VOLUME F6

†PREVIOUSLY PUBLISHED

THE AMERICAN FILM INSTITUTE CATALOG

OF MOTION PICTURES

* FEATURE FILMS 1961-1970

RICHARD P. KRAFSUR

Executive Editor

R. R. BOWKER COMPANY

A Xerox Education Company

New York & London, 1976

Published by R. R. Bowker Co. (A Xerox Education Company)
1180 Avenue of the Americas, New York, N.Y. 10036
Copyright © 1976 by The American Film Institute
International Standard Book Number 0-8352-0453-7
Printed and bound in the United States of America

Library of Congress Cataloging in Publication Data

American Film Institute.
    The American Film Institute catalog of motion pictures produced in the United
States.
    Vol. F6 has title: The American Film Institute catalog of motion pictures.
    Vol. F6: R. P. Krafsur, executive editor.
    Bibliography: v. F6, p.
    CONTENTS:
v. F2: Feature films, 1921-1930. Feature films, 1921-1930, credit & subject indexes.
2v.—   v. F6: Feature films, 1961-1970. Feature films, 1961-1970, indexes, 2v.
    1. Moving-pictures—Catalogs. I. Munden, Kenneth White, ed. II. Krafsur, Richard
P., ed. III. Title.
PN1998.A57   011   79-128587
    ISBN 0-8352-0440-5 (v. 1)

★ *Dedicated to the memory of Kenneth W. Munden, whose inspiration and guidance contributed greatly to the creation of this volume.*

CONTENTS

FOREWORD

★ From its modest beginnings over 100 years ago as an attempt to photograph movement, film has evolved into a mature art form, mirroring customs and attitudes, shaping public opinion, and, arguably, acting as an agent for social and cultural change. It is therefore no wonder that both the amount and quality of scholarship in the field have dramatically increased. More than ever before, film has become a topic of study in our schools, colleges, and universities, while the publishing of materials on film proceeds apace, with books and articles covering every facet of film, from the lives of famous actors and directors to the technical aspects of cinematography.

With this second feature films volume of *The American Film Institute Catalog* we continue our exploration into the past of American motion pictures. This volume covers the decade of the 1960s, following the appearance several years ago of the volume of the 1920s. The Institute's research staff is proceeding with work on the teens decade, and other decades of American filmmaking will follow. The present volume is extremely ambitious in its efforts to be comprehensive. Whereas the volume of the 1920s confined itself to feature films produced in the United States, we felt, in light of the growing internationalism of film, that it would not be enough to produce such a volume for the sixties, when filmmaking was defined less and less by geographic borders. This volume will provide scholars with information on a very comprehensive range of production—from the "New American Cinema" of the experimental filmmakers to the films of countries around the world. This effort to be comprehensive has increased the difficulty of producing the volume but it gives the finished product a much greater utility.

The American Film Institute has shepherded the *Catalog*'s growth into a reference work to answer the needs of historians concerned with the American scene and film scholars as well as fans by providing complete and verifiable information on films in a readily accessible form. This catalog, like its predecessor, records in its Credit Index the careers of individuals who worked both on and in films, whether their contributions were great or small. The stars, both behind and in front of the camera, are here, as are the footsoldiers of *War and Peace*. Production companies range from giants like United Artists to specialized companies such as Bizarre Productions. The efforts of Coppola and Cassavetes, Buñuel and Bergman, are chronicled alongside the productions of writers, producers and directors whose names will never lodge in public memory. A Literary and Dramatic Source Index is included, providing a link between films and the literature upon which they were based. The *Catalog* also contains a Subject Index, through which historians interested in the content of the decade's films can prosecute their search. Present are themes which defined the decade: war, race relations, violence, sexual expression, social criticism. A National Production Index conveniently lists films by the country or countries that produced them, reflecting this volume's coverage of all films released commercially in this country during the decade.

As is evident from the bibliography and the lists of individual and institutional contributors, the *Catalog* staff has consulted a vast amount of written material, first-person sources, and, in many cases, the films themselves. It is our hope and expectation that the result will serve all scholars and researchers who are interested in film.

GEORGE STEVENS, JR.
DIRECTOR, THE AMERICAN FILM INSTITUTE

INTRODUCTION

★ This, the second volume of *The American Film Institute Catalog* to be published, is concerned exclusively with feature-length films which were released and exhibited commercially in the United States between 1 January 1961 and 31 December 1970. To reflect the international nature of filmmaking during the decade and to indicate the extensive financial and artistic involvement of the United States in the production of films abroad, as well as the impact of foreign filmmaking upon American filmmakers and audiences we have expanded our coverage to include not only those productions for which United States participation could be documented, but all films meeting the above criteria of length and release, regardless of country of origin. To be included in the *Catalog* a film must have been exhibited commercially in a motion picture theater, or, in the case of various "experimental" or independent films, in places where a price of admission was required. Furthermore, to be accepted for inclusion each film had to have a running time of 45 minutes or more and had to be available with English-language soundtrack or subtitles. Not found in this volume are films made for television and not theatrically released; foreign-language films released only in original language version; films shown only at academic institutions, museums, or festivals; and educational, industrial, or government films not given commercial exhibition.

We have compiled the information contained in the *Catalog* from a multiplicity of sources in many languages. Among the bodies of records consulted were film periodicals and books, including numerous monographs; reviews of films in the press; the motion picture records of the U. S. Copyright Office; pressbooks, press sheets, and other studio and distributor publicity material; the records of the Maryland State Board of Censors; film catalogs issued by many organizations, including the Canyon Cinema Cooperative, the Center Cinema Cooperative, the Film-Makers' Cooperative, the Film-Mak-ers' Distribution Center, the Independent Film Importers and Distributors of America, and the National Association of Theatre Owners; program notes from a variety of sources, including the Film-Makers' Cinematheque and the Museum of Modern Art Department of Film; film festival programs; directories and catalogs of national production from many countries; published and unpublished screenplays; company records; and, in many cases, the films themselves and individuals involved in their production and distribution. Among the most essential of our reference sources were *Boxoffice,* the British Film Institute *Film Title Index, The Film Daily Year Book of Motion Pictures, Filmens hvem-hvad-hvor, Filmfacts, Index de la Cinématographie française, Monthly Film Bulletin, Motion Picture Exhibitor, The New York Times Film Reviews, Screen World,* and *Variety.*

The *Catalog* project has been granted working space in the Library of Congress, where it has ready access to the Library's resources, including the films preserved in its collections, comprised in part of the American Film Institute Collection. Deserving of special thanks are Edgar Breitenbach, former Chief, Prints and Photographs Division; his successor in that office, Alan M. Fern; and John B. Kuiper, Assistant Chief for Motion Pictures. Staff of the Motion Picture Section whose aid is gratefully acknowledged are Harriet W. Aveney, Rita R. Horwitz, David L. Parker, Barbara S. Rowland, Patrick J. Sheehan, Paul B. Spehr, and Pearline M. Ward.

Institutions whose assistance in the preparation of this volume has been material include the Academy of Motion Picture Arts and Sciences, the Anthology Film Archives, the Museum of Modern Art, and the film organizations noted in the Bibliography, whose publications proved helpful. We are indebted to these institutions and to the individuals and corporations listed below, who contributed important data and support in significant amounts:

John Amero, Per Calum, Alex DeRenzy, Jörn Donner, Dave Eisenstark, Michael Findlay, Ronald L. Freedman, David F. Friedman, Pierre Guinle, Nicholas Hotton IV, David H. Iwaoka, Tod Jonson, Torsten Jungstedt, Lawrence F. Karr, Herschell Gordon Lewis, Barry Mahon, Lia Munden, Thaddeus Y. Ohta, Ruzica Popovitch, Adam Reilly, Barbara Ringer, Michael A. Ripps, Jerome Sandy, Anne Schlosser, Charles Silver, Leokadia Silverstein, Mildred Simpson, David R. Smith, D. John Turner, and Catherine Verret; Ajay Film Co., Allied Artists, American International Pictures, Artkino Pictures, Audubon Films, Bardene International Films, Ben Barry & Associates, Seymour Borde & Associates, Brandon Films, Joseph Brenner Associates, Cambist Films, Cannon Releasing Corp., Chancellor Films, Cinemation Industries, Columbia Pictures, Contemporary Films/McGraw-Hill, Crown International Pictures, Donald A. Davis Productions, Walt Disney Productions, Distribpix, Inc., Emerson Film Enterprises, Gordon Films, J.E.R. Pictures, Sam Lake Enterprises, Manson Distributing Corp., Mature Pictures, Metro-Goldwyn-Mayer, Inc., the Motion Picture Association of America, New Yorker Films, Paramount Pictures, Sack Amusement Enterprises, Schoenfeld Film Distributing Corp., Sherpix, Inc., Shochiku Co., C. Tobalina Productions, Toho Co., Twentieth Century-Fox Film Corp., United Artists, Universal Pictures, Warner Bros., Inc., and Wheeler Film Co.

Work on this volume began under the editorship of the late Kenneth Munden, who also applied the exacting standards of his long experience as an archivist and editor to *The American Film Institute Catalog, Feature Films 1921–1930*. Following an absence of three years, he returned to help us for all too brief a period. We hope this volume will testify to our efforts to maintain the high quality of the scholarship that characterized his work. Kenneth Munden was succeeded as Executive Editor by Stephen Zito, who, since his transfer to other projects within the Institute, has continued to furnish aid and advice.

The American Film Institute, an independent, nonprofit organization, was established in June 1967 by the National Endowment for the Arts to preserve the heritage and to advance the art of film and television in America. The project has been under the supervision of, successively, the American Film Institute's Sam Kula, Sali Ann Kriegsman, Dan Rose, and Win Sharples, Jr., and under the general direction of Richard Carlton, Deputy Director of the Institute. Contributing to the completion of the volume were Kathleen Karr, Anthony Slide, Sally Benbassett, Ann Demeter, Howard Moss, and Sarah Rouse. The computer technology required to process the data and generate the indexes was developed by Auto-Graphics, Inc., which through photocomposition prepared the full text in camera-ready form for publication.

This volume of the *Catalog* was supported with funds provided by the National Endowment for the Humanities, through its Division of Research Grants, and by matching funds from individuals and corporations.

RICHARD P. KRAFSUR

Portions of the material contained in this volume originally appeared in the periodical publication *Filmfacts*, Ernest Parmentier, Editor, and are reprinted by permission.

GUIDE TO ENTRIES

Information about each film, to the extent available, is arranged in the following order.

Film title. Appears in the alphabetical sequence of all titles. The title under which the film was found to have been first shown commercially in the United States is given. The film may be cross-referenced according to alternative titles, including original foreign-language title(s), working or prerelease title(s), and title(s) under which the film was subsequently shown.

Country of origin. Parenthetically follows foreign films and United States coproductions, corresponding to the nationality of the production company or companies.

Reissue. Indicated parenthetically following film title. Films first released before the decade 1961–1970 are included in this volume when they have been retitled or otherwise altered for rerelease in the 1960s.

Entry number. Assigned to each film in alphabetical sequence. The prefix F6 identifies the series of volumes describing feature films and the volume of the present work within that series. In the accompanying indexes the entry number rather than page number is used with each listing.

Producing company or individual. Heads the first paragraph following the title.

Sponsoring company or individual. Preceded by the word *For,* denotes the source of financial support provided to the producing company or individual.

Distributor. Included when it has been determined that it differs from producing company or individual. Multiple distributors for each film within the course of the decade are indicated, while subdistributors are not.

Date of release or earliest commercial showing deter- **mined.** Place of showing is specified. For every film registered for copyright the registration date with the prefix "c" is appended, followed by the copyright registration number.

Sound, silent, or sound-on-tape.

Color indication. The process is noted.

Gauge. Widescreen or special effects process is noted.

Length. Film duration is expressed in minutes.

MPAA rating. A system of evaluation implemented in November 1968 by the Motion Picture Association of America.

Production credits. Expressed in a manner as specific as possible. Preexisting musical or other works incorporated in the film are included in the production credits.

Cast. Roles are stated parenthetically in italics.

Genre. This indication is of necessity general; subject headings clarify the film's classification.

Source. Identifies original preexisting material upon which the film is based.

Synopsis. Recapitulates what occurs in the film.

Subject terms. Reflect the film's content.

Note. Provides additional information, as available, including: original language title(s); release dates in the case of foreign films and coproductions; alternative title(s); location filming information; and pseudonym information. The note also calls attention to conflicts and problems resulting from contradictory sources.

SELECTED BIBLIOGRAPHY

BOOKS

Academy of Motion Picture Arts and Sciences, and the Writers Guild of America, West. *Who Wrote the Movie and What Else Did He Write?* Los Angeles, 1970.

Bartošková, Šárka. *Československé filmy, 1958–1959; filmografie.* Prague, 1960.

————.*Československé filmy, 1960–1965.* 2 vols. Prague, 1966.

Bessy, Maurice, and Chardans, Jean-Louis. *Dictionnaire du cinéma et de la télévision.* 4 vols. Paris, 1965–1971.

Bucher, Felix, and Gmür, Leonhard H. *Germany.* Screen Series. London, 1970.

Cawkwell, Tim, and Smith, John M., eds. *The World Encyclopedia of the Film.* New York, 1974.

Cowie, Peter, and Svensson, Arne. *Sweden.* 2 vols. Screen Series. London, 1970.

Dimmitt, Richard Bertrand. *A Title Guide to the Talkies.* New York, 1965.

Eberhard, Wolfram. *The Chinese Silver Screen.* Taipei, 1972.

Eberhardt, Konrad. *Aktorzy filmu polskiego.* Warsaw, 1962.

Enser, A. G. S. *Filmed Books and Plays.* New York, 1972.

Fuente, María Isabel de la. *Indice bibliográfico del cine mexicano.* Vol. 1 (1930–1965), Vol. 2 (1966-1967). Mexico City, 1967–1968.

Gifford, Denis. *The British Film Catalogue, 1895–1970.* Newton Abbot, 1973.

Hagen, Ordean A. *Who Done It?* New York, 1969.

Halliwell, Leslie. *The Filmgoer's Companion.* 3rd ed. London, 1970.

Hibbin, Nina. *Eastern Europe.* Screen Series. London, 1969.

Janicki, Stanisław. *Film polski od A do Z.* Warsaw, 1972.

Katholische Filmkommission für Österreich. *20 Jahre Film. 1948–1968.* Vienna, 1969.

Lee, Walt. *Reference Guide to Fantastic Films.* 3 vols. Los Angeles, 1972–1974.

Martin, Marcel. *France.* Screen Series. London, 1971.

Méndez-Leite, Fernando. *Historia del cine español.* Madrid, 1965.

Michael, Paul, ed. *The American Movies Reference Book.* Englewood Cliffs, N.J., 1969.

Micheli, Sergio. *Il cinema bulgaro.* Padua, 1971.

Mitropoulos, Aglaé. *Découverte du cinéma grec, histoire, chronologie, biographies, films . . .* French adapt. by Guy Braucourt. Paris, 1968.

Molnár, István, ed. *Magyar Filmográfia: Játékfilmek 1945–1969.* Magyar Filmtudományi Intézet es Filmarchívum. Budapest, 1973.

Morris, Peter, ed. *Canadian Feature Films: 1913–1963.* Part 2 (1941–1963). Canadian Filmography Series, No. 7. Ottawa, 1974.

Moscow. Vsesoyuznyy gosudarstvennyy institut kinematografii. Kafedra kinovedeniya. *Kratkaya istoriya sovetskogo kino. 1917–1967.* Moscow, 1969.

The New York Times Film Reviews, 1913–1968. Vol. 5 (1959–1968), Vol. 6 (Appendix, Index), Supplement (1969–1970). New York, 1970–1971.

Racheva, Mariya. *Presentday Bulgarian Cinema.* trans. by Liliana Vesselinova. Sofia, 1969.

Rasmussen, Bjørn. *Filmens hvem-hvad-hvor.* 5 vols. Copenhagen, 1968–1970.

Renan, Sheldon. *An Introduction to the American Underground Film.* New York, 1967.

Rondolino, Gianni, ed. *Catalogo Bolaffi del cinema italiano.* Turin, 1967.

———. *Dizionario del cinema italiano 1945–1969.* Turin, 1969.

Savez filmskih radnika Jugoslavije. *Dvadeset godina jugoslovenskog filma 1945–1965.* ed. by Dejan Kosanović. Belgrade, 1966.

U. S. Copyright Office. *Catalog of Copyright Entries. Cumulative Series, Motion Pictures, 1960–1969; Third Series, Motion Pictures and Filmstrips, 1970–June 1974.* Washington, D. C., 1971–1974.

Uusitalo, Kari. *Suomalaisen elokuvan vuosikymmenet.* Helsinki, 1965.

Vsesoyuznyy gosudarstvennyy fond kinofilmov. *Sovetskiye khudozhestvennyye filmy.* Vol. 2 (1930–1957), Vol. 3 (Index), Vol. 4 (1958–1963). Moscow, 1961–1968.

Willis, Donald C. *Horror and Science Fiction Films: A Checklist.* Metuchen, N. J., 1972.

Winquist, Sven G. *Författare till svenska långfilmer samt svensk TV-teater.* Stockholm, 1969.

———. *Filmförfattarlexikon 1896–1971.* Stockholm, 1972.

———. *Svenska ljudfilmer 1929–69 och deras regissörer.* Stockholm, 1969.

Winquist, Sven G., and Jungstedt, Torsten. *Svenskt filmskådespelarlexikon.* Stockholm, 1973.

PERIODICALS

Adam Film Quarterly

Adam Film World

Artisex

L'avant-scène du cinéma (France)

Boxoffice

Daily Variety

Film (Poland)

Film Bulletin

Film Culture

The Film Daily

Film-Echo/Filmwoche (West Germany)

Filme cultura (Brazil)

Filmfacts

Filmmakers' Newsletter

Guia de filmes (Brazil)

Hollywood Reporter

Intermezzo (Italy)

Iskusstvo kino (U.S.S.R.)

Kinematograph Weekly (Great Britain)

Monthly Film Bulletin (Great Britain)

Motion Picture Exhibitor

Motion Picture Herald

Variety

ANNUALS AND OTHER SERIALS

Academy of Motion Picture Arts and Sciences. *Academy Players Directory.*

———. *Reminder List of Productions Eligible for Awards.*

Annuaire du spectacle; théâtre, cinéma, musique, radio, télévision (France)

Annuario del cinema italiano (Italy)

Anuario español de cinematografía (Spain)

Årets Film (Denmark)

British Film and Television Year Book (Great Britain)

Evangelischer Film-Beobachter (West Germany)

The Film Daily Year Book of Motion Pictures

Filmårsboken (Säsongens filmer) (Sweden)

Index cinéma (Index de la Cinématographie française) (France)

International Motion Picture Almanac

Kemp's Film and Television Year Book (International) (Great Britain)

Kinematografija u Srbiji (Yugoslavia)

Kinematograph and Television Year Book (Great Britain)

Office catholique national des techniques de diffusion. *Recueil des films.* (Canada)

Screen World

TV Feature Film Source Book

SOURCES OF NATIONAL PRODUCTION CATALOGS AND OTHER DOCUMENTATION

The Danish Government Film Foundation

DEFA-Aussenhandel (East Germany)

Export-Union der Deutschen Filmindustrie (West Germany)

Film Polski (Poland)

Filmbulgaria

The Finnish Film Foundation

Fondo Nacional de las Artes (Argentina)

Hungarofilm (Hungary)

Instituto Nacional do Cinema (Brazil)

National Film Board of Canada

Sovexportfilm (U.S.S.R.)

Svenska Filminstitutet (Sweden)

Uniespaña (Spain)

Unifrance Film (France)

UniJapan Film (Japan)

Unitalia (Italy)

Yugoslavia Film

ABBREVIATIONS

This list, with a few exceptions, is confined to abbreviations denoting motion picture credits. Other abbreviations appearing in this work conform to standard practices.

Accomp accompaniment, accompanying
Adapt adapter, adaptation
Admin administrator, administration
Adtl additional
Adv adviser
Anim animator, animation
Arr arranger, arranged, arrangement
Assoc associate
Asst assistant
b&w black and white
c copyright
ca circa
Camera camera, cameraman
Ch chief
Charact character
Choreog choreographer, choreography
Cinematog cinematographer, cinematography
col color
Collab collaborator, collaboration
Comm commentary
Comp composer, composed
Cond conductor, conducted
Cons consultant
Constr construction
Cont continuity
Coöp cooperator, cooperation
Coörd coordinator, coordination
Cost costume, costumer, costumes
Decor decorator, decoration
Dial dialog
Dir director, direction
Dist distributor
Dsgn designer, design

Dub dubber, dubbing
Ed editor, editorial
Eff effects
Elec electrical
Electrn electrician
Engr engineer

Exec executive
Gen general
Illus illustrator, illustration
Instr instructor, instruction
Lang language
Lyr lyrics
Mgr manager
mm millimeters
min minutes
Mix mixer, mixing
Mus music, musical
Narr narration
Neg negative
Op operator
Orch orchestra, orchestration
Orig original
Perf performed
Pers personal
Photog photographer, photography, photographic
Pres presenter, presented
Proc process
Prod producer, production
Prop property, properties
Rec recorder, recording
Res research
Scen scenarist, scenario
Sd sound
Sec secretary
Seq sequence, sequences
Si silent
Sp special
Stgd staged
Subtitl subtitles
Supv supervisor, supervision
Sync synchronization
Tech technician, technical
Titl title, titles
Vers version
Vis visual
Writ writer, written

VOLUME F6

À BOUT DE SOUFFLE see **BREATHLESS**

A BRIGLIA SCIOLTA see **PLEASE, NOT NOW!**

A CIASCUNO IL SUO see **WE STILL KILL THE OLD WAY**

À COEUR JOIE see **TWO WEEKS IN SEPTEMBER**

A DOPPIA MANDATA see **LEDA**

À DOUBLE TOUR see **LEDA**

A. K. A. CASSIUS CLAY   F6.0001
Sports of the Century, Inc. *Dist* United Artists. 3 Nov **1970** [New York opening; c3 Nov 1970; LP38909]. Sd; b&w and col (Deluxe). 35mm. 79 min. *MPAA rating* GP.
Prod William Cayton. *Dir* Jim Jacobs. *Assoc Dir & Screenplay* Bernard Evslin. *Photog* Izzy Mankovsky. *Assoc Photog* Larry Garinger. *Film Ed* Edward P. Bartsch. *Mus* Teo Macero. *Sd* Barney Beck, Al Schaffer. *Film Cons* Bernie Chertok, Dave Chertok.
Featuring: Muhammad Ali, Cus D'Amato.
Narrator: Richard Kiley.
Sports documentary. After Cassius Clay wins several Golden Glove awards and a gold medal for boxing in the Olympic Games, a group of millionaires from Louisville, Kentucky, invests in him, and his professional boxing career begins. Clay fights Henry Cooper, Cleveland Williams, Floyd Patterson, and finally, in 1964, Sonny Liston for the heavyweight championship. In the meantime, Clay has become influenced by Black Muslim leader Malcolm X; he soon converts to the Muslim faith and changes his name to Muhammad Ali. Because of his religious convictions, Ali refuses induction into the United States Army in 1967 but is denied a conscientious objector's status. The New York State Athletic Commission also refuses to accept his religious beliefs as justification for not serving in the Army, and he is stripped of the heavyweight title and barred from the ring. *Prizefighters. Fight managers. Conscientious objectors. Black Muslims. Boxing. Religious conversion. Military draft. Louisville (Kentucky). Muhammad Ali. Henry Cooper. Cleveland Williams. Floyd Patterson. Sonny Liston. United States Army. New York State Athletic Commission.*

À LA FRANÇAISE see **IN THE FRENCH STYLE**

À L'ITALIENNE see **MADE IN ITALY**

... A PÁTÝ JEZDEC JE STRACH see **THE FIFTH HORSEMAN IS FEAR**

À QUELQUES JOURS PRÈS see **A MATTER OF DAYS**

À TOUT PRENDRE see **TAKE IT ALL**

A-009 MISSIONE HONG KONG see **RED-DRAGON**

AA, KAIGUN see **GATEWAY TO GLORY**

AA RIKUGUN HAYABUSA SENTOTAI see **THE FALCON FIGHTERS**

ABARE GOEMON see **RISE AGAINST THE SWORD**

THE ABC MURDERS see **THE ALPHABET MURDERS**

THE ABC'S OF MARRIAGE   F6.0002
The Institute of Sexual Behavior. *Dist* Hammerhead Films, Ellman Enterprises. May **1970** [New York showing]. Sd; col (Eastmancolor). 35mm. [Feature length assumed.]
In Assoc With The Keaton Marital Institute.
Sex film. No information about the precise nature of this film has been found except that it deals with variations on the love act. *Sex instruction. Marriage.*

ABNORMAL see **HENTAI**

THE ABNORMAL FEMALE   F6.0003
Dove Productions. *Dist* Distribpix, Inc. ca **1969**. Sd; b&w. 35mm. 65 min.
Prod-Dir (see note) George Raders. *Author* Martin Lathrop. *Dir Photog* H. M. Schultz. *Film Ed* Herbert Williger. *Mus* Arthur Lindsay. *Sd* David Laird. *Asst Dir* Samuel Shuman. *Prod Mgr* David Ratti. *Prod Asst* Milton Kapp. *Hairstyles* Ramona Falk.
Cast: Pamela Berkeley, Jeannette Foster, Carroll Wilson, Harriet Stark, Franklin Chambers, Robert Antonius, Diana Powell, Stephen King, Charles Tom, Judy Dru, Jack Nelder, Merrill Brooks, Cornel Lamonica, Danny Barris, Sara Wells.
Drama. A psychiatrist delves into his private files, and a number of extraordinary female sexual practices come to light. Jeannette captures a young man, ties him up, taunts him, and beats him with a whip. The Baronness covers her man with exotic juices and teases him by withholding fruit from his hungry mouth. Sherry, taunted by memories of a youth filled with her mother's harsh

accusations, now enacts all the charges that were unjustly leveled against her. Kathy suffers from an insatiable lust for men. Pete's wife makes love with another woman to arouse her husband, and Barbara can love only women. *Psychiatry. Sadism. Flagellation. Nymphomania. Voyeurism. Lesbianism.*
Note: Producer-director is also credited as George Rodgers.

ABORTION!   F6.0004
Dist Inter-American Film Distributors, Empire Film Distributors. ca **1967**. Sd; b&w. 35mm. 60 min.
Melodrama. A rebellious, flirtatious, teenaged girl encounters a rapist and becomes pregnant; and an attractive young woman, whose husband is sterile, is impregnated by her lover. Both women come to Dr. Martin seeking abortions, but he refuses, offering advice instead. His emotionally disturbed nurse, trying to be helpful, gives the women the name of an abortionist, who performs the operations under unsanitary conditions. The teenager develops an infection, and the young wife dies of a hemorrhage. Growing suspicious of the nurse, Dr. Martin enlists the aid of an attractive law enforcement officer in setting a trap. The abortionist is identified, but he nearly kills the decoy before Dr. Martin arrives to rescue her. *Physicians. Flirts. Nurses. Detectives. Abortion. Rape. Sterility (sexual). Infidelity. Mental illness.*

THE ABSENT-MINDED PROFESSOR   F6.0005
Walt Disney Productions. *Dist* Buena Vista Distribution Co. 16 Mar **1961** [New York opening; c20 Dec 1960; LP18401]. Sd (RCA); b&w. 35mm. 97 min.
A Walt Disney Production. *Assoc Prod* Bill Walsh. *Dir* Robert Stevenson. *2d Unit Dir* Arthur J. Vitarelli. *Screenplay* Bill Walsh. *Anim Eff* Joshua Meador. *Dir Photog* Edward Colman. *Art Dir* Carroll Clark. *Set Decor* Emile Kuri, Hal Gausman. *Film Ed* Cotton Warburton. *Mus* George Bruns. *Orch* Franklyn Marks. *Song:* "Medfield Fight Song" Richard M. Sherman, Robert B. Sherman. *Sd Supv* Robert O. Cook. *Sd Mix* Dean Thomas. *Mus Ed* Evelyn Kennedy. *Asst Dir* Robert Shannon. *Cost* Chuck Keehne, Gertrude Casey. *Makeup* Pat McNalley. *Hairstyles* Ruth Sandifer. *Sp Eff* Peter Ellenshaw, Eustace Lycett. *Sp Photog Eff* Robert A. Mattey, Joshua Meador. *Seq Cons* Don DaGradi.
Cast: Fred MacMurray *(Prof. Ned Brainard)*, Nancy Olson *(Betsy Carlisle)*, Keenan Wynn *(Alonzo Hawk)*, Tommy Kirk *(Bill Hawk)*, Ed Wynn *(fire chief)*, Leon Ames *(Pres. Rufus Daggett)*, Elliott Reid *(Shelby Ashton)*, Edward Andrews *(defense secretary)*, David Lewis *(General Singer)*, Jack Mullaney *(Air Force captain)*, Belle Montrose *(Mrs. Chatsworth)*, Wally Brown *(Coach Elkins)*, Don Ross *(Lenny)*, James Westerfield *(Officer Hanson)*, Charlie Briggs *(Sig)*, Alan Hewitt *(General Hotchkiss)*, Wendell Holmes *(General Poynter)*, Wally Boag *(TV newsman)*, Forrest Lewis *(Officer Kelly)*, Alan Carney *(1st referee)*, Gage Clarke *(Reverend Bosworth)*, Raymond Bailey *(Admiral Olmstead)*, Leon Tyler *(basketball player)*, Ned Wynn.
Comedy. Source: Samuel W. Taylor, "A Situation of Gravity," in *Liberty Magazine* (22 May 1943). Ned Brainard, the science professor at a smalltown college, is so forgetful that he has left his fiancée, Betsy Carlisle, waiting at the altar on two different occasions. Though determined not to miss the third ceremony, he becomes engrossed in an experiment and again fails to appear. He does not become a bridegroom, but he does become the inventor of a black, rubbery, antigravitational substance which rises to a greater height each time it is bounced. After naming the product "flubber," he substitutes it for the motor of his old Model T and is soon soaring through the sky. Giddy with success, he secretly places some flubber on the shoes of the college's basketball players, enabling them to bounce over the heads of their opponents and win an easy victory. Word of his discovery soon attracts the attention of a scheming alumnus, Alonzo Hawk, who steals the professor's car. Ned places some flubber on Alonzo's shoes, however, and leaves him bouncing higher and higher on his front lawn. Then, with the aid of Betsy, he rescues his car and takes off for Washington, D. C. After completely upsetting the Pentagon's defense system, he lands on the White House lawn and becomes a national hero and, finally, Betsy's husband. *Professors. College life. Gravitation. Theft. Inventions. Rubber. Basketball. Ford automobiles. Weddings. Defense—National. Washington (District of Columbia). The White House. The Pentagon.*
Note: *Son of Flubber,* q. v., is a sequel.

LES ABYSSES (France)   F6.0006
Lenox Films. *Dist* Kanawha Films. 23 Nov **1964** [New York opening]. Sd; b&w. 35mm. 90 min.
Prod-Dir Nico Papatakis. *Orig Scen* Jean Vauthier. *Dial* Jean Vauthier. *Dir Photog* Jean-Michel Boussaguet. *Asst Photog* Jean-Claude Hugon, André Dinot. *Film Ed* Denise de Casabianca, Pascale Laverrière, Edwige Bernard. *Orig Mus* Pierre Barbaud. *Mus Dir* Konstantin Simonovic. *Sd Engr* Claude Lerouge. *Asst Dir* Roger Dallier, Robert Maurice. *Makeup* Marie-Louise Gillet. *Studio Tech* Paul Chapalain, André Beaumont.
Cast: Francine Bergé *(Michèle)*, Colette Bergé *(Marie-Louise)*, Pascale de Boysson *(Elisabeth)*, Colette Régis *(Madame Lapeyre)*, Paul Bonifas *(Monsieur*

Lapeyre), Jean-Louis Le Goff (Philippe), Lise Daubigny, Marcel Roche, Robert Benois (buyers).

Drama. Michèle and Marie-Louise, orphaned sisters bound by an unhealthy devotion, are servant girls on the steadily decaying farm of Monsieur Lapeyre, a once-prosperous Bordeaux wine-grower. Dirty and disheveled, the sisters are reduced to virtual slavery, and for 3 years they have worked without pay. Lapeyre and his domineering wife leave for town with their daughter Elisabeth to effect a reconciliation with Elisabeth's estranged husband, Philippe. The girls are left alone, fearful that their masters will find a buyer for the farm and leave them destitute. Terrorized, they alternately quarrel and embrace, and begin to smash and destroy the household in a desperate attempt to prevent the sale. The family returns unexpectedly, and Elisabeth announces her intention to remain at home with Marie-Louise, the object of her affections. Unable to pay the back wages, the Lapeyres endure continual abuse while the destruction continues. Elisabeth, in an act of charity, had promised the sisters ownership of the backyard chicken house, but now she joins her mother in reneging on the offer. The girls grow increasingly hysterical, and when Philippe arrives with a trio of prospective buyers, Elisabeth goes to him, turning her back on the sisters. As the papers are signed, Michèle and Marie-Louise go berserk and barricade themselves in the kitchen. While attempting to reason with them, Madame and Elisabeth are brutally murdered with kitchen utensils, leaving Lapeyre to his conscience. *Sisters. Orphans. Domestics. Vineyardists. Lesbianism. Insanity. Family life. Murder. Bordeaux.*

Note: Paris opening: Apr 1963; running time: 96 min. Inspired by the French Papin sisters murder case of 1933.

AC/DC   **F6.0007**
Kirt Films International. *Dist* Distribpix, Inc. 23 Apr **1969** [Champaign, Illinois, showing]. Sd; b&w. 35mm. 65 min.

Prod Leonard Kirtman. *Dir-Writ* Larry Winters. *Dir Photog* Steven Wingate. *Ed by* Lipskey. *Prod Supv* Dante D'Jock. *Grip* Rene Ginch.

Cast: Jack Simpson, Gale Forester, Judy Sacks, Rachel Stevens, John Forester, Larry Parks, sd, Gale Louis, Mary Arteon, Frank Hanson, Barry Astor, Henry Parks.

Melodrama. A woman gives up the love and protection of Buster, her churlish older brother, when she has an affair with another woman. Buster takes a fancy to the other woman and also begins an affair with her. Using Sis's camera, Lamont, a pet monkey, takes compromising pictures of Buster and the other woman engaged in sexual activity, thereby bringing their clandestine affair into the open. Confronted by the angry sister, the other woman chooses the brother over her, leaving the sister to console herself with the monkey. *Brother-sister relationship. Lesbianism. Incest. Bisexuality. Cameras. Monkeys. Bestiality.*

ACADEMY LEADER   **F6.0008**
Dist Film-Makers' Cooperative. 15 Dec **1965** [New York opening]. Si with sd-on-tape; b&w. 16mm. 45 min.

Dir Gerard Malanga.

Voice: David Murray.No information about the precise nature of this film has been found.

Note: The soundtrack consists of readings from *David Murray's Journals.*

ACAPULCO EXPOSÉ *see* **ACAPULCO UNCENSORED**

ACAPULCO UNCENSORED   **F6.0009**
Hollywood Cinema Associates. *Dist* Crest Film Distributors. 11 Nov **1968** [New York showing]. Sd; col. 35mm. 71 min.

Documentary(?). Hidden cameras penetrate Acapulco's plush hotels, its villas owned by international socialites, and its brothels. The cameramen, posing as visiting yachtsmen, capture scenes of nude swimming, group sex, and young women staging perverted shows to obtain money for marijuana. *Motion picture cameramen. Eavesdropping. Prostitution. Nudity. Group sex. Stag shows. Impersonation. Resorts. Hotels. Upper classes. Whorehouses. Marijuana. Acapulco.*

Note: Made in Acapulco, this film may also be known as *Acapulco Exposé.*

ACCATTONE! (Italy)   **F6.0010**
Cino del Duca–Arco Film. *Dist* Brandon Films. 4 Apr **1968** [New York opening]. Sd; b&w. 35mm. 120 min.

Prod Alfredo Bini. *Dir-Writ* Pier Paolo Pasolini. *Dial Collab* Sergio Citti. *Photog* Tonino Delli Colli. *Camera* Franco Delli Colli. *Art Dir* Flavio Mogherini. *Film Ed* Nino Baragli. *Musical Selections* Johann Sebastian Bach. *Mus Dir* Carlo Rustichelli. *Sd* Luigi Puri, Manlio Magara. *Asst Dir* Leopoldo Savona, Bernardo Bertolucci. *Prod Mgr* Marcello Bollero. *Subtitl* Herman G. Weinberg.

Cast: Franco Citti (Accattone [Vittorio]), Franca Pasut (Stella), Silvana Corsini (Maddalena), Paola Guidi (Ascenza), Adriana Asti (Amore), Renato Capogna (Renato), Mario Cipriani (Balilla), Roberto Scaringella (Cartagine),

Piero Morgia (Pio), Umberto Bevilacqua (The Neapolitan), Elsa Morante (a prisoner), Adele Cambria (Nannina), Polidor (Becchino), Danilo Alleva (Iaio), Luciano Conti (Il Moicano), Luciano Gonino (Piede d'Oro), Gabriele Baldini (intellectual), Adrianno Mazelli, Mario Castaglione (Amore's clients), Dino Frondi, Tommaso Nuevo (Cartagine's friends), Romolo Orazi (Accattone's father-in-law), Silvio Citti (Sabino), Adriana Moneta (Margheritona).

Drama. Source: Pier Paolo Pasolini, *Una vita violenta* (Milan, 1959). In the Roman slum of Pigneto, a young drifter called Accattone, or "Sponger," cheerfully lives off the earnings of Maddalena, his prostitute mistress, all the while flatly refusing to do a day's work. When Maddalena is arrested and jailed, Accattone, after selling all his possessions to keep from starving, decides to return to his wife, Ascenza, who earns a meager living in a bottle-cleaning factory, and their child. His father-in-law throws him out, however, and Accattone steals his child's religious medal in order to buy a present for Stella, a virginal blonde he has recently met. After reluctantly falling in love, he offers to procure for her if she will become a prostitute. Stella agrees but flees in horror from her first client, and Accattone is forced to take a job as a scrap metal loader. He seems on the verge of participating in conventional society; but exhaustion from working and his distaste for a regular job that pays only starvation wages cause him to quit at the close of the first day. Meanwhile, Maddalena, having learned that Accattone has a new woman, informs the authorities that he has corrupted a minor. Now under police surveillance, Accattone attempts a robbery and, as he tries to escape on a motorcycle, he crashes into a passing truck and is killed. *Pimps. Parasites. Prostitutes. Police. Factory workers. Unemployment. Hunger. Poverty. Robbery. Virginity. Infidelity. Slums. Rome. Motorcycle accidents.*

Note: Filmed on location in the slums of Rome using nonprofessional actors. Released in Italy in 1961; running time: 120 min. Originally intended for U. S. release by Astor Films.

ACCIDENT (Great Britain)   **F6.0011**
Royal Avenue Chelsea. *Dist* Cinema V Distributing, Inc. 17 Apr **1967** [New York opening]. Sd; col (Eastman Color). 35mm. 105 min.

Prod Joseph Losey, Norman Priggen. *Dir* Joseph Losey. *Screenplay* Harold Pinter. *Dir Photog* Gerry Fisher. *Camera Op* Derek Browne. *Art Dir* Carmen Dillon. *Film Ed* Reginald Beck. *Mus* John Dankworth. *Sd Rec* Simon Kaye, Gerry Humphreys. *Sd Ed* Alan Bell. *Asst Dir* Richard Dalton. *Prod Supv* Geoffrey Haine. *Cost* Beatrice Dawson. *Sp Cost for Miss Sassard* De Luca of Rome. *Makeup* Bob Lawrence. *Hairstyles* Pearl Tipaldi.

Cast: Dirk Bogarde (Stephen), Stanley Baker (Charley), Jacqueline Sassard (Anna), Michael York (William), Vivien Merchant (Rosalind), Delphine Seyrig (Francesca), Alexander Knox (college provost), Ann Firbank (Laura), Harold Pinter (Bell), Brian Phelan (police sergeant), Terence Rigby (plain clothes policeman), Freddie Jones (man in Bell's office), Jill Johnson (secretary), Jane Hillary (T.V. receptionist), Maxwell Findlater (Ted), Carole Caplin (Clarissa), Nicholas Mosley (Hedges).

Drama. Source: Nicholas Mosley, *Accident* (London, 1965). The sound of a car crash shatters the stillness of the country night and brings Stephen, an Oxford don, from his work to investigate. He finds two of his students—William, an English nobleman who is dead, and Anna, an Austrian princess suffering from shock. Carrying Anna to his house, Stephen recalls recent events involving the students. *During a tutoring session Stephen learns of William's love for Anna, and Stephen, whose wife, Rosalind, expects their third child and who senses the approach of middle age, also is strongly attracted to her. Stephen's frustration is increased by his unsatisfactory attempt to rekindle the passion he once shared with Francesca and the knowledge that Charley is having an affair with Charley, his brash, more successful Oxford colleague. Anna, however, decides to marry William, and she asks Stephen to tell Charley. Before he can do so, William is killed en route to Stephen's home. As Anna regains consciousness, Stephen makes love to her; afterwards he smuggles her into her dormitory. Anna's decision to return to Austria shocks Charley, and Stephen resumes his life with Rosalind. Professors. Students. Nobility. Royalty. Mistresses. College life. Pregnancy. Infidelity. Oxford University. Automobile accidents.*

Note: Filmed on location at Oxford and London. Opened in London in Feb 1967.

ACE HIGH (Italy)   **F6.0012**
Crono Cinematografica–Finanziaria San Marco. *Dist* Paramount Pictures. 3 Sep **1969** [Detroit opening]. Sd; col (Technicolor). 35mm (Techniscope). 122 min. *MPAA rating* M.

Prod Bino Cicogna, Giuseppe Colizzi. *Exec Prod* Massimo De Rossi. *Dir-Writ* Giuseppe Colizzi. *Dir Action Seq* Nando Poggi. *English Dial* Raffaele Mattela. *Photog* Marcello Masciocchi. *Art Dir* Gastone Carsetti. *Film Ed* Marcello Malvestiti. *Mus* Carlo Rustichelli. *Sd* Augusto Troiani. *Asst Dir* Silvana Mangini Colizzi, Luigi Mangini. *Prod Mgr* Renato Moretti. *Cost* Luciana Fortini. *Sp Eff* Eros Bacciucchi.

Cast: Eli Wallach *(Cacopoulos),* Terence Hill *(Cat Stevens),* Bud Spencer *(Hutch Bessy),* Brock Peters *(Thomas),* Kevin McCarthy *(Drake),* Stephen Zacharias *(Harold),* Livio Lorenzon *(Paco Rosa),* Tiffany Hoyveld *(Thomas' wife),* Remo Capitani *(Cangaceiro).*

Western drama. Cacopoulos, a convicted criminal, is saved from the gallows by the local bank president, who hires him to track down two bank robbers, Cat and Hutch. Cacopoulos accepts the offer, and then guns down the bank president after remembering that he was one of three men responsible for sending him to prison 15 years earlier. After recovering the stolen money, Cacopoulos tries to track down his other two accusers but loses the money gambling in a saloon owned by Drake, one of the men he is pursuing. Cat and Hutch arrive in town and form a partnership with Cacopoulos to recover the money. Cat and Hutch force the croupier into an honest match and win back the money, and Cacopoulos kills Drake in a showdown. *Convicts. Robbers. Bounty hunters. Murder. Revenge. Gambling. Saloons.*

Note: Location scenes filmed in Almería, Spain. Released in Italy in 1968 as *I quattro dell'Ave Maria.* Also reviewed as *Aces High.*

THE ACID EATERS   F6.0013

III Lions. *Dist* FPS Ventures, Crest Film Distributors. 28 Mar **1968** [San Francisco showing]. Sd; col. 35mm. 65 min.

Prod-Dir B. Ron Elliott. *Orig Screenplay* Carlos Monsoya. *Dir Photog* Davis Freeman. *Film Ed* Byron Mabe. *Orig Mus Comp* Billy Allen. *Sd* Glen Glenn Sound. *Script Supv* Kelly Ross.

Cast: Buckie Buck *(Artie),* Bric Wahl *(Ollie),* Bob Wren *(Smiley),* John McCloud *(Big Jack),* Judy Wood *(Genna),* Camille Grant *(Chickie),* Sharon Carr *(girl),* Lila Cranston Lamont *(Fran),* Sam Greenwood *(Miner),* Chico Vespa *(John),* Dianne Curtis *(Marsha).*

Drama. Every Friday afternoon, a group of office workers shed their establishment garb and hit the road on their motorcycles, looking for "action." They find it at the "White Pyramid," a 50-foot tower of LSD. *Office clerks. Sexuality. LSD. Motorcycles.*

Note: May also known as *The Acid People.*

ACID MANTRA, OR REBIRTH OF A NATION   F6.0014

Dist Canyon Cinema Cooperative. Oct **1968** [Los Angeles showing]. col. 3×16mm, see note. 113 min.

Prod-Dir Ben Van Meter. *Photog* Ben Van Meter.

Experimental film. The film consists of three sections: "The World Is Coming" shows a variety of people dancing, swimming, and making love; it concludes with the birth of a baby. "Lila" consists of scenes showing well-known faces, cavorting nudes, couples copulating, and musical numbers. In "Make Love Not War, or Brown Rice," a series of permuted images appear, along with segments from the film *Bridge On the River Kwai. Dancers. Swimming. Sexual practices. Childbirth. Nudity.*

Note: The film was originally shown in a multiple projection version: "The World Is Coming" (45 min) utilized 1 projector; "Lila" (38 min), 2 projectors simultaneously; "Make Love Not War, or Brown Rice" (30 min), 3 projectors. The entire film was subsequently released in single projection versions at 50 and 30 min.

THE ACID PEOPLE *see* THE ACID EATERS

ACOSADA *see* THE PINK PUSSY (WHERE SIN LIVES)

ACROSS THE RIVER   F6.0015

Debema Productions. *Dist* R. M. Franchi. 26 Apr **1965** [New York opening]. Sd; b&w. 35mm. 85 min.

Dir Stefan Sharff. *Screenplay* Stefan Sharff, Ed Sherin. *Photog* Tom Mangravite. *Mus Comp* Charles Gross.

Cast: Lou Gilbert *(Obadiah),* Kay Doubleday *(Monica),* Samuel J. McCurry *(superintendent),* Archie Smith *(bum),* Lou Polan *(store owner),* Robert F. Simon *(policeman),* Slavko Novytsky *(sanitation officer).*

Drama. Obadiah, a friendly recluse, lives in a shack on the grounds of a lumber company across the river from Manhattan in the shadow of the Queensboro Bridge. His daily routine includes milking his goat, exchanging the milk for other foods, and collecting and selling junk and paper. One day Obadiah discovers Monica, a young woman being beaten up by a man near the waterfront, and he takes her home. Obadiah's existence gradually changes as he begins to take care of Monica, feeding and clothing her, even stealing a coat for her. Her presence excites a group of derelicts, who slaughter and roast Obadiah's goat. Then the man from whom Obadiah saved Monica returns and takes her away, leaving Obadiah alone. *Recluses. Derelicts. Junk dealers. Theft. New York City. New York City—Queensboro Bridge. Goats.*

Note: Filmed in New York City.

ACT OF MERCY *see* GUNS OF DARKNESS

ACT OF THE HEART (Canada)   F6.0016

Quest Film Productions. *Dist* Universal Pictures. 25 Nov **1970** [New York opening; c24 Sep 1970; LF122]. Sd; col (Eastmancolor, print by Technicolor). 35mm. 103 min. *MPAA rating* GP.

Pres by Jennings Lang. *Prod-Dir-Writ* Paul Almond. *Assoc Prod* Peter Carter. *Photog* Jean Boffety. *Art Dir* Anne Pritchard. *Film Ed* James D. Mitchell. *Cantata:* "The Flame Within" Harry Freedman. *Songs:* "La chanson de Martha," "La chanson du feu et de l'eau" Gilles Vigneault. *Sung by* Geneviève Bujold. *Mus Arr* Paul Almond. *Sd Engr* David Howells. *Asst Dir* John Board, Frank Phillips, asst dir. *Wardrobe* Jean Patou. *Coöp* Canadian Film Development Corp.

Cast: Geneviève Bujold *(Martha Hayes),* Donald Sutherland *(Father Michael Ferrier),* Monique Leyrac *(Johane Foss),* Bill Mitchell, Canadian *(Russell Foss),* Suzanne Langlois *(housekeeper),* Sharon Acker *(Adele),* Ratch Wallace *(Diedrich),* Jean Duceppe *(parks commissioner),* Gilles Vigneault *(Coach Ti-Jo),* Eric House *(choirmaster),* Jean Dalmain, Claude Jutra, François Tasse, Les Hurricane, Emard de Ville, Jean Duceppe.

Drama. Martha Hayes, a religious young woman from a rural province in Canada, arrives in Montreal to earn money for her parents and finds lodgings with Johane Foss, a widow who is seeking a tutor for her son, Russell. A Protestant who sings in the church choir, Martha is thrilled to be selected by Father Michael Ferrier, an Augustinian monk, to sing a solo in the church concert. Working closely with Martha, Father Ferrier explains the strict religious beliefs of his order, including St. Augustine's symbolic association with the flaming heart. Martha soon finds her feelings for Father Ferrier developing into love. When Russell is injured in a hockey game, Martha comforts Johane at the hospital by reminding her that God will look after her son, but when they receive news that Russell has died, Martha feels that God has abandoned her and rushes to Father Ferrier's church. They begin an emotional argument that ends with their making love in the church. Father Ferrier leaves his order to live with Martha, who takes a job singing in a nightclub, and Ferrier begins broadcasting a social crusade on radio and writing for a local newspaper. Disheartened by his crusade's lack of success, he explains to Martha that an "act of the heart" is needed to attract public attention. After Ferrier has left for a television program, Martha goes out to a field, pours gasoline on her head, and sets fire to herself. *Widows. Tutors. Singers. Monks. Children. Religion. Faith. Death. Celibacy. Social consciousness. Self-immolation. Choirs. Nightclubs. Montreal. Catholic Church.*

Note: Location scenes filmed in Montreal and Rivière du Loup, Quebec. Opened in Montreal in Sep 1970 as *Acte du coeur.*

ACT ONE   F6.0017

Dore Schary Productions. *Dist* Warner Bros. Pictures. 26 Dec **1963** [New York opening; c25 Apr 1964; LP29468]. Sd; b&w. 35mm. 110 min.

A Dore Schary Production. *Prod-Dir-Writ* Dore Schary. *Assoc Prod* Walter Reilly. *Photog* Arthur J. Ornitz. *Set Decor & Prod Dsgn* Edward Carrere. *Film Ed* Mort Fallick. *Mus Comp & Cond* Skitch Henderson. *Sd* Maurice Rosenblum. *1st & 2d Asst Dir* Michael Hertzberg, Roger Rothstein. *Prod Supv* Joel Freeman. *Cost* Gene Coffin. *Makeup* Dean Newman.

Cast: George Hamilton *(Moss Hart),* Jason Robards, Jr. *(George S. Kaufman),* Jack Klugman *(Joe Hyman),* Sam Levene *(Richard Maxwell),* Ruth Ford *(Beatrice Kaufman),* Eli Wallach *(Warren Stone),* Joseph Leon *(Max Siegel),* George Segal *(Lester Sweyd),* Martin Wolfson *(Mr. Hart),* Sam Groom *(David Starr),* Sammy Smith *(Sam H. Harris),* Louise Larabee *(Clara Baum),* David Doyle *(Oliver Fisher),* Jonathan Lippe *(Teddy Manson),* Bert Convy *(Archie Leach),* Sylvie Straus *(Mrs. Hart),* Arno Selco *(Bernie Hart),* Allen Leaf *(Harry),* Lulu B. King *(maid),* Earl Montgomery *(Alexander Woollcott),* Bill Desmond *(George Jean Nathan),* Joe Demar *(Heywood Broun),* Drummond Erskine *(Franklin P. Adams),* Kenneth Moss *(Robert E. Sherwood).*

Biographical drama. Source: Moss Hart, *Act One* (New York, 1959). In 1929 young Brooklynite Moss Hart, influenced by the great playwrights, devotes his leisure time to writing for the theater. Failing in his aspirations, however, he accepts a job as social director in the Catskills and then stages plays at the YMHA in Newark. Eventually he takes the advice of agent Richard Maxwell and writes a comedy, *Once in a Lifetime,* which deals with the early days of Hollywood films, despite the fact that his knowledge of the movie industry is derived from the pages of *Variety.* After being subsidized by a friend, Joe Hyman, he sends the manuscript to producer Warren Stone, who promises a decision within a week. When months pass without any word, Hart's friends sneak a copy of the play to Sam Harris, who agrees to produce it if George Kaufman will collaborate on the script and also direct. Although Kaufman consents, the Atlantic City opening is a failure, and he considers quitting until Hart comes up with an idea that both men feel will turn the play into a hit. It finally opens to rave reviews in New York City in September 1930, thus beginning the longlasting Kaufman-Hart collaboration. *Playwrights. Theatrical producers. Theatrical directors. Journalists. Critics. Columnists. Actors. Theater. New York City—Broadway. New York City—Brooklyn. Catskill Mountains. Newark (New Jersey). Atlantic City. Moss Hart. George S. Kaufman. Sam Henry Harris. Archie Leach. Alexander Woollcott. George Jean Nathan. Matthew Heywood Campbell Broun. Franklin Pierce Adams. Robert Emmet Sherwood. Young Men's Hebrew Association. "Once in a Lifetime".*

Note: Filmed in Manhattan. Archie Leach is Cary Grant's real name.

ACTE DU COEUR see **ACT OF THE HEART**

ACTION MAN (France/Italy)   **F6.0018**
Copernic Films–Fida Cinematografica. *Dist* Ben Barry & Associates. **1969**. Sd; col (Eastmancolor). 35mm (Franscope). 95 min.
Prod Raymond Danon. *Dir* Jean Delannoy. *Screenplay* Alphonse Boudard, Jean Delannoy. *Photog* Walter Wottitz. *Film Ed* Henri Taverna. *Mus* Francis Lai.
Cast: Jean Gabin *(Denis Farrand)*, Robert Stack *(Jim Beckley)*, Margaret Lee *(Betty)*, Suzanne Flon *(Marie-Jeanne Farrand)*, Jean Topart *(Monsieur Henri)*, Lucienne Bogaert *(old woman)*, Walter Giller *(Maurice Labrousse)*, Georges Aminel *(Commissioner Leduc)*, Albert Michel, Carol Vell, Mino Doro.
Action melodrama. Source: J. M. Flynn, *The Action Man* (New York, 1961). Reformed ex-convict Denis Farrand, now a respected businessman in his community, teams up with American adventurer Jim Beckley, an old friend, to rob a bank. Though they succeed, a gang of dope smugglers kidnap Denis' wife, Marie-Jeanne, and demand the stolen money as ransom. Jim is killed helping Denis to rescue his wife. *Ex-convicts. Businessmen. Smugglers. Gangsters. Americans in foreign countries. Bank robberies. Kidnaping. Narcotics.*
Note: Opened in Paris in May 1967 as *Le soleil des voyous*; running time: 100 min; in Rome in Sep 1967 as *Il più grande colpo del secolo*; running time: 100 min. Also known as *Leather and Nylon*.

ACTION SET   **F6.0019**
10 Jan **1968** [Boston opening]. Sd; col? 35mm? [Feature film, length unknown.]
Sex film. No information about the precise nature of this film has been found. *Sexuality.*

THE ACTIVIST   **F6.0020**
Jana Film Enterprises. *Dist* Regional Film Distributors. 10 Dec **1969** [Los Angeles opening; c10 Dec 1969; LP42722]. Sd; col (Technicolor, print by CFI). 35mm. 87 min. *MPAA rating X.*
Prod-Writ Art Napoleon, Jo Napoleon. *Assoc Prod* Josh Freeman, Christopher Budd. *Dir* Art Napoleon. *Supv Film Ed* Gilbert D. Marchant. *Film Ed* Michael Kahn. *Mus Ed* Norton Music Service. *Adtl Mus* Ron E. Grant. *Songs Sung by* The J. Henry. *Sd* James G. Stewart.
Cast: Michael Smith, actor *(Mike)*, Leslie Gilbrun *(Lee)*, Tom Maier *(Professor Williams)*, Benbow Ritchie *(home owner)*, Patricia Ritchie *(his wife)*, Brian Murphy, Naome Gilbert, Ben Schwartz, Charles Goldman, Wendel Brunner *(steering committee)*.
Drama. Mike Corbett, a radical student opposed to the Vietnam war, seeks shelter after a demonstration at a girl friend's apartment but instead finds only her roommate, Lee, there. Lee is attracted by Mike's dedication to the cause; they fall in love and begin living together. Lee begins to help Mike in his protest work but does not become wholeheartedly involved. Mike and his radical organization stage a sit-in at the Berkeley draft induction center; the police are called in and attack the demonstrators, arresting Lee and beating Mike into unconsciousness. Lee later rejoins Mike and tries to encourage him to leave the movement and reenter the university from which he has been expelled. They visit Professor Williams, one of Mike's teachers and a former radical, who also tries to persuade Mike to live within the academic world rather than protest against the inequities of society. Mike abandons his two friends, however, and resumes his protest activities. *Students. Professors. Police. College life. Student activism. Military draft. Demonstrations. Sit-ins. Vietnam War 1964–73. Berkeley (California).*
Note: Location scenes filmed in Berkeley and the Big Sur area. Filmed in part in 16mm.

AD OGNI COSTO see **GRAND SLAM**

ADA   **F6.0021**
Avon Productions–Chalmar, Inc. *Dist* Metro-Goldwyn-Mayer, Inc. 25 Aug **1961** [New York opening; c16 Jun 1961; LP20277]. Sd (Westrex); col (Metrocolor). 35mm (CinemaScope). 108 min.
Prod Lawrence Weingarten. *Dir* Daniel Mann. *Screenplay* Arthur Sheekman, William Driskill. *Dir Photog* Joseph Ruttenberg. *Col Cons* Charles K. Hagedon. *Art Dir* George W. Davis, Edward Carfagno. *Set Decor* Henry Grace, Jack Mills. *Film Ed* Ralph E. Winters. *Asst Ed* Rita Roland. *Mus Score* Bronislau Kaper. *Orch Cond* Robert Armbruster. *Song:* "May the Lord Bless You Real Good" Warren Roberts, Wally Fowler. *Sung by* Dean Martin. *Rec Supv* Franklin Milton. *Sd* Conrad Kahn. *Asst Dir* Al Jennings, Michael Messinger. *Cost Dsgn* Helen Rose. *Makeup* William Tuttle. *Hairstyles* Mary Keats. *Sp Vis Eff* Lee LeBlanc.
Cast: Susan Hayward *(Ada)*, Dean Martin *(Bo Gillis)*, Wilfrid Hyde-White *(Sylvester Marin)*, Ralph Meeker *(Colonel Yancey)*, Martin Balsam *(Steve Jackson)*, Frank Maxwell *(Ronnie Hallerton)*, Connie Sawyer *(Alice Sweet)*, Ford Rainey *(speaker)*, Charles Watts *(Al Winslow)*, Larry Gates *(Joe Adams)*, Robert F. Simon *(Warren Natfield)*, William Zuckert *(Harry Davers)*, Mary Treen *(clubwoman)*.
Melodrama. Source: Wirt Williams, *Ada Dallas* (New York, 1959). While campaigning for the governorship of a southern state, Bo Gillis, a politician given to folksy speeches and guitar playing, falls in love with and marries Ada, a reformed prostitute. The young woman's dubious background alarms both Bo's loyal press agent, Steve Jackson, and his political adviser, Sylvester Marin. Ada proves to be an eager and resourceful campaigner; and once Bo is in office, she tries to convince him that the mild-mannered Marin is a ruthless opportunist, supporting Bo only because it suits his own interests. Even though Marin viciously blackmails the honest lieutenant governor into resigning, Bo refuses to see Marin for what he really is. Ada, anxious to succeed on her own, plays up to Marin and is appointed the new lieutenant governor. A short time later, Bo is badly injured in an automobile explosion—the direct result of his failure to accept all of Marin's suggestions. Bo accuses Ada of siding with Marin, and she decides to prove him wrong. After being sworn in as acting governor because of Bo's incapacitation, she openly defies Marin by supporting a series of reform bills introduced by Bo. Marin, assisted by his corrupt police chief, Colonel Yancey, retaliates by threatening to make public a tape recording that could destroy Ada's reputation; but Bo is released from the hospital in time to defend his wife. Following his speech in the state capitol, the reform legislation is passed, and he and Ada are reunited. *Politicians. Southerners. Prostitutes. Press agents. State governors. State lieutenant governors. Opportunists. Police. Reputation. Political campaigns. Blackmail. Women in politics. Political corruption. Law. Explosions.*
Note: Location scenes filmed in Sacramento, California.

ADALEN 31 (Sweden)   **F6.0022**
Svensk Filmindustri. *Dist* Paramount Pictures. 22 Oct **1969** [New York opening]. Sd; col (Technicolor). 35mm (Techniscope). 115 min.
Prod Kenne Fant. *Dir-Writ* Bo Widerberg. *Photog* Jörgen Persson. *Film Ed* Bo Widerberg. *Instrumental Mus:* "Black and Tan Fantasy" Duke Ellington. *Played by* Bubber Miley. *Mus Selections* Frédéric François Chopin. *Sd* Björn Öberg.
Cast: Peter Schildt *(Kjell Andersson)*, Kerstin Tidelius *(Kjell's mother)*, Roland Hedlund *(Harald Andersson)*, Stefan Feierbach *(Åke)*, Martin Widerberg *(Martin)*, Marie De Geer *(Anna)*, Anita Björk *(Anna's mother)*, Olof Bergström *(Anna's father)*, Jonas Bergström *(Nisse)*, Olle Björling *(strikebreaker)*, Pierre Lindstedt *(foreman)*, Tommy Malmström *(angry young communist)*.
Historical drama. In 1931 the workers in a Swedish paper mill in Ådalen go on a 25-week strike for higher pay. The strikers disagree on whether their tactics should remain passive or become violent. Kjell, the son of Harald Andersson, a striker with moderate views, often visits the home of the factory manager because the manager's wife is concerned about Kjell's education, and because he has fallen in love with the daughter Anna. Later, Anna confesses to her mother that she is pregnant by Kjell, and her mother forces her to go to Stockholm for an abortion. As the strike becomes more violent, Harald, who refuses to join the factory owners in bringing in strike-breakers, finds himself an outcast for his non-violent views. At the request of the owners, soldiers arrive in Ådalen to protect the factories. Harald organizes a peaceful demonstration, but the nervous soldiers open fire on the strikers, killing Harald and wounding others. Kjell, dealt a double blow by Anna's departure and by the death of his father, assumes his position as head of the family. *Factory workers. Soldiers. Employer-employee relations. Strikes. Filial relations. Abortion. Ådalen (Sweden).*
Note: Released in Sweden in May 1969 as *Ådalen 31*; running time: 114 min (cut from 125 min).

ADAM AND HIS APPLE see **ADAM LOST HIS APPLE**

ADAM AND SIX EVES   **F6.0023**
Desert Productions. *Dist* Gold Star Pictures. 3 Aug **1962** [Los Angeles showing]. Sd; col (Eastman Color). 35mm. 60 min. [Also reviewed at 56 min.]
Prod Roberto Rico. *Dir* John Wallis. *Writ* Lawrence Donner.
Cast: Randy Brent *(Adam)*, Gabrielle Benett, Mary Ann Bennett, Shelly Forbes, Leigh Sands, Lorraine Sheldon, Barbara Stanley *(The Six Eves)*.

Comedy. Adam, a city slicker obsessed by the lure of buried gold, sets out in the scorching desert accompanied by Smiley, an experienced desert donkey. After wandering in the sun for several days, they stumble upon a mirage come to life: six beautiful semi-nude women who inhabit an oasis. Gradually, Adam's attention is diverted from the buried treasure, which turns out to have been a mirage. *Prospectors. Nudity. Deserts. Treasure. Adam and Eve. Donkeys.*

ADAM AT 6 A.M.　　　　　　　　　　　　　　F6.0024
Solar Productions. *For* Cinema Center Films. *Dist* National General Pictures. 22 Sep **1970** [Kansas City, Missouri, opening; c7 Aug 1970; LP39821]. Sd; col (Technicolor). 35mm. 100 min. *MPAA rating* GP.

Prod Rick Rosenberg, Robert Christiansen. *Exec Prod* Robert E. Relyea. *Dir* Robert Scheerer. *Screenplay* Stephen Karpf, Elinor Karpf. *Photog* Charles Rosher, Jr. *Camera Op* Bob Byrne. *Camera Asst* Matthew F. Leonetti, Ken Hale. *Art Dir* Dale Hennesy. *Set Decor* Robert De Vestel. *Film Ed* Jack McSweeney. *Mus* Dave Grusin. *Sd* Glenn Anderson. *Mix* Jack Solomon. *Rec* John Muchmore. *Boom Op* Michael Mekjian. *Asst Dir* Thomas J. Schmidt, Les Sheldon. *Prod Mgr* Thomas J. Schmidt. *Script Supv* Ray Quiroz. *Cost* Ray Summers, Joanne Haas. *Makeup* Wes Dawn. *Hairdressing* Dionne Taylor. *Prop Master* Tommy Hawkins. *Still Photog* James Coe. *Key Grip* Tom May. *Gaffer* John Baron, gaffer. *Constr Coörd* Glenn Metts.

Cast: Michael Douglas (Adam Gaines), Lee Purcell (Jerri Jo Hopper), Joe Don Baker (Harvey Gavin), Louise Latham (Mrs. Hopper), Charles Aidman (Mr. Hopper), Grayson Hall (Inez Treadley), Marge Redmond (Cleo), Dana Elcar (Van), Ed Call (Orville), Carolyn Conwell (Mavis), Butch Youngblood (Elwood), Greg Joseph (Ed), Timothy Blake (girl), Richard Derr (Roger Gaines), Pat Randall (Pearlie), Jo Ella Defenbaugh (Marylist), Sharon Marshall (Rosalie), David Sullivan (Leroy), Delbert Monroe (Mutt Teavine), Meg Foster (Joyce), Ann Gwynn (Mrs. Gaines), Ned Wertimer (Dr. Peters), Bud Trone (Ray), Jim Lantz (Strawboss).

Melodrama. Adam Gaines, a young university professor in the Los Angeles area, is disenchanted with his life. At his parents' home in fashionable Beverly Hills, he learns that a great-aunt, whom he had always wanted to meet, has died in Cameron, Missouri; aware that no one in his family seems to be affected by the news, Adam decides to drive to the funeral, hoping to meet some less superficial people. After the service, he attempts to talk with his relatives but becomes embroiled in an argument about his convictions and values. Adam then meets 18-year-old Jerri Jo Hopper and asks her out to a drive-in movie. Attracted to Jerri Jo and life in the Ozarks, Adam gets a job working on a power company road crew, where he becomes friends with Harvey Gavin. After Adam injures his hand at work, he goes to visit Jerri Jo, whose parents are away, and they make love. Soon she begins to contemplate marriage, and Mr. Hopper offers to build them a house. Disturbed at the prospect of settling down, Adam spends a night on the town with Harvey, who gets drunk, loses all of their money in a crap game, and after accusing the other players of cheating, starts a fist fight. The following weekend, Adam quits his job and proposes to Jerri Jo. At a party given by her parents, Adam finds that he cannot relate to her family and friends any better than he could to the people in California, and he leaves the party and drives away. *Professors. Laborers. Disillusionment. Family life. Adolescence. Smalltown life. Marriage. Drunkenness. Gambling. Desertion. Funerals. Los Angeles. Beverly Hills. Cameron (Missouri). Ozarks.*

Note: Location scenes filmed in Orrick, Missouri, and other areas near Kansas City.

ADAM LOST HIS APPLE　　　　　　　　　　　F6.0025
D & R Pictures. *Dist* Dore Productions. 20 Oct **1966** [San Francisco showing]. Sd; col (Eastman Color). 35mm. 65 min.

Prod Harry E. Kerwin. *Dir* Earl Wainwright. *Screenplay* Sam Shackman. *Orig Story* Theodor Beltz. *Camera* Irving Cohen. *2d Camera* Solomon Stanley. *Ed* Richman Keith Singer. *Orig Mus* Vito Jones. *Sd Rec* Ned Meeter. *Prod Mgr* Jerry Gamero. *Makeup Artist* Bud Eastmore.

Cast: Gene Burk, Sally Allen, Joan Gordon, Stan Gordon, Monroe Myers, Jean Schwartz, Bill Rogers, Peggy Tera, Rod Bering, William Sanfield, Arnold Randall, Mal Arnold, Pat Casey, Jack Veloni, Mary Tudcase.

Comedy. Ken, a talented young photographer and wealthy oilman, is commissioned by the Bahama Chamber of Commerce to film the beautiful uninhabited islands in the Bahama chain. On the eve of his departure, he throws a party aboard his luxurious yacht and enjoys the passionate company of Joan, his girl friend of the moment. He goes to the island he is to photograph first and finds two women and a man enjoying themselves in the nude. After several misunderstandings have been cleared up, he learns that the strangers are Americans who decided to remain on the island when they were shipwrecked several years before. Ken falls in love with one of the settlers and promises to return. *Photographers. Oilmen. Castaways. Nudity. Motion pictures. Yachts. Bahamas.*

Note: Filmed on location in Miami and Sarasota, Florida, and in Nassau and Little Harbour, Bahamas. Also shown as *Adam and His Apple*.

THE ADDING MACHINE (United States/Great Britain)　F6.0026
Universal Pictures–Associated London Films. *Dist* Regional Film Distributors. 23 Sep **1969** [New York opening; c23 Sep 1969; LP43549]. Sd; col (Technicolor). 35mm. 100 min. *MPAA rating* M.

Prod-Dir-Writ Jerome Epstein. *Photog* Walter Lassally. *Art Dir* Jack Shampan, John Lagen. *Set Decor* Mike Pittel. *Main Titl* Tom Taylor, Caravel Studios, Gerry Hambling. *Mus Comp* Mike Leander, Lambert Williamson. *Mus Dir* Mike Leander. *Sd Ed* Brian Marshall. *Sd Rec* Roy Norman, Charles Bowers. *Asst Dir* Ray Corbett. *Prod Mgr* L. C. Rudkin. *Cost* Gabriella Falk. *Makeup* Alan Brownie. *Hairstyles* Stephanie Kaye.

Cast: Phyllis Diller (Mrs. Zero), Milo O'Shea (Zero), Billie Whitelaw (Daisy Devore), Sydney Chaplin (Lieutenant Charles), Julian Glover (Shrdlu), Raymond Huntley (Smithers), Phil Brown (Don [Ben?]), Libby Morris (Ethel), Hugh McDermott (Harry), Paddie O'Neil (Mabel), Carol Cleveland (Judy), Bruce Boa (detective), Kenny Damon (Joe), John Brandon, Hal Galili, Tony Caunter (jailers), Bill Hutchinson, actor (Judy's lover), Helen Elliott (2d apartment girl), C. Denier Warren (jury foreman), Tom Duggan (Judee [judge?]), John Bloomfield, Helena Stevens, Alan Surtees, Christine Pryor, Cal McCord, Shirley Cooklin, Anthony Harwood (apartment tenants), Bill Nagy (lawyer), Nicholas Stuart (district attorney), Gordon Sterne, Mike Reed (exercise yardguards), Lola Lloyd (coffee girl), George Margo (gateman in arcade), George Roderick (hot dog vendor), Janet Brown (fat woman), Janie Baron (thin woman), John Cook (husband).

Allegory. Source: Elmer Rice, *The Adding Machine* (New York opening: 19 Mar 1923). Mr. Zero has worked for 25 years as a bookkeeper in a large department store. Married to a nagging wife, he dreams of a romance with Daisy, one of his co-workers, but he is too shy to confess his affection for her. Zero is on the verge of asking his boss, Mr. Smithers, for a raise, when he learns that he is to be replaced by an adding machine. In a fit of rage, he murders Smithers with a letter opener. Despite an emotional appeal to the jury at his trial, Zero is convicted and sentenced to death. Awaiting execution, he meets Shrdlu, a religious fanatic who has murdered his mother. The two men are executed and find themselves transported to heaven, which resembles a huge carnival. Zero also finds Daisy, who had loved him so much that she committed suicide shortly after his death. They have a brief romantic interlude, but he is uncomfortable in a place where no one works, so he takes a job in heaven's accounting office. Thirty years later, Zero is called before Lieutenant Charles, the head of the office, and informed that it is time for him to return to Earth to begin a new life. When Zero expresses disbelief at the continuing cycle, the lieutenant tells him that he has been through the process many times before and that with each reincarnation he becomes more of an automaton. Though Zero pleads for compassion, the lieutenant only offers him a final glimpse of Daisy. *Bookkeepers. Accountants. Marriage. Fantasy. Automation. Employer-employee relations. Murder. Matricide. Capital punishment. Death. Suicide. Reincarnation. Department stores. Trials. Heaven.*

Note: Released in Great Britain in 1970.

ADÉLAÏDE (France/Italy)　　　　　　　　　　F6.0027
Les Films Number One–Poste Parisien–Franco Riganti. *Dist* Sigma III Corp. 27 Apr **1969** [New York opening]. Sd; col (Eastman Color). 35mm. 86 min. *MPAA rating* R.

Prod Félix Garas, Pierre Kalfon. *Dir* Jean-Daniel Simon. *Screenplay* Jean-Pierre Petrolacci, Jean-Daniel Simon. *Photog* Patrice Pouget. *Art Dir* Claude Pignot. *Film Ed* Brigitte Dornes. *Mus* Pierre Vassilu. *Sd* Pierre Panier. *Asst Dir* Jean Mylonas. *Prod Mgr* Georges Chappedelaine.

Cast: Ingrid Thulin (Elisabeth Hermann), Jean Sorel (Frédéric Cournot), Sylvie Fennec (Adélaïde Hermann), Jacques Portet (Potier), Jean-Pierre Bernard (Christian), Faith Brook (governess), Joëlle Bernard (Janine), Simone Gusin, Cynthia Grenier, Robert Higgins.

Drama. Source: Joseph Arthur de Gobineau, *Adélaïde* (Paris, 1913). Following the sudden death of her husband, Elisabeth Hermann decides to marry her lover, Frédéric Cournot, a research engineer who is 10 years her junior. Unperturbed by the knowledge that her daughter Adélaïde is also in love with Frédéric, Elisabeth brings them both to her house on the Breton coast. When it becomes apparent that the two young people are having an affair, Elisabeth sends Adélaïde to boarding school and then marries Frédéric. Adélaïde's resolve is as strong as her mother's, and she succeeds in luring Frédéric away to a small hotel. Although Elisabeth pretends to accept the situation, she appeals to Frédéric to resolve the dilemma. Hoping to placate Elisabeth while maintaining his relationship with her daughter, Frédéric introduces his timid clerk Potier to Adélaïde as a potential suitor. Unexpectedly, Adélaïde goes along with the pretense and tells Frédéric that their affair will end when she marries Potier. Distraught, Frédéric provokes Potier into an argument during a hunting party, but Frédéric is wounded when a gun is accidentally triggered. Determined to share Frédéric during his convalescence, the two women dismiss their servant and seal themselves and

Frédéric off from the outside world. One evening, a group of government officials arrives at the house to reward Frédéric for an engineering accomplishment. When there is no response to their knocking, they assume that the house is deserted and drive off. A few moments later, the sound of three muffled shots is heard from within the house. *Widows. Engineers. Clerks. Filial relations. Marriage. Infidelity. Jealousy. Convalescence. Suicide. Brittany.*

Note: Filmed in Saint Malo and other locations on the Breton coast. Opened in Paris in Aug 1968; running time: 100 min. Italian title: *Fino a farti male.*

ADIOS GRINGO (France/Italy/Spain)   F6.0028
Dorica Film-Explorer Film '58–Fono Roma–Trébol Films–Les Films Corona. *Dist* Trans-Lux Distributing Corp. caNov 1967 [New York showing: Jan 1968]. Sd; col (Eastman Color). 35mm (Euroscope). 98 min.

Pres by Official Films. *Prod* Bruno Turchetto. *Exec Prod* Harry Pears, Luis Bucks. *Dir (see note)* George Finley. *Screenplay* José Luis Jerez, Michèle Villerot, Giorgio Stegani. *Photog* Francisco Sempere. *Camera Op* Rafael Pacheco. *Art Dir* Román Calatayud. *Film Ed* Jacqueline Brachet. *Mus* Benedetto Ghiglia. *Titl Song Sung By* Fred Bongusto. *Sd* Guy Ronson. *Asst Dir* Joaquín Vera. *Prod Mgr* Diego Alchimede. *Cost* Ed Michelson.

Cast: Giuliano Gemma *(Brent Landers)*, Evelyn Stewart *(Lucy Tillson)*, Roberto Camardiel *(Doctor Barfield)*, Jesús Puente *(Tex Slaughter)*, Max Dean *(Avery Ranchester)*, Peter Cross *(Clayton Ranchester)*, Grant Laramy *(Stan Clevenger)*, Jean Martin *(Murphy)*, Monique Saint Clare *(Maude Clevenger)*, Claude Servyll, Sterling Regell, Frank Pascal, Francisco Braña, Ramón Pérez, Mimo Billi, Nello Pazzafini.

Western melodrama. Source: Harry Whittington, *Adios* (publication undetermined). Tricked into buying a herd of stolen cattle, Brent Landers arrives in Western City [Johnson City, according to foreign sources] and is branded a rustler by the owner of the herd, Stan Clevenger. Brent kills Clevenger in self-defense, escapes from a lynching party, and sets out to find the cattle thief. In the desert he chances upon Lucy Tillson, who has been raped and left to die by three men she saw robbing a stagecoach. Brent takes her to the nearest town, where she is treated by kindly Dr. Barfield. One day she recognizes her three assailants, who include the man who sold Brent the cattle, as well as Avery Ranchester, the son of the wealthiest rancher in the territory. Because Brent has a price on his head, the local sheriff, Tex Slaughter, is reluctant to believe him or Lucy, but Tex later becomes convinced of Brent's innocence and becomes his ally. The senior Ranchester attempts to protect his son by whipping up the town's anger against Brent. After Avery's two cohorts have been killed in gunfights, the elder Ranchester leads a lynch mob who entrap Brent and Lucy. When Tex arrives, Avery attempts to gun down Brent, but Ranchester intervenes and is accidentally killed by his son. Finally free, Brent sets off with Lucy to seek a new life. *Cattlemen. Ranchers. Robbers. Sheriffs. Physicians. Gunfighters. Frameup. Rustling. Rape. Stagecoach robberies. Lynching. Murder. Filial relations.*

Note: Giorgio Stegani is credited as director under the pseudonym George Finley. Evelyn Stewart is a pseudonym for Ida Galli; Max Dean for Massimo Righi; Peter Cross for Pierre Cressoy; and Grant Laramy for Germano Longo. Released in Italy in 1966; running time: 100 min. Paris opening: Feb 1967; also released in Spain under the same title.

ADMIRAL YAMAMOTO (Japan)   F6.0029
Toho Co. Dec 1968 [Los Angeles showing]. Sd; col (Eastmancolor). 35mm (Tohoscope). 131 min.

Dir Seiji Maruyama. *Screenplay* Katsuya Suzaki, Seiji Maruyama. *Photog* Kazuo Yamada. *Art Dir* Takeo Kita. *Mus* Masaru Sato. *Sp Eff* Eiji Tsuburaya.

Cast: Toshiro Mifune *(Adm. Isoroku Yamamoto)*, Yuzo Kayama, Toshio Kurosawa, Makoto Sato, Koshiro Matsumoto, Masayuki Mori, Daisuke Kato, Yoko Tsukasa, Wakako Sakai, Kenjiro Ishiyama.

War drama. In 1939 Admiral Isoroku Yamamoto is appointed commander-in-chief of the Combined Imperial Japanese Fleet. Although he is opposed to the Anti-Comintern Pact which allied Japan with Germany and later Italy, once war breaks out in Europe and the Japanese attack Pearl Harbor, Yamamoto determines that the war in the Pacific should be ended quickly. Japan advances easily through the islands of the South Pacific during the early months of 1942, but an error at the Battle of Midway marks the turning point in the Pacific War. By the beginning of 1943, Admiral Yamamoto is forced to withdraw Japanese forces from Midway. In the spring of that year, as Yamamoto is flying to the front, his plane is shot down, and Japan loses the leader who hoped for a swift end to the war it is now losing. *World War II. Midway. Isoroku Yamamoto. Japan—Navy.*

Note: Released in Japan in Aug 1968 as *Yamamoto Isoroku.*

THE ADOLESCENT (Japan)   F6.0030
Dist Olympic International Films. 20 Dec 1967 [Fresno, California, showing]. Sd; b&w. 35mm. 66 min.

Dir Osamu Yamaskich. *U. S. Vers Dir* James E. McLarty.

Cast: Reiko Tsumlira, Akifujikama Kazuyataguchi.

Melodrama. Okami, an innocent 14-year-old schoolgirl, discovers her mother making love to a stranger. After Okami is raped by Katsuo, her cousin's boyfriend, she becomes obsessed with her own sexuality; her desires become insatiable; and she abandons all restraints in a passionate relationship with Katsuo. After Katsuo's death in an accident, Okami and her cousin comfort each other and continue the farming begun by Katsuo. *Innocents. Cousins. Farmers. Adolescence. Rape. Filial relations. Sexuality.*

Note: Original title and release date unknown.

LES ADOLESCENTES *see* THE ADOLESCENTS
LE ADOLESCENTI *see* THE ADOLESCENTS

THE ADOLESCENTS (Canada/France/Italy/Japan)   F6.0031
National Film Board of Canada–Films de la Pléiade–IDI Cinematografica–Ninjin Club. *For* National Film Board of Canada. *Dist* Pathé Contemporary Films. 13 Apr 1967 [New York opening]. Sd; b&w. 35mm. 80 min.

Production Credits for "Fiammetta": *Dir-Writ* Gian Vittorio Baldi. *Film Ed* Dominico Gorgolini.

Production Credits for "Geneviève": *Dir* Michel Brault. *Screenplay* Alex Pelletier. *Film Ed* Werner Nold.

Production Credits for "Marie-France and Veronica": *Dir-Writ* Jean Rouch. *Film Ed* Claudine Bouché.

Cast—"Fiammetta": Micaela Esdra *(Fiammetta)*, Esmeralda Ruspoli *(mother)*, Giancarlo Shragia *(Ottavio)*, Muni Castel *(Mino)*, Franco Marino, actor *(Franco)*, Hilde Reiner *(teacher)*.

Cast—"Geneviève": Geneviève Bujold *(Geneviève)*, Louise Marleau *(Louise)*, Bernard Arcand *(Bernard)*.

Cast—"Marie-France and Veronica": Marie-France de Chabaneix *(Marie-France)*, Véronique Duval *(Veronica)*, Nadine Ballot *(Danièle)*, Marc Kalinoski *(Marc)*, Michel Aracheguesne *(Michel)*, Maurice Pialat *(photographer)*, Gilles Quéant *(friend)*.

Drama. FIAMMETTA: Fiammetta is a 14-year-old girl who lives with her mother in a mansion on an old estate near Florence. Each day she watches tourists visiting the grounds of the estate and broods over memories of her deceased father. Sullen in her misery, Fiammetta has forced her mother, a beautiful woman, into giving up her lover. Filled with resentments she is too young to comprehend, the young girl struggles to maintain some form of contact with her mother. GENEVIEVE: Geneviève and Louise are 17-year-olds attending a winter carnival in Montreal. Louise has an early morning date to meet a young man, Bernard, in church, but she oversleeps, and Geneviève goes in her place. After spending the day with Bernard, Geneviève brings him back to her room, and upon noticing that Louise is out, impulsively kisses him. Their embrace is silently witnessed by Louise. On their way home, Geneviève tells her friend that she spent the day alone, and Louise does not challenge her. MARIE-FRANCE AND VERONICA: Two well-to-do, Parisian 16-year-olds, Marie-France and Veronica, are totally different. Veronica travels with a fast set constantly in search of thrills. Bored with her preoccupied father, she submits to a sexual assault and works as a photographer's model in between her numerous flirtatious affairs. She sees no future for herself except a marriage of convenience when she is 25 and life is over. Marie-France, on the other hand, is close to her family and avoids wild parties, preferring instead to read Baudelaire. Although an old friend presumes that family life is dying out, she has decided that family life is still possible for her generation. *Widows. Flirts. Adolescence. Motherhood. Filial relations. Wealth. Death. Friendship. Duplicity. Family life. Manors. Carnivals. Florence. Paris. Montreal.*

Note: Shown at the 1964 Venice Film Festival under the title *La fleur de l'âge, ou les adolescentes*; running time: 110 min. Commercial release in Canada, France, Italy, or Japan is unconfirmed. Italian title: *Le adolescenti.* Alternative U. S. title: *That Tender Age.* The Japanese segment, "Ako," directed by Hiroshi Teshigahara, was deleted in U. S. release version.

ADORABILE IDIOTA *see* A RAVISHING IDIOT
L'ADORABLE CORPS DE DEBORAH *see* THE SWEET BODY OF   DEBORAH

ADORABLE JULIA (Austria/France)   F6.0032
Wiener Mundus Films–Les Productions de l'Etoile. *Dist* See-Art Films, Continental Distributing, Inc. 7 Apr 1964 [New York opening]. Sd; b&w. 35mm. 94 min.

Prod-Dir Alfred Weidenmann. *Screenplay* Guy Bolton, Marc-Gilbert Sauvajon. *Dial* Pascal Jardin. *Austrian Vers* Johanna Sibelius, Eberhard Keindorff. *Photog* Werner Krien. *Art Dir* Leo Metzenbauer. *Film Ed* Renate Jelinek. *Mus* Rolf Wilhelm. *Sd* Kurt Schwarz. *Asst Dir* Karl Kirchner. Heinz Pollak, Gerald Martell. *Prod Supv* Wolfgang Müller, Rudolf Stering. *Cost* Margarete Volters. *Dresses for Lilli Palmer* Pierre Balmain. *Makeup* Hans Nowotny. *English Subtitl* Herman G. Weinberg.

Cast: Lilli Palmer (*Julia Lambert*), Charles Boyer (*Michael Gosselyn*), Thomas Fritsch (*Roger*), Jean Sorel (*Tom Fennel*), Ljuba Welitsch (*Dolly de Fries*), Jeanne Valérie (*Avis Crichton*), Charles Régnier (*Lord Charles Tamerly*), Tilly Lauenstein (*Evie*), Otto Schmöle (*Albert*), Sylvia Lydi (*Miss Philipps*), Herta Risavi (*Margary Michaels*), Peter Schmidberger, Fritz Weiss, Friedrich Neubauer, Herbert Fux, Gustav Elger, Fritz Puchstein, Hannah Ehrenstrasser.

Comedy-drama. Source: Somerset Maugham and Guy Bolton, *Theatre* (New York opening: 12 Nov 1941). Somerset Maugham, *Theatre* (Garden City, N.Y., 1937). After years of marriage, Julia Lambert, a successful actress in London, discovers that life with her producer-director husband, Michael, has become primarily a business arrangement. This depressing revelation is heightened by the fact that she is no longer young and is the mother of a son in college. Consequently, when she is openly and avidly pursued by her husband's young accountant, Tom Fennel, Julia easily succumbs to the boy's advances and becomes his mistress. After becoming indifferent to everything but her meetings with Tom, Julia is infuriated when her young lover introduces her to an ingenue, Avis, whom he suggests for a part in Michael's new play. Fully aware that Tom is infatuated with the girl, Julia insists Avis be given the role and then allows her to steal every scene during rehearsal. On opening night, however, Julia drops her mask and gives such a brilliant performance that Avis is completely overshadowed. She then chooses to avoid the opening night party in favor of going to her favorite restaurant and gorging herself on fattening foods. Michael finds her there and they both realize that their marriage—despite its problems—is fortified by their mutual love of the theater. *Actors. Theatrical directors. Accountants. Mistresses. Ingenues. Marriage. Infidelity. Theater. Middle age. Restaurants. London.*

Note: Released in Austria as *Julia, du bist zauberhaft* at 97 min; opened in Paris in Jun 1962 as *Adorable Julia*. Filmed in Austria (interiors) and Great Britain (exteriors).

ADORABLE SINNER see **MAGNIFICENT SINNER**

ADORABLES CANAILLES see **MICHELLE**

ADUA AND HER COMPANIONS see **LOVE À LA CARTE**

ADUA AND HER FRIENDS see **LOVE À LA CARTE**

ADUA E LE COMPAGNE see **LOVE À LA CARTE**

ADULTEROUS AFFAIR (Canada)   F6.0033
Independent Film Artists. *Dist* Executive Films, Manson Distributing Corp., Sunset International Pictures. Mar **1966** [New York showing]. Sd; b&w. 35mm. 84 min.
Prod Jack Ennis. *Dir-Writ* Ted Leversuch. *Story* Margot Stevens. *Dir Photog* Stanley Lipinski. *Lighting* Alan Rogers. *Camera Asst* Mathias Chromecki. *Art Dir* Peter Douett. *Ed Supv* John Bath. *Mus Dir* John Bath. *Sd* Sam Chandler. *Sd Asst* Ed Leversuch. *Asst Dir* John Ashley, asst dir. *Prod Mgr* Phil Styles. *Prod Asst* Hugh Greer. *Script Asst* Stella Finlayson. *Makeup Artist* Peggy Stevens. *Still Photog* Peter F. Adamson.
Cast: Jean Christopher (*Barbara*), Bruce Gray (*Russ Taren*), Sean Sullivan (*Frank*), Faith Gardiner (*Lola*), Brian James (*Stephen*), Linda Gillespie (*receptionist*), Gillian Taylor (*Tina*), Jean Cavall (*telephone man*), Tony Pacioni (*client*).
Melodrama. Blackmailer Russ Taren rents an apartment from Lola, an ex-stripper. Spying on an adjacent apartment, Russ photographs Barbara cheating on her executive husband, Frank. Russ informs Barbara, vacationing in Niagara Falls with her doctor boyfriend Stephen, that she must make love to him or he will show the compromising photographs to her husband. Frank, becoming suspicious of his wife, trails Barbara and Russ. Barbara tells Stephen of the blackmail plot, but Tina, apparently another of the blackmailer's victims, kills Russ. *Stripteasers. Executives. Housewives. Physicians. Blackmail. Infidelity. Niagara Falls. Photographs.*
Note: Filmed in Toronto. Released in Canada in 1968 as *Room for a Stranger*. U. S. title changed to *The Love Blackmailer*. Actor Brian James is also credited as Brian Hadley-James.

ADVANCE TO THE REAR   F6.0034
Ted Richmond Productions. *Dist* Metro-Goldwyn-Mayer, Inc. 15 Apr **1964** [San Francisco opening; c31 Dec 1963; LP26952]. Sd (Westrex); b&w. 35mm (Panavision). 97 min.
A Ted Richmond Production. *Prod* Ted Richmond. *Dir* George Marshall. *Screenplay* Samuel A. Peeples, William Bowers. *Story* Jack Schaefer. *Dir Photog* Milton Krasner. *Camera Op* Alfred Lebovitz. *Asst Camera Op* Paul Koons, Owen Marsh. *Art Dir* George W. Davis, Eddie Imazu. *Set Decor* Henry Grace, Budd S. Friend. *Film Ed* Archie Marshek. *Asst Ed* Leonard Lieberman. *Mus & Songs:* "Company of Cowards," "This Ol' Riverboat," "Today," "Whistlin' Dixie," "Anything Love Can Buy," "Ladies," "Company Q Whistle

March," "Way Down in Arkansas," "Brackenby's Music Box," "Charleston Town" Randy Sparks. *Adapt & Cond* Hugo Montenegro. *Played & Sung by* New Christy Minstrels. *Rec Supv* Franklin Milton. *Sd Mix* Paul Kamp. *Rec* Walter Goss. *Boom Op* A. Murray Jarvis. *Asst Dir* William McGarry, George Marshall, Jr., Jack Barry. *Script Supv* Cleo Anton. *Men's Wardrobe* Frank Beetson, Lee Plunkett, Luster Bayless. *Women's Wardrobe* Sylvia Posner. *Makeup Supv* William Tuttle. *Makeup* Lynn Reynolds, Terry Miles, Ed Butterworth. *Hairstyles* Sydney Guilaroff, Agnes Flanagan. *Sp Vis Eff* J. McMillan Johnson. *Gaffer* Wesley Shanks. *Head Grip* Hank Forrester. *Prop* Dick Neblett. *Dial Dir* Harold Clifton. *Wrangler-Ramrod* Dick Webb.
Cast: Glenn Ford (*Capt. Jared Heath*), Stella Stevens (*Martha Lou Williams*), Melvyn Douglas (*Col. Claude Brackenby*), Jim Backus (*General Willoughby*), Joan Blondell (*Easy Jenny*), Andrew Prine (*Pvt. Owen Selous*), Jesse Pearson (*Cpl. Silas Geary*), Alan Hale, [Jr.] (*Sgt. Beauregard Davis*), James Griffith (*Hugo Zattig*), Yvonne Craig (*Ora*), Whit Bissell (*Captain Queeg*), Michael Pate (*Thin Elk*), Preston Foster (*general*).
War comedy. Suggested by William Chamberlain, "Company of Cowards," in *Saturday Evening Post* (10 Mar 1956). During the Civil War a Union Army general officer has a comfortable encampment and a pleasant "agreement" with the enemy: every morning his company fires at them, they fire back, and no one gets hurt. When finally he is ordered to attack, his horse bolts and charges to the rear with the infantry following. As punishment for his apparent cowardice he is put in charge of a company of misfits and sent west to Indian Territory. Through an error, the fact that his unit is replacing one that is protecting Union gold has been overlooked. The men journey westward by riverboat and are joined by a group of camp followers led by Easy Jenny and including Martha Lou Williams, a Confederate spy. A romance develops between Martha Lou and Capt. Jared Heath, though he perceives her devious purpose. Her efforts to obtain information while retaining her virtue result in the misfits' losing their horses, their pants, and the Union gold to a group of renegades and then undertaking a counishcharge in their long underwear. They lose their weapons but use their eccentric talents to defend themselves, and they save the gold by building and using a catapult. *Spies. Prostitutes. Cowardice. Gold. Catapults. United States—History—Civil War. Indian Territory. United States Army—Infantry.*
Note: Copyrighted under the working title *Company of Cowards?* The novel *Company of Cowards* was published in 1957 under the authorship of Jack Schaefer.

THE ADVENTURE see **L'AVVENTURA**

THE ADVENTURERS   F6.0035
Adventurers Film–Avco Embassy Pictures–Paramount Pictures. *Dist* Paramount Pictures. 25 Mar **1970** [New York opening; c18 Feb 1970; LP38129]. Sd; col (Technicolor). 35mm (Panavision). 171 min. [Cut from 191 min.] *MPAA rating* M.
Pres by Joseph E. Levine. *Prod-Dir* Lewis Gilbert. *2d Unit Dir* Ernest Day. *Dir of Action Seq* Bob Simmons. *Screenplay* Michael Hastings, Lewis Gilbert. *Dir Photog* Claude Renoir. *2d Unit Photog* Skeets Kelly. *Camera* John Harris. *Art Dir* John Hoesli, Aurelio Crugnola, Jack Maxsted, Harry Pottle. *Set Decor* Vernon Dixon, Franco Fumagalli, Colin Grimes. *Prod Dsgn* Tony Masters. *Film Ed* Anne V. Coates. *Mus* Antonio Carlos Jobim. *Mus Dir & Adtl Mus* Eumir Deodato. *Sd* Vernon Harris, sd. *Sd Rec* Peter Davies, Bob Jones. *1st & 2d Asst Dir* Bill Cartlidge, Terence Churcher. *Prod Supv* Geoffrey Helman. *Asst to the Prod* Timothy Corrie. *Unit Mgr* Juan Estelrich. *Cont* Connie Willis. *Cost* Ronald Paterson. *Makeup Artist* Stuart Freeborn. *Sp Eff* Cliff Richardson. *Prop Supv* Ray Traynor. *Constr Mgr* Dick Frift.
Cast: Bekim Fehmiu (*Dax Xenos*), Charles Aznavour (*Marcel Campion*), Alan Badel (*Rojo*), Candice Bergen (*Sue Ann Daley*), Thommy Berggren (*Sergei Nikovitch*), Delia Boccardo (*Caroline de Coyne*), Ernest Borgnine (*Fat Cat*), Rossano Brazzi (*Baron de Coyne*), Olivia De Havilland (*Deborah Hadley*), Anna Moffo (*Dania Leonardi*), Leigh Taylor-Young (*Amparo*), Christian Roberts (*Robert*), Yorgo Voyagis (*El Lobo*), Fernando Rey (*Jaime Xenos*), John Ireland (*Mr. Hadley*), Jorge Martinez de Hoyos (*El Condor*), Sydney Tafler (*Colonel Gutierrez*), Yolande Donlan (*Mrs. Erickson*), Angela Scoular (*Denisonde*), Milena Vukotic (*April*), Ferdy Mayne (*Sergei's father*), Jacqueline Smith (*Belinda*), Katharine Balfour (*Roberto's mother*), Roberta Donatelli (*Amparo as a child*), Peter Graves, British (*trustee banker*), John Frederick (*Mr. Erickson*), Allan Cuthbertson (*Hugh*), Zienia Merton (*Dax's sister*), Roberta Haynes (*Dax's mother*), Lois Maxwell (*woman at fashion show*), Loris Loddi (*Dax as a child*), Michael Balfour (*detective*), Vanessa Lee (*banker's wife*), Katia Christina (*Natalia*), Katiushka Lanvin (*Marita*), Christine Delit (*brunette at polo game*), Nadia Scarpitia (*Giulia*), Helena Ronee (*Lexie*), Randi Lind (*blonde at polo game*), Linda Towne (*Michelle*), Joal Carlo (*Jose*), Marcus Beck (*Philippe*), Gisela Kopel (*girl in stream with Fat Cat*), David Canon (*Hadley's secretary*), Jose Luis Ospina (*Roberto*), Manuelo Serrano (*rape sergeant*), Rey Vasquez (*Manuelo*), Kiki Goncalves (*general*), Anthony

Hickox (*Robert as a child*), Carl Eklund (*Sergei as a child*), Juan Estelrich (*radio announcer*).

Melodrama. Source: Harold Robbins, *The Adventurers* (New York, 1966). Dax Xenos, a 10-year old boy in the South American country of Corteguay, witnesses the rape and murder of his mother by government soldiers and runs to his father, Jaime, who is with a band of revolutionaries. Jaime's men capture the government soldiers, give Dax the privilege of personally executing his mother's murderers, and then take the boy to their hideout in the mountains where he meets Amparo, the daughter of revolutionary leader Rojo. After the rebels oust the dictator and establish Rojo as president, Dax accompanies his father to Rome, where Jaime is to serve as ambassador. Years later, Jaime returns to Corteguay to find that Rojo has established himself as dictator; he contacts El Condor, the new revolutionary leader, but is killed by Colonel Gutierrez, Rojo's security chief. Dax, now a young man, returns to Corteguay for his father's funeral. Rojo persuades Dax, who does not know the cause of his father's death, to convince El Condor to surrender, but when El Condor surrenders, he is killed•by Gutierrez. Because his promise to El Condor was betrayed, Dax murders Gutierrez, confronts Rojo with his treachery, and returns to Rome. He becomes a gigolo and finally marries millionairess Sue Anne Daley, but they soon divorce. Dax again returns to Corteguay, this time for the unveiling of a statue of his father, and finds himself thrust into yet another revolution. Led this time by El Lobo, the revolution succeeds when Dax murders Rojo. Meanwhile, Dax learns that Amparo has borne him a son. Delighted, he sends her back to Rome with the intention of establishing a democracy in Corteguay and returning to his new family, but he is assassinated by the vengeful son of El Condor. *Children. Revolutionaries. Dictators. Diplomats. Heiresses. Gigolos. Revolutions. Rape. Murder. Filial relations. Revenge. Perfidy. Marriage. Divorce. Illegitimacy. Funerals. South America. Rome.*

Note: Location scenes filmed in Rome and Columbia. First shown on 23 Feb 1970 on a cross-country jet flight.

ADVENTURES OF A NOBLEMAN *see* **THE SARAGOSSA MANUSCRIPT**

ADVENTURES OF A YOUNG MAN *see* **HEMINGWAY'S ADVENTURES OF A YOUNG MAN**

THE ADVENTURES OF BULLWHIP GRIFFIN   F6.0036
Walt Disney Productions. *Dist* Buena Vista Distribution Co. 8 Mar **1967** [New York opening; c9 Dec 1966; LP33839]. Sd (RCA); col (Technicolor). 35mm. 110 min.
Pres by Walt Disney. *Co-prod* Bill Anderson, prod. *Assoc Prod* Louis Debney. *Dir* James Neilson. *2d Unit Dir* Arthur J. Vitarelli. *Screenplay* Lowell S. Hawley. *Dir Photog* Edward Colman. *Art Dir* Carroll Clark, John B. Mansbridge. *Set Decor* Emile Kuri, Hal Gausman. *Cartoon Titl & Bridges* Ward Kimball. *Film Ed* Marsh Hendry. *Mus* George Bruns. *Orch* Walter Sheets. *Songs* Robert B. Sherman, Richard M. Sherman, Mel Leven, George Bruns. *Choreog* Alex Plasschaert. *Sd Supv* Robert O. Cook. *Sd Mix* Dean Thomas. *Mus Ed* Evelyn Kennedy. *Asst Dir* John C. Chulay. *Cost Dsgn* Bill Thomas. *Cost* Chuck Keehne, Neva Rames. *Makeup* Pat McNalley. *Hairstyles* La Rue Matheron. *Sp Eff* Eustace Lycett. *Matte Artist* Peter Ellenshaw.
Cast: Roddy McDowall (*Bullwhip Griffin*), Suzanne Pleshette (*Arabella Flagg*), Karl Malden (*Judge Higgins*), Harry Guardino (*Sam Trimble*), Richard Haydn (*Quentin Bartlett*), Hermione Baddeley (*Miss Irene Chesney*), Bryan Russell (*Jack Flagg*), Liam Redmond (*Captain Swain*), Cecil Kellaway (*Mr. Pemberton*), Joby Baker (*bandido leader*), Mike Mazurki (*"Mountain Ox"*), Alan Carney (*Joe Turner*), Parley Baer (*chief executioner*), Arthur Hunnicutt (*referee*), Dub Taylor (*timekeeper*), Pedro Gonzalez-Gonzalez (*bandido*), Dave Willock.
Adventure comedy. Source: Albert Sidney Fleischman, *By the Great Horn Spoon!* (Boston, 1963). Arabella Flagg and her 14-year-old brother, Jack, are left orphaned and penniless when their grandfather dies in Boston in 1849. Determined to make his own fortune, Jack stows away aboard a ship bound for the California gold rush. He is followed by the family's very proper butler, Eric Griffin, who becomes the ship's cook. Also aboard is the nefarious Judge Higgins, a thief with a disguise for every imaginable crooked caper. As the ship approaches San Francisco, the judge steals the map of a gold mine from Quentin Bartlett, a Shakespearean actor, and sneaks ashore in the only lifeboat. Griffin, Jack, and Bartlett take pursuit and recover the map, only to find it riddled with bullet holes. Nevertheless, they strike a rich gold deposit but lose the gold in a river when the judge, disguised as a Chinese coolie, tries to steal it from them. Arabella arrives in San Francisco to look for Jack and takes a job as a dancehall singer. Griffin, now nicknamed "Bullwhip" because he accidentally knocked unconscious the town bully, "Mountain Ox," decides to enter a boxing match to earn some money. Encouraged by kisses from Arabella, Griffin wins the prize money and proposes to Arabella. The judge, disguised as a bookkeeper, tries

to steal the money, but he is caught by the spectators and forced to lock himself in jail to avoid being lynched. *Orphans. Stowaways. Butlers. Thieves. Actors. Dancehall girls. Brother-sister relationship. Gold rushes. Disguise. Prizefighting. Ships. Boston. California. San Francisco. Documentation.*

THE ADVENTURES OF BUSTY BROWN   F6.0037
Barry Mahon Productions. 17 Sep **1964** [San Francisco showing]. Sd; b&w. 35mm. 61 min.
A Barry Mahon Production.
Cast: Laurie Dane.
Crime melodrama. Busty Brown, one of the country's foremost detectives, comes to San Francisco to take the case of a Chinese client whose daughter has been kidnaped by a crime syndicate. Limey, the British racketeer who heads the syndicate, holds the girl hostage in his nightclub overlooking the Pacific. He warns her father that she will be killed unless he cooperates with the syndicate in the matter of some imports from Hong Kong. Busty's client refuses to be intimidated, and Limey switches his approach. He threatens to make the girl appear nude in the nightclub show and afterwards to submit her to other indignities. Busty poses as a chorus girl and gets into the show by going to bed with the producer. She rescues her client's daughter and pushes Limey, locked in the trunk of his car, off a cliff. *Detectives. Chinese. Racketeers. British. Chorus girls. Kidnaping. Nudity. Murder. Nightclubs. Stag shows. San Francisco.*
Note: Also known as *Busty Brown, Dusty Brown, Lusty Busty Brown,* and *The Adventures of Rusty Brown.*

THE ADVENTURES OF SCARAMOUCHE (France/Italy/Spain)
                                                         F6.0038
Fides–Capitole Films–Producciones Benito Perojo–C. C. M. *Dist* Embassy Pictures. 21 Nov **1964** [New York opening]. Sd; col (Eastman Color). 35mm (Dyaliscope). 98 min.
Dir-Writ Antonio Isasi Isasmendi. *Screenplay* Jorge Illa, Luis Comerón, Arturo Rigel, Antonio Isasi Isasmendi, Colin Mann. *Story* Guido Malatesta. *Photog* Alejandro Ulloa. *Art Dir* Enrique Alarcón. *Film Ed* Petra De Mieva. *Mus* Gregorio García Segura. *Song* Charles Aznavour. *Sung by* Jacqueline François. *Prod Mgr* Miguel Tudela.
Cast: Gérard Barray (*Robert Lafleur [Scaramouche]*), Michèle Girardon (*Diana*), Alberto de Mendoza (*Marquis de la Tour*), Gianna Maria Canale (*Suzanna*), Yvette Lebon (*Madame de Pompignan*), Gonzalo Canas, Andrés Mejuto (*Pietro, see note*), José Bruguera (*Marquis de Souchil*), Georges Rigaud (*Villancourt [Lacoste], see note*), Antonio Gradoli (*Abbé Christian*), Helga Liné, Xan Das Bolas, Gustavo Re, Rafael Durán, Alvaro de Luna, Iran Eory.
Adventure melodrama. Source: Rafael Sabatini, *Scaramouche; a Romance of the French Revolution* (Boston, 1921). Robert Lafleur, a Parisian strolling player nicknamed "Scaramouche" for one of his burlesque characterizations, receives a visit from the Marquis de Souchil, who questions him about the birthmark on his shoulder and then leaves, promising an explanation later. Shortly thereafter Souchil is murdered, and Robert is arrested through the influence of the Marquis de la Tour, who has come into conflict with Robert because the actor, a ladies' man, has been courting La Tour's mistress. Robert escapes with the help of Diana, Souchil's niece [or ward, according to some sources]. Robert discovers that he is the legitimate son of the Duc de Froissart, who died under questionable circumstances, and that La Tour is really the illegitimate son of Froissart's brother, Villancourt. La Tour had been substituted for Robert at birth, and Robert's identifying birthmark was duplicated on La Tour's shoulder. La Tour kidnaps Diana, but Robert, aided by his friend Pietro and other members of his troop, rescues her. La Tour gives a masked ball during which he plans to usurp the title of the Duc de Froissart, but Robert arrives with his actors, pantomimes the murder of his father, exposes La Tour, and finally kills him in a duel. *Actors. Mistresses. Nobility. Cousins. Usurpers. Illegitimacy. Imposture. Murder. Abduction. Mime. Masquerades. Theatrical troupes. Birthmarks. Carnivals. Paris. Duels.*
Note: Released in France in 1963 as *Scaramouche*. Spanish title: *La mascara de Scaramouche*. Italian title: *Le avventure di Scaramouche*. Sources conflict in crediting the role of Pietro and in screenplay credit: several U. S. sources credit Arturo Rigel, Antonio Isasi Isasmendi, and Colin Mann with screenplay; while most European sources credit Rigel, Isasi Isasmendi, Luis Comerón, and Jorge Illa. A French source credits Georges Rigaud's role as that of the government minister Lacoste.

THE ADVENTURES OF THE EXQUISITE CORPSE *see* **KODAK GHOST POEMS—PART 1: THE ADVENTURES OF THE EXQUISITE CORPSE**

THE ADVENTURES OF THE PRINCE AND THE PAUPER *see* **THE PRINCE AND THE PAUPER**

THE ADVERSARY　　　　　　　　　　　　　　F6.0039

Belle–Kay International Pictures. Mar **1970**. Sd; b&w. 35mm. 75 min.

Prod Lee Franklin, Larry Klein. *Dir-Writ* Larry Klein. *Photog* Stephen R. Winsten. *Film Ed* Sam Raleigh. *Sd* Geoffrey Weinstock.

Cast: Howard Lawrence *(Jimmy West)*, Vic Campos *(Johnny Carlos)*, Frank Mangiapane *(Pecky Schwartz)*, Stephanie Waxman *(Lisa Carlos)*, Brian Roberts *(Timothy Benjamin)*, Marvin Davis *(Pinky)*, Chris Assini *(Carrie)*, Natalie Richards *(Muriel)*, Ed Smith *(boxer)*.

Melodrama. Jimmy West abandons his own boxing career to manage Johnny Carlos, a promising fighter who hates boxing. Jimmy fails at his new profession, and as a result of his disappointment with a woman, he turns to homosexual love. *Fight managers. Prizefighters. Prizefighting. Male homosexuality.*

ADVISE AND CONSENT　　　　　　　　　　　　F6.0040

Alpha–Alpina S. A. *Dist* Columbia Pictures. 6 Jun **1962** [New York opening; c1 Jun 1962; LP22238]. Sd (Westrex); b&w. 35mm (Panavision). 140 min.

Pres by Otto Preminger. *Prod-Dir* Otto Preminger. *Screenplay* Wendell Mayes. *Dir Photog* Sam Leavitt. *Camera Op* Saul Midwall, Emil Oster, Jr. *Set Decor* Eli Benneche. *Prod Dsgn* Lyle Wheeler. *Titl Dsgn* Saul Bass. *Film Ed* Louis R. Loeffler. *Mus* Jerry Fielding. *Titl Song* Jerry Fielding, Ned Washington. *Sung by* Frank Sinatra. *Sd* Harold Lewis, William Hamilton. *Mus Rec* Murray Spivack. *Mus Ed* Lee Osborne. *Sd Eff Ed* Leon Birnbaum. *1st, 2d & 3d Asst Dir* L. V. McCardle, Jr., Don Kranze, Larry Powell, Charles Bohart. *Prod Mgr* Jack McEdward. *Unit Mgr* Henry Weinberger. *Asst to the Prod* Max Slater. *Script Supv* Kathleen Fagan. *Prod Sec* Florence Nerlinger. *Wardrobe* Joe King, Adele Parmenter, Michael Harte. *Cost Coörd* Hope Bryce. *Makeup* Del Armstrong, Robert Jiras. *Hairdressing* Myrl Stoltz. *Tech Adv* Allen Drury. *Still Photog* Al St. Hilaire, Josh Weiner. *Constr Mgr* Bud Pine. *Key Grip* Morris Rosen. *Prop Master* Meyer Gordon. *Elec Supv* James Almond.

Cast: Henry Fonda *(Robert Leffingwell)*, Charles Laughton *(Sen. Seabright Cooley)*, Don Murray *(Sen. Brigham Anderson)*, Walter Pidgeon *(Sen. Bob Munson)*, Peter Lawford *(Sen. Lafe Smith)*, Gene Tierney *(Dolly Harrison)*, Franchot Tone *(The President)*, Lew Ayres *(The Vice President)*, Burgess Meredith *(Herbert Gelman)*, Eddie Hodges *(Johnny Leffingwell)*, Paul Ford *(Sen. Stanley Danta)*, George Grizzard *(Sen. Fred Van Ackerman)*, Inga Swenson *(Ellen Anderson)*, Paul McGrath *(Hardiman Fletcher)*, Will Geer *(The Senate Minority Leader)*, Edward Andrews *(Sen. Orrin Knox)*, Betty White *(Sen. Bessie Adams)*, Malcolm Atterbury *(Sen. Tom August)*, J. Edward McKinley *(Sen. Powell Hanson)*, William Quinn *(Sen. Paul Hendershot)*, Tiki Santos *(Senator Kanaho)*, Raoul DeLeon *(Senator Velez)*, Tom Helmore *(British ambassador)*, Hilary Eaves *(Lady Maudulayne)*, Rene Paul *(French ambassador)*, Michele Montau *(Celestine Barre)*, Raj Mallick *(Indian ambassador)*, Russ Brown *(night watchman)*, Paul Stevens *(Louis Newborn)*, Janet Jane Carty *(Pidge Anderson)*, Chet Stratton *(Rev. Carney Birch)*, Larry Tucker *(Manuel)*, John Granger *(Ray Shaff)*, Sid Gould *(bartender)*, Bettie Johnson *(Lafe's girl)*, Cay Forester *(President's secretary)*, William H. Y. Knighton, Jr. *(president of White House Correspondents Association)*, Henry F. Ashurst *(Senator McCafferty)*, Guy M. Gillette *(Senator Harper)*, Irv Kupcinet, Robert C. Wilson, Alan Emory, Jessie Stearns Buscher, Milton Berliner, Allan W. Cromley, Bruce Zortmann, Wayne Tucker *(journalists)*, Al McGranary, Joe Baird, Harry Denny, Leon Alton, George Denormand, Ed Haskett, Virgil Johannsen, Paul Power, Maxwell Reed, Mario Cimino, Edwin K. Baker, Clive L. Halliday, Roger Clark, Robert Malcolm, Dick Ryan, Gene Matthews, Leoda Richards, Bernard Sell, Brandon Beach, Hal Taggart *(senators)*, White House Correspondents Association, White House Press Photographers Association, Meyer Davis and His Orchestra.

Drama. Source: Allen Drury, *Advise and Consent* (Garden City, New York, 1959). Washington is thrown into a turmoil when the seriously ill President of the United States asks the Senate to "advise and consent" to the appointment of Robert Leffingwell, a highly controversial figure, as his new Secretary of State. The President's chief support comes from Bob Munson, the Senate Majority Leader, while the principal opposition is raised by Seab Cooley, a southern senator who uses the testimony of a mentally unbalanced clerk, Herbert Gelman, to brand Leffingwell an ex-Communist. Although Leffingwell confesses the truth of the accusation to the President, his Communist affiliation is dismissed as a youthful indiscretion, and Leffingwell denies the accusation while testifying under oath before the Senate subcommittee. The committee chairman, Brigham Anderson, learns of the perjury and demands the withdrawal of Leffingwell's nomination. When the President refuses, Anderson decides that for the good of the country he must make the truth public. Before he can do so, however, he is threatened with blackmail by Fred Van Ackerman, an overambitious senator who warns Anderson that if he fails to approve the nomination, his own youthful indiscretion (a wartime homosexual experience in Hawaii) will be exposed. Unable to face the shame of his own past and unable to confess the truth to his wife, Anderson slashes his throat with a razor. Following the arrival of the tragic news, the Senate votes on Leffingwell's

nomination. It ends in a deadlock, with the decisive vote going to the Vice President. As he ponders his decision, word arrives that the President has died. The once ineffectual Vice President is suddenly inspired by the monumental responsibility of his new office and announces that he will appoint his own Secretary of State. *Presidents of the United States. Politicians. United States—State Department—Secretary of State. Southerners. Vice Presidents of the United States. Politics. Communism. Perjury. Ambition. Blackmail. Male homosexuality. Suicide. Washington (District of Columbia). United States Congress. United States Capitol.*

Note: Location scenes filmed in Washington, D. C.

THE AEGEAN TRAGEDY (Greece)　　　　　　　　F6.0041

Basil Maros Productions. *Dist* Apollo Films. 30 Jan **1965** [New York opening]. Sd; b&w. 35mm. 63 min.

Prod-Dir Basil Maros. *Screenplay* Angelos Prokopiou. *Film Ed* Basil Maros. *Mus* Yannis Markopoulos. *Sd* Mikes Damalas.

Cast: Vassilis Zochos *(narrator)*.

Documentary. Excerpts from newsreels are used to trace the political developments in Greece from the accession to the throne in 1913 of Constantine I and the end of the Balkan Wars, through World War I, war with Turkey in the 20's, changes of government between the two World Wars, World War II and the German occupation, the end of the war, and finally the defeat of rebelling Communist E.L.A.S. forces. The film focuses on the turmoil and factionalism that shook the country as it passed through war, revolution, monarchy, republican government, and dictatorship. Among the personalities who receive attention are Greek republican leader Eleutherios Venizelos, dictator General Joannes Metaxas, King George II, Mussolini, Hitler, and Winston Churchill. *Resistance (political). Military occupation. Greece—History. World War I. World War II. Balkan Wars. Greco-Turkish War (1921–22). Balkans. Turkey. Constantine I (Greece). Joannes Metaxas. Eleutherios Venizelos. George II (Greece). Benito Mussolini. Adolf Hitler. Winston Leonard Spencer Churchill. Greece—Army.*

Note: Includes documentary footage provided by the Greek National Film Archives. Original Greek title: *Tragodia tou Aegaeou*. May also be known as *Tragedy of the Aegean Sea*.

THE AFFAIR (Japan)　　　　　　　　　　　　　F6.0042

Gendai Eiga. *Dist* Shochiku Films of America. Feb **1969** [Los Angeles showing]. Sd; b&w. 35mm (Shochiku GrandScope). 97 min.

Dir-Writ Yoshishige Yoshida. *Photog* Mitsuji Kanau. *Art Dir* Chiyoo Umeda. *Mus* Shigeru Ikeno.

Cast: Mariko Okada *(Oriko)*, Yoshie Minami *(her mother)*, Tadahiko Sugano *(Furuhata)*, Shigako Shimegi *(his sister)*, Isao Kimura *(Mitsuharu)*, Etsushi Takahashi *(laborer)*.

Melodrama. Based on a work by: Masaaki Tachihara. Oriko rebels against her sexually promiscuous mother, whose life ended in a traffic accident, by marrying Furuhata, a business executive. After five years, Oriko is so indifferent to her husband that she expresses no concern over his extra-marital affair. She meets Mitsuharu, a sculptor and former lover of her mother, and finds that her past hatred for him has given way to more friendly feelings. After a party that evening, Oriko witnesses her sister-in-law's rape in a deserted beach house by a laborer and finds herself fascinated by the man. Returning to the house the next day, she finds that the laborer lives there. She submits to his advances and later tells Mitsuharu about the incident. He suggests she divorce her husband and come to him. When Furuhata accuses her of adultery with the sculptor, she discloses her affair with the laborer. Shocked, Furuhata agrees to a divorce. That night Oriko and Mitsuharu make love for the first time. Although Oriko visits the beach house once more, the laborer has left. Meanwhile, Mitsuharu, crushed under one of his sculptures, is paralyzed below the waist and rendered permanently impotent. Oriko decides to care for him and assume the role of loving mother. *Mistresses. Businessmen. Sculptors. Sisters-in-law. Infidelity. Rape. Impotence. Motherhood.*

Note: Released in Japan in May 1967 as *Joen*.

AN AFFAIR OF THE HEART see LOVE AFFAIR; OR THE CASE OF THE MISSING SWITCHBOARD OPERATOR

AN AFFAIR OF THE SKIN　　　　　　　　　　　F6.0043

Dist Zenith International Film Corp. 20 Nov **1963** [New York opening]. Sd; b&w. 35mm. 102 min.

Prod Ben Maddow, Helen Levitt. *Assoc Prod* Joseph Strick. *Dir-Writ* Ben Maddow. *Photog* Roger Barlow, David Shore. *Musical Selections* Wolfgang Amadeus Mozart. *Mus* Shiko Ozaki, Leroy Vinnegar, Jr. *Prod Mgr* Bernard Gersten.

Cast: Viveca Lindfors *(Victoria)*, Kevin McCarthy *(Allen McCleod)*, Lee Grant *(Katherine McCleod)*, Diana Sands *(Janice)*, Herbert Berghof *(Max)*, Nancy Malone *(Claire)*, Osceola Archer *(Mrs. Cluny)*, Will Lee *(waiter)*.

Drama. Allen McCleod is an unemployed drifter who lives on the income of his wife, Katherine. His friend Max introduces his girl friend, Victoria, a fashion model, to Allen. Aware of Allen's attraction to Victoria, Max tries to interest him in Janice, a brilliant young photographer, but Janice is interested only in her work. Allen finally persuades Victoria to have an affair with him, but he proves to be impotent. Finding no happiness with his wife at home, Allen leaves the house, gets drunk, and at 3 a. m. arrives at Janice's studio with a prostitute. A reprimand from Janice prompts him to write two letters: a love letter to Victoria and a note to Katherine about their marital difficulties. The letter to Katherine becomes an apology and plea for understanding. In his distraught condition, Allen encloses Katherine's letter in the envelope intended for Victoria and Victoria's in the one addressed to Katherine. Meanwhile, despite her love for Allen, Victoria has accepted Max's proposal of marriage and, having recognized Allen's basic weakness and irreponsibility, informs him on their last night together of his error in posting the letters. After saving Katherine from an attempted suicide provoked by her desperate love for him, Allen returns to the confinement of his marriage. *Drifters. Models. Photographers. Prostitutes. Marriage. Infidelity. Impotence. Drunkenness. New York City. Documentation.*

Note: Filmed in New York City.

THE AFFAIR OF VILLA FIORITA see THE BATTLE OF THE VILLA FIORITA

THE AFFAIRS OF APHRODITE   F6.0044

Dist Canyon Distributing Co. 29 Apr **1970** [Norfolk, Virginia, opening]. Sd; col (Eastmancolor). 35mm. 75 min.

Prod Ed DePriest. *Assoc Prod* Red Shryver. *Dir-Writ* Alain Patrick. *Dir Photog* Gary Graver. *Asst Camera* Jim O'Neil. *Set Dsgn* Ron Forman. *Film Ed* Red Shryver. *Mus* John Bath. *Sd* Hollywood Picture Recorders. *Asst Dir* Granville Murphy. *Script Girl* Gail Burton. *Cost Dsgn* Ron Forman. *Makeup* Herb Danforth. *Key Grip* John Aston. *Boom Op* Gene Clark.

Cast: Antoinette Maynard (*Aphrodite*), Christine Murray (*Sappho*), Walt Phillips (*Apollo*), Robin Courtney (*Paris*), Monica Williams (*Katenga*), Wayne Roberts (*Antiochus*), George DePati, Rosemary Chambers, Fred Hansen, Natali Weston, Ken Lerner, Maryanne Hastings.

Drama. Aphrodite and her brother Apollo spend all eternity in the pursuit of depraved sexual pleasures. Antiochus, their benefactor, presents them with a servant from a nearby slave market to assist them in degraded sex rites. Unaware that she is in reality Sappho, the exiled queen of Crete, Aphrodite and Apollo take her back to Mt. Olympus, along with Katenga, a voluptuous Negress they have purchased for themselves. The slaves are forced to submit to interminable acts of perversion. Paris arrives at the Olympian palace to free his lover Sappho, but he fails and is sadistically tortured by Aphrodite and Apollo. Now both captives, the lovers make plans with Katenga to escape. As Katenga steals away to a nearby fishing village to find a small boat for the voyage, she injures herself in a fall. A soldier discovers her helpless condition and rapes her. Paris and Sappho descend the mountain to join Katenga, and arrive just as she is murdered by the rapist. The enraged Paris slays the soldier, but he is overcome by Apollo and returned to Olympus, where Apollo forces him to witness the anal rape of his beloved. Aphrodite then places Paris under a spell, transferring his love to Helen of Troy. Paris is allowed to depart the company of the gods, while Sappho remains behind on Olympus, where her sexual talents have blossomed. *Negroes. Royalty. Soldiers. Brother-sister relationship. Incest. Slavery. Sadism. Anal sex. Rape. Murder. Torture. Sensualism. Personal identity. Crete. Mythological characters. Olympus. Paris Prince of Troy. Helen of Troy. Aphrodite. Apollo.*

L'AFFONDAMENTO DELLA VALIANT see THE VALIANT

AFRICA ABLAZE (Reissue)   F6.0045

Metro-Goldwyn-Mayer, Inc. **1962.** Sd; b&w. 35mm. 113 min.

Note: Originally released in 1957 as *Something of Value* by Loew's Inc.; c28 Feb 1957; LP7731.

AFRICA ADDIO (Italy)   F6.0046

Rizzoli Films. *Dist* Rizzoli Film Distributors, Cinemation Industries. 12 Mar **1967** [New York opening]. Sd; col (Technicolor). 35mm (Techniscope). 120 min. [Also 80 min.]

An Angelo Rizzoli Production. *Prod* Angelo Rizzoli. *Dir–Writ–Conceived by* Gualtiero Jacopetti, Franco Prosperi. *Photog* Antonio Climati. *Film Ed* Gualtiero Jacopetti, Franco Prosperi. *Mus & Theme Song:* "Who Can Say" Riz Ortolani. *Sd* Fausto Ancillai. *Gen Organization* Stanis Nievo.

Narrator: Frank Latimore.

Documentary. The film is a result of 3 years of travel throughout Africa by the directors to capture the racial, ethnic, political, and social upheavals that took place during the continent's transition from colonialism to independence. The sequences include: the uneasy takeover of the Kenyan government from

the British in 1963, the final stages of Mau Mau terrorism, the brutal civil war in the Congo, a race riot in Dar es Salaam, the 2-week revolution in Zanzibar, the genocidal slaughter of the Watusi by the Bahutu in Rwanda, and the nationalist revolt against the Portuguese in Angola. Also included in the footage are scenes of thousands of wild animals being killed in the game parks, rich Africans employing white servants, a Boer trek filmed in a scenic sunset, and the futile efforts of preservation societies to save African wildlife from slaughter. *British. Mau Mau. Watusi. Portuguese. Boers. Colonialism. Nationalism. Terrorism. Revolutions. Riots. Racism. Massacres. Wildlife—Conservation. Africa. Kenya. Zanzibar. Rwanda. Angola. Dar es Salaam. Congo. South Africa. Big game.*

Note: Filmed on location in Africa. Released in Italy in 1966; running time: 138 min. Rereleased in 1970 as *Africa, Blood and Guts*; running time: 83 min.

AFRICA, BLOOD AND GUTS see AFRICA ADDIO

AFRICA EROTICA   F6.0047

International Film Enterprises. *Dist* Manson Distributing Corp. Nov **1970.** Sd; col (Eastman Color, print by Berkey Pathé). 35mm. 95 min. *MPAA rating* R.

Prod-Dir Zygmunt Sulistrowski. *Screenplay* Jordan Arthur Deutsch. *Story* Zygmunt Sulistrowski. *Photog* Herbert Theis, Celeste Sebastiano. *Film Ed* Zygmunt Sulistrowski. *Mus* Moacir Santos, Zygmunt Sulistrowski, Enrico Simonetti. *Prod Asst* Christine Raymann. *Miss Rochelle's Wardrobe* Jeunique Fashions.

Cast: Darr Poran (*Robert*), Carrie Rochelle (*Karen*), Alice Marie.

Adventure melodrama. Robert, a writer-photographer in his early 40's, meets Karen, a naive young woman, in Los Angeles. She agrees to model for Robert, and they travel to Dar es Salaam to begin a tour of Africa. In the wilderness, the couple gradually get to know each other. Because of an incident that occured when she was 17, Karen is terrified of sex, and she is very suspicious of Robert. When the couple reach Murchison Falls, he asks Karen to pose in the nude. Robert's request triggers an emotional outburst in Karen because of her memories, but Robert is able to calm her, and the two grow closer. As they drive their amphibious car down the Nile, Robert tells Karen about a tragic love affair he had in Hong Kong which has haunted him ever since. While remembering the affair, he is interrupted by screams from Karen who sees dangerous rapids ahead. Robert manages to save their lives, but the vehicle is damaged, and they face a struggle for survival. After Robert constructs sails, they reach land and continue toward safety as their relationship develops into love. *Photographers. Models. Frigidity. Memory. Survival. Amphibious vehicles. Los Angeles. Dar es Salaam. Murchison Falls. Nile River. Hong Kong.*

Note: Location scenes filmed in Tanzania and Uganda. Also known as *Happening in Africa* and *Karen, The Lovemaker.*

AFRICA SEXY (Italy)   F6.0048

Cineproduzioni Associate. *Dist* Filmarco. 27 Dec **1963** [New York State license]. Sd; col (Eastmancolor). 35mm (SuperTotalscope). 95 min.

Dir Roberto Bianchi Montero.

Cast: Jimmy Montand, Joe Said, Raymond Loyal.

Documentary. No information about the precise nature of this film has been found. *Sexuality. Africa.*

Note: Opened in Rome in May 1963; running time: 100 min.

AFRICA—TEXAS STYLE! (United States/Great Britain)   F6.0049

Vantors Films. *Dist* Paramount Pictures. 2 Jun **1967** [Miami, Florida, opening; c2 Jun 1967; LP34702]. Sd; col (Eastman Color). 35mm. 110 min.

An Ivan Tors Production. *Prod-Dir* Andrew Marton. *Assoc Prod* John Pellatt. *Screenplay* Andy White. *Lighting Camera* Paul Beeson. *Camera Op* Harry Gillam. *Art Dir* Maurice Fowler. *Film Ed* Henry Richardson. *Mus Comp & Cond* Malcolm Arnold. *Sd Mix* Gerry Turner. *1st & 2d Asst Dir* Ted Sturgis, Ivo Nightingale. *Unit Mgr* Derek Parr. *Cont* Doreen Soan. *Prod Sec* Midge Warnes. *Wardrobe Master* Duncan MacPhee. *Makeup* Eleanor Jones. *Hairdresser* Betty Glasow. *Sp Eff* Thomas "Knobby" Clark. *Casting Dir* Irene Howard. *Still Photog* John Jay. *Prop Master* John Poyner. *Supv Electrn* Tom Heathcoat.

Cast: Hugh O'Brian (*Jim Sinclair*), John Mills (*Wing Commander Hayes*), Nigel Green (*Karl Bekker*), Tom Nardini (*John Henry*), Adrienne Corri (*Fay Carter*), Ronald Howard (*Hugo Copp*), Charles Malinda (*Sampson*), Honey Wamala (*Mr. Oyondi*), Charles Hayes (*veterinary*), Stephen Kikumu (*Peter*), Ali Twaha (*Turk*), Mohammed Abdullah (*witch doctor*), Hayley Mills (*girl at airport*).

Adventure melodrama. Howard Hayes, an English rancher in modern-day Kenya, believes that food can be provided for the starving Masai natives by the herding and domestication of wild game. To help prove his point, he imports two American cowboys, rodeo champion Jim Sinclair and his companion, John Henry, a Navajo Indian. Opposition to the plan comes from Karl Bekker, a cattle rancher who fears that disease from the wild animals may infect his prize cattle. Despite Bekker's interference, the efforts of the two cowboys prove successful; the wild animals quickly adapt to their confinement, and the prospect of breeding them in captivity becomes a reality. During his stay, Jim meets local doctor Hugo Copp, his attractive nurse Fay Carter, and Sampson, a native boy who dreams of going to school in the United States. On the eve of the cowboys' scheduled departure, Bekker opens the animals' pens and drives them into the wilderness. Jim sets out after them, but he is thrown from his horse and attacked by a charging rhinoceros. Sampson helps distract the beast until Jim can rope and tie it. Bekker makes a last attempt to frighten off the now-domesticated wild game, but he is arrested, and the animals return to their corrals. Jim decides to stay in Africa and marry Fay, and John Henry ends up driving the new school bus, with little Sampson as one of his passengers. *Ranchers. Cowboys. Masai. Navajo Indians. Cattlemen. Physicians. Nurses. Americans in foreign countries. Animals—Domestication. Food. Kenya. Big game. Rhinoceros.*

Note: Location scenes filmed in Kenya. Released in Great Britain in Jul 1967; running time: 105 min. Working title: *Cowboy in Africa.*

AFRICAN SAFARI F6.0050
R. E. Shanin Enterprises. *Dist* Crown International Pictures. 27 Nov **1968** [Denver, Colorado, opening; c6 Sep 1963; MP15161]. Sd; col (De Luxe). 35mm. 98 min. [Copyright length: 103 min.] *MPAA rating G.*
Prod-Dir-Writ Ronald E. Shanin. *Photog* Ronald E. Shanin. *Film Ed* Paul Ent, Fred Rowley, John Gates, Floyd Stratton. *Bantu Mus* Radio Bantu S.A.B.C. *Sd* Irene Film Studio (South Africa).
Narrator: Michael Rye.
Documentary. Ronald E. Shanin, an aeronautical engineer turned animal collector, filmed this documentary while traveling 25,000 miles through Africa over a 5 1/2-year period. Included in the footage are scenes of lionesses on the prowl for food and caring for their young; Shanin capturing a cobra and a black mamba with his bare hands; shots of an eagle whose wingspread reaches 7 feet; scenes of leopards, chimpanzees, a hyena, elephants, gazelles, cheetahs, and rhinoceros; and visits with the Bambuti Pygmies and with Masai tribesmen. Shanin is filmed as he hunts a lion which has been killing dogs in a bush village. The final two episodes of the film are devoted to the scaling of the fog-shrouded peaks of the "Mountains of the Moon" to map uncharted glacial floes that form the source of the Nile; and to photographing the newly-erupting Congo volcano Kitsimbanyi both from the air and at a distance of 15 yards as it spreads lava through forests and villages. *Masai. Bambuti. Safaris. Animal life. Mountain climbing. Volcanoes. Glaciers. Africa. Nile River. Congo. Lions. Snakes. Eagles.*
Note: Filmed in 16mm in Central and East Africa. Registered for copyright as *The Rivers of Fire and Ice.* Cape Town opening: Jul 1962.

AFRICANUS SEXUALIS see BLACK IS BEAUTIFUL

AFTER MEIN KAMPF F6.0051
Joseph Brenner Associates. Aug **1961**. Sd; b&w. 35mm. 74 min.
Prod Joseph Brenner. *Prod Assoc* Ted Marshall, prod. *Dir-Writ* Ralph Porter. *Film Ed* Stan Norvin. *Sd* Magno Sound. *Asst to the Dir* Carol Littenberg. *Opticals* Tri-Pix Film Services.
Narrator: Jonathan Farwell.
Documentary drama. Beginning with Hitler as a youth, the film traces Hitler's rise to power; the birth of the Nazi party; the Hindenburg era; the Reichstag fire; internal Nazi Party purges, including the murder of Ernst Röhm; the assassination of Engelbert Dollfuss; the German annexation of Austria and invasion of Czechoslovakia, Holland, France, and Belgium; Nazi atrocities, including shots of the extermination camp of Majdanek in Lublin, Poland, a reenactment of a "scientific" experiment in which prositutes were used to revive near-frozen prisoners, and a reenactment of the rape and murder of a woman by a German soldier; the Munich Pact; the Russo-German nonaggresssion pact; Nazi techniques of spying within families; the use of youth by the Nazi machine; and the war with Russia. Throughout the film, the suggestion is made that Hitler may still be alive. *Nazis. War victims. Prisoners of war. Prostitutes. Military occupation. Murder. Assassination. Rape. Genocide. War crimes. Espionage. Torture. Concentration camps. Munich Pact (1938). World War II. Germany—History—Third Reich. Austria. Czechoslovakia. Netherlands. France. Belgium. Union of Soviet Socialist Republics. Lublin (Poland). Adolf Hitler. Paul von Hindenburg. Ernst Röhm. Engelbert Dollfuss.*
Note: Rereleased in 1964 as *Ravaged*; running time: 64 min.

AFTER THE BALL WAS OVER F6.0052
Dist Distribpix, Inc. 26 Sep **1969** [Champaign, Illinois, showing]. Sd; b&w. 35mm. 64 min.
Cast: Alice Noland, Neal Taylor, Norris Nelson, John Daniels, Celia Adams, Leslie Coates, Mary Myers, Michael Ellis, actor, Floyd Cramer.

Melodrama. Evelyn inherits a small fortune and a thriving business from her father; becomes a playgirl; joins the jet set; and marries Robert Lloyd, a suave "wheeler-dealer." After a while, Robert begins to ignore Evelyn, and she becomes depressed. Robert insists that she see Dr. McCann, a psychiatrist, who recommends therapy. Evelyn is annoyed when, at a dinner party for two of Robert's friends, Robert makes sexual overtures to his friend's wife. Evelyn is horrified when friend Kenneth makes passes at her. After suggesting that she relax and enjoy herself, Robert shows some pornographic films, and Evelyn is appalled. Kenneth's caresses become intimate; Evelyn escapes to her bedroom, but Kenneth follows and rapes her. During the struggle, Evelyn believes that she sees her chauffeur sneak into the room and take photographs. The following day Evelyn reports these incidents to Dr. McCann, who insists that she is fantasizing and gives her some pills that he claims are tranquilizers. At home, she takes two of the pills and discovers that they are hallucinogenic drugs. Slipping in and out of reality, Evelyn is sexually abused by her maid and again sees the chauffeur enter and snap pictures. Evelyn feels that she is going insane when, the next day, Dr. McCann gives her an injection and molests her. Finally, Evelyn overhears Robert plotting to drive her insane and realizes that he has been attempting to gain control of her fortune by tormenting her. Furious, Evelyn tricks Robert into drinking some of the "tranquilizers," and, as he lies helpless on the bed, she smothers him with a pillow. *Playgirls. Fortune hunters. Psychiatrists. Housemaids. Chauffeurs. Inheritance. Rape. Lesbianism. Murder. Hallucinations. Insanity. Marriage. Sex exploitation films. Psychedelic drugs. Tranquilizers.*
Note: Also known as *After the Ball.*

AFTER THE FOX (United States/Great Britain/Italy) F6.0053
Delegate Productions–Nancy Enterprises–Compagnia Cinematografica Montoro. *Dist* United Artists. 23 Dec **1966** [New York opening; c15 Dec 1966; LP40473]. Sd; col (DeLuxe). 35mm (Panavision). 103 min.
Prod John Bryan. *Assoc Prod* Maurizio Lodi-Fe. *Dir* Vittorio De Sica. *2d Unit Dir* Richard Talmadge, Giorgio Stegani. *Screenplay* Neil Simon, Cesare Zavattini. *Story* Neil Simon. *Photog* Leonida Barboni. *Prod Dsgn* Mario Garbuglia. *Main Titl* Maurice Binder. *Film Ed* Russell Lloyd. *Mus* Burt Bacharach. *Titl Song Lyr* Hal David. *Orch* Charles Blackwell. *Sung By* The Hollies, Peter Sellers. *Sd* Sash Fisher. *Asst Dir* Franco Cirino. *Prod Mgr* Orazio Tassara. *Cost* Piero Tosi. *Makeup* Stuart Freeborn, Amato Garbini. *Hairstyles* Gabriella Borzelli.
Cast: Peter Sellers (*Aldo Vanucci*), Victor Mature (*Tony Powell*), Britt Ekland (*Gina Romantica*), Martin Balsam (*Harry Granoff*), Akim Tamiroff (*Okra*), Paolo Stoppa (*Pollo*), Tino Buazzelli (*Siepi*), Mac Ronay (*Carlo*), Lydia Brazzi (*Mama Vanucci*), Lando Buzzanca (*police chief*), Maria Grazia Buccella (*bikini girl*), Maurice Denham (*chief of Interpol*), Tiberio Murgia (*1st detective*), Francesco De Leone (*2d detective*), Carlo Croccolo (*cafe owner*), Nino Musco (*mayor*), Pier Luigi Pizzi (*doctor*), Lino Mattera (*singer*), Piero Gerlini (*jailer*), Daniele Vargas (*prosecuting counsel*), Franco Sportelli (*judge*), Giustino Durano (*critic*), Mimmo Poli (*fat actor*), Enzo Fiermonte (*Raymond*), Roberto De Simone (*Marcel Vignon*), Angelo Spaggiari (*Felix Kessler*), David Lodge (*policeman*), Timothy Bateson (*Michael O'Reilly*), Vittorio De Sica (*himself*).
Farce. Relaxing in jail for the ninth time in 11 years, Aldo Vanucci, alias "The Fox," remains unmoved by a discussion among fellow inmates Pollo, Carlo, and Siepi about a recent gold bullion robbery in Cairo valued at $3 million. However, when he hears rumors that his younger sister Gina has become a girl of the streets, he switches places with the prison doctor who has come to examine him and once again returns to society. Racing to Rome, he catches Gina trying to pick up a fat, middle-aged man on the street. Enraged, Aldo attacks the man, only to discover that his sister is making a cinéma vérité film. The incident provides Aldo with an inspirational idea for helping archcriminal Okra smuggle the stolen gold bullion into Italy. Posing as "new wave" director Federico Fabrizi, Aldo hijacks some motion picture equipment, hires a fading American matinee idol, Tony Powell, as his star, and sets up for location filming at a small Mediterranean fishing village where the bullion is to be brought in by ship from Cairo. He plans to incorporate the landing of the gold into the plot of his film and obtains the assistance of the local police chief. Everything runs smoothly until Tony's manager, Harry Granoff, tips off the police, and Okra pulls a last-minute double-cross which lands everybody in jail after a long chase involving the police and Interpol. To save Gina, Tony, and the innocent villagers, Aldo confesses, but not before hearing his film acclaimed as "the work of a primitive genius." Aldo is again sent back to prison with a 5-year sentence; but, since he has made a date for the following April, he undertakes to escape again. *Hoodlums. Actors. Motion picture directors. Police. Prison escapes. Brother-sister relationship. Prostitution. Smuggling. Robbery. Imposture. Perfidy. Gold. Motion pictures. Rome. INTERPOL. Chases.*

Note: Filmed in Italy. Released in Great Britain and Italy in 1966. Italian title: *Caccia alla volpe.*

AFTER YOU, COMRADE (South Africa) F6.0054

Jamie Uys Film Productions. *Dist* Continental Distributing, Inc. 10 Apr **1967** [New York opening]. Sd; col (Technicolor). 35mm. 84 min.

Prod-Dir-Writ Jamie Uys. *Photog* Manie Botha. *Art Dir* Ian MacLeod, Kay Dubinski. *Backdrops and Titl* Geoff Botha. *Film Ed* Dave Burman. *Mus Comp, Arr & Cond* Sam Sklair. *Sd* Whitney Walls, Gerald Dannaher, Peter Zinner. *Prod Mgr* Ivan Hall. *Miss Maasdorp's Wardrobe* Joey Spiller. *Makeup* Nola Du Preez, Carol Roos.

Cast: Jamie Uys (*Igor Strogoff*), Bob Courtney (*Granger J. Wellborne*), Reinet Maasdorp (*Tanya Orloff*), Angus Neill (*Johnny Edwards*), Joe Stewardson (*Ed Sloane*), Arthur Swemmer (*Anzonia [ambassador]*), Frank Gregory (*Italian mayor*), Mimmo Poli (*Italian butcher*), Marjorie Gordon (*hostel matron*), Emil Nofal (*television announcer*), Sann De Lange (*Yugoslavian mother*), Wilhelm Esterhuizen (*Austrian farmer*), Victor Ivanoff (*chief Russian delegate*), Ricky Arden (*2d Russian delegate*), Keith Stanners-Bloxam (*U. S. delegate*), George Bertolis (*Greek sergeant*), Bill Brewer (*president at conference*).

Comedy. During a world peace conference in Athens, the delegate from the United States, Granger Wellborne, and the Russian representative, Igor Strogoff, become involved in endless bickering that frustrates all hope of progress. As a solution, the ambassador from the tiny utopian country of Anzonia persuades the two men to settle their differences during a walking race from Athens to Paris, thereby affording the conference an opportunity to make headway in their absence. Although outraged by the ludicrous and undignified event, neither the U.S.S.R. nor the U. S. withdraws its man for fear of admitting defeat and losing face. Meanwhile, the contest is televised via Early Bird satellite and receives worldwide publicity. As the two diplomats walk the 1,500 miles without money or passports, they beg and steal food, sneak across borders, and even get drunk together; but there is no break in their bickering. By the time they reach Paris and collapse at the feet of General Charles de Gaulle, however, they have become friends. The race ends in a draw, while the other members of the conference who have postponed peace negotiations in order to devise rules for the contest, continue to argue. *Diplomats. Americans in foreign countries. Russians. Walking contests. Conferences—International. Cold war. Satellites. Imaginary republics. Athens. Paris. Greece. Yugoslavia. Austria. Switzerland. Liechtenstein. Italy. France. Charles De Gaulle. United States—Diplomatic and consular service. Union of Soviet Socialist Republics—Diplomatic and consular service.*

Note: Partially filmed in Greece, Yugoslavia, Austria, Switzerland, Liechtenstein, Italy, and France. Released in South Africa in 1966 as *All the Way to Paris.*

AFTERNOON see THE CHELSEA GIRLS

AGAIN A LOVE STORY see LOVE IS A FUNNY THING

AGE OF CONSENT (Australia) F6.0055

Nautilus Productions. *Dist* Columbia Pictures. Jan **1970** [c8 Mar 1970; LP37891]. Sd; col (Berkey Pathé). 35mm. 98 min. *MPAA rating* R.

A Michael Powell–James Mason Production. *Prod* Michael Powell, James Mason. *Assoc Prod* Michael Pate. *Dir* Michael Powell. *Screenplay* Peter Yeldham. *Dir Photog* Hannes Staudinger. *Camera* John McLean, Graham Lind. *Underwater Photog* Ron Taylor. *Art Dir* Dennis Gentle. *Set Dresser* Bill Piggott. *Film Ed* Anthony Buckley. *Mus Comp & Cond* (see note) Stanley Myers, Peter Sculthorpe. *Sd Rec* Paul Ennis, Lloyd Colman. *Boom Op* Alfred Wiggins. *Sd Ed* Tim Wellburn. *Asst Dir* David Crocker. *Unit Mgr* Kevin Powell. *Prod Supv* Brian Chirlian. *Cont* Rita Cavil. *Wardrobe* Anne Senior. *Makeup* Peggy Carter. *Hairdresser* Robert Hynard. *Prop Master* Marshall Lusted. *Constr Mgr* Reg Bevear. *Ch Grip* Peter Doig. *Ch Electrn* Tony Tegg. *New York Paintings* Paul Delprat. *Casting* Gloria Payten.

Cast: James Mason (*Bradley Morahan*), Helen Mirren (*Cora*), Jack MacGowran (*Nat Kelly*), Neva Carr-Glyn (*Ma Ryan*), Andonia Katsaros (*Isabel Marley*), Michael Boddy (*Hendricks*), Harold Hopkins (*Ted Farrell*), Slim DeGrey (*Cooley*), Max Meldrum (*TV interviewer*), Frank Thring (*Godfrey*), Clarissa Kaye (*Meg*), Judy McGrath (*Grace*), Lenore Caton (*Edna*), Diane Strachan (*Susie*), Roberta Grant (*Ivy*), Prince Nial (*Jasper*), Dora Hing (*receptionist*), Hudson Frausset (*New Yorker*), Peggy Cass (*New Yorker's wife*), Eric Reiman (*an art lover*), Tommy Hanlon, Jr. (*Levi-Strauss*), Geoff Cartwright (*newsboy*).

Comedy-drama. Source: Norman Lindsay, *Age of Consent* (New York, 1938). Bradley Morahan, a highly successful artist, is frustrated working in New York City and decides to return to his native Australia. He first goes to Brisbane, where he spends some time at the racetrack, and then goes to an island off the coast of Queensland that he remembers as being uninhabited. There he establishes himself in a grass hut and prepares to begin work; he is

dismayed, however, to discover that the island is inhabited by an old alcoholic, Ma Ryan, and her beautiful granddaughter, Cora. The young girl gathers shellfish and sells them on the mainland to support her grandmother's drinking habits, but since she is also saving money to become a hairdresser in Melbourne, she gladly accepts a job as Bradley's model. Cora poses in the nude, and a love affair gradually begins to develop. Meanwhile, Nat Kelly, an old friend of Bradley's, suddenly appears, and after an unsuccessful attempt to borrow some money, Kelly steals £300 from the painter and flees the island. Ma Ryan then discovers Cora's savings from modeling and threatens to inform the authorities that Cora is below the age of consent. Their argument precipitates a fight over the money, and in the struggle the old woman falls off a cliff to her death. The police determine that the death was accidental, leaving Bradley and Cora free to continue their affair. *Artists. Grandmothers. Models. Police. Alcoholism. Nudity. Theft. Adolescence. Racetracks. Islands. New York City. Brisbane. Queensland (Australia).*

Note: Filmed on the Great Barrier Reef at Dunk Isle, Queensland, Australia. Opened in Brisbane in Mar 1969; running time: 103 min. Sources conflict in crediting music composer.

AGE OF ILLUSIONS (Hungary) F6.0056

Mafilm Studios. *Dist* Brandon Films. 29 Mar **1967** [New York opening]. Sd; b&w. 35mm. 97 min.

Dir-Writ István Szabó. *Dir Photog* Tamás Vámos. *Asst Photog* József Lőrincz. *Film Ed* Sándor Zákonyi. *Mus* Péter Eötvös. *Sd* György Pintér. *Prod Mgr* György Sivó.

Cast: András Bálint (*János*), Ilona Béres (*Éva*), Judit Halász (*Habgab*), Kati Sólyom (*Annie Klinger*), Béla Asztalos (*Laci*), Tamás Erőss (*Matyi*), László Murányi (*Gergely*), Cecilia Esztergályos (*Ági, ballerina*), Miklós Gábor (*Flesch, the chief engineer*), János Rajz (*Zsoldos*), Imre Sinkovits (*Harrer*), István Bujtor.

Drama. Upon receiving their degrees from the Budapest University, four young television engineers agree to pool their intellectual resources in a combined effort to transform modern society with new social concepts. Although they are part of a communist society, they see themselves first and foremost as engineers. Filled with youthful ardor and enthusiasm, they are so determined to abolish the antiquated ways of their older, more experienced colleagues that they are not discouraged when they are sent to different departments. During a brief holiday, they visit a resort where they share a flirtation. One of the young men, János, is haunted by the image of a young law school graduate, Éva, whose views on the ethical standards of modern society had impressed the engineers when they watched her on the monitor screens of a television car. On New Year's Eve, János meets Éva, and they celebrate together, falling madly in love. Then, one of the engineers is stricken with leukemia and dies. Shocked by this senseless waste of life, János and Éva both plunge into their work in the hope of creating something useful for humanity that will give their life meaning. But their zeal gradually diminishes in the face of everyday sorrows and disappointments, and their love fades as they discover that they no longer inspire each other. For them, the age of illusions is over. *Engineers. Lawyers. Youth. Ethics. Death. Cancer. Communism. Disillusionment. Social consciousness. New Year's Eve.*

Note: Produced in Hungary in 1964 as *Álmodozások kora.*

AGE OF YOUTH (U.S.S.R.) F6.0057

Dovzhenko Film Studio. *Dist* Artkino Pictures. Mar **1961** [Los Angeles showing]. Sd; col. 35mm. 81 min. [Also reviewed at 92 min.]

Dir Aleksey Mishurin. *Screenplay* A. Shaykevich. *Story Ed* A. Pereguda. *Photog* A. Gerasimov. *Sets* G. Prokopets. *Film Ed* Ye. Gerasimov. *Mus* Platon Mayboroda. *Song Lyr* A. Malyshko. *Cond* Ye. Dushchenko. *Dances* A. Berdovskiy. *Sd* S. Sergiyenko. *Asst Dir* N. Sergeyev. *Prod Mgr* N. Sharov. *Cost* A. Chepurko. *Makeup* A. Dubchak, N. Zelenskaya. *Sp Eff* L. Shtifanov, V. Deminskiy.

Cast: Svetlana Zhivankova (*Natasha*), Viktor Rudoy (*Sergey*), V. Kulik (*Volodya*), Aleksandr Khvylya (*Dneprov-Zadunayskiy*), Ye. Mashkara (*Natasha's mother*), M. Yakovchenko (*Uncle Vasya*), A. Sova (*director of "Palace of Culture"*), G. Sklyanskiy (*Kolya*), G. Aladov, L. Anfilova, I. Bondar, G. Gnennaya, V. Draga, F. Dubrovskiy, V. Zinovyev, M. Ivanova, D. Kadnikov, A. Kalaberdin, I. Kuznovich, M. Muravyov, O. Nozhkina, L. Okrent, N. Panasyev, R. Starik, S. Sibel, A. Sumarokov, A. Kharyakov, Yu. Tsupko, S. Shkurat.

Musical comedy. Natasha, a talented dancer, is persuaded to replace Lesik, a young male soloist who has broken his leg, for a concert in the Donbas. Still dressed as a boy, she leaves the hall to catch a train to Kiev in order to audition for admittance to theater school. Discovering that she has forgotten her ticket, she is consoled by Sergey, a young singer and guitarist who is also without a ticket. They ride together on the train roof, and Sergey sings for his companion, still unaware that "Lesik" is a girl. At the audition, Sergey again meets and becomes infatuated with Natasha, who explains that she is Lesik's sister.

Sergey's first test, a reading from *Othello*, goes badly, and Natasha persuades him to perform one of his songs for the final audition. Volodya, a young conductor whose uncle is among the judges, also loves Natasha, and she asks him to approach his uncle to help her and Sergey if necessary. Sergey discovers her intervention and, dismayed at her dishonesty, decides to withdraw and return to the Donbas. Natasha, ashamed, likewise decides to apply honestly the following year. Again dressed as a boy, she once more meets Sergey before their departure from Kiev. They spend the day together, and Sergey at last discovers that "Lesik" is in fact his beloved Natasha. [Synopsis obtained from a Soviet source.] *Students. Dancers. Singers. Orchestra conductors. Youth. Male impersonation. Personal identity. Auditions. Theatrical schools. Kiev. Donbas.*

Note: Released in the U.S.S.R. in Mar 1959 as *Gody molodyye.* Also released as *The Train Goes to Kiev.*

AGENT 8 3/4 (Great Britain)   F6.0058

Rank Organisation. *Dist* Continental Distributing, Inc. 13 Oct **1965** [New York opening]. Sd; col (Eastmancolor). 35mm. 98 min.

A Betty E. Box–Ralph Thomas Production. *Prod* Betty E. Box. *Dir* Ralph Thomas. *Screenplay* Lukas Heller. *Photog* Ernest Steward. *Camera Op* James Bawden. *Art Dir* Syd Cain. *Set Decor* Arthur Taksen. *Film Ed* Alfred Roome. *Mus* Angelo Lavagnino. *Cond* Muir Mathieson. *Sd* Don Sharpe. *Sd Rec* John W. Mitchell, Bill Daniels. *Asst Dir* Simon Relph, Giorgio Gentili. *Prod Mgr* Bill Hill. *Cont* Gladys Goldsmith. *Makeup* William Partleton. *Hairdressing* Stella Rivers. *Still Photog* George Courtney Ward.

Cast: Dirk Bogarde *(Nicholas Whistler),* Sylva Koscina *(Vlasta Simenova),* Robert Morley *(Colonel Cunliffe),* Leo McKern *(Simenova),* Roger Delgado *(Josef),* John Le Mesurier *(Allsop),* Richard Vernon *(Roddinghead),* Amanda Grinling *(Cunliffe's secretary),* Noel Harrison *(Johnnie),* Derek Nimmo *(Fred),* Jill Melford *(Lorna),* Brook Williams *(Leon),* George Pravda *(Pavelka),* Richard Pasco *(Plakov),* Eric Pohlmann *(Galushka),* Gertan Klauber *(German research man),* Alan Tilvern *(Simenova's aide),* Frank Finlay *(embassy janitor),* John Standing *(washroom attendant),* Norman Bird *(labor exchange clerk),* William Mervyn *(business man),* Igor Meggido, Sandra Hampton *(Russian dancers),* Philo Hauser *(Vlacek),* John Junkin *(storeman),* John Fowlds *(burnt man),* André Charise *(waiter).*

Satire. Source: Lionel Davidson, *Night of Wenceslas* (London, 1960). Young Nicholas Whistler, an out-of-work British writer, is hired as a junior executive to glass manufacturer Colonel Cunliffe. Nicholas accepts the position because the pay is high, but what he does not know is that Cunliffe is actually head of British Intelligence and he will be used as a secret agent. Nicholas, who speaks Czech, is told to go to Prague and pick up from a contact at the State glassworks some vital information. He understands that the mission must be done under cover because open trade with Iron Curtain countries is still impossible. Nicholas' password with his Prague contact is "hot enough for June." He is met at the airport by Vlasta Simenova, his chauffeur, who is actually a counterspy working for her father, head of Czech Intelligence. Nicholas and Vlasta have fallen in love by the time he has acquired the paper from his contact, who informs Nicholas that they are both spies. After eluding the Prague police, Nicholas finds refuge in the British Embassy, and he gains passage back to London when embassy officials exchange him for a British-held spy. He is delighted when he is joined on the return trip by Vlasta, who is being sent to London on a "trade" mission. *Authors. Industrialists. Executives. Spies. Police. Chauffeurs. Czechoslovakians. Espionage. Employment. London. Prague. Great Britain—Intelligence service. Documentation.*

Note: Prague location scenes filmed in Padua. Released in Great Britain in 1964 as *Hot Enough for June.* Also reviewed as *Agent 008 3/4.*

AGENT FOR H. A. R. M.   F6.0059

Dimension IV. *Dist* Universal Pictures. 5 Jan **1966** [New York opening; c5 Mar 1966; LP35378]. Sd (TV Recorders); col (Eastman Color). 35mm. 84 min.

A Joseph F. Robertson Production. *Prod* Joseph F. Robertson. *Assoc Prod* Edward F. Abrams, Jack Bartlett. *Created & Writ by* Blair Robertson. *Cinematog* James A. Crabe. *Camera Op* Joe Hanwright. *Art Dir* Normand Boule. *Set Dsgn* CTM Studios. *Film Ed* D. E. Rollins. *Mus* Gene Kauer, Douglas Lackey. *Sd Mix* Ken Carlson, Don Harrold. *Asst Dir* Dave Marks. *Prod Mgr* Lou Place. *Asst to Prod* Ron Terry. *Script Supv* Bri Murphy. *Makeup* Mark Snegoff. *Sp Eff* Harry Woolman. *Still Photog* Peter Sorel. *Key Grip* Tom Ramsey. *Ch Electrn* George Breslaw.

Cast: Mark Richman *(Adam Chance),* Wendell Corey *(Jim Graff),* Carl Esmond *(Prof. Janos Steffanic),* Barbara Bouchet *(Ava Vestok),* Martin Kosleck *(Malko),* Rafael Campos *(Luis),* Alizia Gur *(Mideastern contact),* Donna Michelle *(Marian),* Robert Quarry *(Borg),* Robert Donner *(morgue attendant),* Steve Stevens *(Billy),* Mark Snegoff *(Conrad),* Horst Ebersberg *(Helgar),* Chris Anders *(Schloss),* Ray Dannis *(Manson),* Ronald Von *(police lieutenant),* Robert Christopher *(police officer).*

Action drama. Adam Chance, undercover agent for H. A. R. M. (Human Actiological Relations Machine), is assigned by security chief Jim Graff to investigate the mysterious murder of the assistant to Prof. Janos Steffanic, who escaped from behind the Iron Curtain and has resumed research in the United States. Steffanic is working on an antidote for a spore from outer space that converts human flesh to fungus, and Chance learns from Steffanic that Malko, his former superior, intends to infect American crops with the spore. When two of Malko's henchmen attempt to abduct Steffanic and his niece Ava, Chance kills the henchmen and rescues Ava, but the professor disappears. Chance then goes to Malko's refuge in Mexico, which he has discovered by hiding in Malko's truck; and in a battle between Chance on a motorcycle and Malko and his men in an observer plane, Chance kills all but Malko. In the final struggle, both Steffanic and Malko come into contact with the spore. Malko shrivels and dies immediately, and the professor, though he has taken the antidote, also dies before it takes effect. Chance finds the enemy agent, Ava, who had impersonated Steffanic's long-lost niece, and arrests her. *Scientists. Secret agents. Hired killers. Espionage. Murder. Biological warfare. Abduction. Impersonation. Motorcycles. Airplanes. Mexico. Iron Curtain.*

Note: Working title: *The H. A. R. M. Machine.*

AGENT 38-24-36 (THE WARM-BLOODED SPY) see A RAVISHING IDIOT

AGENT 069   F6.0060

Dist Stacey Distributors. ca **1970**. Sd; col. 16mm. 61-81 min.

Sex film. No information about the precise nature of this film has been found. *Secret agents. Sexuality.*

AGENT 008 3/4 see AGENT 8 3/4

AGENTE 077, MISION BLOODY MARY see MISSION BLOODY MARY

AGENTE LEMMY CAUTION MISSIONE ALPHAVILLE see ALPHAVILLE

AGENTE 077—MISSIONE BLOODY MARY see MISSION BLOODY MARY

AGGIE—THE DIARY OF A NYMPH   F6.0061

Dist Pyramid Productions, Emerson Film Enterprises. **1969.** Sd; col. 35mm. 90 min.

Prod-Dir Ken Kennedy.

Cast: Jamie Karson, Richard Alexander, Burke Rhind, Brandy Cartwright.

Melodrama. Aggie, the devoted protector of her orphaned brother and sister, leads a double life, being driven by uncontrollable sexual urges. Frank, a young friend, regards her as his property, though he continues his search for new conquests. Aggie's own need for illicit adventure leads her to travel into town where another lover awaits her. Violent arguments with Frank always end in passionate reconciliation, but while Aggie is away from the farm, Frank's interest shifts to her inexperienced younger sister. A circus agent asks to post handbills on Aggie's barn. He offers her enough money to buy parts for the tractor her young brother loves, and she concludes the deal by having sex with him. Soon afterwards, she discovers Frank and her sister in the stable; her attempts to dominate the couple lead to their elopement. Unable to renounce Frank, she invites them to live on the farm. She travels to town to satisfy her frustrated desires and finds her lover with another woman. She is picked up in a bar, makes love with a stranger, and then returns home. There her sister surprises her making love with Frank. Infuriated, she pursues Frank with a shotgun as he makes his exit. A motor starts up, she fires, and discovers that she has killed her beloved brother. At daybreak, the sheriff leads her away. *Orphans. Nymphomania. Brother-sister relationship. Farm life. Sexual initiation. Elopement. Murder. Jealousy. Tractors.*

Note: Also known as *Aggie* and *Diary of a Nymph.*

AGI MURAD, IL DIAVOLO BIANCO see THE WHITE WARRIOR

THE AGONY AND THE ECSTASY   F6.0062

International Classics. *Dist* Twentieth Century-Fox Film Corp. 7 Oct **1965** [New York opening; c7 Oct 1965; LP32666]. Sd (Westrex); col (DeLuxe). 35mm & 70mm (Todd-AO). 140 min. [Copyright length: 136 min.]

Prod-Dir Carol Reed. *2d Unit Dir* Robert D. Webb. *Screen Story & Screenplay* Philip Dunne. *Dir Photog* Leon Shamroy. *2d Unit Photog* Piero Portalupi. *Art Dir* Jack Martin Smith. *Set Decor* Dario Simoni. *Prod Dsgn* John De Cuir. *Film Ed* Samuel E. Beetley. *Mus Comp & Cond* Alex North. *Choral Mus Comp & Cond* Franco Potenza. *Orch* Alexander Courage. *Sd* Carlton W. Faulkner, Douglas O. Williams. *Asst Dir* Gus Agosti. *Cost Dsgn* Vittorio Nino Novarese. *Wardrobe* Casa d'Arte-Firenze, R. Peruzzi. *Makeup* Gus Agosti. *Hairstylist* Grazia De Rossi. *Sp Photog Eff* L. B. Abbott, Emil Kosa, Jr. *Prop Master* Sam Gordon.

Cast: Charlton Heston *(Michelangelo),* Rex Harrison *(Pope Julius II),* Diane Cilento *(Contessina de' Medici),* Harry Andrews *(Bramante),* Alberto Lupo

(Duke of Urbino), Adolfo Celi (Giovanni de' Medici), Venantino Venantini (Paris de Grassis), John Stacy (Sangallo), Fausto Tozzi (foreman), Maxine Audley (woman), Tomas Milian (Raphael).

Historical melodrama. Source: Irving Stone, The Agony and the Ecstasy (New York, 1961). In 1508, Pope Julius II, whose army is in constant warfare with neighboring states, has commissioned Michelangelo to create 40 statues for his tomb which is to be located in the new St. Peter's Basilica. The pope later asks Michelangelo to halt work on the tomb and decorate the ceiling of the Sistine Chapel, but the artist argues that he is not a painter. He begins at the pope's insistence, but, discouraged by the mediocrity of his drawings, he destroys them and runs away to the marble quarries in the mountains. While there, he sees visions from Genesis and decides to use them for the theme of the ceiling paintings. He returns to Rome and begs the angered pope to allow him to continue his work. Against many obstacles, including an accidental fall and temporary blindness from the dripping paint, progress continues slowly with constant encouragement from Julius. Fearful that he may not return from battle, the pope orders the artist to let him view the unfinished work, but Michelangelo refuses. While Julius is on the battlefield, however, Michelangelo goes to him at the insistence of the Contessina de' Medici and apologizes for his action. When the wounded pope returns to Rome and is believed to be dying, Michelangelo visits him and persuades him to go to the Easter mass in the chapel. At the mass, Julius is awed by the magnificence of the mural; and Michelangelo requests to continue work on the sculptures for the pope's tomb. Sculptors. Painters. Christianity. Visions. Blindness. Tombs. Rome. Julius II (pope). Michelangelo. The Medici. Sistine Chapel. Saint Peter's Basilica. "Genesis".

Note: Filmed in Rome and other places in Italy.

THE AGONY OF LOVE   F6.0063

Boxoffice International Pictures. Dist Boxoffice International Film Distributors. 7 Dec 1966 [Champaign, Illinois, showing]. Sd; b&w. 35mm. 83 min.

Prod-Dir-Writ William Rotsler. *Exec Prod* Harry H. Hershey, Edward Everett. *2d Unit Dir* Omar Tasmanian. *Dir Photog* Dwayne Rayven. *Lighting* Ed Urbank. *Art Dir* Clint Randall. *Film Ed* William Rotsler. *Mus* Dean Grennell. *Location Rec* Paul Turner. *Sd Eff* Frank Coe. *Sd* Commercial Sound Recorders. *Asst Dir* James Brand. *Cont* Joyce McDaniel. *Prod Asst* July Glidden. *Still Photog* David McDaniel, Ralph Hampton, Bill Pickard.

Cast: Pat Barrington (Barbara Thomas), Sam Taylor (Barton Thomas), Parker Garvey (Jim Osbourne), R. A. Silverberg (The Psychiatrist), Ben Johns (The First Man), Shannon Carse (The Beatnik), Joy Lowe (The Beatchick), Jay Edwards (The Eater), Sherry Shannon (The Conventioneer's Girl), Al Ward, Morton Smith (The Conventioneers), Owen Hannifen (The Second Man), Oswald Fenwick (Julius), Helena Clayton, Tori Lambert (The Girls), Betty Lavender (Betty).

Melodrama. Although she has "everything"—beauty, wealth, a good education, an attractive husband—Barbara Thomas is driven by a compulsion to degrade herself. Ignored by her husband, Barton, who is preoccupied with business, she maintains a separate apartment where she entertains a succession of faceless customers. She gives money to her beatnik lover, who manhandles her, and then takes part in a lovemaking session with a beatnik girl who joins them. After a disturbing dream, Barbara visits her psychiatrist, who tries unsuccessfully to bring her secret compulsions to light. Barbara joins another call girl in a party with two boisterous conventioneers. At Barton's office, a valued client, Jim Osbourne, threatens to take his business elsewhere if Barton does not provide call girls for him and his partner. Another bizarre dream sends Barbara back to her psychiatrist, who finally succeeds in making her understand that money is a poor substitute for love. At this crucial point, Barton calls to say that he will not be home; Osbourne has pressured him into coming along for the party. Abandoned once more, Barbara decides to seek attention as she has in the past. When Barton arrives for the orgy, he finds his wife among the call girls. She protests that her infidelity is a result of her search for the love that has been denied her, and she runs off into the night. After a chase through Hollywood with her husband in pursuit, destiny intervenes, and Barbara meets her death. Housewives. Businessmen. Psychiatrists. Beatniks. Prostitution. Masochism. Infidelity. Troilism. Sadism. Loneliness. Orgies. Hollywood. Chases. Dreams.

Note: Also known as From Lady to Tramp.

AH JONAN see **WEAKER SEX**

AH! LES BELLES BACCHANTES see **PEEK-A-BOO**

AI NO KAWAKI see **LONGING FOR LOVE**

AI TO HONOHO TO see **CHALLENGE TO LIVE**

AI TO SHI NO KIROKU see **THE HEART OF HIROSHIMA**

AIMEZ-VOUS BRAHMS? see **GOODBYE AGAIN**

AIMEZ-VOUS LES FEMMES? see **A TASTE FOR WOMEN**

AIR PATROL   F6.0064

Associated Producers, Inc. Dist Twentieth Century-Fox Film Corp. Jul 1962 [c17 Jun 1962; LP22802]. Sd; b&w. 35mm (CinemaScope). 70 min.

Prod-Dir Maury Dexter. *Screenplay* Henry Cross. *Dir Photog* John Nickolaus, Jr. *Aerial Photog* Jack Woolf. *Set Decor* Harry Reif. *Supv Film Ed* Jodie Copelan. *Mus Comp & Cond* Albert Glasser. *Sd* William Bernds, Harry M. Leonard. *Supv Sd Ed* Jack Cornall. *Asst Dir* Willard Kirkham. *Prod Supv* Harold E. Knox. *Script Supv* Betty Crosby. *Wardrobe* Ray Summers. *Makeup* Bob Mark. *Prop Master* Mike Gordon.

Cast: Willard Parker (Lieut. Vern Taylor), Merry Anders (Mona Whitney), Robert Dix (Sgt. Bob Castle), John Holland (Arthur Murcott), Russ Bender (Sgt. Lou Kurnitz), Douglass Dumbrille (Millard Nolan), George Eldredge (Howie Franklin), Ivan Bonar (Oliver Dunning), Jack Younger, Glen Marshall, Ray Dannis, Stacey Winters, LaRue Farlow.

Crime melodrama. A valuable Fragonard painting is stolen from art dealer Arthur Murcott's office by a thief who carries it to the roof of the building, where a helicopter awaits him. It seems to be a perfect getaway. The Los Angeles Police Department assigns three detectives to investigate the case, and they learn that the night watchman had noticed a helicopter flying over the building on the night of the crime. Sergeant Castle checks on all helicopter operators and becomes suspicious of Oliver Dunning, who has recently acquired a helicopter. Castle's partners question Millard Nolan, an aging actor and art collector who originally commissioned Murcott to buy the painting but was forced to cancel the purchase. Murcott receives a phone call demanding $100,000 ransom for the painting. His secretary, Mona Whitney, prepares to take the money to the Hollywood Bowl, where she is told she will find the Fragonard. Meanwhile, Nolan pushes Dunning from a rooftop and then picks up the ransom money, but he is spotted as he drives onto the freeway. Sergeant Castle takes pursuit by helicopter, and Nolan, cornered on top of a river dam, falls after being shot by the police. Art dealers. Art collectors. Secretaries. Air pilots. Police. Theft. Murder. Paintings. Helicopters. Ransom. Dams. Los Angeles. Jean Honoré Fragonard. Hollywood Bowl. Chases.

Note: Henry Cross is a pseudonym for Harry Spalding.

AIRBORNE   F6.0065

A. Diamond Productions. Dist Gillman Film Corp., Parade Releasing Organization. 30 May 1962 [Los Angeles opening]. Sd; b&w. 35mm. 78 min.

Prod Art Diamond. *Dir-Writ* James Landis. *Photog* Larry Raimond. *Asst Camera* Robert Six. *Art Dir* Fred Worley. *Film Ed* Rocco Moriano. *Mus* Allyn Ferguson, William Hinshaw. *Sd* Ken Babcock, Gil Marchant. *Asst to the Prod* William Wallmark, Raymond Marinelli. *Tech Adv* Ernest L. Basciano, (Capt.).

Cast: Bobby Diamond (Pvt. Eddie Slocum), Carolyn Byrd (Jenny May), Robert Christian (Pvt. Rocky Layman), Mike Angel (Pvt. Mouse Talliaferro), Bill Hale (Sergeant Benner), Robert Hughes (Sergeant White), James Maydock (Private Barnowski), George Marlowe (Private Erski), Keith Babcock (Private Gordblitz), Barbara Markham (Bertha), Robert May, W. Delaney, D. J. Sullivan, L. Blue, John Smothergood, Carl C. Alligood, Ralph Cotner, Ernst Hunter.

Melodrama. One of the new recruits at Fort Bragg, home of the 82nd Airborne Division, is Pvt. Eddie Slocum, a guitar-playing Indiana farm boy. During his 3 weeks training at jump school, he runs afoul of Pvt. Rocky Layman, a bullying braggart jealous of the attention Eddie gets from local beauty Jenny May. Following practice leaps from a high tower, the recruits make their first jump from an airplane. As Eddie floats toward the earth, he spots Rocky's chute drifting close to his own. Although he screams a warning, Rocky fails to hear it and his body becomes entangled in Eddie's chute lines. When his parachute collapses, Rocky crawls down the ropes until Eddie is able to grab him. The youngster holds on to his former enemy until they reach the ground. His brush with death effects a deep change in Rocky, and he apologizes for his past behavior. Bullies. Military life. Jealousy. Parachuting. Fort Bragg (North Carolina). United States Army—Airborne—82nd Division.

Note: Location scenes filmed at Fort Bragg, North Carolina.

AIRLINE STEWARDESS see **THE STEWARDESSES**

AIRPORT   F6.0066

Ross Hunter Productions–Universal Pictures. Dist Universal Pictures. 5 Mar 1970 [New York opening; c5 Mar 1970; LP38968]. Sd; col (Technicolor). 35mm & 70mm (Todd-AO). 137 min. MPAA rating G.

Prod Ross Hunter. *Assoc Prod* Jacque Mapes. *Dir-Writ* George Seaton. *Dir Adtl Seq* (see note) Henry Hathaway. *Dir Photog* Ernest Laszlo. *Art Dir* Alexander Golitzen, Preston Ames. *Set Decor* Jack D. Moore, Mickey S. Michaels. *Film Ed* Stuart Gilmore. *Mus Comp & Cond* Alfred Newman. *Sd*

Waldon O. Watson, David H. Moriarty, Ronald Pierce. *Asst Dir* Donald Roberts, Peter Price. *Prod Mgr* Ray Gosnell. *Script Supv* Betty Abbott. *Cost* Edith Head. *Makeup* Bud Westmore. *Hairstyles* Larry Germain. *Sp Photog Eff* Don W. Weed, James Gordon. *Adv* John N. Denend, Lee Danielson.

Cast: Burt Lancaster *(Mel Bakersfeld)*, Dean Martin *(Capt. Vernon Demerest)*, Jean Seberg *(Tanya Livingston)*, Jacqueline Bisset *(Gwen Meighen)*, George Kennedy *(Pat Patroni)*, Helen Hayes *(Ada Quonsett)*, Van Heflin *(D. O. Guerrero)*, Maureen Stapleton *(Inez Guerrero)*, Barry Nelson *(Lieut. Anson Harris)*, Dana Wynter *(Cindy Bakersfeld)*, Lloyd Nolan *(Harry Standish)*, Barbara Hale *(Sarah Demerest)*, Gary Collins *(Cy Jordan)*, John Findlater *(Peter Coakley)*, Jessie Royce Landis *(Mrs. Harriet DuBarry Mossman)*, Larry Gates *(Commissioner Ackerman)*, Peter Turgeon *(Marcus Rathbone)*, Whit Bissell *(Mr. Davidson)*, Virginia Grey *(Mrs. Schultz)*, Eileen Wesson *(Judy)*, Paul Picerni *(Dr. Compagno)*, Robert Patten *(Captain Benson)*, Clark Howat *(Bert Weatherby)*, Lew Brown *(Reynolds)*, Ilana Dowding *(Roberta Bakersfeld)*, Lisa Garritson *(Libby Bakersfeld)*, Jim Nolan *(Father Steven Lonigan)*, Patty Poulsen *(Joan)*, Ena Hartman *(Ruth)*, Malila Saint Duval *(Maria)*, Sharon Harvey *(Sally)*, Albert Reed *(Lieutenant Ordway)*, Jodean Russo *(Marie Patroni)*, Nancy Ann Nelson *(Bunnie)*, Dick Winslow *(Mr. Schultz)*, Lou Wagner *(Schuyler Schultz)*, Janis Hansen *(Sister Katherine Grace)*, Mary Jackson *(Sister Felice)*, Shelly Novack *(Rollings)*, Chuck Daniel *(Parks)*, Charles Brewer *(Diller)*.

Melodrama. Source: Arthur Hailey, *Airport* (Garden City, New York, 1968). Mel Bakersfeld, general manager of Lincoln International Airport, is beset with problems during one of the worst snowstorms in the history of the Midwest. A disabled jet has blocked the major runway, and the auxiliary runway is too short for takeoffs in bad weather conditions, forcing Mel to call maintenance chief Joe Patroni to solve the crisis; Mel's wife, Cindy, informs him that she wants a divorce; and Tanya Livingston, the Trans Global Airlines passenger agent with whom Mel is having an affair, is distracted by the mischievous Ada Quonsett, an elderly woman who is trying to stow away on a jet to Rome. Meanwhile, the emotionally disturbed D. O. Guerrero comes on board with a bomb in a briefcase, intending to blow up the plane so that his wife, Inez, can collect on the life insurance policy he has just purchased. The jet is piloted by Mel's brother-in-law, Vernon Demerest, who has just learned that his lover, stewardess Gwen Meighen, is pregnant. Shortly after departure, he is warned that Mel and Tanya have determined that Guerrero is carrying a bomb. With Ada's help, Vernon attempts to get the briefcase, then nearly succeeds in persuading Guerrero not to open it, but Guerrero runs into the bathroom and explodes the bomb. Guerrero is blown out of the jet, Gwen suffers a serious eye injury, and the aircraft is severely crippled, but Vernon and co-captain Anson Harris manage to land on Lincoln's runway, which Patroni has just cleared. As the passengers and crew enter the terminal, Vernon's wife, Sarah, observes her husband's obvious concern for Gwen and realizes that he has been unfaithful. *Executives. Mechanics. Stowaways. Air pilots. Brothers-in-law. Airline stewardesses. Divorce. Marriage. Infidelity. Suicide. Pregnancy. Airfields. Airplanes—Jet. Bombs. Insurance. Blizzards. Explosions.*

Note: Location scenes filmed at Minneapolis-St. Paul International Airport. Hathaway directed some scenes during Seaton's illness.

AJIA HIMITSU KEISATSU see **ASIAPOL SECRET SERVICE**

AKAGE see **RED LION**

AKAI SATSUI see **UNHOLY DESIRE**

AKOGARE see **ONCE A RAINY DAY**

AKU NO MONSHO see **BRAND OF EVIL**

AKUTO see **CONQUEST**

ALADDIN AND HIS MAGIC LAMP (U.S.S.R.)　　　　　**F6.0067**
Gorky Film Studio. *Dist* Childhood Productions. 16 Aug **1968** [Charlotte, North Carolina, opening]. Sd; col (Sovcolor). 35mm. 87 min.

Dir Boris Rytsarev. *Screenplay* Viktor Vitkovich, Grigoriy Yagdfeld. *Photog* V. Dultsev, L. Ragozin. *Art Dir* A. Anfilov, K. Zagorskiy. *Mus* Aleksey Muravlev. *Sd* S. Gurin. *Asst Dir* V. Losev. *Prod Mgr* I. Morozov.

Cast: Boris Bystrov *(Aladdin)*, Dodo Chogovadze *(princess)*, Otar Koberidze *(sultan)*, Sarry Karryyev *(genie)*, Ye. Verulashvili *(Aladdin's mother)*, A. Fayt *(Magribinets)*, G. Sadykhov *(grand vizier)*, Georgiy Millyar *(wise man)*, E. Bilanishvili *(night watchman)*, Valentin Bryleyev *(Mubarak)*, Yu. Chekulayev *(Mustafa)*, Boris Andreyev, Ya. Belenkiy, I. Verdin, E. Geller, N. Gorlov, I. Gordzhiy, V. Maslantsov, Z. Mustafin, P. Mukhin, Ye. Pandul, S. Safonov, B. Svetlov, N. Sementsova, Yu. Shmagala, M. Shcherbakov, B. Yegin.

Fantasy. The evil wizard Magribinets learns that Aladdin, the son of a poor widow in Bagdad, is destined to find the magic lamp, and he sets out to find the youth. Magribinets saves Aladdin's life when the youth commits the offense

of gazing into the eyes of Princess Boodoor [Budur], the sultan's daughter. Aladdin in gratitude descends into the underground kingdom to help Magribinets find the lamp, but upon emerging with the treasure he is attacked by the wizard. Aladdin, fearing for his life, accidentally rubs the lamp, and a genie appears to do his bidding. The genie obeys Aladdin's command to bring the princess to him, but their love is hindered by the sultan, who sends his palace guards to arrest the youth. The potentate in vain attempts to persuade the princess that her love for Aladdin has been a dream. Rescued from the sultan's dungeon by the genie, Aladdin is reunited with Boodoor, and her father at last gives his consent to their marriage. *Sorcerers. Royalty. Widows. Genii. Magic. Wish fulfillment. Bagdad. Imaginary kingdoms. Aladdin.*

Note: Released in the U.S.S.R. in 1967 as *Volshebnaya lampa Aladdina.* Based on *The Arabian Nights' Entertainments.*

ALAKAZAM THE GREAT (Japan)　　　　　　　　　　　**F6.0068**
Toei Animation Studio Co. *Dist* American International Pictures. Jul **1961** [c14 Jul 1961; LP20358]. Sd; col (Eastman Color by Pathé). 35mm (Magiscope). 84 min.

Production Credits for U. S. Vers: *Pres by* James H. Nicholson, Samuel Z. Arkoff. *Prod* Lou Rusoff. *Dir* Lee Kresel. *Screenplay* Lou Rusoff, Lee Kresel. *Film Ed* Salvatore Billitteri, Laurette Odney. *Mus* Les Baxter. *Mus Coörd* Al Simms. *Orch* Albert Harris. Songs: "Ali the Great," "Bluebird in the Cherry Tree," "Under the Waterfall," "Aliki-Aliko-Alakazam" Les Baxter. *Sd* Titra Sound Corp. *Sd Ed* Kay Rose. *Mus Ed* Eve Newman, George Brand.

Production Credits for Japanese Vers: *Prod* Hiroshi Okawa. *Dir* Teiji Yabushita, Osamu Tezuka, Daisaku Shirakawa. *Screenplay* Osamu Tezuka. *Scen* Keinosuke Uekusa. *Orig Adapt* Hideyuki Takahashi, Goro Kontaibo. *Orig Drawings* Yasuji Mori, Akira Daikubara. *Anim* Koichi Mori, Yasuo Otsuka, Masao Kumagawa, Akira Daikubara, Hideo Furusawa. *Art Work and Col* Masaaki Yano, Hajime Numai, Koichi Maeba. *Background* Eiko Sugimoto, Kimiko Saito, Kazuko Ozawa, Mataji Urata, Saburo Yokoi. *Photog* Seigo Otsuka, Harusato Otsuka, Komei Ishikawa, Kenji Sugiyama.

Voices: Frankie Avalon *(Alakazam)*, Dodie Stevens *(De De)*, Jonathan Winters *(Sir Quigley Broken Bottom)*, Arnold Stang *(Lulipopo)*, Sterling Holloway *(narrator)*.

Animated fantasy. Alakazam, a shy and modest monkey, is chosen by his peers to be the monarch of all animals on earth. The continued adulation of his constituents soon goes to his head, however, and he becomes even more selfish and arrogant after he compels Merlin, a magician, to disclose the secrets of his tricks. To teach him a lesson, King Amo, ruler of Majutsoland, the celestial island where all retired magicians reside, imprisons Alakazam in a cave; and Alakazam is then abandoned by everyone except De De, a female monkey who has always loved him. Later, Alakazam is released from confinement with the stipulation that he go about the countryside performing good deeds with Amo's son, Prince Amat. The pilgrimage succeeds in humbling Alakazam, and the reformed monkey is allowed to return with De De to the other animals. *Royalty. Magicians. Pilgrims. Pride. Caves. Imaginary kingdoms. Animals. Monkeys.*

Note: Released in Japan in 1960 in ToeiScope as *Saiyu-ki;* running time: 88 min. Reedited by American International Pictures for U. S. release. Copyright claimant: Alta Vista Productions.

ALASKAN SAFARI　　　　　　　　　　　　　　　　　**F6.0069**
Alaskan Shows. *Dist* American National Enterprises. 31 Jan **1968** [Cincinnati, Ohio, opening; c2 Jan 1968; LP40400]. Sd; col (Eastman Color). 35mm. 118 min. [Cut to 93 min.]

A Ron Hayes Production. *Prod-Dir* Ron Hayes, Bev Hayes. *Photog* Ron Hayes.

Documentary. In Alaska, after several scenes of Air Force jets and rockets at NORAD missile sites, and of the breakup of the Knik Glacier in spring, a hunting expedition is formed. In the tundra the hunters seek out ptarmigan, moose, caribou, grizzly bears, and mountain goats. In the arctic regions, they hunt seals and polar bears. There are also scenes of eskimo villages, king crabs being caught, grumbling volcanoes, and salmon spawning. *Eskimos. Hunting. Fishing. Village life. Airplanes—Jet. Missiles. Volcanoes. Glaciers. Alaska. United States Air Force. Ptarmigan. Moose. Caribou. Bears. Goats. Seals. Bears. Crabs. Salmon.*

Note: Filmed in 16mm. This film is a combination of two previously released features: *Arctic Safari* and *Safari in Alaska,* q. v.

L'ALBERO DI NATALE see **THE CHRISTMAS TREE**

ALEX IN WONDERLAND　　　　　　　　　　　　　　**F6.0070**
Coriander Productions. *Dist* Metro-Goldwyn-Mayer, Inc. 17 Dec **1970** [Los Angeles opening; c30 Dec 1970; LP38518]. Sd; col (Metrocolor). 35mm. 109 min. [Copyright length: 112 min.] *MPAA rating* R.

Prod Larry Tucker. *Assoc Prod* Anthony Ray. *Dir* Paul Mazursky. *Screenplay* Larry Tucker, Paul Mazursky. *Dir Photog* Laszlo Kovacs. *Camera*

Op Bob Byrne. *Set Decor* Audrey Blasdel. *Prod Dsgn* Pato Guzman. *Film Ed* Stuart H. Pappé. *Mus Comp & Cond* Tom O'Horgan. *Song:* "Hooray for Hollywood" Richard A. Whiting, Johnny Mercer. *Sung by* Doris Day. *Song:* "Le vrai scandale" Antoine Duhamel, Jeanne Moreau. *Song:* "La rêve est là" Georges Delerue, Jeanne Moreau. *Sung by* Jeanne Moreau. *Song:* "The Little Theatre," "Juliet's Rainbow" *comp by* Nino Rota. *Song:* "Over the Rainbow" Harold Arlen, E. Y. Harburg. *Song:* "Time on Your Side" *comp & perf by* Howlett Smith. *Song:* "Ja-Le-Man-Si," "O-Me-Ya-Wa-Do" John Broughton, Stanley Brown. *Perf by* Hassan and His Afros. *Choreog* Paula Kelly. *Sd* Jerry Jost, Hal Watkins. *Mus Ed* William Saracino. *Asst Dir* Anthony Ray. *Unit Prod Mgr* John G. Wilson. *Location Mgr* Howard Horton. *Script Supv* Marvin Weldon. *Cost* Moss Mabry. *Makeup* John Holden. *Hairstyles* Lola M. Kemp.

Cast: Donald Sutherland *(Alex)*, Ellen Burstyn *(Beth)*, Meg Mazursky *(Amy)*, Glenna Sergent *(Nancy)*, Viola Spolin *(mother)*, Andre Philippe *(Andre)*, Michael Lerner, actor *(Leo)*, Joan Delaney *(Jane)*, Neil Burstyn *(Norman)*, Leon Frederick *(Lewis)*, Carol O'Leary *(Marlene)*, Tox Drohar *(Tox)*, Sophia Krischer *(Sophia)*, Gene Krischer *(Gene)*, Paul Mazursky *(Hal Stern)*, Moss Mabry *(Mr. Wayne)*, Marvin Walkenstein *(Bernie Leavitt)*, Rosemary Edelman *(Stern's secretary)*, Ed Long *(border guard)*, Angelo Rossitto *(Fellini #1)*, John Rico *(Fellini #2)*, Howlett Smith *(piano player)*, Virginia Hawkins *(secretary)*, Richard Geary *(studio cop)*, Frances Nealy *(maid)*, Billy Holms *(public relations man)*, George Reynolds *(chauffeur)*, Federico Fellini, Jeanne Moreau *(themselves)*.

Comedy-drama. Alex, a Hollywood film director with a family and one successful but unreleased film to his credit, begins to search for ideas for his next film. He visits Hal Stern, a producer at Metro-Goldwyn-Mayer, who suggests that they do a film about a black girl who has a heart transplant and falls in love with her white surgeon. Alex rejects the idea and contemplates making a film about the invasion of Beverly Hills by black militants. He also fantasizes about meeting in Rome with director Federico Fellini; filming the machine-gunning of his family on Hollywood Boulevard; and meeting actress Jeanne Moreau, who sings a song to him. Meanwhile, his wife, Beth, grows more impatient with him during their attempts to find a new house. Alex takes LSD with his friend Andre, but when he tries to describe his experience to Beth, she begins crying, frustrated with his aimlessness. At a school play in which his daughter Amy has a role, Alex imagines various characters from Fellini films parading by. Finally he and Beth buy an expensive house, and Alex is momentarily content. *Motion picture directors. Motion picture producers. Psychiatrists. Negroes. Marriage. Fantasy. Family life. LSD. Hollywood. Los Angeles. Beverly Hills. Rome. Federico Fellini. Jeanne Moreau. Metro-Goldwyn-Mayer Studios.*

Note: "The Little Theatre" and "Juliet's Rainbow" are from the score of Fellini's *Juliet of the Spirits,* and "La rêve est là" is the theme music from François Truffaut's *Jules and Jim.*

ALEXANDER see **VERY HAPPY ALEXANDER**

ALEXANDRE LE BIENHEUREUX see **VERY HAPPY ALEXANDER**

ALFIE (Great Britain)   **F6.0071**
Sheldrake Films. *Dist* Paramount Pictures. 24 Aug **1966** [New York opening; c31 Dec 1965; LP33214]. Sd; col (Technicolor). 35mm (Techniscope). 114 min.
Prod-Dir Lewis Gilbert. *Assoc Prod* John Gilbert. *Screenplay* Bill Naughton. *Photog* Otto Heller. *Art Dir* Peter Mullins. *Film Ed* Thelma Connell. *Mus* Sonny Rollins. *Titl Song* Burt Bacharach, Hal David. *Sung by* Cher. *Sd* Peter Davies. *Asst Dir* William P. Cartlidge. *Prod Supv* Denis Johnson. *Makeup* Freddie Williamson. *Hairdresser* Betty Glasow.
Cast: Michael Caine *(Alfie)*, Shelley Winters *(Ruby)*, Millicent Martin *(Siddie)*, Julia Foster *(Gilda)*, Jane Asher *(Annie)*, Shirley Ann Field *(Carla)*, Vivien Merchant *(Lily)*, Eleanor Bron *(woman doctor)*, Denholm Elliott *(Mr. Smith)*, Alfie Bass *(Harry)*, Graham Stark *(Humphrey)*, Murray Melvin *(Nat)*, Sydney Tafler *(Lofty)*.
Drama. Source: Bill Naughton, *Alfie* (London opening: 19 Jun 1963). Alfie is a totally hedonistic Cockney whose main concern is the conquest of women. After a brief affair with Siddie, a young married woman, he involves himself with a plain and simple Cockney, Gilda, who becomes his uncomplaining mistress, expecting neither love nor marriage; but when she has a child and Alfie refuses to marry her, despite obvious affection for his son, Gilda marries a devoted and understanding bus conductor who gives the child his name. Learning that he has a touch of tuberculosis, Alfie goes to a sanitarium where he easily seduces Carla, one of his pretty nurses. After his release, Alfie spends an afternoon with Lily, the wife of another patient, a seemingly harmless dalliance that results in another pregnancy. When the distraught woman turns to Alfie for help, he arranges for an abortion in his flat. The sight of his stillborn child has a shattering effect on Alfie, and he decides to settle down with Ruby, a rich and merry widow; but when he visits her apartment and learns she has a new and younger lover, he suffers still another emotional setback. As even

his former girl friends seem to display a lack of interest in him, Alfie is forced to wonder if perhaps he may have the wrong approach to life. *Cockneys. Philanderers. Mistresses. Nurses. Widows. Infidelity. Hedonism. Seduction. Tuberculosis. Abortion. Illegitimacy. Sanitariums. London—East End.*
Note: Location scenes filmed in London. Opened in London in Mar 1966.

ALFRED THE GREAT (Great Britain)   **F6.0072**
Bernard Smith Films–Metro-Goldwyn-Mayer Pictures. *Dist* Metro-Goldwyn-Mayer, Inc. 8 Oct **1969** [Cleveland opening; c2 Jul 1969; LP37333]. Sd; col (Metrocolor). 35mm (Panavision). 122 min. *MPAA rating* M.
A Bernard Smith–James R. Webb Production. *Prod* Bernard Smith. *Prod Assoc* Michael Killanin. *Dir* Clive Donner. *2d Unit Dir* Brian Cummins. *Screenplay* Ken Taylor, James R. Webb. *Story* James R. Webb. *Dir Photog* Alex Thomson. *Camera Op* Tony Spratling. *Art Dir* Ernest Archer. *Set Decor* Patrick McLoughlin. *Prod Dsgn* Michael Stringer. *Film Ed* Fergus McDonell. *Mus Comp & Cond* Raymond Leppard. *Sd Rec* Cyril Swern. *Sd Ed* Allan Sones. *Asst Dir* Peter Price. *In Charge of Prod* Roy Parkinson. *Cont* Josephine Knowles. *Cost Dsgn* Jocelyn Rickards. *Makeup* Tom Smith. *Hairdresser* Alice Holmes. *Sp Eff* Robert MacDonald. *Battlemaster* Paul Stader. *Casting Dir* John Merrick.
Cast: David Hemmings *(Alfred)*, Michael York *(Guthrum)*, Prunella Ransome *(Aelhswith)*, Colin Blakely *(Asher)*, Ian McKellen *(Roger)*, Peter Vaughan *(Buhrud)*, Alan Dobie *(Ethelred)*, Julian Glover *(Athelstan)*, Vivien Merchant *(Freda)*, Julian Chagrin *(Ivar)*, Jim Norton *(Thanet)*, John Rees *(Cuthbert)*, Christopher Timothy *(Cedric)*, Peter Blythe *(Eafa)*, Sinead Cusack *(Edith)*, Barry Evans *(Ingild)*, Barry Jackson *(Wulfstan)*, Henry Woolf *(Wenda)*, Andrew Bradford *(Edwin)*, Keith Buckley *(Hadric)*, Michael Billington *(Offa)*, David Glaisyer *(Olaf)*, Ralph Nossek *(bishop)*, Eric Brooks *(Brother Thomas)*, Trevor Jones *(Sigurd)*, Russell Campbell.
Historical melodrama. Source: Eleanor Shipley Duckett, *Alfred the Great* (Chicago, 1956). While 9th-century England is being plundered by the fierce Danes, Alfred, who is about to become a priest, is persuaded to lead the Christian armies in the defense of their land. He uses a new concept in battle, the pincer movement, and his forces are victorious. Alfred, however, becomes aware of his own lust for blood. Now a hero, Alfred is offered the hand of Aelhswith, the daughter of Buhrud, King of Mercia, and he marries. Alfred remains chaste, nevertheless, maintaining his intention of becoming a priest. When his weak older brother, Ethelred, dies, Alfred inherits the kingdom of Wessex. He is still caught between the two forces of Church and State, but he finally gives up his priestly ambitions when he violently consummates his marriage. Again he faces Guthrum, leader of the Danes, who have entered England to pillage the countryside. Alfred finally agrees to a treaty—he will give up a huge amount of gold and his wife (of whose pregnancy he is unaware) as hostage. Alfred, after a tragic loss by his army, goes into the marshland to live with bandits, vowing that he will never again take up the sword. The need to resist the Danes, however, changes his mind; and with the help of the nobles and peasant reinforcements, he is victorious. He rescues his wife and newborn child and gains the respect of the Danes, leading Guthrum to believe in the Christian God. Having united England, he becomes known as Alfred the Great. *Royalty. Danes. Soldiers. West Saxons. Brothers. Hostages. Bandits. Christianity. Marriage. Chastity. Treaties. Great Britain—History—Anglo-Saxon period. Wessex. Mercia. Alfred the Great. Ealthswith. Ethelred I. Guthrum. The Church.*
Note: Location scenes filmed in Galway County, Ireland. Opened in London in Jul 1969.

ALICE IN ACIDLAND   **F6.0073**
Unit Ten Productions. *Dist* Bernhard Films. 17 Oct **1969** [Champaign, Illinois, showing]. Sd; col and b&w. 35mm. 67 min.
Prod-Dir John Donne. *Orig Screenplay* Gertrude Steen. *Photog* Lew Jennings. *Art Dir* Jerry Murray, art. *Film Ed* Larry Strange. *Mus* Music Industries. *Sp Color Eff* Thomas Edison Co.
Melodrama. College student Alice Trenton, recovering from the emotional shock of her mother's sudden death and her best friend's suicide, finds companionship with her French teacher, a seemingly sympathetic woman who Alice later discovers is a lesbian. The teacher recruits young women for pleasure, loosens their inhibitions with marijuana and LSD, and then gives them advanced lessons in lovemaking. Introduced to her first experience with LSD, Alice has a variety of sexual encounters and joins in an orgy. *Students. College teachers. French. Death. Lesbianism. Suicide. Inhibition. Seduction. Marijuana. LSD. Orgies.*
Note: May also be known as *Alice in Hippieland.*

ALICE IN HIPPIELAND see **ALICE IN ACIDLAND**

ALICE OF WONDERLAND IN PARIS　　　　　　F6.0074

Rembrandt Films. *Dist* Childhood Productions. 5 Feb **1966** [Milwaukee, Wisconsin, opening]. Sd; col (Eastman Color). 35mm. 52 min.

A William L. Snyder Production. *Prod* William L. Snyder. *Dir* Gene Deitch.

Voices: Carl Reiner, Norma MacMillan, Howard Morris, Allen Swift.

Animated fantasy. Loosely based on: Ludwig Bemelmans, *Madeleine*; *Madeleine and the Gypsies*; *Madeleine and the Bad Hat* (New York, 1939, 1956, 1959). Eve Titus, *Anatole* (New York, 1956). Crockett Johnson, *The Frowning Prince* (New York, 1959). James Thurber, *Many Moons* (New York, 1943). Alice travels to Paris in order to meet little Madeleine. Upon arriving, she encounters a mouse who claims to be the great-grandson of Anatole, the famous cheese-testing mouse of Paris. The mouse gives Alice some magic cheese, and she shrinks to a small size. She accompanies the mouse on a tour of Paris and listens to him relate the story of Anatole. The mouse leads Alice to Madeleine, who is attempting to reform a naughty boy. Next, Alice meets a young prince who frowns so much that he fears it will become permanent, but the frown is removed by a smiling princess. A piece of fragrant cheese causes Alice to dream that she is Princess Lenore, the princess who pines away for the moon. Later, Alice joins Madeleine again, and they visit a Gypsy carnival. Alice eats more magic cheese, returns to her normal size, and leaves Paris for home. *Children. Royalty. Gypsies. Magic. Carnivals. Cheese. Paris. "Alice in Wonderland". Mice.*

Note: Also reviewed as *Alice in Wonderland in Paris*. Alternative title: *Alice of Wonderland in New Adventures*.

ALICE'S RESTAURANT　　　　　　　　　　　F6.0075

Florin Corp. *Dist* United Artists. 20 Aug **1969** [Boston opening; c19 Aug 1969; LP37340]. Sd; col (DeLuxe). 35mm. 111 min. *MPAA rating R.*

Prod Hillard Elkins, Joseph Manduke. *Assoc Prod* Harold Leventhal. *Dir* Arthur Penn. *Screenplay* Venable Herndon, Arthur Penn. *Dir Photog* Michael Nebbia. *Camera Op* Victor Kemper. *Set Decor* John Mortensen. *Scenic Artist* Shelly Bartolini. *Prod Dsgn* Warren Clymer. *Titl Dsgn* Wayne Fitzgerald. *Film Ed* Dede Allen. *Assoc Film Ed* Gerald Greenberg. *Asst Film Ed* Richard Marks, Stephen Rotter. *Mus Supv, Comp & Arr Adtl Mtl* Garry Sherman. *Mus & Songs* Arlo Guthrie. *Songs:* "Pastures of Plenty," "Car Song" Woody Guthrie. *Sung by* Pete Seeger. *Song:* "You're a Fink" Arlo Guthrie, Garry Sherman. *Song:* "Songs to Aging Children" Joni Mitchell. *Adapt:* "Amazing Grace" Arlo Guthrie, Garry Sherman. *Mus Dir* Fred Hellerman. *Sd Mix* Abe Seidman. *Sd Ed* Sanford Rackow, Jack Fitzstephens. *Re-rec* Richard Vorisek. *1st & 2d Asst Dir* William C. Gerrity, Frank Simpson. *Prod Supv* Willard W. Goodman. *Prod Assoc* Gene Lasko. *Asst to the Prod* Florence Nerlinger, Ed Bowes, Bill Liberman. *Script Supv* Barbara Rittenberg. *Cost Dsgn* Anna Hill Johnstone. *Wardrobe Supv* George Newman, Marilyn Putnam. *Makeup* Irving Buchman. *Hairstyles* Philip Naso. *Gaffer* Morton Gorowitz. *Key Grip* Charles Kolb. *Prop Master* Thomas Wright. *Ch Carpenter* Merle Eckhart.

Cast: Arlo Guthrie (*Arlo Guthrie*), Pat Quinn (*Alice Brock*), James Broderick (*Ray Brock*), Michael McClanathan (*Shelly*), Geoff Outlaw (*Roger*), Tina Chen (*Mari-chan*), Kathleen Dabney (*Karin*), William Obanhein (*Officer Obie*), Seth Allen (*evangelist*), Monroe Arnold (*Blueglass*), Joseph Boley (*Woody Guthrie*), James Hannon (*himself, a judge*), Vinette Carroll (*lady clerk*), Sylvia Davis (*Marjorie Guthrie*), Simm Landres (*Jacob*), Eulalie Noble (*Ruth*), Louis Beachner (*Dean*), MacIntyre Dixon (*1st deconsecration minister*), Pierce Middleton (*2d deconsecration minister*), Donald Marye (*funeral director*), Shelley Plimpton (*Reenie*), M. Emmet Walsh (*Group W Sergeant*), Ron Weyand (*cop no. 1*), Eleanor Wilson (*landlady*), Simon Deckard (*medic*), Thomas De Wolfe (*waiter*), Graham Jarvis (*music teacher*), John Quill (*cop no. 2*), Frank Simpson (*sergeant*), Pete Seeger (*himself*), Lee Hays (*himself*), Alice Brock (*Suzy*).

Comedy-drama. Based on real-life incidents and the song by: Arlo Guthrie, "Alice's Restaurant Massacree." After registering for the draft, folk singer Arlo enrolls at Rocky Mountain College in Montana to qualify for an "educational" draft deferment. During matriculation, however, Arlo, disgusted by the school's bureaucracy and the townspeople's antagonism, drops out. Traveling east, he visits his dying father, Woody, in a New York hospital and participates with Stockbridge, Massachusetts, friends Ray and Alice Brock in the founding of a commune in a deconsecrated church and, later, the establishment of a restaurant. Communal harmony is disrupted by Shelly, an incorrigible drug addict to whom Alice compassionately makes love. After an altercation with Ray, Alice runs away to New York, where she encounters Arlo in Greenwich Village. Together they return to the commune for a mammoth Thanksgiving feast. Finding the city dump closed for the holiday, Arlo deposits a half ton of garbage in a ravine. Alerted by a passing motorist, Officer Obie identifies the culprit by means of a letter found in the trash heap and arrests Arlo for littering. At a hearing before a blind justice, Arlo pleads guilty. As a consequence he is declared unfit for military service by the army. After his father dies of Huntington's chorea and Shelly dies of an overdose of heroin, the grieving

communards participate in a ceremony celebrating the renewal of the Brocks' wedding vows. During the festivity, Ray proposes the purchase of farmland in Vermont. The group, its ardor dampened by Shelly's death, is unenthusiastic. Despite Ray's pleas, the former friends separate. As Arlo and his girl friend, Mari-chan, depart, the disconsolate Alice watches from the door of the empty church. *Students. Hippies. Singers. Drug addicts. Police. Military draft. Communal living. Infidelity. Marriage. Drunkenness. Churches. Incurable illness. Drug overdose. Restaurants. Dumps. Funerals. Weddings. Heroin. Trials. Thanksgiving Day. Montana. New York City. New York City—Greenwich Village. Stockbridge. Woody Guthrie. Arlo Guthrie. Rocky Mountain College.*

Note: Filmed on location in and around Stockbridge and in New York City.

ALIKI—MY LOVE (United States/Greece)　　　F6.0076

Finos Films–Aquarius Productions. *Dist* Lionex Films, Jacon Film Distributors. 11 Dec **1963** [Los Angeles opening]. Sd; b&w. 35mm. 90 min. [Cut from 100 min.]

Prod Rudolph Maté, George St. George. *Dir* Rudolph Maté. *Screenplay-Story* George St. George. *Photog* Aristedes Karides-Fuchs. *Art Dir* Markos Zervas. *Mus* Manos Hadjidakis. *Sd* Janis Smyrnios.

Cast: Aliki Vouyouklaki (*Aliki*), Jess Conrad (*Barry Wilson*), Wilfrid Hyde-White (*Richard Caraway*), Katherine Kath (*Anna*), Paris Alexander (*Pastrudis*), John Pardos (*Sparks*), Roland George (*Socrates*).

Comedy. Playboy Barry Wilson, an American of Greek ancestry, believes that he will inherit a hamburger sauce empire from his late uncle. Learning that the recipe for the sauce died with the uncle, Barry's only inherited asset is the Greek island of Eftihia. Arriving there with his hypochondriac lawyer Richard Caraway, Barry tries to sell the island as a potential tourist attraction to Pastrudis, a Greek hotel millionaire. Local schoolteacher Aliki and her mother, Anna, scheme to keep the island from being sold. Charmed into sampling one of Anna's dishes, Caraway realizes that she has the recipe for the special hamburger sauce which can make him rich and save the island from the onslaught of tourists. *Playboys. Americans in foreign countries. Hypochondriacs. Lawyers. Millionaires. Schoolteachers. Inheritance. Food. Islands.*

Note: Filmed on the Greek island of Ios. Also known in the United States as *Aliki*.

ALIMONY LOVERS　　　　　　　　　　　　F6.0077

Clover Films. 2 Apr **1969** [Fresno showing]. Sd; col. 35mm. 74 min.

Prod William Dancer. *Dir* Harold Perkins. *Mus* Nova.

Cast: Will Gary, Lisa Cameron, Joy Kahl, Chris Mathis, Kathy Williams, Cathy Fox, Sebastian Gregory.

Drama. Roger Rose, divorced from his wife, moves into an expensive singles' apartment complex where divorcées live on their ex-husbands' alimony checks and indulge in fantastic sex games in the apartment house's recreation rooms and health club. Rose, bitter from his recent experience with divorce and unable to afford the rent on his apartment because of the alimony he must pay his ex-wife, hits upon a scheme to supplement his income. Taking advantage of the collection of sexual deviates, Rose persuades the women to perform their specialties before a paying audience. The show, which includes fetishistic demonstrations, acts showing sadomasochistic fantasies, and lesbian acts, is shut down by the police. Rose transfers his attention to the young female attorney handling his case. *Opportunists. Lawyers. Divorce. Alimony. Fetishism. Lesbianism. Sadomasochism. Finance—Personal. Sex shows.*

ALIVE AND KICKING (Great Britain)　　　　　F6.0078

Associated British Picture Corp. *Dist* Seven Arts Pictures. 24 Jun **1964** [Los Angeles opening]. Sd; b&w. 35mm. 94 min.

A Victor Skutezky Production. *Prod* Victor Skutezky. *Dir* Cyril Frankel. *Screenplay* Denis Cannan. *Based on an Idea by* William Dinner, William Morum. *Photog* Gilbert Taylor. *Art Dir* Robert Jones. *Film Ed* Bernard Gribble. *Mus* Philip Green. *Lyr* Michael Carr, mus. *Dances* Denys Palmer. *Sd* Richard Bird, Len Shilton. *Asst Dir* Jeremy Summers.

Cast: Sybil Thorndike (*Dora*), Kathleen Harrison (*Rosie*), Estelle Winwood (*Mabel*), Stanley Holloway (*McDonagh*), Joyce Carey (*matron*), Eric Pohlmann (*Russian captain*), Colin Gordon (*birdwatcher*), John Salew (*solicitor*), Liam Redmond (*old man*), Marjorie Rhodes (*old woman*), Richard Harris, Olive McFarland (*lovers*), Anita Sharp Bolster (*postmistress*), Brenden O'Dowda, Joseph MacNally (*singers*), Paul Farrell (*postman*), Patrick McAlinney (*policeman*), Raymond Manthorpe (*little boy*), Tony Quinn, Harry Hutchinson (*villagers*).

Comedy. Three elderly women, Rosie, a sharp-witted Cockney; Dora, a clever organizer; and genteel Mabel, escape from the Sunset Old Folks' Home and accidentally set out to sea in a motorboat. A Russian trawler picks them up and puts them ashore on a secluded Irish island, and there the women commandeer three cottages which they later learn have been bought by

McDonagh, an Irishman who has recently returned as a millionaire from the United States. McDonagh collapses while singing to Rosie, falls into the sea, and is presumed drowned. The women pretend they are McDonagh's nieces, claiming their uncle is ill and bedridden. To support themselves, they knit sweaters made from local wool. Their garments become fashionable in London, and the women organize the islanders into a prosperous knitting industry. A search for additional wool on another island leads to the discovery of McDonagh, who "adopts" the ladies as his nieces and becomes a partner in their sweater business. *Cockneys. Millionaires. Russians. Uncles. Old age. Imposture. Knitting. Old age homes. Fishing boats. Islands. Cottage industries. Ireland.*

Note: Location scenes filmed in Oban, Scotland. Released in Great Britain in 1959.

ALL BAD see **INDECENT**

ALL FALL DOWN   F6.0079

John Houseman Productions. *Dist* Metro-Goldwyn-Mayer, Inc. 28 Mar **1962** [Chicago opening; c21 Feb 1962; LP21395]. Sd (Westrex); b&w. 35mm. 111 min.

Prod John Houseman. *Assoc Prod* Ethel Winant. *Dir* John Frankenheimer. *Screenplay* William Inge. *Dir Photog* Lionel Lindon. *Art Dir* George W. Davis, Preston Ames. *Set Decor* Henry Grace, George R. Nelson. *Film Ed* Fredric Steinkamp. *Mus* Alex North. *Rec Supv* Franklin Milton. *Asst Dir* Hal Polaire. *Cost* Dorothy Jeakins. *Makeup* William Tuttle. *Hairstyles* Sydney Guilaroff. *Sp Vis Eff* Robert R. Hoag.

Cast: Eva Marie Saint *(Echo O'Brien)*, Warren Beatty *(Berry-Berry Willart)*, Karl Malden *(Ralph Willart)*, Angela Lansbury *(Annabel Willart)*, Brandon De Wilde *(Clinton Willart)*, Constance Ford *(Mrs. Mandel)*, Barbara Baxley *(schoolteacher)*, Evans Evans *(Hedy)*, Madame Spivy *(bouncer)*, Jennifer Howard *(Myra)*, Albert Paulsen *(Captain Ramirez)*, Henry Kulky *(sailor)*, Colette Jackson *(Dorothy)*, Robert Sorrells *(waiter in sweet shop)*, Bernadette Withers *(Mildred)*, Carol Kelly *(Flame)*, Paul Bryar *(manager of sweet shop)*.

Drama. Source: James Leo Herlihy, *All Fall Down* (New York, 1960). Fifteen-year-old Clinton Willart arrives in Florida with $200 for his older brother, Berry-Berry, whom he idolizes. Berry-Berry had wired home for cash to go into business; actually he needs the money to pay a jail fine for beating up a prostitute. Once free, Berry-Berry sends Clinton back to Ohio, vaguely promising to return for Christmas. At home with Annabel, his talkative and meddling mother, and Ralph, his likeable but alcoholic father, Clinton views their life as humdrum compared with Berry-Berry's glamorous existence. Excitement suddenly comes into Clinton's life, however, with the appearance of Echo O'Brien, the daughter of Annabel's closest friend. Echo's beauty and charm captivate the entire family, particularly young Clinton. Then Berry-Berry returns. Again his appeal to women proves irresistible, and Echo falls in love with him. Berry-Berry almost returns her love, but when he learns that she is pregnant, his latent misogyny reasserts itself, and he leaves her. Filled with despair, Echo drives her car off a cliff. At first, Clinton decides to kill his brother, but when Berry-Berry breaks down and sobs, Clinton realizes how pathetic his brother really is. No longer shackled by a distorted adoration for his older brother, Clinton leaves Berry-Berry to his own self-inflicted misery. *Brothers. Misogynists. Hero worship. Adolescence. Family life. Alcoholism. Pregnancy. Suicide. Florida. Ohio.*

Note: Some location scenes filmed in Key West, Florida.

ALL GIRL see **ALL WOMAN**

ALL HANDS ON DECK   F6.0080

Twentieth Century–Fox Film Corp. 31 Mar **1961** [New York opening; c24 Mar 1961; LP19561]. Sd (Westrex); col (DeLuxe). 35mm (CinemaScope). 98 min.

Prod Oscar Brodney. *Dir* Norman Taurog. *Screenplay* Jay Sommers. *Dir Photog* Leo Tover. *Art Dir* Jack Martin Smith, Walter M. Simonds. *Set Decor* Walter M. Scott, Lou Hafley. *Film Ed* Fredrick Y. Smith. *Mus* Cyril Mockridge. *Cond* Pete King. *Orch* Arthur Morton, Edward B. Powell, Vic Schoen, Herbert Spencer. *Songs:* "All Hands on Deck," "I've Got It Made," "Somewhere There's Home," "You Mean Everything to You" Ray Evans, Jay Livingston. *Sung by* Pat Boone. *Choreog* Hal Belfer. *Sd* E. Clayton Ward, Frank W. Moran. *Asst Dir* Stanley Hough. *Asst to the Prod* Jack Mintz. *Makeup* Ben Nye. *Hairstyles* Helen Turpin. *Tech Adv* Daniel E. Bergin, (Comdr.), USN), Francis T. Kleber, (Comdr., USN). *Coöp* United States Navy, Officers & Men of LST St. Clair County.

Cast: Pat Boone *(Lieut. Victor Donald)*, Buddy Hackett *(Shrieking Eagle Garfield)*, Dennis O'Keefe *(Lieut. Comdr. Brian O'Gara)*, Barbara Eden *(Sally Hobson)*, Warren Berlinger *(Ensign Rush)*, Gale Gordon *(Admiral Bintle)*, David Brandon *(Lieutenant Kutley)*, Joe E. Ross *(bos'n)*, Bartlett Robinson *(Lieutenant Commander Anthony)*, Paul Von Schreiber *(Mulvaney)*, Ann B. Davis *(Nobby)*, Jody McCrea *(Lieutenant j.g. Schuyler)*, Chet Stratton *(theater manager)*, Pat McCaffrie *(Gruber)*, Owasso.

Comedy. Source: Donald R. Morris, *Warm Bodies* (New York, 1957). Lieut. Victor Donald is the executive officer aboard a Navy LST operating out of Long Beach, California. His chief duty is to keep a watchful eye on the zany antics of Garfield, a Chickasaw Indian who has attracted the attention of Washington politicians because of his wealth. One day at the movies, Garfield becomes upset by the western picture being shown and tears the theater apart. Reporter Sally Hobson arrives to cover the story of the wild Indian, and Donald falls in love with her. The LST is ordered to make a trial run to the Aleutians, and Garfield smuggles aboard a pet turkey, which later mates with a pelican and produces a turkey-pelican egg. When the ship returns to Long Beach, a visiting admiral surprises the captain, Lieut. Comdr. Brian O'Gara, with an inspection tour of the vessel. The admiral not only discovers the turkey and the unhatched egg, but he also uncovers Sally, who had sneaked aboard in an ashcan in order to be near Donald. The admiral's rage quickly subsides when he learns that Sally's uncle is chairman of the Navy Appropriations Committee. *Chickasaw Indians. Reporters. Stowaways. Motion picture theaters. LST's. Eggs. Long Beach (California). Aleutian Islands. United States Navy. Turkeys. Pelicans.*

ALL IN A NIGHT'S WORK   F6.0081

Hal Wallis Productions. *Dist* Paramount Pictures. 22 Mar **1961** [New York opening; c31 Dec 1960; LP18883]. Sd; col (Technicolor). 35mm. 94 min.

Prod Hal B. Wallis. *Assoc Prod* Paul Nathan. *Dir* Joseph Anthony. *Screenplay* Edmund Beloin, Maurice Richlin, Sidney Sheldon. *Dir Photog* Joseph LaShelle. *Col Cons* Richard Mueller. *Art Dir* Hal Pereira, Walter Tyler. *Set Decor* Sam Comer, Arthur Krams. *Ed Supv* Warren Low. *Ed* Howard Smith. *Mus* Andre Previn. *Sd Rec* Gene Merritt, Charles Grenzbach. *Asst Dir* Daniel J. McCauley. *Prod Mgr* Richard Blaydon. *Cost* Edith Head. *Makeup Supv* Wally Westmore. *Hairstyle Supv* Nellie Manley. *Sp Photog Eff* John P. Fulton. *Proc Photog* Farciot Edouart.

Cast: Dean Martin *(Tony Ryder)*, Shirley MacLaine *(Katie Robbins)*, Charlie Ruggles *(Dr. Warren Kingsley, Sr.)*, Cliff Robertson *(Warren Kingsley, Jr.)*, Norma Crane *(Marge Coombs)*, Gale Gordon *(Oliver Dunning)*, Jerome Cowan *(Sam Weaver)*, Jack Weston *(Lasker)*, Ian Wolfe *(O'Hara)*, Mabel Albertson *(Mrs. Kingsley, Sr.)*, Mary Treen *(Miss Schuster)*, Rex Evans *(Carter)*, Roy Gordon *(Albright)*, Charles Evans *(Colonel Ryder)*, Ralph Dumke *(Baker)*, John Hudson *(Harry Lane)*, Rosemary Bowe *(Tony's "friend")*, Gertrude Astor *(customer)*, Jasper *(the dog)*.

Comedy. Source: Owen Elford, an unidentified story. While on vacation in Palm Beach, Katie Robbins, a researcher for a Manhattan publishing house, saves an inebriated millionaire from drowning. When she sheds her wet clothes, however, the grateful millionaire becomes so amorous that Katie is forced to flee, clad only in a towel and earrings. She darts into somebody else's room and finds a man lying in bed with a blissful smile on his face. As she races back into the corridor, the house detective spies her and gives chase. Though she loses him, he finds one of her earrings. Unknown to Katie, the stranger in bed was the deceased head of the publishing firm where she works. Playboy Tony Ryder inherits the company and is warned that the firm will probably be blackmailed by the mystery woman seen running from the dead man's room. Once Tony spots Katie with the missing earring, he immediately leaps to the wrong conclusion and tries to thwart any blackmail attempts by giving Katie a $200 a week raise. Furthermore, he tries to speed up her marriage to veterinarian Warren Kingsley, Jr., in the hope that Katie will ease up on her demands. When this backfires, Tony invites Katie to his apartment for dinner. After filling her with champagne and romantic ideas, he announces that he is willing to forgive her for trying to blackmail the firm. Furious, Katie stalks out. Tony then realizes that Katie is innocent and that he is in love with her. *Researchers. Millionaires. Publishers. Detectives. Playboys. Veterinarians. Mistaken identity. Blackmail. Inheritance. Chases. Palm Beach. New York City.*

Note: Copyright claimants: Hal B. Wallis and Joseph H. Hazen.

ALL MEN ARE APES!   F6.0082

Barnard L. Sackett Productions. *Dist* Adelphia Pictures. 14 Dec **1965**. Sd; b&w. 35mm. 85 min.

Assoc Prod Charles E. Mazin. *Dir* Joseph P. Mawra. *Screenplay* Barnard L. Sackett, Charles E. Mazin. *Camera* Richard E. Brooks. *Asst Camera* Charles Caffall. *Film Ed* Joseph P. Mawra. *Background Mus Arr & Cond* Irv Dweir. *Song:* "Only God Can Understand You" Charles E. Mazin. *Sung by* The Ink Spots. *Songs:* "Voodoo," "All Men Are Apes" Charles E. Mazin. *Sung by* Sandi Brown. *Sd Engr* John Nicholas, sd.

Cast: Stephanie De Passe *(Diane)*, Mark Ryan *(Buddy Saxon)*, Grace Lynn *(Marge)*, Steve Woods *(sailor)*, Steve Vincent *(Rocky Adams)*, Bonny Lee Noll *(stripper)*, Mia Marlowe *(Barbara)*, Ted Teschner *(window strip man)*, Walter Teague *(hotel porter)*, Tom O'Horgan *(Marcel Fires)*, Wendy Winston *(Indian dancer)*, Jeanine Costa *(Plum Girl)*, Brigitte Batit *(Peacock Girl)*, Ceylon *(belly dancer)*, Bob Worms *(muscle man)*, Frank Geraci *(Junior Brighteyes)*, "Harry the Ape".

Comedy-drama. Diane recalls the events that have placed her behind bars: Returning home from school, she finds her mother in bed with a sailor and successfully competes for his attention. To smooth things over, she visits the club where her mother works as a waitress and meets Rocky Adams, an agent who encourages her to become a stripper. Her mother turns her out, and Diane goes to stay the night with Barbara, who tries unsuccessfully to lead her into a lesbian relationship. She moves into Rocky's hotel where a peeping tom watches her strip through a window, and the hotel porter joins her in the shower. To further her career, Rocky takes her to a VIP party where a female impersonator performs a belly dance. The Plum Girl is heaped with fruit, and the Peacock Girl is auctioned for the weekend to the highest bidder. In return for his help, Rocky demands that Diane scrub his back. Her stripping career well established, Diane hires a muscleman as a servant. She falls in love with gangster Buddy Saxon, who rapes her on their first night out; as a result, Barbara gives her a gun for protection. Diane takes a job in a "Beauty and the Beast" dance act with Harry the Ape, a live gorilla. Buddy arrives on the scene, and Diane wildly shoots at him. She misses, but she decides that she has had enough of human company and joins Harry in his cage. *Sailors. Waitresses. Stripteasers. Talent agents. Exotic dancers. Musclemen. Gangsters. Adolescence. Lesbianism. Voyeurism. Female impersonation. Rape. Nightclubs. Apes.*

Note: Produced in Philadelphia.

ALL MY MEN   F6.0083

Dist Sam Lake Enterprises. **1966**. Sd; b&w. 35mm. 70 min.
A Sam Lake Production.

Drama. Kim, a young woman who has decided to become a prostitute, is discouraged by the strange and sometimes perverse desires a prostitute must satisfy. One client demands that she make love with another woman while he watches. After a wild party with all of her associates, Kim elopes with her lover. *Prostitution. Voyeurism. Lesbianism. Elopement. Orgies.*

ALL NEAT IN BLACK STOCKINGS (Great Britain)   F6.0084

Miron Films-Anglo Amalgamated Productions. *Dist* National General Pictures. 17 Sep **1969** [New York opening]. Sd; col (Technicolor). 35mm. 96 min. *MPAA rating* R.

Prod Leon Clore. *Co-prod* John Arnold. *Dir* Christopher Morahan. *Screenplay* Jane Gaskell, Hugh Whitemore. *Dir Photog* Larry Pizer. *Camera Op* Ronnie Maasz. *Art Dir* David Brockhurst. *Film Ed* Misha Norland. *Mus* Robert Cornford. *Song:* "All Neat in Black Stockings" Robert Cornford, Terence Delaney. *Sd* Jim Willis. *Asst Dir* Ted Morley, Ewan Pearson, Philip Livingstone. *Prod Mgr* John Bremer. *Cont* Betty Harley. *Cost* Caroline Mott. *Casting Dir* Miriam Brickman.

Cast: Victor Henry (*Ginger*), Susan George (*Jill*), Jack Shepherd (*Dwyer*), Vanessa Forsyth (*Carole*), Terence De Marney (*Old Gunge*), Anna Cropper (*Sis*), Harry Towb (*Issur*), Jasmina Hamzavi (*Babette*), Deirdre Costello (*new bird*), Nita Lorraine (*Jocasta*), Rosalind Elliot (*1st bird*), Clare Kelly (*mother*), Anna Welsh (*hospital sister*), Geoffrey Reed, Michael McKevitt (*orderlies*), Tanya Trude (*new bird*), Eric Longworth (*businessman*), Shivendra Sinha (*Pakistani*), Gwendolyn Watts (*suburban housewife*), Graham James (*young bloke*), Marc Bergman (*toddler*), John Woodnutt (*vicar*), Andre Dakar (*man with parrot*), Christine Pryor (*waitress in cafe*), Malcolm Tierney (*photographer*), Maurice Travers (*car salesman*), Larry Dann (*new mate*), Neil Wilson (*angry householder*), Carmen Monroe (*nurse*).

Comedy-drama. Source: Jane Gaskell, *All Neat in Black Stockings* (London, 1966). Ginger, a 20-year-old window cleaner working at a hospital in London, is a devoted girl-chaser who shares his women with his best friend, Dwyer. While Ginger is at a pub with Babette, a nurse at the hospital, Dwyer becomes infatuated with Jill, an innocent-looking young woman. He begins to pursue her by dating her roommate Carole, and eventually he persuades her to go out with him. Meanwhile, Ginger is taking care of the house and pets of Old Gunge, a patient in the hospital, and moves into the elderly man's mansion along with his pregnant sister, Issur, her husband, Issur, and Issur's mistress, Jocasta. One evening Ginger returns to the mansion with Jill to find that Issur is holding a wild party. He asks Dwyer to take care of Jill while he gets rid of the rowdy guests and returns to discover that Dwyer has seduced Jill. Ginger's troubles increase when Issur runs away with Jocasta, and Old Gunge comes home to find his house a disaster. Sis is allowed to stay on as the housekeeper, but Ginger is banished. Jill visits Ginger and informs him that she is pregnant, and Ginger agrees to marry her. Jill's domineering mother immediately insists that they live with her. The baby's birth further discourages Ginger, and he has a drunken sexual encounter with his mother-in-law, who henceforth caters to his every need. Back to his old ways again, Ginger sees a pretty waitress at lunch and takes pursuit. *Window washers. Roommates. Mistresses. Mothers-in-law. Waitresses. Bachelors. Pregnancy. Brother-sister relationship. Marriage. Seduction. Infidelity. Drunkenness. Hospitals. London. Animals.*

Note: Opened in London in Apr 1969; running time: 99 min.

ALL NIGHT LONG (Great Britain)   F6.0085

Bob Roberts Productions. *For* Rank Organisation. *Dist* Colorama Features. 17 Apr **1963** [Los Angeles opening]. Sd; b&w. 35mm. 91 min.

Prod Michael Relph. *Exec Prod* Bob Roberts, prod. *Dir* Basil Dearden. *Screenplay* Nel King, Peter Achilles. *Photog* Ted Scaife. *Camera Op* H. A. R. Thomson. *Focus Op* Wally Fairweather. *Camera Grip* Fred Graver. *Art Dir* Ray Simm. *Ch Draughtsman* Alan Fraiser. *Set Dresser* Peter James. *Prod Dsgn* Michael Relph. *Film Ed* John D. Guthridge. *1st Asst Ed* Marcel Durham. *2d Asst Ed* Stephen Durbridge. *Mus Dir* Philip Green. *Songs:* "Dedication to Johnny Hodges," "Frenzy," "Muy Rapido," "Skin Fever," "Wingate's Spot" Philip Green. *Titl Song* Philip Green, Sonny Miller. *Song:* "The Chase" Philip Green, Tubby Hayes. *Song:* "Sax Reference" Philip Green, Kenny Napper. *Song:* "Scott-Free" Johnny Scott. *Sd* Christopher Lancaster. *Sd Rec* Gordon K. McCallum. *Mus Rec* Robert T. MacPhee. *Boom Op* Harry Fairbairn. *Sd Camera Op* Charles Arnold. *1st, 2d & 3d Asst Dir* Stanley Hosgood, Terry Clegg, Alex Carver-Hill. *Prod Mgr* Bill Hill. *Prod Sec* Lorely Farley. *Cost Dsgn* Julie Harris, cost. *Wardrobe Supv* Dorothy Edwards. *Wardrobe Master* Bert Simmonds. *Makeup* Geoffrey Rodway. *Hairdresser* Stella Rivers. *Casting Dir* Weston Drury, Jr.. *Constr Mgr* Ron Udell. *Prop Buyer* Jim Baker. *Still Photog* Ian Jeayes. *Chargehand Prop Dresser* George Ball. *Chargehand Electrn* Tom Heathcoat.

Cast: Patrick McGoohan (*Johnny Cousin*), Marti Stevens (*Delia Lane*), Betsy Blair (*Emily, Johnny's wife*), Keith Michell (*Cass Michaels*), Richard Attenborough (*Rod Hamilton*), Paul Harris (*Aurelius Rex*), Bernard Braden (*Berger*), Maria Velasco (*Benny*), Harry Towb (*Phales*), Dave Brubeck, John Dankworth, Charles Mingus, Tubby Hayes, Keith Christie, Ray Dempsey, Allan Ganley, Ben Courtley, Barry Morgan, Kenny Napper, Colin Purbrook, Johnny Scott, Geoffrey Holder (*themselves*).

Melodrama with music. In a converted warehouse in London's East End, jazz enthusiast Rodney Hamilton stages an all-night anniversary party for successful Negro jazz pianist Aurelius Rex and Delia, his devoted white wife who gave up her singing career for matrimony. Johnny Cousin, Rex's jealous drummer, schemes to break up their marriage by attempting to persuade Delia to sing in a band he would like to start, but she refuses. Spreading rumors about Delia's infidelity, Johnny edits a tape recording of Delia and Cass Michaels, Rex's saxophonist and business manager, to make it appear that they are having an affair. The enraged Rex nearly strangles his wife, but Johnny's treachery is exposed and the couple are reconciled. *Negroes. Pianists. Singers. Drummers. Saxophonists. Business managers. Jazz. Miscegenation. Jealousy. Slander. Jazzbands. Recorders. London—East End.*

Note: Opened in London in Feb 1962; running time: 95 min. Drummer Allan Ganley dubs for Patrick McGoohan.

ALL NIGHT RIDER   F6.0086

Dist Distribpix, Inc. **1969**. Sd; col. 35mm. 60 min.
Prod Jack Bravman, Michael Findlay. *Dir* Michael Findlay. *Photog* Roberta Findlay. *Film Ed* Michael Findlay.

Sex film. No information about the precise nature of this film has been found, but press material suggests that it includes scenes of motorcyclists and lesbianism. *Motorcyclists. Lesbianism.*

ALL OF ME   F6.0087

Dist Joseph Brenner Associates. 23 Oct **1963**. Sd; col (Eastman Color). 35mm. 73 min.

Prod-Dir Jay Martin. *Assoc Prod* Frank Sacco. *Story-Screenplay* William L. Rose. *Dir Photog* Ray Malon. *Camera Op* Ronnie Latore. *Film Ed* Michael James. *Orig Score Comp & Dir* Kai Roberts. *Sd* Bernard Zimney. *Asst Dir* Pierre Gabin. *Script girl* Nina Keller.

Cast: Brenda De Naut (*Danielle*).

Drama. Bill, a television producer, assists a young woman who has been assaulted on the New York City waterfront and takes her to his apartment to recover from the attack. The woman, Dany, relates to Bill her recent adventures in New York: *Frank Terrell, middle-aged owner of a modeling agency, invites Dany, winner of an Iowa beauty contest, to come to New York for a career in fashion modeling. Dany accepts, unaware that her rather full figure would disqualify her as a high fashion model. Bill interrupts her account to ask her along on an excursion he is about to make to film an assignment, but she demurs when told that the locale will be a nudist camp. Terrell's motives become clear as Dany is soon posing for cheesecake photographs. Terrell makes a pass at her, and Dany stalks out of the studio, returns to retrieve her portfolio, and again rejects Terrell's suggestions that she pose nude for him. He follows her, begins to molest her, and runs off when her screams for help attract passerby Bill. Bill, hopeful that he can show her the salutary aspects of nudity, convinces Dany to go along with him to Sunny Rest Lodge. She is at first reluctant, remaining outside the gates, but she soon mingles with the campers, fully enjoying herself.*

Bill and Dany have become friends and admirers. *Models. Photographers. Television producers. Nudism. Nudist camps. New York City—Waterfront. Sunny Rest Lodge.*

ALL THE EVILS OF S—— see ALL THE SINS OF SODOM

ALL THE FALLEN ANGELS see THE WILD ANGELS

ALL THE LOVIN' KINFOLK   F6.0088
Dist Clover Films. ca **1970**. Sd; col (Eastman Color). 35mm. 84 min.
Prod Daniel Cady, John Hayes. *Dir-Writ* John Hayes. *Dir Photog* Paul Hipp. *Camera Op* Ron Johnson. *Mus* Mario Toscana. *Lyr:* "Leavin' These Mountains" Ellen Bender. *Sung by* Larry Adair. *Sd Rec* Sam Rosen. *Prod Mgr* Henning Schellerup. *Cost* Logan Costumes.
Cast: Jay Scott *(Zeb)*, Mady Maguire *(Cindy)*, Ann Ryan *(Tricia)*, Janice Douglas *(Mrs. Pruitt)*, Donna Young *(Sue)*, William Guhl *(Luke)*, Ruth Stanley *(Babs)*, Marland Proctor *(Corporal Simpson)*, Lynn York *(Rose)*, John Dennis *(bartender)*, Buck Stahl *(Mr. Wilson)*, Richard Gentry *(Randy)*.
Rural melodrama. Upon graduating from Glen Holler High School in 1933, Cindy decides to leave behind the dingy mountain hamlet and go to live with her married sister Sue, whose difficult circumstances she believes to be more comfortable with her own. Cindy's distant cousin Zeb has decided to go to work at a gas station on the main highway, and they leave Glen time and, to seek new horizons. That afternoon Cindy meets her salesman boyfriend, and they make love in a field, leaving Zeb to stand watch over the salesman's car. After a night at a roadhouse where the cousins make their first contact with the outside world, they reach Cindy's destination. Cindy bids Zeb a cold farewell, but her expectations are shattered when she discovers that Sue lives in a run-down house and serves as little more than a slave to her husband Luke and his gang of moonshiners. After fending off Luke's determined advances, Cindy is driven out of the town by the mountain folk, who have been told that she made improper advances toward her sister's husband. Determined to rescue her sister, Cindy goes to work as a prostitute in Madam Rose's house. Meanwhile, Zeb has also met with disappointment. After arriving at the gas station, he found that his boss had died, leaving Zeb to look after his widow and daughter, Tricia. Zeb and Tricia are mutually attracted, but he refuses to have sex with him unless he wears a prophylactic. She describes the device to the ignorant Zeb, but he arrives at the drug store at closing time and, disappointed, visits Rose's house. There he is recognized by Cindy, who becomes jealous when she hears of his attraction to Tricia, and she seduces him. Zeb agrees to help Cindy, on the assumption that she will then leave Rose's house; and the following day they rescue Sue, narrowly escaping their pursuers. Cindy rents an apartment for the three of them, but Zeb, realizing that Cindy plans to continue in her chosen profession, leaves to rejoin Tricia. *Cousins. Sisters. Moonshiners. Madams. Widows. Mountain life. Prostitution. Seduction. Birth control. Poverty. Whorehouses. Filling stations.*
Note: Also known as *Kinfolk, Kin Folk,* and *The Closest of Kin.*

ALL THE LOVING COUPLES   F6.0089
Sudan Productions. *Dist* U-M Film Distributors. 19 Mar **1969** [Los Angeles opening]. Sd; col (Eastman Color) with b&w seq. 35mm. 76 min. [Original length: 82 min.] *MPAA rating* X.
Pres by Cottage Films. A Milo O. Frank Production. *Prod* Milo O. Frank, Harold Nebenzal. *Exec Prod* Harold Nebenzal. *Assoc Prod* Marvin Best. *Dir* Mack Bing. *Screenplay* Leo V. Gordon. *Photog* Carl F. Marquard. *Set Decor* Raymond G. Boltz, Jr. *Film Ed* Larry Heath. *Mus* Casanova. *Sd* Ryder Sound Service, Bob Post. *Asst Dir* William Schwartz.
Cast: Norman Alden *(Mitch)*, Gloria Manon *(Liz)*, Scott Graham *(Dale)*, Barbara Blake *(Kathy)*, Paul Lambert *(Irv)*, Lynn Cartwright *(Natalie)*, Paul Comi *(Mike)*, Jackie Russell *(Thelma)*, Anna Hastings, Frank Bueno, Tony Gardner *(actors in stag film)*.
Drama. Impotent Mitch Burnett, a supporter of the John Birch Society, and his bisexual wife Liz give a party at their plush San Fernando Valley home. The first to arrive are Dale and Kathy Osborne, strangers to the Burnetts. Insurance agent Dale hopes that he will be able to garner some lucrative contracts from the guests, who are all mate-swappers. Kathy demurs when she learns the nature of the party, but Dale reminds her of his recent business failures, and she reluctantly consents to remain at the party. Irv and Natalie Soberman, the Osbornes' friends, arrive and warmly greet the Burnetts: Natalie hurries in to help Mitch finish dressing, and Irv and Liz kiss passionately. Mike and Thelma Corey arrive with some stag films. The liquor begins to flow, and soon the Burnetts and the Coreys are expounding on the advantages of mate swapping. A round of "spin the bottle" pits Kathy with Mike, and Dale with Natalie for sexual liaisons. Later, Mitch attempts to make love to Kathy, but his impotence hinders him. When all have returned to the living room, the conversation returns to the subject of mate swapping, and Natalie refuses Dale's request for a private rendezvous, explaining that the group only swaps when they are all together. Over coffee, the group decides to head for Howard Johnson's and

some 4 a.m. ice cream, and they pile into several cars. Kathy senses the honesty and loneliness of the other couples and joins Mitch and Liz, refusing to ride with her husband, whom she sees as a hypocritical opportunist. *Insurance agents. Opportunists. Mate swapping. Bisexuality. Business ethics. Jealousy. Impotence. Hypocrisy. Sex exploitation films. San Fernando Valley (California). John Birch Society.*
Note: Also known as *All the Loving Neighbors.*

ALL THE LOVING NEIGHBORS see ALL THE LOVING COUPLES

ALL THE OTHER GIRLS DO (France/Italy)   F6.0090
Sagittario Film-Tirso Film-Dicifrance. *Dist* Harlequin International Pictures. 11 Nov **1966** [San Francisco opening]. Sd; b&w. 35mm. 90 min.
Pres by Noonan-Warfield Productions. *Dir* Silvio Amadio. *Screenplay* Silvio Amadio, Carlo Romano. *Photog* Franco Villa. *Mus* Gino Peguri.
Cast: Rosemarie Dexter *(Giovenella Magrini)*, Jacques Perrin *(Gabriele)*, Folco Lulli *(Gabriele's father)*, Magali Noël *(Giovenella's sister)*, Bice Valori *(Giovenella's father)*, Gina Rovere *(Giovenella's mother)*, Luisa Della Noce *(Signora Pascutti)*, Arnoldo Foà *(Signora Pascutti)*, Alberto Bonucci, Mario Scaccia, Manuela Kent, Paola Pitti, Myriam Corio, Margaret Robsahm, Vincenzo Talarico.
Romantic melodrama. Gabriele and Giovenella, two teenagers who are in love, find their overly-concerned parents anxious to drive them apart, even though their romance is innocent. Gabriele's father hints that a man need not marry to satisfy his sexual urges. To prove his point, he takes his son to a red light district in Rome, and when this fails, he considers turning over his own mistress to the boy. The father's plan only manages to inflame Gabriele's passion for Giovenella. Gabriele schemes to bring Giovenella to a bachelor apartment, but she ignores his subtle suggestions, thereby doubling his frustration. When they quarrel, Giovenella turns to her older sister who advises her to trust in Gabriele and give herself freely to him. Knowing that the honest love that she and Gabriele have for each other has been threatened by adult interference, Giovenella meets Gabriele at the apartment, and the couple consummate their love. Later that night as they are driving home, they stop to kiss, and a policeman arrests them; but they are released with a warning to be more discreet in the future. The young couple agree to wait until they are married before making love again. *Prostitutes. Sisters. Police. Adolescence. Filial relations. Sexual initiation. Rome.*
Note: Opened in Rome in Mar 1965 as *Oltraggio al pudore;* alternative Italian title: *Tutte le altre ragazze lo fanno.* Also known as *Cheating Italian Style.*

ALL THE ROMAN MUSCLES   F6.0091
30 Jan **1970** [Los Angeles opening]. Sd; col. 35mm? 90 min.
Pres by Jon Pako.
Sex film. A group of musclemen perform their acts against a background of ancient Roman ruins. *Body-builders.*

ALL THE SINS OF SODOM   F6.0092
Morris Kaplan. 17 Jun **1968** [New York opening]. Sd; b&w. 35mm. 88 min.
Pres by Morris Kaplan. *Prod* Morris Kaplan. *Assoc Prod* Peggy Steffans. *Dir-Writ* Joe Sarno. *Camera* Steve Silverman. *Adtl Photog* Bob Bailin.
Melodrama. Renowned fashion photographer Henning is obsessed with finding a model who personifies feminine evil. One day Joyce appears and matches his concept of the sinister woman he wants for his study. As he proceeds to work, Henning is at first oblivious to the effect the diabolical woman is having on his life. One by one, his friends and associates succumb to Joyce's irresistible sexual power. Henning slowly becomes aware of Joyce's evil influence, and he drives himself to complete the project. He then discovers that Joyce is gone and has taken his negatives, and he collapses—a broken man—amidst the collection of proofs which he cannot reproduce. *Models. Photographers. Temptresses. Misogynists. Moral corruption. Theft. Obsession. Sexuality. Photographs.*
Note: Also known as *Sins of Sodom* and *All the Evils of S——.*

ALL THE WAY (Reissue)   F6.0093
Paramount Pictures. Apr **1966**. Sd; b&w. 35mm (VistaVision). 126 min.
Note: Originally released in 1957 as *The Joker Is Wild;* c5 Oct 1957; LP9219.

ALL THE WAY DOWN   F6.0094
Dyle IV Productions-Hollywood Hilltop Productions. *Dist* Canyon Distributing Co. 23 Oct **1968** [Champaign, Illinois, showing]. Sd; b&w. 35mm. 71 min.
Dir Zoltan G. Spencer.
Melodrama. Cindy, a bar girl, substitutes for Sandra and Billie, feature attractions at a topless striptease club, when the very popular sadomasochistic-lesbian-striptease-dance duo fail to appear at the club one busy night. Cindy is encouraged to pursue a career as a striptease dancer by Joe, manager of the club

who develops an offstage relationship with Cindy. Meanwhile, Joe's former stars, Sandra and Billie, aware of Cindy's popularity, believe that Joe has betrayed them, and they set out to destroy Cindy's career. One night at the club, Sandra and Billie force Joe to watch as they mutilate Cindy, thereby evening the score with her, and their revenge is complete when they have Joe arrested for possession of marijuana. Joe is sentenced to 6 months in prison; the club temporarily loses its license; and when Joe gets out of jail, he is unable to find work anywhere in the city. *Bar girls. Nightclub managers. Go-go dancers. Striptease. Sadomasochism. Jealousy. Revenge. Lesbianism. Frameup. Employer-employee relations. Imprisonment. Nightclubs. Marijuana.*

ALL THE WAY HOME   F6.0095

Talent Associates–Paramount, Ltd. *Dist* Paramount Pictures. 17 Oct **1963** [Knoxville, Tennessee, opening; c25 Dec 1963; LP26840]. Sd; b&w. 35mm. 103 min. [Also 97 min.]

A David Susskind Production. *Prod* David Susskind. *Assoc Prod* Jack Grossberg. *Dir* Alex Segal. *Screenplay* Philip Reisman, Jr. *Cinematog* Boris Kaufman. *Art Dir & Prod Dsgn* Richard Sylbert. *Film Ed* Carl Lerner. *Mus* Bernard Green, Alec Wilder. *Sd* Jim Shields. *Asst Dir* Larry Sturhahn, Michael Hertzberg.

Cast: Jean Simmons (*Mary Follet*), Robert Preston (*Jay Follet*), Pat Hingle (*Ralph Follet*), Aline MacMahon (*Aunt Hannah*), Thomas Chalmers (*Joel*), John Cullum (*Andrew*), Ronnie Claire Edwards (*Sally*), Michael Kearney (*Rufus Follet*), John Henry Faulk (*Walter Starr*), Lylah Tiffany (*Great-Great-Granmaw*), Mary Perry (*Grand-Aunt Sadie*), Georgia Simmons (*Jessie*), Edwin Wolfe (*John Henry*), Ferdie Hoffman (*Father Jackson*), Helen Carew (*Mary's mother*).

Domestic melodrama. Source: Tad Mosel, *All the Way Home* (New York opening: 30 Nov 1960). James Agee, *A Death in the Family* (New York, 1957). Rufus Follet is a 7-year-old boy living in a small town in Tennessee in 1915. His chief delights are the hours he spends with his father, Jay, an easygoing man who takes the child to Chaplin movies, the neighborhood saloon, and their "special place" where they can watch trains go by. Although Rufus' pregnant mother, Mary, is often at odds with Jay because of his drinking and lack of interest in religion, their marriage is essentially a happy one. Following a visit to Rufus' elderly grandmother, Jay receives word from his brother Ralph that their father is seriously ill. Returning home from the old man's house, Jay is killed in an automobile accident. For little Rufus, it is the end of his world. Unable to comprehend the meaning of death, he breaks down after the funeral and races to the special place where he and his father shared so many hours. Mary follows, waits until the boy's emotions are spent, and then takes him in her arms. She tells him that the child she is carrying will always remind him of his father; holding hands, the two return home. *Filial relations. Childhood. Pregnancy. Death. Family life. Motion pictures. Funerals. Tennessee. Charles Chaplin. Automobile accidents.*

Note: Location scenes filmed in Knoxville, Tennessee.

ALL THE WAY TO PARIS *see* AFTER YOU, COMRADE

ALL THESE WOMEN (Sweden)   F6.0096

Svensk Filmindustri. *Dist* Janus Films. 5 Oct **1964** [New York opening]. Sd; col (Eastman Color). 35mm. 80 min.

Prod Allan Ekelund. *Dir* Ingmar Bergman. *Screenplay* (see note) Erland Josephson, Ingmar Bergman. *Photog* Sven Nykvist. *Art Dir* P. A. Lundgren. *Film Ed* Ulla Ryghe. *Mus* Erik Nordgren. *Sd* P. O. Pettersson, Tage Sjöberg. *Asst Dir* Lenn Hjörtzberg, Lars-Erik Liedholm. *Prod Mgr* Lars-Owe Carlberg. *Cost* Mago. *Sp Eff* Evald Andersson.

Cast: Jarl Kulle (*Cornelius*), Georg Funkquist (*Tristan*), Eva Dahlbeck (*Adelaïde*), Harriet Andersson (*Isolde*), Karin Kavli (*Madame Tussaud*), Gertrud Fridh (*Traviata*), Bibi Andersson (*Humlan*), Allan Edwall (*Jillker*), Barbro Hiort af Ornäs (*Beatrice*), Mona Malm (*Cecilia*), Gösta Prüzelius (*Swedish radio announcer*), Jan-Olof Strandberg (*German radio announcer*), Göran Graffman (*French radio announcer*), Jan Blomberg (*British radio announcer*), Ulf Johansson, Axel Düberg, Lars-Erik Liedholm (*men in black suits*), Carl Billquist (*a young man, see note*), Lars-Owe Carlberg (*The Driver*), Doris Funcke, Yvonne Igell (*housemaids*).

Farce. Felix, a famous cellist, has died. At his funeral, the last 4 days of his life are recounted. *Cornelius, a conceited, well-known music critic, visits at the summer home of Felix, bringing with him his own musical composition entitled "A Fish's Dream. Abstraction No. 14," which he hopes the "genius" will perform. Also staying at the estate are the numerous women in Felix's life: his wife Adelaïde, his mistress Humlan, his accompanist Beatrice, his housemaid Isolde, his pretty young relative Cecilia, his pupil Traviata, and his patroness Madame Tussaud. Cornelius, denied permission to enter the master's presence, wanders about the huge house attempting to learn something about Felix. Humlan lures him to bed, Traviata attacks him, and he is photographed by Jillker, Felix's concert master, in a compromising position with Beatrice.*

Fleeing to the attic, he finds some letters in which Felix urges Adelaïde to murder him if ever he betrays his art. After causing mass confusion by accidentally setting off a fireworks display, Cornelius attempts to see Felix by dressing as a woman. Failing in this he angrily announces that unless his musical composition is performed by Felix he will not immortalize him in a biography. Although Felix makes no reply, Cornelius'work is announced for the "genius'"s radio concert. But Felix dies before a note can be played. After the funeral Cornelius begins to read Felix's biography to the others. They are interrupted by a young cellist who plays for them. Felix is forgotten as everyone gathers around the new "genius." *Cellists. Critics. Composers. Pianists. Mistresses. Housemaids. Students. Patrons. Authors. Music. Seduction. Disguise. Egotists. Funerals. Photographs. Fireworks. Documentation.*

Note: Released in Sweden in Jun 1964 as *För att inte tala om alla dessa kvinnor.* Buntel Ericsson, credited with screenplay by some sources, is a collective pseudonym for Ingmar Bergman and Erland Josephson. Carl Billquist is credited with the role of Felix by at least one source. Alternative title. *As for All These Women.*

ALL TOGETHER NOW   F6.0097

Cannon Productions–House on 69th Street Co. *Dist* Cannon Releasing Corp. 4 Feb **1970** [Pittsburgh opening]. Sd; col (DynamiColor). 35mm. 78 min.

Prod Christopher Dennis. *Dir-Writ* William Louis Allan. *Adtl Narr* Gayle Greene. *Dir Photog* Bruce Sparks. *Ed* George Thomas. *Mus* Shepard Meyers, Larry Rosen. *Mus Score Prod* Duo/Creatics. *Sd Engr* Marty Endell. *Prod Mgr* David Christopher. *Script Supv* Rita Field. *Makeup Artist* Claire Lune.

Cast: Cileste Eslar (*Marsha*), Thomas Baker (*Julian*), Robert Cordier (*Malcolm*), Ela Mitzo (*Barbara*), Arianna (*girl in novel*), Helen Stewart (*lesbian friend*), Sam Hall (*boatman*), William Fitzgerald (*doctor*).

Melodrama. A boatman fishes the body of a woman from the Central Park Lake. As a crowd of police and newspaper reporters gathers, the woman's voice begins to narrate the tale of the events that led to her death: *Marsha, happily married to Julian, an immature, egotistical artist, is commissioned to write a novel about lesbians. She feels that her inexperience will hamper her understanding of the characters' motivations, and to broaden her perspective she becomes involved in a relationship with lesbian Barbara. She soon finds that her husband is no longer attractive to her, and she leaves him to live with Barbara. She arrives at Barbara's apartment to find her making love with a fat, vulgar libertine, Malcolm. Fearful of being excluded, Marsha nearly yields to Malcolm's advances, but she is finally shaken into a realization that she is headed on the wrong course. She returns home to resume her interrupted marriage but finds that Barbara has, in the interval, seduced her husband. Unable to cope with life, Marsha drowns herself wearing a fur coat.* [Contains scenes of masturbation and urolagnia. According to the press material, Marsha's immature, animalistic husband neglects and mistreats her. She is driven to embark on an affair with a romantic Frenchman, but this likewise ends unhappily. Floundering, she sets out to write a series of love and sex novels. She consults a woman doctor who is considered an authority on the subject of sexuality, and the doctor promptly seduces her. She uses her experiences as the basis for her novels but is finally unable to continue writing; and she takes her own life.] *Novelists. Artists. Physicians. French. Egotists. Suicide. Lesbianism. Infidelity. Bisexuality. Seduction. Autoeroticism. Fetishism. New York City—Central Park.*

ALL WEEKEND LOVERS *see* THE KILLING GAME

ALL WOMAN   F6.0098

Franklin Productions–Three Stories High Co. *Dist* Joseph Brenner Associates. 20 Sep **1967** [Fresno, California, showing; c21 Mar 1961; LU3176]. Sd; b&w. 35mm. 83 min.

Prod-Dir Frank Warren.

Cast: Robert Alda (*Wally*), Rebecca Sand (*Kitty*), William Redfield (*Tod*), Midge Ware (*Martha*), Patricia Alison (*Virginia*), Lonney Lewis (*Marty*), Daniel Negrin (*"Him"*), Kathy Sands (*little girl*), Phil Bruns (*drunk*), Beverly Lawrence (*Birdie*).

Melodrama. Source: Louis S. London, *Schizo* (publication undetermined). Wally, an aspiring young Broadway composer, becomes involved in the lives of Kitty, Martha, and Virginia, three women who successively occupy an apartment in the New York City brownstone where he lives. Kitty, a widow, is beset by nightmares in which she is sexually assaulted by her deceased husband. Wally encourages her to undergo psychiatric treatment, but before the arrangements can be made, Kitty is arrested for murdering her husband. Wally attempts to help Martha, a dancer who has lived and worked hard in the city for 5 years while attempting to break into the Broadway big time with her dancing partner, Tod, whom she loves. Martha becomes discouraged by failure, and she returns to her hometown when Tod appears reluctant to marry her. Six months later, she returns to the city and discovers that Tod has had a homosexual affair with a producer. Martha then realizes that her relationship with Tod has been that of an affectionate mother for her son. The third neighbor Wally befriends is Virginia, a shy young woman who is obsessed with finding her father, a rapid-sketch artist who deserted her mother when Virginia was 7. A stranger who poses as Virginia's father attempts to rape her, but she is rescued by her boyfriend, Marty. *Composers. Neighbors. Widows. Dancers. Murder. Mental illness. Male homosexuality. Rape. New York City—Broadway. Dreams.*

Note: Produced in 1958. Contains subsequently added sex exploitation footage. Registered for copyright as *Schizo*; running time: 80 min. Copyright records give production company as Three Stories High Co. Also advertised as *All Girl.*

ALL WOMEN ARE BAD
F6.0099

Dist American Film Distributing Corp. 5 Mar **1969** [Boston opening]. Sd; b&w. 35mm. 67 min.

Dir Larry Crane.

Cast: Liz Byan, Peter Bradford.

Melodrama. John Steele, a door-to-door salesman, returns home one day to find his wife, Leila, in the arms of another man. John decides to take the ferry to New York City to prove to Leila that he, too, can be unfaithful. He rents a room in a boardinghouse and watches through a keyhole as a female artist sketches a nude male model. The artist and the model begin to make love, and John realizes that the artist is his wife. He goes to a bar that caters to homosexuals and lesbians, and he observes a woman smoking opium. In another part of the bar, John sees a man whipping a woman. John next goes to a theatrical booking office and witnesses a young woman auditioning for a striptease act. He follows her home and finds his wife lying nude in a coffin. At this point, John wakes to find himself at home in bed with Leila, relieved that his nightmare is over. *Salesmen. Artists. Models. Infidelity. Voyeurism. Male homosexuality. Lesbianism. Flagellation. Striptease. Opium. New York City. Dreams.*

Note: May also be known as *Women Are Bad.*

ALLA RICERCA DI GREGORY see IN SEARCH OF GREGORY

THE ALLEY CATS
F6.0100

Spear Productions–J. C. Production Co. *Dist* Audubon Films. 21 Sep **1966** [Fresno, California, showing]. Sd; b&w. 35mm (UltraScope). 83 min.

A Radley H. Metzger Production. *Prod-Dir* Radley H. Metzger. *Script* Peter Fernandez. *Photog* Hans Jura. *Asst Camera* Addi Gerner. *Film Ed* Humphrey Wood. *Prod Mgr* Osman Ragheb.

Cast: Anne Arthur *(Leslie)*, Sabrina Koch *(Irena)*, Karen Field *(Agnes)*, Charles Hickman *(Logan)*, Harold Baerow *(Christian)*, Uta Levka *(Shelia, the dancer).*

Melodrama. At a party given by Irena for her wealthy young friends in Europe's swinging set, Leslie, a beautiful but unfulfilled young woman, finds herself attracted to Christian. Meanwhile, Leslie's unfaithful fiancé, Logan, pursues an affair with her friend Agnes. Leslie and Christian begin to see each other regularly and soon decide to spend the night together. Christian leaves town abruptly the following day, and Leslie realizes that for Christian their affair was only a casual one. Leslie joins her friends at a discotheque and finds to her distress that she responds sexually to an erotic dance by Shelia. Depressed and confused, Leslie leaves the discotheque and climbs to the top of a high tower, seized with the thought of killing herself. Irena fortuitously appears; she comforts Leslie and invites her home for a drink. Along the way, they briefly meet Agnes, who is on her way to meet Logan. Later Irena takes advantage of Leslie's depression to seduce her. The following morning, Agnes informs Logan of Leslie's whereabouts. Logan goes to Irena's apartment and warns her never to see Leslie again. As Logan and Leslie walk in a nearby park, Leslie begins to feel for the first time the security and love for which she has always yearned. *Socialites. Exotic dancers. Lesbianism. Suicide. Infidelity. Seduction.*

Note: Filmed in France.

ALLEY OF NIGHTMARES see SHE FREAK

ALLEY TRAMP
F6.0101

United Pictures Organization–Leon Thirard. *Dist* United Pictures Organization. 12 Jun **1968** [Chicago opening]. Sd; b&w. 35mm. 75 min.

Prod Leon Thirard. *Dir* Armand Parys. *2d Unit Dir* Ramon Delamare. *Screenplay* Paul Gordone. *Story* Jean Michel. *Photog* Georges Parades. *2d Unit Photog* Gaston Palau. *Art Dir* Gerard Bussieres. *Set Dsgn* Rosinne Barillet.

Cast: Anette Courset, Jean Lamee, Lisa Bourdon, Marie Delmonde, Lamone Baimu, Anette Souvet, Jacque Sette.

Melodrama. Marie, a naive teenager, comes home from a date and finds her parents violently making love. She relates the story to her cousin Phillip, who becomes aroused, and the two begin a sexual relationship. One day, Marie returns from one of her adventures with Phillip and finds her mother with a strange man. As the stranger is about to leave, Marie invites him to her bedroom and seduces him. Her mother hears the sounds of passion and is shocked to find the two together, but the undaunted teenager continues to fulfill her desires with other men. Later, Marie becomes ill after having an abortion and is sent to the hospital to recover. There she tries to rape an intern, and finally she is placed in a sanitarium for treatment. *Cousins. Hospital interns. Adolescence. Filial relations. Infidelity. Abortion. Nymphomania. Hospitals.*

Note: Also known as *Alley Tramps.*

ALLEZ FRANCE! see THE COUNTERFEIT CONSTABLE

ÁLMODOZÁSOK KORA see AGE OF ILLUSIONS

ALMOST ANGELS
F6.0102

Walt Disney Productions. *Dist* Buena Vista Distribution Co. 26 Sep **1962** [c1 Aug 1962; LP22955]. Sd (RCA); col (Technicolor). 35mm. 93 min.

A Walt Disney Production. *Dir* Steven Previn. *Screenplay* Vernon Harris. *Based on an Orig Idea & Story by* Robert A. Stemmle. *Dir Photog* Kurt Grigoleit. *Camera Op* Herbert Geier. *2d Unit Photog* Hermann Meroth. *Art Dir* Werner Schlichting, Isabella Schlichting. *Film Ed* Alfred Srp. *Mus Dir-Background Mus* Heinz Schreiter. *Mus Selections Arr & Cond* Helmuth Froschauer. *Songs:* "The Rose in the Meadow," "The Lindon Tree" Franz Peter Schubert. *Song:* "The Blue Danube" Johann Strauss. *Selections From the Works of* Johannes Brahms. *Perf by* Vienna Symphony Orchestra. *Choreog* Norman Thomson. *Sd* Herbert Janeczka, Kurt Schwarz. *Asst Dir* Rudolf Nussgruber. *Prod Supv* Peter V. Herald. *Prod Mgr* Willy Egger, Robert Russ. *Cost* Leo Bei. *Wardrobe* Josef Warnke, Maria Fleischmann. *Makeup* Rudolf Ohlschmidt, Leopold Kuhnert. *Hairstyles* Berta Matula. *Dial Coach* Kent McPherron. *Studio Rep* Harry Tytle.

Cast: Peter Weck *(Max Heller)*, Hans Holt *(Director Eisinger)*, Fritz Eckhardt *(Father Fiala)*, Bruni Löbel *(Frau Fiala)*, Gunther Philipp *(radio commentator)*, Vincent Winter *(Toni Fiala)*, Sean Scully *(Peter Schaefer)*, Denis Gilmore *(Friedel Schmidt)*, Hennie Scott *(Ferdy)*, Heinz Grohmann *(music teacher)*, Rose Renee Roth *(wardrobe mistress)*, Heide Grubl *(seamstress)*, Ferda Maren *(sister-nurse)*, Liselotte Wrede *(woman)*, Hermann Furthmosek, Hans Christian, Walter Regelsberger *(choirmasters)*, Oskar Willner *(Misignore)*, Walter Varndel *(mathematics teacher)*, Bernhard Hindinger *(Felix Meinl)*, Anni Schoenhuber *(woman)*, Elisabeth Stiepl *(mother)*, The Vienna Boys' Choir *(themselves).*

Drama with music. Thirteen-year-old Toni Fiala wins a place in the Vienna Boys' Choir at an audition held by choir director Eisinger. With his mother's encouragement, he overcomes the opposition of his father, a railway engineer, and is permitted to join the choir. Since his scholarly abilities are limited, he faces the problem of maintaining the good grades required by both his father and the choir school. During his first few days at the school, Toni is placed in the care of Peter Schaefer, the oldest member of the choir. Their initial friendship turns to distrust when Peter learns that choirmaster Max Heller is teaching Toni a song that has always been one of Peter's solos. At first, he tries to sabotage Toni's chances of success in the choir, but later he accepts and even helps his young friend. Just before they are scheduled to leave on a tour, the boys discover that Peter's voice has cracked. They attempt to cover for him, but the deception is revealed. Due to his unusual ability to compose and conduct, however, Peter is permitted to go on tour as an assistant conductor. *Students. Music teachers. Filial relations. Adolescence. Friendship. Choirs. Conservatories (schools). Vienna. The Vienna Boys' Choir.*

Note: Location scenes filmed in Vienna, Austria. Prerelease title: *Born To Sing.*

ALONE AGAINST ROME (Italy)
F6.0103

Atlantica Cinematografica. *Dist* Medallion Pictures. Dec **1963** [Los Angeles opening: 18 Mar 1964]. Sd; col (Technicolor). 35mm (Totalscope). 100 min.

Prod Marco Vicario. *Exec Prod* Sante Chimirri. *Dir* Herbert Wise. *Arena Scenes Dir* Riccardo Freda. *Dub Vers Dir* Richard McNamara. *Screenplay* Ennio Mancini, Gianni Astolfi, Gastad Green. *Photog* Silvano Ippoliti. *Art Dir* Piero Poletto. *Film Ed* Roberto Cinquini. *Mus* Armando Trovajoli. *Sd* Roy Mangano.

Cast: Rossana Podestà *(Fabiola)*, Lang Jeffries *(Brenno)*, Philippe Leroy *(Lucius Silla)*, Gabriele Tinti *(Goruk)*, Luciana Angelillo.

Melodrama. Source: Gastad Green, *The Gladiator* (publication undetermined). The rebellious city of Antigonea is subdued by the 13th Roman legion led by Lucius Suetonius. After making a pact with the city, Suetonius leaves Lucius Silla in charge. Silla does not honor the agreement, and to prevent the destruction of the city, the beautiful Fabiola agrees to live with Silla, who sends her betrothed, the mighty Brenno, to gladiator school. Brenno plans a revolt which fails, but in a great spectacle in the arena he defeats all challengers and escapes death between racing chariots. He then claims the right to man-to-man combat with Silla; and Suetonius, who has recently returned to Antigonea, orders him into the arena. Silla is killed, and Suetonius frees Brenno, who is reunited with Fabiola. *Strongmen. Gladiators. Revolts. Chariots. Arenas. Rome—History—Empire.*

Note: Released in Italy in 1962 as *Solo contro Roma.* Herbert Wise is the pseudonym of Luciano Ricci.

ALONE ON THE PACIFIC *see* **MY ENEMY, THE SEA**

THE ALPHABET MURDERS (Great Britain)   **F6.0104**
Metro-Goldwyn-Mayer Pictures. *Dist* Metro-Goldwyn-Mayer, Inc. 2 Mar **1966** [Pittsburgh opening; c21 Dec 1965; LP31995]. Sd (Westrex); b&w. 35mm. 90 min.
Prod Lawrence P. Bachmann. *Assoc Prod* Ben Arbeid. *Dir* Frank Tashlin. *Screenplay* David Pursall, Jack Seddon. *Dir Photog* Desmond Dickinson. *Camera Op* Harry Gillam. *Art Dir* Bill Andrews. *Film Ed* John Victor Smith. *Mus Comp & Cond* Ron Goodwin. *Song:* "Amanda" Brian Fahey, Norman Newell. *Sung by* Ray Peterson. *Rec Supv* A. W. Watkins. *Sd Rec* Sash Fisher. *Dub Mix* Fred Turtle. *Sd Ed* Bill Creed. *Asst Dir* David Tomblin. *Prod Mgr* Albert Becket. *Unit Mgr* Jake Wright. *Mr. Randall's Clothes by* Hardy Amies.
Cast: Tony Randall *(Hercule Poirot),* Anita Ekberg *(Amanda Beatrice Cross),* Robert Morley *(Hastings),* Maurice Denham *(Inspector Japp),* Guy Rolfe *(Duncan Doncaster),* Sheila Allen *(Lady Diane),* James Villiers *(Franklin),* Julian Glover *(Don Fortune),* Grazina Frame *(Betty Barnard),* Clive Morton *("X"),* Cyril Luckham *(Sir Carmichael Clarke),* Richard Wattis *(Wolf),* David Lodge *(scrgeant),* Patrick Newell *(Cracknell),* Austin Trevor *(Judson),* Alison Seebohm *(Miss Sparks),* Windsor Davies *(Dragbot),* Sheila Reid *(Mrs. Fortune),* Margaret Rutherford *(Miss Marple),* Stringer Davis *(Mr. Stringer).*
Mystery comedy-drama. Source: Agatha Christie, *The A. B. C. Murders* (London, 1936). Hercule Poirot, the famous Belgian detective, learns that British Intelligence has assigned one of their men, Hastings, to follow him while he is in London visiting his tailor. Poirot seems to attract crime, and while in London, an aquaclown, Albert Aachen, is found murdered in a swimming pool. Killed by a poisoned dart, Aachen's body is found by police next to a copy of the A. B. C. guide to London. While Poirot and Hastings enjoy a Turkish bath, Amanda Beatrice Cross enters in a frenzy and declares that she is a compulsive murderer; then she vanishes, leaving behind a handbag bearing the initials A. B. C. and a bowling alley score card. Poirot's investigation leads him to Betty Barnard, a bowling instructress who is murdered shortly afterwards, again by a poisoned dart. Since the first two victims had the initials A. A. and B. B., Poirot deduces that the next victim will be C. C., and further inquiries convince him that the killer will strike Sir Carmichael Clarke. Inspector Japp believes the case is solved when Amanda Cross is cornered on a high crane and jumps into the Thames. Poirot, however, continues to investigate and finally proves that Amanda did not perish in her plunge. A schizophrenic, she committed the murders because of her obsession with the alphabet. *Detectives. Clowns. Belgians. Murder. Swimming pools. Turkish baths. London. Thames River. Great Britain—Intelligence service.*
Note: Released in Great Britain in Jul 1966; running time: 85 min. Working titles: *Amanda* and *The ABC Murders.*

ALPHAVILLE (France/Italy)   **F6.0105**
Chaumiane Production-Film Studio. *Dist* Pathé Contemporary Films. 25 Oct **1965** [New York opening]. Sd; b&w. 35mm. 100 min.
Prod André Michelin. *Dir-Writ* Jean-Luc Godard. *Photog* Raoul Coutard. *Film Ed* Agnès Guillemot. *Mus* Paul Misraki. *Sd* René Levert. *Asst Dir* Charles Bitsch, Jean-Paul Savignac, Hélène Kalouguine. *Prod Mgr* Philippe Dussart.
Cast: Eddie Constantine *(Lemmy Caution),* Anna Karina *(Natacha),* Akim Tamiroff *(Henri Dickson),* Howard Vernon *(The Professor),* Laszlo Szabo *(The Engineer),* Michel Delahaye *(assistant to Professor von Braun),* Jean-André Fieschi *(Professor Eckel),* Jean-Louis Comolli *(Professor Jeckel),* Alpha 60 *(itself).*
Science fiction drama. In 1984, Earth sends secret agent Lemmy Caution across the galaxy to Alphaville. In this steel and concrete city of the future, his mission is to capture or dispose of the Earth scientist Professor Leonard Nosferatu, alias von Braun, and to find Henri Dickson, Caution's predecessor. Von Braun rules Alphaville through a giant computer, Alpha 60. This machine controls the lives of the people according to its own logic. It unemotionally orders the executions of those who resist, or still believe in such outmoded concepts as love and conscience. In his disguise as Yvan Johnson, reporter for the *Figaro-Pravda,* Caution proceeds with his investigations while at the same time becoming involved with von Braun's daughter, Natacha. Caution is able to find Dickson, who is hiding in a hotel in another part of the city. Here the men who resist the machine's orders come to kill themselves or be executed. At the hotel the staff consists of robot-like people, their jobs and ranks tattooed on their bodies. Sex is provided by official seductresses. Dickson dies in the hotel, and, disguised again, Caution is taken by von Braun to the nerve center of the city, while the computer decides what to do with him. Just before it decides to execute Caution, the secret agent shoots von Braun, thus ensuring

the destruction of Alpha 60. The inhabitants of the land, by now all mutants, are either killed or made harmless with the death of the machine. Natacha is saved only because she has learned the meaning of love, and she is able to return to Earth with Caution. *Scientists. Reporters. Space travel. Secret agents. Mutation. Alienation. The Future. Disguise. Capital punishment. Computers.*
Note: Filmed on location in Paris. Opened in Paris in May 1965; running time: 90 min. Alternative title: *Une étrange aventure de Lemmy Caution.* Released in Italy as *Agente Lemmy Caution missione Alphaville.* Working title: *Tarzan versus I.B.M.*

ALPINE WORLD   **F6.0106**
15 Jan **1970** [San Diego, California, showing]. Si; col. 35mm. ca120 min.
Pres by Explorama. *A Film by* Eric Pavel.
Travelog. A travel host describes Switzerland, Austria, Italy, and France. Mont Blanc, Geneva, the Jungfrau, St. Bernard Pass, Italian lakes, and Innsbruck are featured. *Travel. Switzerland. Austria. Italy. France. Mont Blanc. Geneva. Alps. Innsbruck.*
Note: Narration delivered live on stage.

ÄLSKANDE PAR *see* **LOVING COUPLES**

ÄLSKARINNAN *see* **THE SWEDISH MISTRESS**

ALTA INFEDELTÀ *see* **HIGH INFIDELITY**

DAS ÄLTESTE GEWERBE DER WELT *see* **THE OLDEST PROFESSION**

ALVAREZ KELLY   **F6.0107**
Ray David Productions. *Dist* Columbia Pictures. 6 Oct **1966** [Baton Rouge, Louisiana, opening; c1 Oct 1966; LP33018]. Sd; col (Pathé). 35mm. 116 min. [Also reviewed at 110 min.]
A Sol C. Siegel Production. *Prod* Sol C. Siegel. *Dir* Edward Dmytryk. *Screenplay* Franklin Coen, Elliott Arnold. *Story* Franklin Coen. *Dir Photog* Joseph MacDonald. *Camera* Duke Callaghan. *Art Dir* Walter M. Simonds. *Set Decor* Morris Hoffman. *Prolog & Main Titl Dsgn* Don Record. *Film Ed* Harold F. Kress. *Mus* John Green. *Titl Song* Johnny Mercer, John Green. *Sung by* The Brothers Four. *Sd* Lambert Day. *Sd Supv* Charles J. Rice. *Asst Sd* Franklin Hansen, Stan Wetzel, Andy Payne, Roger Smedley. *Asst Dir* Frank Baur, Gene Anderson, Jr., Joe De Martini. *Unit Prod Mgr* Lee Lukather. *Wardrobe* Seth Banks, Kathleen McCandless. *Makeup Supv* Ben Lane. *Makeup* Werner Keptler. *Hairstyles* Virginia Jones, Dorothy Andre. *Sp Eff* Ira Anderson, Jr. *Stunt Coörd* Joseph Yrigoyen. *Still Photog* Homer Van Pelt.
Cast: William Holden *(Alvarez Kelly),* Richard Widmark *(Col. Tom Rossiter),* Janice Rule *(Liz Pickering),* Patrick O'Neal *(Maj. Albert Stedman),* Victoria Shaw *(Charity Warwick),* Roger C. Carmel *(Capt. Angus Ferguson),* Richard Rust *(Sergeant Hatcher),* Arthur Franz *(Captain Towers),* Donald Barry *(Lieutenant Farrow),* Duke Hobbie *(John Beaurider),* Harry Carey, [Jr.] *(Corporal Peterson),* Howard Caine *(McIntyre),* Mauritz Hugo *(Ely Harrison),* G. B. Atwater *(General Kautz),* Robert Morgan *(Captain Williams),* Paul Lukather *(Captain Webster),* Stephanie Hill *(Mary Ann),* Indus Arthur *(Melinda),* Clint Ritchie *(Union lieutenant).*
Action drama. During the Civil War, when the Union Army is trying to starve the people of Richmond into submission, renegade adventurer Alvarez Kelly delivers a herd of 2,500 cattle to U. S. Army Maj. Albert Stedman at a Virginia plantation. But Confederate guerrilla Tom Rossiter wins the aid of the plantation owner's daughter, Charity Warwick, in devising a way to steal the herd for the South. Kelly is coerced to aid in the plot when Rossiter kidnaps him, shoots off one of his fingers, and threatens to continue unless he cooperates. Although Kelly agrees to teach the Confederates how to handle cattle, he secretly arranges for Rossiter's reluctant girl friend, Liz Pickering, to escape from the South on a blockade runner. Despite the bitter hatred between the two men, the raid on the Warwick plantation is successful. But the problem then becomes that of transporting the cattle over a bridge which Stedman has fortified with 500 soldiers. Unable to bypass the bridge, Kelly stampedes the cattle into the Union lines. A bloody and disorganized battle follows, during which Kelly risks his life to rescue a Confederate officer and Rossiter shoots one of his own men who has turned against Kelly. When the herd is safely across the bridge, Rossiter frees Kelly to go his own way. *Adventurers. Cattlemen. Guerrillas. Kidnaping. Rustling. Mutilation. Plantations. Bridges. Stampedes. United States—History—Civil War. Richmond (Virginia). Virginia. Cattle.*
Note: Location scenes filmed in and around Baton Rouge, Louisiana.

ALWAYS ON MONDAY *see* **MY TALE IS HOT**

ALWAYS ON SATURDAY   **F6.0108**
Dist Boxoffice International Film Distributors. 2 Nov **1966** [New York showing]. Sd; b&w. 35mm. 60 min.
Comedy. Tom, the town drunk, relates tales to his bartender of the weekend sexual adventures of their neighborhood friends. *Bartenders. Alcoholism. Sexuality.*

AM ANFANG WAR ES SÜNDE *see* THE BEGINNING WAS SIN

AM I FEMALE?   **F6.0109**
California Continental Cinema. 29 Oct **1970** [San Francisco showing]. Sd; col (Eastman Color). 35mm. 82 min.
A Warren St. Thomas Production.
Cast: Warren St. Thomas, Jennifer Kelly, Susan Wright, Barney West.
Melodrama. A desperate young woman who is unable to find sexual satisfaction with either men or women commits suicide. Her father sets out to avenge her death; from Acapulco to the deviant communities and nightclubs of the San Francisco waterfront, he seeks out his daughter's lesbian acquaintances and murders them one by one. *Suicide. Fatherhood. Lesbianism. Revenge. Murder. Nightclubs. Acapulco. San Francisco.*
Note: Also known as *Am I a Female?*

AM I TRYING PART II *see* TORA-SAN PT. 2

AMAI ASE *see* SWEET SWEAT

AMANDA *see* THE ALPHABET MURDERS

L'AMANT DE CINQ JOURS *see* THE FIVE DAY LOVER

L'AMANTE DEL VAMPIRO *see* THE VAMPIRE AND THE BALLERINA

L'AMANTE DI CINQUE GIORNI *see* THE FIVE DAY LOVER

LOS AMANTES DE VERONA *see* ROMEO AND JULIET

LOS AMANTES DEL DESIERTO *see* DESERT WARRIOR

AMANTI *see* A PLACE FOR LOVERS

AMANTI DEL DESERTO *see* DESERT WARRIOR

AMANTI D'OLTRETOMBA *see* NIGHTMARE CASTLE

LES AMANTS DE TERUEL *see* THE LOVERS OF TERUEL

LES AMANTS DU TAGE *see* PORT OF SHAME

THE AMAZING TRANSPLANT   **F6.0110**
Mostest Productions. *Dist* Jerand Film Distributors. ca **1970**. Sd; col. 35mm. 80 min.
Prod-Dir Louis Silverman. *Screenplay* Dawn Whitman. *Dir Photog* C. Davis Smith. *Film Ed* Lou Burdi. *Asst to the Ed* Andrew Pressman. *Mus Score* Music Sound Track Service. *Sd Eff* Emil Haviv. *Sp Eff* Eli Haviv. *Optical Eff* B. & O. Film Specialists.
Cast: Juan Fernandez, Linda Southern, Larry Hunter, Olive Denneccio, Sandy Eden, Kim Pope, E. B. Preist, Suzzan Landow, Pat Barrett.
Melodrama. Detective Bill Barlen investigates his own nephew Arthur, who is missing and is suspected of the sex slaying of Mary Thorne. Barlen interviews several of Arthur's acquaintances: Midge, Edie, and Bobby, three women who claim that Arthur raped them; and Dr. Meade, who performed an appendectomy on Arthur. Meanwhile, Arthur, after setting up his next victim, a prostitute, inexplicably does not harm her. Barlen returns to Meade for further questioning, and Meade tells of Arthur's recent past, revealing that Arthur, envious of the sexual prowess of his friend Felix, blackmailed Meade, an abortionist, into transplanting onto Arthur his friend's sex organ when he knew that Felix was dying of an incurable disease. Arthur is brought to trial when he confesses that he did not mean to kill Mary Thorne; he actually loved her, but that the sight of her gold earrings threw him (as it did Felix) into a fit of violent and uncontrollable lust. Barlen surmises that Felix's acknowledged obsession for gold earrings came with the organ transplant, and that Arthur did not harm the prostitute because she was not wearing gold earrings. *Detectives. Surgeons. Uncles. Prostitutes. Psychopaths. Murder. Rape. Abortion. Blackmail. Envy. Lust. Obsession. Incurable illness. Organ transplants. Appendicitis.*

AMAZONS OF ROME (France/Italy)   **F6.0111**
Cine Italia–Régina–Criterion Film. *Dist* United Artists. 10 Apr **1963** [Los Angeles opening; c6 Mar 1963; LP24643]. Sd; col (Eastmancolor). 35mm. 96 min.
Prod Carlo Ludovico Bragaglia. *Dir* Carlo Ludovico Bragaglia, Vittorio Cottafavi. *Screenplay* Léo Joannon. *French Adapt* Pierre O'Connell. *Story* Luigi Emmanuele, Gaetan Loffredo. *Photog* Marc Fossard. *Art Dir* Raymond Gabutti. *Film Ed* René Le Hénaff. *Mus* Marcel Landowski. *Sd* Pierre-Henri Goumy. *Prod Mgr* Louis de Masure.
Cast: Louis Jourdan *(Drusco)*, Sylvia Syms *(Clelia)*, Nicole Courcel *(Lucilla)*, Ettore Manni *(Coclite)*, Renaud Mary, Jean Chevrier, Nicolas Vogel, Corrado Pani, Paola Falchi, Maria Luisa Rolando, Carlo Giustini, Michel Piccoli, Jacques Dufilho.

Costume melodrama. In 476 B. C., Rome is besieged by the Etruscans, who are aided by Greek soldiers and Gallic horsemen led by Drusco. The Etruscan chief, Porsenna, grants a truce on condition that Rome provide 1000 hostages as security. Drusco, captivated by Clelia, leader of a valiant squadron of Roman women, demands that the women be included among the hostages. Meanwhile, Lucilla, an Etruscan noblewoman, agitates among the Greeks for the destruction of Rome. She arranges to have Drusco's men relieved of the duty of guarding the women, and, when they have left the camp on a mission, she plies the Etruscans with drink in the hope that they will assault the hostages. Clelia and her army escape to Rome, but the truce is now shattered. The Etruscans attack Rome, but Clelia's warriors travel underground through the sewers to attack the enemy from the rear. The Etruscans gain the advantage, but Drusco intervenes, makes peace with Rome, and proposes marriage to Clelia. *Etruscans. Hostages. Nobility. Gauls. Amazons. Drunkenness. Rape. Sewers. Rome—History—Empire. Greece—Ancient. Cloelia. Porsenna.*
Note: Rome opening: Aug 1961 as *Le vergini di Roma*; running time: ca80 min. Paris opening: May 1961 as *Les vierges de Rome*; running time: 98 min.

THE AMBITIOUS (Japan)   **F6.0112**
Nakamura Productions. *Dist* Toho Co. 26 Aug **1970** [Los Angeles opening]. Sd; col. 35mm. 120 min.
Dir-Writ Daisuke Ito. *Photog* Kazuo Yamada. *Art Dir* Juichi Yamada. *Mus* Masaru Sato.
Cast: Kinnosuke Nakamura *(Ryoma Sakamoto)*, Tatsuya Nakadai, Sayuri Yoshinaga, Noboru Nakaya, Katsuo Nakamura, Eitaro Matsuyama, Shigeru Kamiyama, Shinsuke Mikimoto, Keiju Kobayashi, Toshiro Mifune.
Historical melodrama. Ryoma Sakamoto, a 19th-century samurai, is opposed to the feudal structure of Japan with its many warring clans. The far-sighted samurai works for the unification of Japan to prevent its exploitation by foreign powers. *Samurai. Feudalism. Nationalism. Japan—History—Meiji period 1867–1912.*
Note: Released in Japan in Feb 1970 as *Bakumatsu*.

AMBUSH   **F6.0113**
1 Aug **1968** [New York opening]. Sd; col. 16mm. [Feature length assumed.]
Sex film. No information about the precise nature of this film has been found, but press material suggests that it is a sex film with a western setting. *Sexuality.*

THE AMBUSH (Japan)   **F6.0114**
Mifune Productions. *Dist* Toho Co. 18 Dec **1970** [Los Angeles opening]. Sd; col. 35mm. 115 min.
Exec Prod Toshiro Mifune, Yoshio Nishikawa. *Dir* Hiroshi Inagaki. *Screenplay* Kyu Fujiki, Hideo Oguni, Hajime Takaiwa, Ichiro Miyakawa. *Photog* Kazuo Yamada. *Mus* Masaru Sato.
Cast: Toshiro Mifune *(Yojimbo)*, Shintaro Katsu *(Gentetsu)*, Kinnosuke Nakamura *(Heima Ibuki)*, Ruriko Asaoka *(Okuni)*, Yujiro Ishihara *(Yataro)*, Mika Kitagawa, Ichiro Arishima, Yoshio Tsuchiya, Ryunosuke Yamazaki, Jotaro Togami, Chusha Ichikawa, Heima Ibuki.
Action drama. Yojimbo, a masterless samurai, is hired for a mysterious task at the Sanshu Pass. On his way there, he rescues Okuni, a beautiful but ill-treated woman. Because of the danger of his mission, he leaves her at an inn on the Mikuni Pass in Shinshu, now a path for fugitives from the law. Gentetsu, a doctor living in a barn behind the inn, is secretly the head of a Shogunate band planning to attack a clan of samurai carrying gold through the pass. Yojimbo sides with the samurai and in a fierce fight kills every man in the Shogunate band. *Samurai. Outlaws. Rescue. Inns. Gold.*
Note: Released in Japan in Apr 1970 as *Machi-buse*. Subtitle: *Incident at Blood Pass.*

AMBUSH BAY   **F6.0115**
Courageous Films. *Dist* United Artists. 31 Aug **1966** [Baltimore opening; c9 May 1966; LP32948]. Sd; col (DeLuxe). 35mm. 109 min.
A Schenck-Zabel Production. *Prod* Hal Klein. *Exec Prod* Aubrey Schenck. *Dir* Ron Winston. *Screenplay* Marve Feinberg, Ib Melchior. *Dir Photog* Emmanuel Rojas. *Film Ed* John Schreyer. *Mus Comp & Cond* Richard La Salle. *Sd* Burdick S. Trask. *Sd Eff Ed* Del Harris. *Mus Ed* Edna Bullock. *Asst Dir* Read Killgore. *Prod Mgr* Vicente Nayve. *Makeup Artist* Charles Blackman. *Sp Eff* Charles Schulthies. *Photog Eff* Butler-Glouner Inc. *Tech Adv* Clement J. Stadler, (Lieut. Col.).
Cast: Hugh O'Brian *(1st Sgt. Steve Corey)*, Mickey Rooney *(Sgt. Ernest Wartell)*, James Mitchum *(Pfc. James Grenier)*, Tisa Chang *(Miyazaki)*, Pete Masterson *(Sgt. William Maccone)*, Harry Lauter *(Cpl. Alvin Ross)*, Gregg Amsterdam *(Cpl. Stanley Parrish)*, Jim Anauo *(Pvt. Henry Reynolds)*, Tony Smith *(Pvt. George George)*, Clem Stadler *(Capt. Alonzo Davis)*, Amado Abello *(Amado)*, Juris Sulit *(Midori)*, Max Quismundo *(Max)*, Bruno Punzalan *(Ramon)*, Buff Fernandez *(Lieutenant Tokuzo)*, Joaquin Farjado *(Captain Kayamatsu)*, Limbo Lagdameo *(man)*, Nonong Arceo *(soldier)*.

Melodrama. Nine Marines land secretly on a Philippine island in 1944 on a mission to contact a spy who has information to convey concerning General MacArthur's planned invasion of the islands. Sergeant Corey takes charge of the group when their captain is killed. The patrol fights its way through the Japanese defenses, and only five Marines remain when they finally arrive at their destination and rescue the spy, Miyazaki, a Japanese-American woman, from the enemy. Miyazaki reveals that the Japanese have learned MacArthur's planned invasion route and have mined the bay he will use; but the group's radio has been destroyed, and they are unable to communicate this intelligence. Sergeant Wartell stays behind to hold off an enemy patrol, which he destroys at the cost of his own life, as the survivors, Corey and Pfc. Grenier, set out with Miyazaki to detonate the mines. Miyazaki sacrifices herself to save her companions from the Japanese, and the mission is a success, though Corey is killed. Grenier escapes in time to hear the MacArthur radio broadcast: "People of the Philippines, I have returned." *Spies. Japanese. Combat zone life. Self-sacrifice. Mines (war explosives). World War II. Philippines. Douglas MacArthur. United States Marines. Japan—Army.*

Note: Filmed on Luzon in the Philippines.

THE AMBUSHERS   F6.0116

Meadway-Claude Productions #3. *Dist* Columbia Pictures. 20 Dec **1967** [Chicago opening; c1 Dec 1967; LP35419]. Sd; col (Technicolor). 35mm. 102 min.

An Irving Allen Production. *Prod* Irving Allen. *Assoc Prod* Douglas Netter. *Dir* Henry Levin. *2d Unit Dir* James Havens. *Screenplay* Herbert Baker. *Dir Photog* Burnett Guffey, Edward Colman. *2d Unit Camera* Jack Marta, Tony Braun. *Art Dir* Joe Wright. *Set Decor* Richard Spero. *Film Ed* Harold F. Kress. *Mus Comp & Cond* Hugo Montenegro. *Song:* "The Ambushers" Hugo Montenegro, Herbert Baker. *Sung by* Tommy Boyce, Bobby Hart. *Choreog* Mary Jane Mangler. *Sd Supv* Charles J. Rice. *Sd* James Z. Flaster, Jack Haynes. *Asst Dir* Jerome M. Siegel. *Unit Prod Mgr* Howard Pine. *2d Unit Asst* Harold Lewis. *Dresses & Cost* Oleg Cassini. *Dean Martin's Wardrobe Dsgn by* Sy Devore. *Makeup Supv* Ben Lane. *Hairstyles* Virginia Jones. *Sp Eff* Danny Lee. *Prop Master* Max Frankel.

Cast: Dean Martin (*Matt Helm*), Senta Berger (*Francesca Madeiros*), Janice Rule (*Sheila Sommers*), James Gregory (*MacDonald*), Albert Salmi (*José Ortega*), Kurt Kasznar (*Quintana*), Beverly Adams (*Lovey Kravezit*), David Mauro (*Nassim*), Roy Jenson (*Karl*), John Brascia (*Rocco*), Linda Foster (*Linda*), Yumido Ishizuka, Karin Fedderson, Ulla Lindstrom, Marilyn Suka, Lena Cederham, Susannah Moore, Terri Hughes, Penny Brahms, Kyra Bester, Jan Watson, Annabella Incontrera, Dee Duffy, Alena Johnston (*Slaygirls*), Marilyn Tindall, John Indrisano.

Action comedy. Source: Donald Hamilton, *The Ambushers* (New York, 1963). The first U. S. flying saucer sent into space is sabotaged by enemy agent José Ortega, and the pilot, Sheila Sommers, is tortured, whereupon sleuth-photographer Matt Helm is called in to investigate. Matt and Sheila pose as husband and wife and fly to Acapulco, where they are hosted by Quintana, a local brewery tycoon. After discovering that Quintana is working for Ortega, they are nearly killed by the beer baron's henchmen. Francesca Madeiros, a secret agent for another foreign power, helps them escape but is duped into leading Helm and Sheila to Ortega's hideout in the Mexican jungle. Although Francesca attempts to pit Ortega against the two Americans, she is eventually killed by his right-hand man, Nassim. Ortega then follows Sheila into the grounded saucer, unaware that when radioactive controls are set off only a woman can survive the withering blast. Ortega and Quintana are both finally killed, but not before the latter has trapped Sheila in the flying saucer and set it rolling down a railroad track. Helm rescues her, however, with the help of his ray gun and a speedy motorcycle. *Secret agents. Photographers. Brewers. Hired killers. Tycoons. Imposture. Space exploration. Sabotage. Torture. Flying saucers. Motorcycles. Jungles. Acapulco. Mexico. Matt Helm.*

Note: Location scenes filmed in Mexico.

AMERICA AMERICA   F6.0117

Athena Enterprises. *Dist* Warner Bros. Pictures. 15 Dec **1963** [New York opening; c22 Feb 1964; LP29435]. Sd; b&w. 35mm. 174 min. [Cut from 177 min.]

Prod-Dir-Writ Elia Kazan. *Assoc Prod* Charles H. Maguire. *Photog* Haskell Wexler. *Camera Op* Harlowe Stengel. *Art Dir* Gene Callahan. *Film Ed* Dede Allen. *Asst Film Ed* Peter Grivas. *Mus* Manos Hadjidakis. *Lyr* Nikos Gatsos. *Sd Mix* Leroy Robbins. *Re-rec Mix* Richard Vorisek. *Ch Sd Ed* Edward Beyer. *Sd Ed* Jean Bagley, Jack Fitzstephens. *Prod Asst* Burtt Harris. *Set Cont* Marie Kenney. *Cost* Anna Hill Johnstone. *Makeup* Emilio Trani. *Optical Eff* Film Opticals. *Liaison in Greece for Athena Enterprises* Theodore Kritas.

Cast: Stathis Giallelis (*Stavros Topouzoglou*), Frank Wolff (*Vartan Damadian*), Harry Davis (*Isaac Topouzoglou*), Elena Karam (*Vasso Topouzoglou*), Estelle Hemsley (*Grandmother Topouzoglou*), Gregory Rozakis (*Hohanness Gardashian*), Lou Antonio (*Abdul*), Salem Ludwig (*Odysseus Topouzoglou*), John Marley (*Garabet*), Joanna Frank (*Vartuhi*), Paul Mann (*Aleko Sinnikoglou*), Linda Marsh (*Thomna Sinnikoglou*), Robert H. Harris (*Aratoon Kebabian*), Katharine Balfour (*Sophia Kebabian*).

Drama. Source: Elia Kazan, *America America* (New York, 1962). Stavros Topouzoglou, a young Greek, decides to emigrate to America when one of his closest friends is murdered for standing up to Turkish oppression in 1896. As a preliminary step, he journeys to Constantinople in order to join his cousin Odysseus' rug business. His parents, Isaac and Vasso, planning to join their son later, entrust him with the Topouzoglou valuables; but Stavros is robbed on the way by Abdul, a dishonest Turk who previously befriended him. He later avenges the theft by killing Abdul but reaches his cousin's home penniless and disgraced. Odysseus advises Stavros to capitalize on his good looks by marrying a wealthy woman, but Stavros refuses to jeopardize his trip to America. Instead, he joins a group of revolutionaries and is seriously wounded during a raid. After a short affair with Vartuhi, one of the conspirator's daughters, Stavros reconsiders his cousin's suggestion and becomes engaged to Thomna Sinnikoglou, the homely daughter of a rug dealer. He finds that he cannot go through with the marriage, however, and accepts only a fraction of the large dowry offered by Thomna's father—just enough money for a boat trip to America. A day before the ship's departure, Stavros meets Sophia, the wife of American rug buyer Aratoon Kebabian. They have an affair aboard ship, but the romance is quickly aborted when the furious Aratoon discovers them and promises to have the young Greek deported to Turkey. Stavros hides from the authorities but realizes that the most important dream of his life will probably be shattered. His despair over the certain deportation has driven him near the point of nervous collapse when he meets Hohanness Gardashian, a young Armenian who is one of eight indentured shoeshine boys on his way to New York. Just as Stavros' chances for escape seem more remote than ever, Hohanness, who is dying of tuberculosis, jumps over the side of the ship and drowns himself, thereby permitting Stavros to use his name and take over the shoeshine job. The young Greek reaches America at last and begins saving money to bring his family to join him. *Greeks. Turks. Cousins. Merchants. Revolutionaries. Armenians. Bootblacks. Immigration. Murder. Filial relations. Robbery. Revenge. Marriage. Infidelity. Deportation. Tuberculosis. Self-sacrifice. Dowries. Ocean liners. Turkey. Constantinople. New York City.*

Note: Filmed entirely in Greece.

AMERICA BY NIGHT (France/Italy)   F6.0118

Italcaribe Cinematografica–René Thévenet. *Dist* Major Film Distributing Corp. 11 May **1962** [New York State license]. Sd; col (Eastmancolor). 35mm. ca74 min.

Prod Angelo Faccenna, Giuseppe Maria Scotese. *Dir* Giuseppe Maria Scotese. *Unit Dir* Ernesto Guida, Tonti, Rendhel, Louis Duchesne. *Screenplay* Giuseppe Maria Scotese, Ernesto Guida. *Comm* Max Favalelli. *Photog* Massimo Dallamano, Rino Filippini, Alessandro D'Eva. *Mus* Marcello Giombini.

Cast: Holiday on Ice, Le Roy Glaver, Danny Brown New Jewel Box Revue, Chinese Playgal 1961, Tito Leduc, Los Danzantes Mejicanos, Los Caribes, Ricky Renée, Punch Mille of the "River Queen", Vincente Torrealba de Caracas, Danea Venezolanas of the Indios Piaroa, Cobby Yee ("The Dragon Lady"), Bustles and Beaus, Feminine Cup Bearers 1890, The Red Garter Banjos, The New Orleans Jazz, George Aul Sextet, Las Vegas American Girls, The Antogalaxy, Lionel Hampton, Michele, Lou Elliot, Nefra Duval, Lina Lancia's Boulevard 15, Little Joe and His Mascot, Original Poodle Symphony of Sally and Joe Novello, Mighty Sparrow (King of Calypso), Jam Session of "Vieux Carré", Basin Street Show Bar, Tony Wells, Tina Marie, The Desperados Steel Band, Embassy Night Revue, Mauri and Ambar, La Fox, The Sanctified Gospel Singers, Marinho and Luis Bonfa's "Mikimba" de Brasilia, Kean and Gladys in "La Cubanita", Carlos Machados Show of Copacabana, Samba Carnival, Miriam Michelsonn.

Documentary. Among the American floor shows, revues, and cabarets presented are those of Sardi's, the Copacabana, and Greenwich Village clubs; San Francisco burlesque theaters and Chinatown clubs; Trinidad and Cuban carnivals; Havana's Tropicana Club; a modern cabaret in Brasília; *casas* in Panama; Las Vegas floor shows; *piaroas* in Caracas; and the Boca in Buenos Aires. Also investigated are Harlem bands, Basin Street soloists, Louisiana gospel singers, and samba dancing in Rio de Janeiro. *Stripteasers. Dancers. Entertainers. Musicians. Negroes. Singers. Bands. Music. Urban life. Burlesque. Nightclubs. Cabarets. San Francisco. New York City—Harlem. New York City—Greenwich Village. Louisiana. New Orleans. Caracas. Rio de Janeiro. Las Vegas. San Francisco—Chinatown. Brasília. Trinidad. Sardi's (New York City). Boca (Buenos Aires). Copacabana (New York City). Tropicana (Havana).*

Note: Opened in Rome in Apr 1961 as *America di notte*; running time: 100 min; in Paris in Jun 1963 as *Les nuits d'Amérique*; running time: 98 min.

AMERICA DI NOTTE *see* **AMERICA BY NIGHT**

AN AMERICAN DREAM — F6.0119

Warner Bros. Pictures. 24 Aug **1966** [Los Angeles opening; c9 Sep 1966; LP35723]. Sd; col (Technicolor). 35mm. 107 min. [Copyright length: 103 min.]

Exec Prod William Conrad. *Dir* Robert Gist. *Screenplay* Mann Rubin. *Dir Photog* Sam Leavitt. *Camera Op* Al Myers. *Art Dir* LeRoy Deane. *Set Decor* Ralph S. Hurst. *Film Ed* George Rohrs. *Mus* Johnny Mandel. *Song:* "A Time for Love" Johnny Mandel, Paul Francis Webster. *Sung by* Janet Leigh. *Sd* M. A. Merrick. *Boom Op* Eugene O'Brien. *Asst Dir* Sherry Shourds, Edward A. Teets. *Unit Mgr* J. Russell Llewellyn. *Cost Dsgn* Howard Shoup. *Wardrobe* Yvonne Wood, Tye Unsald. *Makeup Supv* Gordon Bau. *Makeup* Harlan Phillips. *Supv Hairstylist* Jean Burt Reilly. *Dial Supv* Bert Steinberger. *Gaffer* Charles O'Bannon. *Prop* Archie Neel.

Cast: Stuart Whitman (*Stephen Rojack*), Janet Leigh (*Cherry McMahon*), Eleanor Parker (*Deborah Rojack*), Barry Sullivan (*Lieutenant Roberts*), Lloyd Nolan (*Barney Kelly*), Murray Hamilton (*Arthur Kabot*), J. D. Cannon (*Sergeant Leznicki*), Susan Denberg (*Ruta*), Les Crane (*Nicky*), Warren Stevens (*Johnny Dell*), Joe De Santis (*Eddie Ganucci*), Stacy Harris (*Detective O'Brien*), Paul Mantee (*Shago Martin*), Harold Gould (*Ganucci's lawyer*), George Takei (*Ord Long*), Kelly Jean Peters (*Freya*).

Drama. Source: Norman Mailer, *An American Dream* (New York, 1965). Former war hero Stephen Rojack is now a successful but controversial television commentator whose specialty is criticizing the police for not curtailing the activities of Cosa Nostra gang leader Ganucci. One evening Rojack receives a phone call from his estranged wife, Deborah, a wealthy and dissipated alcoholic. He visits her in the hope of getting her to agree to a divorce, but she unmercifully goads him into a violent fight which ends when Rojack strangles her and throws her from her 30-story penthouse. When taken to police headquarters, where he insists that his wife's death was a suicide, Rojack runs into Ganucci, the gangster's nephew Nicky, and Nicky's girl friend Cherry McMahon, a nightclub singer who once had an affair with Rojack. After being reluctantly released by the police, Rojack resumes his affair with Cherry, thereby further enraging the Cosa Nostra who decide to eliminate him. Rojack is then visited by Barney Kelly, his dead wife's father, who harasses him into admitting that he killed Deborah. Instead of turning the information over to the police, however, Mr. Kelly leaves Rojack to wrestle with his tormented conscience. Events come to a violent climax when Nicky persuades Cherry to help him trap Rojack in return for a new singing contract. She lures Rojack to her apartment but then tearfully warns him of the danger. No longer able to continue running, Rojack borrows Cherry's revolver, enters the trap, and is gunned down after killing Nicky. *War heroes. Reporters. Police. Uncles. Singers. Fathers-in-law. Alcoholism. Wealth. Murder. Conscience. Bribery. Perfidy. Los Angeles. Mafia.*

Note: Location scenes filmed in Los Angeles.

AMERICAN REVOLUTION 2 — F6.0120

The Film Group. *Dist* Cannon Releasing Corp. 20 Oct **1969** [New York opening]. Sd; b&w. 16mm & 35mm. 80 min.

Documentary. Chicago Mayor Richard Daley's preparations for the 1968 convention of the Democratic Party and ensuing confrontations between police and protestors are investigated. Among the groups represented are the Black Panthers; their white counterparts, the Young Patriots; a society of newly uprooted mountain people from Appalachia; a band of marchers led by comedian Dick Gregory; the National Guard; ghetto residents; liberal whites from the Lincoln Park area; and participants in an Uptown Council model-cities program. Black citizens are interviewed in neighborhood bars, restaurants, and pool halls. When Black Panther Bobby Lee decries police brutality to a district police commissioner, the official blames outside agitators for community conflict. Amid vociferous denials by the audience, the scene shifts to a silent, snow-covered cemetery. *Politicians. Police. Negroes. Riots. Youth. Urban life. Demonstrations. Ghettos. Chicago. Richard J. Daley. Dick Gregory. Bobby Lee. Democratic National Convention 1968. Young Patriots. Black Panthers. National Guard.*

Note: The Film Group functions as a unit and does not itemize individual credits.

THE AMERICANIZATION OF EMILY — F6.0121

Filmways, Inc. *Dist* Metro-Goldwyn-Mayer, Inc. 27 Oct **1964** [New York opening; c17 Jul 1964; LP28978]. Sd (Westrex); b&w. 35mm. 115 min.

A Martin Ransohoff Production. *Prod* Martin Ransohoff. *Assoc Prod* John Calley. *Dir* Arthur Hiller. *Screenplay* Paddy Chayefsky. *Dir Photog* Philip Lathrop. *Adtl Photog* Christopher Challis. *Art Dir* George W. Davis, Hans Peters, Elliot Scott. *Set Decor* Henry Grace, Robert R. Benton. *Film Ed* Tom McAdoo. *Mus* Johnny Mandel. *Song:* "Emily" Johnny Mercer, Johnny Mandel. *Orch Cond* Robert Armbruster. *Sd Rec Supv* Franklin Milton. *Asst Dir* Al Shenberg. *Cost Dsgn* Bill Thomas. *Makeup Supv* William Tuttle. *Hairstyles* Sydney Guilaroff. *Sp Vis Eff* J. McMillan Johnson.

Cast: James Garner (*Lieut. Comdr. Charles E. Madison*), Julie Andrews (*Emily Barham*), Melvyn Douglas (*Adm. William Jessup*), James Coburn (*Lieut. Comdr. "Bus" Cummings*), Joyce Grenfell (*Mrs. Barham*), Edward Binns (*Adm. Thomas Healy*), Liz Fraser (*Sheila*), Keenan Wynn (*old sailor*), William Windom (*Capt. Harry Spaulding*), John Crawford (*C. P. O. Paul Adams*), Douglas Henderson (*Capt. Marvin Ellender*), Edmon Ryan (*Admiral Hoyle*), Steve Franken (*young sailor*), Paul Newlan (*Gen. William Hallerton*), Gary Cockrell (*Lieut. Victor Wade*), Alan Sues (*Enright*), Bill Fraser (*port commander*), Lou Byrne (*nurse captain*), Alan Howard (*port ensign*), Linda Marlowe (*Pat*), Janine Gray, Judy Carne, Kathy Kersh ("*nameless broads*"), Sharon Tate.

War drama. Source: William Bradford Huie, *The Americanization of Emily* (New York, 1959). In wartime London just before D-Day, Lieut. Comdr. Charlie Madison, an aide to eccentric Rear Admiral Jessup, specializes in supplying the top Navy officers with luxuries such as party girls. Madison is an exponent of cowardice as a virtue because he believes reverence of heroism promotes war. He falls in love with Emily Barham, his British motorpool driver, a young woman who has lost her husband and brother in the war. Admiral Jessup is obsessed with the idea that the Army has a better image than the Navy and is determined that the first dead man on Omaha Beach on D-Day be a sailor. Jessup orders Madison to photograph the D-Day landing, and, despite his protests which alienate Emily, Madison is forced at gunpoint to be the first man to land on Omaha Beach. Running from the bombs, Madison trips a land mine and is reported to be the first man killed in the invasion. Photographs of his supposedly dead body appear in the newspapers, and he becomes a hero, but later he is found alive. Admiral Jessup then organizes a hero's welcome for Madison, but he threatens to confess the true story of his cowardice to the press. Emily, in a reversal of sentiment, promises to marry him if he will keep his secret, and Madison agrees to remain quiet. *Eccentrics. Pacifists. British. Widows. War heroes. Cowardice. World War II. D-Day (6 Jun 1944). London. Omaha Beach. United States Navy. United States Army.*

Note: Location scenes filmed in London. Reissued in 1967 as *Emily*.

LE AMICHE (Italy) — F6.0122

Titanus–Trionfalcine. *Dist* Premiere Films. 4 Jan **1962** [New York showing]. Sd; b&w. 35mm. 104 min.

Prod Giovanni Addessi. *Dir* Michelangelo Antonioni. *Screenplay* Suso Cecchi D'Amico, Michelangelo Antonioni, Alba De Cespedes. *Photog* Gianni Di Venanzo. *Art Dir* Gianni Polidori. *Film Ed* Eraldo Da Roma. *Mus* Giovanni Fusco. *Piano Played by* Armando Trovajoli. *Guitar Played by* Libero Tosoni. *Asst Dir* Luigi Vanzi. *Prod Mgr* Pietro Notarianni. *Cost* Sorelle Fontana (Roma).

Cast: Eleonora Rossi-Drago (*Clelia*), Gabriele Ferzetti (*Lorenzo*), Franco Fabrizi (*Cesare Pedoni*), Valentina Cortese (*Nene*), Yvonne Furneaux (*Momina de Stefani*), Madeleine Fischer (*Rosetta Savoni*), Anna Maria Pancani (*Mariella*), Maria Gambarelli (*Clelia's employer*), Ettore Manni (*Carlo*), Luciano Volpato.

Drama. Source: Cesare Pavese, "Tre donne sole," in *La bella estate* (Turin, 1949). Clelia leaves her job as a couturier in a fashionable Rome dress shop and goes home to Turin to set up a boutique. After moving into a hotel, she makes several new friends, including Rosetta Savoni, a next door neighbor who is unable to get along with her wealthy parents; Lorenzo, a painter who is jealous of his wife Nene's artistic abilities; and Momina de Stefani, a bored sophisticate. Rosetta is having an unhappy love affair with Lorenzo and attempts suicide, even though Nene is willing to tolerate their relationship. Meanwhile, Clelia falls in love with Carlo, an architect's assistant, but discards any consideration of marriage because his meager income would force them to live in poverty. When Lorenzo finally admits that he prefers his work to Rosetta and Nene and that both women bore him, Rosetta kills herself, and Lorenzo eventually returns to his wife. Clelia is fired from her job when she becomes hysterical over the death of her friend, and she leaves for Rome. *Couturiers. Neighbors. Painters. Architects. Marriage. Envy. Infidelity. Suicide. Boutiques. Hotels. Turin. Rome.*

Note: Location scenes filmed in Turin. Opened in Rome in Nov 1955. Also known as *The Girl Friends*.

AMICI PER LA PELLE *see* **FRIENDS FOR LIFE**

LES AMITIÉS PARTICULIÈRES *see* **THIS SPECIAL FRIENDSHIP**

AMMAZZALI TUTTI E TORNA SOLO *see* **KILL THEM ALL AND COME BACK ALONE**

L'AMMUTINAMENTO *see* **WHITE SLAVE SHIP**

AMOK see MORO WITCH DOCTOR

AMOK see THE RAPE

AMONG THE PATHS TO EDEN see TRILOGY

AMONG THE THORNS see THE YOUNG SINNER

AMORE A VENT'ANNI see LOVE AT TWENTY

L'AMORE ATTRAVERSO I SECOLI see THE OLDEST PROFESSION

L'AMORE DIFFICILE see OF WAYWARD LOVE

AMORE IN 4 DIMENSIONI see LOVE IN 4 DIMENSIONS

AMORE IN STOCKHOLM see TO BED OR NOT TO BED

L'AMORE PRIMITIVO see PRIMITIVE LOVE

AMORI DI UNA CALDA ESTATE see THE UNINHIBITED

THE AMORISTS (Japan) F6.0123

Nikkatsu Corp. *Dist* Toho Co. Aug **1966** [Los Angeles showing]. Sd; b&w. 35mm (Nikkatsu Scope). [U. S. release length unknown.]

Prod Jiro Romoda. *Dir* Shohei Imamura. *Screenplay* Koji Numata, Shohei Imamura. *Story* Akihiro Nosaka. *Photog* Masahisa Himeda. *Art Dir* Ichiro Takada, Hiromi Shiozawa. *Film Ed* Mutsuo Tanji. *Mus* Toshiro Kusunoki. *Sd* Shinichi Beniya.

Cast: Shoichi Ozawa *(Yoshimoto "Subu" Ogata)*, Sumiko Sakamoto *(Haru Masuda)*, Masafumi Kondo *(Koichi)*, Keiko Sagawa *(Keiko)*, Ganjiro Nakamura *(elderly client)*, Chocho Miyako, Haruo Tanaka, Shinichi Nakano.

Comedy-drama. Yoshimoto "Subu" Ogata, a salesman of medical instruments, also deals in pornographic material of every variety and supplies young girls to businessmen. He has no qualms about his business, asserting that he is bringing pleasure to those in need of sexual satisfaction. His personal life, however, is deeply troubled. He lives with a widow, Haru Masuda, who keeps a carp that she insists is a reincarnation of her husband, and her two teenaged children: a son, Koichi, who is interested in Ogata only for his money, and a daughter, Keiko, who does not resist Ogata's tentative advances toward her. Haru, disturbed by the relationship between Ogata and her daughter, suggests that they get married. After Koichi steals his mother's money and runs off with a prostitute, Haru goes mad, is hospitalized, and dies. While Keiko is holding orgies in the house, Ogata goes through a period of grief and debauchery, finally moving to a houseboat with his assistant, Kabo. There, Ogata fashions a full-size doll in the likeness of Haru, believing that such an invention will make men independent of women. Several years later, Ogata has gone slightly mad and refuses to sell his invention, believing it to be a reincarnation of Haru. The boat slips from its moorings and drifts out to sea, with Ogata aboard singing happily. *Pornographers. Salesmen. Widows. Pimps. Reincarnation. Insanity. Adolescence. Filial relations. Houseboats. Sex aids. Sex exploitation films. Osaka. Fish.*

Note: Filmed on location in Osaka. Released in Japan in Mar 1966 as *Jinruigaku nyumon;* running time: 128 min. May have been significantly cut for distribution in the U. S.

THE AMOROUS ADVENTURES OF MOLL FLANDERS
(Great Britain) F6.0124

Winchester Film Productions. *Dist* Paramount Pictures. 27 May **1965** [New York opening; c26 May 1965; LP30649]. Sd; col (Technicolor). 35mm (Panavision). 126 min.

Prod Marcel Hellman. *Assoc Prod* Richard Hellman. *Dir* Terence Young. *Screenplay* Denis Cannan, Roland Kibbee. *Photog* Ted Moore. *Location Art Dir* Alex Vetchinsky. *Prod Dsgn* Syd Cain. *Film Ed* Frederick Wilson. *Mus Comp & Cond* John Addison. *Sung by* Lionel Long. *Choreog* Pauline Grant. *Sd* Bert Ross, Bob Jones. *Asst Dir* David Anderson. *Prod Supv* Mickey Delamar. *Cost* Elizabeth Haffenden, Joan Bridge. *Period Adv* Vyvyan Holland, James Laver.

Cast: Kim Novak *(Moll Flanders)*, Claire Ufland *(young Moll)*, Richard Johnson *(Jemmy)*, Angela Lansbury *(Lady Blystone)*, Vittorio De Sica *(The Count)*, Leo McKern *(Squint)*, George Sanders *(The Banker)*, Lilli Palmer *(Dutchy)*, Peter Butterworth *(Grunt)*, Dandy Nichols *(orphanage superintendent)*, Noel Howlett *(bishop)*, Cecil Parker *(The Mayor)*, Barbara Couper *(mayor's wife)*, Daniel Massey *(elder brother)*, Derren Nesbitt *(younger brother)*, Ingrid Hafner *(elder sister)*, June Watts *(younger sister)*, Judith Furse *(Miss Glowber)*, Anthony Dawson, British *(The Officer of Dragoons)*, Roger Livesey *(drunken parson)*, Hugh Griffith *(prison governor)*, Jess Conrad *(1st Mohock)*, Noel Harrison *(2d Mohock)*, Alex Scott *(3d Mohock)*, Alexis Kanner *(4th Mohock)*, Mary Merrall *(a lady)*, Richard Wattis *(jeweler)*, Terence Lodge *(draper)*, Reginald Beckwith *(doctor)*, Lionel Long *(singer in prison)*, David Lodge *(ship's captain)*, David Hutcheson *(a*

nobleman)*, Michael Trubshawe *(Lord Mayor of London)*, Richard Goolden *(The Ordinary)*, Leonard Sachs *(prison doctor)*, Basil Dignam *(lawyer)*, Michael Brennan *(The Turnkey)*, Liam Redmond *(convict ship captain)*, Neville Jason *(convict ship officer)*.

Costume comedy. Source: Daniel Defoe, *Moll Flanders* (1721). As Moll Flanders grows up in an orphanage in the 18th century, she dreams of becoming a lady. She first seeks to realize her ambition in the home of a local mayor where she is employed as a servant. She loses her virginity to the older son and marries his younger brother, a drunkard who soon leaves her a widow. She next becomes a personal servant to the wealthy Lady Blystone and travels to London where she encounters a young highwayman, Jemmy. Jemmy thinks that Moll is Lady Blystone, and disguised as a wealthy sea captain, he courts her; but upon discovering their mutual error, they part company. Lady Blystone's Latin lover, the Count, tries to seduce Moll, and when the two are discovered, Moll loses her job. She then marries a prominent banker and promptly abandons him on their wedding night when she sees the militia chasing Jemmy. Searching for her lover, Moll joins a band of thieves led by Dutchy. She is reunited with Jemmy when they both end up in the same jail, awaiting execution. The banker visits the jail one day and dies of heart failure when he sees his wife behind bars. With the fortune left to her by the banker, Moll buys a reprieve for herself and Jemmy. Their sentence is reduced to deportation, and the two are married aboard a ship sailing away from England. *Orphans. Adventuresses. Mayors. Domestics. Widows. Highwaymen. Bankers. Sea captains. Thieves. Courtship. Drunkenness. Marriage. Impersonation. Seduction. Deportation. Social classes. Employer-employee relations. Capital punishment. Inheritance. Jails. London.*

Note: Released in London in Sep 1965.

THE AMOROUS GENERAL see WALTZ OF THE TOREADORS

THE AMOROUS MR. PRAWN see THE PLAYGIRL AND THE WAR MINISTER

THE AMOROUS PRAWN see THE PLAYGIRL AND THE WAR MINISTER

THE AMOROUS SEX (Great Britain) F6.0125

Flamingo Productions. *Dist* Constitution Films, William Mishkin. 29 Oct **1962** [New York showing]. Sd; b&w. 35mm. 66 min.

Prod Jeff Kruger. *Dir* Ronnie Albert. *Screenplay* Ron Ahran. *Photog* S. D. Onions. *Film Ed* Jay Dea. *Mus Dir* Malcolm Lockyer. *Song Sung by* Tony Crombie. *Sd* Charles Green.

Cast: Julie Amber *(Bonnie Martyn)*, Sheldon Lawrence *(Bill Lacey)*, Irv Bauer *(Dave Lefferts)*, Leonie Page *(Tina Miller)*, Dave Browning *(Gerry Turner)*, Al Burnett, Billy Myles, The Mellowkings, Cindy Mann, Miss Jeri Lee, Delilah, Fred Parris and His Satins, Lee Allen and His Band.

Drama. Bonnie Martyn wins a camp beauty contest and a trip to London to participate in the all-England finals. Her fiancé, Bill Lacey, accompanies her. Although Bonnie, a talented singer, does not win the finals, she meets producer Dave Lefferts who arranges some successful recording sessions for her. Dave offers Bonnie a nightclub engagement in New York City, intending to seduce her once she and Bill are separated. In New York, Bonnie soon realizes that she has been tricked; she returns to London to be reconciled with Bill. *Singers. Music producers. Seduction. Beauty contests. Recording. Nightclubs. London. New York City.*

Note: Released in Great Britain in 1959 as *Sweet Beat.*

L'AMOUR À LA CHAÎNE see TIGHT SKIRTS, LOOSE PLEASURES

L'AMOUR À VINGT ANS see LOVE AT TWENTY

AMOUR DE POCHE see NUDE IN HIS POCKET

L'AMOUR EN 4 DIMENSIONS see LOVE IN 4 DIMENSIONS

AN EINEM FREITAG IN LAS VEGAS see THEY CAME TO ROB LAS VEGAS

AN EINEM FREITAG UM HALB ZWÖLF see THE WORLD IN MY POCKET

ANALYZE YOUR SEX F6.0126

Fleetan Films. *Dist* Able Film Co. ca **1970**. Sd; col. 16mm. [Feature length assumed.]

Sex film. No information about the precise nature of this film has been found. *Sexuality.*

THE ANATOMIST (Great Britain) F6.0127

Dola Films. *Dist* Dave Bader. Oct **1961**. Sd; b&w. 35mm. 73 min.

Pres by Dave Bader, Walter Gettinger, Herbert L. Lee. A Harry Alan Towers Production. *Prod* Vincent Johnston. *Dir–Screenplay* Leonard William.

Cast: Alastair Sim *(Dr. Knox)*, George Cole, Jill Bennett, Adrienne Corri, Diarmuid Kelly, Michael Ripper, Margaret Gordon, Peter Halliday, Frank

Wilson Taylor, Jefferson Clifford, Doria Noar, Irene Sunters.

Melodrama. Source: James Bridie, *The Anatomist* (London opening: 7 Oct 1931). Dr. Knox, a professor of anatomy in Edinburgh in 1828, buys bodies from two Irish grave robbers who frequently resort to murder when there is a shortage of bodies. Knox's assistant, George Cole, becomes aware of the origin of the bodies when he recognizes the corpse of Adrienne Corri, a young woman whom he had met at a bar. Cole protests to Knox, but he is rebuffed until an angry mob threatens to hunt down the professor. The grave robbers are arrested; Knox is implicated in the resulting scandal; Cole manages to appease the mob; and the students continue to attend Dr. Knox's lectures. *Professors. Grave robbers. Students. Murder. Anatomy. Scandal. Corpses. Edinburgh.*

ANATOMY OF A MARRIAGE; MY DAYS WITH JEAN-MARC

(France/Italy)   F6.0128

Films Borderie-Terra Films-Jolly Film-Arco Film. *Dist* Janus Films. 26 Oct **1964** [New York opening]. Sd; b&w. 35mm. 96 min.

Prod Raymond Froment. *Dir-Orig Story* André Cayatte. *Dial* Louis Sapin. *Adapt* André Cayatte, Maurice Augergé, Louis Sapin. *Dir Photog* Roger Fellous. *Camera* Adolphe Charlet. *Set Dsgn* Robert Clavel. *Film Ed* Paul Cayatte. *Mus* Louiguy. *Piano* Aldo Ciccolini. *Sd Engr* Jacques Lebreton. *Asst Dir* Pierre Léaud, Jacques Bourdon. *Prod Mgr* Léon Sanz.

Cast: Marie-José Nat *(Françoise)*, Jacques Charrier *(Jean-Marc)*, Michel Subor *(Roger)*, Giani Esposito *(Ettore)*, Michèle Girardon *(Patricia)*, Macha Meril *(Nicole)*, Georges Rivière *(Philippe)*, Jacqueline Porel *(Line)*, Yves Vincent *(Granjouan)*, Yvan Chiffre *(Christian)*, Anne Caprile *(Madame Monier)*, Corinne Armand *(Christina)*, Michel Tureau *(Milou)*, Marie-Claude Breton *(Minouche)*, Rosita Fernandez *(housemaid)*, Blanchette Brunoy *(Suzanne)*, Alfred Adam *(Aubry)*, Jacques Monod *(Rouquier)*, Henri Crémieux *(Rancoule)*, Jean-Henri Chambois *(president of the tribunal)*, Julien Verdier *(porter)*, Marcel Pérès *(tenant)*, Madeleine Suffel *(tenant's wife)*, Micheline Sandrel *(announcer)*, Stéphane Grappelli *(violinist)*, Robert Porte *(intern)*, Nicole Chaumot *(secretary)*, Paul Faivre *(doctor)*, Sybil Saulnier *(Danièle)*, Jean-Jacques Steen *(entrepreneur)*, Lina Roxa *(concierge)*, Jacques Marin, Francomme, Marcelle Ranson, Micheline Cureau, Jean Léon, André Dalibert.

Drama. In 1955, Françoise, an energetic and ambitious young Parisian with well-defined goals, meets fellow law student Jean-Marc, a handsome and charming young man without character or willpower. She breaks her family ties rather than renounce him, convinced that his spinelessness will guarantee the freedom she holds dear, but discovers herself mistaken when she finds that she is pregnant. Nevertheless, she abandons her career and concentrates her ambitions on Jean-Marc, investing him with the courage he lacks. He panics under the weight of his new responsibilites and accepts a position as a provincial magistrate in the Ardennes. Though Françoise holds her boredom and impatience with smalltown life in check, she suddenly realizes that Jean-Marc has limited his sights to a career as a bureaucrat, and she shakes him out of his complacency by creating a scandal. Thanks to her influence, he obtains a position in the office of a famous Parisian lawyer, while she establishes contacts with the help of Roger, a former schoolmate and beau. Jean-Marc's scruples and hesitations inhibit his progress, and soon he is forced to leave the firm. Forced to act as breadwinner for the family, Françoise accepts a position with the public relations firm where Roger works. In spite of her tact and understanding, she cannot soothe Jean-Marc's wounded pride. Though she has ample opportunity for infidelity, she remains faithful to her husband, but he abandons her, stubbornly believing his unfounded suspicions. *Law students. Lawyers. Careerwomen. Magistrates. Marriage. Ambition. Filial relations. Infidelity. Pregnancy. Scandal. Employment—Women. Smalltown life. Paris. Ardennes.*

Note: Opened in Paris in Jan 1964 as *La vie conjugale* in two parts entitled *Jean-Marc* and *Françoise*; running time for each part: 112 min. Italian titles: *La vita conjugale* and *Per il bene e per il male*. The second part was released in the U. S. as *Anatomy of a Marriage; My Nights With Françoise,* q. v.

ANATOMY OF A MARRIAGE; MY NIGHTS WITH FRANÇOISE

(France/Italy)   F6.0129

Films Borderie-Terra Films-Jolly Film-Arco Film. *Dist* Janus Films. 26 Oct **1964** [New York opening]. Sd; b&w. 35mm. 97 min.

Prod Raymond Froment. *Dir-Orig Story* André Cayatte. *Dial* Louis Sapin. *Adapt* André Cayatte, Maurice Augergé, Louis Sapin. *Dir Photog* Roger Fellous. *Camera* Adolphe Charlet. *Set Dsgn* Robert Clavel. *Film Ed* Paul Cayatte. *Mus* Louiguy. *Piano* Aldo Ciccolini. *Sd Engr* Jacques Lebreton. *Asst Dir* Pierre Léaud, Jacques Bourdon. *Prod Mgr* Léon Sanz.

Cast: Jacques Charrier *(Jean-Marc)*, Marie-José Nat *(Françoise)*, Michel Subor *(Roger)*, Giani Esposito *(Ettore)*, Michèle Girardon *(Patricia)*, Macha Meril *(Nicole)*, Georges Rivière *(Philippe)*, Jacqueline Porel *(Line)*, Yves Vincent *(Granjouan)*, Yvan Chiffre *(Christian)*, Anne Caprile *(Madame Monier)*, Corinne Armand *(Christina)*, Michel Tureau *(Milou)*, Marie-Claude Breton *(Minouche)*, Rosita Fernandez *(housemaid)*, Blanchette Brunoy *(Suzanne)*, Alfred Adam *(Aubry)*, Jacques Monod *(Rouguier)*, Henri Crémieux

(Rancoule), Jean-Henri Chambois *(president of tribunal)*, Julien Verdier *(porter)*, Marcel Pérès *(tenant)*, Madeleine Suffel *(tenant's wife)*, Micheline Sandrel *(announcer)*, Stéphane Grappelli *(violinist)*, Robert Porte *(intern)*, Nicole Chaumot *(secretary)*, Paul Faivre *(doctor)*, Sybil Saulnier *(Danièle)*, Jean-Jacques Steen *(entrepreneur)*, Lina Roxa *(concierge)*, Jacques Marin, Francomme, Marcelle Ranson, Micheline Cureau, Jean Léon, André Dalibert.

Drama. Jean-Marc, an easygoing young Parisian student not overly concerned about his future, casually pursues a career in law. His girl friends help him to forget conditions at home, where his widowed mother, attempting to ward off middle age, entertains a stream of young lovers. Jean-Marc's latest conquest is Françoise, a sweetly naive young woman with a taste for the gaudy. When she breaks with her parents, who resent their liaison, Jean-Marc takes care of her, assuming that they will soon work side by side. Unfortunately, he passes his exams, but she fails hers. When she discovers that she is pregnant, he marries her and takes complete responsibility for the three of them. Soon a rift develops between his mother and his wife; to save their marriage, Jean-Marc delays his professional advancement by taking a job as a magistrate in the Ardennes. Though the provincial life is perfect for Françoise, who conquers the local citizenry, she eventually grows impatient for their return to Paris, where her material desires are better satisfied. Jean-Marc perseveres in his career and eventually finds satisfaction in attacking the problem of juvenile delinquency. Having at last found a calling in life, he is forced by Françoise to abandon it when she creates a scandal. Jean-Marc enters the firm of a Parisian lawyer he had met 3 years earlier and soon becomes indispensable, but, unable to endure the constant compromises required of him, he resigns to work on his own. Françoise, anxious for wealth and luxury, accepts a job in a publicity firm and begins to neglect her family. She becomes involved with several men at work, and when Jean-Marc discovers what is going on, he leaves her. *Law students. Lawyers. Widows. Magistrates. Mothers-in-law. Marriage. Ambition. Filial relations. Infidelity. Pregnancy. Scandal. Employment—Women. Smalltown life. Paris. Ardennes.*

Note: Opened in Paris in Jan 1964 as *La vie conjugale* in two parts entitled *Jean-Marc* and *Françoise*; running time for each part: 112 min. Italian titles: *La vita conjugale* and *Per il bene e per il male*. The first part was released in the U. S. as *Anatomy of a Marriage; My Days With Jean-Marc,* q. v.

ANATOMY OF A PSYCHO   F6.0130

Plymouth. *Dist* Unitel of California. 14 Jun **1961** [Los Angeles opening]. Sd; b&w. 35mm. 75 min.

A Brooke L. Peters Production. *Prod-Dir* Brooke L. Peters. *Screenplay* Jane Mann, Larry Lee. *Orig Story* Jane Mann.

Cast: Darrell Howe *(Chet)*, Ronnie Burns *(Mickey)*, Pamela Lincoln *(Pat)*, Judy Howard *(Sandy)*, Russ Bender *(Frank)*, Pat McMahon *(Arthur)*, Frank Kiliman *(Bobbie)*, Mike Grainger *(Lieutenant Mac)*, Don Devlin *(Moe)*, John B. Lee *(district attorney)*, Robert W. Stabler *(prosecuting attorney)*, Charles J. Simon *(judge)*.

Crime melodrama. A young man named Chet seeks revenge upon society for sending his brother to the gas chamber. Certain that his brother was innocent, he plots against all those responsible for his conviction. Aiding him in his vendetta is Sandy, a beautiful but vicious tramp. Sandy's sister, Pat, tries to show Chet that he is wrong, but this only makes him more psychotic and he attempts to frame Pat's boyfriend, Mickey, for a crime he himself committed. But a quick-thinking police lieutenant, Mac, traps Chet into confessing his own crimes and admitting that his brother was guilty. *Brothers. Police. Sisters. Psychopaths. Revenge. Capital punishment. Confession (law).*

AND FATHER CAME TOO *see* **FATHER CAME TOO**

AND FIVE MAKES JASON   F6.0131

Art In Motion (A. I. M.) Productions. *Dist* Grads Corp., Clamil Productions. 17 Dec **1969** [Washington, D.C., opening]. Sd; b&w. 35mm. 62 min.

Prod J. Photo X. *Dir* William Stagg.

Cast: Peter Deb *(Jason)*, Don Auld *(Luke)*, Kathy Williams *(Rena)*, Kathy Harriet *(May)*, Jack Rink *(Lieutenant Lewis)*, Shari Knowles, Sidney Mase, Jay Ray.

Melodrama. Under Luke's ruthless direction, a Nevada gang kidnaps young women, drugs them, rapes them, and conditions them for sale to the highest bidder in the underground sex market. May, a roughneck lesbian, disciplines the women, while Marty, a sex offender, acts as "pickup" man, and Junior, their slow-witted accomplice, serves as errand boy. Rena, a beautiful woman who unwittingly becomes mixed up with the gang, tries to cooperate, but May, crazed by lust, kills her. When normal police methods fail in apprehending the gang, special agent Jason McCoy penetrates their ranks and becomes a gang member. Though he at first must participate in the torture and degradation of the captives, he at last fulfills his mission and destroys the gang. *Detectives. White slave traffic. Rape. Torture. Murder. Lesbianism. Sadism. Narcotics. Nevada.*

AND JENNY MAKES THREE see **JENNY**

... AND NOW MIGUEL   F6.0132

Robert B. Radnitz Productions. *Dist* Universal Pictures. 1 Jun **1966** [Albuquerque, New Mexico, opening; c2 Jul 1966; LP35376]. Sd (Westrex); col (Technicolor). 35mm. 95 min.

A Robert B. Radnitz Production. *Prod* Robert B. Radnitz. *In Charge of Prod* Edward Muhl. *Dir* James B. Clark. *Screenplay* Ted Sherdeman, Jane Klove. *Dir Photog* Clifford Stine. *Camera Op* William Dodds. *Asst Camera* William Reisbord. *Art Dir* Alexander Golitzen, William D. DeCinces. *Set Decor* John McCarthy, Joseph Kish. *Set Coörd* Virgil Clark. *Film Ed* Hugh S. Fowler. *Asst Ed* Fred Chulack. *Mus* Phillip Lambro. *Mus Supv* Joseph Gershenson. *Sd* Waldon O. Watson, David H. Moriarty, Bruce Greiner, Don Bolger, Robert Sheridan. *Asst Dir* Phil Bowles, James Welch. *Unit Prod Mgr* Kenneth L. Grossman. *Cost* Rosemary Odell. *Wardrobe* Martha Bunch, Gordon Murray. *Makeup* Bud Westmore, Dick Dawson, Dick Blair. *Hairstyles* Larry Germain, Clara Holgate. *Tech Adv* John S. Carroll. *Coöp* Gilberto Atencio, James Hall, People of Abequin, People of Santa Fe (New Mexico), People of Ildefonso Pueblo. *Dogs Trained by* Frank Weatherwax. *Still Photog* Jack Geraghty. *Gaffer* Earl Kennedy. *Grip* Steve Rez, Frank Bono. *Prop* Bill Nunley, Frank Nifong.

Cast: Pat Cardi *(Miguel)*, Michael Ansara *(Blas)*, Guy Stockwell *(Perez)*, Clu Gulager *(Johnny)*, Joe De Santis *(Padre de Chavez)*, Pilar Del Rey *(Tomasita)*, Peter Robbins *(Pedro)*, Buck Taylor *(Gabriel)*, Edmund Hashim *(Eli)*, Heil F. Waters *(wool buyer)*, James Hall *(ranger)*, J. Scott Carroll *(shearer)*, Emma Tyson *(Faustina Chavez)*, Ralph W. Pairon *(priest)*, Richard J. Brehm *(Bonifacio Chavez)*, Sister Katrina *(sister)*, Ted Butterfield *(Indian chief)*.

Drama. Source: Joseph Krumgold, *... And Now Miguel* (New York, 1953). Miguel Chavez, a 10-year-old Mexican boy, longs to accompany his father, Blas, to the mountains to graze their sheep, but each year he is told that he is too young. He prays to San Ysidro, the patron saint of farmers, and tries to prove his worth by helping with the shearing and branding. When he is humiliated by falling into a fleece bag, however, Miguel runs to the village to see his artist friend Perez and tells him that San Ysidro has ignored him. Perez advises patience and continued prayer. Shortly afterward, a storm panics the sheep, and they run into the hills. When Blas goes off in search of the flock, Miguel sets out on his own and eventually finds the lost sheep. On the way home, a pack of wolves stalk the boy, and after praying to San Ysidro for help, Miguel hears his father's call. The proud father promises to take Miguel to the mountains on his next trip. *Shepherds. Artists. Farmers. Mexicans. Children. Catholics. Friendship. Filial relations. Faith. Ranches. Mexico. Saint Isidore the Farmer. Storms. Sheep. Wolves.*

Note: Filmed on location in San Ildefonso Pueblo, Abequin, and Santa Fe (New Mexico).

AND SO TO BED (Austria/West Germany)   F6.0133

Team–Film–Stadthallen Produktion. *Dist* Medallion Pictures. 30 Jul **1965** [New York opening]. Sd; b&w. 35mm. 112 min.

Prod Adolf Eder. *Exec Prod* Heinz Pollak. *Dir* Alfred Weidenmann. *Screenplay* Herbert Reinecker. *Photog* Georg Bruckbauer. *Camera Op* Wolfgang Hewecker. *Asst Camera* Karl Kirchner. *Art Dir* Otto Pischinger, Herta Hareiter. *Film Ed* Alfred Srp, Grete Girinec. *Mus* Charly Niessen. *Sd* Otto Untersalmberger, Anton Amlacher. *Asst Dir* Jerzy Macc. *Prod Supv* Karl Spiehs. *Prod Mgr* Gerald Martell, Wolfgang Müller. *Cost* Paul Seltenhammer. *Makeup* Hans Nowotny.

Cast: Hildegard Knef *(Lilo)*, Walter Giller *(policeman)*, Thomas Fritsch *(Hans)*, Alexandra Stewart *(Brigitte)*, Martin Held *(professor)*, Daliah Lavi *(Claudia)*, Peter Van Eyck *(office chief)*, Nadja Tiller *(office chief's wife)*, Peter Parten *(student)*, Danièle Gaubert *(Françoise)*, Angelo Santi *(Octaviano)*, Lilli Palmer *(actress)*, Paul Hubschmid *(diplomat)*, Elisabeth Flickenschildt *(elderly woman)*, Gisela Trowe, Paul Hoffmann, Charles Regnier, Fritz Tillmann, Egon von Jordan, Ulli Lommel.

Comedy-drama. Source: Arthur Schnitzler, *Reigen* (Berlin opening: 23 Dec 1920). Lilo, a high-priced call girl, attends a party given by a group of students, and at their behest, she seduces Hans, an innocent young man. Now experienced, Hans enters a liaison with Brigitte, the wife of his respectable professor. The professor gets drunk while on a trip to Frankfurt and spends the night with Claudia, a secretary. Claudia has a brief encounter with her boss, who then returns to his ex-wife. The ex-wife in turn takes up with an impoverished student, and the student becomes attracted to Françoise, a French general's daughter. Françoise falls for Octaviano, a talented singer working as a waiter in a hotel. A famous actress, impressed by the waiter's talent and good looks, gets him a part in her movie. After the shooting, the actress leaves by train and is invited by a diplomat to share his sleeping compartment. The diplomat is met the next day by an older woman who has been helping him with his career, and when they part, the diplomat meets and makes a date with Lilo. *Prostitutes. Students. Professors. Secretaries. French. Singers. Actors. Diplomats. Waiters.*

Sexual initiation. Seduction. Marriage. Infidelity. Trains. Frankfurt am Main.

Note: Released in West Germany in Nov 1963 as *Das grosse Liebesspiel*; running time: 138 min.

... AND SUDDENLY IT'S MURDER! (France/Italy)   F6.0134

Dino De Laurentiis Cinematografica–Orsay Films. *Dist* Royal Films International. 23 Jan **1964** [New York opening]. Sd; b&w. 35mm (CinemaScope). 90 min.

Prod Dino De Laurentiis. *Dir* Mario Camerini. *Screenplay* Rodolfo Sonego, Giorgio Arlorio, Stefano Strucchi, Luciano Vincenzoni, Oreste Biancoli. *Photog* Gianni Di Venanzo. *Film Ed* Giuliana Attenni. *Mus* Pino Calvi.

Cast: Alberto Sordi *(Alberto Franzetti)*, Vittorio Gassman *(Remo Capretti)*, Silvana Mangano *(Marina Capretti)*, Nino Manfredi *(Quirino Filonzi)*, Franca Valeri *(Giovanna Filonzi)*, Bernard Blier *(police commissioner)*, Dorian Gray *(Eleonora Franzetti)*, Georges Rivière *(man-about-Monte Carlo)*, Sylva Koscina, Lamberto Antinori.

Crime comedy. Three couples from Rome meet on a train bound for Monte Carlo. Remo and Marina, assistants in a hairdressing shop, hope to win enough money to open their own business. Wealthy manufacturer Alberto Franzetti, a gambling addict with a "sure-fire" winning system, neglects his wife, Eleonora, in his concentration on the gaming tables. Quirino and Giovanna Filonzi, poor newspaper vendors, have found a valuable dog and are returning it to a wealthy old woman for a reward. Quirino soon discovers that the old woman has been robbed and murdered, and, in his frantic departure from the scene of the crime, he leaves evidence which implicates all three couples and leads to his arrest. Meanwhile, Remo and Alberto lose heavily at the casino, while Eleonora finds diversion with a local man-about-town. Desperate for funds, Remo steals a suitcase; then discovers the old woman's body inside and makes a frenzied attempt to dispose of the evidence before he, too, is arrested. Finally, Alberto attracts the suspicions of the police commissioner and is arrested in turn. The three are charged with being accomplices in the crime, and they incriminate one another as each attempts to find an alibi. The police commissioner finally discovers that the old woman's housekeeper and butler killed their employer. Returning to Rome after their release, the three couples are the only witnesses to another murder. *... Hairdressers. Manufacturers. Police. Butlers. Housekeepers. Murder. Robbery. Gambling. Infidelity. Circumstantial evidence. Wealth. Casinos. Rewards. Trains. Monte Carlo. Rome. Dogs.*

Note: Released in Italy in Dec 1960 as *Crimen*; running time: ca100 min. Released in France in 1961 as *Chacun son alibi*; running time: 110 min.

... AND THE WILD, WILD WOMEN (France/Italy)   F6.0135

Riama Film–Francinex. *Dist* Trans-Lux Distributing Corp. c24 May **1961** [LP21698; New York State license: 23 Mar 1961]. Sd; b&w. 35mm (Supercinescope). 85 min.

Prod Giuseppe Amato. *Dir* Renato Castellani. *Dial & Adapt* Suso Cecchi D'Amico, Renato Castellani. *Photog* Leonida Barboni, Aiace Parolin. *Art Dir* Ottavio Scotti. *Ed* Iolanda Benvenuti. *Mus* Roman Vlad. *Sd Engr* Enrico Palmieri. *Asst Dir* Rinaldo Ricci. *Prod Mgr* Franco Magli.

Cast: Anna Magnani *(Egle [Aggie])*, Giulietta Masina *(Lina)*, Cristina Gajoni *(Marietta)*, Myriam Bru *(Vittorina)*, Renato Salvatori *(Piero, the mechanic)*, Milly Monti *(Suor Giuseppina)*, Angela Portaluri *(Laura)*, Virginia Benati *(Vera)*, Miranda Campa *(Ida Maroni)*, Marcella Rovena *(Signora Luisa)*, Mirella Gregori *(Adele)*, Marcella Valeri *(Assunta)*, Pia Velsi *(Suora "28")*, Alba Maiolini *(Sara)*, Manzilla Ercolani *(Amelia)*, Luigina Giustini *(Giacomino)*, Lia Grani *(Contessa)*, Saro Urzì *(Maresciallo Carcere)*, Alberto Sordi *(Adonis)*, Anita Durante, Ada Passeri, Umberto Spadaro.

Melodrama. Source: Isa Mari, *Roma, via delle Mantellate* (Rome, 1953). Lina, a naive young woman, joins the company of prostitutes, murderers, and thieves at a large women's prison as she awaits her trial on charges of robbery. She soon finds a friend in Aggie, a hardened prostitute and con woman who decides to school Lina in the ways of the world. Lina tries to convince Aggie that she is innocent: she had come to Rome to work as a housemaid and had fallen in love with Adonis, who promised to marry her. One night they went to a movie; her employer's house was robbed while they were gone, and she was charged with the crime. Aggie insists that Adonis planned the crime. She advises Lina to offer him a proposition: her silence in exchange for a share of the "take." Lina learns that her cynical friend is right: Adonis is a married man with three children, and she is not the first housemaid Adonis has tricked. Acquitted of the crime, Lina leaves her innocence behind in prison. Meanwhile, Aggie's cynical defenses begin to waiver. She is moved by her contact with Marietta, a romantic young thief who has been watching a mechanic working across the street from the prison. Lina secretly brings them together; they fall in love and make plans to marry. Marietta leaves the prison, and Aggie considers the hopelessness of her life, happy that her friends are free. One day Lina returns to the prison transformed into a grotesquely painted prostitute. Aggie feels responsible for the change; in horror she attacks Lina. As she is being dragged off to solitary confinement, Aggie screams for the freedom to change her life. *Housemaids. Innocents. Swindlers. Prostitutes. Thieves. Confidence women. Mechanics. Criminals—Rehabilitation. Moral corruption. Cynics. Robbery. Prisons. Rome.*

Note: Opened in Rome in Nov 1958 as *Nella città l'inferno;* running time: 110 min.; in Paris in Jun 1959 as *L'enfer dans la ville;* running time: 98 min. Also known as *The Wild, Wild Women* and *Hell in the City.*

AND THERE CAME A MAN (France/Italy) F6.0136
Sol Produzioni–Majestic Film–Franco London Film–Harry Saltzman. *Dist* Brandon Films. 4 Apr **1968** [New York opening]. Sd; col (Technicolor). 35mm. 90 min.

Prod Vincenzo Labella. *Dir* Ermanno Olmi. *Screenplay* Ermanno Olmi, Vincenzo Labella. *Photog* Piero Portalupi. *Art Dir* Ennio Michettoni. *Film Ed* Carla Colombo. *Mus* Franco Potenza. *Mus Supv* Pete Kameron. *Asst Dir* Maria Teresa Girosi. *Prod Supv* Gasparo Palumbo.

Cast: Rod Steiger *(The Intermediary),* Adolfo Celi *(Monsignor Radini-Tedeschi),* Rita Bertocchi *(Signora Roncalli),* Pietro Gelmi *(Signor Roncalli),* Antonio Bertocchi *(Uncle Xavier),* Fabrizio Rossi *(Angelo, age 4),* Alberto Rossi *(Angelo, age 7),* Giovanni Rossi, actor *(Angelo, age 10),* Alfonso Orlando *(Abbé François),* Antonio Ruttigni *(Abbé Pierre [Don Pietro]),* Giorgio Fortunato *(Papal secretary),* Ottone Candiani *(drunken priest in Venice).*

Biographical drama. Based on incidents in the life of Pope John XXIII and on: John XXIII (Pope), *Il giornale dell'anima e altri scritti di pietà* (Rome, 1964). The life story of Pope John XXIII is related with the aid of excerpts from his *Giornale dell' anima* and an "intermediary" who stands in for the pontiff: Angelo Giuseppe Roncalli was born into a large and deeply religious farming family at Sotto il Monte on November 25, 1881. As a young child he studied Latin with a village priest, and at the age of 12 he entered the seminary at Bergamo. Because of his special devotion to the Church, he was sent to the Pontifical Seminary at Rome. He placed little value on the pomp of that city, however, preferring the quiet of the Church of Santa Maria in Monte Santo, where he was ordained in 1904. Although he would have liked to become a simple village priest, he was made secretary to Monsignor Radini-Tedeschi, Bishop at Bergamo, a position he held until the bishop's death 10 years later. Following service in the medical corps during World War I, he worked with the Society for the Propagation of the Faith, was consecrated bishop in 1925, and was sent to Bulgaria as Apostolic Visitor. Serving next in Istanbul as Apostolic Delegate to Turkey and Greece, he worked for humanitarian goals during World War II, seeking to guarantee the safety of food cargo ships entering blockaded Greek ports. After serving as Nuncio in Paris from 1944 to 1953, he was appointed Patriarch of Venice, and he regarded his new position as cardinal with great humility. While in Venice, he insisted upon confessing to a drunken priest in order to restore the man's faith. He became Pope John XXIII in 1958, continuing to pursue his main goal of "uniting the souls of men." To this end, he organized an ecumenical council. *Priests. Humanitarianism. Confession. Catholic Church. Seminaries. Ecumenical councils. World War I. World War II. Bergamo. Rome. Vatican. Bulgaria. Turkey. Greece. Paris. Venice. John XXIII (pope). Society for the Propagation of the Faith.*

Note: Released in Italy in 1965 as *E venne un uomo.* U. S. sources credit the film as produced in association with Harry Saltzman.

THE ANDERSON PLATOON (France) F6.0137
Office de Radiodiffusion–Télévision Française. *Dist* Pathé Contemporary Films. 17 Dec **1967** [New York opening]. Sd; b&w. 35mm. 65 min.

Dir-Writ Pierre Schoendorffer. *Photog* Dominique Merlin. *Sd* Raymond Adam.

Cast: Joseph Anderson *(himself),* Pierre Schoendorffer *(narrator).*

Documentary. Commissioned by French national television to film a documentary about Americans in Vietnam, Pierre Schoendorffer and his crew spent 6 weeks in the fall of 1966 with a platoon commanded by a Negro graduate of West Point, Lieut. Joseph Anderson. The platoon, which is characterized by racial harmony and comradeship, has been assigned to a unit ordered to take the crest of a hill about 250 miles north of Saigon. The men are landed by helicopter in the area and inch their way across fields and small rivers under constant enemy fire. During a temporary break in the fighting, one soldier is given leave to go to Saigon. But he quickly squanders his money and returns to the platoon before his pass has expired. Once Lieutenant Anderson and his men have moved into a small village, they are ordered into combat again. As the wounded and dead are removed by helicopter, the battle for the crest of the hill continues. *Negroes. Combat zone life. Military life. Race relations. Vietnam War 1964–73. Republic of Vietnam. Saigon. United States Army.*

Note: Released in France in Jan 1967 as a television documentary entitled *La patrouille Anderson;* running time: 50 min. Presented by CBS Television in Jul 1967.

ANDESU NO HANAYOME *see* **BRIDE OF THE ANDES**

ANDREA (West Germany) F6.0138
Metrostar–HIFI–Stereo. *Dist* Caprice Pictures. 5 Aug **1969** [Maryland license]. Sd; col (Eastman Color). 35mm. 70 min.

Pres by Melvin Warshaw. *Prod* Melvin Warshaw, Harald A. Hoeller. *Dir-Writ* Hans Schott-Schöbinger. *Dir Photog* Hanns Matula. *Art Dir* Nino Borghi. *Mus* Hans Hammerschmid.

Cast: Dagmar Lassander *(Andrea),* Ralph Clemente *(Thomas),* Art Brauss *(Yossi),* Hans von Borsody *(Frederick Jansen),* Joachim Hansen *(Peter),* Herbert Fux *(Felix Klarsen),* Anne Famos *(Mila),* Gita Rena *(Clarissa),* Fred Bernhoff *(Dr. Wagner),* Helmut Alimonta *(Schorsch),* Ingrid Simon *(Luisa).*

Melodrama. Rich and beautiful Andrea visits her ailing father in his country home, where she becomes bored and restless. Searching for sexual fulfillment, she seduces her maid's fiancé and her best friend's husband. After breaking off her engagement to Thomas, she goes to the city and is picked up in a bar by Felix, a brutal pimp who beats and rapes her. She manages to escape and flees to the country. After her father dies, Andrea is lonelier than ever until she meets Frederick, an escaped convict seeking revenge against his mistress who betrayed him. She gives him food and clothes and seduces him, but the next morning he leaves. Realizing that she is in love for the first time, Andrea calls her lawyer to arrange a pardon for Frederick, but he is shot and killed after murdering his two associates. Heartbroken, Andrea suffers a nervous breakdown. After recovering, she marries Thomas and finally finds contentment. *Pimps. Prison escapees. Filial relations. Seduction. Rape. Murder. Mental illness.*

Note: Released in West Germany in Oct 1968 as *Andrea—wie ein Blatt auf nackter Haut;* running time: 90 min.

ANDREA—WIE EIN BLATT AUF NACKTER HAUT *see* **ANDREA**

ANDY F6.0139
Deran Productions. *Dist* Universal Pictures. 21 Jan **1965** [New York opening; c23 Jan 1965; LP33415]. Sd; b&w. 35mm. 86 min.

Prod-Dir-Writ Richard C. Sarafian. *Assoc Prod* Joshua J. Shapiro. *Dir Photog* Ernesto Caparros. *Camera Op* Peter Garbarini. *Asst Camera* Peter Norman, Francis Grumman. *Art Dir* Peter J. Wexler. *Master Scenic Artist* Armand Catenaro. *Film Ed* Aram Avakian, Hugh A. Robertson, Jr. *Asst Ed* Lynn Ratener. *Mus* Robert Prince. *Sd* Willard Goodman, Nat Boxer, Richard Vorisek. *Asst Dir* Larry Sturhahn, Paul Leaf. *Asst to the Prod* Mel Howard. *Script Supv* Maggie James. *Cost Dsgn* Hazel Roy. *Wardrobe* George Newman. *Makeup* Irving Buchman. *Key Grip* Edward Knott. *Gaffer* Mel Brown. *Prop* Richard Tice. *Stills* Muky. *Casting Cons* Michael Shurtleff.

Cast: Norman Alden *(Andy),* Tamara Daykarhanova *(Mrs. Cliadakis),* Zvee Scooler *(Mr. Cliadakis),* Murvyn Vye *(bartender),* Warren Finnerty *(Simovich),* Ann Wedgeworth *(Margie),* William Griffis *(Kennedy),* Al Nesor *(Sommerville),* Sudie Bond *(Thelma),* Judith Lowry, Leon K. Lensky, Cynthia Grover, Henry Sherwood, William Beach, Howland Chamberlain.

Drama. Andy, the mentally retarded 40-year-old son of Greek immigrants, is a trial to his parents, Mr. and Mrs. Cliadakis, and for that reason they decide to send him to an institution. Mrs. Cliadakis gives Andy money to buy a new suit, but he wanders through New York and winds up in a bar. He is a powerful man, having once been a ship's fireman, and when a group of customers in the bar begin to jeer at him, he takes them on in a fight. Later, a prostitute takes Andy home with her. Andy goes home the next morning, and his worried parents realize that Andy needs love, not an institution. They decide to move to the suburbs so that he will have greater freedom and a chance to spend time outdoors. *Greeks. Immigrants. Bartenders. Prostitutes. Mental retardation. Filial relations. Bars. New York City.*

Note: Location scenes filmed in New York City.

ANDY WARHOL SERIAL *see* **KISS**

ANDY WARHOL'S RESTAURANT *see* **NUDE RESTAURANT**

ANGEKLAGT NACH PARAGRAPH 218 *see* **THE DOCTOR SAYS**

ANGEL *see* **THE GRASSHOPPER**

ANGEL, ANGEL, DOWN WE GO F6.0140
Four Leaf Productions. *Dist* American International Pictures. 26 Nov **1969** [Los Angeles opening; c26 Nov 1969; LP37642]. Sd; col (print by Movielab). 35mm. 93 min. *MPAA rating* R.

Pres by James H. Nicholson, Samuel Z. Arkoff. *Prod* Jerome F. Katzman. *Exec Prod* Sam Katzman. *Assoc Prod* Arthur Dreifuss. *Dir-Writ* Robert Thom. *Cinematog* John F. Warren. *Art Dir* Gabriel Scognamillo. *Set Decor* Don Greenwood. *Film Ed* Eve Newman. *Mus Comp & Cond* Fred Karger. *Songs:* "Angel, Angel, Down We Go," "The Fat Song," "Hey, Hey, Hey, and a Hi Ho," "Lady, Lady," "Mother Lover," "Revelation" Barry Mann, Cynthia Weil. *Songs Sung by* Jordan Christopher. *Choreog* Wilda Taylor. *Sd* Fred Faust. *Asst*

Dir John G. Wilson, Robert Dijoux. *Unit Mgr* Robert Stone. *Script Supv* Cosmo Genovese. *Dress Dsgn* Renee Connely. *Wardrobe* Kitty Mager, Gene Ostler. *Makeup* William Tuttle, William Reynolds, makeup. *Hairstyles* Sydney Guilaroff, Helen Parrish. *Collages* Shirley Kaplan. *Parachute Adv* Carl Boenisch. *Prop Master* Carl Bionde. *Gaffer* Don Nygren. *Still Photog* Virgil Apger.

Cast: Jennifer Jones (*Astrid Steele*), Jordan Christopher (*Bogart*), Roddy McDowall (*Santoro*), Holly Near (*Tara Nicole Steele*), Lou Rawls (*Joe*), Charles Aidman (*Willy Steele*), Davey Davison (*Anna Livia*), Marty Brill (*maitre d'*), Hiroko Watanabe (*masseuse*), Carol Costello, Danielle Aubry, Sandrine Gobet, Joan Calhoun, Rudy Battaglia, George Ostos, Ron Allen, Romo Vincent.

Melodrama. Eighteen-year-old Tara Nicole Steele, overweight and insecure, returns home to her wealthy parents in California after having been away for years at a Swiss boarding school. Her homosexual father, Willy, is an airplane manufacturer. Her mother, Astrid, is a former star of stag films and a status seeker who has a passion for jewels. Not quite sure what to do with Tara, her only child, Astrid plans a coming out party for the girl. The extravaganza is actually a showcase for Astrid's jewelry; and Tara, unnoticed, leaves the party and is nearly run over by Bogart, a pop singer who was invited to the affair to perform with his group, Joe, Anna Livia, and Santoro. Bogart invites Tara to go for a ride with him; she accepts and they immediately have sex. Tara's absence eventually begins to worry her parents, and they are about to call the police when Tara returns with Bogart and his group. Bogart announces that he would like to marry Tara, but Tara's initial wonderment turns to bewilderment when Bogart begins to flirt with her mother. Bogart soon embarks on an affair with Astrid, who after much teasing agrees to go skydiving with her future son-in-law and his friends. Tara pilots the plane, and Willy watches from the ground as the group jumps. Once they have all jumped, Bogart and his friends taunt Astrid by passing between them her diamond necklace. All land safely but Astrid, who plunges to her death after her parachute fails to open. Tara returns home and finds her father slain. It is revealed that Bogart had been involved in a homosexual liaison with Willy, and he killed both Astrid and Willy. Unable to accept reality, Tara goes insane. *Manufacturers. Actors. Social climbers. Debutantes. Singers. Musicians. Air pilots. Wealth. Parenthood. Adolescence. Murder. Infidelity. Male homosexuality. Insanity. Skydiving. Airplanes. Boarding schools. Jewels. Switzerland. California.*

Note: Also known as *Cult of the Damned.*

ANGEL BABY   F6.0141

Madera Productions. *Dist* Allied Artists. 10 May **1961** [Detroit opening; c12 May 1961; LP19408]. Sd; b&w. 35mm. 97 min.

A Thomas F. Woods Production. *Prod* Thomas F. Woods. *Assoc Prod* Francis Schwartz. *Dir* Paul Wendkos. *Orig Dir* (see note) Hubert Cornfield. *Screenplay* Orin Borsten, Paul Mason, Samuel Roeca. *Photog* Haskell Wexler, Jack Marta. *Art Dir* Val Tamelin. *Set Dsgn* Sidney Clifford. *Film Ed* Betty J. Lane. *Mus Comp & Cond* Wayne Shanklin. *Orch* Henry Beau. *Songs:* "Jenny Angel," "Little by Little Sinners Will Burn," "Rise Up Singing," "Beulah Land," "Our Love's No Ordinary Thing," "He's My God, Yet" Wayne Shanklin. *Sd Ed* Kay Rose. *Sd Mix* Al Overton. *Mus Ed* Dave Kahn. *Asst Dir* Leonard Katzman. *Prod Supv* Richard Kay. *Cost Dsgn* Marjorie Corso. *Makeup* Stanley Campbell, Guy Del Russo. *Hairstyles* Gale McGarry, Irene Aparicio. *Set Constr* George Troast.

Cast: Salome Jens (*Jenny Brooks, Angel Baby*), George Hamilton (*Paul Strand*), Mercedes McCambridge (*Sarah Strand*), Joan Blondell (*Mollie Hays*), Henry Jones (*Ben Hays*), Burt Reynolds (*Hoke Adams*), Roger Clark (*Sam Wilcox*), Dudley Remus (*Otis Finch*), Victoria Adams (*Ma Brooks*), Harry Swoger (*big cripple*), Barbara G. Biggart (*farm girl*), Davy Biladeau (*little boy*), Eddie Firestone ("*blind*" *man*).

Melodrama. Source: Elsie Oakes Barber, *Jenny Angel* (New York, 1954). Shocked into muteness by a brutal father, young Jenny Brooks tries to escape the loneliness of her life by becoming the town trollop. Then one day a faith-healing preacher named Paul Strand comes to the small southern town where Jenny lives and miraculously restores her power of speech. Deeply moved, she abandons her former ways and joins Paul's troop of touring evangelists. The simple honesty of her faith wins her the friendship of the somewhat alcoholic Mollie and Ben Hays, but the soft beauty of her youth arouses the jealousy of Paul's wife, Sarah, an older, twisted, vindictive woman. After accusing Paul of having adulterous thoughts, Sarah "persuades" Jenny to go out on her own, and, accompanied by Mollie and Ben, the young girl—now billed as Angel Baby, The Preacher of the Ages—begins a tour of the South. An unscrupulous drug manufacturer, Sam Wilcox, becomes her manager and uses the innocence of her spiritual fervor to further his own mercenary ends, even resorting to rigging a phony healing in which the unsuspecting Jenny restores a "blind" man's sight. The night after the "miracle," as hundreds of the ill and maimed wait to be cured, Sarah arrives at the tent, denounces Jenny as a fraud, and

exposes the bogus miracle. As the stunned Jenny staggers from her platform, the crowd riots, and in the ensuing melee, Sarah is killed. Paul seeks out Jenny and tries to persuade her to return to preaching. At first she refuses, but when her prayers help a crippled child to walk again, she rediscovers her faith and decides to join Paul in the continuance of his evangelical work. *Mutes. Promiscuity. Faith cure. Evangelists. Faith. Blindness. Cripples. Jealousy. Miracles. Fraud. United States—South.*

Note: Location scenes filmed in Florida. Hubert Cornfield, the film's original director, was replaced after a week of filming due to disagreements with the producer; approximately 6 minutes of Cornfield's footage was included in the released film.

EL ÁNGEL EXTERMINADOR *see* **THE EXTERMINATING ANGEL**

ANGEL IN A TAXI (Italy)   F6.0142

Ebe Cinematografica. *Dist* Magna Pictures, Albex Films. 13 Nov **1963** [Buffalo, New York, opening]. Sd; b&w. 35mm. 90-96 min.

Prod-Dir-Writ Antonio Leonviola. *Photog* Enzo Serafin. *Film Ed* Roberto Cinquini. *Mus* Piero Morgan.

Cast: Vera Cecova (*Camilla*), Vittorio De Sica (*God*), Marietto (*Marietto*), Gabriele Ferzetti, Roberto Risso, Mario Carotenuto, Pina Renzi, Dolores Palumbo, Erminio Spalla, Gisella Sofio, Dorika Dory, Giacomo Furia, Polidor, Memmo Carotenuto, Mario Riva, Ave Ninchi, Nerio Bernardi.

Fantasy. Marietto, a stubborn little orphan, believes that it is his responsibility to select his own mother. From among the photographs in several magazines, he chooses Camilla, a beautiful ballerina. He runs away from the orphanage to find his adopted "mother" and begins following her everywhere. Despite Camilla's attempts to get rid of him, Marietto plagues her with his mischief. Fans and associates of Camilla believe Marietto is actually her illegitimate son, whom she had hidden in an orphanage. God, in the guise of an ill-tempered but generous and wise man, helps the boy out of his difficulty and unites Marietto with Camilla, who also takes on a man she loves as a husband and father. *Orphans. Dancers. Runaways. Illegitimacy. Adoption. Orphanages.*

Note: Opened in Rome in Jan 1959 as *Ballerina e buon Dio*; running time: 95 min. Also known as *Ballerina and the Good God.*

ANGEL IN MY POCKET   F6.0143

Universal Pictures. 7 Feb **1969** [Atlanta opening; c29 Mar 1969; LP36744]. Sd; col (Technicolor). 35mm (Techniscope). 105 min. *MPAA rating* G.

Prod Edward J. Montagne. *Dir* Alan Rafkin. *Screenplay* Jim Fritzell, Everett Greenbaum. *Photog* William Margulies. *Art Dir* Russell Kimball, Alexander Golitzen. *Set Decor* John McCarthy, John Sturtevant. *Film Ed* Sam E. Waxman. *Mus* Lyn Murray. *Mus Supv* Joseph Gershenson. *Song:* "The Girls of All Nations" Jerry Keller, Dave Blume. *Sd* Waldon O. Watson, Ed Somers. *Asst Dir* Phil Bowles. *Prod Mgr* Wes Thompson. *Asst to the Prod* Billy Sands. *Cost* Grady Hunt. *Makeup* Bud Westmore. *Hairstyles* Larry Germain.

Cast: Andy Griffith (*Sam*), Jerry Van Dyke (*Bubba*), Kay Medford (*Racine*), Lee Meriwether (*Mary Elizabeth*), Henry Jones (*Will Sinclair*), Edgar Buchanan (*Axel Gresham*), Gary Collins (*Art Shields*), Parker Fennelly (*Calvin*), Jack Dodson (*Norman Gresham*), Elena Verdugo (*Lila Sinclair*), Margaret Hamilton (*Rhoda*), Ruth McDevitt (*Nadine*), Richard Van Fleet (*Harry Toback*), Bob Hastings (*Ted Palish*), Jim Boles (*Corby Gresham*), Leonard Stone (*Paul Gresham*), Steve Franken (*Zimmerman*), Larry D. Mann (*Bishop Morenschild*), Al Checco (*Byron*), Margaret Ann Peterson (*Mrs. Harry Toback*), Peggy Mondo (*Charlotte*), Beverly Powers (*Charlene De Gaulle* [see note]), Joy Harmon (*Miss Holland*), Benny Rubin (*Dad Shrader*), Herbie Faye (*Mr. Welch*), George Tapps (*Ace Black*), Eddie Quillan (*Reverend Beckwith*), Michael Barrier (*Mr. Grant*), Buddy Foster (*Sammy*), Todd Starke (*Dink*), Amber Smale (*Rachel*), Susan Seaforth (*Mrs. Grant*), Athena Lorde (*Mrs. Corby Gresham*), Grace Albertson (*Mrs. Will Sinclair*), Robert Lieb (*Cyrus Sinclair*), Claudia Bryar (*Mrs. Axel Gresham*), Tani Phelps (*Mrs. Ted Palish*), Monty Margetts (*Mrs. Chase*), Eve Bruce (*Miss U. S. A.*), Lynn Fields (*Miss France*), Gloria Mills (*Miss Soviet Union*), Chela Bacigalupo (*Miss South America*), Anne Besant (*Miss England*), Linda Carol (*Miss Egypt*), Bonnie Sue Schwartz (*majorette*), Jesslyn Fax (*Mrs. Styles*), Stuart Nisbet (*sheriff*), Ellen Corby (*older woman*), Kathryn Minner (*Mrs. Williams*), Mary Gregory (*secretary*), Rufe Davis (*older man*).

Comedy-drama. Samuel D. Whitehead, a newly-ordained minister who put himself through seminary school by working in a brickyard, is assigned to his first parish in the small town of Wood Falls, Kansas. For years, the town has been beset by the endless bickering of the two founding families, the Sinclairs and the Greshams, and the church has had seven other ministers in the past decade. Upon arriving with his pregnant wife, Mary Elizabeth, his three small children, his complaining mother-in-law, Racine, and his shiftless brother-in-law Bubba, Sam's troubles begin immediately. First, he becomes involved in a sidewalk political brawl between the supporters of Mayor Will Sinclair and his opponent, Axel Gresham. Next, his visit to a burlesque house to arrange for the donation of its unused organ to the church is misinterpreted, and, finally, he performs the marriage ceremony for Lila Sinclair and Norman Gresham, a middle-aged couple who have kept their love a secret for 25 years because of their feuding families. Although Sam plans to keep the wedding a secret, it becomes public knowledge when Bubba and the parsonage caretaker, Calvin Grey, spike the church social punch with liquor made in the basement, and the normally shy Lila blurts out the news. After Will Sinclair and Axel Gresham arrange for Sam to be removed, Sam persuades a young lawyer, Art Shields, to run for mayor. The parades of all three candidates meet on the main street, and the ensuing chaos ends when the distillery explodes, setting the church on fire. As word arrives that Shields has won the election, Sam leaves town with his family, but his car is stopped by a procession led by Sinclair and Gresham. Reconciled and united by their defeat in the mayoral race, they are going to build a new church, and they ask Sam to remain as pastor. Mary Elizabeth announces that she is about to give birth to her fourth child, and Sam shouts his acceptance, turning his car back toward Wood Falls. *Clergymen. Mayors. Lawyers. Smalltown life. Family life. Feuds. Pregnancy. Elections. Political campaigns. Burlesque. Weddings. Drunkenness. Churches. Stills. Kansas. Explosions. Fires.*

Note: Beverly Powers is also known as Beverly Hills.

THE ANGEL LEVINE   **F6.0144**
Belafonte Enterprises. *Dist* United Artists. 28 Jul **1970** [New York opening; c15 Jul 1970; LP38169]. Sd; col (De Luxe). 35mm. 104 min. *MPAA rating* GP.
Prod Chiz Schultz. *Prod Exec* Kenneth Utt. *Dir* Ján Kadár. *Screenplay* Bill Gunn, Ronald Ribman. *Dir Photog* Dick Kratina. *Set Decor* Ben Rutter, Howard Duff, Jr. *Prod Dsgn* George Jenkins. *Film Ed* Carl Lerner. *Mus* Zdenek Liska. *Mus Comp & Cond* William Eaton. *Sd* Lee Bost. *Asst Dir* Paul Ganapoler. *Prod Supv* Hal Schaffel. *Script Supv* Barbara Rittenberg. *Cost* Domingo Rodriguez.
Cast: Zero Mostel (*Morris Mishkin*), Harry Belafonte (*Alexander Levine*), Ida Kaminska (*Fanny Mishkin*), Milo O'Shea (*Dr. Arnold Berg*), Gloria Foster (*Sally*), Barbara Ann Teer (*welfare lady*), Eli Wallach (*store clerk*), Anne Jackson (*lady in the store*).
Fantasy. Source: Bernard Malamud, "Angel Levine," in *Commentary* (Dec 1955). Morris Mishkin, an impoverished Jewish tailor, is beset by difficulties: a backache prevents him from working; his wife, Fanny, is suffering from heart disease; and his daughter has run away with an Italian. Reduced to his last few dollars because of delays in the welfare system, Morris goes to the grocery store for a few meager provisions. On the way, he sees a black man steal a fur coat and yells for the police, but the thief dashes across the street and is killed by a car. Morris returns home to find Fanny's condition worse, and he castigates God for his continued suffering. He then walks into the kitchen and sees the black thief, who claims to be a Jewish angel named Alexander Levine. Levine explains that he must perform a miracle within 24 hours in order to be confirmed as an angel, but Morris is skeptical. Despite an immediate improvement in Fanny's health, Morris refuses to attribute the miracle to God's mercy. Eventually Levine's 24 hours expire, and he leaves the tailor, who still disbelieves. Fanny soon becomes worse, and Morris, now ready to believe in Levine, searches for him in the streets of Harlem, but all he finds is a black feather in a synagogue. *Jews. Tailors. Negroes. Angels. Poverty. Marriage. Heart disease. Theft. Miracles. New York City. New York City—Harlem. Automobile accidents.*
Note: Location scenes filmed in New York City.

AN ANGEL OF LOVE *see* **AN ANGLE OF LOVE**

ANGEL ON EARTH (France/West Germany)   **F6.0145**
CCC-Filmkunst–Régina–Criterion Film. *Dist* Comet Film Distributors. Jan **1966.** Sd; col (Eastman Color). 35mm. 88 min.
Prod Artur Brauner. *Dir* Geza von Radvanyi. *Screenplay* René Barjavel, Geza von Radvanyi. *Photog* Roger Hubert. *Art Dir* Jean d' Eaubonne. *Film Ed* René Le Hénaff. *Mus* Jean Wiener. *Sd* Constantin Evangelou, Julien Coutellier. *Asst Dir* Olivier Gérard. *Prod Dir* Adolf Rosen. *Prod Mgr* Serge Komor.
Cast: Romy Schneider (*air stewardess/guardian angel*), Henri Vidal (*Pierre Chaillot*), Jean-Paul Belmondo (*Michel Barrot*), Michèle Mercier (*Princess Augusta von Münchenberg*), Margarethe Haagen (*archangel*), Erika von Thellmann (*princess*), Ernst Waldow (*manager*), Franz Otto Krüger (*dentist*), Jean Brochard, Paulette Dubost, Jean Tissier, Albert Dinan, Panisse, Combal.
Fantasy. A stewardess for Star Angel Airlines falls in love with race car driver Pierre Chaillot. Jilted in favor of a toreador by Princess Augusta von Münchenberg, Chaillot contemplates suicide but is dissuaded by his guardian angel, who appears in the guise of the enamored stewardess. When his mentor is recalled by her heavenly superiors, the driver resumes his relationship with Augusta. Returning to help Chaillot win the Grand Prix de Monaco, the angel afterwards arranges the marriage of driver and stewardess. *Stock car drivers.*

Airline stewardesses. Royalty. Angels. Bullfighters. Automobile racing. Suicide. Marriage. Miracles. Monaco.
Note: Location scenes filmed on the Côte d'Azur. Opened in Düsseldorf in Aug 1959 as *Ein Engel auf Erden*; running time: 90 min (cut from 94 min); in Paris in Nov 1960 as *Mademoiselle Ange*; running times: 86 and 90 min.

UN ANGEL PASO POR BROOKLYN *see* **THE MAN WHO WAGGED HIS TAIL**

ANGEL UNCHAINED   **F6.0146**
American International Pictures. 19 Aug **1970** [Minneapolis opening; c19 Aug 1970; LP38509]. Sd; col (print by Movielab). 35mm. 92 min. [Also 90 min.] *MPAA rating* GP.
Pres by James H. Nicholson, Samuel Z. Arkoff. *Prod-Dir* Lee Madden. *Co-prod* Norman Herman. *Exec Prod* Hal Klein. *Prod Exec* William J. Immerman. *Screenplay* Jeffrey Alladin Fiskin. *Story* Lee Madden, Jeffrey Alladin Fiskin. *Dir Photog* Irving Lippman. *Camera Op* Hugh Gagnier. *Asst Camera* Ken Hale, John Greer. *Film Ed* Fred Feitshans, Jr. *Mus Supv* Al Simms. *Mus* Randy Sparks. *Mix* Brad Trask. *Boom Op* Harlan Riggs. *Asst Dir* Rusty Meek, Joe Ellis. *Prod Mgr* Rusty Meek. *Script Supv* Stu Lippman. *Post-prod Supv* Salvatore Billitteri. *Post-prod Asst* James Honore. *Wardrobe* Oscar Rodriguez. *Makeup* Fred Blau, Jr. *Sp Eff* Roger George. *Still Photog* Jack Albin. *Prop* Arthur Friedrich. *Gaffer* Ralph McCarthy. *Grip* Bud Gaunt, John Hennessy.
Cast: Don Stroud (*Angel*), Luke Askew (*Tremaine*), Larry Bishop (*Pilot*), Tyne Daly (*Merilee*), Neil Moran (*Magician*), Jean Marie (*Jackie*), Bill McKinney (*Shotgun*), Jordan Rhodes (*Tom*), Peter Laurence (*Dave*), Pedro Regas (*Injun*), Linda Smith (*Wendy*), Nita Michaels (*Matty*), J. Cosgrove Butchie (*Ray*), Tim Ryan (*hood*), Alan Gibbs, J. N. Roberts (*duners*), Bill Burton (*marauder*), Bud Ekins (*Speed*), Jerry Randall (*Candy*), Aldo Ray (*sheriff*).
Action melodrama. When motorcyclist Angel rescues his friend Shotgun from a brawl with members of a rival gang, Shotgun promises to return the favor some day. To begin a new life, however, Angel quits his gang and sets out on a cross-country tour. He stops at a gas station and sees Merilee, a member of a local commune, being harassed by a group of citizens who are trying to force the hippies to leave the area. Accompanying her back to the commune, he meets Tremaine, the pacifist leader, who invites him to stay. Later, when townspeople try to destroy the hippies' crops with their dune buggies, Angel accidentally hits one of the drivers with a pitchfork, thus intensifying the feud. Consequently, Tremaine asks Angel to enlist the aid of his old gang to defend the commune, and Angel reluctantly agrees. Shotgun and the gang arrive, but there is immediate friction between the two groups until the townspeople finally attack; the gang and the commune join forces to drive them away, but Tremaine is killed during the fighting. *Motorcycle gangs. Hippies. Pacifists. Communal living. Feuds. Smalltown life.*
Note: Filmed on location in Arizona. Working title: *Unchained*.

ANGELI BIANCHI ... ANGELI NERI *see* **WITCHCRAFT '70**

ANGELIQUE IN BLACK LEATHER   **F6.0147**
Dist Imperial Pictures. 30 Aug **1968** [Champaign, Illinois, showing]. Sd; col. 35mm. 65 min.
Prod-Dir Angelique Bouchet.
Cast: Angelique Bouchet, Maria Lennard, Solange Canard.
Drama. Angelique's life revolves around Suzanne, a sophisticated lesbian who embodies male strength in her black leather attire. As Angelique watches her lover dress for a date, she is filled with jealous suspicions and resolves to follow behind. Losing Suzanne in the crowd, Angelique meets Domenique. They spend a romantic afternoon together, and Angelique decides to devote herself to her newfound love. She arranges to let Suzanne find her with Jenelle. Together the two women torture Suzanne by arousing her desire and jealousy. *Lesbianism. Fetishism. Jealousy.*
Note: Also known as *Angelique.*

UN ANGELO È SCESO A BROOKLYN *see* **THE MAN WHO WAGGED HIS TAIL**

ANGELS DIE HARD!   **F6.0148**
Angels Productions. *Dist* New World Pictures. 8 Jul **1970** [Dallas opening]. Sd; col (Movielab). 35mm. 86 min. *MPAA rating* R.
A Roger Corman Production. *Prod* Charles Beach Dickerson. *Exec Prod* James Tanenbaum, Jane Schaffer. *Dir-Writ* Richard Compton. *Photog* Arch Archambault. *Film Ed* Tony De Zarraga. *Mus* Marcia Waldorf, Richard Hieronymous, Pettipoint Productions. *Sd* Jim Evergreen. *Asst Dir* John Rico. *Unit Prod Mgr* Mike Stringer. *Custom Motorcycles* Gary Littlejohn.
Cast: Tom Baker (*Blair*), William Smith (*Gentleman Tim*), R. G. Armstrong (*Mel Potter*), Alan DeWitt (*Mr. Sparagut*), Connie Nelson (*Nancy Davis*), Carl Steppling (*Sheriff Dan Davis*), Frank Leo (*Deputy Johnny Martin*), Gary Littlejohn (*Piston*), Rita Murray (*Naomi*), Mike Angel (*Dirty Davie*), William

Bonner *(Houston)*, Michael Donovan O'Donnell *(Monk)*, Leslie Otis *(Tommy)*, Dianne Turley *(Patsy)*, Beach Dickerson *(Shank)*, Mike Stringer *(Seed)*, Richard Compton *(restaurant owner)*, Bambi Allen *(owner's wife)*.

Action melodrama. When 30 Hell's Angels roar into a California town on their motorcycles and create a wild street brawl, the local sheriff holds one of them hostage until the gang leaves town. Although the order is obeyed, the captured motorcyclist is brutally run down and killed as he drives across the county line. Vowing revenge, Blair, the gang's leader, ar.d his buddy Gentleman Tim lead the Angels in a bizarre funeral procession back to the local cemetery. Despite threats by the sheriff and the more militant townsmen to drive out the cyclists, deputy Johnny Martin dissuades them from taking any immediate action. The gang rescues a child trapped in an abandoned mine shaft, but the sheriff's hostility increases when he sees his daughter Nancy talking with Blair. As the townsmen organize for a raid on the Angels' camp, Nancy warns the bikers, but she is later beaten up by one of the local youths. During the bloody fight that ensues, the sheriff sees his badly bruised daughter wandering along a road. Certain that Blair is to blame, he tries to run him down, but Deputy Martin fires a shot at the sheriff's patrol car to prevent Blair's murder. The gunfire sends the patrol car careening off the road into an embankment, and it explodes. *Sheriffs. Hostages. Smalltown life. Murder. Revenge. Funerals. California. Hell's Angels. Automobile accidents. Explosions.*

Note: Location scenes filmed in Kernville, California. Working title: *The Violent Angels.*

ANGELS FROM HELL   F6.0149

Fanfare Film Productions. *Dist* American International Pictures. 29 May **1968** [Wichita, Kansas, opening; c19 Jun 1968; LP35941]. Sd; col (Perfect). 35mm. 86 min.

Prod Kurt Neumann. *Exec Prod* Joe Solomon. *Dir* Bruce Kessler. *Screenplay* Jerome Wish. *Dir Photog* Herman Knox. *Art Decor* Wally Moon. *Set Decor & Titl* Van Dutch. *Film Ed* William Martin. *Mus Comp & Cond* Stu Phillips. *Titl Song* Guy Hemric, Byron Cole, Stu Phillips. *Song:* "Crystal Tear" Guy Hemric, Stu Phillips. *Song:* "Mr. Madison Avenue" Fred Cole, Bob Atkins. *Song:* "No One Says a Word (No Communication)" Jerry Fuller, Stu Phillips. *Song:* "Shake Off the Chains" Ted Markland. *Song:* "Who's It Gonna Be" Fred Cole. *Songs Perf by* The Peanut Butter Conspiracy, Lollipop Shoppe, Stu Phillips Orchestra. *Sd* Keith Wester. *Asst Dir* Ray Gosnell. *Wardrobe* Ron Dawson. *Makeup* Richard Scarso.

Cast: Tom Stern *(Mike)*, Arlene Martel *(Ginger)*, Ted Markland *(Smiley)*, Stephen Oliver *(Speed)*, Paul Bertoya *(Nutty Norman)*, James Murphy *(Tiny Tim)*, Jack Starrett *(Captain Bingham)*, Jay York *(George)*, Pepper Martin *(Dennis)*, Bob Harris *(Baney)*, Saundra Gayle *(Clair)*, Susan Walters *(Millie)*, Luana Talltree *(Angry Annie)*, Susan Holloway *(Jennifer)*, Judith Garwood *(Louise)*. Susanne Sidney *(Buff)*, Steve Rogers *(Dude)*.

Melodrama. Returning from Vietnam as a war hero, Mike, a former motorcycle outlaw, breaks with his wife and sets out to resume his old way of life. Accompanied by his buddy Smiley, he moves to another town to start a new cycle gang. Meeting opposition from rival outlaws, Mike uses his combat experience to establish himself as the uncontested gang leader. When the police intervene, Mike, by now drunk with power, decides to unite all the cycle gangs in the state. As recruits flock to join the gang, the war with the police flares into the open. Then, during a pot-and-sex orgy, one of the gang kills a young girl and is subsequently shot down by the police. Enraged, Mike calls for all-out war but is quickly trapped in his hideout by the police. Defiantly he dies opposing the establishment for which he had fought in Vietnam. *Veterans. Motorcycle gangs. Outlaws. Police. Murder. Orgies. Marijuana. Vietnam War 1964-73.*

Note: Location scenes filmed in California.

ÄNGLAR, FINNS DOM? *see* LOVE MATES

AN ANGLE OF LOVE   F6.0150

Espionage Films. *Dist* Distribpix, Inc. 25 Sep **1968** [Champaign, Illinois, showing]. Sd; b&w. 35mm. 73 min.

Pres by International Visual Images Ltd. *Exec Prod* Vera Mandelova. *Dir* William K. Hennigar. *Camera* John Fisher. *Film Ed* Utopia International Visual Images. *Sd* D'Arcy Raley. *Prod Supv* Dell Raley. *Prod Asst* Jack Russell.

Cast: Coral Byrde *(Gloria)*, Gary Allen, Gregory Hope.

Melodrama. Gloria, a virgin tease, toys with her boyfried, Paul, and although she does not respond sexually to him, she does find sexual gratification when she is brutally raped by a drug addict in her hallway. Gloria becomes obsessed with sex and allows Paul to seduce her. Unsatisfied, Gloria picks up two hippies in a bar, but they also fail to bring her release. Gloria experiments with lesbian love and finds it unrewarding. Gloria finally meets a man who excites her, but his old-fashioned morality repulses her, and she returns to group sex. At an orgy, Gloria meets the man who raped her. She lures him to her apartment and kills him as he brings her to climax. *Virginity. Drug addicts. Hippies. Nymphomania. Rape. Lesbianism. Murder. Frigidity. Orgies.*

Note: Also known as *An Angel of Love.*

THE ANGRY BREED   F6.0151

David Commons Associates-Harold Goldman Associates. *Dist* Commonwealth United Entertainment, Inc. Jun **1968.** Sd; col. 35mm. 89 min. *MPAA rating* M.

Prod-Dir-Writ David Commons. *Exec Prod* Frank Brandt, Fred Maisel. *Story* Rex Carlton. *Photog* Gregory Sandor. *Art Dir* Leon Ericksen. *Film Ed* David Saxon. *Mus* Lawrence Brown, Mike Curb. *Sd* Frank Murphy. *Asst Dir* Elliot Schick, William Lasky. *Wardrobe* Dodie Warren. *Makeup* Louis Lane. *Hairstyles* Gretchen Moon.

Cast: Jan Sterling *(Gloria Patton)*, James MacArthur *(Deek Stacey)*, William Windom *(Vance Patton)*, Jan Murray *(Mori Thompson)*, Murray MacLeod *(Johnny Taylor)*, Lori Martin *(Diane Patton)*, Melody Patterson *(April Wilde)*, Karen Malouf *(Jade)*, Suzie Kaye *(Ginny Morris)*.

Melodrama. While serving in the Army in Vietnam, aspiring actor Johnny Taylor saves the life of a Hollywood writer who rewards him with an original screenplay to be sold only to a producer who will cast Johnny in the lead role. When Johnny returns to California, however, he discovers that while many studios want the script, no one wants him. One evening he rescues Diane Patton, the daughter of a famous producer, from a motorcycle gang. To show his gratitude, Mr. Patton agrees to finance the film and sends Johnny to agent Mori Thompson; but Thompson's favorite client is actor Deek Stacey, the leader of the motorcycle gang, who also wants the part. Deek and Mori conspire to murder Johnny at Patton's Halloween party. They spike the punch with LSD, and Johnny finds himself in a dungeon facing a knife-wielding Deek, but the housekeeper helps him escape. Later, when Patton announces that the picture has been cancelled, his alcoholic wife, Gloria, disgusted with the way her husband uses people, tries to kill him by tampering with the cable car that leads from their house to the beach below. Deek arrives seeking revenge, and he and Patton fight in the cable car, which crashes to the rocks, killing Deek and injuring Patton. Shocked into realizing how much trouble he has caused, Patton is reconciled with his wife, and Johnny and Diane pledge their love. *Veterans. Actors. Motion picture scriptwriters. Motorcycle gangs. Motion picture producers. Theatrical agents. Housekeepers. Rescue. Conspiracy. Murder. Alcoholism. Revenge. LSD. Cable cars. Vietnam War 1964-73. Hollywood.*

Note: Location scenes filmed in Hollywood and Malibu, California.

THE ANGRY SEA (Japan)   F6.0152

Toho Co.-Morishige Productions. *Dist* Toho Co. Feb **1961** [Los Angeles showing]. Sd; col (Eastmancolor). 35mm (Tohoscope). 93 min.

Prod Kazuo Takimura. *Dir* Seiji Hisamatsu. *Screenplay* Mutsuaki Saegusa, Seiji Hisamatsu. *Photog* Seiichi Endo. *Art Dir* Takeo Itita. *Mus* Ikuma Dan.

Cast: Hisaya Morishige *(fisherman)*, Mitsuko Kusabue, Jun Funato, Yoko Tsukasa, Masao Oda, Tsutomu Yamazaki, Ryutaro Nagai, Hiroyuki Ota, Jun Hamamura, Toru Yuri, Zeko Nakamura, Haruya Kato, Senkichi Omura, Hikaru Tashioka, Akira Nishimura.

Drama. Source: Yukio Togawa, *Otsuku rojin* (Tokyo, 1960). A fisherman of the northern islands, too old to ply his trade, becomes a night watchman and net mender at a local fishery. Alone with his cats, the man remembers his dead wife and three sons. He recalls his eldest son drowning while playing on the ice floes; his second son's death while a soldier in China; his third boy's service during World War II and subsequent departure for Tokyo; his wife's death from pneumonia; his son's return from Tokyo, career as a fisherman, and recent death during a typhoon. When the son's fiancée arrives for a visit to her beloved's island, the fisherman escorts her about the island without revealing his identity. The man later drowns while attempting to save one of his beloved pets. *Fishermen. Watchmen. Family life. Loneliness. Death. World War II. Islands. Cats.*

Note: Released in Japan in 1960 as *Chi no hate ni ikuru mono*; running time: 125 min.

THE ANIMAL   F6.0153

R. L. F. Productions. *Dist* Olympic International Films. 3 May **1968** [Champaign, Illinois, showing]. Sd; b&w with col seq. 35mm. 88 min.

Prod-Dir R. L. Frost. *Asst Prod* Wesdon Bishop. *Orig Story* Felix Lomax. *Photog* Charles Langdon. *Film Ed* Thomas L. Myers. *Mus* Mischa Terr. *Asst Dir* James E. McLarty.

Cast: David Holmes, actor *(Ted Andrews)*, Virginia Gordon, Armand Atam, Jay Fineberg, Janis Rhodes, Francie Hyde, Sharon Wells, Linda Stiles, Inez Coup, Capri.

Melodrama. Ted Andrews, whose childhood heritage of severe depression and a hatred of his mother has led him into sadistic activities, terrorizes his neighborhood by spying with a telescope into the intimate lives of his neighbors and making obscene and threatening phone calls. Ted's compulsions surface when he is under the influence of marijuana and LSD. Eventually, he becomes obsessed with a woman of dignity and wealth, and he sets out to degrade and humiliate her. He threatens to kill her 10-year-old son unless she cooperates, and as a result she agrees to perform erotically while he watches through his telescope. Ted later forces her to meet him at a motel in order to degrade her totally. [Includes a shower sequence and scenes of autoeroticism, sadism, lesbianism, and a murder.] *Sex deviates. Neighbors. Sadism. Voyeurism. Lesbianism. Autoeroticism. Filial relations. Murder. Marijuana. LSD.*

ANIMAL LOVE   F6.0154

Kenny Productions. *Dist* Chancellor Films. ca **1969**. Sd; col (Colortone). 35mm. 73 min.

Prod-Dir Kenny. *Camera* Paul Prado. *Film Ed* Rene Powell. *Sd* Frank Pestel. *Rec* Magno Sound.

Cast: Mary Dunn *(Mara Harris)*, Sam King *(Charles Harris)*, Dan Neri *(Hank)*, Henry Nelson *(Doctor Borrow)*, Rose Poey *(Wilma)*.

Drama. Judge Charles Harris strays from his young wife, Mara, and engages in a tempestuous affair with Nicki Longan, who wears a leopard skin sarong to arouse him. Mara also finds a young lover, Hank, a tough ex-convict who introduces her to marijuana. Hank takes her to a party which becomes an orgy, and she mingles with dope addicts. A public scandal occurs when the police raid the orgy, and she breaks away and returns home, but her husband remains distant and preoccupied. The scandal, which threatens to ruin the judge, appears to be a final obstacle to their reconciliation until, one day, she dons a leopard skin coat left behind by the maid. The judge's desire triggered by the sight of the animal skin, he makes wild love to her, and the two recapture their passion for each other. *Newlyweds. Judges. Mistresses. Ex-convicts. Drug addicts. Fetishism. Marriage. Infidelity. Scandal. Marijuana. Orgies.*

THE ANIMALS (France)   F6.0155

Télé-Hachette-Ancinex. *Dist* Emerson Film Enterprises. 20 Jan **1965** [Los Angeles opening]. Sd; b&w. 35mm. 87 min.

Pres by Four Star Productions. *Prod* Nicole Stéphane. *Dir-Writ* Frédéric Rossif. *Adapt & French Vers Narr* Madeleine Chapsal. *English Vers Narr* Arthur Weiss. *Photog* Georges Barsky. *Film Ed* Suzanne Baron, Frédéric Rossif. *Mus* Maurice Jarre. *Sd* Elvire Lerner. *Prod Mgr* Michelle Chamson, Monique Montivier.

English Vers Narrators: Lamont Johnson, Bethel Leslie.

French Vers Narrators: Martine Sarcey, Marcelle Ranson, Jean-Pierre Marielle, Jean-Marc Bory, Maurice Escande.

Documentary. The development of animal life is traced from microscopic cell life to the more complex creatures. Many species throughout the world are examined in their natural habitats as well as in zoos. The insect world is examined, followed by another sequence about animals that haunt our dreams. There are also scenes of the beasts' struggle for survival and mothers caring for their young. Man's cruelty toward wild animals and birds is shown as hunters plan a series of expeditions. *Hunters. Animal life. Biology. Survival. Zoos.*

Note: Filmed over a period of 13 years. Opened in Paris in Dec 1963 as *Les animaux*; running time: 90 min.

ANIMAS TRUJANO *see* **THE IMPORTANT MAN**

LES ANIMAUX *see* **THE ANIMALS**

ANITA   F6.0156

Dist Distribpix, Inc. 15 Oct **1969** [Boston opening]. Sd; col. 35mm. 64 min.

Sex film. Anita comes to New York hoping to become an actress, but work in the theater is hard to find, and she supports herself by modeling. Jack Baron, a promising young photographer, seduces her, and Anita becomes his mistress. Jack introduces her to small-time movie producer Milton Allen. In exchange for Milton's backing in a film project, Jack has promised him a pliant and innocent young girl for the evening—Anita. Eventually, Anita plays the leading role in the movie, a sex exploitation film, and at the same time she meets her next lover, Jerry Reamer, an egotistical young actor. She continues to live with Jack, who has become a drug addict. To support his habit, Jack sells Anita's services to a pornographer who uses her to pose for still photographs of lesbian activity. Jack finally begins to pimp for Anita, and one night he brings home Max, a wealthy sadomasochist. Max takes a fancy to Anita and makes her his mistress. Anita gives a party to celebrate her new life and invites all the people she knows in New York. Among the guests is her friend Gina, with whom Anita has had a longtime intimacy. *Actors. Photographers. Motion picture producers. Drug addicts. Mistresses. Models. Pornography. Lesbianism. Prostitution. Sadomasochism. Seduction. Sex exploitation films. New York City.*

ANN AND EVE (Sweden)   F6.0157

Omega Film. *Dist* Chevron Pictures. 15 Jul **1970** [Los Angeles opening]. Sd; col (Eastmancolor, print by Movielab). 35mm. 89 min. *MPAA rating* X.

Prod Lennart Berns. *Exec Prod* Bert Sundberg. *Dir* Arne Mattsson. *Screenplay* Ernest Hotch. *Camera* Max Wilén. *Art Dir* Željko Senečić. *Film Ed* Wic Kjellin. *Mus Comp* Bengt-Arne Wallin. *Sd* Bo Abrahamsson. *Asst Dir* Matija Milcinski. *Prod Mgr* Erik Rasmussen, Branko Lustig.

Cast: Gio Petré *(Ann)*, Marie Liljedahl *(Eve)*, Heinz Hopf *(Walter, a fisherman)*, Ignac Pavkovic *(2d fisherman)*, Julian Mateos *(hotel porter)*, Olivera Vuco *(nightclub singer)*, Francisco Rabal *(Francesco)*, Bozidarka Frajt *(Walter's mistress)*, Nevenka Filipovic *(Walter's wife)*, Erik Hell *(Chief Braun)*, Agneta Prytz *(film saleswoman)*.

Melodrama. Ann, a Swedish film critic in her early 30's, and Eve, an 18-year-old bride-to-be, vacation for 2 weeks along the Adriatic coast of Yugoslavia. Eve rhapsodizes about her fiancé, while, Ann, cynical about love and determined to prevent Eve from achieving marital happiness, denigrates any type of lasting relationship. Eve eventually allows herself to be seduced by Walter, a fisherman hired by Ann to handle their boat, while Ann makes love to another fisherman in front of Eve. The following morning, Walter's mistress kills him in a jealous rage. Eve temporarily loses interest in the prospect of marriage and abandons herself to sexual pleasure. The two women vie for the hotel porter, who willingly satisfies both women. Eve then becomes involved with a lesbian nightclub singer. Ann meets Italian movie director Francesco at a party, but he rejects her when he senses her destructive nature. (It becomes apparent that Ann drove her film director husband to suicide by professionally criticizing his films.) The women quarrel, and Eve hitchhikes back to her fiancé in Stockholm, but on the way she is raped by four truckdrivers. She finally marries her fiancé, however, and Ann follows Francesco to the Venice Film Festival for a screening of his latest film—which bears the same title as her late husband's last unfinished work. *Critics. Cynics. Fishermen. Mistresses. Porters. Singers. Motion picture directors. Italians. Truckdrivers. Vacations. Seduction. Murder. Lesbianism. Suicide. Rape. Adriatic Sea. Yugoslavia. Stockholm. Venice Film Festival.*

Note: Location scenes filmed in Yugoslavia and Sweden. Released in Sweden in Oct 1970 as *Ann och Eve—De erotiska*; running time: 109 min.

ANN OCH EVE—DE EROTISKA *see* **ANN AND EVE**

ANNA, MY DARLING (Sweden)   F6.0158

Omega Film. *Dist* Shaw-Rubin Organization. Mar **1968** [San Jose, California, showing]. Sd; b&w. 35mm. 86 min.

Dir Håkan Ersgård. *Screenplay* Ove Tjernberg. *1st Camera* Åke Dahlquist. *2d Camera* Lasse Dahlqvist. *Film Ed* Ingemar Ejve. *Mus* Jan Johansson. *Sd* Lars Nordberg. *Prod Mgr* Bert Sundberg. *Script Girl* Kik Reeder. *Wardrobe* Torella.

Cast: Bente Dessau *(Anna)*, Bob Asklöf *(Erik)*, Herman Ahlsell *(Henrik)*, Margit Carlqvist *(Monika)*, Åke Grönberg *(Erik's father)*, Viveka Dahlén *(Yvonne)*, Eva Strömberg, Mimi Nelson.

Drama. Anna, a 36-year-old divorcée with two children, has an affair with 21-year-old Erik, one of the students in the ballet school where she teaches. That summer, Anna takes her children to a cottage by the sea, and Erik visits when he is not helping his father wash taxicabs. Anna's former husband, who deserted her and the children, appears in a new American car and, claiming to have car trouble, spends the night. The next day Erik fixes the car and goes fishing with Anna's son. The ex-husband demands that Anna return to him. They argue and Anna flees when he tries to rape her. Erik, believing that Anna and her ex-husband have been reconciled, drinks too much, takes a swim, and nearly drowns. When he returns to the cottage and finds Anna still gone, he packs his bags and leaves. Anna arrives back at the cottage and thinks Erik has deserted her. Sometime later, Anna discovers that she is pregnant and, with the help of a girl friend, obtains an abortion. Anna calls a friend for comfort; the friend calls Erik, who rushes to Anna. Although they are reunited, it is not certain whether their love will last. *Dance teachers. Students. Middle age. Divorce. Abortion. Family life. Rape. Ballet. Summer.*

Note: Released in Sweden in 1965 as *Ett sommaräventyr*. Working title: *... Då ska du få en gungstol av mig—en blå.*

ANNA'S SIN (Italy)   F6.0159

Giaguaro Film. *Dist* Atlantis Films. Aug **1961**. Sd; b&w. 35mm. 86 min.

Pres by George Morris. *Dir* Camillo Mastrocinque. *Screenplay* Edoardo Anton, Camillo Mastrocinque. *Story* Anna Vita. *Dir Photog* Alvaro Mancori. *Camera Op* Adalberto Albertini. *Prod Dsgn* Carlo Egidi. *Film Ed (see note)* Pier Piccinato, Mario Bonotti. *Mus* Alessandro Cicognini. *Songs:* "Stomping in Rome," "Anna's Theme" perf by Giacomo Rondinella, Roman New Orleans Jazz Band. *Sd Engr* Tullio Parmeggiani.

Cast: Anna Vita *(Anna Curti)*, Ben E. Johnson *(John Ruthford)*, Paul Muller *(Alberto)*, William Demby *(Sam)*, Pamela Winter *(Alley)*, Giovanna Mazzotti *(Laura)*, Rosario Borelli *(impresario)*, Oscar Adriani *(Michael)*, Giacomo Rondinella *(singer)*, Sergio Raimondi, Nino Capozzi, Anna Davila, Marisa Benedetti.

Drama. John Ruthford, an American Negro actor, arrives in Rome to star in a stage production of *Othello* and also to locate Sam, a Negro for whom John served a 7-year prison term in the United States for raping a white girl. John selects Anna Curti to play Desdemona, and during rehearsals, they fall in love.

Alberto, Anna's dishonest manager who is also in love with her and is scheming to get her inheritance, tells her of John's prison record, and she abruptly ends their affair. When she eventually learns the truth, Alberto seeks out Sam and kills him before he can clear John's name. John attacks Alberto and then flees. Believing himself to be a murderer, he decides to commit suicide; but Anna finds him, tells him that Alberto is alive and in police custody, and convinces him of her love. *Americans in foreign countries. Actors. Negroes. Theatrical managers. Injustice. Revenge. Rape. Jealousy. Murder. Suicide. Rehearsals. Inheritance. Rome. "Othello".*

Note: Released in Italy in 1953 as *Il peccato di Anna*. Sources conflict in crediting editor.

ANNE OF THE THOUSAND DAYS (Great Britain)　　　F6.0160

Universal Pictures, Ltd. *Dist* Universal Pictures. 18 Dec **1969** [Los Angeles opening; c18 Dec 1969; LP38938]. Sd; col (Technicolor). 35mm (Panavision, see note). 145 min. *MPAA rating* M.

A Hal Wallis Production. *Prod* Hal B. Wallis. *Assoc Prod* Richard McWhorter. *Dir* Charles Jarrott. *Screenplay* John Hale, Bridget Boland. *Adapt* Richard Sokolove. *Dir Photog* Arthur Ibbetson. *Camera Op* Paul Wilson. *Art Dir* Lionel Couch. *Set Decor* Peter Howitt, Patrick McLoughlin. *Sketch Artist* Andrew Campbell. *Scenic Artist* W. Simpson Robinson, Ferdie Bellan, Frank Graves. *Prod Dsgn* Maurice Carter. *Film Ed* Richard Marden. *Asst Film Ed* Mary Kessell. *Mus* Georges Delerue. *Choreog* Mary Skeaping. *Sd Ed* Don Sharpe, Colin Miller. *Sd Rec* John Aldred. *Sd Boom Op* Robin Clegg. *1st & 2d Asst Dir* Simon Relph, Nigel Wooll, Nicholas Hippisley Coxe. *Prod Supv* James Ware. *Prod Sec* Joan Williams. *Location Mgr* Inez Easton. *Cont* Valerie Booth. *Cost Dsgn* Margaret Furse. *Wardrobe Supv* Ivy Baker. *Wardrobe Mistress* Vi Murray, Maggie Lewin. *Wardrobe Master* Arthur Newman. *Makeup* Tom Smith. *Hairstyles* Joan Carpenter, Anne Triebner. *Tech & Historical Adv* Patrick McLoughlin. *Horse Master* Jeremy Taylor. *Casting Dir* Sally Nicholl. *Constr Mgr* Charles Hammerton. *Still Photog* Norman Gryspeerdt.

Cast: Richard Burton (*King Henry VIII*), Genevieve Bujold (*Anne Boleyn*), Irene Papas (*Queen Catherine of Aragon*), Anthony Quayle (*Cardinal Wolsey*), John Colicos (*Thomas Cromwell*), Michael Hordern (*Thomas Boleyn*), Katharine Blake (*Elizabeth Boleyn*), Valerie Gearon (*Mary Boleyn*), Michael Johnson (*George Boleyn*), Peter Jeffrey (*Norfolk*), Joseph O'Connor (*Fisher*), William Squire (*Thomas More*), Esmond Knight (*Kingston*), Nora Swinburne (*Lady Kingston*), Vernon Dobtcheff (*Mendoza*), Brook Williams (*Brereton*), Gary Bond (*Smeaton*), T. P. McKenna (*Norris*), Denis Quilley (*Weston*), Terence Wilton (*Harry Percy*), Lesley Paterson (*Jane Seymour*), Nicola Pagett (*Princess Mary*), June Ellis (*Bess*), Kynaston Reeves (*Willoughby*), Marne Maitland (*Campeggio*), Cyril Luckham (*Prior Houghton*), Amanda Walker, Charlotte Selwyn, Elizabeth Counsell (*Anne's ladies in waiting*), Juliet Kempson, Fiona Hartford (*Catherine's ladies in waiting [English]*), Lilian Hutchins, Ann Tirard (*Catherine's ladies in waiting [Spanish]*), Amanda Jane Smythe (*child Elizabeth*).

Historical drama. Source: Maxwell Anderson, *Anne of the Thousand Days* (New York opening: 8 Dec 1948). King Henry VIII of England, whose marriage to Catherine of Aragon has failed to produce a male heir to the throne, becomes infatuated with Anne Boleyn, who is in love with Harry Percy. The king prevents their marriage by sending Percy away and ordering that Anne be made a lady-in-waiting to Catherine. Anne, who has acquired a taste for power, consents to have sex with Henry only if he will marry her and make her queen of England. Henry turns to his counselor, Cardinal Wolsey, to intercede for him with the pope in Rome to have his marriage annulled, but the pope is a prisoner of Catherine's father, King Ferdinand of Spain, and refuses to grant the annulment. When Wolsey also fails to get the annulment approved from the local ecclesiastical body, Henry strips him of his position and appoints Thomas Cromwell in his place. As a final recourse, Henry breaks with the Catholic Church and appoints himself head of the Church of England. Henry, who demands an oath of loyalty recognizing himself as head of both church and state, has Sir Thomas More beheaded when he fails to comply. Now free of his ties to Catherine, Henry marries Anne, and soon afterward she bears him a daughter, Elizabeth. When their second child, a son, is stillborn, Henry becomes furious and orders that his new lover, Jane Seymour, be made one of Anne's ladies-in-waiting. At Henry's command, Cromwell fabricates a case of adultery against Anne, and she is convicted by the court. The strong-willed Anne refuses Henry's offer of clemency if she will renounce the marriage, and as she faces the guillotine, Henry rides off to visit Jane. *Royalty. Heirs. Marriage. Marriage—Annulment. Infidelity. Ambition. Church and state. Divorce. Childbirth. Stillbirth. Frameup. Capital punishment. Great Britain—History—Tudors. Henry VIII (England). Catherine of Aragon. Anne Boleyn. Thomas Wolsey. Thomas Cromwell. Thomas More. Jane Seymour. Catholic Church. Church of England.*

Note: Filmed in 35mm and blown up to 70mm for some roadshow presentations. Opened in London in Feb 1970.

L'ANNÉE DERNIÈRE À MARIENBAD *see* **LAST YEAR AT MARIENBAD**

THE ANNIVERSARY (Great Britain)　　　F6.0161

Seven Arts Productions–Hammer Film Productions. *Dist* Twentieth Century–Fox Film Corp. 7 Feb **1968** [Philadelphia opening; c31 Dec 1967; LP35409]. Sd; col (De Luxe). 35mm. 95 min.

Prod-Writ Jimmy Sangster. *Dir* (see note) Roy Ward Baker, Alvin Rakoff. *Dir Photog* Harry Waxman. *Camera Op* Gerry Anstiss. *Prod Dsgn* Reece Pemberton. *Supv Ed* James Needs. *Film Ed* Peter Weatherley. *Mus Supv* Philip Martell. *Titl Mus Played by* The New Vaudeville Band. *Sd Rec* Les Hammond. *Rec Supv* A. W. Lumkin. *Asst Dir* Bert Batt. *Prod Mgr* Victor Peck. *Wardrobe* Mary Gibson. *Makeup* George Partleton. *Hairdresser* A. G. Scott.

Cast: Bette Davis (*Mrs. Taggart*), Sheila Hancock (*Karen Taggart*), Jack Hedley (*Terry Taggart*), James Cossins (*Henry Taggart*), Christian Roberts (*Tom Taggart*), Elaine Taylor (*Shirley Blair*), Timothy Bateson (*Mr. Bird*), Arnold Diamond (*headwaiter*), Albert Shepherd, Ralph Watson, Sally-Jane Spencer.

Comedy-drama. Source: Bill MacIlwraith, *The Anniversary* (London opening: 20 Apr 1966). Though her husband has been dead for 10 years, Mrs. Taggart continues to celebrate her wedding anniversary and thus tighten her hold on her three grown sons. The family gathers for the latest annual dinner party, to which the youngest son, Tom, brings his fiancée, Shirley Blair, who is already pregnant by him. After contemptuously ridiculing Shirley because of her large ears, Mrs. Taggart learns that her second son, Terry, wants to emigrate to Canada with his wife, Karen, before their sixth child is born. Coldly reminding Terry that while still a boy he popped out one of her eyes with an air pistol, Mrs. Taggart dismisses the matter and summons her third son, Henry, from his upstairs bedroom. A transvestite, Henry's periodic stealing of lingerie from neighborhood washlines is indulged by Mrs. Taggart to assure his remaining by her side. Unfortunately, however, Henry has borrowed Terry's car for one of his washline raids, and the police have a report of the license plate number. Mrs. Taggart blackmails Terry into giving up going to Canada by threatening to have Henry committed or to allow the police to believe that Terry is the transvestite for whom the police are searching. When the rebellious Tom and Shirley try to defy Mrs. Taggart by making love in her bed, they find her glass eye under a pillow—a shock so severe that Shirley almost has a miscarriage. Incensed by this final outrage, Tom, Shirley, Terry, and Karen storm out of the house, while Henry retreats to the sanctuary of his bedroom. Undaunted, Mrs. Taggart telephones her lawyer and instructs him to inform the emigration authorities that she holds an unpaid debt from Terry. Satisfied that there will be another anniversary party next year, Mrs. Taggart raises her glass to toast the portrait of her late husband. *Widows. Wedding anniversaries. Motherhood. Filial relations. Transvestism. Theft. Blackmail. Pregnancy. Eyes—Artificial.*

Note: Opened in London in Jan 1968. Director Alvin Rakoff was replaced by Roy Ward Baker, who receives screen credit.

L'ANNO SCORSO A MARIENBAD *see* **LAST YEAR AT MARIENBAD**

ANOMALIES—A WORLD OF DREAMS　　　F6.0162

Fine Products. *Dist* Fine Products, Distribpix, Inc. 8 Oct **1970** [San Francisco showing]. Sd; col. 35mm. 70 min.

Prod Gerald Fine, Jerry Jackson.

Sex instruction film(?). A physician presents several "clinical studies" of sexual inhibitions and deviations. *Physicians. Inhibition. Sexual practices.*

Note: Also known as *Anomalies* and *Anomaly*.

ANOTHER DAY, ANOTHER MAN　　　F6.0163

Juri Productions. *Dist* Jerand Film Distributors, Sack Amusement Enterprises. 19 Oct **1966**. Sd; b&w. 35mm. 70 min.

Prod-Dir Doris Wishman. *Story* Dawn Whitman. *Dir Photog* Nouri Haviv. *Film Ed* Marie Inc. *Mus* Music Sound Recorders. *Sd Titra Sound Corp. *Optical Eff* B & O Film Specialists.

Cast: Tony Gregory, Barbie Kemp, Mary O'Hara, Rod Regan, D. Swanson, Darlene Bennett, J. B. Brandt, Bob Oran.

Melodrama. Ann and Tess are roommates. Ann works in an office and Tess is a prostitute working for a pimp named Bert. Ann is secretly married to Steve Wundit, and she quits her job when Steve gets a raise. A short time later, Steve becomes very ill, and Ann is forced to go to work for Bert to support Steve. Tess becomes pregnant by Bert, but he refuses to marry her, and she informs the police of his prostitution ring. Steve recovers enough to visit Ann at what he supposes is her office. Steve finds her in another man's arms, and he quickly returns home to commit suicide. Ann finds him dead and cries that she became a prostitute for his sake. *Roommates. Office clerks. Prostitutes. Pimps. Prostitution. Suicide. Pregnancy. Self-sacrifice.*

ANOTHER WOMAN, ANOTHER DAY see **THE LOVE MERCHANT**

ANSATSU see **THE ASSASSIN**

THE ANSWER! see **HANDS OF A STRANGER**

ANTIGONE (Greece)   F6.0164

Norma Films Productions. *Dist* Ellis Films. 18 Sep **1962** [New York opening]. Sd; b&w. 35mm. 88 min.

Prod Demetrios Paris. *Exec Prod* Sperie Perakos. *Dir-Writ* George Tzavellas. *Photog* Dinos Katsouridis. *Art Dir* George Anemoyannis. *Mus* Arghyris Kounadis. *Sd* Nikos Despotides. *Cost* George Anemoyannis. *English Subtitl* Noelle Gillmor.

Cast: Irene Papas *(Antigone)*, Manos Katrakis *(Creon)*, Maro Kontou *(Ismene)*, Nikos Kazis *(Haemon)*, Ilia Livikou *(Eurydice)*, Theo Karousos *(Teiresias)*, Yannis Arghyris *(sentry)*, Byron Pallis *(messenger)*, T. Morides *(leader of the chorus)*.

Tragedy. Source: Sophocles, *Antigone*. A film version of Sophocles' tragedy. *Royalty. Sisters. Uncles. Brothers. Prophets. Death. Murder. Suicide. Loyalty. Fratricide. Brother-sister relationship. Rites and ceremonies. Blindness. Exile. Caves. Thebes. Duels.*

Note: Produced in 1961; running time: 93 min.

ANTINEA, L'AMANTE DELLA CITTÀ SEPOLTA see **JOURNEY BENEATH THE DESERT**

ANTONIO DAS MORTES (Brazil)   F6.0165

Produções Cinematográficas Mapa. *Dist* Grove Press. 2 Apr **1970** [New York opening]. Sd; col (Eastman Color). 35mm. 100 min.

Prod Claude-Antoiñe Mapa, Glauber Rocha. *Exec Prod* Zelito Viana. *Dir-Writ* Glauber Rocha. *Photog* Alfonso Beato. *Camera Op* Ricardo Stein. *Art Dir* Glauber Rocha. *Film Ed* Eduardo Escorel. *Asst Film Ed* Amauri Alves. *Mus* Marlos Nobre, Walter Queiroz, Sérgio Ricardo. *Sd* Walter Goulart. *Asst Dir* Antonio Calmon.

Cast: Maurício do Valle *(Antônio das Mortes)*, Odete Lara *(Laura)*, Hugo Carvana *(Police Chief Mattos)*, Othon Bastos *(The Professor)*, Jofre Soares *(Colonel Horacio)*, Lorival Pariz *(Coirana)*, Rosa Maria Penna *(Sanata Bárbara)*, Mário Gusmão *(Antão)*, Vinicius Salvatori *("Mata Vaca")*, Emanuel Cavalcanti *(priest)*, Sante Scaldaferri *(Batista)*, The People of Milagres.

Drama. Colonel Horatio, an old, tyrannical, blind landowner in the *sertão* (backlands) of northeastern Brazil, rules over the poverty-stricken village of Jardim das Piranhas. At his side are Laura, his young and beautiful mistress, whom he saved from a brothel, and a cowardly, ambitious police chief, Mattos, who favors modernization through U. S. capital. A dispirited schoolteacher from the city instructs the town's children in Brazilian history and consoles himself with drink. Horatio's peace is disturbed by the appearance of a starving band of *beatos* (mystical believers from the poorest classes) led by the *cangaceiro* (bandit-rebel) Coirana, who proclaims himself a holy warrior battling the dragon of evil and demands food for his people. To pacify Horatio, Mattos summons Antônio das Mortes, who in years gone by carried out a personal mission of extermination against the *cangaceiros*, killing their leader, Lampião, in 1938. Antônio arrives to verify the report of a new *cangaceiro*, but Horatio is dismayed to learn that he will accept no money for killing Coirana. In a ritual fight with machetes as the *beatos* chant nearby, Antônio wounds Coirana. He feels troubled by his deed, however, and realizes that it is no longer the *cangaceiro* who is his enemy. He seeks counsel from Coirana's "saint," a young woman dressed in white, and she sends him to seek forgiveness along "the fiery roads of earth." Meanwhile, Laura urges Mattos to kill Horatio and usurp his power, and when Mattos vacillates she publicly stabs him to death to retain Horatio's trust. Coirana dies from his wound, and while Antônio carries his body into the *sertão*, Horatio calls in a band of hired killers led by "Mata Vaca" to exterminate the *cangaceiro*'s helpless followers. The village priest seeks in vain for help as the schoolteacher makes love with Laura over Mattos' corpse. Only the saint and an old black disciple survive the slaughter of the *beatos*. Antônio returns and resurrects the schoolteacher from his despair. In front of the village church they meet Mata Vaca and his band in a heroic gun battle. The hired killers are wiped out, and Horatio is killed by the black disciple. The schoolteacher carries the body of Laura, killed in the battle, as Antônio departs along a modern highway. [A prologue describes parallels between the Christian and African religious heritage of Brazil and the importance of the legend of St. George and the Dragon.] *Landowners. Police. Bandits. Peasants. Hired killers. Mistresses. Religious sects. Mysticism. Schoolteachers. Poverty. Blindness. Infidelity. Murder. Massacres. Brazil—Northeast. Saint George.*

Note: Filmed on location in Milagres in the Brazilian Northeast. Rio de Janeiro opening: Jun 1969 as *O dragão da maldade contra o santo guerreiro*; alternative title: *Antônio das Mortes*.

ANTS IN MY PANTS   F6.0166

MJ Productions. *Dist* MarJon Film Distributors. ca **1970**. Sd; col. 16mm. [Feature film, length unknown.]

Sex film. No information about the precise nature of this film has been found. *Sexuality.*

ANY BODY ... ANY WAY   F6.0167

SHB Productions. *Dist* Distribpix, Inc. 11 Dec **1968** [Champaign, Illinois, showing]. Sd; col (Berkey). 35mm. 79 min.

Prod Stanley H. Brasloff. *Dir-Writ* Charles Romine. *Photog* Victor Petrashevic. *Art Dir* John Annus. *Film Ed* Kemper Peacock. *Mus Dir* Harvey R. Kugler. *Sd* John Fodor. *Prod Mgr* Kenneth Rudnick.

Cast: Eve Reeves, Joyce Denner, Daniel Garth, Ivan Hagar, Irene Lawrence, Andrea Beatrice, Allan Michaels, Madeline LeRoux, Michael Lawrence, Christina Piroska.

Melodrama. Strolling through a pastoral glen, Mr. Bradley is drawn to the sounds of rock and roll music in an apparently deserted barn, and discovers a young people's orgy in progress. He climbs to the loft to see better, and there he saves a pretty girl from being raped. The girl, Ann, introduces Bradley to her friend Terry; Bradley soon leaves to rendezvous with his hired hand, Freddy. When Ann and Terry later find their car disabled, they accept Freddy's "help" as he drives them to Bradley's home, and they soon realize they are prisoners of a demented, one-time mortician. Bradley rapes Terry and then shows the fearstruck young women the preserved nude bodies of three who refused to cooperate in Bradley's experimentation. Ann then allows herself to be anointed with special oil and becomes the subject for an unnatural experiment. Ann and Terry then stage a mock brawl and, when Bradley comes to investigate, overcome him and escape, accidentally setting the house afire in their desperate rush to freedom. Bradley is trapped in his flaming mansion and, about to be burned alive, hallucinates that the three naked corpses arise and relentlessly march upon him. *Undertakers. Sex deviates. Rape. Kidnaping. Experiments. Orgies. Fires.*

Note: Also known as *Anybody, Anywhere*.

ANY GUN CAN PLAY (Italy)   F6.0168

Fida Cinematografica. *Dist* Golden Eagle Films, RAF Industries. 13 Sep **1968** [New York opening]. Sd; col (Technicolor). 35mm (Techniscope). 103 min.

Dir-Writ Enzo G. Castellari. *Screenplay* Romolo Guerrieri, George Simonelli, Enzo G. Castellari, Fabio Carpi, Sauro Scavolini. *Photog* Gianni Bergamini. *Mus* Francesco De Masi.

Cast: Edd Byrnes *(Clayton)*, Gilbert Roland *(Monetero)*, George Hilton *(The Bounty Hunter)*, Kareen O'Hara *(Wapa)*, Pedro Sanchez *(Pajondo)*, Gerard Herter *(Backman)*.

Western melodrama. After killing three western bandits in order to collect the reward money on their heads, a bounty hunter decides his next quarry will be the notorious bandito, Monetero. During an attack on a train carrying a safe containing gold from the Southern Bank, Monetero is betrayed by his deputy, Pajondo, who makes off with the loot. Although Monetero tracks him down, Pajondo is killed by an Army sergeant, and Monetero himself is taken prisoner. Before he can be executed, he is rescued by the bounty hunter, who knows that before Pajondo died he gave Monetero a gold medallion, the clue to the treasure's whereabouts. Unfortunately for the two men, the coin has been divided and the other half has fallen into the hands of Clayton, a young Southern Bank official who was also implicated in the train robbery. For a time the three would-be thieves pair off in different partnerships designed to cheat the third party out of a share of the gold. But eventually they all arrive at the hacienda where the cache of gold is hidden. They battle with each other until Backman, an insurance agent, arrives and takes possession of the sacks of gold. As he rides off, however, it is revealed that the sacks contain nothing more than rocks and sand—the gold is still hidden in the pipes of an old church organ. When Monetero's gang show up, they are shot down by the now unified threesome who proceed to shoot holes in the organ pipes and divide the gold. *Bandits. Bounty hunters. Bankers. Train robberies. Cheating. Greed. Murder. Gold.*

Note: Produced in 1967; Italian title: *Vado ... l'ammazzo e torno*. Filmed in whole or in part in Spain.

ANY MAN'S WOMAN (Reissue) (France/Italy)   F6.0169

Globe Omnium Films-Electra Compagnia Cinematografica. *Dist* Ellis Films. Oct **1964**. Sd; b&w. 35mm. 89 min.

Note: Originally released in the United States as *No Escape* (Ellis Films, 1959). Initial French release in 1958 as *Le piège*; running time: 98 min. Released in Italy in 1959 as *La trappola si chiude*.

ANY NUMBER CAN WIN (France/Italy) **F6.0170**
CIPRA–C. C. M.–Cité Films. *Dist* Metro-Goldwyn-Mayer, Inc. 8 Oct **1963** [New York opening; c5 Nov 1963; LP26630]. Sd; b&w. 35mm (CinemaScope). 112 min. [Copyright length: 107 min.]

Prod Jacques Bar. *Dir* Henri Verneuil. *Screenplay* Albert Simonin, Michel Audiard, Henri Verneuil. *Dial* Michel Audiard. *Adapt* Albert Simonin. *Dir Photog* Louis Page. *Set Dsgn* Robert Clavel. *Film Ed* Françoise Bonnot, Michèle Boehm. *Mus* Michel Magne. *Sd Engr* Jean Rieul. *Asst Dir* Claude Pinoteau, Christian de Chalonges. *Prod Mgr* Jacques Juranville.

Cast: Jean Gabin (*Charles*), Alain Delon (*Francis*), Viviane Romance (*Ginette*), Maurice Biraud (*Louis*), Carla Marlier (*Brigitte*), José-Luis de Vilallonga (*Grimp*), Germaine Montéro (*Francis' mother*), Jean Carmet (*barman*), Dora Doll (*countess*), Henri Virlogeux (*Mario*), Rita Cadillac (*Lilliane*), Anne-Marie Coffinet (*Marcelle*), Jimmy Davis (*Sam*), Dominique Davray (*Leone*), Claude Cerval (*inspector*), Ben Tyber Ballet Troupe.

Crime drama. Source: John Trinian, *The Big Grab* (New York, 1960). Charles, an aging Frenchman who has served a 5-year prison term for attempted burglary, ignores the pleas of his wife and makes elaborate plans for robbing the gambling casino at Cannes. Since the plot requires the assistance of others, he brings in Francis, a young man whom he met in prison, and Francis' brother-in-law, Louis. Knowing that the casino proceeds are kept in a basement vault which can be reached only by an elevator, Charles orders Francis to ingratiate himself with the dancers in the casino ballet troupe and learn the exact location of the backstage trapdoor which leads to the elevator shaft. The handsome Francis easily becomes involved in a romantic affair with Brigitte, one of the dancers, and gathers all the necessary data. On the night of the robbery, Francis goes to the casino roof and lowers himself down the elevator shaft; and, wearing a black mask, he confronts the head cashier with a machine gun as he is depositing the night's receipts. After obtaining the keys to the exit door, Francis admits Charles. The two leave with a billion francs, which Francis hides in a swimming pool locker room. They plan to make their getaway the following morning, but Francis notices that his picture appears in a newspaper photo of the casino and overhears the cashier remark that he remembers the suitcase in which the thieves stashed the money. He desperately slips the valise into the pool, but the bag opens and both Charles and Francis sit helplessly by as the franc notes float to the surface of the pool. *Ex-convicts. Brothers-in-law. Thieves. Dancers. Robbery. Casinos. Elevators. Swimming pools. Cannes.*

Note: Opened in Paris in Apr 1963 as *Mélodie en sous-sol*; running time: 120 min; in Italy in 1963 as *Colpo grosso al casino*; running time: 115 min. Working title: *The Big Grab*.

ANY WEDNESDAY **F6.0171**
Warner Bros. Pictures. 13 Oct **1966** [New York opening; c31 Dec 1966; LP36583]. Sd; col (Technicolor). 35mm. 109 min.

Prod-Writ for the Screen Julius J. Epstein. *Dir* Robert Ellis Miller. *Dir Photog* Harold Lipstein. *Art Dir* Alfred Sweeney. *Set Decor* Claude Carpenter. *Film Ed* Stefan Arnsten. *Mus Comp & Cond* George Duning. *Mus:* "*Any Wednesday*" George Duning. *Lyr* Marilyn Bergman, Alan Bergman. *Sd* Everett Hughes. *Asst Dir* Victor Vallejo. *Cost Dsgn* Dorothy Jeakins. *Wigs* Carita. *Makeup Supv* Gordon Bau. *Supv Hairstylist* Jean Burt Reilly.

Cast: Jane Fonda (*Ellen Gordon*), Jason Robards, [Jr.] (*John Cleves*), Dean Jones (*Cass Henderson*), Rosemary Murphy (*Dorothy Cleves*), Ann Prentiss (*Miss Linsley*), Jack Fletcher (*Felix*), King Moody (*milkman*), Kelly Jean Peters (*girl in gallery*), Monty Margetts (*nurse*).

Comedy. Source: Muriel Resnik, *Any Wednesday* (New York opening: 18 Feb 1964). Six days a week, middle-aged industrial millionaire John Cleves leaves his New York City office and returns home to his wife, Dorothy, in New Jersey. On Wednesdays, when he is supposedly away on business trips, he goes to the East Side apartment of his young mistress, Ellen Gordon. Because the apartment is listed in John's expense books as an "executive suite," his new and inexperienced secretary gives the address to Cass Henderson, an out-of-town businessman who can't find a hotel room. Upon discovering Ellen in the apartment, Cass concludes she is a party girl supplied by Cleves. The situation becomes even stickier when the secretary next gives the address to Mrs. Cleves, who arrives at the apartment and assumes that Ellen and Cass are married. Delighted to meet a young couple from Ohio, Dorothy insists that the Hendersons join the Cleves for a night on the town. The evening is a disaster for all concerned, culminating in the breakup of the Cleves' marriage. Although John moves into Ellen's apartment, Ellen becomes friends with Dorothy and offers her the use of the "executive suite" whenever she is in town. As a result, John arrives there one day and discovers his as yet undivorced wife taking a bath. Ellen also bursts in, catches them making love, and, furious, races into the arms of the delighted Cass. John then begs Dorothy to take him back. After consideration, she decides he is very poor husband material; but she assures him that he can call her "any Wednesday." *Industrialists. Millionaires. Mistresses.*

Secretaries. Businessmen. Marriage. Infidelity. Duplicity. Mistaken identity. New York City—East Side.

Note: Location scenes filmed in New York City.

ANYBODY, ANYWHERE *see* **ANY BODY ... ANY WAY**

ANYONE CAN PLAY (Italy) **F6.0172**
Documento Film. *Dist* Paramount Pictures. Sep **1968** [c21 Sep 1967; LF24]. Sd; col (Eastman Color). 35mm. 88 min.

Prod Gianni Hecht Lucari. *Assoc Prod* Fausto Saraceni. *Dir* Luigi Zampa. *Screenplay* Ettore Scola, Ruggero Maccari, Stefano Strucchi. *Dir Photog* Ennio Guarnieri. *Camera Op* Arturo Zavattini. *Camera Asst* Sergio Salvati. *Art Dir* Maurizio Chiari. *Film Ed* Nino Baragli. *Mus* Armando Trovajoli. *English Titl Song Sung by* Mal of the Primitives. *Choreog* Gino Landi. *Sd* Fernando Pescetelli. *Boom* Alvaro Orsini. *Asst Dir* Joe Pollini. *Prod Mgr* Romano Dandi. *Unit Mgr* Egidio Quarantotto. *Script Supv* Mimmola Girosi. *Makeup* Nilo Jacoponi. *Makeup for Ursula Andress* John O'Gorman. *Hairstyles* Jole Cecchini. *Dial Dir* Don Carlos Dunaway. *Ch Elctrn* Amilcare Cuccoli. *Head Grip* Ennio Picconi. *Stillman* Velio Cioni.

Cast: Ursula Andress (*Norma*), Virna Lisi (*Luisa*), Claudine Auger (*Esmeralda*), Marisa Mell (*Paola*), Brett Halsey (*Carlo, Norma's husband*), Jean-Pierre Cassel (*Aldo, Luisa's husband*), Frank Wolff (*Cesare, Paola's husband*), Marco Guglielmi (*Berto, Esmeralda's husband*), Vittorio Caprioli ("*Brigadier*," *thief*), Franco Fabrizi (*Sandro, Luisa's lover*), Luciano Salce (*psychiatrist*), Lando Buzzanca ("*Smoothie*," *blackmailer*), Pietro Morfea (*blackmailer*), Mario Adorf (*traffic cop*), Fred Williams, actor (*accountant, Esmeralda's lover*), Luis Valenzano Aloisi (*blackmailer*), Margherita Guzzinati (*contessa*), Lia Zoppelli (*Luisa's mother*), Stash De Rola (*Luisa's 2d lover*), Arthur Hansell (*playboy*).

Comedy. Esmeralda, left alone after her husband's departure on business, decides to avoid the temptation offered by one of his employees, a handsome accountant, by visiting three college friends who are organizing a charity party in Rome. Although all of the friends have married well to attractive men, they experience feelings of restlessness. Luisa, who has succumbed to extramarital temptations, is being blackmailed by a gang of extortionists who have recorded her in an encounter in the back seat of an automobile. After trying unsuccessfully to help the extortionists rob the charity party's receipts, Luisa resigns herself to suffering the consequences of her infidelity. However, when her husband accidentally hears the tape he believes that one of his own lapses has been recorded and falls prey to the blackmailers himself. Luisa meets another lover and hands him a card on which she has written, "Do what you want but don't take." Norma has recurring nightmares in which she is sexually assaulted by a huge, moustached stranger. Following the advice of her psychiatrist, she has an affair with a traffic policeman who resembles the man in her dreams. As her dreams persist, however, she resorts to seducing other men who resemble the phantom brute, and she encounters a squad of moustached policemen. Paola, normally shy, performs a striptease at the charity party and creates a sensation. Her husband, a public servant, is forced to give up his job, and he becomes his wife's manager and straight man as she turns professional. Esmeralda returns home to consummate the affair with the accountant, but she is relieved when her husband's arrival forestalls her indiscretion. Her fidelity is short-lived, however: her husband announces that he has more work to do and insists that she attend the races at Monte Carlo with the accountant. *Businessmen. Police. Psychiatrists. Accountants. Civil servants. Infidelity. Blackmail. Rape. Striptease. Charity. Rome. Dreams.*

Note: Released in Italy in 1967 as *Le dolci signore*; running time: 110 min. Some sources omit Stefano Strucchi from screenplay credit.

ANYONE FOR VENICE? *see* **THE HONEY POT**

ANYTHING FOR MONEY **F6.0173**
Howard Farber Films. *Dist* Distribpix, Inc. May **1967**. Sd; b&w. 35mm. 81 min.

Exec Prod Howard Farber, Arthur Morowitz. *Dir-Writ* Joe Sarno. *Dir Photog* Bruce Sparks. *Asst Camera* Robert Bailin. *Mus* Burton Greene. *Sd Engr* F. James Datri, Jr., Mark Dichter. *Ch Electrn* Myron Odegaard.

Cast: Joanna Mills (*Judy*), Judson Todd (*Jim*), Patti Paget (*Edna*), Peggy Stephans (*Louise*), Tony King (*Paul*), Michael Lawrence (*Mike*), Barbara Kemp (*Leslie*), Irene De Bari (*Pam*), Victor Bertini (*Duke*), Cathy O'Shea (*Jean*), Pat Barrett (*Sue*), Lucy Lake (*Peggy*), Brigitte Lemar (*Susan*).

Melodrama. Draftsman Jim Cort is transferred from his West Coast job back East, and with his wife Judy moves into the home of her attractive Aunt Edna, a wealthy widow and businesswoman attended only by her strait-laced secretary, Louise. Judy prompts Jim to engage Edna in an affair in order to make permanent their stay in the big house. Louise sees through Judy's deceit, but she is unable to warn Edna, for the older woman is blinded by nostalgia for her husband, aspects of whom she sees in Jim. Edna has meanwhile discovered Porky's Place, a sex club to which she refers Jim and Judy with her membership card. Judy takes advantage of the club's services and engages two of the "hostesses" to come to Edna's the following night; she also invites Paul, an insecure neighborhood youth whom she has seduced. Louise arrives unexpectedly, and Judy prompts Paul to kiss her; but the boy receives a slap in the face for his attentions. Unbalanced and incited, Paul begins to mercilessly beat Louise, who immediately loses all reserve and passionately begins to make love to him, revelling in his cruelty. Edna and Jim return home and retire to another bedroom. Judy, abandoned, cries desperately for her husband and her youthful lover, but is left alone at the mercy of the "hostesses," who take her back to Porky's Place and introduce her to a new life of shame. *Draftsmen. Businesswomen. Aunts. Widows. Secretaries. Newlyweds. Infidelity. Seduction. Sadomasochism. Prostitution. Greed. Sex clubs.*

ANYTHING ONCE F6.0174

Dist Sam Lake Enterprises. 12 Mar **1969** [Champaign, Illinois, showing]. Sd; b&w. 35mm. 78 min.

Pres by Sam Lake. *Prod* Don Walters. *Dir* Graham Place.

Cast: Ann Wells, Peggy Peacock.

Melodrama. Ann Wells wins the lead in an off-Broadway play and begins to learn of stage politics and backstage sexual relations. At first Ann is confused and upset, and she freezes when Neal James, her co-star, makes love to her onstage. She is subjected to the lesbian advances of an older actress, Marion Sheldon. Ann's involvement in the perversions of the bizarre group deepens, but she is saved from depravity by Phil Masters, who falls in love with her. *Actors. Lesbianism. Theater. New York City.*

Note: Also known as *Anything Once, or Twice* and *Anything Once, or Twice if I Like It.*

ANYTHING WITH GIRLS *see* HOW TO DO ANYTHING AT ALL WITH GIRLS

ANZIO (Italy) F6.0175

Dino De Laurentiis Cinematografica. *Dist* Columbia Pictures. 24 Jul **1968** [New York opening; c1 Jul 1968; LP36052]. Sd; col (Technicolor). 35mm (Panavision). 117 min.

Prod Dino De Laurentiis. *Dir English Vers* Edward Dmytryk. *Dir Italian Vers* Duilio Coletti. *English Screenplay* Harry A. L. Craig. *Adapt* Frank DeFelitta, Duilio Coletti, Giuseppe Mangione, Canestri. *Dir Photog* Giuseppe Rotunno. *Camera* Giuseppe Maccari. *Art Dir* Luigi Scaccianoce. *Asst Art Dir* Dante Ferretti. *Set Dressing* Francesco Bronzi, Emilio D'Andria. *Set Constr* Aldo Puccini. *Film Ed* Peter Taylor, Alberto Gallitti. *Mus Comp & Cond* Riz Ortolani. *Song:* "This World Is Yours" Riz Ortolani, Doc Pomus. *Sung by* Jack Jones. *Sd Rec* Aldo De Martini. *Sd Ed* Norman Schwartz. *Asst Dir* Giorgio Gentili, Gianni Cozzo. *Prod Mgr* Mario Del Papa. *Cont* Elvira D'Amico. *Prod Inspectors* Fritz Mueller, Ferdinando Aliverni. *Cost* Ugo Pericoli. *Wardrobe* Anna Maria Fea. *Makeup Supv* Amato Garbini. *Hairdresser* Gabriella Borzelli. *Sp Eff* Walfrido Traversari. *Casting Dir* Guidarino Guidi.

Cast: Robert Mitchum *(Dick Ennis)*, Peter Falk *(Corporal Rabinoff)*, Earl Holliman *(Sergeant Stimler)*, Mark Damon *(Richardson)*, Reni Santoni *(Movie)*, Joseph Walsh *(Doyle)*, Thomas Hunter *(Andy)*, Giancarlo Giannini *(Cellini)*, Anthony Steel *(General Marsh)*, Patrick Magee *(General Starkey)*, Arthur Franz *(General Howard)*, Elsa Albani *(Emilia)*, Wayde Preston *(Colonel Hendricks)*, Venantino Venantini *(Captain Burns)*, Annabella Andreoli *(Anna)*, Wolfgang Preiss *(Marshal Kesselring)*, Tonio Selwart *(General Von Mackensen)*, Stefanella Giovannini *(Diana)*, Marcella Valeri *(Assunta)*, Enzo Turco *(Pepe)*, Elisabeth Tompson *(Raffaella)*, Wolfgang Hillinger *(Hans)*, Dante Maggio *(Neapolitan street hawker)*, Tiberio Mitri *(British Member of Parliament)*, Vittoria Dal Verme, Giorgia Della Giusta, Carmen Scarpitta *(Neapolitan girls)*, Arthur Kennedy *(General Lesly)*, Robert Ryan *(General Carson)*.

War drama. Source: Wynford Vaughan-Thomas, *Anzio* (New York, 1961). On 22 June 1944, Dick Ennis, a cynical American war correspondent, lands at Anzio with the Allied invasion forces. Accompanied by Movie (a ranger) and a commando, Corporal Rabinoff, Ennis drives into Rome without encountering any German troops en route or inside the city. When they report to General Lesly, commander of the Anzio invasion troops, he refuses to advance, suspecting that the Germans are laying a trap. Lesly's decision to reinforce his position permits the Germans to organize their defense; and an eventual Allied raid on a strategic village results in the loss of many Allied lives. Though Ennis, Movie, Rabinoff, and five other men escape, they are trapped behind the Nazi lines. Given temporary refuge by an Italian woman and her teenaged daughters, the men discover a heavily fortified trap being laid by the Germans around the beachhead. Of the eight men, only Ennis, Movie, and Stimler return to Anzio with the information. After a bloody siege of 4 months, the Allies finally rout the Nazis and march victorious into Rome. Ennis watches General Carson play the conquering hero, then turns away, saddened and disillusioned by the incompetence that led to so many deaths. *Reporters. Rangers. Commandos.*

Deception (military). World War II. Anzio. Rome. Albert Kesselring. Eberhard von Mackensen. United States Army. Great Britain—Army. Germany—Army.

Note: Location scenes filmed in and around Rome. Released in 1968 in Italy as *Lo sbarco di Anzio.* Also known as *The Battle for Anzio.*

AOBEKA MONOGATARI *see* THIS MADDING CROWD

AOI YAJU *see* THE BLUE BEAST

APA *see* FATHER

APACHE GOLD (France / Italy / West Germany / Yugoslavia) F6.0176

Rialto-Film Preben Philipsen–Jadran Film–S. N. C.–Atlantis Film. *Dist* Columbia Pictures. Jun **1965**. Sd; col (Eastman Color). 35mm (CinemaScope). 91 min.

Prod Horst Wendlandt. *Exec Prod* Leif Feilberg. *Dir* Harald Reinl. *2d Unit Dir* Stipe Delić. *Screenplay* Harald G. Petersson. *Photog* Ernst W. Kalinke. *Ch Camera* Everhard Dycke. *Asst Camera* Egon Haedler. *Dir Photog 2d Unit* Milorad Marković. *Art Dir* Vladimir Tadej. *Film Ed* Hermann Haller. *Mus* Martin Böttcher. *Sd* Fedor Jeler. *Asst Dir* Charles M. Wakefield, Slavko Andres. *Prod Mgr* Josip Lulić, Frank Goslar, Dusko Ercegović. *Prod Supv* Erwin Gitt. *Cost* Irms Pauli. *Makeup* Walter Wegner, Gerda Wegner. *Sp Eff* Erwin Lange. *Prop* Otto Fechtner, Herbert Kerz. *Still Photog* Gerd-Victor Krau, Karlheinz Vogelmann, Lothar Winkler.

Cast: Lex Barker *(Old Shatterhand)*, Pierre Brice *(Winnetou)*, Mario Adorf *(Santer)*, Marie Versini *(Nscho-tschi)*, Ralf Wolter *(Sam Hawkins)*, Walter Barnes *(Bill Jones [Bancroft])*, Mavid Popović *(Intschu-tschuna)*, Dunja Rajter *(Belle)*, Chris Howland *(British journalist)*, Husein Čokić, Demeter Bitenc, Niksa Stefanini, Vlado Krstulović, Ilija Ivezić, Branko Špoljar, Teddy Sotosek, Tomoslav Erak, Hrvoje Evob, Antun Nalis, Vladimir Bošnjak, Ana Kranjčec.

Western melodrama. Source: Karl Friedrich May, *Winnetou, der röte Gentleman* (Freiberg im Breisgau, 1893). Santer, leader of a desperado band of outlaws and Kiowa Indians, causes the chief engineer of the Great Western Railroad to violate a treaty with the Apache Indians by extending the railroad into Apache territory in an attempt to steal a legendary Apache treasure hoard. Winnetou, son of the Apache chief, leads an uprising against the intruders but is captured and tortured by Santer. Old Shatterhand, a special investigator for the railroad company, arrives on the scene and comes to his rescue, but Winnetou rides off without having recognized the man who saved him. As Old Shatterhand confronts Santer, Winnetou leads an attack against the railroad headquarters, and Old Shatterhand is seriously injured. Winnetou's sister, Nscho-tschi, nurses him back to health, however, and he is forced to undergo a trial by tomahawk and canoe to prove his friendship to the Apaches. Old Shatterhand stands the test of courage, and Nscho-tschi produces evidence that it was he who saved Winnetou's life. United as blood brothers, Winnetou and Old Shatterhand meet Santer and his men in a gunfight, during which Nscho-tschi and the Apache chief are killed, and Santer falls to his death. *Apache Indians. Desperadoes. Kiowa Indians. Outlaws. Blood brothers. Investigators. Revenge. Uprisings. Torture. Friendship. Treaties. Railroads. Gold. Treasure. Great Western Railroad. Winnetou.*

Note: Filmed in Yugoslavia as *Vinetu.* Released in West Germany in Dec 1963 as *Winnetou—I. Teil;* running time: 101 min; opened in Paris in Aug 1964 as *La révolte des indiens apaches.* Italian title: *La valle dei lunghi coltelli.*

APACHE RIFLES F6.0177

Admiral Pictures. *Dist* Twentieth Century–Fox Film Corp. 30 Sep **1964** [Denver, Colorado, opening; c30 Sep 1964; LP29334]. Sd; col (Eastman Color, print by DeLuxe). 35mm. 92 min.

Assoc Prod Grant Whytock. *Dir* William Witney. *Screenplay* Charles B. Smith. *Story* Kenneth Gamet, Richard Schayer. *Dir Photog* Arch R. Dalzell. *Art Dir* Frank Sylos. *Set Decor* Morris Hoffman. *Supv Film Ed* Grant Whytock. *Mus* Richard La Salle. *Sd* Lambert Day. *Sd Ed* James A. Richard. *Mus Ed* Sid Sidney. *Asst Dir* Herbert S. Greene. *Prod Mgr* Joseph Small. *Wardrobe* Alexis Davidoff. *Makeup Artist* Vincent Romaine. *Hairstyles* Gladys Witten. *Prop Master* Max Frankel.

Cast: Audie Murphy *(Jeff Stanton)*, Michael Dante *(Red Hawk)*, Linda Lawson *(Dawn Gillis)*, L. Q. Jones *(Mike Greer)*, Ken Lynch *(Hodges)*, Joseph A. Vitale *(Victorio)*, Robert Brubaker *(Sergeant Cobb)*, Eugene Iglesias *(Corporal Ramirez)*, J. Pat O'Malley *(Captain Thatcher)*, John Archer *(Colonel Perry)*, Charles Watts *(Crawford Owens)*, Howard Wright *(Thompson)*, Peter Hansen, actor *(Captain Green)*, Robert Karnes *(sheriff)*, Hugh Sanders *(Arizona delegate)*, Sydney Smith *(general of the Army)*, S. John Launer *(General Nelson)*, Robert B. Williams *(Miller)*.

Western drama. In the Arizona Territory in 1879, Apaches leave their reservation to wreak vengeance on the farmers and gold miners who have invaded their homeland. Captain Stanton of the U. S. Cavalry captures Red Hawk, son of Apache chief Victorio, and uses him to bargain for a truce, agreeing to see that greedy miners are kept off Indian territory. The unscrupulous white men murder the new Indian agent, however, and the Apaches are blamed. Stanton is replaced by Colonel Perry, who uses the opportunity to ambush Red Hawk and move him to a new reservation in Texas. Stanton feels that he has broken his word to the chief's son and offers to resign. Red Hawk, however, offers his friendship; and Stanton, with his half-breed fiancée, Dawn, decides to remain in the Cavalry. *Apache Indians. Farmers. Gold miners. Indian agents. Halfcastes. Revenge. Race relations. Treaties. Arizona. Texas. United States Army—Cavalry.*

Note: Location scenes filmed in the Mojave Desert. Working title: *Apache Uprising.* Based on a story written by Richard Schayer for *Indian Uprising* (1952).

APACHE UPRISING   F6.0178

A. C. Lyles Productions. *Dist* Paramount Pictures. 19 Jan **1966** [New York opening; c29 Dec 1965; LP32174]. Sd; col (Technicolor). 35mm (Techniscope). 90 min.

Prod A. C. Lyles. *Dir* R. G. Springsteen. *Screenplay* Harry Sanford, Max Lamb. *Dir Photog* W. Wallace Kelley. *Art Dir* Hal Pereira, Franz Bachelin. *Set Decor* Ray Moyer, Sam Comer. *Film Ed* John Schreyer. *Mus* Jimmie Haskell. *Sd* Harry M. Lindgren, John Wilkinson. *Asst Dir* Dale Coleman, Bob Templeton. *Prod Mgr* Howard Roessel. *Wardrobe* Veda Carroll, Tony Scarano. *Makeup* Wally Westmore, Del Acevedo. *Hairstyles* Nellie Manley, Dean Cole. *Proc Photog* Farciot Edouart.

Cast: Rory Calhoun *(Jim Walker)*, Corinne Calvet *(Janice MacKenzie)*, John Russell *(Vance Buckner)*, Lon Chaney, [Jr.] *(Charlie Russell)*, Gene Evans *(Jess Cooney)*, Richard Arlen *(Captain Gannon)*, Robert H. Harris *(Hoyt Taylor)*, Arthur Hunnicutt *(Bill Gibson)*, DeForest Kelley *(Toby Jack Saunders)*, George Chandler *(Jace Asher)*, Johnny Mack Brown *(Sheriff Ben Hall)*, Jean Parker *(Mrs. Hawkes)*, Abel Fernandez *(young Apache chief)*, Robert Carricart *(Chico Lopez)*, Donald Barry *(Henry Belden)*, Paul Daniel *(Old Antone)*, Reg Parton, Roy Jenson, Rodd Redwing, Dan White, Ben Stanton.

Western drama. Source: Harry Sanford and Max Steeber, *Way Station* (New York, 1961). Apaches attack Jim Walker as he heads for Lordsburg to pick up a herd of mustangs. Bill Gibson, a scout, saves him, and they both head for Apache Wells, discovering a massacred family along the way. As they bury the bodies, Apaches attack again, but then retreat. The Indians fear a Cavalry patrol, which Jim and Bill join but are unable to convince of an Apache uprising. At Apache Wells, Vance Buckner plans with Jess Cooney and Toby Jack Saunders to rob a stagecoach outside the town. When the stage leaves, Jim, Bill, Jess, and Toby Jack are aboard. At the station, Jim fights with Toby Jack when he insults Janice, one of the passengers. Buckner arrives and, with Jess and Toby Jack, disarms the passengers and demands that the money carried on the stage be turned over to him. After revealing that the robbery was the scheme of Taylor, the district manager of the stage line, Toby Jack kills him. Jim and Bill forestall Buckner's plan to kill them by revealing that an Indian they picked up is Antone, an Apache chief, and that his tribe will surely attack. Toby Jack kills Bill, however, but is himself killed by the Apaches as he leaves the station. Jim and Janice escape but are then captured by the Indians; Jim tells them of Antone's imprisonment inside the station and that the Indians must free Buckner and Jess in order to save the chief. The Indians agree, and the outlaws flee. Jim follows them and finds Jess shot, but when he overtakes Buckner, he is unable to kill him in cold blood. The Apaches, who have followed, demand that Buckner be turned over to them so that he may pay for past crimes against Indians, but they allow Jim and Janice to escape to Lordsburg. *Scouts— Frontier. Apache Indians. Tribal chiefs. Hostages. Massacres. Stagecoach robberies. Murder. United States Army—Cavalry. Lordsburg. Horses.*

Note: Location scenes filmed in the Vasquez Mountains, Colorado.

APACHE UPRISING see APACHE RIFLES

APARTMENT IN MOSCOW (U.S.S.R.)   F6.0179

Gorky Film Studio. *Dist* Artkino Pictures. 26 May **1962** [New York opening]. Sd; b&w. 35mm. 70 min.

Dir Viktor Eysymont. *Screenplay* Georgiy Mdivani. *Story Ed* S. Klebanov. *Photog* Boris Monastyrskiy. *Camera* I. Zarafyan. *Art Dir* Boris Dulenkov. *Film Ed* V. Vasilyeva, ed. *Mus* Lev Shvarts. *Cond* E. Khachaturyan. *Sd* N. Pisarev. *Asst Dir* I. Safarova. *Prod Mgr* N. Gofman. *Cost* M. Bykhovskaya. *Makeup* S. Filenova. *Sp Eff* F. Shakh, V. Nikitchenko, A. Sokolov, sp eff.

Cast: Yevgeniy Burenkov *(Degtyaryov)*, N. Doroshina *(Liza)*, V. Vladimirova *(Varvara)*, V. Gusev *(Sakharov)*, T. Pelttser *(The Teacher)*, Stasik Lykhin *(Borya)*, Alla Gutchina *(Nadya)*, Ye. Shutov, Georgiy Vitsin, Dima Uspenskiy, A. Vasilyev, Nikolay Novlyanskiy, Seryozha Smirnov, G. Samokhina, Vitya Stulchikov.

Drama. Ivan Degtyaryov, a good-hearted ex-sailor who leads a construction team building a Moscow housing project, befriends Borya, a free-spirited young boy whose mischief frequently leads to trouble. Borya destroys Ivan's flowerbed, and afterwards Ivan has a heart-to-heart talk with the boy, recruiting

him as a helper. Misfortune has befallen Borya's sister, Liza, who is about to give birth to a baby fathered by Pavel Sakharov, a member of Ivan's construction crew, who has jilted her. Pavel's perfidious behavior is sternly condemned by the other members of the crew, and Ivan feels a deep concern for Liza's plight. He tenderly courts her and with tact and understanding helps her to overcome her despair. Liza returns his love, and, beginning a life together, they move into the newly-completed housing. *Construction crews. Children. Housing. Courtship. Illegitimacy. Brother-sister relationship. Desertion. Moscow.*

Note: Released in the U.S.S.R. in Nov 1961 as *Konets staroy Beryozovki*; running time: 73 min.

L'APE REGINA see THE CONJUGAL BED

THE APE WOMAN (France/Italy)   F6.0180

C. C. Champion–Les Films Concordia–Cocinor–Les Films Marceau. *Dist* Embassy Pictures. 22 Sep **1964** [New York opening]. Sd; b&w. 35mm. 92 min. [Also reviewed at 97 min.]

Pres by Joseph E. Levine. *Prod* Carlo Ponti. *Dir-Writ* Marco Ferreri. *Screenplay* Marco Ferreri, Rafael Azcona. *Photog* Aldo Tonti. *Art Dir* Mario Garbuglia. *Film Ed* Mario Serandrei. *Mus Comp & Cond* Teo Usuelli. *Sd* Mario Faraoni, Mario Amari, Vittorio De Sisti. *Asst Dir* Giancarlo Santi. *Prod Mgr* Antonio Altoviti. *Cost* Piero Tosi. *Makeup* Alberto De Rossi.

Cast: Ugo Tognazzi *(Antonio Focaccio)*, Annie Girardot *(Maria)*, Achille Maieroni *(Majeroni)*, Elvira Paoloni *(chambermaid)*, Ugo Rossi *(pensioner)*, Filippo Pompa Marcelli *(Bruno)*, Ermelinda De Felice *(Sister Furgoncino)*.

Melodrama. Antonio, a 40-year-old Neapolitan small-time operator out for the "fast buck," discovers his golden opportunity while showing "cultural" slides of bare-breasted Africans to residents of a home for the poor run by Catholic nuns. Maria, an inmate of the home, is normal in all respects except that her face and body are completely covered by hair. Antonio manages to convince the shy, self-conscious girl to leave with him to become a freak attraction as "The Ape Woman," supposedly captured in Africa. The act attains some financial success, but the humiliation is too much for the girl and she returns to the home. Antonio succeeds in getting her back with a marriage proposal and makes sure that the wedding is well-publicized. Although he tries to avoid consummation, Maria's threats of annulment change his mind. They join a troupe of performers and travel to Paris where Maria's striptease act is a sensation. Maria becomes pregnant and, although advised to have the pregnancy aborted for fear that the child will be abnormal, determines to have the baby. The baby is born completely normal, and Maria's body's reaction to pregnancy and birth causes her to lose the unnatural hair. She is transformed into a normal, attractive woman. Antonio is at first enraged by the loss of his "meal ticket" but finally realizes the blessing of the change for Maria. He takes a steady, honest job to support his family, and they eventually settle into a normal existence. [In the Italian release version, unlike the version shown in Paris, Maria and her baby die during childbirth, and Antonio exhibits their mummies in order to pay his debts.] *Confidence men. Nuns. Freaks. Hirsutism. Freak shows. Marriage. Childbirth. Striptease. Photographs. Paris.*

Note: Released in Italy in 1964 as *La donna scimmia*; running time: 97 min; in France as *Le mari de la femme à barbe* at 92 min. Shown at Cannes Film Festival at 100 min.

APES ON THE ROCK see THE CLUE OF THE MISSING APE

THE APHRODESIANS   F6.0181

Dist Stacey Distributors. ca **1970**. Sd; col. 16mm. 61-81 min.

Sex film. No information about the precise nature of this film has been found. *Sexuality. Aphrodisiacs.*

APOCALYPSE 3:16   F6.0182

Dist Martin Charlot, Film-Makers' Distribution Center. 8 Dec **1964** [Honolulu, Hawaii, opening]. Si (see note); b&w. 16mm. 110 min.

Prod-Dir Martin Charlot. *Photog* Martin Charlot. *Film Ed* Martin Charlot.

Cast: Tom Kealiinohomoku *(young man)*, Myron Van Brundt *(old man)*, Dion Satterfield *(girl on beach)*, Donald McCauley *(man on porch)*, Chester Gorman *(man with book)*, Terry Marsh *(man with flowers)*, Cecilia Souza *(girl)*, Richard Drake *(man in pool hall)*, Connie Hill *(his girl)*, Jean Charlot *(old man [see note])*, Mark Smith, Robert D. Browne, Edmond Browne *(detectives)*, Mercer Mayer *(medic)*, Norman Wright *(body)*, Richard Drake, Jr. *(boy)*, Lyn Gillham, Bart Miller, Jean Reddick, Edward Stasack *(people in forest)*, Patrick Silva *(water body)*.

Drama. At a Hawaiian beach a woman comes from the water to join a young artist, but they are interrupted by an elderly painter who imprints a stigma on the artist's hand. While visiting four friends in their forest cabin, the young artist is enthralled by a Mexican snake mask. He stumbles and falls from the cabin's porch, vomiting in the darkness. Following his victory in a pool match, the artist is beaten and robbed by his opponent. He revenges himself despite the aged painter's efforts to stop him. In Waikiki he again encounters the old man, who leads him to an apartment and instructs him in meditation. As the elderly artist awakens from a trance, his protégé kisses him on the lips, then stabs him repeatedly. After dropping his mentor's corpse in a stream, the artist weights it with rocks. Nevertheless, the body rises to the surface and floats away. In the forest cabin, the young artist kisses the old painter, from whose lips blood flows. A woman pushes the young man down and he begins to choke her. A frail young man wearing a crown of flowers comes to her aid, and the artist assaults him. In the forest the artist kisses the woman's hand and kneels beside the frail young man. Returning to Waikiki, the young artist dances crazily in an old wooden house. Three padlocks fall from the door, and he is visited by the old man. The young artist cuts out his heart and offers it to the old man. *Artists. Old age. Personality. Faith. Murder. Self-sacrifice. Billiard parlors. Hawaii. Honolulu. Waikiki Beach.*

Note: Filmed on location in Hawaii. Film-Makers' Distribution Center released the film in 1967 when it opened in New York City in a 96-min version. Background sounds were added to the film between 1964 and 1967. Jean Charlot completed the role of the old man after the death of Van Brundt.

THE APPALOOSA   F6.0183

Universal Pictures. 15 Sep **1966** [New York opening; c15 Oct 1966; LP34493]. Sd (Westrex); col (Technicolor). 35mm (Techniscope). 98 min.

Prod Alan Miller. *In Charge of Prod* Edward Muhl. *Dir* Sidney J. Furie. *Screenplay* James Bridges, Roland Kibbee. *Dir Photog* Russell Metty. *Camera Op* Edwin Pyle. *Asst Camera* Ledger Haddow. *Art Dir* Alexander Golitzen, Alfred Sweeney. *Set Decor* John McCarthy, Oliver Emert. *Set Coörd* Virgil Clark. *Main Titl* Pacific Title. *Film Ed* Ted J. Kent. *Asst Film Ed* Peter Colbert. *Mus* Frank Skinner. *Mus Supv* Joseph Gershenson. *Choreog* Poppy Del Vando. *Sd* Waldon O. Watson, Lyle Cain, William Griffith, James Alexander, Bruce Smith. *Asst Dir* Douglas Green, Carl Beringer, James Welch. *Unit Prod Mgr* Wallace Worsley, William S. Gilmore, Jr.. *Script Supv* Robert Forrest. *Women's Cost* Rosemary Odell. *Men's Cost* Helen Colvig. *Wardrobe* Olive Koenitz, Norman Mayreis, David Watson. *Makeup Supv* Bud Westmore. *Makeup* Mark Reedall, Hank Edds, Phil Rhodes, Sherrie Rose. *Hairstyles* Larry Germain, Clara Holgate. *Sp Eff* Ben McMahon. *Tech Adv* Salvador Baquez. *Dial Coach* Celia Webb. *Still Photog* Chic Donchin. *Gaffer* Max Nippell. *Prop* Bill Nunley, John Faltis. *Grip* Charles Cowie, Ken Smith.

Cast: Marlon Brando *(Matt Fletcher)*, Anjanette Comer *(Trini)*, John Saxon *(Chuy Medina)*, Emilio Fernandez *(Lazaro)*, Alex Montoya *(Squint-Eye)*, Miriam Colon *(Ana)*, Rafael Campos *(Paco)*, Frank Silvera *(Ramos)*, Larry D. Mann *(priest)*, Argentina Brunetti *(Yaqui woman)*.

Western melodrama. Source: Robert MacLeod, *The Appaloosa* (Greenwich, Connecticut, 1963). Buffalo hunter Matt Fletcher enters a church in the border town of Ojo Prieto. He plans to begin a new life by using his magnificent Appaloosa stallion to start a horsebreeding farm with his old friend Paco, an impoverished Mexican farmer. His hopes are ruined, however, when Trini, a young woman who has been sold by her parents to Mexican bandit Chuy Medina, tells Chuy that Matt molested her in church. When Chuy enters the church, Trini escapes on Matt's Appaloosa, but she is quickly captured and returned by Chuy's pistoleros. Matt's hopes are shattered when Chuy steals the horse and drags Matt by a rope through a rock-strewn brook. After recovering from his injuries, Matt ventures into Chuy's stronghold and confronts him in a hand-wrestling match in which poisonous scorpions await the one whose arm is forced to the table. Matt loses but saves his life by cutting open the wound with a piece of broken glass. Trini comes to his aid and hides him in a shack owned by Ramos, a goatherd, and nurses him back to health. Squint-Eye, another of Chuy's pistoleros, comes to the shack looking for Matt and Trini, and when Ramos refuses to divulge their whereabouts, Squint-Eye kills Ramos. After killing Squint-Eye, Matt then returns to Chuy's stronghold, retrieves the Appaloosa, and flees toward the border with Trini. Chuy follows, and Matt, realizing that Trini means more to him than the horse, sends out the Appaloosa to draw Chuy's fire. As the bandit aims for the horse, Matt fires and kills him. Matt and Trini then cross the border with the Appaloosa to start a new life. *Hunters. Horsebreeders. Mexicans. Farmers. Bandits. Horsethieves. Goatherds. Frameup. Wrestling. Sadism. Murder. Churches. Mexican border. Horses. Scorpions.*

Note: Location scenes filmed in St. George, Utah; Lancaster, California; and in the San Bernardino Mountains near Wrightwood, California. Working title: *Southwest to Sonora.*

THE APPOINTMENT   F6.0184

Marpol Productions. *Dist* Metro-Goldwyn-Mayer, Inc. 20 Mar **1970** [San Francisco opening; c31 Dec 1968; LP36740]. Sd; col (Metrocolor). 35mm. 100 min. [Copyright length: 115 min.] *MPAA rating* R.

A Martin Poll Production. *Prod* Martin Poll. *Dir* Sidney Lumet. *Screenplay* James Salter. *Story* Antonio Leonviola. *Dir Photog* Carlo Di Palma. *1st Camera Op* Alberto Spagnoli. *Art Dir* Piero Gherardi. *Set Dresser* Arrigo Breschi. *Film*

Ed Thelma Connell. *Mus Score Comp & Cond* Stu Phillips. *Song:* "Solo e triste" ("The Empty Man") Stu Phillips, Bob Stone. *Sung by* Eric Karl of Bodine. *Theme Song:* "Beauty of Beginning" Stu Phillips, Bob Stone. *Sung by* Laura Creamer. *Song:* "The Appointment" John Barry. *Adtl Mus & Orch* John Walker. *Sd Rec* David Hildyard. *Sd Ed* Michael Hart. *Dub Mix* Gerry Humphreys. *Asst Dir* Luciano Sacripanti. *Prod Supv* Orazio Tassara. *Cost Dsgn* Piero Gherardi. *Makeup* Otello Fava. *Hairstyles* Renata Magnanti. *Dial Coach* Mickey Knox.

Cast: Omar Sharif *(Federico Fendi)*, Anouk Aimée *(Carla)*, Lotte Lenya *(Emma Valadier)*, Fausto Tozzi *(Renzo)*, Ennio Balbo *(Ugo Perion)*, Didi Perego *(Nany)*, Luigi Proietti, Paola Barbara, Inna Alexeieff, Daniela Calvino, Ermelinda De Felice, Angelo Infanti, Serena Michelotti, Monica Pardo, Rodolfo Valadier.

Romantic drama. In Rome, Federico Fendi, a lawyer, falls in love with and marries Carla, his colleague Renzo's fiancée, despite Renzo's expressed fear that Carla is secretly a high-priced call girl. Federico's suspicion grows; he begins to follow Carla and becomes convinced of the truth of the accusation in the wake of several coincidences. Federico learns that Carla is innocent of any wrongdoing only after she kills herself over what she sees as her husband's obsessively jealous nature. *Lawyers. Italians. Reputation. Prostitution. Marriage. Jealousy. Suicide. Rome.*

Note: Filmed in 1968; locations scenes filmed in and around Rome and at Lake Bolsena, Italy. Following its 1969 Cannes Film Festival showing, the film was reedited and rescored. John Barry's song and John Walker's music are deleted from the U. S. release version.

THE APRIL FOOLS   F6.0185

Jalem Productions. *Dist* National General Pictures. 28 May **1969** [New York opening; c28 May 1969; LP36888]. Sd; col (Technicolor). 35mm (Panavision). 95 min. *MPAA rating* M.

Pres by Cinema Center Films. *Prod* Gordon Carroll. *Assoc Prod* Carter DeHaven, Jr. *Dir* Stuart Rosenberg. *Story-Screenplay* Hal Dresner. *Photog* Michel Hugo. *Camera Op* Roger Sherman, Sr. *Art Dir* Robert Luthardt. *Set Decor* William Kiernan. *Prod Dsgn* Richard Sylbert. *Film Ed* Robert Wyman. *Mus Comp* Marvin Hamlisch. *Cond* Morton Stevens. *Titl Song* Burt Bacharach, Hal David. *Sung by* Dionne Warwick. *Choreog* Marc Wilder. *Sd Mix* Larry Jost. *Asst Dir* Hank Moonjean, Howard W. Koch, Jr. *Unit Mgr* Carter DeHaven, Jr. *Script Supv* Betty Crosby. *Cost Dsgn* Donfeld. *Men's Cost* Ted Tetrick. *Women's Cost* Thalia Phillips. *Makeup* Harry Ray, Fred Williams. *Hairstyles* Simone Kopp, Agnes Flanagan. *Prop Master* William Skammes.

Cast: Jack Lemmon *(Howard Brubaker)*, Catherine Deneuve *(Catherine Gunther)*, Peter Lawford *(Ted Gunther)*, Jack Weston *(Potter Shrader)*, Myrna Loy *(Grace Greenlaw)*, Charles Boyer *(Andre Greenlaw)*, Harvey Korman *(Benson)*, Sally Kellerman *(Phyllis Brubaker)*, Melinda Dillon *(Leslie Hopkins)*, Kenneth Mars *(Don Hopkins)*, Janice Carroll *(Mimsy Shrader)*, David Doyle *(Walters)*, Gary Dubin *(Stanley Brubaker)*, Susan Barrett *(party singer)*, Dee Gardner *(secretary)*, Tom Ahearne *(doorman)*, Tani Phelps, Nancy Howard.

Romantic comedy. Howard Brubaker, a successful Wall Street broker, lives in Darien, Connecticut, with his preoccupied suburban housewife, Phyllis, and a son who ignores him. While attending a cocktail party given by Ted Gunther, his boss, Howard meets Gunther's French-born wife, Catherine. Unaware of her true identity, he invites her out for a drink at a discotheque, and they meet amateur astrologer Grace Greenlaw. Later, at the Greenlaws' mansion, Howard tells Catherine that he has always felt like the fairy-tale prince who has been turned into a frog and must wait for the kiss of a princess to restore him. Catherine reveals that her marriage is miserable and that she is planning to return to Paris the next day. After delivering Catherine to her apartment, Howard wanders into Central Park and decides to quit his job and go to Paris. He confronts Gunther with the news that he is quitting, then returns to Catherine with a toy frog and confesses his love. Undeterred by the knowledge that she is Gunther's wife, he agrees to meet her at Kennedy Airport. As Catherine tries to convince her husband that she is actually leaving him, Howard takes a drunken train ride with his friend, lawyer Potter Shrader, who advises him on obtaining a divorce. His wife greets the news with apparent indifference, and Howard, finally realizing that his marriage is meaningless, races to the airport. Just before take-off, Howard leaps aboard the plane in time to take the place of the toy frog that Catherine has placed in the seat next to her. *Brokers. Housewives. French. Astrologers. Lawyers. Suburban life. Drunkenness. Marriage. Divorce. Infidelity. Discotheques. New York City—Wall Street. Darien (Connecticut). New York City—Central Park. John Fitzgerald Kennedy International Airport. "Frog Prince".*

Note: Location scenes filmed in and around New York City.

THE AQUA SEX   F6.0186

Aquarex. *Dist* Art Films International. 19 Mar **1965** [Los Angeles showing; c1 Aug 1964; LP32312]. Sd; col (Eastman Color). 35mm. 71 min. [Also reviewed at 77-88 min.]

Prod-Dir-Writ John Lamb. *Assoc Prod* Ronald Graham.

Cast: Gaby Martone *(Queen of the Aqua)*, George Rowe *(Dr. Samuel Jamison)*, Timothy Carey *(Milo Sangster)*, Jose Gonzalez-Gonzalez *(Pepe Gallardo)*.

Melodrama. Marine biologist Dr. Samuel Jamison learns that a friend owning a map showing the whereabouts of huge pearls has been murdered. Unaware that the murderer is following him, Jamison sets off for Tiburón, a seemingly deserted island off the coast of Mexico. The island is actually inhabited by "amphibious women" who until the discovery of the pearls lived in peace, undisturbed by man. Jamison, in his underwater expedition, finds the pearls and also forms an attachment to one of the women. Their idyllic existence is disrupted when the murderer, Milo Sangster, reaches the island and while stealing some of the pearls kills one of the women. Pepe, the good-natured Mexican fisherman whose boat and services Sangster hired, is thrown overboard by Sangster to eliminate his only witness. The other sirens lure Sangster back into the sea, where Jamison overpowers him. As Jamison sails back to the mainland, he wonders how much of his adventure was merely a dream. *Marine biologists. Divers. Fishermen. Mermaids and mermen. Murder. Theft. Pearls. Mexico. The Sea. Dreams.*

Note: Adapted from *The Mermaids of Tiburón*, q. v.; additional sex scenes have been added. Also known as *The Virgin Aqua Sex*.

ARABELLA (Italy)   F6.0187

Cram Film. *Dist* Universal Pictures. 9 Oct **1970** [San Francisco showing; c27 Sep 1969; LP40550]. Sd; col (Technicolor). 35mm. 91 min. *MPAA rating* M.

Prod Maleno Malenotti. *Assoc Prod* Salvatore Argento. *Dir* Mauro Bolognini. *Screenplay* Adriano Baracco, Brunello Rondi, Giorgio Arlorio. *Dir Photog* Ennio Guarnieri. *Camera Op* Arturo Zavattini. *Art Dir* Alberto Boccianti. *Film Ed* Eraldo Da Roma. *Mus* Ennio Morricone. *Sd* Mario Faraoni. *Asst Dir* Roberto Malenotti. *Unit Prod Mgr* Mario De Biase. *Cost* Piero Tosi. *English Dial* Alan Hackney.

Cast: Virna Lisi *(Arabella Danesi)*, James Fox *(Giorgio)*, Margaret Rutherford *(Princess Ilaria)*, Terry-Thomas *(hotel manager/general/duke/insurance manager)*, Paola Borboni *(Duchess Moretti)*, Antonio Casagrande *(Filberto)*, Giancarlo Giannini *(Saverio)*, Milena Vukotic *(Graziella)*, Esmeralda Ruspoli, Valentino Macchi, Renato Romano, Renato Chiantoni, Giuseppe Addobbati.

Comedy. In Italy in the 1920's Arabella Danesi is forced to turn to swindling to help keep the home of her mother, Princess Ilaria, from the tax collector. She tricks a hotel manager into giving her a large sum of money by pretending that she is a close friend of Mussolini (the swindle, meanwhile, prevents a burglar named Giorgio from breaking into the hotel's safe). The money is not enough, however, so Arabella postpones her wedding and tries to extort money from a general who was photographed with her in scandalous poses. Giorgio, still upset by the failure of the hotel theft, attempts to blackmail the general, but Arabella persuades the general that she should deliver the blackmail money herself, and when the grateful general hands over £1,000, Arabella takes the money directly to her mother. Her next victim is a duke who hires Arabella to change his son Saverio's indifference toward women so that the young man can marry Graziella, his fiancée. When Arabella approaches Saverio, he readily admits that he is feigning disinterest so that his father will continue to procure beautiful women for him. Agreeing to take a painting for her silence, she promises to sleep with Saverio the following night, but instead she substitutes Graziella, and she and the grateful duke watch the proof of his son's virility. Arabella then goes to a gambling casino in Venice where she sees Giorgio, who, because of a heavy losing streak, is on the verge of suicide. After persuading him not to kill himself, she goes with Giorgio to his room to make love; the next morning Arabella awakens to find herself naked in a museum, surrounded by tourists. She returns to her home to find the tax collectors about to repossess the house. As a last resort, her mother plans to burn down the mansion for the insurance money, but after igniting the fire, she realizes that the insurance policy has been left behind. She rushes in to find it, with Arabella following. Giorgio arrives in time to save them both, and he and Arabella reconcile amidst the ruins. *Swindlers. Revenue agents. Hotelkeepers. Burglars. Nobility. Filial relations. Imposture. Blackmail. Perfidy. Bribery. Suicide. Arson. Taxes. Photographs. Casinos. Museums. Insurance. Venice. Fires.*

Note: Released in Italy in 1967; running time: 105 min.

ARABESQUE (United States/Great Britain)   F6.0188

Stanley Donen Enterprises. *Dist* Universal Pictures. 5 May **1966** [New York opening; c2 Jul 1966; LP34494]. Sd; col (Technicolor). 35mm (Panavision). 105 min.

Prod-Dir Stanley Donen. *In Charge of Prod* Edward Muhl. *Prod Exec* Arthur Carroll. *Assoc Prod* Denis Holt. *Screenplay* Julian Mitchell, Stanley Price, Pierre Marton. *Cont* Constance Willis. *Photog* Christopher Challis. *Camera Op* Austin Dempster. *2d Unit Op* John Jordan. *Art Dir* Reece Pemberton. *Main Titl Dsgn* Maurice Binder. *Film Ed* Frederick Wilson. *Mus* Henry Mancini. *Sd Mix* John W. Mitchell, Colin Le Mesurier. *Dub Ed* Don Sharpe. *Asst Dir* Eric Rattray. *Prod Mgr* David W. Orton. *Miss Loren's Wardrobe* Christian Dior. *Makeup* W. T. Partleton.

Cast: Gregory Peck *(David Pollock)*, Sophia Loren *(Yasmin Azir)*, Alan Badel *(Beshraavi)*, Kieron Moore *(Yussef)*, John Merivale *(Sloane)*, Duncan Lamont *(Webster)*, Carl Duering *(Jena)*, George Coulouris *(Ragheeb)*, Ernest Clark *(Beauchamp)*, Harold Kasket *(Lufti)*, Gordon Griffin *(Fanshaw)*, Sidney James.

Comedy-drama. Source: Alex Gordon, *The Cipher* (New York, 1961). Because of his knowledge of ancient languages, David Pollock, an American professor visiting Oxford, becomes the key figure in deciphering a secret message written in hieroglyphics. First, he is kidnaped by the prime minister of a Middle Eastern nation who asks him to spy on oil magnate Beshraavi in the interest of world peace. Then, while visiting Beshraavi's home, Pollock meets Yasmin Azir, Beshraavi's mistress, who warns him that his life is in danger and helps him escape through the London zoo. Pollock hides the secret message before being captured by Yussef, another conspirator who seems to have a proprietary interest in Yasmin. Once more eluding his captors, Pollock runs into Yasmin, but, unable to figure out which group of spies she is with, he refuses to trust her. However, when both of them are attacked by Yussef and his henchmen, Pollock decides to work with her against Beshraavi. They decipher the cryptogram and learn that the prime minister is about to be assassinated while making a speech at the London airport. Despite their frantic efforts to save him, the man is shot down by Beshraavi. Yasmin then reveals that she is a spy for the real prime minister and that the murdered man was merely one of Beshraavi's employees. The real minister has been kidnaped to prevent him from making a speech denouncing Beshraavi's oil interests. Pollock and Yasmin succeed in rescuing the minister; but as they flee across the open countryside, Beshraavi pursues them in a helicopter. Pollock outwits him by hurling a steel ladder into the aircraft's propeller blades, and Beshraavi crashes to his death. Yasmin decides to retire from international intrigue and follow Pollock back to the peaceful life at Oxford. *Americans in foreign countries. Professors. Prime ministers. Oil magnates. Mistresses. Spies. Espionage. Cryptography. Conspiracy. Kidnaping. Assassination. Helicopters. London. Oxford University. Chases.*

Note: Opened in London in Jul 1966.

ARASHI NO NAKA NO OTOKO *see* **THE MAN IN THE STORM**

L'ARBRE DE NOËL *see* **THE CHRISTMAS TREE**

THE ARCH (Republic of China)   F6.0189

Film Dynasty Productions. *Dist* Paul D. Lee. Dec **1969** [Los Angeles showing]. Sd; b&w. 35mm. 94 min.

Prod-Dir-Writ Shu Shuen. *Asst Prod* Richard Tang. *Photog* Subrata Mitra. *2d Unit Photog* Chi H'u Che. *Set Decor* Pao Tien Ming. *Film Ed* Les Blank, C. C. See. *Mus* Lui Tsun Yuan. *Sd* Del Harris. *Cost* Liu Hsian Hui. *Makeup* Sung Shiao-chiang.

Cast: Lisa Lu *(Madam Tung)*, Roy Chiao Hung *(Captain Yang)*, Hilda Chou Hsuan *(Wei-ling)*, Li Ying *(Old Chang)*, Wen Hsui *(grandmother)*, Liang Jui *(monk)*.

Romantic drama. In southwest China during the Ming Dynasty, Madam Tung, the virtuous widow of an eminent scholar, is held in high regard by her neighbors. In fact, the townspeople petition the emperor to construct an arch celebrating her fidelity to her husband's memory. While the populace awaits the emperor's response, an army enters the village to protect the harvest from plunder. Although Madam Tung is strongly attracted to the captain, she masks her emotions, enabling Captain Yang and her daughter Wei-ling to court and marry. Madam Tung is left alone, and the arch is constructed. *Widows. Soldiers. Village life. Fidelity. Courtship. Marriage. Filial relations. Sculptures. China—History—Ming Dynasty.*

Note: Location scenes filmed in Taiwan in 1967. Shu Shuen is a pseudonym for Cecile Tang.

ARCHIMEDE *see* **SIEGE OF SYRACUSE**

ARCHIMÈDE, LE CLOCHARD *see* **THE MAGNIFICENT TRAMP**

L'ARCIDIAVOLO *see* **THE DEVIL IN LOVE**

ARCTIC SAFARI   F6.0190

Alaskan Shows. 9 Dec **1964** [Portland, Oregon, opening]. Sd; col. 35mm. 80 min.

A Ron Hayes Production. *Prod-Dir* Ron Hayes, Bev Hayes. *Photog* Ron Hayes.

Documentary. The film depicts hunting and fishing expeditions in the 49th state. *Hunting. Fishing. Alaska.*

Note: Filmed in 16mm. Combined with *Safari in Alaska*, q. v., and reedited into the feature *Alaskan Safari*, q. v.

ARE YOU BORED WITH MEN? *see* **DARLING, ARE YOU BORED WITH MEN?**

THE ARISTOCATS   F6.0191

Walt Disney Productions. *Dist* Buena Vista Distribution Co. 11 Dec **1970** [Los Angeles opening; c10 Aug 1970; LP38283]. Sd (RCA); col (Technicolor). 35mm. 78 min. *MPAA rating* G.

Prod Wolfgang Reitherman, Winston Hibler. *Dir* Wolfgang Reitherman. *Screenplay* Larry Clemmons, Vance Gerry, Frank Thomas, Julius Svendsen, Ken Anderson, Eric Cleworth, Ralph Wright. *Story* Tom McGowan, Tom Rowe. *Anim Dir* Milt Kahl, Ollie Johnston, Frank Thomas, John Lounsbery. *Layout* Don Griffith, Basil Davidovich, Sylvia Roemer. *Background* Al Dempster, Bill Layne, Ralph Hulett. *Eff Anim* Dan MacManus, Dick Lucas. *Charact Anim* Hal King, Eric Cleworth, Fred Hellmich, Eric Larson, Julius Svendsen, Walt Stanchfield, Dave Michener. *Prod Dsgn* Ken Anderson. *Film Ed* Tom Acosta. *Mus* George Bruns. *Orch* Walter Sheets. *Titl Song* Robert B. Sherman, Richard M. Sherman. *Sung by* Maurice Chevalier. *Song: "Scales and Arpeggios," "She Never Felt Alone"* Robert B. Sherman, Richard M. Sherman. *Song: "Thomas O'Malley Cat"* Terry Gilkyson. *Sung by* Phil Harris. *Song: "Ev'rybody Wants To Be a Cat"* Floyd Huddleston, Al Rinker. *Sd* Robert O. Cook. *Mus Ed* Evelyn Kennedy. *Asst Dir* Ed Hansen, Dan Alguire. *Prod Mgr* Don Duckwall.

Cast—Voices: Phil Harris (*J. Thomas O'Malley*), Eva Gabor (*Duchess*), Sterling Holloway (*Roquefort*), Scatman Crothers (*Scatcat*), Paul Winchell (*Chinese cat*), Tim Hudson (*English cat*), Vito Scotti (*Italian cat*), Thurl Ravenscroft (*Russian cat*), Dean Clark (*Berlioz*), Liz English (*Marie*), Gary Dubin (*Toulouse*), Nancy Kulp (*Frou Frou*), Pat Buttram (*Napoleon*), George Lindsey (*Lafayette*), Monica Evans (*Abigail*), Carole Shelley (*Amelia*), Charles Lane (*lawyer*), Hermione Baddeley (*Madame Bonfamille*), Roddy Maude-Roxby (*butler*), Bill Thompson (*Uncle Waldo*), Ruth Buzzi ([see note]).

Animated comedy. In 1910 in Paris, a cat named Duchess and her three kittens are made beneficiaries in the will of the wealthy Madame Bonfamille. Edgar, the butler, learning that he will become the heir if misfortune should befall the cats, drugs their milk, takes them to the country, and abandons them. Upon regaining consciousness, they realize that they are lost, but soon they encounter J. Thomas O'Malley, an alley cat who promises to help them return to Paris. On the way, O'Malley dives into a stream to rescue one of the kittens but is himself swept downstream and saved from drowning by the Gabble Sisters, two English geese who are also traveling to Paris. When they arrive in Paris, O'Malley offers his lodgings to Duchess and the kittens in a bohemian quarter of the city; Duchess accepts and they are treated to a jazz concert by a band of O'Malley's alley cat friends. The next day Duchess and the kittens return to their home, but Edgar puts them in a trunk for final disposal. Roquefort, a friendly mouse, runs to inform O'Malley of Duchess' plight, and O'Malley and his gang arrive to release Duchess. In the course of the fighting, Edgar is locked in the trunk intended for Duchess. A truck arrives and the trunk is delivered, as planned, to Timbuktu. *Heirs. Aristocrats. Butlers. Sisters. Jazzbands. Greed. Rescue. Inheritance. Paris. Cats. Mice. Geese.*

Note: Ruth Buzzi sings for the character of Frou Frou.

ARIZONA BILL *see* **THE ROAD TO FORT ALAMO**

ARIZONA BUSHWHACKERS   F6.0192

A. C. Lyles Productions. *Dist* Paramount Pictures. Mar **1968** [c31 Jan, 15 Dec 1967; LP35286, LP35826]. Sd; col (Technicolor). 35mm (Techniscope). 87 min.

Prod A. C. Lyles. *Dir* Lesley Selander. *Screenplay* Steve Fisher. *Story* Steve Fisher, Andrew Craddock. *Art Dir* Hal Pereira, Al Roelofs. *Set Decor* Robert R. Benton, Jerry Welch. *Film Ed* John F. Schreyer. *Mus* Jimmie Haskell. *Sd* Joe Edmondson, John Wilkinson. *Asst Dir* Dale Hutchinson. *Prod Mgr* Robert Goodstein. *Makeup* Wally Westmore. *Hairstyles* Nellie Manley. *Sp Photog Eff* Paul K. Lerpae.

Cast: Howard Keel (*Lee Travis*), Yvonne De Carlo (*Jill Wyler*), John Ireland (*Dan Shelby*), Marilyn Maxwell (*Molly*), Scott Brady (*Tom Rile*), Brian Donlevy (*Mayor Joe Smith*), Barton MacLane (*Sheriff Lloyd Grover*), James Craig (*Ike Clanton*), Roy Rogers, Jr. (*Roy*), Reg Parton (*Curly*), Monty Montana (*stage driver*), Eric Cody (*bushwhacker*), James Cagney (*narrator*).

Western drama. Lee Travis, a captured Confederate riverboat gambler and gunfighter, is given the opportunity to join the Union Army and help bring law and order to the West. When residents of Colton, Arizona, learn that a turncoat is going to replace Sheriff Grover, everyone complains except Mayor Joe

Smith. He hopes that Travis can help rout Tom Rile, who has been bribing the corrupt Grover; in truth, however, Travis is a Southern spy assigned to transport arms and ammunition hidden near the town to a group of Confederate soldiers. Hoping to rid the town of the drunks and bums hanging around Rile's saloon and gambling house, Travis wins the saloon from Rile in a dice game, then closes the place and orders Rile out of town. Travis learns from bar girl Molly, whom he has mistaken for his Confederate contact, that Rile has been selling weapons to Apaches. Realizing that Rile has been availing himself of the hidden Confederate supplies, Travis tries to apprehend him but is shot and taken to a doctor by milliner Jill Wyler, who, he has learned, is his contact. In the meantime, Dan Shelby, Grover's deputy, discovers that Travis and Jill are spies and is about to turn them over to Mayor Smith when Grover returns to announce that the war is over. The ex-sheriff also informs the mayor that Rile and the Indians are about to attack the town. The small band of citizens defend themselves against the raid, killing Rile, his gunmen, and most of the Apaches. Jill and Shelby are romantically united, and Travis gives Molly the deed to the saloon before riding out of town. *Gamblers. Gunfighters. Prisoners of war. Sheriffs. Soldiers. Saloon keepers. Mayors. Barmaids. Milliners. Spies. Apache Indians. Bribery. Mistaken identity. Ammunition. United States—History— Civil War. Arizona.*

ARIZONA COLT *see* **THE MAN FROM NOWHERE**

ARIZONA RAIDERS   F6.0193

Admiral Pictures. *Dist* Columbia Pictures. Jul **1965** [c1 May 1965; LP30823]. Sd; col (Eastmancolor, print by Technicolor). 35mm (Techniscope). 88 min.

Prod Grant Whytock. *Dir* William Witney. *Screenplay* Alex Gottlieb, Mary Willingham, Willard Willingham. *Story (see note)* Frank Gruber, Richard Schayer. *Dir Photog* Jacques Marquette. *Art Dir* Paul Sylos, Jr. *Set Decor* Harry Reif. *Supv Ed* Grant Whytock. *Mus* Richard LaSalle. *Sd Supv* Charles J. Rice. *Sd Ed* Al Bird. *Sd* B. F. Ryan. *Mus Ed* Edna Bullock. *Asst Dir* Jack Lacey. *Prod Supv* Harold E. Knox. *Script Supv* John Gannon. *Wardrobe* Joseph Dimmitt. *Makeup Artist* Dan Greenway. *Hairstyles* Edith Lindon. *Prop Master* Charles Henley.

Cast: Audie Murphy (*Clint*), Michael Dante (*Brady*), Ben Cooper (*Willie Martin*), Buster Crabbe (*Captain Andrews*), Gloria Talbott (*Martina*), Ray Stricklyn (*Danny Bonner*), George Keymas (*Montana*), Fred Krone (*Matt Edwards*), Willard Willingham (*Eddie*), Red Morgan (*Tex*), Fred Graham (*Quantrell*).

Western melodrama. Clint, a Confederate Army hero whose parents were murdered by carpetbaggers after the Civil War, has joined Quantrell's Raiders, a group of guerrillas. After Quantrell is killed, Clint and his friend Willie Martin are captured and tried by Union troops led by Captain Andrews, and they are sentenced to 20 years at hard labor. Andrews is subsequently appointed to lead the newly-formed Arizona Rangers in hunting down remnants of Quantrell's band who have attacked a peaceful Yaqui Indian village and abducted Martina, the chief's daughter. Andrews arranges for Clint and Willie to escape and promises them an unconditional pardon if they will help him round up the outlaws. Clint agrees to the scheme because he wants to take revenge on an old enemy, Montana, who now leads the raiders. Clint tracks Montana to the Indian village and kills him, but he decides to abandon his escape to Mexico when he learns that the gang has killed his younger brother and Willie. Clint returns, and with the help of Captain Andrews and a group of Indian braves he destroys the rest of the gang, rescuing Martina. The mission complete, he embarks on a career as an Arizona Ranger. *Confederate veterans. Brothers. War heroes. Guerrillas. Outlaws. Yaqui Indians. Abduction. Revenge. United States—History—Civil War. Arizona. Mexican border. Arizona Rangers. Quantrill's Raiders.*

Note: Location scenes filmed in Phoenix, Arizona. *The Texas Rangers* (Columbia, 1951) was used for source material; screenplay by Schayer, story by Gruber.

UN ARMA DE DOS FILOS *see* **SHARK!**

ARMORED COMMAND   F6.0194

Allied Artists. 2 Aug **1961** [Omaha, Nebraska, opening; c28 Jul 1961; LP19929]. Sd; b&w. 35mm. 105 min. [Also 99 min.]

Prod-Writ Ron W. Alcorn. *Dir* Byron Haskin. *Photog* Ernest Haller. *Art Dir* Hans Berthel. *Film Ed* Walter Hannemann. *Co-ed* Hanni Ruda. *Mus Comp & Cond* Bert Grund. *Sd* F. W. Dustmann, J. Rapp. *Sd Ed* Luisa Hudeczek. *Asst Dir* Frank Guthke. *Prod Mgr* Lonnie D'Orsa. *Set Cont* Pia Arnold. *Sp Eff* Augie Lohman. *Tech Adv* Thomas A. Ryan. *Coöp* United States Army, United States—Defense Department.

Cast: Howard Keel (*Colonel Devlin*), Tina Louise (*Alexandra Bastegar*), Warner Anderson (*Lieutenant Colonel Wilson*), Earl Holliman (*Sergeant Mike*), Carleton Young (*Captain Macklin*), Burt Reynolds (*Skee*), James Dobson (*Arab*), Marty Ingels (*Pinhead*), Clem Harvey (*Tex*), Maurice Marsac (*Jean Robert*), Thomas A. Ryan (*major*), Peter Capell (*little general*), Charles

Nolte *(Captain Swain),* Brandon Maggart.

War melodrama. In northeastern France, during World War II, a U. S. Army patrol finds a wounded girl, Alexandra, lying on a road in the Vosges Mountains. Unaware that she is a German spy, they move her into an abandoned house and nurse her back to health. She quickly ingratiates herself with the men, offers her services as an interpreter to Army Intelligence, and then passes what information she picks up to the German espionage network. Consequently, the unit is unable to detect any Germans in the area, although the group commander, Colonel Devlin, is certain they are present. Eventually, two German soldiers are captured, and they reveal that a large German force is nearby. When Colonel Devlin learns that Alexandra has been working for Intelligence, he becomes suspicious of her and orders his men to prepare for an attack. The Germans attempt to create disturbances by seeing to it that cognac is made available to the American soldiers, but Devlin has the liquor confiscated. A short time later, the Germans attack; and Alexandra joins in the battle, killing two American soldiers with a shotgun. When young Sergeant Mike, who has fallen in love with Alexandra, sees her shoot Skee, his rival for her affections, he kills her with a blast of machine-gun fire. Reinforcements soon arrive to drive off the enemy and help Devlin hold his position. *Germans. Spies. Interpreters. Espionage. Perfidy. World War II. France. Vosges Mountains. United States Army—Intelligence. Germany—Army.*

Note: Filmed in Munich, West Germany.

ARMS AND THE MAN (West Germany)   **F6.0195**
Bavaria Filmkunst. *Dist* Casino Films. 24 Feb **1962** [New York opening]. Sd; col (AgfaColor). 35mm. 96 min.

Prod H. R. Sokal, P. Goldbaum. *Dir* Franz Peter Wirth. *Screenplay* Johanna Sibelius, Eberhard Keindorff. *Photog* Klaus von Rautenfeld. *Camera Op* Rolf Kästel. *Camera Asst* Knut Seedorf. *Art Dir* Hermann Warm, Bruno Monden. *Film Ed* Claus von Boro. *Mus* Franz Grothe. *Sd* F. W. Dustmann. *Asst Dir* Horst Rainer Erler. *Prod Mgr* Dietrich von Theobald. *Cost* Herbert Ploberger.

Cast: O. W. Fischer *(Captain Bluntschli),* Liselotte Pulver *(Raina Petkoff),* Ellen Schwiers *(Louka),* Jan Hendriks *(Sergius Saranoff),* Ljuba Welitsch *(Katharina),* Kurt Kasznar *(Petkoff),* Manfred Inger *(Nicola).*

Comedy. Source: George Bernard Shaw, *Arms and the Man* (London opening: 21 Apr 1894). In the 1890's, the war between the Bulgarians and the Serbs ends when Bulgarian Lieut. Sergius Saranoff routs the forces of Captain Bluntschli, the Swiss-born mercenary in charge of Serbian artillery. While fleeing from the enemy, Bluntschli takes refuge in the bedroom of Raina Petkoff, Sergius' fiancée. Raina's pride in her fiancé's victory becomes somewhat deflated when she learns that the Serbs fled because their ammunition did not fit their cannon. Bluntschli spends the night in Raina's bedroom but leaves shortly before daybreak. When he returns at the conclusion of the peace negotiations, however, he gives Raina cause to wonder whether she has chosen the right man to wed. Her hesitation makes Sergius increasingly impatient, and he eventually challenges Bluntschli to a duel. When the superior Bluntschli easily knocks the sword out of his opponent's hand, Sergius realizes that he has lost Raina, and he defies all social convention by turning to the sultry Petkoff maid, Louka, and asking her to marry him. The Petkoffs are delighted to welcome Bluntschli, the heir to a number of flourishing Swiss hotels, as their new son-in-law. *Soldiers. Swiss. Mercenaries. Housemaids. War heroes. Heirs. Courtship. Serbo-Bulgarian War 1885. Bulgaria. Serbia. Duels.*

Note: Released in West Germany in 1959 as *Helden;* running time: 96 min.

THE ARMY GAME (France)   **F6.0196**
Films du Carrosse–S. E. D. I. F.–Anray Films. *Dist* Consort/Orion Films. 23 Apr **1963** [New York opening]. Sd; b&w. 35mm (Franscope). 87 min.

Prod Marcel Berbert. *Dir* Claude de Givray, François Truffaut. *Screenplay* Claude de Givray, François Truffaut, Mouëzy-Eon. *Photog* Raoul Coutard. *Film Ed* Claudine Bouché. *Mus* Ricet Barrier.

Cast: Christian de Tilière *(Jean Lerat),* Ricet Barrier *(Joseph),* Jacques Balutin *(corporal),* Serge Davri *(colonel),* Annie Lefébure *(Annie),* Germaine Risse *(aunt),* Annie Augay *(Catherine),* Odile Geoffroy, Serge Korber, Petit-Bobo, Jean-Louis Walmont, Bernadette Lafont, François Truffaut.

Comedy. Source: André Sylvane and André Mouëzy-Eon, *Tire-au-flanc!* (Paris opening: 10 Nov 1904). Aristocrat Jean Lerat, recently called for military service, expects special considerations, particularly as his aunt has spoken of him to the colonel, a family friend. His hopes remain unfulfilled, however, and his snobbery makes him the butt of his comrades' merriment. By coincidence, his chauffeur, Joseph, is drafted into the same unit and now treats Jean as an equal. Joseph obtains leave to visit the Nice Carnival while his former master must remain on guard duty. Jean meets the colonel's daughter, Catherine, and a timid relationship develops between them. Gradually, Jean rids himself of his pretensions and becomes integrated into the group. In a performance of *Tire au flanc* given in celebration of the completion of basic training, Jean plays a valet and Joseph his master. The show is a great success; Jean's performance is a hit, and he wins Catherine's love. *Chauffeurs. Snobbery. Wealth. Social*

classes. France—Army.

Note: Opened in Paris in Dec 1961 as *Tire au flanc 62.*

AROUND THE WORLD IN 80 WAYS!   **F6.0197**
Kirt Films International. *Dist* Distribpix, Inc. 25 Jul **1969** [Champaign, Illinois, showing]. Sd; b&w. 35mm. 60 min.

Prod Leonard Kirtman. *Dir* Tommy Goetz. *Photog* Tommy Goetz. *Supv* Tommy Goetz.

Cast: Lois Lane, Rita Joyce, Mary Aster, Tommy Goetz.

Sex film. A group of wealthy, middle-aged stockbrokers grows tired of speculating on stocks and bonds and hires several couples to perform sex acts for them while the brokers place bets with one another concerning the number of sexual variations each couple can think of. All inhibitions are eventually dropped, and the sex partners join in a wild orgy. *Stockbrokers. Voyeurism. Wagers. Orgies. Sexual techniques.*

AROUND THE WORLD UNDER THE SEA   **F6.0198**
Ivan Tors Enterprises. *Dist* Metro-Goldwyn-Mayer, Inc. 2 Jun **1966** [Miami, Florida, opening; c31 Dec 1965; LP32329]. Sd (Westrex); col (Metrocolor). 35mm (Panavision). 120 min. [Copyright length: 111 min.]

An Ivan Tors Production. *Prod-Dir* Andrew Marton. *Assoc Prod* Ben Chapman. *Diving Seq Dir* Ricou Browning. *Screenplay* Arthur Weiss, Art Arthur. *Story* Elmer Parsons. *Dir Photog* Clifford Poland. *Dir Underwater Photog* Lamar Boren. *Art Dir* Preston Rountree, Mel Bledsoe. *Set Decor* Max Pittman. *Film Ed* Warren Adams. *Mus* Harry Sukman. *Mus Supv* Al Mack. *Sd* Franklin Milton. *Asst Dir* James Gordon McLean. *Unit Prod Mgr* Edward Haldeman. *Asst to the Prod* Norman Siegel. *Sp Eff* Project Unlimited. *Tech Adv* Harry Redmond, Jr. *Coöp* United States Coast Guard, Miami Seaquarium, Marineland of the Pacific, Scripps Institution of Oceanography, United States Department of Defense, University of Miami. *Underwater Engr* Jordan Klein. *Sp Diving Suit* Mordecai Grebow. *Underwater Res* Richard Tubor.

Cast: Lloyd Bridges *(Dr. Doug Standish),* Shirley Eaton *(Dr. Maggie Hanford),* Brian Kelly *(Dr. Craig Mosby),* David McCallum *(Dr. Phil Volker),* Keenan Wynn *(Hank Stahl),* Marshall Thompson *(Dr. Orin Hillyard),* Gary Merrill *(Dr. August Boren),* Ron Hayes *(Brinkman),* George Shibata *(Professor Hamuru),* Frank Logan *(captain of "Diligence"),* Don Wells *(sonar man),* Donald Linton *(vice president),* Jack Ewalt *(superintendent on mining barge),* George De Vries *(lieutenant),* Tony Gulliver *(officer),* Joey Carter *(technician),* Celeste Yarnall *(secretary),* Paul Gray *(pilot).*

Adventure drama. Dr. Doug Standish, his assistant Dr. Craig Mosby, Dr. Phil Volker, Dr. Maggie Hanford, Hank Stahl, and Dr. Orin Hillyard make up a team of specialists in undersea life assembled for an expedition aboard the *Hydronaut,* an atomic-powered submarine. Their mission is to place electronic sensors at strategic places on ocean beds throughout the world to provide an early-warning system for the volcanic eruptions which have caused a worldwide series of earthquake disasters. Volker has consented to join the mission on the condition that a sidetrip be made to locate a sunken treasure containing a cache of valuable crystals. The presence of Hanford, the only female crew member, is an additional source of tension on board the *Hydronaut.* Then Hillyard is injured when he tries to set a sensor near an active volcano, and Stahl narrowly escapes injury from a giant eel. Their job finally completed, the scientists head for the sunken treasure. Just as they find it, they receive an urgent order by radio to place one last sensor near a newly-discovered volcano; and they are forced to abandon the treasure. The volcano erupts as they are fixing the sensor, and the submarine is trapped on the ocean bed by falling rock. In desperation, Standish blows off half of the ship with dynamite, with the result that the other half rises safely to the surface. A helicopter comes to their rescue, but they are unable to return for the treasure. *Scientists. Seismology. Volcanoes. Submarines. Treasure. Earthquakes. Explosions. Eels.*

Note: Location scenes filmed on the Great Barrier Reef, the Bahamas, and in Dade and Broward counties, Florida.

AROUND THE WORLD WITH NOTHING ON   **F6.0199**
Advent Film Productions. *Dist* Union Film Distributors, Kingsley International Pictures. 7 Feb **1963** [San Francisco showing]. Sd; col (Eastman Color). 35mm. 72 min.

Prod Dick Randall. *Exec Prod* Stan Borden. *Dir* Arthur Knight. *Photog* Sherman Price.

Cast: Carole Wilson, Cindy Courtland, Brigette Baum, Donna Scott, Jane Demarest, Beverly Pye, Gretchen Bjorling, Frank Mitchell.

Nudist film. Carole Wilson, a Hollywood starlet, travels to Oakdale, a Southern California nudist resort, to participate in a beauty contest in the hopes of winning the grand prize of a trip around the nudist centers of Europe. Carole loses the contest to Joan and, disappointed, returns to her cabin. Carole falls asleep and dreams that she actually won the contest and the trip around Europe. In Denmark she meets the Danish nudist beauty queen, Gretchen Bjorling, and they tour Copenhagen and Camp Solbakken, the nudist center; then Carole continues to Paris to visit a nudist country club outside the city, Chateau Etienne. In Nice, Carole meets Yvonne, her new hostess, who takes her to the nudist Île du Levant. After visiting Heliopolis, a nudist city overlooking the sea, Carole travels to London, meets her English hostess Jennifer, and visits a nudist estate in South Devonshire. As the day ends, Carole wakes to a knock on the door and finds herself back in Oakdale. Joan has come to give her regrets that Carole cannot make the trip. Carole says goodbye to Joan and winks at the audience. *Actors. Danes. French. English. Nudism. Nudist camps. Beauty contests. Île du Levant. Paris. South Devonshire. Copenhagen. Nice. California. Heliopolis. London. Dreams.*

Note: Film was shot on location at the places noted. Also known as *Searching for Venus, Searching for Venus Around the World,* and *A Trip Around the World.*

AROUND THE WORLD WITH NOTHING ON *see* LUST FOR THE SUN

AROUSED   F6.0200

Plaudit Productions. *Dist* Cambist Films. Jan **1966.** Sd; b&w. 35mm. 78 min.
Prod Ray Jenkins. *Asst Prod* Lee Hessel. *Dir* Anton Holden. *Screenplay* Anton Holden, Raymond Jacobs. *Dir Photog* Gideon Zumbach. *Film Ed* Anton Holden. *Asst Ed* Mark Rappaport. *Mus* Edmund Mitchel.

Cast: Janine Lenon *(Ginny),* Steve Hollister *(Johnny),* Fleurette Carter *(Angela),* Joanna Mills *(Ann),* Tony Palladino *(Louie),* Ted Gelanza, Gus, Marlene Stevens *(Pat).*

Melodrama. Johnny, a detective investigating the brutal murder of a high-priced call girl, becomes involved with two of the victim's friends, Ginny and Angela. Ginny, who has vowed to find and castrate the murderer, suspects Louie, a bartender, when he shows contempt for prostitutes. Her suspicions are confirmed when she follows Louie home and discovers that he has a collection of erotic devices. Angela is attacked and murdered in an elevator, and Johnny is taken off the case. He unwittingly pairs off his wife with Louie and goes to see Ginny. Johnny tells Ginny that Angela has been killed, and they make love to comfort each other. Ginny reveals that she suspects Louie is the murderer, and Johnny, startled, races home to find his wife seriously wounded. Ginny and some of her friends trace Louie to his apartment, surround him, and carry out Ginny's objective before the police arrive. *Psychopaths. Prostitutes. Bartenders. Detectives. Murder. Revenge. Infidelity. Castration. Sex aids.*

THE ARRANGEMENT   F6.0201

Athena Enterprises-Warner Bros.-Seven Arts Productions. *Dist* Warner Bros. Pictures. 18 Nov **1969** [New York opening; c1 Dec 1969; LP37989]. Sd; col (Technicolor). 35mm (Panavision). 127 min. *MPAA rating* R.
Prod-Dir-Screenplay Elia Kazan. *Assoc Prod* Charles Maguire. *Dir Photog* Robert Surtees. *Art Dir* Malcolm C. Bert. *Set Dsgn* Audrey Blasdel. *Prod Dsgn* Gene Callahan. *Film Ed* Stefan Arnsten. *Mus Comp & Cond* David Amram. *Sd* Larry Jost. *Re-Rec* Richard Vorisek. *Asst Dir* Burtt Harris. *Cost Dsgn* Theadora Van Runkle.

Cast: Kirk Douglas *(Eddie/Evangelos),* Faye Dunaway *(Gwen),* Deborah Kerr *(Florence Anderson),* Richard Boone *(Sam),* Hume Cronyn *(Arthur),* Michael Higgins *(Michael),* John Randolph Jones *(Charles),* Carol Rossen *(Gloria),* Ann Hegira *(Thomna),* William Hansen *(Dr. Weeks),* Charles Drake *(Finnegan),* Harold Gould *(Dr. Leibman),* E. J. Andre *(Uncle Joe),* Michael Murphy *(Father Draddy),* Philip Bourneuf *(Judge Morris),* Dianne Hull *(Ellen),* Barry Sullivan *(Collier),* Clint Kimbrough *(Ben),* Ann Doran *(Nurse Costello).*

Drama. Source: Elia Kazan, *The Arrangement* (New York, 1967). Leaving behind his luxurious Los Angeles estate, successful advertising executive Eddie Anderson (a second-generation immigrant) on his way to his agency is triggered into a suicide attempt by the noise and rush of the Los Angeles freeway: he folds his arms and smiles maniacally as his imported sports car rams into a truck. He is not killed, but convalescing at home he refuses to speak except to inform his boss, Finnegan, that he will not return. He daydreams about his stormy relationship with Gwen, a voluptuous research assistant at the agency who has fascinated him by her sneering disdain of his tyrannical success as the idea-man at the agency (selling "clean" Zephyr cigarettes). Psychiatrist Dr. Leibman, engaged to treat him, is told briefly of his history by Eddie's wife, Florence, who knows about Gwen and reveals that Eddie's interest in sex ended when he broke off the affair. That night a horrendous nightmare brings Eddie out of his self-imposed silence, and as he tells Florence of his loathing for his life of perpetual "arrangements," she tries to listen sympathetically, hoping to spur his self-confidence, but periodically lapses into a bitter riposte because of his adultery. She persuades him to return to work, but cries herself bitterly to sleep when they cannot make love or achieve any satisfaction from their new understanding. Eddie's return is dramatic, but he insults an important client, upsets a number of office applecarts, and departs in a small plane with which he crazily buzzes the city. His lawyer, Arthur, prevents his arrest and induces

Eddie to give Florence his power of attorney before he departs for New York to visit his ailing, senile father, Sam. In New York he finds Gwen, who has had a child whose father she will not name; she is now living platonically with Charles, an admirer. When Eddie's brother Michael, sister-in-law Gloria, and Florence arrive and threaten the hospitalized old man with institutionalization, Eddie "kidnaps" and takes him to their old family estate on Long Island, where he induces Gwen to come and resume their affair. They are in bed—Eddie pleading with Gwen to marry him and she furiously recounting with great detail all of the affairs she has had since they parted—when Gloria and Florence burst in. They manage to get old Sam into an ambulance, and Eddie is once again reassured and seduced into accepting "arrangements" by Arthur, Florence, and his daughter, Ellen. Gwen soon leaves with Charles, and after Eddie and Florence have another violent confrontation, he goes to Gwen only to be shot by Charles. He then angrily sets the house on fire and is himself sent to a mental hospital. Gwen induces him to leave the institution and escorts him to his father's funeral. He stares vacantly at the grave, surrounded by wife, mistress, lawyer, and family. *Advertising executives. Psychiatrists. Lawyers. Marriage. Infidelity. Impotence. Mental illness. Suicide. Filial relations. Automobile accidents. Cigarettes. Los Angeles. New York City. Dreams. Old age. Funerals. Illegitimacy.*

Note: Filmed mainly on location in New York City and Long Island.

ARRÊTEZ LES TAMBOURS *see* WOMEN AND WAR

ARRIVANO TITANI *see* MY SON, THE HERO

ARRIVEDERCI, BABY! (Great Britain)   F6.0202

Seven Arts Productions. *Dist* Paramount Pictures. 28 Dec **1966** [New York opening; c16 Dec 1966; LP33625]. Sd; col (Technicolor). 35mm (Panavision). 100 min.
Pres by Ray Stark, Seven Arts Productions. *Prod-Dir-Writ* Ken Hughes. *Assoc Prod* Richard McWhorter, Greg Morrison. *2d Unit Dir* Richard Taylor. *Story* Ken Hughes, Ronald Harwood. *Dir Photog* Denys Coop. *Art Dir* Seamus Flannery. *Set Decor* Patrick McLoughlin. *Film Ed* John Shirley. *Mus Comp & Cond* Dennis Farnom. *Adtl Mus* Tibor Kunstler and His Gypsy Orchestra, The Plainsmen. *Sd* John Mitchell. *Asst Dir* Colin Brewer. *Prod Supv* James Ware. *Location Mgr* John Quested. *Cost* Elizabeth Haffenden, Joan Bridge. *Miss Schiaffino's Gowns* Pierre Balmain. *Makeup* George Frost, Eric Allwright.

Cast: Tony Curtis *(Nick Johnson),* Rosanna Schiaffino *(Francesca de Rienzi),* Lionel Jeffries *(Parker),* Zsa Zsa Gabor *(Gigi),* Nancy Kwan *(Baby),* Fenella Fielding *(Lady Fawcett),* Anna Quayle *(Aunt Miriam),* Warren Mitchell *(Conte de Rienzi/Maximilian),* Mischa Auer *(Romeo),* Noel Purcell *(Captain O'Flannery),* Alan Gifford *(U.S. officer),* Joseph Furst *(German officer),* Monti De Lyle *(butler),* Bernard Spear *(French inspector),* Eileen Way *(Italian dressmaker),* Bruno Barnabe *(head waiter),* Gabor Baraker *(gypsy baron),* Tony Baron *(Baby's boyfriend),* Eunice Black *(matron),* John Brandon, Windsor Davies *(radio engineers),* Franco DeRosa *(Romano),* John Fordyce *(boy in orphanage),* Iole Marinelli *(1st maid),* Miki Iveria *(2d maid),* Henri Vidon *(priest),* Raymond Young *(photographer).*

Comedy. Suggested by: Richard Deming, *The Careful Man* (London, 1962). Nick Johnson's dream of becoming wealthy was realized at the age of 12 when he was adopted by a kindly widow who liked him to call her Aunt Miriam. She jeopardizes Nick's inheritance by becoming romantically involved with a barge captain, and Nick kills her by connecting the strings of her harp to an electric transformer. Continuing his quest for wealth, Nick marries Gigi, a wealthy divorcée, and disposes of her by sending her to outer space in a NATO rocket she is scheduled to launch. His second wife, Lady Fenella Fawcett, a horsewoman, dies in a fall when Nick places a steeplechase hedge in front of a 50-foot deep gravel pit. His third wife, the beautiful Francesca, became a widow when her husband, a 75-year-old count, dropped dead from anticipation en route to his honeymoon villa. As Nick works on his plans for eliminating Francesca, he is unaware that because their marriage to the count was never consummated, it is void in the eyes of the Church and the $5 million inheritance has passed into the hands of the count's brother, Max. Francesca learns of Nick's scheme and decides to kill him for his money. Both hit upon the idea of booby-trapping the other's car. Once the traps have been set they drive off in opposite directions, but neither can go through with the plan, and they race back to warn each other. Deciding that love is more important than money, they settle down for a life of marital bliss. A few years later, Francesca takes in laundry and cooks nightly spaghetti dinners while Nick sits around drinking beer and protecting himself from their two children. *Fortune hunters. Orphans. Widows. Nobility. Equestrians. Inheritance. Adoption. Murder. Marriage. Perfidy. Rockets. Monte Carlo. Riviera. Automobile accidents.*

Note: Released in Great Britain in 1967 as *Drop Dead, Darling.* Locations filmed at Monte Carlo and the Côte d'Azur. Working titles: *My Last Duchess, You Just Kill Me,* and *You're Dead Right.*

ARROWFEATHER see GAS-S-S-S ... OR IT MAY BECOME NECESSARY TO DESTROY THE WORLD IN ORDER TO SAVE IT!

THE ART OF GENTLE PERSUASION   F6.0203
Dist Preferred Enterprises. ca **1970**. Sd; col. 35mm. 65 min.

Prod-Dir Sanford White. *Exec Prod* Hal DeLechere. *Song:* "Sexy World" David Frydmann, Jay Fineberg. *Sung by* Tushi Grabasso.

Sex film. Rolf, a self-assured executive known as "The Boss," runs his home and his business by the same guiding principle: "What's good for the boss—is good for the company." He dominates an assortment of people, including his wife and domestic servants, his friends, and his business associates, and encourages them to participate in a variety of sexual practices—various positions of sexual intercourse, mate swapping, group sex, lesbianism, anal and oral sex. *Businessmen. Domestics. Sexual techniques. Mate swapping. Lesbianism. Group sex. Oral sex. Anal sex. Employer-employee relations.*

Note: Also known as *Gentle Persuasion*.

THE ART OF LOVE   F6.0204
Ross Hunter Productions–Cherokee Productions. *Dist* Universal Pictures. 23 Jun **1965** [Chicago opening; c10 Jul 1965; LP32604]. Sd (Westrex); col (Technicolor). 35mm. 99 min.

Prod Ross Hunter. *Dir* Norman Jewison. *Screenplay* Carl Reiner. *Story* Richard Alan Simmons, William Sackheim. *Dir Photog* Russell Metty. *Art Dir* Alexander Golitzen, George Webb. *Set Decor* Howard Bristol, John P. Austin. *Titl* De Patie-Freleng. *Film Ed* Milton Carruth. *Mus* Cy Coleman. *Mus Supv* Joseph Gershenson. *Choreog* Hal Belfer. *Sd* Waldon O. Watson, Clarence Self. *Asst Sd* Herb Alberty, Roy Steele, Chick Bourland. *Asst Dir* Douglas Green, Carl Beringer. *Unit Prod Mgr* Norman Deming. *Script Supv* Robert Forrest. *Cost Dsgn* Ray Aghayan. *Wardrobe* Bill Jobe, Rita Riggs. *Makeup* Bud Westmore. *Hairstyles* Larry Germain. *Tech Adv* Paul Verdier. *Dial Coach* Herold Goodwin. *Still Photog* Rollie Lane.

Cast: James Garner *(Casey Barnett)*, Dick Van Dyke *(Paul Sloan)*, Elke Sommer *(Nikki Dunay)*, Angie Dickinson *(Laurie)*, Ethel Merman *(Madame Coco La Fontaine)*, Carl Reiner *(Rodin)*, Pierre Olaf *(Inspector Carnot)*, Miiko Taka *(Chou-Chou)*, Roger C. Carmel *(Zorgus)*, Irving Jacobson *(Fromkis)*, Jay Novello *(janitor)*, Naomi Stevens *(Mrs. Fromkis)*, Renzo Cesana *(Pepe de Winter)*, Leon Belasco *(Prince)*, Louis Mercier *(judge)*, Maurice Marsac *(prosecutor)*, Fifi D'Orsay *(Fanny)*, Marcel Hillaire *(executioner)*, Dawn Villere *(Couchette)*, Nan Martin *(Margo)*, Victoria Carroll *(Yvette)*, Sharon Shore *(Betti)*, Astrid De Brea *(Cerise)*, Emile Genest *(Cesar)*, Paul Verdier *(painter)*.

Comedy. Paul, a starving American artist in Paris, shocks his unsuccessful roommate, Casey, a writer, when he decides to go back to his wealthy fiancée, Laurie, in the United States. They carry on a drunken debate on the banks of the Seine, and Casey decides that Paul should fake a suicide, thus enhancing the value of his paintings. As Casey composes a suicide note, Paul jumps off a bridge to save Nikki, who is fleeing lascivious attentions. They safely reach a barge, but Casey believes that Paul has really drowned. With great publicity, the paintings begin to sell, and Paul has to hide out in a nightclub to produce more of them. Casey then falls in love with Laurie, who has come to Paris for a visit. For revenge, Paul fakes evidence that points to his own murder by Casey; and Casey is arrested, tried and sentenced to death by the guillotine. Paul saves Casey at the last moment, and he also saves Nikki from a rich admirer. *Americans in foreign countries. Artists. Authors. Roommates. Drunkenness. Suicide. Revenge. Capital punishment. Fraud. Publicity. Nightclubs. Paris. Seine River.*

Note: Location scenes filmed in Paris.

THE ART OF MARRIAGE   F6.0205
Nevada Institute for Family Studies. 16 Feb **1970** [New York opening]. Sd; col. 35mm. 62 min.

Instructional film. Seeking to examine some of the basic causes of marital incompatibility, the film shows explicit sexual techniques to help couples overcome their inhibitions and lack of sexual knowledge. *Marriage. Sexual techniques. Sex instruction.*

THE ART OF VISION   F6.0206
Dist Film-Makers' Cooperative, Brakhage. 27 Feb **1965** [New York opening]. Si; col with b&w seq (Eastman Color). 16mm. 278 min. [See note.]

Prod-Dir-Writ Stan Brakhage. *Photog* Stan Brakhage. *Adtl Photog* Jane Brakhage. *Film Ed* Stan Brakhage.

Cast: Stan Brakhage *(Dog Star Man)*, Jane Brakhage *(woman)*, Sirius [dog].

Experimental film. See *Dog Star Man*, q. v. *Woodsmen. Death. Parenthood. Dreams. Dogs.*

Note: The film is an elaboration of *Dog Star Man*, q. v., although the rolls of film are superimposed differently. Running times: Prelude, 75 min; Part I, 31 min; Part II, 17 min; Part III, 63 min; and Part IV, 84 min. In the prelude rolls A and B appear first in succession and then superimposed, A over B. Part I consists of a single roll. In Part II, rolls A and B are first superimposed, A over B, then shown in succession. In Part III, A, B, and C rolls appear in succession and then superimposed, A over B, A over C, B over C. In Part IV, rolls A, B, C, and D appear superimposed, A over B over C over D; then in the order of AB, AD, BC, BD, and CD; and, finally, in succession. Each roll contains superimpositions.

THE ARTFUL PENETRATION see BLACK ON WHITE

ARTIST NUDE SECRETS see ARTIST'S STUDIO SECRETS

ARTIST'S MODELS see INTIMATE DIARY OF ARTISTS' MODELS

ARTIST'S STUDIO SECRETS   F6.0207
Dist Boxoffice International Film Distributors. 10 Sep **1964** [San Francisco showing]. Sd; b&w. 35mm. 78 min.

Drama. Percy Green, a fine Greenwich Village artist, develops an aversion to everything concealed or covered, including the models who pose for him, and he loses all desire to paint. In order to save his career, his wife, Hortense, sees to it that Percy never sees his models while they are fully clothed. She convinces her brother to throw a bohemian studio party in order to bolster Percy's career and stimulate his interest in art, while furthering her own ends. All goes well as the party gets underway, but as the night wears on, the atmosphere grows licentious, and recriminations fly. Percy accuses his wife of dominating him and interfering with his creative ability. He sets out to make her jealous by making love with his models, turning the studio into a nest of schemes, intrigues, and jealousy. At last Percy loses his fetish, and peace returns to the Green household. *Painters. Models. Brothers. Nudity. Infidelity. Jealousy. Marriage. Fetishism. Bohemianism. New York City—Greenwich Village.*

Note: Also known as *The Story of an Artist's Studio Secrets* and *Artist Nude Secrets*.

ARTURO'S ISLAND (Italy)   F6.0208
C. C. Champion–Titanus. *Dist* Metro-Goldwyn-Mayer, Inc. 21 Dec **1962** [New York opening]. Sd; b&w. 35mm. 104 min. [Also reviewed at 90 min.]

Prod Carlo Ponti. *Exec Prod* Antonio Altoviti. *Dir* Damiano Damiani. *Screenplay* Damiano Damiani, Ugo Liberatore, Enrico Ribulzi, Cesare Zavattini. *Photog* Roberto Gerardi. *Art Dir* Franco Mancini. *Film Ed* Adriana Novelli. *Mus* Carlo Rustichelli, Nino Rota. *Sd* G. Orleisi. *Prod Mgr* Mario De Biase.

Cast: Reginald Kernan *(Wilhelm)*, Key Meersman *(Nunziata)*, Vanni De Maigret *(Arturo)*, Luigi Giuliani *(Tonino Stella)*, Gabriella Giorgelli *(Teresa)*.

Drama. Source: Elsa Morante, *L'isola di Arturo* (Turin, 1957). Arturo, a 16-year-old boy who is ignorant of the world beyond his home, the island of Procida in the Bay of Naples, lives alone in his father's huge home while waiting for him to return from one of his frequent wanderings. Wilhelm, his father, returns and brings with him a lovely wife, Nunziata, who is barely older than Arturo. Arturo adores Wilhelm, and at first he regards Nunziata as an interloper, but they soon become good friends. His father leaves again, and when the young wife gives birth to a child, Arturo finds that his affection for her has turned to love. However, since the pious Nunziata treats him only as a son, he succumbs to the charms of a seductive village woman, Teresa, whose husband has abandoned her. Wilhelm once more returns, this time on the same ship as Tonino, a young prisoner at the island penitentiary, who refers to Arturo's father as "Pretty Boy" and reveals that Wilhelm has arranged to help him escape. Enraged at the homosexual insinuation, Arturo attacks Tonino but is unmercifully beaten by the stronger man. Wilhelm eventually intervenes to protect his son. After Tonino has gone, Arturo realizes that his father is lost to him forever, and he leaves the island. *Wanderers. Stepmothers. Convicts. Adolescence. Filial relations. Male homosexuality. Seduction. Jealousy. Prisons. Procida. Bay of Naples.*

Note: Filmed on location in the Bay of Naples. Released in Italy in 1962 as *L'isola di Arturo*.

ARU OSAKA NO ONNA see AYAKO

ARU SONAN see DEATH ON THE MOUNTAIN

ARUPUSU NO WAKADAISHO see IT STARTED IN THE ALPS

DER ARZT STELLT FEST ... see THE DOCTOR SAYS

AS FOR ALL THESE WOMEN see ALL THESE WOMEN

AS NATURE INTENDED (Great Britain)   F6.0209
Markten–Compass Films–Cory Films. *Dist* Crown International Pictures. 8 Feb **1963** [Los Angeles opening]. Sd (RCA); col (Eastman Color). 35mm. 65 min.

Prod-Dir Harrison Marks. *Exec Prod* John Brason. *Story* Harrison Marks, Gerald Holgate. *Dir Photog* Roy Pointer. *Camera Op* Terry Maher. *Art Dir*

John Brason. *Main Titl* Compass Films. *Mus* Boosey & Hawkes, Charles Brull Ltd. *Sd* Derek Taylor. *1st & 2d Asst Dir* Peter Dixon, Norman Hoy. *Prod Mgr* Derek Horne. *Cont* Lilian Lee. *Makeup* Gerry Fairbank. *Hairdresser* Daphne Vollmer. *Coöp* Spielplatz Nudist Camp.

Cast: Pamela Green *(Pamela)*, Jackie Salt *(Jackie)*, Petrina Forsyth *(Petrina)*, Bridget Leonard *(Bridget)*, Angela Jones *(Angela)*, Guy Kingsley Poynter, Daws Butler *(commentary)*, Stuart Samuels.

Travelog. Petrina, a secretary; Pamela, a dancer; and Jackie, a shoe saleswoman, rent a car and drive to Devon and Cornwall for a holiday, passing the historic sites of Stonehenge, Tintagel Castle, Clovelly, the Minnack Open-Air Theatre, and Lands End. Bridget and Angela, two gas station attendants also on holiday, hike to their destination, a private beach belonging to a nudist club. The three women meet Bridget and Angela, who convince them to join the club and enjoy the freedom of nudism. *Tourists. Vacations. Nudist camps. Beaches. Somerset (England). Devon (England). Cornwall (England). Clovelly (England). Lands End (England). Stonehenge. Tintagel Castle. Minnack Open-Air Theatre.*

Note: Released in Great Britain in 1961 as *Naked as Nature Intended.*

ASCENSEUR POUR L'ÉCHAFAUD *see* **FRANTIC**

ASCHENPUTTEL *see* **CINDERELLA**

ASFALTO SELVAGEM *see* **LOLLIPOP**

ASHES AND DIAMONDS (Poland)   F6.0210

Kadr Film Unit. *For* Film Polski. *Dist* Janus Films. 29 May **1961** [New York opening]. Sd; b&w. 35mm. 105 min.

Prod Stanisław Adler. *Dir* Andrzej Wajda. *Artistic Asst* Zygmunt Wójcik, Michael Sosiński. *Screenplay* Andrzej Wajda, Jerzy Andrzejewski. *Photog* Jerzy Wójcik. *Asst Photog* Krzysztof Winiewicz, Wiesław Zdort, Zygmunt Krusznicki, Jerzy Szurowski, Bogdan Mysliński. *Art Dir* Roman Mann. *Asst Art Dir* Leszek Wajda, Jarosław Switoniak, Marian Kowaliński. *Film Ed* Halina Nawrocka. *Asst Ed* Irena Choryńska. *Mus* Jan Krenz. "Polonaise" Michael Cleophas Ogiński. *Played by* Wrocław Radio Quintet. *Cond* Filip Nowak. *Sd* Bogdan Bieńkowski. *Asst Dir* Janusz Morgenstern, Andrzej Wróbel, Anna Janeczkowa, Jan Włodarczyk. *Cost* Katarzyna Chodorowicz. *Makeup* Halina Sieńska, Halina Turant, Halina Zając.

Cast: Zbigniew Cybulski *(Maciek)*, Ewa Krzyżewska *(Christine [Krystyna])*, Adam Pawlikowski *(Andrzej)*, Wacław Zastrzeżyński *(Szczuka)*, Bogumił Kobiela *(Drewnowski)*, Jan Ciecierski *(porter)*, Stanisław Milski *(Pieniązek, the journalist)*, Artur Młodnicki *(Kotowicz)*, Halina Kwiatkowska *(Mrs. Staniewicz)*, Ignacy Machowski *(Waga)*, Zbigniew Skowroński *(Slomka)*, Barbara Krafft *(Stefka)*, Aleksander Sewruk *(Swiecki)*, Zofia Czerwińska, I. Orzewska, H. Siekierko, Grażyna Staniszewska, J. Adamczyk, Adolf Chronicki, W. Grotowicz, Mieczysław Łoza, Tadeusz Kalinowski, E. Matysik, Józef Pieracki.

War drama. Source: Jerzy Andrzejewski, *Popiół i diament, powieść* (Warsaw, 1948). On May 7, 1945, V-E Day, Andrzej and Maciek, two resistance fighters in a small Polish town, receive orders from their headquarters in London to assassinate the newly arrived Communist Party secretary, Szczuka. They mistakenly shoot down two innocent workmen, and young Maciek, deeply affected by this needless waste of life, balks at the thought of carrying out his assignment. Despite years of following orders without question, he cannot bring himself to celebrate this first day of peace with the prospect of yet another killing, especially since Szczuka seems to him to be a harmless man. That night Maciek attends a victory banquet, and is strongly attracted to a young barmaid, Christine. After spending the night with her, he decides he is through with killing and will enter a university. Humiliated by charges of desertion, however, he is once more forced to stalk his prey. He kills Szczuka, but Maciek himself is wounded while trying to escape. He runs through the city and dies in agony on a rubbish heap. *Barmaids. Communists. Resistance (political). Conscience. Assassination. Youth. World War II. V-E Day (7 May 1945).*

Note: Released in Poland in Oct 1958 as *Popiół i diament.* Last in an "unplanned trilogy" of films directed by Wajda, following *A Generation* (1954) and *Kanal* (1956). Barbara Krafft is a pseudonym for Barbara Krafftówna.

ASHITA ARU KAGIRI *see* **TILL TOMORROW COMES**

ASHIYA KARA NO HIKO *see* **FLIGHT FROM ASHIYA**

ASIAPOL SECRET SERVICE (Japan)   F6.0211

Nikkatsu Corp. *Dist* Toho Co. Feb **1969** [Los Angeles showing]. Sd; col (Eastmancolor). 35mm (Nikkatsu Scope). 97 min.

Dir Akinori Matsuo. *Screenplay* Iwao Yamazaki. *Photog* Kazumi Iwasa. *Art Dir* Kimihiko Nakamura. *Mus* Toshiro Mayuzumi.

Cast: Hideaki Nitani *(Ryutaro Saeki)*, Joe Shishido *(Georgie Eaton)*, Ruriko Asaoka *(Kyoko Misaki)*, Fang Ying *(Yang Ming Hua)*, Wang Hsieh *(Lai Yu Tien)*.

Action melodrama. Ryutaro Saeki, an agent of Asia Interpol, trails a shipment of contraband gold being shipped from Hong Kong to a Georgie Eaton. The truck is purposely blown up and the company president who sent the cargo is killed while golfing by an explosive golf ball. Saeki follows Eaton's yacht to Hong Kong but he is trapped in a time-bombed car with a Chinese woman, Ming Hua. They escape the trap with the help of the dead president's daughter whom Saeki had suspected of being a member of the smuggling ring. Saeki and Ming Hua board Eaton's yacht and learn that the smuggler is an Eurasian trying to destroy the Japanese economy because his Japanese father had deserted him and his mother. Trapped by Eaton, the pair are again saved by the daughter, now revealed to be Lai Yu Tien, also an Asia Interpol agent. As other agents board the yacht, Eaton is crushed beneath the gold bars he was bringing to Japan. Saeki returns to Tokyo to receive his next assignment. *Secret agents. Chinese. Eurasians. Smuggling. Revenge. Yachts. Golf. Gold. Hong Kong. Explosions.*

Note: Released in Japan in 1966 as *Ajia himitsu keisatsu.*

ASPECTS OF THE COLLEGE *see* **THE COLLEGE**

ASSALTO AO TREM PAGADOR *see* **TRAIN ROBBERY CONFIDENTIAL**

THE ASSASSIN (Japan)   F6.0212

Shochiku Co. 30 Oct **1964** [Los Angeles showing]. Sd; b&w. 35mm (Shochiku GrandScope). 104 min.

Dir Masahiro Shinoda. *Screenplay* Nobuo Yamada. *Story* Ryotaro Shiba. *Photog* Masao Kosugi.

Cast: Tetsuro Tamba, Shima Iwashita, Isao Kimura, Eitaro Ozawa, Eiji Okada, Keiji Sada.

Action melodrama. In 1863, Lord Matsudaira of the Tokugawa Shogunate obtains a pardon for Hachiro Kiyokawa, a free samurai in prison for murdering a police agent. Although Kiyokawa is notoriously anti-Shogunate, Matsudaira figures he can now employ the samurai's oratorical and organizational talents to form a free samurai party which will suppress the anti-Shogunate movement in Kyoto. Matsudaira's fears that Kiyokawa might be assassinated because of his new political stance are confirmed when the samurai's old comrades in the anti-Shogunate movement attempt to kill him. Kiyokawa slays his attackers, but once in Kyoto he announces that he is still opposed to the Shogunate and intends to lead a force against the anti-Royalist movement. Angered at Kiyokawa's treachery, Matsudaira dispatches Tadasaburo Sasaki, a Shogunate guard, to assassinate Kiyokawa, and, at the height of the samurai's popularity, Sasaki kills him on an Edo street. *Samurai. Hired killers. Assassination. Perfidy. Amnesty. Military government. Kyoto. Edo.*

Note: Released in Japan in 1964 as *Ansatsu.*

L'ASSASSIN *see* **THE LADY KILLER OF ROME**

ASSASSINATION (Italy)   F6.0213

Cinegay–Jolly Film. *Dist* Ben Barry & Associates. **1969**. Sd; col (Technicolor). 35mm (Techniscope). 95 min.

Prod Felice Testa Gay. *Dir* Hal Brady. *Screenplay* Lou Strateman, Andy Colbert, Max Hatired. *Story* Emil Bridge. *Photog* Erico Menczer. *Art Dir* Louis Nadeau. *Film Ed* Sergius Hillman. *Mus Comp & Cond* Robby Poitevin. *Sd* Mike Dodge. *Asst Dir* Louis Glidston.

Cast: Henry Silva *(John Chandler/Philip Chandler)*, Fred Beir *(Bob)*, Evelyn Stewart *(Barbara)*, Peter Dane *(Lang)*, Bill Vanders *(Thomas)*, Fred Farrel *(Morrison)*, Bob Molden *(Otto)*, Karl Menzinger *(Hans)*, Gunther Scholtz *(Senator Grahame)*, Gert von Zitweitz *(baron)*, John Schoffield *(Jack)*, Helga Braun *(vendeuse)*.

Action melodrama. CIA agent John Chandler, sentenced to death for the murder of a colleague, secretly is reprieved. Through plastic surgery and psychological brainwashing, he assumes the identity of a nonexistent brother, Philip. In Hamburg he infiltrates an international secret society plotting to assassinate U. S. Senator Grahame and wreck his peace mission. As proof of loyalty to the society, John fights to the death with Bob, a double agent who has since married John's "widow," Barbara. Confessing the truth to his wife, John goes to the Hamburg airport and simulates assassination of the senator. The organization abducts John to Berlin, where he is to be sacrificed in the sabotage of Senator Grahame's peace conference. John thwarts the plot, subdues his enemies, and regains the CIA's trust. En route to Hamburg, however, he is killed by a sniper. *Intelligence agents. Peacemakers. Plastic surgery. Brainwashing. Personal identity. Assassination. Perfidy. Sabotage. Secret societies. Conferences—International. Hamburg. Berlin. United States—Central Intelligence Agency. United States Congress.*

Note: Opened in Rome in Aug 1967; running time: 100 min. Pseudonymns include: Hal Brady (Alfonso Brescia), Sergius Hillman (Sergio Montanari), Evelyn Stewart (Ida Galli), and Fred Farrell (Alfredo Varelli).

THE ASSASSINATION BUREAU (Great Britain)   F6.0214

Heathfield Films. *Dist* Paramount Pictures. 23 Mar **1969** [New York opening; c20 Jan 1969; LP36591]. Sd; col (Technicolor). 35mm. 110 min. [Also reviewed at 106 min.] *MPAA rating* M.

A Basil Dearden–Michael Relph Production. *Prod-Writ* Michael Relph. *Dir* Basil Dearden. *Adtl Dial* Wolf Mankowitz. *Photog* Geoffrey Unsworth. *Art Dir* Roy Smith, Frank White. *Set Decor* Helen Thomas. *Prod Dsgn* Michael Relph. *Main Titl* Robert Ellis. *Film Ed* Teddy Darvas. *Mus* Ron Grainer. *Song:* "*Life Is a Precious Thing*" Hal Shaper, Ron Grainer. *Sung by* Mike Sammes Singers. *Sd Rec* Ken Barker, John Dennis, sd. *Sd Mix* Dudley Messenger. *Sd Supv* John Poyner. *Asst Dir* John Peverall. *Prod Supv* Charles Orme. *Prod Mgr* Barrie Melrose. *Cost Dsgn* Beatrice Dawson. *Hairstyles* Barbara Ritchie. *Sp Eff* Thomas "Knobby" Clark, Les Bowie.

Cast: Oliver Reed (*Ivan Dragomiloff*), Diana Rigg (*Sonya Winter*), Telly Savalas (*Lord Bostwick*), Curt Jurgens (*General von Pinck*), Warren Mitchell (*Herr Weiss*), Philippe Noiret (*Monsieur Lucoville*), Kenneth Griffith (*Monsieur Popescu*), Vernon Dobtcheff (*Mr. Muntzov*), Clive Revill (*Cesare Spado*), Beryl Reid (*Madame Otero*), Annabella Incontrera (*Eleanora*), Jess Conrad (*Angelo*), George Coulouris (*Swiss peasant*), Ralph Michael (*editor*), Katherine Kath (*Madame Lucoville*), Eugene Deckers (*desk clerk*), Olaf Pooley (*Swiss cashier*), George Murcell (*pilot*), Michael Wolf (*officer*), Gordon Sterne (*corporal*), Peter Bowles, William Kendall (*clients at Madame Otero's*), Jeremy Lloyd (*English officer*), Roger Delgado, Maurice Browning, Clive Gazes, Gerik Schjelderup (*bureau members*), Milton Reid, Frank Thornton.

Action melodrama. Source: Jack London and Robert L. Fish, *The Assassination Bureau, Ltd.* (London, 1963). In turn-of-the-century England, Sonya Winter decides to invade the male-dominated world of journalism by proving that a series of murders are the work of a single organization. Once she has persuaded a wealthy newspaper proprietor, Lord Bostwick, to back her venture, Sonya poses as a prospective client and makes contact with the organization's chairman, Ivan Dragomiloff. She learns from him that the Assassination Bureau was founded by Ivan's father for the purpose of eliminating people who deserve to die. After offering £20,000 to dispose of a suitable candidate, Sonya startles Ivan by telling him that he is the man she wants assassinated. Admitting that the bureau has become motivated more by greed than by its original ideals, Ivan accepts the assignment. He assembles the bureau's members, including Lord Bostwick, and informs them that since they all deserve to die he will try to kill them before they can kill him. Lord Bostwick, who dreams of using the bureau to control the world, offers a £10,000 bonus to the successful assassin, but Ivan travels to the Continent with Sonya and uses every conceivable means to outmaneuver and destroy his opponents. By the time they reach Venice, Sonya has fallen in love with Ivan, and she aids him in duping the bureau into believing that he has been poisoned by the widow of Cesare Spado, Bostwick's trusted assistant. Inflated with confidence, Bostwick plots with the German bureau member, General von Pinck, to drop a bomb from a zeppelin on a castle where the kings and queens of Europe have assembled for a peace conference. But Ivan climbs aboard the zeppelin as it departs and corners Bostwick and von Pinck. When Bostwick fires his gun, the zeppelin catches fire and plunges to earth as Ivan alone manages to escape. A grateful Europe decorates Ivan for his gallantry, and Sonya is on hand to offer him her love. *Reporters. Germans. Hired killers. Royalty. Employment— Women. Imposture. Assassination. Megalomania. Greed. Perfidy. Zeppelins. London. Venice.*

Note: Location scenes filmed in London, Paris, Zurich, Vienna, and Venice. Opened in London in Mar 1969. May also be known as *The Assassination Bureau Limited.*

L'ASSASSINO *see* THE LADY KILLER OF ROME

ASSASSINOS *see* THE VIOLENT AND THE DAMNED

ASSAULT ON A QUEEN   F6.0215

Seven Arts Productions–Sinatra Enterprises. *Dist* Paramount Pictures. 15 Jun **1966** [Philadelphia opening; c15 Jun 1966; LP32759]. Sd; col (Technicolor). 35mm (Panavision). 106 min.

Prod William Goetz. *Assoc Prod* William H. Daniels. *Exec Prod* Frank Sinatra. *Dir* Jack Donohue. *2d Unit Dir* Robert D. Webb. *Screenplay* Rod Serling. *Dir Photog* William H. Daniels. *Art Dir* Paul Groesse, Hal Pereira. *Set Decor* John P. Austin. *Film Ed* Archie Marshek, Jack Wheeler. *Mus* Duke Ellington. *Orch* Nathan Van Cleave. *Sd Rec* Stanley Jones, Charles Grenzbach. *Asst Dir* Richard Lang. *Prod Mgr* Gerald D. Wineman. *Prod Supv* Joseph C. Behm. *Script Supv* Dorothy Yutzi. *Unit Prod Mgr* Aldo Silvani. *Miss Lisi's Cost* Edith Head. *Men's Wardrobe* Geoffrey Alan. *Makeup Supv* Wally Westmore. *Hairstyle Supv* Nellie Manley. *Hairstyles* Dorothy White. *Sp Eff* Lee Vasque. *Sp Photog Eff* Lawrence W. Butler, Paul K. Lerpae. *Proc Photog* Farciot Edouart. *Tech Adv* Charles C. Wilbur, (Capt.). *Coöp* Cunard Steam-Ship Co., Officers and Crew of the *Queen Mary*, United States Coast Guard

Headquarters (Washington, D. C.), United States Coast Guard Audio-Visual Unit (Hollywood), Personnel of the United States Coast Guard Cutter *Androscoggin*, Personnel of the United States Coast Guard Cutter *Minnetonka*. *Prop Master* Charles Mason. *Dial Coach* Thom Conroy.

Cast: Frank Sinatra (*Mark Brittain*), Virna Lisi (*Rosa Lucchesi*), Tony Franciosa (*Vic Rossiter*), Richard Conte (*Tony Moreno*), Alf Kjellin (*Eric Lauffnauer*), Errol John (*Linc Langley*), Murray Matheson (*captain*), Reginald Denny (*master-at-arms*), John Warburton (*bank manager*), Lester Matthews (*doctor*), Val Avery (*Trench*), Gilchrist Stuart, Ronald Long, Leslie Bradley, Arthur Gould-Porter (*officers*), Laurence Conroy (*junior officer*).

Adventure melodrama. Source: Jack Finney, *Assault on a Queen* (New York, 1959). After an unsuccessful attempt to recover a lost treasure off the coast of Florida, five adventurers concoct a wild scheme for highjacking the *Queen Mary*. The group consists of beautiful Rosa Lucchesi, an Italian who is financing the venture; Mark Brittain and Linc Langley, partners in a debt-ridden charter boat business; Vic Rossiter, an opportunist with designs on Rosa; and Eric Lauffnauer, a former U-boat commander. Utilizing a World War II German submarine they found during the Florida escapade, they bring in a sixth member, Tony Moreno, an expert in repairing submarine engines and equipment. Once their vessel is ready, they intercept the *Queen Mary* and, by posing as British officers, Mark, Rossiter and Lauffnauer obtain permission to go aboard. Then they warn the ship's captain that unless he turns over the contents of the safe, the *Queen Mary* will be torpedoed. As the men empty the safe, the *Queen Mary* signals an SOS to a U. S. Coast Guard cutter in the area. During the getaway, Rossiter is killed; and Mark and Lauffnauer allow the loot to fall over the side while they frantically make their escape. Back on the sub, Eric decides to torpedo the approaching Coast Guard cutter and kills Moreno for opposing him. Mark hurls himself at Eric as he fires, but the torpedoes miss their target. Rosa, Mark, and Linc escape in a rubber raft as the cutter rams the sub. Lauffnauer goes down with the sub, and the three survivors drift in the direction of South America. *Divers. Thieves. Hijackers. Italians. Germans. Mechanics. Imposture. Robbery. Treasure. Partnerships. Submarines. Florida. United States Coast Guard. S. S. "Queen Mary".*

Note: Location scenes filmed aboard the *Queen Mary*. Copyright claimants: Paramount Pictures and Park Lane Enterprises.

L'ASSEDIO DI SIRACUSA *see* SIEGE OF SYRACUSE

THE ASSIGNMENT *see* ASSIGNMENT TO KILL

ASSIGNMENT—FEMALE   F6.0216

Dist Rialto International Film Releasing Corp. **1966.** Sd; b&w. 35mm. [Feature film, length unknown.]

Prod-Dir-Writ Raymond A. Phelan. *Mus* Ross-Gaffney Inc. *Sd Eff* Ross-Gaffney Inc. *Florida Citrus Water Ski Show Prod* Tommy Bartlett.

Cast: Tony King (*Rob*), Keith Caporal (*Hank*), Jean Sexton (*Carol*), Betsy York (*Anne*), Louisa Moritz (*Miss Mousie*), Claudia Mann (*Miss Cashbox*), Merle Moriarty (*Miss Lush*), Fujiko Asakawa (*Miss Nonins*), Yolanda Signorelli (*model*), Diana Conti (*Marcello's girl*), Jean C. Boudreau (*pimp*), Zafrana (*Oriental dancer*), Roz Croney (*Limbo dancer*).

Comedy-drama. Hank and Rob go to New York City in search of adventure. Hank's objective is to seduce as many women as time and strength will allow. He meets Carol, who so overwhelms him with her sexual prowess that Hank proposes marriage to her. Although Rob is shy and inexperienced, he loses his innocence soon after arriving in New York and partakes in a wild variety of erotic experiences. He returns to his hotel room with a woman as innocent as he was when he arrived in the city. *Playboys. Seduction. Innocents. Sexuality. Marriage. New York City.*

ASSIGNMENT K (Great Britain)   F6.0217

Gildor Films–Mazurka Productions. *Dist* Columbia Pictures. Jun **1968** [c31 Dec 1967; LP36016]. Sd (RCA); col (Technicolor). 35mm (Techniscope). 97 min.

Prod Maurice Foster, Ben Arbeid. *Dir* Val Guest. *Screenplay* Val Guest, Bill Strutton, Maurice Foster. *Dir Photog* Ken Hodges. *Camera Op* Herbert R. Smith. *Art Dir* John Blezard. *Film Ed* Jack Slade. *Asst Ed* Lois Gray. *Mus Comp* Basil Kirchin. *Mus Cond* John A. Coleman. *Sd Rec* Cyril Collick. *Sd Ed* James Shields. *Dub Mix* Ken Scrivener. *Asst Dir* John Stoneman. *Prod Supv* Roy Parkinson. *Cont* Splinters Deason. *Cost Dsgn* Yvonne Blake. *Mr. Boyd's Clothes* by Douglas Hayward. *Wardrobe Supv* Ray Beck. *Makeup* Tony Sforzini. *Hairdresser* Marjorie Whittle.

Cast: Stephen Boyd (*Philip Scott*), Camilla Sparv (*Toni Peters*), Michael Redgrave (*Harris*), Leo McKern (*Smith*), Jeremy Kemp (*Hal*), Robert Hoffmann (*Paul Spiegler*), Jane Merrow (*Martine*), Carl Möhner (*inspector*), Vivi Bach (*Erika Herschel*), Werner Peters (*Kramer*), Dieter Geissler (*Kurt*), John Alderton (*George*), Jan Werich (*Dr. Spiegler*), David Healy (*David*), Ursula Howells (*Estelle*), Basil Dignam (*Howlett*), Joachim Hansen (*Heinrich Herschel*), Geoffrey Bayldon (*boffin*), Marthe Harell (*Mrs. Peters*), Traudi

Hochfilzer *(ski instructress)*, Friedrich von Thun *(Rolfe)*, Catherina von Schell *(Maggi)*, Herbert Fuchs *(Bavarian tourist)*, Peter Capell *(landlord of chalet)*, Heinz Leo Fisher *(Joseph)*, Karl Otto Alberty *(detective)*, Helmut Schneider *(stranger)*, Friedrich von Ledebur *(ski shop proprietor)*, Andrea Allen *(mini skirt)*, Rosemarie Reede *(English nurse)*, Mia Nardi *(German nurse)*, Jenny White *(air hostess)*, Olga Linden *(nightclub blonde)*, Alexander Allerson *(model car salesman)*, Alistair Hunter *(doorman)*, Gert Wiedenhofen *(porter)*.

Melodrama. Source: Hartley Howard, *Department K* (London, 1964). As a toy manufacturer, British Intelligence agent Philip Scott transmits microfilmed messages between Germany and England by hiding them inside dolls. Answerable only to Harris in Department K at the Board of Trade, Philip is a law unto himself, and even Harris is ignorant of the names of Philip's contacts abroad. While visiting an international toy fair in Munich, Scott meets and falls in love with Toni Peters, a Swedish heiress. When Scott's enemies learn his true identity, they kill a member of his unit and then kidnap Toni from Scott's London flat. Smith, the ringleader of the opposition, informs Scott that Toni will be released if they are given the name of Scott's chief contact in Germany. Scott yields to this demand, but Scott and his friend Paul arrange for the contact's death before he can fall into enemy hands. Smith then retaliates by again kidnaping Toni. Scott penetrates Smith's headquarters and disarms his men, only to learn that Toni is actually one of the enemy. When an explosive device placed by Scott in Smith's hiding place detonates, however, Toni saves Scott while permitting her own colleagues to die. Disillusioned with the business of spying and finally aware that Harris is a double agent, Scott confronts Harris. Rather than face justice, Harris commits suicide. Once he is discharged, Scott, now certain that he is no longer willing to make the sacrifices required of a secret agent, drives away, leaving Toni behind. *Manufacturers. Secret agents. Swedes. Heiresses. Imposture. Espionage. Murder. Kidnaping. Duplicity. Suicide. Dolls. Microfilm. Federal Republic of Germany. Munich. Great Britain—Intelligence service. Great Britain—Board of Trade. Documentation. Explosions.*

Note: Location scenes filmed in West Germany, Kitzbühel (Austria), and Great Britain. Opened in London in Feb 1968. Prerelease title: *Department K.*

ASSIGNMENT—OUTER SPACE (Italy)   F6.0218
Ultra Film–Titanus. *Dist* American International Pictures. 13 Dec **1961** [San Diego, California, opening]. Sd; col (Technicolor). 35mm. 79 min.

Prod English Vers Hugo Grimaldi, Four Crown Productions. *Dir* Anthony Daisies. *Screenplay* Vassily Petrov. *Photog* Marcello Masciocchi. *Mus Supv* Gordon Zahler. *Mus* J. K. Broady. *Sd Eff Ed* Joseph Von Stroheim. *Sp Eff* Caesar Peace.

Cast: Rik von Nutter *(Ray Peterson)*, Gabriella Farinon *(Lucy)*, Dave Montresor *(George)*, Archie Savage *(Al)*, Alan Dijon *(The Commander)*, Frank Fantasia, Aldo Pini, Joe Pollini, David Maran, José Néstor, Anita Todesco.

English Vers Narrator: Jack Wallace.

Science fiction melodrama. Spaceship *Alfa II* is spinning uncontrollably around the solar system directed only by an electronic brain due to the pilot's sudden death. Heat from the ship is threatening to bring death and destruction unless *Alfa II* is halted before it moves closer to earth. Reporter Ray Peterson, who is aboard a space station rocket, joins with the commander and Lucy, the route officer, in the expedition to save the earth. After hours of tension and a growing jealousy between the commander and Ray over Lucy, Ray goes into space alone and disconnects the electronic brain. He thus saves the earth and wins Lucy's affection and the commander's respect. *Journalists. Spacemen. Space travel. Heroism. Spaceships. Computers.*

Note: Opened in Rome in Aug in 1960 as *Space Men.* Four Crown Productions apparently had no part in production but was responsible for the English language version. Anthony Daisies is a pseudonym for Antonio Margheriti; Frank Fantasia for Franco Fantasia.

ASSIGNMENT REDHEAD *see* MILLION DOLLAR MANHUNT

ASSIGNMENT TO KILL   F6.0219
Warner Bros.–Seven Arts, Inc. Jan **1969** [c1 Jan 1969; LP37150]. Sd; col (Technicolor). 35mm (Panavision). 102 min. [Copyright length: 98 min.] *MPAA rating* M.

Exec Prod William Conrad. *Dir-Writ* Sheldon Reynolds. *Dir Photog* Harold Lipstein, Enzo Barboni. *Art Dir* John Beckman. *Set Decor* George James Hopkins. *Film Ed* George Rohrs. *Mus* William Lava. *Sd* Stanley Jones. *Asst Dir* Gil Kissel. *Unit Mgr* Charles Bonniwell, Jr. *Makeup Supv* Gordon Bau. *Supv Hairstylist* Jean Burt Reilly.

Cast: Patrick O'Neal *(Richard Cutting)*, Joan Hackett *(Dominique Laurant)*, John Gielgud *(Curt Valayan)*, Herbert Lom *(Matt Wilson)*, Eric Portman *(notary)*, Peter Van Eyck *(Walter Green)*, Oscar Homolka *(Inspector Ruff)*, Leon Greene *(The Big Man)*, Kent Smith *(Mr. Eversley)*, Philip Ober *(Bohlen)*, Fifi D'Orsay *(Mrs. Hennie)*, Eva Soreny *(landlady)*, Cynthia Baxter *(Felice Valayan)*.

Crime melodrama. When two ships belonging to financier Curt Valayan are lost at sea, private investigator Richard Cutting is hired by an insurance underwriting firm to look into possible fraud. Traveling to Switzerland to investigate the wreckage of a small plane supposedly containing the body of Walter Green, an employee of Valayan's, Cutting meets Matt Wilson, Valayan's top aide. After learning that a man walked away from the crash and took a taxi to Zurich, Cutting tracks down Green's secretary, Dominique Laurant, and asks her to arrange a meeting for him with Green. Although Green confesses that he personally sabotaged the two ships and is willing to sign sworn documents to that effect, he is murdered before he can do so by a powerful gunman known only as the Big Man. Disappointed by Cutting's apparent failure, Dominique sets herself up as a "patsy" for the killers by boldly telling Wilson that she has Green's signed confession. This gives Cutting the idea to bribe a notary to sign some documents and date them prior to Green's death. Once this act is accomplished, he returns to Dominique's hotel and discovers that she has been strangled by the Big Man. Determined to avenge her death, Cutting arranges a meeting with Valayan and warns him that unless he returns the insurance money the underwriting firm will plant a phony news story about his oil holdings. After thwarting an attempt on his own life by pushing the Big Man to his death from a balcony, Cutting returns to Valayan's chalet and persuades him that the planted news story is actually true: Green's documents prove that the doublecrossing Wilson has made a deal with a Middle Eastern country to take over Valayan's oil interests. Once the enraged Valayan has turned on Wilson and killed him, Cutting retracts his offer to hand over the Green documents. As Cutting leaves, Police Inspector Ruff arrives in time to find Wilson's murdered body lying in the center of Valayan's living room. *Investigators. Financiers. Secretaries. Hired killers. Police. Fraud. Murder. Insurance. Bribery. Sabotage. Oil. Ships. Switzerland. Documentation.*

Note: Filmed in 1966; locations in Switzerland. Working title: *The Assignment.*

THE ASTRO-ZOMBIES   F6.0220
Ram Ltd.–Ted V. Mikels Film Productions. *Dist* Geneni Film Distributing Co., Seymour Borde & Associates. May **1968.** Sd; col (Eastman Color). 35mm. 94 min. [Also 90 min.]

Prod-Dir Ted V. Mikels. *Exec Prod* Kenneth Altose, Wayne M. Rogers. *Screenplay* Ted V. Mikels, Wayne M. Rogers. *Photog* Robert Maxwell. *Art Dir* Wally Moon. *Film Ed* Art Names. *Mus* Nico Karaski. *Sd* Frank L. Smith.

Cast: Wendell Corey *(Holman)*, John Carradine *(Dr. DeMarco)*, Tom Pace *(Eric Porter)*, Joan Patrick *(Janine Norwalk)*, Rafael Campos *(Juan)*, Tura Satana *(Satanna)*, William Bagdad *(Franchot)*, Vincent Barbi *(Tiros)*, Joseph Hoover *(Chuck Edwards)*, Victor Izay *(Dr. Petrovich)*, Wally Moon *(Mike Webber)*, John Hopkins, sd *(Thompson)*, Egon Sirany *(foreign agent)*, Lynnette Lantz *(Ginger)*, Vic Lance *(chauffeur)*, Janis Saul *(Lynn)*, Rod Wilmoth *(astro-zombie)*.

Horror film. Following several brutal murders in which the victims' vital organs are ripped from their bodies, CIA Chief Holman concludes that Dr. DeMarco, the former head of the Astro Space Laboratory, has created an astro-man with a defective brain. DeMarco, who has been missing since his dismissal from the space center, has hidden himself in an old mansion on the outskirts of the city and, with a deformed assistant, has been experimenting on human bodies. The doctor's work has also aroused the interest of several foreign agents, including the exotic Satanna. When a beautiful lab technician is mutilated, Holman sets a trap for DeMarco by planting another woman in the lab as bait. The scheme works; one of the astro-zombies attacks the woman, is driven off, and then trailed to DeMarco's mansion. Satanna and her henchmen have also located the doctor through a frequency rectifier. Holman and his men quickly surround the house, trapping Satanna inside with DeMarco and the zombies. As the astro-creatures begin butchering indiscriminately, Satanna shoots DeMarco, but not before he has thrown a master switch that destroys the mansion and its occupants. *Foreign agents. Scientists. Zombies. Murder. Experiments. Mutilation. Laboratories. United States—Central Intelligence Agency.*

Note: Location scenes filmed in southern California.

ASU ARU KAGIRI *see* TILL TOMORROW COMES

AT ANY PRICE *see* MACHINE GUN MCCAIN

AT LIL'S PLACE *see* THE ORGY AT LIL'S PLACE

AT THE END OF THE RAINBOW *see* THE PRINCESS AND THE MAGIC FROG

EL ATAUD DEL VAMPIRO *see* VAMPIRE'S COFFIN

ATLANTIC ADVENTURE (Canada)   F6.0221
Inter-TV Films. *Dist* Schoenfeld Film Distributing Corp. 25 Sep **1961** [Boston opening]. Sd; b&w. 35mm. 62 min.

Participants: Henri Beaudout, Marc Modena, Gaston Vanackere, José Martínez *(crew)*. Puce, Guiton *(cats)*.

Narrator: Fred Maness.

Documentary. On 24 May 1956 Henri Beaudout, Marc Modena, Gaston Vanackere, José Martinez, and two cats set out from Halifax, Nova Scotia, on a 17- by 31-foot raft, *L'Egaré II* (The Lost One). Martinez falls ill and must be transferred to a Canadian trawler, but the others, determined to cross the Atlantic, remain at sea for 88 days. Having fought cold, hunger, sharks, exposure, and the unpredictable elements, they finally reach Falmouth, England, on 21 August, thus becoming the first men in history to achieve a west-to-east crossing of the Atlantic on a primitive raft. *Adventurers. Seamen. Survival. Rafts. Fishing boats. Halifax (Nova Scotia). Atlantic Ocean. Falmouth (England). Cats. Sharks.*

Note: Produced for Canadian television.

L'ATLANTIDE *see* **JOURNEY BENEATH THE DESERT**

ATLANTIS, THE LOST CONTINENT F6.0222

Galaxy Productions. *Dist* Metro-Goldwyn-Mayer, Inc. 3 May **1961** [Los Angeles opening; c31 Dec 1960; LP19109]. Sd (Westrex); col (Metrocolor). 35mm. 90 min.

A George Pal Production. *Prod-Dir* George Pal. *Screenplay* Daniel Mainwaring. *Anim* Project Unlimited. *Dir Photog* Harold E. Wellman. *Col Cons* Charles K. Hagedon. *Art Dir* George W. Davis, William Ferrari. *Set Decor* Henry Grace, Dick Pefferle. *Film Ed* Ben Lewis. *Mus Score* Russ Garcia. *Rec Supv* Franklin Milton. *Asst Dir* Ridgeway Callow. *Makeup* William Tuttle. *Hairstyles* Mary Keats. *Sp Eff* A. Arnold Gillespie, Lee LeBlanc, Robert R. Hoag.

Cast: Anthony Hall *(Demetrios)*, Joyce Taylor *(Antillia)*, John Dall *(Zaren)*, Bill Smith *(captain of the guard)*, Frank DeKova *(Sonoy)*, Edgar Stehli *(King Kronas)*, Edward Platt *(Azor)*, Berry Kroeger *(surgeon)*, Wolfe Barzell *(Petros)*, Jay Novello *(Xandros)*, Buck Maffie *(Andes)*, Paul Frees *(narrator)*.

Science fiction melodrama. Source: Gerald P. Hargreaves, *Atalanta, a Story of Atlantis* (a play; London, 1949). Demetrios, a young sailor in ancient Greece, finds an unconscious girl adrift in the Mediterranean. Upon awakening, she informs him that she is the Princess Antillia of Atlantis, and he agrees to take her home. When they arrive in Atlantis, Antillia learns that her father's power has been usurped by Zaren, the minister of war, who plans to conquer the world with a deadly crystal that lies embedded in an extinct volcano. To dislodge the crystal, Zaren has recruited hundreds of slaves, some of whom have been turned into animals by his surgeon. Though Demetrios is also forced into slavery, he wins his freedom when he overpowers a 7-foot man in the Ordeal by Fire and Water. Eventually Zaren succeeds in removing the crystal, but on the day that the great war is to begin, the volcano suddenly erupts. As Demetrios, Antillia, and some of the slaves escape in boats, Zaren turns the deadly rays of the crystal on them. Before he can kill them, however, he is destroyed by his own diabolical weapon. Waves of molten lava pour over Atlantis, and a mammoth tidal wave sweeps over the continent, causing it to sink into the sea. Demetrios, Antillia, and the other survivors sail away in search of a new continent. *Greeks. Royalty. Usurpers. Sailors. Escapees. Megalomania. Slavery. Transmutation. Death rays. Tidal waves. Volcanoes. Mediterranean Sea. Atlantis.*

ATLAS F6.0223

Filmgroup, Inc. *Dist* Realart Pictures. 18 May **1961** [New Orleans opening]. Sd; col (Eastman Color). 35mm (Vistascope). 84 min. [Also reviewed at 78 min.]

Prod-Dir Roger Corman. *Assoc Prod* Charles Griffith. *Story & Screenplay* Charles Griffith. *Photog* Basil Maros. *Film Ed* Michael Luciano. *Mus* Ronald Stein. *Sd Rec* Allen Hershey. *Asst Dir* Henry Yatrou. *Cost* Barbara Comeau.

Cast: Michael Forest *(Atlas)*, Frank Wolff *(Praximedes)*, Barboura Morris *(Candia)*, Walter Maslow *(Garnis)*, Christos Exarchos *(Indros)*, Andreas Philippides *(Talectos)*, Theodore Dimitriou *(Gallus)*, Miranda Kounelaki *(Ariana)*, Sascha Dario *(ballerina)*.

Costume melodrama. For 3 months the citizens of the ancient Grecian city state of Thenis have been holding off the attacking forces of Praximedes, the power-mad ruler of Seronikos. In an effort to avoid more bloodshed, it is agreed that the battle will be decided by a private combat between the leading warrior of each side. Aided by Candia, his seductive mistress, Praximedes persuades Atlas, the Olympic champion, to represent him in the contest. Atlas is victorious over Indros, the champion of Thenis; and the citizens of Thenis are forced to open their gates to the triumphant Praximedes. Upon observing the despot's tyrannical rule, however, Atlas leaves the city with Candia, with whom he has fallen in love. They join forces with rebel troops led by Indros and trick Praximedes into taking his army out of the city. When he returns, Atlas and the rebels are waiting. In the final battle, Atlas slays Praximedes, and peace is restored to Thenis. *Soldiers. Despots. Mistresses. Strongmen. Duels. Greece—Ancient. Atlas.*

Note: Filmed in Greece.

ATLAS AGAINST THE CYCLOPS (Italy) F6.0224

Panda Film. *Dist* Medallion Pictures. 14 Apr **1963** [New York showing]. Sd; col (Eastman Color). 35mm (Dyaliscope). 100 min.

Prod Ermanno Donati, Luigi Carpentieri. *Dir* Antonio Leonviola. *Screenplay* Oreste Biancoli, Gino Mangini. *Story* Oreste Biancoli. *Photog* Riccardo Pallottini. *Art Dir* Alberto Boccianti. *Film Ed* Mario Serandrei. *Mus* Carlo Innocenzi. *Sd* Giannetti Nardi. *Cost* Giuliano Papi.

Cast: Gordon Mitchell *(Maciste)*, Chelo Alonso *(Capys)*, Vira Silenti *(Penelope)*, Dante Di Paolo *(Ifito)*, Aldo Bufi-Landi *(Sirone)*, Paul Wynter *(Mumba)*, Germano Longo *(Agisandro)*, Giotto Tempestini *(Aronio)*, Massimo Righi *(Efros)*, Raffaella Pelloni *(Eber)*, Tullio Altamura *(official)*, Antonio Meschini *(soldier)*, Flavio *(Penelope's son)*, Aldo Padinotti *(cyclops)*.

Action melodrama. Queen Capys of Sadok orders her army to attack a village that houses the descendents of Ulysses, whom she has vowed to destroy. Agisandro, the village governor, is killed in the battle, and several survivors are taken prisoner, but Agisandro's widow, Penelope, and their baby son are rescued by Aronio, a shepherd, and taken to the cave of Maciste. Capys, infuriated that the baby has been permitted to escape, tortures several prisoners in an unsuccessful attempt to learn the child's whereabouts but later falls in love with Maciste when he is captured trying to free the prisoners. Ifito, the queen's commander, who is jealous of Capys' attention to her prisoner, drugs Maciste into divulging the child's hiding place and attempts to sacrifice the baby to a cyclops. Capys decides to aid Maciste and sends him to the cave which houses the beast. The queen is killed rescuing Maciste, and Ifito is eaten by the cyclops, but Penelope and her son are saved. *Royalty. Widows. Infants. Shepherds. Hostages. Torture. Jealousy. Self-sacrifice. Caves. Drugs. Atlas. Maciste. Cyclops.*

Note: Opened in Rome in Apr 1961 as *Maciste nella terra dei ciclopi*. May also be known as *Atlas vs. the Cyclops*.

ATLAS VS. THE CYCLOPS *see* **ATLAS AGAINST THE CYCLOPS**

ATOM AGE VAMPIRE (Italy) F6.0225

Lion Film. *Dist* Topaz Film Corp., Manson Distributing Corp. 29 May **1963** [Los Angeles opening]. Sd; b&w. 35mm. 87 min.

Prod Mario Fava. *Dir-Writ* Anton Giulio Majano. *Dir English Vers* Richard McNamara. *Screenplay* Piero Monviso, Gino De Santis, Alberto Bevilacqua, Anton Giulio Majano. *Screenplay English Vers* John Hart. *Photog* Aldo Giordani. *Art Dir* Walter Martigli, Giuseppe Ranieri. *Mus* Armando Trovajoli. *Sp Eff* Ugo Amadoro.

Cast: Alberto Lupo *(Professor Levyn)*, Susanne Loret *(Jeannette)*, Sergio Fantoni *(Pierre)*, Franca Parisi Strahl *(Monique)*, Ivo Garrani *(police commissioner)*, Andrea Scotti *(gardener)*, Roberto Berta *(Sacha, Professor Levyn's man)*.

Science fiction melodrama. Despondent because she has broken her engagement to Pierre, a merchant seaman whose ship has just set sail, Jeannette, a beautiful dancer, crashes her car and is badly scarred. Professor Levyn, who has done research work on atom bomb victims of Hiroshima and is currently experimenting with human tissue regeneration, successfully treats her with a formula derived from the glands of dead women. When Jeannette's scars begin to reappear, Levyn, now hopelessly enamored of her, turns into a monster and against the advice of Monique, his devoted assistant, kills women for more formula ingredients. Pierre returns in time to alert the police and save Jeannette from a fiendish attack by the jealous professor, who has just murdered Monique. Pierre and Jeannette are reconciled. *Seamen. Dancers. Scientists. Professors. Disfiguration. Murder. Jealousy. Atom bomb. Automobile accidents.*

Note: Released in Italy in 1961 as *Seddok, l'erede di Satana*; running time: 105 min.

THE ATOMIC BRAIN *see* **MONSTROSITY**

ATOMIC NO OBON, ONNA OYABUN TAIKETSU NO MAKI *see* **OBON'S DIPPING CONTEST**

ATRACO AL HAMPA *see* **THE VISCOUNT**

ATRAGON (Japan) F6.0226

Toho Co. *Dist* American International Pictures. 30 Dec **1964** [Cincinnati, Ohio, opening; c23 Dec 1964; LP29781]. Sd; col (Eastmancolor, print by Pathé). 35mm (Tohoscope). 88 min. [Copyright length: 90 min.]

Pres by James H. Nicholson, Samuel Z. Arkoff. *Exec Prod* Tomoyuki Tanaka. *Dir* Inoshiro Honda. *Screenplay* Shinichi Sekizawa. *Photog* Hajime Koizumi. *Mus* Akira Ifukube. *Sp Eff Dir* Eiji Tsuburaya.

Cast: Tadao Takashima *(commercial photographer)*, Yoko Fujiyama *(Captain Shinguji's daughter)*, Yu Fujiki *(Captain Shinguji)*, Kenji Sawara, Akemi Kita, Tetsuko Kobayashi, Akihiko Hirata, Hiroshi Koizumi, Jun Tazaki,

Ken Uehara.

Science fiction melodrama. Over 2,000 years ago, the Mu Kingdom sank beneath the Pacific Ocean when a huge earthquake swept across its continent. Its submerged civilization survived, however, and harnessed the energy from the center of the earth. With this power, the Mu queen plans to conquer and subjugate the world. As disasters, including an earthquake in Tokyo, erupt all over the globe, the United Nations send their newest atomic submarine to search for the Mu Kingdom; but the craft is destroyed by underwater pressure emanating from the undersea empire. The only hope of salvation for the world is the *Atragon*, an extraordinary land-air-sea warship designed by a former Japanese naval commander who disappeared to a remote island when World War II ended in defeat for Japan. Although attempts by the Mu people to kidnap the commander, Captain Shinguji, have failed, they have succeeded in abducting both his daughter and her photographer boyfriend. The young escape, taking the Mu queen captive, and Captain Shinguji consents to send the *Atragon* to defend Japan and the world. The vessel destroys all of the enemy's protective forces, including a monstrous sea creature, and then, by disabling the Mus' power source, destroys the entire Mu Kingdom. *Royalty. Photographers. Megalomania. Abduction. Demolition—Underwater. Submarines. Pacific Ocean. Tokyo. United Nations. Earthquakes. Sea monsters. Imaginary kingdoms.*

Note: Released in Japan in 1964 as *Kaitei gunkan*; running time: 96 min.

ATT ÄLSKA *see* **TO LOVE**

ATTACK ON THE IRON COAST (United States/Great Britain) **F6.0227**
Oakmont Productions. *For* Mirisch Corp. *Dist* United Artists. Mar **1968** [c6 Mar 1968; LP35496]. Sd; col (DeLuxe). 35mm. 89 min.

Pres by Mirisch Films. A John C. Champion Production. *Prod* John C. Champion. *Exec Prod* Irving Temaner. *Assoc Prod* Ted Lloyd. *Dir* Paul Wendkos. *Screenplay* Herman Hoffman. *Story* John C. Champion. *Dir Photog* Paul Beeson. *Camera Op* Neil Binney. *2d Unit Photog* Desmond Dickinson. *Art Dir* Bill Andrews. *Set Decor* Ken Ryan. *Film Ed* Ernest Hosler. *Mus* Gerard Schurmann. *Sd Rec* Cyril Swern. *Asst Dir* Anthony Waye. *Wardrobe* John Briggs. *Makeup Supv* George Blackler. *Sp Eff* Bowie Films. *Props* Dave Jordan.

Cast: Lloyd Bridges (*Maj. James Wilson*), Andrew Keir (*Capt. Owen Franklin*), Sue Lloyd (*Sue Wilson*), Mark Eden (*Lieut. Comdr. Donald Kimberley*), Maurice Denham (*Sir Frederick Grafton*), Glyn Owen (*Lieutenant Forrester*), Howard Pays (*Lieutenant Graham*), George Mikell (*Captain Strasser*), Simon Prebble (*Lieutenant Smythe*), Keith Buckley, Bill Henderson, Gavin Breck (*commandos*), Walter Gotell (*von Horst*), Michael Wolf (*Lieutenant Kramer*), John Welsh (*Cansley*), Joan Crane (*wren officer*), Ernest Clark (*Air Vice Marshal Woodbridge*), Richard Shaw (*German infantry sergeant*), Victor Beaumont (*German battery commander*), John Albineri (*German gunnery sergeant*), John Kelland (*flag lieutenant*), Mark Ward (*Timmy Wilson*), Dick Haydon (*Pringle*), John Golightly (*helmsman*), Murray Evans (*bosun's mate*), Robin Hawdon (*radar man*), Sean Barrett (*radio man*).

War drama. During World War II American commando leader Maj. James Wilson requests permission to cross the English Channel and raid a heavily-guarded German naval installation in France that the Nazis call the "Iron Coast." Although Wilson is opposed by Capt. Owen Franklin, whose son was killed in a previous raid led by Wilson, the British Admiralty is so concerned about Allied shipping losses in the Channel that they give Wilson the go-ahead and order Franklin to assist in the preparations. Lieut. Comdr. Donald Kimberley is blinded during the strenuous training sessions; but Wilson, ready to abandon the mission because of the accident and because of Franklin's continued harassment, is nevertheless convinced by Kimberley of the importance of the mission, and the men embark on the dangerous assignment. Just as the raid is to take place, Wilson receives word that the air cover they expected to have has been destroyed in battle, and that he is to return at once to England. Having secured Franklin's support, Wilson ignores the order and proceeds with the original plan. The commandos board a battered British minesweeper packed with explosives, cross the Channel, and successfully ram the dock where the Nazi high command is located. Although he is badly injured and unable to go ashore with the others to destroy secondary targets, Wilson detonates the explosive device on the minesweeper and sacrifices his life in demolishing the Iron Coast. *Nazis. Commandos. War heroes. Blindness. Self-sacrifice. Explosives. Ships. World War II. English Channel. France. United States Army. Great Britain—Royal Navy.*

Note: Filmed on location in Great Britain and released there in 1968.

ATTEMPT TO KILL (Great Britain) **F6.0228**
Merton Park Studios. *Dist* Schoenfeld Film Distributing Corp. Jul **1966**. Sd (Westrex); b&w. 35mm. 57 min.

Prod Jack Greenwood. *Dir* Royston Morley. *Screenplay* Richard Harris, writ. *Photog* Bert Mason. *Art Dir* Peter Mullins. *Film Ed* Edward Jarvis. *Mus*

Comp & Cond Bernard Ebbinghouse. *Titl Mus Comp* Michael Carr, mus. *Sd Ed* Roy Norman. *Sd Rec* Sidney Rider, Ronald Abbott. *Asst Dir* Peter Price. *Prod Mgr* Joe Levy. *Set Cont* Marjorie Owens. *Casting Dir* Ronald Curtis.

Cast: Derek Farr (*Detective Inspector Minter*), Tony Wright (*Gerry Hamilton*), Richard Pearson (*Frank Weyman*), Freda Jackson (*Mrs. Weyman*), Patricia Mort (*Elisabeth Gray*), J. G. Devlin (*Elliot*), Clifford Earl (*Sergeant Bennett*), Dennis Holmes (*Fraser*), Alan Jeyes (*gardener*), Grace Arnold (*housekeeper*), Trevor Reid (*bank manager*), Frances Bennett (*barmaid*).

Mystery melodrama. Source: Edgar Wallace, *The Lone House Mystery* (London, 1929). Several attempts are made on the life of London business tycoon Frank Weyman, and Scotland Yard Inspector Minter and his assistant, Sergeant Bennett, are called in to investigate. The suspects include Fraser, an embittered former employee of Weyman; Elisabeth Gray, Weyman's secretary and fiancée to whom he has willed a substantial inheritance; the estranged Mrs. Weyman; Elliot, a man whose reputation Weyman once destroyed; and Gerry Hamilton, a garageowner who loves Elisabeth. The case is further complicated by the fatal stabbing of Fraser and another attempt on Weyman's life when his motorboat is blown up. Inspector Minter proves that Elisabeth and Gerry, who are secretly married, are guilty. *Tycoons. Businessmen. Secretaries. Garagemen. Detectives. Murder. Inheritance. London. Scotland Yard. Explosions.*

Note: Released in Great Britain in 1961; running time: 57 min.

ATTONG *see* **THE YOUNG AND THE BRAVE**

ATTRACTION *see* **BLACK ON WHITE**

AU HASARD, BALTHAZAR (France/Sweden) **F6.0229**
Parc Film-Argos Films-Athos Films-Svensk Filmindustri-Svenska Filminstitutet. *Dist* Cinema Ventures. 19 Feb **1970** [New York opening]. Sd; col. 35mm. 96 min.

Prod Mag Bodard. *Dir-Writ* Robert Bresson. *Photog* Ghislain Cloquet. *Art Dir* Pierre Charbonnier. *Film Ed* Raymond Lamy. *Mus: Piano Sonata no. 20* Franz Peter Schubert. *Adtl Mus* Jean Wiener. *Sd* Antoine Archimbaud, Jacques Carrère. *Asst Dir* Jacques Kébadian, Sven Frostenson. *Prod Mgr* Philippe Dussart.

Cast: Anne Wiazemsky (*Marie*), François Lafarge (*Gérard*), Philippe Asselin (*Marie's father*), Nathalie Joyaut (*Marie's mother*), Walter Green (*Jacques*), J. C. Guilbert (*Arnold, the tramp*), Pierre Klossowski (*corn merchant*), Jean Rémignard (*notary*), Jacques Sorbets (*captain of gendarmerie*), Tord Paag (*Louis*), Sven Frostenson, Roger Fjellstrom (*Gérard's friends*), Jean-Joël Barbier (*doyen*), Rémy Brozeck (*Marcel*), Mylène Weyergans (*nurse*), Guy Bréjac (*vet*), François Sullerot (*baker*), M. C. Frémont (*baker's wife*).

Drama. Jacques and Marie, two children who spend summers together in a French town near Switzerland, receive a newborn donkey as a pet and name him Balthazar. A short time later Jacques' father leaves with his family for Paris, entrusting the management of his farm to Marie's father, a local schoolteacher. Some years later, Balthazar, who has been returned to his original owner, only to lead a hard life carting sand, escapes and finds his way back to the farm. Marie, now 16, adores Balthazar, and her father keeps the donkey to pull their donkey cart. Balthazar is eventually sold to the village baker. Jacques returns and, despite a lawsuit that his father has brought against Marie's father over the running of the farm, declares his love for Marie. But Marie is infatuated with Gérard, the baker's delivery boy and leader of a gang of juvenile delinquents. Gérard treats Balthazar cruelly, and he seduces Marie, whose concern for Balthazar's well-being leads her into Gérard's hands. In time Balthazar is passed on to Arnold, a drunken tramp who uses Balthazar to give rides to tourists; then to a circus, where he performs a multiplication act by stamping his feet; and eventually back to Arnold. With Arnold's death, Balthazar is sold to a corn merchant who starves and overworks him until, too sick to work, he is taken back by Marie's parents. Meanwhile, Marie has left home because of her continuing relationship with Gérard, and she offers herself to the corn merchant for a place to stay the night. Gérard, in retribution, beats her, strips her naked, and leaves her in an abandoned house. Taking Balthazar, he and his friends load the donkey's back with contraband goods which they intend to smuggle across the border. They are shot at by customs officials and escape, but Balthazar, mortally wounded, dies on a hillside among a flock of sheep. *Farmers. Juvenile delinquents. Schoolteachers. Bakers. Tramps. Childhood. Adolescence. Village life. Filial relations. Seduction. Alcoholism. Theft. Smuggling. Circus. Pets. Lawsuits. Donkeys.*

Note: Opened in Paris in May 1966; running time: 90 min. Opened in Stockholm in Nov 1967 as *Min vän Balthazar*; running time: 94 min.

AUDACE COLPO DEI SOLITI IGNOTI *see* **FIASCO IN MILAN**

AN AUDIO/VISUAL ROCK THING *see* **POPCORN; AN AUDIO/VISUAL ROCK THING**

AUDITION (Czechoslovakia)   **F6.0230**
Barrandov Film Studio. *For* Československý Film. *Dist* Brandon Films. 3 Jul **1968** [New York opening]. Sd; b&w. 35mm. 47 min.

Assoc Prod Ladislav Dražan, Zdeňka Černá. *Dir* Miloš Forman. *Story & Screenplay* Miloš Forman, Ivan Passer. *Photog* Miroslav Ondříček. *Camera Op* Karel Hejsek. *Camera Asst* Emil Hora. *Film Ed* Miroslav Hájek, Jitka Šulcová. *Mus* Jiří Šlitr. *Lyr* Jiří Suchý. *Sd* Josef Vlček. *Asst Dir* Tomáš Kulík. *Prod Ch* Miloš Bergl.

Cast: Jiří Suchý, Jiří Šlitr *(themselves)*, Markéta Krotká *(Marguerite)*, Věra Křesadlová *(Věra)*, Ladislav Jakim *(Marguerite's boyfriend)*, Petr Brožek, Karel Mareš, František Pokorný, Vladimír Hrabánek, Jiří Planner, Ferdinand Havlík Orchestra, Petr Brožek's Krystal Group, Hana Hegerová, Pavlína Filipovská, Sylva Daníčková, Jana Malknechtová, Pavel Sedláček, Renata Tůmová, Eva Pospíšilová, Bohumír Paleček, Eva Stránská, Bohunka Sladká, Majka Gillarová, Zuzana Opršalová, Zdeňka Lorencová, Dana Urbánková.

Comedy-drama with music. In Prague's Semaphore Theatre, lyricist-dramatist Jiří Suchý and composer Jiří Šlitr audition a group of teenaged girls for a musical revue. Among the singers are Věra, a member of an amateur jazz group, and Marguerite, a pedicurist. One of the girls suffers a bad case of stage fright, and another, supremely over-confident, learns in the end that she has not been selected for the production. *Singers. Composers. Playwrights. Adolescence. Auditions. Musical revues. Prague. Semaphore Theatre (Prague).*

Note: Filmed at the Semaphore Theatre in Prague. Opened in Prague in Feb 1964; the second part of a film entitled *Konkurs*. Alternative U. S. titles: *Talent Competition* and *Competition*.

AURA *see* **THE WITCH**

DAS AUSSCHWEIFENDE LEBEN DES MARQUIS DE SADE *see* **DE SADE**

UNE AUSSI LONGUE ABSENCE *see* **THE LONG ABSENCE**

AUSTRALIA: LAND OF PARADOX   **F6.0231**
1 Feb **1970** [Los Angeles showing]. Si; col. 35mm. ca120 min.
Pres by Explorama. *A Film by* Nicol Smith.

Travelog. A travel host describes Sydney, Canberra, Tasmania, Darwin, the Great Barrier Reef, Brampton Island, the Bondi lifesaving carnival, the aborigines, wild water buffalo, and 100-pound clams. *Aborigines. Travel. Australia. Sydney (Australia). Canberra. Tasmania. Darwin. Great Barrier Reef. Bondi Beach. Water buffalo. Clams.*

Note: Narration delivered live on stage.

UN AUTRE PAYS *see* **DRYLANDERS**

AN AUTUMN AFTERNOON (Japan)   **F6.0232**
Shochiku Co. *Dist* Shochiku Films of America. **1964** [Los Angeles showing]. Sd; col (Agfacolor). 35mm. 113 min.

Prod Shizuo Yamanouchi. *Dir* Yasujiro Ozu. *Screenplay* Yasujiro Ozu, Kogo Noda. *Photog* Yushun Atsuta. *Art Dir* Tatsuo Hamada. *Film Ed* Yoshiyasu Hamamura. *Mus* Takanobu Saito. *Sd* Yoshisaburo Senoo.

Cast: Chishu Ryu *(Shuhei Hirayama)*, Shima Iwashita *(Michiko Hirayama)*, Shin-ichiro Mikami *(Kazuo Hirayama)*, Keiji Sada *(Koichi Hirayama)*, Mariko Okada *(Akiko Hirayama)*, Nobuo Nakamura *(Shuzo Kawai)*, Kuniko Miyake *(Nobuko Kawai)*, Ryuji Kita *(Susumu Horie)*, Eijiro Tono *(Sakuma)*, Teruo Yoshida *(Miura)*, Michiyo Tamaki, Haruko Sugimura, Daisuke Kato, Kyoko Kishida, Toyoko Takahashi.

Domestic drama. Shuhei Hirayama, a widowed former naval officer, lives with his spinster daughter, Michiko, and college student son, Kazuo. Shuhei's simple routine includes regular drinking sessions with his old navy friends. At one such party honoring his former teacher, Sakuma, Shuhei learns of the man's lonely life as a shopkeeper living with an unmarried daughter who has suffered from not having a life of her own. Concerned over his own daughter's position, Shuhei mentions marriage to her, but Michiko insists that her place is in his home. Shuhei learns that Miura, a friend of his married son Koichi, was interested in Michiko at one time. Further investigation, however, discloses that Miura is now engaged to another wowan. Following this revelation, Kazuo finds his sister crying in her room. Michiko later accepts a man selected by the wife of her father's friend Kawai and is married. Alone after the ceremony, Shuhei visits a bar whose proprietress reminds him of his dead wife. Returning home, Shuhei is overwhelmed by loneliness. *Widowers. Spinsters. Family life. Old age. Loneliness. Marriage—Arranged. Weddings.*

Note: Released in Japan in Nov 1962 as *Samma no aji*. Alternative U. S. title: *The Widower*. Yushun Atsuta is also known as Yuharu Atsuta.

AVEC-AVEC *see* **DUFFY**

THE AVENGER (France/Italy)   **F6.0233**
Mercury Film (Rome)–Sirius–C. I. C. C. *Dist* Medallion Pictures. Jun **1964**. Sd; col (Eastman Color). 35mm (Euroscope). 108 min.

Prod Albert Band, Giorgio Venturini. *Dir* Giorgio Rivalta. *Screenplay* Ugo Liberatore, Luigi Mangini, Arrigo Montanari, Nino Stresa. *Photog* Angelo Lotti. *Art Dir* Arrigo Equini. *Film Ed* Antonietta Zita. *Mus* Giovanni Fusco. *Cost* Arrigo Equini.

Cast: Steve Reeves *(Aeneas)*, Carla Marlier *(Lavinia)*, Gianni Garko *(Turno)*, Giacomo Rossi Stuart *(Eurialo)*, Liana Orfei *(Camilla)*, Mario Ferrari *(Latino)*, Enzo Fiermonte *(Acate)*, Nerio Bernardi *(Drance)*, Luciano Benetti *(Sergeste)*, Lula Selli *(Amata)*, Roberto Bettoni *(Pallante)*, Maurice Poli *(Mezensio)*, Benito Stefanelli *(Niso)*, Pietro Capanna *(Bisia)*.

Drama. Derived from: Vergil, *The Aeneid*. Aeneas leads the surviving Trojan warriors to the banks of the Tiber where they settle and plan to build a new city. The king of the province grants them permission to proceed, but a hostile neighboring chief tries to destroy the settlement by stampeding it with bulls. When Aeneas defeats the chief in a tournament, he wins the love of the princess. The chief is angered and turns his people against the Trojans. Before war breaks out, Aeneas enlists the help of the Etruscans and convinces the king of the province that the conflict should be resolved in a hand-to-hand duel. The king agrees, and Aeneas defeats the rival chief, marries the princess, and wins the blessing of the king. *Trojans. Etruscans. Royalty. Tiber River. Rome. Aeneas. Latinus. Turnus. Duels. Stampedes. Bulls.*

Note: Opened in Rome in Dec 1962 as *La leggenda di Enea*; running time: 102 min; in Paris in Apr 1964 as *Conquérants héroïques*; running time: 95 min.

LAS AVENTURAS DEL VIZCONDE *see* **THE VISCOUNT**

L'AVENTURE SAUVAGE *see* **THE TRAP**

LES AVENTURES DU VICOMTE *see* **THE VISCOUNT**

LES AVENTURES EXTRAORDINAIRES DE CERVANTES *see* **THE YOUNG REBEL**

LES AVENTURIERS *see* **THE LAST ADVENTURE**

L'AVEU *see* **THE CONFESSION**

L'AVVENTURA (France/Italy)   **F6.0234**
Cino del Duca–Produzione Cinematografiche Europee–Société Cinématographique Lyre. *Dist* Janus Films. 4 Apr **1961** [New York opening]. Sd; b&w. 35mm. 145 min.

Pres by Raymond Hakim, Robert Hakim. *Prod* Amato Pennasilico. *Dir* Michelangelo Antonioni. *Screenplay* Michelangelo Antonioni, Elio Bartolini, Tonino Guerra. *Photog* Aldo Scavarda. *Art Dir* Piero Poletto. *Film Ed* Eraldo Da Roma. *Mus* Giovanni Fusco. *Sd* Claudio Maielli. *Asst Dir* Franco Indovina, Gianni Arduini, Jack O'Connell. *Prod Mgr* Luciano Perugia.

Cast: Monica Vitti *(Claudia)*, Gabriele Ferzetti *(Sandro)*, Lea Massari *(Anna)*, Dominique Blanchar *(Giulia)*, James Addams *(Corrado, her husband)*, Renzo Ricci *(Anna's father)*, Esmeralda Ruspoli *(Patrizia)*, Lelio Luttazzi *(Raimondo)*, Dorothy De Poliolo *(Gloria Perkins)*, Giovanni Petrucci *(young prince)*, Enrico Bologna, Rita Molè, Franco Cimino, Renato Pinciroli, Giovanni Danesi, Vincenzo Tranchina, Angela Tomasi di Lampedusa.

Drama. A group of wealthy, jaded Italian socialites are the members of a yachting party cruising off the northeast coast of Sicily. Included in the small group are Sandro, a 40-year-old architect who has long since abandoned his artistic principles for a life of easy commercial success; Anna, Sandro's mistress, who is dissatisfied with their almost purely sexual relationship; and Claudia, Anna's friend, who is the one member of the party unaccustomed to a life of wealth. They go ashore to explore a barren, volcanic island. Following a sudden storm, it is discovered that Anna has disappeared. A search of the island proves fruitless, and Claudia blames Anna's apparent suicide on Sandro's heartlessness. Separately, and then together, however, Claudia and Sandro visit places on the mainland where a strange girl is said to have been seen. Gradually, as it becomes more and more apparent that Anna is not going to be found, Claudia and Sandro turn to each other. Though she at first resists his advances, her feelings of shame and guilt are overcome by her passion, and she becomes his mistress. Later, the two lovers rejoin their friends at a party in an elegant hotel in Taormina. That night Claudia awakens to find Sandro gone. She prowls through the hotel until she discovers him clumsily making love to a high-class prostitute. As Claudia stares at him, Sandro realizes the uselessness and emptiness of his actions. Filled with despair, he wanders out into the cold, gray dawn and begins to sob quietly. Claudia follows him and, feeling compassion and desolation, places her hands on his shoulders and wordlessly forgives him. *Idle rich. Socialites. Mistresses. Architects. Prostitutes. Missing persons. Infidelity. Hotels. Yachts. Islands. Taormina. Sicily. Storms.*

Note: Island scenes filmed off the coast of Sicily. Opened in Paris in Sep 1960; running time: 139 min; in Rome in Nov 1960 at 130 min. Also known in the United States as *The Adventure*.

L'AVVENTURA DI UN ITALIANO IN CINA see MARCO POLO

LE AVVENTURE DI SCARAMOUCHE see THE ADVENTURES OF SCARAMOUCHE

LE AVVENTURE DI TOPO GIGIO see THE MAGIC WORLD OF TOPO GIGIO (THE ITALIAN MOUSE)

LE AVVENTURE E GLI AMORI DI MIGUEL CERVANTES see THE YOUNG REBEL

UN AVVENTURIERO A TAHITI see TENDER SCOUNDREL

THE AWFUL DR. ORLOF (France/Spain) F6.0235
Hispamer Films. *Dist* Sigma II! Corp. 7 Oct 1964 [Cincinnati, Ohio, opening]. Sd; b&w. 35mm. 90 min.
A Sergio Newman–Léo Lax Production. *Dir-Writ* Jesús Franco. *Photog* Godofredo Pacheco. *Art Dir* Antonio Simont. *Mus* José Pagán, Antonio Ramírez Angel. *Prod Supv* Manuel Rossón.
Cast: Howard Vernon *(Dr. Orlof)*, Conrado San Martín *(Inspector Tanner)*, Diana Lorys *(Wanda)*, Perla Cristal *(Irma)*, Ricardo Valle *(Marius)*, María Silva *(Jenny)*, Venancio Muro, Mara Laso, Félix Dafauce, Faustino Comejo.
Horror film. Based on a novel by: David Kuhne. At the turn of the century, Dr. Orlof, a respected surgeon, secretly abducts young actresses from cafes in disreputable areas in order to perform skin grafting operations on the features of his horribly disfigured daughter. Aiding him is a criminal, Marius, whom Orlof has blinded and turned into a near robot. Police create a composite portrait of the unknown fiend, but the evidence is inconclusive until Wanda, the ballerina fiancée of Inspector Tanner, decides to act as bait without telling the inspector. Orlof is lured into the trap and takes Wanda to his castle for surgical experimentation. Meanwhile, a necklace belonging to one of the victims is found in a stream flowing through Orlof's property. As police close in, Marius turns on Orlof, who has killed the one woman who has treated him kindly; and the mad doctor is killed as Inspector Tanner rescues his fiancée. *Surgeons. Psychopaths. Dancers. Actors. Monsters. Police. Murder. Disfiguration. Abduction. Cafes. Castles.*
Note: Madrid opening: May 1962 as *Gritos en la noche*; Paris opening: May 1963 as *L'horrible Dr. Orloff*. Sources disagree in assigning production credits.

AYAKO (Japan) F6.0236
Toho Co. Apr 1964 [Los Angeles showing]. Sd; col (Eastmancolor). 35mm (Tohoscope). 90 min.
Exec Prod Sanezumi Fujimoto, Masakatsu Kaneko. *Dir* Eizo Sugawa. *Screenplay* Yoshikata Yoda. *Photog* Seiichi Endo. *Mus* Seiji Hiraoka.
Cast: Reiko Dan *(Ayako)*, Keizo Kawasaki, Kamatari Fujiwara, Kyu Sazanka, Chisako Hara, Hikaru Mayuzumi, Eitaro Ozawa, Homare Suguro.
Melodrama. Ayako, a secretary to the president of a cartel, carries on a secret romance with a clerk in her office. To help pay off her brother's gambling debts, her father steals money from his own firm, planning to replace it with his retirement allowance. Ayako in turn pilfers the same amount from her office and orders her father to repay the money he has stolen. Caught replacing the money, he is fired without a pension. Ayako's boyfriend suggests she become her boss's mistress and milk him for the stolen money; the arrangement works until the boss's wife discovers them together. Ayako then obtains work in a bar through Natsuko, a bar maid, but her affair with a stockbroker ends abruptly when Natsuko, whose lover has deserted her, kills herself. Eager to rid herself of her parasitic boyfriend, Ayako invites him to her apartment. The stockbroker arrives at the same time and in the fight that ensues Ayako smashes the broker over the head with a bottle. At the police station, her father can only wring his hands, while Ayako looks optimistically to the future. *Secretaries. Office clerks. Bar girls. Executives. Stockbrokers. Mistresses. Theft. Suicide. Family life. Infidelity. Debt.*
Note: Released in Japan in 1962 as *Aru Osaka no onna*.

BABES IN THE WOODS F6.0237
Aurora Productions. *Dist* Olympic International Films. 1962. Sd; col. 35mm. ca60 min.
Cast: Pat Bolin, Marge London, Vickie Miles, Karen Moore, Karl Morton.
Nudist film. The late J. Wellington Figby narrates the tale of his widow, Martha, as she attempts to rescue their resort from financial difficulties; she renames the resort "Mrs. Figby's Pine Tree Resort and Planned Vacations for Respectable Busy Business Girls." On their way to the camp, three young women, Mrs. Figby's first guests, refresh themselves with a nude dip at Hidden Falls. They decide to hitchhike when their jeep fails to start. They remove their clothes and hitchhike in the nude, but the sight of Mrs. Figby approaching in her truck sends them scurrying into the bushes to dress. Mrs. Figby treats her guests to a hair-raising airplane tour of the camp. After dinner the women attempt to teach Mrs. Figby to dance the Twist; later they retire to their cabin where Mrs. Figby finds them assuming poses of strippers and pin-up models. Two of the women join their hostess for a fishing trip. While Mrs. Figby wrestles with her elaborate equipment out on the lake, the third woman, following the advice of the incorporeal Figby, remains on the dock and lands a pile of fish with only a piece of string and a bent hairpin. *Widows. Businesswomen. Air pilots. Hitchhikers. Nudity. Resorts. Vacations. Fishing. Airplanes. Twist (dance).*

BABES IN TOYLAND F6.0238
Walt Disney Productions. *Dist* Buena Vista Distribution Co. 14 Dec 1961 [New York opening; c17 Nov 1961; LP20733]. Sd (RCA); col (Technicolor). 35mm. 105 min. [Also 100 min.]
Prod Walt Disney. *Dir* Jack Donohue. *Screenplay* Ward Kimball, Joe Rinaldi, Lowell S. Hawley. *Anim Eff* Joshua Meador. *Dir Photog* Edward Colman. *Art Dir* Carroll Clark, Marvin Aubrey Davis. *Sp Art Styling* A. Kendall O'Connor. *Set Decor* Emile Kuri, Hal Gausman. *Film Ed* Robert Stafford. *Mus Adapt & Cond* George Bruns. *Lyr & Introductory Material* Mel Leven. *Orch* Franklyn Marks. *Choral Arr* Jud Conlon. *Songs:* "I Can't Do the Sum," "Just a Toy," "Floretta," "Castle in Spain," "We Won't Be Happy Till We Get It," "Lemonade," "Just a Whisper Away," "March of the Toys," "Toyland" Victor Herbert, mus. *Songs:* "The Workshop Song," "The Forest of No Return," "Slowly He Sank Into the Sea" George Bruns, Mel Leven. *Choreog* Tom Mahoney. *Sd Supv* Robert O. Cook. *Sd* Dean Thomas. *Mus Ed* Evelyn Kennedy. *Asst Dir* Austen Jewell. *Asst to the Prod* Louis Debney. *Unit Mgr* Arthur J. Vitarelli. *Cost Dsgn* Bill Thomas. *Cost* Chuck Keehne, Gertrude Casey. *Makeup* Pat McNalley. *Hairstyles* Ruth Sandifer. *Sp Eff* Eustace Lycett, Robert A. Mattey. *Toy Seq* Bill Justice, Xavier Atencio, Yale Gracey. *Matte Artist* Jim Fetherolf.
Cast: Ray Bolger *(Barnaby)*, Tommy Sands *(Tom Piper)*, Annette *(Mary Contrary)*, Ed Wynn *(The Toymaker)*, Tommy Kirk *(Grumio)*, Kevin Corcoran *(Boy Blue)*, Henry Calvin *(Gonzorgo)*, Gene Sheldon *(Roderigo)*, Mary McCarty *(Mother Goose)*, Ann Jilliann *(Bo Peep)*, Brian Corcoran *(Willie Winkie)*, Marilee Arnold, Melanie Arnold *(twins)*, Jerry Glenn *(Simple Simon)*, John Perri *(Jack-Be-Nimble)*, David Pinson *(Bobby Shaftoe)*, Bryan Russell *(little boy)*, James Martin *(Jack)*, Ilana Dowding *(Jill)*.
Musical fantasy. Based on the operetta by: Victor Herbert and Glen McDonough, *Babes in Toyland* (Chicago opening: 17 Jun 1903). The villagers in the land of Mother Goose gather in the square to celebrate the coming marriage of Tom Piper and Mary Contrary. Barnaby, Mary's evil tutor, hopes to marry the young girl himself and has Tom abducted by two knaves, Gonzorgo and Roderigo, and then sold to a band of Gypsies. Barnaby ruins Mary's source of income by driving her sheep into the Forest of No Return, but Tom returns in time to foil Barnaby's scheme and lead Mary and her brothers and sisters into the forest to retrieve the missing sheep. The friendly trees escort them to Toyland, where the kindly Toymaker puts them to work in return for his help. Meanwhile, Barnaby uses the Toymaker's latest invention to reduce Tom to toy size and tries to force Mary into marrying him. Tom mobilizes the Army of Wooden Soldiers, however, and once more comes to the rescue. The culprit is reduced in size and imprisoned in a bird cage; Tom (now of normal size) and Mary are finally married. *Tutors. Gypsies. Toymakers. Imaginary kingdoms. Weddings. Abduction. Toys. Trees. Mother Goose. Sheep.*
Note: Previously filmed in 1934 (M-G-M).

BABETTE IN RETURN OF THE SECRET SOCIETY F6.0239
FPS Ventures. 11 Sep 1968 [New York showing]. Sd; b&w. 35mm. 65 min.
Cast: Claudia Cheer, Maxine, Sue Akers, Jo Street.
Sex film. Babette, a bisexual, is an active member of "The Secret Society," a sex club for unusual and bizarre sexual practices. Ramon, leader of the club, begins to compile a library of pornography that the club plans to sell to interested purchasers. Babette meets a married couple who reveal some new techniques in the art of triangular love. She then responds to an advertisement and becomes one of a group of four who explore a wealth of sexual possibilities. *Pornography. Troilism. Bisexuality. Sexual techniques. Group sex. Sex clubs.*
Note: Also known as *Babette* and as *Return of the Secret Society*.

BABO 73 F6.0240
Dist Film-Makers' Cooperative, Film-Makers' Distribution Center. Sep 1964 [Los Angeles opening]. Sd; col and b&w. 16mm. 60 min.
Prod-Dir-Writ Robert Downey. *Photog* William Waering. *Mus* Tom O'Horgan.
Cast: Taylor Mead *(The President)*.
Satire. A Presidential candidate stumbles through his campaign and the early weeks of his administration. Among the subjects treated are: the civil rights movement, the Catholic Church, international diplomacy, shoe fetishism, psychiatry, God, *Time* magazine, and Americans of the North, South, East, and West, as well as the office of the President of the United Status (sic). *Presidents*

of the United States. Civil rights. Diplomacy. Fetishism. Psychiatry. Religion. Political campaigns. Washington (District of Columbia). Catholic Church. "Time".

Note: Filmed in Washington, D. C., New York City, and New Jersey.

BABY, LIGHT MY FIRE   F6.0241

J. R. L. Productions. *Dist* Cinex Film Industries. 1 Jan **1970** [San Francisco showing]. Sd; b&w. 35mm. 95 min.

Prod-Dir Lou Campa. *Exec Prod* John Liggio. *Story* Ronald Edwards. *Dir Photog* B. H. Dial. *Asst Photog* Charles Carmello. *Sets* Charles Carmello. *Film Ed* Lou Campa. *Mus Arr* Dave Herman. *Sd* Tony Donovan. *Sp Eff* Charles Carmello. *Grip* C. Liggio.

Cast: Tina Buckley (*June Wilson*), Larry Hunter (*Pancho*), Olivia Brandon (*Candy*), Vic Donte (*Dr. Gerber*), Marc Kelo (*Brad*), Mae East (*Mexican girl*), Stephanie Bae, Anita Lott (*lesbians*), Alice Halz (*U.N. girl*), Lou Champion (*stag man*), Steve Dickenson (*Dr. Delem*), John Christofori (*U.N. delegate*), John Rock (*servant*), Gerard Damiano (*Foreman*).

Drama. Foreman, head of a drug syndicate, kidnaps 17-year-old anti-drug crusader June Wilson, whose campaign to legalize marijuana so that its sale can be controlled by Congress threatens his organization. Dr. Gerber, formerly a Nazi concentration camp officer, is ordered to brainwash June into becoming a nymphomaniac while hidden cameras record the process. She is raped by "public relations" man Brad Crane, and forced into abnormal sex with Pancho, a degenerate, while his teenage assistant looks on. June then receives orders to seduce a naive new worker and demonstrates the success of her conditioning. June succumbs to Candy's lesbian advances, and Foreman and Gerber plan an orgy for some Washington politicians. While several 15-year-old girls "entertain," Brad Crane, who has fallen in love with June, helps her escape, and they go to the police. Thus June's mission—to smash the pot peddlers—is fulfilled. *Drug dealers. Nazis. Politicians. Kidnaping. Brainwashing. Adolescence. Nymphomania. Rape. Seduction. Lesbianism. Syndicates. Marijuana. Washington (District of Columbia).*

Note: Also known as *Come on Baby, Light My Fire* and *C'mon, Baby, Light My Fire.*

BABY LOVE (Great Britain)   F6.0242

Avton Film Productions. *Dist* Avco Embassy Pictures. 19 Mar **1969** [New York opening]. Sd; col (Eastman Color). 35mm. 98 min. *MPAA rating* R.

Pres by Joseph E. Levine. A Klinger-Shipman Production. *Prod* Guido Coen. *Exec Prod* Michael Klinger. *Dir* Alastair Reid. *Screenplay* Alastair Reid, Guido Coen, Michael Klinger. *Dir Photog* Desmond Dickinson. *Art Dir* Scott MacGregor. *Film Ed* John Glen. *Mus Comp & Cond* Max Harris. *Theme Mus* Enrico Intra. *Songs* Tokenam Aw. *Sung by* Katch 22. *Sd Rec* Brian Marshall. *Asst Dir* Ray Corbett. *Prod Mgr* David Griffith. *Cost* Harry Haynes. *Makeup* Bunty Phillips. *Hairstyles* Ann Box.

Cast: Ann Lynn (*Amy Quayle*), Keith Barron (*Robert Quayle*), Linda Hayden (*Luci Thompson*), Derek Lamden (*Nicholas Quayle*), Diana Dors (*Liz Thompson*), Patience Collier (*Mrs. Carmichael*), Dick Emery (*Harry Pearson*), Sheila Steafel (*Tessa Pearson*), Sally Stephens (*Margo Pearson*), Timothy Carlton (*Jeremy*), Christopher Witty (*Jonathan*), Vernon Dobtcheff (*man in cinema*), Michael Lewis, Julian Barnes (*boys*), Patsy Snell (*girl in discotheque*), Linbert Spencer, Troy Dante.

Melodrama. Source: Tina Chad Christian, *Baby Love* (London, 1968). Returning to her Merseyside slum home one afternoon, 15-year-old Luci Thompson discovers that her mother, Liz, has committed suicide because of terminal cancer. Before slashing her wrists in a steam-filled bathroom, Liz has left a letter to her former lover, Robert Quayle, now a successful doctor in a London suburb, asking him to take care of her illegitimate daughter Luci. Taking pity on the youngster, Robert and his wife, Amy, bring Luci into their home and treat her as one of the family. Luci's desperate need for love and the shock of going from a poverty-stricken environment to one of wealth, causes her to create havoc in the Quayles' home. She flagrantly flirts with the Quayles' teenaged son, Nicholas, coyly teases Robert by reminding him of her mother, and awakens Amy's latent lesbianism by sleeping with her in order to avoid recurring nightmares. Warned by Nicholas that she may be sent away, Luci offers her naked body to Robert but is rejected. Enraged, she slashes her face with a fork as Nicholas watches from a distance. Later, when the boy tries to wash away the revulsion he feels by taking a shower, Luci enters the bathroom. Associating the steam-filled room with her mother's death, Luci attacks Nicholas, and, as he slips unconscious to the tile floor, she confuses him with her mother and begins to sob. Once Nicholas has been moved to a hospital, the Quayles vow that Luci must leave their house. Luci, however, cunningly exposes the sexual hold she has over Amy and forces Robert to admit that he, too, is attracted to her. Confident that the Quayles lack the courage to evict her, Luci changes into a seductive dress and brazenly flirts with a neighbor, when he and his wife stop by for drinks. *Orphans. Physicians. Flirts. Suicide. Cancer. Illegitimacy. Poverty. Adolescence. Lesbianism. Mental illness.*

Wealth. Family life. London. Mersey River (England).

Note: Location scenes filmed in and around London. Released in London in Mar 1969; running time: 93 min.

THE BABY MAKER   F6.0243

Robert Wise Productions. *Dist* National General Pictures. 1 Oct **1970** [New York opening]. Sd; col (Technicolor). 35mm. 109 min. *MPAA rating* R.

A Robert Wise Production. *Prod* Richard Goldstone. *Dir-Writ* James Bridges. *Photog* Charles Rosher, Jr. *Camera Op* Bob Byrne. *Asst Camera* Matthew F. Leonetti, Ken Hale. *Art Dir* Mort Rabinowitz. *Set Decor* Raymond Paul. *Set Dsgn* Francis M. Noden. *Sketch Artist* William B. Major. *Main Titl* Pacific Title. *Film Ed* Walter Thompson. *Asst Ed* John Hanley. *Mus* Fred Karlin. *Songs:* "People Come, People Go," "Lotus Baby Rant'n Mantra Blues," "What Do Ya Do?" Fred Karlin, Tylwyth Kymry. *Sung by* Ole Blue. *Song:* "She's a Fine Looking Lady" Diana Gibson. *Sd* Larry Jost. *Boom Op* Clint Althouse. *Asst Dir* Howard W. Koch, Jr., Joe Ellis. *Prod Mgr* Herbert Willis. *Script Supv* Michael Preece. *Prod Sec* Myrtle Von Stein, Jean Merrick. *Wardrobe* Robert Richards. *Makeup* Wes Dawn. *Hairstyles* Maryce Bates. *Sp Eff* Thol O. Simonson. *Tech Adv* Irwin V. Frankel, Pat Hedruck. *Dial Coach* Geoffrey Horne. *Still Photog* Floyd McCarty. *Gaffer* Pat Blyner.

Cast: Barbara Hershey (*Tish Gray*), Collin Wilcox-Horne (*Suzanne Wilcox*), Sam Groom (*Jay Wilcox*), Scott Glenn (*Tad Jacks*), Jeannie Berlin (*Charlotte*), Lili Valenty (*Mrs. Culnick*), Helena Kallianiotes (*Wanda*), Jeff Siggins (*Dexter*), Phyllis Coates (*Tish's mother*), Madge Kennedy (*Tish's grandmother*), Ray Hemphill (*toystore killer*), Paul Linke (*Sam*), Brenda Sykes (*Frances*), Geoffrey Horne (*Jimmy*), Charles Wagenheim (*toystore owner*), Bob Ennis (*Exotica*), Mimi Doyle (*woman clerk*), Patty Dietz (*nurse*), Pat Hedruck (*childbirth instructress*), Robert Pickett (*Dr. Sims*), Jonathan Green, Michael Scroggins, Samuel Francis, Allen Keesling, Charles Lippincott, Peter Mays, Jeffrey Perkins (*The Single Wing Turquoise Bird Light Show*).

Melodrama. Tish Gray, a California hippie, is introduced to Suzanne and Jay Wilcox, a wealthy Beverly Hills couple who are unable to have a child. They offer Tish a considerable sum of money if she will conceive and bear a child by Jay. Tish, who enjoys being pregnant, agrees to the scheme, and she and Jay go to his cabin in the mountains; shortly after returning to Los Angeles, Tish learns that she is pregnant. Suzanne, who is eager to have the child, makes Tish promise to give up her hippie way of life and the use of drugs. Tension begins to mount between Tish and her boyfriend, Tad Jacks, and after an argument she leaves him and moves into the Wilcox home. Although the household seems peaceful, Jay's feelings for Tish grow stronger while Tish becomes resentful of Tad's infidelity and has doubts about giving up the child to a middle-class family. Furthermore, she is berated by her friend Charlotte for accepting such a lifestyle, but their friendship resumes when Tish agrees to go to a demonstration against war toys. When Tish bears the long-awaited child, the Wilcoxes pay for the balance of the money, take the child, and bid her farewell. *Hippies. Middle classes. Marriage. Childlessness. Infidelity. Pregnancy. Demonstrations. Childbirth. Los Angeles. Beverly Hills.*

Note: Location scenes filmed in Los Angeles.

BABY THE RAIN MUST FALL   F6.0244

Park Place Productions-Solar Productions. *Dist* Columbia Pictures. 13 Jan **1965** [New York opening; c31 Dec 1964; LP29944]. Sd (RCA); b&w. 35mm. 100 min. [Also 93 min.]

An Alan J. Pakula-Robert Mulligan Production. *Prod* Alan J. Pakula. *Dir* Robert Mulligan. *Screenplay* Horton Foote. *Dir Photog* Ernest Laszlo. *Art Dir* Roland Anderson. *Set Decor* Frank Tuttle. *Titl Dsgn* Vance Johnson. *Film Ed* Aaron Stell. *Mus* Elmer Bernstein. *Songs:* "Gospel Time," "Henry's Heap," "Pecan Grove Rock," "Travelin' Lady," "Wagon Wheel Watusi" Elmer Bernstein. *Songs:* "Baby the Rain Must Fall," "Shine for Me," "Treat Me Right" Elmer Bernstein, Ernie Sheldon. *Sd Supv* Charles J. Rice. *Sd* Lambert Day. *Asst Dir* Joseph E. Kenny. *Asst to the Prod* Isabel M. Halliburton. *Script Supv* Meta Rebner. *Makeup Supv* Ben Lane. *Tech Adv* Billy Strange.

Cast: Lee Remick (*Georgette Thomas*), Steve McQueen (*Henry Thomas*), Don Murray (*Slim*), Paul Fix (*Judge Ewing*), Josephine Hutchinson (*Mrs. Ewing*), Ruth White (*Miss Clara*), Charles Watts (*Mr. Tillman*), Georgia Simmons (*Miss Kate*), Carol Veazie (*Mrs. Tillman*), Estelle Hemsley (*Catherine*), Kimberly Block (*Margaret Rose*), Zamah Cunningham (*Mrs. T. V. Smith*), George Dunn (*counterman*).

Drama. Source: Horton Foote, *The Traveling Lady* (New York opening: 27 Oct 1954). Georgette Thomas and her daughter, Margaret Rose, travel by bus to a small Texas town to meet her husband, Henry, when he is released from prison after serving time for stabbing a man during a drunken brawl. Slim, the local sheriff and boyhood friend of Henry, takes Georgette to her husband, a guitar-playing singer still dominated by Miss Kate Dawson, the aging spinster who reared him following the death of his parents. Henry tries to make a home for his wife and daughter, but Miss Kate forbids his singing in local nightclubs, threatening to have him returned to prison if he does not obey her. When Miss

Kate finally dies, with a curse for him on her lips, the frustrated Henry drunkenly destroys her possessions and desecrates her grave. Henry is returned to prison, and Georgette and Margaret Rose leave town with Slim. *Ex-convicts. Orphans. Spinsters. Sheriffs. Singers. Criminals—Rehabilitation. Family life. Drunkenness. Nightclubs. Texas.*

Note: Filmed in and around Wharton and Columbus, Texas. Working title: *Traveling Lady.*

BABY VICKIE   F6.0245

Clover Films. 13 Aug **1969** [Boston opening]. Sd; b&w. 35mm. 72-75 min.

A William Dancer Production. *Dir-Writ* Harold Perkins. *Orig Story* Price Brown. *Camera* John Lyons. *Ed* Harold Perkins.

Cast: Sharon Matt *(Baby Vickie)*, Sebastian Gregory *(Tony)*, Bonnie Clark *(Lorne)*, Bill Moore *(Steve)*, Barbara Kline *(The Stripper)*, Dana Raven *(Vickie's mother)*, Will Gary *(father)*, Dona Lamana.

Melodrama. Sexually repressed, young Vickie enacts fantasies with the dummies in her father's tailor shop. Rejecting Steve, a young man who has her parents' approval, Vickie runs away from his sexual advances to the city's waterfront, and there she is beaten and raped. Vickie's parents try to cover up their daughter's disgrace by arranging her marriage with Steve. Vickie's mind has been warped by her waterfront experience, however, and a year later when she and Steve are married, Vickie fails to adapt to the new life as a young bride. She returns to the waterfront and to the man who raped her. *Filial relations. Seduction. Rape. Moral corruption. Marriage—Arranged.*

THE BABYSITTER   F6.0246

Dundee Productions. *Dist* Crown International Pictures. 21 May **1969** [San Francisco opening]. Sd; b&w. 35mm. 76 min. *MPAA rating* R.

Prod George E. Carey. *Dir* Don Henderson. *Screenplay* James E. McLarty. *Orig Story* George E. Carey, Don Henderson. *Dir Photog* Stanton R. Fox. *Titl Dsgn* Steve Smith. *Ed* Don Henderson. *Mus Comp & Cond* Robert O. Ragland. *Lyr* Sid Wayne. *Mus Perf by* The Food. *Sd* Ken Carlson. *Asst Sd* Charles Henderson, sd. *Asst Dir* Lord Douglas. *Script Supv* Blair Brooks. *Prod Asst* Carolyn Link. *Makeup* Munkrast. *Still Photog* George McDonald. *Lighting Gaffer* Paul Wilmoth.

Cast: Patricia Wymer *(Candy Wilson)*, George E. Carey *(George Maxwell)*, Ann Bellamy *(Edith Maxwell)*, Kathy Williams *(Julie Freeman)*, Robert Tessier *(Laurence Mackey)*, Ken Hooker *(Raymond Willas)*, Ted C. Frank *(Kyle Mackey)*, James E. McLarty *(Inkie)*, Sheri Jackson *(Joan Maxwell)*, Ruth Noonan *(Doris Winkler)*, Warren Rose *(Ben Fredericks)*, Doris Rose *(Aggie Fredericks)*, Charles Messenger *(Frank Harrington)*, Mary Messenger *(Lena Harrington)*, Paul Wilmoth *(Richard)*, Devon Blaine *(first dancer)*, Kari Longacre *(second dancer)*.

Melodrama. Tired of the bridge games that consume his married life, middle-aged Assistant District Attorney George Maxwell finds himself responding to the advances of his teenaged babysitter, Candy. Maxwell has been assigned to prosecute motorcycle gang leader Laurence Mackey for the brutal slaying of Doris Winkler. Mackey's girl friend, Julie, decides to blackmail the prosecutor into dropping the case by gathering evidence of his daughter Joan's lesbian activities, but Julie stumbles upon Maxwell's blossoming romance instead and photographs him with the babysitter. Confronted by the incriminating evidence, Maxwell realizes that both his marriage and his career are at stake and calls Candy to end the affair. She convinces two friends to visit Julie; they force her to divulge the hiding place of the negatives and then plant marijuana where it will be easily discovered when Candy phones the police. The next day, the newspapers are filled with news of Mackey's conviction and with praise for the prosecutor. Maxwell's letter of resignation arrives as the district attorney examines the photographs sent by special delivery, but all goes well. Maxwell's resignation is refused, and his wife, who has also received copies of the photos, concedes that perhaps they have indeed been spending too much time playing bridge. *District attorneys. Babysitters. Hoodlums. Murder. Blackmail. Marriage. Infidelity. Middle age. Lesbianism. Frameup. Marijuana. Bridge.*

Note: Filmed on location in the Los Angeles suburbs.

LE BACCANTI *see* THE BACCHANTES

BACCHANALE   F6.0247

Amero Brothers–Scardera Enterprises. *Dist* Distribpix, Inc. Jun **1970**. Sd; Monochromatic seq & col. 35mm. 78 min. *MPAA rating* X.

An Amero Brothers Production. *Prod-Dir-Script* John Amero, Lem Amero. *Camera* John Amero. *Art Dir* Alexandra D'Largo. *Film Ed* Lem Amero. *Dubbing* Cara Duff, Michael Heller. *Mus Ed* Firth DeMule. *Cost* John Brock Benson. *Col Eff* Paul Guffanti.

Cast: Uta Erickson *(Ruth)*, Darcy Brown *(fashion m.c.)*, Chuck Federico *(guitarist)*, Richard Sherman *(guard)*, Roni Scardera *(lead model)*, Pat Agers *(Louise)*, Ron Babin *(man in coffin)*, Stanley Camel *(lover)*, Steve Gould *(mourner)*, LaRue Watts *(harpie)*, Bob Niles *(slave)*, Linda Joyce *(countess)*, Lydia Burns *(fag hag)*, Donny Lee *(Go-Go)*.

Sex film. Sexually frustrated, Ruth dreams of her sex fantasies: descending an endless fire escape while simultaneously attending a bizarre fashion show/funeral in which she is alternately a model and a corpse. In the graveyard, Ruth has sex with a shrouded spirit while mist rises around them. She is haunted by incestuous thoughts of her brother, a soldier killed in Vietnam. In her dreams she fondles a handsome male corpse. In a climactic cave scene Ruth becomes involved in a ritual with a high priestess and her four slaves. The sequence, which apparently includes incidents of lesbianism, whipping, male homosexuality, masturbation, and heterosexual acts, is interrupted by the appearance of the ghost of Ruth's brother. *Models. Soldiers. Necrophilia. Voyeurism. Incest. Brother-sister relationship. Male homosexuality. Autoeroticism. Lesbianism. Flagellation. Corpses. Rites and ceremonies. Fantasy. Funerals. Fashion shows. Dreams.*

THE BACCHANTES (France/Italy)   F6.0248

Vic Films–Société Cinématographique Lyre. *Dist* Medallion Pictures. **1963**. Sd; col (Eastman Color). 35mm (Techniscope). 100 min.

Dir Giorgio Ferroni. *Screenplay* Giorgio Stegani, Giorgio Ferroni. *Photog* Pierludovico Pavoni. *Mus* Mario Nascimbene.

Cast: Taina Elg *(Dirce)*, Pierre Brice *(Dionysus)*, Alberto Lupo *(Pentheus)*, Alessandra Panaro *(Manto)*, Akim Tamiroff, Raf Mattioli, Erno Crisa, Gérard Landry.

Costume drama. Inspired by: Euripides, *Bacchae*. The people of Thebes are suffering from a severe drought. King Pentheus is told by his mother, Agave, that the people have turned against him because he does not recognize the deity of Dionysus, the god of fertility. The king decides to sacrifice Manto, the niece of a seer, to Demeter, the goddess of earth, but Dirce, the king's betrothed, wants to spare the young woman. She goes to a grotto where the Bacchantae (followers of Dionysus) have gathered and there meets a stranger who leaves for Thebes when Dirce tells him of the pending sacrifice. Lacdamo, the king's cousin, rescues Manto, but the stranger, revealed to be Dionysus, is captured. Dirce visits him in prison, and when he tells her his true identity, the two escape to Mount Cithaeron. During the Thebans' revolt, King Pentheus is killed, and Lacdamo assumes power. Dirce, realizing the futility of her love for a god, remains with the Bacchantae. *Mythological characters. Royalty. Cousins. Drought. Human sacrifice. Revolts. Assassination. Thebes. Cithaeron. Dionysus. Pentheus. Demeter. Agave. Bacchus.*

Note: Opened in Rome in Aug 1961 as *Le baccanti.*

BACHELOR FLAT   F6.0249

Jack Cummings Productions. *Dist* Twentieth Century-Fox Film Corp. 12 Jan **1962** [New York opening; c22 Dec 1961; LP21156]. Sd (Westrex); col (De Luxe). 35mm (CinemaScope). 91 min.

Prod Jack Cummings. *Dir* Frank Tashlin. *Screenplay* Frank Tashlin, Budd Grossman. *Dir Photog* Daniel L. Fapp. *Art Dir* Jack Martin Smith, Leland Fuller. *Set Decor* Walter M. Scott, Paul S. Fox. *Film Ed* Hugh S. Fowler. *Mus* Johnny Williams. *Orch* Robert Franklyn. *Sd* E. Clayton Ward, Warren B. Delaplain. *Asst Dir* Ad Schaumer. *Unit Mgr* Charles Levin. *Script Supv* Doris Drought. *Cost Dsgn* Don Feld. *Makeup* Ben Nye. *Hairstyles* Helen Turpin. *Sp Photog Eff* L. B. Abbott. *Dial Coach* Carl Shain.

Cast: Tuesday Weld *(Libby Bushmill)*, Richard Beymer *(Mike Polaski)*, Terry-Thomas *(Professor Bruce Patterson)*, Celeste Holm *(Helen Bushmill)*, Francesca Bellini *(Gladys)*, Howard McNear *(Dr. Bowman)*, Ann Del Guercio *(Liz)*, Roxanne Arlen *(Mrs. Roberts)*, Alice Reinheart *(Mrs. Bowman)*, Stephen Bekassy *(Paul)*, Margo Moore *(Moll)*, George Bruggeman *(Paul Revere)*, Jessica *(a dachshund)*.

Comedy. Source: Budd Grossman, *Libby* (a play; production undetermined). Bruce Patterson, a mild-mannered professor of archeology who is relentlessly pursued by his amorous female students, leases the apartment of his fiancée, Helen Bushmill, while she is on a trip to Paris. The age-conscious Helen has never told Bruce that she was previously married, or that she has a 17-year-old daughter, Libby. Consequently, when Libby appears at her mother's house, Bruce mistakes her for one of his passionate students and sends her away. Libby pretends to be an unhappy delinquent, however, and the professor allows her to stay. Though Libby's attentions are soon drawn to Bruce's neighbor, law student Mike Polaski, the helpless professor continues to be menaced by love-sick teenagers. Mike finally convinces him that the only way to stop the girls is to do the chasing himself. Bruce takes the advice, gets roaring drunk, and, minus his trousers, chases all the girls on a nearby beach. His escapade is witnessed by the horrified Helen, who has just returned from Paris. At first she breaks off their engagement, but Libby and Mike easily persuade her to change her mind. *Professors. Students. Adolescence. Drunkenness. Beaches.*

BACHELOR GIRL   F6.0250

1968. Sd; b&w? 35mm? [Feature film, length unknown.]

Sex film. No information about the precise nature of this film has been found. *Sexuality.*

BACHELOR IN PARADISE   F6.0251

Ted Richmond Productions. *Dist* Metro-Goldwyn-Mayer, Inc. 1 Nov **1961** [Philadelphia opening; c23 Oct 1961; LP20447]. Sd (Westrex); col (Metrocolor). 35mm (CinemaScope). 109 min.

Prod Ted Richmond. *Dir* Jack Arnold. *Screenplay* Valentine Davies, Hal Kanter. *Story* Vera Caspary. *Dir Photog* Joseph Ruttenberg. *Col Cons* Charles K. Hagedon. *Art Dir* George W. Davis, Hans Peters. *Set Decor* Henry Grace, Keogh Gleason. *Main Titl* Animation Inc. *Film Ed* Richard Farrell. *Mus Score* Henry Mancini. *Titl Song* Henry Mancini, Mack David. *Rec Supv* Franklin Milton. *Asst Dir* Eric Von Stroheim, Jr. *Cost Dsgn* Helen Rose. *Makeup* William Tuttle. *Miss Turner's Hairstyles* Helen Young. *Hairstyles* Mary Keats.

Cast: Bob Hope (*Adam J. Niles*), Lana Turner (*Rosemary Howard*), Janis Paige (*Dolores Jynson*), Jim Hutton (*Larry Delavane*), Paula Prentiss (*Linda Delavane*), Don Porter (*Thomas W. Jynson*), Virginia Grey (*Camille Quinlaw*), Agnes Moorehead (*Judge Peterson*), Florence Sundstrom (*Mrs. Pickering*), John McGiver (*Austin Palfrey*), Clinton Sundberg (*Rodney Jones*), Alan Hewitt (*Backett*), Reta Shaw (*Mrs. Brown*), Mary Treen (*housewife*), Tracy Stratford ("*Mrs. McGonigle*").

Comedy. Adam J. Niles, a writer noted for his series of racy books on the sexual mores of foreign peoples, finds himself in debt to the Internal Revenue Service because of a dishonest personal manager. Forbidden to leave the States, he changes his name, moves into Paradise Village, a California housing development, and secretly begins compiling material for a book on how Americans live. The only bachelor in the community, he quickly becomes the center of attention among the bored housewives. Though his activities are watched with suspicion by Rosemary Howard, the community's secretary, Adam organizes a discussion group in which he advises the women on how to bring romance back into their lives. When the jealous husbands try to have him evicted, Rosemary, who has finally been won over, quits her job and becomes Adam's secretary. Eventually Adam's tax problems are solved, but in the process his true identity is revealed, and he is involved in three Paradise Village divorce suits. Aided by Rosemary's testimony and the enthusiastic support of three wives, Adam persuades the presiding female judge of his innocence. The three wives return to their husbands, and Adam declares his love for Rosemary. *Authors. Sex researchers. Bachelors. Housewives. Secretaries. Judges. Income tax. Personal identity. Suburban life. Marriage. Jealousy. Divorce. Trials. California. United States—Internal Revenue Service.*

BACHELOR OF HEARTS (Great Britain)   F6.0252

Independent Artists. *For* Rank Organisation. *Dist* Coatinental Distributing, Inc. May **1962**. Sd; col (Eastman color). 35mm. 97 min.

A Julian Wintle–Leslie Parkyn Production. *Prod* Vivian A. Cox. *Dir* Wolf Rilla. *Screenplay* Leslie Bricusse, Frederic Raphael. *Dir Photog* Geoffrey Unsworth. *Art Dir* Edward Carrick. *Film Ed* Eric Boyd-Perkins. *Mus* Hubert Clifford. *Sd* Frank Goulding.

Cast: Hardy Krüger (*Wolf Hauser*), Sylvia Syms (*Ann Wainwright*), Ronald Lewis (*Hugo Foster*), Jeremy Burnham (*Adrian Baskerville*), Peter Myers, actor (*Jeremy*), Philip Gilbert (*Conrad Lewis*), Charles Kay (*Tom Clark*), John Richardson (*Robin*), Gillian Vaughan (*Virginia*), Sandra Francis (*Lois*), Miles Malleson (*Dr. Butson*), Eric Barker (*Audrey Murdock*), Newton Blick (*Morgan*), Barbara Steele (*Fiona*).

Comedy. At Cambridge, German exchange student Wolf Hauser is victimized by the exclusive Dodo Club, whose six members set him afire and toss him into the Cam River. Thus initiated into college life, Hauser is befriended by Dodo leader Hugo Foster and Girton College coed Ann Wainwright. Although Hauser is anxious to study, his friends the Dodos involve him in their term objective of bathing in the female lavatory at Girton. During a police raid Foster saves Hauser from arrest. In the third term, the Dodos shun female society until midnight of the annual May Ball, commanding the German to entertain Ann's girl friends. Despite such obligations, Wolf passes his exams and wins Ann's affection. *Students. Germans. Exchange students. Police. College life. Hazing. Friendship. Practical jokes. Secret societies. Cam River. Cambridge University.*

Note: Location scenes filmed in Cambridge, England. Opened in London in Dec 1958. Working titles: *Light Blue, Cambridge Blue,* and *The Freshman.*

BACHELOR TOM AND HIS BIKINI PLAYMATES see BACHELOR TOM PEEPING

BACHELOR TOM PEEPING   F6.0253

Corsican Productions. *Dist* Paul Mart Productions. 2 Feb **1962** [Los Angeles showing]. Sd; col (Eastmancolor). 35mm. 61 min.

A Film by Joe Castagnoli, William Dewar, Jerry Jackson. *Mus Score Comp & Cond* Alex Sandford.

Cast: Brad Dorian, Pat Casse, Sandra Lind.

Comedy. *Reporter Tom Peeping drives past a secluded "sun club" on the way to cover a story for a magazine. He decides to visit but is refused entrance to the women's retreat. He purchases some feminine apparel in a nearby town and returns to the club to mingle with the naked women. Tom takes a swim, his bathing suit soon falls off, and he is tossed out. Undaunted, Tom buys more clothes and returns as an elderly matron. Again, his disguise allows him to enter the club, and he proceeds to take pictures for his magazine. Tom awakes in a sanitarium, finds himself straitjacketed and delirious, and realizes that his adventures were all imaginary. Reporters. Nudism. Female impersonation. Magazines (periodicals). Nudist camps. Sanitariums. Photographs. Dreams.*

Note: Also marketed in an expurgated version known as *Bachelor Tom and His Bikini Playmates* and possibly as *Bikini Playmates.* The unexpurgated version may also be known as *Bachelor Tom Peeking.*

BACHELOR'S DREAM   F6.0254

A. F. P. I. Productions. *Dist* SCA Distributors, Sack Amusement Enterprises. 10 May **1967** [New York showing]. Sd; col. 35mm (Astravision). [Feature length assumed.]

Prod-Dir A. C. Stephen. *Assoc Prod* Don Nagel. *Screenplay* Jason Underwood. *Dir Photog* Robert Wilson. *Art Dir* Bud Costello. *Post Prod* Herr Freed. *Mus Score* Igor Gigagusky.

Sex film. Each day as he returns from the office, shy, meek Abner Biddle retires to the solitary paradise of his "girlie" books, bringing the models to life with his lively imagination. He watches Anita dance sensuously and feasts his eyes on Angie as she plays with her collection of stuffed animals. He watches the models undress and receives their kisses; finally, he invites a beautiful, seductive blonde out on a date. *Office clerks. Bachelors. Models. Dancers. Timidity. Nudity. Voyeurism. Fantasy. Pornography.*

←→ (BACK AND FORTH)   F6.0255

Dist Film-Makers' Cooperative. 21 May **1969** [New York opening]. Sd; col. 16mm. 52 min.

Prod-Dir Michael Snow. *Photog* Michael Snow. *Film Ed* Michael Snow. *Sd* Michael Snow.

Experimental film. Events occur inside and outside a drab, prefabricated school building. The camera pans continuously back and forth, its speed varying in relation to each event. The outside of the building is shown; a janitor crosses from right to left. The camera then moves inside the building; each view is separated from the other by a panning movement. A young woman reads a book near the window; a student responds to her teacher's questions by either nodding or shaking her head; a man and a woman throw a ball to each other; a janitor sweeps the floor; two men at a party fight playfully; a man washes the classroom window; and a policeman peers inside. Midway through the film, the camera increases the tempo of its panning across the empty classroom to a blurry pace, whereupon its motion becomes an up and down movement, which gradually slows to a halt; and the credits appear. The film concludes with the previous images in multiple superimposition.

Note: Also reviewed as *The Double-Headed Arrow.*

BACK DOOR TO HELL (United States/Philippines)   F6.0256

Lippert, Inc.–Medallion Films. *Dist* Twentieth Century-Fox Film Corp. Nov **1964** [c4 Nov 1964; LP29823]. Sd; b&w. 35mm. 68 min. [Copyright length: 70 min.]

Prod Fred Roos. *Assoc Prod* Ronald Remy. *Dir* Monte Hellman. *Screenplay* Richard A. Guttman, John Hackett. *Story* Richard A. Guttman. *Dir Photog* Mars Rasca. *Camera Op* Ricardo Remias. *Film Ed* Fely Crisotomo. *Mus* Mike Velarde. *Sd* Juanito Clemente. *Prod Mgr* Nilo Saez. *Prod Asst* Walter Phelps. *Makeup* Nita Sol Cruz. *Coöp* Philippine Department of National Defense, Armed Forces of the Philippines.

Cast: Jimmie Rodgers (*Lieutenant Craig*), Jack Nicholson (*Burnett*), John Hackett (*Jersey*), Annabelle Huggins (*Maria*), Conrad Maga (*Paco*), Johnny Monteiro (*Ramundo*), Joe Sison (*Japanese captain*), Henry Duval (*Garde*), Ben Perez, Vic Uematsu.

War drama. In World War II, before the Allied reoccupation of the Philippines, U. S. Lieutenant Craig and two other men, Burnett and Jersey, penetrate the enemy occupation to determine the strength and position of the Japanese forces. They contact Paco, a guerrilla leader, who agrees to help them, but the Japanese detect their presence and threaten to destroy a village unless the Americans surrender. Paco and his men, however, are able to capture the village. Craig then meets a local bandit who promises him information about the Japanese in exchange for his radio, but when Craig is delayed while checking the information, the impatient bandit destroys the radio and runs off. Unable to transmit his intelligence, Craig sneaks into a Japanese-held village and sends his message by enemy radio, but he and his men are apprehended. The Americans, with Paco and his guerrillas, battle with the Japanese; and Burnett, Paco, and all his men are killed. Only Craig and Jersey escape. *Guerrillas. Bandits. Informers. Military occupation. Espionage. Radio. World War II. United States Army—Intelligence. Japan—Army.*

Note: Filmed on location in the Bicol region, Philippines.

BACK SEAT CABBIE   F6.0257
Triumph Films. *Dist* Distribpix, Inc. **1969**. Sd; col. 35mm. 63 min.
Prod Bob Mansy. *Dir* C. Walsh. *Mus* The Wild Stones.
Cast: Janet Topaz, Margaret Leigh.
Sex film. On her first day as a cab driver, Gloria is seduced by one of her passengers. She enjoys the experience and decides to become a prostitute; she uses her cab as a mobile brothel and turns tricks with men, women, and mixed couples. *Taxi drivers. Prostitutes. Lesbianism. Seduction. Sexual practices. Taxicabs.*

BACK STREET   F6.0258
Ross Hunter Productions–Carrollton, Inc. *Dist* Universal-International. 11 Oct **1961** [Chicago opening; c20 Aug 1961; LP24728]. Sd; col (Eastman Color by Pathé). 35mm. 107 min.
Prod Ross Hunter. *Dir* David Miller. *Screenplay* Eleanore Griffin, William Ludwig. *Dir Photog* Stanley Cortez. *Art Dir* Alexander Golitzen. *Set Decor* Howard Bristol. *Film Ed* Milton Carruth. *Mus Supv* Joseph Gershenson. *Mus* Frank Skinner. *Titl Song* Frank Skinner, Ken Darby. *Sd* Waldon O. Watson, Frank H. Wilkinson. *Asst Dir* Phil Bowles, James Welch. *Unit Prod Mgr* Lew Leary. *Gowns Dsgn* Jean Louis. *Makeup* Bud Westmore. *Hairstyles* Larry Germain. *Orig Oil Paintings* Alison Hunter. *Dial Dir* Leon Charles.
Cast: Susan Hayward (*Rae Smith*), John Gavin (*Paul Saxon*), Vera Miles (*Liz Saxon*), Charles Drake (*Curt Stanton*), Virginia Grey (*Janie*), Reginald Gardiner (*Dalian*), Tammy Marihugh (*Caroline Saxon*), Robert Eyer (*Paul Saxon, Jr.*), Natalie Schafer (*Mrs. Evans*), Doreen McLean (*Miss Hatfield*), Alex Gerry (*Mr. Venner*), Karen Norris (*Mrs. Panworth*), Hayden Rorke (*Charley Claypole*), Mary Lawrence (*Marge Claypole*), Joe Cronin (*airport clerk*), Ted Thorpe (*hotel clerk*), Joseph Mell (*proprietor*), Dick Kallman (*sailor*), Joyce Meadows (*showroom model*), Lilyan Chauvin (*Paris airport employee*), Joanne Betay, Vivianne Porte, Isabelle Felder, Melissa Weston, Bea Ammidown (*"Harper's Bazaar" models*).
Romantic melodrama. Source: Fannie Hurst, *Back Street* (New York, 1931). Following his discharge from the Marines after World War II, Paul Saxon, heir to a chain of department stores, has an affair with Rae Smith, the owner of a dress shop in Lincoln, Nebraska. However, when Rae learns that Paul is married and has two children, she moves to New York and becomes a successful fashion designer. Paul finds her there, but Rae refuses to become the "other woman" in his life. Years later they meet again in Rome, where Rae, now the partner of the celebrated designer Dalian, has opened a salon. During the 3 days they spend together at Rae's seaside villa, Paul explains to Rae that his alcoholic wife, Liz, refuses to grant him a divorce. After a suicide attempt by Liz, Paul buys Rae a house in the Paris suburbs, and the two lovers continue to meet. Eventually Paul's young son identifies Rae as the mysterious woman in his father's life and orders her to stay away. Then Liz publicly shames Rae during one of her fashion shows. That same night, while driving with Paul, the drunken Liz loses control of the car and is killed in a crash. Paul is taken to a hospital and calls Rae to profess his love before he dies. Later, Rae is visited by Paul's two orphaned children, who now share with her a common bond of loneliness and grief. *Veterans. Heirs. Mistresses. Couturiers. Children. Orphans. Infidelity. Alcoholism. Divorce. Suicide. Filial relations. Fashion shows. Lincoln (Nebraska). New York City. Rome. Paris. London. Automobile accidents.*
Note: Previously filmed in 1932 and 1941.

BACKFIRE (France/Italy/Spain)   F6.0259
Sud Pacifique Films–Capitole Films–Producciones Benito Perojo–Transmonde Film. *Dist* Royal Films International. 26 Apr **1965** [New York opening]. Sd; b&w. 35mm (Franscope). 97 min.
Exec Prod Paul-Edmond Decharme. *Dir* Jean Becker. *Dial* Daniel Boulanger. *Adapt (see note)* Daniel Boulanger, Claude Sautet, Maurice Fabre, Didier Goulard, Jean Becker. *Photog* Edmond Séchan, Jean-Paul Schwartz. *Art Dir* Georges Wakhévitch. *Film Ed* Monique Kirsanoff. *Mus* Martial Solal. *Mus (Spanish vers?)* Gregorio García Segura. *Asst Dir* Constantin Gavras.
Cast: Jean-Paul Belmondo (*David Ladislas*), Jean Seberg (*Olga Célan*), Gert Fröbe (*Fehrman*), Enrico Maria Salerno (*Mario*), Renate Ewert (*The Countess*), Jean-Pierre Marielle (*Hode*), Wolfgang Preiss (*Grenner*), Fernando Rey, Diana Lorys, Michel Beaune, Roberto Camardiel, Xan Das Bolas, Petar Martinovitch, Margarita Gil, Carmen de Lirio, Fernando Sancho, José Jaspe, Rafael Luis Calvo, M. Furia, Jerzy Macc.
Crime comedy-drama. Based on a novel by: Clet Coroner. After successfully completing an assignment for a ring of international smugglers, Parisian David Ladislas receives orders to deliver a shipment of gold to Lebanon using a Triumph convertible for transport. Accompanying him is Olga, who apparently has more knowledge of the operation than David. He tries persistently to woo information from her but learns only that the gold is hidden somewhere in the car. Arriving in Beirut, David decides to doublecross the ruthless organization head, Fehrman, and steal the gold for himself despite Olga's objections. They pass customs safely, and, eluding police, travel first to Athens and then to Naples as David attempts to find a buyer for the contraband gold. Fehrman is alerted and traps David, who is forced to drive the car down a steep embankment; the frightened Olga has meanwhile returned to Germany. David tracks down Olga in Bremen, and they await the arrival of the Triumph, which has been loaded aboard a ship. As the vehicle is being unloaded the next day, it catches fire, and the gold, which was coated on in layers under the paint, begins to melt. David and Olga escape as the police retrieve the fortune in melted gold. *Germans. Police. Smuggling. Perfidy. Organized crime. Gold. Automobiles. Ships. Beirut. Athens. Naples. Bremen. Chases.*
Note: Paris opening: Sep 1964 as *Échappement libre*; running time: 105 min; Italian title: *Scappamento aperto*; Spanish title: *Escape libre*. The screenplay collaboration of Claude Sautet is unconfirmed.

BACKTRACK   F6.0260
MCA-TV. *Dist* Universal Pictures. 26 May **1969** [New York showing]. Sd; col. 35mm. 95 min. *MPAA rating G.*
Prod David J. O'Connell. *Dir* Earl Bellamy. *Screenplay* Borden Chase. *Photog* Richard H. Kline, John L. Russell, Andrew Jackson. *Art Dir* George Patrick, Howard E. Johnson. *Set Decor* John McCarthy, James M. Walters, Sr., Perry Murdock, Oliver Emert. *Film Ed* Michael R. McAdam. *Mus* Jack Marshall. *Sd* Waldon O. Watson, Frank H. Wilkinson, Earl Crain, Jr., Robert R. Bertrand. *Asst Dir* Henry Kline, Carter De Haven, III, James M. Walters, Jr. *Makeup* Bud Westmore. *Hairstyles* Larry Germain.
Cast: Neville Brand (*Reese*), James Drury (*Ramrod*), Doug McClure (*Trampas*), Peter Brown (*Chad*), William Smith (*Riley*), Philip Carey (*Captain Parmalee*), Ida Lupino (*Mama Delores*), Rhonda Fleming (*Carmelita Flanagan*), Fernando Lamas (*Captain Estrada*), Royal Dano (*Faraway*), Gary Clarke (*Steve*), Randy Boone (*Randy*), L. Q. Jones (*Belden*), Carol Byron (*Winnie*), Ross Elliott (*Sheriff Abbott*), Hal Baylor (*Flake*), George Savalas (*Turnkey*), Alberto Morin (*Alvarez*), Teresa Terry (*Estrallita*), Priscilla Garcia (*Gaviota*), Ruben Moreno (*The Yaqui Chief*).
Western comedy-drama. Forced to leave a Western town for gambling with loaded dice, a young maverick cowboy named Trampas makes his way to the Shiloh Ranch and asks the ramrod for a job. Happy to oblige, the ramrod sends Trampas on his first cattle drive and then assigns him to join three other cowhands in transporting a prize bull from a Mexican village back to the Shiloh Ranch. During a return stopover in Laredo, Trampas becomes enamored of Carmelita Flanagan, a saloon owner who is also being eyed by three Texas Rangers, Chad, Reese, and Riley. The rivalry over Carmelita leads to a series of brawls that ends only when Ranger boss Captain Parmalee sends his three men to hunt down a gang of bandits at the Mexican border. With Trampas tagging along, the Rangers happen upon a train that has been robbed. Discovering that an infant is the only survivor, the men stop for milk at a cantina owned by Mama Delores, a fiery widow who has long been trying to get Reese to marry her. During their stay Yaqui Indians attack the village, and a trainman's uniform is found on one of the dead Indians. Certain that the Yaquis robbed the train, the four men investigate Captain Estrada, an officer in the Mexican patrol who secretly has been supplying the Indians with guns. Discovering a new shipment of firearms, the Rangers and Trampas stuff the muzzles with lead before being captured by the Yaquis. They then persuade Captain Estrada to execute them by firing squad and watch with enormous satisfaction as the rifles explode in the faces of the firing squad. Afterwards, Estrada is stabbed by the Indians for selling them faulty guns, and the Rangers and Trampas escape. The adventure over, Trampas bids farewell to the Rangers, smiles goodby to Carmelita, and heads back to Shiloh with the prize bull. *Cowboys. Widows. Saloon keepers. Mexicans. Texas Rangers. Yaqui Indians. Gunrunners. Train robberies. Ranches. Firearms. Laredo. Mexican border.*
Note: Made from excerpts from "Laredo" and "The Virginian," including *We've Lost a Train*, an episode from "The Virginian" telecast on NBC 21 Apr 1965 (c18 Apr 1965; LP32266).

BAD COMPANY (France)   F6.0261
Anouchka Films. *Dist* New Yorker Films. 26 Jan **1969** [New York opening]. Sd; b&w. 35mm. 88 min.
Production Credits for "Robinson's Place": *Dir-Writ* Jean Eustache. *Photog* Philippe Théaudière. *Film Ed* Jean Eustache. *Mus* César Gattegno. *Asst Dir* Jeanne Delos.
Production Credits for "Santa Claus Has Blue Eyes": *Prod* Jean-Luc Godard. *Dir-Writ* Jean Eustache. *Photog* Philippe Théaudière. *Film Ed* Antoine Bonfanti. *Mus* René Coll, César Gattegno.
Cast—"Robinson's Place": Aristide (*1st young man*), Daniel Bart (*2d young man*), Dominique Jayr (*woman*).
Cast—"Santa Claus Has Blue Eyes": Jean-Pierre Léaud (*Daniel*), Gérard Zimmermann (*Dumas*), Henri Martinez (*Martinez*), René Gilson

(photographer), Michel Maynard.

Drama. ROBINSON'S PLACE: Two young Parisians spend a night on the town in Montparnasse, bar-hopping and staring at women. When they encounter a young mother recently separated from her husband, they take her to a couple of dancehalls, but failing to seduce her, they steal her wallet and jokingly dismiss the theft by rationalizing that it will pay for their drinks. They are too guilt-ridden to keep the wallet, however, and finally return it to her in the mail. SANTA CLAUS HAS BLUE EYES: Daniel belongs to a group of French teenagers who spend their time hanging around streets, stealing books, looking for money, and daydreaming about sexual adventures. One day a photographer gives Daniel a job in which he dresses up as Santa Claus and poses with people who pay to have their picture taken with him. Aided by the disguise, he is able to flirt with numerous women, earn enough money to buy a new coat, and pay for a visit to the local bordello. Although he convinces a young woman to date him, he loses her when she sees him without his disguise. *Pickups. Juvenile delinquents. Photographers. Youth. Separation (marital). Theft. Conscience. Adolescence. Disguise. Bars. Dancehalls. Whorehouses. Paris—Montparnasse. Santa Claus.*

Note: Opened in Paris in Jun 1967 as *Les mauvaises fréquentations*. "Robinson's Place" (40 min) was filmed in 1964 as "Du côté de Robinson"; "Santa Claus Has Blue Eyes" (48 min) in 1966 as "Le Père Noël a les yeux bleus."

BAD DIANE see CALL ME BAD

BAD GIRLS DO CRY   F6.0262
Dist Jacqueline Kay, Inc., Box Office Spectaculars. 6 Oct **1965** [Maryland license]. Sd; b&w. 35mm. 63 min.
Prod Howard Freeman. *Dir* Sid Melton.
Cast: Misty Ayers, Bill Page.
Melodrama. A young girl in a small town becomes entangled with a gang who involve her in prostitution. *Gangs. Prostitution. Smalltown life.*
Note: Filmed in Hollywood.

BAD GIRLS DON'T CRY see LA NOTTE BRAVA

BAD GIRLS FOR THE BOYS   F6.0263
Whitehall Pictures–Ahnevant Society of Georgia. *Dist* Sack Amusement Enterprises, Haven International Pictures. 11 May **1966** [Champaign, Illinois, showing]. Sd; col (Eastmancolor). 35mm. 70 min.
A Delta International Pictures Production. *Prod* Robert M. Moscow. *Assoc Prod* Richard Ramsaur. *Dir-Writ* William McGaha. *Based on an Idea by* Paul Jones, writ. *Photog* Julio Roldan. *Film Ed* Paul Jasiukonis. *Orig Mus* Bill Hames, Robert Tarwater. *Mus Dir* Byron Adams. *Sd* Spectra Sound. *Cultural Cons* J. Lee Friedman.
Cast: Bob Johnson, Al Camillo, William McGaha, George Ahnevant, Samantha Scott, Diana Stanley, Mockie Friedman, Robert M. Moscow, Bonnie St. Clair *(unidentified roles)*, Charles Booker *(special guest)*, Mike Dix *(narrator)*, Paul Hargett and The Bikini Sweethearts.
Comedy. No information about the precise nature of this film has been found, but press material suggests that it includes scenes of nudity, voyeurism, mate swapping, group sex, and prostitution. *Voyeurism. Mate swapping. Group sex. Nudity. Prostitution.*

BAD GIRLS GO TO HELL   F6.0264
Doris Wishman. *Dist* Juri Productions, Sam Lake Enterprises. 24 Dec **1965** [Fresno, California, showing]. Sd; b&w. 35mm. 71 min.
A Doris Wishman Production.
Melodrama. Meg Kelton, an attractive young newlywed, is attacked by the janitor in her apartment building. Attempting to drive him away, she inadvertently kills him and, panic stricken, flees to New York City. There Meg becomes involved with a man who is kind when he is sober, but brutal when he gets drunk. She leaves him, and moves in with Della. Her newfound friend makes lesbian advances, and Meg flees again. She rents a room in the home of a married couple, but the husband molests her as she lies sleeping, and once again she is forced to leave. In desperation, Meg takes a job as a companion to a semi-invalid woman. One day, she learns that her employer's son is a detective at work on a murder case. He recognizes Meg from a police photo and accuses her of the murder. She begins to scream, until at last her husband awakens her from her terrible nightmare. When he leaves, Meg goes to the incinerator. She is attacked by the janitor, and screams with the realization that her dream is coming true. *Newlyweds. Janitors. Detectives. Invalids. Rape. Drunkenness. Lesbianism. Murder. Infidelity. New York City. Dreams.*

THE BAD SLEEP WELL (Japan)   F6.0265
Toho Co.–Kurosawa Films. *Dist* Toho International, Inc. 22 Jan **1963** [New York opening]. Sd; b&w. 35mm (Tohoscope). 135 min.
Prod Tomoyuki Tanaka, Akira Kurosawa. *Dir* Akira Kurosawa. *Screenplay* Hideo Oguni, Eijiro Hisaita, Akira Kurosawa, Ryuzo Kikushima, Shinobu Hashimoto. *Photog* Yuzuru Aizawa. *Lighting* Ichiro Inohara. *Art Dir* Yoshiro Muraki. *Mus* Masaru Sato. *Sd Rec* Fumio Yanoguchi, Hisashi Shimonaga.
Cast: Toshiro Mifune *(Koichi Nishi)*, Takeshi Kato *(Itakura)*, Masayuki Mori *(Iwabuchi)*, Takashi Shimura *(Moriyama)*, Akira Nishimura *(Shirai)*, Kamatari Fujiwara *(Wada)*, Kyoko Kagawa *(Keiko)*, Tatsuya Mihashi *(Tatsuo)*, Gen Shimizu *(Miura)*, Kyu Sazanka *(Kaneko)*, Chishu Ryu *(Nonaka)*, Seiji Miyaguchi *(Okakura)*, Nobuo Nakamura *(lawyer)*, Susumu Fujita *(commissioner)*, Koji Mitsui *(journalist)*.
Crime drama. An elaborate wedding reception for Keiko, the daughter of President Iwabuchi of the Unutilized Land Development Corporation, and Koichi Nishi, the president's secretary, is interrupted when corporate executive Wada is arrested on charges of embezzlement. The incident reminds the press of an earlier scandal involving Iwabuchi, administrative officer Moriyama, and contract officer Shirai; the case was hushed up after the apparent suicide of Assistant Chief Furuya. Following the wedding, the police question Wada and accountant Miura about bribery of corporation officials by a construction company. As a result of the inquiry, Miura commits suicide, and Wada attempts to take his own life but is stopped by Nishi, who is revealed to be the son of Furuya. Determined to avenge his father's death, Nishi uses Wada to force Shirai to confess to the murder of Furuya. Nishi then abducts Moriyama and learns the hiding place of the stolen money and records. Nishi's ultimate aim is to destroy President Iwabuchi, but his growing love for Keiko, whom he married initially to further his revenge, causes him to hesitate. Upon learning Nishi's true identity, Iwabuchi arranges for Wada and Nishi to be killed in an automobile crash. *Executives. Businessmen. Embezzlement. Scandal. Bribery. Suicide. Revenge. Abduction. Murder. Personal identity. Fatherhood. Weddings. Automobile accidents.*
Note: Released in Japan in Sep 1960 as *Warui yatsu hodo yoku nemuru*; running time: 151 min.

BADJAO (Philippines)   F6.0266
L. V. N. Pictures of Manila. *Dist* Parallel Film Distributors. 20 Sep **1962** [New York opening]. Sd; b&w. 35mm. 100 min.
Prod Manuel de León. *Exec Prod* Narcisa de León. *Dir* Lamberto V. Avellana. *Screenplay-Story* Rolf Bayer. *Photog* Mike Accion. *Art Dir* Teody Carmona. *Film Ed* Gregorio Caraballo. *Mus* F. Buencamino, Jr. *Sd* July Hidalgo.
Cast: Rosa Rosal *(Bala-amai)*, Tony Santos *(Hassan)*, Leroy Salvador *(Asid)*, Joseph de Cordova *(Datu Tahil)*, Vic Silayan *(Jikiri)*, Oscar Keesee *(pearl dealer)*, Pedro Faustino *(Badjao chief)*, Tony Dantes *(chief's bodyguard)*.
Drama. Hassan, son of the chief of the Badjao tribe of the South Seas, falls in love with Bala-amai, niece of the chief of the rival Moros. To marry Bala-amai, Hassan must abandon his pagan, sea-dwelling tribe and join the Islamic, land-dwelling Moros. In exchange for Bala-amai's hand, Hassan uses his pearl-diving skills to provide the tribe with valuable blue pearls. Soon after Bala-amai bears a child, however, Hassan quarrels with the Moro chief and refuses to dive for more pearls. The Moros burn down their house, and Hassan and Bala-amai flee to the Badjaos. There they are welcomed, and their child passes the test of surviving when thrown into the water and is declared a Badjao. *Tribal chiefs. Children. Paganism. Islam. Marriage. Pearl diving. Rites and ceremonies. South Seas. Sulu Archipelago. Moros.*
Note: Produced in the Philippines in 1957; running time: 105 min. May also be known as *Badjao, the Sea Gypsies*.

BADLANDS see SERGEANTS 3

LA BAIE DES ANGES see BAY OF THE ANGELS

LA BAIE DU DÉSIR see THE EROTIC TOUCH OF HOT SKIN

THE BAILIFF (Japan)   F6.0267
Daiei Motion Picture Co.–Kyoto Studio. *Dist* Brandon Films. Sep **1969** [New York opening]. Sd; b&w. 35mm. 125 min.
Prod Masaichi Nagata. *Dir* Kenji Mizoguchi. *Screenplay* Yahiro Fuji, Yoshikata Yoda. *Photog* Kazuo Miyagawa. *Art Dir* Kisaku Ito. *Mus* Fumio Hayasaka.
Cast: Kinuyo Tanaka *(Tamaki)*, Yoshiaki Hanayagi *(Zushio)*, Kyoko Kagawa *(Anju)*, Eitaro Shindo *(Bailiff Sansho)*, Ichiro Sugai *(Nio)*, Yoko Kosono *(Kohagi)*, Chieko Naniwa *(Ubatake)*, Kikue Mori *(priestess)*, Masao Chimizu *(The Father)*, Ken Mitsuda *(Prime Minister Fujiwara)*, Akitake Kono *(Taro)*, Ryosuke Kagawa, Masahito Kato, Keito Enami.
Drama. Source: Ogai Mori, "Sansho dayu," in *Chuo koron* (Jan 1915). A provincial governor in 11th-century Japan, who protects the peasants in his region from the imperial government's stern laws, is exiled, and his two children, Zushio and Anju, are abducted and delivered into slavery. Their mother, Tamaki, is sold as a courtesan. After 10 years' servitude under the cruel slaveowner Sansho, Zushio, having learned that his mother is still alive, escapes, intent on reuniting his family. Anju drowns herself in the lake so that Zushio

can make good his escape. In Kyoto, Zushio learns that his father, now dead, has been proclaimed a hero; and Zushio is given a governorship in the province where Sansho has his slave compound. He returns to the compound, frees the slaves, and resigns his post to search for his mother. He finds her on a remote island, sitting near her hut by the sea. Though aged, lame, and blind she recognizes her son. *Slavers. Bailiffs. Peasants. Exile. Family life. Abduction. Feudalism. Prostitution. Brother-sister relationship. Suicide. Self-sacrifice. Islands. Kyoto.*

Note: Released in Japan in 1954 as *Sansho dayu* at 130 min. Also known as *Sansho the Bailiff.*

BAISERS VOLÉS *see* **STOLEN KISSES**

BAJA BIG HORN *see* **WHITE FURY**

BAKUMATSU *see* **THE AMBITIOUS**

LE BAL DES VOYOUS *see* **PLAYMATES**

UN BALCÓN SOBRE EL INFIERNO *see* **WEB OF FEAR**

THE BALCONY   F6.0268
Walter Reade-Sterling, Inc.–Allen-Hodgdon Productions–City Film Corp. *Dist* Continental Distributing, Inc. 21 Mar **1963** [New York opening; c10 Dec 1962; LU3227]. Sd; b&w. 35mm. 84 min.

Prod Ben Maddow, Joseph Strick. *Asst Prod* Rosemary Kaye. *Dir* Joseph Strick. *Screenplay* Ben Maddow. *Photog* George Folsey. *Camera Op* Frank Dugas. *Art Dir* John Nicholson, Jean Owens, Gabriel Scognamillo. *Film Ed* Chester W. Schaeffer. *Mus Comp* Igor Stravinsky. *Mus Cond* Robert Craft. *Sd Ed* Verna Fields, Jeanne Turner. *Asst Dir* Helen Levitt. *Prod Mgr* Joel Glickman.

Cast: Shelley Winters *(Madam Irma)*, Peter Falk *(police chief)*, Lee Grant *(Carmen)*, Ruby Dee *(thief)*, Peter Brocco *(judge)*, Kent Smith *(general)*, Jeff Corey *(bishop)*, Joyce Jameson *(penitent)*, Arnette Jens *(horse)*, Leonard Nimoy *(rebel leader)*.

Allegory. Source: Jean Genêt, *Le balcon* (trans. by Bernard Frechtman as *The Balcony*; London opening: 22 Apr 1957). Madam Irma's brothel, The Balcony, is located in a vast, converted movie studio. Although a revolution is raging in the city streets, Irma ignores the turmoil and continues catering to the desires of her clientele. A gas station attendant pretends to be a bishop erotically stimulated by the lewd confessions of a penitent; a milkman posing as a general delights in whipping his female "horse"; and an accountant pretends he is a chief justice trying the case of a petty thief. One day Irma's lover, the chief of police, commandeers the three phony dignitaries and parades them through the streets in the hope that it will quiet the populace. When the men begin to believe their roles, the chief brutally strips them of their illusions. While Irma is pretending to be the queen, the rebel leader arrives at The Balcony and announces that he wants to impersonate the police chief. As he is being seduced by Carmen, Irma's lesbian confidante, he is suddenly confronted by the chief. The two men begin to fight, and Irma orders her women to strip them of their uniforms. Clad only in bath towels, they leave The Balcony as Irma turns to the audience and tells them to go home, where the illusions they practice are even more false than those she sells at her brothel. *Prostitutes. Police. Madams. Clergymen. Soldiers. Judges. Revolutions. Imposture. Fantasy. Lesbianism. Whorehouses. Motion picture studios.*

BALLAD AT DANCERS' ROCK *see* **STAGECOACH TO DANCERS' ROCK**

BALLAD IN BLUE *see* **BLUES FOR LOVERS**

BALLAD OF A GUNFIGHTER   F6.0269
Bill Ward Pictures. *Dist* Parade Pictures. 21 Aug **1963** [San Angelo, Texas, opening]. Sd; col (Eastmancolor). 35mm. 84 min.

Prod-Dir-Writ Bill Ward. *Assoc Prod* Jaime Mendoza-Nava, Charlie Aldrich. *Dir Photog* Brydon Baker. *Camera Op* Jack Willoughby. *Set Decor* Raymond G. Boltz. *Eff Ed* Jack Cornall, Bill Keith. *Neg Cutter* Pat McFall. *Song:* "San Angelo" writ & sung by Marty Robbins. *Song:* "El Paso" writ by Marty Robbins. *Prod Asst* Jerry Vance, Jack Willoughby, Cynthia Goodwins. *Script Supv* Billy Vernon. *Cost Supv* Muriel Pool. *Gaffer* Chet Stafford. *Painting* Ted Withers.

Cast: Marty Robbins *(Marty Robbins)*, Joyce Redd *(Secora)*, Bob Barron *(McCord)*, Nestor Paiva *(Padre)*, Michael Davis *(Miguelito)*, Laurette Luez *(Felina)*, Charlie Aldrich *(Amigo)*, Paul McDonald *(Mr. Baker)*, Cynthia Goodwins, Claudia Aldrich *(nuns)*, Gene Davis *(bartender)*, Tommy Cloud *(blacksmith)*, Rich Arnold, Chuck Bail *(stuntmen)*, Traveler *(a horse)*.

Western melodrama. Gunfighter Marty Robbins robs a stagecoach minutes before a gang led by McCord, the saloon keeper of San Angelo, was to have done so. Marty goes to San Angelo and "plants" the gold for the Padre to find. McCord cannot accuse Marty of the robbery without giving himself away, but

he is provoked into action when they become rivals for Secora, a dancehall girl. On the night Marty and Secora are to depart San Angelo, they are gunned down by the gang, but Marty's last act is to kill McCord. *Gunfighters. Saloon keepers. Clergymen. Dancehall girls. Stagecoach robberies. San Angelo (Texas).*

THE BALLAD OF A HUSSAR (U.S.S.R.)   F6.0270
Mosfilm. *Dist* Artkino Pictures. 13 Jul **1963** [New York opening]. Sd; col (Sovcolor). 35mm. 94 min.

Dir-Screenplay Collab Eldar Ryazanov. *Screenplay* Aleksandr Gladkov. *Story Ed* Ye. Skidanenko. *Photog* Leonid Kraynevich. *2d Camera* Vladimir Nakhabtsev. *Art Dir* Mikhail Bogdanov, Gennadiy Myasnikov. *Film Ed* Ye. Ovsyannikova. *Mus* Tikhon Khrennikov. *Cond* A. Roytman. *Sd* Valeriy Popov. *Asst Dir* Yu. Danilovich. *Prod Mgr* V. Maslov. *Cost* O. Kruchinina. *Makeup* O. Struntsova. *Sp Eff* I. Felitsyn, V. Sevostyanov, A. Klimenko. *Circus Dir* M. Tuganov. *Fencing Master* L. Blokh.

Cast: Larisa Golubkina *(Shura Azarova)*, Yuriy Yakovlev *(Rzhevskiy)*, Igor Ilinskiy *(Kutuzov)*, Tatyana Shmyga *(Masha [Zhermon])*, Nikolay Kryuchkov *(Ivan)*, A. Khodurskiy *(Count Nurin)*, Viktor Koltsov *(Azarov)*, L. Polyakov *(Pelymov)*, A. Polevoy *(Balmashyov)*, V. Shiryayev *(Salgari)*, Yu. Belov, Valentin Bryleyev, Yu. Kireyev, M. Orlov, F. Yavorskiy, Roman Khomyatov, V. Denisov, V. Troshin *(partisans)*, V. Grave, L. Lyubetskiy, P. Shpringfeld, V. Gusev, Yu. Martynov, G. Yudin, B. Ivanov, E. Smirnov, actor.

Operetta film. Source: Aleksandr Gladkov, *Davnym-davno (pitomtsy slavy)* (a play in verse; Moscow, 1942). At the time of the Napoleonic invasion of Russia, the pompous Lieut. Dmitriy Rzhevskiy is affianced to Shura, niece of retired Major Azarov. In order to deflate Rzhevskiy's ego, Shura disguises herself as a hussar and joins the Russian army. She maintains her disguise and impresses her companions with her heroic deeds. Captured during a daring raid against the French, she is rescued by Dmitriy, who finally discovers her identity. *Hussars. War heroes. Disguise. Male impersonation. Napoleonic Wars. Russia—Army.*

Note: Released in the U.S.S.R. in Sep 1962 as *Gusarskaya ballada*. Also known as *Ballad of a Hussar.*

THE BALLAD OF CABLE HOGUE   F6.0271
Phil Feldman Productions. *Dist* Warner Bros. Pictures. 18 Mar **1970** [Los Angeles opening; c1 Mar 1970; LP38145]. Sd; col (Technicolor). 35mm. 121 min. *MPAA rating* R.

Pres by Kinney National Co. A Phil Feldman Production. *Prod-Dir* Sam Peckinpah. *Exec Prod* Phil Feldman. *Assoc Prod* Gordon Dawson. *Co-prod* William Faralla. *Screenplay* John Crawford, writ, Edmund Penney. *Dir Photog* Lucien Ballard. *Art Dir* Leroy Coleman. *Set Decor* Jack Mills. *Main Titl* Latigo Productions. *Film Ed* Frank Santillo, Louis Lombardo. *Mus* Jerry Goldsmith. *Mus Supv* Sonny Burke. *Orch* Arthur Morton. *Song:* "Tomorrow Is the Song I Sing" Richard Gillis, Jerry Goldsmith. *Sung by* Richard Gillis. *Song:* "Wait for Me, Sunrise" comp & sung by Richard Gillis. *Song:* "Butterfly Mornin's" Richard Gillis. *Sung by* Jason Robards, [Jr.], Stella Stevens. *Song:* "Hogan's Saloon Song" Richard Gillis. *Sd* Don Rush. *Asst Dir* John Gaudioso. *Unit Prod Mgr* Dink Templeton. *Cost for Miss Stevens* Robert Fletcher. *Makeup* Gary Liddiard, Al Fleming. *Hairstyles* Kathy Blondell. *Sp Eff* Bud Hulburd. *Dial Supv* Frank Kowalski.

Cast: Jason Robards, [Jr.] *(Cable Hogue)*, Stella Stevens *(Hildy)*, David Warner *(Joshua Sloane)*, Strother Martin *(Bowen)*, Slim Pickens *(Ben Fairchild)*, L. Q. Jones *(Taggart)*, Peter Whitney *(Cushing)*, R. G. Armstrong *(Quittner)*, Gene Evans *(Clete)*, William Mims *(Jensen)*, Kathleen Freeman *(Mrs. Jensen)*, Susan O'Connell *(Claudia)*, Vaughn Taylor *(Powell)*, Felix Nelson *(William)*, Max Evans *(Webb Seely)*, Darwin W. Lamb *(The Stranger)*, James Anderson *(preacher)*, Mary Munday *(Dot)*, William Faralla *(Lucius)*, Matthew Peckinpah *(Matthew)*, Victor Izay *(stage office clerk)*, Easy Pickens *(Easy)*.

Western comedy-drama. Abandoned in the desert by partners Bowen and Taggart, prospector Cable Hogue swears revenge. After four days of aimless wandering and desperate prayer Hogue discovers water. As its site is the only hole within 40 miles and conveniently close to the stagecoach route, Hogue establishes Cable Springs, an oasis for weary travelers. The entrepreneur, however, shoots his first customer when the client refuses to pay the 10-cent drinking fee. His second visitor, Joshua Sloane, a lecherous evangelist, guards the waterhole while Hogue rides into the town of Deaddog to file his claim. Although the stagecoach manager, Quittner, refuses to stake him, town banker Cushing invest $100. The budding entrepreneur hies to Hildy, the town prostitute, who gives him a bath. Hearing a revival outside, Hogue is reminded of Sloane and leaves abruptly without paying the prostitute. His claim secure and business booming, Hogue offers Hildy sanctuary when she is driven from Deaddog by pious citizens. The two fall in love, but Hildy leaves for San Francisco and a rich husband. Her departure coincides with the arrival of Hogue's former partners, intent on the acquisition of their old friend's fortune. The wiley prospector, guessing their purpose, traps the pair in a snakepit, shooting Taggart and sparing Bowen. When the widowed and enriched Hildy arrives to spirit her lover to New Orleans, he is accidentally crushed by her automobile. As he expires Hogue is eulogized by Sloane. *Prospectors. Entrepreneurs. Evangelists. Prostitutes. Bankers. Widows. Revenge. Water rights. Partnerships. Lechery. Stagecoaches. Deserts. Automobile accidents. Snakes.*

Note: Exteriors filmed in Arizona and Nevada.

BALLAD OF GAVILAN F6.0272
International Productions. *Dist* Craddock Films. **1968**. Sd; col. 35mm. ca85 min.

Prod-Dir-Writ William J. Jugo. *Mus Comp & Sung by* Pete Seeger.

Cast: Christopher George, George De Vries.

Western melodrama. To avenge the wrongs done to his family, a son seeks out and kills the man responsible. *Revenge.*

Note: Filmed on location in Immokalee, Florida, in 1966. Working title: *Gavilan.*

THE BALLAD OF JOSIE F6.0273
Universal Pictures. 12 Jan **1968** [New Orleans opening; c24 Feb 1967; LP37902]. Sd (Westrex); col (Technicolor). 35mm (Techniscope). 102 min.

Prod Norman MacDonnell. *Exec Prod* Martin Melcher. *Dir* Andrew V. McLaglen. *Screenplay* Harold Swanton. *Dir Photog* Milton Krasner. *Art Dir* Alexander Golitzen, Addison Hehr. *Set Decor* John McCarthy, James S. Redd. *Main Titl* National Screen Service. *Film Ed* Otho Lovering, Fred Chulack. *Mus De Vol. Mus Supv* Joseph Gershenson. *Song:* "Wait Till Tomorrow" Gene De Paul, Jack Lloyd. *Sung by* The Sun Set Group. *Titl Song* Don Costa, Floyd Huddleston. *Sung by* Ronnie Dante. *Sd* Waldon O. Watson, Frank H. Wilkinson. *Asst Dir* Terry Morse, Jr., Newt Arnold, John Anderson, Jr. *Unit Prod Mgr* Hal Polaire. *Gowns* Jean Louis. *Makeup* Bud Westmore. *Miss Day's Hairstyles* Barbara Lampson. *Supv Hairstyles* Larry Germain. *Matte Supv* Albert Whitlock. *Stunt Coörd* Hal Needham.

Cast: Doris Day *(Josie Minick),* Peter Graves *(Jason Meredith),* George Kennedy *(Arch Ogden),* Andy Devine *(Judge Tatum),* William Talman *(Charlie Lord),* David Hartman *(Sheriff Fonse Pruitt),* Guy Raymond *(Doc),* Audrey Christie *(Annabelle Pettijohn),* Karen Jensen *(Deborah Wilkes),* Elisabeth Fraser *(Widow Renfrew),* Linda Meiklejohn *(Jenny),* Shirley O'Hara *(Elizabeth),* Timothy Scott *(Klugg),* Don Stroud *(Bratsch),* Paul Fix *(Alpheus Minick),* Harry Carey, [Jr.] *(Mooney),* John Fiedler *(Simpson),* Robert Lowery *(Whit Minick),* Teddy Quinn *(Luther Minick).*

Western melodrama. Josie Minick is acquitted for accidentally killing her drunken husband; nevertheless, her 8-year-old son, Luther, is taken to Cheyenne to be cared for by her wealthy father-in-law, Alpheus Minick. Despite the offer of her rancher neighbor Arch Ogden to buy her rundown ranch, Josie decides to renovate the place with her husband's insurance money, but she soon becomes discouraged by her failure to resurrect the place. She tries a job as a waitress but is equally unhappy. Finally she buys a flock of sheep and hires two farmhands to care for them; but local cattlemen revive their long-standing war with the sheepherders as Arch and the other ranchers prepare for a battle against the beleaguered widow. News of the range war reaches Washington, D. C., where the town's district attorney, Charlie Lord, is wrapping up negotiations for Wyoming becoming a state. He hurriedly returns to the town and finds Annabelle Pettijohn, crusader for women's rights, conducting a streetfight against the male ranchers. Furious beyond reason at Josie's part in the squabble, Arch rides out to her ranch and puts a torch to her barn. Jason Meredith, Josie's rugged supporter, eventually stops Arch. Next morning, Charlie negotiates a truce between Arch and Josie whereby the rancher will buy Josie's sheep and sell cattle to her at bargain prices. Delighted, Josie allows Jason to accept the proposition on her behalf—because he will be sharing her life with little Luther from now on. *Widows. Ranchers. Neighbors. Waitresses. Fathers-in-law. District attorneys. Drunkenness. Murder. Motherhood. Child custody. Incendiarism. Employment—Women. Women's rights. Trials. Range wars. Insurance. Wyoming. Cheyenne. Washington (District of Columbia). Sheep. Cattle.*

Note: Prerelease titles: *The Epic of Josie* and *Meanwhile, Back at the Ranch.*

A BALLAD OF LOVE (U.S.S.R.) F6.0274
Riga Film Studio. *Dist* Artkino Pictures. 19 Feb **1966** [New York opening]. Sd; b&w. 35mm. 45 min.

Dir-Writ Mikhail Bogin. *Screenplay* Mikhail Bogin, Yuriy Chulyukin. *Photog* Rikhard Pik, Genrikh Pilipson. *Art Dir* Tamara Antonova. *Mus* Romuald Grinblat. *Sd* G. Koroteyev. *Asst Dir* B. Ruzh.

Cast: Viktoria Fyodorova *(The Girl),* Valentin Smirnitskiy *(The Boy),* V. Zakharov, V. Akurater, T. Vitin, M. Grakhova, R. Dambran, F. Kogan, V. Lyubimov, V. Freymut.

Drama. A young oboist follows a pretty girl in Moscow and is surprised when she fails to respond to his attempts at conversation. Intrigued, he follows her to a circus theater school; finally they meet, and he learns that she has been deaf and dumb since she was injured in an air raid at the age of three. Later, the boy invites the girl to a cafe and is filled with apprehension when a friend of his asks her to dance; but the girl, who is training to become an acrobatic dancer, observes the other couples and is soon completely at ease. The boy and girl grow close, their relationship enriched by the boy's sensitivity and the girl's highly developed senses of vision and touch. She attends a concert at which the boy is performing, and her desperate yearning to understand music causes a melody heard in childhood to well up in her mind, mingled with the sound of the wind and the air raid. Content, she watches the boy perform. *Deafmutes. Students. Musicians. Dancers. Courtship. Adolescence. Cafes. Moscow.*

Note: Released in the U.S.S.R. in 1965 as *Dvoye;* running time: 37 min.

BALLAD OF NARAYAMA (Japan) F6.0275
Shochiku Co. *Dist* Films Around the World, Inc. 19 Jun **1961** [New York opening]. Sd; col (Fujicolor). 35mm (Shochiku Grandscope). 98 min.

Prod Ryuzo Otani, Masaharu Kokaji. *Dir-Screenplay* Keisuke Kinoshita. *Photog* Hiroyuki Kusuda. *Art Dir* Kisaku Ito, Chiyoo Umeda. *Film Ed* Yoshi Sugihara. *Ballad:* "Nagauta" Rokuzaemon Kineya. *Ballad:* "Joruri" Matsunosuke Nozawa. *Sd* Hisao Ono.

Cast: Kinuyo Tanaka *(Orin),* Teiji Takahashi *(Tatsuhei),* Yuko Mochizuki *(Tama-yan),* Danko Ichikawa *(Kesakichi),* Keiko Ogasawara *(Matsu-yan),* Seiji Miyaguchi *(Mata-yan),* Yunosuke Ito *(Mata-yan's son),* Ken Mitsuda *(Teru-yan).*

Drama. Source: Shichiro Fukasawa, *Narayamabushi-ko* (Tokyo, 1957). A tiny village in ancient Japan is so plagued by famine and starvation that it has become traditional for old people, once they have reached the age of 70, to ascend voluntarily the heights of Mount Narayama and serenely await death. Before making such a journey, an elderly matriarch, Orin, sets her house in order by finding a new wife for her recently widowed son, Tatsuhei. Orin is pleased that the woman, Tama-yan, is an ideal mother for Tatsuhei's three children. As the ceremonial feast preceding her sacrifice nears, Orin becomes embarrassed by her strong white teeth, a constant reminder of the food she eats. Determined to look like a toothless old woman ready for death, she breaks them on a mill stone. On the day of his mother's departure, Tatsuhei carries her on his back to the skeleton-covered peaks of Narayama. As he races from the horrifying scene, snow begins to fall. Tama-yan joins her husband in thanking the gods of Narayama for allowing the old woman to die a quick death by freezing rather than a slow and arduous one by starvation. *Famine. Old age. Filial relations. Village life. Social customs. Self-sacrifice.*

Note: Released in Japan in 1958 as *Narayama-bushi-ko.*

LA BALLATA DEL BOIA see **NOT ON YOUR LIFE**

BALLERINA AND THE GOOD GOD see **ANGEL IN A TAXI**

BALLERINA E BUON DIO see **ANGEL IN A TAXI**

THE BALLERS F6.0276
Boss Productions. *Dist* Boss Distributors. 14 May **1969** [Boston opening]. Sd; b&w. 35mm. 69 min.

Prod Enrico Alexandros, Wizard Glick. *Dir* Wizard Glick. *Camera* John Meroa.

Cast: Sheba Swengire, Donna Grande, Sandra Sture, Tulip Moyst, Linda Lust, Sam Bueno, Bill Farmer.

Sex film. No information about the precise nature of this film has been found, but press photographs suggest that it includes scenes of nudity, lesbianism, group sex, and oral intercourse, and that it takes place in a secluded cabin in the north during the winter. *Nudity. Lesbianism. Group sex. Oral sex.*

Note: Also known as *The Callers* and *Lisa and Ballers.*

BALLET OF OTHELLO (U.S.S.R.) F6.0277
Gruziya-Film. *Dist* Artkino Pictures. 2 May **1964** [New York opening]. Sd; col (Sovcolor). 35mm. 95 min.

Dir Vakhtang Chabukiani. *Scen* Yuriy Gelovani, Vakhtang Chabukiani. *Photog* Feliks Vysotskiy. *Camera* A. Parezishvili. *Art Dir* Serapion Vatsadze, Solomon Virsaladze. *Mus* Aleksey Machavariani. *Ballet Master* Vakhtang Chabukiani. *Sd* D. Lomidze. *Asst Dir* Sh. Martishvili. *Sp Eff* O. Magakyan, M. Sekhniashvili.

Featuring: Paliashvili Opera Theatre and Ballet of Tbilisi.

Cast: Vakhtang Chabukiani *(Othello),* Vera Tsignadze *(Desdemona),* Zurab Kikaleyshvili *(Iago),* Eteri Chabukiani *(Bianca),* Liana Mitayshvili *(Emilia),* B. Manavardisashvili *(Cassio),* R. Tsulukidze *(Roderigo),* Mikhail Dudko *(Brabantio),* M. Gelyus *(Montano),* V. Ivashkin *(Duke of Venice),* M. Abdaladze, V. Gunashvili, V. Gorbovich, A. Dvali, T. Kossova, K. Dzneladze, R. Magalashvili, L. Mkhitaryan, L. Nadareyshvili.

Dance film. Source: William Shakespeare, *Othello.* A ballet version of Shakespeare's tragedy. *Moors. Nobility. Soldiers. Perfidy. Jealousy. Ambition. Murder. Suicide. Miscegenation. Fatherhood. Venice. Cyprus.*

Note: Released in the U.S.S.R. in Sep 1961 as *Venetsianskiy mavr.* Vakhtang Chabukiani created the role of Othello for the Paliashvili Opera Theatre and Ballet of Tbilisi in 1957.

BALTIC EXPRESS (Poland)   **F6.0278**

Kadr Film Unit. *For* Film Polski. *Dist* Telepix Corp. Dec **1962**. Sd; b&w. 35mm. 95 min.

Prod Jerzy Rutowicz. *Dir* Jerzy Kawalerowicz. *Screenplay* Jerzy Kawalerowicz, Jerzy Lutowski. *Photog* Jan Laskowski. *Art Dir* Ryszard Potocki. *Mus* Andrzej Trzaskowski. *Based on Mus:* "Moon Rays" Artie Shaw. *Sd* Józef Bartczak, Tadeusz Altman.

Cast: Lucyna Winnicka *(Marthe)*, Leon Niemczyk *(man)*, Teresa Szmigielówna *(blonde)*, Zbigniew Cybulski *(Stachek)*, Roland Głowacki *(sleeper)*, H. Dabrowska, Ignacy Machowski, Aleksander Sewruk, Zygmunt Zintel, M. Gazda.

Drama. Marthe, a young woman, leaves her lover, Stachek, and travels to the seashore. She buys a ticket from a stranger, boards a night train, and finds herself sharing a compartment with a man. Stachek stands on the platform, pleading with Marthe to stay, as the train leaves the station. Marthe ignores him and learns that her traveling companion is a surgeon who is upset over an unsuccessful operation in which a patient died. Marthe and the doctor are drawn to each other. Suddenly, the train stops and police enter, searching for a murderer who is supposed to be in Marthe's compartment. The doctor is suspected at first, until Marthe identifies the stranger in the next compartment as the man who sold her a ticket. He is chased and captured by police, and the train resumes the trip. At the journey's end, the doctor is met by his wife, and Marthe is left alone. *Surgeons. Police. Strangers. Murder. Infidelity. Trains.*

Note: Released in Poland in 1959 as *Pociąg*; running time: 100 min.

BAMBOLE (France/Italy)   **F6.0279**

Documento Film–Orsay Films. *Dist* Royal Films International. 28 Jun **1965** [New York opening]. Sd; b&w. 35mm. 111 min.

Overall Production Credits: *Prod* Gianni Hecht Lucari. *Mus* Armando Trovajoli.

Production Credits—"The Telephone Call": *Dir* Dino Risi. *Story & Screenplay* Rodolfo Sonego. *Photog* Ennio Guarnieri. *Art Dir* Gianni Polidori. *Film Ed* Giuliana Bettoja.

Production Credits—"Treatise in Eugenics": *Dir* Luigi Comencini. *Screenplay* Tullio Pinelli. *Story* Luciano Salce, Steno. *Photog* Carlo Montuori. *Art Dir* Giancarlo Bartolini Salimbeni. *Film Ed* Roberto Cinquini.

Production Credits—"The Soup": *Dir* Franco Rossi. *Story & Screenplay* Rodolfo Sonego, Luigi Magni. *Photog* Roberto Gerardi. *Art Dir* Gianni Polidori. *Film Ed* Giorgio Serralonga.

Production Credits—"Monsignor Cupid": *Dir* Mauro Bolognini. *Screenplay* Leo Benvenuti, Piero De Bernardi. *Photog* Leonida Barboni. *Art Dir* Gianni Polidori. *Film Ed* Roberto Cinquini.

Cast—"The Telephone Call": Virna Lisi *(Luisa, the wife)*, Nino Manfredi *(Giorgio, the husband)*, Alicia Brandet *(Armenia)*.

Cast—"Treatise in Eugenics": Elke Sommer *(Ulla)*, Maurizio Arena *(Massimo)*, Piero Focaccia *(Valerio)*.

Cast—"The Soup": Monica Vitti *(Giovanna)*, John Karlsen *(Alfonso, her husband)*, Orazio Orlando *(Richetto, her lover)*, Roberto DeSimone *(Peppe)*.

Cast—"Monsignor Cupid": Gina Lollobrigida *(Beatrice)*, Akim Tamiroff *(Monsignor Arendi)*, Jean Sorel *(Vincenzo)*, Gianni Rizzo *(hotel manager)*, Camillo Milli.

Comedy. "Monsignor Cupid" episode based on a tale from: Giovanni Boccaccio, *Il decamerone.* THE TELEPHONE CALL: Luisa and Giorgio are newlyweds, but Luisa postpones lovemaking because she is reading a novel. As Giorgio becomes increasingly frustrated, the half-dressed Luisa becomes involved in a seemingly endless telephone conversation with her mother. He overhears her say that their next door neighbor, Armenia, has very loose morals and cannot resist booksellers, whereupon he leaves Luisa on the phone and goes next door with a load of books. TREATISE IN EUGENICS: Ulla, a Swede who does not believe in marriage, has come to Rome to seek a man to father her child according to modern theories of eugenics; her inspection trips are chauffeured by Valerio. Ulla seems to favor the handsome Massimo as a prospective father, but in the end she marries Valerio for love, and they have many children. THE SOUP: Giovanna decides to use the funds she has gained from the settlement of a traffic accident to murder her boorish, middle-aged husband, Alfonso, because she is tired of life in the slums and especially of Alfonso's uncouth eating habits. Through a series of mishaps none of her plans is successful, and she is left listening to Alfonso slurp soup. MONSIGNOR CUPID: Monsignor Arendi has come to Rome for the Ecumenical Council accompanied by his handsome nephew Vincenzo, who serves as his secretary. Beatrice, wife of their hotelkeeper, tries to seduce Vincenzo, but the youth is too innocent to respond. Beatrice, undaunted, complains to his uncle that Vincenzo has been pestering her and that she will leave the hotel to avoid him. When the Monsignor reprimands Vincenzo, he understands Beatrice's intent; and on the pretense of apologizing he goes to her hiding place. They continue their romance in the hotel, which by this time is filled with clergymen. *Swedes. Chauffeurs. Newlyweds. Booksellers. Innocents. Uncles. Priests. Hotelkeepers. Marriage. Eugenics. Murder. Infidelity. Seduction. Etiquette. Telephone. Slums. Food. Rome.*

Note: Opened in Rome caJan 1965 as *Le bambole*, with episodes entitled "La telefonata," "Il trattato di eugenetica," "La minestra," and "Monsignor Cupido"; running time: 100 min. Paris opening in Jul 1965 as *Les poupées*; running time: 105 min. Also reviewed as *The Dolls.*

THE BAMBOO SAUCER   **F6.0280**

Harris Associates–National Telefilm Associates. *Dist* World Entertainment Corp. 23 Oct **1968** [Boston opening; c23 Oct 1968; LP36579]. Sd; col (De Luxe). 35mm. 100 min. [Copyright length: 103 min.] *MPAA rating* G.

A Jerry Fairbanks Production. *Prod* Jerry Fairbanks. *Assoc Prod* Charles E. Burns. *Dir-Writ* Frank Telford. *Orig Story* Rip Von Ronkel, John P. Fulton. *Photog* Hal Mohr. *Camera Op* Jack McCoskey. *Set Lighting* Bob Comer. *Art Dir* Theodore Holsopple. *Film Ed* Richard C. Harris. *Mus* Edward Paul. *Sd* Dean Gilmore. *Asst Dir* Hank Gilbert, Russell Vreeland. *Supv* Grant Spicer. *Prod Mgr* Herbert Willis. *Unit Mgr* Gerald Seth Sindell, Terry Croghan. *Sp Eff* John P. Fulton, Glen Robinson. *Extra Eff* Deon Hanson. *Tech Cons* H. Roy Vanderford.

Cast: Dan Duryea *(Hank Peters)*, John Ericson *(Fred Norwood)*, Lois Nettleton *(Anna Karachev)*, Bob Hastings *(Garson)*, Vincent Beck *(Zagorsky)*, Bernard Fox *(Ephram)*, Robert Dane *(Miller)*, Rico Cattani *(Dubovsky)*, James Hong *(Sam Archibald)*, Bartlett Robinson *(Rhodes)*, Nick Katurich *(Gadyakoff)*, William Mims *(Joe Vetry)*, Nan Leslie *(Dorothy Vetry)*, Andy Romano *(Blanchard)*.

Science fiction melodrama. Fred Norwood is attacked by an unidentified flying object while flying an experimental supersonic jet. He escapes but is fired by the president of the aircraft company for foolishly endangering his plane. Determined to validate his story, Norwood rents a small jet and enlists the aid of his brother-in-law, Joe Vetry, to fly it; but after spotting the UFO by radar and taking pursuit, Vetry crashes and disappears. Hank Peters, a U. S. Secret Service official, shows Norwood a sketch of a craft drawn by a peasant in a remote area of mainland China. Assured by Norwood that the craft could be the same as the UFO he saw, Peters asks Norwood and two technicians, Garson and Ephram, to join him on a mission to find the mysterious object. After parachuting into mountainous Chinese terrain, the men encounter a Russian group—led by Dubovsky and including scientist Anna Karachev—on an identical mission. Agreeing that their best interests will be served by joining together, the two groups locate the UFO in the ruins of a church and, after some discouraging attempts, discover how to enter the craft. Dubovsky at first attempts to achieve glory exclusively for Russia by holding the Americans prisoner and flying the object with his own men; but when it is discovered that Chinese Communist soldiers are about to attack them, the two parties remain together to resist their common enemy. In the battle that follows, everyone except Norwood, Anna, and Garson is killed. The three survivors manage to escape from the Chinese and head for Geneva in the UFO, hoping that their discovery will be beneficial to mankind. *Air pilots. Missing persons. Chinese. Communists. Government agents. Russians. Scientists. Parachuting. Cold war. Airplanes—Jet. United States Secret Service. Unidentified flying objects. People's Republic of China. Geneva. Airplane accidents.*

Note: Working title: *Operation Blue Book.* Rereleased in 1969 as *Collision Course*; running time: 90 min.

BAMSE (Sweden)   **F6.0281**

A-Produktion. *Dist* Chevron Pictures. 23 Mar **1970** [New York opening]. Sd; col (Eastman Color, print by Movielab). 35mm. 110 min. *MPAA rating* GP.

Exec Prod Ewert Granholm. *Dir* Arne Mattsson. *Screenplay* Arne Mattsson, Elsa Prawitz. *Photog* Lars Björne. *Camera* Wic Kjellin. *Art Dir* Harold Garmland. *Film Ed* Wic Kjellin. "Clarinet Quintet" K.581 Wolfgang Amadeus Mozart. *Selections from* "Tales From the Vienna Woods" Johann Strauss. *Sd* Lars Klettner, Hans Andersson. *Prod Mgr* Olle Lenander. *Cost* Per LeKang, Bertha Sånnell.

Cast: Grynet Molvig *(Barbro "Bamse" Persson)*, Folke Sundquist *(Christer Berg)*, Ulla Jacobsson *(Vera Berg)*, Björn Thambert *(Chris, the son)*, Henning Sjöström *(the lawyer)*, Gio Petré *(the blonde)*, Paul Hagen *(Danish porter)*, Gunilla Dahlmann *(brunette)*, Sune Mangs *(drunk)*, Pia Rydwall *(Greta)*, Rune Lindström, Lasse Krantz.

Melodrama. When Christer Berg dies in an automobile accident, a teddy bear is found in the wreckage. Chris, Berg's teenage son, finds that the teddy bear belongs to his father's mistress, Bamse. Chris torments Bamse, forcing her to visit his parents' home, and introduces her to his mother, Vera, as his fiancée. Increasingly fascinated by Bamse, Chris follows her to a resort. Although Bamse falls in love with him, she refuses to allow their relationship to go beyond the platonic. Concerned about her son, Vera follows the couple, but she remains silent, unwilling to disturb their happiness. Returning home, she learns that Bamse has been left a large sum of money in her husband's will. Finally, Chris tells his mother the truth about Bamse. Vera confronts Bamse, and the two women agree that Chris should go abroad for a year. Chris walks along the seashore with Bamse to say goodbye. The parting is interrupted by a telephone call; Bamse learns that she is pregnant by the father, and she disappears by the sea. Chris looks for her, but he finds only the teddy bear. *Mistresses. Infidelity. Filial relations. Adolescence. Inheritance. Pregnancy. Toys. Resorts. Automobile accidents.*

Note: Released in Sweden in Dec 1968. Also known as *The Teddy Bear* and *My Father's Mistress.*.

BANANA PEEL (France/Italy)   **F6.0282**
Sud Pacifique Films–Capitole Films–C. C. M. *Dist* Pathé Contemporary Films. 18 Jan **1965** [New York opening]. Sd; b&w. 35mm (see note). 97 min.
Prod Paul-Edmond Decharme. *Dir* Marcel Ophuls. *Screenplay* Marcel Ophuls, Claude Sautet, Daniel Boulanger. *Photog* Jean Rabier. *Camera* Alain Levent. *Art Dir* Georges Wakhévitch. *Film Ed* Monique Kirsanoff. *Mus* Ward Swingle. *Song:* "*Vive la nuit*" Cyrus Bassiak. *Sd* André Hervée.
Cast: Jeanne Moreau *(Cathy)*, Jean-Paul Belmondo *(Michel)*, Gert Fröbe *(Lachard)*, Claude Brasseur *(Charlie)*, Jean-Pierre Marielle *(Reynaldo)*, Alain Cuny *(Bontemps)*, Charles Regnier.
Comedy. Source: Charles Williams, *Nothing in Her Way* (New York, 1953). Jazz musician Michel Pollard agrees to help Cathy, his ex-wife, take revenge on the two wealthy men whose dishonesty caused her father's ruin. With two accomplices, Reynaldo and Charlie, they go to an island off Brittany where Bontemps, their first target, resides. Posing as an engineer from a German optical firm, Michel cons Bontemps into the belief that the island's sand is extremely valuable, and Bontemps is swindled out of 400,000 francs. When the group returns to Paris, Cathy, with the help of two hired thugs, doublecrosses Reynaldo and Charlie. She and Michel take all the money and go to the Riviera where she has located the second swindler, Lachard, who is addicted to the races. Michel, posing as a veterinarian involved with a gang that drugs racehorses, and Cathy, posing as his wife, swindle Lachard out of 600,000 francs by means of an elaborate betting scheme. Reynaldo and the two thugs catch up with Michel and Cathy, and when they threaten Cathy, Michel gives them the key to the airport locker in which he has supposedly hidden the money. Actually, Michel has checked the money in a flight bag with the airport florist. Michel learns that their first victim was the wrong man. He and Cathy claim the flight bag, return 400,000 francs to Bontemps, and, with the remaining 200,000 francs, fly away for a vacation. On the same flight, openly displaying his diamonds, is a wealthy jeweler. ... *Confidence men. Hoodlums. Musicians. Germans. Veterinarians. Imposture. Perfidy. Horseracing. Wealth. Revenge. Divorce. Airfields. Riviera. Brittany. Paris.*
Note: Opened in Paris in Nov 1964 as *Peau de banane* (in Franscope); Italian title: *Buccia di banana.*

BANCO À BANGKOK *see* **SHADOW OF EVIL**

BAND OF ASSASSINS (Japan)   **F6.0283**
Mifune Productions. *Dist* Toho International, Inc. 15 Apr **1970** [Los Angeles showing]. Sd; col (Eastmancolor). 35mm. 122 min.
Prod Toshiro Mifune, Yoshio Nishikawa, Hiroshi Inagaki. *Dir* Tadashi Sawashima. *Screenplay* Kenro Matsuura. *Photog* Kazuo Yamada. *Art Dir* Hiroshi Ueda. *Mus* Masaru Sato.
Cast: Toshiro Mifune *(Isami Kondo)*, Keiju Kobayashi *(Hijikata)*, Kinya Kitaoji *(Okita)*, Rentaro Mikuni *(Kamo Serizawa)*, Ganemon Nakamura, Katsuo Nakamura, Umenosuke Nakamura, Yoko Tsukasa, Junko Ikeuchi, Yuriko Hoshi, Yumiko Nogawa.
Historical melodrama. In 1863, Isami Kondo and eight of his fencing students travel to Kyoto to defend the Tokugawa Shogunate, which is under heavy attack from radicals who wish to restore the emperor to power. In Kyoto, Kondo obtains permission to set up the Shinsen Group, a paramilitary organization of assassins with severe rules for its members. Kamo Serizawa, co-leader of the group with Kondo, cracks under the pressure, and when he turns to drinking and oversteps the group's restrictions on the use of violence, Kondo is forced to purge him from the group. The Shinsen's prestige is restored when it breaks up a plot to burn the city and abduct the emperor. Public opinion continues to turn against the Shogunate, however; Kondo is finally branded a traitor and executed in 1868. *Royalty. Militants. Treason. Conspiracy. Assassination. Coups d'état. Japan—History—Tokugawa period 1600–1867. Kyoto. Isami Kondo.*
Note: Released in Japan in Jan 1970 as *Shinsengumi.*

BAND OF GOLD *see* **HOW TO SAVE A MARRIAGE—AND RUIN YOUR LIFE**

BAND OF OUTSIDERS (France)   **F6.0284**
Anouchka Films–Orsay Films. *Dist* Royal Films International. 15 Mar **1966** [New York opening]. Sd; b&w. 35mm. 97 min.
Dir-Writ Jean-Luc Godard. *Photog* Raoul Coutard. *Asst Photog* Georges Liron. *Film Ed* Agnès Guillemot, Françoise Collin. *Mus* Michel Legrand. *Prod Mgr* Philippe Dussart.
Cast: Anna Karina *(Odile)*, Sami Frey *(Franz)*, Claude Brasseur *(Arthur)*, Louisa Colpeyn *(aunt)*, Danièle Girard *(English teacher [see note])*, Chantal Darget *(Arthur's aunt [see note])*, Ernest Menzer *(Arthur's uncle)*, Georges Staquet *(Legionnaire)*, Michèle Seghers, Claude Makovski *(pupils)*, Michel Delahaye *(doorman at language school)*, Jean-Luc Godard *(narrator)*.
Crime drama. Source: Dolores (Birk) Hitchens, *Fool's Gold* (Garden City, N. Y., 1958). Odile, who lives in the Paris suburbs as an au pair girl in the home of her aunt, Madame Victoria, enrolls in an English language school and meets Franz, a young hoodlum. She casually mentions that her aunt keeps a large sum of money in a cupboard for her friend Monsieur Stolz. Franz talks of the money to his friend Arthur, who wrangles an introduction to Odile, infatuates her, and persuades her to help them steal the money. While checking on the amount, Odile forgets to replace her aunt's coat over the stash, and the money is gone when the trio arrives to steal it. Arthur beats Odile, who becomes disenchanted with him; and Franz, who loves her, is disturbed by his friend's violence. Arthur's criminal family hear of the affair; and to prevent Arthur's uncle from reaching the money before they do, the three return to the house the next day. When Madame Victoria interrupts them, she is locked in a closet and gagged. The three would-be thieves fail to find the money, and Arthur frees Madame Victoria to question her, but she has apparently suffocated. They flee, but Arthur, realizing that the money must be hidden in the dog kennel, returns on the pretext of finding out whether Madame Victoria is really dead. He finds the money, but his uncle arrives and they are both killed in a shootout. Monsieur Stolz drives up and finds the money just as Madame Victoria, who had only fainted, comes out to meet him. Franz and Odile escape to South America. [In bits of action, the characters parody Hollywood films, and a sequel is promised in CinemaScope and Technicolor. Godard, narrating the film, breaks into the action to explain the characters' feelings.] *Au pair girls. Hoodlums. Aunts. Uncles. Urban life. Robbery. Murder. Motion pictures. Paris.*
Note: Opened in Paris in Aug 1964 as *Bande à part.* Some sources credit Danièle Girard with the role of the English teacher, while Chantal Darget is credited variously as the English teacher, Arthur's aunt, and the mistress.

BANDE À PART *see* **BAND OF OUTSIDERS**

BANDITI A MILANO *see* **THE VIOLENT FOUR**

BANDITI A ORGOSOLO *see* **BANDITS OF ORGOSOLO**

IL BANDITO DELLA 11 *see* **PIERROT LE FOU**

BANDITS OF ORGOSOLO (Italy)   **F6.0285**
Titanus. *Dist* Pathé Contemporary Films. 13 Apr **1964** [New York opening]. Sd; b&w. 35mm. 98 min.
Prod-Dir Vittorio De Seta. *Screenplay* Vittorio De Seta, Vera Gherarducci. *Photog* Vittorio De Seta. *Camera* Luciano Tovolo, Marcello Gallinelli. *Art Dir (see note)* Elio Balletti. *Film Ed* Fernanda Papa, Iolanda Benvenuti, Vittorio De Seta. *Mus Comp* Valentino Bucchi. *Mus Cond* Franco Ferrara. *Sd* Fausto Ancillai, Nino Renda. *Asst Dir* Vera Gherarducci. *Cost* Marilù Carteny.
Cast: Michele Cossu *(Michele)*, Peppeddu Cuccu *(Peppeddu)*, Vittorina Pisano *(Mintonia)*.
Drama. Michele, a simple Sardinian peasant who wants nothing more than to tend his flock of sheep, suddenly finds himself implicated in the robbery of a herd of swine and the murder of a policeman when the bandits responsible for the crimes stop for a rest at his cottage. Following their departure, Michele is questioned by the police; but he refuses to turn informer. Terrified that he will lose his sheep and his only means of existence, he takes his 12-year-old brother, Peppeddu, and drives his flock across the bleak mountains in a desperate attempt to survive. They encounter drought and thinning vegetation, until one by one, the sheep die. Peppeddu becomes ill, and Michele takes him to the nearest village. Penniless and with no employment available, Michele steals a flock of sheep belonging to another peasant and becomes one of the bandits of Orgosolo. *Peasants. Shepherds. Bandits. Brothers. Police. Robbery. Murder. Poverty. Survival. Sardinia. Orgosolo. Sheep.*
Note: Opened in Rome in Nov 1961 as *Banditi a Orgosolo.* The cast is composed of Sardinian peasants. Elio Balletti is credited with adaptation by one source.

BANDITS ON THE WIND (Japan)   F6.0286

Toho Co. 14 Sep **1962** [Los Angeles opening]. Sd; b&w. 35mm (Tohoscope). 113 min.

Exec Prod Tomoyuki Tanaka. *Dir* Hiroshi Inagaki. *Screenplay* Masato Ide, Hiroshi Inagaki. *Photog* Kazuo Yamada. *Mus* Kan Ishii.

Cast: Yosuke Natsuki (*Taro*), Makoto Sato (*Gale*), Somegoro Ichikawa (*Gen*), Izumi Yukimura (*Kayo*), Chishu Ryu (*village priest*), Akiko Wakabayashi (*Sawa*), Mannosuke Nakamura, Jun Tatara, Tadao Nakamaru, Koshiro Matsumoto, Chusha Ichikawa.

Melodrama. In 15th-century Japan, a gang of 11 bandits roam the countryside, robbing the mansions of the rich and killing those who stand in their way. They decide to stop in a nearby village to rest but discover that it is desolate and that the remaining inhabitants are starving. The bandits steal food from another village and return to feed the starving villagers. They take up headquarters in a Buddhist temple, and a priest, recognizing a banner which is part of their loot, hails them as samurai of a powerful clan. Taro, the one-eyed leader of the bandits, takes advantage of the mistake, hoping to use the masquerade for monetary advantage. Gen, a farmer's son, is moved by the villagers' poverty, however, and presents them with the gang's stolen money. Some of the bandits acclaim his kindness, but others condemn it, and dissension develops in the ranks. Later, learning that 25 of the village men are being kept as slaves to assist in the construction of a castle for a provincial lord, the bandits attack and defeat the lord's men, freeing the villagers. But the army of another feudal warlord, fearing the bandits' growing strength, attacks and slays them. *Bandits. Samurai. Peasants. Farmers. Warlords. Feudalism. Robbery. Murder. Poverty. Mistaken identity. Slavery. Buddhism. Hunger.*

Note: Released in Japan in 1961 as *Yato kaze no naka o hashiru*; running time: 111 min.

BANDOLERO!   F6.0287

Twentieth Century-Fox Film Corp. 18 Jun **1968** [Dallas opening; c18 Jun 1968; LP35904]. Sd (Westrex); col (DeLuxe). 35mm (Panavision). 106 min.

Prod Robert L. Jacks. *Dir* Andrew V. McLaglen. *Screenplay* James Lee Barrett. *Dir Photog* William H. Clothier. *Art Dir* Jack Martin Smith, Alfred Sweeney. *Set Decor* Walter M. Scott, Chester L. Bayhi. *Film Ed* Folmar Blangsted. *Mus* Jerry Goldsmith. *Orch* Herbert Spencer. *Sd* Herman Lewis, David Dockendorf. *Asst Dir* Terry Morse, Jr. *Unit Prod Mgr* Jack Stubbs. *Makeup* Dan Striepeke, Del Acevedo. *Hairstyles* Edith Lindon. *Sp Photog Eff* L. B. Abbott, Emil Kosa, Jr. *Stunt Coörd* Hal Needham.

Cast: James Stewart (*Mace Bishop*), Dean Martin (*Dee Bishop*), Raquel Welch (*Maria*), George Kennedy (*Sheriff Johnson*), Andrew Prine (*Roscoe Bookbinder*), Will Geer (*Pop Chaney*), Clint Ritchie (*Babe*), Denver Pyle (*Muncie Carter*), Tom Heaton (*Joe Chaney*), Rudy Diaz (*Angel Muñoz*), Sean McClory (*Robbie*), Harry Carey, [Jr.] (*Cort Hayjack*), Donald Barry (*Jack Hawkins*), Guy Raymond (*Ossie Grimes*), Perry Lopez (*Frisco*), Jock Mahoney (*Stoner*), Dub Taylor (*attendant*), Big John Hamilton (*bank clerk*), Bob Adler (*Ross Harper*), John Mitchum (*bathhouse customer*), Joseph Patrick Cranshaw (*bank clerk*), Roy Barcroft (*bartender*).

Western melodrama. Source: Stanley L. Hough, "Mace" (unpublished story). A band of outlaws led by former Confederate soldier Dee Bishop kill a wealthy rancher during the attempted robbery of a Texas bank. The gang is arrested by Sheriff Johnson, tried, and sentenced to die on the gallows. Dee's older brother, Mace, disguises himself as the hangman and stages a last-minute rescue of the five men. The outlaws flee across the Mexican border, taking the murdered rancher's widow, Maria Stoner, as hostage. While Sheriff Johnson, Deputy Roscoe Bookbinder, and a posse are pursuing the gang, Mace robs the bank and then goes to join his brother's band in a deserted town once ravaged by bandoleros. The fugitives begin arguing among themselves, with Mace, Dee, and Maria on one side, and Pop Chaney and his cowardly son Joe on the other. Eventually, Dee falls in love with Maria and contemplates founding a Montana homestead to atone for his errant past, but his plans are foiled by the arrival of Johnson. Though the sheriff, who is also in love with Maria, captures Dee's men, he is forced to release them when the bandoleros launch an attack. In the slaughter that ensues, Dee and Mace are both killed by the bandolero leader, Angel Muñoz, who is then gunned down by Maria. After burying the two brothers, Johnson and Maria head back to Texas. *Confederate veterans. Outlaws. Ranchers. Sheriffs. Brothers. Executioners. Widows. Hostages. Bandits. Murder. Bank robberies. Capital punishment. Imposture. Texas. Mexico. Chases.*

BANG BANG   F6.0288

Dist Canyon Distributing Co. 15 Jul **1970** [Champaign, Illinois, showing]. Sd; col (Eastman Color). 35mm. 75 min.

Prod-Dir-Writ Alvin Tokunow, Bill Kaplan. *Camera* Alvin Tokunow, Bill Kaplan, David Ming Li Lowe, Dan McLaughlin, Robert Grant. *Film Ed* Alvin Tokunow, Bill Kaplan. *Orig Mus* Milkman. *Sd* Judy Rieder, Alvin Tokunow. *Makeup* Alvin Tokunow, Bill Kaplan. *Sp Eff* Kim R. Gottlieb, Sam

Mangiamelli, Bill Kaplan. *Crew* Earl Sampson, Derek Wicks, Mary Ellen King, Amir Cosen, Bill Stalew, Rowl Murrow.

Cast: Joanne Martin (*Carol*), Dale Struman (*Judy*), Ron Levi (*driver*), Charles Goodman (*John*), Brigit Kempler (*bike lady*), Mike Meyers (*biker*), Robert Haines (*Ron*), Melinda Melana (*hitch-hiker*), Susan Klien (*friend*), Sharmen Lewis (*lesbian*).

Sex film. Two women pick up a hitchhiker in Los Angeles and direct her to her destination, the beach house of an old friend. The hitchhiker buys some new clothes and is almost raped by the next person from whom she accepts a ride. She finally arrives at her friend's house and discovers that he has become a homosexual. Some lesbians attack her, and she runs out into the street and is picked up by a member of the Hell's Angels motorcycle gang. The woman and the motorcyclist have sex; his girl friend returns home unexpectedly, and the three engage in troilism. The hitchhiker leaves them and telephones the two women who earlier gave her directions. She goes to a house and is given an aphrodisiac. There is an orgy, and the woman is served up in a huge tub of spaghetti. *Hitchhikers. Lesbianism. Troilism. Male homosexuality. Group sex. Aphrodisiacs. Hell's Angels.*

THE BANG BANG GANG   F6.0289

E. S. I. Productions. *Dist* Eden International Films. 20 Aug **1970** [trade review]. Sd; col (Eastman Color). 35mm. 93 min.

Prod-Dir-Writ Van Guylder. *Photog* Bob Maxwell. *Art Dir* Bud Costello. *Mus* Allen Alper. *Sd* Clark D. Will. *In Charge of Prod* Roger Gentry. *Makeup* Nora Maxwell.

Cast: Jae Miller (*Tami*), Michael Kirkwood (*Adam*), Revel Quinn (*Dallas*), Marland Proctor (*LeRoy*), Edward Blessington (*Chico*), Bambi Allen (*Lila*).

Crime melodrama. During the 1930's, two holdup men, Adam and LeRoy, join gun molls Tami and Dallas to terrorize the Southwest. Between holdups, they take part in a barroom brawl in which they wound Chico, a gang leader. With his men, Chico finds the two couples, shoots Adam in both hands and beats Dallas with a strap; he then forces Dallas to perform fellatio on him while everyone, including his gang, looks on. Chico shoots Dallas' lover, LeRoy, and then he rapes Dallas and stabs her to make her more responsive. Lila, a lesbian, ties Tami to a wall and rapes her. Tami and Adam escape and eventually exact revenge on Chico's men, while Chico, trying to abscond with the couples' money, is killed by Lila. *Thieves. Molls. Gangs. Revenge. Flagellation. Robbery. Oral sex. Lesbianism. Rape.*

Note: Formerly titled *Kiss Kiss Bang Bang*, the film may also be known as *The Bang Bang Game*.

THE BANG BANG KID (Italy/Spain)   F6.0290

L. M. Films–Domino Film. *Dist* Ajay Film Co. 11 Jun **1968** [Trade screening]. Sd; col (print by Movielab). 35mm. 90 min.

Pres by Westside International. *Prod* Sidney Pink. *Dir (see note)* Stanley Praeger, Luciano Lelli. *Screenplay (see note)* Howard Berk, José Luis Bayonas. *Photog* Antonio Macasoli. *Sets* Wolfgang Burman. *Film Ed* Antonio Ramírez. *Mus* Nico Fidenco. *Asst Dir* Luciano Sacripanti.

Cast: Guy Madison (*Bear Bullock*), Sandra Milo (*Gwenda Skaggel*), Tom Bosley (*Merriweather Newberry*), Riccardo Garrone (*Killer Kissock*), José María Caffarel (*Mayor Skaggel*), Dianik Zurakowska (*Betsy Skaggel*), Giustino Durano (*Hotchkiss*), Eugenio Galadini, Renato Chiantoni, Nazareno Natale.

Western comedy. Wealthy mineowner Bear Bullock, who pictures himself as a medieval lord, controls the little town of Limerick, Arizona. The citizens of Limerick, headed by Mayor Skaggel, attempt to find a sheriff who will subdue Bullock and his men, but the candidates are gunned down in turn. One day Merriweather Newberry, an insignificant-looking, clumsy little man, arrives with his robot, the Bang Bang Kid, and claims that he can relieve the plight of the village. After several embarrasing failures, Newberry finally gets Bang Bang running properly, and the robot defeats Bullock in a showdown at Bullock's imported European castle. His rule at an end, Bullock leaves town accompanied by beautiful Gwenda Skaggel. *Despots. Sheriffs. Mayors. Robots. Castles. Arizona.*

Note: Produced in Spain as *Bang Bang*. Italian title: *Bang Bang Kid*. Sources conflict in crediting director and writer, U. S. sources citing Praeger and Berk and Spanish source citing Lelli and Bayonas.

BANG! BANG! YOU'RE DEAD! (Great Britain)   F6.0291

Towers of London–Marrakesh Film. *Dist* American International Pictures. 31 Aug **1966** [Buffalo, New York, opening]. Sd; col (Eastmancolor, print by Movielab). 35mm. 92 min.

Pres by Landau/Unger Co. *Prod* Harry Alan Towers. *Exec Prod* Oliver A. Unger. *Dir* Don Sharp. *Screenplay* Peter Yeldham. *Story* Peter Welbeck. *Photog* Michael Reed. *Adtl Photog* John Kotze. *2d Unit Photog* Egil Woxholt. *Art Dir* Frank White. *Film Ed* Teddy Darvas. *Mus Comp & Cond* Malcolm Lockyer. *Sd* John Brommage, John Poyner. *Asst Dir* Barrie Melrose. *Prod Mgr* Peter Manley. *Wardrobe* Joanna Wright. *Makeup* Eleanor Jones. *Hairstyles*

Ann Box.

Cast: Tony Randall *(Andrew Jessel)*, Senta Berger *(Kyra Stanovy)*, Terry-Thomas *(El Caid)*, Herbert Lom *(Narim Casimir)*, Wilfrid Hyde-White *(Arthur Fairbrother)*, Grégoire Aslan *(Achmed)*, John Le Mesurier *(George Lillywhite)*, Klaus Kinski *(Jonquil)*, Margaret Lee *(Samia Voss)*, Emile Stemmler *(hotel clerk)*, Helen Sanguineti *(Madame Bouseny)*, Sanchez Francisco *(Martinez)*, William Sanguineti *(police chief)*, Hassan Essakali *(motorcycle policeman)*, Keith Peacock *(Philippe)*, Burt Kwouk *(export manager)*.

Mystery comedy. Among the passengers arriving at Marrakesh Airport is an unknown courier carrying $2 million intended for Narim Casimir, an espionage agent who has agreed to sell secret documents which could shift a crucial United Nations vote in favor of the People's Republic of China. As the passengers check into a hotel, there is a mixup in the rooms assigned to Andrew Jessel, an American architect posing as an oil representative, and beautiful journalist Kyra Stanovy. A corpse is found in Kyra's room, and Jessel tries to help dispose of it. He thereby runs afoul of Casimir's henchmen, who had planted the body in order to incriminate Kyra, whom they know to be an American CIA agent. Jessel becomes even more enmeshed in the intrigue when he goes to Casimir to protest the attempted frameup and inadvertently takes the briefcase containing the secret documents. Now marked for certain death, Jessel and Kyra flee through the streets and bazaars of Marrakesh into the hills. They are aided by desert adventurer Achmed and by El Caid, an English-educated Arab chieftain. Casimir succeeds in capturing both Kyra and El Caid just prior to his rendezvous with the courier, Arthur Fairbrother, an Englishman who has been posing as a sanitary engineer. Jessel, aided by a band of ruffians recruited by Achmed, comes to the rescue and, by capturing both Casimir and Fairbrother, foils the plot to fix the U. N. vote. *Couriers. Americans in foreign countries. Journalists. Adventurers. Arabs. Architects. Espionage. Murder. Imposture. Frameup. Hotels. Deserts. Marrakesh. Morocco. People's Republic of China. United States—Central Intelligence Agency. United Nations. Documentation. Chases.*

Note: Filmed in Marrakesh. Opened in London in May 1966 as *Our Man in Marrakesh*. Peter Welbeck is a pseudonym of Harry Alan Towers.

THE BANK BREAKER see KALEIDOSCOPE

BANKOKKU NO YORU see NIGHT IN BANGKOK

BANNED   F6.0292

Imperial Pictures. *Dist* CIP Ltd. 23 Feb **1966** [San Francisco showing]. Sd; b&w. 35mm. 67 min.

Cast: Judy Adler.

Sex film. The film is about the making of a motion picture subsequently seized by authorities after its first theatrical showing. *Censorship. Sex exploitation films.*

BANNING   F6.0293

Universal Pictures. 30 Jun **1967** [Nashville, Tennessee, opening; c2 Sep 1967; LP37875]. Sd (Westrex); col (Technicolor). 35mm (Techniscope). 102 min.

Prod Dick Berg. *Asst Prod* David A. Hammond. *Dir* Ron Winston. *Screenplay* James Lee. *Story* Hamilton Maule. *Dir Photog* Loyal Griggs. *Art Dir* Alexander Golitzen, Henry Bumstead. *Set Decor* John McCarthy, George Milo. *Main Titl* Cinefx, Phill Norman. *Film Ed* J. Terry Williams. *Mus* Quincy Jones. *Mus Supv* Joseph Gershenson. *Song:* "The Eyes of Love" Quincy Jones, Bob Russell. *Sung by* Gil Bernal. *Sd* Waldon O. Watson, William Russell. *Asst Dir* Edward K. Dodds. *Unit Prod Mgr* Wallace Worsley. *Gowns* Jean Louis. *Makeup* Bud Westmore. *Hairstyles* Larry Germain.

Cast: Robert Wagner *(Mike Banning)*, Anjanette Comer *(Carol Lindquist)*, Jill St. John *(Angela Barr)*, Guy Stockwell *(Jonathan Linus)*, James Farentino *(Chris Patton)*, Susan Clark *(Cynthia Linus)*, Howard St. John *(J. Pallister Young)*, Mike Kellin *(Harry Kalielle)*, Gene Hackman *(Tommy Del Gaddo)*, Sean Garrison *(Richard Tyson)*, Logan Ramsey *(Doc Brewer)*, Edmon Ryan *(Stuart Warren)*, Oliver McGowan *(Senator Brady)*, Lucille Meredith *(Maggi Andrews)*, William Cort *(Tony)*.

Melodrama. Although professional golfer Mike Banning has been inactive for over 5 years, he takes a job as assistant pro at the El Presidente Country Club to help pay the gambling debt of his old friend Doc Brewer. His presence immediately arouses the interest of two aggressive women—Angela Barr, a wealthy socialite, and Cynthia, the wife of top pro Jonathan Linus. Banning, however, finds himself attracted to social director Carol Lindquist, unaware that she is Linus' mistress and a widow with a young daughter. After Banning learns that Cynthia helps her father, J. Pallister Young, cheat at poker, he blackmails Young into staging a "calcutta," a special tournament with an enormous cash prize. The leading partners in the match are Banning and Richard Tyson (Young's nephew), who are opposing Young and caddy Chris Patton. Before the tournament, Patton's resentment of Banning's position in the

club results in a fist fight, and Patton ends up with a broken wrist. He is replaced by Linus, who attempts to disqualify Banning by pointing out that he once tried to throw a match; Young, however, has learned from Cynthia that Linus had framed Banning, and so the calcutta takes place on schedule. Banning and Tyson win, and Banning leaves his share of the money to pay for Doc Brewer's debt; he then leaves the country club, hinting to Carol that he may send for her and the child. *Socialites. Social directors. Mistresses. Widows. Caddies. Golf. Debt. Filial relations. Cheating. Blackmail. Frameup. Country clubs. Poker. Tournaments.*

BAR MAID   F6.0294

Kirt Films International. *Dist* Distribpix, Inc. 19 Aug **1970** [Champaign, Illinois, showing]. Sd; col. 35mm. 64 min.

Sex film. Cherry, a smalltown girl, goes to the big city and finds work as a barmaid at Betty's Place, a bar that has sex parties in the back room. Cherry becomes a prostitute and has a variety of sexual experiences there. *Barmaids. Prostitutes. Sexuality. Bars.*

BARABBAS (Italy)   F6.0295

Dino De Laurentiis Cinematografica. *Dist* Columbia Pictures. 10 Oct **1962** [New York opening; c1 Dec 1962; LP23761]. Sd; col (Technicolor). 35mm & 70mm (Technirama 70). 144 min. [Also reviewed at 134 min.]

A Dino De Laurentiis Production. *Prod* Dino De Laurentiis. *Assoc Prod* Luigi Luraschi. *Dir* Richard Fleischer. *Screenplay* Christopher Fry, Ivo Perilli, Diego Fabbri, Nigel Balchin. *Photog* Aldo Tonti. *Art Dir* Mario Chiari. *Set Decor* Maurizio Chiari. *Film Ed* Raymond Poulton, Alberto Gallitti. *Mus Comp* Mario Nascimbene. *Mus Cond* Franco Ferrara. *Asst to the Prod* Ralph Serpe. *Cost* Maria De Matteis.

Cast: Anthony Quinn *(Barabbas)*, Silvana Mangano *(Rachel)*, Arthur Kennedy *(Pontius Pilate)*, Katy Jurado *(Sara)*, Harry Andrews *(St. Peter)*, Vittorio Gassman *(Sahak)*, Jack Palance *(Torvald)*, Ernest Borgnine *(Lucius)*, Valentina Cortese *(Julia)*, Arnoldo Foà *(Joseph of Arimathaea)*, Norman Wooland *(Rufio)*, Enrico Glori *(important gentleman)*, Carlo Giustini *(officer)*, Rina Braido *(reveller in tavern)*, Douglas Fowley *(potter)*, Laurence Payne *(disciple)*, Michael Gwynn *(Lazarus)*, Gustavo De Nardo *(man in potter's store)*, Tullio Tomadoni *(blind man)*, Maria Zanoli *(beggar)*, Friedrich Ledebur *(second officer)*, Guido Celano *(Scorpio)*, Spartaco Nale *(overseer)*, Gianni Di Benedetto *(3d officer)*, Vladimiro Picciafuochi *(farm superintendent)*, Bobby Hall *(commander of gladiators)*, Joe Robinson *(gladiator)*, Ivan Triesault *(emperor)*, Roy Mangano, actor *(Christ)*, Nando Angelini, Marcello Di Martire.

Religious epic. Source: Pär Lagerkvist, *Barabbas* (Stockholm, 1950). Each year at Passover, the people of Jerusalem are permitted to grant freedom to one of two condemned prisoners. It is thus that Barabbas, an assassin and thief, is pardoned by popular acclaim while Jesus is sent to be crucified. Upon his release, Barabbas discovers that his beloved, Rachel, has become a follower of Christ; and she tells him of the Resurrection. Unable to comprehend her faith in Christ as the Messiah, Barabbas meets with Saint Peter and Christ's disciples and hears Lazarus' story, but he remains unconvinced and returns to his old way of life after Rachel is stoned to death as a heretic. Inevitably, he is again taken prisoner, and this time he is sentenced to a lifetime of slave labor in the sulphur mines of Sicily. In the years that follow he is chained to a Christian, Sahak, who wins his admiration, but Barabbas still refuses to admit the existence of a God. Barabbas and Sahak emerge the sole survivors when the mine collapses, and they are eventually taken to Rome, where they are trained as gladiators. Because of his faith, Sahak refuses to kill, and he is put to death. Barabbas vanquishes Torvald, the sadistic captain of the gladiators, in the circus arena. As a reward for his courage, he is granted his freedom by the emperor. After giving Sahak a Christian burial in the catacombs, Barabbas discovers that Rome is on fire. Believing the Roman charge that the Christians are responsible for the deed, Barabbas decides to help those whom he has denied; and he adds a torch to the flames. He is captured and sentenced to be crucified along with many Christians. *Gladiators. Thieves. Religious conversion. Christianity. Slavery. Conscience. Crucifixion. Incendiarism. Capital punishment. Sulfur. Mines. Rome—History—Empire. Jerusalem. Sicily. Barabbas. Pontius Pilate. Jesus. Lazarus. Saint Peter. Fires. The Resurrection.*

Note: Opened in Rome in Dec 1961 as *Barabba*.

BARB WIRE see SHOOT OUT AT BIG SAG

BARBARA   F6.0296

Druidstone-Hottentot Production Corp. *Dist* Olympia Films. 10 Aug **1970** [New York opening; c10 Aug 1970; MP21107]. Sd; b&w. 16mm. 91 min.

Prod Walter Burns, Josef Bush, Bill Haislip. *Dir* Walter Burns. *Screenplay* Josef Bush. *Camera* Oswaldo Novaes. *Asst Camera* Francisco Novaes. *Film Ed* Walter Burns, Josef Bush, Bill Haislip, Neil Irwin. *Film Cutter* Francisco Novaes. *Song:* "Candy Bar" writ & perf by Michael Lytle, Ronnie Franklin. *Songs:* "Just a Little Bit of Love," "The Ordinary Country Wife," "A Song To

Console You," "Numbers, Places, Change Partners, and Dance" writ & perf by Joseph Bomarito, Joseph Currie. *Guitar* Ellen Kole. *Piano* Frank Mele. *Bass Guitar* Russ O'Hara. *Drums* Buddy Saltzman. *Organ Mus Perf by* Mildred V. Larson. *Asst Dir* Daniel Landau. *Movie Stills* Dion McGregor Collection.

Cast: Jack Rader *(Max)*, Nancy Boyle *(Leslie)*, Robert McLane *(Tom)*, Barbara *(Barbara)*, John Kuhner *(Franz)*, Melba La Rose, Jr. *(Gemma)*, Bill Haislip *(Zoltan)*, Myron "Butch" Ogelsby *(Sam)*, Erika Freeman *(waitress)*, Tequila Mockingbird *(Supernnom)*, Will Gary *(Frank)*, Francisco Novaes *(laborer)*, Robert Floria, Art Hill *(fishermen)*, Elsa Tresko *(woman)*, Ute Sielaff *(Doris)*, Victor Smith *(sentry)*, Marcia Mohr *(suburban housewife)*.

Comedy-drama. Source: Frank Newman, *Barbara* (New York, 1968). Teenaged Barbara spends the summer on Fire Island with her parents and brother. She is sexually initiated by a "guru," and with another couple, she experiments with sex. While on a macrobiotic diet, the young people practice sodomy, homosexuality, and lesbianism, as well as heterosexual relations. Barbara seduces her younger brother, and together they attempt to convert their parents to the new lifestyle. *Adolescence. Filial relations. Sexual initiation. Male homosexuality. Lesbianism. Incest. Brother-sister relationship. Vacations. Fire Island.*

Note: Filmed on Fire Island.

BARBARELLA (France/Italy) **F6.0297**
Marianne Productions–Dino De Laurentiis Cinematografica. *Dist* Paramount Pictures. 11 Oct **1968** [New York opening; c4 Oct 1968; LF29]. Sd; col (Technicolor). 35mm (Panavision). 98 min.

A Dino De Laurentiis Production. *Prod* Dino De Laurentiis. *Dir* Roger Vadim. *2d Unit Dir* Alberto Cardone. *Screenplay* Terry Southern, Brian Degas, Jean-Claude Forest, Clement Biddle Wood, Roger Vadim, Claude Brulé, Tudor Gates, Vittorio Bonicelli. *Dir Photog* Claude Renoir. *2d Unit Photog* Wladimir Ivanov. *Art Dir* Enrico Fea. *Set Dir* Giorgio Herman. *Prod Dsgn* Mario Garbuglia. *Main Titl* Arcady. *Film Ed* Victoria Mercanton. *Mus* Maurice Jarre. *Songs:* "Barbarella," "Love, Love, Love Drags Me Down," "I Love All the Love in You" Charles Fox, Bob Crewe. *Sung by* The Glitterhouse. *Song:* "An Angel Is Love" Charles Fox, Bob Crewe. *Perf by* The Bob Crewe Generation. *Instrumental:* "The Black Queen's Beads" Charles Fox, Bob Crewe. *Sd Mix* David Hildyard. *Asst Dir* Carlo Lastricati. *Prod Supv* Guy Luongo. *Prod Mgr* Roberto Cocco. *Cost Dsgn* Jacques Fonteray. *Cost for Barbarella in Last Seq* Paco Rabanne. *Hairstyles* Amalia Paoletti. *Sp Eff* Augie Lohman. *Artistic Cons* Jean-Claude Forest.

Cast: Jane Fonda *(Barbarella)*, John Phillip Law *(Pygar)*, Anita Pallenberg *(The Black Queen)*. Milo O'Shea *(Durand-Durand, the concierge)*. David Hemmings *(Dildano)*, Marcel Marceau *(Professor Ping)*, Ugo Tognazzi *(Mark Hand)*. Claude Dauphin *(President of Earth)*, Antonio Sabato *(Jean-Paul)*, Talitha Pol *(pipe-smoking girl)*, Serge Marquand *(Captain Sun)*, Véronique Vendell *(Captain Moon)*, Maria Theresa Orsini *(The Suicide Girl)*, Catherine Chevalier *(Stomoxys)*, Marie Thérèse Chevalier *(Glossina)*, Sergio Ferrero *(The Black Queen's messenger)*, Giancarlo Cobelli *(The Revolutionary)*, Nino Musco *(The Generale)*, Chantal Cachin *(The Female Revolutionary)*, Romolo Valli, Franco Gulà, Barbara Winner, Carla Rousso, Umberto Di Grazia.

Science fiction satire. Based on the comic strip by: Jean-Claude Forest, *Barbarella* (Paris, 1964). Barbarella, a beautiful 41st-century astronaut, is ordered by the President of Earth to find Durand-Durand, an Earth scientist who has disappeared with the secret of the Positronic Ray, a powerful new weapon. Landing on the planet Lythion, Barbarella is attacked by carnivorous dolls manipulated by two seemingly sweet twin girls. Bearded hunter Mark Hand rescues her and reveals that Durand-Durand is in the city of Sogo. Barbarella shows her appreciation by making love to him in the "old-fashioned" way that has long been replaced on Earth by exaltation-transference pills. Taking off again, Barbarella accidentally crashes into a labyrinth inhabited by outcasts from Sogo. Once the kindly orchid-chewing Professor Ping has repaired her spaceship, the blind angel Pygar flies her to Sogo after his will to fly is restored by Barbarella during a sexual therapy session in his nest. The pair are soon captured by Sogo's Black Queen and her concierge; Pygar is subjected to a mock crucifixion and then seduced by the Queen, while Barbarella barely escapes being pecked to death by hundreds of birds. Dildano, her rescuer and head of the local underground revolutionaries, agrees to help her find Durand-Durand; in return, Barbarella shows him how to make love by means of finger-touching while under the influence of the exaltation-transference pills. But Dildano's bumbling assistance only leads to Barbarella's recapture by the concierge, who is revealed as none other than Durand-Durand himself. The wicked scientist tries to kill Barbarella by sealing her in a machine that induces fatal sexual pleasure; instead, Barbarella's stamina causes the machine to blow all its fuses. Durand-Durand then attempts to destroy the Black Queen, but she retaliates by releasing the viscous substance that surrounds the city and has fed off its evil. As Sogo crumbles around them, Pygar clutches Barbarella and the Black Queen in his arms and flies off with them. When Barbarella asks Pygar

why he saved the evil but seductive Queen, he smiles slyly and says, "An angel has no memory." *Astronauts. Space creatures. Royalty. Professors. Scientists. Twins. Angels. Revolutionaries. Hunters. Sexual practices. Seduction. Blindness. Space travel. Death rays. Imaginary planets. The Future.*

Note: Opened in Paris in Oct 1968; released in Italy in 1968.

THE BARBARIANS (Reissue) (Italy) **F6.0298**
Laura Film–Oro. *Dist* Hemisphere Pictures. 24 Jun **1964** [periodical notice]. Sd; b&w. 35mm. 83 min.

Pres by William M. Pizor.

Note: Released in 1957 by Allied Artists as *The Pagans*; released in Italy in 1952 as *Il sacco di Roma*.

BARBIE'S HOSPITAL AFFAIR **F6.0299**
Dist Hollywood Cinema Associates, Distribpix, Inc. ca **1970**. Sd; col (Eastman Color). 35mm. [Feature length assumed.]

Pres by Carl R. Carter. *Prod-Dir-Writ* Arnold Roberts. *Camera* William Cole. *Art Dept* Jack Sossaman. *Sets* Ty Fowler. *Mus* Eddie Levine. *Sd* Fred Meeks. *Makeup* Colier. *Still Photog* Jim Beckham. *Gaffer* Robert Jay.

Cast: Lee Baker, Sterling Eilert, III, Eugene Wilkins, Eddie Levine, Connie Edwards, Ann Box, actress, Angel Albright, Ronnie Gilbert, actor, Luann Cox, Bill Bagley, Lennie London, Ann Rodgers.

Melodrama. Barbie, who is suffering from amnesia, is brought to the hospital after an accident. The relationships between hospital personnel are revealed: a doctor is involved with a nurse; the head nurse blackmails a doctor's girl friend into lesbian acts; a love affair develops between an orderly and a nurse's aide; and an intern falls in love with Barbie. The intern and Barbie marry, and on their wedding night Barbie regains her memory. Barbie was a top call girl, and her amnesia was caused by a severe beating she received from three men who forced her to have sex with them all simultaneously. Barbie's husband is understanding, and Barbie decides to leave the past behind her. *Physicians. Nurses. Hospital interns. Orderlies (hospital). Prostitutes. Amnesia. Blackmail. Lesbianism. Marriage. Hospitals.*

LES BARBOUZES *see* **THE GREAT SPY CHASE**

THE BARE AND THE SHAPELY *see* **THE RUINED BRUIN**

THE BARE HUNT; OR MY GUN IS JAMMED **F6.0300**
August Films. *Dist* Olympic International Films. **1963**. Sd; b&w. 35mm. 69 min.

Comedy. Private detective Max T. Unimportant, a self-styled master of disguises, attempts to solve the crime of the year. His investigation leads him to the fringe of the sex exploitation world where he finds beautiful figure models and starlets who are anxious to appear nude before the movie camera. Among those he meets are: the Gypsy Fortune Teller, the women at Madam Myrtle's Model Agency, Cleopatra, and the Boobsy Twins. Max enjoys himself thoroughly, though he fails to catch the suspect. *Detectives. Models. Actors. Fortune-tellers. Disguise. Nudity. Sex exploitation films.*

Note: Also known as *The Bear Hunt* and *My Gun Is Jammed*.

BARE LADY *see* **MY BARE LADY**

BARE WITH ME *see* **CHERRY'S HOUSE OF NUDES**

BARE WORLD *see* **MY BARE LADY**

BAREFOOT IN THE PARK **F6.0301**
Nancy Enterprises–Paramount Pictures. *Dist* Paramount Pictures. 25 May **1967** [New York opening; c25 May 1967; LP34529]. Sd; col (Technicolor). 35mm. 105 min.

A Hal Wallis Production. *Prod* Hal B. Wallis. *Assoc Prod* Neil Simon, Paul Nathan. *Dir* Gene Saks. *Screenplay* Neil Simon. *Cinematog* Joseph La Shelle. *Art Dir* Hal Pereira, Walter Tyler. *Set Decor* Robert R. Benton, Arthur Krams. *Film Ed* William A. Lyon. *Mus* Neal Hefti. *Titl Song* Johnny Mercer, Neal Hefti. *Sd* Harold Lewis, Charles Grenzbach. *Asst Dir* Howard Grace. *Unit Prod Mgr* William W. Gray, Frank Caffey. *Script Supv* Charlsie Bryant. *Cost Dsgn* Edith Head. *Makeup* Wally Westmore, Frank McCoy. *Hairstyles* Nellie Manley. *Sp Photog Eff* Paul K. Lerpae. *Proc Photog* Farciot Edouart.

Cast: Robert Redford *(Paul Bratter)*, Jane Fonda *(Corie Bratter)*, Charles Boyer *(Victor Velasco)*, Mildred Natwick *(Mrs. Ethel Banks)*, Herbert Edelman *(telephone man)*, James Stone *(delivery man)*, Ted Hartley *(Frank)*, Mabel Albertson *(Aunt Harriet)*, Fritz Feld *(restaurant proprietor)*, John Indrisano *(cop)*, Paul E. Burns *(bum in park)*.

Romantic comedy. Source: Neil Simon, *Barefoot in the Park* (New York opening: 23 Oct 1963). After spending their entire 6-day honeymoon in a suite at New York's Plaza Hotel, Corie and Paul Bratter move into their Greenwich Village apartment. For the optimistic Corie, the whole adventure of making a home is pure enchantment; but Paul, a conservative lawyer, is dismayed by the inconvenience and general drabness. Their upstairs neighbor, Victor Velasco, is a self-admitted rake accustomed to using their bedroom window to reach his own quarters because he has been evicted by the landlord. Corie is fascinated by Victor's continental manner, and she decides that he would be the perfect companion for her widowed mother. When they all go to an Albanian restaurant on Staten Island, Corie's mother, Mrs. Banks, drinks and eats everything that is bad for her ulcer, falls down a flight of stairs, and ends up spending the night at Victor's. The evening also precipitates a quarrel between Corie and Paul, and Corie demands a divorce. Paul goes on a binge, gives his topcoat to a tramp in Washington Square, and starts running barefoot in the 30-degree weather. After a talk with her mother, who admits to a pleasant but harmless evening with Victor, Corie realizes that marriage should be more than a lark. Repentant, she goes to find Paul and bring him home; but, drunkenly determined to live up to Corie's idea of fun, he crawls out on the roof through their skylight and teeters on the ledge. Corie climbs after him and assures him that she does not want him to change. A crowd of sidewalk spectators, including Mrs. Banks and Victor, break into spontaneous applause as the newlyweds reconcile. *Newlyweds. Lawyers. Rakes. Neighbors. Mothers-in-law. Widows. Honeymoons. Marriage. Filial relations. Bohemianism. Drunkenness. New York City—Greenwich Village. New York City—Staten Island. New York City—Central Park. Plaza Hotel (New York City).*

Note: Location scenes filmed in New York City.

THE BAREST HEIRESS see **THE SHAMELESS**

EL BARÓN DEL TERROR see **THE BRAINIAC**

BARQUERO   F6.0302
Aubrey Schenck Enterprises. *Dist* United Artists. 15 May **1970** [Dallas opening; c15 May 1970; LP38059]. Sd; col (De Luxe). 35mm. 108 min. [See note.] *MPAA rating* GP.

An Aubrey Schenck Production. *Exec Prod* Aubrey Schenck. *Dir* Gordon Douglas. *Screenplay* George Schenck, William Marks. *Dir Photog* Gerald Finnerman. *Adtl Photog* Dale Deverman. *Camera Op* Joe Jackman, Ned Davenport. *Camera Asst* Eric Anderson, photog, Dale Siegler, Steve Yaconelli. *Art Dir* Allen E. Smith. *Film Ed* Charles Nelson. *Mus* Dominic Frontiere. *Sd Rec* Robert J. Miller, Bill Tremellen. *Boom* Ben Sad. *Asst Dir* Rusty Meek, Nat Holt, Jr. *Script Supv* Malcolm Atterbury, Jr.. *Asst to the Prod* Ann Tait. *Cost* Ray Phelps, Carl Erbele, Thalia Phillips. *Makeup* Fred Blau, Bob Romero, makeup. *Sp Eff* Horace L. Hulburd, Allen Bastien. *Still Photog* John Monte. *Ch Electrn* Howard Ex. *Prop Master* Arthur Friedrich. *Wrangler* Ivan Conner.

Cast: Lee Van Cleef (*Travis*), Warren Oates (*Remy*), Forrest Tucker (*Mountain Phil*), Kerwin Mathews (*Marquette*), Mariette Hartley (*Anna*), Marie Gomez (*Nola*), Armando Silvestre (*Sawyer*), John Davis Chandler (*Fair*), Craig Littler (*Pitney*), Ed Bakey (*Happy*), Richard Lapp (*Poe*), Harry Lauter (*Steele*), Frank Babich (*Roland*), Armand Alzamora (*Lopez*), Terry Leonard (*Hawk*), Thad Williams (*Gibson*), Bennie Dobbins (*Encow*), Rita Conde (*Layeta*), Brad Weston (*driver*).

Western melodrama. Jake Remy's marauders attack and loot the town of Buckskin, Arizona. Anxious to cross the Paria River into Mexico, three of the bandits enter the town of Lonely Dell, intending to commandeer the ferry operated by Travis. Taken prisoner, the ferryboat captain is rescued by Mountain Phil. Killing two of the bandits, Travis and Mountain Phil keep the third as a hostage. Arriving in Lonely Dell, Remy learns that Travis has transported the town's population to the other side of the river. Although Remy offers booty for passage, Travis refuses. Unaware that Lonely Dell is occupied by the band, villager Roland, hunting during the town's evacuation, falls into Remy's hands. When the bandit offers to exchange Roland for use of the ferry, Travis refuses, despite the sexual favors promised by the hostage's wife. That night, however, Travis and Mountain Phil swim the Paria, stampede Remy's horses, and rescue Roland. The hostage's wife then honors the agreement. Desperate, the band builds a raft and crosses the river. In midstream the barque is intercepted by Travis' ferry. On board are the townspeople, who slaughter the marauders. *Bandits. Hostages. Frontier and pioneer life. Infidelity. Murder. Stampedes. Ferryboats. Arizona. Paria River. Mexico.*

Note: Location scenes filmed in Colorado. Cut from 114 min; also reviewed at 104 min.

BARREN LIVES (Brazil)   F6.0303
Luiz Carlos Barreto-Herbert Richers-Darulo Trellers. *Dist* Pathé Contemporary Films. 5 Jun **1969** [New York opening]. Sd; b&w. 35mm. 100 min.

Prod Luiz Carlos Barreto, Herbert Richers, Darulo Trellers. *Dir-Writ* Nelson Pereira dos Santos. *Photog* Luiz Carlos Barreto, José Rosa. *Film Ed* Rafael Justo.

Cast: Átila Iório (*Fabiano*), Maria Riberio (*Sinhá Vitória*), Jofre Soares (*policeman*), Orlando Macedo (*rancher*), Gilvan, Genivaldo (*children*).

Drama. Source: Graciliano Ramos, *Vidas sêcas* (Rio de Janeiro, 1938). In 1940, a severe drought in the *sertao*, the backland of sparse vegetation in northeastern Brazil, forces a poor family to abandon their home in the hope of finding a patch of soil that will support them. After the mother, Sinhá Vitória, has killed their pet parrot to feed her husband, Fabiano, and two small sons, the family comes to an abandoned, dilapidated shack that belongs to a cattle rancher. In return for being allowed to live in the hut, Fabiano agrees to care for the rancher's livestock. The family are virtual slaves of the rancher; the pittance gained from the year's work allows them no hope of amelioration in their lives. On the day of a festival, Fabiano takes his insignificant earnings, drinks in the village, and is lured into a card game by a cruel policeman. When a quarrel ensues and Fabiano is beaten up by soldiers and thrown into jail, he offers little resistance. The drought returns, decimating the rancher's cattle. Baleia, the family dog, formerly a valued member of the work force, sickens, and Fabiano shoots her. The cattle are moved away, and the family, left with no means of living, gather up their meager possessions and once more set out in search of a better place to live. *Ranchers. Police. Cowboys. Social classes. Drought. Poverty. Survival. Family life. Brazil—Northeast. Dogs. Cattle.*

Note: Produced in Brazil in 1963 as *Vidas sêcas*; running time: 105 min(?).

THE BASHFUL ELEPHANT   F6.0304
McGowan International, Inc. *Dist* Allied Artists. Feb **1962** [c9 Jan 1962; LP20940]. Sd; b&w. 35mm. 82 min. [Copyright length: 85 min.]

Prod-Dir-Writ Dorrell McGowan, Stuart E. McGowan. *Dir Photog* George Tysen. *Camera* Werner Jansen. *Art Dir* Wolf Witzemann. *Film Ed* Hans Nikel. *Mus & Lyr* Ronald Stein. *Sung by* Raffaela. *Asst Dir* Rudolf Zehetruber. *Prod Mgr* Fritz Weiss. *Still Photog* Arthur Hammerer.

Cast: Molly Mack (*Tristy*), Helmut Schmid (*Kurt*), Kai Fischer (*Steffi*), Buddy Baer (*tavern owner*), Fritz Weiss (*Father Francis*), Arnulf Schröder (*police inspector*), Hans Schumm (*Fritz*), Hans Pössenbacher (*constable*), Gernot Duda (*policeman*), Jeffrey (*dog*), Valle (*elephant*).

Melodrama. Aided by a border dog, 12-year-old orphan Tristy escapes from Hungary into Austria where she hopes to find a "papa and mama." Apprehended by police who intend to return her to an orphanage in Hungary, Tristy again escapes and joins a circus. The circus owner's girl friend, captivated by the waif, wants them to marry so that they may adopt Tristy. The Austrian police attempt to take Tristy away, and when they are defied by the girl's dog and a friendly elephant they threaten to shoot the animals. Tristy decides to give herself up, but she is followed by the animals and instead, runs away from the police, taking refuge in a church. Accidentally knocked unconscious by a fall down a flight of stairs, Tristy is picked up by the elephant and carried back to the circus. All ends happily as the circus owner agrees to marry his girl friend and adopt Tristy. *Refugees. Orphans. Police. Circus. Adoption. Marriage. Churches. Hungary. Austria. Dogs. Elephants.*

Note: Filmed in Austria. Some sources suggest that this is a U.S./Austria coproduction.

THE BASTARD WENCH FROM CHICAGO see **THE FABULOUS BASTARD FROM CHICAGO**

LA BATAILLE DE CORINTHE see **THE CENTURION**

LA BATAILLE DE SAN SEBASTIAN see **GUNS FOR SAN SEBASTIAN**

BATANGAS see **MISSION BATANGAS**

BATMAN   F6.0305
Greenlawn Productions. *Dist* Twentieth Century-Fox Film Corp. 30 Jul **1966** [Austin, Texas, opening; c3 Aug 1966; LP32999]. Sd (Westrex); col (DeLuxe). 35mm. 105 min.

Prod William Dozier. *Assoc Prod* Charles B. FitzSimons. *Dir* Leslie H. Martinson. *2d Unit Dir* Ray Kellogg. *Story & Screenplay* Lorenzo Semple, Jr. *Dir Photog* Howard Schwartz. *2d Unit Photog* Jack Marta. *Aerial Photog* Nelson Tyler. *Art Dir* Jack Martin Smith, Serge Krizman. *Set Decor* Walter M. Scott, Chester L. Bayhi. *Main Titl* Richard Kuhn, National Screen Service. *Film Ed* Harry Gerstad. *Mus* Nelson Riddle. "Batman Theme" Neal Hefti. *Orch* Gil Grau. *Sd* Roy Meadows, Harry M. Leonard. *Asst Dir* William Derwin, David Whorf. *Unit Prod Mgr* Sam Strangis. *Script Supv* Duane Toler. *Wardrobe* Jan Kemp, Lee Harmer, Pat Barto. *Makeup* Ben Nye, Bruce Hutchinson. *Hairstyles Supv* Margaret Donovan. *Sp Photog Eff* L. B. Abbott. *Batboat* Glastron. *Prop* Jack Briggs, Walt Douglas, Wes Lee. *Grip* Sam Bishop. *Gaffer* Bill Neff.

Cast: Adam West (*Bruce Wayne [Batman]*), Burt Ward (*Dick Grayson [Robin]*), Lee Meriwether (*Kitka [The Catwoman]*), Cesar Romero (*The Joker*), Burgess Meredith (*The Penguin*), Frank Gorshin (*The Riddler*), Alan Napier (*Alfred*), Neil Hamilton (*Commissioner Gordon*), Stafford Repp (*Chief O'Hara*), Madge Blake (*Aunt Harriet Cooper*), Reginald Denny (*Commodore Schmidlapp*), Milton Frome (*Vice Admiral Fangschliester*), Gil Perkins (*Bluebeard*), Dick Crockett (*Morgan*), George Sawaya (*Quetch*), Sterling Holloway (*Colonel Terry*).

Crime comedy. Based on characters created by: Bob Kane. Batman, the caped crusader, and Robin, the boy wonder, learn that Commodore Schmidlapp, a millionaire distiller, is in danger aboard his yacht and rush to his aid by batcopter, but the yacht disappears beneath Batman as he is descending the batladder. The dynamic duo learns that The Catwoman, The Joker, The Penguin, and The Riddler have joined forces to eliminate Batman and Robin and eventually control the world. (The vanishing yacht was a decoy to lure Batman and Robin from the place where the villains were hijacking the yacht of Commander Redhead and holding him prisoner because they want his invention, a dehydrator that turns humans into dust that can be returned to human form with the addition of water.) After many encounters the villains are still loose, and The Penguin goes to Security Council headquarters. There he turns nine diplomats into dust, which he places in nine test tubes. Batman and Robin, however, outwit and capture the quartet of criminals and rescue Commander Redhead. As they are about to reconstitute the nine diplomats, the commander sneezes on the test tubes, scattering the dust. Batman does his best to sort the dust into nine homogeneous piles, but when the dust is restored to human form, the Russian speaks Greek, the Greek speaks English, and so on. But Batman is satisfied that the world is safe from the four fiends for the time being. *Distillers. Millionaires. Hijackers. Diplomats. Inventors. Conspiracy. Dehydration. Yachts. Helicopters. United Nations—Security Council. Batman.*

Note: The film was inspired by the ABC Television series, *Batman*.

BATS WITH BABY FACES see **GYPSY GIRL**

LA BATTAGLIA DEI MODS see **THE BATTLE OF THE MODS**

LA BATTAGLIA DI ALGERI see **THE BATTLE OF ALGIERS**

LA BATTAGLIA DI FORT APACHE see **SHATTERHAND**

BATTLE ABOARD THE DEFIANT see **DAMN THE DEFIANT!**

BATTLE AT BLOODY BEACH   F6.0306
Associated Producers, Inc. *Dist* Twentieth Century-Fox Film Corp. 7 Jun 1961 [Buffalo, New York opening; c1 Jun 1961; LP19569]. Sd; b&w. 35mm (CinemaScope). 80 min. [Also 83 min.]

A Robert L. Lippert Production. *Prod-Story* Richard Maibaum. *Dir* Herbert Coleman. *Screenplay* Richard Maibaum, Willard Willingham. *Dir Photog* Kenneth Peach. *Art Dir* John Mansbridge. *Set Decor* Harry Reif. *Supv Film Ed* Jodie Copelan. *Mus Comp & Cond* Henry Vars. *Sd* Frank McWhorter, Jack Solomon. *Supv Sd Ed* Jack Cornall. *Asst Dir* Francisco Day, George Batcheller. *Prod Supv* Harold E. Knox. *Script Supv* George Rutter. *Wardrobe* Robert Olivas. *Makeup* Vincent Romaine. *Coöp* United States—Defense Department, United States Navy. *Prop Master* Wilbur Russell.

Cast: Audie Murphy *(Craig Benson)*, Gary Crosby *(Marty Sackler)*, Dolores Michaels *(Ruth Benson)*, Alejandro Rey *(Julio Fontana)*, Marjorie Stapp *(Caroline Pelham)*, Barry Atwater *(Jeff Pelham)*, E. J. Andre *(Dr. Van Bart)*, Dale Ishimoto *(Blanco)*, Miriam Colon *(Nahni)*, Pilar Seurat *(Camota)*, Lillian Bronson *(Delia Ellis)*, William Mims *(M'Keever)*, Ivan Dixon *(Tiger Blair)*, Kevin Brodie *(Timmy Thompson)*, Sara Anderson *(Mrs. Thompson)*, Lloyd Kino *(Japanese lieutenant)*.

War melodrama. During the Japanese invasion of the Philippines, American civilian Craig Benson works with guerrilla fighters on the islands, delivering supplies and evacuating stranded civilians. For some time he has been searching for his wife, Ruth, who became separated from him when the Japanese attacked Manila. Aided by easygoing Marty Sackler, a U. S. Marine radio operator, Benson contacts guerrilla leader Julio Fontana, who agrees to round up Americans hiding in the hills in exchange for U. S. ammunition. Benson also discovers that his wife, thinking that he had been killed, has joined the guerrillas and is now Fontana's mistress. Eventually, Benson and Fontana manage to get a small group of civilians down to a beach where they are scheduled to be met by a submarine. The Japanese suddenly attack, and Marty tries to swim to his radio shack to call for help; but he is killed by a shark. Benson, however, slips away and rounds up a group of guerrilla fighters who defeat the enemy forces. As the submarine arrives to pick up the survivors, Ruth decides to leave Fontana and return to her husband. *Guerrillas. Mistresses. Missing persons. Infidelity. Ammunition. Submarines. World War II. Philippines. Japan—Army. United States Marines. Sharks.*

Note: Francisco Day is also known as Chico Day.

BATTLE BENEATH THE EARTH (United States/Great Britain) F6.0307
Reynolds-Vetter Productions-DDD Productions-Cherokee Productions. *Dist* Metro-Goldwyn-Mayer, Inc. 15 May 1968 [Los Angeles opening; c31 Dec 1967, 6 Feb 1968; LP35455, LP35487]. Sd; col (Technicolor). 35mm. 92 min.

Prod Charles Reynolds. Charles Vetter. *Dir* Montgomery Tully. *Orig Story-Screenplay* Lance Z. Hargreaves. *Photog* Kenneth Talbot. *Camera Op* Alan McCabe. *Art Dir* Jim Morahan. *Supv Ed* Sidney Stone. *Mus* Ken Jones. *Rec Supv* A. W. Watkins. *Sd Rec* J. B. Smith, Gerry Turner. *Dub Ed* Stanley Smith.

Asst Dir Pat Kelly. *Prod Mgr* Ronnie Bear. *Sp Eff* Tom Howard.

Cast: Kerwin Mathews *(Comdr. Jonathan Shaw)*, Viviane Ventura *(Tila Yung)*, Robert Ayres *(Adm. Felix Hillebrand)*, Peter Arne *(Arnold Kramer)*, Al Mulock *(Sgt. Marvin Mulberry)*, Martin Benson *(General Chan Lu)*, Peter Elliott, actor *(Kengh Lee)*, Earl Cameron *(Sgt. Seth Hawkins)*, John Brandon *(Maj. Frank Cannon)*, Edward Bishop *(Lieut. Comdr. Vance Cassidy)*, Bill Nagy *(Col. Talbot Wilson)*, Sarah Brackett *(Meg Webson)*, Paula Li Shiu *(Dr. Arnn)*, David Spenser *(Major Chai)*, Michael McStay *(train commander)*, Carl Jaffe *(Dr. Galissi)*, Norma West *(Susan Kramer)*, Larry Cross *(broadcaster)*, Bessie Love *(matron)*, Bee Duffell *(matron's friend)*, Bill Hutchinson, actor *(Lanchek)*, Martin Terry *(mine foreman)*, Frank Lieberman, Roy Pattison *(police)*, Chela Matthison *(nurse)*.

Science fiction melodrama. Scientist Arnold Kramer's theory that an enemy power is digging a complex of tunnels beneath United States soil is verified by findings of the Los Alamos Atomic Detection Center. The Pentagon determines that the Communist Chinese are building the subterranean network and orders Comdr. Jonathan Shaw to help Kramer avert disaster. Their assignment is to prevent the Chinese from detonating the stockpiled nuclear weapons that they have delivered into the tunnels by a single supply shaft under the Pacific Ocean. After Shaw has set up his staff, including geologist Tila Yung, inside an extinct Hawaiian volcano, he prepares to attack the Chinese supply tunnel, while Kramer builds a borer equipped with a laser beam head. Before the mission can be accomplished, however, Shaw, Kramer, Tila Yung, and the others are captured by General Chan Lu. Kramer heroically gives his life to save the others, who escape. Shaw then activates the mechanism on one of the nuclear weapons, and a tremendous blast erupts inside the tunnel, destroying the Chinese forces and creating an enormous mushroom cloud over the Pacific. *Scientists. Chinese. Communists. Geologists. Cold war. Self-sacrifice. Tunnels. Nuclear weapons. Laser. Volcanoes. Los Alamos. Pacific Ocean. Hawaii. United States Army. United States Navy. The Pentagon.*

Note: Released in Great Britain ca1969; running time: 83 min.

BATTLE BEYOND THE STARS see **THE GREEN SLIME**

BATTLE BEYOND THE SUN (U.S.S.R.)   F6.0308
Dovzhenko Film Studio. *Dist* American International Pictures. 13 Feb 1963 [Detroit opening]. Sd; col (Sovcolor). 35mm. 75 min. [Also reviewed at 67 min.]

Production Credits for "Nebo Zovyot": *Dir* A. Kozyr, M. Karyukov. *Screenplay* A. Sazonov, Ye. Pomeshchikov. *Screenplay Collab* M. Karyukov. *Story Ed* R. Korol. *Photog* Nikolay Kulchitskiy. *Art Dir* Yu. Shvets. *Sets* A. Borin. *Film Ed* L. Mkhitaryants. *Mus* Yu. Meytus. *Cond* V. Tolba, V. Meshcherin. *Sd* G. Parakhnikov. *Asst Dir* V. Fokin. *Artistic Supv* T. Levchuk. *Prod Mgr* T. Kulchitskaya. *Cost* G. Glinkova. *Makeup* Ye. Odinovich. *Sp Eff* F. Semyannikov, N. Ilyushin, Yu. Shvets, G. Lukashov.

Production Credits for U. S. Release Vers (see note): *Prod* Filmgroup Inc. *Prod-Dir* Thomas Colchart. *Exec Prod* Roger Corman. *Screenplay* Nicholas Colbert, Edwin Palmer. *English Vers Adapt* Francis Ford Coppola.

Cast—"Nebo Zovyot": Ivan Pereverzev *(Kornev)*, A. Shvorin *(Gordiyenko)*, K. Bartashevich *(Klark)*, G. Tonunts *(Verst)*, V. Chernyak *(Somov)*, V. Dobrovolskiy *(Demchenko)*, A. Popova *(Korneva)*, T. Litvinenko *(Lena)*, L. Borisenko *(Olga)*, L. Lobov *(Sashko)*, S. Filimonov *(Troyan)*, M. Samoylova *(Klark's mother)*.

Cast—U. S. Release Vers (see note): Edd Perry, Arla Powell, Andy Stewart, Bruce Hunter, Gene Tonner, Barry Chertok, Lawrence Loben, Kirk Barton, Frederick Farley, Thomas Littleton, Mary Kannon, Linda Barrett.

Science fiction melodrama. Sometime in the future, the Earth is divided into North Hemis and South Hemis, two great nations with coinciding plans to explore Mars. As the North Hemis spaceship prepares to blast off from a space station, the South Hemis spaceship lands on the same platform and unexpectedly takes off for Mars, thus forcing the other spaceship into a race. But the South Hemis spaceship is drawn toward the Sun, forcing its rivals to perform a rescue mission and take its members aboard. Now perilously low on fuel because of the rescue maneuver, the North Hemis ship must land on Astar, a celestial body in the orbit of Mars. The men appear doomed: one of the South Hemis crew becomes delirious and envisions a nightmarish battle between two grotesque space creatures. As he awakens, another spaceship lands on Astar, piloted by a crew member injured during the unexpected take-off by South Hemis. He brings sufficient fuel for the stranded craft to return to Earth, but he dies from the effects of the hard journey. The two crews subsequently unite and dedicate their space pursuits to his memory. [In the original version, a Soviet writer visits a space research center and that evening imagines future space travel. The space exploration involves rocket ships from the Soviet Union and a foreign nation.] *Astronauts. Space creatures. Space exploration. Space rescue. Self-sacrifice. Spaceships. The Sun. Mars (planet). The Future. Dreams.*

Note: Released in the U.S.S.R. in Sep 1959 as *Nebo zovyot*; running time: 77 min. Additional footage may have been added for U. S. release. Thomas Colchart, Nicholas Colbert, and Edwin Palmer appear to be pseudonyms for

Soviet director and writers. U. S. cast credits are pseudonyms for Soviet actors: Edd Perry (Ivan Pereverzev), Arla Powell (A. Popova), Andy Stewart (A. Shvorin), Gene Tonner (G. Tonunts), Barry Chertok (V. Chernyak), Lawrence Loben (L. Lobov), Kirk Barton (K. Bartashevich), and Linda Barrett (L. Borisenko).

THE BATTLE FOR ANZIO *see* ANZIO

BATTLE FOR KHARTOUM *see* KHARTOUM

THE BATTLE HOURS *see* COUNTERPOINT

THE BATTLE OF ALGIERS (Algeria/Italy)   **F6.0309**

Igor Film-Casbah Films. *Dist* Rizzoli Film Distributors, Allied Artists. 21 Sep **1967** [New York opening]. Sd; b&w. 35mm (CinemaScope). 120 min. [Also 125 min.]

Pres by Gene Wesson, Albert Schwartz, Harry Diamond. *Prod* Antonio Musu, Yacef Saadi. *Dir* Gillo Pontecorvo. *Assoc Dir (see note)* Ali Yahia. *2d Unit Dir* Giuliano Montaldo. *Screenplay* Franco Solinas. *Story* Gillo Pontecorvo, Franco Solinas. *Dir Photog* Marcello Gatti. *Art Dir-Set Decor* Sergio Canevari. *Film Ed* Mario Serandrei, Mario Morra. *Mus* Ennio Morricone, Gillo Pontecorvo. *Asst Dir* Fernando Morandi, Moussa Haddad. *Prod Mgr* Sergio Merolle, Nour Eddine Bhahimi. *Sp Eff* Tarcisio Diamanti, Aldo Gasparri.

Cast: Jean Martin (*Colonel Mathieu*), Yacef Saadi (*Saari Kader*), Brahim Haggiag (*Ali la Pointe*), Tommaso Neri (*Captain Dubois*), Fawzia El-Kader (*Halima*), Samia Kerbash (*Fathia*), Mohamed Ben Kassen (*Petit Omar*), Ugo Paletti (*The Captain*).

Historical drama. In October 1957, Ali la Pointe, a leader of the Algerian FLN (Front de Liberation Nationale), is trapped by the French in his house in the Casbah. He reflects back to the time 3 years earlier in 1954 when he became involved in the struggle for freedom: *Ali, who had been a petty thief, joins the guerrilla movement after his release from prison. He soon becomes a leader in the struggle to rid the Casbah of its brothels and other vice. Under the leadership of Saari Kader, the Arabs undertake terrorist activities against the European community in Algiers, including the shooting of policemen to obtain weapons. Although the Governor attempts to squelch the uprising by sealing off the Casbah (where most of the FLN are in hiding), the attacks continue. Then a journalist belonging to a French extremist group which includes a number of police officials takes advantage of his press card to gain entry into the Casbah and plant a bomb which kills scores of Arabs. In retaliation, Kader has three Arab women leave the Casbah in European dress and plant time bombs in a crowded cafe, a dance bar, and an air terminal. By 1957 the French are desperate and bring in the 10th Paratroop Division headed by Colonel Mathieu. Quick to understand that the FLN is set up like a pyramid in which no one member knows the identity of more than three others, Mathieu uses torture to force captured terrorists to reveal the names of their comrades. When the FLN orders an 8-day general strike while the United Nations debates the crisis, Mathieu intensifies his efforts to break down the structure of the pyramid and capture Kader, Larbi Ben M'Hidi, and the other group leaders. By the time the United Nations has decided not to intervene, Mathieu has eliminated all but one of the FLN chiefs—Ali la Pointe. Eventually, the address of Ali's hideout is discovered, and he and three others, including a young boy, Omar, are trapped behind the wall of a bedroom. Mathieu delivers the ultimatum that unless they surrender, the house will be blown up.* Ali and his comrades refuse to yield and, as Arabs throughout the Casbah pray, the last four survivors of the FLN die. For over 3 years, until December 1960, there is relative quiet. Then, without warning, rioting erupts anew as thousands upon thousands of Algerians roar through the streets shouting their cry of freedom. The struggle continues until finally—on July 3, 1962—Algeria wins its independence. *French. Journalists. Revolutionaries. Police. Nationalism. Terrorism. Poverty. Strikes. Torture. Bombs. Algeria—History—1945-62. Algeria—History—War of Independence. Algiers. Ammar Ali. Larbi Ben M'Hidi. France—Army.*

Note: Filmed in Algiers in 1965 as *Maarakat Alger*. Released in Italy in 1966 as *La battaglia di Algeri*; running time: 135 min. The production was subsidized by the Algerian government; the people of Algiers served as its cast. Samia Kerbash is also known as Michèle Kerbash. Associate director credit is unconfirmed.

BATTLE OF BRITAIN (Great Britain)   **F6.0310**

Spitfire Productions. *Dist* United Artists. 20 Oct **1969** [New York opening; c15 Sep **1969**; LF54]. Sd; col (Technicolor). 35mm (Panavision). 132 min. *MPAA rating* G.

Prod Harry Saltzman, S. Benjamin Fisz. *Assoc Prod* John Palmer. *Dir* Guy Hamilton. *Aerial & 2d Unit Dir* David Bracknell. *Screenplay* James Kennaway, Wilfred Greatorex. *Dir Photog* Freddie Young. *2d Unit Photog* Bob Huke. *Aerial Photog* Skeets Kelly, John Jordan. *Supv Art Dir* Maurice Carter. *Art Dir* Bert Davey, Jack Maxsted, William Hutchinson, Gil Parrondo. *Main Titl*

Maurice Binder. *Film Ed* Bert Bates. *Mus Comp & Cond* Ron Goodwin. *Comp:* "Battle in the Air" William Walton. *Cond* Malcolm Arnold. *Sd Ed* James Shields, Ted Mason. *Sd* Gordon Everett, Gordon McCallum. *Asst Dir* Derek Cracknell. *Prod Supv* Sydney Streeter. *Spanish Prod Mgr* Agustin Pastor. *Prod Mgr* Claud Hudson. *Aerial Unit Prod Mgr* Bernard Williams. *Cont* Elaine Schreyeck. *Wardrobe Supv* John Wilson-Apperson. *Wardrobe Mistress* Brenda Dabbs. *Ch Makeup* George Frost, Eric Allwright. *Hairstyles* A. G. Scott. *Sp Eff* Cliff Richardson, Glen Robinson, Wally Veevers, Ray Caple. *British Technical & Tactical Adv* Hamish Mahaddie, (Group Capt.), Tom Gleave, (Group Capt.), Robert Stanford-Tuck, (Wing Comdr.), Robert Wright, (Wing Comdr.), Ginger Lacey, (Sqn. Ldr.), B. Drobinski, (Sqn. Ldr.), Claire Legge, (Wing Comdr.). *German Technical & Tactical Adv* Adolf Galland, (Lieut. Gen.), Hans Brustellin, (Col.), Franz Frodl, (Maj.). *Prop* John Bennett. *Casting Dir* Maude Spector. *German Casting & Dial Dir* Carl Duering.

Cast: Laurence Olivier (*Air Chief Marshal Sir Hugh Dowding*), Robert Shaw (*Squadron Leader Skipper*), Christopher Plummer (*Sqn. Ldr. Colin Harvey*), Susannah York (*Section Officer Maggie Harvey*), Ian McShane (*Sergeant Pilot Andy*), Michael Caine (*Squadron Leader Canfield*), Kenneth More (*Group Captain Baker*), Trevor Howard (*Air Vice Marshal Keith Park*), Patrick Wymark (*Air Vice Marshal Trafford Leigh-Mallory*), Ralph Richardson (*British minister in Switzerland*), Curt Jürgens (*Baron von Richter*), Harry Andrews (*Sir Francis Stokes*), Michael Redgrave (*Air Vice Marshal Evill*), Nigel Patrick (*Group Captain Hope*), Michael Bates (*Warrant Officer Warrick*), Isla Blair (*Andy's wife*), John Baskcomb (*farmer*), Tom Chatto (*Willoughby's assistant*), James Cosmo (*Jamie*), Robert Flemyng (*Wing Commander Willoughby*), Barry Foster (*Squadron Leader Edwards*), Edward Fox (*Pilot Officer Archie*), W. G. Foxley (*Squadron Leader Evans*), David Griffin (*Sergeant Pilot Chris*), Jack Gwillim (*senior air staff officer*), Myles Hoyle (*Peter*), Duncan Lamont (*Flight Sergeant Arthur*), Sarah Lawson (*Skipper's wife*), Mark Malicz (*Pasco*), André Maranne (*French N.C.O.*), Anthony Nicholls (*minister*), Nicholas Pennell (*Simon*), Andrzej Scibor (*Ox*), Jean Wladon (*Jean-Jacques*), Wilfried van Aacken (*General Osterkamp*), Karl Otto Alberty (*Jeschonnek*), Alexander Allerson (*Major Brandt*), Dietrich Frauboes (*Field Marshal Milch*), Alf Jungermann (*Brandt's navigator*), Peter Hager (*Field Marshal Kesselring*), Wolf Harnisch (*General Fink*), Reinhard Horras (*Bruno*), Helmut Kircher (*Boehm*), Paul Neuhaus (*Major Foehn*), Malte Petzel (*Col. Beppo Schmid*), Manfred Reddemann (*Major Falke*), Hein Riess (*Reichs Marshal Goering*), Rolf Stiefel (*Hitler*).

Historical epic. Partially based on the book by: Derek Wood and Derek Dempster, *The Narrow Margin* (London, 1961). After the evacuation of Dunkirk and Britain's rejection of Hitler's offer for an armistice, the British hope to gain time to rearm for the inevitable clash with the Luftwaffe. Following Goering's plan to destroy British air power on the ground, the Luftwaffe attacks airfields in southern England, causing heavy losses. The RAF is able to fight back effectively, however, thus vindicating Air Chief Marshal Hugh Dowding's policy of maintaining protective strength in Britain during the battle for France. Continuous assaults by the Germans begin to place a strain on the RAF's most experienced pilots, such as Squadron Leaders Skipper and Harvey, and inexperienced fliers are hurriedly trained for the daily operations. When a German plane accidentally bombs London, the British retaliate by shelling Berlin; Hitler, furious that the enemy was able to penetrate his country, calls for the destruction of London and other British cities. The RAF uses the time of the blitzkrieg to rebuild the destroyed airfields and to regroup with the aid of the Polish Freedom Fighters; Goering's massive attack is met by a strong RAF, and the order to invade Britain is cancelled. *Air pilots. Aerial bombardment. Airfields. World War II. Dunkirk. France. London. Adolf Hitler. Hermann Göring. Hugh Caswall Dowding. Great Britain—Royal Air Force. Germany—Air Force.*

Note: Location scenes filmed at Duxford, Hawkinge, North Weald, and Northold airfields in England, and at the Tablana airfield in Spain. Opened in London in Sep 1969.

BATTLE OF THE ASTROS *see* MONSTER ZERO

BATTLE OF THE BULGE   **F6.0311**

United States Productions-Sidney Harmon-Cinerama, Inc. *Dist* Warner Bros. Pictures. 16 Dec **1965** [Los Angeles opening; c18 Jun 1966; LP33759]. Sd (Westrex); col (Technicolor). 35mm & 70mm (Ultra-Panavision, see note). 162 min. [Copyright length: 140 min.]

Prod Milton Sperling, Philip Yordan. *Dir* Ken Annakin. *Screenplay* Philip Yordan, Milton Sperling, John Melson. *Dir Photog* Jack Hildyard. *2d Unit Photog* John Cabrera. *Camera Op* Dudley Lovell. *Camera Asst* Ronald Anscombe. *Aerial Photog* Jack Willoughby. *Art Dir* Eugene Lourié. *Supv Ed* Derek Parsons. *Mus Comp & Cond* Benjamin Frankel. *Played by* New Philharmonia Orchestra. *Song:* "Panzerlied" Kurt Wiehle, Benjamin Frankel. *Sd Ed* Kurt Herrnfeld, Alban Streeter. *Sd Rec* David Hildyard, Gordon McCallum. *Asst Dir* José López Rodero, Martín Sacristan, Luis García. *Prod*

Supv Bernard Glasser. *Post-prod Exec* Lester A. Sansom. *Prod Mgr* Tibor Reves, Gregorio Sacristan. *Unit Mgr* Leon Chooluck, Miguel Pérez, Juan Estelrich. *Prod Coörd* Lou Brandt. *Script Supv* Joy Mercer, Marie Wachsman. *Wardrobe* Charles Simminger. *Cost Dsgn* Laure de Zarate. *Makeup* Trevor Crole-Rees, José Maria Sánchez. *Sp Eff Ch* Alex Weldon. *Sp Eff* Richard Parker, Kit West, Basilio Cortijo. *Adv* Meinrad von Lauchert, (Maj. Gen.), Luis Martin Pozuelo, (Lieut. Col.), Sherman Joff, (Lieut. Col.), Edward King. *Dial Coach* Janet Brandt. *Miniature Constr* Henri Assola.

Cast: Henry Fonda *(Lieutenant Colonel Kiley)*, Robert Shaw *(Colonel Hessler)*, Robert Ryan *(General Grey)*, Dana Andrews *(Colonel Pritchard)*, George Montgomery *(Sergeant Duquesne)*, Ty Hardin *(Schumacher)*, Pier Angeli *(Louise)*, Barbara Werle *(Elena)*, Charles Bronson *(Wolenski)*, Hans Christian Blech *(Conrad)*, Werner Peters *(General Kohler)*, James MacArthur *(Lieutenant Weaver)*, Telly Savalas *(Sergeant Guffy)*, Karl Otto Alberty *(von Diepel)*, William Conrad *(narrator)*, Steve Rowland, Robert Woods, Charles Stalnaker, David Thomson, actor, Sebastian Cavalieri, Raoul Pérez, Jack Gaskins, Janet Brandt, Max Slaten, Carl Rapp, Axel Anderson, Donald Pickering, Bud Strait, Peter Herendeen, Ben Tatar, Paul Eshelman, Richard Zeidman, John Schereschewsky, Victor Brandt, Richard Baxter, William Boone, John Clarke, Ward Maule, Paul Polansky, Freddie Toehl, Leland Wyler, Quinn Donoghue, John Friess, Reginald Gillam, Peter Grzcegorczyk, Richard Laver, Harry Van Der Linden, Derek Robertson, Martin Rolin, Robert Royal, Russ Stoddard.

War drama. In December 1944 Allied soldiers are anticipating victory in Europe and the end of the war. U. S. intelligence officer Lieutenant Colonel Kiley, however, believes that the German Army is planning to launch a major, last-ditch offensive in the Ardennes Forest in Belgium. Kiley's superiors, Colonel Pritchard and General Grey, take no action because they believe the Germans to be too exhausted to carry out such an attack. In fact, famed German tank commander Colonel Hessler has been recalled from the Russian front to lead a fullscale attack using troops and a throng of new Tiger tanks. The Germans wait for bad weather to ground the Allies' superior air support and then make their assault. Moreover, the Germans place English-speaking saboteurs, uniformed as military police, behind the lines to cause confusion among the Allies. The force of the assault having lowered the morale of the American troops, Kiley watches as they retreat, and he suddenly deduces that the Germans will soon run out of gasoline; they have been foraging from captured supply dumps now in the hands of the saboteurs. Lieutenant Weaver recognizes the saboteurs for what they are, and, encouraged by the wounded Kiley, he and a small group recapture the largest of the dumps to prevent it from falling to Hessler. As the German tanks approach the dump, Weaver and his men roll the drums of gasoline toward the tanks and ignite them, setting the fleet ablaze and averting the last serious threat of the German Army. *Combat zone life. Sabotage. Disguise. Tanks (armored cars). Gasoline. World War II. Battle of the Bulge. Ardennes. United States Army. United States Army—Intelligence. Germany—Army.*

Note: Filmed in Spain. Roadshow presentations in Cinerama.

BATTLE OF THE JAPAN SEA (Japan)　　　　　　　　**F6.0312**
Toho Co. 30 Oct **1970** [Los Angeles showing]. Sd; col. 35mm. 128 min. *MPAA rating* G.

Exec Prod Tomoyuki Tanaka. *Dir* Seiji Maruyama. *Screenplay* Toshio Yazumi. *Photog* Hiroshi Murai. *Art Dir* Takeo Kita. *Mus* Masaru Sato. *Sp Eff* Eiji Tsuburaya.

Cast: Toshiro Mifune *(Admiral Togo)*, Tatsuya Nakadai *(Major Akashi)*, Yuzo Kayama *(Commander Hirose)*, Chishu Ryu *(General Nogi)*, Susumu Fujita, Mitsuko Kusabue, Ryutaro Tatsumi, Koshiro Matsumoto, Toshio Kurosawa, Yoko Tsukasa.

Historical drama. At the turn of the century, diplomatic relations between Japan and Russia are broken when, following the Boxer Rebellion, Russia refuses to remove its troops from Manchuria. Admiral Togo, commander-in-chief of the combined Japanese fleet, plans to destroy the Russian Asiatic fleet at Port Arthur and Vladivostok and sends Commander Hirose to blockade Port Arthur. Despite an attack by Japanese land forces, the Russian fleet runs the blockade to join the Vladivostok squadron. In Oct 1904, the Russian Baltic fleet, led by Admiral Rozhdestvenski, leaves Libau; Togo assumes they are headed for the Japan Sea. On May 27, 1905, the Japanese fleet soundly defeats the Baltic fleet in the Tushima Strait before the Russians can reach embattled Port Arthur. *Russo-Japanese War 1904–05. China—History—Boxer Rebellion. Port Arthur (China). Vladivostok. Tsushima. Heihachiro Togo. Zinovi Petrovich Rozhdestvenski. Russia—Navy. Japan—Navy.*

Note: Released in Japan in Aug 1969 as *Nihonkai Daikaisen*.

THE BATTLE OF THE MODS (Italy/West Germany)　　　**F6.0313**
Ultra Film-Roxy Film. *Dist* G. G. Productions. caSep **1968**. Sd; col (Eastmancolor). 35mm. 97 min.

Pres by Nick W. Russo. *Prod* Luggi Waldleitner. *Dir* Franco Montemurro. *Screenplay* Ennio De Concini, Adriano Bolzoni, Michael A. Scheiber. *Photog* Mario Montuori. *Mus* Robby Poitevin. *Title Song Sung by* Udo Jürgens.

Cast: Ricky Shayne, Joachim Fuchsberger, Elga Andersen, Eleonora Brown, Orchidea De Santis, Enzo Cerusico, Solveig D'Assunta, Cristina Gajoni, Udo Jürgens, Jürgen Draeger, Rudolf Lenz, Hans Elwenspoek, Solvi Stübing.

Melodrama. Ricky Fuller, a 20-year-old Liverpool guitar-player and member of the Mods, takes part in a gang war against the Rockers. His girl friend is killed in the fracas, and Ricky flees with the police in pursuit. He travels from London to Paris and Genoa and finally to Rome, where he seeks out his father, Robert, an oil tycoon. The meeting does nothing to bridge the gap between Ricky and his father, who is planning a second marriage to Sonia, a member of Italian high society. Sonia attempts to seduce Ricky, and the rivalry between father and son eventually drives Ricky from the comfortable surroundings of Robert's house. He becomes involved in the decadent life of young performers in Rome, meanwhile falling in love with Martine, Sonia's sister. Finally, Ricky succeeds in escaping with Martine from the morass of decadence in which they have been engulfed. *Oil magnates. Guitarists. Upper classes. Mods. Rockers. Youth. Filial relations. Jealousy. Seduction. Gang wars. Liverpool. London. Paris. Genoa. Rome.*

Note: Opened in Rome in Aug 1966 as *La battaglia dei Mods*; in West Germany in Sep 1966 as *Siebzehn Jahr, blondes Haar*. Also known as *Crazy Baby*.

THE BATTLE OF THE VILLA FIORITA (United States/Great Britain)　　**F6.0314**
Warner Bros. Pictures. 26 May **1965** [New York opening; c10 May 1965; LP30547]. Sd; col (Technicolor). 35mm (Panavision). 111 min.

A Delmer Daves Production. *Prod-Dir-Writ* Delmer Daves. *Dir Photog* Oswald Morris. *Art Dir* Carmen Dillon. *Film Ed* Bert Bates. *Mus Comp & Cond* Mischa Spoliansky. *Sd Rec* Les Hammond, Len Shilton. *Prod Supv* Victor Peck. *Sp Wardrobe Dsgn for Miss O'Hara* Biki of Milano, Emilio Pucci. *Makeup* Tony Sforzini. *Hairstyles* A. G. Scott. *Casting* Robert Lennard.

Cast: Maureen O'Hara *(Moira)*, Rossano Brazzi *(Lorenzo)*, Richard Todd *(Darrell)*, Phyllis Calvert *(Margot)*, Martin Stephens *(Michael)*, Elizabeth Dear *(Debby)*, Olivia Hussey *(Donna)*, Maxine Audley *(Charmian)*, Ursula Jeans *(Lady Anthea)*, Ettore Manni *(Father Rossi)*, Richard Wattis *(travel agent)*, Finlay Currie *(master of ceremonies)*, Clelia Matania *(Celestina)*, Rosi Di Pietro *(Giulietta)*.

Domestic drama. Source: Rumer Godden, *The Battle of the Villa Fiorita* (London, 1963). Moira Clavering, a middle-class British housewife, meets and falls in love with Italian concert pianist Lorenzo Tassara during one of the numerous absences of her husband, Darrell. When Darrell finds out about his wife's affair, he suggests that she go to Italy with her lover and decide what she must do. Darrell then takes the responsibility of telling their children, Michael and Debby. Unable to accept their mother's departure, the children follow Moira to Italy, where they confront Moira and Lorenzo. To add to the confusion, Lorenzo's daughter, Donna, also arrives and joins the battle to break up the romance between Moira and her father. The three children try everything from hunger strikes to temper tantrums; when all this fails, Michael and Donna go sailing during a storm. After the children are safely rescued, Moira decides that she must return to London and resume her family life. *Italians. Pianists. Housewives. Children. Infidelity. Family life. Sailboats. London. Italy. Storms.*

Note: Location scenes filmed on the Italian Riviera. Released in Great Britain in 1965; running time: 105 min. Also known as *The Affair of Villa Fiorita*.

BATTLE OF THE WORLDS (Italy)　　　　　　　　**F6.0315**
Ultra Film-Sicilia Cinematografica. *Dist* Topaz Film Corp., Manson Distributing Corp. Mar **1963**. Sd; col. 35mm. 84 min.

Prod Supv Tommaso Sagone. *Dir* Anthony Dawson. *Screenplay* Vassily Petrov. *Cinematog* Cesare Allione. *Film Ed* George Serallon.

Cast: Claude Rains *(Prof. Benjamin Benson)*, Bill Carter *(Fred Steel)*, Maya Brent *(Eva)*, Umberto Orsini *(Bob Cole)*, Jacqueline Derval *(Cathy)*, Renzo Palmer *(General Verrick)*, Carol Danell *(Mrs. Collins)*.

Science fiction melodrama. A planet from another galaxy speeds on a collision course toward Earth, but 95,000 miles away it goes into orbit and sends out flying saucers. News of a possible invasion from outer space creates panic, and Earth's space force leads an attack on the invaders. One of the saucers is maneuvered to land on Earth, and Prof. Benjamin Benson, head of a Pacific island observatory, learns the secret of its electronic brain and uses it to destroy the other saucers. Professor Benson, his assistant Fred Steel, and Fred's fiancée, Eva, receive permission to explore the strange planet to discover the reason for its threat to Earth. They land on the planet, and in a crystal cave, they find thousands of steel skeletons, automatons of an extinct race. Fred and Eva flee the planet, but Benson, intent on discovering the power that brought the planet millions of miles through space, remains behind as rockets from Earth destroy the planet. *Scientists. Space warfare. Space exploration. Flying saucers. Spaceships. Computers. Imaginary planets.*

Note: Released in Italy in 1961 as *Il pianeta degli uomini spenti.* Anthony Dawson is a pseudonym for Antonio Margheriti.

THE BAY OF SAINT-MICHEL *see* **PATTERN FOR PLUNDER**

BAY OF THE ANGELS (France)   **F6.0316**
Sud Pacifique Films. *Dist* Pathé Contemporary Films. 24 Nov **1964** [New York opening]. Sd; b&w. 35mm (CinemaScope). 85 min.

Prod Paul-Edmond Decharme. *Dir-Writ* Jacques Demy. *Dir Photog* Jean Rabier. *Art Dir* Bernard Evein. *Film Ed* Anne-Marie Cotret. *Mus* Michel Legrand. *Sd* André Hervée. *Asst Dir* Constantin Gavras.

Cast: Jeanne Moreau *(Jackie Demaistre),* Claude Mann *(Jean Fournier),* Paul Guers *(Caron),* Henri Nassiet *(Jean's father).*

Drama. Jean Fournier, a young, underpaid Parisian bank clerk, is tempted into trying his luck at the gambling tables at Enghien by a friend, Caron, who has won a considerable sum there. Jean wins, but when he tells his father that he plans to spend his vacation gambling at Nice rather than visiting relatives, his father disowns him. At Nice, Jean meets Jackie Demaistre, a compulsive gambler who has sacrificed her husband and child to her obsession. Together Jackie and Jean win a huge sum of money, but after a spending spree they return to the gaming tables and lose everything. Penniless, Jackie spends the night with Jean. The following day Jean reveals that he has extra funds, and with this money they win fabulously, buy a car, and drive to Monte Carlo. Jean tries to convince Jackie to give up gambling and return to Paris with him, but she tells him that she has only stayed with him because he brings her luck. They lose everything again and return to Nice where Jean's father, who has forgiven him, wires him money to return home. Jean tries to get Jackie to come with him, but instead she pawns her watch and goes to the casino. Sincerely in love with her, Jean follows Jackie to the casino where he again pleads with her. Again she refuses, but when she sees Jean leaving the casino she rushes after him. *Bank clerks. Gamblers. Roulette. Filial relations. Monte Carlo. Nice.*

Note: Opened in Paris in Mar 1963 as *La baie des anges;* running time: 89 min.

BAYOU *see* **POOR WHITE TRASH**

BE CAREFUL HOW YOU WISH *see* **THE INCREDIBLE MR. LIMPET**

BE GLAD ... (Great Britain)   **F6.0317**
Cosmologies Productions. *Dist* Razzmatazz Films. 20 Dec **1970** [New York opening]. Sd; col (Eastman Color). 16mm. 50 min.

Pres by Jay K. Hoffman. *Prod* Austin John Marshall. *Assoc Prod* Joe Boyd. *Dir-Writ* Peter Neal. *Photog* Brian Grainger, David MacDonald, photog, Peter Neal. *Photog on* "The Pirate and the Crystal Ball—A Fable" Peter Neal. *Film Ed* Peter Neal. *Mus & Songs:* "All Writ Down," "Mercy I Cry City," "The Iron Stone" The Incredible String Band. *Location Sd* Derek Rye, Michael Cox, sd, Paul Robinson. *Studio Sd* John Wood, sd.

Cast—Featuring: Mike Heron, Robin Williamson, Rose, Licorice, Dick Steele, John Bailey.

Cast—"The Pirate and the Crystal Ball—A Fable": Rakis *(pirate/miller's son),* Malcolm le Maistre *(bird/hern),* Rose, Licorice, Uiscoba *(fates),* Mike Heron, Robin Williamson *(gods).*

Documentary. The Incredible String Band (Mike Heron and Robin Williamson) is shown in a March 1968 Royal Festival Hall concert, in interview with *Newsweek* reporter Dick Steele, and being visited at their home by their friends, including "groupies" Rose and Licorice, their constant companions. They describe their interest in mysticism and witchcraft, and they display their talent with a variety of western and eastern instruments (guitar, lute, violin, harpsichord, recorder, and sitar). The film ends with an original mimed playlet, "The Pirate and the Crystal Ball—A Fable," which concerns a pirate's attempt to steal a crystal ball from three fates and thus alter destiny. *Musicians. Reporters. Groupies. Pirates. Mysticism. Witchcraft. Mime. Interviews. Folk music. Crystal balls. The Incredible String Band. Royal Festival Hall (London).*

Note: "The Pirate and the Crystal Ball—A Fable" filmed on location in Wales. Released in Great Britain in 1970 as *BE GLAD for the Song Has No Ending.*

BEACH BALL   **F6.0318**
The Patton Co.-La Honda Service Productions. *Dist* Paramount Pictures. 13 Oct **1965** [Louisville, Kentucky, opening; c29 Sep 1965; LP31680]. Sd; col (Technicolor). 35mm. 83 min.

Prod Bart Patton. *Dir* Lennie Weinrib. *Screenplay* David Malcolm. *Photog* Alfred Taylor. *Prod Dsgn* Ray Storey. *Film Ed* Karl Wald. *Mus* Frank Wilson. *Songs:* "I Feel So Good," "Surfin' Shinding," "Wiggle Like You Tickled" Chester Pipkin, Frank Wilson. *Song:* "We've Got Money" Al Capps. *Theme*

Song: "Come to the Beach Ball With Me" & *Song:* "Surfer Boy" Eddie Holland, Brian Holland, Lamont Dozier. "Come to the Beach Ball With Me" sung by The Supremes. *Asst Dir* Gary Kurtz. *Prod Mgr* Peter Broadrick. *Wardrobe* Sharon Compton. *Girls' Beach Wear* Rose Marie Reed. *Makeup* June Gilham. *Hairstyles* George Spicer.

Cast: Edd Byrnes *(Dick Martin),* Chris Noel *(Susan),* Robert Logan *(Bango),* Gail Gilmore *(Deborah),* Aron Kincaid *(Jack),* Mikki Jamison *(Augusta),* Don Edmonds *(Bob),* Brenda Benet *(Samantha),* Anna Lavelle *(Polly),* James Wellman *(Mr. Wolf),* The Supremes, The Four Seasons, The Righteous Brothers, The Hondells, The Walker Brothers *(themselves),* Jack Bernardi, Dick Miller, Bill Sampson, Lee Krieger, John Hyden.

Comedy with music. Dick Martin, manager of the musical group The Wigglers (Bango, Jack, and Bob), is notified by Mr. Wolf that the group owes him $1,000 for their instruments. To obtain the payment demanded, Dick tells Susan, credit union manager of the college they attend, that he needs a sum to continue his research in African tribal rhythms. In fact, he and The Wigglers have dropped out of school and are enjoying life among the surfers and hot rodders at Malibu. Susan and finance committee members Augusta, Samantha, and Deborah decide to deliver the money in person; but upon arriving at the beach, they learn that they have been duped and tear up the check. The four women then don bikinis and join the party in progress in hopes of persuading the men to return to school. Mr. Wolf, frustrated in his attempts to collect the money or repossess the instruments, summons the police; but the musicians evade them by appearing at the "Hot Rod and Musical Show" dressed in women's clothes. The group wins first prize in the competition, and the musicians pay their debts and return to college having won the affections of the four financiers. *Students. Musicians. Merchants. Police. Surfers. Rock and roll. College life. Debt. Female impersonation. Loans. Contests. Beaches. Malibu (California).*

BEACH BLANKET BINGO   **F6.0319**
American International Pictures. Apr **1965** [c14 Apr 1965; LP30614]. Sd; col (Pathé). 35mm (Panavision). 98 min.

Prod James H. Nicholson, Samuel Z. Arkoff. *Co-prod* Anthony Carras. *Dir* William Asher. *Screenplay* William Asher, Leo Townsend. *Photog* Floyd Crosby. *Art Dir* Howard Campbell. *Film Ed* Fred Feitshans, Eve Newman. *Mus* Les Baxter. *Mus Supv* Al Simms. *Songs* Jerry Styner, Guy Hemric. *Perf by* The Hondells. *Choreog* Jack Baker. *Sd* James Nelson. *Asst Dir* Dale Hutchinson. *Cost* Marjorie Corso.

Cast: Frankie Avalon *(Frankie),* Annette Funicello *(Dee Dee),* Deborah Walley *(Bonnie Graham),* Harvey Lembeck *(Eric Von Zipper),* John Ashley *(Steve Gordon),* Jody McCrea *(Bonehead),* Donna Loren *(Donna),* Marta Kristen *(Lorelei),* Linda Evans *(Sugar Kane),* Timothy Carey *(South Dakota Slim),* Donna Michelle *(Animal),* Mike Nader *(Butch),* Patti Chandler *(Patti),* The Hondells *(themselves),* Don Rickles *(Big Drop),* Paul Lynde *(Bullets),* Buster Keaton *(himself),* Earl Wilson *(himself),* Bobbi Shaw *(Bobbi),* Andy Romano, Alan Fife, Jerry Brutsche, John Macchia, Bob Harvey, Alberta Nelson, Myrna Ross *(Rat Pack).*

Comedy with music. Frankie and Dee Dee and their beach friends watch a parachute jump concocted by press agent Bullets as a publicity stunt for singer Sugar Kane. The group become interested in skydiving and arrange to take lessons at Big Drop's school. Later, at a party given for Sugar Kane, Bonnie flirts with Frankie, sending Dee Dee into a jealous rage, but the quarreling is interrupted when Eric Von Zipper's Rat Pack motorcycle gang crashes the party. Meanwhile, Bonehead, one of the surfer group, is saved from drowning by Lorelei, a beautiful mermaid, and he falls in love with her. Believing that Bullets has devised another publicity stunt, Sugar Kane allows herself to be kidnaped by Von Zipper; but the surfers lead a wild chase to save her with the aid of Lorelei and Bonehead. As Lorelei returns to the sea, Bonehead finds solace with Sugar Kane, and Frankie and Dee Dee resolve their differences. *Surfers. Motorcycle gangs. Singers. Mermaids and mermen. Press agents. Publicity. Skydiving. Jealousy. Flirtation. Kidnaping. Beaches. Chases.*

BEACH GIRLS *see* **THE GIRLS ON THE BEACH**

THE BEACH GIRLS AND THE MONSTER   **F6.0320**
American Academy Productions. *Dist* U. S. Films. 15 Sep **1965** [Los Angeles opening]. Sd; b&w with col seq (Technicolor). 35mm. 70 min.

An Edward Janis Production. *Prod* Edward Janis. *Dir* Jon Hall. *Orig Story & Screenplay* Joan Gardner. *Photog Col Seq* Dale Davis. *Mus* Frank Sinatra, Jr.. *Mus Arr & Cond* Chuck Slagle. *Song:* "Monster in the Surf" Walker Edmiston, Elaine DuPont. *Song:* "More Than Wanting You" Arnold Lessing. *Prod Mgr* William Larkin.

Cast: Jon Hall *(Otto Lindsey),* Sue Casey *(Vicki),* Walker Edmiston *(Mark),* Arnold Lessing *(Richard Lindsey),* Elaine DuPont *(Jane Howard),* Read Morgan *(sheriff),* Clyde Adler *(deputy),* Gloria Neil *(Bunny),* Tony Roberts *(Brad),* Dale Davis *(Tom),* Carolyn Williamson *(Sue).*

Horror film. Richard has not become an oceanographer as his father (a professor at the Oceanic Research Laboratory) has wished, and he spends his time surfing with his friends. He and his fiancée, Jane, find the mutilated body of a girl on the beach, and later, at a beach party, Mark, a loner, discovers that his friend Tom also has been murdered. The evidence points to a sea monster, and Mark is suspected of disguising himself and committing the crime. He begins to investigate and finds footprints that lead him to Richard's house, where Richard's young and attractive stepmother, Vicki, tries to seduce him. The monster suddenly enters the room and kills Vicki, but in its struggle with Mark is unmasked to reveal Otto, Richard's father. As the police approach, Otto escapes by automobile, but after a chase through Hollywood Hills, he crashes and dies. *Surfers. Oceanographers. Professors. Stepmothers. Mutilation. Murder. Seduction. Filial relations. Disguise. Sea monsters. Hollywood. Chases. Automobile accidents.*

Note: Location scenes filmed in and around Los Angeles. The 5-min color sequence consists of surfing scenes filmed in Hawaii and off the coast of California. Working title: *Surf Terror*. Also known as *Monster From the Surf*.

BEACH HOUSE PARTY see WILD ON THE BEACH

BEACH PARTY   F6.0321

Alta Vista Productions. *Dist* American International Pictures. 7 Aug **1963** [c14 Aug 1963; LP26482]. Sd; col (PathéColor). 35mm (Panavision). 101 min.

A James H. Nicholson–Samuel Z. Arkoff Production. *Prod* James H. Nicholson, Lou Rusoff. *Exec Prod* Samuel Z. Arkoff. *Assoc Prod* Robert Dillon. *Dir* William Asher. *Screenplay* Lou Rusoff. *Dir Photog* Kay Norton. *Camera* Richard Kelley, Al Berkson, Bob Simpson. *Art Dir* Daniel Haller. *Set Decor* Harry Reif. *Prod Dsgn* Daniel Haller. *Main Titl* Butler-Glouner Inc. *Film Ed* Homer Powell. *Mus Score* Les Baxter. *Mus Coörd* Al Simms. *Songs:* "Beach Party," "Swingin' and A-Surfin'," "Secret Surfin' Spot" Gary Usher, Roger Christian. *Songs:* "Promise Me Anything (Give Me More)," "Treat Him Nicely" Guy Hemric, Jerry Styner. *Sung by* Annette Funicello. *Song:* "Don't Stop Now" Bob Marcucci, Russ Faith. *Sd* Don Rush, Roger White. *Sd Ed* Al Bird. *Sd Asst* Carl Daniels, Elmer Norman. *Mus Ed* Eve Newman. *Asst Dir* Clark Paylow, Lew Borzage. *Prod Supv* Bartlett A. Carre. *Unit Mgr* Robert Agnew. *Prod Asst* Jack Cash. *Script Supv* Jeanne Lippman. *Cost Supv* Marjorie Corso, Tom Welsh. *Makeup* Carlie Taylor. *Hairdresser* Scotty Rackin. *Photog Sp Eff* Butler-Glouner Inc. *Constr Coörd* Ross Hahn. *Prop* Karl Brainard, Dick Rubin, John Cengia. *Grip* Lawrence Milton, Joe Michelski. *Gaffer* Cliff Hutchinson. *Best Boy* Chet Fowler. *Still Photog* Bill Creamer.

Cast: Bob Cummings *(Professor Sutwell)*, Dorothy Malone *(Marianne)*, Frankie Avalon *(Frankie)*, Annette Funicello *(Dolores)*, Harvey Lembeck *(Eric Von Zipper)*, Jody McCrea *(Deadhead)*, Morey Amsterdam *(Cappy)*, John Ashley *(Ken)*, Eva Six *(Ava)*, Dick Dale and the Del Tones *(musicians)*, David Landfield *(Ed)*, Dolores Wells *(Sue)*, Valora Noland *(Rhonda)*, Bobby Payne *(Tom)*, Duane Ament *(Big Boy)*, Andy Romano, John Macchia, Jerry Brutsche, Bob Harvey *(motorcycle rats)*, Linda Rogers, Alberta Nelson *(motorcycle mice)*, Candy Johnson *(perpetual motion dancer)*, Roger Bacon *(tour guide)*, Yvette Vickers, Sharon Garrett *(yogi girls)*, Mickey Dora, John Fain, Pam Colbert, Donna Russell, Mike Nader, Ed Garner, Laura Lynn, Susan Yardley, Brian Wilson *(surfers)*, Lorie Summers, Meredith MacRae, Luree Nicholson, Paulette Rapp, Marlo Baers *(beach girls)*, John Beach, Bill Slosky, Brent Battin, Roger Christian, Gary Usher, Bill Parker *(beach boys)*, Vincent Price *(Big Daddy)*.

Comedy with music. Frankie takes his girl friend, Dolores, to a beach house in southern California for a surfing vacation. Upon arrival, he is dismayed to find a crowd of their friends there, invited by Dolores. From an adjoining house, their beach antics are observed by anthropology professor Sutwell and his secretary, Marianne, who are doing research on the sex play of teenagers. Meanwhile, Frankie has become angry with Dolores and plans to avenge himself by feigning a romance with voluptuous Ava, a waitress at the local beer and rock and roll establishment. When the professor rescues Dolores from the unwelcome attentions of Eric Von Zipper, a leather-jacketed motorcyclist, they become friends, and Frankie becomes jealous. As the apparent romances develop, the teenagers discover the professor's research papers and realize what he is doing. At the beer hall, Professor Sutwell is confronted by the irate youngsters and the cyclists. A pie-throwing brawl ensues which finally clears up the misunderstandings, and Frankie and Dolores are reconciled, while Professor Sutwell realizes that Marianne is the woman for him. *Professors. Sex researchers. Secretaries. Surfers. Waitresses. Motorcyclists. Vacations. Jealousy. Rock and roll. Appearances. Beaches. Bars. California.*

Note: Filmed on the coast of southern California at Balboa, Laguna, Malibu, and Newport.

BEACH PARTY IN A HAUNTED HOUSE see THE GHOST IN THE INVISIBLE BIKINI

BEACH PARTY ITALIAN STYLE see EIGHTEEN IN THE SUN

BEACH RED   F6.0322

Theodora Productions. *Dist* United Artists. 3 Aug **1967** [New York opening; c3 Aug 1967; LP34789]. Sd; col (De Luxe). 35mm. 105 min.

Prod-Dir Cornel Wilde. *Screenplay* Clint Johnston, Donald A. Peters, Jefferson Pascal. *Photog* Cecil Cooney. *Art Dir* Francisco Balangue. *Titl Backgrounds* Michael W. Green, Takashi Tanaka. *Film Ed* Frank P. Keller. *Mus Arr & Cond* Antonio Buenaventura. *Sp Arr* Marty Paich. *Titl Song* Elbey Vid. *Sung by* Jean Wallace. *Sd* James Chapman. *Asst Dir* Derek Cracknell, Francisco MacLang. *Prod Mgr* Vicente Nayve. *Prod Supv* Harry F. Hogan. *Wardrobe* Vicente Cabrera. *Makeup* Neville Smallwood. *Sp Eff* Paul Pollard. *Tech Adv* James C. Murray.

Cast: Cornel Wilde *(Captain MacDonald)*, Rip Torn *(Sergeant Honeywell)*, Burr De Benning *(Egan)*, Patrick Wolfe *(Cliff)*, Jean Wallace *(Julia MacDonald)*, Jaime Sanchez *(Colombo)*, Genki Koyama *(Captain Sugiyama)*, Gene Blakely *(Goldberg)*, Norman Pak *(Nakano)*, Dewey Stringer *(Mouse)*, Fred Galang *(Lieutenant Domingo)*, Hiroshi Kiyama *(Michio)*, Michael Parsons *(Sergeant Lindstrom)*, Dale Ishimoto *(Captain Tanaka)*, Linda Albertano *(Egan's girl friend)*, Jan Garrison *(Susie)*, Michio Hazama *(Captain Kondo)*, Masako Otsuki *(colonel's wife)*, Kiyoma Takezawa *(Japanese soldier)*, George Bayot, John Allen, Ed Finlan, Bill Dunbar, Mike McMichael, Ernie Holt, Phil Beinke, Dennis Ullman, Rod Meir, Jun Bona, Pat Whitlock, Charles Weaver.

War drama. Source: Peter Bowman, *Beach Red* (New York, 1945). During the bloodiest days of World War II, a battalion of U. S. Marines led by Captain MacDonald and his sadistic sergeant, Honeywell, land on the beach of a Japanese-held island off the Philippines. Inching their way forward, they suffer heavy casualties until they reach the comparative safety of a dense forest. Despite a shoulder wound, MacDonald supervises setting up camp and organizes the search for the enemy. Whenever there is a lull in the fighting, MacDonald and his men lapse into nostalgic remembrances of their civilian lives. Similarly, the nearby Japanese soldiers are recalling their own peacetime lives with their families. Eventually, MacDonald sends Cliff, a nervous 18-year-old whose father is a minister, and Egan, a hillbilly ladies' man, on a scouting mission. Though they are successful in radioing back the enemy's exact position, they run into an ambush on their way back to camp. Egan is killed, and Cliff and a young Japanese soldier, Nakano, are seriously wounded. Cliff looks compassionately at his enemy counterpart and tosses him his water canteen. Understanding the gesture, Nakano offers Cliff a cigarette. At this point Honeywell bursts into the clearing and savagely kills the young Japanese. As Captain MacDonald stares at the carnage around him, he contemplates the futility of war. *Combat zone life. Nostalgia. Memory. World War II. Philippines. United States Marines. Japan—Army.*

Note: Filmed in the Philippines and Japan.

THE BEAR (France/Italy)   F6.0323

Filmsonor–Intermondia Films–Titanus. *Dist* Embassy Pictures. Jan **1963**. Sd; col (Eastmancolor). 35mm. 85 min.

Dir Edmond Séchan. *Screenplay* Roger Mauge, Edmond Séchan. *Orig Story* Roger Mauge. *Dir Photog* André Villard. *Art Dir* René Renoux. *Film Ed* Jacqueline Thiédot. *Mus* Jean Prodromidès. *Sd* Raymond Gauguier.

Cast: Renato Rascel *(Lucien Ménard)*, Francis Blanche *(Chappuis)*, Gôcha *(himself, the bear)*, Daniel Lecourtois *(director)*, Yvette Etiévant, Cora Camoin, Gaby Basset, Hélène Tossy, Marcel Loche, Jean Bellanger, Hubert de Lapparent.

Fantasy. Lucien Ménard, a newly hired zoo keeper, is assigned to take care of a bear named Gôcha. At first he is afraid of the bear and Chappuis, the tyrannical boss at the zoo, but Ménard's fears evaporate when he discovers that Gôcha can speak. He learns that the fearsome attitude of the bear is merely a result of his loneliness. Ménard teaches Gôcha to read and to play cards, and he arranges for him to spend a night with his true love, a polar bear in the next cage. Chappuis finds out about the talking bear, but no one believes him, and he is fired for drunkenness. Ménard replaces him as head zoo keeper and arranges for Gôcha to be returned to the wild. *Zoo keepers. Employer-employee relations. Zoos. Bears.*

Note: Opened in Paris in Dec 1960 as *L'ours*. The role of the bear was played by both a man and a trained Russian bear. May also be known as *The Talking Bear*.

THE BEAR HUNT see THE BARE HUNT; OR MY GUN IS JAMMED

BEARDED GENERAL (South Korea)   F6.0324

Tai Chang Enterprise Co. Dec **1969** [Los Angeles showing]. Sd; col (Eastman Color). 35mm (Taichang-scope). 90 min.

Prod Kim Tai Soo. *Dir* Lee Sungkoo. *Screenplay* Kim Sungok. *Photog* Chang Suk Keun. *Film Ed* Yoo Jai Won. *Mus* Joe Kim Hee.

Cast: Shin Sungil, Yoon Chunghi, Kim Sungho, Kim Sungok.

Melodrama. Kim Chulhun, a news cameraman, is found dead, and Detective Park is assigned to the case. He finds a letter written by Kim to a writer whom he locates. The writer tells Park about Kim's intended novel which concerns an alienated youth who dies a tragic death. Park thinks that Kim is similar to the hero of the book, and his suspicions are confirmed after he talks with Shinhai, Kim's former mistress. Kim had been writing a story on dancehalls when he met Shinhai, an unhappy taxi dancer whose fiancée was killed in the Korean War. Kim promised to keep secret her past, and they began an affair. Their life was unhappy, however, because Kim was immature in his approach to their relationship. When Kim completed his novel, Shinhai left him. Park next talks with Kim's mother and is told that Kim was a lonely child. After interviewing Kim's friends, Park talks with a model who was Kim's latest girl friend; she relates that Kim seemed to be a normal, sympathetic man. Kim's death is never satisfactorily resolved, and Park concludes that he may have committed suicide or have been killed by his mistress. Nevertheless, Kim was similar to the hero in his own novel—at odds with the world around him. *Photographers. Novelists. Detectives. Authors. Mistresses. Taxi dancers. Models. Death. Alienation. Loneliness. Suicide. Murder.*

Note: Released in South Korea in 1968 as *Changgun ui suyum*.

THE BEARDLESS WARRIORS *see* **THE YOUNG WARRIORS**

BEAST ALLEY (Japan)   F6.0325
Toho Co. Jul **1966** [Los Angeles showing]. Sd; b&w. 35mm (Tohoscope). 142 min.

Exec Prod Sanezumi Fujimoto, Masakatsu Kaneko. *Dir* Eizo Sugawa. *Screenplay* Yoshio Shirasaka, Eizo Sugawa. *Photog* Yasumichi Fukuzawa. *Mus* Toru Takemitsu.

Cast: Junko Ikeuchi *(Tamiko)*, Keiju Kobayashi, Ryo Ikebe, Yunosuke Ito, Eitaro Ozawa.

Melodrama. Tamiko, working as a chambermaid to support her bedridden husband, meets a man who promises her happiness and financial security. She accepts his offer and soon finds herself a sexual toy passed from hand to hand. Driven to the point of burning down her own home to murder her husband, Tamiko comes to realize that her new way of life is one of degradation from which she—and her male associates—cannot escape. *Chambermaids. Invalids. Infidelity. Murder. Promiscuity. Arson.*

Note: Released in Japan in 1965 as *Kemonomichi*.

BEAST AND THE BODY *see* **BEAUTY AND THE BODY**

BEAST OF BLOOD (United States/Philippines)   F6.0326
Beast of Blood Production Co.-Sceptre Industries. *Dist* Hemisphere Pictures. Aug **1970** [c6 May 1970; LP38823]. Sd; col. 35mm. 90 min. *MPAA rating* GP.

Prod-Dir-Screenplay Eddie Romero. *Exec Prod* Kane W. Lynn. *Assoc Dir* Armando Herrera. *Story* Beverly Miller. *Dir Cinematog* Justo Paulino. *2d Unit Camera* Edmund Cupcupin. *Asst Camera* José Totanis. *Art Dir* Ben Otico. *Set Decor* Bobby Bautista. *Graphics* Magi-Philippines. *Supv Film Ed* Ben Barcelón. *Mus Comp & Cond* Tito Arevalo. *Sd Dir* Tommy Santos. *Sd Rec* Ernesto Cajucom. *Sd Eff* Tony Gosalves. *Asst Dir* Maria Abelardo. *Prod Mgr* Mario David, prod mgr. *Unit Mgr* Cenon Gonzalez. *Wardrobe* Paquito Salcedo. *Makeup Supv* Tony Artieda. *Sp Eff* Teofilo Hilario. *Medical Cons* Bienvenido Aldanese. *Head Gaffer* Fausto Lopez. *Dial Supv* Tita Muñoz.

Cast: John Ashley *(Bill Foster)*, Celeste Yarnall *(Myra)*, Eddie Garcia *(Dr. Lorca)*, Liza Belmonte *(Laida)*, Alfonso Carvajal, actor *(Ramu)*, Bruno Punzalán *(Razak)*, Beverly Miller *(captain)*, Angel Buenaventura, Johnny Long.

Horror film. Returning to Blood Island via a small cargo boat, Bill Foster meets Myra, a reporter who is investigating several mysterious incidents for a possible story. Informed by the native chief, Ramu, that Don Ramon, the green-blooded monster, is stalking the island, Bill leads Myra and some frightened natives into a decaying mansion where they discover a decomposed corpse chained to the floor and a decapitated head. Later, Myra is kidnaped by Razak and taken to Dr. Lorca's hideout in the Valley of the Red Mist. Hideously disfigured from a struggle with the legendary blood monster, Lorca keeps the monster's severed head and body in his laboratory. In an attempt to purge the monster's brain of evil impulses, Lorca beheads a native and unsuccessfully tries to graft the body onto the monster's head. Meanwhile, coming to Myra's rescue, Bill and the natives attack Lorca's hideout. During the melee, the body of the monster, guided by the head, murders Lorca and demolishes the laboratory before being gunned down by the invaders. With Lorca's domain in flames, Bill, Myra, and the natives leave, taking with them the head of the blood monster. *Physicians. Monsters. Reporters. Decapitation. Experiments. Kidnaping. Rescue. Murder. Laboratories. Corpses. Ships. Islands. South Seas.*

Note: This is a sequel to the film *Mad Doctor of Blood Island*, q. v. Filmed in the Philippines. Originally known as *Return to the Horrors of Blood Island*.

BEAST OF MOROCCO *see* **THE HAND OF NIGHT**

BEAST OF PARADISE ISLE (Reissue)   F6.0327
RKO Radio Pictures. *Dist* Realart Pictures. 16 Jul **1961** [New York showing]. Sd; b&w. 35mm. 65 min.

Note: Originally released as *Port Sinister* by RKO Radio Pictures in 1953; c31 Dec 1952; LP2532.

THE BEAST OF YUCCA FLATS   F6.0328
Anthony Cardoza-Roland Morin. *Dist* Crown International Pictures. May **1961**. Sd; b&w. 35mm. 60 min.

Prod Anthony Cardoza, Roland Morin. *Dir-Writ* Coleman Francis. *Photog* John Cagle. *Film Ed* Coleman Francis. *Mus* Irwin Nafshun, Al Remington. *Asst Dir* Austin McKinney.

Cast: Tor Johnson *(The Beast)*, Douglas Mellor, Larry Aten, Barbara Francis, Bing Stafford, Linda Bielima, John Morrison, actor, Tony Cardoza, Bob Labansat, Jim Oliphant.

Horror film. A scientist is chased into Yucca Flats, an atomic bomb test area, by communist spies. Because of the contamination of radioactivity on his body, the scientist slowly changes into a horrifying monster that terrorizes all who come within his range. *Scientists. Communists. Spies. Monsters. Atom bomb. Radiation. Yucca Flats.*

Note: Film may have been released in 1964 as *Girl Madness*.

THE BEAST THAT KILLED WOMEN   F6.0329
Barry Mahon Productions. 5 Aug **1965** [San Francisco showing]. Sd; col. 35mm. 61 min.

A Barry Mahon Production. *Prod-Dir* Barry Mahon. *Exec Prod* Bob Gordon. *Photog* Barry Mahon. *Ed* Rick Carrier. *Asst Dir* Byron Mabe. *Opticals* Eastern Effects.

Horror film. A horrible murder interrupts a happy weekend at a nudist camp, and the police begin searching for a sex maniac. The following night, the police learn that the murderer is actually a giant beast with a gorilla-like appearance, who has found his way into the woods near the lake. He apparently hates women, and when he mistakenly attacks his intended victim's husband, he throws the man from the dock and runs into the woods. With the news that a monster is running loose, the camp empties. The police decide to use a female decoy to trap the beast; an attractive policewoman is assigned to sleep near the lake. Once again the beast attacks, but he is killed before the woman can be harmed. *Misogynists. Police. Murder. Nudist camps. Monsters. Apes.*

BEAT GIRL *see* **WILD FOR KICKS**

THE BEATLES *see* **A HARD DAY'S NIGHT**

BEAU GESTE   F6.0330
Universal Pictures. Jul **1966** [New York opening: 7 Sep; c3 Sep 1966; LP35382]. Sd (Westrex); col (Technicolor). 35mm (Techniscope). 104 min.

Prod Walter Seltzer. *In Charge of Prod* Edward Muhl. *Dir-Screenplay* Douglas Heyes. *2d Unit Dir* Joe Kane. *Dir Photog* Bud Thackery. *Art Dir* Alexander Golitzen, Henry Bumstead. *Set Decor* John McCarthy, James S. Redd. *Titl* Pacific Title. *Film Ed* Russell F. Schoengarth. *Mus* Hans J. Salter. *Mus Supv* Joseph Gershenson. *Song:* "Beau Geste March" Hal Hopper. *Sd* Waldon O. Watson, David H. Moriarty. *Asst Dir* Terry Morse, Jr., John Anderson, Jr. *Prod Mgr* James C. Pratt. *Unit Prod Mgr* Wes Thompson. *Cost* Rosemary Odell. *Makeup* Bud Westmore. *Hair Stylist* Larry Germain. *Matte Supv* Albert Whitlock. *Tech Adv* D. R. O. Hatswell. *Dial Coach* Rand Brooks. *Stunt Coörd* Hal Needham.

Cast: Guy Stockwell *(Beau)*, Doug McClure *(John)*, Leslie Nielsen *(Lieutenant De Ruse)*, Telly Savalas *(Sergeant-Major Dagineau)*, David Mauro *(Boldini)*, Robert Wolders *(Fouchet)*, Leo Gordon *(Krauss)*, Michael Constantine *(Rostov)*, Malachi Throne *(Kerjacki)*, Joe De Santis *(Beaujolais)*, X. Brands *(Vallejo)*, Michael Carr *(sergeant)*, George Keymas *(platoon sergeant)*, Patrick Whyte *(surgeon)*, Ted Jacques *(captain)*, Ava Zamora *(dancer)*, Jeff Nelson, David Gross, Hal Hopper, Chuck Wood, Duane Grey, Vic Lundin *(legionnaires)*, Arthur Atkinson, Albert Canter, Claude Chastanet, Boris Nico Dellwoy, Dimitri Drobatschewsky, John Du Mortier, Edward Erdmann, Antoine Figr, Frank Fuessler, Paul L. Jumet, Andrew G. Lontai, Maurice Malinowski, Yervand Markarian, George Olesnicki, Ulrich Schelling, Gunther Schumacher, Ernest Seidl, François Slistan, Douglas M. Smith, Charles Stransky, Henryk Szarek, Joseph Szepesy, Paul Villarose, Robert Vowels, Wesley T. Williams *(French Foreign Legion veterans)*.

Adventure melodrama. Source: Percival Christopher Wren, *Beau Geste* (New York, 1925). In 1906, young Beau Graves takes the blame for a crime committed by his business partner and leaves his home in the United States to join the French Foreign Legion. He is sent to Fort Zinderneuf in the Arabian Desert where he immediately runs afoul of the brutal and sadistic Sergeant-Major Dagineau, who suspects Beau of sending him an unsigned threatening letter. Beau wins the admiration of the other men, however, when he stands up to Dagineau. He also wins the friendship of the weak and drunken commander, Lieutenant De Ruse, who nicknames him "Geste" upon learning that Beau's sacrifice at home was unnecessary since his partner confessed and committed suicide shortly after Beau's departure for the Legion. Later, Beau is joined by his devoted brother John, and Dagineau becomes more convinced than ever that Beau plans to murder him. Lieutenant De Ruse is wounded by an Arab, and before dying he confesses to Beau that it was he who wrote the anonymous letter in the hope that fear might make Dagineau more humane. Dagineau, driven to the point of near-madness by the prospect of sudden death, subjects his men to torturous desert marches and cruel punishments. As the Arabs prepare for a massive assault, Beau manages to quell a mass mutiny among the men. In the subsequent attack, the legionnaires are killed off one by one until only Beau and Dagineau remain. A death struggle between the two men ensues, and Beau is found alive when a relief column arrives at the fort. *Brothers. Arabs. French. Americans in foreign countries. Self-sacrifice. Paranoia. Exile. Sadism. Mutiny. Alcoholism. Forts. Deserts. Arabia. France—Army—Foreign Legion. Documentation.*

Note: Previously filmed by Paramount Pictures in 1926 and 1939.

BEAUCOUP TROP POUR UN SEUL HOMME see THE CLIMAX

THE BEAUTIFUL AND THE BLOODY see THE BEAUTIFUL, THE BLOODY, AND THE BARE

THE BEAUTIFUL SWINDLERS (France/Italy/Japan/Netherlands)
F6.0331
Ulysse Productions-Primex Films-Lux Film-Vides-Toho Co.-Caesar Films. *Dist* Ellis Films, Continental Distributing, Inc. 12 Sep **1967** [Chicago opening]. Sd; b&w. 35mm (Franscope). 90 min.
   Overall Production Credits: *Prod* Pierre Roustang. *Engl Subtitl* Herman G. Weinberg.
   Production Credits—"Amsterdam": *Dir* Roman Polanski. *Screenplay* Roman Polanski, Gérard Brach. *Photog* Jerzy Lipman. *Film Ed* Rita von Royen. *Mus* Krzysztof Komeda.
   Production Credits—"Naples": *Dir* Ugo Gregoretti. *Photog* Tonino Delli Colli. *Mus* Piero Umiliani.
   Production Credits—"Paris": *Dir* Claude Chabrol. *Photog* Jean Rabier. *Film Ed* Jacques Gaillard. *Mus* Pierre Jansen.
   Production Credits—"Tokyo": *Dir* Hiromichi Horikawa. *Photog* Asakazu Nakai. *Mus* Keitaro Miho.
   Cast—"Amsterdam": Nicole Karen, Jan Teulings, Arnold Gelderman.
   Cast—"Naples": Gabriella Giorgelli, Beppe Mannaiuolo, Guido Giuseppone.
   Cast—"Paris": Jean-Pierre Cassel, Catherine Deneuve, Francis Blanche, Sacha Briquet, Jean-Louis Maury.
   Cast—"Tokyo": Mie Hama, Ken Mitsuda.
   Comedy. AMSTERDAM: A young Parisian woman in Amsterdam cons a middle-aged Dutchman into buying her a diamond necklace, presumably with the promise that she will in return give him certain "favors." She flees from his house with the expensive jewelry, however, before fulfilling her end of the bargain. But her motives are entirely unmercenary: she trades her acquisition for a parrot being sold by a waterfront bum who is unaware of the necklace's value. NAPLES: To avoid being evicted from the city as an undesirable citizen, a prostitute marries a man from an old people's home. Her pimp decides to repeat the process with all the streetwalkers, thus making him the richest procurer in the city. The newly married old men are devoted to their young wives, however, and will no longer permit them to work at night. PARIS: An ingenious swindler sells the Eiffel Tower to a gullible German, who is taken into custody by the welfare authorities when he shows his "title deed." TOKYO: A barmaid becomes the mistress of a wealthy man, then watches happily as he chokes to death eating noodles. She attempts to pawn his false teeth, believing them to be made of platinum, but learns that they are worthless. Foiled by his "false" teeth and equally false bank notes, she is, nonetheless, arrested for his murder. *Swindlers. Prostitutes. Pimps. Germans. Barmaids. Mistresses. Theft. Old age. Marriage. Fraud. Gullibility. Greed. Murder. Amsterdam. Naples. Paris. Tokyo. Eiffel Tower. Documentation. Parrots.*

Note: Opened in Paris in Aug 1964 as *Les plus belles escroqueries du monde;* released in Italy in 1964 as *Le truffe più belle del mondo.* Originally produced as a 5-part anthology in color. One of the segments (directed by Jean-Luc Godard and featuring Jean Seberg, Charles Denner, and Laszlo Szabo) was deleted before its Paris premiere and later released in France as a short entitled *Le grand escroc.* Scheduled for U. S. distribution by Continental Distributing, Inc. as *World's Greatest Swindles.*

THE BEAUTIFUL, THE BLOODY, AND THE BARE
F6.0332
Dist Esquire Pictures, Boxoffice International Film Distributors. 8 Dec **1964** [New York showing]. Sd; col (Eastman Color). 35mm. 66 min.

Prod Al C. Ruban. *Dir* Sande N. Johnsen. *Cinematog* Jerry Denby. *Art Dir* Neil Fallon. *Film Ed* Jay DeAre. *Mus Comp* Steve Karmen. *Sd* A. Morris. *Asst Dir* Sol Lowe. *Script Clerk* Bente Claussen. *Makeup* Anne Shirley.
   Cast: Jack Lowe, Marlene Denes, Debra Page.
   Melodrama. Leo and Mona Vincente, who operate an art school using nude models, receive a visit from Leo's school friend Pete Abbott. At dinner Pete relates his activities since college graduation. While traveling around Europe, Pete became interested in blood rites practiced in northern Italy and actually participated in some of the secret ceremonies. In an effort to help his friend Pete become reestablished in the States, Leo offers Pete, a professional photographer, the use of the art school's facilities, including the nude models. Pete hesitates, then accepts Leo's offer. Soon other models flock to him, anxious to be photographed for posterity by so fine an artist. During the course of the shooting, Pete's bloodlust surfaces. He throws his full energies into his work, but he nevertheless struggles in vain to contain his passion. Finally, he murders a model who is posing for him in the park. He returns to the studio and murders another model; before his frenzy has subsided, Mona walks in, sees a dead body, and screams. Pete lunges for her, but Leo arrives and chases Pete over the rooftops. At last Pete takes his own life. *Models. Photographers. Art teachers. Nudity. Murder. Suicide. Rites and ceremonies. Chases.*

Note: Also known as *Bloody, Bare, and Beautiful* and *The Beautiful and the Bloody.*

BEAUTY AND THE BEAST   **F6.0333**
Harvard Film Corp. *Dist* United Artists. 13 Feb **1963** [San Francisco opening; c28 Nov 1962; LP23762]. Sd; col (Technicolor). 35mm. 77 min.
   Prod Robert E. Kent. *Dir* Edward L. Cahn. *Screenplay* George Bruce, Orville H. Hampton. *Camera* Gilbert Warrenton. *Art Dir* Franz Bachelin. *Film Ed* Robert Carlisle. *Sd Mix* Fred Lau. *Asst Dir* Herbert S. Greene. *Makeup* Jack P. Pierce.
   Cast: Joyce Taylor (*Lady Althea*), Mark Damon (*Duke Eduardo*), Eduard Franz (*Baron Orsini*), Michael Pate (*Prince Bruno*), Merry Anders (*Princess Sybil*), Dayton Lummis (*Count Roderick*), Walter Burke (*Grimaldi*).
   Fantasy. In the medieval duchy of Allena, Lady Althea, a lovely young noblewoman, discovers that her fiancé, Duke Eduardo, is the innocent victim of an ancient curse which turns him into a beast at night. Ambitious for the throne, the evil Prince Bruno incites a mob to burn the duke at the stake. At the last moment, however, the duke is saved when Althea kisses his beast-face, thereby breaking the spell. The unscrupulous prince is banished, and Althea and the duke are married. *Nobility. Royalty. Ambition. Metamorphosis. Curses. Banishment.*

BEAUTY AND THE BEAST see DAY OF A STRIPPER

BEAUTY AND THE BODY   **F6.0334**
Paul Mart Productions. *Dist* Manson Distributing Corp. Aug **1963**. Sd; col (Eastman Color). 35mm. 62 min. [Also reviewed at 70 min.]
   Prod-Dir Paul Mart. *Exec Prod* Edmund Goldman. *Assoc Prod* Milton Mann. *Screenplay* Richard Tyler. *Photog* William Dewar. *Main Titl* Consolidated Film Industries. *Film Ed* Richard Tyler. *Sd* Ryder Sound Service. *Prod Mgr* Ronald A. Haddad. *Prod Asst* Gary A. Stromberg. *Tech Adv* Michael F. Goldman.
   Cast: Kip Behar (*Body*), Judy Miller (*Beauty*).
   Travelog. A beautiful girl and an "All-American" athlete, both supposedly vacationing, meet on a Santa Monica beach and decide to go to numerous shows, pageants, and sports events in California and Mexico [see subject references below]. In 3 days they fall in love, only to have to say goodby. Subsequently, they discover the truth about each other when he applies for a dishwashing job at the drive-in where she is a carhop. Promising never to lie again, they decide to face the future together. *Dishwashers. Waitresses. Ice skating. Karate. Skydiving. Diving. Swimming. Bullfighting. Rodeos. Jai alai. California. Santa Monica. Mexico.*

Note: Also known as *Beast and the Body.*

BEAUTY AND THE BULLFIGHTER (Reissue) (France)   **F6.0335**
Cité Films-Cocinor. *Dist* Hoffberg Productions. May **1967**. Sd (Western Electric); col (Eastmancolor). 35mm. 70 min.
   Note: Released in 1958 as *Love in a Hot Climate* by Hoffberg Productions. Released in France in 1954 as *Sang et lumières.*

THE BEAUTY JUNGLE see CONTEST GIRL

BEAUTY #2   **F6.0336**
Dist Film-Makers' Cooperative. 17 Jul **1965** [New York opening]. Sd; b&w. 16mm. 70 min.
   Prod-Dir Andy Warhol. *Writ* Chuck Wein. *Asst Dir* Chuck Wein. *Prod Asst* Gerard Malanga, Buddy Wirtschafter.
   Cast: Edie Sedgwick (*girl*), Gino Piserchio (*Beauty #2*), Gerard Malanga, Chuck Wein (*off-camera voices*), Horse (*a dog*).

Satire. A young woman is in bed with her current boyfriend, Beauty #2, when the voice of her former lover interrupts them. In the ensuing dialogue between the woman and the voice, details about her past are revealed. From time to time she toys with a drink and some cigarettes. A Doberman pinscher is also present. *Dogs.*

BEBO'S GIRL (France/Italy)   F6.0337
Lux Film-Vides-Ultra Film-C. C. F. Lux. *Dist* Continental Distributing, Inc. 11 Nov **1964** [New York opening]. Sd; b&w. 35mm. 106 min.
Pres by Walter Reade-Sterling Inc. *Prod* Franco Cristaldi. *Dir* Luigi Comencini. *Screenplay* Marcello Fondato, Luigi Comencini. *Dir Photog* Gianni Di Venanzo. *Art Dir* Piero Gherardi. *Film Ed* Nino Baragli. *Orig Mus* Carlo Rustichelli. *Sd* Claudio Maielli. *Asst Dir* Leopoldo Macchina. *Cost* Otello Fava.
Cast: Claudia Cardinale *(Mara)*, George Chakiris *(Bebo [Bube])*, Marc Michel *(Stefano)*, Dany Paris *(Liliana)*, Emilio Esposito *(Mara's father)*, Monique Vita *(Incs)*, Mario Lupi *(Lidori)*, Pier Luigi Catocci *(Father Ciolfi)*, Carla Calò *(Mara's mother)*, Bruno Scipioni *(Mauro)*, Ugo Chitti *(Arnaldo)*.
Drama. Source: Carlo Cassola, *La ragazza di Bube* (Turin, 1960). When the war in Italy ends in 1944 and partisan fighters make their way back to their homes, a young partisan nicknamed Bebo stops off at a village in Tuscany to pay his respects to the family of his closest friend, who was killed by the Germans. During his short stay, he meets his dead comrade's naive and innocent half-sister, Mara. They begin to date; Mara is bored with her peasant life and finds excitement in spending time with a local hero. Later, Bebo is involved in a flareup between partisans and Fascists and kills the son of the local police chief. He asks Mara's father for her hand in marriage; later, he is warned that he must go into hiding, and Mara consents to accompany him after he buys her a pair of high-heeled shoes and takes her out to a restaurant. On the road, Bebo saves the life of Father Ciolfi, a collaborationist priest. Mara becomes increasingly attracted to Bebo, but they are separated when he is forced to flee the country. Mara finds work at a city print shop and meets Stefano, a serious, sensitive writer who falls in love with her. Mara begins to wonder if her feelings for Bebo were anything more than infatuation, but when she learns that he has been returned from France and is about to stand trial she visits him in prison. She tries to help him at the trial but is tongue-tied before the judge; and when Bebo is sentenced to 14 years in prison she realizes that she has remained "Bebo's girl" and decides to wait for him. *Peasants. Fugitives. War heroes. Fascists. Resistance (political). Courtship. Fidelity. World War II. Tuscany.*
Note: Released in Italy in 1963 as *La ragazza di Bube*; running time: 110 min; Paris opening: Sep 1964 as *La ragazza.*

BECKET (United States/Great Britain)   F6.0338
Paramount Film Service-Keep Films. *Dist* Paramount Pictures. 11 Mar **1964** [New York opening; c9 Mar 1964; LP28979]. Sd; col (Technicolor). 35mm & 70mm (Panavision). 165 min. [Also 148 min.]
Prod Hal Wallis. *Dir* Peter Glenville. *Screenplay* Edward Anhalt. *Cinematog* Geoffrey Unsworth. *Art Dir* Maurice Carter. *Set Decor* Robert Cartwright. *Prod Dsgn* John Bryan. *Film Ed* Anne V. Coates. *Mus Score* Laurence Rosenthal. *Cond* Muir Mathieson. *Sd* Buster Ambler. *Asst Dir* Colin Brewer. *Prod Mgr* Denis Holt. *Asst to the Prod* Richard McWhorter. *Cost Dsgn* Margaret Furse. *Cost* Phyllis Dalton. *Makeup* Charles Parker. *Hairstyles* Joan Smallwood.
Cast: Richard Burton *(Thomas Becket)*, Peter O'Toole *(King Henry II)*, John Gielgud *(King Louis VII of France)*, Donald Wolfit *(Gilbert Folliot, Bishop of London)*, Martita Hunt *(Queen Matilda)*, Pamela Brown *(Queen Eleanor)*, Paolo Stoppa *(Pope Alexander III)*, Gino Cervi *(Cardinal Zambelli)*, David Weston *(Brother John)*, Felix Aylmer *(Archbishop of Canterbury)*, Percy Herbert, Niall MacGinnis, Christopher Rhodes, Peter Jeffrey, Michael Miller, Peter Prowse *(Henry II's barons)*, Inigo Jackson *(Robert de Beaumont, Duke of Leicester)*, Sian Phillips *(Gwendolen)*, Veronique Vendell *(French girl)*, Gerald Lawson *(old peasant)*, Jennifer Hilary *(peasant's daughter)*, John Phillips, British *(Bishop of Winchester)*, Frank Pettingell *(Bishop of York)*, Hamilton Dyce *(Bishop of Chichester)*, Paul Farrell *(farmer)*, Rose Howlett *(farmer's wife)*, Linda Marlowe *(farmer's daughter)*, Patrick Newell *(William of Corbeil)*, Riggs O'Hara *(Prince Henry)*, Geoffrey Bayldon *(Brother Philip)*, Graham Stark *(pope's secretary)*, Victor Spinetti *(French tailor)*, Magda Knopke *(girl on balcony)*, Wilfrid Lawson *(old soldier)*, Edward Woodward *(Clement)*, Tutte Lemkow, Michael Anthony *(courtiers)*.
Historical drama. Source: Jean Anouilh, *Becket, ou l'honneur de Dieu* (Paris opening: 1 Oct 1959). In 12th-century England, King Henry II, descendant of Norman conquerors, is at odds with the church because he spends most of his time hunting, drinking, and womanizing with his Saxon friend Thomas Becket, who also advises him on matters of state. Antagonism between church and state mounts when the church refuses to allocate funds for Henry's battle with France. To tie Becket closer to his court, Henry makes him Chancellor of England, and from this position Becket fights the church on Henry's behalf. The

two continue to rule England as steadfast friends until Henry impetuously demands payment for a past favor and asks for Becket's mistress, Gwendolen. The honor-bound Becket submits to the king's request, but Gwendolen takes her own life. Following the death of the Archbishop of Canterbury, Henry appoints Becket to the archbishopric, despite the protests of most of the clergy and Becket himself, who claims that he cannot serve both God and the king. Becket assumes his office with religious dignity and, finding himself in opposition to Henry's interference in the church, resigns as Chancellor of England. Furious because he mistakenly believed that installing his best friend as archbishop would give him control of the church, Henry joins forces with Becket's enemy, Folliot, the Bishop of London, in an attempt to bring Becket to trial on false charges of embezzlement. Becket escapes to France where King Louis VII helps him reach the Vatican. Pope Alexander III offers him sanctuary in a monastery, and Louis arranges for a final meeting between Becket and Henry. The confrontation between the two former friends is an emotional one, and Henry guarantees Becket's safe conduct back to England. There, the Saxons give Becket a warm welcome. The frustrated Henry impulsively calls for the elimination of the meddlesome priest, however, and four barons murder Becket before the altar in Canterbury Cathedral. Stricken by the loss of his friend and filled with guilt, Henry allows himself to be flogged by Saxon monks and then proclaims Becket a saint. *Royalty. Philanderers. Normans. Saxons. Clergymen. Church and state. Friendship. Frameup. Assassination. Guilt. Flogging. Monasteries. France. Vatican. Henry II (England). Thomas à Becket. Louis VII (France). Alexander III (pope). Catholic Church. Canterbury Cathedral.*
Note: Opened in London in Mar 1964; running time: 149 min. Filmed in 35mm and blown up to 70mm for some roadshow presentations.

THE BED AND HOW TO MAKE IT!   F6.0339
Howard Farber Films. *Dist* Distribpix, Inc. 4 Dec **1966** [New York opening]. Sd; b&w. 35mm. 91 min.
Exec Prod Howard Farber, Arthur Morowitz. *Dir-Writ* Joe Sarno. *Dir Photog* Bruce Sparks. *Asst Camera* Robert Bailin. *Sd Engr* James Lynch. *Ch Electrn* Moe Odegaard.
Cast: Francine Ashley *(Ellen)*, Judson Todd *(Russ)*, Loraine Claire *(Connie)*, Peggy Stephans *(Dot)*, Barbara Kemp *(Peg)*, Victor Bertini *(Nick)*, Rita Bennett *(Karen)*, Nick Linkov *(Vince)*, Tony King *(Darrell)*, Gail Sedrish *(Edna)*.
Melodrama. Suspended from school and banished from home by her mother, Ellen Cooper takes work as a chambermaid in her Aunt Connie's motel. Connie, an alcoholic, determines to fire Ellen when she suspects that her husband Russ is having an affair with the young woman. Knowing that her aunt has no resistance to alcohol, Ellen devises a plan to destroy Connie. She leaves a bottle of liquor in Connie's room, and when Connie is helplessly drunk, invites three strange men from nearby Haven Bar to molest her. During the wild party that ensues, Ellen brings Russ to witness his wife's depravity. Then Ellen, her co-worker Dottie, and Nick France, owner of the Haven Bar, plan a party to make Connie repeat her drunken performance and to blackmail her with photographs they intend to take of Connie having intercourse with the three men from the bar. Nick France and his girl friend Karen, both sex perverts, welcome the chance for some weird entertainment and agree to stage the party at their house. Unaware that his wife is the "guest of honor," Russ is startled when two women drag Connie, drunk and half naked, into a room and throw her onto the floor before him. Russ tries to protect Connie when the three barflies begin to paw her, but he is helpless. Meanwhile, Dottie continues to snap pictures. Ellen, frightened and confused, tells the guests that Dottie is taking pictures to blackmail them, and the guests turn on Dottie. Then Ellen's lie is exposed, and she is abandoned to the perverted Nick and Karen, who delighted, begin to undress her. *Chambermaids. Aunts. Uncles. Saloon keepers. Alcoholism. Blackmail. Sadism. Infidelity. Motels. Bars.*

THE BED AND THE BEAUTIFUL see CARGO OF LOVE

BED OF FIRE see THE GLASS CAGE

BED OF VIOLENCE   F6.0340
Chellee Films. 31 Aug **1967** [San Francisco showing]. Sd; b&w. 35mm. 95 min.
Prod Chellee Wilson. *Asst Prod* Ken Rowley. *Dir-Writ* Joe Sarno. *Dir Photog* Bruce Sparks. *Asst Camera* Bob Bailin. *Mus* Pir Marini. *Sd* James Lynch. *Prod Asst* Gillian Mills. *Electrn* Steve Silverman.
Cast: Riley, Cleo Nova, Nick Dundas, Tony Giarratano, Ginger Stevens, Rip Atlanta, Kip Rivas, Sue Evans, Lilian Dillon, Richard Michaels, Ron Vial, David Blackhurst, David Bruno.
Melodrama. Racketeers Robbie LaRose, Frank Valle, and Vince DeMotte run a numbers game in a nightclub that contains private rooms. In one of them, Robbie is carrying on his affair with Joan, Frank's wife, when a disagreement leads her to knife him. Overhearing a phone call Joan makes while disposing of the corpse, Pam, a young woman who works at the club, assumes that Joan

is turning to her husband Frank for help. Downstairs, Robbie's cousin Iggy Di Anthony waits for him with a friend, Paul Musa, whom he hopes Robbie will hire. When Robbie doesn't appear, Paul asks his sister Rose, who lives in the same building as Frank and Joan Valle, to plead with Frank to hire her brother; and after a heated sexual encounter, she succeeds in getting Paul the job. Frank and Vince temporarily re-divide the business between them until Robbie shows up, but Iggy lets it be known that Robbie must appear or suffer the consequences. Another Musa, Paul's cousin Annette, also comes to town looking for work, and she is soon attacked by a drunken Iggy and then rescued by Frank. The two spend a long night together and fall in love. Pam, the woman who overheard Joan's preparations to dispose of Robbie's body, makes an anonymous phone call to Frank. He becomes suspicious of Joan, who in turn flees to her accomplice, the third partner, Vince DeMotte. Vince is disturbed by her panic and knifes her, and then utilizes Pam's erroneous belief that Frank is the conspirator by sending her to Iggy, who has sworn revenge on Robbie's murderer. Iggy then gets a second visit, this one from Rose, who is jealous of Annette, having listened to her innocent confession of love for Frank, the man whom Rose once loved. Iggy makes violent love to Rose and learns that Annette is planning to return for her belongings before running away with Frank. He trails the young woman to Frank and shoots him in the shoulder. He is then about to execute Annette when Rose kills Iggy. *Racketeers. Cousins. Murder. Revenge. Infidelity. Marriage. Brother-sister relationship. Drunkenness. Mistaken identity. Prostitution. Nightclubs. Partnerships. Gambling. Employment.*

THE BED SITTING ROOM (Great Britain)   F6.0341

Oscar Lewenstein Productions. *Dist* Lopert Pictures. 28 Sep **1969** [New York opening; c28 Sep 1969; LP40173]. Sd (RCA); col (Eastman Color, print by DeLuxe). 35mm. 90 min. *MPAA rating* M.

Pres by United Artists. *Prod-Dir* Richard Lester. *Exec Prod* Oscar Lewenstein. *Assoc Prod* Roy Stevens. *Screenplay* John Antrobus. *Adapt* Charles Wood. *Dir Photog* David Watkin. *Camera Op* Paul Wilson, Freddie Cooper, Mervyn Wilson. *Art Dir* Michael Seymour. *Prod Dsgn* Assheton Gorton. *Film Ed* John Victor Smith. *Mus Comp & Cond* Ken Thorne. *Sd Ed* Stephen Warwick. *Sd Mix* Peter Sutton. *Dub Mix* Gerry Humphreys. *Asst Dir* Richard Burge. *Cont* Valerie Booth. *Sp Eff* Phil Stokes.

Cast: Rita Tushingham (*Penelope*), Ralph Richardson (*Lord Fortnum*), Peter Cook (*police inspector*), Dudley Moore (*police sergeant*), Spike Milligan (*Mate*), Michael Hordern (*Capt. Bules Martin*), Roy Kinnear (*Plastic Mac Man*), Richard Warwick (*Alan*), Arthur Lowe (*father*), Mona Washbourne (*mother*), Ronald Fraser (*The Army*), Dandy Nichols (*Mrs. Ethel Shroake*), Frank Thornton (*The BBC*), Harry Secombe (*Shelter Man*), Jimmy Edwards (*Nigel*), Henry Woolf (*electricity man for the whole nation*), Jack Shepherd (*underwater vicar*), Marty Feldman (*Nurse Arthur [National Health Service]*), Bill Wallis (*The Prime Minister*), Gordon Rollings (*drip feed patient*), Ronnie Brody (*dwarf chauffeur*), Cecil Cheng (*Chinaman*), Eddie Malin (*club waiter*), Chris Konyils (*policeman*), Ron Moody.

Allegory. Source: Spike Milligan and John Antrobus, *The Bed Sitting Room* (London opening: 31 Jan 1963). Three years after the shortest war in history has ended in nuclear holocaust, a handful of survivors grope their way among the rubble that was London. Penelope, 17 months pregnant, lives with her lover, Alan, and her parents in the underground. Other survivors include Capt. Bules Martin, who holds a "Defeat of England" medal for failing to save the royal palace from "the thing" during the war; Lord Fortnum, afraid that he will mutate into a bed sitting room; a fireguard, Mate; Shelter Man, a regional head of government; a male nurse, the National Health Service; and two policemen who hover over the survivors in a balloon and shout "keep moving" to prevent people from becoming easy targets in the event of another war. Fortnum goes to 20 Cul de Sac Place and eventually does become a bed sitting room. Penelope's mother is presented with her own death certificate and turns into a cupboard. Penelope, despite her love for Alan, is forced to marry Martin because of his bright future. Her father is selected to be prime minister because of his 22-inch leg length, but he turns into a parrot and is cooked and eaten. Penelope finally gives birth to a monster that quickly dies. Martin, lacking sexual power, yields his nuptial honors to Alan. Penelope quickly gives birth to a second child, who is normal, and the country is saved: she and Alan walk off together with the child as a band pays homage to Mrs. Ethel Shroake, closest in succession to the throne. *Police. Royalty. Prime ministers. Monsters. Nuclear warfare. Mutation. Pregnancy. Survival. Family life. Subways. London. The Future.*

Note: Filmed on location in England. Opened in London in Mar 1970; running time: 91 min.

BEDAZZLED (Great Britain)   F6.0342

Stanley Donen Enterprises. *Dist* Twentieth Century-Fox Film Corp. 10 Dec **1967** [New York opening; c9 Dec 1967; LP35498]. Sd; col (De Luxe). 35mm (Panavision). 107 min.

A Stanley Donen Production. *Prod-Dir* Stanley Donen. *Prod Exec* Arthur Carroll. *Screenplay* Peter Cook. *Story* Peter Cook, Dudley Moore. *Anim* Bailey-Pettengell Design Ltd. *Dir Photog* Austin Dempster. *Camera Op* Herbert R. Smith. *Art Dir* Terence Knight. *Asst Art Dir* Ted Tester. *Set Decor* Leon Davis. *Main Titl* Maurice Binder. *Film Ed* Richard Marden. *Asst Ed* Mary Kessell. *Mus* Dudley Moore. *Songs Comp by* Peter Cook. *Song:* "Bedazzled" sung by Peter Cook. *Song:* "Love Me" sung by Dudley Moore. *Sd Mix* John Purchese, Doug Turner. *Dub Ed* Terry Rawlings. *1st & 2d Asst Dir* John Quested, Jonathan Benson. *Prod Supv* James Ware. *Cont* Valerie Booth. *Fashion Cons* Clare Rendlesham. *Cost Supv* Yvonne Caffin. *Miss Bron's Clothes Dsgn by* Jean Muir. *Makeup* Jill Carpenter, Alex Garfath. *Hairdresser* Olga Angelinetta. *Miss Bron's Hairstyles* Alexandre of Paris, Hartnell of London. *Casting Dir* Maude Spector. *Constr Mgr* Leon Davis. *Elec* Lee Electrics.

Cast: Peter Cook (*George Spiggot*), Dudley Moore (*Stanley Moon*), Eleanor Bron (*Margaret Spencer*), Raquel Welch (*Lilian Lust*), Alba (*Vanity*), Robert Russell (*Anger*), Barry Humphries (*Envy*), Parnell McGarry (*Gluttony*), Daniele Noel (*Avarice*), Howard Goorney (*Sloth*), Michael Bates (*Inspector Clarke*), Bernard Spear (*Irving Moses*), Robin Hawdon (*Randolph*), Michael Trubshawe (*Lord Dowdy*), Evelyn Moore (*Mrs. Wisby*), Charles Lloyd Pack (*vicar*), Lockwood West (*Saint Peter*), Betty Cooper (*Sister Phoebe*), Peter Hutchins (*P. C. Roberts*), Max Faulkner (*priest*), John Steiner (*television announcer*), Erik Chitty (*Seed*), Robin Tolhurst (*Daphne*), Anna Turner (*shop assistant*), Michael Boddy (*cardinal*).

Comedy. Stanley Moon, a short order cook in a London hamburger bar, is desperately in love with Margaret, the waitress, but is too timid to approach her. Depressed by his dreary life and his inability to express his love, he decides to hang himself. Failing at even this, he is suddenly confronted by the mysterious George Spiggot, who is in fact the Devil. The forlorn Stanley agrees to sell his soul for seven wishes in the hope of winning Margaret's love. Spiggot consents to allow Stanley an escape clause should he find the fulfillment of his wishes unsatisfactory. He wishes first to become an articulate intellectual; but he makes the mistake of talking himself into almost raping poor Margaret. Next, he becomes a wealthy tycoon who lavishes everything upon Margaret, now his wife, only to discover that what she really wants is other men. His third wish makes Stanley a pop-singing idol; but he loses Margaret's love when she swoons over a more exciting newcomer who looks remarkably like Spiggot. Spiggot next tricks Stanley into squandering one of his wishes when Stanley wishes out loud to know what Margaret is doing at that moment. They become flies on a wall and are able to observe Margaret talking with Inspector Clark, who is investigating Stanley's disappearance. Becoming desperate, Stanley decides to be a man of irresistible sex appeal. Despite Margaret's passion, however, she cannot bring herself to be unfaithful to her saint-like husband, who resembles Spiggot. As his next request Stanley pleads to be "a warm, loving, outgoing person and Margaret the same." The wish is granted, and they are transformed into nuns of the Order of the Leaping Berelians, whose mother superior again resembles Spiggot. After explaining to Stanley that one of his wishes was wasted on an ice lolly, Spiggot announces that he has reached his quota and that his soul will be restored to him in the hope that he, Spiggot, may reenter heaven. As Stanley returns to his hamburger bar, Spiggot is refused heavenly pardon because of his excessive pride. *Cooks. Waitresses. Intellectuals. Singers. Detectives. Nuns. Tycoons. Lovelorn. Timidity. Suicide. Wish fulfillment. Wealth. Marriage. Infidelity. Pride. Restaurants. Contracts. London. The Devil. The Soul.*

Note: Opened in London in Dec 1967; running time: 103 min.

THE BEDFORD INCIDENT (United States/Great Britain)   F6.0343

Bedford Productions. *Dist* Columbia Pictures. 11 Oct **1965** [New London, Connecticut, opening; c1 Aug 1965; LP31742]. Sd (Westrex); b&w. 35mm. 102 min.

A James B. Harris–Richard Widmark Production. *Prod-Dir* James B. Harris. *Assoc Prod* Denis O'Dell. *Co-prod* Richard Widmark. *Screenplay* James Poe. *Dir Photog* Gilbert Taylor. *Camera Op* Derek Browne. *Art Dir* Arthur Lawson. *Assoc Art Dir* Lionel Couch. *Film Ed* John Jympson. *Asst Film Ed* Pamela Tomling, Roy Benson. *Mus Comp & Cond* Gerard Schurmann. *Sd Rec* Leslie Hammond, Bob Jones. *Sd Ed* Winston Ryder. *Asst Dir* Clive Reed. *Prod Mgr* Victor Peck. *Cont* Phyllis Crocker. *Makeup* Eric Allwright. *Tech Adv* Ian Cox, (Lieut. Comdr., Royal Navy Ret.), James D. Ferguson, (Capt. USN Ret.). *Casting Dir* James Liggat.

Cast: Richard Widmark (*Capt. Eric Finlander*), Sidney Poitier (*Ben Munceford*), James MacArthur (*Ensign Ralston*), Martin Balsam (*Lieut. Comdr. Chester Potter*), Wally Cox (*Seaman Merlin Queffle*), Eric Portman (*Commodore Wolfgang Schrepke*).

Cast—Bridge: Michael Kane (*Commander Allison*), Colin Maitland (*Seaman Jones*), Michael Graham (*Lieutenant Krindlemeyer*), Billy Edwards (*Lieutenant Hazelwood*), Paul Tamarin, Stephen Von Schreiber, Eugene

Leonard (seamen 2d class), Frank Lieberman, James Caffrey, Burnell Tucker, Ronald Rubin (seaman 1st class).

Cast—C. I. C.: Gary Cockrell (Lieutenant Bascombe), George Roubicek (Lieutenant Berger), Roy Stephens, Glenn Beck (seamen 2d class), John McCarthy, actor, Shane Rimmer (seaman 1st class).

Cast—Communications: Brian Davies (Lieutenant Beckman), Edward Bishop (Lieutenant Hacker), Paul Carson (seaman 1st class), Laurence Herder (petty officer).

Cast—Sick Bay: Phil Brown (Chief Hospitalman McKinley), Donald Sutherland (Hospitalman Nerney), Warren Stanhope (Hospitalman Strauss).

Melodrama. Source: Mark Rascovich, The Bedford Incident (New York, 1963). U. S. Navy Capt. Eric Finlander is the tough, efficient commander of the Bedford, an ultra-modern submarine-chasing destroyer. He has the complete loyalty of his crew, who both fear and respect him. His assistant, Commodore Schrepke, a German former U-boat commander in World War II now on assignment to NATO, is the only one who dares to question Finlander's orders or intent. The Navy permits Ben Munceford, a liberal Negro journalist, to come aboard for the purpose of writing a story about Finlander and his crew. Another newcomer, ship's doctor Lieut. Comdr. Chester Potter, discovers to his amazement that the crew never report for sick call. The Bedford is on its usual patrol off the coast of Greenland when expert sonar man Merlin Queffle detects a Russian submarine. Finlander wants to force the submarine to surface but is prohibited by fleet headquarters from doing so. Finlander stalks the submarine, keeping an around-the-clock watch, waiting for it to surface for air. Despite the warnings of Schrepke and Munceford, who sense that this mock war has gotten out of hand and fear that the Russians may show force, Finlander rams the submarine, now in international waters, when the Russians refuse to identify themselves. The crew of the Bedford is exhausted and near to cracking under the strain of keeping constant vigilance at their stations; Queffle has collapsed; and young Ensign Ralston, the butt of Finlander's criticisms, is dangerously jittery. Ralston misunderstands a command and fires a nuclear missile at the submarine, which is sunk but not before launching its own torpedoes to destroy the Bedford. Ship crews. Journalists. Negroes. Germans. Russians. Physicians. Obsession. Cold war. Sonar. Submarines. Battleships. Nuclear weapons. Greenland. United States Navy. North Atlantic Treaty Organization.

Note: Filmed in Great Britain. London opening: Oct 1965.

BEDROOM VENDETTA see THE GREEN MARE

THE BEDSPREAD   **F6.0344**
Kirt Films International. Dist Distribpix, Inc. **1969**. Sd; col. 35mm. 65 min.

Sex film. Alone in the big city, Rita, a destitute young woman, finds work as a chambermaid and discovers that she is working in a hotel catering to prostitutes and their clients. As she goes from room to room, Rita willingly becomes involved in a variety of sexual experiences, and she soon becomes the leader of the hotel's nonstop parties. Eventually, the parties become wilder, the people more depraved, and the action hotter until the film explodes in a climactic ending. Chambermaids. Prostitution. Sexuality. Hotels. Whorehouses. Orgies.

BEDTIME STORY   **F6.0345**
Lankershim Co.-Pennebaker, Inc. Dist Universal Pictures. 10 Jun **1964** [New York opening; c4 Jul 1963; LP32601]. Sd (Westrex); col (Eastman Color by Pathé). 35mm. 99 min.

Prod Stanley Shapiro. Exec Prod Robert Arthur. Dir Ralph Levy. Screenplay Stanley Shapiro, Paul Henning. Dir Photog Clifford Stine. Art Dir Alexander Golitzen, Robert Clatworthy. Set Decor Oliver Emert. Titl Pacific Title. Film Ed Milton Carruth. Mus Hans J. Salter. Mus Supv Joseph Gershenson. Sd Waldon O. Watson, Corson Jowett. Asst Dir Joseph E. Kenny. Unit Prod Mgr Kenneth L. Grossman. Gowns Dsgn Jean Louis. Makeup Bud Westmore. Hairstyles Larry Germain.

Cast: Marlon Brando (Freddy Benson), David Niven (Lawrence Jamison), Shirley Jones (Janet Walker), Dody Goodman (Fanny Eubank), Aram Stephan (André), Parley Baer (Colonel Williams), Marie Windsor (Mrs. Sutton), Rebecca Sand (Miss Trumble), Frances Robinson (Miss Harrington), Henry Slate (Sattler), Norman Alden (Dubin), Susanne Cramer (Anna Kroeger), Cynthia Lynn (Frieda), Ilse Taurins (Hilda), Francine York (Gina).

Romantic comedy. Cpl. Freddy Benson is a successful smalltime con artist who, while stationed in Europe, seduces women, accepts money and gifts from them, and then moves on. Discharged from the Army because of an affair with a mayor's daughter, he heads for the French Riviera. There he meets another womanizer, Lawrence Jamison, a sophisticated counterpart who works on a much grander scale, posing as royalty. Freddy begins to encroach on Jamison when he appears as the "prince's" idiot brother. With the arrival of Janet Walker, an American reputed to be a "soap queen," they wager on who will be the first to divest her of $25,000 and the one to remain on the Riviera. Freddy

plays a psychosomatic cripple who has lost the use of his legs because of an unfaithful sweetheart. He pretends that he needs money to engage the services of a Swiss psychiatrist, Dr. Schaffhausen. As a counter to Freddy's charade, Jamison poses as Schaffhausen. Freddy's charm triumphs until it is found that Janet is not a soap heiress but rather the winner of a beauty contest. Because Freddy has fallen in love with her and wants to marry her, he concedes the victory to Jamison, who then continues unchallenged in his field. Confidence men. Americans in foreign countries. Philanderers. Heiresses. Psychiatrists. Royalty. Mistaken identity. Imposture. Wagers. Psychosomatic illness. Riviera. United States Army.

Note: Working title: King of the Mountain.

BEFORE DAWN (Japan)   **F6.0346**
Kindai Eiga Kyokai–Mingei Theatrical Troupe. Dist Toho Co. 4 Nov **1966** [Los Angeles opening]. Sd; b&w. 35mm. 142 min. [Cut to 120 min.]

Dir Kimisaburo Yoshimura. Screenplay Kaneto Shindo. Photog Yoshio Miyajima. Mus Akira Ifukube.

Cast: Osamu Takizawa (Hanzo Aoyama), Nobuko Otowa (his daughter), Shin Date (his father), Chikako Hosokawa (his mother), Fukuko Sayo (his wife), Akira Yamanouchi (his son), Masao Shimizu (Juheiji), Jukichi Uno (Kanekicki), Taiji Tonoyama (ox-cart driver).

Historical drama. Source: Toson Shimazaki, Yoake mae (Tokyo, 1935). In 19th-century Magome, Hanzo Aoyama is the proprietor of an inn frequented by wealthy lords who traverse the rugged Kiso Trail, connecting Kyoto and Edo. In return for status and privilege, his family remains loyal to the ruthless Tokugawa shogunate general, who has refused the poverty-stricken Magome villagers permission to log the surrounding cypress forests. As the struggle for imperial restoration continues in the 1860's, there is great social and political upheaval; famine, labor strikes, and many assassinations lead to the War of the Restoration. When the emperor is reinstated in 1867, Aoyama opens his heart to his fellow villagers and appeals on their behalf to the new regime. His cause denied by Emperor Meiji, the embittered Aoyama dies insane at the age of 56. Dictators. Feudalism. Village life. Poverty. Famine. Strikes. Assassination. Insanity. Inns. Forests. Japan—History—Tokugawa period 1600–1867. Japan—History—Meiji period 1867–1912. Japan—History—Restoration 1853–70. Magome (Japan).

Note: Filmed on location in Magome, Japan. Released in Japan in 1953 as Yoake mae. Director Kimisaburo Yoshimura is also known as Kozaburo Yoshimura.

BEFORE THE REVOLUTION (Italy)   **F6.0347**
Iride Cinematografica. Dist New Yorker Films. 21 Jul **1965** [New York opening]. Sd; b&w. 35mm. 112 min.

Dir-Writ Bernardo Bertolucci. Screenplay Collab Gianni Amico. Photog Aldo Scavarda. Film Ed Roberto Perpignani. Mus Gino Paoli, Ennio Morricone. Mus Dir Franco Ferrara. Songs: "Ricordati," "Vivere ancora" writ & sung by Gino Paoli. Song: "Avero 15 anni" sung by Ennio Ferrari. Sd Romano Pampaloni. Asst Dir Gianni Amico.

Cast: Adriana Asti (Gina), Francesco Barilli (Fabrizio), Allen Midgette (Agostino), Morando Morandini (Cesare), Domenico Alpi (Fabrizio's father), Giuseppe Maghenzani (Fabrizio's brother), Cecrope Barilli (Puck), Cristina Pariset (Clelia), Emilia Borghi (Fabrizio's mother), Iole Lunardi (Fabrizio's grandmother), Evelina Alpi (girl), Gianni Amico (friend), Goliardo Padova (The Painter), Guido Fanti (Enore), Salvatore Enrico (sacristan), Ida Pellegri (Clelia's mother).

Drama. Fabrizio, 20-years-old and caught up in Marxist ideology, rejects the stagnation of the Parmesian middle class background he shares with his fiancée, Clelia. Two friends encourage him: Cesare, a schoolteacher who serves as his guide in Marxism, and Agostino, the son of a prosperous manufacturer. He breaks with Clelia, and his dismayed parents invite his young aunt, Gina, to stay for a while in the hope that she can communicate with him. Then Agostino is drowned, and Fabrizio draws closer to Gina in his need for a close friend. She reciprocates his friendship, and they become secret lovers. Fabrizio finds difficulty in coping with Gina's unpredictable moods, however, and when one day he sees her emerging from a hotel with a chance acquaintance, his bitterness leads to a deterioration in their relationship. Finally Cesare helps Gina pack her suitcases to leave. Fabrizio becomes politically disillusioned and returns to Clelia, whose uncomplicated acceptance provides him with the security he needs. Although he encounters Gina again at the opera and discovers that his fascination with her remains, he marries Clelia. Cesare preaches revolution to a new generation of students and Gina tearfully embraces Fabrizio's younger brother. Middle classes. Revolutionaries. Schoolteachers. Aunts. Incest. Marxism. Youth. Friendship. Disillusionment. Parma.

Note: Rome opening: Nov 1964 as Prima della rivoluzione; running time: 115 min.

BEFORE WINTER COMES (Great Britain)   **F6.0348**
Windward Films. *Dist* Columbia Pictures. 24 Mar **1969** [New York opening; c1 Apr 1969; LP36822]. Sd (RCA); col (Technicolor, print by Perfect). 35mm. 108 min.
Prod Robert Emmett Ginna. *Dir* J. Lee Thompson. *Screenplay* Andrew Sinclair. *Dir Photog* Gilbert Taylor. *Camera Op* Herbert R. Smith. *Art Dir* John Blezard. *Film Ed* Willy Kemplen. *Mus* Ron Grainer. *Sd Rec* Cyril Collick. *Sd Ed* Winston Ryder. *Dub Mix* Ken Scrivener. *Asst Dir* Jake Wright. *Prod Mgr* Bruce Sharman. *Location Mgr* Robert Simmonds. *Cont* Kay Mander. *Wardrobe Supv* Eddie Boyce. *Makeup* Constance Reeve. *Hairdressing* Marjorie Whittle. *Casting Dir* Maude Spector.
Cast: David Niven *(Major Burnside)*, Topol *(Janovic)*, Anna Karina *(Maria)*, John Hurt *(Lieutenant Pilkington)*, Anthony Quayle *(Brigadier Bewley)*, Ori Levy *(Captain Kamenev)*, John Collin *(Sergeant Woody)*, Karel Stepanek *(Count Kerassy)*, Guy Deghy *(Kovacs)*, Mark Malicz *(Komenski)*, Gertan Klauber *(Russian major)*, Hana-Maria Pravda *(Beata)*, George Innes *(Bill)*, Tony Selby *(Ted)*, Hugh Futcher *(Joe)*, Christopher Sandford *(Johnny)*, Colin Spaull *(Alf)*, Larry Dann *(Al)*, Jeffry Wickham *(Captain Roots)*, Alysoun Austin *(A.T.S. driver)*, John Savident *(British corporal)*, Constantin De Goguel *(Russian corporal)*, Jerry Tarrant *(2d British corporal)*, Joseph Roubalik *(Russian soldier)*, David Carson *(1st British soldier)*, Albert Shepherd *(2d British soldier)*, Bruno W. Pantel *(Anatol)*, Hans Epskamp *(priest)*, Nora Minor *(witch)*, Lieselotte Quilling *(Frau Komenski)*, Karin Schroeder *(pregnant girl)*, Hans Schumm *(The Camp Doctor)*, Harry Kalenberg *(policeman)*, Eduard Linkers *(businessman)*, Peter Mathes *(Malik)*, Gisela Fritsch *(Anna)*, Britt Bern *(Marta)*.
Drama. Source: Frederick L. Keefe, "The Interpreter," in *New Yorker* (10 Dec 1966). In 1945, British Maj. Giles Burnside is assigned to an Austrian border camp for displaced persons and ordered to determine whether the swarms of refugees should be sent to the American or the Russian zone. Although conscientious, the Major dislikes his task and hopes for a transfer, despite the realization that he has been removed from active service because of a courageous but ill-fated disregard for orders which resulted in the tragic loss of 200 men and left him with a partially disabled leg. His determination to adhere strictly to regulations is handicapped by the inexperience of his young interpreter, Lieut. Francis Pilkington, who speaks only Greek, Latin, and a little French. But the dilemma is resolved when one of the refugees, a man who calls himself Janovic, steps forth and announces that he speaks a multitude of languages. Quickly enrolled as an interpreter, Janovic soon turns out to be much more. He acts as a mediator between Major Burnside and his Russian counterpart, Captain Kamenev; he puts the camp in shape for an inspection by Brigadier General Bewley; and, in effect, he takes over the running of the entire station. He also finds time to romance the owner of the inn, Maria Holz, a young woman whose husband was presumably killed at Stalingrad. But Janovic's love for Maria turns to anger when he discovers that she is insuring her relationship with the British by also giving herself to Major Burnside. Then, as the last of the refugees are readied for departure, Captain Kamenev learns that Janovic is a Russian army deserter and, under the Allied agreement, must be returned to Russia for execution. Unwilling to put his trust in Burnside's promise of help, Janovic tries to escape, but he is captured and brought back to the camp. The incident ties Burnside's hands and he is forced to put Janovic on a truck bound for the Russian zone. But there is a glimmer of hope as Janovic notices that Captain Kamenev, by now an old friend, is the officer in charge of the convoy. With work at the camp completed, Major Burnside receives the bitter honor of being assigned to another refugee center in recognition of his accomplishment. *Refugees. Interpreters. Russians. Innkeepers. Widows. Deserters—Military. Survival. World War II. Austria. Great Britain—Army. Union of Soviet Socialist Republics—Army.*
Note: Location scenes filmed near Salzburg, Austria. Released in Great Britain in 1969.

THE BEGINNERS *see* **THE FIRST TIME**

THE BEGINNERS THREE *see* **THE FIRST TIME**

THE BEGINNING WAS SIN (West Germany/Yugoslavia)   **F6.0349**
Saphir Film-Triglav Film. *Dist* Globe Releasing, John Alexander Film Associates. 1 Aug **1962** [Philadelphia opening]. Sd; b&w. 35mm. 88 min.
Prod Peter Bamberger. *Dir-Writ* Franz Čap. *Photog* Bruno Stephan. *Art Dir* Mirko Lippo. *Film Ed* Hilde Grebner, Klaus Eckstein. *Mus* Bojan Adamič. *Prod Mgr* Helmut Bamberger.
Cast: Ruth Niehaus *(Rosalie)*, Viktor Staal *(Jacob Bauer)*, Hansi Knotecks *(Anna)*, Peter Carsten *(Marko)*, Laya Raki *(gypsy dancer)*, Petr Unkel, Franz Muxeneder, Edith Schultze-Westrum.
Romantic melodrama. Source: Guy de Maupassant, "Histoire d'une fille de ferme," in *Revue Politique et Littéraire* (20 Mar 1881). Jacob Bauer, a rich farmer, is unhappy that his wife is sterile. Unknown to him, his maid Rosalie

is raped and becomes pregnant by Marko, a farmhand who deserts her when she suggests marriage. Rosalie goes to her mother's home, gives birth to a son, and returns to Jacob, whose wife has died. Pleased with her work, Jacob proposes marriage; she hesitates because of her illegitimate child, but later accepts, keeping her secret. Jacob soon begins to torment her for not having a child by him. During a violent quarrel, she declares that it is he who is sterile, revealing that she has already borne a child. Humbled, Jacob adopts the boy. *Farmers. Housemaids. Farmhands. Widowers. Childlessness. Sterility (sexual). Rape. Pregnancy. Illegitimacy. Marriage. Adoption.*
Note: Location scenes filmed in Yugoslavia. Opened in Essen in Oct 1954 as *Am Anfang war es Sünde*; running time: 96 min. Yugoslavian title: *Greh.*

BEHIND CLOSED DOORS *see* **DADDY, DARLING**

BEHIND THE IRON CURTAIN *see* **GRAND TOUR OF EASTERN EUROPE: BEHIND THE IRON CURTAIN**

BEHIND THE NUDIST CURTAIN   **F6.0350**
Juri Productions. *Dist* Atlantic Pictures. 11 Sep **1964** [Los Angeles showing]. Sd; col (Eastman Color). 35mm (Techniscope). 71 min.
Prod-Dir Doris Wishman. *Screenplay* Martin Samuels. *Narr* Melvin Stanley. *Film Ed* Al Nahmias. *Mus* Picture Scores. *Sd* Titra Sound Corp. *Optical Eff* B & O Film Specialists.
Cast: Brett Morrison *(narrator)*, William Mayer, Maria Stinger, Betty Andrews, Harry W. Stinger, Janice Coughlin, Martha J. Pryor, Christy Fanshee, Lee Abell, Sandy Sinclair, Betsi Warton.
Nudist film. Sam Dennison, a vacationing detective, is negotiating the purchase of a nudist camp from its owner, Martha, when he receives an assignment to locate Mr. X, an international spy who receives information from entertainers around the world. Sam travels to Las Vegas, Hong Kong, Thailand, Paris, Haiti, Mexico, Hawaii, Berlin, and Tokyo, stopping between trips at Martha's nudist camp. Mr. X is captured and Sam returns to the nudist camp for a deserved rest. Sam marries Martha and is reluctantly persuaded to spend their honeymoon traveling around the world. *Detectives. Spies. Nudist camps. Las Vegas. Thailand. Haiti. Hawaii. Hong Kong. Paris. Mexico. Tokyo. Berlin.*
Note: Also known as *Nature Girls Unlimited*, and possibly as *Nudist Curtain.* Location shooting at Sunny Palms Lodge, Homestead, Florida; and Spartans, Miami, Florida. Certain nightclub sequences appeared earlier in the film *Playgirls International*, q. v.

BEHOLD A PALE HORSE   **F6.0351**
Highland–Brentwood Productions. *Dist* Columbia Pictures. 13 Aug **1964** [New York opening; c1 Aug 1964; LP29281]. Sd; b&w. 35mm. 112 min. [Cut from 118 min.]
A Fred Zinnemann Production. *Prod-Dir* Fred Zinnemann. *Assoc Prod* Alexander Trauner. *Screenplay* J. P. Miller. *Photog* Jean Badal. *Camera Op* Henri Tiquet. *Art Dir* Auguste Capelier. *Set Decor* Maurice Barnathan. *Prod Dsgn* Alexander Trauner. *Film Ed* Walter Thompson. *Mus Comp & Cond* Maurice Jarre. *Sd* Jean Monchablon. *Asst Dir* Paul Feyder. *Prod Mgr* Louis Wipf. *Cont* Alice Ziller. *Cost Dsgn* Elizabeth Haffenden, Joan Bridge. *Makeup* Michel Deruelle. *Hairstyles* Marc Blanchard. *Casting* Margot Capelier. *Dial Coach* Ruth Roberts, Walter Kelley. *Opening Montage Courtesy of* Nicole Stéphane, Frédéric Rossif.
Cast: Gregory Peck *(Manuel Artiguez)*, Anthony Quinn *(Captain Vinolas)*, Omar Sharif *(Father Francisco)*, Mildred Dunnock *(Pilar)*, Raymond Pellegrin *(Carlos)*, Paolo Stoppa *(Pedro)*, Daniela Rocca *(Rosanna)*, Christian Marquand *(Lieutenant Zaganar)*, Marietto Angeletti *(Paco Dages)*, Perrette Pradier *(Maria)*, Zia Mohyeddin *(Luis)*, Rosalie Crutchley *(Teresa)*, Molly Urquhart, Jean-Paul Moulinot, Laurence Badie, Martin Benson, Jean-Claude Bercq, Claude Berri, Claude Confortes, Michel Lonsdale, Alain Saury, José-Luis de Vilallonga, Elisabeth Wiener.
Drama. Source: Emeric Pressburger, *Killing a Mouse on Sunday* (London, 1961). Twenty years after the Spanish Civil War, Manuel Artiguez, a guerrilla fighter who has found sanctuary in the French town of Pau, receives word from Carlos, a smuggler, that his mother, Pilar, is dying in a San Martín hospital. Pilar learns that her son's bitter enemy, San Martín police chief Vinolas, with the aid of Carlos, has set a trap for Artiguez, and she persuades a local priest, Father Francisco, to carry a letter of warning to her son begging him not to come. Paco, an 11-year-old whose father was killed by Vinolas, destroys the letter, hoping that Artiguez will meet and kill Vinolas. When Paco sees Artiguez with the traitor Carlos, however, he tells Artiguez of his mother's death and the letter that he destroyed. Artiguez travels to Lourdes where Father Francisco confirms Paco's story, but he decides to follow Carlos to Spain anyway. Aided by Paco, Artiguez enters the San Martín hospital and manages to reach the roof, where he overpowers one of Vinolas' snipers and then kills Carlos. Artiguez is also killed in the gunfire, and Vinolas is left triumphant but wondering why the guerrilla chose to enter Spain and face his enemy. *Guerrillas. Smugglers. Police. Priests. Duplicity. Filial relations. Revenge. Hospitals. Spain—History—Civil*

War 1936–39. Pau. San Martín del Rey Aurelio. Lourdes. Documentation.
    Note: Location scenes filmed in southwest France in Bayonne, Lourdes, and the Pyrénées. Opening montage borrowed from *To Die in Madrid,* q. v.

BEL AMI 2000 ODER: WIE VERFÜHRT MAN EINEN PLAYBOY? *see* HOW TO SEDUCE A PLAYBOY

LE BEL ANTONIO *see* BELL'ANTONIO

BELI DJAVO *see* THE WHITE WARRIOR

BELL, BARE AND BEAUTIFUL   F6.0352
    Griffith Productions. 13 Sep **1963** [Los Angeles showing]. Sd; col (Eastman Color). 35mm. 64 min.
    Prod Davis Freeman. *Exec Prod* Leroy C. Griffith, Eli Jackson. *Dir* Lewis H. Gordon. *Screenplay* Leroy C. Griffith. *Photog* Lewis H. Gordon. *Film Ed* Carroll Wurkes. *Mus* L. W. Ellington. *Sd* Davis Mason.
    Cast: Virginia Bell *(Gina)*, Thomas Sweetwood *(Rick)*, Joy Hodges *(Betty)*, Sunny Dare *(Elsa)*, Dave Friedman *(Barney)*, Al Golden *(Dr. Everett)*, Roland Porter *(Roland)*, Harry Shurgin *(gangster)*, Leroy C. Griffith *(theatre manager)*, Ben Melton *(Mickey)*, Jerome Eden *(artist)*, Craig Maudslay, Jr. *(bellboy)*, Huntington Hall *(doctor)*, Cindy Craig, Sheryl Nichols, Barbara Taylor, Fraiah Payne, Joyce Lewis, Sandra Sinclair.
    Nudist film. Young millionaire Rick Bradshaw consults his psychiatrist Dr. Everett about his persistent dream about an unknown, beautiful woman. Dr. Everett takes Rick to an artist, who sketches a likeness of Rick's dream girl, and the picture is run in the newspapers. Rick is swamped with replies from women, but the genuine one comes from the agent of burlesque queen Gina Adair. Rick follows Gina and her act to Miami, searching in vain for her in her favorite nudist camp. Rick approaches Gina at the theater where she works, but he is assaulted by her manager, Barney, who controls Gina because of a large unpaid loan once given her father. Rick later repays the loan when he finally sees Gina at the nudist camp. Barney sends a gangster friend after Rick to recover the loan note. Rick detains the gangster, informs the police, and goes off with Gina to discuss their marriage. *Millionaires. Stripteasers. Psychiatrists. Theatrical managers. Gangsters. Nudism. Burlesque. Nudist camps. Loans. Miami. Dreams.*
    Note: Nature camp sequences filmed at Spartan's Tropical Gardens, Miami, Florida.

BELLA DI GIORNO *see* BELLE DE JOUR

BELL'ANTONIO (France/Italy)   F6.0353
    Cino del Duca–Arco Film–Société Cinématographique Lyre. *Dist* Embassy Pictures. 2 Apr **1962** [New York opening]. Sd; b&w. 35mm. 101 min.
    Pres by Raphael Hakim. *Prod* Alfredo Bini. *Dir* Mauro Bolognini. *Screenplay* Pier Paolo Pasolini, Gino Visentini. *Photog* Armando Nannuzzi. *Art Dir* Carlo Egidi, Piero Tosi. *Film Ed* Nino Baragli. *Mus Comp & Cond* Piero Piccioni. *Asst Dir* Nicolo Ferrari, Luigi Bazzoni. *Prod Mgr* Manolo Bolognini.
    Cast: Marcello Mastroianni *(Antonio Magnano)*, Claudia Cardinale *(Barbara Puglisi)*, Pierre Brasseur *(Alfio Magnano)*, Rina Morelli *(Signora Magnano)*, Tomas Milian *(Eduardo)*, Fulvia Mammi *(Elena)*, Patrizia Bini *(Santuzza)*, Anna Arena, Maria Luisa Crescenzi, Cesarina Gherardi, Gina Mattarolo, Alice Sandro, Nino Camarada, Guido Celano, Maurizio Conti, Salvatore Fazio, Rino Giusti, Enzo Tiribelli, Ugo Torrente.
    Comedy-drama. *Source: Vitaliano Brancati, Il bell'Antonio* (Milan, 1950). After spending 3 years in Rome, handsome Antonio Magnano returns to his native Catania. His reputation as a lady-killer has been fostered largely by his boastful father, Alfio, who equates honor with virility. Consequently Antonio finds himself besieged by women, a situation from which he escapes by agreeing to his father's wish that he marry Barbara Puglisi, the naive and innocent daughter of a wealthy and politically prominent family. For the first time in his life, Antonio becomes involved in a relationship based on love rather than pure eroticism, and the shock makes him impotent. For almost a year Antonio and Barbara appear to be blissfully happy, but when it becomes common knowledge that their union is still unconsummated, Barbara's outraged parents have the marriage annulled. The public disgrace falls heavily on Signor Magnano, and he tries to reestablish the family reputation by distinguishing himself at the neighborhood brothel, a course of action which proves fatal to the diabetic old man. Filled with remorse and still in love with Barbara, who has since remarried, Antonio has a fling with the family maid. She becomes pregnant, and the overjoyed Signora Magnano proclaims the news of her son's virility throughout the town. Antonio finds little solace in his regained manhood, however, in the face of his unfulfilled love for Barbara. *Sicilians. Playboys. Braggarts. Housemaids. Impotence. Marriage—Annulment. Manhood. Reputation. Filial relations. Whorehouses. Catania.*
    Note: Opened in Rome in Feb 1960 as *Il bell'Antonio,* and in Paris in Jul 1961 as *Le bel Antonio;* French running time: 92 min.

THE BELLBOY AND THE PLAYGIRLS *see* THE PLAYGIRLS AND THE BELLBOY

LA BELLE AMÉRICAINE (France)   F6.0354
    C. C. F. C.–Panoramas Films–Le Film d'Art–Carlton Continental–Corflor. *Dist* Continental Distributing, Inc. 17 Dec **1961** [New York opening]. Sd; b&w. 35mm. 100 min.
    Prod Henri Diamant-Berger, Arthur Lesser. *Assoc Prod* Walter Rupp. *Dir* Robert Dhéry. *Screenplay* Robert Dhéry, Pierre Tchernia, Alfred Adam. *Photog* Ghislain Cloquet. *Art Dir* Lucien Aguettand. *Film Ed* Albert Jurgenson. *Mus* Gérard Calvi. *Sd* Robert Teisseire. *Asst Dir* Tony Aboyantz. *English Titl* Herman G. Weinberg.
    Cast: Robert Dhéry *(Marcel)*, Colette Brosset *(Paulette)*, Alfred Adam *(Alfred)*, Louis de Funès *(factory supervisor/police station chief)*, Bernard Lavalette *(Minister of Commerce)*, Christian Marin *(ice cream vendor)*, Catherine Sola *(his girl friend)*, Robert Rollis *(barber)*, Jacques Fabbri *(grocer)*, Jacques Legras *(barkeeper)*, Michel Serrault *(Marcel's army buddy)*, Annie Ducaux *(Madame Lucanzas)*, Eliane d'Almeida *("secretary")*, Hélène Dieudonné *(Granny)*, Robert Burnier *(Minister's aide)*, Pierre Dac *(colonel)*, Didier Daix *(Minister's aide)*, Robert Destain *(Marseilles inspector)*, Max Favalelli *(The Ambassador)*, Bernard Dhéran *(factory manager)*, Maurice Gardett *(gendarme)*, Gilberte Géniat *(Madame Zoutin)*, Jean Richard *(locksmith)*, Pierre Tchernia *(tv announcer)*, Jean Carmet *(tramp on the road)*, Jacques Charrier *(obliging motorist)*, Roger Pierre *(snob in the sports car)*, Jean-Marc Thibault *(effeminate young man)*, Jean Lefebvre, René Sarvil.
    Comedy. Madame Lucanzas, furious because her late husband has willed his enormous American convertible to his "private secretary," sells the car to Marcel, a factory worker, for 500 francs ($100) in order to deprive the "secretary" of her inheritance. Being the owner of such an elegant car, dubbed "La Belle Américaine," causes Marcel innumerable difficulties. Gasoline consumption threatens to bankrupt him; his envious boss fires him; his wife Paulette turns a televised exhibit of dogs, fashions, and luxury cars into a shambles; the secretary locks Marcel in the trunk of the car when he refuses to sell it back to her; he mistakenly drives into an automatic car wash with the top down; and he becomes embroiled in a traffic jam involving official government cars. The last misfortune, however, proves to be a lucky break, for the Minister of Commerce becomes so impressed with "La Belle" that he strikes up a friendship with Marcel. Consequently, when the car is lost, the Minister uses his influence to see that it is promptly returned to Marcel. The problem of what to do with the car is finally solved when Paulette crashes it into an ice cream cart, and "La Belle Américaine" is converted into a palatial ice cream stand that creates a sensation at the race track. *Factory workers. Secretaries. Widows. Employer-employee relations. Jealousy. Automobile accidents. Finance—Personal. Automobiles. Traffic.*
    Note: Released in Paris in Sep 1961. May also have been released in the U. S. as *What a Chassis!*

BELLE DE JOUR (France/Italy)   F6.0355
    Paris-Films Production–Five Film. *Dist* Allied Artists. 10 Apr **1968** [New York opening; c24 May 1967; LF30]. Sd; col (Eastman Color). 35mm. 100 min. [Copyright length: 104 min.]
    Prod Robert Hakim, Raymond Hakim. *Dir* Luis Buñuel. *Screenplay* Luis Buñuel, Jean-Claude Carrière. *Photog* Sacha Vierny. *Adtl Photog* Philippe Brun. *Art Dir* Robert Clavel. *Set Decor* Maurice Barnathan. *Film Ed* Louisette Hautecoeur, Walter Spohr. *Sd Engr* René Longuet. *Asst Dir* Jacques Fraenkel, Pierre Lary. *Prod Mgr* Henri Baum. *Miss Deneuve's Cost* Yves Saint Laurent. *Wardrobe* Hélène Nourry. *Makeup* Janine Jarreau. *Hairstyles* Simone Knapp.
    Cast: Catherine Deneuve *(Séverine Sérizy)*, Jean Sorel *(Pierre Sérizy)*, Geneviève Page *(Madame Anaïs)*, Michel Piccoli *(Henri Husson)*, Pierre Clementi *(Marcel)*, Macha Méril *(Renée Févret)*, Francisco Rabal *(Hyppolite)*, Georges Marchal *(The Duke)*, Françoise Fabian *(Charlotte)*, Maria Latour *(Mathilde)*, Francis Blanche *(Monsieur Adolphe)*, Iska Khan *(Asian client)*, Muni *(Pallas)*, François Maistre *(The Professor)*, Bernard Fresson *(Le Grêle)*, Dominique Dandrieux *(Catherine)*, Brigitte Parmentier *(Séverine as a child)*, Michel Charrel *(footman)*, D. de Roseville *(coachman)*, Marcel Charvey *(Professor Henri)*, Pierre Marcay *(intern)*, Adélaïde Blasquez *(maid)*, Marc Eyraud *(barman)*, Bernard Musson *(majordomo)*, Claude Cerval.
    Drama. *Source: Joseph Kessel, Belle de jour* (Paris, 1928). Séverine is the beautiful wife of a young, successful surgeon, Pierre Sérizy. Although she loves her husband, Séverine is sexually unmoved by his too-gentle lovemaking and is haunted by fantasies in which Pierre orders her pulled from a horsedrawn carriage and whipped by two liveried coachmen. One day Séverine learns that a respectable married woman she knows has been earning extra spending money by working part time in a brothel. Intrigued, Séverine visits the establishment and, following a talk with Madame Anaïs, agrees to work there every afternoon under the name "Belle de jour." Now sexually fulfilled, Séverine finds that her relationship with Pierre is improving. But one of

Séverine's regular clients, Marcel, a cocky, gold-toothed hoodlum, becomes so enamored of her that he asks her to go away with him. When she refuses, Marcel finds out her true identity, shoots Pierre, and is himself killed by the police. As a result of the shooting, Pierre is left paralyzed, blind, and speechless. Séverine feels responsible for her husband's tragedy, and her masochistic needs are perhaps fulfilled by the realization that she will have to wait on Pierre for the rest of his life. Pierre's friend Henri Husson, who has visited Madame Anaïs' establishment and seen Séverine there, arrives to tell Pierre about Séverine's other life. Henri leaves, and Séverine turns toward Pierre, who has begun to weep. He suddenly gets up as though nothing were wrong with him, and they look out the window as the horsedrawn carriage goes past, empty. *Surgeons. Madams. Hoodlums. Police. Marriage. Masochism. Prostitution. Sexual practices. Jealousy. Paralysis. Blindness. Fantasy.*

Note: Opened in Paris in May 1967; in Rome in Sep 1967 as *Bella di giorno.*

LA BELLE ET LE CAVALIER see MORE THAN A MIRACLE

BELLE SOMMERS   F6.0356
Astron Productions. *Dist* Columbia Pictures. 30 May **1962** [New York opening; c1 Mar 1962; LP21507]. Sd (Westrex); b&w. 35mm. 62 min.

Prod William Sackheim. *Dir* Elliot Silverstein. *Screenplay* Richard Alan Simmons. *Dir Photog* Charles S. Welborn. *Art Dir* Robert Peterson. *Set Decor* Louis Diage. *Film Ed* Asa Clark. *Mus Supv* Irving Friedman. *Mus* Harry Sukman. *Song:* "Exactly Like You" Dorothy Fields, Jimmy McHugh. *Sung by* Polly Bergen. *Song:* "Once I Had a True Love" sung by Polly Bergen. *Asst Dir* Herbert Wallerstein. *Prod Supv* Seymour Friedman. *Makeup Supv* Ben Lane.

Cast: Polly Bergen (*Belle Sommers*), David Janssen (*Danny Castle*), Warren Stevens (*Lew Burton*), Jay Adler (*Jack Hiker*), Joan Staley (*Ruth Killiam*), Carroll O'Connor (*Jerry Griffith*), Eddie Ryder (*Cliff Short*), Robert Brubaker (*Herb Palette*), Reedy Talton (*Detective Lieutenant Perelli*).

Melodrama. Belle Sommers, once a leading nightclub and recording star, is no longer in the public eye because of her former association with the promotion rackets. In an effort to make a comeback, she asks an old friend, press agent Danny Castle, to help her. Danny learns that Belle has been blacklisted for ending her relationship with racketeer Jack Hiker, who is determined to see that she remains in obscurity. Consequently, when Danny tries to arrange engagements for Belle, Jack sends one of his henchmen, Lew Burton, to threaten Belle and beat up Danny. Nevertheless, Danny manages to book Belle on a telethon, which leads to a booking at a top New York nightclub. Jack warns Belle that if she appears he will divulge her prison record. Undaunted, Belle confesses her indiscretion to the opening night audience and then goes on to a stunning triumph. Knowing that Belle has attained her goal and no longer needs him, Danny gracefully bows out of the picture. *Singers. Press agents. Ex-convicts. Racketeers. Reputation. Blacklisting. Revenge. Nightclubs. New York City.*

Note: Location scenes filmed in Hollywood and New York.

BELLES DAMES, VILAINS MESSIEURS see THE BIRDS, THE BEES, AND THE ITALIANS

THE BELT AND SUSPENDERS MAN   F6.0357
Sherfield Productions. 11 Jun **1970** [San Francisco, showing; c2 Nov 1969; LP38142]. Sd; col. 16mm. 85 min. [Copyright length: 125 min.]

Prod-Dir-Writ Donald J. Levy. *Photog* Jack Graham. *Film Ed* Lela Smith. *Asst Dir* Doyne Mraz.

Cast: Donald J. Levy, Halcyon Makapagal.

Comedy-drama. Dudley Gray, a bumbling postman, lives with his selfish wife and in-laws in a small northwestern town in 1928. His life is filled with small annoyances—barking dogs, runaway baby chicks, wet sheets of postage stamps, irate alarm clocks, and rebounding doors. One day at work he meets frail Laura Eros, who comes to the post office every morning and afternoon to ask, in vain, about a letter from her husband, Peter. Dudley soon discovers that Peter was killed while trying to commit a robbery. Aware that Laura's health is failing, Dudley begins to send her love letters using Peter's name. Laura is cheered by the letters, but she is soon bedridden by a new attack. Dudley begins to enclose money in the forged letters, and he confesses his love for her to a friend. Consulting with her doctor, he learns that the best remedy for her condition is the dry pollution-free climate of New Mexico. Meanwhile, Laura learns of Dudley's kindness and begins to write him a letter expressing her gratitude and love. Before she can finish, however, she dies, spilling ink onto the paper, obliterating the message and shattering Dudley's dream. *Mail carriers. In-laws. Widows. Marriage. Health. Death. Documentation. Chickens. Dogs.*

Note: Filmed in Lodi, California.

BENEATH THE PLANET OF THE APES   F6.0358
APJAC Productions. *Dist* Twentieth Century-Fox Film Corp. 26 May **1970** [Los Angeles opening; c31 Dec 1969; LP37952]. Sd (Westrex); col (DeLuxe). 35mm (Panavision). 95 min. *MPAA rating* G.

An Arthur P. Jacobs Production. *Prod* Arthur P. Jacobs. *Assoc Prod* Mort Abrahams. *Dir* Ted Post. *2d Unit Dir* Chuck Roberson. *Screenplay* Paul Dehn. *Story* Mort Abrahams, Paul Dehn. *Dir Photog* Milton Krasner. *Camera Asst* Arthur Gerstle, Mervin Becker. *Art Dir* Jack Martin Smith, William Creber. *Set Decor* Walter M. Scott, Sven Wickman. *Film Ed* Marion Rothman. *Asst Ed* Richard Lane. *Mus* Leonard Rosenman. *Orch* Ralph Ferraro. *Sd* Steve Bass, David Dockendorf. *Boom Op* Orrick Barrick. *Asst Dir* Fred Simpson, Milt Trager, Murray Schwartz. *Unit Prod Mgr* Joseph C. Behm. *Location Mgr* William Venegas. *Script Supv* Joan Bremin. *Cost Dsgn* Morton Haack. *Creative Makeup Dsgn* John Chambers. *Makeup Supv* Dan Striepeke. *Hairstyles* Edith Lindon. *Sp Photog Eff* L. B. Abbott. *Art Cruickshank, Art Illus* Fred Harpman. *Still Photog* George Hurrell. *Gaffer* Fred Hall. *Prop* Pat O'Connor.

Cast: James Franciscus (*Brent*), Charlton Heston (*Taylor*), Kim Hunter (*Zira*), Maurice Evans (*Dr. Zaius*), Linda Harrison (*Nova*), Paul Richards (*Mendez*), Victor Buono (*fat man*), James Gregory (*Ursus*), Jeff Corey (*Caspay*), Natalie Trundy (*Albina*), Thomas Gomez (*minister*), David Watson (*Cornelius*), Don Pedro Colley (*Negro*), Tod Andrews (*skipper*), Gregory Sierra (*Verger*), Eldon Burke (*gorilla sergeant*), Lou Wagner (*Lucius*), Roddy McDowall (*intro voice*).

Science fiction melodrama. Based on characters created by: Pierre Boulle. Taylor, an astronaut, has crashlanded on an unknown planet. Having escaped from his captors—uniformed gorillas on horseback—Taylor, accompanied by his mute female companion Nova, is riding on horseback over a wasteland, an area feared by the apes as the "forbidden zone," when he encounters the remnants of the Statue of Liberty, half buried in the sand, and he realizes that his 20th-century world has been destroyed. Suddenly the earth splits before them, and Taylor vanishes into the rock formation after telling Nova to return to Zira, a scientist and one of the friendly apes who helped them escape. En route Nova meets another astronaut, Brent, who has been sent to find Taylor, and takes him to Taylor's friends in the city of the apes. They are captured after learning that the militaristic apes plan to destroy the remaining life in the forbidden zone. Zira helps Brent and Nova escape into the forbidden zone, and there they stumble onto the subterranean ruins of New York City. The labyrinth is populated by human beings, 40th-century mutations who conceal their disfigurations with masks, worship a live atom bomb, and communicate telepathically. Brent is captured, interrogated about the planned ape attack, and thrown into a cell with Taylor. Their guard orders them by telepathy to kill each other, but Nova interrupts the guard's thought, and in the ensuing respite, Taylor and Brent overpower the guard. Meanwhile, the apes attack the city, in spite of the mutants' attempts to repel them. Brent and Taylor try to prevent the detonation of the atom bomb, which they realize is a doomsday machine capable of destroying the world. Nova is killed, along with the mutants' leader. Taylor is shot; Brent is killed; and, seeing that the apes can easily win, Taylor presses the button which releases the bomb. *Astronauts. Mutes. Scientists. Evolution. Mutation. Mental telepathy. Human race. Atom bomb. Holocausts. New York City. Statue of Liberty. Chases. The Future. Doomsday. Apes.*

Note: A sequel to *Planet of the Apes,* q. v.

BENGELCHEN HAT'S WIRKLICH SCHWER see 24-HOUR LOVER

BENGELCHEN LIEBT KREUZ UND QUER see 24-HOUR LOVER

BENITO MUSSOLINI see BLOOD ON THE BALCONY

BENJAMIN (France)   F6.0359
Marianne Productions-Parc Film. *Dist* Paramount Pictures. 25 Mar **1968** [New York opening; c12 Jan 1968; LF28]. Sd; col (Technicolor?). 35mm. 100 min. *MPAA rating* X.

A Mag Bodard Production. *Prod* Mag Bodard. *Dir* Michel Deville. *Screenplay* Nina Companeez. *Story* Nina Companeez, Michel Deville. *Photog* Ghislain Cloquet. *Art Dir* Claude Pignot. *Film Ed* Nina Companeez. *Mus (see note)* Jean Wiener, André Girard. *Mus Selections* Luigi Boccherini, Joseph Haydn, Wolfgang Amadeus Mozart, Jean Philippe Rameau. *Choreog* Reno Adipietro. *Sd* André Hervée, Jean Nény. *Asst Dir* Jean Lefèvre. *Prod Mgr* Philippe Dussart. *Unit Mgr* Michel Choquet. *Cost* Rita Bayance. *Makeup* Alexandre Marcus. *Hairstyles* Carita. *Casting* René Pascal.

Cast: Michèle Morgan (*Countess de Valandry*), Catherine Deneuve (*Anne de Clécy*), Pierre Clémenti (*Benjamin*), Michel Piccoli (*Count Philippe de Saint-Germain*), Francine Bergé (*Marion*), Anna Gaël (*Célestine*), Catherine Rouvel (*Victorine*), Jacques Dufilho (*Camille*), Odile Versois (*married woman*), Simone Bach (*Madame La Tour*), Angelo Bardi (*Basile*), Sacha Briquet (*Célestin*), Lyne Chardonnet (*Jacotte*), Madeleine Damien (*The Old Lady*), Jacques Filh (*Adrien*), Tania Torrens (*Madame de Chartres*), Cécile Vassort (*Aline*), Jean Lefèvre (*Pascaline*), Brigitte DeFrance (*Pascaline*), Danièle Girard (*Lisette*), René Bazart (*Monsieur du Plessis*), Eve Cloquet (*Fanchon*), Magali Louis, Diana Lepvrier.

Costume comedy. In 18th-century France, Benjamin, a 17-year-old orphan of noble birth, sets off with his faithful guardian, Camille, to visit his wealthy aunt, the Countess de Valandry. Benjamin's good looks charm his aunt, and she amusedly indulges his boorish manners. Benjamin's naiveté in sexual matters prompts the countess' lover, Count Philippe, to take the lad under his wing for tutelage. He brings him to visit another 17-year-old orphaned virgin, the exquisite Anne de Clécy, under the pretext of inviting her to a party at the countess' chateau the next evening. Before they depart, Benjamin is able to observe Philippe's flirtatious behavior with Anne. Next, Philippe allows Benjamin to watch, through a window, his seduction of a married woman. The two then return for a nighttime visit to Anne's bedroom, but she successfully, if teasingly, evades Philippe's advances. The following day, Benjamin makes arrangements for various amorous assignations (with servant girls Marion, Célestine, and Victorine, and the married woman whose seduction he witnessed), but each tryst is prematurely interrupted. In the meantime, Philippe, impressed with Anne's resistance the night before, asks her to marry him; and though she refuses him, she is secretly pleased. When some stray fireworks set afire the stable where Benjamin has been romping with two of the servant girls, he is forced to return to his room for a change of clothing. There he discovers the waiting Anne, who explains that, though she has decided to marry Philippe, she wants him, another innocent, to deflower her and thus deny Philippe that satisfaction. While the others are distracted by the fire, Anne and Benjamin at last make love. The following morning, Anne makes the latest entry in the diary that Benjamin has been keeping—an inscription that attests to his new sexual status. *Nobility. Orphans. Guardians. Innocents. Aunts. Domestics. Virginity. Seduction. Sexual initiation. Infidelity. Diaries. Fireworks. Fires.*

Note: Filmed on location at the Chateau St. Brice near Cognac. Paris opening: Jan 1968 as *Benjamin ou les mémoires d'un puceau*; running times: 105 and 100 min. One U. S. source gives running time as 108 min. Sources disagree on composer of original music. Advertised as *Benjamin; The Diary of an Innocent Young Boy.*

BENJAMIN OU LES MÉMOIRES D'UN PUCEAU see **BENJAMIN**

BEREGIS AVTOMOBILYA! see **AN UNCOMMON THIEF**

BERLIN IST EINE SÜNDE WELT see **THAT WOMAN**

BERLINO, APPUNTAMENTO PER LE SPIE see **SPY IN YOUR EYE**

BERNADETTE OF LOURDES (France/Italy)   F6.0360
E. D. I. C.–Société d'Etudes et de Négociations Cinématographiques–Zebra Film–Cineriz–Les Films Tamara. *Dist* Janus Films. 29 Jan **1962** [New York opening]. Sd; b&w. 35mm. 93 min. [Also reviewed at 105 min.]
Prod Georges de La Grandière. *Dir* Robert Darène. *Screenplay* Gilbert Cesbron. *Adapt* Gilbert Cesbron, Robert Darène. *Photog* Marcel Weiss. *Art Dir* Robert Dumesnil. *Film Ed* Germaine Artus. *Mus* Maurice Thiriet. *Sd* Michel Fano. *Prod Mgr* Jacqueline Rémy.
Cast: Danièle Ajoret (*Bernadette Soubirous*), Nadine Alari (*Mother Marie-Thérèse*), Robert Arnoux (*Dr. Dozous*), Blanchette Brunoy (*Mother Nathalie*), Jean Clarieux (*attorney general*), Lise Delamare (*mother superior*), Jean-Jacques Delbo (*Chief of Police Jacomet*), Françoise Engel (*Sister Damien*), Michèle Grellier (*Sister Bernard Dalias*), Bernard Lajarrige (*François Soubirous*), Renaud Mary (*Bishop of Nevers*), Charles Moulin (*Gendarmerie Commander d'Angla*), Henri Nassiet (*Abbé Peyramale*), Françoise Saint-Laurent (*Sister Eugénie*), Madeleine Sologne (*Louise Soubirous*), André Reybaz, André Chanu, Véronique Deschamps, José Steiner, Jean Morel, Annie Sinigalia, Grégoire Aslan.
Biographical drama. In 1858, while gathering wood in a grotto near Lourdes, Bernadette Soubirous, the sickly, uneducated daughter of a poverty-stricken family, sees a white-clad "lady" who speaks to her in a soft voice. When news of this vision circulates throughout the village, the girl's parents forbid her to return to the grotto. But her friends persuade her father to allow her to go back, and each time she does so the vision reappears. On a subsequent visit, Bernadette follows the lady's instructions and scratches at the earth until a spring bursts forth. Opinion remains divided, however, as to the validity of Bernadette's reports, and the local priest questions her about the identity of the lady. Bernadette again goes to the grotto and returns with the lady's response, "I am the Immaculate Conception." Later, a sick child drinks from the spring and is cured. As word of this miracle spreads and thousands of believers journey to the spring to pray and be cured, the governor erects barricades around the grotto. However, Emperor Napoleon III eventually decrees that free access to the miraculous spring is to be granted to all. Bernadette retreats to a convent at Nevers and becomes Sister Maria Bernarde. Even here, she is the object of curiosity and misunderstanding as well as reverence. Her delicate health gradually weakened by asthma attacks, she dies on April 16, 1879. *Nuns. Peasants. Priests. Faith cure. Religion. Springs. Convents. Lourdes. Nevers.*

Bernadette of Lourdes. Catholic Church. Miracles. Visions. Virgin Mary.
Note: Paris opening: Jan 1961 as *Il suffit d'aimer*; running time: 102 min.

BERSERK (Great Britain)   F6.0361
Herman Cohen Productions. *Dist* Columbia Pictures. 6 Dec **1967** [Pittsburgh opening; c31 Dec 1967; LP35900]. Sd (Westrex); col (Technicolor). 35mm. 96 min.
Prod Herman Cohen. *Assoc Prod* Robert Sterne. *Dir* Jim O'Connolly. *Orig Story-Screenplay* Aben Kandel, Herman Cohen. *Dir Photog* Desmond Dickinson. *Camera Op* Norman Jones. *Art Dir* Maurice Pelling. *Set Decor* Helen Thomas. *Film Ed* Raymond Poulton. *Mus Comp & Cond* Patrick John Scott. *Sd Ed* Mike Le Mare. *Sd Mix* Bert Ross. *Sd Supv* John Cox. *Asst Dir* Barry Langley. *Prod Mgr* Laurie Greenwood. *Cont* Betty Harley. *Prod Sec* Vickie Emery. *Wardrobe* Joyce Stoneman. *Cost* Jay Hutchinson Scott. *Makeup* George Partleton. *Hairdresser* Pearl Tipaldi. *Casting* Maude Spector. *Constr Mgr* Fred Bennett.
Cast: Joan Crawford (*Monica Rivers*), Ty Hardin (*Frank Hawkins*), Diana Dors (*Matilda*), Michael Gough (*Dorando*), Judy Geeson (*Angela Rivers*), Robert Hardy (*Detective Superintendent Brooks*), Geoffrey Keen (*Commissioner Dalby*), Sydney Tafler (*Harrison Liston*), George Claydon (*Bruno*), Philip Madoc (*Lazlo*), Ambrosine Phillpotts (*Miss Burrows*), Thomas Cimarro (*Gaspar*), Peter Burton (*Gustavo*), Golda Casimir (*bearded lady*), Ted Lune (*skeleton man*), Milton Reid (*strong man*), Marianne Stone (*Wanda*), Miki Iveria (*Gypsy fortune-teller*), Howard Goorney (*Emil*), Reginald Marsh (*Detective Sergeant Hutchins*), Bryan Pringle (*Detective Constable Bradford*), Billy Smart Circus.
Mystery melodrama. Monica Rivers, the ambitious owner and ringmaster of a traveling circus, is so determined to draw capacity crowds that when her star highwire performer is murdered during a performance, she orders her manager-partner, Dorando, to make the most of the subsequent publicity. A short time later, a young man named Frank Hawkins presents himself and demonstrates his own highwire act. Monica not only hires him but also takes him on as a lover. As business flourishes, tragedy continues to plague the circus. Late one night, Dorando is found dead; and a short time later, the drunken Matilda, who suspected Monica herself of committing the murders to gain publicity, is sawed in half by her partner, Lazlo the Illusionist. Then after Frank has forced Monica to give him a share of the profits, Monica's rebellious 16-year-old daughter, Angela, arrives with word that she has been expelled from a private school. Quickly persuading her mother to let her remain, Angela insists upon performing as the target in a knife-throwing act. When she learns of her mother's relationship with Frank, a bitter quarrel ensues. That night, while Frank is doing his act, a knife plunges into his back, and he falls to his death onto the bed of spikes. On hand is Scotland Yard Superintendent Brooks, who traps the hysterical Angela. Convinced that the circus had taken her father away from her, she committed the murders in the hope of forcing her mother to give up her career. After confessing, Angela tries to escape, trips over a wire, and is electrocuted. *Careerwomen. Widows. Ringmasters. Tightrope walkers. Ambition. Murder. Partnerships. Publicity. Adolescence. Filial relations. Confession (law). Circus. Scotland Yard.*
Note: Released in Great Britain in 1967. Working title: *Circus of Blood.*

THE BEST HOUSE IN LONDON (Great Britain)   F6.0362
Bridge Films. *Dist* Metro-Goldwyn-Mayer, Inc. 30 Jul **1969** [New York opening; c31 Dec 1968; LP36723]. Sd (RCA); col (Eastman Color). 35mm. 105 min. [Copyright length: 98 min.] *MPAA rating* X.
A Carlo Ponti Production. *Prod* Philip Breen, Kurt Unger. *Assoc Prod* Clifford Parkes. *Dir* Philip Saville. *Orig Screenplay* Denis Norden. *Dir Photog* Alex Thomson. *Camera Op* Tony Spratling. *Art Dir* Fred Carter. *Prod Dsgn* Wilfrid Shingleton. *Titl Dsgn* Shirt Sleeve Studio. *Film Ed* Peter Tanner. *Mus Comp* Mischa Spoliansky. *Mus Cond* Eric Rogers. *Song:* "The Birds of London Town" Ronald Cass, Peter Myers. *Sung by* Tessie O'Shea. *Song:* "My Little Pussy" Ronald Cass. *Sd Rec* Dickie Bird, Nolan Roberts. *Sd Ed* Roy Hyde. *Asst Dir* David Tringham. *Prod Mgr* Ted Wallis. *Cont* Annabel Davis-Goff. *Cost Dsgn* Yvonne Blake. *Makeup* Neville Smallwood. *Hairdresser* Joan Smallwood. *Sp Eff* Ted Samuels. *Casting Dir* Paul Lee Lander.
Cast: David Hemmings (*Walter Leybourne/Benjamin Oakes*), Joanna Pettet (*Josephine Pacefoot*), George Sanders (*Sir Francis Leybourne*), Dany Robin (*Babette*), Warren Mitchell (*Count Pandolfo*), John Bird (*Home Secretary*), William Rushton (*Sylvester Wall*), Bill Fraser (*Inspector Macpherson*), Maurice Denham (*editor of "The Times"*), Wolfe Morris (*Chinese trade attaché*), Martita Hunt (*headmistress*), Arnold Diamond (*Charles Dickens*), Hugh Burden (*Lord Tennyson*), John De Marco (*Oscar Wilde*), George Reynolds (*Lord Alfred Douglas*), Jan Holden (*Lady Dilke*), Mike Lennox (*Algernon Charles Swinburne*), Arthur Howard (*Mr. Fortnum*), Clement Freud (*Mr. Mason*), Neal Arden (*Dr. Livingstone*), Walter Brown (*Mr. Barrett*), Suzanne Hunt (*Miss Elizabeth Barrett*), Carol Friday (*Flora*), Marie Rogers (*Phoebe*), Tessie O'Shea (*singer*), Avril Angers (*Flora's mother*), Betty

Marsden (Felicity), Ferdy Mayne, William Mervyn, Eric Barker, John Cleese, Peter Jeffrey, Charles Lloyd Pack, Joe Lynch.

Comedy. Two diverse factions in Victorian England have vowed to do something about the prostitution in London's streets. On the one hand, a delegation of government officials has decided to try the "French system" by sponsoring an official brothel to be situated in an ancestral home belonging to Sir Francis Leybourne; on the other hand, Sir Francis' niece, Josephine Pacefoot, is engaged in starting a rehabilitation center for wayward girls. When Sir Francis is called away to India, where he maintains a large opium plantation, he turns the administration of the government brothel over to his mistress, Babette, who turns it over to her lover, Sir Francis' disinherited son, Walter. Here in this luxurious bordello many famous Victorians, including Charles Dickens, Lord Tennyson, Oscar Wilde, Lord Alfred Douglas, Lady Dilke, Algernon Charles Swinburne, and Elizabeth Barrett Browning, make brief appearances. Benjamin Oakes, a young publicity consultant who has been promoting an airship invented by Count Pandolfo, aligns himself with Josephine's group in order to expose the widespread prostitution. Conversely, Walter is luring Josephine's reformed prostitutes to Babette's establishment. Then the natives on Sir Francis' opium plantation slay him, and Josephine inherits both the ancestral brothel and the plantation. Determined that he shall have control of his father's assets, Walter schemes to get rid of the troublesome Benjamin by framing him on a rape charge and then seducing and marrying Josephine. But his evil plot goes awry when the Chinese trade attaché, disturbed by the sale of Indian-grown opium to his country, kidnaps Josephine and threatens her with a horrible, Oriental-style death unless she turns over the deed to the plantation. Although Benjamin, temporarily released in order to clear himself of the rape charge, attempts to rescue her, he ends up being captured himself. But, with the disclosure of an unlikely filial relationship between the Chinese trade attaché and the Leybournes, and the imminent possibility of a raid, Josephine and Benjamin escape to freedom. Following the confusion that ensues, Josephine converts her uncle's ancestral home into a rehabilitation school, while the former occupants, including Babette, are hired by the French Ambassador to take up residence in Count Pandolfo's newly-invented airship—the first international flying brothel. *Landed gentry. Nobility. Uncles. Mistresses. Publicists. Inventors. Chinese. French. Diplomats. Cousins. Prostitution. Social reform. Murder. Inheritance. Frameup. Rape. Seduction. Filial relations. Marriage. Abduction. Opium. Whorehouses. Dirigibles. India. London. Charles Dickens. Alfred Tennyson. Oscar Wilde. Alfred Bruce Douglas. Emilia Frances Dilke. Algernon Charles Swinburne. David Livingstone. Elizabeth Barrett Browning. Charles Darwin. Prince Albert. William Ewart Gladstone. Soames Forsyte. Sherlock Holmes.*

Note: Released in Great Britain in 1969; running time: 96 min. Location scenes filmed in and around London. Several other real and fictional Victorians appear in the film, among them Charles Darwin, Prince Albert, Soames Forsyte, Sherlock Holmes, and William Gladstone.

THE BEST KEPT SECRET OF THE WAR see THE SECRET WAR OF HARRY FRIGG

THE BEST MAN   F6.0363
Millar/Turman Productions. *Dist* United Artists. 6 Apr **1964** [New York opening; c6 Apr 1964; LP27773]. Sd; b&w. 35mm. 102 min.

Prod Stuart Millar, Lawrence Turman. *Prod Assoc* Tom Mankiewicz. *Dir* Franklin J. Schaffner. *Screenplay* Gore Vidal. *Dir Photog* Haskell Wexler. *Art Dir* Lyle Wheeler. *Set Decor* Richard Mansfield. *Main Titl* DePatie–Freleng. *Film Ed* Robert Swink. *Mus* Mort Lindsey. *Sd Mix* Jack Solomon. *Sd Ed* Don Hall, Jr.. *Mus Ed* James Henrikson. *Asst Dir* Dick Moder. *Prod Supv* Ben Hersh. *Asst to Prod* Marion Rosenberg. *Cost Supv* Dorothy Jeakins. *Prop* Max Frankel.

Cast: Henry Fonda (*William Russell*), Cliff Robertson (*Joe Cantwell*), Edie Adams (*Mabel Cantwell*), Margaret Leighton (*Alice Russell*), Shelley Berman (*Sheldon Bascomb*), Lee Tracy (*Art Hockstader*), Ann Sothern (*Mrs. Gamadge*), Gene Raymond (*Don Cantwell*), Kevin McCarthy (*Dick Jensen*), Mahalia Jackson (*herself*), Howard K. Smith (*himself*), John Henry Faulk (*T. T. Claypoole*), Richard Arlen (*Oscar Anderson*), Penny Singleton (*Mrs. Claypoole*), George Kirgo (*speechwriter*), George Furth (*Tom*), Anne Newman (*Janet*), Mary Lawrence (*Mrs. Merwin*), H. E. West (*Senator Lazarus*), Michael MacDonald (*zealot*), William R. Eberson (*Governor Merwin*), Natalie Masters (*Mrs. Anderson*), Blossom Rock (*cleaning woman*), Bill Stout (*himself*), Tyler McVey (*chairman*), Sherwood Keith (*doctor*).

Drama. Source: Gore Vidal, *The Best Man* (New York opening: 31 Mar 1960). At a U. S. presidential nominating convention in Los Angeles, the leading presidential candidates are William Russell, former Secretary of State, and Joe Cantwell, an unscrupulous conservative senator. To avoid scandal, Russell and his estranged wife have reconciled for the duration of the campaign. Cantwell, however, plans to exploit Russell's past history of mental illness. Both candidates seek the endorsement of Art Hockstader, a devious former

president, who dies during the convention. Although he is told that Cantwell was an active homosexual in the Army, Russell refuses to divulge this information to the press. Sickened by such slander, Russell ends his candidacy, throwing his support to a third contender. In so doing, he regains his wife's love. *Presidents of the United States. Politicians. Ambition. Marriage. Blackmail. Mental illness. Political corruption. Male homosexuality. Political conventions. Los Angeles. United States Congress.*

Note: Includes newsreel footage of the 1960 U. S. presidential nominating conventions.

THE BEST OF CINERAMA   F6.0364
Cinerama, Inc. 25 Dec **1963** [New York opening]. Sd; col (Technicolor). 3× 35mm (Cinerama). 142 min.

Co-prod Merian C. Cooper, Thomas Conroy. *Exec Prod* Max E. Youngstein. *Supv Film Ed* Lovel S. Ellis. *Film Ed* Norman Karlin, William E. Wild.

Narrator: Lowell Thomas.

Compilation film. Excerpts are presented from five Cinerama feature films: *This Is Cinerama* (1952), *Cinerama Holiday* (1955), *Seven Wonders of the World* (1956), *Search for Paradise* (1957), and *Cinerama South Seas Adventure* (1958).

THE BEST OF ENEMIES (Great Britain/Italy)   F6.0365
Dino De Laurentiis Cinematografica. *Dist* Columbia Pictures. 6 Aug **1962** [New York opening; c1 Sep 1962; LP22998]. Sd; col (Technicolor). 35mm (Technirama). 104 min.

Prod Dino De Laurentiis. *Assoc Prod* Luigi Luraschi. *Asst Prod* Ralph Serpe. *Dir* Guy Hamilton. *Screenplay* Jack Pulman. *Adapt* Age & Scarpelli, Suso Cecchi D'Amico. *Story* Luciano Vincenzoni. *Photog* Giuseppe Rotunno. *Art Dir* Mario Garbuglia. *Set Decor* Giorgio Herman. *Film Ed* Bert Bates. *Mus* Nino Rota. *Sd* Piero Cavazutti, Bruno Brunacci. *Asst Dir* Mario Maffei, Yoel Zilberg. *Prod Mgr* Bruno Tolusso, Lazare Bianco. *Cost* Ezio Frigerio, Dario Cecchi. *Dial Dir* Manuel Del Campo.

Cast: David Niven (*Major Richardson*), Alberto Sordi (*Captain Blasi*), Michael Wilding (*Lieutenant Burke*), Amedeo Nazzari (*Major Fornari*), Harry Andrews (*Captain Rootes*), David Opatoshu (*Captain Bernasconi*), Aldo Giuffrè (*Sergeant Todini*), Tiberio Mitri (*Corporal Moccaia*), Kenneth Fortescue (*Lieutenant Thomlinson*), Duncan Macrae (*Sergeant Trevethan*), Noel Harrison (*Lieutenant Hilary*), Robert Desmond (*Private Slinger*), Michael Trubshawe (*Colonel Brownlow*), Bernard Cribbins (*Private Tanner*), Ronald Fraser (*prefect*), Pietro Marescalchi (*Corporal Brotolin*), Alessandro Ninchi (*Lieutenant Del Pra*), Pippo Fazio (*Sergeant Spadoni*), Bruno Cattaneo (*Private Mattone*), Luigi Bracale (*Guddu*).

War comedy-drama. In 1941 a British officer, Major Richardson, and his reconnaissance pilot, Lieutenant Burke, fall into the hands of an Italian patrol when their plane crashes in the Abyssinian desert. Although an immediate dislike springs up between Richardson and his captor, Captain Blasi, the Italian, hoping to conserve his scant rations, allows the two Englishmen to escape on condition that the British do not pursue his patrol. Later, when Richardson is ordered by his commanding officer to attack the fort in which the Italians are hiding, Blasi regards the action as an ungentlemanly act of treachery. Following a forest fire which drives both sides to the safety of a small island, Richardson captures Blasi and his men and sets out in the general direction of his base. Hopelessly lost, he leads the two groups to a deserted Italian fort, where they meet hostile native tribesmen who take their rifles and shoes. The blunders made by the two officers help to thaw their animosity, and a grudging friendship develops between them. Eventually they stumble into Addis Ababa, which is now, unexpectedly, in the hands of the British. As Blasi and his men are lined up for shipment to a prisoner of war camp, Richardson and his men dignify the Italians' defeat by giving them a respectful military salute. *Air pilots. Prisoners of war. Friendship. Combat zone life. Islands. World War II. Addis Ababa. Ethiopia. Great Britain—Army. Italy—Army. Airplane accidents. Forest fires.*

Note: Location scenes filmed in Israel. Rome opening: Oct 1961 as *I due nemici*; London opening: Jan 1962. Working title: *Two Enemies*; prerelease length: 109 min. Columbia Pictures participated in the financing of the film.

THE BEST OF LAUREL AND HARDY   F6.0366
James Wolcott Productions. *Dist* U-M Film Distributors. Feb **1969**. Sd; b&w. 35mm. 84 min.

A James L. Wolcott Production. *Prod* James L. Wolcott. *Prod Assoc* Paul M. Heller. *Ed Cons* Morrie Roizman.

Compilation film. The evolution of the comedy team of Stan Laurel and Oliver Hardy is shown by compiling excerpts from short subjects and two features originally presented by Hal Roach. The sequences, each introduced by a still photograph with legend, include: *Night Owls and Alley Cats* [from *Night Owls*] (1930); *Music Hath Charms* [*Below Zero*] (1930); *The $125 Misunderstanding* [*One Good Turn*] (1931); *A Dollar a Head* [*The Live Ghost*]

(1934); *Crime and Punishment* [*Pardon Us*] (1931); *Man's Best Friend* [*Laughing Gravy*] (1931); *Tallyho!* [*Be Big*] (1930); *How To Visit a Sick Friend* [*County Hospital*] (1932); *Moonlight and Romance* [*Our Wife*] (1931); *Three's a Crowd* [*Their First Mistake*] (1932); and *Double Trouble* [*Our Relations*] (1936). *Actors. Motion pictures—History. Stan Laurel. Oliver Hardy.*

THE BEST OF W. C. FIELDS   **F6.0367**
Dist Joseph Brenner Associates. 20 Jun **1969** [Chicago opening]. Sd; b&w. 35mm. 62 min.
   Anthology. The film consists of three W. C. Fields short comedies, *The Barbershop, The Pharmacist,* and *The Fatal Glass of Beer,* all produced by Mack Sennett and distributed by Paramount Pictures in 1933. *Actors. Motion pictures—History. W. C. Fields.*
   Note: Also known as *W. C. Fields Film Festival* and *One Hour With W. C. Fields.*

LA BESTIA HUMANO *see* **THE HUMAN BEAST**

DER BESUCH *see* **THE VISIT**

BETA SOM *see* **TORPEDO BAY**

THE BETRAYAL *see* **FRAULEIN DOKTOR**

BETRAYAL *see* **UPTIGHT**

DAS BETT EINER JUNGFRAU *see* **THE PSYCHIC LOVER**

DAS BETT EINER JUNGFRAU *see* **SWEET SMELL OF LOVE**

BETTER A WIDOW (France/Italy)   **F6.0368**
Ultra Film–Universal Productions France. *Dist* Universal Pictures. Feb **1969** [c29 Mar 1968; LP38887]. Sd; col (Technicolor). 35mm. 101 min. *MPAA rating* M.
   A Ennio De Concini Production. *Prod* Turi Vasile. *Dir* Duccio Tessari. *Screenplay* Adriano Baracco, Brian Degas, Tudor Gates, Duccio Tessari. *Story* Ennio De Concini. *Dir Photog* Ennio Guarnieri. *Camera Op* Arturo Zavattini. *Asst Camera Op* Emilio Loffredo, Sergio Salvati, Carlo De Biase. *Art Dir* Luigi Scaccianoce. *Asst Art Dir* Dante Ferretti. *Set Decor* Bruno Casari. *Film Ed* Romano Trina, Mario Morra. *Mus* Carlo Rustichelli. *Mus Cond* Bruno Nicolai. *Band of Noto Cond* Francesco Mulè. *Sd* Claudio Maielli. *Sd Ed* Alfred Cox. *Dub Mix* Alberto Bartolomei, Danilo Moroni. *Asst Dir* Mario Forges Davanzati, Louise Vincent. *Prod Mgr* Danilo Marciani. *Asst to the Prod* Don Bruno. *Script Supv* Rita Agostini. *Prod Asst* Michele Marsala, Antonio Mazza. *Cost Dsgn* Adriana Berselli. *Wardrobe* Ceraceni, Tirelli of Rome, Tiziani of Rome, Vongher. *Makeup* Nilo Jacoponi. *Hairstyles* Jole Cecchini. *Still Photog* G. B. Poletto.
   Cast: Virna Lisi (*Rosa Minniti*), Peter McEnery (*Tom Proby*), Gabriele Ferzetti (*Don Calogero Minniti*), Lando Buzzanca (*Massito*), Jean Servais (*Baron Misceni*), Agnès Spaak (*prostitute*), Nino Terzo (*Carmelo*), Carla Calò (*Rosa's governess*), Salvatore Fucile (*Don Santo*), Roy Bosier (*orchestra conductor*), Bruno Lauzi (*hotel manager*), Adriano Vitale (*Misceni's chauffeur/killer*), Francesco Leone, Luciano Taccone, Oreste Palella, Giorgio Cholet, Raniero Di Giovanbattista, Ivan Scratuglia, Sebastiano Rossito, Salvatore Spadaro, Gaetano Tomaselli.
   Comedy-drama. When Tom Proby, a young British engineer, arrives in Sicily to select the site for a new petroleum refinery, the local Mafia splits into two factions. The progressives, headed by Don Calogero Minniti, favor the enterprise, while the arch-conservatives, led by Baron Misceni, oppose it. Once the progressives have won the dispute, Don Calogero assigns a local journalist, Massito, to escort Proby around the countryside in the hope of influencing his decision, but Proby proves to be a man of such integrity that Baron Misceni initiates a campaign to drive the young engineer out of Sicily. Proby, however, remains unharmed and has the audacity to pursue romantically Don Calogero's daughter Rosa, who is engaged to marry Misceni. Through continued harassment, Misceni eventually succeeds in persuading Proby to leave Sicily. Don Calogero tries to delay him by sending a prostitute to his room, but Rosa telephones Proby and changes his mind. The subsequent public lovemaking between Rosa and Proby creates a scandal, and the outraged Misceni decides it is time to do away with the troublesome Englishman. When several assassination attempts fail, the Mafia chieftain orders Misceni into retirement and decrees that his estate, which Proby has selected for the oil refinery, be sold. Misceni ignores the decision, however, and abducts Rosa just as Proby has won the approval of her father. In order to preserve her honor, Rosa must marry Baron Misceni, and although the wedding takes place, the baron is killed as he leaves the church. With Rosa's reputation unblemished, she is free to marry Proby and return with him to England. *English. Sicilians. Engineers—Mining. Newspapermen. Prostitutes. Abduction. Scandal. Assassination. Oil fields. Weddings. Sicily. Mafia.*

Note: Location scenes filmed in Siracusa, Italy, and in Sicily. Released in Italy in 1968 as *Meglio vedova.*

BETWEEN TEARS AND SMILES (Hong Kong)   **F6.0369**
Shaw Brothers (H. K.) Ltd. ca28 Apr **1965** [New York showing]. Sd; b&w. 35mm. 135 min.
   Dir Lo Chen. *Screenplay* Ching Wei. *Photog* Liu Chi. *Mus Comp* Wang Fu-ling.
   Cast: Li Li Hua (*Shen Fung Hsien/Ho Li Ya*), Ivy Ling Po (*Kwan Shiu-chu*), Kwan Shan (*Fan Chia Soo*), Chen Yen-yen (*Mrs. Shen*), Ching Niao (*General Chang*), Chiang Kuang-chao (*Uncle Shen*), Kao Pao-shu (*Mrs. Tao*).
   Melodrama. In the early days of the Chinese Republic wealthy student Fan Chia Soo becomes romantically involved with three young women. Although one of them is his social equal and another is an attractive acrobat, the youth falls in love with the third, a singer in second-rate bars. Their affair is interrupted, however, when the student is called away and the singer is kidnaped by Chang, a lascivious general. *Students. Upper classes. Singers. Acrobats. Kidnaping. Bars. Republic of China.*
   Note: Released in Hong Kong in 1964 as *Sun tai sil yen yin.*

THE BEVERLY HILLS CALL BOYS *see* **THE UPSTAIRS ROOM**

BEWARE OF CHILDREN (Great Britain)   **F6.0370**
G. H. W. Productions. *For* Anglo-Amalgamated Film Distributors. *Dist* American International Pictures. Apr **1961.** Sd; b&w. 35mm. 80 min. [Also 87 min.]
   Prod Peter Rogers. *Assoc Prod* Basil Keys. *Dir* Gerald Thomas. *Screenplay* Norman Hudis, Robin Estridge. *Dir of Photog* Alan Hume. *Art Dir* Carmen Dillon. *Film Ed* John Shirley. *Mus Comp & Cond* Bruce Montgomery. *Sd* Jim Sibley, Robert T. MacPhee, Bill Daniels. *Asst Dir* Jack Causey. *Cost* Joan Ellacott. *Makeup* Eddie Knight. *Hairstyles* Stella Rivers.
   Cast: Leslie Phillips (*David Robinson*), Geraldine McEwan (*Catherine Robinson*), Julia Lockwood (*Vanilla*), Noel Purcell (*Tandy*), Irene Handl (*Mrs. Spicer*), Joan Hickson (*cook*), June Jago (*matron*), Cyril Raymond (*Colonel Matthews*), Esma Cannon (*district nurse*), Alan Gifford (*Edgar Treadgold*), Sydney Tafler (*Mr. Rockbottom*), Brian Oulton (*vicar*), Eric Pohlmann (*king*), Brian Rawlinson (*Will*), Michael Sarne (*Henri*), Joy Shelton (*Mrs. Rockbottom*), Patricia Jessel (*queen*), Earl Cameron (*colored father*), Pearl Prescod (*colored mother*), Peter Howell (*Angus' father*), Marian Mather (*Helen Treadgold*), Peggy Simpson (*Angus' mother*), Noël Hood (*vicar's wife*), Cyril Chamberlain (*cafe owner*).
   Cast—The Children: Christopher Witty (*Richard Robinson*), Martin Stephens (*Angus*), Francesca Annis (*Priscilla*), Haydn Evans (*Lionel*), Michael Gowdy (*Dandy Big*), Jeanette Bradbury (*Dandy Little*), Keith Lacey (*Hassan*), Mark Mileham (*Suleiman*), Louise Redman (*Margaret*), Millicent Kerr (*Eileen*).
   Comedy-drama. Source: Verily Anderson, *Beware of Children* (London, 1958). When David Robinson and his wife, Catherine, inherit an old English manor house, they decide to turn it into a vacation resort for children whose wealthy parents are too busy to care for their offspring. A strange assortment of children, including the sons and daughters of Arabian monarchs, American industrialists, and wealthy divorcees, arrive on opening day. Trouble develops when most of the youngsters turn out to be unruly, spoiled brats who chop down trees, steal off in a station wagon for midnight snacks, and tear down draperies to make costumes. Further complications arise when the cook proves to have an unquenchable passion for alcohol, and local councilwoman Mrs. Spicer objects to the enterprise, saying that the home should be used for underprivileged children. The domestic problem is solved when one of the children dresses up as a ghost and terrifies the cook into taking the pledge. And when, at end of summer, the children refuse to go home unless their parents promise to give them more time and attention, Mrs. Spicer realizes how much good the Robinsons are doing and she withdraws her objections to their home. *Children. Politicians. Cooks. Children's homes. Wealth. Alcoholism. Manors. Resorts. Summer.*
   Note: Opened in London in Dec 1960 as *No Kidding*; running time: 87 min.

BEWARE THE BLACK WIDOW   **F6.0371**
Nadir Films. *Dist* Goldstone Film Enterprises. 24 Apr **1968** [New York showing]. Sd; b&w. 35mm. 72 min.
   Prod-Dir Larry Crane. *Screenplay* Walter M. Berger. *Dir Cinematog* Glen Tracy. *Camera* Bob Castle. *Ed* Glen Tracy. *Songs and Mus* Larry Crane. *Mus Arr & Cond* Lorenzo Fuller. *Songs:* "Beware the Black Widow," "I'm Cute" *Sung by* Larry Crane. *Song:* "I Want a Doll for Christmas" *Sung by* Vince Hawley. *Songs:* "A Man Isn't Old," "Bijou" *Sung by* Dino Laudicina. *Song:* "Make Me Over" *Sung by* Shirley Koshler. *Sd Eff* Joe Karpisek, Hollis Video Arts.
   Cast: Sharon Kent, Don Canfield, Luke St. Clair, Gia Nina, Dean Larents, Danny Nugent, Edmund Nightwood, Mario Manzini, Rose Conti, Ensley

Everett, Harry Miller, Peter LoPicolo, Frank MacIntosh, Essie Brown, Luis De Ybarrondo.

Crime melodrama. Mafia henchmen are being killed off by a mysterious figure dressed in mourning who is known only as "The Black Widow." The editor and a reporter from a crusading newspaper investigate the killings, and the reporter persuades one of the mob prostitutes to talk to him: *Italian-born, she is raped by a Mafia gunman. She and her boyfriend, whose face is severely scarred when the gunman's companions burn him with a torch, then separately emigrate to the United States.* The Mafia chief is lured by the reporter to a store in Chinatown. The Black Widow arrives, there is a fight, and the Black Widow, who is revealed to be the vengeful Italian with the scarred face, is killed. One of the Mafia henchmen turns out to be an undercover agent, and he arrests the Mafia boss. The reporter and the prostitute who gave him his first lead in the case leave together to start a new life. *Gangsters. Newspapermen. Detectives. Prostitutes. Chinese. Italians. Disguise. Murder. Disfiguration. Revenge. New York City—Chinatown. Mafia.*

Note: May also be known as *Black Widow* and *Beware the Widow Spider.*

BEYOND ALL LIMITS (Mexico)   F6.0372
Cinematográfica Latino Americana. *Dist* Sutton Pictures, Omat Films. 18 Jan **1961** [Buffalo, New York, opening]. Sd; col (Eastman Color). 35mm. 100 min.

Pres by Lester Braunstein, Howard J. Beck. *Prod* Olallo Rubio, Jr. *Dir* Roberto Gavaldón. *Screenplay* Edwin Harvey Blum, Julien Silva. *Adapt* Iñigo de Martino. *Story* Libertad Blasco Ibañez. *Photog* Gabriel Figueroa. *Art Dir* Manuel Fontanals. *Film Ed* Gloria Schoemann. *Mus* Gustavo César Carrión. *Sd* José B. Carles.

Cast: Jack Palance *(Gatsby)*, María Félix *(Magdalena)*, Pedro Armendáriz *(Pepe)*, Juanito Múzquiz *(Juanito)*, Carlos Montalbán, Domingo Soler, Enrique Lucero, Paul Stewart, Emma Roldan, Jorge Martínez de Hoyos.

Drama. Source: Vicente Blasco Ibáñez, *Flor de mayo* (Valencia, 1895). After an absence of 5 years, American adventurer Gatsby returns to the Mexican fishing village where he had an affair with Magdalena, the wife of a well-to-do fisherman, Pepe. Although Magdalena now has a 5-year-old son, Juanito, Gatsby is hopeful of resuming their clandestine affair. In order to be near Magdalena, he proposes that Pepe join him in an illegal shrimp-smuggling venture. Pepe, however, distrusts Gatsby and suspects him of being Juanito's father. When his suspicions are confirmed, Pepe rejects the child and threatens to kill Gatsby, unaware that the two lovers have rekindled their passion and decided to run off and take the boy with them. Juanito's tender devotion to Pepe has such a sobering effect on the three adults that they put aside their personal feelings for the sake of the child. Gatsby sails away alone, and Magdalena and Pepe decide to try and rebuild their shattered marriage. *Adventurers. Americans in foreign countries. Children. Fishermen. Infidelity. Fatherhood. Jealousy. Smuggling. Marriage. Fishing villages.*

Note: Location scenes filmed in and around Topolobampo. Produced in Mexico in 1957 as *Flor de mayo.*

BEYOND CONTROL (Italy/West Germany)   F6.0373
Rinco-Film–United Pictures. *Dist* William Mishkin. 4 Nov **1970** [Hartford, Connecticut, opening]. Sd; col (Eastman Color). 35mm. 89 min.

Prod Peter Hellstern, Martin Hellstern. *Exec Prod* Ernst Steinlechner. *Dir* Helmut Förnbacher. *Screenplay (see note)* Martin Roda-Becher, Charly Niessen, Helmut Förnbacher, Eli Marcus, Joe Juliano. *Photog* Igor Luther. *Art Dir* Guy Sheppard. *Film Ed* Clara Fabry. *Mus* Charly Niessen. *Asst Dir* Martin Roda-Becher. *Cost* Brigitte Lange.

Cast: William Berger *(Jimmy Velte)*, Helmut Förnbacher *(Frank Sandweg)*, Helga Anders *(Monika)*, Georgia Moll *(Brigitte)*, Grit Böttcher *(Christina)*, Willy Birgel *(prosecutor)*, Benno Hoffmann, Harald Dietl, Rüdi Walter, Schaggi Streuli, Mäni Weber, Margrit Rainer, Paul Bühlmann.

Crime melodrama. As Hitler rises to power in Germany in 1934, a high-ranking Nazi official discourses on the virtues of German youth while his wife seduces Frank Sandweg, a younger man. Bored by the official's lecture, Frank's friend Jimmy Velte ushers the Nazi into the bedroom where his wife and Frank are making love. The older man pulls a gun, and the youths beat him up, but they are apprehended and sent to prison. Undaunted, they engineer an escape, steal a car, and embark on a life of crime that includes riddling their victims with bullet holes ("freckles"). After meeting Brigitte, a young woman who becomes Frank's mistress, the two fugitives execute a series of daring bank robberies, calling a halt to their raids only when the authorities get too close for comfort. Jimmy flees to Switzerland and falls in love with Brigitte's friend Monika, who knows nothing of the trio's notorious reputation. All goes well until money runs out, and Brigitte deserts Frank for an older, wealthier man. Frank and Jimmy return to robbing banks, then head for Marseilles and a ship that will take them to South America. But Jimmy wants to see Monika once more, and, although they are sought by the police of three nations, Frank accompanies his friend back to Switzerland. By now, however, Monika knows

the truth; and after rejecting Jimmy, she cooperates with the police by helping them trap the fugitives in a park. Although Monika begs them to surrender, Frank and Jimmy refuse to be taken alive. Exchanging a brief farewell, they face each other, take out their revolvers, and open fire. *Nazis. Fugitives. Mistresses. Police. Youth. Murder. Bank robberies. Prison escapes. Germany—History—Third Reich. France. Switzerland. Marseilles.*

Note: Location scenes filmed in West Germany, Switzerland, and southern France. Released in West Germany in Oct 1968 as *Sommersprossen;* running time: 90 min. Writing contribution of Marcus and Juliano is unconfirmed.

BEYOND THE GREAT WALL (Hong Kong)   F6.0374
Shaw Brothers (H. K.) Ltd. *Dist* Frank Lee International. 24 Aug **1967** [New York showing]. Sd; col. 35mm. 100 min.

Prod Run Run Shaw. *Dir* Li Han-hsiang.

Cast: Lin Dai *(concubine)*, Chao Lei *(emperor)*, Hung Po *(court painter)*, Li Yang *(Hun army chieftain)*, Chiang Kuang-chao, Chang Tsui-hing.

Melodrama with music. A Chinese emperor, who chooses his favorites from their portraits, is misled into ignoring the presence of a beautiful concubine in his palace because she refuses to bribe the court artist to paint an accurate likeness. The emperor meets the woman by chance and falls in love with her, forcing the artist to flee and seek protection with the Huns. For revenge, the artist presents the Hun leader with an accurate portrait of the woman, telling him that the emperor offers her in marriage. The emperor's enraged treatment of the Hun's emissaries and wedding gifts rouses the chieftain to send his army against the emperor. Seeking to avert bloodshed, the woman offers to marry the Hun chieftain, who showers her with gifts and affection and orders the artist's execution. The woman extracts pledges of peace and drowns herself on the eve of her wedding. *Royalty. Painters. Mistresses. Huns. Perfidy. Revenge. Suicide. Bribery. Self-sacrifice. Portraits (paintings). China—History.*

BEYOND THE LAW   F6.0375
Supreme Mix. *Dist* Grove Press. 23 Oct **1968** [New York opening]. Sd; b&w. 16mm & 35mm. 110 min. [Also revewed at 96 min.]

Prod Buzz Farbar, Norman Mailer. *Dir* Norman Mailer. *Improvised by the Actors From a Story Outline by* Norman Mailer. *Photog* D. A. Pennebaker, Nicholas Proferes, Jan Welt. *Film Ed* Jan Welt, Norman Mailer, Lana Jokel. *Mus* Frank Conroy. *Sd* Nina Schulman, Tim Cunningham, Peter Hansen.

Cast: Rip Torn *(Popcorn)*, George Plimpton *(The Mayor)*, Norman Mailer *(Lieut. Francis Xavier Pope)*, Mickey Knox *(Detective Mickey Berk)*, Buzz Farbar *(Detective Rocco Gibraltar)*, Beverly Bentley *(Mary Pope)*, Mara Lynn *(Ilse Fuchs)*, José Torres, boxer *(Jose)*, Tom Baker *(Irish)*, Lee Roscoe *(Lee Ray Rogers)*, Marcia Mason *(Marcia Stillwell)*, Mary Wilson Price *(Judy Grundy)*, Noel Parmentel *(assistant district attorney)*, Jack Richardson *(Jack Scott)*, Harold Conrad *(Perry Fuchs)*, Joe Shaw *(Joe Brown)*, Tom Quinn *(Tom Finley)*, Roger Donahue *(detective)*, Michael McClure *(Grahr)*, Edward Bonetti *(wife-killer)*, Peter Rosoff *(subway arrestee)*, John Maloon *(John Francis)*, Jimmy Reardon *(Detective Callahan)*, Tim Hickey *(Buffalo)*, Bryan Hamill *(Buffalo's kid brother)*, Pedro Ortiz *(Mario)*, Dolores Elbert *(Dolores)*, Sylvia Allen *(Sylvia)*.

Drama. While detectives Mickey Berk and Rocco Gibraltar are having dinner with their dates, Marcia Stillwell and Judy Grundy, they talk about their jobs at a New York City precinct. Early in the evening, Lieutenant Francis X. Pope brutishly interrogates several suspects—an accused child molester, a suspected homosexual, a married couple who run a "whipping club," a mugger named Jose, and a man who admittedly ax-murdered his wife. The intense investigations being conducted by Pope and an assistant district attorney are suspended, however, when two motorcyclists, Popcorn and Grahr, are dragged in for questioning and start a free-for-all by attacking the detectives. Soon thereafter, the mayor of the city arrives, ostensibly on a walking tour; but he actually has come because of complaints about the mistreatment of minorities. When Jose supplies the bruises on his face as evidence, Pope admits that his men do get "a little over-eager" at times, but he promises to take care of the matter. Once the mayor has left, Pope goes to a nearby restaurant for dinner with his wife, Mary. Expressing her unhappiness over Pope's being, in effect, "married to the police force," she asks for a divorce and states that she has been having an affair with detective Gibraltar. Now drunk, Pope spots Gibraltar and questions him privately about the affair. After Pope's obnoxious behavior has chased Marcia and Judy away, he also leaves. Although he soon returns with Lee, a prostitute he had questioned earlier, Mary gets rid of the woman and reconciles her problems with Pope. By this time, however, he is too inebriated to do anything more than prop himself up on the bar and trade tired quips with Berk and Gibraltar. *Detectives. Mayors. Prostitutes. Muggers. Motorcyclists. Interrogation. Male homosexuality. Murder. Child molesting. Police brutality. Drunkenness. Divorce. Infidelity. New York City.*

Note: Filmed in New York City in 16mm and blown up to 35mm. Released as an Evergreen Film. Rereleased in 1972 as *Beyond the Law—Blue,* a reedited version running 100 min and containing sex exploitation footage.

BEYOND THE MOUNTAINS see **THE DESPERATE ONES**

BEYOND THE STARS see **THE UNEARTHLY STRANGER**

BEYOND THE VALLEY OF THE DOLLS　　　　　F6.0376

Twentieth Century-Fox Film Corp. 17 Jun 1970 [Los Angeles opening; c26 Jun 1970; LP38187]. Sd (Westrex); col (De Luxe). 35mm (Panavision). 109 min. *MPAA rating X.*

Prod-Dir Russ Meyer. *Assoc Prod* Red Hershon, Eve Meyer. *Screenplay* Roger Ebert. *Story* Roger Ebert, Russ Meyer. *Dir Photog* Fred Koenekamp. *Art Dir* Jack Martin Smith, Arthur Lonergan. *Set Decor* Walter M. Scott, Stuart A. Reiss. *Film Ed* Dann Cahn, Dick Wormel. *Mus* Stu Phillips. *Mus Supv* Igo Kantor. *Adtl Mus* William Loose. *Voc Coörd* Lynn Carey. *Songs:* "In the Long Run," "Look On Up at the Bottom," "Come With the Gentle People," "Sweet Talkin' Candy Man" Stu Phillips, Bob Stone. *Songs:* "Find It," "Once I Had Love" Stu Phillips, Lynn Carey. *Titl Song* Stu Phillips, Bob Stone. *Sung* by The Sandpipers. *Songs:* "A Girl From the City," "I'm Comin' Home" Paul Marshall. *Sung* by The Strawberry Alarm Clock. *Sd* Richard Overton, Don Minkler. *Mus Ed* Robert Simard. *Asst Dir* David Hall, C. E. Dismukes. *Unit Prod Mgr* Norman Cook. *Asst to the Prod* Manny Diez. *Fashions* David Hayes. *Makeup Supv* Dan Striepeke. *Makeup* Willard Buell. *Hairstyles* Edith Lindon. *Sp Photog Eff* Jack Harmon. *Prop Master* Syd Greenwood.

Cast: Dolly Read (*Kelly MacNamara*), Cynthia Myers (*Casey Anderson*), Marcia McBroom (*Petronella Danforth*), John LaZar (*Ronnie "Z-Man" Barzell*), Michael Blodgett (*Lance Rocke*), David Gurian (*Harris Allsworth*), Edy Williams (*Ashley St. Ives*), Erica Gavin (*Roxanne*), Phyllis Davis (*Susan Lake*), Harrison Page (*Emerson Thorne*), Duncan McLeod (*Porter Hall*), James Iglehart (*Randy Black*), Charles Napier (*Baxter Wolfe*), Henry Rowland (*Otto*), Princess Livingston (*matron*), Stan Ross (*disciple*), Lavelle Roby (*Vanessa*), Angel Ray (*girl-in-tub*), Veronica Erickson (*blond date*), Haji (*cat woman*), Karen Smith (*redhead*), Sebastian Brook (*art director*), Bruce V. McBroom (*photographer*), Ian Sander (*boy-in-tub*), Koko Tani (*assistant*), Samantha Scott (*Cynthia*), Tea Crawford (*Kathy Page*), Heath Jobes (*makeup man*), John Logan (*escort*), Susan Reed (*fashion model*), Robin Bach (*gay boy*), Ceil Cabot (*mother*), Mary Carroll (*middle-aged woman*), Joseph Cellini (*man—flowered pants*), Jackie Cole (*1st woman*), Cissy Colpitts (*2d woman*), Frank Corsentino (*hippie boy*), Mibb Curry (*white-haired gentleman*), Coleman Francis (*rotund drunk*), Charles Fox, actor (*earnest man*), Pamela Grier (*4th woman*), T. J. Halligan (*science teacher*), Rick Holmes (*man with glasses*), Marshall Kent (*Dr. Downs*), Michael Kriss (*young actor*), Tim Laurie (*2d gay man*), Bebe Louie (*hippie girl*), Lillian Martin (*nurse*), Ashley Phillips (*fashion model*), Garth Pillsbury (*man with newspaper*), "Big Jack" Provan (*father*), Joyce Ree (*Marion Harrisburg*), Christopher Riordan (*gay boy*), Bert Santos (*taxi driver*), George Strattan (*3d gay man*), The Strawberry Alarm Clock, The Sandpipers (*themselves*).

Melodrama. Tired of playing to high school audiences, Kelly, Casey, and Pet, members of a rock trio, travel to Hollywood, accompanied by Harris Allsworth, the band's manager and Kelly's lover. There they are befriended by Kelly's Aunt Susan, an advertising executive, who, despite the misgivings of her lawyer, Porter Hall, decides to share with Kelly the family fortune. At an orgy the band is discovered by the effeminate entrepreneur host, Ronnie "Z-Man" Barzell, who rechristens them "The Carrie Nations." Among lovers quickly acquired at Ronnie's party are Lance, a boorish gigolo, who enters into a liaison with Kelly; Emerson, a law student who wins Pet's love; and Roxanne, a lesbian designer who captures Casey's heart. As the celebrated trio perform on national television, Harris, distraught by Kelly's infidelity and Casey's impregnation by him, hurls himself from the catwalk. He is rushed to the hospital, where Dr. Scholl informs Kelly that Harris can look forward to life as a paraplegic. Realizing that Harris is her true love, Kelly devotes herself to his care. Touched by Casey's plight, Roxanne arranges an abortion. Ronnie invites Lance, Roxanne, and Casey to a private party, at which costumes are distributed. Dressed as Superwoman, Ronnie attempts to seduce Lance, who is attired in a loin cloth. Rejected, Ronnie binds the gigolo. After revealing that he is, in fact, a woman, Ronnie bares her breasts, brandishes a sword, and chops off Lance's head. She then plunges a gun into the sleeping Roxanne's mouth and fires. Terrified, Casey phones her friends, who rush to her rescue but arrive too late. As Emerson and Kelly attempt to subdue Ronnie, the gun discharges, killing the transvestite. During the fray, however, the crippled Harris is miraculously cured. In a triple wedding ceremony, Kelly and Harris, Pet and Emerson, and Aunt Susan and an old love are united. *Bands. Gigolos. Theatrical managers. Law students. Couturiers. Paraplegics. Murder. Male homosexuality. Transvestism. Lesbianism. Abortion. Rock and roll. Decapitation. Television. Weddings. Orgies. Hollywood.*

BGS OF GINZA (Japan)　　　　　F6.0377

Shochiku Co. *Dist* Shochiku Films of America. Apr 1970 [Los Angeles showing]. Sd; col. 35mm. [Feature film, length unknown.]

Dir Umeji Inoue. *Screenplay* Umeji Inoue, Akira Saiga. *Photog* Keiji Maruyama. *Art Dir* Gohei Morita. *Mus* Kenjiro Hirose.

Cast: Yoshiko Kayama (*Miwa*), Yumiko Nogawa (*Yuka*), Kikko Matsuoka (*Hideko*), Etsuko Nami (*Kiriko*), Bontaro Miake (*Nonomiya*), Yasunori Irikawa (*Shunichi*), Takuya Fujioka (*Gondo*), Sentaro Tatsuya (*Oki*), Rumi Koyama, Saroi Yuki, Taiichiro Hirokawa, Yasushi Nagata, Jun Kajima, Chikako Kaga, Hiroshi Aoyama, Noboru Nakada, Kentaro Imai, Ryusuke Kita, Kenji Nagisa, Daisuke Nakano, Kosaku Yamayoshi, Shuichi Oki, Akiye Kokubu, Rutaro Hanai.

Melodrama. In the Ginza district, Miwa runs the bar "Erica" which is owned by her patron, Nonomiya. Her top hostess Hideko is conducting an affair with Tatsuya, a popular singer and ex-lover of Miwa. After a quarrel with Hideko, Miwa plots to break up Hideko's romance by using a new girl, Yuka, to lure Tatsuya away. The scheme succeeds and Hideko quits the Erica, moves to another bar in the Ginza, and takes with her several hostesses. Miwa now becomes jealous of Yuka and Tatsuya. An article about the couple in a national magazine causes a scandal which forces the couple to break up. Yuka learns that the article was written by Miwa, and she gains her own revenge by informing Nonomiya that his mistress is having an affair with the Erica's manager, Oki. Nonomiya breaks off relations with Miwa, who marries Oki and leaves the city. Yuka now takes over Miwa's job and apartment after seducing Nonomiya, while insisting she is his business partner rather than his mistress. Yuka has problems at the Erica because Hideko has taken away many of her hostesses, and she decides, over Nonomiya's objections, to change the club into a go-go bar. The new business is a success until Nonomiya suddenly dies, and coincidentally the Erica's license is revoked because minors were employed at the club. Shunichi, Nonomiya's son and the new owner, wants to sell out to Yuka, who now loves him, but she insists that he sell instead to Hideko. Yuka soon discovers that Hideko was responsible for the Erica's license being suspended, but Yuka can hold no grudges against her former rival. *Nightclub hostesses. Bar girls. Mistresses. Singers. Nightclub owners. Go-go dancers. Jealousy. Revenge. Scandal. Infidelity. Business competition. Business management. Seduction. Magazines (periodicals). Tokyo—Ginza District.*

Note: Released in Japan in May 1965 as *Yoru no nettaigyo.*

BIANCO, ROSSO, GIALLO, ROSA see **LOVE FACTORY**

LA BIBBIA see **THE BIBLE ... IN THE BEGINNING**

THE BIBLE ... IN THE BEGINNING (United States/Italy)　F6.0378

Dino De Laurentiis Cinematografica. *Dist* Twentieth Century-Fox Film Corp., Seven Arts Pictures. 28 Sep 1966 [New York opening; c6 Oct 1966; LP34869]. Sd (RCA); col (Technicolor, print by DeLuxe). 35mm & 70mm (Dimension 150). 174 min.

Pres by Dino De Laurentiis. *Prod* Dino De Laurentiis. *Assoc Prod* Luigi Luraschi. *Dir* John Huston. *2d Unit Dir for "The Creation"* Ernst Haas. *Screenplay* Christopher Fry. *Screenplay Asst* Jonathan Griffin, Ivo Perilli, Vittorio Bonicelli. *Story Cons* Emilio Villa. *Dir Photog* Giuseppe Rotunno. *Camera Op* Giuseppe Maccari. *Art Dir* Mario Chiari. *Assoc Art Dir* Stephen Grimes. *Asst Art Dir* Pasquale Romano. *Set Constr* Mario Scisi, Aldo Puccini. *Set Dressing* Enzo Eusepi, Bruno Avesani. *Set Dressing Accessories* Tani-Cappellini. *Film Ed* Ralph Kemplen. *Asst to Film Ed* Eunice Mountjoy. *Mus Score* Toshiro Mayuzumi. *Cond* Franco Ferrara. *Perf by* Orchestra Cinefonica Italiana, Chorus Carapellucci. *Choreog* Katherine Dunham. *Sd Rec Supv* Fred Hynes. *Sd Rec* Murray Spivack, Basil Fenton-Smith. *Sd Ed* Leslie Hodgson. *Mus Ed* Gilbert D. Marchant. *Mix* Mario Celentano. *Asst Dir* Vana Caruso, Ottavio Oppo. *Prod Mgr* Bruno Todini. *Prod Asst* Romano Dandi, Giorgio Morra. *Asst to Prod* Ralph Serpe. *Assoc to Dir* Gladys Hill. *Script Girl* Yvonne Axworthy. *Prod Insp* Marco Tamburella, Antonio Girasante, Fernando Cinquini. *Cost* Maria De Matteis, Tigano & Lo Faro. *Miss Gardner's Cost* Sorelle Fontana (Roma). *Makeup Supv* Alberto De Rossi. *Makeup* Giuliano Laurenti. *Hairstyles* Elda Magnanti. *Sp Eff* Augie Lohman. *Sp Optical Eff* Technicolor Limited, Linwood Dunn, Film Effects of Hollywood. *Sun Eff & Sp Projector* Zeus-Janiro. *Cons* W. M. Merchant, (Rev.), Salvatore Garofalo, (Msgr.). *Coöp* Corrado Gagli, Mirko. *Zoological Cons* Angelo Lombardi. *Casting Dir* Guidarino Guidi. *Still Photog* Paul Ronald, Louis Goldman.

Cast: Michael Parks (*Adam*), Ulla Bergryd (*Eve*), Richard Harris (*Cain*), John Huston (*Noah/narrator*), Stephen Boyd (*Nimrod*), George C. Scott (*Abraham*), Ava Gardner (*Sarah*), Peter O'Toole (*The Three Angels*), Zoe Sallis (*Hagar*), Gabriele Ferzetti (*Lot*), Eleonora Rossi Drago (*Lot's wife*), Franco Nero (*Abel*), Pupella Maggio (*Noah's wife*), Alberto Lucantoni (*Isaac*), Luciano Conversi (*Ishmael*), Robert Rietty (*Abraham's steward*), Adriana Ambesi, Maria Grazia Spina (*Lot's daughters*), Claudie Lange (*The Queen, Nimrod's wife*), Angelo Boscariol (*Shem*), Peter Heinze (*Ham*), Anna Maria Orso (*Shem's wife*), Eric Leutzinger (*Japheth*), Rossana Di Rocco (*Japheth's wife*), Gabriella Pallotta (*Ham's wife*), Flavio Bennati (*serpent*), Roger Beaumont, Gianluigi Crescenzi, Michael Steinpichler, Giovanna Galletti.

Biblical epic. This film portrays the first 22 chapters of Genesis, depicting: The Creation; Adam and Eve and the expulsion from Eden; Cain and Abel; Noah and the Flood; Nimrod and the Tower of Babel; Abraham, his wife, Sarah, her handmaiden Hagar, and the birth of Ishmael; the destruction of Sodom and Gomorrah; and Abraham and Isaac. *Jews. Murder. Vanity. Self-sacrifice. Human sacrifice. Moral corruption. Angels. Floods. Biblical characters. Adam and Eve. Cain and Abel. Noah. Abraham. Sarah. Sodom and Gomorrah. Lot. Ildith. Isaac. Tower of Babel. Animals.*

Note: Filmed in Rome, Sicily, Sardinia, and northern Egypt. Opened in Rome in 1966 as *La Bibbia*. Also known as *The Bible*. The St. James version of the Bible is read in the narration.

LES BICHES (France/Italy)   **F6.0379**

Les Films La Boétie-Alexandra Produzione. *Dist* VIP Distributors, Goldstone Film Enterprises. 28 Sep **1968** [New York opening; c12 May 1968; LF33]. Sd; col (Eastman Color). 35mm. 104 min.

Pres by Jack H. Harris. *Prod* André Génovès. *Assoc Prod* Georges Casati. *Dir* Claude Chabrol. *Screenplay* Paul Gégauff, Claude Chabrol. *Dial* Paul Gégauff. *Photog* Jean Rabier. *Camera* Claude Zidi. *1st Asst Camera* Paul Bonis. *2d Asst Camera* Jeanine Rabier. *Art Dir* Marc Berthier. *Film Ed* Jacques Gaillard. *Asst Film Ed* Frédéric de Châteaubriant. *Mus* Pierre Jansen. *Mus Cond* Jacques Baudry. *Sd* Guy Chichignoud. *Boom Op* Gérard Daquay. *Asst Dir* Claude Bakka. *Prod Mgr* Patrick Delauneux. *Script Girl* Aurore Paquiss. *Admin* Henri Dutrannoy. *Cost* Maurice Albray. *Makeup* Louis Bonnemaison, Maud Begon. *Still Photog* Helga Romanoff.

Cast: Stéphane Audran (*Frédérique*), Jacqueline Sassard (*Why*), Jean-Louis Trintignant (*Paul Thomas*), Nane Germon (*Violetta*), Serge Bento (*bookseller*), Dominique Zardi (*Riais*), Henri Attal (*Robègue*), Claude Chabrol (*filmmaker*), Henri Frances.

Drama. On the Pont des Arts in Paris, the wealthy and beautiful Frédérique meets Why, a poor bohemian of vague origin trying to eke out a living by chalking does, her favorite subject, on sidewalks. Finding her attractive, Frédérique drops a bill at Why's feet, brings her to her apartment, seduces her, and takes her to her villa in Saint-Tropez, where their leisurely life is interrupted only by the antics of Robègue and Riais, two homosexual parasite-buffoons whom Frédérique finds amusing. At a party given by Frédérique, Why is drawn to Paul Thomas, a successful architect, and leaves the party with him. They are followed by the two parasites, who, under Frédérique's orders, watch from a distance as Paul makes love to the virginal Why. Irritated at Paul's intrusion, Frédérique visits him, and in spite of herself falls in love with him. Paul, who only considered his relationship with Why a passing affair, returns Frédérique's love. They drive to Paris, leaving Why to put up with Robègue and Riais at the villa. Upon their return, Frédérique is still unwilling to give up Why and asks her to remain when Paul moves in. The parasites scheme to get rid of the male intruder, but their machinations are suspected by Frédérique, and they are expelled from the villa. Despite her emotional uncertainty, Why mutely accepts her position, though it is Paul and Frédérique who retire to the bedroom each night. One morning Why finds a note saying that Paul and Frédérique have gone to Paris, and she follows them and goes to Frédérique's apartment. Discovering Frédérique alone, Why confesses in a jealous, love-hate outburst of feelings her need of both Frédérique and Paul. When Frédérique tells Why that she finds her love repulsive and orders her from the house, Why stabs Frédérique with a poisoned dagger. She telephones Paul, pretending to be Frédérique, and invites him to the apartment. When he arrives Why is waiting for him dressed in Frédérique's clothes. *Artists. Architects. Wealth. Virginity. Seduction. Lesbianism. Male homosexuality. Jealousy. Murder. Personal identity. Paris. Saint-Tropez.*

Note: Location scenes filmed in Paris and Saint-Tropez. Opened in Paris in Mar 1968 at 88 min; released in Italy in 1968. Copyright claimant: Blue Chip Productions.

IL BIDONE (France/Italy)   **F6.0380**

Titanus-S. G. C. *For* Mario De Vecchi Films. *Dist* Astor Pictures, Pathé Contemporary Films. Oct **1962** [Los Angeles showing: Jul 1963]. Sd; b&w. 35mm. 92 min.

Dir Federico Fellini. *Story-Screenplay* Federico Fellini, Tullio Pinelli, Ennio Flajano. *Photog* Otello Martelli. *Sets* Dario Cecchi. *Film Ed* Mario Serandrei, Giuseppe Vari. *Mus* Nino Rota. *Sd* Giovanni Rossi.

Cast: Broderick Crawford (*Augusto*), Richard Basehart (*Picasso*), Franco Fabrizi (*Roberto*), Giulietta Masina (*Iris*), Giacomo Gabriello (*Vargas*), Alberto De Amicis (*Rinaldo*), Lorella De Luca (*Patrizia*), Sue Ellen Blake (*Anna*), Irene Cefaro (*Marisa*), Xenia Valderi, Mario Passante.

Comedy-drama. Augusto, a shallow, middle-aged, petty confidence man, travels through the Italian countryside with his two companions, the cynical Roberto, and Picasso, the family man, appealing to the greed of the poor in order to pull off cheap swindles. In a favorite ploy, Augusto dresses as a bishop and visits small farms, pretending to find treasure buried by a departed murderer. He turns the "treasure" over to the farmers in exchange for money to celebrate masses for the sinner's soul. Rinaldo, a newcomer who has made money in the drug trade, invites them to his gaudy New Year's Eve party to ridicule their shabbiness. One day Augusto meets his 18-year-old daughter, Patrizia, an enthusiastic student with bright hopes for the future. His paternal feelings aroused, he takes her to a movie where he is shamed and humiliated as one of his victims identifies him and he is arrested before Patrizia's eyes. Upon his release from prison, Augusto finds that Picasso has abandoned the group to rejoin his wife, who has been hurt by the discovery of his criminal activities. Growing increasingly uneasy, Augusto assembles a new crew of con men. In a mechanical repetition of the timeworn treasure swindle, he meets a crippled peasant girl. Forced to hear the confession of a true believer, Augusto is troubled and tries to cheat his companions in order to gain money to help his daughter obtain a job. The other men discover Augusto's duplicity and viciously attack him. Left alone through the night, Augusto dies in anguish. *Confidence men. Farmers. Peasants. Priests. Drug dealers. Cheating. Poverty. Filial relations. Conscience. Middle age. Religion. Imposture.*

Note: Filmed in Italy and released there in 1955. Shown at the Venice Festival at 109 min; cut to 100 min for Rome opening; Paris opening: Feb 1956; running time: 108 min. Also known in the U. S. as *The Swindle*.

BIG BAD WOLF (West Germany)   **F6.0381**

Schongerfilm. *Dist* Childhood Productions. Oct **1966**. Sd; col (Agfacolor). 35mm. 53 min.

A Hubert Schonger Production. *Dir* Peter Podehl. *Screenplay* Konrad Lustig. *Photog* Peter Puluj. *Mus* Fred Sporer.

Cast: Paul Tripp (*narrator*), Harriet Gessner, Jürgen von Alten, Johannes Buzalski.

Fantasy. *Source:* Jakob Grimm and Wilhelm Grimm, "Der Wolf und die sieben jungen Geisslein". A mother goat and her seven little kids live in the hollow trunk of a tree. While the mother is busy with the household chores, her kids play with a wise old goat whose most important lesson is to beware of the big bad wolf. One day the mother goat goes shopping and cautions her kids not to open the door for anyone but her. Shortly after her departure, the big bad wolf tries twice to gain entry; on his third try, he tricks the kids into opening the door. Mother goat returns just in time and, with the help of her smallest kid, outsmarts the wolf. *Motherhood. Rescue. Goats. Wolves.*

Note: Released in West Germany in 1957 as *Der Wolf und die sieben jungen Geisslein*; running time: 58 min.

THE BIG BANKROLL see **KING OF THE ROARING 20'S—THE STORY OF ARNOLD ROTHSTEIN**

BIG BEAVER   **F6.0382**

John Samuels Films, Ltd. *Dist* Stacey Distributors. ca **1970**. Sd; col. 16mm. 61-81 min.

Prod Jack Koff. *Dir* Semore Lavender. *Screenplay* Carry Longer. *Col Camera* Harold Square.

Cast: MacHenry (*Toronto*), Mary Thackery (*Blue Moon*), Thelma Handy (*Head Piece*).

Sex film. Indian brave Toronto and his girl friend Head Piece ravish Blue Moon during an inter-tribal massacre. *Indians of North America. Group sex.*

THE BIG BOSTON ROBBERY see **BLUEPRINT FOR ROBBERY**

THE BIG BOUNCE   **F6.0383**

Greenway Productions. *Dist* Warner Bros.-Seven Arts, Inc. 5 Mar **1969** [New York opening; c1 Mar 1969; LP37234]. Sd; col (Technicolor). 35mm (Panavision). 102 min. MPAA rating R.

A William Dozier Production. *Prod* William Dozier. *Dir* Alex March. *Screenplay* Robert Dozier. *Dir Photog* Howard Schwartz. *Set Decor* Audrey Blasdel, James Roach. *Prod Dsgn* Serge Krizman. *Film Ed* William Ziegler. *Mus* Mike Curb. *Titl Song* Mike Curb, Guy Hemric. *Orch* Jerry Styner. *Sd* Robert J. Miller. *Asst Dir* Steven Bernhardt, Alan Rudolph, Bob Birnbaum. *Asst to the Prod* Charles B. FitzSimons. *Unit Mgr* Sam Strangis. *Cost Coörd* Pat Barto. *Makeup Supv* Gordon Bau. *Supv Hairstylist* Jean Burt Reilly. *Constr Coörd* Thomas Dries.

Cast: Ryan O'Neal (*Jack Ryan*), Leigh Taylor-Young (*Nancy Barker*), Van Heflin (*Sam Mirakian*), Lee Grant (*Joanne*), James Daly (*Ray Ritchie*), Robert Webber (*Bob Rogers*), Cindy Eilbacher (*Cheryl*), Noam Pitlik (*Sam Turner*), Victor Paul (*Comacho*), Kevin O'Neal (*boy in dune buggy*), Charles Cooper (*senator*), Paul Sorensen (*senator's associate*), Phyllis Davis (*girl in bikini*).

Melodrama. *Source:* Elmore Leonard, *Big Bounce* (New York, 1969). Jack Ryan, a young Vietnam War veteran with a criminal record, works as a migrant laborer on a California produce farm. He gets into a fight with a Mexican laborer and is told by camp manager Bob Rogers to get out of town. Ryan hitches a ride with Ray Ritchie, the owner of the farm, and Nancy Barker, his secretary and mistress. Later, Ryan meets Sam Mirakian, a justice of the peace who offers him a job at his motel. The two men run into Nancy and Rogers at a bar, and Nancy tries to goad Rogers into fighting Ryan, but Mirakian stops them. After Mirakian leaves, Ryan picks up Joanne, an unhappy divorcée, and he soon becomes involved with her. Most of his time, however, is taken up by Nancy, who taunts him into shattering windows with rocks, breaking into beach houses, and making love in a cemetery. Then Ritchie forces Nancy to give herself to an influential senator, and she plots to have her revenge by robbing Ritchie's safe of $50,000 in payroll money. Nancy forces an occupied dune buggy over a cliff and warns Ryan that unless he joins her in the theft, she will tell the police that he was the guilty party. After learning that Joanne has committed suicide, Ryan sets out for the safe-cracking job, unaware that Nancy plans to kill him. Instead, Nancy shoots the Mexican laborer who has come to the house looking for Ryan. When Ryan arrives, he realizes that he was the intended victim and walks out on Nancy. Nancy stuffs the dead man's pockets with money, pleads attempted robbery, and is acquitted on grounds of justifiable homicide. As Ryan leaves town, Nancy follows and tries to pick him up. He refuses and she drives away, mocking him with an obscene gesture. *Veterans. Migratory workers. Mexicans. Farm foremen. Justices of the peace. Mistresses. Vandalism. Sadism. Revenge. Murder. Blackmail. Suicide. Robbery. Justifiable homicide. Bars. Cemeteries. California.*

Note: Location scenes filmed in Carmel and Monterey, California.

THE BIG CITY (India)　　　　　　　　　　　F6.0384

R. D. B. & Co. *Dist* Harrison Pictures. Aug **1967**. Sd; b&w. 35mm. 125 min.

Prod R. D. Bansal. *Dir-Writ* Satyajit Ray. *Photog* Subrata Mitra. *Art Dir* Bansi Chandragupta. *Film Ed* Dulal Dutta. *Mus* Satyajit Ray. *Prod Mgr* Bimal Dey.

Cast: Madhabi Mukherjee *(Arati)*, Anil Chatterjee *(Subrata)*, Haradhan Banerjee *(Mukherjee)*, Haren Chatterjee *(father)*, Vicky Redwood *(Edith Simmons)*, Jaya Bhaduri *(sister)*, Shephalika Devi, Pramanik Sarkar.

Domestic drama. Source: Narendranath Mitra, *Abataranika* (Calcutta, 1963). Subrata, a mild-mannered and underpayed Calcutta bank clerk, supports his wife, Arati, their small son, his aged parents, and his younger sister. When his meager salary fails to meet the daily needs of the family, Arati takes a job selling knitting machines to wealthy housewives. Outraged by this violation of propriety, Subrata's father, a half-blind retired schoolteacher, shuns Arati and looks upon his son with contempt. Subrata, however, tries to accept the practicality of his wife's working, despite the severe blow to his ego and the diminishment of his importance as head of the household. As Arati gradually becomes accustomed to the outside world and the art of selling, she begins to enjoy her new independence, delighting in meeting new people and assuming new responsibilities. When Subrata's bank is forced to close down, Arati becomes the only breadwinner in the family. Emotionally broken by his failure as a provider, Subrata is on the verge of demanding that his wife stop working when she quits her job because of her employer's prejudiced attitude toward Edith Simmons, an Anglo-Indian salesgirl. United by a mutual determination to overcome adversity, Subrata and Arati set out together to look for employment. *Bank clerks. Saleswomen. Family life. Employment—Women. Pride. Prejudice. Unemployment. Calcutta.*

Note: Released in India in 1963 as *Mahanagar*; running time: 133 min.

THE BIG CUBE (United States/Mexico)　　　　　　F6.0385

Motion Pictures International-Producciones Anco. *Dist* Warner Bros.-Seven Arts, Inc. 30 Apr **1969** [Cincinnati, Ohio, opening; c1 May 1969; LP37258]. Sd (RCA); col (Eastman Color, print by Technicolor). 35mm. 98 min. *MPAA rating* M.

A Francisco Diez Barroso Production. *Prod* Lindsley Parsons. *Dir* Tito Davison. *Screenplay* William Douglas Lansford. *Story* Tito Davison, Edmundo Báez. *Dir Photog* Gabriel Figueroa. *Art Dir* Manuel Fontanals. *Titl Dsgn* Pacific Title, Ben Krasnow. *Film Ed* Carlos Savage. *Mus Comp & Cond* Val Johns. *Song:* "Lean on Me" Val Johns, Howard Finkelstein. *Sung by* The Finks. *Sd Supv* James L. Fields. *Rec* Manuel Topete, Galdino Samperio. *Asst Dir* Winfield Sánchez. *Prod Ch* Enrique Morfin. *Prod Mgr* Felipe Subervielle. *Asst to the Prod* Jon A. Cutaia. *Gowns* Travilla. *Cost Coörd* Consuelo Mugica. *Makeup* Ana Guerrero, Rosa Guerrero. *Hairstylist* Esperanza Gómez. *Sp Eff* Charlatan Productions. *Sp Lighting Eff* Omega's Eye. *Sp Transitional Seq* Mobile Color FX of Hollywood. *Casting* James Lister.

Cast: Lana Turner *(Adriana Roman)*, George Chakiris *(Johnny Allen)*, Richard Egan *(Frederick Lansdale)*, Dan O'Herlihy *(Charles Winthrop)*, Karin Mossberg *(Lisa Winthrop)*, Pamela Rodgers *(Bibi)*, Carlos East *(Lalo)*, Augusto Benedico *(Dr. Lorenz)*, Victor Junco *(Delacroix)*, Norma Herrera *(Stella)*, Pedro Galvan *(university dean)*, Regina Torne *(Queen Bee)*, The Finks *(The Finks)*.

Melodrama. Broadway actress Adriana Roman abandons her career to become the wife of tycoon Charles Winthrop. His daughter, Lisa, disapproves of the marriage and begins to associate with a group of abandoned, drug-using hippies. Winthrop drowns trying to save Adriana when his yacht is wrecked in a storm, and Adriana, rescued by fishermen, becomes Lisa's guardian. Lisa's inheritance is placed in Adriana's trust, subject to her approval of Lisa's marriage. The resentful stepdaughter and her greedy boyfriend, Johnny Allen, a medical student and frequent LSD user, mix an LSD cube with Adriana's sedatives when she fails to approve their marriage. Adriana eventually goes insane, and, suffering from amnesia, she is placed in a mental hospital. Playwright-director Frederick Lansdale, a close friend of Adriana's, suspects that something is amiss. Lisa discovers Johnny's infidelity on their wedding night, and, realizing that he courted her only for her fortune, she confesses the entire affair to Frederick. Frederick writes a play based on Adriana's traumatic experiences and persuades her to act in it. On opening night, Adriana regains her memory, recognizing her nightmares as instigated by Johnny to force her to suicide. The fully recovered Adriana returns home to the repentant Lisa and the loving Frederick, while Johnny is destroyed by drugs. *Actors. Hippies. Tycoons. Stepmothers. Playwrights. Guardians. Medical students. Filial relations. Inheritance. Greed. Amnesia. Insanity. Suicide. LSD. Hallucinations.*

BIG DADDY　　　　　　　　　　　　　　　F6.0386

Syzygy Productions. *Dist* United Film Organization. 11 Jun **1969** [El Paso, Texas, opening]. Sd; col. 35mm. [Feature film, length unknown.]

Pres by M. A. Ripps. *Prod-Dir-Writ* Carl K. Hittleman. *Assoc Prod* Reed Sherman. *Asst Prod* Herbert G. Luft. *Photog* Morrison B. Paul. *Asst Photog* Harry Underwood, John D. Taylor. *Art Dir* Rudi Feld. *Set Decor* Fred Price. *Film Ed* Carlo Lodato, Margaret Royce. *Mus* Alan Hyams. *Sd* Wallace R. Bearden. *Asst Dir* Hank Gilbert, Wendell Franklin. *Script Supv* Robert Gary. *Wardrobe* Sabine Manela, Wayne A. Reed. *Makeup* Charles Blackman. *Alligators Created by* Wah Chang. *Still Photog* Madison Lacy.

Cast: Victor Buono *(A. Lincoln Beauregard)*, Joan Blondell, Chill Wills, Tisha Sterling, Reed Sherman, Billy Benedict, John Hale, actor, Virginia Sale, Tanya Lemani, Ned Romero, Don McArt, Kelton Garwood, Wendy Wickstrom, Carol Schmidt, Rhonda Scott, Lennie Geer, Louis Hart, William Foster, Hank Worden, Arline Hunter.

Adventure melodrama. In the Florida Everglades, a man [Reed Sherman] falls in love with an illiterate swamp girl and vies for her affections with A. Lincoln Beauregard. In the course of his adventures he encounters a voodoo doctor and faces danger in the alligator-infested swamps. *Adventurers. Voodoo. Illiteracy. Florida Everglades. Alligators.*

Note: Filmed in 1965 as *Paradise Road.*

BIG ENOUGH N' OLD ENOUGH　　　　　　　　F6.0387

Trans-International Films. Apr **1968**. Sd; col (Eastman Color). 35mm (Colorscope). 79 min. *MPAA rating* R.

Prod K. Gordon Murray. *Dir-Writ* Joseph Prieto. *Screenplay* Reuben Guberman. *Photog* J. R. Remy.

Cast: Cyril Poitier *(Reuben)*, Bobbie Byers *(Lucy)*, Diwaldo Myers *(Marco)*, Viola Lloyd *(Teresa)*, William P. Kelley *(High Test)*.

Melodrama. High Test, outlaw leader of "The Black Angels," a motorcycle gang, becomes interested in Teresa, the teenaged daughter of a Mexican-American migrant laborer. Teresa's brother Marco is employed as a skilled mechanic by Reuben, the black owner of a service station and roadside bar. High Test, after finding his steady girl friend Lucy flirting with Reuben, beats the black. He then abducts Teresa and attempts to rape her, but she kills him in the struggle and is rescued by Marco. *Mexicans. Migratory workers. Mechanics. Negroes. Adolescence. Brother-sister relationship. Jealousy. Abduction. Rape. Manslaughter. Motorcycle gangs. Filling stations.*

Note: Filmed in Florida. Also known as *Savages From Hell.*

THE BIG GAMBLE　　　　　　　　　　　　　F6.0388

Darryl F. Zanuck Productions. *Dist* Twentieth Century-Fox Film Corp. 1 Sep **1961** [New York opening; c31 Dec 1960; LP20361]. Sd (Westrex); col (De Luxe). 35mm (CinemaScope). 100 min.

A Darryl F. Zanuck Production. *Prod* Darryl F. Zanuck. *Dir* Richard Fleischer. *African Action Seq Dir* Elmo Williams. *Screenplay* Irwin Shaw. *Dir Photog* William C. Mellor. *African Action Seq Photog* Henri Persin. *Art Dir* Jean d' Eaubonne. *Film Ed* Roger Dwyre. *Mus Comp & Cond* Maurice Jarre. *Sd* Jo de Bretagne. *Supv Sd Ed* Leon Birnbaum. *Asst Dir* Paul Feyder, Bernard Farrel. *Prod Mgr* Julien Derode. *Prod Asst* Christian Ferry. *Script Girl* Lucie Lichtig. *Optical Eff* Lax.

Cast: Stephen Boyd *(Vic Brennan)*, Juliette Greco *(Marie Brennan)*, David Wayne *(Samuel Brennan)*, Gregory Ratoff *(Kaltenberg)*, Sybil Thorndike *(Aunt Cathleen)*, Fernand Ledoux *(customs official)*, Marie Kean *(Cynthia)*, Harold Goldblatt *(priest)*, Maureen O'Dea *(Margaret Brennan)*, J. G. Devlin *(driving instructor)*, Philip O'Flynn *(John Brennan)*, Fergal Stanley *(Davey Brennan)*, Jess Hahn *(1st mate)*, Alain Saury *(Lieutenant François)*, Jacques Marin *(hotel clerk)*. Members of the Abbey Theatre Company, Ulster Theatre, Comédie-Française *(participating players)*.

Adventure melodrama. Irish seaman Vic Brennan persuades his Dublin family to finance a truck-hauling business in the remote African town of Jebanda. The only stipulation is that his cousin Samuel, a timid bank clerk, accompany Vic and his Corsican bride, Marie, to Africa and protect the family fortune. When the trio arrive at a small settlement on the Ivory Coast, Samuel loses their customs papers, and their truck is impounded. Fortunately, Marie meets an old friend, a French naval lieutenant; and despite Vic's jealous nature, she uses her wiles to get the truck released from custody. Before they leave, Vic buys 300 cases of beer, certain he can double his money once they reach Jebanda. After a short time on the road, the truck crashes against a fallen tree. Vic, however, resourcefully rounds up some natives to remove the tree in return for a few cases of beer. Further on, they encounter a gruff German, Hans Kaltenberg, who offers to be their guide and then tries to steal their cargo; but Vic overpowers him and drives him off. The blazing African sun eventually proves too much for Samuel, and he comes down with a fever. As Marie cares for him, he deliriously declares his love for her. By the time his fever has abated, the truck has reached a raging river. While crossing, Vic is knocked unconscious by a log and sent reeling downstream. Samuel suddenly finds the courage and strength to drag his cousin ashore. As they start down a steep hillside, the brakes of the truck give way, and it crashes between two trees and turns over; but the trio discover that Jebanda is just ahead. *Irish. Seamen. Cousins. Bank clerks. Corsicans. Brides. French. Germans. Guides. Trucking agencies. Customs (tariff). Courage. Gold Coast. Dublin. Ivory Coast. Automobile accidents.*

Note: Location scenes filmed on the Gold Coast, Africa; in Dublin, Ireland; and in southern France.

THE BIG GRAB *see* ANY NUMBER CAN WIN

THE BIG GUNDOWN (Italy/Spain)   F6.0389
P. E. A.–Tulio Demicheli. *Dist* Columbia Pictures. 21 Aug **1968** [New York opening; c1 Jul 1968; LP36168]. Sd; col (Technicolor). 35mm (Techniscope). 90 min.

Prod Alberto Grimaldi. *Dir* Sergio Sollima. *Screenplay* Sergio Donati, Sergio Sollima, Tulio Demicheli. *Story* Franco Solinas, Fernando Morandi. *Dir Photog* Carlo Carlini. *Art Dir* Raphael Perri, Enrique Alarcón. *Sets* Carlo Simi. *Supv Ed* Adriana Novelli. *Ed* Adriana Peñalba. *Mus* Ennio Morricone. *Cond* Bruno Nicolai. *Song:* "Run, Man, Run" sung by Cristy. *Sd* Pietro Spadoni. *Asst Dir* Nino Zanchin. *Prod Mgr* Valentin Panero, Fernando Cinquini. *Cost* Carlo Simi. *Makeup* Rino Carboni. *Hairstyles* Vittoria Silvi. *Sp Eff* Eros Bacciucchi.

Cast: Lee Van Cleef *(Jonathan Corbett),* Tomas Milian *(Cuchillo),* Luisa Rivelli *(Lizzie),* Fernando Sancho *(Captain Sergura),* Nieves Navarro *(widow),* Benito Stefanelli *(Jess),* Walter Barnes *(Brokston),* Angel Del Pozo *(Brokston's son-in-law),* María Granada *(Rosita),* Lanfranco Ceccarelli *(Jack),* Roberto Camardiel *(Jellicol),* Nello Pazzafini *(Hondo),* Spartaco Conversi *(Mitchell),* Romano Puppo *(Rocky),* Tom Felleghi *(Chet),* Calisto Calisti *(Miller),* Antonio Casas *(Dance),* José Torres *(Nathan),* Gerard Herter, Antonio Molino Rojo.

Western melodrama. Brokston, an influential Texas railroad speculator, offers to help lawman Jonathan Corbett with his bid to enter politics if Corbett captures Mexican outlaw Cuchillo, who is suspected of raping and murdering a young white girl. Corbett traces Cuchillo to a Mormon camp, to a ranch belonging to a sadistic widow, to a jail where he is in the custody of an uncomprehending sheriff, and to a brothel—but the wily Mexican escapes each time. When Corbett eventually captures Cuchillo, he is tricked into believing that he has been bitten by a snake and that he must untie Cuchillo so that Cuchillo can draw out the poison. Although Cuchillo now has the opportunity to kill Corbett, he leaves him unharmed, choosing only to make his escape. As Corbett begins to doubt Cuchillo's guilt, he is joined in his search by Brokston's son-in-law. When the two men trap Cuchillo in the desert, it becomes apparent to Corbett that the son-in-law is the real rapist-murderer and that Cuchillo was merely a witness to the crime. Forgetting his animosity toward the fugitive, Corbett allows the two men to attack each other. Cuchillo stabs his adversary in the forehead, and Corbett kills Brokston. Corbett and Cuchillo now part as friends. *Sheriffs. Mexicans. Outlaws. In-laws. Widows. Politics. Rape. Murder. Perfidy. Railroads. Ranches. Jails. Whorehouses. Snakebites. Deserts. Church of Jesus Christ of Latter-day Saints.*

Note: Exteriors filmed in Spain. Released in 1968 in Italy as *La resa dei conti;* opened in Madrid in Mar 1968 as *El halcón y la presa;* running time: 107 min.

A BIG HAND FOR THE LITTLE LADY   F6.0390
Eden Productions. *Dist* Warner Bros. Pictures. 31 May **1966** [Houston opening; c7 Feb 1966; LP32661]. Sd; col (Technicolor). 35mm. 95 min.

Prod-Dir Fielder Cook. *Assoc Prod* Joel Freeman. *Screenplay* Sidney Carroll. *Dir Photog* Lee Garmes. *Set Decor* Ralph S. Hurst. *Prod Dsgn* Robert Smith. *Film Ed* George Rohrs. *Mus Comp & Cond* David Raksin. *Sd* Everett Hughes. *Asst Dir* Joseph E. Kenny. *Makeup Supv* Gordon Bau. *Supv*

Hairstylist Jean Burt Reilly. *Dial Supv* Norman Stuart.

Cast: Henry Fonda *(Meredith),* Joanne Woodward *(Mary),* Jason Robards, [Jr.] *(Henry Drummond),* Paul Ford *(Ballinger),* Charles Bickford *(Benson Tropp),* Burgess Meredith *(Doc Scully),* Kevin McCarthy *(Otto Habershaw),* Robert Middleton *(Dennis Wilcox),* John Qualen *(Jesse Buford),* Gerald Michenaud *(Jackie),* James Kenny *(Sam Rhine),* Allen Collins *(Toby),* Jim Boles *(Pete),* Virginia Gregg *(Mrs. Drummond),* Chester Conklin *(old man in saloon),* Mae Clarke *(Mrs. Craig),* Ned Glass *(Owney Price),* James Griffith *(Mr. Stribling),* Noah Keen *(Sparrow),* Milton Selzer *(Fleeson),* Louise Glenn *(Celie Drummond),* William Cort *(Arthur).*

Western comedy. Source: Sidney Carroll, *Big Deal in Laredo* (a teleplay; NBC, 7 Oct 1962). In 1896, the five richest men in the Laredo territory are entrenched in the back room of a saloon for their annual poker game. Seated at the table are Henry Drummond, who walked out on his daughter's wedding rather than be late for the game; Benson Tropp, a woman-hating undertaker; Otto Habershaw, a dapper lawyer who, in order not to miss the game, abandoned a client facing hanging; Dennis Wilcox, a wealthy cattleman; and Jesse Buford, a miserly local merchant. The game is still going the next day when Meredith, a timid farmer who has sworn to give up gambling, arrives in town with his wife, Mary, and their young son Jackie. While Mary goes to have their damaged wagon repaired, Meredith watches the men play cards. Unable to resist temptation, he takes his homestead money and joins the game; but by the time Mary returns, he needs an additional $500 to stay in the game. The excitement and suspense, coupled with Mary's indignation, prove too much for Meredith's heart, and he collapses. Doc Scully is summoned, and Meredith is removed from the game, but not before asking Mary to play out his hand. Although she knows nothing about poker, Mary staunchly agrees to protect the family money. She uses her poker hand as collateral and asks banker C. P. Ballinger for a loan. The other players' amused looks turn to stunned disbelief when the banker accepts the offer and raises the bet $5,000 per player. Unable to compete, the men throw in their cards and leave Mary with $16,000. They are comforted only by knowing that they have lost to a gallant and courageous woman. The men are unaware, however, that both Meredith and Mary are professional gamblers and that Ballinger and Doc Scully concocted the whole plot to cheat the big-time gamblers. *Gamblers. Undertakers. Lawyers. Cattlemen. Merchants. Farmers. Bankers. Swindlers. Poker. Male chauvinism. Conspiracy. Saloons. Laredo.*

THE BIG HUNT   F6.0391
Sherwood-Dungan Productions. *Dist* Crown International Pictures. Nov **1969**. Sd; col. 35mm (Metroscope). 94 min. [Original length: 54 min.]

An Ellis Dungan Production. *Assoc Prod* Stanley Willis. *Dir-Writ* George Sherwood. *Photog* Ellis Dungan, E. R. Cooper, A. Vasant, Mesbahn Amen, S. C. Ghatak. *Film Ed* Stanley Willis. S. K. Dutto. *Mus Comp* Allan Gray. *Mus Dir* Ludo Philipp. *Sd Ed* Patricia Holmes. *Sd Mix* J. J. Y. Scarlett. *Sd Rec* S. B. Mani. *Prod Mgr* R. A. Zuberi.

Cast: Ellis Dungan *(himself),* Sidney Hertzberg *(commentator).*

Documentary. In India and Pakistan, American Ellis Dungan captures and trains wild elephants and a rhinoceros. Also shown are a 10-day religious festival honoring the Hindu goddess Durga and a tiger hunt with the Maharaja of Cooch Behar. *Americans in foreign countries. Royalty. Hunting. Rites and ceremonies. Hinduism. India. Pakistan. Cooch Behar. Elephants. Rhinoceros. Tigers.*

Note: Filmed in 16mm. Produced in 1958.

THE BIG MONEY (Great Britain)   F6.0392
Rank Organisation. *Dist* Lopert Pictures. Mar **1962**. Sd; b&w (see note). 35mm (VistaVision). 89 min.

Prod (see note) Joseph Janni. *Exec Prod* Earl St. John. *Dir* John Paddy Carstairs. *Story & Screenplay* John Baines. *Adtl Material* Patrick Campbell. *Dir Photog* Jack Cox. *Camera* Jack Cardiff. *Art Dir* Cedric Dawe. *Film Ed* Alfred Roome. *Re-ed (see note)* Hugh Stewart. *Mus* Van Phillips. *Sd* Don Sharpe, Desmond Saunders. *Prod Mgr* Jack Swinburne.

Cast: Ian Carmichael *(Willie Frith),* Belinda Lee *(Gloria),* Kathleen Harrison *(Mrs. Frith),* James Hayter *(Mr. Frith),* Jill Ireland *(Doreen Frith),* Renee Houston *(Bobby),* Michael Brennan *(Bluey),* Digby Wolfe *(Harry Mason),* Robert Helpmann *(The Reverend),* George Coulouris *(The Colonel),* Leslie Phillips *(The Receptionist),* Harold Berens *(The Bookmaker).*

Crime comedy. The Frith family supports itself by picking pockets and shoplifting. The family is chagrined, however, by eldest son Willie's criminal incompetence. When the youth steals a suitcase filled with money from a clergyman, the loot is found to be bogus. Although his family suggests burning the counterfeit currency, Willie converts the bills to legal tender and takes up with Gloria, a barmaid in a London hotel. Disguised as Arabs, the clerical counterfeiter and his henchmen track Willie to the hotel. A brawl ensues, and Willie and the gangsters are arrested. Humiliated by their son's conviction, the Friths disown Willie. Despite this desertion Willie enters prison happily, secure in the knowledge that Gloria has promised to wait for him. *Pickpockets. Thieves. Clergymen. Counterfeiters. Barmaids. Police. Family life. Shoplifting. Disguise. Hotels. London.*

Note: Location scenes filmed in London and Ascot. Produced in 1956; opened in London in Technicolor in May 1958; running time: 86 min. Prior to British release the film was reedited by Hugh Stewart; producer Janni removed his name from the screen credits.

THE BIG MOUTH F6.0393

Jerry Lewis Films. *Dist* Columbia Pictures. 21 Jun **1967** [Saint Louis opening; c1 Jun 1967; LP34743]. Sd; col (Pathé). 35mm. 107 min.

A Jerry Lewis Production. *Prod-Dir* Jerry Lewis. *Assoc Prod* Joe E. Stabile. *Screenplay* Jerry Lewis, Bill Richmond. *Story* Bill Richmond. *Dir Photog* W. Wallace Kelley. *Adtl Photog* Ernest Laszlo. *Camera Op* Richard Johnson, photog. *Set Decor* Frank Tuttle. *Prod Dsgn* Lyle Wheeler. *Film Ed* Russel Wiles. *Asst Ed* Joe Luciano. *Mus Comp & Cond* Harry Betts. *Sd* Al Overton, Jr., Jack Haynes, Charles J. Rice. *1st & 2d Asst Dir* Rusty Meek, Hal Bell. *Unit Prod Mgr* Howard Pine. *Script Supv* Hazel Hall. *Cost Dsgn* Moss Mabry. *Men's Wardrobe* Guy Verhille. *Makeup Supv* Ben Lane. *Makeup* Jack Stone. *Hairdresser* Joyce Morrison. *Coöp* Hilton Inn (Mission Bay, San Diego), Sea World (San Diego). *Prop* Richard M. Rubin.

Cast: Jerry Lewis *(Gerald Clamson)*, Harold J. Stone *(Thor)*, Susan Bay *(Suzie Cartwright)*, Buddy Lester *(Studs)*, Del Moore *(Mr. Hodges)*, Paul Lambert *(Moxie)*, Jeannine Riley *(Bambi Berman)*, Leonard Stone *(Fong)*, Charlie Callas *(Rex)*, Frank De Vol, actor *(Bogart)*, Vern Rowe *(Gunner)*, Dave Lipp *(Lizard)*, Vincent Van Lynn *(Fancher)*, Mike Mahoney, Walter Kray *(detectives)*, John Nolan *(FBI agent)*, Eddie Ryder *(Specs)*, William Wellman, Jr., Ben Gazzara, Howard Morris, Paul Burke, Vince Barnett *(uncredited appearances)*.

Comedy. While surf fishing in the Pacific, eccentric Gerald Clamson hooks a frogman on his line. The frogman, who looks exactly like Gerald, mumbles something about stolen diamonds hidden in or around a nearby hotel and then warns Gerald to run before he is caught by pursuing gangsters. Attempting to solve the mystery, Gerald finds the hotel and is unable to get a room, but he meets a pretty airline hostess, Suzie, and an attractive social director, Bambi, who is in league with the gangsters. When the list of treasure seekers grows to two rival gangs and other disreputable people, as well as the police, Gerald assumes various disguises in the hope of outwitting his would-be captors. Mayhem is added to confusion as all concerned become involved in a mad chase through San Diego that ends when the crooks follow a false lead that lands them in the ocean. Although Gerald never recovers the diamonds, he is more than willing to settle for the adoring Suzie. *Eccentrics. Frogmen. Doubles. Airline stewardesses. Social directors. Gangsters. Disguise. Treasure. Hotels. San Diego. Chases.*

THE BIG NOISE see DEAD HEAT ON A MERRY-GO-ROUND

THE BIG PARADE OF COMEDY see MGM'S BIG PARADE OF COMEDY

BIG RED F6.0394

Walt Disney Productions. *Dist* Buena Vista Distribution Co. 13 Jun **1962** [c6 Apr 1962; LP21936]. Sd (RCA); col (Technicolor). 35mm. 89 min.

Pres by Walt Disney. *Prod* Walt Disney. *Co-prod* Winston Hibler. *Assoc Prod* Erwin L. Verity. *Dir* Norman Tokar. *Screenplay* Louis Pelletier. *Dir Photog* Edward Colman. *Art Dir* Carroll Clark, Marvin Aubrey Davis. *Set Decor* Emile Kuri, Hal Gausman. *Film Ed* Grant K. Smith. *Mus* Oliver Wallace. *Orch* Walter Sheets. *Songs:* "Big Red Theme," "Mon Amour Perdu," "Emile's Reel" Richard M. Sherman, Robert B. Sherman. *Sd* Robert O. Cook. *Sd Mix* Dean Thomas. *Mus Ed* Evelyn Kennedy. *Asst Dir* Arthur J. Vitarelli. *Cost* Chuck Keehne. *Makeup* Pat McNalley. *Irish Setters Trained by* William R. Koehler.

Cast: Walter Pidgeon *(James Haggin)*, Gilles Payant *(Rene Dumont)*, Emile Genest *(Emile Fornet)*, Janette Bertrand *(Therese Fornet)*, Georges Bouvier *(baggageman)*, Doris Lussier *(Farmer Mariot)*, Rolland Bédard *(conductor)*, Teddy Burns Goulet *(engineer)*, Champion Red Aye "Scraps" *(Big Red)*.

Melodrama. Source: James Arthur Kjelgaard, *Big Red* (New York, 1945). Rene Dumont, a 14-year-old orphan who lives in the woods of northern Canada, is hired to exercise Big Red, a champion Irish setter that belongs to James Haggin. When the dog becomes so attached to the boy that he refuses to take orders from anyone else, Haggin separates them. In a desperate effort to return to Rene, Big Red is seriously injured, and Haggin decides to have the animal put to sleep. Rene takes the dog away, nurses him back to health, and then reluctantly returns him to Haggin, who offers Rene his old job. When Rene refuses, Haggin, hurt by the boy's rejection, ships Big Red and his mate, Mollie, to Montreal for sale. The two dogs escape from the train and disappear into the pine forest. Rene finds them in a cave where Mollie has given birth to a litter of puppies. Meanwhile, Haggin realizes his growing affection for Rene and

pursues them, but he is thrown from his horse and trapped in a rocky gorge. Big Red and Rene arrive in time to save him from a menacing mountain lion. As they head for home, Haggin offers to adopt Rene, and the boy, knowing that he will never again be separated from Big Red, gladly accepts. *Orphans. Adolescence. Animal care. Friendship. Adoption. Employer-employee relations. Canada. Montreal. Dogs. Lions.*

Note: Location scenes filmed in Quebec.

THE BIG RISK (France/Italy) F6.0395

Mondex Films–Les Films Odéon–Filmsonor–Zebra Film. *Dist* United Artists. Jul **1963** [c9 May 1963; LP25090]. Sd; b&w. 35mm. 111 min.

Pres by Robert Amon. *Prod* Jean Darvey. *Dir* Claude Sautet. *Screenplay-Adapt* Jose Giovanni, Claude Sautet, Pascal Jardin. *Dir Photog* Ghislain Cloquet. *Film Ed* Albert Jurgenson. *Mus* Georges Delerue. *Sd* Jacques Lebreton. *Asst Dir* Jean Lefèvre. *Prod Mgr* Jacques Plante.

Cast: Lino Ventura *(Abel)*, Sandra Milo *(Liliane)*, Jean-Paul Belmondo *(Stark)*, Marcel Dalio *(Gibelin)*, Jacques Dacqmine *(Commissioner Blot)*, Claude Cerval *(Fargier)*, Bernard Dheran *(Blastone)*, Michel Ardan *(Vintran)*, Corrado Guarducci *(Ferucci)*, Simone France *(Thérèse)*, Stan Kroll *(Raymond Naldi)*, René Génin *(Chapuis)*, Charles Blavette *(Bénazet)*, Michele Meritz *(Sophie Fargier)*, France Asselin *(Madame Vintran)*, Robert Desnoux *(Pierrot)*, Thierry Lavoye *(Daniel)*.

Crime melodrama. Source: José Giovanni, *Le trou* (Paris, 1957). Abel, a gangster, his wife Thérèse, two young sons, and Raymond Naldi, his companion, fight a gun battle with Italian frontier guards, while trying to escape from Italy to France, and Naldi and Thérèse die of gunshot wounds. Abel and his sons escape with the aid of a stranger named Stark when Abel's underworld gang in Paris refuses to help them. En route to Paris in an ambulance with his three charges, Stark saves the life of Liliane, a beautiful young woman, and falls in love with her. Abel's Paris gang fears that Abel will avenge their betrayal of him, and they plan to kill him before he reaches Paris. Stark uncovers the plot and kills the assassins before they can harm Abel and his sons. Police await them at their destination, the home of Abel's uncle, and a gunfight ensues. Wounded, Stark turns himself over to the law, and Abel, aware of his guilt and the trouble he has caused others, surrenders to the police, in hopes of setting a better example for his young sons. *Gangsters. Police. Fugitives. Border police. Filial relations. Self-sacrifice. Murder. Perfidy. Ambulances. Italy. Paris. Chases.*

Note: Opened in Paris in Mar 1960 as *Classe tous risques*; running time: 110 min.

THE BIG SEARCH see EAST OF KILIMANJARO

THE BIG SHOW F6.0396

Associated Producers, Inc. *Dist* Twentieth Century-Fox Film Corp. 10 May **1961** [New York opening; c4 May 1961; LP19488]. Sd (Westrex); col (DeLuxe). 35mm (CinemaScope). 113 min.

Prod Ted Sherdeman, James B. Clark. *Exec Prod* Robert L. Lippert. *Dir* James B. Clark. *Writ* Ted Sherdeman. *Dir Photog* Otto Heller. *Art Dir* Ludwig Reiber. *Film Ed* Benjamin Laird. *Mus* Paul Sawtell, Bert Shefter. *Sd Rec* Walter Rühland, Don McKay. *Asst Dir* Herman Goebel. *Prod Mgr* Clarence Eurist. *Cost Dsgn* Teddy Turai-Rossi. *Makeup* Josef Coesfeld, Klara Kraft. *Coöp* Circus Krone (Munich), Carl Sembach, Erhardt Plath, Christol Sembach.

Cast: Esther Williams *(Hillary Allen)*, Cliff Robertson *(Josef Everard)*, Nehemiah Persoff *(Bruno Everard)*, Robert Vaughn *(Klaus Everard)*, Margia Dean *(Carlotta Martinez)*, David Nelson *(Eric Solden)*, Carol Christensen *(Garda Everard)*, Kurt Pecher *(Hans Everard)*, Renata Mannhardt *(Teresa Vizzini)*, Franco Andrei *(Fredrik Everard)*, Peter Capell *(Vizzini)*, Stefan Schnabel *(lawyer)*, Carleton Young *(Judge Richter)*, Philo Hauser *(ringmaster)*, Mariza Tomic *(Frau Stein)*, Gerd Vespermann *(prosecutor)*, Pierre Alizée, Jacques Nicolet, Marlies Tanz, Gerhard Stapper, Rudolph Stey High Wire Troupe *(trapezists)*, Doris Arndt and the Ice Bears, The Wandruschka Family.

Melodrama. Bruno Everard, the mercenary, power-mad owner of a traveling German circus, exploits everyone, including his family of four sons and a daughter, all of whom are trained performers. His oldest son, Klaus, who has always resented his father's obvious preference for the younger and more talented Josef, tries to endear himself to Bruno by marrying Teresa Vizzini, the daughter of a menagerie owner with whom Bruno has long wished to merge. In so doing Klaus infuriates young Carlotta Martinez, an aerialist whom he had promised to marry. Meanwhile, Josef has fallen in love with a wealthy American, Hillary Allen, but when she asks him to abandon the circus and return to the United States as her business manager, Josef breaks off the romance. At the same time, Bruno's daughter, Garda, defies her father by marrying an American soldier, Eric Solden. Eventually Teresa realizes that Klaus married her only to gain control of her father's menagerie. Overcome by despair, she commits suicide by allowing herself to be mauled in a polar bear act. Shortly thereafter, Carlotta is seriously injured in a high wire accident.

When she charges Bruno with negligence, Josef assumes full responsibility for the faulty equipment and is sentenced to a prison term. While he is away the other children renounce their father and take the circus away from him. The old man tries to make a comeback but suffers a fatal heart attack while performing on an outdoor trapeze. When Josef is released from prison, he turns on his brothers, blaming them for their father's death. Klaus tries to knife Josef but is himself killed by the same polar bear that took Teresa's life. The tragedy has a sobering effect upon the remaining members of the family, and they decide to reorganize the family circus. At last, Hillary agrees to marry Josef on his terms. *Acrialists. Soldiers. Brothers. Germans. Americans in foreign countries. Filial relations. Circus. Family life. Marriage. Breach of promise. Suicide. Heart disease. Bears.*

Note: Filmed in part in Munich. One source suggests that the film is based on Jerome Weidman's novel ... *I'll Never Go There Any More* (New York, 1941).

BIG SIN CITY   F6.0397

Frank & Efrain Productions. *Dist* Fine Products. 9 Mar **1970** [Maryland license]. Sd; col (Eastman Color). 35mm. 73 min.

A Frank-Efrain Production. *Dir* Carlos Tobalina. *Screenplay* Ed Sands. *Orig Story* Frank Tulak. *Mus Comp & Score* William St. Pierre. *Rock and Roll Perf by* The Solid Mists. *Orig Songs:* "Don't Wiggle the Toes," "Big Sin City," "Watching the Girls" Nat Combo, E. Tobalina.

Cast: Art August *(Tom)*, Brigette Douche *(French girl)*, Jay Colonna *(Jay)*.

Sex film. Jay and Carlos, pursuing the exotic pleasures of the "big sin city," find a beautiful French dancer with exceptional control of the muscles of her body. In the meantime, Tom takes Jerry to visit the seashore where they meet some man-hungry nude sunbathers. Jay and Carlos leave the Frenchwoman and meet a woman who derives sexual pleasure with a boa constrictor. Jay and Carlos next watch two lesbian stripteasers perform. Later, Jay is surprised by a policeman as he spies on a man and woman having sexual intercourse, and Carlos is shot by an irate husband. *French. Exotic dancers. Hedonism. Striptease. Voyeurism. Bestiality. Nudity. Lesbianism. Sunbathing. Snakes.*

Note: Also known as *Notorious Big Sin City.*

THE BIG SWITCH (Great Britain)   F6.0398

Miracle Film Productions. *Dist* ScreenCom International. 3 Dec **1970** [San Francisco showing]. Sd; col (Eastmancolor). 35mm. 80 min.

Prod-Dir-Writ Pete Walker. *Dir Photog* Brian Tufano. *Photog* Richard Scott. *Camera Op* Ernest Kerry. *Supv Film Ed* Peter Austen-Hunt. *Film Ed* Nehama Milner. *Mus Comp & Cond* Harry South. *Sd Rec* Peter O'Connor. *Asst Dir* John Regan. *Prod Mgr* John Regan.

Cast: Sebastian Breaks *(John Carter)*, Virginia Wetherell *(Karen)*, Jack Allen *(Hornsby-Smith)*, Derek Aylward *(Karl Mendez)*, Erika Raffael *(Samantha)*, Douglas Blackwell *(Bruno Miglio)*, Julie Shaw *(Cathy)*, Jane Howard *(Jane)*, Roy Stone *(Al)*, Nicholas Hawtrey *(Gerry)*, Brian Weske *(Mike)*, Gilly Grant *(Sally)*, Desmond Cullum-Jones *(chief inspector)*, Derek Martin *(1st heavy)*, Steve Emerson *(2d heavy)*, Tracey Yorke *(1st stripper)*, Lena Ellis *(2d stripper)*.

Mystery melodrama. John Carter, London man-about-town, meets Samantha at a Chelsea discotheque, and, at her suggestion, they return to her flat for the night. After going for cigarettes, John returns to the apartment to find that Samantha has been murdered in her bathroom. He fears implication and decides not to call the police when he discovers evidence that Samantha was using drugs. The next day he is summarily dismissed by Hornsby-Smith, his supervisor, and he returns home to find three hoodlums and a woman playing strip poker in his flat. They beat him up for a large gambling debt they claim he owes. Next, he is blackmailed into taking a trip to Brighton with a frightened young woman, Karen. The blackmailer, Mendez, has two of his gang, Cathy and Jane, photograph John and Karen and record their exact measurements. John seduces Cathy and learns that he and Karen are to be murdered and their identities assumed by a deported gangster and his wife who are being smuggled back into England. John, Cathy, and Karen escape, but Cathy is shot by the pursuing gangsters. During the climactic gun battle between the police and Mendez' gang, John learns that Hornsby-Smith is the evil force behind his plight, and that Samantha's death was a hoax intended to facilitate his blackmail. John and Karen return to London together. *Playboys. Gangsters. Murder. Employer-employee relations. Smuggling. Blackmail. Seduction. Discotheques. Narcotics. Poker. Imposture. London—Chelsea. Brighton (England).*

Note: British release caNov 1968 as *Strip Poker.* Exteriors filmed in Brighton.

THE BIG T.N.T. SHOW   F6.0399

American International Pictures. 19 Jan **1966** [Los Angeles opening]. Sd; col (Technicolor). 35mm (Electorama). 93 min.

A Henry G. Saperstein Production. *Prod* Phil Spector. *Exec Prod* James H. Nicholson, Samuel Z. Arkoff, Henry G. Saperstein. *Assoc Prod* Jerry Goldstein. *Dir* Larry Peerce. *Dir Photog* Robert Boatman. *Camera* John Braislin, Ernest Hall, Kenneth Lamkin, Gary Stanton. *Video Engr* Carl Hanseman. *Art Dir* Lawrence Klein. *Film Ed* Ronald Sinclair, Eve Newman. *Mus Dir* Phil Spector. *Asst Mus Dir* Don Randi. *Songs:* "Dang Me," "Engine, Engine No. 9," "England Swings," "King of the Road" *writ & sung by* Roger Miller. *Song:* "Five Hundred Miles" Hedy West. *Sung by* Joan Baez. *Song:* "There but for Fortune" Phil Ochs. *Sung by* Joan Baez. *Song:* "You've Lost That Lovin' Feelin'" Barry Mann, Cynthia Weil, Phil Spector. *Sung by* Joan Baez. *Song:* "Georgia on My Mind" Hoagy Carmichael, Stuart Gorrell. *Sung by* Ray Charles. *Song:* "Let the Good Times Roll" Leonard Lee. *Sung by* Ray Charles. *Song:* "What'd I Say" *writ & sung by* Ray Charles. *Song:* "One, Two, Three" John Madara, David White, mus, Leonard Borisoff. *Perf by* Ray Charles Orchestra. *Orch Cond* David McCallum. *Song:* "(I Can't Get No) Satisfaction" Mick Jagger, Keith Richard. *Perf by* Ray Charles Orchestra. *Orch Cond* David McCallum. *Songs:* "Blues," "My Sweet Joy," "Universal Soldier," "Summer Day Reflection" *writ & sung by* Donovan. *Songs:* "Downtown," "My Love" Tony Hatch. *Sung by* Petula Clark. *Song:* "You're the One" Tony Hatch, Petula Clark. *Sung by* Petula Clark. *Songs:* "The Bells of Rhymney," "Turn, Turn, Turn" Pete Seeger. *Sung by* The Byrds. *Song:* "Mr. Tambourine Man" Bob Dylan. *Sung by* The Byrds. *Song:* "Do You Believe in Magic?" John Sebastian. *Sung by* The Lovin' Spoonful. *Song:* "You Didn't Have To Be So Nice" John Sebastian, Steve Boone. *Sung by* The Lovin' Spoonful. *Song:* "Shake" Sam Cooke. *Sung by* Ike and Tina Turner. *Song:* "Please, Please, Please" James Brown, singer, Johnny Terry. *Sung by* Ike and Tina Turner. *Songs:* "Goodbye, So Long," "A Fool in Love," "It's Gonna Work Out Fine" *sung by* Ike and Tina Turner. *Song:* "Be My Baby" Terry Wayne. *Sung by* The Ronettes. *Song:* "Shout" O'Kelly Isley, Ronald Isley, Rudolph Isley. *Sung by* The Ronettes. *Songs:* "Bo Diddley," "The Break," "Road Runner" *writ & sung by* Bo Diddley. *Backup for Bo Diddley* Chester Lindsay, Clifton James, mus, Dee Dee, Bee Bee, Gloria. *Uncredited Mus Perf by* The Modern Folk Quartet. *Choreog & Asst Choreog* Ward Ellis, Teri Robinson. *Sd Rec* Don Dunbar. *Audio Engr* Lionel St. Peter. *Asst Dir* Anthony Ray. *Prod Mgr* Del Jack. *Post-prod Supv* S. Richard Krown. *Tech Supv* Oscar E. Wilson. *Tech Dir* Ray Conners. *Wardrobe* Marjorie Holcomb. *Audio Cons* Larry Levine.

Featuring: Roger Miller, Joan Baez, Ray Charles, Ray Charles Orchestra, Donovan, Petula Clark, The Byrds, The Lovin' Spoonful, Ike and Tina Turner, The Modern Folk Quartet, The Ronettes, Bo Diddley, David McCallum.

Musical revue. David McCallum dashes into a Hollywood auditorium called The Moulin Rouge, and thousands of teenagers mob him. Finally reaching the orchestra, he waves a baton and introduces the first in a succession of musical entertainers who perform their hit recordings. Highlights include: Joan Baez singing "Five Hundred Miles," Roger Miller singing "King of the Road," Ray Charles singing "Georgia on My Mind," Petula Clark singing "Downtown," Donovan singing "Universal Soldier," The Byrds with "Mr. Tambourine Man," The Lovin' Spoonful singing "You Didn't Have To Be So Nice," and Ike and Tina Turner performing many of their hits. *Singers. Musicians. Orchestra conductors. Rock and roll. Folk music. Country music. Hollywood.*

Note: Filmed before a live audience 29 Nov 1965. Prerelease title: *This Could Be the Night.*

THE BIG WAVE (United States/Japan)   F6.0400

Stratton Productions-Toho Co. *Dist* Allied Artists. Apr **1962** [c2 Apr 1962; LP21652]. Sd; b&w. 35mm. 73 min. [Also reviewed at 98 min.]

Prod-Dir Tad Danielewski. *Exec Prod* Pearl S. Buck. *Screenplay* Pearl S. Buck, Tad Danielewski. *Photog* Ichio Yamazaki. *Art Dir* Itsuro Hirata. *Film Ed* Akikazu Kono. *Mus* Toshiro Mayuzumi. *Mus Cond* Hiroshi Yoshizawa. *Song:* "Be Ready at Dawn" Tad Danielewski, Toshiro Mayuzumi. *Sd Rec* Hidejiro Yotsuie. *Sd Mix* Michio Okazaki. *Asst Dir* Joseph E. Markarof. *Prod Mgr* Clark Paylow. *Prod Supv* Masayuki Nakajima. *Script Supv* Noriko Maebatake. *Wardrobe* Yoshiaki Murata, Ikue Tsuda. *Makeup* Haruhiko Yamada. *Sp Eff* Kenji Inagawa. *Dial Coach* Sylvia Danielewski. *Gaffer* Yokichi Hishinuma. *Prop* Satoru Sango.

Cast: Sessue Hayakawa *(Old Gentleman)*, Ichizo Itami *(Toru)*, Mickey Curtis *(Yukio)*, Koji Shitara *(Toru, as a boy)*, Hiroyuki Ota *(Yukio, as a boy)*, Rumiko Sasa *(Setsu)*, Juddy Ongg *(Setsu, as a girl)*, Reiko Higa *(Haruko)*, Sachiko Atami *(Haruko, as a girl)*, Henry Okawa *(Yukio's father)*, Chieko Murata *(Yukio's mother)*, Tetsu Nakamura *(Toru's father)*, Frank Tokunaga *(Toru's grandfather)*, Shigeru Nihonmatsu *(old servant)*, Noriko Sengoku *(Toru's mother)*.

Melodrama. Source: Pearl S. Buck, *The Big Wave* (New York, 1948). Farmboy Yukio and fisherboy Toru live in a small Japanese village that is periodically threatened by a volcano on one side and tidal waves on the other. The village and most of its inhabitants are destroyed by a tidal wave after not heeding the warning of the Old Gentleman. Ten years pass, and now Toru and Yukio, who survived the big wave, are like brothers. Setsu, Yukio's sister, and Toru plan their marriage and their future as fisherfolk. The Old Gentleman offers them a farm in the village, but they turn him down, knowing that he will always warn them of future tidal waves. *Farmers. Fishermen. Prophets. Village life. Friendship. Volcanoes. Tidal waves. Fishing villages.*

THE BIG WEEKEND *see* **DEAR HEART**

BIG WIND FROM TOKYO (Japan)   **F6.0401**
   Toho Co. Oct **1967** [Los Angeles showing]. Sd; col 35mm (Tohoscope). 90 min.
   Dir Seiji Maruyama.
   Cast: Akira Takarada, Toshio Kurosawa, Keiko Sawai, Megumi Matsumoto.No information about the nature of this film has been found. *Tokyo.*
   Note: Released in Japan in Dec 1966 as *Ishinaka sensei gyojoki.*

BIGFOOT   **F6.0402**
   Gemini-American Productions. *Dist* Ellman Enterprises. 21 Oct **1970** [Dallas opening]. Sd; col (Eastman Color, print by DeLuxe). 35mm. 95 min. *MPAA rating GP.*
   Pres by Universal Entertainment Corp. *Prod* Anthony Cardoza. *Exec Prod* Eric Tomlin. *Assoc Prod* Bill Reardon. *Exec in Charge of Prod* Fred Packard. *Dir-Orig Story* Robert F. Slatzer. *Screenplay* Robert F. Slatzer, James Gordon White. *Dir Photog* Wilson S. Hong. *Camera Op* Frank Ruttencutter. *1st Asst Camera* Richard Eisman. *2d Unit Camera Op* Henning Schellerup. *Art Dir* Norman Houle. *Main Titl* Ray Mercer. *Film Ed* Bud Hoffman, Hugo Grimaldi. *Asst Film Ed* Ted Prado. *Mus Score* Richard A. Podolor. *Song:* "Bigfoot" sung by Don Jones, mus. *Rec Engr* Bill Cooper. *Sd* Bob Dietz, Ken Carlson. *Boom Op* Lowell Brown, Murray Cohen. *Asst Dir* Anthony M. Lanza, Israel Shaked, Christopher Mitchum. *Unit Mgr* Arthur Gilbert. *Prod Mgr* Derwin Abbe. *Prod Assoc* Edward Sherman. *Asst to the Prod* Rick De Costa. *Prod Coörd* Ronald Kurtz. *Wardrobe* Joann Sigal. *Makeup* Louis Lane, John Elliott. *Sp Eff* Harry Woolman. *Set Constr* John DeBiasio. *Prop* Earl Phillips, Rick Phillips.
   Cast: Chris Mitchum (*Rick*), John Carradine (*Jasper B. Hawks*), Joi Lansing (*Joi Landis*), Lindsay Crosby (*Wheels*), Judy Jordan (*Chris*), James Craig (*Sheriff Cyrus*), John Mitchum (*Elmer Briggs*), Joy Wilkerson (*Peggy*), James Stellar (*Bigfoot*), Ken Maynard (*Mr. Bennett*), Doodles Weaver (*forest ranger*), Dorothy Keller (*Nellie*), Noble "Kid" Chissell (*Hardrock*), Nick Raymond (*Slim*), Sonny West (*Mike*), Walt Zachrich (*Deputy Hank*), Ray Cantrell (*Dum Dum*), Suzy Marlin Crosby (*Suzy*), Lois Red Elk (*Falling Star*), Jenifer Bishop (*Bobbi*), Holly Kamen (*Cyclist*), Walt Swanner (*Henry*), Billy Record (*Billy*), Carolyn Gilbert (*Mrs. Cummings*), Sonny Incontro (*Omaha*), Kathy Andrews (*Kathy*), Haji Lammé (*Haji*), Kim Oliphant, Eric Tomlin (*rangers*), Denise Gilbert (*child in store*), Kim Cardoza (*Kim*), Charles Harter (*Chuck*), William Bonner (*Lucky*), Diane Hardin (*Sally*), Tony Cardoza (*fisherman*), Louis Lane (*observer*), Kenny Marlowe (*little boy*), Jerry Maren (*baby creature*), Nick Raymond (*evil creature*), Gloria Hill, Nancy Hunter, A'Leshia Lee (*female creatures*), Ian Flynn, Marina Ghané, Carolyn McNichol.
   Horror film. When her plane develops engine trouble, Joi Landis parachutes into a rugged, inaccessible area of the American Northwest and is captured by a giant ape-like creature. Meanwhile, several weekend trail-bike riders stop for supplies at a general store owned by Mr. Bennett. After Rick and Chris separate from their friends Wheels and Peggy, they are attacked by a beast similar to the one encountered by Joi, and Chris is carried off. At the store, the sheriff is skeptical about Rick's story, but itinerant peddlers Jasper B. Hawks and Elmer Briggs, realizing the potential fortune to be made with a sideshow attraction featuring the beast, agree to help Rick search the dense forest. Captured by the beasts, the men learn from Joi of the legendary Bigfoot, a dying, sub-human race who have captured the women for mating purposes. Wheels arrives with other motorcyclists and Hardrock, a vengeful trapper. The creatures are dispersed, and all the captives except Joi are rescued. Saved by her Bigfoot captor from a mountain lion and a bear, Joi is taken to the beast's lair. She escapes when Hardrock wounds the Bigfoot; and the beast is sealed in a cave when one of the bikers dynamites the entrance. Having failed to secure a living specimen, Hawks hopes to persuade the women to relate their experiences as a traveling sideshow attraction. *Motorcyclists. Peddlers. Monsters. Sheriffs. Trappers. Entrepreneurs. Abduction. Rescue. Reproduction. Forests. General stores. Caves. California. Explosions. Cougars. Bears.*
   Note: Location scenes filmed in the Tehachapi Mountains, California.

THE BIGGEST BUNDLE OF THEM ALL (United States/Italy) **F6.0403**
   Metro-Goldwyn-Mayer, Inc. 17 Jan **1968** [New York opening; c31 Oct 1967; LP34813]. Sd (Westrex); col (Metrocolor). 35mm (Panavision). 110 min. [Also 106 min.]
   A Josef Shaftel–Sy Stewart Production. *Prod–Story* Josef Shaftel. *Assoc Prod* Sy Stewart. *Dir* Ken Annakin. *Screenplay* Sy Salkowitz, Josef Shaftel, Riccardo Aragno. *Dir Photog* Piero Portalupi. *Camera Op* Dudley Lovell. *Art Dir* Arrigo Equini. *Film Ed* Ralph Sheldon. *Mus Comp & Cond* Riz Ortolani.

Titl Song Ritchie Cordell, Sal Trimachi. *Titl Song Sung by* Eric Burdon. *Song:* "Most of All There's You" Riz Ortolani, Norman Newell. *Sung by* Johnny Mathis. *Guitar* Ivor Mairant. *Sd Rec* Kurt Doubravsky. *Dub Mix* J. B. Smith. *Sd Ed* David Hawkins. *Asst Dir* Victor Merenda. *Prod Supv* Basil Keys. *Prod Mgr* Fred S. Wallach. *Unit Mgr* Mario Pisani. *Cont* Joy Mercer. *Cost Dsgn* Itala Scandariato. *Sp Eff* Robert MacDonald.
   Cast: Vittorio De Sica (*Cesare Celli*), Raquel Welch (*Juliana*), Robert Wagner (*Harry*), Godfrey Cambridge (*Benny*), Davy Kaye (*Davey*), Francesco Mulè (*Tozzi*), Edward G. Robinson (*Professor Samuels*), Victor Spinetti (*Captain Giglio*), Yvonne Sanson (*Teresa*), Mickey Knox (*Joe Ware*), Femi Benussi (*Uncle Carlo's bride*), Paola Borboni (*Signora Rosa*), Andrea Aureli (*carabiniere*), Aldo Bufi Landi (*Capitano del Signore*), Carlo Croccolo (*Franco*), Roberto De Simone (*Uncle Carlo*), Piero Gerlini (*Captain Capuano*), Giulio Marchetti (*Naldi*), Ermelinda De Felice (*Emma*), Lex Monson (*Percy Peckinpaugh*), Giulio Donnini (*priest*), Massimo Sarchielli (*Paqueletto*), Clara Bindi (*Davey's wife*), Milena Vukotic (*Angelini*), Gianna Dauro (*Signora Clara*), Carlo Rizzo (*maître d'hôtel*), Nino Musco (*chef*), Nino Vingelli (*restaurant manager*), Calisto Calisti (*Inspector Bordoni*), The Counts (*themselves*).
   Crime comedy. Harry Price and his inept crew of amateur criminals kidnap Cesare Celli, an exiled American gangster living in Italy and hold him for ransom. When it turns out that none of Celli's friends will bail him out, he conceives the idea of a $5 million platinum robbery both as a way of repaying Price and his gang for their kidnaping effort and to retaliate against a world that has passed him by. Celli puts the novice criminals through rigorous physical training and brings in the renowned Professor Samuels to mastermind the heist. The gang encounters numerous difficulties in raising capital for the robbery, but finally they are ready to put their plan into action. The special railway car carrying the platinum will be blocked by a surplus tank, and the loot will be loaded onto a hijacked bomber for transport to a fence in Morocco. Despite consistent bumbling and threats by Harry and his girl friend Juliana to betray Celli and abscond with the platinum, the robbery is successful and the plane makes its getaway. All the gang's efforts come to naught, however, when the plane's bomb doors are accidentally opened and the platinum descends into the waiting arms of the police. *Expatriates. Masterminds. Police. Hijackers. Kidnaping. Revenge. Train robberies. Ransom. Platinum. Bombers. Tanks (armored cars). Morocco.*
   Note: Location scenes filmed in Italy and France.

THE BIGGEST FIGHT ON EARTH *see* **GHIDRAH, THE THREE-HEADED MONSTER**

BIKE BOY   **F6.0404**
   Factory Films. *Dist* Andy Warhol Films, Film-Makers' Cooperative. 5 Oct **1967** [New York opening]. Sd; col (Eastman Color). 16mm. 96 min.
   Prod-Dir-Story Andy Warhol. *Photog* Paul Morrissey.
   Cast: Joe Spencer (*The Motorcyclist*), Ed Wiener (*his buddy*), Vera Cruz (*other cyclist*), George Ann, Bruce Ann (*salesmen*), Ed Hood (*florist*), Brigid Polk (*woman with husband*), Ingrid Superstar (*girl in kitchen*), Ann Wehrer (*woman wearing wig*), Viva (*girl on couch*), Clay Bird, Bettina Coffin, Valerie Solanis.
   Satire. A motorcyclist has just arrived in New York City from California. He takes a shower and combs his hair very slowly. In a men's boutique, where the male staff find him very attractive, the motorcyclist tries on underwear and other clothes. At a florist's shop, he meets a woman who discusses flagellation with him. An older woman wearing a blonde wig attempts to lure him into giving her a ride on his motorcycle. Another acquaintance strips in her kitchen in an effort to arouse him, meanwhile delivering a lengthy monolog on the pleasures of cooking and the methods of preparing eggs. Still another woman, who is "stoned" on amphetamines, mocks his sexuality as her impotent husband looks on. Finally, a woman on a couch browbeats him into having sex with her. *Motorcyclists. Flagellation. Male homosexuality. Seduction. Impotence. Boutiques. Amphetamines. Eggs. New York City.*

BIKINI *see* **OPERATION BIKINI**

BIKINI BEACH   **F6.0405**
   Alta Vista Productions. *Dist* American International Pictures. 22 Jul **1964** [Chicago opening; c22 Jul 1964; LP29248]. Sd; col (PathéColor). 35mm (Panavision). 100 min.
   Pres by James H. Nicholson, Samuel Z. Arkoff. *Prod* James H. Nicholson, Samuel Z. Arkoff. *Co-prod* Anthony Carras. *Dir* William Asher. *2d Unit Dir* Anthony Carras. *Writ* William Asher, Leo Townsend, Robert Dillon. *Dir Photog* Floyd Crosby. *Art Dir & Prod Dsgn* Daniel Haller. *Set Decor* Harry Reif. *Titl* Butler-Glouner Inc. *Film Ed* Fred Feitshans. *Mus Score* Les Baxter. *Mus Coörd* Al Simms. *Songs:* "Bikini Beach," "Love's a Secret Weapon," "Gimme Your Love," "How About That!" "This Time It's Love," "Happy Feeling (Dance and Shout)," "Because You're You" Guy Hemric, Jerry Styner.

Songs: "*Bikini Drag*," "*Record Run*" Gary Usher, Roger Christian. *Song:* "*Got You Where I Want You*" Jack Merrill, Red Gilson. *Choreog* Tom Mahoney. *Sd* Don Rush. *Sd Ed* Kay Rose. *Mus Ed* Eve Newman. *Asst Mus Ed* Milton Lustig. *Asst Dir* Clark Paylow. *Prod Supv* Joe Wonder. *Prod Asst* Jack Cash. *Cost* Marjorie Corso. *Hairdressing* Eve Newing. *Sp Photog Eff* Butler-Glouner Inc. *Sp Eff* Roger George, Joe Zomar. *Tech Adv* Von Deming. *Coöp* Dean Jeffries. *Prop* Karl Brainard. *Constr Coörd* Ross Hahn.

Cast: Frankie Avalon (*Frankie/The Potato Bug*), Annette Funicello (*Dee Dee*), Martha Hyer (*Vivien Clements*), Harvey Lembeck (*Eric Von Zipper*), Don Rickles (*Big Drag*), John Ashley (*Johnny*), Jody McCrea (*Deadhead*), Candy Johnson (*Candy*), Danielle Aubry (*Lady Bug*), Meredith MacRae (*Animal*), Dolores Wells (*Sniffles*), Paul Smith, actor 1, James Westerfield (*officers*), Donna Loren (*Donna*), Little Stevie Wonder (*himself*), The Pyramids (*themselves*), The Exciters Band (*themselves*), Janos Prohaska (*Clyde, the chimpanzee*), Timothy Carey (*South Dakota Slim*), Val Warren (*The Teenage Werewolf Monster*), Keenan Wynn (*Harvey Huntington Honeywagon*), Boris Karloff (*art dealer*), Renie Riano.

Comedy with music. Frankie, Dee Dee, and their surfing friends arrive at Bikini Beach for a vacation and meet The Potato Bug, a British recording star also vacationing there. Newspaper publisher Huntington Honeywagon, who is trying to obtain the beach for a senior citizens' retirement community, menaces the youngsters' beach fun, claiming that they have sunk to animal level. (Honeywagon uses his pet chimpanzee, Clyde, to demonstrate his point.) The youngsters have allies in Vivien Clements, a teacher, and Big Drag, operator of a teenagers' hangout. The Potato Bug is interested in drag racing, and when Frankie expresses a similar interest, Dee Dee, out of spite, flirts with the Britisher. Eric Von Zipper and his motorcycle gang join Honeywagon's campaign against the surfers. Meanwhile, under Vivien's influence, Honeywagon begins to change his opinion of the youngsters. When Frankie and The Potato Bug plan to compete in a drag race, Von Zipper sabotages what he thinks is the Britisher's car, hoping that Frankie will be blamed. The sabotaged car is Frankie's, and he barely escapes when the car crashes after the race ends in a dead heat. Von Zipper is found out, and he and his gang are defeated in a fight at Big Drag's place and are sent away. The Potato Bug leaves, Frankie and Dee Dee are reconciled, and Vivien and Honeywagon become friends. *Surfers. Singers. British. Schoolteachers. Publishers. Motorcycle gangs. Adolescence. Rock and roll. Automobile racing. Flirtation. Jealousy. Beaches. Vacations. Automobile accidents. Chimpanzees.*

BIKINI BEACH *see* **OPERATION BIKINI**

BIKINI PARADISE   F6.0406
A. C. E. Films–Security Pictures. *Dist* Allied Artists. Apr 1967. Sd; col (Eastman Color). 35mm. 89 min.
A Philip Yordan Production. *Prod* Lester A. Sansom, Bernard Glasser. *Dir* Gregg Tallas. *Screenplay* Howard Berk. *Story* Howard Berk, Daniel Aubrey. *Photog* Manuel Berenguer. *Art Dir* Eugene Lourie. *Film Ed* Kurt Herrnfeld. *Mus Comp & Cond* Johnny Douglas. *Asst Dir* José Ochoa.
Cast: Janette Scott (*Rachel*), Kieron Moore (*Lieut. Allison Fraser*), John Baer (*Lieut. Anthony Crane*), Kay Walsh (*Harriet Pembroke*), Alexander Knox (*Commissioner Lighton*), Anna Brazzou (*Maya*), Sylvia Sorente (*Daphne*), Margaret Nolan (*Margarita*), Michele Mahaut (*Lisa*), Francine Welch (*Charlotte*), Pilar Clemens (*Julia*), Aida Power (*Ingrid*), Robert Beatty (*commissioner*), Shirley Faulls (*girl in park*), Graham Sumner (*officer*).
Comedy. Navy Lieut. Allison Fraser is sent by Commissioner Lighton to search the Pacific islands for Harriet Pembroke, a teacher who disappeared with her female pupils during World War II while escaping from the Japanese. Fraser and his colleague, Lieut. Anthony Crane, are captured by eight women, who apparently have never seen men before, and taken to their leader, Harriet Pembroke herself. After interrogating and then feasting the men, Miss Pembroke tells them they will be used for mating purposes and then done away with. Fraser and Crane escape on the night of their "marriages" to Rachel and Maya by disguising themselves as women. When another naval search party arrives, they are told that Fraser and Crane have disappeared. But the two men suddenly reappear, and the entire naval party heads for their cabin cruiser. Upon discovering that it is gone and that they are all trapped together, the marooned sailors and the women begin pairing off, certain they will establish a remote island paradise. *Schoolteachers. Reproduction. United States Navy. Missing persons. Disguise. Marriage—Arranged. World War II. South Sea Islands.*
Note: Filmed in the Canary Islands in 1964; working title: *White Savage.*

BIKINI PARTY IN A HAUNTED HOUSE *see* **THE GHOST IN THE INVISIBLE BIKINI**

BIKINI PLAYMATES *see* **BACHELOR TOM PEEPING**

DAS BILDNIS DES DORIAN GRAY *see* **DORIAN GRAY**

BILL WALLACE OF CHINA   F6.0407
Logos Productions. 30 May 1967 [Miami, Florida, opening]. Sd; col. 35mm (see note). 103 min.
Prod Gregory Walcott. *Dir-Writ* Douglas Green, dir. *Photog* Charles Wong. *Prod Dsgn* T. C. Wang. *Sd* Shung-ichi Yasuda. *Asst Dir* Kam Pak Kin.
Cast: Gregory Walcott (*Bill Wallace*), Jo Helton, Fung Yi, Peter Chan, H. K. Sheung.
Biographical drama. The film is a story of Bill Wallace, a Tennessee doctor who worked for years in a missionary hospital in China. *Americans in foreign countries. Physicians. Hospitals. Missions. China.*
Note: Filmed in Hong Kong. Press material indicates widescreen process.

BILLIE   F6.0408
Chrislaw Productions. *Dist* United Artists. 1 Sep 1965 [Chicago opening; c1 Sep 1965; LP32217]. Sd; col (Technicolor). 35mm (Techniscope). 87 min. [Also 83 min.]
Prod-Dir Don Weis. *Exec Prod* Peter Lawford. *In Charge of Prod* Milton Ebbins. *Assoc Prod* John Ross. *Screenplay* Ronald Alexander. *Dir Photog* John L. Russell. *Camera Op* Paul Hill. *Art Dir* Hal Pereira, Arthur Lonergan. *Set Decor* Sam Comer, James Payne. *Titl Dsgn* Richard Kuhn, National Screen Service. *Film Ed* Adrienne Fazan. *Asst Ed* Neil Travis. *Mus* Dominic Frontiere. *Titl Song* Dominic Frontiere, Diane Lampert. *Mus:* "Victory Dance" Dominic Frontiere. *Songs:* "Lonely Little In-Between," "Funny Little Butterflies," "The Girl Is a Girl Is a Girl" Lor Crane, Bernice Ross, Jack Gold, mus. *Songs Sung by* Patty Duke. *Vocals Supv by* Jack Gold, mus. *Arr by* Arnold Goland. *Choreog & Asst Choreog* David Winters, Donna McKechnie. *Sd Mix* Harry Lindgren. *Asst Dir* Dick Moder, Dale Coleman. *Prod Mgr* John Clarke Bowman. *Asst to the Prod* H. Bud Otto. *Prod Sec* Matty Lake. *Script Supv* Stanley Scheuer. *Miss Duke's Wardrobe Coörd* George Drew. *Women's Cost* Dolores Sheppard. *Men's Cost* Jerry Alpert. *Makeup* Del Acevedo. *Hairstyles* Dean Cole. *Athletic Tech Adv* Rafer Johnson. *Prop Master* Everett Israelson. *Co. Grip* Herb Weltz. *Gaffer* Norman Cassidy.
Cast: Patty Duke (*Billie Carol*), Jim Backus (*Howard G. Carol*), Jane Greer (*Agnes Carol*), Warren Berlinger (*Mike Benson*), Billy De Wolfe (*Mayor Davis*), Charles Lane (*Coach Jones*), Dick Sargent (*Matt Bullitt*), Susan Seaforth (*Jean Matthews*), Ted Bessell (*Bob Matthews*), Richard Deacon (*Principal Wilson*), Bobby Diamond (*Eddie Davis*), Michael Fox (*Ray Case*), Clive Clerk (*Ted Chekas*), Harlan Warde (*Dr. Hall*), Jean MacRae (*Nurse Webb*), Allan Grant (*himself*), Georgia Simmons (*Mrs. Hosenwacker*), Arline Anderson (*Mrs. Clifton*), Layte Bowden (*Miss Channing*), Matty Jordan (*reporter*), Shirley J. Shawn (*Mrs. Harper*), Maria Leonard (*Adele Colin*), Breena Howard (*Mary Jensen*), Craig W. Chudy (*starter*).
Domestic comedy with music. Source: Ronald Alexander, *Time Out for Ginger* (New York opening: 26 Nov 1952). Billie Carol, a 16-year-old athlete, consistently out-runs all the boys on her high school track team. Her prowess leads to trouble with her boyfriend, Mike Benson, who is ashamed of always losing to a girl, and with her father, who had been running for mayor on a platform of no competition between the sexes. Her father changes his position to a more liberal one after he and Billie are featured in *Life* magazine, but his opponent, Mayor Davis, still wages a dirty campaign. Mayor Davis, besides involving Billie, makes use of the fact that her unmarried sister Jean is pregnant. Jean reveals that she has been secretly married for a year before the election, and Mr. Carol wins. Billie becomes more feminine and puts on a dress for the first time to go out on a date with Mike. *Women athletes. Mayors. Political campaigns. Filial relations. High school life. Pregnancy. Adolescence. Track.* "*Life*" (*magazine*).
Note: Copyright claimant: Chrislaw–Patty Duke Productions.

BILLION DOLLAR BRAIN (Great Britain)   F6.0409
Lowndes Productions. *Dist* United Artists. 20 Dec 1967 [Los Angeles opening]. Sd; col (Technicolor, print by DeLuxe). 35mm (Panavision). 108 min.
Prod Harry Saltzman. *Exec Prod* Andre De Toth. *Dir* Ken Russell. *Screenplay* John McGrath. *Dir Photog* Billy Williams. *Camera* David Harcourt. *Art Dir* Bert Davey. *Prod Dsgn* Syd Cain. *Film Ed* Alan Osbiston. *Mus Comp & Cond* Richard Rodney Bennett. *Sd* John Mitchell. *Asst Dir* Jack Causey, Jim Brennan. *Prod Mgr* Eva Monley. *Wardrobe* John Brady, Maggie Lewin. *Makeup* Freddie Williamson, Benny Royston. *Hairstyles* Joan Smallwood.
Cast: Michael Caine (*Harry Palmer*), Karl Malden (*Leo Newbegin*), Ed Begley (*General Midwinter*), Oscar Homolka (*Colonel Stock*), Françoise Dorléac (*Anya*), Guy Doleman (*Colonel Ross*), Vladek Sheybal (*Dr. Eiwort*), Milo Sperber (*Basil*), Mark Elwes (*Birkinshaw*), Stanley Caine (*G. P. O. delivery boy*).

Mystery melodrama. Source: Len Deighton, *Billion Dollar Brain* (London, 1966). Harry Palmer has quit the British Intelligence service to operate a private detective agency. British Intelligence head Colonel Ross tries to induce him to return to work, but Palmer refuses. Shortly thereafter Palmer gets an assignment to deliver some eggs to Finland. In Helsinki he meets Anya, who takes him to an old friend, ex-CIA agent Leo Newbegin, to collect his fee. Palmer is blackmailed by the British service into pretending to join Newbegin's organization, which is headed by a zealous anti-Communist, Texas billionaire General Midwinter. Palmer is trapped at the Latvian border and nearly killed by Anya, whereupon he learns that Midwinter is attempting to foment revolution in Soviet satellite countries before leading his own army in an attack on Russia—an attack planned by his billion-dollar computer. Newbegin, who has been doublecrossing Midwinter, escapes from Helsinki with Anya; she in turn doublecrosses Newbegin and hands him over to Palmer. Aware that the eggs are filled with a lethal virus, Anya flees with them to Russia, for which she has been working as a spy. Midwinter and his army advance toward Russia but sink through thin ice when Colonel Stok, head of the Russian secret service, dispatches several planes to drop a few well-placed bombs on the ice. Palmer, the only survivor, is rescued by Stok, an old friend of Palmer's; and Stok and Anya, satisfied at having thwarted Midwinter's plot, hand the eggs over to Palmer. *Detectives. Spies. Fanatics. Russians. Texans. Millionaires. Biological warfare. Espionage. Anti-communism. Blackmail. Perfidy. Computers. Eggs. Latvia. Helsinki. Union of Soviet Socialist Republics. Great Britain—Intelligence service. Harry Palmer.*

Note: Filmed on location in Helsinki and Latvia. Opened in London in Nov 1967 at 111 min. This is the third in a series of films based on the Harry Palmer character.

THE BILLION DOLLAR CAPER *see* **THE MONEY JUNGLE**

BILLY BRIGHT *see* **THE COMIC**

BILLY BUDD (Great Britain)   F6.0410
Anglo-Allied Pictures. *Dist* Allied Artists. 30 Oct **1962** [New York opening; c1 Nov 1962; LP23189]. Sd; b&w. 35mm (CinemaScope). 123 min. [Also reviewed at 112 min.]

Prod-Dir Peter Ustinov. *Exec Prod* A. Ronald Lubin. *Prod Assoc* Arthur S. Ferriman. *Screenplay (see note)* Peter Ustinov, DeWitt Bodeen, Robert Rossen. *Dir Photog* Robert Krasker. *Camera Op* John Harris. *Focus* Kelvin Pike, Bernard Ford. *Art Dir* Peter Murton. *Prod Dsgn* Don Ashton. *Film Ed* Jack Harris. *Mus* Anthony Hopkins, mus. *Played by* The Philharmonic Orchestra. *Sd* Charles Crafford, Charles Poulton, Len Shilton. *Sd Camera Op* Gordon Hooton. *Boom Op* Tom Buchanan. *1st & 2d Asst Dir* Michael Birkett, Claude Watson. *Prod Mgr* Victor Peck. *Prod Sec* Joan Parcell. *Cost Dsgn* Anthony Mendleson. *Wardrobe Master* Ron Beck. *Wardrobe Mistress* Laura Nightingale. *Makeup* Bob Lawrence. *Hairdresser* Henry Montsash. *Sp Eff* George Blackwell. *Constr Mgr* Stanley Gale. *Still Photog* George Higgins. *Chargehand Prop* F. Pratt. *Chargehand Electrn* Wally Thompson. *Nautical Rigger* D. Harrison.

Cast: Terence Stamp (*Billy Budd*), Peter Ustinov (*Capt. Edward Fairfax Vere*), Robert Ryan (*Master-at-Arms John Claggart*), Melvyn Douglas (*The Dansker*), Ronald Lewis (*Jenkins*), David McCallum (*Lieutenant Wyatt*), John Neville (*Lieut. John Ratcliffe*), Paul Rogers (*Lieut. Philip Seymour*), Lee Montague (*Squeak*), Thomas Heathcote (*Payne*), Ray McAnally (*O'Daniel*), Robert Brown (*Talbot*), John Meillon (*Kincaid*), Cyril Luckham (*Hallam*), Niall MacGinnis (*Captain Graveling*), Victor Brooks, Barry Keegan.

Drama. Source: Herman Melville, "Billy Budd, Foretopman," in *Billy Budd, and Other Prose Pieces* (London, 1924). Louis O. Coxe and Robert Chapman, *Billy Budd* (New York opening: 10 Feb 1951). In 1797 a young merchant seaman, Billy Budd, is impressed into service by the British Navy for the war between England and France. His innate goodness blinds him to the evil in other men, and when he proves to be an excellent sailor, Billy soon becomes the most popular member of the crew. Only the sadistic and hated master-at-arms, Claggart, remains aloof; unable to comprehend the boy's simple and honest nature, Claggart attempts to bring about his downfall by falsely accusing him of instigating a mutiny. The ship's captain, Edward Fairfax Vere, knows that Claggart is lying and calls upon Billy to deny the charge, but the boy is so stunned by the accusation that an impediment in his speech renders him incapable of uttering a word; instead, he strikes Claggart, causing him to fall, fracture his skull, and die. At the shipboard court-martial, all the officers agree that the death was accidental and Billy should therefore be acquitted, but Vere points out that they must deal with naval law, not justice, and that Billy must pay the death penalty for killing a superior officer. The board is forced to make the agonizing decision that Billy be hanged, but as the rope is placed around his neck, he prevents a possible mutiny among the crew by crying out, "God bless Captain Vere." The latter is so emotionally moved by the words that he considers himself unfit for command, but the crew rallies when a French ship

appears on the horizon. Vere dies in the ensuing engagement. *Innocents. Sailors. Sadism. Mutiny. Manslaughter. Capital punishment. Courts-martial. Napoleonic Wars. Great Britain—Royal Navy.*

Note: Location scenes filmed in Spain. Opened in London in Sep 1962. Rossen is not officially credited for writing the screenplay.

BILLY LIAR (Great Britain)   F6.0411
Vic Films–Waterhall Productions. *Dist* Continental Distributing, Inc. 16 Dec **1963** [New York opening]. Sd; b&w. 35mm (CinemaScope). 96 min.

Prod Joseph Janni. *Assoc Prod* Jack Rix. *Dir* John Schlesinger. *Screenplay* Keith Waterhouse, Willis Hall. *Photog* Denys Coop. *Camera Op* Jack Atchelor. *Camera Asst* Neil Binney, Michael Rutter. *Art Dir* Ray Simm. *Set Dresser* Ken Bridgeman. *Draughtsman* Martin Atkinson. *Film Ed* Roger Cherrill. *1st Asst Ed* Jack Gardner. *2d Asst Ed* Jean Short. *Mus Comp* Richard Rodney Bennett. *Cond* John Hollingsworth. *Sd Mix* Peter Handford. *Boom Op* Tom Buchanan. *Sd Camera Op* Doug Barnett. *1st & 2d Asst Dir* Frank Ernst, Jim Brennan. *Prod Mgr* Charles Blair. *Pers Asst to the Prod* John Goldstone. *Prod Sec* Ann Skinner. *Cont* Pamela Mann. *Wardrobe Supv* Laura Nightingale. *Wardrobe Master* Ron Beck. *Makeup* Bob Lawrence. *Hairdresser* Joyce James. *Grip* Albert Lott. *Casting Dir* Miriam Brickman. *Still Photog* Harry Gillard. *Ch Electrn* Frank Robertson. *Prop Buyer* Dennis Maddison. *Prop* John Feehan, Phil Meighan, Tom Brooker.

Cast: Tom Courtenay (*Billy Fisher*), Julie Christie (*Liz*), Wilfred Pickles (*Geoffrey Fisher*), Mona Washbourne (*Alice Fisher*), Ethel Griffies (*Grandmother Florence*), Finlay Currie (*Duxbury*), Rodney Bewes (*Arthur Crabtree*), Helen Fraser (*Barbara*), George Innes (*Eric Stamp*), Leonard Rossiter (*Shadrack*), Gwendolyn Watts (*Rita*), Patrick Barr (*Inspector MacDonald*), Godfrey Winn (*disc jockey*), Ernest Clark (*prison governor*), Leslie Randall (*Danny Boon*), Anna Wing (*Mrs. Crabtree*), Elaine Stevens (*Danny's secretary*), George Ghent (*Danny's P. R. O.*), Flo Fallows (*1st prostitute*), Alice Woods (*2d prostitute*), Douglas Clarke (*serviceman*), Jack Cunningham, actor (*ticket examiner*), Lester Legh (*bandleader*).

Comedy-drama. Source: Keith Waterhouse and Willis Hall, *Billy Liar* (London opening: 13 Sep 1960). Keith Waterhouse, *Billy Liar* (London, 1959). Billy Fisher's wild imagination is his only escape from a humdrum life in a northern England town. Whenever his stifling job as a clerk in an undertaker's office becomes too much for him or when his family's nagging efforts to make him conform overpower him, Billy retreats to "Ambrosia," a mythical kingdom conjured up in his mind. In "Ambrosia," Billy is king, general, lover, or any idealized hero that the situation of the moment makes him desire. Billy's dream of becoming a television scriptwriter in London has been encouraged by a well-known comedian to whom he sent samples of his writing. Before he can take any decisive step, however, Billy has two problems to settle: he is engaged to two different girls and in love with a third, and he must dispose of his employer's advertising calendars which he was unable to mail months earlier because he spent the postage money. On the day the comedian is scheduled to make an appearance in town, Billy offers his resignation to his employer, Mr. Shadrack. He is informed, however, that Shadrack knows about the calendars and that he will either have to make restitution or work off the debt. Later that afternoon, in a meeting with the comedian, Billy learns that the encouragement he received was merely a form letter. And at a dance that night, Billy's efforts to divide his time between both fiancées fail. The women come face to face and get into a hair-pulling battle, and both subsequently break their engagements to Billy. He escapes to a nearby park with Liz, the wild, unconventional woman he really loves. Liz convinces him to take his chances at making a success of his writing and leave with her for London at midnight. When he goes home to pack and inform his parents of his departure, he learns that his grandmother has been hospitalized. At the hospital, Billy is told of his grandmother's death, but he still plans to leave and bids farewell to his mother. He and Liz board the London train, but at the last moment he gets off, and the train leaves with Liz. Billy returns to the monotony of his small town life and to the security of "Ambrosia." *Television scriptwriters. Undertakers. Office clerks. Entertainers. Family life. Employer-employee relations. Duplicity. Fantasy. Imaginary kingdoms.*

Note: Opened in London in Aug 1963; running time: 98 min.

BILLY ROSE'S JUMBO *see* **JUMBO**

BILLY THE KID VS. DRACULA   F6.0412
Circle Productions. *Dist* Embassy Pictures. 30 Mar **1966** [New Haven, Connecticut, opening]. Sd; col (Pathé). 35mm. 72 min. [Cut from 84 min.]

Prod Carroll Case. *Assoc Prod* Howard W. Koch, Jr. *Dir* William Beaudine, [Sr.]. *Story & Screenplay* Carl K. Hittleman. *Dir Photog* Lothrop Worth. *Art Dir* Paul Sylos. *Set Decor* Harry Reif. *Film Ed* Roy Livingston. *Mus* Raoul Kraushaar. *Sd Rec* Harold Lewis. *Asst Dir* Max Stein. *Prod Mgr* Sam Manners. *Makeup* Ted Coodley. *Sp Photog Eff* Cinema Research Corp.

Cast: Chuck Courtney (*Billy the Kid*), John Carradine (*Count Dracula*), Melinda Plowman (*Betty Bentley*), Virginia Christine (*Eva Oster*), Walter Janovitz (*Franz Oster*), Bing Russell (*Red Thorpe*), Lennie Geer (*Yancy*), Roy Barcroft (*Marshal Griffin*), Olive Carey (*Dr. Henrietta Hull*), Hannie Landman (*Lila Oster*), Marjorie Bennett (*Mrs. Ann Bentley*), William Forrest (*James Underhill*), George Cisar (*Joe Flake*), Charlita (*Nana*), Harry Carey, Jr. (*Ben*), Richard Reeves, Max Kleven, Jack Williams, William Challee.

Horror melodrama. Arriving by stagecoach at Wickenburg, a small Southwestern village, Count Dracula poses as the uncle of Betty Bentley, who owns the Bar-B ranch. Almost immediately he arouses the suspicions of the ranch foreman, the reformed outlaw Billy the Kid. As Billy sets out to prove the "uncle" an imposter, he is unaware that Dracula already has Betty in his power. The local doctor eventually comes to Billy's aid by holding a mirror up to Dracula's face and exposing him as a vampire when no reflection appears in the glass. Although Dracula escapes, Billy, the doctor, and the marshal trace him to a silver mine. Bullets proving to be of no help, Billy fights off Dracula's attack with a scalpel and drives it into the vampire's heart. As his body dissolves, Betty recovers from the mesmerized state in which Dracula had placed her. *Ranchers. Ranch foremen. Uncles. Vampires. Physicians. United States marshals. Imposture. Silver mines. William H. Bonney. Dracula.*

BIMBO THE GREAT (West Germany)   F6.0413

Corona Filmproduktion. *Dist* Warner Bros. Pictures. 28 Jun **1961** [New York opening; c17 Jun 1960; LP25364]. Sd; col (Eastmancolor by Pathé). 35mm. 96 min. [Also reviewed at 92 min.]

Pres by Joseph E. Levine. *Prod* Alexander Grüter. *Dir* Harald Philipp. *Screenplay* Hans Raspotnik, Harald Philipp, Erich Kröhnke. *Photog* Willy Winterstein. *Mus* Theo Mackeben, Klaus Ogermann. *Song:* "The Torch Burns at Midnight" Mitchell Parish, Vic Mizzy. *Song:* "Angel Baby" Mitchell Parish. *Choreog* John Schapar.

Cast: Claus Holm (*Bimbo Tagore*), Germaine Damar (*Lilo*), Elma Karlowa (*Yvonne*), Marina Orschel (*Marianne*), Helmut Schmid (*Kovacs*), Paul Hartmann (*Williams*), Lisa Gussack (*Monica*), Loni Heuser (*circus agent*), Hans von Borsody, Elke Aberle.

Melodrama. Trapeze artists Bimbo Tagore and his wife, Marianne, star in a European traveling circus. Before one of their performances, Bimbo's jealous half brother, Kovacs, tampers with the trapeze equipment in the hope that Bimbo will fall to his death. The plan backfires, however, and Marianne is killed. A court inquiry acquits Bimbo after he is falsely implicated in his wife's death, but the tragedy leaves him shattered, and he begins to drink heavily. As a result, Yvonne's lion taming act replaces Bimbo's high-wire act; and his daughter, Monica, is taken away from him and placed in the custody of her aunt. Learning that Kovacs plans to take over the trapeze act, Bimbo straightens himself out and returns to rehearse his act with Yvonne, who replaces his wife. A fight with Kovacs causes a fire in the circus tent. Bimbo braves the flames to rescue Kovacs, who, before dying, confesses to the earlier crime and also admits that he has again tampered with the trapeze equipment. Bimbo manages to repair it in time, and he and Yvonne are a huge success. Reunited with little Monica, he announces that he and Yvonne will soon wed. *Trapezists. Lion tamers. Brothers. Widowers. Jealousy. Murder. Alcoholism. Frameup. Parenthood. Circus. Fires.*

Note: Produced in West Germany in 1958 as *Rivalen der Manege.* Copyright claimant: Embassy Pictures. Some cast names may have been anglicized for U. S. release: Claus Holm became Charles Holm, Elma Karlowa became Eleanor Marlowe, Helmut Schmid became Henry Smith, Marina Orschel became Maryanne Shields, and Lisa Gussack became Lisa Stack.

LA BIONDA DI PECHINO see PEKING BLONDE

THE BIRD WITH THE CRYSTAL PLUMAGE (Italy/West Germany)   F6.0414

Seda Spettacoli–CCC-Filmkunst. *Dist* U-M Film Distributors. 22 Jul **1970** [New York opening]. Sd; col (Eastman Color). 35mm (Techniscope). 98 min. *MPAA rating* GP.

Pres by Sidney Glazier. *Prod* Salvatore Argento. *Dir-Writ* Dario Argento. *Dir Photog* Vittorio Storaro. *Camera* Enrico Umetelli. *Art Dir* Dario Micheli. *Film Ed* Franco Fraticelli. *Mus* Ennio Morricone. *Sd* Carlo Diotallevi. *Asst Dir* Roberto Pariante. *Prod Mgr* Camillo Teti. *Wardrobe* Dario Micheli.

Cast: Tony Musante (*Sam Dalmas*), Suzy Kendall (*Julia*), Eva Renzi (*Monica Ranieri*), Enrico Maria Salerno (*Morosini*), Mario Adorf (*Berto*), Renato Romano (*Dover*), Umberto Raho (*Ranieri*), Raf Valenti, Giuseppe Castellano.

Mystery melodrama. Based on a novel by: Bryan Edgar Wallace. Sam Dalmas, a writer from Philadelphia who is vacationing in Rome, sees through the window of an art gallery a woman struggling with a man. Suddenly the man, brandishing a knife, runs away, and the woman collapses to the floor. Police question Sam, the only witness to the attack; and Inspector Morosini, taking Sam's passport, advises him to remain in the city. Gallery owner Alberto Ranieri identifies the injured woman as his wife and business partner, Monica. Sam begins his own investigation of the incident, both out of curiosity and because he is anxious to depart Italy as soon as possible. He visits the Ranieri apartment but is unable to interview Monica because she is recuperating from the attack. Meanwhile, police, having linked the attack with the recent stabbing deaths of three other women, learn of a fourth murder. Several attempts are made on Sam's life, and he is told in an anonymous telephone call (which he tape-records) that his girl friend, Julia, a model with whom he lives, will die unless they both leave the country. Sam reports the threat to the police and turns over to them the tape recording he has made of the caller's voice, which, as it turns out, does not match the voice in a call police have received from a man claiming to be the murderer. Moreover, Sam's tape contains a peculiar squeaking sound in the background. Morosini, concerned about Sam's safety, returns his passport and releases him from his promise to remain in Rome. Dover, an ornithologist friend of Sam's, believes that the squeaking on the tape is the call of a rare bird which is housed in the city zoo. Sam, Dover, and Julia meet Inspector Morosini at the zoo, and there Sam observes that a window of the Ranieri apartment looks out upon the bird's cage. Alerted by a scream from the Ranieri apartment, police break in there to find husband and wife fighting over a knife. In the struggle Ranieri falls [or throws himself] from the open window, and, dying, he confesses to the four stabbing murders. Sam soon realizes that Monica is the murderer and that Ranieri was protecting his deranged wife, but before she is apprehended, Monica kills Dover and nearly makes victims of Sam and Julia. *Authors. Detectives. Art dealers. Models. Ornithologists. Police. Murder. Confession (law). Insanity. Suicide. Art galleries. Recorders. Zoos. Rome. Documentation. Birds.*

Note: Released in Italy in 1970 as *L'uccello dalle piume di cristallo;* in West Germany in Jun 1970 as *Das Geheimnis der schwarzen Handschuhe;* running time: 94 min.

BIRDMAN OF ALCATRAZ   F6.0415

Norma Productions. *Dist* United Artists. 3 Jul **1962** [Los Angeles opening; c3 Jul 1962; LP23015]. Sd; b&w. 35mm. 147 min. [Also 143 min.]

Pres by Harold Hecht. *Prod* Stuart Millar, Guy Trosper. *Exec Prod* Harold Hecht. *Dir* John Frankenheimer. *Screenplay* Guy Trosper. *Photog* Burnett Guffey. *Co-Photog* Robert Krasker. *Art Dir* Fernando Carrere. *Film Ed* Edward Mann. *Mus* Elmer Bernstein. *Sd* George Cooper. *Sd Eff* Robert Reich, James Nelson. *Asst Dir* Dave Silver. *Prod Mgr* Gilbert Kurland. *Makeup* Robert Schiffer. *Bird Handler* A. W. Kennard.

Cast: Burt Lancaster (*Robert Stroud*), Karl Malden (*Harvey Shoemaker*), Thelma Ritter (*Elizabeth Stroud*), Betty Field (*Stella Johnson*), Neville Brand (*Bull Ransom*), Edmond O'Brien (*Tom Gaddis*), Hugh Marlowe (*Roy Comstock*), Telly Savalas (*Feto Gomez*), Whit Bissell (*Dr. Ellis*), Crahan Denton (*Kramer*), Leo Penn (*Eddie Kassellis*), James Westerfield (*Jess Younger*), Lewis Charles (*Chaplain Wentzel*), Arthur Stewart (*guard captain*), Raymond Greenleaf (*judge*), Nick Dennis (*crazed prisoner*), William Hansen (*Fred Daw*), Harry Holcombe (*city editor*), Robert Burton (*Sen. Ham Lewis*), Len Lesser (*Burns*), Chris Robinson (*Logue*), George Mitchell (*Father Matthieu*), Edward Mallory (*John Clary*), Adrienne Marden (*Mrs. Woodrow Wilson*), Harry Jackson (*reporter*).

Biographical drama. Source: Thomas E. Gaddis, *Birdman of Alcatraz; The Story of Robert Stroud* (New York, 1955). In 1909, Robert Stroud kills a man in Alaska and is sentenced to 12 years imprisonment. He forfeits his chance for parole when he knifes another prisoner. While serving time at Leavenworth, he murders a prison guard who refuses to let his mother visit him, and he is condemned to death. Before his execution can be carried out, however, his mother visits Mrs. Woodrow Wilson, who persuades the president to commute Stroud's sentence to life imprisonment. The prison warden, Harvey Shoemaker, informs Stroud that he will spend the rest of his life in solitary confinement. One day during exercise period in the isolation yard, he finds a wounded sparrow and takes it to his cell. Secretly he nurses the bird back to health and then teaches it to perform tricks. When Warden Shoemaker is replaced by a kindlier man, Stroud is given permission to keep his pet and also to have other birds in his cell. Through endless study, he becomes an authority on caged birds and eventually writes a textbook on their diseases. After winning a prize in a magazine competition, he is visited by Stella Johnson, a lonely widow who suggests that they manufacture his remedies. A change in the prison set-up threatens to deprive Stroud of his birds, but he finds a legal loophole that will permit him to marry Stella while he is still in solitary confinement. The newspaper publicity which is created permits him to carry on his work. Then he is abruptly transferred to Alcatraz where his old nemesis, Shoemaker, is warden. When Stroud is informed that he can no longer keep his birds, he shifts his interest to caged men and writes a book on penology. Shoemaker, however, has the work confiscated. Stroud acts as a peacemaker in a prison riot and is transferred to a minimum security farm at Springfield, Missouri. As he leaves

Alcatraz, he is met by Tom Gaddis, a social worker and writer who became Stroud's defender by writing *Bird Man of Alcatraz* in 1955. *Prison wardens. Authors. Widows. Social workers. Murder. Capital punishment. Filial relations. Criminals—Rehabilitation. Ornithology. Marriage. Publicity. Penology. Prison revolts. Prisons. Alaska. Robert Stroud. Edith Bolling Galt Wilson. Leavenworth (U. S. penitentiary). Alcatraz. Birds.*

Note: Some location scenes filmed in San Francisco.

THE BIRDS F6.0416

Alfred J. Hitchcock Productions. *Dist* Universal Pictures. 28 Mar **1963** [New York opening; c28 Mar, 20 Apr 1963; LP25722, LP35397]. Sd; col (Technicolor). 35mm. 120 min.

Prod-Dir Alfred Hitchcock. *Screenplay* Evan Hunter. *Dir Photog* Robert Burks. *Set Decor* George Milo. *Prod Dsgn* Robert Boyle. *Main Titl* James S. Pollak. *Film Ed* George Tomasini. *Electronic Sd Prod & Comp* Remi Gassman, Oskar Sala. *Sd Rec* Waldon O. Watson, William Russell. *Sd Cons* Bernard Herrmann. *Asst Dir* James H. Brown. *Prod Mgr* Norman Deming. *Asst to Mr. Hitchcock* Peggy Robertson. *Script Supv* Lois Thurman. *Wardrobe Supv* Rita Riggs. *Miss Hedren's Cost Dsgn* Edith Head. *Makeup* Howard Smit. *Hairstyles* Virginia Darcy. *Sp Eff* Lawrence A. Hampton. *Pictorial Dsgn* Albert Whitlock. *Sp Photog Adv* Ub Iwerks. *Bird Trainer* Ray Berwick.

Cast: Rod Taylor *(Mitch Brenner)*, Tippi Hedren *(Melanie Daniels)*, Jessica Tandy *(Mrs. Brenner)*, Suzanne Pleshette *(Annie Hayworth)*, Veronica Cartwright *(Cathy Brenner)*, Ethel Griffies *(Mrs. Bundy)*, Charles McGraw *(Sebastian Sholes)*, Ruth McDevitt *(Mrs. MacGruder)*, Joe Mantell *(traveling salesman)*, Doreen Lang *(hysterical woman)*, Malcolm Atterbury *(Deputy Al Malone)*, Karl Swenson *(drunk)*, Elizabeth Wilson *(Helen Carter)*, Lonny Chapman *(Deke Carter)*, Doodles Weaver *(fisherman)*, John McGovern *(postal clerk)*, Richard Deacon *(man in elevator)*, William Quinn.

Horror film. Source: Daphne Du Maurier, "The Birds," in *The Apple Tree* (London, 1952). While in a San Francisco pet shop, wealthy Melanie Daniels becomes attracted to Mitch Brenner, a young lawyer who is trying unsuccessfully to find a pair of lovebirds for his little sister Cathy. Acting on a sudden impulse, Melanie buys two of the birds and decides to deliver them to Mitch's home on an island in Bodega Bay. After secretly leaving the birds in the Brenner house, she is returning to the mainland by motor boat when a seagull swoops down on her, gashes her forehead, and then flies away. Mitch meets her at the mainland pier and brings her back to his home. The next day a group of birds attack Cathy and her friends during a birthday party. That evening hundreds of finches fly down a chimney and terrorize Melanie and the Brenners. Panic in the small town mounts as birds murder a chicken farmer by pecking him to death, create a flash fire at a gas station, and swarm over the local children as they leave school. Following the death of schoolteacher Annie Hayworth, most of the townspeople leave their homes and head for San Francisco. Mitch boards up all entrances to his home and awaits the onslaught. The birds dive against the house, tearing at shingles and gnawing at doors, but they are unable to get inside. When Melanie goes to the attic, however, she is attacked by a roomful of crows who have made a hole in the roof. Mitch manages to rescue her but realizes the house is no longer safe. With the coming of morning, the birds are momentarily quiet. Taking advantage of the silence, he puts Melanie and his family into his car and leaves for San Francisco as thousands of birds watch their departure. *Lawyers. Children. Schoolteachers. Brother-sister relationship. Filial relations. Fear. Evacuation. Smalltown life. Pet shops. Islands. Birthdays. San Francisco. Birds.*

BIRDS DO IT F6.0417

Ivan Tors Enterprises. *Dist* Columbia Pictures. Aug **1966** [c27 Jul 1966; LP32996]. Sd; col (Pathé). 35mm. 95 min.

Prod Stanley Colbert. *Prod Exec* Ben Chapman. *Exec Prod* Ivan Tors. *Dir* Andrew Marton. *Screenplay* Arnie Kogen. *Story* Leonard Kaufman. *Dir Photog* Howard Winner. *Art Dir* Mel Bledsoe. *Set Decor* Don Ivey. *Set Dsgn* Preston Rountree. *Film Ed* Erwin Dumbrille. *Mus Comp & Cond* Samuel Matlovsky. *Titl Song* Howard Greenfield, Jack Keller. *Sd* Howard Warren. *Asst Dir* James Gordon McLean. *Prod Mgr* Edward Haldeman. *Script Supv* Joseph Gannon. *Wardrobe* Peggy Kunkle, Mildred Simpkins. *Soupy Sales' Wardrobe* Andrew Pallack. *Makeup Supv* George Fiala. *Hairstyles* Irene Aparicio. *Sp Eff* Howard A. Anderson Co. *Prop* Jack Johnson, prop.

Cast: Soupy Sales *(Melvin Byrd)*, Tab Hunter *(Lieutenant Porter)*, Arthur O'Connell *(Professor Wald)*, Edward Andrews *(General Smithburn)*, Doris Dowling *(Congresswoman Clanger)*, Beverly Adams *(Claudine Wald)*, Louis Quinn *(Sergeant Skam)*, Frank Nastasi *(Yellow Cab driver)*, Burt Taylor *(Devlin)*, Courtney Brown *(Arno)*, Russell Saunders *(Clurg)*, Julian Voloshin *(Professor Nep)*, Bob Bersell *(doorman)*, Warren Day *(Curtis)*, Jay Laskay *(Willie)*, Burt Leigh *(radio operator)*.

Comedy. When a dust particle ruins a space rocket being constructed at Cape Kennedy, Melvin Byrd becomes a "top secret" janitor equipped with

selfpropulsion cleaning utensils. Since his duties are not divulged to outsiders, enemy agents infiltrate the base and unsuccessfully attempt to eliminate him. Melvin's affection for Judi, an astrochimp, results in his accidentally becoming "negatively ionized" so that he not only floats and flies like a bird but becomes irresistible to women. As Melvin soars away over the base, he is watched by a stunned group of visiting congressmen, field personnel, and the enemy agents. And young Claudine Wald, the daughter of Melvin's superior, forgets her usual indifference to Melvin and races after him, wildly screaming her love. Melvin's journey over the bay creates havoc among commercial and private planes and among the boats in the harbor. But just as the Coast Guard arrives on the scene, the "ionizer" at the base is turned off and Melvin descends to the ground. The Coast Guard gathers all of his pursuers into a huge cargo net, picks out the enemy agents, and releases the others. Despite the loss of his extraordinary powers, a delighted Melvin discovers that Claudine still finds him irresistible. *Janitors. Foreign agents. Ionization. Rockets. Cape Kennedy. United States Congress. United States Coast Guard. Chimpanzees.*

BIRDS IN PERU (France) F6.0418

Universal Productions France. *Dist* Regional Film Distributors. 6 Nov **1968** [New York opening]. Sd; col (Technicolor). 35mm (Franscope). 95 min. *MPAA rating X.*

Prod Jacques Natteau. *Dir-Writ-Adapt-Dial* Romain Gary. *Photog Dir* Christian Matras. *Art Dir* Jacques Brizzio. *Set Decor* Fernand Cjaivoret. *Film Ed* Denise Charvein. *Mus* Kenton Coe. *Sd* Guy Chichignoud. *Asst Dir* Michel Wyn. *Prod Mgr* Fred Surin. *Makeup* Phuong Maittret. *Hairstyles* Valentine Montero.

Cast: Jean Seberg *(Adriana)*, Maurice Ronet *(Rainier)*, Pierre Brasseur *(The Husband)*, Jean-Pierre Kalfon *(The Chauffeur)*, Michel Buades *(Alejo)*, Danielle Darrieux *(Madame Fernande)*, Pierre Koulak *(The Bouncer)*, Henry Czarniak *(truck driver)*, Jackie Lombard *(Rita)*.

Drama. Source: Romain Gary, "Les oiseaux vont mourir au Pérou," in *Gloire à nos illustres pionniers; nouvelles* (Paris, 1962). In the early morning hours after a Peruvian carnival, a young woman named Adriana lies naked and exhausted on a lonely stretch of beach—the final resting place for dying gulls from the nearby Guano Islands. The night before, Adriana left her sadomasochistic millionaire husband and came to the beach with four costumed revelers with whom she hoped to find sexual fulfillment. Tormented by nymphomania, and knowing that her husband and his chauffeur-bodyguard will soon come for her, Adriana dresses herself and wanders into a beachside brothel owned by Madame Fernande. At first Adriana gives herself to the madame and offers to work for her as a prostitute but then changes her mind and returns to the beach. Remembering her agreement that the chauffeur could kill her if she ever succumbed again to her sickness, she attempts to drown herself, but she is rescued by Rainier, a poet and self-confessed failure, who runs a beach cafe that no one frequents. While they make love, Rainier implies that they could be each other's salvation. His suggestions are interrupted, however, by the arrival of the chauffeur and the whisky-sodden husband, who have come to carry out the agreed-upon ritualized execution. Rainier intervenes and is knocked unconscious; a young Indian boy called Alejo, who has been following Adriana, leaps out from a hiding place and plunges a knife into the chauffeur. Ignoring the others, Adriana wanders off alone as her husband picks up the dead chauffeur's cap and hands it to Rainier, who accepts it. As the two men set off after Adriana, the young boy races headlong into the sea. *Millionaires. Chauffeurs. Peruvians. Madams. Poets. Indians of South America. Nymphomania. Sadomasochism. Lesbianism. Suicide. Murder. Marriage. Infidelity. Cafes. Whorehouses. Carnivals. Beaches. Peru. Birds.*

Note: Opened in Paris in Jun 1968 as *Les oiseaux vont mourir au Pérou.* Filmed on the coast of Spain and in Mauritania.

BIRDS OF A FEATHER ... FLOCKING TOGETHER see **THE WILD FEMALES**

THE BIRDS, THE BEES, AND THE ITALIANS (France/Italy) F6.0419

Dear Film-R. P. A.-Les Films du Siècle. *Dist* Claridge Pictures. 7 Aug **1967** [New York opening]. Sd; b&w. 35mm. 115 min.

Prod Robert Haggiag, Pietro Germi. *Dir* Pietro Germi. *Screenplay* Age & Scarpelli, Luciano Vincenzoni, Pietro Germi. *Orig Story* Luciano Vincenzoni, Pietro Germi. *Photog* Aiace Parolin. *Art Dir* Carlo Egidi. *Film Ed* Sergio Montanari. *Mus* Carlo Rustichelli. *Cond* Pierluigi Urbini. *Sd* Vittorio Trentino. *Asst Dir* Francesco Massaro. *Prod Mgr* Gianni Cecchin. *Cost* Angela Sammaciccia.

Cast: Virna Lisi *(Milena Zulian)*, Gastone Moschin *(Osvaldo Bisigato)*, Nora Ricci *(Gilda Bisigato)*, Alberto Lionello *(Toni Gasparini)*, Olga Villi *(Ippolita Gasparini)*, Franco Fabrizi *(Lino Benedetti)*, Beba Loncar *(Noemi Castellan)*, Gigi Ballista *(Dr. Giacinto Castellan)*, Aldo Puglisi *(Officer Mancuso)*, Giulio Questi *(Franco Zaccaria)*, Gustavo D'Arpe *(Sante Scarabello)*, Quinto Parmeggiani *(Nane Soligo)*, Gia Sandri *(Betty Soligo)*, Moira Orfei *(Giorgia*

Casellato), Alberto Rabagliati *(Giacomo Casellato),* Patrizia Valturri *(Alda Cristofoletto),* Carlo Bagno *(Bepi Cristofoletto),* Virgilio Scapin *(Don Schiavon),* Ilia Guiotto *(Bepi Scodeller),* Tity Karish *(Bianca Scodeller),* Giacomo Rizzo *(Egisto Scodeller),* Sergio Fincato *(Attorney Maschio),* Ruggero Dal Fabbro *(Attorney Tonello),* Lauro Rubin *(Ivo Bastanzi),* Giancarlo Fontanieri *(Bank Director Padovan),* Giuseppe Perini *(Marshall Potenza),* Virgilio Gazzolo, Stefano Satta Flores, Giulio Onesti, Antonio Acqua.

Comedy. During a bawdy party in the Italian town of Treviso, the unhappily married Toni Gasparini confides to his friend, Dr. Castellan, that he is impotent. As a result, the doctor allows his attractive young wife, Noemi, to leave the party early in Toni's company. When a local gossip informs the doctor that Toni is considered to be one of the most virile men in town, the doctor hurries home to discover that the gossip spoke the truth. To preserve appearances he makes the lovers promise to keep the adultery secret. Elsewhere in Treviso, the henpecked Osvaldo Bisigato, a bank clerk, falls madly in love with a cafe cashier, Milena Zulian, and eventually leaves home to join her. But the jealous husbands in the town unite with Osvaldo's wife, and the lovers lose their jobs. When they are arrested as adulterers, Milena leaves town and Osvaldo is confined in a sanitarium after attempting suicide. Later, as Osvaldo returns to his nagging wife, he plugs his ears with cotton. During an afternoon of shopping in town, Alda Cristofoletto, a young farm girl, is seduced by a number of the town's principal citizens, who do not realize that she is under age. When she tells her father of her adventure, he files charges against the prominent men. A collection is quickly taken; the father is paid off with the help of the wife of one of the men; and the community's "honor" is saved. *Physicians. Bank clerks. Cashiers. Infidelity. Hypocrisy. Appearances. Impotence. Bribery. Seduction. Suicide. Statutory rape. Treviso (Italy).*

Note: Rome opening: Feb 1966 as *Signore e signori.* Paris opening: Jun 1966 as *Ces messieurs dames;* running time: 90 min. Other French titles: *Belles dames, vilains messieurs; Mesdames et messieurs.*

THE BIRTH OF A NATION (Reissue)   F6.0420
Epoch Producing Corp. *Dist* Joseph Brenner Associates. 11 Mar **1970** [Rosslyn, Virginia, opening]. Sd eff & mus score; b&w. 35mm. 105 min. *MPAA rating G.*

Note: Originally released in silent version in 1915; length: 11,586 ft. A new sound effects track and titles are used in this version.

THE BIRTH OF JUDO (Japan)   F6.0421
Shochiku Co. *Dist* Shochiku Films of America. 9 Jul **1965** [Los Angeles showing]. Sd; col. 35mm. [Feature film, length unknown.]
Dir-Writ Kunio Watanabe. *Story* Tsuneo Tomita. *Photog* Takeo Kawarazaki. *Art Dir* Seiichi Toriizuka. *Mus* Eiichi Yamada.

Cast: Shoichi Hirai *(Shogoro Yano),* Yoko Matsuyama *(Suga Yano),* Shintaro Kuraoka *(Yujiro Toda),* Ryohei Uchida *(Gennosuke Egaki),* Tetsuro Tamba *(Shuzo Izawa).*

Drama. In late 19th-century Japan, Shogoro Yano, a young student of jujitsu, attempts unsuccessfully to unite the competing schools of the newest form of martial arts. His sister, Suga, is engaged to the son of Viscount Seikanji, an influential politician who has helped Yano obtain a position at the Imperial Academy. The viscount, opposed to jujitsu, orders Yano to give it up or leave the university. Yano refuses to abandon his study of jujitsu, and the viscount cancels his son's engagement with Suga. A rich businessman attempts to arrange a marriage with the viscount's son for his daughter, Sanae, a friend of both Suga and Yano, but Sanae refuses to go through with the marriage, and she offers her apologies to Suga and Yano. While on an errand, Toda, Yano's only disciple, is attacked and nearly killed by Kakefuda, an undisciplined student of jujitsu. Later, when an anonymous politician offers a new gymnasium to anyone who can beat Yano in a match, Toda substitutes for his teacher and gains revenge by overcoming Kakefuda. Yano, who has gained two more followers, decides to develop a purer form of jujitsu and name it judo, or "the way of nature." *Nobility. Students. Politicians. Businessmen. Brother-sister relationship. Marriage—Arranged. Wealth. Revenge. Jujitsu. Judo. Duels.*

Note: Released in Japan in Mar 1965 as *Yawara sempu.*

BIRTH OF TRIPLETS   F6.0422
Alexander Enterprises. 26 Aug **1964** [Cincinnati, Ohio, opening]. Sd; col. 35mm. [Feature film, length unknown.]
Prod Claude Alexander.

Documentary. No information about the precise nature of this film has been found except that actual scenes of five different births are shown. *Triplets. Childbirth.*

Note: Also known as *The Story of Birth* and *The Wondrous Story of Birth.*

THE BIRTHDAY PARTY (Great Britain)   F6.0423
Palomar Pictures International. *Dist* Continental Distributing, Inc. 9 Dec **1968** [New York opening]. Sd; col (Technicolor). 35mm. 123 min. *MPAA rating G.*

Prod Max J. Rosenberg, Milton Subotsky. *Exec Prod* Edgar J. Scherick. *Dir* William Friedkin. *Screenplay* Harold Pinter. *Photog* Denys Coop. *Prod Dsgn* Edward Marshall. *Film Ed* Antony Gibbs. *Sd* Norman Bolland. *Asst Dir* Andrew Grieve. *Prod Mgr* Teresa Bolland.

Cast: Robert Shaw *(Stanley Weber),* Patrick Magee *(Shamus McCann),* Dandy Nichols *(Meg Bowles),* Sydney Tafler *(Nat Goldberg),* Moultrie Kelsall *(Petey Bowles),* Helen Fraser *(Lulu).*

Drama. Source: Harold Pinter, *The Birthday Party* (London opening: 19 May 1958). Meg and Petey Bowles are the slovenly proprietors of a rundown seaside boardinghouse. Their only boarder is Stanley, an unshaven and mysterious nonconformist. Prior to moving in a year or so ago, he may have been a concert pianist, or perhaps a deserter from a criminal organization. One day two strangers—urbane and jovial Nat Goldberg and grim and servile Shamus McCann—arrive at the boardinghouse and easily insinuate themselves into Meg's good graces by asking for one of her "splendid accommodations." Their apparent purpose is to give Stanley a birthday party and to bring him back to the underworld organization. Goldberg and McCann manage to catch Stanley alone, and they interrogate him until he retaliates by kicking Goldberg in the groin. Despite Stanley's protests that it is not his birthday, Meg insists that the party be held that evening with Lulu, a neighborhood woman, as the only guest. As the evening progresses and the guests play a wild game of blind man's buff, Stanley gradually weakens in his resistance to the threatening intimations of the two strangers. The party finally ends when Stanley steps on Meg's gift, a toy drum, and reduces the inebriated Meg to a state of mournful reverie. The next morning as Meg and Petey go about their chores, Goldberg and McCann take Stanley, now verging on a mental breakdown, away to meet an unknown fate. *Landladies. Landlords. Nonconformists. Gangsters. Drunkenness. Boardinghouses. Birthdays.*

Note: Released in Great Britain in 1970; running time: 124 min.

BIRTHDAY PARTY   F6.0424
28 Aug **1970** [Los Angeles showing]. Sd; col. 16mm? [Feature length assumed.]
Cast: Xis, Lars.

Sex film. No information about the precise nature of this film has been found. *Sexuality.*

BIRTHPLACE OF THE HOOTENANNY see GREENWICH VILLAGE STORY

BIRUMA NO TATEGOTO see THE BURMESE HARP

BIS ZUM ENDE ALLER TAGE see GIRL FROM HONG KONG

LA BISBETICA DOMATA see THE TAMING OF THE SHREW

THE BITE (Japan)   F6.0425
Dist Olympic International Films. ca **1965.** Sd; b&w. 35mm. 62 min. *Dir* Kan Mukai.

Melodrama. A wealthy socialite relieves her boredom by hiring a handsome slum youth to seduce young girls, while she watches with her friends through a two-way mirror. The youth, kept in a state of humiliating dependency, is forced to bring lesbians and sadists to the secret room. Finally, he is joined by the voyeur herself. In a burst of bitter defiance, he rapes the woman's 12-year-old daughter, while the mother watches, horrified, through the mirror. *Socialites. Prostitutes. Voyeurism. Seduction. Poverty. Sadomasochism. Lesbianism. Revenge. Rape.*

Note: Original title and release undetermined. Probably altered for U. S. release.

THE BIZARRE ONES   F6.0426
Dist Sam Lake Enterprises. Oct **1968** [New York opening]. Sd; b&w. 35mm. 73 min.
A Sam Lake Production. *Dir-Writ* Ron Sullivan.

Cast: Claire Eclaire, Cherie Winters, Tracy Lee, Judy Caine, Marianne Lord.

Melodrama. Diedra, a voluptuous blonde, picks up a hitchhiker and seduces him in her car. She leaves him in chains, without his pants, and continues driving to an isolated farmhouse. There she comes upon a sadist torturing a blindfolded girl. When he leaves the room to help another man start an electric sex machine, Diedra begins to make love with his victim. Enraged, the sadist enlists the help of the other inhabitants to tie Diedra to the roof of her car. As the group drives off to torture a new victim, the hitchhiker arrives at the farmhouse. He finds a gun and sets out to kill Diedra. *Hitchhikers. Sadism. Torture. Seduction. Lesbianism. Murder. Bisexuality. Sex aids.*

BIZARRO *see* MONDO BIZARRO

BLACK ANGELS   F6.0427

Merrick International Pictures. 14 Oct **1970** [Chicago opening]. Sd; col (print by Movielab). 35mm. 92 min. *MPAA rating* R.

Prod Leo Rivers. *Exec Prod* Laurence Merrick. *Assoc Prod* A. J. Krupsaw. *Dir-Writ* Laurence Merrick. *Dir Photog* Laurence Merrick. *Camera* Paul Hipp. *Asst Camera* Henning Schellerup. *Main Titl* Photo Effex. *Film Ed* Clancy Syrko. *Mus Dir* Lou Peralta. *Song:* "What's Going On" *Comp by* Bobby Stevens. *Sung by* Tom Markham. *Song:* "What You Don't Know Won't Hurt You Is a Lie" *Comp & Sung by* Bobby Stevens. *Song:* "Cigarettes" *Comp & Sung by* Smokey Roberds. *Songs:* "Black Angel," "Confrontation" *Comp & Sung by* Morgan Cavett. *Song:* "Beautiful" *Comp & Sung by* Jack Bedient. *Song:* "Multileveller Conversational Tightrope Walking Shoes" *Comp & Perf by* Judy Fine. *Songs:* "Military Disgust," "Everything Is Alright" *Perf by* Mad Dog. *Song:* "Lord Give Us Peace" *Comp & Perf by* Alan Brackett. *Sd* Ted Botkin. *Cont* Jill Murphy. *Makeup* Gerald Sutcliffe. *Eff Ed* Dan Finnerty. *Stunts* George Baudin.

Cast: Des Roberts *(Chainer)*, John King, III *(Johnny Reb)*, Linda Jackson *(Jackie)*, James Young-El *(Jimmy)*, Clancy Syrko *(Lieutenant Harper)*, Beverly Gardner *(Wallflower)*, James Whitworth *(Big Jim)*, John Donovan *(Frenchy)*, Gene Stowell *(Fixer)*, Miller Pettit *(One-Eye)*, Channon Scot *(Jaw-Bone)*, Robert Johnson *(Knifer)*, Frank Donato *(Clyde)*, Sumner Spector *(Daddy)*, The Choppers Gang *(themselves)*, Harry Hampton *(drunk)*, Irma Smith *(waitress)*, Charlie James, Nate White *(Black Panthers)*, Fabian Cativiela *(Machetti)*, Joanne Strum, Margaret Kingman *(club girls)*, Bill Hooks *(Knifer's right hand)*, Sandy Friedberg *(singer)*, Kent Wyatt *(chauffeur)*, Adam Lahav *(boy on bike)*.

Melodrama. For years, two motorcycle gangs—the white Serpents and the black Choppers—have been locked in fierce rivalry, united only by their mutual hatred for a local police officer, Lieutenant Harper, who would like to see the two groups destroy each other. A newly-initiated Chopper is killed in a fight with Chainer, the leader of the Serpents, and Harper's wish moves closer to becoming a reality. After the Serpents accept new biker Johnny Reb into their ranks, they ride into town to mete out punishment to a renegade member. There Chainer is ambushed by four Choppers, but Johnny Red mysteriously appears and saves his life. Returning to their hideout, the gang launches a wild party, which Johnny Reb further enlivens by passing out illegal pills. As the gang eventually becomes drowsy and vulnerable from the pills' aftereffects, one of the cyclists, Frenchy, discovers that Johnny Reb is actually a black Chopper passing for white. Before Frenchy can warn the others, however, Johnny Reb stabs him to death and then signals the Choppers to attack. The two evenly matched gangs massacre each other while Lieutenant Harper happily observes the bloodbath from a distant hilltop. *Motorcycle gangs. Negroes. Police. Traitors. Gang wars. Imposture. Murder. Drugs.*

Note: Filmed in California.

BLACK AUTUMN *see* VIOLENT MIDNIGHT

THE BLACK CAT   F6.0428

Falcon International Corp. *Dist* Hemisphere Pictures. May **1966**. Sd; b&w. 35mm. 73 min. [Cut from 77 min.]

Prod Patrick Sims. *Dir–Screenplay* Harold Hoffman. *Photog* Walter Schenk. *Art Dir* Robert Dracub. *Film Ed* Charles Schelling. *Sp Eff* Manuel De Aumente.

Cast: Robert Frost *(Lew)*, Robyn Baker *(Diana)*, Sadie French *(Lillith)*, Scotty McKay, George Russell, Tommie Russell.

Horror film. Source: Edgar Allan Poe, "The Black Cat," in *United States Saturday Post* (19 Aug 1843). On their first wedding anniversary, Diana gives Lew a black cat to add to his menagerie. Lew comes to believe that the cat is a reincarnation of his hated father, and one day, after a drinking bout, he gouges out one of its eyes. Lew eventually kills the cat, and that night the house burns down. Learning that the house was not insured, Lew goes berserk and is sent to a sanitarium for psychiatric care. Upon his release, he returns to Diana and brings home a stray black cat. Diana notices that this cat also has a bad eye, and Lew begins to have nightmares. Fearing that he is being haunted by it, Lew attacks the cat but accidentally kills Diana. Lew walls up her body in the cellar, but the former housekeeper, Lillith, alerts the police, who arrive and find nothing until a meow is heard coming from behind the wall. The police tear it down and find Diana's body and the live cat. Lew escapes in his car, sees a black cat in the road, and is killed when he crashes to avoid the animal. *Housekeepers. Police. Wedding anniversaries. Drunkenness. Superstition. Insanity. Reincarnation. Mutilation. Manslaughter. Sanitariums. Automobile accidents. Fires. Cats.*

Note: Filmed on location in Dallas and Fort Worth, Texas.

THE BLACK CAT *see* KURONEKO

THE BLACK DOOR *see* THE BRAIN THAT WOULDN'T DIE

THE BLACK DUKE (Italy/Spain)   F6.0429

Rodes Cinematografica–Hispamer Films. *Dist* Production Releasing Corp., Eldorado Pictures International. Feb **1964** [New York showing]. Sd; col (Eastman Color). 35mm. 105 min. [Also reviewed at 90 min.]

Pres by East/West Films. *Prod* Tullio Bruschi. *Dir* Pino Mercanti. *Story & Screenplay* Mario Amendola. *Photog* Antonio Macasoli. *Art Dir* Teddy Villalba, Mario Montori. *Film Ed* Iolanda Benvenuti, Rosa Graceli-Salgado. *Mus* Giorgio Fabor. *Prod Supv* Angel Rosson.

Cast: Cameron Mitchell *(Cesare Borgia)*, Gloria Milland *(Caterina Sforza)*, Conrado Sanmartín, Franco Fantasia, Robert Dean, Dina De Santis, Maria Grazia Spina, Gloria Osuna, Rafael Cores.

Historical melodrama. Cesare Borgia, a Roman duke famous for his military conquests and for his power over women, has seized territories in all parts of Italy at the beginning of the 16th century. Caterina Sforza, who controls the fortress of Forlì, attempts to assassinate the duke in order to retain the independence of her territory. She gains the loyalty of the duke's most trusted lieutenant and directs him to have Borgia murdered, but Borgia uncovers the plot. In another attempt to eliminate her enemy, Caterina sends a beautiful woman named Genevieve to the duke's palace to romance and then poison him. Borgia's charm overcomes the young woman, however, and she drinks the poison herself to save his life. Borgia learns from the woman's dying confession that his lieutenant is conspiring to murder him. The lieutenant flees to Forlì, and the duke and his forces follow. They seize the fortress, and Borgia kills the traitor. When Caterina finally confronts Borgia, she agrees to return to Rome with the charming duke—not as a captive but as his guest. *Nobility. Traitors. Assassination. Poisoning. Conspiracy. The Renaissance. Rome. Forlì. Cesare Borgia. Caterina Sforza.*

Note: Released in Italy in 1963 as *Il duca nero*; running time: 103 min; opened in Madrid in Mar 1963 as *El duque negro*.

BLACK FOX   F6.0430

Image Productions–Animated Productions–Al Stahl–LeVien International Productions. *Dist* Capri Films, Arthur Steloff, Astor Pictures, Heritage International. Dec **1962** [Los Angeles showing]. Sd; b&w. 35mm. 89 min.

Prod-Dir-Writ Louis Clyde Stoumen. *Exec Prod* Jack LeVien. *Assoc Prod* Don Devlin. *Anim Supv* Al Stahl. *Film Ed* Kenn Collins, Mark Wortreich. *Mus Comp & Cond* Ezra Laderman. *Played by* New York Chamber Orchestra, Julliard String Quartet. *Sd* Richard Vorisek. *Prod Supv* Richard Kaplan. *Prod Asst* Angela Grieg Stoumen.

Cast: Marlene Dietrich *(Narrator)*.

Documentary. Based in part on: Johann Wolfgang von Goethe, *Reineke Fuchs* (1794). This documentary intertwines the story of Reynard the Fox, the symbol of political ruthlessness adapted by Goethe from a medieval fable, and the life of Adolf Hitler. As Reynard, through guile and demagogy, uses every psychological ruse and gimmick to persuade the other animals of his righteousness and his right to be their leader, so Hitler is shown from his beginnings as a cunning conspirator and tremendously effective orator playing on the bitterness and passions of the defeated German people. Paralleling the newsreel shots of Hitler's early rise to power are the surrealistic drawings Doré made for Dante's *Inferno* and Kaulbach's 19th-century illustrations for Goethe's *Reynard the Fox*. Hitler's accession to the German chancellorship under von Hindenburg, his maneuverings vis-à-vis Communism both as an enemy and an ally, and his almost unparelleled indulgence in savagery toward helpless victims are given an ironic counterpoint in the story of Reynard's dealings with the animal community. Hitler's destructive and self-destructive cataclysmic career is seen through World War II and the Götterdämmerung of his death in a Berlin bunker, and an estimate of his impact on modern civilization is symbolically represented. *Dictators. Germans. Nazism. Communism. Militarism. Germany—History—Third Reich. World War II. Berlin. Adolf Hitler. Paul von Hindenburg. "Reynard the Fox."*

Note: In addition to Paul Gustave Doré's illustrations from Dante's *Inferno* and Wilhelm von Kaulbach's etchings from Goethe's *Reineke Fuchs*, the film makes use of drawings of Byron Goto, Pablo Picasso, and George Grosz. Also known as *The Black Fox*. Subtitled as *The True Story of Adolf Hitler*.

BLACK GIRL (France/Senegal)   F6.0431

Les Actualités Françaises–Les Films Domirêve. *Dist* New Yorker Films. Jan **1969**. Sd; b&w. 35mm. 60 min.

Dir-Writ Ousmane Sembene. *Photog* Christian Lacoste. *Asst* Pathé Diop. *Film Ed* André Gaudier. *Asst Dir* Ibrahima Barro, Pathé Diop. *Prod Mgr* André Zwobada.

Cast: Mbissine Thérèse Diop *(The Maid)*, Anne-Marie Jelinck *(Madame)*, Momar Nar Sene *(young man)*, Robert Fontaine *(Master)*, Ibrahima Boy *(boy with mask)*, Bernard Delbard, Nicole Donati, Raymond Lemery, Suzanne

Lemery *(guests)*.

Voices: Toto Bissainthe, Robert Marcy, Sophie LeClerc.

Drama. Source: Ousmane Sembene, *Voltaïque* (Paris, 1962). In Dakar, a young black girl is hired by a vacationing European couple to work for them as a governess in Antibes. Upon arriving in her new surroundings, the girl discovers that the couple's children are away at school, and she is reduced to being nothing more than their maid. Restricted to cooking and cleaning, she begins to think of herself as a slave, and her hostility is increased by the woman's overbearing and patronizing manner. Although the man is more considerate, he lacks the understanding necessary to comprehend that the young girl is developing racist tendencies. Gradually becoming more and more despondent, the girl retreats into a state of despair that leads to her suicide. When the man returns her few pitiful belongings to Senegal, he suddenly becomes frightened and uneasy while in the presence of her people. *Governesses. Housemaids. Negroes. Racism. Social classes. Suicide. Employment—Women. Employer-employee relations. Antibes. Dakar.*

Note: Filmed in southern France and Dakar, Senegal. Opened in Paris in Apr 1967 as *La noire de ...* and in Senegal in Feb 1969; running time: 70 min.

BLACK GOLD   F6.0432

Warner Bros. Pictures. Jun **1963** [c1 Jun 1963; LP29444]. Sd; b&w. 35mm. 99 min.

Prod Jim Barnett. *Dir* Leslie H. Martinson. *Screenplay* Bob Duncan, Wanda Duncan. *Photog* Harold Stine. *Art Dir* William Campbell, art dir. *Set Decor* William Stevens. *Film Ed* Leo H. Shreve. *Mus* Howard Jackson. *Sd* Samuel F. Goode. *Asst Dir* Claude Binyon, Jr. *Makeup* Gordon Bau. *Hairstyles* Jean Burt Reilly.

Cast: Philip Carey *(Frank McCandless)*, Diane McBain *(Ann Evans)*, James Best *(Jericho Larkin)*, Fay Spain *(Julie)*, Claude Akins *(Chick Carrington)*, William Phipps *(Albert Mailer)*, Dub Taylor *(Doc)*, Ken Mayer *(Felker)*, Iron-Eyes Cody *(Charlie Two-Bits)*, Vincent Barbi *(Klein)*, Rusty Wescoatt *(Wilkins)*.

Melodrama. Source: Harry Whittington, "Wyoming Wildcatters" (a short story; publication undetermined). In the 1920's, Frank McCandless crashlands his plane on the Oklahoma farm run by Ann Evans, whose father was killed in an oil field accident. Frank, attracted to Ann, realizes the land is oil rich, so he sells his plane and leases the property for drilling. With additional money borrowed from Julie, the girl friend of his long-time buddy, Jericho, they begin drilling, but the oil fails to appear. Julie, a nightclub singer, is tired of waiting for Jericho to marry her and weds Frank's enemy and ex-employer, Chick Carrington, a ruthless oil promoter who needs a wife to further his political ambitions. When Jericho and Frank try for another strike, Carrington tries to dynamite their equipment, but Frank brings the sheriff and forces Carrington to use the explosive to shoot the well. The black gold gushes forth, and Ann joins Frank in his search for new oil fields. *Farmers. Air pilots. Oilmen. Singers. Sheriffs. Marriage. Sabotage. Oil fields. Oil wells. Explosives. Oklahoma. Airplane accidents.*

BLACK IS BEAUTIFUL   F6.0433

Institute for Adult Education. 15 Apr **1970** [Los Angeles opening]. Sd; b&w. 35mm. 60 min.

Documentary. The film is a "documentary" on black sexuality. The narrator asserts that Africans possess a special sexual prowess and discusses African sexual and marriage customs. A Los Angeles couple demonstrate a number of positions of sexual intercourse, including oral intercourse, reputedly practiced among various African tribes. *Negroes. Africans. Sexual practices. Rites and ceremonies. Oral sex. Tribal life. Los Angeles.*

Note: Also known as *Africanus Sexualis*.

THE BLACK KLANSMAN   F6.0434

SGS Productions. *Dist* U. S. Films. 25 May **1966** [Detroit opening]. Sd; b&w. 35mm. 88 min.

Pres by Joe Solomon. *Prod-Dir* Ted V. Mikels. *Exec Prod* Joe Solomon. *Screenplay* John T. Wilson, Arthur Names. *Cinematog* Robert Caramico. *Art Dir* Wally Moon. *Film Ed* Ted V. Mikels. *Mus Score* Jaime Mendoza-Nava. *Titl Song* Tony Harris. *Sd* Austin McKinney. *Asst Dir* Arthur Names. *Wardrobe* Vana Carroll. *Makeup* Byrd Holland.

Cast: Richard Gilden *(Jerry Ellsworth)*, Rima Kutner *(Andrea)*, Harry Lovejoy *(Rook)*, Max Julien *(Raymond)*, Jackie Deslonde *(Farley)*, Jimmy Mack *(Lonnie)*, Maureen Gaffney *(Carole Ann)*, William McLennan *(Wallace)*, Gino De Agustino *(Sawyer)*, Tex Armstrong *(Jenkins)*, Byrd Holland *(Buckley)*, Whitman Mayo *(Alex)*, Frances Williams *(Ellis Madison)*, Ray Dannis *(Sloane)*.

Melodrama. Widower Jerry Ellsworth, a light-skinned Negro nightclub entertainer living in Los Angeles, learns that his 6-year-old daughter has been killed in a Ku Klux Klan church bombing in Alabama. In order to track down

the murderer, Jerry leaves behind his white mistress, Andrea, and goes to Alabama. Passing for white, he joins the Klan at the invitation of the local Klan leader, Rook. Meanwhile, the brother of another bombing victim hires two gangsters from Harlem to deal with the Klansmen. The pair attack a Klan rally, shooting several people. Jerry, who has been having an affair with Rook's daughter, learns that Andrea has arrived from Los Angeles with Lonnie, a Negro friend, to look for him. The new arrivals are quickly seized by the sheriff, who plans to lynch them along with the New York gangsters. The gangsters are hanged, but Jerry rescues Andrea and Lonnie. He shoots Rook in self-defense, revealing the Klan leader's responsibility for his daughter's death. The town's white mayor, a changed man, agrees to work for racial harmony, and Jerry decides to remain in Alabama among his people. *Entertainers. Negroes. Mistresses. Sheriffs. Mayors. Gangsters. Widowers. Racism. Lynching. Murder. Miscegenation. Imposture. Revenge. Churches. Bombs. Los Angeles. Alabama. Ku Klux Klan.*

Note: Also known as *I Crossed the Color Line*.

BLACK LIKE ME   F6.0435

Julius Tannenbaum–Hilltop Productions. *Dist* Continental Distributing, Inc. 20 May **1964** [New York opening]. Sd; b&w. 35mm. 107 min.

Pres by Victor Weingarten. *Prod* Julius Tannenbaum. *Dir* Carl Lerner. *Screenplay* Gerda Lerner, Carl Lerner. *Photog* Victor Lukens, Henry Mueller, II. *Titl Dsgn* Everett Aison. *Film Ed* Lora Hays. *Mus Comp & Cond* Meyer Kupferman. *Sd* Stanley Kasper. *Sd Re-rec* Richard Vorisek. *Asst Dir* Edward Wells. *Asst to the Prod* Bernard Cherin. *Asst to the Dir* John G. Avildsen. *Tech Dir* Tony La Marca. *Makeup* Herman Buchman.

Cast: James Whitmore *(John Finley Horton)*, Clifton James *(Eli Carr)*, Lenka Peterson *(Lucy Horton)*, Roscoe Lee Browne *(Christopher)*, Sorrell Booke *(Dr. Jackson)*, Stanley Brock *(salesman)*, Will Geer *(farmer)*, Robert Gerringer *(Ed Saunders)*, Eva Jessye *(Mrs. Townsend)*, P. J. Sidney *(Frank Newcomb)*, Al Freeman, Jr. *(Tom Newcomb)*, Dan Priest *(bus driver)*, Walter Mason *(Mason)*, John Marriott *(Hodges)*, Richard Ward *(Burt Wilson)*, David Huddleston *(young man in car)*, Thelma Oliver *(Georgie)*, Billie Allen *(Vertell)*, Llewellyn B. Skinner *(Stretch)*, Matt Clark *(hoodlum)*, Sarah Cunningham *(Mary Saunders)*, Alan Bergmann *(Charles Maynard)*, Ralph Dunn *(priest)*.

Drama. Source: John Howard Griffin, *Black Like Me* (Boston, 1961). John Finley Horton, a white Southern newspaperman, darkens his skin and begins to live as a black while writing a series of magazine articles about his experiences. Horton has a number of harrowing encounters, both with whites and blacks, as he travels from town to town in his disguise. His treatment brings him close to hysteria, and he seeks temporary refuge with some white friends before resuming his masquerade. One of Horton's last encounters is with black Frank Newcomb and his son Tom. Frank believes integration will be accomplished only through love, but Tom feels differently and is cynical about Horton's articles and outraged when he learns that Horton is really white. It is pointed out that Horton, unlike a real Negro, can always shed his blackness. Horton returns to his own world unsure if his articles had any beneficial effect, but with the satisfaction of having told the story. *Newspapermen. Negroes. Imposture. Racial prejudice. Race relations. United States—South.*

Note: Location scenes filmed in Maryland, Virginia, Washington, D. C., and the west coast of Florida. Working title: *No Man Walks Alone*.

BLACK LIZARD (Japan)   F6.0436

Shochiku Co. Jul **1969** [Los Angeles showing]. Sd; col (Eastmancolor). 35mm (Shochiku GrandScope). 86 min.

Dir Kinji Fukasaku. *Screenplay* Masashige Narusawa. *Adapt* Yukio Mishima. *Story* Rampo Edogawa. *Photog* Hiroshi Dowaki. *Art Dir* Kyohei Morita. Isao Tomita.

Cast: Akihiro Maruyama *(Black Lizard)*, Isao Kimura *(Detective Akechi)*, Junya Usami *(jeweler)*, Kikko Matsuoka *(Sanae)*, Toshiko Kobayashi *(Hina)*, Yukio Mishima, Tetsuro Tamba.

Crime melodrama. The Black Lizard, a skillful woman jewel thief, kidnaps Sanae, the daughter of a jewel merchant in charge of the valuable Star of Egypt diamond. Famed detective Akechi frees the girl, but the Lizard kidnaps her again and demands the Star of Egypt as ransom. After the payment is made, the Lizard decides to keep the girl and add her to her collection of living statues. Akechi makes a final attempt to rescue Sanae, but, to all appearances, he is killed. As the Lizard sets off for her island hideaway, she discovers that Sanae is really a substituted double and that Matsu, the Lizard's confidant, is Akechi in disguise. Cornered, the Lizard takes poison and as she dies in the detective's arms, both realize they have come to love each other. *Thieves. Detectives. Diamond merchants. Hostages. Domestics. Kidnaping. Disguise. Suicide. Poisoning. Diamonds. Islands.*

Note: Released in Japan in Aug 1968 as *Kurotokage*.

BLACK LOVE—WHITE LOVE see SWEET LOVE, BITTER

BLACK NYLONS see SPIKED HEELS AND BLACK NYLONS

BLACK ON WHITE (Italy) F6.0437

Lion Film. *Dist* Audubon Films. 9 Oct **1969** [New York opening]. Sd; col (Eastman) with b&w seq. 35mm. 89 min. *MPAA rating X.*

Pres by Radley Metzger. *Prod-Dir-Story* Tinto Brass. *Screenplay* Tinto Brass, Franco Longo. *Photog* Silvano Ippoliti. *Art Dir* Peter Murray. *Film Ed* Tinto Brass. *Mus* Freedom. *Mus Supv* Vittorio Gelmetti. *Asst Dir* Alan Sekers, Giorgio Patrono, Sheila Rubin. *Prod Mgr* Marcello Bollero.

Cast: Anita Sanders *(Barbara, the girl)*, Terry Carter *(The Stranger [young Negro])*, Nino Segurini *(Paolo, the lover)*, Umberto Di Grazia, Freedom.

Melodrama. Barbara, an Italian woman with her husband in London, tours the city alone and notices a handsome, young Negro following her. His presence sparks a series of fantasies showing her sexual frustrations, her anxieties, and her prejudices. She vividly imagines concentration camps, war atrocities, an eyeball being slit by a razor, rape, and having sex with strangers. She finally confronts the stranger and makes love with him in Hyde Park. Her husband drives up and she joins him, her inhibitions resolved. *Negroes. Strangers. Racial prejudice. Miscegenation. Inhibition. Rape. War crimes. London. London—Hyde Park. Fantasy.*

Note: Location scenes filmed in London. Released in Italy in 1969 as *Nero su bianco.* This film is also known as *The Artful Penetration; The Artful Penetration of Barbara; Shameful;* and *Attraction.*

BLACK PIT OF DR. M (Mexico) F6.0438

Alameda Films. *Dist* United Producers Releasing Organization, Joseph Brenner Associates. 11 Oct **1961** [Los Angeles opening; c8 Apr 1961; LP19603]. Sd; b&w. 35mm. 71 min.

Prod Alfred Ripstein, Jr. *Dir* Fernando Méndez. *Story-Adapt* Ramón Obón. *Photog* Victor Herrera. *Scenery* Gunther Gerszo. *Film Ed* Charles Kimball. *Asst Film Ed* George Azcarate. *Mus Dir* Gustavo César Carrión. *Sd* Rodolfo Solís. *Asst Dir* A. Fernandez. *Prod Mgr* Carl Ventimillia. *Prod Ch* Jorge Cardena.

Cast: Rafael Bertrand *(Dr. Harrison Aldaman)*, Gastón Santos *(Dr. Masali)*, Mapy Cortés *(Patricia Aldaman)*, Carlos Ancira *(Edward Jameson)*, Carolina Barret, Beatriz Aguirre, Luis Aragón, Antonio Raxell, Lupe Carriles.

Horror film. Two physicians who work in an insane asylum make a pact. On his deathbed Dr. Aldaman is reminded by Dr. Masali that according to the pact, the first to die must return and help the other learn the secret of what is beyond death and then return him to life. Through a medium, Masali invokes Aldaman's spirit and receives a clue: 3 months hence a door will close and there will be no turning back. Aldaman's daughter, Patricia, believes that her father died when she was a small child, but a stranger appears and tells her that her father actually abandoned her mother when she was a baby and has recently died, leaving her an inheritance. He gives her a key to take to Masali, who tells her that the stranger she saw was actually her father. Masali uses the key to open a chest belonging to Aldaman, containing Patricia's birth certificate, some jewels, and a dagger. While Patricia is at the asylum, she sees a young intern, Edward Jameson; each has dreamed of the other, though they have never met. Patricia agrees to stay at the asylum and work as a nurse in order to be with Edward. Meanwhile, Elmer, an assistant, is badly disfigured when a violent patient throws acid in his face. Elmer returns and murders the patient with the dagger from the chest. Dr. Masali is found locked in the room with the body and convicted of the crime. Thinking that this is all a part of Aldaman's plan, Masali waits to be rescued. Elmer, however, dies while attempting to deliver a written confession. As Masali is executed, Elmer's body rises from the grave. Dr. Gonzalez, who had tried to dissuade Masali from probing the secrets of the next world, realizes that Masali has returned to life in Elmer's body, complete with scarred face. The resurrected "Dr. M" confesses to Gonzalez that he is madly in love with Patricia, and he tries to disfigure her with acid so that he will be the only one to love her. Edward intervenes, and as they fight, he throws acid on Dr. M, who catches fire and dies. *Physicians. Seances. Ghosts. Supernatural. Murder. Disfiguration. Desertion. Inheritance. Capital punishment. Reviviscence. Insane asylums. Dreams.*

Note: Produced in Mexico in 1958 as *Misterios de ultratumba.* Released in the United States in May 1959 in the original language version by Clasa-Mohme, Inc.

BLACK RAINBOW F6.0439

Dist Michael Zuckerman. 2 Nov **1966** [New York opening]. Si?; b&w. 16mm. 60 min.

Dir Michael Zuckerman. No information about the precise nature of this film has been found.

BLACK REVENGE see SCORPIO '70

BLACK ROOTS F6.0440

Impact Films. 24 Sep **1970** [New York opening]. Sd; col. 16mm. 61 min.

Prod-Dir Lionel Rogosin. *Photog* Robert Wagoner. *Song:* "In This Land" sung by Gary Davis. *Mus Cons* Alan Lomax, Anna Lomax, Shunmagun A. Pillay.

Featuring: Frederick D. Kirkpatrick, Gary Davis, Jim Collier, Larry Johnson, actor, Wende Smith, Florynce Kennedy.

Documentary. As black leaders recall individual incidents of racial oppression, mostly in the South, black musicians provide blues accompaniment. Included is footage of urban street life. *Negroes. Musicians. Racism. Urban life. United States—South.*

BLACK ROSE (Japan) F6.0441

Shochiku Co. *Dist* Shochiku Films of America. Jul **1969** [Los Angeles showing]. Sd; col (Eastmancolor). 35mm (Shochiku GrandScope). 90 min.

Dir Kinji Fukasaku. *Screenplay* Hiroo Matsuda, Kinji Fukasaku. *Photog* Ko Kawamata. *Art Dir* Masao Kumagi. *Mus* Hajime Kaburagi.

Cast: Akihiro Maruyama *(Ryuko)*, Eitaro Ozawa *(Kyohei)*, Masakazu Tamura *(Wataru)*, Ayako Hosho *(Kyohei's wife)*.

Crime melodrama. Source: Yukio Mishima, *Kurobara no yakata* (a play; production undetermined). Kyohei, owner of the private club "Black Rose," hires Ryuko, a mysterious woman whose popularity immediately increases the club's business. Several men claiming to be Ryuko's lovers appear, only to meet violent and inexplicable deaths. Kyohei's obsessive love for Ryuko is complicated by the return of his gangster son, Wataru, who also falls under the mysterious woman's spell. Persuading Ryuko to leave with him, Wataru plans a robbery to raise the needed expenses and is wounded during the attempt. Kyohei pleads with his son to be reasonable, but to no avail. As Wataru and Ryuko set out to sea in a motorboat, they collide with a ship and both are drowned. Kyohei is left alone in his club. *Nightclub owners. Gangsters. Obsession. Robbery. Filial relations. Motorboats. Nightclubs.*

Note: Released in Japan in Jan 1969 as *Kurobara no yakata.*

BLACK SABBATH (United States/France/Italy) F6.0442

Emmepi Cinematografica-Société Cinématographique Lyre-Galatea-American International Pictures. *Dist* American International Pictures. 6 May **1964** [Detroit opening; c6 May 1964; LP28250]. Sd; col (PathéColor). 35mm. 99 min. [Copyright length: 96 min.]

Pres by James H. Nicholson, Samuel Z. Arkoff. *Assoc Prod* Salvatore Billitteri. *Dir* Mario Bava. *Screenplay* Marcello Fondato. *Screenplay Collab* (see note) Alberto Bevilacqua, Mario Bava, Ugo Guerra. *Dir Photog* Ubaldo Terzano. *Art Dir* Giorgio Giovannini. *Set Dresser* Riccardo Domenici. *Film Ed* Mario Serandrei. *English Vers Mus* Les Baxter. *Mus Coörd* Al Simms. *Italian Vers Mus* Roberto Nicolosi. *Sd* Titra Sound Corp. *Sd Ed* Al Bird, Kay Rose, Ernest Reichert. *Mus Ed* Eve Newman. *Prod Mgr* Paolo Mercuri. *Cost Dsgn* Tina Grani. *Makeup* Otello Fava. *Hairdresser* Renata Magnanti.

Cast—"The Drop of Water": Jacqueline Pierreux *(Helen Corey)*, Milly Monti *(Miss Perkins' maid)*.

Cast—"The Telephone": Michèle Mercier *(Rosy)*, Lidia Alfonsi *(Mary)*, Gustavo De Nardo.

Cast—"The Wurdalak": Boris Karloff *(Gorca)*, Susy Andersen *(Sdenka)*, Mark Damon *(Vladimir D'Urfé)*, Glauco Onorato *(Giorgio)*, Rika Dialina *(Giorgio's wife)*, Massimo Righi *(Pietro)*.

Master of Ceremonies: Boris Karloff.

Horror film. Based on stories by: Anton Pavlovich Chekhov, F. G. Snyder and Leo Nikolaevich Tolstoy. THE DROP OF WATER: Nurse Helen Corey is called to the home of Madame Perkins, a clairvoyant, but finds the woman dead when she arrives. The nurse steals a diamond ring from the hand of the corpse and puts it on when she gets home. That night she becomes terrified at the sound of dripping water; finally Madame Perkins' ghost appears and forces her to strangle herself. The next day the police find Helen dead of an apparent heart attack, her finger bruised as if a ring had been wrenched from it. THE TELEPHONE: Rosy, a prostitute, receives threatening phone calls from a man she once betrayed and who is now dead. Terrified, she asks a friend, Mary, to stay with her, but the caller enters the house and kills Mary by mistake. Rosy then stabs the man, but the telephone rings again and his voice tells her that she can never kill him. THE WURDALAK: Vladimir, a young nobleman traveling in Eastern Europe, spends the night with a family who fear that their father, Gorca, has become a wurdalak, a species of vampire that thirsts for the blood of its loved ones. Gorca has killed Alibeck, a bandit and vampire, but neglected to drive a stake through his heart. Gorca kills his relatives one by one, and they, in turn, become vampires. Meanwhile, Vladimir and Gorca's daughter, Sdenka, fall in love; they escape to a convent but Gorca finds them and, unknown to Vladimir, transforms Sdenka into a wurdalak. When Vladimir kisses her, she kills him, turning him into a vampire. *Nurses. Vampires. Clairvoyants. Ghosts.*

Nobility. Prostitutes. Fear. Hallucinations. Revenge. Theft. Family life. Jewels. Telephone.

Note: Opened in Rome in Sep 1963 as *I tre volti della paura*, with episodes entitled "I wurdalak," "La goccia d'acqua," and "Il telefono"; running time: 100 min. Opened in Paris in Nov 1965 as *Les trois visages de la peur*; running time: 95 min. One Italian source credits Ugo Guerra as screenwriter. Jacqueline Pierreux is a pseudonym of Jacqueline Soussard. "The Drop of Water" is based on a story by Chekhov; "The Telephone" on a story by F. G. Snyder; and "The Wurdalak" on a story by Tolstoy. Copyright claimant: Alta Vista Productions.

THE BLACK SLEEP *see* **DR. CADMAN'S SECRET**

BLACK SPURS   F6.0443
A. C. Lyles Productions. *Dist* Paramount Pictures. 28 May **1965** [New York opening; c31 Dec 1964; LP30825]. Sd; col (Technicolor). 35mm (Techniscope). 81 min.
Prod A. C. Lyles. *Dir* R. G. Springsteen. *Screenplay* Steve Fisher. *Camera* Ralph Woolsey. *Art Dir* Hal Pereira, Al Roelofs. *Set Decor* Ray Moyer, Sam Comer. *Film Ed* Archie Marshek. *Mus* Jimmie Haskell. *Titl Song* "By" Dunham, Jimmie Haskell. *Sung by* Jerry Cole. *Sd* Hugo Grenzbach. *Asst Dir* James Rosenberger, Dale Coleman. *Sp Photog Eff* Paul K. Lerpae.
Cast: Rory Calhoun *(Santee)*, Terry Moore *(Anna)*, Linda Darnell *(Sadie)*, Scott Brady *(Tanner)*, Lon Chaney, [Jr.] *(Kile)*, Bruce Cabot *(Henderson)*, Richard Arlen *(Pete)*, Patricia Owens *(Clare Grubbs)*, James Best *(Sheriff Elkins)*, Jerome Courtland *(Sam Grubbs)*, DeForest Kelley *(first sheriff)*, James Brown *(Sheriff Nemo)*, Joseph Hoover *(Swifty)*, Manuel Padilla *(Manuel)*, Sandra Giles, Sally Nichols, Rusty Allen *(Sadie's girls)*, Jeanne Baird *(Mrs. Nemo)*, Chuck Roberson *(Norton)*, Robert Carricart, Barbara Wilkin, Joe Forte, Guy Wilkerson, Lorraine Bendix, Read Morgan, Patricia King, Howard Joslin, Max Power, William Bickmore.
Western melodrama. In Kansas of the 1880's, in order to buy a ranch and settle down with his fiancée, Anna, Santee sets out to become a bounty hunter. He returns 8 months later to find that Anna has married Ralph Elkins, Sheriff of Lark. Santee approaches landowner Gus Kile with a plan for discrediting the town of Lark so that the new railroad will be routed instead through Kile's town and thus increase property values. Sheriff Nemo of the town of Kile persuades the landowner that he can carry out the scheme more efficiently, but when Nemo tries to kill Santee, he is gunned down. Santee then forces Pete, Lark's saloon keeper, to finance the importation of bouncer Henderson, gambler Swifty, and a group of dancehall girls in the employ of Sadie, a madam from New Orleans. Santee, however, repudiates Henderson and his vicious gang after they tar and feather Sheriff Elkins and injure Tanner, the local preacher. Vowing to clean up the town he himself has brought to ruin, Santee destroys the gunslingers and leaves with the good wishes of Anna and her husband. *Bounty hunters. Sheriffs. Saloon keepers. Gamblers. Madams. Prostitutes. Preachers. Bouncers. Marriage. Revenge. Land speculation. Law and order. Railroads. Saloons. Kansas.*

BLACK SUN (France/Italy)   F6.0444
Copernic Films–Medusa Film. *Dist* Ben Barry & Associates. 1969. Sd; col (Eastmancolor). 35mm (Franscope). 90 min.
Dir Denys de La Patellière. *Screenplay* Denys de La Patellière, Pascal Jardin. *Photog* Armand Thirard. *Film Ed* Jacqueline Thiedot.
Cast: Michèle Mercier *(Béatrice [Christine])*, Daniel Gélin *(Guy Rodier)*, David O'Brien *(Eliott)*, Michel de Ré *(Ergy)*, Jean Topart *(Bayard)*, Valentina Cortese *(Maria)*.
Melodrama. After the death of wealthy industrialist Gaston Rodier in Paris, his daughter Béatrice [Christine] promises to find her brother, Guy, a Nazi collaborator in World War II and now self-exiled in Africa. She finds him in the isolated desert town of Tombor, but he refuses to return with her. Although courted by Eliott, an American pilot, Béatrice pretends to be attracted to Ergy, an unscrupulous adventurer who dominates Tombor, in order to rouse Guy from his relationship with Maria, a desperate woman kept alive by his companionship. Rescued from Ergy by Guy, Béatrice leaves her brother and flees with Eliott by plane. *Traitors. Americans in foreign countries. Air pilots. Adventurers. Brother-sister relationship. Exile. Deserts. Paris. Africa.*
Note: Opened in Paris in Nov 1966 as *Soleil noir*; running time: 100 min.

BLACK SUNDAY (Italy)   F6.0445
Galatea–Jolly Film. *Dist* American International Pictures. 15 Feb **1961** [Cleveland opening; c3 Feb 1961; LP20329]. Sd; b&w. 35mm. 84 min.
Overall Production Credits: *Prod* Massimo De Rita. *Dir* Mario Bava. *Screenplay* Ennio De Concini, Mario Serandrei, Mario Bava, Marcello Coscia. *Photog* Ubaldo Terzano, Mario Bava. *Art Dir* Giorgio Giovannini, Mario Bava. *Film Ed* Mario Serandrei. *Mus* Roberto Nicolosi. *Asst Dir* Vana Caruso. *Prod Asst* Paolo Mercuri, Armando Govoni. *Script Girl* Bona Magrini. *Wardrobe* Tina Grani.

Production Credits—U. S. Vers: *Pres by* James H. Nicholson, Samuel Z. Arkoff. *Prod* Lou Rusoff, Titra Sound Corp. *Dir* Lee Kresel. *Film Ed* Salvatore Billitteri. *Mus* Les Baxter. *Mus Coörd* Al Simms. *Sd* Robert Sherwood.
Cast: Barbara Steele *(Princess Asa/Princess Katia)*, John Richardson *(Dr. Andrej Gorobek)*, Ivo Garrani *(Prince Vajda)*, Andrea Checchi *(Dr. Choma Kruvajan)*, Arturo Dominici *(Javutich)*, Enrico Olivieri *(Constantino)*, Antonio Pierfederici *(priest)*, Clara Bindi *(innkeeper)*, Germana Dominici *(her daughter)*, Mario Passante *(Nikita)*, Tino Bianchi *(Ivan)*, Renato Terra.
Horror film. Source: Nikolay Vasilyevich Gogol, "Viy," in *Mirgorod* (Saint Petersburg, 1835). Black Sunday, the one day in each century when Satan walks among the living, occurs in 1830. On this day in Moldavia, Dr. Choma Kruvajan, a traveling physician, accidentally spills blood on the coffin of the Princess Asa of the House of Vajda, unwittingly restoring the witch to life. Two centuries earlier, Asa and her serf, Igor Javutich, at the direction of her Inquisitor brother, had been tortured and burned at the stake. In revenge, Asa laid a curse on the House of Vajda. Now roused by the scent of blood, Asa commands Javutich to rise from his grave and help her destroy her brother's three remaining descendants. Her first victim is Dr. Kruvajan, who has been called in to care for the elderly Prince Vajda. Once Asa has turned the doctor into a vampire, she forces him to suck the blood of the ailing prince. The next morning, the doctor's young assistant, Andrej Gorobek, comes to Vajda castle to investigate his friend's disappearance and is attracted by the beauty of the Princess Katia, who is the image of Asa. Katia's brother, Constantino, is thrown down a ravine; an old servant is discovered hanged; and Katia suddenly finds herself in the grip of the evil Asa. As the young woman's youth is being drawn into the vampire's body, Andrej bursts into the room. He identifies the real Katia by the crucifix she is wearing and then turns Asa over to the local priest, who burns the vampire. *Witches. Physicians. Vampires. Royalty. Priests. Torture. Revenge. Brother-sister relationship. Castles. Curses. Moldavia. The Inquisition.*
Note: Opened in Rome in Aug 1960 as *La maschera del demonio*. The U. S. version contains additional sound effects and modified musical score. Copyright claimant: Alta Vista Productions.

BLACK TIGHTS (France)   F6.0446
Grandes Projections Cinématographiques–Talma Films–Doperfilme–Joseph Kaufman. *Dist* Magna Pictures. Feb **1962**. Sd; col (Technicolor). 35mm (Super Technirama 70). 120 min.
Overall Production Credits: *Prod* Joseph Kaufman. *Assoc Prod* Simon Schiffrin. *Dir* Terence Young. *Photog* Henri Alekan. *Art Dir* Georges Wakhevitch, Henri Morin. *Film Ed* Françoise Javet. *Mus Dir* Marius Constant. *Orch* Concerts Lamoreaux. *Choreog* Roland Petit. *Sd* Jacques Lebreton. *Asst Dir* Bernard Farrel. *Maître de Ballet* Françoise Adret, Raoul Celada.
Production Credits—"The Diamond Cruncher": *Lyr* Raymond Queneau. *English Vers* Herbert Kretzmer. *Story* Roland Petit, Alfred Adam. *Set Decor* Georges Wakhevitch. *Mus* Jean-Michel Damase. *Cost* Georges Wakhevitch.
Production Credits—"Cyrano de Bergerac": *Story* Roland Petit. *Decor* Bazarte. *Mus* Marius Constant. *Cost* Yves Saint-Laurent.
Productions Credits—"A Merry Mourning": *Story* Roland Petit. *Decor* Antoni Clavé. *Mus* Maurice Thiriet. *Cost* Antoni Clavé.
Production Credits—"Carmen": *Decor & Cost* Antoni Clavé.
Cast: Maurice Chevalier *(introduction)*, Ballets de Roland Petit.
Cast—"The Diamond Cruncher": Zizi Jeanmaire *(The Diamond Cruncher)*, Dirk Sanders *(Pierrot)*, Bertie Eckhart *(The Patron [proprietor])*.
Cast—"Cyrano de Bergerac": Moira Shearer *(Roxane)*, Roland Petit *(Cyrano)*, Georges Reich *(Christian)*.
Cast—"A Merry Mourning": Cyd Charisse *(The Widow)*, Roland Petit *(The Young Man)*, Hans Van Manen *(The Husband)*, Gérard Lemaitre *(The Waiter)*, Danielle Jossi, Régine Boury *(soubrettes)*, Maurice Chevalier *(narrator)*.
Cast—"Carmen": Zizi Jeanmaire *(Carmen)*, Roland Petit *(Don José)*, Henning Kronstam *(toreador)*, Josette Clavier *(woman bandit)*, Fredbjørn Bjørnsson *(smuggler)*, Hans Van Manen *(bandit)*.
Dance film. Source: Edmond Rostand, *Cyrano de Bergerac* (Paris, 1898). Georges Bizet, Henri Meilhac and Ludovic Halévy, *Carmen* (Paris opening: 3 Mar 1875). Four tales are performed by the Ballets de Roland Petit: THE DIAMOND CRUNCHER: A beautiful pickpocket in the market area of Paris has a passion for eating stolen diamonds, to the despair of her gangster companions. She is finally broken of the habit by a truckdriver, Pierrot, who convinces her that true happiness is to be found not in diamonds, but in cabbages. CYRANO DE BERGERAC: An unhappy poet with an enormous nose writes love letters for his friend Christian to send to the lovely Roxane. When Christian is killed in battle, Roxane, unaware it is really Cyrano she loves, enters a convent. On the day Cyrano comes to visit Roxane, he is mortally wounded by his enemies; and he dies in her arms after confessing his love. A MERRY MOURNING: A young wife longs for a beautiful black dress she has seen in a shop window. When her jealous husband is killed in a duel with a rival suitor, the widow wears the dress

as her mourning gown and gaily dances with the man who, only hours before, killed her husband on the dueling grounds. CARMEN: In 1820 Seville, Carmen, a fiery cigarette girl, talks her lover, matador Don José, into joining a group of bandits and killing a man. Carmen abandons Don José for a toreador, and he confronts her outside the bullfight arena and stabs her to death. *Pickpockets. Hoodlums. Truckdrivers. Poets. Soldiers. Widows. Bullfighters. Bandits. Cigarette girls. Imposture. Duels. Jealousy. Murder. Courtship. Diamonds. Convents. Documentation. Paris. Seville.*

Note: Shown at the Venice Film Festival in 1960 as *Un, deux, trois, quatre!*; running time: 140 min. Opened in Paris in Jun 1962 as *Les collants noirs.* The first act was entitled "La croqueuse de diamants," and the third "Deuil en 24 heures."

THE BLACK TORMENT (Great Britain)   **F6.0447**
Compton-Tekli Film Productions. *Dist* Governor Films. Dec **1964**. Sd; col (Eastman Color). 35mm. 85 min.
Prod-Dir Robert Hartford-Davis. *Assoc Prod* Robert Sterne. *Exec Prod* Tony Tenser, Michael Klinger. *Screenplay* Donald Ford, Derek Ford. *Dir Photog* Peter Newbrook. *Art Dir* Allan Harris. *Film Ed* Alastair McIntyre. *Mus Comp & Dir* Bobby Richards. *Sd Supv* John Cox. *Sd Rec* Red Law. *Asst Dir* Ted Sturgis.
Cast: Heather Sears (*Lady Elizabeth Fordyke*), John Turner (*Sir Richard Fordyke*), Ann Lynn (*Diane*), Peter Arne (*Seymour*), Norman Bird (*Harris*), Raymond Huntley (*Colonel Wentworth*), Annette Whiteley (*Mary*), Joseph Tomelty (*Sir Giles Fordyke*), Patrick Troughton (*ostler*), Francis De Wolff (*Black John*), Edina Ronay (*Lucy Judd*), Roger Croucher (*apprentice*), Charles Houston (*Jenkins*), Derek Newark (*coachman*), Cathy McDonald (*Kate*), Jack Taylor, Bill Cummings, Frank Hayden (*soldiers*).
Horror film. In the spring of 1780 widower Sir Richard Fordyke returns from London to his family's country estate, accompanied by Elizabeth, his new bride, and learns that the manor tenants suspect him of practicing witchcraft. During his absence, young Lucy Judd was brutally raped and murdered; Lucy allegedly uttered Sir Richard's name before dying, and local residents claim to have seen Sir Richard in the countryside on the night Lucy was slain. Sir Richard's first wife committed suicide, and his father, Sir Giles, is a mute paralytic who is attended by Diane, the sister of Sir Richard's first wife. Disturbing events begin to occur: Sir Richard sees the ghost of his first wife in the garden; the window from which she jumped to her death refuses to stay shut; and Richard is chased by the same apparition on horseback. Mary, the maid, is murdered, and Sir Giles is found hanging from a chandelier. Finally, Sir Richard learns that he has a twin brother who, insane from birth, has been kept closeted for many years. Diane, believing that Sir Richard murdered her sister because she did not produce an heir, discovered the existence of the madman and, with the help of her cousin Seymour, the steward, whose motive is to gain control of the estate by depriving Sir Richard of his inheritance, contrived to use the mad brother to drive Richard insane. The mad brother attacks Elizabeth, and she shoots him. Seymour betrays Diane and kills her, and Sir Richard murders Seymour. *Widowers. Nobility. Brothers. Twins. Stewards. Mutes. Murder. Insanity. Witchcraft. Inheritance. Ghosts. Manors.*
Note: Opened in London in Oct 1964.

A BLACK VEIL FOR LISA (Italy/West Germany)   **F6.0448**
Filmes Cinematografica-Pan Film-Top Film. *Dist* Commonwealth United Entertainment, Inc. Aug **1969**. Sd; col (Eastman Color). 35mm. 88 min. *MPAA rating* R.
Prod Giorgio Venturini. *Dir* Massimo Dallamano. *Screenplay* Giuseppe Belli, Vittorio Petrilli, Massimo Dallamano, Audrey Nohra. *Story* Giuseppe Belli. *Dir Photog* Angelo Lotti. *Art Dir* Giorgio Aragno. *Film Ed* Harry Eisen, Mike Pozen, Daniele Alabiso, Stanley Frazen. *Mus (see note)* Richard Markowitz, Giovanni Fusco, Gianfranco Reverberi. *Mus Cond* Igo Kantor. *Orch* Willard Jones. *Song:* "Melodie de Lisa" Alan Gordon, Gary Bonner. *Asst Dir* Monica Felt.
Cast: John Mills (*Franz Bulov*), Luciana Paluzzi (*Lisa*), Robert Hoffmann (*Max*), Tullio Altamura (*Ostermeyer*), Renate Kasche (*Marianne*), Carlo Hintermann (*Mansfield*), Enzo Fiermonte (*Siegert*), Loris Bazzocchi (*Kruger*), Giuseppe Terranova ("*Rabbit*"), Rodolfo Licari (*Olaf*), Bernardino Solitari (*Müller*), Vanna Polverosi (*Ursula*), Robert Van Daalen (*Dr. Gross*), Carlo Spadoni (*Erick*), Jimmy Soffrano, Paola Natale, Mirella Pamphili.
Crime melodrama. Investigating a major drug ring, Bulov, head of Hamburg's police narcotics division, is under pressure because a number of informants are killed before they are able to talk. Bulov also suspects that his much younger wife, Lisa, has committed adultery. His assumptions lead him to allow the drug ring's hired killer, Max, to remain free under the condition that Lisa will be killed. Bulov comes to believe, however, that Lisa has not been unfaithful to him; but before he can reach Max to countermand his instructions, Max and Lisa become attracted to each other. Bulov tries to rearrest Max, but Max stabs him to death. Lisa then returns to her real lover, Schoerman, the head

of the dope ring, but he rejects her because of her affair with Max. *Police. Informers. Hired killers. Narcotics. Murder. Infidelity. Jealousy. Hamburg.*
Note: Released in Italy in 1968 as *La morte non ha sesso*; in West Germany in Mar 1969 as *Das Geheimnis der jungen Witwe*; running time: 95 min. Fusco is credited as composer of music by Italian sources; Reverberi by German sources.

BLACK WIDOW *see* **BEWARE THE BLACK WIDOW**

BLACK ZOO   **F6.0449**
Herman Cohen Productions. *Dist* Allied Artists. 15 May **1963** [New York opening; c20 May 1963; LP24880]. Sd; col (Eastman Color). 35mm (Panavision). 88 min.
Prod Herman Cohen. *Dir* Robert Gordon. *Orig Story–Screenplay* Aben Kandel, Herman Cohen. *Dir Photog* Floyd Crosby. *Camera Op* Harry Underwood. *Asst Camera Op* Al Baerthlein. *2d Asst Camera Op* David McEwen. *Art Dir* William Glasgow. *Set Dresser* Budd S. Friend. *Film Ed* Michael Luciano. *Mus Comp & Cond* Paul Dunlap. *Titl Song* Robert Marcucci, Russell Faith. *Perf by* Russell Faith Orchestra. *Sd* John Bury. *Sd Eff Ed* Harold McGhan. *Sd Rec* Brad Trask. *Mus Ed* Charles Brown. *Boom Op* Richard Overton. *Asst Dir* William McGarry, Arthur Broidy. *Prod Mgr* Edward Morey, Jr. *Script Supv* Mary Gibsone. *Prod Sec* Rita Calmanson. *Wardrobe* Jack Master, Norah Sharpe. *Makeup* Philip Scheer. *Hairstyles* Peggy Shannon. *Sp Eff* Pat Dinga. *Optical Eff* Howard A. Anderson. *Animal Supv* Ralph Helfer. *Prop Master* Arthur Friedrich. *Constr Supv* James West. *Still Photog* Ed Jones. *Grip* Charles Hannawalt. *Gaffer* Harry Sundby.
Cast: Michael Gough (*Michael Conrad*), Jeanne Cooper (*Edna Conrad*), Rod Lauren (*Carl*), Virginia Grey (*Jenny*), Jerome Cowan (*Jeffrey Stengel*), Elisha Cook (*Joe*), Warrene Ott (*Mary Hogan*), Marianna Hill (*Audrey*), Oren Curtis (*Radu*), Eileen Janssen (*bride*), Eric Stone (*groom*), Dani Lynn, Susan Slavin (*art students*), Edward Platt (*Detective Rivers*), Douglas Henderson (*Lieutenant Duggan*), Jerry Douglas (*lab technician*), Claudia Brack (*Carl's mother*), Daniel Kurlick (*Carl as a child*), Byron Morrow (*coroner*), Michael St. Angel (*Officer Donovan*), Joseph Mell.
Melodrama. Los Angeles zoo-owner Michael Conrad, insanely devoted to his animals, stops at nothing to eliminate obstacles to his work. While the police investigate two deaths by wild-animal maulings, Michael commands one of his lions to kill Jeffrey Stengel because of Stengel's insistence that Michael sell his zoo terrain for a housing development. Michael's wife, Edna, is suspicious of his actions and also resents his harsh treatment of the mute keeper, Carl. After an argument, she decides to leave Michael and resume her circus career. Her agent, Jenny, is killed by a gorilla after Michael overhears her make a tempting job offer to his wife. Meanwhile, Edna and Carl prepare to run away but are discovered by Michael; in a rage, he beats Edna and reveals that Carl is his own son, mute since childhood when he watched a lioness kill his mother on Michael's command. Michael commands a lion to kill Edna; Carl goes to her aid and is forced to kill his father in self-defense. The dying Michael calls in vain for his beloved beasts to save him. *Animal trainers. Psychopaths. Zoo keepers. Talent agents. Police. Mutes. Murder. Filial relations. Personal identity. Real estate. Zoos. Circus. Los Angeles. Apes. Lions.*
Note: Also known as *Horrors of the Black Zoo.*

BLACKBEARD'S GHOST   **F6.0450**
Walt Disney Productions. *Dist* Buena Vista Distribution Co. 8 Feb **1968** [Los Angeles opening; c13 Oct 1967; LP35091]. Sd (RCA); col (Technicolor). 35mm. 107 min.
Pres by Walt Disney. *Co-prod* Bill Walsh. *Dir* Robert Stevenson. *2d Unit Dir* Arthur J. Vitarelli. *Screenplay* Bill Walsh, Don DaGradi. *Dir Photog* Edward Colman. *Art Dir* Carroll Clark, John B. Mansbridge. *Set Decor* Emile Kuri, Hal Gausman. *Film Ed* Robert Stafford. *Mus* Robert F. Brunner. *Orch* Cecil A. Crandall. *Sd Supv* Robert O. Cook. *Sd Mix* Dean Thomas. *Mus Ed* Evelyn Kennedy. *Asst Dir* Paul Cameron, Paul Feiner, Christopher Hibler. *Unit Mgr* Joseph L. McEveety. *Cost Dsgn* Bill Thomas. *Cost* Chuck Keehne, Neva Rames. *Makeup* Gordon Hubbard. *Hairstyles* La Rue Matheron. *Sp Eff* Eustace Lycett, Robert A. Mattey. *Matte Artist* Peter Ellenshaw.
Cast: Peter Ustinov (*Captain Blackbeard*), Dean Jones (*Steve Walker*), Suzanne Pleshette (*Jo Anne Baker*), Elsa Lanchester (*Emily Stowecroft*), Joby Baker (*Silky Seymour*), Elliott Reid (*TV commentator*), Richard Deacon (*Dean Wheaton*), Norman Grabowski (*Virgil*), Kelly Thordsen (*motorcycle officer*), Michael Conrad (*Pinetop Purvis*), Herbie Faye (*croupier*), George Murdock (*head official*), Hank Jones (*Gudger Larkin*), Ned Glass (*teller*), Gil Lamb (*waiter*), Alan Carney (*bartender*), Ted Markland (*Charles*), Lou Nova (*Leon*), Charlie Brill (*Edward*), Herb Vigran, William Fawcett, Betty Bronson, Elsie Baker, Kathryn Minner, Sara Taft.
Comedy. Source: Ben Stahl, *Blackbeard's Ghost* (Boston, 1965). Blackbeard's Inn, a small hotel on the Carolina coast, is run by the Daughters of the Buccaneers, a group of little old ladies all claiming to be descendants of

the notorious Edward Teach, known as Blackbeard. When Steve Walker, the new track coach for Godolphin College, registers at the inn, he learns that the Daughters are desperately trying to pay off their mortgage in order to prevent a takeover by the local gambling czar, Silky Seymour. Encouraged by Jo Anne Baker, a college instructor, Steve helps the old ladies' cause by buying an antique bedwarmer at a charity auction and discovers that it was once owned by Blackbeard's 10th wife. Before being burned as a witch, she had condemned her philandering husband to wander in limbo until he performed one good deed. By accident, Steve conjures up the devilish pirate's spirit and persuades him to help the Daughters. Since Blackbeard is invisible to all but Steve, he easily steals $900 of the mortage money that Jo Anne has raised and places a bet with Silky that Steve's track team will win the upcoming relays. Utilizing his invisible powers, Blackbeard creates havoc among the opposing team and literally hurls the Godolphins to victory; but Silky welshes on the bet and agrees only to return the $900. Steve, relying on Blackbeard's help, storms into Silky's gaming room, slaps down the money at the roulette table, and watches as the pirate helps him win $38,000. Following a confrontation with Silky and his hoods, Steve and Jo Anne hand the money over to the Daughters and save the inn. Suddenly Blackbeard materializes, ritually burns the mortgage, and then—free at last from the curse of his wife—majestically departs. *Athletic coaches. Innkeepers. College teachers. Witches. Pirates. Ghosts. Philanderers. Ancestry. Gambling. Auctions. Robbery. Track. Supernatural. Curses. Wagers. Hotels. Mortgages. United States—South. Edward Teach.*

Note: Location scenes filmed in California.

BLACKMAILED WIVES　　　　　　　　　　　　　　　　**F6.0451**
Mitam Productions. 9 Aug 1968 [Champaign, Illinois, showing]. Sd; b&w. 35mm. 63 min.
Dir Adam Clay.
Melodrama. Mrs. Mason, a contented housewife who wishes to earn extra money, answers an advertisement seeking women to model swimming suits and clothes. She goes to an agency and, while undressing for her first assignment, is kissed by a male model, who then apologizes, explaining that he mistook her for another model. She returns to the agency several days later for another assignment and is confronted with nude pictures of the illicit kiss. Mr. Chaney, the ruthless owner of the agency, uses the pictures to blackmail Mrs. Mason into having an affair with Lloyd. More pictures are taken, and Chaney forces Mrs. Mason into daytime prostitution. Mrs. Cole reveals how she too was blackmailed into prostitution by Mr. Chaney, and she relives her first experience with a customer. Mr. Chaney summons all of the prostitutes to an orgy at his house, and when one of them is late, he tries to force her to commit lesbian acts with another prostitute; then he beats her and rapes her. Lloyd and Fred call an ambulance, and the police arrest Chaney's gang. *Housewives. Models. Blackmail. Prostitution. Group sex. Lesbianism. Rape. Photographs. Whorehouses.*

BLAGO U SREBRNOM JEZERU *see* **TREASURE OF SILVER LAKE**

THE BLAST *see* **EXPLOSION**

BLAST OF SILENCE　　　　　　　　　　　　　　　　**F6.0452**
Alfred W. Crown–Dan Enright. *Dist* Universal–International Films. Jul 1961. Sd; b&w. 35mm. 77 min.
Prod Merrill Brody. *Dir-Writ* Allen Baron. *Narr* Mel Davenport. *Photog* Merrill Brody. *Camera* Erich Kollmar. *Art Dir* Charles Rosen. *Titl* Gary Lobby. *Film Ed* Peggy Lawson. *Mus* Meyer Kupferman. *Sd* Lee Bost, John Strauss, Albert Gramaglia. *Asst Dir* Carole Brody. *Prod Mgr* Joel Mandel. *Story Cons* Will Sparks.
Cast: Allen Baron (*Frank Bono*), Molly McCarthy (*Lorrie*), Larry Tucker (*Big Ralph*), Peter Clune (*Troiano*), Danny Meehan (*Petey*), Milda Memonas (*Troiano's girl*), Dean Sheldon (*nightclub singer*), Charles Creasap (*contact man*), Bill Da Prato (*sailor*), Erich Kollmar (*bellhop*), Ruth Kaner (*building superintendent*), Don Saroyan (*Lorrie's boyfriend*), Jeri Sapanen (*waiter*), Mel Sponder (*drummer*), Betty Kovac (*Troiano's wife*), Joe Bubbico, Gil Rogers, Jerry Douglas, Bob Taylor, Ernest Jackson (*gangsters*), Lionel Stander (*narrator*).
Crime melodrama. Frank Bono, a professional gunman from Cleveland, is hired by a New York City syndicate to kill local racketeer Troiano. Bono arrives in town on Christmas Eve, collects half of his payment, and methodically trails his victim. As he maps out his murder method, Bono arranges to acquire a gun and silencer from Big Ralph, a repulsive, overweight fence. That night Bono encounters Lorrie, a woman he dated years earlier and accepts her invitation for dinner, only to discover later, when he tries to kiss her, that she was being kind to him only out of pity. Big Ralph learns that Bono's victim is an important racketeer, and he demands more money from Bono, threatening him with blackmail. Infuriated, Bono murders Big Ralph. In a moment of panic, Bono tries to back out of killing Troiano, but he is warned that the deed *must* be done. Bono finally corners Troiano and kills him. He goes to collect his fee and is

instead ambushed and killed by syndicate thugs. *Hired killers. Gangsters. Fences (for stolen goods). Murder. Blackmail. Syndicates. New York City.*
Note: Filmed in New York City.

BLAST-OFF *see* **THOSE FANTASTIC FLYING FOOLS**

BLAST-OFF GIRLS　　　　　　　　　　　　　　　　**F6.0453**
Creative Film Enterprises. *Dist* Dominant Pictures, Box Office Spectaculars. 5 Oct 1967 [New Orleans opening]. Sd; col 35mm. 85 min.
Prod-Dir-Orig Screenplay Herschell Gordon Lewis. *Exec Prod* Sidney J. Reich. *Camera* Roy Collodi. *2d Unit Camera* Steve Poster. *Lighting Engr* Cornelius Smith. *Sd* William R. Johnson. *Sd Asst* James Nelson, actor. *Asst Dir* Louise Downe. *Prod Mgr* Paul Hunter. *Prod Coörd* Robert Enrietto. *Prod Asst* Spyros Hortis. *Asst to the Prod* Alex Ameripoor. *Crew Ch* Dean Alexander. *Still Photog* Leonard Pretto.
Cast: Dan Conway (*Boojie Baker*), Ray Sager (*Gordie*), Tom Tyrell, Ron Liace, Dennis Hickey, Chris Wolski, Ralph Mullin ("*The Big Blast*" ["*The Faded Blue*"]), Steve White, Tom Eppolito, Bob Compton, Ray Barry, Tony Sorci ("*Charlie*"), Lawrence J. Aberword (*Marty Dunne*), Paul Hunter (*Lieutenant Kronski*), Don Logay (*Michael Blake*), Jack Horner (*Mr. Roswell*), Sherri Lane (*Kim*), Sharon Camille (*Maxine*), Ann Heath (*Harriet*), Vicki Tenerrelli (*Sally*), Julia Ames (*Barbara*), Sarasue Gleiss (*Laurie*), Barbara Harrison (*Angel*), Col. Harlan Sanders (*himself*).
Melodrama with music. Boojie Baker, a manager of rock and roll groups, is fired from his job for withholding money from his associates. He goes to a cheap bar, sees a ragged group of musicians, and signs them to a contract which states that the profits from their performances will be divided equally with him. The band is named "The Big Blast," and their first concert proves successful when Baker arranges for a group of girls to run onto the stage and rip off the boys' shirts. The band's success—ensured by the women Boojie makes available to promoters—leads the group to rebel at the terms of the contract. Inviting the boys to an orgiastic party that night, Boojie has a man pose as a policeman, raid the party, and arrange fake arrests in order to blackmail the boys into signing another contract giving Boojie an even larger share of the profits. "The Big Blast" soon loses its enthusiasm and the group's popularity begins to wane. Television appearances, recording sessions, and concerts end in disaster. Finally, the boys rip up the contract and humiliate Boojie, who leaves them to look for another band to manage. *Talent agents. Musicians. Embezzlement. Publicity. Disguise. Blackmail. Rock and roll. Orgies. Contracts.*

BLAZE STARR GOES BACK TO NATURE *see* **BLAZE STARR GOES NUDIST**

BLAZE STARR GOES NUDIST　　　　　　　　　　　　　　　　**F6.0454**
Juri Productions. *Dist* Doe–Rae Pictures. 1 Jul 1962 [Los Angeles showing; cl Jul 1962; LP23375]. Sd; col (Eastman Color). 35mm. 79 min.
Prod-Dir Doris Wishman. *Screenplay* Melvin Stanley. *Dir Photog* Raymond Pheelan. *Film Ed* Martin Samuels. *Songs:* "*The Moon Is the Lamp of Love*," "*Going Back to Nature*" J. J. Kendall. *Sung by* Ralph Young. *Sd* Titra Sound Corp. *Optical Eff* B & O Film Specialists.
Cast: Blaze Starr, Russ Martine, Gene Burk, William Mayer, Sandra Sinclair, Stephen Bloom, Bunny Downe, James Antonio, Warrene Gray, Richard Johnson, actor, Mary Jo Walls, Joan Bamford, Craig Maudslay, Jr., Dolores K. Norris, Ingrid Martinsen, Lee Abell, Shirley Perratto, William Barrett.
Nudist film. Blaze Starr, a well-known screen actress, quarrels with her agent-fiancé Tony over his constant invasion of her privacy for publicity purposes. Retreating to a movie theater for asylum, Blaze becomes intrigued with the nudist colony life depicted in the film. The next day Blaze drives to the nudist camp and is persuaded to join by the director, Andy Sims. In the next few weeks, Blaze spends her weekends at the camp, refusing to tell Tony of her whereabouts. One day Tony follows her to the camp and is disturbed by the effect adverse publicity would have on contract negotiations with her producer, D. W. Wolfe. Blaze breaks an important meeting with Wolfe to be at the camp. Later that day, Blaze meets Wolfe at the nudist camp and discovers that he is a veteran nudist. *Actors. Motion picture producers. Talent agents. Publicity. Nudism. Nudist camps. Contracts.*
Note: Shot on location at Sunny Palms Lodge, Homestead, Florida. Also known as *Blaze Starr Goes Back to Nature* and *Busting Out.*

THE BLIND BEAST (Japan)　　　　　　　　　　　　　　　　**F6.0455**
Daiei Motion Picture Co. Apr 1969. Sd; col (Daiei Color-Scope). 35mm. 90 min.
A Kazumasa Nakano Production. *Dir* Yasuzo Masumura. *Screenplay* Yoshio Shirasaka. *Orig Story* Rampo Edogawa. *Photog* Setsuo Kobayashi. *Art Dir* Shigeo Mano. *Sd* Takeo Suda.
Cast: Eiji Funakoshi (*Michio Sofu*), Mako Midori (*Aki Shima*), Noriko Sengoku (*Shino*).

Melodrama. A blind sculptor, aided by his mother, abducts a model and takes her to his warehouse studio. The girl gives in to his sexual desires, hoping for a chance to escape. The dim light in the warehouse causes her to lose her sight, and sexual relations with her captor turn into a sadomasochistic contest. They torture each other until the model, seeking the ultimate masochistic experience, asks her cut off her arms and legs—an act performed with a meat cleaver. The son accidentally kills his mother and then commits suicide. *Sculptors. Models. Abduction. Sadomasochism. Matricide. Suicide. Amputation. Blindness.*

Note: Released in Japan in Jan 1969 as *Moju.*

BLIND CORNER *see* MAN IN THE DARK

BLINDFOLD   F6.0456

Universal Pictures. 25 May **1966** [New York opening; c11 Jun 1966; LP35377]. Sd (Westrex); col (Technicolor). 35mm (Panavision). 102 min.

Prod Marvin Schwartz. *In Charge of Prod* Edward Muhl. *Exec Prod* Robert Arthur. *Asst Prod* Ernest B. Wehmeyer. *Dir* Philip Dunne. *Screenplay* Philip Dunne, W. H. Menger. *Dir Photog* Joseph MacDonald. *Camera Op* Duke Callaghan. *Asst Camera* Bob Thomas. *Art Dir* Alexander Golitzen, Henry Bumstead. *Set Decor* John McCarthy, George Milo. *Set Coörd* Virgil Clark. *Main Titl* Pacific Title. *Film Ed* Ted J. Kent. *Mus* Lalo Schifrin. *Mus Supv* Joseph Gershenson. *Sd* Waldon O. Watson, William Russell, Bill Schwartz, James Alexander, Bruce Smith. *Asst Dir* Terence Nelson, Bill Gilmore, Burt Astor. *Unit Prod Mgr* Wallace Worsley. *Script Supv* Robert Forrest. *Gowns Dsgn by* Jean Louis. *Wardrobe* Peter Saldutti, Thomas Costich, Grace Harris. *Makeup* Bud Westmore, Mark Reedall, Jack Freeman, Alberta Olds. *Hairstyles* Larry Germain, Gladys Witten. *Matte Supv* Albert Whitlock. *Dial Coach* Bert Steinberger. *Still Photog* Frank Shugrue. *Gaffer* Les Everson. *Grip* Dean Paup, George Hudder. *Prop* Blackie Rosenkrantz, Harry Ott.

Cast: Rock Hudson *(Dr. Bartholomew Snow)*, Claudia Cardinale *(Vicky Vincenti)*, Jack Warden *(General Pratt)*, Guy Stockwell *(Fitzpatrick)*, Brad Dexter *(Harrigan)*, Anne Seymour *(Smitty)*, Alejandro Rey *(Arthur Vincenti)*, Hari Rhodes *(Captain Davis)*, Vito Scotti *(Michelangelo Vincenti)*, Angela Clarke *(Lavinia Vincenti)*, John Megna *(Mario Vincenti)*, Paul Comi *(Barker)*, Ned Glass *(Lippy)*, Mort Mills *(Homburg)*, Jack De Mave *(Homburg)*, Robert F. Simon *(police lieutenant)*.

Mystery comedy. Source: Lucille Fletcher, *Blindfold* (New York, 1960). Psychiatrist Bartholomew Snow is called into a secret meeting with General Pratt, a U. S. Security Chief, and ordered to treat government scientist Arthur Vincenti, a former patient who has suffered a mental breakdown. Because Security fears an international ring of kidnapers who sell scientific geniuses, Vincenti is kept in hiding at a mysterious Base X in the Southern swamps, and Snow is blindfolded for each visit to his patient. Snow's life becomes more complicated when the scientist's sister, nightclub singer Victoria Vail *(Vicky Vincenti)*, accuses him of abducting her brother. She causes an argument which leads to their arrest, and Snow avoids curious reporters by announcing their engagement. Snow is then visited by Fitzpatrick, a young man who claims that General Pratt is an enemy agent; Fitzpatrick reveals his true motives, however, by trying to force Snow to disclose the location of Base X. Snow realizes that he must remove himself from the case, and he recommends a substitute, but Fitzpatrick poses as the new psychiatrist and is taken to the base. Upon learning of the imposture, Snow, accompanied by Victoria, retraces his trips to the base by recalling sounds and the length of each journey. When he and Victoria arrive, they find both the scientist and General Pratt being held prisoner by Fitzpatrick. The ensuing battle is broken up by the arrival of the U. S. Army. Fitzpatrick and his men are captured, and Snow and Victoria are left to decide whether to remain engaged. *Psychiatrists. Scientists. Secret agents. Singers. Espionage. Mental illness. Brother-sister relationship. Kidnaping. Imposture. Swamps. United States Army—Intelligence.*

THE BLISS OF MRS. BLOSSOM (Great Britain)   F6.0457

Paramount British Pictures. *Dist* Paramount Pictures. 25 Sep **1968** [Detroit opening; c1 Sep 1968; LP36395]. Sd; col (Technicolor). 35mm. 93 min. *MPAA rating* M.

A Josef Shaftel Production. *Prod-Story* Josef Shaftel. *Dir* Joseph McGrath. *Screenplay* Alec Coppel, Denis Norden. *Dir Photog* Geoffrey Unsworth. *Art Dir* George Lack, Bill Alexander. *Prod Dsgn* Assheton Gorton. *Film Ed* Ralph Sheldon. *Mus Comp & Cond* Riz Ortolani. *Song:* "I Think I'm Beginning To Fall in Love" Riz Ortolani, Norman Newell. *Song:* "The Way That I Live" Geoff Stephens. *Sung by* Jack Jones. *Sd Mix* Laurie Clarkson, David Hawkins. *Sp Sd Eff* Richard Parker. *1st & 2d Asst Dir* David Bessgrove, Michael Guest. *Prod Mgr* Fred Slark. *Cont* Margaret Unsworth. *Cost Dsgn* Jocelyn Rickards. *Wardrobe Supv* Bridget Sellers. *Makeup* Trevor Crole-Rees. *Hairdresser* Bernadette Ibbetson.

Cast: Shirley MacLaine *(Harriet Blossom)*, Richard Attenborough *(Robert Blossom)*, James Booth *(Ambrose Tuttle)*, Freddie Jones *(Detective Sergeant*

Dylan), William Rushton *(Dylan's assistant)*, Bob Monkhouse *(Dr. Taylor)*, Patricia Routledge *(Miss Reece)*, John Bluthal *(judge)*, Harry Towb *(doctor)*, Barry Humphries *(Mr. Wainwright)*, Michael Segal *(Robert's counsel)*, Sandra Caron, Sheila Steafel, Clive Dunn, Frank Thornton, Geraldine Sherman, Julian Chagrin, John Cleese, Bruce Lacey, Tony Grey, Douglas Grey, Leslie Dwyer, Ronnie Brody, Bob Godfrey, John Mulgrew, Marjorie Gresley, Freddie Earlle, Marianne Stone, Keith Smith, The New Vaudeville Band.

Domestic comedy. Source: Alec Coppel, *A Bird in the Nest* (a play; publication undetermined). Robert Blossom, an over-worked English brassiere manufacturer, spends his spare hours "conducting" great symphony recordings while his neglected wife Harriet busies herself with painting and needlework. One day Harriet's sewing machine breaks down, and Robert sends a factory worker, Ambrose Tuttle, to repair it. Upon discovering that she shares a wildly imaginative fantasy life with Ambrose, Harriet installs him in her attic and conceals his presence from Robert. While Scotland Yard searches for the missing factory worker, Ambrose divides his time between studying a wide variety of self-education books and recreating with Harriet great love stories of the past. As the years pass, Ambrose's newfound talents enable him to transform the attic into a beautifully designed showplace; while Robert, driven to distraction by strange noises and by articles missing from his home, consults a psychiatrist. The strain proves too much for Robert, and he eventually collapses and is hospitalized. Utilizing his self-taught knowledge of investments and banking, Ambrose passes stock market tips on to Harriet who, in turn, forwards them to Robert. Inevitably, Robert amasses a fortune and quickly proceeds to perfect the international brassiere. When he decides to move to a home without an attic in Geneva, Ambrose sabotages a convention by arranging for Robert's inflatable brassieres to swell to such enormous proportions that the wearers float skyward. After being forced to return home, Robert finally discovers the truth about the man who has lived in his attic for nearly 4 years. Announcing his intention of returning to his first love, music, Robert divorces his wife and gives Ambrose and Harriet his factory for a wedding present. Before long, it is the over-worked Ambrose who leaves for work each morning, while Harriet pushes a button to summon her new lover, Robert, up from the basement. *Manufacturers. Housewives. Factory workers. Psychiatrists. Fantasy. Marriage. Infidelity. Sabotage. Divorce. Music. Lingerie. Stock market. Scotland Yard.*

Note: Released in Great Britain in Dec 1968. Location scenes filmed in London.

THE BLOCK   F6.0458

Dist American Film Distributing Corp. 15 Apr **1964** [periodical review]. Sd; b&w. 35mm. 67 min.

Prod James E. Myers, Norman "Red" Benson. *Assoc Prod* C. Davis Smith. *Dir* Tony Orlando. *Screenplay* Tony Orlando, Ronald Collier. *Photog* Manuel Whitaker. *Film Ed* C. Davis Smith. *Song:* "Blues on the Block" *Sung by* Joan Weber. *Sd* Fred Bowman. *Asst to Dir* Iris Hunter.

Cast: Dick Lee *(Frank)*, Joan Weber *(Penny)*, Norman Brooks *(Brand)*, Lillian Reis *(Vi)*, Norman "Red" Benson *(commentator)*, James E. Myers *(inspector)*, Lorrie Cummings *(Sydney)*, Ron Logan *(boy)*, Iris Hunter *(Julie)*, Lisette Diamond *(Sylvia)*, Phil Diamond *(Dr. Shelley)*, Phil Jaye *(strange man)*, Bob London *(desk clerk)*, Monte Barry *(Lieutenant Reeves)*, Phil Lane *(conventioneer)*, Diane Muller, Anne Wright *(dancers)*, Terri Sawyer Quartet, Paul Mitchell, Johnny Cymbal, Louis Melisse.

Melodrama. Violet is a b-girl and dancer at the notorious Celebrity Club. Frank, a wealthy playboy, visits the club, meets Penny, another entertainer, and becomes involved in the lives of the two women. Brand, Vi's boyfriend, arranges a modeling session for Vi; his intention is to obtain pornographic photographs with which to blackmail Vi. During the session, Brand arrives unexpectedly and rapes Vi, thus providing the photographer with enough "material" to make movies and snap photographs. Meanwhile, Brand seduces Penny and coerces her into prostitution. Penny's first client is Frank. Brand kills Vi when she tries to go to the police, and he hides in Penny's apartment. He tortures Penny and is about to kill her when Frank arrives, causing Brand accidentally to kill himself. *Bar girls. Stripteasers. Playboys. Pimps. Blackmail. Rape. Prostitution. Perfidy. Pornography. Murder. Nightclubs. Photographs.*

Note: Made in Philadelphia and Atlantic City, New Jersey.

DEN BLODIGA TIDEN *see* MEIN KAMPF

THE BLOND WIFE *see* KISS THE OTHER SHEIK

LA BLONDE DE PÉKIN *see* PEKING BLONDE

BLONDE ON A BUM TRIP   F6.0459

Niles Street Films. *Dist* Distribpix, Inc. 24 Jul **1968** [New York opening]. Sd; b&w. 35mm. 65 min.

Prod Jack Bravman, Ed Adlam. *Exec Prod* Leo Cooper. *Dir* Ralph Mauro.

Cast: Carol Trent, Alexis Wassel, Barbara Spiegelberg, Martha Rabell.

Documentary (?). This film purports to be a "documentary" on the hippie subculture of New York's East Village. It details the effects of hallucinogenic drugs on those who use them. Included are scenes of lust, sadism, and mutilation. *Hippies. Sadism. Mutilation. Lust. Psychedelic drugs. New York City—East Village.*

Note: Also known as *Blonde on a Bum Rap.*

DIE BLONDE VON PEKING *see* **PEKING BLONDE**

BLOOD AND BLACK LACE (France/Italy/West Germany)   **F6.0460**
Emmepi Cinematografica–Productions Georges de Beauregard–Top Film. *Dist* Allied Artists, Woolner Bros. Pictures. 2 Apr **1965** [Chicago opening]. Sd; col (Technicolor). 35mm. 90 min.

Pres by Woolner Bros. Pictures. *Prod* Massimo Patrizi, Alfred Mirabel. *Prod English Vers* Lou Moss. *Dir* Mario Bava. *Screenplay* Marcel Fondat, Joe Barilla, Mario Bava. *Photog* Herman Tarzana. *Art Dir* Harry Brest. *Film Ed* Mark Suran. *Mus* Carl Rustic.

Cast: Eva Bartok (*Cristina*), Cameron Mitchell (*Max Martan*), Thomas Reiner (*Inspector Silvester*), Arianna Gorini (*Nicole*), Mary Arden (*Peggy*), Franco Ressel (*Marquis Richard Morell*), Lea Krüger (*Isabella*), Claude Dantes (*Tao-li*), Massimo Righi (*Marco*), Giuliano Raffaelli (*Zanchin*), Luciano Pigozzi (*Cesare Lazzarini*), Dante Di Paolo (*Frank Scalo*), Harriet White (*Clarice*), Enzo Cerusico, Nadia Anty, Heidi Stroh, Mara Carmosino.

Crime melodrama. Cristina and her lover Max Martan own a luxurious fashion salon which is a coverup for illegal activities such as traffic in drugs. Isabella, a model, is strangled, and when Nicole, her roommate, finds her diary, she too is murdered by a masked killer. Next, Peggy is tortured and killed; and after Peggy's death, another woman is murdered. It is divulged that Martan was responsible for the murder of the four women, and he convinces Cristina to murder a fifth, Tao-li, as she attempts to escape. Coveting Cristina's wealth, Martan then arranges for her to fall from a balcony, but before dying, Cristina manages to telephone the police and shoot Martan. *Couturiers. Models. Roommates. Drug dealers. Murder. Torture. Diaries.*

Note: Released in Italy in 1964 as *Sei donne per l'assassino*; in Paris in Dec 1964 as *Six femmes pour l'assassin* at 85 min; in West Germany in Nov 1964 as *Blutige Seide* at 88 min. The following appear under pseudonyms: Arrigo Breschi (Harry Brest), Ubaldo Terzano (Herman Tarzana), Mario Serandrei (Mark Suran), Carlo Rustichelli (Carl Rustic), Marcello Fondata (Marcel Fondat), and Alfredo Mirabile (Alfred Mirabel). U. S. prerelease title: *Fashion House of Death.*

BLOOD AND ROSES (France/Italy)   **F6.0461**
Films E. G. E.–Documento Film. *Dist* Paramount Pictures. 2 Sep **1961** [Pittsburgh opening; c1 Sep 1961; LP20276]. Sd; col (Technicolor). 35mm (Technirama). 74 min.

Prod Raymond Eger. *Dir* Roger Vadim. *Screenplay* Roger Vadim, Roger Vailland, Claude Brulé, Claude Martin. *Dial* Roger Vailland. *English Dial* Peter Viertel. *Dir Photog* Claude Renoir. *Art Dir & Set Dsgn* Jean André, Robert Guisgand. *Film Ed* Victoria Mercanton. *Mus Comp & Cond* Jean Prodromidès. *Sd* Robert Biart, Julien Coutellier. *Asst Dir* Jacques Poitrenaud. *Cost* Marcel Escoffier. *Makeup* Amato Garbini.

Cast: Mel Ferrer (*Leopoldo De Karnstein*), Elsa Martinelli (*Georgia Monteverdi*), Annette Vadim (*Carmilla von Karnstein*), Jacques-René Chauffard (*Dr. Verari*), Marc Allégret (*Judge Monteverdi*), Alberto Bonucci (*Carlo Ruggieri*), Serge Marquand (*Giuseppe*), Gabriella Farinon (*Lisa*), Renato Speziali (*Guido Naldi*), Edith Peters (*The Cook*), Gianni Di Benedetto (*The Police Marshal*), Camilla Stroyberg (*Martha*), Nathalie Leforet (*Marie*).

Horror film. Source: J. Sheridan Le Fanu, "Carmilla," in *In a Glass Darkly* (London, 1872). At an old country villa near modern Rome, the aristocratic Leopoldo De Karnstein makes final preparations for a masked ball celebrating his approaching marriage to Georgia Monteverdi. Also present is Leopoldo's cousin Carmilla, who is fascinated by the legend that their ancestors were vampires, one of whom, Millarca, was never destroyed. Carmilla is secretly in love with Leopoldo and bitterly resents his marrying the beautiful Georgia. On the evening of the ball, Carmilla appears wearing Millarca's dress, a flowing white gown that she has taken from the family museum. Later that night, while wandering about the estate, Carmilla stumbles upon the crypt where Millarca was entombed and becomes possessed by the evil spirit of her ancestor. A few days later, the dead body of a servant girl, Lisa, is found, with the marks of the vampire on her neck. Subsequently, Carmilla goes to Georgia's bedroom, where at that moment Georgia is having a nightmare. Leopoldo is wakened by terrified screams, rushes into Georgia's room, and finds her in a coma with marks on her neck. Carmilla flees to Millarca's grave just as the police are preparing to detonate some abandoned German mines dating from World War II. The force of the explosion hurls Carmilla against a fence, and a wooden stake pierces her heart. Weeks later, Leopoldo and Georgia leave on their honeymoon, unaware

that the spirit of Millarca travels with them. *Vampires. Aristocrats. Cousins. Domestics. Ancestry. Weddings. Honeymoons. Jealousy. Masquerades. Tombs. Mines (war explosives). Rome. Dreams.*

Note: Location scenes filmed at Hadrian's Villa in Italy. Opened in Paris in Sep 1960 as ... *Et mourir de plaisir*; running time: 80-90 min; in Rome in Jan 1961 as *Il sangue e la rosa*; running time: 100 min.

BLOOD BATH   **F6.0462**
Jack Hill Productions. *Dist* American International Pictures. 2 Mar **1966** [Cincinnati, Ohio, opening; c2 Mar 1966; LP32465]. Sd; b&w. 35mm. 80 min. [See note.]

Prod Jack Hill. *Exec Prod* Roger Corman. *Dir-Writ* Jack Hill, Stephanie Rothman. *Dir Photog* Alfred Taylor. *Art Dir* James Brunner. *Film Ed* Mort Tubor. *Mus* Mark Lowry. *Mus Supv* Ronald Stein. *Sd* Gary Kurtz. *Prod Mgr* Bart Patton. *Script Supv* Sharon Compton. *Makeup* William Condos.

Cast: William Campbell (*Antonio Sordi*), Marissa Mathes (*Daisy Allen*), Lori Saunders (*Dorian/Melissa*), Sandra Knight (*Donna Allen*), Karl Schanzer, Jeff Elliot, Sid Haig, Jonathan Haze, David Ackles, Thomas Karnes, Frank Church, David Miller, actor, Jeff Nichols.

Horror film. Behind the mysterious disappearances of several women in Venice is artist Antonio Sordi, who becomes a vampire at night and either kills his victims on the street or lures them to his belltower studio where he drops their corpses into boiling wax and then uses them as inspiration for his paintings. By day Sordi has a strange romance with Dorian, an aspiring American ballerina, who resembles Melissa, a mistress to Sordi's 15th century ancestor, Erno Sordi, a prominent artist who was burned at the stake for sorcery. Daisy Allen, Dorian's friend, is killed by Sordi in his studio. Several days later, Donna, Daisy's sister, learns from Max, Daisy's boyfriend, that she had been to see Sordi. After the artist denies having met Daisy, Donna tries to convince Max of the parallel between the legend of the Sordi belltower—in which the soul of Erno Sordi returns from the dead as a vampire, seeking revenge against Melissa, who betrayed him—and the disappearances of her sister and the other women. Trailing Sordi, Donna is discovered by the vampire and killed by him while seeking safety on a nearby merry-go-round. After killing Linda Moreno, a stripteaser, and her jealous husband, Sordi, as a vampire, attacks Dorian on the beach. Unaware that Sordi is the vampire, she seeks refuge in the artist's studio. There, the crazed Sordi, believing himself to be his reincarnated ancestor and Dorian to be Melissa, tries to kill her but is himself destroyed when the waxed bodies of his victims suddenly come to life and drive him into the vat of wax. *Vampires. Painters. Missing persons. Americans in foreign countries. Dancers. Sisters. Stripteasers. Revenge. Murder. Impotence. Ancestry. Merry-go-rounds. Beaches. Corpses. Venice.*

Note: Also reviewed at 69 min; copyright length: 62 min. Lori Saunders is screen credited as Linda Saunders.

BLOOD BEAST FROM HELL *see* **THE VAMPIRE BEAST CRAVES BLOOD**

BLOOD BEAST FROM OUTER SPACE (Great Britain)   **F6.0463**
New Art Productions. *For* Armitage Films. *Dist* World Entertainment Corp. Nov **1966** [Texas showing; c16 Jun 1966; LP32985]. Sd; b&w. 35mm. 84 min.

Pres by Harris Associates. *Prod* Ronald Liles. *Exec Prod* John Phillips, British. *Dir* John Gilling. *Screenplay* Jim O'Connolly. *Photog* Stephen Dade. *Art Dir* Harry White. *Film Ed* Philip Barnikel. *Mus Comp & Cond* Johnny Gregory. *Titl Mus* Joe Glenn, Larry Greene, Bob Sande. *Sd* John Cox. *Sd Rec* Kevin Sutton. *Asst Dir* Ray Frift.

Cast: John Saxon (*Jack Costain*), Maurice Denham (*Professor Morley*), Patricia Haines (*Ann Barlow*), John Carson (*Army major*), Jack Watson (*Sergeant Hawkins*), Alfred Burke (*Detective Superintendent Hartley*), Stanley Meadows (*Grant*), Warren Mitchell (*Lilburn*), Marianne Stone (*Mrs. Lilburn*), Aubrey Morris (*Thorburn*), Geoffrey Lumsden (*Colonel Davy*), Ballard Berkeley (*Commander Savage*), Barbara French (*Joyce Malone*), Anthony Wager (*Private Higgins*), David Gregory (*Private Jones*), Tom Gill (*police commissioner's secretary*), Vincent Harding (*1st R/T soldier*), Douglas Livingstone (*2d R/T soldier*), Romo Gorrara (*lieutenant*), John Sherlock (*TV newscaster*), Robert Crewdson (*Medra*).

Science fiction melodrama. Source: Frank Crisp, *The Night Callers* (London, 1960). Scientists Jack Costain, Ann Barlow, and Professor Morley visit the landing site of a UFO whose course they have traced by radar but find only a 6-inch sphere, which they take to their research laboratory. Ann, working late one night, encounters a scaly-clawed creature. The major in charge of the Army unit guarding the sphere disbelieves her story, but Jack finds a giant footprint leading from the window of the storeroom. Morley speculates that the sphere is a receiver for the transmission of matter from another planet but dies as he attempts to observe its activation. The alien disappears with the sphere, and the major is killed shortly afterwards. In the weeks that follow, several young women are reported missing. Superintendent Hartley of Scotland Yard learns that all of them answered a classified advertisement soliciting models and contacted "Medra" at a Soho bookshop. Ann answers the advertisement and discovers that Medra is the alien being, a creature half-human and half-beast who has come from Jupiter's third moon, Ganymede. Jack and Hartley break into the bookshop and find Ann strangled. Following the disappearance of another woman, they trace Medra to a farm. He explains that he came to Earth to gather women for genetic experiments to benefit Ganymede's population, a race of mutants descended from survivors of atomic warfare long ago. His mission complete, he enters the sphere and returns to Ganymede. *Scientists. Space creatures. Mutation. Eugenics. Nuclear warfare. Abduction. Bookshops. London—Soho. Ganymede (satellite). Jupiter (planet). Scotland Yard. Great Britain—Army.*

Note: Released in Great Britain in Feb 1968 as *The Night Caller*; running time: 82 min. Also known as *Night Caller From Outer Space.*

THE BLOOD BEAST TERROR see **THE VAMPIRE BEAST CRAVES BLOOD**

BLOOD BRIDES see **BRIDES OF BLOOD**

BLOOD CREATURE (Reissue) (United States/Philippines)   **F6.0464**
Lynn-Romero Productions. *Dist* Hemisphere Pictures. 5 Feb **1965** [Boston opening]. Sd; b&w. 35mm. 89 min.

Note: Originally released in 1959 as *Terror Is a Man* by Valiant Films.

THE BLOOD CROWD see **THE MCMASTERS**

THE BLOOD DEMON (West Germany)   **F6.0465**
Constantin-Film. *Dist* Hemisphere Pictures. 21 May **1969** [Dayton, Ohio, opening]. Sd; col (Eastman Color). 35mm. ca73 min. *MPAA rating* M.

Prod Wolfgang Kühnlenz. *Prod Supv* Erwin Gitt. *Dir* Harald Reinl. *Screenplay* Manfred R. Köhler. *Photog* Ernst W. Kalinke. *Art Dir* Gabriel Pellon, Werner Achmann. *Film Ed* Hermann Haller. *Mus* Peter Thomas. *Sd* Hans Joachim Richter. *Prod Mgr* Robert Goeb. *Cost* Irms Pauli. *Sp Eff* Erwin Lange.

Cast: Christopher Lee (*Count Regula*), Lex Barker (*Roger Montelis*), Karin Dor (*Lilian von Brandt*), Carl Lange (*Anatole*), Vladimir Medar (*Fabian*), Christiane Rücker (*Babette*), Dieter Eppler (*Kutscher*).

Horror film. Inspired by: Edgar Allan Poe, "The Pit and the Pendulum," in *The Gift* (Philadelphia, 1843). Forty years after Count Regula is beheaded and dismembered for murdering 12 virgins, Baroness Lilian von Brandt, her maid, Babette, and her attorney, Roger Montelis, are summoned by a mysterious messenger to the legendary Blood Castle where the murders were committed. They are joined by Fabian, a thief disguised as a monk, who hopes to rob the castle. As they travel through the ghostly forest festooned with corpses, Roger rescues Lilian and Babette from mummy-like hooded riders, but in the darkness of midnight the women become lost. Not until Roger and Fabian reach the ruins of the castle do they find Lilian and Babette, imprisoned by Anatole, Count Regula's indestructible servant. The dismembered Count Regula, revived by Anatole, announces that he needs the blood of a 13th virgin to achieve immortality and that he is ready to sacrifice Lilian. While Lilian is suspended above a pit of spiders and snakes and subjected to mental torture, Roger is thrown into a pit to be executed by a razor-sharp swinging pendulum. Roger manages to free himself, and, armed with Lilian's diamond-studded cross, he destroys Anatole and Count Regula. The castle crumbles as the four captives make their escape, Roger with Lilian and Fabian with Babette. *Vampires. Lawyers. Virginity. Chambermaids. Monks. Thieves. Decapitation. Mutilation. Murder. Torture. Immortality. Disguise. Castles. Snakes. Spiders.*

Note: Originally released in West Germany in 1967 as *Die Schlangengrube und das Pendel*; running time: 85 min.

BLOOD DOCTOR see **MAD DOCTOR OF BLOOD ISLAND**

THE BLOOD DRINKERS (United States/Philippines)   **F6.0466**
Dist Hemisphere Pictures. May **1966.** Sd (Westrex); col. 35mm. 87 min.
A Cirio H. Santiago Production. *Prod* Danilo Santiago. *Exec Prod* Cirio H. Santiago. *Dir* Gerardo de Leon. *Screenplay* Cesar Amigo. *Story* Rico Omagap. *Photog* Felipe Sacdalan. *Art Dir* Ben Otico. *Film Ed* Salvador. *Mus Dir* Tito Arevalo. *Mus Arr* Vic Marqueses. *Sd* Pat Del Rosario, Demetrio de Santos. *Sd Eff* Tony Gosalves. *Makeup* Tony Artieda & Associates. *Sp Eff* Hilario Brothers.

Cast: Amalia Fuentes (*Charita/Christine*), Ronald Remy (*Marco*), Eddie Fernandez (*Victor*), Eva Montez, Celia Rodriguez, Paquito Salcedo, Felisa Salcedo, Vicky Velasquez, Jess Roma, Mary Walter, Renato Robles, Evelyn Shreve.

Horror film. Marco, a vampire, and his associates, Tanya and La Gordo, a dwarf, invade a small village where Charita, the twin sister of Marco's dying lover, Christine, lives with her foster parents. Marco plans to transfer the healthy heart of Charita into Christine's body, which is being kept alive by

transfusions of Charita's blood. Charita is kept under Marco's spell, and she responds to a vampire bat who acts as his messenger. When the twins' mother, Doña Marisa, tries to intervene, she is killed by the bat. Victor, a young man, comes to the village and falls in love with Charita. With the help of a priest and the police, he leads a party of villagers, armed with burning crosses, to Marco's hideout. Marco, who is rendered harmless by the light, escapes, and stakes are driven into the hearts of the remaining vampires. Victor rescues Charita, and the village returns to its normal state. *Vampires. Twins. Sisters. Police. Priests. Dwarfs. Village life. Blood transfusion. Spells. Murder. Organ transplants. Impalement. Bats.*

Note: Rereleased as *Vampire People.*

BLOOD FEAST   **F6.0467**
Box Office Spectaculars. Jul **1963** [Peoria, Illinois, showing]. Sd; col (Eastman Color). 35mm. 75 min. [Cut to 58 min.]

A David F. Friedman–Herschell G. Lewis Production. *Prod* David F. Friedman, Stanford S. Kohlberg, Herschell G. Lewis. *Dir* Herschell G. Lewis. *Screenplay* Allison Louise Downe. *Photog* Herschell G. Lewis. *Film Ed* Robert Sinise, Frank Romolo. *Orig Mus* Herschell G. Lewis. *Sd* David F. Friedman. *Sp Eff* Herschell G. Lewis. *Crew Ch* Harry Kerby. *Ch Electrn* Lorin D. Hall.

Cast: Thomas Wood (*Pete Thornton*), Mal Arnold (*Ramses*), Connie Mason (*Suzette*), Scott H. Hall (*police captain*), Lyn Bolton (*Mrs. Fremont*), Toni Calvert (*Trudy*), Gene Courtier (*Tony*), Ashlyn Martin (*girl on beach*), Sandra Sinclair (*girl in apartment*), Jerome Eden (*high priest*), Al Golden (*Dr. Flanders*), Craig Maudslay, Jr. (*truck driver*).

Horror film. Ramses, an exotic caterer and a fanatic worshiper of the devil-cult of Ishtar, convinces a woman to give her daughter an "Egyptian feast," in which he secretly plans to serve parts of girls' bodies. As the day of the party approaches, a series of bloody murders occur. The girl's fiance, a police lieutenant, arrives just in time to prevent her being vivisected for the feast. Fleeing from the police across the city dump, the fiendish cultist is accidentally mangled to death beneath the blades of a garbage truck. *Caterers. Police. Demonology. Cannibalism. Ritual murder. Cults. Ishtar.*

BLOOD FIEND (Great Britain)   **F6.0468**
Pennea Productions. *Dist* Hemisphere Pictures. Nov **1967.** Sd; col (Technicolor). 35mm (Techniscope). 88 min.

Prod Michael Smedley-Aston. *Exec Prod* William Gell. *Dir* Samuel Gallu. *Screenplay* Ellis Kadison, Roger Marshall. *Photog* Gilbert Taylor. *Art Dir* Peter Proud. *Film Ed* Barry Vince. *Mus* Elisabeth Lutyens. *Mus Dir* Philip Martell. *Sd Rec* A. W. Lumkin.

Cast: Christopher Lee (*Philippe Darvas*), Lelia Goldoni (*Dani Gireaux*), Jenny Till (*Nicole Chapel*), Julian Glover (*Charles Marquis*), Ivor Dean (*Inspector Micheaud*), Evelyn Laye (*Madame Angèle*), Joseph Fürst.

Horror film. A series of murders bearing signs of vampirism are committed in Paris during the staging of Philippe Darvas' macabre productions at the Theatre of Death. Inspector Micheaud is aided in his investigation of the blood-drinking murders by a young surgeon, Charles Marquis, whose girl friend, Dani Gireaux, is an actress at the theater. Charles becomes increasingly suspicious of the sinister-looking Darvas, particularly after he watches Darvas hypnotize Dani's roommate, Nicole, at a party, and she appears to be subservient to his will. However, Charles's hypothesis is disproved when Darvas is murdered, and the bizarre killings continue. Dani later finds an unfinished play by Darvas in which he reveals Nicole as a necrophiliac whose vampirism originated in her infancy, when she was kept alive by draughts of human blood. Nicole confronts Dani underneath the stage of the Theatre of Death during the performance of a voodoo dance. Nicole is accidentally killed by a spear plunged through the floorboards, and Dani is saved. *Vampires. Theatrical directors. Playwrights. Actors. Police. Surgeons. Roommates. Murder. Hypnotism. Necrophilia. Theater. Voodoo. Paris.*

Note: Released in Great Britain in 1967 as *Theatre of Death*; running time: 91 min.

BLOOD KIN see **THE LAST OF THE MOBILE HOTSHOTS**

BLOOD MANIA   **F6.0469**
Jude Productions. *Dist* Crown International Pictures. 28 Oct **1970** [Los Angeles opening]. Sd; col (DeLuxe). 35mm. 88 min. *MPAA rating* R.

Prod Chris Marconi, Peter Carpenter. *Asst Prod* Tony Crechales. *Dir* Robert V. O'Neil. *Screenplay* Toby Sacher, Tony Crechales. *Based on an Orig Story* by Peter Carpenter. *Photog* Bob Maxwell, Gary Graver. *Art Dir* Pierre Decorative Design. *Titl & Opticals* Image Inc. *Film Ed* Patrick Kennedy. *Mus* Don Vincent. *Mus Supv* John Caper, Jr. *Sd* Clark D. Will. *Electronic Sd* Wurlitzer. *Prod Mgr* Gary Kent. *Painting by* Mendij.

Cast: Peter Carpenter (*Dr. Craig Cooper*), Maria De Aragon (*Victoria Waterman*), Vicki Peters (*Gail Waterman*), Reagan Wilson (*Cheryl*), Jacqueline Dalya (*Kate*), Leslie Simms (*Nurse Turner*), Eric Allison (*Ridgeley Waterman*), Arell Blanton (*blackmailer*), Alex Rocco (*lawyer*), Reid Smith (*pool boy*).

Melodrama. Because he performed illegal abortions during his days as an intern, hospital staff doctor Craig Cooper now finds himself being blackmailed by a one-time college friend. Aware that his hospital superior's daughter, Victoria Waterman, has long been sexually attracted to him, Cooper tells the neurotic young woman that he needs $50,000 for taxes and then seduces her. The following morning, Cooper is summoned to the Waterman residence and informed that the doctor died during his sleep. When Victoria, while painting furiously at her easel, admits that she administered an undetectable poison to her father in order to hasten the receipt of her inheritance, Cooper suppresses an impulse to notify the police and reports the cause of death as a stroke. In the meantime, Cooper's mistress Cheryl has secretly tried to help by arranging a rendezvous with the blackmailer; but although she submits to the blackmailer's brutal lovemaking, she fails to dissuade him from pressuring Cooper. At the reading of Dr. Waterman's will, Victoria is stunned to learn that she has inherited only a small monthly allowance; the bulk of the estate has gone to her sister Gail. Driven to a psychotic rage, Victoria attacks her sister in the bathroom, murders her with a brass candelabra, and then feverishly resumes painting at her easel. Upon discovering the body, Cooper carries it to his car, conceals it in the back seat, and returns to Victoria. A few moments later, however, the couple are horrified to see Gail's blood-spattered body standing in the doorway. Then the figure slumps to the floor and the blackmailer, smiling demonically at Cooper, steps out of the shadows. As Cooper turns away, he catches a glimpse of the canvas Victoria has been painting. It is a portrait of himself cradled in the arms of death. *Physicians. Mistresses. Sisters. Abortion. Blackmail. Insanity. Seduction. Murder. Poisoning. Inheritance. Hospitals. Paintings. Wills. Corpses.*

Note: Location scenes filmed in Los Angeles.

BLOOD OF DRACULA'S CASTLE   F6.0470

Paragon International Pictures–A & E Film Corp. *Dist* Crown International Pictures. 14 May **1969** [Charlotte, North Carolina, opening]. Sd; col (Pathé). 35mm. 84 min. *MPAA rating* M.

Prod Al Adamson, Rex Carlton. *Exec Prod* Martin B. Cohen. *Assoc Prod* Ewing Brown, Jerome Wexler. *Dir* Al Adamson. *Screenplay* Rex Carlton. *Dir Photog* Leslie Kovacs. *Supv Ed* Ewing Brown. *Ed* Peter Perry. *Mus* Lincoln Mayorage. *Sung by* Gil Bernal. *Prod Sd* Jerry Hansen. *Prod Mgr* Bud Cardos. *Script Supv* Joyce King. *Cost Coörd* Jon Shannon. *Makeup* Jean Hewitt. *Sp Makeup* Kent Osborne. *Eff Ed* Fred Badiyan. *Coöp* Marineland. *Still Photog* Peter Sorel.

Cast: John Carradine *(George)*, Paula Raymond *(Countess Townsend)*, Alex D'Arcy *(Count Townsend)*, Robert Dix *(Johnny)*, Gene Shane *(Glen Cannon)*, Barbara Bishop *(Liz Arden)*, Vicki Volante *(Ann)*, Ray Young *(Mango)*, John Cardos, Kent Osborne.

Horror film. Glen Cannon, a photographer, receives a telegram that informs him that he has inherited Falcon Rock Castle from his late uncle. Glen and his fiancée, Liz, visit the castle to give notice to the current occupants, Count and Countess Townsend. They learn from George, the butler, that the Townsends will join them only after sunset. After a dinner in which the Townsends drink a deep red liquid, Glen's car mysteriously breaks down, and they are forced to spend the night at the castle. A wolf-like scream in the night horrifies the couple: they investigate and find nothing, but the next day they find several women chained to a wall in the castle's basement. One of the women, Ann, tells them that the Townsends are really the Count and Countess Dracula, vampires who sleep in coffins. That night, under a full moon, Glen and Liz witness a woman being sacrificed to the "Great God Luna." They free the other women following the deaths of the butler and Mango, a grotesque servant, and the destruction of the vampires by the dawn light. Then they leave the castle behind them. *Photographers. Butlers. Vampires. Human sacrifice. Inheritance. Rites and ceremonies. Castles. Dracula.*

Note: Produced in 1967. Sources conflict in crediting production company. Filmed with the cooperation of Walter Gaynor, owner of Castle Ranch.

THE BLOOD OF FU MANCHU *see* KISS & KILL

BLOOD ON THE ARROW   F6.0471

Leon Fromkess–Sam Firks. *Dist* Allied Artists. 11 Nov **1964** [Los Angeles opening]. Sd; col (DeLuxe). 35mm. 91 min.

Prod Leon Fromkess. *Dir* Sidney Salkow. *Screenplay* Robert E. Kent. *Story* Robert E. Kent, Mark Hanna. *Photog* Kenneth Peach. *Film Ed* William Austin. *Mus* Richard La Salle. *Sd* Glen Glenn Sound. *Asst Dir* Nate Levinson. *Prod Mgr* Herbert G. Luft. *Asst to the Prod* Rita Fromkess. *Sp Eff* Pat Dinga.

Cast: Dale Robertson *(Wade Cooper)*, Martha Hyer *(Nancy Mailer)*, Wendell Corey *(Clint Mailer)*, Dandy Curran *(Tim)*, Paul Mantee *(Segura)*, Robert Carricart *(Kai-La)*, Ted de Corsia *(Jud)*, Elisha Cook *(Tex)*, John Matthews *(Mike)*, Tom Reese *(Charlie)*, Bloyce Wright *(Captain Stanhope)*, Michael Hammond, Leland Wainscott.

Western drama. Prisoner of a U. S. Cavalry patrol, outlaw Wade Cooper is the only survivor of an Apache attack. Nancy Mailer rescues Wade and brings him to her husband Clint's trading post, where she nurses the outlaw back to health over the objections of her husband, a cowardly miser. The Apaches raid the post, kidnaping the Mailers' son and demanding rifles in exchange for his release. Clint Mailer obtains the aid of an outlaw band to steal the rifles from an Army post, but they are caught by soldiers and killed. Wade rescues the boy by leading the Indians into a booby trap in Clint's gold mine, and he and Nancy, who have fallen in love, start a new life together. *Outlaws. Apache Indians. Misers. Kidnaping. Cowardice. Gold mines. Trading posts. United States Army—Cavalry.*

BLOOD ON THE BALCONY (Italy)   F6.0472

Etrusca Cinematografica–Galatea. *Dist* Jillo Film Productions. 29 Jun **1964** [New York opening]. Sd; b&w with col seq. 35mm. 92 min.

Prod Roberto Rossellini. *Dir* Pasquale Prunas. *Narr* Enzo Biagi, Sergio Zavoli. *Scen* G. B. Cavallero, G. Laura. *Film Ed* Romeo Ciatti, Mario Serandrei. *Mus Score* Roberto Nicolosi.

Documentary. The film traces the life of Benito Mussolini from 1914 to his death at the hands of Italian partisans in 1945. Authentic newsreel footage shows the rise of fascism in Italy. There are scenes of Mussolini as the crusading editor of a Milanese newspaper, the founding of the Fascist Party in 1919, the march on Rome in 1922, and the collapse of King Vittorio Emmanuel's reign. In addition, scenes of Mussolini's private life are shown, as are scenes of major historical events, including the Ethiopian campaign, the alliance with Hitler, and Italy's participation in World War II. *Dictators. Fascism. World War II. Benito Mussolini. Victor Emmanuel III (Italy). Adolf Hitler. Italy—Army.*

Note: Opened in Rome in May 1962 as *Benito Mussolini*; running time: 105 min.

THE BLOOD ROSE (France)   F6.0473

Transatlantic Productions. *Dist* Allied Artists. 28 Oct **1970** [Detroit opening]. Sd; col (Eastman Color). 35mm. 92 min. *MPAA rating* R.

Prod Edgar Oppenheimer. *Dir* Claude Mulot. *Screenplay* Claude Mulot, Edgar Oppenheimer, Jean Carriaga. *Photog* Roger Fellous. *Art Dir* Franco Davila. *Film Ed* Monique Kirsanoff. *Mus* Jean-Paul Dorsay. *Mus Dir* Eliane Dorsay. *Asst Dir* Jean Carriaga. *Prod Mgr* Georges Dybman. *Sp Eff* Guy Delecluse.

Cast: Philippe Lemaire *(Frédéric Lansac)*, Anny Duperey *(Anne)*, Howard Vernon *(Professor Rohmer)*, Elisabeth Teissier *(Barbara)*, Olivia Robin, Michèle Perello, Valérie Boisgel, Gérard Huart, Johnny Cacao.

Horror film. Frédéric Lansac, a portraitist and botanist whose beauty salon specializing in herbal remedies is patronized by wealthy and beautiful Parisian women, meets and falls in love with Anne at a fancy dress ball, and soon thereafter they marry. They move into Frédéric's secluded château and are attended by two dwarf servants. Shortly afterwards Anne's face is burned and horribly scarred when a jealous woman pushes her into a bonfire during an exhibition of Frédéric's paintings. As a result, Anne secludes herself and slowly goes insane. Frédéric discovers that Dr. Rohmer, an employee of Frédéric's beauty parlor, is a skilled plastic surgeon who has been disqualified from practicing medicine and has resorted to performing plastic surgery on wanted criminals. Frédéric blackmails Rohmer into attempting to perform a grafting operation on his wife's scarred face. Frédéric lures two of his clients to the château, but both die horribly, and the search for a donor continues. Barbara, the sister of the nurse who had been attending Anne and whom Anne killed, arrives at the château. Anne finds her to be pretty and demands that she become the donor. Anne is thwarted when Barbara escapes and Rohmer commits suicide. Frédéric, recognizing the extent of his wife's madness, has her killed by his servants and then gives himself up to the police. *Painters. Botanists. Surgeons. Nurses. Sisters. Dwarfs. Domestics. Marriage. Wealth. Jealousy. Disfiguration. Insanity. Blackmail. Murder. Suicide. Plastic surgery. Castles. Beauty shops. Art exhibits. Herbs. Fires.*

Note: Opened in Paris in Sep 1970 as *La rose écorchée*; running time: 95 min. Film allegedly contained a subplot involving lesbianism, which was deleted from the U. S. release version.

THE BLOOD SEEKERS *see* CAIN'S WAY

THE BLOOD SUCKERS *see* DR. TERROR'S GALLERY OF HORRORS

BLOODLUST   F6.0474

Cinegraf Productions. *Dist* Crown International Pictures. 13 Sep **1961** [San Diego, California, opening]. Sd; b&w. 35mm. 68 min.

Prod-Dir-Writ Ralph Brooke. *Photog* Richard E. Cunha. *Mus* Manuel Francisco. *Sd* Robert Post, Ken Corson, Gene Garvin. *Asst Dir* Leonard Shapiro, John C. Chulay. *Prod Mgr* Bri Murphy. *Script Supv* Diana Loomis. *Makeup* Jack Dusek. *Prop* Richard M. Rubin, John Cengia. *Gaffer* Charles

Beckett.

Cast: Wilton Graff (*Dr. Albert Balleau*), Lilyan Chauvin (*Sandra Balleau*), Robert Reed (*Johnny Randall*), June Kenny (*Betty Scott*), Gene Persson (*Pete Garwood*), Joan Lora (*Jean Perry*), Walter Brooke (*Dean Gerrard*), Troy Patterson, Bobby Hall, Bill Coontz.

Horror film. Source: Richard Edward Connell, "The Most Dangerous Game," in *Collier's* (19 Jan 1924). While vacationing in the tropics, four young adventurers—Johnny, Betty, Pete, and Jean—go ashore on a small island and meet the sinister Dr. Balleau, a madman who spends his time hunting vicious wild animals with which he has stocked the island. The four visitors learn that the doctor also enjoys hunting human beings and then displaying them, by means of taxidermy, after they have met horrible deaths. After murdering his wife and houseguest, Balleau sets the four young people free and tells them he will hunt them down with a crossbow. Before he can do so, however, he is crushed to death by a crazed aide, and the four vacationers are saved. *Psychopaths. Adventurers. Houseguests. Hunting. Murder. Taxidermy. Vacations. Crossbows. Tropics. Islands. Animals.*

Note: Filmed in 1959.

BLOODTHIRSTY BUTCHERS   F6.0475
Constitution Films. *Dist* William Mishkin. Jan **1970**. Sd; col. 35mm. 85 min. [Trade review length: 79 min.] *MPAA rating* R.

Prod William Mishkin. *Dir* Andy Milligan. *Script* Andy Milligan, John Borske. *Photog* Andy Milligan. *Art Dir* James Fox, art.

Cast: John Miranda, Annabella Wood, Berwick Kaler, Jane Helay, Michael Cox, Linda Driver, Jonathan Holt, Ann Arrow.

Horror film. Sweeney Todd, a barber, and Maggie Lovett, a baker, join forces to commit a series of brutal, gory murders in London. Tobias Ragg, an employee of the bakery, abducts a number of customers from the barber shop and kills them. The victims include his own girl friend, the barber's wife, Becky, and Maggie's invalid husband. The bakery begins to offer "meat pies" for sale. Johanna Jeffrey, Maggie's unsuspecting salegirl, goes to the police when her boyfriend Jarvis Williams disappears. The police arrive and save Jarvis; Tobias and Sweeney hack each other to death. *Barbers. Bakers. Invalids. Salesclerks. Missing persons. Murder. Cannibalism. Bakeries. Barbershops. London.*

BLOODY, BARE, AND BEAUTIFUL see **THE BEAUTIFUL, THE BLOODY, AND THE BARE**

THE BLOODY BROOD (Canada)   F6.0476
Meridian Films–Key Film Productions. *Dist* Sutton Pictures, Astor Pictures. Jun **1962**. Sd; b&w. 35mm. 69 min.

Prod-Dir Julian Roffman. *Exec Prod* Yvonne Taylor, Ralph Foster. *Screenplay* Elwood Ullman, Ben Kerner, Des Hardman. *Orig Script* Anne Howard Bailey. *Dir Photog* Eugen Shuftan. *Art Dir* David S. Ballou. *Sets* Robert Byrnes. *Film Ed* Robert Johnson, ed. *Mus* Harry Freedman. *Cond* Louis Applebaum. *Prod Coörd* Herbert S. Alpert.

Cast: Peter Falk (*Nico*), Jack Betts (*Cliff Bowers*), Ronald Hartmann (*Francis*), Barbara Lord (*Ellie*), Robert Christie (*Detective McLeod*), William Brydon (*Studs*), George Sperdakos (*Ricky*), Ronald Taylor (*Dave*), Michael Zenon (*Weasel*), Billy Kowalchuk (*Roy*), Sammy Sales (*Louis*), Kenneth Wickes (*Paul*), Carol Starkman (*blonde neighbor*), Rolf Colstan (*Stephanex*), Anne Collings (*model*).

Melodrama. A gang of beatniks who deal dope are led by psychopath Nico and his partner Francis. One evening they give a messenger boy a hamburger containing ground glass just for the "kick" of watching him die. The victim's brother, Cliff Bowers, is told by the police that they have been unable to solve the murder, so Bowers conducts his own investigation. At Nico's hangout, he meets Ellie, a young woman who tells him about Nico and his gang. Two of Nico's henchmen, Studs and Weasel, learn of Bowers' search and beat him up, but afterwards they are betrayed by Nico in a drug transaction and are themselves attacked. Ellie has now fallen in love with Bowers and helps him set a trap for Nico at the hangout. As the police arrive, Nico flees but is killed by his betrayed henchmen. Francis confesses to the police and is arrested. *Brothers. Police. Psychopaths. Drug dealers. Beatniks. Gangs. Sadism. Murder. Perfidy.*

Note: Released in Canada in 1959; running time: 68 min. Cut from 80 min.

BLOODY MAMA   F6.0477
American International Pictures. 24 Mar **1970** [Little Rock, Arkansas, opening; c25 Mar 1970; LP37775]. Sd; col (print by Movielab). 35mm. 90 min. *MPAA rating* R.

Pres by James H. Nicholson, Samuel Z. Arkoff. *Prod-Dir* Roger Corman. *Exec Prod* Samuel Z. Arkoff, James H. Nicholson. *Co-prod* Norman Herman. *Screenplay* Robert Thom. *Story* Robert Thom, Donald A. Peters. *Photog* John Alonzo, photog. *Camera Op* John Elsenbach. *Asst Camera* Joseph Marquette, Jr., Roy Hogstedt. *Titl Dsgn* Pacific Title. *Film Ed* Eve Newman. *Mus Comp & Dir* Don Randi. *Mus Supv* Al Simms. *Titl Song* Don Randi, Guy Hemric,

Bob Silver. *Perf by* Bigfoot. *Sd Mix* Charles Knight. *Boom Op* Don Sharpless. *Sd Eff* Edit-International. *Asst Dir* Gary Grillo. *Prod Mgr* Elliot Schick. *Script Supv* Tom Moore, script supv. *Cost* Thomas Costich. *Makeup Artist* David Grayson. *Hairdresser* Betty Iverson. *Sp Eff* A. D. Flowers. *Optical Eff* Cinefx. *Vis Cons* Michael Levesque. *Gaffer* Robert E. Thomas. *Prop Master* Michael Ross. *Key Grip* Richard King. *Stunt Coörd* Bud Walls. *Our Man in Arkansas* William Bond, Jr. *Still Photog* Michael J. Freeman.

Cast: Shelley Winters (*Kate "Ma" Barker*), Pat Hingle (*Sam Adams Pendlebury*), Don Stroud (*Herman Barker*), Diane Varsi (*Mona Gibson*), Bruce Dern (*Kevin Dirkman*), Clint Kimbrough (*Arthur Barker*), Robert De Niro (*Lloyd Barker*), Robert Walden (*Fred Barker*), Alex Nicol (*George Barker*), Michael Fox (*Dr. Roth*), Scatman Crothers (*Moses*), Stacy Harris (*Agent McClellan*), Pamela Dunlap (*Rembrandt*), Lisa Jill (*young Kate*), Steve Mitchell (*sheriff*), Roy Idom (*ferryboat passenger*).

Crime melodrama. Raped by her brothers at age seven, Ma Barker exacts absolute loyalty from her four sons, sadistic Herman, narcotics addict Lloyd, soft-spoken Arthur, and homosexual Fred. During the Depression Ma and her brood leave passive Pa Barker and the Ozarks to begin a criminal career. While robbing a ferryboat eldest son Herman loses his temper and stomps a passenger to death. To console Herman, Ma sleeps with him. Apprehended robbing a picnic, Fred and Herman are incarcerated. In prison Fred succumbs to the advances of Kevin Dirkman, who becomes Ma's lover upon release. Over her protests Herman introduces his mistress, the prostitute Mona, into the band. After Lloyd rapes local resident Rembrandt, Ma, Herman, and Kevin drown the girl in the bathtub. Later Lloyd dies of a drug overdose. The gang then kidnaps congenial multi-millionaire Sam Adams Pendlebury. Upon payment of the ransom Ma insists that the hostage be killed. Her sons, however, release the multi-millionaire and Herman assumes command of the band. At their Lake Weir hideout Herman and Kevin unknowingly reveal their identities by firing machine guns at an alligator. Trapped by police, the Barkers fight to the finish, Ma being the last to fall. *Gangsters. Drug addicts. Prostitutes. Mistresses. Millionaires. Theft. Murder. Motherhood. Filial relations. Incest. Rape. Male homosexuality. Kidnaping. Drug overdose. Prisons. The Great Depression (1929–34). Ozarks. Lake Weir (Florida). Kate "Ma" Barker. Alligators.*

Note: Filmed on location in Arkansas.

BLOODY PIT OF HORROR (United States/Italy)   F6.0478
M. B. S. Cinematografica–International Entertainment Corp.–Ralph Zucker. *Dist* Pacemaker Pictures. Oct **1967**. Sd; col (Eastman Color). 35mm. 74 min.

Prod Francesco Merli. *Exec Prod* Felix C. Ziffer, J. R. Coolidge. *Dir* Max Hunter. *Screenplay* Roberto Natale, Romano Migliorini. *Photog* Luciano Trasatti. *Art Dir* Frank Arnold. *Film Ed* Robert Ardis. *Mus* Gino Peguri.

Cast: Mickey Hargitay (*Anderson*), Louise Barrett (*Edith*), Walter Brandt, Moa Thai, Femi Martin, Alfred Rice, Rita Klein, John Turner, Ralph Zucker, Barbara Nelly, Albert Gordon, Nando Angelini.

Horror film. Inspired by the writings of: Donatien Alphonse François (Marquis de) Sade. Rick, a writer, his publisher, Parks, and his secretary, Edith—along with a photographer and five seductive models—break into a seemingly deserted medieval castle to take some photographs for horror story bookjackets. The castle is occupied, however, by a former actor named Anderson, a psychopathic sadist who has shut himself off from the world. Initially, he intends to send the group away, but he recognizes Edith as his former fiancée. Although he puts the dungeon off-limits, they proceed to take pictures there with the models posed in provocative costumes. This arouses Anderson's bloodlust, and he assumes the identity of the "Crimson Executioner" who was hanged centuries before for having a private torture chamber. Anderson, using many of the executioner's sadistic devices, eventually kills everyone except Edith and Rick; but he himself is done in by the poisoned barbs of the "Lover-of-Death" machine. Edith and Rick then leave the castle. *Authors. Photographers. Publishers. Secretaries. Models. Actors. Psychopaths. Sadism. Torture. Murder. Personal identity. Castles.*

Note: Produced in Italy in 1965 as *Il boia scarlatto*; also known as *Il castello di Artena*. U. S. alternative titles: *The Crimson Executioner* and *The Red Hangman*. The following are credited under pseudonyms: Massimo Pupillo (Max Hunter), Walter Brandi (Walter Brandt), Luisa Baratto (Louise Barret), Eufamia Benussi (Femi Martin), Alfredo Rizzo (Alfred Rice).

BLOODY SEA (Mexico)   F6.0479
Dist K. Gordon Murray Productions, Trans-International Films. ca **1965**. Sd; b&w. 35mm. 80 min.

Pres by K. Gordon Murray. *Prod English Vers* K. Gordon Murray.

Horror film. No information about the precise nature of this film has been found.

THE BLOODY VAMPIRE (Mexico)   F6.0480
Tele-Talía Films. *Dist* K. Gordon Murray Productions, Trans-International Films. ca **1965**. Sd; b&w. 35mm. 98 min.

Pres by K. Gordon Murray. *Prod* Rafael Pérez Grovas. *Prod English Vers* K. Gordon Murray. *Dir-Story-Screenplay* Michael Morayta. *Dir English Vers* Manuel San Fernando. *Photog* Raúl Martínez Solares. *Art Dir* Manuel Fontanals. *Film Ed* Gloria Schoemann. *Mus* Luis Hernández Bretón. *Sd* Jesús González Gancy.

Cast: Carlos Agosti (*Count Frankenhausen*), Antonio Raxell (*Count Cagliostro*), Begoña Palacios (*Ines Cagliostro*), Raúl Farell (*Richard*), Erna Martha Bauman (*Countess Frankenhausen*), Bertha Moss (*Hildegard*), Francisco Córdova, Lupe Carriles, Rafael Etienne, Enrique Lucero.

Horror film. Count Cagliostro, whose family has tried for generations to rid the world of vampires, instructs his daughter, Ines, and her fiancé, the physician Richard, to protect several valuable documents. When the doctor is summoned to the bedside of the ailing Countess Frankenhausen, Ines enters the castle disguised as a servant. In this guise she attracts the amorous count, who is unaware of her conviction that he is a vampire, and incurs the wrath of Hildegard, the jealous housekeeper. Although the countess confides her fear of her husband to Richard, the doctor chooses to believe the vampire's assertion that his wife is mad. Unmasked by the angry Frankenhausen, Ines is rescued by Richard. The enraged vampire kills his wife, quaffs her blood, and escapes. *Nobility. Vampires. Physicians. Housekeepers. Housemaids. Filial relations. Disguise. Jealousy. Castles.*

Note: Produced in Mexico in 1962 as *El vampiro sangriento;* running time: 110 min.

BLOW THE MAN DOWN   F6.0481
Dyle IV Productions-M'Lew Productions. *Dist* Canyon Distributing Co. 11 Oct **1968** [Champaign, Illinois, showing]. Sd; col (Eastman Color). 35mm. 71 min.

Prod H. P. Edwards. *Dir-Writ* Hayes Dupree. *Film Ed* Christopher Darque. *Mus Score* Robin Herth. *Sd* Spectra Sound.

Cast: Sharon Wells (*Melessa*), Michael Wellington (*Burt*), Camille Grant (*Anna*), Pat Neice (*Liz*), Michelle Egan (*Michelle*), Janice Mackey (*Terri*), Mary West (*Grace*), Karen Wickline (*Wendy*), Linda Powers (*Helen*), Bill Marxs (*Lance*), Ron Garcia (*Ricky*), John DeBella (*Barry*).

Sex film. Three women are enslaved by a free love society from which there is no escape. Melessa, a virgin tease, is given LSD and is raped by three lesbians. Liz, a young starlet, roams the streets and meets gangster Burt Genopolis in a bar. Unaware of Burt's reputation, Liz makes a play for him and is subjected to a night of endless lust. Anna, a voyeur, also figures in the film. *Virginity. Actors. Teases. Gangsters. Lesbianism. Voyeurism. Rape. Satyriasis. LSD. Free love.*

BLOW-UP (Great Britain/Italy)   F6.0482
Bridge Films. *For* Metro-Goldwyn-Mayer Pictures. *Dist* Premier Productions. 18 Dec **1966** [New York opening; c31 Dec 1966; LP33773]. Sd; col (Metrocolor). 35mm. 110 min.

Prod Carlo Ponti. *Exec Prod* Pierre Rouve. *Dir-Story* Michelangelo Antonioni. *Screenplay* Michelangelo Antonioni, Tonino Guerra. *English Dial Collab* Edward Bond. *Dir Photog* Carlo Di Palma. *Camera Op* Ray Parslow. *Art Dir* Assheton Gorton. *Film Ed* Frank Clarke. *Mus Comp* Herbie Hancock. *Song:* "Stroll On" *writ & perf by* The Yardbirds. *Sd Rec* Robin Gregory. *Sd Ed* Mike Le Mare. *Dub Mix* J. B. Smith. *Asst Dir* Claude Watson. *Prod Mgr* Donald Toms. *Cont* Betty Harley. *Location Mgr* Bruce Sharman. *Dress Dsgn* Jocelyn Rickards. *Wardrobe Supv* Jackie Breed. *Makeup* Paul Rabiger. *Hairdresser* Stephanie Kaye. *Dial Asst* Piers Haggard. *Photog Murals* John Cowan.

Cast: Vanessa Redgrave (*Jane*), Sarah Miles (*Patricia*), David Hemmings (*Thomas*), John Castle (*Patricia's artist husband*), Jane Birkin, Gillian Hills (*teenagers*), Peter Bowles (*Ron*), Verushka (*herself*), Julian Chagrin, Claude Chagrin (*mimes*), Reg Wilkins (*Thomas' assistant*), Tsai Chin (*Thomas' receptionist*), Susan Broderick (*antique shop owner*), Harry Hutchinson (*shopkeeper*), Mary Khal (*fashion editor*), The Yardbirds (*themselves*), Ronan O'Casey (*Jane's lover in park*), Jill Kennington, Peggy Moffitt, Rosaleen Murray, Ann Norman, Melanie Hampshire (*models*).

Mystery drama. Source: Julio Cortázar, "Final del juego," in *Final del juego; [cuentos]* (Buenos Aires, 1964). Thomas, a successful London photographer, spends a night in a flophouse, photographing derelicts for the book he is preparing. The following day he photographs a fashion layout and then speeds off in his Rolls Royce to inspect an antique shop he intends to buy. He strolls into a nearby park and catches sight of a couple playfully making love. Amused, he proceeds to take pictures of their apparent bliss until the woman, Jane, sees him and asks for the roll of film. He refuses, and later she traces him to his studio and flatly offers herself in exchange for the negatives. After tricking her into accepting a different roll of film, Thomas develops his pictures. An expression on Jane's face as she appears to be glancing toward some bushes arouses his curiosity, and he starts making blowups of the frames of film. Thomas feverishly enlarges each photo in sequence until suddenly he sees the

shadowy figure of a man with a gun lurking in the bushes. The paradoxical nature of his discovery—the difference between what he thought he saw and what actually took place—irritates and confuses him, as does his sudden passion to know the truth. In an interlude, he indulges himself with two teenaged would-be models who visit his studio, but, inevitably, he is drawn back to the park, and he finds the dead body of the man he photographed with Jane. He races back to his studio, but the photographs and negatives have been stolen. When he returns to the park again there is no longer a body. All he sees is a group of mimes playing an imaginary game of tennis. He joins in their game for a moment by tossing an invisible ball back to them, and then he walks slowly away. *Photographers. Models. Photography. Murder. Mime. Seduction. Parks. Antiques. Documentation. London.*

Note: Location scenes filmed in London. Released in Great Britain in 1967. Metro-Goldwyn-Mayer, originally scheduled to distribute the film, removed its name when the seal of the Production Code of America was denied and released the film through a subsidiary company, Premier Productions.

BLUE   F6.0483
Kettledrum Productions. *Dist* Paramount Pictures. 23 Apr **1968** [Salt Lake City, Utah, opening; c31 Mar 1968; LP36393]. Sd; col (Technicolor). 35mm (Panavision). 113 min.

Prod Judd Bernard, Irwin Winkler. *Prod Exec* John Bloom. *Assoc Prod* Patricia Casey. *Dir* Silvio Narizzano. *2d Unit Dir* Yakima Canutt. *Screenplay* Meade Roberts, Ronald M. Cohen. *Story* Ronald M. Cohen. *Photog* Stanley Cortez. *Art Dir* Hal Pereira, Albert Brenner, Al Roelofs. *Set Decor* Claude Carpenter. *Film Ed* Stewart Linder. *Mus* Manos Hadjidakis. *Orch* Leo Arnaud. *Sd Rec* John Carter, John Wilkinson. *Asst Dir* Joseph Lenzi. *2d Unit Asst Dir* Jack Corrick. *Unit Prod Mgr* Joseph Kenny. *2d Unit Prod Mgr* John Morrison. *Script Supv* Doris Grau. *Men's Wardrobe* Pat Kelley. *Women's Wardrobe* Ann Landers. *Makeup Supv* Wally Westmore. *Makeup Artist* Gary Morris. *Hairstyle Supv* Nellie Manley. *Hairstylist* Maryce Bates. *Proc Photog* Farciot Edouart. *Vis Cons* Anthony Pratt. *Prop Master* Anthony Wade. *Dial Coach* Sally Kirkland.

Cast: Terence Stamp (*Blue [Azul]*), Joanna Pettet (*Joanne Morton*), Karl Malden (*Doc Morton*), Ricardo Montalban (*Ortega*), Anthony Costello (*Jess Parker*), Joe De Santis (*Carlos*), James Westerfield (*Abe Parker*), Stathis Giallelis (*Manuel*), Carlos East (*Xavier*), Sara Vardi (*Inez*), Robert Lipton (*Antonio*), Kevin Corcoran (*Rory Calvin*), Ivalou Redd (*Helen Buchanan*), Dorothy Konrad (*Alma Wishoff*), Helen Kleeb (*Elizabeth Parker*), Michael Bell (*Jim Benton*), Wes Bishop (*settler*), Marian Mason (*Mrs. Kramer*), Alma Beltrand (*cantina proprietress*), Sally Kirkland (*Sara Lambert*), Peggy Lipton (*Laurie Kramer*), Jerry Gatlin (*Wes Lambert*), William Shannon (*police chief*), Michael Nader (*Mexican assassin*).

Western melodrama. Azul, the adopted son of Ortega, a Mexican revolutionary bandit, is as cruel as Ortega's three real sons—Manuel, Xavier, and Antonio. During a raid on a Texas settlement in 1880, however, Azul kills Manuel to prevent him from raping Joanne, a young Texas woman. In the ensuing battle with the settlers, Antonio is killed and Azul wounded. Joanne and her father, Doc Morton, offer Azul refuge during his convalescence, and the two young people slowly come to trust each other. Azul, now called Blue, realizes that in killing Manuel he has severed his ties with the Mexicans, and he agrees to help Doc run his farm. After some reluctance on the part of Joanne's former suitor, Jess Parker, all of the settlers accept Blue, and he and Joanne fall in love. Meanwhile, Ortega, depressed by the loss of his adopted son, seeks him out; but their reunion quickly turns into a fight when Blue rejects the old man. His pride hurt, Ortega vows to return with a fighting force, and Blue reluctantly agrees to lead the Texas community against his foster father whom he still loves. The ambush organized by Blue to trap Ortega and his band at the Rio Grande is successful, and both Xavier and Ortega are killed. Feeling guilty for having betrayed his own people, Blue honors Ortega's last request that he be carried to the Mexican side of the river for burial. In so doing, Blue becomes a target for Carlos, a dying Mexican gunman who uses his last bullet to kill Blue. As the settlers pick up their dead, Joanne swims out to bring Blue's body back to Texas soil. *Texans. Mexicans. Foster fathers. Revolutionaries. Bandits. Settlers. Murder. Rape. Filial relations. Perfidy. Texas. Mexican border. Rio Grande.*

Note: Location scenes filmed in Moab, Utah.

THE BLUE BEAST (Japan)   F6.0484
Toho Co. 29 Jan **1965** [New York opening]. Sd; b&w. 35mm (Tohoscope). 95 min.

Prod Sanezumi Fujimoto, Masakatsu Kaneko. *Dir* Hiromichi Horikawa. *Screenplay* Yoshio Shirasaka. *Photog* Asaichi Nakai. *Mus* Sei Ikeno.

Cast: Tatsuya Nakadai (*Yasuhiko Kuroki*), Yoko Tsukasa (*Ayako Eto*), Koreya Senda (*Ayako's father*), Ichiro Nakaya (*Goda*), Jun Tazaki (*Ogawa*), Keiko Awaji (*Yoshie*).

Melodrama. Yasuhiko Kuroki is determined to make his fortune by any means possible, including the use of women and treachery. Yoshie, his former college mistress and socialist colleague, helps him acquire a job with a large publishing company owned by Eto. To win Eto's favor Kuroki informs him of the plans of his socialist friends for a union strike; as a result the union is broken, and the strike fails. To accelerate his rise to the top Kuroki seduces Ayako, Eto's daughter, and she becomes pregnant. The two are married, but Kuroki resumes his relationship with Yoshie, who is now married to the union leader. When Yoshie's husband discovers them together, Yoshie betrays Kuroki and informs the union about his part in the abortive strike. Kuroki returns to his apartment one night and is stabbed to death by one of the outraged union leaders. *Informers. Socialists. Mistresses. Publishers. Ambition. Perfidy. Strikes. Infidelity. Murder. Labor unions.*

Note: Released in Japan in 1960 as *Aoi yaju.*

BLUE HAWAII   F6.0485
Hal Wallis Productions. *Dist* Paramount Pictures. 22 Nov **1961** [Los Angeles opening; c1 Nov 1961; LP20763]. Sd; col (Technicolor). 35mm (Panavision). 101 min.

A Hal Wallis Production. *Prod* Hal B. Wallis. *Assoc Prod* Paul Nathan. *Dir* Norman Taurog. *Screenplay* Hal Kanter. *Story* Allan Weiss. *Dir Photog* Charles Lang, Jr. *2d Unit Photog* W. Wallace Kelley. *Col Cons* Richard Mueller. *Art Dir* Hal Pereira, Walter Tyler. *Set Decor* Sam Comer, Frank McKelvy. *Ed Supv* Warren Low. *Ed* Terry O. Morse. *Mus Scored & Cond* Joseph J. Lilley. *Vocal Accompaniment* The Jordanaires. *Titl Song* Leo Robin, Ralph Rainger. *Song:* "Almost Always True" Fred Wise, Ben Weisman. *Song:* "Aloha Oe" Lydia Kamekeha Liliuodalani. *Arr & Adapt* Elvis Presley. *Song:* "No More" Don Robertson, Hal Blair. *Songs:* "I Can't Help Falling in Love," "Ku-U-I-Po" Hugo Peretti, Luigi Creatore, George David Weiss. *Song:* "Rock-a-Hula Baby" Fred Wise, Ben Weisman, Dolores Fuller. *Song:* "Moonlight Swim" Sylvia Dee, Ben Weisman. *Songs:* "Ito Eats," "Slicin' Sand," "Hawaiian Sunset," "Beach Boy Blues," "Island of Love" Sid Tepper, Roy C. Bennett. *Song:* "Hawaiian Wedding Song" Charles E. King, Al Hoffman, Dick Manning. *Songs Sung by* Elvis Presley. *Mus Numbers Staged by* Charles O'Curran. *Sd Rec* Philip Mitchell, Charles Grenzbach. *Asst Dir* D. Michael Moore. *Cost* Edith Head. *Makeup Supv* Wally Westmore. *Hairstyles* Nellie Manley. *Sp Photog Eff* John P. Fulton. *Proc Photog* Farciot Edouart. *Tech Adv* Col. Tom Parker. *Dial Coach* Jack Mintz.

Cast: Elvis Presley *(Chad Gates)*, Joan Blackman *(Maile Duval)*, Nancy Walters *(Abigail Prentace)*, Roland Winters *(Fred Gates)*, Angela Lansbury *(Sarah Lee Gates)*, John Archer *(Jack Kelman)*, Howard McNear *(Mr. Chapman)*, Flora Hayes *(Mrs. Manaka)*, Gregory Gay *(Mr. Duval)*, Steve Brodie *(Mr. Garvey)*, Iris Adrian *(Mrs. Garvey)*, Darlene Tompkins *(Patsy)*, Pamela Akert *(Sandy)*, Christian Kay *(Beverly)*, Jenny Maxwell *(Ellie)*, Frank Atienza *(Ito O'Hara)*, Lani Kai *(Carl)*, Jose De Vega *(Ernie)*, Ralph Hanalie *(Wes)*, Hilo Hattie, Mike Ross *(Lieutenant Grey)*, Richard Reeves *(harmonica-playing convict)*, Tiki Hanalie.

Comedy-drama with music. After two years in the Army, Chad Gates returns to Hawaii, where he defies his wealthy and domineering Southern mother by refusing to take a job in his father's prosperous pineapple business. Instead, he goes to work as a guide for the tourist agency where Maile, his French-Hawaiian girl friend, is employed. His first assignment is to escort schoolteacher Abigail Prentace and four teenaged girls around the island. At a luau, Chad gets into a fight with a drunken tourist who has made advances toward one of the teenagers, and he is hauled off to jail. Later, Chad is reprimanded by his mother, who blames the row on Maile's influence. Maile, on the other hand, is suspicious of Abigail's interest in Chad; she is unaware that it is Chad's uncle, Jack Kelman, with whom the young teacher has fallen in love. All misunderstandings are resolved, however, and Chad and Maile plan to marry and open their own tourist agency. Chad's father, with the sly assistance of Uncle Jack, agrees to let Chad and Maile handle all the arrangements for his company's next convention on the island. Even Mrs. Gates is won over during the colorful Hawaiian wedding. *Southerners. Businessmen. Hawaiians. Guides. Schoolteachers. Uncles. Filial relations. Wealth. Jealousy. Tourism. Luaus. Weddings. Hawaii.*

Note: Location scenes filmed in Hawaii. Prerelease title: *Hawaii Beach Boy.* Copyright claimants: Hal B. Wallis and Joseph H. Hazen.

THE BLUE MAX (Great Britain)   F6.0486
Twentieth Century-Fox Productions. *Dist* Twentieth Century-Fox Film Corp. 21 Jun **1966** [New York opening; c22 Jun 1966; LP33515]. Sd (Westrex); col (DeLuxe). 35mm (CinemaScope). 156 min.

Prod Christian Ferry. *Exec Prod* Elmo Williams. *Dir* John Guillermin. *Aerial Unit Dir* Anthony Squire. *Screenplay* David Pursall, Jack Seddon, Gerald Hanley. *Adapt* Ben Barzman, Basilio Franchina. *Dir Photog* Douglas Slocombe. *Aerial Unit Photog* Skeets Kelly. *Camera Op* Chic Waterson. *Art Dir* Fred Carter. *Prod Dsgn* Wilfrid Shingleton. *Film Ed* Max Benedict. *Asst*

Ed Elizabeth Thoyts. *Assembly Cutter* Norman Cohen. *Mus Comp & Cond* Jerry Goldsmith. *Sd* Claude Hitchcock, John Cox, Bob Jones. *Sd Ed* Chris Greenham. *Asst Dir* Jack Causey, Derek Cracknell. *Prod Mgr* René Dupont. *Cont* Helen Whitson. *Irish Prod Liaison* William O'Kelly. *Miss Andress' Wardrobe* John Furness. *Wardrobe Supv* Elsa Fennell. *Head Makeup* Charles Parker. *George Peppard's Makeup* Tony Sforzini. *Ursula Andress' Makeup* John O'Gorman. *Hairdresser* Pat McDermott. *Sp Eff* Karl Baumgartner, Maurice Ayers, Ron Ballanger. *Air Supv* Allen Wheeler, (Commodore). *Air Engr* Johnny Maher. *Flyers* Derek Pigott, Ken Byrnes, Tim Clutterbuck, Pat Cranfield, Peter Hillwood, Tim Healey, Darby Kennedy, Roger Kennedy, Joan Hughes, Liam Mulligan, Taffy Rich. *Casting Dir* Stuart Lyons.

Cast: George Peppard *(Bruno Stachel)*, James Mason *(Count von Klugermann)*, Ursula Andress *(Countess Kaeti)*, Jeremy Kemp *(Willi von Klugermann)*, Karl Michael Vogler *(Heidemann)*, Anton Diffring *(Holbach)*, Harry Towb *(Kettering)*, Peter Woodthorpe *(Rupp)*, Derek Newark *(Ziegel)*, Derren Nesbitt *(Fabian)*, Loni von Friedl *(Elfi von Friedl)*, Friedrich Ledebur *(Field Marshal von Lenndorf)*, Carl Schell *(Baron von Richthofen)*, Hugo Schuster *(Hans)*, Alex Scott *(orator)*, Roger Ostime *(crown prince)*, Ray Browne, Timothy Parkes, Ian Kingsley *(pilots)*, John Harvey.

Historical drama. Source: Jack D. Hunter, *The Blue Max* (New York, 1964). Toward the end of World War I, a newly-trained German fighter pilot, Bruno Stachel, becomes unpopular with his fellow pilots because of his determination to win the Blue Max, an award given to German pilots who shoot down 20 enemy planes. When he captures a British observation plane and coldbloodedly shoots it down in order to score a "kill," his action wins the approval of high-ranking Count von Klugermann, who openly applauds the will to win at any cost. Competing with Bruno for top flying honors is the count's nephew, Willi, who is having an affair with his uncle's wife, Kaeti. The calculating Bruno not only takes Kaeti for himself but also maneuvers his rival into a fatal crash and then claims two of Willi's kills as his own. Now eligible for the Blue Max, Bruno refuses to leave the country with Kaeti though he is certain of Germany's eventual defeat. In revenge, Kaeti exposes his false claims at the same moment a court-martial is ordered to investigate Willi's death and other instances of Bruno's disregard for human life. The count, unwilling to permit the hero to be disgraced, deliberately permits Bruno to test a new plane he knows to be faulty. Consequently, Bruno takes flight before a huge crowd and does a spectacular series of air maneuvers before the plane breaks apart in mid-air. *Germans. Air pilots. Ambition. Infidelity. Revenge. Courts-martial. World War I. Germany.*

Note: Filmed in Ireland. Opened in London in Jun 1966.

BLUE MOVIE   F6.0487
Factory Films. *Dist* Andy Warhol Films. 13 Jun **1969** [New York opening]. Sd; col (Eastman Color). 16mm. 90 min. [See note.]

Exec Prod Paul Morrissey. *Prod-Dir* Andy Warhol. *Photog* Andy Warhol. *Sd* Jed Johnson.

Cast: Viva *(Viva)*, Louis Waldon *(Louis)*.

Satire. Viva and Louis spend an afternoon in a Manhattan apartment. While lying on a bed, they discuss such topics as strychnine in drugs and whether it is responsible for hallucinations; the paintings of Franz Kline; Viva's concern about getting old; how athlete's foot and gonorrhea are contracted; and the possibility that they will get married. Louis removes Viva's clothes as well as his own, and they continue their discussions while they examine each other's bodies and have sexual intercourse. Later, Viva relates an incident in which she was stopped by police in East Hampton, Long Island, for not wearing a brassiere. They go on to discuss Mayor Lindsay of New York, the predicament of U. S. involvement in Vietnam, and the futility of war. Kneeling near the bed, they watch television for a while; they then get dressed. Viva prepares a meal; they discuss oral sex and Louis' unhappy marriage; and finally they move to the bathroom. Louis gets into the shower fully clothed, and Viva admits that she is "stoned." They disrobe and enjoy some sexual horseplay in and out of the bathtub until Viva looks at the camera, asks, "Is it on? Is it still on?" and flees. *Oral sex. Television. Marriage. Psychedelic drugs. Poisoning. Venereal disease. Athlete's foot. Vietnam War 1964–73. New York City. Franz Kline. John Vliet Lindsay.*

Note: Filmed on location in New York City. Subsequent to the New York opening at 90 min, the film was screened for the press at 140 min; 105-min general release version opened 21 Jul 1969. Also known as *Fuck* and *F**k.*

BLUE SURFARI *see* SURFARI

BLUEBEARD *see* LANDRU

BLUEPRINT FOR ROBBERY   F6.0488
Paramount Pictures. 18 Jan **1961** [Boston opening; c31 Dec 1960; LP18279]. Sd; b&w. 35mm. 87 min.

Prod Bryan Foy. *Dir* Jerry Hopper. *Screenplay* Irwin Winehouse, A. Sanford Wolf. *Dir Photog* Loyal Griggs. *Art Dir* Hal Pereira, Al Roelofs. *Set Decor* Sam Comer, Ray Moyer. *Film Ed* Terry O. Morse. *Mus Score* Nathan Van Cleave.

Sd Rec Hugo Grenzbach, Charles Grenzbach. *Asst Dir* C. C. Coleman, Jr. *Makeup Supv* Wally Westmore. *Hairstyle Supv* Nellie Manley. *Proc Photog* Farciot Edouart. *Adv (see note)* Preston G. Smith.

Cast: J. Pat O'Malley (*Pop Kane*), Robert J. Wilke (*Captain Swanson*), Robert Gist (*Chips McGann*), Romo Vincent (*Fatso Bonneli*), Jay Barney (*Red Mack*), Henry Corden (*Preacher-Doc*), Tom Duggan (*James Livingston*), Sherwood Price (*Gus Romay*), Robert Carricart (*Gyp Grogan*), John Indrisano (*Nick Tony*), Paul Salata (*Rocky*), Joe Conley (*Jock McGee*), Marion Ross (*young woman*), Barbara Mansell (*bargirl*).

Crime melodrama. Boston nightclub owner Chips McGann organizes a group of mobsters to rob an armored car service. Ex-convict Red Mack is masterminding the plan on the condition that they wait for his old friend Pop Kane to finish a jail sentence. When Pop is released, the plans are completed, and several weeks are devoted to careful preparations. The gang then don grotesque Halloween masks, enter the armored car building, and make off with more than $2 million. As previously agreed, McGann is to keep all the money until the Massachusetts statute of limitations runs out in 3 1/2 years. A short time after the heist, Red is jailed on a minor robbery charge, but McGann refuses, despite Pop's pleas, to furnish the bail. Red is paroled, and McGann attempts to have him killed, but Red survives. The police become suspicious, revoke his parole, and lock him up again. When he refuses to talk, they tell him that they plan to arrest Pop on a parole violation charge and send him back to prison for life. Red then agrees to provide the evidence if Pop is cleared of all charges and permitted to return to his native Ireland. After the remainder of the gang have been apprehended, a meeting is arranged between Pop and Red. Pop, unaware that Red has saved him from life imprisonment, accuses him of being an informer and walks out of the room. *Nightclub owners. Gangsters. Ex-convicts. Police. Informers. Robbery. Parole. Armored car services. Masks. Boston.*

Note: Based on a 1950 armored car robbery in Boston. The film's advisor, Preston G. Smith, served as warden of the U. S. Federal Prison at Terminal Island, California. Working title: *The Big Boston Robbery.*

BLUES FOR LOVERS (Great Britain)   **F6.0489**
Alsa Films. *Dist* Twentieth Century–Fox Film Corp. 7 Sep **1966** [New York opening; c31 Dec 1965; LP33481]. Sd (RCA); b&w. 35mm. 89 min.

Pres by Alexander Salkind. *Prod* Herman Blaser. *Exec Prod* Alexander Salkind, Miguel Salkind. *Dir* Paul Henreid. *Screenplay* Burton Wohl. *Story* Paul Henreid, Burton Wohl. *Photog* Bob Huke. *Camera Op* Ron Taylor. *Art Dir* Lionel Couch. *Film Ed* Raymond Poulton. *Asst Ed* John Lee, ed. *Mus Dir* Ray Charles. *Songs:* "Let the Good Times Roll," "Lucky Old Sun," "Hallelujah, I Love Her So," "Talking About You," "Cry," "What'd I Say," "Unchain My Heart," "I Got a Woman," "Careless Love" *perf by* Ray Charles Orchestra, The Raelets. *Song:* "Light Out of Darkness" Ray Charles, Rick Ward, Stanley Black. *Sd Rec* Claude Hitchcock, John Aldred. *Dub Ed* James Shields. *Asst Dir* Stuart Freeman, Alex Carver-Hill, Nigel Watts. *Prod Supv* Wilfred Eades. *Prod Mgr* R. L. M. Davidson. *Cont* Eileen Head. *Wardrobe Mistress* Jackie Cummins. *Makeup* George Partleton. *Hairdresser* Henry Montsash.

Cast: Ray Charles (*himself*), Tom Bell (*Steve Collins*), Mary Peach (*Peggy Harrison*), Dawn Addams (*Gina Graham*), Joe Adams (*Fred*), Betty McDowall (*Mrs. Babbidge*), Lucy Appleby (*Margaret*), Monika Henreid (*Antonia*), Piers Bishop (*David*), Brenda Agnew (*Antonia's protector*), Dennis Brennan (*George Stewart*), John Cowley (*Arthur Penrose*), Richard Condon (*standee*), Rosette Devereaux (*girl dancer*), Dennis Franks (*theater porter*), Bob Gallico (*journalist*), Vernon Hayden (*headmaster*), Albert Healy (*bass player*), Richard De Lisle (*drummer*), Joan Mayne (*girl dancer*), Peter Maycock (*Eric*), Leo McCabe (*Roger*), Nuala Moiselle (*nurse*), Antonio Navarro (*guitarist*), Anne Padwick (*bus conductress*), Albert Regent (*dancer*), Hal Roach, mus (*guitarist*), Dawn Robinson (*Mrs. Penrose*), Robert Lee Ross (*John*), Middleton Woods (*theater porter*).

Drama with music. American jazz pianist Ray Charles entertains at a London institute for blind children and meets David, a blind 8-year-old boy, and his widowed mother, Peggy Harrison. Charles becomes fond of the boy; but he and Steve Collins, a young composer-pianist romantically involved with Peggy, worry about her overprotective attitude toward David. Steve does some arrangements for Charles's band, and Charles asks Steve to accompany the band to Paris. Peggy wants Peggy and David to come along, but she is afraid that the trip would be harmful to David. In Paris, Steve resumes an affair with Gina, a socialite. Peggy and David come to Paris, however, when Charles tells him that he has met an eye surgeon who believes there is a chance to restore the boy's sight by a dangerous operation, for which Charles wants to pay. Peggy is grateful but apprehensive until Gina persuades her to take the risk. The operation is performed on the day that Charles presents Steve's first major composition. David's operation is successful and there appears to be a good chance that his sight will return; Steve's composition is well received, and he

and Peggy are reunited. *Americans in foreign countries. Musicians. Pianists. Widows. Composers. Socialites. Surgeons. Children. Blindness. Motherhood. Eye surgery. Jazzbands. London. Paris.*

Note: Location scenes filmed in London and Paris. Opened in London in Feb 1965 as *Ballad in Blue.*

BLUTIGE SEIDE *see* **BLOOD AND BLACK LACE**

THE BOATNIKS   **F6.0490**
Walt Disney Productions. *Dist* Buena Vista Distribution Co. 1 Jul **1970** [New York opening; c21 May 1970; LP38057]. Sd (RCA); col (Technicolor). 35mm. 100 min. *MPAA rating* G.

Prod Ron Miller. *Assoc Prod* Tom Leetch. *Dir* Norman Tokar. *2d Unit Dir* Arthur J. Vitarelli. *Screen Story & Screenplay* Arthur Julian. *Story* Marty Roth. *Dir Photog* William Snyder. *Camera Op* Roger Sherman. *Asst Camera* Jim Luske, James Mathews. *Art Dir* Hilyard Brown, John Mansbridge. *Set Decor* Emile Kuri, Frank R. McKelvy. *Film Ed* Cotton Warburton. *Mus* Robert F. Brunner. *Orch* Franklyn Marks. *Song:* "Boatniks" Robert F. Brunner, Bruce Belland. *Sd Supv* Robert O. Cook. *Sd Mix* Dean Thomas. *Mus Ed* Evelyn Kennedy. *Boom Op* Frank Regula. *Asst Dir* Christopher Hibler, Robert M. Webb. *Unit Mgr* Irving Temaner. *Script Supv* Eylla Jacobus. *Cost* Emily Sundby, Chuck Keehne. *Makeup* Robert J. Schiffer. *Hairstyles* La Rue Matheron, Joan Phillips. *Sp Eff* Eustace Lycett, Robert A. Mattey. *Matte Artist* Alan Maley. *Still Photog* Floyd McCarty. *Gaffer* Otto Meyer. *Prop Master* Wilbur Russell. *Key Grip* Stan Reed.

Cast: Robert Morse (*Ens. Thomas Garland*), Stefanie Powers (*Kate Fairchild*), Phil Silvers (*Harry Simmons*), Norman Fell (*Max Mason*), Mickey Shaughnessy (*Charlie Long*), Wally Cox (*Jason Bennett*), Don Ameche (*Commander Taylor*), Joey Forman (*Lieutenant Jordan*), Vito Scotti (*Pepe Galindo*), Tom Lowell (*Wagner*), Bob Hastings (*Chief Walsh*), Sammy Jackson (*Garlotti*), Joe E. Ross (*nutty sailor*), Judy Jordan (*Tina*), Al Lewis (*Bert*), Midori (*Chiyoko Kuni*), Kelly Thordsen (*motorcycle cop*), Gil Lamb (*Mr. Mitchell*).

Comedy. Ensign Thomas Garland takes command of a busy harbor in Newport Beach, California. Although senior officer Commander Taylor is eager to have the son of an illustrious World War II hero under him, enthusiasm wanes upon discovery of the officer's incompetence. After introducing himself to rental operator Kate Fairchild by spilling yellow paint over her, Garland attempts to rescue a rowboat, in the process grounding his Coast Guard cutter. As three thieves, Harry, Max, and Charlie, escape through the fogbound harbor, they collide with Garland's vessel. The jewels, hidden in a picnic basket, sink to the ocean floor. To recover the basket the trio recruits a voluptuous Japanese pearl diver, thereby exciting the ensign's suspicion. Informed of these events by Garland, Taylor is incredulous until Moby Dick, Kate's pet pelican, pilfers a jewel-encrusted pickle. During the thieves' flight by submarine and seaplane the jewels are jettisoned. Garland recovers the cache, selecting from it an engagement ring for Kate. *Thieves. Japanese. Diving. Shipwrecks. Picnics. Fog. Motorboats. Jewels. Submarines. Seaplanes. Newport Beach (California). United States Coast Guard. Chases. Pelicans.*

Note: Location scenes filmed at Newport Beach, California.

BOB & CAROL & TED & ALICE   **F6.0491**
Frankovich Productions–Coriander Productions. *Dist* Columbia Pictures. 8 Oct **1969** [New York opening; c1 Dec 1969; LP37646]. Sd; col (Technicolor). 35mm. 104 min. *MPAA rating* R.

An M. J. Frankovich Production. *Prod* Larry Tucker. *Exec Prod* M. J. Frankovich. *Dir* Paul Mazursky. *Writ* Paul Mazursky, Larry Tucker. *Dir Photog* Charles Lang. *Art Dir* Pato Guzman. *Set Decor* Frank Tuttle. *Film Ed* Stuart H. Pappé. *Mus* Quincy Jones. *Song:* "What the World Needs Now Is Love" Hal David, Burt Bacharach. *Sung by* Jackie De Shannon. *Song:* "I Needs To Be Be'd With" Ernie Shelby, Quincy Jones. *Sung by* Johnnie Wesley. *Song:* "Burbank Brown" Ray Greathouse, Morris Bachemin. *Instrumental* Sweet Progress. *Choreog* Miriam Nelson. *Sd Supv* Charles J. Rice. *Sd* Dean Thomas, Arthur Piantadosi. *Asst Dir* Anthony Ray. *Exec Prod Mgr* William O'Sullivan. *Cost Dsgn* Moss Mabry. *Makeup Supv* Ben Lane. *Hairstyles* Virginia Jones. *Prop Master* Max Frankel.

Cast: Natalie Wood (*Carol Sanders*), Robert Culp (*Bob Sanders*), Elliott Gould (*Ted Henderson*), Dyan Cannon (*Alice Henderson*), Horst Ebersberg (*Horst*), Lee Bergere (*Emilio*), Donald F. Muhich (*psychiatrist*), Noble Lee Holderread, Jr. (*Sean*), K. T. Stevens (*Phyllis*), Celeste Yarnall (*Susan*), Lynn Borden (*Cutter*), Linda Burton (*stewardess*).

Cast—Institute Group: Greg Mullavey (*group leader*), André Philippe (*Oscar*), Diane Berghoff (*Myrna*), John Halloran (*Conrad*), Susan Merin (*Toby*), Jeffrey Walker (*Roger*), Vicki Thal (*Jane*), Joyce Easton (*Wendy*), Howard Dayton (*Howard*), Alida Ihle (*Alida*).

Cast—Family Friends: John Brent (*Dave*), Garry Goodrow (*Bert*), Carol O'Leary (*Sue*), Constance Egan (*Norma*).

Comedy. While doing research for a documentary, filmmaker Bob Sanders takes his wife, Carol, to an Esalen-type "sensitivity" institute in Southern California. Enlightened by the experience, the couple vow to expand their capacities for love and understanding by sharing everything with each other. So great is their enthusiasm that they decide to share their newfound "liberation" with their closest friends, lawyer Ted Henderson and his wife, Alice. But the Hendersons, particularly the somewhat inhibited Alice, remain skeptical. Following a trip to San Francisco, Bob confesses to his wife that he had a brief extramarital fling with his production secretary. Deeply moved by Bob's frankness and trust, Carol repeats Bob's confession to Ted and Alice, but the revelation leaves Alice so aghast that she feels compelled to visit a psychiatrist to discuss her sexual life with Ted. Upon returning from another trip, Bob finds that Carol spent the previous night with Horst, the tennis instructor from their club. Stifling his initial hostility in favor of a more "civilized" attitude, Bob insists that Horst sit down and join him in a friendly drink. A short time later Bob and Carol and Ted and Alice go off to Las Vegas for a weekend. Before leaving to catch Tony Bennett's dinner show, Bob relates Carol's experience with Horst, and Ted is moved to admit that he, too, recently indulged in a brief adulterous episode. Unhinged by what has happened, Alice defiantly demands that they have an orgy before going out to dinner. After some hesitation and discussion, the two couples agree to the proposal and all four climb into one large bed. Despite some preliminaries, however, they find that they are unable to go through with it. Filled with good will toward each other, Bob and Carol and Ted and Alice get dressed, leave the hotel, and join the throngs of people milling about outside. *Motion picture directors. Lawyers. Secretaries. Psychiatrists. Tennis instructors. Infidelity. Mate swapping. Friendship. Encounter groups. California. Las Vegas.*

Note: Location scenes filmed in California.

THE BOB HOPE VIETNAM CHRISTMAS SHOW   F6.0492

Bob Hope Enterprises. *Dist* Interstate Circuit, Inc. 6 Apr **1966** [Dallas opening]. Sd; col. 35mm. ca72 min. [See note.]

Exec Prod Bob Hope. *Dir* Mort Lachman. *Screenplay* Mort Lachman, Bill Larkin, Lester White, Charles Lee, John Rapp, Gig Henry. *Dir Photog* Alan Stensvold. *Film Ed* Richard Belding, Louis Lombardo. *Asst to Exec Prod* Sil Caranchini. *Program Coörd* George Hope. *Unit Mgr* Tom Hulbert. *Script Cons* Norm Sullivan.

Featuring: Bob Hope, Carroll Baker, Kaye Stevens, Jack Jones, Joey Heatherton, Anita Bryant, Jerry Colonna, Nicholas Bros., Diana Lynn Batts, Les Brown and His Band, Peter Leeds.

Film Clips of: Martha Raye, Eddie Fisher, John Bubbles, Francis Cardinal Spellman.

Documentary. Bob Hope and his entourage entertain U. S. troops in Vietnam, Thailand, the Philippines, Guam, Wake Island, and aboard a ship in the Pacific. *Vietnam. Thailand. Philippines. Guam. Wake Island. Pacific Ocean. United States Army. United States Marines. United States Air Force. United States Navy.*

Note: First shown 19 Jan 1966 on NBC-TV. An introduction by Hope and additional scenes were added for theatrical release.

THE BOBO (Great Britain)   F6.0493

Gina Productions. *Dist* Warner Bros.–Seven Arts, Inc. 11 Aug **1967** [Boston opening; c19 Aug 1967; LP35725]. Sd; col (Technicolor). 35mm. 103 min.

A Jerry Gershwin–Elliott Kastner Production. *Prod* Jerry Gershwin, Elliott Kastner. *Assoc Prod* David R. Schwartz. *Assoc to Prod* Aldo Piga. *Dir* Robert Parrish. *Screenplay* David R. Schwartz. *Photog* Gerry Turpin. *Camera Op* Ron Taylor. *Art Dir* Elven Webb. *Set Dresser* Franco Fumagalli. *Prod Dsgn* Don Ashton. *Main Titl* National Screen Service Ltd. *Film Ed* John Jympson. *Asst Ed* Pamela Tomling. *Mus* Francis Lai. *Songs:* "The Bulls of Salamanca," "The Girl From Barcelona" George Martin, Herbert Kretzmer. *Songs:* "Imagine," "The Song of the Blue Matador" Francis Lai, Sammy Cahn. *Sd Rec* Sash Fisher, Gordon K. McCallum. *Sd Ed* Rusty Coppleman. *Asst Dir* Gus Agosti. *Prod Supv* Denis Holt. *Prod Mgr* Orazio Tassara. *Cont* Yvonne Axworthy. *Asst to Prod* Marion Rosenberg, Franca Tasso. *Cost* Adriana Berselli. *Mr. Sellers' Makeup* Harry Frampton. *Miss Ekland's Makeup* John O'Gorman. *Hairdressing* Amalia Paoletti. *Dial Dir* Alfredo Lettieri, Raffaele Mottola.

Cast: Peter Sellers *(Juan Bautista)*, Britt Ekland *(Olimpia Segura)*, Rossano Brazzi *(Carlos Matabosch)*, Adolfo Celi *(Francisco Carbonell)*, Hattie Jacques *(Trinity Martinez)*, Ferdy Mayne *(Silvestre Flores)*, Kenneth Griffith *(Pepe Gamazo)*, Alfredo Lettieri *(Eugenio Gomez)*, Marne Maitland *(Luis Castillo)*, John Wells *(Pompadour major-domo)*, Don Lurio *(Ramon Gonzales)*, Giustino Durano *(druggist)*, Alfredo Chetta *(Ilya)*, La Chana *(Flamenco dancer)*, Los Tarantos *(Flamenco company)*.

Comedy. Source: David R. Schwartz, *The Bobo* (a play; production undetermined). Burt Cole, *Olimpia* (New York, 1959). Having failed to win fame in the bullring, impoverished Juan Bautista goes to Barcelona in the hope of making a name for himself as a singing matador. So persistent is he that

impresario Francisco Carbonell agrees to give him a booking if, within 3 days, he can seduce the beautiful Olimpia, Barcelona's most celebrated "courtesan." Undaunted by the fact that the young woman has become wealthy by bestowing nothing more than promises, Juan poses as the trusted emissary of a wealthy count who is prepared to pay a fortune just to meet Olimpia on a platonic level. Intrigued by the proposal, Olimpia accepts Juan's check for 25,000 pesetas and consents to meet the count. But when he fails to appear at each of their scheduled meetings, Olimpia is obliged to pass the time with Juan. On the third day, she purchases a mink coat with the check and, lightheaded from too much wine, invites Juan to spend the night with her. In the morning, however, she discovers that the check was worthless. When Juan confesses his guilt, the enraged Olimpia forces him at gunpoint to bathe in a tub of blue dye guaranteed to last for 2 years. Although Juan has won the wager, he is too much of a gentleman to give Carbonell the details of his night with Olimpia, and he loses his contract. Some time later, Olimpia and Matabosch, one of her wealthy conquests, see a poster advertising Juan as Spain's only singing blue matador. *Bullfighters. Singers. Impresari. Prostitutes. Wagers. Imposture. Seduction. Wealth. Drunkenness. Duplicity. Dye. Barcelona.*

Note: Location scenes filmed in Barcelona, Spain. Released in Great Britain in 1967.

BOCCACCIO '70 (France/Italy)   F6.0494

Concordia Compagnia Cinematografica–Cineriz–Francinex–Gray Films. *Dist* Embassy Pictures. 26 Jun **1962** [New York opening]. Sd; col (Technicolor, U. S. print by Eastmancolor). 35mm. 165 min.

Overall Production Credits: *Pres by* Joseph E. Levine. *Prod* Carlo Ponti, Antonio Cervi. *Devised by* Cesare Zavattini.

Production Credits—"The Temptation of Dr. Antonio": *Dir* Federico Fellini. *Screenplay* Federico Fellini, Ennio Flajano, Tullio Pinelli. *Photog* Otello Martelli. *Set Dsgn* Piero Zuffi. *Film Ed* Leo Catozzo. *Mus* Nino Rota.

Production Credits—"The Job": *Dir* Luchino Visconti. *Screenplay* Luchino Visconti, Suso Cecchi D'Amico. *Photog* Giuseppe Rotunno. *Set Dsgn* Mario Garbuglia. *Film Ed* Mario Serandrei. *Mus* Nino Rota.

Production Credits—"The Raffle": *Dir* Vittorio De Sica. *Screenplay* Cesare Zavattini. *Photog* Otello Martelli. *Set Dsgn* Elio Costanzi. *Film Ed* Adriana Novelli. *Mus* Armando Trovajoli.

Cast—"The Temptation of Dr. Antonio": Anita Ekberg *(Anita)*, Peppino De Filippo *(Dr. Antonio)*, Dante Maggio, Alberto Sorrentino, Giacomo Furia, Mario Passante, Silvio Bagolini.

Cast—"The Job": Romy Schneider *(Pupe)*, Tomas Milian *(The Count)*, Romolo Valli *(The Lawyer)*, Paolo Stoppa, Amedeo Girard.

Cast—"The Raffle": Sophia Loren *(Zoe)*, Luigi Giuliani *(Gaetano)*, Alfio Vita *(The Sexton)*.

Comedy-drama. Source: Giovanni Boccaccio, *Il decamerone.* THE TEMPTATION OF DR. ANTONIO: Dr. Antonio, a self-appointed crusader against vice and immorality in Rome, is outraged when a gigantic poster of a seductive blonde holding a glass of milk is erected on the vacant lot facing his apartment. To placate him the authorities cover the poster with paper, but the covering comes off during a storm, and the obsessed moralist imagines that the giant woman on the poster has come to life. Ignoring his squealing protests, she playfully picks him up, holds him to her bosom, and dances through the streets with voluptuous abandon. He is driven mad by the encounter, and, with the coming of morning the police find him clinging to the top of the billboard. A huge crowd gathers as he is lifted down and carried away to an asylum. THE JOB: Bored with his idle existence, a young Milanese count creates a scandal by consorting with $1000-a-night call girls. Although the news infuriates his German father-in-law, who controls the family funds, his beautiful wife, Pupe, remains calmly indifferent. She tells him that she has made a wager with her father that she can support herself for a year. As preparation for her job, she has visited the count's female companions and learned the secrets of their profession. She then suggests that the count avoid any further notoriety by paying her whenever he feels the need for sexual intimacy. The count agrees and goes to write a check as his wife prepares for bed with tears running down her face. THE RAFFLE: Zoe, a lusty young woman, works with a traveling carnival belonging to her brother-in-law. Each Saturday night in a different village in the Po Valley, she offers herself as the prize of a $5-a-ticket raffle to help support her pregnant sister. One night she falls in love with a handsome stranger, Gaetano, and becomes reluctant to accommodate the latest winner, a meek sexton named Cuspet, who has declined all offers to purchase his ticket. Rather than embarrass the sexton in front of his friends, Zoe covers him with lipstick, gives him all the prize money, and then politely ushers him out of her bedroom. As the proud Cuspet is carried through the streets of the town, Zoe races off to meet Gaetano. *Nobility. Fathers-in-law. Germans. Sextons. Censorship. Prostitution. Wagers. Obsession. Employment—Women. Lotteries. Infidelity. Fatherhood. Billboards. Carnivals. Rome. Milan. Po River. Hallucinations.*

Note: Opened in Rome in Feb 1962 in a 210-min version including four episodes: "Renzo e Lucia," directed by Mario Monicelli; "Le tentazioni di Dottor Antonio"; "Il lavoro"; and "La riffa." Monicelli's episode was omitted outside of Italy. Opened in Paris in Aug 1962 as *Boccace 70*; running time: 156 min.

BOCCACE 70 *see* **BOCCACCIO '70**

THE BODY (Japan)   **F6.0495**
  Shochiku Co. *Dist* Shochiku Films of America. 24 Feb **1964** [Los Angeles opening]. Sd; col (Eastmancolor). 35mm (Shochiku GrandScope). 85 min.
  Exec Prod Masao Shirai, Shigeru Wakatsuki. *Dir-Writ* Masashige Narusawa. *Photog* Ko Kawamata. *Art Dir* Koji Uno, art. *Mus* Toru Takemitsu, Joji Iwata.
  Cast: Michiko Saga (*Sakiko Okamu*), Ichiro Sugai (*her father*), Kumeko Urabe (*her mother*), Kazuko Matsuo (*Kimiko*), Mitsuko Takara (*Marie Angel*), Minoru Chiaki (*Sasaki*), Yusuke Kawazu (*Sota*), Hiroyuki Nagato (*Takasugi*), Eitaro Shindo (*Hyodo*), Isuzu Yamada (*proprietress of sex club*), Chieko Naniwa (*Naka*), Isao Sasaki (*the handsome boy*).
  Melodrama. Source: Kafu Nagai, *Ratai* (Tokyo, 1954). Sakiko comes to Tokyo from a small fishing village where her humble parents work in a public bathhouse. Finding work in the city, Sakiko becomes her boss's mistress. He forces her to keep close account of her daily expenses, allowing her no money to spend on herself. After he is arrested for tax evasion, she leaves him and, on the advice of her ballet teacher, takes a job in a sex club where she meets Hyodo, a member of parliament. Not wishing to become involved with her, Hyodo after a time rejects her. Aspiring to a life of luxury, and well aware of her physical attractiveness to both men and women, Sakiko becomes a prostitute after being taught the skills of the profession. One night she picks up a sincere and handsome young man, but he soon flees from her when she forces herself on him too strongly. Alone again, Sakiko returns to the streets. *Prostitutes. Mistresses. Misers. Politicians. Dance teachers. Ambition. Urban life. Sex clubs. Tokyo.*
  Note: Released in Japan in 1962 as *Ratai*; running time: 98 min.

THE BODY BENEATH   **F6.0496**
  Cinemedia Films. *Dist* Nova International. 4 Dec **1970** [Buffalo, New York, opening]. Sd; col. 35mm. 85 min.
  Dir-Writ Andy Milligan. *Photog* Andy Milligan. *Sets* James Fox, art. *Film Ed* Gerald Jackson. *Prod Mgr* Graham Steane.
  Cast: Jackie Skarvellis (*Miss Ford*), Emma Jones, Susan Clark [2], Colin Gordon (*Ford relatives*), Gavin Reed (*vampire*), Susan Heard (*wife of vampire*), Richmond Ross (*artist*), Berwick Kaler (*hunchback*), Felicity Sentance (*maid*).
  Horror film. Arriving in London, a British vampire and his wife seek the remaining relations of the Fords, whose blood has nourished their family for centuries. A female descendant, who has become pregnant by an artist, is confronted by the vampire in preacher's guise. His identity so concealed, the vampire, hoping to obtain both blood and baby, proposes to perform the ceremony uniting woman and artist. Another female Ford, bitten by the fiend, permits the vampire's entourage to feast on her husband. A maid is killed with knitting needles, a hunchbacked servant is burned alive, and another Ford is slain. At a blood feast, the vampire persuades his disciples to emigrate to America, leaving the ancestral Carfax Abbey to the newlywed vampires. *British. Vampires. Artists. Newlyweds. Hunchbacks. Housemaids. Pregnancy. Marriage. Disguise. Murder. London.*
  Note: Filmed in England. Shot in 16mm.

BODY OF A FEMALE   **F6.0497**
  Amlay Pictures. *Dist* Joseph Brenner Associates. 7 Jan **1965** [New York State license; Fresno, California, showing: 6 Aug 1965]. Sd; b&w. 35mm. 71 min.
  Prod-Dir J. Ellsworth, Julian Marsh. *Screenplay* Francis Ellie. *Camera* Douglas Fenway, John Firth. *Lighting* Robert Marx. *Film Ed* Michael Crane.
  Cast: Anna Riva (*Cindy*), Lem Amero (*Spencer*), Robert West (*Bruno*), Kate Swanson (*Mrs. Arnold*), Sally Wood, actress (*Norma*), Peggy Johnson, Jack Ballard, Bette Page, Linda Moray, Billie Malone, Jean Cloud.
  Melodrama. Cindy, a Cuban stripper who works in a noisy lowlife dive near Coney Island, is seen one night by Spencer, a jaded New England heir who hires young drifter Bruno to get the woman for him. Bruno drugs Cindy and drives her to Spencer's decaying mansion where she willingly remains, tempted by Spencer's promise of a handsome reward. She performs a private striptease for Spencer, and he barely manages to suppress his longing to whip her. Bruno has lingered near the mansion, and he drives there hoping to see Cindy once more. Spencer is away in town, and his terrified housekeeper, Mrs. Arnold, tells Bruno of the state to which her employer's obsessive fantasies have reduced him. Bruno runs to the pond where Cindy is swimming in the nude, but she flees to the house before he can warn her. Spencer is driven frantic by her near nudity; he lashes her to a bed and whips her. Bruno intervenes, overcomes Spencer, and

takes Cindy away with him. Bent on vengeance, Spencer hunts them down and confronts them on a deserted beach. Bruno disarms the desperate madman and drowns him in the surf. *Stripteasers. Heirs. Wanderers. Housekeepers. Abduction. Flagellation. Sadism. Nudity. Revenge. Insanity. Beaches. Coney Island.*

THE BODY STEALERS (United States/Great Britain)   **F6.0498**
  Tigon British Film Productions–Sagittarius Productions. *Dist* Allied Artists. 19 Aug **1970** [Tulsa, Oklahoma, opening; c22 Jul 1969; LP37545]. Sd; col (Eastman Color). 35mm. 91 min. *MPAA rating* R.
  Prod Tony Tenser. *Dir* Gerry Levy. *Screenplay* Mike St. Clair. *Adtl Material* Peter Marcus. *Photog* John Coquillon. *Camera Op* Peter Hendry. *Art Dir* Wilfred Arnold. *Film Ed* Howard Lanning. *Mus & Mus Dir* Reg Tilsley. *Sd* Robert Peck, Hugh Strain. *Asst Dir* John Workman. *Prod Mgr* John Workman. *Wardrobe* Frank Vinall. *Sp Eff* Tom Wadden.
  Cast: George Sanders (*General Armstrong*), Maurice Evans (*Dr. Matthews*), Patrick Allen (*Bob Megan*), Neil Connery (*Jim Radford*), Hilary Dwyer (*Julie Slade*), Robert Flemyng (*Wing Commander Baldwin*), Lorna Wilde (*Lorna*), Allan Cuthbertson (*Hindesmith*), Michael Culver (*Lieutenant Bailes*), Sally Faulkner (*Joanna*), Shelagh Fraser (*Mrs. Thatcher*), Carl Rigg (*Pilot Officer Briggs*), Carol Anne Hawkins (*Paula*), Michael Graham, Brian Harrison (*pilots*), Dixon Adams (*David*), Derek Pollitt (*Davies*), Max Latimer (*guard sergeant*), Ralph Carrigan (*military policeman*), Johnny Wade (*orderly*), Edward Kelsey, Dennis Chinnery (*control officers*), Colin Rix (*control sergeant*), Michael Warren (*Harry*), Steve Kirby (*driver*), Leslie Schofield (*gate guard*), Arnold Peters (*Mr. Smith*), Clifford Earl (*sergeant in laboratory*), Larry Dann (*jeep driver*), Michael Goldie (*dispatch driver*), Wanda Moore (*new secretary*), Jan Miller (*Sally*).
  Science fiction drama. At an air show attended by top NATO observers, a group of parachutists demonstrating a new parachute designed by Jim Radford disappear into a red cloud and never reach the ground. General Armstrong and Wing Commander Baldwin hire Bob Megan, a former U. S. Air Force investigator, to look into the strange occurrence. Bob discusses the matter with Dr. Matthews, the head of the local space research laboratory, and his assistant Julie Slade. When one of the missing parachutists is found and discovered to have been chemically altered from human form, Bob decides to make a jump himself. He vanishes into the red cloud but reappears in a state of unconsciousness. When he revives, Bob discovers that Lorna, a mysterious woman to whom he has been attracted, is an alien being and that Jim Radford was killed while following her. Bob also learns that Dr. Matthews' body has been taken over by one of the aliens on a mission to repopulate his planet with humans. The alien attempts to kill Bob, but Lorna kills him in order to save Bob. Lorna agrees to return the remaining parachutists, who have been kept in a state of suspended animation, and in return Bob agrees to help Lorna's people by finding volunteers to live on her planet. *Scientists. Investigators. Missing persons. Spacemen. Parachuting. Transmutation. Suspended animation. Airfields.*
  Note: Released in Great Britain in 1969. Copyrighted as *Thin Air*. Also known as *Invasion of the Body Stealers*.

BOEING BOEING   **F6.0499**
  Hal Wallis Productions. *Dist* Paramount Pictures. 22 Dec **1965** [Los Angeles opening; c17 Dec 1965; LP32165]. Sd; col (Technicolor). 35mm. 102 min.
  Pres by Hal Wallis. *Prod* Hal B. Wallis. *Assoc Prod* Paul Nathan. *Dir* John Rich. *Screenplay* Edward Anhalt. *Dir Photog* Lucien Ballard. *Camera Op* Richard Batcheller, John Thoney, Paul Waddel. *Art Dir* Hal Pereira, Walter Tyler. *Set Decor* Sam Comer, Ray Moyer. *Film Ed* Warren Low, Archie Marshek. *Mus* Neal Hefti. *Sd* Harold Lewis, Charles Grenzbach. *Rec* Jim Miller. *Boom Op* Glenn Anderson. *Asst Dir* Daniel J. McCauley, Howard Joslin, Nat Holt, Jr. *Asst to the Prod* Jack Saper. *Unit Prod Mgr* William W. Gray. *Script Supv* Marvin Weldon. *Cost Dsgn* Edith Head. *Cost* John A. Anderson, Glenita Dineen. *Makeup Supv* Wally Westmore. *Makeup* Allan Snyder. *Hairstyle Supv* Nellie Manley. *Sp Photog Eff* Paul K. Lerpae. *Proc Photog* Farciot Edouart. *Prop* Martin Pendleton, Anthony Wade. *Grip* Arthur Gaunt. *Gaffer* Chet Stafford. *Still Photog* Sterling Smith.
  Cast: Jerry Lewis (*Robert Reed*), Tony Curtis (*Bernard Lawrence*), Dany Saval (*Jacqueline Grieux*), Christiane Schmidtmer (*Lise Bruner*), Suzanna Leigh (*Vicky Hawkins*), Thelma Ritter (*Bertha*), Lomax Study (*Pierre*), Françoise Ruggieri (*taxi driver*), Nai Bonet, Miko Mayama.
  Romantic comedy. Source: Marc Camoletti, *Boeing-Boeing* (Paris opening: 14 Dec 1960). Bernard Lawrence, an American correspondent stationed in Paris, has tricked each of three women into believing she is his fiancée. They are British Vicky Hawkins, German Lise Bruner, and French Jacqueline Grieux. Each of them, stewardesses for their respective national airlines, has a different schedule, enabling Bernard to share his apartment with them one at a time. Bertha, the housekeeper, arranges the apartment into different styles of furniture and food for each of the women. This arrangement is disturbed when

the airlines switch to the new powerful jets, enabling the women to spend more time in Paris. Robert Reed, Bernard's friend, arrives in Paris without a hotel room and stays in Bernard's apartment. Robert soon realizes Bernard's trouble and forces him to let him move into the apartment. Both men attempt to keep the women from discovering the arrangement, but after a series of incidents, they give up and flee in a taxi from the angry women. They discover that the driver, a pretty young woman, has two roommates who also drive the taxi on the other two shifts. Bernard begins to make plans for a new arrangement. *Journalists. Airline stewardesses. Housekeepers. British. French. Germans. Americans in foreign countries. Taxi drivers. Airplanes—Jet. Paris.*

Note: Filmed in part in Paris. Copyright claimants: Hal B. Wallis and Joseph B. Hazen.

THE BOFORS GUN (Great Britain)   F6.0500

Capelfilms—Everglades Productions. *For* Universal Pictures, Ltd. *Dist* Regional Film Distributors. 22 Sep **1968** [New York opening; c13 Sep 1969; LP39251]. Sd; col (Technicolor). 35mm. 106 min.

Prod Robert Goldston, Otto Plaschkes. *Dir* Jack Gold. *Screenplay* John McGrath. *Photog* Alan Hume. *Art Dir* Terence Knight. *Set Decor* Jack Holden. *Film Ed* Anne V. Coates. *Mus* Carl Davis. *Sd* Derek Ball. *Asst Dir* Barry Langley. *Prod Mgr* Clive Reed. *Cost* Duncan MacPhee. *Makeup* Benny Royston. *Hairstyles* Henry Montsash.

Cast: Nicol Williamson *(Gunner Danny O'Rourke)*, Ian Holm *(Gunner Flynn)*, David Warner *(Lance-Bombardier Terry Evans)*, Richard O'Callaghan *(Rowe)*, Barry Jackson *(Shone)*, Donald Gee *(Crawley)*, John Thaw *(Featherstone)*, Peter Vaughan *(Sergeant Walker)*, Gareth Forwood *(Lieutenant Pickering)*, Geoffrey Hughes *(Cook Private Samuel)*, John Herrington *(German painter)*, Barbara Jefford *(NAAFI girl)*, Glynn Edwards, Lindsay Campbell.

Drama. Source: John McGrath, *Events While Guarding the Bofors Gun* (London opening: 12 Apr 1966). In 1954, British Army Lance-Bombardier Terry Evans is put in command of a small squadron of men in Germany assigned to guard an obsolete Bofors gun. Evans, who is scheduled to return to England the following day for review by the War Office Selection Board, is aware that his chance for a commission rests upon his having a clean record, and he faces this unexpected assignment with apprehension. One of the gunners under his command, Danny O'Rourke, is a loud and cynical Irish anarchist; he chooses the eve of his 30th birthday to mount a furious attack against the establishment in general and Evans in particular. Enraged by Evans' middle-class platitudes about responsibility, O'Rourke defiantly leaves his post, gets drunk, chops down the company flagpole, and jumps out of a window in an abortive suicide attempt. Convinced that he is acting purely out of concern for O'Rourke, Evans covers up for him and refuses to file a report on the incident, but Flynn, another gunner, forces Evans to face the fact that the real reason for his action is not O'Rourke's welfare but a selfish desire to protect his own service record. At midnight, O'Rourke stabs himself with a bayonet, killing himself and destroying Evans' career. *Irish. Anarchists. Military life. Ambition. Drunkenness. Death. Birthdays. Germany. Great Britain—Army.*

Note: Opened in London in Aug 1968.

LA BOHÈME (Switzerland)   F6.0501

Cosmotel. *Dist* Warner Bros. Pictures. 20 Oct **1965** [New York opening; c21 Oct 1965; LP32328]. Sd; col (Technicolor). 35mm. 107 min.

Pres by Herbert von Karajan. *Dir* Franco Zeffirelli. *Assoc Dir* Wilhelm Semmelroth. *Artistic Dir* Herbert von Karajan. *Libretto* Giuseppe Giacosa, Luigi Illica. *Camera* Werner Krien. *Camera Op* Gerhard Girbig. *Set Builder* Paul Haferung. *Prod Dsgn* Franco Zeffirelli. *Film Ed* Alice Seedorf, G. Ricordi. *Mus Comp* Giacomo Puccini. *Cond* Herbert von Karajan. *Chorus Dir* Roberto Benaglio. *Sd* Günter Hermanns. *Prod Mgr* Willy Zeyn. *Cost* Marcel Escoffier. *Makeup* Arthur Schramm, Anni Revel.

Cast: Gianni Raimondi *(Rodolfo)*, Rolando Panerai *(Marcello)*, Gianni Maffeo *(Schaunard)*, Ivo Vinco *(Colline)*, Carlo Badioli *(Benoit/Alcindoro)*, Virgilio Carbonari *(Alcindoro)*, Mirella Freni *(Mimi)*, Adriana Martino *(Musetta)*, Franco Ricciardi *(Parpignol)*, Giuseppe Morresi *(sergeant at the customs)*, Carlo Forti *(customs official)*, Angelo Mercuriali *(fruit vendor)*, La Scala Orchestra, La Scala Chorus.

Opera film. Source: Giacomo Puccini, Giuseppe Giacosa and Luigi Illica, *La Bohème* (first performance: Turin, 1 Feb 1896). Henri Murger, "Scènes de la vie de Bohème," in *Le Corsair* (1847–49). This version of Puccini's opera based on the Murger tale of Bohemian life and love in the Latin Quarter of Paris in the 1830's was filmed in a Munich studio using La Scala Company's settings, costumes, and cast. *Poets. Playwrights. Painters. Musicians. Philosophers. Landlords. Neighbors. Seamstresses. Bohemianism. Jealousy. Poverty. Courtship. Death. Cafes. Tuberculosis. Christmas. Paris—Quartier Latin.*

Note: Released in Switzerland in 1965; running time: 112 min. Sources conflict in crediting the actors portraying the roles of Benoit and Alcindoro.

IL BOIA SCARLATTO see BLOODY PIT OF HORROR

BOIN–N–G   F6.0502

Dist Box Office Spectaculars. 18 Apr **1963** [San Francisco showing]. Sd; col (Eastman Color). 35mm. 70 min.

Prod Davis Freeman. *Dir* Lewis H. Gordon. *Screenplay* Davis Freeman, Lewis H. Gordon. *Camera* Marvin Lester. *Ed Supv* Valerie Hawthorne. *Sd* Davis Mason. *Prod Mgr* William Kurbee. *Asst* Andy Romanoff.

Cast: Thomas Sweetwood *(Al Harding)*, Bill Johnson *(Bob Stevens)*, Vickie Miles *(Francine)*, Christina Castel *(Audrey)*, Robbie Bee *(Schmurtz)*, Lawrence Wood *(Sonny Halitosis)*, Marge London, Joanne Stuart, Marlene Gage.

Nudist film. No information about the precise nature of this film has been found, but press material suggests that it is a story about two men who set out to make a nudist movie. *Nudism. Sex exploitation films.*

BOÎTE DE NUIT see HOTBED OF SIN

BOKUTO KIDAN see THE TWILIGHT STORY

BOLD NEW APPROACH   F6.0503

Mental Health Film Board. Nov **1966**. Sd; 62 min.

Dir-Writ Irving Jacoby.

Narrator: Archie R. Foley.

Documentary. Archie R. Foley, M. D., a psychiatric consultant, narrates a number of case histories in order to demonstrate the need for a community mental health center where troubled people can find aid through inpatient and outpatient treatment, 24-hour hospital clinics, emergency services, intercommunity consultation agencies, and preventive programs. *Psychiatrists. Mental illness. Health. Hospitals.*

BOLSHOI BALLET 67 (U.S.S.R.)   F6.0504

Mosfilm. *Dist* Paramount Pictures. 29 Sep **1966** [New York opening; c1 May 1966; MP15967]. Sd; col (print by Technicolor). 35mm (see note). 75 min. [Copyright length: 82 min.]

Dir Leonid Lavrovskiy, Aleksandr Shelenkov. *Scen* Lev Arnshtam, Leonid Lavrovskiy, Aleksandr Shelenkov. *English Narr* Sidney Carroll. *Camera* Aleksandr Shelenkov, Iolanda Chen. *Camera* S. Armand. *Art Dir* A. Parkhomenko. *Film Ed* L. Feyginova. *Sp Mus Comp & Arr* Nikolay Yakovlev. *Mus Perf by* Bolshoi Theater Orchestra, Bolshoi Symphony Orchestra of Radio and Television. *Cond* Gennadiy Rozhdestvenskiy. *Concertmaster* I. Zaytseva, mus. *Mus Perf by* Bolshoi Theater Violin Ensemble. *Cond* Y. Reyentovich. "Valses nobles et sentimentales," "Bolero" Maurice Joseph Ravel. "Giselle" Adolphe Charles Adam. "Laurencia" ("Laurensiya") Aleksandr Abramovich Kreyn. "Don Quixote" ("Don Kikhot") Ludwig Minkus. "The Dying Swan" ("Le cygne") Camille Saint-Saëns. "The Stone Flower" ("Skaz o kamennom tsvetke") Sergei Sergeevich Prokofiev. "Rhapsody on a Theme by Paganini" Sergei Rachmaninoff. *Mus Selections* Petr Ilich Tchaikovsky. *Ballet Dir* T. Kuyava-Dzhevetska, T. Ustinova, S. Golovkina. *Choreog* Leonid Lavrovskiy. *Sd Op* B. Volskiy, Grigoriy Korenblyum. *Asst Dir* L. Brozhovskiy. *Mgr of the Prod* I. Khlopyeva. *Cost* A. Danduryan. *Cost for Ballet "Paganini"* V. Ryndina. *Makeup* M. Maslova, T. Krylova. *Sp Eff* G. Ayzenberg, N. Spiridonova, Ya. Korablyov. *English Vers Supv* Celebrity Concert Corp.

Featured Performers and Dancers: Natalya Bessmertnova, Mikhail Lavrovskiy ("Valses nobles et sentimentales"), Nina Sorokina ("Giselle"), Nina Timofeyeva ("Laurencia"), Mayya Samokhvalova ("Don Quixote"), Yaroslav Sekh, Yekaterina Maksimova ("Paganini"), Yelena Kholina, Aleksandr Lavreniuk, S. Radchenko ("Bolero"), A. Osipenko ("The Dying Swan"), Raisa Struchkova, Yu. Grigoryev, Vladimir Levashyov, Natalya Kasatkina, A. Simachyov ("The Stone Flower"), Bolshoi Theater Ballet, Students of the Moscow Choreographic School.

Narrator: Ariane (narrator).

Dance film. In Moscow, a young girl who dreams of becoming a prima ballerina enters the famed Bolshoi Theater school. The students undergo rigorous training sessions and exercises; and from time to time they watch the leading stars of the Bolshoi in rehearsal and during actual performances. After 10 years of study, the young woman completes her apprenticeship and prepares for her first appearance before the public as a member of the corps de ballet. *Dancers. Students. Ballet. Moscow. Bolshoi Theater (Moscow).*

Note: Released in the U.S.S.R. in 1965 as *Sekret uspekha;* running time: 86 min. Registered for copyright in 70mm.

A BOMB FOR A DICTATOR (France)   F6.0505

Coopérative Générale du Cinéma–Régent–Cinégraph. *Dist* Medallion Pictures. Feb **1963**. Sd (Western Electric); b&w. 35mm. 73 min.

Assoc Prod Pierre Lévy. *Dir* Alex Joffé. *Screenplay* Alex Joffé, Jean Lévitte. *Dir Photog* L.-H. Burel. *Camera* Henri Raichi. *Art Dir* Jacques Paris. *Set Decor* Marius Martin. *Film Ed* Raymond Lamy. *Mus* Paul Misraki. *Sd Dir* M. Lebreton. *Sd Rec* Claude Orhon. *Boom Op* Charles Akerman. *Asst Dir* Robert Menegoz. *Prod Mgr* Irénée Leriche. *Location Mgr* Emerio Genini. *Prod Sec*

Elise Marion. *Script Girl* Colette Robin. *Wardrobe Mistress* Germaine Hoden. *Wardrobe Master* Claude Coustaud. *Makeup* Igor Keldich. *Hairstyles* Claude Uselmann. *Still Photog* Jean-Louis Castelli. *Prop* Raymond Lemarchand, Jacques Martin.

Cast: Pierre Fresnay *(Luis)*, Michel Auclair *(Franco)*, Grégoire Aslan *(General Ribera)*, Betty Schneider *(Lili)*, Françoise Fabian *(air hostess)*, Tilda Thamar *(Madame Ribera)*, José Lewgoy *(Ramirez)*, Pierre Tabard *(Savelli)*.

Melodrama. Luis and Franco, two South American revolutionaries, plan to assassinate their country's dictator, General Ribera, as he returns by private plane from a holiday in France. Ribera decides to fly by commercial airliner instead, and the two men are forced to examine their ethics and patriotic zeal. Franco, who objects to killing the 50 other passengers, tries to prevent Luis from carrying a time-bomb onto the plane, but Luis kills him and boards with the bomb hidden in a typewriter. When Luis confronts Ribera, however, the dictator dies of a heart attack. Unable to disarm the bomb, Luis breaks a pressurized window, forcing the plane to crash-land on the island of Elba. Luis then carries the bomb into the sea, where it explodes and kills him. *South Americans. Dictators. Revolutionaries. Ethics. Assassination. Bombs. Airplanes. Heart disease. Nice. Elba. Explosions.*

Note: Location scenes filmed in Nice. Opened in Paris in Nov 1957 as *Les fanatiques*; running time: 90 min.

BOMB IN THE HIGH STREET (Great Britain)　　　　　F6.0506
Elthea Productions. *Dist* Hemisphere Pictures. Jul **1964**. Sd; b&w. 35mm. 60 min.
Prod Zichy. *Exec Prod* Ethel Linder Reiner. *Dir* Terry Bishop, Peter Bezencenet. *Screenplay* Benjamin Simcoe. *Dir Photog* Gordon Dines. *Art Dir* Peter Mullins, Lionel Couch. *Film Ed* John Trumper. *Mus & Mus Dir* Wilfred Josephs. *Song:* "Make Room for Miracles" Richard Kayne. *Sung by* Johnny Towers. *Sd* Bill Bristow. *Asst Dir* William Lang.

Cast: Ronald Howard *(Manning)*, Terry Palmer *(Mike)*, Suzanna Leigh *(Jackie)*, Jack Allen *(Superintendent Halsey)*, Peter Gilmore *(Shorty)*, Russell Waters *(Trent)*, Maurice Good *(Feeney)*, James Villiers *(Stevens)*, Geoffrey Bayldon *(Clay)*, Jack Lambert *(police sergeant)*, A. J. Brown *(nightwatchman)*, Humphrey Lestocq *(reporter)*, Leonard Sachs *(Freeling)*, Gerald Case *(Ventry)*, Margaret Lacey *(woman at barrier)*.

Melodrama. A watchman claiming to have found an unexploded bomb, a relic of World War II, on a building site, notifies Superintendent Halsey, who evacuates the neighborhood. The watchman tells police that he has already alerted a bomb disposal squad, who, in reality, are a gang of bank robbers. Led by Manning, the robbers work on the bank vault as the police innocently keep their distance. The robbery is unexpectedly foiled when Jackie and Mike, a teenage couple who are running away from home, emerge from a half-built house where they have been sleeping. The robbers attempt to escape, but Mike follows them on his motorbike as Jackie calls the police, who eventually apprehend the gang and reward the youngsters. *Police. Watchmen. Robbers. Runaways. Bank robberies. Adolescence. Bombs. Vaults.*

Note: Released in Great Britain in 1963.

BOMBAY TALKIE (India)　　　　　F6.0507
Merchant–Ivory Productions. *Dist* Dia Films. 18 Nov **1970** [New York opening]. Sd; col (Eastman Color). 35mm. 112 min. *MPAA rating* GP.
Prod Ismail Merchant. *Dir* James Ivory. *Screenplay* James Ivory, Ruth Prawer Jhabvala. *Story* Ruth Prawer Jhabvala. *Photog* Subrata Mitra. *Art Dir* A. Ranga Raj. *Main Titl* Tilak. *Film Ed* David Gladwell. *Mus* Shankar Jaikishan. *Lyr* Hasrat Jaipuri. *Songs Sung by* Asha Bhonsle, Kishore Kumar, Mohamed Rafi. *Sd Ed* Prabhakar Supare. *Sd Rec* Narendra Singh. *Sd Re-rec* Mangesh Desal, A. K. Parmar. *Asst Dir* Tom Reeves. *Prod Mgr* Narendra Kumar. *Asst to the Prod* Mohan Nadkarni, Asha Seth. *Tech Adv* J. F. H. Van Der Auwera.

Cast: Shashi Kapoor *(Vikram)*, Jennifer Kendal *(Lucia Lane)*, Zia Mohyeddin *(Hari)*, Aparna Sen *(Mala)*, Utpal Dutt *(Bose)*, Nadira *(Anjana Devi)*, Pincho Kapoor *(Swamiji)*, Helen *(heroine in gold)*, Usha Iyer *(cabaret singer)*, Sulochana *(Gopal Ma)*, Prayag Raaj *(director)*, Jalal Agha, Anwar Ali, Mohan Nadkarni *(young men)*, Sukhdev, Darshan *(men at bar)*, Mirza Musharaff *(fan)*, Sonoo Arora *(heroine in red)*, Iftikhar *(Vizarat Khan)*, Datta Ram *(playback singer)*, Mohan Dingra *(jeweller)*, Peter Howard, Angelika Saleh, Nicholas Lear, Sudarshan Dhir.

Melodrama. Lucia Lane, an Anglo-American writer of lurid novels, comes to India in search of inspiration and meets Hari, a screenwriter, who takes her to the Bombay film company where he works. There she meets Vikram, an Indian matinee idol, and begins an affair with him. Despite the extreme jealousy of his wife, Mala, Vikram wants to continue the affair, but Lucia, advised by a fortune-teller that she will ruin the men in her life, abandons Vikram and goes to a religious retreat. She soon discovers, however, that a life of prayer is not enough for her, and she returns to the secular world. To celebrate her birthday she goes drinking with Vikram and Hari, and the three become recklessly

drunk. When Mala threatens to turn Vikram out unless he stops seeing Lucia, he is at first indecisive, but then he tells Lucia that he is going to return to his wife. Lucia asks Hari to intervene for her, and he goes to talk with Vikram, but when Vikram insults Lucia, Hari, who is in love with Lucia, stabs Vikram to death. *Novelists. Americans in foreign countries. Motion picture scriptwriters. Actors. Fortune-tellers. Infidelity. Jealousy. Drunkenness. Murder. Motion picture studios. Birthdays. Bombay.*

Note: Filmed on location in Bombay in 1970.

BOMBS OVER CHINA (Reissue)　　　　　F6.0508
Paramount Pictures. *Dist* Citation Films. 8 Nov **1962** [Maryland license]. Sd; col. 35mm. 91 min.
Note: Originally released by Paramount Pictures in 1951 as *Hong Kong*; c13 Nov 1951; LP1459.

BON VOYAGE!　　　　　F6.0509
Walt Disney Productions. *Dist* Buena Vista Distribution Co. 17 May **1962** [New York opening; c21 Feb 1962; LP21935]. Sd (RCA); col (Technicolor). 35mm. 130 min.
Pres by Walt Disney. A Walt Disney Production. *Assoc Prod* Bill Walsh, Ron Miller. *Dir* James Neilson. *Screenplay* Bill Walsh. *Dir Photog* William Snyder. *Art Dir* Carroll Clark, Marvin Aubrey Davis. *Set Decor* Emile Kuri, Hal Gausman. *Sp Titl* Bill Justice, Xavier Atencio. *Film Ed* Cotton Warburton. *Mus* Paul Smith. *Orch & Dance Mus* Franklyn Marks. *Titl Song* Richard M. Sherman, Robert B. Sherman. *Sd Supv* Robert O. Cook. *Sd Mix* Dean Thomas. *Mus Ed* Evelyn Kennedy. *Asst Dir* Joseph L. McEveety. *French Prod Supv* Sacha Kamenka. *Cost Dsgn* Bill Thomas. *Cost* Chuck Keehne, Gertrude Casey. *Makeup* Pat McNalley. *Hairstyles* Ruth Sandifer. *Sp Eff* Eustace Lycett.

Cast: Fred MacMurray *(Harry Willard)*, Jane Wyman *(Katie Willard)*, Michael Callan *(Nick O'Mara)*, Deborah Walley *(Amy Willard)*, Jessie Royce Landis *(La Countessa)*, Tommy Kirk *(Elliott Willard)*, Georgette Anys *(Madame Clebert)*, Kevin Corcoran *(Skipper Willard)*, Ivan Desny *(Rudolph)*, Françoise Prévost *(girl)*, Alex Gerry *(Horace)*, Howard I. Smith *(Judge Henderson)*, Philip Coolidge *(passport clerk)*, Casey Adams *(tight suit)*, James Millhollin *(librarian)*, Marcel Hillaire *(sewer guide)*, Richard Wattis *(Englishman)*, Carol White *(Penelope)*, Marie Sirago *(Florelle)*, Doris Packer *(Mrs. Henderson)*, Ana Maria Majalca *(Shamra)*, Hassan Khayyam *(Shamra's father)*, Elizabeth Talbot Martin, Frances Mercer, Jacques Hilling.

Comedy. Source: Marijane Hayes and Joseph Hayes, *Bon Voyage* (New York, 1957). Harry Willard, a Terre Haute plumbing contractor, and Katie, his wife, have spent years planning and saving for a trip abroad. Finally their dream is realized, and along with their three children—teenagers Amy and Elliott, and 12-year-old Skipper—they arrive in New York to board the Europe-bound S.S. *United States*. Even before the ship has left the pier, Harry's troubles begin when Amy becomes involved with playboy Nick O'Mara, the son of a giddy American who has married into European royalty. Once in Paris, Katie acquires a chic coiffure which captures the eye of Rudolph, a handsome Hungarian, and Elliott falls for an intriguing French girl. Harry, on the other hand, tries to please little Skipper by taking him on a tour of the Paris sewer system, and the two become hopelessly lost in the underground labyrinth. The family then moves on to the Riviera where Harry manages to straighten out everyone's romantic problems, but not before he knocks Rudolph unconscious at a cocktail party given by Nick's countess mother. Their vacation over, the Willards return to the comparative peace and quiet of their Terre Haute home. *Plumbers. Contractors. Children. Playboys. Hungarians. French. Tourists. Nobility. Family life. Vacations. Adolescence. Sewers. Terre Haute. New York City. Paris. Riviera. S.S. "United States".*

Note: Location scenes filmed on the S.S. *United States*, in Paris, and on the Riviera.

LE BONHEUR (France)　　　　　F6.0510
Parc Film. *Dist* Clover Films Corp. 23 May **1966** [New York opening]. Sd; col (Eastman Color). 35mm. 87 min.
Pres by George Roth. *Prod Mag* Bodard. *Dir-Writ* Agnes Varda. *Photog* Jean Rabier, Claude Beausoleil. *Art Dir* Hubert Monloup. *Film Ed* Janine Verneau. *Mus Selections (see note)* Wolfgang Amadeus Mozart. *Sd* Antoine Bonfanti, Louis Hochet. *Asst Dir* Jean-Paul Savignac. *Prod Mgr* Philippe Dussart. *English Titl* Ursule Molinaro.

Cast: Jean-Claude Drouot *(François)*, Claire Drouot *(Thérèse)*, Sandrine Drouot *(Gisou)*, Olivier Drouot *(Pierrot)*, Marie-France Boyer *(Emilie)*.

Romantic drama. François, a young carpenter, lives a happy, uncomplicated life with his wife Thérèse, a seamstress, and their two small children, Gisou and Pierrot, in the Paris suburb of Fontenay. On weekends he delights in taking his family on picnics in the nearby woods. One day at Vincennes he meets Emilie, a clerk in the local post office. Their first few casual encounters gradually develop into a passionate affair, unencumbered by guilt. This new and different love adds to François' happiness, and he becomes more gentle, relaxed, and tender with Thérèse. Emilie accepts the fact that François loves his wife also. One day he tries to explain to Thérèse the change that has come over him. Although he assures her that his new relationship only increases his joy at being a husband and father, Thérèse is unable to understand. She quietly submits to his lovemaking one more time and then drowns herself. François mourns his wife's death for a long time and no longer visits Emilie. Eventually, however, he is drawn back to her, and they resume their former relationship. She accepts the two children as her own and joins the family on picnics, and one day François makes her his wife. *Carpenters. Seamstresses. Postal clerks. Mistresses. Infidelity. Suicide. Family life. Marriage. Fontenay-sous-Bois. Vincennes (France).*

Note: Opened in Paris in Feb 1965. Also released in the United States as *Happiness.* Mozart selections include: the Piano Quintet in E-flat Major (K.452); Music for Two Pianos; a movement from an uncompleted symphony; the Fugue in C Minor for Piano, Four Hands (K.426); and the Adagio and Fugue in C-Minor for String Orchestra (K.546).

BONITINHA, MAS ORDINÁRIA *see* **PRETTY BUT WICKED**

LA BONNE SOUPE (France/Italy)   **F6.0511**
Belstar Productions–Les Films du Siècle–Dear Film. *Dist* International Classics. Apr **1964** [c31 Dec 1963; LP28208]. Sd; b&w. 35mm (CinemaScope). 97 min.

An André Hakim Production. *Prod* André Hakim. *Dir-Writ* Robert Thomas. *Dir Photog* Roger Hubert. *Camera* André Dumaitre. *Art Dir* Jacques Saulnier. *Set Decor* Charles Merangel. *Credit Titl* Jean Fouchet. *Film Ed* Henri Taverna. *Asst Ed* Marie-Claude Bariset. *Mus* Raymond Le Sénéchal. *Mus Arr* Hubert Rostaing. *Orch Cond* Jacques Metehen. *Sd* Jean Rieul. *Asst Dir* Jacques Rouffio. *Prod Mgr* Jacques Juranville. *Unit Mgr* Rene Fargeas. *Cost Dsgn* Maurice Albray. *Makeup* Lina Gallet. *Sp Eff* Jean Fouchet.

Cast: Annie Girardot (*Marie-Paule [young]*), Marie Bell (*Marie-Paule [older]*), Gérard Blain (*painter*), Bernard Blier (*Monsieur Joseph*), Jean-Claude Brialy (*Jacquot*), Blanchette Brunoy (*Angèle*), Claude Dauphin (*Monsieur Oscar*), Sacha Distel (*Roger*), Daniel Gélin (*Raymond*), Denise Grey (*Madame Boudard*), Jane Marken (*Madame Alphonse*), Christian Marquand (*Lucien Volard*), Félix Marten (*Odilon*), Raymond Pellegrin (*Armand*), Franchot Tone (*Montasi, Jr.*), Danielle Volle (*Janine*).

Comedy-drama. Source: Félicien Marceau, *La bonne soupe* (Paris, 1958). Marie-Paule is a handsome, middle-aged women whose sole distraction from boredom is gambling. While at the casino at Cannes she relates the story of her life to Mr. Oscar, chief of the casino croupiers. At an early age, while working in a clothing store, she was seduced by her employer whom she persuaded to take her to Paris. But he soon abandoned her and she drifted into a series of brief, meaningless love affairs. Eventually she met a kindly older man, Joseph, who told his naive wife that Marie was his secretary. One night, however, she made the mistake of making love to Joseph's brother-in-law, Raymond. Despite the scandal, Joseph bought her a small tavern. There Marie fell in love with her handsome barman, Jacquot, but her happiness was cut short when he was fatally wounded during a robbery. Learning that she was pregnant, she married Armand Buvard, the owner of a biscuit factory. As the years passed she remained a loyal and devoted wife and mother and arranged a marriage for her daughter to the wealthy Lucien Volard. Upon discovering that Lucien was unfaithful, the outraged Marie went to his flat to reproach him for his behavior. Instead she succumbed to his advances and allowed him to make love to her. They were discovered by her husband and daughter, and all that Marie-Paule had strived for crumbled in an instant, and she was banished from her home. After finishing her tale, she catches sight of a millionaire-playboy, John Montasi, who invites her to join him for a cruise on his yacht. As the ship leaves port, Marie-Paule bids Mr. Oscar a fond adieu and sails off to new adventure. *Adventuresses. Croupiers. Clerks. Storekeepers. Manufacturers. Bartenders. Millionaires. Middle age. Gambling. Employer-employee relations. Seduction. Pregnancy. Marriage. Yachts. Cannes. Paris.*

Note: Opened in Paris in Jan 1964. Also known *Careless Love.*

LES BONNES CAUSES *see* **DON'T TEMPT THE DEVIL**

LES BONNES FEMMES (France/Italy)   **F6.0512**
Paris-Films Production–Panitalia. *Dist* Harold Cornsweet Productions. 12 May **1966** [New York opening]. Sd; b&w. 35mm. 95 min.

Prod Raymond Hakim, Robert Hakim. *Dir-Adapt* Claude Chabrol. *Screenplay-Dial* Paul Gégauff. *Photog* Henri Decaë. *Art Dir* Jacques Mély. *Film Ed* Jacques Gaillard. *Mus* Paul Misraki, Pierre Jansen. *Sd* Jean-Claude Marchetti. *Prod Mgr* Ralph Baum.

Cast: Bernadette Lafont (*Jane*), Lucile Saint-Simon (*Rita*), Clotilde Joano (*Jacqueline*), Stéphane Audran (*Ginette*), Mario David (*motorcyclist [Ernest]*), Ave Ninchi (*Madame Louise*), Jean-Louis Maury (*young playboy [Marcel]*), Albert Dinan (*Albert, his older companion*), Sacha Briquet (*Henri*), Claude Berri (*André*), Pierre Bertan (*Monsieur Belin*), Serge Bento (*delivery man*),

Karen Blanguernon (*girl in dancehall*), Claude Chabrol.

Drama. Jane, Ginette, Rita, and Jacqueline are young Parisians working in an electric appliance store. Bored with their humdrum working day, they seek glamour, happiness, and love during their free evenings. Jane is engaged to a soldier but, because of his absence and her hunger for excitement, she allows herself to be picked up by strangers who promise a night of carousing. Ginette, oldest and most secretive of the group, finds her escape by donning a black wig and singing Italian songs in a second-rate theatre. Her pleasure abruptly ends when the other girls discover her carefully guarded secret. Rita believes herself in love with the son of a shopkeeping family until she meets his penny-pinching parents and realizes that marriage to him would be merely changing her environment. Jacqueline, youngest and most innocent of the quartet, demurely permits herself to be followed everywhere by a young man on a motorcycle. One Sunday afternoon, he approaches her and takes her to the country. They have lunch at an old inn, and then he takes her for a walk in the nearby woods and brutally murders her. *Salesclerks. Pickups. Singers. Motorcyclists. Infidelity. Disguise. Courtship. Storekeepers. Murder. Employment—Women. Paris.*

Note: Opened in Paris in Apr 1960; running time: 104 min. Released in Italy in 1964 as *Le donne facili.*

BONNIE AND CLYDE   **F6.0513**
Tatira–Hiller Productions. *Dist* Warner Bros.–Seven Arts, Inc. 13 Aug **1967** [New York opening; c30 Sep 1967; LP35800]. Sd; col (Technicolor). 35mm. 111 min.

Prod Warren Beatty. *Dir* Arthur Penn. *Writ* David Newman, Robert Benton. *Dir Photog* Burnett Guffey. *Art Dir* Dean Tavoularis. *Set Decor* Raymond Paul. *Film Ed* Dede Allen. *Mus Comp* Charles Strouse. *Song:* "Foggy Mountain Breakdown" Earl Scruggs. *Played by* Lester Flatt, Earl Scruggs. *Sd* Francis E. Stahl. *Asst Dir* Jack N. Reddish. *Prod Mgr* Russ Saunders. *Asst to the Prod* Elaine Michea. *Script Supv* John Dutton. *Cost Dsgn* Theadora Van Runkle. *Women's Wardrobe* Norma Brown. *Men's Wardrobe* Andy Matyasi. *Makeup Created by* Robert Jiras. *Hair Stylist* Gladys Witten. *Sp Eff* Danny Lee. *Sp Cons* Robert Towne.

Cast: Warren Beatty (*Clyde Barrow*), Faye Dunaway (*Bonnie Parker*), Michael J. Pollard (*C. W. Moss*), Gene Hackman (*Buck Barrow*), Estelle Parsons (*Blanche*), Denver Pyle (*Frank Hamer*), Dub Taylor (*Ivan Moss*), Evans Evans (*Velma Davis*), Gene Wilder (*Eugene Grizzard*), James Stiver (*grocery store owner*).

Crime drama. During the depression in the early 1930's, Bonnie Parker meets Clyde Barrow when he tries to steal her mother's car. Intrigued by his brazen manner and bored with her job as a waitress, she decides to become his partner in crime. Together they stage a series of amateur holdups that provide them with excitement but little monetary reward. Eventually they take on C. W. Moss, a dimwitted garage mechanic, who serves as their getaway driver. Finally they are joined by Clyde's brother Buck, recently released from prison, and his wife, Blanche, a whining preacher's daughter. As they add bank robbery and murder to their list of crimes, the quintet quickly becomes the object of statewide manhunts. While holed up in a rented apartment in Joplin, Missouri, they make the first of their incredible escapes from the police. Fascinated by the legendary reputation growing around them, they brag about their exploits, take pictures of each other, and, on one occasion, force a Texas Ranger to pose with them. Through it all a love relationship develops between Bonnie and Clyde that endures despite Clyde's impotence. After a visit with Bonnie's mother, the gang is surrounded in Dexter, Iowa. Buck dies with half of his face shot away, Blanche is blinded and captured, and Bonnie is wounded in the shoulder. The three survivors find a temporary hideout with C. W.'s father in a Louisiana town, and there Bonnie and Clyde finally consummate their love. Bonnie recovers from her wounds, and they plan to move on again; but C. W.'s father, hoping to lighten his son's punishment, has cooperated with the police in setting a trap. In May of 1934, Bonnie and Clyde ride into a police ambush and die as their bodies are riddled with a thousand rounds of ammunition. *Gangs. Waitresses. Drifters. Brothers. Police. Texas Rangers. Garagemen. Theft. Bank robberies. Murder. Impotence. Perfidy. Filial relations. Manhunts. Reputation. The Great Depression (1929–34). Texas. Joplin (Missouri). Dexter (Iowa). Louisiana. Bonnie Parker. Clyde Barrow. "Gold Diggers of 1933".*

Note: Location scenes filmed in Texas. Includes sequence from *Gold Diggers of 1933.*

BOOM! (United States/Great Britain)   **F6.0514**
World Film Service Productions–Moonlake Productions. *Dist* Universal Pictures. 26 May **1968** [New York opening; c10 Aug 1968; LP37968]. Sd (RCA); col (Technicolor). 35mm (Panavision). 110 min.

A John Heyman Production. *Prod* John Heyman, Norman Priggen. *Assoc Prod* Lester Persky. *Dir* Joseph Losey. *Screenplay* Tennessee Williams. *Lighting Camera* Douglas Slocombe. *Camera Op* Chic Waterson. *Art Dir* Richard MacDonald. *Prod Dsgn* Richard MacDonald. *Film Ed* Reginald Beck.

Mus Comp & Cond John Barry. *Indian Sitar Mus* Nazirali Jairazbhoy, Viram Jasani. *Song:* "Hideaway" John Dankworth, Don Black. *Sung by* Georgie Fame. *Sd Rec* Leslie Hammond, Gerry Humphreys. *Dub Ed* Alan Bell. *Asst Dir* Carlo Lastricati. *Prod Supv* Ottavio Oppo. *Unit Mgr* Valerio De Paolis. *Cont* Helen Whitson. *Miss Taylor's Wardrobe* Tiziani of Rome. *Wardrobe Supv* Annalisa Nasalli-Rocca. *Mr. Coward's Cost* Douglas Hayward. *Miss Taylor's Makeup* Frank La Rue. *Mr. Burton's Makeup* Ron Berkeley. *Miss Taylor's Hairstyles* Alexandre of Paris.

Cast: Elizabeth Taylor (*Flora Goforth*), Richard Burton (*Chris Flanders*), Noel Coward (*The Witch of Capri*), Joanna Shimkus (*Blackie*), Michael Dunn (*Rudy*), Romolo Valli (*Dr. Lullo*), Fernando Piazza (*Etti*), Veronica Wells (*Simonetta*), Claudie Ettori (*manicurist*), Howard Taylor (*journalist*), Gens Block (*photographer*), Franco Pesce (*villager*), Sergio Carozzi, Giovanni Paganelli.

Drama. Source: Tennessee Williams, *The Milk Train Doesn't Stop Here Anymore* (New York opening: 16 Jan 1963). Tennessee Williams, "Man Bring This up Road," in *Mademoiselle* (Jul 1959). Flora Goforth, a millionairess widowed six times, retires each summer to her private island in the Mediterranean. This summer, however, she learns that she is going to die and begins to dictate her memoirs to Blackie, her abused secretary. One day an aging poet, Chris Flanders, arrives on the island and is attacked by Mrs. Goforth's dwarf bodyguard and his pack of vicious dogs. Although Mrs. Goforth's friend, an epicene bachelor known as the Witch of Capri, tells her that Chris has been called the "Angel of Death" because of his frequent association with dying wealthy women, she tolerates the intruder and permits him to remain in one of the guest houses adjacent to her lavish villa. Alternately repelled and attracted by the poet, Mrs. Goforth begins to rely more and more on his presence as her health gradually wanes. Ultimately forced to accept the inevitable, she invites Chris into her bedroom and collapses. As he sits by her side and prepares her for death, Chris slowly removes her fortune in jewels. After she has died, he wanders out onto the terrace, pours himself a large snifter of brandy, drops a huge diamond into it, and lets the glass fall to the sea below. *Millionaires. Widows. Secretaries. Poets. Dwarfs. Bodyguards. Bachelors. Incurable illness. Death. Islands. Jewels. Summer. Mediterranean Sea. Dogs.*

Note: Location scenes filmed in Sardinia. Opened in London in Dec 1968; running time: 113 min. Working titles: *Sunburst* and *Goforth.*

BORA BORA (France/Italy)   **F6.0515**
Finarco Film–Franco London Film. *Dist* American International Pictures. Feb **1970** [c25 Feb 1970; LP38189]. Sd; col (Technicolor). 35mm (Techniscope). 90 min. *MPAA rating* R.

Prod Alfredo Bini. *Assoc Prod* Eliseo Boschi. *Dir-Writ* Ugo Liberatore. *Dir Photog* Leonida Barboni. *Art Dir* Piero Cicoletti. *Film Ed* Giancarlo Cappelli. *Mus English Lang Vers* Les Baxter. *Mus Italian Lang Vers* Piero Piccioni. *Cost* Piero Cicoletti.

Cast: Haydée Politoff (*Marita Ferris*), Corrado Pani (*Roberto Ferris*), Doris Kunstmann (*Susanne*), Rosine Copie (*Tehina*), Antoine Coco Puputauki (*Mani*).

Drama. Following a marital rift, cynical Roberto Ferris follows his wife, Marita, to Tahiti but learns that she has checked out of her hotel without leaving a forwarding address. He meets Susanne, a masochistic nymphomaniac who has chosen the Polynesian way of life because it allows her to indulge her sensualism. Eventually Ferris learns that his wife is living on the island of Bora Bora with Mani, her young Polynesian lover. Upon arriving on Bora Bora and having his offer of reconciliation rejected by Marita, Ferris decides to stay on in order to discover what it is about the island that fascinates her. The natives offer him a place to sleep and a 15-year-old virgin for a companion. To prove his virility to Marita, Ferris takes a native woman, Tehina, for his mistress. The islanders build the couple a beach shack, and Marita, almost in spite of herself, supervises the construction. When the indolent Tehina eventually leaves, Marita moves into her husband's shack; then, to prove himself as a lover, Ferris offers both his home and wife to Mani. Afterwards, overcome by jealousy, Ferris attacks Mani as he emerges from the shack. Mani, however, easily defeats Ferris with a few well-placed kicks and walks away. Realizing that they are incapable of adapting to Polynesian life, Ferris and his wife burn the beach shack and leave the island. *Polynesians. Mistresses. Infidelity. Marriage. Hedonism. Polygamy. Nymphomania. Jealousy. Tahiti. Bora Bora.*

Note: Released in Italy in 1968; running time: 100 min. Opened in Paris in Nov 1969. Filmed in the Society Islands.

BORN FREE (Great Britain)   **F6.0516**
Open Road Films–Atlas Films. *Dist* Columbia Pictures. 6 Apr **1966** [Los Angeles opening; c31 Dec 1965; LP32471]. Sd (Westrex); col (Eastmancolor, print by Pathé). 35mm (Panavision). 95 min.

Pres by Highroad Productions. *Prod* Sam Jaffe, Paul Radin. *Exec Prod* Carl Foreman. *Dir* James Hill. *Orig Dir* (see note) Tom McGowan. *Writ for the*

Screen by Gerald L. C. Copley. *Dir Photog* Kenneth Talbot. *Camera Op* Rodney Anstiss. *Camera Asst* Marc Hymes. *Camera Grip* Wally Wheatley. *Film Ed* Don Deacon. *Asst Ed* Gordon Davie. *Mus Comp & Cond* John Barry. *Titl Song* John Barry, Don Black. *Sd Rec* Claude Hitchcock, Bob Jones. *Sd Ed* Chris Greenham. *1st & 2d Asst Dir* William P. Cartlidge, Paul Herd. *Prod Coörd* Hal Mason. *Cont Asst* Kay Rawlings. *Prod Mgr* L. C. Rudkin. *Prod Supv* Sidney G. Barnsby. *Prod Sec* Jane Oscroft. *Location Mgr* Pat Fisher. *Ch Tech Adv* George Adamson. *Coöp* Haile Selassie, Game Department of Uganda. *Animal Supv* Peter Whitehead, animal supv. *Gaffer* Tom Watson. *Still Photog* John Jay.

Cast: Virginia McKenna (*Joy Adamson*), Bill Travers (*George Adamson*), Geoffrey Keen (*Kendall*), Peter Lukoye (*Nuru*), Omar Chambati (*Makkede*), Bill Godden (*Sam*), Bryan Epsom (*Baker*), Robert Cheetham (*Ken*), Robert Young, British (*James*), Geoffrey Best (*Watson*), Surya Patel (*Indian doctor*), Mara (*Elsa, a lion*), Girl (*Elsa as a cub*), Boy, Ugas, Henrietta (*lions*), Pati (*Pati, a hyrax*).

Adventure drama. Source: Joy Adamson, *Born Free* (London, 1960). George Adamson, a senior game warden in Kenya, kills a man-eating lion and is forced to shoot the lion's mate when she attacks him. He then brings home three orphaned female lion cubs. His wife, Joy, rears the baby animals, overcoming their initial refusal to accept milk, and becomes particularly attached to the smallest, Elsa. When it is time to send the cubs to a zoo, Joy is reluctant to part with Elsa, so George sends only the other two cubs. Elsa becomes a member of the family, freely roaming through the house and the vicinity but rarely venturing into the jungle. When Elsa reaches full size, the district commissioner points out that her presence has become a major concern and suggests that she should be sent to a zoo. Joy rebels against the idea of Elsa living in confinement, and she wins 2 months to teach Elsa to fend for herself in the jungle. Since the lion is completely domesticated and has never had to kill for food or defend herself, the Adamsons have a difficult time making Elsa understand what is expected of her. In her first introduction to hunting, she is chased by a warthog. The Adamsons finally succeed in reconditioning Elsa to life in the wild, however, and at the next mating season she goes off alone into the jungle. The following year, after a trip to England, the Adamsons return to Kenya. One day Elsa appears at their camp with three of her own cubs. She spends the day with her friends and then returns to her mate. *Game wardens. Survival. Animals— Domestication. Animal life. Jungles. Kenya. Joy Adamson. George Adamson. Lions.*

Note: Filmed on location in Naro Moru, Maralal, and Malindi, Kenya, and Doldol, Ethiopia. London opening: Mar 1966. Original director Tom McGowan resigned after several months of production.

BORN IN SIN (Japan)   **F6.0517**
Toho Co. 24 May **1963** [Los Angeles showing]. Sd; col (Eastmancolor). 35mm (Tohoscope). 116 min.

Exec Prod Sanezumi Fujimoto, Masakatsu Kaneko. *Screenplay* Toshiro Ide. *Story* Yojiro Ishizaka. *Photog* Rokuro Nishigaki. *Mus* Toshiro Mayuzumi.

Cast: Yuzo Kayama, Yuriko Hoshi, So Yamamura, Mitsuko Kusabue, Daisuke Kato, Chikage Awashima.

Domestic melodrama. Overhearing an argument between her mother Tomoko and family friend Sawada, Taneko, a sheltered 21-year-old student, discovers that her father Shinzo has been formerly married, and that her mother enticed Shinzo from her own second cousin, Asako. During a flight to Tokyo Shinzo chances to meet Asako, now married, whom he has not seen for 20 years. At the airport, while waiting for her father, Taneko meets Shintaro, a fellow student to whom she has been attracted for some time. He is at the airport waiting for Asako, who is his mother. During the summer vacation the students fall in love, but Taneko is shocked when Shintaro discloses his earlier involvement with a promiscuous woman employed at his father's hotel. At an art exhibition Shinzo and Asako again meet by accident and discover that they both have hoped for such a meeting. Asako, curious about Shinzo's present family, unexpectedly arrives at his home one evening. [Sources do not disclose the film's ending.] *Students. Cousins. Personal identity. Family life. Promiscuity. Marriage. Tokyo.*

Note: Released in Japan as *Kawano hotoride.*

THE BORN LOSERS   **F6.0518**
Otis Productions. *Dist* American International Pictures. 18 Aug **1967** [New York opening; c12 Jul 1967; LP34699]. Sd; col (PathéColor). 35mm. 112 min.

Prod Donald Henderson. *Exec Prod* Delores Taylor. *Assoc Prod* Jay Loughrin. *Dir* T. C. Frank. *Screenplay* E. James Lloyd. *Photog* Gregory Sandor. *Camera* Frank Ruttencutter, Herman Knox. *Art Dir* Rick Beck-Meyer. *Film Ed* John Winfield. *Sd* Leroy Robbins. *Asst Dir* Paul Lewis. *Prod Mgr* Jonathan Haze. *Makeup* Louis Lane.

Cast: Tom Laughlin (*Billy Jack*), Elizabeth James (*Vicky Barrington*), Jane Russell (*Mrs. Shorn*), Jeremy Slate (*Danny Carmody*), William Wellman, Jr. (*Child*), Robert Tessier (*Cue Ball*), Jeff Cooper (*Gangrene*), Edwin Cook

(Crabs), Tex (himself), Paul Prokop (Speechless), Julie Cahn (Lu Ann Crawford), Susan Foster (Linda Prang), Janice Miller (Jodell Shorn), Stuart Lancaster (sheriff), Jack Starrett (deputy), Paul Bruce (district attorney), Robert Cleaves (Mr. Crawford), Ann Bellamy (Mrs. Prang), Gordon Hoban (Jerry Carmody).

Crime melodrama. A motorcycle gang is terrorizing a California mountain town. When an innocent young man is brutally beaten, half-breed Billy Jack goes to the boy's aid but lands in jail. He vows revenge against the gang after he is released. Meanwhile, attractive teenager Vicky Barrington is kidnaped by the hoodlums and taken to their hangout, where a wild orgy involving some of the town's teenagers is in progress. Vicky escapes, but the other girls do not, and a rape scandal ensues. While the district attorney attempts to build an airtight case, gang leader Danny Carmody initiates a fear campaign to prevent anyone from testifying. Vicky, who thinks she is safe, is viciously assaulted in an isolated field by Speechless, a mute member of the gang. All victims and witnesses are intimidated as gang rule grips the town and the sheriff's efforts to maintain law and order are stymied. After Vicky is released from the hospital, Billy hides her in his mountain hideout, but they are discovered and Vicky is kidnaped again. Billy defeats gang member Gangrene in a gas station battle but is unable to beat the entire gang, so he enlists police aid to rescue Vicky. But the police are delayed, and Vicky is brutally raped by Gangrene. Forced to act on his own, Billy breaks into the hangout, lines the gang up at gunpoint, shoots Carmody dead, and forces two other members to take Vicky to the hospital. Billy is forcing the others to go outside when the police arrive. As he rides off for the hospital on his motorcycle, one of the policemen mistakes him for a fleeing hoodlum and shoots him. Though badly wounded, he makes it to his hideout. Vicky, partially recovered, leads a helicopter rescue squad, and Billy is evacuated for medical treatment. *Motorcycle gangs. Halfcastes. Police. District attorneys. Mutes. Adolescence. Abduction. Rape. Revenge. Murder. Law and order. California.*

Note: Donald Henderson, T. C. Frank, and E. James Lloyd are pseudonyms of Tom Laughlin.

BORN TO BUCK F6.0519
Pandora Pictures. 26 Jun **1968** [Pierre, South Dakota, opening]. Sd; col (Eastman Color). 35mm. ca90 min.
Prod-Dir Casey Tibbs. *Screenplay* Mollie Carle. *Photog* Dick McCarthy. *Mus Comp* Dick Stabile.
With: Casey Tibbs, Jack Hart, Albert Lopez, John Tibbs, Norval Cooper, Roy Houck.
Narrators: Henry Fonda, Rex Allen.
Documentary. Bronco riders travel through the Lower Brule Reservation in the South Dakota hills and round up 400 wild horses, which are in danger of extinction. The herd is driven to Fort Pierre where the horses are ridden by broncobusters in rodeo competition. *Broncobusters. Roundups. Rodeos. South Dakota. Fort Pierre (South Dakota). Horses.*
Note: Filmed on location in South Dakota.

BORN TO SING see **ALMOST ANGELS**

BORN WILD see **THE YOUNG ANIMALS**

BORSALINO (France/Italy) F6.0520
Adel Productions–Marianne Productions–Mars Film Produzione. *Dist* Paramount Pictures. 13 Aug **1970** [New York opening; c20 Mar 1970; LF63]. Sd; col (Eastman Color). 35mm. 128 min. *MPAA rating* GP.
Prod Alain Delon. *Assoc Prod* Pierre Caro. *Dir* Jacques Deray. *Screenplay* Jean-Claude Carrière, Claude Sautet, Jacques Deray, Jean Cau. *Dial* Jean-Claude Carrière. *Photog* Jean-Jacques Tarbes. *Camera Op* Jean Charvein. *Asst Camera* Claude Bourgoin. *Art Dir* François de Lamothe. *Asst Art Dir* Jacques Brizzio, Pierre Duquesne, Robert André. *Set Decor* Robert Christides. *Main Titl* Jean Fouchet, Eurocitel. *Film Ed* Paul Cayatte. *Asst Ed* Liane Morice. *Mus* Claude Bolling. *Sd* Jacques Maumont. *1st & 2d Asst Dir* Olivier Gérard, Jean Patrick Lebel, Jean-François Delon, Michèle Sennet. *Prod Mgr* Pierre Saint-Blancat. *Unit Mgr* Jean-Marc Isy, Alain Belmondo, Jean Drouin, Roch Siffredi. *Script Girl* Annie Rozier. *Cost Dsgn* Jacques Fonteray. *Wardrobe Master* Pierre Nourry. *Wardrobe Mistress* Tanine Autre. *Makeup* Michel Deruelle. *Still Photog* Pierre Manciet. *Propmen* André Pierdel, Michel Sune.
Cast: Jean-Paul Belmondo (Capella), Alain Delon (Siffredi), Michel Bouquet (Rinaldi), Catherine Rouvel (Lola), Françoise Christophe (Madame Escarguel), Corinne Marchand (Madame Rinaldi), Julien Guiomar (Boccace), Arnoldo Foà (Marello), Nicole Calfan (Ginette), Christian de Tilière ("The Dancer"), Mario David (Mario), André Bollet (Poli), Laura Adani (Siffredi's mother), Daniel Ivernel (police inspector), Denis Berry (Nono), Hélène Rémy (Lydia), Mireille Darc (whore), Odette Piquet (singer), Lionel Vitrant (Fernand), Jean Aron (accountant), Pierre Koulak (Spada), Yvan Chiffre, Claude Cerval.
Crime melodrama. Source: Eugène Saccomare, *Bandits à Marseille* (Paris, 1968). Siffredi, a smalltime Marseilles gangster in the 1930's, is released from

prison and searches for his former girl friend, Lola. He finds her with Capella, another gangster, and after they fight over Lola, the two men become friendly and decide to form a partnership. For a while they fix horseraces and prizefights until they are contacted by Rinaldi, a lawyer who works for Marello and Poli, the gangsters who control crime in Marseilles. Rinaldi suggests that Siffredi and Capella seize control of Marello's hold on the fish market business. They succeed in ousting Marello, but they are no longer content to remain in the background. In an attempt to gain control of Poli's meat market operations, Siffredi and Capella are nearly killed by Poli's henchmen, and they are forced to go into hiding. They emerge armed with machine guns and murder Poli. After Rinaldi is killed by "The Dancer," another aspiring gangster, Capella and Siffredi dispose of his body and establish themselves as the rulers of the Marseilles crime world. The two men become extremely wealthy, but Capella tells his partner that he is leaving Marseilles before they begin to fight with each other over control of their organization. As Capella departs, Siffredi sees him slain by a waiting assassin; Siffredi then realizes that his own position in Marseilles is tenuous and that he must leave. *Ex-convicts. Gangsters. Lawyers. Partnerships. Organized crime. Murder. Horseracing. Prizefighting. Marseilles.*
Note: Location scenes filmed in Marseilles. Opened in Paris in Mar 1970. Released in Italy in 1970.

LE BOSSU DE ROME see **THE HUNCHBACK OF ROME**

THE BOSTON STRANGLER F6.0521
Twentieth Century–Fox Film Corp. 16 Oct **1968** [New York opening; c16 Oct 1968; LP36281]. Sd (Westrex); col (DeLuxe). 35mm (Panavision). 116 min.
Prod Robert Fryer. *Assoc Prod* James Cresson. *Dir* Richard Fleischer. *Screenplay* Edward Anhalt. *Dir Photog* Richard H. Kline. *Art Dir* Jack Martin Smith, Richard Day. *Set Decor* Walter M. Scott, Stuart A. Reiss, Raphael Bretton. *Film Ed* Marion Rothman. *Mus* Lionel Newman. *Sd* Don Bassman, David Dockendorf. *Asst Dir* David Hall. *Unit Prod Mgr* Eric Stacey. *Cost Supv* Travilla. *Makeup* Dan Striepeke. *Hairstyles* Edith Lindon. *Sp Photog Eff* L. B. Abbott, Art Cruickshank, John C. Caldwell. *Tech Adv* John S. Bottomly, Phillip DiNatale. *Prod Film Treatment* Fred Harpman.
Cast: Tony Curtis (Albert DeSalvo), Henry Fonda (John S. Bottomly), George Kennedy (Phil DiNatale), Mike Kellin (Julian Soshnick), Hurd Hatfield (Terence Huntley), Murray Hamilton (Frank McAfee), Jeff Corey (John Asgeirsson), Sally Kellerman (Dianne Cluny), William Marshall (Edward W. Brooke), George Voskovec (Peter Hurkos), Leora Dana (Mary Bottomly), Carolyn Conwell (Irmgard DeSalvo), Jeanne Cooper (Cloe), Austin Willis (Dr. Nagy), Lara Lindsay (Bobbie Eden), George Furth (Lyonel Brumley), Richard X. Slattery (Ed Willis), William Hickey (Eugene T. Rourke), Eve Collyer (Ellen Ridgeway), Gwyda Donhowe (Alice Oakville), Alex Dreier (news commentator), John Cameron Swayze (television narrator), Shelley Burton (David Parker), Elizabeth Baur (Harriet Fordin), James Brolin (Sergeant Lisi), George Tyne (Dr. Kramer), Dana Elcar (Luis Schubert), William Traylor (Arnie Carr), Carole Shelley (Dana Banks), Karen Huston (Pat Bruner), Enid Markey (Edna), Dorothy Blackburn (Minnie), Almira Sessions (Emma Hodak), Isabella Hoops (Bertha Blum), Richard Krisher (Tom), Arthur Hanson (commissioner), Walter Klavun (chief of police), Tim Herbert (Cedric), Matt Bennett (Harold), Penny Williams (Mae), Janis Young (Louise Parker), George Fisher (Mr. Taylor), David Lewis (Judge Schroeder), Pam McMyler (Grace), Greg Benedict (Dick Matheson), Tom Aldredge (Harold Lacey), Marie Thomas (Gloria), Gina Harding (Audri), Nancie Phillips (Barbara Wise), Tommy Flanders.
Drama. Source: Gerold Frank, *The Boston Strangler* (New York, 1966). When several middle-aged women are found strangled and sexually assaulted in the Back Bay area of Boston, the police round up numerous suspects but fail to uncover any leads. As the stranglings continue, Massachusetts Atty. Gen. Edward W. Brooke, Jr., persuades Asst. Atty. Gen. John S. Bottomly to set up a bureau to coordinate information concerning the slayings. While women report possible suspects, an ESP expert, Peter Hurkos, is brought in to conjure up a vision of the murderer. Elsewhere in the city, plumber Albert DeSalvo stops watching the funeral of President Kennedy on television and tells his wife that he must check on a customer's furnace. Instead, he gains access to a young woman's home and murders her. He continues his attacks but is finally apprehended when he is chased into the street by the husband of an intended victim and struck by a police car. DeSalvo is sent to Boston City Hospital for observation, while Bottomly and Det. Phillip J. DiNatale question a surviving victim who recalls that she bit her attacker on the thumb. Discovering that DeSalvo has a bite mark on his thumb, Bottomly and DiNatale check his place of employment and discover that his absences from work correspond with the dates of the murders. Aware that DeSalvo may be a schizophrenic incapable of total recall, Bottomly places him in a room with his wife and watches from behind a glass wall as the confrontation triggers DeSalvo's subconscious and compels him to clutch his wife by the throat. There is insufficient evidence to

prove that DeSalvo is the strangler, but Bottomly is certain that he has the right man when DeSalvo later reveals additional details about the murders. *Psychopaths. Sex deviates. Plumbers. Police. Lawyers. Murder. Marriage. Extrasensory perception. Schizophrenia. Circumstantial evidence. Boston. Boston—Back Bay. Edward W. Brooke, Jr. Albert DeSalvo. John S. Bottomly. Peter Hurkos. Phillip J. DiNatale. Boston City Hospital.*

Note: Location scenes filmed in Boston.

BOUDU SAUVÉ DES EAUX see BOUDU SAVED FROM DROWNING

BOUDU SAVED FROM DROWNING (France)   F6.0522

Michel Simon–Jean Gehret. *Dist* Pathé Contemporary Films. 23 Feb 1967 [New York opening]. Sd; b&w. 35mm. 87 min. [Also 84 min.]

Prod Michel Simon, Jean Gehret. *Dir* Jean Renoir. *Screenplay* Jean Renoir, Albert Valentin. *Photog* Marcel Lucien, Asselin. *Art Dir* Hughes Laurent, Jean Castanier. *Film Ed* Suzanne de Troye, Marguerite Renoir. *Mus* Raphaël, Jean Boulze, Edouard Dumoulin. "The Blue Danube" Johann Strauss. *Sd* Kalinowski. *Asst Dir* Jacques Becker. *Studio Mgr* Clément Oliver.

Cast: Michel Simon *(Boudu)*, Charles Granval *(Monsieur Lestingois)*, Marcelle Hainia *(Madame Lestingois)*, Séverine Lerczynska *(Anne-Marie)*, Jean Dasté *(student)*, Max Dalban *(Godin)*, Jean Gehret *(Vigour)*, Jacques Becker *(poet on beach)*, Jane Pierson *(Rose)*, Georges Darnoux *(wedding guest)*.

Comedy-drama. Source: René Fauchois, *Boudu sauvé des eaux* (Paris opening: 1919). Depressed by the loss of his pet dog, Boudu, a tramp, throws himself into the Seine. He is rescued and nursed back to health by a kindly bookdealer, Monsieur Lestingois. Instead of being grateful, however, Boudu maintains that his savior is now responsible for his well-being. All attempts to adjust Boudu to a middle-class way of life fail, and he carelessly defaces priceless first edition books, floods the kitchen, and creates other outrageous disturbances. Additionally, he manages to seduce Madame Lestingois as well as interrupt his host's nightly visits to the maid, Anne-Marie, by insisting upon sleeping in the hall corridor between their rooms. Then Boudu wins a lottery with a ticket given to him by Monsieur Lestingois, and he decides to marry Anne-Marie. Following their wedding, they are drifting down the Seine in a river punt and Boudu begins to long for his former freedom. As a result, the boat is "accidentally" tipped over and Boudu disappears. While the others are mourning his death, he wades ashore, changes clothes with a scarecrow, and happily sets out on the road again. *Tramps. Booksellers. Middle classes. Housemaids. Suicide. Rescue. Marriage. Seduction. Infidelity. Bookshops. Lotteries. Weddings. Seine River. Paris. Joinville (Haute-Marne).*

Note: Filmed on location in Paris and Joinville. Released in France in 1932 as *Boudu sauvé des eaux.*

THE BOUNTY KILLER   F6.0523

Premiere Productions. *Dist* Embassy Pictures. Jun 1965. Sd; col (Technicolor). 35mm (Technicolor). 92 min.

Prod Alex Gordon. *Exec Prod* Pat B. Rooney. *Dir* Spencer Gordon Bennet. *Screenplay* R. Alexander, Leo Gordon. *Photog* Frederick E. West. *Art Dir* Don Ament. *Film Ed* Ronald Sinclair. *Mus* Ronald Stein. *Sd* Harry Lindgren. *Asst Dir* Clark Paylow.

Cast: Dan Duryea *(Willie Duggan)*, Rod Cameron *(Johnny Liam)*, Audrey Dalton *(Carole Ridgeway)*, Richard Arlen *(Ridgeway)*, Buster Crabbe *(Mike Clayman)*, Fuzzy Knight *(Luther)*, Johnny Mack Brown *(Sheriff Green)*, Peter Duryea *(youth)*, Bob Steele *(Red)*, Eddie Quillan *(pianist)*, Norman Willis *(Hank Willis)*, Edmund Cobb *(townsman)*, Duane Ament *(Ben Liam)*, Grady Sutton *(minister)*, Emory Parnell *(Sam)*, Daniel M. White *(Marshal Davis)*, I. Stanford Jolley *(Sheriff Jones)*, John Reach *(Jeb)*, Red Morgan *(Seddon)*, Dolores Domasin *(waitress)*, Dudley Ross *(Indian)*, Ronn Delanor *(Joe)*, Tom Kennedy *(waiter)*, G. M. "Broncho Billy" Anderson *(man in the cantina)*, Frank Lacteen, Michael Hinn.

Western melodrama. Upon arriving in a Western mining town, mild-mannered Easterner Willie Duggan is brutally beaten for talking to dancehall hostess Carole Ridgeway. The thrashing, however, is terminated by Johnny Liam, who shoots and kills Duggan's assailant. Duggan finds work with a transport company, delivering the miners' payroll. When Duggan and his assistant Luther are ambushed Duggan kills the robber. After discovering that rewards are given for such slaughter, Duggan and Luther become bounty hunters. Although they capture outlaw Mike Clayman, his henchmen follow the pair, killing Luther and wounding Duggan. The unconscious victim is found by rancher Ridgeway, whose daughter Carole restores the gunman to health. Despite his love for Carole, Duggan resolves to avenge his partner's death and launches a campaign to exterminate outlaws. In his zeal Duggan kills an innocent man, becoming a criminal in his own right. While eloping with Carole, Duggan himself is slain by a bounty hunter. *Bounty hunters. Dancehall girls. Outlaws. Ranchers. Murder. Revenge. Manslaughter. Rewards. Mining towns.*

THE BOUNTY KILLER see THE UGLY ONES

BOURBON STREET see PASSION STREET, U. S. A.

BOURBON ST. SHADOWS   F6.0524

Dist MPA Feature Films. 5 Jun 1962 [Maryland license]. b&w. 35mm. 70 min.

Prod-Dir Ben Parker. *Screenplay* George Bellak, Betty Jeffries. *Photog* Willis Winford, Joseph Wheeler. *Set Decor* Sam Leve, Bernard Weist. *Film Ed* John Hemel. *Mus Supv* Edward Dutreil. *Sd* Dennis Fretwell. *Makeup* Eddie Senz.

Cast: Richard Derr *(Lamont Cranston)*, Mark Daniels *(Jogendra)*, Helen Westcott *(Tara)*, Jeanne Neher *(Felicia Ramirez)*, Dan Mullin *(Pablo Ramirez/ Victor Ramirez)*, Lee Edwards *(colonel)*, Jack Donner *(Billy)*, Steve Dano *(Tony Alcade)*, Leo Bruno *(Rocco)*, Sam Page *(Charlie)*.

Adventure melodrama. Pablo Ramirez, exiled Santa Cruz president hiding out in a Bourbon Street apartment in New Orleans, and his daughter, Felicia, are the objects of an assassination plot headed by Pablo's despotic twin brother, Victor, who has betrayed Pablo and assumed power in the Latin American republic. Musician Tony Alcade, who was helping Pablo, is murdered while talking long-distance with Lamont Cranston, a crime fighter who can become invisible at will. Cranston comes to New Orleans and, with his aide Jogendra, uses his mysterious power to rescue Pablo and Felicia, who had been kidnaped by Victor. The way is thus paved for Pablo to return to power. *Presidents. Musicians. Despots. Twins. Exile. Murder. Invisibility. Kidnaping. Perfidy. Assassination. Latin America. New Orleans. Imaginary republics.*

Note: Filmed in New Orleans.

THE BOX BOY   F6.0525

Dist Xerxes Productions. Jan 1970. Sd; col. 16mm. [Feature film, length unknown.]

Sex film. A delivery boy has sexual relations with a maid, two teenaged girls, and a housewife. Upon returning home after work, he collapses when his wife suggests that they make love. Included are scenes of autoeroticism, lesbianism, and group sex. *Delivery boys. Housewives. Housemaids. Autoeroticism. Adolescence. Group sex. Lesbianism.*

BOY (Japan)   F6.0526

Sozo-sha–A. T. G. *Dist* Grove Press. 9 Apr 1970 [New York opening]. Sd; col (Eastman Color) with b&w sequences. 35mm (CinemaScope). 97 min.

Prod Masayuki Nakajima, Takuji Yamaguchi. *Dir* Nagisa Oshima. *Screenplay* Tsutomu Tamura. *Photog* Yasuhiro Yoshioka, Seizo Sengen. *Art Dir* Jusho Toda. *Film Ed* Sueko Shiraishi. *Mus* Hikaru Hayashi. *Sd* Hideo Nishizaki. *Sd Eff* Akira Suzuki. *Asst Dir* Kiyoshi Ogasawara, Yun-do Yun, Daiji Ozeki. *Prod Mgr* Toshimi Kinoshita.

Cast: Tetsuo Abe *(Toshio)*, Fumio Watanabe *(father)*, Akiko Koyama *(stepmother)*, Tsuyoshi Kinoshita *(little brother)*.

Drama. Toshio, a 10-year-old boy, lives with his father, a shiftless ex-soldier, his stepmother, and his toddler half brother. The family gains a livelihood by means of a swindle in which Toshio's stepmother rushes into the path of oncoming traffic and feigns being struck by a car in order to hound a quick cash "settlement" from the driver. Eventually, Toshio is trained to assume her function, and the family moves from city to city to avoid detection. Their nomadic lifestyle isolates Toshio, who often retreats into fantasies. He attempts to run away to his grandmother's house in Kochio, but, unable to afford the fare, he buys a ticket to a less distant location and after sleeping on a beach returns to his parents. With police now alerted to the family's activities, they travel north to snowy Hokkaido. The boy's parents quarrel: his stepmother hopes to gather enough money in a short time to make a better life for them, while his father believes that they should refrain from repeating the swindle until the danger has passed. They discuss separating for a time and argue over who will take Toshio, the breadwinner. The father, in an outburst, flings away the watch Toshio's stepmother has given him. The toddler wanders into the road to retrieve it and causes an accident that results in the deaths of a man and a little girl. Later, the despondent Toshio builds a snowman and tells his little brother of a benevolent man from outer space who will right all wrongs; then, recognizing his own impotence, he attacks the snowman. The family settles down and again moves south, but the police arrest them. Under questioning, the boy admits only that he was in Hokkaido and witnessed the accident. *Children. Wanderers. Police. Extortion. Family life. Trains. Hokkaido. Automobile accidents.*

Note: Released in Japan in 1969 as *Shonen.*

A BOY … A GIRL   F6.0527

Cinema J Productions. *Dist* Jack Hanson, Four Star Excelsior Releasing Co., Cannon Releasing Corp. 25 Apr 1969 [Los Angeles showing]. Sd; col. 35mm (see note). 69 min. [See note.]

Pres by Jack Hanson. *Prod* Jack Hanson. *Dir-Writ* John Derek. *Photog* John Derek. *Film Ed* John H. Post, Bob Raff, Sonic Editorial Service. *Mus* Joe Greene. *Lyr* John Derek. *Sp Mus Writ & Rec* The Jamme. *Cost Dsgn* John Derek.

Cast: Dino Martin, Jr. *(The Boy)*, Airion Fromer *(The Girl)*, Karen Steele *(Elizabeth)*, Kerwin Mathews *(Mr. Christian)*, Peggy Lipton, Trace Vernell, Gene Walker, Michael-Maxim Nader.

Drama. A boy and a girl, both 15, meet and fall in love. Shattered by his first encounter with death in a motorcycle race, the Boy makes love for the first time; he feels confused and seeks advice from an attractive older woman, who helps him explore his consciousness with LSD. Mr. Christian, a sympathetic and wealthy stable owner, offers the Girl his love along with the gift of a horse. Tiring of the Boy's monotonous declarations of devotion, the Girl runs off to Mr. Christian, leaving behind the days of innocent awakening. ... *Innocents. Sexual initiation. Adolescence. Seduction. Middle age. Wealth. Motorcycle accidents. LSD. Horses.*

Note: Filmed in 16mm and blown up to 35mm. The film was re-edited with plot changes by producer Hanson and film exhibitor Marshall Naify after its initial preview; rereleased in Jul 1970 by Four Star-Excelsior as *The Sun Is Up*; running time: 76 and 85 min.

THE BOY CRIED MURDER (Great Britain/West Germany/Yugoslavia)
F6.0528

CCC-Filmkunst-Carlos Films-Avala Film-Bernard Luber. *Dist* Universal Pictures. 13 Apr **1966** [New York opening; c2 Apr 1966; LP34790]. Sd; col (Eastman Color). 35mm. 86 min.

Prod Philip N. Krasne. *Exec Prod* Bernard Luber. *Dir* George P. Breakston. *Screenplay* Robin Estridge. *Dir Photog* Milorad Marković. *Film Ed* Milanka Nanović. *Comp & Mus Dir* Martin Slavin. *Sd* Dušan Aleksić. *Asst Dir* Časlav Damjanović, Branka Soldo. *Prod Mgr* Ante Milić.

Cast: Fraser "Fiz" MacIntosh *(Jonathan "Jonno" Durrant)*, Veronica Hurst *(Clare Durrant)*, Phil Brown *(Tom Durrant)*, Tim Barrett *(Mike)*, Beba Lončar *(Susie)*, Edward Steel *(Colonel Wetherall)*, Anita Sharp Bolster *(Mrs. Wetherall)*, Sonja Hlebš *(Marianne)*, Alex MacIntosh *(police sergeant)*, Vuka Dundzerović *(Mrs. Bosnic)*.

Mystery melodrama. Source: Cornell Woolrich, "The Boy Cried Murder," in *Mystery Book Magazine* (Mar 1947). Jonno, jealous of his stepfather, Tom, invents stories and makes mischief to attract attention. As the family travels by steamer along the Adriatic Coast, Jonno sees a man fall into the water and claims he was pushed. The man is rescued and explains that he simply had too much to drink, and Jonno receives a scolding. The family arrives at the small resort town of Budva, and the boy again attracts attention by freeing a tame bear. During their holiday Clare and Tom become friendly with Susie and her boyfriend, Mike, a ne'er-do-well who relies on his great charm and sex appeal to get along. Mike receives a visit from Marianne, a former girl friend who intends to tell the police about a sum of money he took from her. Trailing Mike as he chases after Marianne to stop her, Jonno stumbles over her corpse. No one believes Jonno's story, however, because the body cannot be found and because of his earlier lie. When Jonno's parents go to a dance one night, Mike breaks into the boy's room, but Jonno escapes, pursued through the town by the murderer. Clare and Tom discover Jonno's disappearance, and the police begin a search for him after Susie confirms Mike's guilt in the murder. Mike catches Jonno in a citadel overlooking the sea and uses the boy as a shield. At last, however, he thrusts Jonno into Tom's arms and falls to his death on the rocks below. *Stepfathers. Children. Ne'er-do-wells. Murder. Filial relations. Mendacity. Steamboats. Resorts. Budva. Adriatic Sea. Chases. Bears.*

Note: Filmed on the coast of Montenegro. Released in Great Britain in Nov 1966; running time: 81 min; in West Germany in Sep 1966 as *Ein Junge schrie Mord*; running time: 84 min; in Yugoslavia in 1967 as *Dečak je vikao ubistvo*. The Cornell Woolrich story was previously filmed as *The Window* (RKO, 1949).

BOY, DID I GET A WRONG NUMBER!
F6.0529

Admiral Pictures. *Dist* United Artists. 8 Jun **1966** [New York opening; c8 Jun 1966; LP33582]. Sd; col (DeLuxe). 35mm. 99 min.

An Edward Small Production. *Prod* Edward Small. *Assoc Prod* George Beck. *Dir* George Marshall. *Screenplay* Burt Styler, Albert E. Lewin, George Kennett. *Story* George Beck. *Dir Photog* Lionel Lindon. *Art Dir* Frank Sylos. *Set Decor* H. Web Arrowsmith. *Supv Film Ed* Grant Whytock. *Mus* Richard LaSalle, "By" Dunham. *Sd* Clarence Peterson. *Sd Eff Ed* Al Bird. *Mus Ed* Clarence Peterson. *Asst Dir* Herbert S. Greene. *Prod Supv* Harold E. Knox. *Fashion Dsgn* Marjorie Corso. *Wardrobe* Morris Brown, Einar Bourman. *Makeup for Miss Sommer & Miss Lord* Hal Lierley, Mike Moschella. *Hairstyles* Jane Chabra.

Cast: Bob Hope *(Tom Meade)*, Elke Sommer *(Didi)*, Phyllis Diller *(Lily)*, Cesare Danova *(Pepe)*, Marjorie Lord *(Martha Meade)*, Kelly Thordsen *(Schwartz)*, Benny Baker *(Regan)*, Terry Burnham *(Doris Meade)*, Joyce

Jameson *(telephone operator)*, Harry Von Zell *(newscaster)*, Kevin Burchett *(Larry Meade)*, Keith Taylor *(Plympton)*, John Todd Roberts *(newsboy)*.

Comedy. When Didi, the bubble bath queen of the French cinema, arrives in Hollywood for her first dramatic film and discovers that the script once more calls for her to immerse herself in suds, she leaves in a rage and takes refuge in a hotel in Rocky Point, Oregon. Tom Meade, the real estate operator in the area, tries to get his wife, Martha, on the telephone and by mistake is connected with Didi. Immediately grasping the publicity possibilities of the situation, he sneaks her some food, tries to persuade her to stay at one of his cabins, and gets thrown out of his car. After promising to take his wife to their cabin for the weekend, Tom learns that Didi has changed her mind and is staying at the cabin. Meanwhile, his maid, Lily, has been listening on the telephone and knows of the mixup. Tom tells his wife that he must go to the cabin alone because forest rangers have reported a broken waterpipe. No sooner does he arrive and find Didi sleeping in her bubble bath than Lily arrives on a motorcycle to warn him that Martha is on her way. Frantically, Tom and Lily hide Didi in a wall bed, then in the basement, and finally in a fire locker behind the house. But all attempts to conceal Didi fail. Martha storms out, but Didi drives off in her car, hits a bump, and plunges into the lake. The police are alerted about the movie star's disappearance, Tom becomes the prime suspect, and the police arrest him. He escapes in a police car, unaware that Didi is sleeping in the back seat. The chase ends when Tom hits a fire hydrant and crashes into a soap factory. And all ends well as Didi makes an appearance covered in bubbles. *French. Actors. Real estate agents. Housemaids. Police. Marriage. Motion pictures. Hotels. Telephone. Motorcycles. Soap. Hollywood. Oregon. Chases.*

BOY INTO MAN
F6.0530

Aug **1970** [Los Angeles showing]. Sd; col (Eastman Color). 35mm? 120 min. *Dir* Mark Eden, dir.

Sex film. No information about the precise nature of this film has been found, but press material suggests that it concerns male homosexuality. *Male homosexuality.*

A BOY NAMED CHARLIE BROWN
F6.0531

Cinema Center Films-United Features Syndicate. *Dist* National General Pictures. 4 Dec **1969** [New York opening]. Sd; col (Technicolor). 35mm. 85 min. *MPAA rating* G.

A Lee Mendelson-Bill Melendez Production. *Prod* Lee Mendelson, Bill Melendez. *Dir* Bill Melendez. *Screenplay* Charles M. Schulz. *Graphic Dsgn* Edward Levitt, Bernard Gruver, Evert Brown, Ruth Kissane, Charles McElmurry, Dean Spille, Ellie Bonnard, Jan Green, Al Shean. *Anim* Don Lusk, Frank Smith, Rudy Zamora, Bob Carlson, Bill Littlejohn, Ken O'Brien, Bob Matz, Russ Van Neida, Barry Nelson, anim, Ken Champin, Spencer Peel, Hank Smith, Sam Jaimes, Maggie Bowen, Herm Cohen, Lew Irwin, Bror Lansing, Jay Sarbry, Gerry Kane. *Inkers & Painters* Beverly Robbins, Eleanor Warren, Faith Kovaleski, Manon Washburn, Debbie Abbot, Joice Lee Marshall, Gwenn Dotzler, Karen Oglesby, Dawn Smith, Chandra Poweris, Florence Hammontre, Connie Crawley, Celine Miles. *Adtl Art* Philip Roman, Richard Thompson, Frank Braxton. *Camera* Nick Vasu. *Film Ed* Robert T. Gillis, Charles McCann, Steve Melendez. *Neg Cutting* Alice Keillor. *Titl Song Writ & Sung by* Rod McKuen. *Songs:* "Failure Face," "Champion Charlie Brown," "We Lost Again," "Class Champion," "You'll Either Be a Hero ... or a Goat," "Bus Station," "National Spelling Bee," "B-E-A-G-E-L," "I'm Never Going to School Again" Rod McKuen. *Songs:* "Big City," "Homecoming" Rod McKuen, Vince Guaraldi. *Song:* "I Before E" John Scott Trotter, Bill Melendez, Al Shean. *Piano Sonata no. 8, op. 13 (Pathétique)* Ludwig van Beethoven. *Played by* Ingolf Dahl. *Orig Mus Score* Vince Guaraldi. *Mus Dir* John Scott Trotter. *Choreog for Snoopy's skating* Skippy Baxter.

Cast—The Voices: Peter Robbins *(Charlie Brown)*, Pamelyn Ferdin *(Lucy Van Pelt)*, Glenn Gilger *(Linus Van Pelt)*, Andy Pforsich *(Schroeder)*, Sally Dryer *(Patty)*, Anne Altieri *(Violet)*, Erin Sullivan *(Sally)*, Linda Mendelson *(Frieda)*, Christopher De Faria *(Pig Pen)*, David Carey *(2d boy)*, Guy Pforsich *(3d boy)*, Bill Melendez *(Snoopy)*.

Animated comedy. Source: Charles M. Schulz, *Peanuts* (a comic strip appearing daily through United Features Syndicate). When his football team achieves its 99th consecutive loss, second-grader Charlie Brown consults Lucy, the neighborhood psychiatrist, who advises him to build up skill and confidence by place-kicking. When he attempts to follow her advice, however, she perversely snatches the ball away. Charlie then enters and, with the help of the beagle Snoopy and Lucy's brother Linus, wins his school's spelling contest, having been given such familiar words as "failure" and "insecure". Sponsored by "Lucy Van Pelt Inc.," Charlie participates in a national spelling bee in New York City. During his absence, Lucy hints at a forthcoming marriage to Schroeder, a protégé pianist and Beethoven enthusiast. In quest of the blanket to which he is symbiotically attached, Linus, accompanied by Snoopy, follows Charlie to New York. There Snoopy dances on the ice of Rockefeller Center, and Linus finds his blanket, now a discarded shoe rag. Although Charlie survives the preliminary competition, he is eliminated in the final round of the spelling tournament, when he is unable to spell the word "beagle." Disheartened, he returns home, and is again bested by Lucy while attempting to placekick. *Songs:* "Cloud Dreams" (Lucy, Linus & Charlie Brown); "Charlie Brown and His All-Stars" (The Team); "We Lost Again" (Charlie Brown & Linus); "Blue Charlie Brown" (Charlie Brown & Lucy); "Time To Go to School" (Linus & Lucy); "I Only Dread One Day at a Time" (Charlie Brown, Linus, Lucy, Violet & Patty); "Failure Face" (Lucy, Violet & Patty); "By Golly I'll Show 'Em" (Charlie Brown & Friends); "Class Champion," "I Before E" (Charlie Brown & Linus); "School Spelling Bee" (Charlie Brown, Linus & Lucy); "Champion Charlie Brown" (The Gang); "Start Boning up on Your Spelling, Charlie Brown" (Charlie Brown & Friends); "You'll Either Be a Hero ... or a Goat" (Charlie Brown, Linus & Sally); "Bus Station" (The Gang); "Do Piano Players Make a Lot of Money" (Lucy & Schroeder); "I've Got To Get My Blanket Back" (Linus & Lucy); "Big City," "Found Blanket" (Charlie Brown & Linus); "National Spelling Bee," "B-E-A-G-E-L" (Charlie Brown & Friends); "Homecoming" (Charlie Brown & Linus); "I'm Never Going to School Again" (Charlie Brown, Linus & Sally); "Welcome Home, Charlie Brown" (Charlie Brown & Lucy). *Children. Psychiatrists. Self-confidence. Obsession. Football. Spelling. Elementary school life. Television. New York City. Ludwig van Beethoven. Dogs.*

BOY OF TWO WORLDS (Denmark)   F6.0532

Laterna Film. *Dist* G. G. Productions. Apr **1970**. Sd; col (Eastman Color). 35mm. 88 min. *MPAA rating G.*

Dir Astrid Henning-Jensen. *Screenplay* Astrid Henning-Jensen, Bjarne Henning-Jensen. *Photog* Henning Bendtsen, Niels Carstens, Arthur Christiansen. *Film Ed* Anker. *Mus* Herman D. Koppel. *Sd* Georg Jensen, Peter Willemoes. *Prod Supv* Mogens Skot-Hansen.

Cast: Jimmy Sterman (*Paw*), Edvin Adolphson (*Anders Nilsson*), Ninja Tholstrup (*Aunt Frieda*), Asbjørn Andersen (*Yvonne*), Sacha Wamberg (*squire*), Freddy Pedersen (*Marius*), Karl Stegger, Preben Neergaard, Karen Lykkehus, Helge Kjaerulff-Schmidt, Grethe Høholdt, Poul Smyrner, Mogens Hermansen, Finn Lassen, Svend Bille, Arthur Jensen, Ebba Amfeldt, Otto Hallstrøm, Rigmor Hvidtfeldt, Ego Brønnum-Jacobsen.

Drama. Source: Torry Gredsted, *Paw, der Indianerjunge* (Cologne, 1931). Paw, the orphaned son of a West Indian woman and a Danish sea captain, is sent to live with his Aunt Frieda in Copenhagen. When his aunt dies, the townspeople display their prejudice against the dark-skinned boy until Anders Nilsson, a poacher, takes him in. Nilsson eventually is caught and fined for poaching, and Paw is sent to reform school. Paw escapes and goes to live in the woods with a baby fox. Later he is wounded by a duck poacher and then taken in by a squire and his daughter Yvonne. The squire hires Nilsson to be his gamekeeper, and Paw becomes his helper. *Orphans. Halfcastes. Children. Aunts. Poachers. Gamekeepers. Racial prejudice. Filial relations. Reformatories. Fox.*

Note: Released in Denmark in Dec 1959 as *Paw*; running time: 100 min. Also known as *The Lure of the Jungle.*

A BOY TEN FEET TALL (Great Britain)   F6.0533

Great Shows, Ltd. *Dist* Paramount Pictures. 8 Jan **1965** [New Orleans opening; c31 Dec 1963; LP29476]. Sd; col (Eastmancolor, print by Technicolor). 35mm (CinemaScope). 88 min.

Pres by Bryanston Films, Seven Arts Productions. A Michael Balcon Production. *Prod* Hal Mason. *Exec Prod* Michael Balcon. *Dir* Alexander Mackendrick. *Screenplay* Denis Cannan. *Dir Photog* Erwin Hillier. *Camera Op* Robert Kindred. *2d Unit Photog* Norman Warwick. *Focus* George Pink, Roy Ford. *2d Unit Focus* Peter Hendry, Lou Lavelly. *Art Dir* Ted Tester. *Asst Art Dir* Scott Slimon. *Set Decor* Scott Slimon. *Film Ed* Jack Harris. *1st Asst Ed* Mary Kessell. *2d Asst Ed* John Rogers, ed. *Mus* Tristram Cary. *Sd Rec* H. L. Bird. *Sd Camera Op* Sandy Fairlie. *Boom Op* Ken Ritchie. *1st, 2d & 3d Asst Dir* Peter Price, Richard Gill, Terry Lens, Michael Meighan. *Prod Mgr* Philip Shipway. *Prod Sec* Doris Prince. *Cont* Joan Kirk. *Wardrobe Master* Ernie Farrer. *Wardrobe Mistress* Jean Fairlie. *Makeup* Philip Leakey. *Hairdresser* Henry Montsash. *Tech Adv* John Kingsley Heath. *Grip* Tommy Miller. *Still Photog* Laurie Turner. *Prop* Henry Frewer, Derek Creedon. *Supv Electrn* Robert Canning.

Cast: Edward G. Robinson (*Cocky Wainwright*), Fergus McClelland (*Sammy*), Constance Cummings (*Gloria von Imhoff*), Harry H. Corbett (*Lem*), Paul Stassino (*Spyros Dracondopolous*), Zia Mohyeddin (*Syrian*), Orlando Martins (*Abu Lubaba*), John Turner (*Heneker*), Zena Walker (*Aunt Jane*), Jack Gwillim (*district commissioner*), Patricia Donahue (*Cathie*), Jared Allen (*Bob*), Guy Deghy (*doctor*), Marne Maitland (*Hassan*), Steven Scott (*Egyptian policeman*), Frederick Schiller (*head porter*), Tajiri, Swaleh, Faith Brown (*members of Cocky's camp*).

Adventure melodrama. Source: W. H. Canaway, *Sammy Going South* (London, 1961). Sammy, a 10-year-old boy whose parents were killed in the bombing of Port Said during the Suez Crisis, sets out for Durban to visit his Aunt Jane, unaware that he must trek 5,000 miles across an entire continent. He is picked up by a Syrian peddler who plans to exploit him, but the man has an accident and dies. Sammy then encounters Gloria von Imhoff, a rich American tourist, but he distrusts her and runs away. His next acquaintance is Cocky Wainwright, a diamond smuggler and hunter who becomes fond of the lad and takes him to his hideout, teaches him to shoot, and reminisces about his past. Their happy relationship is abruptly ended when Cocky is arrested and taken to jail. He is visited there by Sammy's aunt, who accepts Cocky's advice that the boy be permitted to finish his journey alone. When Sammy finally reaches his aunt's hotel in Durban, she is there to greet him. *Orphans. Aunts. Syrians. Peddlers. Americans in foreign countries. Tourists. Smugglers. Childhood. Friendship. Jails. Suez Crisis. Port Said. Durban.*

Note: Location scenes filmed in South Africa. Opened in London in Mar 1963 as *Sammy Going South*; running time: 128 min.

THE BOY WHO CAUGHT A CROOK   F6.0534

Harvard Film Corp. *Dist* United Artists. 25 Oct **1961** [Los Angeles opening; c27 Sep 1961; LP21186]. Sd; b&w. 35mm. 72 min.

Prod Robert E. Kent. *Dir* Edward L. Cahn. *Screenplay* Nathan Juran. *Photog* Gilbert Warrenton. *Art Dir* Harry Reif. *Film Ed* Robert Carlisle. *Mus* Richard La Salle. *Sd* Al Overton. *Asst Dir* Herbert S. Greene. *Prod Mgr* Joseph Small. *Wardrobe* Douglas Stevens. *Makeup* Harry Thomas. *Hairstyles* Frances Sperry.

Cast: Wanda Hendrix (*Laura*), Roger Mobley (*kid*), Don Beddoe (*The Colonel*), Richard Crane (*Connors*), Johnny Seven (*Rocky Kent*), Robert J. Stevenson (*sergeant*), Bill Walker (*keeper*), Henry Hunter (*Flannigan*).

Melodrama. One day a small newsboy and his old hobo friend, The Colonel, find a briefcase in an open lot. The old man opens it privately and tells the disappointed boy that it is empty. Later, the lad learns from a radio broadcast that the briefcase was used in a $100,000 robbery; and Laura, the boy's widowed mother, insists that he turn over the briefcase to the authorities. After notifying the police, the boy is accosted by the robber, Rocky Kent, who accuses him of stealing the money and forces him to lead the way to The Colonel's house. In an effort to save the boy from harm, The Colonel says that he took the money and offers to lead Kent to the hiding place. Returning home, however, the boy learns that the money was found in the possession of a drunken tramp; and, realizing that The Colonel lied to save him, the boy leads the police to The Colonel and Kent. The robber is apprehended, and the boy and the hobo receive a $1,000 reward. *Newsboys. Hoboes. Widows. Police. Robbery. Honesty. Filial relations. Rewards. Los Angeles.*

Note: Location scenes filmed in Los Angeles. Working titles: *The Boy Who Found $100,000* and *The Colonel of Bunker Hill.*

THE BOY WHO FOUND $100,000 *see* THE BOY WHO CAUGHT A CROOK

THE BOYS (Great Britain)   F6.0535

Galaworldfilm Productions–Atlas Productions. *Dist* Screen Entertainment Co. **1963**. Sd (RCA); b&w. 35mm (CinemaScope). 123 min.

Pres by Henry G. Saperstein. *Prod-Dir* Sidney J. Furie. *Exec Prod* Kenneth Rive. *Screenplay* Stuart Douglass. *Photog* Gerald Gibbs. *Camera Op* Chic Waterson. *Art Dir* John Earl. *Titl Dsgn* James Baker. *Film Ed* Jack Slade. *Mus Comp & Played by* The Shadows. *Mus Dir* Bill McGuffie. *Sd* Claude Hitchcock, Len Shilton. *Dub Ed* James Shields. *Asst Dir* David Bracknell. *Prod Mgr* Fred Slark. *Cont* Kay Mander. *Casting Dir* Robert Lennard.

Cast: Richard Todd (*Victor Webster*), Robert Morley (*Lewis Montgomery*), Felix Aylmer (*judge*), Dudley Sutton (*Stan Coulter*), Ronald Lacey (*Billy Herne*), Tony Garnett (*Ginger Thompson*), Jess Conrad (*Barney Lee*), Wilfrid Brambell (*Robert Brewer*), Allan Cuthbertson (*Randolph St. John*), Wensley Pithey (*Mr. Coulter*), Colin Gordon (*Gordon Lonsdale*), Kenneth J. Warren (*George Tanner*), Laurence Hardy (*Patmor*), Harold Scott (*Caldwell*), Betty Marsden (*Mrs. Herne*), Carol White (*Evelyn May*), Patrick Magee (*Mr. Lee*), Ian Fleming, David Lodge, Rita Webb, Hilda Fenemore, Olga Dickie, Roy Kinnear, Mavis Villiers, Lloyd Lamble, Charles Morgan, Patrick Newell, Tom Chatto, George Moon.

Crime drama. In London, working-class youths Stan Coulter, Barney Lee, Billy Herne, and Ginger Thompson are accused of murdering an elderly garage attendant and stealing 15 shillings from his cash box. During their trial at the Old Bailey, prosecution attorney Victor Webster calls numerous witnesses who describe the teenagers as reckless Teddy boys who planned the robbery, a factor that makes the offense capital. Defense counsel Lewis Montgomery in turn provides persuasive arguments that conflict with the views of the Crown witnesses. Webster, himself beginning to doubt the boys' guilt, traps Stan into a confession. Stan receives the death sentence; juveniles Barney and Billy are convicted as accomplices; and Ginger is acquitted. *Garagemen. Lawyers. Teddy boys. Juvenile delinquents. Murder. Robbery. Adolescence. Capital punishment. Trials. Confession (law). London. Old Bailey.*

Note: Location scenes filmed in and around London. Opened in London in Sep 1962.

THE BOYS FROM BEVERLY HILLS *see* THE UPSTAIRS ROOM

BOYS IN CHAINS   F6.0536
27 Feb **1969** [San Francisco showing]. Sd; col. 35mm. [Feature film, length unknown.]

Sex film. Although no information on the precise nature of this film has been found, press material indicates that it concerns male homosexuality. *Male homosexuality.*

THE BOYS IN THE BAND   F6.0537
Leo Productions, Ltd. *For* Cinema Center Films. *Dist* National General Pictures. 17 Mar **1970** [New York opening; c6 Mar 1970; LP38966]. Sd; col (Deluxe). 35mm. 120 min. *MPAA rating* R.

Prod-Writ Mart Crowley. *Exec Prod* Dominick Dunne, Robert Jiras. *Assoc Prod* Kenneth Utt. *Dir* William Friedkin. *Dir Photog* Arthur J. Ornitz. *Camera Op* Richard Mingalone. *Asst Camera* Felix Trimboli. *Prod Dsgn* John Robert Lloyd. *Asst Art Dir* Robert Wightman. *Set Decor* Philip Smith. *Master Scenic Artist* Edward Garzero. *Set Dresser* Robert Klatt. *Main Titl* Everett Aison. *Film Ed* Jerry Greenberg, Carl Lerner. *Asst Ed* Lynn Lewis Lovett. *Song:* "Anything Goes" Cole Porter. *Sung by* Harpers Bizarre. *Song:* "The Look of Love" Burt Bacharach, Hal David. *Perf by* Burt Bacharach. *Song:* "Heat Wave" Eddie Holland, Lamont Dozier, Brian Holland. *Sung by* Martha and the Vandellas. *Song:* "The Frog" João Donato de Oliveira. *Perf by* Sergio Mendes and Brasil '66. *Song:* "Good Lovin' Ain't Easy To Come By" Nicholas Ashford, Valerie Simpson. *Sung by* Marvin Gaye, Tammi Terrell. *Sd* Jack C. Jacobsen. *Sd Ed* Jack Fitzstephens, Sanford Rackow, Vincent Connelly. *Sd Mix* Al Gramaglia. *Dub Ed* Jean Bagley. *Asst Dir* William C. Gerrity, Fred Gallo. *Prod Mgr* Paul Ganapoler. *Script Supv* Nancy Tonery. *Prod Sec* Adeline Leonard. *Cost Dsgn* W. Robert La Vine. *Wardrobe Supv* Joseph W. Dehn. *Makeup Supv* Robert O'Bradovich. *Makeup* John Jiras. *Hairstyles* Vern Caruso. *Ch Electrn* Willie Meyerhoff, Sal Martorano. *Key Grip* Mike Mahony. *Head Carpenter* Ken Paquette. *Prop Master* Joe Caracciolo. *Still Photog* Muky. *Casting* Victor-Jay Agency.

Cast: Kenneth Nelson *(Michael)*, Leonard Frey *(Harold)*, Frederick Combs *(Donald)*, Cliff Gorman *(Emory)*, Reuben Greene *(Bernard)*, Robert La Tourneaux *(Cowboy)*, Laurence Luckinbill *(Hank)*, Keith Prentice *(Larry)*, Peter White *(Alan)*.

Comedy-drama. Source: Mart Crowley, *The Boys in the Band* (New York opening: 14 Apr 1968). Homosexuals Donald and Michael are discussing a birthday party the latter is giving for their friend Harold, when Alan, an old heterosexual college acquaintance of Michael's, telephones and asks if he can visit. Michael reluctantly agrees, even though the party guests are due to arrive at his Greenwich Village apartment. Emory, an interior decorator, is first to come, and he is soon followed by lovers Hank and Larry, and Bernard, a black. As the six of them dance raucously, Alan arrives and immediately is made uncomfortable by the situation; in addition, he and Emory instantly dislike each other. After the appearance of Cowboy, who has been rented by Emory as a birthday gift for Harold, the guest of honor arrives, and Michael suggests they play a game in which each person telephones the one he has loved most in his life. Both Bernard and Emory make unsatisfactory calls to men they have desired for years, and Hank calls Larry's answering service to declare his love. Michael then accuses Alan of being a "closet" homosexual and goads him into calling a former college friend whose advances Alan had once spurned; Alan dials a number and blurts out his love to the person on the other end, but Michael's brief victory is ruined when the person turns out to be Alan's estranged wife. The festivities begin to pall, and the guests start to leave, but not before Harold devastates Michael by characterizing him as a neurotic, unable to live in either the homosexual or heterosexual world. *Interior decorators. Prostitutes. Negroes. Male homosexuality. Telephone. Neurosis. Birthdays. New York City—Greenwich Village.*

Note: Location scenes filmed in New York City.

BOYS' NIGHT OUT   F6.0538
Filmways, Inc.-Kimco Pictures-Embassy Pictures. *Dist* Metro-Goldwyn-Mayer, Inc. 21 Jun **1962** [New York opening; c20 Apr 1962; LP22235]. Sd; col (Metrocolor). 35mm (CinemaScope). 114 min.

Pres by Joseph E. Levine. A Martin Ransohoff Production. *Prod* Martin Ransohoff. *Assoc Prod* James C. Pratt. *Dir* Michael Gordon. *Screenplay* Ira Wallach. *Adapt* Marion Hargrove. *Story* Arne Sultan, Marvin Worth. *Dir Photog* Arthur E. Arling. *Camera Op* Dick Towers. *Col Cons* Charles K. Hagedon. *Art Dir* George W. Davis, Hans Peters. *Set Decor* Henry Grace, Jerry Wunderlich. *Main Titl Dsgn* Playhouse Pictures. *Film Ed* Tom McAdoo.

Mus Frank DeVol. *Songs:* "Boys' Night Out," "Cathy" Sammy Cahn, James Van Heusen. *Sung by* Patti Page. *Rec Supv* Franklin Milton. *Mix* William E. Edmondson. *Boom Op* Mal Rennings. *Rec* John Chandler. *Asst Dir* James Welch, Ronald Florance. *Asst to the Dir* Ivan Volkman. *Miss Novak's Cost* Kim Novak, Bill Thomas. *Executed by* Elizabeth Courtney. *Wardrobe* Carl Garrison, Roselle Fetherston. *Makeup* William Tuttle. *Hairstyles* Mary Keats, Maudlee McDougall. *Dial Coach* Mike Ross. *Still Photog* M. B. Paul. *Gaffer* Perry O'Brien. *Grip* Mervyn Price.

Cast: Kim Novak *(Cathy)*, James Garner *(Fred Williams)*, Tony Randall *(George Drayton)*, Howard Duff *(Doug Jackson)*, Janet Blair *(Marge Drayton)*, Patti Page *(Joanne McIllenny)*, Jessie Royce Landis *(Ethel Williams)*, Oscar Homolka *(Dr. Prokosch)*, Howard Morris *(Howard McIllenny)*, Anne Jeffreys *(Toni Jackson)*, Zsa Zsa Gabor *(girl friend)*, Fred Clark *(Mr. Bohannon)*, William Bendix *(Slattery)*, Jim Backus *(Peter Bowers)*, Larry Keating *(Mr. Bingham)*, Ruth McDevitt *(Beulah Partridge)*.

Comedy. Bachelor Fred Williams and his three married friends, George, Doug, and Howard, are Manhattan commuters from Connecticut who decide to rent an apartment in New York City and furnish it with a beautiful blonde to be available to each of them on different nights of the week. In answer to a *New York Times* advertisement, Cathy, an attractive young woman, accepts the position. Unknown to the "boys," she is actually a sociology student preparing a thesis on the sexual patterns of the suburban male. By clever maneuvering, she manages to subdue their amorous intentions. Although their evenings with Cathy are completely innocent, the three married men lie to Fred about their torrid evenings at the apartment. Wildly jealous, he proposes to Cathy, and she accepts. Meanwhile, the three wives have learned of the situation through a private investigator, and they arrive at the apartment in a rage. All misunderstandings are cleared up, however, when Cathy reveals her true motive for accepting the housekeeper job. Furious at having been duped, Fred walks out, but the wives, aided by Fred's mother, promptly drag him back. He decides to become the fourth member of a quartet of husbands who spend a weekly night on the town—with their wives. *Bachelors. Suburbanites. Students. Detectives. Sex research. Imposture. Jealousy. Infidelity. Marriage. New York City. Connecticut. "New York Times".*

THE BOYS OF PAUL STREET (United States/Hungary)   F6.0539
Mafilm Studios-Bohgros Films. *Dist* Twentieth Century-Fox Film Corp. 23 Jun **1969** [New York opening]. Sd; col (Eastman Color, print by DeLuxe). 35mm (Agascope). 105 min. *MPAA rating* G.

Prod Endre Bohém. *Exec Prod* Bud Groskopf. *Dir* Zoltán Fábri. *Screenplay* Zoltán Fábri, Endre Bohém. *Dir Photog* György Illés. *Camera* József Lőrincz. *Lighting* László Kocsenda. *Col Cons* Géza Dobranyi, Magda Boros. *Art Dir* József Romvári. *Set Dsgn* Tilda Gáti. *Architect* Eva Martin. *Film Ed* Ferencné Szécsényi. *Asst Film Ed* Mária Magyar. *Mus Comp* Emil Petrovics. *Sd Engr* György Pintér. *Prod Exec* Ottó Föld. *Prod Mgr* József Bajusz. *Unit Mgr* István Szücs, György Rozsasi. *Cost Dsgn* Judit Schaffer. *Wardrobe* Irene Juhasz. *Makeup* Ottilia Pasztory. *Dial Dir* Katalin Haasz. *Casting* John Owen. *2d Asst* Ferenc Andras, Zsuzsa Paál.

Cast—The Boys of Paul Street: Anthony Kemp *(Nemecsek)*, William Burleigh *(Boka)*, John Moulder-Brown *(Gereb)*, Robert Efford *(Csonakos)*, Mark Colleano *(Csele)*, Gary O'Brien *(Weisz)*, Martin Beaumont *(Kolnay)*, Paul Bartlett *(Barabas)*, Earl Younger *(Leszik)*, György Vizi *(Richter)*.

Cast—The Red Shirts: Julien Holdaway *(Feriats)*, Peter Delmar *(older Pasztor)*, Miklós Jancsó *(younger Pasztor)*, Attila Németh *(Wendaver)*, Imre Ebergényi *(Szebenits)*, Sándor Kentner *(Torok)*.

Cast—Other Youngsters: András Avar *(Szabo)*, János Pach *(younger Szabo)*, István Séri *(bespectacled boy)*, Orsolya Zeitler *(girl with Diabolo)*.

Cast—Adults: Mari Törőcsik *(Nemecsek's mother)*, Sándor Pécsi *(Professor Racz)*, László Kozák *(Jano)*, László Paál *(Nemecsek's father)*, Árpád Téry *(The Doctor)*.

Comedy-drama. Source: Ferenc Molnár, *A Pál utcai fiúk* (1907). In turn-of-the-century Budapest, two groups of teenage boys engage in a mock war over one of the few vacant lots remaining in the city. The Paul Street boys have long regarded the lot as their exclusive property; now the fearsome Red Shirts have decided to drive them out and take over. As preparations begin for the battle and each side plans its strategy, Private Nemecsek, the smallest, youngest, pluckiest Paul Street boy, aspires to becoming an officer. Spying on the Red Shirts, he is forced to hide in the water to avoid discovery and catches cold. Then, when Gereb, a Paul Street boy, defects to the Red Shirts, Nemecsek sneaks into the enemy camp to find out what secrets the traitor has divulged. Hearing the Red Shirts disparaging his comrades, Nemecsek speaks out in their defense and is thrown into a lake. As a result, Nemecsek falls ill with pneumonia, much to the concern of Boka, the general of the Paul Street boys, who has become fond of the small but courageous private. Finally, the battle formally begins. Although gravely ill, Nemecsek gets out of bed and goes to the battlefield, determined to fight. Delirious and dying, he falls upon the leader of the Red Shirts and is hailed for winning the battle for the Paul Street troops. The battle is over and Nemecsek is at last a "hero"—albeit a dead hero. Saddened and disillusioned by the price of victory, Boka returns to the vacant lot and learns that the city has claimed it for the site of a new apartment house. *Gangs. Spies. Traitors. Adolescence. Heroism. Disillusionment. Gang wars. Pneumonia. Budapest.*

Note: Filmed in Budapest in 1968 in both English and Hungarian versions; released in Hungary in Apr 1969 as *A Pál utcai fiúk* at 112 min.

THE BRAIN (Great Britain/West Germany)   **F6.0540**
Raymond Stross Productions–CCC-Filmkunst. *Dist* Governor Films. Dec 1964. Sd; b&w. 35mm. 83 min.
Prod Raymond Stross. *Exec Prod* Artur Brauner. *Dir* Freddie Francis. *Screenplay* Robert Stewart, Philip Mackie. *Dir Photog* Bob Huke. *Camera Op* Eric Besche. *Focus Puller* Ronnie Fox-Rogers. *Art Dir* Arthur Lawson. *Asst Art Dir* Don Picton. *Scenic Artist* Ted Barnes. *Draughtsman* Raymonde Reilly. *Film Ed* Oswald Hafenrichter. *1st Asst Ed* David Nimmo. *Mus* Ken Jones. *Sd Dir* Stephen Dalby. *Sd Mix* Bill Bulkley. *Boom Op* Fred Tomlin. *Sd Camera Op* Dave Goghan. *1st, 2d, & 3d Asst Dir* Buddy Booth, Ernie Lewis, Don Webb. *Prod Supv* George Fowler. *Prod Sec* Angela Cockill. *Cont* Pamela Davies. *Wardrobe Mistress* Jackie Cummins. *Makeup Artist* George Frost. *Hairdresser* Mervyn Medalie. *Still Photog* Ted Reed. *Prod Buyer* Ronald Baker. *Grip* Ted Tucker. *Rigger* H. Paton. *Chargehand Prop* Alfred Pegley.
Cast: Anne Heywood *(Anna)*, Peter Van Eyck *(Dr. Peter Corrie)*, Cecil Parker *(Stevenson)*, Bernard Lee *(Frank Shears)*, Ellen Schwiers *(Ella)*, Maxine Audley *(Marion)*, Jeremy Spenser *(Martin)*, Siegfried Lowitz *(Walters)*, Hans Nielsen *(Immerman)*, Miles Malleson *(Dr. Miller)*, Jack MacGowran *(Furber)*, George A. Cooper *(Gabler)*, Irene Richmond *(Mrs. Gabler)*, Ann Sears *(secretary)*, Victor Brooks *(farmer)*, Alistair Williams *(Inspector Pike)*, Kenneth Kendall *(newscaster)*, John Junkin *(Frederick)*, Frank Forsyth *(Francis)*, Bandana Das Gupta *(Miss Soong)*, Allan Cuthbertson *(Dr. Silva)*, Richard McNeff *(Parkin)*, John Watson *(priest)*, Patsy Rowlands *(dancehall girl)*, Bryan Pringle *(master of ceremonies)*, Dieter Borsche.
Science fiction melodrama. Source: Curt Siodmak, *Donovan's Brain* (New York, 1943). Dr. Peter Corrie and his assistant, Frank Shears, investigate an airplane accident near their laboratory. They take the only survivor inside, remove his brain when his heart stops beating, and keep it alive in an experimental solution. The brain, which belonged to ruthless tycoon Max Holt, soon begins to take control of Dr. Corrie's mind. At Holt's funeral Corrie meets the dead man's daughter, Anna; his rebellious son, Martin; and his unethical lawyer, Stevenson. Corrie suspects that Holt was murdered, and under the strange hypnotic influence of the brain he searches for the killer. He encounters Holt's mistress, Marion Fare, and his chauffeur, Gable; and when Gable is murdered, Corrie is framed by Holt's associates. Controlled by the brain, Corrie almost murders a man, but Shears is able to stop him by removing the brain from the solution. Corrie later discovers that Anna killed her father because of his monopoly of a new drug. *Scientists. Tycoons. Chauffeurs. Disembodiment. Experiments. Murder. Frameup. Patricide. Laboratories. Airplane accidents.*
Note: Released in Great Britain in Dec 1963 as *Vengeance*; running time: 83 min; in West Germany in Oct 1962 as *Ein Toter sucht seinen Mörder*; running time: 84 min. Previously filmed in 1944 as *Lady and the Monster* (Republic) and in 1953 as *Donovan's Brain* (United Artists).

THE BRAIN (France/Italy)   **F6.0541**
Gaumont International–Dino De Laurentiis Cinematografica. *Dist* Paramount Pictures. 13 Nov 1969 [New York opening; c7 Mar 1969; LF55]. Sd; col (Eastman Color). 35mm (Franscope). 100 min.
Prod Alain Poiré. *Dir* Gérard Oury. *2d Unit Dir* Claude Clément. *Screenplay* Gérard Oury, Marcel Jullian, Danièle Thompson. *Dir Photog* Wladimir Ivanov. *Tech Adv for Photog* Armand Thirard. *Prod Dsgn* Jean André. *Film Ed* Albert Jurgenson. *Mus* Georges Delerue. *Titl Song* Eddie Snyder, Larry Kulck. Jean Rieul, Louis Hochet. *Asst Dir* Marc Monnet, Gérard Guérin. *Prod Supv* Paul Joly. *Cost Dsgn* Tanine Autre. *Hairstyles* Alex Archambault.
Cast: David Niven *(The Brain)*, Jean-Paul Belmondo *(Arthur)*, Bourvil *(Anatole)*, Eli Wallach *(Scannapieco)*, Silvia Monti *(Sofia)*, Fernand Valois *(Bruno)*, Raymond Gérôme *(commissioner)*, Jacques Balutin *(Pochet)*, Jacques Ciron *(Duboeuf)*, Fernand Guiot *(Mazurel)*, Jean Le Poulain *(man from 5th floor)*, Robert Dalban *(Belgian with cold)*, Raoul Delfosse, Pierre Tornade, Paul Mercey *(Belgians)*, Henri Genès *(chief guard)*, Yves Barsacq, Dominique Zardi *(guards)*, Tom Duggan *(Superintendent Cummings)*, Guy Delorme, Michel Garland *(Brain's accomplices)*, Patrick Préjean.
Crime comedy. The Brain, wanted by the police for the Glasgow-London train robbery, leaves his villa in Sicily, hires Mafia chief Scannapieco, and heads for Paris, where he is assigned as security guard for a train carrying $12 million to NATO headquarters in Brussels. Intending to repeat his earlier successful robbery, The Brain encounters competition from Arthur, an escaped convict, and his friend Anatole. The two men get away with the money but throw the

bags over a bridge and into the arms of The Brain. Scannapieco then doublecrosses his partner because The Brain has been having an affair with the Mafia chief's sister, Sofia. At the dock at Le Havre, Scannapieco is arrested by the police, who believe him to be The Brain; meanwhile, Arthur discovers that Scannapieco had hidden the money inside a replica of the Statue of Liberty being shipped from France to New York. When the bottom of the statue is opened, however, the $12 million is scattered by the wind. Anatole, Arthur, and The Brain arrive in New York Harbor aboard the ship as The Brain plans to lead an assault on a $50 million gold shipment destined for Fort Knox. *Thieves. Gangsters. Fugitives. Police. Train robberies. Perfidy. Mistaken identity. Ships. Gold. Sicily. Paris. Le Havre. New York City. Statue of Liberty. Mafia.*
Note: Opened in Paris in Mar 1969 as *Le Cerveau* and in Italy in 1969 as *Il Cervello*. Original running time: 115 min.

THE BRAIN THAT WOULDN'T DIE   **F6.0542**
Rex Carlton Productions. *Dist* American International Pictures. May 1962. Sd; b&w. 35mm. 71 min. [Also reviewed at 81 min.]
Prod Rex Carlton. *Assoc Prod* Mort Landberg. *Dir-Writ* Joseph Green, dir. *Orig Story* Rex Carlton, Joseph Green, dir. *Photog* Stephen Hajnal. *Art Dir* Paul Fanning. *Film Ed* Leonard Anderson, Marc Anderson. *Mus* Abe Baker, Tony Restaino. *Asst Dir* Tony La Marca. *Prod Mgr* Alfred H. Lessner. *Makeup* George Fiala. *Sp Eff* Byron Baer.
Cast: Virginia Leith *(Jan Compton)*, Herb Evers *(Dr. Bill Cortner [see note])*, Adele Lamont *(Doris Powell)*, Bruce Brighton *(Dr. Cortner)*, Doris Brent *(nurse)*, Leslie Daniel *(Kurt)*, Bonnie Shari *(stripper)*, Paula Maurice *(B-girl)*, Lola Mason *(Donna Williams)*, Audrey Devereau *(Jeannie)*, Bruce Kerr *(announcer)*, Eddie Carmel *(monster)*.
Horror film. Surgeon Bill Cortner, who robs graves to obtain organs for his transplant experiments, has an automobile wreck in which his fiancée, Jan, is decapitated. He rushes her head to his laboratory where, with various drugs and equipment, he is able to keep the brain alive. Although Jan pleads with Cortner to let her die, he abducts Doris Powell, a disfigured photographer's model with a beautiful body, which he intends to attach to his fiancée's head. Jan, however, manages to communicate with a demented, captive monster created by Cortner's previous operations; when the creature escapes and sets the laboratory on fire, killing both the doctor and his assistant, Doris is freed and Jan's suffering ends. *Surgeons. Grave robbers. Models. Monsters. Organ transplants. Decapitation. Abduction. Disfiguration. Experiments. Laboratories. Automobile accidents. Fires.*
Note: Location scenes filmed near Tarrytown, New York, in 1959. Prerelease title: *The Black Door*. Also known as *The Head That Wouldn't Die*. Herb Evers is also credited as Jason Evers.

THE BRAINIAC (Mexico)   **F6.0543**
Cinematográfica A. B. S. A. *Dist* Trans-International Films. 9 Apr 1969 [Trenton, New Jersey, opening]. Sd; b&w. 35mm. 77 min.
Dir Chano Urueta. *Screenplay* Federico Curiel, Antonio Orellan. *Adapt* Adolfo Torres Portillo. *Photog* José Ortiz Ramos. *Art Dir* Javier Torres Torija. *Film Ed* Alfredo Rosas Priego. *Mus* Gustavo César Carrión. *Sd* Jesús González Gancy.
Cast: Abel Salazar, Rubén Rojo, Rosa María Gallardo, David Silva, Federico Curiel, Germán Robles, René Cardona, Luis Aragón, Ariadne Welter, Víctor Velázquez, Ofelia Guilmáin, Carmen Montejo, Federico Garcés.
Horror film. Burned at the stake in 1661 as a sorcerer, a baron curses the descendants of his accusers. When a comet passes over the site 300 years later, he returns as a brain-eating monster. *Nobility. Sorcerers. Monsters. Executioners. Reviviscence. Curses. Comets.*
Note: Produced in Mexico in 1961 as *El barón del terror*. First released in the United States in a Spanish version in Aug 1963.

BRAINSTORM   **F6.0544**
Warner Bros. Pictures. 5 May 1965 [Denver, Colorado, opening; c8 May 1965; LP31749]. Sd; b&w. 35mm (Panavision). 114 min. [Copyright length: 105 min.]
Prod-Dir William Conrad. *Screenplay* Mann Rubin. *Story* Lawrence B. Marcus. *Dir Photog* Sam Leavitt. *Camera Op* Al Myers, William Renaldi, Charles W. Short. *Art Dir* Robert Smith. *Set Decor* Hoyle Barrett. *Film Ed* William Ziegler. *Mus* George Duning. *Sd* M. A. Merrick, William Thompson, Ben Sad. *Asst Dir* Howard Grace, Monty Masters. *Unit Mgr* James T. Vaughn. *Script Supv* Karen Wookey. *Wardrobe* Ken Laurence, Rose Brandi. *Makeup Supv* Gordon Bau. *Hairstyles* Jean Burt Reilly. *Dial Supv* James Lydon. *Still Photog* Jack Woods, still photog.
Cast: Jeff Hunter *(Jim Grayam)*, Anne Francis *(Lorrie Benson)*, Dana Andrews *(Cort Benson)*, Viveca Lindfors *(Dr. Elizabeth Larstadt)*, Stacy Harris *(Josh Reynolds)*, Kathie Browne *(Angie DeWitt)*, Phillip Pine *(Dr. Ames)*, Michael Pate *(Dr. Mills)*, Robert McQueeney *(Sergeant Dawes)*, Strother Martin *(Mr. Clyde)*, Joan Swift *(Clara)*, George Pelling *(butler)*, Victoria

Meyerink *(Julie)*, Stephen Roberts *(judge)*, Pat Cardi *(Bobby)*.

Drama. Jim Grayam, a research analyst in California, rescues his boss's wife, Lorrie Benson, from a car stalled on a railroad track. He discovers that the accident was really a suicide attempt made because Cort Benson is so cruel to her. Lorrie, afraid to leave her husband out of concern for their child, starts an affair with Jim. Cort discovers the affair and also learns that Jim was once treated for mental illness. Cort attempts to avenge himself on Jim by framing him on charges made by Angie DeWitt, but police Sergeant Dawes spoils this attempt. Cort next takes advantage of Jim's mental history to convince others that Jim is going mad. Jim and Lorrie grow closer and evolve a plan whereby Jim will study the symptoms of mental illness and then pretend to be insane, finally murdering Cort. He will be able to plead not guilty at his trial by reason of insanity and after acquittal will be reunited with Lorrie. The plan works up to a point; Dr. Larstadt agrees that Jim is insane, but after the trial she refuses to release him from institutional care. Jim cannot adjust to the asylum, and when he finds out that Lorrie has another boyfriend, he goes completely insane. *Researchers. Psychiatrists. Employer-employee relations. Revenge. Infidelity. Marriage. Murder. Insanity. Trials. Suicide. Frameup. Insane asylums. California.*

Note: Location scenes filmed in the San Fernando Valley and at Greystone Mansion in Beverly Hills, California.

BRAINWASHED (West Germany)   **F6.0545**
Roxy Film. *Dist* Allied Artists. Jun **1961** [c1 Jun 1961; LP19550]. Sd; b&w. 35mm. 102 min.
Prod Luggi Waldleitner. *Dir* Gerd Oswald. *Screenplay* Harold Medford, Gerd Oswald. *English Dial Asst* Wolf Vollmar. *Adapt* Herbert Reinecker. *Dir Photog* Günter Senftleben. *Camera Op* Fritz Anton, Willi Schöne. *Art Dir* Wolf Englert, Ernst Richter. *Film Ed* Klaus Eckstein. *Mus* Hans-Martin Majewski. *Sd* Bernard Reicherts. *Asst Dir* Jochen Wiedermann. *Prod Mgr* Johannes J. Frank. *Cost Supv* Ursula Stutz.
Cast: Curd Jürgens *(Werner von Basil)*, Claire Bloom *(Irene Andreny)*, Hansjörg Felmy *(Hans Berger)*, Mario Adorf *(Mirko Centowic)*, Albert Lieven *(Hartmann)*, Alan Gifford *(MacIver)*, Dietmar Schönherr *(rabbi)*, Karel Stepanek *(Baranow)*, Wolfgang Wahl *(Moonface)*, Rudolf Forster *(hotel manager)*, Albert Bessler *(scientist)*, Jan Hendriks *(1st officer)*, Harald Maresch *(ballet master)*, Dorothea Wieck *(countess)*, Ryk de Gooyer *(Berger's secretary)*, Susanne Körber *(young lady)*, Hans Söhnker *(Bishop Ambrosse)*.
Drama. Source: Stefan Zweig, *Schachnovelle* (Buenos Aires, 1942). In 1938, shortly after the Nazi invasion of Austria, a prominent Viennese intellectual, Werner von Basil, is arrested for smuggling art treasures out of the country. When he refuses to collaborate, Hans Berger, a Gestapo official, tries to break his will by imprisoning him in a hotel room without mental sustenance of any kind. Irene Andreny, a young ballerina with whom Berger is in love, tries to intercede on von Basil's behalf but to no avail. During a visit to Berger's office, von Basil manages to steal a small book on chess which he studies voraciously in order to keep his mind alert. Even when the book is taken away from him, he continues to mentally play the game. So complete is his concentration that when Berger finally succeeds in breaking him down, von Basil suffers a total mental collapse, rendering him useless to his captors. When he is eventually released, he is joined by Irene, who helps him regain his sanity. *Intellectuals. Smugglers. Dancers. Nazis. Brainwashing. Chess. Art. Hotels. Vienna. Austria. Gestapo.*
Note: Filmed in Austria and Czechoslovakia. Released in West Germany in 1960 as *Die Schachnovelle*. Also known as *The Royal Game*.

BRANCHES   **F6.0546**
Cornell University Cinema. *Dist* Cornell University Cinema, New Line Cinema. 6 Nov **1970** [Ithaca, New York, opening]. Sd; b&w. 16mm. 103 min.
Prod Gordon Beck. *Conceived & Dir by* Ed Emshwiller. *Anim* Jody Uttal, Diane Egbert, Bruce Ferguson. *Photog* Peter Scheer. *Camera* Ralph Perri, Don Milici, Jim Skydell, Pat Lee, Stewart Owre. *Titl & Credits* Ellie Beth Leass, Richard Perlmutter, Jim Skydell. *Film Ed* Larry McConkey, Karen Kramer, David Fogel, Ted Gulick, Peter Scheer, Wade Mann, Richard Perlmutter, Brian McLernan, Ellie Beth Leass, Judy Rabinovitz, Jeanne Kolker, Stewart Owre. *Mus Comp* David Borden. *Perf by* Mother Mallard. *Titl Song* John Hostetter. *Jug Band Mus Perf by* Cosmic Daddy Dancers. *Sd* John D. Anderson. *Sd Crew* Pat Lee, Jeanne Kolker, Judy Rabinovitz, Bruce Ferguson, Stewart Owre, Ellie Beth Leass. *Prod Crew* Ellie Beth Leass, Don Milici, Ralph Perri, Wade Mann, Harold Zimmerman, P. S. Wright, Jim Skydell, Brian McLernan. *Tech Asst* Skip Landen. *Sp Thanks* Instructional Resources Center (Ithaca College).
Cast: Bill Weidner *(Bill)*, Connie Brady *(pretty girl)*, Al Capogrossi *(her other boyfriend)*, Richard Perlmutter *(Bill's side kick)*, Erica Saxe *(girl after Bill)*, Christian Larson *(storyteller)*, Sam Hay *(black power theoretician)*, David Connor, Susan Miller, Tina Graybard, Bruce Ferguson, Ernest Wright, Andrew Smallwood, Pat Lee, Diane Egbert, Rich Hamilton, Jeanne Kolker, Stewart Owre, Don Milici, Ellie Beth Leass, Richard Lieberman, Joe Gilchrist, Brian

McLernan, Harold Zimmerman.
Experimental film. While a friend relates a sexual escapade, Bill, a bearded college student, fantasizes about various sexual experiences with a pretty girl. Clad in an undershirt marked with the number "1," Bill encounters an art-as-politics freak, a black power theoretician, and an amorous female. In the confusion, Bill tries to understand himself and his environment. *Students. Fantasy. Sexuality. College life.*
Note: Filmed in and around Ithaca, New York.

THE BRAND *see* **BRAND OF SHAME**

BRAND OF EVIL (Japan)   **F6.0547**
Takarazuka Motion Picture Co. *Dist* Toho Co. 12 Feb **1965** [Los Angeles showing]. Sd; b&w. 35mm (Tohoscope). 133 min.
Prod Sanezumi Fujimoto, Reiji Miwa. *Dir* Hiromichi Horikawa. *Screenplay* Shinobu Hashimoto, Sakae Hirosawa. *Photog* Minoru Aizawa. *Mus* Toshiro Mayuzumi.
Cast: Tsutomu Yamazaki *(Detective Kikuchi)*, Michiyo Aratama, Kyoko Kishida, Keiji Sada, Eijiro Yanagi, Shiro Osaka.
Crime melodrama. While investigating the murder of a housemaid, Detective Kikuchi is implicated by a trap set by the killer. The detective is sentenced to a prison term and the case is closed. Several years later, released on parole, Kikuchi joins a private detective agency and begins to work in his spare time on solving the murder. Hired by Mitsue Takazawa, the wife of the chairman of a cartel, to investigate her husband's private life, Kikuchi learns that Mitsue is actually after information beneficial to her husband in his dealings with Shibata, the president of a large trading firm. Kikuchi continues investigating the murder even when Setsuko, a woman with whom he is in love, becomes implicated. He finally deduces that Shibata murdered his own housemaid because she knew he was blackmailing Mitsue's husband, who had hastened the death of his foster father to gain control of the cartel. Shibata's body is found, and Kikuchi sets a trap for the second killer. [Sources do not disclose the film's ending.] *Detectives. Executives. Housemaids. Foster fathers. Murder. Frameup. Blackmail. Business competition. Parole. Cartels.*
Note: Released in Japan in 1964 as *Aku no monsho*. Minoru Aizawa may also be known as Jo Aizawa.

BRAND OF SHAME   **F6.0548**
B & B Productions. *Dist* FPS Ventures. 19 Jul **1968** [Champaign, Illinois, showing]. Sd; col. 35mm. 74 min.
Prod-Dir B. Ron Elliott. *Screenplay* Gene Radford, David F. Friedman. *Camera* Sy Klops. *Mus* Billy Allen. *Sd* Sam Kopetzky.
Cast: Donna Duzzit *(Rachel)*, Steve Stunning *(Steve)*, Bart Black *(Craig)*, Vanessa Van Dyke *(Mollie)*, Paula Pleasure *(Delilah)*, Ora Fiss *(Stella)*, Vic Sav *(Red)*, Ronnie Runningboard *(George)*.
Western melodrama. Based on the novella by: David F. Friedman, "Brand of Shame," in *Spicy Western Stories* (publication undetermined). Schoolteacher Rachel Clark, a virgin, arrives in town on the same stagecoach as Steve Turner, whose expert shooting has just thwarted a robbery. Rachel plans to exploit her dead father's gold mine, and she takes a room in the town's only hotel, owned by Mollie, a lesbian whose dancehall girls satisfy the sexual needs of ranchers and cowboys. Craig conspires with Mollie and his girl friend, Delilah, to rob Rachel of the map showing the location of the gold mine. Steve and Rachel, strongly attracted to each other, ride out into the desert and make passionate love. Later, Delilah is sent to seduce Steve while Craig kidnaps Rachel and whips her. She remains silent until Craig allows one of his henchmen, George, a halfwit, to molest her. Steve repulses Delilah, saves Rachel from George, and kills Craig's other henchmen. As Craig prepares to kill Steve, Rachel shoots the bandit. *Schoolteachers. Gunfighters. Bandits. Dancehall girls. Hotelkeepers. Halfwits. Theft. Torture. Lesbianism. Prostitution. Abduction. Seduction. Virginity. Stagecoach robberies. Gold mines. Flogging. Documentation.*
Note: May also be known as *The Brand*.

BRAND X   **F6.0549**
Trax Productions. *Dist* C. M. B. Films, New Line Cinema. 18 May **1970** [New York opening]. Sd; col (Eastman Color). 35mm. 87 min.
Prod-Dir-Writ Win Chamberlain. *Photog* John Harnish. *Film Ed* John Harnish, Karen Edwards, Win Chamberlain, Mike Misch, Frank Cavestani. *Mus* Ken Lauber. *Song:* "Pennies From Heaven" sung by Ultra Violet.
Cast: Taylor Mead *(viewer/nurse/president/minister)*, Sally Kirkland *(patient/president's wife)*, Tally Brown *(talk show hostess)*, Frank Cavestani *(doctor)*, Abbie Hoffman *(policeman, Lawren O·der)*, Ultra Violet *(singer)*, Susanna Baumgart *(patient)*, Candy Darling *(Marlene D-Train)*, Paul Fagan *(surfer)*, Baby Jane Holzer, Sam Shepard.
Satire. A bedraggled man wakes up amidst the clutter of his bedroom and immediately turns on his television set. What follows is a series of skits lampooning television programming and commercials, in which many of the

central characters resemble the viewer. A morning fitness show is led by an emaciated host whose favorite exercise is to curl up into a fetal position. On a talk show called "Boy's Talk" a group of musclemen are fondled by their female host. In "What's My Sex," a panel attempts to decide whether the contestants are men or women. A hospital drama, "Everybody's Nurse," is also included in the programming. A policeman is interviewed while defecating and later while bathing in paper money. The President of the United States conducts a press conference as his retarded wife is displayed nearby. Another program burlesques a Confederate soldier returning home from war. "The Tomorrow Show," a late-night talk show, features a singer and a surfer. News, weather, and stock market reports are interspersed in the programming. Commercials throughout the day feature the "Old Colonial Dope Company," "Dirt," "Sweat," computer dating, athletic supporters, and peanut butter. The evening closes with a nightly sermonette in which a minister renders his interpretation of the Crucifixion; and the national anthem follows. *Clergymen. Presidents of the United States. Nurses. Confederate veterans. Physicians. Musclemen. Police. Television. Politics. Religion. Female impersonation. Television commercials. Drugs. Sexuality. Physical training.*

Note: Taylor Mead's dialog improvised by the actor; other dialog credited to the group.

BRANDY IN THE WILDERNESS   F6.0550

Dist Stanton Kaye, New Line Cinema. 18 Jun **1969** [New York opening]. Sd; b&w. 16mm. 72 min. [See note.]

Prod-Writ Michaux French, Stanton Kaye. *Dir* Stanton Kaye. *Dir Photog* Stanton Kaye.

Cast: Michaux French *(Brandy)*, Stanton Kaye *(Simon Weiss)*.

Autobiographical drama. Simon, an independent filmmaker in his early 20's, travels from his native Los Angeles to New York City to join his patron, Brandy, who subsequently becomes his girl friend. Their relationship and its difficulties are explored alongside the making of the film, which chronicles Simon's and Brandy's odyssey across the American landscape and Simon's frustrated quest to recapture what has been lost from his past. En route by car to Los Angeles, they visit Brandy's father in Chicago, but the meeting of the generations only discourages Simon's hope of finding a foundation in the past. Brandy becomes pregnant, and they return to Manhattan, where, lacking a sense of stability, Simon neglects Brandy. Exasperated, she nearly leaves him. They confront their problems, however, and are able to devote themselves once again to their lives together with their infant child and to the film. *Filmmakers. Patrons. Nostalgia. Pregnancy. Motion pictures. Travel. New York City. Chicago. Los Angeles.*

Note: Subsequently released in 87 and 95 min versions.

THE BRASS BOTTLE   F6.0551

Universal Pictures–Scarus, Inc. *Dist* Universal Pictures. 12 Feb **1964** [Houston opening; c28 Mar 1963; LP32602]. Sd (Westrex); col (Eastman Color by Pathé). 35mm. 89 min.

Prod Robert Arthur. *Dir* Harry Keller. *Screenplay* Oscar Brodney. *Dir Photog* Clifford Stine. *Camera Op* William Dodds. *Asst Camera* William Reisbord, Ed Hearn. *Art Dir* Alexander Golitzen, Henry Bumstead. *Set Decor* Oliver Emert. *Set Coörd* Fred Knoth. *Titl* Pacific Title. *Film Ed* Milton Carruth, Ted J. Kent. *Asst Ed* Fred Chulack. *Mus* Bernard Green. *Mus Supv* Joseph Gershenson. *Choreog* Hal Belfer. *Sd* Waldon O. Watson, Frank H. Wilkinson. *Sd Asst* John Oliver, Harold King, Victor Goode. *Asst Dir* Joseph Kenny, Carl Beringer. *Unit Prod Mgr* Norman Deming. *Script Supv* Cliff Bole. *Cost Dsgn* Rosemary Odell. *Wardrobe* Grady Hunt, Dorothy Drake. *Makeup Supv* Bud Westmore. *Makeup* George Lane, Jack Freeman, Imogene Abbott. *Hairstylist* Larry Germain, Kay Reed. *Sp Photog Eff* Roswell Hoffman. *Dial Coach* Herold Goodwin. *Still Photog* Rollie Lane. *Gaffer* William Harmon. *Grip* Walter Woodworth, Carl Johnston. *Prop* Sol Martino, John Faltis.

Cast: Tony Randall *(Harold Ventimore)*, Burl Ives *(Fakrash-el Aamash)*, Barbara Eden *(Sylvia Kenton)*, Kamala Devi *(Tezra)*, Edward Andrews *(Anthony Kenton)*, Richard Erdman *(Seymour Jenks)*, Kathie Browne *(Hazel Jenks)*, Ann Doran *(Martha Kenton)*, Philip Ober *(William Beevor)*, Parley Baer *(Sam Wackerbath)*, Howard I. Smith *(Senator Grindl)*, Lulu Porter *(dancer)*, Alex Gerry *(Dr. Travisley)*, Herb Vigran *(Eddie)*, Alan Dexter *(Joe)*, Robert Lieb *(Lawyer Jennings)*, Jan Arvan *(Seneschal)*, Nora Marlowe *(Mrs. McGruder)*, Aline Towne *(Miss Gidden)*.

Comedy. Source: F. Anstey, *The Brass Bottle* (London, 1900). Architect Harold Ventimore buys an antique brass bottle as a gift for his future father-in-law, Anthony Kenton, an Egyptologist, but he decides the bottle is a fake and keeps it for himself. He breaks the seal, thereby releasing a genie, Fakrash, who is ready to serve him. Almost immediately, Fakrash obtains for Harold a multimillion-dollar housing contract from tycoon Sam Wackerbath. When, Harold's fiancée, Sylvia, comes to dinner with her parents, Fakrash turns Harold's house into a sultan's palace complete with dancing girls. The guests are outraged, and Harold blames Fakrash for alienating Sylvia, whereupon the

genie gives him a gift of Tezra, a houri. Harold cannot rid himself of Tezra, and matters are further complicated when Fakrash performs more tricks, such as producing a herd of elephants at rush hour to distract a policeman from giving a summons to Harold. When Harold explains to authorities the reasons for the unusual occurrences, he is restrained with a straight-jacket. Fakrash then tries to explain to a government panel that he is a genie, but his words fall on unbelieving ears until he demonstrates his power by miniaturizing the panel members. Fakrash also succeeds, at Harold's request, in erasing all that he has done, including the very memory of his existence. Sam Wackerbath comes to Harold's office to hire him and introduces him to his new partner and the partner's wife—Fakrash and Tezra! *Architects. Archeologists. Genii. Tycoons. Houris. Fathers-in-law. Magic. Housing. Elephants.*

Note: A previous film version of the Anstey novel was released by Associated First National Pictures in 1923.

THE BRAVE LITTLE TAILOR (East Germany)   F6.0552

DEFA. *Dist* Childhood Productions. 4 Oct **1969** [Brooklyn, New York, opening]. col (Agfacolor, print by DeLuxe). 35mm. [Feature film, length unknown.]

Prod English Vers William L. Snyder. *Dir* Helmut Spiess.

Cast: Kurt Schmidtchen, Christel Bodenstein.

Fantasy. Source: Jakob Grimm and Wilhelm Grimm, "Das tapfere Schneiderlein". The brave little tailor kills seven flies with one blow and embroiders a belt depicting the details of his conquest. He sets out to tell the world of his conquest and encounters many difficult situations in which he proves his courage. As reward, he is offered the hand of the beautiful princess. *Tailors. Royalty. Courage. Rewards. Flies.*

Note: Released in East Germany in 1956 as *Das tapfere Schneiderlein*.

DER BRAVE SOLDAT SCHWEJK see THE GOOD SOLDIER SCHWEIK

BRAVO PORTUGAL   F6.0553

31 Mar **1970** [San Diego, California, showing]. Si; col. 35mm. ca120 min. *Pres by* Explorama. *A Film by* Lisa Chickerling, Jeanne Porterfield.

Travelog. Two travel hosts describe the Campino fair at Santarém, the last race of the Tall Ships, the pilgrimage to the Shrine of the Virgin Mary in Fátima, bullfights, and Lisbon. *Travel. Bullfighting. Portugal. Santarém (Portugal). Fátima (Portugal). Lisbon. Virgin Mary.*

Note: Narration delivered live on stage.

BRAVO, YOUNG GUY (Japan)   F6.0554

Toho Co. May **1970** [Los Angeles showing]. Sd; col. 35mm. 90 min. *Dir* Katsumi Iwauchi.

Cast: Yuzo Kayama, Wakako Sakai, Kunie Tanaka.

Comedy. No information about the precise nature of this film has been found.

Note: Released in Japan in Jan 1970 as *Burabo! Yangu gai*.

THE BRAZEN WOMEN OF BALZAC (West Germany)   F6.0555

Lisa-Film. *Dist* Globe Pictures. 19 Feb **1970** [Madison, Wisconsin, opening]. Sd; col. 35mm. 80 min. *MPAA rating* X.

Pres by Joseph Green, Martin Gottlieb. *Dir* Josef Zacher. *Screenplay* Kurt Nachmann. *Photog* Kurt Junek. *Film Ed* Traude Kappl. *Mus* Claudius Alzner. *Asst Dir* Claudio Schreiber.

Cast: Joachim Hansen *(Fabian)*, Edwige Fenech *(Felizitas)*, Angelika Ott *(Arabella)*, Michaela May *(Eugénie)*, Katharina Alt *(Sophie [see note])*, Francy Fair *(Annette)*, Ivan Nesbitt *(Manuel)*, Walter Buschhoff *(Leuwenstam)*, Sieghardt Rupp *(George)*, Ralf Wolter, Sissi Löwinger, Gustav Knuth, Mathilde Schmid.

Comedy. Source: Honoré de Balzac, *Les contes drôlatiques* (1832–37). At their chateau dilettante Fabian, mistress Eugénie, and niece Annette, host a succession of lovers, including Arabella and the wealthy Leuwenstam, who have not yet consummated their marriage, and the estranged aristocrats, Manuel and Felizitas. Inspired by the reading of Balzac, the party plans an orgiastic grape festival. During the orgy Sophie, the maid, sequesters Annette and Manuel. Surprised by Fabian, the aristocrat requests his niece's hand. Under cover of blackness Sophie pairs Leuwenstam and Felizitas, whom he mistakes for his wife. Discovering his error, Leuwenstam consents to a divorce, then proposes marriage to the willing Felizitas. Following suit, Fabian weds Eugénie. *Mistresses. Houseguests. Housemaids. Uncles. Aristocrats. Infidelity. Divorce. Marriage. Mistaken identity. Orgies. Honoré de Balzac.*

Note: Released in West Germany in Apr 1969 as *Die tolldreisten Geschichten des Honoré de Balzac*; running time: 84 min. Original German title: *Komm, liebe Maid und mache*. Reedited, possibly with additional sex footage, for U. S. release. Some sources credit Katharina Alt as Caterina Altieri.

THE BREAK (Great Britain)   F6.0556

Mancunian Film Corp. *Dist* Planet Films, Union Film Distributors. Apr **1963**. Sd; b&w. 35mm. 75 min.

Prod Tom Blakeley. *Dir* Lance Comfort. *Screenplay* Pip Baker, Jane Baker. *Photog* Basil Emmott. *Art Dir* George Provis. *Film Ed* Peter Pitt. *Mus Comp & Cond* Brian Fahey. *Sd Rec* Buster Ambler. *Asst Dir* Roy Baird. *Prod Mgr* John Comfort.

Cast: Tony Britton *(Greg Parker)*, William Lucas *(Jacko Thomas)*, Eddie Byrne *(Judd Tredgar)*, Robert Urquhart *(Pearson)*, Sonia Dresdel *(Sarah)*, Edwin Richfield *(Moses)*, Christina Gregg *(Sue Thomas)*, Gene Anderson *(Jean Tredgar)*, Patrick Jordan *(driver)*, John Junkin *(Harry)*, Marshall Jones *(Jim)*.

Melodrama. Jacko Thomas, an escaped convict, hides out at a country inn owned by Judd Tredgar, a smuggler who is arranging for Jacko's getaway. Also at the inn are the convict's sister, Sue; a novelist, Greg Parker; and Pearson, a private detective trying to get information about Parker for use by Parker's wife in a divorce suit. Jacko murders Pearson when Pearson discovers Tredgar's smuggling activities, and Jacko also kills one of the inn's servants, Moses, when Moses pleads for permission to take Pearson's body to a church. Sarah, the servant's mute sister, retaliates by killing Jacko. *Prison escapees. Detectives. Smugglers. Novelists. Mutes. Murder. Inns.*

Note: Released in Great Britain in Jul 1963; running time: 76 min.

BREAKFAST AT TIFFANY'S   F6.0557

Jurow–Shepherd Productions. *Dist* Paramount Pictures. 5 Oct **1961** [New York opening; c5 Oct 1961; LP20389]. Sd; col (Technicolor). 35mm. 114 min.

Prod Martin Jurow, Richard Shepherd. *Dir* Blake Edwards. *Screenplay* George Axelrod. *Dir Photog* Franz F. Planer. *Col Cons* Richard Mueller. *Art Dir* Hal Pereira, Roland Anderson. *Set Decor* Sam Comer, Ray Moyer. *Film Ed* Howard Smith. *Mus* Henry Mancini. *Song:* "Moon River" Henry Mancini, Johnny Mercer. *Sung by* Audrey Hepburn. *Sd Rec* Hugo Grenzbach, John Wilkinson. *Asst Dir* William McGarry. *Cost Supv* Edith Head. *Miss Hepburn's Wardrobe* Givenchy. *Miss Neal's Wardrobe* Pauline Trigere. *Makeup Supv* Wally Westmore. *Hairstyle Supv* Nellie Manley. *Sp Photog Eff* John P. Fulton. *Proc Photog* Farciot Edouart.

Cast: Audrey Hepburn *(Holly Golightly)*, George Peppard *(Paul Varjak)*, Patricia Neal *("2E")*, Buddy Ebsen *(Doc Golightly)*, Martin Balsam *(O. J. Berman)*, Mickey Rooney *(Mr. Yunioshi)*, Vilallonga *(José)*, Dorothy Whitney *(Mag Wildwood)*, Stanley Adams *(Rusty Trawler)*, Alan Reed, Sr. *(Sally Tomato)*, John McGiver *(Tiffany's salesman)*, Beverly Hills *(nightclub dancer)*, Claude Stroud *(Sid Arbuck)*, Elvia Allman *(librarian)*, Michael Quinn *(man with eye patch)*, James Lanphier *(The Cousin)*, Dick Crockett *(taxi driver)*, Kip King *(delivery boy)*, Joan Staley *(girl in low cut dress)*, Gil Lamb, Annabella Soong, Wilson Wood, William Benegal Rav, Tommy Farrell, Hanna Landy, Fay McKenzie, Helen Spring *(party guests)*, Putney *(Cat, a cat)*.

Romantic comedy-drama. Source: Truman Capote, *Breakfast at Tiffany's* (New York, 1958). Holly Golightly lives in a brownstone on Manhattan's swank East Side. Totally madcap, she has a partially furnished apartment, owns a cat with no name, gets rid of the "mean reds" by visiting Tiffany's, and is forever misplacing her door key, much to the dismay of her upstairs neighbor Mr. Yunioshi, a Japanese photographer. Holly makes her living in two ways: she receive $50 from her gentlemen escorts whenever she needs powder room money, and she is paid $100 for each weekly trip she makes to Sing Sing, where she visits Sally Tomato, an ex-mobster. One day Paul Varjak, a young writer who is supported by an older woman nicknamed "2E," comes into Holly's life. Following one of Holly's wild cocktail parties, Paul unexpectedly meets Doc Golightly, a gentle Texan whom Holly married when she was only 15 years old. Holly explains to Paul that the marriage was annulled long ago, and he helps her send the heartbroken Doc away. After a day on the town together, Paul realizes that he is in love with Holly and proposes to her; but she is determined to marry José, a South American millionaire. However, when it is publicly revealed that Holly has been innocently carrying narcotics ring information from Sally Tomato to his New York associates, the stuffy José abandons her. Furious at everything and everyone, Holly throws Cat into the rain and decides to leave town, but Paul lectures her and then goes out to find Cat. Holly realizes how much she is giving up and races through the wet streets to a happy reunion with Paul and Cat. *Eccentrics. Authors. Japanese. Photographers. Convicts. Millionaires. South Americans. Marriage—Annulment. Materialism. Narcotics. New York City—East Side. Sing Sing. Tiffany's (New York City). Cats.*

Note: Location scenes filmed in New York City.

THE BREAKING POINT *see* THE GREAT ARMORED CAR SWINDLE

BREATHLESS (France)   F6.0558

Productions Georges de Beauregard–S. N. C. *Dist* Films Around the World, Inc. 7 Feb **1961** [New York opening]. Sd; b&w. 35mm. 89 min.

Prod Georges de Beauregard. *Dir-Screenplay* Jean-Luc Godard. *Story* François Truffaut. *Photog* Raoul Coutard. *Camera Op* Claude Beausoleil. *Ed (see note)* Cécile Decugis, Jean-Luc Godard. *Asst Ed* Lila Herman. *Mus* Martial Solal. *Clarinet Concerto (K. 622)* Wolfgang Amadeus Mozart. *Sd* Jacques Maumont. *Asst Dir* Pierre Rissient. *Artistic Supv* Claude Chabrol.

Cast: Jean Seberg *(Patricia Franchini)*, Jean-Paul Belmondo *(Michel Poiccard, alias Laszlo Kovacs)*, Liliane David *(Liliane)*, Daniel Boulanger *(inspector)*, Jean-Pierre Melville *(Parvulesco)*, Henri-Jacques Huet *(Berrouti)*, Claude Mansard *(used car dealer)*, Van Doude *(editor)*, Jean-Luc Godard *(informer)*, François Moreuil *(newsreel cameraman)*, Claude Chabrol, François Truffaut, Michel Fabre, Roger Hanin, Jean-Louis Richard, André S. Labarthe, Jacques Scellier, Philippe de Broca, Guido Orlando, José Bénazéraf, Jean Douchet.

Drama. Michel Poiccard, a self-centered and amoral young Frenchman with no visible means of support, has patterned his character after Humphrey Bogart's screen image, taking what he wants when he wants it. One day while loafing around Marseilles, he casually steals a car. He heads north, and, finding a gun in the glove compartment, cold-bloodedly kills a policeman who attempts to stop him. Back in Paris, he makes a date with Patricia Franchini, a young American expatriate who sells the *Herald Tribune* on the Champs-Elysées. Shaking off police, he mugs and robs a man in a restaurant men's room and then lets himself into Patricia's apartment. They make love, and she reveals that she may be pregnant as a result of an earlier encounter. He suggests that they go to Italy, but she guards against sacrificing her independence and her aspirations as a journalist. Threatened by police, she accompanies Michel to a friend's house; but, concerned about her freedom, she then impulsively betrays him in hopes of forcing him to leave without her. Not even the thought of death, however, can move Michel, and he lingers about the house until the police arrive on the scene. As he runs down the cobblestoned street, he is hit from behind by gunfire. When Patricia reaches him, he looks up at her, makes their private funny face, curses her, and then dies. *Americans in foreign countries. Police. Journalists. Fugitives. Hoodlums. Murder. Theft. Pregnancy. Perfidy. Marseilles. Paris. Humphrey Bogart. "New York Herald Tribune".*

Note: Paris opening: Mar 1960 as *À bout de souffle*. The film is dedicated to Monogram Pictures. Much of the dialogue was improvised during or just before shooting. Only one source credits Godard as editor.

THE BREMEN TOWN MUSICIANS (West Germany)   F6.0559

Schongerfilm. *Dist* Childhood Productions. Oct **1965**. Sd; col. 35mm. 66 min.

Prod Hubert Schonger. *Dir* Rainer Geis. *Screenplay* Dolores Devine. *Mus* Raimund Rosenberger. *Mus Cond* Lehman Engel. *Songs* Anne Delugg, Milton Delugg.

Cast: Paul Tripp *(narrator)*, Peter Thom, Max Bössl, Christa Welzmüller, Toni Mang, Peter Brand, Otto Friebel, Paul Bös, Edgar Wenzel.

Fantasy. Source: Jakob Grimm and Wilhelm Grimm, "Die Bremer Stadtmusikanten". A musically inclined donkey travels to Bremen to participate in a music contest. Along the way, he unchains a mistreated dog, which joins him on his journey. Next, they pick up a cat and a rooster. Stopping to rest in a house in the forest, they find the house occupied by thieves, but accidentally they scare the thieves away. By setting traps, the animals keep the thieves at a distance, and they decide to stay in the house and play their instruments, rather than attending the contest in Bremen. *Musicians. Thieves. Contests. Bremen. Donkeys. Dogs. Cats. Roosters.*

Note: Released in West Germany in Sep 1959 as *Die Bremer Stadtmusikanten*; running time: 77 min.

DIE BREMER STADTMUSIKANTEN *see* THE BREMEN TOWN MUSICIANS

DAS BRENNENDE GERICHT *see* THE BURNING COURT

BREWSTER MCCLOUD   F6.0560

Adler–Phillips–Lion's Gate Films. *Dist* Metro-Goldwyn-Mayer, Inc. 5 Dec **1970** [Houston opening; c2 Dec 1970; LP38779]. Sd; col (Metrocolor). 35mm (Panavision). 104 min. *MPAA rating* R.

Prod Lou Adler. *Assoc Prod* Robert Eggenweiler, James Margellos. *Dir* Robert Altman. *2d Unit Dir* Louis Lombardo. *Writ* Doran William Cannon. *Dir Photog* Lamar Boren, Jordan Cronenweth. *2d Unit Photog* Don McClendon. *Art Dir* George W. Davis, Preston Ames. *Film Ed* Louis Lombardo. *Asst Ed* Ross Levy. *Mus Score & Cond* Gene Page. *Titl Song:* "The Star-Spangled Banner" Francis Scott Key. *Song:* "Lift Every Voice and Sing" Rosamund Johnson, James Weldon Johnson. *Sung by* Merry Clayton. *Song:* "White Feather Wings" John Phillips. *Sung by* Merry Clayton. *Songs:* "Last of the Unnatural Acts," "The First and Last Thing You Do," "I Promise Not To Tell" *writ & sung by* John Phillips. *Sd* Harry W. Tetrick, William McCaughey. *Asst Dir* Tommy Thompson. *Asst to the Prod* Ross Levy. *Wardrobe* Jack Sandeen, Jean Marie Andrzejewski. *Makeup* Ed Butterworth. *Hairdresser* Dorothy White. *Sp Eff* Marcel Vercoutere. *Wings Dsgn by* Leon Ericksen. *Casting* Gary Wayne Chason.

Cast: Bud Cort *(Brewster McCloud)*, Sally Kellerman *(Louise)*, Michael Murphy *(Frank Shaft)*, William Windom *(Haskell Weeks)*, Shelley Duvall *(Suzanne)*, Rene Auberjonois *(The Lecturer)*, Stacy Keach *(Abraham Wright)*, John Schuck *(Alvin Johnson)*, Margaret Hamilton *(Daphne Heap)*, Jennifer Salt *(Hope McFarland)*, Corey Fischer *(Lieutenant Hines)*, G. Wood *(Captain Crandall)*, Bert Remsen *(Douglas Breen)*, Angelin Johnson *(Mrs. Breen)*, Dean Goss *(Officer Eugene Ledbetter)*, William Baldwin *(Bernard)*, William Henry Bennet *(band conductor)*, Gary Wayne Chason *(camera store clerk)*, Ellis Gilbert *(butler)*, Verdie Henshaw *(Feathered Nest Sanatorium manager)*, Bob Warner *(camera store assistant manager)*, Keith V. Erickson *(Professor Aggnout)*, Thomas Danko *(color lab man)*, W. E. Terry, Jr. *(police chaplain)*, Ronnie Cammack *(Wendel)*, Dixie M. Taylor *(manager, Tanninger's Nursing Home)*, Pearl Coffey Chason *(nursing home attendant)*, Amelia Parker *(nursing home manageress)*, David Welch *(Breen's son)*.

Fantasy. While living in a bomb shelter beneath the Houston Astrodome, adolescent Brewster McCloud is employed as chauffeur to 120-year-old flying ace Abraham Wright. Striving to become a modern Icarus, McCloud subjects himself to a rigid regimen of exercise, nourishes himself with health food, and perfects a pair of wings. His movements are observed by a pedantic ornithologist, The Lecturer, and applauded by Hope, an adolescent fan who is stimulated to orgasm by his exercises. McCloud's mentor in this undertaking, however, is Louise, a buxom guardian angel who wears only a trenchcoat. As McCloud prepares for flight, Houston witnesses a series of bizarre murders, commencing with those of the miserly Wright, whose wheelchair careens wildly while the old man is collecting rent from a bankrupt nursing home, and Astrodome anthem singer Daphne Heap, whose corpse is discovered beneath a birdcage. A clue is provided by the bird dung coating both corpses, but, baffled by it, Houston police recruit San Francisco detective Frank Shaft. When narcotics agent Douglas Breen suggests that he will forego arresting McCloud for possession of marijuana upon receipt of the youth's camera, he is pelleted by bird droppings and dies shortly thereafter. While chasing a stolen car in which McCloud is riding, Shaft crashes into a pond, crushing his legs, and afterwards he shoots himself. McCloud loses his virginity to Astrodome guide Suzanne, thereby sacrificing the protection of Louise. Trusting her completely, McCloud confides his participation in the murders to Suzanne, who promptly informs Bernard, aide to politician Haskell Weeks. Although he quickly eliminates Weeks, McCloud, deserted by Louise and Suzanne, is trapped by police inside the Astrodome. Donning his wings, McCloud flies about the stadium, finally fluttering to his death. *Inventors. Landlords. Police. Singers. Guides. Chauffeurs. Detectives. Narcotics agents. Informers. Politicians. Lecturers. Adolescence. Sexual initiation. Murder. Suicide. Ornithology. Bomb shelters. Marijuana. Cameras. Houston. Houston Astrodome. Chases. Automobile accidents. Birds.*

Note: Location scenes filmed in and around the Astrodome in Houston, Texas. Working title: *Brewster McCloud's Flying Machine.*

BREWSTER'S MILLIONS *see* **THREE ON A SPREE**

THE BRICK DOLLHOUSE   **F6.0561**
FPS Ventures. 13 Sep **1967** [Boston opening]. Sd; col (Eastmancolor). 35mm. 61 min.
Prod-Dir Tony Martinez. *Assoc Prod* Eric Marlo. *Story-Screenplay* Joe Delg. *Dir Photog* G. Oniag. *Camera* G. Glenn, Jr. *Film Ed* Ernie B. Sitam. *Sd* Ryder Sound Service. *Asst Dir* Fletcher Fist. *Wardrobe* Richard Wyke. *Makeup* Sue Hamilton, makeup.

Cast: Tina Vienna *(Carmen)*, Lee Cory *(Danielle)*, Peggy Ann Malone *(Sherry)*, Joyana *(Min Lee)*, George French *(Lieutenant Parker)*, Steve Powers *(Rod)*, Frankie O'Brien *(Sandy)*, Helena Clayton *(Linda)*, Carolyn Malborough *(Dina)*, Federico Steward *(Doctor)*.

Melodrama. Min Lee, a Eurasian exotic dancer living in a luxurious Hollywood singles apartment building, is found murdered in her bedroom. Her five roommates, Carmen, Danielle, Sherry, Linda, and Sandy, Min Lee's lesbian lover, are questioned by Lieutenant Parker. Each one tells Parker of her activities prior to Min Lee's death, including graphic details of her active sex life. Parker has no suspects until Linda relates that she lent her wig and a dress to Min Lee the night before the murder. Parker cleverly tricks Linda's ex-suitor, Rod, into confessing that he killed Min Lee, mistaking her for Linda. *Exotic dancers. Roommates. Detectives. Eurasians. Murder. Sexuality. Jealousy. Mistaken identity. Lesbianism. Hollywood.*

Note: Also known as *The Doll House* and *The House of Brick Dolls.*

THE BRIDE *see* **THE OLD MAN'S BRIDE**

THE BRIDE AND THE BEASTS   **F6.0562**
Unit Ten Productions. *Dist* Bernhard Films. 8 Oct **1969** [New York showing]. Sd; b&w. 35mm. [Feature length assumed.]
Exec Prod Charles H. Leonard. *Dir* John Donne. *Photog* Pierrot Mattiss. *Asst Dir* Andre Renoir.

Cast: Ingrid Bjornstaad.

Melodrama. Angela Cartwright attends a bridal shower given in her honor by a former girl friend of her fiancé, unaware that the rejected mistress has spitefully invited Angela's ex-boyfriend. According to her plan, the ex-boyfriend would crash the party with a few of his friends dressed as hippies and carrying knives and bike chains but would leave as soon as they had a few free drinks. Instead, they run amok and turn a peaceful bridal shower into an orgy of rape, torture, and plunder. *Brides. Mistresses. Hippies. Disguise. Rape. Revenge. Torture. Practical jokes. Orgies.*

Note: Country of origin undetermined; an unconfirmed source attributes production to Sweden.

A BRIDE FOR BRENDA   **F6.0563**
Kirt Films International. *Dist* Distribpix, Inc. **1969**. Sd; b&w. 35mm. 62 min.
Dir Tommy Goetz. *Writ* Ron Rheego. *Asst Camera* Jack Ried. *Asst Ed* Eric Oner. *Mus* Blairs Symphony Orchestra. *Sd* Larry Parks, sd. *Rec* Fred Turner. *Asst Dir* Sam Parks. *Prod Asst* Mary Blanch. *Tech Cons* Marvin Stikes.

Cast: Roger Willock, Steve Mason, George Blau, Lois Lane, Rita Joyce, Mary Aster.

Melodrama. Shortly after she arrives in the big city from the Midwest, Brenda, an innocent virgin, goes to her landlady's apartment and finds her making love with a woman. Her curiosity and lust aroused, Brenda goes to her boyfriend and loses her virginity. Brenda returns to the landlady's apartment and is initiated into lesbianism. Later, while her boyfriend, bound and tortured, looks on, Brenda is "married" to one of her lesbian acquaintances. *Virginity. Landladies. Lesbianism. Sadism. Torture. Marriage—Lesbian.*

BRIDE OF THE ANDES (Japan)   **F6.0564**
Tokyo Eiga Co.-Hani Productions. *Dist* Toho Co. May **1967** [Los Angeles showing]. Sd; col (Eastmancolor). 35mm (Tohoscope). 108 min.
Dir-Writ Susumu Hani. *Photog* Juichi Nagano. *Mus* Hikaru Hayashi.

Cast: Sachiko Hidari *(Tamiko)*, Ancermo Fukuda *(Taro)*, Koji Takahashi *(Sasaki)*, Don Mateo *(Quisquis)*, Takeshi Hika *(Takeshi)*.

Drama. Tamiko, a mail-order bride with a son from a previous marriage, arrives in Peru to meet her new husband, a Japanese archeologist working on Incan ruins. At first Tamiko has difficulty adjusting to life in the village where her husband works, and just as she gains the acceptance of the villagers, her husband is killed in an accident while excavating for Incan gold. The money from the treasure is given to the village, and Tamiko decides to stay and carry on her husband's work. *Mail-order brides. Archeologists. Village life. Mountain life. Treasure. Marriage. Peru.*

Note: Location scenes filmed in Peru and Bolivia. Released in Japan in 1966 as *Andesu no hanayome.*

LA BRIDE SUR LE COU *see* **PLEASE, NOT NOW!**

THE BRIDE WORE BLACK (France/Italy) **F6.0565**
Films du Carrosse–Les Productions Artistes Associés–Dino De Laurentiis Cinematografica. *Dist* Lopert Pictures. 25 Jun **1968** [New York opening; c19 Feb 1968; LF41]. Sd; col (DeLuxe). 35mm. 107 min.
Pres by Oscar Lewenstein, Woodfall Films. *Prod* Marcel Berbert. *Dir* François Truffaut. *Adapt-Dial* François Truffaut, Jean-Louis Richard. *Dir Photog* Raoul Coutard. *Camera* Georges Liron. *Art Dir* Pierre Guffroy. *Film Ed* Claudine Bouché. *Mus* Bernard Herrmann. *Mus Dir* André Girard. *Sd Dir* René Levert. *Asst Dir* Jean Chayrou, Roland Thénot. *Prod Mgr* Georges Charlot. *Makeup Dir* Louis Bonnemaison. *Hairdresser* Simone Knapp. *Still Photog* Marilou Parolini.

Cast: Jeanne Moreau *(Julie Kohler)*, Jean-Claude Brialy *(Corey)*, Michel Bouquet *(Robert Coral)*, Charles Denner *(Fergus)*, Claude Rich *(Bliss)*, Daniel Boulanger *(Holmes)*, Michel Lonsdale *(René Morane)*, Alexandra Stewart *(Miss Becker)*, Serge Rousseau *(David)*, Jacques Robiolles *(Charlie)*, Luce Fabiole *(Julie's mother)*, Sylvine Delannoy *(Mrs. Morane)*, Jacqueline Rouillard *(maid)*, Van Doude *(Inspector Fabri)*, Paul Pavel *(mechanic)*, Maurice Garrel *(plaintiff)*, Frédérique Fontanarosa, Renaud Fontanarosa *(musicians)*, Christophe Brunot *(Morane's son)*, Gilles Quéant *(examining magistrate)*, Elisabeth Rey *(Julie as a child)*, Jean-Pierre Rey *(David as a child)*, Dominique Robier *(Sabine)*, Michèle Viborel *(Gilberte, Bliss's fiancée)*, Michèle Montfort *(model)*, Daniel Pommereulle *(Fergus's friend)*.

Drama. Source: William Irish, *The Bride Wore Black* (New York, 1940). During a cocktail party celebrating his engagement, a young Frenchman named Bliss is lured onto the terrace of his elegant Côte d'Azur apartment and pushed to his death by a mysterious woman dressed in white. A short time later, the woman appears in a rural mountain village. After enticing Robert Coral, a timid bank clerk, into inviting her to his dingy bachelor apartment, the woman kills him with poisoned wine. The third victim is René Morane, an aspiring politician with a wife and son. Once the wife has been tricked into leaving their suburban home to visit her mother, the woman poses as the son's teacher and gains entry into Morane's house; she locks him in a storage cupboard and leaves him to suffocate. Before each victim dies, the woman reveals that her name is Julie Kohler, the widow of a man who was shot to death on the steps outside the church where they were married. The fatal bullet had come from a building across the street where five men had been playing with a rifle which accidentally fired. After her mother prevented her from committing suicide, Julie vowed to have revenge on all of her husband's killers. Fourth on the list is Holmes, a dishonest car dealer, who is saved from Julie's vengeance when he is arrested by the police for handling stolen merchandise. Going on to her final victim, a painter known as Fergus, Julie agrees to be his model for a series of illustrations depicting Diana the Huntress. Although he eventually expresses his love for her, Julie kills him with the bow-and-arrow prop she used while posing. By deliberately not blacking out a wall painting Fergus made of her and then appearing at his funeral, Julie is easily recognized by Corey, a close friend of both the first and fifth victims. Openly admitting her guilt in the four murders, Julie is handed over to the police and imprisoned in the same jail where the fraudulent car dealer, Holmes, is now an inmate. While helping the matrons serve food to the prisoners, Julie takes a carving knife and completes her revenge by stabbing Holmes. *Brides. Widows. Bank clerks. Politicians. Salesmen. Painters. Models. Revenge. Murder. Poisoning. Imposture. Suffocation. Confession (law). Imprisonment. Funerals. Prisons. Riviera.*

Note: Location scenes filmed in and around Paris and in Versailles, Chevilly-Larue, Senlis, and Cannes. Opened in Paris in Apr 1968 as *La mariée était en noir*; in Italy in 1968 as *La sposa in nero*.

BRIDES OF BLOOD (United States/Philippines)   **F6.0566**
Hemisphere Pictures. *Dist* Hemisphere Pictures, Premier Pictures. May **1968**. Sd; col. 35mm. 92 min.

Prod Eddie Romero. *Exec Prod* Kane W. Lynn. *Dir* Eddie Romero, Gerardo de Leon.

Cast: John Ashley (*Jim Farrel*), Kent Taylor (*Dr. Paul Henderson*), Beverly Hills (*Carla Henderson*), Mario Montenegro (*Stephen Powers*), Eva Darren (*Alma*), Oscar Keesee, Ely Ramos, Jr., Bruno Punzalan, Andres Centenera, Pedro Navarro, Carmelita Estrella, Quiel Mendoza, Willie Tomada, Ben Sanchez, Angelita Alba.

Horror film. The Atomic Energy Commission sends three Americans, naturalist Paul Henderson, his wife, Carla, and Peace Corpsman Jim Farrel, to Blood Island in the Pacific to investigate rumors of plant and animal mutations caused by atomic radiation. They are shocked when they see the severed head and arm of a girl, although the native chief insists that the death was accidental. After they become the houseguests of epileptic landowner Stephen Powers, several strange phenomena are observed by the visiting party: man-eating trees and vines, a ferocious cockroach, a vicious butterfly, and a monster which devours nude virgins sacrificed by the natives. When Alma, a lovely native girl to whom Jim is attracted, is chosen as the monster's next victim, Jim convinces the villagers that the mutants must be destroyed. The beast kills Carla when she approaches it to satisfy his sexual desires; and the natives finally consent to help when the monster kills Paul. They trap the monster in a bamboo hut, set it afire, and watch the mutated body of Stephen Powers emerge. *Monsters. Americans in foreign countries. Naturalists. Houseguests. Radiation. Mutation. Animal life. Carnivorous plants. Decapitation. Human sacrifice. Epilepsy. South Sea Islands. Atomic Energy Commission. Fires.*

Note: Filmed in the Philippines. Working titles: *Terror on Blood Island* and *Orgy of Blood*. Also known as *Blood Brides* and *Brides of Death*.

BRIDES OF DEATH *see* **BRIDES OF BLOOD**

THE BRIDES OF FU MANCHU (Great Britain)   **F6.0567**
Hallam Productions-Fu Manchu Films. *Dist* Seven Arts Pictures. 14 Dec **1966** [Providence, Rhode Island, opening]. Sd; col (Eastmancolor). 35mm. 94 min.

Prod Harry Alan Towers. *Exec Prod* Oliver A. Unger. *Dir* Don Sharp. *2d Unit Dir* David Eady. *Screenplay* Peter Welbeck. *Dir Photog* Ernest Steward. *2d Unit Photog* John Kotze. *Camera Op* Dudley Lovell. *Art Dir* Frank White. *Asst Art Dir* George Lack. *Film Ed* Allan Morrison. *Mus Comp* Johnny Douglas, Bruce Montgomery. *Mus Cond* Philip Martell. *Sd Rec* John Brommage, Ken Cameron. *Sd* Fred Hughesdon. *Asst Dir* Barrie Melrose. *Prod Mgr* John Comfort. *Location Mgr* Bruce Sharman. *Cont* Josie Fulford. *Cost* Harry Haynes, T. Haynes. *Makeup* George Partleton. *Hairstyles* Ann Box.

Cast: Christopher Lee (*Fu Manchu*), Douglas Wilmer (*Nayland Smith*), Marie Versini (*Marie Lentz*), Heinz Drache (*Franz Baumer*), Howard Marion-

Crawford (*Dr. Ronald Petrie*), Tsai Chin (*Lin Tang*), Kenneth Fortescue (*Sergeant Spicer*), Joseph Furst (*Otto Lentz*), Carole Gray (*Michèle Merlin*), Harald Leipnitz (*Nikki Sheldon*), Roger Hanin (*Insp. Pierre Grimaldi*), Rupert Davies (*Jules Merlin*), Burt Kwouk (*Feng*), Eric Young (*Feng's assistant*), Poulet Tu (*Lotus*), Salmaan Peer (*Abdul*), Wendy Gifford (*Louise*), Dani Sheridan (*Shiva*), Lucille Soong (*Yewar*), Maureen Beck (*nurse*), Clive Swift (*porter*), Kitty Attwood (*cleaner*), Christopher Kum (*wireless operator*), Tommy Yapp, Cecil Cheng (*dacoits*), Denis Holmes (*constable*), Nicholas Courtney (*sergeant*), Desmond Gill (*warder*), Christine Rau (*Austrian bride*), Danièle Defrère (*Belgian bride*), Yvonne Ekman (*Danish bride*), Janette Napper (*English bride*), Evelyne Dheliat (*French bride*), Katatina Quest (*German bride*), Anje Langstraat (*Dutch bride*), Grete-Lill Henden (*Norwegian bride*), Gaby Schar (*Swiss bride*).

Adventure melodrama. Based on the characters created by: Sax Rohmer. As part of his plan for world domination, the evil Fu Manchu has taken as hostages the daughters of 12 political or industrial figures. Scotland Yard's Nayland Smith and Dr. Petrie are unable to prevent the kidnaping of Marie Lentz, a famed scientist's daughter who is brought to Fu Manchu's North African headquarters in the Sahara, only to learn that Fu Manchu possesses a lethal death ray. In time, Smith, Dr. Petrie, and Marie's fiancé, Franz Baumer, make their way to Fu Manchu's temple, but the death ray apparatus has already been set on a destructive course. Fu Manchu's "brides" barricade the doors against him and assist Smith and Dr. Petrie in resetting the death ray's tracking device, and the temple explodes after they have escaped. As he watches, Nayland Smith believes he hears the words, "the world will hear from me again," coming to him across the desert. *Scientists. Detectives. Masterminds. Hostages. Brides. Kidnaping. Megalomania. Death rays. Explosions. Sahara. Scotland Yard. Fu Manchu.*

Note: Released in Great Britain Dec 1966. Peter Welbeck is a pseudonym of Harry Alan Towers. This is a sequel to *The Face of Fu Manchu*, q. v.

THE BRIDGE (West Germany)   **F6.0568**
Fono-Film–Jochen Severin. *Dist* Allied Artists. 1 May **1961** [New York opening; c22 Oct 1959; LP21653]. Sd; b&w. 35mm. 102 min.

Prod Hermann Schwerin. *Dir* Bernhard Wicki. *Screenplay* Bernhard Wicki, Michael Mansfeld, Karl-Wilhelm Vivier. *Photog* Gerd von Bonin. *Camera Asst* Horst Fehlhaber, Franz Ausböck. *Art Dir* Peter Scharff, Heinrich Graf Brühl. *Film Ed* Carl Otto Bartning. *Mus* Hans-Martin Majewski. *Sd* Willy Schwardorf. *Asst Dir* Holger Lussmann. *Prod Asst* Hans Wolff. *Dir Prod* J. M. von Wolffersdorff. *Prod Mgr* Withold Grünberg, Karl Helmer. *Still Photog* Chargesheimer.

Cast: Volker Bohnet (*Hans Scholten*), Fritz Wepper (*Albert Mutz*), Michael Hinz (*Walter Forst*), Frank Glaubrecht (*Jürgen Borchert*), Karl Michael Balzer (*Karl Horber*), Volker Lechtenbrink (*Klaus Hager*), Günther Hoffmann (*Sigi Bernhard*), Cordula Trantow (*Franziska*), Wolfgang Stumpf (*Stern, the teacher*), Günter Pfitzmann (*Corporal Heilmann*), Heinz Spitzner (*Captain Fröhlich*), Siegfried Schürenberg (*lieutenant colonel*), Ruth Hausmeister (*Mrs. Mutz*), Eva Vaitl (*Mrs. Borchert*), Edith Schultze-Westrum (*Mrs. Bernhard*), Hans Elwenspoek (*Mr. Forst*), Trude Breitschopf (*Mrs. Forst*), Klaus Hellmold (*Mr. Horber*), Inge Benz (*Sigrun*), Edeltraut Elsner (*Barbara*), Til Kiwe, Alexander Hunzinger, H. Bergmann, Johannes Buzalski, Loriot, Heini Göbel, H. Habernoll, J. Herrmann, H. Hochwarter, Emiljosef Hunek, A. Lach, E. Lehn, H. Oetl, H. Struck, A. Teuber, H. Winninger.

War drama. Source: Manfred Gregor, *Die Brücke* (Vienna, 1958). In late April, 1945, the German army is facing defeat; Nazi officials are deserting their posts; and the Wermacht is in a state of disorganized retreat. Nevertheless, German schoolboys are still being drafted in a last desperate attempt to halt the Allied advance. In one small German village, seven 16-year-old boys proudly leave their homes and families for military duty; and after only one day's training, they are ordered into combat. Their former schoolteacher intercedes on their behalf, however, and they are assigned to a corporal, who places them on guard duty at the small bridge at the edge of their town. The bridge has no military importance, and the corporal knows, as the boys do not, that it is to be destroyed by a demolition squad in the morning. That night the corporal is killed by two SS men, and the boys, left on their own, dig in to defend their post. The youngest and smallest boy, Sigi, is killed by a strafing plane. Moments later, American tanks arrive. Though one of the boys scores a lucky hit, their little victory is short-lived: Jürgen, who proudly went to war carrying his late father's army pistol, is shot down by a sniper; Karl, who innocently and naively loved his father's mistress, is killed by shrapnel; Klaus, who thought only of his beloved Franziska, cracks under the strain of battle and runs into the line of fire; and Walter, who despised his Nazi father, is crushed to death by the falling debris of a bombed-out farmhouse. When the Americans retreat momentarily, a German demolition squad arrives to blow up the bridge, but the two remaining boys, unwilling to accept the idea that their comrades may have died in vain, refuse to yield their position and open fire on the squad. Though the squad withdraws, it also opens fire and kills the sixth boy, Hans, a handsome idealist. The sole survivor is young Albert; dazed and bewildered, he staggers alone across the bridge. The next day the war in Europe ends. *Nazis. Students. Schoolteachers. Mistresses. Idealists. Adolescence. Demolition. Filial relations. Village life. Bridges. V-E Day (7 May 1945). World War II. Germany—Army. United States Army—Armored Forces. SS.*

Note: Released in West Germany in Oct 1959 as *Die Brücke.*

THE BRIDGE AT REMAGEN   F6.0569

Wolper Pictures. *Dist* United Artists. 25 Jun **1969** [Huntington, West Virginia, opening; c25 Jun 1969; LP37146]. Sd; col (DeLuxe). 35mm (Panavision). 116 min. *MPAA rating* M.

Prod David L. Wolper. *Assoc Prod* Julian Ludwig, Theodore Strauss. *Dir* John Guillermin. *2d Unit Dir* William Kronick. *Screenplay* Richard Yates, William Roberts, Ray Rigby. *Screen Story* Roger Hirson. *Dir Photog* Stanley Cortez. *Camera Op* Cecil Cooney, Gordon Meagher. *Art Dir* Alfred Sweeney. *Film Ed* William Cartwright. *Mus* Elmer Bernstein. *Sd* Don Wortham, Al Overton. *Asst Dir* Reggie Callow. *Prod Supv* Harvey Bernhard. *Exec Prod Mgr* Milton Feldman. *Cost* Frank Balchus. *Makeup* Milan Jandera. *Sp Eff* Logan Frazee. *Adv* Cecil E. Roberts, (Col. USA Ret.), Kenneth William Hechler. *Stunt Supv* Hal Needham.

Cast: George Segal *(Lieut. Phil Hartman)*, Robert Vaughn *(Maj. Paul Kreuger)*, Ben Gazzara *(Sergeant Angelo)*, Bradford Dillman *(Major Barnes)*, E. G. Marshall *(Brigadier General Shinner)*, Peter Van Eyck *(General von Brock)*, Matt Clark *(Corporal Jellicoe)*, Fritz Ford *(Colonel Dent)*, Tom Heaton *(Lieutenant Pattison)*, Bo Hopkins *(Corporal Grebs)*, Robert Logan *(Private Bissell)*, Paul Prokop *(Captain Colt)*, Steve Sandor *(Private Slavek)*, Frank Webb *(Private Glover)*, Hans Christian Blech *(Capt. Carl Schmidt)*, Joachim Hansen *(Capt. Otto Baumann)*, Gunter Meisner *(SS General Gerlach)*, Richard Munch *(Field Marshal von Sturmer)*, Heinz Reincke *(Emil Holzgang)*, Sonja Ziemann *(Greta Holzgang)*, Vit Olmer *(Lieutenant Zimring)*, Rudolf Jelinek *(Private Manfred)*, Anna Gael *(girl).*

War drama. Source: Kenneth William Hechler, *Bridge at Remagen* (New York, 1957). By early 1945, the last remaining span across the Rhine into Germany is the Ludendorff bridge at Remagen. When General von Brock, the German commander in the area, receives orders to destroy the bridge, he delays rather than abandon 50,000 of his men to the onrushing American soldiers. Placing the aristocratic Maj. Paul Kreuger in charge, von Brock instructs him to hold the bridge as long as possible. At the same time, U. S. Brigadier General Shinner hopes to trap the retreating Germans by ordering an armored infantry division to spearhead a drive for the Rhine. Leading the offensive is Major Barnes, an ambitious career officer who is disliked by most of his men, particularly Lieut. Phil Hartman, his platoon leader. Hartman is also at odds with Sergeant Angelo, a scavenger who searches for valuables on the bodies of the dead German soldiers. Upon reaching a town near Remagen, the Americans prepare to billet for the night, but they are ordered to push on toward the Rhine. Kreuger, meanwhile, is trying to rally his defense forces while waiting for explosives to arrive. Although the Americans meet stiff opposition as they enter Remagen, their tanks crash the barricades and head for the bridge. Kreuger delays dynamiting the bridge to allow a German train to attempt a crossing and then sets off his explosives, only to discover that they are defective. Seizing upon the German failure, General Shinner orders that the bridge be taken intact. By night, the Americans have crossed the bridge after heavy fighting which unites Hartman and Angelo in a common cause. Kreuger, refusing to admit defeat, asks for reinforcements, but he is shot by an SS firing squad for failing to destroy the bridge. The American victory becomes meaningless, however, when in March 1945, the bridge collapses. *Profiteers. Bridges. Tanks (armored cars). Explosives. World War II. Remagen. Rhine River. United States Army. Germany—Army. SS.*

Note: Filmed on location in Czechoslovakia, West Germany, and Italy.

BRIDGE TO THE SUN (United States/France)   F6.0570

Cité Films. *Dist* Metro-Goldwyn-Mayer, Inc. 4 Oct **1961** [Washington, D.C., opening; c7 Aug 1961; LP20070]. Sd (Westrex); b&w. 35mm. 112 min.

Prod Jacques Bar. *Dir* Etienne Périer. *Screenplay* Charles Kaufman. *Photog* Marcel Weiss, Seiichi Kizuka, Bill Kelly. *Camera Op* Raymond Picon-Borel. *Art Dir* Hiroshi Mizutani. *Set Decor* Robert Bouladoux. *Set Dsgn* Jean-Jacques Caziot. *Film Ed* Robert Isnardon, Monique Isnardon. *Mus* Georges Auric. *Orch Cond* Jacques Metehen. *Asst Dir* Jacques Rouffio, Takashi Fugie, Olivier Gérard. *Prod Mgr* Jacques Juranville. *Unit Mgr* Hiroshi Moroishi, Haven Falconer. *Cont* Francine Corteggiani. *Makeup* René Daudin. *Hairstyles* Mary Roche-Faye. *Sp Eff* Kenji Inagawa.

Cast: Carroll Baker *(Gwen Terasaki)*, James Shigeta *(Hidenari Terasaki [Terry])*, James Yagi *(Hara)*, Tetsuro Tamba *(Jiro)*, Sean Garrison *(Fred Tyson)*, Ruth Masters *(Aunt Peggy)*, Nori Elisabeth Hermann, Emi Florence Hirsch *(Mako Terasaki, at different ages)*, Hiroshi Tomono *(Ishi)*, Kyoko Takahashi, Yoshiko Hiromura, Lee Payant.

Biographical drama. Source: Gwen (Harold) Terasaki, *Bridge to the Sun* (Chapel Hill, North Carolina, 1957). In 1930, while vacationing in Washington, D. C., Tennessee-born Gwen Harold falls in love with and marries Japanese diplomat Hidenari (Terry) Terasaki, despite her family's objections. When the Japanese attack Pearl Harbor in 1941, Gwen, Terry, and their daughter, Mako, are sent to Japan in exchange for American diplomats stationed there. Because of Terry's long opposition to the war party, he is stripped of all his stations and carefully watched by the Kempei-tai, the secret police. Furthermore, Gwen, torn between allegiance to her native country and affection for her new home, is often treated with hostility by the Japanese. An additional problem occurs when a friend of Mako's is killed during an Allied bombing, and Mako becomes embittered against her mother's country. When Japan eventually surrenders, Terry is appointed to act as a liaison between Emperor Hirohito and General MacArthur; but the war years have taken a heavy toll upon Terry's health, and he discovers that he has only a short time to live. To spare his wife and child, he suggests that they return to the United States where he will join them later. Though Gwen has learned of Terry's fatal illness, she respects her husband's wishes, and she and Mako leave Japan. *Japanese. Diplomats. Americans in foreign countries. Miscegenation. Racial prejudice. Family life. Patriotism. Incurable illness. World War II. Pearl Harbor Attack 1941. Washington (District of Columbia). Japan. Gwen Terasaki. Hidenari Terasaki. Douglas MacArthur. Hirohito. Kempei-tai.*

Note: Location scenes filmed in Japan and Washington, D. C. Opened in Paris in Mar 1964 as *Le pont vers le soleil;* running times: 115 and 88 min.

THE BRIG   F6.0571

White Line Productions. *Dist* David C. Stone, Film-Makers' Cooperative, Film-Makers' Distribution Center. 4 Mar **1965** [New York showing]. Sd; b&w. 16mm & 35mm. 68 min. [Cut from 120 min.]

Prod David C. Stone. *Dir* Jonas Mekas, Adolfas Mekas. *Stage Prod Dir* Judith Malina. *Screenplay* Kenneth H. Brown. *Photog* Jonas Mekas. *Stage Prod Dsgn* Julian Beck. *Film Ed* Adolfas Mekas.

Cast: Warren Finnerty, Jim Anderson, Henry Howard, Tom Lillard *(guards)*, James Tiroff, Steven Ben Israel, Gene Lipton, Rufus Collins, Mike Elias, William Shari, Viktor Allen, George Bartenieff, Gene Gordon, Mark Duffy *(prisoners)*, Henry Proach *(new prisoner)*, Carl Einhorn, Luke Theodore *(stretcher bearers/prison chasers).*

Drama. Source: Kenneth H. Brown, *The Brig* (New York opening: 13 May 1963). In a United States Marines brig, which resembles a large chicken-wire cage within an area set off by barbed wire, prison guards awaken the 10 prisoners at 4:30 a.m. by scraping garbage-can lids along the mesh of their communal cell. The prisoners are ordered to clean their quarters, shower, dress, and eat breakfast in double time. They are forbidden to talk with one another, and during the time allowed for smoking, they are forced to inhale and exhale in unison. To cross one of the white lines that indicate right angles in the brig, a prisoner must ask permission from the guards. "Relaxation" consists of standing at attention while reading from the book of prison regulations. Throughout the course of the day, the men do compulsory exercises, scrub the brig thoroughly, perform rigorous drills, and undergo punishment for their "offenses." As a result of this routine, Prisoner Number Five collapses and is straitjacketed. A new prisoner becomes Prisoner Number Five. At bedtime, the prisoners undress and climb into bed, all the while moving in double time. *Prison guards. Sadism. Insanity. Prisons. United States Marines. The Living Theatre.*

Note: Filmed in 16mm at an actual performance of the Living Theatre production in New York City.

THE BRIGAND OF KANDAHAR (Great Britain)   F6.0572

Hammer Film Productions. *Dist* Columbia Pictures. caNov **1965** [c1 Jul 1965; LP31679]. Sd (RCA); col (Eastman Color by Pathé). 35mm (CinemaScope). 81 min.

Prod Anthony Nelson Keys. *Dir-Writ* John Gilling. *Dir Photog* Reg Wyer. *Camera Op* Harry Gillam. *Art Dir* Don Mingaye. *Prod Dsgn* Bernard Robinson. *Supv Ed* James Needs. *Ed* Tom Simpson. *Mus Comp* Don Banks. *Mus Supv* Philip Martell. *Rec Supv* A. W. Lumkin. *Sd Rec* Simon Kaye. *Sd Ed* Roy Hyde. *Asst Dir* Frank Nesbitt. *Prod Mgr* Don Weeks. *Cont* Pauline Harlow. *Wardrobe Mistress* Rosemary Burrows. *Makeup* Roy Ashton, Richard Mills. *Hairstyles* Frieda Steiger. *Sp Eff* Syd Pearson. *Fight Arr* Peter Diamond.

Cast: Ronald Lewis *(Lieutenant Case)*, Oliver Reed *(Eli Khan)*, Duncan Lamont *(Colonel Drewe)*, Yvonne Romain *(Ratina)*, Catherine Woodville *(Elsa Connelley)*, Glyn Houston *(Marriott)*, Inigo Jackson *(Captain Boyd)*, Sean Lynch *(Rattu)*, Walter Brown *(Hitala)*, Jeremy Burnham *(Captain Connelley)*, Joe Powell *(color sergeant)*, Henry Davies *(2d Lieutenant Crowe)*, John Southworth *(2d Lieutenant Barlow)*, Caron Gardner *(serving maid).*

Adventure drama. In 1850 Lieutenant Case, a halfcaste officer in the Bengal Lancers, is falsely accused of having abandoned a colleague, Captain Connelley, to the Gilzhai, a rebel band the Lancers are trying to suppress, allegedly because

Case loves Connelley's wife, Elsa. Discharged by Colonel Drewe, Case, enraged both by this injustice and by Elsa's belief that he is guilty, escapes from prison and joins the Gilzhai. He finds the captured Connelley, who has been tortured by Eli Khan, the leader of the Gilzhais, and shoots him out of mercy. Elsa and a London journalist, Marriott, who have been captured by the rebels, accuse him of murder. Case kills Khan for torturing Connelley, frees Elsa and Marriott, and, with Khan's sister, Ratina, leads the Gilzhai against the British. His forces are routed, and he and Ratina are killed, but not before he has killed Colonel Drewe. Marriott, who now understands that Case was a victim of racial prejudice, goes to London to tell Case's story. *Halfcastes. Journalists. Prison escapes. Infidelity. Injustice. Torture. Courts-martial. Racial prejudice. Mercy killing. Kandahar. Great Britain—Army—Bengal Lancers.*

Note: Opened in London in Aug 1965. Includes footage from *Zarak* (Columbia, 1957).

BRIGHTY OF THE GRAND CANYON   **F6.0573**
Stephen F. Booth Productions. *Dist* Feature Film Corp. of America. 24 Nov **1966** [Detroit opening; c20 Jun, 22 Nov 1966; LU3438, LP33764]. Sd; col (DeLuxe). 35mm. 89 min.
Prod Stephen F. Booth. *Dir-Writ* Norman Foster. *Photog* Ted Saizis, Vincent Saizis. *Film Ed* Joseph Dervin. *Orig Mus Score* Richard Lavsky, Phyllis Lavsky. *Sd & Mus Eff* E. Robert Velazco.
Cast: Joseph Cotten *(Jim Owen)*, Pat Conway *(Jake Irons)*, Dick Foran *(Old Timer)*, Karl Swenson *(Theodore Roosevelt)*, Dandy Curran *(Homer Hobbs)*, Jiggs *(Brighty, a burro)*, Jason Clarke.
Western melodrama. Source: Marguerite Henry, *Brighty of the Grand Canyon* (New York, 1953). In the Southwest of the early 1900's, countless wild burros run free and unharmed in the Grand Canyon area. One day a gold prospector known as Old Timer befriends one of the little animals, names him Brighty, and takes him along while panning for gold. When Old Timer hits a rich vein, the villainous Jake Irons murders him and makes off with the gold. Left alone, Brighty wanders into the camp of Jim Owen, a noted mountain lion hunter, who is alerted by the animal's presence that something may have happened to Old Timer. While Owen and Theodore Roosevelt are on a hunting trip, Brighty covers himself with glory by fighting off an attacking mountain lion. In the spring, the burro leads Owen back down to Old Timer's gold mine. Although he is wounded by Jake Irons, Brighty helps Owen bring his former master's killer to justice. *Prospectors. Hunters. Murder. Gold. Grand Canyon. Theodore Roosevelt. Donkeys. Lions.*
Note: Filmed on location in Arizona and Utah.

BRIGITTA   **F6.0574**
Dist I. R. M. I. Films. 13 Dec **1967** [New York showing]. Sd; b&w. 63 min. A Franz Hollen Production.
Cast: Elke Cole, Eva Richter.
Sex film. No information about the precise nature of this film has been found, but press material suggests that it is the story of a young German prostitute. *Prostitutes. Germans.*

BRINK OF LOVE *see* **STARK FEAR**

BRITISH SOUNDS *see* **SEE YOU AT MAO**

BROADWAY PIN-UP HONEYS *see* **NUDES, INC.**

THE BROKEN LAND   **F6.0575**
Associated Producers, Inc. *Dist* Twentieth Century-Fox Film Corp. Apr **1962** [c31 Dec 1961; LP21177]. Sd; col (De Luxe). 35mm (CinemaScope). 60 min.
Prod Leonard A. Schwartz. *Dir* John Bushelman. *Writ* Edward J. Lakso. *Dir Photog* Floyd Crosby. *Art Dir* John Mansbridge. *Supv Film Ed* Carl Pierson. *Mus Comp & Cond* Richard La Salle. *Sd* Frank McWhorter. *Supv Sd Ed* Jack Cornall. *Asst Dir* Frank Parmenter. *Prod Mgr* Harold E. Knox. *Script Supv* Dixie McCoy. *Wardrobe* Ray Summers, Paula Giokaris. *Makeup* Bob Mark. *Prop Master* Ted Ross. *Ch Grip* Chuck Hanawalt.
Cast: Kent Taylor *(Jim Kogan)*, Diana Darrin *(Marva Aikens)*, Jody McCrea *(Ed Flynn)*, Robert Sampson *(Gabe Dunson)*, Jack Nicholson *(Will Broicous)*, Gary Sneed *(Billy Bell)*, Don Orlando, Helen Joseph, H. Tom Cain, Bob Pollard.
Western melodrama. Sadistic Jim Kogan, U. S. marshal in a small western town, unjustly imprisons Will Broicous, the son of a famous gunfighter, along with Gabe and Billy, two men who attempt to help Will. Marva Aikens, a pretty waitress, helps them escape; but Kogan and his deputy pursue and capture them. Kogan kills Billy and his own deputy and brings the others back to town, where Marva informs the townspeople of Kogan's cruel deeds. Stripped of his badge and power, Kogan is left kneeling in the street, while Marva, Gabe, and Will are set free. *United States marshals. Gunfighters. Waitresses. Injustice. Sadism. Prison escapes. Murder.*

Note: Filmed at Apache Junction, Arizona; working title: *Vanishing Frontier.*

THE BROKEN LARIAT *see* **THE WILD WESTERNERS**

BROKEN SWORDS (Japan)   **F6.0576**
Daiei Motion Picture Co. Nov **1969** [Los Angeles showing]. Sd; col (Fuji Color). 35mm (Daiei Scope). 90 min.
Dir Kazuo Ikehiro. *Screenplay* Daisuke Ito. *Story* Kosuke Gomi. *Photog* Chishi Makiura. *Art Dir* Shigenori Shimoishizaka. *Mus* Takeo Watanabe.
Cast: Hiroki Matsukata *(Tenzen Tange)*, Kojiro Hongo *(Yasubei Nakayama)*, Tomomi Iwai *(Chiharu)*, Shigeru Tsuyuguchi *(Ryunoshin Nagao)*, Yoshi Kato, Tatsuo Matsumura.
Action melodrama. During the peaceful Genroku Era, the arts flourish while political morality declines. In contrast to the penchant of the times for material possessions, two young samurai, Tenzen Tange and Yasubei Nakayama, members of different fencing schools, devote their lives to the study of martial arts. The two meet on the way to Takada-no-Baba, where Yasubei intends to avenge his uncle, who was slain by 36 swordsmen belonging to Tenzen's school. Singlehandedly, Yasubei kills all of them. Under the samurai code, Tenzen is expelled for not helping his men, as is Yasubei, for pursuing a private feud. Lords Asano and Uesugi, two powerful daimyo impressed by Yasubei's skills, compete for his service. Yasubei is undecided between the two offers until he meets Chiharu, the sister of Ryunoshin Nagao, a Uesugi retainer. Yasubei's love for Chiharu leads him to decide in favor of Uesugi until he learns that Chiharu is Tenzen's fiancée, at which point he becomes Lord Asano's vassal. [Sources are unclear regarding the ending of the film.] *Samurai. Nobility. Uncles. Revenge. Feuds. Japan—History—Genroku Era.*
Note: Released in Japan in May 1969 as *Hiken yaburi.*

THE BROKEN WINGS (Lebanon)   **F6.0577**
Atlas Film (Lebanon). *Dist* Continental Distributing, Inc. 22 Dec **1965** [Los Angeles opening]. Sd; b&w. 35mm. 90 min.
Prod Toufic Kayrouz, Antoine Khoury. *Dir* Yusuf Malouf. *Screenplay* Saeed Akal. *Photog* Robert Sabagha.
Cast: Pierre Bordey *(Kahlil Gibran)*, Saladin Nader *(Mansour Bey Galib)*, Nidal Ash Kar *(Selma Karamy)*, Philip Akiki *(Ferris Affandi Karamy)*, Joseph Gabrail Salim *(Gibran's friend)*.
Biographical melodrama. Source: Kahlil Gibran, *The Broken Wings* (New York, 1957). Budding poet and philosopher Kahlil Gibran, despite his solitary preoccupations, falls in love with Selma Karamy, the beautiful daughter of the wealthy Ferris Affandi Karamy. Unfortunately, Selma's father has already been persuaded to marry her to a bishop's nephew, Mansour Bey Galib, and the two lovers are forced to part. Five years of marriage to her drunken, gambling, lecherous husband oppress the fragile Selma, and a reunion with Gibran reveals the continued strength of their love. Romantic meetings in the moonlight are all that are left the couple, however, as Selma determines to remain faithful to her husband, despite his philandering with a nightclub dancer. Finally Selma's prayers for a child are answered, but she dies after giving birth to a son. Gibran is left grief-stricken and soon leaves Beirut for New York City's Greenwich Village. *Poets. Philosophers. Philanderers. Marriage—Arranged. Infidelity. Childbirth. Beirut. Kahlil Gibran.*
Note: Produced in Lebanon in 1964 as *Lal aghnihat elmoutakasra.*

BRÖLLOPSBESVÄR *see* **SWEDISH WEDDING NIGHT**

BROOKS WILSON LTD. *see* **LOVING**

BROTHEL   **F6.0578**
Dist Film-Makers' Cooperative. 6 Feb **1966** [New York opening]. Si with sd-on-tape; col. 16mm. 48 min.
Prod-Dir Bill Vehr.
Cast: Mario Montez, Jack Smith, Lohr Wilson, Linda Sampson, Piero Heliczer, Jeanne Phillips, Tosh Carillo, Suzanne DeMaria, Sterling Houston, Ray Hagen, Ronni Love, Paul Warner, Ira Kaufman, Bruce Rudo, Lynn Johnson, Ricardo Capurta, Larry Rey, Mimi Stark, Will Inman, Francis Francine, Mark Saffron, David Adorno.
Satire. In a decadent "Arabian" bordello setting in the art nouveau tradition, extravagantly made up and costumed characters, including transvestites, perform erotic actions. The scene soon becomes a drunken orgy of bisexual behavior. *Transvestism. Male homosexuality. Bisexuality. Orgies. Drunkenness. Whorehouses.*

BROTHER, CRY FOR ME   **F6.0579**
International Center Productions. *Dist* Fine Products. Mar **1970**. Sd; col. 35mm. 95 min. *MPAA rating* G.
Pres by Gerald Fine. *Prod* Hubie Jay Kerns, William White. *Assoc Prod* Ron Brown. *Dir* William White. *Film Ed* Andrew Herbert, Carl Monson, Ed Hunt. *Mus* Jaime Mendoza.

Cast: Steve Drexel (*Geoffrey Noble*), Larry Pennell (*Jim Noble*), Leslie Parrish (*Jenny*), Richard Davalos (*Michael Noble*), Kahana (*Pablo*), Anthony Caruso, Ron Brown, Jay Adler.

Adventure melodrama. Noble, an old man who is unhappy with his three greedy sons, gives each of them a map leading to a hidden treasure in South America. Noble hopes that their greed will destroy them all. The brothers arrive in South America at the same time. Michael's beautiful wife, Jenny, loves his brother Jim, while Geoffrey, the greediest of the three, hopes to possess both the woman and the treasure. The interior is accessible only by boat, and Geoffrey manages to kidnap Jenny as he begins the journey. Michael accidentally kills a policeman in his frantic search for his wife; he makes his way into the jungle with the authorities on his trail. Jim finds Jenny under the guard of Geoffrey's accomplice, frees her, and scuttles his brother's boat. Pablo, a friendly native, leads them to the ancient Inca ruins. Jenny, bathing under a waterfall, stumbles upon the entrance to the cave, but she and Jim are soon confronted by Geoffrey and his accomplice. The police arrive next, claiming the treasure as the property of the government, and all of them are pinned down by the insane Michael's rifle fire. Michael pursues Geoffrey into the jungle, kills him, and threatens to murder Jim before he is gunned down by the police inspector. Jenny and Jim sadly leave the scene of the tragedy. *Brothers. Police. Greed. Infidelity. Abduction. Sabotage. Fratricide. Manslaughter. Jungles. Treasure. Insanity. South America. Documentation.*

THE BROTHERHOOD   F6.0580

Brotherhood Co. *Dist* Paramount Pictures. 25 Dec **1968** [Los Angeles opening; c28 Aug 1968; LP36835]. Sd; col (Technicolor). 35mm. 96 min. *MPAA rating* M.

Overall Production Credits: A Martin Ritt Production. *Prod* Kirk Douglas. *Dir* Martin Ritt. *Screenplay* Lewis John Carlino. *Photog* Boris Kaufman. *Art Dir* Tambi Larsen. *Asst Art Dir* Charles Bailey. *Set Decor* Bob Drumheller. *Scenic Artist* Murray Stern. *Film Ed* Frank Bracht. *Mus* Lalo Schifrin. *Song:* "Moon River" Johnny Mercer, Henry Mancini. *Song:* "Tarantella Abballa Abballa" Ignazio Privitera. *Sd Rec* Jack C. Jacobsen. *Asst Dir* Peter Scoppa. *Prod Mgr* David Golden. *Tech Supv* Lewis John Carlino. *Cost Dsgn* Ruth Morley. *Men's Wardrobe* James Hagerman. *Women's Wardrobe* Marilyn Putnam. *Makeup* Martin Bell. *Hairstyles* Betty De Stefano. *Gaffer* Howard Fortune. *Key Grip* Robert Ward.

Production Credits for Sicilian Locations: *2d Unit Dir* Francesco Cinieri. *2d Unit Camera* Amerigo Gengarelli. *Art Dir* Toni Sarzi-Braga. *Set Dresser* Giorgio Postiglione. *Asst Dir* Giorgio Gentili.

Cast: Kirk Douglas (*Frank*), Alex Cord (*Vince*), Irene Papas (*Ida*), Luther Adler (*Bertolo*), Susan Strasberg (*Emma*), Murray Hamilton (*Egan*), Eduardo Ciannelli (*Don Peppino*), Joe De Santis (*Pietro Rizzi*), Connie Scott (*Carmela*), Val Avery (*Jake Rotherman*), Val Bisoglio (*Cheech*), Alan Hewitt (*Solly Levin*), Barry Primus (*Vido*), Michele Cimarosa (*Toto*), Louis Badolati (*Don Turridu*).

Crime melodrama. Following his discharge from the Army, Vince Ginetta, a young Italian-American, marries his girl friend, Emma, and at their wedding celebration a Sicilian folk song, "Vitti 'na Crozza," is sung. He then goes to work for the Mafia in New York City as a bookkeeper. Obviously pleased by the decision is Vince's older brother, Frank, a syndicate board member who adheres to old customs and opposes expanding into new activities such as electronics unions. Despite their mutual affection, the two brothers clash when Frank vetoes any involvement that might cause trouble with the Federal government. As Vince's father-in-law, Bertolo, who is also a board member, instigates a move to replace Frank with his brother, deposed Mafia leader Don Peppino tells Frank that his father and 40 other loyal Mafia members were betrayed by Bertolo and massacred by the new regime. Compelled by tradition to avenge the killings, Frank brutally murders Bertolo and flees to Sicily with his wife, Ida, and his daughter, Carmela. When Vince arrives sometime later, Frank readily understands that his brother has been assigned to murder him in order to test his loyalty to the Mafia. After saying goodby to his wife, Frank takes Vince for a walk and hands him a rifle that belonged to their father. Fully aware that Vince's family will be murdered if he fails to carry out his assignment, Frank kisses his brother and asks for the fatal bullet. Once he has killed his brother, Vince permits Frank's chauffeur to drive him to the airport. *Veterans. Italians. Bookkeepers. Gangsters. Brothers. Fathers-in-law. Weddings. Gang wars. Revenge. Murder. Loyalty. Fratricide. Mafia. Sicily. New York City.*

Note: Filmed on location in New York City and in Sicily.

BROTHERLY LOVE (Great Britain)   F6.0581

Metro-Goldwyn-Mayer Pictures–Windward Films–Keep Films. *Dist* Metro-Goldwyn-Mayer, Inc. 22 Apr **1970** [New York opening; c9 Apr 1970; LP37892]. Sd; col (Metrocolor). 35mm. 112 min. *MPAA rating* R.

Prod Robert Emmett Ginna. *Assoc Prod* Denis Johnson. *Dir* J. Lee Thompson. *Screenplay* James Kennaway. *Dir Photog* Ted Moore. *Camera Op* Robert Kindred. *Art Dir* Maurice Fowler. *Asst Art Dir* Ken Jones, art. *Set Dresser* John Jarvis. *Main Titl* Maurice Binder. *Film Ed* Willy Kemplen. *Mus Comp & Cond* John Addison. *Scottish Mus* Jimmy Blue and His Band. *Scottish Dances Arr by* Bobby Watson. *Sd Ed* Jim Groom. *Sd Rec* Simon Kaye. *Dub Mix* Gerry Humphreys. *Asst Dir* Jake Wright. *Prod Mgr* Bernard Williams. *Unit Mgr* Terry Clegg. *Asst to the Prod* Peter Perkins. *Cont* Kay Mander. *Prod Sec* Loretta Ordewer. *Miss York's Cost* Yvonne Blake. *Wardrobe Supv* Betty Adamson. *Makeup Supv* Bill Lodge. *Hairdressing Supv* Maud Onslow. *Constr Mgr* Dick Frift. *Casting Dir* Maude Spector. *Dial Dir* Ewan Roberts.

Cast: Peter O'Toole (*Sir Charles Henry Arbuthnot Pinkerton Ferguson*), Susannah York (*Hilary Dow*), Michael Craig (*Douglas Dow*), Harry Andrews (*Brigadier Crieff*), Cyril Cusack (*Dr. Maitland*), Judy Cornwell (*Rosie*), Brian Blessed (*Jock Baird*), Robert Urquhart (*auctioneer*), Mark Malicz (*Benny-the-Pole*), Lennox Milne (*Miss Mailer*), Jean Anderson (*matron*), Marjorie Dalziel (*Bank Lizzie*), Helena Gloag (*Auntie Belle*), Madeleine Christie (*Bun McKenzie*), Roy Boutcher (*MacLachlan-Forbes*), Peter Reeves (*Alex Smart*), Leonard Maguire (*storekeeper*), Paul Farrell (*Alec-the-Gillie*), Rona Newton-John (*Miss Scott*), Ewan Roberts (*Mr. Hutchison*), Frances De La Tour (*nurse*), Patrick Gardiner (*ambulance driver*), Alex McAvoy (*hen farmer*), John Malloy (*ginger-haired farmer*), Harry Jones (*wee farmer*), Geoffrey Golden (*bearded farmer*), John Shedden (*slim farmer*), Bernadette Gallagher (*Ina*), Maura Keely (*Ina's mother*), John Kelly (*Ina's father*), Clare Mullen (*barmaid*), Eamonn Keane (*Fred-who-is-Bob*), Desmond Perry (*Dr. Soames*), Helen Norman (*cook*), Wallace Campbell (*hotel manager*), Tom Irwin (*Ramsay*), Mary Larkin (*Hilary's friend*).

Drama. Source: James Kennaway, *Country Dance* (London opening: 27 Jun 1967). James Kennaway, *Household Guests* (London, 1961). Sir Charles (Pink) and his sister Hilary, who is separated from her husband, live on a farm in Scotland. One day at a sheep auction, Hilary runs into Douglas, her husband, and discovers that they are still in love, and she asks him to meet her at a country dance that night. Pink learns of his sister's plan and plots to prevent their reconciliation; at the dance, he constantly interposes himself between Hilary and Douglas. When Rosie, a former maid on Pink's farm, arrives and asks Hilary the whereabouts of Douglas, Hilary comes to the conclusion that Douglas is the father of Rosie's illegitimate child. She confronts Douglas with this information, but before he can deny the accusation, Hilary goes on a spree and first propositions the band leader, but settles for Jock, the local constable who is the real father of Rosie's child. On his way to a duck hunt the next day, Pink discovers Hilary sleeping in his car, and she confesses her actions of the previous night. Pink, realizing that he is about to lose her, shoots his ear off at the hunt in an attempt to elicit sympathy from her. Reduced to alcoholic desperation, Pink confesses his incestuous love for Hilary. Douglas and Hilary, who have agreed to a reconciliation, decide that they have no choice but to commit Pink to a mental institution. *Landed gentry. Housemaids. Constables. Brother-sister relationship. Separation (marital). Jealousy. Illegitimacy. Hunting. Mutilation. Alcoholism. Incest. Insanity. Scotland.*

Note: Location scenes filmed in Wicklow County (Ireland) and Perthshire (Scotland). Opened in London in Mar 1971 as *Country Dance*.

BRUCIA, RAGAZZO, BRUCIA *see* A WOMAN ON FIRE

DIE BRÜCKE *see* THE BRIDGE

UNA BRUJA SIN ESCOBA *see* A WITCH WITHOUT A BROOM

BRUSHFIRE!   F6.0582

Obelisk, Inc. *Dist* Paramount Pictures. 21 Feb **1962** [New York opening; c31 Jan 1962; LP21461]. Sd; b&w. 35mm. 80 min.

Prod-Dir Jack Warner, Jr.. *Assoc Prod–Story* Irwin R. Blacker. *Screenplay* Irwin R. Blacker, Jack Warner, Jr. *Dir Photog* Ed Fitzgerald. *Art Dir* Ted Holsopple. *Set Dresser* Ray Boltz. *Film Ed* Roy Livingston. *Mus Comp & Cond* Irving Gertz. *Sd* Clarence Peterson. *Asst Dir* Robert Farfan. *Prod Supv* Hugh McCollum. *Wardrobe* Claire Cramer. *Makeup* Larry Butterworth.

Cast: John Ireland (*Jeff Saygure*), Everett Sloane (*Chevern McCase*), Jo Morrow (*Easter Banford*), Al Avalon (*Tony Banford*), Carl Esmond (*Martin*), Howard Caine (*Vladimar*), Beal Wong (*Tamboura*), Gerald Jann, Jon Lormer, Maria Tsien McClay, James Hong, Guy Lee, Kim Loui.

Adventure melodrama. In Southeast Asia, guerrilla rebels kidnap an American couple, Easter and Tony Banford, and hold them for a ransom of guns and ammunition. Realizing that the rebels must be stopped, Chevern McCase, a former World War II guerrilla fighter, joins his friend Jeff Saygure in organizing a rescue party. While they are leading a team of plantation workers to the rebel headquarters, Easter is brutally raped by Martin, the guerrilla leader, as Tony watches helplessly. Eventually Chevern and his men reach the guerrilla headquarters, destroy their radio communications, and rescue the young couple. As they make their getaway by sampan, Martin and the rebels attack. Tony hastily misfires when he sees Martin about to shoot Jeff and is himself killed by a blast from the enemy leader's gun. Jeff counters by hurling a hand grenade at Martin and killing him. Seeing their leader fall, the guerrillas flee in disorganized retreat. Jeff then consoles Easter and explains that the rescue effort was worth the cost because it kept the uprising from developing into a fullscale revolt. *Guerrillas. Americans in foreign countries. Kidnaping. Rape. Sabotage. Uprisings. Ransom. Southeast Asia.*

THE BRUTE AND THE BEAST (Italy)　　　　　　　　**F6.0583**
Mega Film–Colt Produzioni Cinematografiche–L. F. Produzioni Cinematografiche. *Dist* American International Pictures. Dec **1968** [c4 Dec 1968; LP36820]. Sd; col (Perfect). 35mm. 88 min.
Dir Lucio Fulci, Terry Vantell. *Screenplay* Fernando Di Leo. *Photog* Riccardo Pallottini. *Art Dir* Sergio Canevari. *Set Decor* Mario Giorsi. *Film Ed* Ornella Micheli. *Mus* Lallo Gori. *Sd* Fernando Pescetelli. *Asst Dir* Giovanni Fago. *Prod Mgr* Livio Maffei. *Cost* Silvano Giusti. *Makeup* Andrea Riva. *Hairstyles* Marcella De Marzi.
Cast: Franco Nero *(Tom)*, George Hilton *(Jeff)*, Nino Castelnuovo *(Jason)*, Lyn Shayne *(Brady)*, John MacDouglas *(Mr. Scott)*, Rina Franchetti *(Mercedes)*, Aysanoa Runachagua, Tchang Yu, Tom Felleghi, Franco Morici.
Western melodrama. While panning for gold in a remote area of the Old West, Tom, a young prospector, receives a mysterious note urging him to return to the town he had left while still a child. He discovers upon his arrival that neither his alcoholic half brother, Jeff, nor the loyal family housekeeper, Mercedes, is able to provide any information concerning the urgent request. Tom learns that the town is under the tyrannical control of an old man, Scott, and his sadistic, crazed son, Jason, who has usurped the ranch belonging to Tom's family. Attempting to confront Scott at the ranch, Tom is brutally bullwhipped by Jason and his henchmen. When Mercedes is killed by Jason's men, Jeff sobers up and accompanies Tom on a second visit to the ranch. The men gun down the guards to gain entrance to Scott, who confesses that he sent the note and that he is Tom's father. Scott reveals that Jason is responsible for all the bloodshed, whereupon Jason turns on his father and kills him. Tom and Jeff then shoot down Jason's henchmen, and Tom kills Jason in a gunfight, thus regaining the ranch that is his birthright and setting the town free from tyranny. *Prospectors. Brothers. Hired killers. Alcoholism. Fatherhood. Murder. Patricide. Fratricide. Insanity. Ranches. Documentation.*
Note: Released in Italy in 1966 as *Tempo di massacro.*

THE BUBBLE　　　　　　　　　　　　　　　　　　　**F6.0584**
Midwestern Magic-Vuers. *Dist* Arch Oboler. 21 Dec **1966** [Chicago opening]. Sd; col. 35mm (Space-Vision). 112 min.
Prod-Dir-Writ Arch Oboler. *Assoc Prod* Marvin Chomsky. *Dir Photog* Charles Wheeler. *Art Dir* Marvin Chomsky. *Film Ed* Igo Kantor. *Mus* Paul Sawtell, Bert Shefter. *Sd* Al Overton, Carl Daniels. *Asst Dir* Richard Dixon. *Tech Dir* Robert V. Bernier. *Photog Dsgn* Arch Oboler.
Cast: Michael Cole *(Mark)*, Deborah Walley *(Catherine)*, Johnny Desmond *(Tony)*, Kassie McMahon, Barbara Eiler, Virginia Gregg, Victor Perrin, Olan Soule, Chester Jones.
Science fiction drama. Catherine, in her 9th month of pregnancy, begins to have labor pains while on vacation in the mountains. Her husband, Mark, charters a plane from Tony, a former Korean War pilot, in the hope of reaching a hospital before the baby is born. Forced to make an emergency landing when they become lost in a storm, they find themselves in a strange community whose residents move mechanically, as if under a hypnotic spell. A characteristically afflicted doctor from the community delivers Catherine's baby safely. Later, the visitors discover that the area is covered by a huge, transparent dome and that once a week a resident disappears, presumably to be studied by the aliens who have trapped the community in a "zoo." Mark and Catherine take refuge in an old mill in the countryside while Mark attempts to dig an escape tunnel under the dome. Mark and Tony discover a mysterious rock structure in which they find a seat. Tony receives a convulsive shock when he sits in the seat, and grotesque faces swirl around him. Permanently affected by the experience, Tony eventually disappears. Mark then destroys the seat in an attempt to enlist the aid of the doctor. The community's source of food is thereby discontinued, and the starving citizens eventually follow Mark and Catherine to their unfinished escape route. *Air pilots. Spacemen. Physicians. Childbirth. Hypnotism. Airplanes. Tunnels. Zoos. Storms. Hallucinations.*
Note: Space-Vision is a single-camera, single-projector 3-D process in which images appear to leave the screen and move in space.

BUCCIA DI BANANA *see* **BANANA PEEL**

BUCHAMUKURE DAIHAKKEN *see* **COMPUTER FREE-FOR-ALL**
BUCKSKIN　　　　　　　　　　　　　　　　　　　　**F6.0585**
A. C. Lyles Productions. *Dist* Paramount Pictures. May **1968** [c20 Mar 1968; LP35658]. Sd; col (Pathé). 35mm. 98 min.
Prod A. C. Lyles. *Dir* Michael Moore. *Screenplay* Michael Fisher. *Dir Photog* W. Wallace Kelley. *Art Dir* Al Roelofs. *Set Decor* Jerry Miggins. *Film*

Ed Jack Wheeler. *Mus* Jimmie Haskell. *Sd Rec* John Carter, John Wilkinson. *Asst Dir* Joseph Kenny. *Unit Prod Mgr* Howard Roessel. *Men's Wardrobe* Jesse Munden. *Ladies' Wardrobe* Ruth Stella. *Makeup* Bill Wood, Louis Haszillo. *Hairstylist* Maryce Bates.
Cast: Barry Sullivan *(Chaddock)*, Joan Caulfield *(Nora Johnson)*, Wendell Corey *(Rep Marlowe)*, Lon Chaney, [Jr.] *(Sheriff Tangley)*, John Russell *(Patch)*, Barbara Hale *(Sarah Cody)*, Barton MacLane *(Doc Raymond)*, Bill Williams *(Frank Cody)*, Richard Arlen *(townsman)*, Leo Gordon *(Travis)*, Gerald Michenaud *(Akii)*, George Chandler *(storekeeper Perkins)*, Aki Aleong *(Sung Li)*, Michael Larrain *(Jimmy Cody)*, Craig Littler *(Browdie)*, James X. Mitchell *(Baker)*, Emile Meyer *(Corbin)*, Robert Riordan *(telegrapher)*, LeRoy Johnson *(bartender)*, Manuela Thiess *(Moni)*.
Western melodrama. In 1881 Rep Marlowe, a ruthless land baron, has bought up most of the area surrounding the small town of Gloryhole, Montana, and is driving out the homesteaders by building a dam to cut off their water supply. Opposing him is Montana territorial marshal Chaddock, a widowed former army scout with a 10-year-old halfbreed son. By promising to open the dam, Chaddock manages to persuade some of the settlers, particularly the Cody family, to postpone their move to Oregon. Chaddock also wins the support of one-time schoolteacher Nora Johnson, who has become an embittered saloon woman after being assaulted by a group of miners. Although Chaddock blows up the dam, young Jimmy Cody is killed, and Chaddock is bitten by a rattlesnake. While he is recuperating at the Cody ranch, Marlowe and his henchman Patch, who had served with Chaddock in the army before being dishonorably discharged, make plans to force the settlers out of town by shooting Chaddock. But, when Chaddock returns to town to face Marlowe and his men, some of the townspeople support him. In the final gun battle, Marlowe and Patch are killed, and although Chaddock is wounded, peace is restored to the valley. *Land barons. Homesteaders. United States marshals. Widowers. Barroom hostesses. Gunfighters. Water rights. Dams. Snakebites. Montana. Explosions.*
Note: Working title: *The Frontiersman.*

IL BUCO *see* **THE NIGHT WATCH**

BUDDENBROOKS (West Germany)　　　　　　　　**F6.0586**
Filmaufbau–Hans Abich. *Dist* Casino Films. 15 Jun **1962** [Chicago opening]. Sd; b&w. 35mm. 199 min.
A Hans Abich Production. *Dir* Alfred Weidenmann. *Screenplay* Erika Mann, Harald Braun, Jacob Geis. *Photog* Friedl Behn-Grund. *Camera Asst* Günther Knuth, Thomas Kapiewicz. *Art Dir* Robert Herlth, Arno Richter, Kurt Herlth. *Film Ed* Caspar van den Berg, Ursula van den Berg. *Mus* Werner Eisbrenner. *Sd* Werner Schlagge. *Prod Mgr* Gustl Gotzler, Manfred Kercher, Kurt Heinz. *Prod Dir* Eberhard Krause. *Cost* Herbert Ploberger, Vera Otto. *Wardrobe* Fritz Strack, Anni Loretto, Heinrich Meyer. *Makeup* Franz Mayrhofer, Gerda Scholz-Grosse, Gertrud Weinz-Werner. *Prop* Horst Mischke, Georg Attlfellner. *Still Photog* Wolfgang Brünjes.
Cast: Liselotte Pulver *(Antonie Buddenbrook)*, Nadja Tiller *(Gerda Buddenbrook)*, Hansjörg Felmy *(Tom Buddenbrook)*, Hanns Lothar *(Christian Buddenbrook)*, Lil Dagover *(Frau Consul Elizabeth Buddenbrook)*, Werner Hinz *(Consul Jean Buddenbrook)*, Günther Lüders *(Corle)*, Robert Graf *(Bendix Grünlich)*, Wolfgang Wahl *(Wagenström)*, Walter Sedlmayr *(Alois Permaneder)*, Horst Janson *(Morten Schwartzkopf)*, Gustav Knuth *(commander)*, Joseph Offenbach *(banker)*, Ellen Roedler *(flower girl)*, Rudolf Platte, Maria Sebaldt, Mathias Fuchs, Carsta Löck, Paul Hartmann, Hans Leibelt, Gustl Halenke, Fritz Schmiedel, Hans Paetsch, Peter Lühr, Josef Dahmen, Karl Ludwig Lindt, Frank Freytag, Camilla Spira, Rudolf Fernau, Erika Mann, Eva Maria Meineke.
Domestic drama. Source: Thomas Mann, *Buddenbrooks* (Berlin, 1901). Since 1875 the wealth and reputation of the Buddenbrook family have steadily declined. In Lübeck, Consul Jean Buddenbrook, having inherited his father Johann's business, marries his daughter Antonie to Hamburg merchant Bendix Grünlich, despite her love for medical student Morten Schwartzkopf. The marriage ends in divorce, however, when Jean learns that Grünlich has fraudulently used his daughter's dowry to prevent bankruptcy. Jean's eldest son, Tom, assumes leadership of the family business upon his father's death, while his younger brother Christian, having shown a distaste for the Buddenbrook interests, is sent to Munich for his health. Tom marries Dutch heiress Gerda Arnoldsen and arranges his sister's second marriage, a short-lived union with Munich brewer Alois Permaneder. Following the death of Frau Buddenbrook, the family haggles over the inheritance. The marriage of Antonie's daughter Erica Grünlich to Hugo Weinschenk ends in scandal and is followed soon after by the death of Tom. After marrying his mistress, a former chorus girl, Christian is institutionalized. The death of Tom and that of Gerda's sickly 15-year-old son, Hanno, during a typhoid epidemic, concludes the demise of the Buddenbrooks. *Civil servants. Merchants. Medical students. Dutch. Heiresses. Brewers. Chorus girls. Mistresses. Family life. Wealth.*

Marriage. Marriage—Arranged. Divorce. Bankruptcy. Health. Inheritance. Scandal. Dowries. Typhus. Lübeck. Hamburg. Munich.

Note: Opened in Lübeck in Nov 1959; running times: 110 min (Part I), 109 min (Part II). Cut to 93 min (Part I) and 106 min (Part II) for U. S. distribution.

BUDDHA (Japan)   F6.0587

Daiei Motion Picture Co. *Dist* Lopert Pictures. 2 Jul **1963** [San Francisco opening]. Sd; col (Technicolor). 35mm (Technirama, see note). 139 min. [Also 134 min.]

Prod Masaichi Nagata. *Assoc Prod* Akinari Suzuki. *Dir* Kenji Misumi. *Screenplay* Fuji Yahiro. *Anim* Tomio Sagisu. *Drawings* Yoshio Watanabe, anim. *Dir Photog* Hiroshi Imai. *Lighting* Kenichi Okamoto. *Col Cons* Yoshiaki Kiura. *Art Dir* Kisaku Ito. *Art* Akira Naito. *Set Decor* Teruo Kajitani. *Decor Cons* Toshiharu Takatsu. *Film Ed* Kanji Suganuma. *Mus* Akira Ifukube. *Mus Cond* Jin Ueda. *Perf by* Tokyo Symphony Orchestra. *Choreog* Kiitsu Sakakibara. *Sd Rec Supv* Masao Osumi. *Asst Dir* Akira Inoue, Yoshiyuki Kuroda. *Prod Mgr* Masatsugu Hashimoto. *Cost Dsgn* Hachiro Nakajima. *Cost Cons* Yoshio Ueno. *Sp Eff* Tatsuyuki Yokota, So-Ichi Aisaka. *Sp Photog Eff* Tooru Matoba, Chishi Makiura. *Tech Adv* Gakuro Nakamura, Takio Nakamura.

Cast: Kojiro Hongo *(Siddhartha)*, Charito Solis *(Yashodhara)*, Shintaro Katsu *(Devadatta)*, Machiko Kyo *(Nandabala)*, Raizo Ichikawa *(Kunala)*, Fujiko Yamamoto *(Usha)*, Hiroshi Kawaguchi *(Ajatashatru)*, Katsuhiko Kobayashi *(Ananda)*, Tamao Nakamura *(Auttami)*, Junko Kano *(Matangi)*, Mieko Kondo *(Amana)*, Tokiko Mita *(Sari)*, Hiromi Ichida *(Naccha)*, Michiko Ai *(Kilika)*, Matasaburo Niwa *(Sonna)*, Keizo Kawasaki *(Upali)*, Reiko Fujiwara *(child's mother)*, Gen Mitamura *(Shariputra)*, Ryuzo Shimada *(Bhutika)*, Joji Tsurumi *(Arama)*, Shiro Otsuji *(Kalodayi)*, Yoshiro Kitahara *(Kaundinya)*, Jun Negami *(Mahakashyapa)*, Ganjiro Nakamura *(Ashoka)*, Toshio Chiba *(Graha)*, Ryuichi Ishii *(Bandhu)*, Yoichi Funaki *(Maudgaliputra)*, Sanemon Arashi *(Rayana)*, Osamu Maryuama *(Jivaka)*, Gen Shimizu *(Kisaka)*, Isuzu Yamada *(Kalidevi)*, Yumeji Tsukioka *(Takshakara)*, Tanie Kitabayashi *(Sumi)*, Chikako Hosokawa *(Maya)*, Haruko Sugimura *(Vaidehi)*, Koreya Senda *(Shuddhodana)*, Eijiro Tono *(Suratha)*, Bontaro Miyake *(Channa)*, Osamu Takizawa *(Ajita)*, Jukai Ichikawa *(Bimbisara)*, Koichi Katsuragi *(Suprabuddha)*, Ryonosuke Azuma *(Bashpa)*, Shintaro Nanjyo *(Mahanaman)*, Kinya Ichikawa *(Chunda)*, Seishiro Hara *(Bhadrika)*, Saburo Date *(Ashvajit)*, Kongo Reiko *(Sabhaya)*, Kimiko Tachibana *(Amita)*.

Religious epic. Prince Siddhartha is born to a royal family; although it is not spring, the trees blossom, and the air is filled with music. The prince grows up in luxury, and when he is 20 years old, he wins the hand of Princess Yashodhara. They live in wealthy seclusion until Siddhartha discovers that the world outside his palace walls is full of poverty, sickness, and hunger; he leaves the palace in search of spiritual guidance. While he is away, his evil cousin Devadatta attacks Yashodhara, and she commits suicide because of her disgrace. The tragedy does not deter Siddhartha from his meditations, however, and after 6 years, enlightenment comes to him under the sacred tree. He is spiritually reborn as Buddha and begins to teach and perform miracles. Meanwhile, Devadatta uses thousands of slaves to build a temple to the evil gods of the occult and orders the murder of all the Buddhist priests. This activity brings about an earthquake and fires that destroy the evil temple, and Devadatta falls into the earth during the quake. He is saved and forgiven by Buddha. At the end of his life, Buddha bids farewell to his people and enters Nirvana. *Royalty. Religious persecution. Religious conversion. Miracles. Suicide. Temples. Gautama Buddha. Buddhism. Fires. Earthquakes.*

Note: Released in Japan in 1963 as *Shaka*; running time: 156 min.

BUFFALO GUN   F6.0588

A. R. Milton–Gannaway Productions. *Dist* Globe Pictures. 23 May **1961** [Maryland license]. Sd; b&w. 35mm. 72 min.

Prod-Writ A. R. Milton. *Dir* Albert C. Gannaway. *Photog* Gerald Finnerman. *Art Dir* George Troast. *Film Ed* Carl Pingitore. *Mus* Ramez Idriss. *Sd* Phil Mitchell. *Sd Eff* Kay Harris.

Cast: Marty Robbins, Webb Pierce, Carl Smith *(themselves)*, Wayne Morris *(Rocca)*, Mary Ellen Kay *(Clementine)*, Don "Red" Barry *(Murdock)*, Douglas Fowley *(sheriff)*, Harry Lauter *(telegraph operator)*, The Jordanaires.

Western melodrama. In the 1870's, U. S. Marshal Webb Pierce, along with deputies Marty Robbins and Carl Smith, is sent to investigate the robbery of supply trains containing food, clothing, and weapons for the Indians. They learn that the culprits are Sam Rocca, a man posing as an Indian agent; his partner, Murdock; and a telegraph operator. Pierce and his deputies discover the stolen weapons in Rocca's hayloft, but they do not arrest him immediately. Rocca holds a barn dance, during which he stages a cattle stampede to divert the townspeople. As the people are chasing the cattle, Rocca and his accomplices unload the weapons, but they are caught by the government agents. Pierce and Smith then leave town; but Robbins remains to marry Clementine, a woman he had met at the barn dance. *United States marshals. Indians of North America.*

Train robberies. Imposture. Firearms. Stampedes. Cattle.

Note: Produced in 1958.

LA BUGIARDA *see* **SIX DAYS A WEEK**

BULL OF THE CAMPUS (Japan)   F6.0589

Toho Co. May **1962** [Los Angeles showing]. Sd; col (Eastmancolor). 35mm (Tohoscope). 94 min.

Exec Prod Sanezumi Fujimoto. *Dir* Toshio Sugie. *Screenplay* Ryozo Kasahara, Yasuo Tanami. *Photog* Takeshi Suzuki. *Mus* Kenjiro Hirose.

Cast: Yuzo Kayama *(Yuichi)*, Yuriko Hoshi, Reiko Dan, Ken Uehara, Yoko Fujiyama, Akemi Kita, Machiko Naka, Tatsuyoshi Ebara, Asami Kuzi, Ichiro Arishima, Choko Ida.

Romantic melodrama. Yuichi, a college student and star swimmer, has problems both with his family and his love life. At home, he often quarrels with his old-fashioned father but is the favorite of his grandmother. Yuichi invites Sumiko to a dance, but when she arrives, he is so busy leading the band and socializing with his friends that she leaves with Shinjiro, his rival. Back at home, Yuichi finds his spendthrift sister has secretly stolen funds from their father's restaurant. Yuichi tries to replace the money with his own funds, but his sister confesses the theft and the father, blaming Yuichi for not telling the family, throws him out of the house. He moves to a resort town and takes a job as a lifeguard. After he rescues from drowning the daughter of a local millionaire, the man offers his daughter's hand in marriage as a reward. Yuichi, who has reconciled with Sumiko, refuses the offer, but Sumiko learns of the proposal and once again Yuichi is without a girl friend. At the intercollegiate swimming meet, Yuichi is told just before the big race that his grandmother has been hit by a car driven by Shinjiro. In spite of the pressure, he wins the race and Sumiko returns to him. *Students. Grandmothers. Millionaires. Lifeguards. Family life. Courtship. Jealousy. Theft. Swimming. Automobile accidents. Resorts.*

Note: Released in Japan in 1962 as *Daigaku no wakadaisho*.

BULLET FOR A BADMAN   F6.0590

Gordon Kay & Associates. *Dist* Universal Pictures. 2 Sep **1964** [Los Angeles opening; c29 Sep 1964; LP34784]. Sd (Westrex); col (Eastman Color by Pathé). 35mm. 80 min.

Prod Gordon Kay. *Dir* R. G. Springsteen. *Screenplay* Mary Willingham, Willard Willingham. *Dir Photog* Joseph Biroc. *Art Dir* Alexander Golitzen, Henry Bumstead. *Set Decor* Oliver Emert. *Film Ed* Russell F. Schoengarth. *Mus* Frank Skinner. *Mus Supv* Joseph Gershenson. *Sd* Waldon O. Watson, Joe Lapis. *Asst Dir* Phil Bowles, Carl Beringer. *Unit Prod Mgr* Howard Pine. *Cost Supv* Edward Armand, Olive Koenitz. *Makeup* Bud Westmore. *Hairstyles* Larry Germain.

Cast: Audie Murphy *(Logan Keliher)*, Darren McGavin *(Sam Ward)*, Ruta Lee *(Lottie)*, Beverley Owen *(Susan)*, Skip Homeier *(Pink)*, George Tobias *(Diggs)*, Alan Hale, [Jr.] *(Leach)*, Berkeley Harris *(Jeff)*, Edward Platt *(Tucker)*, Kevin Tate *(Sammy)*, Cece Whitney *(Goldie)*, Mort Mills, Buff Brady, Bob Steele, Ray Teal.

Western drama. Source: Marvin H. Albert, *Renegade Posse* (New York, 1958). Sam Ward, serving a life sentence for murder, escapes to kill Logan Keliher. Former Texas Rangers who fought together, they became enemies when Sam turned bank robber. Animosity between them was intensified when Logan married Sam's ex-wife, Susan, and accepted their son as his own. The two men accidentally meet in the town of Griffin when Sam's gang holds up the bank while Logan is arranging for a loan. Although the rest of his gang is killed, Sam escapes and visits Susan to warn her that he plans to have revenge on her new husband. Logan eventually captures Sam but is forced to untie him when they are attacked by Apaches. They survive the raid, but both men are badly wounded and Logan takes Sam to his shack, where he sees his son for the first time. Pink, a conniving posse member, arrives and tries to take the bank loot. Sam takes a bullet meant for Logan, and after Logan has killed Pink, Sam dies in his former buddy's arms, but not before the two men have been reunited in friendship. *Texas Rangers. Outlaws. Gangs. Apache Indians. Posses. Stepfathers. Prison escapes. Murder. Revenge. Bank robberies. Jealousy. Fatherhood. Self-sacrifice. Friendship.*

Note: Location scenes filmed in Utah. Working title: *Renegade Posse.*

BULLET FOR BILLY THE KID (Mexico)   F6.0591

Alameda Films. *Dist* A. D. P. Productions. Nov **1963**. Sd; col (Eastman Color). 35mm. 61 min.

Prod Alfred Ripstein, Jr. *Prod English Vers* Jerry Warren. *Dir* Rafael Baledón. *Screenplay* Ramón Obón. *Photog* Raúl Martínez Solares. *Film Ed* Juan José Marino. *Mus* Gustavo César Carrión. *Sd* Rodolfo Solís.

Cast: Gaston Sands, Steve Brodie, Lloyd Nelson, Marla Blaine, Richard McIntyre, Gilbert Cramer, Rita Mace, Peter Gillon.

Western melodrama. Having decided to start a new life, Billy the Kid starts his dangerous 1,000-mile journey to a ranch that he and his sister own. Plagued and trailed by both lawmen and gunslingers, he writes his sister to have friends on guard at the ranch. No sooner does he arrive than the killers, who have intercepted the letter, surround the ranch. Escaping into the night after a blazing gun battle, he realizes that Billy the Kid can never find peace. *Outlaws. Gunfighters. Ranches. William H. Bonney.*

## A BULLET FOR PRETTY BOY								F6.0592

American International Pictures. 15 Jul 1970 [Dallas opening; c15 Jul 1970; LP38507]. Sd; col (print by Movielab). 35mm. 88 min. [Cut from 91 min?] *MPAA rating GP.*

A Larry Buchanan Production. *Prod-Dir* Larry Buchanan. *Screenplay* Henry Rosenbaum. *Story* Enrique Touceda, Larry Buchanan. *Dir Photog* James R. Davidson. *Film Ed* Miguel Levin. *Mus Score* Harley Hatcher. *Mus Supv* Al Simms. *Theme Song:* "It's Me I'm Running From" Harley Hatcher, Guy Hemric. *Song:* "I'm Gonna Love You ('Til I Die)" Harley Hatcher. *Song:* "Gone Tomorrow" Richard Bowen. *Song* "Ruby, Ruby" Richard Bowen, Harold Finch, Jr., Robert Gilly, Danny Heald. *Songs Perf by* The Source. *Sd* Lawrence Gianneschi, Sr. *Script Supv* Joretta Cherry. *Wardrobe* Ron Scott. *Makeup Artist* Lynn Brooks. *Ch Electrn* Robert Creasy. *Key Grip* R. H. Christensen, Sr.

Cast: Fabian Forte *(Charles "Pretty Boy" Floyd)*, Jocelyn Lane *(Betty)*, Astrid Warner *(Ruby)*, Michael Haynes *(Ned Short)*, Adam Roarke *("Preacher")*, Robert Glenn *(Hossler)*, Anne MacAdams *(Beryl)*, Camilla Carr *(Helen)*, Jeff Alexander, actor *(Wallace)*, Desmond Dhooge *(Harvey)*, Bill Thurman *(Huddy)*, Hugh Feagin *(Jack Dowler)*, Jessie Lee Fulton *(Mrs. Floyd)*, James Harrell *(Mr. Floyd)*, Gene Ross *(William)*, Ed Lo Russo *(Bo)*, Charlie Dell *(Charlie)*, Eddie Thomas *(Ben Dowler)*, Frank DeBenedett *(Lester Floyd)*, Ethan Allen *(Seth)*, Troy K. Hoskins *(Sheriff Taylor)*, Lucky Mosley, Charles Redding, David Beuret, Walt Becklund, Ron Scott *(deputies)*.

Crime melodrama. At a reception following his wedding, Oklahoma farmer Charles Floyd demands an apology from Jack Dowler for insulting his bride, Ruby; Dowler's references to his previous sexual relations with Ruby force Charles to beat an apology out of the intruder. Dowler swears revenge for his public humiliation, and that night he tries to ambush Charles but accidentally kills his rival's father. When Charles goes to Dowler's farm the next morning to elicit a confession, they fight and Dowler is killed. Consequently, Charles is convicted of manslaughter and sent to prison. Four years later he escapes and seeks refuge in a Kansas City brothel run by Beryl, where Betty, one of the prostitutes, is attracted to him. Her affection infuriates Beryl's brother Wallace, who is in love with Betty, and in retaliation, he starts referring to Charles as "Pretty Boy," a nickname that gains national acceptance when Charles joins Ned Short's gang of bank robbers. After several bank holdups, Pretty Boy is captured, but he kills a guard and escapes from the train taking him to jail. He returns to Oklahoma for a brief reunion with Ruby, but even though they are still in love, she realizes that she cannot live the kind of life her husband must now live. "Preacher," a local drunkard, accompanies Pretty Boy back to Beryl's, where they join Betty and Ned Short's gang in a widely publicized crime spree. Short and Preacher are killed in a police stakeout, however, and Pretty Boy and Betty escape to a shack near his old home. After a last goodbye with Ruby, the gang's two survivors rob Pretty Boy's hometown bank. Betty escapes, but Pretty Boy is trapped in a ranch house and dies in a hail of bullets. *Farmers. Gangsters. Fugitives. Prostitutes. Police. Preachers. Revenge. Manslaughter. Murder. Prison escapes. Jealousy. Bank robberies. Alcoholism. Weddings. Whorehouses. Oklahoma. Kansas City (Missouri). Charles "Pretty Boy" Floyd.*

Note: Filmed on location in Texas.

## A BULLET FOR SANDOVAL (Italy/Spain)					F6.0593

Leone Film–Daiano Film–Atlántida Films. *Dist* U-M Film Distributors. caJun 1970. Sd; col (Eastman Color, print by Movielab). 35mm. 91 min. *MPAA rating GP.*

Pres by UMC Pictures. *Prod* Elio Scardamaglia, Ugo Guerra. *Dir* Julio Buchs. *Screenplay-Story* Ugo Guerra, José Luis Martínez Mollá, Federico de Urrutia, Julio Buchs. *Photog* Francisco Sempere. *Art Dir* José Luis Galicia, Jaime Pérez Cubero, Giancarlo Bartolini Salimbeni. *Set Decor* Giuseppe Bassan. *Film Ed* Daniele Alabiso, Magdalena Pulido. *Mus Comp & Dir* Gianni Ferrio. *Sd* Antonio Forrest. *Prod Mgr* Domenico De Martino, Valentin Panero. *Wardrobe* Peris.

Cast: Ernest Borgnine *(Don Pedro Sandoval)*, George Hilton *(Warner)*, Alberto de Mendoza *(Lucky Boy)*, Leo Anchóriz *(Padre)*, Antonio Pica *(Sam)*, José Manuel Martín *(cross-eyed man)*, Manuel de Blas *(Gonzales)*, Manuel Miranda *(Francisco)*, Gustavo Rojo *(Guadalupano)*, Annabella Incontrera *(Rosa)*, Andrea Aureli *(Morton)*, José Guardiola, Claudio Trionfo, Alfonso Rojas.

Western melodrama. Warner deserts the Confederate Army when he learns that Rosa, the Mexican woman he loves, is ill with cholera and about to give birth to his child. Recaptured by the Confederates and placed on a burial detail, he escapes with his friends Lucky Boy and Sam and travels to Rosa's hometown near the Mexican border, where a cholera epidemic now rages. Don Pedro

Sandoval, Rosa's father, who had forbidden her to marry Warner because he was a "gringo," informs him of her death and drives him away with his newborn son. Joined by an ex-monk, Warner and his friends are unable to obtain food. A farmer, fearful of exposure to cholera, spills a pail of milk rather than give it to the baby. The infant dies, and Warner swears revenge, drowning the farmer in a trough filled with milk and raiding the countryside with a desperado band. Sandoval's oldest son is killed, and his body dumped on Sandoval's doorstep. As Warner and his men flee to Mexico, Sandoval pursues the outlaw, and during a religious festival the two men confront each other. Fighting with knives on a catwalk over a bullpen, both men fall into the ring, and Sandoval is gored to death. Warner and his band find themselves trapped in the arena, surrounded by a troop of Mexican soldiers. The outlaws begin to fire against hopeless odds and are gunned down. *Mexicans. Desperadoes. Gravediggers. Infants. Deserters—Military. Monks. Revenge. Cholera. Epidemics. Prejudice. Murder. Starvation. Bullfighting. Childbirth. United States—History—Civil War. Mexican border.*

Note: Filmed in 1969; location scenes filmed in Almería, Spain. Released in Spain and Italy in Techniscope. Spanish title: *Los desesperados*; running time: 100 min. Italian title: *Quei disperati che puzzano di sudore e di morte.*

## A BULLET FOR THE GENERAL (Italy)					F6.0594

M. C. M. *Dist* Avco Embassy Pictures. Sep 1968 [New York opening: 30 Apr 1969]. Sd; col (Technicolor, print by Pathé). 35mm (Techniscope). 115 min.

Prod Bianco Manini. *Dir* Damiano Damiani. *Story & Screenplay* Salvatore Laurani. *Adapt & Dial* Franco Solinas, Damiano Damiani. *Photog* Antonio Secchi. *Art Dir* Sergio Canevari. *Film Ed* Renato Cinquini. *Mus* Luis Enriquez Bacalov. *Mus Supv* Ennio Morricone. *Sd* Renato Cinquini. *Prod Mgr* Ofelia Minaldi, Ferruccio De Martino. *Cost* Marilu Carteny.

Cast: Gian Maria Volontè *(El Chuncho)*, Lou Castel *(Bill Tate)*, Klaus Kinski *(El Santo)*, Martine Beswick *(Adelita)*, Jaime Fernández *(General Elias)*, Andrea Checchi *(Don Felipe)*, Spartaco Conversi *(Cirillo)*, Joaquín Parra *(Picaro)*, José Manuel Martín *(Raimundo)*, Santiago Santos *(Guapo)*, Valentino Macchi *(Pedrito)*, Carla Gravina *(Felipe's wife)*, Aldo Sambrell.

Action melodrama. During the 1910 Mexican revolution, a band of guerrillas led by El Chuncho attack a train carrying government arms, troops, and munitions. Bill Tate, an American passenger, helps the revolutionaries by killing the train's engineer. El Chuncho then seizes the munitions and rides off, taking along Tate, whom he has been told is a criminal awaiting execution. With Tate now part of his rebel army, El Chuncho steals more weapons and sets out to sell them to General Elias of the revolutionary army. En route the guerrillas stop at San Miguel, a revolutionary stronghold that is facing a military attack. Tate and several other guerrillas, convinced that the town will be destroyed, desert their leader. El Chuncho is persuaded to leave and proceeds to General Elias's camp with the weapons. At the general's headquarters, however, El Chuncho is accused of treason and sentenced to death. Accepting his fate, El Chuncho asks that he be executed by his brother El Santo, a religious fanatic. But Tate kills El Santo and shoots General Elias with a golden bullet, thereby revealing that he was hired by the Mexican government to kill the revolutionary general. Tate receives a reward and offers to share it with El Chuncho, provided the latter will help to form a civil union. El Chuncho refuses to compromise his principles, however, and while singing a revolutionary hymn, he kills the startled American. *Mexicans. Guerrillas. Revolutionaries. Americans in foreign countries. Train robberies. Treason. Assassination. Mexico—History—1910-17. Mexico—Army.*

Note: Filmed in Spain. Released in Italy in 1967 as *Quien sabe?*; running time: 135 min.

## BULLET WOUND (Japan)								F6.0595

Toho Co. *Dist* Toho International, Inc. 28 Mar 1970 [Los Angeles showing]. Sd; col (Eastmancolor). 35mm. 94 min.

Exec Prod Tomohiro Kaiyama. *Dir* Shiro Moritani. *Screenplay* Hidekazu Nagahara. *Camera* Takao Saito. *Art Dir* Yoshiro Muraki. *Mus* Toru Takemitsu.

Cast: Yuzo Kayama *(Takimura)*, Kiwako Taichi *(Saori)*, Kei Sato, Eiji Okada.

Melodrama. Terrorists attacking a special U. S. envoy are thwarted by a sniper in a helicopter who sends their car hurtling over a cliff. The sniper is Takimura, a Nisei CIA agent assigned to Japan. Takimura next helps Yang, a trade show delegate from the People's Republic of China, seek asylum in the U. S. Embassy. A Chinese sniper fires at Takimura but instead wounds Saori, a sculptress. After Takimura kills a North Korean who is revealed to be a Chinese spy, the CIA senses that the spy is connected with Yang's defection and forces him to admit that the delegation has come to Japan to buy arms from American gunrunner Tony Rose. Challenged to a duel by the sniper who wounded Saori, Takimura kills his opponent. Dying, the sniper reveals that Yang lied to the CIA and identified the wrong man as Tony Rose; the real Tony Rose was hospitalized after completing the deal. Saori, with whom Takimura is having an affair, tries to convince the agent to quit his job and move with her to South America, but Takimura hunts down Rose and kills him; however, CIA agents kill Takimura when he next meets with Saori. *Nisei. Americans in foreign countries. Gunrunners. Secret agents. Sculptors. Chinese. Perfidy. Duels. People's Republic of China. United States—Central Intelligence Agency.*

Note: Released in Japan in Sep 1969 as *Dankon.*

BULLITT   F6.0596

Solar Productions. *Dist* Warner Bros.–Seven Arts, Inc. 17 Oct **1968** [New York opening; c1 Dec 1968; LP38106]. Sd; col (Technicolor). 35mm. 114 min. *MPAA rating* M.

Prod Philip D'Antoni. *Exec Prod* Robert E. Relyea. *Dir* Peter Yates. *Screenplay* Alan R. Trustman, Harry Kleiner. *Dir Photog* William A. Fraker. *Art Dir* Albert Brenner. *Set Decor* Ralph S. Hurst, Philip Abramson. *Main Titl* Pablo Ferro Films. *Film Ed* Frank P. Keller. *Asst Ed* Ralph H. Martin. *Mus* Lalo Schifrin. *Sd* John Kean. *Asst Dir* Tim Zinnemann, Daisy Gerber. *Prod Mgr* Jack N. Reddish. *Unit Mgr* Joe L. Cramer. *Script Supv* Marshall Wolins. *Cost Dsgn* Theadora Van Runkle. *Cost* Alan Levine. *Makeup* Emile LaVigne. *Hairstyles* Pat Davey. *Sp Eff* Sass Bedig.

Cast: Steve McQueen *(Frank Bullitt)*, Robert Vaughn *(Walter Chalmers)*, Jacqueline Bisset *(Cathy)*, Don Gordon *(Delgetti)*, Robert Duvall *(Weissberg)*, Simon Oakland *(Captain Bennett)*, Norman Fell *(Captain Baker)*, Carl Reindel *(Stanton)*, Felice Orlandi *(Renick)*, Pat Renella *(Johnny Ross)*, Georg Stanford Brown *(Dr. Willard)*, Justin Tarr *(Eddy, the informer)*, Victor Tayback *(Peter Ross)*, Paul Genge *(hired killer)*, Ed Peck *(Wescott)*, Robert Lipton *(1st aide)*, John Aprea *(killer)*, Al Checco *(desk clerk)*, Bill Hickman *(Phill)*.

Crime melodrama. Source: Robert L. Pike, *Mute Witness* (Garden City, New York, 1963). Chicago hoodlum Johnny Ross defrauds his Mafia associates and escapes to San Francisco where he agrees to testify before a Senate subcommittee on crime headed by ambitious politician Walter Chalmers. At the request of Chalmers, Det. Lieut. Frank Bullitt is assigned to protect Ross who is hiding out in a dilapidated hotel; two gunmen manage to enter Ross's room, however, and seriously wound him. Chalmers then warns Bullitt that he will destroy his career if Ross dies. When Ross is stabbed to death in the hospital, Bullitt persuades a member of the hospital staff, Dr. Willard, to help conceal the death, and he sets out to investigate the case. The Mafia gangsters follow him, but Bullitt escapes in an automobile chase through San Francisco that ends when the Mafia car crashes into a gasoline pump and explodes. Despite the objections of his girl friend Cathy, Bullitt retraces Ross's movements and eventually learns that the dead man was a decoy, and that the real Ross plans to leave the country under the name of Albert Renick. Tracing a phone call Ross had made to a San Mateo motel, Bullitt drives there with Cathy and finds a murdered woman with $30,000 in traveler's checks made out to Albert and Dorothy Renick. Bullitt then learns that Ross has booked a seat on a night plane to London. He races to stop him at the airport, but runs into Chalmers, who admits that he sent him to guard the wrong man and demands that the real Ross be taken alive. After an angry exchange with Chalmers, Bullitt goes after Ross, chases him from a departing plane onto the runway, and finally kills him as he tries to escape. *Gangsters. Detectives. Police. Physicians. Politicians. Perfidy. Murder. Imposture. Hotels. Hospitals. Airfields. San Francisco. San Mateo. United States Congress. Mafia. Chases. Automobile accidents.*

Note: Location scenes filmed in San Francisco.

BUMERANG *see* **CRY DOUBLE CROSS**

BUNDFALD *see* **SIN ALLEY**

BUNNY & CLOD   F6.0597

Kingslee Film. *Dist* Grads Corp. 15 Apr **1970** [Champaign, Illinois, showing]. Sd; col. 35mm. 62 min.

Prod Robert A. Poore. *Exec Prod* James Randel Kingslee. *Prod Mgr* Kelly Ross.

Cast: Diane Evans, Joe Brock, Kathy Feirek, Casey Larrain.

Comedy. On a hot East Texas day, Bunny sets out to release his girl friend and partner in crime, Clod, from the Cooz City jail. With Sheriff Hammerhead, pride of the East Texas Rangers, hot on his trail, Bunny gives a lift to a young hitchhiking couple. He then proceeds to assault the girl sexually in the back seat while her boyfriend is forced to drive the car. Later, at a filling station, Bunny makes love with two young ladies before Sheriff Hammerhead catches up with him. Bunny makes his escape while the women detain the sheriff. Bunny then enters the Cooz City jail disguised in women's clothes in order to find Clod. After observing a lesbian encounter between two inmates, Bunny successfully frees Clod, and they speed away. Sheriff Hammerhead and a posse eventually catch up with the two, however, and they take care of them in the gangster tradition. *Gangsters. Sheriffs. Hitchhikers. Lesbianism. Prison escapes. Filling stations. Texas. Texas Rangers.*

BUNNY BLOSSOM FOR PRESIDENT   F6.0598

Topar Productions. *Dist* Probe Films. Feb **1970** [Los Angeles showing]. Sd; col. 16mm. [Feature film, length unknown.]

Comedy. Bunny Blossom runs for president of her college, because she very much wants to head the student body. *College life.*

BUNNY LAKE IS MISSING (Great Britain)   F6.0599

Wheel Productions. *Dist* Columbia Pictures. 3 Oct **1965** [New York opening; c1 Oct 1965; LP32274]. Sd (Westrex); b&w. 35mm (Panavision). 107 min.

Pres by Otto Preminger. *Prod-Dir* Otto Preminger. *Assoc Prod* Martin C. Schute. *Screenplay* John Mortimer, Penelope Mortimer. *Dir Photog* Denys Coop. *Camera Op* Gerry Fisher. *Camera Grip* Dick Savery. *Set Decor* Elven Webb, Scott Slimon. *Prod Dsgn* Don Ashton. *Main Titl* Saul Bass. *Film Ed* Peter Thornton. *Mus* Paul Glass. *Sd Rec* Claude Hitchcock, Red Law. *Sd Ed* Jonathan Bates. *Mus Ed* Valerie Lesser. *Asst Dir* Bryan Coates, Bernie Williams, Ivo Nightingale. *Cont Supv* Pam Carlton. *Prod Mgr* Eva Monley, Douglas Peirce. *Asst to the Prod* Max Slater. *Prod Sec* Noreen Hipwell. *Wardrobe Master* Ray Beck. *Cost Coörd* Hope Bryce. *Wardrobe Mistress* Evelyn Gibbs. *Makeup* Neville Smallwood. *Hairdressing* Maud Onslow. *Sp Eff* Charles Staffell. *Casting* James Liggat. *Ch Electrn* Peter Carey. *Prop Master* Henry Newman.

Cast—In Order of Appearance: Keir Dullea *(Steven)*, Carol Lynley *(Ann)*, Lucie Mannheim *(cook)*, Noel Coward *(Wilson)*, Delphi Lawrence, Suzanne Neve *(mothers at school)*, Adrienne Corri *(Dorothy)*, Kika Markham *(nurse)*, Jill Melford *(teacher)*, Anna Massey *(Elvira Smollet)*, Martita Hunt *(Ada Ford)*, Laurence Olivier *(Newhouse)*, Clive Revill *(Sergeant Andrews)*, Damaris Hayman *(Daphne)*, Patrick Jordan *(policeman)*, Jane Evers *(policewoman)*, John Sharp *(fingerprint man)*, Geoffrey Frederick *(police photographer)*, Percy Herbert *(policeman at station)*, Michael Wynne *(Rogers)*, Bill Maxam *(barman)*, Tim Brinton *(newscaster)*, The Zombies *(themselves)*, Victor Maddern *(taxi driver)*, Fred Emney *(man in Soho)*, Finlay Currie *(doll maker)*, Richard Wattis *(clerk in shipping office)*, David Oxley *(doctor)*, John Forbes-Robertson *(hospital attendant)*, Megs Jenkins *(hospital sister)*, Suky Appleby *(Bunny)*.

Mystery melodrama. Source: Evelyn Piper, *Bunny Lake Is Missing* (New York, 1957). Ann Lake arrives in London from America to join her brother, Steven, a journalist. She hurriedly enrolls her illegitimate, 4-year-old child, Bunny, in a nursery school and sees only the waiting room and the school cook. When Ann returns to the school to collect Bunny, the child is missing—none of the staff has seen her, and the cook has walked out on her job. Police Inspector Newhouse is called in and attempts to put some clues together. He finds that he is not quite sure that Bunny even exists. Steven seems more concerned about Ann's mind than about the child; nobody at the school has ever heard of Bunny; all of Bunny's possessions that Ann claims were in the new house are missing; and Ann once had an imaginary playmate named Bunny. Nearly in shock, Ann finds a repair stub for one of Bunny's dolls that leads her to a doll repair shop. Before she can take the evidence to the police, she is knocked unconscious by Steven, who steals the doll and burns it. Ann is taken to a hospital, but she escapes in time to see Steven take Bunny, drugged, from his car trunk. He is about to strangle her when Ann diverts his attention and suggests to him moments from their childhood when he, possessive of his sister, tried to destroy her imaginary playmate. She keeps Steven occupied with children's games until the police, at last aware of the truth, arrive to take him away. *Journalists. Children. Cooks. Police. Americans in foreign countries. Illegitimacy. Brother-sister relationship. Missing persons. Abduction. Mental illness. Child care—Day nurseries. Dolls. London.*

Note: Filmed on location in London. Opened in London in Feb 1966.

BUNNY YEAGER'S NUDE CAMERA   F6.0600

Dist Cinema Syndicate, Inc. 28 May **1963** [New York showing]. Sd; col (Eastman Color). 35mm. 73 min.

Prod-Dir Barry Mahon. *Photog* Barry Mahon. *Asst Dir* Sande Johnsen. *Optical Eff* B & O Film Specialists.

Cast: Bunny Yeager, Lisa Winters, John Nevins, Davee Decker.

Comedy-drama. Bunny Yeager, an ex-model and photographer of nudes, notices a beautiful girl on a bus and tries to convince her to model for her. Lisa is hesitant, but after observing Bunny at work in her studio during the day, she agrees to model pending her boyfriend's approval. Meanwhile, Bunny receives a proposal from a men's magazine: they will pay $15,000, to be split between photographer and model, for the most beautiful pinup photograph in the world. Convinced that Lisa is the girl for the job, Bunny is relieved when Lisa assents. Bunny neglects her husband and children, who would like to see more of her, and spends the next several days hard at work in her studio. On the day of the magazine's deadline, Bunny rushes to the airport to mail the photographs. She starts to go home, but she stops to convince a glamorous stewardess to model for her. *Photographers. Models. Airline stewardesses. Photographs. Nudity.*

Magazines (periodicals).

Note: Filmed in Miami. Also known as *Nude Camera.*

BUNNY YEAGER'S NUDE LAS VEGAS   F6.0601

Barry Mahon Productions. *Dist* Cinema Syndicate, Inc. 19 Feb **1964** [Trade review]. Sd; col (Eastman Color). 35mm. 69 min.

A Barry Mahon Production. *Prod-Dir* Barry Mahon. *Screenplay* Maurice McEndree. *Photog* Barry Mahon. *Film Ed* Maurice McEndree. *Mus Comp* Henri Woode. *Sd* Al Ruban. *Asst Dir* Sande N. Johnsen. *Script Clerk* Clelle Mahon.

Cast: Bunny Yeager *(herself),* Bud Irwin, Peggy Pepper, Maurice McEndree, Al Ruban.

Comedy-drama. Bunny Yeager, a prominent photographer of nudes, goes to Las Vegas with her husband for a vacation. While Charlie, a tout, escorts them around the clubs and casinos, they meet a friend of Bunny's from Miami. The friend is waiting for her husband, who will join her to celebrate their first wedding anniversary, and she has squandered her expense money at the dice table. Though her husband is very wealthy, he cannot tolerate gambling. Now she is trying desperately to replace the money before his arrival. In order to help, Bunny gives up her vacation to produce a magazine layout for a New York editor, featuring her friend, who has never modeled before. The two set out to complete the assignment as quickly as possible. With Charlie's help, they round up the best-known showgirls to use as background for the feature. They mail the exposed film to the publisher and await the money. The friend's husband sends a telegram to say that he will arrive a day early. After some desperate maneuvering to cover up, they replace the money at the last minute. *Photographers. Showgirls. Models. Gambling. Nudity. Finance—Personal. Magazines (periodicals). Wedding anniversaries. Las Vegas.*

Note: Also known as *Nude Las Vegas.*

BUONA SERA, MRS. CAMPBELL   F6.0602

Connaught Productions. *Dist* United Artists. 12 Feb **1969** [New York opening; c20 Dec 1968; LP36624]. Sd; col (Technicolor). 35mm. 111 min. *MPAA rating* M.

A Melvin Frank Production. *Prod-Dir* Melvin Frank. *Exec Prod* C. O. Erickson. *2d Unit Dir* Robert L. Lawrence. *Screenplay* Melvin Frank, Denis Norden, Sheldon Keller. *Photog* Gabor Pogany. *Art Dir* Arrigo Equini. *Set Decor* Giuseppe Chevalier. *Film Ed* William Butler. *Mus Comp & Cond* Riz Ortolani. *Song:* "Buona Sera, Mrs. Campbell" Melvin Frank, Andrew Frank, Riz Ortolani. *Sung by* Jimmy Roselli. *Sd* David Hildyard. *Sd Ed* Wally Nelson. *Asst Dir* Franco Cirino. *Prod Mgr* Giorgio Zambon, Luciano Piperno. *Wardrobe Dsgn* Morton Haack. *Makeup* Amato Garbini.

Cast: Gina Lollobrigida *(Carla [Mrs. Campbell]),* Shelley Winters *(Shirley Newman),* Phil Silvers *(Phil Newman),* Peter Lawford *(Justin Young),* Telly Savalas *(Walter Braddock),* Lee Grant *(Fritzie Braddock),* Janet Margolin *(Gia),* Marian Moses *(Lauren Young),* Naomi Stevens *(Rosa),* Philippe Leroy *(Vittorio),* Giovanna Galletti *(countess),* Renzo Palmer *(mayor),* Dale Cummings *(Pete),* James Mishler *(Stubby).*

Comedy. Source: Aiken Morewood, "Buona Sera, Mrs. Campbell" (publication undetermined). During World War II, a young Italian girl (Carla) "comforted" three members of the U. S. Army Air Force at her home in the village of San Forino. When she found herself pregnant shortly after their squadron was transferred, Carla wrote each of the three men a letter implying that he was the father. And each responded by promising to send her a monthly allotment check. To save face in her village, Carla made up an imaginary husband, named him Capt. Eddie Campbell after a can of American soup and then claimed he was killed in action. With the three monthly checks coming in regularly for the past 20 years, Carla has been able to live comfortably and send her daughter, Gia, to a fashionable Swiss boarding school. But now she learns that the three men—Phil Newman, Justin Young, and Walter Braddock—are bringing their wives and children to San Forino for a squadron reunion. Stunned by the realization that each man will expect to see his child, Carla's distress turns to panic when she discovers that her lover, Vittorio, has suggested to Gia that she return for the happy event and meet her father's Air Force buddies. When one and all descend on the village, Carla makes a gallant attempt to preserve everyone's illusions—but to no avail, for Gia and the three couples learn the truth about Mrs. Campbell and her "dead" husband. Once their anger has subsided, however, the men and their wives share a paternal concern when the heartbroken girl runs off to join a married man on a trip to Brazil. Racing after the fleeing girl, they bring her back to San Forino for the dedication of the chapel the squadron is presenting to the village. At the ceremony, Carla tries to confess the truth, but she is stopped by the Americans, who have united to preserve the name of "Captain Campbell" and his courageous "wife." *Veterans. Widows. Italians. Illegitimacy. Reunions. Village life. Motherhood. World War II. Italy. United States Army—Air Force.*

Note: Filmed in Italy.

IL BUONO, IL BRUTTO, IL CATTIVO *see* THE GOOD, THE BAD, AND THE UGLY

BURABO! YANGU GAI *see* BRAVO, YOUNG GUY

BURAIKAN *see* THE SCANDALOUS ADVENTURES OF BURAIKAN

BURARI BURABURA MONOGATARI *see* MY HOBO

THE BURMESE HARP (Japan)   F6.0603

Nikkatsu Corp. *Dist* Brandon Films. 28 Apr **1967** [New York opening]. Sd; b&w. 35mm. 116 min.

Prod Masayuki Takagi. *Dir* Kon Ichikawa. *Screenplay* Natto Wada. *Orig Story* Michio Takeyama. *Photog* Minoru Yokoyama. *Art Dir* Takashi Matsuyama. *Film Ed* Masanori Tsujii. *Mus* Akira Ifukube. *Sd* Masakazu Kamiya.

Cast: Shoji Yasui *(Private Mizushima),* Rentaro Mikuni *(Captain Inouye),* Tatsuya Mihashi *(defense commander),* Tanie Kitabayashi *(old woman),* Yunosuke Ito *(village head).*

War drama. Private Mizushima is part of a Japanese fighting unit stationed in Burma during the final days of World War II. Popular with his fellow soldiers, he often plays for them on a handmade Burmese harp, which he also occasionally uses as a warning signal. When the war ends and the British move his unit to a prisoner-of-war camp at Mudan, Mizushima volunteers to persuade a garrison of mountain fighters to surrender. He fails in his mission; the garrison is destroyed, and he barely escapes with his life. After being nursed back to health by a Buddhist monk, Mizushima takes one of the monk's robes and sets out on the long road back to Mudon. Along the way, he passes countless battlefields strewn with the corpses of his dead countrymen, and whenever he is able, he buries or burns their bodies. Before reaching his destination, he is deeply moved by the scene of a group of British soldiers and nurses holding a memorial service for unknown Japanese dead. When he arrives at Mudan, the men of his unit are uncertain as to whether or not this mysterious monk is their friend. On the day of their departure for Japan, however, they learn that Mizushima has resolved to remain in Burma to bury the thousands of Japanese soldiers killed in battle. *Monks. Prisoners of war. Harpists. Combat zone life. Disguise. Death. Rites and ceremonies. World War II. Burma. Japan—Army. Great Britain—Army.*

Note: Released in Japan in 1956 as *Biruma no tategoto.*

BURN! (France/Italy)   F6.0604

P. E. A.–Les Productions Artistes Associés. *Dist* United Artists. 21 Oct **1970** [New York opening; c19 Dec 1969; LF76]. Sd; col (De Luxe, print by Technicolor). 35mm. 112 min. *MPAA rating* GP.

Prod Alberto Grimaldi. *Dir* Gillo Pontecorvo. *Screenplay* Franco Solinas, Giorgio Arlorio. *Story* Gillo Pontecorvo, Franco Solinas, Giorgio Arlorio. *Photog* Marcello Gatti, Giuseppe Ruzzolini. *Camera Op* Otello Spila, Elio Polacchi. *Art Dir* Sergio Canevari. *Set Decor* Francesco Bronzi. *Prod Dsgn* Piero Gherardi. *Supv Film Ed* Enzo Ocone. *Film Ed* Mario Morra. *Mus* Ennio Morricone. *Mus Dir* Bruno Nicolai. *Sd Rec* Eugenio Rondani. *1st & 2d Asst Dir* Rinaldo Ricci, Salvo Basile. *Prod Supv* Mario Del Papa. *Unit Mgr* Sergio Merolle, Averoe Stefani. *Script Clerk* Annamaria Montanari. *Cost* Piero Gherardi. *Wardrobe Coörd* Marilu Carteny. *Makeup* Mauro Gavazzi. *Marlon Brando's Makeup* Phil Rhodes. *Hairdresser* Anna Graziosi. *Sp Eff* Aldo Gasparri. *Armaments Cons* Alessandro Sozzi. *Percussion Adv* Franco Giordano. *Constr Supv* Franco Vanorio. *Set Constr* Alvaro Belsole. *Props* Carlo Ferri. *Dial Coach* Anna Korda. *Marlon Brando's Dial Coach* Sam Gilman.

Cast: Marlon Brando *(Sir William Walker),* Evaristo Marquez *(José Dolores),* Renato Salvatori *(Teddy Sanchez),* Norman Hill *(Shelton),* Tom Lyons *(General Prada),* Wanani *(Guarina),* Joseph Persaud *(Juanito),* Giampiero Albertini *(Henry),* Carlo Palmucci *(Jack),* Cecily Browne *(Lady Bella),* Dana Ghia *(Francesca),* Mauricio Rodriguez *(Ramon),* Alejandro Obregon *(English major).*

Drama. In 1845 Sir William Walker is sent to the Caribbean island of Queimada by the British government to disrupt the Portuguese colonial sugar monopoly. Taking notice of the execution of Santiago, the leader of a slave insurrection, Sir William decides to foment a revolt under the leadership of José Dolores, a dock porter. Sir William first persuades Dolores to commit a bullion robbery, which forces him to massacre pursuing Portuguese troops. Soon slaves from the plantations join Dolores' band of robbers, and Teddy Sanchez, the liberal spokesman for the plantation owners, is persuaded by Sir William to assassinate the Portuguese governor and thereby gain independence for the colonists. The insurrection succeeds, but after Sir William convinces Dolores that he lacks the economic knowledge necessary to run the country, the plantation owners gain control, and the slaves return to chopping sugar cane. His mission completed, Sir William leaves Queimada to continue his work elsewhere. Ten years later Sir William, a drunken derelict in London, is recruited by the British Sugar Company to put down another revolt led by

Dolores. He returns to Queimada to lead British troops against Dolores, whom he himself had trained in guerrilla warfare. When Teddy Sanchez, the present governor of Queimada, objects to Sir William's ruthless tactics, Sir William has him assassinated and helps establish a military dictatorship. Eventually, Sir William captures Dolores and offers him clemency if he will leave the island, but Dolores rejects the offer; understanding Sir William's mode of operation, he prefers to be executed and thus serve his cause. The insurrection is finally quelled, and Sir William prepares to leave the island, but he is assassinated by a dock porter who offers to carry his bags. *British. Foreign agents. Portuguese. Landed gentry. Revolutionaries. Guerrillas. Colonial administration. Imperialism. Slavery. Robbery. Revolts. Assassination. Coups d'état. Alcoholism. Military government. Capital punishment. Islands. Plantations. Sugar. Caribbean. London.*

Note: Location scenes filmed in Colombia and Morocco. Opened in Rome in Dec 1969 as *Quemada!*; in Paris in Jan 1971 as *Queimada!* Prerelease running time: 132 min.

BURN, BABY, BURN see **THE CAROLYN LIMA STORY**

BURN, WITCH, BURN (Great Britain)   F6.0605
Independent Artists. *Dist* American International Pictures. 25 Apr **1962** [Buffalo, New York, opening; c10 Mar 1962; LP22125]. Sd (RCA); b&w. 35mm. 90 min.

Pres by James H. Nicholson, Samuel Z. Arkoff. A Julian Wintle–Leslie Parkyn Production. *Prod* Albert Fennell. *Exec Prod* Julian Wintle, Leslie Parkyn. *Dir* Sidney Hayers. *Screenplay* Charles Beaumont, Richard Matheson, George Baxt. *Dir Photog* Reginald Wyer. *Camera Op* Gerry Turpin. *Art Dir* Jack Shampan. *Set Dresser* Peter Lamont. *Film Ed* Ralph Sheldon. *Mus Comp* William Alwyn. *Mus Cond* Muir Mathieson. *Sd Ed* Alastair McIntyre, Ted Mason. *Sd Rec* Eric Bayman, Len Shilton. *Sd* John W. Mitchell, Ken Cameron. *Asst Dir* David Bracknell. *Prod Supv* Arthur Alcott. *Prod Mgr* Geoffrey Haine. *Cont* Jane Buck. *Wardrobe Mistress* Maude Churchill. *Wardrobe* Sophie Devine. *Makeup* Basil Newall. *Hairstyles* Iris Tilley.

Cast: Janet Blair *(Tansy Taylor)*, Peter Wyngarde *(Norman Taylor)*, Margaret Johnston *(Flora Carr)*, Anthony Nicholls *(Harvey Sawtelle)*, Colin Gordon *(Prof. Lindsay Carr)*, Kathleen Byron *(Evelyn Sawtelle)*, Reginald Beckwith *(Harold Gunnison)*, Jessica Dunning *(Hilda Gunnison)*, Norman Bird *(doctor)*, Judith Stott *(Margaret Abbott)*, Bill Mitchell *(Fred Jennings)*, George Roubicek *(cleaners' man)*, Frank Singuineau *(truck driver)*, Gary Woolf *(his mate)*.

Horror film. Source: Fritz Leiber, *Conjure Wife* (New York, 1953). Tansy Taylor, the wife of an English university professor, secretly practices witchcraft to further her husband, Norman's, career. When he accidentally discovers her secret, he destroys her instruments of black magic. Following Tansy's warning that his action has left him vulnerable to evil forces, Norman's luck changes: a girl student charges him with rape, her boyfriend threatens him, and his car runs into a ditch. Then, one evening, Tansy disappears; Norman finds her nearly dead in a graveyard. When he brings her home, she attempts to kill him and later turns on the wife of one of his colleagues. Eventually, Norman learns that Flora Carr, the crippled wife of his rival for the chairmanship of the sociology department, is also a practitioner of witchcraft and has hypnotized Tansy into obeying her commands. That night, the Taylor home catches fire, and a huge stone eagle from one of the university buildings suddenly comes to life and attacks Norman. Later, the masonry supporting the eagle collapses, and Flora is killed as the stone edifice crashes to the earth. *Professors. Cripples. Witchcraft. Spells. Marriage. Hypnotism. Ambition. Cemeteries. Fires. Eagles.*

Note: Location scenes filmed in Penzance (Cornwall); working title: *Conjure Wife.* Opened in London in May 1962 as *Night of the Eagle*; running time: 87 min. Copyright claimant: Alta Vista Productions.

THE BURNING COURT (France/Italy/West Germany)   F6.0606
International Productions–UFA Comacico–Laura Cinematografica–Mondex Films–Taurus Cinematografica. *Dist* Trans-Lux Distributing Corp. 31 Jul **1963** [New York opening]. Sd; b&w. 35mm. 102 min.

Prod Yvon Guézel. *Assoc Prod* Ralph Baum. *Dir* Julien Duvivier. *Screenplay* Julien Duvivier, Charles Spaak. *Dial* Charles Spaak. *Photog* Roger Fellous. *Camera Op* Robert Schneider. *Asst Camera* René Schneider. *Art Dir* Willi Schatz. *Film Ed* Paul Cayatte. *Asst Ed* Nicole Cayatte. *Mus* Georges Auric. *Sd* Guy Chichignoud. *Asst Dir* Michel Romanoff. *Prod Mgr* Jochen Graubner, René Grobert. *Script Girl* Annie Maurel. *Prod Sec* Gisela Sixt. *Cost* Tanine Autre. *Wardrobe* Suzanne Pinoteau, H. Langhammer, H. Böhm. *Makeup* Yvonne Fortuna, Werner Schröder, Nicole Bouban. *Prop* Peter Martin, Michel Suné, E. Birk. *Still Photog* Rolf Lantin.

Cast: Nadja Tiller *(Myra)*, Jean-Claude Brialy *(Marc Desgrèz)*, Perrette Pradier *(Lucie Desgrèz)*, Claude Rich *(Stéphane Desgrèz)*, Duvallès *(Mathias Desgrèz)*, Walter Giller *(Michel Boissard)*, Edith Scob *(Marie Boissard)*, Antoine Balpêtré *(Dr. Hermann)*, René Génin *(Henderson)*, Héléna Manson

(Madame Henderson), Dany Jacquet *(Frieda)*, Catherine Thévenin *(maid)*, Carl Brake *(police inspector)*.

Mystery melodrama. Source: John Dickson Carr, *The Burning Court* (New York, 1959). According to legend there is a curse on the ancient castle of the Desgrèz family. Years before, the mistress of one of their ancestors was accused of witchcraft; and when she was burned at the stake, she cursed her lover and his descendants. Now living at the castle is Mathias Desgrèz, an ailing eccentric who is a student of black magic and sorcery. Visiting the old man are his two bickering nephews, Stéphane and Marc, and the latter's wife, Lucie. Also present are mystery writer Michel Boissard and his wife, Marie. On the night of a costume ball the housekeeper sees a shadowy figure, which she believes to be Lucie, give a drink to Mathias. The next morning the old man is found dead from poisoning, and Lucie becomes the chief suspect since she and Marc are the beneficiaries of Mathias' will. It is then disclosed that Mathias' nurse, Myra, is Marc's mistress and that she has been administering cumulative doses of arsenic to Mathias but was not responsible for the final, lethal drink. The two lovers quarrel violently over the sudden turn of events, and Marc drowns Myra. Though Marc confesses to his crime, the murder of Mathias remains unsolved. *Eccentrics. Uncles. Mistresses. Authors. Nurses. Housekeepers. Murder. Witchcraft. Curses. Poisoning. Inheritance. Castles. Masquerades.*

Note: Released in West Germany as *Das brennende Gericht* in Feb 1962; running time: 113 min; opened in Paris in Mar 1962 as *La chambre ardente*; running time: 110 min; released in Italy as *I peccatori della foresta nera.*

THE BURNING MAN see **THE CAROLYN LIMA STORY**

THE BUS   F6.0607
Haskell Wexler. *Dist* Harrison Pictures. 6 Apr **1965** [New York opening]. Sd; b&w. 35mm. 62 min.

Pres by Edward Harrison. *Prod-Dir* Haskell Wexler. *Photog* Haskell Wexler. *Asst Photog* Michael Philip Butler. *Film Ed* Conrad Bentzen. *Mus* Richard Markowitz. *Sd* Nell Cox.

Documentary. A group of San Franciscans, blacks and whites, take a 3-day cross-country bus trip to participate in the historic "March on Washington" in the summer of 1963. Ideas, comments, and arguments of the riders regarding the state of civil rights and racial integration are recorded, as well as the singing of inspirational and folk songs. The Charles Franklin family gives an introduction, and the rest of the film consists of recorded conversations and a final scene of the mass rally on the Washington Monument grounds. *Negroes. Demonstrations. Race relations. Civil rights. Travel. Social classes. Buses. San Francisco. Washington (District of Columbia). Washington Monument (District of Columbia).*

BUS RILEY'S BACK IN TOWN   F6.0608
Universal Pictures. 24 Mar **1965** [Los Angeles opening; c17 Apr 1965; LP33408]. Sd (Westrex); col (Eastman Color). 35mm. 93 min. [Copyright length: 100 min.]

Prod Elliott Kastner. *Dir* Harvey Hart. *Screenplay (see note)* Walter Gage. *Dir Photog* Russell Metty. *Camera Op* Edwin Pyle. *Asst Camera* Ledger Haddow, John Hussey. *Art Dir* Alexander Golitzen, Frank Arrigo. *Set Decor* John McCarthy, Oliver Emert. *Set Coörd* Jerry MacDonald. *Main Titl* Pacific Title. *Film Ed* Folmar Blangsted. *Asst Ed* Monte Hellman. *Mus* Richard Markowitz. *Mus Supv* Joseph Gershenson. *Songs:* "I Want You To Know," "Got a Surfboard Ten Feet Long" Richard Markowitz, Jacques Wilson. *Sung by* Dobie Gray. *Choreog* David Winters. *Sd* Waldon O. Watson, Lyle Cain, Corson Jowett, Ed Borschell, John Erlinger, Victor Goode. *Asst Dir* Terence Nelson, Bill Gilmore. *Unit Prod Mgr* John Morrison. *Script Supv* Luanna Poole. *Ann-Margret's Gowns Dsgn* Jean Louis. *Cost* Rosemary Odell. *Wardrobe* Bucky Rous, Viola Thompson. *Makeup* Bud Westmore, Frank McCoy, Dick Cobos, Dorothy Parkinson. *Hairstyles* Larry Germain, Jean Austin. *Dial Coach* Bert Steinberger. *Still Photog* Jack Geraghty. *Gaffer* Max Nippell. *Grip* Charles Cowie, Ken Smith. *Prop* Sol Martino, John Faltis.

Cast: Ann-Margret *(Laurel)*, Michael Parks *(Bus Riley)*, Janet Margolin *(Judy)*, Brad Dexter *(Slocum)*, Crahan Denton *(Spencer)*, Jocelyn Brando *(Mrs. Riley)*, Kim Darby *(Gussie)*, Larry Storch *(Howie)*, Mimsy Farmer *(Paula)*, Brett Somers *(Carlotta)*, Nan Martin *(Mrs. Nichols)*, Lisabeth Hush *(Joy)*, Ethel Griffies *(Mrs. Spencer)*, Alice Pearce *(housewife)*, Chet Stratton *(Benji)*, David Carradine *(Stretch)*, Marc Cavell *(Egg Foo)*, Parley Baer *(Mr. Griswald)*.

Drama. Veteran Bus Riley returns to his hometown, his mother, and Gussie, his younger sister, to find that Laurel, his former fiancée, has married a wealthy older man. Unwilling to return to his old job as a garage mechanic, Bus becomes a vacuum-cleaner salesman. Laurel learns of Bus's return and, with her husband out of town, easily persuades Bus to resume their relationship. Judy, a friend of Gussie, loses her mother in a fire and comes to live with the Rileys, who try to promote a romance between her and Bus. Sometime later, Judy leaves town to go to live with her father, and Bus misses her. He becomes disgusted with the tactics his boss urges him to use in selling vacuum cleaners, and, depressed by the emptiness of his relationship with Laurel and attracted by the possibility of a romance with Judy, he quits his job, ends his affair with Laurel, and goes back to work as an auto mechanic. *Veterans. Salesmen. Mechanics. Family life. Infidelity. Brother-sister relationship. Fires.*

Note: Walter Gage is a pseudonym for William Inge, who requested that his name be removed from the credits.

THE BUSH WHACKER *see* THE BUSHWHACKER

THE BUSHBABY (Great Britain)   **F6.0609**
Velvet Film Productions. *Dist* Metro-Goldwyn-Mayer, Inc. Nov **1970** [c31 Dec 1969; LP38192]. Sd; col (Metrocolor). 35mm. 100 min. *MPAA rating* G.
Prod Robert Maxwell, prod, John Trent. *Assoc Prod* Dennis Bertera. *Dir* John Trent. *Screenplay* Robert Maxwell, prod, William H. Stevenson. *Dir Photog* Davis Boulton. *Camera Op* Stan Mestel. *Art Dir* Jack Shampan. *Film Ed* Raymond Poulton. *Mus Supv* Philip Martell. *Mus Comp* Les Reed. *Swahili Lyr for "Kwaheri"* Roger Magwaza. *Song: "Onward Christian Soldiers"* Arthur Sullivan. *Arr* S. Baring-Gould. *Rec Supv* A. W. Watkins. *Sd Rec* Gerry Turner. *Sd Ed* Arthur Ridout. *Asst Dir* Jake Wright. *Prod Mgr* Tom Sachs. *Cost* Joanna Wright. *Makeup* Stella Morris. *Hairstyles* Susie Hill. *Cons Naturalist* Grahame Dangerfield.
Cast: Margaret Brooks *(Jackie Leeds)*, Lou Gossett *(Tembo)*, Donald Houston *(John Leeds)*, Laurence Naismith *(Professor "Cranky" Crankshaw)*, Marne Maitland *(The Hadj)*, Geoffrey Bayldon *(Tillson)*, Jack Gwillim *(Ardsley)*, Noel Howlett *(Reverend Barlow)*, Charles Hyatt *(Gideon)*, Tommy Ansah *(policeman)*, Jumoke Debayo *(bus woman)*, Harold Goodwin *(steward)*, Willy Jonah *(police sergeant)*, Simon Lack *(first officer)*, Victor Maddern *(barman)*, Illario Pedro *(policeman)*, Martin Wyldeck *(captain)*, Sid Hunt *(second officer)*, Mohinder Singh *(Sikh inspector)*, Johan Mkopi *(police constable)*, Kisesa Mayega *(elephant poacher)*.
Adventure drama. Source: William H. Stevenson, *The Bushbabies* (Boston, 1965). Jackie, daughter of widower John Leeds, an East African game warden, receives as a pet the small bushbaby Komba. As the Leedses board a ship to return to England, Jackie learns that she cannot take her pet. When she leaves the liner to restore the animal to its habitat, the ship departs without her. Jackie is found beside the dock by Tembo, the Leeds' black servant. She dissuades him from calling the police, preferring to visit a family friend. Upon arriving, however, they find his home deserted. Jackie's disappearance having been detected, the police assume her abduction by Tembo and launch a manhunt for the innocent black. The Hadj, a local ivory poacher fearing discovery during the police investigation, commands his minions to kill Tembo. Overtaken by the henchmen, Jackie is accidentally wounded by a poisoned arrow and sinks into a coma. The fugitives, however, are found by Professor Crankshaw, who gives Jackie an antidote. Unwilling to risk her life in the professor's ancient airplane, Tembo takes Jackie to the land of Masai. When the police locate the pair in a hut, they plan Tembo's execution. Although Tembo is wounded by their bullets, Leeds arrives in time to save the black from further harm. *Masai. Domestics. Police. Fugitives. Poachers. Professors. Race relations. Colonial administration. Filial relations. Poisoning. Ships. Airplanes. British East Africa. Chases. Lemurs.*
Note: Exterior scenes filmed in Tanzania; working title: *The Bushbabies*. Produced with the cooperation the Tanzanian government.

BUSHIDO (Japan)   **F6.0610**
Toei Co. 12 Sep **1964** [New York opening]. Sd; b&w. 35mm (ToeiScope). 123 min.
Prod Hiroshi Okawa. *Dir* Tadashi Imai. *Screenplay* Naoyuki Suzuki. *Orig Story* Norio Nanjo. *Camera* Makoto Tsuboi. *Mus* Toshiro Mayuzumi.
Cast: Kinnosuke Nakamura *(Iikura)*, Masayuki Mori *(Lord Hori)*, Kyoko Kishida *(Lady Hagi)*, Yoshiko Mita *(Kyoko)*, Ineko Arima, Shinjiro Ebara.
Epic. At the turn of the 17th century in Japan Jirozaemon Iikura signs an oath of obedience pledging the service and loyalty of his descendents to the feudal Lord Hori. Through four generations the Iikura family suffer torture and shame in order to uphold the pact in accordance with the tenets of *bushido*. the original signer, believing that he has not lived up to his master's standards, commits harakiri after the Christian rebellion of 1637, as does his son Sajiemon. Shinzo Iikura grows up to become the involuntary homosexual partner of Takabumi Hori. When the master discovers that Shinzo has made love to one of the ladies of the court, he castrates him and forces him to marry the woman. Before the marriage, however, the bride is impregnated so that the family line will continue. [According to another source, Shinzo Iikura discovers that his fiancée has been raped by the lunatic Takabumi Hori and decides to give his allegiance not to the emperor. He dies courageously in a war against the Chinese.] Shinzo's son becomes a grave samurai skilled in the "occult cut," a practice which involves lopping two equally-sized edges off a wooden shield. His master sexually assaults his wife, and the samurai protests. As punishment he is

blindfolded and made to perform the "occult cut" on two people, whom he discovers to be his daughter and her fiancé. The tradition of *bushido* remains evident in Japan during World War II with the suicide actions of kamikaze pilots, such as Osamu Iikura. Finally, Susumu Iikura breaks with the bushido tradition, achieving individual success with a construction project and happiness with his fiancée, Kyoko. *Nobility. Samurai. Kamikazes. Feudalism. Loyalty. Suicide. Castration. Male homosexuality. Torture. Rape. Hara-kiri. World War II.*
Note: Released in Japan in 1963 as *Bushido zankoku monogatari*; running time: 125 min.

BUSHIDO ZANKOKU MONOGATARI *see* BUSHIDO

THE BUSHWHACKER   **F6.0611**
Eliot Enterprises. *Dist* Falcon Film Distributors, Chancellor Films. Nov **1968**. Sd; col (Eastman Color). 35mm. 86 min.
Prod-Dir B. Ron Elliott. *Screenplay* Torn Pages. *Film Ed* Rip N. Tear. *Mus* Tone Deff. *Sd* Sam Kopetzky.
Cast: Merci Mee *(Dawn)*, Acee Decee *(Moureen)*, Ronnie Runningboard *(Bushwhacker)*, Rita Roundheels *(Sherry)*, Baron von Flipover *(Dan)*.
Melodrama. A pilot, Dan, is faced with the task of protecting his three female passengers—Dawn, Sherry, and Moureen—against a demented sniper who has shot down their plane in mid-desert. While keeping watch and defending themselves against the hardships of the desert, the group amuse themselves by pairing off for sexual activities. Dawn, the most aggressive of the women, seduces Dan while lesbian Moureen passes the time with Sherry. The watchful bushwhacker, anxious to participate, captures Sherry, ties her to a tree, and tortures her with a red-hot knife before strangling her. [According to one source, Moureen then makes love to Sherry's corpse.] Before Dan can catch up with him, the bushwhacker also captures Dawn and rapes and mutilates her. Dan and Moureen then set a trap for the madman. Moureen entices him, and as he advances toward her, Dan shoots him with a flare gun. *Psychopaths. Air pilots. Rape. Mutilation. Murder. Torture. Lesbianism. Voyeurism. Sadism. Necrophilia. Deserts. Airplane accidents.*
Note: Also known as *The Bush Whacker*, *The Bushwacker*, and *Bushwackers.*

THE BUSINESSMAN'S LUNCH *see* MID-DAY MISTRESS

BUSTING OUT *see* BLAZE STARR GOES NUDIST

BUSTY BROWN *see* THE ADVENTURES OF BUSTY BROWN

THE BUSY BODY   **F6.0612**
William Castle Enterprises. *Dist* Paramount Pictures. 13 Jan **1967** [New Orleans opening; c13 Jan 1967; LP33769]. Sd; col (Technicolor). 35mm (Techniscope). 101 min. [Also reviewed at 90 min.]
Prod-Dir William Castle. *Assoc Prod* Dona Holloway. *Screenplay* Ben Starr. *Dir Photog* Hal Stine. *Art Dir* Hal Pereira, Roland Anderson, Al Roelofs. *Set Decor* Jack Mills, Robert R. Benton. *Film Ed* Edwin H. Bryant. *Mus* Vic Mizzy. *Song: "Out of Nowhere"* Edward Heyman, Johnny Green. *Perf by* Arlene Golonka. *Sd Rec* Harold Lewis, Ray Cossar, John Wilkinson. *Asst Dir* Andrew J. Durkus, Charles Bohart. *Prod Mgr* Frank Caffey. *Asst Prod Mgr* Curtis Mick. *Unit Prod Mgr* Kenneth DeLand. *Makeup* Wally Westmore, Monte Westmore. *Hairstyles* Nellie Manley, Hedvig Mjorud. *Proc Photog* Farciot Edouart. *Sp Photog Eff* Paul K. Lerpae.
Cast: Sid Caesar *(George Norton)*, Robert Ryan *(Charley Barker)*, Anne Baxter *(Margo Foster)*, Kay Medford *(Ma Norton)*, Jan Murray *(Murray Foster)*, Richard Pryor *(Whittaker)*, Arlene Golonka *(Bobbi Brody)*, Charles McGraw *(Fred Harwell)*, Ben Blue *(Mr. Rose)*, Dom DeLuise *(Kurt Brock)*, Godfrey Cambridge *(Mike)*, Marty Ingels *(Willy)*, Paul Wexler *(Merriwether)*, Bill Dana *(Archie Brody)*, George Jessel *(Mr. Fessel)*, Audrie Magee *(Mrs. Fessel)*, Mickey Deems *(cop no. 1)*, Choo Choo Collins *(woman no. 1)*, Marina Koshetz *(Marcia Woshikowski)*, Norman Bartold, Mike Wagner, Larry Gelman, Don Brodie, actor *(board members)*.
Comedy. Source: Donald E. Westlake, *The Busy Body* (New York, 1966). Gang leader Charley Barker orders one of his flunkies, George Norton, to dig up the corpse of Archie Brody, a crime syndicate money collector, because Brody was buried in a blue suit that had $1,000,000 sewn in its lining. George digs up the body twice: the first time he finds an empty coffin. George tries again a few days later and finds the body of a total stranger. Suspicion points to the funeral parlor, but when both the mortician and his assistant are murdered, Barker, implying that George stole the money, has him "taken for a ride." George escapes, visits Brody's widow, an ex-stripper named Bobbi, and learns that her neighbors, the Fosters, are somehow involved. George's sleuthing proves that Margo Foster had attempted to pass off Brody's charred body as her husband in order to collect his insurance; and Murray Foster had killed the two morticians to insure secrecy. Once the couple are arrested, George returns to Bobbi's apartment and discovers that she is color blind—her

husband had been buried in his *brown* suit, and the blue suit in his closet does not have any money sewn into its lining. It becomes apparent that Barker stole the syndicate's money himself and was also responsible for Brody's murder. The gang leader tries to kill George, but in a climactic rooftop struggle, George's possessive mother and Bobbi come to his rescue, and Barker falls to his death. *Gangsters. Widows. Murder. Perfidy. Theft. Fraud. Syndicates. Corpses. Insurance.*

Note: Location scenes filmed in Chicago.

BUTA TO GUNKAN *see* **THE FLESH IS HOT**

BUTCH CASSIDY AND THE SUNDANCE KID   F6.0613

Campanile Productions. *Dist* Twentieth Century–Fox Film Corp. 23 Sep **1969** [New Haven, Connecticut, opening; c23 Sep 1969; LP38925]. Sd (Westrex); col (DeLuxe). 35mm (Panavision). 110 min. *MPAA rating* M.

Pres by Paul Newman, John Foreman. A George Roy Hill–Paul Monash Production. *Prod* John Foreman. *Exec Prod* Paul Monash. *Dir* George Roy Hill. *2d Unit Dir* Michael Moore. *Screenplay* William Goldman. *Dir Photog* Conrad Hall. *2d Unit Photog* Harold E. Wellman. *Art Dir* Jack Martin Smith, Philip Jefferies. *Set Decor* Walter M. Scott, Chester L. Bayhi. *Main Titl* Glenn Advertising Inc. *Film Ed* John C. Howard, Richard C. Meyer. *Graphic Montage* John Neuhart. *Mus Comp & Cond* Burt Bacharach. *Song:* "Rain Drops Keep Fallin' on My Head" Burt Bacharach, Hal David. *Sung by* B. J. Thomas. *Orch* Leo Shuken, Jack Hayes. *Sd* William E. Edmondson, David Dockendorf. *Asst Dir* Steven Bernhardt. *Asst to the Prod* Ron Preissman. *Prod Mgr* Lloyd Anderson. *Cost* Edith Head. *Makeup* Dan Striepeke. *Hairstyles* Edith Lindon. *Sp Photog Eff* L. B. Abbott, Art Cruickshank. *Sp Still Photog* Lawrence Schiller. *Dial Coach* Robert Crawford, Jr.

Cast: Paul Newman *(Butch Cassidy),* Robert Redford *(The Sundance Kid),* Katharine Ross *(Etta Place),* Strother Martin *(Percy Garris),* Henry Jones *(bike salesman),* Jeff Corey *(Sheriff Bledsoe),* George Furth *(Woodcock),* Cloris Leachman *(Agnes),* Ted Cassidy *(Harvey Logan),* Kenneth Mars *(marshal),* Donnelly Rhodes *(Macon),* Jody Gilbert *(large woman),* Timothy Scott *(News Carver),* Don Keefer *(fireman),* Charles Dierkop *(Flat Nose Curry),* Francisco Cordova *(bank manager),* Nelson Olmsted *(photographer),* Paul Bryar, Sam Elliott *(card players),* Charles Akins *(bank teller),* Eric Sinclair *(Tiffany's salesman).*

Western comedy-drama. Butch Cassidy and the Sundance Kid, two affable outlaws, have become notorious in the early 20th-century West for the audacity with which they and their gang pull off bank and train robberies. Recently, however, a number of holdups have ended in comic failure, and when, after a poker-playing vacation, Butch and Sundance return to the gang, they find open rebellion. After suppressing the uprising, Butch accepts a suggestion that the gang undertake their most daring exploit—a double holdup of the Union Pacific Railroad. The first stage of the robbery is successful, but on the return journey, railroad president E. H. Harriman anticipates the gang's plan and sends out a well-trained posse to subvert the attack. Butch and Sundance escape and find refuge with schoolteacher Etta Place, Sundance's girl friend. Butch realizes that the posse is still on their trail and suggests that he, Etta, and Sundance flee to New York and take a boat to South America. After a brief stay in New York, the trio arrive in Bolivia, where they successfully pull off several heists. Eventually, the leader of the Union Pacific posse shows up, and Etta, tired of bandit life, refuses to stand by and watch the men die. After she leaves, Butch and Sundance decide to go straight, but on their first honest job, as payroll guards, they are ambushed by bandits. They kill the robbers, conclude that their past is irrevocable, and take off with the money. They manage to elude their pursuers until a few Bolivian soldiers ambush them. Cornered in a small stucco structure, the badly-wounded Butch talks about a new life in Australia. Nurtured by the fantasy and unaware that an entire Bolivian Army regiment is waiting for them, the two outlaws rush out of the building and into a barrage of bullets. *Outlaws. Gangs. Schoolteachers. Guards. Soldiers. Train robberies. Bank robberies. Murder. Poker. New York City. Bolivia. George "Butch" Cassidy. Harry Longabaugh. Union Pacific Railroad. Chases.*

Note: Filmed on location in Mexico, Wyoming, Colorado, and Utah.

BUWANA TOSHI NO UTA *see* **BWANA TOSHI**

BWANA TOSHI (Japan)   F6.0614

Toho Co.–Hani Productions. *Dist* Brandon Films. Jun **1967** [Los Angeles showing]. Sd; col (Eastman Color). 35mm (Tohoscope). 98 min.

Prod Nobuyo Horiba. *Dir* Susumu Hani. *Screenplay* Susumu Hani, Kunio Shimizu. *Camera* Manji Kanau, Mitsuji Kaneko. *Mus* Toru Takemitsu.

Cast: Kiyoshi Atsumi *(Toshi),* Tsutomu Shimomoto *(Onishi),* Hamisi Salehe *(Toshi's assistant),* Bibi Agnes, Haide Gitaposta, Gilba Haide.

Melodrama. Based on a novel by: Toshishide Katayori. Toshi, a Japanese engineer, arrives in Tanganyika to assemble prefabricated houses for a Japanese geological expedition and discovers that the expedition has moved to another site. Toshi decides to go ahead with the construction, hoping that his limited knowledge of the Swahili language will assist him. Toshi struggles with the strange African culture and at one point finds himself on trial for striking a native. Eventually, through mutual understanding, the camp is completed, and Toshi is accepted as a friend of the Africans. *Engineers. Construction workers. Africans. Race relations. Trials. Swahili. Tanganyika.*

Note: Location scenes filmed in Africa. Released in Japan in 1965 as *Buwana Toshi no uta;* running time: 115 min.

BY LOVE POSSESSED   F6.0615

Mirisch Pictures–Seven Arts Productions–Miral Productions. *Dist* United Artists. 13 Jun **1961** [Los Angeles opening; c14 Jun 1961; LP20328]. Sd; col (De Luxe). 35mm. 115 min.

Prod Walter Mirisch. *Dir* John Sturges. *Screenplay* John Dennis, writ. *Screenplay Revision* Isobel Lennart, William Roberts, Ketti Frings. *Cinematog* Russell Metty. *Art Dir* Malcolm Brown. *Set Decor* Edward G. Boyle. *Film Ed* Ferris Webster. *Mus Score Comp & Cond* Elmer Bernstein. *Titl Song* Elmer Bernstein, Sammy Cahn. *Sd* Franklin Hansen. *Asst Dir* Sam Nelson. *Prod Supv* Allen K. Wood. *Prod Mgr* William Calihan. *Wardrobe Dsgn* Bill Thomas. *Makeup* Del Armstrong, Layne Britton. *Prop* Jack Carter, prop.

Cast: Lana Turner *(Marjorie Penrose),* Efrem Zimbalist, Jr. *(Arthur Winner),* Jason Robards, Jr. *(Julius Penrose),* George Hamilton *(Warren Winner),* Susan Kohner *(Helen Detweiler),* Barbara Bel Geddes *(Clarissa Winner),* Thomas Mitchell *(Noah Tuttle),* Everett Sloane *(Reggie),* Yvonne Craig *(Veronica Kovacs),* Jean Willes *(Junie McCarthy),* Frank Maxwell *(Jerry Brophy),* Gilbert Green *(Mr. Woolf),* Carroll O'Connor *(Bernie Breck).*

Romantic melodrama. Source: James Gould Cozzens, *By Love Possessed* (New York, 1957). Arthur Winner, Julius Penrose, and Noah Tuttle are partners in the leading law firm in a small Massachusetts town. For some time, the marriages of both Arthur and Julius have been on shaky ground—Arthur's because his wife, Clarissa, feels that their union is merely a business merger, and Julius' because of an automobile accident that has left him impotent. After several chance meetings, Arthur enters into an adulterous affair with Julius' frustrated, alcoholic wife, Marjorie. Simultaneously, Arthur begins having trouble with his rebellious young son, Warren, who has no intention of either practicing law with his father or of marrying Helen Detweiler, Noah's wealthy ward. Instead, the young man takes up with Veronica Kovacs, the local prostitute. When he tires of her, she falsely accuses him of rape, and he flees town. Suddenly aware of his failure as both husband and father, Arthur resolves to start a new life with Clarissa; and he begins by breaking off his relationship with Marjorie. That night the heartbroken Helen commits suicide by drinking cleaning fluid. As the stunned Arthur goes through the papers of her estate, he discovers that Noah has embezzled over $60,000 from her account. Since the old man used the money to repay investors in his bankrupt trolley line and is slowly repaying it, Arthur and Julius decide to remain silent about the discovery. Young Warren learns of Helen's suicide when he returns to town to borrow money from Marjorie. Though she is willing to let him have it, she tells him that running away from a problem is only a temporary solution. Sobered by the advice, Warren decides to remain and face Veronica's charges. After he has left, Marjorie realizes that her advice to Warren also applies to herself, and she returns to Julius. *Lawyers. Wards. Prostitutes. Smalltown life. Marriage. Impotence. Alcoholism. Infidelity. Filial relations. Wealth. Rape. Suicide. Embezzlement. Bankruptcy. Massachusetts.*

Note: John Dennis is a pseudonym for Charles Schnee, who requested that his name be removed from screen credits following a revision of the original screenplay.

BYAKUYA NO YOJO *see* **THE TEMPTRESS AND THE MONK**

BYE BYE BIRDIE   F6.0616

Kohlmar-Sidney Co. *Dist* Columbia Pictures. 4 Apr **1963** [New York opening; c1 Jun 1963; LP25369]. Sd (RCA); col (Eastman Color, print by Technicolor). 35mm (Panavision). 112 min.

A Fred Kohlmar–George Sidney Production. *Prod* Fred Kohlmar. *Dir* George Sidney. *Screenplay* Irving Brecher. *Dir Photog* Joseph Biroc. *Camera Op* Andrew McIntyre. *Camera Asst* Al Bettcher. *Set Decor* Arthur Krams. *Prod Dsgn* Paul Groesse. *Film Ed* Charles Nelson. *Songs* Charles Strouse, Lee Adams. *Mus Arr & Cond* Johnny Green. *Mus Coörd* Fred Karger. *Orch* Johnny Green, Al Woodbury. *Choreog & Asst Choreog* Onna White, Tom Panko. *Sd Supv* Charles J. Rice. *Sd* James Z. Flaster. *Rec* Harry Foy. *Asst Dir* Dave Silver, Pat Corleto. *Prod Asst* Milton Feldman. *Unit Location Mgr* Norman August. *Script Supv* Marshall Wolins. *Wardrobe Coörd & Women's Wardrobe* Marjorie B. Wahl. *Miss Leigh's Cost by* Pat Barto. *Men's Wardrobe* Ed Ware. *Makeup Supv* Ben Lane. *Teenage Makeup Created by* Helena Rubenstein. *Makeup* Joe Di Bella. *Miss Leigh's Hairstyles* Larry Germain. *Sp Eff* Geza Gaspar. *Still Photog* Mel Traxel. *Gaffer* Seldon White. *Ch Grip* Ed Blaisdell. *Prop Master* Charles Granucci.

Cast: Janet Leigh (*Rosie DeLeon*), Dick Van Dyke (*Albert Peterson*), Ann-Margret (*Kim McAfee*), Maureen Stapleton (*Mama Peterson*), Bobby Rydell (*Hugo Peabody*), Jesse Pearson (*Conrad Birdie*), Ed Sullivan (*himself*), Paul Lynde (*Mr. McAfee*), Mary LaRoche (*Mrs. McAfee*), Michael Evans (*Claude Paisley*), Robert Paige (*Bob Precht*), Gregory Morton (*Borov*), Bryan Russell (*Randolph McAfee*), Milton Frome (*Mr. Maude*), Ben Astar (*ballet manager*), Trudi Ames (*Ursula*), Cyril Delevanti (*Mr. Nebbitt*), Frank Albertson (*mayor*), Beverly Yates (*mayor's wife*), Frank Sully (*bartender*), Bo Peep Karlin (*Ursula's mother*), Melinda Marx (*teenager*), Mell Turner, Gil Lamb (*Shriners*), Lee Aaker (*leader*), Karel Shimoff (*prima ballerina*), Donald Lawton (*Russian consul*), Yvonne White (*telephone operator*), Debbie Stern (*Debbie*), Sheila Denner (*Sheila*), Pete Menefee (*Harvey*), George Spicer (*Tommy*), Dick Winslow (*leader, firemen's band*), Hazel Shermet (*Marge, Birdie's secretary*), John Daly (*himself*).

Musical comedy. Source: Michael Stewart, Charles Strouse and Lee Adams, *Bye Bye Birdie* (New York opening: 14 Apr 1960). The news that Conrad Birdie, a rock-n-roll idol, is to be drafted creates a national crisis among his teenaged worshipers and spells doom for Albert Peterson, an impoverished song writer who wrote the title song for a film Conrad had planned to make. Adding to Albert's woe are the attempts of his domineering mother to break up his romance with Rosie DeLeon, his long-suffering secretary. In an effort to solve the dilemma, Rosie induces Albert to write a special farewell song that Conrad will sing to a fan on the Ed Sullivan show. The lucky girl selected to receive a parting kiss from Conrad is 16-year-old Kim McAfee of Sweet Apple, Ohio; but the singer's arrival there creates a near riot; Kim's boyfriend Hugo Peabody, becomes jealous, her father refuses to let Conrad stay in his home, and, even worse, Albert's mother arrives on the scene. The final blow comes when word arrives that Albert's spot on the TV show will be limited to 30 seconds because the Russian ballet troupe scheduled to appear before Conrad needs an extra 4 minutes. In desperation, Albert and Rosie slip some pills that speed up nerve reflexes into a glass of milk; the Russian conductor drinks it, and the ballet turns into a farce. Conrad performs Albert's song, but as he sings to Kim, Hugo socks the singer on the jaw in full sight of all. All ends happily, however, as Kim is reunited with Hugo, Albert finally decides to marry Rosie, and even Mama finds a Sweet Apple resident who wants to marry her. *Songs:* "Bye Bye Birdie" (Kim); "The Telephone Hour" (Hugo, Chorus); "How Lovely To Be a Woman" (Kim); "Put on a Happy Face" (Rosie, Albert); "One Boy" (Kim, Hugo); "Honestly Sincere" (Conrad); "Hymn for a Sunday Evening" (Kim, Mr. McAfee, Mrs. McAfee, Randolph); "One Last Kiss" (Conrad); "Kids" (Mama, Mr. McAfee, Albert, Randolph); "A Lot of Living To Do" (Kim, Hugo, Conrad); "Rosie" (Rosie, Albert); "The Shriners' Ballet" (Rosie, Dancers). *Singers. Composers. Secretaries. Russians. Orchestra conductors. Dancers. Smalltown life. Rock and roll. Military draft. Adolescence. Jealousy. Filial relations. Ballet. Marriage. Television. Drugs. Ohio. New York City. Ed Sullivan Show.*

BYE BYE BRAVERMAN　　　　　　　　　　　　　　　　　F6.0617

Warner Bros.-Seven Arts, Inc. 21 Feb **1968** [New York opening; c1 Apr 1968; LP37152]. Sd; col (Technicolor). 35mm. 94 min.

Prod-Dir Sidney Lumet. *Assoc Prod* Charles Maguire. *Screenplay* Herbert Sargent. *Dir Photog* Boris Kaufman. *Camera Op* Hank Muller. *Art Dir* Ben Kasazkow. *Set Decor* John Godfrey. *Scenic Artist* Stanley Cappiello. *Film Ed (see note)* Gerald Greenberg, Ralph Rosenblum. *Asst Film Ed* Lynn Lewis. *Mus* Peter Matz. *Lyr* Herbert Sargent. *Sd Engr* Fred Bosch. *Sd Ed* Alan Heim. *Sd Mix* Dick Vorisek. *1st & 2d Asst Dir* Burtt Harris, Alan Hopkins. *Prod Supv* Kenneth Utt. *Script Supv* Maggie James. *Wardrobe* George Newman. *Cost Dsgn* Anna Hill Johnstone. *Makeup* Bill Herman. *Hairdresser* William Chiarelli. *Key Gip* Charles Kolb. *Gaffer* Willie Meyerhoff. *Master Prop* Ken Fitzpatrick.

Cast: George Segal (*Morroe Rieff*), Jack Warden (*Barnet Weiner*), Joseph Wiseman (*Felix Ottensteen*), Sorrell Booke (*Holly Levine*), Jessica Walter (*Inez Braverman*), Phyllis Newman (*Myra Mandelbaum*), Zohra Lampert (*Etta Rieff*), Godfrey Cambridge (*taxicab driver*), Alan King (*rabbi*), Anthony Holland (*Max Ottensteen*), Susan Wyler (*Pilar*), Lieb Lensky (*custodian*), Graham Jarvis, Peter Gumeny.

Comedy-drama. Source: Wallace Markfield, *To an Early Grave* (New York, 1964). Early one Sunday morning in New York, Morroe Rieff is shocked to learn that his friend Leslie Braverman, a fellow writer and intellectual, is dead. Morroe visits his friend's widow, Inez, and receives the second shock of the day when the supposedly bereaved widow tries to make love to him. Pulling himself together, Morroe prepares to attend the funeral services in Brooklyn with Braverman's three other close friends—Barnet Weiner, who gives up a Sunday in bed with his mistress Myra Mandelbaum; Felix Ottensteen, the oldest of the group; and Holly Levine, the most commercially successful writer of the quartet. Meeting in Greenwich Village, the four friends pile into Holly's Volkswagen, set out for the synagogue, and get lost. An accident with a Negro

cab driver almost creates a brawl; but when it is discovered that the cabbie, like themselves, is Jewish, hard feelings mellow into streetcorner philosophizing and drinking. Eventually, the four friends reach the synagogue and dutifully sit through a marathon sermon before realizing they are attending the funeral services of a total stranger. Despite their exhaustion, they continue on until they locate Braverman's gravesite. When Morroe returns home that night and attempts to tell his wife about all the events of the day, he suddenly stops talking and begins to weep. *Authors. Intellectuals. Widows. Jews. Negroes. Taxi drivers. Rabbis. Death. Friendship. Funerals. Volkswagen automobiles. New York City—Greenwich Village. New York City. New York City—Brooklyn. Automobile accidents.*

Note: Filmed in New York City. Sources conflict in crediting film editor.

C. C. AND COMPANY　　　　　　　　　　　　　　　　　F6.0618

Rogallan Productions-Namanco. *Dist* Avco Embassy Pictures. 14 Oct **1970** [New York opening]. Sd; col (De Luxe, print by Movielab). 35mm. 94 min. MPAA rating R.

Prod Allan Carr, Roger Smith. *Exec Prod* Joseph E. Levine. *Dir* Seymour Robbie. *Screenplay* Roger Smith. *Dir Photog* Charles Wheeler. *Camera Op* Roger Sherman, Jr. *Asst Camera* Ron Vargas, Frank Palmer. *Main Titl* Pacific Title. *Film Ed* Fred Chulack. *Mus* Lenny Stack. *Song:* "Today" Lenny Stack, Janelle Cohen. *Sung by* Ann-Margret. *Song:* "I Can't Turn You Loose" Otis Redding. *Sung by* Wayne Cochran and The C. C. Ryders. *Songs:* "Jenny Take a Ride," "See See Rider" *sung by* Mitch Ryder. *Sd Rec* Robert Martin. *Boom Op* Norman Webster. *Asst Dir* Dennis Donnelly, Joe Nayfack. *Prod Supv* Frank Baur. *Prod Asst* Michael Rachmil. *Prod Sec* Jo Warner. *Script Supv* Meta Rebner. *Cost Dsgn* Jon Shannon. *Wardrobe* Ron Ross. *Makeup* Frank McCoy. *Sp Eff* Henry Millar, Jr. *Still Photog* Jack Geraghty. *Gaffer* Harry Sundby.

Cast: Joe Namath (*C. C. Ryder*), Ann-Margret (*Ann McCalley*), William Smith (*Moon*), Jennifer Billingsley (*Pom Pom*), Don Chastain (*Eddie Ellis*), Teda Bracci (*Pig*), Mike Battle (*Rabbit*), Sid Haig (*Crow*), Greg Mullavey (*Lizard*), Bruce Glover (*Captain Midnight*), Tedd King (*Suicide Sam*), Gary Littlejohn (*Sitting Bull*), Frank Noel (*Kraut*), Kiva Kelly (*Eva*), Jackie Rohr (*Zit Zit*), Bob Keyworth (*Charlie Hopkins*), Alan Pappe (*photographer*), Ned Wertimer (*motorcycle salesman*), William Baldwin (*nightwatchman*), Shirley Eder (*lady ticket taker*), John Wasserman (*store manager*), Bonnie Emerson, Paula Warner (*models*), Wayne Cochran and The C. C. Ryders (*themselves*).

Action melodrama. C. C. Ryder, Lizard, and Crow, members of The Heads motorcycle gang, come upon Ann McCalley, a beautiful fashion correspondent whose limousine has broken down. Lizard and Crow attempt to rape her, but C. C. overpowers them and saves the young woman. The next day, as The Heads disrupt a motorcycle race, C. C. sees Ann photographing Eddie Ellis, one of the racers, and to impress her, C. C. steals a motorcycle and wins $600 in the race. Moon, the leader of The Heads, is already angry at C. C. for interfering with the rape of Ann and demands that C. C. turn the money over to the gang's treasury. When C. C. refuses, Moon beats him up and takes the money, but later that night, C. C. seduces Pom Pom, Moon's girl friend, and steals back the money. He then moves in with Ann, but The Heads kidnap and hold her for $1,000 ransom. C. C. makes a counteroffer of double or nothing in a race against Moon. During the race, Moon's cycle swerves out of control, and he is killed. After setting fire to The Heads' motorcycles, C. C. runs away with Ann. *Motorcycle gangs. Fashion editors. Photographers. Rape. Motorcycle racing. Theft. Seduction. Kidnaping. Ransom. Arson. Motorcycle accidents.*

ÇA S'EST PASSÉ À ROME see **FROM A ROMAN BALCONY**

LA CABEZA VIVIENTE see **THE LIVING HEAD**

THE CABINET OF CALIGARI　　　　　　　　　　　　　　F6.0619

Associated Producers, Inc. *Dist* Twentieth Century-Fox Film Corp. 26 May **1962** [New York opening; c23 May 1962; LP21993]. Sd (Westrex); b&w. 35mm (CinemaScope). 104 min.

A Robert L. Lippert Production. *Prod-Dir* Roger Kay. *Screenplay* Robert Bloch. *Dir Photog* John L. Russell. *Set Decor* Howard Bristol. *Prod Dsgn* Serge Krizman. *Film Ed* Archie Marshek. *Mus* Gerald Fried. *Sd Rec* Jack Solomon. *Asst Dir* Lee Lukather, Harold E. Knox. *Prod Mgr* Lee Lukather. *Script Supv* Dixie McCoy. *Men's Wardrobe* Wes Jeffries. *Women's Wardrobe* Kathleen McCandless. *Makeup* Gene Hibbs. *Hairdresser* Jane Shugrue. *Prop Master* Tom Coleman. *Ch Set Electrn* George H. Merhoff.

Cast: Glynis Johns (*Jane Lindstrom*), Dan O'Herlihy (*Paul/Caligari*), Richard Davalos (*Mark*), Lawrence Dobkin (*David*), Constance Ford (*Christine*), J. Pat O'Malley (*Martin*), Vicki Trickett (*Jeanie*), Estelle Winwood (*Ruth*), Doreen Lang (*Vivian*), Charles Fredericks (*Bob*), Phyllis Teagardin (*little girl*).

Melodrama. Source: Robert Wiene, *Das Kabinett des Dr. Caligari* (a film; Decla, 1919). While driving along a lonely country road one evening, Jane Lindstrom has a flat tire and seeks help at a gloomy mansion. She is greeted by Caligari, a bearded stranger who suggests that she spend the night. After meeting the other guests in the bizarre house, she is drugged and then questioned by her host. Realizing that she is a prisoner and is being spied upon, Jane makes an unsuccessful attempt to escape. Her only visitor is a young man, Mark, who seems to love her but is unable to stay at the house and is apparently unwilling to help her leave. In seemingly rapid succession, the young woman is subjected to a series of violent shocks in which she and the other guests are tortured and then later consoled by Paul, a sympathetic doctor who bears a marked resemblance to the sadistic Caligari. Eventually, Jane is forced into a final nerve-shattering encounter with her captor. She awakens to the realization that she is a middle-aged woman undergoing treatment in a mental institution. Exhausted, but cured of her fantasies, she is taken home by her devoted and loving son—Mark. *Physicians. Hallucinations. Torture. Mental illness. Filial relations. Drugs. Hospitals.*

CABRIOLA *see* **EVERY DAY IS A HOLIDAY**

CACCIA AI VIOLENTI *see* **ONE STEP TO HELL**

CACCIA AL MASCHIO *see* **MALE HUNT**

CACCIA ALLA VOLPE *see* **AFTER THE FOX**

CACTUS FLOWER   F6.0620
   Frankovich Productions. *Dist* Columbia Pictures. 16 Dec **1969** [New York opening; c1 Dec 1969; LP37305]. Sd; col (Technicolor). 35mm. 103 min.
   Prod M. J. Frankovich. *Dir* Gene Saks. *Screenplay* I. A. L. Diamond. *Dir Photog* Charles Lang. *Set Decor* Edward G. Boyle. *Prod Dsgn* Robert Clatworthy. *Film Ed* Maury Winetrobe. *Mus* Quincy Jones. *Song:* "*A Time for Love Is Anytime*" Quincy Jones, Cynthia Weil. *Sung by* Sarah Vaughan. *Choreog* Miriam Nelson. *Sd* Bill Ford, Arthur Piantadosi. *Asst Dir* Anthony Ray. *Exec Prod Mgr* William O'Sullivan. *Cost Dsgn* Moss Mabry. *Men's Wardrobe* Guy Verhille. *Ingrid Bergman's Makeup Supv* John O'Gorman. *Prop Master* Max Frankel.
   Cast: Walter Matthau *(Julian Winston)*, Ingrid Bergman *(Stephanie Dickinson)*, Goldie Hawn *(Toni Simmons)*, Jack Weston *(Harvey Greenfield)*, Rick Lenz *(Igor Sullivan)*, Vito Scotti *(Señor Sanchez)*, Irene Hervey *(Mrs. Durant)*, Eve Bruce *(Georgia)*, Irwin Charone *(store manager)*, Matthew Saks *(nephew)*.
   Comedy. Source: Abe Burrows, *Cactus Flower* (New York opening: 8 Dec 1964). Pierre Barillet and Jean Pierre Gredy, *Fleur de Cactus* (Paris opening: 19 Sep 1964). When middle-aged New York dentist Julian Winston breaks their date, his 21-year-old mistress, Toni Simmons, attempts suicide. She is rescued, however, by Igor Sullivan, an aspiring young author and her neighbor. Despite his bachelor status, Winston has told Toni that he is married and the father of three. Impressed by Toni's abortive attempt on her life, Winston considers marrying her. Knowing that he hates liars, the dentist fabricates a divorce from his nonexistent wife. In so doing he elicits the cooperation of his spinster assistant, Stephanie Dickinson, who, unbeknownst to the dentist, has loved him for 10 years. Stephanie plays the role of wife so well that Toni relents, and Winston realizes that his nurse is not only the perfect professional associate but the ideal mate. *Dentists. Nurses. Authors. Spinsters. Bachelors. Mendacity. Mistresses. Marriage. Middle age. Suicide.*

LA CADUTA DEGLI DEI *see* **THE DAMNED**

CAESAR THE CONQUEROR (Italy)   F6.0621
   Metheus Film. *Dist* Medallion Pictures. **1963.** Sd; col (Eastman Color). 35mm (Totalscope). 103 min.
   Prod Roberto Capitani, Luigi Mondello. *Dir* Amerigo Anton. *Screenplay* Arpad De Riso, Nino Scolaro. *Photog* Romolo Garroni. *Art Dir* Amedeo Mellone. *Film Ed* Beatrice Felici. *Mus* Gian Stellari, Guido Robuschi. *Cost* Maria Luisa Panaro.
   Cast: Cameron Mitchell *(Julius Caesar)*, Rick Battaglia *(Vercingetorix)*, Dominique Wilms *(Queen Astrid)*, Ivo Payer *(Claudius Valerian)*, Raffaella Carrà *(Publia)*, Nerio Bernardi *(Cicero)*, Carla Calò *(Calpurnia)*, Cesare Fantoni *(Caius Oppio)*, Carlo Tamberlani *(Pompey)*, Lucia Randi *(Clelia)*, Giulio Donnini *(Eporidorige)*, Bruno Tocci *(Mark Antony)*, Aldo Pini *(Quintus Cicero)*, Fedele Gentile *(centurion)*, Enzo Petracca *(Titus Azius)*.
   Historical melodrama. Source: Gaius Julius Caesar, *De bello Gallico.* In 52 B. C. Emperor Julius Caesar, anxious to secure more troops to suppress the rebellion in Gaul, is rejected by the senate opposition under the leadership of Cicero. Caesar subsequently orders Publia, his adopted ward, to marry Quintus Cicero, the senator's brother and a Roman soldier fighting in Gaul. Publia and her lover Claudius Valerian, Caesar's messenger, are captured by Vercingetorix, the Gaul patriot leader, but Queen Astrid, ally and jealous mistress of Vercingetorix, frees them. Vercingetorix burns the Gallic towns in Caesar's path to prevent him from living off the land and attacks the besieged Roman legions in Alesia. When Caesar's reinforcements, alerted by Publia and

Claudius, arrive, Astrid is killed in battle, and Vercingetorix is forced to surrender. *Gauls. Soldiers. Wards. Messengers. Royalty. Mistresses. Revolts. Marriage—Arranged. Jealousy. Rome—History—Empire. Gaul. Alesia. Gaius Julius Caesar. Marcus Tullius Cicero. Vercingetorix.*
   Note: Released in Italy in 1963 as *Giulio Cesare il conquistatore delle Gallie.* Amerigo Anton is a pseudonym for Tanio Boccia.

CAGED DESIRES   F6.0622
   Hollywood Cinema Associates. 8 Apr **1970** [Washington, D. C., opening]. Sd; b&w. 35mm. 75 min.
   Prod-Dir Don Davis. *Screenplay* Barbara Peeters, Bryon Predika. *Photog* Henning Schellerup. *Camera Op* Wayne Carter. *Film Ed* Donna Davis. *Mus* Chet More, Jim More. *Sd* Fred Why.
   Cast: Barbara Peeters, Connie Barney, Susan Francis, Lu Tomeny, Fern Holbrook, Victoria Carbe, Thareen Auroraa, Buzz Hinkley, Willa Arste, Linda Jeanne.
   Drama. Maggie, a shy 16-year-old who has been jailed for performing an illegal, fatal abortion, is placed in a cell with lesbians Brucie and Cat and Angel, a sensitive Spanish-American girl. Cat and Brucie compete for the newcomer, and Maggie resists them despite warnings that if she does not cooperate she will be forcibly taken and subjected to torture. Brucie and Cat sexually attack Maggie, and Cat forces her to perform cunnilingus. Cat is Maggie's "protector" until Brucie "wins" Maggie in a fight. For revenge, Cat forces Maggie to have relations with a male prison physician the women have captured and gang raped. To complete her revenge, Cat reveals Maggie's crime—using a coathanger to abort a girl friend. Maggie and Angel become lovers, but their affair ends disastrously when the prison matron discovers them in mutual cunnilingus. Whip in hand, she leads Angel off to solitary confinement. *Prison matrons. Spanish. Physicians. Abortion. Lesbianism. Sadism. Rape. Oral sex. Prisons.*

CAGED WOMEN   F6.0623
   Cosmos Films. *Dist* Able Film Co. ca **1970.** Sd; col. 16mm. [Feature length assumed.]
   Sex film. Sexual perverts, nymphomaniacs, and lesbians are all thrown together in an exposé of life in a women's prison. *Lesbianism. Sex deviates. Nymphomania. Prisons.*

CAINE *see* **SHARK!**

CAIN'S CUTTHROATS *see* **CAIN'S WAY**

CAIN'S WAY   F6.0624
   J. C. Productions. *Dist* M. D. A. Associates, Colby Productions, Fanfare Films. 28 Jan **1970** [Baltimore opening]. Sd; col (Eastman Color). 35mm. 97 min. [Also reviewed at 93 min.] *MPAA rating* R.
   Pres by Herbert Nitke. A Cort Production. *Prod* Kent Osborne, Budd Dell. *Assoc Prod (see note)* Ralph Luce, Jack Hammond. *Exec Prod* Gerald Fine. *Dir* Kent Osborne. *Screenplay* Wilton Denmark. *Adtl Dial* Ralph Luce, Kent Osborne. *Photog* Ralph Waldo. *Mus Score* Harley Hatcher. *Prod Mgr* Sheldon Lee, Donna Thorne. *Prod Coörd* Edward Gruskin.
   Cast: John Carradine *(Preacher Sims)*, Scott Brady *(Captain Cain)*, Adair Jameson *(Cain's girlfriend)*, Robert Dix *(gang leader)*, Teresa Thaw, Don Epperson, Darwin Joston, Willis Martin, Russ McCubbin, Bruce Kimball, Tom Wytowitch, Andy Moon, Valda Mansen, John Crofton.
   Melodrama. In 1970 a motorcycle gang wearing Confederate insignia terrorize a town, forcing a woman to undress, and beating the black sheriff. The narrator attempts to explain their behavior, and, as the scene shifts to 1870, a gang of former Confederate marauders, Cain's Cutthroats, murder several Union soldiers, rob their strongbox, and mutilate one Yankee. They return to their wartime leader, Justice Cain, who is now a married homesteader, and ask him to lead the gang once more. When he refuses, they rape and kill Cain's black wife and shoot him and his son. Cain joins forces with bounty hunter Preacher Sims to track down the gang. One by one, members of the gang are found and killed, Sims keeping their heads in brine to preserve them for the reward. Cain becomes so obsessed with vengeance that Sims finally leaves him. When he tries to interfere with the execution of the gang's leader, Cain is shot by soldiers. *Motorcycle gangs. Confederate veterans. Homesteaders. Bounty hunters. Preachers. Revenge. Murder. Rape. Robbery. Capital punishment. Miscegenation. Mutilation.*
   Note: Working title: *Justice Cain.* Released by Fanfare as *Cain's Cutthroats*; running time: 81 min. Also known as *The Blood Seekers.* Sources conflict in crediting associate producer.

CAIRO (United States/Great Britain)   F6.0625
   Metro-Goldwyn-Mayer, Inc. Jan **1963** [c16 Jan 1963; LP23692]. Sd (Westrex); b&w. 35mm. 91 min.
   Prod Ronald Kinnoch. *Exec Prod* Lawrence P. Bachmann. *Dir* Wolf Rilla. *Screenplay* Joanne Court. *Dir Photog* Desmond Dickinson. *Camera Op* Dia

Elmahdy. *Art Dir* Ivan King, Maher Abdel Nour. *Film Ed* Bernard Gribble. *Mus Comp & Cond* Kenneth V. Jones. *Sd Rec* Fred Turtle. *Dub Ed* Alban Streeter. *Dub Rec* J. B. Smith. *Asst Dir* Simon Saleh, George Pollard. *Prod Mgr* Raphael Jabbour, Ted Wallis. *Location Mgr* Hassan Abdel Wahab. *Cont* Doreen Dearnaley. *Wardrobe* Aziza Murad Ibraham Osman. *Makeup* Jim Hydes. *Hairstyles* Iris Tilley. *Stills* Ali Gamal-El-Din. *Dial Coach* Peter Elliott, actor.

Cast: George Sanders *(Major Pickering)*, Richard Johnson *(Ali)*, Faten Hamama *(Amina)*, John Meillon *(Willy)*, Ahmed Mazhar *(Kerim)*, Eric Pohlmann *(Nicodemos)*, Walter Rilla *(Kuchuk)*, Kamal El Shennawy *(Ghattas)*, Salah Nazmi *(commandant)*, Chewikar *(Marie)*, Mona *(Bamba)*, Abdel Khalek Saleh *(assistant minister)*, Said Abu Bakr *(Osman)*, Salah Mansour *(doctor)*, Mohamed El Sayed *(1st officer)*, Youssef Shaaban *(2d officer)*, Ezzat El Alaili *(3d officer)*, Mohammed Abdel Rahman *(4th officer)*, Nahed Sabri *(1st dancer)*, Aziza Hassan *(2d dancer)*.

Crime drama. Source: W. R. Burnett, *The Asphalt Jungle* (New York, 1949). Upon his release from a German jail, Major Pickering goes to Egypt to rob the Cairo museum of ancient gems. Involved in the scheme are Nicodemus, a nightclub owner; Willy, an explosives expert; Ali, a drug addict in love with a dancer, Amina; and Kuchuk, a fence. During the robbery an alarm is accidentally triggered, and the police arrive. Although the gang escapes with the gems, the police track down Nicodemus and force him to provide information about the crime. Kuchuk kills himself rather than go to jail, Willy dies of wounds received during the escape, and Ali, also seriously wounded, expires in the arms of Amina. The major almost escapes with the gems but lingers to admire a belly dancer and is captured. *Nightclub owners. Drug addicts. Fences (for stolen goods). Police. Exotic dancers. Robbery. Suicide. Gems. Museums. Explosives. Cairo.*

Note: Location scenes filmed in Egypt. Opened in London in Mar 1963. A remake of *The Asphalt Jungle* (1950).

LA CALDA PELLE *see* **DE L'AMOUR**

LA CALDA VITA (France/Italy)   **F6.0626**
Jolly Film–Agiman. *Dist* Magna Pictures Distribution Corp. Mar **1967**. Sd; col (Technicolor). 35mm. 110 min.

Dir Florestano Vancini. *Screenplay* Marcello Fondato, Elio Bartolini, Florestano Vancini. *Photog* Roberto Gerardi. *Art Dir* Flavio Mogherini. *Film Ed* Roberto Cinquini. *Mus* Carlo Rustichelli. *Song sung by* Catherine Spaak.

Cast: Catherine Spaak *(Sergia)*, Gabriele Ferzetti *(Guido)*, Jacques Perrin *(Fredi)*, Fabrizio Capucci *(Max)*.

Comedy-drama. Source: Pier Antonio Quarantotti Gambini, *La calda vita* (Turin, 1958). Sergia, a curious adolescent girl, vacations on an island near Sardinia with Fredi, a sentimental Frenchman, and Max, an extroverted but moody young man. At first she is attracted to Fredi but then becomes involved with Guido, an older man who owns the villa where they are staying. After the despondent Fredi commits suicide, Sergia decides to leave the island by herself. *Adolescence. Suicide. Vacations. Islands. Sardinia.*

Note: Location scenes filmed on an island near Sardinia. Opened in Rome in Feb 1963. Foreign sources indicate film was presented in Techniscope.

CALENDAR PIN-UP GIRLS   **F6.0627**
Conde Productions. *Dist* Conde Productions, Paul Mart Productions. caMay **1966**. Sd; col. 35mm. [Feature length assumed.]

Pres by Manuel S. Conde. *Prod* Manuel S. Conde. *Dir-Writ* John Roscoe. *Dir Photog* Manuel S. Conde. *Prod Mgr* Chester Phebus. *Script Cont* Maria D. Maury. *Makeup* Gomery.

Cast: Dolores Carlos, Christy Foushee, Roblan, Nobel Vega.

Sex film. At a movie studio aspiring starlets assist artists, photographers, and technicians in the production of a nude calendar. *Actors. Models. Commercial artists. Photographers. Nudity.*

Note: Also known as *Calendar Pin-Ups.*

THE CALICO QUEEN *see* **THE HANGING OF JAKE ELLIS**

THE CALICO SHERIFF *see* **THE SECOND TIME AROUND**

CALIFORNIA   **F6.0628**
Caren Productions. *Dist* American International Pictures. Mar **1963**. Sd; b&w. 35mm. 86 min.

Prod-Dir Hamil Petroff. *Assoc Prod* Vernon Keays. *Screenplay* James West, writ. *Photog* Ed Fitzgerald. *Art Dir* Theodore Holsopple. *Film Ed* Bert Honey. *Mus Comp & Cond* Richard La Salle. *Sd* Clarence Peterson. *Asst Dir* Arthur J. Vitarelli.

Cast: Jock Mahoney *(Don Michael O'Casey)*, Faith Domergue *(Carlotta Torres)*, Michael Pate *(Don Francisco Hernandez)*, Susan Seaforth *(Marianna De La Rosa)*, Rodolfo Hoyos *(Padre Soler)*, Penny Santon *(Dona Ana Sofia Hicenta)*, Jimmy Murphy *(Jacinto)*, Nestor Paiva *(General Micheltorena)*, Roberto Contreras *(Lieutenant Sanchez)*, Felix Locher *(Don Pablo*

Hernandez)*, Charles Horvath *(Manuel)*.

Historical drama. In 1841, near Monterey, California, the people are uniting to break from Mexican rule and seek admission to the United States. Collaborator Don Francisco leads Mexican troops in terrorizing the region while Don Michael, his half brother from Los Angeles, heads the revolutionaries. Carlotta, Don Francisco's mistress, collaborates with the revolutionaries and then kills herself. Don Francisco is killed by one of his own men after the Mexicans are defeated, leaving his fiancée, Marianna De La Rosa, an heiress from a neighboring estate, free to marry Don "Mike" who now takes rightful possession of his father's lands. *Revolutionaries. Mexicans. Brothers. Mistresses. Soldiers. Suicide. Inheritance. Monterey (California).*

Note: Working title: *Don Mike.*

CALL GIRL 77 *see* **SURFTIDE 77**

CALL GIRLS OF COPENHAGEN *see* **VILLA-VENNELY: HOME OF COPENHAGEN CALL GIRLS**

CALL GIRLS OF FRANKFURT (Austria)   **F6.0629**
Intercontinental Film. *Dist* Manson Distributing Corp. Aug **1968**. Sd; b&w. 35mm. 85 min.

Prod Karl Spiehs. *Dir-Writ* Rolf Olsen. *Photog* Karl Löb. *Camera Op* Ernst Zahrt. *Art Dir* Fritz Jüptner-Jonstorff. *Film Ed* Grete Girinec. *Mus* Erwin Halletz. *Sd* Kurt Schwarz. *Asst Dir* Lucie Berndsen. *Prod Dir* Günter Eulau. *Prod Mgr* Erich Tomek, Klaus Jüptner-Jonstorff. *Cost* Frauke Sthamer. *Makeup* Ladislaus Valiček. *Hairstyles* Lilly Zangerie.

Cast: Vera Tschechowa *(Vera Paterny)*, Erik Schuman *(Alphons Tewes)*, Claude Ringer *(Peter Seitz)*, Walter Kohut *(Harry Schimek)*, Barbara Valentin *(Sonja)*, Christiane Rücker *(Lilo)*, Harald Dietl *(Dieter Lorenz)*, Fritz Tillmann *(Rudolf Nickel)*, Hans Zander *(Fritzchen)*, Walter Breuer *(Mr. Bosse)*, Ilse Peternell *(Edith Freytag)*, Angelika Krüger *(Erika)*, Rolf Kutschera *(Franz)*, Wolfried Lier *(Felix)*, Wolfgang Litto *(Kurt)*, Wilbert Gurley *(Joe)*, Ingeborg Gruber *(Tina)*, Richard Münch *(Dr. Freytag)*, Konrad Georg *(Inspector Reinisch)*, Angelika Ott, Marisa Fiori.

Melodrama. Arriving in Frankfurt for a visit with his fiancée, Vera Paterny, Peter Seitz discovers her corpse in her luxury apartment. Vera's former pimp and lover, Alphons Tewes, strongly suggests that Seitz return to Vienna. Ignoring his advice, Seitz consults Harry Schimek, a rival racketeer, who informs him of Vera's past. When Seitz returns to her flat to recover his valise, he is arrested. A gang war between the underworld rivals ensues, in which the prostitutes are stripped and humiliated. Under pressure from police inspector Reinisch, the gangsters launch their own investigation of the murder. Having identified laundry delivery man Dieter Lorenz as the culprit, the band pursues him to a railroad yard, where he is run over by a train. *Gangsters. Prostitutes. Police. Delivery men. Pimps. Murder. Gang wars. Organized crime. Trains. Frankfurt am Main.*

Note: Released in Austria in 1966 as *In Frankfurt sind die Nächte heiss;* running time: 96 min. Also known as *Playgirls of Frankfurt.*

CALL ME A CAB *see* **CARRY ON CABBY**

CALL ME BAD (Mexico)   **F6.0630**
Cinematográfica Calderón. *Dist* K. Gordon Murray Productions. 25 May **1962** [Atlanta showing]. Sd; col. 35mm. 88 min.

Pres by K. Gordon Murray. *Prod* Guillermo Calderón. *Dir* Tito Davison. *Screenplay* Rafael García Travesi. *Adapt* Julio Alejandro de Castro, Tito Davison. *Photog* Jack Draper. *Art Dir* Manuel Fontanals. *Film Ed* Jorge Bustos. *Mus* Antonio Díaz Conde. *Sd* Luis Fernández.

Cast: Ana Luisa Peluffo, Armando Calvo, Roberto Cañedo, Francisco Jambrina, Hortensia Santoveña, Rosario Gálvez, Antonio Raxell, Raúl Meraz.

Melodrama. A model is torn between her wish to remain faithful to an invalid husband and her sexual desire for the artist she loves. *Models. Artists. Invalids. Marriage. Infidelity.*

Note: Produced in Mexico in 1956 and released there as *La Diana cazadora.* Also released in the U. S. as *Diana* and *Bad Diane.*

CALL ME BWANA (Great Britain)   **F6.0631**
Eon Productions–Danjaq, S. A. *Dist* United Artists. 5 Jun **1963** [Boston opening; c6 Jun 1963; LP25388]. Sd; col (Eastman Color). 35mm. 103 min.

Pres by Harry Saltzman, Albert R. Broccoli. *Prod* Albert R. Broccoli. *Exec Prod* Harry Saltzman. *Assoc Prod* Stanley Sopel. *Dir* Gordon Douglas. *2d Unit Dir* Henry Geddes, Bluey Hill. *Screenplay* Nate Monaster, Johanna Harwood. *Dir Photog* Ted Moore. *Camera Op* John Winbolt. *Focus* John Shinerock. *2d Unit Photog* Skeets Kelly, John Coquillon. *Camera Grip* Reg Hall. *Art Dir* Syd Cain. *Asst Art Dir* John Graysmark. *Set Decor* Peter Russell. *Ch Draughtsman* Alan Tomkins. *Film Ed* Peter Hunt. *Asst Film Ed* Norman Wanstall. *2d Asst Film Ed* Stephen Warwick. *Mus Comp* Muir Mathieson, Monty Norman. *Mus Cond* Muir Mathieson. *Titl Song* Monty Norman. *Sd Rec* Bill Daniels, John Mitchell. *Sd Boom Op* Roy Charman. *Sd Camera Op* Ken Barker. *1st & 2d Asst*

Dir Clive Reed, Bob Howard. *Prod Mgr* Bill Hill. *Location Mgr* John Meadows. *Cont* Kay Rawlings. *Wardrobe Mistress* Eileen Sullivan. *Wardrobe Master* Ray Beck. *Makeup* Basil Newall, Tony Sforzini. *Hairstyles* Eileen Warwick, Ann Box. *Sp Eff* John Stears. *Prop Buyer* Jim Baker. *Constr Mgr* Ron Udell. *Still Photog* Arthur Evans. *Elec Supv* Reg Blackburn. *Chargehand Prop* P. Weymouth.

Cast: Bob Hope *(Matt Merriwether)*, Anita Ekberg *(Luba)*, Edie Adams *(Frederica Larsen)*, Lionel Jeffries *(Dr. Ezra Mungo)*, Arnold Palmer *(himself)*, Percy Herbert *(1st henchman)*, Paul Carpenter *(Colonel Spencer)*, Orlando Martins *(tribal chief)*, Al Mulock *(2d henchman)*, Bari Johnson *(Uta)*, Peter Dyneley *(Williams)*, Robert Nichols *(American major)*, Robert Arden, Kevin Scott *(CIA men)*, Mei Ling *(Hyacinth)*, Mark Heath *(Koba)*, Neville Monroe, Michael Moyer, Richard Burrell *(reporters)*.

Comedy. Matt Merriwether has built up a phony reputation as an intrepid explorer of darkest Africa by writing books based on the secret diaries of his uncle. Consequently, when an American moon capsule containing vital data crashes into an uncharted region inhabited by the savage Ekele tribe, Matt is assigned the task of recovering the capsule because of his supposed expert knowledge of the locale. Equipped with a do-it-yourself suicide kit and accompanied by an attractive security agent, Frederica Larsen, Matt arrives in Africa. Also on the scene are two foreign agents—Luba, a voluptuous blonde, and Dr. Ezra Mungo, her "missionary father"—who have orders to obtain the capsule at any cost. Overcome by Luba's charms, Matt invites her to join his safari, professedly searching for a rare elephant; and, though he has several nearly fatal accidents, he never suspects his companions. When they finally stumble into Ekele territory, they discover that the natives regard the capsule as a divine symbol dropped by the gods. After Matt has received a royal welcome in honor of his late uncle, Mungo and his henchman try to steal the capsule. But they are captured and prepared for that night's dinner, as Luba, who has fallen in love with Matt, joins him and his party in racing to the capsule. Reaching it, they take off and arrive safely in Florida. *Explorers. Foreign agents. Missionaries. Cannibals. Plagiarism. Imposture. Safaris. Space capsules. Religious objects. Diaries. Africa. Florida. Elephants.*

Note: Opened in London in Apr 1963.

CALL ME GENIUS (Great Britain)   **F6.0632**
Associated British Productions. *Dist* Continental Distributing, Inc. 16 Oct 1961 [New York opening]. Sd; col (Technicolor). 35mm. 105 min.

Prod W. A. Whittaker. *Dir* Robert Day. *Screenplay* Alan Simpson, Ray Galton. *Orig story* Tony Hancock, Alan Simpson, Ray Galton. *Photog* Gilbert Taylor. *Art Dir* Robert Jones. *Film Ed* Richard Best. *Mus* Frank Cordell. *Mus Dir* Stanley Black. *Sd* Len Shilton, Len Abbott. *Paintings* Alistair Grant.

Cast: Tony Hancock *(Anthony Hancock)*, George Sanders *(Sir Charles Brouard)*, Paul Massie *(Paul)*, Margit Saad *(Margot Carreras)*, Grégoire Aslan *(Aristotle Carreras)*, Dennis Price *(Jim Smith)*, Irene Handl *(Mrs. Crevatte)*, Mervyn Johns *(London art gallery manager)*, Peter Bull *(Paris art gallery manager)*, John Le Mesurier *(office manager)*, Liz Fraser *(waitress)*, Nanette Newman *(Josey)*, Marie Burke *(Madame Laurent)*, Marie Devereux *(Yvette)*, John Wood *(poet)*, Mario Fabrizi *(bar attendant)*, Sandor Eles, Oliver Reed, Gary Lockwood, Neville Becker *(artists)*.

Comedy. Bored with the dull routine of his office job and yearning to be an artist, Anthony Hancock leaves London and moves to Paris. He becomes friendly with a young painter from England, Paul, and the two share a garret studio on the Left Bank. Though Anthony's colossal sculptures and infantile paintings are totally lacking in merit, a bogus intellectual set adopts him and proclaims him a genius. Paul, who cannot comprehend his friend's "theories," becomes disheartened and returns to London, leaving his paintings behind. Paul's paintings are seen by Sir Charles Brouard, an art connoisseur who mistakes them for Anthony's and promotes a highly successful exhibit. As his fame increases, Anthony is commissioned by a Greek shipping magnate, Aristotle Carreras, to immortalize his wife in stone. The finished product, however, is a disaster, and Anthony flees to London. He discovers that Paul has adopted his "infantile" technique and has done numerous paintings. Brouard arranges a showing, and Anthony is once more hailed a genius. Realizing how completely he has hoodwinked the art world, Anthony confesses at the exhibition that the paintings are Paul's. He then returns to his former flat to continue painting and sculpting, confident that someday his talent will be recognized. *Office clerks. Painters. Sculptors. Art collectors. Art patrons. Greeks. Shipping magnates. Hoaxes. Snobbery. Self-confidence. Art exhibits. London. Paris—Left Bank.*

Note: Released in Great Britain in 1961 as *The Rebel*.

THE CALL OF FLESH (Japan)   **F6.0633**
Toho Co. *Dist* Gold Star Pictures. Aug 1966 [Los Angeles showing]. Sd; b&w. 35mm (Tohoscope). 97 min.

Exec Prod Hisao Ichikawa. *Dir-Writ* Hideo Onchi. *Photog* Masaharu Utsumi. *Mus* Toru Takemitsu.

Cast: Reiko Dan, Koji Nambara, Yuko Kusunoki, S. Sakamoto.

Drama. Maya and Sen, two old companions who have not seen each other in 18 years, meet in a department store. Maya, now the wife of a tailor, and Sen, the owner of a nightclub, recall their experiences after World War II as prostitutes with three other women. *One day, Ibuki, a wounded fugitive, seeks refuge in their house. As he is nursed back to health, he witnesses the prostitutes brutally punishing one of the women for falling in love with a customer and not accepting payment from him. Maya falls in love with Ibuki, and after they make love on a barge, she, too, is whipped for breaching the prostitutes' code. Sen confesses to Maya that she also had sex with Ibuki, and Maya's passion is rekindled. When Ibuki calls her a few days later, she decides to return to him since her marriage has left her sexually unsatisfied. Prostitutes. Fugitives. Nightclub owners. Infidelity. Whorehouses. World War II.*

Note: Released in Japan in 1964 as *Jotai*.

CALL OF THE NORTH   **F6.0634**
Alaska Outdoors Picture Corp. 25 Mar 1970 [Salt Lake City, Utah, opening]. Sd; col. 35mm. [Feature film, length unknown.]

Prod-Dir Darrell Thompson.

Documentary. No information about the precise nature of this film has been found, but press material suggests that it contains scenes of fishing and hunting moose, sheep, and brown bear in Alaska. *Fishing. Hunting. Alaska. Moose. Sheep. Bears.*

CALL SURFTIDE 77 see **SURFTIDE 77**

THE CALLERS see **THE BALLERS**

LES CAMARADES see **THE ORGANIZER**

CAMBRIDGE BLUE see **BACHELOR OF HEARTS**

CAMELOT   **F6.0635**
Warner Bros.-Seven Arts, Inc. 25 Oct 1967 [New York opening; c21 Oct 1967; LP38107]. Sd; col (Technicolor). 35mm (Panavision, see note). 179 min.

Prod Jack L. Warner. *Dir* Joshua Logan. *Dir Action Seq* Tap Canutt, Joe Canutt. *Screenplay* Alan Jay Lerner. *Dir Photog* Richard H. Kline. *Art Dir & Sets* Edward Carrere. *Set Decor* John W. Brown. *Prod Dsgn* John Truscott. *Film Ed* Folmar Blangsted. *Songs* Alan Jay Lerner, Frederick Loewe. *Mus Supv & Cond* Alfred Newman. *Assoc Mus Supv* Ken Darby. *Orch* Leo Shuken, Jack Hayes, Pete King, Gus Levene. *Mus Staging Assoc* Buddy Schwab. *Mus Liaison* Trude Rittman. *Sd* M. A. Merrick, Dan Wallin. *Asst Dir* Arthur Jacobson, Jack Aldworth. *Asst to the Prod* Joel Freeman. *Cost Dsgn* John Truscott. *Makeup Supv* Gordon Bau. *Hairstyles* Jean Burt Reilly. *Speech Cons* Daniel Vandraegen.

Cast: Richard Harris *(King Arthur)*, Vanessa Redgrave *(Guenevere)*, Franco Nero *(Lancelot Du Lac)*, David Hemmings *(Mordred)*, Lionel Jeffries *(King Pellinore)*, Laurence Naismith *(Merlyn)*, Pierre Olaf *(Dap)*, Estelle Winwood *(Lady Clarinda)*, Gary Marshall *(Sir Lionel)*, Anthony Rogers *(Sir Dinaden)*, Peter Bromilow *(Sir Sagramore)*, Sue Casey *(Lady Sybil)*, Garry Marsh *(Tom of Warwick)*, Nicolas Beauvy *(King Arthur as a boy)*.

Musical drama. Source: Alan Jay Lerner and Frederick Loewe, *Camelot* (New York opening: 3 Dec 1960). T. H. White, *The Once and Future King* (London, 1958). In England long ago, King Arthur first encounters his bride-to-be, Guenevere, in the enchanted forest surrounding his castle at Camelot. Following their royal wedding, Arthur's happiness inspires him to establish The Knights of the Round Table, an order of chivalry in which all members would be bound by a common desire to aid the oppressed, keeping faith with trust and honor. A young knight, Lancelot Du Lac, journeys to England to join the order when Arthur's call reaches France. Brave and purehearted, Lancelot quickly becomes the most celebrated of all Arthur's knights. Guenevere at first resents his popularity, but after watching him apparently breathe life back into the body of a knight he has wounded in a jousting match, her scorn turns to admiration and ultimately to love. Despite their deep affection for Arthur, Guenevere and Lancelot become secret lovers. Arthur refuses to pay heed to the rumors circulating throughout his court and sends into exile all those who defile the names of Lancelot and Guenevere. Arthur's illegitimate son, Mordred, arrives at Camelot to seek a declaration of his identity, and when he is refused, he spitefully wins the aid of several knights in trapping Lancelot and Guenevere in a love tryst. Lancelot escapes, but Guenevere is found guilty at a trial by jury and sentenced to be burned at the stake. Forced to support the ruling of his own court, Arthur watches in grateful silence when Lancelot rides into the courtyard, frees Guenevere, and carries her to safety. Guenevere enters a convent, and as Arthur and Lancelot prepare to battle, Arthur reflects sadly on the dream that was to have been Camelot. *Songs:* "I Wonder What the King Is Doing Tonight" (King Arthur); "The Simple Joys of Maidenhood" (Guenevere); "Camelot" (chorus & King Arthur); "C'est moi" (Lancelot); "The Lusty Month of May" (Guenevere & chorus); "Follow Me," "Children's Chorus" (chorus); "How To Handle a Woman" (King Arthur); "Take Me to the Fair" (Guenevere, Sir Lionel, Sir Dinaden & Sir Sagramore); "If Ever I Would Leave You" (Lancelot); "What Do the Simple Folks Do?" (King Arthur & Guenevere); "I Loved You Once in Silence" (Guenevere); "Guenevere" (chorus). *Royalty. French. Nobility. Knighthood. Infidelity. Jousting. Illegitimacy. Capital punishment. Weddings. Trials. Convents. Age of Chivalry. King Arthur. Round Table. Guinevere. Lancelot. Camelot.*

Note: Location scenes filmed in Spain. Blown up to 70mm for some roadshow engagements.

CAMILLE 2000   **F6.0636**

Spear Productions. *Dist* Audubon Films. 16 Jul **1969** [New York opening]. Sd; col (Technicolor). 35mm (Panavision). 115 min.

Prod-Dir Radley Metzger. *Screenplay* Michael DeForrest. *Photog* Ennio Guarnieri. *Sets* Enrico Sabbatini. *Supv Film Ed* Humphrey Hinshelwood. *Film Ed* Amadeo Safa. *Mus Comp* Piero Piccioni. *Sd Rec* Mario Celentano. *Asst Dir* Francesco Cinieri. *Dir Prod* Mario Mariani. *Cost* Enrico Sabbatini.

Cast: Danièle Gaubert *(Marguerite Gautier)*, Nino Castelnuovo *(Armand)*, Eleonora Rossi-Drago *(Prudence)*, Philippe Forquet *(DeVarville)*, Roberto Bisacco *(Gaston)*, Massimo Serato *(Armand's father)*, Silvana Venturelli *(Olympe)*, Zachary Adams *(Gody)*, Dominique Badescu *(see note)*.

Romantic drama. *Source:* Alexandre Dumas, fils, *La dame aux camélias* (1848). Armand Duval, the son of a wealthy industrialist, arrives in Rome in the company of his worldly cousin Gaston. At a society party, he meets Marguerite Gautier, the beautiful, drug-addicted, openly unfaithful mistress of a wealthy elderly patron. Hopelessly infatuated, Armand ignores Marguerite's notorious reputation and begs her to accept his love. She does, but she continues to have liaisons with other men, including DeVarville, a wealthy young nobleman from whom she accepts money. Shocked by her behavior, Armand now demands absolute fidelity, and Marguerite, steadily weakening from the effect of drugs and tiring of her senseless pleasure-seeking, yields to his wish. To celebrate their reconciliation, the couple travel to a small coastal town in the south of France for an idyllic interlude. Their brief happiness is shattered when Armand's father secretly visits Marguerite and convinces her that she is ruining his son's life. Marguerite stages an argument and coldly announces that she is returning to DeVarville. Filled with despair, Armand retaliates by beginning a flamboyant affair with a boutique model, Olympe, and even makes passionate love to her at an orgiastic party while in the presence of Marguerite. Then, at a subsequent society party, he humiliates Marguerite before the guests by flinging money at her and calling her a whore. Prior to his departure for America, Armand catches a chance remark made by his father and suddenly understands the motives for Marguerite's behavior. By now, however, the drugs have taken their toll and Marguerite is dying of an overdose in a nearby hospital. Armand reaches her in time to reaffirm his love, and Marguerite, begging forgiveness, dies in his arms. *Mistresses. French. Upper classes. Models. Drug addicts. Infidelity. Promiscuity. Orgies. Jealousy. Hedonism. Drug overdose. Self-sacrifice. Filial relations. Rome. France.*

Note: Filmed in Rome and Porto Ercole. One source credits Dominique Badescu with an unspecified acting role.

CAMP   **F6.0637**

Dist Film-Makers' Cooperative. 22 Nov **1965** [New York opening]. Sd; b&w. 16mm. 70 min.

Prod-Dir Andy Warhol. *Prod Asst* Gerard Malanga, Buddy Wirtschafter.

Cast: Paul Swan, Baby Jane Holzer, Mar-Mar Donyle, Jodie Babs, Tally Brown, Jack Smith, Fu-Fu Smith, Tosh Carillo, Mario Montez *(performers)*, Gerard Malanga *(host)*.

Musical satire. In a home theater setting, performers sing, dance, do comedy bits, and otherwise entertain. Each takes a turn performing while the others watch and applaud. *Entertainers. Theater—Amateur.*

CAMPANADAS A MEDIANOCHE *see* **FALSTAFF**

CAMPUS A GO-GO (Japan)   **F6.0638**

Toho Co. Sep **1966** [Los Angeles showing]. Sd; col. 35mm (Tohoscope). 94 min.

Dir Katsumi Iwauchi.

Cast: Yuzo Kayama, Yuriko Hoshi, Choko Iida, Kinuyo Tanaka, Ichiro Arishima.

Romantic drama. No information about the precise nature of this film has been found. *Students. College life.*

Note: Released in Japan in 1966 as *Ereki no wakadaisho*.

CAMPUS CONFIDENTIAL   **F6.0639**

Gulf-United Productions. 21 Aug **1968** [New York showing]. Sd; b&w. 35mm. 73 min.

Dir Charles Edwards. *Script* Phillip Raye. *Photog* John Douglas, photog. *Titl* Conway & Sons. *Sd* Glen Glenn Sound.

Cast: Barbara Laine, June Sundae, Sandra McKinney, Susan Williams, Bobbi Davis *(The Girls)*, Warren Sherwood, Richard Sennete, Tom Krim, Max McQuire *(The Boys)*.

Drama. Three college co-eds, Bobbi, June, and Barbara, share an expensive off-campus apartment and seek bizarre sexual adventures. Barbara and June are engaged in a lesbian affair, while Bobbi seeks heterosexual kicks. Bobbi sneaks into a radio station one night and seduces the disc jockey during his program. At the same time, two other students, Sandy and Susie, smoke marijuana at a party and take LSD. They shed their clothes and seduce Warren, left alone with them to experience the high. *Students. Roommates. Disc jockeys. College life. Lesbianism. Seduction. Marijuana. LSD.*

Note: Filmed in Florida.

CAMPUS HEAT   **F6.0640**

Cinex Film Industries. 6 Feb **1969** [New York showing]. Sd; b&w. 35mm. 70 min.

Prod Phil Slade. *Assoc Prod* Terry Merrill. *Dir* Tom Rich. *Screenplay* Wayne Rafferty. *Dir Photog* Tom Barnett. *Camera Op* Earl Wainwright. *Asst Camera* Kerry Whitenack. *Set Dsgn* Pierre Du Kane. *Ed* Earl Wainwright, Harry Kerwin. *Mus* Sol Tosco. *Sd Mix Rec* John McGrath, sd. *Boom* Harold Glaze. *Asst Dir* Joan Wainwright. *Prod Mgr* Bob Davidson. *Script Supv* Betty Kerwin. *Makeup* Edith Johns. *Hairstylist* Jere. *Still Photog* James Bice. *Head Electrn* Claude Pounds. *Key Grip* Bob Barnett. *Casting Dir* Jeff Partin.

Cast: Susan Cline, Mary Moore, Jean Marker, Lois Kent, Betsy Wright, Joan Reed *(night club performers)*, Beverly Phillips, Louise Jones, Sue Ect, Linda Ware, Brenda Bliven, Mindy Suskin, Darlene Hunt, Chrisy Enlow, June Wiles *(college coeds)*, Fred Kaye, Hal Singer, Mort Ostroff, Joe Dodds, Harry Moore *(college male students)*, Bob Decker, Sylvia Speas *(communal living couple)*, Jim Booker *(professor, State University)*, Anna Wong, Sylvia Speas, Ermma Bennett *(call girls)*, Earl De Lema.

Drama. Young women thrust into the sexually charged atmosphere of the college campus experiment eagerly with diverse forms of sexual activity, including lesbianism, autoeroticism, sadomasochism, and group sex. One student joins her boyfriend in a commune and enjoys the pleasures of marriage without the legal constraints. Others throw off all restrictions to become part of wild sex party groups, discovering new worlds of sexual experience, while campus authorities, surrendering to the new morality, dispense free contraceptives and allow dating behind locked dormitory doors. *Students. College life. Sexual initiation. Lesbianism. Autoeroticism. Sadomasochism. Group sex. Birth control. Communal living.*

CAN HEIRONYMUS MERKIN EVER FORGET MERCY HUMPPE AND FIND TRUE HAPPINESS? (Great Britain)   **F6.0641**

Taralex Corp.–Universal Pictures, Ltd. *Dist* Regional Film Distributors. 19 Mar **1969** [New York opening; c7 Jun 1969; LP38884]. Sd (RCA); col (Technicolor). 35mm. 104 min. *MPAA rating* X.

Prod-Dir Anthony Newley. *Assoc Prod* George Fowler. *Screenplay* Anthony Newley, Herman Raucher. *Dir Photog* Otto Heller. *Camera Op* Bernard Ford, Neil Ginger Gemmell. *Art Dir* William Constable. *Asst Art Dir* Don Mingaye. *Set Decor* Scott Slimon. *Main Titl* Richard Williams Studio. *Film Ed* Bernard Gribble. *Mus Dir* Philip Martell. *Mus Arr* Peter Knight, Harry Robinson, David Lindup. *Songs* Anthony Newley, Herbert Kretzmer. *Songs:* "I'm All I Need," "Once Upon a Time," "Lullaby," "Sweet Love Child," "If All the World's a Stage," "Oh, What a Son of a Bitch I Am" sung by Anthony Newley. *Song:* "Piccadilly Lily" sung by Anthony Newley, Bruce Forsyth. *Song:* "Chalk and Cheese" sung by Joan Collins. *Song:* "When You Gotta Go" sung by George Jessel. *Song:* "On the Boards" sung by Bruce Forsyth. *Choreog* Johnny Greenland. *Sd* Wally Milner. *Sd Mix* Ken Scrivener. *Asst Dir* Ray Frift. *Prod Mgr* Dennis Gardiner. *Cont* Connie Willis. *Cost Dsgn* Loudon St. Hill. *Wardrobe* Hilda Geerdts. *Makeup* R. L. Alexander. *Hairstyles* Mervyn Medalie. *Sp Eff* Peter Hutchinson.

Cast: Anthony Newley *(Heironymus Merkin)*, Joan Collins *(Polyester Poontang)*, Milton Berle *(Good Time Eddie Filth)*, George Jessel *(The Presence)*, Stubby Kaye *(fat writer)*, Bruce Forsyth *(Uncle Limelight)*, Patricia Hayes *(Grandma)*, Victor Spinetti *(Sharpnose)*, Tom Stern *(Producer Ron)*, Connie Kreski *(Mercy Humppe)*, Judy Cornwell *(Filigree Fondle)*, Berri Cornish *(Fran)*, Roy Desmond *(The Mask)*, Sally Douglas *(Automation Bunny)*, Desmond Walter Ellis *(Philip Bluster)*, Gilly Grant *(Miss Maidenhead Fern)*, Isabel Hurll *(Marge)*, Rosalind Knight *(Penelope)*, Aleta Morrison *(Harriet)*, Louis Negin *(Producer Peter)*, Tara Newley *(Thumbelina)*, Alexander Newley *(Thaxted)*, Margaret Nolan *(Little Assistance)*, Julian Orchard *(The Red Cardinal)*, Ronald Radd *(Bentley)*, Ronald Rubin *(skinny writer)*, Margo Segrave *(Miss Hope Climax)*, Sue Shepherd *(Miss Quiche Lorraine)*, Bernard Stone *(Icicle Ike)*, Yolanda (British) *(Trampolena Whambang)*, Lynda Baron *(Baby Boobala)*, Joyce Blair *(Oat-O-Rinos girl)*, Robin Bullivant *(Oat-O-Rinos teenager)*, Laurie Leigh *(Toothpaste Mother)*, Robert Hutton *(insurance agent)*, Eve Pearce *(Floor Wax housewife)*, John

Poore (*Toothpaste teenager*), Muriel Young (*Liz Harper, Brentwood 8*), Sasha Newley.

Comedy with music. Aware that at the age of 40 his life is more than half over, Heironymus Merkin brings his mother and his two children to a deserted beach to show them a filmed account of his life. *As a child, he is persuaded by his dying Uncle Limelight, an old vaudevillian, to embark upon a stage career. Under the supervision of his agent, a leering minion of Satan named Good Time Eddie Filth, Heironymus rapidly achieves success, and, despite the objections of Eddie Filth, he marries Filigree Fondle, a young woman whom he has impregnated.* While Heironymus is projecting the film, the production crew that helped shoot it arrives on the beach. *He continues to dally with other women, however, right up to the birth of his child. When the baby is stillborn, a white-clad Presence appears before Heironymus, just as it did when Uncle Limelight died. To Heironymus' delight, Filigree eventually runs off with another man, thereby leaving Heironymus free to pursue the beautiful Polyester Poontang.* Meanwhile, the film crew, the producers, and the writers are fretting because Heironymus has not yet devised an ending for his picture, and also because a trio of film critics are now present at the beach. *After impregnating Polyester, Heironymus marries again. While Polyester is bearing him two children, Heironymus takes up with the seductive Mercy Humppe, but when Polyester loses her third child, and the Presence once again appears,* Heironymus finally decides that it is time to settle down. With the coming of dawn, the film ends and Heironymus' producers continue to berate him. Then, a police car arrives, and a furious Polyester threatens to divorce Heironymus for keeping their two children out all night. *Motion picture producers. Motion picture directors. Uncles. Vaudevillians. Theatrical agents. Motion picture crews. Motion picture scriptwriters. Critics. Middle age. Filial relations. Childhood. Death. Marriage. Pregnancy. Infidelity. Stillbirth. Childbirth. Motion pictures. Beaches. Visions.*

Note: Location scenes filmed on Malta. Opened in London in Jun 1969; running time: 107 min. (cut from 117 min).

THE CANADIANS (United States/Canada/Great Britain)   **F6.0642**
  Twentieth Century-Fox Productions–Associated Producers, Inc. *Dist* Twentieth Century-Fox Film Corp. 22 Feb **1961** [Buffalo, New York, opening; c24 Feb 1961; LP18880]. Sd; col (De Luxe). 35mm (CinemaScope). 85 min.
  Prod Herman Webber. *Dir-Writ* Burt Kennedy. *Dir Photog* Arthur Ibbetson. *Film Ed* Douglas Robertson. *Mus Comp* Douglas Gamley. *Cond* Muir Mathieson. *Songs:* "This Is Canada," "Sioux Lullaby," "The Night" Ken Darby. *Sd Mix* Arthur Bradburn. *Prod Mgr* Douglas Twiddy. *Cont* Connie Willis. *Wardrobe (see note)* Jan Kemp, Jim Dunlevy. *Makeup* Alex Garfath.
  Cast: Robert Ryan (*Inspector William Gannon*), John Dehner (*Frank Boone*), Torin Thatcher (*Master Sergeant McGregor*), Burt Metcalfe (*Constable Springer*), John Sutton (*Superintendent Walker*), Jack Creley (*Greer*), Scott Peters (*Ben*), Richard Alden (*Billy*), Teresa Stratas (*The White Squaw*), Michael Pate (*Chief Four Horns*).
  Northwest melodrama. The Sioux Indians, led by Chief Four Horns, flee to Canada following the slaughter of General Custer's troops at Little Big Horn. They are intercepted by Inspector William Gannon of the Royal Northwest Mounted Police, who tells them that they may remain in Canada provided they obey the laws. The Indians agree, but trouble arises when Montana rancher Frank Boone and three of his gunmen come north to recover some horses they believe were stolen by the Indians. When Boone and the gunmen massacre a small village of Sioux and abduct a white squaw, the Mounties, fearful of reprisal by the Sioux, quickly take the marauders into custody; however, they escape, taking the white squaw as hostage. The Mounties pursue them, and in the gun battle that follows, the woman is killed while saving Gannon's life. The escaping men then reach the top of Buffalo Cliffs. There they are confronted by the Sioux, who start a horse stampede and drive Boone and his men over the edge of the cliff. With peace restored, the Mounties return to their headquarters. *Sioux Indians. Refugees. Ranchers. Hostages. Massacres. Chases. Custer's Last Stand. Canada. Little Big Horn. Northwest Mounted Police. Stampedes. Horses.*
  Note: Location scenes filmed in the Cyprus Hills of Saskatchewan, Canada. Sources conflict in crediting wardrobe designer.

THE CANDIDATE   **F6.0643**
  Cosnat Productions. *Dist* Atlantic Pictures. 7 Oct **1964** [Dallas opening]. Sd; b&w. 35mm. 84 min.
  Pres Jerry Blaine. *Prod* Maurice Duke. *Dir* Robert Angus. *Screenplay* Joyce Ann Miller, Quenton Vale, Frank Moceri. *Photog* Stanley Cortez. *Art Dir* Archie Bacon. *Film Ed* William Martin. *Mus* Steve Karmen, Sid Robin. *Sd* Lambert Day. *Prod Supv* Maurie M. Suess. *Prod Mgr* Clancy Herne. *Asst to Prod* Marvin Fisher.
  Cast: Mamie Van Doren (*Samantha Ashley*), June Wilkinson (*Angela Wallace*), Ted Knight (*Frank Carlton*), Eric Mason (*Buddy Barker*), Rachel Romen (*Mona Archer*), Robin Raymond (*Attorney Rogers*), William Long, Jr.

(*Fallon*), John Matthews (*Senator Harper*), Herb Vigran (*Dr. Endicott*), Art Allessi (*psychiatrist*), Phil Arnold (*plumber*), Carol Ann Lee, Joyce Nizzari, Beverly St. Lawrence, Susan Kelly, Sharon Rogers, Suzzanne Hiatt (*party girls*).
  Drama. A U. S. Senate committee is investigating the moral fitness of Buddy Barker to continue as congressional coordinator. During the closed hearings, Barker's "social secretary," Samantha Ashley, recalls the events leading up to the investigation: Samantha, a hotel hostess, meets Buddy in Miami. He persuades her—for a price—to keep company with Massachusetts senatorial candidate Frank Carlton. Samantha goes to work for Buddy, moving into his home in Chevy Chase, and continues to see Frank. While accompanying Frank on a campaign trip to Boston, Samantha meets English beauty Angela, whom she persuades to "be nice" to Frank. Buddy arranges a fundraising party for Frank in Washington, and there Frank becomes involved with party girl Mona Archer. Mona becomes pregnant, and Samantha takes her to a prominent Washington physician for an abortion. Instead, the doctor allegedly rapes her. Frank and Angela announce their plans to marry, but the following day during the hearings a stag film of Angela burlesquing a rape by a Chaplinesque character is shown, causing Frank to have a fatal heart attack. Samantha leaves Buddy, and his career ends in failure and loneliness. *Politicians. Prostitutes. Secretaries. English. Physicians. Political campaigns. Moral corruption. Pregnancy. Abortion. Rape. Heart disease. Scandal. Hotels. Sex exploitation films. Miami. Chevy Chase (Maryland). Massachusetts. Washington (District of Columbia). United States Congress.*
  Note: Title later changed to *Party Girls for the Candidate.*

THE CANDIDATE see **THE GOOD, THE BAD AND THE BEAUTIFUL**

CANDIDATE FOR MURDER (Great Britain)   **F6.0644**
  Merton Park Studios. *Dist* Schoenfeld Film Distributing Corp. 5 Sep **1966** [New York showing]. Sd; b&w. 35mm. 60 min.
  Prod Jack Greenwood. *Dir* David Villiers. *Screenplay* Lukas Heller. *Photog* Bert Mason. *Art Dir* Peter Proud. *Film Ed* Bernard Gribble. *Mus* Charles Blackwell. *Titl Mus* Michael Carr, mus. *Sd* Sid Rider, Ronald Abbott. *Asst Dir* Ted Lewis.
  Cast: Michael Gough (*Donald Edwards*), Erika Remberg (*Helene Edwards*), Hans von Borsody (*Kersten*), John Justin (*Robert Vaughan*), Paul Whitsun-Jones (*Phillips*), Vanda Godsell (*Betty Conlon*), Jerold Wells (*police inspector*), Annika Wills (*Jacqueline*), Victor Charrington (*barman*), Ray Smith (*chauffeur*).
  Crime melodrama. Source: Edgar Wallace, "The Best Laid Plans of a Man in Love" (publication undetermined). Mistakenly believing that his actress wife, Helene, is having an affair with young barrister Robert Vaughan, jealous socialite Donald Edwards decides to murder her. Donald hires Kersten, a professional killer, to do the job during a farewell party for Helene before she leaves London for the United States. Donald telephones his wife to say that he will not be able to attend her party. Kersten, however, tells Helene of her husband's plot, hides her in his cottage, and demands his fee from Donald. Donald, who is planning to murder Kersten to protect himself, insists on proof that his wife is dead. Kersten indignantly replies that he has committed the perfect crime but agrees to show Donald the corpse. He shows Donald what appears to be a body in the back of his car, and Donald, crazed and unable to look at his wife, hands over the money. After Kersten has pulled back the blanket revealing only pillows, Donald shoots him and then runs him down while driving away. Upon arriving at Kersten's cottage, Donald meets Robert and is preparing to shoot him when the mortally wounded Kersten appears and kills Donald before dying. Robert comforts Helene, who plans to resume her acting career in the United States. *Socialites. Actors. Barristers. Hired killers. Jealousy. Infidelity. Murder. Perfidy. London.*
  Note: Released in Great Britain in Apr 1962.

CANDIDE (France)   **F6.0645**
  C. L. M.–Pathé Cinéma. *Dist* Union Film Distributors. 19 Nov **1962** [New York opening]. Sd; b&w. 35mm. 90 min.
  Prod Clément Duhour. *Dir* Norbert Carbonnaux. *Dial* Norbert Carbonnaux, Albert Simonin. *Adapt* Norbert Carbonnaux. *Photog* Robert Lefebvre. *Art Dir* Jean Douarinou. *Film Ed* Paulette Robert. *Mus* Hubert Rostaing. *Sd* Jean Bertrand. *Prod Dir* André Deroual.
  Cast: Jean-Pierre Cassel (*Candide*), Dahlia Lavi (*Cunegonde*), Pierre Brasseur (*Pangloss*), Nadia Gray (*ubiquitous lady*), Michel Simon (*Nanar*), Jean Richard (*black marketeer*), Louis de Funès (*Gestapo officer*), Poiret and Serrault (*police*), Robert Manuel (*all German officers*), Jean Tissier (*Doctor Jacques*), Tino Rossi, Luis Mariano, Dario Moreno (*South American dictators*), Jean Constantin (*Fourak*), Albert Simonin (*Major Simpson*), Jacqueline Maillan (*American mother*), Don Ziegler (*American father*), John William (*chef*), Harold Kay, Mathilde Casadesus, Michel Garland, Michèle Verez,

O'Det.

Comedy. Adapted from: Voltaire, *Candide; ou, l'optimisme* (1759). Reared in the chateau of a baron who manufactures antique helmets, the orphan Candide is brought up by his tutor, Pangloss, to believe that he is living in "the best of all possible worlds." Candide falls in love with the baron's daughter, Cunegonde, and is thrown out of the house when her father surprises them in an innocent kiss. War breaks out in 1939, and Candide is called into the army. Captured by the Germans, he escapes to Switzerland and becomes a member of the International Red Cross. After smuggling Pangloss out of a concentration camp, Candide is rescued from a firing squad by a mysterious lady who reunites him with his beloved Cunegonde, now being shared by a Gestapo officer and a black marketeer. Candide kills the officer, and the lovers flee to South America to remain there through a series of revolutions before returning to France. Back home, Candide is acclaimed a hero for murdering the Gestapo officer, but Cunegonde is condemned as a Nazi collaborator. Candide secures her release through blackmail and travels to Indonesia (where he escapes from native guerillas) and Moscow (where he accidentally precipitates a missile conflict between the United States and the U.S.S.R.). He next visits America, becomes involved in a racial clash, and is quickly married and divorced. Once back home, he is reunited with Cunegonde, Pangloss, and the mysterious lady. They all retire to a country house where Pangloss persuades Candide to write his memoirs on this best of all possible worlds. *Orphans. Tutors. Nazis. Germany—Army. France—Army. Nobility. Guerrillas. Traitors. Blackmail. Philosophy. Race relations. Missiles. Black market. Revolutions. Concentration camps. World War II. Indonesia. South America. Switzerland. Moscow. Gestapo. Red Cross.*

Note: Released in Paris in Dec 1960 as *Candide, ou l'optimisme au XXᵉ siècle.*

CANDIDE, OU L'OPTIMISME AU XXᴱ SIÈCLE *see* **CANDIDE**

CANDY (United States/France/Italy)   F6.0646
Selmur Pictures–Dear Film–Les Films Corona. *Dist* Cinerama Releasing Corp. 17 Dec **1968** [New York opening]. Sd; col (Technicolor). 35mm. 119 min. *MPAA rating* R.

Prod Robert Haggiag. *Exec Prod* Selig J. Seligman, Peter Zoref. *Dir* Christian Marquand. *Assoc Dir* Giancarlo Zagni. *Screenplay* Buck Henry. *Italian Vers Screenplay* Enrico Medioli. *Dir Photog* Giuseppe Rotunno. *Art Dir* Dean Tavoularis. *Set Decor* Robert Nelson. *Set Dsgn* Boris Juraga. *Asst Set Dir* Joe Chevalier. *Supv Film Ed* Frank Santillo. *Film Ed* Giancarlo Cappelli. *Mus Comp & Cond* Dave Grusin. *Song:* "Child of the Universe" Dave Grusin, Roger McGuinn. *Perf* by The Byrds. *Song:* "Magic Carpet Ride" John Kay, Rushton Moreve. *Perf by* Steppenwolf. *Song:* "Rock Me" John Kay. *Perf by* Steppenwolf. *Choreog* Don Lurio. *Sd* Basil Fenton-Smith. *Sd Rec* Mario Celentano. *Sd Ed* Gordon Daniel. *Mus Ed* Stanley Davis. *Asst Dir* Francesco Cinieri, Luciano Sacripanti. *Prod Supv* Vico Pavoni. *Post Prod Supv* Tom Walker. *Prod Mgr* Mario Mariani, Gray Frederickson. *Cost Dsgn* Enrico Sabbatini. *Asst Cost Dsgn* Nadia Vitali. *Cost for Richard Burton, Ewa Aulin, Florinda Bolkan, Marilù Tolo & Nicoletta Machiavelli Dsgn by* Mia Fonssagrives, Vicki Tiel. *Sp Eff* Augie Lohman. *Sp Vis Eff* Harold Wellman. *Opening & Closing Seq* Douglas Trumbull.

Cast: Ewa Aulin *(Candy)*, Charles Aznavour *(The Hunchback)*, Marlon Brando *(Grindl)*, Richard Burton *(McPhisto)*, James Coburn *(Dr. Krankeit)*, John Huston *(Dr. Dunlap)*, Walter Matthau *(General Smight)*, Ringo Starr *(Emmanuel)*, John Astin *(Daddy/Uncle Jack)*, Elsa Martinelli *(Livia)*, Sugar Ray Robinson *(Zero)*, Anita Pallenberg *(Nurse Bullock)*, Lea Padovani *(Silvia)*, Florinda Bolkan *(Lolita)*, Marilù Tolo *(Conchita)*, Nicoletta Machiavelli *(Marquita)*, Umberto Orsini *(1st hood)*, Joey Forman *(The Cop)*, Fabian Dean *(The Sergeant)*, Peggy Nathan *(Miss Quimby)*, Neal Noorlac *(Harold)*, Peter Dane *(Luther)*, Tony Foutz *(1st weirdo)*, Tom Keyes *(2d weirdo)*, Micaela Pignatelli *(girl)*, Mark Salvage *(Dr. Harris)*, Enzo Fiermonte *(2d hood)*, Enrico Maria Salerno *(Jonathan J. John)*, Members of the Living Theatre.

Comedy. Source: Terry Southern and Mason Hoffenberg, *Candy* (New York, 1964). After being reprimanded for her lack of intellectual interests by her father, Candy, a naive adolescent, attends a reading given by the alcoholic, Welsh poet McPhisto, who plies her with drink. In her gameroom she is assaulted by Emmanuel, the Mexican gardener. Displeased to discover her in Emmanuel's embrace, her schoolteacher father decides to exile Candy to New York City. En route to the airport, however, Candy is pursued by Emmanuel's three sisters, outraged because he has forsaken his priestly ambition. After an altercation, Candy boards the plane of General Smight, who exacts her favors in exchange for a transfusion for her injured father. In New York her father is the patient of egomaniacal brain surgeon Krankeit. Following the operation, the patient wanders away unnoticed. Candy visits Greenwich Village and participates in a pornographic film shot in a public lavatory by Jonathan J. John. She then encounters a benevolent hunchback in Central Park, who is afterwards revealed to be an archcriminal. In the trailer of a truck Candy discovers Grindl

the Guru, a magus who teaches her the secrets of life during a drive to California. Searching for the Great Buddha, Candy finds a filthy hermit. He escorts her to a temple, where the pair have sexual relations. As a deluge destroys the temple and cleanses the hermit, Candy discovers that her lover has been her apparently amnesiac father. At a love-in, Candy is reunited with her many sexual partners, all in hippy garb, and afterwards assumed into the heavens. *Schoolteachers. Poets. Welsh. Mexicans. Gardeners. Soldiers. Physicians. Motion picture directors. Hunchbacks. Gurus. Hermits. Hippies. Adolescence. High school life. Filial relations. Drunkenness. Seduction. Rape. Lechery. Brain surgery. Buddhism. Incest. Sex exploitation films. Airplanes. Hospitals. Love-ins. New York City. New York City—Greenwich Village. New York City—Central Park. California.*

Note: Filmed on location in Rome, New York City, and in the desert near Barstow, California. Original running time: 124 min. Opened in Paris in Aug 1970; running time: 110 min. Italian title: *Candy e il sul pazzo mondo.*

CANDY BABY   F6.0647
Cinex Film Industries. 22 Jan **1969** [Champaign, Illinois, showing]. Sd; col. 35mm. 75 min.

Prod-Dir B. H. Dial. *Assoc Prod* Gillian Vastlake. *Writ* Gillian Vastlake. *Camera* Cecil R. Jones. *Asst Camera* Myron Mogul, IV. *Ed* Jacques Chien-Lit. *Asst Ed* Naja Nitlodge. *Sd* Humphrey Groundloupe. *Script Girl* Basta Laparola. *Stills* Herman Q. Muscleman.

Cast: Raphaela, Tina Bopper, Jody Graber, Georgy Girl, Katherine Howard, Judy Caine, Joseph Andrews, Elliot Rico, George Wilson, Steve De Naut, Laura Lynn, pseud, Cherie Winters, Maharishi Narish Yogi, Natasha George, Myron Mogul, IV, Hilliard Hotridge, Morris Towne, Bill McRoberts, Guiseppe Verdi.

Sex film. Elliot, a conservative newspaper reporter, is assigned to cover one of Peter's wild parties for a series on the "swinging generation." Peter offers candy to all of the guests; only Elliot is unaware that it contains a hallucinogenic drug. Ronnie, a "hip" reporter, explains that appearances are misleading. Toni, who appears to be happily married as she talks with her husband, is actually caught up in a fantasy of lesbian love. Across the room, a guru preaches to a teenybopper. She tries to relate a sexual encounter with Jody, another young guest, when her mind drifts back to the past: she recalls the boy's virgin awkwardness and her knowledgeable sexual instruction. Her thoughts return to the present, and she pulls the guru down onto the pillows. Elliot, now under the influence of the "candy," cannot resist the urge to look within the minds of other guests: a bored young woman sitting at the other side of the room joins a hippie boy in tying a hippie girl to a bed and forcing her to watch as they make love. Elliot tries to leave, but he is trapped in his own fantasy. A sophisticated blonde reaches out to him, and they begin to make love. He is surrounded by nude women who run their hands over his body and smile at his horror. He struggles to his feet and runs out the door in the grip of a drug-induced nightmare. *Reporters. Gurus. Hippies. Photographers. Lesbianism. Seduction. Sexual initiation. Psychedelic states. Sadism. Sensualism. LSD. Hallucinations.*

Note: Original title: *Candy.* Also known as *Dreamy Love Bed.*

THE CANDY MAN   F6.0648
Sagittarius Productions. *Dist* Allied Artists. Feb **1969** [c19 Feb 1969; LU3576]. Sd; col (Eastmancolor, print by DeLuxe). 35mm. 97 min. *MPAA rating* G.

Prod-Dir-Screenplay Herbert J. Leder. *Story* Francis Swann. *Photog* Gabriel Torres. *Art Dir* José Rodriguez Granada. *Film Ed* Juan José Marino. *Prod Mgr* Alfonso Sánchez Tello.

Cast: George Sanders *(Sidney Carter [Candy Man])*, Leslie Parrish *(Julia Evans)*, Manolo Fabregas *(Lieutenant Garcia)*, Gina Romand *(Greta Hansen)*, Carlos Cortez *(Rick Pierce)*, Pedro Galvan *(Roger West)*, Pixie Hopkins *(Maria Lopez)*, Nancy Rodman *(Gwen)*, Chuck Anderson *(Lee Stevens)*, Felix Gonzalez *(Felipe)*, Lupita Ferrat *(Jenny)*.

Crime melodrama. Sidney Carter, a British drug pusher in Mexico City who is known as the Candy Man, plans to kidnap the small daughter of Julia Evans, an American actress, with the help of addict Rick Pierce and his girl friend Greta. The plot fails when Greta, hired as the child's nursemaid, refuses to go through with the scheme and fights with Rick while another woman makes off with the child. Carter finds the woman, who is deranged over the loss of her own child, and he continues his plan to demand a ransom. The police, headed by Lieutenant Garcia, are brought into the case by Julia's manager, Roger, and her ex-husband, Lee, and they track him down after the payment is made. Cornered on a hotel window ledge with the child after a chase, Carter falls to his death as the police save the child. Julia is reunited with Lee and their daughter. *Drug dealers. Drug addicts. Actors. Americans in foreign countries. British. Police. Kidnaping. Marriage. Mexico City. Chases.*

Note: Location scenes filmed in Mexico City.

THE CANDY WEB see **13 FRIGHTENED GIRLS**

CANDY'S LUSTFUL NATURE F6.0649

Dist Emerson Film Enterprises. 26 Apr **1967** [Baltimore opening]. Sd; b&w. 35mm. 60 min.

Prod Michael Billings. *Dir* Nicholas Millard.

Cast: Lorna Vidman, Herman Rose, Nadia Witt.

Sex film. No information about the precise nature of this film has been found. *Sexuality.*

Note: Advertised as *Candy's Nature*; may also be known as *$100 Is My Price.*

CANNIBAL ORGY, OR THE MADDEST STORY EVER TOLD see **SPIDER BABY**

CANNON FOR CORDOBA F6.0650

Mirisch Productions. *Dist* United Artists. 7 Oct **1970** [Boston opening; c7 Oct 1970; LP38251]. Sd; col (DeLuxe). 35mm (Panavision). 104 min. *MPAA rating* GP.

Prod Vincent M. Fennelly. *Assoc Prod & Screenplay* Stephen Kandel. *Dir* Paul Wendkos. *Dir Photog* Antonio Macasoli. *Camera Op* Ricardo Navarrete. *Art Dir* José María Tapiador. *Set Decor* Rafael Salazar. *Film Ed* Walter Hannemann. *Mus* Elmer Bernstein. *Sd Mix* Roy Charman. *Sd* George Rice. *Asst Dir* José María Ochoa. *Prod Supv* Robert Goodstein. *Prod Mgr* Eduardo G. Maroto. *Script Supv* Eva del Castillo. *Wardrobe* Eric Seelig. *Makeup* Ricardo Vazquez. *Hairdressing* Adela del Pino. *Sp Eff* Alex Weldon. *Prop Master* Art Cole.

Cast: George Peppard (*Capt. Rod Douglas*), Giovanna Ralli (*Leonora*), Raf Vallone (*Cordoba*), Pete Duel (*Andy Rice*), Don Gordon (*Sgt. Jackson Harkness*), Nico Minardos (*Peter Andros*), John Russell (*Brig. Gen. John J. Pershing*), Francine York (*Sophia*), John Larch (*Harry Warner*), Charles Stalnaker (*Captain Riggs*), John Clarke (*Major Wall*), Gabriele Tinti (*Lieut. Antonio Gutierrez*), Hans Meyer (*Svedborg*), Janis Hansen (*girl*), Lionel Murton, Richard Pendry, Takis Emmanuel.

Western melodrama. Hector Cordoba, a bandit who is also a general in Pancho Villa's Mexican revolutionary army, attacks a United States Army fort a short distance over the border. Gen. John Pershing blames Captain Douglas for not alerting the soldiers to the impending attack; he orders Douglas to capture Cordoba and bring him back to the United States for trial. For the mission, Douglas assembles a small commando band, including Andy Rice, Sgt. Jackson Harkness, Peter Andros, and Lieut. Antonio Gutierrez, the Mexican envoy. They depart for Mexico where they are to meet Leonora, a young woman who had been raped by Cordoba and is now willing to lead the commandos to his fortress headquarters. According to their plan, Leonora and Gutierrez are to pose as deserters to gain entry; once inside, Leonora is to seduce Cordoba and allow the commandos to capture him. Instead, Leonora betrays Gutierrez when they meet Cordoba, and Cordoba imprisons the entire commando unit. Douglas escapes from the jail, frees Rice and Gutierrez, and they seize Cordoba. Dynamite and flamethrowers are used to destroy the fortress, and Cordoba is shot by one of his own men as the commandos make their escape. *Bandits. Commandos. Revolutionaries. Imposture. Seduction. Perfidy. Prison escapes. Forts. Dynamite. Flamethrowers. Mexico—History—1910–17. Mexican border. John Joseph Pershing. United States Army.*

Note: Filmed on location in Spain. Prerelease title: *Dragon Master.*

I CANNONI DI SAN SEBASTIAN see **GUNS FOR SAN SEBASTIAN**

LOS CAÑONES DE SAN SEBASTIÁN see **GUNS FOR SAN SEBASTIAN**

CAPE FEAR F6.0651

Melville-Talbot Productions. *Dist* Universal-International. 12 Apr **1962** [Miami, Florida, opening; c18 Dec 1961; LP24729]. Sd; b&w. 35mm. 105 min.

Prod Sy Bartlett. *Dir* J. Lee Thompson. *Screenplay* James R. Webb. *Photog* Sam Leavitt. *Art Dir* Alexander Golitzen, Robert Boyle. *Set Decor* Oliver Emert. *Film Ed* George Tomasini. *Mus* Bernard Herrmann. *Sd* Waldon O. Watson, Corson Jowett. *Asst Dir* Ray Gosnell, Jr. *Prod Mgr* Ernest B. Wehmeyer. *Cost* Mary Wills. *Makeup* Frank Prehoda, Tom Tuttle. *Hairstyles* Virginia Darcy.

Cast: Gregory Peck (*Sam Bowden*), Robert Mitchum (*Max Cady*), Polly Bergen (*Peggy Bowden*), Lori Martin (*Nancy Bowden*), Martin Balsam (*Mark Dutton*), Jack Kruschen (*Dave Grafton*), Telly Savalas (*Charles Sievers*), Barrie Chase (*Diane Taylor*), Paul Comi (*Garner*), John McKee (*Officer Marconi*), Page Slattery (*Deputy Kersek*), Ward Ramsey (*Officer Brown*), Edward Platt (*judge*), Will Wright (*Dr. Pearsall*), Joan Staley (*waitress*), Norma Yost (*ticket clerk*), Mack Williams (*Dr. Lowney*), Thomas Newman (*Lieutenant Gervasi*), Alan Reynolds (*Vernon*), Herb Armstrong (*waiter*), Bunny Rhea (*pianist*), Carol Sydes (*Betty*), Alan Wells, Allan Ray (*young blades*), Paul Levitt (*police operator*).

Melodrama. Source: John D. MacDonald, *The Executioners* (New York, 1958). Following a 6-year imprisonment for committing a sadistic sex crime, Max Cady arrives in a small southern town to seek revenge on the man responsible for his conviction, counselor Sam Bowden. Although Cady makes no direct threats, it is apparent that he is after Sam's wife, Peggy, and his 12-year-old daughter, Nancy. Because he has broken no law, neither Sam nor the police are able to take any legal action against him. Consequently, Sam cannot prevent Cady from poisoning the family dog, menacing Nancy when she leaves school, and whispering obscenities to Peggy over the telephone. Furthermore, Cady refuses to be bribed or bullied out of town. Desperate, Sam decides to take the law into his hands and lay a trap for Cady. After hiding his wife and daughter in a houseboat on the Cape Fear River, he leaves town. He then secretly returns, hopeful that Cady has discovered the hiding place. The ruse works, and Cady arrives on the scene late one night. Following a furious struggle in the river, Sam overpowers Cady and once more is instrumental in sending him to prison. *Lawyers. Sex deviates. Police. Family life. Ex-convicts. Sadism. Smalltown life. Revenge. United States—South. Houseboats. Cape Fear River. Dogs.*

THE CAPER OF THE GOLDEN BULLS F6.0652

Greene-Rouse Productions. *For* Paramount Pictures/Embassy Pictures. *Dist* Embassy Pictures. 24 May **1967** [Detroit opening]. Sd; col (Pathé Color). 35mm. 105 min.

Pres by Joseph E. Levine. *Prod* Clarence Greene. *Exec Prod* Joseph E. Levine. *Dir* Russell Rouse. *Screenplay* Ed Waters, David Moessinger. *Photog* Hal Stine. *Art Dir* Hal Pereira, Arthur Lonergan. *Set Decor* Arthur Krams, Robert R. Benton. *Film Ed* Chester W. Schaeffer, Robert Wyman. *Mus & Main Theme* Vic Mizzy. *Sd* Terry Kellum, Ray Cossar, John Wilkinson. *Asst Dir* Danny McCauley. *Prod Mgr* Maurie M. Suess, Robert Goldstein, Frank Caffey. *Cost* Edith Head. *Men's Wardrobe* Robert Magahay. *Makeup* Wally Westmore, Hal Lierley. *Hairstyles* Nellie Manley, Hedvig Mjorud. *Dial Coach* Leon Charles.

Cast: Stephen Boyd (*Peter Churchman*), Yvette Mimieux (*Grace Harvey*), Giovanna Ralli (*Angela Tresler*), Walter Slezak (*Antonio Gonzalez*), Vito Scotti (*François Morel*), Clifton James (*Philippe Lemoins*), Lomax Study (*Paul Brissard*), Tom Toner (*Canalli*), Henry Beckman (*Bendell*), Noah Keen (*Ryan*), Jay Novello (*Carlos*), Arnold Moss (*Mr. Shahari*), Leon Askin (*Morchek*), Leon Charles (*deafmute*), J. G. Devlin.

Crime melodrama. Source: William P. McGivern, *The Caper of the Golden Bulls* (New York, 1966). During World War II, bomber pilot Peter Churchman accidentally destroyed a French cathedral while on a mission to Germany. Following the war, he and his crew robbed several banks in Germany to pay anonymously for the restoration of the cathedral. Having later become a respected restaurateur in the Spanish town of Santa Maria, Peter thoroughly enjoys both his position and his relationship with another American expatriate, Grace Harvey, to whom he is engaged. One day he receives a visit from Angela Tresler, a wartime accomplice, who threatens to expose his past unless he masterminds and executes the robbery of the bank at Pamplona during the annual Fiesta of San Fermin. Moreover, Angela has sent for Peter's bomber crew and coerced them into also joining in the venture. Forced to yield to her demands, Peter and his crew, accompanied by Grace, travel to Pamplona. As the fiesta begins, the men tape explosives and tools to their chests and join the local male populace in the traditional running before the bulls through the narrow town streets. As they reach a storeroom adjoining the bank, they dash into an alley, break into the basement, and blast their way into the bank, synchronizing the explosion with a cannon blast from the bull ring. Once inside the bank, Peter crawls along a high ledge, disconnects the alarm system, and opens a vault containing the jewels intended for the adornment of religious statues used in the procession. As planned, the gems are passed through a transom into a huge hollow carnival statue carried by one of Angela's accomplices. Peter and his cohorts escape to safety, but they discover that Angela does not have the jewels. Acting on her own, Grace hid in a duplicate carnival statue, took the jewels as they were passed through the transom, and turned them over to police inspector Gonzalez to embellish the shabby and weathered statue of the Virgin of Santa Maria. Enraged, Angela leaves Pamplona as Peter and Grace join in the fiesta. *Air pilots. Veterans. Restaurateurs. Expatriates. Police. Aerial bombardment. Bank robberies. Blackmail. Cathedrals. Jewels. Carnivals. World War II. Pamplona. Explosions. Bulls.*

Note: Location scenes filmed in Pamplona and Madrid.

LA CAPERUCITA ROJA see **LITTLE RED RIDING HOOD**

CAPERUCITA Y PULGARCITO CONTRA LOS MONSTRUOS see **LITTLE RED RIDING HOOD AND THE MONSTERS**

CAPERUCITA Y SUS TRES AMIGOS see **LITTLE RED RIDING HOOD AND HER FRIENDS**

CAPITAINE MORGAN see **MORGAN THE PIRATE**

LE CAPORAL ÉPINGLÉ see **THE ELUSIVE CORPORAL**

CAPRICE   F6.0653

Melcher-Arcola Productions. *Dist* Twentieth Century-Fox Film Corp. 7 Jun **1967** [New York opening; c24 May 1967; LP34467]. Sd (Westrex); col (De Luxe). 35mm (CinemaScope). 98 min.

An Aaron Rosenberg-Martin Melcher Production. *Prod* Aaron Rosenberg, Martin Melcher. *Assoc Prod* Barney Rosenzweig. *Dir* Frank Tashlin. *Screenplay* Jay Jayson, Frank Tashlin. *Story* Martin Hale, Jay Jayson. *Dir Photog* Leon Shamroy. *Aerial Photog* Nelson Tyler. *Art Dir* Jack Martin Smith, William Creber. *Set Decor* Walter M. Scott, Jerry Wunderlich. *Titl* National Screen Service. *Film Ed* Robert Simpson. *Mus* De Vol. *Orch* Al Woodbury. *Song:* "Caprice" Larry Marks. *Sung by* Doris Day. *Sd* Harry M. Lindgren, David Dockendorf. *Asst Dir* David Silver. *Unit Prod Mgr* Francisco Day. *Cost Dsgn* Ray Aghayan. *Makeup* Ben Nye, Harry Maret. *Miss Day's Hair Styles* Barbara Lampson. *Hair Styles Supv* Margaret Donovan. *Sp Photog Eff* L. B. Abbott, Emil Kosa, Jr. "Batman" television seq based on characters created by Bob Kane.

Cast: Doris Day (*Patricia Fowler [Foster]*), Richard Harris (*Christopher White*), Ray Walston (*Stuart Clancy*), Jack Kruschen (*Matthew Cutter*), Edward Mulhare (*Sir Jason Fox*), Lilia Skala (*Madame Piasco*), Irene Tsu (*Su Ling*), Larry D. Mann (*Inspector Kapinsky*), Maurice Marsac (*Auber*), Michael Romanoff (*butler*), Lisa Seagram (*Mandy*), Michael J. Pollard (*Barney*), Fritz Feld (*Swiss innkeeper*), Leon Shamroy.

Comedy. Pat Fowler, an industrial spy employed by Sir Jason Fox of Femina Cosmetics, is arrested in Paris for attempting to sell the formula for a new deodorant to a rival firm owned by Matt Cutter. The arrest is actually a ruse concocted by Sir Jason to trick Cutter into hiring Pat. The scheme works, and Pat sets out to steal the secret formula for a spray that prevents hair from getting wet even when under water. The spray is the invention of the eccentric Dr. Stuart Clancy, Cutter's top cosmetician. Also involved in the espionage is Christopher White, a double agent who lures Pat to his apartment, drugs her, and tape records all she knows about Sir Jason's enterprises. He also learns that Pat's father, an Interpol agent, was shot to death on a Swiss ski slope while on the trail of a narcotics ring. Upon discovering that all of Clancy's preparations are actually formulated in Switzerland by his mother-in-law, Madame Piasco, Pat flies there and steals a vial of the hair spray from the woman's cosmetics shop. Afterwards, she goes skiing on the slope where her father was killed and is saved from a similar fate by Christopher, who comes to the rescue in a helicopter. Now certain that Clancy is her father's murderer, Pat confides in Christopher and learns that he is her father's Interpol replacement. After uncovering evidence which proves that Sir Jason and Clancy are concealing narcotics in a brand of face powder which the innocent Cutter retails, Pat is trapped by a menacing scrubwoman—Clancy in disguise. Clancy meets his own death when he tries to kill Pat. But Pat is again trapped, this time by Sir Jason, who forces her into a waiting helicopter. When it takes off, Christopher fires a shot and kills Sir Jason. His body falls from the open helicopter, and the terrified Pat is left alone in the cockpit. Miraculously she manages to fly to Paris and makes a 2-point landing on top of the Eiffel Tower. Scrambling out of the plane, she races into the arms of the waiting Christopher. *Spies. Businesswomen. Eccentrics. Business ethics. Skiing. Murder. Disguise. Imposture. Cosmetics. Secret formulas. Narcotics. Helicopters. Paris. Switzerland. INTERPOL. Eiffel Tower.*

Note: Location scenes filmed in Switzerland, Paris, and California.

LES CAPRICES DE MARIE see **GIVE HER THE MOON**

CAPRICIOUS SUMMER (Czechoslovakia)   F6.0654

Barrandov Film Studio. *For* Československý Film. *Dist* Sigma III Corp. 24 Sep **1968** [New York opening]. Sd; col (Eastman Color). 35mm. 75 min.

Pres by Carlo Ponti. *Prod* Jan Libora, Vladimír Kalina. *Dir* Jiří Menzel. *Screenplay* Jiří Menzel, Václav Nývlt. *Dir Photog* Jaromír Šofr. *Art Dir* Ladislav Winkelhofer. *Prod Dsgn* Oldřich Bosák. *Film Ed* Jiřina Lukešová. *Mus* Jiří Šust. *Choreog* Luboš Oboun. *Sd* Jiří Pavlík. *Asst Dir* Miloš Kohout. *Prod Mgr* Olga Dimitrovová. *Cost Dsgn* Olga Dimitrovová.

Cast: Rudolf Hrušínský (*Antonín Dura*), Vlastimil Brodský (*Major Hugo*), František Řehák (*Canon Roch*), Míla Myslíková (*Katerine Durová*), Jana Drchalová (*Anna*), Jiří Menzel (*Arnostek*), Bohuš Záhorský, K. Hovorka, A. Pražák.

Comedy. Source: Vladislav Vančura, *Rozmarné léto* (Prague, 1926). At the turn of the century in a small town, three middle-aged men—Dura, a bathhouse owner; Major Hugo, a retired army officer; and Canon Roch, the local abbé— witness the arrival of Arnostek, a touring tightrope walker, and his young

assistant, Anna. The three men attend the tightrope walker's performance in the town square that evening, and they all become enchanted with Anna. Encouraged by her flirtatious manner, Dura attempts to seduce her in his bathhouse, but they are interrupted by the sudden appearance of Katerine, Dura's plumpish wife. Katerine, infatuated with Arnostek, packs her things and moves into his caravan. The next evening, Canon Roch is visiting Anna, ostensibly to read to her, when some village toughs barge in and start a fight. On the third night, Major Hugo lures Anna to his home for an elegant feast, but the food and wine prove too much for him, and he falls asleep on Anna's lap. By the next morning, Arnostek has become so bored by Katerine's smothering attentions that he sends her back to Dura and goes to fetch Anna. Somewhat wiser after their brush with seduction, the three friends and Katerine resume their summer existence, and the little caravan leaves town. *Clergymen. Veterans. Baths. Tightrope walkers. Smalltown life. Middle age. Flirtation. Infidelity. Seduction. Drunkenness. Carnivals. Summer.*

Note: Released in Czechoslovakia in 1968 as *Rozmarné léto.*

CAPTAIN CLEGG see **NIGHT CREATURES**

CAPTAIN MILKSHAKE   F6.0655

Richmark Productions. 10 Nov **1970** [San Diego, California, opening]. Sd; col with b&w seq (Technicolor). 35mm (Techniscope). 89 min. *MPAA rating* R.

A Joint Adventure Production. *Prod-Dir* Richard Crawford. *Exec Prod* Lloyd Marcus. *Co-prod* Harvey B. Levitt. *Screenplay* Richard Crawford, Barry Leichtling. *Dir Photog* Robert A. Sherry. *Slow Motion & Combat Photog* Joe Purcell. *Film Ed* David Korn, Richard Crawford. *Song:* "Children of the Future" Steve Miller. *Perf by* Steve Miller Band. *Song:* "Who Do You Love" Gene McDaniels. *Sung by* Quicksilver Messenger Service. *Song:* "Untitled Protest" Joe McDonald. *Sung by* Country Joe & the Fish. *Song:* "Oh, Death" J. Reedy. *Perf by* Kaleidoscope. *Song:* "Lie to Me" David Lindley, Solomon Feldthouse, Stuart A. Brotman, Paul Lagos, Templeton Parcely. *Sung by* Kaleidoscope. *Songs:* "Fall in Love With Life," "Run With My Rhythm" writ & sung by Eric Selten. *Song:* "Minor Miracle" writ & sung by Richard Johnson, mus. *Song:* "Who's Zoo" writ & sung by Bud Conway. *Song:* "Untitled Guitar Song" writ & sung by Wayne Stromberg. *Song:* "Ballad of Tommy Udo" David Lindley. *Songs:* "Tanya," "Ballad of Tommy Udo" sung by Kaleidoscope. *Sd* Richard Pitstick. *Asst Dir* Don Russell. *Sp Vis Eff* Phra Visuals, Vega Visuals, Reggie Hager. *Sp Combat Eff* Harry Woolman. *Sp Photog Eff* Cinedepth.

Cast: Geoff Gage (*Paul Fredericks*), Andrea Cagan (*Melissa Hamilton*), David Korn (*Thesp*), Ronald Barca (*Anchovy*), Evelyn King (*Evelyn*), Belle Greer (*Mrs. Fredericks*), Joanne Moore Jordan (*Mrs. Randolph*), Darlene Conley (*Mrs. Hamilton*), James Ashton (*Uncle Jimson*), Stuart Lancaster (*cabby*), Wally Starr (*Mr. Toliver*), Buddy Pantsari (*priest*), Barry Leichtling (*Lightning*), Rob Reece (*Frank*), Kip Winsett (*Kip*), Hal Neilsen, James Hourigan (*border guards*), Paul Lagos (*Bubber*), Edward O'Brien (*O. B.*), George Driver (*Loose George*), Richard Morrill (*Dr. Haskell*), Trans Love Airways.

Melodrama. On emergency leave from Vietnam to attend the funeral of his stepfather, U. S. Marine Paul Fredericks arrives in San Diego and is given a lift by college student Melissa Hamilton, who is meeting Thesp, the leader of the hippie commune to which she belongs. Paul, attracted to Melissa, joins her and her friends, who introduce him to marijuana. Paul accompanies Melissa, Anchovy, another commune member, and Thesp, who is also a drug dealer, on a smuggling run (ostensibly a holiday) across the Mexican border. They are searched on their return, but border guards do not find the hidden marijuana; and Paul accuses Melissa of having known they were carrying contraband. On his last day of leave, Paul seeks out Melissa at an antiwar demonstration in Berkeley, but she breaks off with him. Returning to Vietnam, Paul is killed in action. *Hitchhikers. Students. Hippies. Drug dealers. Border police. Communal living. Smuggling. Disillusionment. Funerals. Marijuana. Demonstrations. Vietnam War 1964–73. San Diego. Mexican border. Berkeley (California). United States Marines.*

Note: Location scenes filmed in and around San Diego and in Berkeley during an antiwar demonstration held in People's Park.

CAPTAIN NEMO AND THE UNDERWATER CITY (Great Britain)   F6.0656

Omnia Films. *Dist* Metro-Goldwyn-Mayer, Inc. Mar **1970** [c19 Jan 1970; LP37531]. Sd; col (Metrocolor). 35mm (Panavision). 106 min.

A Bertram Ostrer-Steven Pallos Production. *Prod* Bertram Ostrer. *Exec Prod* Steven Pallos. *Dir* James Hill. *Screenplay* Pip Baker, Jane Baker, R. Wright Campbell. *Dir Photog* Alan Hume. *Underwater Photog* Egil S. Woxholt. *Camera Op* Godfrey Godar. *Art Dir* Bill Andrews. *Film Ed* Bill Lewthwaite. *Mus* Wally Stott. *Mus Cond* Marcus Dods. *Rec Supv* A. W. Watkins. *Sd Ed* Jim Sibley. *Sd Rec* Cyril Swern. *Dub Mix* Bob Jones. *Asst Dir* Ted Lewis. *Prod Supv* Albert Becket. *Prod Mgr* Terry Lens. *Cont* June Randall.

Cost Dsgn Olga Lehmann. *Makeup* Ernest Gasser. *Hairstyles* Alice Holmes. *Sp Eff* Jack Mills, photog, George Gibbs, Richard Conway.

Cast: Robert Ryan *(Captain Nemo)*, Chuck Connors *(Sen. Robert Fraser)*, Nanette Newman *(Helena)*, John Turner *(Joab)*, Luciana Paluzzi *(Mala)*, Bill Fraser *(Barnaby)*, Kenneth Connor *(Swallow)*, Allan Cuthbertson *(Lomax)*, Christopher Hartstone *(Philip)*, Vincent Harding *(mate-navigator)*, Ralph Nossek *(engineer)*, Michael McGovern, Alan Barry, Anthony Bailey *(sailors)*, Ann Patrice, Margot Ley, Patsy Snell *(barmaids)*, Ian Ramsey *(Adam)*, John Moore, actor *(Skipper)*.

Science fiction melodrama. Inspired by characters created by: Jules Verne. In the early 1860's, the submarine *Nautilus I* picks up six survivors shipwrecked in an Atlantic storm. The submarine takes the survivors to Templemer, a self-contained underwater city ruled by Captain Nemo, who is attempting to establish an underwater utopia. Lomax, one of those rescued, is claustrophobic and dies while frantically trying to escape. U. S. Senator Fraser tries to persuade Nemo to allow him to continue his diplomatic mission, the prevention of the spread of the American Civil War to Europe. Two brothers, Barnaby and Swallow, also wish to depart, but for a different motive: Templemer is rich with gold extracted from the sea, and the brothers plan to steal the gold and carry it to the mainland. They persuade Joab, Nemo's first mate, to allow them to commandeer the smaller *Nautilus II* which Nemo has based in the glass-domed city. Meanwhile, Senator Fraser and Nemo succeed in destroying Mobula, an enormous sea monster that had been threatening the city; Fraser then joins Barnaby and Swallow in an attempt to reach the surface in the stolen submarine. In the course of their escape, the ship is wrecked and Barnaby is killed, but Fraser and Swallow are rescued on the surface by a passing ship. *Ship crews. Sea captains. Diplomats. Brothers. Ship crews. Sea rescue. Claustrophobia. Utopia. Theft. Submarines. Underwater cities. Gold. United States Congress. Shipwrecks. Sea monsters.*

Note: Opened in London in Dec 1969.

CAPTAIN NEWMAN, M. D. F6.0657

Brentwood Productions-Reynard Productions. *Dist* Universal Pictures. 25 Dec **1963** [Los Angeles opening; c4 Apr 1964; LP34721]. Sd (Westrex); col (Eastman Color by Pathé). 35mm. 126 min.

Prod Robert Arthur. *Dir* David Miller. *2d Unit Dir* Robert D. Webb. *Screenplay* Richard Breen, Phoebe Ephron, Henry Ephron. *Dir Photog* Russell Metty. *Camera Op* Ed Pyle. *Asst Camera* Ledger Haddow, Eugene Lenoir. *Art Dir* Alexander Golitzen, Alfred Sweeney. *Set Decor* Howard Bristol. *Set Coörd* Fred Knoth. *Main Titl* Pacific Title. *Film Ed* Alma Macrorie. *Asst Ed* Edward Broussard. *Mus Supv* Frank Skinner. *Mus Supv* Joseph Gershenson. *Sd* Waldon O. Watson, William Russell. *Sd Asst* John Oliver, John Erlinger, Henry Janssen. *Asst Dir* Phil Bowles, Bill Gilmore, Terry Morse, Jr. *Unit Prod Mgr* Joseph Behm. *Script Supv* Marshall Schlom. *Cost Dsgn* Rosemary Odell. *Wardrobe* Seth Banks, John Lucas, Norman Mayreis, Dina Joseph. *Makeup Supv* Bud Westmore. *Makeup* Frank Prehoda, Frank McCoy, Jean Abbott. *Hairstyles* Larry Germain, Emma Di Vittorio. *Matte* Albert Whitlock. *Sp Eff* Walter Hammond. *Tech Adv* B. A. Whitaker, (Maj. USAF), Sherwyn Woods, (Capt. USAF). *Dial Coach* Leon Charles. *Still Photog* Rollie Lane. *Grip* Charles Cowie, Ken Smith. *Prop* Tony Lombardo, Jeff Stanton, Al Larusch.

Cast: Gregory Peck *(Capt. Josiah J. Newman)*, Tony Curtis *(Corp. Jackson Laibowitz)*, Angie Dickinson *(Lieut. Francie Corum)*, Bobby Darin *(Corp. Jim Tompkins)*, Eddie Albert *(Col. Norval Algate Bliss)*, Bethel Leslie *(Mrs. Paul Cabot Winston)*, Larry Storch *(Corporal Gavoni)*, Jane Withers *(Lieut. Grace Blodgett)*, Dick Sargent *(Lieutenant Alderson)*, Syl Lamont *(Sergeant Kopp)*, James Gregory *(Col. Edgar Pyser)*, Robert F. Simon *(Lieutenant Colonel Larrabee)*, Paul Carr *(Werbel)*, Vito Scotti *(Maj. Alfredo Fortuno)*, Crahan Denton *(Major General Snowden)*, Gregory Walcott *(Captain Howard)*, Charles Briggs *(Gorkow)*, Robert Duvall *(Capt. Paul Cabot Winston)*, Penny Santon *(waitress at Blue Grotto)*, Amzie Strickland *(Kathie)*, Barry Atwater *(Major Dawes)*, Ann Doran *(Mrs. Pyser)*, Joey Walsh *(Maccarades)*, Byron Morrow *(Hollingshead)*, David Landfield *(corporal)*, Ron Brogan *(chaplain [priest])*, Robert Strong *(chaplain [rabbi])*, John Hart *(officer)*, Sammy Reese *(Haskell)*, Ted Bessell *(Carrozzo)*, Martin West, David Winters, Marc Cavell, Seamon Glass, Jack Grinnage *(patients)*.

Comedy-drama. Source: Leo Rosten, *Captain Newman, M. D.* (New York, 1961). Captain Newman, head of the neuropsychiatric section at a Southwestern Army air base during World War II, is badgered by his commanding officer because he grounds so many men and is slow in returning them to active duty. Newman is assisted by Lieut. Francie Corum, a nurse with whom he has an affair; Lieut. Grace Blodgett, another nurse, who provides the patients with a "mother" image; and Corp. Jackson Laibowitz, a New Jersey Jew and Newman's chief orderly, who, although untrained in medical arts, has an innate understanding of human behavior. Among Newman's patients is Colonel Bliss, who has a guilt complex about the many men he has sent into combat never to return. Bliss does not respond to treatment and ultimately

commits suicide by jumping off a water tower. Corporal Tompkins, another patient, considers himself a coward for failing to rescue a buddy from a burning plane, although Tompkins has been decorated for his bravery in 34 missions. He is cured by Newman, only to be killed in combat upon returning to active duty. Captain Winston, brought in in a catatonic state, is successfully treated with the help of his wife and set on the path to complete recovery. Newman, Corum, Laibowitz, and Blodgett continue their discouraging job of curing men and sending them back to the front. *Physicians. Air pilots. Jews. Nurses. War heroes. Orderlies (hospital). Psychiatry. Battle fatigue. Guilt. Suicide. Cowardice. Catalepsy. Hospitals. World War II. United States Army—Air Force.*

Note: Locations filmed in Arizona.

CAPTAIN SINBAD F6.0658

King Brothers Productions. *Dist* Metro-Goldwyn-Mayer, Inc. 19 Jun **1963** [Boston opening; c16 May 1963; LP26348]. Sd; col (Technicolor). 35mm. 85 min.

Prod Frank King, Herman King. *Dir* Byron Haskin. *Orig Story-Screenplay* Samuel B. West, Harry Relis. *Dir Photog* Günter Senftleben. *Photog* Eugen Shuftan. *Camera Op* Ernst Wild. *Art Dir* Werner Schlichting, Isabella Schlichting. *Set Dressing* Arno Richter. *Film Ed* Robert Swink. *Assoc Ed* Eric Boyd-Perkins. *Asst Ed* George E. Swink, Hal Ashby. *Mus Comp* Michel Michelet. *Symphonic Orch Cond* Kurt Graunke. *Choreog* Gene Reed. *Sd Ed* Don Hall, Jr. *Sd Engr* Walter Ruhland. *1st Asst Dir* Frank Guthke. *Asst Dir-Prod Supv* Leon Chooluck. *Asst to the Prod* James Dobson. *Unit Mgr* Wolfgang von Schiber, Karl-Heinz Eisner. *Script Supv* Trudy von Trotha. *Supv Wardrobe* Harry Haynes. *Wardrobe Mistress* Tina Swanson. *Ballet Cost Dsgn* Ingrid Winter. *Cost* Nathans of London. *Makeup Artist* Josef Coesfeld. *Sp Eff* Lee Zavitz, Augie Lohman. *Sp Photog Eff* Tom Howard. *Animal Handler* Hans Paul Eiber.

Cast: Guy Williams *(Captain Sinbad)*, Heidi Brühl *(Princess Jana)*, Pedro Armendariz *(El Kerim)*, Abraham Sofaer *(Galgo)*, Bernie Hamilton *(Quintus)*, Helmut Schneider *(Bendar)*, Margaret Jahnen *(lady-in-waiting)*, Rolf Wanka *(The King)*, Walter Barnes *(Rolf)*, James Dobson *(Iffrich)*, Maurice Marsac *(Ahmed)*, Henry Brandon *(Colonel Kabar)*, John Crawford *(Aram)*, Geoffrey Toone *(Mohar)*, John Schapar, Anna Luise Schubert *(dance soloists)*, The Reed-Schapar Dancers, Lawrence Montaigne, Guy Doleman, Charles Fawcett, Peter Brace, Burr Jerger, Ludwig Schultze, Hans Schumm, David Wilding, Fred Haggerty, Joe Powell.

Fantasy. In ancient Baristan, Captain Sinbad falls in love with the beautiful Princess Jana, whose father, the king, is under the evil spell of a villainous tyrant, El Kerim. El Kerim has seized control of the kingdom and plans to marry Princess Jana. Upon learning that El Kerim is indestructible because his heart is locked in an ivory tower guarded by multiheaded, fire-breathing monsters, Sinbad and his loyal followers set out to find the tower. After encountering numerous perils (an invisible monster, a nine-headed scylla, an attack upon their ship by giant prehistoric birds), they finally reach the tower. El Kerim has also arrived by magic to protect his heart, but Sinbad slays the tyrant and saves Princess Jana from the death El Kerim had planned for her. *Royalty. Despots. Magic. Invisibility. Imaginary kingdoms. Sinbad. Monsters.*

Note: Filmed in Munich. Also reviewed as *Captain Sindbad*.

THE CAPTIVES (Denmark) F6.0659

BT København. *Dist* Phoenix International Films. 17 Jul **1970** [Kansas City, Kansas, opening]. Sd; col. 35mm. [Feature film, length unknown.]

Dir Carl Borch. *Photog* E. R. Frederiksen. *Ed Supv* Peter Cooke, ed. *Sd Rec* Hans Sørensen. *Asst Dir* Brüel Marquart.

Cast: Brigit Krøyer *(Avi)*, Karl Hansen *(Max C. Kragh)*, Orla Nsu *(Edith)*, Leif Betheas *(Jorgen)*, Annelise Dette *(Liala)*, Emil Kjarum *(Steen)*.

Drama. Source: T. J. Møller, *Fire* (publication undetermined). While driving to their rural retreat, wealthy industrialist Max. C. Kragh and his wife, Edith, are abducted by four drug-crazed, adolescent hitchhikers—Avi, Steen, Jorgen, and Liala. The four break into a vacant house, where they subject the couple to a night of terror, raping Edith in the presence of her helpless husband. *Industrialists. Hitchhikers. Abduction. Rape. Adolescence. Narcotics.*

Note: Original title and release undetermined.

THE CAPTIVES see **ESCAPE TO BERLIN**

CAPTURE THAT CAPSULE! F6.0660

Riviera Productions. 16 Aug **1961** [Detroit opening; c6 Jun 1961; LP19506]. Sd; b&w. 35mm. 75 min.

Prod-Dir Will Zens. *Assoc Prod* Mar Nelson. *Story-Screenplay* Jan Elblein, Will Zens. *Photog* Vilis Lapenieks. *Art Dir* Cliff Bertrand. *Film Ed* Bill Schaefer. *Mus Comp* Arthur Hopkins. *Sd Rec* Floyd Crow. *Sd Eff* Leif Rise. *Asst Dir* David Bradley. *Prod Mgr* John P. Bradley.

Cast: Richard Miller *(Ed Nowak)*, Dick O'Neill *(Al)*, Richard Jordahl *(Henry)*, Pat Bradley *(Jack Reynolds)*, Carl Rogers *(Hamilton)*, Dorothy

Schiller (Mary), Ed Siani (Borman), Doug Hughes (Joe), Wylie Carter (Mac), Michael David (boy), LaRae Phillips (beach girl), Jack Treacy (Art), Ed Gangel (Webster), Richard Twohy (Persinger), Miriam Wilson (party girl), Ron Wright, Lee Fortner (boat men), Gene Garner, Web Smith (fish and game officers).

Melodrama. As a special rocket missile with a secret data capsule is fired from Cape Canaveral, a spy ring plots its course by means of technical information received from a contact. Unknown to the spies, the Air Force, the CIA, and the FBI have been aware of the conspiracy and have been supplying false information through their own plants. To further confuse the enemy, a dummy capsule is dropped into the area where the spies are searching. The conspirators retrieve their prize, unaware that the capsule contains a miniature radio transmitter, which informs government agents of the spies' whereabouts. A chase develops over land and sea, highlighted by a murderous encounter with skin divers, a careening ride in a stolen sports car, and the frustrating pursuit of a small boy, who, upon discovering the capsule, scampers off with it. The government agents eventually outwit the spies and bring them to justice. *Spies. Divers. Children. Conspiracy. Theft. Rockets. Radio. Cape Canaveral. United States Air Force. United States—Central Intelligence Agency. United States— Federal Bureau of Investigation. Chases.*

Note: Location scenes filmed in California.

LA CARA DEL TERROR see **FACE OF TERROR**

LES CARABINIERS (France/Italy)   **F6.0661**
Rome-Paris Films–Laetitia Films–Les Films Marceau-Cocinor. *Dist* West End Films, Inc., New Yorker Films. 25 Apr **1968** [New York opening]. Sd; b&w. 35mm. 80 min.

Prod Georges de Beauregard, Carlo Ponti. *Dir* Jean-Luc Godard. *Screenplay* Roberto Rossellini, Jean Gruault, Jean-Luc Godard. *Photog* Raoul Coutard. *Asst Photog* Claude Beausoleil. *Art Dir* Jean-Jacques Fabre. *Film Ed* Agnès Guillemot. *Mus* Philippe Arthuys. *Asst Dir* Charles Bitsch, Jean-Paul Savignac. *Prod Mgr* Roger Scipion.

Cast: Geneviève Galéa (Venus), Catherine Ribeiro (Cleopatra), Marino Masè (Michelangelo), Albert Juross (Ulysses), Gérard Poirot, Jean Brassat, Alvaro Gheri (carabiniers), Barbet Schroeder (car salesman), Jean Gruault (baby's father), Jean-Louis Comolli (soldier with fish), Odile Geoffroy (girl revolutionary), Catherine Durant ("la femme du monde"), Jean Monsigny, Gilbert Servien (soldiers), Wladimir Faters (revolutionary), Roger Coggio, Pascale Audret (couple in car).

Allegory. Source: Benjamin Joppolo, *I carabinieri* (adapted by Jacques Audiberti; Paris opening: 28 May 1958). In response to a summons from the king of an unspecified country, two oafish brothers, Ulysses and Michelangelo, leave their ramshackle home to go off to war. The summons is delivered by two military policemen (carabiniers) who describe the joys of being soldiers in foreign countries and doing such splendid deeds as stealing juke boxes, breaking old men's eye glasses, setting fire to women, informing on people, and leaving restaurants without paying the bill. Once they have joined the war, the two men bumble their way from Egypt through Rostov to American, all the while merrily reporting by postcard to their women, Cleopatra and Venus, on the fine summer they are having. As Ulysses kills a Marxist revolutionary woman, Michelangelo cheers for more and Ulysses continues to shoot her dead body. Besides the usual horrors associated with war, the brothers see all the artistic treasures of man's civilization. The fighting continues for 3 years without a sign of peace; the brothers' enthusiasm begins to wane, and they discover that their letter from the king will not enable them to acquire the new sportscar they had been promised. Eventually, however, the brothers return home with a suitcase of picture postcards showing the treasures of the world. When the war ends, they are instructed to exchange the cards for the treasures as a reward for their service to the king. But after the peace treaty has been signed, Ulysses and Michelangelo are unable to collect their bounty; fighting has broken out in the streets, and the king has been deposed by a revolution. The two brothers are arrested and shot as war criminals. Their executioners are the same carabiniers who persuaded them to join the army. *Brothers. Soldiers. War victims. Military life. Capital punishment. War crimes. Revolts. Imaginary kingdoms. Art.*

Note: Opened in Paris in May 1963 at 75 min.

THE CARDINAL   **F6.0662**
Gamma Productions. *Dist* Columbia Pictures. 12 Dec **1963** [Boston opening; c1 Dec 1963; LP26806]. Sd (Westrex); col (Technicolor). 35mm (Panavision). 175 min.

Prod-Dir Otto Preminger. *Assoc Prod* Martin C. Schute. *Screenplay* Robert Dozier. *Dir Photog* Leon Shamroy. *2d Unit Camera* Piero Portalupi. *Camera Op* Jack Atcheler, Saul Midwall, Paul Uhl. *Art Dir Vienna Seq* Otto Niedermoser. *Set Decor* Gene Callahan. *Prod Dsgn* Lyle Wheeler. *Titl* Saul Bass. *Film Ed* Louis R. Loeffler. *Mus* Jerome Moross. "Jubilate Alleluia" Wolfgang Amadeus Mozart. *Perf by* Wilma Lipp, The Wiener Jeunesse Choir. *Liturgical Chants* Monks of the Abbey at Casamari, Don Nivardo Buttarazzi,

(Abbot at Casamari), Don Raffaele Scaccia, (Rector at Casamari). *Lyr:* "They Haven't Got the Girls in the U.S.A." Al Stillman. *Choreog* Buddy Schwab. *Sd* Harold Lewis, Red Law, Walter Goss, Morris Feingold. *Mus Ed* Leon Birnbaum. *Sd Eff Ed* Peter Thornton. *Asst Dir* Gerry O'Hara, Bob Vietro, Bryan Coates, Hermann Leitner, Robert Fiz, Eric Von Stroheim, Jr. *Prod Mgr* Harrison Starr, Eva Monley, Henry Weinberger. *Prod Mgr Courtesy of Danubia Films–Vienna* Paul Waldherr. *Prod Mgr Courtesy of International Film Services–Rome* Guy Luongo. *Script Supv* Kathleen Fagan. *Exec Asst to the Prod* Nat Rudich. *Cost Dsgn* Donald Brooks. *Cost Coörd* Hope Bryce. *Wardrobe* Joe King, Flo Transfield, George Newman. *Jewelry* Paltscho of Vienna. *Makeup* Dick Smith, Robert Jiras. *Hairdressing* Frederic Jones. *Tech Adv* Donald Hayne. *Ch Gaffer* Fred Hall. *Constr Grip* Fred Bockstahler. *Key Grip* Leo McCreary, Morris Rosen. *Prop Master* Tom Frewer, Art Cole. *Dial Asst* Max Slater. *Casting* Bill Barnes.

Cast: Tom Tryon (Stephen Fermoyle)

Cast—Boston: Carol Lynley (Mona), Dorothy Gish (Celia), Maggie McNamara (Florrie), Bill Hayes (Frank), Cameron Prud'Homme (Din), Cecil Kellaway (Monsignor Monaghan), Loring Smith (Cornelius J. Deegan), John Saxon (Benny Rampell), James Hickman (Father Lyons), Bernice Gahm (Mrs. Rampell), John Huston (Cardinal Glennon), José Duval (Ramon Gongaro), Peter MacLean (Father Callahan), Robert Morse (Bobby [& His Adora-Belles]), Billy Reed (master of ceremonies).

Cast—L'Enclume: Pat Henning (Hercule Menton), Burgess Meredith (Father Ned Halley), Jill Haworth (Lalage Menton), Russ Brown (Dr. Heller).

Cast—Rome: Raf Vallone (Cardinal Quarenghi), Tullio Carminati (Cardinal Giacobbi), Ossie Davis (Father Gillis), Don Francesco Mancini, of Veroli (master of ceremonies at the ordination), Dino Di Luca (Italian monsignor).

Cast—New York Pier: Carol Lynley (Regina Fermoyle), Donald Hayne (Father Eberling).

Cast—Lamar, Georgia: Chill Wills (Monsignor Whittle), Arthur Hunnicutt (Sheriff Dubrow), Doro Merande (woman picket), Patrick O'Neal (Cecil Turner), Murray Hamilton (Lafe).

Cast—Vienna: Romy Schneider (Annemarie), Peter Weck (Kurt von Hartman).

Cast—Additional players: Rudolf Forster (drinking man at ball), Josef Meinrad (Cardinal Innitzer), Dagmar Schmedes (Madame Walter), Eric Frey (Seyss-Inquart), Josef Krastel (Von Hartman butler), Mathias Fuchs (Father Neidermoser), Vilma Degischer (Sister Wilhelmina), Wolfgang Preiss (SS major), Jurgen Wilke (army lieutenant), Eric Van Nuys, Stephen Skodler.

Religious drama. Source: Henry Morton Robinson, *The Cardinal* (New York, 1950). In 1917 young Stephen Fermoyle returns to his native Boston as a newly ordained Roman Catholic priest. Upon learning that their daughter, Mona, is planning to marry a Jewish boy, the strong-willed Fermoyle family is so openly rude that the lad changes his mind. Consequently, Mona runs away and becomes the partner of a tango dancer. Stephen's arrogant nature causes the crusty but humane Archbishop Glennon to send him to a remote country parish, and there he learns his first lesson in humility from the dying Father Halley. He discovers that Mona is about to have an illegitimate child and that her life can be saved only if the infant's cranium is crushed. All too aware of Catholic dogma, Stephen denies permission and Mona dies. Haunted by the incident, he takes a year's leave of absence from his position with the Vatican diplomatic corps and becomes a teacher in Vienna. After a romantic but unfulfilled encounter with Anna, one of his students, he decides that the Church is his true vocation. Upon his return to Rome, he irritates most of his superiors by defending the rights of a Negro priest to have a parish in Georgia. As a result of his courageous fight against the Ku Klux Klan, he is promoted to Bishop. Just prior to World War II, he is sent to Austria in an unsuccessful attempt to persuade Cardinal Innitzer to oppose the Nazis. Subsequently, the two have a narrow escape when the Nazis attack the Austrian diocese. As the war begins, Fermoyle is appointed Cardinal, and his proud family travels from America to watch their son assume the robes of his office. *Priests. Catholics. Irish. Jews. Dancers. Schoolteachers. Negroes. Brother-sister relationship. Anti-Semitism. Illegitimacy. Childbirth. Death. Racial prejudice. Nazism. Catholic Church. World War II. Rome. Vatican. Boston. Vienna. Georgia. Theodor Innitzer. Artur von Seyss-Inquart. Ku Klux Klan.*

Note: Location scenes filmed in Boston, Stamford, Connecticut, Rome, Vienna, and Stowe, Vermont. Filmed in 35mm and blown up to 70mm for some roadshow presentations.

CAREER BED   **F6.0663**
Movimarc, Inc. Productions. *Dist* Provocative Films. 20 Jun **1969** [Champaign, Illinois, showing]. Sd; b&w. 35mm. 79 min.

Prod Jeff Gold. *Dir-Writ* Joel M. Reed. *Photog* Ron Dorfman. *Asst Camera* Michael Becker. *Sets* Dan Landi. *Film Ed* Ron Dorfman. *Mus Writ & Sung by* Vic Spina. *Played by* The Lost Children. *Sd* George Honchar. *Prod Mgr* Elliott R. Reed. *Asst to Mr. Reed* Joan MacKenzie.

Cast: Liza Duran (*Susan Potter*), Honey Hunter (*Emily Potter*), James David (*Bob Dartfield*), Merle Miller (*Miss Reynolds*), John Cardoza (*Jack Landive*), Donald Walters (*David Smith*), Stioge Glyspayne (*Gerald Ramer*), Charles Buffum (*Ross Miller*), Lance Hirsch (*waiter*), Dennis Lord (*Boris Rachman*), Jeff Reed (*actor*), Gale McCarty (*reporter*), Ann Wells (*new girl*).

Drama. Widowed Emily Potter drags her pretty daughter Susan away from her boyfriend, Bob Dartfield, and comes to New York City, intent on forcing Susan up Broadway's ladder to success. Bob follows them and, to insure that Susan will not weaken from the resolve her mother has forced upon her, Emily seduces Bob, telling him that Susan is having an affair with a producer, a blatant lie. Emily forces Susan to have relations with Miss Reynolds, a lesbian agent, and tries later to do the same with David Smith, a television producer. Susan's rebellion subsides when Emily attempts suicide, thereby coercing her daughter into total obeisance. Susan falls prey to Gerald Ramer, an "agent" who promises her to film producer Ross Miller. Both Ramer and Emily try to obtain a contract from Miller by using Susan as a pawn, but the young woman manages to convince Miller that she really loves him and they marry. Thoroughly corrupted by her experiences, Susan ruthlessly begins to use her body to advance her career. Emily, cast aside, is planning the future of another ingenue. *Widows. Innocents. Actors. Theatrical agents. Television producers. Motion picture producers. Motherhood. Ambition. Seduction. Suicide. Lesbianism. Moral corruption. Employment—Women. New York City—Broadway.*

CARELESS LOVE *see* **LA BONNE SOUPE**

CARESSED (Canada)   F6.0664
Laurence L. Kent. *Dist* Joseph Brenner Associates. 10 Nov 1965 [Denver, Colorado, opening; c15 May 1965; LF20]. Sd; b&w. 35mm. 81 min.

Prod-Dir-Writ Laurence L. Kent. *Cinematog* Richard Bellamy. *Graphics* Sonja Arentzson. *Film Ed* Sheila Reljac. *Mus* Jack Dale. *Sd* Robin Spurgeon.

Cast: Robert Howay (*Tom*), Angela Gann (*Elaine*), Lanny Beckman (*Bill*), Carol Pastinsky (*Kathy*), Bob Silverman (*Al*), Bill Hartley, Mitzi Hurd, Virginia Dunsaith.

Melodrama. Tom and Bill, high school seniors, have lively discussions on the sexual experiences they both hope to enjoy. Elaine, a buxom tease whom Tom begins to date, sees love and sex in terms of marriage. On one occasion, Tom and Bill and some of their friends visit a girl with a reputation for loose morals; another time, Tom procures a prostitute but flees when she undresses. Meanwhile, Tom is being helped in his studies by Kathy, a bright classmate, and he discusses his hopes and dreams with her. One evening they make love, and later Kathy learns that she is pregnant. Tom obtains a scholarship to continue his education, ignores his responsibility to Kathy, and becomes engaged to Elaine. *Students. Prostitutes. High school life. Sexual initiation. Adolescence. Pregnancy. Scholarships.*

Note: Filmed on location in Vancouver. Shown in Canada in Nov 1964 as *Sweet Substitute*; running time: 90 min.

THE CARETAKER *see* **THE GUEST**

THE CARETAKERS   F6.0665
Hall Bartlett Productions. *Dist* United Artists. 21 Aug 1963 [New York opening; c1 May 1963; LP25246]. Sd; b&w. 35mm. 97 min.

A Hall Bartlett Production. *Prod-Dir* Hall Bartlett. *Prod Exec* Nat James. *Assoc Prod* Jerry Paris. *Screenplay* Henry F. Greenberg. *Story* Hall Bartlett, Jerry Paris. *Photog* Lucien Ballard. *1st Camera* James Mathews. *Camera Op* Ed Garvin. *Asst Camera* George Elliott. *Art Dir* Rolland M. Brooks, Claudio Guzman. *Set Decor* Frank Tuttle. *Titl Drawings* Irving Block. *Film Ed* William B. Murphy. *Mus* Elmer Bernstein. *Mix* Tom Thompson. *Rec* Ken Wesson. *Boom Op* Jim Gibbs. *Asst Dir* Joe Demartini. *Prod Mgr* Sydney M. Fogel. *Prod Sec* Jeanne Reddeman. *Script Supv* Winifred Gibson. *Men's Wardrobe* Frank Delmar. *Women's Wardrobe* Ann Helfgott. *Makeup* Frank Prehoda. *Hairstyles* Pat Westmore. *Proc Photog* Ed Hammers. *Still Photog* Ed Cronenweth, Don Christie. *Dial Coach* Haile Chace. *Prop Master* Tom Coleman. *Gaffer* George Satterfield.

Cast: Robert Stack (*Dr. Donovan MacLeod*), Polly Bergen (*Lorna Melford*), Joan Crawford (*Lucretia Terry*), Janis Paige (*Marion*), Diane McBain (*Alison Horne*), Van Williams (*Dr. Larry Denning*), Constance Ford (*Nurse Bracken*), Sharon Hugueny (*Connie*), Herbert Marshall (*Dr. Jubal Harrington*), Ana St. Clair (*Anna*), Barbara Barrie (*Edna*), Robert Vaughn (*Jim Melford*), Susan Oliver (*Cathy Clark*), Ellen Corby (*Irene*).

Melodrama. Source: Dariel Telfer, *The Caretakers* (New York, 1959). Following the death of her small son in an automobile accident, Lorna Melford suffers a nervous collapse and is confined in a mental institution. Despite her homicidal tendencies, Dr. Donovan MacLeod decides that Lorna is a "borderline case" and places her in a group therapy ward where the patients are given considerable freedom. The group includes also the nymphomaniac Marion; Connie, who hears imaginary voices; Anna, who saw her parents killed in wartime; senile Irene; and Edna, mute and a pyromaniac. Lucretia Terry, the

hospital's head nurse, who advocates the use of force in handling the patients, strongly opposes MacLeod's methods. He is almost discredited when Marion steals some alcohol and stages a wild party that ends in brawling and fighting. Lucretia brings charges against him and tries to have him replaced, but the hospital's board of directors gives him a little more time to justify his theories. The crucial moment arrives when Edna, with a torch she has made, attempts to set fire to the group therapy ward. The strong-arm methods of Lucretia's nurses fail to subdue the girl, but Lorna soothingly induces Edna to give up her torch and to speak the first word she has uttered in years. Lorna's apparent cure prompts the hospital board to grant MacLeod permission to open a day clinic for borderline cases. *Psychiatrists. Nurses. Motherhood. Mutes. Pyromaniacs. Psychiatry. Group therapy. Mental illness. Nymphomania. Hospitals. Automobile accidents.*

CARGO OF LOVE   F6.0666
Charles Abrams Productions. *Dist* Abrams & Parisi, Inc. 7 Mar 1968 [New York opening]. Sd; b&w. 35mm. 70 min.

Prod-Dir Anton Holden.

Cast: Sheba Britt (*Ellie*), Gloria Irrizary, Sam Stewart, Tony Pascal.

Melodrama. Seduced and abandoned by the man she loves, Ellie flees in shame from her community. She becomes a companion to a wealthy woman, and when she arrives she is drugged at Senora Lupo's luxurious East Side New York apartment and driven to a secluded estate. The estate is a playground for wealthy men, and the Lupo sisters run a white slave racket to keep the place supplied with innocent young women. She awakens to the screams of an inmate being flogged and is alerted to the danger of attempting to escape when another inmate is tortured to death and burned. Pregnancy or illness means certain death; local police cooperate to make escape impossible. At last, tipped off by the disappearance of young women in a number of cities, the FBI investigates. A young female agent, equipped with electronic surveillance devices, answers the ad, and the gang is brought to justice. *Racketeers. Sisters. Police. Abduction. White slave traffic. Torture. Flagellation. Murder. Bribery. Electronic surveillance. New York City—East Side. United States—Federal Bureau of Investigation.*

Note: Allegedly based on a true story. Also known as *The Bed and the Beautiful.*

CARIBE *see* **WHEN THE GIRLS TAKE OVER**

CARLA'S THING   F6.0667
Dist Stacey Distributors. ca 1970. Sd; col. 16mm. 61-81 min.

Sex film. No information about the precise nature of this film has been found. *Sexuality.*

Note: Also known as *Carla's Bed.*

CARMEN (Switzerland)   F6.0668
Cosmotel. *Dist* Beta Film. 26 Jul 1970 [New York opening]. Sd; col (Eastman Color). 35mm. 167 min.

Prod Fritz Buttenstedt. *Dir* Herbert von Karajan. *Libretto* Henri Meilhac, Ludovic Halévy. *Photog* Ernst Wild, François Reichenbach. *Art Dir* Georges Wakhévitch. *Set Decor* Theo Otto. *Film Ed* Gérard Patris. *Mus:* "Carmen" Georges Bizet. *Mus Played by* Vienna Philharmonic Orchestra. *Mus Cond* Herbert von Karajan. *Mus Sung by* Vienna State Opera Chorus. *Chorus Master* Walter Hagen-Groll. *Sd* Horant H. Hohlfeld. *Cost* Georges Wakhévitch.

Cast: Grace Bumbry (*Carmen*), Jon Vickers (*Don José*), Mirella Freni (*Micaëla*), Justino Diaz (*Escamillo*), Olivera Miljakovic (*Frasquita*), Julia Hamari (*Mercédès*), Robert Kerns (*Morales*), Anton Diakov (*Zuniga*), Kurt Equiluz (*El Dancairo*), Milen Paunov (*El Remendado*), Mariemma and the Ballet de España.

Opera film. Sources: Georges Bizet, Henri Meilhac and Ludovic Halévy, *Carmen* (first performance: Paris, 3 Mar 1875). Prosper Mérimée, "Carmen," in *La revue des deux mondes* (15 Oct 1845). A film of the 1966 Salzburg Festival performance of *Carmen. Flirts. Soldiers. Spanish. Gypsies. Cigarette girls. Bullfighters. Deserters—Military. Infidelity. Jealousy. Murder. Seville.*

Note: Produced in Switzerland in 1967.

CARMEN, BABY   F6.0669
Amsterdam Film Corp. *Dist* Audubon Films. 10 Oct 1967 [New York opening]. Sd; col (Eastman Color). 35mm (Ultrascope). 90 min.

Pres by Radley Metzger. *Prod-Dir* Radley Metzger. *Screenplay* Jesse Vogel. *Photog* Hans Jura. *Film Ed* Humphrey Wood. *Mus* Daniel Hart. *Prod Mgr* Osman Ragheb. *Cost* Milena Kumar. *Makeup* Katschi Walzel.

Cast: Uta Levka (*Carmen*), Claude Ringer (*policeman*), Carl Möhner (*Medico*), Barbara Valentin (*Dolores*), Walter Wilz (*Baby Lucas*), Christiane Rücker (*Misty*), Michael Münzer (*magistrate*), Doris Arden, Doris Pistek (*Darcy, see note*), Christian Fredersdorf, Artur Brass.

Melodrama. Carmen, a cafe waitress who engages in prostitution, seduces a young policeman in order to escape a knifing charge. He serves a short prison term for his professional lapse, and afterwards Carmen accepts him as her lover, although she continues to have affairs with other men. When the policeman discovers Carmen with his superior, he becomes enraged and kills his rival. Now a fugitive, the policeman flees with Carmen to a villa where they join another couple in smuggling and in blackmailing tourists searching for sexual diversion. While at a gambling casino, Carmen picks up Medico, the head of the state parole board, and accompanies him to his home for a sexual threesome with the maid, who turns out to be Medico's wife. In return, Medico later arranges for the release of Carmen's imprisoned husband. The final blow to the policeman's pride comes when Carmen deserts him in favor of a popular rock and roll singer, Baby Lucas. Beside himself with jealousy, the policeman picks an argument with the ex-convict husband and kills him. He then follows Carmen and Baby Lucas to the night club where the latter is performing. He forces Carmen to step outside with him, quarrels with her in the city square, and stabs her to death. *Waitresses. Prostitutes. Police. Singers. Ex-convicts. Parole officers. Murder. Jealousy. Seduction. Blackmail. Troilism. Casinos. Carmen.*

Note: Filmed on location in Piran and Portoroz, Yugoslavia, and at studios in Munich. Pressbook and foreign sources credit actress Doris Arden with the role of Darcy, while many U. S. sources credit Doris Pistek; one name may be a pseudonym for the other. Barbara Valentin is credited by U. S. sources as Barbara Valentine.

CARMEN, LA DE RONDA see **THE DEVIL MADE A WOMAN**

CARMILLA see **WHAT NEXT?**

CARNABY, M. D. (Great Britain)   F6.0670

Rank Organisation. *Dist* Continental Distributing, Inc. Aug **1967**. Sd; col (Eastman Color). 35mm. 101 min.

A Betty E. Box–Ralph Thomas Production. *Prod* Betty E. Box. *Dir* Ralph Thomas. *Screenplay* Jack Davies. *Photog* Ernest Steward. *Art Dir* Alex Vetchinsky. *Film Ed* Alfred Roome. *Mus Dir* Johnny Scott. *Songs:* "Doctor in Clover," "Take a Look at Me" Rick Jones, Johnny Scott. *Songs Sung by* Kiki Dee. *Sd Rec* Dudley Messenger, Gordon K. McCallum. *Asst Dir* Simon Relph. *Prod Mgr* Ian Lewis.

Cast: Leslie Phillips (*Dr. Gaston Grimsdyke*), James Robertson-Justice (*Sir Lancelot Spratt*), Shirley Ann Field (*Nurse Bancroft*), John Fraser (*Dr. Miles Grimsdyke*), Joan Sims (*Matron Sweet*), Arthur Haynes (*Tarquin Wendover*), Fenella Fielding (*Tatiana Rubikov*), Jeremy Lloyd (*Lambert Symington*), Noel Purcell (*O'Malley*), Robert Hutton (*Rock Stewart*), Eric Barker (*Professor Halfback*), Terry Scott (*Robert*), Norman Vaughan (*TV commentator*), Elizabeth Ercy (*Jeannine*), Alfie Bass (*Fleming*), Anne Cunningham (*women's ward sister*), Suzan Farmer (*Nurse Holiday*), Harry Fowler (*Grafton*), Peter Gilmore (*Len*), Nicky Henson (*salesman*), Bill Kerr (*digger*), Justine Lord (*new matron*), Roddy Maude-Roxby (*Tristram*), Lionel Murton (*publicity man*), Anthony Sharp (*Dr. Loftus*), Dandy Nichols (*fat woman patient*), Ronnie Stevens (*TV producer*), Robin Hunter (*Sydney*), Barry Justice (*Beckwith*).

Comedy. Source: Richard Gordon, *Doctor in Clover* (London, 1960). Dr. Gaston Grimsdyke, an accident-prone, 35-year-old philanderer who has lost his job as a prison medical officer, enrolls in the Hampden Cross Hospital medical school for a refresher course with his former professor, Sir Lancelot Spratt. There Gaston falls in love with Jeannine, a French physiotherapist, and attempts to find a job at the hospital to stay and enjoy her company. Gaston's situation is complicated by the presence of Dr. Miles Grimsdyke, his cousin, who wants the same job in order to be with Nurse Holiday. Gaston flirts with Jeannine, but she prefers the company of Lambert Symington, a handsome medical student. Instructed by the professor to "soften up" Matron Sweet, a tough middle-aged careerwoman, Gaston sends love notes to her and signs them "L. S." Matron Sweet mistakenly interprets the signature as that of old Sir Lancelot Spratt. One evening Sir Lancelot accidentally receives a rejuvenation injection meant for Gaston and causes chaos at a party when he tries to sexually assault the matron. The next morning, Matron Sweet announces her departure in order to avoid a romance that could hamper her career. Gaston dresses in mod clothing to impress Jeannine, but she still refuses to abandon Lambert for him. Sir Lancelot announces that the hospital job will be given to Miles, and as consolation to the downcast Gaston, Sir Lancelot proposes that he romance the new matron. Gaston sees the pretty young woman and cheerfully accepts the assignment. *Physicians. Philanderers. Nurses. French. Medical students. Cousins. Careerwomen. Rejuvenation. Hospitals.*

Note: Opened in London in Mar 1966 as *Doctor in Clover.*

CARNAL KNOWLEDGE   F6.0671

Cosmos Films. *Dist* Able Film Co. ca **1970**. Sd; col. 16mm. [Feature length assumed.]

Sex film. Willie, a traveling man, has a friend, a pimp, who provides Willie's customers with prostitutes. Willie enters into festivities that lead to a surprise present for his birthday. *Traveling salesmen. Pimps. Prostitutes.*

CARNIVAL OF CRIME   F6.0672

Twin Film Productions. *Dist* Crown International Pictures. Jun **1964**. Sd; b&w. 35mm. 83 min.

Prod-Dir George M. Cahan. *Exec Prod* Federico J. Aicardi. *Screenplay* Bill Barret. *Photog* Americo Hoss. *Orig Mus & Songs:* "Amor en amor," "Viver so de voce," "Amore en Brasília," "Voce chegou sorrindo" *writ & perf by* Luiz Bonfa.

Cast: Jean-Pierre Aumont (*Mike Voray*), Alix Talton (*Lynn Voray*), Tonia Carrero (*Marina Silvera*), Luis Dávila (*Ray Donato*), Alberto Dalbes (*photographer*), Nathan Pinzon (*inspector*), Jardel Filho (*Paulo*), Norma Benguell (*model*), Norma Blum (*secretary*), Alicia Bonnet (*lady of the night*).

Action melodrama. Source: Winston Graham, *The Sleeping Partner* (London, 1961). Returning to his Rio de Janeiro home after an inspection trip in Brasília, prominent builder Mike Voray discovers his wife, Lynn, missing. After learning that she is divorcing him, Mike explains to his secretary Marina Silvera, who is secretly in love with him, that he suspects Lynn of having an affair with his partner Paulo. Attempting to contact his wife, Mike is assaulted at an address given him by Lynn's lawyer. Recovering, he learns from Marina that Lynn has been found dead. Marina also confirms Mike's belief that his wife committed adultery with several men, including Ray Donato. Mike confronts Donato, who reveals that Lynn was his mistress. Lynn, threatening to tell Donato's fiancée of their relationship, fell and struck her head in a struggle with him after he tried to break off the affair. As the police arrive, Donato flees into a crowd of people attending a carnival. Pursued by Mike, Donato falls to his death from a staircase. Mike and Marina return to Brasília as newlyweds. *Contractors. Missing persons. Secretaries. Mistresses. Police. Newlyweds. Divorce. Infidelity. Carnivals. Brasília. Rio de Janeiro. Chases.*

Note: Location scenes filmed in Brasília and Rio de Janeiro. Produced in 1961; working title: *Sleeping Partners.*

CARNIVAL OF SOULS   F6.0673

Harcourt Productions. *Dist* Herts–Lion International Corp. Sep **1962**. Sd; b&w. 35mm. 80 min. [Cut from 91 min.]

Prod-Dir Herk Harvey. *Writ* John Clifford, writ. *Dir Photog* Maurice Prather. *Titl* Dan Fitzgerald. *Film Ed* Dan Palmquist, Bill De Jarnette. *Mus* Gene Moore. *Sd Ed* Brown, Don Jessup. *Asst Dir* Raza Badiyi. *Prod Mgr* Larry Sneegas. *Asst Prod Mgr* Larry Fellers, Richard Walker. *Hairstyles* George Corn.

Cast: Candace Hilligoss (*Mary Henry*), Herk Harvey (*The Man*), Frances Feist (*landlady*), Sidney Berger (*John Linden*), Stan Levitt (*doctor*), Art Ellison (*minister*), Tom McGinnis, Dan Palmquist, Steve Boozer, Pamela Ballard, Larry Sneegas, Cari Conboy, Karen Pyles, Forbes Caldwell, Bill De Jarnette, T. C. Adams, Sharon Scoville, Mary Ann Harris, Peter Schnitzler, Bill Sollner.

Horror film. Mary Henry and two other young women are apparently drowned when their car is forced off the road during a drag race and plunges over a bridge. While searchers look for the car, Mary emerges alive from the water and, after being treated for injuries, leaves the area to pursue her career as an organist in a nearby state. As she drives to her new position, Mary passes a deserted carnival pavilion and a sinister figure looming in her path. Mary is haunted by the phantom figure, but she takes these apparitions as signs of shock from which she will soon recover. Although Mary tries to start a new life, the phantom periodically reappears, and she is strangely drawn to the carnival grounds. One day when Mary is shopping, the apparition overtakes her. A passing doctor sees that Mary is a victim of hysteria; he takes her to his office and listens to her strange story. One night while she is practicing on the church organ, the phantom again overtakes her. The minister hears the strange music Mary feels compelled to play, and he dismisses her. John Linden, a fellow boarder whom she had earlier scorned, makes advances to her in her room; she sees the phantom again, and her screams frighten Linden away. The next day Mary is drawn to the carnival grounds. There a "carnival of dancing souls" reaches out for her, and she sees herself dancing with the phantom. Later, at the site of the accident, the submerged car is found with the bodies of all three women, including Mary's, in it. *Visions. Organists. Clergymen. Physicians. Zombies. Psychic phenomena. Death. Dance of death. Supernatural. Automobile racing. Automobile accidents.*

Note: Filmed in Lawrence, Kansas.

CARNY GIRL   F6.0674

Gartmil Productions. *Dist* Chancellor Films. 25 May **1970** [Champaign, Illinois, showing]. Sd; col (Eastmancolor). 35mm. 67 min.

Prod-Dir-Writ Frank Garto. *Assoc Prod* Jerry Millard.

Cast: Lucky Kargo, Suzzan Landow, Debby Lynn.

Melodrama. Smalltown girl Barbara joins a traveling carnival and soon becomes one of the most enticing of the carnival's exotic dancers and strippers. Russ, the carnival owner, must quell the sex-crazed men in the audience when

Barbara comes on stage to perform. Barbara is assaulted by the obese hot dog vendor, Bingo, and escapes being raped only to fall under the influence of Ella, a domineering lesbian. The carnival life from which Barbara cannot escape eventually includes prostitution by day and lesbian activity at night with the women in the troupe. *Exotic dancers. Food vendors. Stripteasers. Rape. Lesbianism. Prostitution. Carnivals.*

THE CAROLYN LIMA STORY F6.0675

Continental American Artists. *Dist* Fiesta Artists Pictures, Colonial International Pictures. 9 Apr **1966** [Houston opening]. Sd; b&w. 35mm. 90 min.

Prod Charles Martinez. *Assoc Prod* Dale Berry. *Dir* John Rowe. *Tech Adv* Carolyn Lima.

Cast: Dana Sherry *(Carolyn Lima)*, Alfredo Criado, Skip Gerson, Van Lister, Jane Brantley, Tiera Edwards, Ann Morgan, John Rowe, Princess Taboo, Doris Masters, David Jessie, Josette.

Melodrama. Based on an incident in the life of Carolyn Lima. Actress Carolyn Lima, released from prison after serving a sentence for murder, meets Mark Kimmery, and the two plan to marry despite objections from his mother and his friends. Dressing in front of a mirror, Mark reconstructs Carolyn's past. *As a young woman, Carolyn is seduced by the syndicate into a life of prostitution. There is a murder, and Carolyn is imprisoned.* The syndicate, believing that they can pull Carolyn back into a life of crime, kidnap Carolyn and Mark to force her to cooperate in the payroll robbery of the large store where she works. The gangsters intend to murder Carolyn and Mark, but they themselves die at the hands of both the police and a gang of women who are former associates of Carolyn. Carolyn and Mark marry and plan to begin a new life. *Actors. Gangsters. Prostitution. Criminals—Rehabilitation. Marriage. Murder. Reputation. Kidnaping. Robbery. Syndicates. Carolyn Lima.*

Note: Filmed in Houston, Texas. Working and alternative release title: *Burn, Baby, Burn.* Pre-release title: *The Burning Man.*

CAROSELLO NAPOLETANO see NEAPOLITAN CAROUSEL

THE CARPETBAGGERS F6.0676

Embassy Pictures-Paramount Pictures. *Dist* Paramount Pictures. 9 Apr **1964** [Denver, Colorado, opening; c31 Dec 1963; LP28322]. Sd; col (Technicolor). 35mm (Panavision, see note). 150 min.

Prod Joseph E. Levine. *Dir* Edward Dmytryk. *Screenplay* John Michael Hayes. *Cinematog* Joseph MacDonald. *Camera Op* Duke Callaghan. *Asst Camera* Dewey Wrigley, Jr. *Technicolor Cons* Richard Mueller. *Art Dir* Hal Pereira, Walter Tyler. *Set Decor* Arthur Krams, Sam Comer. *Film Ed* Frank Bracht. *Mus Comp & Cond* Elmer Bernstein. *Sd* John Carter, Charles Grenzbach. *Rec* Jim Miller. *Boom Op* Bud Parman. *Asst Dir* D. Michael Moore, James Rosenberger, Dale Coleman. *Prod Mgr* Frank Caffey. *Unit Prod Mgr* William W. Gray. *Script Supv* Claire Behnke. *Cost Dsgn* Edith Head. *Cost* Ruth Stella, Glenita Dineen, John A. Anderson, Gildo Scarano. *Makeup* Wally Westmore, Gary Morris. *Hairstyles* Sherry Wilson. *Hairstyle Supv* Nellie Manley. *Sp Photog Eff* Paul K. Lerpae. *Process Photog* Farciot Edouart. *Prop* Gordon Cole, Robert McCrillis. *Dial Coach* Frank London. *Still Photog* Art Say. *Grip* Dominic Seminerio, Norbert Haring. *Gaffer* Chet Stafford.

Cast: George Peppard *(Jonas Cord, Jr.)*, Carroll Baker *(Rina Marlowe)*, Alan Ladd *(Nevada Smith)*, Bob Cummings *(Dan Pierce)*, Martha Hyer *(Jennie Denton)*, Elizabeth Ashley *(Monica Winthrop)*, Martin Balsam *(Bernard B. Norman)*, Lew Ayres *(McAllister)*, Ralph Taeger *(Buzz Dalton)*, Archie Moore *(Jedediah)*, Leif Erickson *(Jonas Cord, Sr.)*, Tom Lowell *(David Woolf)*, Arthur Franz *(Morrissey)*, Tom Tully *(Amos Winthrop)*, Audrey Totter *(prostitute)*, Anthony Warde *(Moroni)*, John Conte *(Ellis)*, Francesca Bellini *(Cynthia Randall)*, Vaughn Taylor *(doctor)*, Lynn Borden *(starlet)*, Gladys Holland *(French nurse)*, Victoria Jean *(Jo-Ann Cord)*, Charles Lane *(Denby)*, Frankie Darro *(bellboy)*, Lisa Seagram *(Moroni's secretary)*, Ann Doran *(woman reporter)*, Joseph Turkel *(reporter)*, Donald Barry *(sound man)*, Peter Duryea *(assistant director)*.

Melodrama. Source: Harold Robbins, *The Carpetbaggers* (New York, 1961). In 1925, playboy Jonas Cord, Jr., inherits the Cord Chemical factory after his father dies from a stroke in the midst of their quarrel. Jonas immediately buys out all shares of Cord Chemical; the transactions include making a financial settlement with his stepmother, Rina, who jilted him to marry the senior Cord for his money, and liquidating the stock belonging to Nevada Smith, a cowhand who acted as father to him during his childhood. Later, Rina becomes a top fashion model in Paris, and Nevada becomes a popular silent screen cowboy star, while Jonas enlists the aid of McAllister, his father's attorney, and engineer Buzz Dalton to build the business into a multimillion dollar empire pioneering in plastics and aeronautics. On a whim, Jonas marries, then neglects, Monica Winthrop, after ruining her father's business. With the coming of talking pictures, Nevada's career at Bernard B. Norman's Film Studios is threatened until Jonas offers financial backing for a film to star both the aging star and Rina, who has returned to the United States; in addition, Jonas decides to direct

the film himself and hires Nevada's agent, Dan Pierce, as his public relations man. Jonas' behavior forces Monica to leave him, while the nymphomaniacal Rina, now married to Nevada, becomes an alcoholic and dies in a car accident; Norman and Pierce, however, arrange to withhold the news from Jonas long enough to sell him the studio, which is virtually worthless now that its biggest star is dead. Jonas goes on a binge but recovers when he meets call girl Jennie Denton, who resembles Rina; Jonas turns her into a star and proposes marriage, but she is horrified to learn that Jonas relishes her degraded past. His treatment of Jennie so disgusts his associates that Dalton quits, and even Nevada is appalled to the point of provoking a bloody fistfight, which Nevada wins. Jonas, who has lived for years in fear of hereditary insanity because of his twin brother who died, insane, in infancy, then learns from Nevada that the infant was not a full brother; he then returns to Monica, who learned the truth years before, to begin a new life with their daughter. *Millionaires. Playboys. Businessmen. Motion picture producers. Actors. Widows. Cowboys. Fortune hunters. Models. Lawyers. Talent agents. Stepmothers. Engineers. Prostitutes. Filial relations. Inheritance. Insanity. Childhood. Heredity. Business ethics. Marriage. Alcoholism. Friendship. Infidelity. Public relations. Nymphomania. Factories. Strokes. Aeronautics. Motion pictures—History. Paris. Hollywood. Automobile accidents.*

Note: Location scenes filmed in and around Hollywood, Pasadena, and the Mojave Desert town of Boron. Blown up to 70mm for some roadshow presentations.

CARRY IT ON F6.0677

The New Film Co.-United Productions of America. *Dist* Maron Films. 26 Aug **1970** [New York opening]. Sd; b&w. 35mm (see note). 80 min. [Cut from 84 min.] *MPAA rating* GP.

Prod-Dir-Writ James Coyne, Robert C. Jones, Christopher Knight. *Assoc Prod* Robert Silverthorne. *Photog* James Coyne, Robert C. Jones, Christopher Knight. *Film Ed* James Coyne, Robert C. Jones, Christopher Knight. *Asst Ed* Miriam Weinstein. *Titl Song* Gil Turner. *Song:* "Last Thing on My Mind" Tom Paxton. *Song:* "Hickory Wind" Gram Parsons, Bob Buchanan. *Song:* "Suzanne" Leonard Cohen. *Song:* "Miller's Cave" Jack Clement. *Song:* "Land of a Thousand Dances" Chris Kenner. *Song:* "Cinammon Girl" Neil Young. *Song:* "Down So Low" Tracy Faye Nelson. *Song:* "Mother Earth" Memphis Slim. *Song:* "Oh Happy Day" *Arr by* Edwin Hawkins. *Song:* "We Shall Overcome" Pete Seeger, Guy Carawan, Zilphia Horten, Frank Hamilton, mus. *Song:* "All I Have To Offer You Is Me" Dallas Frazier, Alan Range. *Song:* "I Shall Be Released" Bob Dylan. *Song Sung by* Joan Baez. *Concert Sd* Mark Levinson.

Featuring: Joan Baez, David Harris, activist.

Documentary. The film presents an interview with folksinger Joan Baez and her husband, David Harris. In 1969 David is about to be taken to jail on charges of draft evasion, and the couple discuss how David's 3-year prison term will affect their lives. David, a pacifist, explains his philosophy regarding military service and the turbulent situation on American university campuses. Although Joan is pregnant, she goes on with her summer concert tour. *Singers. Pacifists. Draft dodgers. Military draft. Imprisonment. College life. Pregnancy. Folk music. Joan Baez. David Harris.*

Note: Filmed in 16mm.

CARRY ON CABBY (Great Britain) F6.0678

Adder Productions. *For* Anglo Amalgamated Film Distributors. *Dist* Governor Films. caJan **1967**. Sd; b&w. 35mm. 89 min.

Prod Peter Rogers. *Assoc Prod* Frank Bevis. *Dir* Gerald Thomas. *Screenplay* Talbot Rothwell. *Story* Sidney C. Green, Richard M. Hills. *Dir Photog* Alan Hume. *Camera Op* Godfrey Godar. *Focus Op* Steve Claydon. *Camera Grip* Fred Graver. *Art Dir* Jack Stephens. *Set Dresser* Helen Thomas. *Ch Draughtsman* Bob Laing. *Film Ed* Archie Ludski. *1st Asst Ed* Rod Keys. *2d Asst Ed* Jean Sheffield. *Mus Comp & Cond* Eric Rogers. *Sd Mix* Bill Daniels. *Boom Op* Gus Lloyd. *Sd Camera* R. Hogben. *Dub Ed* Arthur Ridout. *1st, 2d & 3d Asst Dir* Peter Bolton, Kits Browning, Michael Klaw. *Unit Mgr* Donald Toms. *Prod Sec* Lana Stephens. *Cont* Penny Daniels. *Cost Dsgn* Joan Ellacott. *Wardrobe Mistress* Pat Baden. *Wardrobe Master* John Hilling. *Makeup* Geoffrey Rodway. *Hairdresser* Biddy Chrystal. *Casting Dir* Betty White, casting. *Constr Mgr* Bert Mansell. *Prop Buyer* Harry Hannay. *Still Photog* Albert Clarke. *Supv Electrn* John Swan.

Cast: Sidney James *(Charlie Hawkins)*, Hattie Jacques *(Peggy Hawkins)*, Kenneth Connor *(Ted Watkins)*, Charles Hawtrey *("Pintpot")*, Esma Cannon *(Flo)*, Liz Fraser *(Sally)*, Bill Owen *(Smily Sim)*, Milo O'Shea *(Len)*, Judith Furse *("Battleaxe")*, Ambrosine Phillpotts *(aristocratic lady)*, Renee Houston *(Molly)*, Jim Dale *(small man)*, Amanda Barrie *(Anthea)*, Carole Shelley *(dumb girl)*, Cyril Chamberlain *(Sarge)*, Norman Chappell *(Allbright)*, Peter Gilmore *(Dancy)*, Michael Ward *(man in tweeds)*, Noel Dyson *(district nurse)*, Michael Nightingale *(business man)*, Ian Wilson *(clerk)*, Peter Byrne *(bridegroom)*, Darryl Kavann *(Punchy)*, Peter Jesson *(car salesman)*, Don McCorkindale

(Tubby), Charles Stanley *(Geoff)*, Marion Collins *(bride)*, Frank Forsyth *(chauffeur)*.

Comedy. Charlie Hawkins is so busy running his fleet of taxicabs that he leaves his wife, Peggy, alone on their wedding anniversary. Further trouble looms when his union threatens to strike if the wife of an ailing driver is permitted to take her husband's place. The incident gives Peggy the idea of starting a rival taxi chain, Glamcabs, staffed with women drivers garbed in revealing costumes. Peggy keeps her business venture a secret from Charlie and adds insult to injury by financing it with his business profits, which happen to be banked in her name. As Charlie's competition increases, he declares all-out war and even resorts to having his manager, Ted Watson, disguise himself as a Glamcab driver. The ruse is discovered, and the battle rages on until Charlie learns the identity of his rival. Peggy's victory turns out to be a hollow one, however, when Charlie's ego is totally destroyed. But a reconciliation is effected when the Glamcabs are hijacked and Charlie's drivers race to the rescue. After the hijackers are captured, Charlie learns that he may soon have to change the name of his business to "Hawkins & Son." *Taxi drivers. Businesswomen. Hijackers. Women's rights. Female impersonation. Pregnancy. Labor unions. Wedding anniversaries. Chases.*

Note: Opened on the island of Jersey in Aug 1963; running time: 91 min. Working title: *Call Me a Cab.*

CARRY ON CLEO (Great Britain)　　　　　　　　　　　　　**F6.0679**
Adder Productions. *For* Anglo Amalgamated Productions. *Dist* Governor Films. 22 Oct **1965** [New York opening]. Sd; col (Eastmancolor). 35mm. 92 min.

Prod Peter Rogers. *Assoc Prod* Frank Bevis. *Dir* Gerald Thomas. *Screenplay* Talbot Rothwell. *Dir Photog* Alan Hume. *Art Dir* Bert Davey. *Film Ed* Archie Ludski. *Mus* Eric Rogers. *Sd* Bill Daniels. *Asst Dir* Peter Bolton. *Cost* Julie Harris, cost.

Cast: Sidney James *(Mark Antony)*, Kenneth Williams *(Julius Caesar)*, Kenneth Connor *(Hengist Pod)*, Charles Hawtrey *(Seneca)*, Joan Sims *(Calpurnia)*, Jim Dale *(Horsa)*, Amanda Barrie *(Cleopatra)*, Victor Maddern *(sergeant major)*, Julie Stevens *(Gloria)*, Sheila Hancock *(Senna Pod)*, Jon Pertwee *(soothsayer)*, Francis De Wolff *(Agrippa)*, Michael Ward *(Archimedes)*, Brian Oulton *(Brutus)*, Warren Mitchell *(Spencius)*, David Davenport *(Bilius)*, Tanya Binning *(Virginia)*, Tom Clegg *(Sosages)*, Peter Gilmore *(galley master)*, Gertan Klauber *(Marcus)*, Ian Wilson *(messenger)*, Brian Rawlinson *(Hessian driver)*, E. V. H. Emmett *(narrator)*.

Farce. Suggested by: William Shakespeare, *Antony and Cleopatra, Julius Caesar*. In ancient Britain, Mark Antony captures two men—Hengist Pod, an inventor working on a square wheel, and Horsa, a member of the Saxon underground movement—and takes them to Rome to be sold as slaves. Horsa escapes, but the weak Hengist is mistaken for a brave warrior and selected to be Caesar's bodyguard. Caesar dispatches Antony to Egypt to force Cleopatra from the throne and install Ptolemy. Antony and Cleopatra fall in love, however, and Antony disposes of Ptolemy before returning to Rome with plans to lure Caesar to Egypt and assassinate him. Hengist and Horsa clumsily contribute to the downfall of Antony's conspiracy and are rewarded with their freedom. *Bodyguards. Inventors. Saxons. Slavery. Conspiracy. Rome— History—Empire. Egypt. Gaius Julius Caesar. Mark Antony. Cleopatra.*

Note: Opened in London in Dec 1964.

CARRY ON CONSTABLE (Great Britain)　　　　　　　　　**F6.0680**
G. H. W. Productions. *Dist* Governor Films. Feb **1961**. Sd; b&w. 35mm. 86 min.

Prod Peter Rogers. *Dir* Gerald Thomas. *Screenplay* Norman Hudis. *Based on an Idea by* Brock Williams. *Dir Photog* Ted Scaife. *Camera Op* Alan Hume. *Focus* Ken Withers. *Camera Grip* Reg Hall. *Art Dir* Carmen Dillon. *Set Dresser* Vernon Dixon. *Ch Draughtsman* Bob Laing. *Film Ed* John Shirley. *1st Asst Ed* Jim Sibley. *2d Asst Ed* Peter Andrews. *Mus Comp & Cond* Bruce Montgomery. *Sd Mix* Robert MacPhee. *Boom Op* Tony Cripps. *Sd Camera Op* Ron Butcher. *1st, 2d & 3d Asst Dir* Peter Manley, Eric Rattray, Ray Freeborn. *Prod Mgr* Frank Bevis. *Prod Sec* Jean Hall. *Cont* Joan Davis. *Dress Dsgn* Yvonne Caffin. *Men's Wardrobe* Duncan MacPhee. *Women's Wardrobe* Maggie Lewin. *Makeup* George Blackler, Eddie Knight. *Hairdresser* Stella Rivers. *Casting Dir* Betty White, casting. *Still Photog* George Ward. *Chargehand Prop* Dingle Bell. *Prop Buyer* Ron Quelch. *Constr Mgr* Bert Mansell. *Ch Electrn* Harry Black.

Cast: Sidney James *(Sgt. Frank Wilkins)*, Eric Barker *(Inspector Mills)*, Kenneth Connor *(Constable Charlie Constable)*, Charles Hawtrey *(Special Constable Gorse)*, Kenneth Williams *(Constable Benson)*, Leslie Phillips *(Constable Potter)*, Joan Sims *(Policewoman Gloria Passworthy)*, Hattie Jacques *(Sgt. Laura Moon)*, Shirley Eaton *(Sally Barry)*, Cyril Chamberlain *(Constable Thurston)*, Joan Hickson *(Mrs. May)*, Irene Handl *(distraught woman)*, Terence Longdon *(Herbert Hall)*, Jill Adams *(Policewoman Harrison)*, Esma Cannon *(deaf lady)*, Freddie Mills *(crook)*, Brian Oulton *(store*

manager), Victor Maddern *(criminal type)*, Joan Young *(suspect)*, Hilda Fenemore *(agitated woman)*, Noel Dyson *(vague woman)*, Michael Balfour *(Matt)*, Diane Aubrey *(Honoria)*, Dorinda Stevens *(young woman)*, Marv Law *(1st shop assistant)*.

Farce. Due to a flu epidemic which leaves a British police station in dire need of replacements, three police rookies are given a chance to show their mettle. They are: Tom Potter, an ex-playboy and would-be Don Juan; Stanley Benson, a snobbish intellectual with his own views on criminology; and Charlie Constable, a superstitious amateur astrologer. Assisted by effeminate Special Officer Timothy Gorse, the trio bungle every attempt at maintaining law and order. They inadvertently help thieves escape with their loot; Gorse gets caught in midair on a bell tower rope while chasing a cat; Potter investigates a noise and bursts in upon pretty Sally Barry while she is in her bath; Benson arrests a plain-clothes policeman because he looks like the "criminal type"; and Gorse and Benson are arrested when they impersonate women in a disastrous effort to catch shoplifters. Despite all this, the rookies miraculously manage to apprehend a gang of crooks who have robbed an armored payroll truck. Because of their heroic deed, their two astounded superiors, Inspector Mills and Sergeant Wilkins, are given promotions. *Constables. Thieves. Law and order. Female impersonation. Robbery. Armored cars. Cats.*

Note: Opened in London in Feb 1960.

CARRY ON REGARDLESS (Great Britain)　　　　　　　　**F6.0681**
Anglo Amalgamated Productions–G. H. W. Productions. *Dist* Governor Films. 10 May **1963** [Los Angeles opening]. Sd; b&w. 35mm. 86 min.

Prod Peter Rogers. *Assoc Prod* Basil Keys. *Dir* Gerald Thomas. *Screenplay* Norman Hudis. *Photog* Alan Hume. *Camera Op* Dudley Lovell. *Focus* Steve Claydon. *Camera Grip* Reg Hall. *Art Dir* Lionel Couch. *Set Dresser* Josie MacAvin. *Draughtsman* Robert Laing. *Film Ed* John Shirley. *Asst Ed* David Campling, Peter Andrews. *Mus Dir* Bruce Montgomery. *Sd Mix* Robert MacPhee. *Boom Op* Harry Fairbairn. *Sd Camera Op* Ted Karnon. *1st, 2d & 3d Asst Dir* Jack Causey, Jim Brennan, Terry Clegg. *Unit Mgr* Claude Watson. *Prod Sec* Rhonda Grogan. *Cont* Gladys Goldsmith. *Cost Dsgn* Joan Ellacott. *Women's Wardrobe* Marie Feldwick. *Men's Wardrobe* Duncan MacPhee. *Makeup* George Blackler. *Hairdresser* Biddy Chrystal. *Casting Dir* Betty White, casting. *Still Photog* Albert Clarke. *Constr Mgr* Bert Mansell. *Prop Buyer* John Higgs. *Chargehand Electrn* Tom Heathcoat.

Cast: Sidney James *(Bert Handy)*, Kenneth Connor *(Sam Twist)*, Charles Hawtrey *(Gabriel Dimple)*, Joan Sims *(Lily Duveen)*, Kenneth Williams *(Francis Courtenay)*, Bill Owen *(Mike Weston)*, Liz Fraser *(Delia King)*, Terence Longdon *(Montgomery Infield-Hopping)*, Hattie Jacques *(frosty-faced sister)*, Stanley Unwin *(Stanley)*, Esma Cannon *(Miss Cooling)*, Joan Hickson *(matron)*, Sydney Tafler *(club manager)*, Betty Marsden *(Mata Hari)*, Julia Arnall *(Trudi Trelawney)*, Fenella Fielding *(Penny Panting)*, Terence Alexander *(Trevor Trelawney)*, David Lodge *(wine connoisseur)*, Jerry Desmonde *(Martin Paul)*, Eric Pohlmann *(sinister man)*, June Jago *(1st sister)*, Jimmy Thompson *(Mr. Delling)*, Carole Shelley *(Mrs. Delling)*, Kynaston Reeves *(millionaire)*, Molly Weir *(bird woman)*, Michael Ward *(photographer)*, Freddie Mills *(Lefty Vincent)*, Ambrosine Phillpotts.

Farce. Bert Handy sets up an employment agency called "Helping Hands, Ltd." He hires refugees from the Labour Exchange Staff to do odd jobs: Francis Courtenay walks a chimpanzee around London; Gabriel Dimple substitutes as a bouncer at a bar; Lily Duveen demonstrates bubble bath; Delia King models underwear; and Sam Twist demonstrates the bed of the century. They all mismanage one unusual job after another. Stanley Unwin, the landlord, tries to remove them from the premises by raising their rent, but all agree to accept Unwin's offer to clean up an old house in return for a 99-year lease on the agency's property. As a result of their bungling, however, Unwin must demolish the property and erect a new structure. Handy and his crew carry on with their work as usual. *Handymen. Landlords. Bouncers. Models. Employment agencies. Chimpanzees.*

Note: Opened in London in Mar 1961; running time: 90 min.

CARRY ON SPYING (Great Britain)　　　　　　　　　　　**F6.0682**
Anglo Amalgamated Productions–Adder Productions. *Dist* Governor Films. 30 Dec **1964** [Los Angeles opening]. Sd; b&w. 35mm. 87 min.

A Peter Rogers Production. *Prod* Peter Rogers. *Assoc Prod* Frank Bevis. *Dir* Gerald Thomas. *Screenplay* Talbot Rothwell, Sid Colin. *Dir Photog* Alan Hume. *Art Dir* Alex Vetchinsky. *Film Ed* Archie Ludski. *Mus Comp & Cond* Eric Rogers. *Song:* "Too Late" Alex Alstone, Geoffrey Parsons. *Song:* "The Magic of Love" Eric Rogers. *Sd* C. C. Stevens. *Asst Dir* Peter Bolton.

Cast: Kenneth Williams *(Desmond Simkins)*, Barbara Windsor *(Daphne Honeybutt)*, Bernard Cribbins *(Harold Crump)*, Charles Hawtrey *(Charlie Bind)*, Eric Barker *(chief)*, Dilys Laye *(Lila)*, Jim Dale *(Carstairs)*, Richard Wattis *(Cobley)*, Eric Pohlmann *("The Fat Man")*, Victor Maddern *(Milchmann)*, Judith Furse *(Dr. Crow)*, John Bluthal *(headwaiter)*, Frank Forsyth *(Professor Clark)*, Gertan Klauber *(code clerk)*, Jill Mai Meredith *(cigarette girl)*, Nora Gordon *(elderly woman)*, Angela Ellison *(cloakroom girl)*, Norman Mitchell *(native policeman)*, Hugh Futcher *(scrawny native)*, Tom Clegg *(doorman)*, Renee Houston *(madame)*, Derek Sydney *(Algerian gent)*, Jack Taylor, Bill Cummings *(thugs)*, Anthony Baird, Patrick Durkin *(guards)*.

Comedy. When BOSH (British Operational Security Headquarters) learns that a STENCH (Society for Total Extinction of Non-Conforming Humans) agent named Milchmann has stolen a secret formula, four bumbling BOSH agents—Desmond Simkins, Harold Crump, Charlie Bind, and Daphne Honeybutt—are assigned to get it back. In Vienna they find Milchmann murdered and the formula missing, but in Algiers they recover the formula from a STENCH agent called "The Fat Man." They are pursued by STENCH agents led by Lila; but before they are captured, Daphne, who has a photographic memory, memorizes the formula and destroys it. Dr. Crow, STENCH's chief, is driven mad in her attempts to brainwash the brainless Daphne. The BOSH agents are ordered killed but are saved by Lila, who turns out to be a counteragent for SNOG (Society for Neutralization of Germs). They set a time bomb to blow up STENCH underground headquarters and escape by the emergency exit only to find themselves in BOSH headquarters directly over the STENCH headquarters—due to blow up momentarily. *Secret agents. Espionage. Brainwashing. Murder. Bombs. Secret formulas. Vienna. Algiers.*

Note: Opened in London in Aug 1964.

CARRY ON TEACHER (Great Britain)   F6.0683

Beaconsfield Films–Anglo Amalgamated Productions. *Dist* Governor Films. 30 May 1962 [Los Angeles opening]. Sd; b&w. 35mm. 86 min.

Prod Peter Rogers. *Exec Prod* Nat Cohen, Stuart Levy. *Dir* Gerald Thomas. *Screenplay* Norman Hudis. *Dir Photog* Reginald Wyer. *Camera Op* Alan Hume. *Focus Asst* Steve Claydon. *Art Dir (see note)* Alex Vetchinsky, Lionel Couch. *Set Dresser* Terence Morgan, II. *Draughtsman* Bob Laing. *Film Ed* John Shirley. *Asst Ed* Jim Sibley, Vera Dover. *Mus* Bruce Montgomery. *Sd Supv* Cyril Crowhurst. *Sd Mix* Robert MacPhee. *Boom Op* Gus Lloyd. *Sd Camera Op* Ken Barker. *1st, 2d & 3d Asst Dir* Bert Batt, David Tringham, Ian Goddard. *Prod Mgr* Frank Bevis. *Prod Sec* Sheila Hill. *Cont* Tilly Day. *Wardrobe Mistress* Laurel Staffell. *Men's Wardrobe* H. Brown. *Makeup* George Blackler. *Hairdressing* Olga Angelinetta. *Casting* Betty White, casting. *Constr Mgr* Bert Mansell. *Prop Buyer* John Higgs.

Cast: Ted Ray *(William Wakefield)*, Kenneth Connor *(Gregory Adams)*, Leslie Phillips *(Alistair Grigg)*, Charles Hawtrey *(Michael Bean)*, Joan Sims *(Sarah Allcock)*, Kenneth Williams *(Edwin Milton)*, Hattie Jacques *(Grace Short)*, Rosalind Knight *(Felicity Wheeler)*, Cyril Chamberlain *(Alf)*, Richard O'Sullivan *(Robin Stevens)*, Carol White *(Sheila Dale)*, Paul Cole *(Atkins)*, Jane White, British *(Irene)*, Larry Dann *(boy)*, Diana Beevers *(Penny Lee)*, George Howell *(Billy Haig)*, Jacqueline Lewis *(Pat Gordon)*, Roy Hines *(Harry Bird)*.

Farce. William Wakefield, a popular headmaster, has applied for the headmaster's job at a new country school after spending 20 years at his present job. Because he is a kind and gentle man, none of his students want him to leave. They find out that Felicity Wheeler and psychologist Alistair Grigg from the Ministry of Education are coming to inspect the school to determine Wakefield's qualifications. They decide to sabotage the school's normal routine, thus ruining Wakefield's chances for the new job. The students employ a full range of pranks, from itching powder and booby traps to blowing up the restrooms. Their wild behavior comes to a climax at the school play, *Romeo and Juliet*, which they transform into a burlesque show. When Wakefield realizes the reason for the trouble, he is touched and agrees to stay. *Headmasters. Students. Psychologists. High school life. Practical jokes. Great Britain—Ministry of Education. "Romeo and Juliet".*

Note: Opened in London in Sep 1959. Sources conflict in crediting art director.

CARTAGINE IN FIAMME *see* **CARTHAGE IN FLAMES**

CARTHAGE EN FLAMMES *see* **CARTHAGE IN FLAMES**

CARTHAGE IN FLAMES (France/Italy)   F6.0684

Lux Film–Gallone Produzione–C. C. F. Lux. *Dist* Columbia Pictures. 25 Jan 1961 [New York opening; c1 Mar 1961; LP20461]. Sd; col (Technicolor). 35mm (Technirama, see note). 93 min. [Cut from 111 min.]

Prod Guido Luzzato, Carmine Gallone. *Assoc Prod* Marino Vacca, Carmine Gallone, Jr. *Dir* Carmine Gallone. *Screenplay* Ennio De Concini, Duccio Tessari, Carmine Gallone. *English Vers* William De Lane Lea. *Photog* Piero Portalupi. *Art Dir* Guido Fiorini, Amedeo Mellone. *Film Ed* Nicolo Lazzari. *Mus Comp* Mario Nascimbene. *Cond* Franco Ferrara. *Sd* Renato Cadueri. *Asst Dir* Franco Cirino, Andrea Volpe. *Cost* Veniero Colasanti. *Sp Eff* Ottavio Mannini.

Cast: Anne Heywood *(Fulvia)*, José Suárez *(Hiram)*, Ilaria Occhini *(Ophir)*, Daniel Gélin *(Phegor)*, Pierre Brasseur *(Sidone)*, Paolo Stoppa *(Astarito)*, Mario Girotti *(Tsour)*, Aldo Silvani *(Hermon)*, Edith Peters *(nurse)*, Erno

Crisa, Ivo Garrani, Cesare Fantoni, Gianrico Tedeschi, Fernand Ledoux.

Historical drama. Source: Emilio Salgari, *Cartagine in fiamme* (Genoa, 1908). In 146 B. C., as Roman legions lay siege to Carthage, Hiram, an exiled soldier-statesman, rescues a beautiful Roman, Fulvia, from a sacrificial altar. Hiram's enemy, the wily Phegor, pursues them; but after a battle at sea, Hiram eludes Phegor and returns in secret to Carthage, where he learns that his beloved Ophir has been betrothed by her father to wed a young warrior, Tsour. Hiram abducts Ophir and takes to sea once more. Phegor then captures Fulvia, whom he covets, and Hiram again tries to rescue her, but this time he is caught. Fulvia, in love with Hiram, arranges for his escape by promising to give herself to Phegor. As the Roman legions advance, Hiram appears before the grand council and volunteers to lead an army. Tsour, sensing the sincerity of the offer, aligns himself with Hiram and joins him in going to meet the Romans; but they are unable to win the battle, and Tsour dies in combat. Hiram flees with Ophir to the safety of his ship as the Romans enter Carthage. Fulvia seeks out Phegor, embraces him, and drags him to his death in the flaming ruins of the city. *Soldiers. Exile. Human sacrifice. Marriage—Arranged. Abduction. Rescue. Ships. Punic wars. Rome—History—Monarchy & Republic. Carthage. Fires.*

Note: Opened in Rome in Jan 1960 as *Cartagine in fiamme*; running time: 120 min; in Paris in Mar 1960 as *Carthage en flammes*; running time: 115 min. Foreign release in Super-Technirama 70.

CARTOUCHE (France/Italy)   F6.0685

Ariane–Filmsonor–Vides. *Dist* Embassy Pictures. 21 Jul 1964 [New York opening]. Sd; col (Eastman Color). 35mm (Dyaliscope). 115 min.

Prod Georges Dancigers. *Dir-Writ* Philippe de Broca. *Screenplay* Daniel Boulanger, Philippe de Broca. *Screenplay Collab* Charles Spaak. *Dial* Daniel Boulanger. *Photog* Christian Matras. *Art Dir* François de Lamothe. *Film Ed* Laurence Méry. *Mus* Georges Delerue. *Sd* Jean Rieul.

Cast: Jean-Paul Belmondo *(Cartouche)*, Claudia Cardinale *(Venus)*, Odile Versois *(Isabelle de Ferrussac)*, Philippe Lemaire *(de Ferrussac)*, Marcel Dalio *(Malichot)*, Noël Roquevert *(recruiting sergeant)*, Jess Hahn *(La Douceur)*, Jean Rochefort *(La Taupe)*, Alain Dekock *(Louison)*, Jacques Charon *(colonel)*, Lucien Raimbourg *(marshal)*, Pierre Repp, Jacques Balutin, René Marlic, Paul Préboist, Jacques Hilling, Philippe de Broca.

Adventure comedy-drama. In 18th-century France, Cartouche, a cooper's son, robs from the rich, gives to the poor, and earns a comfortable income by his thievery. Rebelling against the authority of Malichot, leader of the pickpockets, he is forced to flee Paris and enlist in the army. He joins forces with La Douceur and La Taupe; together they steal their regiment's cashbox, but Cartouche is captured and imprisoned. He escapes, at the same time rescuing Venus, a gypsy pickpocket who becomes his mistress. Cartouche takes over Malichot's organization and turns it into an extremely successful crime syndicate. The vengeful Malichot turns informer, uniting against his rival with de Ferrussac, the cruel Paris chief of police. La Douceur is captured and tortured by de Ferrussac but refuses to betray Cartouche. In retaliation, Cartouche loots the Ottoman Embassy and invades the convent school run by de Ferrussac's beautiful, aristocratic wife, Isabelle. Captivated by Isabelle, Cartouche presents her with Ottoman treasures; finally she agrees to meet him, but her aged confidante betrays them, and de Ferrussac and 50 men descend upon the waiting Cartouche. He is rescued by Venus and his sidekicks, but Venus sacrifices her life to save him. Cartouche pursues the de Ferrussacs at a ball and robs the guests of their finery and jewels. These he drapes over Venus in her hearse, a beautiful, golden coach. Cartouche causes the coach to sink into the Seine and sets out to avenge Venus through continued theft and lawlessness. *Outlaws. Deserters—Military. Police. Gypsies. Mistresses. Informers. Aristocrats. Robbery. Revenge. Loyalty. Organized crime. Self-sacrifice. Convents. Paris. Louis Dominique Bourguignon.*

Note: Opened in Paris and Rome in Mar 1962.

LA CASA DE LAS MIL MUÑECAS *see* **HOUSE OF A THOUSAND DOLLS**

LA CASA DEL TERROR *see* **FACE OF THE SCREAMING WEREWOLF**

LA CASA EMBRUJADA *see* **THE CURSE OF THE CRYING WOMAN**

CASABLAN (Greece)   F6.0686

Frisch–Natas Productions–Cinematographic Enterprises Anzervos Corp. *Dist* Noel Meadow Associates. 12 Dec 1964 [New York opening]. Sd; b&w. 35mm. 63 min.

Prod Alec Natas. *Dir* Larry Frisch. *Screenplay* Alex Maimon. *Photog* Grigoris Danalis. *Art Dir* Petros Kapares. *Film Ed* Gerassimos Papadatos. *Mus Comp & Cond* Kostas Kapnissis.

Cast: Nikos Kourkoulos *(Casablan)*, Maria Xenia *(Rachel)*, Lykourgos Kallergis *(Abramov)*, Demetris Ballas *(Yosh)*, Mitsos Lygizos *(Feldman)*, Dimos Starenios *(Mushiko)*, Aspa Nakopoulou *(Gina)*, Artemis Matsas

(Neuberg).

Drama. Source: Yigal Mossensohn, *Casablan* (a play; Tel Aviv, 1958). Casablan, a quick-tempered young Moroccan, emigrates to Israel in 1948 to fight in the war of independence, but his lack of education and training makes him an outcast in post-war society. After he is arrested by police inspector Abramov and falsely accused of murdering a petty criminal, Casablan is defended by Yosh, his former army commander; in the process, Yosh falls in love with Rachel, Casablan's girl friend. Gina, a prostitute who loves Casablan, helps secure his acquittal by providing an alibi. Later, Casablan is jailed once again for fighting as Yosh and Rachel go away together. *Immigrants. Moroccans. Lawyers. Prostitutes. Police. Injustice. Murder. Trials. Israeli-Arab War 1948–49. Israel.*

Note: Location scenes filmed in Athens.

CASANOVA *see* **CASANOVA '70**

CASANOVA '70 (France/Italy)　　　　　　　　　　　　　**F6.0687**
C. C. Champion-Les Films Concordia. *Dist* Embassy Pictures. 20 Jul **1965** [New York opening]. Sd; col. 35mm. 113 min.

Pres by Joseph E. Levine. A Carlo Ponti Production. *Prod* Carlo Ponti. *Dir* Mario Monicelli. *Screenplay* Furio Scarpelli, Agenore Incrocci, Mario Monicelli, Suso Cecchi D'Amico. *Story* Tonino Guerra, Giorgio Salvioni. *Dir Photog* Aldo Tonti. *Camera* Luigi Kuveiller. *Art Dir* Mario Garbuglia. *Set Decor* Giorgio Herman. *Film Ed* Ruggero Mastroianni. *Mus* Armando Trovajoli. *Sd* Ennio Sensi. *Asst Dir* Renzo Marignano. *Cost Dsgn* Giulio Coltellacci. *Cost* Annamode.

Cast: Marcello Mastroianni (*Maj. Andrea Rossi-Colombetti*), Virna Lisi (*Gigliola*), Michèle Mercier (*Noelle*), Marisa Mell (*Thelma*), Marco Ferreri (*Count Ferreri*), Enrico Maria Salerno (*psychoanalyst*), Guido Alberti (*The Monsignor*), Margaret Lee (*Dolly Greenwater*), Rosemarie Dexter (*chambermaid*), Iolanda Modio (*Addolarata*), Seyna Seyn (*Indonesian airline hostess*), Moira Orfei (*Santina*), Liana Orfei (*lion tamer*), Beba Loncar (*girl in museum*), Frank Gregory (*General Greenwater*), Luciana Paoli (*grocer's wife*), Augusta Checcotti (*Gigliola's mother*), Mario Banchelli (*Gigliola's father*), Bernard Blier (*commissioner*).

Comedy. Maj. Andrea Rossi-Colombetti, an Italian officer attached to the NATO headquarters in Naples, consults a psychiatrist because of a unique problem: he is so handsome and women are so liberated that there is no longer any challenge in the art of seduction. The loss of the elements of danger and suspense has rendered the major impotent. The psychiatrist, who harbors unusual sexual preferences himself, advises Andrea to concentrate on platonic relationships. The major goes for a skiing vacation in the Swiss Alps, and there he meets and becomes engaged to the virginal Gigliola. The engagement does not solve his problem, however, and he is unable to resist such temptations as kissing a woman lion tamer in a cage full of lions; posing as a doctor to seduce a peasant girl in Sicily; and pursuing a prostitute reputed to possess evil powers. The climax of his adventures comes in the seduction of the wife of a jealous count. The old count, who pretends to be deaf, overhears their plans and plots to murder the major but accidentally kills himself. The major is brought to trial for murder, but he is finally acquitted when his problem is explained and the count's feigned deafness is discovered. Andrea and Gigliola are then married, and the major satisfies his quest for danger by walking on a ledge six floors above the ground to reach his wife's bedroom. *Philanderers. Psychiatrists. Sicilians. Nobility. Lion tamers. Prostitutes. Impotence. Seduction. Murder. Virginity. Infidelity. Deafness. Imposture. Ski resorts. Trials. Alps. Naples. Switzerland. North Atlantic Treaty Organization.*

Note: Rome opening: Oct 1965; Paris opening: Aug 1965; French title: *Casanova.*

THE CASE AGAINST PAUL RYKER *see* **SERGEANT RYKER**

LA CASE DE L'ONCLE TOM *see* **UNCLE TOM'S CABIN**

THE CASE OF PATTY SMITH　　　　　　　　　　　　　**F6.0688**
Impact Films. *Dist* Ellis Gordon Films, Topaz Film Corp. 8 Jun **1962** [Los Angeles showing]. Sd; b&w. 35mm. 93 min.

A Leo Handel Production. *Prod-Dir-Story-Screenplay* Leo Handel. *Assoc Prod* Ib Melchior. *Photog* Howard Schwartz. *Art Dir* Ted Holsopple. *Set Decor* Ray Boltz. *Film Ed* Stanford Tischler. *Mus* Ingram P. Walters. *Sd* Denzil Daniels. *Asst Dir* Nathan R. Barragar, William Derwin. *Wardrobe* Ray Boltz. *Makeup* Jean Udko. *Hairstyles* Bob Wolfe. *Prop* Tom Coleman.

Cast: Merry Anders (*Mary*), J. Edward McKinley (*Dr. Miller*), Dani Lynn (*Patty*), Carleton Crane (*Allan*), Robert Rudelson (*Top*), Speer Martin (*Sidy*), Sean Brian (*Reep*), David McMahon (*Father O'Brian*), Bruno Ve Sota (*Colbert*), Jack Haddock (*Lieutenant Powell*), Joe Conley (*Johnny*), Leif Lindstrom (*Dr. Nielson*), Mary Patton (*Myra*), Sid Kane (*Crawford*), Sherwood Keith (*Dr. Fridden*), Phil Clarke (*pawnbroker*), Harrison Lewis (*bartender*), Adrienne Hayes (*Jean*), Mary Benoit (*Dr. Miller's nurse*), Sally

Hughes (*Dr. Fridden's nurse*), Ralph Neff (*"Doctor"*), Barney Biro (*narrator*).

Melodrama. Patty Smith is raped by three hoodlums on a Los Angeles beach. Young, inexperienced, and away from her Kansas home, she neglects to inform the proper authorities. Finding herself pregnant, she consults Dr. Miller, who explains that it is legally impossible for him to abort her pregnancy. She seeks advice from a priest, Father O'Brian, who criticizes her desire not to have the baby. Another physician, Dr. Fridden, offers to perform the abortion, but his price of $600 is impossible for Patty to meet. As her condition becomes apparent, most of her friends desert her. In desperation, she goes to the contact man of an abortion ring. He tells her that the operation can be arranged for $200, and, after Patty agrees to pay the price, the abortion is performed in a massage parlor. Soon afterwards, Patty is rushed to a hospital suffering great pain, and she dies. The rapists and the abortion ring members are apprehended by the police through information supplied by Patty's roommate, Mary. *Hoodlums. Physicians. Roommates. Priests. Rape. Abortion. Pregnancy. Manslaughter. Hospitals. Massage parlors. Los Angeles.*

Note: Also known as *The Shame of Patty Smith.*

THE CASE OF THE EXCITING WIVES *see* **THE CASE OF THE STRIPPING WIVES**

THE CASE OF THE MISSING SWITCHBOARD OPERATOR *see* **LOVE AFFAIR; OR THE CASE OF THE MISSING SWITCHBOARD OPERATOR**

THE CASE OF THE STRIPPING WIVES　　　　　　　　　**F6.0689**
Griffith & Borden. *Dist* American Film Distributing Corp. 24 Mar **1966** [New York showing]. Sd; col (Eastman Color). 35mm. 74 min.

Pres by Leroy C. Griffith. *Prod* Leroy C. Griffith. *Asst Prod* Chester Phebus. *Dir* (see note) Manuel S. Conde. *Dir-Script* (see note) Maria D. Maury. *Narr* Lisette Bourbeau. *Photog* Manuel S. Conde. *Ed* Sam Aniego. *Sd* Condi Studio.

Cast: Cindy Embers, Natasha, Libby Jones, Pagan Jones, Electrique, Jack Cole, Abe Atkinson, Aly Weiner, Sam Alport.

Drama. A group of beautiful housewives who are bored with their lives, and in particular with their husbands, look for excitement in a nudist camp. While their husbands are away on business, the women enter a striptease and beauty contest held in a local theater and compete with some of the most famous strippers in the profession. *Housewives. Striptease. Marriage. Nudist camps. Beauty contests.*

Note: Sources credit the film's director variously as Manuel S. Conde and as Maria D. Maury. Also known as *Stripping Wives, The Case of the Exciting Wives,* and *Exciting Wives.* Location scenes filmed in Miami, Florida.

CASH ON DEMAND (Great Britain)　　　　　　　　　　**F6.0690**
Hammer Film Productions-Woodpecker Productions. *Dist* Columbia Pictures. 20 Dec **1961** [Los Angeles opening; c1 Jan 1962; LP21392]. Sd (RCA); b&w. 35mm. 84 min. [Copyright length: 77 min.]

Prod Michael Carreras. *Assoc Prod* Anthony Nelson Keys. *Dir* Quentin Lawrence. *Screenplay* David T. Chantler, Lewis Greifer. *Dir Photog* Arthur Grant. *Camera Op* Len Harris. *Art Dir* Don Mingaye. *Prod Dsgn* Bernard Robinson. *Supv Ed* James Needs. *Ed* Eric Boyd-Perkins. *Mus Comp* Wilfred Josephs. *Mus Supv* John Hollingsworth. *Sd Rec* Jock May. *Sd Ed* Alban Streeter. *Asst Dir* John Peverall. *Prod Mgr* Clifford Parkes. *Cont* Tilly Day. *Wardrobe Supv* Molly Arbuthnot. *Wardrobe Mistress* Rosemary Burrows. *Makeup Artist* Roy Ashton. *Hairstyles* Frieda Steiger. *Casting* Stuart Lyons.

Cast: Peter Cushing (*Fordyce*), André Morell (*Hepburn*), Richard Vernon (*Pearson*), Norman Bird (*Sanderson*), Kevin Stoney (*Detective Inspector Mason*), Barry Lowe (*Peter Harvill*), Edith Sharpe (*Miss Pringle*), Lois Daine (*Sally*), Alan Haywood (*Kane*), Charles Morgan (*Collins*), Vera Cook (*Mrs. Fordyce*), Gareth Tandy (*Tommy*), Fred Stone (*window cleaner*).

Drama. Source: Jacques Gillies, *The Gold Inside* (a teleplay; ATV London, 24 Sep 1960). Hepburn, a suave crook, poses as an insurance investigator in order to loot the provincial bank managed by Fordyce, a strict disciplinarian who is unpopular with his staff. The robber persuades Fordyce that, unless he assists in the robbery and getaway, his wife and son will be killed; thoroughly intimidated, Fordyce agrees to help. When a bank aide discovers that Hepburn is an imposter, the manager must plead with the staff not to inform the police so that his family can be saved. They agree, unaware that Hepburn has already been arrested. Fordyce later realizes that he owes the bank staff a debt of gratitude. *Insurance agents. Bankers. Imposture. Extortion. Bank robberies. Employer-employee relations.*

Note: Released in Great Britain in Dec 1963; running time: 66 min.

CASINO ROYALE (Great Britain)　　　　　　　　　　　**F6.0691**
Famous Artists Productions. *Dist* Columbia Pictures. 28 Apr **1967** [New York opening; c1 Apr 1967; LF13]. Sd; col (Technicolor). 35mm (Panavision). 130 min.

Pres by Charles K. Feldman. *Prod* Charles K. Feldman, Jerry Bresler. *Assoc Prod* John Dark. *Dir* John Huston, Ken Hughes, Val Guest, Robert Parrish, Joseph McGrath. *Adtl Seq* Val Guest. *2d Unit Dir* Richard Talmadge, Anthony Squire. *Screenplay & Adapt* Wolf Mankowitz, John Law, writ, Michael Sayers. *Adtl Writ (see note)* Billy Wilder, Ben Hecht, John Huston, Val Guest, Joseph Heller, Terry Southern. *Photog* Jack Hildyard. *Adtl Photog* John Wilcox, Nicolas Roeg. *Art Dir* John Howell, Ivor Beddoes, Lionel Couch. *Set Decor* Terence Morgan, II. *Prod Dsgn* Michael Stringer. *Titl* Richard Williams. *Film Ed* Bill Lenny. *Montage Eff* Richard Williams. *Mus Comp & Cond* Burt Bacharach. *Main Titl Theme Perf by* Herb Alpert, The Tijuana Brass. *Song:* "The Look of Love" Burt Bacharach, Hal David. *Sung by* Dusty Springfield. *Choreog* Tutte Lemkow. *Sd* John W. Mitchell, Sash Fisher, Bob Jones, Dick Langford, Chris Greenham. *Asst Dir* Roy Baird, John Stoneman, Carl Mannin. *Prod Mgr* Douglas Peirce, John Merriman, Barrie Melrose. *Cost* Julie Harris, cost. *Cost for Misses Andress and Pettet* Bermans of London. *Makeup* Neville Smallwood. *Makeup for Miss Andress* John O'Gorman. *Hairstyles* Joan Smallwood. *Sp Eff* Cliff Richardson, Roy Whybrow. *Sp Matte Work* Les Bowie.

Cast: David Niven (*Sir James Bond*), Peter Sellers (*Evelyn Tremble, 007*), Ursula Andress (*Vesper Lynd, 007*), Orson Welles (*Le Chiffre*), Joanna Pettet (*Mata Bond*), Daliah Lavi (*The Detainer, 007*), Woody Allen (*Jimmy Bond/Dr. Nosh*), Terence Cooper (*Cooper, 007*), Barbara Bouchet (*Moneypenny*), Deborah Kerr (*Lady Fiona/Agent Mimi*), William Holden (*Ransome*), Charles Boyer (*Le Grand*), John Huston (*McTarry/M*), Kurt Kasznar (*Smernov*), George Raft (*himself*), Jean-Paul Belmondo (*French legionnaire*), Peter O'Toole (*Scottish piper*), Angela Scoular (*Buttercup*), Gabriella Licudi (*Eliza*), Tracey Crisp (*Heather*), Elaine Taylor (*Peg*), Jacqueline Bisset (*Miss Goodthighs*), Alexandra Bastedo (*Meg*), Anna Quayle (*Frau Hoffner*), Stirling Moss (*driver*), Derek Nimmo (*Hadley*), Ronnie Corbett (*Polo*), Colin Gordon (*casino director*), Bernard Cribbins (*taxi driver*), Tracy Reed (*Fang leader*), John Bluthal (*casino doorman/M1.5*), Geoffrey Bayldon (*Q*), John Wells (*Q's assistant*), Duncan Macrae (*Inspector Mathis*), Graham Stark (*cashier*), Chic Murray (*Chic*), Jonathan Routh (*John*), Richard Wattis (*British Army officer*), Vladek Sheybal (*Le Chiffre's representative*), Percy Herbert (*1st piper*), Penny Riley (*control girl*), Jeanne Roland (*captain of the guard*), Arthur Mullard.

Action comedy. Suggested by: Ian Fleming, *Casino Royale* (London, 1953). The original James Bond (007) retired following his star-crossed love affair with Mata Hari and watched with disdain as his gimmick-laden imitators sullied his name. But as the international crime organization known as SMERSH threatens world domination, he agrees to come out of retirement. After his longtime superior McTarry ("M") is killed, Bond goes to Scotland to console McTarry's widow, Lady Fiona, unaware that the woman he encounters is actually a SMERSH agent. Bond's charms are such, however, that Lady Fiona gives up her life of espionage and retires to a convent when Bond declines her offer of love. To outwit his enemy, Bond decides there should be more than one 007 agent. He enlists the services of Vesper Lynd, the world's richest and most seductive spy; Evelyn Tremble, the inventor of a foolproof gambling system; Cooper, a strong-arm agent trained to resist women; and Bond's own daughter, Mata Bond. While Mata is outwitting SMERSH in Berlin, Bond sends Tremble and Vesper to the famed Casino Royale, and there SMERSH agent Le Chiffre is attempting to replenish his organization's finances by playing baccarat. Although Tremble defeats Le Chiffre at the gaming tables, Vesper is kidnaped as they leave. In pursuit, Tremble is captured, tortured, and eventually shot. Mata is also abducted and carried off in a flying saucer. SMERSH begins to get the upper hand, and Bond swings into action. Upon learning that the casino is merely a front and that SMERSH is headed by his own fiendish nephew, Jimmy Bond, Sir James utilizes the charms of The Detainer (another 007) to induce Jimmy to swallow an explosive capsule. Bond then calls for his allies—the French Foreign Legion, tribes of American Indians, the U. S. Cavalry, United Nations paratroopers, and the Keystone Cops—to invade the casino. During the ensuing melee, Bond makes a strategic exit as Jimmy's internal bomb goes off and the casino and its occupants are blown up. *Secret agents. Widows. Nobility. Uncles. Retirement. Organized crime. Murder. Espionage. Gambling. Kidnaping. Torture. Casinos. Flying saucers. Scotland. Berlin. France. Margaretha Geertruida Zelle. James Bond. Explosions.*

Note: Location scenes filmed in England, Ireland, and France. Released in Great Britain in 1967; running time: 131 min. Wilder, Hecht, Huston, Guest, Heller, and Southern are uncredited screenplay writers.

CAST A GIANT SHADOW   F6.0692

Mirisch Corp.-Llenroc Productions-Batjac Productions. *Dist* United Artists. 30 Mar **1966** [New York opening; c29 Mar 1966; LP32500]. Sd; col (DeLuxe). 35mm (Panavision). 141 min. [Copyright length: 139 min.]

Pres by Mirisch Corp. *Prod-Dir-Writ* Melville Shavelson. *Co-prod* Michael Wayne. *2d Unit Dir* Jack Reddish. *2d Unit Photog* Aldo Tonti. *2d Unit Photog* Marko Yakovlevich. *Art Dir* Arrigo Equini. *Prod Dsgn* Michael Stringer. *Main Titl* Pacific Title. *Film Ed* Bert Bates, Gene Ruggiero. *Mus* Elmer Bernstein.

Mus: "Next Year in Jerusalem" Dov Seltzer. *Hebrew Lyr:* "Lila Lel" Dan Almagor. *Orch* Leo Shuken, Jack Hayes. *Sd* David Bowen, Chuck Overhulser. *Asst Dir* Charles Scott, Jr., Tim Zinnemann. *Prod Supv* Allen K. Wood. *Prod Mgr* Nate H. Edwards. *Unit Mgr* Patrick J. Palmer. *Italian Prod Coörd* Guy Luongo. *Israeli Unit Prod Mgr* Shlomo Mograbi. *Cost* Margaret Furse. *Makeup* David Grayson, Euclide Santoli. *Hairstyles* Vasco Reggiani. *Sp Eff* Sass Bedig.

Cast: Kirk Douglas (*Col. David "Mickey" Marcus*), Senta Berger (*Magda Simon*), Angie Dickinson (*Mrs. Emma Marcus*), James Donald (*Safir*), Stathis Giallelis (*Ram Oren*), Luther Adler (*Jacob Zion*), Haym Topol (*Abou Ibn Kader*), Frank Sinatra (*Vince*), Yul Brynner (*Comdr. Asher Gonen*), John Wayne (*Gen. Mike Randolph*), Gary Merrill (*Pentagon Chief of Staff*), Ruth White (*Mrs. Chaison*), Gordon Jackson (*James MacAfee*). Michael Hordern (*British ambassador*), Allan Cuthbertson (*British immigration officer*), Jeremy Kemp (*senior officer*), Sean Barrett (*junior officer*), Michael Shillo (*André Simon*), Rina Ganor (*Rona*), Roland Bartrop (*Bert Harrison*), Vera Dolen (*Mrs. Martinson*), Robert Gardett (*General Walsh*), Michael Balston, Claude Aliotti (*sentries*), Samra Dedes (*belly dancer*), Michael Shagrir (*truck driver*), Frank Latimore, Ken Buckle (*U. N. officers*), Rod Dana (*aide to Randolph*), Robert Ross, actor (*aide to Chief of Staff*), Arthur Hansell (*officer*), Don Sturkie (*parachute sergeant*), Hilel Raveh (*Yaakov*), Shlomo Hermon (*Yussuff*).

War drama. Source: Ted Berkman, *Cast a Giant Shadow* (New York, 1962). In late 1947 the British plan to withdraw from Palestine and the Arabs openly ignore the announcement of the United Nations to partition Palestine into separate Arab and Jewish states. Col. David "Mickey" Marcus, West Point graduate, military adviser to Franklin Roosevelt, and D-Day veteran, is asked to reorganize the Haganah. Despite the objections of his wife, Emma, and Pentagon officials, Marcus accepts the responsibility. Upon his arrival in Palestine, he is informed that the underground army is outnumbered 60 to 1 and that its striking force is weakened by internal differences. Aiding Marcus in his program is Magda Simon, a soldier with whom he becomes romantically involved. Disturbed by news of Emma's ill health resulting from a miscarriage and the Haganah's reluctance to accept him as a leader, Marcus returns to the United States. While attempting to see whether the U. S. will be the first in the United Nations to recognize Israel, he becomes aware of his Jewish heritage and decides to go back and serve the new nation. He is reunited with Magda as the U. S. recognizes Israel. When word arrives that the U. N. has called for a cease-fire, Marcus is ordered to break through to Jerusalem before the truce takes effect. Several attacks fail until Marcus rallies the Jews to build a mountain pass. As victory comes, Marcus receives a letter from Emma offering him a divorce. Realizing how much he loves her, he says goodby to Magda and strolls into a monastery courtyard. Unable to speak or understand Hebrew, he ignores a sentry's warning and is accidentally killed a few hours before the truce takes effect. *Military life. Infidelity. Israeli-Arab War 1948–49. Palestine. Jerusalem. David "Mickey" Marcus. Israel—Army. United States Army. United Nations.*

Note: Location scenes filmed in Israel and Italy.

IL CASTELLO DI ARTENA see BLOODY PIT OF HORROR

IL CASTELLO IN SVEZIA see NUTTY, NAUGHTY CHATEAU

THE CASTILIAN (United States/Spain)   F6.0693

Cinemagic, Inc.-Producciones M. D. *Dist* Warner Bros. Pictures. 6 Sep **1963** [Chicago opening]. Sd; col (Eastmancolor, print by Panacolor). 35mm. 129 min.

Prod-English Screenplay & Dial Sidney W. Pink. *Exec Prod* Richard C. Meyer. *Assoc Prod* Michael Hamilburg, Joseph Leonard. *Dir* Javier Setó. *Dir Action Scenes* Al Wyatt. *Screenplay* Paulino Rodrigo Díaz, Javier Setó, Luis de los Arcos. *Photog* Mario Pacheco. *Camera Op* Rafael Pacheco. *Art Dir* José Antonio de la Guerra. *Supv Film Ed* Richard C. Meyer. *Film Ed* Margarita Ochoa. *Mus Comp & Cond* José Buenagu. *Song:* "Song of Fernan" José Buenagu, Robert Marcucci. *Songs:* "Valley of the Swords," "Song of Love" Russell Faith, Robert Marcucci. *Asst Dir* José Puyol. *Prod Mgr* Pérez Gómez. *Cost* José Zamora. *Dial Dir* Eric Chapman.

Cast: Cesar Romero (*Jerónimo*), Frankie Avalon (*Jerifan*), Broderick Crawford (*Don Sancho*), Alida Valli (*Queen Teresa*), Spartaco Santoni (*Fernán Gonzáles*), Teresa Velázquez (*Sancha*), Fernando Rey (*King of León [Ramiro III]*), George Rigaud (*Saint Millan*), Germán Cobos (*Adberramán*), Julio Peña (*Santiago*), Angel Del Pozo (*Don Sancho's son*), Linda Darnell, Hugo Pimentel, Beny Deus, Tomás Blanco, Rafael Durán, Roberto Rey, Francisco Morán.

Historical drama. Based on a 13th-century Spanish epic poem, *El poema de Fernán Gonzáles*. In 10th-century Spain Fernán Gonzáles, a Castilian nobleman, emerges from a self-imposed exile after the death of his older brother, the ruler of the city of Lara. Assisted by his loyal companion, Jerónimo, he leads a resistance army against the ruthless Navarrese troops and the Moors. After becoming enamored of the beautiful Sancha, the niece of Queen Teresa of León, Fernán kills Sancha's father, Don Sancho, the ruthless King of

Navarre, who has attacked the Castilians in Valpierre. Fernán orders the dead of both sides to be buried together in the hope that this act will be accepted as a gesture of peace, but the late ruler's son and new king betrays Fernán and imprisons him in a dungeon. Aided by Sancha, he escapes and is reunited with Jerónimo to lead his small partisan force in a series of raids against the invading Moors. The vast Moorish army assembles under the command of Adberramán for an attack against the Castilians, but two patron saints of Spain, Millan and Santiago, come to earth in human form and counsel Fernán. Fortified by this divine intervention, the Castilians are able to rout the Moors. Following the victory the patron saints gallop into the sky, carrying with them the dead body of Jerónimo. The Castilians and the Navarrese come to a harmonious agreement, and Fernán and Sancha prepare for a peaceful rule over the grateful Castilian people. *Nobility. Brothers. Peacemakers. Moors. Royalty. Exile. Military invasion. Prison escapes. Perfidy. Miracles. Spain—History—Arab period 711-1492. Castile. Navarre. Fernán González. Ramiro II (León).*

Note: Filmed in Spain; exteriors filmed in Burgos. Madrid opening: Apr 1963 as *El valle de las espadas*. May also be known in the United States under the working title *Valley of the Swords*.

CASTING CALL　　　　　　　　　　　　　　　　　　　　F6.0694

Gentlemen II Productions. *Dist* Sack Amusement Enterprises. ca **1970**. Sd; col. 35mm. ca76 min.

Prod Robert Leigh. *Dir* Ken Stewart. *Dir Photog* Stan Slate. *Camera* Bill Coors. *Film Ed* Ken Stewart. *Mus* Oliver Howard. *Sd Rec* Gary Pierce. *Prod Mgr* Russell Booth. *Makeup* Harry Hash. *Key Grip* Robert Rubio. *Gaffer* Lance Cott.

Cast: John Long *(Les Heyer)*, Stephen Treadwell *(Jay Robbins)*, Susan Bergdahl *(Charlotte)*, Heidi Sohler *(Hanna Hightower)*, Valerie Lauron *(Bobbi)*, Zoltan Narish *(Harry Kelp)*, Sarah Warren *(Abbey)*, Judy Angel *(Sherry)*, Michael Valentine *(attendant)*, Lainie McCrea *(Lulu)*, Linda Vroom *(big blonde)*, Olivia Cavery *(girl)*, Thad Paine *(boy hippy)*, Constance Petty *(girl hippy)*, Linda York *(girl in rape)*, Jeff Goodman, Stacey Daniels, Cecelia Smith *(rapists)*.

Melodrama. Sex exploitation film director Les Heyer, a decadent and insatiable man, satisfies his unnatural desires by sleeping with the women who answer his casting calls. Among the women who enter his office are: Charlotte, who is unsatisfied in her marriage; Bobbi, a flower child who has sex for money in order to release a friend from jail; Hanna, a bisexual; and Sherri, a hopeful starlet and Heyer's mistress, who invents new thrills for Heyer in hopes of starring in his next film. Heyer has two assistants, flesh peddler Harry Kelp, who more than matches the director's capacity for evil, and Jay Robbins, a wholesome young man who seems to be out of place in Heyer's world. Jay's fiancée, Abbey, an actress who is desperate for a break, falls into Heyer's trap, and his activities with her climax the film. *Motion picture directors. Actors. Hippies. Mistresses. Satyriasis. Bisexuality. Moral corruption. Prostitution. Ambition. Employer-employee relations. Sex exploitation films.*

THE CASTING COUCH　　　　　　　　　　　　　　　　　F6.0695

Dist Stacey Distributors. ca **1970**. Sd; col. 16mm. 61-81 min.

Sex film. No information about the precise nature of this film has been found. *Actors. Sexuality.*

THE CASTLE (Switzerland/West Germany)　　　　　　　　　F6.0696

Alfa Film–Glarus–Rudolf Noelte Filmproduktion. *Dist* Continental Distributing, Inc. 9 Mar **1969** [New York opening]. Sd; col (U. S. print by Movielab). 35mm. 93 min.

Prod Maximilian Schell. *Dir-Writ* Rudolf Noelte. *Photog* Wolfgang Treu. *Art Dir* Otto Pischinger, Herta Pischinger. *Film Ed* Dagmar Hirtz. *Mus (see note)* Herbert Trantow. *Sd* Oskar Haarbrandt. *Asst Dir* Ilona Perl, Peter Pauker. *Prod Mgr* Josef Hadrawa, Helmut Bauer. *Cost* Barbara Bilabel. *Makeup* Evelynne Maino. *English Subtitl* Herman G. Weinberg.

Cast: Maximilian Schell *(K.)*, Cordula Trantow *(Frieda)*, Trudik Daniel *(innkeeper's wife)*, Helmut Qualtinger *(Burgel)*, Franz Misar *(Arthur)*, Johann Misar *(Jeremiah)*, Hanns Ernst Jager *(landlord)*, Friedrich Maurer *(mayor)*, Else Ehser *(Mizzi)*, Iva Janzurova *(Olga)*, Martha Wallner *(Amalia)*, Georg Lehn *(Barnabas)*, Karl Hellmer *(schoolmaster)*, Ilse Kunkele *(schoolmistress)*, Benno Hoffmann *(uniformed man)*, E. O. Fuhrmann *(Momus)*, Leo Mally *(Gerstaecker)*, Hans Possenbacher *(innkeeper)*, Armand Ozory *(Erlanger)*.

Allegory. Source: Franz Kafka, *Das Schloss* (Munich, 1926). K., a land surveyor, is summoned to an unnamed village by unseen authorities who rule from an oppressive Castle on a nearby hill. Although supposedly called to practice his profession, he is told that there is no work for him; and the villagers regard him with open fear and mistrust. Confused, K. tries to establish contact with the Castle, but each attempt is met with a new barrier as the innkeeper, the innkeeper's wife, the mayor, and the peasants all stand firm in their resolve that K. shall not contact the Castle. He is unable even to obtain an explanation as to why he should be barred, and his resolve to confront the hierarchy soon

becomes an obsession. The only person who offers friendship is the local barmaid, Frieda. She, too, turns against him when she realizes that he makes use of anyone, including the woman he loves, to gain admittance to the Castle. Eventually, K. nearly succeeds in meeting one of the visiting secretaries from the Castle. At the last minute, however, the coach carrying the official heads back to the Castle. Denounced and humiliated, K. races after the rapidly departing coach. [When first shown at the 1968 Venice Film Festival, the film ended with the death of K.] *Barmaids. Innkeepers. Surveyors. Peasants. Village life. Obsession. Totalitarianism. Bureaucracy. Castles.*

Note: Filmed in Austria in 1968 as *Das Schloss*. Music credited by German source only.

CASTLE KEEP　　　　　　　　　　　　　　　　　　　　　F6.0697

Filmways, Inc. *Dist* Columbia Pictures. 23 Jul **1969** [New York opening; c1 Jul 1969; LP36998]. Sd; col (Technicolor). 35mm (Panavision). 105 min. [Copyright length: 119 min.] *MPAA rating* R.

A Martin Ransohoff Production. *Prod* Martin Ransohoff, John Calley. *Assoc Prod* Edward L. Rissien. *Prod Exec* Ben Kadish. *Dir* Sydney Pollack. *2d Unit Dir* Ray Kellogg. *Screenplay* Daniel Taradash, David Rayfiel. *Dir Photog* Henri Decaë. *Aerial Photog* Tyler Camera Systems. *Art Dir* Max Douy, Jacques Douy, Mort Rabinowitz. *Set Dresser* Charles Merangel. *Prod Dsgn* Rino Mondellini. *Titl* Phill Norman, Cinefx. *Film Ed* Malcolm Cooke. *Asst Film Ed* Michele Robert. *Mus Comp & Cond* Michel Legrand. *Choreog* Dirk Sanders. *Sd* Antoine Petitjean, Yves Dacquay. *Asst Dir (see note)* Marc Maurette, Stevo Petrovic, Pierre Roubaud. *Prod Mgr* Ludmilla Goulian. *Unit Mgr* Suzanne Wiesenfeld. *Cost Dsgn* Jacques Fonteray, Jack Martell. *Makeup* Robert J. Schiffer. *Hairstyles* Anna Cristofani. *Sp Eff* Lee Zavitz. *Casting* Lynn Stalmaster.

Cast: Burt Lancaster *(Major Falconer)*, Patrick O'Neal *(Captain Beckman)*, Jean-Pierre Aumont *(The Count)*, Peter Falk *(Sergeant Rossi)*, Astrid Heeren *(Thérèse)*, Scott Wilson *(Corporal Clearboy)*, Tony Bill *(Lieutenant Amberjack)*, Al Freeman, Jr. *(Private Benjamin)*, James Patterson *(Elk)*, Bruce Dern *(Billy Bix)*, Michael Conrad *(Sergeant De Vaca)*, Caterina Boratto *(Red Queen)*, Bisera Vukotić *(baker's wife)*, Elisabeth Teissier, Marja Allanen, Anne Marie Moskovenko, Eya Tuli, Elizabeth Darius, Karen Blanguernon, Maria Danube *(Red Queen girls)*, Jancika Kovac *(David)*, Ernest Clark *(British colonel)*, Harry Baird *(dancing soldier)*, Dave Jones *(one-eared soldier)*, Jean Gimello *(Puerto Rican)*.

War drama. Source: William Eastlake, *Castle Keep* (New York, 1965). In the winter of 1944 as World War II nears its end, one-eyed Infantry Major Abraham Falconer leads a group of seven battle-weary soldiers to a medieval castle on the Belgian side of the French border. The owner of the castle, the Comte de Maldorais, permits the men to be billeted in one of the castle turrets, but he urges the major not to make a stand against an expected German attack because the castle is filled with priceless art treasures. Although this plea is seconded by Captain Beckman, one of Falconer's officers and an art historian, the rest of the men in the squad occupy themselves with other matters. Sergeant Rossi, a civilian baker, assists and makes love to the local baker, a widow; Corporal Clearboy, a dour ex-cowboy, becomes enamored of a captured Volkswagen; Lieut. Amberjack, a former divinity student, tries, unsuccessfully, to have as good a time at the nearby brothel as his comrades, the hard-drinking Sergeant De Vaca and a sharp-tongued Indian, Pvt. Henry Three Ears of an Elk; and the youngest of the lot, Private Benjamin, a Negro intellectual, is writing a novel, *Castle Keep*, about his war experiences. As the men await the German advance toward Bastogne, the impotent count encourages a romance between his youthful wife and niece, Thérèse, and Falconer in the hope that their union will provide an heir to the Maldorais line. When the Germans finally march on the castle, the count tries to save the works of art by leading the enemy to an underground entrance to the castle, but he dies in the attempt. Despite Falconer's order that the secret passage be dynamited, thus destroying the art treasury, his men, including Beckman, rally to his call. During the desperate fighting that ensues the brothel girls hurl Molotov cocktails on the invading Nazi tanks, and the GI's take a deadly toll of the enemy, but one after another they are cut down. Only Private Benjamin escapes, taking Thérèse with him, as the castle is destroyed in the holocaust. *Nobility. Art historians. Bakers. Widows. Negroes. Novelists. Indians of North America. Ministerial students. Combat zone life. Impotence. Infidelity. Art. Castles. Whorehouses. World War II. Belgium. France. Bastogne. United States Army—Infantry. Germany—Army.*

Note: Filmed in Yugoslavia. Some sources list Roubaud as assistant director instead of Petrovic.

CASTLE OF BLOOD (France/Italy)　　　　　　　　　　　　F6.0698

Vulsinia Film–Jolly Film–Ulysse Productions–Léo Lax Films. *Dist* Woolner Bros. Pictures. 29 Jul **1964** [Los Angeles opening]. Sd; b&w. 35mm. 85 min.

Prod Frank Belty, Walter Sarch. *Dir* Anthony Dawson. *Story & Screenplay* Jean Grimaud, Gordon Wilson, Jr. *Photog* Richard Kramer. *Art Dir* Warner

Scott. *Film Ed* Otel Langhel. *Mus Comp & Cond* Riz Ortolani. *Asst Dir* Roger Duke.

Cast: Barbara Steele *(Elizabeth Blackwood)*, Georges Rivière *(Alan Foster)*, Margaret Robsahm *(Julia)*, Sylvia Sorente *(Eli)*, Henry Kruger *(Dr. Carmus)*, Montgomery Glenn, Raoul H. Newman, Phil Karson, John Peters, Ben Steffen, Salvo Randone.

Horror film. Source: Edgar Allan Poe, "Danse Macabre" (a short story; publication undetermined). Journalist Alan Foster finds Edgar Allan Poe in a London tavern on All Souls' Eve. Lord Blackwood accompanies him and backs up Poe's claim that his writings about the living dead are not fiction; the two men bet Foster that he cannot survive one night alone in the Blackwood Castle. Foster accepts the bet and encounters Blackwood's sister Elizabeth in the castle. Horrified to find that she has no heartbeat, Foster learns from Dr. Carmus, a necromancer who also inhabits the castle, that All Souls' Day is the one day of the year when the dead return to life and reenact their final moments of life. Foster watches several murders involving Elizabeth, her husband, her jealous lover, and a lesbian admirer; he is then told by Dr. Carmus that the spirits need warm blood to complete their ritual. Realizing that he is intended as a sacrificial victim, Foster flees with Elizabeth from the castle only to be impaled on an iron gate outside. In the morning, Lord Blackwood removes the wager from the dead journalist's wallet. *Journalists. Zombies. Witchcraft. Wagers. Reviviscence. Murder. Human sacrifice. Castles. All Souls' Eve. Edgar Allan Poe.*

Note: Released in Italy in 1964 as *Danza macabra*; opened in Paris in Apr 1965 as *Danse macabre*; running time: 87 min. Anthony Dawson is a pseudonym for Antonio Margheriti, Walter Sarch for Giovanni Addessi, Jean Grimaud for Gianni Grimaldi, Gordon Wilson, Jr., for Sergio Corbucci, Richard Kramer for Riccardo Pallottini, Otel Langhel for Otello Colangeli, and Frank Belty for Marco Vicario. Also known as *Tombs of Horror, Coffin of Terror*, and *Edgar Allan Poe's Castle of Blood*.

CASTLE OF EVIL   F6.0699

National Telefilm Associates. *Dist* World Entertainment Corp., United Pictures. Nov **1966** [Texas showing]. Sd; col (Eastman Color). 35mm. 81 min.

Prod Earle Lyon. *Exec Prod* Fred Jordan. *Assoc Prod* Wendell Niles, Jr. *Dir* Francis D. Lyon. *Screenplay* Charles A. Wallace. *Dir Photog* Brick Marquard. *Art Dir* Paul Sylos, Jr. *Supv Ed* Robert S. Eisen. *Mus* Paul Dunlap. *Sd* John Bury. *Prod Mgr* Joe Wonder. *Makeup* Bob Dawn. *Sp Eff* Roger George.

Cast: Scott Brady *(Matt Granger)*, Virginia Mayo *(Sable)*, David Brian *(Robert Hawley)*, Lisa Gaye *(Carol Harris)*, Hugh Marlowe *(Dr. Corozal)*, Shelley Morrison *(Lupe Tekal d'Esperanza)*, Ernest Sarracino *(Tunki)*, William Thourlby *(electronic man)*, Natividad Vacio *(Machado)*.

Horror film. The heirs of eccentric chemist Kovec are summoned to a remote castle on a wind-swept Caribbean island for the reading of the dead man's will. Upon their arrival, the guests (all of whom were present when Kovec was disfigured by phosphorous salts) are informed by the housekeeper, Lupe, that if any of them should die before the will is probated the survivors will share the extra portion. At this point Kovec's apparition comes before the heirs and declares that one of them was responsible for his disfiguration. That night, Kovec's doctor, Robert Hawley, is murdered, and a short time later Lupe is attacked. Before dying, Lupe explains that Kovec created an electronic man in his own image for purposes of revenge; but, bent on securing his fortune for herself, she programmed the monster to kill the heirs one by one. Now something obviously has gone wrong, for the creature is acting under its own volition. As it goes about its business of attempting to kill the rest of the guests—especially Kovec's ex-mistress, Sable—engineer Matt Granger finds a laser gun in the castle laboratory and destroys the electronic man. *Heirs. Chemists. Physicians. Housekeepers. Mistresses. Engineers. Disfiguration. Murder. Revenge. Castles. Robots. Laser. Caribbean. Wills.*

Note: Working title: *The Haunting of Castle Montego.*

I CASTRATI *see* **WHITE VOICES**

CASTRO, CUBA, AND COMMUNISM   F6.0700

Mel O'Dee Productions-Parallel Film Distributors. *Dist* Sam Lake Enterprises. May **1962** [Los Angeles showing]. Sd; b&w. 35mm. 60 min.

Cast: Westbrook Van Voorhis *(narrator)*.

Documentary. This film uses television newsreel footage to document Fidel Castro's rise to power in Cuba. Coverage includes: the Batista government; the incitement to revolution; Castro as a student agitator; the July 26th massacre; Castro uniting the rebel forces in the mountains; guerrilla warfare; Che Guevara's attack on Santa Clara; riots in Havana; Castro's rise from freedom fighter to dictator; Chinese and European Communists arriving in Cuba; the Communist takeover in Cuba; and Russia's military presence in the Western Hemisphere. *Students. Guerrillas. Cubans. Chinese. Dictators. Russians. Communism. Revolutions. Massacres. Riots. Coups d'état. Cuba. Fidel Castro Ruz. Fulgencio Batista y Zaldívar. Ernesto Che Guevara.*

Note: Also known as *Danger on Our Doorstep.*

THE CAT   F6.0701

World–Cine Associates. *Dist* Embassy Pictures. Jun **1966**. Sd; col (PathéColor). 35mm. 87 min.

Prod-Dir Ellis Kadison. *Assoc Prod* William Schwartz. *Screenplay* William Redlin, Laird Koenig. *Photog* Monroe Askins. *Camera Op* Harry May. *Supv Ed* Douglas Robertson. *Ed* Jack Cornall. *Mus Comp & Score* Stan Worth. *Sd* John W. Barry, Roy Harvery. *Asst Dir* Grayson Rogers. *Script Supv* Patricia Lamb. *Wardrobe* Bill Edwards. *Makeup* Phil Rhodes. *Hairdresser* Linda Trainoff. *Dial Coach* Carl Shain. *Still Photog* Roger Mace. *Grip* Harry Stern, Butch Hazel. *Gaffer* Ted Garber. *Prop* Oscar Lau, Charles West.

Cast: Roger Perry *(Pete Kilby)*, Peggy Ann Garner *(Martha Kilby)*, Barry Coe *(Walt Kilby)*, Dwayne Redlin *(Toby)*, George Fisher *(Bill Krim)*, Ted Darby *(Art)*, John Todd Roberts *(Jesse)*, Richard Webb *(Sheriff Vern)*, Leslie Bradley *(Mike)*.

Adventure melodrama. Martha and Walt Kilby and their 8-year-old son, Toby, leave the city for the California mountain country. There, Walt's brother Pete offers them a home on his ranch property. Pete tells them of a band of rustlers that plague the area, despite strong security measures. Martha, Walt, and Toby meet Bill, a trapper who keeps a mountain lion caged in his truck. The animal appears docile in Toby's presence but escapes and wanders off when the cage falls off the truck. Toby then tells his father that a mountain lion is prowling outside, and Walt is furious when he finds nothing. As punishment, Walt orders Toby to remain in the cabin while he is out with Pete, but the boy wanders off and witnesses a forest ranger photographing and then fighting one of the rustlers. This man, Art, brutally kills the ranger but sees that he has been observed by Toby. When Walt returns, Bill tells him that his lion has escaped, and Walt realizes that Toby was not lying. Pete sets out with a search party, and the group finds the dead ranger. Art joins the search party, hoping to find and kill Toby before he can talk. Toby is approached by the mountain lion, who acts quite friendly, and the animal's warmth protects Toby through the freezing night. Meanwhile, Bill has developed the ranger's photograph, which serves to implicate Art, and warns the search party. Art has already found Toby alone while the lion is away searching for food. The lion hears Toby's cries and returns in time to prevent his murder by chasing Art and causing him to fall off a cliff. The lion runs off when the search party approaches. After being reunited with Toby, Walt decides to go back to the city. As they drive off, Toby waves goodby to the lion, who is once more in its natural habitat. *Children. Forest rangers. Rustlers. Trappers. Brothers. Mountain life. Murder. Ranches. Photographs. California. Lions.*

Note: Working title: *Cat.*

CAT AND MOUSE (Poland/West Germany)   F6.0702

Modern Art Film–RYTM Film Unit-Film Polski. *Dist* Grove Press. 4 Feb **1970** [New York opening]. Sd; b&w. 35mm. 92 min.

Dir-Writ Hansjürgen Pohland. *Photog* Wolf Wirth. *Film Ed* Christa Pohland. *Mus* Attila Zoller.

Cast: Lars Brandt *(young Mahlke)*, Peter Brandt *(older Mahlke)*, Wolfgang Neuss *(Pilenz)*, Claudia Bremer *(Tulla)*, Herbert Weissbach *(Klohse)*, Ingrid van Bergen *(aunt)*, Michael Hinz *(pilot)*, Helmut Kircher *(lieutenant-commander)*, Hans-Peter Brandes *(Esch)*.

Drama. Source: Günter Grass, *Katz und Maus* (Neuweid am Rhein, 1961). Twenty years have passed since the years of the Third Reich when Pilenz was a student in Danzig. Now he returns to visit his old school and recalls his friend Mahlke: Young Mahlke possesses an exceptionally large Adam's apple, a condition for which he compensates by striving very hard to excel in school and at sports. An exceptionally strong swimmer, he is the only one of his friends who can dive and reach a sunken wreck in the harbor waters. Mahlke dreams of winning the Iron Cross, with the hope that the medal, when worn around his neck, will attract attention away from his Adam's apple. A war hero who won the medal visits the school, and Mahlke is unable to resist the impulse to steal it. The theft is discovered, Mahlke confesses, and Klohse, the rigidly authoritarian school principal, has him expelled. Mahlke joins the German Navy and wins the Iron Cross for bravery. He returns to his school to recount his adventures but is forced to leave by the unforgiving Klohse. Mahlke deserts from the Navy and with his longtime friend Pilenz visits the sunken wreck where as students they spent so much time. Mahlke bids farewell to Pilenz, dives to the wreck, and does not return. *Students. School principals. Deserters—Military. War heroes. Adolescence. Swimming. Theft. Suicide. Iron Cross. World War II. Germany—History—Third Reich. Danzig. Germany—Navy.*

Note: Location scenes filmed in and around Gdańsk. Released in West Germany in Feb 1967 as *Katz und Maus*; running time: 88 min. Polish title: *Kot i mysz.*

CAT BALLOU　　　　　　　　　　　　　　　F6.0703

Harold Hecht Corp. *Dist* Columbia Pictures. 7 May **1965** [Denver, Colorado, opening; c1 Jun 1965; LP30839]. Sd; col (Eastman Color by Pathé). 35mm. 96 min.

A Harold Hecht Production. *Prod* Harold Hecht. *Assoc Prod* Mitch Lindemann. *Dir* Elliot Silverstein. *2d Unit Dir* Yakima Canutt. *Screenplay* Walter Newman, Frank R. Pierson. *Dir Photog* Jack Marta. *Art Dir* Malcolm Brown. *Set Decor* Richard Mansfield. *Film Ed* Charles Nelson. *Mus* De Vol. *Songs* Mack David, Jerry Livingston. *Songs Sung by* Nat King Cole, Stubby Kaye. *Choreog* Miriam Nelson. *Sd Supv* Charles J. Rice. *Sd* Earl Snyder. *Asst Dir* Lee Lukather, Ray Gosnell. *Miss Fonda's Gowns* Bill Thomas. *Makeup Supv* Ben Lane. *Hairstyles* Virginia Jones.

Cast: Jane Fonda *(Cat Ballou)*, Lee Marvin *(Kid Shelleen/Tim Strawn)*, Michael Callan *(Clay Boone)*, Dwayne Hickman *(Jed)*, Nat King Cole, Stubby Kaye *(shouters)*, Tom Nardini *(Jackson Two-Bears)*, John Marley *(Frankie Ballou)*, Reginald Denny *(Sir Harry Percival)*, Jay C. Flippen *(Sheriff Cardigan)*, Arthur Hunnicutt *(Butch Cassidy)*, Bruce Cabot *(Sheriff Maledon)*, Burt Mustin *(accuser)*, Paul Gilbert *(train messenger)*, Robert Phillips *(Klem)*, Charles Wagenheim *(James)*, Duke Hobbie *(Homer)*, Ayllene Gibbons *(Hedda)*, Everett L. Rohrer *(train engineer)*, Harry Harvey, Sr. *(train conductor)*, Hallene Hill *(honey girl)*, Gail Bonney *(Mabel Bentley)*, Joseph Hamilton *(Frenchie)*, Dorothy Claire *(singing tart)*, Charles Horvath *(Hardcase)*, Chuck Roberson *(armed guard)*, Nick Cravat *(Ad-Lib)*, Ted White *(gunslinger)*, Erik Sorenson *(valet)*, Ivan L. Middleton *(train fireman)*, Carol Veazie *(Mrs. Parker)*.

Western comedy. Source: Roy Chanslor, *The Ballad of Cat Ballou* (Boston, 1956). Catherine Ballou, an aspiring schoolteacher, is traveling by train to Wolf City, Wyoming, to visit her rancher father, Frankie Ballou. En route she unwittingly helps accused cattle rustler Clay Boone elude his captor, the sheriff, when Boone's Uncle Jed, a drunkard disguised as a preacher, distracts the lawman. She reaches the ranch to find that the Wolf City Developing Company is trying to take away the ranch from her father, whose only defender is an educated Indian, Jackson Two-Bears. Clay and Jed appear and reluctantly offer to help Catherine. She also wires legendary gunfighter Kid Shelleen to come and help protect her father from fast-drawing Tim Strawn, alias Silvernose, the hired killer who is threatening Frankie. Shelleen arrives, a drunken stumblebum who is literally unable to hit the side of a barn when he shoots and whose pants fall down when he draws his gun. Strawn kills Frankie, but the townspeople refuse to bring him to justice, and Catherine becomes a revenge-seeking outlaw known as Cat Ballou. She and her four associates rob a train carrying the Wolf City payroll, and Shelleen, inspired by his love for Cat (unrequited because she loves Clay), shapes up and kills Strawn. Later he casually admits that Strawn was his brother. Cat poses as a prostitute and confronts town boss Sir Harry Percival, owner of the Wolf City Developing Company. A struggle ensues; Harry is killed; and Cat is sentenced to be hanged. Just as the noose is being placed around her neck, however, her gang arrives and stages a daring rescue. *Ranchers. Schoolteachers. Rustlers. Preachers. Fugitives. Hired killers. Indians of North America. Gunfighters. Outlaws. Brothers. Filial relations. Alcoholism. Extortion. Murder. Revenge. Imposture. Robbery. Capital punishment. Trains. Wyoming. George "Butch" Cassidy.*

THE CAT BURGLAR　　　　　　　　　　　　F6.0704

Harvard Film Corp. *Dist* United Artists. Jul **1961**. Sd; b&w. 35mm. 65 min.

Prod Gene Corman. *Dir* William Witney. *Screenplay* Leo Gordon. *Photog* Taylor Byars. *Art Dir* Daniel Haller. *Film Ed* Mort Tubor. *Mus* Buddy Bregman. *Sd* Herman Lewis. *Asst Dir* Paul Rapp. *Makeup* Harry Thomas.

Cast: Jack Hogan *(Jack Coley)*, June Kenney *(Nan Baker)*, Gregg Palmer *(Reed Taylor)*, Will J. White *(Leo Joseph)*, Gene Roth *(Pete)*, Bruno Ve Sota *(Muskie)*, Billie Bird *(Mrs. Prattle)*, Tommy Ivo *(Willie Prattle)*, Hal Torey *(Officer Regan)*, John Baer *(Alan Sheridan)*.

Crime melodrama. While ransacking Nan Baker's apartment, Jack Coley, a smalltime burglar, steals a briefcase belonging to Nan's boy friend, Alan Sheridan. The briefcase contains plans for a secret defense formula which Alan plans to sell to a foreign power, and his superiors warn Alan that if the papers are not recovered, he will have to face the consequences. When he fails to retrieve them, his superiors murder him and go after Jack. Realizing the true value of the papers and refusing to commit treason, Jack prepares for the attack and kills the two conspirators, though he himself is mortally wounded. Following his death, Nan returns the vital formulas to the proper authorities. *Burglars. Theft. Treason. Murder. Documentation. Secret formulas.*

THE CAT IN THE SACK (Canada)　　　　　　F6.0705

Office National du Film—Canada. *Dist* Pathé Contemporary Films. 11 May **1967** [New York opening]. Sd; b&w. 35mm. 74 min.

Prod Jacques Bobet. *Dir-Writ* Gilles Groulx. *Photog* Jean-Claude Labrecque. *Mus Selections* John Coltrane, Antonio Vivaldi, François Couperin. *Sd* Marcel Carrière. *Sd Ed* Marguerite Payette, Sydney Pearson. *Mix* Roger Lamoureux.

Cast: Claude Godbout *(Claude)*, Barbara Ulrich *(Barbara)*, Manon Blain *(Manon J'sais-pas-qui)*, Jean-Paul Bernier *(Jean-Paul)*, Véronique Vilbert *(Véronique)*, André Leblanc *(Toulouse)*, Paul-Marie Lapointe, Pierre Maheu, Jean-V. Dufresne.

Drama. Claude, a 23-year-old journalist in Montreal, questions the value of the society in which he lives and his responsibility as a French Canadian, and seeks his own identity. Like many other youths in Quebec, he is faced with the alternatives of adjusting to a way of life that does not correspond to his ideals or seeking to change the society. Claude expresses his rebellion in articles which are rejected by publishers. His girl friend, Barbara, a Jewish drama student, is too preoccupied with the pursuit of her art and the tangible pleasures of life to concern herself with abstract social problems. Feeling the need to think things out alone, Claude retires to a snowy hideaway in the north of Quebec. As he meditates in the isolated countryside, he loses contact with Barbara, who becomes increasingly involved in her own pursuits. *French Canadians. Jews. Actors. Students. Journalists. Alienation. Social consciousness. Winter. Montreal. Quebec.*

Note: Opened in Montreal in Sep 1964 as *Le chat dans le sac.*

CATACOMBS see THE WOMAN WHO WOULDN'T DIE

CATALINA CAPER　　　　　　　　　　　　F6.0706

Executive Pictures. *Dist* Crown International Pictures. 26 Apr **1967** [San Diego, California, opening]. Sd; col (Eastman Color). 35mm. 84 min.

Prod Bond Blackman, Jack Bartlett. *Exec Prod* Sherman H. Dryer. *Assoc Prod* Willis Osborn, Salvatore Mungo. *Dir* Lee Sholem. *Screenplay* Clyde Ware. *Story* Sam Pierce. *Dir Photog* Ted V. Mikels. *Camera* Robert Caramico. *Film Ed* Herman Freedman. *Mus Comp* Jerry Long. *Mus Supv* John Caper, Jr. *Song:* "Scuba Party" *sung by* Little Richard. *Song:* "Book of Love" *sung by* Carol Connors. *Song:* "There's a New World Opening for Me" *sung by* The Cascades. *Song:* "Never Steal Anything Wet" *sung by* Mary Wells. *Choreog* Michael Blodgett. *Sd Rec* Rod Sutton. *Asst Dir* Dick Dixon, Wendell Franklin. *Prod Mgr* Ron Terry. *Asst to the Prod* Bruce Clark. *Wardrobe* Dorothy Worner. *Makeup* Mark Snegoff. *Prop Master* Earl Phillips.

Cast: Tommy Kirk *(Don Pringle)*, Del Moore *(Arthur Duval)*, Peter Duryea *(Tad Duval)*, Robert Donner *(Fingers O'Toole)*, Ulla Stromstedt *(Katrina)*, Jim Begg *(Larry Colvis)*, Sue Casey *(Anne Duval)*, Venita Wolf *(Tina Moss)*, Brian Cutler *(Charlie Moss)*, Peter Mamakos *(Borman)*, Lyle Waggoner *(Angelo)*, Lee Deane *(Lakopolous)*, Michael Blodgett *(Bob Draper)*, Bonnie Lomann *(redhead)*, Britt Nilsson *(brunette)*, Donna Russell *(blonde)*, James Almanzar *(Sid)*, Carol Connors, Little Richard, Timothy Garland, The Cascades, Adrian Teen Models.

Action comedy. College pals Don Pringle and Charlie Moss are spending their summer on Santa Catalina Island scuba diving and girl chasing. At the same time, Arthur Duval and his incompetent accomplice, Larry Colvis, are plotting to sell a fake Chinese scroll to a Greek millionaire who specializes in buying stolen art. As part of their scheme, Duval and Colvis have stolen the genuine scroll from a museum in order to convince the millionaire's art expert, Borman, of the authenticity of their merchandise. When the real scroll falls overboard during a scuffle on Duval's rented yacht, Don and Charlie are enlisted to recover the treasure. The plot is complicated by the arrival of criminal Fingers O'Toole and by the growing suspicions of the harbor patrol, but the scroll is eventually returned safely to the museum. *Students. Art collectors. Greeks. Divers. Millionaires. Fraud. Theft. Scrolls. Museums. Yachts. Santa Catalina (California).*

Note: Filmed on location in Santa Catalina and Malibu, California. Working title: *Never Steal Anything Wet.*

CATCH AS CATCH CAN (Italy)　　　　　　F6.0707

Fair Film. *Dist* Embassy Pictures. **1968**. Sd; col (Technicolor). 35mm. 95 min.

Prod Mario Cecchi Gori. *Dir* Franco Indovina. *Screenplay* Tonino Guerra, Luigi Malerba, Franco Indovina. *Photog* Aldo Tonti. *Film Ed* Marcello Malvestiti. *Mus* Luis Enriquez Bacalov.

Cast: Vittorio Gassman *(Bob Chiaramonte)*, Martha Hyer *(Luisa Chiaramonte)*, Gila Golan *(Emma)*, Karin Skorreso *(girl model)*, Massimo Serato *(agent)*, Carmelo Bene *(priest)*, Stephen Zacharias *(police inspector)*, Jacques Herlin *(zoology professor)*, Claudio Gora *(cabinet minister)*, Luigi Proietti, Ivan Scratuglia.

Comedy. Bob Chiaramonte, a successful actor and model who specializes in commercials and billboards, finds the animal kingdom suddenly turning against him. On location, a dog soils his pants, a bull attacks him, and bees and ants disturb his concentration. Harassed and unable to work, Bob takes a vacation, only to be bothered by a fly which gives him no peace until he finally kills it. On the verge of a nervous collapse, Bob visits a zoo and, trying to prove his superiority to an ape, climbs into the animal's cage and is left there by the

keepers. *Actors. Models. Mental illness. Zoos. Dogs. Bulls. Bees. Flies. Apes.*
Note: Released in Italy in 1967 as *Lo scatenato*. Alternative title: *Tutti Frutti*.

CATCH ME WHEN I FALL　　　　　　　　　　　　　　**F6.0708**
Jul **1970** [Los Angeles showing]. Sd; col. 35mm? [Feature length assumed.]
Sex film. No information about the precise nature of this film has been found, but press material suggests that it features an all-male orgy. *Male homosexuality. Orgies.*

CATCH 69　　　　　　　　　　　　　　　　　　　　**F6.0709**
Kirt Films International. *Dist* Distribpix, Inc. 9 Sep **1970** [Champaign, Illinois, showing]. Sd; col. 35mm. [Feature film, length undetermined.]
Drama. Two highly successful career women share both an apartment in the big city and a highly satisfying sex life together. The ex-boyfriend of one of the women returns to the city on leave from the army, and both women, needing to reassure themselves that lesbianism is more satisfactory than heterosexual love, separately go to bed with him. Each woman tries to persuade the young man that she is the more exciting sex partner but neither of them enjoys it. The G.I. returns to the army, and the women decide that no pleasure is more intense or more satisfying than their lesbian love. *Careerwomen. Roommates. Soldiers. Lesbianism.*

CATCH-22　　　　　　　　　　　　　　　　　　　　**F6.0710**
Paramount Pictures–Filmways, Inc. *Dist* Paramount Pictures. 24 Jun **1970** [New York opening; c5 Jun 1970; LP38130]. Sd; col (Technicolor). 35mm (Panavision). 122 min. *MPAA rating* R.
A Mike Nichols Production. *Prod* John Calley, Martin Ransohoff. *Assoc Prod* Clive Reed. *Dir* Mike Nichols. *2d Unit Dir* Andrew Marton, John Jordan, Alan McCabe. *Screenplay* Buck Henry. *Dir Photog* David Watkin. *2d Unit Photog* Harold Wellman. *Helicopter Photog* Nelson Tyler. *Camera Op* Alan McCabe. *1st Asst Camera* Peter Ewens. *2d Unit Camera Op* John C. Stevens. *Art Dir* Harold Michelson. *Set Decor* Ray Moyer. *Prod Dsgn* Richard Sylbert. *Titl Layout* Wayne Fitzgerald. *Film Ed* Sam O'Steen. *Ed Asst* Stewart Linder. *Mus Cond* Fritz Reiner. *Mus:* "Thus Spake Zarathustra" Richard Strauss. *Sd Rec* Larry Jost, Elden Ruberg. *Supv Sd Eff Ed* Gordon Daniel. *Sd Eff Ed* Howard Beals. *1st & 2d Asst Dir* Edward A. Teets, Martin Cohan, Ron Grow. *Prod Mgr* Jack Corrick. *Script Supv* Meta Rebner. *Unit Prod Mgr* Joe L. Cramer. *Rome Prod Coörd* Baccio Bandini. *Cost Supv* Ernest Adler. *Men's Wardrobe* Lambert Marks. *Makeup Supv* Del Armstrong. *Hairstyle Supv* Ernest Adler. *Sp Eff* Lee Vasque. *Sp Photog Eff* Albert Whitlock. *Tech Adv* Alexander Gerry. *Flying Seq* Tallmantz Aviation. *Flying Supv* Frank Tallman. *Dial Coach* Geoffrey Horne. *Casting* Alan Shayne. *Prop Master* Robert Schultz. *Key Grip* Bud Gaunt. *Gaffer* Earl Gilbert.
Cast: Alan Arkin (*Captain Yossarian*), Martin Balsam (*Colonel Cathcart*), Richard Benjamin (*Major Danby*), Art Garfunkel (*Captain Nately*), Jack Gilford (*Doc Daneeka*), Buck Henry (*Lieutenant Colonel Korn*), Bob Newhart (*Major Major*), Anthony Perkins (*Chaplain Tappman*), Paula Prentiss (*Nurse Duckett*), Martin Sheen (*Lieutenant Dobbs*), Jon Voight (*Milo Minderbinder*), Orson Welles (*General Dreedle*), Seth Allen (*Hungry Joe*), Bob Balaban (*Captain Orr*), Susanne Benton (*General Dreedle's WAC*), Peter Bonerz (*Captain McWatt*), Norman Fell (*Sergeant Towser*), Charles Grodin (*Aarfy Aardvark*), Austin Pendleton (*Colonel Moodus*), Gina Rovere (*Nately's whore*), Olympia Carlisi (*Luciana*), Marcel Dalio (*old man*), Evi Maltagliati (*old woman*), Liam Dunn (*father*), Elizabeth Wilson (*mother*), Richard Libertini (*brother*), Jon Korkes (*Snowden*), John Brent (*Cathcart's receptionist*), Collin Wilcox-Horne (*Nurse Cramer*), Phil Roth, Bruce Kirby, Jack Riley (*doctors*), Felice Orlandi (*man in black*), Wendy D'Olive (*Aarfy's girl*), Fernanda Vitobello (*kid sister*).
War comedy-drama. Source: Joseph Heller, *Catch-22* (New York, 1961). Captain Yossarian, stationed on a Mediterranean island during World War II, begs Doc Daneeka to certify him unfit for flying. Daneeka explains, however, that "Catch-22" prevents him from grounding Yossarian for insanity since anyone who voluntarily flies a bombing mission is crazy; therefore, anyone requesting to be grounded must be sane. Meanwhile, the ambitious Colonel Cathcart, who longs to be the subject of a feature article in *The Saturday Evening Post*, forces more missions on the men, and the inevitable strain results in bizarre behavior on the part of all. Milo Minderbinder sells parachutes and morphine from the flyers' first aid kits as part of his black market operation; Major Major agrees to admit visitors to his office only when he is away from the premises; the idealistic Captain Nately decides to marry an Italian whore, but he is killed in a bombardment of the airbase arranged by Milo in another of his financial schemes; General Dreedle awards medals to the participants of a mission who dropped their bombs in the sea; Yossarian arrives naked at the ceremony because Gunner Sergeant Snowden died in his arms and drenched his uniform with blood; Yossarian's attempt to make love with Nurse Duckett on the beach fails, and she kicks him in the groin; and Captain McWatt, flying

over the ocean, slices fellow airman Hungry Joe in half with his propeller. Yossarian goes AWOL to inform Nately's whore in Rome of her lover's death and discovers that all the prostitutes now work for Milo's corporation. Later, Colonel Cathcart offers to send Yossarian back to the United States if he promises to go on a public relations tour for their unit. On the way back from the colonel's office, however, Yossarian is stabbed by Nately's whore who is disguised as a soldier. While recuperating in the hospital, he learns from Chaplain Tappman that Orr, who has crashed many planes, is now in Sweden after paddling across the sea for 16 weeks. Inspired by Orr's success, Yossarian jumps out of the hospital window, races to a rubber raft, and begins paddling across the Mediterranean. *Physicians. Air pilots. Italians. Prostitutes. Chaplains. Deserters—Military. Insanity. Battle fatigue. Combat zone life. Black market. Aerial bombardment. Death. Mutilation. Revenge. Disguise. Islands. Awards. Airfields. Beaches. Hospitals. World War II. Mediterranean Sea. Rome. United States Air Force.*
Note: Location scenes filmed in Mexico and Rome.

CATCH US IF YOU CAN *see* **HAVING A WILD WEEKEND**

THE CATS (Sweden)　　　　　　　　　　　　　　　**F6.0711**
Lorens Marmstedt–Cat-Film. *Dist* National Showmanship Films. 24 Mar **1969** [New York opening]. Sd; b&w. 35mm. 93 min. *MPAA rating* R.
Prod Lorens Marmstedt. *Dir* Henning Carlsen. *Screenplay* Walentin Chorell, Henning Carlsen. *Photog* Mac Ahlberg, Per Staehr. *Mus* Krzysztof Komeda. *Sd* Lars Nordberg. *Script Girl* Sigyn Sahlin. *Studio Mgr* Bengt Lindstrom. *English Titl* Rose Sokol.
Cast: Eva Dahlbeck (*Marta*), Gio Petré (*Rike*), Monica Nielsen (*Mirka*), Lena Granhagen (*Ragni*), Hjördis Petterson (*Anna*), Isa Quensel (*Tora*), Ruth Kasdan (*Xenia*), Inga Gill (*Klara*), Lena Hansson (*Sally*), Per Myrberg (*Jonny*).
Drama. Source: Walentin Chorell, *Kattorna* (Helsinki opening: 12 Jan 1961). Working within the stultifying confines of a commercial laundry, a group of love-starved women pass their time conversing about their sexual appetites and frustrations. Although they occasionally discuss the sole male employee, Jonny, the delivery man, most of the women's gossip centers around their antagonism toward Marta, the cool, aloof laundry manager. The most volatile of the group is Rike, a woman with nymphomaniac tendencies who, following a dissolute weekend, returns to the laundry in an embittered mood and falsely accuses Marta of making lesbian advances toward her. Eager to believe the worst, the other women stage a sit-in, refusing to return to their jobs until Marta resigns. Rike watches with sadistic pleasure as Marta is taunted and humiliated, but she eventually breaks down and admits that she lied. The women redirect their hostility toward Rike, but Marta goes to her defense and ultimately confesses that in truth, she does harbor suppressed lesbian desires toward Rike. Moved by the confession, Rike offers herself to the older woman, but Marta refuses to submit to her own latent lesbianism. As work at the laundry resumes, both Marta and Rike return to their separate loveless worlds. *Laundresses. Gossip. Employment—Women. Employer-employee relations. Nymphomania. Lesbianism. Slander. Confession. Laundries.*
Note: Released in Sweden in 1965 as *Kattorna*.

CATTLE KING　　　　　　　　　　　　　　　　　　**F6.0712**
Missouri Productions. *Dist* Metro-Goldwyn-Mayer, Inc. Jun **1963** [c14 Jun 1963; LP24664]. Sd (RCA); col (Metrocolor). 35mm (Metroscope). 88 min.
Prod Nat Holt. *Assoc Prod* Thomas Thompson. *Dir* Tay Garnett. *Screenplay* Thomas Thompson. *Dir Photog* William Snyder. *Art Dir* Walter Holscher. *Set Decor* Ted Driscoll. *Film Ed* George White. *Mus Score* Paul Sawtell, Bert Shefter. *Sd Ed* Bill Naylor. *Rec Supv* Clarence Peterson. *Mus Ed* George E. Marsh. *Asst Dir* Henry E. Brill. *Prod Mgr* William Persons. *Wardrobe* Seth Banks. *Makeup* Grant R. Keats. *Casting* Harvey Clermont.
Cast: Robert Taylor (*Sam Brassfield*), Joan Caulfield (*Sharleen Travers*), Robert Loggia (*Johnny Quatro*), Robert Middleton (*Clay Mathews*), Larry Gates (*President Chester A. Arthur*), Malcolm Atterbury (*Clevenger*), William Windom (*Harry Travers*), Virginia Christine (*Ruth Winters*), Ray Teal (*Ed Winters*), Richard Devon (*Vince Bodine*), Robert Ivers (*Webb Carter*), Maggie Pierce (*June Carter*), Woodrow Palfrey (*Stafford*), Richard Tretter (*Hobie*), John Mitchum (*Tex*).
Western melodrama. In Wyoming during the 1880's, Sam Brassfield, a successful rancher who fences in his land for controlled grazing, opposes the National Cattle Trail, which would open up vast territories and eventually destroy the rich grasslands. His principal opponent is Clay Mathews, a ruthless cattle speculator who has won the support of Harry Travers, the cowardly brother of Brassfield's fiancée, Sharleen. As the situation worsens, Mathews' men cut fences, shoot one of Brassfield's ranch hands, and raid the ranch of homesteader Abe Clevenger, placing the blame on Brassfield. Clevenger tries to kill Brassfield, but he is wounded, and while recuperating at the Brassfield ranch, Clevenger learns the truth about Mathews' plans and his strong-handed tactics. Brassfield travels to Cheyenne and makes a protest to President Chester

Arthur who, after paying a surprise visit to Brassfield, sides with the ranchers. Believing that Travers has also been won over, Mathews attempts to have him killed, but it is Sharleen who is fatally wounded. Supported by Clevenger and the other homesteaders, Brassfield and his men are able to defeat Mathews in a final gun battle. *Ranchers. Cattlemen. Range wars. Homesteaders. Land rights. Wyoming. Cheyenne. Chester Alan Arthur.*

Note: Location scenes filmed in California. Also known as *Guns of Wyoming.*

CAUGHT IN THE ACT! F6.0713

Extraordinary Films. *Dist* William Mishkin. 14 Sep **1966** [Fresno, California, showing]. Sd; b&w. 35mm. 82 min.

Prod William Mishkin. *Dir* J. Nehemiah. *Writ* Charles Ross.

Cast: Brigitte Evans (*Cherry Holloway*), Steve Hollister (*Bob Murphy*), April Maye (*Helen Desmond*), Viki Polin (*Clarice Foster*), Cathy Scott (*Barbara*), Steve Prince (*Warren Curtis*), Bernard Weit (*Walter Harris*), Jackie Richards (*Mrs. Harris*), Reg Perri (*Andre*), Johnny Kuhl (*Jimmy*), Anna Karol (*Anne*), Don Carmen (*David*).

Melodrama. Beautiful Cherry Holloway comes to New York City seeking romance and a career and finds a job with Clarice Foster, whose model agency is a front for a call girl racket. Cherry falls in love with artist Bob Murphy, who convinces her to move into his apartment after she is nearly raped by a client. They make plans to marry, and Cherry poses in the nude for Bob. Heiress Helen Desmond sees one of the paintings and lures Bob away from Cherry. Cherry is soon living on Park Avenue supported by wealthy Mr. Harris, but she is caught in bed with her benefactor by a detective and photographer sent by Harris' wife. Meanwhile, nymphomaniac Helen wears Bob out, forcing him to leave her. He becomes an alcoholic and feels guilty about leaving Cherry. He tries to commit suicide, but his failed attempt brings Cherry back to him. *Models. Artists. Mistresses. Prostitution. Rape. Guilt. Alcoholism. Wealth. Infidelity. Nymphomania. Model agencies.*

Note: Also known as *Caught in the Act—Naked.*

CAUGHT IN THE CAN F6.0714

Dist Stacey Distributors. ca **1970**. Sd; col. 16mm. 61-81 min.

Sex film. No information about the precise nature of this film has been found. *Sexuality.*

THE CAVALCADE OF LAUGHS F6.0715

Walter A. Futter. 15 Feb **1963** [Maryland license]. Sd; b&w. 35mm. 64 min.

Anthology. Four films from the early career of Charlie Chaplin are presented: *Dough and Dynamite* (1914), *Caught in a Cabaret* (1914), *His Trysting Place* (1914), and *A Night Out* (1915). *Motion pictures—History. Charles Chaplin.*

CAVALCADE OF RUSSIAN BALLET AND DANCE (U.S.S.R.) F6.0716

Artkino Pictures. 29 May **1965** [New York opening]. Sd; b&w with col seq. 35mm. 100 min. [Also 70 min.]

Compilation by Rose Madell. *Mus Selections:* "Waltz of the Flowers" from "The Nutcracker" ("Casse-noisette," "Shchelkunchik"), "The Swan Lake" ("Lebedinoye ozero") Pëtr Ilich Tchaikovsky. "The Dying Swan" ("Le cygne") Camille Saint-Saëns. *Choreog* Michel Fokine. *Ballet:* "Taras Bulba" Vasiliy Pavlovich Solovyov-Sedoy. *Mus:* "Taras Bulba" Mikola Vitaliyovich Lisenko. "Paquita" Ludwig Minkus. *Staged by* Marius Petipa. "The Fountain of Bakhchisaray" ("Bakhchisarayskiy fontan") Boris Vladimirovich Asafyev. "Polovetskian dance" from "Prince Igor" ("Knyaz Igor") Aleksandr Porfiryevich Borodin. "Le corsaire" Robert Boscha.

Featured Ensembles: State Symphonic Ensemble and Corps de Ballet, State Ensemble of Folk Dances, Moiseyev Ensemble, Turkmenian Ensemble.

Featured Performer—"The Dying Swan": Galina Ulanova.

Performers Featured in Turkmenian Ensemble: Ati Ogebayev, S. Aymambetov, B. Kulbevdiyev.

Featured Performers—"The Swan Lake": Galina Ulanova, Konstantin Sergeyev.

Cast—"Taras Bulba": Mikhail Dudko (*Taras*), Vakhtang Chabukiani (*Andrey*), Sergey Koren (*Ostap*), Ukrainian State Corps de Ballet.

Cast—"Paquita": Galya Pirozhaya, Andrey Khamzin, Maly Leningrad Ballet Ensemble.

Featured Performers—"The Fountain of Bakhchisaray": Galina Ulanova (*Mariya*), Maya Plisetskaya (*Zarema*), Pavel Gusev (*Girey*).

Cast—"Polovetskian dance" from "Prince Igor": Olga Lepeshinskaya, Bolshoi Theater Ballet.

Featured Graduating Class Performers: Yekaterina Maksimova, Alla Sizova, Rudolf Nureyev.

Dance film. A survey of Soviet dance, incorporating film clips dating back to the early 1930's. The selections include the "Waltz of the Flowers" from *The Nutcracker*, performed by the State Symphonic Ensemble and Corps de Ballet; scenes of the young Galina Ulanova performing in *The Dying Swan*;

performances of the Moldavian dance "Moldavenets," the Belorussian dance "Kriznachek," and the Azerbaidzhan dance "Kazaki" by the State Ensemble of Folk Dances; a performance by the Turkmenian Ensemble; an excerpt from *The Swan Lake*, danced by Galina Ulanova and Konstantin Sergeyev; "Quadrille," performed by the Moiseyev Ensemble; selections from *Taras Bulba*, featuring Mikhail Dudko, Vakhtang Chabukiani, Sergey Koren, and the Ukrainian State Corps de Ballet; from *Paquita*, performed by the Maly Leningrad Ballet Ensemble, featuring Galya Pirozhaya and Andrey Khamzin; and from *The Fountain of Bakhchisaray*, featuring Galina Ulanova, Maya Plisetskaya, and Pavel Gusev; "Polovetskian dance" from Borodin's *Prince Igor*, featuring Olga Lepeshinskaya and the Bolshoi Theater Ballet; and performances by members of the 1958 graduating class of the Soviet National Ballet Schools, including Yekaterina Maksimova dancing in *The Nutcracker*, and Alla Sizova and Rudolf Nureyev dancing in *Le corsaire*. *Folk dancing. Ballet. Dance schools.*

Note: Assembled by Artkino Pictures from footage on deposit at the National State Cinema Archives in Moscow.

LES CAVALIERS ROUGES see **SHATTERHAND**

CAVALLERIA COMMANDOS see **CAVALRY COMMAND**

CAVALLERIA RUSTICANA (Austria/Switzerland/West Germany)
F6.0717

Cosmotel–Zweiten Deutschen Fernsehen–Österreichischen Rundfunk-Fernsehen. *Dist* Beta Film. 25 Jul **1970** [New York opening]. Sd; col (Eastman Color). 35mm. 76 min.

Prod Fritz Buttenstedt. *Dir* Åke Falck. *Artistic Dir* Herbert von Karajan. *Orig Staging* Giorgio Strehler. *Libretto* Giovanni Targioni-Tozzetti, Guido Menasci. *Photog* Ernst Wild. *2d Unit Photog* Mac Ahlberg. *Art Dir* Luciano Damiani. *Mus* Pietro Mascagni. *Mus Cond* Herbert von Karajan. *Mus Played by* La Scala Orchestra. *Sung by* La Scala Chorus. *Sd* Hans Weber, Günter Hermanns. *Asst Dir* Peter Busse. *Prod Asst* Dieter Meyer, Horant H. Hohlfeld. *Cost* Luciano Damiani.

Cast: Fiorenza Cossotto (*Santuzza*), Gianfranco Cecchele (*Turiddu*), Anna Di Stasio (*Lucia*), Giangiacomo Guelfi (*Alfio*), Adriana Martino (*Lola*).

Opera film. Source: Pietro Mascagni, Giovanni Targioni-Tozzetti and Guido Menasci, *Cavalleria rusticana* (first performance: Rome, 17 May 1890). Giovanni Verga, "Cavalleria rusticana," in *Cavalleria rusticana ed altre novelle* (Milan, 1880). In a small Sicilian village, Turiddu and Lola are having an affair, a situation simplified by her husband's frequent business trips. The couple were in love years before, but when Turiddu returned home from army service, he discovered that the impatient Lola had married Alfio. Later, Turiddu began courting Santuzza, but Lola quickly became bored with her stolid husband and succeeded in tempting Turiddu to resume their affair. On Easter Sunday, Turiddu follows Lola into church, and when Santuzza tries to stop him, he throws her to the ground. Alfio appears, and Santuzza, in her despair, blurts out the truth about Lola's infidelity. The cuckolded husband challenges Turiddu to a duel, and Turiddu is killed. *Veterans. Cuckolds. Marriage. Infidelity. Jealousy. Easter. Sicily. Duels.*

Note: Location scenes filmed in Sicily. Produced in 1968.

CAVALLERIA RUSTICANA see **FATAL DESIRE**

CAVALRY CHARGE (Reissue) F6.0718

Paramount Pictures. *Dist* Citation Films, Paramount Pictures. 14 Apr **1961** [Maryland license]. Sd; col. 35mm. 88 min.

Note: Originally released in 1951 as *The Last Outpost*; c11 May 1951; LP910.

CAVALRY COMMAND (United States/Philippines) F6.0719

Peoples Pictures–Parade Pictures. *Dist* Parade Pictures. Nov **1963** [Los Angeles showing]. Sd; col (Technicolor). 35mm. 80 min.

Pres by Riley Jackson, Robert Patrick. *Prod* Cirio H. Santiago. *Assoc Prod* Harry Smith, prod. *Dir-Writ* Eddie Romero. *Dir Photog* Felipe Sacdalan. *Film Ed* Gervacio Santos, Ted Smith. *Mus Dir* Tito Arevalo, Ariston Avelino. *Sd* H. R. Smith.

Cast: John Agar (*Sergeant Norcutt*), Richard Arlen (*Sergeant Heisler*), Myron Healey (*Lieutenant Worth*), Alicia Vergel (*Laura*), Pancho Magalona (*Captain Magno*), William Phipps (*Private Haines*), Eddie Infante (*priest*), Boy Planas (*Tibo*).

Action drama. During the American occupation of the Philippines in 1902, Lieutenant Worth and his cavalry troops befriend the people of San Pascual with food and medicine. Despite this aid, the fanatic Captain Magno persists in resisting the Americans with guerrilla tactics. Beleaguered by a tribe of wild Igorot bandits, Magno falls into the hands of the Americans, but Worth refuses him a martyr's execution and imprisons him instead. Worth receives orders to move on and leaves three men—Sergeant Norcutt, Sergeant Heisler, and Private Haines—to continue helping the community. After Magno's release, one of the Igorots tries to kill him, and the captain insists that the Americans were involved. He manages to overcome the three soldiers, but his small band deserts him when he burns down the new school that the Americans had helped build. Magno then decides to single-handedly attack a supply convoy headed for San Pascual, but some Igorots have the same idea, and Magno ends up siding with the Americans to prevent the burning of the only bridge that links the town with the mainland. His change of heart is complete when he sees that the convoy contains food and medicine rather than weapons. *Guerrillas. Bandits. Military occupation. Igorots. United States—History—War of 1898. United States Army—Cavalry.*

Note: Released in the Philippines as *Cavalleria commandos.*

CAVE OF THE LIVING DEAD (West Germany/Yugoslavia)   F6.0720
Objektiv Film–Triglav Film. *For* Film Development Corp. *Dist* Trans-Lux Distributing Corp. Jul **1966**. Sd; b&w. 35mm. 87 min.

Pres by Richard Gordon. *Prod-Dir-Story* Akos von Rathony. *Screenplay* C. von Rock. *Photog* Hrvoje Sarić. *Art Dir* Ivan Pengov. *Film Ed* Klaus Dudenhöfer. *Mus* Herbert Jarczyk. *Sd* Franco Jurjek. *Prod Supv* Gerd F. Reetz. *Prod Mgr* Jancz Krizaj.

Cast: Adrian Hoven *(Inspector Doren)*, Karin Field *(Karin)*, Erika Remberg *(Maria)*, Wolfgang Preiss *(Professor Adelsberg)*, Emmerich Schrenk *(Thomas)*, John Kitzmiller *(John)*, Carl Möhner, Vida Juvan, Stane Sever, Danilo Turk, Laci Cigoj, Tito Strozzi.

Horror film. Because local police are unable to solve the mysterious murders of seven young women in a small village, Inspector Doren of INTERPOL is assigned to the case. As a result of a talk with an old witch, the inspector begins to suspect that the killings are the work of a vampire. He learns more from some of the villagers, who link the murders to caves under an ancient castle where Professor Adelsberg and his secretary, Karin, are conducting scientific experiments. After tracking the professor to his underground headquarters, Doren finds the seven living dead and discovers that Adelsberg is the vampire. Karin is to be his next victim. With the help of the witch, Doren is able to save Karin and kill Adelsberg by driving a stake through his heart. *Police. Detectives. Vampires. Secretaries. Professors. Witches. Murder. Experiments. Impalement. Castles. Caves. INTERPOL.*

Note: Released in West Germany in 1964 as *Der Fluch der grünen Augen*; running time: 89 min. According to some sources, filmed in English in West Germany and produced by Richard Gordon for Film Development Corp. Other sources credit only Objektiv Film and Triglav Film as production companies and Akos von Rathony as producer.

LE CAVE SE REBIFFE see THE COUNTERFEITERS OF PARIS

THE CAVERN (Italy/West Germany)   F6.0721
Cine Doris–Ernst Neubach. *For* Melcher Co. *Dist* Twentieth Century-Fox Film Corp. Nov **1965** [c24 Dec 1964; LP32172]. Sd; b&w. 35mm. 83 min. [Copyright length: 95 min.]

Prod-Dir Edgar G. Ulmer. *Exec Prod* Martin Melcher. *Collab Dir* Paolo Bianchini. *Story & Screenplay* Michael Pertwee, Jack Davies. *Italian Vers* Alberto Bevilacqua. *Camera* Gabor Pogany. *Film Ed* Renato Cinquini. *Mus Comp* Carlo Rustichelli. *Adtl Mus* Gene Di Novi. *Cond* Franco Ferrara. *Titl Song* Carroll Coates. *Sung by* Bobby Bare. *Sd* Bruno Moreal. *Makeup* Euclide Santoli. *Sp Eff* Joseph Natanson.

Cast: John Saxon *(Pvt. Joe Kramer)*, Rosanna Schiaffino *(Anna)*, Larry Hagman *(Captain Wilson)*, Peter L. Marshall *(Lieut. Peter Carter)*, Nino Castelnuovo *(Mario)*, Brian Aherne *(General Braithwaite)*, Hans von Borsody *(Hans)*, Joachim Hansen *(German soldier)*, Alfredo Varelli, Renato Terra.

War drama. In Italy during World War II, German soldiers trap Anna; U. S. Army Pvt. Joe Kramer; U. S. Army Captain Wilson; American General Braithwaite; Mario, an Italian soldier; Hans, a German soldier; and Lieut. Peter Carter, a Canadian pilot who escaped from a prisoner-of-war camp, in an Alpine cavern that has served as a German storehouse. Falling explosives seal the entrances, and they spend weeks seeking a means of exit. Captain Wilson, an alcoholic, finds a cache of liquor and later shares it with fellow drinker General Braithwaite. Meanwhile, Kramer falls in love with Anna, against the wishes of Mario. Hans discovers a way out, but Italian partisans kill him before he can return to notify the others. Later, Carter dies trying to find an escape route, and Captain Wilson drowns in a drunken stupor. When General Braithwaite goes insane and attempts suicide with a grenade, the explosion creates a passageway to the outside, and the captives leave the cavern. *Escapees. Prisoners of war. Canadians. Alcoholism. Survival. Suicide. Resistance (political). Caves. World War II. Alps. United States Army. Italy—Army. Germany—Army. Explosions.*

Note: Filmed in Italy and Yugoslavia. Released in Italy as *Sette contro la morte* in 1965; German title: *Helden—Himmel und Hölle.*

LA CAZA see THE HUNT
CE SACRÉ GRAND-PÈRE see THE MARRIAGE CAME TUMBLING DOWN
CELEBRATION see THE STRIPPER
CENSORED   F6.0722
Barry Mahon Productions. *Dist* Cinema Syndicate, Inc. 28 May **1965** [Los Angeles opening]. Sd; b&w. 35mm. 61 min.

A Barry Mahon Production. *Prod-Dir* Barry Mahon. *Photog* Rick Carrier. *Film Ed* Byron Mabe. *Sd* Magno Sound.

Compilation film. Noted lecturer and critic Sid Berry presents a collection of film clips which have been deleted from various sex exploitation films to comply with the demands of censorship. He begins his discussion with the nudist camp movies, and moves on to the group of "nudie" films depicting artists, models, and photographers at work. Sadism and violence then come under his scrutiny, as he shows a white slaver kidnaping an innocent girl, and a sex maniac dismembering his victim. Bedroom scenes of all varieties provide a comprehensive view of the sex exploitation field, so that the audience can decide on the merits of censorship. *Lecturers. Artists. Models. Photographers. Censorship. Sex exploitation films. White slave traffic. Mutilation. Sadism. Nudism. Nudist camps.*

Note: Also known as *This Picture Is Censored.*

CENSORED   F6.0723
R. W. Cresse. *Dist* International Theatrical Amusements. ca **1966**. Sd; b&w. 35mm? 60 min.

Prod R. W. Cresse. *Dir* R. L. Frost. *Photog* R. L. Frost.

Cast: James Arena, Virginia Gordon, Tom McFadden.

Compilation film. A compilation of scenes that have been censored from various films. *Censorship.*

CENSORSHIP IN DENMARK: A NEW APPROACH see PORNOGRAPHY IN DENMARK: A NEW APPROACH
CENT BRIQUES ET DES TUILES see HOW NOT TO ROB A DEPARTMENT STORE
CENT MILLE DOLLARS AU SOLEIL see GREED IN THE SUN
CENTO DOLLARI D'ODIO see UNCLE TOM'S CABIN
100 RAGAZZE PER UN PLAYBOY see HOW TO SEDUCE A PLAYBOY
CENTOMILA DOLLARI AL SOLE see GREED IN THE SUN

THE CENTURION (France/Italy)   F6.0724
Europa Cinematografica–C. F. P. C. *Dist* Producers International Pictures. caAug **1962**. Sd; col (Eastman Color). 35mm (Euroscope). 77 min.

Pres by William Hunter. *Prod* Manlio Morelli. *Dir* Mario Costa. *Story & Screenplay* Nino Stresa. *Photog* Pier Ludovico Pavoni. *Film Ed* Albert Salvadori. *Mus* Carlo Innocenzi. *Prod Supv* Gino Fanano. *Cost* Mario Giorsi. *Sp Eff* Antonio Visone.

Cast: Jacques Sernas *(Caius Vinicius)*, John Drew Barrymore *(Diaeus)*, Geneviève Grad *(Hebe)*, Gianna Maria Canale *(Artemide)*, Gordon Mitchell *(General Metellus)*, Gianni Santuccio *(Critolaus)*, Nando Tamberlani *(Callicrates)*, Ivano Staccioli *(Hippolytus)*, Andrea Fantasia *(Lucius Mummius)*, Gianni Solaro *(Caesar)*, José Jaspe *(traitor)*, Vassili Karamis *(Egeo)*, Dina De Santis *(Chimene)*, Milena Vukotic *(Ancella)*, Adrian Vianello *(Cleo)*.

Historical melodrama. In 146 B. C. the Roman centurion Caius Vinicius is sent to Greece in an attempt to persuade the Achaean League, led by Corinth, to accept the terms of the Roman "moral rule." He is wounded in a fight between Critolaus, the anti-Roman Corinthian leader, and Callicrates, head of a minority group in favor of accepting Roman rule; and he unwittingly hides in Critolaus' villa. In secret, Vinicius is restored to health by Hebe, Critolaus' daughter, and they fall in love. Callicrates' wife, Artimede, is likewise attracted to Vinicius and becomes insanely jealous. Meanwhile, the Romans send Lucius Mummius to lead an attack against Corinth, and the jealous Artimede betrays Vinicius to the anti-Roman authorities, who arrest him. Diaeus, a treacherous Corinthian military commander, threatens to have Vinicius killed unless Hebe agrees to marry him. Callicrates rescues Vinicius, and with the help of Metellus, a Roman general, they attempt to prevent the destruction of Corinth. However, Diaeus discovers Callicrates' plan and has him killed before the peaceful surrender of the city can be accomplished; Lucius Mummius then sets the city aflame. Artimede dies in an attempt to kill Hebe. Vinicius rescues Hebe from Diaeus, and together they make their way to safety. *Centurions. Peacemakers. Revolts. Resistance (political). Perfidy. Jealousy. Incendiarism. Rome—History—Empire. Corinth. Greece—Ancient. Critolaus. Callicrates of Leontium. Lucius Mummius. Metellus. Achaean League.*

Note: Released in Italy and France in 1962; Italian title: *Il conquistatore di Corinto;* French title: *La bataille de Corinthe.*

THE CENTURIONS *see* **LOST COMMAND**

C'ERA UNA VOLTA *see* **MORE THAN A MIRACLE**

C'ERA UNA VOLTA IL WEST *see* **ONCE UPON A TIME IN THE WEST**

LA CEREMONIA *see* **THE CEREMONY**

THE CEREMONY (United States/Spain)   **F6.0725**
Laurence Harvey Productions–Magla. *Dist* United Artists. 25 Dec **1963** [Los Angeles opening]. Sd; b&w. 35mm. 105 min.
Prod-Dir Laurence Harvey. *Screenplay* Ben Barzman. *Adtl Dial* Laurence Harvey, Alun Falconer. *Photog (see note)* Brian West, Oswald Morris. *2d Unit Camera* Antonio Macasoli. *Art Dir* Ramiro Gómez. *Film Ed* Ralph Kemplen. *Mus* Gerard Schürmann. *Sd* Brendan Redmond. *Asst Dir* John Quested, Pedro Vidal. *Asst to the Prod* Alan Kaplan. *Prod Supv* David Middlemas. *Prod Mgr* Jesús García Gárgoles. *Cost* Moss Mabry. *Sp Eff* Manolo Vaquero, Arthur Reavis.
Cast: Laurence Harvey *(Sean McKenna)*, Sarah Miles *(Catherine)*, Robert Walker, [Jr.] *(Dominic)*, John Ireland *(prison warden)*, Ross Martin *(LeCoq)*, Lee Patterson *(Nicky)*, Jack MacGowran *(O'Brien)*, Murray Melvin *(1st gendarme)*, Carlos Casaravilla *(Ramades)*, Fernando Rey *(Sanchez)*, Fernando Sánchez *(Shaoush)*, José Nieto *(inspector)*, Noel Purcell *(Finigan)*, Xan Das Bolas *(Arab peasant)*, Barta Barri *(death house guard)*, Edward St. John *(special guard)*, José Guardiola *(gate guard)*, José Trinidad *(police chauffeur)*, José Manuel Martín, Juan Olaguibel, Juan García Delgado, Julio Tabuyo, James Brown, Rafael Albaicín, Ricardo Rodriguez, Manuel Peña, Carlos Chemenal, Alvaro Varela, Enrique Closas *(gendarmes)*, Francisco Montalvo, José Riesgo *(guards)*, Eduardo García *(truckdriver)*, Phil Posner *(prison official)*.
Melodrama. Source: Frédéric Grendel, *La cérémonie* (Paris, 1951). After a bank holdup in Tangiers, in the course of which a guard is killed, Irishman Sean McKenna, the leader of the gang responsible for the crime, is arrested for the murder. Though he is innocent, the sadistic French public prosecutor, LeCoq, is determined that an example be made, and Sean is sentenced to death by the firing squad. Catherine, his girl friend, persuades his brother, Dominic, to help arrange an escape by promising to run away with him once Sean is freed; and they are aided in the plan by Sean's friend Nicky. Aided by a bribed jailer, Dominic disguises himself as a priest and is permitted to enter the death cell. After changing clothes with his brother, Dominic blows up the prison power house and then escapes by rope ladder. Garbed in the priest's clothing, Sean walks out of the prison gates during the confusion. Reunited with Catherine and Dominic, Sean learns of their affair, and a violent fight ensues. With the arrival of the police, the three escape. As Dominic leads police away from his brother, his car crashes and bursts into flame. His face burned beyond recognition, Dominic is mistaken for Sean and brought back to the prison. The priest, Father O'Brien, hears Dominic's confession but is unable to give absolution because Dominic refuses to reveal his true identity. Sean learns of the situation and rushes to the prison, but Dominic has already been executed, even though most of the firing squad refused to fire their guns. Sean carries his dead brother's body into the prison. *Irish. Brothers. French. Priests. Prison wardens. Public prosecutors. Capital punishment. Prison escapes. Bank robberies. Mistaken identity. Self-sacrifice. Impersonation. Tangiers. Automobile accidents. Chases.*
Note: Filmed in Spain. Spanish title: *La ceremonia.* Sources conflict in crediting photographer.

CERVANTES *see* **THE YOUNG REBEL**

LE CERVEAU *see* **THE BRAIN**

IL CERVELLO *see* **THE BRAIN**

CES MESSIEURS DAMES *see* **THE BIRDS, THE BEES, AND THE ITALIANS**

CESTA DO PRAVĚKU *see* **JOURNEY TO THE BEGINNING OF TIME**

CHACUN SON ALIBI *see* **... AND SUDDENLY IT'S MURDER!**

CHAFED ELBOWS   **F6.0726**
Goosedown Productions. *Dist* Film-Makers' Distribution Center, Vulcan Projections. 4 Jan **1967** [New York opening]. Sd; b&w and col. 16mm & 35mm. 63 min.
Prod-Dir-Writ Robert Downey. *Photog* William Waering, Stan Warnow. *Film Ed* Fred Von Bernewitz, Robert Soukis. *Mus* Tom O'Horgan.
Cast: George Morgan *(Walter Dinsmore)*, Elsie Downey *(his mother/the other women)*, Lawrence Wolf *(Dr. Oliver Sinfield/34 voices)*, Robert (Chinese) *(God)*, Dan List, Ralph Blasi, Ben Bagley, Ronald Nealy, Lafayette Malatsun, Steve Harris, Jack Harvey, Jack Jobson, Tom O'Horgan, Stan Warnow.
Satire. Walter Dinsmore's annual January breakdown begins shortly after he leaves his mother's apartment. He is delivered by caesarian section [or through a hysterectomy?] of 189 ten-dollar bills, an accumulation which is the result of swallowing a nickel when he was a child. Psychoanalysis proves of little help to him inasmuch as he sees nothing wrong with being in love with his mother. Death offers no solution; Heaven promptly rejects Walter and sends him back to Earth, whereupon he is sold as a pop art creation. He takes an acting job as a policeman in an underground film but finds that "all the action takes place behind the camera." After the movie project folds because someone knocks over the camera, Walter keeps his policeman's uniform, directs traffic at Times Square, and accepts bribes from pornography peddlers. He helps cater potato salad at a Bar Mitzvah and meets a woman who is hiding under a table. When their rooftop orgy is interrupted by the caterer, Walter flings him to the street below. Walter's cousin, in a telephone call from the Dixie Hotel on 43d Street, complains that Walter has made her pregnant. He throws her from the window, and she lands on a theater marquee, gaining instant "star billing." After becoming a rock and roll singing sensation with a song entitled "In Your Black Leather Negligee," Walter returns home and finds that his father has died. Walter marries his mother, becomes a proud father, moves to the suburbs, and lives happily on welfare. [The order of events is uncertain.] *Police. Pornographers. Psychiatrists. Caterers. Cousins. Oedipus complex. Death. Incest. Murder. Motherhood. Surgery. Sexuality. Art. Motion pictures. Rock and roll. Bar Mitzvah. New York City. New York City—Times Square. Dixie Hotel (New York). Heaven.*
Note: Subsequently released in a 57-min version. A large portion of the film is composed of still shots and stop-motion camera effects.

THE CHAIN *see* **THE DAISY CHAIN**

THE CHAIN *see* **THE VIOLENT ONES**

CHAINED GIRLS   **F6.0727**
Dist American Film Distributing Corp. 25 Mar **1965** [San Francisco showing]. Sd; b&w. 35mm. 65 min.
Pres by Stan Borden. *Prod* George Weiss. *Dir* Joseph P. Mawra. *Narr* Perry Peters. *Greenwich Village Photog* Harold Casanova. *Apartment Seq Photog* Werner Rose. *Sd* Magno Sound.
Sex film. The film examines various aspects of lesbianism. *Lesbianism.*

CHAINWORK LOVE *see* **TIGHT SKIRTS, LOOSE PLEASURES**

CHAIR DE POULE *see* **HIGHWAY PICKUP**

THE CHAIRMAN (United States/Great Britain)   **F6.0728**
APJAC Productions–Twentieth Century-Fox Productions. *Dist* Twentieth Century-Fox Film Corp. 25 Jun **1969** [New York opening; c25 Jun 1969; LP37416]. Sd (Westrex); col (DeLuxe). 35mm (Panavision). 104 min. *MPAA rating* M.
An Arthur P. Jacobs Production. *Prod* Mort Abrahams. *Assoc Prod* Pepi Lenzi. *Dir* J. Lee Thompson. *Screenplay* Ben Maddow. *Dir Photog* John Wilcox. *Photog* Ted Moore. *Camera Op* Robert Kindred. *Art Dir* Peter Mullins. *Set Dresser* Arthur Taksen. *Titl Seq Dsgn* Paul Brown-Constable. *Film Ed* Richard Best. *Mus Comp & Cond* Jerry Goldsmith. *Sd Rec* Dudley Messenger, Gordon K. McCallum. *Dub Ed* William Trent. *Asst Dir* Ferdinand Fairfax. *Prod Supv* John Merriman. *Prod Mgr* David Korda. *Cont* Kay Mander. *Location Mgr* Tim Hampton. *Cost Dsgn* Anna Duse. *Wardrobe Supv* Tiny Nicholls. *Makeup* Trevor Crole-Rees. *Hairdresser* Bernadette Ibbetson. *Casting* Weston Drury, Jr. *Constr Mgr* Leon Davis.
Cast: Gregory Peck *(Dr. John Hathaway)*, Anne Heywood *(Kay Hanna)*, Arthur Hill *(Shelby)*, Alan Dobie *(Benson)*, Conrad Yama *(The Chairman)*, Zienia Merton *(Ting Ling)*, Ori Levy *(Shertov)*, Eric Young *(Yin)*, Burt Kwouk *(Chang Shou)*, Alan White *(Gardner)*, Keye Luke *(Professor Soong Li)*, Francisca Tu *(Soong Chu)*, Mei Ling *(stewardess)*, Janet Key *(1st girl student)*, Gordon Sterne *(U. S. Air Force sergeant)*, Robert Lee *(hotel night manager)*, Helen Horton *(Susan Wright)*, Keith Bonnard *(Chinese officer)*, Cecil Cheng *(soldier)*, Laurence Herder *(Russian border guard officer)*, Simon Cain *(U. S. Signals captain)*, Anthony Chinn *(Chinese officer)*, Edward Cast *(audio room technician)*.
Melodrama. Source: Jay Richard Kennedy, *The Chairman* (New York, 1970). Dr. John Hathaway, a widowed Nobel Prize winning American scientist teaching at a London university, is asked by Lieutenant General Shelby of the American Embassy to visit the People's Republic of China for the purpose of obtaining an enzyme, developed by Hathaway's former teacher Soong Li, which will enable crops to grow in any climate. Because the formula would guarantee world domination to the power holding its secret, Shelby explains that both the United States and the Soviet Union have an interest in seeing that its monopoly does not remain with the Chinese. Hathaway hesitates to make the trip both because of his romantic involvement with college professor Kay Hanna and

because of his opposition to America's Far East policy; but a telephone call from the President persuades him to undertake the project. In preparation for the trip, a transmitter is implanted in Hathaway's skull so that he can communicate with officials in London by satellite. Unbeknownst to Hathaway, the transmitter is also equipped with an explosive device that can be detonated from London should it be deemed necessary. Arriving in Hong Kong, Hathaway is escorted to China by Yin, the chief of Chinese security forces, who introduces him to the Chairman of the Communist party. During a ping-pong game in which they trade viewpoints, the Chairman persuades Hathaway to help with the production of the enzyme by assuring him that China plans to share the discovery with the world. With the help of Soong Li's daughter, Soong Chu, a brilliant scientist and member of the Red Guard, Hathaway and Soong Li perfect the enzyme, but their experiments are stopped when Red Guards storm the laboratory and attack Soong Li because he is opposed to the new movement in China. Hathaway decides to steal the microfilm on which the formula is recorded but discovers that the film has been removed. Soong Li commits suicide, leaving Hathaway only a book of the Chairman's quotations. He flees, aided by Yin's lieutenant, Chang Shou, who is actually a Soviet agent, but Yin has detected the transmitter in Hathaway's skull by radar, and the Chinese take pursuit. Hathaway makes his way to the electrified wire fence at the Sino-Soviet border, but Shelby in London decides to activate the explosive device when Hathaway is unable to reach Soviet soil. However, Russian soldiers blow up a section of fence, enabling Hathaway to cross the border. Safe in London, Hathaway discovers that the book given to him by Soong Li contains the enzyme formula. He also learns that the Anglo-American authorities, like the Chinese, intend to keep the formula secret, and decides with Kay to fight the decision in the interests of humanity. *Scientists. Widowers. Professors. Americans in foreign countries. Chinese. Russians. Secret agents. Espionage. Electronic surveillance. Suicide. Communism. Explosives. London. People's Republic of China. Hong Kong. Union of Soviet Socialist Republics. Mao Tse-tung. United States Army—Intelligence. Great Britain—Intelligence service. People's Republic of China, Red Guards. Nobel Prize. Union of Soviet Socialist Republics—Army. "Quotations From Chairman Mao Tse-tung".*

Note: Location scenes filmed in London, Wales, and Taiwan. Opened in London in Jul 1969 as *The Most Dangerous Man in the World*; running time: 99 min.

CHALEURS D'ÉTÉ *see* **HEAT OF THE SUMMER**

THE CHALK GARDEN (Great Britain)   F6.0729
Quota Rentals. *Dist* Universal Pictures. 21 May **1964** [New York opening; c13 Jun 1964; LP35380]. Sd (Westrex); col (Technicolor). 35mm. 106 min.

A Ross Hunter Production. *Prod* Ross Hunter. *In Charge of Prod* Edward Muhl. *Dir* Ronald Neame. *Screenplay* John Michael Hayes. *Dir Photog* Arthur Ibbetson. *Camera Op* Paul Wilson. *Art Dir* Carmen Dillon. *Set Decor* John Jarvis. *Film Ed* Jack Harris. *Mus Comp & Cond* Malcolm Arnold. *Sd* A. W. Watkins, Gerry Turner. *Sd Ed* James Shields. *Asst Dir* Basil Rayburn. *Prod Mgr* Harold Buck. *Cont* Pamela Davies. *Cost Dsgn* Julie Harris, cost. *Makeup* Ernest Gasser. *Hairstyles* Gordon Bond.

Cast: Deborah Kerr (*Madrigal*), Hayley Mills (*Laurel*), John Mills (*Maitland*), Edith Evans (*Mrs. St. Maugham*), Felix Aylmer (*Judge McWhirrey*), Elizabeth Sellars (*Olivia*), Lally Bowers (*Anna*), Toke Townley (*shop clerk*), Tonie MacMillan (*Mrs. Williams*).

Drama. Source: Enid Bagnold, *The Chalk Garden* (New York opening: 26 Oct 1955). Madrigal, an Englishwoman recently released from prison after serving time for murder, arrives at the home of Mrs. St. Maugham to apply for the position of governess and companion to the elderly woman's 16-year-old granddaughter, Laurel. She is hired, despite her lack of references, primarily for her knowledge of gardening because Mrs. St. Maugham has difficulty raising anything in the chalky earth of her garden. Madrigal keeps her past a secret, but Laurel, who lives in a partial fantasy world (she hates her mother whom she believes abandoned her when she divorced and remarried) tries to uncover the secrets of her new governess. Maitland, the butler, becomes attracted to Madrigal and tells her that Laurel's wild tales are untrue. When the judge who convicted Madrigal comes to lunch, he does not recognize her, but they get into a heated discussion about the case. Laurel suspects that Madrigal is the murderess in question but makes a pact with Maitland never to reveal her suspicion. Madrigal realizes that Laurel is much the same as she was at 16 and fears that Laurel might make the same mistakes if she is not told the truth about her mother. She tells Mrs. St. Maugham that Laurel's mother should be allowed to have her, and Laurel, overhearing them, realizes that she was never abandoned. When her mother arrives, Laurel is ready to go with her, and Madrigal remains at the house as companion to Mrs. St. Maugham. *Ex-convicts. Governesses. Grandmothers. Butlers. Judges. Murder. Gardeners. Duplicity. Personal identity. Adolescence. Filial relations.*

Note: Opened in London in Apr 1964.

THE CHALLENGE *see* **IT TAKES A THIEF**

A CHALLENGE FOR ROBIN HOOD (Great Britain)   F6.0730
Hammer Film Productions-Seven Arts Productions. *Dist* Twentieth Century-Fox Film Corp. caJun **1968** [c31 Dec 1967; LP36111]. Sd (RCA); col (DeLuxe). 35mm. 85 min. [Copyright length: 96 min.]

Prod Clifford Parkes. *Exec Prod* Michael Carreras. *Dir* C. M. Pennington-Richards. *Screenplay* Peter Bryan. *Dir Photog* Arthur Grant. *Camera Op* Moray Grant. *Art Dir* Maurice Carter. *Supv Ed* James Needs. *Ed* Chris Barnes. *Mus Comp* Gary Hughes. *Mus Supv* Philip Martell. *Sd Mix* George Stephenson. *Sd Rec* Laurie Barnett. *Sd Ed* Jack Knight. *Asst Dir* Ray Corbett. *Prod Mgr* Bryan Coates. *Cont* Elizabeth Wilcox. *Wardrobe Mistress* Dulcie Midwinter. *Makeup* Michael Morris. *Hairstyles* Bill Griffiths. *Sp Eff* Bowie Films. *Casting* Irene Lamb. *Fights Arr* Peter Diamond.

Cast: Barrie Ingham (*Robin Hood*), James Hayter (*Friar Tuck*), Leon Greene (*Little John*), Peter Blythe (*Roger de Courtenay*), Gay Hamilton (*Maid Marian*), Alfie Bass (*pie merchant*), Jenny Till ("*Lady Marian*"), John Arnatt (*Sheriff of Nottingham*), Eric Flynn (*Alan-a-Dale*), John Gugolka (*Stephen*), Reg Lye (*Much*), William Squire (*Sir John*), Donald Pickering (*Sir Jamyl de Penitone*), Eric Woofe (*Henry de Courtenay*), John Harvey (*Wallace*), Douglas Mitchell (*Will Scarlet*), John Graham, British (*Justin*), Arthur Hewlett (*Edwin*), Norman Mitchell (*dray driver*).

Adventure drama. In the era when Richard the Lion-Hearted is absent on his Crusade and his evil brother John is ruling England with a tyrannical hand, Sir John de Courtenay dies and bequeaths his estate to his two sons, Roger and Henry, and their cousin, Robin. When Roger murders his brother and tries to incriminate Robin, Robin flees with the loyal Friar Tuck to the relative safety of Sherwood Forest. Upon encountering a band of outlaws, Robin displays such skill with the bow and arrow that he is elected their leader. Before long, he becomes the legendary Robin Hood, robbing the rich to help the poor, while outwitting Roger and the Sheriff of Nottingham. Determined to lure Robin into a trap, the sheriff and Roger decide to hang an innocent man at a fair. Robin and his men save the man, however, and later storm Courtenay Castle to rescue Lady Marian, the sister of one of Robin's men. Though Roger is killed, the sheriff escapes. Robin then marries Maid Marian and returns with Friar Tuck to his band of Sherwood Forest outlaws. *Outlaws. Sheriffs. Cousins. Brothers. Monks. Fratricide. Frameup. Robbery. Archery. Capital punishment. Fairs. Castles. Sherwood Forest. Nottingham. Richard the Lion-Hearted. Robin Hood.*

Note: Released in Great Britain in Dec 1967; running time: 96 min. Working title: *The Legend of Robin Hood*.

CHALLENGE TO LIVE (Japan)   F6.0731
Toho Co. *Dist* Toho International, Inc. Mar **1962** [Los Angeles showing]. Sd; col (Eastman Color). 35mm (Tohoscope). 99 min.

Prod Masumi Fujimoto. *Exec Prod* Sanezumi Fujimoto. *Dir* Eizo Sugawa. *Screenplay* Kaneto Shindo. *Photog* Fukuzo Koizumi. *Art Dir* Iwao Akune. *Mus* Masaru Sato. *Sd* Masanao Uehara.

Cast: Tatsuya Mihashi (*Izaki*), Yoko Tsukasa (*Saeko Sawada*), Yumi Shirakawa (*Keiko Takamine*), Masayuki Mori (*Sawada resident*), V. S. Shes (*Prime Minister Mesacin*), Chanty Zebery (*Effran*), Schuan (*Maft*), Kumi Mizuno, Takashi Shimura.

Drama. Source: Shintaro Ishihara, *Chosen* (Tokyo, 1960). Stranded on a raft in the Pacific Ocean during World War II, Izaki is implored by a dying friend to put an end to his suffering; finally Izaki accedes to his friend's wish. Haunted by the experience after the war, he finds no purpose in life, and when his girl friend pleads with him to join her in a suicide pact, he agrees. The lovers take pills, but though she dies, Izaki survives. He returns to his job at an oil company headed by Mr. Sawada, who tries to help him develop his talents and asks him to help solve the problem of a dwindling oil supply. Meanwhile, Izaki meets Mr. Sawada's daughter Saeko, who has become embittered by an unhappy love affair. The two disillusioned young people find many parallels in their lives, and as they grow close Izaki discovers that the friend he killed was Saeko's brother. Izaki suggests to Mr. Sawada that he can break up an international cartel by sending tankers to Iraq to purchase oil. Mr. Sawada at first doubts the soundness of the suggestion, but eventually his reservations are overcome and a contract with the foreign oil dealers is signed. Though Izaki appears to have contracted tuberculosis, he decides to board the tanker to Iraq to supervise the oil deal. He accomplishes his objective and regains a sense of self-respect; but on the return voyage, the tuberculosis becomes increasingly serious, and he dies before reaching Japan. *Mercy killing. Oil business. Suicide. Disillusionment. Tuberculosis. Cartels. World War II. Iraq.*

Note: Released in Japan in Jun 1961 as *Ai to honoho to*.

LA CHAMADE (France/Italy)   F6.0732
Ariane-Les Productions Artistes Associés-P. E. A. *Dist* Lopert Pictures. 27 Jul **1969** [New York opening; c30 Oct 1968; LF87]. Sd; col (De Luxe). 35mm.

102 min. *MPAA rating* R.

Dir Alain Cavalier. *Adapt & Dial* Françoise Sagan, Alain Cavalier. *Dir Photog* Pierre Lhomme. *Camera* Jean Chiabaut. *Set Decor* Jacques Dugied. *Film Ed* Pierre Gillette. *Mus* Maurice Le Roux. *Sd Engr* Jacques Maumont. *Asst Dir* Florence Malraux. *Prod Mgr* Jean Drouin. *Prod Dir* Pierre Laurent. *Catherine Deneuve's Wardrobe* Yves Saint-Laurent. *Makeup* Odette Berroyer. *Still Photog* Jurgen Vollmer.

Cast: Catherine Deneuve (*Lucile*), Michel Piccoli (*Charles*), Roger Van Hool (*Antoine*), Irène Tunc (*Diane*), Jacques Sereys (*Johnny*), Philippine Pascal (*Claire*), Souad Amidou (*Etienne*), Monique Lejeune (*Marianne*), Louise Rioton (*Pauline*), Matt Carney (*Destret*), Christiane Lasquin (*Madeleine*).

Drama. Source: Françoise Sagan, *La chamade* (Paris, 1965). Lucile is the beautiful mistress of Charles, a wealthy, middle-aged Parisian businessman. Accustomed to luxury, Lucile devotes her time exclusively to concerts, parties, and fashion. By chance, she meets Antoine, a handsome but indigent publisher's reader who has been introduced into the social set by his mistress, Diane. After a tenuous beginning, the relationship between Lucile and Antoine develops into love. Although Antoine ends his affair with Diane, Lucile is unable to break with Charles and accompanies him to Saint-Tropez. Upon learning that Lucile has started drinking excessively, Antoine goes to her, persuades her to leave Charles, and takes her back to his apartment in Paris. For a time, Lucile is happy, allowing Antoine to arrange a job for her as a magazine file clerk, but after only one month, she quits without informing Antoine. Eventually he discovers the ruse and is furious but decides to let Lucile have her own way. When she becomes pregnant, Lucile hurts Antoine by first refusing to bear the child and then by allowing Charles to pay for an abortion at an expensive Swiss clinic. Some time later, Lucile accepts Charles's invitation to accompany him to a concert. After spending the night with him, she returns to Antoine and finds him asleep, with a list of instructions for the day tacked to the wall. Unable to resist the lure of her former life, Lucile calls Antoine from a nearby pay phone, tells him that their affair is over, and returns to Charles. *Mistresses. Businessmen. Clerks. Poverty. Alcoholism. Pregnancy. Abortion. Paris. Saint-Tropez.*

Note: Location scenes filmed in Paris and Saint-Tropez. Opened in Paris in Oct 1968; running time: 105 min; released in Italy in 1969.

CHAMBER OF HORRORS   F6.0733

Warner Bros. Pictures. 31 Aug **1966** [Charlotte, North Carolina, opening; c15 Jul 1966; LP33598]. Sd; col (Technicolor). 35mm. 99 min.

Prod-Dir Hy Averback. *Assoc Prod* Jim Barnett. *Screenplay* Stephen Kandel. *Story* Ray Russell, Stephen Kandel. *Dir Photog* Richard Kline. *Art Dir* Art Loel. *Set Decor* William L. Kuehl. *Film Ed* David Wages. *Mus* William Lava. *Sd Engr* M. A. Merrick. *Asst Dir* Sam Schneider. *Unit Mgr* Sherry Shourds. *Makeup Supv* Gordon Bau. *Supv Hairstylist* Jean Burt Reilly.

Cast: Patrick O'Neal (*Jason Cravette*), Cesare Danova (*Anthony Draco*), Wilfrid Hyde-White (*Harold Blount*), Laura Devon (*Marie Champlain*), Patrice Wymore (*Vivian*), Suzy Parker (*Barbara Dixon*), Tun Tun (*Señor Pepe de Reyes*), Philip Bourneuf (*Inspector Strudwick*), Jeanette Nolan (*Mrs. Ewing Perryman*), Marie Windsor (*Madame Corona*), Wayne Rogers (*Sergeant Albertson*), Vinton Hayworth (*Judge Randolph*), Richard O'Brien (*Dr. Cobb*), Inger Stratton (*Gloria*), Berry Kroeger (*Chun Sing*), Charles Seel (*Dr. Hopewell*), Ayllene Gibbons (*barmaid*), Tony Curtis (*Mr. Julian*).

Horror film. In turn-of-the-century Baltimore, madman Jason Cravette forces a minister to marry him to the corpse of a woman he has strangled with her own hair. After the macabre ceremony, the minister races to the police and relates his story to Inspector Strudwick. Also present are Anthony Draco and Harold Blount, who, along with a Spanish dwarf called Pepe, are co-owners of the House of Wax, a museum specializing in the re-creation of infamous murders. When a police search uncovers only Cravette's dead bride, Draco tracks the sadistic killer to a brothel. Cravette is captured, a trial is held, and he is sentenced to be hanged. He escapes from a train passing over a river and survives only by hacking off his manacled hand. His body is never recovered, and he is assumed dead. The House of Wax adds a Baltimore Strangler tableau to its displays. Cravette, meanwhile, has acquired a wooden hand stump that can be fitted with hooks, scalpels, or cleavers; and he plans to murder all those connected with his death sentence. So clever is he in carrying out his vendetta that each one of his intended victims except Draco comes to a violent end. He goes to the wax museum to complete his revenge by slashing Draco's throat, but he himself dies when he is impaled on a hook protruding from his own wax effigy. *Psychopaths. Police. Dwarfs. Spanish. Detectives. Sadism. Murder. Revenge. Amputation. Capital punishment. Waxworks. Trials. Weddings. Corpses. Baltimore.*

Note: Expanded from an unsold TV pilot film based on *House of Wax* (Warner Bros., 1953).

LA CHAMBRE ARDENTE *see* THE BURNING COURT

LA CHAMBRE OBSCURE *see* LAUGHTER IN THE DARK

CHAMPAGNE FLIGHT *see* COME FLY WITH ME

THE CHAMPAGNE MURDERS (France)   F6.0734

Universal Productions France. *Dist* Universal Pictures. Mar **1968** [c30 Mar 1968; LP41197]. Sd; col (Technicolor). 35mm (Techniscope). 98 min.

Prod Raymond Eger. *Assoc Prod* Jacques Natteau. *Dir* Claude Chabrol. *Screenplay* Claude Brulé, Derek Prouse. *Dial* Paul Gégauff. *Story* William Benjamin. *Dir Photog* Jean Rabier. *Camera Op* Claude Zidi. *Asst Camera Op* Paul Bonis. *Art Dir* Rino Mondellini. *Asst Art Dir* Jacques Brizzio. *Main Titl* Jean Fouchet. *Film Ed* Jacques Gaillard. *Mus Comp* Pierre Jansen. *Cond by* André Jouve. *Sd Engr* Guy Chichignoud. *1st & 2d Asst Dir* Pierre Gauchet, Vincent Gardair. *Prod Mgr* Fred Surin. *Unit Mgr* Pierre Cottance. *Cont* Denise Gaillard. *Cost Dsgn* Maurice Albray. *Makeup* Anatole Paris. *Hairstyles* Janou Pottier. *Coöp* Société Pommery-Greno.

Cast: Anthony Perkins (*Christopher Balling*), Maurice Ronet (*Paul Wagner*), Stéphane Audran (*Jacqueline/Lydia*), Yvonne Furneaux (*Christine Balling*), Suzanne Lloyd (*Evelyn Wharton*), Catherine Sola (*Denise*), Christa Lang (*Paula*), Henry Jones (*Mr. Clarke*), George Skaff (*Mr. Ffeifer*), Marie-Ange Agnès (*Michèle*), Annie Vidal (*blonde*).

Mystery melodrama. American-born ex-gigolo Christopher Balling is married to a wealthy Frenchwoman, Christine, who wants to sell her champagne company to a U. S. syndicate. However, the champagne's brand name is owned by Christopher's closest friend, playboy Paul Wagner, who refuses to sell. To make matters worse, Paul, emotionally unstable as a result of an incident in which he was inexplicably attacked and a female companion murdered, becomes drunk at a party and insults the American bidders. With her negotiations imperiled, Christine asks Christopher to accompany Paul on a trip to Hamburg, hoping that he can persuade Paul to sign the agreement. After a visit to a Hamburg nightclub, Christopher goes off with an attractive blonde, leaving Paul with a prostitute, Paula. Paul eventually passes out from drink, and, upon waking in the morning, he discovers that Paula has disappeared. In fact she is dead. Christine is informed of the murder by a newspaper clipping sent through the mail, and she attempts to blackmail Paul into selling the brand name. Paul, now on the verge of a breakdown, goes with Christopher to a party and is openly enticed by the hostess, sculptress Evelyn Wharton. Again Paul passes out, and, upon regaining consciousness, he finds himself alone with Evelyn's murdered body. He visits Christine and agrees to sign the necessary papers for the American deal, but later he finds Christine murdered in her bed. Exploring further, he discovers Christopher with the blonde woman he met in Germany. It is revealed that she is the murderess; in the guise of a plain-looking secretary she has worked for Christine, living in the same house, and has schemed to give Christopher control of his wife's fortune. She tries to shoot Paul, and as Christopher attempts to protect his friend, the three struggle on the floor. *Playboys. Businesswomen. Prostitutes. Secretaries. Expatriates. Sculptors. Murder. Blackmail. Alcoholism. Infidelity. Personal identity. Greed. Disguise. Wealth. Mental illness. Wine. Hamburg.*

Note: Opened in Paris in Mar 1967 as *Le scandale*; running time: 107 min. William Benjamin is a pseudonym for Raymond Eger. Filmed simultaneously in French and English.

LA CHANCE D'ÊTRE FEMME *see* WHAT A WOMAN!

CHANGE OF HABIT   F6.0735

Universal Pictures–NBC Productions. *Dist* Universal Pictures. Nov **1969** [c10 Nov 1969; LP39252]. Sd; col (Technicolor). 35mm. 93 min. *MPAA rating* G.

Prod Joe Connelly. *Assoc Prod* Irving Paley. *Dir* William Graham. *Screenplay* James Lee, S. S. Schweitzer, Eric Bercovici. *Story* John Joseph, Richard Morris. *Photog* Russell Metty. *Camera Op* Wilbur Gossman. *Asst Camera* William Renaldi. *Art Dir* Alexander Golitzen, Frank Arrigo. *Asst Art Dir* Joe Alves. *Set Decor* John McCarthy, Ruby Levitt. *Film Ed* Douglas Stewart. *Mus* Ben Weisman, William Goldenberg. *Mus Supv* Stanley Wilson. *Songs:* "Change of Habit," "Let Us Pray" Ben Weisman, Buddy Kaye. *Sung by* Elvis Presley. *Mus:* "Rubberneckin'" Bunny Warren, Dory Jones. *Sd* Waldon O. Watson, Lyle Cain, Ronald Pierce. *Boom Op* Perry Devore. *Rec* Bill Schwartz. *Asst Dir* Phil Bowles, Jack Terry, Richard C. Bennett. *Unit Prod Mgr* Joseph Kenny. *Script Supv* Diana Loomis. *Prod Coörd* Walter Woodworth. *Cost* Helen Colvig. *Wardrobe* Don Snyder, cost, Austin Felious, May Booth. *Makeup Supv* Bud Westmore. *Makeup* Tom Tuttle, James McCoy. *Hairstyles* Larry Germain, Clara Holgate. *Gaffer* Edward Hobson. *Grip* Ollie Hansel. *Prop* Bill Nunley, Bill Smallback. *Casting Dir* Bob Edmiston.

Cast: Elvis Presley (*Dr. John Carpenter*), Mary Tyler Moore (*Sister Michelle*), Barbara McNair (*Sister Irene*), Jane Elliot (*Sister Barbara*), Leora Dana (*Mother Joseph*), Edward Asner (*Lieutenant Moretti*), Robert Emhardt

("The Banker"), Regis Toomey (Father Gibbons), Doro Merande (Rose), Ruth McDevitt (Lily), Richard Carlson (Bishop Finley), Nefti Millet (Julio Hernandez), Laura Figueroa (Desiree), Lorena Kirk (Amanda), Virginia Vincent (Miss Parker), David Renard (Colom), Ji-Tu Cumbuka (Hawk), Bill Elliott (Robbie), Rodolfo Hoyos (Mr. Hernandez).

Melodrama. John Carpenter, a young doctor operating a free clinic in a ghetto, looks with apprehension at the arrival of three nuns who have been granted special dispensation to wear laymen's clothing and help him with his work. Gradually gaining the respect of the community are: Sister Michelle, a speech therapist, who is able to help Julio Hernandez, the leader of a gang of juvenile delinquents, and who also works with an autistic child; Sister Irene, a Negro, who demonstrates her own sense of ghetto wisdom; and Sister Barbara, who becomes involved in protesting the unfair prices that a local food market charges the residents. Dr. Carpenter, who is unaware that the women are nuns, falls in love with Sister Michelle, but she gently rebuffs him and becomes even more involved in community affairs. Despite interference from her superior, Bishop Finley, Sister Michelle organizes a block party to bring the black and Puerto Rican elements of the community together. At the party, "The Banker," a local black gangster, slaps Sister Irene for meddling in his business affairs, but Dr. Carpenter knocks the gangster down. Later, Sister Michelle is nearly raped by Julio Hernandez, and again Dr. Carpenter comes to the rescue. Meanwhile, Sister Barbara, who has been picketing the market, is arrested, and Mother Joseph, the nun in charge of the convent, orders all three women to leave the project. Sister Michelle, who is now in love with Carpenter, must choose between him and the Church. *Physicians. Nuns. Speech therapists. Puerto Ricans. Juvenile delinquents. Negroes. Clergymen. Gangsters. Mistaken identity. Race relations. Rape. Clinics. Ghettos. Demonstrations.*

A CHANGE OF HEART see **TWO AND TWO MAKE SIX**

CHANGE OF MIND   F6.0736

Sagittarius Productions. *Dist* Cinerama Releasing Corp. 1 Oct **1969** [New York opening; c1 Oct 1969; LP38181]. Sd; col (Eastman Color). 35mm. 103 min. [Also 98 min.] *MPAA rating* R.

Prod-Writ Seeleg Lester, Dick Wesson. *Exec Prod* Henry S. White. *Dir* Robert Stevens. *Dir Photog* Arthur J. Ornitz. *Art Dir* Harold Maxfield. *Main Titl* Wally Gentleman. *Film Ed* Donald Ginsberg. *Mus Comp & Cond* Duke Ellington. *Sd Mix* Joe Grimaldi. *Sd Des* Dollery. *Asst Dir* Kris Paterson. *Prod Mgr* Clark Paylow. *Wardrobe Dsgn* Gail Ansell. *Makeup* Ken Brooke. *Hairdresser* James Keeler. *Tech Adv* Norrie Swanson. *Casting* Frances Egan.

Cast: Raymond St. Jacques (David Rowe), Susan Oliver (Margaret Rowe), Janet MacLachlan (Elizabeth Dickson), Leslie Nielsen (Sheriff Webb), Donnelly Rhodes (Roger Morrow), David Bailey (Tommy Benson), Andre Womble (Scupper), Clarisse Taylor (Rose Landis), Jack Creley (Bill Chambers), Cosette Lee (Angela Rowe), Larry Reynolds (Judge Forrest), Hope Clarke (Nancy), Rudy Challenger (Howard Culver), Henry Ramer (Chief Enfield), Franz Russell (Mayor Farrell), Joseph Shaw (Governor La Tourette), Sydney Brown (Attorney Nash), Tony Kamreither (Dr. Bornear), Ronald Hartmann (Dr. Kelman), Murray Westgate (Judge Stanton), Guy Sanvido, Chuck Samata, Dan MacDonald, Joseph Wynn (reporters), Charles Elder (Mako), Horace Bailey (Moorland), Buddy Ferens (officer), Don Crawford (Callicot), Pat Collins (Mrs. Robinson), Sean Sullivan (Mr. Robinson), Vivian Reis (Gloria), Ellen Flood (mother), Danny McIlravey (little boy), Keith Williams (guest), Clarence Haynes (butler).

Drama. The brain of David Rowe, a white liberal district attorney dying of cancer, is transplanted into the body of a recently killed black man. After being legally certified as the same person, Rowe attempts to resume his personal and professional life; but his mother can no longer accept him, and his wife, Margaret, is unable to overcome a certain amount of sexual frigidity. Furthermore, Rowe soon learns that he is rejected by his white colleagues as well as the black community, and that his political party is planning to drop him at the next election. Reduced to despair, Rowe seeks consolation in the company of Elizabeth Dickson, the widow of the man whose body he now inhabits. Upon resuming his professional life, Rowe prepares to prosecute Sheriff Webb, a bigoted white man accused of murdering his black mistress. When the governor tries to stop the trial for political reasons, Rowe once more turns to Elizabeth for solace, but she can no longer accept him. Then, as Rowe is about to win his case against Webb, he uncovers evidence that establishes the sheriff's innocence and implicates a black man. By dismissing the case, Rowe becomes something of a hero to both blacks and whites, and it is suggested that he run for state attorney general. Even though his wife now seems willing to accept him, Rowe decides to leave town. *District attorneys. Negroes. Widows. Sheriffs. Organ transplants. Personal identity. Race relations. Marriage. Filial relations. Frigidity. Infidelity. Miscegenation. Murder. Cancer. Trials.*

Note: Location scenes filmed around Toronto, Canada.

CHANGES   F6.0737

Hall Bartlett, Inc. *Dist* Cinerama Releasing Corp. 11 Feb **1969** [New York opening; c11 Feb 1969; LP38512]. Sd; col (Eastman Color). 35mm (Panavision). 93 min. [Copyright length: 98 min.] *MPAA rating* M.

A Hall Bartlett Production. *Prod-Dir* Hall Bartlett. *Screenplay* Bill E. Kelly, Hall Bartlett. *Adtl Dial* Tracy Butler. *Dir Photog* Richard Moore. *Art Dir* Jack Poplin. *Main Titl* Sandy Dvore. *Film Ed* Peter Zinner, Earle Herdan. *Mus & Songs* Tim Buckley, Kim Weston, Mickey Stevenson, Neil Young, Marty Paich, Charles Greene. *Titl Song Comp & Sung by* Kim Weston. *Song:* "Both Sides Now" Joni Mitchell. *Sung by* Judy Collins. *Song:* "Expecting To Fly" Neil Young. *Sung by* Condello. *Sd* Norval Crutcher, Kay Rose. *Sd Rec* Robert Martin. *Asst Dir* Bill Thomas. *Prod Mgr* Emmett Emerson. *Sp Eff* George Ross, sp eff.

Cast: Kent Lane (Kent), Michele Carey (Julie), Manuela Thiess (Bobbi). Jack Albertson (Kent's father), Maris Fehr (Kent's mother), Marcia Strassman (Kristine), Tom Fielding (Kent's roommate), Bill E. Kelly (Kent's friend), Kenneth Washington (Negro man), Kim Weston, Doug Dowell, Doug Bell, Buddy Hart, Cindy Mitchum, Monica Petersen, Christopher Hayden, Clarice Gillis, Katherine Victory, Sam Chew, Jr., Sherry Mitchell, Sammy Vaughn, Grant Conroy, Terry Garr, Sammy Tanner, John Moio, Jesus Alonzo, Jr., Vincent George.

Melodrama. Alienated from his family and friends, Kent, a West Coast student, drops out of college and takes to the road in his sports car. While driving along the Big Sur coastline, he thinks about his hometown girl friend Bobbi's dependence on his love, his college roommate's acceptance of establishment rules, and his parents' failure to understand the problems of youth. At one point Kent had tried to explain to Bobbi why he felt that he could not assume responsibility for her, but the lonely girl's feeling of rejection had driven her to suicide. The recollection of Bobbi's tragedy causes Kent to lose control of his car, and he crashes over an embankment. He hitchhikes aimlessly until he is picked up by Kristine, a free-lance reporter who conducts campus interviews. After covering a peace demonstration, they spend the night together, but Kent leaves when he realizes that she also has needs that he is unwilling to fulfill. Finally, Kent wanders into a carnival, where he meets Julie, an independent young woman who gets him a job and allows him to move into her apartment. For a time Kent is happy, but soon he feels the need to move on. When Julie asks to go with him and is refused, she rebukes Kent for his selfishness and lack of purpose. Although he leaves again, Julie's words have reached him, and he sets off determined to make his life meaningful. *Students. Wanderers. Roommates. Hitchhikers. Reporters. Memory. Suicide. Guilt. Sports cars. Demonstrations. Carnivals. Big Sur. California. Automobile accidents.*

Note: Location scenes filmed at Big Sur, California.

CHANGES   F6.0738

Cinex Film Industries. *Dist* Cinex International Film Distributors. 28 Dec **1970** [New Haven, Connecticut, opening]. Sd; col. 35mm. 90 min.

Prod-Dir-Writ Gerard Damiano. *Dir Photog* Arthur Marks. *Asst Camera* George Feinberg. *2d Unit Camera* Ron Wortham, Charles Carmello, Tony Foresto. *Titl & Eff* Grimm Graphics. *Film Ed* Mark Ross, Gerard Damiano. *Mus* Alan Baker. *Song:* "Getting Off" *Writ & Sung by* Monti Rock, III. *Sd Man* Bernie Brandt. *Prod Mgr* Mark Ross. *Prod Coörd* George Delemos. *Cont* Lucy Grant. *Stills* Richard Start. *Ch Grip* Gerodias Filmore. *Res* Harvey Green.

Cast—In Order of Appearance: Grace Tarpey (lounge owner), Dr. Arthur Greenspan (psychiatrist), Larry Hunter (store clerk), Melvin Frest (theatre manager), Carol Barr (stripper), Mary Philips (member N.O.W. and editor of "New Broadside"), Marty Adler (model studio owner), Jack Nichols, Lige Clark (editors, "Gay Magazine"), Arthur Irving (member G.A.A.), Al Goldstein (editor, "Screw Magazine"), Jim Buckley (publisher, "Screw Magazine"), Marcea Blackman (ad director).

Cast—"The Making of a Peep Show" with hidden camera: Nancy (actress) (sculptress), Gerard Damiano, Jr.

Documentary. This film uses interviews and detailed coverage of live events to explore the changing attitude of society toward pornography, sexual permissiveness, sexual deviation, and the women's liberation movement. Individuals working in or commenting on the sexual underground are interviewed, and there are scenes of nudity and explicit sexual activity in bars, bookstores, model studios, movie theaters, and burlesque houses. *Sexuality. Pornography. Feminism. Stag shows. Magazines (periodicals).*

CHANGGUN UI SUYUM see **BEARDED GENERAL**

CHANS see **JUST ONCE MORE**

CHANTAL   F6.0739

C. I. T. Films. *Dist* I. R. M. I. Films. 13 Mar **1968** [New York showing]. Sd; b&w. 62 min.

Prod Jack Stram. *Dir* Allan Lindus.
Cast: Lily Damon, Herb Canover.

Sex film. Aspiring actress Chantal Duval goes to Hollywood to become a star but is refused jobs by the major studios. Disgusted by predatory lesbians and phony directors, and unwilling to accept work in sex films, Chantal forfeits the hope of a film career and returns home. *Actors. Motion picture directors. Lesbianism. Disillusionment. Employment—Women. Sex exploitation films. Hollywood.*

THE CHAPLIN REVUE   F6.0740
Roy Export Co.-United Artists. *Dist* United Artists. 27 Jan **1964** [New York opening; c25 Sep 1959; LP29374]. Sd; b&w. 35mm. 117 min.
Prod-Dir-Writ Charles Chaplin. *Mus* Charles Chaplin.
Commentator: Charles Chaplin.

Compilation film. Charles Chaplin presents three of his early films: *A Dog's Life* (1918), *Shoulder Arms* (1918), and *The Pilgrim* (1923). *Motion pictures— History. Charles Chaplin.*

CHAPLIN'S ART OF COMEDY   F6.0741
Pizor Classic Films. *Dist* Hemisphere Pictures. Sep **1966**. Sd; b&w. 35mm. 85 min.
Prod-Writ Samuel M. Sherman. *Exec Prod* Irwin Pizor. *Anim* Bob Lebar. *Titl* Bob Lebar. *Mus* Elias Breeskin. *Audio Control* Maurice Manne. *Narr Rec* William R. Sheridan. *Track* Cinema Recording Corp.. *Re-rec* Val Peters. *Script Cons* Ruth Riva Sherman, Jack Melnick. *Prod & Ed Services* Signature Films.
Narrator: Dave Anderson, narrator.

Compilation film. A survey of Charles Chaplin's early career using re-edited footage from: *The Tramp* (1915), *Bank* (1915), *Champion* (1915), *His New Job* (1915), *A Night Out* (1915), *Police* (1916), *A Night in the Show* (1915), *In the Park* (1915), and *A Woman* (1915). *Motion pictures—History. Charles Chaplin.*

THE CHAPMAN REPORT   F6.0742
Darryl F. Zanuck Productions. *Dist* Warner Bros. Pictures. 5 Oct **1962** [Chicago opening; c13 Oct 1962; LP29373]. Sd; col (Technicolor). 35mm. 125 min.
A Darryl F. Zanuck Production. *Prod* Richard D. Zanuck. *Dir* George Cukor. *Screenplay* Wyatt Cooper, Don M. Mankiewicz. *Adapt* Grant Stuart, Gene Allen. *Photog* Harold Lipstein. *Col Coörd* Hoyningen-Huene. *Art Dir* Gene Allen. *Set Decor* George James Hopkins. *Titl Dsgn* Hoyningen-Huene. *Film Ed* Robert Simpson. *Mus* Leonard Rosenman. *Sd* Stanley Jones. *Asst Dir* Sergei Petschnikoff, James T. Vaughn. *Cost* Orry-Kelly. *Makeup* Gordon Bau. *Hairstyles* Jean Burt Reilly.
Cast: Efrem Zimbalist, Jr. *(Paul Radford)*, Shelley Winters *(Sarah Garnell)*, Jane Fonda *(Kathleen Barclay)*, Claire Bloom *(Naomi Shields)*, Glynis Johns *(Teresa Harnish)*, Ray Danton *(Fred Linden)*, Ty Hardin *(Ed Kraski)*, Andrew Duggan *(Dr. George C. Chapman)*, John Dehner *(Geoffrey Harnish)*, Harold J. Stone *(Frank Garnell)*, Corey Allen *(Wash Dillon)*, Jennifer Howard *(Grace Waterton)*, Cloris Leachman *(Miss Selby)*, Chad Everett *(water boy)*, Henry Daniell *(Dr. Jonas)*, Hope Cameron *(Ruth Linden)*, Roy Roberts *(Alan Roby)*, Evan Thompson *(Cass Kelly)*, John Baer *("Boy" Barclay)*, Jack Cassidy *(Ted Dyson)*, Grady Sutton *(Simon)*, Alex Viespi *(Bardelli)*, William Hummer *(Johnny Dillon)*, Pamela Austin, Jack Littlefield, Ray Foster, Fern Barry.
Melodrama. Source: Irving Wallace, *The Chapman Report* (New York, 1960). Dr. George C. Chapman, a famous psychologist, and his assistant, Paul Radford, arrive in a Los Angeles suburb to conduct a survey on the sex habits of American women. After their first lecture on the project, four women volunteer as subjects. Sarah Garnell, a middle-aged wife and mother, is having an affair with a young theater director, Fred Linden. She decides to run away with him, but he rejects her, and she returns to her husband. Teresa Harnish, married to an art dealer, believes that they have a perfect relationship until she meets handsome football player Ed Kraski. When she discovers his rough aggressiveness, however, she turns back to the safety of her home. Naomi Shields, an alcoholic nymphomaniac, becomes involved with a jazz musician who allows his drunken friends to rape her at a party; she subsequently commits suicide. The fourth woman, Kathleen Barclay, a young widow who believes that she is frigid, breaks down during questioning and leaves the doctor's office. Paul traces her to her home and, by becoming personally involved, convinces her that her fears are unfounded. Dr. Chapman then reveals that the four cases are exceptions to the rule; most American marriages are happy ones. *Psychologists. Suburbanites. Housewives. Theatrical directors. Art dealers. Athletes. Musicians. Widows. Sex research. Marriage. Infidelity. Alcoholism. Nymphomania. Rape. Suicide. Frigidity. Los Angeles.*

CHAPPAQUA   F6.0743
Conrad Rooks. *Dist* Regional Film Distributors, Minotaur Releasing Co. 5 Nov **1967** [New York opening; c1 Aug 1966; MP16926]. Sd; b&w with col seq (Eastmancolor). 35mm. 92 min. [Also reviewed at 82 min.]

Prod-Dir-Writ Conrad Rooks. *Dir Photog* Robert Frank. *Camera* Etienne Becker. *Photog* David Larcher. *Photog Cons* Eugen Shuftan. *Art Dir* Régis Pagniez. *Film Ed* Kenout Peltier. *Asst Film Ed* Claudine Merlin, Claude Le Gallou, Catherine Peltier. *Orig Mus Comp & Dir* Ravi Shankar. *Orig Mus Perf by* Ravi Shankar, Alla Rakha, Keshav Sathe. *Excerpts from "Saint Matthew's Passion"* Johann Sebastian Bach. *Song:* "Buttercups" Trude Heller. *Adtl Mus Perf by* The Fugs, Donovan. *Mus Cons* Phil Glass. *Sd* I. M. Sommerville, Peter Pilafian. *Unit Mgr* Francis Bouche. *Cons Mgr* Louis Emile Galey. *Wardrobe* Agnès Senne. *Makeup* Jean Pipard, Jacqueline Pipard. *Still Photog* David Larcher.
Cast: Jean-Louis Barrault *(Dr. Benoit)*, Conrad Rooks *(Russel Harwick)*, William S. Burroughs *(Opium Jones)*, Allen Ginsberg *(Messiah)*, Ravi Shankar *(Sun God)*, Paula Pritchett *(Water Woman)*, Ornette Coleman *(Peyote Eater)*, Swami Satchidananda *(The Guru)*, Moondog *(The Prophet)*, Jill Lator *(Sacrificed One)*, John Esam *(The Connection)*, The Fugs, Rita Renoir, Penny Brown, Jacques Seiler, Moustique, Sophie Steboun, Elder Wilder, Peter Orlovsky, Pascal Aubier, France Crémieux, Mr. & Mrs. René Serisier, Donovan.
Autobiographical drama. Russel Harwick, the son of a wealthy American business executive, has been an alcoholic since he was 14 and a drug addict since he was 19. At 27 he is in the final stages of heroin addiction, when his father's death shocks him into wanting to be cured. He arrives in Paris for a sleep cure and is driven to a rest home on the outskirts of the city. During Russel's withdrawal period presided over by Doctor Benoit, he frequently has fantasies and nightmarish visions. He imagines himself under the wing of an Indian guru, floating through space with an ethereal and loving woman, and fighting off the persistent lures of his friends—especially Opium Jones, a sinister pusher. Russel is eventually cured and released from the clinic. As he leaves in a helicopter, he turns to look back, only to see himself on a balcony of the chateau that has been his hospital-clinic. *Americans in foreign countries. Physicians. Gurus. Drug addicts. Drug dealers. Alcoholism. Heroin. Sanitariums. Hallucinations. Paris.*
Note: Filmed in France, Mexico, India, England, Ceylon, Jamaica, and the United States. Rooks bought the rights from Universal in Jan 1968 and rereleased *Chappaqua* in Nov 1970 through his Minotaur Releasing Co.

CHARADE   F6.0744
Stanley Donen Productions. *Dist* Universal Pictures. 5 Dec **1963** [New York opening]. Sd; col (Technicolor). 35mm. 113 min.
Prod-Dir Stanley Donen. *Assoc Prod* James Ware. *Prod Exec* Arthur Carroll. *Screenplay* Peter Stone. *Photog* Charles Lang, Jr. *Art Dir* Jean d' Eaubonne. *Film Ed* James Clark. *Mus* Henry Mancini. *Titl Song* Henry Mancini, Johnny Mercer. *Sd* Jacques Carrère, Bob Jones. *Asst Dir* Marc Maurette. *Prod Mgr* Léopold Schlosberg. *Miss Hepburn's Clothes* Givenchy. *Makeup* Alberto De Rossi, John O'Gorman.
Cast: Cary Grant *(Peter Joshua/Alexander Dyle/Adam Canfield/Brian Cruikshank)*, Audrey Hepburn *(Reggie Lambert)*, Walter Matthau *(Hamilton Bartholomew/Carson Dyle)*, James Coburn *(Tex Panthollow)*, George Kennedy *(Herman Scobie)*, Ned Glass *(Leopold Gideon)*, Jacques Marin *(Inspector Grandpierre)*, Paul Bonifas *(Félix)*, Dominique Minot *(Sylvie Gaudet)*, Thomas Chelimsky *(Jean-Louis Gaudet)*.
Mystery comedy-melodrama. Source: Peter Stone and Marc Behm, "The Unsuspecting Wife" (publication undetermined). Returning to Paris from an Alpine ski holiday, Reggie Lambert finds her husband, Charles, murdered. A vacation acquaintance, Peter Joshua, offers his services and assists her in finding a hotel room. Lambert's funeral is attended by three strange Americans. Summoned to the U. S. Embassy, Reggie is informed by supposed C.I.A. official Hamilton Bartholomew that Lambert and four accomplices had pilfered $250,000 in gold destined for the French Resistance during World War II, and that the government would appreciate her assistance in finding the loot. He further confides his fear for her life. Reggie assures Bartholomew, however, that she has no idea where the money is. The agent further informs the widow that among Lambert's former associates only Carson Dyle is deceased; the others attended her husband's funeral. Threatened by the trio, Reggie confides in Joshua, who reveals that he is Dyle's vengeful brother Alexander. Informed by Bartholomew that Dyle had no brother, Reggie confronts Joshua, who now asserts that he is thief Adam Canfield. When the American trio is murdered, Reggie assumes that her friend is, in fact, Alexander Dyle. En route to deliver the three rare stamps representing the purloined $250,000 Reggie meets Joshua, who discloses that Bartholomew is in reality Carson Dyle. Unmasked, the murderer flees to the Comédie Française, where he falls to his death through an open trap door. Joshua thereupon reveals to Reggie that he is U. S. Treasury agent Brian Cruikshank, accepts the stamps, and embraces the widow. *Widows. Americans in foreign countries. Thieves. Secret agents. Imposture. Murder. Perfidy. Personal identity. Resistance (political). Hotels. Funerals. Philately. World War II. Alps. Paris. Comédie Française. United States—Central*

Intelligence Agency. United States—Treasury Department.
Note: Filmed in Paris, Megève, and the French Alps.

THE CHARGE OF THE LIGHT BRIGADE (Great Britain)   **F6.0745**
Woodfall Films. *Dist* United Artists. 6 Oct **1968** [New York opening; c11 Apr 1968; LF23]. Sd; col (DeLuxe). 35mm (Panavision). 128 min. [Copyright length: 143 min]
Prod Neil Hartley. *Dir* Tony Richardson. *2d Unit Dir* Christian de Chalonges. *Screenplay* Charles Wood. *Anim* Richard Williams. *Photog* David Watkin. *2d Unit Photog* Peter Suschitzky. *Col Adv* Lila De Nobili. *Art Dir* Edward Marshall. *Assoc Art Dir* Julia Trevelyan Oman. *Main Titl* Richard Williams. *Supv Ed* Kevin Brownlow. *Ed* Hugh Raggett. *Mus Comp* John Addison. *Sd* Simon Kaye, Peter Handford. *Asst Dir* Clive Reed. *Action Arr* Robert Simmonds. *Prod Supv* Roy Stevens. *Prod Mgr* Julian Mackintosh. *Cost* David Walker. *Sp Eff* Robert MacDonald, Paul Pollard. *Period Cons* Lila De Nobili. *Historical Res* John Mollo.
Cast: Trevor Howard *(Lord Cardigan)*, Vanessa Redgrave *(Clarissa)*, John Gielgud *(Lord Raglan)*, Harry Andrews *(Lord Lucan)*, Jill Bennett *(Mrs. Duberly)*, David Hemmings *(Captain Nolan)*, Peter Bowles *(Paymaster Duberly)*, Mark Burns *(Captain Morris)*, Howard Marion Crawford *(Sir George Brown)*, Mark Dignam *(Airey)*, Alan Dobie *(Mogg)*, Willoughby Goddard *(squire)*, T. P. McKenna *(Russell)*, Corin Redgrave *(Featherstonehough)*, Norman Rossington *(Corbett)*, Ben Aris *(Maxse)*, Leo Britt *(Scarlett)*, Helen Cherry *(Lady Scarlett)*, Ambrose Coghill *(Douglas)*, Douking *(St. Arnaud)*, Andrew Faulds *(Quaker preacher)*, Ben Howard *(Pridmore)*, Rachel Kempson *(Mrs. Codrington)*, Roger Mutton *(Codrington)*, Valerie Newman *(Mrs. Mitchell)*, Donald Wolfit *("Macbeth")*, Peter Woodthorpe *(valet)*, Michael Miller *(Sir Colin Campbell)*, Micky Baker *(Trooper Metcalfe)*, John Carney *(Trooper Mitchell)*, Chris Cunningham *(Farrier)*, Christopher Chittell, Clive Endersby, Derek Fuke *(troopers)*, John Hallam *(officer)*, Barbara Hicks *(Mrs. Duberly's maid)*, Declan Mulholland *(Farrier)*, Roy Pattison *(sergeant major)*, Dino Shafeek *(Indian servant)*, John Trenaman *(Sergeant Smith)*, Colin Vancao *(Captain Charteris)*.
Historical drama. Partially based on: Cecil Woodham-Smith, *The Reason Why* (London, 1953). In 1854, 39 years after Napoleon's defeat at Waterloo, a group of aristocratic British army officers, including the arrogant Lord Cardigan, become restless for an opportunity to seek military glory. While Cardigan is eagerly planning to lead an army in the Crimean expedition to protect the Ottoman Empire from the invading Russians, he is also involved in a dispute with Captain Lewis Nolan, an outspoken young officer recently returned to Britain from India. As the two men's mutual acrimony reaches its peak, the British declare war, join forces with the French, and set sail for Turkey. Left behind in England is an officer's wife, Clarissa Morris, with whom Nolan has been having an affair. Once in the Crimea, the British army, although poorly-provisioned and cholera-ridden, wins an initial victory over the Russians and quickly becomes complacent about its power. Failing to follow through on his forces' advantage, the doddering Lord Raglan ponders his next course of action, while Cardigan dallies with Mrs. Duberly, the unfaithful paymaster's wife, who cheers on the soldiers by day and their commanding officer by night. Infuriated by the lack of immediate retaliation as the Battle of Balaklava begins, Nolan takes it upon himself to deliver one of Raglan's incoherent military orders to Cardigan and his brother-in-law, Lord Lucan. In the confusion, Cardigan's Light Brigade veers into the wrong valley and heads straight into the waiting Russian cannons. Though Nolan attempts to halt the charge, he is killed by an aerial burst, as the brigade stubbornly continues its suicidal march. Following the slaughter, Cardigan rides his horse over Nolan's corpse and joins the other officers in bickering over where the blame for the senseless debacle should be laid. *Aristocrats. Brothers-in-law. Military life. Infidelity. Ambition. Cholera. Crimean War. Ottoman Empire. Russia. James Thomas Brudenell Cardigan. Fitzroy James Henry Somerset Raglan. Great Britain—Army. Russia—Army.*
Note: Location scenes filmed in Turkey. Opened in London in Apr 1968; running time: 141 min. Previously filmed in the United States in 1903, 1912, and 1936; previously filmed in Great Britain in 1931.

CHARLENE'S INJUSTICE   **F6.0746**
Dist Chancellor Films. Sep **1969**. Sd; col. 35mm. 67 min.
Melodrama. Anne and Charlene become pregnant by the same man. Charlene, a poor girl, dies as the result of a botched illegal abortion. Anne, a rich girl, has a successful abortion and decides to become prudent in her sexual relationships. *Pregnancy. Abortion. Wealth. Poverty. Promiscuity.*

CHARLES LLOYD—JOURNEY WITHIN   **F6.0747**
Eric Sherman. Jun **1969** [c16 May 1968; MU7918]. Sd; b&w. 16mm. 58 min.
Prod-Dir Eric Sherman. *Photog* Eric Sherman. *Film Ed* Eric Sherman. *Mus Perf by* Charles Lloyd. *Sd Rec* Eric Sherman.

Documentary. The music and life of black jazz musician Charles Lloyd are examined. Included are excerpts from concert performances in both America and Europe. *Negroes. Musicians. Jazz. Charles Lloyd.*
Note: Location scenes filmed in Memphis, Tennessee.

CHARLIE BUBBLES (Great Britain)   **F6.0748**
Memorial Enterprises–Universal Pictures. *Dist* Regional Film Distributors. 11 Feb **1968** [New York opening; c30 Mar 1968; LP41196]. Sd (Westrex); col (Technicolor). 35mm. 91 min.
Prod Michael Medwin. *Assoc Prod* George Pitcher. *Dir* Albert Finney. *Screenplay-Orig Story* Shelagh Delaney. *Dir Photog* Peter Suschitzky. *Camera Op* Jimmy Turrell. *Art Dir* Edward Marshall. *Set Decor* Josie Macavin. *Film Ed* Fergus McDonell. *Mus Comp & Cond* Misha Donat. *Sd Rec* Peter Handford, Hugh Strain. *Sd Ed* Dino Di Campo. *1st Asst Dir* Terry Clegg. *Prod Mgr* Ian Lewis. *Cont* Doreen Dearnaley. *Asst to the Prod* David Barber. *Cost Dsgn* Yvonne Blake. *Wardrobe Mistress* Rosemary Burrows. *Makeup* Jock Alexander. *Hairdresser* Joyce James. *Process Photog* Charles Staffell.
Cast: Albert Finney *(Charlie Bubbles)*, Colin Blakely *(Smokey Pickles)*, Billie Whitelaw *(Lottie Bubbles)*, Liza Minnelli *(Eliza)*, Timothy Garland *(Jack Bubbles)*, Richard Pearson *(accountant)*, Nicholas Phipps *(agent)*, Peter Sallis *(solicitor)*, Charles Hill *(head waiter)*, Charles Lamb *(Mr. Noseworthy)*, Margery Mason *(Mrs. Noseworthy)*, Diana Coupland *(Maudie)*, George Innes *(garage attendant)*, Arthur Pentelow *(man with car)*, Alan Lake *(airman)*, Yootha Joyce *(woman in motorway cafe)*, Peter Carlisle *(man in motorway cafe)*, Wendy Padbury *(girl in motorway cafe)*, Susan Engel *(nanny)*, Rex Boyd *(receptionist)*, Joe Gladwin *(waiter in hotel)*, John Ronane *(Gerry)*, Albert Shepherd *(policeman)*, Ted Norris *(1st reporter)*, Bryan Mosley *(2d reporter)*.
Drama. Despite the advantages and luxuries that a successful writing career have brought him, Charlie Bubbles is bored with his life. At a plush London restaurant, he runs into an old friend, Smokey Pickles, and joins him for a drunken tour of London's haberdasheries, pool halls, and pubs. Charlie returns to his expensive townhouse with Smokey, slumps before the closed-circuit television monitors in his office, and disinterestedly watches the movements of his servants and secretary. An angry phone call from his ex-wife Lottie, who lives in a farmhouse in the country, reminds Charlie that he had promised to take their 9-year-old son, Jack, to a soccer match. Not particularly anxious to make the trip alone, he takes his American secretary Eliza along. They spend the early morning hours at a hotel in Manchester, and he passively permits her to make love to him. Upon arriving at Lottie's the next morning, Charlie is greeted with indifference almost equal to his own. In an attempt to communicate with his son, he takes the boy to the soccer match but loses him in the crowd. After searching for hours, he notifies the police and returns to the farmhouse, where he finds Jack contentedly watching television with his mother. Realizing that even his son has no real need of him, Charlie crawls into bed and falls asleep. The next morning he arises early and walks to a nearby meadow where a huge observation balloon is moored. He climbs into it, cuts the ropes, and rises slowly into the sky. *Authors. Americans in foreign countries. Secretaries. Wealth. Disillusionment. Drunkenness. Divorce. Parenthood. Television. Balloons (ascent). Soccer. London. Manchester (England).*
Note: Released in Great Britain in Sep 1968; running time: 89 min.

CHARLIE, THE LONESOME COUGAR   **F6.0749**
Walt Disney Productions–Cangary, Ltd. *Dist* Buena Vista Distribution Co. 18 Oct **1967** [c29 Sep 1967; LP34867]. Sd; col (Technicolor). 35mm. 75 min.
Pres by Walt Disney. A Walt Disney Production. *Co-prod* Winston Hibler. *Dir* Winston Hibler. *Screenplay* Jack Speirs. *Story* Jack Speirs, Winston Hibler. *Photog* Lloyd Beebe, William W. Bacon, III, Charles L. Draper. *Film Ed* Gregg McLaughlin. *Mus* Franklyn Marks. *Song:* "Talkin' About Charlie" Jack Speirs, Franklyn Marks. *Orch* Wayne Robinson. *Sd* Robert O. Cook. *Mus Ed* Rusty Jones. *Field Prod* Lloyd Beebe, Charles L. Draper, Ford Beebe. *Prod Mgr* Erwin L. Verity. *Prod Coörd* Robert F. Metzler. *Coöp* Potlatch Forests Inc., Weyerhauser Co. *Animal Supv* Marinho Correia, Dell May.
Cast: Ron Brown *(Jess Bradley)*, Bryan Russell *(Potlatch)*, Linda Wallace *(Jess's fiancée)*, Jim Wilson *(farmer)*, Clifford Peterson *(mill manager)*, Lewis Sample *(chief engineer)*, Edward C. Moller *(mill hand)*, Rex Allen *(narrator)*, Charlie *(himself, a cougar)*.
Comedy-drama. While harvesting in the Pacific Northwest pine country, lumberman Jess Bradley finds an orphaned cougar kitten and adopts it as a pet. Nicknamed Goodtime Charlie, the little animal quickly makes friends with the lumbermill workers and is more or less permitted to run free. But during a huge lumber drive downriver Charlie upsets a kitchen wanigan and thus irritates the cook and the crew foreman. As a result, Jess is forced to keep his pet locked in a cage. The confinement proves too much for Charlie, and one night he escapes after hearing the call of a female cougar. Unaccustomed to fending and hunting for himself, Charlie heads for the nearest farm, but he is driven away by a blast of buckshot. He spends a long and lonely winter in the forest until

he finally makes his way back to Jess's camp. Upon being discovered, the terrified animal panics and races through the mill until he is cornered in an elevator shaft. Just as the manager is about to shoot Charlie, Jess arrives to rescue his former pet. Realizing that Charlie is no longer compatible with civilization, Jess takes him to a wildlife refuge. There Charlie finds a female cougar with whom to share his new home. *Lumberjacks. Cooks. Animals— Domestication. Lumbering. Wildlife refuges. United States—Northwest. Cougars.*

Note: Filmed in Washington and Idaho.

CHARLIE'S BIG ROMANCE (Reissue)   **F6.0750**
Keystone Film Co.–Ras Films International. *Dist* Crystal Pictures. **1967**. Sd eff & mus score; b&w. 35mm. 75 min.
Sd Vers Prod Sidney Tager.
Note: A Chaplin film originally released in Nov 1914 as *Tillie's Punctured Romance;* c4 Dec 1914; LU4875.

CHARLY   **F6.0751**
Selmur Pictures–Robertson Associates. *Dist* Cinerama Releasing Corp. 23 Sep **1968** [New York opening]. Sd; col (Technicolor). 35mm (Techniscope). 106 min.
A Ralph Nelson Production. *Prod-Dir* Ralph Nelson. *Exec Prod* Selig J. Seligman. *Screenplay* Stirling Silliphant. *Dir Photog* Arthur J. Ornitz. *Camera Op* Victor Kemper. *Art Dir* Charles Rosen. *Set Decor* Clint Marshall. *Titl & Montage* Richard Kuhn. *Film Ed* Fredric Steinkamp. *Mus Comp, Dir & Perf* by Ravi Shankar. *Sd Dir* Jim Shields. *Asst Dir* Louis A. Stroller, Mike Blum. *Prod Asst* Steve Mussman, Burt Bluestein. *Asst to the Prod* Doris Quinlan. *Script Supv* Betty Todd. *Prod Mgr* Henry Spitz. *Wardrobe* Hazel Roy. *Makeup* Vincent Kehoe. *Prop Master* Conrad Brink. *Gaffer* Norman Leigh. *Key Grip* Walter Engels.
Cast: Cliff Robertson (*Charly Gordon*), Claire Bloom (*Alice Kinian*), Lilia Skala (*Dr. Anna Straus*), Leon Janney (*Dr. Richard Nemur*), Dick Van Patten (*Bert*), William Dwyer (*Joey*), Ed McNally (*Gimpy*), Dan Morgan (*Paddy*), Barney Martin (*Hank*), Ruth White (*Mrs. Apple*), Frank Dolan (*Eddie*), Ralph Nelson (*convention speaker*).
Drama. Source: Daniel Keyes, *Flowers for Algernon* (New York, 1966). Charly Gordon, a retarded 30-year-old with the mind of a child, works as a sweeper in a Boston bakery, where he is often the victim of cruel jokes made by co-workers whom he considers his best friends. In a fruitless attempt to better himself, he diligently attends evening classes taught by Alice Kinian. Touched and impressed by Charly's intense desire to learn, Alice arranges to have him examined by Dr. Richard Nemur, a neurosurgeon, and Dr. Anna Straus, a psychiatrist. The two doctors have surgically cured mentally defective mice and are looking for a human subject. In his initial tests, Charly scores lower than Algernon, a mouse; but after experimental surgery, Charley rapidly improves, and his operation is considered a success. He quits the bakery job to devote all of his time to his studies, and his mental capacity soon reaches genius proportions. Charly develops slower emotionally, however; and, misinterpreting Alice's attentions, he tries forcibly to make love to her. Shamed by the rebuff, Charly runs away and briefly assumes a hippy lifestyle. When he returns to resume his studies, he has clearly become a mature adult. Charly and Alice then realize that they are in love, and they spend a idyllic holiday together before Charly is scheduled to speak to a gathering of distinguished scientists. Before going on stage, however, Charly discovers that Algernon is dead, and the other experimental mice have begun to revert to their former mental states. Aware that he probably faces a similar fate, Charly startles the assembly with a bitter attack on modern civilization. Although Dr. Nemur and Dr. Straus desperately attempt to prevent his regression, it soon becomes apparent that their efforts are in vain. Finally recognizing defeat, Charly returns to his room to face it alone, despite Alice's pleas that she be allowed to remain with him. *Schoolteachers. Surgeons. Psychiatrists. Scientists. Mental retardation. Self-confidence. Brain surgery. Experiments. Education. Bakeries. Boston. Mice.*
Note: Filmed on location in and around Boston; split-screen techniques are used in several sequences. The original story ("Flowers for Algernon," in *The Magazine of Fantasy and Science Fiction*, Apr 1959) was first produced in 1961 as *The Two Worlds of Charly Gordon* on CBS-TV's "U. S. Steel Hour" and starred Cliff Robertson in the original role of Charly.

CHARRO!   **F6.0752**
National General Pictures. 13 Mar **1969** [San Antonio, Texas, opening]. Sd; col (Technicolor). 35mm (Panavision). 98 min. *MPAA rating* G.
Pres by Cinema Center Films. *Prod-Dir-Writ* Charles Marquis Warren. *Exec Prod* Harry A. Caplan. *Assoc Prod* Dink Templeton. *Story* Frederic Louis Fox. *Dir Photog* Ellsworth Fredricks. *Art Dir* James Sullivan. *Set Decor* Charles Thompson. *Film Ed* Al Clark. *Post Prod Ed Supv* Jack Kirschner. *Mus Comp & Cond* Hugo Montenegro. *Titl Song* (see note) Marilyn Bergman, Alan Bergman, Billy Strange, Scott Davis. *Sung by* Elvis Presley. *Sd Mix* Roy

Meadows. *Sd Rec* Urey Kauk. *Mus Ed* John Mick. *1st & 2d Asst Dir* Dink Templeton, Les Sheldon, Joe Nayfack. *Unit Prod Mgr* Maurie M. Suess. *Makeup* William Reynolds, makeup. *Sp Eff* George C. Thompson, Woodrow Ward, Robert Beck. *Dial Dir* Roy Lindberg.
Cast: Elvis Presley (*Jess Wade*), Ina Balin (*Tracy*), Victor French (*Vince*), Barbara Werle (*Sara Ramsey*), Lynn Kellogg (*Marcie*), Solomon Sturges (*Billy Roy*), Paul Brinegar (*Opie Keetch*), James Sikking (*Gunner*), Harry Landers (*Heff*), Tony Young (*Lieutenant Rivera*), James Almanzar (*Sheriff Ramsey*), Charles H. Gray (*Mody*), Rodd Redwing (*Lige*), Garry Walberg (*Martin Tilford*), Duane Grey (*Gabe*), J. Edward McKinley (*Henry Carter*), John Pickard (*Jerome Selby*), Robert Luster (*Will Joslyn*), Christa Lang (*Christa*), Robert Karnes (*Harvey, the bartender*).
Western melodrama. In 1870, reformed outlaw Jess Wade is tricked into believing that his former girl friend Tracy urgently wants to see him. Riding into a small Mexican border town, Jess is captured by the band of outlaws, led by Vince and his deranged brother Billy Roy, that he had abandoned a year before in order to lead an honest life. Jess is taken to the gang's mountain hideout and shown the legendary Victory Gun—the cannon that fired the last shot against Maximilian and won freedom for Mexico—as well as a counterfeit poster proclaiming that he is wanted dead or alive by both Mexico and the United States for the theft of the cannon. Jess manages to get away, and he seeks safety in the village of Rio Seco, where Tracy operates the local saloon and Sheriff Ramsey is a trusted friend. Billy Roy appears on the scene and seriously wounds the sheriff in a gunfight. After subduing Billy Roy and dragging him off to jail, Jess arms the townspeople for a possible attack by Vince's gang. But Vince eliminates outside reinforcements by ambushing a platoon of Mexican cavalry, and he threatens to turn the Victory Gun on Rio Seco unless Billy Roy is freed. To back up his warning, Vince fires several shots that topple the church steeple and kill Sheriff Ramsey. Jess takes Billy Roy up to the mountain hideout when the panic-stricken citizens insist that the prisoner be released. During the fighting that ensues, several gang members are slain, and Billy Roy is killed when the wagon holding the cannon breaks loose and crushes him. Jess takes the defeated prisoner and drives the cannon wagon back into Rio Seco. Although the grateful townspeople ask Jess to remain on as sheriff, he declines, stating that he must take the cannon and Vince back to Mexico. Before riding out of town, however, Jess promises Tracy that he will send for her. *Outlaws. Saloon keepers. Sheriffs. Gangs. Criminals—Rehabilitation. Frameup. Theft. Blackmail. Ordnance. Jails. Mexican border. Mexico—Army. Documentation.*
Note: Filmed on location in Arizona at Superstition Mountain and Apache Junction. Sources conflict in crediting title song: press material lists Alan and Marilyn Bergman as lyricists, while the music copyright register credits words and music by Billy Strange and Scott Davis.

THE CHASE   **F6.0753**
Lone Star Pictures–Horizon Pictures. *Dist* Columbia Pictures. 17 Feb **1966** [Boston opening; c1 Feb 1966; LP32290]. Sd (RCA); col (Technicolor). 35mm (Panavision). 135 min. [Copyright length: 132 min.]
Prod Sam Spiegel. *Dir* Arthur Penn. *2d Unit Dir* James Havens. *Screenplay* Lillian Hellman. *Dir Photog* Joseph La Shelle. *Camera Op* William Lloyd Norton. *Asst Camera* Bob Hosler, Eugene Lenoir. *Adtl Photog* Robert Surtees. *Art Dir* Robert Luthardt. *Set Decor* Frank Tuttle. *Prod Dsgn* Richard Day. *Main Titl* Maurice Binder. *Film Ed* Gene Milford. *Mus Comp & Cond* John Barry. *Sd Supv* Charles J. Rice. *Sd* James Z. Flaster. *Mus Rec* Eric Tomlinson. *Sd Dub* John Cox. *Rec* Harold Lee. *Boom Op* Doug Grant. *Asst Dir* Russell Saunders, Bob Templeton, C. M. Florance. *Unit Prod Mgr* Joe Wonder. *Script Supv* Marshall Schlom. *Cost Dsgn* Donfeld. *Wardrobe* Seth Banks, Jim George, Marie Osborne, Virginia Pherrin. *Makeup Supv* Ben Lane. *Makeup* Harry Maret. *Hairstyles* Virginia Jones. *Sp Eff* David Koehler. *Still Photog* John Monte. *Prop* Clarence Peet, Bill Kantor. *Gaffer* Seldon White. *Constr Coörd* Ed Shanley.
Cast: Marlon Brando (*Sheriff Calder*), Jane Fonda (*Anna Reeves*), Robert Redford (*Bubber Reeves*), E. G. Marshall (*Val Rogers*), Angie Dickinson (*Ruby Calder*), Janice Rule (*Emily Stewart*), Miriam Hopkins (*Mrs. Reeves*), Martha Hyer (*Mary Fuller*), Richard Bradford (*Damon Fuller*), Robert Duvall (*Edwin Stewart*), James Fox (*Jason "Jake" Rogers*), Diana Hyland (*Elizabeth Rogers*), Henry Hull (*Briggs*), Jocelyn Brando (*Mrs. Briggs*), Katherine Walsh (*Verna Dee*), Lori Martin (*Cutie*), Marc Seaton (*Paul*), Paul H. Williams (*Seymour*), Clifton James (*Lem*), Malcolm Atterbury (*Mr. Reeves*), Nydia Westman (*Mrs. Henderson*), Joel Fluellen (*Lester Johnson*), Steve Ihnat (*Archie*), Maurice Manson (*Moore*), Bruce Cabot (*Sol*), Stephen Whittaker (*Slim*), Pamela Curran (*Mrs. Sifftifieus*), Ken Renard (*Sam*), Eduardo Ciannelli, Richard Collier (*guests at Rogers' party*), Grady Sutton (*Mr. Sifftifieus*), Amy Fonda (*young Anna in photograph*), Ralph Moody, George Winters, Howard Wright, Monte Hale, Mel Gallagher, Ray Galvin, Davis Roberts.
Drama. Source: Horton Foote, *The Chase* (New York, 1956). Horton Foote, *The Chase* (New York opening: 15 Apr 1952). Tarl, a Texas town virtually

owned by wealthy banker Val Rogers, is thrown into an uproar when it is learned that Bubber Reeves has escaped from the state penitentiary with another convict. The latter kills a motorist for his car and clothing and then leaves Bubber to shift for himself. Some of the Tarl residents believe Bubber guilty but others think him innocent. One of these is Sheriff Calder, who feels that Bubber will try to come home. The gossip, speculations, and predictions about Bubber's fate serve as the catalyst that alters the lives of some of the townspeople. There is his unfaithful wife, Anna, who has been having an affair with her husband's best friend, Jake, the only son of Rogers, who is himself unhappily married. Also affected are Calder's wife, Ruby, who devotedly tries to guide and protect her husband; Emily Stewart, the bored wife of the bank vice-president, who openly admits her sexual feelings for her husband's colleague Damon Fuller; and the latter's wife, Mary, driven to alcoholism by her loveless marriage. After a wild birthday party for Rogers, Sheriff Calder is mercilessly beaten by those opposing his strict maintenance of law and order. At the same time, Bubber arrives in town and seeks help from his wife and Jake Rogers. The news leaks out that he is hiding in an auto junkyard, and the whole town goes there to smoke him out. During the confusion, Jake is fatally injured by a gasoline explosion. Calder takes Bubber into custody and is leading him to jail when one of the town troublemakers, Archie, kills the young fugitive. Calder thrashes Archie, but Calder, aware that the situation is hopeless, leaves town with his wife to seek a better place to live. *Bankers. Prison escapees. Sheriffs. Vigilantes. Wealth. Murder. Law and order. Marriage. Infidelity. Alcoholism. Smalltown life. Manhunts. Texas. Explosions. Chases.*

CHASING TWO HARES see **A KIEV COMEDY**

LA CHASSE À L'HOMME see **MALE HUNT**

CHASTITY   F6.0754

Progress Motion Pictures. *Dist* American International Pictures. Jun **1969**. Sd; col (Berkey Pathé). 35mm. 85 min. *MPAA rating* R.

A Sonny Bono Production. *Prod-Writ* Sonny Bono. *Dir* Alessio De Paola. *Photog* Ben Coleman. *Film Ed* Hugo Grimaldi. *Mus Comp* Sonny Bono. *Mus Arr & Cond* Don Peake. *Sd* Gilbert D. Marchant, Duane Hensel. *Asst Dir* William Lukather. *Prod Coörd* Frank Leonetti. *Cost* Sadie Hayes. *Makeup* Stanley Campbell. *Hairstyles* Ray Foreman.

Cast: Cher (*Chastity*), Barbara London (*Diana Midnight*), Stephen Whittaker (*Eddie*), Tom Nolan (*Tommy*), Danny Zapien (*cab driver*), Elmer Valentine (*1st truckdriver*), Burke Rhind (*salesman*), Richard Armstrong (*husband*), Joe Light (*master of ceremonies*), Dolly Hunt (*church lady*), Jason Clarke (*2d truckdriver*), Autumn.

Drama. Unhappy with her life but unable or unwilling to confront the reasons for her unhappiness, a young woman who calls herself Chastity hitchhikes through the Southwest. Determined to live up to the name she has chosen for herself, she cruelly rebuffs a friendly truckdriver and then accepts a ride from Eddie, a young law student. Though he gives her a bed for the night and makes no physical demands upon her, Chastity runs away from him, takes $5 from a gas station, steals a car, and eventually hitches a ride to Mexico. Following an encounter with a cab driver who is a procurer, she visits a bordello owned by Diana Midnight and cheats a gullible young man out of his money by getting him to pay for an evening of "sexual entertainment" which never progresses beyond washing his hair. Despite the use of Diana's beach house, Chastity once more takes to the road when she discovers that her patroness is a lesbian. Returning to Eddie in the middle of the night, she spends some time with him but leaves abruptly the next morning. Chastity recalls her past and the trauma of her early home life, with its incestuous overtones. Racing to the highway, she stands there with tears streaming down her face as another truck driver pulls over to offer her a ride. *Hitchhikers. Prostitutes. Pimps. Truckdrivers. Law students. Chastity. Theft. Duplicity. Lesbianism. Incest. Whorehouses. Mexico.*

THE CHASTITY BELT see **ON MY WAY TO THE CRUSADES, I MET A GIRL WHO ...**

LE CHAT DANS LE SAC see **THE CAT IN THE SACK**

CHÂTEAU EN SUÈDE see **NUTTY, NAUGHTY CHATEAU**

CHAUD LES SECRETS see **DEAD RUN**

CHE!   F6.0755

Sy Bartlett-Richard Fleischer. *Dist* Twentieth Century-Fox Film Corp. 29 May **1969** [New York opening; c29 May 1969; LP36853]. Sd (Westrex); col (DeLuxe). 35mm (Panavision). 96 min. *MPAA rating* M.

Prod Sy Bartlett. *Dir* Richard Fleischer. *Screenplay* Michael Wilson, Sy Bartlett. *Story* Sy Bartlett, David Karp. *Dir Photog* Charles Wheeler. *Art Dir* Jack Martin Smith, Arthur Lonergan. *Prod Illus* Fred Harpman. *Set Decor* Walter M. Scott, Stuart A. Reiss. *Film Ed* Marion Rothman. *Mus Comp & Cond* Lalo Schifrin. *Sd* Don Bassman, David Dockendorf. *Asst Dir* Richard

Glassman. *Unit Prod Mgr* David Hall. *Makeup Supv* Dan Striepeke. *Makeup Artist* Del Acevedo. *Hairstyles* Edith Lindon. *Sp Photog Eff* L. B. Abbott, Art Cruickshank, John C. Caldwell.

Cast: Omar Sharif (*Che Guevara*), Jack Palance (*Fidel Castro*), Cesare Danova (*Ramon Valdez*), Robert Loggia (*Faustino Morales*), Woody Strode (*Guillermo*), Barbara Luna (*Anita Marquez*), Frank Silvera (*goatherd*), Albert Paulsen (*Captain Vasquez*), Linda Marsh (*Tania*), Tom Troupe (*Felipe Muñoz*), Rudy Diaz (*Willy*), Perry Lopez (*Rolando*), Abraham Sofaer (*Pablo Rojas*), Richard Angarola (*Colonel Salazar*), Sarita Vara (*Celia Sanchez*), Paul Bertoya (*Raul Castro*), Sid Haig (*Antonio*), Adolph Caesar (*Juan Almeida*), Paul Picerni (*Hector*), Ray Martell (*Camilo Cienfuegos*), Valentin De Vargas (*Captain Flores*), Miguel Suarez (*guide*), Jess Franco (*Sergeant Terraza*).

Biographical drama. In 1956 Fidel Castro and a band of 82 rebel fighters land on the Cuban coast and begin waging guerrilla warfare against the military forces of President Batista. Included among the rebels is Ernesto "Che" Guevara, a young Argentine doctor who, despite periodic asthma attacks, soon proves his mettle as a guerrilla fighter. As additional volunteers join the small army, Che assumes leadership of a patrol, delegating the medical supervision to nurse Anita Marquez, and proves himself to be such a brilliant tactician in jungle fighting, as well as a stern disciplinarian, that Castro makes him his chief advisor. When the guerrillas, after 2 years of fighting, finally defeat Batista's troops and march triumphantly into Havana, Che directs the massive reprisals, explaining to Castro that he is preventing a larger bloodbath by taking vengeance out of the hands of the people. Before long, Che becomes bored with directing affairs of state and dreams of starting another revolution encompassing all of South America. In 1962, when Castro backs down during the U. S.-Russian missile crisis, Che accuses the dictator of being a puppet of the Soviet Union, and 3 years later, despite Castro's pleadings, Che leaves Cuba. Traveling incognito to Bolivia, Che joins forces with another revolutionary, Tania, and begins a new guerrilla campaign. But the movement fails to win popular support from the peasants, and Che's starving troops are forced to steal food from the same people they are trying to liberate. They are eventually caught in an ambush by a Bolivian Army patrol; Tania is killed, Che is wounded and captured, and the revolution goes down in defeat. Che is taken to a village schoolhouse, and there an army officer confronts him with an old peasant who says that all the people really want is to be left alone. Then, without a trial, Che is shot to death on October 9, 1967. The next day his corpse is shown to the press along with reports that Che Guevara was killed in a battle between his guerrillas and Bolivian Army rangers. *Guerrillas. Physicians. Argentineans. Revolutionaries. Cuba—History—1958 Revolution. Cuban Missile Crisis 1962. Havana. Bolivia. Fidel Castro Ruz. Ernesto "Che" Guevara. Fulgencio Batista y Zaldívar.*

Note: Location scenes filmed in Puerto Rico.

EL CHE GUEVARA (Italy)   F6.0756

Inducine. *Dist* RAF Industries. 11 Jun **1969** [Philadelphia opening]. Sd; col (Eastman Color). 35mm. 89 min. *MPAA rating* G.

Assoc Prod Enrico Verga, Corrado Ferlaino. *Dir* Paolo Heusch. *Story-Screenplay* Adriano Bolzoni. *Dir Photog* Luciano Trasatti. *Art Dir* Piero Filippone. *Film Ed* Eugenio Alabiso. *Mus* Nico Fidenco. *Prod Supv* Lucio Bompani. *Cost* Rosalba Menichelli.

Cast: Francisco Rabal (*Che Guevara*), John Ireland (*CIA Agent Stuart*), Jack Stuart (*Prado*), Susanna Martinkova (*Simona*), Howard Ross (*Pepe*), Empedocle Buzzanca (*Soto*), Remo De Angelis (*Chino*), Sergio Doria (*Clemente*), Corinne Fontaine (*Efisia*), Guido Lollobrigida (*Vicente*), Andrea Checchi (*Selnich*), Vittorio Sanipoli (*Ayoroa*), Lex Monson (*Acacio*), Piero Morgia (*Willy*), Romano Moschini (*Sebastian*), Giancarlo Prete (*Miranda*), Gianni Pulone (*sergeant*), Andrea Scotti (*Ramirez*), Raf Sparanero (*Aguilera*), José Torres (*Ruiz*).

Biographical melodrama. Source: Adriano Bolzoni, *El Chè Guevara* (Rome, 1967). In Bolivia, Cuban guerrilla Che Guevara and his comrades are attempting to incite a Marxist revolution, despite the apathy of the civilian population. After embarrassing the Bolivian army and frustrating the CIA, Che is pursued through the jungles and finally captured in a battle. On orders from La Paz, the military unofficially executes him on 9 October 1967 so that he will not appear to be a martyr and further strain delicate Latin American foreign relations. *Cubans. Guerrillas. Revolutionaries. Marxism. Jungles. Bolivia. Ernesto "Che" Guevara. United States—Central Intelligence Agency.*

Note: Location scenes filmed in Sardinia. Released in Italy in 1968; running time: 95 min. Jack Stuart is a pseudonym for Giacomo Rossi Stuart; Howard Ross for Renato Rossini.

CHÉ IS ALIVE see **DIALOGO CON CHÉ**

THE CHEATERS (France/Italy)   F6.0757

Silver Films–Cinétel–Zebra Film. *Dist* Continental Distributing, Inc. 4 Jun **1961** [New York opening]. Sd; b&w. 35mm. 117 min.

Prod Robert Dorfmann. *Dir* Marcel Carné. *Dial* Jacques Sigurd. *Adapt* Marcel Carné, Jacques Sigurd. *Story* Charles Spaak. *Photog* Claude Renoir. *Art Dir* Paul Bertrand. *Film Ed* Albert Jurgenson. *Jazz Recordings* Maxime Saury, Ray Brown, Roy Eldridge, Herb Ellis, mus, Stan Getz, Dizzy Gillespie, Coleman Hawkins, Gus Johnson, Oscar Peterson, Sonny Stitt, Norman Granz. *Sd* Antoine Archimbaud. *Asst Dir* Serge Friedman, Paul Seban. *Prod Mgr* Louis Wipf. *Cost* Mayo. *Gowns* Christian Dior, Heim, Virginie.

Cast: Jacques Charrier (*Bob Letellier*), Pascale Petit (*Mic*), Andréa Parisy (*Clo*), Laurent Terzieff (*Alain*), Roland Lesaffre (*Roger*), Dany Saval (*Nicole*), Jacques Portet (*Guy*), Pierre Brice (*Bernard*), Alfunso Mathis (*Peter*), Jean-Paul Belmondo (*Lou*), Denise Vernac (*Mic's mother*), Roland Armontel.

Melodrama. Bob Letellier, a student from a well-to-do family, drifts into the company of a group of Left Bank Parisians united by a common determination to defy social and moral conventions. At a party given by Clo, the promiscuous daughter of an aristocratic family, the young people dance to American jazz records. Bob gets drunk, is seduced by his hostess, and afterwards becomes enamored of her best friend, nicknamed Mic. The attraction is mutual, but the couple hide their romantic feelings since the code of the group denies the existence of love. Mic becomes involved in a blackmail scheme that will bring her enough money to realize her life's ambition—to purchase a British sports car. Bob's reluctance to assist in the project is interpreted as cowardice by Mic. Finally he goes through with the scheme, but when he delivers the money he finds Mic in bed with the cynical Alain. Outraged, Bob hurls the money at Mic, denounces her, and storms out. A short time later, he and Mic meet at another of Clo's parties. The group play the "game of truth," in which they are cross-examined by Alain. Eager to hurt Bob, Mic states that Alain is a much better lover than Bob. Bob counters by denying that he ever loved Mic and then announces that he will marry the pregnant Clo. Stunned, Mic rushes out of the apartment and speeds off in her car. Bob races after her, screaming that he cheated at the game of truth. Mic cannot hear him, however, and she is killed as her car crashes into a gasoline truck. *Students. Youth. Promiscuity. Bohemianism. Blackmail. Drunkenness. Jealousy. Alienation. Jazz. Sports cars. Paris. Automobile accidents.*

Note: Paris opening: Oct 1958 as *Les tricheurs*; running time: 125 min. Rome opening: Jan 1959 as *Peccatori in blue-jeans*; running time: 95 min.

CHEATING ITALIAN STYLE see ALL THE OTHER GIRLS DO

CHECKERBOARD (France/Italy)   F6.0758
Zodiaque Productions–Lodice–Globe Films International. *Dist* American Film Distributing Corp. Feb **1969**. Sd; b&w. 35mm. 105 min.

Pres by Stan Borden. *Assoc Prod* Emile Darbel. *Dir-Writ* Claude Bernard-Aubert. *Dial* Claude Accursi. *Dir Photog* Jean Isnard. *Camera* Robert Schneider, Robert Alliel, Jean Collomb. *Art Dir* J.-Paul Coutan-Laboureur. *Asst Art Dir* Robert Taillandier. *Film Ed* Gabriel Rongier. *Asst Film Ed* André Davanture. *Mus* André Hodeir. *Sd* André Louis. *Sd Rec* Urbain Loiseau. *Sd Boom* Alexis Bodik. *Asst Dir* Raoul Sangla. *Prod Mgr* Louis Manella. *Location Mgr* Pierre Vouillon. *Script Girl* Geneviève Cortier. *Prod Sec* Ginette Heftler. *Cost* Catherine Giboyau. *Makeup* Serge Groffe. *Prop* Emile Dechelle. *Still Photog* François Dieudonné.

Cast: Jacques Richard (*Bob Stanley*), Toto Bissainthe (*Bessie Vance*), Samba Ababaka (*Vance*), Grégoire Aslan (*Stanley*), Roger Blin, Nico Pepe, Doudou Babet, Anne Carrère, Guy Tréjan, Douta Seck, Alice Sapritch, Lucien Raimbourg, Hubert de Lapparent, Mara Berni, Milly Vitale, Nicole Dieudonné, André Certes, Théo Bipolet, Lud Germain, Paul Bisciglia, J.-P. Dréan, Jacques Bézard, Bob Ingarao, Alain Roulleau.

Melodrama. In the racially segregated desert town of Cicada, Bob, a former paratrooper, and Bessie, a black woman, fall in love. The townspeople violently oppose the affair, and there is a confrontation between the lovers' fathers. Although the two men prepare to fight in the desert, their hatred dissolves when they discover a spring. They return to the town with the hope of bringing the people together. Spurned by the populace, the two families leave to form their own community. *Negroes. Racial prejudice. Smalltown life. Filial relations. Miscegenation. Deserts. Springs.*

Note: Location scenes filmed in and around Causses, Millau, and Nice. Released in Paris in May 1959 as *Les tripes au soleil*; in Rome in Sep 1959 as *Questione di pelle*.

THE CHECKERED FLAG   F6.0759
Guild Studios 5 Inc. *Dist* Motion Picture Investors, Mercury Pictures. 29 May **1963** [Kansas City, Missouri, opening]. Sd; col (Eastman Color). 35mm. 110 min. [Also reviewed at 83 min.]

A Herb Vendig Production. *Prod* Herb Vendig. *Dir-Writ* William Grefé. *Photog* J. R. Remy. *Art Dir* Ken Miller. *Film Ed* Edward B. Mulloy. *Orig Mus* Alice Simms. *Songs:* "*Bikini Baby,*" "*Hip-So Calypso,*" "*(Take Me) Far Away*" Alice Simms. *Song:* "*Coconut, Fall on de Head*" Alice Simms, George Symonette. *Sd* Edward B. Mulloy.

Cast: Charles G. Martin (*Rutherford*), Evelyn King (*Bo Rutherford, his wife*), Joe Morrison (*Bill Garrison*), Peggy Vendig (*Ginger*).

Action melodrama. Bo Rutherford, the alcoholic wife of a millionaire playboy and racing car driver, is threatened with divorce because of her many adulterous affairs. She entices Bill Garrison, a new driver on the circuit, to help plot Rutherford's death so she can inherit his fortune. The first attempts fail, and Rutherford and Garrison become friends temporarily at a drunken outing with two women; tempers flare the next morning, however, and the two men are bitter enemies by the next race. Their cars crash on the track, and Rutherford is killed; Bill loses both legs, and Bo is disfigured and blinded in an explosion when she tries to rescue him. Although the crippled lovers can now live a wealthy life together, Bill is determined to end it for both of them. *Millionaires. Playboys. Cripples. Automobile racing. Infidelity. Murder. Alcoholism. Disfiguration. Blindness. Amputation. Automobile accidents. Explosions.*

Note: Filmed in the Bahamas and in Sebring and Miami, Florida.

CHELKASH (U.S.S.R.)   F6.0760
Mosfilm. *Dist* Artkino Pictures. 25 Jan **1964** [New York opening]. Sd; b&w. 35mm. 45 min.

Dir Fyodor Filippov. *Screenplay* A. Simukov. *Photog* Era Savelyeva. *Art Dir* Ye. Chernyayev. *Film Ed* V. Massino. *Mus* I. Boldyrev. *Lyr* Maxim Gorky. *Cond* A. Roytman. *Sd* A. Pavlov. *Artistic Supv* Mikhail Romm. *Prod Mgr* V. Biyazi. *Cost* A. Danduryan. *Makeup* A. Maslova. *Sp Eff* N. Renkov, F. Krasnyy.

Cast: Andrey Popov (*Chelkash*), Viktor Matveyev (*Gavrila*), Aleksey Boyko (*Semyonych*).

Melodrama. Source: Maxim Gorky, "Chelkash," in *Russkoye bogatstvo* (no. 6, 1895). Chelkash, a well-known tramp and thief on the waterfront of a southern port, meets Gavrila, a simple young peasant. Gavrila, hoping to earn enough money to return to his village a free and independent man, accepts Chelkash's offer of a night's employment as an oarsman. Not until he has rowed out to sea with Chelkash does he realize that he is an accomplice in a robbery, and he is filled with fear. Chelkash warns him to keep silent and talks with him about the good peasant life. When they return to shore, the boat laden with goods stolen from a warehouse, Chelkash visits a smuggler. With the profits from the theft he pays Gavrila handsomely, but greed has now been awakened in the young man. Chelkash's plan to spend the remaining money in one night of revelry makes Gavrila mad with frustration, and he yearns to keep the entire sum for himself. They struggle, and, in a rage, Gavrila throws a rock at the departing Chelkash, knocking him to the ground. Terrified at what he has done, the young peasant drops to his knees and begs forgiveness. With disdain, Chelkash flings the money at the corrupted young man. *Peasants. Tramps. Theft. Greed. Moral corruption. Waterfronts. Rowboats.*

Note: Released in the U.S.S.R. in Jun 1957.

CHELOVEK IDYOT ZA SOLNTSEM see SANDU FOLLOWS THE SUN

THE CHELSEA GIRLS   F6.0761
Andy Warhol. *Dist* Film-Makers' Cooperative, Film-Makers' Distribution Center, Andy Warhol Films. 15 Sep **1966** [New York opening]. Sd; b&w and col (Eastman Color). 2 × 16mm (see note). 195 min. [General release version: 205 min; also reviewed at 210 min.]

Prod-Dir Andy Warhol. "*Hanoi Hanna*" and other unspecified segments writ by Ronald Tavel. *Photog* Andy Warhol. *Mus* The Velvet Underground. *Prod Asst* Paul Morrissey. *Strobe Lighting for "The Trip" and "Their Town" Segments* Billy Linich.

Cast—"The Pope Ondine Story": Ondine ("*Pope*"), Angelina "Pepper" Davis, Ingrid Superstar, Albert René Ricard, Mary Might, International Velvet, Ronna.

Cast—"The Duchess": Brigid Polk.

Cast—"The John": Ed Hood (*Ed*), Patrick Flemming (*Patrick*), Mario Montez (*transvestite*), Angelina "Pepper" Davis, International Velvet, Mary Might, Gerard Malanga, Albert René Ricard, Ingrid Superstar.

Cast—"Hanoi Hanna (Queen of China)": Mary Might (*Hanoi Hanna*), International Velvet, Ingrid Superstar, Angelina "Pepper" Davis.

Cast—"The Gerard Malanga Story": Marie Menken ("*mother*"), Gerard Malanga ("*son*"), Mary Might (*girl friend*).

Cast—"The Trip" and "Their Town (Toby Short)": Eric Emerson.

Cast—"Afternoon": Edie Sedgwick (*Edie*), Ondine, Arthur Loeb, Donald Lyons, Dorothy Dean.

Cast—"The Closet": Nico, Randy Borscheidt.

Cast—Reel 1: Nico, Eric Emerson, Ari.

Experimental film. (Reel 1) In a small apartment kitchen, Nico cuts her hair, converses with her boyfriend, Eric, and plays with her son, Ari. (Reel 2) THE POPE ONDINE STORY: A self-proclaimed "pope" receives penitents and complains of his weighty responsibilities as a patriarch. Ingrid discusses her sex life with him. He grows tired of remaining in front of the camera. (Reel 3) THE DUCHESS: A young woman gives herself an amphetamine injection while discussing Andy Warhol with a friend over the telephone. (Reel 4) THE JOHN: Ed lounges on a bed, fussing and bickering with Patrick, an Irish youth whom he has just picked up. They are interrupted by friends and neighbors. (Reel 5) HANOI HANNA (QUEEN OF CHINA): Hanoi Hanna subjects the other women to sadistic verbal and physical games. (Reel 6) Hanoi Hanna continues her onslaught as another woman enters the group. (Reel 7) Ed and Patrick are interrupted by Mario, a transvestite, who insists on entertaining them and sings two songs. The youths' objections become increasingly insulting, and Mario departs in a huff. (Reel 8) THE GERARD MALANGA STORY (col): A young man is lectured at length by his "mother," as his girl friend looks on in silence. (Reel 9) THE TRIP (col): A young man on an LSD trip discourses on his sexuality, fondles himself, and teasingly removes his clothes as colored lights are projected over his body. (Reel 10) THEIR TOWN (TOBY SHORT) (col): The young man appears with the group of actors in the colors of a light show. (Reel 11) After injecting himself with methedrine, Pope Ondine receives a final penitent. She calls him a phony, thereby enraging him; he shouts verbal abuse, slaps her, and chases her around the room as persons off-camera attempt to calm him. (Reel 12) Nico, alone in her room, lies on a bed and cries to herself. Toward the end of the reel, soft rock music is heard on the soundtrack. [This description refers to the general release version; running time: 205 min. Advertisements for the New York opening refer to the following segments: "Room 723—Pope Ondine," "Room 422—The Gerard Malanga Story," "Room 946—George's Room," "Room 202—Afternoon," "Room 116—Hanoi Hanna," "Room 632—The John," "Room 416—The Trip," "Room 822—The Closet." GEORGE'S ROOM remains unidentified. In AFTERNOON, Edie entertains friends in her room. THE CLOSET involves two "children" who live in a closet.] Male homosexuality. Lesbianism. Sexuality. Transvestism. Sadomasochism. Urban life. Confession. Filial relations. Narcissism. Hotels. LSD. Amphetamines. Chelsea Hotel (New York City).

Note: A few segments were filmed in the Chelsea Hotel in New York City; most were filmed elsewhere in New York City and in Cambridge, Massachusetts. Uncut reels, each 33–35 minutes in length, were projected side by side; in the general release version, the first reel appeared on the right side of the screen, and a few minutes later, the second reel began on the left. Mary Might is a pseudonym for Mary Woronov; Ingrid Superstar for Ingrid Von Scheven; International Velvet for Susan Bottomly; and Ondine for Bob Olivio.

CHERRY, HARRY & RAQUEL   F6.0762

Panamint Films–Eve Productions. *Dist* Eve Productions. 26 Nov **1969** [Atlanta opening; c7 Nov 1969; LP37261]. Sd; col (DeLuxe). 35mm. 71 min. *MPAA rating X.*

Prod-Dir-Story Russ Meyer. *Assoc Prod* Anthony James Ryan, Thomas J. McGowan, Eve Meyer. *Screenplay* Tom Wolfe, Russ Meyer. *Cinematog* Russ Meyer. *Asst Cinematog* John Koester. *Film Ed* Russ Meyer, Richard Brummer. *Asst Film Ed* Robert Pergament. *Mus* Igo Kantor, William Loose. *Song:* "Toys of Our Time" sung by Jack and the Balls. *Sd* Richard Brummer. *Prod Mgr* Anthony James Ryan. *Asst Prod Mgr* Jacqueline Ryan.

Cast: Larissa Ely *(Raquel)*, Linda Ashton *(Cherry)*, Charles Napier *(Harry)*, Bert Santos *(Enrique)*, Franklin H. Bolger *(Mr. Franklin)*, Astrid Lillimor *(Soul)*, Michele Grand *(Millie)*, John Milo *(Apache)*, Robert Aiken *(Tom)*, Michaelani *(Dr. Lee)*, John Koester *(gas attendant)*, Daniel Roberts *(delivery boy)*, Russ Meyer.

Melodrama. Although confined to an Arizona hospital, Franklin masterminds a massive narcotics operation. From his bed the patient commands his minions, including deputy sheriff Harry, Mexican-American syndicate driver Enrique, English nurse Cherry, and mistress Raquel. Among their assignments is the murder of Apache, an Indian competitor. When Harry and Enrique attempt to ambush the dealer, however, he eludes them. Returning with a marijuana shipment from Mexico, Enrique is waylaid and slain by the Indian. Apache's next victim is Franklin, whom he kills in his hospital bed. Raquel arrives to cheer Franklin and makes love to his corpse before realizing that the invalid is dead. Shocked by the discovery, she rushes to Cherry, who offers her marijuana and love. As Harry and Apache fight to the finish, the entire plot is revealed to have been the product of author Raquel's imagination. *Drug dealers. Masterminds. Sheriffs. Nurses. Apache Indians. Mistresses. Authors. Smuggling. Mexicans. Necrophilia. Lesbianism. Murder. Hospitals. Marijuana. Mexico. Arizona.*

Note: Also known as *Three Ways To Love*. Astrid Lillimor is a pseudonym for Uschi Digart.

CHERRY'S HOUSE OF NUDES   F6.0763

Artists Productions. *Dist* Ascot Productions, Ltd., Gillman Film Corp. 17 Jan **1964** [San Francisco opening]. Sd; col. 35mm. [Feature length assumed.]

Prod Bill Spallas. *Dir* Wade Williams.

Cast: Kathy Fields, [2], Pat Shelley, Earl D'Eon.

Comedy. No information about the precise nature of this film has been found, but press material suggests that it concerns a naive man in a whorehouse. *Prostitution. Innocents. Whorehouses.*

Note: Also known as *Cherry's House* and *Bare With Me*. May also be known as *Sherry's House of Nudes.*

CHERYOMUSHKI *see* SONG OVER MOSCOW

CHEYENNE AUTUMN   F6.0764

Ford–Smith Productions. *Dist* Warner Bros. Pictures. 3 Oct **1964** [Cheyenne, Wyoming, opening; c2 Jan 1965; LP32384]. Sd; col (Technicolor). 35mm & 70mm (Super Panavision 70). 158 min. [See note.]

Prod Bernard Smith. *Dir* John Ford. *Assoc Dir* Ray Kellogg. *Screenplay* James R. Webb. *Dir Photog* William Clothier. *Art Dir* Richard Day. *Set Decor* Darrell Silvera. *Film Ed* Otho Lovering. *Mus Comp & Cond* Alex North. *Sd Ed* Francis E. Stahl. *Sd* Jack Solomon. *Asst Dir* Wingate Smith, Russ Saunders. *Cost Dsgn* Ann B. Peck. *Cost Coörd* Frank Beetson, Sr. *Makeup* Norman Pringle. *Hairstyles* Sherry Wilson, Fae Smith. *Sp Eff* Ralph Webb.

Cast: Richard Widmark *(Capt. Thomas Archer)*, Carroll Baker *(Deborah Wright)*, Karl Malden *(Captain Wessels)*, Sal Mineo *(Red Shirt)*, Dolores Del Rio *(Spanish woman)*, Ricardo Montalban *(Little Wolf)*, Gilbert Roland *(Dull Knife)*, Arthur Kennedy *(Doc Holliday)*, Patrick Wayne *(2d Lieutenant Scott)*, Elizabeth Allen *(Miss Guinevere Plantagenet)*, John Carradine *(Maj. Jeff Blair)*, Victor Jory *(Tall Tree)*, James Stewart *(Wyatt Earp)*, Edward G. Robinson *(Carl Schurz, Secretary of the Interior)*, Mike Mazurki *(Sr. 1st Sgt. Stanislas Wichowsky)*, George O'Brien *(Major Braden)*, Sean McClory *(Dr. O'Carberry)*, Judson Pratt *(Mayor "Dog" Kelly)*, Carmen D'Antonio *(Pawnee woman)*, Ken Curtis *(Joe)*, John Qualen *(Svenson)*, Shug Fisher *(Skinny, trail boss)*, Nancy Hsueh *(Little Bird)*, Walter Baldwin *(Jeremy Wright)*, Chuck Roberson *(platoon sergeant)*, Harry Carey, Jr. *(Trooper Smith)*, Ben Johnson *(Trooper Plumtree)*, Jim O'Hara, Chuck Hayward *(troopers)*, Lee Bradley, Frank Bradley *(Cheyennes)*, Walter Reed *(Lieutenant Peterson)*, Willis Bouchey *(colonel)*, Carleton Young *(aide to Carl Schurz)*, Denver Pyle *(Senator Henry)*, Nanomba "Moonbeam" Morton *(Running Deer)*, Dan Borzage, Dean Smith, David Humphreys Miller, Bing Russell *(troopers)*.

Western epic. Source: Mari Sandoz, *Cheyenne Autumn* (New York, 1953). In the 1870's, the Cheyenne Indians are taken from their Wyoming homelands and moved to a barren Oklahoma reservation. After a year of waiting for Federal aid that never arrives, the original band of 1,000 has been reduced by disease and starvation to a mere 286. Desperate, the survivors decide to make a 1,500-mile trek to their former Yellowstone hunting grounds. Accompanying them is Deborah Wright, a Quaker schoolteacher sympathetic to their plight. And pursuing them is a cavalry troop headed by Captain Thomas Archer, Deborah's betrothed, who hopes to resolve the dilemma without bloodshed. But a young hotheaded Cheyenne brave named Red Shirt precipitates several skirmishes in which U. S. soldiers are killed. When the newspapers play up the incidents by depicting the Cheyennes as "marauding savages," Wyatt Earp and Doc Holliday are pressured into organizing a war party. Earp, however, deliberately leads his drunken posse in the wrong direction and remains on the trail until public panic subsides. With the coming of winter, the Cheyennes split into two groups: half continue their journey; half surrender to the brutal Captain Wessels at Fort Robinson. Upon learning that Wessels intends to march the Indians back to Oklahoma, Captain Archer goes to Washington to seek the help of the Secretary of the Interior. Before he can do so, the Indians revolt, kill Wessels, and flee into the snow. As they are trapped by troops prepared to massacre them, Archer arrives with the Secretary, who negotiates a treaty which permits the Cheyennes to return to their homeland. Once there, Red Shirt and Chief Little Wolf face each other with pistols to settle their dispute over the latter's wife. Red Shirt is killed, and Little Wolf, having broken his vow never to kill another Cheyenne, goes into self-imposed exile. As peace is restored, Archer and Deborah decide to remain with the Indians who have survived the historic ordeal. *Cheyenne Indians. Quakers. Schoolteachers. Soldiers. Racism. Dispossession. Starvation. Murder. Survival. Duels. Winter. Wyoming. Oklahoma. Wyatt Earp. John H. "Doc" Holliday. Carl Schurz. United States—Interior Department. United States Army—Cavalry.*

Note: Location scenes filmed in Utah and Colorado, including Monument Valley. Sources give running times varying from 145 to 170 min.

THE CHEYENNE SOCIAL CLUB   F6.0765

National General Pictures. 12 Jun **1970** [Chicago opening]. Sd; col (Technicolor). 35mm (Panavision). 103 min. *MPAA rating GP.*

Prod-Dir Gene Kelly. *Exec Prod & Screenplay* James Lee Barrett. *Dir Photog* William H. Clothier. *Set Decor* James Hopkins. *Prod Dsgn* Gene Allen. *Main Titl* Pacific Title. *Film Ed* Adrienne Fazan. *Mus & Mus Dir* Walter Scharf. *Songs:* "Rolling Stone," "One Dream" Walter Scharf, Al Kasha,

Joel Hirschhorn. *Song:* "Rolling Stone" sung by James Stewart, Henry Fonda. *Sd* Fred Faust. *Mus Ed* John Mick. *Asst Dir* Paul Helmick. *Unit Prod Mgr* Paul Helmick. *Unit Mgr* Richard Kobritz. *Cost* Yvonne Wood. *Makeup Supv* Frank Westmore. *Hairstyles* Vivienne Walker.

Cast: James Stewart *(John O'Hanlan)*, Henry Fonda *(Harley O'Sullivan)*, Shirley Jones *(Jenny)*, Sue Ane Langdon *(Opal Ann)*, Elaine Devry *(Pauline)*, Robert Middleton *(barman at Great Plains Saloon)*, Arch Johnson *(Marshal Anderson)*, Dabbs Greer *(Willowby)*, Jackie Russell *(Carrie Virginia)*, Jackie Joseph *(Annie Jo)*, Sharon De Bord *(Sara Jean)*, Richard Collier *(Nathan Potter)*, Charles Tyner *(Charlie Bannister)*, Jean Willes *(Alice)*, Robert J. Wilke *(Corey Bannister)*, Carl Reindel *(Pete Dodge)*, J. Pat O'Malley *(Dr. Foy)*, Jason Wingreen *(Dr. Farley Carter)*, John Dehner *(Clay Carroll)*, Hal Baylor *(barman at Lady of Egypt)*, Charlotte Stewart *(Mae)*, Alberto Morin *(ranch foreman)*, Myron Healey *(Deuter)*, Warren Kemmerling *(Kohler)*, Dick Johnstone *(Mr. Yancey)*, Phil Mead *(cook)*, Hi Roberts *(scared man)*, Ed Pennybacker *(teamster)*, Red Morgan *(Hansen)*, Dean Smith, Bill Hicks, Bill Davis, Walt Davis, actor, John Welty *(The Bannister Gang)*.

Western comedy. In 1870, Texas cowboy John O'Hanlan receives a letter from Willowby, a lawyer in Cheyenne, Wyoming, informing him that he has inherited an establishment called the Cheyenne Social Club. O'Hanlan immediately sets out with his close friend Harley O'Sullivan to claim the property, and after a year's journey, he arrives in Cheyenne to receive the accrued profits and set himself up as a man of means and an upright citizen. When he discovers that the Cheyenne Social Club is a brothel, however, he makes plans to fire the women and convert the building into a boardinghouse. The whole town tries to dissuade him; Willowby explains that the house is on railroad property and that he will lose it if he closes it down. When Jenny, the madam of the house, is beaten up by Corey Bannister, O'Hanlan challenges him to a gunfight and, through an improbable stroke of luck, kills him. O'Hanlan and O'Sullivan soon find themselves the object of the Bannister brothers' revenge. Despite their ineptitude as gunfighters, O'Hanlan and O'Sullivan manage to defeat the Bannisters, only to find themselves sought by the entire 200-member Bannister clan. Realizing that their luck is running out, they deed the Cheyenne Social Club to Jenny and hastily leave town. *Cowboys. Lawyers. Prostitutes. Madams. Gunfighters. Revenge. Feuds. Frontier and pioneer life. Inheritance. Whorehouses. Texas. Cheyenne.*

Note: Location scenes filmed in Santa Fe, New Mexico.

CHI NO HATE NI IKURU MONO *see* **THE ANGRY SEA**

CHI TO SUNA *see* **FORT GRAVEYARD**

CHIANG SHAN MEI JEN *see* **THE KINGDOM AND THE BEAUTY**

THE CHICAGO KID *see* **THE FABULOUS BASTARD FROM CHICAGO**

CHICAGO 70　　　　　　　　　　　　　　　　**F6.0766**
Monitor Productions. *Dist* CM. Jun **1970**. Sd; col. 16mm & 35mm. 93 min.
Prod-Dir Kerry Feltham. *Photog* Mogens Gander, Henri Fiks. *Film Ed* Italo Costa, Featherstone Fanshaw.

Cast: Mel Dixon *(Bobby Seale)*, Jim Lawrence *(Mark Lane)*, Calvin Butler *(Arlo Guthrie)*, Neil Walsh *(Mayor Daley/Country Joe)*, George Metesky *(Allen Ginsberg)*, Peter Faulkner *(Abbie Hoffman)*, Diane Grant *(Linda Morse)*, François Klanfer *(DJ)*, Ray Whelan, Rick McKenna, Carol Carrington.

Experimental film. Source: The Toronto Workshop, *Chicago 70* (New York opening: 25 May 1970). This film is an exact representation of the off-Broadway play performed by the Toronto Workshop. The transcript of the "Chicago Seven" conspiracy trial stemming from demonstrations at the 1968 Democratic National Convention is juxtaposed with Lewis Carroll's *Alice in Wonderland*, and the cast members take turns playing the various principals in the trial, including the defendants—Abbie Hoffman, Jerry Rubin, John Froines, Tom Hayden, David Dellinger, Lee Weiner, Rennie Davis and Bobby Seale; the attorneys—William Kunstler and Lenny Weinglass; several witnesses—Mark Lane, Arlo Guthrie, Mayor Richard Daley, Allen Ginsberg, Country Joe McDonald, and Linda Morse; and the presiding judge, Julius Hoffman. The actors improvise much of the action; however, the testimonies of Guthrie, Ginsberg, McDonald, and Abbie Hoffman are taken directly from the transcript. As occurred in the trial, Bobby Seale is bound and gagged by order of Judge Hoffman, thus leaving seven defendants. Throughout the proceedings, members of the cast ride bicycles and hop on pogo sticks in the courtroom. *Judges. Lawyers. Conspiracy. Trials. Demonstrations. Radicalism. Democratic National Convention 1968. Chicago. Abbie Hoffman. Jerry C. Rubin. John R. Froines. Tom Hayden. David T. Dellinger. Lee Weiner. Rennie Davis. Bobby G. Seale. William M. Kunstler. Leonard I. Weinglass. Mark Lane. Arlo Guthrie. Richard J. Daley. Allen Ginsberg. Country Joe McDonald. Linda Morse. Julius J. Hoffman. "Alice in Wonderland". Documentation.*

Note: Filmed in Chicago. Also known as *The Conspiracy Circus—Chicago '70*.

CHICHI TO KO *see* **OUR SILENT LOVE**

CHICHIKO GUSA *see* **GREEN LIGHT TO JOY**

CHIEKO-SHO *see* **PORTRAIT OF CHIEKO**

LES CHIENS DANS LA NUIT *see* **THE GIRL CAN'T STOP**

CHIKUMAGAWA ZESSHO *see* **RIVER OF FOREVER**

A CHILD IS WAITING　　　　　　　　　　　　**F6.0767**
Larcas Productions. *Dist* United Artists. 14 Jan **1963** [Minneapolis opening: c1 Nov 1962; LP23686]. Sd; b&w. 35mm. 102 min.
Prod Stanley Kramer. *Assoc Prod* Philip Langner. *Dir* John Cassavetes. *Orig Screenplay* Abby Mann. *Cinematog* Joseph LaShelle. *Prod Dsgn* Rudolph Sternad. *Film Ed* Gene Fowler, Jr. *Mus* Ernest Gold. *Sd* James Speak. *Asst Dir* Lindsley Parsons, Jr., Douglas Green. *Prod Mgr* Nate H. Edwards.

Cast: Burt Lancaster *(Dr. Matthew Clark)*, Judy Garland *(Jean Hansen)*, Gena Rowlands *(Sophie Widdicombe)*, Steven Hill *(Ted Widdicombe)*, Bruce Ritchey *(Reuben Widdicombe)*, Gloria McGehee *(Mattie)*, Paul Stewart *(Goodman)*, Elizabeth Wilson *(Miss Fogarty)*, Barbara Pepper *(Miss Brown)*, John Marley *(Holland)*, June Walker *(Mrs. McDonald)*, Mario Gallo *(Dr. Lombardi)*, Fred Draper *(Dr. Sack)*, Lawrence Tierney *(Douglas Benham)*.

Drama. Source: Abby Mann, *A Child Is Waiting* (first presented on CBS TV's "Studio One," 11 Mar 1957). Dr. Matthew Clark is the head of a state institution for mentally retarded children. Jean Hansen, a former music teacher anxious to give her life some meaning, joins the staff of the hospital. Jean, who tries to shelter the children with her love, suspiciously regards Clark's stern training methods. She becomes emotionally involved with 12-year-old Reuben Widdicombe, who has been abandoned by his divorced parents. Jean defies Clark by sending for the child's parents when Reuben stubbornly refuses to obey orders. Mrs. Widdicombe, however, concurs with the doctor's decision that it would be damaging for the boy to see her. As she leaves, Reuben catches sight of her and chases her departing car; and the incident so emotionally upsets the boy that he runs away from the school. Clark returns him the next morning, whereupon Jean, realizing her mistake, offers to resign. Clark, however, suggests that she remain on and continue her preparations for a Thanksgiving show in which all the children will participate. On the day of the show, Reuben's father arrives to take his son to a private school; but when he hears Reuben haltingly recite a poem and then respond to the audience's applause, he understands his son's desperate need to achieve something for himself. *Physicians. Music teachers. Children. Mental retardation. Divorce. Parenthood. Hospitals. Thanksgiving Day.*

Note: The children in the film, with the exception of Bruce Ritchey, were patients at the Pacific State Hospital in Pomona, California.

CHILDISH THINGS　　　　　　　　　　　　　**F6.0768**
Filmworld Productions. 2 Jul **1969** [Los Angeles opening]. Sd; col (Eastman Color, print by Pathé). 35mm. 93 min.
A Sinners Co. Production. *Prod-Writ* Don Murray. *Assoc Prod* Maurice Wright. *Dir* John Derek. *Photog* John Derek. *Art Dir* John Harris, art dir. *Main Titl* Cinefx, Phill Norman. *Film Ed* Maurice Wright. *Mus* Joe Greene. *Song Sung by* Rod Lauren. *Sd* Rod Sutton. *Asst Dir* Jonathan Haze.

Cast: Don Murray *(Tom Harris)*, Linda Evans *(Pat Jennings)*, David Brian *(Jennings)*, Angelique Pettyjohn *(Angelique)*, Don Joslyn *(Kelly)*, Gypsy Boots *(Gypsy)*, Rod Lauren *(Rod)*, LeRoy Jenkins *(preacher)*, Logan Ramsey *(Mr. Simmons)*, Erik Holland *(1st fighter)*, Jack Griffin *(Jack)*, Valerie Brooke *(girl)*, Gene LaBelle *(peanut man)*, Ed Bennett *(carousel man)*, Seamon Glass *(ex-fighter)*, George Atkinson *(last fighter)*, Peter Tenen *(Gene)*, Claire Kelly *(Sharon)*.

Melodrama. Tom Harris, a dissolute boxer, ravishes Pat, the innocent 19-year-old daughter of a former alcoholic, and thereafter attempts to court her. Jennings, her father, operates a farm for dipsomaniacs and celebrates annually his own Last Supper. *Boxers. Rape. Alcoholism. Filial relations.*

Note: Filmed in 1966 as *Tale of the Cock*. Location scenes filmed in Los Angeles and Las Vegas.

CHILDREN OF THE DAMNED (Great Britain)　　　**F6.0769**
Metro-Goldwyn-Mayer Pictures. *Dist* Metro-Goldwyn-Mayer, Inc. 29 Jan **1964** [New York opening; c31 Dec 1963; LP26847]. Sd (Westrex); b&w. 35mm. 90 min. [Also reviewed at 81 min.]
A Lawrence P. Bachmann Production. *Assoc Prod* Ben Arbeid. *Exec Prod* Lawrence P. Bachmann. *Dir* Anton M. Leader. *Orig Screenplay* John Briley. *Dir Photog* Davis Boulton. *Art Dir* Elliot Scott. *Film Ed* Ernest Walter. *Mus Comp & Cond* Ron Goodwin. *Rec Supv* A. W. Watkins. *Sd Rec* David Bowen. *Dub Mix* J. B. Smith. *Sd Ed* Allan Sones. *Asst Dir* Ted Sturgis, Terry Lens, Roger Simons. *Prod Mgr* Albert Becket. *Cont* Betty Harley. *Sp Eff* Tom

Howard. *Casting Dir* Irene Howard.

Cast: Ian Hendry (*Dr. Tom Lewellin*), Alan Badel (*Dr. David Neville*), Barbara Ferris (*Susan Eliot*), Alfred Burke (*Colin Webster*), Sheila Allen (*Diana Looran*), Ralph Michael (*Minister of Defense*), Martin Miller (*Professor Gruber*), Harold Goldblatt (*Harib*), Patrick White (*Mr. Davidson*), Andre Mikhelson (*Russian official*), Bessie Love (*Mrs. Robbin*), Tom Bowman (*General Miller*), Clive Powell (*Paul*), Lee Yoke-Moon (*Mi Ling*), Roberta Rex (*Nina*), Gerald Delsol (*Aga*), Mahdu Mathen (*Raschid*), Frank Summerscale (*Mark*).

Science fiction drama. Based on characters created by: John Wyndham. A UNESCO survey reveals six children, all the same age, in six countries who show identical and impossibly high scores in intelligence tests. The four boys and two girls, who come from Russia, the United States, Great Britain, India, China, and Africa, are brought to their respective embassies in London so that scientists may study their ability to communicate telepathically with each other, their power to impose their will on others, and other supernatural abilities. Their mothers, who are unable to explain the phenomenon, all insist that the children had no fathers. The children, led by the English boy, Paul, escape and hide in an abandoned church, taking with them Susan Eliot, Paul's young aunt. With their powers they turn away fearful government officials who have decided that the children must be destroyed. A scientist, Dr. Tom Lewellin, shocked by the government's plan to kill the six, persuades the chief of the UNESCO project to talk to the children. The children demonstrate their own higher morality but not in enough time to save themselves. An attack is accidentally launched, and the church and the children are destroyed. *Children. Russians. Americans in foreign countries. East Indians. Chinese. Africans. Scientists. Mental telepathy. Murder. Churches. London. United Nations Educational Scientific and Cultural Organization.*

Note: Released in Great Britain in Apr 1964.

CHILDREN'S FILM FESTIVAL (Canada)   F6.0770
Boxoffice Attractions–National Film Board of Canada. 28 Nov **1968** [Washington, D. C., opening]. Sd; col. 35mm. 88 min.
Prod Sheldon Tromberg.
Anthology. A program of seven short films, produced by the National Film Board of Canada, including: *Christmas Cracker; Paddle-to-the-Sea; The Story of Cinderella; Ti-Jean Goes Lumbering; Norman McLaren's Opening Speech; Dimensions;* and *The Bear and the Mouse.*

THE CHILDREN'S HOUR   F6.0771
Mirisch-World Wide Productions. *Dist* United Artists. 20 Dec **1961** [Los Angeles opening; c20 Dec 1961; LP21849]. Sd; b&w. 35mm. 107 min.
Pres by Mirisch Co. A William Wyler Production. *Prod-Dir* William Wyler. *Assoc Prod* Robert Wyler. *Screenplay* John Michael Hayes. *Adapt* Lillian Hellman. *Cinematog* Franz F. Planer. *Art Dir* Fernando Carrere. *Set Decor* Edward G. Boyle. *Film Ed* Robert Swink. *Mus* Alex North. *Sd* Fred Lau, Don Hall, Jr. *Asst Dir* Robert E. Relyea, Jerome M. Siegel. *Prod Mgr* Allen K. Wood. *Asst to the Prod* Clarence Marks. *Cost* Dorothy Jeakins. *Wardrobe* Bert Henrikson, Irene Caine, Ruth Stella. *Makeup* Emile La Vigne, Frank McCoy. *Hairstyles* Joan St. Oegger.

Cast: Audrey Hepburn (*Karen Wright*), Shirley MacLaine (*Martha Dobie*), James Garner (*Dr. Joe Cardin*), Miriam Hopkins (*Mrs. Lily Mortar*), Fay Bainter (*Mrs. Amelia Tilford*), Karen Balkin (*Mary Tilford*), Veronica Cartwright (*Rosalie*), Jered Barclay (*grocery boy*), Mimi Gibson, Debbie Moldow, Diane Mountford, William Mims, Florence MacMichael, Sallie Brophy, Hope Summers.

Drama. Source: Lillian Hellman, *The Children's Hour* (New York opening: 20 Nov 1934). Karen Wright and Martha Dobie are the head-mistresses of a small private school for girls. Their major disciplinary problem is 12-year-old Mary Tilford, the granddaughter of the town's most influential citizen. When the child is punished for telling a lie, she runs to her grandmother and tells another—and much more devastating—lie from which it may be inferred that the two teachers are having an "unnatural" relationship. Although Mary herself only dimly understands what she has said, the effect upon her shocked grandmother is obvious; and Mary elaborates upon her story. Horrified, Mrs. Tilford takes Mary out of the school and urges other guardians and parents to do the same. Karen and Martha, forced into taking drastic action, bring a slander suit against Mrs. Tilford but lose the much-publicized case when their chief witness, Martha's irresponsible Aunt Lily, deserts them under pressure and refuses to testify in their behalf. Not only is the school destroyed, but Karen realizes that Mary's lie has even created doubts in the mind of her fiancé, Dr. Joe Cardin. After she has released him, Karen suggests to Martha that they go away somewhere to make new lives for themselves. But the scandal has brought to Martha the terrible realization that the child's lie has uncovered a suppressed emotion, and she hysterically confesses her love for Karen. Then, sick with despair, she hangs herself. The vicious lie is eventually exposed, but for Karen it is too late: following Martha's funeral, she walks silently past Joe, Mrs.

Tilford, and the other repentant townspeople. *Headmistresses. Grandmothers. Aunts. Children. Mendacity. Lesbianism. Slander. Scandal. Suicide. Trials. Boarding schools.*

Note: William Wyler also directed the original filmed version of Lillian Hellman's play, *These Three* (United Artists, 1936). Working title: *Infamous.*

CHIMES AT MIDNIGHT *see* **FALSTAFF**

CHIN NU YU HUN *see* **THE ENCHANTING SHADOW**

CHIN-P'ING-MEI *see* **THE CONCUBINES**

CHINA! (Great Britain)   F6.0772
Felix Greene. *Dist* Felix Greene, Janus Films. 25 May **1965** [New York opening]. Sd; col. 16mm & 35mm. 65 min.
Pres by Felix Greene. *Prod-Writ* Felix Greene. *Asst Prod* L. W. Cole. *Photog* Felix Greene, Hsu Chih-chiang. *Film Ed* John Jeremy. *Sd Ed* Walter Storey.
Narrator: Alexander Scourby.
Documentary. The film surveys life in modern-day Communist China and contains newsreel footage dating back to 1949. Among the social and economic topics covered are industry, sports, drama, music, and education. The cities of Peking and Shanghai are spotlighted, where old slums are replaced with new facilities to create a better life for the workers. In rural China, farmers are shown living a happy life on the productive agricultural communes. There are also scenes of nomads and their camels crossing the snowy deserts of Mongolia. Another segment contains an interview with Premier Chou En-lai. The film ends with a 14-minute segment of the Peking Symphony Orchestra, under the direction of Li Tehlun and featuring pianist Yin Chang-tuang, performing western music in their new concert hall. *Chinese. Communism. Urban life. Rural life. Communal living. Slums. People's Republic of China. Peking. Shanghai. Mongolia. Chou En-lai.*

Note: Released in Great Britain in 1965; running time: 70 min. Originally commissioned as a television documentary by British ATC-TV. The musical score includes Chinese folk music as well as western classical music.

CHINA (Denmark)   F6.0773
22 Apr **1970** [Santa Monica, California, showing]. Si; col. 35mm. ca120 min.
Pres by Explorama. *A Film by* Jens Bjerre.
Travelog. A travel host describes various aspects of the Communist Chinese revolution. Departing from Moscow, the Peking Express traverses Asia, offering glimpses of Siberia, Mongolia, and the Great Wall, before arriving in Peking. Also featured are Hangchow, Shanghai, and Soochow. *Travel. Trains. People's Republic of China. Moscow. Siberia. Mongolia. Great Wall of China. Peking. Hangchow. Shanghai. Soochow.*

Note: Narration delivered live on stage.

CHINA IS NEAR (Italy)   F6.0774
Vides. *Dist* Royal Films International. 8 Jan **1968** [New York opening]. Sd; b&w. 35mm. 108 min.
Prod Franco Cristaldi. *Exec Prod* Oscar Brazzi. *Dir-Story* Marco Bellocchio. *Screenplay* Marco Bellocchio, Elda Tattoli. *Dir Photog* Tonino Delli Colli. *Camera Op* Franco Di Giacomo. *Asst Camera* Giuseppe Lanci. *Art Dir* Rodolfo Frattaioli, Ugo Novello. *Set Decor* Mimmo Scavia. *Film Ed* Roberto Perpignani. *Asst Ed* M. Teresa Bernabei, Augusto Aquilani. *Mus Comp* Ennio Morricone. *Mus Cond* Bruno Nicolai. *Song:* "Poesia" sung by Don Backy. *Song:* "E la cosa si ripete" sung by Cristiano Metz. *Sd* Vittorio De Sisti. *Mix* Renato Cadueri. *Prod Supv* Rodolfo Frattaioli, Ugo Novello. *Signor Mauri's Clothes* by Roberto Wougher. *Artistic Collab* Elda Tattoli. *Coöp* Carla Marzari, Giuliano Todeschini, Gustavo Mazzini, Francesco Arcangeli, Irma Silimbani, Giuseppe Longanesi, Ondina Longanesi, Remigio Bettoli, Giambattista Bassi, Sandro Berdondini, Sofia Zanelli, Izza Mazzini, Luigi Vannini, Renato Reggi, Claudio Tura, Giuseppe Mugnani, Gianmaria Mariani, The Boys of the Collegio S. Caterina di Imola, The People of Imola, Sofia Serristori. *Still Photog* Gianfranco Fontana.

Cast: Glauco Mauri (*Vittorio*), Elda Tattoli (*Elena*), Paolo Graziosi (*Carlo*), Daniela Surina (*Giovanna*), Pierluigi Aprà (*Camillo*), Alessandro Haber (*Rospo*), Claudio Trionfo (*Giacomo*), Laura De Marchi (*Clotilde*), Claudio Cassinelli (*Furio*), Renato Jalenti (*Don Pino*), Mimma Biscardi.

Comedy. When Vittorio, a bumbling 35-year-old professor of political science from a land-owning family in northern Italy, decides to run for office on the Socialist ticket, he incurs the wrath of his young brother Camillo, a Maoist seminarian. His sister, Elena, is impregnated by his working-class campaign manager, Carlo, who hopes to marry into the family fortune. Giovanna, Vittorio's secretary and Carlo's mistress, follows suit. Inspired by her lover's example, she attempts to conceive by her boss. The candidate's mastery of birth control, however, frustrates her design. Conspiring with Carlo, she becomes pregnant. His preventative measures notwithstanding, she informs Vittorio that he is about to become a father. Sensing political advantage, Vittorio acquiesces and informs the voters that, despite his superior social standing, he will marry a member of the proletariat. Meanwhile, Elena, disregarding Carlo's objections, attempts to obtain an abortion. As a physician prepares to perform the illegal operation, a protesting Capuchin monk at Carlo's instigation falls on his knees before the doctor. Fearing imprisonment, the abortionist begs the priest to hear his confession. At a victory celebration for his brother, Camillo and his cronies let loose a cat and police dogs. *Professors. Brothers. Socialists. Maoists. Catholics. Physicians. Monks. Political campaigns. Social classes. Brother-sister relationship. Marriage. Pregnancy. Birth control. Abortion. Confession. Dogs. Cats.*

Note: Released in Italy in 1967 as *La Cina è vicina*; running time: 116 min.

THE CHINA STORY *see* SATAN NEVER SLEEPS

THE CHINA STORY: ONE-FOURTH OF HUMANITY (Great Britain)
F6.0775

Victor-Parks Productions. *Dist* Rogosin Films. 2 Oct **1968** [New York opening]. Sd; b&w and col. 35mm. 74 min.

An Edgar Snow Production. *Prod* Bernard Victor, John Parks. *Dir-Writ* Edgar Snow. *Photog* Edgar Snow. *Photog Asst* Chu Kai-chu. *Mus Perf by* Shanghai Conservatory of Music, Central Conservatory of Music of Peking, Peking Symphony Orchestra, Shanghai Symphony Orchestra. *Prod Asst* P. B. O'Casey.

Narrator: Edgar Snow.

Documentary. Assembled largely from journalist Edgar Snow's private collection of film taken during his 30 years as a foreign correspondent in China, the film opens with sequences of the student rebellion of 1935—the beginning of Mao Tse-tung's rise to power. The footage also includes the Chinese Red Army's Long March, scenes of athletic training programs, agricultural advancements through the development of communes, medical research, and Premier Chou En-lai commenting on the use of atomic power. Also shown is Mr. Snow's interview with Chairman Mao in 1965. *Chinese. Revolts. Communism. Communal living. Nuclear weapons. China—History—Republic 1912-49. China—History—Long March 1934-35. People's Republic of China. Mao Tse-tung. Chou En-lai.*

Note: Also known as *One-Fourth of Humanity: The China Story*.

LA CHINOISE (France)
F6.0776

Anouchka Films-Productions de la Guéville-Parc Film-Simar Films-Athos Films. *Dist* Leacock Pennebaker, Inc. 3 Apr **1968** [New York opening]. Sd; col (Eastmancolor). 35mm. 95 min.

Dir-Writ Jean-Luc Godard. *Photog* Raoul Coutard. *Camera Op* Georges Liron. *Film Ed* Agnès Guillemot, Delphine Desfons, Marguerite Renoir. *Mus Selections from* Karl-Heinz Stockhausen, Antonio Vivaldi. *Selections from Piano Sonata in A Major opus 120* Franz Peter Schubert. *Sd* René Levert. *Asst Dir* Charles Bitsch. *Prod Mgr* Philippe Dussart. *English Subtitl* Mark Woodcock.

Cast: Anne Wiazemsky *(Véronique)*, Jean-Pierre Léaud *(Guillaume Meister)*, Michel Sémeniako *(Henri)*, Lex de Bruijn *(Kirilov)*, Juliette Berto *(Yvonne)*, Omar Diop *(Comrade X, Omar)*, Francis Jeanson *(Francis)*, Blandine Jeanson *(Blandine)*, Eliane Giovagnoli.

Drama. During the summer of 1967 five Maoists form the Rosa Luxemburg cell in a suburban apartment. Among its founders are students Guillaume Meister, Henri, and Véronique, the peasant Yvonne, and the painter Kirilov. So sequestered, the revolutionaries develop personal programs of political action. While Nanterre philosophy student Véronique plans to reform the university by destroying it, Guillaume envisions a theatre in which only the works of Brecht are performed. Disappointed because Véronique declares herself to be the more suitable assassin, Kirilov commits suicide. Exposed as a revisionist, Henri takes to the streets to sell the Communist paper, *l'Humanité*. Although she mistakenly slays an innocent person, Véronique confidently fulfills her self-appointed murder mission and assassinates a Soviet official. When vacation ends Véronique returns to the university, while Yvonne distributes *l'Humanité* and Guillaume takes his dramas to an audience of housewives. *Revolutionaries. Maoists. Students. Painters. Actors. Peasants. Russians. Suicide. Assassination. Terrorism. Social classes. Paris. Nanterre. Bertolt Brecht. Rosa Luxemburg. Mao Tse-tung.*

Note: Location scenes filmed in Paris. Opened in Paris in Aug 1967; running time: 90 min. Also known as *La Chinoise, ou plutôt à la chinoise*.

CHINTAO YOSAI BAKUGEKI MEIREI *see* SIEGE OF FORT BISMARCK

CHISTOYE NEBO *see* CLEAR SKIES

CHISUM
F6.0777

Batjac Productions. *Dist* Warner Bros. Pictures. 24 Jun **1970** [Dallas opening; c25 Jun 1970; LP40896]. Sd; col (Technicolor). 35mm (Panavision). 111 min. *MPAA rating* G.

Prod-Writ Andrew J. Fenady. *Exec Prod* Michael Wayne. *Dir* Andrew V. McLaglen. *Dir Photog* William H. Clothier. *Camera Op* George Nogle. *Asst Camera* Richard Barth, Fred J. Smith. *Art Dir* Carl Anderson. *Set Decor* Ray Moyer. *Main Titl* Larry Bees, Art Shinbo. *Film Ed* Robert Simpson. *Mus* Dominic Frontiere. *Mus Supv* Sonny Burke. *Song:* "Turn Me Around" Dominic Frontiere, Norman Gimbel. *Song:* "Ballad of John Chisum" Dominic Frontiere, Andrew J. Fenady. *Sung by* Merle Haggard. *Sd* John Ferguson. *Asst Dir* Fred R. Simpson, Joe Nayfack, Harry S. Franklin. *Prod Mgr* Joseph C. Behm. *Script Supv* Marshall Wolins. *Wardrobe* Michael Harte, Luster Bayless. *Makeup* David Grayson. *Sp Eff* Howard Jensen. *Paintings* Russ Vickers. *Prop Master* Ray Thompson. *Key Grip* Carl Gibson. *Gaffer* James Vaiana. *Stunt Coörd* Cliff Lyons.

Cast: John Wayne *(John Chisum)*, Forrest Tucker *(Lawrence Murphy)*, Christopher George *(Dan Nodeen)*, Ben Johnson *(James Pepper)*, Glenn Corbett *(Pat Garrett)*, Bruce Cabot *(Sheriff Brady)*, Andrew Prine *(Alex McSween)*, Patric Knowles *(J. H. Tunstall)*, Richard Jaeckel *(Jess Evans)*, Geoffrey Deuel *(Billy "The Kid" Bonney)*, Pamela McMyler *(Sally Chisum)*, Lynda Day *(Sue McSween)*, John Agar *(Patton)*, Lloyd Battista *(Neemo)*, Robert Donner *(Morton)*, Ray Teal *(Justice Wilson)*, Edward Faulkner *(Dolan)*, Ron Soble *(Bowdre)*, John Mitchum *(Baker)*, Glenn Langan *(Dudley)*, Alan Baxter *(Governor Axtell)*, Alberto Morin *(Delgado)*, William Bryant *(Jeff)*, Pedro Armendariz, Jr. *(Ben)*, Christopher Mitchum *(O'Folliard)*, Abraham Sofaer *(White Buffalo)*, Gregg Palmer *(Riker)*, Trinidad Villa *(blacksmith)*, Josh McLaglen, Mari McLaglen.

Western melodrama. In 1878 John Chisum, the owner of a huge New Mexico cattle ranch, discovers that Lawrence Murphy, a corrupt businessman, is trying to gain control of the surrounding land by illegally foreclosing mortgages. When Chisum comes upon some of Murphy's men rustling cattle, he enlists the aid of J. H. Tunstall, his English neighbor, and the notorious Billy "The Kid" Bonney to gun the cowboys down. Stranger Pat Garrett arrives and informs Chisum of Murphy's growing power and particularly his influence on Sheriff Brady, who was appointed by Murphy. When the ranchers attempt to set up a general store of their own and Murphy's men interfere, Tunstall decides to report his actions to the governor; on his way, however, Tunstall is killed by Sheriff Brady. Billy, enraged by the murder of his friend, shoots Brady and his deputies in revenge. Chisum's niece Sally, who had been attracted to Billy, realizes the extent of his violent character and turns her affection to Pat Garrett. Murphy then uses the killings to persuade the governor to send bounty hunter Dan Nodeen to apprehend Billy and his gang. Murphy joins Nodeen in the fierce gunfight against Billy; Chisum stampedes his cattle through town and in the resulting confusion, Billy chases Nodeen out of town and Chisum kills Murphy. The town is left in ruins, but Garrett is appointed sheriff, and Chisum is once again in control of his cattle empire. *Ranchers. Gunfighters. English. Cowboys. Sheriffs. Territorial governors. Bounty hunters. Greed. Rustling. Range wars. Murder. Revenge. Ranches. Mortgages. New Mexico. William H. Bonney. Pat Garrett. John Simpson Chisum. Stampedes. Cattle.*

Note: Location scenes filmed in Durango, Mexico.

CHITTY CHITTY BANG BANG (Great Britain)
F6.0778

Warfield Productions-Dramatic Features. *Dist* United Artists. 18 Dec **1968** [New York opening; c17 Dec 1968; LP36650]. Sd; col (Technicolor). 35mm & 70mm (Super Panavision 70). 145 min. *MPAA rating* G.

Prod Albert R. Broccoli. *Assoc Prod* Stanley Sopel. *Dir* Richard Taylor. *Screenplay* Roald Dahl, Ken Hughes. *Adtl Dial* Richard Maibaum. *Photog* Christopher Challis. *2d Unit Photog* Skeets Kelly. *Aerial Photog* John Jordan. *Art Dir* Harry Pottle. *Prod Dsgn* Ken Adam. *Film Ed* John Shirley. *Mus Supv & Cond* Irwin Kostal. *Mus & Lyr* Richard M. Sherman, Robert B. Sherman. *Mus Numbers Staged by* Marc Breaux, Dee Dee Wood. *Sd* John Mitchell, Fred Hynes. *Mus Ed* Robin Clarke. *Asst Dir* Gus Agosti. *Prod Supv* David Middlemas. *Prod Assoc* Peter Hunt. *Loc Mgr* Frank Ernst. *Cost* Elizabeth Haffenden, Joan Bridge. *Sp Eff* John Stears. *Potts' Inventions Created by* Rowland Emett.

Cast: Dick Van Dyke *(Caractacus Potts)*, Sally Ann Howes *(Truly Scrumptious)*, Lionel Jeffries *(Grandpa Potts)*, Gert Fröbe *(Baron Bomburst)*, Anna Quayle *(Baroness Bomburst)*, Benny Hill *(toymaker)*, James Robertson-Justice *(Lord Scrumptious)*, Robert Helpmann *(child catcher)*, Heather Ripley *(Jemima Potts)*, Adrian Hall *(Jeremy Potts)*, Barbara Windsor *(blonde)*, Davy Kaye *(admiral)*, Alexander Dore *(1st spy)*, Bernard Spear *(2d spy)*, Stanley Unwin *(chancellor)*, Peter Arne *(captain of guard)*, Desmond Llewelyn *(Coggins)*, Victor Maddern *(junkman)*, Arthur Mullard *(big man)*, Ross Parker *(chef)*, Gerald Campion, Felix Felton, Monti De Lyle *(ministers)*. Totti Truman-Taylor *(duchess)*, Larry Taylor *(lieutenant)*, Max Bacon *(orchestra)*, Max Wall, John Heawood, Michael Darbyshire, Kenneth Maller, Gerald Taylor, Eddie Davis, British actor *(The Inventors)*, John Raddock *(Minister of Finance)*, Richard Wattis *(secretary at sweet factory)*, Colin Rix *(chauffeur)*, John Baskcomb *(castle chef)*, Janette Rowsell, Miranda Hampton *(scullery* *maids),* Jessie Robins *(pastry cook),* John Crocker *(under chef),* Theo Agar *(4th minister),* Gabrielle Daye *(lady in waiting),* Grace Newcombe *(2d duchess),* Kay Hamilton *(3d duchess),* Dickie Owen *(major domo),* Teddy Kiss.

Musical comedy. Source: Ian Fleming, *Chitty Chitty Bang Bang; the Magical Car* (London, 1964). Caractacus Potts is a woefully unsuccessful inventor who lives in an Edwardian mill house with his two small children, Jemima and Jeremy, and their eccentric grandfather. In an attempt to raise 30 shillings so that the children can purchase a dilapidated racing car from a junk dealer, Potts tries to sell his latest invention, whistling sweets, to Lord Scrumptious, the owner of the local candy factory. The demonstration at Scrumptious' factory is a catastrophe; but the undaunted Potts performs with a troupe of folk dancers at a country fair and earns the money to buy the car. Using a few odds and ends, plus a great deal of hard work and imagination, Potts converts the old wreck into a shiny new contraption which is affectionately named Chitty Chitty Bang Bang. While on a seaside picnic with the children and Truly, Lord Scrumptious' beautiful daughter, Potts weaves a story about the magical powers of the car ... *The evil Baron Bomburst of Vulgaria, who has learned that Chitty Chitty can sail on the water and soar through the sky, is determined to have Potts make him a duplicate model. But it is Grandpa Potts that the Baron's pirates kidnap by mistake and carry away by airship. Witnessing the abduction, Potts, Truly, and the children give chase by flying in Chitty Chitty to far-off Vulgaria. There they learn that Baroness Bomburst so despises children that she has forbidden them in the kingdom. Because of this, Jemima and Jeremy become victims of the royal Child Catcher and are imprisoned in the castle. Aided by the village toymaker and all the children who have escaped capture by hiding in an underground cave, Potts and Truly masquerade as life-sized puppets and gain entry to the Baron's birthday party. At a given signal, all the children rush in and lead a successful mutiny in freeing Vulgaria from tyranny. With Grandpa, Jemima, and Jeremy rescued, Potts and Truly fly home in Chitty Chitty.* After the picnic, Lord Scrumptious offers Potts a contract for manufacturing the whistling sweets as candies for dogs. As Potts, Truly, and the children drive off, their happiness is such that they are unaware that Chitty Chitty Bang Bang has once more taken to the skies. *Songs:* "You Two" (Potts, Jeremy & Jemima); "Toot Sweets" (Potts, Truly, Jeremy, Jemima & Chorus); "Hushabye Mountain" (Potts); "Me Ol' Bam-Boo" (Potts & Dance Ensemble); "Truly Scrumptious" (Truly, Jeremy & Jemima); "Chitty Chitty Bang Bang" (Potts, Truly, Jeremy & Jemima); "Lovely Lonely Man" (Truly); "Posh!" (Grandpa); "Hushabye Mountain" (Reprise by Potts & Truly); "The Roses of Success" (Grandpa & Inventors); "Chu-Chi Face" (Baron & Baroness); "Doll on a Music Box," "Truly Scrumptious" (Potts & Truly); "Chitty Chitty Bang Bang" (Potts, Truly & Chorus). Inventors. Eccentrics. Children. Grandfathers. Pirates. Manufacturers. Nobility. Family life. Magic. Kidnaping. Disguise. Mutiny. Automobiles. Candy. Imaginary kingdoms. Puppets.

Note: Released in Great Britain in 1968.

CHIVATO   **F6.0779**
Dist International Film Distributors. 27 Jan **1961** [Miami, Florida, opening]. Sd; b&w. 35mm. 85 min.

Prod-Dir Albert C. Gannaway. *Asst Prod* John Roscoe. *Screenplay* Frank Graves, writ, Mark Hanna. *Photog* Ernest Haller.

Cast: Bill Fletcher *(Ramón),* Jake LaMotta *(Julio),* Lon Chaney, [Jr.] *(Gordo),* Sonia Marrero *(Sonia Velasco),* Dan Gould *(Eduardo),* George Rodríguez *(Molito),* Barbara Lea *(Elena).*

Drama. Produced in 1961, the film presents a description of the possible political situation in Cuba in 1962. A revolt takes place on the Isle of Pines against the Communist government of Fidel Castro, and the Castro forces are soundly defeated. Communists. Revolts. Cuba. Fidel Castro Ruz.

Note: Filmed in Cuba and in South Miami, Florida. Title changed to *Rebellion in Cuba.*

CHOKOSO NO AKEBONO *see* **SKY SCRAPER!**

CHOLPON—UTRENNYAYA ZVEZDA *see* **MORNING STAR**

THE CHOPPERS   **F6.0780**
Rushmore Productions. *Dist* Fairway-International Films. 30 Nov **1961** [Maryland license]. Sd; b&w. 35mm. 66 min.

Pres by Alvin Schoncite. *Prod-Story-Screenplay* Arch Hall, [Sr.]. *Dir* Leigh Jason. *Photog* Clark Ramsey. *Film Ed* Jack Ogilvie. *Mus Comp & Cond* Al Pellegrini. *Songs:* "Konga Joe," "Monkey in My Hatband" comp & sung by Arch Hall, Jr. *Asst Dir* Elmer Decker.

Cast: Arch Hall, Jr. *(Crusier),* Marianne Gaba *(Liz),* Robert Paget *(Torch),* Tom Brown, U. S. actor *(Tom Hart),* Rex Holman *(Flip),* Mickey Hoyle *(Snooper),* Chuck Barnes *(Ben),* Bruno Ve Sota *(Moose McGill),* Britt Woods *(Cowboy Boggs),* Dee Dee Green *(Gypsy),* William Shaw *(Lieutenant Fleming),* Pat Hawley *(Officer Jenks),* Richard S. Cowl *(Mr. Lester).*

Crime melodrama. Crusier, a teenager, steals some hubcaps for his homemade hotrod. Encouraged by his success, he steals more automobile parts and soon organizes four friends into a gang of thieves who operate out of a drive-in restaurant. The police name their gang "The Choppers," and insurance investigator Tom Hart is called to investigate the claims for stolen car accessories. The Choppers dispose of their loot through a fence, junk dealer Moose McGill, but the case is broken when Hart's car is stripped at the gang's headquarters. His secretary, Liz, finds chicken feathers at the scene of the crime, and this leads to the discovery of the use of a poultry truck as part of the gang's operation. The police set up a decoy, and Hart catches Crusier and the gang at the junkyard, but not before Crusier has killed McGill. Juvenile delinquents. Gangs. Investigators. Fences (for stolen goods). Secretaries. Police. Theft. Automobiles.

Note: Produced in 1959.

CHORUS AT DAWN (Japan)   **F6.0781**
Toho Co. Apr **1965** [Los Angeles showing]. Sd; col? 35mm. [Feature film, length unknown.]

Cast: Akira Takarada, Michiyo Aratama, So Yamamura, Chisako Hara. No information about the nature of this film has been found.

Note: Original title and release undetermined.

LES CHOSES DE LA VIE *see* **THE THINGS OF LIFE**

THE CHRISTINE JORGENSEN STORY   **F6.0782**
Edprod Pictures. *Dist* United Artists. 17 Jun **1970** [Los Angeles opening; c17 Jun 1970; LP38112]. Sd; col (De Luxe). 35mm. 89 min. *MPAA rating* R.

Pres by Edward Small. *Prod* Edward Small. *Assoc Prod* Robert E. Kent. *Dir* Irving Rapper. *Screenplay* Robert E. Kent, Ellis St. Joseph. *Dir Photog* Jacques Marquette. *Art Dir* Frank Sylos. *Set Decor* Morris Hoffman. *Supv Film Ed* Grant Whytock. *Mus* Paul Sawtell, Bert Shefter. *Sd* Brad Trask. *Asst Dir* Howard Kazanjian. *Prod Supv* Harold E. Knox. *Cost* Moss Mabry. *Makeup* Louis LaCava. *Sp Eff* Roger George. *Tech Adv* Christine Jorgensen, Robert O. Pearman.

Cast: John Hansen *(George/Christine Jorgensen),* Joan Tompkins *(Aunt Thora),* Quinn Redeker *(Tom Crawford),* John Himes *(George Jorgensen, Sr.),* Ellen Clark *(Mrs. Florence Jorgensen),* Rod McCary *(Jess Wanner),* Will Kuluva *(Professor Estabrook),* Oscar Beregi *(Dr. Victor Dahlman),* Lynn Harper *(Dolly as an adult),* Trent Lehman *(George, age seven),* Pamelyn Ferdin *(Dolly as a child),* Bill Erwin *(pastor),* Joyce Meadows *(Tani),* Sondra Scott *(Angela),* Don Pierce *(Jack),* Elaine Joyce *(Loretta),* Eddie Frank *(George as a very young child),* Dee Carroll *(Mrs. Whalstrom),* Peter Bourne *(Mr. Whalstrom).*

Biographical melodrama. Source: Christine Jorgensen, *Christine Jorgensen: A Personal Autobiography* (New York, 1967). Fascinated by all things feminine since childhood, George Jorgensen, Jr., secures a position as a fashion photographer for a top advertising agency. During an assignment in Southampton, however, the models dispute Jorgensen's masculinity, and his mentor, homosexual executive Jess Wanner, attempts to rape him. The photographer contemplates suicide, but instead participates in a series of hormone experiments conducted by Professor Estabrook and agrees to a sex change operation performed by Denmark's leading surgeon, Dr. Victor Dahlman. While recuperating from the successful operation, the first of its kind, Jorgensen remains in Copenhagen living with his supportive Aunt Thora and assuming the name of her dead daughter Christine. Dreading publicity, the photographer shuns all reporters except magazine writer Tom Crawford. During an extensive interview in a secluded mountain cabin the two fall in love, and Crawford persuades Jorgensen to return to New York and begin life anew. Photographers. Physicians. Professors. Advertising executives. Reporters. Aunts. Models. Americans in foreign countries. Sex change operations. Male homosexuality. Childhood. Rape. Suicide. Experiments. Copenhagen. Denmark. Southampton (New York). Christine Jorgensen.

Note: Prerelease title: *Christine.* Original running time: 98 min.

THE CHRISTINE KEELER AFFAIR (Great Britain)   **F6.0783**
Topaz Film Corp. (British). *Dist* JaGold Pictures. ca3 Jun **1964** [Daytona Beach, Florida, opening]. Sd; b&w. 35mm. 90 min.

Pres by John Nasht. *Prod* John Nasht. *Dir* Robert Spafford. *Screenplay* Matt White, Ronald Maxwell, Robert Spafford. *Dir Photog* Michel Rocca. *Mus (see note)* Roger Connock, Roger Bourdin.

Cast: Yvonne Buckingham *(Christine Keeler),* John Drew Barrymore *(Dr. Stephen Ward),* Alicia Brandet *(Mandy Rice-Davies),* Mel Welles *(Capt. Yevgeni Ivanov),* Peter Prowse *(Domaren),* Mimi Heinrich *(Marianne),* Christine Keeler *(herself),* Jimmy Moore, Gunnar Lemvigh, Carl Ottosen, Carl Ishøj, Bent Thalmay, Lise Henningsen, Anita Rieneck, Knud Hallest.

Biographical melodrama. Prefaced by an interview with its subject, the film chronicles the rise of demimondaine Christine Keeler. Coming to London as a girl, Christine finds employment first as a photographer's model and then as a hostess. At the Murray Club she meets Mandy Rice-Davies, who introduces her to society osteopath Stephen Ward. Although Christine moves into Ward's apartment, she tires of their platonic relationship and leaves the osteopath briefly for West Indian musician Johnny Edgecomb. Following her return, Ward escorts her about town on a dog leash. At a wild swimming pool party she meets British Minister of War John Profumo and Soviet naval attaché Yevgeni Ivanov. Christine's liaisons with both are revealed when disgruntled former lover Edgecomb fires pistol shots through her apartment door, and Scotland Yard is summoned. The ensuing scandal forces Profumo's resignation and Ivanov's return to Russia. Stephen Ward commits suicide, and Christine is sent to prison. *Mistresses. Models. Nightclub hostesses. Diplomats. Physicians. Socialites. Russians. Musicians. West Indians. Scandal. Swimming pools. London. Christine Keeler. Stephen Ward. Yevgeni Ivanov. John Profumo. Mandy Rice-Davies. Scotland Yard.*

Note: Filmed in Denmark. The film was banned in Great Britain. Sources conflict in music credit. Also known as *The Keeler Affair.* Advertised as *Scandal '64.*

THE CHRISTMAS KID (United States/Spain)   F6.0784

Westside International–L. M. Films. *Dist* Producers Releasing Organization. Jul **1967.** Sd; col (Eastmancolor, print by Movielab). 35mm. 90 min.

Prod-Dir Sidney Pink. *Exec Prod* José López Moreno. *Screenplay* Jim Henaghan, Rodrigo Rivero. *Photog* Manuel Hernández Sanjuán. *Art Dir* Wolfgang Burman. *Set Decor* Augusto Lega. *Film Ed* John Horvath, Antonio Ramírez. *Mus* Fernando García Morcillo. *Asst Dir* Philip Pink, Paul Gonzales. *Prod Mgr* Angel Monis.

Cast: Jeffrey Hunter *(Joe Novak),* Louis Hayward *(Mike Culligan),* Perla Cristal *(Marie Lefleur),* Gustavo Rojo *(Mayor Louis Carrillo),* Luis Prendes *(Judge Perkins),* Reginald Gillam *(Dr. Fred Carter),* Fernando Hilbeck *(Jud Walters),* Jack Taylor *(John Novak),* Eric Chapman *(Percy Martin),* Dennis Kilbane *(Luke Acker),* Russ Stoddard *(Pete Prima),* Carl Rapp *(Sheriff Anderson),* Guillermo Méndez *(Karl Humber),* Alvaro de Luna *(Burt Froelich),* Alejandra Nilo *(Marika Novak).*

Western drama. On Christmas Day in 1855 near Jasper, Arizona, a blacksmith's wife dies while giving birth to a son. When the embittered father, John Novak, names the child Cain, three of Jasper's prominent citizens— Mayor Carrillo, Dr. Carter, and Judge Perkins—baptize the boy Joe and practically adopt him. Known as the Christmas Kid, the rebellious Joe grows up; and when the welfare of Jasper is threatened by the unscrupulous gambler and promoter Mike Culligan, he reluctantly agrees to replace the spineless Sheriff Anderson. Culligan, however, uses his girl friend, Marie Lefleur, to charm Joe, and she soon has him under Culligan's control. When Joe's drunken father is killed in a barroom brawl, Joe despairs, hands in his badge, and forsakes guns and killing. As a romance develops between Marie and Joe, he persuades her to leave Culligan and return to her home; but, as she is leaving, she is gunned down by two of Culligan's henchmen, Karl and Burt. The crime spurs Joe back into action and so enrages the townspeople that they burn down Culligan's gambling-dance hall. Culligan then uses Joe's weakling childhood friend, Jud Walters, to frame the Christmas Kid as a killer-thief. With evidence stacked against him, Joe is sentenced to be hanged along with Karl and Burt. When the latter two are swept from their horses to swing in the air, however, Joe's horse does not move, for his loyal friends who know of Joe's innocence have hobbled the animal's legs. At this point Jud comes forth to tell the truth about Culligan's villainy. Though the trapped Culligan kills Jud, he himself is shot to death by Mayor Carrillo. Joe, the Christmas Kid, is now free to bring peace again to Jasper. *Blacksmiths. Gamblers. Sheriffs. Mayors. Childbirth. Smalltown life. Filial relations. Murder. Arson. Frameup. Capital punishment. Dancehalls. Bars. Christmas. Arizona.*

Note: Produced in Spain in 1966 and released there as *Joe Navidad;* running time: 85 min.

A CHRISTMAS MEMORY see TRILOGY

THE CHRISTMAS THAT ALMOST WASN'T (United States/Italy)   F6.0785

Bambi Film. *Dist* Childhood Productions. 23 Nov **1966** [New York opening]. Sd; col (Eastman Color). 35mm. 95 min.

Prod Barry B. Yellen. *Dir* Rossano Brazzi. *Screenplay-Orig Story* Paul Tripp. *Photog* Alvaro Mancori. *Settings* A. Danilo Zanetti. *Film Ed* Maurizio Lucidi. *Mus, Orch & Mus Dir* Bruno Nicolai. *Songs:* "Christmas Is Coming," "The Christmas That Almost Wasn't," "Hustle Bustle," "I'm Bad," "Kids Get All the Breaks," "The Name of the Song Is Prune," "Nothing To Do but Wait," "Santa Claus (Round)," "Time for Christmas," "What Are Children Like When They're Fast Asleep," "Why Can't Every Day Be Christmas" Ray Carter, Paul Tripp. *Titl Song Sung by* Glenn Yarbrough. *Cost* A. Danilo Zanetti.

Cast: Rossano Brazzi *(Phineas T. Prune),* Paul Tripp *(Sam Whipple),* Lydia Brazzi *(Mrs. Santa Claus),* Alberto Rabagliati *(Santa Claus),* Mischa Auer *(Johnathan, the bookkeeper),* Sonny Fox *(Mr. Prim),* John Karlsen *(Blossom).*

Fantasy. Phineas T. Prune, an ill-tempered millionaire industrialist who hates Christmas, purchases the North Pole and plans to evict Mr. and Mrs. Santa Claus from their home unless their back rent is paid by Christmas Eve. Hoping to earn some money, Santa takes the advice of his lawyer friend Sam Whipple and goes to work in Prim's Department Store. But Prune buys out Mr. Prim and fires Santa. As Christmas Eve approaches, a small boy learns of Santa's dilemma and races to tell everyone that Santa Claus needs money. The children of the world respond by running to Santa with their pennies. With the rent paid, Santa loads his sleigh and streaks through the sky to deliver his presents. The last one is for Phineas T. Prune. It is a sailboat that he asked for when he was 5 years old, but the postcard had been lost in the mail. Upon receiving the gift, Prune's faith in Christmas and Santa Claus is restored. *Millionaires. Industrialists. Lawyers. Children. Eviction. Finance—Personal. Department stores. Christmas. North Pole. Santa Claus.*

Note: Filmed in Rome in 1965. Italian release title: *Il Natale che quasi non fu.*

THE CHRISTMAS TREE (France/Italy)   F6.0786

Les Films Corona–Jupiter Film. *Dist* Continental Distributing, Inc. 25 Sep **1969** [New York opening]. Sd; col (Eastmancolor, print by Movielab). 35mm. 110 min. *MPAA rating* G.

Prod Robert Dorfmann. *Dir-Writ* Terence Young. *2d Unit Dir* Bernard Farrel. *Photog* Henri Alekan. *2d Unit Photog* Raymond Picon-Borel. *Art Dir* Tony Roman, Robert André, Eugène Roman. *Set Decor* Fernand Bernardi, Robert Turlure. *Prod Dsgn* Jean André. *Film Ed* Johnny Dwyre. *Mus* Georges Auric. *Sd* William R. Sivel. *Asst Dir* Paul Feyder. *Prod Supv* Georges Valon. *Cost* Tanine Autre. *Makeup* Marie-Madeleine Paris. *Hairstyles* Alain Scemama. *Sp Eff* Karl Baumgartner, Daniel Braunschweig.

Cast: William Holden *(Laurent),* Virna Lisi *(Catherine),* Bourvil *(Verdun),* Brook Fuller *(Pascal),* Madeleine Damien *(Marinette),* Friedrich Ledebur *(Vernet),* Mario Feliciani *(doctor).*

Melodrama. Source: Michel Bataille, *L'arbre de Noël* (Paris, 1967). Laurent, a widowed French-American millionaire, and his 10-year-old son, Pascal, are fishing near a desolate Corsican beach when a plane carrying an atomic weapon explodes overhead. Because Laurent is swimming underwater at the time, he suffers no harmful effects, but Pascal is exposed to radiation and develops leukemia. Upon learning that his son has only a few months to live, Laurent stops working and takes Pascal to his country chateau. With the aid of his fiancée, Catherine, an art director for *Paris Match,* his wartime friend Verdun, who works as a caretaker at the chateau, and Verdun's wife, Marinette, Laurent tries to indulge the child's every whim. It soon becomes apparent that Pascal is aware of his fatal illness and calmly accepts the approach of death. Pascal loves his surroundings, and his father buys him a blue tractor and trailer to drive around the chateau grounds. Because the boy shows an interest in wolves, Laurent and Verdun break into a Paris zoo and steal two of the animals so that Pascal may train them as pets. After one of the wolves is rescued from a fall into a well, the boy nurses the animal. Later, a wild stallion colt attacks Pascal while he plays, and the wolves come to his rescue. On Christmas Eve, while Verdun is dressing for dinner and Laurent and Catherine are out doing last-minute shopping, Pascal begins to weaken. Upon returning to the chateau, Laurent discovers that his son has died at the foot of the Christmas tree, surrounded by his opened presents and guarded by his two howling pet wolves. Pascal's last gift to his father is a hand-carved wooden plaque wishing him and his friends good luck. *Widowers. Millionaires. Caretakers. Fatherhood. Childhood. Cancer. Theft. Death. Tractors. Castles. Radiation. Zoos. Christmas. Corsica. "Paris Match". Wolves. Horses.*

Note: Location scenes filmed in Nice and Corsica. Paris opening: Oct 1969 as *L'arbre de Noël;* running time: 107 min. Italian title: *L'albero di Natale.*

CHRISTOPHER WOTAN see THE YOUNG SINNER

CHRONICLE OF A SUMMER (France)   F6.0787

Argos Films. *Dist* Pathé Contemporary Films. 6 May **1965** [New York opening]. Sd; b&w. 35mm. 90 min.

Prod Anatole Dauman, Philippe Lifschitz. *Dir-Writ* Jean Rouch, Edgar Morin. *Photog* Roger Morillère, Raoul Coutard, Jean-Jacques Tarbès, Michel Brault. *Film Ed* Jean Ravel, Néna Baratier, Françoise Colin. *Sd* Guy Rophe, Michel Fano, Barthélémy. *Asst Dir* Claude Beausoleil, Louis Boucher. *Prod Mgr* André Heinrich. *Coöp* Comité du Film Ethnographique, Musée del'Homme (Paris), André Coutant.

Cast: Jean Rouch, Edgar Morin, Marceline, Angelo, Marilou, Jean-Pierre *(main participants),* Jean, Jacques *(factory workers),* Régis, Céline, Jean-Marc, Nadine, Landry, Raymond *(students),* Jacques, Simone *(office workers),* Henri, Madi, Catherine *(artists),* Sophie *(model).*

Documentary. Ethnographer-filmmaker Jean Rouch and sociologist-film critic Edgar Morin, assisted by a motion picture crew, interview people on the streets of Paris during the summer of 1960. Marceline asks passersby on the

Place de la Concorde if they are happy. She discusses her childhood spent in a concentration camp and the death of her parents. Two African friends wonder why she has a tattoo on her arm. Rouch and Morin talk with an artist couple who are happy with the bohemian life and later with a bourgeois couple who work in an office. Angelo, a worker at the Renault factory, meets Negro student Landry, and they discuss their philosophies. Another student, Jean-Pierre, Marceline's former boyfriend, is also interviewed at length. Marilou, an Italian working as a secretary at *Cahiers du Cinéma* is interviewed twice. On the first occasion, she finds little meaning in life; later she falls in love, and during the second interview, she discusses her new perspective. At a beach resort in Saint-Tropez, Sophie talks about her career as a cover girl. Rouch and Morin then assemble everyone in a screening room where they view the edited film and comment on cinema verité. Finally, walking through the corridors of the Musée de l'Homme, Rouch and Morin analyze their subjects' reactions. *Filmmakers. Anthropologists. Sociologists. Models. Students. Secretaries. Artists. Italians. Jews. Factory workers. Africans. Urban life. Concentration camps. Resorts. Summer. World War II. Paris. Saint-Tropez. Musée de l'Homme (Paris). "Cahiers du Cinéma".*

Note: Paris opening: Oct 1961 as *Chronique d'un été*; running time: 85 min.

CHRONICLE OF ANNA MAGDALENA BACH (Italy/West Germany)
F6.0788

Franz-Seitz Filmproduktion-Kuratorium Junger Deutscher Film-Hessisches Rundfunk—Straub—Huillet—Filmfonds—Telepool—IDI Cinematografica—RAI. *Dist* New Yorker Films. 7 Apr **1969** [New York showing]. Sd; b&w. 35mm. 94 min.

Prod Gian Vittorio Baldi. *Dir* Jean-Marie Straub. *Screenplay* Jean-Marie Straub, Danièle Huillet. *Photog* Ugo Piccone. *Camera Op* Saverio Diamanti, Giovanni Canfarelli. *Film Ed* Danièle Huillet, Jean-Marie Straub. *Mus Selections* Johann Sebastian Bach. *Orch* Concentus Musicus (Vienna). *Mus Cond* Nikolaus Harnoncourt. *Concert Group* Schola Cantorum Basilienses. *Concert Group Cond* August Wenzinger. *Choir* Hanover Boys' Choir. *Choir Dir* Heinz Hennig. *Orch* Musica Antica Ensemble. *Sd* Louis Hochet, Lucien Moreau. *Sd Rec* Paul Schöler. *Prod Mgr* Danièle Huillet. *Prod Asst* Georg Focking, Aldo Passalacqua, Joachim Wolf. *Cost* Casa d'Arte Firenze, Vera Poggioni, Renata Morroni.

Cast: Gustav Leonhardt *(Johann Sebastian Bach)*, Christiane Lang *(Anna Magdalena Bach)*, Paolo Carlini *(Hölzel)*, Ernst Castelli *(Steger)*, Hans-Peter Boye *(Born)*, Joachim Wolf *(rector)*, Rainer Kirchner *(superintendent)*, Eckart Brüntjen *(Prefect Kittler)*, Walter Peters *(Prefect Krause)*, Kathrien Leonhardt *(Catherina Dorothea Bach)*, Anja Fährmann *(Regine Susanna Bach)*, Katja Drewanz *(Christine Sophie Henrietta Bach)*, Bob van Aspern *(Johann Elias Bach)*, Andreas Pangritz *(Wilhelm Friedemann Bach)*, Bernd Weikl *(singer in Cantata no. 205)*, Wolfgang Schöne *(singer in Cantata no. 82)*, Karl-Heinz Lampe *(singer in Cantata no. 42)*, Nikolaus Harnoncourt *(Prince of Anhalt-Cöthen)*, Karl-Heinz Klein *(bass voice for duet in Cantata no. 140)*, Bernhard Wehle *(soprano voice in Cantata no. 140)*, Christa Degler *(voice of Anna Magdalena Bach in Cantata no. 244a)*.

Biographical drama. Anna Magdalena Bach recounts the last years of the life of her husband, Johann Sebastian, from the time of their marriage in 1721 until his death in 1750. Most of the film is devoted to the performance of Bach's musical works, although the basic facts of his life are illustrated with photographs, letters, original manuscripts, and other documents. *Musical selections include:* Brandenburg Concerto no. 5, Prelude 6 from the *Little Clavier Book for Wilhelm Friedemann Bach*, Minuet 2 of the Suite in D Minor from the *Little Clavier Book for Anna Magdalena Bach*, Sonata no. 2 in D Major for Viola and Harpsichord, Partita in E Minor from the *Little Clavier Book for Anna Magdalena Bach*, Trio-sonata no. 2 in C Minor, Magnificat in D Major, *St. Matthew Passion*, Prelude in B Minor for Organ, Mass in B Minor, Ascension Oratorio, Clavier-Übung, Italian Concerto, "Goldberg Variations," *Musical Offering, Art of the Fugue*, Chorale for Organ, Cantatas no. 205, no. 198, no. 244a, no. 42, no. 215, no. 140, and no. 82. *Musicians. Composers. Marriage. Family life. Music. Johann Sebastian Bach. Anna Magdalena Bach.*

Note: Released in West Germany in 1968 as *Chronik der Anna Magdalena Bach*; in Italy as *Cronaca di Anna Magdalena Bach*.

CHRONIK DER ANNA MAGDALENA BACH *see* **CHRONICLE OF ANNA MAGDALENA BACH**

CHRONIQUE D'UN ÉTÉ *see* **CHRONICLE OF A SUMMER**

CHUBASCO
F6.0789

Warner Bros.-Seven Arts, Inc. 5 Jun **1968** [Los Angeles opening; c1 Jun 1968; LP35853]. Sd; col (Technicolor). 35mm (Panavision). 100 min.

Exec Prod William Conrad. *Exec Asst Prod* James Lydon. *Dir-Writ* Allen H. Miner. *Dir Photog (see note)* Lew Jennings, Paul Ivano, Robert Burks. *Camera Op* Roger Williams, photog. *Asst Camera* Elmer Faubion. *Art Dir* Howard Hollander. *Set Decor* William L. Kuehl. *Film Ed* John W. Holmes. *Mus* William Lava. *Song:* "*To Love You*" William Lava, William Conrad. *Song:* "*If It's Love*" William Lava, Gordon Jenkins. *Sd* Stanley Jones. *Asst Dir* Fred Gammon. *Unit Mgr* Sherry Shourds. *Script Supv* Jules Miliman. *Location Mgr* Charles Caramelli. *Wardrobe* William Smith, cost. *Makeup Supv* Gordon Bau. *Makeup* Gary Liddiard. *Supv Hairstylist* Jean Burt Reilly. *Dial Supv* Rick Miner. *Prop* Ben Goldman. *Grip* Harold Noyes, Leonard Bukey. *Electrn* LeRoy Thompson. *Still Photog* John Monte.

Cast: Richard Egan *(Sebastian)*, Christopher Jones *(Chubasco)*, Susan Strasberg *(Bunny)*, Ann Sothern *(Angela)*, Simon Oakland *(Laurindo)*, Audrey Totter *(Theresa)*, Preston Foster *(Nick)*, Peter Whitney *(Matt)*, Edward Binns *(Judge North)*, Joe De Santis *(Benito)*, Norman Alden *(Frenchy)*, Stewart Moss *(Les)*, Ron Rich *(Juno)*, Milton Frome *(police sergeant)*, Toni Gerri *(Aunt Mary)*.

Melodrama. Police arrest Chubasco, a wild 20-year-old, and his girl friend Bunny when a gang of motorcyclists ride through a California beach party. Bunny is bailed out by her irate father, Sebastian, and the sympathetic judge prevails upon executive Nick Kassel to find work for Chubasco aboard one of his tuna boats. Despite his rebellious attitude, Chubasco wins the approval of Captain Laurindo. Later, Chubasco goes to work for an elderly skipper, Benito, who takes a paternal interest in him and helps him to arrange an elopement with Bunny. The wedding, which takes place in a brothel owned by Benito's friend Angela, is a raucous affair which ends sadly when Benito suffers a fatal heart attack. Chubasco ships out on another tuna boat and leaves Bunny in the care of Angela. Although Chubasco's new skipper turns out to be Bunny's father, the two men get along well enough until Sebastian learns that Chubasco has married Bunny. Unwilling to accept the young man, he attacks Chubasco but is himself knocked overboard during the fight. Despite Chubasco's saving his life, Sebastian vows to put him ashore at the next port. When Chubasco accidentally falls over the side, Sebastian rescues him. The two men are united by the incident, and when their ship reaches port, Sebastian smiles as Chubasco embraces Bunny. *Motorcycle gangs. Judges. Executives. Sea captains. Police. Elopement. Fatherhood. Employer-employee relations. Rescue. Fishing boats. Weddings. Whorehouses. California.*

Note: Location scenes filmed in San Diego, California. Burks was replaced as photographer early in production.

CHUKA
F6.0790

Rodlor, Inc. *Dist* Paramount Pictures. 3 May **1967** [New Haven, Connecticut, opening; c3 May 1967; LP34355]. Sd; col (Technicolor by Pathé). 35mm. 105 min.

Prod Rod Taylor, Jack Jason. *Dir* Gordon Douglas. *2d Unit Dir* Ray Kellogg. *Screenplay* Richard Jessup. *Photog* Harold Stine. *2d Unit Photog* Irmin Roberts. *Art Dir* Hal Pereira, Tambi Larsen. *Set Decor* Robert R. Benton, Jack Mills. *Film Ed* Robert Wyman. *Mus Comp & Cond* Leith Stevens. *Orch* Nathan Van Cleave, Herbert Spencer. *Sd* Garry Harris, John Wilkinson. *Asst Dir* Howard Roessel. *Prod Mgr* John Coonan. *Asst to the Prod* Fred Hakim. *Cost Dsgn* Edith Head. *Makeup* Wally Westmore. *Hairstyles* Nellie Manley. *Sp Photog Eff* Paul K. Lerpae.

Cast: Rod Taylor *(Chuka)*, Ernest Borgnine *(Sgt. Otto Hansbach)*, John Mills *(Col. Stuart Valois)*, Luciana Paluzzi *(Veronica Kleitz)*, James Whitmore *(Trent)*, Angela Dorian *(Helena Chavez)*, Louis Hayward *(Major Benson)*, Michael Cole *(Private Spivey)*, Hugh Reilly *(Captain Carrol)*, Barry O'Hara *(Slim)*, Joseph Sirola *(Baldwin)*, Marco Antonio *(Hanu)*, Gerald York *(Lieutenant Daly)*, Herlinda Del Carmen *(Indian girl)*, Lucky Carson *(stage driver)*.

Western melodrama. Source: Richard Jessup, *Chuka* (Greenwich, Connecticut, 1961). While on the trail, a gunfighter known as Chuka gives some of his food to Hanu, chief of a tribe of starving Arapahoe Indians. A short time later, they come upon a disabled stagecoach, and Hanu repays his debt to Chuka by sparing the lives of the passengers, including Veronica, a widowed Mexican aristocrat with whom Chuka had been in love: Veronica was forced to reject him because of his lowly status. Chuka leads the stranded travelers to a nearby fort garrisoned by an undisciplined company of misfits and commanded by Colonel Valois, a martinet tortured by the memory that, while he was a British officer in India, his entire regiment had been slaughtered while he was in a drunken stupor. When the Arapahoes surround the fort and capture a scouting party, Chuka rescues Trent, the sole survivor of the party, and returns to warn Valois that an Indian attack is imminent and to advise him to take the offensive against the Indians. Valois scorns the suggestion, however, and ignores that his men have taken to quarreling among themselves, sleeping with Indian women, and discussing a possible mutiny. On the eve of the attack, Chuka is reunited with Veronica; suddenly, an Indian woman stabs her sleeping partner and sets fire to the fort. The Arapahoes swarm over the walls, and Valois, impeccably dressed for battle, is killed along with everyone else by the marauding Indians. Later a cavalry troop arrives at the fort, and among the blackened ruins they find a "single grave—Veronica's—marked with a cross and an empty gun holster. There is no sign of Chuka. *Gunfighters. Arapahoe Indians. Widows. Aristocrats. Mexicans. British. Hunger. Alcoholism. Massacres. Forts. United States Army—Cavalry. Fires.*

CHUSHINGURA (Japan)   **F6.0791**
Toho Co. *Dist* Toho International, Inc., Berkeley Cinema Guild. 3 Oct **1963** [New York opening]. Sd; col (Eastman Color). 35mm (Tohoscope). 108 min.

Exec Prod Sanezumi Fujimoto, Tomoyuki Tanaka, Hiroshi Inagaki. *Dir* Hiroshi Inagaki. *Screenplay* Toshio Yazumi. *Photog* Kazuo Yamada. *Art Dir* Kisaku Ito. *Mus* Akira Ifukube. *Choreog* Kiyokata Seruwaka. *Asst Dir* Teruo Maru. *English Titl* Herman G. Weinberg.

Cast: Koshiro Matsumoto *(Kuranosuke Oishi)*, Yuzo Kayama *(Takuminokami Asano)*, Chusha Ichikawa *(Kouzuke Kira)*, Toshiro Mifune *(Genba Tawaraboshi)*, Yoko Tsukasa *(Yozenin)*, Setsuko Hara *(Riku)*, Tatsuya Mihashi *(Yasubei Horibe)*, Yosuke Natsuki *(Kinemon Okano)*, Ichiro Arishima *(Denpachiro Tamon)*, Norihei Miki *(Gayboy Geisha)*, Frankie Sakai *(Carpenter Goro)*, Keiju Kobayashi *(Lord Awaji)*, Yuriko Hoshi *(Otsuya)*, Yumi Shirakawa *(Ume)*, Kumi Mizuno *(Saho)*, Akira Takarada *(Gunpei Takada)*, Takashi Shimura *(Hyobe Chishaka)*, Michiyo Aratama.

Historical drama. Based on a Kabuki play-cycle by: Izumo Takeda, Senryu Namiki and Shoraku Miyoshi, *Kanadehon Chushingura* (first performance: Osaka, 1748). In March of 1701, the incorruptible young Lord Asano of Ako is appointed to receive and entertain imperial envoys calling on the shogun in Edo. Lord Kira, his supervisor, expects graft payments for every bit of advice, but Asano will have no part of bribery. Kira goads Asano beyond endurance, and the young lord finally draws his sword and wounds Kira. Asano is ordered to commit harakiri and his fief is forfeited. Chamberlain Oishi, Asano's chief retainer, calls a meeting of Asano's men, and they swear to avenge the injustice to their late master. To insure his family's safety, Oishi divorces his wife and sends her away with their children. Oishi then moves to Kyoto and descends to a life of debauchery to mislead Kira, who surrounds himself with bodyguards, fearing a vendetta. Twenty-one months later, after much spying on both sides, the group of 47 avengers acquire the plans of Kira's mansion, complete their plot, and attack. After decapitating Kira they march to Lord Asano's grave where the populace greets them as heroes. After deliberation, the sentence of death is passed on the 47 retainers, but in recognition of their loyalty to their lord and the approval of the populace, they are not executed like common criminals but are allowed to die by their own hands as befits true samurai. *Samurai. Nobility. Political corruption. Feudalism. Hara-kiri. Revenge. Government—Local. Injustice. Decapitation. Loyalty. Kyoto. Asano Naganori. Kira Yoshinaka. Oishi Yoshio.*

Note: Released in Japan in 1962 as a 2-part film; combined running time: 204 min. Rereleased in uncut version in 1966 by the Berkeley Cinema Guild. According to a U. S. source, film was subtitled *47 Samurai.*

CHUZHIYE DETI *see* **STEPCHILDREN**

ČIČA TOMINA KOLIBA *see* **UNCLE TOM'S CABIN**

THE CICADA IS NOT AN INSECT *see* **THE GAMES MEN PLAY**

EL CID (United States/Italy)   **F6.0792**
Samuel Bronston Productions–Dear Film–Allied Artists. *Dist* Allied Artists. 14 Dec **1961** [New York opening; c6 Dec 1961; LP27968]. Sd; col (Technicolor). 35mm & 70mm (Super Technirama). 184 min. [Copyright length: 181 min.]

Pres by Samuel Bronston. *Prod* Samuel Bronston. *Assoc Prod* Jaime Prades, Michael Waszynski. *Dir* Anthony Mann. *2d Unit Dir* Yakima Canutt. *Screenplay* Philip Yordan, Fredric M. Frank. *Orig Story* Fredric M. Frank. *Dir Photog* Robert Krasker. *Dir Photog 2d Unit* Manuel Berenguer. *Art Dir* Veniero Colasanti, John Moore. *Murals* Maciek Piotrowski. *Film Ed* Robert Lawrence. *Mus* Miklos Rozsa. *Love Theme* Miklos Rozsa, Paul Francis Webster. *Sd Rec* Jack Solomon. *Re-rec* Gordon K. McCallum. *Sd Ed* Verna Fields. *Mus Ed* Edna Bullock. *Asst Dir* Luciano Sacripanti, José María Ochoa, José López Rodero. *Prod Mgr* Leon Chooluck, Guy Luongo. *Script Supv* Pat Miller. *Cost Dsgn* Veniero Colasanti, John Moore. *Wardrobe Dir* Gloria Mussetta. *Makeup Created by* Mario Van Riel. *Hairstyles* Grazia De Rossi. *Sp Eff* Alex Weldon, Jack Erickson. *Master of Prop* Stanley Detlie. *Supv Tech* Carl Gibson. *Supv Electn* Norton Kurland.

Cast: Charlton Heston *(El Cid)*, Sophia Loren *(Chimene)*, Raf Vallone *(Count Ordoñez)*, Geneviève Page *(Princess Urraca)*, John Fraser *(Prince Alfonso)*, Gary Raymond *(Prince Sancho)*, Hurd Hatfield *(Arias)*, Massimo Serato *(Fanez)*, Herbert Lom *(Ben Yussuf)*, Frank Thring *(Al Kadir)*, Douglas Wilmer *(Moutamin)*, Michael Hordern *(Don Diego)*, Andrew Cruickshank *(Count Gormaz)*, Tullio Carminati *(Don Pedro)*, Ralph Truman *(King Ferdinand)*, Christopher Rhodes *(Don Martin)*, Gérard Tichy *(King Ramiro)*, Carlo Giustini *(Bermudez)*, Paul Müller, Katina Noble, Fausto Tozzi, Barbara Everest, Franco Fantasia.

Biographical melodrama. In 11th-century Spain, the Christian kingdoms of Castile, Leon, and Aragon face the constant threat of the warring Moors and their determination to spread the Islamic culture throughout all of Europe. Into this arena of violence rides Rodrigo Diaz de Vivar, whose courage, wisdom, and spiritual strength earn him the sobriquet El Cid, or "The Lord." Following one particular battle, El Cid liberates some Moorish emirs on their vow never again to attack Castile. His act of mercy is misinterpreted as treason by Count Gormaz, the father of his beloved Chimene, and to protect the family honor El Cid is forced to slay the Count in a duel. Although Chimene vows to have her revenge, she is obliged to marry El Cid upon the bidding of King Ferdinand, but they do not consummate the marriage, and Chimene enters a convent. A short time later Ferdinand dies, and his kingdom is divided amongst his three quarrelsome children, Alfonso, Sancho, and Urraca. Before long, the weak, ambitious Alfonso arranges the assassination of Sancho. When El Cid refuses to vow allegiance unless Alfonso swears himself innocent of his brother's death, he is banished from Castile. But through the long years that follow, El Cid continues to battle the Moors, and his ranks increase as loyal subjects join him by the score. Eventually his noble nature wins over even Chimene, and she again declares her love for him. When the Moorish leader, Ben Yussuf, begins planning a massive invasion of Valencia, Alfonso recalls El Cid from exile and places him in charge of the army. For days the battle rages and on the eve of the last great Moorish onslaught El Cid is mortally wounded by a stray arrow. Attended by Chimene, he makes her promise that, alive or dead, he will lead the next day's charge. Obedient to her husband's wishes, Chimene has El Cid's dead body mounted firmly on his white charger and placed before his troops. And when the Moors see the seemingly invincible El Cid riding once more into battle, terror and confusion overtake them, and they flee in disorganized panic toward their ships. *Royalty. War heroes. Soldiers. Spanish. Moors. Treason. Marriage—Arranged. Regicide. Exile. Islam. Christianity. Spain—History—Arab period 711–1492. Valencia. Castile. Aragon. El Cid. Ferdinand I (Castile and León). Alfonso VI (Castile and León). Sancho II (Castile). Urraca. Jimena Diaz. Yusuf Ibn-Tashfin. al- Mutamid. Kadir. Duels.*

Note: Filmed in Madrid and Rome. Released in Italy in 1961; running time: 176 min.

LE CIEL ET LA BOUE *see* **THE SKY ABOVE—THE MUD BELOW**

LA CIGARRA NO ES UN BICHO *see* **THE GAMES MEN PLAY**

LA CINA È VICINA *see* **CHINA IS NEAR**

THE CINCINNATI KID   **F6.0793**
Filmways, Inc.–Solar Productions. *Dist* Metro-Goldwyn-Mayer, Inc. 15 Oct **1965** [New Orleans opening; c21 Sep 1965; LP31708]. Sd (Westrex); col (Metrocolor). 35mm. 113 min. [Also reviewed at 105 min.]

Prod Martin Ransohoff. *Assoc Prod* John Calley. *Dir* Norman Jewison. *Screenplay* Ring Lardner, Jr., Terry Southern. *Dir Photog* Philip H. Lathrop. *Art Dir* George W. Davis, Edward Carfagno. *Set Decor* Henry Grace, Hugh Hunt. *Film Ed* Hal Ashby. *Orch Cond* Robert Armbruster. *Mus* Lalo Schifrin. *Theme Song:* "The Cincinnati Kid" Dorcas Cochran. *Sung by* Ray Charles. *Rec Supv* Franklin Milton. *Asst Dir* Kurt Neumann. *Cost Dsgn* Donfeld. *Makeup Supv* William Tuttle. *Hairstyles* Sydney Guilaroff.

Cast: Steve McQueen *(The Cincinnati Kid)*, Edward G. Robinson *(Lancey Howard)*, Ann-Margret *(Melba)*, Karl Malden *(Shooter)*, Tuesday Weld *(Christian)*, Joan Blondell *(Lady Fingers)*, Rip Torn *(Slade)*, Jack Weston *(Pig)*, Cab Calloway *(Yeller)*, Jeff Corey *(Hoban)*, Theo Marcuse *(Felix)*, Milton Selzer *(Sokal)*, Karl Swenson *(Mr. Rudd)*, Emile Genest *(Cajun)*, Ron Soble *(Danny)*, Irene Tedrow *(Mrs. Rudd)*, Midge Ware *(Mrs. Slade)*, Dub Taylor *(dealer)*, Joyce Perry *(Mrs. Hoban)*, Olan Soule *(desk clerk)*, Barry O'Hara *(Eddie)*, Pat McCaffrie, John Hart *(poker players)*, Howard Wendell *(Charlie, poker player)*, Mimi Dillard *(Slade's girlfriend)*, Gregg Martell *(Danny's henchman)*, Harry Hines, Burt Mustin, William Challee, Charles Wagenheim *(old men)*, Virginia Harrison *(employee)*, Breena Howard *(Cajun's woman)*, Robert DoQui *(Tillie)*.

Drama. Source: Richard Jessup, *The Cincinnati Kid* (Boston, 1963). The Cincinnati Kid is king of the local stud poker players in New Orleans in the 1930's, but Lancey "The Man" Howard is the national champion. Howard comes to New Orleans for a private match with Slade, a wealthy local businessman, on whom he inflicts heavy losses. The Kid's friend Shooter, known for his honesty, is dealer for these private games and suggests a match between Howard and The Kid. Christian, The Kid's girl friend, leaves town to visit her parents. Slade, betting heavily on the match in an attempt to recoup his losses, puts pressure on Shooter to slip The Kid winning cards. The Kid learns of the machinations during the long game and, even though he could easily win, substitutes Lady Fingers for Shooter as dealer. Melba, Slade's wife, taking advantage of Christian's absence, starts an affair with The Kid during a break in the game. The climax of the match occurs when The Kid loses everything on a full house to Howard's straight flush. The Kid also loses

Christian when she finds out about his affair with Melba. The Kid starts out again on the streets, playing for coins against a shoeshine boy but still retaining his honor. *Gamblers. Cheating. Infidelity. Honesty. Poker. New Orleans.*

Note: Sam Peckinpah, originally slated to direct the film, was replaced shortly after shooting began. It is not known how much, if any, of his footage is in the film.

CINDERBALLER   F6.0794

Dist Stacey Distributors. ca **1970**. Sd; col. 16mm. 61-81 min.

Sex film. No information about the precise nature of this film has been found. *Sexuality.*

CINDERELLA (U.S.S.R.)   F6.0795

Gorky Film Studio. *Dist* Janus Films. 20 Dec **1961** [New York opening]. Sd; col (Magicolor). 35mm. 84 min. [Also reviewed at 80 min.]

Pres by Sovexportfilm. *Dir* Aleksandr Rou, Rostislav Zakharov. *Story Ed* V. Biryukova. *Scen-Choreog Plan* Aleksandr Gintsburg, Rostislav Zakharov, Aleksandr Rou. *Photog* Aleksandr Gintsburg. *Art Dir* M. Petrovskiy. *Sets* A. Ivashchenko. *Sets From Sketches by* Peter Williams. *Film Ed* Ye. Abdirkina. *Mus* Sergei Sergeevich Prokofiev. *Book* Nikolay Dimitriyevich Volkov. *Mus Cond* Yuriy Fayyer. *Mus Perf* Bolshoi Theater Orchestra. *Ballet Master* Rostislav Zakharov. *Sd* Anatoliy Dikan. *Cost From Sketches by* Peter Williams. *Makeup* N. Mardisova, V. Sharov, Yu. Sharova, V. Zhabokpitskaya. *Sp Eff* L. Akimov, Arseniy Klopotovskiy.

Cast: Raisa Struchkova *(Cinderella)*, Gennadiy Ledyakh *(prince)*, Yelena Vanke *(stepmother)*, Natalya Ryzhenko *(1st stepsister)*, Lesma Chadarayn *(2d stepsister)*, Aleksandr Pavlinov *(Cinderella's father)*, V. Kudryashov, Nina Simonova *(Andalusian dancers)*, Yekaterina Maksimova *(spring fairy)*, Yelena Ryabinkina *(summer fairy)*, Marina Kolpakchi *(autumn fairy)*, Natalya Taborko *(winter fairy)*, Yu. Vyrenkov *(jester)*, Aleksandr Radunskiy *(master of ceremonies)*, G. Tarasov *(steward)*, Aleksandr Lapauri, V. Zakharov, Yu. Ignatov *(foreign guests)*, L. Shvachkin *(midnight gnome)*, Yu. Skott *(snake dancer)*, V. Fearbakh, N. Papko *(mazurka soloists)*.

Dance film. Source: Charles Perrault, "Cendrillon," in *Recueil de pièces curieuses et nouvelles* (Paris, 1697). Sergei Sergeevich Prokofiev and Nikolay Dmitriyevich Volkov, *Zolushka* (Moscow performance: 21 Nov 1945). A screen version of the Prokofiev ballet originally produced by Rostislav Zakharov in 1945. *Royalty. Stepmothers. Stepsisters. Dancers. Fairies. Charwomen. Magic. Filial relations. Shoes. Balls (formal gatherings).*

Note: Released in the U.S.S.R. in Feb 1961 as *Khrustalnyy bashmachok*; running time: 80 min.

CINDERELLA (West Germany)   F6.0796

Fritz Genschow-Film. *Dist* Childhood Productions. 22 Oct **1966** [New York showing]. Sd; col (Agfacolor). 35mm. 72 min.

Prod-Dir-Writ Fritz Genschow. *Screenplay Collab* Renée Stobrawa. *Photog* Gerhard Huttula. *Art Dir* Waldemar Volkmer. *Film Ed* Albert Baumeister. *Mus German Vers* Richard Stauch. *Mus Dir U. S. Vers* Milton Delugg. *Songs* Milton Delugg, Anne Delugg. *Mus Supv U. S. Vers* George Brackman. *Dances* Carola Krauskopf. *Sd* Heinz Weissert. *Cost* Waldemar Volkmer.

Cast: Rita-Maria Nowotny *(Cinderella)*, Renée Stobrawa *(fairy godmother)*, Fritz Genschow *(father)*, Aenne Bruck *(stepmother)*, Maria Axt, Renate Fischer *(stepsisters)*, Rüdiger Lichti *(prince)*, Werner Stock *(elf)*, Paul Tripp *(narrator U. S. Vers)*, Herbert Weissbach, Joachim Rödel, Gisela Schauroth.

Fantasy. Source: Jakob Grimm and Wilhelm Grimm, "Aschenputtel". A live action, musical version of the Grimm brothers fairytale, filmed in natural settings. *Stepmothers. Stepsisters. Drudges. Royalty. Fairies. Godmothers. Jealousy. Balls (formal gatherings). Shoes.*

Note: Released in West Germany in 1955 as *Aschenputtel*.

CINDERELLA AND THE GOLDEN DRESS *see* **SINDERELLA AND THE GOLDEN BRA**

CINDERELLER AND HER FELLER *see* **RINDERCELLA**

CINDY AND DONNA   F6.0797

Tempo Enterprises. *Dist* Crown International Pictures. Jun **1970**. Sd; col (De Luxe). 35mm. 84 min. *MPAA rating* X.

Prod Robert J. Anderson, Terry Anderson. *Assoc Prod* Bill Anderson, prod-ed. *Dir* Robert J. Anderson. *Screenplay* Barry Clark. *Dir Photog* J. Barry Herron. *Film Ed* Bill Anderson, prod-ed. *Mus Comp* Robert O. Ragland. *Prod Supv* Bill Savoy.

Cast: Debbie Osborne *(Cindy)*, Nancy Ison *(Donna)*, Cheryl Powell *(Karen)*, Max Manning *(father)*, Suzy Allen *(mother)*, Tom Koben *(Greg)*.

Melodrama. Half sisters Cindy, 15, and Donna, 17, live in the suburbs with their parents. Their mother, a heavy drinker, is married to Cindy's roaming father. Cindy watches Donna and her boyfriend, Greg, smoke marijuana and make love, and she becomes curious about her own sexual nature, but she is afraid to experiment. One day she discovers her father in bed with Donna, who is high on drugs. Their parents leave for a weekend, and the girls each embark on an adventure: Donna agrees to "pose" for two of Greg's friends and has sex with all three of them; and Cindy goes to the beach with her friend, Karen. The two girls are picked up by local youths, but Cindy refuses her date's advances. The girls then go to Cindy's house and smoke some of Donna's marijuana. There Cindy has her first sexual experience—with Karen. Cindy decides to learn about sex from Greg, and they make a date, but Donna interrupts their lovemaking and orders Greg to leave. Greg throws Donna out of the house, and she is struck by a car. Horrified and ashamed, Cindy ends her quest for sexual experience. *Sisters. Parenthood. Adolescence. Alcoholism. Infidelity. Lesbianism. Group sex. Sexual initiation. Suburban life. Marijuana. Automobile accidents.*

CINÉMA VÉRITÉ   F6.0798

C. I. T. Films. *Dist* I. R. M. I. Films. 1 Feb **1968** [New York showing]. Sd; b&w. 35mm. 61 min.

Dir Allan Lindus.

Documentary. As a motion picture producer, a director, and an author discuss censorship and pornographic films, their conversation is punctuated by footage of stripteasers and lesbians. *Motion picture producers. Motion picture directors. Authors. Censorship. Lesbianism. Striptease. Sex exploitation films.*

CINERAMA'S RUSSIAN ADVENTURE (United States/U.S.S.R.)   F6.0799

J. Jay Frankel–Central Documentary Film Studio–Moscow Popular Science Studio. *Dist* United Roadshow Presentations. 29 Mar **1966** [Chicago opening]. Sd; col (Technicolor). 3x35mm & 70mm (Cinerama, see note). 122-162 min. [See note.]

Production Credits for Film Excerpts: *Dir* Leonid Kristi, Roman Karmen, Boris Dolin, Oleg Lebedev, Solomon Kogan, Vasiliy Katanyan, V. Komissarzhevskiy. *Photog* Nikolay Generalov, Sergey Medynskiy, Anatoliy Koloshin, E. Ezov, Ilya Gutman, A. Missyura, Vladimir Vorontsov, V. Ryklin, Georgiy Kholnyy. *Orig Mus* Aleksandr Lokshin, Ilya Shveytser, Yuriy Yefimov.

Production Credits for U. S. Compilation: *Pres by* Harold J. Dennis, J. Jay Frankel. A J. Jay Frankel Production. *Narr & Prolog* Homer McCoy. *Mus Ed* William E. Wild. *Prod Supv* Thomas Conroy.

Narrator: Bing Crosby.

Featuring: Bolshoi Theater Ballet, Bolshoi Theater Orchestra, Moscow State Circus, Moiseyev Ensemble, Piatnitsky State Chorus and Dance Ensemble.

Documentary. Following an introduction by Bing Crosby, the Cinerama screen widens for scenes of landscapes, cities, peoples, and entertainments of the Soviet Union. Highlights include Moscow's historic buildings and churches, including the Kremlin, its subway and streets, a spring carnival, the seaside resorts on the Black Sea, a trip down the Volga River, skiers, a troika racing along a snow-covered road, a helicopter view of the North Pole, an Antarctic whale hunt, the capture of a wild boar in the Moyun-Kum of Central Asia, a race by reindeer-drawn sleds, divers in the Sea of Okhotsk, battling an octopus, the capture of antelope, rafting logs down the Tisza River, and the development of new towns in Siberia. Other scenes include a visit to the Moscow Circus, where the renowned clown Oleg Popov performs, the dancing of the Moiseyev and Piatnitsky companies, and excerpts from the repertoire of the Bolshoi Theater Ballet. *Clowns. Whaling. Hunting. Diving. Lumbering. Skiing. Sledding. Subways. Resorts. Circus. Helicopters. Carnivals. Troikas. Rafts. Moscow. Black Sea. Volga River. North Pole. Antarctic regions. Siberia. Tisza River. Moyun-Kum. Sea of Okhotsk. The Kremlin (Moscow). Wild hogs. Antelope. Reindeer. Octopi.*

Note: This is a U. S. compilation of footage included in a number of Soviet Kinopanorama releases, including *Shiroka strana moya ...* (produced in 1957 by the Moscow Popular Science Studio, 90 min), *Volshebnoye zerkalo* (produced in 1958 by the Central Documentary Film Studio, ca140 min), *Chas neozhidannykh puteshestviy. V polyote na vertolyote* (produced in 1960 by the Central Documentary Film Studio, ca100 min), *Chetvyortaya programma panoramnykh filmov: "Tsirkovoye predstavleniye" i "Na Krasnoy ploshchadi"* (produced in 1961 by the Central Documentary Film Studio, ca100 min), *Udivitelnaya okhota* (produced in 1961 by the Moscow Popular Science Studio, 78 min), *SSSR s otkrytym serdtsem* (produced in 1961 by the Moscow Popular Science Studio), and *V Antarktiku za kitami*. Shown in the U. S. in Cinerama and 70mm. Longer running time may include an overture and intermission.

CINQ FILLES EN FURIE *see* **FIVE WILD GIRLS**

CINQ GARS POUR SINGAPOUR *see* **SINGAPORE, SINGAPORE**

CINQUE MARINES PER SINGAPORE *see* **SINGAPORE, SINGAPORE**

CINQUE ORE IN CONTANTI see **FIVE GOLDEN HOURS**

CINQUE TOMBE PER UN MEDIUM see **TERROR-CREATURES FROM THE GRAVE**

LA CINTURA DI CASTITÀ see **ON MY WAY TO THE CRUSADES, I MET A GIRL WHO ...**

LA CIOCIARA see **TWO WOMEN**

CIRCLE OF DECEPTION (Great Britain)   **F6.0800**
Twentieth Century-Fox Film Corp. 8 Feb **1961** [Saint Louis opening; c30 Dec 1960; LP18567]. Sd (Westrex); b&w. 35mm (CinemaScope). 100 min.
Prod Tom Morahan. *Dir* Jack Lee, dir. *Screenplay* Nigel Balchin, Robert Musel. *Dir Photog* Gordon Dines. *Camera Op* Cecil Cooney. *1st Focus* Brian Cummins. *2d Focus* Michael Wilson, photog. *Art Dir* J. Elder Wills, Maurice Pelling. *Set Decor* Andrew Low. *Draughtsman* Henry Lee, Royce Baxter. *Scenic Artist* Ted Barnes. *Prod Dsgn* Tom Morahan. *Film Ed* Gordon Pilkington. *Assembly Ed* Deveril Goodman. *2d Asst Ed* Tony West. *Mus Comp* Clifton Parker. *Played by* The Symphonic Orchestra. *Cond* Dock Mathieson. *Sd Mix* Claude Hitchcock. *Sd Ed* Don Challis. *Sd Camera* Margery Lindop. *Boom Op* David Jones. *1st & 2d Asst Dir* Clive Reed, David Tringham. *Prod Mgr* Frederick Gunn. *Prod Asst* Howard Connell. *Prod Sec* Jill Langley. *Cont* Eileen Hildyard. *Cost Dsgn* Joan Ellacott. *Wardrobe Mistress* Evelyn Gibbs. *Makeup* George Partleton. *Hairstyles* Betty Glasow. *Sp Eff* Peter Neilson. *Tech Adv* Christopher Burney. *Constr Mgr* F. E. Trussett. *Prop Buyer* Bryn Siddall. *Still Photog* Harold Hanscomb. *Casting Dir* Nora Roberts. *Gaffer* G. Bignall.
Cast: Suzy Parker (*Lucy Bowen*), Bradford Dillman (*Paul Raine*), Harry Andrews (*Captain Rawson*), Robert Stephens (*Captain Stein*), Paul Rogers (*Major Spence*), John Welsh (*Major Taylor*), Ronald Allen (*Abelson*), A. J. Brown (*Frank Bowen*), Martin Boddey (*Harry [Henry] Crow*), Charles Lloyd Pack (*Ayres*), Jacques Cey (*curé*), John Dearth (*Captain Ormrod*), Norman Coburn (*Carter*), André Charise (*Lohman*), Stephen Dartnell (*Brunner*), David Palmer, Hennie Scott (*small boy [see note]*), Maurice Belfer (*cobbler*), Meier Tzelniker (*barman*), Richard Shaw (*Liebert*), Roland Brand (*Captain Von Horst*), Duncan Lamont (*Ballard*), Walter Gotell (*phoney Ballard*), Tony Doonan (*R. A. F. sergeant*), Arthur Gross (*Maquis man*), Michael Ripper (*Chauval*), Brian Hankins (*German sergeant*), Basil Beale (*Price*), Jean Harvey (*F. A. N. Y.*), Mickey Wood (*instructor*), Jean Briant (*Lohman's assistant*), Frank Forsyth (*club member*), Richard Marner (*German colonel*), George Mikell (*German officer*), John Serret, Michael Shaw, Tony Quinn, Theodore Wilhelm.
War melodrama. Source: Alec Waugh, "Small Back Room in St. Marylebone," in *Esquire* (Mar 1953). In 1945, shortly before the Allied invasion of Europe, British Intelligence formulates a plan for outwitting the Germans in occupied France. Selecting an officer, they will deliberately give him false information and parachute him into Normandy on the theory that, if captured, he will crack under torture and reveal what he knows. The ruse can only succeed, however, if the officer believes that his mission is real. After lengthy psychological testing, Paul Raine, a young Canadian, is chosen for the job by the Intelligence chief, Captain Rawson. Partially responsible for the selection is Lieut. Lucy Bowen, who, though in love with Paul and opposed to the inhuman maneuver, reluctantly agrees with the decision. Everything works as planned; once in France, Paul is captured by the Gestapo, imprisoned, and relentlessly tortured. When close to the breaking point, he bites down on the cyanide pellet concealed in his hollow tooth. However, Rawson has seen to it that the capsule contains no poison; Paul "breaks" and tells the Germans everything. A short time later the French underground storms the prison and Paul is freed. Tortured with the thought that he betrayed his country, he flees to Tangiers and takes refuge in alcohol. As he hovers on the brink of suicide, Lucy finds him, tells him the truth, and restores his will to live. *Canadians. Prisoners of war. Espionage. Deception (military). Torture. Suicide. Guilt. Alcoholism. World War II. France—History—German occupation 1940–45. Tangiers. France. Great Britain—Intelligence service. Gestapo. Maquis.*
Note: Location scenes filmed in France. Opened in London in Jan 1961. Working title: *Destruction Test*. Cutting continuity lists David Palmer in the role of "small boy," while other sources credit Hennie Scott.

CIRCLE OF LOVE (France/Italy)   **F6.0801**
Paris-Films Production–Interopa Film-Pathé Cinéma. *Dist* Continental Distributing, Inc. 24 Mar **1965** [New York opening]. Sd; col (Eastman Color, print by Technicolor). 35mm (Franscope). 105 min. [Also 108 min.]
Prod Robert Hakim, Raymond Hakim. *Dir* Roger Vadim. *Screenplay* Jean Anouilh. *Photog* Henri Decaë. *Art Dir* François de Lamothe. *Main Titl* Maurice Binder. *Film Ed* Victoria Spiri-Mercanton. *Mus* Michel Magne. *Sd* Robert Biart. *Prod Mgr* Ralph Baum. *Cost* Marc Doelnitz.

Cast: Marie Dubois (*prostitute*), Claude Giraud (*soldier*), Anna Karina (*maid*), Valérie Lagrange (*her friend*), Jean-Claude Brialy (*young man*), Jane Fonda (*married woman*), Maurice Ronet (*husband*), Catherine Spaak (*midinette*), Bernard Noël (*author*), Francine Bergé (*actress*), Jean Sorel (*young officer*), Françoise Dorléac.
Drama. Source: Arthur Schnitzler, *Reigen* (Berlin opening: 23 Dec 1920). In 1913, a sentimental Parisian prostitute offers herself freely to a handsome soldier because he resembles her true love. Seeking to take advantage of all opportunities for lovemaking, the soldier seduces a lonely housemaid and then goes off to make other conquests. Returning home, the despondent maid allows her employer's son to make love to her. Encouraged by the experience, the young gentleman consummates his desire for a married woman. Refreshed by the love session, the married woman makes bold overtures to her stuffy husband. Later, he takes a midinette for his mistress, but the ambitious young woman forsakes him for an author she hopes will write a play for her. Instead, he pursues an established actress with whom he had an affair years before. He has little success, however, for the actress finds satisfaction only with young men, and she has a brief affair with the Count, a young officer. Following their encounter, the Count embarks on a night of wild revelry. Morning finds him in the flat of the sentimental prostitute, who this time collects a fee for her services. The cycle of love is now complete. *Soldiers. Prostitutes. Actors. Authors. Shopgirls. Chambermaids. Aristocrats. Infidelity. Sexuality. Seduction. Paris.*
Note: Opened in Paris in Oct 1964 as *La ronde*; running time: 110 min; in Rome in Sep 1965 as *Il piacere e l'amore*.

THE CIRCUS (Reissue)   **F6.0802**
United Artists. 15 Dec **1969** [New York opening]. Sd eff & mus score; b&w. 35mm. 72 min. MPAA rating G.
Mus & Theme Song: "Swing, Little Girl" comp & sung by Charles Chaplin.
Note: Originally released in silent version in Jan 1928; c6 Jan 1928; 7 reels.

CIRCUS FRIENDS (Great Britain)   **F6.0803**
Femina Films–London Independent Producers. *For* Children's Film Foundation. *Dist* Continental Distributing, Inc. 11 May **1962** [Maryland license]. Sd; b&w. 35mm. 63 min.
Prod-Writ Peter Rogers. *Dir* Gerald Thomas. *Photog* Otto Heller. *Film Ed* Peter Boita. *Mus* Bruce Montgomery. *Sd Rec* Francis Flynn. *Asst Dir* George Provis.
Cast: Alan Coleshill (*Nicky*), Carol White (*Nan*), David Tilley (*Martin*), Pat Belcher (*Beryl*), Meredith Edwards (*Farmer Beasley*), John Horsley (*Bert Marlow*), Sam Kydd (*George*).
Drama. Circus proprietor Bert Marlow, unable to pay the rental fee on a field leased from Farmer Beasley, satisfies his debt by giving him Pinto, the pet pony of niece Nan and nephew Nicky. Pinto, however, is rescued from the farmer by Judy, a pet Alsacian, and concealed with village friends by Nan and Nicky. At the performance the following day, Pinto performs successfully, enabling Marlow to discharge his financial obligation to the farmer. *Circus performers. Farmers. Landlords. Children. Uncles. Debt. Abduction. Circus. Horses. Dogs.*
Note: Released in Great Britain in 1956.

CIRCUS OF BLOOD see **BERSERK**

CIRCUS OF FEAR see **PSYCHO-CIRCUS**

CIRCUS WORLD   **F6.0804**
Bronston-Midway Productions. *Dist* Paramount Pictures. 25 Jun **1964** [New York opening; c25 Jun 1964; LP30326]. Sd; col (Technicolor). 35mm & 70mm (Super Technirama 70). 135 min. [Copyright length: 131 min.]
Pres by Samuel Bronston. *Prod* Samuel Bronston. *Exec Assoc Prod* Michael Waszynski. *Dir* Henry Hathaway. *2d Unit Dir* Richard Talmadge. *Screenplay* Ben Hecht, Julian Halevy, James Edward Grant. *Story* Philip Yordan, Nicholas Ray. *Photog* Jack Hildyard. *2d Unit Photog* Claude Renoir. *Prod Dsgn* John De Cuir. *Main Titl* Dong Kingman. *Film Ed* Dorothy Spencer. *Mus* Dimitri Tiomkin. *Sd* David Hildyard. *1st & 2d Unit Asst Dir* Jose Lopez Rodero, Terry Yorke. *Prod Mgr* C. O. Erickson. *Cont* Elaine Schreyeck, Kay Rawlings. *Cost* Renie. *Makeup* Mario Van Riel. *Hairstyles* Grazia De Rossi. *Sp Eff* Alex Weldon. *Tech Adv* Alfredo Marquerie. *Coörd of Circus Operations* Frank Capra, Jr. *Circus Adv* Franz Althoff.
Cast: John Wayne (*Matt Masters*), Rita Hayworth (*Lili Alfredo*), Claudia Cardinale (*Toni Alfredo*), Lloyd Nolan (*Cap Carson*), Richard Conte (*Aldo Alfredo*), John Smith (*Steve McCabe*), Henri Dantes (*Emile Schuman*), Wanda Rotha (*Mrs. Schuman*), Katharyna (*Giovana*), Kay Walsh (*Flo Hunt*), Margaret McGrath (*Anna*), Katherine Ellison (*Molly*), Miles Malleson (*Billy Rogers*), Katherine Kath (*Hilda*), Moustache (*bartender*), Franz Althoff and His Circus, José María Caffarel, François Galepides.
Action melodrama. Matt Masters, an American circus impresario in the early 1900's, decides to take his circus and Wild West Show to Europe, with

the ulterior motive of finding Lili Alfredo, mother of Toni, the young circus performer whom Matt has protected since Lili's disappearance 14 years earlier. Lili had been married to an aerialist though in love with Matt; and when her husband fell to his death, it was rumored that he committed suicide because of Lili's unfaithfulness. The troupe puts on a show aboard the circus boat in Barcelona; when a performer falls overboard, the huge audience surges to the railing, causing the ship to capsize. No lives are lost, but the circus is destroyed. Matt, Toni, and Steve McCabe, Toni's boyfriend, join a touring Wild West Show and are a great success. Matt plans to put together another show and rehearse it in Spain during the winter before touring. In Madrid, Lili turns up in the audience and later tells Matt that Toni is better off not knowing about her mother. Later, Lili asks for a job in the circus, but she is still determined to keep her identity a secret, until Tojo, a clown, tells Toni about Lili and about her father's suicide. Toni becomes hysterical and is about to confront Lili in hatred when Matt stops her and tells her that her mother was refused a divorce by her father. A fire breaks out, and Toni and Lili, scaling a rope to the top of the tent, save the major part of the big top from burning. When the fire is extinguished, Lili and Toni embrace; and at the opening of the circus the next night, the two perform an aerial act. At the end, Matt and Lili marry, and Toni and Steve also marry. *Impresari. Americans in foreign countries. Aerialists. Clowns. Suicide. Infidelity. Shipwrecks. Circus. Personal identity. Wild West shows. Barcelona. Madrid. Fires.*

Note: Presented in Cinerama for roadshow engagements.

CISKE (Netherlands/West Germany) **F6.0805**
Filmproductie Maatschappij "Amsterdam" N.V.–Omega Filmgesellschaft. *Dist* Bakros Corp. 2 Aug **1963** [New York opening]. Sd; b&w. 35mm. 88 min.
Prod J. J. ter Linden, Alfred Bittins. *Dir-Writ* Wolfgang Staudte. *Dir Photog* Otto Baecker, P. Dekeukelaire. *Art Dir* Nicole van Baarle. *Mus Comp* Steye van Brandenburg, Herbert Windt.
Cast—Dutch version (see note): Dick van der Velde (*Ciske*), Kees Brusse (*The Teacher*), Riek Schagen (*Aunt Jans*), Rob de Vries (*The Father*), Jenny van Maerlant (*The Mother*), Heidi Everts (*The Girl Student*), Piet van Leeuwen (*The Cripple*), Johan Valk (*The Inspector*), Paul Steenbergen (*The Priest*), Johan Kaart, Lies Franken, Berhard Droog.
Cast—German version (see note): Heli Finkenzeller (*Aunt Jans*), Berta Drews (*The Mother*), Alexander Kerst (*The Father*), Günther Lüders (*The Priest*), Walter Janssen (*The Inspector*), Hermann Speelmans.
Melodrama. Source: Piet Bakker, *Ciske de Rat* (Amsterdam, 1941). Thirteen-year-old Ciske, a victim of parental neglect, becomes neurotic and terrorizes his school. His father, a sailor, is indifferent, but his mother abuses him until he kills her. Ciske is sentenced to the reformatory and is rehabilitated; but after his release, he is tormented about his past by the other children in school and their parents. Ciske's future, though, looks bright and loving, thanks to the help of such sympathetic adults as his teacher and his Aunt Jans, a shopkeeper. *Children. Sailors. Schoolteachers. Storekeepers. Parenthood. Matricide. Neurosis. Criminals—Rehabilitation. Reformatories.*
Note: Released in West Germany in 1955 as *Ciske, ein Kind braucht Liebe*; running time: 96 min. Released in the Netherlands as *Ciske de Rat*. Also known as *Ciske the Rat*. German and U. S. sources differ in cast credit. According to one source, German credits refer to voices dubbed for German release.

LA CITTÀ PRIGIONIERA see **CONQUERED CITY**

CITY IN THE SEA see **WAR-GODS OF THE DEEP**

CITY OF FEAR (Great Britain) **F6.0806**
Towers of London–Javelin Productions. *Dist* Allied Artists. Sep **1965**. Sd; b&w. 35mm. 90 min.
Prod (see note) Sandy Howard, Arthur Steloff, Harry Alan Towers. *Dir* Peter Bezencenet. *Screenplay* Peter Welbeck. *Adtl Dial* Max Bourne. *Photog* Martin Curtis. *Art Dir* Peter Best. *Set Dsgn* Richard Over. *Film Ed* Peter Boita. *Mus* Johnny Douglas. *Sd* Freddie Norkus.
Cast: Paul Maxwell (*Mike Foster*), Terry Moore (*Suzan*), Marisa Mell (*Ilona*), Albert Lieven (*Paul*), Pinkas Braun (*Ferenc*), Zsu Zsu Banki (*Magda*), Maria Takacs (*Marika*), Birgit Heiberg (*Zsu Zsu*), Maria Rohm (*maid*), Helga Lehner (*Eva*).
Melodrama. Mike Foster, a Canadian newspaperman, is en route to Budapest when in the Vienna airport he is approached by Ferenc, a man posing as a Hungarian refugee. Ferenc persuades Mike to deliver a package which, he says, contains medicine for his sister's ailing child in Hungary. When Mike arrives in Budapest, he discovers that he has lost the woman's telephone number and arranges a radio appeal for her address. At his hotel, he meets Suzan, an American fashion expert, and they fall in love. Mike is then approached by Ilona, who claims to be Ferenc's sister, and he discovers that the package contains not medicine but two forged passports. Ilona tells him the passports are for herself and her scientist father, Paul, who wish to escape to Austria. Mike agrees to drive them over the border in Suzan's car, but en route

they are stopped by Ferenc and other police spies. Ilona, too, is exposed as a police agent, and they reveal their plans to capture Mike in order to use him as an exchange hostage for a Hungarian spy captured by the Americans. Before they are able to apprehend him, however, Mike disarms a guard and with Suzan and Paul crosses the frontier. *Political refugees. Canadians. Americans in foreign countries. Newspapermen. Couturiers. Spies. Secret agents. Scientists. Forgery. Perfidy. Passports. Vienna. Budapest.*
Note: Filmed in Austria and Hungary. Released in Great Britain in 1966; running time: 75 min. Sources conflict in crediting producer. Peter Welbeck is a pseudonym for Harry Alan Towers.

CITY OF SECRETS (West Germany) **F6.0807**
Real-Film. *Dist* Bakros Corp. 26 Jul **1963** [New York opening]. Sd; b&w? 35mm. 88 min.
Dir Fritz Kortner. *Screenplay* Fritz Kortner, Curt Johannes Braun. *Photog* Albert Benitz. *Art Dir* Herbert Kirchhoff, Dieter Bartels. *Film Ed* Klaus Dudenhöfer. *Mus* Michael Jary. *Sd* Werner Schlagge. *Prod Dir* Heinz-Günter Sass. *Prod Mgr* Georg Siebert, Joachim Hess.
Cast: Annemarie Düringer (*Ernie Lauer*), Erich Schellow (*engineer*), Walther Süssenguth (*Boehnke*), Margot Trooger (*Paula*), Paul Hörbiger (*Herbert Klein*), Eva-Ingeborg Scholz (*telephonist*), Bruni Löbel (*Susi Ecker*), Adrian Hoven (*Gerhard Scholz*), Grethe Weiser (*Frida Binder*), Carl Ludwig Diehl (*Professor Siebrecht*), Lucie Mannheim (*Karina*), Werner Fuetterer (*Dr. Günther*), Karl Heinz Schroth.
Melodrama. Source: Curt Johannes Braun, *Die Stadt ist voller Geheimnisse* (a play; production undetermined). Boehnke, the boss of a factory in West Germany, is forced to close his business due to financial difficulties. In a series of vignettes, the private lives of some of the unemployed workers are examined. Frida Binder, the cleaning woman who secretly lives rent-free at the plant, is reunited with cashier Herbert Klein after 30 years; the office telephone girl is having a romance with publicist Gerhard Scholz; and Ernie Lauer, the office secretary, spends a day with the plant engineer. One of the former employees commits suicide, and although it is not directly linked to the closing, Boehnke is persuaded by his daughter Paula to reopen the factory. *Factory management. Factory workers. Charwomen. Cashiers. Publicists. Secretaries. Employer-employee relations. Unemployment. Suicide. Factories.*
Note: Released in West Germany in 1955 as *Die Stadt ist voller Geheimnisse*; running time: 100 min. Also known as *Secrets of the City*.

CITY OF SIN (Reissue) (United States/Philippines) **F6.0808**
Lynn-Romero Productions. *Dist* Hemisphere Pictures. caSep **1966**. Sd; b&w. 35mm. 79 min.
Note: Originally released in 1959 as *The Scavengers*.

THE CITY OF THE DEAD see **HORROR HOTEL**

CITY UNDER THE SEA see **WAR-GODS OF THE DEEP**

LA CIUDAD SAGRADA see **THE MIGHTY JUNGLE**

CIVILISATION: THE SKIN OF OUR TEETH (Great Britain) **F6.0809**
British Broadcasting Corp. *Dist* Time–Life Films. 14 Mar **1970** [New York opening]. Sd; col (Eastmancolor). 35mm. 52 min.
Prod Michael Gill, Peter Montagnon. *Asst Prod* Ann Turner. *Dir* Michael Gill. *Narr* Kenneth Clark. *Lighting Camera* A. A. Englander. *Camera Op* Kenneth MacMillan. *Camera Asst* Colin Deehan. *Lighting* Dave Griffiths, Jack Probert, Joe Cooksey, John Taylor. *Supv Film Ed* Allan Tyrer. *Ed* Jesse Palmer, Michael Shah Dayan, Peter Heelas, Roger Crittenden. *Sd Rec* Basil Harris. *Sd Asst* Malcolm Webberley. *Asst to the Prod* Carol Jones, Maggie Houston. *Res* Ann Turner. *Res Asst* June Leech. *Grip* Bill Paget.
Narrator: Kenneth Clark.
Documentary. Sir Kenneth Clark's personal history of Western civilization, as reflected in its art, architecture, and technical achievements, examines Western Europe from the fall of the Roman Empire to the year 1,000. The dispersion of Christian culture by the barbarian conquerors of Rome gave rise to Islam during the 7th century. As the new faith swept through the Mediterranean lands, migrant Christians settled in Scotland, the Hebrides, and Ireland. In the West they encountered Viking explorers, for whom the ship was as much a work of art as the temple had been for the ancient Greeks. Because literacy was confined to the higher clerics of the time, many works of classical literature were left uncopied or destroyed since they might detract from study of the scriptures. Only through the efforts of Charlemagne, the first man since the fall of Rome to achieve political unity in Europe and encourage the arts, were many secular manuscripts preserved. The act of preservation, which included elaborate ornamentation and design, carried on the meticulous craftsmanship of the wandering barbarians, who had deemphasized man as a subject of their art in favor of birds and other animals. After the breakup of the Frankish kingdom, the dominance of the Church over both man and nature is reflected; the crucifix and other religious objects became vehicles for artistic

expression. With a new cultural focus and the dissolution of barbarian dominance, Europe in the year 1,000 was prepared to embark upon its first great age of civilization. *Vikings. Christianity. Art. Islam. Literature. Documentation. Ships. Europe—History—392-814. Europe. Ravenna (Italy). Hebrides. Paris. Oslo. Aix-la-Chapelle. Nimes. Charlemagne.*

Note: Location scenes filmed in Paris, Ravenna, Hebrides, Oslo, Aix-la-Chapelle, and Nimes. First shown in Great Britain 23 Mar 1969 on BBC 2; the first in Sir Kenneth Clark's series on the history of Western civilization. Also known as *The Frozen World.*

CIVILISATION: THE GREAT THAW (Great Britain)   F6.0812

British Broadcasting Corp. *Dist* Time–Life Films. 14 Mar **1970** [New York opening]. Sd; col (Eastmancolor). 35mm. 52 min.

Prod Michael Gill, Peter Montagnon. *Asst Prod* Ann Turner. *Dir* Peter Montagnon. *Narr* Kenneth Clark. *Lighting Camera* A. A. Englander. *Camera Op* Kenneth MacMillan. *Camera Asst* Colin Deehan. *Lighting* Dave Griffiths, Jack Probert, Joe Cooksey, John Taylor. *Supv Film Ed* Allan Tyrer. *Ed* Jesse Palmer, Michael Shah Dayan, Peter Heelas, Roger Crittenden. *Sd Rec* Basil Harris. *Sd Asst* Malcolm Webberley. *Asst to the Prod* Carol Jones, Maggie Houston. *Res* Ann Turner. *Res Asst* June Leech. *Grip* Bill Paget.

Narrator: Kenneth Clark.

Documentary. The film concentrates on the 12th century, when many of Europe's most famous cathedrals, monasteries, and abbeys were constructed. According to Sir Kenneth Clark, the triumph of the Roman Catholic Church resulted in more stability, infusing artists and artisans alike with a tremendous amount of energy; the first visible sign of this spirit was in the elaborately ornamented Abbey of Cluny. Opposed to the Cluniac style was St. Bernard of Clairvaux, whose influence resulted in the Cistercian style, closer to modern architectural ideals of simplicity and function. The release of energy also resulted in crusades and pilgrimages to the Holy Land, and art began to reflect Eastern influences brought back by returning crusaders and pilgrims. One of the most influential figures of the century was Abbot Suger, who believed that through the effect of beautiful things on the senses, one could understand absolute beauty, or God. His philosophy, embodied in the St. Denis Cathedral, is considered to be the rationale for the modern belief in the virtue of art. The Cathedral of Chartres, according to Clark, "is a masterpiece of harmonious proportion"; constructed by people from all over France, the cathedral was destroyed by fire in 1194 and rebuilt when a valuable relic of the Virgin Mary was discovered intact among the ruins. Chartres, the bridge between Romanesque and Gothic architecture, is cited as the culmination of the first awakening of Western civilization. *Architecture. Middle Ages. The Crusades. Europe. Durham (England). Moissac (France). Vézelay (France). Autun (France). Bernard of Clairvaux. Suger (abbot of Saint Denis). Catholic Church. Chartres Cathedral. Saint Denis Cathedral. Abbey of Cluny.*

Note: Location scenes filmed in Durham, England; and Moissac, Vézelay, Autun, and Chartres, France. First shown in Great Britain on 2 Mar 1967 on BBC 2; the second in Sir Kenneth Clark's series on the history of Western civilization.

CIVILISATION: ROMANCE AND REALITY (Great Britain)   F6.0813

British Broadcasting Corp. *Dist* Time–Life Films. 21 Mar **1970** [New York opening]. Sd; col (Eastmancolor). 35mm. 52 min.

Prod Michael Gill, Peter Montagnon. *Asst Prod* Ann Turner. *Dir* Michael Gill. *Narr* Kenneth Clark. *Lighting Camera* A. A. Englander. *Camera Op* Kenneth MacMillan. *Camera Asst* Colin Deehan. *Lighting* Dave Griffiths, Jack Probert, Joe Cooksey, John Taylor. *Supv Film Ed* Allan Tyrer. *Ed* Jesse Palmer, Michael Shah Dayan, Peter Heelas, Roger Crittenden. *Sd Rec* Basil Harris. *Sd Asst* Malcolm Webberley. *Asst to the Prod* Carol Jones, Maggie Houston. *Res* Ann Turner. *Res Asst* June Leech. *Grip* Bill Paget.

Narrator: Kenneth Clark.

Documentary. The film explores the Gothic world of 14th century Europe, an age of chivalry, courtesy, and romance. Architecture reached a point of unequaled extravagance, and the image of women in art reflected a uniquely chivalrous approach, with the madonna as the highest representation of this ideal. Courtly love was the subject of lengthy stories and poems which influenced romantic writers of later centuries. Among the great patrons of art and learning was Jean de France, the Duke of Berry, whose manuscripts depicted court life and country scenes in medieval France. Francis of Assisi, rejecting material comforts for a life of poverty dedicated to aiding the unfortunate and rebuilding churches, was so influential that Pope Innocent III gave him permission to found a new order. The basilica erected after his death and decorated by all the famous painters of 13th and 14th century Italy was a masterpiece of Gothic architecture and an ironic memorial to the man whose cult of poverty would be belied by the Church and its expanding financial empire. Banking and capital were concentrated in a few families; the bankers were also art patrons, encouraging artists like Giotto, whose figures reflected a solidity and concrete reality that anticipated the Renaissance. Dante's

writing, particularly *The Divine Comedy*, belonged to the earlier Gothic era of great cathedrals; his counterpart in sculpture was Giovanni Pisano. *Art patrons. Bankers. Art. Architecture. Literature. Sculpture. Age of Chivalry. France. Italy. Tuscany. Umbria. Pisa. Florence. Jean de France (Duke of Berry). Francis of Assisi. Innocent III (pope). Giotto. Giovanni Pisano. Dante Alighieri. Cluny Museum (Paris). Arena Chapel (Padua). "Divine Comedy".*

Note: Location scenes filmed in Tuscany, Umbria, and Pisa, Italy; and at the Cluny Museum in Paris and the Arena Chapel in Padua. First shown in Great Britain 9 Mar 1969 on BBC 2; the third in Sir Kenneth Clark's series on the history of Western civilization.

CIVILISATION: MAN—THE MEASURE OF ALL THINGS
(Great Britain)   F6.0814

British Broadcasting Corp. *Dist* Time–Life Films. 21 Mar **1970** [New York opening]. Sd; col (Eastmancolor). 35mm. 52 min.

Prod Michael Gill, Peter Montagnon. *Dir* Ann Turner. *Narr* Kenneth Clark. *Lighting Camera* A. A. Englander. *Camera Op* Kenneth MacMillan. *Camera Asst* Colin Deehan. *Lighting* Dave Griffiths, Jack Probert, Joe Cooksey, John Taylor. *Supv Film Ed* Allan Tyrer. *Ed* Jesse Palmer, Michael Shah Dayan, Peter Heelas, Roger Crittenden. *Sd Rec* Basil Harris. *Sd Asst* Malcolm Webberley. *Asst to the Prod* Carol Jones, Maggie Houston. *Res* Ann Turner. *Res Asst* June Leech. *Grip* Bill Paget.

Narrator: Kenneth Clark.

Documentary. Continuing his personal history of Western civilization, Sir Kenneth Clark discusses the Italian Renaissance. At the beginning of the 15th century, optimistic citizens of the Florentine republic revived the virtues of ancient Greece and Rome. The first 30 years of the century was the age of scholarship; new classical texts were discovered and old ones re-edited. To house these valuable texts, Cosimo de Medici built the library of San Marco. Architecture, under the influence of Brunelleschi, became light and economical, no longer directed toward God but toward the needs of man. Perspective, the rendering of the exact position of a figure in space through mathematical calculation, became central for artists such as Ghiberti and remained part of artists' training for centuries to come. Florentine craftsmen and artists were encouraged in a unique atmosphere of healthy criticism and a disdain for mediocrity. The idea of fame replaced the chivalric ideal, as wealthy Florentines attempted to immortalize themselves in realistic portraits, such as those of the Flemish artist, Jan Van Eyck. The middle part of the century was dominated by Lorenzo de Medici, a poet and politician, whose cousin Lorenzino commissioned paintings by Botticelli. In the last quarter of the century, activity centered in the small courts of northern Italy, especially Urbino and the famous Ducal Palace, which influenced the manners of the period, uniting medieval chivalry and the Platonic ideal. Artists began to develop a view of nature as an idyllic retreat, as reflected in the paintings of Giorgione. In Urbino, as in Florence, the Renaissance depended upon a small minority; consequently, the movement lost impetus after the death of the first two generations of humanists. *Art. Architecture. The Renaissance. Italy. Florence. Urbino. Mantua. Cosimo de Medici. Filippo Brunelleschi. Lorenzo Ghiberti. Jan Van Eyck. Lorenzo de Medici. Lorenzino de Medici. Sandro Botticelli. Il Giorgione. Library of San Marco. Ducal Palace (Urbino).*

Note: Location scenes filmed in Florence, Urbino, and Mantua, Italy. First shown in Great Britain 16 Mar 1969 on BBC 2; the fourth in Sir Kenneth Clark's series on the history of Western civilization.

CIVILISATION: THE HERO AS ARTIST (Great Britain)   F6.0815

British Broadcasting Corp. *Dist* Time–Life Films. 4 Apr **1970** [New York opening]. Sd; col (Eastmancolor). 35mm. 52 min.

Prod Michael Gill, Peter Montagnon. *Asst Prod* Ann Turner. *Dir* Michael Gill. *Narr* Kenneth Clark. *Lighting Camera* A. A. Englander. *Camera Op* Kenneth MacMillan. *Camera Asst* Colin Deehan. *Lighting* Dave Griffiths, Jack Probert, Joe Cooksey, John Taylor. *Supv Film Ed* Allan Tyrer. *Ed* Jesse Palmer, Michael Shah Dayan, Peter Heelas, Roger Crittenden. *Sd Rec* Basil Harris. *Sd Asst* Malcolm Webberley. *Asst to the Prod* Carol Jones, Maggie Houston. *Res* Ann Turner. *Res Asst* June Leech. *Grip* Bill Paget.

Narrator: Kenneth Clark.

Documentary. Sir Kenneth Clark examines the Italian Renaissance of the early 16th century, when the center of activity shifted from Florence to Rome; a political factor in the shift was the return of the papacy to Vatican City after years in exile. Among the popes of the period who encouraged the revitalization of Rome was Julius II, under whom Michelangelo, Bramante, and Raphael became famous. Julius began the reconstruction of St. Peter's Basilica under Bramante's plans. A main work of the High Renaissance was Michelangelo's "David," sculptured in Florence in 1501; its heroic proportions set the tone for the art of the period. The thoughts of the Italian Renaissance were expressed largely in visual imagery, as seen in Michelangelo's ceiling of the Sistine Chapel and Raphael's frescoes for Julius' study. While Michelangelo seemed to belong to any era, Raphael was strictly a man of his age, harmonizing the various strains and influences of the time. Leonardo da Vinci, sometimes called a typical Renaissance man, was a man of consuming curiosity; his series of sketches depicting the world overwhelmed by water prophesied the end of a golden age, during which humanism and intelligence combined with the heroic ideal to express man's highest aspirations. *Art. Architecture. Sculpture. The Renaissance. Italy. Florence. Rome. Vatican. Julius II (pope). Bramante. Michelangelo. Raphael. Leonardo da Vinci. Saint Peter's Basilica. Sistine Chapel.*

Note: Location scenes filmed in the Vatican. First shown in Great Britain on 23 Mar 1969 on BBC 2; the fifth in Sir Kenneth Clark's series on the history of Western civilization.

CIVILISATION: PROTEST AND COMMUNICATION (Great Britain)
F6.0816

British Broadcasting Corp. *Dist* Time–Life Films. 11 Apr **1970** [New York opening]. Sd; col (Eastmancolor). 35mm. 52 min.

Prod Michael Gill, Peter Montagnon. *Asst Prod* Ann Turner. *Dir* Peter Montagnon. *Narr* Kenneth Clark. *Lighting Camera* A. A. Englander. *Camera Op* Kenneth MacMillan. *Camera Asst* Colin Deehan. *Lighting* Dave Griffiths, Jack Probert, Joe Cooksey, John Taylor. *Supv Film Ed* Allan Tyrer. *Ed* Jesse Palmer, Michael Shah Dayan, Peter Heelas, Roger Crittenden. *Sd Rec* Basil Harris. *Sd Asst* Malcolm Webberley. *Asst to the Prod* Carol Jones, Maggie Houston. *Res* Ann Turner. *Res Asst* June Leech. *Grip* Bill Paget.

Narrator: Kenneth Clark.

Members of the Royal Shakespeare Company: William Devlin, Ronald Lacey, Eric Porter, Ian Richardson, Patrick Stewart.

Documentary. Sir Kenneth Clark examines 16th-century northern Europe and the Reformation in this chapter of his history of Western civilization. Following the achievements of Michelangelo, Raphael, and da Vinci, there was a period of turbulence in which accepted beliefs were questioned and defied. In Germany, wealthy merchants commissioned elaborate sculptures for their churches, but the German temperament contained a streak of hysteria which would eventually lead to outward rebellion against the Church. The invention of the printing press spurred the dissemination of thought by word rather than visual imagery and helped writers such as Erasmus gain a larger audience for their ideas. The woodcut, as perfected by Albrecht Dürer, also took advantage of the new invention to illustrate the workings of the human psyche, implementing the use of perspective to heighten the sense of reality. Printing also made possible translations of the Bible into contemporary languages, thus enabling it to reach a greater number of people. Martin Luther crystalized much of the doubt and questioning of the time in his protests, although he disapproved of the resulting violence and destruction. The images in the churches—the stained glass illustrations and the statues—were destroyed as symbols of the old order. The Reformation promoted a new figure in European civilization: the intellectual recluse, typified by Michel de Montaigne. After 1570, Elizabethan England became the only country where intellectual freedom was prized and artistic achievement encouraged, giving rise to original architecture and the writings of Marlowe, Spenser, and Shakespeare. The latter's skepticism was a culmination of the protests and doubts of the Reformation. *Art. Architecture. Literature. The Reformation. Würzburg. Germany. England. Desiderius Erasmus. Albrecht Dürer. Martin Luther. Michel Eyquem de Montaigne. Christopher Marlowe. Edmund Spenser. William Shakespeare.*

Note: Location scenes filmed in Würzburg, Germany. First shown in Great Britain on 30 Mar 1969 on BBC 2; the sixth in Sir Kenneth Clark's series on the history of Western civilization.

CIVILISATION: GRANDEUR AND OBEDIENCE (Great Britain)
F6.0817

British Broadcasting Corp. *Dist* Time–Life Films. 11 Apr **1970** [New York opening]. Sd; col (Eastmancolor). 35mm. 52 min.

Prod Michael Gill, Peter Montagnon. *Asst Prod* Ann Turner. *Dir* Peter Montagnon. *Narr* Kenneth Clark. *Lighting Camera* A. A. Englander. *Camera Op* Kenneth MacMillan. *Camera Asst* Colin Deehan. *Lighting* Dave Griffiths, Jack Probert, Joe Cooksey, John Taylor. *Supv Film Ed* Allan Tyrer. *Ed* Jesse Palmer, Michael Shah Dayan, Peter Heelas, Roger Crittenden. *Sd Rec* Basil Harris. *Sd Asst* Malcolm Webberley. *Asst to the Prod* Carol Jones, Maggie Houston. *Res* Ann Turner. *Res Asst* June Leech. *Grip* Bill Paget.

Narrator: Kenneth Clark.

Documentary. This chapter of Sir Kenneth Clark's history of Western civilization explores the grandeur of Rome during the Counter-Reformation. Papal Rome, a magnificent example of town planning, was constructed only 50 years after the city was almost totally destroyed by northern barbarians. As a result of the reconstruction, the Church regained much of its spiritual force; and a belief in its authority, inspired by the saints of the 16th century, sparked a renewal of creative energy between 1620 and 1660. The quality of architecture remained superior because architects such as Della Porta, Michelangelo, and

Bernini were artists whose aesthetic principles found their greatest expression in the completion of St. Peter's Basilica. The Church's response to Protestant criticism was to glorify the very beliefs attacked during the Reformation. Baroque art, commissioned by affluent papal families, appealed to deep-seated religious impulses and gained more popularity than the intellectual art of the Renaissance. The grandeur of the period concealed a certain hollowness, however, since the wealthy families competed among themselves out of greed and vanity rather than idealism. Art exploited the popular feelings of its time and lost touch with the humanism of the Renaissance. *Art. Architecture. Sculpture. The Counter-Reformation. Rome. Vatican. Michelangelo. Giacomo Della Porta. Giovanni Lorenzo Bernini. Catholic Church. Saint Peter's Basilica.*

Note: Location scenes filmed in Rome and Vatican City. First shown in Great Britain 7 Apr 1969 on BBC 2; the seventh in Sir Kenneth Clark's series on the history of Western civilization.

CIVILISATION: THE LIGHT OF EXPERIENCE (Great Britain)
F6.0818

British Broadcasting Corp. *Dist* Time–Life Films. 18 Apr **1970** [New York opening]. Sd; col (Eastmancolor). 35mm. 52 min.

Prod Michael Gill, Peter Montagnon. *Asst Prod* Ann Turner. *Dir* Michael Gill. *Narr* Kenneth Clark. *Lighting Camera* A. A. Englander. *Camera Op* Kenneth MacMillan. *Camera Asst* Colin Deehan. *Lighting* Dave Griffiths, Jack Probert, Joe Cooksey, John Taylor. *Supv Film Ed* Allan Tyrer. *Ed* Jesse Palmer, Michael Shah Dayan, Peter Heelas, Roger Crittenden. *Sd Rec* Basil Harris. *Sd Asst* Malcolm Webberley. *Asst to the Prod* Carol Jones, Maggie Houston. *Res* Ann Turner. *Res Asst* June Leech. *Grip* Bill Paget.

Narrator: Kenneth Clark.

Documentary. This chapter of Clark's history of Western civilization explores the first scientific era, when divine authority was replaced by experience, experiment, and observation. Early 17th-century Holland, more tolerant of religious differences than the rest of Europe, was first to profit from the change. The bourgeoisie of Amsterdam, eager to immortalize themselves, had portraits painted of their business groups. Rembrandt, the most influential painter of his time, interpreted biblical history in light of his own experience. Mathematics was the dominating faith of such thinkers as Descartes, who wished to discard preconceptions in favor of direct experience, as did Vermeer in his paintings. Vermeer's concern for the effects of light had its scientific counterpart in the invention of the lens for use in scientific instruments. In the 1660's, intellectual leadership shifted from Holland to England, where the formation of the Royal Society and the publication of Newton's *Principia* marked the summit of the era of observation. After the disastrous fire in 1666, London was rebuilt according to Christopher Wren's plan, which called for the construction of 30 city churches, including St. Paul's Cathedral. The Age of Experience also saw the first conscious division between science and the poetic imagination as well as the emergence of a clearer prose style. Few men realized that the growth of capitalism and the development of rational thought would lead to a new barbarism marked by increased greed, the loss of traditional skills, and a pecuniary and pragmatic rather than aesthetic approach to the arts. *Art. Architecture. Literature. Science. Netherlands. England. Amsterdam. Greenwich (England). London. Rembrandt. René Descartes. Jan Vermeer. Christopher Wren. Isaac Newton. Saint Paul's Cathedral (London).*

Note: Location scenes filmed in Amsterdam, London, and Greenwich. First shown in Great Britain on 14 Apr 1969 on BBC 2; the eighth in Sir Kenneth Clark's series on the history of Western civilization.

CIVILISATION: THE PURSUIT OF HAPPINESS (Great Britain)
F6.0819

British Broadcasting Corp. *Dist* Time–Life Films. 18 Apr **1970** [New York opening]. Sd; col (Eastmancolor). 35mm. 52 min.

Prod Michael Gill, Peter Montagnon. *Asst Prod* Ann Turner. *Dir* Peter Montagnon. *Narr* Kenneth Clark. *Lighting Camera* A. A. Englander. *Camera Op* Kenneth MacMillan. *Camera Asst* Colin Deehan. *Lighting* Dave Griffiths, Jack Probert, Joe Cooksey, John Taylor. *Supv Film Ed* Allan Tyrer. *Ed* Jesse Palmer, Michael Shah Dayan, Peter Heelas, Roger Crittenden. *Sd Rec* Basil Harris. *Sd Asst* Malcolm Webberley. *Asst to the Prod* Carol Jones, Maggie Houston. *Res* Ann Turner. *Res Asst* June Leech. *Grip* Bill Paget.

Narrator: Kenneth Clark.

Documentary. Sir Kenneth Clark's history of Western civilization examines 18th-century music and Rococo architecture, both characterized by qualities of fluidity, symmetry, and decoration, reflecting a less serious attitude toward life than obtained in the previous century. Rococo was preceded by an austere period of classicism in France, although it was more directly influenced by Italian Baroque. The great art of the period remained religious; church music, encouraged by Lutheran reforms and the German bourgeoisie, found its greatest composer in Johann Sebastian Bach, who transcended the Baroque influences to which Handel remained faithful throughout his career. Balthasar Neumann's Vierzehnheiligen Abbey Church at Neresheim was the architectural illustration of the music of Handel and Bach. Watteau's painting reflected the Rococo reaction against classicism and its extension of the Baroque into realms of free association. The two great composers of the second half of the century were Haydn and Mozart; the drama intrinsic to the latter's music spurred the development and popularity of opera, which expressed more complex emotions than Rococo. *Art. Architecture. Music. Opera. Germany. Italy. Würzburg. Neresheim. Johann Sebastian Bach. George Frederick Handel. Balthasar Neumann. Joseph Haydn. Wolfgang Amadeus Mozart. Vierzehnheiligen Abbey Church.*

Note: Location scenes filmed in Würzburg and Neresheim, West Germany. First shown in Great Britain on 21 Apr 1969 on BBC 2; the ninth in Sir Kenneth Clark's series on the history of Western civilization.

CIVILISATION: THE SMILE OF REASON (Great Britain)   F6.0810
British Broadcasting Corp. *Dist* Time-Life Films. 25 Apr **1970** [New York opening]. Sd; col (Eastmancolor). 35mm. 52 min.
Prod Michael Gill, Peter Montagnon. *Asst Prod* Ann Turner. *Dir* Michael Gill. *Narr* Kenneth Clark. *Lighting Camera* A. A. Englander. *Camera Op* Kenneth MacMillan. *Camera Asst* Colin Deehan. *Lighting* Dave Griffiths, Jack Probert, Joe Cooksey, John Taylor. *Supv Film Ed* Allan Tyrer. *Ed* Jesse Palmer, Michael Shah Dayan, Peter Heelas, Roger Crittenden. *Sd Rec* Basil Harris. *Sd Asst* Malcolm Webberley. *Asst to the Prod* Carol Jones, Maggie Houston. *Res* Ann Turner. *Res Asst* June Leech. *Grip* Bill Paget.

Narrator: Kenneth Clark.

Documentary. Clark discusses the Enlightenment of the 18th century, when the emphasis on natural law, justice, and toleration was best expressed in the writings of Voltaire. England, acknowledged by the French philosophers as the origin of the Enlightenment, encouraged a kind of amateurism in the arts by men of wealth and leisure. The development in France of the salon, conducted by gracious hostesses, renewed the awareness of feminine qualities and provided a forum for intellectuals such as Diderot, the guiding force behind the first French encyclopedia. The Scots, practical and energetic, contributed Adam Smith, David Hume, and James Watt to the world of ideas and science. Humanism, no longer bound to the Church as in the Renaissance, constructed a new morality based on natural law and the stoicism of ancient republican Rome, a morality expressed most clearly in the paintings of David. In America, Thomas Jefferson typified the universal man of the 18th century, his genius most apparent in his designs for Monticello and the University of Virginia. The design for Washington, D. C., laid out by L'Enfant under the direction of Jefferson, also reflected the influence of the Enlightenment on the American heritage. *Art. Architecture. Science. Age of Enlightenment. France. England. Scotland. Charlottesville. Richmond (Virginia). Washington (District of Columbia). Voltaire. Denis Diderot. Adam Smith. David Hume. James Watt. Thomas Jefferson. Jacques Louis David. Pierre Charles L'Enfant. University of Virginia. Monticello.*

Note: Location scenes filmed in Charlottesville and Richmond, Virginia, and Washington, D. C. First shown in Great Britain on 28 Apr 1969 on BBC 2; the 10th in Sir Kenneth Clark's series on the history of Western civilization.

CIVILISATION: THE WORSHIP OF NATURE (Great Britain) F6.0811
British Broadcasting Corp. *Dist* Time-Life Films. 25 Apr **1970** [New York opening]. Sd; col (Eastmancolor). 35mm. 52 min.
Prod Michael Gill, Peter Montagnon. *Dir* Michael Gill, Ann Turner. *Narr* Kenneth Clark. *Lighting Camera* A. A. Englander. *Camera Op* Kenneth MacMillan. *Camera Asst* Colin Deehan. *Lighting* Dave Griffiths, Jack Probert, Joe Cooksey, John Taylor. *Supv Film Ed* Allan Tyrer. *Ed* Jesse Palmer, Michael Shah Dayan, Peter Heelas, Roger Crittenden. *Sd Rec* Basil Harris. *Sd Asst* Malcolm Webberley. *Asst to the Prod* Carol Jones, Maggie Houston. *Res* Ann Turner. *Res Asst* June Leech. *Grip* Bill Paget.

Narrator: Kenneth Clark.

Poetry Read by: C. Day Lewis.

Documentary. Sir Kenneth Clark's history of Western civilization turns to the 18th and 19th centuries, when a belief in the divinity of nature replaced Christianity as the chief creative force. Rousseau's philosophy asserted the innocence and beauty of both nature and natural man. Goethe's view of nature contained a pre-Darwinian concept of evolution, while Coleridge took a mystical and Wordsworth a religious approach in their poems. English painting expressed the desire for the simple life in the art of Constable and Turner. Ruskin studied nature to prove that it illustrated moral law. French artists less interested in the picturesque, painted either naturalistic landscapes or, influenced by Turner's emphasis on pure color, depicted the dominance of light in any setting. The Impressionism of Renoir and Monet split into several schools after only 20 years, but its influence on modern art is undeniable. Monet's final attempts to immerse himself totally in nature symbolized the need that man felt for rebirth through the love of nature. *Art. Poetry. Nature. England. France. Switzerland. Jean Jacques Rousseau. Johann Wolfgang von Goethe. Samuel Taylor Coleridge. William Wordsworth. John Constable.*

Joseph Mallord William Turner. John Ruskin. Pierre Auguste Renoir. Claude Monet. William Collins.

Note: Location scenes filmed in Switzerland and England. First shown in Great Britain on 5 May 1969 on BBC 2; the 11th in Sir Kenneth Clark's series on the history of Western civilization. C. Day Lewis reads from the poetry of William Wordsworth, Samuel Taylor Coleridge's "Hymn Before Sunrise in the Vale of Chaumouni," and William Collins' "Ode to Evening."

CIVILIZATION AND ITS DISCONTENTS   F6.0820
Dist Film-Makers' Cooperative. 2 Jan **1964** [New York opening]. Si with sd-on-tape; b&w. 16mm. 45 min.
Prod-Dir Paul Morrissey.
Cast: Marco St. John, Robin Brooks, Jared Martin, Pierre Blanchard, Virginia Bell. No information about the precise nature of this film has been found.

CLAMBAKE   F6.0821
Rhodes Pictures. *Dist* United Artists. Oct **1967** [New York opening: 13 Dec; c18 Oct 1967; LP35089]. Sd; col (Technicolor). 35mm (Techniscope). 100 min.
A Levy-Gardner-Laven Production. *Prod* Jules Levy, Arthur Gardner, Arnold Laven. *Assoc Prod* Tom Rolf. *Dir* Arthur H. Nadel. *Story-Screenplay* Arthur Browne, Jr. *Photog* William Margulies. *Art Dir* Lloyd S. Papez. *Set Decor* James S. Redd. *Film Ed* Tom Rolf. *Mus Comp & Cond* Jeff Alexander. *Song:* "Clambake" Sid Wayne, Ben Weisman. *Songs:* "Who Needs Money?" "The Girl I Never Loved" Randy Starr. *Songs:* "Confidence," "A House That Has Everything" Sid Tepper, Roy C. Bennett. *Song:* "Hey, Hey, Hey" Joy Byers. *Songs Sung by* Elvis Presley. *Choreog* Alex Romero. *Sd* Frank H. Wilkinson. *Asst Dir* Claude Binyon, Jr., Bill Green. *Prod Mgr* Ben Bishop. *Wardrobe* May Booth, Hugh McFarland. *Makeup* Dan Greenway, Howard Smit. *Hairstyles* Judy Alexander. *Sp Eff* Bob Warner, sp eff.
Cast: Elvis Presley *(Scott Heyward)*, Shelley Fabares *(Dianne Carter)*, Will Hutchins *(Tom Wilson)*, Bill Bixby *(James Jamison III)*, James Gregory *(Duster Heyward)*, Gary Merrill *(Sam Burton)*, Amanda Harley *(Ellie)*, Suzie Kaye *(Sally)*, Angelique Pettyjohn *(Gloria)*, Olga Kaya *(Gigi)*, Arlene Charles *(Olive)*, Jack Good *(Mr. Hathaway)*, Hal Peary *(doorman)*, Sam Riddle *(race announcer)*, Sue England *(cigarette girl)*, Lisa Slagle *(Lisa)*, Lee Krieger *(bartender)*, Melvin Allen *(crewman)*, Herb Barnett *(waiter)*, Steve Cory *(bellhop)*, Robert Lieb *(Barasch)*, Bob "Red" West *(ice cream vendor)*.
Comedy with music. Texas oil heir Scott Heyward rejects the offer of a vice presidency in his father's company and sets out to make good on his own. En route to Florida, he switches identities with a young motorcyclist named Tom Wilson and takes the latter's job as a water ski instructor at a Miami hotel. While Tom, posing as Scott, checks into the hotel's presidential suite, Scott starts giving skiing lessons to fortune hunter Dianne Carter, who is out to snare playboy James Jamison III, a competitor in the annual Orange Bowl Power Boat Regatta. Although Scott is eager to impress Dianne by also competing in the event, he refuses to use one of the three boats he owns in Texas. Instead, he sticks to his vow of living only on his hotel earnings by offering to drive a boat designed by Sam Burton. Since Burton's craft went to pieces in the last race because of defective protective coating, Scott sends for an experimental hardener called "Goop," which he himself developed in his father's laboratory. On the eve of the regatta, a clash between Scott and Jamison results in Dianne's admitting that her values were warped and that she is now rooting for Scott to win. He does win, and that evening, as Scott proposes to Dianne, the true identities of Scott and Tom are revealed. Stunned to learn she is actually engaged to a multimillionaire, Dianne faints dead away. *Texans. Heirs. Millionaires. Playboys. Motorcyclists. Fortune hunters. Impersonation. Boat racing. Filial relations. Water skiing. Hotels. Motorboats. Inventions. Miami.*
Note: Location scenes filmed in Florida. One source lists "You Don't Know Me" as an additional song performed in the film.

LE CLAN DES SICILIENS see THE SICILIAN CLAN

LES CLANDESTINES see VICE DOLLS

CLARENCE, THE CROSS-EYED LION   F6.0822
Ivan Tors Enterprises. *Dist* Metro-Goldwyn-Mayer, Inc. 14 Apr **1965** [Cincinnati, Ohio, opening; c1 Mar 1965; LP29820]. Sd (Westrex); col (Metrocolor). 35mm. 98 min. [Copyright length: 92 min.]
An Ivan Tors Production. *Prod* Leonard Kaufman. *Assoc Prod* Harry Redmond, Jr. *Dir* Andrew Marton. *Screenplay* Alan Caillou. *Story* Art Arthur, Marshall Thompson. *Dir Photog* Lamar Boren. *Art Dir* George W. Davis, Eddie Imazu. *Set Dsgn* Henry Grace, Jack Mills. *Supv Film Ed* Warren Adams. *Film Ed* John B. Woelz. *Mus Supv* Al Mack. *Mus Cond* Robert Armbruster. *Main Titl Mus* Shelly Manne. *Rec Supv* Franklin Milton. *Sd Rec* Philip Mitchell. *Asst Dir* G. Rex Bailey. *Asst to the Prod* Norman Siegel. *Makeup Supv* William Tuttle. *Tech Adv* Ralph Helfer.

Cast: Marshall Thompson (*Dr. Marsh Tracy*), Betsy Drake (*Julie Harper*), Richard Haydn (*Rupert Rowbotham*), Cheryl Miller (*Paula*), Alan Caillou (*Carter*), Rockne Tarkington (*Juma*), Maurice Marsac (*Gregory*), Robert DoQui (*sergeant*), Albert Amos (*Husseini*), Dinny Powell (*Dinny*), Mark Allen (*Larson*), Laurence Conroy (*tourist*), Allyson Daniell (*tourist's wife*), Janee Michelle (*girl in pit*), Naaman Brown, Napoleon Whiting (*villagers*), Chester Jones (*old man*), Clarence (*himself, a lion*), Doris (*herself, a chimpanzee*), Mary Lou (*herself, a python*).

Comedy. Dr. Marsh Tracy and his teenaged daughter, Paula, are working in an African game preserve when a harmless lion begins to wander through the villages, frightening the natives. Dr. Tracy traps the lion, examines him, and discovers that the cross-eyed animal cannot see well enough to hunt. Paula names the lion Clarence, and the two become great friends. Paula's British tutor, Rupert Rowbotham, is terrified of Clarence and the other animals on the preserve—Doris the chimpanzee and Mary Lou the python. Meanwhile, Dr. Tracy has become romantically interested in Julie Harper, an anthropologist studying gorillas in a nearby rain forest. When the news arrives that rebel terrorists are heading for the rain forest to capture gorillas to trade for weapons, Dr. Tracy rushes to the camp to save Julie; but both are captured. Rowbotham, fleeing the preserve in fear of the animals, drives into the scene, not knowing that Clarence has hidden in the back seat of his car. Clarence helps defeat the terrorists and save Dr. Tracy and Paula. *Veterinarians. British. Tutors. Anthropologists. Terrorists. Adolescence. Eyesight. Abduction. Game preserves. Africa. Apes. Lions. Chimpanzees. Snakes.*

CLASH BY NIGHT see ESCAPE BY NIGHT

CLASS OF 69   F6.0823
Janus II Productions–Academy Productions. *Dist* Jo-Jo Distributors, Exhibitors Distributing, Ltd. ca **1970**. Sd; col. 16mm. ca60 min,

Sex film. A story about the reunion of the "class of 69," this film deals with love, sex, and dope. *Sexuality. Class reunions. Narcotics.*

CLASSE TOUS RISQUES see THE BIG RISK

CLAUDE see THE TWO OF US

CLAUDE ET GRETA see HER AND SHE AND HIM

CLAUDELLE INGLISH   F6.0824
Warner Bros. Pictures. 20 Sep **1961** [New York opening; c9 Sep 1961; LP27097]. Sd; b&w. 35mm. 99 min.

Prod-Screenplay Leonard Freeman. *Dir* Gordon Douglas. *Photog* Ralph Woolsey. *Art Dir* Malcolm C. Bert. *Set Decor* Alfred E. Kegerris. *Film Ed* Folmar Blangsted. *Mus* Howard Jackson. *Sd* Francis M. Stahl. *Asst Dir* William Kissel. *Cost* Howard Shoup. *Makeup* Gordon Bau. *Hairstyles* Jean Burt Reilly.

Cast: Diane McBain (*Claudelle Inglish*), Arthur Kennedy (*Clyde Inglish*), Will Hutchins (*Dennis Peasley*), Constance Ford (*Jessie Inglish*), Claude Akins (*S. T. Crawford*), Frank Overton (*Harley Peasley*), Chad Everett (*Linn Varner*), Robert Colbert (*Rip Guyler*), Ford Rainey (*Reverend Armstrong*), James Bell (*Josh*), Robert Logan (*Charles Henry*), Jan Stine (*Dave Adams*), Hope Summers (*Ernestine Peasley*).

Melodrama. Source: Erskine Caldwell, *Claudelle Inglish* (Boston, 1959). Claudelle Inglish, the teenage daughter of a Georgia sharecropper, is in love with Linn Varner, a farmboy. Claudelle's mother, Jessie, all too aware of her own drab existence, tries to discourage the romance by urging Claudelle to marry S. T. Crawford, an older, wealthy farmowner. But Claudelle refuses, and she remains faithful to Linn even when he is drafted into the Army. When he writes that he is planning to marry someone else, however, Claudelle brazenly turns into the town trollop. Her first affair is with Dennis Peasley, whose father owns the general store. Dennis falls in love with her, but Claudelle begins "accepting gifts" from most of the other men of the town, including Dennis' father. When Clyde Inglish, Claudelle's father, learns of his daughter's reputation and accuses her of being a tramp, Claudelle angrily confronts him with the news that Jessie has been seen making love to S. T. Crawford in a parked car. A short time later, Dennis and local tough Rip Guyler come to blows over Claudelle. Their bloody fight ends in death when Rip runs his car into the hysterical Dennis. The next morning, a repentant Claudelle tells her father that Jessie has left home. Sobered by the news, father and daughter decide to move away and begin a new life. But Harley Peasley, deranged by his son's death, arrives at the Inglish farm, corners Claudelle, and shoots her. Clyde rushes into the house and embraces his daughter as she dies. *Farmers. Adolescence. Reputation. Infidelity. Filial relations. Murder. Georgia.*

Note: Location scenes filmed in northern California.

CLEAR SKIES (U.S.S.R.)   F6.0825
Mosfilm. *Dist* Eagle Film Distribution Corp. 26 Nov **1963** [New York opening]. Sd; col (Sovcolor). 35mm. 90 min.

Dir Grigoriy Chukhray. *Screenplay* Daniil Khrabrovitskiy. *Story Ed* M. Rooz. *Photog* Sergey Poluyanov. *Camera* O. Zguridi. *Art Dir* Boris Nemechek. *Film Ed* M. Timofeyeva. *Mus* Mikhail Ziv. *Cond* A. Roytman. *Sd* L. Bulgakov. *1st & 2d Asst Dir* Vladimir Glazkov, R. Bove, V. Tiunova. *Prod Mgr* V. Kantorovich. *Cost* V. Perelyotov. *Makeup* S. Kalinin. *Sp Eff* V. Rylach, A. Klimenko. *Cons* P. Kotov.

Cast: Nina Drobysheva (*Sasha Lvova*), Yevgeniy Urbanskiy (*Aleksey Astakhov*), N. Kuzmina (*Lyusya*), Vitaliy Konyayev (*Petya*), G. Kulikov (*Mitya*), L. Knyazev (*Ivan Ilich*), Oleg Tabakov, Alik Krylov (*Sergey*), G. Georgiu (*Nikolay Avdeyevich*), Vitalik Bondarev (*Yegorka*), A. Aleksandrushkin, V. Anisko, K. Bartashevich, A. Dubov, P. Kiryutkin, Tamara Nosova, N. Khryashchikov.

Drama. On New Year's Eve 1941, test pilot Aleksey Astakhov because of a misunderstanding attends a party at the home of the Lvovs to which he has not been invited. When the mistake becomes clear, he leaves, and though Sasha Lvova recognizes him and wants him to return, it is too late. When the city is evacuated, Sasha remains behind to work at a factory. During an air raid, Aleksey and Sasha meet again, and in the few free evenings they spend together, they fall in love. A short time later, Sasha hears a radio report that Aleksey has been lost in action; and posthumously he is made a Hero of the Soviet Union. Sasha gives birth to their son and continues to hope that Aleksey is alive. Finally, with the end of the war, Aleksey returns from a German prison camp scarred and prematurely aged. In the post-war years, under Stalin's leadership, Aleksey's wartime surrender to the Germans creates suspicion of disloyalty. His Party membership is revoked and he is prevented from working as a pilot. Aleksey loses hope and begins drinking heavily, but Sasha maintains her faith in him and attempts to encourage him to look toward the future. After Stalin's death, Aleksey's case is reviewed and all of his honors are restored. Once again Aleksey's test plane flies through the skies. *Air pilots. War heroes. Prisoners of war. Communists. Injustice. Stalinism. Alcoholism. Illegitimacy. World War II.*

Note: Released in the U.S.S.R. in May 1961 as *Chistoye nebo*; running time: 109 min.

CLÉO DE 5 À 7 see CLEO FROM 5 TO 7

CLEO FROM 5 TO 7 (France)   F6.0826
Rome-Paris Films. *Dist* Zenith International Film Corp. 4 Sep **1962** [New York opening]. Sd; b&w with credit titl seq in col (Eastman Color). 35mm. 90 min.

Prod-Exec Prod Georges de Beauregard. *Assoc Prod* Bruna Drigo. *Exec Prod* Carlo Ponti. *Dir-Screenplay-Adapt-Dial* Agnès Varda. *Dir Photog* Jean Rabier. *Camera Op* Alain Levent. *Asst Camera Op* Paul Bonis. *Art Dir* Bernard Evein. *Film Ed* Janine Verneau. *Asst Film Ed* Pascale Laverrière. *Mus & Songs* Michel Legrand. *Lyr* Agnès Varda. *Sd Engr* Jean Labussière, Julien Coutellier. *Sd Ed* Jacques Maumont. *Asst Dir* Bernard Toublanc-Michel, Marin Karmitz. *Prod Mgr* Edith Tertza, Jean-François Adam. *Script Girl* Aurore Paquiss. *Cost Dsgn* Bernard Evein. *Cost* Alyette Samazeuilh. *Makeup* Aïda Carange. *Apprentice* Noune Serra, Claude Laporte. *Still Photog* Liliane de Kermadec. *English Titl* Rose Sokol.

Cast: Corinne Marchand (*Cléo*), Antoine Bourseiller (*Antoine*), Dorothée Blank (*Dorothée*), Michel Legrand (*Bob, the pianist*), Dominique Davray (*Angèle*), José-Luis de Vilallonga (*Cléo's lover*), Jean-Luc Godard, Anna Karina, Eddie Constantine, Sami Frey, Danièle Delorme, Jean-Claude Brialy, Yves Robert, Alan Scott (*actors in comedy film*), Robert Postec, Lucienne Marchand.

Drama. One afternoon in Paris, Cléo, a beautiful chanteuse, awaits the results of tests to determine whether or not she has cancer. In the interval, she visits a fortune-teller and is horrified when the tarot cards confirm her fears. She seeks consolation with Angèle, her companion and manager, in a cafe. They visit a shop where Cléo views herself in a mirror, obtaining reassurance that she is still young and beautiful, and buys a hat. Returning to her Montparnasse home, Cléo is visited by her lover, a busy man who can offer her only a moment of polite concern. Her songwriter and pianist arrive to rehearse a new number, but the song suddenly recalls her fears and she leaves, unable to tolerate the banter of the musicians. At a cafe she plays one of her own recordings, but no one listens. She visits her friend Dorothée, an artist's model, and together they deliver some film to Dorothée's lover, a motion picture projectionist. He projects a short comedy film for them, and Cléo momentarily forgets her anxiety. Dorothée breaks her mirror as they leave, and again Cléo becomes upset and wanders about the city. As 7 o'clock approaches, she strolls through the Parc Montsouris and meets Antoine, a young and good-natured soldier enjoying his last few hours of leave before returning to Algeria. She tells him of her situation, and he promises to accompany her to the doctor's office. Cléo is now able to face the verdict with courage. *Singers. Fortune-tellers. Physicians. Composers. Musicians. Models. Motion picture projectionists. Soldiers. Death. Cancer. Fear. Friendship. Cafes. Rehearsals. Motion pictures.*

Parks. Paris—Montparnasse. Paris.
   Note: Paris opening: Apr 1962 as *Cléo de 5 à 7.*

CLEOPATRA (United States/Great Britain)   **F6.0827**
   Twentieth Century-Fox Film Productions–MCL Films–Walwa Films. *Dist* Twentieth Century-Fox Film Corp. 12 Jun **1963** [New York opening; c19 Jun 1963; LP28304]. Sd (Westrex); col (De Luxe). 35mm & 70mm (Todd-AO). 243 min. [Cut to 222 min.]
   Production Credits: *Prod* Walter Wanger. *Dir* Joseph L. Mankiewicz. *2d Unit Dir* Ray Kellogg, Andrew Marton. *Screenplay* Joseph L. Mankiewicz, Ranald MacDougall, Sidney Buchman. *Dir Photog* Leon Shamroy. *2d Unit Photog* Claude Renoir, Piero Portalupi. *Col Cons* Leonard Doss. *Art Dir* Jack Martin Smith, Hilyard Brown, Herman Blumenthal, Maurice Pelling, Elven Webb, Boris Juraga. *Set Decor* Walter M. Scott, Paul S. Fox, Ray Moyer. *Prod Dsgn* John De Cuir. *Film Ed* Dorothy Spencer. *Mus Comp & Cond* Alex North. *Assoc Mus Cond* Lionel Newman. *Choreog* Hermes Pan. *Sd Rec Supv* Fred Hynes, James Corcoran. *Sd Rec* Bernard Freericks, Murray Spivack. *Asst Dir* Fred R. Simpson. *Prod Mgr* Forrest E. Johnston, C. O. Erickson. *2d Unit Prod Mgr* Saul Wurtzel. *Elizabeth Taylor's Cost* Irene Sharaff. *Men's Cost* Vittorio Nino Novarese. *Women's Cost* Renie. *Makeup* Alberto De Rossi. *Miss Taylor's Hairstylist* Vivienne Zavitz. *Sp Photog Eff* L. B. Abbott, Emil Kosa, Jr.
   Original Production Staff (see note): *Dir* Rouben Mamoulian. *Screenplay* Nigel Balchin, Ludi Claire, Dale Wasserman, Lawrence Durrell. *Script Cons* Nunnally Johnson, Marc Brandel. *Lighting Camera* Jack Hildyard. *Casting Cons* Stuart Lyons.
   Cast: Elizabeth Taylor (*Cleopatra*), Richard Burton (*Mark Antony*), Rex Harrison (*Julius Caesar*), Pamela Brown (*High Priestess*), George Cole (*Flavius*), Hume Cronyn (*Sosigenes*), Cesare Danova (*Apollodorus*), Kenneth Haigh (*Brutus*), Andrew Keir (*Agrippa*), Martin Landau (*Rufio*), Roddy McDowall (*Octavian*), Robert Stephens (*Germanicus*), Francesca Annis (*Eiras*), Grégoire Aslan (*Pothinos*), Martin Benson (*Ramos*), Herbert Berghof (*Theodotos*), John Cairney (*Phoebus*), Jacqui Chan (*Lotos*), Isabelle Cooley (*Charmian*), John Doucette (*Achillas*), Andrew Faulds (*Canidius*), Michael Gwynn (*Cimber*), Michael Hordern (*Cicero*), John Hoyt (*Cassius*), Marne Maitland (*Euphranor*), Carroll O'Connor (*Casca*), Richard O'Sullivan (*Ptolemy*), Gwen Watford (*Calpurnia*), Douglas Wilmer (*Decimus*), Marina Berti (*Queen at Tarsus*), John Karlsen (*High Priest*), Loris Loddi (*Caesarion, age 4*), Jean Marsh (*Octavia*), Gin Mart (*Marcellus*), Furio Meniconi (*Mithridates*), Del Russell (*Caesarion, age 7*), Kenneth Nash (*Caesarion, age 12*), John Valva (*Valvus*), Finlay Currie (*Titus*), Laurence Naismith (*Archesilius*), John Alderson, Peter Forster, Gesa Meiken, Marie Devereux, Michèle Bally, Kathy Martin, Maria Badmajev, Maureen Lane, Simon Mizrahi, John Gayford.
   Historical epic. Based upon ancient sources, including histories by: Plutarch, Suetonius and Appianus. Charles Marie Franzero, *The Life and Times of Cleopatra* (London, 1957). In 48 B. C. Caesar pursues Pompey from Pharsalia to Egypt. Ptolemy, now sovereign after deposing his older sister, Cleopatra, attempts to curry favor with Caesar by presenting the conquerer with the head of Pompey, borne by his satraps, Pothinos and Achillas. To win Caesar's support from her brother, Cleopatra hides herself in a rug, which Apollodorus, her minion, presents to Caesar. The Roman is immediately infatuated; banishing Ptolemy, he declares Cleopatra Egypt's sole sovereign and takes her as his concubine. A son, Caesarion, is born of their union. Caesar, however, must return to Italy. Although he is briefly reunited with Cleopatra during a magnificent reception for the queen in Rome, Caesar is assassinated shortly thereafter, and his paramour returns to Egypt. When Mark Antony, Caesar's protege, beholds Cleopatra aboard her barque at Tarsus some years later, he is smitten and becomes both her lover and military ally. Their liaison notwithstanding, Antony, to consolidate his position in Rome, marries Octavia, sister of the ambitious Octavian. The marriage satisfies no one: Cleopatra is infuriated, and Antony, tiring of his Roman wife, returns to Egypt. There he flaunts his liaison by marrying Cleopatra in a public ceremony. Sensing Antony's weakness, Octavian attacks and defeats his forces at Actium. Alarmed, Cleopatra withdraws her fleet and seeks refuge in her tomb. Falsely informed that she is dead, Antony stabs himself. Borne to her sanctuary, he expires in her arms. In despair, Cleopatra applies an asp to her breast and dies of its poison. *Royalty. Soldiers. Egyptians. Politics. Military life. Marriage. Assassination. Infidelity. Suicide. Tombs. Weddings. Rome—History— Empire. Egypt—Ancient. Gaius Julius Caesar. Cleopatra. Mark Antony. Octavia. Pompey the Great. Ptolemy XIII. Gaius Julius Caesar Octavianus. Snakes.*
   Note: Location scenes filmed in Italy (Torre Astura, Anzio, Ischia, and Lanuvio); Egypt (Alexandria, Edkou, and desert locales); and Spain (Almeria). Opened in London in Aug 1963; running time: 215 min. Earlier footage by Mamoulian included in the final version.

CLEOPATRA'S DAUGHTER (France/Italy)   **F6.0828**
   Explorer Film–C. F. P. C. *Dist* Medallion Pictures. Feb **1963**. Sd; col (Eastman Color, print by Technicolor). 35mm (Ultrascope). 93 min.
   Dir Fernando Cerchio. *Dub Vers Dir* Richard McNamara. *Screenplay* Fernando Cerchio, Damiano Damiani. *Photog* Anchise Brizzi. *Art Dir* Arrigo Equini. *Film Ed* Antonietta Zita. *Mus* Antonio Fusco. *Sd* Mario Amari, Ovidio Del Grande. *Asst Dir* Giuliano Betti. *Prod Mgr* Manlio Morelli. *Cost* Giancarlo Bartolini Salimbeni.
   Cast: Debra Paget (*Shila*), Ettore Manni (*Resi*), Erno Crisa (*Kefren*), Robert Alda (*Inuni*), Corrado Pani (*Nemorat*), Yvette Lebon (*Queen Tegi*), Andreina Rossi (*Kefren's mistress*), Ivano Staccioli, Renato Mambor.
   Adventure melodrama. Following the Egyptian defeat of the Syrians, Tegi, the cruel Queen Mother of Egypt, imprisons Shila, Cleopatra's Syrian daughter. Tegi forces Shila to marry her son Nemorat, the Pharoah, thereby uniting Egypt and Syria; but before the marriage is consummated, Nemorat is poisoned by his scheming uncle, Kefren. Shila, falsely accused of the crime, is sentenced to be buried alive with her husband's body. Resi, the court physician, has fallen in love with Shila and gives her a potion which induces a state simulating death. After Shila is entombed in the pyramid, Resi, aided by tomb robbers, abducts Inuni, the head pyramid architect, and forces him to lead them to the treasure-filled burial chamber. Here the greedy robbers are immured, but Inuni helps Shila and Resi to escape although he is trapped in the tomb. Kefren is unmasked as the murderer, and the two lovers flee to the desert with a passing caravan. *Syrians. Royalty. Uncles. Physicians. Grave robbers. Architects. Abduction. Marriage—Arranged. Poisoning. Murder. Frameup. Capital punishment. Potions. Deserts. Vaults. Egypt. Cleopatra. Pyramids (Egypt).*
   Note: Opened in Rome and Paris in Jun 1961; running time: 102 min. Italian title: *Il sepolcro dei re;* French title: *La vallée des Pharaons.* Also known as *Daughter of Cleopatra.*

THE CLIMAX (France/Italy)   **F6.0829**
   Produzioni Associate Delphos–Les Productions Artistes Associés–R. P. A.– Compagnia Cinematografica Montoro–Dear Film. *Dist* Lopert Pictures. 11 Sep **1967** [New York opening]. Sd; b&w. 35mm. 97 min.
   Pres by Dear Film. *Prod-Dir* Pietro Germi. *Exec Prod* Robert Haggiag. *Screenplay-Story* Pietro Germi, Alfredo Giannetti, Tullio Pinelli, Carlo Bernari. *Photog* Aiace Parolin. *Set Decor* Andrea Fantacci. *Prod Dsgn* Carlo Egidi. *Film Ed* Sergio Montanari. *Mus* Carlo Rustichelli. *Sd* Guido Ortensi. *Asst Dir* Francesco Massaro. *Dir Prod* Luigi Giacosi. *Prod Mgr* Gianni Cecchin. *Wardrobe* Angela Sammaciccia. *Makeup* Raffaele Cristini. *Hairstyles* Martina Patacca.
   Cast: Ugo Tognazzi (*Sergio Masini*), Stefania Sandrelli (*Marisa Malagugini*), Renée Longarini (*Giulia Masini*), Maria Grazia Carmassi (*Adela Baistrocchi*), Gigi Ballista (*Don Michele*), Sergio Fincato (*Colasanti*), Marco Della Giovanna (*Riccardo Massini*), Ildebrando Santafé (*Caputo*), Riccardo Billi (*Filiberto Malagugini*), Carlo Bagno (*Mr. Malagugini*), Lina Lagalla (*Mrs. Malagugini*), Stefano Chierchie (*Bruno*), Costantino Bramini (*Nini*), Cinzia Sperapani (*Luisa*), Mimosa Gregoretti (*Mita*), Giorgio Bianchi (*head clinic doctor*), Giovanna Lenzi (*nurse*).
   Domestic comedy. Sergio Masini, a concert violinist in an Italian symphony orchestra, is deeply devoted to three separate families. His legal wife of eighteen years, Giulia, bore him a son and two daughters. Then 8 years later, he met Adela, a singer who lost her voice while they were with a touring opera company. Sergio made her his mistress, fathered her two children, and showed her as much consideration as he bestowed upon his wife. Lastly, he was attracted to a young music student, Marisa, who won him over with her simplicity and her need for someone to love. While Marisa is in a clinic awaiting the birth of a child, Sergio wanders into a church and unburdens himself to a priest, describing his efforts to support his three households equally. He maintains three sets of insurance, buys three sets of Christmas presents, honors all birthdays, and, on occasion, even eats three evening meals at three different homes. To make ends meet, he sings in a cabaret during late hours. Upon hearing the story, the startled priest warns Sergio that he cannot continue such a pace and hints that a divorce might be the answer. Shocked, Sergio leaves the church and returns to the clinic where Marisa has given birth to a boy. Seeing how tired Sergio looks, Marisa, who knows about his wife and other mistress, suggests that he take a rest at the seashore with Giulia. But when he goes to telephone her, he suffers a heart attack and dies. Sergio watches his funeral from the hereafter and tries to discern from his wife's face whether she suspected the truth about his other families, but all that Giulia reveals is an enigmatic smile. *Violinists. Singers. Mistresses. Students. Priests. Infidelity. Family life. Marriage. Fatherhood. Childbirth. Heart disease. Confession. Funerals. Heaven.*
   Note: Released in Italy in 1967 as *L'immorale;* in Paris in Apr 1968 as *Beaucoup trop pour un seul homme.* Also known as *Too Much for One Man.* Sources conflict in crediting production companies: Italian references list R. P.

A., Delphos, and Les Productions Artistes Associés, with Dear Film as distributor; several American sources credit Dear Film as presentor; and other American sources mention Montoro Films and Dear Film.

THE CLOCK STRIKES THREE see **WHEN THE CLOCK STRIKES**

CLOPORTES (France/Italy)   **F6.0830**

Les Films du Siècle-Produzioni Artistiche Internazionali. *Dist* International Classics. 18 Apr **1966** [New York opening; c31 Dec 1965; LF7]. Sd; b&w. 35mm (CinemaScope). 102 min.

Prod Bertrand Javal. *Dir* Pierre Granier-Deferre. *Dial* Michel Audiard. *Adapt* Albert Simonin. *Dir Photog* Nicolas Hayer. *Camera* Philippe Brun. *Asst Camera* Yves Rodallec, Arlette Massay. *Set Dsgn* Jacques Saulnier. *Asst Set Dsgn* Georges Glon, Gérard Viard. *Main Titl* Jean Fouchet. *Film Ed* Jean Ravel. *Asst Ed* Hélène Muller, Mireille Joly. *Mus Comp & Perf* Jimmy Smith. *Sd Engr* Jean Labussière. *Sd Asst* Yves Dacquay, Jean Bareille. *Asst Dir* Jean-Michel Lacor, Jean-Pierre Petrolacci, Patrice de Balliencourt. *Prod Mgr* Paul Joly. *Script Girl* Hélène Sébillotte. *Prod Asst* Paulette Boréal. *Wardrobe* Charles Merangel. *Makeup* Georges Bouban. *Makeup for Miss Irina Demick* John O'Gorman. *Still Photog* Dimitry Fedotoff.

Cast: Lino Ventura *(Alphonse)*, Charles Aznavour *(Edmond)*, Irina Demick *(Catherine)*, Maurice Biraud *(Arthur)*, Georges Géret *(Rouquemoute)*, Pierre Brasseur *(Tonton)*, Françoise Rosay *(Gertrude)*, Annie Fratellini *(Leone)*, Georges Blaness *(Omar)*, François Mirante *(1st inspector)*, François Dalou *(2d inspector)*, Patricia Scott *(Elizabeth)*, Marie-Hélène Dasté *(Mme. Clancul)*, Daniel Ceccaldi *(Lescure)*, Georges Chamarat *(Clancul)*, Norman Bart, Dorothée Blank, J. P. Caussade, Marcel Charvey, Michel Dacquin, Carlos Da Silva, Michel Duplaix, Michel Garland, Donald O'Brien, Renée Passeur, André Thorent, François Valorbe.

Crime comedy-drama. Source: Alphonse Boudard, *La métamorphose des cloportes* (Paris, 1962). Three French thieves—Edmond, Arthur and Rouquemoute—make plans to rob a money-lending establishment situated next door to a funeral parlor. Needing money for a blowtorch, they bring in Alphonse, a former boxer now dealing in stolen art, by exaggerating the potential gain. He raises the necessary cash by selling a Braque to a sly fence named Tonton. The robbery, however, is a dismal failure and Alphonse is captured as his cronies make off in the getaway car. Rather than be branded a stool pigeon, Alphonse serves a 5-year prison term only to discover that the three thieves have looted his apartment of everything of any value. When he is released, he sets a plan of revenge into action and eliminates his double-crossing pals. Before Rouquemoute dies, he confesses that Tonton was behind the robbery of Alphonse's apartment. Already in love with Tonton's girl friend Catherine, Alphonse now makes plans to take over both Tonton's art gallery and girl. But Catherine proves to be the best of the *cloportes*: she shoots Tonton, makes Alphonse appear to be guilty, sees him taken to jail, and then settles down to enjoy the fruits of her work. *Thieves. Fences (for stolen goods). Boxers. Mistresses. Robbery. Revenge. Perfidy. Murder. Frameup. Prisons. Art galleries.*

Note: Released in France in 1965 as *La métamorphose des cloportes*; Italian release title: *Sotto il tallone.*

CLOSELY WATCHED TRAINS (Czechoslovakia)   **F6.0831**

Barrandov Film Studio. For Československý Film. *Dist* Sigma III Corp. 15 Oct **1967** [New York opening]. Sd; b&w. 35mm. 89 min.

Pres by Carlo Ponti. *Prod* Zdeněk Oves. *Dir* Jiří Menzel. *Screenplay* Jiří Menzel, Bohumil Hrabal. *Dir Photog* Jaromír Šofr. *Camera* Jaromír Huik. *Lighting* Zak. *Art Dir* Oldřich Bosák. *Asst Art Dir* Bohumil Nový. *Sets* Jiří Cvrček. *Film Ed* Jiřina Lukešová. *Asst Ed* Štěpánka Stříbrná. *Mus* Jiří Šust. *Playcd by* The Film Symphony Orchestra. *Mus Cond* Štěpán Koníček. *Mus of the Czechoslovak Army Cond* Eduard Kudelašek. *Sd* Jiří Pavlík. *Asst Dir* Bohumil Kouba. *Prod Sec* Manuela Peterová. *Prod Asst* Jaroslav Vagner. *Cont* Jana Novotná. *Wardrobe* Olga Dimitrovová. *Cost Supv* Jaroslav Holub. *Cost Prod* Růžena Bulicková. *Makeup* Miroslav Koubek. *Expert Adv* J. Šimak, Colonel Golyser. *Coöp* B. Cajthaml. *Still Photog* Jiří Stach. *English Subtitl* M. A. Gebert. *Production Group* Šmída–Fikar.

Cast: Václav Neckář *(Trainee Miloš Hrma)*, Jitka Bendová *(Conductor Maša)*, Vladimír Valenta *(stationmaster)*, Libuše Havelková *(stationmaster's wife)*, Josef Somr *(train dispatcher Hubicka)*, Alois Vachek *(station assistant)*, Jitka Zelenohorská *(telegraphist)*, Vlastimil Brodský *(Councilor Zedniček)*, Ferdinand Kruta *(Uncle Noneman)*, Květa Fialová *(The Countess)*, Naďa Urbánková *(Victoria Freie)*, Jiří Menzel *(Dr. Brabec)*, Nadežda Gayerová.

Comedy-drama. Source: Bohumil Hrabal, *Ostře sledované vlaky* (Prague, 1965). In German-occupied Czechoslovakia, Miloš becomes an apprentice train dispatcher at a small railway station. Inexperienced and impressionable, Miloš watches with awe and envy as his superior, Hubicka, performs his duties while concentrating on making sexual conquests on the station house sofa. Hubicka thus comes into conflict with the pompous stationmaster, a pigeon-

fancier. Hopeful of ending his virginity, Miloš embarks on a romance with Maša, a pretty train conductor. But when he spends the night with her at her uncle's photographic studio, he finds himself impotent. Despondent over his failure, he rents a hotel room and slashes his wrists, but his suicide attempt fails. A sympathetic doctor suggests that he find an experienced woman to instruct him sexually, but Miloš cannot find anyone willing to be his teacher. Meanwhile, Hubicka secretly plans to blow up a German munitions train when it passes through the town. On the eve of the train's arrival, an ex-circus performer working with the resistance brings explosives to the station house. Noticing Miloš' scarred wrists and hearing of his dilemma, she serves as his teacher. Early the next morning, as the munitions train approaches, Hubicka is detained by a pro-Nazi councilor and obliged to stand trial for using official rubber stamps to make imprints on the buttocks of his teenaged telegraphist. During the hearing, Miloš makes off with the dynamite, climbs the signal tower, and hurls the explosives onto the train as it passes beneath him. A German soldier shoots him, however, and he falls onto one of the railway cars. While Maša waits to declare her love for Miloš, the air is shattered by the blast from the exploding munitions train. *Nazis. Railroad dispatchers. Railroad conductors. Stationmasters. Virginity. Sexual initiation. Resistance (political). Sabotage. Suicide. Seduction. Military occupation. Explosives. World War II.*

Note: Location scenes filmed in Loděnice with the cooperation of the Loděnice railway stationmaster, B. Cajthaml, and the CSD employees. Released in Czechoslovakia in 1966 as *Ostře sledované vlaky*; running time: 92 min. First shown in the United States in 1966 at the Museum of Modern Art as *A Difficult Love.*

THE CLOSER TO THE BONE THE SWEETER THE MEAT   **F6.0832**

Dist Distribpix, Inc. **1969**. Sd; col. 35mm. 63 min.

Prod Jack Bravman, Michael Findlay. *Dir* Michael Findlay. *Photog* Roberta Findlay. *Film Ed* Michael Findlay.

Sex film. No information about the specific nature of this film has been found, but pressbook materials suggest that it includes scenes of troilism, lesbianism, and flagellation. *Troilism. Lesbianism. Flagellation.*

THE CLOSEST OF KIN see **ALL THE LOVIN' KINFOLK**

THE CLOSET see **THE CHELSEA GIRLS**

CLOUDS OVER ISRAEL (Israel)   **F6.0833**

Israel Co-Production Films-Harold Cornsweet Productions-Du-Or Films. *Dist* Harold Cornsweet Productions, Hemisphere Pictures. 3 Nov **1965** [Cleveland opening]. Sd; b&w. 35mm. 85 min.

Prod Mati Raz, Harold Cornsweet. *Dir* Ivan Lengyel. *Screenplay* Moshe Hadar. *Photog* Marko Yakovlevich. *Film Ed* Dani Schick. *Mus* Naom Sheriff. *Sd* Zalman Nachtigal.

Cast: Yiftah Spector *(Dan)*, Ehud Banai, El-Or *(Bedouin boy)*, Dina Doronne *(Bedouin woman)*, Hadara Azulai *(Sinaia)*, Shaika Levi *(enemy pilot)*, Itzhak Benyamini *(enemy scout)*, Itzhak Barzilai *(enemy soldier)*, Ygal Alon *(enemy jeep soldier)*, Shimon Israeli *(Uri)*, Sinaia Hamdan.

War drama. During the Israeli-Arab War of 1956, Dan, a young Israeli pilot, is forced to bail out of his plane inside enemy-held desert territory. The plane crash destroys a Bedouin encampment, leaving only a Bedouin woman, her 5-year-old son, and an infant girl. When Dan finds them, the woman is severely burned, suffering from shock, and unable to nurse her baby. He cares for her and nourishes the child with goat's milk. Later, the woman repays his kindness by hiding him from an Egyptian patrol. Eventually, a lost Israeli army officer joins them and nearly guns down the woman to protect his security; but the pilot restrains him, and together they attempt to repair a small reconnaissance plane. As the three survivors work together, national differences disappear, and the officer is deeply touched when the Arab boy asks him to become his new father. Consequently, when the plane is repaired, the officer remains behind as Dan takes off with the Bedouin family; but the plane crashes, and only the infant girl, Sinaia, survives. The officer takes the child in one arm and a submachine gun in the other and heads toward the desert. *Air pilots. Bedouins. War victims. Orphans. Soldiers. Survival. Deserts. Israeli-Arab War 1956. Airplane accidents.*

Note: Location scenes filmed in the Negev. Released in Israel in 1962 as *Sinaia*. Photographer Marko Yakovlevich is also credited as Marco Ya'acobi. El-Or may be a pseudonym for Ehud Banai.

THE CLOWN AND THE KID   **F6.0834**

Harvard Film Corp. *Dist* United Artists. 27 Dec **1961** [Los Angeles opening]. Sd; b&w. 35mm. 65 min.

Prod Robert E. Kent. *Dir* Edward L. Cahn. *Screenplay* Herbert Abbott Spiro, Jerry Sackheim. *Photog* Gilbert Warrenton. *Set Decor* Don Webb. *Film Ed* Irving Berlin, ed. *Sd* Stan Cooley. *Asst Dir* Kenny Walters, Buddy Messinger. *Prod Mgr* Joseph Small. *Unit Mgr* Herbert S. Greene. *Script Supv* Richard Walton. *Wardrobe* Bill Edwards, Barbara Maxwell. *Makeup* Tom

Miller, Jr. *Hairstyles* Helen Lierly. *Sp Eff* Barney Wolff. *Still Photog* Madison Lacy.

Cast: John Lupton *(Peter Stanton)*, Mike McGreevey *(Shawn)*, Don Keefer *(Moko)*, Mary Webster *(Robin)*, Mary Adams *(mother superior)*, Peggy Stewart *(Sister Grace)*, Barry Kelley *(Detective Barker)*, Ken Mayer *(trooper)*, Charles G. Martin *(Daly)*, Victor French *(1st patrolman)*, James Parnell *(2d patrolman)*, Edith Evanson.

Melodrama. Moko, the clown, knowing he has but a short time to live, is taking his son, Shawn, to a convent school in Darwin, Texas. Moko dies on the way, and Shawn unwittingly takes up with an escaped convict, Peter, who uses Moko's makeup and identity to conceal himself from the authorities. Peter and Shawn take jobs with an amusement park owned by Robin, who falls in love with Peter. Learning of Peter's true identity, Shawn rides off on his horse, "King," into a raging tornado. The police arrive for Peter, but he escapes to search for Shawn. Finding him unconscious from a fall, Peter brings him back for aid, knowing he must give himself up to the police. *Clowns. Prison escapees. Orphans. Police. Filial relations. Incurable illness. Disguise. Self-sacrifice. Convents. Amusement parks. Texas. Tornadoes. Horses.*

THE CLOWN AND THE KIDS (United States/Bulgaria)　　**F6.0835**
Brown-Fox Film Productions-Bulgarian State Films. *Dist* Childhood Productions. Oct **1968**. Sd; col (Eastman Color). 35mm. 75 min.

Prod Silas Fox. *Assoc Prod* Leonard Green. *Dir-Writ* Mende Brown. *Photog* Dimo Kolarov. *Mus & Songs:* "Good Friends, Good-Bye," "Happiness Will Be Your Reward," "I Hate Kids," "I Mean He's Mean," "I Used To Be a Griper," "I've Got a Brother (I've Got a Sister)," "Love and Be Loved," "My House Is Empty," "The Piper's Song," "Waltz for a Circus Elephant," "What Is a Circus" Tony Velona. *Asst Dir* Violeta Lazarova, Nikolay Popov. *Prod Mgr* Kiro Kirov.

Cast: Emmett Kelly *(The Piper)*, Burt Stratford *(Mark, his son)*, Katie Dunn *(Freny, his daughter)*, Mikhail Mikhailov *(Mr. Scrag)*, Leo Conforti *(mayor)*, Bogomil Simeonov *(Scrag's lieutenant)*, Oleg Kovachev *(Billy)*, Naicho Petrov.

Musical comedy-drama. Based on a story by: Wilhelm Hauff. The Piper Family Circus arrives in the Balkan village of Scragsville, where the somber inhabitants are forbidden by the rich miller Scrag to have fun. Disobeying Scrag, the children rush to greet Piper the clown and tell him of the miller's cruelty. At the clown's suggestion, the children begin to cry, thereby forcing Scrag to permit them to attend the circus. After the performance, Piper teaches the children a song and tells them to respect their parents. When Scrag attempts to prevent the circus from leaving town, Piper plays his song on a flute and summons the children. Scrag is defeated by the youngsters and the circus leaves the happy village. *Millers. Children. Clowns. Flutists. Circus. Balkans.*

Note: Location scenes filmed in Koprivshtitsa. Bulgarian title: *Svirachŭt.* U. S. working titles: *The Piper* and *The Pied Piper.*

CLOWNS IN CLOVER *see* **LIFE IS A CIRCUS**

THE CLUE OF THE MISSING APE (Great Britain)　　**F6.0836**
Gaumont-British Picture Corp. *For* Children's Film Foundation. *Dist* Continental Distributing, Inc. 26 Apr **1962** [Maryland license]. sd; b&w. 35mm. 58 min.

Prod Frank Wells. *Dir-Script* James Hill. *Story* Frank Wells, Donald Carter, Commander Hackforth-Jones. *Photog* James Allen. *Art Dir* Jack Stephens. *Film Ed* Arthur Stevens. *Asst Ed* Mary Ross-Wood. *Mus* Jack Beaver. *Sd* Maurice Askew. *Asst Dir* Laurie Hardy Brown. *Cont* Audrey Salter. *Makeup* Harry Richmond.

Cast: Nati Banda *(Pilar Ellis)*, Roy Savage, British *(Jimmy Sutton)*, George Cole *(Gobo)*, Patrick Boxill *(Mr. Palmer)*, William Patrick *(Lieutenant-Commander Collier)*, Marcus Simpson *(Petty Officer Ellis)*, Bill Shine *(henchman in opening sequence)*, John Ocello, Peter Copley, Evelyn Roberts, Harold Siddons, John Welsh, Julian Somers, William Walter, Luis Ellul, Carla Challoner.

Action melodrama. Having heroically rescued a pilot from his burning plane, young Jimmy Sutton is rewarded with a trip to Gibraltar, where he befriends Pilar, daughter of host Petty Officer Ellis. Although the children uncover a plot by international spies both to undermine morale by killing the famous Gibraltar apes and to decimate the Royal Navy, their elders are unbelieving. Jimmy and Pilar steal the plans for the fleet's destruction, however, enabling frogmen to deactivate limpet mines attached to the ship *Vanguard* and facilitate apprehension of the saboteurs. *Children. Spies. Frogmen. Heroism. Demolition—Underwater. Sabotage. Mines (war explosives). Gibraltar. Great Britain—Royal Navy. Airplane accidents. Chases. Apes.*

Note: Location scenes filmed on Gibraltar; working title: *Apes on the Rock.* Released in Great Britain in 1953 as *Gibraltar Adventure.*

CLUE OF THE TWISTED CANDLE (Great Britain)　　**F6.0837**
Merton Park Studios. *Dist* Schoenfeld Film Distributing Corp. Jul **1968**. Sd; b&w. 35mm. 61 min.

Prod Jack Greenwood. *Assoc Prod* Jim O'Connolly. *Dir* Allan Davis. *Screenplay* Philip Mackie. *Photog* Brian Rhodes. *Camera Op* Alf Hicks. *Art Dir* Wilfred Arnold. *Film Ed* Bernard Gribble. *Mus* Francis Chagrin. *Titl Mus* Michael Carr, mus. *Sd Rec* Sid Rider, Ronald Abbott. *Sd Ed* Derek Holding. *Asst Dir* Jimmy Komisarjevsky. *Prod Mgr* Harry Kratz. *Wardrobe* Freda Gibson. *Makeup* Michael Morris.

Cast: Bernard Lee *(Superintendent Meredith)*, David Knight *(John Lexman/Dr. Griswold)*, Francis De Wolff *(Ramon Karadis)*, Colette Wilde *(Grace Neilson)*, Christine Shaw *(Belinda Holland)*, Stanley Morgan *(Sergeant Anson)*, A. J. Brown *(police commissioner)*, Richard Caldicot *(Pike Fisher)*, Edmond Bennett *(manservant)*, Simon Lack *(Jock)*, Anthony Baird *(Sergeant Butterfield)*, Gladys Henson *(landlady)*, Alfred Maron *(Finch)*, Richard Vernon *(Viney)*, Kenneth Fortescue *(secretary, C.I.D.)*, Hazel Hughes *(Miss Cunningham)*, Harry Locke *(Amis)*, Roy Purcell *(Brennan)*.

Mystery melodrama. Source: Edgar Wallace, *Clue of the Twisted Candle* (Boston, 1916). Fearing that his life is in danger, wealthy Greek financier Ramon Karadis installs a direct line to Scotland Yard in his suburban London home. During a visit to Karadis' estate, Superintendent Meredith is notified by the Yard that London playboy John Lexman has confessed to a shooting. While investigating the murder, Meredith learns that the gun Lexman used was given to him by Karadis. Meredith's suspicions that Karadis tricked Lexman into committing the crime increase when the suicide of a rich widow reveals that the woman was being blackmailed by Karadis. Lexman escapes from prison and arranges to meet Meredith at his office. Meanwhile, an eccentric novelist, Dr. Griswold, is seen leaving the Karadis estate. Just after Lexman arrives at Scotland Yard for his appointment, the Karadis direct line rings. Meredith and Lexman rush to the mansion and find Karadis' corpse in a room locked from the inside. The only clues are two partly burned candles—one near the door and one near the telephone. Reconstructing the murder, Meredith shows how the killer gained time for an alibi by using burning candles: as they melted, they caused the door latch to lock and the direct telephone line to activate. Finally, Meredith reveals that Dr. Griswold is still abroad and that Lexman disguised himself as the author in order to kill Karadis. Lexman, Karadis' junior partner in a blackmail racket, committed the murder in order to take over the business. *Greeks. Financiers. Novelists. Detectives. Playboys. Murder. Blackmail. Prison escapes. Impersonation. Telephone. London. Scotland Yard.*

Note: Released in Great Britain in Oct 1960.

THE CLUE TO A CRIME OF LUST *see* **GRAFFITI**

C'MON, LET'S LIVE A LITTLE　　**F6.0838**
Allstar Pictures-Hertelandy Associates. *Dist* Paramount Pictures. caMay **1967** [New York opening: 3 May; c31 Dec 1966; LP34356]. Sd; col (Technicolor). 35mm (Techniscope). 85 min.

Exec Prod Alex Alexander. *Prod* June Starr, John Hertelandy. *Dir* David Butler. *Screenplay* June Starr. *Photog* Carl Berger. *Art Dir* Frank Sylos. *Film Ed* Eve Newman. *Mus* Don Ralke. *Songs:* "C'mon, Let's Live a Little," "Instant Girl," "Baker Man," "What Fool This Mortal Be," "Tonight's the Night," "For Granted," "Back-Talk," "Over and Over," "Let's Go Go," "Way Back Home" Don Crawford. *Asst Dir* Glenn N. Cook.

Cast: Bobby Vee *(Jesse Crawford)*, Jackie De Shannon *(Judy Grant)*, Eddie Hodges *(Eddie Stewart)*, Suzie Kaye *(Bee Bee Vendemeer)*, Patsy Kelly *(Mrs. Fitts)*, Ethel Smith *(An' Effel)*, Bo Belinsky *(Bo-Bo)*, John Ireland, Jr. *(Rego)*, Don Crawford *(Jeb Crawford)*, Mark Evans *(Tim Grant)*, Russ Conway *(John W. Grant)*, Jill Banner *(Wendy)*, Kim Carnes *(Melinda)*, Joy Tobin *(Joy)*, Frank Alesia *(Balta)*, Ken Osmond *(The Beard)*, Tiger Joe Marsh *(Spuko)*, Ben Frommer *(Jake)*, The Pair Extraordinaire.

Drama with music. Jesse Crawford, a young Arkansas folk singer, heads for the college town of Waymount in hopes of getting an education. En route, he rescues the dean's pretty daughter, Judy Grant, from an automobile accident and is rewarded with an opportunity to take entrance exams, which he passes. Jesse's singing ability is soon discovered and he becomes an innocent instrument for the campus politicking of the school radical, an egotistical senior, Rego, who has started a "free speech" movement directed against Dean Grant. Rego is planning a big rally in the college auditorium and decides to use Jesse to draw a crowd. Although Jesse's singing is a huge success, he realizes too late that in allowing himself to be victimized he has hurt both Judy and her father. Angry and ashamed, he hits Rego and walks out of the rally. As he packs his bags to leave, Dean Grant makes a surprise appearance at the rally and completely wins over the student body. And Jesse is persuaded to remain on campus to continue both his studies and his romance with Judy. *Singers. Students. Deans. Freedom of speech. College life. Student activism. Demonstrations. Politics. Arkansas. Automobile accidents.*

COAST OF SKELETONS (Great Britain)   **F6.0839**
Towers of London. *Dist* Seven Arts Pictures. 3 Nov **1965** [Cincinnati, Ohio, opening]. Sd; col (Technicolor). 35mm (Techniscope). 90 min.
Pres by Seven Arts Productions. *Prod* Harry Alan Towers, Oliver A. Unger. *Dir* Robert Lynn. *2d Unit Dir* Egil S. Woxholt. *Screenplay* Anthony Scott Veitch. *Story* Peter Welbeck. *Dir Photog* Stephen Dade. *Camera* Ronnie Maasz. *2d Unit Photog* Egil S. Woxholt. *Film Ed* John Trumper. *Mus Comp & Cond* Christopher Whelen. *Miss Andersen's Dresses by* Louis Féraud.
Cast: Richard Todd *(Harry Sanders)*, Dale Robertson *(A. J. Magnus)*, Heinz Drache *(Janny von Koltze)*, Marianne Koch *(Helga)*, Elga Andersen *(Elizabeth von Koltze)*, Dietmar Schönherr *(Piet van Houten)*, Derek Nimmo *(Tom Hamilton)*, George Leech *(Carlo Seton)*, Gabriel Bayman *(Charlie Singer)*, Josh Du Toit *(Hajo Petersen)*, Gordon Mulholland *(Mr. Spyker)*.
Adventure drama. Source: Edgar Wallace, *Sanders of the River* (London, 1911). Harry Sanders loses his job as a conservation officer in Africa and is hired by a London insurance company to investigate the loss of a diamond dredge owned by wealthy Texan A. J. Magnus, who is heavily insured. Magnus buys a new dredge, and Sanders, assisted by Tom Hamilton, boards the vessel and meets its German captain, von Koltz, an ex-submarine commander. Sanders also meets the captain's wife, Elizabeth (who is having an affair with her husband's boss, Magnus), and his sister, Helga, with whom Sanders falls in love. Sanders quarrels with Carlo Seton, one of Magnus' henchmen, while von Koltz anchors the dredge and explores underwater. His curiosity aroused, Sanders follows von Koltz underwater and is instrumental in saving his life. After the rescue, von Koltz confides to Sanders his plan to find a secret gold consignment that was carried on a ship he sank in wartime. With the assistance of Charlie Singer, Sanders discovers that Magnus' lost dredge is stranded on the sandy shore of the "Coast of Skeletons." Sanders also discovers that the diamond dredging is a front to hide the fact that the wreck contains the gold that von Koltz seeks. Magnus, who, along with Elizabeth and Carlo, has been planning to doublecross von Koltz and Singer, finds the gold, and Carlo shoots Singer. Before dying, Singer ignites a cache of dynamite, and Magnus and his companions die in the explosion. Sanders, Helga, Hamilton, and von Koltz witness the explosion and escape from the danger, planning to return later to recover the gold. *Texans. Germans. Investigators. Sea captains. Sisters. Perfidy. Infidelity. Murder. Insurance. Gold. Diamonds. Dredges. Submarines. Africa. Ship explosions.*
Note: Filmed in Africa. Released in Great Britain in Aug 1965; running time: 91 min. Sources conflict in crediting producer. Peter Welbeck is a pseudonym for Harry Alan Towers.

THE COBRA (Italy/Spain)   **F6.0840**
Italian International Film–P. E. F. S. A. Films. *Dist* American International Pictures. Dec **1967** [c27 Dec 1967; LP35443]. Sd; col (Technicolor). 35mm (Techniscope). 93 min. [Copyright length: 97 min.]
Prod Fulvio Lucisano. *Dir* Mario Sequi. *Screenplay* Gumersindo Mollo. *Story* Adriano Bolzoni. *Photog* Enrique Torán, Claudio Racca. *Decor* Adolfo Cofino. *Mus* Antón García Abril. *Asst Dir* Stefano Rolla.
Cast: Dana Andrews *(Chief Kelly)*, Peter Martell *(Mike Rand)*, Anita Ekberg *(Lou)*, Elisa Montés *(Corianne)*, Jesús Puente *(Stiarkos)*, Peter Dane *(Hullinger)*, Luciana Vincenzi *(Ulla)*, George Histman *(Crane)*, Omar Zoulfikar *(Sadek)*, Giovanni Petrucci *(King)*, Chang'e *(Li Fang)*, Ehshane Sadek *(Gamel)*, Lidia Biondi.
Drama. In Istanbul, U. S. Secret Service Chief Kelly recruits former agent Mike Rand to discover the identity of The Cobra, the head of a criminal organization that has been smuggling pure opium into the United States. To avenge the death of a girl friend recently killed by the syndicate, Rand gives up his easy life and accepts the mission. Through interrogation of one of The Cobra's agents, Rand obtains a code providing details of the gang's operations. Continuing his search across the Middle East, Rand learns that the opium arrives from China and then is parachuted into the desert, packed into plastic tubes, and shipped through a petroleum pipeline to The Cobra's secret warehouse before being smuggled into the United States. With the assistance of Lou, a woman The Cobra has introduced to drugs, Rand discovers that The Cobra is the well-known financier and shipowner, Stiarkos. In a final gunfight between Stiarkos' men and Secret Service agents, Lou is killed while saving Rand's life, but the consignment of drugs is destroyed. After capturing Stiarkos, Rand decides not to risk the possibility of Stiarkos' evading trial, and so he shoots him. Then, after rejecting Kelly's offer of a high position, Rand exchanges his gun for a few bottles of whiskey and returns to his former aimless existence in Istanbul. *Wanderers. Financiers. Shipowners. Smuggling. Cryptography. Revenge. Murder. Organized crime. Opium. Deserts. Istanbul. Middle East. China. United States Secret Service.*
Note: Filmed on location in the Near and Middle East. Released in Italy in 1967 as *Il cobra*; in Spain as *El cobra*; running time: 89 min. U. S. sources credit Roman Dollar Films as the Italian production company.

THE COCKEYED COWBOYS OF CALICO COUNTY   **F6.0841**
Universal Pictures. Apr **1970** [c22 Mar 1970; LP38970]. Sd; col (Technicolor). 35mm. 99 min. *MPAA rating G.*
Prod-Writ Ranald MacDougall. *Dir* Tony Leader. *Photog* Richard L. Rawlings. *Art Dir* Alexander Golitzen, George Patrick. *Set Decor* John McCarthy, James M. Walters, Jr. *Film Ed* Richard G. Wray. *Mus* Lyn Murray. *Mus Supv* Stanley Wilson. *Sd* Waldon O. Watson, Roger H. Heman, Jr. *Asst Dir* Gene H. Law. *Asst to the Prod* Heather MacDougall. *Unit Prod Mgr* Ben Bishop. *Cost* Helen Colvig. *Makeup* Universal Pictures Professional Cosmetics. *Hairstyles* Larry Germain.
Cast: Dan Blocker *(Charley Bicker)*, Nanette Fabray *(Sadie)*, Jim Backus *(Staunch)*, Wally Cox *(Mr. Bester)*, Jack Elam *(Kittrick)*, Henry Jones *(Hanson)*, Stubby Kaye *(bartender)*, Mickey Rooney *(Indian Tom)*, Noah Beery *(Eddie)*, Marge Champion *(Mrs. Bester)*, Donald Barry *(Rusty)*, Hamilton Camp *(Mr. Fowler)*, Tom Basham *(traveler)*, Iron Eyes Cody *(Crazy Foot)*, James McCallion *(Dr. Henry)*, Byron Foulger *(Reverend Marshall)*, Ray Ballard *(Carson)*, Jack Cassidy *(Roger Hand)*.
Western comedy. Charley Bicker, a blacksmith with more brawn than brains, orders a mail-order bride from Boston. On the day of her scheduled arrival, the entire town of Calico turns out at the railroad depot to greet her, but she is not on the train. Despondent, Charley decides to leave Calico County, but the townspeople, who depend on his services, devise a plan to convince him to stay. Staunch, the unofficial mayor, persuades Sadie, a bar girl at the local saloon, to pose as the missing bride from Boston. The drunken Charley does not recognize her, and at first Sadie goes along with the scheme, but when Roger Hand, Sadie's boyfriend, tries to provoke Charley into a gunfight, she returns to the saloon, and the angered townspeople throw Roger into jail. Kittrick, a nearsighted bounty hunter, arrives in Calico and is told that Roger is an outlaw; when Roger is banished from the town, Kittrick follows him. Charley, given a second chance, is informed of Sadie's whereabouts by the townswomen, who are eager to have Sadie married; when he goes after her, she punches him in the mouth. A minister arrives and performs the marriage ceremony as Sadie tends his wound. *Blacksmiths. Mail-order brides. Mayors. Bar girls. Bounty hunters. Clergymen. Smalltown life. Imposture. Drunkenness. Perfidy. Marriage. Saloons. Jails.*
Note: Originally intended, but never shown, as an NBC-TV feature entitled *A Woman for Charlie*; slightly revised for theatrical release.

LE COCU MAGNIFIQUE *see* **THE MAGNIFICENT CUCKOLD**

CODE NAME: OPERATION CROSSBOW *see* **OPERATION CROSSBOW**

CODE 7, VICTIM 5! (Great Britain)   **F6.0842**
Towers of London. *Dist* Columbia Pictures. 10 Feb **1965** [Detroit opening; c26 Dec 1964; LP29396]. Sd (RCA); col (Technicolor). 35mm (TechniScope). 88 min.
Prod (see note) Harry Alan Towers, Skip Steloff. *Dir* Robert Lynn. *2d Unit Dir* Egil S. Woxholt. *Screenplay* Peter Yeldham. *Orig Story* Peter Welbeck. *Dir Photog* Nicolas Roeg. *Underwater Photog* Egil S. Woxholt. *Camera Op* Alex Thomson, Kevin Kavanagh. *Film Ed* John Trumper. *Mus Comp & Cond* Johnny Douglas. *Sd* Ken Cameron. *Sd Mix* Fred Hughesdon. *Sd Ed* Roy Taylor. *Asst Dir* Roy Baird. *Prod Mgr* John Comfort. *Cont* Muirne Mathieson. *Location Contact* Alan Girney. *Coöp* South African Association for Marine Biological Research.
Cast: Lex Barker *(Steve Martin)*, Ronald Fraser *(Inspector Lean)*, Walter Rilla *(Wexler)*, Ann Smyrner *(Helga Swenson)*, Veronique Vendell *(Gina)*, Gustel Gundelach *(Kramer)*, Dietmar Schönherr *(Dr. Paul)*, Percy Sieff *(Anderson)*, Gert Van den Bergh *(Vanberger)*, Howard Davies *(Rawlings)*, Sophia Spentzos *(Leila)*.
Crime melodrama. American private eye Steve Martin flies to Cape Town at the behest of Wexler, a copper tycoon who fears that his life is in danger following the murder of his butler. Martin is met at the airport by Wexler's secretary, Helga, and almost immediately an attempt is made on their lives. The members of Wexler's household, all of whom attract suspicion, include Gina, the millionaire's sensual stepdaughter; Paul, his personal physician and his daughter's boyfriend; and Anderson, the manager of Wexler's copper mine. Also working on the case is philandering police chief Inspector Lean, who has discovered an old photograph of four prisoners of war, including Wexler and the murdered butler. Ostrich farmer Vanberger, also among the prisoners in the photograph, soon meets his death, and Wexler, too, is eventually murdered. The two sleuths discover that the man responsible for the crimes is Paul, whose father, the fourth man in the photograph, was murdered by Wexler many years ago after discovering a rich copper deposit. Paul falls to his death after a chase along the cliffs of Table Mountain, and Martin returns to the United States with Helga, whom he plans to marry. *Americans in foreign countries. Detectives. Millionaires. Secretaries. Mine foremen. Police. Prisoners of war. Physicians.*

Murder. Filial relations. Revenge. Photographs. Cape Town. Table Bay (South Africa).

Note: Location scenes filmed in Cape Town and surrounding areas, including Table Mountain. Released in Great Britain caMar 1965 as *Victim Five.* Title changed from *Table Bay.* Towers produced the film; however, Skip Steloff receives screen credit. Peter Welbeck is a pseudonym for Towers.

LE COEUR BATTANT *see* **THE FRENCH GAME**

UN COEUR GROS COMME ÇA! *see* **THE WINNER**

LES COEURS VERTS *see* **NAKED HEARTS**

THE COFFEE FORTUNE TELLER *see* **THE FORTUNE TELLER**

COFFIN OF TERROR *see* **CASTLE OF BLOOD**

UN COIN TRANQUILLE À LA CAMPAGNE *see* **A QUIET PLACE IN THE COUNTRY**

COL CUORE IN GOLA *see* **DEADLY SWEET**

COL FERRO E COL FUOCO *see* **INVASION 1700**

A COLD WIND FROM HELL *see* **PYRO**

A COLD WIND IN AUGUST　　　　　　　　　　　　　　**F6.0843**
Troy Films. *Dist* Aidart Pictures. 26 Jul **1961** [New York opening]. Sd; b&w. 35mm. 80 min.
Prod Phillip Hazelton. *Assoc Prod* Robert L. Ross. *Dir* Alexander Singer. *Screenplay* Burton Wohl. *Photog* Floyd Crosby. *Credit Titl* Gene Grand, Leo Monahan. *Film Ed* Jerry Young. *Mus* Gerald Fried.
Cast: Lola Albright *(Iris Hartford),* Scott Marlowe *(Vito Perugino),* Herschel Bernardi *(Juley Franz),* Joe De Santis *(Papa Perugino),* Clarke Gordon *(Harry),* Janet Brandt *(Shirley),* Skip Young *(Al),* Ann Atmar *(Carol),* Jana Taylor *(Alice),* Dee Dee Green *(Mary).*
Melodrama. Source: Burton Wohl, *Cold Wind in August* (New York, 1960). While spending the summer in her New York apartment, Iris Hartford, a lonely burlesque stripper who has been married three times, becomes physically attracted to 17-year-old Vito Perugino, a janitor's son. The seduction of young Vito is relatively simple for the older woman, and before long he has become hopelessly enamored of her. Drawn by Vito's innocence, Iris finds herself falling in love with him, much to the dismay of her most recent lover, industrialist Juley Franz. Iris conceals her occupation from Vito, but one day her estranged husband Harry, an unsuccessful impresario, persuades her to interrupt her 3-month vacation to make a 1-week appearance at a Newark burlesque house. A group of Vito's friends take him to watch Iris, and he is horrified to see her flaunting her nakedness before leering strangers. Vito's romantic ideal is shattered, and he lashes out at Iris while she, in turn, rebukes him for his arrogance and intolerance. Despite the quarrel, Iris realizes that she still loves Vito, and she makes a feeble attempt at reconciliation, but she is unable to win back his love. *Stripteasers. Industrialists. Impresari. Seduction. Burlesque. Nudity. Disillusionment. Adolescence. Nightclubs. New York City. Newark (New Jersey).*

COLÈRE FROIDE *see* **THUNDER IN THE BLOOD**

LES COLLANTS NOIRS *see* **BLACK TIGHTS**

THE COLLECTION　　　　　　　　　　　　　　　　**F6.0844**
Project One. 9 Sep **1970** [Los Angeles opening]. col (Eastman Color). [Feature film, length unknown.]
Cast: Max Blue *(The Collector),* David Michaels, Ash Grover, Poco Alan.
Melodrama. The collector captures and enslaves men to satisfy his homosexual lust. *Collectors. Male homosexuality. Abduction.*

THE COLLECTOR (United States/Great Britain)　　　**F6.0845**
The Collector Co. *Dist* Columbia Pictures. 17 Jun **1965** [New York opening; c1 Jun 1965; LP31745]. Sd; col (Technicolor). 35mm. 119 min.
Overall Production Credits: A William Wyler Production. *Prod* Jud Kinberg, John Kohn. *Dir* William Wyler. *2d Unit Dir* Robert Swink. *Screenplay* Stanley Mann, John Kohn. *Art Dir* John Stoll. *Film Ed* Robert Swink. *Mus* Maurice Jarre.
Production Credits—American Staff: *Dir Photog* Robert Surtees. *Camera Op* Andrew McIntyre. *Set Decor* Frank Tuttle. *Main Titl* Richard Kuhn, National Screen Service. *Sd Supv* Charles J. Rice. *Sd* Jack Solomon. *Re-rec* Clem Portman. *Mus Ed* Richard C. Harris. *Asst Dir* Sergei Petschnikoff. *Unit Location Mgr* Norman August. *Script Supv* Isabel Blodgett. *Men's Wardrobe* Jack Martell. *Women's Wardrobe* Vi Alford. *Makeup Supv* Ben Lane. *Hairstyles* Virginia Jones, Ruby Felker. *Drawings* Robin Vaccarino. *Prop Master* Tom Plews. *Dial Coach* Kathleen Freeman.
Production Credits—British Staff: *Dir Photog* Robert Krasker. *Camera Op* John Harris. *2d Unit Camera* Norman Warwick. *Film Ed* David Hawkins. *Sd*

Rec Cyril Collick. *Asst Dir* Roy Baird. *Prod Mgr* Philip Shipway. *Wardrobe Mistress* Brenda Dabbs. *Makeup Artist* Harold Fletcher. *Hairstyles* Pearl Tipaldi.
Cast: Terence Stamp *(Freddie Clegg),* Samantha Eggar *(Miranda Grey),* Mona Washbourne *(Aunt Annie),* Maurice Dallimore *(The Neighbor),* William Beckley *(Crutchley),* Gordon Barclay, David Haviland *(clerks).*
Drama. Source: John Fowles, *The Collector* (London, 1963). Freddie Clegg, a neurotic London bank clerk and amateur lepidopterist, wins a football pool. Now financially secure, he resigns from the bank and purchases an estate in Sussex, which he furnishes in anticipation of a visitor. He then abducts Miranda Grey, an art student. Certain that in time she will come to love him, he sequesters her in a basement apartment in his manor. At first bewildered, Miranda unsuccessfully attempts to cajole, then seduce, her keeper. Desperate, she smites him with a spade. Stunned, Freddie nevertheless again imprisons her. He goes for medical attention, returning 3 days later to find his prisoner expiring, the basement furnace having given out in his absence. After burying Miranda, Freddie searches for a substitute. He decides that a nurse will be a most suitable specimen for his collection. *Bank clerks. Students. Collectors. Insanity. Abduction. Imprisonment. Gambling. Sussex. London. Butterflies.*
Note: Partially filmed in London and on location in England. Opened in London in Oct 1965; running time: 120 min.

THE COLLEGE　　　　　　　　　　　　　　　　　　**F6.0846**
Documentary Film Group (University of Chicago). *Dist* Film-Makers' Cooperative. 10 Mar **1964** [New York opening; c9 Apr 1964; MU7402]. Sd; b&w. 16mm. 55 min.
Prod Gerald Temaner. *Dir* Vernon Zimmerman. *Photog* Vernon Zimmerman. *Film Ed* Vernon Zimmerman. *Asst Dir* Gordon Quinn.
Documentary. An exploration of the life of the University of Chicago community. Among the subjects are classroom situations (with taped interviews juxtaposed to provide commentary), group activities, student and faculty discussions, a folk festival, the "Wash Prom," a demonstration by the Congress of Racial Equality, a "twist night," alumni reminiscences, and a Humanities Committee tea. Newsreel footage of the old intercollegiate football team and years later of scientists working on the clandestine Manhattan Project at Stagg Field contrast with views of Stagg Field as it is today. *College life. Folk music. Football. Twist (dance). Manhattan Project. Chicago. University of Chicago. Congress of Racial Equality.*
Note: Working title: *Aspects of the College.*

COLLEGE CORRUPTION　　　　　　　　　　　　　**F6.0847**
Cosmos Films. *Dist* Able Film Co. ca **1970.** Sd; col. 16mm. [Feature length assumed.]
Sex film. A college professor ensures that her students get good grades by involving them in sexual activities with her. *Professors. Students. Sexuality. College life.*

COLLEGE GIRLS　　　　　　　　　　　　　　　　　**F6.0848**
A. F. P. I. Productions. *Dist* SCA Distributors, Sack Amusement Enterprises. 14 Aug **1968** [New York showing]. Sd; b&w. 35mm. 85 min.
Prod-Dir A. C. Stephen. *Orig Story-Adapt* Bruce Mitchell. *Photog* Robert Maxwell. *Ed* Sam Sharpe. *Still Photog* CinemaGraphics.
Cast: Forman Shane, Capri, Sean O'Hara, Marsha Jordan, Randy Lee, Gee Gentell, Linda Styles, Ron Negri, Dianna Rosano, Ray Cyr.
Drama. Behind the ivy-covered walls of an American university, students pursue a variety of erotic activities. Professor Bryce prefers sex "research" to teaching biology; no female student ever fails his course. Rosie and Fluff take charge of initiating the virgin Wistful into Lambda Sigma Delta (LSD) fraternity. At the celebration that follows, inhibitions are released with a variety of stimulants. Harry, a roughneck football player, rapes Janie, who is comforted by Professor Bryce's lesbian wife. "He-man" Charlie, head of the fraternity, class president, football hero, and playboy, downs too many LSD tablets and attempts to fly off the balcony. He awakens in a doctor's office and swears off drug-induced excitement. *Students. Professors. Playboys. College life. Seduction. Lesbianism. Rape. Sexual initiation. Troilism. Fraternities. LSD.*

LES COLLÉGIENNES *see* **THE TWILIGHT GIRLS**

COLLISION COURSE *see* **THE BAMBOO SAUCER**

THE COLONEL OF BUNKER HILL *see* **THE BOY WHO CAUGHT A CROOK**

LA COLONNA INFAME *see* **LIPSTICK**

COLOR ME BLOOD RED　　　　　　　　　　　　　**F6.0849**
Box Office Spectaculars. *Dist* Jacqueline Kay, Inc. 13 Oct **1965** [Baltimore opening]. Sd; col. 35mm. 74 min.
A Friedman–Lewis Production. *Prod* David F. Friedman. *Dir-Writ* Herschell G. Lewis. *Photog* Herschell G. Lewis. *Asst Camera* Andy Romanoff.

Film Ed Robert Sinise. *Sd* David F. Friedman. *Crew Ch* Lorin D. Hall. *Paintings* Chuck Scott, Dave Seidel.

Cast: Don Joseph *(Adam Sorg)*, Candi Conder *(April)*, Elyn Warner *(Gigi)*, Scott H. Hall *(Farnsworth)*, Jerome Eden *(Rolf)*, Patricia Lee, actress *(Sydney)*, James Jaeckel *(Jack)*, Iris Marshall *(Mrs. Carter)*, William Harris *(Gregorovich)*, Cathy Collins *(Mitzi)*.

Horror film. A mad artist kills his models in macabre fashion to obtain their blood, which he uses to make his paint. *Psychopaths. Painters. Models. Murder. Axes.*

Note: Filmed on location in Sarasota, Florida.

COLOR ME DEAD (Australia)   **F6.0850**
Goldsworthy Productions. *Dist* Commonwealth United Entertainment, Inc. 17 Sep **1969** [Miami, Florida, opening]. Sd; col (Eastmancolor). 35mm. 97 min. *MPAA rating* R.
Prod-Dir Eddie Davis. *Exec Dir* Reginald Goldsworthy. *Photog* Mick Bornemann. *Art Dir* Sid Fort. *Film Ed* Warren Adams. *Mus* Bob Young. *Sd* John Appleton. *Asst Dir* Warwick Freeman. *Prod Mgr* Kit Denton. *Wardrobe* Heather Burlison. *Makeup* Gaye Evans.
Cast: Tom Tryon *(Frank Bigelow)*, Carolyn Jones *(Paula Gibson)*, Rick Jason *(Bradley Taylor)*, Patricia Connolly *(Marla Rakubian)*, Tony Ward *(Halliday)*, Penny Sugg *(Miss Foster)*, Reginald Gillam *(Eugene Phillips)*, Margot Reid *(Mrs. Phillips)*, Peter Sumner *(Stanley Phillips)*, Michael Lawrence [2] *(George Reynolds)*, Sandy Harbott *(Chester)*.
Melodrama. Source: Russell Rouse and Clarence Greene, screenplay for *D. O. A.*, 1949. A playgirl distracts public accountant Frank Bigelow as radioactive poison is slipped into his drink. The next day, he suffers from stomach pains and goes to a clinic and finds that he has been poisoned and that he has only a short time to live. Searching for a motive that would lead him to his killer, Frank recalls a suspicious uranium sale he recently notarized. Despite a sniper's attempt on his life, a murder, and two more poisonings, Bigelow learns that the uranium was part of a complicated swindle and the killer is Halliday, comptroller to Phillips, an unwitting participant in the swindle. Bigelow confronts Halliday, who falls to his death from the catwalk of an ocean liner. The accountant then staggers to a police station, relates the entire story behind his own murder, and dies. *Playgirls. Accountants. Swindlers. Poisoning. Murder. Uranium.*
Note: Filmed in Sydney, Australia.

COLORADO (Reissue)   **F6.0851**
Paramount Pictures. *Dist* Citation Films, Paramount Pictures. **1961** [New York showing: 30 Jan 1963]. Sd; col (Technicolor). 35mm (VistaVision). 92 min.
Note: Originally released as *Run for Cover* by Paramount Pictures in 1955; c1 Apr 1955; LP4801.

EL COLOSO DE RODAS *see* **THE COLOSSUS OF RHODES**

LE COLOSSE DE RHODES *see* **THE COLOSSUS OF RHODES**

IL COLOSSO DI RODA *see* **THE COLOSSUS OF RHODES**

COLOSSUS 1980 *see* **THE FORBIN PROJECT**

THE COLOSSUS OF RHODES (France/Italy/Spain)   **F6.0852**
Cineproduzioni Associate–C. F. P. C.–C. T. I.–Procusa. *Dist* Metro-Goldwyn-Mayer, Inc. 13 Dec **1961** [New York opening; c31 Dec 1961; LP21311]. Sd (Westrex); col (Eastman Color). 35mm (Totalscope). 128 min. [Copyright length: 121 min.]
Prod Michele Scaglione. *Dir* Sergio Leone. *Screenplay* Ennio De Concini, Sergio Leone, Luciano Martino, Cesare Seccia, Duccio Tessari, Age Gavioli, Carlo Gualtieri, Luciano Chittarini. *Dir Photog* Antonio L. Ballesteros. *Photog* Emilio Foriscot, Mariano Ruiz Capillas. *Set Dsgn* Jesús Mateos, Ramiro Gómez. *Film Ed* Eraldo Da Roma. *Mus* Angelo Francesco Lavagnino. *Prod Mgr* Cesare Ceccia. *Cost* Vittorio Rossi. *Wigs* Palombi. *Weapons & Accessories* Rancati Sormani. *Constr* Francisco R. Asensio.
Cast: Rory Calhoun *(Dario)*, Lea Massari *(Diala)*, Georges Marchal *(Peliocles)*, Conrado San Martín *(Thar)*, Angel Aranda *(Koros)*, Mabel Karr *(Mirte)*, Jorge Rigaud *(Lissipo)*, Roberto Camardiel *(Serse)*, Mimmo Palmara *(Arcs)*, Félix Fernández *(Carete)*, Carlo Tamberlani *(Xenon)*, Alfio Caltabiano *(Creonte)*, José McVilches *(Eros)*, Antonio Casas *(Phoenician ambassador)*, Yann Larvor *(Mahor)*, Fernando Calzado *(Sirone)*, Ignazio Dolce, Arturo Cabre.
Adventure drama. In 224 B. C., a gigantic bronze statue (Colossus) is erected at the entrance to the port of Rhodes. The tiny island is beset by political intrigue because the evil Prime Minister Thar plans to turn Rhodes over to the Phoenicians and thus threaten Greek trade routes in the Mediterranean. Opposing Thar are five Greek brothers who have learned of the scheme and are determined to destroy the Colossus. A Greek captain, Dario, becomes

involved with the brothers and decides that the only way to penetrate the Colossus is through its architect. Consequently, he arranges a meeting with the designer's daughter Diala, unaware that she is Thar's mistress. When she betrays them, the brothers are sentenced to die in the arena; but Dario gains the attention of the Rhodes citizenry and reveals the Phoenician plot. His disclosure generates a battle between Phoenicians and the people of Rhodes, culminating in an earthquake that topples the Colossus into the sea. *Prime ministers. Phoenicians. Greeks. Brothers. Architects. Mistresses. Trade. Perfidy. Capital punishment. Arenas. Rhodes. Greece—Ancient. Mediterranean Sea. Colossus of Rhodes. Earthquakes.*
Note: Location scenes filmed in Spain. Opened in Rome in Sep 1961 as *Il colosso di Roda* at 110 min; in Paris in Aug 1961 as *Le colosse de Rhodes* at 145 min; and in Madrid in Jun 1961 as *El coloso de Rodas* at 123 min.

COLOSSUS—THE FORBIN PROJECT *see* **THE FORBIN PROJECT**

COLPO GROSSO A GALATA BRIDGE *see* **THAT MAN IN ISTANBUL**

COLPO GROSSO A PARIGI *see* **HOW NOT TO ROB A DEPARTMENT STORE**

COLPO GROSSO AL CASINO *see* **ANY NUMBER CAN WIN**

COLPO GROSSO MA NON TROPPO *see* **THE SUCKER**

IL COLPO SEGRETO DI D'ARTAGNAN *see* **THE SECRET MARK OF D'ARTAGNAN**

THE COLT (U.S.S.R.)   **F6.0853**
Lenfilm. *Dist* Artkino Pictures. 3 Jun **1961** [New York opening]. Sd; b&w. 35mm. 42 min. [Also reviewed at 47 min.]
Dir Vladimir Fetin. *Screenplay* Arnold Vitol. *Story Ed* S. Ponomarenko. *Photog* Yevgeniy Kirpichyov. *Art Dir* A. Rudyakov. *Film Ed* K. Kozyreva. *Mus* Vasiliy Pavlovich Solovyov-Sedoy. *Cond* K. Eliasberg. *Sd* A. Volokhova. *Asst Dir* L. Makhtin. *Creative Supv* Grigoriy Kozintsev. *Prod Mgr* B. Griner. *Military Cons* N. Oslikovskiy. *Cons* S. Turkova-Sholokhova.
Cast: Yevgeniy Matveyev *(Trofim)*, Leonid Parkhomenko *(squadron commander)*, G. Karelina *(Cossack woman)*, S. Polezhayev *(officer)*, A. Trusov *(cavalry sergeant-major)*.
War melodrama. Source: Mikhail Aleksandrovich Sholokhov, "Zherebyonok" (a short story; Moscow?, 1926). After years of arduous fighting in a Red Army cavalry unit during the Russian civil war, Trofim gains a renewed sense of warmth and humanity when his mare gives birth to a foal. He is ordered to destroy the newborn animal but cannot bring himself to carry out the order. The colt survives in the midst of battle and follows Trofim's unit. Losing its way, it strays behind enemy lines and nearly drowns as it tries to cross a river to reach its mother. Trofim rescues the colt but is mortally wounded as he reaches the riverbank. Before dying, he sees the colt rejoin its mother. *Soldiers. Combat zone life. Russia—History—1917–21 Revolution. Horses.*
Note: Released in the U.S.S.R. in Mar 1960 as *Zherebyonok*.

I COLTELLI DEL VENDICATORE *see* **KNIVES OF THE AVENGER**

IL COLTELLO NELLA PIAGA *see* **FIVE MILES TO MIDNIGHT**

THE COLUMBIA REVOLT   **F6.0854**
Newsreel. 7 Oct **1968** [New York opening]. Sd; b&w. 16mm. 50 min.
Prod Staff (see note) Stewart Bird, Eric Breitbart, Jonathan Chernoble, Lynn Costello, Michael Dannenberg, Norris Eisenbrey, Marvin Fishman, Bill Floyd, Ellin Hirst, Alan Jacobs, Ken Kaiser, Janet Kranzberg, Rene Lichtman, Jerry Long, Liz Mamorsky, Larry Mead, Karen Mitnick, Melvin Morgulis, Masanori Oe, Charles Pasternak, Lynn Phillips, Richard Pike, Mike Robinson, Stephen Sbarge, Dan Shafarman, Allan Siegel, Bill Speiser, David C. Stone, Pat Tan, Shawn Walker.
Documentary. This combination of motion picture and still photography chronicles the takeover of Columbia University in the spring of 1968 by a coalition of radical groups, among them Students for a Democratic Society. The film shows Columbia's President Grayson Kirk praising the modern university; highlights the takeover of the campus in New York City's Morningside Heights and occupation of the administrators' offices, culminating in the police "bust"; and shows commencement exercises as staged by both the radical and the non-radical student factions. *Students. Police. Radicalism. College life. Student activism. Revolts. New York City—Morningside Heights. Grayson Kirk. Columbia University. Students for a Democratic Society.*
Note: The 30 artists and technicians involved are known collectively as "Newsreel" and are responsible for production, direction, photography, editing, and recording.

THE COMANCHEROS   F6.0855

Twentieth Century-Fox Film Corp. 1 Nov **1961** [New York opening; c1 Nov 1961; LP20766]. Sd (Westrex); col (DeLuxe). 35mm (CinemaScope). 107 min.

Prod George Sherman. *Dir* Michael Curtiz. *Action Seq Dir* Cliff Lyons. *Screenplay* James Edward Grant, Clair Huffaker. *Dir Photog* William H. Clothier. *Art Dir* Jack Martin Smith, Alfred Ybarra. *Set Decor* Walter M. Scott, Robert Priestley. *Film Ed* Louis R. Loeffler. *Mus* Elmer Bernstein. *Orch* Leo Shuken, Jack Hayes. *Dances Staged by* Hal Belfer. *Sd* Alfred Bruzlin, Warren B. Delaplain. *Asst Dir* Jack R. Berne. *Cost Dsgn* Marjorie Best. *Makeup* Ben Nye. *Hairstyles* Helen Turpin.

Cast: John Wayne *(Jake Cutter)*, Stuart Whitman *(Paul Regret)*, Ina Balin *(Pilar)*, Nehemiah Persoff *(Graile)*, Lee Marvin *(Crow)*, Michael Ansara *(Amelung)*, Patrick Wayne *(Tobe)*, Bruce Cabot *(Major Henry)*, Joan O'Brien *(Melinda)*, Edgar Buchanan *(Judge Bean)*, Guinn "Big Boy" Williams *(Ed McBain)*, Jack Elam *(Horseface)*, Henry Daniell *(Gireaux)*, Richard Devon *(Estevan)*, Steve Baylor *(Comanchero)*, John Dierkes *(Bill)*, Roger Mobley *(Bub Schofield)*, Bob Steele *(Pa Schofield)*, Luisa Triana *(Spanish dancer)*, Iphigenie Castiglioni *(Josefina)*, Aissa Wayne *(Bessie)*, George J. Lewis *(Iron Shirt)*, Tom Hennessy *(Graile's bodyguard)*, Jackie Cubat, Leigh Snowden *(hotel girls)*.

Western melodrama. Source: Paul I. Wellman, *The Comancheros* (Garden City, N. Y., 1952). In 1843 Texas Ranger Jake Cutter arrests gambler Paul Regret in Galveston and heads for Louisiana. There Paul is wanted for killing a man in a pistol duel. En route, Paul catches Jake off guard, clouts him with a shovel, and makes his escape. Jake returns to Ranger headquarters and is ordered to impersonate a gun smuggler in order to ferret out the secret stronghold of the Comancheros, a band of white renegades selling liquor and guns to the marauding Comanches. While stopping off at a small town, Jake again runs into Paul and again takes him into custody. After helping some ranchers ward off an Indian attack, the two men reach the Comancheros' hideout, where Paul encounters Pilar, an adventuress he knew and loved in Galveston. Aware that Jake is a Ranger, Pilar decides to join him and Paul in their fight against her father, Graile, the Comanchero leader. Early one morning, they sneak out of the stronghold and set fire to the gun powder magazines. Before they can reach safety, however, they are attacked by bloodthirsty Comanches, but the Rangers ride to the rescue and repulse the attack. After saying goodbye to Pilar and Paul, Jake rides off into the sunset. *Texas Rangers. Gamblers. Smugglers. Gangs. Comanche Indians. Disguise. Firearms. Duels. Texas. Galveston.*

Note: Location scenes filmed in Moab, Utah.

COME BACK BABY   F6.0856

Dist Film-Makers' Distribution Center. 13 Jun **1968** [New York opening]. Sd; b&w. 16mm. 100 min.

A David Allen Greene Production. *Prod-Dir-Writ* David Allen Greene. *Photog* David Allen Greene. *Film Ed* David Allen Greene. *Mus* Musicues. *Adtl Mus* David Allen Greene, J. T. Riebling, Lightnin' Hopkins, Lonnie Mack. *Chief Prod Asst* John Terry Riebling.

Cast: John Terry Riebling *(Cal Thacker)*, Barbara Teitelbaum *(Carrie Da Silva)*, Mark Weishaus *(Mike Rubel)*, Craig Bovia *(Richard Stoney Morgan)*, Barbara Rubel *(Stoney's sister)*, Mary Anne Seibert *(Silvia)*, Colette Bablon *(Stoney's intended victim)*, Jaqueline Uytenbogaart *(girl in bed)*, Jane Hornick *(girl at party)*, Steve Steinhauer *(boy at party)*, Barbara Riebling *(prostitute)*, George Gerdes *(thief)*, John McDonald, U.S. actor *(mugging victim)*, Felicia Waynesboro *(streetwalker)*, Henry Gribbin, Len Wanetik, Dave Stegstra *(policemen)*.

Melodrama. Cal Thacker, a would-be artist, shares his slum living quarters with Mike Rubel, a pusher who exists in a private drug-centered world, and Richard Stoney Morgan, an embittered drifter who sponges from the other two. Cal's girl friend, Carrie, who has provided his only meaningful human contact, finds him in bed with another girl and breaks with him. In despair, Cal tries unsuccessfully to obtain funds by selling his paintings. His motorcycle is wrecked in a crash, though Cal miraculously escapes injury. Later in the day, the three roommates meet at the apartment and attempt to obliterate their problems with cheap whiskey. The liquor only creates new problems, however; Mike and Cal become involved in a violent argument with Stoney, who eventually leaves. Seeking revenge, Stoney reports Mike to the police as a marijuana pusher and then returns to the apartment with a knife. In the fight that ensues, Cal kills Stoney; but Cal is then gunned down by police. *Artists. Drifters. Drug dealers. Roommates. Police. Urban life. Infidelity. Murder. Drunkenness. Revenge. Marijuana. Motorcycle accidents.*

Note: Filmed in Pittsburgh.

COME BLOW YOUR HORN   F6.0857

Essex Productions-Tandem Enterprises. *Dist* Paramount Pictures. 5 Jun **1963** [New York opening; c6 Jun 1963; LP26150]. Sd; col (Technicolor). 35mm (Panavision). 112 min.

Prod Norman Lear, Bud Yorkin. *Exec Prod* Howard W. Koch. *Dir* Bud Yorkin. *Screenplay* Norman Lear. *Photog* William H. Daniels. *Art Dir* Hal Pereira, Roland Anderson. *Set Decor* Sam Comer, James Payne. *Film Ed* Frank P. Keller. *Mus* Nelson Riddle. *Orch* Gil Grau. *Titl Song* Sammy Cahn, James Van Heusen. *Sung by* Frank Sinatra. *Sd* John Carter. *Asst Dir* Daniel J. McCauley. *Cost* Edith Head. *Makeup* Wally Westmore. *Hairstyles* Christine Widmeyer, Gene Shacove, Frederic Jones. *Sp Photog Eff* Paul K. Lerpae.

Cast: Frank Sinatra *(Alan Baker)*, Lee J. Cobb *(Mr. Baker)*, Molly Picon *(Mrs. Baker)*, Barbara Rush *(Connie)*, Jill St. John *(Peggy)*, Tony Bill *(Buddy Baker)*, Dan Blocker *(Mr. Eckman)*, Phyllis McGuire *(Mrs. Eckman)*, Herbie Faye *(waiter)*, Romo Vincent *(barber)*, Charlotte Fletcher *(manicurist)*, Greta Randall *(tall girl)*, Dean Martin *(The Bum)*, Joyce Nizzari *(Snow)*, Carole Wells *(Eunice)*.

Comedy. Source: Neil Simon, *Come Blow Your Horn* (New York opening: 22 Feb 1961). Bored with living at home with his older, Jewish parents, young Buddy Baker packs his bags and arrives unannounced at the luxurious Manhattan apartment of his older brother, Alan, a fast-living, girl-chasing bachelor who never allows his duties at his father's artificial fruit factory to interfere with his pleasures. Pleased at his brother's show of independence, Alan buys Buddy a flashy new wardrobe and introduces him to New York night life. Their father becomes enraged at Alan's poor example and at his irresponsible loss of an important account. Buddy is such an apt pupil that he soon takes over his brother's private stock of liquor and begins dating his girl friends. After giving up Peggy, the woman upstairs, to Buddy, Alan is beaten up by the husband of another woman friend. He becomes frightened at the prospect of a serious relationship, alienating his favorite girl friend, Connie. Suddenly realizing the futility of his life, Alan urges Buddy to end his carousing and settle down, but Buddy is having too good a time. Their argument jolts Alan into maturity, and he decides to propose to Connie. Following their marriage, Alan discovers that his mother has left his father because of his bad temper, but Alan effects their reconciliation, successfully concludes a business deal, and bequeaths his bachelor apartment to the delighted Buddy. *Brothers. Businessmen. Playboys. Bachelors. Jews. Marriage. Filial relations. Fruit—Artificial. New York City.*

COME DANCE WITH ME *see* **COME PLAY WITH ME**

COME DREAM WITH ME   F6.0858

RAM Films. 10 Jul **1969** [San Francisco showing]. Sd; col. 16mm. [Feature length assumed.]

Dir Jack Evans. *Story* Richard Z. Evans.

Sex film. In anticipation of her boyfriend's arrival, a woman cooks a meal and prepares herself sexually for his visit. When he comes in drunk, she is unable to arouse him so she turns to masturbation for satisfaction. She smokes marijuana and dreams of other sexual affairs, including an encounter in which she and her lesbian lover force a man to make love to them. *Sexuality. Food preparation. Drunkenness. Autoeroticism. Marijuana. Lesbianism. Troilism. Dreams.*

COME DRINK WITH ME (Hong Kong)   F6.0859

Shaw Brothers (H. K.) Ltd. Jul **1966** [Los Angeles showing]. Sd; col (Eastman Color). 97 min.

Prod Run Run Shaw. *Dir-Writ* Chin Chaun.

Cast: Cheng Pei-pei, Yueh Hua, Cheng Hung-li, Li Yu-chung, Yang Chih-chang, Feng I, Wang Chung, Shen Lao.

Adventure drama. Adventuress Golden Swallow and her Indian sidekick, Tonto, triumph over several sword-wielding bandits. *Adventuresses. Bandits. East Indians.*

COME FLY WITH ME (United States/Great Britain)   F6.0860

Metro-Goldwyn-Mayer, Inc. 27 Mar **1963** [Kansas City, Missouri, opening; c13 Feb 1963; LP23853]. Sd; col (Metrocolor). 35mm (Panavision). 109 min.

Prod Anatole De Grunwald. *Assoc Prod* Roy Parkinson. *Dir* Henry Levin. *Story-Screenplay* William Roberts. *Dir Photog* Oswald Morris. *Camera Op* Brian West. *Art Dir* William Kellner. *Film Ed* Frank Clarke. *Assemby Ed* Philip Barnikel. *Mus* Lyn Murray. *Song:* "La chansonnette" Philippe Gérard. *French Lyr* Jean Dréjac. *Arr* Lyn Murray, Wally Stott. *Sung by* Simone Langlois. "In einem kleinem Cafe in Hernals" Hermann Leopoldi. *Arr* Wally Stott. *Titl Song* James Van Heusen, Sammy Cahn. *Arr* Lyn Murray. *Sung by* Frankie Avalon. *Rec Supv* A. W. Watkins. *Sd Rec* Gerry Turner. *Sd Ed* Bill Creed. *Dub Mix* J. B. Smith. *Asst Dir* Jimmy Komisarjevsky. *Prod Mgr* Albert Becket. *Cont* Elaine Schreyeck. *Wardrobe Supv* Felix Evans. *Miss Addams' Wardrobe* Pierre Balmain. *Makeup* Tom Smith. *Hairdressing* Joan Johnstone. *Sp Eff* Tom Howard. *Coöp* Authorities of Orly Airport (Paris), Authorities of Schwechat Airport (Vienna), Authorities of New York International Airport.

Cast: Dolores Hart *(Donna Stuart)*, Hugh O'Brian *(1st Officer Ray Winsley)*, Karl Boehm *(Baron Franz von Elzingen)*, Karl Malden *(Walter Lucas)*, Pamela Tiffin *(Carol Brewster)*, Lois Nettleton *(Hilda "Bergie"*

Bergstrom), Dawn Addams (*Katy Rimard*), Richard Wattis (*Oliver Garson*), Andrew Cruickshank (*Cardwell*), James Dobson (*Teddy Shepherd*), Lois Maxwell (*Gwen*), John Crawford (*captain*), Robert Easton (*navigator*), Guido Wieland (*Armand*), Maurice Marsac (*Rimard*), Bibi Morat (*French urchin*).

Romantic comedy. Suggested by: Bernard Glemser, *Girl on a Wing* (New York, 1960). During a flight from New York to Paris and Vienna, airline employees and passengers fall in love. Cub stewardess Carol Brewster is attracted to copilot Ray Winsley, 1st-class hostess Donna Stuart is charmed by Austrian Baron Franz von Elzingen, and veteran flight attendant "Bergie" Bergstrom is captivated by Walter Lucas, a shy Texan traveling tourist class. On land, however, the idealistic Carol learns of the copilot's past liaison with married Katy Rimard, materialistic Donna discovers that the baron is a jewel smuggler, and wary Bergie finds her Texan to be a recently bereaved widower. Despite these revelations, the affairs end happily. After Donna pledges fidelity, the baron surrenders to police. Lucas discloses that he is also a millionaire, and escorts Carol and Bergie aboard a chartered jet flown by Ray, intended as a honeymoon express. *Airline stewardesses. Widowers. Air pilots. Texans. Millionaires. Nobility. Smugglers. Marriage. Infidelity. Travel. Airplanes. Jewels. New York City. Paris. Vienna.*

Note: Exteriors filmed in Paris, New York City, Vienna, and elsewhere in Austria; interiors in England. Opened in London in Apr 1963. Working titles: *Champagne Flight* and *The Friendliest Girls in the World*.

COME MARRY ME (Japan)   F6.0861
Toho Co. Sep **1967** [Los Angeles showing]. Sd; col. 35mm (Tohoscope). 84 min.

Dir Ishiro Honda.

Cast: Yuzo Kayama, Yoko Naito, Keiko Sawai, Ichiro Arishima. No information about the nature of this film has been found. *Marriage.*

Note: Released in Japan in 1966 as *Oyome ni oide*.

COME ON BABY, LIGHT MY FIRE *see* **BABY, LIGHT MY FIRE**

COME ONE, COME ALL!   F6.0862
Sebastian Gregory. *Dist* Entertainment Ventures, Inc. Oct **1970**. Sd; col (Eastmancolor). 35mm. 74 min.

Pres by Sebastian Gregory. *Prod-Dir-Writ* Sebastian Gregory. *Camera* Henning Schellerup. *Sets* Byron Falbrook. *Mus* David Kenzie. *Sd* Sam Rosen. *Post Prod Supv* Bob Freeman. *Cost* Danielle.

Cast: Sebastian Gregory (*himself*), Gina Montaine (*Geraldine*), Henry Dillon (*Michael*), Diane Lamport (*Louise*), Roberta Landis (*Monica*), Loretta Tyler (*Shirley*), Dorothy Campbell (*dancer*), Christine March (*Goldilocks*), Peter Ferris.

Comedy-drama. Sebastian Gregory, a handsome rake, lies in his coffin and thinks about the adventure that put him there: *Sebastian arrives in Hollywood hoping to become a famous movie star; failing that, he becomes a gigolo, seduces a wealthy older woman, and acquires a nine-bedroom mansion which he turns into a pleasure-house. One night, five of his regular clients arrive at the same time and make their demands for his "special" services. The activity exhausts Sebastian, and he realizes that he can escape his plight only by feigning death and hoping that his guests will all go home. He plans an elaborate funeral and prepares for his disappearance. At the funeral, however, his mourners, all avid fans of Sebastian, begin to take off their clothes in the funeral parlor, and Sebastian, his lust aroused, is compelled to reveal his hoax.* Rakes. Gigolos. Actors. Prostitution. Fraud. Nudity. Death. Funerals. Hollywood.*

Note: Sebastian Gregory is a pseudonym of Anthony Vorno.

COME PLAY WITH ME   F6.0863
Nova Pictures. *Dist* Trans-Universe Pictures, Goldstone Film Enterprises. May **1968**. Sd; b&w. 35mm. 72 min.

A Nick Cosentino Production. *Prod-Dir-Writ* Nick Cosentino. *Dir Photog* William Reilly. *Art Dir* Jock Stockwell. *Film Ed* Albert Atkins. *Sd* Fred Kamiel.

Cast: Charline Tesar (*Jan Cousins*), Jeremy Langham (*Roger Stevens*), Linda Lawrence (*Clarice Wilson*), Christine Cybelle (*Charlotte Green*), Steven Harrison (*George Blake*), Rose Conti (*Marge*), Janet Banzet (*Ruthie*), Vincent Marr (*Dr. Cole*), George Loros (*Biff Giles*), Michael Alaimo (*Professor Holden*), Robert Dark (*Stu White*), Lucy Marks (*Sophie*).

Melodrama. Jan Cousins, brutally raped by her date, returns to boarding school, and there she is comforted by Clarice, a lesbian who seduces her. Jan seeks sexual fulfillment with her boyfriend, Roger, but his strict upbringing has left him with a perverse need to be spanked. Roger appeals first to a prostitute, then to Clarice, and finally to Jan for a spanking, but she reacts with shock and tears. Her psychiatrist suggests that she find a normal man, but her successive dates are even more abnormal than Roger. She modifies her standards of normality and begins to accept all types of behavior. She does some research on flagellation, whips Roger, and finally achieves sexual satisfaction. *Students. Psychiatrists. Rape. Lesbianism. Seduction. Sadomasochism. Flagellation.*

Boarding schools.

Note: Also known as *Come Dance With Me.*

COME PLAY WITH ME   F6.0864
Golden Hawk Productions. ca **1970**. Sd; col. 35mm. [Feature length assumed.]

Prod Alex Blanchard. *Dir* James Fergeson.

Cast: Chet Labb, Jan Fawn.

Sex film. A young man is initiated into the art of sex by an experienced prostitute who teaches him copulation and oral intercourse. *Prostitutes. Sex instruction. Sexual initiation. Oral sex.*

COME PLAY WITH ME *see* **GRAZIE, ZIA**

COME RIDE THE WILD PINK HORSE   F6.0865
Chellee Films. *Dist* Chancellor Films. 9 Aug **1967** [New York opening]. Sd; b&w. 35mm. 86 min.

Prod Chellee Wilson. *Asst Prod* Ken Rowley. *Dir-Writ* Joe Sarno. *Dir Photog* Bruce Sparks. *Asst Camera* Bob Bailin. *Film Ed* Kemper Peacock. *Mus* Pir Marini. *Sd* James Lynch. *Prod Mgr* Steve Silverman. *Script Girl* Gillian Mills. *Gaffer* Pete Marberry.

Cast: Mona Marshal, Cleo Nova, Steppen Wolf, Rene Valli, Sheila Britt, Pete Hall, Judson Todd, Rex Barton, Christina Dalon, Sue Evans, Nick Dundas, Dom Tatlock, Ginger Stevens, Richard Nichols, Kip Rivas, David Marks, Michael Lawrence.

Melodrama. Jennifer Weller, though satisfied with her marriage to Eddie, finds her role as a suburban housewife oppressive and begins to accompany Marian Harris, a restless neighbor, on jaunts into the city. At first, Marian is the more adventurous of the two, quickly accommodating two young traveling salesmen they meet at the Deep Six Bar, but Jennifer has second thoughts, and she leaves the mens' motel room. Returning to the bar, she meets Seth Leonard, the guitar-playing leader of a free-living artists' commune. Hoping that the suburban adventurers will help the group out of financial difficulty, Seth and his girl friend Alexis arrange an erotic dance session. Marian is immediately drawn into the excitement; Jennifer, though repelled, is haunted by the music. Late one night, she slips from Eddie's bed and goes to make love with Seth, as Alexis looks on. Thereafter, Jennifer and Marian participate actively in the life of the art colony, until Alexis' mounting jealousy spurs her to demand $1,000 from Jennifer. Jennifer is forbidden to return when she cannot raise the money. She begins to fill her afternoons with other extra-marital affairs. Seth grows depressed at the separation, and the colony begins to collapse. Marian discovers that her husband, Len, is among Jennifer's afternoon lovers. Len is confronted with Jennifer's recitation of his wife's infidelity, and the marriage is destroyed. Seth leaves the commune and calls on Jennifer. She haughtily rejects him and leaves him alone as she romances another daytime lover. *Housewives. Artists. Neighbors. Traveling salesmen. Suburbanites. Infidelity. Revenge. Promiscuity. Marriage. Communal living. Jealousy. Extortion. Perfidy. Voyeurism. Bars. Art colonies.*

COME SEPTEMBER   F6.0866
7 Pictures-Raoul Walsh Enterprises. *Dist* Universal-International. 9 Aug **1961** [Minneapolis opening; c10 Aug 1961; LP25106]. Sd; col (Technicolor). 35mm (CinemaScope). 112 min.

Prod Robert Arthur. *Assoc Prod* Henry Willson. *Dir* Robert Mulligan. *Screenplay* Stanley Shapiro, Maurice Richlin. *Dir Photog* William H. Daniels. *Art Dir* Henry Bumstead. *Set Decor* John P. Austin. *Film Ed* Russell F. Schoengarth. *Mus Supv* Joseph Gershenson. *Mus* Hans J. Salter. *Songs:* "Come September," "Multiplication" *writ & sung by* Bobby Darin. *Sd* Waldon O. Watson, Sash Fisher. *Asst Dir* Joseph Kenny. *Prod Mgr* Ernest B. Wehmeyer. *Gowns* Morton Haack. *Gowns Executed by* Shuberth of Rome. *Makeup* Bud Westmore, Jack Freeman. *Hairstyles* Larry Germain.

Cast: Rock Hudson (*Robert Lawrence Talbot*), Gina Lollobrigida (*Lisa Fellini*), Sandra Dee (*Sandy Stevens*), Bobby Darin (*Tony*), Walter Slezak (*Maurice Clavell*), Brenda De Banzie (*Margaret Allison*), Rossana Rory (*Anna*), Ronald Howard (*Spencer*), Joel Grey (*Beagle*), Ronnie Haran (*Sparrow*), Chris Seitz (*Larry*), Cindy Conroy (*Julia*), Joan Freeman (*Linda*), Nancy Anderson (*Patricia*), Michael Eden (*Ron*), Claudia Brack (*Carol*), Charles Fawcett (*Warren*), John Stacy (*Douglas*), Katherine Guildford (*Claire*), Betty Foa (*Elena*), Helen Stirling (*Katherine*), Del Balzo (*mother superior*), Anna Maestri, Stella Vitelleschi, Milena Vukotic, Edy Nogara (*Lisa's maids*), Francesco Tensi (*Robert's secretary*), Liliana Celli (*seamstress*).

Comedy. For the past 6 years American millionaire Robert Talbot has been spending September with his 1-month-a-year mistress, Lisa Fellini, at his villa in Portofino. This year he arrives unannounced in July, however, and discovers that his major-domo, Maurice, has been making a tidy profit 11 months of the year by converting the villa into an elegant hotel—La Dolce Vista. Outraged, Robert demands that the guests—six American teenaged girls and a chaperon—leave immediately. Before the eviction can be accomplished, however, the chaperon slips on a champagne cork and injures her back; and Robert is stuck with his "guests." Another setback occurs when four American college boys pitch a tent just outside the villa and begin courting the girls. Apprehensive lest he be liable for arrest on a morals charge, Robert, accompanied by Lisa, sets himself up as both guardian and chaperon of the girls. His primary concern is keeping the most amorous of the boys, Tony, from seducing young Sandy Stevens. When Lisa learns that Robert has warned Sandy that men don't marry girls who "give away free samples," she indignantly storms out of the villa and returns to Rome to rejoin her stuffy British fiancé, Spencer. Robert follows but, despite a marriage proposal, he is unable to stop the infuriated Lisa. After a chat with Sandy, however, Lisa has a change of heart and races, in her wedding gown, to catch Robert. Following their marriage, they return to the villa for their honeymoon. They are appalled to discover that it is once more Hotel La Dolce Vista. This time Robert is confronted with a different problem—his "guests" are nine vacationing nuns! *British. Millionaires. Americans in foreign countries. Chaperons. Mistresses. Majordomos. Tourists. Double standard. Weddings. Adolescence. Seduction. Hotels. Portofino. Rome.*

Note: Filmed in Italy.

COME SPY WITH ME   **F6.0867**
MPO Pictures–ABC Films. *Dist* Twentieth Century–Fox Film Corp. 18 Jan **1967** [Los Angeles opening; c31 Dec 1966; LP34448]. Sd; col (DeLuxe). 35mm. 85 min.

Pres by Futurama Entertainment Corp. *Prod* Paul M. Heller. *Exec Prod* Alan V. Iselin. *Dir* Marshall Stone. *Screenplay* Cherney Berg. *Orig Story* Stuart James. *Photog* Zoli Vidor. *Underwater Photog* Jordan Klein. *Art Dir* Howard Barker. *Titl Dsgn* Paul Petroff. *Film Ed* Hy Goldman. *Mus Comp & Cond* Bob Bowers. *Titl Song* William "Smokey" Robinson, Jr. *Sung by* The Miracles. *Song:* "The Shark" *lyr by* Jerry Butler. *Sd* John W. Barry. *Asst Dir* Charles Okun. *Prod Mgr* Eva Monley. *Cost* Georganne Aldrich. *Makeup* Clay Lambert. *Coöp* Jamaica Tourist Bureau.

Cast: Troy Donahue *(Pete Barker)*, Andrea Dromm *(Jill Parsons)*, Albert Dekker *(Walter Ludeker)*, Lucienne Bridou *(Linda)*, Mart Hulswit *(Larry Claymore)*, Valerie Allen *(Samantha)*, Dan Ferrone *(Augie)*, Howard Schell *(Corbett)*, Chance Gentry *(Chance)*, Louis Edmonds *(Gunther Stiller)*, Kate Aldrich *(Chris)*, Pam Colbert *(Pam)*, Gil Pratley *(Kieswetter)*, Georges Shoucair *(Pantin)*, Alston Bair *(Keefer)*, Tim Moxon *(Morgan)*, Eric Coverly *(Karl)*, Jack Lewis *(Brooks)*.

Action melodrama. U. S. Intelligence assigns Jill Parsons to investigate the mysterious deaths of two secret agents in the Caribbean. The agency fears that the deaths may indicate danger to a meeting of foreign ministers scheduled to be held aboard an aircraft carrier in the area. Jill infiltrates a local skindiving competition to be held off a charter boat belonging to young Pete Barker. Meanwhile, the activities of the skindivers are being carefully observed by enemy agent Walter Ludeker, who has been laying highly explosive equipment across the ocean beds. In an attempt to learn if a U. S. agent is among the divers, he persuades his nephew Larry to enter the competition. Though another woman, Samantha, is wrongly suspected and kidnaped, Ludeker later realizes that it is Jill he wants, and he abducts her also. When U. S. Intelligence learns of Jill's disappearance, they raid Ludeker's stronghold, rescue the two women, and destroy the network of underwater explosives. With the completion of her assignment, Jill is free to reveal her romantic interest in Pete. *Secret agents. Divers. Uncles. Murder. Conspiracy. Abduction. Contests. Explosives. Caribbean.*

Note: Location scenes filmed in Jamaica. Working title: *Red Over Red*.

COME TO THE PARTY *see* **THE YOUNG SWINGERS**

THE COMEDIANS (United States/Bermuda/France)   **F6.0868**
Metro-Goldwyn-Mayer, Inc.-Maximillian Productions-Trianon Productions. *Dist* Metro-Goldwyn-Mayer, Inc. 31 Oct **1967** [New York opening; c2 Nov 1967; LP34814]. Sd; col (Metrocolor). 35mm (Panavision). 160 min.

A Peter Glenville Production. *Prod-Dir* Peter Glenville. *Screenplay* Graham Greene. *Dir Photog* Henri Decaë. *Camera Op* Ernest Day. *Art Dir* François de Lamothe. *Set Dresser* Robert Christides. *Film Ed* Françoise Javet. *Mus Comp & Cond* Laurence Rosenthal. *Sd Rec* Cyril Swern. *Sd Ed* Jonathan Bates. *Dub Mix* Jacques Carrere. *Asst Dir* Jean-Michel Lacor. *Prod Supv* Louis Wipf. *Asst to the Prod* Judith Coxhead. *Unit Mgr* Lucien Lippens. *Cont* Alice Ziller. *Miss Taylor's Gowns* Tiziani of Rome. *Miss Taylor's Hairstyles* Alexandre of Paris.

Cast: Richard Burton *(Brown)*, Elizabeth Taylor *(Martha Pineda)*, Alec Guinness *(Major Jones)*, Peter Ustinov *(Ambassador Pineda)*, Paul Ford *(Smith)*, Lillian Gish *(Mrs. Smith)*, Raymond St. Jacques *(Captain Concasseur)*, Zaeks Mokae *(Michel)*, Roscoe Lee Browne *(Petit Pierre)*, Douta Seck *(Joseph)*, Albia Peters *(César)*, Gloria Foster *(Madame Philipot)*, Robin Langford *(Angelito)*, Georg Stanford Brown *(Henri Philipot)*, James Earl Jones

(Dr. Magiot), Cicely Tyson *(Marie Thérèse)*.

Drama. Source: Graham Greene, *The Comedians* (New York, 1966). Under the dictatorship of "Papa Doc" Duvalier and his secret police (the Tontons Macoute), Haiti has become a land of violence and terror, with only a handful of rebels daring to oppose the reign of tyranny. Because of this situation, a ship arriving at Port-au-Prince brings with it only four passengers. One of them, Brown, is a politically uncommitted cynic who has returned to the island to reopen his deserted hotel and to resume his love affair with Martha Pineda, the bored wife of a Latin American ambassador. The other three new arrivals are Mr. and Mrs. Smith, an American couple who have made the trip in the hope of establishing a vegetarian center, and the somewhat mysterious Jones, a British "major" who delights in boasting of his military experiences in Burma. Upon stepping ashore, Jones is immediately arrested and thrown into jail; and, a short time later, Brown finds the murdered body of a former government minister lying at the bottom of his empty swimming pool. The Smiths attend the dead minister's funeral and witness the brutal abuse of his widow at the hands of the Tontons. Indignant, they persuade Brown to assist in arranging for Jones's release. Although their efforts are successful, they are unaware that Jones has made a bargain with the Tontons to provide them with arms and ammunition from Miami. After the Smiths have accepted the futility of their mission and returned to the United States, Jones discovers that he is unable to put through his armaments deal, and he seeks sanctuary at the Pinedas' embassy home. As a warm relationship develops between Martha and Jones, the jealous Brown tricks Jones into volunteering to organize the rebels being banded together by Henri Philipot, the artist nephew of the murdered minister. At a meeting at the Pineda home, Dr. Magiot, a distinguished Haitian patriot, arranges for Jones to be smuggled into the hills and also makes an attempt to appeal to Brown for assistance. Although Dr. Magiot has his throat slashed by the Tontons, Jones, disguised as a native woman and accompanied by Brown, makes his way to the rebel rendezvous in a cemetery. During their all-night vigil, Jones confesses to Brown that his whole military background is a fraud but that he is resolved to go through with his mission in an attempt to do one worthwhile thing with his life. At dawn the two men are discovered by the Tontons, and Jones is shot and killed. But the rebels arrive in time to rescue Brown and gun down Jones's killers. Brown, no longer able to remain indifferent to the Haitian cause, allows Henri to persuade him to take Jones's place in the desperate chance it will bolster the rebels' morale in their almost hopeless fight for freedom. As the Pinedas also leave the island, Martha looks down from the plane that is taking her away from Haiti and speculates on the destiny of her lost lover fighting in the hills below. *Hotelkeepers. Diplomats. Americans in foreign countries. Vegetarians. British. Soldiers. Haitians. Guerrillas. Gunrunners. Braggarts. Infidelity. Political corruption. Imposture. Murder. Haiti. François Duvalier. Tontons Macoute.*

Note: Location scenes filmed in Dahomey and in the south of France. The film was cut heavily for second-run theaters. Many of Guinness's scenes were excised, and the narrative ends earlier than in the original version. Opened in Paris in Feb 1968 as *Les comédiens*.

LES COMÉDIENS *see* **THE COMEDIANS**

THE COMEDY OF TERRORS   **F6.0869**
Alta Vista Productions. *Dist* American International Pictures. 25 Dec **1963** [Detroit opening; c1 Jan 1964; LP27172]. Sd; col (PathéColor). 35mm (Panavision). 88 min. [Copyright length: 83 min.]

Pres by James H. Nicholson, Samuel Z. Arkoff. *Prod* James H. Nicholson, Samuel Z. Arkoff. *Co-prod* Anthony Carras. *Assoc Prod-Screenplay* Richard Matheson. *Dir* Jacques Tourneur. *Dir Photog* Floyd Crosby. *Camera Op* Harry Underwood. *Art Dir-Prod Dsgn* Daniel Haller. *Set Decor* Harry Reif. *Film Ed* Anthony Carras. *Mus* Les Baxter. *Sd* Don Rush. *Asst Dir* Robert Agnew, Lew Borzage. *Prod Supv* Joe Wonder. *Prod Asst* Jack Cash. *Script Supv* Emile Ehrlich. *Cost Supv* Marjorie Corso. *Wardrobe* Jerry Alpert. *Makeup Artist* Carlie Taylor. *Hairstyles* Betty Pedretti, Scotty Rackin. *Sp Eff* Pat Dinga. *Prop Master* Karl Brainard. *Still Photog* Tim Vanick. *Dial Dir* Wayne Winton.

Cast: Vincent Price *(Waldo Trumbull)*, Peter Lorre *(Felix Gillie)*, Boris Karloff *(Amos Hinchley)*, Basil Rathbone *(John F. Black)*, Joe E. Brown *(cemetery keeper)*, Joyce Jameson *(Amaryllis Trumbull)*, Beverly Hills *(Mrs. Phipps)*, Paul Barselow *(Riggs)*, Linda Rogers *(Phipps' maid)*, Luree Nicholson *(Black's servant)*, Luree Holmes *([see note])*, Buddy Mason *(Mr. Phipps)*, "Rhubarb" the Cat *(Cleopatra)*, Alan DeWitt, Doug Williams.

Horror comedy. In the 1890's, the small New England funeral business of Hinchley and Trumbull is in difficulty because of the laziness and drunkenness of Trumbull, who married the 92-year-old Hinchley's daughter, Amaryllis, to gain control of the business. Trumbull works only at moments of financial crisis, "creating" new customers with the help of Felix Gillie, whom Trumbull blackmails into being his assistant. Amaryllis is unhappy about her husband's abusiveness, his destruction of her hopes of becoming an opera singer, and his threats to kill her senile father with poison kept in a bottle which the old man thinks contains medicine. She and the sympathetic, tone-deaf Felix fall in love. Trumbull's landlord, John F. Black, threatens to evict him unless he pays a year's back rent, and Trumbull decides to get the money by providing an expensive funeral for a wealthy man whom he and Felix murder. Their plan backfires when the man's widow skips town without paying for the funeral. Trumbull next decides to kill Black. During the attempted murder, Black, a catalepsy victim, has what appears to be a fatal stroke. When his "corpse" stirs just before the funeral, Trumbull knocks him out and ties and gags him. According to the terms of Black's will, he is interred in a mausoleum, where he revives once again. The cemetery keeper, hearing his pounding, releases him; the now-maddened Black goes to the funeral parlor seeking revenge; but Trumbull finally kills him. Trumbull then turns on Amaryllis and Felix, rendering them unconscious. When the police arrive, Trumbull feigns unconsciousness to escape the blame for Black's death. Hinchley sees him and, thinking him ill, pours the poisoned medicine down his throat, killing him. Felix and Amaryllis find love together, and Hinchley goes on his merry, innocent way. *Undertakers. Singers. Landlords. Widows. Drunkenness. Blackmail. Eviction. Murder. Catalepsy. Funerals. Old age. Insanity. Partnerships. Strokes. Poisoning. Cemeteries. Opera. Tombs. New England. Cats.*

Note: Rereleased in Mar 1965 as *The Graveside Story.* One source credits Luree Holmes in place of Luree Nicholson.

THE COMIC   F6.0870

Acre Enterprises. *Dist* Columbia Pictures. 19 Nov **1969** [New York opening; c1 Nov 1969; LP37546]. Sd; col (Berkey Pathé Color). 35mm. 94 min. *MPAA rating* M.

Prod-Writ Carl Reiner, Aaron Ruben. *Dir* Carl Reiner. *Photog* W. Wallace Kelley. *2d Unit Photog* Donald Glouner. *Set Decor* Morris Hoffman. *Prod Dsgn* Walter Simonds. *Film Ed* Adrienne Fazan. *Mus* Jack Elliott. *Titl Song Perf by* Dennis Yost, The Classics IV. *Sd Supv* Charles J. Rice. *Sd* Les Fresholtz, Arthur Piantadosi. *Asst Dir* Rusty Meek. *Unit Prod Mgr* Russell Saunders. *Cost* Guy Verhille. *Makeup Supv* Ben Lane. *Hairstyles* Virginia Jones. *Spec Photog Eff* Butler-Glouner Inc.

Cast: Dick Van Dyke *(Billy Bright),* Michele Lee *(Mary Gibson),* Mickey Rooney *(Cockeye),* Cornel Wilde *(Frank Powers),* Nina Wayne *(Sybil),* Pert Kelton *(Mama),* Steve Allen *(himself),* Barbara Heller *(Ginger),* Ed Peck *(Edwin G. Englehardt),* Jeannine Riley *(Lorraine),* Gavin MacLeod *(1st director),* Jay Novello *(Miguel),* Craig Huebing *(doctor),* Paulene Myers *(Phoebe),* Fritz Feld *(Armand),* Jerome Cowan *(Lawrence),* Isabell Sanford *(woman),* Jeff Donnell *(nurse),* Carl Reiner *(Al Schilling).*

Comedy-drama. At his funeral the corpse of silent film comedian Billy Bright recalls his early vaudeville career; a stormy marriage to starlet Mary Gibson; divorce; marriage in Mexico to a wanton alcoholic; a prolonged sojourn in Europe; rediscovery by Steve Allen; a late career as the star of television commercials; engagement to an adolescent fortune hunter; his collapse at the altar rail; and a final visit from his son, an effeminate fashion designer. *Actors. Fortune hunters. Couturiers. Filial relations. Funerals. Motion pictures. Vaudeville. Television. Divorce. Mexico.*

Note: Working title: *Billy Bright.*

COMING APART   F6.0871

Kaleidoscope Films. 26 Oct **1969** [New York opening]. Sd; b&w. 35mm. 110 min.

Prod Israel Davis, Andrew J. Kuehn. *Dir-Writ* Milton Moses Ginsberg. *Camera* Jack Yager. *Film Ed* Lawrence Tetenbaum. *Sd* Thomas M. Daniel. *Cost* Francesca Davis.

Cast: Rip Torn *(Joe Glazer),* Sally Kirkland *(JoAnn),* Viveca Lindfors *(Monica),* Megan McCormick *(Joy),* Lois Markle *(Elaine),* Lynn Swann *(Anita),* Phoebe Dorin *(Karen),* Nancy MacKay *(Amy),* Julie Garfield *(Eugene McCarthy worker),* Kevin O'Connor *(Armand),* Robert Blankshine *(Sarabell),* Michael McGuire, Darlene Cotton *(couple at party),* Jane Marla Robbins *(Mrs. Glazer),* Joanna Vischer *(dancing lady).*

Drama. Joe Glazer, a New York psychiatrist, leaves the hospital where he works, rents a Kips Bay apartment under an assumed name, and installs a movie camera to record the events of his life. Although his wife is in the process of divorcing him, Joe does not lack female companionship; in fact, most of the people who visit the apartment are women. Among the visitors recorded on film are: Elaine, who wants Joe to add to the collection of cigarette burns on her body; Anita, a blonde tease who brings along a portfolio of nude photographs of herself, as well as a baby in a carriage; two female campaigners for Eugene McCarthy, who are merely passing by; JoAnn, a former patient who uses rock music to stimulate her nude dancing gyrations and to accompany the act of fellatio she performs on Joe; Karen, the wife of one of his best friends; Monica, an ex-mistress who, although worried about Joe's mental condition, would like to continue their affair; and a party guest who foils Joe's attempted pass and turns out to be a transvestite. The camera records the actions and words of Joe and finally, his mental breakdown. *Psychiatrists. Mistresses. Lovelorn.*

Divorce. Mental illness. Masochism. Oral sex. Transvestism. Nudity. Exhibitionism. Home movies. Political campaigns.

A COMING-OUT PARTY (Great Britain)   F6.0872

Independent Artists. *For* Rank Organisation. *Dist* Union Film Distributors. 30 Jul **1962** [New York opening]. Sd; b&w. 35mm. 98 min.

Pres by J. Arthur Rank. A Julian Wintle–Leslie Parkyn Production. *Prod* Julian Wintle, Leslie Parkyn. *Dir* Ken Annakin. *Screenplay* Jack Davies, Henry Blyth. *Photog* Ernest Steward. *Camera Op* James Bawden. *Focus Puller* Ian McMillan. *Art Dir* Harry Pottle. *Draughtsman* Eric Saw, Terence Marsh. *Scenic Artist* Alan Maley. *Film Ed* Ralph Sheldon. *Asst Ed* Pamela Tomling. *2d Asst Ed* James Langfield. *Mus* Reg Owen. *Sd Ed* Stan Fiferman. *Sd Rec* Ken Cameron, John W. Mitchell. *Sd Camera Op* Ron Butcher. *Boom Op* Tony Cripps. *1st, 2d & 3d Asst Dir* Clive Reed, Ron Jackson, Bernie Williams. *Prod Supv* Arthur Alcott. *Unit Mgr* Geoffrey Haine. *Cont* Joy Mercer. *Prod Sec* Norma Garment. *Wardrobe Mistress* Vi Murray. *Makeup Artist* Trevor Crole-Rees. *Hairdresser* Maud Onslow. *Still Photog* Ian Jeayes. *Constr Mgr* Bert Roberts. *Prop Master* Fred Eames. *Prop Buyer* Frederick Hasler.

Cast: James Robertson-Justice *(Sir Ernest Pease),* Leslie Phillips *(Jimmy Cooper),* Stanley Baxter *(Everett/Major Stampfel),* Eric Sykes *(Willoughby),* Richard Wattis *(Woodcock),* Godfrey Winn *(himself, an interviewer),* Colin Gordon *(Briggs),* Joan Haythorne *(Miss Rogers),* John Forrest *(Grassy Green),* Jeremy Lloyd *("Bonzo" Baines),* Peter Myers, actor *(Shaw),* Ronald Leigh Hunt *(Clynes),* John Ringham *(Plum Pouding),* John Le Mesurier *(Piggott),* Norman Bird *(Travers),* Ronnie Stevens *(Hankley),* Vincent Ball *(Higgins),* Ed Devereaux *(Webber),* Brian Oulton *(scientist),* Nancy Nevinson, Heidi Erich *(German fraus).*

War comedy-drama. Sir Ernest Pease, a famous aeronautical scientist, is a guest on the British version of the television program *This Is Your Life* and recalls an incident in 1942: *Flying over Germany to observe first hand the results of one of his radar experiments, his plane is hit by antiaircraft fire, forcing Pease to parachute to earth. Captured, he is sent to a POW camp, where his fellow prisoners suspect him of being a German spy because of his aloof, taciturn nature and his ability to speak German. After word arrives from the War Office that he is a VIP, all hands join in effecting his escape. Following several unsuccessful attempts, Pease decides to take command of the situation. He hides while his mates pretend there has been an escape. Once certain that German commandant Major Stampfel believes him to be among the missing, Pease and two other prisoners pose as members of the Swiss Red Cross Commission and quietly walk out of the camp. Pease and his friends are reunited on the television program.* Scientists. Prisoners of war. Prison escapes. Imposture. Aeronautics. Radar. Television. World War II. Germany. Great Britain—War Office. Red Cross. "This Is Your Life".

Note: Opened in London in Apr 1961 as *Very Important Person.*

COMING OUT PARTY   F6.0873

Dist Stacey Distributors. ca **1970.** Sd; col. 16mm. 61-81 min.

Sex film. No information about the precise nature of this film has been found. *Sexual initiation.*

THE COMING THING   F6.0874

Beyond the Pleasure Principle. *Dist* Sherpix, Inc. 17 Dec **1970** [San Francisco opening]. Sd; col. 35mm. 83 min.

Prod-Dir David Reberg.

Sex film. No information about the precise nature of this film has been found. *Sexuality.*

COMMANDO (Belgium/Italy/Spain/West Germany)   F6.0875

Tempo Film-Galatea-Fl. C. IT.-Midega Film-Monachia-Zeyn-Film-produktion. *Dist* American International Pictures. Feb **1964** [c26 Feb 1964; LP27907]. Sd; b&w. 35mm. 98 min. [Also reviewed at 95 min.]

Dir Frank Wisbar. *Screenplay* Giuseppe Mangione, Mino Guerrini, William Demby, Milton Krims, Frank Wisbar, Eric Bercovici. *Story* Arturo Tofanelli. *Photog* Cecilio Paniagua. *Art Dir* Enrique Alarcón. *Film Ed* Mario Serandrei. *Mus* Angelo Francesco Lavagnino. *Sd* Luigi Puri. *Asst Dir* Antonio Linares, Wieland Liebske. *Prod Mgr* Gabriele Silvestri.

Cast: Stewart Granger *(Captain Le Blanc),* Dorian Gray *(Nora),* Maurizio Arena *(Dolce Vita),* Ivo Garrani *(Colonel Dionne),* Fausto Tozzi *(Brascia),* Riccardo Garrone *(Paolo),* Carlos Casaravilla *(Ben Bled),* Peter Carsten *(Barbarossa),* Hans von Borsody *(Fritz),* Rafael Luis Calvo *(Kappa-kappa),* Dietmar Schönherr *(Petit Prince),* Leo Anchóriz *(Garcia),* Alfredo Mayo, Guillermo Carmona, Pablito Alonso, Jaime de Pedro, Francisco Cornet.

War drama. During the Algerian War of 1961, Captain Le Blanc of the French Foreign Legion receives orders to capture the leader of the resistance movement, Ben Bled, and bring him to French headquarters. Le Blanc and 12 of his legionnaires carry out their mission and take their prisoner to a rendezvous spot where a helicopter is waiting to take them to safety. But the helicopter is shot down, and the party, which now includes a French prostitute named Nora and an Arab boy, is forced to make a long and dangerous trek through partisan territory. They hide in an abandoned church, and Le Blanc's men are forced to fight for a cause they already know to be lost. The battle is long and bloody, and one by one the legionnaires are killed. Le Blanc and the remnants of his once proud force arrive with their prisoner at headquarters, and learn that all the fighting and dying has been in vain: the political situation has changed and Ben Bled is now an important figure who will help negotiate a peace treaty. Bitter and confused, Le Blanc considers killing his prisoner. But he changes his mind and is left to wonder about the lives he sacrificed in carrying out his orders. *Algerians. French. Guerrillas. Prostitutes. Resistance (political). Combat zone life. Helicopters. Algeria—History—War of Independence. France—Army—Foreign Legion.*

Note: Filmed in Italy. Released in Munich in Feb 1963 as *Marschier oder krepier;* running time: 99 min; in Rome in Nov 1962 as *Marcia o crepa;* in Madrid in Jan 1963 as *Marcha o muere;* and in Belgium as *Héros sans retour.*

THE COMMITTEE *see* **A SESSION WITH THE COMMITTEE**

COMMON-LAW CABIN! *see* **HOW MUCH LOVING DOES A NORMAL COUPLE NEED?**

COMMON LAW WIFE　　　　　　　　　　　　　　　**F6.0876**
Texas Film Producers. *Dist* Cinema Distributors of America. 28 Oct **1963** [trade review; c21 Aug 1963; LP26826]. Sd; b&w. 35mm. 81 min. [Copyright length: 77 min.]

Pres by M. A. Ripps. *Prod* Fred Kadane. *Dir* Eric Sayers. *Screenplay* Grace Knowland.

Cast: Lacy Kelly *(Jonelle ["Baby Doll"])*, Shugfoot Rainey *(Uncle Chug),* Annabelle Lee *(Linda),* Jody Works *(Sheriff Jody),* Bull Connors *(Bull),* Emma Lou Watkins *(Brenda),* Anne MacAdams, George Edgley.

Rural melodrama. Uncle Chug has been living in the rural South with his common-law wife, Linda, for 5 years when their relationship is suddenly threatened by the arrival of Chug's sensuous niece, Jonelle. Competition arises between the two women for Chug's love and money, although Linda reminds Chug that she can prove the legality of their common-law marriage with a motel receipt from the first night they spent together. Jonelle, who is interested only in the money, performs a striptease in a restaurant and becomes involved with Bull, the local moonshiner. The two kill Uncle Chug by poisoning his whiskey. Linda realizes that Jonelle was at least partially responsible for Chug's death, and, after conning Jonelle into riding to see her "dying" uncle, Linda pushes her out of the car and shoots her. Then Linda kills herself by drinking the poisoned whiskey. *Uncles. Sheriffs. Moonshiners. Marriage—Common law. Greed. Striptease. Poisoning. Rural life. Murder. Suicide. Liquor. United States—South. Documentation.*

THE COMMUNE　　　　　　　　　　　　　　　　　　**F6.0877**
Mar **1970** [Los Angeles showing]. Sd; col. 16mm? [Feature length assumed.]

Cast: Robert Harry.

Melodrama. A cult lives in the desert, where they practice bestiality and sexual cruelty. *Cults. Bestiality. Sadism. Deserts.*

COMMUTER GAME　　　　　　　　　　　　　　　　　**F6.0878**
Horst Productions. *Dist* Abrams & Parisi, Inc. Mar **1969**. Sd; b&w. 35mm. 78 min.

Dir Fred Kamiel.

Comedy. Two suburbanites who tell their wives that they have to work late in the city go to their rented apartment and entertain women. They even fix up their conservative doctor friend with a woman who poses as a patient and then acts as the seducer. Soon their wives get wise to their husbands' scheme, go to the city, get picked up, and take the strangers to the apartment. After chases and arguments, the husbands are forgiven and the couples return to the suburbs. *Suburbanites. Physicians. Marriage. Infidelity. Pickups.*

I COMPAGNI *see* **THE ORGANIZER**

COMPAÑERAS AND COMPAÑEROS　　　　　　　　　**F6.0879**
Monument Film Corp. *Dist* New Yorker Films. 3 Dec **1970** [New York opening]. Sd; col (Eastman Color). 16mm. 90 min.

Prod-Dir-Writ David C. Stone, Barbara Stone, Adolfas Mekas. *Photog* Robert Machover, Robert Lacativa. *Film Ed* David C. Stone, Barbara Stone, Adolfas Mekas.

Documentary. The continued spirit of the Cuban revolution is evidenced in the activities and viewpoints of members of five groups of Cuban youth: soldiers from various battalions who are joined in a champion brigade to cut a quota of sugar cane in Oriente province for the 1970 harvest; the "Orientadores," who assist peasants in isolated rural and mountainous regions of Pinar del Río province, aiding them in building schools, hospitals, and other essential communal facilities and encouraging them to work collectively; a crew of young women from underprivileged backgrounds who have volunteered to develop

the agriculture of the province of Camagüey, at the same time attending classes; a group of engineering students working to double the productivity of a sugar mill in Oriente province; and students selected from each province to study the sciences at a specialized boarding school near Havana, sharing responsibility for the operation of the school with their teachers. The young people discuss their backgrounds, their emergence and functions in a revolutionary society, their revolutionary, third world consciousness, their theories on Latin American revolution and guerrilla warfare, their economy, their nation's future, and their commitment to the development of the "New Man" envisaged by "Che" Guevara. *Soldiers. Students. Peasants. Revolutionaries. Engineers. Social classes. Youth. Construction. Farming. Communism. Education. Sugar. Boarding schools. Factories. Cuba—History—1958 Revolution. Cuba. Camagüey. Oriente. Havana. Pinar del Río. Ernesto "Che" Guevara.*

Note: In Spanish with English subtitles. Filmed in Cuba Jun-Oct 1969; subsequently released in 80-min and 45-min versions.

COMPANY OF COWARDS? *see* **ADVANCE TO THE REAR**

COMPANY OF KILLERS　　　　　　　　　　　　　　**F6.0880**
Universal Pictures. 26 Aug **1970** [Los Angeles opening; c29 Jul 1970; LP39191]. Sd; col (Technicolor). 35mm. 86 min. *MPAA rating* G.

Prod E. Jack Neuman, Jerry Thorpe. *Assoc Prod* Lloyd Richards. *Dir* Jerry Thorpe. *Screenplay* E. Jack Neuman. *Photog* Jack Marta. *Art Dir* Alexander Golitzen, Joe Alves. *Set Decor* John McCarthy, Claire P. Brown. *Film Ed* John Elias. *Mus* Richard Hazard. *Mus Supv* Stanley Wilson. *Sd* Waldon O. Watson, Frank H. Wilkinson. *Asst Dir* Paul Cameron. *Unit Prod Mgr* Arthur S. Newman, Jr. *Cost* Burton Miller. *Makeup* Bud Westmore. *Hairstyles* Larry Germain.

Cast: Van Johnson *(Sam Cahill),* Ray Milland *(George DeSalles),* John Saxon *(Dave Poohler),* Brian Kelly *(Nick Andros),* Fritz Weaver *(John Shankalien),* Clu Gulager *(Frank Quinn),* Susan Oliver *(Thelma Dwyer),* Diana Lynn *(Edwina DeSalles),* Robert Middleton *(Owen Brady),* Terry Carter *(Jaffie),* Anna Capri *(Maryjane),* Anthony James *(Jimmy),* Marian Collier *(Sylvia),* Nate Esformes *(Peterson),* Mercer Harris *(Luke),* Joyce Jameson *(Marnie),* Gerald Hiken *(Chick),* Vince Howard *(Dale Christian),* Larry Thor *(Clarington),* Donna Michelle *(Gloria),* Jeanne Bal *(Patricia Cahill).*

Crime melodrama. In a midwestern city Dave Poohler is hospitalized when found unconscious in a park. While delirious, he confesses to being a hired killer, but he escapes when he regains consciousness. Police Chief Sam Cahill, tipped by attending physician Nick Andros and prodded by reporter Frank Quinn, issues an alert for the man. Dave contacts his girl friend Thelma Dwyer and their boss John Shankalien, who is arranging the murder of multimillionaire Owen Brady for fellow businessman George DeSalles. Dave trails Brady to a cocktail lounge, picks up go-go dancer Maryjane, and is spotted by a passing patrolman. Dave is wounded in a shoot-out at Maryjane's apartment, but he again escapes and confronts Brady at his home. Brady flees when Dave loses his gun, but he is chased by Dave in his car. Cahill, notified by Brady's girl friend Gloria, stops the would-be assassin, who perishes in a fiery crash. Dave's co-conspirators are apprehended. *Hired killers. Police. Physicians. Reporters. Millionaires. Businessmen. Go-go dancers. Murder. Conspiracy. Hospitals. Bars. Automobile accidents. Chases.*

Note: Location scenes filmed in Denver. Produced in 1968 as *The Protectors,* intended as a television feature.

COMPARTIMENT TUEURS *see* **THE SLEEPING CAR MURDER**

COMPETITION *see* **AUDITION**

COMPUTER FREE-FOR-ALL (Japan)　　　　　　　　**F6.0881**
Toho Co. Apr **1969** [Los Angeles showing]. Sd; col (Eastmancolor). 35mm. 84 min.

Dir Kengo Furusawa. *Screenplay* Yasuo Tanami. *Photog* Senkichi Nagai. *Art Dir* Kazuo Ogawa. *Mus* Naozumi Yamamoto.

Cast: Hajime Hana *(Hanakawado),* Hitoshi Ueki *(Uemura),* Kei Tani *(Tanii),* Hiroshi Inuzuka, Senri Sakurai, Eitaro Ishibashi, Shin Yasuda.

Comedy. Hanakawado, a computer salesman, desperately needs to complete an important deal to pay his enormous bar tab. Using company funds, he pays Uemura, the owner of the bar, in advance, but subsequently loses the deal and a promotion. Furthermore, he discovers that through a computer error, the bill has been far overpaid. Together with Tanii, who is in charge of the computers and fears he will lose his job, Hanakawado and Uemura go to the apartment of Yoshiko, who works at the bar and into whose bank account the money was paid. However, the trio finds her murdered, and Tanii decides to use the computer to revive her. Given a second life, the shrewish Yoshiko becomes a sweet young girl. The money is recovered, and all charges of embezzling are dropped. *Salesmen. Embezzlement. Debt. Reviviscence. Murder. Bars. Computers.*

Note: Released in Japan in Jan 1969 as *Buchamukure daihakken.*

COMPUTER GAME   **F6.0882**

Kirt Films International. *Dist* Distribpix, Inc. **1969**. Sd; col. 35mm. 63 min.

Melodrama. Tony, a sexually obsessed madman, utilizes a computer dating service to procure unsuspecting women for his private use, and then makes them perform lesbian and autoerotic acts. Although the women sometimes enjoy this abasement, the police arrest Tony and put an end to his perverse practices. *Sadism. Insanity. Sex deviates. Lesbianism. Autoeroticism. Computer dating services.*

THE COMPUTER WORE TENNIS SHOES   **F6.0883**

Walt Disney Productions. *Dist* Buena Vista Distribution Co. 11 Feb **1970** [Los Angeles opening; c3 Oct 1969; LP37331]. Sd (RCA); col (Technicolor). 35mm. 90 min. *MPAA rating G.*

Prod Bill Anderson, prod. *Assoc Prod & Writ* Joseph L. McEveety. *Dir* Robert Butler. *2nd Unit Dir* Arthur J. Vitarelli. *Dir Photog* Frank Phillips. *Art Dir* John B. Mansbridge. *Set Decor* Emile Kuri, Hal Gausman. *Main Titl* Alan Maley. *Film Ed* Cotton Warburton. *Mus* Robert F. Brunner. *Orch* Walter Sheets. *Titl Song* Robert F. Brunner, Bruce Belland. *Sd Supv* Robert O. Cook. *Sd Mix* Dean Thomas. *Mus Ed* Evelyn Kennedy. *Asst Dir* Christopher Hibler. *Cost* Chuck Keehne, Emily Sundby. *Makeup* Robert J. Schiffer. *Hairstyles* La Rue Matheron. *Tech Adv* Ko Suzuki.

Cast: Kurt Russell *(Dexter)*, Cesar Romero *(A. J. Arno)*, Joe Flynn *(Dean Higgins)*, William Schallert *(Professor Quigley)*, Alan Hewitt *(Dean Collingsgood)*, Richard Bakalyan *(Chillie Walsh)*, Debbie Paine *(Annie)*, Frank Webb *(Pete)*, Michael McGreevey *(Schuyler)*, Jon Provost *(Bradley)*, Frank Welker *(Henry)*, Alexander Clarke *(Myles)*, Bing Russell *(Angelo)*, Pat Harrington *(moderator)*, Fabian Dean *(Little Mac)*, Fritz Feld *(Sigmund Van Dyke)*, Pete Renoudet *(Lieutenant Hannah)*, Hillyard Anderson *(J. Reedy)*.

Comedy. Unbeknownst to the administrators of Medfield College, an interview during which Dean Higgins denies Professor Quigley a much-needed computer is broadcast to the assembled student body. Outraged by this refusal, the students persuade entrepreneur Arno to donate his old computer in lieu of the customary $20,000 contribution to the college. Arno is delighted, as the computer is worth considerably less than his usual donation. When student leader Dexter attempts to repair the machine, lightning strikes and he is instantly infused with the electronic brain's memory bank. Among its information is a chronicle of Arno's illegal gambling operations. Dexter's remarkable new knowledge endears him to Dean Higgins, who enrolls the student in a televised competition for $100,000. During the contest, however, the word "applejack" triggers an enumeration of Arno's illegal activities. Enraged, the gangster abducts the contestant, sequestering Dexter at his country estate. Disguised as house painters, Dexter's classmates paint the stately mansion orange and green. While so doing, they rescue the student, dropping the trunk in which he is locked two stories into a waiting truck. The fall destroys Dexter's memory bank. Returned to the contest, Dexter is unable to respond to the key question, which is answered correctly by a slow-witted associate, who thereby wins for Medfield the $100,000. *Students. Deans. Professors. Racketeers. Rescue. Gambling. Abduction. College life. Computers. Television. Lightning. Contests.*

LE COMTE DE MONTE CRISTO *see* **THE STORY OF THE COUNT OF MONTE CRISTO**

LE CONCERTO DE LA PEUR *see* **NIGHT OF LUST**

THE CONCRETE JUNGLE (Great Britain)   **F6.0884**

Merton Park Studios. *Dist* Fanfare Films. 6 Jun **1962** [Philadelphia opening]. Sd; b&w. 35mm. 86 min.

A Nat Cohen–Stuart Levy Production. *Prod* Jack Greenwood. *Assoc Prod* Jim O'Connolly. *Dir* Joseph Losey. *Screenplay* Alun Owen. *Story* Jimmy Sangster. *Photog* Robert Krasker. *Camera Op* John Harris. *1st Camera Asst* Peter Jessop. *Art Dir* Scott MacGregor. *Asst Art Dir* Leonard Townsend. *Draughtsman* John Graysmark. *Prod Dsgn* Richard MacDonald. *Film Ed (see note)* Reginald Mills, Geoffrey Muller. *Asst Ed* Brian Blamey. *Mus Comp & Cond* John Dankworth. *Song:* "Prison Blues" sung by Cleo Laine. *Sd* Sidney Rider, Ronald Abbott. *Boom Op* Tom Otter. *Sd Camera Op* Arthur Vincent. *Dub Ed* Derek Holding. *1st, 2d & 3d Asst Dir* Buddy Booth, N. C. V. Miller, Timothy Burrill, John Quested. *Prod Mgr* Bill Shore. *Prod Sec* Doris Prince. *Cont* Pamela Davies. *Wardrobe Supv* Ron Beck. *Wardrobe Mistress* Laura Nightingale. *Makeup Supv* George Partleton. *Hairdresser* Helen Penfold. *Still Photog* Eddie Orton. *Ch Electrn* Jim Axtell. *Prop Buyer* A. E. Waters. *Casting Dir* Ronald Curtis. *Constr Mgr* Curtis Turner.

Cast: Stanley Baker *(Johnny Bannion)*, Sam Wanamaker *(Mike Carter)*, Margit Saad *(Suzanne)*, Patrick Magee *(Chief Warder Barrows)*, Noel Willman *(prison governor)*, Grégoire Aslan *(Frank Saffron)*, Jill Bennett *(Maggie)*, Kenneth J. Warren *(Clobber)*, Nigel Green *(Ted)*, Kenneth Cope *(Kelly)*,

Patrick Wymark *(Sol)*, Jack Rodney *(Scout)*, John Molloy *(Snipe)*, Brian Phelan *(Pauly Larkin)*, Murray Melvin *(Antlers)*, John Van Eyssen *(Formby)*, Laurence Naismith *(Mr. Town)*, Rupert Davies *(Edwards)*, Tom Bell *(Flynn)*, Neil McCarthy *(O'Hara)*, Edward Judd *(young warder)*, Dorothy Bromiley *(Angela)*, Derek Francis *(priest)*, Redmond Phillips *(prison doctor)*, Paul Stassino *(Alfredo Fanucci)*, Jerold Wells *(Warder Brown)*, Keith Smith *(Hanson)*, Tom Gerard *(Quantock)*, Larry Taylor *(Charles)*, Sydney Bromley *(frightened prisoner)*, Luigi Tiano *(Italian-speaking prisoner)*, Richard Shaw *(warder in van)*, Charles Lamb *(Mr. Able)*, Maxwell Shaw, Victor Beaumont *(men at party)*, Ronald Brittain *(kitchen warder)*, Thomas Eytle, Maitland Williams *(West Indian prisoners)*, Dickie Owen *(1st man in prison)*, Roy Dotrice *(Nicholls)*, Bobby Naidoo *(Serang)*.

Crime drama. While serving a 3-year prison sentence, Johnny Bannion plans a racetrack robbery. Once out of prison, Johnny and his partner, Mike Carter, carry out the plan and escape with $100,000. The fence demands a higher percentage than previously agreed upon, however, so Johnny buries the money in a field after taking $1,500 to buy a ring for his girl friend, Suzanne. Betrayed by a former girl friend who tips off the police, Johnny is returned to prison for 15 years. Carter uses his prison contacts to torture Johnny, but he refuses to divulge the location of the money. Carter's mob, holding Suzanne as a hostage, arranges for Johnny to escape so they can trick him into leading them to the cache. Johnny rescues Suzanne, but one of Carter's over-anxious gunmen mortally wounds him. He dies without revealing the hiding place, leaving Carter and his men still searching for the money. *Convicts. Fences (for stolen goods). Hostages. Robbery. Partnerships. Perfidy. Murder. Torture. Prison escapes. Racetracks.*

Note: Location scenes filmed in London. Released in Great Britain in 1960 as *The Criminal*; running time: 97 min. British working title: *The Concrete Jungle*. Prerelease information credits Muller as film editor.

CONCRETE WILDERNESS *see* **MEDIUM COOL**

THE CONCUBINES (Japan)   **F6.0885**

Unicorn Productions. *Dist* Boxoffice International Pictures. Jul **1969**. Sd; col (Eastman Color). 35mm (Cinema Scope). 90 min.

Pres by Harry Novak. *Prod* Kiyoshi Ogasawara. *Asst Prod* Hideo Tomohisa. *Dir* Koji Takamatsu. *Screenplay* Jiku Yamatoya. *English Vers* James E. McClarty. *Dir Photog* Hideo Ito. *Lighting* Hajime Isomi. *Art Dir* Shukei Hirataka. *Sets* Ogawa Kogei. *Film Ed* Tadashi Tsuji. *Mus* Masao Yagi. *Sd* Takashi Sugizaki. *Asst Dir* Michio Akiyama, Isao Okijima. *Prod Mgr* Masayuki Yayama. *Cost* Tokyo Costumes Co.

Cast: Tomoko Mayama *(Pan Chin Lien)*, Shikyoku Takashima *(Wu Sung)*, Juuzo Itami *(Hsi Men Ching)*, Ruriko Asari *(Li Ping-Brh)*, Riko Kurenai *(Chun Mei)*, Hatsuo Yamatani *(Wu Ta)*, Ko Hei Tsusaki *(Ying)*, Yuzo Tachikawa *(Hau Yung)*.

Drama. Based on the 16th-century novel presumably written by: Shih-chen Wang, *Chin P'ing Mei*. Toward the end of the decline of the Sung dynasty in 13th-century China, Wu Sung, the captain of the guards, spurns the advances of his sister-in-law, Pan Chin Lien, known as "The Golden Lotus." She turns to Hsi Men Ching, a wealthy, decadent man, and becomes his fifth wife when her husband is killed. Wu Sung tries to avenge his brother's death in which Hsi Men Ching was implicated, but he is banished to a remote prison. Wu Sung is rescued by revolutionary forces who kill the man responsible for the imprisonment. Pan Chin Lien again tries for Wu Sung's declaration of love, but instead, she receives a sword through her heart. *Soldiers. Chinese. Sisters-in-law. Revolutionaries. Brothers. Seduction. Murder. Marriage. Revenge. Prisons. Polygamy. China—History—Sung Dynasty.*

Note: Japanese title *Chin-P'ing-Mei*. Also known as *The Notorious Concubines*.

THE CONDEMNED OF ALTONA (France/Italy)   **F6.0886**

Titanus–S. G. C. *Dist* Twentieth Century-Fox Film Corp. Sep **1963** [New York opening: 30 Oct; c31 Dec 1962; LP26629]. Sd; b&w. 35mm (CinemaScope). 114 min.

Prod Carlo Ponti. *Dir* Vittorio De Sica. *Dir Theatrical Seq* Manfred Wekwerth. *Screenplay (see note)* Abby Mann, Cesare Zavattini. *Dir Photog* Roberto Gerardi. *Art Dir* Ezio Frigerio. *Asst Art Dir* Carlo Tommasi. *Film Ed* Manuel Del Campo, Adriana Novelli. *Symphony no. 11* ("The Year 1905"), *3d Movement:* "In Memorium" Dmitriy Dmitriyevich Shostakovich. *Cond* Franco Ferrara. *Mus Comment* Nino Rota. *Sd Engr* Ennio Sensi. *Asst Dir* Luisa Alessandri, Giuseppe Menegatti. *Exec in Charge of Prod* Luciano Perugia. *Asst to the Prod* Tommaso Sagone, Mario De Biase, Jerzy Macc. *Cont Girls* Barbara Fuchs, Pina Zani. *Wardrobe Dsgn* Pier Luigi Pizzi. *Makeup* Nilo Jacoponi. *Makeup for Sophia Loren* Giuseppe Annunziata. *Hairdresser for Sophia Loren* Ada Palombi. *Hairdresser* Carlo Sindici. *Drawings* Renato Guttuso. *Dial Dir* George Tyne.

Cast: Sophia Loren *(Johanna)*, Maximilian Schell *(Franz)*, Fredric March *(Gerlach)*, Robert Wagner *(Werner)*, Françoise Prévost *(Leni)*, Alfredo Franchi *(grounds keeper)*, Lucia Pelella *(wife of grounds keeper)*, Roberto Massa *(driver)*, Antonia Cianci *(maid)*, Carlo Antonini *(police official)*, Armando Sifo *(policeman)*, Aldo Pecchioli *(cook)*, Ekkehard Schall.

Drama. Inspired by: Jean-Paul Sartre, *Les séquestrés d'Altona* (Paris opening: 23 Sep 1959). Upon learning that he will die of cancer in a few months, Gerlach, head of West Germany's greatest industrial combine, summons his younger son, Werner, and Werner's wife, Johanna, an actress, to the family home in Altona. Gerlach wants Werner to assume control of the business, but Werner disapproves of the power his father has amassed by openly supporting any government that would enable him to make money. Although Johanna has been told the elder Gerlach son, Franz, had been killed several years after being cited at the Nuremberg trials for war crimes, she discovers he is actually living in the attic of the house. Walled up in a room without windows and surrounded by relics of the Nazi era, he is totally insane and sees no one except his sister Leni, who brings him food and tells him that Germany is in poverty and ruins. Johanna manages to gain entrance to the room and, after several talks, tells him that Germany is enjoying enormous prosperity. Johanna begins to pity Franz; the embittered and possessive Leni tells the truth about Franz's long career as a soldier who enjoyed torturing and killing his victims. Franz, in desperation, leaves his self-imposed confinement and seeks out his father. The elder Gerlach takes Franz to the shipyards and proudly shows him his empire. As they travel to the observation platform, Franz, in an attempt to erase the guilt of his father and himself, leaps to his death, dragging his father with him. *Industrialists. Brothers. Actors. Nazis. Death. Cancer. Filial relations. Wealth. Business ethics. War crimes. Insanity. Murder. Suicide. Guilt. International Military Tribunal. Federal Republic of Germany. Altona. Bertolt Brecht.*

Note: Exteriors filmed in Hamburg. Released in Italy in 1962 as *I sequestrati di Altona* and in France in 1963 as *Les séquestrés d'Altona*. The film includes a scene in a theater where Sophia Loren interprets the "Referendum" scene from Bertolt Brecht's *A Private Life of the Master Race*, and Ekkehard Schall interprets a scene from *The Resistable Rise of Arturo Ui*, as presented by the Berliner Ensemble. Cesare Zavattini does not receive U. S. screen credit.

CONE OF SILENCE *see* **TROUBLE IN THE SKY**

THE CONFESSION (France/Italy)   F6.0887
Les Films Corona–Films Pomereu–Fono Roma–Selenia Cinematografica. *Dist* Paramount Pictures. 9 Dec **1970** [New York opening]. Sd; col (Eastman Color). 35mm. 138 min. *MPAA rating GP.*
Prod Robert Dorfmann, Bertrand Javal. *Dir* Costa-Gavras. *Screenplay* Jorge Semprun. *Photog* Raoul Coutard. *Asst Photog* Chris Marker. *Art Dir* Bernard Evein. *Film Ed* Françoise Bonnot. *Sd* William Sivel. *Asst Dir* Alain Corneau. *Prod Mgr* Claude Hauser.
Cast: Yves Montand *(Gérard)*, Simone Signoret *(Lise)*, Gabriele Ferzetti *(Kohoutek)*, Michel Vitold *(Smola)*, Jean Bouise *(man in factory)*, Laszlo Szabo *(secret policeman)*, Monique Chaumette, Guy Mairesse, Marc Eyraud, Gérard Darrieu, Gilles Ségal, Charles Moulin, Nicole Vervil, Georges Aubert, André Cellier, Pierre Delaval, William Jacques, Henri Marteau, Michel Robin, Antoine Vitez, Michel Beaune, Marc Bonseignour, Thierry Bosc, Jean-Paul Cisife, Marcel Cuvelier, Pierre Decazes, Basile Diamantopoulos, Jacques Emin, Jean-François Gobbi, Maurice Jacquemont, Jean-Pierre Janic, Patrick Lancelot, Jean Lescot, François Marthouret, Pierre Moncorbier, Umberto Raho, Jacques Rispal, Paul Savatier, Claude Vernier, Pierre Vielhescazes.
Historical drama. Source: Artur London, *L'aveu, dans l'engrenage du procès de Prague* (Paris, 1968). In 1951 Gérard, a Jew and Czechoslovakian Under-Secretary of Foreign Affairs, is abducted by Prague Intelligence and charged with conspiracy against the Communist party. His suspicious past activities include participation in the International Brigade in Spain, incarceration in a German concentration camp, and confinement in a Swiss tuberculosis sanitarium. After months of torture conducted by secret policemen Smola and Kohoutek, Gérard is persuaded to confess to false charges for the sake of party loyalty. With 13 codefendants, 11 of whom are also Jewish, Gérard stands trial; all make false confessions because of absolute allegiance to the party. Eleven receive death sentences; Gérard and the others are sentenced to life imprisonment. When she hears his confession broadcast over public radio, Gérard's French Communist wife, Lise, denounces him. After Stalin's death Gérard is released and vindicated. Reunited with his wife and children, he moves to Paris, where he chronicles his trial and imprisonment. He returns to Prague as the Russians begin occupation of Czechoslovakia. *Communists. Czechoslovakians. Expatriates. Secret agents. Secret police. Political corruption. Anti-Semitism. Confession (law). Interrogation. Torture. Trials. Espionage. Prisons. Concentration camps. Czechoslovakia—Politics and Government—1945-. Czechoslovakia—History—Soviet Intervention 1968. Prague. Joseph Stalin. Artur Gérard London. Lise Ricol-London.*

Note· Opened in Paris in Apr 1970 as *L'aveu*; running time: 138 min. Cut from 150 min?

CONFESSION OF A DIRTY PAIR *see* **CONFESSIONS OF A WILD PAIR**

CONFESSIONS OF A BAD GIRL   F6.0888
Barry Mahon Productions. *Dist* Little Pictures. 12 Nov **1965** [Los Angeles showing]. Sd; b&w. 35mm. 63 min.
A Barry Mahon Production. *Prod-Dir* Barry Mahon. *Photog* Rick Carrier. *Ed* John John. *Sd* Magno Sound.
Cast: Judy Adler.
Drama. A young woman who came to New York City seeking fame and fortune recalls the road to success: Arriving alone in the city, she is unable to get a start in show business until she learns that she must supplement her talents as a model with sexual favors to those in a position to boost her career. As a garment district fashion model, she must submit to the embraces of influential buyers, and cooperate with Madison Avenue photographers who believe that a woman posing nude is a willing sex partner and with film producers and their Texas backers. Wild parties at the local motel, sexual encounters at the studio, and weekend "dates" form a necessary part of the "cooperative" woman's activities. *Models. Buyers. Photographers. Motion picture producers. Promiscuity. Ambition. Motion pictures. New York City—Madison Avenue. New York City—Garment district.*
Note: Filmed in New York City.

CONFESSIONS OF A DIVORCEE *see* **THE DIVORCEE**

CONFESSIONS OF A PSYCHO CAT   F6.0889
Dist Chancellor Films. Feb **1968**. Sd; b&w. 35mm. 70 min.
Pres by Herb Stanley, Bob Page. *Prod-Dir* Herb Stanley.
Cast: Eileen Lord, Ed Brandt, Frank Grace, Dick Lord.
Sex film. Little information about the precise nature of this film has been found, but press material with accompanying photographs suggest that it concerns the adventures of Virginia, a schizophrenic sensualist and that it includes scenes of troilism, lesbianism, sadism, and oral and anal intercourse. *Sensualists. Schizophrenia. Troilism. Lesbianism. Sadism. Oral sex. Anal sex.*

CONFESSIONS OF A VAHINE *see* **MAEVA**

CONFESSIONS OF A WILD PAIR   F6.0890
C. I. T. Films. *Dist* I. R. M. I. Films. 19 Oct **1967** [New York opening]. Sd; b&w. 35mm. 66 min.
A Film by Max Böll. *Dir* Joe Davis. *Scen* Hans Dedow. *Mus Score* Al Deline.
Cast: Sybille Renza *(Margo)*, Karin Franke.
Sex film. Margo, an amoral young American and an aspiring writer, travels through Europe to gain different experiences. Included in the film are striptease and lesbian lovemaking scenes. *Americans in foreign countries. Authors. Travel. Striptease. Lesbianism. Europe.*
Note: Filmed in Munich. Also released as *Confession of a Dirty Pair.*

CONFESSIONS OF AN OPIUM EATER   F6.0891
Photoplay Associates. *Dist* Allied Artists. Jun **1962** [c27 Apr 1962; LP21768]. Sd (Westrex); b&w. 35mm. 85 min.
An Albert Zugsmith Production. *Prod-Dir* Albert Zugsmith. *Assoc Prod (see note)* Robert Hill, Eugene Lourie. *Writ (see note)* Robert Hill, Seton I. Miller. *Dir Photog* Joseph Biroc. *Art Dir* Eugene Lourie. *Set Decor* Joe Kish. *Film Ed (see note)* Roy Livingston, Robert S. Eisen, Edward Curtiss. *Mus* Albert Glasser. *Choreog* Jon Gregory. *Sd* Ralph Butler. *Sd Ed* Charles Schelling. *Mus Ed* Victor Lewis. *Asst Dir* Lindsley Parsons, Jr. *Prod Mgr* Edward Morey, Jr. *Unit Prod Mgr* Lonnie D'Orsa. *Set Cont* Eylla Jacobus. *Wardrobe* Roger J. Weinberg, Norah Sharpe. *Makeup Artist* Bill Turner. *Hairdresser* Alice Monte. *Sp Eff* Milt Olsen. *Prop Master* Ted Mossman. *Constr Supv* James West. *Stunt Dir* Paul Stader.
Cast: Vincent Price *(De Quincey)*, Linda Ho *(Ruby Low)*, Philip Ahn *(Ching Foon)*, Richard Loo *(George Wah)*, June Kim *(Lotus)*, Yvonne Moray *(child)*, Alicia Li *(Ping Toy)*, John Mamo *(auctioneer)*, Arthur Wong *(Kwai Tong)*, Jo Anne Miya *(1st dancing girl)*, Geri Hoo *(2d dancing girl)*, Keiko *(3d dancing girl)*, Carol Russell *(slave girl)*, Terence De Marney *(scrawny man)*, Vincent Barbi *(captain)*, Caroline Kido *(Lo Tsen)*, Gerald Jann *(fat Chinese)*, Vivianne Manku *(catatonic girl)*, Miel Saan *(Look Gow)*, Victor Sen Yung *(Wing Young)*, Ralph Ahn *(Wah Chan)*, Richard Fong.
Melodrama. Source: Thomas De Quincey, *Confessions of an English Opium-eater*, in *London Magazine* (Sep-Oct 1821). In the early 1900's, a Chinese junk smuggles slave girls into San Francisco's Chinatown to be sold at auction. George Wah, a crusading newspaper editor and tong leader, attempts to save the girls but fails when a rival tong appears. He escapes with the help of Lotus, one of the slave girls, who herself manages to escape. The supposition

that Wah is dead precipitates a tong war. Adventurer Gil De Quincey arrives to help Wah by joining a rival tong led by Ruby Low, who secretly has killed and is impersonating Tang, the real tong leader. At the underground auction, Wah, disguised as an elderly man, buys Lotus, who has been recaptured, for a large amount of opium. Gil, in the meantime, has found his way to the room with the help of a Chinese "slave child." Wah and Gil are exposed, but an explosion helps them escape to a labyrinth of tunnels. In a subsequent struggle in a drain under the city streets, Gil and Ruby drown in a lovers' embrace. *Chinese. Newspapermen. Editors. Adventurers. Slavery. Smuggling. Gang wars. Murder. Disguise. Male impersonation. Tongs. Tunnels. Opium. San Francisco—Chinatown.*

Note: Copyright material credits Seton I. Miller as co-screenplay writer, Ed Curtiss as film editor, and Eugene Lourie as associate producer/production designer; Miller and Curtiss do not receive screen credit; Lourie is credited on screen as art director. Actress Keiko Nishimura receives screen credit as Keiko. Alternative title: *Souls for Sale.* Rerelease title: *Secrets of a Soul.*

CONFETTI AL PEPE see **SWEET AND SOUR**

CONFIDENTIAL REPORT see **MR. ARKADIN**

CONGIURA DI SPIE see **TO COMMIT A MURDER**

THE CONJUGAL BED (France/Italy)   F6.0892
Sancro Film-Fair Film-Cocinor-Les Films Marceau. *Dist* Embassy Pictures. 16 Sep **1963** [New York opening]. Sd; b&w. 35mm. 90 min.
Pres by Joseph E. Levine. *Prod* Henryk Chroscicki, Alfonso Sansone. *Dir* Marco Ferreri. *Screenplay* Goffredo Parise, Marco Ferreri, Rafael Azcona. *Screenplay Collab* Pasquale Festa Campanile, Massimo Franciosa, Diego Fabbri. *From an Outline by* Goffredo Parise. *Dir Photog* Ennio Guarnieri. *Camera* Danilo Desideri. *Asst Camera* Franco Marino. *Art Dir* Massimiliano Capriccioli. *Asst Art Dir* Franco Maciocia. *Set Dresser* Rosa Sansone. *Film Ed* Lionello Massobrio. *Mus* Teo Usuelli. *1st & 2d Asst Dir* Giancarlo Santi, Misha Asherov. *Prod Mgr* Illio Rovelli. *Cont* Francesco Degli Espinosa. *Set Mgr* Antonio Negri. *Prod Asst* Ezio Ranzini. *Cost Dsgn* Luciana Marinucci. *Dressmaker* Marcella Giovanetti. *Makeup* Nilo Jacoponi.
Cast: Ugo Tognazzi *(Alfonso)*, Marina Vlady *(Regina)*, Walter Giller *(Father Mariano)*, Linda Sini *(Mother Superior)*, Riccardo Fellini *(Riccardo)*, Achille Maieroni *(Aunt Mafalda)*, Pietro Tattanelli *(Uncle Don Giuseppe)*, Jusupoff Ragazzi *(Aunt Jolanda)*, Igi Polidoro *(Igi)*, Melissa Drake *(Maria Costanza)*, Sandrino Pinelli *(Maria Costanza's fiancé)*, Mario Giussani *(Count Ribulsi)*, Polidor *(Brother Lorenzo)*, Jacqueline Perrier, Nino Vingelli.
Comedy-drama. At the age of 40, Alfonso, a partner in a successful automobile dealership, decides that the time has come to take a wife. Rejecting the female companions of his single days, he is assisted by a school friend, Father Mariano, in meeting Regina, a virginal, middle-class young woman. Following their wedding, Alfonso moves into his bride's home, a beehive of widowed aunts and cousins who anxiously await word of Regina's pregnancy. Regina's belief that a woman's function is to bear children leads her to make enormous physical demands upon her husband. His heart weakening under the strain, Alfonso appeals to Father Mariano, who assures him that Regina is a model wife. Alfonso is forced to submit to a painful series of hormone injections aimed at enhancing his virility. Finally he collapses and goes to the seashore to recuperate. Regina visits him periodically, and after a violent lovemaking session, Alfonso suffers a heart seizure. At last he learns that he has fulfilled his function and will become a father. Regina henceforth denies herself to her husband, and while Alfonso, now an invalid, is relegated to a maid's room, Regina consults with his partner at the automobile agency. Left alone to enjoy a short period of happy independence, Alfonso dies before the baby's birth. *Bachelors. Newlyweds. Catholics. Widows. Aunts. Priests. Middle classes. Invalids. Pregnancy. Motherhood. Marriage. Sexuality. Heart disease. Sterility (sexual). Automobile agencies.*
Note: Opened in Rome in Apr 1963 as *Una storia moderna (L'ape regina)*; running time 105 min; in Paris in Jun 1963 as *Le lit conjugal*; running time: 95 min. Alernative Italian title: *L'ape regina.* U. S. prerelease title: *Queen Bee.*

CONJUGAL CABIN see **HOW MUCH LOVING DOES A NORMAL COUPLE NEED?**

CONJURE WIFE see **BURN, WITCH, BURN**

THE CONNECTION   F6.0893
The Connection Co.-Allen-Hodgdon Productions. *Dist* Films Around the World, Inc., Film-Makers' Distribution Center. 15 Feb **1962** [Scottsdale, Arizona, opening]. Sd; b&w. 35mm. 103 min. [See note.]
Prod Lewis Allen, Shirley Clarke. *Assoc Prod* Jim Di Gangi. *Dir* Shirley Clarke. *Screenplay* Jack Gelber. *Photog* Arthur J. Ornitz. *Art Dir* Albert Brenner. *Set Decor* Gene Callahan. *Prod Dsgn* Richard Sylbert. *Film Ed* Shirley Clarke. *Mus* Freddie Redd. *Sd* Jim Shields. *Sd Eff* Tony Schwartz. *Cost*

Ruth Morley.
Cast—Principals: William Redfield *(Jim Dunn)*, Warren Finnerty *(Leach)*, Garry Goodrow *(Ernie)*, Jerome Raphel *(Solly)*, James Anderson *(Sam)*, Carl Lee *(Cowboy)*, Barbara Winchester *(Sister Salvation)*, Roscoe Lee Browne *(J. J. Burden)*, Henry Proach *(Harry)*.
Cast—Musicians: Freddie Redd *(piano)*, Jackie McLean *(alto sax)*, Michael Mattos *(bass)*, Larry Ritchie *(drums)*.
Drama. Source: Jack Gelber, *The Connection* (New York opening: 15 Jul 1959). Eight drug addicts are gathered in a Manhattan loft apartment belonging to Leach. In order to pay their "connection" when he arrives with heroin, the men have agreed for a fee to allow Jim Dunn, a would-be documentary filmmaker, and his cameraman, J. J. Burden, to photograph them. While they are waiting for their "fix," four of the men play jazz; the others somewhat self-consciously relate anecdotes about themselves and their backgrounds. Eventually the "connection," a black named Cowboy, arrives. He is accompanied by a street salvationist; he has brought her along to distract the police. As the addicts file into the bathroom one by one for their shots, the bewildered old woman begins to suspect that they are drinking. She so accuses them and is politely but firmly ushered from the loft. The men then persuade Dunn to try some heroin so that he will have a deeper understanding of the subject of his film. After taking the drug, he becomes violently ill and tells J. J. to take over. While Dunn is sleeping, Leach gives himself an overdose of heroin and goes into a coma. After Cowboy has given physical aid, Dunn awakens. Realizing his experiment is a failure, he tells J. J. to keep the footage. *Drug addicts. Motion picture directors. Motion picture cameramen. Negroes. Drug dealers. Police. Drug overdose. Heroin. Jazz. New York City. Salvation Army. Documentation.*
Note: Filmed on location in New York City. Original running time: 110 min. Also reviewed at 93 min.

CONQUÉRANTS HÉROÏQUES see **THE AVENGER**

CONQUERED CITY (Italy)   F6.0894
Maxima Film-Lux Film-Galatea. *Dist* American International Pictures. Jan **1965** [c13 Jan 1965; LP29779]. Sd; b&w. 35mm. 91 min.
Dir Joseph Anthony. *Screenplay* Guy Elmes, Eric Bercovici, Marc Brandel. *Photog* Leonida Barboni. *Art Dir* Mario Chiari. *Film Ed* Marion Bonitti, Raymond Poulton, Michael Billingsley. *Mus* Piero Piccioni.
Cast: David Niven *(Maj. Peter Whitfield)*, Lea Massari *(Lelia)*, Ben Gazzara *(Capt. George Stubbs)*, Daniela Rocca *(Doushka)*, Martin Balsam *(Feinberg)*, Michael Craig *(Captain Elliot)*, Clelia Matania *(Miss Climedes)*, Giulio Bosetti *(Narriman)*, Percy Herbert *(Sergeant Reed)*, Ivo Garrani *(Mavroti)*, Odoardo Spadaro *(Mendoris)*, Roberto Risso *(Corporal Loveday)*, Venantino Venantini *(General Ferolou)*, Carlo Hintermann *(sergeant)*, Adelmo Di Fraia *(Andrea)*, Massimo Righi *(Pollit)*, Francesco Tensi *(General Bennet)*, Renato Moretti *(The "Saint")*, Lamberto Antinori.
War drama. Source: John Appleby, *The Captive City* (New York, 1955). As the Germans retreat northward out of Greece in 1945, the city of Athens is contested by rival political factions, and British Maj. Peter Whitfield finds himself commanding the defense of the Hotel Zeus in the middle of the besieged city. The hotel is surrounded by Greek rebels led by Mavroti, and trapped inside are Captain Elliot, a British officer; several Greek loyalists; two American soldiers, Captain Stubbs and Private Feinberg; and hotel owner Janny Mendoris and his daughter Lelia. Whitfield learns from Mendoris that the hotel contains a large cache of weapons desperately needed by the rebel fighters, and he determines to withstand the rebels' repeated attacks. Captain Stubbs is at first reluctant to join in the defense, but the heat of battle finally diverts him from his romantic pursuit of both Lelia and Doushka, a fiery refugee. With the help of Stubbs, Whitfield successfully defends the hotel until movements in the enemy camp indicate that a traitor is aiding the Greeks from within the hotel. Stubbs disappears, and Whitfield assumes that he has gone over to the rebels. After making plans to blow up the hotel and the cache of arms when his people are free, Whitfield goes to negotiate with the rebels. There he finds that the rebels have tortured Stubbs into revealing where the arms are located, and Whitfield realizes that the traitor is still in the hotel. Under the guise of defeat, Whitfield returns to the hotel and agrees to vacate his remaining forces. He discovers that Captain Elliot is the traitor, and after a gunfight in the hotel basement, Whitfield manages to set off an explosion which rips through the basement fortress and destroys Elliot and the munitions. Whitfield and the remaining patriots escape to join the British. *Soldiers. Greeks. Germans. British. Hotelkeepers. Traitors. Refugees. Guerrillas. Torture. Hotels. Firearms. World War II. Athens. Explosions.*
Note: Rome opening in Dec 1962 as *La città prigioniera*; running time: 108 min.

CONQUEROR WORM (Great Britain)   **F6.0895**
Tigon British Film Productions–American International Productions. *Dist* American International Pictures. 15 May **1968** [Los Angeles opening; c15 May 1968; LP35942]. Sd; col (Eastman Color, print by Perfect). 35mm. 87 min.
Prod Arnold Louis Miller. *Exec Prod* Tony Tenser. *Co-prod* Louis M. Heyward. *Assoc Prod* Philip Waddilove. *Dir* Michael Reeves. *Screenplay* Michael Reeves,. Tom Baker, writ. *Adtl Scenes Writ* Louis M. Heyward. *Photog* John Coquillon. *Camera Op* Brian Elvin, Gerry Anstiss. *Camera Asst* Tony Breeze, Chris Reynolds. *Art Dir* Jim Morahan. *Asst Art Dir* Peter Shields. *Set Dresser* Jimmy James, writ. *Film Ed* Howard Lanning. *Asst Ed* Marion Curren. *Mus Comp & Cond* Paul Ferris. *Sd Rec* Paul Le Mare. *Sd Mix* Hugh Strain. *Dub Ed* Dennis Lanning. *Asst Dir* Ian Goddard, Iain Lawrence. *Prod Mgr* Ricky Coward. *Location Mgr* Ewan Pearson. *Cont* Lorna Selwyn. *Prod Sec* Pat O'Donnell. *Wardrobe* Jill Thomson. *Makeup* Dore Hamilton. *Hairdresser* Henry Montsash. *Sp Eff* Roger Dicken. *Casting Dir* Freddie Vale. *Prop* Sid Davies, Fred Harrison. *Still Photog* Jack Dooley. *Grip* Freddie Williams. *Constr Mgr* Dennis Cantrell. *Gaffer* Laurie Shane.
Cast: Vincent Price *(Matthew Hopkins)*, Ian Ogilvy *(Richard Marshall)*, Rupert Davies *(John Lowes)*, Hilary Dwyer *(Sara)*, Robert Russell *(John Stearne)*, Patrick Wymark *(Oliver Cromwell)*, Wilfrid Brambell *(Master Loach)*, Nicky Henson *(Trooper Swallow)*, Tony Selby *(Salter)*, Bernard Kay *(fisherman)*, Godfrey James *(Webb)*, Michael Beint *(Captain Gordon)*, John Trenaman *(Trooper Harcourt)*, Bill Maxwell *(Trooper Gifford)*, Morris Jar *(Paul)*, Maggie Kimberley *(Elizabeth Clark)*, Peter Haigh *(Lavenham magistrate)*, John Kidd *(magistrate)*, Hira Talfrey *(hanged woman)*, Ann Tirard *(old woman)*, Peter Thomas, actor *(farrier)*, Edward Palmer *(shepherd)*, David Webb, actor *(jailer)*, Paul Dawkins *(farmer)*, Lee Peters *(infantry sergeant)*, David Lyell *(foot soldier)*, Alf Joint *(sentry)*, Martin Terry *(Hoxne innkeeper)*, Jack Lynn *(Brandeston innkeeper)*, Beaufoy Milton *(priest)*, Dennis Thorne, Michael Segal *(villagers)*, Toby Lennon *(old man)*, Gillian Aldham *(young woman in cell)*, Paul Ferris *(young husband)*, Margaret Nolan, Sally Douglas, Donna Reading, Tasma Brereton, Sandy Seager *(wenches at inn)*, Philip Waddilove, Derek Ware, Susi Field.
Horror film. Source: Ronald Bassett, *Witchfinder General* (London, 1966). In an England torn apart by the civil war that followed Cromwell's victory at Naseby in 1645, Matthew Hopkins and his henchman Stearne pose as witchhunters, extracting money for their services from magistrates and torturing suspects into falsely confessing their guilt before being executed. One of their victims is John Lowes, a village priest whose niece, Sara, attempts to save her uncle's life by giving herself to Hopkins. Later, however, Stearne rapes Sara and then persuades Hopkins to hang Lowes before leaving the vicinity. When Sara's betrothed, Richard Marshall, learns of her humiliation, he quickly marries her and vows vengeance on Hopkins. When the "witchfinder general," as Hopkins is now known, learns of Richard's relentless pursuit of him, he lays a trap that eventually leads to the capture of both Richard and Sara. Hopkins tortures Sara in front of Richard, hoping to force a confession of witchcraft from the young man; but just as Hopkins is about to brand the sign of the cross on Sara's back, several of Richard's comrades storm the prison and rescue the young lovers. In a frenzy, Richard gouges out one of Stearne's eyes and then begins dismembering Hopkins with an ax. Horrified by the spectacle, one of the soldiers shoots the dying Hopkins. *Magistrates. Priests. Uncles. Soldiers. Witchcraft. Torture. Self-sacrifice. Rape. Revenge. Murder. Mutilation. Naseby. Great Britain—History—Civil War and Commonwealth. Oliver Cromwell.*
Note: Location scenes filmed in Suffolk, England. Opened in London in May 1968 as *Witchfinder General*. Also known as *Edgar Allan Poe's Conqueror Worm*. Sources conflict in crediting set dresser.

CONQUEST (Japan)   **F6.0896**
Kindai Eiga Kyokai. *Dist* Toho Co. Sep **1966** [Los Angeles showing]. Sd; b&w. 35mm (Tohoscope). 122 min.
Dir-Screenplay Kaneto Shindo. *Orig Story* Junichiro Tanizaki. *Photog* Kiyoshi Kuroda. *Mus* Hikaru Hayashi.
Cast: Kyoko Kishida *(Kaoyo)*, Eitaro Ozawa, Nobuko Otowa, Ko Kimura, Taiji Tonoyama.
Drama. Based on the prolog and first act of the play by: Izumo Takeda, Senryu Namiki and Shoraku Miyoshi, *Kanadehon Chushingura* (first performed in Osaka in 1748). Moronao, a provincial governor in 18th-century Japan, is attracted to Kaoyo, the wife of a court magistrate. Moronao commissions a love poem to be written and sent to her, but she returns it with an admonition. He orders the magistrate into combat and begins to plan her seduction of Kaoyo the widow. The magistrate, anticipating Moronao's superior strength, takes Kaoyo with him to the battlefield. Moronao is enraged by the magistrate's cleverness and sends his army to kill the magistrate and bring back Kaoyo. To Moronao's chagrin, the army kills Kaoyo and returns with only her head. *Territorial governors. Magistrates. Seduction. Japan—*

History—Tokugawa period 1600-1867.
Note: Released in Japan in 1965 as *Akuto*.

CONQUEST OF MYCENE (France/Italy)   **F6.0897**
Explorer Film '58–C. F. P. C. *Dist* Embassy Pictures. 15 Dec **1965** [New York showing]. Sd; col (Eastman Color). 35mm (Euroscope). 102 min.
Prod Bruno Turchetto. *Dir* Giorgio Ferroni. *Screenplay* Remigio Del Grosso, Giorgio Ferroni. *Photog* Augusto Tiezzi. *Art Dir* Arrigo Equini. *Mus* Carlo Rustichelli.
Cast: Gordon Scott *(Glauco [Glaucus]/Hercules)*, Rosalba Neri *(Pasifae)*, Alessandra Panaro *(Medea)*, Michel Lemoine *(Oineo)*, Arturo Dominici, Jany Clair, Nerio Bernardi.
Action melodrama. As the King of Mycene lies dying after an earthquake has destroyed his city, he leaves Medea, a daughter from his first marriage, in the care of Pasifae, his pregnant wife. Later, the queen has a son, and to commemorate the event a second Mycene is built at the child's birthplace. Pasifae claims that her son is the embodiment of the god Moloch, whose followers frequently offer hostages as human sacrifices. In nearby Tirinto [Tiryns], one of the cities which unwillingly provides the captives, the king's son Glauco takes the name of Hercules and enters Mycene with a group of hostages. Secretly planning to lead a revolt, Hercules first wins the support of Pasifae, but the queen turns against him when she discovers that he and Medea have fallen in love. Pasifae's attempts to kill Hercules and to have her stepdaughter sacrificed fail when Tirinto's army aids the people of Mycene in a revolt. *Royalty. Stepmothers. Hostages. Human sacrifice. Filial relations. Revolts. Mycenae. Greece—History. Earthquakes. Hercules. Pasiphaë. Medea. Moloch. Tiryns.*
Note: Opened in Rome in 1964 as *Ercole contro Molock*; in Paris in Sep 1964 as *Hercule contre Moloch*; running time: 98 min.

THE CONQUESTS OF MR. ROSE see **THE EROTIC MR. ROSE**

IL CONQUISTATORE DI CORINTO see **THE CENTURION**

THE CONSPIRACY CIRCUS—CHICAGO '70. see **CHICAGO 70**

CONSTANCE AUX ENFERS see **WEB OF FEAR**

CONSTANTINE AND THE CROSS (Italy)   **F6.0898**
Jonia Film. *Dist* Embassy Pictures. 21 Nov **1962** [Detroit opening]. Sd; col (Eastman Color). 35mm (Totalscope). 120 min. [Also reviewed at 110 min.]
Pres by Joseph E. Levine. *Prod* Ferdinando Felicioni. *Dir* Lionello De Felice. *Screenplay* Ennio De Concini, Ernesto Guida, Lionello De Felice, Diego Fabbri, Fulvio Palmieri, Franco Rossetti, Guglielmo Santangelo. *Photog* Massimo Dallamano. *Art Dir* Franco Lolli. *Film Ed* Mario Serandrei, Gabriele Varriale. *Mus* Mario Nascimbene. *Cost* Giancarlo Bartolini Salimbeni. *U. S. Dub Vers* Beaver-Champion Attractions.
Cast: Cornel Wilde *(Constantine)*, Christine Kaufmann *(Livia)*, Belinda Lee *(Fausta)*, Elisa Cegani *(Helena)*, Massimo Serato *(Maxentius)*, Fausto Tozzi *(Hadrian)*, Tino Carraro *(Maximian)*, Carlo Ninchi *(Constantius Chlorus)*, Vittorio Sanipoli *(Apuleius)*, Franco Fantasia, Nando Tamberlani, Annibale Ninchi, Loris Gizzi, Nando Gazzolo, Enrico Glori, Jole Mauro, Renato Terra, Lia Angeleri.
Historical melodrama. In the early years of the 4th century A. D., the warrior Constantine aids his father, Emperor Constantius Chlorus, in fighting the barbarians and is summoned to receive honors in Rome. En route to the city with his friend Hadrian, a centurion, he is ambushed by the soldiers of Maxentius, his political rival, who shifts the blame for the attack to the Christians. After leaving the wounded Hadrian in the care of Livia, a Christian maiden, Constantine arrives in Rome. Livia is imprisoned for her beliefs but is released through the intervention of Constantine, who is accused of treachery and forced to flee the city, leaving behind his betrothed, Fausta, Maxentius' sister. Subsequently, Constantius reveals before his death that Constantine's mother, Helena, is also a Christian. Constantine is acclaimed Emperor of the West; and he announces a position of toleration towards the Christians. He weds Fausta, but her father, Maximian, urged by Maxentius, attempts to assassinate him and commits suicide when the plot fails. Maxentius becomes ruler of Rome, continues the cruel persecution of the Christians, and has Livia tortured and killed. Fausta travels to Rome to sway him, but he holds her prisoner and conspires to attack Constantine's forces in Gaul. Encouraged by a vision of the cross bearing the inscription, "By This Sign Conquer," Constantine defeats his enemies, rescues Fausta and his mother, and assures freedom of worship to the Christians. *Royalty. Centurions. Assassination. Religious persecution. Religious conversion. Torture. Suicide. Perfidy. Rome—History—Empire. Constantine I. Constantius Chlorus. Fausta. Maxentius. Maximian. Helena (mother of Constantine I). Christianity. Visions.*
Note: Battle scenes filmed in Yugoslavia; Yugoslavian coproduction status unconfirmed. Opened in Rome in Jan 1961 as *Costantino il Grande*; running time: 95 min; cut from 120 min. Alternative Italian title: *Costantino il Grande—*

In hoc signo vinces. Sources vary in rendering historical names; anglicized versions have been chosen.

CONSTELLATION: VIRGO see **SIGN OF THE VIRGIN**

CONSTRUCTION GANG   F6.0899

Dist Distribpix, Inc. 17 Jul **1970** [Champaign, Illinois, showing]. Sd; col. 35mm. 64 min.

Drama. After several weeks of marriage, Audrey finds that her husband will not have intercourse with her. She becomes increasingly frustrated and finally accedes to the advances of a handsome construction worker, a virile man who knows all there is to know about sex. Audrey comes home with the construction worker one evening and finds her husband with another woman. The four of them engage in an orgy, and Audrey is initiated into lesbianism and group sex. *Newlyweds. Construction workers. Infidelity. Orgies. Lesbianism.*

IL CONTE DI MONTECRISTO see **THE STORY OF THE COUNT OF MONTE CRISTO**

CONTEMPT (France/Italy)   F6.0900

Rome–Paris Films–Les Films Concordia–C. C. Champion. *Dist* Embassy Pictures. Oct **1964** [New York opening: 18 Dec]. Sd; col (Technicolor). 35mm (CinemaScope, see note). 103 min. [Also reviewed at 99 min.]

Pres by Joseph E. Levine. *Prod* Carlo Ponti, Georges de Beauregard. *Dir-Writ* Jean-Luc Godard. *Photog* Raoul Coutard. *Film Ed* Agnès Guillemot, Lila Lakshmanan. *Mus* Georges Delerue. *Sd Engr* William Sivel. *Asst Dir* Charles Bitsch. *Prod Mgr* Philippe Dussart. *Co-prod Mgr* Carlo Lastricati. *Script Girl* Suzanne Schiffman. *Wardrobe* Tanine Autre. *Makeup* Odette Berroyer. *Still Photog* Vicky Dussart.

Cast: Brigitte Bardot *(Camille Javal)*, Jack Palance *(Jeremy Prokosch)*, Michel Piccoli *(Paul Javal)*, Giorgia Moll *(Francesca Vanini)*, Fritz Lang *(himself, the director)*, Jean-Luc Godard *(assistant director)*, Linda Véras *(siren)*.

Drama. Source: Alberto Moravia, *Il disprezzo* (Milan, 1954). Paul Javal, a young French dramatist who has found commercial success in Rome, accepts an offer from vulgar American producer Jeremy Prokosch to rework the script for German director Fritz Lang's screen adaptation of *The Odyssey.* Paul's wife, Camille, joins him on the first day of the project at Cinecitta. As the first discussions are completed, Prokosch invites the crew to join him at his villa, offering Camille a ride in his two-seat sportscar. Camille looks to Paul to decline the offer, but he submissively withdraws to follow by taxi. He does not catch up with them until 30 minutes later, explaining that he was delayed by a traffic accident. Camille grows uneasy, secretly doubting his integrity and suspecting that he is using her to cement his ties with Prokosch. The feelings of doubt are heightened when she sees him exchange familiarities with Prokosch's secretary, Francesca. Back at their apartment Paul and Camille discuss the subtle uneasiness that has come between them in the first few hours of the project, and Camille suddenly announces to her bewildered husband that she no longer loves him. Hoping to rekindle Camille's love, Paul convinces her to accept Prokosch's invitation to join them for filming in Capri. Prokosch and Lang are locked in a conflict over the correct interpretation of Homer's work, an impasse exacerbated by the difficulty of communication between the German director, French script writer, and American producer. Francesca acts as interpreter, mediating all conversations. When Paul sides with Prokosch against Lang by suggesting that Odysseus actually left home because of his wife's infidelity, Camille's suspicions of her husband's servility are confirmed. She deliberately allows him to find her in Prokosch's embrace, and in the ensuing confrontation she declares that her respect for him has turned to contempt because he has bartered her to Prokosch. He denies this accusation, offering to sever his connection with the film and leave Capri; but she will not recant and leaves for Rome with the producer. After an auto crash in which Camille and Prokosch are killed, Paul prepares to leave Capri and return to the theater. Lang continues to work on the film. *Playwrights. Motion picture producers. Motion picture directors. Germans. Americans in foreign countries. Secretaries. Interpreters. Marriage. Jealousy. Infidelity. Ethics. Motion pictures. Cinecitta (Rome). Rome. Capri. Fritz Lang. Automobile accidents. "The Odyssey".*

Note: Filmed on location in Rome and Capri. Opened in Paris in Dec 1963 as *Le mépris* at 100 min; in Italy in Oct 1963 as *Il disprezzo* at 87 min. Filmed in Franscope.

THE CONTEST   F6.0901

Cosmos Films. *Dist* Able Film Co. ca **1970**. Sd; col. 16mm. [Feature length assumed.]

Sex film. Contruction workers enter into a sex marathon with a group of women. *Construction workers. Sexuality. Contests.*

CONTEST GIRL (Great Britain)   F6.0902

Val Guest Productions. *For* Rank Organisation. *Dist* Continental Distributing, Inc. May **1966**. Sd; col (Eastman Color). 35mm (CinemaScope). 99 min. [Also reviewed at 82, 83, and 102 min.]

Prod-Dir Val Guest. *Exec Prod* Earl St. John. *Assoc Prod* Frank Sherwin Green. *Screenplay* Val Guest, Robert Muller. *Dir Photog* Arthur Grant. *Art Dir* Maurice Carter. *Film Ed* Bill Lenny. *Mus Comp & Cond* Laurie Johnson. *Sd Ed* James Shields. *Sd Rec* Claude Hitchcock, Ken Cameron. *Asst Dir* Roy Baird. *French Asst Dir* Daniel Wronecki. *Prod Mgr* Robert Lynn. *French Prod Mgr* Louis Fleury. *Cost* Beatrice Dawson. *Makeup* Tony Sforzini. *Hairdressing* Biddy Chrystal.

Cast: Ian Hendry *(Don Mackenzie)*, Janette Scott *(Shirley Freeman)*, Ronald Fraser *(Walter Carey)*, Edmund Purdom *(Rex Carrick)*, Jean Claudio *(Roger Armand)*, Kay Walsh *(Mrs. Freeman)*, Norman Bird *(Mr. Freeman)*, Janina Faye *(Elaine Freeman)*, Tommy Trinder *(Charlie Dorton)*, David Weston *(Harry)*, Francis Matthews *(Taylor)*, Jerry Desmonde *("Rose of England" organizer)*, Peter Ashmore *(Lucius)*, Jacqueline Jones *(Jean Watson)*, Jackie White *(Barbara)*, Leila Williams *(2d chaperon)*, Paul Carpenter, Henry McCarthy *(American tourists)*, Raymond Young *("Globe" organizer)*, Marianne Stone *(typist)*, Sylvia Steel *(Janet)*, Eve Eden *(Angela)*, Jacqueline Wallis *(Julie)*, Margaret Nolan *(Caroline)*, Nicki Peters *(Cora)*, Linda Christian *(herself)*, Alizia Gur *(Miss Peru)*, Arlette Dobson *(Miss America)*, Margaret Bristow *(Miss France)*, Barbara von der Heyde *(Miss Germany)*, Yuriko Nakahara *(Miss Japan)*, Gillian French *(Miss Italy)*, Donna Pearson *(Miss Sweden)*, Rosemarie Frankland *(Miss Australia)*, Ting Ling *(Miss China)*, Vera Novac *(Miss Malaysia)*, Shirley Hadler *(Miss Belgium)*, Kathy Highland *(Miss Eire)*, Gloria Wenlock *(Miss Denmark)*, Julie Devonshire *(Miss Greece)*, Jackie Durham *(Miss Poland)*, Sandy Sarjeant *(Miss Spain)*, Sidney James, Stirling Moss, Duchess of Bedford, Joe Brown, British, Lionel Blair, Norman Hartnell.

Melodrama. Shirley Freeman, a typist, is vacationing at the beach when she is approached by newspaper reporter Don Mackenzie and persuaded to enter a beauty contest. Don and his photographer friend, Walter, write a newspaper article on Shirley with pin-up pictures. Shirley's parents and her boyfriend, Harry, express their disapproval of her activities, but Shirley decides to pursue her new career. After winning the "Rose of England" contest, Shirley becomes a professional beauty contestant. Don, her promoter, has fallen in love with Shirley, but she does not return his attentions. When movie actor Rex Carrick also falls in love with her, he tries to persuade Shirley to quit the beauty business. Instead, Shirley becomes more obsessed with fame and goes on to enter the "Miss Globe" contest in southern France and to seduce one of the organizers in hopes of winning. Miss Peru, who also seduced a contest organizer, is declared the winner, however. Greatly disillusioned, Shirley returns to England, where her participation in beauty contests is limited to judging. One day Shirley recognizes her younger sister, Elaine, as one of the contestants and panics as she recalls her own experiences. She flees from her judge's chair, and runs into Don, who seems to understand her reaction. *Typists. Models. Reporters. Actors. Peruvians. Sisters. Ambition. Fame. Seduction. Disillusionment. Beaches. Beauty contests. England. France. Riviera.*

Note: Location scenes filmed on the Riviera, in Monaco, Nice, Cannes, and Monte Carlo. Opened in London in Sep 1964 as *The Beauty Jungle;* running time: 114 min.

THE CONTINENTAL TWIST see **TWIST ALL NIGHT**

LES CONTREBANDIÈRES see **THE SMUGGLERS**

CONVICT STAGE   F6.0903

Steve Production. *Dist* Twentieth Century-Fox Film Corp. 17 Jun **1965** [New York opening; c2 Jun 1965; LP31311]. Sd; b&w. 35mm. 71 min.

Prod Hal Klein. *Dir* Lesley Selander. *Screenplay* Daniel Mainwaring. *Story* Donald Barry. *Dir Photog* Gordon Avil. *Camera Op* Edward L. Davenport. *Film Ed* John F. Schreyer. *Mus Comp & Cond* Richard LaSalle. *Sd Mix* Burdick S. Trask. *Asst Dir* Joe Wonder. *Script Supv* Billy Vernon. *Cost* Patrick Cummings. *Makeup Artist* Gustaf M. Norin. *Hairstyles* Ann Kirk. *Sp Eff* Roger George. *Photog Eff* Butler-Glouner Inc. *Prop Master* Charles Chichetti. *Key Grip* Harry Stern. *Ch Electrn* Ross Maehl.

Cast: Harry Lauter *(Ben Lattimore)*, Donald Barry *(Marshal Karnin)*, Jodi Mitchell *(Sally)*, Hanna Landy *(Ma Simes)*, Joseph Patridge, Eric Matthews, Walter Reed, Michael Carr, Fred Krone, George Sawaya, Karl MacDonald.

Western drama. Ben Lattimore swears revenge on the Simes Brothers, members of a notorious outlaw gang who killed his sister during a stagecoach hold-up. He trails the brothers but stops after Ma Simes shoots and wounds him. Ben's girl friend Sally nurses him back to health and urges him to entrust the pursuit to Marshal Karnin. Ben, however, decides to pick up the trail of the Simes Brothers, even though his action threatens to separate him from Sally.

He learns that Marshal Karnin and a posse have captured the Simes Brothers and plan to escort them to prison in a stagecoach. Ben approaches the stagecoach, hoping to kill the brothers, but Karnin convinces him that a fair trial will bring the outlaws to justice. Ben rides along to protect the other passengers in the stagecoach from the rest of the outlaw gang which is still at large. Marshal Karnin and he do not realize that Ma Simes is also a passenger. When the travelers spend the night in a deserted town, Ma Simes attempts to free her sons, and a gunfight ensues. Marshal Karnin and Ben kill Ma Simes and bring the rest of the gang to trial, and Ben returns to Sally. *Brothers. Outlaws. United States marshals. Revenge. Filial relations. Stagecoach robberies.*

CONVICTS 4   F6.0904

Kaufman-Lubin Productions. *Dist* Allied Artists. 15 Jun **1962** [Philadelphia opening; c4 Apr 1962; LP21654]. Sd; b&w. 35mm. 105 min.

Prod A. Ronald Lubin. *Dir-Screenplay* Millard Kaufman. *Cinematog* Joseph Biroc. *Art Dir* Howard Richmond. *Set Decor* Joseph Kish. *Film Ed* George White. *Mus Comp & Cond* Leonard Rosenman. *Sd* Ralph Butler. *Mus Ed* Eve Newman. *Sd Ed* Archie Dattelbaum. *Asst Dir* Clark Paylow, Arthur Broidy, Mickey Lewis. *Asst to Prod* Doane Harrison. *Prod Supv* Edward Morey, Jr. *Location Mgr* James E. Henderling. *Set Cont* Robert Gary. *Wardrobe* Roger J. Weinberg, Wally Harton, Norah Sharpe. *Makeup* William Turner. *Hairstyles* Janette Marvin. *Sp Eff* Milt Olsen. *Tech Adv* John Resko. *Prop Master* Ted Mossman. *Constr Supv* James West.

Cast: Ben Gazzara (*John Resko*), Stuart Whitman (*principal keeper*), Ray Walston (*Iggy*), Vincent Price (*Carl Carmer*), Rod Steiger (*Tiptoes*), Broderick Crawford (*warden*), Dodie Stevens (*Resko's sister*), Jack Kruschen (*Resko's father*), Sammy Davis, Jr. (*Wino*), Naomi Stevens (*Resko's mother*), Carmen Phillips (*Resko's wife*), Susan Silo (*Resko's daughter*), Timothy Carey (*Nick*), Roland LaStarza (*Duke*), Tom Gilson (*Lefty*), Arthur Malet (*storekeeper*), Lee Krieger (*Stanley*), Myron Healey (*Gunther*), Josip Elic (*barber*), Jack Albertson (*art teacher*), Robert H. Harris (*commissioner*), Andy Albin (*con*), Burt Lange (*gallery man*), John Kellogg, Adam Williams, Robert Christopher, Warren Kemmerling, Kreg Martin, John Close, Billy Varga (*guards*), Reggie Nalder (*Greer*), John Dierkes (*cell block guard*).

Biographical drama. Source: John Resko, *Reprieve; the Testament of John Resko* (Garden City, New York, 1956). During the Great Depression, John Resko kills a storekeeper for trying to prevent him from taking a toy for his infant child. As he awaits execution at Sing Sing, his sentence is commuted to life imprisonment, and he is transferred to Dannemora Prison. Surly and belligerent, he is in constant trouble with both the authorities and his fellow inmates, notably Iggy, a comical near-psychotic, and Wino, the black "Halloween Bandit." Resko's state of mind is hardly improved by the news that his wife has left him and that his father died while saving a child's life in an effort to atone for his son's crime. Following two unsuccessful escape attempts and several long stretches in solitary confinement, Resko's ability to paint is discovered by the prison's new and more compassionate principal keeper. At first reluctant to participate in the prison's art class, Resko gradually finds himself becoming more and more absorbed in his drawings; and almost without his realizing it, a gradual rehabilitation takes place. His work is eventually discovered and introduced to the outside world by noted art critic Carl Carmer. Then, in 1949, after 18 years in prison, Resko is paroled. As he leaves Dannemora, his grownup daughter and his first grandchild are waiting for him. *Storekeepers. Psychopaths. Negroes. Painters. Prison wardens. Criminals—Rehabilitation. Murder. Theft. Capital punishment. Prison escapes. Parole. The Great Depression (1929–34). John Resko. Carl Carmer. Sing Sing. Clinton State Prison.*

Note: Location scenes filmed at Folsom Prison. Working and alternative title: *Reprieve.*

COOGAN'S BLUFF   F6.0905

Malpaso Co. *Dist* Universal Pictures. 2 Oct **1968** [New York opening; c30 Nov 1968; LP37073]. Sd (Westrex); col (Technicolor). 35mm. 94 min. [Copyright length: 100 min.]

Prod-Dir Donald Siegel. *Exec Prod* Richard E. Lyons. *Assoc Prod* Irving Leonard. *Stunt Coörd* Paul Baxley. *Screenplay* Herman Miller, Dean Riesner, Howard Rodman. *Story* Herman Miller. *Photog* Bud Thackery. *Art Dir* Alexander Golitzen, Robert MacKichan. *Set Decor* John McCarthy, John Austin. *Titl* Universal Title. *Film Ed* Sam E. Waxman. *Mus Supv* Stanley Wilson. *Mus* Lalo Schifrin. *Songs:* "Pigeon-Toed Orange Peel," "Everybody" Wally Holmes, Lalo Schifrin. *Sung by* The Pigeon-Toed Orange Peels. *Sd* Waldon O. Watson, Lyle Cain, Jack Bolger. *Asst Dir* Joseph Cavalier. *Prod Mgr* Robert E. Larson. *Cost Dsgn* Helen Colvig. *Makeup* Bud Westmore. *Hairstyles* Larry Germain. *Dial Coach* Scott Hale.

Cast: Clint Eastwood (*Walt Coogan*), Lee J. Cobb (*Lieutenant McElroy*), Susan Clark (*Julie Roth*), Tisha Sterling (*Linny Raven*), Don Stroud (*James Ringerman*), Betty Field (*Mrs. Ringerman*), Tom Tully (*Sheriff McCrea*), Melodie Johnson (*Millie*), James Edwards (*Jackson*), Rudy Diaz (*Running Bear*), David Doyle (*Pushie*), Louis Zorich (*taxi driver*), Meg Myles (*Big Red*), Marjorie Bennett (*Mrs. Fowler*), Seymour Cassel (*young hood*), John Coe (*bellboy*), Skip Battyn (*Omega*), Albert Popwell (*Wonderful Digby*), Conrad Bain (*Madison Avenue man*), James Gavin (*Ferguson*), Albert Henderson (*desk sergeant*), James McCallion (*room clerk*), Syl Lamont (*manager*), Jess Osuna (*prison hospital guard*), Jerry Summers (*Good Eyes*), Antonia Rey (*Mrs. Amador*), Marya Henriques (*go-go dancer*).

Crime melodrama. Arizona Deputy Sheriff Walt Coogan is sent to New York City to extradite escaped killer James Ringerman. Accustomed to getting his man in the old-West tradition, Coogan is frustrated by legal snarls when Manhattan Detective Lieutenant McElroy tells him Ringerman is at Bellevue Hospital recuperating from an overdose of LSD and cannot be moved until the doctors release him. After whiling away some time with probation officer Julie Roth, Coogan bluffs his way into Bellevue and tricks the attendants into handing Ringerman over to him. On the way to the airport to catch a plane for Arizona, however, he is outwitted by Ringerman's freaked-out girl friend Linny and beaten unconscious by a thug, and Ringerman escapes. Now Coogan tries another tack; he visits Julie in her apartment, gets Linny's address from Julie's files, and tracks her to a psychedelic club. After accompanying Linny back to her apartment, he makes love to her and extracts from her a promise to lead him to Ringerman. Instead, she takes him to a pool hall where he is attacked in a bloody battle with pool balls and cues. Coogan returns to Linny's apartment and, by knocking her around, bluffs her into believing he'll kill her if she does not lead him to Ringerman. She takes him to the Cloisters where Ringerman, armed with a gun stolen from Coogan, attempts to escape on his motorcycle. But Coogan gives chase on another cycle and then on foot until he eventually tackles his man. When McElroy and his men arrive, Coogan claims he is making a citizen's arrest. Later, as he and Ringerman wait on top of the Pan Am Building for the helicopter that will take them to the airport and on to Arizona, Julie runs up to say goodbye. *Sheriffs. Escapees. Police. Probation officers. Hippies. Murder. Extradition. Seduction. LSD. Billiard parlors. Motorcycles. Arizona. New York City. New York City—Cloisters. Chases.*

Note: Location scenes filmed in New York City.

COOL HAND LUKE   F6.0906

Jalem Productions. *Dist* Warner Bros.–Seven Arts, Inc. 1 Nov **1967** [New York opening; c27 Jul 1967; LP35742]. Sd; col (Technicolor). 35mm (Panavision). 126 min. [Also reviewed at 129 min.]

Prod Gordon Carroll. *Assoc Prod* Carter DeHaven, Jr. *Dir* Stuart Rosenberg. *Screenplay* Donn Pearce, Frank R. Pierson. *Dir Photog* Conrad Hall. *Art Dir* Cary Odell. *Set Decor* Fred Price. *Film Ed* Sam O'Steen. *Mus* Lalo Schifrin. *Sd* Larry Jost. *Asst Dir* Hank Moonjean. *Unit Mgr* Arthur S. Newman, Jr. *Cost Dsgn* Howard Shoup. *Makeup Supv* Gordon Bau. *Supv Hairstylist* Jean Burt Reilly.

Cast: Paul Newman (*Luke Jackson*), George Kennedy (*Dragline*), J. D. Cannon (*Society Red*), Lou Antonio (*Koko*), Robert Drivas (*Loudmouth Steve*), Strother Martin (*Captain*), Jo Van Fleet (*Arletta*), Clifton James (*Carr*), Morgan Woodward (*Boss Godfrey*), Luke Askew (*Boss Paul*), Marc Cavell (*Rabbitt*), Richard Davalos (*Blind Dick*), Robert Donner (*Boss Shorty*), Warren Finnerty (*Tattoo*), Dennis Hopper (*Babalugats*), John McLiam (*Boss Kean*), Wayne Rogers (*Gambler*), Dean Stanton (*Tramp*), Charles Tyner (*Boss Higgins*), Ralph Waite (*Alibi*), Anthony Zerbe (*Dog Boy*), Buck Kartalian (*Dynamite*), Joy Harmon (*girl*), James Gammon (*Sleepy*), Joe Don Baker (*Fixer*), Donn Pearce (*Sailor*), Norman Goodwins (*Stupid Blondie*), Chuck Hicks (*Chief*), John Pearce (*John Sr.*), Eddie Rosson (*John Jr.*), Rush Williams (*patrolman*), James Jeter (*Wickerman*), Robert Luster (*Jabo*), Rance Howard (*sheriff*), James Bradley, Jr., Cyril "Chips" Robinson (*Negro boys*).

Drama. Source: Donald Pearce, *Cool Hand Luke* (New York, 1965). Luke Jackson is arrested for unscrewing the tops from a row of parking meters while on a drunken spree in a small Southern town. After the trial, he is sentenced to 2 years of labor on a chain gang. A loner who maintains his aloofness even while working in the blazing sun, Luke soon antagonizes another prisoner, Dragline, the acknowledged leader of the chain gang. The tension between the two men mounts until they finally have a fight in which Dragline beats Luke but is unable to make him give up. Luke's skill at poker, plus his refusal to break under pressure from the sadistic guards, win him the respect of Dragline and the admiration of the other inmates. A short time after Luke receives a farewell visit from his dying mother, a telegram arrives informing him that she is dead. Unable to bear his confinement, Luke saws a hole in the floor under his bunk and escapes; but he is captured, brutally beaten, and put in ankle chains. Undaunted, he breaks out again but is recaptured. Every effort is made to break his will, and he is bludgeoned and overworked until he begs the guards for mercy. Upon seeing Luke betray the myth of the indomitable hero, the other men treat him with contempt. Then, without warning, he escapes in a dump truck, followed by Dragline. Taking refuge in a church, Luke sends Dragline away and attempts to settle his score with God. Partly out of love for Luke, partly out of fear for his own safety, Dragline returns with the guards. Rather than surrender, Luke stands before a window and shouts his defiance until he is silenced by a bullet. The hysterical Dragline is beaten into submission and then returns to the chain gang where he perpetuates the legend of Cool Hand Luke. *Prison guards. Fugitives. Drunkenness. Sadism. Filial relations. Friendship. Prison escapes. Chain gangs. Churches.*

Note: Location scenes filmed in the San Joaquin River Delta area near Stockton, California.

COOL IT, BABY   F6.0907

Cam-Scope Pictures. *Dist* Boxoffice International Film Distributors. 17 May **1967** [New York showing]. Sd; b&w. 35mm. 75 min.

Prod Lou Campa. *Dir* Lou Champion. *Screenplay* L. A. Cideck. *Story* Louis Palisano. *Set Dir* W. L. Walter. *Ed* Lew Waldeck. *Sd Rec* W. W. Lister. *Post Sd* Lew Waldeck. *Asst Dir* Fred Campa. *Grip* Tom Fluery.

Cast: Beverly Baum (*Monica*), Joe Marzano (*Herman*), Christine Cybelle (*Valerie*), Elenora (*Connie*), Ronald O'Flynn (*Jack Price*), Robert James (*Assistant D. A.*), Anita Fisher (*policewoman*), Hal Wall (*district attorney*), Walt Sears (*judge*), Lou Ponzia (*Paul James*), Yolanda Signorelli (*model*), Susan Charge, Marilyn Pulaski, James Lodato, Fred Nelson, Augie Piccin, Jr., C. M. Champion, Loretta Flower, Tom Flower.

Melodrama. The showing of a stag film to Connie and Monica is interrupted by Connie's screams as she watches herself perform in the film under the influence of drugs. Connie has realized that Monica will blackmail her because of this movie, but suddenly she finds herself in a witness chair testifying against Monica. She and the other witnesses relate their stories. Connie was tricked into posing for pornographic pictures by Herman, who invited her to a party when they met at the bar. No one else was present, and her drink contained an aphrodisiac. Connie becomes hysterical, and her husband, Jack, a vice squad detective, must continue the story. He was watching Monica's house and then raided it, finding an orgy taking place. Everyone except Connie was able to escape. Herman takes the stand to reveal that the real head of the operation was the assistant district attorney. He and Monica would torture any girl who threatened to expose them, and Monica's tortures had already resulted in one girl's death. Herman wanted to leave after the girl died but was unable to do so because a raid was due that night. Valerie, one of Monica's victims, testifies next. She relates how the assistant district attorney placed her in Monica's house instead of prosecuting her on some charges. Valerie fought against Monica's lesbianism and her other sexual practices, but under torture had to relent. Connie is called back to be the last witness, and the case seems to be resolved. Jack and Connie are back together, and all seems well except for an evil grin on Monica's face, which seems to say the sordid affair is not really over. *District attorneys. Sexual practices. Detectives. Blackmail. Murder. Torture. Political corruption. Lesbianism. Orgies. Trials. Sex exploitation films. Aphrodisiacs.*

Note: Also known as *Cool, Baby.*

THE COOL ONES   F6.0908

Warner Bros. Pictures. 12 Apr **1967** [Kansas City, Missouri, opening; c1 Feb 1967; LP35727]. Sd; col (Technicolor). 35mm (Panavision). 95 min. [Copyright length: 93 min.]

A William Conrad Production. *Exec Prod* William Conrad. *Dir* Gene Nelson. *Screenplay–Story* Joyce Geller. *Adapt* Gene Nelson, Robert Kaufman. *Dir Photog* Floyd Crosby. *Camera Op* Jack Whitman. *Asst Camera* Alfred Baalas. *Art Dir* LeRoy Deane. *Asst Art Dir* Tracy Bousman. *Set Decor* Ralph S. Hurst. *Set Coörd* Glenn Metts. *Film Ed* James Heckert. *Asst Ed* John C. Horger. *Mus Supv* Lee Hazlewood. *Orig Mus Score* Ernie Freeman. *Mus Arr* Billy Strange. *Songs:* "The Cool Ones," "A Bad Woman's Love," "Whiz Bam Opener," "This Town," "High," "Up Your Totem Pole With Love," "Tantrum," "It's Your World," "Hands," "Baby, Baby, Your Love Is All I Need" Lee Hazlewood. *Song:* "Where Did I Go Wrong" Billy Strange, Jack Lloyd. *Sung by* Nita Talbot, Jim Begg, Roddy McDowall. *Song:* "It's Magic" Sammy Cahn, Jule Styne. *Choreog* Toni Basil. *Sd* Everett Hughes, Dan Wallin. *Rec* Robert J. Miller. *Boom Op* Ora Hudson. *Asst Dir* Gil Kissel, Gary Grillo. *Unit Mgr* J. Russell Llewellyn. *Script Supv* Marshall Wolins. *Cost Dsgn* Howard Shoup. *Wardrobe* Tye Oswald, Yvonne Wood. *Makeup Supv* Gordon Bau. *Makeup* Bill Phillips. *Body Makeup* Dorothy Parkinson. *Supv Hairstylist* Jean Burt Reilly. *Dial Supv* Julie Gibson. *Gaffer* LeRoy Thompson. *Prop Master* Archie Neel. *Key Grip* Kenneth Taylor. *Still Photog* Bert Six.

Cast: Roddy McDowall (*Tony Krum*), Debbie Watson (*Hallie Rodgers*), Gil Peterson (*Cliff Donner*), Phil Harris (*Fred MacElwaine*), Elvira Miller (*Mrs. Miller*), Robert Coote (*Stanley Krumley*), Nita Talbot (*Dee Dee*), George Furth (*Howie*), Jim Begg (*Charles Forbes*), James Millhollin (*manager*), Phil Arnold (*Uncle Steve*), Melanie Alexander (*Sandy*), The Bantams, Glen Campbell, The Leaves, T. J. & the Fourmations.

Comedy with music. At the age of 23, singer Cliff Donner becomes an overnight failure when his latest album proves unsuccessful. Although

disillusioned with show business, he agrees to perform at a club for teenagers in Palm Springs, California. At the same time Hallie Rodgers, a pretty teenager, loses her job as a TV go-go dancer when she leaves her cage and starts singing and dancing before the cameras. Eventually the two young people are signed as a team by Tony Krum, a young, self-made rock and roll millionaire tycoon. Without telling Cliff, Tony arranges a publicity buildup whereby Hallie and Cliff will gradually fall in love while performing on TV within view of thousands of delighted teenagers. Everything works as planned until Cliff learns of Tony's scheme and quits the show. Cliff is persuaded to return, but he treats Hallie with cold indifference. Determined to prove that Cliff means more to her than a career, Hallie fails to appear for their biggest TV engagement. As Cliff is about to perform alone, he suddenly understands Hallie's motive, and leaves the stage to find her. Mrs. Miller, the cleaning woman, fills in for them and becomes an instant success. *Singers. Go-go dancers. Tycoons. Charwomen. Rock and roll. Adolescence. Show business. Publicity. Television. Nightclubs. Palm Springs.*

Note: Location scenes filmed in Palm Springs, California.

THE COOL WORLD   F6.0909

Wiseman Film Productions. *Dist* Cinema V Distributing, Inc. 20 Apr **1964** [New York opening]. Sd; b&w. 35mm. 105 min. [See note.]

Prod Frederick Wiseman. *Dir* Shirley Clarke. *Screenplay* Shirley Clarke, Carl Lee. *Photog* Baird Bryant. *Adtl Photog* Leroy McLucas. *Interior Lighting* Tom Mangravite. *Sets* Roger Furman. *Film Ed* Shirley Clarke. *Mus Comp & Arr* Mal Waldron. *Jazz Mus Perf by* Dizzy Gillespie, Yusef Lateef, Mal Waldron, Aaron Bell, Arthur Taylor. *Rock and Roll Mus Perf by* Herb Lowell, Charles Jackson, Julian Euell, Hal Singer. *Gospel Mus* Barbara Webb. *Calliope Played by* Stan Free. *Sd Ed* Hugh A. Robertson, Jr. *Sd Rec* Richard Vorisek, David Jones. *Mus Rec* Bill Blachy. *Asst Dir* Alex Goitein. *Prod Mgr* Dorothy Oshlag. *Cont* Madeline Anderson.

Cast: Hampton Clanton (*Richard "Duke" Custis*), Yolanda Rodriguez (*Luanne*), Carl Lee (*Priest*), Georgia Burke (*Grandma*), Bostic Felton (*Rod*), Charles Richardson (*Beep Bop*), Bruce Edwards (*Warrior*), Teddy McCain (*Saint*), Gary Bolling (*Littleman*), Ronald Perry (*Savage*), Lloyd Edwards (*Foxy*), Ken Sutherland (*Big Jeff*), Billy Taylor (*Mission*), Jay Brooks (*Littleman's father*), Clarence Williams, III (*Blood*), Claude Cave (*Hardy*), Marilyn Cox (*Miss Dewpont*), Gloria Foster (*Mrs. Custis*), Jerome Raphel (*Mr. Shapiro*), Joe Oliver (*Angel*), J. C. Lee (*Coolie*), John Marriott (*Hurst*), Bert Donaldson (*45*), Joseph Dennis (*Douglas Thurston*), Maurice Sneed (*Rocky*), William Ford (*Ace*), Alfred Callymore (*China*), Ted Butler (*Mr. Osborne*), Pheta Canegata (*Pheta*), Nettie Avery (*Big Daddy*), Riley Mac (*Mac*), Sandra McPherson (*Coney Island girl*), Wilbur Green (*Priest's buddy*), Val Bisoglio, Vic Romano (*gangsters*), Dean Cohen, Peter De Anda, Alan Mercer, William Canegata (*cops*), George W. Goodman (*newscaster*), Richard Ward (*street speaker*), Esther Bodie, Irma Williams (*ladies*), Milton Williams, Evadney Canegata.

Drama. Source: Warren Miller, *The Cool World* (Boston, 1959). Warren Miller and Robert Rossen, *The Cool World* (New York opening: 22 Feb 1960). Duke, a black adolescent and member of the Royal Pythons, lives in Harlem with his mother and grandmother. Following the departure of their friend Littleman's father, the Pythons appropriate the apartment, installing Luanne as resident prostitute. Despite the fact that Luanne is Python president Blood's girl friend, she and Duke fall in love. Discovering that Blood is a heroin addict, Duke assumes leadership of the gang. During an idyll at Coney Island, however, Luanne vanishes, and Duke returns to Harlem. During a halfhearted battle with the Wolves, a rival gang, Duke stabs an antagonist. Seeking refuge, he rushes to Python headquarters, where he discovers the corpse of a friend. At home he is apprehended by police. *Prostitutes. Street gangs. Police. Drug addicts. Negro life. Urban life. Adolescence. Murder. Theft. Gang wars. Filial relations. New York City—Harlem. Coney Island.*

Note: Filmed on location in Harlem. Venice Film Festival (1963) running time: 125 min.

COP-OUT (Great Britain)   F6.0910

Selmur Productions. *Dist* Cinerama Releasing Corp. 5 Jan **1968** [New Orleans opening]. Sd; col (Eastman Color). 35mm. 95 min.

An Anatole De Grunwald Production. *Prod* Dimitri De Grunwald. *Exec Prod* Selig J. Seligman. *Dir-Writ* Pierre Rouve. *Dir Photog* Ken Higgins. *Camera Op* Ray Parslow. *Art Dir* Tony Woollard. *Film Ed* Ernest Walter. *Mus Comp & Cond* Patrick John Scott. *Song:* "Ain't That So" Vic Briggs, Patrick John Scott. *Sung by* Eric Burdon, The Animals. *Sd Rec* Cyril Swern. *Dub Mix* J. B. Smith. *Sd Ed* Allan Sones. *Asst Dir* Jimmy Komisarjevsky. *Prod Controller* Roy Parkinson. *Prod Mgr* Donald Toms. *Cont* Pam Carlton. *Wardrobe Supv* Felix Evans. *Makeup* Richard Mills. *Hairstyles* Barbara Ritchie.

Cast: James Mason (*John Sawyer*), Geraldine Chaplin (*Angela Sawyer*), Bobby Darin (*Barney Teale*), Paul Bertoya (*Jo Christophorides*), Ian Ogilvy (*Desmond Flower*), Bryan Stanyon (*Peter Hawkins*), Pippa Steel (*Sue Phillips*),

Clive Morton (*Colonel Flower*), James Hayter (*Harry Hawkins*), Megs Jenkins (*Mrs. Christophorides*), Lisa Daniely (*Diana*), Moira Lister (*Mrs. Flower*), Yootha Joyce (*girl at shooting range*), John Henderson (*old clerk*), Rita Webb (*Mrs. Plaskett*), Danvers Walker (*Chetham*), Julian Orchard (*policeman*), Ivor Dean (*Inspector Colder*), Marjie Lawrence (*Brenda*), Lindy Aaron (*Angela as a child*), Lucy Griffiths (*library cleaner*), Charlotte Selwyn (*salesgirl*), Melinda May (*librarian*), Tom Kempinski (*shop assistant*), Sheila White (*Hazel*), Toni Palmer (*doorwoman*), Michael Standing (*fashion photographer*), Anne Hart (*barmaid*).

Mystery melodrama. Source: Georges Simenon, *Les inconnus dans la maison* (Paris, 1940). John Sawyer, once a prominent barrister, is now an alcoholic recluse living in Winchester, England, with Angela, his 20-year-old daughter. Angela treats him with open contempt, preferring to spend her time looking for amusement at local discotheques and coffee bars. One day Angela's group of friends is infiltrated by Barney Teale, a sinister American ship steward. A short time later, Barney's dead body is found by Sawyer in his home. When Angela's boyfriend, Jo Christophorides, is accused of the murder, Sawyer decides to come out of retirement and defend the young man, although he is haunted by his last murder case which resulted in his client's execution. Jo's chances appear slim until Sawyer learns that another of Angela's friends, Desmond Flower, is impotent—a secret that Barney had also discovered. Barney had sadistically forced Desmond into a sexual encounter with a young woman in order to expose his weakness, and Desmond killed him, planting false evidence implicating Jo. Once Desmond's alibi is broken and Jo's innocence established, Sawyer and his estranged daughter are reconciled. *Barristers. Recluses. Americans in foreign countries. Stewards. Alcoholism. Filial relations. Murder. Frameup. Impotence. Trials. Winchester (England).*

Note: Location scenes filmed in Southampton, England. Released in Great Britain in Jul 1967 as *Stranger in the House*; running time: 104 min. Previously filmed in France in 1942 as *Les inconnus dans la maison* and released in the United States in 1949 by Lopert Pictures as *Stranger in the House*.

COPACABANA PALACE see **GIRL GAME**

COPENHAGEN CALL GIRLS see **VILLA-VENNELY: HOME OF COPENHAGEN CALL GIRLS**

LA CORDE RAIDE see **LOVERS ON A TIGHTROPE**

CORDILLERA see **FLIGHT TO FURY**

LE CORNIAUD see **THE SUCKER**

THE CORPORATE QUEEN   F6.0911
Dist Victoria Films. 1970. Sd; b&w. 35mm. 82 min.
Prod-Dir-Writ John Amero, Lem Amero. *Camera* John Amero. *Lighting* Phoebe Dinsmore. *Film Ed* Lem Amero. *Mus* Firth DeMule. *Audio* Chuck Federico. *Cost* John Brock Benson. *Casting* Haymarket.
Cast: Renay Claire (*Crystal Laverne*), Marie Brent (*Edna*), Tony Vito (*Chino*).
Melodrama. Elegant Crystal Laverne, who rules over one of the largest prostitution empires in the country, dismisses her followers from the plush New York City penthouse where she holds court and relates the story of her success to her efficient, man-hating private secretary, Edna: *Suffering financially from a police crackdown, Crystal picks up Chino, a handsome young man who has been sleeping near her door. He has nothing to offer her but his bounteous sex drive, and they pool their talents to open a massage service. Chino accepts clients of both sexes, and business booms. They move to new quarters, expanding the facilities to serve men and women of every sexual inclination, including clients seeking sexual experiences with lesbians, nymphomaniacs, and foot fetishists. Crystal falls in love with Chino and showers him with gifts, but he devotes his time to his work. She momentarily suspects him of infidelity, but he allays her suspicions, and she takes him out for a night on the town which ends up in a private club where they watch an erotic show. Chino proposes marriage, and Crystal gladly accepts. Crystal leaves for an appointment with a real estate agent in preparation for her forthcoming marriage, and Edna climbs into her employer's bed to make love with Chino, demanding that he perform a variety of sex acts. Crystal returns unexpectedly to retrieve some papers and watches through her two-way mirror as Edna and Chino plot to murder her by causing a gas explosion. She turns the tables on her perfidious lover and secretary and laughs sadistically as the bedroom explodes. Madams. Secretaries. Prostitution. Bisexuality. Male homosexuality. Lesbianism. Fetishism. Murder. Perfidy. Nymphomania. Sex shows. Massage parlors. Explosions. New York City.*

LE CORPS ET LE FOUET see **WHAT!**

CORPSE IN THE MORGUE (Reissue)   F6.0912
Universal Pictures. 18 Jul **1962** [Maryland license]. Sd; b&w. 35mm. 67 min.
Note: Originally released in 1938 as *Lady in the Morgue*; running time: 70 min; c21 Apr 1938; LP7980.

THE CORPSE MAKERS see **TWICE TOLD TALES**

THE CORPSE OF BEVERLY HILLS (West Germany)   F6.0913
Modern Art Film. *Dist* Medallion Pictures. Nov **1965**. Sd; b&w with col seq (Eastman Color). 35mm (Franscope). 85 min.
Prod Hansjürgen Pohland. *Dir* Michael Pfleghar. *Screenplay* Peter Laregh, Hansjürgen Pohland, Michael Pfleghar. *Photog* Ernst Wild. *Asst Camera* Jürgen Jürges. *Film Ed* Margot von Schlieffen. *Mus* Heinz Kiessling. *Asst Dir* Erika Hinze-Selch. *Prod Mgr* Harald Zimmer. *Prod Asst* Peter Genée. *Cost* Helmut Holger. *Wardrobe* Sybille Jackstadt. *Makeup* Erich-Lothar Schmekel, Anni Führkötter.
Cast: Heidelinde Weis (*Lu Sostlov*), Klausjürgen Wussow (*C. G.*), Horst Frank (*Manning/Dr. Steininger*), Wolfgang Neuss (*Ben*), Ernst Fritz Fürbringer (*Professor Sostlov*), Peter Schütte (*Swendka*), Bruno Dietrich (*Peter de Lorm*), Alice Kessler, Ellen Kessler (*The Tiddy Sisters*), Herbert Weissbach (*priest*), Walter Giller.
Crime melodrama. Source: Kurt Götz, *Die Tote von Beverly Hills* (Berlin, 1951). The naked corpse of a 26-year-old woman is found in a wooded area of Beverly Hills, and Detective Ben determines that the body is that of Lu Sostlov, the unfaithful wife of an immigrant Czech scientist. The victim's diary, which is filled with tales of her many affairs, allows Ben to reconstruct her past. *At the age of 17, Lu is seduced by an opera tenor; her lover is killed, however, by Manning, a lawyer. Following several other illicit interludes in Berlin, Lu travels to the United States, marries the Czech scientist, and enjoys a brief affair with a Las Vegas entertainer before leaving her husband for Peter de Lorm, a German film writer. She has her portrait painted by the wealthy Dr. Steininger, whom she learns is Manning in disguise, and then becomes involved with a Swiss sportswriter, the man who later discovers her corpse.* After tracing a lead to the Tiddy Sisters, members of a Las Vegas theatrical troupe, Ben solves the murder. *Detectives. Czechoslovakians. Immigrants. Scientists. Singers. Lawyers. Entertainers. Motion picture scriptwriters. Artists. Swiss. Sportswriters. Sisters. Murder. Infidelity. Disguise. Seduction. Diaries. Portraits (paintings). Beverly Hills. Las Vegas. Hollywood. Berlin.*
Note: Filmed in Hollywood, Beverly Hills, and Berlin. Released in West Germany in Apr 1964 as *Die Tote von Beverly Hills*; running time: 110 min. May also be known as *That Girl From Beverly Hills*. Flashback sequences filmed in color.

CORRIDORS OF BLOOD (Great Britain)   F6.0914
Producers Associates. *Dist* Altura Films International, Metro-Goldwyn-Mayer, Inc. 5 Jun **1963** [New York opening]. Sd; b&w. 35mm. 85 min. [Also reviewed at 87 min.]
Prod John Croydon, Charles Vetter. *Exec Prod* Richard Gordon. *Dir* Robert Day. *Screenplay* Jean Scott Rogers. *Photog* Geoffrey Faithfull. *Art Dir* Tony Masters. *Film Ed* Peter Mayhew. *Mus Comp* Buxton Orr. *Mus Dir* Frederick Lewis. *Sd* Cyril Swern. *Dub Ed* Peter Musgrave. *Asst Dir* Peter Bolton. *Prod Mgr* George Mills. *Cont* Sue Dyson. *Makeup* Wally Schneiderman. *Hairstyles* Eileen Warwick.
Cast: Boris Karloff (*Dr. Bolton*), Betta St. John (*Susan*), Francis Matthews (*Dr. Jonathan Bolton*), Francis De Wolff (*Black Ben*), Adrienne Corri (*Rachel*), Frank Pettingell (*Blount*), Finlay Currie (*Dr. Matheson*), Christopher Lee (*Resurrection Joe*), Marian Spencer (*Mrs. Matheson*), Carl Bernard (*Ned the Crow*), Charles Lloyd Pack (*Hardcastle*), Yvonne Warren (*Rosa*), Robert Raglan (*Wilkes*), Basil Dignam (*chairman*), John Gabriel (*dispenser*), Nigel Green (*Inspector Donovan*), Howard Lang (*chief inspector*), Julian D'Albie (*bald man*), Roddy Hughes (*man with watch*).
Horror film. Before the discovery of anesthesia, operations were bloody, screaming ordeals from which the patient often emerged insane. In 1840, London surgeon Dr. Bolton tries to remedy the situation, but he becomes addicted to his experimental drugs. Following a demonstration during which one of his patients rises from the operating table and attacks the attending doctors and students, the humiliated Bolton takes an overdose of drugs and enters a tavern in the slum district of Seven Dials. There he falls prey to Black Ben and Resurrection Joe, whose main activity is supplying the hospital with bodies for dissection. In exchange for stolen drugs, Bolton is forced to supply signed death certificates for their victims. When one of the grave robbers murders a hospital guard, the police apprehend the criminals, but not before Bolton is stabbed to death. Bolton's son Jonathan continues his father's experiments and becomes instrumental in developing anesthetics. *Surgeons. Drug addicts. Grave robbers. Experiments. Murder. Anesthetics. Pubs. London.*

Note: Released in Great Britain in Sep 1962; running time: 86 min. Working title: *The Doctor of Seven Dials.*

LES CORROMPUS see **THE CORRUPT ONES**

THE CORRUPT ONES (France/Italy/West Germany) **F6.0915**
CCC-Filmkunst–Criterion Film–Senior Cinematografica. *Dist* Warner Bros. Pictures. 15 Feb **1967** [San Francisco opening; c1 Feb 1967; LP35724]. Sd; col (Technicolor). 35mm (Techniscope). 92 min.
Prod Artur Brauner. *Exec Prod* Nat Wachsberger. *Dir (see note)* James Hill. *Action Dir* Bill Catching. *Screenplay* Brian Clemens. *Writ (see note)* Harry Jack Bloom. *Dial* Georges Farrel. *Orig Story* Ladislaus Fodor, Arp Brown. *Dir Photog* Heinz Pehlke. *Asst Photog* Günther Knuth, Horst Chlupka. *Art Dir* Hans-Jürgen Kiebach, Ernst Schomer. *Ed* Alfred Srp. *Mus Comp* Georges Garvarentz. *Song:* "The Corrupt Ones" Buddy Kaye, Georges Garvarentz. *Sung by* Dusty Springfield. *Asst Dir (see note)* Frank Winterstein. *Prod Supv* Peter Hahne. *Prod Mgr* Wolfram Kohtz, Harry Wilbert. *Cost Dsgn* Paul Seltenhammer. *Makeup* Heinz Stamm, Jupp Paschke.
Cast: Robert Stack *(Cliff Wilder)*, Elke Sommer *(Lily Mancini)*, Nancy Kwan *(Tina)*, Christian Marquand *(Joey Brandon)*, Maurizio Arena *(Danny Mancini)*, Richard Haller *(Kau-Song)*, Dean Heyde *(Hugo)*, Ah-Yue-Lou *(Chow)*, Marisa Merlini *(Madame Vulcano)*, Werner Peters *(Pinto)*, Heide Bohlen *(Jasmine)*, Rosemary Bowe, Maria Minh.
Melodrama. Cliff Wilder, a free-lance photographer on assignment in mainland China, is surprised taking unauthorized photographs and narrowly escapes capture. As he flees to Macao, he is aided by Danny Mancini, a stranger who gives him a package containing the Peking Medallion, on which is inscribed the clue to a lost fortune. Before he can retrieve the package, Danny is captured and murdered by the Fu Song Tong. Summoned by Police Chief Pinto to the city morgue, Cliff is confronted with Danny's corpse, upon which he secretes the medallion. He then makes the acquaintance of Lily, Danny's former wife, in whom he confides; Tina, leader of a murderous tong; and Joey Brandon, owner of an American casino. Tina and Joey join forces to kidnap Lily, whom Cliff ransoms with the medallion, having already decoded its message and made a deal with Chief Pinto to retrieve the treasure. As all concerned converge upon the underground tomb that is the site of the treasure, its crumbling walls collapse. To the party's surprise, an exit from the tomb opens into mainland China. Although Tina and Joey are slain, Lily, Cliff, and Chief Pinto escape across the border. *Photographers. Chinese. Police. Widows. Casino owners. Murder. Gangs. Treasure. Tombs. People's Republic of China. Macao.*
Note: Location scenes filmed in Macao and Hong Kong. Released in Italy in 1966 as *Il sigillo de Pechino*; in West Germany in Jan 1967 as *Die Hölle von Macao*; running time: 93 min; opened in Paris in Feb 1967 as *Les corrompus*; running time: 90 min. Sources conflict on directing and writing credits. Copyright claimant: Omnia Deutsche Film Export and Waterview Productions. Also known as *The Peking Medallion* and *Hell to Macao.*

CORRUPTION (Great Britain) **F6.0916**
Titan International Productions–Oakshire Co. *Dist* Columbia Pictures. 4 Dec **1968** [New York opening; c1 Dec 1968; LP36396]. Sd; col (Perfect Color). 35mm. 91 min. *MPAA rating* R.
A Peter Newbrook–Robert Hartford-Davis Production. *Prod* Peter Newbrook. *Dir* Robert Hartford-Davis. *Screenplay for Dorak Productions* Donald Ford, Derek Ford. *Dir Photog* Peter Newbrook. *Camera Op* Norman Jones. *Prod Dsgn* Bruce Grimes. *Film Ed* Don Deacon. *Asst Ed* Maxine Julius. *Mus Comp & Cond* Bill McGuffie. *Sd Supv* Cyril Collick. *Dub Mix* Peter Gilpin, George Willows. *Asst Dir* Ken Softley. *In Charge of Prod* Robert Sterne. *Cont* Splinters Deason. *Makeup* John O'Gorman. *Hairdresser* Biddy Chrystal. *Sp Eff* Michael Albrechtsen. *Casting Dir* James Liggat.
Cast: Peter Cushing *(Sir John Rowan)*, Sue Lloyd *(Lynn Nolan)*, Noel Trevarthen *(Steve Harris)*, Kate O'Mara *(Val Nolan)*, David Lodge *(Groper)*, Anthony Booth *(Mike Orme)*, Wendy Varnals *(Terry)*, Billy Murray *(Rik)*, Vanessa Howard *(Kate)*, Jan Waters *(girl in the flat)*, Phillip Manikum *(Georgie)*, Alexandra Dane *(Sandy)*, Valerie Van Ost *(girl in the train)*, Diana Ashley *(Claire)*, Victor Baring *(mortuary attendant)*, Shirley Stelfox *(girl at the party).*
Horror film. Eminent British surgeon Sir John Rowan falls asleep in his apartment before he is to attend a party with Lynn Nolan, his fashion model fiancée. *At the party, Lynn introduces him to photographer Mike Orme, who persuades Lynn to pose for him. There is a jealous fight between the two men, and a floodlight topples on Lynn and disfigures her face. To overcome Lynn's despair, Sir John attempts to restore her beauty by injecting into her face a pituitary extract and operating with a laser beam. Using a gland stolen from a hospital corpse, Sir John surgically recaptures Lynn's loveliness and takes her on a holiday; but the remedy proves to be short-lived, and Lynn's face again becomes a hideous mask. In the desperate hope that live tissues will be more*

permanent, *Sir John decapitates a Soho prostitute and operates again. This remedy also proves to be temporary, and Sir John realizes that he will have to continue killing in order to preserve Lynn's appearance. Sir John's associate, Dr. Stephen Harris, perceives what Sir John has been doing to restore Lynn's beauty. Unaware that Lynn has encouraged Sir John to commit the murders, Stephen and Lynn's sister, Val, rush to warn her. Meanwhile, Sir John and Lynn are being harassed in their country home by hoodlum friends of their lastest victim, a young woman named Terry. After killing Terry's husband, the now-deranged Lynn activates the laser beam and demands that Sir John operate once more. The laser goes out of control, however, and kills the hoodlums as well as Sir John, Lynn, and the newly-arrived Stephen and Val. The house, littered with corpses, burns to the ground.* Sir John arrives at the party where Lynn introduces him to her photographer friend. *Surgeons. Nobility. Models. Photographers. Prostitutes. Sisters. Hoodlums. Jealousy. Disfiguration. Murder. Decapitation. Plastic surgery. Vanity. Laser. Fires. Dreams.*
Note: Released in Great Britain in Dec 1968. Location scenes filmed in London.

CORRUPTION OF THE DAMNED **F6.0917**
Dist Film-Makers' Cooperative, Film-Makers' Distribution Center, Canyon Cinema Cooperative. 18 Sep **1965** [New York opening]. Sd; b&w. 16mm. 55 min.
Prod-Dir George Kuchar. *Photog* George Kuchar.
Cast: Mary Flanagan *(Cora)*, Gina Zuckerman *(Aunt Anna)*, Donna Kerness *(medium)*, Francis Leibowitz *(mother)*, Floraine Connors *(Connie)*, Steve Packard *(Paul)*, Mike Kuchar *(youth)*, Lawrence Leibowitz *(brother)*, Michael Zuckerman *([businessman]).*
Satire. A youth searches for his unfaithful lover and along the way encounters orgies and various forms of sexual depravity. In one incident, the youth, followed by his listless, mollycoddle brother, who wears earflaps in evidence of his dependency, meets his mother in a junkyard. She threatens to shoot her sons with a machine gun unless they return home to eat dinner, but when she is unable to follow through with her threat, the boys depart and she stabs herself. Ignorant of his mother's action, the brother is transformed by his odyssey, and in a spiteful fit he tosses away his earflaps, achieving manhood. *Brothers. Filial relations. Sexual practices. Orgies. Moral corruption. Suicide. Infidelity. Manhood.*

COSÌ FAN TUTTE (Austria/West Germany) **F6.0918**
Unitel Film–Neue Thalia. *Dist* Beta Film. 23 Jul **1970** [New York opening]. Sd; col (Eastman Color). 35mm. 159 min.
Exec Prod Fritz Buttenstedt. *Dir* Vaclav Kaslik. *Libretto* Lorenzo Da Ponte. *Photog* Jan Stallich. *Art Dir* Milos Ditrich. *Film Ed* Gela-Marina Runne. *Mus* Wolfgang Amadeus Mozart. *Perf by* Vienna Philharmonic Orchestra. *Cond* Karl Böhm. *Cost* Jan Skalicky.
Cast: Gundula Janowitz *(Fiordiligi)*, Christa Ludwig *(Dorabella)*, Olivera Miljakovic *(Despina)*, Luigi Alva *(Ferrando)*, Hermann Prey *(Guglielmo)*, Walter Berry *(Don Alfonso).*
Opera film. Source: Wolfgang Amadeus Mozart and Lorenzo Da Ponte, *Così fan tutte, ossia la scuola degli amanti* (first performance: Vienna, 26 Jan 1790). A film of Mozart's opera. *Soldiers. Duplicity. Courtship. Disguise. Military draft. Weddings.*
Note: Produced in 1970 for West German television.

COSTANTINO IL GRANDE see **CONSTANTINE AND THE CROSS**

COTTON COMES TO HARLEM **F6.0919**
Formosa Productions. *Dist* United Artists. 27 May **1970** [Chicago opening; c27 May 1970; LP38052]. Sd; col (De Luxe). 35mm. 97 min. *MPAA rating* R.
Prod Samuel Goldwyn, Jr. *Exec in Charge of Prod* Stanley Neufeld. *Dir* Ossie Davis. *2d Unit Dir & Stunt Coörd* Max Kleven. *Screenplay* Arnold Perl, Ossie Davis. *Dir Photog* Gerald Hirschfeld. *2d Unit Photog* Gil Geller. *Camera Op* Enrique Bravo. *Art Dir* Manny Gerard. *Set Decor* Bob Drumheller. *Main Titl* F. Hillsberg Inc. *Film Ed* Robert Q. Lovett, John Carter, ed. *Mus* Galt MacDermot. *Songs:* "Cotton Comes to Harlem," "Goin' Home" Galt MacDermot, Joseph S. Lewis. *Song:* "Ain't Now but It's Going To Be" Galt MacDermot, Ossie Davis. *Song:* "Down in My Soul" Galt MacDermot, William Dumaresq. *Song:* "My Salvation" Galt MacDermot, Paul Laurence Dunbar. *Choreog* Louis Johnson. *Sd Supv* Newton Avrutis. *Asst Dir* Domenic D'Antonio, John Cates, Samuel N. Bennerson. *Cost* Anna Hill Johnstone. *Makeup Supv* Irving Carlton. *Hairstyles for Miss Pace* Walter Fountaine. *Sp Eff* Sol Stern.
Cast: Godfrey Cambridge *(Gravedigger Jones)*, Raymond St. Jacques *(Coffin Ed Johnson)*, Calvin Lockhart *(Rev. Deke O'Malley)*, Judy Pace *(Iris)*, Redd Foxx *(Uncle Bud)*, John Anderson *(Bryce)*, Emily Yancy *(Mabel)*, J. D. Cannon *(Calhoun)*, Mabel Robinson *(Billie)*, Dick Sabol *(Jarema)*, Theodore Wilson *(Barry)*, Eugene Roche *(Anderson)*, Frederick O'Neal *(Casper)*, Vinette Carroll *(Reba)*, Gene Lindsey *(Luddy)*, Van Kirksey *(Early Riser)*, Cleavon

Little (Lo Boy), Helen Martin (Church Sister), Turk Turpin (Dum-Dum), Tom Lane (44), Arnold Williams (Hi Jenks), Lou Jacobi (Goodman), Leonardo Cimino (Tom), Maxwell Glanville, Irwin C. Watson.

Crime comedy. Source: Chester Himes, *Cotton Comes to Harlem* (New York, 1965). At an outdoor barbecue, charismatic confidence man Rev. Deke O'Malley defrauds Harlem residents of $87,000 intended to transport blacks back to Africa. The money, however, is immediately seized by the black minister's white partner, Calhoun, who flees the scene in a meat truck, having secreted the money in a bale of cotton. O'Malley follows in an armored car, himself pursued by black police detectives Coffin Ed Johnson and Gravedigger Jones. The bale bounces from the truck during the chase, is found by Uncle Bud, a junkman, and sold as a prop to Mabel, an inventive stripteaser. As Mabel begins her act in Harlem's Apollo Theater, Calhoun and O'Malley appear onstage in "blackface," and fruitlessly comb the cotton for money. While so doing, the two are exposed and arrested by Coffin Ed and Gravedigger. The detectives subsequently coerce a Mafia don to compensate O'Malley's disgruntled congregation for the elusive $87,000. The pair later receives a postcard from Uncle Bud, who discloses that he has absconded with the missing money to Africa, where he is enjoying a new lifestyle. *Negroes. Preachers. Confidence men. Detectives. Junk dealers. Stripteasers. Theft. Extortion. Fraud. Perfidy. Cotton. New York City—Harlem. Africa. Mafia. Apollo Theater (New York). Chases.*

Note: Location scenes filmed in Harlem.

COTTONPICKIN' CHICKENPICKERS   F6.0920
Southeastern Pictures–Southern Musical Productions, Inc. *Dist* Southeastern Pictures. May **1967**. Sd; col (Eastman Color). 35mm. 92 min.

Prod-Dir Larry E. Jackson. *Exec Prod* Charles W. Broun, Jr. *Assoc Prod* David B. Putnam. *Co-prod & N. Y. Rep* Dick Randall. *Screenplay* Bob Baron, Larry E. Jackson. *Dir Photog* Gerhard Maser. *Camera* Virgil Phifer. *Lighting* J. P. Wicks. *Art Dir* Peter Rotondo. *Sets* James Williams. *Film Ed* Signpost Inc. *Song*: "Cottonpickin' Chickenpickers" comp & sung by Hank Mills. *Song*: "This Must Be the Bottom" Del Reeves, Ellen Reeves. Sung by Del Reeves. *Songs*: "Almost Persuaded," "Where Could I Go (But to Her)" Glenn Sutton, Billy Sherrill. Sung by David Houston. *Song*: "Comin' on Strong" Lyn Parker. Sung by David Wilkins. *Song*: "Dirty Ole Egg Suckin' Dog" sung by Mel Tillis. *Song*: "Not Me" sung by Margie Bowes. *Song*: "Messed Up" sung by Hugh X. Lewis. *Sd* Hack Swain. *Asst Dir* Robert M. Newsom. *Asst to the Prod* Harry C. Anderson. *Script Supv* Gary Goch. *Wardrobe* Wanda Mack. *Makeup Supv* Lillian Lawson. *Makeup Artist* Edna Miller. *Hairstyles* Nora Eaton. *Carpenter* William Weaver. *Prop* William Wenzel. *Key Art* Chuck Kennedy.

Cast: Del Reeves (Darby Clyde Fenster), Hugh X. Lewis (Jerry Martin), Sonny Tufts (Cousin Urie), David Houston (Deputy Burke), Greta Thyssen (Greta), Slapsy Maxie Rosenbloom (mailman), Lila Lee (Viola Zickafoose), Tommy Noonan (Bird-Dog Berrigan), Hank Mills (Deputy Will), Philip Hunter (Judge Beale), Margie Bowes (Susie Zickafoose), David Wilkins (David), J. D. Marshall (Dreama Sue), Birgitta Andersson (Brigit), Ted Lehmann (Uncle Ned), Christian Anderson (Cousin Elwood), Mel Tillis (Hound-Dog Berrigan), Jack Morey (Sheriff Mathis), Buck Bayliss (Liquid Louie Tallfeathers).

Comedy with music. Darby Clyde Fenster and Jerry Martin, broke and hungry, think they are on a train to Hollywood, California, but they actually are aboard a freight train to Hollywood, Florida. Hunger pangs force them to get off, and they are soon offered a ride by Maxie the Mailman. Passing by a chicken farm, the boys cannot resist plucking some chickens for themselves, but they are caught by owners Viola and Susie Zickafoose and Uncle Ned. A chase through the swamps ensues, with most of the local townspeople in hot pursuit. Aviator Bird-Dog Berrigan and his brother Hound-Dog help to track Darby Clyde and Jerry in their plane but cause Liquid Louie Tallfeathers and Cousin Elwood, who think that their illegal still is under attack, to launch homemade rockets. Bird-Dog is downed, but not before the still blows up around Cousin Urie, who is so drunk that he has been oblivious to the battle. Before everyone's personal dilemma is resolved, high octane booze, a highpowered Everglades airboat, and lots of war paint figure prominently in another mighty explosion. *Mail carriers. Thieves. Air pilots. Moonshiners. Rural life. Railroads. Swamps. Stills. Hollywood. Hollywood (Florida). Explosions. Chases. Chickens.*

THE COUCH   F6.0921
Warner Bros. Pictures. 21 Feb **1962** [New York opening; c26 Oct 1961; LP27100]. Sd; b&w. 35mm. 100 min.

Prod-Dir Owen Crump. *Screenplay* Robert Bloch. *Story* Blake Edwards, Owen Crump. *Photog* Harold Stine. *Art Dir* Jack Poplin. *Set Decor* William L. Kuehl. *Film Ed* Leo H. Shreve. *Mus* Frank Perkins. *Sd* Stanley Jones. *Asst Dir* James T. Vaughn. *Makeup* Gordon Bau. *Hairstyles* Jean Burt Reilly.

Cast: Grant Williams (Charles Campbell), Shirley Knight (Terry), Onslow Stevens (Dr. Janz), William Leslie (Lindsay), Anne Helm (Jean Quimby), Simon Scott (Lieutenant Kritzman), Michael Bachus (Sergeant Bonner), John Alvin (Sloan), Harry Holcombe (D. A.), Hope Summers (Mrs. Quimby).

Crime melodrama. Following a 2-year prison term for rape, young Charles Campbell is paroled on condition that he undergo daily psychiatric treatment. Maintaining a calm appearance, he conceals both his hatred of Dr. Janz, who represents all father-like authority, and his dislike of the analyst's couch, the symbol of his guilt. One day Campbell phones the police and announces that a murder will be committed at 7 o'clock. A few minutes before the hour he stabs a stranger with an icepick and then reports to Dr. Janz for his daily session. Several days later he commits another murder in the same manner. Eventually Campbell decides that Dr. Janz will be his next victim. After stabbing the doctor in a crowded passageway, Campbell goes to Janz's office and attempts to seduce his niece, Terry. They are interrupted by a phone call notifying Terry that her uncle is alive but unconscious in a hospital. Campbell races there, conceals his identity by wearing an operating gown and mask, and enters the recovery room in which Dr. Janz is lying. Before the deranged killer can complete his third murder, however, he is apprehended by the police. *Psychiatrists. Psychopaths. Police. Uncles. Rape. Seduction. Parole. Murder. Disguise.*

COUGAR COUNTRY   F6.0922
American National Enterprises–North American Wildlife Productions. *Dist* American National Enterprises. Nov **1970** [c7 Jan 1970; LP40399, LP40474]. Sd; col. 35mm. 106 min. *MPAA rating G.*

Exec Prod David W. Meyer. *Photog* Ernest Wilkinson, Wilford L. Miller, Mel Hardman, Dick Robinson, Robert W. Davison. *Film Ed* James W. Dearden, Almon R. Teeter, Mel Hardman. *Mus* William Loose.

Cast: Tabby (Whiskers, a cougar), Tawny (his mother), Michael Rye (narrator).

Documentary. Whiskers, a cougar cub from a litter of three, familiarizes himself with his habitat in Colorado's Rocky Mountains. Among the animals observed are banded Canadian geese, badgers, beavers, grizzly bears, marmots, big horn sheep, and skunks. Whiskers soon learns to avoid porcupines, snakes, and coyotes. Although an eagle attempts to abduct him, his mother rescues the cub. At 2 years of age, Whiskers becomes independent. An expert hunter, he enjoys elk, rabbit, and trout. Treed by men and dogs, his natural enemies, the cougar nevertheless manages to escape. *Animal life. Hunting. Colorado. Rocky Mountains. Cougars. Geese. Dogs. Porcupines. Snakes. Beavers. Skunks. Eagles. Sheep. Bears.*

Note: Filmed on location in Colorado. The preface consists of a 25-min short, *Where the Wild Goose Goes*, produced in 1970 by North American Wildlife Productions.

COULD I BUT LIVE (Japan)   F6.0923
Tokyo Eiga Co. *Dist* Toho International, Inc. 19 Jan **1965** [New York opening]. Sd; b&w. 35mm (Tohoscope). 110 min.

Exec Prod Ichiro Sato, Hideyuki Shiino. *Dir-Writ* Zenzo Matsuyama. *Photog* Hiroshi Murai. *Mus* Masaru Sato.

Cast: Keiju Kobayashi (Sakata), Hideko Takamine (mistress), Yoshie Mizutani, Kon Omura, Shiro Otsuji, Kin Sugai, Kikue Mori.

Melodrama. Sakata, a minor bureaucrat in the Ministry of Agriculture, is completely unaware that a polio epidemic is sweeping Japan in 1960. By accident he receives a phone call from a distraught mother whose child has contracted the disease. Concerned for his own children and shocked that the government is keeping the threat a secret, Sakata and some friends begin collecting statistics and handing out information about polio. At his mistress' bar, Sakata is told by a television reporter of an experimental Russian vaccine that could help stop the epidemic. Sakata offers his own two children for the tests, which prove successful. The vaccine stops the epidemic, and Sakata is a hero. *Bureaucrats. Epidemics. Experiments. Heroism. Poliomyelitis. Medicines.*

Note: Released in Japan in 1965 as *Ware hitotsubu no mugi naredo.*

THE COUNT OF MONTE CRISTO see THE STORY OF THE COUNT OF MONTE CRISTO

COUNT THE POSSIBILITIES see TO INGRID MY LOVE, LISA

COUNT YORGA, VAMPIRE   F6.0924
Erica Productions. *Dist* American International Pictures. 10 Jun **1970** [Los Angeles opening; c10 Jun 1970; LP39862]. Sd; col (print by Movielab). 35mm. 92 min. *MPAA rating GP.*

Prod Michael Macready. *Dir-Writ* Robert Kelljan. *Photog* Arch Archambault. *Camera Op* Pat O'Mara, Jr. *Art Dir* Bob Wilder. *Film Ed* Tony De Zarraga. *Mus* William Marx. *Sd Rec* Robert Dietz, Lowell Brown. *Sd Asst* George Garrin. *Sd Eff* Edit International. *Prod Supv* Robert V. O'Neil. *Script Supv* Pat Townsend. *Wardrobe* Nancy Stom. *Makeup* Mark Rogers, Master Dentalsmith. *Sp Eff* James Tanenbaum. *Ch Electrn* John Murphy. *Key Grip* Jim Getty. *Prop* James Stinson. *Animal Owner & Trainer* Vel Kasegan.

Cast: Robert Quarry (Count Yorga), Roger Perry (Dr. Hayes), Michael Murphy (Paul), Michael Macready (Michael), Donna Anders (Donna), Judy

Lang (*Erica*). Edward Walsh (*Brudah*), Julie Conners (*Cleo*), Paul Hansen (*Peter*). Sybil Scotford (*Judy*), Marsha Jordan (*mother*), Deborah Darnell (*vampire*). Erica Macready (*nurse*). George Macreday (*narrator*).

Horror film. Michael and Donna and another couple, Paul and Erica, attend a seance at Count Yorga's Victorian mansion outside Los Angeles to summon Donna's deceased mother. During the seance Donna faints, and Count Yorga uses the occasion to hypnotize both Donna and Erica. The four leave Yorga's mansion, and Paul drives Michael and Donna to their homes. Afterwards, Paul's camper becomes bogged down in mud. He and Erica decide to spend the night in the camper rather than seek shelter in Yorga's mansion nearby, but in the night they are awakened by howling noises. Paul goes out to investigate and is knocked unconscious by a darkly clad figure. Soon thereafter, Erica becomes a victim of the vampire Count Yorga. The next day Paul finds Erica behaving strangely—she gesticulates wildly, knocks over furniture, and attempts to eat a live cat. Paul consults Dr. Hayes, who, after examining Erica, testing her blood for vampire venom, and noting the marks on her neck, swears that she has been bitten by a vampire. Erica and Donna are abducted by Yorga, and Paul goes to Yorga's mansion to search for them. Michael and Dr. Hayes become alarmed when Paul fails to return, but when they inform the police, the police believe the two are insane. Armed with wooden stakes, Michael and Dr. Hayes go to the mansion and find it swarming with vampires. Yorga has killed Paul. Dr. Hayes is attacked and killed, but Michael drives stakes into the hearts of Erica and Yorga and rescues Donna. He spirits her away, unaware that she too has become a vampire. *Nobility. Vampires. Physicians. Police. Hypnotism. Abduction. Murder. Seances. Cats.*

Note: Location scenes filmed in the Los Angeles area.

COUNTDOWN   F6.0925
Warner Bros.–Seven Arts, Inc. Feb **1968** [New York opening: 1 May; c1 Feb 1968; LP37142]. Sd; col (Technicolor). 35mm (Panavision). 101 min.

A William Conrad Production. *Exec Prod* William Conrad. *Dir* Robert Altman. *Screenplay* Loring Mandel. *Photog* William W. Spencer. *Art Dir* Jack Poplin. *Set Decor* Ralph S. Hurst. *Film Ed* Gene Milford. *Mus Comp & Cond* Leonard Rosenman. *Sd* Everett A. Hughes. *Asst Dir* Victor Vallejo. *Unit Mgr* J. Russell Llewellyn. *Makeup Supv* Gordon Bau. *Supv Hair Stylist* Jean Burt Reilly. *Dial Supv* Stacy Harris.

Cast: James Caan (*Lee*), Joanna Moore (*Mickey*), Robert Duvall (*Chiz*), Barbara Baxley (*Jean*), Charles Aidman (*Gus*), Steve Ihnat (*Ross*), Michael Murphy (*Rick*), Ted Knight (*Larson*), Stephen Coit (*Ehrman*), John Rayner (*Dunc*), Charles Irving (*Seidel*), Bobby Riha (*Stevie*).

Drama. Source: Henry Searls, *The Pilgrim Project* (New York, 1964). Astronauts Chiz, Rick, and Lee are ordered to halt their simulated space flight by NASA executive Ross when it is learned that the Russians are already circling the moon and may shortly attempt a landing. As a consequence, an American astronaut must be selected, trained, and sent to the moon as soon as possible. There he will exist in a shelter for approximately a year until the more up-to-date Apollo can be sent to bring him back. Because of his experience, Chiz is the front-runner for the job, but he loses out to Lee when the President decides that the man making the moon shot should be a civilian. Chiz bitterly agrees to help Lee in his final series of rigorous tests; even so, Lee nearly loses his life in one of them but is saved by his best friend, flight surgeon Gus. When word comes that the Russians are definitely going to land on the moon, Chiz overcomes his animosity and wholeheartedly backs up Lee in a hastily-scheduled launching. Lee makes a successful landing on the moon but is unable to find the shelter. He finds the Russian crew dead and plants the flags of both countries; he finally spots the blinking of the shelter's beacon and walks toward what will be his home for the next year. *Astronauts. Russians. Space flights. Jealousy. The Moon. United States—National Aeronautics and Space Administration. Apollo Project.*

Note: Location scenes filmed in Cocoa Beach, Florida. Working title: *Moonshot.*

THE COUNTERFEIT CONSTABLE (France)   F6.0926
Le Film d'Art–Les Films Arthur Lesser–C. I. C.–Films Borderie. *Dist* Seven Arts Associated Corp. 21 Nov **1966** [New York opening]. Sd; col (Eastman Color). 35mm. 87 min.

Prod Henri Diamant-Berger. *Dir* Robert Dhéry. *Screenplay* Robert Dhéry, Pierre Tchernia, Jean Lhote, Colette Brosset. *Photog* Jean Tournier, Henri Tiquet. *Art Dir* Jean Mandaroux. *Film Ed* Albert Jurgenson. *Mus* Gérard Calvi. *Sd* Jean Monchablon. *Prod Mgr* Maurice Hartwig. *English Subtitl* Noelle Gillmor.

Cast: Robert Dhéry (*Henri*), Colette Brosset (*Yvette, Lady Brisbane*), Ronald Fraser (*Yvette's husband [see note]*), Diana Dors (*herself*), Pierre Olaf (*police telephone operator*), Arthur Mullard (*bank robber*), Bernard Cribbins (*police sergeant*), Catherine Sola (*sister*), Robert Rollis (*desk sergeant*), Henri Genès (*friend*), Ferdy Mayne (*Diana Dors' agent*), Richard Vernon, Jean Richard, Raymond Bussières, Jean Carmet, Pierre Doris, Godfrey Quigley,

Pierre Dac, Percy Herbert, Bernard Lajarrige, Robert Burnier, Pierre Tchernia, Billy Kearns, Robert Destain, Jacques Legras, Colin Blakely, Tim Brinton, Margaret Whiting, Colin Gordon, Georgina Cookson, Jean Lefebvre.

Farce. A few days before his wedding, Henri, without telling his fiancée, joins a group of friends for a weekend trip to London for the championship Anglo-French rugby match. When an overenthusiastic spectator knocks out Henri's two front teeth, he frantically searches for a dentist, an almost impossible task on a Sunday in London. After his teeth have been repaired, Henri is cautioned by the dentist not to open his mouth under any circumstances until the final touches are applied to his capped teeth. Bored with waiting, he slips on the jacket and helmet of a British bobby while the patrolman is in the dentist's chair. Wearing the uniform, he frightens off a mugger molesting film star Diana Dors and is hailed as a hero. Unable to open his mouth to explain, Henri races from the scene, whereupon Miss Dors and her press agent, hoping to use the incident for publicity, take pursuit. Meanwhile, Henri's future sister-in-law and her pompous husband, who spotted Henri at the rugby game, are also searching for him, as are his chums from Paris. And finally the police join in when they learn an imposter in a bobby's uniform is on the loose. After a series of adventures, Henri returns to the dentist's office and from there to the airport to catch a plane for Paris. But Henri tries on a pilot's cap and jacket in the airport and is whisked off by the crew. *British. Actors. Theatrical agents. Constables. Dentists. Mistaken identity. Publicity. Weddings. Rugby. London.*

Note: Filmed in London. Opened in Paris as *Allez France!* in Oct 1964; running time: 90 min. A British source credits Fraser with the role of the chief constable and Richard Vernon as Lord Brisbane.

THE COUNTERFEIT KILLER   F6.0927
Universal Pictures. Jul **1968** [c10 Aug 1968; LP37966]. Sd (Westrex); col (Technicolor). 35mm. 95 min.

Prod Harry Tatelman. *TV Prod (see note)* Stanley Chase. *Dir* Josef Leytes. *TV Dir* Stuart Rosenberg. *Screenplay* Harold Clements, Steven Bocho. *Dir Photog* Benjamin H. Kline, John F. Warren. *Col Coörd* Robert Brower. *Art Dir* John J. Lloyd, Henry Larrecq. *Set Decor* John McCarthy, Robert C. Bradfield, Don Webb. *Film Ed* Tony Martinelli. *Mus Score* Quincy Jones. *Mus Supv* Stanley Wilson. *Sd* Waldon O. Watson, Ed Somers, Earl Crain, Jr. *Asst Dir* Lester William Berke, Roger Slager. *Unit Prod Mgr* George Lollier, Abby Singer. *Makeup* Bud Westmore. *Hairstyles* Larry Germain.

Cast: Jack Lord (*Don Owens*), Shirley Knight (*Angie Peterson*), Jack Weston (*Randolph Riker*), Charles Drake (*Dolan*), Joseph Wiseman (*Rajeski*), Don Hanmer (*O'Hara*), Robert Pine (*Ed*), George Tyne (*George*), Cal Bartlett (*Reggie*), Dean Heyde (*Keyser*), L. Q. Jones (*hotel clerk*), David Renard (*ambulance driver*), Nicholas Colasanto (*plainclothesman*), Mercedes McCambridge (*Frances [see note]*).

Crime drama. Source: Harry Kliner, *The Faceless Man* (a teleplay; first presented on "Bob Hope Presents The Chrysler Theater," 4 May 1966). The bodies of five unidentified foreign sailors are found murdered on the San Pedro, California, waterfront. Soon afterwards, more than $1 million in counterfeit bills appears in circulation. Secret Service Chief Dolan, who suspects that the sailors' deaths and the counterfeit money are linked, sends undercover agent Don Owens to San Pedro to investigate. Carrying a high-powered rifle, Owens checks into a seedy hotel and offers a reward for information about a missing shipmate. Pawnbroker Randolph Riker offers to help; instead he has Owens robbed. Owens is nursed by Angie Peterson, an embittered, divorced cocktail waitress, who becomes emotionally involved with him. The next day, Owens is the victim of a frameup when Riker plants a stolen necklace in Owens' room and then calls the police. Convinced that Owens is a professional killer, Riker bails him out of jail and puts him in touch with three foreigners headed by a trader, Rajeski. Owens is taken to an airport and ordered to kill Dolan when he arrives with East European forger Strega, who is suspected of being part of the counterfeit ring. At the last minute, however, Owens kills one of Rajeski's henchmen. The gang members are rounded up during the pandemonium that ensues, and Dolan arranges for Owens to make his getaway, issuing a press release stating that the sniper-killer escaped capture. *Sailors. Secret agents. Pawnbrokers. Waitresses. Hired killers. Police. Gangs. Murder. Counterfeiting. Conspiracy. Impersonation. Robbery. Frameup. Firearms. Airfields. San Pedro (California). United States Secret Service.*

Note: This film is an expanded version of the teleplay, including additional scenes with Mercedes McCambridge.

THE COUNTERFEIT TRAITOR   F6.0928
Perlsea Co. *Dist* Paramount Pictures. 13 Apr **1962** [Los Angeles opening: c31 Dec 1961; LP22370]. Sd (Westrex); col (Technicolor). 35mm. 140 min.

A Perlberg-Seaton Production. *Prod* William Perlberg. *Dir-Writ* George Seaton. *Dir Photog* Jean Bourgoin. *Camera Op* Louis Stein. *Art Dir* Tambi Larsen, Hal Pereira. *German Art Dir* Mathias Matthies. *Danish Art Dir* Henning Bahs. *Set Decor* Sam Comer, Ellen Schmidt. *Film Ed* Alma Macrorie.

Mus Comp Alfred Newman. *Orch* Edward B. Powell. *Sd Rec* Hans Ebel, Charles Grenzbach. *Asst Dir* Tom Pevsner. *Asst to the Prod* Theodore Taylor. *Exec Prod Mgr* Robert Snody. *German Prod Mgr* Helmut Ungerland. *Danish Prod Mgr* Mogens Skot-Hansen. *Swedish Prod Mgr* Gustav Roger. *Script Girl* Kathleen Fagan. *Cost* Edith Head. *Wardrobe Coörd* Frank Salvi. *Makeup* Neville Smallwood.

Cast: William Holden (*Eric Erickson*), Lilli Palmer (*Marianne Mollendorf*), Hugh Griffith (*Collins*), Erica Beer (*Klara Holtz*), Eva Dahlbeck (*Ingrid Erickson*), Helo Gutschwager (*Hans Holtz*), Holger Hagen (*Carl Bradley*), Ulf Palme (*Max Gumpel*), Carl Raddatz (*Otto Holtz*), Charles Regnier (*Wilhelm Kortner*), Ernst Schröder (*Baron Gerhard Von Oldenbourg*), Ingrid van Bergen (*Hulda Windler*), Werner Peters (*Bruno Ulrich*), Stefan Schnabel (*Jaeger*), Wolfgang Preiss (*Col. Martin Nordoff*), Jochen Blume (*Dr. Jacob Karp*), Dirk Hansen (*Lieutenant Nagler*), Ludwig Maybert (*stationmaster*), Klaus Kinski (*Kindler*), Erik Schuman (*Nazi gunboat officer*), Gunter Meisner (*priest*), Martin Berliner (*porter*), Phil Brown (*Harold Murray*), Peter Capell (*Unger*), Max Buchsbaum (*Fischer*), Ejner Federspiel (*Professor Christiansen*), Eva Fiebig (*Frau Hecker*), Kai Holm (*Gunnar*), Reinhard Kolldehoff (*Colonel Erdmann*), Louis Miehe-Renard (*Poul*), Jens Osterholm (*Lars*), Poul Reichhardt (*fishing boat skipper*), Bendt Rothe (*Mogens*), Albert Rueprecht (*Captain Barlach*), Ted Taylor (*monitor man*), Werner van Deeg (*oil refinery manager*), Georg Voelmmer (*Lieutenant Bretz*), John Wittig (*Sven*), Jørgen Krough, Preben Neergaard, Sven-Knute Nilsson.

Adventure melodrama. Source: Alexander Klein, *The Counterfeit Traitor* (New York, 1958). In 1942, Eric Erickson, an American-born naturalized Swedish citizen, is placed on the Allied blacklist for trading in oil with Nazi Germany. A few days later he is approached by Collins, a British Intelligence agent, who promises that if he will cooperate with the Allies by feeding them any information he picks up on his trips to Germany, his name will be cleared at the end of the war. Erickson knows he has no choice but to accept. By pretending to be pro-Nazi, he wins the confidence of high German officials, but the pretense causes his wife to leave him, and he is branded a traitor by his friends and countrymen. While on a trip to Berlin he meets Marianne Mollendorf, who later becomes his confederate and mistress. By inventing a plan to build an oil refinery in neutral Sweden to guarantee a fuel supply for Germany, Erickson gains permission to tour German refineries, the exact locations of which he passes on to Collins. At the same time, he is placed under surveillance by the Germans, and eventually the Gestapo discover that Marianne is working with the Allies and send her to Moabit Prison. Erickson also is arrested and is forced to watch her execution from a cell window. Though he is totally shattered by the experience, his claim that he never knew she was a spy is believed, and he is released. A short time later, however, he is exposed by a 12-year-old member of the Hitler Youth, the son of a friend whose support Erickson had enlisted. But with the help of the German underground Erickson escapes into Denmark, whence he is taken to Sweden aboard a Danish fishing boat. He is met by Collins and Max Gumpel, the one friend who never believed he was a traitor. *Spies. Traitors. Businessmen. Mistresses. Nazis. Espionage. Resistance (political). Oil business. Blacklisting. Prisons. Fishing boats. Germany—History—Third Reich. World War II. Sweden. Germany. Berlin. Denmark. Eric Siegfried Erickson. Wilhelm Kortner. Bruno Ulrich. Marianne Mollendorf. Great Britain—Intelligence service. Gestapo. Hitler Youth. Moabit Prison.*

Note: Location scenes filmed in West Berlin, Hamburg, Copenhagen, Stockholm, and coastal villages of Sweden and Denmark.

THE COUNTERFEITERS OF PARIS (France/Italy)   F6.0929

Cité Films–C. C. M. *Dist* Metro-Goldwyn-Mayer, Inc., Times Film Corp. 17 Jul **1962** [New York opening; c31 Dec 1961; LP24326]. Sd (Western Electric); b&w. 35mm. 99 min. [Copyright length: 96 min.]

Prod Jacques Bar. *Dir* Gilles Grangier. *Screenplay* Albert Simonin, Michel Audiard, Gilles Grangier. *Dial* Michel Audiard. *Dir Photog* Louis Page. *Photog* Marcel Dole. *Camera* Marc Champion. *1st Asst Camera Op* Raymond Menvielle. *2d Asst Camera Op* René Chabal. *Set Dsgn* Jacques Colombier. *Asst Set Dsgn* Olivier Girard, James Allan, Jacques Paris. *Film Ed* Jacqueline Thiédot. *Asst Ed* Colette Charbonneau. *Mus* Francis Lemarque, Michel Legrand. *Ch Sd Engr* Jean Rieul. *Rec* Gabriel Salagnac. *Boom Op* Marcel Corvaisier. *1st & 2d Asst Dir* Paul Feyder, Serge Piollet. *Prod Dir* Jacques Juranville. *Script Girl* Martine Guillou. *Cont* Albert Volper. *Outdoor Shooting Mgr* Jean Chaplain. *Gen Mgr* Georges Testard. *Chief Makeup* Yvonne Gasperina. *Miss Carol's Hairstyles* Carita.

Cast: Jean Gabin (*The Boss*), Bernard Blier (*Charles*), Martine Carol (*Solange*), Françoise Rosay (*Pauline*), Ginette Leclerc (*Lea*), Antoine Balpêtré (*Lucas*), Maurice Biraud (*Robert*), Frank Villard (*Eric*), Clara Gansard (*Georgette*), Heinrich Gretler (*Tauchmann*), Albert Dinan, Gérard Buhr, Lisa Jouvet, Gabriel Gobin, Robert Dalban, Jacques Marin, Paul Faivre, Hélène Dieudonné, Claude Ivry, René Hell, Max Doria, Charles Bouillaud, Albert

Michel, Marcel Charvey, Jean Moulart, Antonio Ramirez, actor.

Crime comedy-drama. Source: Albert Simonin, *Le Cave se rebiffe* (Paris, 1954). Charles, a crafty Parisian driven out of the prostitution business by a government crackdown, agrees to the suggestion of an associate, Eric, that they use the brothel as headquarters for a counterfeiting ring. After enlisting the talents of Lucas, a banker, and Robert, a young engraver whose wife, Solange, is having an affair with Eric, Charles tries to interest The Boss, a retired counterfeiter, in the scheme. At first The Boss, who has been living a life of ease in South America, refuses, but he eventually agrees to come and take a look at the setup. Intrigued by the idea and impressed with Robert's skill, he consents to supervise the operation in return for a 50 percent share of the profits. The others, resentful of his exorbitant share, plan to double-cross him by secretly printing more money than had been planned. The Boss outwits them, however, and he and Robert abscond with all of the money to South America. *Pimps. Bankers. Engravers. Counterfeiters. Prostitution. Counterfeiting. Perfidy. Infidelity. Whorehouses. Paris.*

Note: Released in France in 1961 as *Le cave se rebiffe*. Italian title: *Il re dei falsari*. Also released in America as *Money, Money, Money*.

COUNTERPOINT   F6.0930

Universal Pictures. Jan **1968** [New York opening: 13 Mar; c3 Feb 1968; LP36856]. Sd (Westrex); col (Technicolor). 35mm (Techniscope). 106 min.

Prod Dick Berg. *Dir* Ralph Nelson. *Screenplay* James Lee, Joel Oliansky. *Dir Photog* Russell Metty. *Art Dir* Alexander Golitzen, Carl Anderson. *Set Decor* John McCarthy, George Milo. *Main Titl* Universal Title. *Film Ed* Howard Epstein. *Mus Supv* Joseph Gershenson. *Mus* Bronislaw Kaper. *Selections from Symphony no. 1* Johannes Brahms. *Selections from Symphony no. 5* Ludwig van Beethoven. *Selections from "Unfinished Symphony"* Franz Peter Schubert. *Selections from "Swan Lake"* Pëtr Ilich Tchaikovsky. *"Tannhäuser Overture"* Richard Wagner. *Played by* Los Angeles Philharmonic Orchestra. *Symphonic Selections Cond by* Lawrence Foster. *Sd* Waldon O. Watson, William Russell. *Asst Dir* Wallace Worsley. *Unit Prod Mgr* William S. Gilmore, Jr. *Asst to the Prod* David A. Hammond. *Cost* Burton Miller. *Makeup* Bud Westmore. *Hairstylist* Larry Germain. *Matte Supv* Albert Whitlock. *Tech Adv* D. R. O. Hatswell. *Dial Coach* Dan Frazer. *Conducting Coach for Charlton Heston* Leo Damiani.

Cast: Charlton Heston (*Evans*), Maximilian Schell (*Schiller*), Kathryn Hays (*Annabelle*), Leslie Nielsen (*Victor*), Anton Diffring (*Arndt*), Linden Chiles (*Long*), Pete Masterson (*Calloway*), Curt Lowens (*Klingerman*), Neva Patterson (*Dorothy*), Cyril Delevanti (*Tartzoff*), Gregory Morton (*Jordon*), Parley Baer (*Hook*), Dan Frazer (*Chaminant*), Ed Peck (*Prescott*), Ralph Nelson (*Belgian officer*).

War drama. Source: Alan Sillitoe, *The General* (New York, 1961). In December of 1944, Lionel Evans, an internationally renowned American conductor, is on a USO tour with his 70-piece symphony orchestra in newly-liberated Belgium. While fleeing from a German counterattack, Evans and his orchestra members are captured by a Panzer division and taken to an old chateau in Luxembourg. Despite orders to execute every prisoner, General Schiller, an avid music lover, commands Evans to give a private concert for him. Evans refuses in order to barter for more time. The presence of two U. S. servicemen hiding among the orchestra members further endangers the group's safety. The two men try to escape during a rehearsal, and one is shot down and the other killed by a land mine. Evans finally consents to give Schiller his concert if he will release Annabelle Rice, the wife of first violinist Victor and Evans' former mistress, who has futilely attempted to bargain for the players' lives. As the performance nears its end, Schiller leaves and gives his aide, Colonel Arndt, permission to kill the musicians. Armed partisans attack the remaining Germans, however, and help most of the orchestra members to escape. Although Evans is left to face Arndt, his life is spared when Schiller returns and shoots Arndt. *Orchestra conductors. Musicians. Nazis. Mistresses. Prisoners of war. Resistance (political). Murder. Orchestras. World War II. Belgium. Luxembourg. United Service Organizations. Germany—Army.*

Note: Working title: *The Battle Hours*.

A COUNTESS FROM HONG KONG (Great Britain)   F6.0931

Universal Pictures. 16 Mar **1967** [New York opening; c29 Apr 1967; LP35390]. Sd (Westrex); col (Technicolor). 35mm. 108 min. [Copyright length: 113 min.]

Pres by Charles Chaplin. *Prod* Jerome Epstein. *Dir-Writ* Charles Chaplin. *Dir Photog* Arthur Ibbetson. *Camera Op* Paul Wilson. *Art Dir* Bob Cartwright. *Set Dresser* Vernon Dixon. *Scenic Artist* Alan Evans. *Prod Dsgn* Don Ashton. *Main Titl* Gordon Shadrick Enterprises. *Film Ed* Gordon Hales. *Asst Film Ed* Richard Hiscott, Brian Sinclair. *Mus Comp & Songs:* "This Is My Song," "My Star" Charles Chaplin. *Mus Arr & Cond* Lambert Williamson. *Mus Assoc* Eric James. *Sd Ed* Michael Hopkins. *Sd Rec* Bill Daniels, Ken Barker. *Asst Dir* Jack Causey. *Prod Supv* Denis Johnson. *Wardrobe Supv* Rosemary Burrows. *Hairdresser* Helen Penfold.

Cast: Marlon Brando *(Ogden Mears)*, Sophia Loren *(Natascha)*, Sydney Chaplin *(Harvey Crothers)*, Tippi Hedren *(Martha)*, Patrick Cargill *(Hudson)*, Michael Medwin *(John Felix)*, Oliver Johnston *(Clark)*, John Paul *(captain)*, Angela Scoular *(society girl)*, Margaret Rutherford *(Miss Gaulswallow)*, Peter Bartlett *(steward)*, Bill Nagy *(Crawford)*, Dilys Laye *(saleswoman)*, Angela Pringle *(baroness)*, Jenny Bridges *(countess)*, Arthur Gross *(immigration officer)*, Balbina *(French maid)*, Anthony Chin, José Sukhum Boonlve *(Hawaiians)*, Geraldine Chaplin, Janine Hill *(girls at dance)*, Burnell Tucker *(hotel receptionist)*, Leonard Trolley *(purser)*, Len Lowe *(electrician)*, Francis Dux *(head waiter)*, Cecil Cheng *(taxi driver)*, Ronald Rubin, Michael Spice, Ray Marlow *(American sailors)*, Josephine Chaplin, Victoria Chaplin *(young girls)*, Kevin Manser *(photographer)*, Marianne Stone, Lew Luton, Larry Cross, Billy Edwards, Drew Russell, John Sterland, Paul Carson, Paul Tamarin *(reporters)*, Carol Cleveland *(nurse)*, Charles Chaplin *(old steward)*.

Romantic comedy. On the eve of his departure from Hong Kong, wealthy American diplomat Ogden Mears spends a night ashore in the company of the beautiful Countess Natascha, an impoverished Russian emigrée who, from the age of 13, has survived by working as a dancehall girl. When Ogden's ship sails the next morning, he discovers Natascha hiding in his stateroom. Determined to reach the United States, she threatens to accuse Ogden of abduction and assault if he exposes her as a stowaway. Because Ogden has just been appointed ambassador to Saudi Arabia and is already in trouble with his wife, he submits to the blackmail. The voyage becomes a frenzied game of hide-and-seek, with Natascha popping in and out of closets and the bathroom to avoid discovery. Ogden is faced also with the problem of obtaining American citizenship for Natascha. A marriage of convenience is hastily arranged between Natascha and Ogden's manservant, Hudson, with the understanding that once ashore at Honolulu, Natascha will obtain both a passport and a divorce. But when the ship docks and Ogden's wife, Martha, comes aboard to effect a reconciliation, Natascha changes into native garb and dives into the bay. Ten minutes with his wife is enough to convince Ogden that Natascha is more important to him than his diplomatic career. Abandoning all else for love, he joins Natascha at the Waikiki Hotel. *Diplomats. Russians. Dancehall girls. Stowaways. Valets. Wealth. Nobility. Blackmail. Marriage of convenience. Marriage. Passports. Hong Kong. Honolulu. Waikiki Beach.*

Note: Opened in London in Jan 1967; running time: 120 min.

COUNTRY BOY   F6.0932

Ambassador Films. *Dist* Howco International, Donald A. Davis Productions. 23 Sep **1966** [Charlotte, North Carolina, opening; c20 Sep 1966; LP33778]. Sd; col (Technicolor). 35mm (Techniscope). 84 min.

Prod E. Stanley Williamson. *Assoc Prod* Neil E. Jackson, Jr. *Dir* Joe Kane. *Story* Paul Crabtree. *Dir Photog* Alan Stensvold. *Art Dir* J. Don Fields. *Film Ed* Verna Fields. *Country Mus Coörd* Hillous Butrum. *Titl Song* Paul Crabtree. *Sung by* Sheb Wooley. *Song:* "Draggin' the River" *writ & sung by* Sheb Wooley. *Song:* "Cry, Cry Lily," "A Little Hunk of America" Paul Crabtree. *Sung by* Randy Boone. *Song:* "Somewhere" Paul Crabtree. *Sung by* Skeeter Davis. *Song:* "First Kiss" Paul Crabtree. *Sung by* Sheb Wooley, Randy Boone. *Song:* "She Passed My Way" Paul Crabtree. *Sung by* Ray Pillow. *Song:* "Would You Believe" Paul Crabtree. *Sung by* Randy Boone, Lois Johnson. *Song:* "Wanted Dead or Alive" Paul Crabtree. *Sung by* Glaser Brothers. *Songs:* "Tomorrow," "Baby, They're Playing Our Song" *sung by* Randy Boone. *Song:* "Fifteen Cents Worth of Pinto Beans" *sung by* Lonzo & Oscar. *Song:* "The Grass Grows Greener" *sung by* Hillous Butrum. *Song:* "Cindy" *sung by* Grandpa Jones. *Sd Engr* Vilmars Zile. *Mus Ed* Bobby Dyson. *Unit Prod Mgr* Jack Barry. *Prod Sec* Cynthia Beeler. *Casting Cons* Marvin Paige.

Cast: Randy Boone *(Link Byrd, Jr.)*, Sheb Wooley *(himself)*, Paul Brinegar *(Mr. Byrd)*, Paul Crabtree *(Fats Jackson)*, Majel Barrett *(Miss Wynn)*, James Dobson *(George Washington Byrd)*, Sondra Rodgers *(Mrs. Byrd)*, John Pickard *(Claude Springer)*, Maurice Dembsky *(Dave Rupp)*, Chuck Doughty *(Thomas Jefferson Byrd)*, Ed Livingston *(John Adams Byrd)*, Pauletta Leeman *(Lucinda May)*, Bob Stewart *(Ernie)*, Ivan Purser *(Mr. Bean)*, R. N. Pelot *(Mr. Potts)*, Dick Brackett *(reporter)*, C. B. Anderson *(angry man)*, Bob Jennings *(television announcer)*, Ruth Charron *(angry woman)*, Joe Kane *(The President)*.

Country Music Guest Stars: Skeeter Davis, Grandpa Jones, Lonzo & Oscar, Glaser Brothers, Ray Pillow, Lois Johnson, Stoney Mountain Cloggers, Hillous Butrum, Bobby Dyson, James Steward, Jane Colvard, Walter Haynes, Beegie Cruser.

Comedy with music. Mechanic Link Byrd, Jr., is asked to repair the bus of country music star Sheb Wooley when it breaks down en route to Nashville. Link, an amateur guitarist, joins Sheb for an informal music session, and, encouraged by Sheb's secretary and agent Miss Wynn, Link decides to go to Nashville. Link's father and girl friend are opposed to the idea, but he stows away on Sheb's bus when it departs. In Nashville, Link accidentally appears on stage, and when Sheb invites him to sing, the youngster's stage fright overcomes

him, and he runs off. Returning to the bus, Link asks Miss Wynn to give him another chance, but instead she gives him money to return home. An unscrupulous agent who learns that Link's name is Abraham Lincoln Byrd, Jr., dresses Link as the 16th president and has him perform a rock and roll act. The audience reaction is so violent that the President of the United States summons Link's father to Washington and asks him to do something about his son. Mr. Byrd travels to New York where Link is to appear on television, forces his way into the studio, and berates Link in front of the audience. As he is about to leave the stage, Link sings a patriotic song, for which he receives a standing ovation. He then returns home with his family. *Mechanics. Guitarists. Singers. Talent agents. Secretaries. Country music. Ambition. Family life. Buses. Television. Nashville (Tennessee). New York City. Washington (District of Columbia). Presidents of the United States.*

Note: Later retitled *Here Comes That Nashville Sound.*

COUNTRY DANCE *see* BROTHERLY LOVE

THE COUNTRY DOCTOR *see* LIFE OF A COUNTRY DOCTOR

COUNTRY GIRL   F6.0933

Carl R. Carter Productions. ca **1968**. Sd; col (Eastman Color). 35mm. 65 min.

A Carl R. Carter Production. *Dir-Writ* Bobby Davis. *Camera* Rob Miklas. *Film Ed* John Flag. *Sd* Ralf Evans. *Prod Mgr* Bob Inzer. *Script Girl* Amy Lee. *Wardrobe* Ty Webster. *Makeup* Cindy Bern. *Gaffer* Billy Farris.

Cast: Marie Campbell, Jean Wilson, Tommy Ruble, Roy Ace Epps, Sue Sennet, Ruth Stafford, Robert Gladney.

Sex film. Country girl Marie and her boyfriend Josh make love, thereby revealing that sexual pleasure in the country is not all that different than that in the city where young married couple Fred and Angie make love. Back in the country, staid housewives Ruth and Honey Bee demonstrate lesbian love. Fred and Angie embark on a fishing trip, encounter Everett and Marie, and the four swap mates. Marie and Angie experiment with lesbian pleasures while their husbands are out fishing. Fred runs into Honey Bee and begins to make love to her, only to be interrupted by her husband. *Sexuality. Mate swapping. Lesbianism. Fishing.*

COUNTRY MUSIC CARAVAN   F6.0934

Colorama Roadshows. 9 Sep **1964** [Cincinnati, Ohio, showing]. Sd; col (Eastman Color). 35mm. 83 min.

Participants: Jim Reeves, Marty Robbins, Carl Smith, Ray Price, Minnie Pearl, Ernest Tubb, Faron Young, Jean Shepard, The Jordanaires, Lonzo & Oscar, The Duke of Paducah, Goldie Hill, June Carter, Billy Byrd, World's Champion Square Dancers.

Musical revue. Seventeen country music performers, some of them veteran entertainers, play 27 different country-and-western hits to the accompaniment of 7 different bands. Various comedy acts and the World's Champion Square Dancers also perform, with most of the entertainment originating from Nashville, Tennessee. *Singers. Country music. Folk dancing. Nashville (Tennessee).*

Note: Also reviewed as *Country Music Carnival.*

COUNTRY MUSIC CARNIVAL *see* COUNTRY MUSIC CARAVAN

COUNTRY MUSIC JAMBOREE   F6.0935

Williams and Jetton Productions. 6 Jan **1970** [Parkin, Arkansas, opening]. Sd; col (Eastman Color). 35mm. [Feature film, length unknown.] *MPAA rating* G.

Exec Prod Andy Jetton. *Dir* Gene Williams.

Cast: Gene Williams, Andy Jetton, Carole Williams, Charlie Fritts, Danny Byrd, Teresa Leggett, The Country Junction Boys.

Drama with music. An aspiring country music performer leaves his hometown of Parkin, Arkansas, and seeks fame in the big city. He becomes homesick for his old friends, but eventually finds success, enabling him to return to Parkin and give a show for those who inspired him as a young man. *Musicians. Rural life. Country music. Parkin (Arkansas).*

Note: Filmed in Parkin, Arkansas.

COUNTRY MUSIC ON BROADWAY   F6.0936

Marathon Pictures. *Dist* Howco International. 2 Apr **1964** [Maryland license]. Sd; col (Eastmancolor). 35mm. 95 min.

Prod Victor Lewis. *Dir* Victor Duncan. *Songs:* "Cold, Cold Heart," "Jambalaya," "I'm a Long Gone Daddy," "Hey, Good Lookin'" Hank Williams. *Song:* "Waterloo" Marijohn Wilkin, John D. Loudermilk. *Song:* "I'm Moving On" Hank Snow. *Song:* "Flint Hill Special" Earl Scruggs. *Song:* "There's a Big Wheel" Don Gibson. *Song:* "A Fool Such as I" Bill Trader. *Song:* "Po' Folks" Bill Anderson. *Song:* "White Lightning" J. P. Richardson. *Song:* "Big Midnight Special" Wilma Lee Cooper. *Song:* "Second Hand Rose" Harlan Howard.

Featuring: Hank Snow, Ferlin Husky, Lester Flatt, Earl Scruggs, Skeeter Davis, George Jones, Buck Owens, Porter Wagoner, Hank Williams, Jr., Roy Drusky, Stonewall Jackson, Bill Anderson, Audrey Williams, The Wilburn Brothers, The Anita Kerr Singers, Wilma Lee, Stoney Cooper, Ralph Emery, Merle Kilgore, The Duke of Paducah, Bobby Smith, singer.

Musical revue. A group of country musicians give a concert in New York City. The master of ceremonies links the acts with country jokes, while backstage the spirit of Hank Williams, the great country singer, is evoked. *Singers. Country music. New York City. Hank Williams.*

Note: A number of additional songs were performed in the film; the titles are undetermined.

COUNTRY MUSIC, U. S. A. see LAS VEGAS HILLBILLYS

COUNTRY WESTERN HOEDOWN   F6.0937
Jam Art Pictures. 30 Nov **1967** [Maryland license]. Sd; col (Eastman Color). 35mm. 83 min.

Prod Arthur W. Stanisch, James F. Sullivan. *Dir* William R. Johnson. *Screenplay* Delores Klaft, Robert Sullivan, Wanda Receiver. *Photog* William R. Johnson, Jay Schiff, Jim Pasternak. *Lighting* Jack Branscombe. *Song:* "Petticoat Junction" Paul Henning, Curt Massey. *Song:* "Woodchoppers' Ball" Woody Herman, Joe Bishop. *Song:* "San Antonio Rose" Bob Wills. *Song:* "My Heart Needs Your Heart" Neal Burris, Ruby (Dunne) Burris, J. L. Frank. *Song:* "Indian Love Dance" Minn-O-Gee-Shik. *Song:* "You Belong to Me" Pee Wee King, Redd Stewart, Chilton Price. *Song:* "Anytime" Herbert Happy Lawson. *Song:* "If You Don't, Somebody Else Will" Johnny Mathis, Jimmy Fautherlee, Geraldine Hamilton. *Song:* "Make Believe" Billy Walker, Jerry Robinson. *Song:* "Silver and Gold" Henry Prichard, Del Sharbutt, Bob Crosby. *Song:* "You'll See the Day" Pee Wee King, J. L. Frank. *Song:* "Oh, Lonesome Me" Don Gibson. *Song:* "Bonaparte's Retreat" Pee Wee King. *Song:* "Dis Train" Jester Hairston. *Song:* "Bimbo" Rod Morris. *Song:* "I'm a Stranger in My Home" Pee Wee King, Redd Stewart, Neal Burris. *Song:* "Looking Back To See" Jim Edward Brown, Maxine Brown. *Songs:* "No One but You," "Why Don't You All Go Home" Pee Wee King, Redd Stewart. *Song:* "Slow Poke" Pee Wee King, Chilton Price. *Song:* "(Soldier's) Deck of Cards" T. Texas Tyler. *Sd* Robert Huffstater. *Unit Prod Asst* Sharon Davison, Deborah Stanisch, Helen Paritz, Gordon Paritz.

Cast: Pee Wee King, Redd Stewart, Little Eller Long, Collins Sisters, Ginger Callahan, Jack Leonard, singer, Red Murphy, Chuck Wiggins, Chellette Sisters, Neal Burris, Bonnie Sloan, Golden West Cowboys, Estil McNew and His "Kentucky Briar Hoppers", Red Herron, Shorty Hayes, Sticks McDonald, Russ Caswell, Terry Tichy, Jack Brengle, Gene Engle, Jim Vest.

Musical revue. Filmed at seven barn dance stages—the Grand Ole Opry in Nashville, Tennessee; the Renfro Valley in Renfro Valley, Kentucky; the National and Midwestern Hayride in Chicago; the Town Hall Party in California; the Old Dominion in Richmond, Virginia; and the Ozark Jubilee—this musical revue features 15 country and western acts performing 33 songs. *Additional Songs:* "Blow Out the Candles," "Cripple Creek," "It Ain't What You Want, It's What You Got," "Jani," "Louisville Bogie," "Old Joe Clark," "Poor Little Me," "Seven Come Eleven," "Skip to My Lou," "There's Been Too Much Said Already," "Tin Type Song," "Winking at Me." *Musicians. Singers. Country music. Nashville (Tennessee). Renfro Valley (Kentucky). Chicago. California. Richmond (Virginia). Grand Ole Opry.*

Note: Also known as *Pee Wee King's "Country Western Hoedown".*

THE COUPLE see THERE WAS AN OLD COUPLE

A COUPLE OF TROUBLE   F6.0938
Dist I. R. M. I. Films. 16 Apr **1969** [New York showing]. Sd; b&w. 35mm. 69 min.

Cast: Justine D'Ore.

Sex film. No information about the precise nature of this film has been found. *Sexuality.*

COURT MARTIAL (West Germany)   F6.0939
Arca-Film. *Dist* United Artists. Dec **1962**. Sd; b&w. 35mm. 82 min.

A Helmut Volmer Production. *Prod* Helmut Volmer. *Dir* Kurt Meisel. *Screenplay* Will Berthold, Heinz Oskar Wuttig. *Photog* Georg Krause. *Mus* Werner Eisbrenner.

Cast: Karlheinz Böhm *(Lieutenant Duren)*, Christian Wolff *(Stahmer)*, Klaus Kammer *(Hinze)*, Werner Peters *(Brenner)*, Sabina Sesselmann *(Frau Duren)*, Hans Nielsen, Carl Wery, Berta Drews, Robert Meyn, Charles Regnier, Herbert Tiede, Edith Hancke, Albert Heyn, Carola von Kayser.

War melodrama. Source: Will Berthold, *Kriegsgericht* (Munich, 1959). During World War II, three survivors of the sunken German ship *Pommern* are rescued, returned to Germany, and hailed as heroes. An investigation follows, however, and the three men are arrested and charged with desertion. Court martial evidence proves that the sea battle lasted 3 hours after the men had abandoned the ship in a raft. The court finds them guilty and orders the death penalty for all three. *Deserters—Military. Courts-martial. Capital punishment. World War II. Germany—Navy. "Pommern".*

Note: Released in West Germany in 1959 as *Kriegsgericht*; running time: 85 min.

THE COURTSHIP OF EDDIE'S FATHER   F6.0940
Euterpe, Inc.–Venice Productions. *Dist* Metro-Goldwyn-Mayer, Inc. 6 Mar **1963** [New York opening; c31 Dec 1962; LP24327]. Sd (Westrex); col (Metrocolor). 35mm (Panavision). 117 min.

Prod Joe Pasternak. *Dir* Vincente Minnelli. *Screenplay* John Gay. *Dir Photog* Milton Krasner. *Art Dir* George W. Davis, Urie McCleary. *Set Decor* Henry Grace, Keogh Gleason. *Film Ed* Adrienne Fazan. *Mus* George Stoll. *Song:* "The Rose and the Butterfly" Victor Young, Stella Unger. *Rec Supv* Franklin Milton. *Asst Dir* William McGarry. *Asst to the Prod* Irving Aaronson. *Cost* Helen Rose. *Makeup* William Tuttle. *Hairstyles* Sydney Guilaroff. *Sp Vis Eff* Robert R. Hoag.

Cast: Glenn Ford *(Tom Corbett)*, Shirley Jones *(Elizabeth Marten)*, Stella Stevens *(Dollye Daly)*, Dina Merrill *(Rita Behrens)*, Roberta Sherwood *(Mrs. Livingston)*, Ronny Howard *(Eddie)*, Jerry Van Dyke *(Norman Jones)*, John La Salle Jazz Combo.

Comedy. Source: Mark Toby, *The Courtship of Eddie's Father* (New York, 1961). Recently widowed Tom Corbett, advertising director of a radio station, hires a day housekeeper to help care for his 6 1/2-year-old son, Eddie. The boy, however, would like his father to become romantically involved with a woman such as their attractive neighbor, divorcée Elizabeth Marten, who nursed Eddie when he was ill. When Eddie fails to interest his father in a relationship with Elizabeth, he strikes up a friendship with a shy beauty contestant from Montana, Dollye Daly; but she falls in love with Norman Jones, a disc jockey who is also a friend of Tom's. Tom next meets Rita Behrens, a chic fashion consultant of whom Eddie disapproves. When Tom announces that he plans to marry Rita, Eddie runs away from summer camp and takes refuge in Elizabeth's apartment. As a result, Tom breaks with Rita, and little Eddie at long last makes his father realize that Elizabeth is the best possible choice for a wife. *Children. Advertising executives. Widowers. Housekeepers. Disc jockeys. Careerwomen. Neighbors. Matchmakers. Fatherhood. Radio.*

LE COUTEAU DANS LA PLAIE see FIVE MILES TO MIDNIGHT

A COVENANT WITH DEATH   F6.0941
Warner Bros. Pictures. 27 Jan **1967** [Albuquerque, New Mexico, opening; c1 Jan 1967; LP35721]. Sd; col (Technicolor). 35mm. 97 min.

Exec Prod William Conrad. *Dir* Lamont Johnson. *Screenplay* Lawrence B. Marcus, Saul Levitt. *Dir Photog* Robert Burks. *Art Dir* Howard Hollander. *Set Decor* Ralph S. Hurst. *Film Ed* William Ziegler. *Mus Comp & Cond* Leonard Rosenman. *Sd* Stanley Jones. *Asst Dir* Gil Kissel. *Unit Mgr* J. Russell Llewellyn. *Makeup Supv* Gordon Bau. *Supv Hairstylist* Jean Burt Reilly. *Dial Supv* Stacy Harris.

Cast: George Maharis *(Ben Lewis)*, Laura Devon *(Rosemary)*, Katy Jurado *(Eulalia Lewis)*, Earl Holliman *(Bryan Talbot)*, Arthur O'Connell *(Judge Hochstadter)*, Sidney Blackmer *(Colonel Oates)*, Gene Hackman *(Harmsworth)*, John Anderson *(Dietrich)*, Wende Wagner *(Rafaela)*, Emilio Fernandez *(Ignacio)*, Kent Smith *(Parmalee)*, Lonny Chapman *(Musgrave)*, Jose De Vega *(Digby)*, Larry D. Mann *(Chillingworth)*, Whit Bissell *(Bruce Donnelly)*, Russell Thorson *(Dr. Shilling)*, Paul Birch *(governor)*, Erwin Neal *(Willie Wayte)*, Robert Dunlap *(policeman)*, Jadine Vaughn *(Louise Talbot)*, Albuquerque Polo Club, Santa Fe County Sheriff's Posse *(polo players)*.

Drama. Source: Stephen Becker, *A Covenant With Death* (New York, 1964). In the Southwest in the 1920's, a young woman is found strangled in her bedroom. Her husband, Bryan Talbot, the town libertine, is found drunk and incoherent. He is arrested and subsequently convicted of murder by circumstantial evidence stemming from his frequent violent outbursts on the promiscuous conduct of his wife. Judge Hochstadter leaves on a fishing trip, thereby placing a younger judge, Ben Morealis Lewis, in charge of Talbot's hanging. A Mexican-American, Lewis is having an affair with a Swedish woman, Rosemary Berquist, despite the objections of his somewhat domineering mother. On the day of the hanging, Talbot goes berserk at the gallows. During his frenzied outburst proclaiming his innocence, he pushes the hangman from the scaffolding and kills him. A few moments later Lewis learns that one of Talbot's neighbors, Bruce Donnelly, has confessed to the murder in a suicide note. Although absolved of his wife's death, Talbot is arrested for the murder of the hangman. Before the second trial begins, Lewis ends his affair with Rosemary and begins a new one with a young Mexican woman, Rafaela. He also runs into Talbot in a tavern and is nearly killed in a fight when the drunken Talbot accuses him of infidelities with his late wife. Forgetting personal feelings, Lewis acquits Talbot on the grounds that an innocent man, even under sentence of death, has the right to defend himself against a society that has unjustly convicted him, threatening to take his life. *Judges. Mexicans. Swedes. Executioners. Jealousy. Murder. Alcoholism. Promiscuity. Injustice. Capital punishment. Suicide. Infidelity. Confession (law). Documentation.*

Note: Location scenes filmed in Santa Fe, New Mexico.

COVER ME BABE   F6.0942

Twentieth Century-Fox Film Corp. 1 Oct **1970** [New York opening; c31 Dec 1969; LP43774]. Sd; col (De Luxe). 35mm. 89 min. *MPAA rating* R.

Prod Lester Linsk. *Dir* Noel Black. *Screenplay* George Wells. *Dir Photog* Michel Hugo. *Camera Op* Jack Courtland. *Camera Asst* Brad Six, Gary Armstrong. *Art Dir* Jack Martin Smith, Dale Hennesy. *Set Decor* Walter M. Scott, Robert De Vestel. *Film Ed* Harry Gerstad. *Mus* Fred Karlin. *Perf by* Bread, Art and Honey, Stony Brook People. *Sd* Richard Overton, David Dockendorf. *Asst Dir* Richard Glassman. *Unit Prod Mgr* Eric Stacey. *Prod Mgr* Edward Haldeman. *Script Supv* Teresa Brachetto. *Wardrobe* Jerry Kobald, Bruce Walkup. *Photog Eff* Art Cruickshank. *Constr Coörd* Ben Benson. *Gaffer* Ralph McCarthy. *Grip* Alonzo Parker.

Cast: Robert Forster *(Tony)*, Sondra Locke *(Melisse)*, Susanne Benton *(Sybil)*, Robert Fields *(Will)*, Ken Kercheval *(Jerry)*, Sam Waterston *(cameraman)*, Michael Margotta *(Steve)*, Mike Kellin *(derelict)*, Floyd Mutrux *(Ronnie)*, Maggie Thrett *(prostitute)*, Jeff Corey *(Paul)*, Regis Toomey *(Michael)*, Mitzi Hoag *(mother)*, Franklin Townsend *(transvestite)*, Mello Alexandria *(male puppet)*, Linda Howe *(female puppet)*, Michael Payne, Carmen Argenziano *(students)*.

Melodrama. Tony, a film student at a Los Angeles university, throws a party to celebrate a prize he has won, and after the party, Melisse, the star of his film stays, and they make love. The next day Melisse leaves Will, a film instructor at the university, and moves into Tony's apartment. When Tony applies for a grant to finance his next film, Will refuses and refers him to Paul, a Hollywood talent agent. Tony decides to go ahead and shoot the film, a documentary on human depravity, without the grant. He films footage of a couple making love in a car, interviews an alcoholic derelict, and stages an argument between Melisse and student actor Jerry which nearly turns into a rape scene. Tony's agent arranges an interview for him with a studio executive, but Tony's arrogance costs him a job offer. Now obsessed with the documentary, Tony hires a prostitute to masturbate in front of the camera, despite Will's protests. Sybil, Tony's former girl friend, agrees to try to seduce Ronnie, a homosexual, but Will breaks in and disrupts the shooting. Melisse, who is totally disillusioned with the filmmaker, moves out. Undaunted by her departure, as well as the rejection by the studio, Tony jogs down the beach alone. *Filmmakers. Students. College teachers. Talent agents. Actors. Prostitutes. Moral corruption. Autoeroticism. Seduction. Motion pictures. Motion picture studios. Los Angeles. Hollywood.*

Note: Working title: *Run Shadow Run*.

THE COW AND I (France/Italy/West Germany)   F6.0943

Les Films du Cyclope-Omnia Film-Da. Ma. Film. *Dist* Zenith International Film Corp. 5 Jun **1961** [New York opening]. Sd; b&w. 35mm. 98 min.

Dir Henri Verneuil. *Dial* Henri Jeanson. *Adapt* Henri Verneuil, Jean Manse, Henri Jeanson. *Story* Jacques Antoine. *Photog* Roger Hubert. *Art Dir* Franz Bi, Jacques Chalvet, Max Seefelder. *Film Ed* James Cuenet, Gabriel Rongier. *Mus* Paul Durand. *Sd* Antoine Petitjean. *Prod Mgr* Walter Rupp, René G. Vuattoux. *English Titl* Rose Sokol.

Cast: Fernandel *(Charles Bailly)*, René Havard *(Bussière)*, Albert Rémy *(Colinet)*, Bernard Musson *(Pommier)*, Maurice Nasil *(Bertoux)*, Pierre-Louis, Richard Winckler *(officers)*, Ingeborg Schöner *(Helga)*, Franciska Kinz *(Helga's mother)*, Ellen Schwiers *(Joséphine)*, Benno Hoffmann *(camp guard)*, Marguerite *(herself, a cow)*.

Comedy. Charles Bailly, a World War II French prisoner of war, devises a clever means of escaping from a German prison farm. A farmer's wife, Helga, lends him one of the cows, Marguerite, and a milk pail. Charles sets out to walk to Stuttgart and to reach the border by posing as a laborer from a nearby farm. En route, he is briefly forced to work at a lumber camp; Marguerite has a romantic interlude with an amorous bull; and Charles robs a German supply truck, only to find he has taken nothing but candles and medical supplies. When he and Marguerite reach the Danube, Charles discovers that all the bridges have been destroyed by air raids. With only a rowboat available, he sadly bids Marguerite goodby, but the resourceful cow crosses the river on a pontoon bridge. Reunited, Charles and Marguerite resume their journey and safely reach Stuttgart. Now Charles must leave Marguerite, and after a tearful farewell, he hops a freight train and arrives in France. He runs into the collaborating French security police, however, and is forced to jump another train to escape them. Unhappily, Charles boards one going in the wrong direction, and he is carried back into Germany. *Prisoners of war. Police. Farmers. Prison escapes. Imposture. Robbery. Rowboats. Bridges. Trains. World War II. Germany. Stuttgart. Danube River. Cows.*

Note: Opened in Paris in Dec 1959 as *La vache et le prisonnier;* running time: 119 min; in Rome in Apr 1960 as *La vacca e il prigioniero;* running time: 90 min.

COWARDS   F6.0944

Jaylo International Films. 23 Jul **1970** [New York opening]. Sd; col (Eastman Color). 35mm. 89 min.

A Lewis Mishkin–Simon Nuchtern Production. *Prod-Dir-Writ* Simon Nuchtern. *Photog* Robert T. Megginson. *Film Ed* Robert T. Megginson. *Mus Comp* Stephen Lerner. *Mus Perf by* The Merry-Go-Round. *Sd* Nigel Noble.

Cast: John Ross, actor *(Philip Haller)*, Susan Sparling *(Joan Boyd)*, Will Patent *(Peter Yates)*, Thomas Murphy *(Howard Yates)*, Philip B. Hall *(Father Reis)*, Alexander Gellman *(Gregory Haller)*, Edith Briden *(Nancy Haller)*, Stephen Snow *(Terry)*, George Linjeris *(Jim)*, Spalding Gray *(radical)*, Kelly Houser *(man at physical)*, Larry Hunter *(detective)*.

Drama. Philip Haller, who opposes American involvement in Vietnam, is about to be drafted when his parents find him a job which will qualify him for a deferment. He rejects this solution, however, and Joan, a Greenwich Village coffeehouse waitress who becomes his girl friend, puts him in touch with a group of draft evaders who are planning to emigrate to Canada. Philip grapples with the question of whether to escape across the border or to continue to resist the draft at home. A series of events combines to influence his decision: his father accuses him of cowardice for evading the draft, and word arrives that Joan's brother has been killed in Vietnam. Later, Philip visits his friend Peter in a military hospital. Peter, the son of a zealous patriot, was wounded almost immediately after his arrival in Vietnam and returned home a hopeless invalid. Philip decides to remain in the United States to fight the draft. He joins Father Reis and an anti-war group in the destruction of a draft board office and is arrested and sent to jail. *Draft dodgers. Priests. Waitresses. Invalids. Military draft. Conscience. Demonstrations. Filial relations. Imprisonment. Hospitals. Vietnam War 1964–73. Canada. New York City—Greenwich Village. United States Army.*

Note: Filmed in New York City.

COWBOY IN AFRICA see **AFRICA—TEXAS STYLE!**

CRACK IN THE WORLD   F6.0945

Security Pictures. *Dist* Paramount Pictures. 24 Feb **1965** [Los Angeles opening; c31 Dec 1964; LP29816]. Sd; col (Technicolor). 35mm. 96 min.

A Philip Yordan Production. *Prod* Bernard Glasser, Lester A. Sansom. *Exec Prod* Philip Yordan. *Dir* Andrew Marton. *Screenplay* Jon Manchip White, Julian Halevy. *Story* Jon Manchip White. *Dir Photog* Manuel Berenguer. *Art Dir* Eugene Lourie. *Film Ed* Derek Parsons. *Mus* Johnny Douglas. *Sd* Kurt Herrnfeld. *Sd Rec* David Hildyard, Maurice Askew. *Asst Dir* José-María Ochoa. *Prod Mgr* Tibor Reves. *Cost* Laure de Zarate. *Sp Eff Dir* Eugene Lourie. *Sp Eff* Alex Weldon.

Cast: Dana Andrews *(Dr. Stephen Sorensen)*, Janette Scott *(Mrs. Maggie Sorensen)*, Kieron Moore *(Ted Rampion)*, Alexander Knox *(Sir Charles Eggerston)*, Peter Damon *(Masefield)*, Gary Lasdun *(Markov)*, Mike Steen *(Steele)*, Todd Martin *(Simpson)*, Jim Gillen *(Rand)*, Alfred Brown, Emilio Carrere, Sydna Scott, John Karlsen, Ben Tatar.

Science fiction drama. Dr. Stephen Sorensen, an aging scientist dying of cancer, is head of Project Inner Space, a plan to expose the earth's core (magma) as a new source of energy. Against the advice of his wife, Maggie, and his associate, geologist Ted Rampion, Sorensen explodes a powerful atomic bomb. The blast cracks the rock layer surrounding the magma, but the scientists' happiness over the success of the project is short-lived when it is learned that earthquakes have erupted along the volatile Macebo Fault. With the help of Maggie, Rampion concludes that the only way to stop the reaction is by detonating another bomb. The second explosion is set off inside a volcano, but the crack created by the first explosion merely reverses its course, threatening to split the earth. Sorensen tricks Rampion and Maggie into leaving him behind, and they escape just as a large wedge of earth flies into space to form another moon. *Scientists. Geologists. Cancer. Experiments. Nuclear energy. Atom bomb. Volcanoes. Earthquakes. Explosions.*

Note: Produced in Spain.

CRACK-UP   F6.0946

Dist Distribpix, Inc. **1969.** Sd; col. 35mm. 64 min.

Prod Jack Bravman, Michael Findlay. *Dir* Michael Findlay. *Photog* Roberta Findlay. *Film Ed* Michael Findlay.

Sex film. No information about the precise nature of this film has been found. *Sexuality.*

CRAIG   F6.0947

Coldwater Clam. 13 Nov **1970** [Los Angeles opening]. Sd; col. 35mm? [Feature film, length unknown.]

Cast: Scot Arden.

Sex film. No information about the precise nature of this film has been found, but press material suggests that it is about male homosexual oral sex. *Male homosexuality. Oral sex.*

THE CRAWLING HAND F6.0948

Joseph F. Robertson Productions. *Dist* Hansen Enterprises, American International Pictures. 4 Sep **1963** [Hartford, Connecticut, opening]. Sd; b&w. 35mm. 89 min.

Prod Joseph F. Robertson. *Dir* Herbert L. Strock. *Screenplay* Herbert L. Strock, William Idelson. *Story* Robert Young, Joseph Cranston. *Photog* Willard Van Der Veer. *Film Ed* Herbert L. Strock. *Sd* Earl Snyder. *Asst Dir* Michael Messinger, Wilbur D'Arcy.

Cast: Peter Breck *(Steve Curan)*, Kent Taylor *(Doc Weitzberg)*, Rod Lauren *(Paul Lawrence)*, Sirry Steffen *(Marta Farnstrom)*, Alan Hale, [Jr.] *(sheriff)*, Arline Judge *(Mrs. Hotchkiss)*, Richard Arlen, Ross Elliott, Allison Hayes, Ed Wermer, Tris Coffin, Syd Saylor, G. Stanley Jones, Ashley Cowan, Jock Putnam, Beverly Lunsford, Andy Andrews.

Horror film. An astronaut in space pleads for death because he has become possessed by an unknown form of outer space life, and scientists explode his craft. A California student finds the astronaut's dismembered arm on a beach and takes it to his roominghouse, where it comes to life and strangles his landlady. Though the student is eventually cleared of the murder when the fingerprints on the body prove to be those of the astronaut, the forces in the arm begin to possess the student. He makes a number of murder attempts before, in a battle with the arm, he wrenches it from his throat and throws it to a pack of hunger-crazed cats who devour it. *Scientists. Astronauts. Students. Landladies. Murder. Mutilation. Roominghouses. Cats.*

Note: Working title: *Tomorrow You Die.* Alternative title: *Strike Me Deadly.*

THE CRAWLING MONSTER *see* **THE CREEPING TERROR**

CRAZY BABY *see* **THE BATTLE OF THE MODS**

A CRAZY DAY *see* **FROM A ROMAN BALCONY**

CRAZY DESIRE (Italy) F6.0949

Dino De Laurentiis Cinematografica. *Dist* Embassy Pictures. 2 Jul **1964** [New York opening]. Sd; b&w. 35mm (Totalscope). 108 min.

Pres by Joseph E. Levine. *Prod* Isidoro Broggi, Renato Libassi. *Dir* Luciano Salce. *Screenplay* Luciano Salce, Franco Castellano, Pipolo. *Ch Camera* Erico Menczer. *Art Dir* Nedo Azzini. *Film Ed* Roberto Cinquini. *Mus* Ennio Morricone. *Prod Mgr* Alessandro Von Norman.

Cast: Ugo Tognazzi *(Antonio Berlinghieri)*, Catherine Spaak *(Francesca)*, Gianni Garko *(Piero)*, Béatrice Altariba *(Silvana)*, Jimmy Fontana *(boyfriend)*, Franco Giacobini *(Alberghetti)*, Fabrizio Capucci, Margherita Girelli, Oliviero Prunas, Diletta D'Andrea, Stelvio Rosi, Lylia Neyung *(Francesca's friends)*, Luciano Salce.

Comedy-drama. Source: Enrico Stella, "Una ragazza di nome Francesca" (publication undetermined). While driving to visit his child at a boarding school in Pisa, Antonio Berlinghieri, a successful 39-year-old electrical engineer, is nearly forced off the road by two cars driven by reckless teenagers. Later, he comes across the two cars, which have run out of gas, and he is waved to a stop by Francesca, a 16-year-old. Francesca flirts with Antonio while the other teenagers siphon out his gas. The teenagers drive away, and shortly thereafter Antonio runs out of gas and has to push his car to a service station. He sees the same group coming out of the station's bar. One of the boys cons Antonio into paying the bill and driving him to the beach cottage where the group is vacationing. Antonio becomes infatuated with Francesca, who encourages his attentions simply to amuse her friends. Meanwhile, he becomes involved in a number of foolish and embarrassing situations in his attempt to prove himself the equal of the younger men in the group. Finally, he fights with Francesca's boyfriend. He receives a sound beating but wins the fight with a lucky blow; and the group declares him their new leader. After a torchlight celebration on the beach, Antonio and Francesca fall asleep in each other's arms. The following morning, however, Antonio awakens alone, surrounded by extinguished torches. Antonio's illusion of recaptured youth disappears with the teenagers. *Engineers. Adolescence. Middle age. Youth. Vacations. Sexuality. Beaches. Gasoline. Automobiles.*

Note: Opened in Rome in Mar 1962 as *La voglia matta;* running times: 100, 105, and 120 min.

CRAZY PARADISE (Denmark) F6.0950

Palladium. *Dist* Sherpix, Inc. 30 Jun **1965** [Kansas City, Missouri, opening]. Sd; col (Eastman Color). 35mm. 95 min.

Pres by Louis K. Sher, Gloria Sher. *Exec Prod* John Hilbard. *Dir* Gabriel Axel. *Screenplay* Bob Ramsing. *Photog* Henning Bendtsen. *Art Dir* Kai Rasch. *Dsgn* Willy Berg Hansen. *Film Ed* Lars Brydesen. *Mus Comp & Cond* Ib

Glindemann. *Sd* Kai Gram Larsen, Knud Kristensen. *Asst Dir* Morten Schyberg, Jens Ravn. *Prod Mgr* Erik Overbye. *Cost* Edith Sørensen, Bente Riber. *Makeup* Bodil Rasmussen.

Cast: Dirch Passer *(Angelus Goat)*, Hans W. Petersen *(Thor Goat)*, Ove Sprogøe *(Simon)*, Ghita Nørby *(Edith Paste)*, Paul Hagen *(Vicar Paul Paste)*, Bodil Steen *(Foreign Minister Bertha Virginius)*, Karl Stegger *(Per Mortensen)*, Lone Hertz *(Greta)*, Lily Broberg *(Anne)*, Judy Gringer *(Ursula)*, Kjeld Petersen *(Ove Bierman, reporter)*, Kai Holm *(prime minister)*, Jørgen Ryg *(Von Adel, his secretary)*, Axel Strøbye *(Hjalmar, the blacksmith)*, Gunnar Lemvigh *(Trommesen)*, Poul Müller *(Thomas Asmussen, editor)*, Valsø Holm *(Janus)*, Keld Markuslund *(Casper Cash, grocer)*, Arthur Jensen *(Tripledick)*, Hugo Herrestrup *(Frederik)*, Gunnar Strømvad *(Laurids)*, Helge Scheuer *(Jens)*, Lotte Tarp *(Karen)*, Erik Paaske *(Borge)*, Elsebeth Larsen *(Betsy Buttock)*, Henning Moritzen *(narrator)*, Jørgen Beck.

Comedy. Source: Ole Juul, *Det tossede paradis* (Copenhagen, 1953). Aphrodisiac eggs produced by hens on a tiny Danish island, Trang, have made aging Thor Goat exceedingly virile, with an ability to drive the local women to sexual frenzy. Meanwhile, Thor's son Angelus, founder of the "Blessed Be Our Bliss" political party, wins the election as chairman of the parish council on a platform of separatism from Denmark, but the Danish government, upon hearing that Trang has declared itself an independent republic, sends a warship carrying Foreign Minister Bertha Virginius to investigate. Angelus' defeated opponent, Per Mortensen, attempts to sabotage the island state, but Thor Goat, helped by the power of the eggs, sexually arouses the foreign minister and returns with her to the mainland. Angelus, finally partaking of the eggs for the first time, inherits his father's calling and quickly arouses the ladies of Trang. *Politicians. Sexuality. Filial relations. Diplomacy. Aphrodisiacs. Eggs. Elections. Islands. Imaginary republics. Chickens.*

Note: Copenhagen opening: Jul 1962 as *Det tossede paradis;* running time: 104 min.

CRAZY QUILT F6.0951

Farallon Productions. *Dist* Continental Distributing, Inc. 3 Oct **1966** [New York opening]. Sd; b&w. 35mm. 75 min.

Prod-Dir-Writ John Korty. *Photog* John Korty. *Film Ed* John Korty. *Assoc Ed* David Schickele. *Mus* Peter Schickele. *Asst Dir* David Schickele. *Cost* Celine Harbeck. *Makeup* Barbara Hiken.

Cast: Tom Rosqui *(Henry)*, Ina Mela *(Lorabelle)*, David Winters *(Baby)*, S. Maloch Gospe *(doctor)*, George William Meyers *(minister)*, Harry Hunt *(Cyrus)*, Calvin Kentfield *(Jim)*, Robert Marquis *(Dr. Milton Tugwell)*, Pavel Wald *(big-game hunter)*, Jerry Mander *(voice teacher)*, Sonia Berman *(fortune-teller)*, Ellen Frye *(Noel)*, Vicki Miller *(Noel, as a child)*, Doug Korty *(Falback Wheeling)*, Burgess Meredith *(narrator)*.

Comedy-drama. Source: Allen Wheelis, "The Illusionless Man and the Visionary Maid," in *Commentary* (May 1964). In San Francisco, Henry, an iconoclastic exterminator, marries Lorabelle, a frivolous romantic. After Lorabelle suffers a miscarriage, for which she blames Henry, she embarks on numerous affairs, including disappointing liaisons with an actor, a fisherman, an Italian voice instructor, and an elderly liar. Indifferent to her comings and goings, Henry combats his ennui by drinking and sleeping. Eventually, Lorabelle settles down and conceives a daughter. During adolescence, the daughter elopes with a motorcyclist, leaving Henry and Lorabelle to their own limited resources. *Exterminators. Idealists. Motorcyclists. Vocal instructors. Actors. Italians. Fishermen. Miscarriage. Marriage. Alcoholism. Infidelity. Disillusionment. Filial relations. San Francisco.*

CRAZY WILD AND CRAZY F6.0952

Barry Mahon Productions. **1965** [intended release; Los Angeles showing: 4 Mar 1966]. Sd; col. 35mm. 63 min.

A Barry Mahon Production. *Prod-Dir* Barry Mahon. *Camera* Barry Mahon. *Ed* Chuck Smith. *Asst Dir* Byron Mabe. *Opticals* Eastern Effects.

Cast: Tony Bogart *(Bob Meyer)*.

Comedy. Bob Meyer buys himself some movie equipment, hires 20 models, and enthusiastically sets out to make nude movies. When his first film is completed, he is startled at the results. He has produced a wild comedy: a volleyball game is ridiculously speeded up, while swimming and diving scenes have been caught in slow motion. Four images of the same woman suddenly appear together, and then seem to turn upside-down. *Motion picture cameramen. Models. Nudity. Sex exploitation films.*

CRAZY WORLD *see* **MONDO PAZZO**

THE CRAZY WORLD OF LAUREL AND HARDY F6.0953

Jay Ward Productions. *Dist* Joseph Brenner Associates. 21 Dec **1967** [New York opening; c1 Jun 1965; LP37887]. Sd; b&w. 35mm. 83 min.

A Hal E. Roach, Sr.-Jay Ward Production. *Prod* Hal E. Roach, Sr. *Exec Prod* Jay Ward, Bill Scott. *Assoc Prod* Raymond Rohauer. *Scenario* Bill Scott. *Film Ed* Skip Craig, Roger Donley. *Mus* Jerry Fielding.

Cast: Stan Laurel (*The Skinny One*), Oliver Hardy (*The Fat One*), Garry Moore (*Narrator*).

Compilation film. This film traces the team of Laurel and Hardy from 1929 to 1938. Shown are excerpts from 21 of their films: *Bacon Grabbers* (1929); *The Hoosegow* (1929); *The Perfect Day* (1929); *Blotto* (1930); *Hog Wild* (1930); *Come Clean* (1931); *Chickens Come Home* (1931); *Helpmates* (1931); *Beau Hunks* (1930); *The Music Box* (1932); *Any Old Port* (1932); *Towed in a Hole* (1933); *Dirty Work* (1933); *Me and My Pal* (1933); *Busy Bodies* (1933); *Sons of the Desert* (1933); *Going Bye-Bye* (1934); *The Bohemian Girl* (1936); *Way Out West* (1937); *Swiss Miss* (1938); and *Blockheads* (1938). *Motion pictures—History. Stan Laurel. Oliver Hardy.*

THE CREATION OF THE HUMANOIDS   F6.0954
Genie Productions. *Dist* Emerson Film Enterprises. 3 Jul **1962** [Los Angeles opening]. Sd; col (Eastman Color). 35mm. 75 min.

Prod Edward J. Kay, Wesley E. Barry. *Dir* Wesley E. Barry. *Screenplay & Story* Jay Simms. *Photog* Hal Mohr. *Art Dir* Ted Rich. *Film Ed* Leonard W. Herman. *Makeup* Jack P. Pierce.

Cast: Don Megowan, Erica Elliot, David Cross, Frances McCann, Don Doolittle, George Milan, Reid Hamilton, Richard Vath, Malcolm Smith, Dudley Manlove.

Science fiction melodrama. Following an atomic explosion in the 23d century, 92 percent of the human race is destroyed. The survivors, their birth rate below 1.4 per couple, make use of purplish-green robots with electronic brains. Intellectually infallible, physically perfect, and possessing absolute emotional stability, these "humanoids" help the flesh-and-blood people to rebuild their cities and maintain a high standard of living. A mad scientist, by giving blood transfusions to the creatures, is making them more human. The hero (Don Megowan) learns that his girl friend has fallen in love with a humanoid, and a crisis ensues. *Robots. Scientists. Nuclear warfare. Human race. Survival. Blood transfusion. The Future.*

THE CREATURE CALLED MAN (Japan)   F6.0955
Toho Co. 7 Oct **1970** [Los Angeles opening]. Sd; col (Eastmancolor). 35mm (Panavision). 93 min.

Exec Prod Yorihiko Yamada. *Dir* Kiyoshi Nishimura. *Screenplay* Hiroshi Nagano, Yoshihiro Ishimatsu. *Photog* Kazutami Hara. *Art Dir* Shinobu Muraki. *Mus* Mitsuhiko Sato.

Cast: Yuzo Kayama (*Toda*), Jiro Tamiya (*Kujo*), Mariko Kaga (*Toda's assistant*), Nancy Sommers (*Kujo's girl friend*), Nobuo Nakamura (*head of N-Bussan*), Shigeru Koyama.

Melodrama. President Jakar of Southnesia flees to Japan after his government is overthrown in a revolution. Although N-Bussan, a corporation supplying arms to the Jakar regime, has aided his flight, the company also has an agreement to do business with the revolutionary government if the company can eliminate Jakar. N-Bussan hires Kujo, a professional killer, before the revolutionary government can send its own assassins. The Japanese government assigns Toda, a top police inspector and an Olympic sharpshooter, to protect Jakar. Toda wards off many attempts on Jakar's life, and during a demonstration against the deposed president's presence in Japan he accidentally kills Kujo's American girl friend. Kujo kills Toda's assistant, and Toda and Kujo then engage in a duel to settle their personal and political differences. *Presidents. Hired killers. Americans in foreign countries. Detectives. Bodyguards. Sharpshooters. Assassination. Duplicity. Revolutions. Demonstrations. Duels. Imaginary republics.*

Note: Released in Japan in Apr 1970 as *Jaga wa hashitta*.

CREATURE FROM THE HAUNTED SEA   F6.0956
Filmgroup, Inc. Jun **1961**. Sd; b&w. 35mm. 60 min.

A Roger Corman Production. *Prod-Dir* Roger Corman. *Dir Pre-Titl Seq* Monte Hellman. *Screenplay* Charles Griffith. *Photog* Jacques Marquette. *Film Ed* Angela Scellars. *Mus* Fred Katz. *Asst Dir* Jack Bohrer. *Location Mgr* Kinta Zertuche.

Cast: Antony Carbone (*Renzo Capeto*), Betsy Jones-Moreland (*Mary-Belle*), Edward Wain (*Sparks Moran*), Edmundo Rivera Alvarez (*Colonel Tostada*), Robert Bean (*Jack*), Sonya Noemi (*Mango*), Beach Dickerson, Roger Corman.

Horror film. During a revolution on a small Caribbean island, international playboy and promoter Renzo Capeto uses his boat to help a group of loyalists headed by Colonel Tostada escape with the national treasury which they plan to use to stage a counterrevolution. Capeto plans to seize the money and claim that a mythological monster rose out of the sea and devoured the loyalists. Unknown to him, a real monster lurks in the very waters where he plans to kill his passengers. When the creature upsets his plans, Capeto decides to sink his boat in 30 feet of water and then retrieve the treasure. Using a nearby island for a base, he and his gang attempt to salvage the loot, but the monster picks them off one by one, except for secret service agent Sparks Moran and his girl

friend Mango. *Playboys. Sea captains. West Indians. Gangs. Theft. Murder. Revolutions. Treasure. Islands. Sea monsters. Caribbean. Government agents.*

Note: Filmed in Puerto Rico in 1959. Edward Wain is a pseudonym for Robert Towne.

CREATURE OF THE WALKING DEAD (Mexico)   F6.0957
Alameda Films. *Dist* A. D. P. Productions. 15 Jun **1965** [Maryland license]. Sd; b&w. 35mm. 74 min.

Pres by Jerry Warren. *Prod English Vers* Jerry Warren. *Dir* Fernando Cortés. *Screenplay* Alfredo Varela, Jr., Fernando Cortés. *Story* José María Fernández Unsáin. *Photog* José Ortiz Ramos. *Photog Adtl U. S. Seq* Richard Wallace. *Art Dir* Gunther Gerszo. *Prod Dsgn* Luis de León. *Film Ed* Alfredo Rosas Priego. *Mus* Gustavo César Carrión. *Sd* Rodolfo Solís. *Sp Eff* Nicolas Reye.

Cast—Orig Vers: Fernando Casanova, Sonia Furió, Edmundo Espino, Hortensia Santoveña, Pedro d'Aguillón, Aurora Alvarado, Rosa María Gallardo.

Cast—English Vers: Rock Madison, Ann Wells, Willard Gross, George Todd, Bruno Ve Sota, Katherine Victor.

Horror film. Discovering the laboratory of his dead grandfather, a scientist experiments in immortality. He revives the patriarch, who is eventually destroyed by the need for human blood. *Grandfathers. Scientists. Immortality. Reviviscence. Laboratories. Experiments.*

Note: Produced in Mexico in 1960 as *La marca del muerto*. First released in the United States in a Spanish version in Feb 1962. Additional footage added for English version.

LES CRÉATURES (France/Sweden)   F6.0958
Parc Film–Madeleine Films–Sandrews. *Dist* New Yorker Films. 9 Apr **1969** [Los Angeles opening]. Sd; col and b&w. 35mm (Franscope). 91 min. [Also 102 min.]

Prod Mag Bodard. *Dir-Writ* Agnès Varda. *Dir Photog* Willy Kurant. *Sets* Claude Pignot. *Film Ed* Janine Verneau. *Mus* Pierre Barbaud.

Cast: Catherine Deneuve (*Mylène*), Michel Piccoli (*Edgar*), Eva Dahlbeck (*Michèle Quellec*), Jacques Charrier (*René de Montyon*), Nino Castelnuovo (*Jean Modet*), Ursula Kubler (*vamp*), Britta Pettersson (*Lucie de Montyon*), Louis Falavigna (*Pierre Roland*), Marie-France Mignal (*Viviane Quellec*), Bernard Lajarrige (*doctor*), Pierre Danny (*Max Picot*), Alain Roy (*Père Quellec*), Lucien Bodard (*recluse*), Jeanne Allard, Roger Dax.

Drama. Edgar, a novelist, is scarred, and his pregnant wife, Mylène, is left mute as a result of an automobile accident caused by his speeding. They go to live on the Île de Noirmoutier, and here Edgar begins to write a novel in which the townspeople are depicted. An old recluse who lives in a tower is represented as manipulating the actions of the residents; he manufactures iron disks, which, when placed in the clothing of his subjects, allow him to stimulate their primitive instincts. Edgar, who expresses "confidence in humanity," goes to the tower and enters into a contest with the proprietor. They draw cards bearing the townspeople's likenesses and wrestle over their fates by throwing dice, manipulating them on a television chessboard. On the verge of losing the game, Edgar destroys the equipment. Soon afterwards, the old man dies, and the complications in the lives of the subjects are resolved by love. Edgar's novel nears completion, and Mylène, her muteness cured, has her baby. *Novelists. Mutes. Masterminds. Recluses. Pregnancy. Magic. Village life. Thought control. Contests. Chess. Television. Île de Noirmoutier. Automobile accidents.*

Note: Paris opening: Sep 1966; running time: 100 min; Malmö opening: Oct 1966 as *Varelserna*. Original running time: 105 min.

CREATURES OF THE PREHISTORIC PLANET *see* HORROR OF THE BLOOD MONSTERS

THE CREEPERS *see* ISLAND OF TERROR

THE CREEPING TERROR   F6.0959
Metropolitan International Pictures. *Dist* Teledyn. ca **1964**. Sd; b&w. 35mm. 75 min.

Prod Argyle Nelson, Jr. *Screenplay* Robert Silliphant, Alan Silliphant. *Photog* Irving Phillips. *Art Dir* John Lackey. *Film Ed* Argyle Nelson, Jr. *Sd* Larry Offerd. *Asst Dir* Randy Starr. *Prod Mgr* Robert Silliphant.

Cast: Vic Savage, Shannon O'Neil, William Thourlby.

Horror film. A spaceship carrying two creatures from outer space lands in a desert area of the western United States. Scientists and military officers approach the site with cameras, planning to transmit information about the invaders to closed-circuit television receivers. One of the monsters escapes from the craft and later emerges from Lake Tahoe; it then eats a series of victims, including a man and his grandson who are fishing, some teenagers having a party on the beach, a chorus girl at Harrah's Club, and patrons at a drive-in movie, before the Army finally blows it apart with a bazooka. One of the scientists rushes back to the spaceship and succeeds in killing the surviving monster with a flamethrower, but not before the victims have been analyzed and their knowledge transmitted by the monsters back to their planet. *Space creatures. Scientists. Spaceships. Television. Flamethrowers. Motion picture theaters—Drive-ins. Lake Tahoe. United States Army. Harrah's Club (Lake Tahoe).*

Note: Location scenes filmed at Lake Tahoe, Nevada. Also known as *The Crawling Monster.*

THE CREST OF MAN (Japan)　　　　　　　**F6.0960**
Nikkatsu Corp. *Dist* Toho Co. Oct **1965** [Los Angeles showing]. Sd; col? 35mm. [Feature film, length unknown.]

Cast: Sayuri Yoshinaga, Mitsuo Hamada, Seiji Miyaguchi, Tanie Kitabayashi.No information about the nature of this film has been found.

Note: Original title and release undetermined.

LE CRI DE LA CHAIR *see* **SIN ON THE BEACH**

CRIME AU CONCERT MAYOL *see* **PALACE OF NUDES**

LE CRIME DE MONSIEUR LANGE *see* **THE CRIME OF MONSIEUR LANGE**

CRIME DOES NOT PAY (France/Italy)　　　　**F6.0961**
Transworld Production-G. E. F.-Cosmos Film-Télédis Films. *Dist* Embassy Pictures. 16 Oct **1962** [New York opening]. Sd; b&w. 35mm (Dyaliscope). 159 min.

Overall Production Credits: *Pres by* Joseph E. Levine. A Gilbert Bokanowski Production. *Prod* Gilbert Bokanowski. *Dir* Gérard Oury. *Screenplay* Jean-Charles Tacchella, Paul Gordeaux, Gérard Oury. *Dir Photog* Christian Matras. *Scenery* Georges Wakhévitch. *Film Ed* Roger Dwyre, Raymond Lamy. *Mus* Georges Delerue. *Sd* Jean Monchablon. *Dir Prod* Adeline Crouset. *Cost* Georges Wakhévitch.

Production Credits for "The Mask": *Adapt-Dial* Jean Aurenche, Pierre Bost.

Production Credits for "The Hugues Case": *Adapt-Dial* Henri Jeanson, René Wheeler.

Production Credits for "The Fenayrou Case": *Dial* Jacques Sigurd. *Adapt* Pierre Boileau, Thomas Narcejac.

Production Credits for "The Man on the Avenue": *Adapt-Dial* Frédéric Dard.

Cast—"The Mask": Edwige Feuillère (*Dona Lucrezia*), Gabriele Ferzetti (*Giraldi*), Rosanna Schiaffino (*Francesca*), Laura Efrikian (*Antonella*), Gino Cervi, Rina Morelli, Serge Lifar.

Cast—"The Hugues Case": Michèle Morgan (*Jeanne Hugues*), Lucienne Bogaert (*Madame Lenormand*), Jean Servais (*Vaughan*), Renaud Mary (*Monsieur Lenormand*), Philippe Noiret (*Monsieur Hugues*), Marie Daems, Claude Cerval.

Cast—"The Fenayrou Case": Annie Girardot (*Gabrielle Fenayrou*), Pierre Brasseur (*Martin Fenayrou*), Christian Marquand (*Louis Aubert*), Paul Guers (*The Doctor*).

Cast—"The Man on the Avenue": Richard Todd (*Colonel Roberts*), Danielle Darrieux (*Madame Marsais*), Perrette Pradier (*Hélène*), Louis de Funès (*bartender*), Raymond Loyer (*Pierre Marsais*).

Cast—Unidentified roles: Frank Villard, Yves Brainville.

Melodrama. Source: Stendhal, *Chroniques italiennes* ("The Mask" seq based on; Paris, 1829). Paul Gordeaux, Cartoon Strip in "France-Soir". A young Parisian, Pierre Marsais, visits a Champs-Elysées movie house to see *Crime Does Not Pay*, a film based on three celebrated crimes. The first part, THE MASK, concerns a 15th-century Venetian duchess, Dona Lucrezia, who invites her unfaithful lover, the Chevalier Giraldi, to what will be his own funeral and then has him murdered. The duchess pays for her crime when her maid, who secretly loved Giraldi, coats the beauty mask she wears at night with acid. In the second episode, THE HUGHES CASE, Clovis Hugues, a radical member of parliament, becomes involved in a scandal when his wife, Jeanne, is unjustly accused of being the mistress of Monsieur Lenormand. In reality, Madame Lenormand had hired a detective, Morin, to find proof of her husband's infidelity so that she can obtain a divorce, and Morin had invented the evidence. Jeanne sues Morin for libel, but Morin wins an acquittal by bribing the jury. Jeanne then takes the law into her own hands and shoots the detective. At her own trial for murder, she is vindicated by the courts. The third segment, THE FENAYROU CASE, takes place in 1913 and concerns Gabrielle Fenayrou, an adulteress who maneuvers her aged husband into killing Aubert, a lover who plans to marry another woman. She then betrays her husband to the police so that she can enter into a new affair with her young doctor. The two toast their love from a bottle of poisoned wine the husband had prepared for Aubert. In the final episode, THE MAN ON THE AVENUE, Marsais leaves the theater at the end of the film and is fatally injured in an automobile accident. The driver of the car, an American colonel, calls on Marsais' widow, an

alcoholic. A subsequent investigation reveals that Marsais, aided by his mistress Hélène, had been plotting to kill his wife. *Chambermaids. Physicians. Mistresses. Nobility. Soldiers. Detectives. Politicians. Murder. Scandal. Infidelity. Alcoholism. Bribery. Automobile accidents. Marriage. Revenge. Trials. Conspiracy. Poisoning. Perjury. Motion pictures. Funerals. Paris. Venice.*

Note: Opened in Paris in Jul 1962 as *Le crime ne paie pas.* "The Hugues Case" was also known as "The Spider's Web." A two-part version of the film known as *The Gentle Art of Murder,* running 79 min and containing "The Fenayrou Case" and "The Man on the Avenue" was released in 1963. Italian title: *Il delitto non paga.*

LE CRIME NE PAIE PAS *see* **CRIME DOES NOT PAY**

THE CRIME OF MONSIEUR LANGE (France)　　**F6.0962**
Obéron. *Dist* Brandon Films. 3 Apr **1964** [New York opening]. Sd; b&w. 35mm. 90 min.

Dir Jean Renoir. *Scen* Jean Castanier, Jean Renoir, Jacques Prévert. *Dial* Jacques Prévert. *Story* Jean Castanier. *Photog* Jean Bachelet. *Set Dsgn* Jean Castanier, Robert Gys. *Asst Set Dsgn* Roger Blin. *Film Ed* Marguerite Renoir. *Mus* Jean Wiener. *Song* Joseph Kosma. *Sung by* Florelle. *Sd* Moreau, L. Bogé, Robert Teisseire. *Asst Dir* Pierre Prévert, Georges Darnoux. *Prod Supv* André Halley des Fontaines. *Still Photog* Dora Maar.

Cast: René Lefèvre (*Monsieur Amédée Lange*), Florelle (*Valentine*), Henri Guisol (*Meunier*), Marcel Levesque (*Bessard, the concierge*), Odette Talazac (*Madame Bessard*), Maurice Baquet (*Charles*), Nadia Sibirskaia (*Estelle*), Jules Berry (*Batala*), Sylvia Bataille (*Edith*), Marcel Duhamel, Guy Decomble, Jean Dasté, Paul Grimault (*printers*), Jacques Brunius (*Baigneur*), Sylvain Itkine (*retired police inspector*), Edmond Beauchamp (*priest on the train*), René Génin (*customer in café*), Paul Demange (*creditor*), Claire Gérard (*prostitute*), Henri Saint-Isles, Max Morise, Fabien Loris, Yves Deniaud, Pierre Huchet, Marcel Lupovici, Jean Brémaud, Janine Loris, Charbonnier.

Comedy-drama. Amédée Lange, an aspiring novelist, works in a Parisian publishing house that specializes in pulp novels. Batala, Lange's cruel and exploitative boss, signs him to a contract for his "Arizona Jim" series of novels and cheats Lange out of his money. Batala then steals the company's funds, flees the city to escape his creditors, and is later reported dead in a train wreck. Lange, the rest of the employees, and the chief creditor form a cooperative business and achieve great success with Lange's western novels. Happy now, the workers in the publishing house fall in love with those in the neighboring laundry, among them Lange and Valentine and Estelle and the concierge's son. Just as everything is going well, Batala comes back disguised as a priest; he had survived the train wreck and exchanged clothes with one of the victims, a priest. He wants to hold Lange to the old contracts and take advantage of the firm's new wealth. Lange realizes the only way to stop such an evil man is to kill him. This done, he and Valentine escape to the frontier, where in a cafe he tells his story to some workers who recognize them. The workers are happy to help them escape. *Novelists. Publishers. Launderers. Swindlers. Priests. Murder. Employer-employee relations. Bankruptcy. Disguise. Contracts. Cooperatives. Paris. Train wrecks.*

Note: Location scenes filmed in Paris and Tréport. Opened in Paris in Jan 1936 as *Le crime de Monsieur Lange;* running time: 84 min. Also known in France as *Le crime de M. Lange.* Working title: *Sur la cour.*

CRIMEN *see* **... AND SUDDENLY IT'S MURDER!**

CRIMES IN THE WAX MUSEUM *see* **NIGHTMARE IN WAX**

THE CRIMINAL *see* **THE CONCRETE JUNGLE**

THE CRIMINAL LIFE OF ARCHIBALDO DE LA CRUZ (Mexico)
　　　　　　　　　　　　　　　　　　　　　　　F6.0963
Alianza Cinematográfica. *Dist* Dan Talbot. 27 Nov **1962** [New York opening]. Sd; b&w. 35mm. 91 min.

Prod Alfonso Patiño Gomez. *Assoc Prod* Roberto Figueroa. *Dir* Luis Buñuel. *Screenplay* Luis Buñuel, Eduardo Ugarte Pages. *Photog* Agustín Jiménez. *Art Dir* Jesús Bracho. *Film Ed* Jorge Bustos. *Mus* Jorge Pérez. *Sd Rec* Ernesto Caballero. *Sd (see note)* Rodolfo Benitez.

Cast: Ernesto Alonso (*Archibaldo de la Cruz*), Miroslava (*Lavinia*), Rita Macedo (*Patricia*), Ariadne Welter, Rodolfo Landa, Andrea Palma, Carlos Riquelme, José María Linares Rivas, Leonor Llausás, Eva Calvo, Carlos Martínez Baena, Roberto Meyer.

Comedy-drama. Based on an unidentified work by: Rodolfo Usigli. Archibaldo de la Cruz, the spoiled child of wealthy parents, curses his governess with a music box which he believes has the power to will death. The woman is killed by a stray bullet, and her disarrayed skirt exposes to Archibaldo's view her beautiful, shapely legs. As a result of this erotic image, Archibaldo grows into manhood associating desire with murder, and he fabricates elaborate plans for killing women. However, his attempts are all thwarted as his intended victims die of natural causes, accidents, or at the hands of others. While recovering from a nervous breakdown, Archibaldo threatens to murder his nurse, but before he can act, she falls down an elevator shaft. Archibaldo later makes plans to murder an unfaithful lover, but another man robs him of the satisfaction. One of his "victims," a model for store dummies, evades death completely, whereupon Archibaldo burns her wax image in an oven. Mentally distraught, he confesses his "crimes" to the police, but unconcerned with psychic guilt, they pay him no heed. In a gesture of liberation, he throws the music box into a pond just as the model whose effigy he burned passes by; apparently cured of his childish obsession, Archibaldo smiles at her, and the two walk away together hand in hand. *Governesses. Models. Police. Nurses. Death. Eroticism. Murder. Obsession. Guilt. Childhood. Magic. Necrophilia. Wealth. Music boxes. Elevators. Dummies. Waxworks.*

Note: Produced in Mexico in 1955 as *Ensayo de un crimen*. A Mexican source gives Rodolfo Benitez sound credit, while other sources credit Ernesto Caballero as sound recordist.

I CRIMINALI DELLA GALASSIA see **THE WILD, WILD PLANET**

THE CRIMSON ALTAR see **THE CRIMSON CULT**

THE CRIMSON BLADE (Great Britain)   **F6.0964**
Hammer Film Productions. *Dist* Columbia Pictures. May **1964** [c1 Mar 1964; LP28064]. Sd (RCA); col (Eastman Color by Pathé). 35mm (Megascope). 83 min.

Prod Anthony Nelson Keys. *Dir & Orig Screenplay* John Gilling. *Dir Photog* Jack Asher. *Camera Op* Cece Cooney. *Art Dir* Don Mingaye. *Asst Art Dir* Ken Ryan. *Prod Dsgn* Bernard Robinson. *Film Ed* John Dunsford. *Supv Ed* James Needs. *Mus Comp* Gary Hughes. *Mus Supv* John Hollingsworth. *Sd* James Groom. *Sd Rec* Ken Rawkins. *Boom Op* Peter Pardo. *Sd Camera Op* Al Thorne. *Sd Transfer Op* Michael Sale. *1st, 2d & 3d Asst Dir* Doug Hermes, Hugh Harlow, Stephen Victor. *Prod Mgr* Clifford Parkes. *Cont* Pauline Wise. *Prod Sec* Barbara Allen. *Wardrobe Supv* Molly Arbuthnot. *Wardrobe Mistress* Rosemary Burrows. *Makeup Artist* Roy Ashton. *Hairstyles* Frieda Steiger. *Sp Eff* Les Bowie. *Still Photog* Tom Edwards. *Camera Grip* Albert Cowland. *Studio Mgr* A. F. Kelly. *Constr Mgr* Arthur Banks. *Ch Electrn* Jack Curtis, electrn. *Prop Buyer* Eric Hillier. *Prop Master* Tommy Money.

Cast: Lionel Jeffries *(Colonel Judd)*, Oliver Reed *(Sylvester)*, Jack Hedley *(Edward Beverley)*, June Thorburn *(Clare Judd)*, Duncan Lamont *(Major Bell)*, Suzan Farmer *(Constance)*, Michael Ripper *(Pablo)*, Charles Houston *(Drury)*, Harold Goldblatt *(Jacob)*, Clifford Elkin *(Philip)*, Michael Byrne *(Lieutenant Hawke)*, John Harvey *(Sergeant Grey)*, John Stuart *(Beverley)*, Harry Towb *(Cobb)*, Robert Rietty *(King Charles I)*, John Watson *(Fitzroy)*, Douglas Blackwell *(Blake)*, Leslie Glazer *(Gonzales)*, John Woodnutt *(Lieutenant Wyatt)*, Eric Corrie *(Duncannon)*, Denis Holmes *(chaplain)*.

Historical melodrama. In 17th century England, King Charles I and his Royalist followers go into hiding after Charles' defeat at Naseby. Colonel Judd, a ruthless Cromwell disciple, ferrets out the Royalists and takes over the castle of one of his victims; but he is unaware that his daughter, Clare, who joins him at the castle, is a Royalist, and that Sylvester, his aide, loves Clare and has also joined the Royalists. Sylvester learns that Clare and Edward Beverley, the Royalist leader known as "The Scarlet Blade," are in love, and he threatens to betray them. Edward is captured. Judd, learning of Sylvester's Royalist activities, arrests him, but Sylvester counters by revealing Clare's Royalist involvement. Judd kills Sylvester, and Clare and Edward escape together and hide at a gypsy camp. Judd locates them but feigns ignorance of their hiding place and, rather than expose them, orders his troops to depart. *Soldiers. Roundheads. Jealousy. Fatherhood. Courtship. Great Britain—History—Civil War and Commonwealth. Charles I (England). Oliver Cromwell.*

Note: Released in Great Britain in Aug 1963 as *The Scarlet Blade* running time: 82 min.

THE CRIMSON CULT (Great Britain)   **F6.0965**
Tigon British Film Productions–American International Pictures. *Dist* American International Pictures. 15 Apr **1970** [Los Angeles opening]. Sd; col (Movielab). 35mm. 87 min. *MPAA rating* GP.

A Tony Tenser Production. *Prod* Louis M. Heyward. *Exec Prod* Tony Tenser. *Assoc Prod* Gerry Levy. *Dir* Vernon Sewell. *Screenplay* Mervyn Haisman, Henry Lincoln. *Adtl Material* Gerry Levy. *Photog* John Coquillon. *Art Dir* Derek Barrington. *Film Ed* Howard Lanning. *Mus* Peter Knight. *Asst Dir* Dennis Lewis. *Prod Mgr* Alex Carver-Hill. *Cost* Michael Southgate. *Makeup* Pauline Worden, Betty Blattner.

Cast: Boris Karloff *(Professor Marsh)*, Christopher Lee *(J. D. Morley)*, Mark Eden *(Robert Manning)*, Virginia Wetherell *(Eve)*, Barbara Steele *(Lavinia Morley)*, Rupert Davies *(vicar)*, Michael Gough *(Elder, the butler)*, Rosemarie Reede *(Esther)*, Derek Tansley *(judge)*, Michael Warren *(chauffeur)*, Ron Pember *(gas station attendant)*, Denys Peek *(Peter Manning/blacksmith)*, Nita Lorraine *(woman with whip)*, Carol Anne, Jenny Shaw *(virgins)*, Vivienne

Carlton *(sacrifice victim)*, Roger Avon *(Sergeant Tyson)*, Paul McNeil *(party guest)*, Christine Pryor, Kerry Dean, Stephanie Marrion, Rosalind Royale *(party girls)*, Millicent Scott *(stripper at party)*, Vicky Richards *(belly dancer at party)*, Tasma Bereton *(painted girl at party)*, Kevin Smith *(drunk at party)*, Lita Scott *(girl with cockerel)*, Terry Raven, Douglas Mitchell *(drivers in car chase)*, Nova St. Claire *(girl in car chase)*.

Horror film. Suggested by: H. P. Lovecraft, "The Dreams in the Witch-House," in *The Mountains of Madness and Other Novels* (Sauk City, Wisconsin, 1964). Robert Manning, an antique dealer, travels to Greymarsh Lodge in search of his brother who failed to return from a buying trip. Morley, the owner of the lodge, tells Robert that his brother never stayed there, but Robert is suspicious since he received a letter from the lodge only 10 days ago. His first night at Greymarsh is Witch's Night, a local holiday which commemorates the burning of Lavinia, a witch who once inhabited the lodge. Robert is warned by Elder, the butler, to stay away, but Robert is intrigued by Morley's niece Eve and decides to stay. On two successive nights Robert is summoned in his dreams by his brother who takes him to Lavinia's chamber; Lavinia tries to force him to sign a confession, and on the second night, he awakens with a knife wound in his arm. The next day, Professor Marsh, an expert on the occult, informs Robert that he is a descendant of the principal accuser at Lavinia's trial and that she swore revenge on the Manning bloodline. Robert and Eve set out to locate the witch's chamber and find the body of the butler in a secret passageway. Morley, who believes that he is a warlock with the task of avenging his dead ancestor, traps them in the chamber and is about to kill them when Professor Marsh and the police arrive. Before Morley can be apprehended, he sets fire to Greymarsh and dies in the flames. *Antique dealers. Brothers. Innkeepers. Butlers. Witches. Professors. Sorcerers. Missing persons. Occult. Revenge. Ancestry. Suicide. Lodges (inns). Dreams. Fires.*

Note: Released in Great Britain in Dec 1968 as *Curse of the Crimson Altar*; running time: 89 min. Also known as *The Crimson Altar*.

THE CRIMSON EXECUTIONER see **BLOODY PIT OF HORROR**

CRISS CROSS see **P. J.**

CRITIC'S CHOICE   **F6.0966**
Warner Bros. Pictures. 3 Apr **1963** [San Francisco opening; c13 Apr 1963; LP29443]. Sd; col (Technicolor). 35mm (Panavision). 100 min.

Prod Frank P. Rosenberg. *Dir* Don Weis. *Screenplay* Jack Sher. *Dir Photog* Charles Lang. *Art Dir* Edward Carrere. *Set Decor* William L. Kuehl. *Main Titl* Pacific Title. *Film Ed* William Ziegler. *Mus* George Duning. *Orch* Arthur Morton. *Sd* Stanley Jones. *Asst Dir* Russell Llewellyn. *Cost* Edith Head. *Makeup* Gordon Bau. *Miss Ball's Hairstyles* Irma Kusley. *Hairstyles* Jean Burt Reilly.

Cast: Bob Hope *(Parker Ballantine)*, Lucille Ball *(Angela Ballantine)*, Marilyn Maxwell *(Ivy London)*, Rip Torn *(Dion Kapakos)*, Jessie Royce Landis *(Charlotte Orr)*, John Dehner *(S. P. Champlain)*, Jim Backus *(Dr. William von Hagedorn)*, Rick Kelman *(John Ballantine)*, Dorothy Green *(Mrs. Champlain)*, Marie Windsor *(Sally Orr)*, Evan McCord *(Phil Yardley)*, Richard Deacon *(Harvey Rittenhouse)*, Joan Shawlee *(Marge Orr)*, Jerome Cowan *(Joe Rosenfield)*, Donald Losby *(Godfrey von Hagedorn)*, Lurene Tuttle *(mother)*, Ernestine Wade *(Thelma)*, Stanley Adams *(bartender)*.

Comedy. Source: Ira Levin, *Critic's Choice* (New York opening: 14 Dec 1960). Broadway drama critic Parker Ballantine is horrified when his wife, Angela, announces that she wants to write a play about her mother and her four zany sisters. Although Parker calls the completed script a disaster, Angela manages to find both a producer and director. While the play is in Boston for tryouts, the nervous Angela begs Parker to disqualify himself as a critic. After quarreling with Angela over director Dion's attentions to her, Parker gets drunk with his ex-wife Ivy, and staggers into the theater. The reviews are all unfavorable, and Parker's is the most vitriolic. The wounded Angela threatens to leave with Dion, but Parker affects a reconciliation by apologizing for his behavior—but not his review—and persuading his wife that he still loves her. *Critics. Playwrights. Theatrical producers. Theatrical directors. Marriage. Jealousy. Drunkenness. Theater. New York City—Broadway. Boston.*

LA CROIX DES VIVANTS see **CROSS OF THE LIVING**

IL CROLLO DI ROMA see **THE FALL OF ROME**

CROMWELL (Great Britain)   **F6.0967**
Irving Allen Ltd. *Dist* Columbia Pictures. 26 Oct **1970** [New York opening; c16 Jul 1970; LF64]. Sd; col (Technicolor). 35mm (Panavision). 139 min. *MPAA rating* G.

Prod Irving Allen. *Assoc Prod* Andrew Donally. *Dir-Writ* Ken Hughes. *2d Unit Dir* Harold F. Kress. *Photog* Geoffrey Unsworth. *2d Unit Photog* Wilkie Cooper. *Camera Op* Peter MacDonald. *Art Dir* Herbert Westbrook. *Asst Art Dir* Bill Bennison. *Set Dresser* Arthur Taksen. *Prod Dsgn* John Stoll. *Film Ed* Bill Lenny. *Mus Comp & Cond* Frank Cordell. *Sd Ed* Alfred Cox. *Sd Rec* Leslie

Hammond, Bob Jones. *Asst Dir* Ted Sturgis. *Prod Supv* Frank Bevis. *Cont* Margaret Unsworth. *Cost Dsgn* Vittorio Nino Novarese. *Wardrobe Supv* John Wilson-Apperson. *Makeup* Neville Smallwood. *Hairdressing* Bobbie Smith. *Sp Eff* Bill Warrington. *Script Cons* Ronald Harwood. *Coöp* Spanish Army. *Stunt Supv* Gerry Crampton. *Spanish Army Liaison* Antonio Sanz Ridruejo. *Casting* Maude Spector.

Cast: Richard Harris *(Oliver Cromwell)*, Alec Guinness *(King Charles I)*, Robert Morley *(Earl of Manchester)*, Dorothy Tutin *(Queen Henrietta Maria)*, Frank Finlay *(John Carter)*, Timothy Dalton *(Prince Rupert)*, Patrick Wymark *(Earl of Strafford)*, Patrick Magee *(Hugh Peters)*, Nigel Stock *(Sir Edward Hyde)*, Charles Gray *(Lord Essex)*, Michael Jayston *(Henry Ireton)*, Richard Cornish *(Oliver Cromwell II)*, Anna Cropper *(Ruth Carter)*, Michael Goodliffe *(solicitor general)*, Jack Gwillim *(General Byron)*, Basil Henson *(Hacker)*, Patrick Holt *(Captain Lundsford)*, Stratford Johns *(President Bradshaw)*, Geoffrey Keen *(John Pym)*, Anthony May *(Richard Cromwell)*, Ian McCulloch *(John Hampden)*, Patrick O'Connell *(John Lilburne)*, John Paul *(General Digby)*, Llewellyn Rees *(The Speaker)*, Robin Stewart *(Prince of Wales)*, Andre Van Gyseghem *(Archbishop Rinuccini)*, Zena Walker *(Mrs. Cromwell)*, John Welsh *(Bishop Juxon)*, Douglas Wilmer *(Thomas Fairfax)*, Anthony Kemp *(Henry Cromwell)*, Stacy Dorning *(Mary Cromwell)*, Melinda Churcher *(Bridget Cromwell)*, George Merritt *(old man/William)*, Gerald Rowland *(drummer boy)*, Josephine Gillick *(Elizabeth)*, Bryan Pringle *(Trooper Hawkins)*.

Historical drama. In 1640 England, Oliver Cromwell, a Puritan member of Parliament, is disturbed by the growing injustices of King Charles's reign and fears that Queen Henrietta Maria, a French Catholic, is influencing her husband to modify the rituals of the Church of England. At first Cromwell decides to take his family to Scotland, but later he is convinced to remain and aid his Puritan friends, the Roundheads, against the Cavaliers, the royalist allies in Parliament. Encouraged by the strong influence of his Catholic queen and the loyal Earl of Strafford, as well as by his own belief in the divine right of the monarchy, Charles demands that Parliament finance a war on Scotland; when Parliament refuses the order, Charles sends troops into the house to regain control, and Cromwell and others accuse him of treason. A civil war develops between the forces of Parliament and the king's troops. After his Puritan forces suffer a resounding defeat at Edgehill, Cromwell takes it upon himself to train the troops, and they subsequently defeat the king's men at Naseby. The queen and the Prince of Wales flee, but King Charles is caught and brought to trial before Parliament; in 1649, Charles is found guilty and beheaded. After a brief and ineffective rule by Parliament, Cromwell returns to London, dissolves Parliament, and has himself appointed Lord Protector, a position which gives him almost dictatorial control over England. *Puritans. Catholics. Roundheads. Cavaliers. Soldiers. Religious persecution. Treason. Capital punishment. Great Britain—History—Stuarts. Great Britain—History—Civil War and Commonwealth. Edgehill (England). Naseby. London. Oliver Cromwell. Charles I (England). Henrietta Maria. Thomas Wentforth, (Earl of Strafford). Henry Montagu, (Earl of Manchester). Great Britain—Parliament. Church of England.*

Note: Location scenes filmed in Spain. Opened in London in Jul 1970.

CRONACA DI ANNA MAGDALENA BACH *see* **CHRONICLE OF ANNA MAGDALENA BACH**

CRONACA FAMILIARE *see* **FAMILY DIARY**

CRONACHE DI UN CONVENTO *see* **THE RELUCTANT SAINT**

THE CROOKED ROAD (Great Britain/Yugoslavia)　　　**F6.0968**
Argo Film Productions-Triglav Film-Trident Films. *Dist* Seven Arts Pictures. 3 Feb **1965** [New York opening]. Sd; b&w. 35mm. 90 min.

Prod David Henley. *Exec Prod* Jack O. Lamont. *Dir* Don Chaffey. *Screenplay* Jay Garrison, Don Chaffey. *Photog* Stephen Dade. *Film Ed* Peter Tanner. *Mus* Bojan Adamič.

Cast: Robert Ryan *(Richard Ashley)*, Stewart Granger *(Duke of Orgagna)*, Nadia Gray *(Cosima)*, Marius Goring *(Harlequin)*, George Coulouris *(Carlos)*, Catherine Woodville *(Elena)*, Robert Rietty *(police chief)*, Milan Mićić, Demeter Bitenc, Murray Kash.

Melodrama. Source: Morris L. West, *The Big Story* (London, 1957). An exposé of the Duke of Orgagna, the ruthless dictator of a small Balkan country, is being compiled by crusading American journalist Richard Ashley. The story will be the biggest in his career, and he needs only certain photostats to document his evidence before releasing the exposé. As he is awaiting the photostats in a cafe, the contact man informs him that the price for them has been raised from $5,000 to $10,000. The enraged Ashley threatens the man and is on the verge of violence when the appearance of Cosima, Orgagna's wife, calms him. Years before, Cosima and Ashley had been lovers, but she rejected him to marry Orgagna. After reminiscing a bit, Ashley and Cosima go for a drive in the country, during the course of which the body of a man falls in the car's path. Upon examining the body, Ashley discovers it is that of the contact man who was to deliver the photostats to him. Ashley takes the corpse to the police and is allowed his freedom on the condition that he remain in the country. Later, after further questioning, he is placed in the Duke of Orgagna's custody at the duke's island villa in order to avoid an international incident. Despite Orgagna's pleas, Ashley tells him he plans to print the exposé. It is revealed that the photostats are in the possession of Elena, Orgagna's mistress, who is the sister of the man who planned to sell them to Ashley. Elena gives Ashley the photostats when she learns that Orgagna killed her brother. The desperate Orgagna attempts to poison Ashley and obtain the photostats, but Elena's father, having learned that his daughter is Orgagna's mistress, fatally stabs the duke. Orgagna's death makes Ashley's exposé unnecessary, and he and Cosima are happily reunited. *Americans in foreign countries. Nobility. Dictators. Journalists. Police. Mistresses. Political corruption. Murder. Poisoning. Infidelity. Brother-sister relationship. Evidence. Cafes. Corpses. Islands. Balkans. Documentation. Automobile accidents.*

Note: Released in Yugoslavia in 1965 as *Krivi put*; running time: 93 min; in Great Britain in Feb 1967; running time: 86 min. The novel *The Big Story* was published in the United States as *The Crooked Road* (New York, 1957).

CROOKS AND CORONETS *see* **SOPHIE'S PLACE**

CROOKS ANONYMOUS (Great Britain)　　　**F6.0969**
Independent Artists. *Dist* Janus Films. 20 Feb **1963** [Los Angeles opening]. Sd; b&w. 35mm. 87 min.

Prod Julian Wintle, Leslie Parkyn. *Assoc Prod* Jack Davies. *Dir* Ken Annakin. *Screenplay* Jack Davies, Henry Blyth. *Photog* Ernest Steward. *Art Dir* Harry Pottle. *Film Ed* John Trumper. *Mus* Muir Mathieson, Henry Martin. *Mus Dir* Muir Mathieson. *Sd* Lionel Selwyn.

Cast: Leslie Phillips *(Dandy Forsdyke)*, Stanley Baxter *(R. S. Widdowes)*, Wilfrid Hyde-White *(Montague)*, Julie Christie *(Babette)*, James Robertson-Justice *(Sir Harvey Russellrod)*, Michael Medwin *(Ronnie)*, Pauline Jameson *(Prunella)*, Robertson Hare *(Grimsdale)*, Charles Lloyd Pack *(Fletcher)*, Bryan Coleman *(Holding)*, Harry Fowler *(Woods)*, Raymond Huntley *(Wagstaffe)*, John Bennett *(Thomas)*, Arthur Mullard *(Grogan)*, Arthur Lovegrove *(Jones)*, Joyce Blair *(Carol)*, Colin Gordon *(drunk)*, Dick Emery *(Cundall)*, Norma Foster, Dandy Nichols, David Drummond, Alfred Burke, Timothy Bateson.

Crime comedy. Dandy Forsdyke, a petty thief who is unable to control his "itchy fingers," is the despair of his fiancée, Babette La Verne, a stripteaser. Babette's friend Carol suggests that Dandy enlist in "Crooks Anonymous," a society for reforming criminals headed by Senior Brother Montague, an ex-convict. After surviving several grueling tests administered by Montague's tough assistant, Brother Widdowes, Forsdyke is pronounced cured. He graduates to an honest job as a Santa Claus in a London department store, but when accidentally locked in the store at night with the Christmas receipts of £250,000, he places an emergency phone call to "Crooks Anonymous" to rescue him from temptation. Montague and the organization arrive in force, but they succumb to the lure of the untraceable bills and steal the money. Babette, informed of their adventure, threatens to expose the crooks unless they return the money. After the hazardous replacement of the money is accomplished, Babette marries Dandy and becomes an honorary member of the reform group. *Thieves. Stripteasers. Ex-convicts. Criminals—Rehabilitation. Honesty. Theft. Syndicates. Department stores. London. Santa Claus.*

Note: Released in Great Britain in 1962.

THE CROSS AND THE SWITCHBLADE　　　**F6.0970**
Dick Ross & Associates-Q. E. D. Productions. *Dist* Dick Ross & Associates, Gateway Films. 3 Jun **1970** [Los Angeles opening]. Sd; col (Eastman Color, print by Technicolor). 35mm. 106 min. *MPAA rating* GP.

Prod Dick Ross. *Assoc Prod* Tom Harris, Ken Curtis. *Dir* Don Murray. *Screenplay* Don Murray, James Bonnet. *Photog* Julian Townsend. *Art Dir* Charles Bailey. *Film Ed* Angelo Ross. *Mus Comp & Cond* Ralph Carmichael. *Sd* Chris Newman. *Asst Dir* Steven M. Marshall, Samuel N. Bennerson. *Prod Mgr* Robert Baron. *Cost* Pearl Somner. *Makeup* John Jiras. *Tech Adv* David Wilkerson, Nicky Cruz.

Cast: Pat Boone *(David Wilkerson)*, Erik Estrada *(Nicky Cruz)*, Jackie Giroux *(Rosa)*, Jo-Ann Robinson *(Little Bo)*, Dino DeFilippi *(Israel)*, Don Blakely *(Abdullah)*, Gil Frazier *(Big Cat)*, Don Lamond *(Sergeant Delano)*, Sam Capuano *(Mr. Gomez)*, Alex Colon *(Mingo)*, Hector Mercado *(Moonlight)*, Stew Silver *(Augie)*, Dorothy James *(Mrs. Gomez)*, David Connell *(pusher)*, Michelle Galjour *(Angela)*, Jackie Cronin *(Norma)*, Virginia Alonso *(Mary)*, Darryl Speer *(Bottlecap)*, Thomas Mooney *(Chance)*, Vincent O'Brien *(judge)*, Jay Devlin *(district attorney)*, Paul Haney *(lawyer)*, Darrel Adleman *(pawnbroker)*, Victor Bumbalo *(Hugo)*, Stanley Finesmith *(trial defendant)*, Sal Christi *(court policeman)*, Andrew T. Murphy *(reporter)*, Kleg Seth *(photographer)*, Laura Figueroa *(Mau Mau deb)*, Jonelle Allen *(Bishop deb)*, Mark Dawson *(policeman)*, Dolores Raskin *(elderly woman)*, Norman

Bly *(heckler)*, Tim Pelt *(bishop)*.

Biographical drama. Source: David Wilkerson, John Sherrill and Elizabeth Sherrill, *The Cross and the Switchblade* (New York, 1963). The Reverend David Wilkerson, a Pennsylvania country preacher, comes to New York to aid a group of teenaged gang members on trial for the murder of a young boy; but when he enters a courtroom to beg permission to meet the defendants, he is seized and frisked by suspicious court officers. After failing to help the accused youngsters, Wilkerson, refusing to be discouraged, remains in New York in the hope of reaching other slum victims. In time, he meets both Nicky Cruz, the leader of a Puerto Rican gang called the Mau Maus, and Nicky's hated enemy Abdullah, the leader of a black gang known as the Bishops. Through his friendship with a homeless black girl, Little Bo, Wilkerson visits the Mau Maus' headquarters and learns of a forthcoming rumble with the Bishops to determine control of the neighborhood. Despite Wilkerson's sincerity, the teenagers look upon him with open distrust. Nicky demonstrates his hostility by spitting on Wilkerson; but the preacher responds by assuring the boy that God will never forsake him. When the rumble results in the death of one of the Mau Maus, Wilkerson becomes more determined than ever to win over the gang members. Then, because the Bishops disrupt the funeral services of the dead youth, another gang fight breaks out, and Nicky suffers a near-fatal beating. Wilkerson visits him and is again rejected, though he senses that he is making some headway toward Nicky's eventual conversion. But the reverend receives another setback when the gangs' leaders vote to fight to the death. Actual violence is curtailed, however, by Wilkerson's persuasive preaching and by his previous assistance in curing Nicky's ex-girl friend Rosa of heroin addiction. Encouraged by this initial success, Wilkerson vows to organize youth rehabilitation centers in all of New York's slum districts. *Puerto Ricans. Negroes. Drug addicts. Police. Clergymen. Street gangs. Adolescence. Gang wars. Religious conversion. Trials. Slums. Funerals. New York City. David Wilkerson.*

Note: Filmed on location in New York City.

CROSS OF THE LIVING (France) F6.0971

Christina Films. *Dist* Cari Releasing Corp. 4 Feb **1963** [New York opening]. Sd; b&w. 35mm. 90 min.

Prod Christine Dumoutier, Jean-Claude Dumoutier. *Dir* Yvan Govar. *Orig Screenplay* Christine Dumoutier, Jean-Claude Dumoutier, Alain Cavalier. *Dial* Maurice Clavel. *Photog* André Bac. *Art Dir* Léon Barsacq. *Film Ed* Paul Cayatte. *Sd* Antoine Archimbaud. *Prod Mgr* Jean-Claude Dumoutier.

Cast: Pascale Petit *(Marie)*, Karlheinz Böhm *(Gus)*, Giani Esposito *(Yan)*, Gabriele Ferzetti *(abbé)*, Christine Darvel, Marie Dubois *(Nell [see note])*, Roger Dumas *(Sylvain)*, Jacques Richard *(Franz)*, Max de Rieux *(Karl)*, Alain Cuny *(count)*, Madeleine Robinson *(Madame Dorneck)*, Marika Green.

Melodrama. Yan returns home to his village in Flanders after being acquitted of killing his stepfather. His old friends, including Franz, a mechanic, have deserted him, and the villagers are still suspicious of him. Yan's only friends are revealed to be Gus, who finds him a job, and the village abbé. Gus intends to marry his mistress Marie, but Marie and Yan feel an increasing attraction to each other. Marie goes to the abbé to confess her problems, but he is not kind to her, possibly because he too is attracted to her. While Gus is out of town, Yan and Marie consummate their love for each other, but at the local dance Franz beats up Yan while calling him a murderer. Yan offers no defense to the beating. Gus returns home, learns of the affair, and sets out to murder Yan, but he cannot kill his friend. Yan realizes that he cannot hurt Gus, his only real friend, and tells Marie that he will not run away with her. Heartbroken, she runs into the forest and is killed in an automobile accident by Gus's mother, Madame Dorneck. Gus brings her body to the village, and the villagers think Yan has killed her. Franz inflames the vigilante atmosphere and, guns in hand, the villagers try to attack Yan. He is defended by the abbé, who is killed when Franz fires his gun. The abbé's body joins Marie's in the church. *Priests. Mechanics. Vigilantes. Friendship. Village life. Infidelity. Automobile accidents. Confession. Flanders.*

Note: Opened in Paris in Jul 1962 as *La croix des vivants*. Sources conflict in crediting actor playing Nell.

CROSSWINDS *see* **JUNGLE ATTACK**

A CROWD FOR LISETTE *see* **LISETTE**

THE CROWN CAPER *see* **THE THOMAS CROWN AFFAIR**

I CRUDELI *see* **THE HELLBENDERS**

CRUNCH *see* **24-HOUR LOVER**

CRY BLOOD, APACHE F6.0972

Dist Golden Eagle International, Goldstone Film Enterprises. Sep **1970**. Sd; col (Eastman Color). 35mm. 82 min. *MPAA rating* R.

Prod Jody McCrea, Harold Roberts. *Dir* Jack Starrett. *Screenplay* Sean MacGregor. *Story* Harold Roberts. *Photog* Bruce Scott, photog. *Film Ed* T. Robinson. *Mus* Elliot Kaplan. *Perf by* The Munich Sinfonetta.

Cast: Jody McCrea *(Pitcalin)*, Dan Kemp *(Vittorio)*, Marie Gahva *(Jemme)*, Don Henley *(Benji)*, Rick Nervick *(Billy)*, Robert Tessier *(Two Card)*, Jack Starrett *(Deacon)*, Carolyn Stellar *(Cochalla)*, Carroll Kemp *(old Indian)*, Barbara Sanford *(mother)*, Dawn Stellar *(child)*, Andy Anza *(crippled Indian)*, Joel McCrea *(older Pitcalin)*.

Western melodrama. Pitcalin, an old frontiersman, recalls his days as a youth just after the Mexican-American War, when he and four prospectors (Billy, Benji, Two Card, and Deacon) came across a band of Apaches who knew the location of a gold mine. When the Indians refused to reveal its whereabouts, the prospectors slaughtered all but a young squaw, Jemme, who then agreed to lead them across the desert to the treasure. A bond developed between Pitcalin and Jemme, causing the prospectors to suspect a conspiracy against them, particularly after their horses disappeared. Only after Billy was hit by an arrow did they realize that an Apache was pursuing them. Later the stalking Indian drowned Benji, killed Two Card by placing a sack containing a snake over his head, and so terrorized Deacon that he lapsed into raving madness. Finally, when the Apache confronted Pitcalin, Jemme revealed that he was her vengeful brother, Vittorio. Before Vittorio could force the frontiersman into a battle for his life, however, Jemme killed her brother so that Pitcalin could live. *Prospectors. Apache Indians. Frontier and pioneer life. Murder. Revenge. Insanity. Fratricide. Gold. Deserts. Snakes.*

Note: Location scenes filmed in Arizona and Sequoia National Park, California.

CRY DOUBLE CROSS (West Germany) F6.0973

Roxy Film. *Dist* Atlantic Pictures. Feb **1962**. Sd; b&w. 35mm. 65 min.

Prod Luggi Waldleitner. *Dir* Alfred Weidenmann. *Screenplay* Herbert Reinecker. *Photog* Kurt Hasse. *Asst Camera* Lothar Kern. *Art Dir* Wolf Englert, Ernst Richter. *Film Ed* Lilian Seng. *Mus* Hans-Martin Majewski. *Sd* Hans Löhmer. *Asst Dir* Wieland Liebske. *Prod Mgr* Kurt Paetz, Fritz Anton. *Dir Prod* Heinrich Schier. *Wardrobe* Walter Schreckling, Margarete Markwordt. *Cost* Ursula Stutz. *Makeup* Max Patyna, Jutta Haase. *Props* Max Freude, Helmut Künecke, Fritz Moritz.

Cast: Hardy Krüger *(Robert Wegner)*, Martin Held *(Police Commissioner Stern)*, Mario Adorf *(Georg Kugler)*, Horst Frank *(Willy Schneider)*, Ingrid van Bergen *(Else)*, Peer Schmidt *(police sergeant)*, Cordula Trantow *(Helga)*, Ernst Waldow, Lu Säuberlich, Wega Jahnke, Marie Luise Nagel, Kurt Pratsch-Kaufmann.

Crime melodrama. Source: Igor Sentjurc, *Bumerang* (Bad Wörishofen, 1959). After Robert Wegner, Georg Kugler, and Willy Schneider have laid out their plans for cracking the safe at the West Berlin Labor Office, Georg accidentally sees his mistress, Else, with Robert. Jealously misconstruing the situation, Georg anonymously informs the police of the impending theft. As a result, the thieves are caught during the robbery. In the ensuing gun battle, Robert is badly wounded but manages to escape. He is recognized, however, by Police Commissioner Stern as the man who saved his life during World War II. The sad but relentless Stern pursues Robert and, upon finding him, tries to persuade him to give himself up. Stern reaches to shake hands with the man who had once saved his life, but Robert knocks him out and steals his gun, only to be shot down by the waiting police. *Safecrackers. Mistresses. Informers. Police. Robbery. Jealousy. Perfidy. Berlin—West.*

Note: Location scenes filmed in West Berlin. Released in West Germany in 1960 as *Bumerang*; running time: 92 min.

CRY FOR HAPPY F6.0974

William Goetz Productions. *Dist* Columbia Pictures. 10 Feb **1961** [Honolulu, Hawaii, opening; c1 Mar 1961; LP19587]. Sd (RCA); col (Eastman Color by Pathé). 35mm (CinemaScope). 110 min.

A William Goetz Production. *Prod* William Goetz. *Dir* George Marshall. *Screenplay* Irving Brecher. *Dir Photog* Burnett Guffey. *Art Dir* Walter Holscher. *Set Decor* William Kiernan. *Film Ed* Chester W. Schaeffer. *Mus* George Duning. *Orch* Arthur Morton. *Rec Supv* Charles J. Rice. *Sd* Lambert Day. *Asst Dir* George Marshall, Jr. *Prod Asst* Milton Feldman. *Cost Dsgn* Norma Koch. *Makeup Supv* Ben Lane. *Hairstyles* Helen Hunt. *Adv* Robert F. Hickey, (Vice-Adm. USN, Ret.). *Coöp* United States—Defense Department, United States—Navy Department. *Tech Cons* Aki Mizuno.

Cast: Glenn Ford *(Andy Cyphers)*, Donald O'Connor *(Murray Prince)*, Miiko Taka *(Chiyoko)*, James Shigeta *(Suzuki)*, Miyoshi Umeki *(Harue)*, Michi Kobi *(Hanakichi)*, Howard St. John *(Admiral Bennett)*, Joe Flynn *(McIntosh)*, Chet Douglas *(Lank)*, Tsuruko Kobayashi *(Koyuki)*, Harriet MacGibbon *(Mrs. Bennett)*, Robert Kino *(Endo)*, Bob Okazaki *(Izumi)*, Harlan Warde *(chaplain)*, Nancy Kovack *(Miss Cameron)*, Ted Knight *(Lieutenant Glick)*, Bill Quinn *(Lymon)*, Chiyo Nakasone *(Keiko)*.

Comedy. Source: George Campbell, *Cry for Happy* (New York, 1958). While recuperating in Japan after a Korean combat mission, four Navy photographers—Cyphers, Prince, Suzuki, and Lank—billet themselves in an off-limits geisha house they believe to be vacant. Though they discover four of the girls are still living there, their delight turns to disappointment when they learn that geishas are not exactly what they had imagined. Nevertheless, romance blossoms and the four men happily submit to a life of luxurious pampering. Then a tongue-in-cheek story Cyphers once told some newsmen—that he was fighting the Korean War to help Japanese orphans—gets considerable publicity in the States, and the Navy Department asks for details. The sailors and the geishas quickly borrow some neighbors' children and convert the geisha house into an orphanage. The hoax is a huge success, donations begin to pour in, and Cyphers is able to make the orphanage a reality. At a double wedding, Prince and Suzuki marry two of the girls, while Cyphers and Lank strongly consider following suit. *Photographers. Geishas. Orphans. Orphanages. Hoaxes. Weddings. Korean War 1950–53. Japan. United States Navy.*

Note: Location scenes filmed in Japan.

CRY FREEDOM (Philippines)　　　　　　　　　　　　　　　**F6.0975**
Edith Perez de Tagle. *Dist* Parallel Film Distributors. May **1961**. Sd; b&w. 35mm. 93 min.

Prod Edith Perez de Tagle. *Dir* Lamberto V. Avellana. *Screenplay* Rolf Bayer. *Photog* Mike Accion. *Mus* Restie Umali.

Cast: Pancho Magalona *(Marking)*, Rosa Rosal *(Yay)*, Johnny Reyes *(Cabalhim)*, Jack Forster *(Sid)*, Charles Kelly *(Lieutenant Stoddard)*, Tony Santos *(Juanito)*.

War drama. Source: Yay Marking, *The Crucible* (publication undetermined). Escaping from behind enemy lines in World War II, Marking, a young Filipino truckdriver, takes to the hills and joins a band of freedom fighters who are conducting guerrilla warfare against the conquering Japanese forces. Because of his courage and initiative, he is made their leader, taking over the function from Cabalhim. His forces grow constantly, and against overwhelming odds his harassment of the Japanese becomes increasingly costly to them. Joining his band are Sid, an American they have freed from a prison camp, and Yay, a newspaper correspondent with whom Marking falls in love. Ultimately, the work of Marking's guerrillas attracts the attention of the U. S. Army, and he is sent technical assistance and modern munitions. From then on he and Yay fight side by side with the liberation army toward the day of complete destruction of the enemy; the differences in their classes and education are surmounted by their shared experiences and love. *Truckdrivers. Journalists. Guerrillas. Resistance (political). Military occupation. Social classes. War matériel. World War II. Yay Marking. United States Army. Japan—Army.*

Note: Produced in the Philippines in 1959.

CRY OF BATTLE (United States/Philippines)　　　　　　　**F6.0976**
Petramonte Productions. *Dist* Allied Artists. 11 Oct **1963** [New York opening; c12 Sep 1963; LP26349]. Sd; b&w. 35mm. 99 min.

Prod Joe Steinberg. *Assoc Prod* Eddie Romero. *Dir* Irving Lerner. *Screenplay* Bernard Gordon. *Dir Photog* Felipe Sacdalan. *Camera Op* Edmundo Bautista. *Art Dir* Benjamin Rosella. *Supv Film Ed* Verna Fields. *Asst Ed* Harry Kaye. *Mus* Richard Markowitz. *Guitarist* Pedro Concepción. *Sd Ed* Jeanne Turner. *Sd Mix* Pat Del Rosario. *Mus Ed* Theodore Roberts. *1st & 2d Asst Dir* José Dagumboy, D. K. Trofeo. *Prod Mgr* Artemio Tecson. *Unit Mgr* Carpi Asturias. *Script Supv* Marilou Soriano. *Cost* Felisa Salcedo. *Makeup Man* Ray Salamat. *Makeup Woman* Remy Amazan. *Sp Eff* Hilario Brothers. *Tech Adv* Elwood J. Nicholson. *Prop Master* David Delina. *Dial Dir* Sidney Clute. *Ch Grip* Perfecto Navarro. *Philippine Army Liaison* J. Juban, (Capt.).

Cast: Van Heflin *(Joe Trent)*, Rita Moreno *(Sisa)*, James MacArthur *(David McVey)*, Leopoldo Salcedo *(Manuel Careo)*, Sidney Clute *(Colonel Ryker)*, Marilou Muñoz *(Pinang)*, Oscar Roncal *(Atong)*, Liza Moreno *(Vera)*, Michael Parsons *(Captain Davis)*, Claude Wilson *(Matchek)*, Vic Solyin *(Captain Garcia)*, Oscar Keesee.

War melodrama. Source: Benjamin Appel, *Fortress in the Rice* (Indianapolis, 1951). Just after the Japanese attack on Pearl Harbor, young Dave McVey, son of a wealthy plantation owner, arrives in the Philippines and is rescued from attacking bandits by Manuel Careo, leader of a resistance group. Sheltered by the guerrillas, Dave meets cynical, brutal Joe Trent, an American who takes the youth under his protection. Joe drunkenly rapes a young Filipina, and Dave, realizing that both of them will be held responsible, joins him in flight. They meet Sisa, a young Filipina guerrilla who speaks English, and accompany her group to the headquarters of an American guerrilla unit. Joe has an affair with Sisa and shoots Atong, the bandit who had assumed the role of her protector. Meanwhile, Dave and Sisa fall in love. Dave leaves Joe, who has been wounded in an enemy raid, in order to seek help from their allies, and Joe forces his attentions on Sisa. Resistance leader Careo pursues Joe and places

him under arrest for rape and murder, but Dave refuses to testify against his protector. During a Japanese attack, Joe escapes with Dave and Sisa, and he later tries to gun down Careo. To prevent the murder of the guerrilla leader, Dave shoots Joe; he and Sisa then join the Filipino guerrillas in their fight against the Japanese. *Refugees. Guerrillas. Soldiers. Filipinos. Japanese. Combat zone life. Murder. Rape. Manhood. Loyalty. Drunkenness. Jungles. World War II. Pearl Harbor Attack 1941. Philippines.*

Note: Filmed in the Philippines, mostly in the jungles outlying Manila. Working title: *To Be a Man.*

THE CRY OF LAUGHING OWLS see **JOHNNY TIGER**

CRY OF THE BANSHEE (Great Britain)　　　　　　　　　　**F6.0977**
American International Productions. *Dist* American International Pictures. 22 Jul **1970** [Chicago opening; c29 Jul 1970; LP38510]. Sd; col (print by Movielab). 35mm. 87 min. *MPAA rating* GP.

Prod-Dir Gordon Hessler. *Exec Prod* Louis M. Heyward. *Assoc Prod* Clifford Parkes. *Screenplay* Tim Kelly, Christopher Wicking. *Story* Tim Kelly. *Lighting Camera* John Coquillon. *Camera Op* Les Young. *Art Dir* George Provis. *Set Dresser* Scott Slimon. *Titl Dsgn* Cinefx. *Film Ed* Oswald Hafenrichter. *Asst Ed* Ean Wood. *Post Prod Supv* Salvatore Billitteri. *Mus Comp & Cond* Les Baxter. *Mus Supv* Al Simms. *Sd Mix* Kevin Sutton. *Dub Mix* Peter Lodge. *Dub Ed* Michael Redbourn. *Asst Dir* Ariel Levy. *Cont* Zelda Barron. *Wardrobe* Dora Lloyd. *Makeup* Tom Smith, Betty Blattner. *Hairstyles* Ivy Emmerton. *Constr Mgr* Bill Miller, constr.

Cast—The Establishment: Vincent Price *(Lord Edward Whitman)*, Essy Persson *(Lady Patricia)*, Hilary Dwyer *(Maureen)*, Carl Rigg *(Harry Whitman)*, Stephen Chase *(Sean)*, Marshall Jones *(Father Tom)*, Andrew McCulloch *(Bully Boy)*, Michael Elphick *(Burke)*, Pamela Moiseiwitsch *(maid)*, Joyce Mandre, Robert Hutton, Peter Forest, Guy Deghy *(party guests)*.

Cast—Witches: Elizabeth Bergner *(Oona)*, Patrick Mower *(Roderick)*, Pamela Farbrother *(Margaret)*, Quinn O'Hara *(Maggie)*, Jane Deady *(naked girl)*.

Cast—Villagers: Hugh Griffith *(Mickey)*, Janet Rossini *(Bess)*, Sally Geeson *(Sarah)*, Godfrey James *(head villager)*, Gertan Klauber *(tavern keeper)*, Peter Benson *(brander)*, Terry Martin *(rider)*, Richard Everett *(Timothy)*, Louis Selwyn *(apprentice)*, Micky Baker *(rider)*, Carol Desmond *(girl)*, Ann Barrass, Nancy Meckler, Hugh Portnow, Stephen Rea, Maurice Colbourne, Dinah Stabb, Tony Sibbald, Neil Johnston, Rowan Wylie, Tim Thomas, Ron Sahewk, Maya Roth, Philly Howell, Guy Pierce.

Horror film. Lord Edward Whitman, a 16th-century magistrate in England, organizes the people of his hamlet against Oona, the leader of a cult of Druids. When Whitman captures and kills two of Oona's children, Oona swears revenge against Lord Whitman and his entire family. She summons a demon which assumes the form of Roderick, a handsome young man who finds employment in the Whitman household as a groom and soon falls in love with the magistrate's daughter Maureen. Lord Whitman has meanwhile located the Druids' worship site and plans to eliminate the cult at their next ceremony. The night of the ceremony, Oona returns Roderick to his banshee form and sends him to kill Maureen; soon afterwards, Lord Whitman's men arrive and murder Oona and her followers. When Whitman returns to his manor, he finds Maureen on the verge of death; Roderick comes out of hiding and attacks Lord Whitman, but Maureen kills the banshee. Whitman then puts Maureen and his son Harry in a carriage to leave the cursed district and returns to assure himself of Roderick's death, but he finds the coffin empty. Hurrying to the carriage, he finds Harry and Maureen murdered. The coachman reveals himself to be Roderick and rides off with Lord Whitman inside, thus completing Oona's revenge. *Magistrates. Druids. Evil spirits. Murder. Revenge. Transmutation. Religious persecution. Filial relations. Rites and ceremonies. Manors. Curses.*

Note: Filmed on location in Middlesex, England. Opened in London in Nov 1970.

CRY OF THE BEWITCHED see **YOUNG AND EVIL**

CRY OF THE MOUNTAIN (Japan)　　　　　　　　　　　　　**F6.0978**
Toho Co. Oct **1969** [Los Angeles showing]. Sd; col? 35mm. 93 min.
Dir Tadashi Sawashima.

Cast: Yuriko Hoshi, Kinya Kitaoji.

Romantic drama. Although no information on the precise nature of this film has been found, sources indicate that it concerns a man's loss of memory following an accident. *Amnesia.*

Note: Released in Japan in Sep 1968 as *Kitahodaka zessho.*

CSILLAGOSOK, KATONÁK see **THE RED AND THE WHITE**

LAS CUATRO VERDADES see **THREE FABLES OF LOVE**

LA CUCARACHA (Mexico)   F6.0979

Películas Rodríguez. *Dist* Azteca Films. 1 Nov **1961** [New York opening]. Sd; col (Eastman Color). 35mm. 90 min.

Prod-Dir Ismael Rodríguez. *Screenplay* José Bolaños Prado, Ismael Rodríguez. *Adapt* Ismael Rodríguez, José Luis Celis, Ricardo Garibay. *Photog* Gabriel Figueroa. *Art Dir* Edward Fitzgerald. *Film Ed* Fernando Martínez. *Mus* Raúl Lavista. *Sd* Manuel Topete, James L. Fields.

Cast: Maria Félix *(La Cucaracha)*, Emilio Fernández *(Colonel Zeta)*, Dolores del Río *(Chabela)*, Pedro Armendáriz *(Razo)*, Antonio Aguilar *(Captain Ventura)*, Ignacio López Tarso, Flor Silvestre, Cuco Sánchez, Lupe Carriles, Miguel Manzano, Alicia del Lago.

War melodrama. During the Mexican revolution, one of Pancho Villa's loyal officers, Colonel Zeta, is forced to conscript all able-bodied males in a small town. The tiny, ragged army is roused from their demoralized apathy by a woman soldier called La Cucaracha, who subsequently falls in love with Zeta. The Colonel is also attracted to the more demure Chabela, a soldier's widow. Following a gun battle in which he kills a rival, Razo, Zeta abandons La Cucaracha in favor of Chabela. Several months and battles later, La Cucaracha, who is pregnant with Zeta's child, meets the army and learns that Zeta has been killed. Seeing the silent Chabela, who has become a soldier herself, La Cucaracha follows the weary men as they move towards the mountains. *Revolutionaries. Widows. Military draft. Pregnancy. Mexico—History—1910–17. Francisco "Pancho" Villa. Mexico—Army.*

Note: Released in Mexico in 1958. Flor Silvestre is a pseudonym for Guillermina Jiménez.

CUCINA AL BURRO see **MY WIFE'S HUSBAND**

LA CUISINE AU BEURRE see **MY WIFE'S HUSBAND**

CUL-DE-SAC (Great Britain)   F6.0980

Compton-Tekli Film Productions. *Dist* Sigma III Corp. 7 Nov **1966** [New York opening]. Sd; b&w. 35mm. 107 min. [Also 104 min.]

Pres by Filmways Inc. A Michael Klinger–Tony Tenser Production. *Prod* Gene Gutowski. *Exec Prod* Sam Waynberg. *Dir* Roman Polanski. *Orig Screenplay* Roman Polanski, Gerard Brach. *Photog* Gilbert Taylor. *Art Dir* Voytek. *Film Ed* Alastair McIntyre. *Mus Comp & Cond* Christopher Komeda. *Sd* Stephen Dalby. *Asst Dir* Ted Sturgis. *Prod Mgr* Don Weeks. *Sp Eff* Bowie Films.

Cast: Donald Pleasence *(George)*, Françoise Dorléac *(Teresa)*, Lionel Stander *(Richard)*, Jack MacGowran *(Albert)*, Iain Quarrier *(Christopher)*, Geoffrey Sumner *(Christopher's father)*, Renée Houston *(Christopher's mother)*, William Franklyn *(Cecil)*, Trevor Delaney *(Nicholas)*, Marie Kean *(Mrs. Fairweather)*, Robert Dorning *(Mr. Fairweather)*, Jacqueline Bisset *(Jacqueline)*.

Drama. Two wounded gangsters escape to an old island castle on the coast of Northumberland. The castle is inhabited by George, an effeminate, middle-aged, retired businessman, and his young, bored, promiscuous, French wife, Teresa, who is having an affair with a neighboring summer resident. When one of the gangsters, Albert, dies from his bullet wounds, his brutish American companion, Richard, takes over the castle while awaiting telephone instructions from Kattlebach, the boss of his gang. Relations among the three bizarre characters are anything but harmonious as George becomes increasingly neurotic, Teresa more bored and mischievous, and Richard more violent. During a visit from some of George's wealthy, class-conscious mainland friends, Richard poses as a manservant while Teresa openly flirts with Cecil, one of the guests. When Richard finally learns that he can expect no help from his boss, he orders George to drive him off the island, which is connected by a causeway to the mainland. George, however, responds with wild violence; completely berserk, he seizes a gun and kills Richard. Cecil returns for a shotgun, and Teresa leaves with him. Alone, George walks to the beach, sits on a rock in the rising tide, and weeps for his lost wife. *Gangsters. French. Americans in foreign countries. Hostages. Businessmen. Marriage. Imposture. Promiscuity. Infidelity. Effeminacy. Retirement. Middle age. Wealth. Murder. Islands. Castles. Northumberland.*

Note: Filmed on location at Holy Island, Northumberland. Opened in London in Jun 1966; running time: 111 min.

CULT OF THE DAMNED see **ANGEL, ANGEL, DOWN WE GO**

THE CUPS OF SAN SEBASTIAN see **THE FICKLE FINGER OF FATE**

LA CURÉE see **THE GAME IS OVER**

THE CURIOUS DR. HUMPP (Argentina)   F6.0981

Productores Argentinos Asociados. *Dist* Unicorn Releases. 14 May **1970** [San Francisco showing]. Sd; b&w. 35mm. 85 min. [Also 80 min.]

Pres by Jerald Intrator. A Forbes–Unistar Films Production. *Prod* Orestes Trucco. *Exec Prod* Coca Blasco. *Dir-Screenplay* Emilio Vieyra. *Story* Raul Zorrilla. *Dir Photog* Aníbal González Paz. *Camera* Victor Caula. *Film Ed* Jacinto Cascales. *Mus* Víctor Buchino. *Asst Dir* Juan C. Codazzi.

Cast: Ricardo Bauleo, Gloria Prat, Aldo Barbero, Susana Beltrán, Justin Martin, Michel Angel, Mary Albano, Al Bugatti, Hector Biuchet, Greta Williams, Alex Klapp, Norbert Nelson.

Melodrama. The police of an unidentified city have organized a manhunt for a number of people missing and believed to have been kidnaped. The chief investigator scoffs at a reporter's theory that the kidnaper is a sadistic, sex-crazed scientist who achieved notoriety in some European newspapers 20 years previously. A nightclub owner provides a description of the man he believes abducted his star stripteaser, and a drugstore clerk is murdered when he calls the reporter about a customer fitting the description. The customer's order was for a large quantity of aphrodisiacs, and the police place stakeouts at all the pharmacies in hopes that the suspect will return for more supplies. The mad scientist is actually controlled by a human brain kept alive in the laboratory, and he performs tests on human response to sexual stimuli; the victims are either disposed of or made into robots. The reporter, who has joined in a stakeout, spots the scientist making another purchase and follows him to the laboratory site. He is taken prisoner and is shown the experiment he will participate in. He persuades the scientist's assistant to aid him and the other victims. A savage gun battle between the police and the scientist results in the scientist's death and the end of the experimentation. *Police. Reporters. Scientists. Clerks. Abduction. Sadism. Murder. Sex research. Disembodiment. Manhunts. Experiments. Aphrodisiacs. Laboratories.*

Note: Produced in Argentina in 1967 as *La venganza del sexo*.

THE CURIOUS FEMALE   F6.0982

Fanfare Film Productions. 1 Oct **1969** [Detroit opening]. Sd; col (Eastmancolor). 35mm. 87 min.

Prod-Dir Paul Rapp. *Exec Prod* Joe Solomon. *Screenplay* Winston R. Paul. *Dir Photog* Don Birnkrant. *Set Dresser* Ray Boltz. *Film Ed* Reg Browne. *Mus Comp & Cond* Stu Phillips. *Titl Song* Stu Phillips, Bob Stone. *Sung by* Barry Mitchell. *Rec Producers* Sound Service. *Post-prod* Synchrofilm. *Sd Eff* Edit-Rite Inc. *1st Asst Dir* Russell Vreeland. *Prod Asst* Peter Fain. *Script Supv* Marie Messinger. *Cost Supv* Marjorie Plecher. *Makeup* Harry Thomas. *Prop Master* Lou Donelan. *Gaffer* Bobby Petzoldt. *Key Grip* John Murray. *Casting Dir* Pearl Kempton.

Cast: Angelique Pettyjohn *(Susan Rome)*, Charlene Jones *(Pearl Lushcomb)*, Bunny Allister *(Liana/Joan)*, David Westberg *(Jorel/Paul Emerson)*, Julie Conners *(Andrée)*, Michael Greer *(Bixby)*, Sebastian Brook *(Mr. Burton)*, Ron Gans *(Jerome Bruce)*, David Pritchard *(Guy Ryan)*, Slim Gaillard *(Mr. Lushcomb)*, Elaine Edwards *(Mrs. Wilde)*, Carol Jean Thompson *(Gloria)*, Harry Sodoni *(Harry)*, Lincoln Kilpatrick *(Uncle Charlie)*, Mildred Harrison *(Mrs. Lushcomb)*, Randee Jensen *(Joy)*, David Buchanan *(young man)*, Mary Virginia Pittman *(Scarlet)*, Junero Jennings *(Roy)*, Betty Gumn *(girl)*, Mike Castle *(Everet)*, Christopher Riordan *(Troy/Lad)*, Ron Graham *(bouncer)*, Josh Bryant *(Mr. Tower)*, David Osterhout *(Hinkley)*, Al Quick *(Weeny)*.

Comedy. In the sexually liberated but totalitarian world of 2177 A.D., the Master Computer rules a society devoid of love, romance, and families. Liana and Jorel decide to break the law and view old films. One of them, a 1969 release entitled *The Three Virgins*, depicts how three women, the only virgin students at a university, are brought together by CUPID, a computer dating service, to talk over their problems. Joan has broken up with medical student Paul because of his demand for pre-marital sex in return for a vague promise of marriage; Pearl Lushcomb, a beautiful black girl, is frigid because of her lecherous uncle's advances; and Susan Rome has been reared to resist sex without love. The women's sexual curiosity is aroused after their discussion, and they act in accordance with their individual desires. At the end of the movie, Liana, Jorel, and their audience are discovered and arrested, and the Master Computer decides to re-run the film for its own enlightenment. *Students. Negroes. Social customs. Virginity. Frigidity. Totalitarianism. Lechery. Law. Sexuality. Computers. Motion pictures. Computer dating services. The Future.*

Note: Also known as *Curious Females*. Working title: *Love, Computer Style*.

CURIOUS YELLOW BIRD see **YELLOW BIRD**

THE CURSE OF HER FLESH   F6.0983

Rivamarsh Productions. *Dist* American Film Distributing Corp. 19 Dec **1968** [San Francisco showing]. Sd; b&w. 35mm. 75 min.

Prod-Writ Julian Marsh, Anna Riva. *Dir* Julian Marsh. *Photog* Anna Riva. *Lighting* Robert Marx. *Film Ed* Julian Marsh. *Mus* Robin Aden. *Sd* Chico Buck. *Cost* Mr. Mike. *Grip* G. (N.Y.C.). *Stills* Marvin Flower.

Cast: Eve Bork, Robert Weste, Dick Feeler, Elaine Margo, Lena Brice, John Ellie, Sally Farb, Steve Roule, Jane Bond.

Melodrama. Richard Jennings, who has vowed revenge on Steve Blakeney, an actor who had been his wife's lover, disguises himself as porter in the theater where Blakeney works. He is about to stab Blakeney when it occurs to him to torture his victim first. Jennings follows Blakeney to a nightclub and watches two women clad only in g-strings perform an erotic dance and engage in lesbian lovemaking. Later, Jennings follows one of the women home, grills her about Blakeney, and causes her death by applying poison to the paws of her cat and dragging the animal across her body. Jennings causes the deaths of three more women who knew Blakeney, all lesbian performers in a sadomasochistic nightclub act. Six months after the series of bizarre killings, Jennings surfaces again. His victim is Paula, Blakeney's new bride. Jennings causes Blakeney to murder Paula, who has led Blakeney to believe that she is a virgin when, in fact, as Blakeney learns from a pornographic film of Paula which Jennings mails to him, Paula is a sexually experienced woman who, before her marriage to Blakeney, had her virginity surgically "restored." Immediately after Blakeney kills his wife with a harpoon, Jennings arrives armed with a machete. He and Blakeney grapple, and, after a climactic chase, Jennings catches up with Blakeney and castrates him as they hang from the tailgate of a speeding truck. *Psychopaths. Actors. Exotic dancers. Newlyweds. Revenge. Murder. Sadomasochism. Lesbianism. Virginity. Castration. Poisoning. Stag shows. Sex exploitation films. Cats.*

Note: This is a sequel to *The Touch of Her Flesh*, q. v. Alternative title: *The Curse of the Curious*; may also be known as *The Curse of the Flesh*.

CURSE OF SIMBA see **CURSE OF THE VOODOO**

THE CURSE OF THE AZTEC MUMMY (Mexico)   F6.0984
Cinematográfica Calderón. *Dist* K. Gordon Murray Productions, Trans-International Films. ca **1965**. Sd; b&w. 35mm. 65 min.
Pres by K. Gordon Murray. *Prod* William Calderon Stell. *Prod English Vers* K. Gordon Murray. *Dir* Rafael Portillo. *Screenplay* Alfredo Salazar. *Story* William Calderon Stell, Alfredo Salazar. *Photog* Enrique Wallace. *Art Dir* Javier Torres Torija. *Film Ed* Jorge Bustos. *Mus* Antonio Díaz Conde. *Sd* Luis Fernández.
Cast: Ramón Gay, Rosita Arenas, Crox Alvarado, Luis Aceves Castañeda, Angel d' Esteffani, Jesús Velázquez, Alejandro Cruz, Enrique Yáñez, Alberto Yáñez, Francisco Segura, Jaime González Quiñones, Arturo Martínez, Guillermo Hernández, Julián de Meriche.
Horror film. When archcriminal Dr. Krupp, alias The Bat, escapes from the police, Dr. Ramon and his fiancée, Flora, are warned by a hooded benefactor, The Angel, of the villain's escape. The Bat plots the theft of an entombed Aztec treasure, guarded by the mummified warrior, Popoca. Flora, whom Krupp believes to be Popoca's beloved princess incarnate, is abducted by The Bat. Ramon and The Angel are captured by The Bat, but Bobby, Ramon's young brother, is alerted by wrist radio and saves them. At the pyramid in which the treasure is hoarded, Ramon and The Angel are recaptured by The Bat's henchmen. With Flora as hostage, The Bat coerces Ramon into deciphering the hieroglyphics, which are the key to the treasure. Although The Angel is unmasked as Ramon's timid helper Pinkate, Popoca emerges from his tomb to subdue The Bat and his minions. *Aztec Indians. Mummies. Royalty. Brothers. Hostages. Disguise. Theft. Reincarnation. Abduction. Treasure. Hieroglyphics. Tombs.*
Note: Produced in Mexico in 1959 as *La maldición de la momia azteca*. William Calderon Stell is an anglicized rendering of Guillermo Calderón.

CURSE OF THE BLOOD-GHOULS (Italy)   F6.0985
Mercury Film International. *Dist* Pacemaker Pictures. 4 Jun **1969** [Boston opening]. Sd; col. 35mm. 72 min. *MPAA rating* G.
A Walter Manley Enterprises Production. *Prod* Dino Sant'Ambrogio. *Dir-Screenplay* Roberto Mauri. *Dir Photog* Ugo Brunelli. *Art Dir* Giuseppe Ranieri. *Film Ed* Jenner Menghi. *Mus* Aldo Piga. *Sd Rec* Nino Renda, Fausto Ancillai. *Asst Dir* Franco Longo. *Prod Mgr* Luigi D'Oliva. *Makeup* Carlo Grillo. *English Vers* Nevada SPA.
Cast: Dieter Eppler (*The Blood Ghoul Vampire*), Walter Brandi, Graziella Granata, Paolo Solvay, Gena Gimmy, Alfredo Rizzo, Edda Ferronao, Carla Foscari, Marietta Procaccini.
Horror film. Wolfgang and Louise give a party in the castle that they have recently purchased near Vienna, and while playing the piano, Louise is struck by a strange sensation and retires to her room. A black-caped vampire attacks her and then visits her on subsequent occasions. Wolfgang calls a doctor, but Louise dies before he arrives. The doctor diagnoses the cause of death, but Louise reappears and attacks Wolfgang. Finding Louise's hiding place and that of another female vampire, the doctor destroys them both. Wolfgang, meanwhile, finds the hiding place of Louise's vampire lover and destroys him by driving an iron stake through his heart. *Vampires. Physicians. Impalement. Castles. Vienna.*

Note: Released in Italy in 1962 as *La strage dei vampiri*; running time: 84 min. Also known as *The Slaughter of the Vampires* and *Curses of the Ghouls*.

CURSE OF THE CRIMSON ALTAR see **THE CRIMSON CULT**

THE CURSE OF THE CRYING WOMAN (Mexico)   F6.0986
Cinematográfica A. B. S. A. *Dist* Trans-International Films. 9 Apr **1969** [Trenton, New Jersey, opening]. Sd; b&w. 35mm. 74 min.
Pres by K. Gordon Murray. *Prod* Abel Salazar. *Dir* Rafael Baledón. *Screenplay* Rafael Baledón, Fernando Galiana. *Adapt* Fernando Galiana. *Photog* José Ortiz Ramos. *Art Dir* Roberto Silva. *Film Ed* Alfredo Rosas Priego. *Mus* Gustavo César Carrión. *Sd* Javier Mateos.
Cast: Rosita Arenas, Abel Salazar, Rita Macedo, Carlos López Moctezuma, Mario Sevilla, Enrique Lucero, Domingo Soler.
Horror film. A young woman, a descendant of the "Crying Woman," inherits a house and is threatened by ghosts and witches. *Inheritance. Curses. Ghosts. Witches.*
Note: Released in Mexico in 1961 as *La maldición de la llorona*; also known as *La casa embrujada*.

THE CURSE OF THE CURIOUS see **THE CURSE OF HER FLESH**

THE CURSE OF THE DOLL PEOPLE (Mexico)   F6.0987
Cinematográfica Calderón. *Dist* Trans-International Films. 2 Mar **1968** [Jacksonville, Florida, opening]. Sd; b&w. 35mm. 83 min.
Pres by K. Gordon Murray. *Prod* William Calderon Stell. *Prod English Vers* K. Gordon Murray. *Dir* Benito Alazraki. *Dir English Vers* Paul Nagle. *Screenplay* Alfredo Salazar. *Photog* Enrique Wallace. *Art Dir* Manuel Fontanals. *Film Ed* Alfredo Rosas Priego. *Mus* Antonio Díaz Conde. *Sd* Ernesto Caballero.
Cast: Elvira Quintana, Ramón Gay, Roberto G. Rivera, Quintín Bulnes, Alfonso Arnold, Jorge Mondragón, Javier Loyá, Nora Veyrán, Luis Aragón.
Horror film. Four adventurers in Haiti witness a voodoo ceremony that is taboo to strangers, and the high priest puts a curse on them which later is fulfilled. *Adventurers. Voodoo. Curses. Rites and ceremonies. Haiti.*
Note: Released in Mexico in 1960 as *Muñecos infernales*.

THE CURSE OF THE FLESH see **THE CURSE OF HER FLESH**

CURSE OF THE FLY (Great Britain)   F6.0988
Lippert Films. *Dist* Twentieth Century–Fox Film Corp. May **1965** [c31 Mar 1965; LP30832]. Sd (Westrex); b&w. 35mm (CinemaScope). 86 min.
Prod Robert L. Lippert, Jack Parsons. *Dir* Don Sharp. *Writ* Harry Spalding. *Dir Photog* Basil Emmott. *Camera Op* Frank Drake. *Art Dir* Harry White. *Titl* Francis Rodker. *Supv Film Ed* Robert Winter. *Asst Ed* Colin Miller. *Mus Comp* Bert Shefter. *Played by* New Philharmonia Orchestra. *Orch* Johnny Pearson. *Sd Ed* Clive Smith. *Sd Rec* Jock May. *Asst Dir* Gordon Gilbert. *Prod Mgr* Teresa Bolland. *Cont* Renee Glynne. *Prod Sec* Angela Cockill. *Makeup* John O'Gorman, Eleanor Jones. *Sp Eff Makeup* Harold Fletcher. *Hairdresser* Barbara Barnard.
Cast: Brian Donlevy (*Henri Delambre*), George Baker (*Martin Delambre*), Carole Gray (*Patricia Stanley*), Yvette Rees (*Wan*), Burt Kwouk (*Tai*), Michael Graham (*Albert Delambre*), Jeremy Wilkin (*Inspector Ronet*), Charles Carson (*Inspector Charas*), Mary Manson (*Judith*), Rachel Kempson (*Madame Fournier*), Warren Stanhope (*hotel manager*), Mia Anderson (*nurse*), Arnold Bell (*porter*), Stan Simmons.
Horror film. For the past three generations the Delambre family has been attempting to disintegrate matter in one place (Montreal) and then transport and reintegrate it in another locale (London). Young Martin Delambre has just married Patricia Stanley, unaware that, though sane, she is an escapee from a mental institution. While staying at the Delambre Canadian estate with Martin and his father, Henri, Patricia begins to doubt her sanity. She learns not only of the ghastly experiments but also that Martin's former wife and two laboratory assistants are locked in the stables—all victims of the Delambres' past failures, which have left them part human and part fly. The experiments have also afflicted Martin with a mysterious recurring malady. Meanwhile, Wan, the Chinese housekeeper, persecutes Patricia because she has usurped the place of Martin's first wife, Judith. When police investigating Patricia's disappearance arrive at the estate, Henri decides that all the residents must be "teleported" to London. However, Martin's brother Albert destroys the London receiving equipment, and Henri becomes lost in the fourth dimension. Having no antidote serum, Martin takes on the metabolism of a fly, and his brief life span expires just as Patricia is rescued by the police. *Monsters. Escapees. Police. Chinese. Housekeepers. Teleportation. Experiments. Mental illness. Marriage. Filial relations. Hospitals. Laboratories. Canada. Montreal. London. Flies.*
Note: Released in Great Britain in Jan 1966. This film is a sequel to *The Fly* (Twentieth Century–Fox, 1958) and *Return of the Fly* (Twentieth Century–Fox, 1959). Working title: *The Curse of the Fly*.

CURSE OF THE GOLEM see **IT!**

THE CURSE OF THE LIVING CORPSE							F6.0989
Deal Films. *Dist* Twentieth Century-Fox Film Corp. 1 Apr **1964** [Detroit opening; c31 Dec 1963; LP27971]. Sd; b&w. 35mm. 84 min.

An Alan V. Iselin-Del Tenney Production. *Prod-Dir-Screenplay* Del Tenney. *Assoc Prod* Alan V. Iselin. *Photog* Richard Hilliard. *Art Dir* Robert Verberkmoss. *Film Ed* Gary Youngman, Jack Hirshfeld. *Mus* Bill Holmes.

Cast: Helen Waren *(Abigail Sinclair)*, Roy Scheider *(Philip Sinclair)*, Margot Hartman *(Vivian Sinclair)*, Robert Milli *(Bruce Sinclair)*, Hugh Franklin *(James Benson)*, Candace Hilligoss *(Deborah Benson)*, Dino Narizzano *(Robert Harrington)*, Linda Donovan *(Letty Crews)*, J. Frank Lucas *(Seth Lucas)*, Jane Bruce *(cook)*, Paul Haney *(Constable Barnes)*, George Cotton *(Constable Winters)*, William Blood *(minister)*.

Horror film. Tyrannical millionaire Rufus Sinclair is obsessed with a fear of premature burial. In his will, he stipulates that if buried alive, he will return from the grave and murder his heirs in the manner each of them fears most: his wife, Abigail, will die by fire; his sons, Bruce and Philip, will die by disfiguration and suffocation respectively; and Philip's wife, Vivian, will drown. Several days after Rufus' death and burial, his corpse vanishes from its crypt, and the murders begin to occur as predicted; in addition, both the family's maid and servant are killed, and the latter's body is found in Rufus' tomb. The deaths continue until Rufus' nephew, Robert Harrington, confronts the murderer in a quicksand bog and reveals him to be the millionaire's weakling son, who has been trying to obtain the family's wealth for himself. *Millionaires. Heirs. Psychopaths. Uncles. Domestics. Death. Murder. Greed. Disfiguration. Suffocation. Reviviscence. Wills. Corpses. Fires.*

Note: Filmed in Stamford, Connecticut.

THE CURSE OF THE MUMMY'S TOMB (Great Britain)			F6.0990
Hammer Film Productions-Swallow Productions. *Dist* Columbia Pictures. 17 Feb **1965** [Detroit opening; c31 Dec 1964; LP31460]. Sd; col (Technicolor). 35mm (Techniscope). 81 min.

Prod-Dir Michael Carreras. *Assoc Prod* Bill Hill. *Screenplay* Henry Younger. *Dir Photog* Otto Heller. *Camera Op* Robert Thomson. *Prod Dsgn* Bernard Robinson. *Supv Ed* James Needs. *Ed* Eric Boyd-Perkins. *Mus Comp* Carlo Martelli. *Mus Supv* Philip Martell. *Sd Ed* James Groom. *Sd Rec* Claude Hitchcock. *Asst Dir* Bert Batt, Hugh Harlow. *Cont* Eileen Head. *Wardrobe* Betty Adamson, John Briggs. *Makeup Artist* Roy Ashton. *Hairstyles* Iris Tilley. *Tech Adv* Andrew Low. *Casting* David Booth.

Cast: Ronald Howard *(John Bray)*, Terence Morgan *(Adam Beauchamp)*, Fred Clark *(Alexander King)*, Jeanne Roland *(Annette Dubois)*, George Pastell *(Hashmi Bey)*, Jack Gwillim *(Sir Giles Dalrymple)*, John Paul *(Inspector MacKenzie)*, Dickie Owen *(The Mummy)*, Michael McStay *(Ra-Antef)*, Harold Goodwin *(Fred)*, Michael Ripper *(Achmed)*, Vernon Smythe *(Jessop)*, Jill Mai Meredith *(Jenny)*, Bernard Rebel *(Professor Dubois)*, Marianne Stone *(landlady)*, Jimmy Gardner.

Horror film. The tomb of Ra-Antef, the pharaoh, is excavated in 1900, and soon afterwards archeologist Professor Dubois is murdered. American showman Alexander King, who is financing the expedition, wants to take the remains and artifacts on an exhibition tour, despite the warnings of archeologists and Hashmi Bey, the Egyptian advisor, that violating the tomb activates its curse. En route to London, the party experiences the effects of the curse. John Bray, the boyfriend of Professor Dubois' daughter Annette, is attacked but is saved by Adam Beauchamp, who falls in love with Annette. As the exhibition is about to open, the mummy case is found to be empty. Ra-Antef fulfills the curse by murdering King, expedition leader Sir Giles Dalrymple, and Hashmi Bey and by abducting Annette. Beauchamp, really Ra-Antef's brother, is revealed to be cursed with immortality because he killed Ra-Antef. He confronts his brother in the sewers, asking Ra-Antef to kill him and also Annette so that they may spend eternity together. John Bray and Inspector MacKenzie are able to rescue Annette as Ra-Antef destroys both himself and his brother. *Archeologists. Professors. Royalty. Brothers. Mummies. Americans in foreign countries. Showmen. Fratricide. Curses. Immortality. Abduction. Murder. Tombs. Sewers. Egypt. London.*

Note: Released in Great Britain in Oct 1964.

CURSE OF THE STONE HAND							F6.0991
Dist Associated Distributors Pictures. Apr **1965**. Sd; b&w. 35mm. 72 min.
Prod Jerry Warren. *Dir* Jerry Warren, Carl Schleipper. *Screenplay* Amos Powell, Marie Laurent. *Photog* Ricardo Younis.

Cast: John Carradine *(hypnotist)*, Ernest Walch, Sheila Bon, Katherine Victor, Lloyd Nelson.

Horror film. Hands sculpted in stone, hidden in the niches of an ancient house, are regarded as sources of a curse by the present inhabitant, a country gentleman addicted to gambling; and indeed he does go to an early grave after experiencing bankruptcy. The house then passes to another family, one of whose sons becomes obsessed with the hands. This son develops sadistic tendencies and, acquiring hypnotic powers, finds himself exercising a mystical control over a brother's fiancée. She repels him, however, and in doing so breaks the spell. The hypnotist, turning to the stone hands, is killed. *Hypnotists. Gamblers. Brothers. Curses. Bankruptcy. Obsession. Sadism. Spells. Sculptures.*

Note: Filmed in Mexico in 1959 as a 2-part feature. Footage added for U.S. release.

CURSE OF THE VAMPIRE see **THE PLAYGIRLS AND THE VAMPIRE**

CURSE OF THE VAMPIRES (United States/Philippines)			F6.0992
Sceptre Industries. *Dist* Hemisphere Pictures. Aug **1970**. Sd; col (Eastman Color). 35mm. 90 min.

Exec Prod Amalia Muhlach. *Dir* Gerardo de Leon. *Screenplay* Ben Feleo, Pierre L. Salas. *Story* Ben Feleo. *Dir Photog* Mike Accion. *Asst Camera* Edmundo Bautista. *Col Cons* Johnny Fornoles. *Set Dir* Ben Otico. *Film Ed* Ben Barcelón. *Asst Film Ed* Narciso Galang. *Mus Comp & Cond* Tito Arevalo. *Lyr* Robert Arevalo. *Orch Vic* Marqueses, Pepe Manuel. *Sd* Salustiano Evarle. *Rec* Vincente Dona, Tony Evarle, Pedro Nicolas. *Sd Eff* Tony Gosalves. *Sd Engr* Demetrio de Santos. *Asst Dir* D. K. Trofeo. *Prod Supv* Alvaro Muhlach. *Men's Wardrobe* F. P. Bautista. *Makeup Artist* Baby Buencamino. *Miss Fuentes' Hairstyles* Lagring of D'Milling.

Cast: Amalia Fuentes *(Leonora)*, Eddie Garcia *(Eduardo)*, Romeo Vasquez *(Daniel)*, Mary Walter *(Mother)*, Johnny Monteiro, Rosario del Pilar, Francisco Cruz, Paquito Salcedo, Quiel Mendoza, Andres Benitez, Luz Angeles, Tessie Hernandez, Linda Rivera.

Horror film. At the turn of the century, Eduardo and his sister Leonora return to their parents' mansion on an island in the Philippines. Upon discovering that their anguished father has imprisoned their mother in the basement because she is a vampire, the horrified Leonora breaks off her engagement with her childhood sweetheart. When Eduardo visits his mother, the old woman attacks him, sinks her fangs into his neck, and turns him into a vampire. As a result, Eduardo, now among the accursed, vampirizes his sweetheart before marrying her. Learning of these happenings, Eduardo's distraught father drives a stake through his wife's heart, but is himself murdered by Eduardo. A short time later, Leonora's fiancée is thrown from his horse and killed when the animal is frightened by the vampire-mother's ghost. Eduardo and his wife strive to turn Leonora into a vampire but are thwarted in their first attempt by the appearance of her fiancé's ghost. After opening her dead lover's coffin to prove to herself that he is indeed dead, the grief-stricken Leonora returns home and is attacked and bitten by Eduardo, his wife, and three other female vampires. The following evening, the local priest and doctor lead a mob of townspeople to the house in order to rescue Leonora, but it is too late. Lying in bed, Leonora's face has twisted into the hideous visage of a vampire, with fangs protruding from her mouth. Suddenly, the ghost of her lover appears, kneels beside her bed, and begins to pray. Presently, a crucifix floats through the air, levitates over Leonora, and plunges itself through her heart. As the villagers set fire to the mansion, destroying all its unearthly inhabitants, the departed Leonora, freed from the curse of the vampires, is reunited in the afterlife with the spirit of her lover. *Vampires. Ghosts. Priests. Family life. Marriage. Murder. Fires. Impalement. Islands.*

Note: Filmed in the Philippines.

CURSE OF THE VOODOO (United States/Great Britain)			F6.0993
Galaworldfilm Productions-Gordon Films. *Dist* Allied Artists. 22 Sep **1965** [Ohio opening]. Sd; b&w. 35mm. 77 min.

Pres by Futurama Entertainment Corp. *Exec Prod* Kenneth Rive. *Dir* Lindsay Shonteff. *Screenplay* Tony O'Grady. *Adtl Scenes & Dial* Leigh Vance. *Dir Photog* Gerald Gibbs. *Art Dir* Tony Inglis. *Film Ed* Barry Vince. *Mus Comp & Cond* Brian Fahey. *Nightclub Mus* Bobby Breen Quintet. *Sd Rec* Jock May. *Asst Dir* Bill Snaith. *Prod Mgr* Fred Slark.

Cast: Bryant Halliday *(Mike Stacey)*, Dennis Price *(Major Lomas)*, Lisa Daniely *(Janet Stacey)*, Mary Kerridge *(Janet's mother)*, Ronald Leigh Hunt *(doctor)*, Jean Lodge *(Mrs. Lomas)*, Dennis Alaba Peters *(Saidi)*, Tony Thawnton *(Radlett)*, Michael Nightingale *(2d hunter)*, Andy Myers *(Tommy Stacey)*, Louis Majoney *(African expert)*, Jimmy Felgate *(barman)*, Nigel Feyistan *(Simbasa in London)*, Beryl Cunningham *(nightclub dancer)*, Bobby Breen Quintet *(nightclub band)*, John Witty, Danny Daniels, Valli Newby.

Melodrama. Mike Stacey, a big game hunter, travels to Simbasi territory while on an African safari. There he kills a lion, an animal sacred to the Simba tribe, and is consequently cursed by the tribal chief, M'Gobo. The Simbas capture Saidi, Mike's aide, and when they torture him, Mike also feels the pain. Moreover, Mike returns to Johannesburg to learn that his wife, Janet, has left him. He follows her to London and continues to suffer great physical and mental anguish, including fever, wounds, and hallucinations. Janet consults an

African expert and learns that Mike must kill M'Gobo to rid himself of the curse. He returns to Africa, kills M'Gobo by running him down with his jeep, and lifts the curse. *Hunters. Tribal chiefs. Simbas. Torture. Voodoo. Safaris. Curses. Africa. Johannesburg. London. Hallucinations. Big game. Lions.*

Note: Filmed in England and released there in 1965 as *Curse of Simba*; running time: 61 min.

THE CURSE OF THE WEREWOLF (Great Britain)   **F6.0994**
Hammer Film Productions-Hotspur Films. *Dist* Universal-International Films. 7 Jun **1961** [New York opening; c19 Dec 1960; LP24730]. Sd; col (Eastman Color). 35mm. 91 min.

Prod Anthony Hinds. *Assoc Prod* Anthony Nelson Keys. *Exec Prod* Michael Carreras. *Dir* Terence Fisher. *Screenplay* John Elder. *Dir Photog* Arthur Grant. *Camera Op* Len Harris. *Art Dir* Thomas Goswell. *Asst Art Dir* Don Mingaye. *Prod Dsgn* Bernard Robinson. *Supv Ed* James Needs. *Ed* Alfred Cox. *Mus Comp & Cond* Benjamin Frankel. *Sd* Jock May. *Sd Ed* Alban Streeter. *1st & 2d Asst Dir* John Peverall, Dominic Fulford. *Prod Mgr* Clifford Parkes. *Cont* Tilly Day. *Wardrobe Mistress* Molly Arbuthnot. *Makeup* Roy Ashton. *Hairdresser* Frieda Steiger. *Sp Eff* Les Bowie. *Casting Dir* Stuart Lyons. *Still Photog* Tom Edwards.

Cast: Clifford Evans *(Don Alfredo Carido)*, Oliver Reed *(León)*, Yvonne Romain *(servant girl)*, Catherine Feller *(Cristina Fernando)*, Anthony Dawson, British *(Marqués Siniestro)*, Hira Talfrey *(Teresa)*, Richard Wordsworth *(beggar)*, Warren Mitchell *(Pepe Valiente)*, George Woodbridge *(Dominique)*, John Gabriel *(priest)*, Ewen Solon *(Don Fernando)*, Peter Sallis *(Don Enrique)*, Michael Ripper *(old soaker)*, Sheila Brennan *(Vera)*, Martin Matthews *(José)*, David Conville *(Rico Gómez)*, Anne Blake *(Rosa Valiente)*, Denis Shaw *(gaoler)*, Josephine Llewellyn *(Marquesa)*, Justin Walters *(young León)*, Renny Lister *(Yvonne)*, Joy Webster *(Isabel)*, John Bennett *(policeman)*, Charles Lamb *(chef)*, Desmond Llewelyn, Gordon Whiting *(footmen)*, Hamlyn Benson *(landlord)*, Serafina Di Leo *(Señora Zumara)*, Kitty Attwood *(midwife)*, Howard Lang *(irate farmer)*, Stephen W. Scott *(another farmer)*, Ray Browne *(official)*, Frank Sieman *(gardener)*, Max Butterfield *(cheeky farmer)*, Michael Peake *(farmer at cantina)*, Rodney Burke, Alan Page, Richard Golding *(customers)*, Michael Lewis *(page)*, Loraine Caruana *(servant girl as a child)*.

Horror film. Source: Guy Endore, *The Werewolf of Paris* (New York, 1933). In 18th-century Spain, the sadistic Marqués Siniestro imprisons a beggar in a dungeon and treats him as a dog, naming him Fido. Ten years later the poor creature is joined by a deafmute servant girl who is being punished for rejecting the marqués' advances. Maddened by his long confinement, the beggar savagely molests the girl and then perishes, a victim of his own metamorphosis into an animal. The ravished girl escapes, kills the marqués, and then tries to drown herself in a river. She is saved by a kindly professor, Alfredo Carido, who takes care of her until she dies giving birth to the beggar's son. Carido christens the child León and adopts him as his own son. As the years pass it becomes apparent that the lad has werewolf tendencies, and by the time he reaches manhood he is responsible for several brutal murders. Realizing the awful truth about himself and fearful that he may someday harm his beloved Cristina, León begs Carido for help. Carido has him sent to a monastery, where he is kept in chains; but eventually León escapes, attempts to elope with Cristina, and is captured and jailed by the police. On the night of the next full moon, León breaks out of his cell and scrambles to the rooftops of the village. The grief-stricken Carido finally kills him with a special bullet—a silver pellet carved from a blessed crucifix. *Nobility. Monsters. Professors. Deafmutes. Rape. Metamorphosis. Murder. Adoption. Jailbreaks. Monasteries. Spain. Werewolves.*

Note: Opened in London in Apr 1961; running time: 88 min. John Elder is a pseudonym for Anthony Hinds.

CURSES OF THE GHOULS *see* **CURSE OF THE BLOOD-GHOULS**

CUSTER *see* **CUSTER OF THE WEST**

THE CUSTER MASSACRE *see* **THE GREAT SIOUX MASSACRE**

CUSTER OF THE WEST   **F6.0995**
Security Pictures. *Dist* Cinerama Releasing Corp. 24 Jan **1968** [Houston opening; c9 Nov 1967; LP38108]. Sd; col (Technicolor). 35mm & 70mm (Super Technirama). 143 min. [Also 140 min; cut to 120 min.]

Prod Philip Yordan, Louis Dolivet. *Exec Prod* Irving Lerner. *Prod Exec* Lester A. Sansom. *Dir* Robert Siodmak. *Dir Civil War Seq* Irving Lerner. *Screenplay* Bernard Gordon, Julian Halevy. *Dir Photog* Cecilio Paniagua. *Art Dir* Jean d' Eaubonne, Eugene Lourie, Julio Molina. *Set Dressing* Antonio Mateos. *Film Ed* Maurice Rootes. *Mus Comp & Cond* Bernardo Segáll. *Songs:* "Marching Song," "Maxwell House," "Heroes Die" Bernardo Segáll, Will Holt. *Song: "Follow Custer"* Bernardo Segáll, Robert Shaw. *Mus Perf by* Royal Philharmonic Orchestra. *Sd Ed* Kurt Herrnfeld, Alban Streeter. *Asst Dir* José María Ochoa. *Prod Supv* Gregorio Sacristan. *Prod Mgr* José Manuel M.

Herrero. *Unit Mgr* Alejandro Peria. *Script Supv* Eva del Castillo. *Dial Cont* John Kirby. *Cost Dsgn* Laure de Zarate. *Wardrobe* Charles Simminger. *Makeup Artist* Julian Ruiz. *Casting* Lillian Kelly.

Cast: Robert Shaw *(Gen. George Armstrong Custer)*, Mary Ure *(Elizabeth Custer)*, Jeffrey Hunter *(Lieutenant Benteen)*, Ty Hardin *(Maj. Marcus Reno)*, Charles Stalnaker *(Lieutenant Howells)*, Robert Hall *(Sergeant Buckley)*, Lawrence Tierney *(Gen. Philip Sheridan)*, Kieron Moore *(Chief Dull Knife)*, Marc Lawrence *(The Goldminer)*, Robert Ryan *(Sergeant Mulligan)*, Jack Gaskins, John Clarke, Bill Christmas, Joe Zboran, Jack Cooper, Carl Rapp, Bud Strait, Dennis Kilbane, Jack Taylor, Fred Kohler, Luis Rivera, Clemence Bettany, Barta Barri, John Dillon, John Underhill, Robert Reynolds.

Western epic. After a flamboyantly successful career in the Civil War, young Gen. George Armstrong Custer goes West, accompanied by his wife, Elizabeth, to take command of the 7th Cavalry. As he sets out to subdue the Indians, who are rebelling against the government's reservation policies, he overcomes initial conflicts with the hard-drinking Maj. Marcus Reno and with Lieutenant Benteen, who is sympathetic toward the Indians' plight, and tightens discipline among his men. Custer receives a surprise visit from Gen. Philip Sheridan, who orders him to attack a Cheyenne village as appeasement for Washington politicians. Custer complies, but his troops run wild and massacre women and children. Though he refuses to take a conciliatory approach toward Chief Dull Knife, he concludes that government responsiveness to private interests must be curbed if peace is to be secured. A patrol of Custer's men deserts after gold is discovered on the reservation, and he is forced to execute the leader, Sergeant Mulligan; meanwhile, efforts to gain Washington's adherence to the terms of the Indian treaties fail totally. Following an Indian ambush of a new railroad that runs through their land, Custer is called to Washington. He exposes top-level politicians in President Grant's administration who have been bribed to serve as spokesmen for railroad and mining interests, and as a result he is relieved of his command. He is disheartened to hear that his men are about to march against the Indians without him. Through the diplomacy of his wife, however, Custer is permitted to return to Dakota to lead his men in battle. At Little Big Horn, his troops are overwhelmed by the Indians, and Custer is the last to die. *Cheyenne Indians. Sioux Indians. Political corruption. Massacres. Railroads. Gold. United States—History—Civil War. United States—History—Indian campaigns. Battle of Washita. Little Big Horn. George Armstrong Custer. Elizabeth Bacon Custer. Philip Henry Sheridan. Marcus A. Reno. Frederick W. Benteen. Dull Knife. Ulysses Simpson Grant. United States Army—Cavalry.*

Note: Filmed in Spain. Presented in Cinerama for some roadshow engagements. Also known as *A Good Day for Fighting*. Working title: *Custer*.

CYBÈLE *see* **SUNDAYS AND CYBÈLE**

CYBORG 2087   **F6.0996**
United Pictures-Harold Goldman Associates-Television Enterprises Corp. *Dist* Feature Film Corp. of America. Oct **1966** [c23 Nov 1966; LP34214]. Sd; col (Eastmancolor). 35mm. 90 min. [Copyright length: 86 min.]

Prod Earle Lyon. *Exec Prod* Fred Jordan. *Dir* Franklin Adreon. *Screenplay* Arthur C. Pierce. *Art Dir* Paul Sylos, Jr. *Film Ed* Frank P. Keller. *Mus* Paul Dunlap.

Cast: Michael Rennie *(Garth)*, Karen Steele *(Sharon)*, Wendell Corey *(sheriff)*, Warren Stevens *(Dr. Zeller)*, Eduard Franz *(Professor Marx)*, Harry Carey, Jr. *(Jay C.)*, Adam Roarke, Chubby Johnson, Tyler MacDuff, Dale Van Sickel, Troy Melton, Jimmy Hibbard, Sherry Alberoni, Betty Jane Royale, John Beck, actor, George Fisher.

Science fiction drama. In 1966, Professor Marx discovers a means of controlling human beings by radio telepathy. By the year 2087, Professor Marx's discovery has been used by evil men to create Cyborgs, automatons having human form. A few Cyborgs who have achieved mental freedom send Garth, one of their kind, back in time to 1966, shortly before the professor is to make known his discovery. Garth's mission is to persuade Marx to keep secret his discovery. Pursued by two "Tracers" who have been sent by the evil men to kill him, Garth convinces Sharon, the professor's assistant, that she must help him to remove a mechanical device from his body, thus making finding him more difficult. She summons a friend, Dr. Zeller, who successfully performs the operation. Garth and Dr. Zeller then attempt to electrocute the Tracers; and, failing to destroy them, Garth escapes to a nearby ghost town. By controlling Sharon's mind, Garth induces her to bring the professor to him. He then overcomes the Tracers, and he and the professor depart for the future. Marx sees the uses to which his discovery will be made, and he decides to guard his secret. Sharon and Dr. Zeller discover they are in love, and life goes on as if there had been no Cyborgs. *Scientists. Professors. Androids. Physicians. Mental telepathy. Time travel. Radio. The Future.*

THE CYCLE SAVAGES
F6.0997

Maurice Smith Productions. *Dist* American International Pictures, Trans-American Films. 22 Aug **1969** [Charlotte, North Carolina, opening; c12 Apr 1969; LP38104]. Sd; col (Movielab). 35mm. 82 min. *MPAA rating* R.

A Maurice Smith-Ray Dorn Production. *Prod* Maurice Smith. *Assoc Prod* Arthur Gilbert, Frank Ragusa. *Exec Prod* Mike Curb, Casey Kasem. *Dir-Writ* Bill Brame. *Dir Photog* Frank Ruttencutter. *Asst Camera* Manuel Shain. *Art Dir* Ray Markham. *Art Work* Ray Robles. *Film Ed* Herman Freedman. *Mus* Jerry Styner, Sidewalk Productions. *Sd* Joe Dixon. *Prod Mgr* Herman Freedman. *Script Supv* Sanan Pierson. *Wardrobe* Sally Jordan. *Makeup* Louis Lane. *Vis Eff* Modern Film Effects. *Tech Adv* Lynn Steed. *Stunt Coörd* Chuck Bail. *Gaffer* John Murray. *Key Grip* Russ Nannarello. *Still Photog* Tom Hohl.

Cast: Bruce Dern (*Keeg*), Melody Patterson (*Lea*), Chris Robinson (*Romko*), Maray Ayres (*Sandy*), Karen Ciral (*Janie*), Mick Mehas (*Bob*), Jack Konzal (*bartender*), Walter Robles (*Tom [Walter?]*), Daniel Ghaffouri (*Marvin*), Anna Sugano (*motorcycle girl*), Gary Littlejohn (*motorcycle boy*), Ron Godwin (*Walter*), Lee Chandler (*Doug*), Marjorie Dayne (*motorcycle girl*), Randee Lee (*one of the girls*), Jerry Taylor (*storekeeper*), Denise Gilbert (*little girl*), Peter Fain, Steve Brodie (*police detectives*), Virginia Hawkins (*woman*), Tom Daly (*Docky*), Casey Kasem (*Keeg's brother*), Scott Brady (*vice squad detective*), Joe McManus, Linda Banks.

Action melodrama. Keeg, the leader of a Los Angeles motorcycle gang, attacks Romko, an artist who is sketching the gang, and takes away his drawings. When Romko again attempts to sketch the gang, he is beaten up and his hands are slashed. Keeg warns the members of the gang that the sketches can be incriminating because of the gang's white slavery operations in Las Vegas. Lea, a follower of the gang, invites Romko into her apartment and summons Docky to attend to Romko's injured hands. Working with the gang to detain Romko long enough for Keeg to ransack his apartment of all the remaining sketches, Lea offers to pose in the nude for Romko. He visits her the next day, and they make love. Meanwhile, the motorcycle gang has kidnaped Janie from the local high school with the intention of making her a prostitute. The entire gang rapes her, and Keeg gives her a large dose of LSD. Keeg then forces another girl, Sandy, to have sex with one of the members of the gang. The police arrive at Lea's apartment to investigate the attack that had been made on Romko. Romko refuses to cooperate with the police, and he and Lea are arrested but are released from jail the next day. Members of the gang capture Romko, take him to a cellar, and torture him by squeezing his hands in a vise. Lea arrives with a gun, but she lacks the courage to shoot, and Sandy grabs the gun from her hand and shoots Keeg. The police then arrive and arrest the members of the gang for raping Janie. *Motorcycle gangs. Artists. Police. Prostitution. Rape. Mutilation. Kidnaping. Torture. White slave traffic. LSD. Los Angeles.*

D GIRLS see **THE DIRTY GIRLS**

DA NEW YORK: MAFIA UCCIDE! see **HAIL! MAFIA**

DÅ SKA DU FÅ EN GUNGSTOL AV MIG—EN BLÅ see **ANNA, MY DARLING**

DA UOMO A UOMO see **DEATH RIDES A HORSE**

ĎÁBLOVA PAST see **THE DEVIL'S TRAP**

DADDY, DARLING
F6.0998

Cinetex Industries. 18 Nov **1970** [Philadelphia opening]. Sd; col (Eastman Color). 35mm. 96 min. *MPAA rating* X.

Pres by Kenn Collins. *Prod* Kenn Collins. *Dir-Writ* Joseph W. Sarno. *Dir Photog* Mikael Salomon. *Set Dsgn* Togo Esben. *Film Ed* Renée Lichtig. *Mus Comp & Cond* Tony Hazzard. *Songs:* "Hello, World," "Fade Away, Maureen," "Hello It's Me," "Me, the Peaceful Heart," "You Won't Be Leaving" Tony Hazzard. *Sd* Paul Boistelle. *Prod Mgr* Palle Schnedler-Sørensen. *Script Girl* Suzanne Bruhn. *Wardrobe* Peggy Stephans. *Makeup* Else Hennings. *Dial Dir* Hal Brav.

Cast: Helle Louise (*Katia Holmqvist*), Gio Petré (*Svea*), Ole Wisborg (*Eric Holmqvist*), Lise Henningsen (*Lena Belling*), Søren Strømberg (*Lars*), Lise Thomsen (*Eva*), Tove Maës (*Segrid*), Fezex Kyo (*Lise*), Inger Gleerup (*Marie*), Jeanette Swensson (*Tonja*).

Domestic drama. In Copenhagen, Katia Holmqvist, a 19-year-old design student, is jealous of her widowed father Eric's fiancée, Svea. Following the couple's marriage and honeymoon, Katia, frustrated by her failure to seduce her father, breaks down after attending class. Miss Den, her sympathetic instructress, introduces Katia to Lena Balling, a successful artist, who agrees to give Katia lessons. Excited by Lena's instruction, Katia warms slightly toward Svea. During her father and stepmother's holiday in Norway, Katia seduces Lars, a boy her own age, whom, she pretends, is her father. Several days later, Katia overhears Eric and Svea making love. After rushing to her teacher's studio for consolation, Katia is fondled by Lena and Tonja, Lena's model and

lover. Finding Katia unresponsive, however, Lena orders her to leave. When Eric later goes to Stockholm on business, Katia seduces her stepmother; but, realizing the futility of her incestuous attraction to Eric, she leaves home the following morning. *Students. Widowers. Artists. Stepmothers. Models. Adolescence. Jealousy. Filial relations. Seduction. Incest. Lesbianism. Copenhagen.*

Note: Location scenes filmed in and around Copenhagen. Working title: *Behind Closed Doors.*

DADDY SAID THE WORLD WAS LOVELY see **PSYCHOUT FOR MURDER**

DADDY'S DELECTABLE DOZEN see **THE TURKISH CUCUMBER**

DADDY'S GONE A-HUNTING
F6.0999

Red Lion Productions. *Dist* National General Pictures. 2 Jul **1969** [Columbus, Ohio, opening]. Sd; col (Technicolor). 35mm (Panavision). 108 min. *MPAA rating* M.

A Mark Robson Production. *Prod-Dir* Mark Robson. *Screenplay* Larry Cohen, Lorenzo Semple, Jr. *Photog* Ernest Laszlo. *Art Dir* James Sullivan. *Set Decor* Charles Thompson. *Main Titl* Pacific Title. *Film Ed* Dorothy Spencer. *Mus Comp & Cond* Johnny Williams. *Titl Song* Johnny Williams, Dory Previn. *Sung by* Lyn Roman. *Sd* Clarence Peterson. *Asst Dir* Fred Simpson. *Prod Mgr* Harry Caplan. *Cost* Travilla. *Makeup* Paul Stanhope. *Hairstyles* Scotty Rackin.

Cast: Carol White (*Cathy Palmer*), Scott Hylands (*Kenneth Daly*), Paul Burke (*Jack Byrnes*), Mala Powers (*Meg Stone*), Rachel Ames (*Dr. Parkington's nurse*), Barry Cahill (*FBI Agent Crosley*), Matilda Calnan (*Ilsa, the maid*), Andrea King (*Brenda Frazier*), Gene Lyons (*Dr. Blanker*), Ron Masak (*Paul Fanning*), Dennis Patrick (*Dr. Parkington*), James Sikking (*FBI Agent Menchell*), Harry Holcombe (*Inspector Dixon*).

Melodrama. Newly arrived in San Francisco to seek a career in advertising, young Englishwoman Cathy Palmer meets and falls in love with Kenneth Daly, an out-of-work photographer. After some months, Cathy learns she is pregnant. Although Kenneth is delighted by the news and wants to get married at once, Cathy by now realizes that Kenneth is violent and emotionally unstable, and she takes the advice of her friend, Meg Stone, by having an abortion. Upon learning what she has done, Kenneth violently accuses her of murdering his child, and then disappears. In time, Cathy marries Jack Byrnes, a successful lawyer with political aspirations. After becoming pregnant again, Cathy begins to suspect that Kenneth is following her, and the ultimate confirmation of her suspicions sends her into premature labor. In the hospital waiting room, Kenneth strikes up a conversation with Jack and wins his sympathy by telling him that his own baby is dead; and he subsequently arrives at the Byrnes home to photograph the new baby. Frightened, Cathy conceals the truth from Jack and goes to visit Kenneth in the hope of reasoning with him, unaware that he has already murdered Dr. Parkington, who had performed the abortion. During their confrontation, Kenneth demands that Cathy kill Jack's baby to atone for murdering his. Terrified, Cathy rushes to Jack and confesses everything, but it is too late. When they return home, they find the baby and the cat's carrying case missing. Cathy then receives a telephone call from Kenneth instructing her to bring the baby's formula to his hotel room. While FBI agents are monitoring the call, Cathy arrives at the hotel and is about to feed her baby when she realizes that Kenneth has poisoned the formula. Before she can escape with her baby, Kenneth knocks her unconscious, places the baby in the carrying case, and flees. Once the FBI and Jack have revived Cathy, they trace Kenneth to the top of the Mark Hopkins Hotel. Overcoming her fear of heights, Cathy climbs up after Kenneth, and after promising to hurl her baby to its death and divorce Jack, she makes a desperate attempt to shove Kenneth aside and grab the carrying case. During the struggle, Cathy saves her child, but Kenneth loses his footing and plummets to his death. *English. Careerwomen. Photographers. Infants. Lawyers. Abortion. Kidnaping. Murder. Parenthood. Pregnancy. Insanity. San Francisco. United States—Federal Bureau of Investigation. Mark Hopkins Hotel. Cats.*

Note: Filmed on location in San Francisco.

DAFFODIL KILLER see **THE DEVIL'S DAFFODIL**

DAFFY see **WILD SEED**

DAGGERS OF BLOOD see **INVASION 1700**

DAI SANJI SEKAI TAISEN—YONJU-ICHI JIKAN NO KYOFU see **THE FINAL WAR**

DAI TATSUMAKI see **WHIRLWIND**

DAIBOKEN see **DON'T CALL ME A CON MAN**

DAIBOSATSU TOGE *see* **THE SWORD OF DOOM**

DAIGAKU NO WAKADAISHO *see* **BULL OF THE CAMPUS**

DAIKAIJU BARAN *see* **VARAN THE UNBELIEVABLE**

DAIKAIJU GAMERA *see* **GAMMERA THE INVINCIBLE**

DAIKANBU *see* **THE GANGSTER VIP**

DAIKON TO NINJIN *see* **TWILIGHT PATH**

DAIKU TAIHEIKI *see* **TALE OF A CARPENTER**

THE DAILY DOUBLE *see* **6-9 THE DAILY DOUBLE**

DAIMAJIN *see* **MAJIN**

DAIROKU NO YOGISHA *see* **SIX SUSPECTS**

DAISIES (Czechoslovakia)   **F6.1000**
Barrandov Film Studio. *For* Československý Film. *Dist* Sigma III Corp. 25 Oct **1967** [New York opening]. Sd; col with b&w seq. 35mm. 74 min.
   Pres by Carlo Ponti. *Dir* Věra Chytilová. *Screenplay* Věra Chytilová, Ester Krumbachová. *Story* Věra Chytilová, Pavel Juráček, Ester Krumbachová. *Photog* Jaroslav Kučera. *Art Dir* Karel Lier. *Film Ed* Miroslav Hájek. *Mus* Jiří Šlitr, Jiří Šust. *Sd* Ladislav Hausdorf. *Cost* Anna Beranková. *Production Group* Šmida–Fikar.
   Cast: Jitka Crhová (*Marie I*), Ivana Karbanová (*Marie II*), Julius Albert (*man-about-town with butterfly collection*), Marie Cesková, Jiřína Cesková, Jiřína Myšková, Jan Klusák.
   Allegory. Having concluded that everything in the world is spoiled, two teenaged girls, both named Marie, decide that they also should be spoiled. They order dinner at an elderly man's expense, running up an exorbitant restaurant bill without in any way reciprocating his generosity. They steal money from the ladies' room attendant, dress extravagantly and provoke public astonishment, destroy each other's clothing, set little fires, tear out each other's hair—all to prove that "we exist." Marie II tires of the butterfly collector with whom she has been having an affair. After creating scenes at a nightclub, in the countryside, and on a train, they wander into a hotel where they find an elegant banquet table, which is an irresistible object for their playful destructiveness. They throw pies and salads at each other, break dishes, overturn furniture, and finally swing from a chandelier that crashes through an open window under their weight, throwing them into the river. Remorseful at the havoc they have wrought on the dining room, they go back and diligently return it to a lunatic facsimile of its former state. They lie down on the table to rest after making futile restorative efforts, wondering if they are really happy, and again the chandelier falls from the ceiling, this time with a mushroom-like explosion. And with this action come the words: "Dedication—To all those whose indignation is limited to a smashed-up salad." *Philosophers. Collectors. Existentialism. Theft. Incendiarism. Adolescence. Food. Hotels. Nightclubs. Trains. Explosions. Butterflies.*
   Note: Produced in Czechoslovakia in 1966 as *Sedmikrásky*; running time: 76-78 min.

THE DAISY CHAIN   **F6.1001**
Hollywood Cinema Associates. *Dist* Crest Film Distributors. 29 Aug **1969** [Champaign, Illinois, showing]. Sd; col. 35mm. 73 min.
   Prod-Dir Don Davis. *Screenplay* Jason Hunter.
   Cast: Marsha Jordan, Linda Lorrigan, Samantha Scott, Ingred Hansen, Helen Baker, Maria Bonner, Forman Shain.
   Drama. The airline pilots, stewardesses, and executive passengers who comprise "The Daisy Chain Club" are dedicated to sex. Recognizing one another by their special daisy-shaped lapel pins, they participate in sex orgies during dull lay-overs and amuse themselves in the air while the auto-pilot controls the plane. When the mother of a club member, looking for her daughter, eavesdrops on a club orgy, in horror she calls the police. By the time they arrive, the errant daughter has joined the nude revel around an ornate fountain. *Air pilots. Airline stewardesses. Businessmen. Promiscuity. Orgies. Sex clubs. Airplanes.*
   Note: May also be known as *The Chain*.

DAITOZOKU *see* **SAMURAI PIRATE**

DALEKS—INVASION EARTH 2150 A. D. (Great Britain)   **F6.1002**
Aaru–Amicus Productions. *Dist* Continental Distributing, Inc. Jun **1967**. Sd; col (Technicolor). 35mm (Techniscope). 84 min.
   Prod Max J. Rosenberg, Milton Subotsky. *Exec Prod* Joe Vegoda. *Dir* Gordon Flemyng. *Screenplay* Milton Subotsky. *Adtl Dial* David Whitaker, writ. *Photog* John Wilcox. *Art Dir* George Provis. *Set Decor* Maurice Pelling. *Film Ed* Ann Chegwidden. *Mus Comp & Cond* Bill McGuffie. *Electronic Mus* Barry Gray. *Sd* John Cox. *Sd Rec* Buster Ambler. *Asst Dir* Anthony Waye.

Prod Mgr Ted Wallis. *Wardrobe* Jackie Cummins. *Makeup* Bunty Phillips. *Hairstyles* Bobbie Smith. *Sp Eff* Ted Samuels.
   Cast: Peter Cushing (*Dr. Who*), Bernard Cribbins (*Tom Campbell*), Ray Brooks (*David*), Andrew Keir (*Wyler*), Roberta Tovey (*Susan*), Jill Curzon (*Louise*), Roger Avon (*Wells*), Keith Marsh (*Conway*), Geoffrey Cheshire (*RoboMan*), Steve Peters (*leader RoboMan*), Philip Madoc (*Brockley*), Eddie Powell (*Thompson*), Godfrey Quigley (*Dortmun*), Tony Reynolds (*man on bicycle*), Bernard Spear (*man with carrier bag*), Sheila Steafel (*young woman*), Eileen Way (*old woman*), Kenneth Watson (*Craddock*), John Wreford (*robber*), Robert Jewell (*leader Dalek operator*).
   Science fiction melodrama. Based on the BBC TV serial *Dr. Who* by: Terry Nation. Tom Campbell, a London constable, mistakes Dr. Who's time machine for an alarm box in his haste to report a robbery in progress and inadvertently joins Dr. Who, his niece Louise, and his granddaughter Susan on a journey to the year 2150 A. D. They discover that London has been desolated by meteorites and cosmic rays and its inhabitants converted into robots by Daleks, mechanical invaders from another planet. While exploring the ruins, Tom and Dr. Who are captured by Daleks, but Louise and Susan are rescued by underground resistance fighters David, Wyler, and Dortmun. Gallantly attacking the aliens with makeshift bombs, David helps Dr. Who escape, but Louise and Tom are left behind inside the Dalek spacecraft. [According to one source, Dortmun initiates the bomb attack.] Wyler and Susan flee to the outskirts of London, narrowly escaping an attack by Daleks, but Dortmun loses his life. Betrayed by a family desperate for food, Wyler and Susan are taken as prisoners to a huge mine worked by slaves under orders from the Daleks. Here they meet Tom and Louise, who have escaped from the spaceship, as well as David and Dr. Who, who have learned that the Daleks are planning to blast out the earth's metallic core with a bomb and use the planet as a giant spaceship. At the last moment, however, Dr. Who successfully deflects the bomb and releases a powerful magnetic force which sucks the invaders into the core of the earth, thus restoring the planet to its human inhabitants. The four Britons return to their own time, and Tom single-handedly catches the robbers. *Scientists. Constables. Uncles. Grandfathers. Space creatures. Resistance (political). Perfidy. Magnetism. Time machines. Robots. Mines. Spaceships. Bombs. London. The Future.*
   Note: Opened in London in Jul 1966. This is the second film based on the *Dr. Who* television series, following *Dr. Who and the Daleks*, q. v. Also known as *Invasion Earth 2150 A. D.*

DALLE ARDENNE ALL'INFERNO *see* **DIRTY HEROES**

DÁMA NA KOLEJÍCH *see* **THE LADY ON THE TRACKS**

DAMA S SOBACHKOY *see* **THE LADY WITH THE DOG**

DAMA SPATHI *see* **LOVE CYCLES**

DAMAGED GOODS *see* **V. D.**

LA DAME DANS L'AUTO AVEC DES LUNETTES ET UN FUSIL *see* **THE LADY IN THE CAR WITH GLASSES AND A GUN**

LES DAMES DE PORT ROYAL *see* **LES DAMES DU BOIS DE BOULOGNE**

LES DAMES DU BOIS DE BOULOGNE (France)   **F6.1003**
Films Raoul Ploquin. *Dist* Brandon Films. 3 Apr **1964** [New York opening]. Sd; b&w. 35mm. 84 min.
   Prod Raoul Ploquin. *Dir-Writ* Robert Bresson. *Dial* Jean Cocteau. *Photog* Philippe Agostini, Maurice Pecqueux, Marcel Weiss. *Art Dir* Max Douy, James Allan, Robert Clavel. *Film Ed* Jean Feyte. *Mus* Jean-Jacques Grünenwald. *Asst Dir* Roger Mercanton. *Prod Mgr* Robert Lavallée. *English Subtitl* Herman G. Weinberg.
   Cast: Maria Casarès (*Hélène*), Elina Labourdette (*Agnès*), Lucienne Bogaert (*Madame D.*), Paul Bernard (*Jean*), Jean Marchat (*Jacques*), Bernard Lajarrige, Marcel Rouze, Emma Lyonel, Lucy Lancy, Madame de Morlay.
   Drama. Based on an incident in the novel by: Denis Diderot, *Jacques le Fataliste* (1796). Hélène and Jean are lovers who have agreed to be totally honest with each another. Sensing that Jean no longer cares for her, Hélène feigns indifference, but to her dismay, Jean confirms her worst suspicions. To avenge herself, she introduces him to Agnès, whom Hélène has "rescued" from a sordid life as a cabaret dancer and call girl. Jean is instantly attracted to Agnès, but Hélène's plan demands marriage for completion. As the wedding day nears, Agnès tries to confess her past to Jean, but he will not listen. Hélène invites a collection of Agnès' former friends and clients to the wedding and then tells Jean of his bride's background. But Jean thwarts Hélène's triumph by forgiving Agnès and begging her to continue living with him. *Prostitutes. Revenge. Weddings. Paris—Bois de Boulogne.*
   Note: Opened in Paris in Sep 1945; running time: 90 min. Working title: *Les dames de Port Royal*. Also known as *Ladies of the Park*.

DAMN THE DEFIANT! (Great Britain)   **F6.1004**
G. W. Films. *Dist* Columbia Pictures. 28 Aug **1962** [New London, Connecticut, opening; c1 Sep 1962; LP22966]. Sd; col (Eastman Color by Pathé). 35mm (CinemaScope). 101 min.
A John Brabourne Production. *Prod* John Brabourne. *Dir* Lewis Gilbert. *Screenplay* Nigel Kneale, Edmund H. North. *Dir Photog* Christopher Challis. *Camera Op* Austin Dempster. *Focus* John Jordan, Roy Ford. *Camera Grip* Jack Roche. *Art Dir* Arthur Lawson. *Asst Art Dir* Don Picton. *Set Dresser* Terence Morgan, II. *Scenic Artist* Ted Barnes. *Draughtsman* Ted Tester, Bill Bennison. *Film Ed* Peter Hunt. *Asst Ed* Norman Wanstall, Gerry Arbeid. *Mus Comp* Clifton Parker. *Mus Cond* Muir Mathieson. *Sd Rec* H. L. Bird, Red Law. *Boom Op* Ken Ritchie. *Dub Ed* Winston Ryder. *1st & 2d Asst Dir* Jack Causey, Claude Watson, Jim Brennan. *Prod Mgr* Richard Goodwin. *Location Mgr* Richard Porter. *Cont* Shirley Barnes. *Prod Sec* Marguerite Green. *Wardrobe Supv* Jean Fairlie. *Makeup* Freddie Williamson, Michael Morris. *Hairdresser* Gordon Bond. *Sp Eff Supv* Howard Lydecker. *Sp Eff Tech* Ernie Sullivan. *Sp Eff Prop* J. Ryan. *Tech Adv* D. H. Angel, (Comdr.). *Fight Arr* William Hobbs. *Still Photog* Bert Cann. *Constr Mgr* W. Mclaren. *Prop* Tom Frewer. *Chargehand Electrn* Jackie Sullivan. *Casting Adv* John Bird.
Cast—Ship's Officers: Alec Guinness (*Captain Crawford*), Dirk Bogarde (*Lieutenant Scott-Padget*), Maurice Denham (*Surgeon Goss*), Nigel Stock (*Senior Midshipman Kilpatrick*), Richard Carpenter (*Lieutenant Ponsonby*), Peter Gill (*Lieutenant D'Arblay*), David Robinson (*Harvey Crawford*), Robin Stewart (*Pardoe*), Ray Brooks (*Hayes*), Peter Greenspan (*Johnson*).
Cast—Ship's Crew: Anthony Quayle (*Vizard*), Tom Bell (*Evans*), Murray Melvin (*Wagstaffe*), Victor Maddern (*Dawlish*), Bryan Pringle (*Sergeant Kneebone*), Johnny Briggs (*Wheatley*), Brian Phelan (*Grimshaw*), Toke Townley (*"Silly Billy" Whiting*), Declan Mulholland (*Morrison*).
Cast—Other Characters: Walter Fitzgerald (*Admiral Jackson*), Joy Shelton (*Mrs. Crawford*), Anthony Oliver (*tavern leader*), Russell Napier (*flag captain*), Michael Coles (*flag lieutenant*), André Maranne (*Colonel Giraud*), Ann Lynn (*young wife*).
Historical drama. Source: Frank Tilsey, *Mutiny* (London, 1958). During the Napoleonic Wars, Captain Crawford of H. M. S. *Defiant* is warned that his second in command, Lieutenant Scott-Padget, is a brutal sadist who has connections with the Admiralty. What the captain does not know is that a fleet-wide mutiny is underway and that his crew is planning to take over the *Defiant* before it reaches Corsica. The conflict of wills between Crawford and Scott-Padget is intensified when the latter heaps unjust punishment upon the captain's son, who is a midshipman aboard the vessel. En route to Corsica, the *Defiant* encounters and captures a French frigate, but not before Captain Crawford has lost an arm in the battle. An officer from the enemy ship reveals that the French are planning to invade England while the British fleet is immobilized by the mutiny. The crew takes over the *Defiant*, but Captain Crawford persuades Vizard, the head mutineer, to take the ship back to England and give warning of the invasion plan. Word then arrives that the mutiny has taken place and that the king has agreed to meet the demands of the men. The restored harmony is disturbed, however, when a crewman fatally knifes Scott-Padget. As Vizard heads the ship for open sea, they meet a French fireship. Rallying the men, Vizard redeems himself in action; and the crew responds to the challenge. *Sea captains. Sadism. Mutiny. Mutilation. Murder. Napoleonic Wars. Mediterranean Sea. Great Britain—Royal Navy. France—Navy.*
Note: Location scenes filmed off the Spanish coast near Denia. Opened in London in Feb 1962 as *H. M. S. Defiant.* Working title: *The Mutineers*; prerelease title: *Battle Aboard the Defiant.*

THE DAMNED (Italy/West Germany)   **F6.1005**
Pegaso Film–Italnoleggio–Eichberg Film–Praesidens. *Dist* Warner Bros.–Seven Arts, Inc. 18 Dec **1969** [New York opening; c3 Oct 1969; LP40890]. Sd (Westrex); col (Technicolor). 35mm. 155 min. [Also reviewed at 160 min.] *MPAA rating* X.
Prod Alfredo Levy, Ever Haggiag. *Exec Prod* Pietro Notarianni. *Dir* Luchino Visconti. *Screenplay* Nicola Badalucco, Enrico Medioli, Luchino Visconti. *Dir Photog* Armando Nannuzzi, Pasquale De Santis. *Camera Op* Nino Cristiani, Giuseppe Berardini, Mario Cimini. *Art Dir* Pasquale Romano. *Asst Art Dir* Giuseppe Ranieri. *Set Dsgn* Enzo Del Prato. *Film Ed* Ruggero Mastroianni. *Asst Film Ed* Lea Mazzocchi. *Mus Comp & Dir* Maurice Jarre. *Rec Dir* Vittorio Trentino. *Sd Mix* Renato Caderi. *Asst Dir* Albino Cocco, Fanny Wessling. *Prod Mgr* Giuseppe Bordogni. *Unit Mgr* Anna Davini, Gilberto Scarpellini, Umberto Sambuco, Bruno Sassaroli, Hugo Leeb, Ernst Egerer. *Script Girl* Rometta Pietrostefani. *Cost* Piero Tosi, Vera Marzot. *Makeup* Mauro Gavazzi. *Hairstyles* Luciano Vito. *Sp Eff* Aldo Gasparri. *Still Photog* Mario Tursi.
Cast: Dirk Bogarde (*Friedrich Bruckmann*), Ingrid Thulin (*Baroness Sophie von Essenbeck*), Helmut Griem (*Aschenbach*), Helmut Berger (*Martin von Essenbeck*), Charlotte Rampling (*Elisabeth Thallman*), Florinda Bolkan (*Olga*),

Reinhard Kolldehoff (*Baron Konstantin von Essenbeck*), Umberto Orsini (*Herbert Thallman*), Albrecht Schönhals (*Baron Joachim von Essenbeck*), Renaud Verley (*Guenther von Essenbeck*), Nora Ricci (*governess*), Irina Wanka (*Lisa Keller*), Valentina Ricci (*Thilde Thallman*), Karin Mittendorf (*Erika Thallman*), Peter Dane (*steelworks employee*), Wolfgang Hillinger (*Yanek*), Bill Vanders (*commissar*), Howard Nelson Rubien (*rector*), Werner Hasselmann (*Gestapo official*), Mark Salvage (*police inspector*), Karl Otto Alberty, John Frederick, Richard Beach (*army officers*), Claus Höhne, Ernst Kühr (*SA officers*), Wolfgang Ehrlich (*SA soldier*), Esterina Carloni, Antonietta Fiorita (*chambermaids*), Jessica Dublin (*nurse*).
Drama. Joachim von Essenbeck, a powerful German industrialist, celebrates his birthday in February 1933. The party is first disrupted by a transvestite performance by his grandson Martin, and then by the news that the Reichstag has been burned. A power struggle over control of the von Essenbeck steelworks develops among Konstantin, Joachim's nephew; Aschenbach, a member of the family and an SS leader; Herbert Thallman, a liberal married to Joachim's grand-niece; and Sophie, Joachim's widowed daughter-in-law who has aligned herself with Friedrich Bruckmann, the executive director of the steelworks. Sophie conspires with Aschenbach to denounce Thallman, a vice-president of the firm, as an anti-fascist, and Herbert is forced to flee the forthcoming political purge. Sophie then persuades Friedrich to kill Joachim with Herbert's gun, and with the aid of her son Martin, she places Friedrich at the head of the firm. Konstantin learns of Martin's sexual desire for young children and blackmails him over Lisa Keller, one of his victims, who hanged herself after being molested. Martin, the major stockholder of the company, transfers his support to Konstantin, but Konstantin's power is short-lived. The SA holds a homosexual orgy at the resort town of Wiesee, and during the Night of the Long Knives, the SS troops arrive and slaughter Konstantin and the others. Sophie and Friedrich attempt to regain power, but Aschenbach, eager to have the steel industry under SS control, tells Martin that it was Friedrich who killed Joachim. Playing upon Martin's hatred of his domineering mother, Aschenbach turns Martin against Sophie; Martin has intercourse with her and forces her to marry Friedrich in a macabre ceremony. Martin's wedding gift to his mother is two capsules of cyanide, which Sophie and Friedrich willingly consume. Aschenbach, who now thoroughly dominates Martin, has finally become the undisputed heir to the von Essenbeck steelworks. *Industrialists. Nazis. Executives. Widows. Sex deviates. Family life. Transvestism. Conspiracy. Murder. Filial relations. Suicide. Frameup. Blackmail. Male homosexuality. Rape. Incest. Matricide. Steel industry. Orgies. Weddings. Poisoning. Birthdays. Germany—History—Third Reich. SS. SA.*
Note: Released in Italy in 1969[?] as *La caduta degli dei (Götterdämmerung).* Original running time: 164 min.

THE DAMNED *see* **THESE ARE THE DAMNED**

DAMON AND PYTHIAS (United States/Italy)   **F6.1006**
International Motion Picture Enterprises–Metro-Goldwyn-Mayer, Inc. *Dist* Metro-Goldwyn-Mayer, Inc. 5 Sep **1962** [New York opening]. Sd; col (Eastman Color). 35mm. 99 min.
U. S. Prod Sam Jaffe. *Italian Prod* Franco Riganti. *Assoc Prod* Samuel Marx. *Dir* Curtis Bernhardt. *Assoc Dir* Alberto Cardone. *U. S. Vers Screenplay* Bridget Boland, Barry Oringer. *Italian Vers Screenplay* Paolo Ojetti, Franco Riganti. *Orig Story* Samuel Marx, Barry Oringer, Franco Riganti. *Photog* Aldo Tonti. *Art Dir* Alberto Boccianti. *Film Ed* Nicolò Lazzari. *Mus* Angelo Francesco Lavagnino. *Mus Dir* Franco Ferrara. *Cost* Adriana Berselli.
Cast: Guy Williams (*Damon*), Don Burnett (*Pythias*), Ilaria Occhini (*Nerissa*), Liana Orfei (*Adriana*), Arnoldo Foà (*Dionysius the Elder*), Maurizio Baldoni (*Dionysius the Younger*), Carlo Giustini (*Cariso*), Franco Fantasia (*fencing master*), Marina Berti, Carla Bonavera (*Mereka [see note]*), Lawrence Montaigne (*flutist*), Andrea Bosic (*Arcanos*), Osvaldo Ruggeri (*Demetrius*), Carlo Rizzo (*Libia*), Gianni Bonagura (*Philemon*), Aldo Silvani (*Digenis*), Carolyn Fonseca (*Chloë*), Giovanna Maculani (*Hermione*), Enrico Salvatore, Tiberio Murgia, Enrico Glori, Luigi Bonos, Vittorio Bonos, Franco Ressel, Tiberio Mitri.
Costume drama. In 400 B. C., Pythias travels from Athens to Syracuse to persuade the philosopher Arcanos to come to Athens and teach the Pythagorean theory of the brotherhood of man. Arcanos has been forced into hiding by the tyrant Dionysius the Elder, who is opposed to a doctrine that forbids violence and killing. In Syracuse, Pythias hires Damon, an adventurous outlaw, to help in the search. At first Damon betrays Pythias, but when the latter refuses to do him harm, Damon helps Arcanos escape from the Storian Guard. Arcanos and Damon reach safety, but Pythias is captured and sentenced to death. Damon then offers himself as a substitute if Dionysius will permit Pythias to pay a farewell visit to Nerissa, his pregnant wife. The tyrant accepts the proposition, although he does not intend to allow Pythias to leave. Aided by Damon's band of robbers, however, Pythias overcomes Dionysius' men and returns to Syracuse. Deeply moved by such loyalty, the citizens of Syracuse

force Dionysius to spare the lives of both men. *Philosophers. Despots. Outlaws. Robbers. Nonviolence. Humanitarianism. Perfidy. Friendship. Capital punishment. Self-sacrifice. Loyalty. Syracuse. Athens. Pythagoras. Damon and Pythias.*

Note: Filmed on location in Italy. Opened in Rome in Sep 1962 as *Il tiranno di Siracusa*; running time: 102 min. Alternative Italian title: *Damone e Pitias*. Sources conflict in crediting the role of Mereka.

DAMONE E PITIAS *see* DAMON AND PYTHIAS

DANCE MOVIE   F6.1007
Dist Film-Makers' Cooperative. 16 Mar **1964** [New York opening]. Si; b&w. 16mm. 45 min.

Prod-Dir Andy Warhol. *Prod Asst* Gerard Malanga.

Cast: Freddie Herko.

Satire. A man continually skates across the frame on one roller skate, occasionally in an indoor setting but for the most part in the streets of New York City, including Brooklyn Heights and Gramercy Park. He is seen at various times of the day and night. *Roller skating. New York City.*

Note: Also known as *Roller Skate*.

DANCE OF THE VAMPIRES *see* THE FEARLESS VAMPIRE KILLERS; OR, PARDON ME BUT YOUR TEETH ARE IN MY NECK

DANDY   F6.1008
Dynacom Productions. *Dist* General Film Corp. 4 Nov **1970** [Chicago opening]. Sd; col (Eastmancolor). 35mm. 82 min.

Prod Ramon Ponce, R. Charleton Wilson. *Dir-Writ* R. Charleton Wilson. *Mus* Billy Dee.

Cast: Cynthia Denny *(Dandy)*, John Alderman *(Larry Lebot)*, Ed Kelly *(Anson)*, Steve Vincent *(Arlen)*, Luanne Roberts *(Ruth)*, David Roya *(Jocko)*, L. L. Cuddles *(Leroy)*, Bob Potter *(Guy)*, Lynn Lyons *(Loreen)*, Al Wilson *(Bateman)*, Frank Cuva *(Penrod)*, Joe Dunnigan, Philip Fields, Michael Cheal, Woody Lee, Tony Giegen *(salesmen)*.

Melodrama. Dandy is bored and unhappy with her life, and she runs away from home to live with her boyfriend. He gets her a job with a models' agent, but the agent turns out to be a procurer. Dandy returns to her boyfriend, only to find that he has another girl. After several adventures, Dandy meets and falls in love with a man with whom she enjoys a tender and beautiful relationship. Eventually, however, she is alone again, and after an interlude with a lesbian she attends a Hollywood party in which group sex is performed. There, she realizes that her sexual nature is to give, rather than take. *Runaways. Pimps. Salesmen. Prostitutes. Models. Lesbianism. Group sex. Hollywood.*

A DANDY IN ASPIC (Great Britain)   F6.1009
Columbia Pictures. 2 Apr **1968** [New York opening; c1 Mar 1968; LP35854]. Sd; col (Technicolor). 35mm (Panavision). 107 min.

An Anthony Mann Production. *Prod-Dir* (see note) Anthony Mann. *Assoc Prod* Leslie Gilliat. *Screenplay* Derek Marlowe. *Photog* Christopher Challis. *Camera Op* Austin Dempster. *Art Dir* Carmen Dillon, Patrick McLoughlin. *Main Titl Dsgn* Michael Graham Smith. *Film Ed* Thelma Connell. *Asst Ed* Stephen Warwick. *Mus Comp & Cond* Quincy Jones. *Song:* "If You Want Love" Ernie Sheldon, Quincy Jones. *Sung by* Shirley Horn. *Sd Rec* Peter Davies, Gerry Humphreys. *Dub Ed* Chris Greenham. *Asst Dir* Jimmy Komisarjevsky. *Prod Mgr* Harold Buck. *Unit Mgr* Eddie Pike. *Cont* Elaine Schreyeck. *Wardrobe* Betty Adamson. *Cost for Laurence Harvey and Mia Farrow* Pierre Cardin. *Makeup* Jill Carpenter. *Hairdresser* Ann Box. *Casting* Maude Spector.

Cast: Laurence Harvey *(Eberlin)*, Tom Courtenay *(Gatiss)*, Mia Farrow *(Caroline)*, Harry Andrews *(Fraser)*, Peter Cook *(Prentiss)*, Lionel Stander *(Sobakevich)*, Per Oscarsson *(Pavel)*, Barbara Murray *(Heather Vogler)*, John Bird *(Henderson)*, Norman Bird *(Copperfield)*, Geoffrey Bayldon *(Lake)*, Calvin Lockhart *(Brogue)*, James Cossins *(Heston-Stevas)*, Michael Trubshawe *(Flowers)*, Lockwood West *(Quince)*, Geoffrey Lumsden *(Ridley)*, Elspeth March *(Lady Hetherington)*, Richard O'Sullivan *(Nevil)*, Geoffrey Denton *(Pond)*, Mike Pratt *(Greff)*, Monika Dietrich *(Hedwig)*, George Murcell *(Sergeant Harris)*, Vernon Dobtcheff *(Stein)*, Stefan Gryss *(Russian)*, Arthur Hewlett *(Moon)*, Paulene Stone *(Red Bird)*, Peter Hutchins *(youth)*, Andre Charise *(head waiter)*.

Drama. Source: Derek Marlowe, *A Dandy in Aspic* (London, 1966). Because Russian secret agent Alexander Eberlin has infiltrated British Intelligence, his request to be allowed back into his native country is turned down by Soviet officials who wish him to continue working in the West. At a briefing session conducted by British Intelligence Chief Fraser, Eberlin is ordered to kill a Russian double agent who is responsible for the deaths of three British spies. Although the Russian infiltrator, known to the British as Krasnevin, is Eberlin himself, the security heads believe it is Pavel, Eberlin's

London contact. After first warning the drug-addicted Pavel, Eberlin later realizes that he must eliminate his contact in order to preserve his own cover; but Pavel has already been murdered by the Russians. After a London meeting with Gatiss, his ruthless arch-rival, Eberlin goes to Berlin but is prevented from escaping into East Germany. His attempt to hide out with Caroline, an Englishwoman, is thwarted when Gatiss finds him and forces him to help ambush a Russian double agent, Henderson. Eberlin shoots Henderson before the spy can reveal that Eberlin is Krasnevin, and Gatiss agrees to pay Soviet espionage chief Sobakevich $100,000 in return for the elusive Krasnevin. But Sobakevich tricks Gatiss by murdering another British agent and passing him off as Eberlin. Cheated out of taking his man alive, Gatiss shoots Sobakevich in the back rather than pay him the $100,000. His mission in Berlin over, Eberlin is ordered to return to London with Gatiss. While telephoning his Soviet chief, Eberlin suddenly realizes that Chief Fraser has known his true identity from the start and has used him to uncover the Russian network in Berlin. Now deserted by his Russian superiors as well as the British, Eberlin faces Gatiss on the West Berlin airport landing strip, and the two men kill each other. *Secret agents. Drug addicts. Espionage. Murder. Perfidy. London. Berlin—West. German Democratic Republic. Great Britain—Intelligence service. Union of Soviet Socialist Republics—Intelligence service.*

Note: Location scenes filmed in London, Surrey, and West Berlin. Opened in London in Mar 1968. Mann died during filming and was replaced by Laurence Harvey.

DANGER: DIABOLIK (France/Italy)   F6.1010
Dino De Laurentiis Cinematografica–Marianne Productions. *Dist* Paramount Pictures. May **1968** [New York opening: 11 Dec 1968; c26 Jan 1968; LF26]. Sd; col (Technicolor). 35mm. 99 min.

Prod Dino De Laurentiis. *Dir* Mario Bava. *Screenplay* Dino Maiuri, Adriano Baracco, Mario Bava. *Adtl Dial* (see note) Brian Degas, Tudor Gates. *Photog* Antonio Rinaldi. *Art Dir* Flavio Mogherini. *Film Ed* Romana Fortini. *Mus* Ennio Morricone. *Sd* Mario Celentano. *Asst Dir* Lamberto Bava. *Prod Mgr* Bruno Todini. *Cost* Luciana Marinucci, Piero Gherardi.

Cast: John Phillip Law *(Diabolik)*, Marisa Mell *(Eva Kant)*, Michel Piccoli *(Inspector Ginco)*, Adolfo Celi *(Ralph Valmont)*, Terry-Thomas *(minister of finance)*, Claudio Gora *(police chief)*, Edward Febo Kelleng *(Sir Harold Clark)*, Caterina Boratto *(Lady Clark)*, Giulio Donnini *(Dr. Vernier)*, Annie Gorassini *(Rose)*, Renzo Palmer *(minister's assistant)*, Mario Donen *(Sergeant Danek)*, Andrea Bosic *(bank manager)*, Lucia Modugno *(prostitute)*, Giorgio Gennari *(Rudy)*, Giorgio Sciolette *(morgue doctor)*, Carlo Croccolo *(lorry driver)*, Giuseppe Fazio *(Tony)*, Lidia Biondi *(policewoman)*, Isarco Ravaioli, Federico Boito, Tiberio Mitri, Wolfgang Hillinger *(Valmont's henchmen)*.

Crime melodrama. Based on the illustrated feature by: Luciana Giussani and Angela Giussani. Diabolik, a daring international master thief, has climaxed a series of robberies by hijacking a $10 million gold shipment, and frustrated Inspector Ginco attempts to set a trap for him by using a million-dollar necklace as bait. When Diabolik again gets safely away with the loot, Ginco aligns himself with underworld boss Ralph Valmont to work out a scheme to trap the elusive thief. Valmont kidnaps Diabolik's girl friend, Eva Kant, and holds her for ransom, but Diabolik rescues his girl, escapes from Ginco's trap, and blows up the nation's tax records to the delight of the populace and the dismay of the minister of finance. In a desperate effort to capture Diabolik, all the remaining gold reserve is melted down for one huge ingot that is encased in steel. Unaware that the ingot has been made radioactive, Diabolik makes off with it, puts on a special protective suit, and begins to melt it down in his underground hideout. While the police follow the radioactive trail, the ingot suddenly explodes and covers Diabolik with molten gold, turning him into a statue. The gilded figure is put on display, and Eva comes to visit it before she is arrested by Ginco as an accomplice. She is startled to see the statue wink at her; and reassured that Diabolik has outwitted his adversaries once again, she leaves with Ginco. *Thieves. Police. Gangsters. Kidnaping. Gold. Radiation. Sculptures. Diabolik.*

Note: Released in Italy in 1968 as *Diabolik*; Paris opening: Apr 1968 as *Danger Diabolik*; running time: 105 min. Some U. S. sources credit the screenplay to Dino Maiuri, Brian Degas, Tudor Gates, and Mario Bava, based on a story by Angela and Luciana Giussani, Dino Maiuri, and Adriano Baracco.

DANGER ON OUR DOORSTEP *see* CASTRO, CUBA, AND COMMUNISM

DANGER ROUTE (Great Britain)   F6.1011
Amicus Productions. *Dist* United Artists. 14 Feb **1968** [Omaha, Nebraska, opening; c16 Nov 1967; LP35522]. Sd (RCA); col (De Luxe). 35mm. 91 min.

Prod Max J. Rosenberg, Milton Subotsky. *Assoc Prod* Ted Wallis. *Dir* Seth Holt. *Screenplay* Meade Roberts. *Adtl Material* Robert Stewart. *Dir Photog* Harry Waxman. *Camera Op* Gerry Anstiss. *2d Unit Camera* Cece Cooney. *Art Dir* Don Mingaye. *Set Dresser* Andrew Low. *Prod Dsgn* Bill Constable. *Film Ed* Oswald Hafenrichter. *Mus Comp* John Mayer. *Mus Dir* Philip Martell. *Titl*

Song Comp Lionel Bart. *Sung by* Anita Harris. *Sd Rec* Nolan Roberts. *Sd Mix* Sydney Squires. *Sd Ed* Clive Smith. *Asst Dir* Stephen Christian. *Prod Mgr* Tony Wallis. *Location Mgr* Derek Parr. *Cont* Kay Mander. *Cost Dsgn* Yvonne Caffin. *Wardrobe Mistress* Evelyn Gibbs. *Makeup* George Partleton. *Hairdresser* Ann Fordyce. *Constr Mgr* Bill Waldron.

Cast: Richard Johnson *(Jonas Wilde)*, Carol Lynley *(Jocelyn)*, Barbara Bouchet *(Mari)*, Sylvia Syms *(Barbara Canning)*, Diana Dors *(Rhoda Gooderich)*, Harry Andrews *(Chief Canning)*, Gordon Jackson *(Brian Stern)*, Maurice Denham *(Peter Ravenspur)*, Sam Wanamaker *(Lucinda)*, David Bauer *(Bennett)*, Julian Chagrin *(Matsys)*, Reg Lye *(Balin)*, Robin Bailey *(Parsons)*, Leslie Sands *(man in cinema)*, Timothy Bateson *(Halliwell)*.

Melodrama. Source: Andrew York, *The Eliminator* (London, 1966). Jonas Wilde, a British secret service agent licensed to kill, returns from a successful mission determined to resign. Canning, his London superior, agrees to forward his resignation if Wilde eliminates a Czechoslovakian scientist defector now being held by the Americans. With the help of a housekeeper, Rhoda Gooderich, Wilde kills the scientist but is himself captured and interrogated by CIA agent Lucinda. After Lucinda tells Wilde that someone in his organization is causing fellow British agents to be killed by mistake, Wilde escapes to look for Canning, who mysteriously has disappeared. Accompanied by Canning's wife, Barbara, Wilde heads for the leader's base in the Channel Islands and learns from Stern, a fellow agent, that still another member of their unit, Peter Ravenspur, has been murdered. Wilde and Stern then take Mari, who has claimed to be Ravenspur's niece, aboard Stern's boat for questioning. Stern then exposes himself as the double agent and is killed by Wilde. Mari, who has actually been working for Lucinda, is killed by a stray bullet, while Wilde escapes. Back in London, he kills his girl friend, Jocelyn, after realizing that she has been working for Stern. Leaving Jocelyn's flat, Wilde runs into Canning, who explains to him that he is too valuable an agent to be allowed to resign and advises him to go under cover until he is again needed. *Secret agents. Czechoslovakians. Scientists. Defectors. Housekeepers. Murder. Espionage. Channel Islands. London. Great Britain—Intelligence service. United States—Central Intelligence Agency.*

Note: Released in Great Britain in Dec 1967; running time: 92 min. Working title: *The Eliminator.*

LE DANGER VIENT DE L'ESPACE *see* **THE DAY THE SKY EXPLODED**

DANGEROUS CHARTER   F6.1012

Dangerous Charter Productions. *Dist* Crown International Pictures. 19 Sep **1962** [Los Angeles opening]. Sd (Panasound); col (Technicolor). 35mm (Panavision). 76 min.

Prod Robert Gottschalk, John R. Moore. *Dir-Orig Story* Robert Gottschalk. *Screenplay* Paul Strait. *Photog* Meredith M. Nicholson. *Film Ed* George White. *Asst Ed* Carl Mahakian. *Mus* Ted Dale. *Song:* "The Sea Is My Woman" Rod Sherwood. *Sd* Franklin Milton, Jean Valentino. *Asst Dir* Joe Boyle, Robert C. Scrivner.

Cast: Chris Warfield *(Marty McMahon)*, Sally Fraser *(June Smith)*, Richard Foote *(Dick Kanc)*, Peter Forster *(Sidney Manet)*, Chick Chandler *(Kick Smith)*, Wright King *(Joe Gallardo)*, Carl Milletaire, Steve Conte, John Zaremba, John Pickard, Alex Montoya.

Crime melodrama. Three fishermen—Marty, Kick, and Joe—find an abandoned yacht with a corpse aboard. They report the discovery to the Coast Guard and are offered the vessel as a charter boat if they will be on the lookout for the yacht's owners, suspected dope smugglers. Marty's girl friend, June, brings the first charter customer, Dick Kane, who soon involves them all in the smuggling of $500,000 in heroin which he knows is on board. After picking up Dick's boss, Sidney Manet, in La Paz, Mexico, Marty is ordered to go to Catalina. Once there the thugs take the heroin and leave in a speedboat. As they disembark, Dick gives June a note telling her that Manet has placed a time bomb in the engine room. Marty throws the bomb overboard and Manet sees the explosion. Realizing his plot has failed, Manet heads the speedboat back towards the yacht. The two vessels collide, and the speedboat is sheared in half. *Fishermen. Smugglers. Hoodlums. Yachts. Corpses. Heroin. Speedboats. Bombs. La Paz (Mexico). Santa Catalina (California). United States Coast Guard. Ship explosions. Chases.*

Note: Location scenes filmed in 1958 on Santa Catalina Island, in the San Pedro harbor, and off the coast of California.

THE DANGEROUS KISS (Japan)   F6.1013

Toho Co. 24 Feb **1961** [Los Angeles opening]. Sd; col (Eastmancolor). 35mm (Tohoscope). [Feature film, length unknown.]

Dir Yuzo Kawashima.

Cast: Akira Takarada, Michiyo Aratama, Reiko Dan, Mitsuko Kusabue, Akemi Kita, Ichiro Nakatani, Seizaburo Kawazu, Haruko Togo, Takao Zushi, Kichijiro Ueda, Shintaro Ishihara, Sachio Sakai, Ichiro Arishima, Yuriko Hoshi,

Sadako Sawamura.

Comedy. Although no information about the precise nature of this film has been found, press material indicates that it concerns a boxer's relations with four attractive women. *Boxers.*

Note: Released in Japan ca1960.

DANGEROUS LOVE AFFAIRS *see* **LES LIAISONS DANGEREUSES**

DANIELLA BY NIGHT (France/West Germany)   F6.1014

Contact Organisation–Paris Inter Productions–Cinelux-Film–Pandora–Film. *Dist* Cambist Films, Audubon Films. Nov **1962.** Sd; b&w. 35mm. 83 min.

Exec Prod Leopold Branonver, René Thevenet. *Dir* Max Pécas. *Screenplay* Wolfgang Steinhardt, Grisha M. Dabat, Max Pécas, Jean Clouzot. *Dial* Grisha M. Dabat. *Dir Photog* André Germain. *Sets* Sidney Bettex, Bob Luchaire. *Film Ed* Paul Cayatte. *Mus* Charles Aznavour, Georges Garvarentz. *Sd* Séverin Frankiel. *Dir Prod* Jacques Garcia. *Prod Mgr* Theo Michel, Helmut Deutschman. *Prod Supv* Joel Lifschutz.

Cast: Elke Sommer *(Daniella)*, Ivan Desny *(Count Castellani)*, Danik Patisson *(Claudine)*, Claire Maurier *(Esmeralda)*, Helmut Schmid *(Karl Bauer)*, René Dary *(Lanzac)*, Sandrine *(mannequin)*, Käthe Haack, Romana Rombach, France Lonbard, Brigitte Banz, Rudy Lenoir, Albert Dinan.

Melodrama. Daniella, a beautiful model, leaves her native France for Italy and begins work at one of the leading fashion houses in Rome. Daniella and her employer, Count Castellani, are mutually attracted, and the Count's mistress, Esmeralda, becomes jealous. During a lavish party, Esmeralda tells the Count that she is pregnant, but he ignores her and continues negotiating to sell microfilm to Lanzac, an enemy agent. Esmeralda threatens to expose Castellani's espionage activities, and a few minutes later she is found dead by Daniella. Castellani hides the microfilm in Daniella's lipstick case. Another member of the gang goes to the nightclub run by Lanzac, and sells it to him. Daniella witnesses the sale and steals the microfilm, but Lanzac immediately discovers the theft and sends two thugs after her. She runs out onto the nightclub's stage, and the men strip her in full view of the audience. She keeps the microfilm, however, and returns it to Castellani, whom she still trusts. Daniella is pursued by Lanzac's agents across Europe. Karl, a journalist, helps her to discover that Count Castellani is really in league with Lanzac. Castellani and Lanzac are killed, and Daniella's friendship for Karl threatens to turn to love. *Models. Couturiers. French. Italians. Nobility. Foreign agents. Mistresses. Espionage. Murder. Jealousy. Employer-employee relations. Theft. Nightclubs. Rome. Documentation.*

Note: Released in Paris in 1961 as *De quoi tu te mêles, Daniela!*; running time: 90 min. German title: *Zarte Haut in schwarzer Seide.*

DANISH & BLUE   F6.1015

Satyr IX Productions. *Dist* Sack Amusement Enterprises. 14 Sep **1970** [Dallas opening]. Sd; col. 35mm. 63 min.

Prod-Dir Spence Crilly.

Drama. Johnny, a sexually troubled American tourist in Copenhagen, visits a sex show starring a black female impersonator. Additional stimulation is provided by two blondes who arouse a brunette, leaving her to be satisfied by two entertainers in Viking garb. Having purchased pornography, the American returns to his hotel and meets Ketti, the brunette from the show. After he fumbles an attempt to have intercourse with her on a picnic, she directs him to the sexologist Erika. Erika explores techniques of stimulation with him, and he practices Erika's sexual prescriptions with Ketti. Johnny rids himself of his sexual difficulties and returns home a virile and experienced lover. [Press material suggests that the film contains scenes of sadomasochism.] *Americans in foreign countries. Negroes. Tourists. Sex researchers. Lesbianism. Female impersonation. Sex instruction. Sexual techniques. Sadomasochism. Sex shows. Pornography. Copenhagen.*

Note: Filmed in Denmark.

DANISH BLUE (Denmark)   F6.1016

Axel Film. *Dist* Grove Press. 25 Nov **1970** [Los Angeles opening]. Sd; col & b&w. 35mm. 72 min.

Prod-Dir-Writ Gabriel Axel. *Photog* Rolf Rønne. *Art Dir* Peter Hojmark. *Film Ed* Edith Nisted. *Mus* Bertrand Bech. *Sd* Ole Orsted. *Prod Mgr* Werner Hedmann, Aage Hansen. *Cost* Lone Ernst.

Cast: Gurli Taschener, Birgit Brüel, Henrik Wiehe, Aage Fønss, Susanne Jagd, Kurt Erik Nielsen, Eddie Karnel, Paul Møller, Arne Hansen, Poul Kelvin, Hans Ejner Jensen, Isa Sørensen, Anne-Marie Poulsen, Kirsten Norholt, Hans Jacob Kolgard, Kurt Rahvig, Per Pallsen, Hardi Rafn.

Documentary. The film surveys the growing interest in pornography in Denmark since the relaxation of the censorship laws. People are interviewed in the street and seen looking at erotica exhibits or browsing through pornography shops. Staged scenes depict the self-conscious buyer of sex materials and the elaborate explanations concocted for the benefit of the store owner; a couple attempting to follow the instructions in a sex manual; and a demonstration of how to make a "blue movie." *Censorship. Pornography. Sex instruction. Motion pictures. Bookshops.*

Note: Produced in Denmark in 1968 as *Det kaere legetøj*; running time: 91 min.

DANKON *see* **BULLET WOUND**

DANS LES GRIFFES DU MANIAQUE *see* **THE DIABOLICAL DR. Z**

DANSE MACABRE *see* **CASTLE OF BLOOD**

DANSK SEXUALITET *see* **SEXUAL FREEDOM IN DENMARK**

DANZA MACABRA *see* **CASTLE OF BLOOD**

THE DAPHNE (Japan)   F6.1017
Toho Co. Aug **1967** [Los Angeles showing]. Sd; col (Eastmancolor). 35mm (Tohoscope). 106 min.
Prod Masumi Fujimoto. *Dir* Yasuki Chiba. *Screenplay* Zenzo Matsuyama. *Photog* Choichi Nakai. *Mus* Toshiro Mayuzumi.
Cast: Machiko Kyo *(1st daughter)*, Haruko Sugimura *(Daphne)*, Reiko Dan *(3d daughter)*, Yuriko Hoshi *(4th daughter)*, Yoko Tsukasa *(2d daughter)*, Yosuke Natsuki *(4th daughter's husband)*, Daisuke Kato, Akira Takarada, Makoto Sato, Tadao Takashima, Hiroshi Koizumi, Keiju Kobayashi, Tatsuya Nakadai.
Domestic drama. Based on the television serial by: Zenzo Matsuyama, *Haruya haru.* Daphne, a widow with four daughters, attempts to keep her family happy despite many problems. Her two youngest daughters are married, but the oldest, a dentist, and the second, her assistant, remain unwed. *Dentists. Widows. Filial relations. Marriage.*
Note: Released in Japan in 1966 as *Jinchoge.*

DARE THE DEVIL   F6.1018
Century Films. *Dist* Cinar Productions. caNov **1969**. Sd; col (Technicolor). 35mm (Techniscope). 72 min. *MPAA rating* R.
Pres by G. B. Roberts. *Prod-Dir* Robert J. Emery. *Screenplay* Kevin Kelly.
Cast: Raymond Wise *(David Kelly)*, Sofia Halkias *(Molly)*, Sherry Avazzano, Elmer Chapel.
Melodrama. David Keller and his fiancée are attacked on the beach by hoodlums. They overpower David and rape the girl. David is frustrated until he meets Molly, an attractive older woman, who introduces him to sex and liquor. *Hoodlums. Rape. Adolescence. Sexual initiation. Beaches.*

DAREDEVIL IN THE CASTLE (Japan)   F6.1019
Toho Co. *Dist* Frank Lee International. 6 Jun **1961** [San Francisco opening]. Sd; col (Eastman Color). 35mm (Tohoscope). 97 min.
Dir Hiroshi Inagaki. *Screenplay* Hiroshi Inagaki, Takeshi Kimura. *Orig Story* Genzo Murakami. *Photog* Kazuo Yamada. *Mus* Yoshio Nishikawa. *Sp Eff* Eiji Tsuburaya.
Cast: Toshiro Mifune *(Mohei)*, Kyoko Kagawa *(Ai)*, Isuzu Yamada *(Yodogimi)*, Yuriko Hoshi *(Senhime)*, Yoshiko Kuga *(Kobue)*, Akihiko Hirata *(Hayato)*, Takashi Shimura, Hanshiro Iwai, Seizaburo Kawazu, Yu Fujiki, Jun Tazaki, Danko Ichikawa, Yosuke Natsuki, Susumu Fujita.
Action melodrama. In a fierce battle between the Toyotomi and Tokugawa clans of early 17th-century Japan, the Toyotomis are defeated, although they still occupy their castle at Osaka. As another bloody conflict appears imminent, Mohei, a samurai who lost his family in the battle, arrives and becomes embroiled in a fight with the city's war profiteers. During the clash, he sees his foster brother Hayato and a young woman named Ai being pursued by a band of warrior-monks. After helping them escape, Mohei himself is rescued by a magician. Shortly thereafter, a Portuguese vessel loaded with firearms casts anchor in the Osaka harbor, and Hayato orders a rich merchant to purchase the weapons before they fall into the hands of the Tokugawa army. The treacherous merchant has captured the beautiful Ai, however, and he offers her to the Portuguese captain in return for reselling the weapons to the Tokugawa clan. Mohei and the magician, disguised as laborers, are also aboard the vessel, and they thwart the merchant's scheme by rescuing Ai and recovering the weapons. Consequently, when the castle is besieged by the Tokugawa army, the defenders are able to hold them back. Eventually peace is declared, but the castle is destroyed by flames. Mohei is awarded rank and money for his heroic exploits, but he rejects the bounty and elects to live as a commoner with Ai, whom he has grown to love. *Samurai. Foster brothers. Magicians. Merchants. Portuguese. Feuds. Kidnaping. Disguise. Rescue. Heroism. Castles. Firearms. Merchant ships. Japan—History—Tokugawa period 1600–1867. Osaka. Fires.*
Note: Released in Japan in 1961 as *Osaka-jo monogatari*. May also have been known in the United States as *Devil in the Castle.*

DARING GAME   F6.1020
Ivan Tors Films. *Dist* Paramount Pictures. 19 Mar **1968** [New York opening; c31 Dec 1967; LP35690]. Sd; col (Eastman Color). 35mm. 101 min.

Prod Gene Levitt. *Exec Prod* Ivan Tors. *Dir* Laslo Benedek. *2d Unit Dir* Ben Chapman. *Underwater Unit Dir* Ricou Browning. *Aerial Seq Dir* Ben Chapman. *Screenplay* Andy White. *Story* Art Arthur, Andy White. *Dir Cinematog* Edmund Gibson. *Underwater Photog* Lamar Boren. *Freefall Photog* Bob Sinclair. *Film Ed* John B. Woelz. *Mus Comp & Cond* George Bruns. *Sd* Howard Warren. *Asst Dir* Gordon McLean. *Prod Mgr* Edward Haldeman.
Cast: Lloyd Bridges *(Vic Powers)*, Nico Minardos *(Ricardo Balboa)*, Joan Blackman *(Kathryn Carlyle)*, Michael Ansara *(President Delgado)*, Shepperd Strudwick *(Dr. Carlyle)*, Alex Montoya *(General Tovrea)*, Irene Dailey *(Mrs. Carlyle)*, Brock Peters *(Jonah Hunt)*, Michael Walker *("Bink")*, Barry Bartle *(Larry Sedgewick)*, Perry Lopez *(Reuben)*, Marie Gomez *(Maria)*, Oren Stevens *(Miguel)*, Oswaldo Calvo, Mark Harris, Rafael Reyes, Laurence Jon Lehr, Frank Schuller, Bill Higbie, Lanita Kent, Judy Jordan, Juan Somoza.
Adventure melodrama. Survival Devices, Inc., is an organization of specialists dedicated to performing missions beneficial to the free world. To aid them in their operations, Vic Powers and his team of air and underwater experts known as the "Flying Fish" have perfected an igloo which can be inflated beneath the sea. Mrs. Carlyle, a long-time friend, asks Vic to help rescue her political scientist husband, Henry, and their daughter, Kathryn, who have disappeared on a Caribbean island ruled by dictator President Delgado. Vic agrees, partially because of his romantic interest in Kathryn. Following an unsuccessful rescue attempt, Vic enlists the aid of Ricardo Balboa, who locates the prison where the Carlyles are being held, and the men parachute into the ocean to set up an underwater escape. Dr. Carlyle refuses to leave the island, however, until he has had a chance to talk to President Delgado, one of his former pupils. Vic forces the dictator to meet with Carlyle on the igloo, and Delgado adamantly defends his totalitarian government. Meanwhile, Delgado's zealous aide, General Tovrea, has learned of the abduction and dispatches a sonar-equipped gunboat to locate the Flying Fish. Through deft maneuvering, Vic avoids the gunboat, but before the Flying Fish can return to the igloo, General Tovrea orders his shore batteries to open fire. Reverting to his former democratic beliefs, Delgado countermands the order, thereby enabling the Flying Fish to sink the menacing gunboat. As the men and the Carlyles head for home, Vic's renewed romance with Kathryn is interrupted when he and his team receive orders for another mission. *Frogmen. Professors. Political prisoners. Dictators. Rescue. Abduction. Parachuting. Filial relations. Totalitarianism. Gunboats. Caribbean.*
Note: Location scenes filmed in Florida and the Bahamas. Working title: *The Unkillables.*

THE DARK *see* **HORROR HOUSE**

DARK INTRUDER   F6.1021
Shamley Productions. *Dist* Universal Pictures. 21 Jul **1965** [New York opening; c6 Nov 1965; LP33833]. Sd; b&w. 35mm. 59 min.
Prod Jack Laird. *Dir* Harvey Hart. *Dir Photog* John F. Warren. *Art Dir* Lloyd S. Papez. *Set Decor* John McCarthy, Julia Heron. *Titl* Pacific Title. *Film Ed* Edward W. Williams. *Mus Supv* Stanley Wilson. *Mus* Lalo Schifrin. *Sd* Waldon O. Watson, Robert R. Bertrand. *Asst Dir* Edward K. Dodds. *Cost Supv* Vincent Dee. *Makeup* Bud Westmore. *Hairstylist* Virginia Darcy.
Cast: Leslie Nielsen *(Brett Kingsford)*, Mark Richman *(Robert Vandenburg)*, Judi Meredith *(Evelyn Lang)*, Gilbert Green *(Harvey Misbach)*, Charles Bolender *(Nikola)*, Werner Klemperer *(Professor Malaki)*, Vaughn Taylor *(Dr. Burdett)*, Peter Brocco *(Chi Zang)*, Bill Quinn *(neighbor)*, Ken Hooker *(1st sergeant)*, Richard Venture *(1st man)*, Mike Ragan *(plainclothesman)*, Ingvard Nielsen *(2d man)*, Claudia Donelly *(woman)*, Anthony Lettier *(2d sergeant)*, Chester Jones *(doorman)*, Harriett Vine *(Hannah)*.
Melodrama. Criminologist Brett Kingsford, who poses as a wealthy playboy to disguise his identity as a detective, is called upon by police to solve a series of related murders in turn-of-the-century San Francisco. The victims were found clawed, a small Oriental statue beside each corpse. Kingsford learns from Chi Zang, an old Chinese, that an ancient demon spirit, represented by the statue, chooses a living person to possess and carry out its evil deeds; but before it can enter the body, it must murder seven times. Kingsford visits his friend Robert Vandenburg, who is engaged to marry Evelyn Lang. Robert appears ill-at-ease and, at the mention of the killings, loses consciousness. Kingsford then learns from Professor Malaki, a fortune-teller, that Robert had a twin brother from whom he was separated at birth. Both the doctor and nurse who were present at their births were among the recent victims, and Kingford concludes that the evil brother, who is deformed, desires to take over his brother's body and is killing all those who could verify Robert's existence. In the belief that the next murder will take place at the wedding, Kingsford arrives in time to save Evelyn from being murdered by the already-possessed Robert. *Criminologists. Playboys. Chinese. Fortune-tellers. Twins. Brothers. Murder. Wealth. Supernatural. Jealousy. Evil spirits. Weddings. San Francisco.*

DARK ODYSSEY   F6.1022

Era K M Films. *Dist* Era K M Films, Audubon Films. 24 Jun **1961** [New York opening]. Sd; b&w. 35mm. 85 min. [Also 75 and 82 min.]

Prod-Dir William Kyriakys, Radley Metzger. *Assoc Prod* James Vlamos. *Screenplay* William Kyriakys, Radley Metzger, James Vlamos. *Photog* Peter Erik Winkler. *Film Ed* Radley Metzger, William Kyriakys. *Mus* Laurence Rosenthal. *Sd* David Jones. *Cont* LaVerne Owens.

Cast: Athan Karras *(Yianni Martakis)*, Jeanne Jerrems *(Niki Vassos)*, David Hooks *(George Andros)*, Rosemary Torri *(Helen Vassos)*, Edward Brazier *(Jack Fields)*, Ariadne Zapnoukayas *(Mrs. Vassos)*, Nicholas Zapnoukayas *(Mr. Vassos)*, Warren Houston *(bartender)*, Chris Marks *(freighter captain)*, Maggie Owens *(cleaning woman)*.

Melodrama. Yianni, a young Greek sailor, jumps ship in New York City in order to pursue a compatriot, Pano Coupas, whom he intends to kill. Yianni meets Niki Vassos, a Greek-American, and she invites him to stay with her family at their Washington Heights home. Mrs. Vassos, a Greek immigrant, distrusts the stranger, and she finds his gun. Confronted by Niki, Yianni reveals that, years before, Coupas visited his village in Greece and disgraced his sister, proposing marriage and then seducing her. Yianni's sister killed herself in shame, and the custom of the mountain village dictated revenge. Niki tries to persuade Yianni to leave behind Old World customs and begin a new life in America, and he wavers. Later at a party to celebrate the baptism of a child, Yianni is persuaded to perform a Greek sword dance, and his emotions are aroused. He seeks out Coupas and shoots him; then he flees to his ship, pursued by police. Niki tries to persuade Yianni to give himself up, but in the struggle, his gun goes off and kills him. *Sailors. Greeks. Immigrants. Revenge. Murder. Brother-sister relationship. Suicide. Social customs. Rites and ceremonies. New York City—Washington Heights. New York City—Waterfront.*

Note: Filmed in New York City in 1958 and released in 1961 in simultaneous English and dubbed Greek versions by Era K M Films. Re-released as *Passionate Sunday* in 1965 by Audubon Films.

DARK OF THE SUN (Great Britain)   F6.1023

George Englund Enterprises. *Dist* Metro-Goldwyn-Mayer, Inc. 3 Jul **1968** [New York opening; c31 Dec 1967; LP35101]. Sd; col (Metrocolor). 35mm (Panavision). 101 min. [Also reviewed at 105 min.]

A George Englund Production. *Prod* George Englund. *Dir* Jack Cardiff. *Screenplay* Quentin Werty, Adrian Spies. *Dir Photog* Edward Scaife. *Camera Op* Alan McCabe. *Art Dir* Elliot Scott. *Film Ed* Ernest Walter. *Mus Comp & Cond* Jacques Loussier. *Rec Supv* A. W. Watkins. *Sd Rec* Gerry Turner. *Dub Mix* J. B. Smith. *Sd Ed* Roy Baker. *Asst Dir* Ted Sturgis. *Prod Mgr* Douglas Twiddy. *Prod Supv* John Palmer. *Sp Eff* Cliff Richardson.

Cast: Rod Taylor *(Curry)*, Yvette Mimieux *(Claire)*, Peter Carsten *(Henlein)*, Jim Brown *(Ruffo)*, Kenneth More *(Dr. Wreid)*, Andre Morell *(Bussier)*, Olivier Despax *(Surrier)*, Guy Deghy *(Delage)*, Bloke Modisane *(Kataki)*, Calvin Lockhart *(Ubi)*, Alan Gifford *(Jansen)*, David Bauer *(Adams)*, Murray Kash *(Cochrane)*, John Serret *(Father Dominic)*, Danny Daniels *(General Moses)*, Monique Lucas *(Madame Bussier)*, Louise Bennett *(Mrs. Ubi)*, Paul Jantzen *(Captain Hansen)*, Emery J. Ujvari *(functionary)*, Alex Gradussov *(Belgian refugee)*.

Action melodrama. Source: Wilbur A. Smith, *The Dark of the Sun* (London, 1965). In 1960, Capt. Bruce Curry, a mercenary, leads a Congolese troop and a small crew of his own men—Sergeant Ruffo, a Congolese patriot educated in the United States; sadistic ex-SS officer Henlein; young Belgian officer Surrier; and the alcoholic British Dr. Wreid—into the Congo aboard a train. Their mission is to rescue the white inhabitants of Port Reprieve, which is about to be attacked by rebel Simba soldiers, and also to bring back uncut diamonds valued at millions of dollars for Congolese President Ubi. En route, Curry and his men rescue a blonde Belgian refugee named Claire and stave off a series of attacks by an enemy plane. When the train arrives at Port Reprieve, the group learn that the time vault containing the diamonds will not open for another 3 hours. In the interval, Wreid attends an African woman in childbirth and decides to stay with his patient rather than escape. Finally, the diamonds and refugees are loaded aboard the train, but the Simbas uncouple the coach containing the diamonds just as the train pulls out. Curry and Ruffo lead a commando raid to retake the town. Though Surrier and Wreid are killed, the raid is successful, but on the way to a nearby town the group almost run out of gas. Curry uses what little gas is left to go on and radio for help, leaving Ruffo, Henlein, Claire, and the refugees behind. Henlein, mistakenly believing that Ruffo has the diamonds, kills him and then flees into the jungle. When Curry returns and finds his friend dead, he pursues and brutally kills Henlein. Curry then returns to Claire and the refugees, and with Ruffo's principles in mind, he surrenders his authority to the native corporal and turns himself in for court-martial. *Mercenaries. Physicians. Soldiers. Refugees. Belgians. Congolese. Germans. Simbas. Patriotism. Murder. Alcoholism. Racism. Revolts. Friendship. Diamonds. Trains. Vaults. Jungles. Democratic Republic of the Congo. SS.*

Note: Released in Great Britain in 1968 as *The Mercenaries*. Location scenes filmed in Jamaica.

DARK PURPOSE (United States/France/Italy)   F6.1024

Galatea–Société Cinématographique Lyre–Brazzi-Barclay-Hayutin. *Dist* Universal Pictures. 5 Feb **1964** [New York opening]. Sd; col (Technicolor). 35mm. 97 min.

Prod Steve Barclay. *Exec Prod* Paul Baron, Harvey Hayutin. *Assoc Prod* Federico D'Avack. *Dir U. S. Vers (see note)* George Marshall. *Dir Italian Vers (see note)* Vittorio Sala. *Screenplay (see note)* David P. Harmon, Massimo D'Avack, Steve Barclay. *Photog* Gabor Pogany. *Art Dir* Massimo Tavazzi. *Film Ed* Giancarlo Cappelli. *Mus Comp* Angelo Francesco Lavagnino. *Mus Cond* Franco Ferrara. *Theme Mus:* "Ravello" Paul Baron. *Sd* Kurt Doubravsky. *Asst Dir* Frank Marchione. *Prod Mgr* Tommaso Sagone. *Gowns* Balestra. *Makeup* Euclide Santoli. *Hairstyles* Italia Cambi.

Cast: Shirley Jones *(Karen Williams)*, Rossano Brazzi *(Count Paolo Barbarelli)*, George Sanders *(Raymond Fontaine)*, Georgia Moll *(Cora Barbarelli)*, Micheline Presle *(Monique Bouvier)*, Charles Fawcett.

Melodrama. Source: Doris Hume, *Dark Purpose* (New York, 1960). Art appraiser Raymond Fontaine and his secretary, Karen Williams, visit the clifftop villa of Count Paolo Barbarelli in Ravello to appraise his art treasures. They meet Cora, a 19-year-old girl who lost her memory in a skiing accident some years before; Paolo claims her as his daughter. Karen and Paolo fall in love, but Cora begs Paolo to send Karen away. Karen, attempting to win Cora's friendship, brings her a gift of a Christmas tree, and, while they talk, Cora's mind clears temporarily. She reveals that she is really Paolo's wife and that he is using her family's money to buy art treasures, but Paolo arrives before she can produce documentation to prove her story. Paolo tells Karen that Cora's story is only a fantasy of her disturbed mind. Next morning, Cora is found dead at the foot of the cliff, and though the police attribute the death to suicide, Karen finds Cora's shawl nearby; moreover, caught in the shawl is a cufflink from a set given Paolo by Karen. Through a secret passage, Karen finds the other link in Cora's bedroom and also discovers the passport and birth certificate that prove the truth of Cora's story. Later, while Karen is struggling with the murderous Paolo in the garden, Paolo's savage watchdog lunges at her back, causing Paolo to fall into the fountain. Though Karen tries to rescue him, the vicious dog prevents her from getting near her master, and she is forced to stand by helplessly while Paolo drowns. Fontaine arrives in time to witness the end of the incident. *Art appraisers. Secretaries. Americans in foreign countries. Art collectors. Nobility. Amnesia. Murder. Ravello. Documentation. Dogs.*

Note: Opened in Rome in 1964 as *L'intrigo*. According to some Italian sources, Vittorio Sala directed under George Marshall's supervision; other sources credit Marshall as director of U. S. version and Sala as director of Italian version. An Italian source credits David P. Harmon, Massimo D'Avack, and Steve Barclay as screenwriters and D'Avack with adaptation; elsewhere Harmon is credited as author of screenplay for U. S. version and D'Avack as author of Italian version.

DARK SHADOWS *see* HOUSE OF DARK SHADOWS

THE DARK SIDE OF TOMORROW   F6.1025

David Novik. *Dist* Able Films. Jul **1970**. Sd; col (Eastmancolor). 35mm. 84 min. *MPAA rating* R.

Prod-Story David Novik. *Assoc Prod* George Watters. *Dir* Barbara Peeters, Jacque Deerson. *Screenplay* Barbara Peeters. *Photog* Jacque Deerson. *Film Ed* Richard Weber, ed. *Mus* Jerry Wright, The Friends, London Dri, Queen Mary Dancers. *Sd* Clark D. Will.

Cast: Elizabeth Plumb *(Denise)*, Alisa Courtney *(Adria)*, John Aprea *(Jim)*, Wayne Want *(David)*, Marland Proctor *(Casey)*, Luanne Roberts *(producer's wife)*, Elizabeth Knowles, Jamie Cooper, Sally Fedem, Linda Handelman, Vince Romano, Laura Patton, Geretta Taylor, Russ Milburn.

Melodrama. Two Los Angeles housewives, Adria and Denise, bored by their husbands' prolonged absence on government business, enter into a lesbian relationship. Unsure of their real feelings for each other, however, the two quarrel. Denise subsequently becomes involved with a woman fashion designer who seduces her at a party, while Adria takes an unemployed actor as a lover. Adria and her actor-lover are discovered together by Adria's husband, who savagely beats them before announcing that the marriage is ended. Free of both husband and male lover, Adria happily returns to her former relationship with Denise. *Housewives. Actors. Couturiers. Marriage. Lesbianism. Infidelity. Los Angeles.*

DARK THE MOUNTAIN SNOW (Japan)   F6.1026

Toho Co. Sep **1966** [Los Angeles showing]. Sd; b&w. 35mm. [Feature film, length unknown.]

Exec Prod Ichiro Sato, Hideyuki Shiino. *Dir-Writ* Zenzo Matsuyama. *Photog* Kozo Okazaki. *Mus* Masaru Sato.

Cast: Hideko Takamine *(Ine Rokujo)*, Frankie Sakai *(Jiro)*, Keiju Kobayashi *(Kyuemon's brother)*, Mayumi Ozora *(Jiro's fiancée)*, Kikue Mori *(Kyuemon's mother)*, Shigeru Shamiyama *(Kyuemon Rokujo)*.

Drama. In the snow country of northern Japan the aristocratic Rokujo family has for the past 200 years operated a firm that manufactures a unique fabric called "Yukiyama Tsumugi." Kyueomon, a widower and the ninth head of the family, decides to marry a geisha over the objections of his mother and the rest of the family. Kyuemon then throws the family heavily into debt constructing a new factory in the belief that demand for the fabric will increase. However, competition from the new chemical fibers cuts into the Rokujo business, and Kyuemon, feeling he has disgraced his family name, commits suicide. The family now attempts to drive off Ine, Kyuemon's geisha wife, but because she is one of the few people aware of the true financial condition of the business, she stays on, attempting to save the firm from bankruptcy. She is aided in her efforts by Jiro, a loyal employee of the business, and their close association prompts rumors, spread by Kyuemon's mother, of a romance between them. Jiro's fiancée, believing the stories of her lover's infidelity, commits suicide. Finally, Ine's struggle to save the business succeeds when the government declares the fabric an "intangible cultural property." Ine leaves with Jiro, allowing the business to be passed on to her son, but even Jiro, unable to forget the past, eventually leaves her. *Widowers. Widows. Geishas. In-laws. Aristocrats. Textile manufacture. Suicide. Gossip. Debt. Factories.*

Note: Released in Japan in 1965 as *Rokujo Yukiyama Tsumugi.*

THE DARK TUNNEL F6.1027

Dist Lawrence Leibowitz. 25 Jun **1965** [New York opening]. Si?; 8mm. 45 min.

Dir Lawrence Leibowitz. No information about the precise nature of this film has been found.

DARKER THAN AMBER F6.1028

Major Pictures–Rodlor, Inc. *For* Cinema Center Films. *Dist* National General Pictures. 12 Aug **1970** [Dallas opening; c10 Jun 1970; LP39246]. Sd; col (Technicolor). 35mm. 97 min. *MPAA rating* R.

Prod Walter Seltzer, Jack Reeves. *Dir* Robert Clouse. *Screenplay* Ed Waters. *Camera* Frank Phillips. *Camera Op* James Pergola. *1st Asst Camera* Mike Davis. *2d Asst Camera* Mike McGowan. *Art Dir* Jack Collis. *Set Decor* Don Ivey. *Film Ed* Fred Chulack. *Asst Film Ed* Steve Cuiffo. *Mus* John Parker, mus. *Sd Mix* Howard Warren. *Rec* Dale Armstrong. *Boom Op* Bill Johnson. *1st & 2d Asst Dir* Ted Swanson, Charles W. Persons. *Prod Mgr* Frank Baur. *Script Supv* Jack Cowden. *Prod Sec* Shirley Cohen. *Cost* Richard Bruno, Peggy Kunkle. *Makeup* Guy Del Russo, Marie Del Russo. *Hairdresser* Irene Aparicio. *Sp Eff* Bob Raley. *Prop Master* Jack Johnson, prop. *Still Photog* Steve Wever. *Stunt Coörd* Roger Creed, Courtney Brown. *Constr Coörd* Bob Krume. *Gaffer* Walter Morris, Jr. *Key Grip* Perry Jones.

Cast: Rod Taylor *(Travis McGee)*, Suzy Kendall *(Vangie Bellemer/Merrimay Lane)*, Theodore Bikel *(Meyer)*, Jane Russell *(Alabama Tiger)*, James Booth *(Burk)*, Janet MacLachlan *(Noreen Walker)*, William Smith *(Terry)*, Ahna Capri *(Del)*, Robert Phillips *(Griff)*, Chris Robinson *(Roy)*, Jack Nagle *(Farnsworth)*, Sherry Faber *(Nina)*, James H. Frysinger *(Dewey Powell)*, Oswaldo Calvo *(Manuel)*, Jeff Gillen *(morgue attendant)*, Michael De Beausset *(Dr. Fairbanks)*, Judy Wallace *(Ginny)*, Harry Wood *(Ed Judson)*, Marcy Knight *(landlady)*, Warren Bauer, Wayne Bauer *(Roy's companions)*, Don Schoff *(steward)*.

Crime melodrama. Source: John D. MacDonald, *Darker Than Amber* (Greenwich, Connecticut, 1966). Private detective Travis McGee and his friend Meyer are fishing near the Florida Keys when they see a woman with an iron boot attached to her foot being thrown from a bridge. They rescue her and take her aboard McGee's houseboat, but she is only willing to divulge her name, Vangie Bellemer. Meanwhile, Terry, one of her assailants, sadistically kills McGee's friend Burk when he refuses to reveal the whereabouts of the detective and Vangie. After the houseboat arrives in Fort Lauderdale, Vangie slips ashore to get some money from her apartment, where Terry and Griff, the other assailant, are waiting for her. They murder her and then make it appear as if she had been killed in a hit-and-run accident, but when McGee identifies the body in the city morgue, he realizes that she was murdered. McGee, who had become fond of Vangie, learns her address, goes to her apartment, and discovers Griff searching for her money. Griff forces McGee to a deserted beach to kill him, but in the ensuing struggle Griff is killed. McGee learns from black maid Noreen that Vangie and Del, one of her friends, had been used as bait to lure wealthy, middle-aged men aboard cruise ships so that Terry could rob them and dump them overboard. In Nassau, McGee convinces Del to cooperate and also enlists the aid of underwater ballerina Merrimay Lane, who looks exactly like Vangie, to impersonate the murder victim. Terry goes into a rage and kills Del when he discovers the iron boot in his bathtub; later, when he sees Merrimay waving at him from the gangway, he goes berserk. After the case is closed, Merrimay tries to seduce McGee, but he rejects her. *Detectives.*

Negroes. Housemaids. Swindlers. Doubles. Fishing. Rescue. Murder. Robbery. Impersonation. Houseboats. Beaches. Florida Keys. Fort Lauderdale.

Note: Location scenes filmed in Florida and Nassau.

DARLING (Great Britain) F6.1029

Vic Films–Appia Films. *Dist* Embassy Pictures. 3 Aug **1965** [New York opening]. Sd; b&w. 35mm. 122 min.

Pres by Joseph E. Levine. A Joseph Janni Production. *Prod* Joseph Janni. *Assoc Prod* Victor Lyndon. *Dir* John Schlesinger. *Screenplay* Frederic Raphael. *Story* Frederic Raphael, John Schlesinger, Joseph Janni. *Dir Photog* Ken Higgins. *Art Dir* Ray Simm. *Set Decor* David Ffolkes. *Scenic Artist* Ted Barnes. *Film Ed* James Clark. *Mus Comp & Cond* John Dankworth. *Sd* Malcolm Cooke. *Sd Rec* Peter Handford, John Aldred. *Prod Mgr* Ed Harper. *Cost* Julie Harris, cost. *Makeup* Bob Lawrence. *Hairdresser* Joyce James.

Cast: Julie Christie *(Diana Scott)*, Dirk Bogarde *(Robert Gold)*, Laurence Harvey *(Miles Brand)*, Roland Curram *(Malcolm)*, Alex Scott *(Sean Martin)*, Basil Henson *(Alec Prosser-Jones)*, Helen Lindsay *(Felicity Prosser-Jones)*, Tyler Butterworth *(William Prosser-Jones)*, Pauline Yates *(Estelle Gold)*, Peter Bayliss *(Lord Grant)*, José-Luis de Vilallonga *(Prince Cesare Della Romita)*, Jean Claudio *(Raoul Maxim)*, Ernst Walder *(Kurt)*, Lucille Soong *(Allie)*, Sidonie Bond *(Gillian)*, John G. Heller *(Gerhard)*, James Cossins *(Basildon)*, Lydia Sherwood *(Lady Brentwood)*, Georgina Cookson *(Carlotta Hale)*, Brian Wilde *(Willett)*, David Harrison *(Charles Glass)*, Irene Richmond *(Mrs. Glass)*, Ann Firbank *(Sybil)*, Richard Bidlake *(Rupert Crabtree)*, Trevor Bowen *(Tony Bridges)*, Helen Stirling *(governess to Cesare)*, Annette Carell *(Billie Castiglione)*, Hugo Dyson *(Matthew Southgate)*, Angus MacKay *(Ivor Dawlish)*, Margaret Gordon *(Helen Dawlish)*, Jane Downes *(Julie)*, Carlo Palmucci *(Curzio)*, Dante Posani *(Gino)*, Umberto Raho *(Palucci)*.

Drama. Diana Scott, an Italian princess by marriage and a famous member of the jet set, is being interviewed by a reporter from a woman's magazine at her Italian villa. She relates the story of her life and how she came to be what she is. ... Born into an upper-middle-class family, she is spoiled as a child because she is so beautiful. Disregarding advice, she is married very young to an equally immature young man. This first marriage fails, and Diana, a model, starts to live her own life in the world of London television and advertising. She meets and falls in love with television journalist Robert Gold, who is so infatuated that he leaves his wife and children for her. But Diana, trying to further her career as a model, abandons him temporarily for an executive, Miles Brand, who finds her a small part in a horror film. After the opening of the film Diana tells Robert that she is pregnant; both are initially pleased and want the child, but soon Diana decides to have an abortion. Taking the matter very lightly, she tells Robert she never got any satisfaction from sex. While recovering at her sister's country home, she is bored and returns to Robert. Once more, however, she leaves him for Miles, who takes her to Paris to experience the wild bisexual parties of his crowd. When Diana returns to London, Robert walks out on her. Diana takes up with homosexual photographer Malcolm, who takes her to Italy to film commercials. Here she meets Prince Cesare Della Romita, a widower with six children. He proposes marriage, but she rejects him. Diana returns once more to London and Robert, but this time she realizes that their affair is truly over. In a search for security, she agrees to marry the prince, but he finds little time for her in his busy schedule. Bored and lonely, she returns to Robert for the last time. They spend a night together and make love, but in the morning Robert sends Diana back to Italy. Diana weeps as she contemplates her affluent but empty life. *Photographers. Actors. Models. Journalists. Royalty. Widowers. Executives. Upper classes. Jet set. Abortion. Sexuality. Promiscuity. Advertising. Orgies. Bisexuality. Male homosexuality. Marriage. Television. Motion pictures. London. Paris. Italy.*

Note: Location scenes filmed in Capri, Florence, London, and France. Opened in London in Sep 1965 as *Darling ...*; running time: 127 min.

DARLING, ARE YOU BORED WITH MEN? F6.1030

Dist I. R. M. I. Films. **1968** [Boston showing: 5 May 1970]. Sd; b&w. 35mm. 70 min.

Prod John Michaels. *Dir* John Meyer.

Cast: Rosemary Klein, Aldo Frank.

Sex film. No information about the precise nature of this film has been found, but press material suggests that it is a black comedy about women who impersonate men. *Male impersonation.*

Note: May also be known as *Are You Bored With Men?* and *Do I Bore You Darling?*

DARLING LILI F6.1031

Geoffrey Productions. *Dist* Paramount Pictures. 24 Jun **1970** [Los Angeles opening; c31 Dec 1969; LP38095]. Sd; col (Technicolor). 35mm (Panavision). 136 min. *MPAA rating* G.

A Blake Edwards Production. *Prod-Dir* Blake Edwards. *Exec Prod* Owen Crump. *Assoc Prod* Ken Wales. *2d Unit Dir* Dick Crockett. *Dir Aerial Seq* Anthony Squire. *Screenplay* Blake Edwards, William Peter Blatty. *Dir Photog* Russell Harlan. *2d Unit Photog* Harold E. Wellman. *Aerial Seq Photog* Guy Tabary. *Camera Op* Jack Whitman. *Camera Asst* Frank Stanley. *Set Decor* Reg Allen, Jack Stevens. *Prod Dsgn* Fernando Carrère. *Film Ed* Peter Zinner. *Mus* Henry Mancini. *Songs:* "Whistling Away the Dark," "The Girl in No Man's Land," "Smile Away Each Rainy Day," "I'll Give You Three Guesses" Henry Mancini, Johnny Mercer. *Songs Sung by* Julie Andrews. *Song:* "Your Good-Will Ambassador" Henry Mancini, Johnny Mercer. *Sung by* Gloria Paul. *Choral Supv* Alan Copeland. *French Lyr Transl* Danielle Mauroy, Michel Legrand. *Song:* "La Marseillaise" Claude Joseph Rouget de Lisle. *Mus Numbers Stgd by* Hermes Pan. *Prod Rec* John Carter. *Supv Stereo Re-rec* Fred Hynes. *Asst Dir* Mickey McCardle, Gene Marum, William R. Poole. *Prod Mgr* John Coonan. *Unit Prod Mgr* Jack McEdward, Curtis Mick, Fred Lemoine, Howard Roessel. *Script Supv* Lois Thurman. *Cost Dsgn* Jack Bear. *Cost for Miss Andrews* Donald Brooks. *Jewelry for Miss Andrews* Marvin Hime. *Makeup for Mr. Hudson* Allan Snyder. *Makeup for Miss Andrews* Willard Buell. *Makeup* Lynn Reynolds. *Hairstyles* Lorraine Roberson. *Sp Photog Eff* Rex Wimpy, Linwood Dunn, Van Der Veer Photo Co. *Sp Eff* Bob Peterson. *Mus Adv* Danny Gould. *Coöp* Derek Piggott, Derek Goddard, Irish Air Corps. *Dial Coach* James Lanphier. *Asst Choreog* Bea Busch. *Vocal Coach* Harper MacKay. *Prop Master* Wally Oliver.

Cast: Julie Andrews (*Lili Smith*), Rock Hudson (*Maj. William Larrabee*), Jeremy Kemp (*Kurt von Ruger*), Lance Percival (*Lieut. Carstairs (T. C.) Twombley-Crouch*), Michael Witney (*Youngblood Carson*), Gloria Paul (*Crêpe Suzette*), Jacques Marin (*Major Duvalle*), André Maranne (*Lieutenant Liggett*), Bernard Kay (*Bedford*), Doreen Keogh (*Emma*), Carl Duering (*Kessler*), Vernon Dobtcheff (*Kraus*), Laurie Main, Louis Mercier (*French generals*), Arthur Gould-Porter (*Sergeant Wells*), Ingo Mogendorf (*The Red Baron*), Niall MacGinnis (*von Hindenburg*), Mimi Monti (*chanteuse*).

Comedy with music. During the Great War, Lili Smith, a popular singer with London audiences, acts as a German agent. Her assignment, relayed by superior Kurt von Ruger, is to develop a friendship with American officer Maj. William Larrabee. While in France to receive the Legion of Honor award for patriotism, Lili meets the flier. Impressed by her compassion for the wounded and infatuated by her charm, Larrabee courts her, employing gypsy violinists to serenade her. As a result, Lili easily elicits military information from him. Discovering the security leak and suspecting the American, French intelligence officers enlist Lili's aid in unmasking the spy. Informed by von Ruger that Larrabee is involved in Operation Crêpe Suzette, Lili discovers that Suzette is Larrabee's stripper mistress and denounces her rival as the German agent. While on a rescue mission the flier is downed. Commandeering the plane of German ace von Richthofen, however, he escapes to England. When Larrabee is arrested for espionage, Lili comes to his aid, proclaiming her identity and outraging her German superiors. Fearing for Lili's life, Larrabee once again takes command of von Richthofen's plane and saves her train from a German air attack. From the sky the flier throws his scarf as a symbol of their love. After the armistice Lili resumes her singing career. During a performance Larrabee steps from the stage wing and embraces her. *Traditional songs:* "It's a Long, Long Way to Tipperary," "Pack Up Your Troubles in Your Old Kit Bag and Smile, Smile, Smile," "Keep the Home Fires Burning," and "Mademoiselle From Armentières" (sung by Lili and chorus). *Secret agents. Singers. Air pilots. Mistresses. Stripteasers. English. Gypsies. Germans. French. Espionage. Courtship. Jealousy. Airplanes. World War I. London. France. Manfred von Richthofen. France—Army—Intelligence service.*

Note: Location scenes filmed in Dublin, Brussels, and Paris. Aerial sequences filmed over Ireland.

THE DAUGHTER; I, A WOMAN PART III (Denmark)   **F6.1032**
Novaris Film. *Dist* Chevron Pictures. 31 Jul 1970 [San Francisco opening]. Sd; col (Eastman Color, print by Movielab). 35mm. 85 min. *MPAA rating* X.
Prod-Writ Peer Guldbrandsen. *Dir* Mac Ahlberg. *Photog* Mac Ahlberg, Aage Wiltrup. *Camera Asst* Alan Ashton. *Art Dir* Erik Björk. *Film Ed* Edith Nisted. *Mus* Sven Gyldmark, Bertrand Bech. *Sd* Jarno Dupont, Torben Øksnebjerg, Jon Branner. *Asst Dir* Susanne Lange. *Unit Prod Mgr* Palle Schnedler-Sørensen. *Prod Asst* Ole Guldbrandsen. *Makeup* Else Hennings. *Ch Electrn* Henning Larsen. *Prop Master* Palle Arrestrup.
Cast: Inger Sundh (*Birthe*), Tom Scott (*Stephen*), Ellen Faison (*Lisa*), Gun Falck (*Siv*), Klaus Pagh (*Leo Smith*), Susanne Jagd (*hippie dancer*), Sören Strömberg (*Egon*), Bent Warburg (*Max*), Helle Louise (*patient*), Tove Bang, Tove Maës (*older women*), Benny Hansen, Paul Glargaard (*Hell's Angels*), John Larsen (*television reporter*).

Drama. Seventeen-year-old Birthe arrives home from boarding school earlier than expected and finds her mother, Siv, in bed with Leo, a doctor at the hospital where Siv is chief nurse. Upset by the spectacle, Birthe flees to a

discotheque, a hangout for hippies and young "toughs." There Stephen, a young American Negro who is a medical student at the hospital where Siv and Leo work, while keeping an eye on his sister Lisa, a go-go dancer, notices Birthe as a newcomer to the club and is immediately attracted to her. But before he can speak to Birthe, she is picked up by Max, a hippie who takes her to a tenement party where hashish is being smoked and some of the guests are engaging in sex play. Max tries to force himself on Birthe; she fights him off; her bag falls to the floor and an erotic photo of her mother drops out. Birthe is accused of being a lesbian. While she is struggling to retrieve the photo from her tormentors, Stephen appears and rescues her. Stephen takes her to the apartment he shares with Lisa and privately announces his intention to marry Birthe. Lisa scorns his hopes of marrying a white woman. Actually, Lisa, a lesbian, intends to compete with her brother for Birthe's affection. Lisa achieves partial success and seduces Birthe, but she eventually loses when Birthe concludes that she was over-reacting to her mother's sexuality, and she decides that she loves Stephen. They are married, and Siv confesses to Leo that she is disturbed by her daughter's marrying a Negro. *Nurses. Physicians. Hippies. Negroes. Medical students. Go-go dancers. Adolescence. Filial relations. Seduction. Brother-sister relationship. Lesbianism. Miscegenation. Discotheques. Hashish. Photographs. Americans in foreign countries.*

Note: Released in Denmark in Feb 1970 as *Tre slags kaerlighed*; running time: 83 min. Original running time: 92 min. Also known as *I, A Woman—3*, and *I Am a Woman III.*

DAUGHTER OF CLEOPATRA see **CLEOPATRA'S DAUGHTER**

DAUGHTER OF SATAN   **F6.1033**
Janus II Productions–Academy Productions. *Dist* Exhibitors Distributing, Ltd., Stacey Distributors. ca 1970. Sd; col. 16mm. ca60 min.
Sex film. Satan, ruler of evil, turns a pure virgin into a wanton nymph. She can do whatever she wishes merely by imagining it. *Virginity. Nymphomania. Lesbianism. The Devil.*
Note: Also known as *Daughter of the Devil.*

DAUGHTER OF THE SUN GOD   **F6.1034**
Condor Productions. *Dist* Herts-Lion International Corp. Oct 1962. Sd; col (Eastman Color). 35mm. 75 min.
Prod Edward A. Biery. *Dir-Writ* Kenneth Herts. *Mus* Les Baxter.
Cast: William Holmes (*Kent*), Lisa Montell (*Christine*), Harry Knapp (*Dr. Howard Knapp*), Juanita Llosa (*Daughter of the Sun God*), Al Bello, Emilio Meiners, Juan Caycho.
Adventure drama. Kent, an American writer and explorer vacationing in Peru, is approached by Christine, whose uncle, an authority on Incan and pre-Columbian cultures, has disappeared. Christine wants Kent to help her find a stolen map of the legendary lost city of gold, where the Incas live today as they had 2,000 years ago. Dr. Howard Knapp, an American archeologist, joins Kent's expedition as a guide. After surviving many perils in the Peruvian desert—snakes, crocodiles, and hostile natives—the group negotiates jungle quicksand and jaguar attacks. Dr. Knapp, revealed to be responsible for stealing the map, separates from Kent and Christine. The couple make their way to the Incan city and warn the natives, who overcome the doctor and his mountain bandits. *Americans in foreign countries. Incas. Authors. Explorers. Uncles. Missing persons. Archeologists. Guides. Bandits. Thieves. Survival. Vacations. Gold. Deserts. Jungles. Quicksand. Peru. Documentation. Snakes. Crocodiles. Jaguars.*
Note: Location scenes filmed in Peru and Brazil.

DAUGHTERS OF LESBOS see **DOMINIQUE**

THE DAVE CLARK FIVE RUNS WILD see **HAVING A WILD WEEKEND**

DAVID AND GOLIATH (Italy)   **F6.1035**
Ansa Cinematografica. *Dist* Allied Artists. May 1961 [c16 May 1961; LP19430]. Sd; col (Eastman Color). 35mm (Totalscope). 95 min.
Pres by Beaver-Champion Attractions. *Exec Prod* Emimmo Salvi. *Dir* Richard Pottier, Ferdinando Baldi. *Screenplay* Umberto Scarpelli, Gino Mangini, Ambrogio Molteni, Emimmo Salvi. *Dir Photog* Carlo Fiore, Adalberto Albertini. *Scenic Photog* Christiano Civirani. *Art Dir* Oscar D'Amico. *Film Ed* Franco Fraticelli. *Mus Comp* Carlo Innocenzi. *Orch Cond* Giuseppe Savagnone. *Choreog* Carla Renalli. *Sd* Pietro Ortolani, Bruno Moreal. *Asst Dir* Gianfranco Baldanello. *Admin Dir* Decio Salvi. *Cost* Ditta Peruzzi, Giovanna Natili. *Makeup Artist* Guglielmo Bonotti. *Hairstyles* Giovanni Palombi.
Cast: Orson Welles (*King Saul*), Ivo Payer (*David*), Edward Hilton (*Prophet Samuel*), Massimo Serato (*Abner*), Eleonora Rossi Drago (*Merab*), Giulia Rubini (*Michal*), Pierre Cressoy (*Jonathan*), Furio Meniconi (*King Asrod*), Kronos (*Goliath*), Dante Maggio (*Cret*), Luigi Tosi (*Benjamin di Gaba*), Umberto Fiz (*Lazar*), Ugo Sasso (*Huro*), Carlo D'Angelo, Gabriele Tinti, Ileana

Danelli, Carla Foscari, Fabrizio Capucci, Roberto Miali, Renato Terra, Emma Baron.

Religious drama. King Saul of Israel, once fair and just but now mad with power, is denounced by the prophet Samuel, who predicts that a young monarch of extraordinary intelligence and goodness will succeed to the throne. Guided by the Lord, Samuel chooses David, the youngest son of a Bethlehem shepherd, and has him brought to the court of Saul. When the youth's goodness and wisdom begin to attract a following—particularly Saul's son and daughter, Jonathan and Michal—the evil prime minister, Abner, advises the king to send David to arrange a truce with the Philistines, with whom Israel has long been warring. David confronts King Asrod of the Philistines, who, impressed by the boldness of the youth, agrees to a truce if David can slay Goliath, the powerful Philistine giant. Armed only with a sling, David deftly evades Goliath's javelins, fells him with a stone, and then kills him with his own sword. David returns in triumph to Israel; Abner attempts to strike him down; but Saul kills his prime minister and then, mindful of Samuel's prophesy, offers David the hand of Michal. *Royalty. Prophets. Prime ministers. Shepherds. Philistines. Giants. Ambition. Slingshots. Israel. Bethlehem. Saul. David. Goliath. Samuel. Jonathan. Michal. Abner.*

Note: Location scenes filmed in Jerusalem and Yugoslavia. Rome opening: Mar 1960 as *David e Golia*; running time: ca110 min.

DAVID AND LISA F6.1036
Lisa & David Co. *Dist* Continental Distributing, Inc. 18 Dec **1962** [Los Angeles opening]. Sd; b&w. 35mm. 94 min.

A Paul M. Heller–Frank Perry Production. *Prod* Paul M. Heller. *Assoc Prod* Vision Associates Inc. *Dir* Frank Perry. *Screenplay* Eleanor Perry. *Photog* Leonard Hirschfield. *Art Dir* Paul M. Heller. *Set Decor* Gene Callahan. *Film Ed* Irving Oshman. *Mus Comp* Mark Lawrence, mus. *Mus Cond* Norman Paris. *Sd* Karl Storr. *Asst Dir* Tony La Marca. *Cost* Anna Hill Johnstone.

Cast: Keir Dullea (*David Clemens*), Janet Margolin (*Lisa*), Howard Da Silva (*Dr. Alan Swinford*), Neva Patterson (*Mrs. Clemens*), Clifton James (*John*), Richard McMurray (*Mr. Clemens*), Nancy Nutter (*Maureen*), Matthew Anden (*Simon*), Jaime Sanchez (*Carlos*), Coni Hudak (*Kate*), Janet Lee Parker (*Sandra*), Karen Gorney (*Josette*).

Drama. Source: Theodore Isaac Rubin, *Lisa and David* (New York, 1961). David Clemens is an emotionally disturbed adolescent who lives in constant terror of being touched. When his mother places him in a home for disturbed youngsters, he rejects both the other children and his psychiatrist, Alan Swinford. Gradually, however, he becomes interested in Lisa, a 15-year-old schizophrenic: as "Muriel" she is completely mute, and as Lisa she talks only in rhyme. As the relationship between the two develops, David's attitude toward Alan relaxes, and he begins to talk with the doctor. David's mother, however, is unsatisfied with her son's progress and removes him from the home. Unable to bear his mother's domination and his parents' quarreling, David runs away and returns to the home. Lisa is so delighted at his return that she ceases speaking in rhyme. During a student party the two youngsters quarrel, and Lisa runs away; after an all-night search, David finds her at a nearby museum. To persuade her to return to Alan, David shows his trust by finally reaching out to touch her, and two walk off together, holding hands. *Psychiatrists. Mutes. Mental illness. Adolescence. Schizophrenia. Family life. Hospitals. Museums.*

Note: Location scenes filmed in Philadelphia.

DAVID, CAROL, DON, WILL: A PORTRAIT F6.1037
Dist Ron Mottram. 15 Oct **1966** [New York opening]. Si; b&w and col. 16mm. 50 min.

Dir Ron Mottram.

Drama? A family settles in Vermont during late summer and early fall. *Family life. Rural life. Vermont.*

Note: Also known as *Portrait*.

DAVID E GOLIA see DAVID AND GOLIATH

DAVID HOLZMAN'S DIARY F6.1038
Jim McBride. *Dist* Paradigm Films. 1 Oct **1968** [New York showing]. Sd; b&w. 16mm. 74 min.

Prod-Dir-Writ Jim McBride. *Camera* Michael Wadleigh. *Adtl Photog* Paul Glickman, Paul Goldsmith. *Film Ed* Jim McBride.

Cast: L. M. Kit Carson (*David Holzman*), Eileen Dietz (*Penny Wohl*), Louise Levine (*Sandra*), Lorenzo Mans (*Pepe*), Fern McBride (*girl on the subway*), Mike Levine (*Sandra's boyfriend*), Bob Lesser (*Max, Penny's agent*), Jack Baran (*cop*).

Drama. On July 14, 1967, young filmmaker David Holzman reveals his plans to make a film diary about his life. Sitting in his West Side New York City apartment against a background of books, posters, and other allusions to films and filmmakers, Holzman quotes Jean-Luc Godard's dictum, "film is truth 24 times a second," and talks about how the truth of the film he is about to make will allow him to understand the truth of his own life. For the next 9 days

Holzman records and examines his life and the events surrounding him, concentrating on his relationship with his girl friend, Penny, who is a model. Scenes of David's life and surroundings are interspersed with scenes of David discussing himself and the film process. Penny becomes increasingly annoyed at being filmed and leaves David's apartment more than once to escape the camera, and David's painter friend, Pepe, also requests that the camera be turned off because he disagrees with David's concept. He films many other acquaintances and strangers—some don't mind; others do—and he experiments in other directions by recording a complete night of television programming and by filming on the street with his new fisheye lens. David's relationship with Penny disintegrates, and he shows increased interest in sexual matters, even indulging in voyeuristic filming of Sandra, his name for a woman who lives across the street. On July 21, David has nothing to report; the project is not coming out as he intended. He rails against his equipment, then apologizes to it. The next day he announces there will be no filming; he must attend his uncle's funeral. Later that day, David announces from a telephone booth that his equipment has been stolen and the film is over. He regrets that he has learned nothing from his experience. *Filmmakers. Models. Painters. Voyeurism. Motion pictures. Diaries. New York City.*

Note: Filmed on location in New York City. The soundtrack includes selections from various New York City radio stations, including music and newscasts of the Newark, New Jersey, riots, the war in Vietnam, and a United Nations roll call.

THE DAY AFTER see UP FROM THE BEACH

THE DAY AND THE HOUR (France/Italy) F6.1039
Cipra–Terra Films–Société Nouvelle des Films Cormoran–C. C. M.–Monica Film. *Dist* Metro-Goldwyn-Mayer, Inc. 19 Feb **1964** [New York opening; c31 Dec 1963; LP29210]. Sd; b&w. 35mm (Franscope). 115 min. [Copyright length: 104 min.]

Prod Jacques Bar. *Assoc Prod* Raymond Froment. *Dir* René Clément. *Screenplay* René Clément, Roger Vailland. *Dial* Roger Vailland. *English Dial* Clement Biddle Wood. *Story* André Barret. *Dir Photog* Henri Decaë. *Camera Op* Alain Douarinou. *Set Dsgn* Bernard Evein. *Film Ed* Fedora Zincone. *Mus* Claude Bölling. "*La Romance de Paris*" interpreted by Charles Trenet. *Sd* Pierre Calvet. *Asst Dir* Claude Pinoteau, Constantin Gavras. *Prod Mgr* Léon Sanz. *Unit Mgr* Michel Choquet.

Cast: Simone Signoret (*Thérèse Dutheil*), Stuart Whitman (*Capt. Allen Morley*), Geneviève Page (*Agathe*), Michel Piccoli (*Antoine*), Reggie Nalder (*German policeman*), Pierre Dux (*Inspector Marboz*), Billy Kearns (*Pat Riley*), Mark Burns, Roger Kemp (*English air pilots*), Henri Virlogeux (*pharmacist*), Colette Castel (*Lucie*), Edward Meeks (*3d English air pilot*), Marcel Bozzufi (*Inspector Lerat*), Jean Gras ("*Gorilla*" *Richebois*), Hubert de Lapparent (*prosecutor*), Georges Staquet (*innkeeper*), Maurice Garrel (*head militiaman*), Guy Dakar (*militiaman*), Robert Bazil (*peasant*), Marcel Gassouk (*another peasant*), Etienne Dirand (*informer*), Fred Fisher (*German officer*), Henia Suchar (*girl in blue*), Marie Mergey (*innkeeper's wife*), Anthony Stuart (*wing commander*), Carl Studer (*Major Gordon*), Clara Gansard (*member of the Maquis*), Yvette Etiévant (*cashier*), Hugues Wanner (*retired army officer*), Gessie Azoulai (*Michou*), Catherine Azoulai (*Charlotte*).

Drama. In Nazi-occupied Paris in 1944, wealthy Thérèse Dutheil is oblivious to the hardships and sufferings brought on by war. Her husband, an officer, has been captured by the Germans, and Thérèse lives in an elegant apartment with her two young daughters. After a trip to a country farm to obtain food, Thérèse returns to Paris with the farmer's son and discovers that three Allied soldiers are hidden in their truck. When the farmer's son disappears, Thérèse, furious at becoming involved, leads the soldiers to a Resistance hideout. Because there isn't room for them all, she is forced to hide American Capt. Allen Morley in her home. When the Resistance sends Allen on an escape route to the Spanish border, Thérèse accompanies him. Along the way a Gestapo agent attempts to arrest him, and they are arrested by local police at Toulouse, but they are allowed to escape because the police chief realizes that this act will place him in a good position with the Allies. Now deeply in love, Allen and Thérèse bicycle to the border. Allen's request that Thérèse be allowed to accompany him to freedom is refused, and he is forced to leave before saying goodby to her. Unable to return to Paris, Thérèse decides to remain at the border to aid other escaping Allied soldiers. As she enters Resistance headquarters, a radio announces the date—6 June 1944. *Idle rich. Soldiers. Nazis. Police. Escapees. Maquis. Family life. World War II. D-Day (6 Jun 1944). France—History—German occupation 1940-45. Paris. Toulouse.*

Note: Paris opening: Apr 1963 as *Le jour et l'heure*; running time: 110 min. Rome opening: Jun 1963 as *Il giorno e l'ora*; running time: 110 min; alternative Italian title: *Viviamo oggi*. Also known as *Today We Live*.

DAY-DREAM (Japan)   **F6.1040**

Daisan Productions–Shochiku Co. *Dist* Joseph Green Pictures. 4 Dec **1964** [Los Angeles showing]. Sd; b&w with col seq. 35mm (Shochiku GrandScope). 92 min.

Overall Production Credits: *Prod* Toyojiro Nagashima. *Dir-Screenplay* Tetsuji Takechi. *Photog* Masayoshi Kayanuma. *Ed* Hanjiro Kaneko. *Mus Comp* Sukehisa Shiba.

Production Credits for Dream Seq: *Prod-Dir* Joseph Green, dir. *Photog* Victor Peters. *Asst Camera* Glen Tracy. *Art Dir* Anne George. *Ed* Nat Greene. *Masks Created by* Anne George.

Cast: Kanako Michi *(Chieko)*, Akira Ishihama *(Kurahashi)*, Chojuro Hanakawa *(The Dentist)*, Yasuko Matsui *(The Nurse)*.

Drama. Source: Jun-ichiro Tanizaki, "Hakujitsumu yume," in *Chuo Koron* (Sep 1926). Chieko, a singer, and Kurahashi, an art student, meet in a dentist's office and become attracted to each other. While the dentist is treating Chieko, Kurahashi's sedation begins to take effect, and he falls into a dreamy sleep. *Kurahashi witnesses the dentist and his nurse take advantage of Chieko when she faints in the dentist's chair. Kurahashi attempts to help her when he next sees her in a deserted nightclub, but Chieko, unable to overcome the dentist's demonic hold on her, is compelled to yield to his sadistic and perverse desires. Kurahashi's love turns into hatred when he witnesses Chieko revel in sensual delight. He finally catches up with her and stabs her while a crowd of people, indifferent to the event, walk by.* Kurahashi awakens from his slumber as Chieko is leaving the dentist's office. She offers him a ride, and as they drive off, Chieko notices teeth marks on her breast. *Singers. Students. Dentists. Nurses. Sadomasochism. Rape. Anesthetics. Nightclubs. Dreams.*

Note: Released in Japan in 1964 as *Hakujitsumu*. U. S.-produced dream sequences added after 1966 San Francisco showing.

A DAY IN COURT (Italy)   **F6.1041**

Excelsa Film–Documento Film–Bellotti Film. *Dist* Ultra Pictures. 10 May **1963** [New York opening]. Sd; b&w. 35mm. 70 min.

Exec Prod Carlo Ponti, Dino De Laurentiis. *Assoc Prod* Paolo Frasca. *Dir* Steno. *Screenplay* Lucio Fulci, Alberto Sordi, Alessandro Continenza. *Based on an Orig Idea by* Lucio Fulci. *Photog* Marco Scarpelli. *Art Dir* Piero Filippone. *Mus* Armando Trovajoli.

Cast: Sophia Loren *(Anna)*, Alberto Sordi *(Meniconi)*, Silvana Pampanini *(Gloriana)*, Walter Chiari *(Don Michele)*, Peppino De Filippo *(Magistrate Del Russo)*, Tania Weber *(Elena)*, Leopoldo Trieste, Virgilio Riento.

Comedy-drama. Magistrate Del Russo presides over four cases brought before him. ADULTERY IN 16MM: Elena brings her traveling salesman husband to court on charges of abandonment, but he claims that he has evidence collected by hidden home movie cameras that Elena has been having an affair with another man. Despite objections by Elena and, oddly, her husband's lawyer, the films are shown in court and the "other man" proves to be the lawyer. THE PRIEST AND THE PROSTITUTE: Don Michele, a young priest, is charged with wrecking a pool room. He explains that he was robbed by Anna, a prostitute, who gave the money to her procurer. In an attempt to retrieve the money he followed the pimp to a pool room and a fight ensued. However, when the priest insists that he gave the money to Anna to start a new life and that he will take the punishment, the judge, humbled by Don Michele's goodness, gives the priest a suspended sentence. INDECENT EXPOSURE: Meniconi is arrested for indecent exposure but insists that he is an innocent health buff. As part of his regimen he often goes swimming in the nude in a big ditch outside of Rome. One day his clothes are stolen, and while hunting for them, he wanders into a palatial villa during a party in search of help. Though Meniconi is convicted, his sentence is suspended; however, appalled that his clean record is spoiled, he leaves the court threatening revenge on the magistrate. THE LUSTFUL LIEUTENANT: Gloriana, a middle-aged prostitute, is brought before Magistrate Del Russo on charges of soliciting. Her fading beauty is reminiscent of a Gloriana the judge knew during the war, when he was a shy lieutenant. She was a startling beauty and a great singing star who restored Del Russo's self-respect and dignity by inviting him to "share" her room in front of an assemblage of jeering officers. The magistrate is unsure if this Gloriana is the same one, but he returns a verdict of "not guilty." *Magistrates. Lawyers. Prostitutes. Priests. Pimps. Soldiers. Singers. Trials. Infidelity. Home movies. Desertion. Theft. Nudity. Middle age. Circumstantial evidence. World War II. Rome.*

Note: Released in Italy in 1954 as *Un giorno in pretura*; running time: 88 min. Most U. S. sources credit Bellotti Film with production; foreign sources credit Documento Film and Excelsa Film.

THE DAY MARS INVADED EARTH   **F6.1042**

Associated Producers, Inc. *Dist* Twentieth Century–Fox Film Corp. 9 Jan **1963** [Los Angeles opening; c6 Dec 1962; LP23852]. Sd; b&w. 35mm (CinemaScope). 70 min.

Prod-Dir Maury Dexter. *Screenplay* Harry Spalding. *Dir Photog* John Nickolaus, Jr. *Set Decor* Harry Reif. *Supv Film Ed* Jodie Copelan. *Mus Comp & Cond* Richard La Salle. *Sd* Carlton W. Faulkner, Harry M. Leonard. *Supv Sd Ed* Jack Cornall. *Asst Dir* Clarence Eurist. *Prod Supv* Harold E. Knox. *Script Supv* Dixie McCoy. *Wardrobe* John Intlekofer. *Makeup* Harry Ross. *Prop Master* Jockey Liebgold.

Cast: Kent Taylor *(Dr. David Fielding)*, Marie Windsor *(Claire Fielding)*, William Mims *(Dr. Web Spencer)*, Betty Beall *(Judi Fielding)*, Lowell Brown *(Frank)*, Gregg Shank *(Rocky Fielding)*, Henrietta Moore, Troy Melton, George Riley.

Science fiction melodrama. Dr. David Fielding and his assistant Dr. Web Spencer succeed in landing a communications device on Mars but are puzzled by the tremendous strength of the radio signals emitted just after the device mysteriously explodes. David leaves Cape Canaveral to vacation on a friend's estate in Los Angeles with his wife, Claire, who is contemplating leaving him because of his negligence, and their two children, Judi and Rocky. Upon his arrival David discovers his own double and doubles of the members of his family roaming the estate. He learns that the lookalikes are Martians whose mission is to prevent further landings on Mars by reducing to ashes all those involved in the recent landing and taking their places; and he is unable to prevent the completion of the mission. *Scientists. Space exploration. Vacations. Missiles. Space creatures. Doubles. Marriage. Mars (planet). Cape Canaveral. Los Angeles.*

Note: Location scenes filmed at Greystone Mansion, Beverly Hills. Working title: *Spaceraid 63.*

DAY OF A STRIPPER   **F6.1043**

American Art Films. 22 May **1964** [Champaign, Illinois, showing; c14 Apr 1964; LP28743]. Sd; col. 35mm. 67 min.

Pres by The Saint. *Prod* Warren St. Thomas.

Cast: Tiger Lilly *(herself, a stripper)*, Tempest Storm, Bambi, Vicki O'Day *(themselves, striptease artists)*, Revere and Roche, Billie Jean and Kavich *(themselves, nightclub acts)*.

Documentary. Tiger Lilly's day begins in the afternoon, with a swim and some trampoline exercise. Night finds her preparing for her act at a strip club, while Bambi performs on stage. As the next act, Revere and Roche, is performing "Beauty and The Beast" onstage, a similar drama is going on in a backstage dressing room where beauteous Billy Jean is pursued by her partner, Kavich, a tiger. After Vicki O'Day's tassel-twirling striptease, Tiger Lilly descends in a gilded elevator cage for her own act. She is followed by Tempest Storm. Tiger Lilly returns to her dressing room with Billy Jean and soaks away the greasepaint in a bubble bath. *Stripteasers. Showgirls. Entertainers. Burlesque. Nightclubs. Rehearsals. "Beauty and The Beast". Tigers.*

Note: Possible alternative title: *Beauty and the Beast.*

DAY OF ANGER (Italy/West Germany)   **F6.1044**

Sancrosiap–Corona Filmproduktion–Divina Film. *Dist* National General Pictures. 5 Nov **1969** [Houston opening]. Sd; col (Technicolor). 35mm (Techniscope). 112 min. *MPAA rating* M.

Prod Alfonso Sansone, Enrico Chroscicki. *Dir* Tonino Valerii. *Screenplay* Ernesto Gastaldi, Renzo Genta, Tonino Valerii. *Dir Photog* Enzo Serafin. *Art Dir* Piero Filippone. *Film Ed* Franco Fraticelli. *Mus Comp & Dir* Riz Ortolani. *Cost* Carlo Simi.

Cast: Giuliano Gemma *(Scott Mary)*, Lee Van Cleef *(Frank Talby)*, Walter Rilla *(Murphallan)*, Andrea Bosic *(Murray Abel)*, Ennio Balbo *(Turner)*, Lukas Ammann *(Judge Cutchel)*, Christa Linder *(judge's daughter)*, Pepe Calvo *(Blind Bill)*, Yvonne Sanson *(Vivien Skill)*, Giorgio Gargiullo, Virgilio Gazzolo, Franco Balducci, Eleonora Morana, Giorgio Di Segni, Anna Maria Orso, Karl Otto Alberty, Benito Stefanelli, Nino Nini.

Western melodrama. Source: Ron Barker, *Der Tod ritt Dienstags* (Rastatt, 1963). Gunfighter Frank Talby rides into Clifton in search of a former partner who cheated him of $50,000. He befriends Scott, a youth whose illegitimate birth has made him the town underdog, and invites him for a drink at the saloon. One of the patrons objects to Scott's presence, and Talby shoots him in a gunfight, winning Scott's adulation. Intent on learning the gunfighter's lessons, the youth follows Talby away from Clifton on a donkey borrowed from Murph, a stable hand who once was marshal of Abilene and has been Scott's only friend among the townspeople. The two men find Talby's former partner, but he is unable to repay the debt, having been swindled himself some years before by the prominent citizens of Clifton. Talby outdraws his partner and returns to Clifton with Scott, whom he hires as an assistant and provides with a pair of guns. Together they take control of the town, extorting money from the bank president and the saloon owner and emerging victorious from a series of gun battles. A gunman hired by the guilty citizens to assassinate Talby is killed by him in a rifle duel. Murph in vain warns Scott that Talby has purposely provided him with inferior guns to maintain his superior position. Murph becomes the town marshal and is heartlessly gunned down by Talby. Scott claims the inheritance left him by the old man—a gun that once belonged to Doc Holliday—and challenges Talby to a duel. Scott outdraws and wounds Talby; and remembering the gunfighter's admonition never to allow a wounded man to live, kills him and then throws his gun away. *Gunfighters. Swindlers. Sheriffs. Illegitimacy. Revenge. Perfidy. Extortion. Hero worship. Youth. Saloons. Guns. John H. "Doc" Holliday.*

Note: Location scenes filmed in Spain. Rome opening: caDec 1967 as *I giorni dell'ira*. Released in West Germany in Jan 1968 as *Der Tod ritt Dienstags*; running time: 115 min. MPAA rating later changed to GP.

DAY OF THE EVIL GUN   F6.1045

Metro-Goldwyn-Mayer, Inc. Mar **1968** [c20 Feb 1968; LP35456]. Sd; col (Metrocolor). 35mm (Panavision). 95 min.

Prod-Dir Jerry Thorpe. *Assoc Prod* Lloyd Richards. *Screenplay* Charles Marquis Warren, Eric Bercovici. *Story* Charles Marquis Warren. *Dir Photog* W. Wallace Kelley. *Art Dir* George W. Davis, Marvin Summerfield. *Set Decor* Henry Grace, Ernesto Carrasco. *Film Ed* Alex Beaton. *Mus* Jeff Alexander. *Rec Supv* Franklin Milton. *Asst Dir* Jack Aldworth. *Unit Prod Mgr* James T. Vaughn.

Cast: Glenn Ford *(Lorn Warfield)*, Arthur Kennedy *(Owen Forbes)*, Dean Jagger *(Jimmy Noble)*, John Anderson *(Capt. Jefferson Addis)*, Paul Fix *(Sheriff Kelso)*, Nico Minardos *(DeLeón)*, Dean Stanton *(Sergeant Parker)*, Pilar Pellicer *(Lydia Yearby)*, Parley Baer *(Willford)*, Royal Dano *(Dr. Eli Prather)*, Ross Elliott *(Reverend Yearby)*, Barbara Babcock *(Angie Warfield)*, James Griffith *(storekeeper)*.

Western drama. Three years after leaving home, gunfighter Lorn Warfield returns to find his ranch in ruin and to hear from a neighbor, Owen Forbes, that his wife, Angie, and two daughters have been taken by the Apaches. The minister's wife, Lydia Yearby, was also captured but was mysteriously returned. Lydia provides Lorn with little information about his family, but he learns more from Jimmy Noble, an old trader who feigns insanity as protection against the Indians. Accompanied by Forbes, who reveals that Angie has consented to marry him because she believes Lorn to be dead, Lorn sets out in search of his family. Lorn and Forbes are captured by Indians but are saved by DeLeón, a Mexican bandit. Continuing their search, they reach a town being held by a band of Confederate renegades led by Capt. Jefferson Addis. The town is attacked by Indians, who leave with two wagons loaded with munitions. Lorn and Forbes follow the wagon tracks to the Indian camp and rescue Angie and the two children. Once safely home, Angie chooses to remain with her husband, whereupon Forbes challenges Lorn to a duel; but Lorn, who has exchanged his gun for food and clothing for his family, refuses to fight. Nevertheless, Forbes wounds Lorn and is about to shoot again when he is himself shot by the storekeeper, using Lorn's traded gun. *Gunfighters. Apache Indians. Traders. Bandits. Traitors. Storekeepers. Confederate veterans. Mexicans. Abduction. Insanity.*

Note: Filmed on location in Durango, Mexico; working title: *Evil Gun.*

THE DAY OF THE HANGING *see* LAW OF THE LAWLESS

DAY OF THE LANDGRABBER *see* LAND RAIDERS

DAY OF THE NIGHTMARE   F6.1046

Screen Group, Inc. *Dist* Herts-Lion International Corp., Governor Films. ca **1965**. Sd; b&w. 35mm. 89 min.

Prod Leon Bleiberg. *Exec Prod* Michael Kraike. *Dir* John Bushelman. *Writ* Leonard Goldstein. *Dir Photog* Ted V. Mikels. *Asst Photog* Bob Maxwell. *Mus* Andre Brummer. *Sd* Don Harrold. *Prod Mgr* Joe Boyle. *Script Supv* Art Names. *Asst Prod Mgr* Gabe Dellutri. *Makeup* Ron Wilson. *Dial Dir* Paul Gibran.

Cast: John Ireland, Elena Verdugo, John Hart, Jimmy Cross, Maralou Gray, Michael Kray, Bette Treadville, Liz Renay, Beverly Bain, Cliff Fields.

Mystery melodrama. Shortly after a woman returns home, neighbors hear a scream and a loud thud coming from her apartment. A few minutes later, Jonathan Crane drags a trunk from the woman's apartment to his car. Summoned by one of the neighbors the next day, the police break into the woman's apartment, find signs of violence, and assume that the woman is missing and possibly dead. Sergeant Harmon of the homicide squad visits Jonathan, who is a commercial artist. Jonathan protests his innocence, and because they lack evidence the police do not arrest him. That same day Barbara, Jonathan's wife, sees the strange trunk in their garage, but night comes before she finds the courage to open it, and Jonathan's sudden return home prevents her from seeing what is inside. Barbara goes to Jonathan's father, a psychiatrist, for help. They find only a sketch of Barbara in the trunk. Barbara is left alone, and the missing woman comes to her house and attempts to kill her. The missing woman appears at the house of Jonathan's father and kills the old man, but not before he recognizes the "woman" as his own son dressed in feminine apparel. Barbara becomes suspicious of Jonathan and follows him to an apartment. Jonathan discovers her presence and attempts to kill her. Sergeant

Harmon arrives to prevent the murder and gives chase, whereupon Jonathan runs from the police and falls off a dock into the path of an oncoming yacht. *Commercial artists. Psychopaths. Police. Psychiatrists. Missing persons. Female impersonation. Dual personality. Patricide. Trunks. Drawings.*

Note: Working title: *Don't Scream, Doris Mays!*

THE DAY OF THE TRIFFIDS (Great Britain)   F6.1047

Security Pictures. *Dist* Allied Artists. Apr **1963** [c18 Feb 1963; LP23722]. Sd; col (Eastman Color). 35mm (CinemaScope). 93 min.

Prod George Pitcher. *Exec Prod–Screenplay* Philip Yordan. *Dir* Steve Sekely. *Dir Photog* Ted Moore. *Camera Op* John Winbolt. *Focus Puller* John Shinerock, Hugh Davey. *Art Dir* Cedric Dawe. *Scenic Artist* Ted Barnes. *Draughtsmen* Neil MacPhee, Michael Lamont. *Supv Film Ed* Spencer Reeve. *Film Ed* Bill Lewthwaite. *Asst Ed* Michael Rabiger, Adrian McDonald. *Mus Comp & Cond* Ron Goodwin. *Adtl Mus* Johnny Douglas. *Sd Ed* Matt McCarthy. *Sd Rec* Bert Ross, Maurice Askew. *1st, 2d, & 3d Asst Dir* Douglas Hermes, Joe Mark, Henry Emery. *Prod Mgr* George Fowler. *Location Dir* Bill Lewthwaite. *Cont* Pamela Davies. *Prod Sec* Curlie Flower. *Wardrobe* Bridget Sellers. *Makeup* Paul Rabiger. *Hairdresser* Eileen Warwick. *Sp Photog Eff* Wally Veevers. *Casting* Thelma Graves. *Prod Buyer* Jim Foster. *Still Photog* Albert Clarke. *Chargehand Prop* Jack Bark. *Chargehand Electrn* Bill Chitty.

Cast: Howard Keel *(Bill Masen)*, Nicole Maurey *(Christine Durrant)*, Janette Scott *(Karen Goodwin)*, Kieron Moore *(Tom Goodwin)*, Mervyn Johns *(Professor Coker)*, Janina Faye *(Susan)*, Alison Leggatt *(Miss Coker)*, Ewan Roberts *(Dr. Soames)*, Colette Wilde *(Nurse Jamieson)*, Carole Ann Ford *(Bettina)*, Geoffrey Matthews *(Luis de la Vega)*, Gilgi Hauser *(Teresa de la Vega)*, Katya Douglas *(Mary)*, Victor Brooks *(Poiret)*, Thomas Gallagher *(burly man)*, Sidney Vivian *(ticket agent)*, Gary Hope *(pilot)*, John Simpson *(blind man)*.

Science fiction drama. Source: John Wyndham, *The Day of the Triffids* (Garden City, New York, 1951). American seaman Bill Masen, whose eyes have been bandaged after an operation, is one of the few people on Earth left with sight after a meteor shower. Upon leaving a London hospital, he rescues Susan, a little girl whose sight has also been spared, and together they flee to France to warn people against burgeoning triffids—voracious, self-locomoted, man-eating plants dropped by the meteors. Meanwhile, Tom and Karen Goodwin, marine biologists doing research in a deserted lighthouse, have killed an attacking triffid and are trying to discover its source of life. Bill and Susan are joined by Christine Durrant, a Frenchwoman whose neighbors have been victimized by the plants, and the threesome head for Spain, where submarines are evacuating survivors. Concurrently, the Goodwins are attacked by hundreds of plants and are apparently doomed; Tom, however, douses the triffids with sea water, causing them to wither and die. Bill and his friends meet the submarine with news that the world is saved. *Seamen. Americans in foreign countries. Marine biologists. Survival. Eye surgery. Blindness. Meteors. Carnivorous plants. Submarines. London. France. Spain.*

Note: Opened in London in May 1963.

THE DAY THE EARTH CAUGHT FIRE (Great Britain)   F6.1048

Melina Productions. *For* Pax Films/British Lion Films. *Dist* Universal-International Films. 15 Mar **1962** [New York opening; c5 Oct 1961; LP24723]. Sd; b&w. 35mm (Dyaliscope). 90 min.

A Val Guest Production. *Prod-Dir* Val Guest. *Assoc Prod* Frank Sherwin Green. *Screenplay* Wolf Mankowitz, Val Guest. *Dir Photog* Harry Waxman. *Camera Op* Moray Grant. *Focus* Wally Byatt, Jimmy Devis. *Camera Grip* Tommy Miller. *Art Dir* Tony Masters. *Asst Art Dir* Geoffrey Tozer. *Set Decor* Scott Slimon. *Scenic Artist* Peter Melrose. *Draughtsmen* Martin Atkinson, Bill Bennison. *Film Ed* Bill Lenny. *1st & 2d Asst Ed* Michael Round, Gillian Scott. *Mus Dir* Stanley Black. *Sd Rec* Buster Ambler. *Dub Ed* Chris Greenham. *Boom Op* Peter Dukelow. *Sd Camera Op* Jimmy Dooley. *1st, 2d & 3d Asst Dir* Philip Shipway, Terry Lens, Bernard Williams. *Prod Mgr* Clifton Brandon. *Cont* Pamela Carlton. *Prod Sec* Jill Langley. *Cost Dsgn & Supv* Beatrice Dawson. *Wardrobe Mistress* Dulcie Midwinter. *Makeup* Tony Sforzini. *Hairdresser* Joyce James. *Sp Eff* Les Bowie. *Tech Adv* Arthur Christiansen. *Still Photog* John Jay. *Prop Buyer* Harry Parr. *Chargehand Electrn* Bert Owen. *Chargehand Prop* Ernie Kell.

Cast: Edward Judd *(Peter Stenning)*, Janet Munro *(Jeannie Craig)*, Leo McKern *(Bill Maguire)*, Michael Goodliffe *(night editor)*, Bernard Braden *(news editor)*, Reginald Beckwith *(Harry)*, Gene Anderson *(May)*, Arthur Christiansen *(editor)*, Austin Trevor *(Sir John Kelly)*, Renee Asherson *(Angela)*, Peter Butterworth *(2d sub editor)*, Charles Morgan *(foreign editor)*, Edward Underdown *(Sanderson)*, John Barron *(1st sub editor)*, Geoffrey Chater *(Holroyd)*, Ian Ellis *(Michael)*, Jane Aird *(nanny)*, Robin Hawdon *(Ronnie)*.

Science fiction melodrama. Newsmen at the London *Daily Express* are baffled by reports of strange phenomena occurring all over the world, such as flooding in the Sahara, unseasonable blizzards in New York, and violent tornadoes in the Soviet Union. London is suffering from scorching temperatures and heavy mists. Though no official explanation of the events is given, the newspaper's science editor Bill Maguire and hard-drinking veteran reporter Peter Stenning discover that the disasters began after two simultaneous nuclear tests were made, one at the North Pole by the Soviet Union, the other at the South Pole by the United States. Stenning learns from Jeannie Craig, a telephone operator at the meteorological office, that the two explosions shifted the earth's orbit and set it hurling toward the sun. The *Express* prints this information and causes a sensation. As temperatures rise and water becomes scarce, governments take emergency measures to curb mounting hysteria, rampant looting, and rioting by teenagers. Scientists from many countries confer and conceive a proposal to explode simultaneously four large bombs to restore the earth's orbit. On detonation day, the populace goes underground, but Stenning waits in the newsroom for the results of the blasts; meanwhile, typesetters have prepared two front pages—one bearing the headline "World Saved," the other "World Doomed." *Reporters. Editors. Telephone operators. Weather. Riots. Looting. Hysteria. Nuclear weapons. Conferences—International. London. Union of Soviet Socialist Republics. North Pole. South Pole. Sahara. "Daily Express" (London). Explosions. Blizzards. Floods. Tornadoes.*

Note: Opened in London in Nov 1961; running time: 99 min.

THE DAY THE EARTH FROZE (Finland/U.S.S.R.)   **F6.1049**
Mosfilm–Suomi-Filmi. *Dist* Renaissance Films, American International Pictures. Apr **1964**. Sd; col (Sovcolor). 35mm (VistaScope). 67 min.
Production Credits for U. S. Vers: *Prod* Julius Strandberg. *Dir* Gregg Sebelious. *Camera* Sid Roth. *Art Dir* Bart Donner. *Mus* Otto Strode. *Sd* Jim Wilson, sd. *Asst Dir* Herman Erkko. *Cost* Eigrid Mannson. *Makeup* Sheron Copler. *Sp Eff* Gerome Langstrome. *Prop* Mike Makir.
Original Production Credits: *Dir* Aleksandr Ptushko. *Co-dir* Holger Harrivirta. *Screenplay* Viktor Vitkovich, Grigoriy Yagdfeld. *Story Ed* I. Rostovtsev. *Photog* G. Tsekaviy, V. Yakushev. *Art Dir* L. Milchin. *Set Decor* A. Makarov. *Mus* Igor Morozov. *Cond* S. Sakharov. *Sd* M. Blahina. *Asst Dir* B. Yevgenev, A. Vanichkin. *Prod Mgr* A. Stefanskiy, G. Kuznetsov. *Cost* R. Karpio. *Makeup* M. Rozhkov. *Sp Eff* A. Renkov, L. Dovgvillo, Z. Moryakova. *Cons* Veine Kaukonen, Kustaa Vilkuna. *Constr* V. Smirnov, constr.
Cast—U. S. Vers: Nina Anderson (*Anniky*), Jon Powers (*Lemminkainen*), Ingrid Elhardt (*Loukhy the Witch*), Peter Sorenson (*Ilmarinen*), Marvin Miller (*narrator*).
Original Cast: Urho Somersalmi (*Väinämöinen*), A. Orochko (*Louhi*), I. Voronov (*Ilmarinen*), Andris Oshin (*Lemminkäinen*), Ada Voytsik (*his mother*), Eve Kivi (*Annikki*), Georgiy Millyar (*sorcerer*), Mark Troyanovskiy (*soothsayer*), L. Laurmää, T. Rompainen, E. Hippelainen, N. Kollen, A. Barantsev, V. Uralskiy, V. Boriskin, P. Modnikov, Valentin Bryleyev, A. Macheret, A. Lenskaya.
Fantasy. Based on the Finnish oral poetry cycle compiled by: Elias Lönnrot, *Kalevala.* Young Lemminkainen goes logging in the country of Kalevala and falls in love with the beautiful Anniky. Anniky's brother Ilmarinen, a blacksmith who possesses magic powers, is happy to hear of Anniky's new love. Five elders ask Ilmarinen to forge for the people of Kalevala the "sampo," a magic mill that produces grain, salt, and gold. Ilmarinen possesses the necessary skill, but the witch Loukhy, the Queen of Pokhiola [Pohjola], has stolen the blacksmith's fire to forge the sampo for herself. Loukhy learns from one of her sorcerers that Ilmarinen alone can construct the sampo, and she sends the sorcerer with her magic cloak to kidnap Anniky in hopes of luring Lemminkainen and Ilmarinen to Pokhiola to rescue Anniky. The plan works, and Loukhy sets tasks for them both in exchange for Anniky's release: Lemminkainen bare-handed must plow a field infested with deadly snakes, while Ilmarinen is to forge the sampo. Each succeeds at his task, and Anniky is set free. Lemminkainen returns to Pokhiola after the three have begun the journey homeward and destroys the sampo, taking with him a fragment that remains. Loukhy vengefully seizes the sun, causing Kalevala to be covered with snow and ice. The Kalevalans attack Pokhiola, but the battle is a stalemate until the Kalevalan army lay down their weapons and take up the sacred harps. The sound of their playing mesmerizes the Pokhiolans, and Loukhy is frozen [or turned to stone]. The sun shines again, and all Kalevala rejoices. *Sorcerers. Witches. Legendary characters. Blacksmiths. Harpists. Brother-sister relationship. Magic. Kidnaping. Revenge. Mills. Imaginary kingdoms. Gold. "Kalevala". The Sun. Väinämöinen. Ilmarinen. Lemminkäinen. Sampo. Snakes.*
Note: Filmed in Finland. Released in Finland and the U.S.S.R. in 1959 as *Sampo;* running time: 96–99 min. U. S. credits appear to be pseudonyms.

THE DAY THE FISH CAME OUT (Great Britain/Greece)   **F6.1050**
Michael Cacoyannis Productions. *Dist* International Classics. 2 Oct **1967** [New York opening; c2 Oct 1967; LP35251]. Sd; col (Deluxe). 35mm. 109 min.
Prod-Dir-Writ Michael Cacoyannis. *Dir Photog* Walter Lassally. *Art Dir* Spyros Vassilou. *Titl Dsgn* Maurice Binder. *Film Ed* Vassilis Syropoulos. *Mus*

Comp & Cond Mikis Theodorakis. *Choreog* Arthur Mitchell. *Sd* Mikes Damalas. *Asst Dir* Tom Pevsner. *Dir Prod* Yannoulla Wakefield. *Cont* May Kapsaskis. *Location Mgr* Vassilis Mariolis. *Unit Mgr* Yannis Petropoulakis. *Wardrobe Supv* Aliki Haritopoulou. *Cost Dsgn* Michael Cacoyannis. *Wardrobe Mistress* Diane Iona. *Cost Executed by* Anna Stavropoulou. *Makeup* Tom Smith, Katia Stefanidou. *Hairdresser* Grigoris Verekos. *Casting* George Kosmatos.
Cast: Tom Courtenay (*The Navigator*), Colin Blakely (*The Pilot*), Sam Wanamaker (*Elias*), Candice Bergen (*Electra*), Ian Ogilvy (*Peter*), Dimitris Nikolaides (*dentist*), Nikos Alexiou (*goatherd*), Patricia Burke (*Mrs. Mavroyannis*), Paris Alexander (*Fred*), Arthur Mitchell (*Frank*), Marlena Carrere (*goatherd's wife*), Tom Klunis (*Mr. French*), William Berger (*man in bed*), Kostas Papakonstantinou (*Manolios*), Dora Stratou (*travel agent*), Alexander Lykourezos (*director of tourism*), Tom Whitehead (*Mike*), Walter Granecki (*base commander*), Demetris Loakimides (*policeman*), Lynn Bryant, James Connolly, Assaf Dayan, Robert Killian, Derek Kulai, Alexis Mantheakis, Raymond McWilliams, Michael Radford, Peter Robinson, Grigoris Stefanides, James Smith, Peter Stratful, Kosta Timvios, Herbert Zeichner (*tourists*).
Satire. In the year 1972, a bomber of an unnamed world power develops engine trouble while flying over the Aegean Sea. The pilot and navigator bail out after disposing of their cargo—two atom bombs and a mysterious metal box. Clad only in their undershorts, the two men wade ashore to the barren island of Karos. To recover the cargo without causing widespread panic, the government of the world power disguises some 20 soldiers, led by Elias, as hotel experts and sends them to Karos under the pretext of studying the island's tourist possibilities. They soon recover the two bombs, but they are unable to locate the metal box, which has already been found by a goatherd who has been unable to open it. As word spreads that Karos is the new status resort, the island quickly fills with tourists, much to the dismay of Elias and the consternation of the two crewmen, who are unaware of the true identity of the hotel experts. Among the influx is Electra, a beautiful American archeologist who flirts with Peter, one of the disguised military men. While they are having a drink, the goatherd steals a powerful acid that Electra uses in her work, and he succeeds in opening the metal box. Disappointed at finding only brown stones, he tosses the box into the sea, and his wife throws a couple of the seemingly worthless objects into the town's water reservoir. Meanwhile, the two pilots, after becoming separated, are reunited and overjoyed because one of them has begged enough money to telephone a report to their headquarters. As they join the tourists wildly dancing on the beach, they notice the countless bodies of dead fish floating to the surface near the harbor. *Air pilots. Navigators. Goatherds. Archeologists. Americans in foreign countries. Soldiers. Disguise. Tourism. Radiation. Bombers. Atom bomb. Resorts. Aegean Sea. Káros.*
Note: Location scenes filmed at Galaxidhion, Greece. Released in Great Britain in 1967.

THE DAY THE HOT LINE GOT HOT (France/Spain)   **F6.1051**
Balcázar P. C.–Inter Continental Production. *Dist* Commonwealth United Entertainment, Inc., American International Pictures. 24 Dec **1969** [San Francisco opening]. Sd; col (Eastman Color). 35mm. 100 min. *MPAA rating* GP.
Prod Francisco Balcázar. *Dir* Etienne Périer. *Assoc Dir* Antonio Liza. *Screenplay* Paul Jarrico. *Story* Guerdon Trueblood, Dominique Fabre. *Photog* Manuel Berenguer. *Art Dir* Juan Alberto Soler. *Film Ed* Teresa Alcocer, Renée Lichtig. *Mus* Paul Misraki.
Cast: Charles Boyer (*Vastov*), Robert Taylor (*Anderson*), George Chakiris (*Eric Ericson*), Marie Dubois (*Natasha*), Marta Grau, Irene D'Astrea, Josefina Tapias, Gérard Tichy, Gustavo Re, Oscar Pellicer, Frank Oliveras.
Comedy. Eric, a computer operator at the IBM center in Stockholm, requests a transfer to Barcelona. For his trip he buys a trunk at a shop where three old ladies are buying an identical one, which they prepare so as to accommodate a human body. These three women are pawns of Truman, an international double agent. They blackmail Natasha, the telephone operator at the hot line center in Stockholm, to send insulting messages to American and Russian leaders. The resulting political crisis will benefit Truman. They then conceal Natasha in their trunk and fly to Barcelona on the same flight with Eric. When the group gets off the plane, their luggage is accidentally exchanged. Unpacking in his hotel room, the astonished Eric discovers Natasha in his trunk and calls the police. When they arrive, they find the trunk empty and the hotel porter dead. Natasha and Eric have been abducted by the geriatric trio. During a gun battle between Anderson, the head of American intelligence, and Vastov, his Soviet counterpart, the couple escapes. Natasha is quickly recaptured by the dowagers who have enlisted the aid of a troupe of nimble Chinese acrobats. Although Eric, having persuaded the police of his innocence, rescues Natasha, Truman and his elderly minions elude capture, much to the consternation of their dupes, Anderson and Vastov. *Telephone operators. Spies. Computer programmers. Russians. Blackmail. Espionage. Abduction. Rescue. Perfidy.*

Stockholm. Barcelona. Hot line. International Business Machines Corp. United States—State Department. Union of Soviet Socialist Republics—Intelligence service.

Note: French title: *Le rouble à deux faces*; Spanish title: *El rublo de las dos caras.* May also be known as *The Hot Line.*

THE DAY THE SKY EXPLODED (France/Italy)   F6.1052

Lux Film–C. C. F. Lux–Royal Film. *Dist* Excelsior Pictures. 27 Sep **1961** [Los Angeles opening]. Sd; b&w. 35mm. 80 min.

Prod Guido Giambartolomei. *Dir* Paolo Heusch. *English Vers Dir* William De Lane Lea. *Screenplay* Marcello Coscia, Alessandro Continenza. *Story* Virgilio Sabel. *Photog* Mario Bava. *Art Dir* Beni Montresor. *Film Ed* Otello Colangeli. *Mus* Carlo Rustichelli. *Prod Mgr* Ione Tuzi.

Cast: Paul Hubschmid (*John MacLaren*), Madeleine Fischer (*Katy Dandridge*), Fiorella Mari (*Mary MacLaren*), Ivo Garrani (*Herbert Weisser*), Dario Michaelis (*Pierre Leducq*), Sam Galter (*Randowsky*), Jean-Jacques Delbo (*Sergei Boetnikov*), Peter Meersman (*General Wandorf*), Massimo Zeppieri (*Dennis MacLaren*), Giacomo Rossi Stuart, Annie Berval, Gérard Landry.

Science fiction melodrama. American, British, and Russian scientists collaborate on an atomic rocket. The rocket is launched from Australia, carrying astronaut John MacLaren. Before he leaves the earth's atmosphere, a breakdown occurs and he is forced to detach himself from the main rocket, which goes on to crash into the sun. The enormous force of the explosion sends a group of asteroids hurtling toward the earth. Strange phenomena, including animal migrations, tidal waves, typhoons, heatwaves, and other catastrophes, inspire panic on earth. The scientists reveal their true mettle; some panic and others go mad. Some, MacLaren among them, resolve their personal problems and study the situation. In his desperate effort to save the earth, MacLaren organizes an international scientific team, and all governments are persuaded to cooperate. At a given time, rockets carrying the world's stockpile of atomic weapons are launched from all over the earth, and the asteroids are exploded. *Scientists. British. Russians. Astronauts. Doomsday. Nuclear energy. Animal life. Insanity. Phenomena. Rockets. Nuclear weapons. Australia. Asteroids. The Sun. Tidal waves. Typhoons. Explosions.*

Note: Rome opening: Sep 1958 as *La morte viene dallo spazio*; running time: ca85 min. Cannes opening: Feb 1959 as *Le danger vient de l'espace*; running time: 81 min. U. S. prerelease title: *Death From Outer Space.*

THE DAY THE SUN ROSE (Japan)   F6.1053

Nihon Eiga Fukko Kyokai. *Dist* Shochiku Films of America. Feb **1969** [Los Angeles showing]. Sd; col. 35mm. [Feature film, length unknown.]

Dir Tetsuya Yamanouchi. *Screenplay* Hisayuki Suzuki, Kunio Shimizu. *Planned by* Daisuke Ito. *Coöp* Kyoto Prefecture, Kyoto City.

Cast: Kinnosuke Nakamura (*Shinkichi*), Toshiro Mifune (*Kuma*), Shima Iwashita (*Ayame*), Yunosuke Ito (*Akamatsu*), Takahiro Tamura (*Sukematsu*), Takashi Shimura (*Tsuneemon*), Eitaro Ozawa (*Kadokura*), Kamatari Fujiwara.

Action melodrama. Source: Katsumi Nishiguchi, *Gionmatsuri* (Tokyo, 1968). In 16th-century Japan, Kyoto is torn by civil discord. Among the factions are clan rulers, their warrior minions, wealthy merchants, farmers, and outcasts. The conflict is exacerbated by a high tax levied on food. In desperation, the farmers organize into roving bands, harassing the wealthy townspeople who hire a group of samurai for protection. Together, the two groups attack the farmers, who are organized under a group of mounted coolies led by Kuma. In the face of fierce resistance, the samurai retreat, leaving many townspeople to die. Protesting against the failure of the samurai and the despotism of the clan warriors, the townspeople refuse to pay the taxes. Under the leadership of Shinkichi, the people also decide to revive the Gion Festival as a symbol of their desire for peace. The authorities raise the food taxes even further, however, and to prevent mass starvation, Shinkichi negotiates with Kuma for the coolies to bring in food from the farms. At first Kuma refuses to help, but eventually he relents. The coolies' delivery of food symbolizes a new unity among the townspeople, the farmers, and the outcasts, and as a result, the Gion Festival takes place. In the midst of the festivities, Shinkichi is shot by a samurai, and Kuma goes after him, but Shinkichi insists that the festival proceed. The people march toward a band of samurai blocking their way, and the samurai retreat from the three groups who are at last united for peace. *Farmers. Samurai. Merchants. Lower classes. Class conflict. Taxes. Food. Gion Festival. Kyoto.*

Note: Released in Japan in 1968 as *Gion matsuri.*

THE DAY THE WAR ENDED (U.S.S.R.)   F6.1054

Gorky Film Studio. *Dist* Artkino Pictures. 28 Jan **1961** [New York opening]. Sd; b&w. 35mm. 90 min.

Dir Photog Yakov Segel. *Screenplay* Iosif Olshanskiy, Nina Rudneva. *Camera* I. Zarafyan. *Art Dir* Boris Dulenkov. *Film Ed* L. Rodionova. *Mus* M. Fradkin. *Song Lyr* Yu. Kamenetskiy, V. Lazarev. *Cond* G.

Gamburg. *Sd* A. Izbutskiy. *Asst Dir* K. Alperova. *Prod Mgr* Ya. Svetozarov. *Story Ed* N. Torchinskaya. *Cost* Ye. Aleksandrova. *Makeup* G. Petrov. *Cons* N. Oslikovskiy, L. Ostrovskaya.

Cast: Valeriy Vinogradov (*Mikhail Platonov*), Lyudmila Butenina (*Olya*), Pyotr Shcherbakov (*Captain Nefyodov*), A. Vovsi (*surgeon*), G. Dunts (*colonel*), Lyudmila Ovchinnikova (*Natasha*), I. Pushkaryov (*Petya Kovalyov*), A. Fayt (*old German*), N. Menshikova (*Frau Fisher*), Kh. Braun (*SS officer*), A. Temerin (*priest*), V. Zakharchenko (*Fisher*), Yu. Fomichyov (*Semyonych, orderly*), E. Knausmyuller (*Kuntse*), Galya Karakulova, A. Danilova, S. Yurtaykin, Ye. Kudryashov, V. Korneyev, A. Vasilyev, A. Sezemann, V. Chumak, R. Daglish.

War melodrama. On 9 May 1945, Soviet truce envoy Mikhail Platonov, carrying a white flag, approaches the cathedral of a German town. Three SS officers within, determined to continue fighting, refuse to surrender with their compatriots. Earlier that day, Platonov, a former language teacher now serving as an interpreter with the Soviet occupation forces, met Olya, a Soviet field nurse. The couple were introduced to each other by Captain Nefyodov, a mutual friend long in love with Olya. Despite their wish not to hurt their friend, it quickly became clear that Olya and Mikhail were in love. Their plans for the future—happier days free of the hatred and violence of war—are cut short, however, when Mikhail is shot and killed by one of the escaping SS men. *Interpreters. Nazis. Nurses. Surgeons. Military occupation. Cathedrals. World War II. V-E Day (7 May 1945). Germany. Union of Soviet Socialist Republics—Army. SS. Germany—Army.*

Note: Released in the U.S.S.R. in Aug 1959 as *Pervyy den mira*; running time: 95 min.

THE DAY THE WORLD CHANGED HANDS *see* THE FORBIN PROJECT

A DAY WITH THE RUSSIANS (U.S.S.R.)   F6.1055

Central Documentary Film Studio. *Dist* Artkino Pictures. 11 Mar **1961** [New York opening]. Sd; col (Sovcolor). 35mm. 120 min.

Production Credits—"September 16th": *Dir* Roman Karmen. *Screenplay* G. Shergova. *Photog* Daniil Kaspiy, Vladislav Mikosha. *Mus* Aleksandr Lokshin.

Production Credits—"Concert of Youth": *Dir* V. Boykov. *Scen* V. Komissarzhevskiy. *Photog* Daniil Kaspiy, Vladislav Mikosha, M. Prudnikov, I. Filatov, D. Rymaryov. *Mus:* "Spartacus" ("Spartak") Aram Ilich Khachaturyan.

Anthology. SEPTEMBER 16: A pictorial record of a day in the Soviet Union in 1959, touching on events and activities of people in different regions and walks of life—farmers, scientists, fashion models, housewives, veterans, etc. Included are shots of Premier Nikita Khrushchev embarking for his trip to New York, and scenes of the young actress Tatyana Samoylova at work on a new film. CONCERT OF YOUTH: A trip from city to city along the Volga River. Students from each region give musical performances, including folk dancing and ballet. An excerpt from Khachaturyan's ballet *Spartacus* (*Spartak*) is included. *Musicians. Dancers. Students. Actors. Folk dancing. Folk music. Ballet. Youth. Volga River. Tatyana Samoylova. Nikita Sergeyevich Khrushchev.*

Note: *September 16* was released in the U.S.S.R. in 1960 as *Den nashey zhizni*; *Concert of Youth* in 1959 as *Zveni, nasha yunost!* Also known as *One Day With the Russians.*

THE DAYDREAMER   F6.1056

Videocraft International Productions. *Dist* Embassy Pictures. Jun **1966**. Sd; col (Eastman Color). 35mm (Animagic, see note). 101 min. [Also 115 min.]

Pres by Joseph E. Levine. *Prod-Writ* Arthur Rankin, Jr. *Assoc Prod* Larry Roemer. *Exec Prod* Joseph E. Levine. *Dir* Jules Bass. *Live-Action Seq Staged by* Ezra Stone. *Anim Seq Staged by* Don Duga. *Live-Action Photog* Daniel Cavelli. *Animagic Photog* Tad Mochinaga. *Art Dir* Maurice Gordon. *Songs* Maury Laws, Jules Bass. *Titl Song Sung by* Robert Goulet. *Song:* "Wishes and Teardrops" sung by Hayley Mills. *Song:* "Luck To Sell" sung by Paul O'Keefe. *Song:* "Happy Guy" sung by Patty Duke. *Song:* "Who Can Tell" sung by Ray Bolger. *Song:* "Simply Wonderful" sung by Ed Wynn, Chorus of Ministers. *Song:* "Isn't It Cozy Here" sung by Sessue Hayakawa. *Sd* Bernard Cowan. *Asst Dir* Kizo Nagashima.

Cast: Paul O'Keefe (*Chris [Hans Christian Andersen]*), Jack Gilford (*Papa Andersen*), Ray Bolger (*The Pieman*), Margaret Hamilton (*Mrs. Klopplebobbler*), Robert Harter (*Big Claus*).

Voices: Cyril Ritchard (*The Sandman*), Hayley Mills (*The Little Mermaid*), Burl Ives (*Father Neptune*), Tallulah Bankhead (*The Sea Witch*), Terry-Thomas (*tailors*), Ed Wynn (*The Emperor*), Victor Borge (*tailors*), Patty Duke (*Thumbelina*), Boris Karloff (*The Rat*), Sessue Hayakawa (*The Mole*), Robert Goulet (*The Singer*).

Fantasy. Source: Hans Christian Andersen, "Den lille havfrue," "Kejserens nye klaeder," "Tommelise," "Paradisets have" (1835–38). Thirteen-year-old Hans Christian Andersen, the son of a poor shoemaker in Odense, Denmark, is an incurable daydreamer. His father tells him about a legendary Garden of Paradise, and one day Chris runs away to find it. In an abandoned boat he meets The Sandman; and before long, young Chris is dreaming of Father Neptune's realm under the sea. There, The Little Mermaid falls in love with him, but, failing to win Chris's love, she is left stranded on a rock. Chris next visits The Emperor's palace and witnesses the old ruler being tricked by two tailors into believing his nakedness is actually a magnificent set of robes. After being magically reduced to the tiny size of Thumbelina and escaping from the evil Rat and Mole, Chris finally enters the Garden of Paradise. Puck, a boy who looks very much like Chris, persuades him to eat from the Tree of Knowledge, and he is plunged into the Valley of Nothingness. Chris awakens from his bad dream and is joyfully reunited with his father. The Sandman makes a last appearance to suggest that perhaps Chris found his own Garden of Paradise through the wonderful tales; Chris ponders his adventures and finally writes them down on paper. *Cobblers. Runaways. Mermaids and mermen. Royalty. Adolescence. Duplicity. Magic. Odense (Denmark). Hans Christian Andersen. Dreams. Imaginary kingdoms. Rats. Moles.*

Note: Filmed in New York, Denmark, Japan, Canada, France, and England. Animagic process involves stop-motion photography of stationary three-dimensional forms.

DAYS OF SIN AND NIGHTS OF NYMPHOMANIA (Denmark)
F6.1057

Pingvin Film. *Dist* Audubon Films. 23 Jul **1965** [Fresno, California, showing]. Sd; b&w. 35mm. 74 min.

Pres by Radley H. Metzger. *Dir-Writ* Poul Nyrup. *Photog* Søren Ingemann. *Film Ed* Edith Nisted Nielsen. *Mus* George Craig. *Mus Comp* Hans Vangkilde. *Perf by* The Weedons. *Sd* Preben Mortensen, Kurt Aalstrup.

Cast: Poul Martin *(Rabbit)*, Marianne Themsen *(Inge)*, Annette Post *(Tove)*, Preben Ploug *(Kim)*, Preben Nicolaisen *(Quickie)*, Tage Røpke *(Søren)*, Anders Dahlerup *(Charles)*, Lars Lie *(Kaj)*, Bjørn Jensen, Rigmor Post, Gunnar Stephan, Tove Nystein, Helle Jensen, Ina Kartin, Jørgen Malling, Erna Tønnesen, Inge Lise Borup.

Melodrama. Kim, a member of a lively young group, is released from jail after having served time for attempted rape. To celebrate his release, Quickie and Rabbit, the group's leaders, organize a wild party in Rabbit's summer house. During the party, stag films are shown, and an orgy develops. Søren, another member of the group, has brought a new girl, Inge, to the party; these two dislike the activities and leave. Inge's sister, Tove, a prostitute, resents the relationship she sees developing between Søren and her sister and arranges to have her parents forbid Inge to see Søren again. The despondent Inge is injured in an automobile accident, and in revenge for her role in separating his friends, Kim kidnaps Tove and holds her in Rabbit's house. Tove is killed accidentally when Kim tries to attack her, and the police send him back to prison. Reunited, Inge and Søren decide to get married. *Ex-convicts. Playboys. Police. Prostitutes. Sisters. Rape. Kidnaping. Revenge. Manslaughter. Sex exploitation films. Orgies. Automobile accidents.*

Note: Released in Denmark in Jul 1963 as *Mellem venner*; running time: 90 min. Also known as *Days of Sin, Nights of Nymphomania*; *Days of Sin and Nights of Madness*; and *Days of Shame and Nights of Excess*.

DAYS OF THRILLS AND LAUGHTER
F6.1058

Robert Youngson Productions. *Dist* Twentieth Century–Fox Film Corp. 21 Mar **1961** [New York opening; c21 Mar 1961; LP19553]. Sd (sd eff & mus score); b&w. 35mm. 93 min.

Prod-Writ Robert Youngson. *Asst Prod* John E. Allen, Alfred Dahlem. *Mus Writ & Cond* Jack Shaindlin. *Orch* Ted Royal. *Rec* Albert Gramaglia. *Ed Supv of Mus* Angelo Ross. *Mus Rec* Aaron Nathanson. *Sd Eff* Alfred Dahlem, Ralph F. Curtiss. *Aerial Image Opticals* Maurice Levy, Samuel Levy. *Film Quality Control* Paul Guffanti.

Narrator: Jay Jackson.

Compilation film. Excerpts from film comedies and thrillers made before the introduction of sound motion pictures. Highlights include: (1) a 1904 French comedy called *The Bath Chair Man;* (2) Mack Sennett's Keystone Cops and Bathing Beauties; (3) Charlie Chaplin in two of his early comedies, *The Adventurer* and *The Cure;* (4) Douglas Fairbanks in a western spoof called *Wild and Wooly;* (5) scenes of Stan Laurel and Oliver Hardy before they became a team; (6) Ben Turpin playing checkers with Cameo, the Wonder Dog; (7) Harry Langdon in a World War I comedy; (8) Houdini rescuing a heroine from the brink of Niagara Falls in *Man From Beyond;* (9) serial queens Pearl White and Ruth Roland escaping from countless dangers, including Warner Oland and Boris Karloff; (10) Monty Banks and his girl friend trapped on a runaway train in *Play Safe;* (11) Charlie Chase in one of his early comedies; and (12) excerpts from the comedies of Al St. John and Snub Pollard. *Motion pictures—History.*

DAYS OF WINE AND ROSES
F6.1059

Martin Manulis–Jalem Productions. *Dist* Warner Bros. Pictures. 26 Dec **1962** [Los Angeles opening; c30 Nov 1962; LP27113]. Sd; b&w. 35mm. 117 min.

Prod Martin Manulis. *Dir* Blake Edwards. *Writ* J. P. Miller. *Dir Photog* Philip H. Lathrop. *Camera Op* Richard H. Kline. *Asst Camera* Cliff King, Gerald Finnerman. *Art Dir* Joseph Wright. *Set Decor* George James Hopkins. *Film Ed* Patrick McCormack. *Mus* Henry Mancini. *Titl Song* Henry Mancini, Johnny Mercer. *Sd* Jack Solomon. *Mix* Russell Ashley. *Boom Op* Ora Hudson. *Cable* Robert Dunning. *Asst Dir* Carter DeHaven, Jr., Jack Cunningham, William F. Sheehan. *Unit Mgr* Jack McEdward. *Script Supv* Betty Abbott. *Cost* Don Feld. *Wardrobe* Forrest T. Butler, Florence Crewell. *Makeup Supv* Gordon Bau. *Makeup* Henry Villardo, Hal Lierley. *Hairstyles* Jean Burt Reilly, Myrl Stoltz. *Sp Eff* Horace L. Hulburd. *Dial Supv* James Lanphier. *Still Photog* Sherman Clark. *Gaffer* Lee Wilson. *Grip* William Classen, Malcolm Matheson. *Prop* Robert Turner, Ben Greenberg.

Cast: Jack Lemmon *(Joe Clay)*, Lee Remick *(Kirsten Arnesen)*, Charles Bickford *(Ellis Arnesen)*, Jack Klugman *(Jim Hungerford)*, Alan Hewitt *(Leland)*, Tom Palmer *(Ballefoy)*, Debbie Megowan *(Debbie Clay)*, Maxine Stuart *(Dottie)*, Jack Albertson *(Trayner)*, Ken Lynch *(liquor store proprietor)*, Katherine Squire *(Mrs. Nolan)*, Gail Bonney *(Gladys)*, Mary Benoit, Ella Ethridge, Rita Kenaston, J. Pat O'Malley, Robert "Buddy" Shaw, Al Paige *(tenants)*, Doc Stortt, Rus Bennett, Dick Crockett *(boors)*, Roger Barrett *(Abe)*, Jack Railey *(waiter)*, Lisa Guiraut *(belly dancer)*, Carl Arnold *(loud man)*, Tom Rosqui *(bettor)*, Barbara Hines, Charlene Holt *(guests)*.

Drama. Source: J. P. Miller, *Days of Wine and Roses* (a teleplay; first presented on CBS's "Playhouse 90" 2 Oct 1958). Joe Clay, a hard-working, hard-drinking public relations man in San Francisco, meets Kirsten Arnesen, a young secretary who adores chocolate but hates liquor. Joe, however, quickly converts her to drink, and within a few months after their marriage, she is able to match him drink for drink. After losing five jobs within the next 4 years, Joe decides that he and Kirsten must go on the wagon. They move in with Kirsten's father at his nursery and stay off alcohol for several weeks. But one night they go on a monumental bender, and Joe, after destroying the greenhouse looking for a bottle he has hidden, ends up in a hospital drying-out tank. Hungerford, an ex-addict, encourages him to join Alcoholics Anonymous, but he is lured back to drink by Kirsten. Realizing that they are doomed as long as she refuses to admit to her alcoholism, Joe takes their child and moves into another apartment. With the help of AA, he is able to reestablish his career and regain his self-respect. One night Kirsten visits him and begs to take him back, but Joe sends her away when she refuses to give up drinking. *Public relations men. Secretaries. In-laws. Marriage. Alcoholism. Employment. Nurseries (horticultural). Hospitals. San Francisco. Alcoholics Anonymous.*

DAYTONA BEACH WEEKEND
F6.1060

Sixtieth Arts. *Dist* Dominant Pictures. 14 Apr **1965** [New Orleans opening]. Sd; col (Ansco Color). 35mm. ca87 min.

Prod-Dir Robert Welby.

Cast: Del Shannon, Houston & Dorsey, Rayna, Sue Skeen, Don Jackson, The Offbeets.

Melodrama. Although no information about the precise nature of this film has been found, press material suggests that it includes scenes of adolescents vacationing in Daytona Beach. *Adolescence. Vacations. Daytona Beach.*

Note: Filmed in Daytona Beach in 16mm.

DAYTON'S DEVILS
F6.1061

Madison Productions–Commonwealth United Productions. *Dist* Commonwealth United Entertainment, Inc. 2 Oct **1968** [New York opening]. Sd; col (Eastmancolor). 35mm. 101 min. [Cut from 103 min.]

Pres by Harold Goldman Associates. *Prod* Robert W. Stabler. *Dir* Jack Shea. *Story & Screenplay* Fred De Gorter. *Photog* Brick Marquard. *Art Dir* Paul Sylos, Jr. *Main Titl* Consolidated Film Industries. *Film Ed* Fred W. Berger. *Mus* Marlin Skiles. *Song:* "Sunny" sung by Lainie Kazan. *Sd* John Bury. *Asst Dir* Elliot Schick. *Prod Mgr* George Fenaja. *Sp Eff* Woodrow Ward.

Cast: Rory Calhoun *(Mike Page)*, Leslie Nielsen *(Frank Dayton)*, Lainie Kazan *(Leda Martell)*, Hans Gudegast *(Max Eckhart)*, Barry Sadler *(Barney Barry)*, Pat Renella *(Claude Sadi)*, Georg Stanford Brown *(Theon Gibson)*, Rigg Kennedy *(Sonny Merton)*, Rodolfo Acosta *(captain)*, Hap Holmwood, Danny Stone.

Adventure melodrama. After masterminding a plan to rob Palomar Air Force Base of a $2.5 million payroll, former U. S. Air Force Col. Frank Dayton assembles a group of adventurers at the Mexican villa of his friend Max Eckhart. As Dayton forces his band of misfits (including artist turned forger Claude Sadi and psychopathic murderer Barney Barry) to undergo extensive physical and technical training, he meets opposition from two of his men— Mike Page and Sonny Merton—but nevertheless succeeds in shaping the group into a crack military-like unit. They are then smuggled to the Santa Barbara coast on a Mexican fishing boat. Equipped with forged identity cards and stolen Air Force uniforms, the men commandeer two military vehicles and enter the base under the pretext of being a special committee investigating finance and payroll mismanagement. After destroying the base's communications and making off with the payroll, they use their truck to block their pursuers and then make their getaway in a station wagon driven by Dayton's girl friend, Leda, a nightclub singer with a shady past. Upon reaching the beach, they unearth buried scuba-diving equipment and swim out with the money to the waiting Mexican fishing boat. But the greedy captain of the boat turns on them in the hope of getting all the money for himself. In the ensuing free-for-all, both the captain and Dayton are killed; a stray bullet causes a fire in the engine room; and soon the boat is aflame. Attracted by the fire, a Navy patrol boat races to the scene as the remnants of "Dayton's Devils" stand helplessly by, laughing hysterically as the loot goes up in smoke. *Singers. Painters. Adventurers. Psychopaths. Diving. Disguise. Robbery. Forgery. Greed. Ship fires. Fishing boats. Santa Barbara. Mexico. United States Air Force. United States Navy.*

DE L'AMOUR (France/Italy)   **F6.1062**
Films de la Pléiade–Cocinor–Les Films Marceau–Cinesecolo. *Dist* Goldstone Film Enterprises. 16 Oct **1968** [San Francisco opening]. Sd; b&w. 35mm. 90 min.
Prod Pierre Braunberger. *Dir* Jean Aurel. *Screenplay* Cécil Saint Laurent, Jean Aurel. *Dial* Cécil Saint Laurent. *Photog* Edmond Richard. *Art Dir* Eric Simon. *Film Ed* Agnès Guillemot, Geneviève Vaury. *Mus* André Hodeir. *Sd* Michel Fano. *Asst Dir* Jean-José Richer. *Prod Mgr* Roger Fleytoux.
Cast: Anna Karina (*Hélène*), Philippe Avron (*Serge*), Michel Piccoli (*Raoul*), Elsa Martinelli (*Mathilde*), Jean Sorel (*Antoine*), Joanna Shimkus (*Sophie*), Bernard Garnier (*Werther*), Cécil Saint Laurent (*man who reads Stendhal*), Isabelle Lunghini.
Romantic comedy-drama. Source: Stendhal, *De l'amour* (Paris, 1822). Serge meets Hélène on a Paris street; she has just broken with her dentist lover, Raoul, a philanderer. Serge takes Hélène to a restaurant and later contrives to have her invite him to her apartment. Werther escorts Sophie to Raoul, who takes advantage of her defenseless position in the dentist's chair to seduce her. For her part, Sophie asks Raoul to drive her to see her ex-husband, telling him that she is visiting her cousin. While he waits restlessly in his car for Sophie, Raoul sees Mathilde, who is sitting in her car next to his in the middle of a traffic jam. Raoul speeds off after Mathilde just as Sophie is about to enter his car. His first encounter with Mathilde is a fiasco, since she is as ruthless a lover as he, and his confidence is shaken. He shows her films of his past conquests, including Hélène and Sophie, and assures her that he loves her. On another day, a new conquest finds herself watching films of Mathilde. *Dentists. Philanderers. Seduction. Home movies. Paris.*
Note: Opened in Paris in Feb 1965; released in Italy in 1965 as *La calda pelle*.

DE QUOI TU TE MÊLES, DANIELA! *see* **DANIELLA BY NIGHT**

DE SADE (United States/West Germany)   **F6.1063**
American International Productions–Trans-Continental Film–CCC–Filmkunst. *Dist* American International Pictures. 25 Sep **1969** [New York opening; c27 Aug 1969; LP37715]. Sd; col (Movielab). 35mm. 113 min. *MPAA rating X.*
Prod Samuel Z. Arkoff, James H. Nicholson. *Exec Prod* Louis M. Heyward, Artur Brauner. *Assoc Prod* Pat Green. *Dir* Cy Endfield. *Uncredited Adtl Dir* Roger Corman, Gordon Hessler. *Screenplay* Richard Matheson, Peter Berg. *Photog* Heinz Pehlke, Richard Angst. *Camera* Herbert Geier, Lothar Hohlfield. *Art Dir* Jürgen Kiebach. *Titl Dsgn* Sandy Dvore. *Film Ed* Max Benedict, Hermann Haller. *Mus Comp & Cond* Billy Strange. *Mus Perf* The Berlin Symphony. *Sd* Ryder Sound Service. *Asst Dir* Alexander Ebermayer von Richthofen. *Prod Supv* Peter Hahne. *Prod Dir* Wolfram Kohtz. *Prod Mgr* Peter Zeumer. *Cost* Vangie Harrison. *Makeup* Freddy Arnold, Barbara Naujok. *Optical Eff* Cinefx.
Cast: Keir Dullea (*Marquis de Sade*), Senta Berger (*Anne de Montreuil*), Lilli Palmer (*Madame de Montreuil*), John Huston (*Abbé de Sade*), Anna Massey (*Renée de Montreuil*), Uta Levka (*Rose Keller*), Herbert Weissbach (*Monsieur de Montreuil*), Christiane Laura Krüger (*De Sade's mistress*), Sonja Ziemann (*Le Beauvoisin*), Max Kiebach (*De Sade as a boy*), Barbara Stanyk (*Colette*), Maria Caleita (*Marie*), Heinz Spitzner (*Inspector Marais*), Friedrich Schönfelder (*De Sade's father*), Susanne von Almassy (*De Sade's mother*), Tilly Lauenstein, Ortrud Gross, Susanne Hsiao, Rolf Eden, Eva-Maria Gebel.
Biographical drama. Based on the correspondence of the Marquis de Sade and: Gilbert Lely, *Vie du Marquis de Sade* (Paris, 1952-57). The Marquis de Sade escapes from an insane asylum where he has been confined for committing unnatural sex acts and for his opposition to the French royalty. The marquis takes refuge in the ruined mansion where he was reared, and there he meets his uncle, the Abbé de Sade, who forces the marquis to remember his past life.

The abbé has the marquis beaten by a young maidservant until the young man is unable to distinguish between pleasure and pain. Eventually, the marquis develops sexual proclivities for flagellation and orgies. He is sent to prison to correct his behavior, but he reacts by writing bitter attacks on the government. Upon his release, he is forced to wed the unattractive Renée de Montreuil; the marquis finally consents to the marriage because he has fallen in love with Anne de Montreuil, the sister of his fiancée. De Sade continues his debaucheries in brothels, pursued by the police. He attempts to elope with Anne, but she dies of the plague. De Sade then leaves his uncle, who has evidently enjoyed inflicting pain on his nephew. *Aristocrats. Uncles. Clergymen. Housemaids. Sisters. Sadism. Masochism. Marriage—Arranged. Elopement. Insane asylums. Prisons. Whorehouses. Plague. France. Donatien Alphonse François [Marquis de] Sade.*
Note: Location scenes filmed in Berlin, Charlottenburg, and Coburg. Released in West Germany in Aug 1970 as *Das ausschweifende Leben des Marquis de Sade*; running time: 100 min. Alternative German title: *Der Marquis de Sade.*

DEAD BIRDS (United States/Netherlands)   **F6.1064**
Peabody Museum–The Netherlands Government. *Dist* Contemporary Films. Jan **1965** [San Francisco showing]. Sd; col (Technicolor). 16mm. 85 min.
Dir Robert Gardner. *Writ* Peter Mathieson. *Photog* Eliot Elisofon. *Main Titl* Peter Chopra, Joyce Chopra. *Film Ed* Robert Gardner, Jestrup Lincoln. *Sd* Michael Rockefeller. *Ethnography* Karl Helder.
Narrator: Robert Gardner.
Documentary. This study of the Dani, a tribe of Western New Guinea, concentrates on one man and his family. The pattern of life alternates between laborious farm work, carried on mainly by the women and children, and fierce battles, waged by the male warriors. *Dani. Tribal life. New Guinea.*
Note: Produced in 1962-63.

DEAD EYES OF LONDON (West Germany)   **F6.1065**
Rialto–Film. *Dist* Magna Pictures Distribution Corp. 18 Feb **1965** [Dallas opening]. Sd; b&w. 35mm. 104 min.
Prod Herbert Sennewald. *Exec Prod* Horst Wendlandt. *Dir* Alfred Vohrer. *Screenplay* Trygve Larsen. *Photog* Karl Löb. *Art Dir* Mathias Matthies. *Film Ed* Ina Orberg. *Mus* Heinz Funk.
Cast: Joachim Fuchsberger (*Inspector Larry Holt*), Karin Baal (*Nora Ward*), Dieter Borsche (*Reverend Dearborn*), Wolfgang Lukschy (*Steven Judd*), Eddi Arent (*Sergeant Harvey*), Klaus Kinski (*Jack*), Harry Wustenhagen, Adi Berber, Bobby Todd, Rudolf Fenner, Ann Savo, Hans Paetsch, Ida Ehre, Fritz Schröder-Jahn, Walter Ladengast.
Mystery melodrama. Source: Edgar Wallace, *The Dark Eyes of London* (London, 1924). Scotland Yard is called in to investigate the seemingly accidental deaths of several heavily-insured foreign gentlemen. When a body is fished out of the Thames, clues lead the Yard to a conglomeration of blind peddlers known as the Dead Eyes of London. An ex-nurse who has worked in an asylum for the blind leads an inspector to the heads of the organization; these men have been paying the blind peddlers to commit the murders, resulting in enormous insurance payments. *Peddlers. Nurses. Blindness. Murder. Insurance. London. Thames River. Scotland Yard.*
Note: Released in West Germany in Apr 1961 as *Die toten Augen von London*; running time: 100 min.

DEAD HEAT ON A MERRY-GO-ROUND   **F6.1066**
Crescent Productions. *Dist* Columbia Pictures. 12 Oct **1966** [New York opening; c1 Oct 1966; LP34216]. Sd; col (Eastman Color, print by Pathé). 35mm. 108 min.
A Carter DeHaven, III–Bernard Girard Production. *Prod* Carter DeHaven, III. *Dir-Writ* Bernard Girard. *Dir Photog* Lionel Lindon. *Art Dir* Walter M. Simonds. *Set Decor* Frank Tuttle. *Film Ed* William A. Lyon. *Mus* Stu Phillips. *Sd Supv* Charles J. Rice. *Sd* Josh Westmoreland. *Asst Dir* William Kissel. *Unit Prod Mgr* M. Frankovich, Jr. *Makeup Supv* Ben Lane. *Hairstyles* Virginia Jones.
Cast: James Coburn (*Eli Kotch*), Camilla Sparv (*Inger Knudson*), Aldo Ray (*Eddie Hart*), Nina Wayne (*Frieda Schmid*), Robert Webber (*Milo Stewart*), Rose Marie (*Margaret Kirby*), Todd Armstrong (*Alfred Morgan*), Marian Moses (*Dr. Marion Hague*), Michael Strong (*Paul Feng*), Severn Darden (*Miles Fisher*), James Westerfield (*Jack Balter*), Phillip Pine (*George Logan*), Simon Scott (*William Anderson*), Ben Astar (*General Mailenkoff*), Michael St. Angel (*Capt. William Yates*), Larry D. Mann (*Officer Howard*), Alex Rodine (*translator*), Albert Nalbandian (*Willie Manus*), Tyler McVey (*Lyman Mann*), Roy Glenn (*Sgt. Elmer K. Coxe*), Joey Faye (*taxi driver*), Mary Young (*Mrs. Galbrace*), George Wallace (*police chief Captain Yates*), Tanya Lemani, Harrison Ford, Stephanie Hill.
Comedy. Confidence man Eli Kotch charms a comely prison psychologist into arranging for his parole from a California prison and picks up, for a $5,000

down payment, the blueprints for a bank at Los Angeles International Airport. Needing a balance of $45,000 in 90 days, he travels to Denver, poses as a Swiss shoeclerk, seduces a German housemaid, and robs her wealthy employer. Moving on to Boston, he hires an electronics expert for the planned bank robbery and, while posing as a termite exterminator and would-be writer, gains entry into the home of prominent Mrs. Galbrace. Eli quickly woos and weds the lady's beautiful secretary, Inger, and sends her to Los Angeles to set up their home, explaining he will follow by truck. Instead, he robs still another rich woman, Margaret Kirby, and then gets a flight to Los Angeles on a chartered plane by posing as a delegate to a Knights of Columbus convention. After paying for the bank blueprints with the proceeds from his robberies, Eli enlists two men, Eddie Hart and Paul Feng, to aid him in the heist. Even the unknowing Inger assists by taking pictures of the bank for a magazine article she believes Eli is writing. The robbery is timed to coincide with the arrival of the Russian premier, and Eli goes to the airport dressed as an Australian police inspector taking a handcuffed extradited prisoner (Eddie Hart) out of the country. Eli even gets the police to help him and his prisoner board a plane bound for Mexico. As he makes a successful getaway with the bank money and contemplates his next identity, he is totally unaware that Inger has been frantically trying to find him—she has inherited $7 million from her former employer, Mrs. Galbrace. *Confidence men. Psychologists. Swiss. Salesclerks. Germans. Housemaids. Exterminators. Columnists. Secretaries. Russians. Australians. Police. Parole. Bank robberies. Imposture. Wealth. Seduction. Robbery. Inheritance. Desertion. Electronics. Prisons. Los Angeles International Airport. California. Denver. Boston. Documentation.*

Note: Location scenes filmed in Boston and Los Angeles. Working titles: *Eli Kotch* and *The Big Noise.*

DEAD I DICK   F6.1067

Dist Stacey Distributors. ca **1970**. Sd; col. 16mm. 61-81 min.

Sex film. No information about the precise nature of this film has been found. *Sexuality.*

DEAD OR ALIVE *see* A MINUTE TO PRAY, A SECOND TO DIE

DEAD RINGER   F6.1068

Warner Bros. Pictures. 29 Jan **1964** [Los Angeles opening; c1 Feb 1964; LP29434]. Sd; b&w. 35mm. 115 min.

Prod William H. Wright. *Dir* Paul Henreid. *Screenplay* Albert Beich, Oscar Millard. *Story* Rian James. *Photog* Ernest Haller. *Art Dir* Perry Ferguson. *Set Decor* William Stevens. *Film Ed* Folmar Blangsted. *Mus* André Previn. *Sd* Robert B. Lee. *Asst Dir* Charles L. Hansen, Lee White, Phil Ball. *Script Supv* Irva Ross. *Cost Dsgn* Don Feld. *Wardrobe* Geoffrey Alan, Ruth Hancock. *Makeup Supv* Gordon Bau. *Miss Davis' Makeup* Gene Hibbs. *Hairstyles* Florence Guernsey. *Dial Coach* Bert Steinberger. *Still Photog* Bert Six. *Gaffer* Gibby Germaine. *Grip* Kenneth Taylor. *Prop* Weldon H. Patterson.

Cast: Bette Davis *(Margaret de Lorca/Edith Philips)*, Karl Malden *(Sgt. Jim Hobbson)*, Peter Lawford *(Tony Collins)*, Philip Carey *(Sgt. Ben Hoag)*, Jean Hagen *(Dede Marshall)*, George Macready *(Paul Harrison)*, Estelle Winwood *(matriarch)*, George Chandler *(George)*, Mario Alcalde *(Garcia)*, Cyril Delevanti *(Henry)*, Monika Henreid *(Janet)*, Bert Remsen *(Dan)*, Charles Watts *(apartment manager)*, Ken Lynch *(Captain Johnson)*.

Crime melodrama. After a separation of 18 years, Edith Philips meets her twin, Margaret de Lorca, at the funeral of the latter's husband, whom Edith also loved. When Edith learns that Margaret had tricked the man into marriage, she becomes so filled with hatred that she lures Margaret to her apartment, signs her own name to a suicide note, and then shoots her sister. After changing clothes with the corpse, she moves into the de Lorca mansion and begins living her sister's life. The masquerade works until she meets Tony Collins, Margaret's secret lover. When he learns of the deception and threatens to blackmail her, Edith realizes that he and Margaret conspired to murder de Lorca. A fight ensues, and Tony is killed by the family's Great Dane. The police become suspicious and exhume the body of the dead husband. Arsenic is found, and Edith is arrested for murder. Although she tries to convince her former suitor, Sgt. Jim Hobbson, that she is really Edith, he refuses to believe her story, and she is sentenced to the gas chamber. *Twins. Sisters. Police. Sororicide. Murder. Impersonation. Suicide. Blackmail. Infidelity. Wealth. Poisoning. Capital punishment. Dogs.*

Note: Location scenes filmed at Greystone Mansion in Beverly Hills.

DEAD RUN (France/Italy/West Germany)   F6.1069

S. N. C.-Intermondia Films-T. C. Productions-CCC-Filmkunst-C. G. R. C.-Metheus Film. *Dist* Universal Pictures. Mar **1969**. Sd; col (Eastman Color). 35mm. 98 min. *MPAA rating* R.

Prod Peter Hahne. *Exec Prod* René Pignères. *Dir* Christian-Jaque. *Screenplay* (see note) Michel Levine, Christian-Jaque, Pascal Jardin, Dany Tyber. *Photog* Pierre Petit. *Art Dir* Jürgen Kiebach. *Film Ed* Jacques Desagneau. *Mus* Gérard Calvi. *Sd* Werner Müssig. *Prod Mgr* Wolfram Kohtz.

Cast: Georges Geret *(Carlos)*, Peter Lawford *(Dain)*, Ira von Fürstenberg *(Suzanne)*, Maria Grazia Buccella *(Anna)*, Horst Frank *(Manganne)*, Werner Peters *(Bardieff)*, Jean Tissier *(Adelgate)*, Bernard Tiphaine *(embassy official)*, Wolfgang Kieling *(Wolfgang)*, Pierre Cordier *(fence)*, Eva Pflug *(Klaus's secretary)*, Wolfgang Preiss, Siegfried Wischnewski, Dean Heyde, Henri Guégan, Michel Charrel, Roger Tréville, Guy Delorme.

Adventure comedy-drama. Source: Robert Sheckley, *Dead Run* (New York, 1961). A band of thugs disguised as ambulance attendants murder an American courier in Berlin and steal his suitcase filled with secret NATO papers. In turn, petty pickpocket Carlos steals the documents and makes off with them, unaware that he has been observed by Suzanne, a wealthy tourist who is later recruited by CIA agent Stephen Dain to identify the thief. Carlos offers the papers to a fence who suggests he contact a jeweler in Lucerne. Manganne and Bardieff, two members of the gang, kill the fence after obtaining the jeweler's address and then murder the contact in Lucerne before the sale can be made. Unaware that he is being followed by Dain and Suzanne, Carlos catches a train to Paris and en route strikes up an acquaintance with Anna, who helps pay for his train fare. In a Parisian nightclub, Carlos attempts to sell the papers to an American embassy official, who—believing Carlos to be joking—tells him to go to Vienna and speak with the Russians. In Vienna Carlos sends Anna to negotiate the deal with a Dr. Klaus. Klaus's secretary, an American undercover agent, notifies Dain that Anna has already handed over half the papers. Manganne and Bardieff murder Klaus and force Anna to call Carlos and ask him to deliver the remainder of the documents. Dain and the police arrive just as Carlos and Anna are about to be killed. The papers recovered, Dain plans to take a holiday in Mexico with Suzanne, until he learns that Carlos has stolen his wallet containing the airline tickets. *Gangsters. Government agents. Americans in foreign countries. Couriers. Pickpockets. Tourists. Fences (for stolen goods). Jewelers. Secretaries. Police. Murder. Theft. Trains. Nightclubs. Berlin. Lucerne. Paris. Vienna. United States—Diplomatic and consular service. United States—Central Intelligence Agency. North Atlantic Treaty Organization. Documentation. Chases.*

Note: Opened in Paris in Aug 1967 as *Deux billets pour Mexico* (also known as *Chaud les secrets*); running time: 95 min; released in West Germany in Sep 1967 as *Geheimnisse in goldenen Nylons* at 86 and 91 min; in Italy in 1968 as *Segreti che scottano*. Sources conflict in crediting screenplay author. Alan Collins is a pseudonym for Luciano Pigozzi.

DEAD TO THE WORLD   F6.1070

National Film Studios. *Dist* United Artists. 27 Oct **1961** [Maryland license]. Sd; b&w. 35mm. 87 min.

Prod F. William Hart. *Exec Prod* Harold A. Keats. *Dir* Nicholas Webster. *Screenplay* John Roeburt. *Photog* Bert Spielvogel. *Mus* Charlie Byrd, Eddie Phyfe Jazz Ensemble.

Cast: Reedy Talton *(Barney Cornell)*, Jana Pearce *(Laura)*, Ford Rainey *(Congressman Keach)*, Casey Peyson *(Karen Stone)*, John McLiam *(Goody)*, John Dorman *(Hannigan)*, Joel Thomas *(Paul Evarts)*, Joseph Julian *(Kelly)*, Leon B. Stevens *(Jason Stone)*, Philip Kenneally *(Sam Hand)*, Len Doyle *(De Luca)*, Maggie O'Neill *(Helga)*, Michael Gorrin *(Milo Crespi)*, Drew Pearson *(narrator)*.

Melodrama. Source: Edward Ronns, *State Department Murders* (New York, 1950). Barney Cornell, a State Department employee in Washington, D. C., has been accused by a Congressional committee of turning top secret material over to a Bulgarian family that saved his life during World War II. With the aid of his superior, Paul Evarts, and a former sweetheart, Laura, he goes about trying to prove his innocence. During this time, he is also falsely accused of the murder of Jason Stone, a political boss. Further investigation enables him to expose Paul as the real traitor, and Cornell is returned to governmental favor. *Bulgarians. Bureaucrats. Politicians. Treason. Murder. Espionage. Washington (District of Columbia). United States—State Department. United States Congress.*

Note: Location scenes filmed in Washington, D. C.

DEADFALL (Great Britain)   F6.1071

Salamander Film Productions. *Dist* Twentieth Century-Fox Film Corp. 11 Sep **1968** [New York opening; c11 Sep 1968; LP36076]. Sd (Westrex); col (Eastman Color by DeLuxe). 35mm. 120 min.

Prod Paul Monash. *Assoc Prod* Jack Rix. *Dir-Writ* Bryan Forbes. *Photog* Gerry Turpin. *Camera Op* Ron Taylor. *Camera Asst* Michael Sarafian. *Camera Grip* Ted Lockhart. *Set Dsgn* Ray Simm. *Set Dresser* Peter James. *Main Titl* Tom Taylor, Caravel Studios. *Film Ed* John Jympson. *Asst Ed* Alan Strachan. *Mus Comp, Cond & Arr* John Barry. *Song:* "My Love Has Two Faces" John Barry, Jack Lawrence. *Sung by* Shirley Bassey. *Soloist in* "Romance for Guitar and Orchestra" Renata Tarrago. *Orch* London Philharmonic Orchestra. *Sd Rec* Bill Daniels, Gordon McCallum. *Dub Ed* Janet Davidson. *Sd Asst* Gus Lloyd. *Asst Dir* Christopher Dryhurst, José López Rodero. *Prod Mgr* Donald Toms. *Spanish Prod Mgr* Fernando Navarro Correcher. *Location Mgr* Teresa Bolland.

Asst to the Prod John L. Hargreaves. *Cont* Penny Daniels. *Cost Dsgn* Julie Harris, cost. *Wardrobe Mistress* Laurel Staffell. *Wardrobe Master* John Hilling. *Jewelry Dsgn & Created by* Roger Milner King. *Makeup* Basil Newall, Freddie Williamson. *Hairdresser* Barbara Ritchie. *Still Photog* George Courtney Ward. *Constr Mgr* Bill Surridge. *Ch Electrn* Bill Walpole, Miguel Sancho Ruiz. *Prop Master* George Ball, Paddy Bennett.

Cast: Michael Caine *(Henry Clarke)*, Giovanna Ralli *(Fe Moreau)*, Eric Portman *(Richard Moreau)*, Nanette Newman *(The Girl)*, David Buck *(Salinas)*, Carlos Pierre *(Antonio)*, Leonard Rossiter *(Fillmore)*, Emilio Rodríguez *(Police Inspector Ballastero)*, Vladek Sheybal *(Dr. Delgado)*, George Ghent *(Stresemann)*, Carmen Dene *(masseuse)*, Geraldine Sherman *(Delgado's receptionist)*, Antonio Sampere *(Lagranja)*, Reg Howell *(Spanish chauffeur)*, Santiago Rivero *(armed guard)*, Philip Madoc *(bank manager)*, John Barry *(orchestra conductor)*.

Drama. Source: Desmond Cory, *Deadfall* (London, 1965). To gain the confidence of multimillionaire Salinas, master jewel thief Henry Clarke has himself committed to a sanitarium for alcoholics. On the day he is to be released, Henry is approached by the beautiful Fe Moreau. Attracted to Fe and aware that her husband, Richard, is a homosexual, Henry agrees to join forces with the couple. Before tackling the Salinas job, however, the trio perfect their technique by robbing a less difficult house, where Henry rips the safe from the wall and carries it out on his back. While Henry is recuperating from the physical strain, he becomes Fe's lover; and Richard becomes involved with Antonio, a young Italian prostitute. When Fe goes to Tangiers to dispose of some jewels, Henry learns from Richard why Fe is so devoted to her husband despite his sexual inclinations. Years before, Richard betrayed his male lover to the Nazis and then, wracked with guilt, joined the Resistance. To avenge himself on a Gestapo collaborator, Richard seduced the man's wife, an act that resulted in Fe's birth. Later, Richard married her without disclosing her true identity. Stunned to learn that Fe is Richard's daughter as well as his wife, Henry goes alone to rob Salinas' house. Meanwhile, Fe returns from Tangiers, learns the secret of her birth, and rushes to the Salinas mansion to join Henry. She arrives just as Henry falls to his death after being shot by a guard. Richard shoots himself, Fe is arrested, and Antonio drives off in Henry's car. *Millionaires. Thieves. Italians. Prostitutes. Alcoholism. Male homosexuality. Incest. Perfidy. Seduction. Infidelity. Resistance (political). Suicide. Jewels. Sanitariums. World War II. Tangiers. Gestapo.*

Note: Location scenes filmed in Majorca and Madrid. Opened in London in Oct 1968.

DEADLIER THAN THE MALE (Great Britain)   **F6.1072**
Santor Film Productions-Inflight Motion Pictures. *Dist* Universal Pictures. 21 Feb **1967** [New York opening; c1 Apr 1967; LP35387]. Sd; col (Technicolor). 35mm (Techniscope). 98 min.

Pres by Rank Organisation. A Sydney Box–Charles Bruce Newbery Production. *Prod* Betty E. Box. *Dir* Ralph Thomas. *Screenplay* Jimmy Sangster, David Osborn, Liz Charles-Williams. *Orig Story* Jimmy Sangster. *Dir Photog* Ernest Steward. *Camera Op* James Bawden, John Morgan, Michael Smith, Reg Hall. *Art Dir* Alex Vetchinsky. *Asst Art Dir* Ted Clements. *Set Dresser* Helen Thomas. *Scenic Artist* Jack Cook. *Draughtsman* Jim Morahan. *Film Ed* Alfred Roome. *Asst Ed* Jack Gardner, Rita Burgess. *Mus Comp & Cond* Malcolm Lockyer. *Titl Song* John Franz, Scott Engel. *Sung by* The Walker Brothers. *Sd Rec* Dudley Messenger, Gordon K. McCallum. *Sd Ed* Don Sharpe. *Boom Op* J. W. N. Daniel. *Sd Camera Op* Terry Hill. *Asst Dir* Simon Relph, Giorgio Gentili, Allan James, Patrick O'Brien. *Prod Mgr* Eric Rattray. *Unit Mgr* Bernard Hanson. *Cont* Gladys Goldsmith. *Location Mgr* Giorgio Zambon. *Cost Dsgn* Cynthia Tingey, Yvonne Caffin. *Wardrobe* John Hilling, Betty Knight. *Makeup* Geoffrey Rodway, John Wilcox, makeup. *Hairdressing* Maud Onslow. *Sp Eff* Kit West, Pat Moore. *Constr Mgr* Ken Softley. *Still Photog* John Jay. *Ch Electrn* Bill Walpole.

Cast: Richard Johnson *(Hugh "Bulldog" Drummond)*, Elke Sommer *(Irma Eckman)*, Sylva Koscina *(Penelope)*, Nigel Green *(Carl Petersen)*, Suzanna Leigh *(Grace)*, Steve Carlson *(Robert Drummond)*, Virginia North *(Brenda)*, Justine Lord *(Miss Ashenden)*, Leonard Rossiter *(Bridgenorth)*, Laurence Naismith *(Sir John Bledlow)*, Zia Mohyeddin *(King Fedra)*, Lee Montague *(Boxer)*, Milton Reid *(Chang)*, Yasuko Nagazumi *(Mitsouko)*, Didi Sydow *(Anna)*, George Pastell *(Carloggio)*, Dervis Ward *(Keller)*, John Stone *(Wyngarde)*, William Mervyn.

Action melodrama. Based on the characters created by: Herbert Cyril ("Sapper") McNeile. Hugh "Bulldog" Drummond, an insurance investigator for Lloyd's of London, is sent to investigate the mysterious deaths of two oil company magnates. Behind the murders are Irma Eckman and her assistant, Penelope, who work for Carl Petersen, the head of a syndicate that arranges for major business deals through devious means. A servant of one of the murdered men brings Drummond part of a taped message, but Drummond is unable to decipher it. Following two attempts on his life, he attends a meeting at the Pan-

Arabian Oil Company, where Irma, representing an unknown oil company, offers to sell the oil rights of the Kingdom of Akmata for a substantial fee. At the meeting, an executive unwittingly provides Drummond with a clue to the tape when he states that the only way to obtain oil concessions from Akmata is to kill the young king, Fedra. Drummond, now suspicious of Irma, follows her home after the meeting is adjourned and discovers that Robert, his nephew who has arrived from the United States for a visit, has been bound and tortured by Penelope. Convinced that Fedra, who turns out to be one of Robert's university friends, is the next victim, Drummond joins Robert and Fedra on a Mediterranean cruise. While on board the boat, Drummond receives an invitation to visit an ancient castle which he believes holds the answer to the mysterious murders. There he meets Irma, Penelope, and other women who are members of an assassination ring headed by Petersen. Although Drummond seems trapped, he manages to outwit Petersen and thwart his plan to kill Fedra; the assassins are killed when their boat explodes. *Detectives. Oil magnates. Uncles. Royalty. Assassination. Torture. Abduction. Murder. Syndicates. Cruisers. Castles. Mediterranean Sea. Lloyd's of London. Explosions.*

Note: Opened in London in Dec 1966.

DEADLOCK see MAN-TRAP

THE DEADLY AFFAIR (Great Britain)   **F6.1073**
Sidney Lumet Film Productions. *Dist* Columbia Pictures. 26 Jan 1967 [New York opening; c1 Mar 1967; LP34166]. Sd (Westrex); col (Technicolor). 35mm. 107 min.

Prod-Dir Sidney Lumet. *Assoc Prod* Denis O'Dell. *Dir Royal Shakespeare Company Seq* Peter Hall. *Screenplay* Paul Dehn. *Dir Photog* Freddie Young. *Camera Op* Brian West. *Art Dir* John Howell. *Set Dresser* Pamela Cornell. *Film Ed* Thelma Connell. *Mus* Quincy Jones. *Orch* Leo Shuken, Jack Hayes. *Theme Song: "Who Needs Forever"* sung by Astrud Gilberto. *Sd Rec* Leslie Hammond, Gerry Humphreys. *Sd Ed* Chris Greenham. *Asst Dir* Ted Sturgis, Brian Cook, Michael Meighan. *Prod Mgr* Victor Peck. *Cont* Phyllis Crocker. *Cost Dsgn* Cynthia Tingey. *Wardrobe Master* Ron Beck. *Makeup Artist* Jill Carpenter. *Hairdresser* Betty Glasow. *Casting* James Liggat. *Constr Mgr* Gus Walker. *Camera Grip* Ted Tucker. *Ch Electrn* Jack Napper. *Ch Prop* Alfred Pegley.

Cast: James Mason *(Charles Dobbs)*, Simone Signoret *(Elsa Fennan)*, Maximilian Schell *(Dieter Frey)*, Harriet Andersson *(Ann Dobbs)*, Harry Andrews *(Inspector Mendel)*, Kenneth Haigh *(Bill Appleby)*, Roy Kinnear *(Adam Scarr)*, Max Adrian *(adviser)*, Lynn Redgrave *(virgin)*, Robert Flemyng *(Samuel Fennan)*, Corin Redgrave *(director)*, Les White *(Harek)*, June Murphy *(1st witch)*, Frank Williams *(2d witch)*, Rosemary Lord *(3d witch)*, Kenneth Ives *(stagehand)*, John Dimech *(waiter)*, Julian Sherrier *(head waiter)*, Petra Markham *(daughter at theater)*, Denis Shaw *(landlord)*, Maria Charles *(blonde)*, Amanda Walker *(brunette)*, Sheraton Blount *(Eunice Scarr)*, Janet Hargreaves *(ticket clerk)*, Michael Brennan *(barman)*, Richard Steele, Gertan Klauber *(businessmen)*, Margaret Lacey *(Mrs. Bird)*, Judy Keirn *(Stewardess)*, Leslie Sands.

Cast—Members of the Royal Shakespeare Company: David Warner *(King Edward)*, Michael Bryant *(Gaveston)*, Stanley Lebor *(Lancaster)*, Paul Hardwick *(Young Mortimer)*, Charles Kay *(Lightborn)*, Timothy West *(Matrevis)*, Jonathan Wales *(Gurney)*, William Dysart, Murray Brown, Paul Starr, Peter Harrison, David Quilter, Terence Sewards, Roger Jones *(nobles)*.

Mystery drama. Source: John Le Carré, *Call for the Dead* (London, 1961). Charles Dobbs, a security agent for the British Foreign Office, is assigned to do a routine check on a government employee who anonymously has been accused of being a Communist. Shortly after clearing the man, Dobbs is stunned to learn he has committed suicide, leaving behind a typed suicide note stating that his career had been ruined by paid informers. Dobbs is so outraged when his superiors insist upon closing the case that he resigns his post and sets out to prove that the man was murdered. After enlisting the aid of a retired police officer, Mendel, Dobbs visits the dead man's widow, Elsa Fennan, a Jewish victim of Nazi concentration camps. His suspicions are further aroused when he catches her in a lie and then later learns that the anonymous letter to the Foreign Office accusing Fennan of being a Communist and the suicide note both came from the same typewriter. Returning home, Dobbs is greeted by an old friend, Dieter Frey, who has arrived in London to do business for a Zurich candy firm. And Dobb's problems are compounded by the discovery that his frequently unfaithful wife, Ann, has seduced Dieter. Resuming their investigation, Dobbs and Mendel uncover clues which lead them first to a garage, then to an office building, and finally to a repertory theater. When it becomes apparent that Elsa Fennan is a Communist, Dobbs realizes her husband must also have discovered this and, therefore, had to be silenced. Certain that Elsa meets her contact at the repertory theater, Dobbs and Mendel set a trap; during a performance of Marlowe's *Edward II* they catch her sitting next to the Russian agent—Dieter Frey. Quick to sense he has been tricked, Dieter murders Elsa in her seat and makes a getaway during the confusion.

Dobbs and Mendel give chase and corner him on a houseboat in Chelsea. Although Dieter kills Mendel, he hesitates to shoot his wartime comrade. Dobbs, however, takes advantage of the respite; overpowering Dieter, he savagely beats him and then watches as his body falls into the water and is crushed between two houseboats. The affair over, Dobbs flies to Zurich to inform his wife that Dieter will not make their planned rendezvous. *Spies. Communists. Government agents. Jews. Widows. Suicide. Murder. Espionage. Infidelity. Theater. London. London—Chelsea. Zurich. "Edward II". Documentation.*

Note: Location scenes filmed in London. Released in Great Britain in Feb 1967. Some sources indicate film was shot in Panavision.

THE DEADLY BEES (Great Britain)   F6.1074

Amicus Productions. *Dist* Paramount Pictures. 19 May **1967** [New York opening; c31 Dec 1966; LP34445]. Sd; col (Technicolor). 35mm (Techniscope). 85 min.

Prod Max J. Rosenberg, Milton Subotsky. *Dir* Freddie Francis. *Screenplay* Robert Bloch, Anthony Marriott. *Dir Photog* John Wilcox. *Art Dir* Bill Constable. *Set Decor* Andrew Low. *Film Ed* Oswald Hafenrichter. *Mus* Wilfred Josephs. *Mus Cond* Philip Martell. *Sd* Michael Pidcock. *Sd Rec* Ken Rawkins. *Asst Dir* Anthony Waye. *Prod Mgr* Derrick Farr. *Sp Eff* Michael Collins. *Sp Photog Eff* John Mackey.

Cast: Suzanna Leigh (*Vicky Robbins*), Frank Finlay (*Manfred*), Guy Doleman (*Ralph Hargrove*), Catherine Finn (*Mrs. Hargrove*), John Harvey (*Thompson*), Michael Ripper (*Hawkins*), Anthony Bailey (*compère*), Tim Barrett (*Harcourt*), James Cossins (*coroner*), Frank Forsyth (*doctor*), Katy Wild (*Doris Hawkins*), Greta Farrer (*sister*), Gina Gianelli (*secretary*), Michael Gwynn (*Dr. Lang*), Maurice Good (*Vicky's agent*), Alister Williamson (*inspector*).

Melodrama. Source: H. F. Heard, *A Taste for Honey* (New York, 1941). Pop singer Vicky Robbins collapses from exhaustion, and her doctor orders her to take an extended vacation on a small island off the coast of England. She rents a small cottage on a farm belonging to Ralph Hargrove, a taciturn man interested only in tending his beehives. Hargrove is constantly irritated by Manfred, another beekeeper, who allows his bees to swarm over the adjoining property. For some time local police have been receiving what they consider crank letters from someone on the island who claims to have developed a strain of killer bees; unless his achievement is recognized, he threatens to unloose them on the populace. Upon learning of the threats, Vicky becomes suspicious of her host, whom she has caught secretly taking blood from his horse in the middle of the night. Mrs. Hargrove's pet dog is inexplicably stung to death by bees, and Vicky's shock quickly turns to terror when Mrs. Hargrove is also found dead, her face horribly distorted by bee stings. After narrowly escaping an attack herself, Vicky races to Manfred's home for shelter. Only then does she learn that it is Manfred who has developed the deadly bees and has unloosed them because Hargrove is trying to learn his secret. Manfred accidentally becomes smeared with the bait that attracts the deadly insects and is stung to death. *Singers. Apiarists. Police. Murder. Vacations. Islands. Experiments. Bees.*

Note: Released in Great Britain in 1967. Original running time: 123 min.

THE DEADLY CIRCLE see **HONEYMOON OF HORROR**

THE DEADLY COMPANIONS   F6.1075

Carousel Productions. *Dist* Pathé-America Distributing Co., Motion Picture Investors. 6 Jun **1961** [Tucson, Arizona, opening]. Sd; col (Pathé Color). 35mm (Panavision). 90 min.

Prod Charles B. FitzSimons. *Dir* Sam Peckinpah. *Screenplay* Albert Sidney Fleischman. *Dir Photog* William H. Clothier. *Film Ed* Stanley E. Rabjohn. *Mus* Marlin Skiles. *Mus Cond* Raoul Kraushaar. *Titl Song:* "A Dream of Love" Marlin Skiles, Charles B. FitzSimons. *Sung by* Maureen O'Hara. *Guitar Solo* Laurindo Almeida, Robert Bain. *Sd* Gordon Sawyer, Robert J. Callen. *Sd Eff Ed* Kurt Herrnfeld. *Mus Ed* Peter Zinner. *Prod Mgr* Lee Lukather. *Wardrobe* Frank Beetson, Sr., Sheila O'Brian. *Makeup* James Barker. *Hairstyles* Fae Smith. *Sp Eff* David Koehler. *Prop Master* Tom Coleman. *Stunt* Chuck Hayward.

Cast: Maureen O'Hara (*Kit Tilden*), Brian Keith (*Yellowleg*), Steve Cochran (*Billy*), Chill Wills (*Turk*), Strother Martin (*parson*), Will Wright (*doctor*), Jim O'Hara (*Cal*), Peter O'Crotty (*mayor*), Billy Vaughan (*Mead*), Robert Sheldon, John Hamilton (*gamblers*), Hank Gobble (*bartender*), Buck Sharpe (*Indian*).

Western melodrama. Source: Albert Sidney Fleischman, *Yellowleg* (New York, 1960). In the late 1860's, a former Union Army sergeant, Yellowleg, hunts down a Rebel deserter, Turk, who tried to scalp him as he lay wounded on a battlefield. He finds him in a bordertown cantina and, without revealing his true motive, persuades him and his trigger-happy sidekick, Billy, to join forces with him in robbing the bank in Gila City, Arizona. Once there, however, the men discover that other outlaws are in town for the same reason; a gun

battle breaks out, and Yellowleg accidentally kills the 9-year-old son of dancehall hostess Kit Tilden. When the woman decides to bury her child next to her husband's grave in Siringo, a ghost town, the remorseful Yellowleg forces his companions to join him in accompanying Kit through the Apache-inhabited desert; but en route, Billy is thrown out of camp for attempting to rape Kit, and Turk deserts. Shortly after arriving in Siringo, Kit and Yellowleg are rejoined by the two outlaws, who have just robbed the bank at Gila City. Yellowleg, despite his growing love for Kit, decides to take his revenge on Turk, but a shoulder wound causes him to miss his mark; instead, it is Billy who shoots Turk. The old man is only wounded, however, and is able to turn on his former friend and kill him. A posse arrives to take Turk back to Gila City as Kit and Yellowleg ride off together. *Veterans. Confederate veterans. Deserters— Military. Outlaws. Dancehall hostesses. Widows. Apache Indians. Children. Revenge. Bank robberies. Rape. Deserts. Ghost towns. United States— History—Civil War. Arizona.*

Note: Filmed on location in and around Tucson, Arizona. Rereleased in 1965 by Motion Picture Investors as *Trigger Happy*.

DEADLY DUO   F6.1076

Harvard Film Corp. *Dist* United Artists. Feb **1962** [c17 Jan 1962; LP21185]. Sd; b&w. 35mm. 70 min.

Prod Robert E. Kent. *Dir* Reginald Le Borg. *Screenplay* Owen Harris. *Photog* Gordon Avil. *Set Decor* Harry Reif. *Film Ed* Kenneth Crane. *Mus* Richard LaSalle. *Sd* Earl Schwartz. *Asst Dir* Frank Mayer. *Prod Mgr* Joseph Small. *Cost* Einar Bourman, Sabine Manela.

Cast: Craig Hill (*Preston Morgan*), Marcia Henderson (*Sabena/Dara*), Robert Lowery (*Jay Flagg*), Dayton Lummis (*Thorne Fletcher*), Carlos Romero (*Lieutenant Reyes*), David Renard (*Manuel*), Irene Tedrow (*Leonora*), Peter Oliphant (*Billy*), Manuel Lopez (*policeman*), Marco Antonio (*Luis*).

Crime melodrama. Source: Richard Jessup, *The Deadly Duo* (New York, 1960). Playboy Robbie Spence is killed in a racing car crash, and Leonora, his wealthy mother, hires attorney Preston Morgan to help her gain custody of her grandson from Robbie's wife, Sabena. Sabena refuses to part with the child, even when offered $500,000; but Sabena's twin sister, Dara, plots with husband Jay Flagg to get the money for themselves. Pretending to be Sabena, Dara signs the necessary papers giving custody of the boy to his grandmother and then arranges for her sister to have an accident on a narrow cliff road. A mechanic spots Flagg tampering with Sabena's car, however, and alerts the police. Dara and Flagg are arrested; Leonora sees the error of her ways and invites Sabena and the child to live with her; and Preston finds romance with Sabena and becomes a partner in a large law firm. *Lawyers. Grandmothers. Widows. Sisters. Twins. Mechanics. Impersonation. Bribery. Child custody. Motherhood. Greed. Automobile accidents.*

THE DEADLY ORGAN (Argentina)   F6.1077

Productores Argentinos Asociados. *Dist* Cambist Films. Oct **1967**. Sd; b&w. 35mm. 75 min.

Pres by Unistar Films. *Prod* Orestes Trucco. *Assoc Prod* (?) Gloria Prat. *Dir* Emilio Vieyra. *Screenplay* Antonio Rosso. *Dir Photog* Aníbal González Paz. *Camera* Víctor Hugo Gaula. *Film Ed* Jacinto Cascales. *Mus* Víctor Buchino.

Cast: Gloria Prat, Mauricio de Ferraris, Ricardo Bauleo, Susana Beltrán, Alberto Candeau, Eduardo Muñoz, Blanca Burgueno, Justin Martín, Eduardo Kliche.

Crime melodrama. A series of sex murders committed by a man wearing a hideous mask creates panic among members of the jet set at the Uruguayan summer resort of Punta Ballena. Police are puzzled upon learning that the victims were attracted to the murder spot by the sound of organ music; and there, having been injected with a "love potion" [heroin, according to an Argentine source], they lavished delights on the masked man, who then killed them by plunging a hypodermic syringe into their breasts. Acting as a decoy to assist the police in identifying the man, a woman narrowly escapes being raped and killed. Finally, the killer is revealed to be a police coroner who went insane after his wife left him for a younger man. Subsequently, driving under the influence of drugs, the couple died in an automobile accident. *Jet set. Police. Coroners. Murder. Rape. Insanity. Infidelity. Masks. Music. Resorts. Heroin. Aphrodisiacs. Uruguay. Automobile accidents.*

Note: Released in Argentina in 1967 as *Placer sangriento*.

THE DEADLY SILENCE see **TARZAN'S DEADLY SILENCE**

DEADLY SWEET (France/Italy)   F6.1078

Panda Film–Les Films Corona. *Dist* Films Distributing Corp., Avco Embassy Pictures. 7 Sep **1969** [Portland, Oregon, opening]. Sd; col with b&w seq (Technicolor). 35mm. 101 min. *MPAA rating* X.

Prod Ermanno Donati, Luigi Carpentieri. *Dir* Tinto Brass. *Screenplay* Tinto Brass, Francesco Longo, Pierre Lévy-Corti. *Photog* Silvano Ippoliti. *Mus* Armando Trovajoli.

Cast: Jean-Louis Trintignant (Bernard), Ewa Aulin (Jane), Roberto Bisacco (David), Charles Kohler (Jerome), Luigi Bellini (Jelly-Roll), Monique Scoazec (Veronica), Vira Silenti (Marta), Enzo Consoli (bartender).

Crime melodrama. Source: Sergio Donati, Il sepolcro di carta (publication undetermined). Bernard, a French actor working in London, returns to his hotel room to find a woman, Jane, looking upon the corpse of Prescott, a nightclub owner. Soon after, Bernard is pursued and tortured by criminals who want a diary which he stole from Prescott's room. While attempting to help Jane evade the criminals, Bernard discovers that she killed Prescott because he was extorting money from her and that she has also murdered several people involved in the investigation. Despite her love for Bernard, Jane shoots him when confronted with the evidence of her guilt. Actors. Nightclub owners. Murder. Extortion. Torture. Theft. Diaries. London.

Note: Released in Italy in 1967 as Col cuore in gola; running time: 107 min.

DEADWOOD '76   F6.1079
Fairway Productions. Dist Fairway International Films. 30 Jun 1965 [Cincinnati, Ohio, opening]. Sd; col (Technicolor). 35mm (Techniscope). 100 min.

An Arch Hall, [Sr.] Production. Prod Nicholas Merriwether. Dir James Landis. Screenplay Arch Hall, Jr., William Watters. Story William Watters. Photog William Zsigmond. Camera Asst Lewis J. Guinn. Art Dir David Reed, III. Film Ed Anthony M. Lanza. Mus Manuel Francisco. Song: "Deadwood" Harper MacKay, Arch Hall, Jr. Sung by Rex Holman. Sd Robert Dietz. Asst Dir Bud Cardos. Indian Wardrobe Eldean Ressl. Makeup Lyn Sherry. Hairstyles Lyn Sherry.

Cast: Arch Hall, Jr. (Billy May), Jack Lester (Tennessee Thompson), Melissa Morgan (Poker Kate), William Watters (Boone May), Robert Dix (Wild Bill Hickok), LaDonna Cottier (Little Bird), Richard S. Cowl (Preacher Smith), David Reed (Fancy Poggin), Rex Marlow (Sam Bass), Gordon Schwenk (Spotted Snake), John Bryant (Hubert), Barbara Moore (Montana), Ray Zachary (Spec Greer), Willard Willingham (Deputy Harding), Harold Bizzy, Read Morgan, John Cardos, Little Jack Little, Bobby Means, Ray Vegas.

Western melodrama. Young Billy May saves Tennessee Thompson from the Indians of the Dakota Bad Lands, and together they travel to the town of Deadwood in the Dakota Territory. The townspeople mistake Billy May for Billy the Kid and place bets on his impending fight with Wild Bill Hickok. In the meantime, Tennessee has purchased a gold claim, but his partner, Billy, is captured during an Indian raid. When they reach the Indian camp, Billy meets his father, Boone May, an ex-Confederate soldier who has joined the Indians in hopes of destroying Custer's troops and establishing a new Confederate state. Billy also meets and falls in love with Little Bird, a young Indian woman. Later he escapes from the camp and shoots two outlaws who have raped Little Bird. By the time he returns to Deadwood, Wild Bill Hickok has arrived, but when Hickok learns Billy's true identity, he decides not to fight him. A young boy, Hubert, tricks Billy into a gunfight, however, and Billy shoots the boy in self-defense. He is hunted down and lynched by a mob of townspeople; when Preacher Smith tries to intervene, he is also shot. Indians of North America. Confederate veterans. Outlaws. Preachers. Mistaken identity. Gold mining. Rape. Lynching. Deadwood (South Dakota). Bad Lands of Dakota. Dakota Territory. George Armstrong Custer. James Butler Hickok. William H. Bonney.

Note: William Watters and Nicholas Merriwether are pseudonyms for Arch Hall, Sr.

THE DEAN'S WIFE   F6.1080
Twin Peaks Productions. Dist Perpetual Films. 28 May 1970 [San Francisco showing]. Sd; col (print by Movielab). 35mm. 75 min.

Prod-Writ L. K. Farbella. Assoc Prod Roger Gentry. Dir Benjamin Onivas. Dir Photog Henning Schellerup.

Cast: Christine Murray (Grace Walker?), Jim Gentry, Mark Edwards, Guy Anthony, Trace Mills, Prudence Smythe, Lynn Lyon, Jeanette Mills, Lloyd Allen, Anita Joyce, Linda Marie, Lee Sommers, Ben Dover, Roy Morgan.

Melodrama. Grace Walker, the nymphomaniac wife of college dean Calvin Walker, takes advantage of her husband's preoccupation with student unrest to satisfy her lust with other members of the campus community. Both students and professors exchange their sexual services for Grace's intervention on their behalf with Calvin. During a student love-in, Peter, a dissident leader, incites a group of students to confront the dean with their demands. The group arrives at the Walker home, and the dean rejects the students' demands, but a spark passes between Peter and Grace. Sometime later, Grace becomes involved in a sexual threesome with Professor Clove, a specialist in erotica, and his wife. The sight of Grace making love with the professor and his wife shatters the dean, and he falls prey to a student plot. Peter slips the dean some LSD and, intending to blackmail him, leads him to an orgy. The dean comes to his senses in the midst of the orgy and is so shaken when he sees his wife and Peter making love that he commits suicide. Deans. Students. Professors. College life.

Nymphomania. Infidelity. Student activism. Troilism. Love-ins. Blackmail. Suicide. Orgies. LSD.

Note: Also known as The Tale of the Dean's Wife.

DEAR BRIGITTE   F6.1081
Fred Kohlmar Productions. Dist Twentieth Century-Fox Film Corp. 27 Jan 1965 [New York opening; c27 Jan 1965; LP29821]. Sd (Westrex); col (DeLuxe). 35mm (CinemaScope). 100 min.

A Fred Kohlmar Production. Prod-Dir Henry Koster. Screenplay Hal Kanter. Dir Photog Lucien Ballard. Art Dir Jack Martin Smith, Malcolm Brown. Set Dsgn Walter M. Scott, Steven Potter. Film Ed Marjorie Fowler. Mus George Duning. Orch Arthur Morton. Sd Alfred Bruzlin, Elmer Raguse. Asst Dir Fred R. Simpson. Cost Dsgn Moss Mabry. Makeup Ben Nye. Hairstyles Margaret Donovan. Spec Photog Eff L. B. Abbott, Emil Kosa, Jr.

Cast: James Stewart (Professor Robert Leaf), Fabian (Kenneth), Glynis Johns (Vina), Cindy Carol (Pandora), Billy Mumy (Erasmus), John Williams (Peregrine Upjohn), Jack Kruschen (Dr. Volker), Charles Robinson (George), Howard Freeman (Dean Sawyer), Jane Wald (Terry), Alice Pearce (unemployment clerk), Jesse White (Argyle), Gene O'Donnell (Lieutenant Rink), Orville Sherman (Von Schlogg), Maida Severn (school teacher), Pitt Herbert (bank manager), Adair Jameson (saleslady), Marcel De la Brosse (taxi driver), Ed Wynn (captain), Brigitte Bardot (herself), Bob Biheller.

Domestic comedy. Source: John Haase, Erasmus With Freckles (New York, 1963). Robert Leaf, poet and professor teaching at a California college, lives on an old ferryboat with his wife and family and is devoted to the arts but detests science. Unnerved when he discovers that his 8-year-old son, Erasmus, is both tone-deaf and colorblind, he is further horrified to learn that Erasmus is a mathematical genius, and Leaf does his best to keep this a secret. Leaf's daughter, Pandora, begins having her brother do her homework, and she and her boyfriend Kenneth soon have Erasmus handicapping horses for them. They begin to pile up money while Erasmus saves the fees he charges them for a trip to Paris to meet Brigitte Bardot, to whom he has written many letters. A con man calling himself Dr. Peregrine Upjohn makes a proposition to Leaf that they finance a Leaf Foundation to set up scholarships for students of the arts and humanities by having Erasmus handicap horses, and Leaf agrees. The foundation's assets soar until Erasmus refuses to perform his function unless he can accept an invitation he has received to visit Brigitte Bardot in Paris. Leaf takes him to Paris, where he actually meets Bardot, and while they are gone Upjohn plans to abscond with the money. An Internal Revenue agent claims the money from Upjohn, but Leaf and Erasmus arrive in time to inform the agent that the foundation is nonprofit and therefore tax exempt. Leaf takes the money, and life on the ferryboat returns to its usual pattern. Poets. Professors. Mathematicians. Confidence men. Revenue agents. Filial relations. Brother-sister relationship. Horseracing. Gambling. Ferryboats. California. Paris. Brigitte Bardot. United States—Internal Revenue Service.

Note: Working title: Erasmus With Freckles.

DEAR HEART   F6.1082
Out-of-Towners Co. Dist Warner Bros. Pictures. 2 Dec 1964 [Los Angeles opening; c27 Mar 1965; LP32382]. Sd; b&w. 35mm. 114 min.

A Martin Manulis Production. Prod Martin Manulis. Dir Delbert Mann. Story & Screenplay Tad Mosel. Dir Photog Russell Harlan. Art Dir Joseph Wright. Set Decor Howard Bristol. Film Ed Folmar Blangsted. Mus Henry Mancini. Titl Song Henry Mancini, Jay Livingston, Ray Evans. Sd Robert B. Lee. Asst Dir Carter DeHaven, Jr. Script Supv Dorothy Aldrin. Cost Dsgn Don Feld. Makeup Supv Gordon Bau. Supv Hairstylist Jean Burt Reilly. Dial Supv Norman Stuart.

Cast: Glenn Ford (Harry Mork), Geraldine Page (Evie Jackson), Michael Anderson, Jr. (Patrick), Barbara Nichols (June), Charles Drake (Frank Taylor), Patricia Barry (Daphne Mitchell), Angela Lansbury (Phyllis), Ruth McDevitt (Miss Tait), Neva Patterson (Connie), Alice Pearce (Miss Moore), Richard Deacon (Mr. Cruikshank), Joanna Crawford (Emile Zola Bernkrand), Peter Turgeon (Peterson), Ken Lynch ("The Masher"), Mary Wickes (Miss Fox), James O'Rear (Marvin), Nelson Olmsted (Herb), Steven Bell.

Comedy-drama. Evie Jackson, a smalltown postmistress whose compulsive friendliness causes men to avoid her, arrives in New York City to attend a postmasters' convention and meets Harry Mork, a recently-promoted greeting card salesman staying at the same hotel. Harry, who is engaged to Phyllis, a widow from Altoona, Pennsylvania, looks forward to settling down after years on the road. Like other men, he is wary of Evie, but after an unhappy rendezvous with June, a magazine salesgirl, he accepts Evie's invitation to a party. He enjoys her company, and she begins to fall in love with him. Evie learns of Harry's forthcoming wedding when he takes her to see the apartment he has rented for himself and his wife, and she decides to return home. Phyllis arrives in New York and visits the apartment with Harry. They find Phyllis' teenaged son, Patrick, living there with his beatnik girl friend, Zola, and learn that the boy plans to stay. Phyllis announces that she prefers to live in hotels because she is tired of housekeeping, and it becomes apparent that she plans to marry Harry to unburden herself of responsibilities and chiefly of the problems involved in raising a son. Harry leaves her and rushes to Pennsylvania Station in time to prevent Evie's departure. *Postmistresses. Salesmen. Widows. Beatniks. Marriage. Courtship. Filial relations. Conventions. Hotels. New York City. New York City—Pennsylvania Station. Altoona.*

Note: Prerelease titles: *The Out-of-Towners* and *The Big Weekend*.

DEAR JOHN (Sweden)   F6.1083

Sandrews. *Dist* Sigma III Corp. 8 Mar **1966** [New York opening]. Sd; b&w. 35mm. 115 min.

Prod Göran Lindgren. *Exec Prod* Bo Jonsson. *Dir-Writ* Lars Magnus Lindgren. *Photog* Rune Ericson. *Art Dir* Jan Boleslaw. *Film Ed* Lennart Wallén. *Mus* Bengt-Arne Wallin. *Cost* Gunilla Pontén.

Cast: Jarl Kulle *(John)*, Christina Schollin *(Anita)*, Helena Nilsson *(Helena)*, Morgan Andersson *(Raymond)*, Synnöve Liljebäck *(Dagny)*, Erik Hell *(Lindgren)*, Emy Storm *(Mrs. Lindgren)*, Håkan Serner *(Erwin)*, Hans Wigren *(Elon)*, Erland Nordenfalk *(Kurt)*, Bo Wahlström *(Bosse)*, Stig Woxter *(taxi driver)*.

Romantic drama. Source: Olle Länsberg, *Käre John* (Stockholm, 1959). Anita, a young unmarried mother, works as a waitress in a small Swedish coastal community near Malmö, where she lives with her daughter Helena and her overprotective brother Raymond. One day a cargo vessel, the *Elsa,* anchors nearby for a weekend, and Anita recognizes John, its captain, as a man who insulted her while drunk two years before. He asks her for a date that evening, but she suggests the following night, when she can get a babysitter for her daughter. In the early morning, they meet while swimming, drink coffee together, and decide to take Helena for a day's outing in Copenhagen, where all three enjoy a pleasant afternoon at the zoo. That evening, after Helena has gone to sleep and Raymond has left for a party, John and Anita have supper in her cottage. Although mutually attracted, they are wary and apprehensive because both have been hurt before. Eventually, after a brief misunderstanding, they make love and spend an ecstatic night together. In the morning, John returns to his boat and departs, leading Anita to believe he was only philandering. John is serious, however, and he returns with a gift for her. Discovering that Anita has left the village for a holiday, John telephones her to propose marriage and she accepts. *Waitresses. Sea captains. Motherhood. Illegitimacy. Village life. Courtship. Brother-sister relationship. Copenhagen. Malmö.*

Note: Released in Sweden in Nov 1964 as *Käre John*; running time: 111 min.

DEAR MARTHA see THE HONEYMOON KILLERS

THE DEATH BLOW see TOUCH OF LEATHER

DEATH CURSE OF TARTU   F6.1084

Falcon International Productions. *Dist* Thunderbird International Pictures. 25 Jan **1967** [New Orleans opening; c16 Oct 1966; LP33765]. Sd; col (Eastman Color). 35mm. 87 min.

Prod Joseph Fink, Juan Hidalgo-Gato. *Dir-Screenplay* William Grefé. *Dir Photog* Julio C. Chavez. *2d Unit Camera* Thomas Casey. *Asst Camera* Osvaldo Sanchez. *Set Dsgn* Thomas Casey. *Titl* Chelo Garcia, Nohemy Someillan. *Film Ed* Julio C. Chavez. *Asst Ed* Oneida Rodriguez. *Songs* Al Greene, Al Jacobs. *Sd* Armando Fernandez. *Asst Dir* Earl Wainwright. *Prod Asst* Bob Hocke. *Script Clerk* Doris Bernhardt. *Makeup* Marie Del Russo. *Stills* Tony Gulliver. *Head Grip* Sandy Perales. *Prop* Georgina Gomez. *Animal Trainer* Frank Weed.

Cast: Fred Pinero *(Ed Tison)*, Babette Sherrill *(Julie Tison)*, Mayra Cristine *(Cindy)*, Sherman Hayes *(Johnny)*, Gary Holtz *(Tommy)*, Maurice Stewart *(Joann)*, Frank Weed *(Sam Gunter)*, Doug Hobart *(Tartu)*, William Marcos *(Billy/The Indian)*.

Horror film. While searching for Indian artifacts in the Florida Everglades, Ed Tison, his wife, Julie, and four archeology students chance upon the burial mound of Tartu, a Seminole witch doctor. Four hundred years ago, Tartu had placed a curse on his grave, vowing that if anyone ever disturbed it, he would return and kill the desecrators of his final resting place. The legend becomes a reality when Tartu comes to life and takes the lives of the four students by transforming himself into a shark, a snake, and an alligator. The Tisons decide that their only hope of survival is to pry open Tartu's coffin and destroy his remains. When they do so, however, Tartu appears as a young Indian warrior and immediately engages Ed in a death struggle. But Ed knocks him into a pit of quicksand, thus fulfilling the prophesy that Tartu could only be destroyed by the forces of nature. *Archeologists. Students. Witch doctors. Ghosts. Seminole Indians. Curses. Burial grounds. Quicksand. Everglades. Sharks. Snakes. Alligators.*

Note: Filmed on location in the Florida Everglades.

DEATH FROM OUTER SPACE see THE DAY THE SKY EXPLODED

DEATH IS A WOMAN see LOVE IS A WOMAN

DEATH OF A GUNFIGHTER   F6.1085

Universal Pictures. 8 May **1969** [Chicago opening; c14 Jun 1970; LP38888]. Sd; col (Technicolor). 35mm. 94 min. [Copyright length: 97 min.] *MPAA rating* M.

Prod Richard E. Lyons. *Dir* Allen Smithee. *Screenplay* Joseph Calvelli. *Dir Photog* Andrew Jackson. *Art Dir* Alexander Golitzen, Howard E. Johnson. *Set Decor* Sandy Grace, John McCarthy. *Main Titl* Universal Title. *Film Ed* Robert F. Shugrue. *Mus* Oliver Nelson. *Mus Supv* Stanley Wilson. *Song:* "Sweet Apple Wine" Oliver Nelson, Carol Hall. *Sung by* Lena Horne. *Sd* Waldon O. Watson, Melvin M. Metcalfe, Sr. *Asst Dir* Joe Boston. *Unit Prod Mgr* Kenneth L. Grossman. *Cost* Helen Colvig. *Makeup* Bud Westmore. *Hairstyles* Larry Germain.

Cast: Richard Widmark *(Marshal Frank Patch)*, Lena Horne *(Claire Quintana)*, John Saxon *(Lou Trinidad)*, Carroll O'Connor *(Lester Locke)*, David Opatoshu *(Edward Rosenbloom)*, Kent Smith *(Andrew Oxley)*, Jacqueline Scott *(Laurie Mills)*, Morgan Woodward *(Ivan Stanek)*, Larry Gates *(Mayor Chester Syre)*, Dub Taylor *(Doc Adams)*, Darleen Carr *(Hilda Jorgenson)*, Michael McGreevey *(Dan Joslin)*, Royal Dano *(Arch Brandt)*, James Lydon *(Luke Mills)*, Kathleen Freeman *(Mary Elizabeth)*, Harry Carey, Jr. *(Reverend Rork)*, Amy Thomson *(Angela)*, Mercer Harris *(Will Oxley)*, Jim O'Hara *(Father Sweeney)*, Walter Sande *(Paul Hammond)*, Victor French *(Phil Miller)*, Robert Sorrells *(Chris Hogg)*, Charles Kuenstle *(Roy Brandt)*, Sara Taft *(Mexican woman)*.

Western drama. Source: Lewis B. Patten, *Death of a Gunfighter* (New York, 1968). For 20 years, Marshal Frank Patch has maintained law and order in the Western town of Cottonwood Springs, but now, as the citizens begin to think of themselves as "progressives," he is looked upon as an anachronism. Only his longtime mistress, Claire Quintana, owner of the local bar and brothel, and young Dan Joslin still respect him. After Patch shoots drunken Luke Mills in self-defense, the town leaders decide to ask for his resignation. When newspaper publisher Andrew Oxley presses the issue, Patch not only refuses to give up his badge but humiliates Oxley in front of his son Will. As a result, Oxley commits suicide, and Will swears revenge. Meanwhile, county sheriff Lou Trinidad is brought in to persuade his old friend to resign before he is killed, but again Patch refuses to submit to the demands. Aware that his days are numbered, Patch convinces Claire to marry him. Following the wedding ceremony, young Will Oxley shoots Patch in the shoulder, and Patch returns the fire, fatally wounding Will. Using the outbreak of renewed gunfighting as an excuse, the saloon keeper and his gang ambush Patch. Bleeding badly, Patch attends the funeral services for Luke, but as he leaves the church, members of the mayor's council open fire and shoot him down in the street. *United States marshals. Mistresses. Madams. Newspapermen. Sheriffs. Gunfighters. Saloon keepers. Justifiable homicide. Drunkenness. Suicide. Revenge. Murder. Saloons. Whorehouses. Weddings. Funerals.*

Note: Allen Smithee is a pseudonym for directors Robert Totten and Don Siegel; Totten directed the film for 25 days and was replaced by Siegel. Working titles: *Patch* and *The Last Gunfighter*. Cutting continuity credits Dan Farron as director, but this may be another pseudonym for Totten and Siegel.

DEATH OF A NYMPHETTE   F6.1086

T. H. All Productions. *Dist* Chancellor Films. Jun **1967**. Sd; b&w. 35mm. 71 min.

Prod-Dir-Writ Malcolm Furri. *Camera* Ted Kalmuk. *Film Ed* Bruce Johnson.

Cast: Derf Renrug *(Robert)*, Cleo Nova *(Peggy)*, Rusti Carter *(Gloria)*, Yolanda *(Frenchy)*.

Melodrama. Recently divorced, Robert Allan meets Peggy at a party, and she soon becomes his mistress. The affair ends, however, when Robert discovers that Peggy is a nymphomaniac. Robert next has an affair with Gloria, but it also ends when he discovers that Gloria, unresponsive with men, is a lesbian. Robert finds happiness at last with Frenchy, but their idyl is shattered when two men break into the apartment, overcome Robert, and assault and murder Frenchy. Her death drives Robert insane. *Mistresses. Nymphomania. Lesbianism. Murder. Insanity.*

THE DEATH OF TARZAN (Czechoslovakia)   F6.1087

Barrandov Film Studio. *For* Československý Film. *Dist* Brandon Films. 3 Jul **1968** [New York opening]. Sd; b&w. 35mm. 72 min.

Dir Jaroslav Balík. *Screenplay* Josef Nesvadba, Jaroslav Balík. *Story* Josef Nesvadba. *Photog* Josef Hanuš. *Asst Camera* Ladislav Chroust, Michal Kulič. *Art Dir* Bohuslav Kulič. *Asst Art Dir* Marta Kaplerová, Věra Líznerová. *Film Ed* Jiřina Lukešová. *Asst Ed* Štěpánka Stříbrná. *Mus* Evžen Illín. *Lyr* Pavel Kopta. *Mus Perf by* Karl Krautgartner and His Orchestra, The Film Symphony Orchestra. *Sd* Miloslav Hůrka. *Asst Sd* Josef Weishaupt. *Asst Dir* Tomáš

Svoboda. *In Charge of Prod* Ladislav Kalaš. *Vice Prod Head* Josef Mathauser, Adolf Široký. *Asst to the Dir* Dagmar Nováková, Marie Kaplanová. *Prod Asst* Luděk Marold. *Cost* Theodor Pistek. *Production Unit* Novotný-Kubala.

Cast: Rudolf Hrušínský (*Wolfgang [Tarzan]*). Jana Stěpánková (*Regina*), Martin Růžek (*Baron Heinrich von Hoppe*), Vlastimil Hašek (*Dr. Foreyt*), Slávka Budínová (*ring director*), Ilya Racek (*usher*), Miroslav Homola (*SA man*), Nina Popelíková (*lady with buckteeth*), Elena Hálková (*The Baroness*), Karel Peyer (*boss*), Ela Poznerová (*lady*), Rudolf Pellar (*scientist*), Josef Beyvl (*manager*), Zdena Hadrbolcová (*German woman*), Josef Hlinomaz (*chimney sweeper*), Viktor Maurer (*vicar*), Jan Tříska (*clown*).

Satire. In 1904, 4-year-old Wolfgang von Hoppe is taken by his parents to live in Africa, where they hope to escape the evils of civilization. When the family is reported dead, cousin Baron Heinrich von Hoppe falls heir to their fortune. But his windfall is threatened some 30 years later when Wolfgang is found in the jungle by big game hunters and returned to his father's villa. Heinrich hires Regina, an English governess, to give the primitive Wolfgang enough training to pass a mental fitness test, but he secretly bribes her to ensure Wolfgang's failure. Regina, however, has her own scheme; she oversees Wolfgang's successful completion of the examination and then marries the wealthy ape-man. While German and British businessmen are squabbling over Wolfgang's oil-rich African property, Heinrich and Regina continue to plot and counterplot. Meanwhile, the simple Wolfgang preaches love and kindness, blindly admiring how idealistic and unselfish civilized humans are compared to the jungle's animals. Upon realizing how bestial humans really are, he violently lashes out at them and then flees—horrified by his own return to savagery. Captured by a circus troupe and exhibited in a cage as a half-man, half-ape called Tarzan, he is finally tracked down by the avaricious Regina and Heinrich. Sensing the futility and total misery of his existence, he shoots himself in front of an audience that includes his two greedy betrayers. *Cousins. Governesses. British. Ape-men. Germans. Businessmen. Idealists. Inheritance. Primitive life. Mental incompetency. Bribery. Greed. Suicide. Jungles. Circus. Africa.*

Note: Location scenes filmed in Prague, Dobříš, Karlovy Vary, and Mariánské Lázně. Released in Czechoslovakia in Jan 1963 as *Tarzanova smrt*. Also known as *Death of the Ape Man*.

DEATH OF THE APE MAN *see* **THE DEATH OF TARZAN**

DEATH ON THE MOUNTAIN (Japan)　　　　　　　　　**F6.1088**
Tokyo Eiga Co. *Dist* Toho Co. Nov **1961** [Los Angeles showing]. Sd; b&w. 35mm (Tohoscope). 87 min.
Exec Prod Ichiro Nagashima. *Dir* Toshio Sugie. *Screenplay* Teruo Ishii. *Story* Seicho Matsumoto. *Photog* Tokuzo Kuroda. *Mus* Yoshiyuki Kozu.

Cast: Hisaya Ito, Takashi Wada, Kiyoshi Kodama, Kyoko Kagawa, Yoshio Tsuchiya.

Drama. Eda, Urahashi, and Iwase, friends who work in the same bank, go mountain climbing during the holidays. Iwase, unable to sleep on the train, grows tired during the climb and frequently falls behind the others. Even at the mountain camp he cannot sleep, and the second day out finds him wearier than before. During the descent the men encounter a bank of thick fog and must decide between two routes: a shortcut known to Iwase, or a longer but safer route advocated by Eda. The men decide on Eda's choice, but they lose their way, and when Eda goes for help, Iwase, exhausted and delirious, wanders off a cliff. The next winter, Eda climbs the same mountain with Makita, Iwase's cousin, who suspects foul play in Iwase's death. Confronted with the evidence and Makita's threat to report it to the police, Eda admits he murdered Iwase, who was having an affair with his wife. Eda murders Makita to suppress the evidence, but an avalanche kills Eda. *Bank clerks. Cousins. Mountain climbing. Murder. Infidelity. Revenge. Fog. Avalanches.*

Note: Released in Japan in 1961 as *Aru sonan*.

DEATH RIDES A HORSE (Italy)　　　　　　　　　　**F6.1089**
P. E. C. *Dist* United Artists. 25 Jun **1969** [Denver, Colorado, opening]. Sd; col (Technicolor). 35mm (Techniscope). 114 min. *MPAA rating* M.
Prod Alfonso Sansone, Enrico Chroscicki. *Dir* Giulio Petroni. *Screenplay* Luciano Vincenzoni, Giulio Petroni. *Photog* Carlo Carlini. *Art Dir* Franco Bottari, Rosa Sansone. *Set Decor* Rosa Gristina. *Film Ed* Eraldo Da Roma. *Mus* Ennio Morricone. *Sd* Elio Pacella. *Asst Dir* Giancarlo Santi, Mario Molli. *Prod Mgr* Gianni Minervini. *Cost* Enzo Bulgarelli. *Makeup* Maurizio Giustini. *Sp Eff* Eros Bacciucchi.

Cast: John Phillip Law (*Bill*), Lee Van Cleef (*Ryan*), Luigi Pistilli (*Wolcott*), Anthony Dawson (*Manina*), José Torres (*Pedro*), Mario Brega (*One-Eye*), Carla Cassola (*Betsy*), Archie Savage (*Vigro*), Guglielmo Spoletini (*Manuel*), Giuseppe Castellano (*sheriff*), Felicita Fanny, Ignazio Leone, Elena Hall, Carlo Pisacane, Nino Vingelli, Romano Puppo, Giovanni Petrucci, Franco Balducci, Nazareno Natale.

Western melodrama. The sole survivor of his family's massacre by outlaws, 5-year-old Bill plans revenge. Fortified by memories of the rapes of his sister

and mother, the boy devotes the ensuing 15 years to marksmanship. Fixed in his mind are the murderer's distinguishing characteristics, including a gypsy earring, a tattoo representing four aces, a skull necklace, and an unusual spur. As the moment of reckoning approaches, Bill's antagonist, Ryan, is released from prison, having served a 15-year sentence for armed robbery. Framed by his former fellows, the embittered Ryan, assisted by Bill, systematically slays the assassins. During the final retributive murder, however, the youth espies the skull about the outlaw's neck. Bound by honor, the orphan insists on a duel. When Ryan participates with an empty pistol, Bill is unable to shoot his former adversary, however, and the two go their separate ways. *Orphans. Outlaws. Gunfighters. Convicts. Murder. Rape. Revenge. Frameup. Tattoos.*

Note: Anthony Dawson is a pseudonym for Antonio Margheriti. Opened in Rome in Sep 1967 as *Da uomo a uomo*.

DEATH TRAP (Great Britain)　　　　　　　　　　**F6.1090**
Anglo Guild Productions. *Dist* Schoenfeld Film Distributing Corp. 23 Nov **1966** [Copiague, New York, opening]. Sd; b&w. 35mm. 56 min.
Prod Jack Greenwood. *Dir* John Moxey. *Screenplay* John Roddick. *Photog* Bert Mason. *Art Dir* Peter Mullins. *Film Ed* Derek Holding. *Mus* Bernard Ebbinghouse. *Sd* Brian Blamey.

Cast: Albert Lieven (*Paul Heindrik*), Barbara Shelley (*Jean Anscomb*), John Meillon (*Ross Williams*), Mercy Haystead (*Carol Halston*), Kenneth Cope (*Derek Maitland*), Leslie Sands (*Detective-Inspector Simons*), Barry Linehan (*Detective-Sergeant Rigby*), Richard Bird (*Ted Cupps*), Murray Hayne (*Ramsey*), Barbara Windsor (*Babs Newton*), Gladys Henson (*housekeeper*).

Mystery drama. Based on a story by: Edgar Wallace. Fashion model Carol Halston visits financier Paul Heindrik to inquire about a withdrawal of £7,000 made by her sister before her suicide. Although Heindrik denies receiving the money, his secretary discovers an incriminating bank slip and attempts to blackmail the financier through her ex-convict boyfriend, Ross. When Ross is fatally injured by a hit-and-run driver, a Scotland Yard investigation focuses on Heindrik, who is revealed to be the murderer of Carol's sister. *Models. Financiers. Ex-convicts. Secretaries. Investigators. Hit-and-run drivers. Murder. Blackmail. Suicide. Scotland Yard. Automobile accidents.*

Note: Released in Great Britain in 1962.

DEATH TRAP *see* **TAKE HER BY SURPRISE**

DEATHSHEAD VAMPIRE *see* **THE VAMPIRE BEAST CRAVES BLOOD**

DEATHWATCH　　　　　　　　　　　　　　　　　**F6.1091**
Deathwatch Co. *Dist* Beverly Pictures, Altura Films International. 20 Jan **1966** [San Francisco opening]. Sd; b&w. 35mm. 88 min.
Prod Leonard Nimoy, Vic Morrow. *Dir* Vic Morrow. *Screenplay* Barbara Turner, Vic Morrow. *Photog* Vilis Lapenieks. *Art Dir* James G. Frieburger. *Supv Ed* Irving Lerner. *Ed* Verna Fields. *Mus* Gerald Fried.

Cast: Leonard Nimoy (*Jules LeFranc*), Michael Forest (*Greeneyes*), Paul Mazursky (*Maurice*), Robert Ellenstein (*guard*), Gavin MacLeod (*Emil*).

Drama. Source: Jean Genêt, *Haute surveillance* (Paris opening: 26 Jan 1949; trans. by Bernard Frechtman as *Deathwatch*; New York opening: 9 Oct 1958). Sharing a dank cell in a French prison are Jules LeFranc, a social outcast serving time for a minor theft, and Greeneyes, a convicted murderer awaiting the guillotine. Embarrassed by the pettiness of his offense against a society he detests, Jules openly worships the infamous Greeneyes and longs to be his friend. Greeneyes, an illiterate, passively accepts Jules' adoration and allows him to read and write his letters. In this way, permitted to share the innermost thoughts of his idol, Jules is able to become vicariously the great killer he has always desired to be. Then Maurice, an overt homosexual, is brought into the cell. Unabashed in his courtship of Greeneyes, he caters to his every whim and sexual need. Now the relationships in the cell explode into a violent struggle for love and identity as Jules and Maurice compete for the attention of Greeneyes. Desperate to prove himself worthy of respect, Jules commits murder by strangling Maurice. But his deed earns him nothing but contempt; Greeneyes' crime was one of passion, whereas Jules' was an act of the will. Branded as an outsider in the world of the criminal, Jules is left totally alone. *Convicts. Thieves. Male homosexuality. Murder. Illiteracy. Prisons. France.*

THE DEBAUCHERS　　　　　　　　　　　　　　　**F6.1092**
Dist Sam Lake Enterprises, Mature Pictures. ca **1970**. Sd; col. 35mm. 76 min.
Prod Jean Jacques Robeau. *Dir* Sidney Knight. *Writ* William Ray. *Camera* Robert Morgenstern. *Film Ed* Sidney Knight. *Sd* Ronald Nort. *Asst Sd* Luigi D'Arc.

Cast: Angela Snenck (*May*), Claude Rube (*Tom*), Dana Barton (*Joan*), Terry DeLane (*Frank*), Robert M. Stol (*Jack*), Daniel Harin (*Dr. Clayton*).

Melodrama. May takes a modeling job at a private estate in order to help her boyfriend Jack buy an automobile. She is greeted at the estate by Joan, the maid, and Dr. Clayton, who warns her that Tom, her millionaire employer, is a bit peculiar. For her first assignment, Tom has May undress and pose lewdly. May is upset and wants to leave, but she is persuaded to stay by Jack, to whom Tom has offered a large sum of money in return for May's cooperation in the making of a film. The next day, Tom offers Jack a big bonus if he will make love to May while Tom films the proceedings. Frank, the butler, and Joan join in. Tom then orders the four to switch partners, and May is forced to submit to Frank. The next day, May tries to leave the house but discovers Frank guarding the locked doors. In a final attempt to escape, May seduces the sympathetic Dr. Clayton who tells her that he, too, is a prisoner. He is able to warn her that for the final scene of the film, Tom has arranged for Jack to murder her. May heeds the warning and straps a kitchen knife to her thigh. The following day, Jack tries to drown her in the swimming pool, but she stabs and kills him. Finally satisfied, Tom tells May she is free to go; he did not care who was killed as long as he was able to film the slaying. With this final defeat, May breaks down. *Models. Housemaids. Physicians. Millionaires. Eccentrics. Psychopaths. Butlers. Murder. Group sex. Rape. Seduction. Sex exploitation films. Swimming pools.*

DEČAK JE VIKAO UBISTVO *see* **THE BOY CRIED MURDER**

DECAMERON '69 (France)   F6.1093
Dist Silver Screen Film Distributors. 20 Aug **1969** [Boston opening]. Sd; b&w with col seq. 35mm. ca74 min.
Prod Bernard Morath. *Dir* Bernard Clarens, Jean Desaillers, Serge Korber, Jean Herman, Louis Grospierre.
Cast: Dick Brown, Pamela Walbert.
Drama. No information about the precise nature of this film has been found, but press material suggests that its subjects include prostitution, lesbianism, and promiscuity. *Prostitution. Lesbianism. Promiscuity.*
Note: A series of vignettes presumably produced in France; additional sex footage added for U. S. release.

THE DECEIVERS *see* **INTIMACY**

LA DECIMA VITTIMA *see* **THE 10TH VICTIM**

DECLINE AND FALL ... OF A BIRD WATCHER (Great Britain)
                                                                 F6.1094
Ivan Foxwell Enterprises. *Dist* Twentieth Century–Fox Film Corp. 26 Jan **1969** [New York opening; c30 Dec 1968; LP36652]. Sd (Westrex); col (DeLuxe). 35mm. 113 min. [Copyright length: 90 min.]
Prod Ivan Foxwell. *Assoc Prod* Sydney Streeter. *Dir* John Krish. *Adapt for the Screen by* Ivan Foxwell. *Adtl Scenes by* Alan Hackney, Hugh Whitemore. *Dir Photog* Desmond Dickinson. *Camera Op* Tony White. *2d Unit Camera* Wally Fairweather. *Art Dir* Jonathan Barry. *Titl* Morton M. Lewis. *Film Ed* Archie Ludski. *Mus Comp & Cond* Ron Goodwin. *Sd Rec* John Bramall, Maurice Askew. *Sd Ed* Peter Keen. *Asst Dir* Douglas Hermes, Peter Bolton. *Prod Mgr* Edward Dorian. *Cont* Doris Martin. *Cost Dsgn* Anna Duse. *Miss Page's Cost Dsgn* Julie Harris, cost. *Wardrobe Master* Ernie Farrer. *Makeup* Ernest Gasser. *Hairstyles* Alice Holmes.
Cast: Robin Phillips *(Paul Pennyfeather)*, Michael Elwyn *(Alastair-Vane-Trumpington)*, Norman Scace *(dean)*, John Glynne Jones *(warden)*, Donald Sayne-Smith *(bursar)*, John Cater *(Blackall)*, Kenneth Griffith *(Mr. Church)*, Donald Wolfit *(Dr. Fagan)*, Colin Blakely *(Philbrick)*, Jonathan Collins *(Clutterbuck)*, Robert Harris *(Prendergast)*, Leo McKern *(Captain Grimes)*, Michael Newport *(Lord Tangent)*, Patience Collier *(Flossie Fagan)*, David McAlister *(Peter Beste-Chetwynde)*, Katy Wild *(giggling girl)*, Geneviève Page *(Margot Beste-Chetwynde)*, Michael Nightingale *(Colonel Clutterbuck)*, Helen Christie *(Mrs. Clutterbuck)*, Joan Sterndale-Bennett *(Lady Circumference)*, Clifton Jones *(Chokey)*, Ann Lancaster *(Mrs. Grimes)*, Michael Hawkins *(Stubbs)*, Roland Curram *(Otto Silenus)*, Griffith Jones *(Sir Humphrey Maltravers)*, Jeremy Child *(Nigel)*, Anne De Vigier *(Nigel's girlfriend)*, Joan Haythorne *(Miss Hart)*, Rodney Bewes *(Arthur Potts)*, Sarah Atkinson *(Jane)*, Jill Kerman *(Sophie)*, George Pravda *(harbour policeman)*, Marne Maitland *(junior policeman)*, Duncan Lamont *(Inspector Bruce)*, Ivor Dean *(Old Bailey policeman)*, Felix Aylmer *(judge)*, Victor Maddern, John Trenaman, Kenneth J. Warren, Tom Clegg *(warders)*, Christopher Banks *(clerk of the court)*, Jack Watson *(gallery warder)*, Donald Sinden *(The Prison Governor)*, Paul Rogers *(chief warder)*, Roy Evans *(Boney)*, Patrick Magee *(maniac)*, Ken Wynne *(drunken surgeon)*, Paul Curran *(clergyman)*.
Comedy. Source: Evelyn Waugh, *Decline and Fall* (London, 1928). Bird watching is the favorite pastime of Paul Pennyfeather, a sensitive, serious young divinity student at Oxford. After being set upon by some drunken undergraduates who remove his trousers, he stumbles over a girl and is expelled for indecent conduct. Through a disreputable employment agency, he gets a teaching job at a seedy Welsh boarding school for boys presided over by the flamboyant Dr. Fagan. Also on the staff are Mr. Prendergast, an old-maidish

former clergyman; Captain Grimes, a one-legged bigamist who has opportunistic designs on Fagan's unattractive daughter Flossie; and Solomon Philbrick, a criminal who serves as Fagan's butler. On Sports Day, everything goes wrong as rain pours down, Prendergast accidentally shoots a student in the foot with the starter's gun, and the nefarious Philbrick sees to it that the silver trophies are stolen. For Paul, however, the day is saved when he meets a wealthy patron named Margot Beste-Chetwynde, who asks him to tutor her son at her lavish estate. After being easily seduced, Paul proposes marriage to Margot and is accepted. Before the ceremony, Margot gets Paul to go to Tangier on a seemingly innocent business trip. As a result, Paul finds himself convicted of trafficking in prostitution and sent to prison. There he encounters two old acquaintances, Philbrick and Captain Grimes. Margot, after marrying the Home Secretary, arranges for Paul's release by a complicated maneuver in which it is stated that Paul died in Dr. Fagan's new nursing home. And a corpse for Paul is provided when Prendergast conveniently comes to an untimely end. Now officially dead, Paul is able to assume a new identity and set out on a new life. *Bird watchers. Ministerial students. Schoolteachers. Thieves. Butlers. Students. Amputees. Patrons. Bigamy. Wealth. Seduction. Prostitution. Personal identity. Employment agencies. Boarding schools. Prisons. Oxford University.*
Note: Released in Great Britain in 1968.

DECOY *see* **MYSTERY SUBMARINE**

EL DEDO DEL DESTINO *see* **THE FICKLE FINGER OF FATE**

EL DEDO EN EL GATILLO *see* **FINGER ON THE TRIGGER**

DEEP DESIRE OF GODS *see* **KURAGEJIMA—LEGENDS FROM A SOUTHERN ISLAND**

DEEP IN LOVE *see* **SKIN DEEP IN LOVE**

DEEP INSIDE   F6.1095
Cannon Productions. *Dist* Cannon Releasing Corp. 14 Feb **1968** [periodical notice]. Sd; b&w. 35mm. 77-87 min. [See note.]
Prod Donald Havens, Jr. *Dir-Writ* Joe Sarno. *Dir Photog* Bruce Sparks. *Asst Camera* Robert Bailin. *Ed* Kemper Peacock. *Orig Score* Pir Marini. *Sd Engr* David Jones, James Hubbard. *Asst to the Dir* Gillian Mills. *Ch Electrn* Myron Odegaard.
Cast: Lara Danielli *(Pamela Lewis)*, Esme Kane *(Millicent Redmond)*, Nick Dundas *(Bill Lewis)*, Ron Vial *(Don Vincent)*, Sheila Britt *(Jean)*, Monique Drevon *(Joy Ponds)*, Bella Donna *(Mavis Kitchell)*, Michelle Fox *(Norma)*, Aaron Green *(Pete)*, Mary Park *(Linda)*, Justin Moreau *(Harry)*, Tia Waters *(Neva)*, Tony Garette *(Martin Ponds)*, Pete Hall *(Jay)*, Jeremy Langham *(Roger)*, Gordon Knotts.
Melodrama. Millicent Redmond, a powerful, frigid woman, is the informal leader of a group of women who live near a beach during one summer. Millicent delights in manipulating her friends by exploiting their weaknesses. She maneuvers Linda, a nymphomaniac, into making desperate attempts to find satisfaction; toys with Neva and Jean, her lesbian roommates from college days; caters to Mavis, an older woman who craves young lovers; and helps to draw Pam Lewis into an affair with a psychotic artist. Millicent maintains control until her games lead to murder. Finally, her friends see Millicent's evil motives and turn on her. ... *Evildoers. Roommates. Artists. Psychopaths. Lesbianism. Nymphomania. Murder. Revenge. Vacations.*
Note: This film was released in three versions; its full running time was 87 min, and edited versions were available at 77 and 80 min.

THE DEFECTOR (France/West Germany)   F6.1096
P. E. C. F.–Rhein-Main Film. *Dist* Seven Arts Pictures. 16 Nov **1966** [New York opening]. Sd; col (Eastman Color). 35mm. 106 min.
Prod-Dir Raoul Lévy. *Exec Prod* Julien Derode. *Screenplay* (see note) Robert Guenette, Raoul Lévy, Lewis Gannet, Peter Francke. *Adapt* Jean Clouzot, Raoul Lévy. *Photog* Raoul Coutard. *Art Dir* Pierre Guffroy, Jürgen Kiebach, Ernst Schomer. *Film Ed* Albert Jürgenson, Roger Dwyre. *Mus* Serge Gainsbourg. *Sd* Joseph de Bretagne. *Asst Dir* Thomas Grimm. *Prod Mgr* Hans Sommer, Jean-Paul Delamotte. *Prod Dir* Hans Seitz. *German Prod Dir* Heinrich Moll. *Prod Sec* Madeleine von Crobath. *Cost* Ingeborg Wilfert. *Makeup* Raimund Stangl.
Cast: Montgomery Clift *(Prof. James Bower)*, Hardy Krüger *(Peter Heinzman)*, Macha Méril *(Frieda Hoffman)*, Roddy McDowall *(CIA agent Adam)*, David Opatoshu *(Orlovsky)*, Christine Delaroche *(Ingrid)*, Hannes Messemer *(Dr. Saltzer)*, Karl Lieffen *(The Major)*, Jean-Luc Godard *(Orlovsky's friend)*, Uta Levka.
Melodrama. Source: Paul Thomas, *L'espion* (Paris, 1965). While visiting in Leipzig, American physicist James Bower is recruited by CIA agent Adam and instructed to assist in the defection of Russian scientist Goshenko. Learning of the plan, Peter Heinzman, an East German scientist and communist agent,

confronts Bower, sequesters him in a hotel room, and interrogates him. Although Bower refuses to cooperate, he learns from the communist that Goshenko is already dead. Prior to his death, however, the Russian had disposed of an important microfilm. Eluding Heinzman, Bower obtains the film from Dr. Saltzer, a contact who dies shortly thereafter. Frustrated, Heinzman invites the American to defect to the East, but Bower refuses. Heinzman is then ordered to cross the border and, gaining Bower's confidence, convert him to the communist cause. During the bogus escape the German is struck and killed by a truck driven by agents of the CIA. *Physicists. Secret agents. Russians. Americans in foreign countries. Defectors. Communists. Scientists. Espionage. Murder. Leipzig. United States—Central Intelligence Agency. Automobile accidents.*

Note: Location scenes filmed in Munich. Opened in Paris in Nov 1966 as *L'espion*; in West Germany in Nov 1966 as *Lautlose Waffen*. Sources conflict on screenplay credit.

DÉFI À GIBRALTAR see **TORPEDO BAY**

DEFIANT DAUGHTERS see **THE SHADOWS GROW LONGER**

THE DEFILERS   F6.1097
Dist Sonney Amusement Enterprises. 1 Oct **1965** [Champaign, Illinois, showing]. Sd; b&w. 35mm. [Feature length assumed.]
    Prod-Writ David F. Friedman. *Dir* R. Lee Frost. *Photog* R. Lee Frost.
    Cast: Mai Jansson (*Jane Collins*).
    Melodrama. Carl and Jamie pick up four girls at a beach party. Carl is rejected by one, then beats another into submission. Later, Carl off-handedly proposes that he and Jamie kidnap a girl and keep her as a slave. After spying on virgin Jane Collins, they lure her to a basement where Carl repeatedly rapes her. Days later, Jamie wants to take part, but he is repelled by Carl's sadism. In a vicious fight, Carl is accidentally killed, and Jamie rushes off to aid Jane. *Virginity. Sadism. Rape. Abduction.*

THE DEGENERATES   F6.1098
Dist J. E. R. Pictures. 5 Apr **1967** [Champaign, Illinois, showing]. Sd; b&w. 35mm. 73 min.
    Prod-Dir Andy Milligan.
    Cast: Bryarly Lee (*Violet*), Marcia Howard (*Iris*), Anne Linden (*Daisy*), Susan Howard (*Rose*), Laura Weiss (*Lily*), Hope Stansbury (*Ivy*), Robert Burgos (*Jim*), Vernon Newman (*GoGo*), David Haine (*Frank*).
    Melodrama. In the year 2000, after a nuclear war has destroyed most of human life, Jim, Frank, and GoGo search for other survivors. Their car crashes, and Jim injures his leg. The three find a farmhouse inhabited by five sisters. Violet, who burned alive her father for making unnatural advances, is their leader. Three of the sisters, Iris, Daisy, and Lily, succumb to the males' sexual advances while Rose remains untouched. Violet knifes GoGo and pins Frank to the barn wall with a pitchfork. After killing Frank, she accidentally stabs Rose, and Ivy, suffering from a childhood trauma, sets her on fire. Jim and Iris leave the farm to start a new life together, and Lily stays behind to take care of Ivy. *Sisters. Patricide. Incest. Seduction. Murder. Incendiarism. Insanity. Nuclear warfare. The Future.*

A DEGREE OF MURDER (West Germany)   F6.1099
Rob Houwer Film. *Dist* Universal Pictures. Jun **1969**. Sd; col (Technicolor). 35mm. 87 min. *MPAA rating* R.
    Prod Rob Houwer. *Dir* Volker Schlöndorff. *Screenplay* Volker Schlöndorff, Gregor von Rezzori, Niklas Franz, Arne Boyer. *Photog* Franz Rath. *Art Dir* Wolfgang Hundhammer. *Film Ed* Claus von Boro. *Mus Comp* Brian Jones. *Sd* Klaus Ekelt. *Asst Dir* Herbert Rimbach, Klaus Müller-Laue. *Prod Mgr* Jürgen Dohme.
    Cast: Anita Pallenberg (*Marie*), Hans P. Hallwachs (*Günther*), Manfred Fischbeck (*Fritz*), Werner Enke (*Hans*), Angela Hillebrecht, Sonja Karzau, Kurt Bula, Willi Harlander.
    Crime melodrama. Marie, a cafe waitress, accidentally kills Hans, her former lover, during a quarrel. The following day she approaches a stranger named Günther and offers him money to help her dispose of the body. They go to her apartment and make love while waiting for nightfall so that they can remove the corpse without being seen. Günther and a friend, Fritz, carry the body to the car, and the three drive to the countryside where they bury Hans near a road construction site. Returning to Munich, Fritz and Marie drive recklessly and collide with another car. To appease the family in the other car, they give them part of the cash that Marie paid the two men. Fritz and Günther begin to fight over Marie's attentions, and in the confusion, the rest of the money blows away. The next day at the cafe, Marie considers joining a customer for a holiday in Greece, while at the construction site a steam shovel unearths the body of Hans. *Waitresses. Manslaughter. Jealousy. Road construction. Munich. Automobile accidents.*

Note: Released in West Germany in Apr 1967 as *Mord und Totschlag*; running time: 87 min.

DELIGHTFUL DILEMMA   F6.1100
Janus II Productions–Academy Productions. *Dist* Able Film Co. Sep **1970** [periodical notice]. Sd; col. 16mm. [Feature length assumed.]
    Prod-Dir Richard Z. Evans. *Asst Dir* Charlie Talley.
    Sex film. While at a party a woman daydreams instead of dances. She imagines nude sexual encounters among the other guests. *Nudity. Sexuality. Dreams.*

DELILAH   F6.1101
Dist Distribpix, Inc. 26 Dec **1969** [Champaign, Illinois, showing]. Sd; col. 35mm. 64 min.
    Drama. Marylyn and Rod, a young married couple, have trouble in bed: Marylyn is nervous and worried about her sexuality, while Rod, sensitive and kind, is bewildered and hurt because his wife cannot reach fulfillment with him. Instead of talking about their problem the two drift apart. Rod turns to fellow engineer David for advice, and David suggests wife-swapping, explaining to the startled Rod that this has been of great help to him and his wife Delilah. On the same day, Delilah visits Marylyn and, hearing of Marylyn's difficulties, seduces her on the pretext of helping her to lose her inhibitions. That weekend, Marylyn and Rod visit David and Delilah at their country house. Fears about her own inadequacy, however, prevent Marylyn from giving in to David's advances, and she retires for the night with Rod, and again makes love and fails to achieve satisfaction. Marylyn later hears David and Delilah making love and secretly leaves her bedroom to watch them. The following weekend, Rod and Marylyn return to the country, and Marylyn finally allows herself to be seduced by David, thereby finding sexual satisfaction at last. The next weekend, Rod and Marylyn again go to David's house and find themselves at an orgy. They are sickened by the spectacle and leave, having decided that they prefer their own private lovemaking. *Engineers. Marriage. Frigidity. Lesbianism. Seduction. Orgies. Mate swapping. Voyeurism.*

IL DELITTO DUPRÉ see **DON'T TEMPT THE DEVIL**

IL DELITTO NON PAGA see **CRIME DOES NOT PAY**

THE DELTA FACTOR   F6.1102
Spillane-Fellows Productions. *Dist* Continental Distributing, Inc. 15 May **1970** [Nashville, Tennessee, opening]. Sd; col (print by Movielab). 35mm. 91 min. *MPAA rating* R.
    Pres by Walter Reade Organization. A Mickey Spillane Production. *Prod-Dir-Writ* Tay Garnett. *Photog* Ted Saizis, Vincent Saizis. *Art Dir* Jack Collis, Benjamin Resella. *Film Ed* Richard Farrell. *Mus* Howard Danziger, Raoul Kraushaar. *Sd* Clem Portman. *Asst Dir* Dink Templeton. *Prod Mgr* Frank Baur, Dink Templeton. *Wardrobe* Soni Karp. *Vis Cons* Dan Fitzgerald. *Stunt Driving* Roger Creed, Jim Climer.
    Cast: Yvette Mimieux (*Kim Stacy*), Christopher George (*Morgan*), Diane McBain (*Lisa Gordot*), Ralph Taeger (*Art Keefer*), Yvonne De Carlo (*Valerie*), Sherri Spillane (*Rosa*), Ted De Corsia (*Ames*), Rhodes Reason (*Dr. Fredericks*), Joseph Sirola (*Sal Dekker*), Richard Ianni, George Ash, Fred Marsell.
    Adventure melodrama. Source: Mickey Spillane, *The Delta Factor* (New York, 1969). After escaping from a maximum-security prison where he was being held for stealing $40 million, Morgan, an international privateer, is recaptured and offered a choice: either return to prison (though he swears he is innocent) or participate in the rescue of a scientist held captive by a Caribbean island dictator. Choosing the latter, Morgan is forced to marry Kim Stacy, a beautiful CIA agent. Posing as a drug dealer, Morgan gains entry to the fortress where the scientist and hundreds of other political prisoners are being held. There he familiarizes himself with the various security measures and formulates a rescue plan; then, after arranging to have a CIA plane meet Kim, the scientist, and himself on a designated airstrip, he returns to the fortress, releases all the prisoners, and escapes with the scientist. Morgan also manages to hold off with gunfire both the pursuing dictator and a carload of soldiers but is thwarted when he reaches the plane and finds Kim held at gunpoint by Sal Dekker, an old war buddy who actually stole the $40 million and framed Morgan. After baiting Dekker into confessing his guilt, Morgan kills him and frees Kim. Then, once the plane is airborne for the States with the scientist safely aboard, Morgan exchanges a loving glance with Kim and, with her assistance, bails out to search for the $40 million and clear his name. *Prison escapees. Scientists. Political prisoners. Dictators. Soldiers. Theft. Frameup. Airplanes. Forts. Caribbean. United States—Central Intelligence Agency.*

DÉMANTY NOCI see **DIAMONDS OF THE NIGHT**

DEMENTIA 13 (United States/Ireland)   **F6.1103**
Filmgroup, Inc.–Garrick, Ltd. *Dist* American International Pictures. 25 Sep 1963 [Los Angeles opening]. Sd; b&w. 35mm. 81 min.

Prod (see note) Charles Hannawalt, R. Wright Campbell. *Exec Prod* Roger Corman. *Assoc Prod* Marianne Wood. *Dir-Writ* Francis Coppola. *Orig Screenplay* Charles Hannawalt. *Photog* (see note) Charles Hannawalt, William Cathcart. *Camera* John Vicario. *Art Dir* Albert Locatelli. *Film Ed* Stewart O'Brien. *Mus* Ronald Stein. *Asst Dir* Richard Dalton. *Tech Adv* William Joseph Bryan, Jr.

Cast: William Campbell (*Richard Haloran*), Luana Anders (*Louise Haloran*), Bart Patton (*Billy Haloran*), Mary Mitchell (*Kane*), Patrick Magee (*Justin Caleb*), Eithne Dunne (*Lady Haloran*), Peter Read (*John Haloran*), Karl Schanzer (*Simon*), Ron Perry (*Arthur*), Derry O'Donovan (*Lilian*), Barbara Dowling (*Kathleen*).

Horror film. In Ireland near their family castle John Haloran and his wife, Louise, argue over the will of John's half-crazy mother, Lady Haloran, and in the heat of the discussion, John dies of a heart attack. Louise, whose primary concern is to gain control of the family wealth, conceals his death, fearing that she will be cut off from the inheritance. The Halorans, including Billy, Richard, and Richard's fiancée, Kane, gather for a memorial ceremony at the gravesite of Kathleen, their sister who was drowned in a nearby lake 8 years earlier. Meanwhile, the scheming Louise plots to drive Lady Haloran insane by making her believe that she can communicate with the dead child; before she can carry out her plan, however, Louise is brutally axed to death. Justin Caleb, the sinister family doctor, becomes suspicious of everyone, and after Lady Haloran is found murdered, he orders the lake drained. A wax statue of Kathleen is found; Billy appears, brandishing an axe; but he is overcome and killed. It is revealed that Billy, a homicidal maniac, also was responsible for his sister's death. *Physicians. Psychopaths. Family life. Murder. Inheritance. Insanity. Heart disease. Castles. Axes.*

Note: Location scenes filmed in Ireland. Irish release undetermined; released in Great Britain in 1964 as *The Haunted and the Hunted.* Production information credits Hannawalt and Campbell as producers and Corman as executive producer; release information credits only Corman as producer. Cathcart is credited as photographer only in production material. Working title: *Dementia.*

LES DEMOISELLES DE ROCHEFORT see **THE YOUNG GIRLS OF ROCHEFORT**

THE DEMON see **ONIBABA**

LE DÉMON DE 11 HEURES see **PIERROT LE FOU**

THE DEMON FROM DEVIL'S LAKE   **F6.1104**
Phillips-Marker Productions. **1964**. Sd; b&w. 35mm. [Feature length assumed.]
Dir-Writ Russ Marker.
Cast: Dave Heath.
Science fiction drama. "Operation Noah's Ark" involves a space capsule filled with a variety of mammals, birds, and reptiles. The spacecraft crashes in a lake, exposing the occupants to different rays. They merge to form one single monster. *Monsters. Transmutation. Space capsules. Radiation. Animals. Birds. Reptiles.*
Note: Location scenes filmed on Lake Texoma and in Sherman, Texas.

DEN NASHEY ZHIZNI see **A DAY WITH THE RUSSIANS**

DENKI KURAGE see **PLAY IT COOL**

LA DÉNONCIATION see **THE IMMORAL MOMENT**

DENSO NINGEN see **SECRET OF THE TELEGIAN**

DENTIST IN THE CHAIR (Great Britain)   **F6.1105**
Briand Film Productions. *Dist* Ajay Film Co., Manhattan Films International. Apr **1961** [Los Angeles opening]. Sd; b&w. 35mm. 84 min.
Prod Bertram Ostrer. *Dir* Don Chaffey. *Screenplay* Val Guest. *Adtl Dial* Bob Monkhouse, George Wadmore. *Photog* Reginald Wyer. *Art Dir* Bill Andrews. *Film Ed* Bill Lenny. *Mus Comp & Cond* Ken Jones. *Prod Mgr* Albert Becket.
Cast: Bob Monkhouse (*David Cookson*), Peggy Cummins (*Peggy Travers*), Kenneth Connor (*Sam Field*), Eric Barker (*The Dean*), Vincent Ball (*Michaels*), Ronnie Stevens (*Brian Dexter*), Eleanor Summerfield (*Ethel Field*), Reginald Beckwith (*Watling*), Stuart Saunders (*Inspector Richardson*), Ian Wallace (*dentist*), Peggy Simpson (*Miss Brent*), Jean St. Clair (*Lucy*), Charlotte Mitchell (*woman in surgery*), Philip Gilbert (*man in surgery*), Jeremy Hawk (*instructor*), Harry Hutchinson (*porter*), Alfred Dean (*wrestler*), Sheree Winton (*Jayne*), Rosie Lee (*Maggie*), Michael Fry (*Jones*), Michael Hawkins (*Brown*), David Glover (*Newman*).

Comedy. Source: Matthew Finch, *Dentist in the Chair* (London, 1955). Dental student David Cookson and his roommate, Brian Dexter, unwittingly purchase some dental equipment stolen by Sam Field, a petty thief. After selling the equipment to their fellow students as "bankrupt stock," they discover themselves to be accomplices to the crime and try to buy the loot back. Peggy, David's girl friend, who is the niece of the hospital dean, serves as an unwilling aid in the mixup. They run into further difficulties when Sam masquerades first as a student and then as a patient. The roommates embark on a series of escapades to recover the equipment, but with their dental exams at hand and Scotland Yard closing in, Sam finally admits to the theft. *Medical students. Roommates. Uncles. Deans. Theft. Imposture. Hospitals. Confession (law). Scotland Yard.*
Note: Released in Great Britain in 1960; running time: 88 min.

DENTIST ON THE JOB see **GET ON WITH IT**

LES DENTS DU DIABLE see **THE SAVAGE INNOCENTS**

DEO GRATIAS see **THANK HEAVEN FOR SMALL FAVORS**

LE DÉPART (Belgium)   **F6.1106**
Elisabeth Films. *Dist* Pathé Contemporary Films. 21 Apr **1968** [New York opening]. Sd; b&w. 35mm. 89 min.
Prod Bronka Ricquier. *Dir* Jerzy Skolimowski. *Screenplay* Jerzy Skolimowski, Andrzej Kostenko. *Photog* Willy Kurant. *Film Ed* Bob Wade. *Mus* Krzysztof Komeda. *Song Sung by* Christiane Legrand. *Sd* Philip Cape. *Asst Dir* Jean-Emile Caudron. *Prod Mgr* Maurice Urbain.
Cast: Jean-Pierre Léaud (*Marc*), Catherine Duport (*Michèle*), Léon Dony (*boss* [see note]), Paul Roland (*friend*), Jacqueline Bir (*older woman*), John Dobrynine (*The Maharajah*), Georges Aubrey (*dealer in used articles*), Maxane (*superintendent*), Lucien Charbonnier, Bernard Graczyk, Marthe Dugard, Jacques Cortois.
Comedy. Marc, a 19-year-old hairdresser's assistant in Brussels, has one passion—automobiles. He has already signed up to drive a Porsche, though he does not own one, in a race scheduled to take place in 2 days. At the last minute, however, Marc's employer, whose Porsche he has intended to use, decides to use his car himself over the weekend. Marc then persuades his best friend, a fellow hairdresser, to disguise himself as a maharajah, and Marc, posing as the maharajah's secretary, takes a Porsche out of its showroom for a "trial run." Using the car, he delivers several wigs for his employer, then meets a young woman, Michèle. Once back at the shop, Marc talks with a seductive older woman, a Porsche owner, who tells him that a car may be rented or borrowed; and she gives Marc her telephone number for use if he should need her help. Instead, he calls a car rental agency and is quoted a deposit price of 15,000 francs. Marc, now frantic, takes Michèle to an auto show in the hope of stealing spare parts that can be sold. When this tactic fails, both Michèle and Marc's friend reluctantly offer to help raise the needed money. Despite a plait of hair worth 10,000 francs and some marketable items Michèle has gathered together, Marc is unable to raise the deposit money. Desperate, he remembers the seductive woman and decides to accept her offer of help, but when he discovers that Michèle has cut her long tresses in the hope of selling them to a wigmaker, he is so touched that he forgets all about the older woman. The rental agency then informs Marc that he is too young in any case to rent a car, and in consequence he makes several futile attempts to steal one. His boss, meanwhile, returns unexpectedly. With Michèle as his navigator, Marc "borrows" the Porsche and sets out for the big race. On their way, the couple stop at a hotel to sleep. Marc sleeps on the floor and dreams of the race and Michèle. When Michèle wakes up, she sees Marc sadly standing at the window; he has overslept, and the race has begun. Now acknowledging a passion no longer obfuscated by automobiles, Marc turns from the window toward the bed. *Hairdressers. Automobile racing. Robbery. Imposture. Automobile rental agencies. Brussels. Porsche automobiles.*
Note: Filmed in Brussels in 1966. Some sources credit the actor playing the role of the boss as Léon Dory. Bracketed roles are unconfirmed.

DEPARTMENT K see **ASSIGNMENT K**

DEPRAVED!   **F6.1107**
Dist J. E. R. Pictures. 27 Sep **1967** [Fresno, California, showing]. Sd; b&w. 35mm. 75 min.
Prod-Dir Andy Milligan.
Cast: Anne Linden (*Vera*), Robert Burgos (*Bob*), Carol Vogel (*Linda*), Josef Bush (*Rod*), Stephen Hart (*Mark*), Ellen Oyam (*Polly*), Hope Stansbury (*Lee*).
Melodrama. Three couples—Bob and Polly, Rod and Linda, and Vera and Mark—experiment with drugs and swap mates. Daylight reveals that each of the swingers has sex problems: Vera, a bisexual, is pregnant and wants an abortion. She is seduced in a bar by Lee, a lesbian who drugs Vera's drink. Linda, Rod's wife, is shown having intercourse with Hank, her brother-in-law. She complains about her need for a "real man." Polly's history of lesbianism

is revealed when she attends a transvestite party where some of the guests come dressed in "drag." Polly escapes the advances of Rocky, a bisexual, and returns home. There, her husband rapes her when she refuses to have sex with him. The three couples assemble for an LSD party. Rod shocks Bob (a sadist) by making a pass at him in the bathroom, and Bob pushes Rod's head into the toilet. The party ends when Vera, hallucinating, jumps out an upstairs window to her death. *Marriage. Infidelity. Mate swapping. Lesbianism. Male homosexuality. Abortion. Transvestism. Bisexuality. Sadism. Rape. Suicide. LSD. Drugs.*

DER KOM EN SOLDAT see **SCANDAL IN DENMARK**

LE DERNIER DES VIKINGS see **LAST OF THE VIKINGS**

LA DERNIÈRE ATTAQUE see **WARRIORS 5**

DES FEMMES DISPARAISSENT see **THE ROAD TO SHAME**

DESAFÍO EN RÍO BRAVO see **GUNMEN OF THE RIO GRANDE**

LES DÉSARROIS DE L'ÉLÈVE TÖRLESS see **YOUNG TORLESS**

DESERT ODYSSEY see **THE HAREM BUNCH; OR WAR AND PIECE**

DESERT PATROL (Great Britain)   **F6.1108**
Tempean Films. *For* Rank Organisation. *Dist* Universal–International Films. 17 Jan **1962** [New York opening]. Sd; b&w. 35mm. 78 min. [Also 73 min.]
Pres by J. Arthur Rank. *Prod* Robert S. Baker, Monty Berman. *Dir* Guy Green. *Screenplay* Robert Westerby. *Orig Story* Sean Fielding. *Photog* Wilkie Cooper. *Art Dir* Maurice Pelling. *Film Ed* Gordon Pilkington. *Mus Comp* Clifton Parker. *Mus Cond* Muir Mathieson. *Sd Rec* Bob Jones. *Asst Dir* Denis O'Dell. *Prod Mgr* George Fowler. *Wardrobe* Jack Verity. *Makeup* Roy Ashton. *Sp Eff* Cliff Richardson, Roy Whybrow.
Cast: Richard Attenborough (*Trooper Brody*), John Gregson (*Capt. Bill Williams*), Michael Craig (*Capt. Tom Cotton*), Vincent Ball (*Sergeant Nesbitt*), Percy Herbert (*Trooper White*), Barry Foster (*Corporal Matheson*), Andrew Faulds (*Sergeant Parker*), George Murcell (*Corporal Simms*), Ray McAnally (*Sergeant Hardy*), Harold Goodwin (*1st road watch*), Tony Thawnton (*Captain Giles*), Dermot Walsh (*Major Jeffries*), Wolf Frees (*German sergeant*), George Mikell (*German officer*).
War drama. During the World War II battle for Africa, a British patrol is sent on a 400-mile journey to Amara with orders to blow up one of Rommel's petroleum dumps. Newly arrived in the Long Range Desert Group is Captain Williams, a mines expert who doesn't take to the easygoing attitude of the other men, particularly that of the group commander, Captain Cotton. En route to Amara, the patrol encounters a German tank which costs them several men and vehicles. After another run-in with the enemy, they reach Amara and accomplish their mission, but, in escaping, their loss of men is heavy and their radio is destroyed. Williams, Cotton, and a handful of survivors now must try to walk out of the desert. They spot a British and a German patrol, each unaware of the other. Williams sacrifices himself by attacking the German patrol car and thus alerting the British. They are able to rout the Germans, rescue the five survivors, and deliver important information for the forthcoming battle of El Alamein. *Germans. Sabotage. Self-sacrifice. Combat zone life. Tanks (armored cars). Radio. Gasoline. Dumps. World War II. Sahara. Amara. El Alamein. Erwin Rommel. Great Britain—Army. Explosions.*
Note: Filmed on location in Libya. Released in Great Britain in Oct 1958 as *Sea of Sand*; running time: 97 min.

THE DESERT RAVEN   **F6.1109**
Cal Dunn Studios. *Dist* Allied Artists. Oct **1965**. Sd; b&w. 35mm. 90 min.
Prod Cal Dunn. *Dir* Alan S. Lee. *Orig Story & Screenplay* Rachel Romen, Alan S. Lee. *Cinematog* Taylor Byars. *Film Ed* John F. Link. *Titl Song* John Steele. *Sung by* Sondra Steele. *Background Mus* Richard La Salle. *Sd Mix* Burdick S. Trask. *Asst Dir* Stanley Brooks, Vernon Keays. *Prod Mgr* Vernon Keays. *Script Supv* Michael Preece. *Prod Asst* Alfred Taylor. *Makeup* Donald W. Roberson.
Cast: Rachel Romen (*Raven*), Rosalind C. Roberts (*Margo*), Robert Terry (*Bert*), Robert Ward, actor (*Ed Crane*), Bea Silvern (*Rena*), Rance Howard (*Reggie*), Paul L'Amoreaux (*deputy*), Edward Schaaf (*Red Banion*), Stuart Walsh (*Jim*), Bill Lloyd (*Al*), Joe Slattery, Gregg Donovan (*radio voices*).
Crime melodrama. A gang of outlaws, among them Bert, the leader; trigger man Ed Crane; stripper Margo; and the youth Reggie, flees to the desert after robbing and killing a wealthy old woman. When Ed kills a gas station attendant, the gang takes cover in the shack of an alcoholic who has been killed by his Indian wife, Rena, for making advances toward his stepdaughter, Raven. Discovering the husband's body, the thieves force the women to hide them. Having fallen in love, Reggie and Raven plan to expose the gang and return the stolen money. During a gun battle with the authorities, Bert is killed while trying to escape, and Raven loses her mother. Raven accepts a reward, which

she will share with Reggie when he is released from prison. *Outlaws. Stripteasers. Filling station attendants. Indians of North America. Stepfathers. Theft. Murder. Filial relations. Alcoholism. Deserts. Rewards.*
Note: Location scenes filmed in the Mojave Desert; working title: *Fly, Raven, Fly.*

LE DÉSERT ROUGE see **RED DESERT**

DESERT WARRIOR (Italy/Spain)   **F6.1110**
Producciones Benito Perojo–Roma Films–Parc Film. *Dist* Medallion Pictures. 8 Nov **1961** [San Francisco opening]. Sd; col (Eastman Color). 35mm (CinemaScope). 87 min.
A Benito Perojo Production. *Dir* Fernando Cerchio, Goffredo Alessandrini, León Klimovsky, Gianni Vernuccio, Ricardo Muñoz Suay. *Screenplay Spanish Vers* Alfonso Pase, Mariano Ozores. *Story* Manuel Villegas López. *Photog* Antonio L. Ballesteros, Mario Damicelli. *Art Dir* Sigfrido Burman, Francisco R. Asensio, Mario Garbuglia. *Film Ed* Antonio Ramírez. *Mus* Michel Michelet. *Prod Mgr* Miguel Tudela.
Cast: Ricardo Montalban (*Prince Said*), Carmen Sevilla (*Princess Amina*), Gino Cervi (*Ibrahim*), José Guardiola (*Selim*), Anna Maria Ferrero, Franca Bettoja, Mariangela Giordano, Manuel Guitián, Domingo Rivas, Manuel Alcón, Arnoldo Foà, Savia Gamal.
Adventure melodrama. Following the assassination of his father, Prince Said of Arabia flees into the desert with a band of his loyal followers. In order to procure arms for a revolt against the new sheik, Ibrahim, Prince Said and his men attack passing caravans. During one such raid, Princess Amina, Ibrahim's daughter, is taken prisoner. Prince Said, however, having mistaken her for a palace singer, Fatima, sets her free. Later, while disguised as a bird charmer, Prince Said again meets Amina and falls in love with her, although he remains unaware of her identity. Eventually Ibrahim is murdered by the evil Selim, who proclaims himself the new sultan. The populace revolts and storms the palace when Selim captures Prince Said and imprisons him. Prince Said kills Selim in a duel and assumes his rightful place on the throne with Amina as his bride. *Royalty. Arabs. Sheiks. Usurpers. Assassination. Revolts. Disguise. Arabia. Duels.*
Note: Filmed in Spain. Opened in Madrid in Jan 1958 as *Los amantes del desierto*. Released in Italy as *Amanti del deserto*; alternative Italian title(?): *La figlia dello sceicco*. Original running time: 91 min. Italian sources credit only Cerchio as director. Sources conflict in crediting Italian production company. One U. S. source credits the film as a Rialto production.

THE DESERTER AND THE NOMADS (Czechoslovakia/Italy)   **F6.1111**
Koliba Film Studio–Československý Film–Ultra Film. *Dist* Royal Films International. Oct **1969**. Sd; col (Eastman Color). 35mm. 103 min.
Prod Moris Ergas. *Exec Prod* Turi Vasile. *Dir* Juro Jakubisko. *Screenplay* Juro Jakubisko, Paolo Rugiero, Karol Sidon, Alberto Liberati, Ladislav Ťažký. *Photog* Juro Jakubisko. *Camera* Stanislav Doršič. *Art Dir* Ivan Vaníček. *Film Ed* Maximilián Remeň, Alfréd Benčič. *Mus* Štěpán Koníček. *Sd* Alexander Pallós. *Asst Dir* Pier Francesco Poli. *Prod Mgr* Ladislav Ondrejka. *Cost* Anna Lidaková.
Cast: Stefan Ladižinský (*Martin/Russian captain*), August Kubáň (*Smrt, the Hussar/Death*), Ferenc Gejza (*Kálmán*), Jana Stehnová (*bride/Nevesta*), Helena Grodová (*Lila*), Alexandra Sekulová (*Mara*), Vašek Kovařík (*crippled Christ*), František Petö (*groom*), Albert Pagáč (*Berger*), Magda Vasaryová (*peasant*), Olga Adamčíková, Katarina Tekelová, Olga Vroňská, Samuel Adamčík.
War drama. Source: Ladislav Ťažký, *Zběhové* (publication undetermined). A trilogy of episodes illustrate the consequences of war. THE DESERTER concerns Kálmán, a gypsy who deserts the army during World War I and returns to his wife, Lila. At a wedding, Kálmán disguises himself as a gypsy bride but is recognized by Smrt, a White Russian Hussar who pursues and kills him. Meanwhile, another deserter in the village incites a riot directed against two wealthy landowners; the Hussars are called in and ruthlessly quash the revolt. SUNDAY deals with the commander of a patrol of Russian partisans who set up quarters in a farmhouse at the close of World War II. An itinerant egg seller comes to the farmhouse, and the Russians accuse him of being a German spy and execute him. News arrives of the end of the war, but a German patrol attacks the village, engaging the Russians in a bloody battle. THE NOMADS takes place in a futuristic world after World War III. In an underground cell, a group of elderly people persecute a man whom they believe represents death. Nevesta, a young woman, takes pity on him, and together they leave the shelter to search for survivors of the nuclear holocaust. When they find no signs of life, both the man and Nevesta die. *Deserters—Military. Gypsies. Hussars. Russians. Germans. Disguise. Murder. Revolts. Resistance (political). Injustice. Nuclear warfare. Weddings. World War I. World War II. The Future.*
Note: Produced in Czechoslovakia in 1968 as *Zbehovia a putníci*. Italian title: *Il disertore e i nomadi*. Original running time: 120 min.

DESERTER USA (Sweden)   **F6.1112**
Sandrews. *Dist* Kanawha Films. 24 Nov **1969** [New York opening]. Sd; b&w. 35mm. 97 min. [Also 145 min (unconfirmed).]
    Prod Lars Lambert. *Exec Prod* Tomas Dyfverman. *Dir-Writ* Lars Lambert, Olle Sjögren. *Camera* Roland Lundin. *Mus* Grapes of Wrath, Christer Eklund.
    Cast: Bill Jones, actor *(John Lane)*, Mark Shapiro *(Ben Rosen)*, John Ashley *(Alan Miller)*, Jim Dotson *(Richard Brown)*, Steve Gershater *(Joe Camden)*, Warren Hamerman *(Walt)*, John Toler *(Fabian)*, John Arinfield *(John)*, Terry Whitmore *(disc jockey)*, Rudi Pastor *(Robert Fletcher)*, Lennart Schlytern.
    Documentary drama. The film is a dramatic reenactment of the experiences shared by United States military deserters and members of the American Deserters Committee living in Sweden. The cast features actual deserters with fictional names whose reactions to the United States Army, the Vietnam War, the Central Intelligence Agency, Swedish "secret police," alleged harassment by the United States, and American imperialism are explored. *Deserters— Military. Police. United States Army—Desertion. Vietnam War 1964–73. American Deserters Committee (Sweden). United States—Central Intelligence Agency.*
    Note: Released in Sweden in Apr 1969; running time: 103 min.

IL DESERTO ROSSO see **RED DESERT**

LOS DESESPERADOS see **A BULLET FOR SANDOVAL**

DESIRE UNDER THE PALMS   **F6.1113**
Rasnel Films. *Dist* A. L. Shackleton Films. **1969**. Sd; b&w. 35mm. 81 min. *Dir-Writ* Joseph W. Sarno.
    Cast: Barbara Lance *(Betty Williams)*, Howard Dale *(Walter Williams)*, Rene Howard *(Doris Perry)*, Tina Raymond *(Tenny Sylvester)*, Sidney Laird *(Jarman Perry)*, Suzan Thomas *(Christine Jessup)*, Jeanne Duval *(Stacy Carter)*, Donna Greene *(Janet Tyson)*, Jean Muniz *(Diane Delon)*.
    Melodrama. Betty Williams writes while her husband Walter, a salesman, is away during the day. She turns out flat, dull stories, however, in contrast to her erotic, passion-filled dreams of lesbian lovemaking. She makes friends with teenager Tenny Sylvester, and meets Tenny's brother-in-law, publisher Jarman Perry. Jarman's brutal, offhand manner impresses her, and she succumbs to his advances. To assuage her feelings of guilt, she persuades Tenny to seduce her husband. She seeks comfort in Jarman's arms, but he forces her to engage in sex play with his young maid while he watches. Fearful that she has lost Walter to her teenaged friend, she meets the publisher again. Jarman's wife, Doris, interrupts their tryst, terrorizes Betty with a gun, and beats her unconscious with the handle of a whip. Betty revives to see Tenny making love to Jarman, while Doris and the maid embrace passionately. Relieved to find that Tenny and Walter are not lovers, Betty flees the orgy in disgust. She returns home to Walter, and they exchange forgiveness. *Authors. Salesmen. Publishers. Housemaids. Lesbianism. Infidelity. Seduction. Voyeurism. Marriage. Group sex. Dreams.*

LE DÉSORDRE see **DISORDER**

LE DÉSORDRE ET LA NUIT see **NIGHT AFFAIR**

THE DESPERADO TRAIL (West Germany / Yugoslavia)   **F6.1114**
Rialto-Film Preben Philipsen–Jadran Film. *Dist* Columbia Pictures. Feb **1967**. Sd; col (Eastmancolor by Pathé). 35mm (Ultrascope). 92 min.
    Prod Horst Wendlandt. *Dir* Harald Reinl. *2d Unit Dir* Stipe Delić. *Screenplay* Harald G. Petersson, Joachim Bartsch. *Photog* Ernst W. Kalinke. *2d Unit Photog* Krešo Grčević. *Art Dir* Vladimir Tadej. *Film Ed* Jutta Hering. *Mus* Martin Böttcher. *Asst Dir* Charles M. Wakefield. *Prod Mgr* Erwin Gitt, Stipe Gurdulić. *Cost* Irms Pauli. *Still Photog* Gerd-Victor Krau, Lothar Winkler, Karl Reiter.
    Cast: Lex Barker *(Old Shatterhand)*, Pierre Brice *(Winnetou)*, Rik Battaglia *(Rollins)*, Ralf Wolter *(Sam Hawkins)*, Carl Lange *(governor)*, Sophie Hardy *(Ann)*, Veljko Maričić *(Vermeulen)*, Aleksandar Gavrić *(Kid)*, Ilija Ivezić *(Klark)*, Miha Baloh *(Gomez)*, Sime Jagarinac, Ivan Novak, Milan Mićić, Dragomir Felba, Dušan Vujisić.
    Western melodrama. Source: Karl Friedrich May, *Winnetou, der röte Gentleman* (Freiberg im Breisgau, 1893). Rollins, the unscrupulous director of a land trust engaged in speculation, becomes enraged when Apache leader Winnetou thwarts his attempt to provoke the Indian tribes into war. The governor asks Winnetou and his white blood brother, Old Shatterhand, to arrange a peace treaty with White Buffalo, an Indian chieftain who has fallen under Rollins' influence through numerous gifts of whiskey and firearms. An agent for the land trust finds out about the mission and informs Rollins, who sets a trap for Winnetou and Old Shatterhand. After an ambush fails, Rollins frames Winnetou for the murder of White Buffalo's son, but Sam Hawkins, an elderly scoundrel, saves Winnetou. Forced to engage in warfare, Winnetou leads his warriors against the united forces of White Buffalo's braves and Rollins' gunmen. The Apaches, close to being defeated, make their last stand,

and the cavalry, dispatched by the governor to insure peace, arrives too late to save Winnetou, who dies intercepting a bullet meant for Old Shatterhand. *Real estate agents. Apache Indians. Blood brothers. Territorial governors. Peacemakers. Land speculation. Friendship. Bribery. Murder. Frameup. Self-sacrifice. Business ethics. Treaties. United States Army—Cavalry. Winnetou.*
    Note: Filmed in Yugoslavia. Released in West Germany in 1965 as *Winnetou—III. Teil.* Yugoslavian title: *Vinetu III.*

THE DESPERADOS   **F6.1115**
Meadway Productions. *Dist* Columbia Pictures. 30 Apr **1969** [Houston opening; c1 May 1969; LP36891]. Sd (Westrex); col (Technicolor). 35mm. 90 min.
    An Irving Allen Production. *Prod* Irving Allen. *Assoc Prod* Andrew Donally. *Dir* Henry Levin. *2d Unit Dir* John Danischewsky. *Screenplay* Walter Brough. *Story* Clarke Reynolds. *Dir Photog* Sam Leavitt. *2d Unit Camera* John Cabrera. *Camera Op* Frank Drake. *Art Dir* José Alguero. *Film Ed* Geoffrey Foot. *Mus Comp & Cond* David Whitaker. *Sd Rec* George Stephenson, Hugh Strain. *Sd Ed* Charles Crafford. *Asst Dir* Pedro Vidal. *Prod Supv* Luis Roberts. *Prod Mgr* Miguel Gil. *Cont* Angela Allen. *Wardrobe Supv* Antonio Pueo. *Makeup* Jose Antonio Sanchez. *Hairdressing* Carmen Sanchez. *Sp Eff* Bill Warrington. *Prop Master* Eddie Fowlie. *Horsemaster* Juan Maján. *Stunt Supv* Gerry Crampton.
    Cast: Vince Edwards *(David Galt)*, Jack Palance *(Parson Josiah Galt)*, George Maharis *(Jacob Galt)*, Neville Brand *(Sheriff Kilpatrick)*, Sylvia Syms *(Laura)*, Christian Roberts *(Adam Galt)*, Kate O'Mara *(Adah)*, Kenneth Cope *(Carlin)*, John Paul *(Lacey)*, Patrick Holt *(Haller)*, Christopher Malcolm *(Gregg)*, John Clarke *(bandit)*, Benjamin Edney *(Pauly)*.
    Western drama. In the closing days of the Civil War, fanatical Parson Josiah Galt and his three sons, Adam, Jacob, and David, are leaders of a gang of southern marauders. Josiah, driven by his lust for revenge for the death of his Indian wife, attacks the Kansas town of St. Thomas. David, recalling his dead mother's prophecy of doom upon the family and repulsed by the carnage caused by his father and brothers, breaks with the gang after his brother Adam tries to rape one of the town's young girls. David is captured by his own men and brought before his father, who accuses him of treason and sentences him to be executed. David escapes, joins his wife, Laura, and together they flee to Texas, where they live for 6 years under an assumed name. After the war, Parson Galt and his sons continue to loot and pillage, and they eventually reach the Texas town where David, Laura, and their young son, Pauly, live. David recognizes the wagons of Carlin's Entertainers, a band of prostitutes who also serve as Galt's spies. Knowing that an attack is imminent, David reveals his true identity to Sheriff Kilpatrick, and together they set a trap for the Galts. David kills Adam, thereby setting off a chain of events that destroys nearly the whole family. To avenge Adam's death, Josiah abducts Pauly and tramples Laura, who dies in David's arms. Setting out on his father's trail, David hunts down Carlin and forces from him facts about a train robbery his father is planning. David helps to foil the robbery but in so doing kills his other brother Jacob. In a final confrontation with his father, David saves Pauly's life, but in the struggle over his son, both David and Josiah fall to their deaths. *Preachers. Fanatics. Desperadoes. Indians of North America. Halfcastes. Brothers. Sheriffs. Prostitutes. Looting. Revenge. Filial relations. Fratricide. Abduction. Rape. Murder. Massacres. Train robberies. United States—History—Civil War. Kansas. Texas. Chases.*

THE DESPERATE ONES (United States / Spain)   **F6.1116**
Pro Artis Ibérica–David Productions–Landau/Unger Co. *Dist* American International Pictures. Mar **1968** [c27 Nov 1967; LP35444]. Sd; col (Eastman Color). 35mm. 104 min.
    Pres by Commonwealth United Entertainment Inc., Jack Grynberg. *Prod-Dir-Writ* Alexander Ramati. *Exec Prod* Henry T. Weinstein. *Assoc Prod* Anthony B. Unger. *Dir Photog* Christian Matras. *Camera Op* Ricardo Navarrete. *Art Dir* Antonio Cortés. *Sp Art Cons* Félix Fabian. *Film Ed* Peter Weatherley. *Mus Comp & Cond* Cristobal Halffter. *Comp* "Ajmi" *Theme* Jean Freber. *Choreog* Gene Collins. *Sd Ed* Peter Keen. *Sd* Wally Milner, Gordon K. McCallum. *Asst Dir* Daniel Mendoza. *Prod Mgr* Jesús Sánchez. *Cont* Margarita Pardo. *Makeup* Emilio Puyol.
    Cast: Maximilian Schell *(Marek)*, Raf Vallone *(Victor)*, Irene Papas *(Ajmi)*, Theodore Bikel *(Kisielev)*, Maria Perschy *(Marusia)*, Fernando Rey *(Ibram)*, George Voskovec *(doctor)*, Alberto de Mendoza *(Hamlat)*, Antonio Vico *(Ulug Beg)*, Vincente Sangiovanni *(Shura)*, Robert Palmer *(Ukranian NKVD)*, Danny Stone *(NKVD guard)*, Mariela Chatlak *(Aka)*, Carmen Carbonell *(Ulug Beg's wife)*, Fernando Hilbeck, Andres Monreal, Maruchi Fresno, Mark Malicz, Max Slaten, Alexander Ramati, Ricardo Palacios, Cris Huerta, Antonio Duque, Luis Castro, actor, Luis Tejada.
    War melodrama. Source: Alexander Ramati, *Beyond the Mountains* (London, 1958). Two Polish brothers, Victor and Marek, imprisoned in a Siberian labor camp since the partition of Poland, escape and make their way

to Kermine, Uzbekistan, en route to join the Polish Army—in exile across the mountain border in Afghanistan. While they await a meeting with Hamlat, a smuggler who will guide them out of the U.S.S.R., the brothers rent a room in the home of Ibram Shukunov and his beautiful wife, Ajmi. Marek immediately falls in love with Ajmi, and Victor becomes enamored of waitress Marusia. Meanwhile, Kisielev, the local NKVD head, keeps the brothers under surveillance. Marek, the younger and weaker of the two, suffers from lingering night blindness as a result of his confinement, and his growing despair brings him into conflict with Victor. On the day of the planned escape, Victor is stricken with typhus. Hamlat is arrested and sent to stand trial in nearby Bokhara, but he flees when his train is bombed. Marek learns that Victor needs adrenalin to survive, but he is denied a travel visa; and Ibram volunteers to go to the black market in Bokhara. Left alone, Marek and Ajmi consummate their love; afterwards, Ajmi, burdened by guilt, attempts to take her own life. Marek saves her, Ibram returns with the adrenalin, and Hamlat is contacted for a last-ditch effort. Marusia is tricked by Kisielev into informing, but she warns Victor and Marek in time. As the brothers set out across the border with Hamlat, Hamlat's children, Ibram, and Ajmi, Marek sacrifices his life by drawing the fire of the border patrol, thereby allowing the others to escape. *Poles. Brothers. Escapees. Smugglers. Spies. Marriage. Infidelity. Suicide. Self-sacrifice. NKVD. Typhus. Epinephrine. Black market. Border police. World War II. Uzbek Soviet Socialist Republic. Bukhara. Afghanistan. Poland.*

Note: Opened in Madrid in Mar 1967 as *Mas alla de las montañas.* U.S. title changed from *Beyond the Mountains.* Copyright claimant: Commonwealth United Entertainment.

LOS DESPIADADOS *see* **THE HELLBENDERS**

DESTINATION HOLY LAND *see* **GRAND TOUR '70: DESTINATION HOLY LAND**

DESTINATION INNER SPACE   F6.1117

United Pictures–Harold Goldman Associates. *Dist* Magna Pictures Distribution Corp. Jun **1966** [c11 May 1966; LP34276]. Sd; col (Eastman Color). 35mm. 83 min.

Prod Earle Lyon. *Exec Prod* Fred Jordan, *Assoc Prod* Wendell Niles, Jr. *Dir* Francis D. Lyon. *Screenplay* Arthur C. Pierce. *Dir Photog* Brick Marquard. *Art Dir* Paul Sylos, Jr. *Set Decor* Harry Reif. *Supv Film Ed* Robert S. Eisen. *Mus* Paul Dunlap. *Mus Ed* George C. Emick. *Sd Mixer* John Bury. *Sd Eff Ed* Joseph Von Stroheim, Douglas H. Grindstaff. *Sd* Glen Glenn Sound. *Asst Dir* Joe Wonder. *Prod Mgr* Joe Wonder. *Script Supv* Stan Olsen. *Makeup* Bob Dawn. *Hairdresser* Linda Trainoff. *Sp Eff* Roger George. *Amphibian Created by* Richard Cassarino. *Gaffer* Lee Cannon. *Prop Master* Ted Cooper. *Casting* Kerwin Coughlin, Jasper Russell.

Cast: Scott Brady *(Commander Wayne)*, Sheree North *(Sandra)*, Gary Merrill *(Dr. Le Satier)*, Mike Road *(Hugh Maddox)*, Wende Wagner *(Rene)*, John Howard *(Dr. James)*, William Thourlby *(Tex)*, Biff Elliott *(Dr. Wilson)*, Glen Spies *(Mike)*, Richard Niles *(Ellis)*, Roy Barcroft *(Skipper)*, Ken Delo *(radio man)*, Ron Burke *(The Thing)*, James Hong *(Ho Lee)*, Ed Charles Sweeny.

Science fiction melodrama. Scientists aboard the Institute of Modern Science's undersea laboratory enlist the aid of Navy Commander Wayne to identify an underwater moving object detected by their radar instruments. Aboard the laboratory are chief scientist Dr. Le Satier; Sandra, a photographer; and Hugh, a former Navy diver. Friction develops when Wayne accuses Hugh of a cowardly act which caused the deaths of several sailors during his Navy days. Wayne identifies the object as being from outer space when it passes close by the lab. Later, Wayne boards the alien vehicle and returns with a pod-shaped container which, once in the laboratory, begins to expand, eventually erupting to produce a gigantic amphibian monster that destroys the lab's air line connection, leaving only a 12-hour air supply. A monster gains entrance to the lab, killing and injuring some crewmen before returning to its own craft. Hugh sacrifices his life in destroying the spacecraft, thus atoning for his previous act of cowardice by saving the lives of his companions aboard the laboratory. *Oceanographers. United States Navy. Divers. Photographers. Space creatures. Sea monsters. Cowardice. Self-sacrifice. Underwater laboratories. Submarines. Radar.*

DESTROY ALL MONSTERS (Japan)   F6.1118

Toho Co. *Dist* American International Pictures. 28 May **1969** [Cincinnati, Ohio, opening; c28 May 1969; LP37499]. Sd; col (Eastman Color, print by Berkey Pathé). 35mm (Tohoscope). 88 min. *MPAA rating* G.

Exec Prod Tomoyuki Tanaka. *Dir* Ishiro Honda. *Screenplay* Kaoru Mabuchi, Ishiro Honda. *Photog* Taiichi Kankura. *Art Dir* Takeo Kita. *Film Ed* Ryohei Fujii. *Mus* Akira Ifukube. *Sd* Shoichi Yoshizawa, Hisashi Shimonaga. *Asst Dir* Seiji Tani. *Sp Eff* Eiji Tsuburaya, Sadamasa Arikawa.

Cast: Akira Kubo *(Capt. Katsuo Yamabe)*, Jun Tazaki *(Dr. Yoshido)*, Yoshio Tsuchiya *(Dr. Otani)*, Kyoko Ai *(Queen of the Kilaaks)*, Yukiko Kobayashi *(Kyoko)*, Kenji Sawara *(Nishikawa)*, Andrew Hughes *(Dr. Stevenson)*, Nadao Kirino, Susumu Kurobe, Hisaya Ito, Yoshifumi Tajima, Naoya Kusakawa, Ikio Sawamura, Wataru Omura, Kazuo Suzuki, Yutaka Sada.

Science fiction melodrama. By 1999, all the monsters that have terrorized mankind have been corralled on the Japanese island of Ogasawara for scientific observation. One day, the sudden appearance of a strange gas destroys the island's electronic barriers and frees the creatures. Soon Godzilla attacks Paris, Mothra invades Peking, Manda (a giant lizard) devastates London, and Rodan threatens Moscow. After scientific experts determine that an extraterrestrial force controls the monsters, Captain Yamabe of Moon Rocket SY-3 is instructed to land his spaceship on Ogasawara and contact the scientists there. On the island, Yamabe is introduced to a zombie-like woman who claims to be from the planet Kilaak, whose people intend to conquer Earth by imbedding remote-controlled devices in the necks of the scientists and monsters. As the creatures attack Tokyo, the experts determine that this is only a diversionary tactic; the Kilaaks' real objective is to build a subterranean base beneath Japan. Yamabe and his crew find and demolish the Kilaaks' lunar control base, and the invaders, flushed from their simulated environment, turn to stone. To save themselves from the monsters, now controlled by earth scientists, the Kilaaks summon space dragon Ghidrah and a fiery flying saucer to crush the Earth monsters. Ghidrah is defeated, SY-3 stops the saucer, and Godzilla destroys the Kilaaks' base. The monsters then return to their peaceful retreat on Ogasawara. *Scientists. Monsters. Zombies. Space creatures. Space warfare. Thought control. Lethal gas. Spaceships. Flying saucers. Ogasawara Islands. Moscow. Peking. Paris. London. Tokyo. The Moon. Imaginary planets. The Future. Rodan. Godzilla. Mothra. Ghidrah. Lizards.*

Note: Released in Japan in Aug 1968 as *Kaiju soshingeki.* Includes scenes from *The War of the Gargantuas,* q. v.

DESTROY, SHE SAID (France)   F6.1119

Ancinex–Madeleine Films. *Dist* Grove Press. 6 Apr **1970** [New York opening]. Sd; b&w. 35mm. 100 min.

Prod Nicole Stéphane. *Dir-Writ* Marguerite Duras. *Photog* Jean Penzer. *Camera* Michel Lebon. *Film Ed* Henri Colpi. *Sd* Luc Périni. *Prod Dir* Monique Montivier.

Cast: Catherine Sellers *(Elisabeth Alione)*, Nicole Hiss *(Alissa Thor)*, Henri Garcin *(Max Thor)*, Michel Lonsdale *(Stein)*, Daniel Gélin *(Bernard Alione)*.

Drama. Source: Marguerite Duras, *Détruire, dit-elle* (Paris, 1969). In a secluded hotel circumscribed by a dense forest Max and Alissa Thor meet Stein and Elisabeth. Max, a professor of future history and an aspiring author, is immediately attracted to the brooding wife of industrialist Bernard Alione, Elisabeth, who is recovering from a miscarriage. Stein, a German Jew and potential writer, is infatuated with Alissa, Max's young wife and former student. During their sojourn the guests' identities gradually meld. While playing cards, for example, each guest anticipates the others' observations. Although her friends remain at the resort, the insecure Elisabeth leaves upon the arrival of her worldly husband. *Authors. Professors. Students. Industrialists. Jews. Marriage. Infidelity. Miscarriage. Forests. Hotels.*

Note: Opened in Paris in Dec 1969 as *Détruire, dit-elle;* running time: 90 min.

DESTRUCTION TEST *see* **CIRCLE OF DECEPTION**

THE DESTRUCTORS   F6.1120

United Pictures–Harold Goldman Associates. *Dist* Feature Film Corp. of America, Commonwealth United Entertainment, Inc. Jan **1968**. Sd; col. 35mm. 97 min.

Prod Earle Lyon. *Dir* Francis D. Lyon. *Screenplay* Arthur C. Pierce, Larry E. Jackson. *Photog* Alan Stensvold. *Art Dir* Paul Sylos. *Set Decor* Raymond G. Boltz. *Film Ed* Robert S. Eisen. *Mus* Paul Dunlap. *Sd* John Erlinger. *Asst Dir* William Schwartz. *Prod Mgr* Joe Wonder. *Sp Eff* Roger George.

Cast: Richard Egan *(Dan Street)*, Patricia Owens *(Charlie Street)*, John Ericson *(Dutch Holland)*, Michael Ansara *(Count Mario Romano)*, Joan Blackman *(Stassa Gertmann)*, David Brian *(Hogan)*, Johnny Seven *(Spaniard)*, Khigh Dhiegh *(King Chou Lai)*, Gregory Morton *(Dr. Frazer)*, John Howard *(Bushnell)*, Eddie Firestone *(Barnes)*, Jayne Massey *(Suzie)*, Michael Dugan *(Parkhouse)*, Jim Adams *(Wayne)*, Olan Soule, Mary Lou Cook, Adele Claire, James Seay, Walter Reed, Douglas Kennedy, Virginia Wood, John Lawrence, Lennie Geer, Robert Riordan, Richard Norris, Linda Kirk, Rick Traeger, King Moody, Cal Currens, Tommy McDonald, Karen Norris, Dodie Warren, Horace Brown, Tex Armstrong, Jim Kline.

Action melodrama. Three espionage agents—Dutch Holland, Spaniard, and Gertmann—blow up an optical company and make off with a tray of laser rubies, though Gertmann is killed in the getaway. National Intelligence Agency investigator Dan Street learns that Gertmann had been employed by an electronics firm that has just perfected a laser-ray gun capable of disintegrating any target from great distances. While Street continues his investigations (to the disappointment of his wife, Charlie) fashion designer Count Mario Romano, accompanied by Dutch and Spaniard, meets with King Chou Lai to sell him the stolen rubies necessary for operation of the ray gun. Street finds Gertmann's widow, Stassa, who is now having an affair with Dutch, and learns that they both work for Romano. Finally realizing that the enemy's objective is to delay completion of the gun, Street doublechecks with the Defense Department and discovers that Romano's yacht is anchored near the fortress-like electronics building where the gun is kept. Street enters an underground tunnel extending from the building to the sea and eventually encounters Romano and his team of "destructors," who have already worked their way through the waterpipes into the electronics building. Dutch, who was brainwashed by Communists in the Korean War and dishonorably discharged as a turncoat, has a change of heart and helps Street prevent the theft of the gun. Though Dutch sacrifices his own life, Romano and Stassa also are killed. *Thieves. Couturiers. Widows. Veterans. Investigators. Robbery. Jewels. Electronics. Laser. Yachts. Brainwashing. Communists. Factories. United States—Defense Department.*

Note: Filmed in 1966.

DET KOM EN SOMMAR see SHORT IS THE SUMMER

THE DETECTIVE   F6.1121

Arcola-Millfield Productions. *Dist* Twentieth Century-Fox Film Corp. 28 May **1968** [New York opening; c29 May 1968; LP35830]. Sd (Westrex); col (DeLuxe). 35mm (Panavision). 114 min.

Prod Aaron Rosenberg. *Dir* Gordon Douglas. *Screenplay* Abby Mann. *Dir Photog* Joseph Biroc. *Art Dir* Jack Martin Smith, William Creber. *Set Decor* Walter M. Scott, Jerry Wunderlich. *Film Ed* Robert Simpson. *Mus* Jerry Goldsmith. *Orch* Warren Barker. *Sd* Harry M. Lindgren, David Dockendorf. *Asst Dir* Richard Lang. *Unit Prod Mgr* David Silver. *Cost Dsgn* Moss Mabry. *Makeup* Dan Striepeke. *Mr. Sinatra's Makeup* Layne Britton. *Hairstyles* Edith Lindon. *Sp Photog Eff* L. B. Abbott, Art Cruickshank. *Tech Adv* Arthur E. Schultheiss, (Lieut.).

Cast: Frank Sinatra *(Joe Leland)*, Lee Remick *(Karen Leland)*, Jacqueline Bisset *(Norma MacIver)*, Ralph Meeker *(Lieutenant Curran)*, Jack Klugman *(Dave Schoenstein)*, Horace McMahon *(Farrell)*, Lloyd Bochner *(Dr. Wendell Roberts)*, William Windom *(Colin MacIver)*, Tony Musante *(Felix Tesla)*, Al Freeman, Jr. *(Robbie Loughren)*, Robert Duvall *(Nestor)*, Pat Henry *(Mercidis)*, Patrick McVey *(Tanner)*, Dixie Marquis *(Carol Linjack)*, Sugar Ray Robinson *(Kelly)*, Renee Taylor *(Rachel Schoenstein)*, James Inman *(Teddy Leikman)*, Tom Atkins *(Harmon)*, James Dukas *(medical examiner)*, Sharon Henesy *(Sharon)*, Jan Farrand *(Karen's friend at theater)*, Marion Brash *(prostitute)*, Earl Montgomery *(desk clerk)*, Peg Murray *(girl at party)*, Frank Reiter *(tough homosexual)*, Peter York *(decent boy)*, Mark Dawson *(desk sergeant)*, José Rodriguez *(boy in police station)*, Tom Gorman *(prison priest)*, Lou Nelson *(procurer)*, Richard Krisher *(Matt Henderson)*, Jilly Rizzo *(bartender)*, Arnold Soboloff, George Plimpton, Phil Sterling, Don Fellows, Paul Larson, Ted Beniades *(reporters)*.

Crime drama. Source: Roderick Thorp, *The Detective* (New York, 1966). New York City Detective Joe Leland is assigned to investigate the grisly murder of Teddy Leikman, the homosexual son of a politically influential department store owner. Aware that a quick arrest and conviction will further his chances of promotion, Leland brings in the dead man's psychopathic former roommate, Felix Tesla, and succeeds in extracting a confession from him. After witnessing Tesla's death by execution and receiving a promotion, Leland makes a futile attempt to patch up his marriage to Karen. A short time later, he receives a visit from Norma MacIver, the wealthy widow of an accountant who fell to his death from the grandstand roof of a race track. Certain that her husband was murdered, Norma explains to Leland that all her efforts to investigate the death have been thwarted. In attempting to reopen the case, Leland encounters strong police opposition, particularly from a fellow officer, Lieutenant Curran, who hints that certain people would be willing to pay a large sum of money if the case remained closed. Following an attempt on his life, Leland examines MacIver's files and discovers that the accountant was involved with several members of the Borough Planning Commission in corrupt land speculation. Suspecting that MacIver's psychiatrist neighbor, Dr. Wendell Roberts, is concealing evidence, Leland breaks into his office. When Roberts unexpectedly comes in, Leland forces him to play a tape recording of one of MacIver's visits. The recording reveals not only MacIver's bisexuality but the fact that after being picked up at a bar by Leikman, his detestation of homosexuality caused him to commit the murder and then take his own life. Realizing that as a police officer he has been instrumental in sending an innocent man to his death, Leland removes his badge and decides to devote himself to exposing police and government corruption. *Detectives. Roommates. Widows. Police. Psychiatrists. Neighbors. Murder. Male homosexuality. Suicide. Capital punishment. Marriage. Political corruption. Land speculation. Bisexuality. Recorders. New York City.*

Note: Location scenes filmed in New York City and the Los Angeles area.

UN DETECTIVE see DETECTIVE BELLI

DETECTIVE BELLI (Italy)   F6.1122

Fair Film. *Dist* Plaza Pictures. 16 Dec **1970** [New York opening]. Sd; col (Technicolor). 35mm. 103 min. *MPAA rating* R.

Prod Mario Cecchi Gori. *Dir* Romolo Guerrieri. *Screenplay* Franco Verucci, Alberto Silvestri, Massimo D'Avack. *Dir Photog* Roberto Gerardi. *Art Dir* Giantito Burchiellaro. *Film Ed* Marcello Malvestiti. *Mus* Fred Bongusto. *Song:* "The World of the Blues" sung by Shirley Harmer. *Sd* Guido Ortensi. *Asst Dir* Renzo Genta.

Cast: Franco Nero *(Stefano Belli)*, Florinda Bolkan *(Vera Fontana)*, Adolfo Celi *(Fontana)*, Delia Boccardo *(Sandy Bronson)*, Susanna Martinkova *(Emmanuelle)*, Renzo Palmer *(Baldo)*, Roberto Bisacco *(Claude)*, Maurizio Bonuglia *(Mino Fontana)*.

Crime melodrama. Source: Ludovico Dentice, *Macchie di belletto* (Milan, 1968). During Christmas season in Rome lawyer Fontana visits Belli, an unscrupulous police detective, and requests that the lawman investigate Romani, an associate of his son Mino and head of Embassy Records, a firm in which the attorney's wife, Vera, is planning to invest. The lawyer also asks Belli to arrange the deportation of English model Sandy Bronson, his son's paramour. When the detective arrives at Romani's apartment he finds the entrepreneur dead. The mutilated photograph of a nude woman suggests a female assassin, and Romani's role as a blackmailer is revealed. Belli, however, is unable to prevent further murders, including that of Mino, who is killed in a brawl with a photographer, and of Sandy. The woman in the photograph is identified as pop singer and drug addict Emmanuelle, and Romani is linked to the world of narcotics traffic. Accompanied by Fontana, Belli confronts the murderess, Vera, who shoots both her husband and the detective. *Detectives. Lawyers. Models. Entertainers. Drug addicts. Blackmail. Narcotics. Filial relations. Murder. Marriage. Photographs. Christmas. Rome.*

Note: Location scenes filmed in and around Rome. Released in Italy in 1969 as *Un detective*. U. S. prerelease title: *A Detective*.

DETENTION GIRLS   F6.1123

Dist Sam Lake Enterprises. Oct **1969**. Sd; b&w. 35mm. 77 min.
A Sam Lake Production.

Melodrama. A young woman's initiation into the nightmare world of women's prisons begins with her arrest at a campus demonstration. The guards take advantage of the prisoners' helplessness to consolidate their own power. The sadistic warden dispenses her brutal discipline on the slightest pretext. The prison doctor insinuates himself into the power structure of the prison while he develops profitable associations in the underworld. Deprived of male companionship, and corrupted by the warden and guards, the prisoners must turn to one another for consolation. Minor flirtations, passionate love affairs, and violent rapes shape the daily lives of the demoralized and degraded women. *Students. Innocents. Prison guards. Prison wardens. Physicians. Lesbianism. Sadism. Organized crime. Prisons. Demonstrations.*

DETOUR (Bulgaria)   F6.1124

Sofiya Film Studios. *For* Bulgarian State Films. *Dist* Brandon Films. 11 Aug **1969** [New York opening]. Sd; b&w. 35mm. 78 min. *MPAA rating* M.

Dir Grisha Ostrovski, Todor Stoyanov. *Story & Screenplay* Blaga Dimitrova. *Photog* Todor Stoyanov. *Mus* Milcho Leviev.

Cast: Nevena Kokanova *(Neda)*, Ivan Andonov *(Boyan)*.

Drama. Boyan, a successful engineer, is forced to make a detour to avoid construction on the road to Sofia. He stops near some archeological diggings to ask directions and is surprised to meet Neda, the woman he loved during his university days 17 years before. She rides into town with him, and they recall their first meeting. *Boyan is a dynamic post-war revolutionary espousing the importance of the Communist Party over petty romantic entanglements, and Neda wagers with her friends that she can make the disciplined idealist fall in love with her.* Although the two share a passionate 10-day affair, they end their romance so that Neda can go to Moscow to continue her education. The parting is painful, but the lovers are willing to sacrifice their personal happiness for a meaningful contribution to a future society. Now middle-aged and married to others, they discover their passion rekindled but fear that a scandal will develop if their friends see them together. By the time Neda accompanies Boyan to the airport, his views are so changed that he offers to forego an important meeting in Vienna if Neda will go away with him. Neda, however, sensing the futility of it all, leaves the airport, and Boyan boards the plane alone. *Engineers. Students. Communists. College life. Nostalgia. Marriage. Middle age. Wagers. Airfields. Sofia.*

Note: Released in Bulgaria in May 1967 as *Otklonenie*; running time: 90 min.

DÉTOURNEMENT DE MINEURES see **THE PRICE OF FLESH**

DÉTRUIRE, DIT-ELLE see **DESTROY, SHE SAID**

DEUX BILLETS POUR MEXICO see **DEAD RUN**

DEUX OU TROIS CHOSES QUE JE SAIS D'ELLE see **TWO OR THREE THINGS I KNOW ABOUT HER**

LES DEUX RIVALES see **TIME OF INDIFFERENCE**

DEUX VOIX   **F6.1125**
Dist Film-Makers' Cooperative. 12 Jul **1966** [New York opening]. Sd; b&w. 16mm. 80 min.
  Prod-Dir Rosalind A. Stevenson. *Orig Mus Comp & Perf* by Steve McCord.
  Cast: Elektrah Lobel *(Her)*, John Heuer *(Him)*, Finnegan *(a cat)*.
  Drama. Anxious and alienated, a woman shares her room with a cat. Although admonished to communicate with no one, she makes the acquaintance of a stranger at a playground. Despite his regular visits to her room, the woman remains emotionally indifferent to him. *Recluses. Loneliness. Cats.*
  Note: Also known as *Two Voices.*

DEVETI KRUG see **THE NINTH CIRCLE**

DEVI (India)   **F6.1126**
Satyajit Ray Productions. *Dist* Harrison Pictures. 7 Oct **1962** [New York opening]. Sd; b&w. 35mm. 95 min.
  Pres by Edward Harrison. *Prod-Dir-Writ* Satyajit Ray. *Photog* Subrata Mitra. *Art Dir* Bansi Chandragupta. *Film Ed* Dulal Dutta. *Mus* Ali Akbar Khan. *Sd* Durgadas Mitra. *Prod Mgr* Anil Chowdhury.
  Cast: Chhabi Biswas *(Kalikinkar)*, Soumitra Chatterjee *(Umaprasad)*, Sharmila Tagore *(Doyamoyee)*, Purnendu Mukherjee *(Taraprasad)*, Karuna Bannerjee *(Harasundari)*, Arpen Choudhury *(Khoka)*, Anil Chatterjee *(Bhudev)*, Mohamed Ibn Israel *(sick boy's father)*, Kali Sarkar *(Professor Jarkar)*, Khagesh Chakravarty *(doctor)*, Nagendra Nath *(priest)*.
  Drama. Based on the works of: Prabhatkumar Mukherjee and Rabindranath Tagore. The rich and religious patriarch Kalikinkar dreams that his adolescent daughter-in-law Doyamoyee is a reincarnation of the Hindu goddess Kali. Proclaiming his vision, he places the girl on an altar outside his home, where she is universally venerated. When a sick child is cured, her divinity is confirmed, and Doyamoyee begins to doubt her own humanity. Returning from his studies in Calcutta, her husband, Umaprasad, demands that the rituals cease and that Doyamoyee come away with him. Fearing divine retribution, his wife refuses. Unable to save her stricken nephew Khoka from death, she becomes insane. [In the original version, Doyamoyee dies by the river as Umaprasad returns.] *Patriarchs. Students. Aunts. Children. In-laws. Upper classes. Hinduism. Adolescence. Family life. Reincarnation. Superstition. Insanity. Miracles. Calcutta. Dreams.*
  Note: Released in India in 1960. 1962 Cannes Film Festival running time: 98 min. Also known as *The Goddess.*

DEVICHYA VESNA see **SPRINGTIME ON THE VOLGA**

THE DEVIL AND THE TEN COMMANDMENTS (France/Italy)
                                                         F6.1127
  Mondex Films-Filmsonor-Procinex-Incei Film-Inter Continental Production. *Dist* Union Film Distributors. 14 Oct **1963** [New York opening]. Sd; b&w. 35mm (Franscope). 120 min.
  Pres by Pathé Cinema Corp. *Prod* Robert Amon, Claude Jaeger. *Dir* Julien Duvivier. *Screenplay* Michel Audiard, René Barjavel, Henri Jeanson, Pascal Jardin, Julien Duvivier, Maurice Bessy. *Photog* Roger Fellous. *Art Dir* François de Lamothe. *Ed* Paul Cayatte. *Mus* (see note) Guy Magenta, Michel Magne, Georges Garvarentz, Charles Aznavour, Jacques Brel, Gilbert Bécaud. *Sd* Guy Chichignoud. *Prod Mgr* Ralph Baum.
  Cast—Episode 1: Michel Simon *(Jérome Chambard)*, Lucien Baroux *(bishop)*, Claude Nollier *(mother superior)*.
  Cast—Episode 2: Dany Saval *(Tania)*, Henri Tisot *(admirer)*.
  Cast—Episode 3: Charles Aznavour *(Denis Mayeux)*, Lino Ventura *(Garigny)*, Maurice Biraud *(police inspector)*, Henri Vilbert *(Alexandre)*, Maurice Teynac *(father superior)*.
  Cast—Episode 4: Françoise Arnoul *(Françoise Beaufort)*, Micheline Presle *(Micheline)*, Mel Ferrer *(Philip Allan)*, Claude Dauphin *(Georges Beaufort)*.
  Cast—Episode 5: Fernandel *(God)*, Germaine Kerjean *(grandmother)*, Gaston Modot *(grandfather)*, Josette Vardier *(mother)*, René Clermont *(father)*, Claudine Maugey.
  Cast—Episode 6: Alain Delon *(Pierre Messager)*, Danielle Darrieux *(Clarisse Ardant)*, Madeleine Robinson *(Madame Messager)*, Georges Wilson *(Monsieur Messager)*, Roland Armontel *(Mercier)*.

  Cast—Episode 7: Jean-Claude Brialy *(Didier Marin)*, Louis de Funès *(Vaillant)*, Armande Navarre *(Janine)*, Noël Roquevert *(inspector)*, Denise Gence *(churchwoman)*, Jean-Paul Moulinot *(bank director)*, Jean Carmet *(tramp)*, Gabriello *(policeman)*.
  Comedy. EPISODE 1: Jérome Chambard, a handyman in a convent, is warned that he will lose his job if he continues to swear. When a boyhood friend, now a bishop, visits the convent, the handyman forgets the warning and, in a dinner discussion, he does swear. He loses his job, but the bishop intercedes and he is reinstated after promising to study the ten commandments anew. EPISODE 2: A young man enamored of a stripper calls on her only to find her married to a janitor who doesn't know what kind of dancing his wife performs. While she is out shopping, the visitor describes her dancing to the husband, who leaves when his wife returns. The stripper demonstrates her new routine for her admirer, but the young man, disillusioned at finding the stripper an ordinary housewife, leaves; then the husband returns and demands that his wife show him her striptease act. EPISODE 3: Denis, a Jesuit novice, leaves the order to avenge his sister's suicide, which was provoked by Garigny, a racketeer who seduced her into prostitution and drug addiction. After instructing a detective to come to his room at a specific hour, Denis persuades Garigny to come a few moments earlier. He provokes the racketeer to murder him, and Garigny is arrested by the detective. EPISODE 4: Philip buys a necklace for Micheline, his mistress, though he is bored with her. Françoise, the wife of a struggling playwright, accompanies the couple at the time of the purchase and admires another necklace. Attracted to Françoise, Philip later buys the other necklace and offers it to her if she will have an affair with him. She agrees and later, to conceal her adultery from Georges, her husband, arranges for him to "find" the necklace amidst some imitation jewelry. Micheline learns of the liaison between Philip and Françoise and seduces Georges, who offers her the choice of a piece of jewelry from Françoise's collection. She recognizes the expensive necklace and chooses it. Françoise is speechless when she later sees Micheline proudly displaying her new acquisition. EPISODE 5: A man claiming to be God visits a humble mountain cottage. A child and her grandparents are at home, and the elderly woman berates "God" for her miserable existence and demands a miracle. "God" causes her allegedly crippled husband to walk again. The old woman dies, and "God" blesses her and departs, leaving renewed faith and hope behind him. He accepts a lift from two men in a van and is driven unknowingly to the nearby psychiatric hospital. EPISODE 6: Pierre learns from his father that his real mother is not Germaine but a famous actress who refused marriage. He goes to see her, but before he can identify himself, she begins a flirtation, assuming him to be another youthful admirer. When he finally reveals himself as her son, she confesses that the man he thinks is his father, Monsieur Messager, is not actually so. But she cannot remember who his real father was, there having been so many men in her life. Pierre, more bewildered than before, leaves his mother to her many lovers and goes home better satisfied with the Messagers as parents. EPISODE 7: Didier, a bank teller, is held up on the job and robbed of 50 million francs. Later he learns the robber's address and steals a suitcase containing the loot. Seated in a cafe next to a tramp, Didier tells Janine, his fiancée, of his new wealth and together they plan to elope. While they are packing, a policeman invites Didier to identify a suspect. Though this man is the guilty one, Didier disclaims any resemblance. After leaving the police station, the released robber chases Didier, and they fight over the suitcase. When a policeman orders them to open it, the contents are revealed as merely food and wine. A bit later, the policeman comes across a hungry tramp whose lunch has turned into 50 million francs! [EPISODE 8 (European version only): One Sunday afternoon, when Jérome Chambard and the bishop are eating, the Devil appears as a serpent. Rather than throwing it into the fire, where Jérome supposes it might be comfortable, he casts it into a well.] *Handymen. Clergymen. Bank clerks. Stripteasers. Racketeers. Detectives. Mistresses. Grandparents. Actors. Police. Janitors. Tramps. Brother-sister relationship. Infidelity. Seduction. Insanity. Revenge. Murder. Religion. Miracles. Parentage. Bank robberies. Convents. Jewels. The Devil. The Commandments. Society of Jesus.*
  Note: Paris opening: Sep 1962 as *Le diable et les dix commandements;* running times: 120 and 130 min. Rome opening: Sep 1962 as *Le tentazioni quotidiane;* running time: 107 min; alternative title: *Il diavolo e i dieci comandamenti.* Also shown in Europe in a 143-min version. Most sources omit Intercontinental Production from production company credit; its role is undetermined. Sources disagree on music credit.

THE DEVIL AT 4 O'CLOCK   **F6.1128**
  Fred Kohlmar Productions. *Dist* Columbia Pictures. 18 Oct **1961** [New York opening; c1 Oct 1961; LP20765]. Sd (RCA); col (Eastman Color by Pathé). 35mm. 127 min.
  A Mervyn LeRoy-Fred Kohlmar Production. *Prod* Fred Kohlmar. *Dir* Mervyn LeRoy. *Screenplay* Liam O'Brien. *Dir Photog* Joseph Biroc. *Art Dir* John Beckman. *Set Decor* Louis Diage. *Film Ed* Charles Nelson. *Mus* George

Duning. *Orch* Arthur Morton. *Sd* Charles J. Rice. *Sd Rec* Josh Westmoreland. *Asst Dir* Carter De Haven, Jr., Floyd Joyer. *Prod Asst* Milton Feldman. *Makeup Supv* Ben Lane. *Sp Eff* Larry Butler, Willis Cook.

Cast: Spencer Tracy *(Father Matthew Doonan)*, Frank Sinatra *(Harry)*, Kerwin Mathews *(Father Joseph Perreau)*, Jean-Pierre Aumont *(Jacques)*, Grégoire Aslan *(Marcel)*, Alexander Scourby *(The Governor)*, Barbara Luna *(Camille)*, Cathy Lewis *(matron)*, Bernie Hamilton *(Charlie)*, Martin Brandt *(Doctor Wexler)*, Lou Merrill *(Aristide)*, Marcel Dalio *(Gaston)*, Tom Middleton *(Paul)*, Ann Duggan *(Clarisse)*, Louis Mercier *(corporal)*, Michele Montau *(Margot)*, Nanette Tanaka *(Fleur)*, Tony Maxwell *(Antoine)*, Jean Del Val *(Louis)*, Moki Hana *(Sonia)*, Warren Hsieh *(Napoleon)*, William Keaulani *(constable)*, "Lucky" Luck *(Captain Olsen)*, Norman Josef Wright *(Fouquette)*, Robin Shimatsu *(Marianne)*.

Melodrama. Source: Max Catto, *The Devil at Four O'Clock* (London, 1958). A seaplane en route to Tahiti with three convicts—Harry, a white American, Marcel, a Frenchman, and Charlie, a Negro American—makes a stopover on a tiny volcanic island in the South Pacific. The pilot deposits his fourth passenger, young Father Perreau, the replacement for aging, bad-tempered Father Matthew Doonan, whom the natives consider slightly insane because of his devotion to a mountain-top hospital he has built for children afflicted with leprosy, and who has eased his frustration with drink. The convicts are recruited to make repairs at the hospital, and Harry falls in love with a beautiful, blind nurse, Camille. One day the volcano erupts and threatens to destroy the entire island. The governor orders everyone evacuated but decides there will not be time to rescue the hospital children. By promising the three convicts paroles, Father Doonan gets them to volunteer for a rescue mission while Father Perreau nurses a broken leg. After being parachuted onto the mountain top, Father Doonan and his volunteers round up the children and personnel and begin the long, tortuous descent of the mountainside. During the trek, Harry and Camille are married by Father Doonan. As the volcano continues erupting, the journey becomes more perilous, and Marcel perishes in a quicksand mire. Later, Father Doonan and Charlie become trapped on a narrow ledge when a footbridge collapses. Harry leads the others to the safety of the beach and a waiting schooner and then races back to rescue Father Doonan and Charlie. It is too late, however, and all three men die as the island blows itself out of the sea with an ear-shattering explosion. *Convicts. Priests. French. Negroes. Americans in foreign countries. Nurses. Children. Leprosy. Self-sacrifice. Alcoholism. Blindness. Parachuting. Hospitals. Volcanoes. Quicksand. South Sea Islands.*

Note: Location scenes filmed on the island of Maui, Hawaii.

THE DEVIL BY THE TAIL (France/Italy) F6.1129
Fildebroc–Les Productions Artistes Associés–P. E. A. *Dist* Lopert Pictures. 29 Jun **1969** [New York opening; c7 Feb 1969; LF51]. Sd; col (De Luxe). 35mm. 93 min. *MPAA rating* M.
Dir Philippe de Broca. *Screenplay* Daniel Boulanger. *Dial* Daniel Boulanger, Philippe de Broca. *Dir Photog* Jean Penzer. *Camera* Gilles Bonneau. *Art Dir* Dominique André. *Film Ed* Françoise Javet. *Mus* Georges Delerue. *Sd* Jean Labussière. *1st & 2d Asst Dir* Georges Pellegrin, Christian Fuin. *Prod Mgr* Jean Pieuchot. *Script Girl* Suzanne Durrenberger. *Cost Dsgn* Jacques Fonteray. *Makeup* Jackie Reynal. *Coiffure* Evelyne Iafrate. *Still Photog* Dolly Schmidt.
Cast: Yves Montand *(Cesar Maricorne)*, Maria Schell *(Diane)*, Jean Rochefort *(Georges)*, Jean-Pierre Marielle *(Leroy-Martin)*, Madeleine Renaud *(La Marquise)*, Marthe Keller *(Amelie)*, Clotilde Joano *(Jeanne)*, Claude Pieplu *(Monsieur Patin)*, Xavier Gélin *(Charlie)*, Tanya Lopert *(Cookie)*, Jacques Balutin *(Balaze)*, Pierre Tornade *(Schwartz)*, Janine Berdin *(Madame Passereau)*, Eddy Roos *(Monsieur Passereau)*.
Crime comedy. An aristocratic French family has become so financially ruined that the matriarchal Marquise has had to turn the family's chateau into a hotel. There are few guests, however, until the Marquise's granddaughter Amelie seduces her boyfriend Charlie, the local garage mechanic, into sabotaging the automobiles that stop for gas and sending the stranded drivers up to the chateau. Soon business is booming, and the ladies of the house, including Amelie's virginal sister Jeanne and their mother, Diane, busy themselves making the guests content. Then Cesar Maricorne arrives, and despite his assertion that he is a diplomat, it is apparent that he is something else, particularly since his male "secretaries" carry guns. Cesar's amorous antics and his behavior have a bad influence on the other visitors at the chateau, and it is decided that he must leave. He and his companions run into a police roadblock, and in the ensuing confusion, the two secretaries and their car sink in a lake, but Cesar returns to the chateau with his attaché case. Thinking himself alone, he telephones for a rescue plane and is overheard by Amelie, who deduces that Cesar is the man who recently robbed a bank of over a million francs. The family agrees that although Cesar must go, his money must remain. They attempt to dispose of him by various means, but the indestructible Cesar survives. When he sets out signal lanterns for the rescue plane, Jeanne, who has

fallen in love with him, moves the lanterns and diverts the plane into a river. Cesar gladly returns to the chateau with Jeanne, and within a few months, the chateau has been converted into an elegant resort, and Cesar has given up his life of crime. *Aristocrats. Mechanics. Diplomats. Gangsters. Police. Family life. Seduction. Sabotage. Imposture. Bank robberies. Castles. Hotels. Resorts. Airplane accidents.*

Note: Opened in Paris in Feb 1969 as *Le diable par la queue*; running time: 95 min. Italian title: *Non tirate il diavolo per la coda*.

DEVIL DOLL (United States/Great Britain) F6.1130
Galaworldfilm Productions–Gordon Films. *Dist* Associated Film Distributors. Sep **1964**. Sd; b&w. 35mm. 80 min.
Prod-Dir Lindsay Shonteff. *Exec Prod* Kenneth Rive, Richard Gordon. *Screenplay* George Barclay, Lance Z. Hargreaves. *Based on a Story by* Frederick E. Smith. *Photog* Gerald Gibbs. *Art Dir* Stan Shields. *Film Ed* Ernest Bullingham. *Sd* Derek McColm. *Prod Mgr* Fred Slark.
Cast: Bryant Halliday *(The Great Vorelli)*, William Sylvester *(Mark English)*, Yvonne Romain *(Marianne)*, Sandra Dorne *(Vorelli's assistant)*, Karel Stepanek *(Dr. Heller)*, Francis De Wolff *(Dr. Keisling)*, Nora Nicholson *(Aunt Eva)*, Philip Ray *(Uncle Walter)*, Alan Gifford *(Bob Garrett)*, Pamela Law *(Garrett's girl friend)*, Heidi Erich *(Grace)*, Anthony Baird *(soldier)*, Trixie Dallas *(Miss Penton)*, Margaret Durnell *(The Countess)*, Ray Landor *(twist dancer)*, Ella Tracey *(Louisa)*, Guy Deghy *(Hans)*, David Charlesworth *(Hugo)*, Lorenza Coalville *(Mercedes)*, Jackie Ramsden *(The Nurse)*.
Horror film. At a London performance given by a ventriloquist-hypnotist called The Great Vorelli, newspaperman Mark English is puzzled by the tension that seems to exist between Vorelli and his dummy, Hugo. Marianne, English's fiancée, persuades her aunt to have Vorelli perform at a charity ball in her home so that English can get a closer look at the dummy. He finds nothing unusual about the dummy, but he awakens that night to find the dummy standing near his bed seeking help and telling English to "find me in Berlin 1948." English goes to Berlin, and he learns that Vorelli had worked there in 1948 with two partners, and that one of them was named Hugo. English locates the other partner, who confesses to seeing Vorelli kill Hugo and transfer his soul to a dummy. Returning to London, English finds Marianne under the hypnotic influence of Vorelli, who plans to transfer her soul to a female dummy. Hugo revolts, destroys the female dummy, and attacks Vorelli. Vorelli's soul then becomes confined to the dummy, and Hugo's soul enters Vorelli's body. *Hypnotists. Newspapermen. Ventriloquism. Partnerships. Murder. Puppets. London. Berlin. The Soul.*

Note: Filmed in Great Britain in 1963 and released there in 1965 at 70 min.

THE DEVIL GOT ANGRY see **MAJIN**

THE DEVIL IN LOVE (Italy) F6.1131
Fair Film. *Dist* Warner Bros.–Seven Arts, Inc. 15 May **1968** [Boston opening]. Sd; b&w (see note). 35mm. 97 min.
Prod Mario Cecchi Gori. *Dir* Ettore Scola. *Story-Screenplay* Ruggero Maccari, Ettore Scola. *Photog* Aldo Tonti. *Art Dir* Luciano Ricceri. *Set Decor* Ezio Altieri. *Film Ed* Marcello Valvestito, Tatiana Casini. *Mus* Armando Trovajoli. *Sd* Guido Ortensi. *Asst Dir* Don Carlos Dunaway, Dino De Palma. *Prod Mgr* Armando Morandi. *Prod Coörd* Pio Angeletti. *Cost* Maurizio Chiari.
Cast: Vittorio Gassman *(Belfagor)*, Claudine Auger *(Magdalena)*, Mickey Rooney *(Adramalek)*, Gabriele Ferzetti *(Lorenzo de Medici)*, Ettore Manni *(captain of guard)*, Annabella Incontrera *(Lucretia)*, Liana Orfei *(innkeeper's wife)*, Luigi Vannucchi *(Prince Franceschetto)*, Sherill Morgan *(Clarice)*, Giorgia Moll *(aristocrat's wife)*, Paolo Di Credico *(Cardinal Giovanni)*.
Costume comedy. Irked by the 1478 peace treaty between Rome and Florence, Beelzebub sends the Archdevil Belfagor and his impish servant, Adramalek, to rekindle the war between the two cities. Once on Earth, Belfagor seduces an innkeeper's wife and then sets out to disrupt the pending political wedding of Franceschetto, the son of Pope Innocent VIII, and Magdalena, the daughter of Lorenzo il Magnifico, the ruling prince of Florence. After inveigling Franceschetto into gambling for his life in a game of tarok, Belfagor easily defeats him and then assumes his identity. With the invisible Adramalek at his side, Belfagor/Franceschetto attends the nuptials but to everyone's amazement announces that he prefers war to marriage to Magdalena. Despite his daughter's humiliation, Lorenzo still advocates peace even though his advisors recommend war. Hoping to disgrace Magdalena further, Belfagor slips into her room, undresses her, leads her to the balcony for all the populace to see, and then, using Leonardo da Vinci's canvas wings, flees with the Florentine guards in pursuit. Engaging the captain of the guard, Belfagor knocks him unconscious but discovers that the captain is actually Magdalena in disguise. His "strange" feeling for her prevents him from killing her, and because of this emotion Beelzebub takes away his devilish powers. Now as vulnerable as any mortal in love, Belfagor is captured and sentenced to burn at the stake. At the last minute, Magdalena throws herself onto the pyre with Belfagor. But Lorenzo stops the

execution—and peace is restored when he consents to the marriage of Belfagor/Franceschetto to Magdalena. *Royalty. Guards. Impersonation. Seduction. Immortality. Marriage. Weddings. Tarok. Rome. Florence. Innocent VIII (pope). Lorenzo de Medici. Hell. The Devil.*

Note: Rome opening: Dec 1966 as *L'arcidiavolo*; running time: ca100 min; alternative title: *Il diavolo innamorato*. Italian version released in Technicolor. Sherill Morgan is a pseudonym for Hélène Chanel.

DEVIL IN SILK (West Germany) **F6.1132**
Fono-Film. *Dist* United Film Enterprises. 5 Jan **1968** [Chicago opening]. Sd; b&w. 35mm. 102 min.
Dir Rolf Hansen. *Screenplay* Jochen Huth. *Photog* Franz Weihmayr. *Art Dir* Robert Herlth, Arno Richter, Peter Röhrig. *Film Ed* Anna Höllering. *Mus* Mark Lothar. *Sd* Eduard Kessel. *Asst Dir* Hans Stumpf. *Prod Dir* Heinz Abel. *Prod Mgr* Hajo Wieland, Wolfgang Völker, Willy Egger.
Cast: Lilli Palmer *(Melanie)*, Curd Jürgens *(Thomas Ritter)*, Winnie Markus *(Sabine)*, Adelheid Seeck, Hans Nielsen, Wolfgang Büttner, Hilde Körber, Paul Bildt, Helmut Rudolph, Paul Bösiger, Robert Meyn, Otto Graf, Wolfgang Martini.
Drama. Source: Gina Kaus, *Teufel in Seide* (Gütersloh, 1956). Thomas Ritter, an unknown composer, meets and marries Melanie, a wealthy young widow, despite his grave doubts about their social differences. Melanie, a fierce egotist, forbids Thomas to devote himself to his music and his friends; she must be his sole passion. Her efforts to separate Thomas from Sabine, a pretty secretary, cause him to become Sabine's lover. Informed by Thomas that he is seeking a divorce, Melanie simulates a suicide; but Thomas is contemptuous of her theatrics, and Melanie kills herself. Indicted for murder, Thomas must persuade a jury of his innocence and confront his own feelings of remorse. *Composers. Widows. Egotists. Social classes. Secretaries. Infidelity. Suicide. Trials.*
Note: Opened in Düsseldorf in Jan 1956 as *Teufel in Seide*; running time: 105 min.

DEVIL IN THE CASTLE *see* **DAREDEVIL IN THE CASTLE**

DEVIL IN VELVET **F6.1133**
Lark Film Productions. *Dist* Boxoffice International Film Distributors. Jan **1968**. Sd; b&w. 35mm. 75 min.
Prod Lou Campa. *Exec Prod* Larry Crane. *Dir* Larry Crane. *Screenplay* Walter M. Berger. *Sets* Thomas Truvato, Donald Purdy. *Ed* Lew Waldeck. *Song:* "The Devil in Velvet" Larry Crane. *Sung by* Sandy Warryn, Larry Crane. *Mus Arr & Incidental Mus* Lorenzo Fuller. *Sd Rec* Dave McKenna. *Cost* Ian Macbeth. *Makeup* Ian Macbeth. *Sp Art Eff* Ian Orlando Macbeth. *Portrait* Fred Speone.
Cast: Edmund Nightwood *(Chancellor Marboeuf)*, Bernard Gilmore *(Maître Charles Haricot)*, Peter Bradford *(Maître Jean-Philippe Epinard)*, Luke St. Clair *(Clerk of the Court)*, Mary Macken *(Madame Brissaut)*, Christine Cybelle *(Louise Montreuil)*, Lou Champion *(Fernand Latour)*, Millie Pitt *(Annette Soupolais)*, Darlene Cotton *(Marianne Lucherne)*, Pauline Marvel *(Isabelle Fanchot)*, Gloria Singer *(Marguerite Coste)*, Irina *(Rosine Coste)*, Ian Orlando Macbeth *(Duc de Guise)*, Calvin Beck *(Comte de Lille)*, Jack Kugel *(Alphonse Framboise)*, June Kent *(Mariette Borelly)*, Natasha *(Suzanne Legume)*, Betty Thomas *(centerpiece)*, Eva *(serving wench)*, Dmitri Nikas *(scribe)*, John Mathews *(Dauphin of France)*, Karl Steen *(Marquis de Sade as a boy)*.
Comedy. The Marquis de Sade is brought to trial before Chancellor Marboeuf on charges of poisoning three prostitutes after a bawdy-house orgy. As the witnesses file past, the Marquis' strange and imaginative sexual practices are revealed, along with his outrageous sense of humor. After the orgy in question, each girl was presented with a box of candies, which the plaintiffs claim were poisoned. The testimony reveals that the candies actually contained a laxative. It becomes evident that the Marquis' gross sensualism is devoid of malice, and the Chancellor becomes convinced that the charges against him are an insult to the nobility of France. Before sentence is passed, however, the Marquis is permitted to speak. The contempt he expresses for the entire court enrages the judge, who sentences him to life imprisonment in the Bastille. Having spent 13 years in confinement, The Marquis makes imprudent remarks about the prison governor, and he is transferred to the Asylum for the Insane at Charenton 11 days before the Revolution would have freed him. Regretfully, he contemplates his former life. *Sensualists. Prostitutes. Nobility. Judges. Trials. Poisoning. Sexual practices. Orgies. France—History—Revolution 1789–93. Donatien Alphonse François [Marquis de] Sade. La Bastille. La Maison de Santé de Charenton.*
Note: Role of the Marquis de Sade apparently uncredited.

THE DEVIL INSIDE *see* **OFFBEAT**

THE DEVIL MADE A WOMAN (Spain) **F6.1134**
Producciones Benito Perojo. *Dist* Medallion Pictures. Feb **1962**. Sd; col (Eastman Color, print by Technicolor). 35mm. 87 min.
Prod Benito Perojo. *Assoc Prod* Miguel Tudela. *Dir* Tulio Demicheli. *Screenplay* Jesús María de Arozamena, Antonio Mas Guindal, Tulio Demicheli, Jean-Pierre Feydeau. *Dir Photog* Antonio L. Ballesteros. *Sets* Enrique Alarcón. *Ed* Antonio Ramirez. *Mus* Gregorio García Segura.
Cast: Sarita Montiel *(Carmen)*, George Mistral *(Antonio)*, Maurice Ronet *(José)*, Amedeo Nazzari *(colonel)*, Gerald Cobos *(Lucas)*, Maria Harte *(Micaela)*, José Marco Davó, Felix Fernandez, Santiago Rivero.
Drama. Source: Georges Bizet, Henri Meilhac and Ludovic Halévy, *Carmen* (Paris opening: 3 Mar 1875); Prosper Mérimée, "Carmen," in *La revue des deux mondes* (15 Oct 1845). Antonio, leader of the Spanish guerrillas in 1812, is wounded during an attack on a patrol of the Napoleonic occupying force in his country, and he takes refuge with Carmen, his mistress, a cabaret singer. That evening, while Carmen is singing in the tavern, she meets and becomes infatuated with José, a French sergeant. Micaela, a jealous woman rejected by Antonio, betrays him to the French, and he is captured despite Carmen's attempt to thwart the arrest. Several nights later, while Carmen is entertaining the French troops, Antonio is freed by his men. Carmen is accused of taking part in the escape plot, and in an effort to defend her, José shoots the French colonel. Forced to flee, José and Carmen join Antonio, whose jealousy leads the two men into a fight in which José is severely wounded. Just then the French storm the rebel hideout, and Carmen and José escape back to Carmen's room, seen only by Micaela. Micaela finds José alone, convinces him of Carmen's intention to betray him, and goes to the French headquarters to disclose the location of José's hideout. As the French arrive at the tavern, José confronts Carmen; but before she can respond, the French open fire, and Carmen throws herself in the path of a bullet meant for José. José dies with Carmen just as Antonio and his men launch their offensive. *Guerrillas. French. Mistresses. Singers. Soldiers. Jealousy. Perfidy. Self-sacrifice. Resistance (political). Murder. Military occupation. Cabarets. Napoleonic Wars.*
Note: Opened in Madrid in Sep 1959 as *Carmen, la de Ronda*; running time: 98 min. The following cast names were changed for American release: Sara Montiel to Sarita Montiel; Jorge Mistral to George Mistral; German Cobos to Gerald Cobos; Maria de los Angeles Hortelano to Maria Harte. Also known as *A Girl Against Napoleon*.

THE DEVIL NEVER SLEEPS *see* **SATAN NEVER SLEEPS**

THE DEVIL RIDES OUT *see* **THE DEVIL'S BRIDE**

THE DEVIL-SHIP PIRATES (Great Britain) **F6.1135**
Hammer Film Productions. *For* Associated British-Pathé, Ltd. *Dist* Columbia Pictures. May **1964** [c1 May 1964; LP28065]. Sd (RCA); col (Eastmancolor by Pathé). 35mm (Megascope). 89 min. [Copyright length: 86 min.]
Prod Anthony Nelson Keys. *Dir* Don Sharp. *Screenplay* Jimmy Sangster. *Dir Photog* Michael Reed. *Camera Op* Alan Hall. *Art Dir* Don Mingaye. *Prod Dsgn* Bernard Robinson. *Supv Ed* James Needs. *Mus Comp* Gary Hughes. *Mus Supv* John Hollingsworth. *Sd Rec* Ken Rawkins. *Sd Dir* Roy Hyde. *Asst Dir* Bert Batt. *Prod Mgr* Don Weeks. *Cont* Pauline Hardow. *Wardrobe Mistress* Rosemary Burrows. *Makeup Artist* Roy Ashton. *Hairstyles* Frieda Steiger. *Sp Eff* Les Bowie. *Fight Arr* Peter Diamond, W. Garwood, (Capt. R. N.).
Cast: Christopher Lee *(Captain Robeles)*, Andrew Keir *(Tom)*, John Cairney *(Harry)*, Duncan Lamont *(Bosun)*, Michael Ripper *(Pepe)*, Ernest Clark *(Sir Basil)*, Barry Warren *(Manuel)*, Suzan Farmer *(Angela)*, Natasha Pyne *(Jane)*, Annette Whiteley *(Meg)*, Charles Houston *(Antonio)*, Philip Latham *(Miller)*, Harry Locke *(Bragg)*, Leonard Fenton *(Quintana)*, Jack Rodney *(Mandrake)*, Barry Linehan *(Gustavo)*, Bruce Beeby *(Pedro)*, Michael Peake *(Grande)*, Johnny Briggs *(Pablo)*, Michael Newport *(Smiler)*, Peter Howell *(The Vicar)*, June Ellis *(Mrs. Blake)*, Joseph O'Connor *(Don José)*.
Historical melodrama. The *Diablo*, a pirate ship commissioned to serve with the Spanish Armada, leaves the Armada when it is defeated by Drake, and Captain Robeles sails the crippled *Diablo* into Cornwall. Jane, a local girl, is taken prisoner before she can tell the villagers of the Spanish defeat. Robeles convinces the villagers that Drake was defeated, and he and his pirates take over the town. Jane escapes with the help of her brother, Harry, but Robeles hangs their father. Manuel, one of Robeles' men, goes over to the side of the villagers when he finds that the pirates do not intend to return to Spain and, instead, will return to piracy once the ship has been mended. Robeles kills both Manuel and Sir Basil Smeeton, the local Lord of the Manor, in duels. But thanks to Manuel's earlier help, the *Diablo* and her crew are blown up as they leave port, and Harry is reunited with Angela, his sweetheart, who had been a pirate hostage. *Spanish. Pirates. Hostages. Ship crews. Duels. Ships. Spanish Armada. Cornwall (England). Ship explosions.*
Note: Released in Great Britain in June 1964.

THE DEVIL STRIKES AT NIGHT *see* **NAZI TERROR AT NIGHT**

DEVIL WOMAN *see* **ONIBABA**

DEVIL'S ANGELS   F6.1136

American International Productions. *Dist* American International Pictures. Apr **1967** [c26 Apr 1967; LP34277]. Sd; col (Pathécolor). 35mm (Panavision). 84 min.

A Roger Corman Production. *Prod* Burt Topper. *Exec Prod* James H. Nicholson, Samuel Z. Arkoff. *Dir* Daniel Haller. *Screenplay* Charles Griffith. *Photog* Richard Moore. *Film Ed* Ronald Steiner, Kenneth Crane. *Mus* Mike Curb. *Titl Song* Mike Curb, Guy Hemric, Jerry Styner. *Mus Supv* Al Simms. *Sd* Phil Mitchell. *Asst Dir* Dale Hutchinson. *Prod Mgr* Jack Bohrer. *Prod Assoc* Jack Cash. *Script Supv* Bonnie Prendergast. *Cost* Richard Bruno. *Makeup* Jack Obringer. *Hairstyles* Ray Foreman. *Prop* Karl Brainard, Richard M. Rubin.

Cast: John Cassavetes *(Cody)*, Beverly Adams *(Lynn)*, Mimsy Farmer *(Marianne)*, Maurice McEndree *(Joel-the-Mole)*, Marc Cavell *(Billy-the-Kid)*, Salli Sachse *(Louise)*, Nai Bonet *(Tonya)*, Buck Taylor *(Gage)*, Marianne Kanter *(Rena)*, Leo Gordon *(Sheriff Henderson)*, Buck Kartalian *(Funky)*, John Craig *(Robot)*, Kip Whitman *(Roy)*, George Sims *(Leroy)*, Mitzi Hoag *(Karen)*, Russ Bender *(Royce)*, Wally Campo *(Grog)*, Richard Anders *(Bruno)*, Paul Myer *(mayor)*, Lee Wainer *(Cane)*, Roy Thiel, Ronnie Dayton *(deputies)*, Henry Kendrick *(store owner)*.

Melodrama. Two members of a motorcycle club called The Skulls become involved in a fatal accident, and their leader, Cody, decrees that the group will avoid a confrontation with the police by moving to Hole-in-the-Wall, a West Coast haven for renegade cyclists. After breaking a fellow member out of the local jail, they head for the outlaw sanctuary. En route they stop off at a small town where a carnival is in progress. Although most of the townspeople are frightened by the leather-jacketed pack, a young girl named Marianne joins them for a party on the beach. But, under the influence of too much liquor, she fears she will be attacked and races hysterically back to town. The sheriff mistakenly assumes she has been raped and orders Cody jailed. Upon learning the truth, the sheriff releases Cody with the understanding that he and his group will leave immediately, but another cycle club has arrived to exact revenge. Quickly taking over the town, the two gangs ignore Cody's pleas and embark on a night of wholesale destruction. Realizing that his hope of finding a haven has been destroyed, Cody mounts his motorcycle and rides off alone. *Motorcycle gangs. Fugitives. Sheriffs. Smalltown life. Drunkenness. Rape. Carnivals.*

Note: Location scenes filmed in Arizona.

THE DEVIL'S BEDROOM   F6.1137

Rebel Productions. *Dist* Manson Distributing Corp. Sep **1964**. Sd; b&w (see note). 35mm. 78 min.

Prod George Gunter, L. Q. Jones. *Assoc Prod* Alvy Moore. *Dir* L. Q. Jones. *Screenplay* Claude Hall, Morgan Woodward. *Orig Story* Claude Hall. *Cinematog* George Gunter, Maitland Stewart. *Set Decor* Judy Masters. *Post Prod Supv* Jim Bullock. *Mus Supv* Edward J. Forsyth. *Mus Comp* William Loose, Emil Cadkin. *Sd Rec* Ben C. Gray, Johnny Kerns. *Sd Ed* Marvin Walowitz. *Prod Mgr* Gene Hall. *Script Clerk* Marta Smith. *Wardrobe* Daisy Gunter. *Key Grip* Leland Priestley. *Still Photog* Jim Mac Gammon. *Prop* Ralph G. Edwards. *Gaffer* Roy Moore. *Wrangler* Charles Jacobs. *Casting* Donald G. Seagull.

Cast: John Lupton *(Jim)*, Valerie Allen *(Della)*, Dick Jones *(Norm)*, Alvy Moore, Morgan Woodward, Justice McQueen, Mrs. Arch Pearson, Claude Hall, Bill Buckner, Thomas Commack, Merv Dawson, E. B. Jolly, Lawrence Mooney, W. H. Handley, Ken Ariola, Ralph G. Edwards.

Action melodrama. Norm cannot convince his brother Jim to sell his ranch, which is located on oil-rich land in Texas. Della, failing to win Jim's affection and his property, marries Norm in revenge, then accuses Jim of trying to rape her. Persuaded by Della that Jim is insane, Norm has his brother placed in a mental institution, but Jim escapes. Norm dies mysteriously in Jim's barn, and Crow, an agitator, arouses the townspeople against Jim. The mob becomes inflamed when Della is found drowned in a well at Jim's farm. Although the sheriff determines both deaths to be accidental, he arrives too late to prevent the crazed mob from burning Jim to death. *Brothers. Ranchers. Sheriffs. Marriage. Revenge. Rape. Insanity. Lynching. Injustice. Murder. Oil. Insane asylums. Texas.*

Note: Filmed in color. Working title: *The Fury of Vengeance.*

THE DEVIL'S BOOK STORE   F6.1138

Dist American Film Distributing Corp. 16 Dec **1969** [Maryland license]. Sd; b&w. 35mm. 63 min.

Compilation Supv Bernard Lust. *Based on an Idea by* Samuel Oliver Bandler.

Crime melodrama. A compilation of footage from *The Filth Shop* and *Meet the Sex,* q. v. *Racketeers. Youth. Pornography. Male homosexuality. Lesbianism. Narcotics. Syndicates. Body painting.*

THE DEVIL'S BRIDE (Great Britain)   F6.1139

Hammer Film Productions–Seven Arts Productions. *Dist* Twentieth Century–Fox Film Corp. 18 Dec **1968** [New York opening; c31 Dec 1967; LP36697]. Sd (RCA); col (DeLuxe). 35mm. 95 min.

Prod Anthony Nelson Keys. *Dir* Terence Fisher. *Screenplay* Richard Matheson. *Dir Photog* Arthur Grant. *Camera Op* Moray Grant. *Supv Art Dir* Bernard Robinson. *Supv Ed* James Needs. *Ed* Spencer Reeve. *Mus Comp* James Bernard. *Mus Supv* Philip Martell. *Choreog* David Toguri. *Sd Rec* Ken Rawkins. *Sd Ed* Arthur Cox, A. W. Lumkin. *Asst Dir* Bert Batt. *Prod Mgr* Ian Lewis. *Cont* June Randall. *Wardrobe Supv* Rosemary Burrows. *Wardrobe Mistress* Janet Lucas. *Makeup* Eddie Knight. *Hairstylist* Pat McDermott. *Sp Eff* Michael Stainer-Hutchins. *Casting* Irene Lamb.

Cast: Christopher Lee *(Duc de Richleau)*, Charles Gray *(Mocata)*, Nike Arrighi *(Tanith)*, Leon Greene *(Rex)*, Patrick Mower *(Simon)*, Gwen Ffrangcon-Davies *(countess)*, Sarah Lawson *(Marie)*, Paul Eddington *(Richard)*, Rosalyn Landor *(Peggy)*, Russell Waters *(Malin)*, Mohan Singh, Keith Pyott, John Brown, British.

Horror film. Source: Dennis Wheatley, *The Devil Rides Out* (London, 1935). In the late 1920's, the Duc de Richleau and his friend Rex Van Ryn arrive at the home of the Duc's protégé, Simon Aron, and find that he is hosting a party for an international secret society he has just joined. After learning that the society is actually a cult of Satanists led by the high priest Mocata and the Countess d'Urfe, the Duc and Van Ryn discover that the real purpose of the gathering is to make plans for initiating Simon and the countess' beautiful niece, Tanith, into the coven. Despite the efforts of the Duc to thwart the plan, Mocata uses his hypnotic powers to lure both Simon and Tanith to a wooded glade for the initiation. But the Duc and Van Ryn succeed in destroying the Devil, conjured up by Mocata's incantation, and lead Simon and Tanith to the home of mutual friends, the Eaton family. Tanith, however, refuses to endanger the Eatons by staying at their house and goes off alone. Van Ryn, who has fallen in love with her, follows but is too late to save her from death. Quick to act, the Duc shields the others at the Eaton home by drawing out a protective circle and warding off the powers of darkness with ritualistic and holy symbols. During the night of terror that follows, young Peggy Eaton succumbs to Mocata's powers and is prepared for the Devil's sacrificial altar. As the Satanists summon the Angel of Death to ride out and claim his victim, the Duc and his friends intervene and rescue Peggy from the altar. Deprived of his intended victim, the Devil—following the ancient tradition that decrees he must carry off someone when called out—seizes Mocata as his own. Tanith is restored to life, and the cult is destroyed. *Nobility. Demonology. Cults. Rites and ceremonies. Hypnotism. Human sacrifice. Secret societies. The Devil.*

Note: Released in Great Britain in 1968 as *The Devil Rides Out.*

THE DEVIL'S BRIGADE   F6.1140

Wolper Pictures. *Dist* United Artists. 15 May **1968** [Detroit opening; c14 May 1968; LP36811]. Sd; col (DeLuxe). 35mm (Panavision). 130 min.

Pres by David L. Wolper. *Prod* David L. Wolper. *Assoc Prod* Theodore Strauss, Julian Ludwig. *Dir* Andrew V. McLaglen. *Screenplay* William Roberts. *Photog* William H. Clothier. *Camera Op* Al Myers. *Art Dir* Alfred Sweeney. *Set Decor* Morris Hoffman. *Main Titl* Don Record. *Film Ed* William Cartwright. *Mus Comp & Cond* Alex North. *Orch* Henry Brant. *Sd* Al Overton, Clem Portman. *Asst Dir* Terry Morse, Jr., Newt Arnold, Dennis Donnelly. *Prod Supv* Clarence Eurist. *Prod Mgr* Howard Joslin. *Makeup* Donald W. Roberson. *Sp Eff Supv* Logan Frazee. *Stunt Supv* Hal Needham.

Cast: William Holden *(Lt. Col. Robert T. Frederick)*, Cliff Robertson *(Maj. Alan Crown)*, Vince Edwards *(Maj. Cliff Bricker)*, Andrew Prine *(Pvt. Theodore Ransom)*, Claude Akins *(Rocky Rockman)*, Richard Jaeckel *(Omar Greco)*, Jack Watson *(Cpl. Wilfred Peacock)*, Jeremy Slate *(Patrick O'Neill)*, Richard Dawson *(Hugh MacDonald)*, Dana Andrews *(Brig. Gen. Walter Naylor)*, Michael Rennie *(Lt. Gen. Mark Clark)*, Carroll O'Connor *(Maj. Gen. Maxwell Hunter)*, Gretchen Wyler *(a lady of joy)*, Tom Stern *(Captain Cardwell)*, Tom Troupe *(Al Manella)*, Luke Askew *(Hubert Hixon)*, Bill Fletcher *(Bronc Guthrie)*, Jean-Paul Vignon *(Henri Laurent)*, Harry Carey, Jr. *(Captain Rose)*, Norman Alden *(M.P. lieutenant)*, Paul Hornung *(lumberjack)*, Gene Fullmer *(bartender)*, Patric Knowles *(Adm. Lord Louis Mountbatten)*, Don Megowan *(Luke Phelan)*, David Pritchard *(Corporal Coker)*, Paul Busch *(German captain)*, James Craig *(American officer)*.

War drama. Source: Robert H. Adleman and George Walton, *The Devil's Brigade* (Philadelphia, 1966). While awaiting the massing of United States power during the bleakest phase of World War II, England begins preparing for commando raids against Nazi-occupied Europe. As part of the desperate operation, the Allies create the 1st Special Service Force to plan and carry out an attack on Norway in hopes of tying up large numbers of German troops. The force of efficiently trained Canadian soldiers and rebellious American G.I. misfits is trained in Montana under the leadership of Lt. Col. Robert T. Frederick, a desk-bound army intellectual who has never before held a field command. Antagonism between the Canadians and the Americans, as well as between their respective leaders, Maj. Alan Crown and Maj. Cliff Bricker, at first threatens to disrupt the guerrilla training. But Frederick uses the men's mutual enmity as the basis for a rivalry that eventually welds them together as one highly disciplined fighting force. Shortly before they are scheduled for embarkation to Europe, the Canadians and Americans engage in a tavern brawl with some local lumberjacks, and, as a result of the free-for-all, the two groups of soldiers discover a camaraderie that had not heretofore existed on the surface. Then, when Frederick feels his outfit is ready for combat, he receives word that the Norway operation has been cancelled and the unit is to be disbanded. Appealing to Washington, he is granted a different assignment for his men—patrolling near the German lines in southern Italy. After capturing an enemy-held village, the unit is given the seemingly impossible task of taking Mt. La Difensa. Although the men accomplish their mission by scaling the precipitous mountainside, their losses are far greater than anticipated. Nonetheless, it is a telling victory—and one which earns for the 1st Special Service Force the grudging admiration of the Germans and the title "The Devil's Brigade." *Intellectuals. Guerrillas. Lumberjacks. Germany—Army. World War II. Montana. Mount La Difensa. Robert T. Frederick. Walter Naylor. Mark Wayne Clark. Maxwell Hunter. Louis Mountbatten. United States Army—Special Forces. Canada—Army.*

Note: Location scenes were filmed on the Wasatch Mountain, Utah, and at Santa Elia Fiume Rapido in Italy.

DEVIL'S CAMERA *see* **SCUM OF THE EARTH!**

THE DEVIL'S DAFFODIL (Great Britain/West Germany)   **F6.1141**
Omnia Films-Rialto Film. *For* Britannia Film Distributors. *Dist* Goldstone Film Enterprises. 25 Oct **1967** [New York opening]. Sd; b&w. 35mm. 86 min.
Prod Steven Pallos, Donald Taylor. *Prod Supv* Horst Wendlandt. *Dir* Akos von Rathony. *Screenplay* Basil Dawson, Donald Taylor. *Dir Photog* Desmond Dickinson. *Photog* Harry Gillam. *Art Dir* William Hutchinson, Jim Sawyer. *Film Ed* Peter Taylor. *Mus* Keith Papworth. *Choreog* Patricia Kirschner. *Sd* Bob Jones, Bert Ross. *Asst Dir* Tom Pevsner. *Prod Mgr* Philip Shipway. *Makeup* Stuart Freeborn.

Cast: William Lucas *(Jack Tarling)*, Joachim Fuchsberger *(Jack Tarling, German vers)*, Penelope Horner *(Anne Rider)*, Sabina Sesselmann *(Anne Rider, German vers)*, Colin Jeavons *(Peter Keene)*, Klaus Kinski *(Peter Keene, German vers)*, Christopher Lee *(Ling Chu)*, Ingrid van Bergen *(Gloria)*, Albert Lieven *(Raymond Lyne)*, Marius Goring *(Oliver Milburgh)*, Jan Hendriks *(Charles)*, Peter Illing *(Jan Putek)*, Walter Gotell *(Superintendent Whiteside)*, Dawn Beret *(Katya)*, Bettine Le Beau *(Trudi)*, Campbell Singer *(Sir Archibald)*, Lance Percival *(French gendarme)*, Frederick Bartman *(detective)*, Nancy Nevinson *(sluttish woman)*, Martin Lyder *(Max)*, Gundel Sargent *(hotel receptionist)*, Irene Prador *(Maisie)*, Edwina Carroll *(Chinese girl)*, Grace Denbeigh-Russell *(Mrs. Rider)*.

Crime melodrama. Source: Edgar Wallace, *The Daffodil Mystery* (London, 1920). Superintendent Whiteside of Scotland Yard deduces that a homicidal maniac is at large when several people are found murdered in London, each with a daffodil placed across his body. Airways security agent Jack Tarling and his detective friend Ling Chu, however, connect the killings with a Hong Kong dope-smuggling ring which they have come to London to investigate. Their theory is confirmed when heroin is found concealed in a shipment of artificial daffodils delivered to a mercantile firm headed by Raymond Lyne. Police discover that all of the murder victims were members of the Cosmos Club, and it is learned that Lyne had recently persuaded Jan Putek, the owner of the club, to hire a drug-addicted ex-convict named Peter Keene. Lyne has kept Keene supplied with heroin in exchange for his services as a hired killer. Lyne, the chief suspect, is found murdered, followed by Putek, Lyne's wife Gloria, and Oliver Milburgh, the manager of the club. Whiteside discovers that the daffodil killer's next victim is to be Anne Rider, Lyne's secretary. The insane Keene lures her to a cemetery and drags her into a mausoleum. Ling Chu, waiting in the shadows, springs from his hiding place in time to trap and knife the killer. Anne is led out of the cemetery by Jack Tarling, who has fallen in love with her. *Detectives. Secretaries. Ex-convicts. Drug addicts. Merchants. Hired killers. Chinese. Murder. Smuggling. Insanity. Flowers. Cemeteries. Clubs. Heroin. London. Hong Kong. Scotland Yard.*

Note: German and English versions simultaneously filmed in London. Released in West Germany in 1961 as *Das Geheimnis der gelben Narzissen*, in Great Britain in May 1961. Also known as *Daffodil Killer.*

DEVIL'S DOLL *see* **THE DEVIL'S HAND**

THE DEVIL'S 8   **F6.1142**
American International Pictures. 19 Mar **1969** [New York opening; c19 Mar 1969; LP36701]. Sd; col (Pathé). 35mm. 97 min. *MPAA rating* M.
Prod-Dir Burt Topper. *Assoc Prod* Jack Cash. *Screenplay* James Gordon White, William Huyck, John Milius. *Story* Larry Gordon. *Dir Photog* Richard C. Glouner. *Art Dir* Paul Sylos. *Set Dsgn* Harry Reif. *Film Ed* Fred Feitshans, Jr. *Mus* Mike Curb. *Mus Supv* Al Simms. *Titl Song* Mike Curb, Guy Hemric. *Sd* Al Overton. *Asst Dir* James Petsch, Lew Borzage. *Prod Mgr* Jack Bohrer. *Script Supv* Lynn Aber. *Wardrobe* Richard Bruno. *Sp Eff* Roger George. *Stunt Coörd* Chuck Bail. *Constr Supv* Ross Hahn.

Cast: Christopher George *(Ray Faulkner)*, Ralph Meeker *(Burl)*, Fabian *(Sonny)*, Tom Nardini *(Billy Joe)*, Leslie Parrish *(Cissy)*, Ross Hagen *(Frank Davis)*, Larry Bishop *(Chandler)*, Cliff Osmond *(Bubba)*, Robert DoQui *(Henry Reed)*, Ron Rifkin *(Stewart Martin)*, Baynes Barron *(bureau chief)*, Joseph Turkel *(Sam)*, Lada Edmund, Jr. *(Inez)*, Marjorie Dayne *(Hallie)*.

Melodrama. Hoping to destroy the corrupt power structure of a southern state, Federal agent Ray Faulkner poses as a road gang convict, engineers the escape of a group of hardened chain-gang criminals, and persuades them to work on the side of the law by promising them paroles. After training the men in high-speed driving and hurling lighted bombs at pinpoint targets, Faulkner prepares to move against a statewide moonshine syndicate. One of Faulkner's convicts, Frank Davis (a former driver for the syndicate), is at first hostile to the idea, but he becomes an eager convert when Faulkner reveals that the mob murdered his brother. Also assisting Faulkner is young Stewart Martin, a Federal agent on his first assignment. Once ready, the team of eight starts intercepting the moonshiners' delivery cars until the syndicate leader, Burl, is forced to give Faulkner and his men a share of the illegal whiskey operation and let them make the deliveries. But Burl pulls a double-cross by arranging for Faulkner and Martin to be ambushed by crooked police while making a moonshine run, and Martin is shot down from a police helicopter. By now, however, Sonny, one of Faulkner's men, has learned the location of Burl's stills and "the devil's eight" attack with their specially equipped cars and carefully timed explosives. During the battle, Burl tries to escape by using his mistress Cissy (who was once Davis' girl friend) as a hostage, but Faulkner succeeds in apprehending him. Cissy is reunited with a reformed Davis, and as Burl is being led away to face trial, Faulkner becomes confident that the power structure will soon crumble. *Government agents. Moonshiners. Chain gangs. Police. Hostages. Criminals—Rehabilitation. Imposture. Political corruption. Perfidy. Syndicates. Explosives. Helicopters. United States—South.*

Note: Location scenes were filmed at Camp Pinecrest, California.

THE DEVIL'S EYE (Sweden)   **F6.1143**
Svensk Filmindustri. *Dist* Janus Films. 30 Oct **1961** [New York opening]. Sd; b&w. 35mm. 90 min.
An Ingmar Bergman Production. *Prod* Allan Ekelund. *Dir-Writ* Ingmar Bergman. *Photog* Gunnar Fischer. *Art Dir* P. A. Lundgren. *Film Ed* Oscar Rosander. *Musical Selections* Domenico Scarlatti. *Sd* Stig Flodin, Staffan Dalin. *Asst Dir* Lenn Hjörtzberg. *Prod Mgr* Lars-Owe Carlberg.

Cast: Jarl Kulle *(Don Juan)*, Bibi Andersson *(Britt-Marie)*, Axel Düberg *(her fiancé)*, Nils Poppe *(The Pastor, her father)*, Gertrud Fridh *(The Pastor's Wife)*, Sture Lagerwall *(Pablo)*, Stig Järrel *(Satan)*, Gunnar Björnstrand *(The Actor)*, Georg Funkquist *(Count Armand de Rochefoucauld)*, Gunnar Sjöberg *(Marquis Giuseppe de Maccopazza)*, Allan Edwall *(The Ear Devil)*, Torsten Winge *(old man)*, Kristina Adolphsson, Ragnar Arvedson, Börje Lundh, Lenn Hjörtzberg.

Comedy. Freely adapted from a Danish radio play by: Oluf Bang, *Don Juan Vender tillbage* (broadcast 30 Aug 1940). One day in the pit of Hell, Satan becomes afflicted with a painful sty. The cause, his ministers advise him, is Britt-Marie, the virginal daughter of a country pastor, a young girl who is stubbornly determined to remain pure until her wedding day. As a remedy, Satan removes Don Juan from his personal hell (seduction without fulfillment) and sends him back to Earth with orders to seduce the young woman. Accompanying Don Juan on his journey are an old watchdog devil and Don Juan's lusty servant, Pablo, who immediately defies his instructions by attempting to seduce the childish pastor's frustrated wife. For Don Juan it is a more complicated matter; the 20th century Britt-Marie is almost totally indifferent to his old-fashioned charm, and his outpourings of love merely serve to amuse her. One night, frustrated and close to desperation, Don Juan sneaks into Britt-Marie's bedroom only to be thoroughly startled by her sudden willingness to submit to him—but out of pity and compassion for his loneliness, not out of love or passion. Humiliated, Don Juan declines her offer and once more returns to Hell. Only then does he fully grasp the extent of his future torment; for the first time in eternity, Don Juan is completely and hopelessly in love. Meanwhile, Pablo's success in seducing the pastor's wife has opened the eyes of the married couple to what has been lacking in their relationship. Satan forces Don Juan to listen to Britt-Marie in bed on her wedding night, and the Devil's eye finally heals, when she tells her husband that she has never been kissed by another man. *Virginity. Clergymen. Indentured servants. Seduction. Chastity. Infidelity. Hell. The Devil. Don Juan.*

Note: Released in Sweden as *Djävulens öga* in Oct 1960.

THE DEVIL'S HAND   F6.1144

Rex Carlton Productions. *Dist* Crown International Pictures. 13 Sep **1961** [San Diego, California, opening]. Sd; b&w. 35mm. 71 min.

Prod (see note) Alvin K. Bubis, Rex Carlton. *Exec Prod* Jack Leroy Miles. *Assoc Prod* Rickey Newberry. *Dir* William J. Hole, Jr. *Screenplay* Jo Heims, Rex Carlton. *Photog* Meredith M. Nicholson. *Film Ed* Howard Epstein. *Makeup* Jack P. Pierce.

Cast: Linda Christian *(Bianca)*, Robert Alda *(Rick)*, Neil Hamilton *(Frank)*, Ariadne Welter *(Donna)*, Gene Craft, Jeannie Carmen, Julie Scott, Diana Spears.

Horror film. Rick awakens from an oft-repeated dream about a beautiful woman and wanders into a curio shop exhibiting lifelike dolls. In the shop, which is actually a front for a voodoo, devil-worshiping cult, he purchases a doll which is an exact replica of the girl in his dreams. The shopowner, Frank, tells him that the doll is modeled after a woman named Bianca, and he gives him her address. As Rick leaves the shop, Frank, who is the high priest of the voodoo cult, sticks a pin into a doll replica of Rick's girl friend, Donna; and the young woman is immediately stricken and rushed to a hospital. Rick visits Bianca, who offers him her love on condition that he join the cult. After his initiation, he removes the pin from Donna's doll so that she will recover. When his disloyalty to the cult is discovered, Frank takes Donna prisoner and orders that she be prepared for sacrifice, but Rick kills Frank and escapes with Donna as the voodoo temple goes up in flames. Bianca's fate, however, is unknown, and Rick wonders if he and Donna are free of her evil influence. *Storekeepers. Priests. Voodoo. Human sacrifice. Demonology. Dolls. Cults. Dreams. Fires.*

Note: Filmed in 1959 as *The Naked Goddess.* Prerelease title: *Devil's Doll.* Alternative title: *Live To Love.* Carlton and Newberry receive no screen credit; Bubis was the film's original associate producer.

THE DEVIL'S MATE   F6.1145

Mitam Productions. *Dist* Filmex Distributing Co. 3 Aug **1966** [Champaign, Illinois, showing]. Sd; b&w. 35mm. 66 min.

Dir T. G. Zorfa.

Cast: John Barry, actor, Jerry Harris *(Brad, see note)*, Arlene Janice, June Scott, Dodie Johns.

Melodrama. Brad, a young rancher, visits the city and invites Patty, a previous acquaintance, to a nightclub. Afterwards, they go to her apartment where Brad tries to rape Patty, and when she resists his advances, her roommate, Lorraine, awakened by Patty's screams, throws acid in Brad's face, leaving one side horribly burned. Brad returns to his ranch to have his wounds tended by his faithful ranch hand, Jess. Brad becomes self-conscious about the disfiguration and seeks sexual gratification with prostitutes. One of these sexual contacts, Randy, antagonizes him, and he goes berserk and murders her. Brad then seeks revenge against the two women who caused his downfall. He kidnaps Lorraine, beats her into submission, and periodically tortures her at his ranch. One day he allows her to escape, recaptures her, and flogs her to death. Now completely demented, Brad seeks out Patty, but the police intercede and extract a confession from him. Brad is killed while attempting to flee from the police. *Ranchers. Roommates. Prostitutes. Psychopaths. Police. Rape. Disfiguration. Flagellation. Murder. Revenge. Sadism. Abduction.*

Note: Conflicting sources suggest that Jerry Harris and John Barry are the same person. Also known as *Satan's Mistress* and *Satan's Woman.*

THE DEVIL'S MESSENGER (United States/Sweden)   F6.1146

Herts-Lion International Corp. 24 Oct **1962** [Los Angeles opening]. Sd; b&w. 35mm. 72 min.

Prod Kenneth Herts. *Dir* Herbert L. Strock. *Orig Screenplay (see note)* Curt Siodmak. *Adapt* Leo Guild. *Photog* William Troiano. *Art Dir* Kenneth Herts. *Mus* Alfred Gwyn. *Sd* Continental Sound Corp. *Asst Dir* David McDonald.

Cast: Lon Chaney, [Jr.] *(The Devil)*, Karen Kadler *(Satanya)*, Michael Hinn *(John Radian)*, Gunnel Broström, Tammy Newmara, John Crawford, Jan Blomberg, Ralph Brown, Ingrid Bedoya, Bertil Johnson, Eve Hossner, Charles Goodlin.

Horror film. One of the recent sinners to arrive in Hell is Satanya, a beautiful young suicide. The Devil orders her to act as a messenger for him to recruit possible new candidates from earth. In return for her work, she is promised clemency. Her first target is a New York photographer, to whom she brings a new camera; subsequently, he kills one of his models. His death and consequent descent into Hell are caused by the repeated appearance of the dead model's face in his photographs. Satanya's next assignment is an anthropologist, whose present from the Devil is a pick. He has fallen in love with a beautiful young woman who has been trapped and frozen in a glacier for a million years. His

entry to Hell is assured when he kills the frozen woman, who drowns as he melts her icy grave. For Satanya, these two missions have been nightmares, but her next assignment brings her great pleasure. The potential victim is the man for whose sake she committed suicide. She ascends to earth as a fortune-teller and is approached by her ex-lover, who wishes her to read his fortune from a crystal ball. As foreseen in their session together, the building collapses and they are both killed. In Hell, the couple are assigned to deliver to the people of earth an envelope containing the formula for an atom bomb. Soon after the formula has been delivered, the human race is destroyed by an atomic explosion, and all are consigned to Hell. *Photographers. Models. Anthropologists. Fortune-tellers. Suicide. Murder. Holocausts. Cameras. Atom bomb. Glaciers. The Devil. Hell.*

Note: Filmed in part in Sweden in 1959 as *No. 13 Demon Street,* a 13-episode TV series written by Curt Siodmak (Leo Guild is generally credited with the screenplay); revised for U. S. theatrical release.

THE DEVIL'S MISTRESS   F6.1147

WGW Pictures. *Dist* Holiday Pictures, Emerson Film Enterprises. **1966.** Sd; col (Eastman Color). 35mm. 66 min.

Prod Wes Moreland. *Dir-Writ* Orville Wanzer. *Photog* Teddy Gregory. *Mus* Billy Allen, Douglas Warren. *Prod Supv* Austin Green.

Cast: Joan Stapleton *(Liah)*, Robert Gregory *(Frank)*, Forrest Westmoreland *(Charlie)*, Douglas Warren *(Joe)*, Oren Williams *(Will)*, Arthur Resley *(Jeroboam)*.

Horror film. Four cowboys who are escaping from the law in the 1870's, flee to the mountains of New Mexico. Sadistic Charlie and Joe hope to find Apache Indian women to rape and murder, but Frank, the youngest of the group, tells Will that he wants no part of murder. The four desperadoes come to an isolated cabin where they find Jeroboam, a frontiersman in Puritan dress, and his bewitching, half-Indian mistress, Liah. Charlie and Joe murder Jeroboam and rape Liah, taking her with them. That night, Liah responds to Charlie's advances with a passionate kiss that makes him slowly weaken and die. The next day, Joe is bitten by a rattlesnake, and he dies in a fall off a rocky cliff. Will refuses to stay at the camp with Frank and Liah because of a recurring nightmare in which he sees a man hanging from a tree. Will's body is later found just as it appeared in the dream. Finally, Liah bewitches Frank, smothering him with kisses until he dies. The revenge complete, Jeroboam emerges from the woods to be reunited with Liah. *Desperadoes. Apache Indians. Halfcastes. Mistresses. Murder. Rape. Sadism. Revenge. Witchcraft. Snakebites. New Mexico. Dreams. The Devil.*

Note: Filmed in Las Cruces, New Mexico. Wes Moreland and Forrest Westmoreland are the same person.

DEVILS OF DARKNESS (Great Britain)   F6.1148

Planet Film Productions. *Dist* Twentieth Century-Fox Film Corp. May **1965.** Sd; col (Eastmancolor, print by De Luxe). 35mm. 88 min.

Prod Tom Blakeley. *Dir* Lance Comfort. *Orig Story & Screenplay* Lyn Fairhurst. *Photog* Reg Wyer. *Camera Op* Frank Drake. *Art Dir* John Earl. *Film Ed* John Trumper. *Mus* Bernie Fenton. *Mus Adv* Frank Patten. *Sd* Robert T. MacPhee, Gordon K. McCallum. *Asst Dir* Roy Baird. *Prod Mgr* John Comfort. *Cont* Muirne Mathieson. *Cost* Muriel Dickson. *Makeup* George Blackler.

Cast: William Sylvester *(Paul Baxter)*, Hubert Noel *(Count Sinistre/Armond du Moliere)*, Tracy Reed *(Karen)*, Carole Gray *(Tania)*, Diana Decker *(Madeline Braun)*, Rona Anderson *(Anne Forest)*, Peter Illing *(Inspector Malin)*, Gérard Heinz *(Bouvier)*, Victor Brooks *(Inspector Hardwick)*, Avril Angers *(Midge)*, Brian Oulton *(The Colonel)*, Marie Burke *(old gypsy woman)*, Marianne Stone *(The Duchess)*, Rod McLennan *(Dave)*, Geoffrey Kenion *(Keith Forest)*, Burnell Tucker *(Derek)*, Julie Mendez *(snake dancer)*, Eddie Byrne.

Horror film. Paul, Keith, and Anne, vacationing in Brittany, scoff at the local gypsies' stories about Count Sinistre, a vampire executed in the 16th century and later returned to life. In 1800 the count married Tania, a young gypsy woman whom he killed and then raised from the dead. Keith goes to explore some local caves and is found dead. Later a handsome Frenchman and his wife come to console Anne. While standing with the Frenchman beside a lake, Anne notices that he casts no reflection: he is Count Sinistre himself. Shortly afterwards, Anne's body is found in the lake. The police call it suicide, but Paul decides to investigate. The bodies of Anne and Keith disappear from the coffins en route to England, and a scientist whom Paul consults is subsequently killed in his laboratory. Seeking further information, Paul meets Karen, a model, who is soon abducted by Count Sinistre. Paul manages to uncover Sinistre's scheme, and, upon returning to Brittany, he unmasks the evil count and saves Karen. The count, frustrated and defeated, trips over a cemetery cross, ages rapidly, and dies. *Vampires. Nobility. French. Scientists. Models. Gypsies. Murder. Abduction. Coffins. Corpses. Vacations. Brittany.*

Note: Opened in London in Sep 1965; running time: 90 min.

THE DEVIL'S OWN (Great Britain)   F6.1149

Seven Arts Productions-Hammer Film Productions. *Dist* Twentieth Century-Fox Film Corp. 25 Jan **1967** [Detroit opening; c31 Dec 1966; LP34064]. Sd (RCA); col (De Luxe). 35mm. 90 min.

Prod Anthony Nelson Keys. *Dir* Cyril Frankel. *Screenplay* Nigel Kneale. *Dir Photog* Arthur Grant. *Camera Op* Cece Cooney. *Art Dir* Don Mingaye. *Prod Dsgn* Bernard Robinson. *Supv Ed* James Needs. *Ed* Chris Barnes. *Mus Comp* Richard Rodney Bennett. *Mus Supv* Philip Martell. *Choreog* Denys Palmer. *Sd Rec* Ken Rawkins. *Sd Roy* Hyde. *Asst Dir* David Tringham. *Prod Mgr* Charles Permane. *Cont* Anne Deeley. *Wardrobe Master* Harry Haynes. *Wardrobe Supv* Molly Arbuthnot. *Makeup* George Partleton. *Hairstyles* Frieda Steiger. *Casting* Irene Lamb.

Cast: Joan Fontaine *(Gwen Mayfield)*, Kay Walsh *(Stephanie Bax)*, Alec McCowen *(Alan Bax)*, Ann Bell *(Sally)*, Ingrid Brett *(Linda)*, John Collin *(Dowsett)*, Michele Dotrice *(Valerie)*, Gwen Ffrangcon-Davies *(Granny Rigg)*, Duncan Lamont *(Bob Curd)*, Leonard Rossiter *(Dr. Wallis)*, Martin Stephens *(Ronnie Dowsett)*, Carmel McSharry *(Mrs. Dowsett)*, Viola Keats *(Mrs. Curd)*, Shelagh Fraser *(Mrs. Creek)*, Bryan Marshall *(Tom)*.

Mystery melodrama. Source: Peter Curtis, *The Devil's Own* (London, 1960). While teaching at a mission school in central Africa, Gwen Mayfield is subjected to a traumatic encounter with a voodoo witch doctor and suffers a nervous collapse. Once recovered, she returns to England and accepts a position as headmistress of a small private school run by Alan Bax, who poses as a priest, and his sister Stephanie, a journalist with a strong interest in witchcraft. Although the village and school are pleasant, Gwen soon senses that her brightest pupil, 13-year-old Linda Rigg, is looked upon with suspicion by most of the townspeople. Further investigation proves that Linda's best friend, Ronnie Dowsett, is being kept away from the girl because of the belief that a local voodoo cult is planning to offer her as a virgin sacrifice. Matters come to a head when Ronnie becomes seriously ill, and a voodoo image of a young boy is found with pins stuck in it. Soon after, Ronnie's father meets a strange death while attempting to find the reason for his son's illness. Gwen plans to speak out at the dead father's inquest, but that night a horrifying voodoo image appears in her bedroom, and she again suffers a nervous breakdown. While at a nursing home, she recovers her memory and escapes back to the village. Aided by Alan, she makes her way to a secret cave and learns that Stephanie has the entire village in her control through the practice of witchcraft. In the cave, Stephanie is preparing to immortalize herself by sacrificing Linda. Gwen is forcibly initiated into the cult, but by spilling her own blood, she is able to break the spell and bring about Stephanie's death. With the village freed of the practitioners of black magic, Gwen chooses to remain on as headmistress of Alan's school. *Schoolteachers. Headmistresses. Students. Journalists. Priests. Voodoo. Witchcraft. Mental illness. Imposture. Brother-sister relationship. Human sacrifice. Rites and ceremonies. Boarding schools. Cults. Caves. Africa.*

Note: Released in Great Britain in 1966 as *The Witches*.

THE DEVIL'S PARTNER   F6.1150

Huron Productions. *Dist* Filmgroup, Inc. 8 Sep **1961** [Atlanta showing]. Sd; b&w. 35mm. 75 min. [Cut to 61 min.]

Prod Hugh M. Hooker. *Dir* Charles R. Rondeau. *Screenplay* Stanley Clements, Laura J. Mathews, Dorrell McGowan. *Photog* Edward Cronjager. *Art Dir* Daniel Haller. *Film Ed* Howard Epstein. *Mus* Ronald Stein. *Asst Dir* Richard Dixon.

Cast: Ed Nelson *(Nick/Pete)*, Jean Allison *(Nell)*, Edgar Buchanan *(Doc)*, Richard Crane *(David)*, Spencer Carlisle *(Tom)*, Byron Foulger *(Papers)*, Claire Carleton *(Ida)*.

Horror film. Nick comes to remote Furnace Flats, Texas, to make the funeral arrangements for his recently deceased, eccentric Uncle Pete. Soon the townspeople come to realize that Nick engages in activities similar to those of his uncle, such as the slaughtering of goats, drawing symbols on the floor with goat's blood, and the muttering of incantations. Nevertheless, Nick ingratiates himself with everyone. He lends money to David, the filling station owner, so that David can marry Nell, daughter of the doctor. Then peculiar things begin to happen. David is attacked by his own dog, seriously scarring his face, and a horse tramples the town drunk to death. When the doctor and the sheriff go to Nick's cabin to investigate, they witness Nick's rites and incantations. David, his appearance badly marred, gives up Nell, and Nick easily takes his place. The sheriff visits Nick's cabin again and is confronted by a large snake. When he fires bullets into the serpent's body, it slowly transforms itself into Nick and eventually into old Pete. A priest is called in to minister to the dying man-snake and to exorcise the devil from his soul. *Sorcerers. Uncles. Priests. Sheriffs. Physicians. Funerals. Murder. Rites and ceremonies. Metamorphosis. Disfiguration. Exorcism. Texas. The Devil. Goats. Horses. Snakes.*

Note: Produced in 1958.

THE DEVIL'S SISTERS   F6.1151

Mustang Productions. *Dist* Thunderbird International Pictures. 19 May **1966** [Miami, Florida, opening; c19 May 1966; LP33142]. Sd; b&w. 35mm. 90 min.

Prod Joseph Fink, Juan Hidalgo-Gato. *Dir* William Grefe. *Screenplay* John Nicholas, William Grefe. *Story* John Nicholas. *Dir Photog* Julio C. Chavez. *Camera Crew* John Whitmore, Mario T. Wilkerson. *Lighting Cons* Thomas Casey. *Titl* Chelo Garcia, Nohemy Someillan. *Film Ed* Julio C. Chavez. *Asst Ed* Justine S. Clegg. *Mus* Al Jacobs. *Mus Arr & Perf by* Dell Staton. *Sd Rec* Armando Fernandez. *Boom* Julio Roldan. *Asst Dir* Robert P. Schneider. *Script Clerk* Betty Kerwin. *Prop* Pat Erle.

Cast: Sharon Saxon *(Teresa)*, Fred Pinero *(Antonio Sanchez)*, Velia Martinez *(Carmen Alvarado)*, Anita Crystal *(Rita Alvarado)*, Ramiro Gomez Kemp *(Roberto Fernandez)*, William Marcos *(Jose Rodriguez)*, Beryl Taylor *(Mrs. Hernandez)*, Mildred Rodesky *(Marta)*, Babette Sherrill *(Ester)*, Toni Camel *(Dolores)*, Joan Jacobs *(Victoria)*, Nora Alonzo *(Emilia)*, Tammy Simms *(first girl)*, Michael De Beausset *(Englishman)*, Mark Harris *(henchman)*.

Melodrama. Captain Fernandez of the police listens as Teresa relates a tale of horror at the hands of a white slavery ring. *Humiliated and disillusioned by Antonio Sanchez, the man she loves, Teresa leaves her hometown to seek a new life in Tijuana. Answering an advertisement soliciting a domestic servant, Teresa travels to a secluded hacienda owned by the Alvarado sisters. Teresa follows Jose, the manservant, and discovers that she is being held captive in a windowless room. In the days that follow, Teresa is beaten and starved. Eventually Rita Alvarado forces her to accept the advances of a procession of men. One evening, Antonio, now a corrupt police officer, comes to the house and becomes enraged to find Teresa in a bordello. To avoid trouble with the police, Rita sends Teresa to a secluded barn in the country where sick, pregnant, or rebellious women await their sale to white slavers. Marta, a sadistic, cigar-smoking tyrant, serves as guardian. Teresa is tortured with the other victims and warned by Carmen Alvarado against trying to escape. While a prospective buyer inspects Teresa and another captive, Teresa's companion hits him over the head with a bottle. The offender is killed, and Teresa is stripped, bound with barbed wire, and left to die. As a result of this outrage, the women revolt, and Teresa manages to escape.* The police investigate and a gun battle ensues in which Rita and her guards are killed. Carmen escapes to the barn and is beaten to death by the enraged captives before the police arrive. *Madams. Police. Sisters. White slave traffic. Employment—Women. Sadism. Torture. Disillusionment. Whorehouses. Tijuana (Mexico).*

Note: Filmed in Miami.

THE DEVIL'S SPAWN see THE LAST GUNFIGHTER

DEVIL'S TEMPLE (Japan)   F6.1152

Daiei Motion Picture Co. Nov **1969** [Los Angeles showing]. Sd; col (Eastmancolor). 35mm (Daiei Scope). 76 min.

Dir Kenji Misumi. *Screenplay* Kaneto Shindo. *Story* Junichiro Tanizaki. *Photog* Kazuo Miyagawa. *Art Dir* Akira Naito. *Mus* Akira Ifukube.

Cast: Shintaro Katsu *(Mumyo Taro)*, Hideko Takamine *(Kaede)*, Michiyo Aratama *(Aizen)*, Kei Sato *(high priest)*.

Melodrama. Mumyo Taro, a thief, lives in an old temple with Aizen, a hedonistic woman who totally dominates him. His wife, Kaede, discovers their hiding place and refuses to leave Taro, becoming involved with the couple in a relationship of love and hate. A high priest happens upon the temple, and when Taro attempts to steal his golden image of Buddha, the priest utters an incantation which leaves Taro helpless. Aizen enters the room and the priest starts with recognition, for she is the same woman over whom he had once fought a duel and entered the priesthood. Aizen leaves with the priest, assuring Taro she will gain revenge for him. A while later Taro and Kaede find Aizen standing over the priest, who is groveling at her feet. Suddenly regaining his wits, the priest bites out his tongue and dies, as Aizen exults over his body. Taro, revolted by the scene, kills Aizen with his sword. The next morning, dressed as a priest, Taro leaves the temple with Kaede. *Thieves. Priests. Hedonism. Revenge. Infidelity. Spells. Temples.*

Note: Released in Japan in May 1969 as *Oni no sumu yakata.*

THE DEVIL'S TRAP (Czechoslovakia)   F6.1153

Barrandov Film Studio. For Československý Film. *Dist* Salisbury Films. 13 Aug **1964** [New York opening]. Sd; b&w. 35mm. 85 min.

Pres by Barry Green. *Dir* František Vláčil. *Screenplay* František A. Dvořák, Miloš V. Kratochvíl. *Dir Photog* Rudolf Milič. *Camera Asst* Miroslav Sinkule, Rudolf Milič, Jr. *Art Dir* Karel Škvor. *Asst Art Dir* Oldřich Okáč. *Ed* Miroslav Hájek. *Asst Ed* Jitka Šulcová. *Mus* Zdeněk Liška. *Sd* František Fabián. *Asst Dir* Jaroslav Beránek, Zdena Pavlátová, Milan Kadlec. *In Charge of Prod* Věra Kadlecová. *Prod Asst* Karel Škorpík, Václav Havlík, Miroslav Dousek. *Sp Coöp* Václav Mencl. *Production Group* Kubala–Novotný.

Cast: Vítězslav Vejražka (Spálený), Miroslav Macháček (Prokus), Čestmír Řanda (Regent Válečsky z Valče), Vlastimil Hašek (Filip), Vít Olmer (Jan), Karla Chadimová (Martina), František Kovářík (shepherd), Bedřich Karen (Bishop Dittrichštejn), Josef Hlinomaz (servant), Zdeněk Kutil (gamekeeper), Jaroslav Moučka (Jakub), Ladislav Kazda (miller), Jiří Vršťala (cavalry officer), Dagmar Kofroňová (miller's wife), Richard Záhorský (parish clerk), Viktor Očásek (writer), Zlatomír Vacek (vicar), František Nechyba (steward), Jiřina Bílá (servant).

Drama. Source: Alfred Technik, Mlýn na ponorné řece (Prague, 1958). During a drought in 16th-century Czechoslovakia Spálený, a charitable miller and amateur scientist, searches for and locates an underground spring. This act of mercy prompts an investigation by the fanatical priest Prokus, an agent of the Inquisition, who suspects that the miller has sold his soul to the Devil. Millers. Priests. Fanatics. Witchcraft. Drought. Springs. The Inquisition. Catholic Church. The Devil.

Note: Exterior scenes filmed at Skalní Mill in Blansko, in the Beroun area, and in Žvahov, Czechoslovakia. Released in Czechoslovakia in Apr 1962 as Ďáblova past; running time: ca88 min.

THE DEVIL'S WANTON (Sweden)   F6.1154
Terrafilm. Dist Embassy Pictures. 4 Jul 1962 [New York opening]. Sd; b&w. 35mm. 72 min.

Pres by Joseph E. Levine. Prod Lorens Marmstedt. Dir-Writ Ingmar Bergman. Photog Göran Strindberg. Art Dir P. A. Lundgren. Film Ed Lennart Wallén. Mus Erland von Koch. Sd Olle Jakobsson. Prod Mgr Allan Ekelund.

Cast: Doris Svedlund (Birgitta-Carolina Söderberg), Birger Malmsten (Thomas), Eva Henning (Sofi), Hasse Ekman (Martin Grandé), Stig Olin (Peter), Irma Christensson (Linnéa), Anders Henrikson (Paul), Marianne Löfgren (Mrs. Bolin), Curt Masreliez (Alf), Carl-Henrik Fant (Arne), Inger Juel (Greta), Åke Fridell (Magnus), Birgit Lindkvist (Anna), Arne Ragneborn (Anna's lover).

Drama. Upon release from a mental institution, Paul, a former mathematics teacher, visits Martin, a motion picture director, and suggests a film depicting earth as Hell, in which human destiny is dictated by the Devil. Although Martin ridicules the idea, he relates it to Thomas, an alcoholic journalist. The writer is reminded of the life of Birgitta-Carolina Söderberg, a prostitute whose pimp, Peter, kills their illegitimate infant. Birgitta-Carolina falls in love with Thomas, who is estranged from his wife, Sofi, but returns to Peter when he threatens to disrupt the writer's life. In despair she slashes her wrists. Upon consideration Martin rejects the possibility of a film about the meaninglessness of life. Schoolteachers. Motion picture directors. Journalists. Prostitutes. Mistresses. Pimps. Mental illness. Alcoholism. Illegitimacy. Separation (marital). Suicide. Infanticide. The Devil. Hell.

Note: Opened in Stockholm in Mar 1949 as Fängelse; running time: 80 min.

THE DEVIL'S WOMAN see EVA

DEVYAT DNEY ODNOGO GODA see NINE DAYS OF ONE YEAR

LE DIABLE ET LES DIX COMMANDEMENTS see THE DEVIL AND THE TEN COMMANDMENTS

LE DIABLE PAR LA QUEUE see THE DEVIL BY THE TAIL

THE DIABOLICAL DR. Z (France/Spain)   F6.1155
Hesperia Films–Speva Films–Ciné-Alliance. Dist U. S. Films. 15 Feb 1967 [Los Angeles opening]. Sd; b&w. 35mm. 86 min. [Also 83 min.]

Prod Serge Silberman, Michel Safra. Dir Jesús Franco. Screenplay Jesús Franco, Jean-Claude Carrière. Dir Photog Alejandro Ulloa. Camera Clemente Manzano. Art Dir Antonio Cortés. Film Ed Jean Feyte. Mus Daniel White. Sd Louis Hochet. Asst Dir Robert Demollière. Prod Dir Henri Baum. Prod Mgr José Alted. Script Girl Nicole Guettard.

Cast: Mabel Karr (Irma), Fernando Montes (Philip), Estella Blain (Nadia), Antonio J. Escribano (Dr. Von Zimmer), Howard Vernon (Vikass), Guy Mairesse, Marcelo Arroita, Lucía Prado, Ana Castor, Alberto Dalbes, José María Prada.

Horror film. Based on a novel by: David Kuhne. Dr. Von Zimmer goes before the medical council with a request to experiment on condemned criminals with his new invention that will change personality. He is turned down and so abused that he suffers a heart attack and dies. His daughter Irma vows revenge on the three council members who opposed her father. She murders a young woman hitchhiker and mutilates the body beyond recognition in order to convince the authorities that the corpse is hers. Now free to work in secret, Irma manages to control the mind of Nadia, a cabaret dancer known in her act as "Miss Death." Irma hopes to use Nadia, endowed with abnormally long fingernails, to murder the three men. The first killing goes as planned, but Irma's control over Nadia begins to falter because of the dancer's innate decency and her love for Philip, one of the council members and Irma's former boyfriend. When Nadia fails to accomplish the second murder, Irma decides to

eliminate her with the aid of her father's machine. She also attempts to do away with Philip, but the police arrive, and Irma is killed in the fracas. Physicians. Hitchhikers. Dancers. Experiments. Personality. Filial relations. Revenge. Murder. Mutilation. Thought control.

Note: Opened in Madrid in Aug 1966 as Miss Muerte; running time: 86 min; in Paris in Nov 1967 as Dans les griffes du maniaque; running time: 90 min.

IL DIABOLICO DR. MABUSE see THE 1000 EYES OF DR. MABUSE

DIABOLIK see DANGER: DIABOLIK

LE DIABOLIQUE DOCTEUR MABUSE see THE 1000 EYES OF DR. MABUSE

DIALOGO CON CHÉ   F6.1156
Dist Film-Makers' Cooperative. 23 Apr 1969 [New York opening]. Sd; b&w. 16mm. ca120 min.

Dir José Soltero. Conceived by José Soltero. Photog José Soltero. Sd Charles Frehse.

Cast: Rolando Peña (Ernesto "Ché" Guevara), Taylor Mead, Ana Maria, Joseph Aliaga, Salvador Cruz, Cesar Vallejo, Carlos Anduze, Raymond Piñero, Santos Negron.

Film essay. Following a scene which occurs "somewhat ahead of chaos, perhaps on the first or second day of creation," an actor portraying Ernesto "Ché" Guevara reads portions of the introduction to Ché's writings on revolution in Latin America. Subsequently, the actor, who is improvising the characterization, and the filmmaker, out of frame, reject the creation of a representational role and condemn the "destructive casting" of the commercial film, typified by the selection of a movie star to portray Ché in the Hollywood version of his life. The actor continues to read, and the dialogue with the filmmaker continues, relating to such themes as the exploitation of Latin America, the fraudulent process of filmmaking, and the moral corruption and arrogance of American society. Ché summons a teacher to the scene and discusses education. Eventually, Ché is shot and killed, and the filmmaker and actors prepare for the final scene, which opened the film. Revolutionaries. Guerrillas. Actors. Motion pictures. Cuba—History—1958 Revolution. Latin America. Hollywood. Ernesto "Che" Guevara.

Note: Also known as Ché Is Alive and Dialogue With Ché. Also shown in a dual-screen version in which identical reels were projected side by side, with a 3-min interval between starting times. Dedicated to Bertolt Brecht.

DIALOGUE (Hungary)   F6.1157
Hunnia Filmstudios. Dist Rogosin Films. 10 Oct 1967 [New York opening]. Sd; b&w. 35mm. 130 min.

Dir-Writ János Herskó. Photog György Illés. Asst Photog Tibor Vagyóczky. Art Dir József Romvári. Film Ed Zoltán Kerényi. Mus Imre Vincze, György Gara. Sd János Arató. Asst Dir István Szabó. Prod Mgr András Németh. Script Ed Zsuzsa Biró. Cost Piroska Katona.

Cast: Anita Semjén (Judit Barna), Imre Sinkovits (László Horváth), István Sztankai (Sándor Kocsis), Mari Törőcsik (Éva), László Csákányi (Uncle Dönci), Sándor Pécsi (Mihály Safrankó), Tibor Molnár (Géza), Katalin Berek (Olga, his wife), István Avar (Sáfár), Miklós Gábor (Szalkay), Margit Bara (Szalkayné), Ilona Béres (Jutka), Tibor Bitskey (actor), Károly Bicskey (Béla), Elma Bulla (Kocsis' landlady), Hilda Gobbi (actress), Flórián Kaló (Lukács), Manyi Kiss (workwoman), János Pásztor (actor), Mária Majczen (Bori), Gyula Szabó (Jani), János Rajz, Ernő Szabó, Miklós Szakáts, Ádám Szirtes, János Árva, József Zsudi, György Miklósy, László György, Erzsi Pártos, Andor Dárday, Bertalan Solti, György Győrffy, Zoltán Makláry, István Nagy, Árpád Gyenge, János Herskó.

Drama. In 1945, László, a young militant Hungarian, marries 17-year-old Judit, who has just been released from a concentration camp following World War II. Fortified by their love and a common desire to work for a better Hungary, their first few months together are happy ones. Then, László is arrested and sent to prison for holding political views different from those of the pro-Stalin regime. During her husband's confinement, Judit resumes a childhood friendship with Sándor Kocsis, a poet, and becomes his mistress. Four years later, when the Stalinist era ends and László is released, he and his wife discover that they have become emotional and political strangers. The estrangement continues until the social upheaval that brings about the revolution of 1956. When Russian tanks move into the country, Judit recalls that it was by this means that she was liberated from the prison camp years before. More understanding of László's belief in the Hungarian Communist experiment, she returns to him as the struggle for Hungarian unity continues. Militants. Political prisoners. Poets. Marriage. Infidelity. Communism. Stalinism. Concentration camps. Hungary—History—Revolt 1956. Russia—Army.

Note: Released in Hungary in Oct 1963 as Párbeszéd; running time: 149 min.

DIALOGUE WITH CHÉ *see* DIALOGO CON CHÉ

DIAMANTES A GO-GO *see* GRAND SLAM

DIAMOND COUNTRY *see* RUN LIKE A THIEF

DIAMOND HEAD   F6.1158
Jerry Bresler Productions. *Dist* Columbia Pictures. 30 Jan **1963** [Honolulu, Hawaii, opening; c1 Feb 1963; LP25375]. Sd (RCA); col (Eastman Color by Pathé). 35mm (Panavision). 107 min.

Prod Jerry Bresler. *Dir* Guy Green. *Screenplay* Marguerite Roberts. *Dir Photog* Sam Leavitt. *Camera Op* Andrew McIntyre. *Asst Camera* Arnold Rich, Eugene Lenoir. *Set Decor* William Kiernan. *Prod Dsgn* Malcolm Brown. *Film Ed* William A. Lyon. *Mus* Johnny Williams. *Orch* Arthur Morton. *Titl Theme* Hugo Winterhalter. *Sd Supv* Charles J. Rice. *Sd* James Z. Flaster. *Rec* Harold Lee. *Boom Op* William Randall, Jr. *Asst Dir* Herbert E. Mendelson, Sam Nelson, Jack Roe, Frank Capra, Jr. *Script Supv* Frances McDowell. *Cost Dsgn* Pat Barto. *Wardrobe* Edna Taylor, Israel Berne. *Makeup Supv* Ben Lane. *Makeup* Joseph Di Bella, Dick Cobes. *Body Makeup* Rose Lehman. *Hairstyles* Carol Michaels. *Location Rep* Marvin Miller. *Still Photog* M. B. Paul, Charles Stapleton. *Grip* Al Becker, John Aker, Charles Gibbs, Willard Klug. *Elec Gaffer* Seldon White.

Cast: Charlton Heston *(Richard "King" Howland)*, Yvette Mimieux *(Sloan Howland)*, George Chakiris *(Dr. Dean Kahana)*, France Nuyen *(Mei Chen)*, James Darren *(Paul Kahana)*, Aline MacMahon *(Kapiolani Kahana)*, Elizabeth Allen *(Laura Beckett)*, Vaughn Taylor *(Judge James Blanding)*, Richard Loo *(Yamagata [see note])*, Marc Marno *(Bobbie Chen)*, Philip Ahn *(Emekona)*, Harold Fong *(Coyama)*, Edward Mallory *(Robert Parsons)*, Lou Gonsalves *(Mario)*, Frank Morris *(Felipe)*, Clarence Kim *(Sammy)*, Jack Matsumoto *(photographer)*, Yankee Chang *(newspaperman)*, Kam Fong Chun *(Loe Kim Lee)*, Leo Ezell *(pianist)*, Alan LeBuse *(heckler)*, R. Ramos *(nurse)*, Seagai Faumunina *(Blue Goose)*.

Drama. Source: Peter Gilman, *Diamond Head* (New York, 1960). Richard "King" Howland, a ruthless and bigoted land monarch on the Hawaiian island of Kauai, is bitterly upset when his younger sister, Sloan, announces that she wants to marry a full-blooded Hawaiian, Paul Kahana, although he himself is having a clandestine affair with the native-born Mei Chen. At the young couple's engagement party, Mei Chen's drunken brother attacks Howland with a knife, and Paul is accidentally stabbed to death when he intercedes. Blaming her brother for Paul's death, Sloan refuses to speak to him and goes to Honolulu. There Paul's brother, Dean, finds her in a drunken stupor and takes her to live at his mother's home. A short time later, Mei Chen dies while giving birth to a son, but Howland refuses to accept the child, and Sloan decides to care for it. Following a fight with Howland, Sloan and Dean take the child and leave, but Howland, forced to accept the fact that he will soon have a halfcaste brother-in-law, finally decides to give his son the family name. *Land barons. Hawaiians. Mistresses. Brothers. Halfcastes. Bigotry. Brother-sister relationship. Marriage—Mixed. Drunkenness. Childbirth. Illegitimacy. Murder. Kauai (Hawaii). Honolulu.*

Note: Location scenes filmed in Hawaii. Richard Loo's participation is unconfirmed.

DIAMOND HUNTERS *see* RUN LIKE A THIEF

DIAMOND STUD   F6.1159
Walnut International Productions. *Dist* Grads Corp. 8 Apr **1970** [Champaign, Illinois, showing]. Sd; col (Eastmancolor). 35mm. 82 min.

Prod Jay Fineberg. *Asst Prod* Jerome Knell. *Exec Prod* Vincent Miranda. *Dir* Greg Corarito. *Writ* Maurice Smith. *Cinematog* Gary Graver. *Titl* David Kelly. *Ed* Ed Hunt. *Sd* Robert Dietz. *Prod Mgr* Buck Buckalew. *Script Supv* Pam Eady. *Wardrobe* Sandy Root. *Makeup* Tony Demarco. *Prop* Dick Ozmun. *Gaffer* John Willheim. *Grip* Ted Mathew.

Cast: Robert Hall *(Diamond Jim)*, John Alderman, Monika Henreid, Victoria Carbé, Michael Greer, Ann Dee, Richard Compton, Jimmie Johnson, Julie Cannons.

Western drama. Rugged entrepreneur Diamond Jim proposes that railroad cars be made of steel instead of wood, and he offers to ride a fully-loaded train of steel cars across a weak wooden tressel to prove that the cars are safe. As the train approaches this crucial test, Diamond Jim contemplates his career. *Diamond Jim, gifted with a magnetic personality, meets the beautiful Sarah and falls in love with her. Diamond Jim's brother Dan is an evil person who leads a low, vulgar life. Diamond Jim's best friend Mark is a dashing figure who takes his place in high society.* The train rolls safely across the tressel, and Diamond Jim calls for a celebration at his mansion that includes Lillian, a tempestuous singer. Jim's boon companion, hard-drinking John L. Sullivan, celebrates in his own fashion in a low-life bar across town and watches a ribald fight between two women. In 1906, Mark and Lillian travel to San Francisco and are caught in the earthquake. Mark suffers a broken leg and returns to Jim's mansion to recuperate. Jim suffers a heart attack, and while he is in the hospital, Mark and Jim's beloved Sarah fall in love. Dan breaks into Jim's house and is shot to death while attempting to steal Jim's diamonds. Jim's doctor tells him that his penchant for overeating could prove fatal, and when Jim is confronted with the love of Mark and Sarah, he orders a huge meal and begins to gorge himself. *Entrepreneurs. Brothers. Singers. Friendship. Theft. Jealousy. Gluttony. Suicide. Railroads. Heart disease. Gay Nineties. James Buchanan Brady. San Francisco—Earthquake 1906.*

DIAMONDS OF THE NIGHT (Czechoslovakia)   F6.1160
Barrandov Film Studio. *For* Československý Film. *Dist* Impact Films. 14 Mar **1968** [New York opening]. Sd; b&w. 35mm. 70 min. [Also 75 min.]

Dir Jan Němec. *Screenplay* Arnošt Lustig, Jan Němec. *Photog* Jaroslav Kučera. *Camera Op* Miroslav Ondříček. *Asst Camera* Petr Čech. *Art Dir* Oldřich Bosák. *Film Ed* Miroslav Hájek. *Asst Ed* Jitka Šulcová. *Sd* František Černý. *Asst Dir* Hynek Bočan. *Prod Mgr* Miloš Bergl. *Asst Prod Mgr* Josef Mára, Zdeňka Černá. *Cost* Ester Krumbachová. *Production Group* Švabík–Procházka.

Cast: Ladislav Janský *(1st boy)*, Antonín Kumbera *(2nd boy)*, Ilse Bischofová *(The Woman)*, Jan Říha, Ivan Asič, August Bischof, Josef Koggel, Oskar Müller, Anton Schich, Rudolf Stolle, Josef Koblížek, Josef Kubát, Rudolf Lukásek, Bohumil Moudrý, Karel Navrátil, Evžen Pichl, František Procházka, Františck Vrána.

Drama. Source: Arnošt Lustig, "Tma ne má stín," in *Démanty noci* (Prague, 1958). During World War II, two Czechoslovakian Jewish boys escape from a train carrying them to the gas chambers in a Nazi concentration camp. Exhausted and starving, they struggle through a forest for days in a desperate attempt to make their way home. When they spy an old woman carrying lunch to her husband in a nearby field, the boys decide to follow her to her cottage and steal food. They spare her life but cannot eat the food they have stolen because their lips are too swollen and cracked. After returning to the old woman's hut to drink some milk, they are captured by a group of feeble old men who take them to the mayor of the village. While the men feast and dance at an inn, the two boys wait for the mayor to decide their fate. After a mock execution by a firing squad, the terrified youngsters are set free. Once again they head for the forest to continue their dangerous journey home. *Jews. Escapees. Refugees. Adolescence. Survival. Theft. Concentration camps. Trains. Forests. World War II.*

Note: Location scenes filmed at Nový Bor. Released in Prague in Sep 1964 as *Démanty noci*.

DIANA *see* CALL ME BAD

LA DIANA CAZADORA *see* CALL ME BAD

DIARIES, NOTES AND SKETCHES   F6.1161
Dist Film-Makers' Distribution Center. Dec **1969** [New York opening]. Sd; col. 16mm. 185 min.

Prod-Dir Jonas Mekas. *Photog* Jonas Mekas. *Ed* Jonas Mekas. *Mus* Jonas Mekas. *Mus Selections* The Velvet Underground, Jim Kweskin Jug Band, Frédéric François Chopin, Dietrich Buxtehude. *Organist* E. Power Biggs. *Song:* "Give Peace a Chance" John Lennon, Paul McCartney.

With the appearances of: Jonas Mekas, David C. Stone, Barbara Stone, Tony Conrad, Beverly Grant, Timothy Leary, David Brooks, Harry Smith, Pola Chapelle, Adolfas Mekas, Ed Emshwiller, Barbara Rubin, P. Adams Sitney, Stan Brakhage, Jane Brakhage, Carl Th. Dreyer, Amy Taubin, Jerome Hill, Ken Kelman, Barbet Schroeder, Gerard Malanga, Jack Smith, Mario Montez, Nico, Edie Sedgwick, The Velvet Underground, Andy Warhol, Naomi Levine, Ken Jacobs, Judith Malina, Gregory J. Markopoulos, Storm De Hirsch, Herman G. Weinberg, Lionel Rogosin, Louis Brigante, The Fugs, Allen Ginsberg, Peter Orlovsky, Norman Mailer, Ernie Gehr, Hans Richter, Standish Lawder, Paul Krassner, Willard Van Dyke, Gideon Bachmann, Shirley Clarke, Jud Yalkut, Marie Menken, Peter Kubelka, James Broughton, Michael Snow, Joyce Wieland, John Lennon, Yoko Ono, Nat Hentoff, Peter H. Beard, John V. Lindsay, Thomas Hoving, Jacob Javits, Frank Kuenstler, Bibbe Hansen, Leo Adams, Gretchen Weinberg.

Film diary. A personal record spanning 5 years in the life of filmmaker Jonas Mekas. Included are the subjects listed below. *Filmmakers. Friendship. Family life. Weddings. New York City. New York City—Central Park. New York State. Colorado. Connecticut. Massachusetts. New Jersey. Texas. Millbrook (New York). Austin (Texas). Montreal. Roxbury (Massachusetts). Hudson River. Marseilles. Cassis. Jean Cocteau. Julian Beck. Judith Malina. John of the Cross. Film-Makers' Cinematheque. Film-Makers' Cooperative. Anthology Film Archives. Marlboro College. Cranbrook Academy of Art. Rutgers University. United Nations. University of Delaware. Documentation. "Film Culture". "Galaxie". "Walden". "Village Voice". Animals.*

Note: Filmed 1964–69 in New York City, Colorado, Connecticut, Delaware, Massachusetts, New Jersey, New York State, Texas, etc. Released as a work in progress. Subsequently distributed in four parts entitled: *Walden: Reel One*; *Walden, Reel Two*; *Walden, Reel Three*; *Walden, Reel Four*. Film's soundtrack contains subway noises, street noises, a variety of musical selections, Mekas playing and singing, and readings from *Walden*, the works of Saint John of the Cross, and a text on Julian Beck and Judith Malina.

IL DIARIO DI UNA CAMERIERA see DIARY OF A CHAMBERMAID

DIARIO DI UNA SCHIZOFRENICA see DIARY OF A SCHIZOPHRENIC GIRL

DIARY OF A BACHELOR   F6.1162

Homer Productions. *Dist* American International Pictures. 18 Sep **1964** [Macon, Georgia, opening; c16 Sep 1964; LP29780]. Sd; b&w. 35mm. 89 min.

Prod-Dir Sandy Howard. *Exec Prod* Abraham P. Levine. *Assoc Prod* Ted Devlet. *2d Unit Dir* Ted Devlet. *Screenplay* Ken Barnett. *Photog* Julian Townsend. *Set Dsgn* Earl Janson. *Film Ed* Angelo Ross. *Mus Comp & Cond* Jack Pleis. *Sd* Jim Shields. *Sd Eff* Ross-Gaffney Inc. *Mus Ed* John McManus. *Asst Dir* Richard Frank. *Prod Mgr* Robert Baron. *Asst to the Prod* Diana Wenman. *Fashion Coörd* Helen Grobin. *Makeup* Saul Meth. *Hairstyles* Mary Roche. *Optical Eff* Tri-Pix Film Services. *Beauty Cons* David Malovny.

Cast: William Traylor *(Skip O'Hara)*, Dagne Crane *(Joanne)*, Joe Silver *(Charlie Barrett)*, Denise Lor *(Jane Woods)*, Susan Dean *(Barbara)*, Eleni Kiamos *(Angie Pisano)*, Jan Crockett *(Jennifer Watters)*, Arlene Golonka *(Louis)*, Joan Holloway *(Nancy Feather)*, Mickey Deems *(Barney Washburn)*, Dom De Luise *(Marvin Rollins)*, Jackie Kannon *(Bob Haney)*, Leora Thatcher *(Mother O'Hara)*, Bradley Bolke *(Bugsy)*, Jim Alexander *(Harley Peterson)*, Joey Faye *(bartender)*, Beatrice Pons *(Thelma)*, Joy Claussen *(Susan)*, Chris Noel *(Carol)*, Saliha Tekneci *(belly dancer)*, Bonnie Jones *(Wanda Smith)*, Joanne MacCormack *(Cynthia Brooks)*, Ellen Nevdal *(Victoria Ampolsk)*, Paula Stewart *(Carlotta Jones)*, Greta Randall, Carolyn Lasater, Darlene Enlow, Nai Bonet, Len Hammer, Larry Navarro.

Comedy. New York City bachelor Skip O'Hara decides to give up the single life to marry Joanne. When Skip is suddenly called away for a business conference, Joanne finds her fiancé's diary and discovers that Skip has been having affairs with numerous young women. The indignant Joanne storms out on Skip shortly before Nancy Feather, an airline hostess who figures prominently in the diary, arrives at Skip's apartment. Joanne returns to apologize to Skip for her hasty judgement only to find Nancy very much at home at Skip's place. Joanne leaves him for good. The passage of a year finds Skip married to Nancy. His bachelor days are over, but Nancy continues to live as she did prior to marriage; her bags are packed for another of her frequent trips to visit old boyfriends. *Bachelors. Playboys. Airline stewardesses. Marriage. Infidelity. Diaries. New York City.*

Note: Filmed on location in New York City.

DIARY OF A CHAMBERMAID (France/Italy)   F6.1163

Speva Films–Filmsonor–Ciné-Alliance–Dear Film. *Dist* International Classics. 9 Mar **1965** [New York opening]. Sd; b&w. 35mm (Franscope). 97 min.

Prod Serge Silberman, Michel Safra. *Assoc Prod* Henri Baum. *Dir* Luis Buñuel. *Screenplay* Luis Buñuel, Jean-Claude Carrière. *Photog* Roger Fellous. *Camera Op* Adolphe Charlet. *Camera Op* René Schneider, Agathe Beaumont. *Art Dir & Set Dsgn* Georges Wakhevitch. *Asst Art Dir* René Calviera. *Scenic Artist* Charles Merangel. *Film Ed* Louisette Hautecoeur-Taverna. *Asst Ed* Arlette Lalande. *Sd Engr* Antoine Petitjean. *Asst Sd* Robert Cambourakis. *Asst Dir* Juan Luis Buñuel, Pierre Lary. *Prod Mgr* André Retbi. *Script Girl* Suzanne Durrenberger. *Prod Sec* Odette Laeupplée. *Wardrobe Supv* Jacqueline Moreau. *Cost* Georges Wakhevitch. *Makeup Supv* Maguy Vernadet. *Hairstyles* Simone Knapp. *Still Photog* Jean-Louis Castelli.

Cast: Jeanne Moreau *(Célestine)*, Georges Géret *(Joseph)*, Michel Piccoli *(Monsieur Monteil)*, Françoise Lugagne *(Madame Monteil)*, Daniel Ivernel *(Capitaine Mauger)*, Jean Ozenne *(Monsieur Rabour)*, Jean-Claude Carrière *(curé)*, Gilberte Géniat *(Rose)*, Bernard Musson *(sacristan)*, Muni *(Marianne)*, Claude Jaeger *(The Judge)*, Dominique Sauvage-Dandieux *(Claire)*, Madeleine Damien, Geymond Vital, Jean Franval, Marcel Rouzé, Jeanne Pérez, Andrée Tainsy, Françoise Bertin, Pierre Collet, Aline Bertrand, Joëlle Bernard, Michel Dacquin, Marcel Le Floch, Marc Eyraud, Gabriel Gobin, Marguerite Bour, Dominique Zardi.

Drama. Source: Octave Mirbeau, *Le journal d'une femme de chambre* (Paris, 1900). In 1930, Célestine, a 32-year-old chambermaid, takes a position at the Normandy estate of the Monteil family. She soon becomes well acquainted with the idiosyncrasies of the household. The elder Monteil is an affable, harmless boot-fetishist; his daughter is a sickly and frigid woman who conducts private "experiments" in her room instead of maintaining sexual relations with

her wastrel husband; the husband works off his excess energy by hunting and by trying to seduce the female servants; and Joseph, the gamekeeper and handyman, is a surly racist who delights in brutally killing small animals. Also on hand is a neighbor, Monsieur Rabour, a fascistic, retired military man who throws garbage into the Monteil garden to continue an old feud. One day the village is thrown into an uproar when the elder Monteil dies in his bed clutching his collection of boots; and a little girl whom Célestine had befriended is found raped and murdered. Célestine, despite her sexual attraction for Joseph, is certain that he is the guilty party and arranges for incriminating evidence to be found. The proof is insufficient, however, and the freed Joseph goes to Cherbourg to open a café. Left alone, Célestine settles for a life of bourgeois contentment by agreeing to marry Rabour. *Fascists. Chambermaids. Handymen. Gamekeepers. Veterans. Fetishism. Filial relations. Frigidity. Marriage. Sadism. Racism. Feuds. Murder. Rape. Frameup. Normandy. Cherbourg.*

Note: Opened in Paris in Mar 1964 as *Le journal d'une femme de chambre*; running time: 98 min; alternative French running time: 85 min. Italian title: *Il diario di una cameriera*. Previously filmed in 1946 by Jean Renoir.

DIARY OF A MAD HOUSEWIFE   F6.1164

Frank Perry Films. *Dist* Universal Pictures. 10 Aug **1970** [New York opening; c10 Aug 1970; LP38194]. Sd; col (Technicolor). 35mm. 95 min. *MPAA rating* R.

Prod-Dir Frank Perry. *Screenplay* Eleanor Perry. *Photog* Gerald Hirschfeld. *Set Decor* Sam Robert, Bob Drumheller. *Prod Dsgn* Peter Dohanos. *Film Ed* Sidney Katz. *Sd* Charles Federmack. *Asst Dir* Charles Okun. *Prod Mgr* Phil Goldfarb. *Asst to the Prod* Lydia Wilen. *Cost Dsgn* Ruth Morley. *Women's Wardrobe* Flo Transfield. *Men's Wardrobe* James Hagerman. *Makeup* Josephine Cianelli. *Hairstyles* Colleen Callaghan. *Gallery Seq* R. L. Felgen & Co. *Paintings from the Exhibition of* Allen Jones.

Cast: Richard Benjamin *(Jonathan Balser)*, Frank Langella *(George Prager)*, Carrie Snodgress *(Tina Balser)*, Lorraine Cullen *(Sylvie Balser)*, Frannie Michel *(Liz Balser)*, Lee Addoms *(Mrs. Prinz)*, Peter Dohanos *(Samuel Keefer)*, Katherine Meskill *(Charlotte Rady)*, Leonard Elliott *(M. Henri)*, Valma *(Margo)*, Hilda Haynes *(Lottie)*, Lester Rawlins *(Dr. Linstrom)*, Jeanette Dubois *(Vera)*, William Kiehl *(Elliot Asher)*, Don Symington *(pediatrician)*, Allison Mills *(women's lib girl)*, Peter Boyle *(man in group therapy session)*, Alice Cooper Band *(themselves)*, Cash Baxter, John Tillenger, Lydia Wilen, Beverly Ballard.

Domestic drama. Source: Sue Kaufman, *Diary of a Mad Housewife* (New York, 1967). New York housewife Tina Balser resents the manipulation of her nagging husband, Jonathan, a status-seeking attorney, and the complaints of her spoiled daughters, Sylvie and Liz. At a gallery opening egocentric author George Prager propositions her, and she subsequently becomes his mistress. During an afternoon rendezvous, however, Tina's aggressive lover reveals certain affinities with her abusive husband. As the affair disintegrates, one of Jonathan's pet projects, a fabulous party, aborts. In its aftermath he confesses to Tina that he has mismanaged the couple's savings, endangered his position in the firm, and committed adultery. Tina responds by leaving George, whom she labels a latent homosexual, and participating in group therapy. *Housewives. Social climbers. Lawyers. Mistresses. Authors. Egotists. Middle classes. Male chauvinism. Marriage. Infidelity. Family life. Social conformity. Alienation. Male homosexuality. Art galleries. Group therapy. New York City.*

Note: Filmed on location in New York City.

DIARY OF A MADMAN   F6.1165

Admiral Pictures. *Dist* United Artists. Mar **1963**. Sd; col (Technicolor). 35mm. 96 min.

Prod-Writ Robert E. Kent. *Dir* Reginald Le Borg. *Dir Photog* Ellis W. Carter. *Art Dir* Daniel Haller. *Set Decor* Victor Gangelin. *Film Ed* Grant Whytock. *Mus* Richard La Salle. *Sd* Ralph Butler. *Asst Dir* Al Westen. *Prod Mgr* Joseph Small. *Cost* Marjorie Corso. *Sp Eff* Norman Breedlove.

Cast: Vincent Price *(Simon Cordier)*, Nancy Kovack *(Odette Duclasse)*, Chris Warfield *(Paul Duclasse)*, Elaine Devry *(Jeanne D'Arville)*, Stephen Roberts *(Rennedon)*, Lewis Martin *(priest)*, Ian Wolfe *(Pierre)*, Edward Colmans *(André D'Arville)*, Mary Adams *(Louise)*, Harvey Stephens *(Louis Girot)*, Nelson Olmsted *(Dr. Borman)*, Joseph Ruskin *(The Horla)*, Dick Wilson, Gloria Clark, George Sawaya, Wayne Collier, Don Brodie, actor, Joseph Del Nostro, Jr.

Horror film. Source: Guy de Maupassant, "Le Horla," in *Gil Blas* (26 Oct 1886). In 1886, French magistrate Simon Cordier kills a condemned murderer in self-defense, thereby inheriting the Horla, an evil spirit that had possessed his victim. Following several mysterious occurrences, Cordier is visited by the Horla and ordered to kill his pet bird. His will all gone, he has no choice but to obey. In an attempt to quiet his nerves, Cordier resumes his hobby of sculpting and falls in love with his model, Odette Duclasse. She neglects to tell the magistrate of Paul, her estranged artist husband, but agrees to run away with him; on the eve of their departure, however, Cordier obeys the Horla's command to murder her. The following morning, unaware of what he has done, Cordier goes to his attic and is horrified to discover Odette's decapitated head resting on the bust he has sculpted. When police arrest Paul for the murder, Cordier maintains silence, even though Jeanne, daughter of art gallery owner Andre D'Arville, pleads with the magistrate to protest her lover's innocence. The Horla then orders Cordier to murder Jeanne, but the reflection of a crucifix awakens him from his murderous trance, and he decides to destroy the evil spirit. Sensing its vulnerability to fire, Cordier awaits the Horla's next visit, then sets his study aflame, killing both himself and his oppressor. As Cordier's will and diary are read, a priest who has been telling the story remarks that the Horla will continue to live wherever evil exists in the heart of man. *French. Magistrates. Models. Sculptors. Artists. Murder. Justifiable homicide. Infidelity. Injustice. Decapitation. Self-sacrifice. Evil spirits. Diaries. Fires. Birds.*

Note: Working title: *The Horla.*

DIARY OF A MODEL *see* **INTIMATE DIARY OF ARTISTS' MODELS**

DIARY OF A NUDIST *see* **NATURE CAMP CONFIDENTIAL**

DIARY OF A NYMPH *see* **AGGIE—THE DIARY OF A NYMPH**

DIARY OF A SCHIZOPHRENIC GIRL (Italy)   F6.1166
Idi Cinematografica. *Dist* Allied Artists. 29 Apr **1970** [New York showing]. Sd; col (Eastman Color). 35mm. 94 min. *MPAA rating* GP.

Pres by Emanuel L. Wolf. *Prod* Gian Vittorio Baldi. *Dir* Nelo Risi. *Screenplay* Nelo Risi, Fabio Carpi. *Photog* Franco Fornari. *Camera* Giulio Albonico. *Mus* Ivan Vandor. *Song* (U. S. vers?) sung by Julius La Rosa. *Scientific Cons* Franco Fornari.

Cast: Ghislaine d' Orsay *(Anna)*, Umberto Raho *(father)*, Marija Tocinowsky *(mother)*, Margarita Lozano *(Blanche [Bianca])*, Gabriella Mulachiè *(nurse)*, Manlio Busoni, Giuseppe Liuzzi *(doctors)*, Sara Ridolfi *(housekeeper)*.

Drama. Source: Renée, *Journal d'une schizophrène; auto-observation d'une schizophrène pendant le traitement psychothérapique par M. A. Sèchehaye* (Paris, 1950). At a Lucerne clinic, Blanche, a psychiatrist, treats Anna, a 17-year-old schizophrenic who has attempted suicide. Consultations with the patient and her mother reveal a history of parental rejection, as well as maternal preference for a younger sister, Mirella. To compensate for this neglect the psychiatrist assumes the role of mother, providing Anna with an alternative childhood and thereby curing her. *Psychiatrists. Sisters. Adolescence. Childhood. Schizophrenia. Filial relations. Suicide. Psychiatry. Clinics. Lucerne.*

Note: Location scenes filmed in Lucerne, Switzerland. Produced in Italy in 1968 as *Diario di una schizofrenica*; running time: 108 min. U. S. prerelease title: *Why Anna?*

DIARY OF A SWINGER   F6.1167
De Lem Films. *Dist* Boxoffice International Film Distributors. 11 Sep **1967** [Boston opening]. Sd; b&w. 35mm. 75 min.

An Amero Brothers Production. *Prod-Dir* John Amero, Lem Amero. *Exec Prod* George Delemos, Martin Avedisian. *Writ* Robert Parker. *Narr* Cara McCormick. *Cinematog* John Amero. *Lighting* Firth De Mule. *Set Decor* Phoebe Dinsmore. *Ed* Lem Amero. *Mus* Thomas J. Valentino. *Adtl Orig Mus* Jason Chamberlain, The Hobbits. *Song:* "Swinger" Dick Wright, Tony Eire. *Song Arr* Dick Wright. *Sung by* Cindy Evans. *Song Dir* Sam Cammarata, Joe Melino. *Sd* Harrison Carroll. *Prod Coörd* John Amero. *Cost* Brock Frocks.

Cast: Joanna Cunningham *(Jeannie)*, Rose Conti *(Vi)*, Biff Field *(Jim)*, Ronald Durling, Joe Harris, Larry Costner, Al "Bomba" Gilman, Pat Barrett, Roni Scardera, Michael Ann Burns, Rina Baron, Jack Benson, Lisa King, Pat Winner, Chuck Federico, Lena Lamont, Darcy Brown.

Melodrama. After an attempt at suicide, Jeannie is forced to accept psychiatric care, and she reveals through flashbacks the events that led her on her desperate course: *Raped near her home in the farmlands of New England, she faces the reproach of the townspeople, who refuse to believe that she has been taken by force. She comes to New York City, hoping to lose herself in the crowd, and shares an apartment with Vivian, a self-sufficient woman who has no use for men. A secretarial job in a theatrical agency leads Jeannie into a romance with Jim, an egotistical young actor, but her need for love remains unsatisfied, and she runs away when Jim tries to seduce her. After being assaulted by her boss, Jeannie becomes a high fashion model, but she once again finds frustration in a world of superficial relationships. When Jim returns from a tour, Jeannie offers him her love. He takes her to a jet-set orgy and taunts her by making love to another woman. Distraught, Jeannie returns to her apartment and surprises a burglar. Attacked and raped, she tries to end her unhappy existence. The psychiatrist tries to reach out to help Jeannie, but she*

is beyond believing that it is possible to enjoy happy relationships with men. Not knowing where else to turn, Jeannie reluctantly accepts the relative security of Vivian's love. *Psychiatrists. Models. Secretaries. Roommates. Actors. Suicide. Rape. Seduction. Lesbianism. Smalltown life. Orgies. Jet set. New York City. New England.*

Note: Filmed in New York City and New Jersey.

DIARY OF A VOYAGE IN THE SOUTH PACIFIC *see* **NUDE ODYSSEY**

THE DIARY OF AN INNOCENT YOUNG BOY *see* **BENJAMIN**

DIARY OF ARTISTS AND MODELS *see* **INTIMATE DIARY OF ARTISTS' MODELS**

THE DIARY OF FANNY HILL   F6.1168
5 Jul **1964** [San Francisco opening]. Sd; col. 35mm? [Feature length assumed.]

Sex film. No information about the precise nature of this film has been found. *Sexuality. Fanny Hill.*

DIARY OF KNOCKERS MCCALLA   F6.1169
Barry Mahon Productions. *Dist* Chancellor Films. May **1968**. Sd; b&w. 35mm. 67 min.

A Barry Mahon Production.

Drama. Beverly "Knockers" McCalla finds that being endowed with powerful sexual drives as well as a very large bust are two big advantages on the road to riches. Having had an affair with her stepfather, she leaves home. When a young man picks her up, she has sex with him in the back seat of the car. He drives her to a roadhouse which operates as an undercover brothel; she is an enormous success. After a run-in with one of the patrons, she moves on to Kansas City and works for one of the largest call girl syndicates in the state. When the police close in, she is sent to New York to become part of the party girl racket. A gangland killing interrupts her climb to riches. Fleeing from the scene of the crime, "Knockers" is picked up by Peter Stackpoole, a wealthy man who proves his honest intentions by marrying her. He dies on their wedding night, leaving "Knockers" $10 million. *Racketeers. Millionaires. Stepfathers. Prostitution. Organized crime. Murder. Marriage. Wealth. Inheritance. Whorehouses. Kansas City (Missouri). New York City.*

Note: Also known as *Diary of Love McCalla. Diary of Kay McAllister* is probably the same film.

IL DIAVOLO *see* **TO BED OR NOT TO BED**

IL DIAVOLO E I DIECI COMANDAMENTI *see* **THE DEVIL AND THE TEN COMMANDMENTS**

IL DIAVOLO INNAMORATO *see* **THE DEVIL IN LOVE**

DICE OF GOD *see* **THE GLORY GUYS**

DICIOTTENNI AL SOLE *see* **EIGHTEEN IN THE SUN**

DICTIONARY OF SEX   F6.1170
Audubon Films. Jan **1964**. Sd; b&w. 35mm. 72 min.

Pres by Radley Metzger. *Compilation Supv* Radley Metzger.

Guest Appearances: Agnès Laurent, Brigitte Juslin, Christian Marquand, Dora Doll, Pierre Brice, Nicole Burgot, Sheba Britt.

Compilation film. This film includes scenes of strippers, female nudity, lesbianism, and a "love duet" dance sequence. *Stripteasers. Dancers. Nudity. Lesbianism.*

Note: Includes footage from *The Fourth Sex, The Twilight Girls,* and *Soft Skin on Black Silk,* q. v. Also known as *Dictionary of Love.*

DID YOU HEAR THE ONE ABOUT THE TRAVELING SALESLADY?   F6.1171
Universal Pictures. 22 Feb **1968** [New Orleans opening; c23 Mar 1967; LP38594]. Sd (Westrex); col (Technicolor). 35mm (Techniscope). 96 min.

Prod Si Rose. *Exec Prod* Edward J. Montagne. *Dir* Don Weis. *Screenplay* John Fenton Murray. *Story* Jim Fritzell, Everett Greenbaum. *Dir Photog* Bud Thackery. *Art Dir* Alexander Golitzen, Robert MacKichan. *Set Decor* John McCarthy, Ralph Sylos. *Main Titl* Pacific Title. *Film Ed* Edward Haire, Dale Johnson. *Mus* Vic Mizzy. *Mus Supv* Joseph Gershenson. *Sd* Waldon O. Watson, Melvin M. Metcalfe, Sr. *Asst Dir* Phil Bowles, Robin Clark. *Unit Prod Mgr* John Morrison. *Miss Diller's Cost* Omar of Omaha. *Makeup* Bud Westmore. *Hairstyles* Larry Germain. *Dial Coach* Rand Brooks. *Stunt Coörd* Chuck Courtney.

Cast: Phyllis Diller *(Agatha Knabenshu)*, Bob Denver *(Bertram Webb)*, Joe Flynn *(Hubert Shelton)*, Eileen Wesson *(Jeanine Morse)*, Jeanette Nolan *(Ma Webb)*, Paul Reed *(Pa Webb)*, Bob Hastings *(Lyle Chatterton)*, David Hartman *(constable)*, Jane Dulo *(Clara Buxton)*, Kelly Thordsen *(Scraggs)*, Charles Lane *(Mr. Duckworth)*, George Neise *(Ben Milford)*, Dal McKennon *(old soldier)*,

Herb Vigran (baggage man), Lloyd Kino (laundry man), Warde Donovan, Eddie Quillan, Eddie Ness (salesmen).

Comedy. In 1910, as Primrose Junction, Kansas, prepares for its annual county fair, traveling saleslady Agatha Knabenshu arrives at the Sunflower Hotel to sell player pianos. When Bertram Webb, the town's unsuccessful young inventor, reduces Agatha's demonstration piano to shambles, he tries to make amends by inviting her to stay at his parents' farm and to repay her by winning $1,000 at the fair with his automatic cow-milking machine. The contraption backfires, however, and sends the cows stampeding through the town, resulting in almost $1,500 in property damages. Meanwhile, the Webbs, bankrupt because of Bertram's inventions, have been informed by banker Hubert Shelton that they have only 24 hours to meet their mortgage. In a desperate attempt to raise the money, Bertram decides to enter his wood-burning automobile in the county fair race, which offers a $1,500 prize. Disguised as racing drivers, Agatha and Bertram pull up to the starting line, but Bertram is discovered; Agatha is not recognized, however, and after a series of wild misadventures, she wins the race. *Traveling saleswomen. Inventors. Bankers. Debt. Bankruptcy. Automobile racing. Disguise. Fairs. Pianos. Inventions. Mortgages. Automobiles. Kansas. Stampedes. Cows.*

DIE! DIE! MY DARLING! (Great Britain)   **F6.1172**
Hammer Film Productions–Seven Arts Productions. *Dist* Columbia Pictures. 12 May **1965** [Philadelphia opening; c1 Mar 1965; LP30840]. Sd (RCA); col (Eastman Color, print by Pathé). 35mm. 97 min.
Prod Anthony Hinds. *Exec Prod* Michael Carreras. *Dir* Silvio Narizzano. *Screenplay* Richard Matheson. *Dir Photog* Arthur Ibbetson. *Camera Op* Paul Wilson. *Prod Dsgn* Peter Proud. *Supv Ed* James Needs. *Ed* John Dunsford. *Mus Comp* Wilfred Josephs. *Mus Supv* Philip Martell. *Sd Rec* Ken Rawkins. *Sd Ed* Roy Hyde. *Asst Dir* Claude Watson. *Prod Mgr* George Fowler. *Cont* Renee Glynne. *Wardrobe Mistress* Mary Gibson. *Makeup* Roy Ashton, Richard Mills. *Hairstyles* Olga Angelinetta.
Cast: Tallulah Bankhead (Mrs. Trefoile), Stefanie Powers (Patricia Carroll), Peter Vaughan (Harry), Maurice Kaufmann (Alan Glentower), Yootha Joyce (Anna), Donald Sutherland (Joseph), Gwendolyn Watts (Gloria), Robert Dorning (Ormsby), Philip Gilbert (Oscar), Winifred Dennis (shopkeeper), Diana King (woman shopper).
Melodrama. Source: Anne Blaisdell, *Nightmare* (New York, 1961). Mrs. Trefoile, an aging religious fanatic who lives in a desolate country home in an English village, devotes her days to reading the Bible and mourning her son, Stephen, who died a few years earlier in a car crash. Her only companions are a sullen housekeeper, Anna; the woman's brutish husband, Harry; and an imbecile gardener, Joseph. One day she receives a courtesy visit from her dead son's former fiancée, Patricia Carroll. Upon learning that Patricia is soon to marry, Mrs. Trefoile locks the young girl in the attic and prepares to "cleanse her soul" so that she will be fit to be reunited with Stephen in the hereafter. All of Patricia's efforts to escape are thwarted until she tempts the lecherous Harry into releasing her, but the plan fails when the now totally deranged Mrs. Trefoile kills Harry in the basement of the house. Eventually, Patricia's fiancé, Alan Glentower, becomes so worried about her absence that he drives to the village. Mrs. Trefoile tells him Patricia has already left, but he discovers the truth and breaks down the cellar door just as the crazed woman is about to perform a death ritual over the terrified Patricia. While Alan telephones the police, Anna, having discovered her dead husband's body in the basement, stabs the old woman in the back. As she dies, Mrs. Trefoile embraces her dead son's portrait and murmurs, "Stephen, they hurt me." *Fanatics. Housekeepers. Gardeners. Motherhood. Death. Employer-employee relations. Village life. Murder. Insanity. The Bible.*
Note: Released in Great Britain in Mar 1965 as *Fanatic.*

DIE, MONSTER, DIE! (United States/Great Britain)   **F6.1173**
Alta Vista Film Productions. *Dist* American International Pictures. 27 Oct **1965** [Boston opening; c27 Oct 1965; LP32041]. Sd; col (Pathécolor). 35mm (Colorscope). 80 min. [Copyright length: 72 min.]
Pres by Samuel Z. Arkoff, James H. Nicholson. *Prod* Pat Green. *Exec Prod* James H. Nicholson, Samuel Z. Arkoff. *Dir* Daniel Haller. *Screenplay* Jerry Sohl. *Dir Photog* Paul Beeson. *Camera Op* Cecil Cooney. *Art Dir* Colin Southcott. *Main Titl* Bowie Films. *Film Ed* Alfred Cox. *Mus Comp* Don Banks. *Mus Dir* Philip Martell. *Sd Rec* Ken Rawkins, Bob Jones. *Sd Ed* Alban Streeter, Alan Corder. *Asst Dir* Dennis Hall. *Cont* Tilly Day. *Wardrobe Mistress* Laurel Staffell. *Makeup Artist* Jimmy Evans. *Hairdresser* Bobbie Smith. *Sp Eff* Wally Veevers, Ernie Sullivan.
Cast: Boris Karloff (Nahum Witley), Nick Adams (Stephen Reinhart), Freda Jackson (Letitia Witley), Suzan Farmer (Susan Witley), Terence De Marney (Merwyn), Patrick Magee (Dr. Henderson), Paul Farrell (Jason), George Moon, Harold Goodwin (cab driver [see note]), Gretchen Franklin, Sheila Raynor (Miss Bailey), Sydney Bromley (Pierce), Billy Milton (Henry), Leslie Dwyer (Potter).

Horror film. Source: H. P. Lovecraft, "The Colour Out of Space," in *Amazing Stories* (Sep 1927). An American scientist, Stephen Reinhart, goes to the village of Arkham, England, to visit Susan Witley, the woman he hopes to marry, and to meet her parents. He is put off by the villagers' lack of warmth, by the bleak grounds surrounding the Witley house, and by the cold reception given him by Susan's father, Nahum. Susan's mother, the bedridden and veiled Letitia, greets him warmly, however, and pleads with him to take Susan away. That night he encounters frightening apparitions and sees from his window the burial of Nahum's manservant Merwyn. The next day he goes to the village to find out about the strange occurrences at the Witley house, but he learns nothing. Later, Stephen and Susan investigate the Witley greenhouse, from which an unearthly glow emanates, and there they discover grotesque plants and organisms. In the cellar of the Witley house they find a huge, radioactive meteorite, which Nahum has been using to create mutations. Letitia, already disfigured from overexposure, is subsequently killed; and Nahum, also exposed to the radiation, dies in a fire which engulfs the house as Susan and Stephen escape. *Americans in foreign countries. Invalids. Scientists. Radiation. Mutation. Village life. Plant life. Disfiguration. Meteors. Ghosts. Fires.*
Note: Opened in London in Feb 1966 as *Monster of Terror*; running time: 80 min. Working title: *House at the End of the World.* Sources conflict in crediting the roles of cab driver and Miss Bailey.

DIFFERENT SONS (Japan)   **F6.1174**
Toho Co. 19 Oct **1962** [Los Angeles opening]. Sd; col (Eastmancolor). 35mm (Tohoscope). 95 min.
Exec Prod Sanezumi Fujimoto. *Dir* Yasuki Chiba. *Screenplay* Zenzo Matsuyama. *Photog* Masao Tamai. *Mus* Akira Ifukube.
Cast: Akira Takarada (Kensuke), Yuzo Kayama (Shoji), Kamatari Fujiwara (father), Yuko Mochizuki (mother), Yumi Shirakawa (Kensuke's wife), Yoko Fujiyama (daughter), Mie Hama, Chisako Hara, Hiroshi Koizumi, Masami Taura, Yu Fujiki, Takashi Shimura.
Domestic melodrama. Kensuke has been nearly disowned by his parents because he married a bar hostess. He has a fine job with a good future, however, and lives in middle class surroundings. His parents, younger brother Shoji, and sister Noriko live in poverty, fighting over the occasional egg on the dinner table. The father finally loses his job and cannot find work. It is now the duty of the children to provide for their parents. Kensuke, bitter because of his rejection, suggests they go to an old age home, but Shoji takes out a loan and becomes a taxi driver to support the family, even though he, too, is bitter at not having been sent to college as was his brother. Noriko, who had been the beloved of a janitor, begins seeing a widowed executive from Kensuke's firm, as urged on by her brother. When he asks her to marry him, Noriko drops the janitor in hopes of a better station in life. Shoji, now working 15 hours a day, wrecks his cab while driving a prostitute home and is threatened by a large lawsuit. His brother does not come to the aid of the family, even now. Further tragedy strikes as Noriko's former suitor, the janitor, arranges her death: she is run over by a train. The father is overwhelmed and tries to kill himself, stopped only by his wife. Kensuke, after being accused of causing all of the family's problems, agrees to help out and gives monetary aid. *Middle classes. Brothers. Taxi drivers. Janitors. Executives. Barroom hostesses. Filial relations. Poverty. Brother-sister relationship. Unemployment. Parenthood. Old age. Loans. Lawsuits. Automobile accidents. Murder. Jealousy. Suicide.*
Note: Released in Japan in 1962 as *Futari no musuko.*

A DIFFICULT LOVE see **CLOSELY WATCHED TRAINS**

DIG THAT JULIET see **ROMANOFF AND JULIET**

LES DIMANCHES DE VILLE D'AVRAY see **SUNDAYS AND CYBÈLE**

DIME WITH A HALO   **F6.1175**
Metro-Goldwyn-Mayer, Inc. May **1963** [c30 Jan 1963; LP23727]. Sd (Westrex); b&w. 35mm. 94 min.
Prod-Writ Laslo Vadnay, Hans Wilhelm. *Co-prod* Anthony Barr, Pat B. Rooney. *Dir* Boris Sagal. *Dir Photog* Philip H. Lathrop. *Art Dir* Charles Myall. *Set Decor* Karl Brainard, Bruce MacDonald. *Film Ed* Ralph E. Winters. *Mus* Ronald Stein. *Sd* Fred Faust. *Asst Dir* Jack Gertsman, Harold H. Herman. *Prod Supv* George Moskov. *Casting Cons* Marvin Paige.
Cast: Barbara Luna (Juanita), Rafael Lopez (Chuy Perez), Roger Mobley (Jose), Paul Langton (Mr. Jones), Robert Carricart (cashier), Manuel Padilla (Rafael), Larry Domasin (Cesar), Tony Maxwell (Domingo), Vito Scotti (doorman), Jay Adler (Mr. Lewis), Theodore Newton (Consul Glenson), Steven Geray (priest), Jeno Mate (Mr. Gonzales), Joan Connors (stripper), Tina Menard (Mexican woman), Raymond Sanchez (newsboy).
Comedy-drama. In the hope of winning a fortune, five Tijuana street urchins pool their meager earnings each week in order to buy a $2 ticket at the Caliente racetrack. Friendly American Mr. Jones places their bets, although he

disapproves of their selections. After losing for 11 consecutive weeks, the boys decide to make Jesus a partner in their venture. They steal a dime from the church poor box, add it to their cash, place their bet, and win $81,513. But they cannot find Mr. Jones, and they refuse to trust any other adult to cash the ticket for them. Juanita, the sister of one of the boys, contacts Jones in Los Angeles, and he promises to drive down the next day. But as he approaches the pay window he suffers a fatal heart attack, and the ticket blows off into a pile of rubbish. After a futile search for the lost ticket, the five boys return to the church and replace the dime they had "borrowed" from the poor box. *Waifs. Mexicans. Gambling. Horseracing. Poverty. Heart disease. Theft. Churches. Tijuana (Mexico).*

DIMENSION 5   F6.1176

United Pictures–Harold Goldman Associates. *Dist* Feature Film Corp. of America. Oct 1966 [c23 Nov 1966; LP34215]. Sd; col (Technicolor). 35mm. 91 min.

Prod Earle Lyon. *Exec Prod* Fred Jordan. *Dir* Franklin Adreon. *Screenplay* Arthur C. Pierce. *Photog* Alan Stensvold. *Art Dir* Paul Sylos, Jr. *Set Decor* Ray Boltz. *Film Ed* Robert S. Eisen. *Mus* Paul Dunlap. *Sd* Vic Appel. *Asst Dir* Joe Wonder.

Cast: Jeffrey Hunter (*Justin Power*), France Nuyen (*Kitty*), Harold Sakata (*Big Buddha*), Donald Woods (*Cane*), Linda Ho (*Nancy Ho*), Robert Ito (*Sato*), David Chow (*Stoneface*), Lee Kolima (*Genghis*), Jon Lormer, Bill Walker, Virginia Lee, Ken Spalding, Carol Byron, Kam Tong, Tad Horino, Gerald Jann, Maggie Thrett, Kay Michaels, Marianna Case, Deanna Lund, Robert Phillips, Allen Jung, John McKee, Ruth Foster, Tex Armstrong, Ed Parker, Tita Marsell.

Science fiction melodrama. Secret agent Justin Power narrowly escapes from enemy agents and reports to Cane, his superior at Espionage, Inc., who informs him that the National Intelligence Agency has captured a member of Dragon, a Communist Chinese organization. From the prisoner they learn that the Chinese are plotting to destroy Los Angeles with an H-bomb. With the help of Kitty Tu, his assistant from Hong Kong, Power learns that Ming Products, an import company, is the front for Dragon, whose leader, Big Buddha, is expecting a shipment in 3 weeks. Using their time-converter belts, Power and Kitty advance themselves to the arrival of the expected ship and discover, hidden in a shipment of rice, component parts of an H-bomb. Before they have a chance to act, though, they are captured by Big Buddha and his men, but they escape with the help of Nancy Ho, a Dragon agent who knows Power. Big Buddha and his men are killed, and Los Angeles is saved. Power and Kitty go back in time to pick up the 3 weeks they lost. *Secret agents. Chinese. Communists. Importers. Hired killers. Espionage. Smuggling. Hydrogen bomb. Time travel. Rice. Los Angeles. The Future.*

DIMKA (U.S.S.R.)   F6.1177

Gorky Film Studio. *Dist* Artkino Pictures. 20 Mar 1964 [New York opening]. Sd; b&w. 35mm. 77 min.

Dir Ilya Frez. *Screenplay* Volf Dolgiy. *Story Ed* V. Biryukova. *Photog* Mikhail Kirillov. *Art Dir* Sergey Serebrenikov. *Film Ed* V. Mironova. *Mus* Nikolay Yakovlev. *Cond* A. Roytman. *Sd* D. Flyangolts. *Asst Dir* Z. Danilova. *Prod Mgr* Ya. Zvonkov, N. Gofman. *Cost* N. Muller. *Makeup* D. Tsesarskaya. *Sp Eff* V. Lozovskiy, S. Ivanov.

Cast: Alyosha Zagorskiy (*Dimka*), Olga Lysenko (*his mother*), Vladimir Treshchalov (*Andrey*), S. Ageyeva, M. Gavrilko, V. Klyukin, A. Kasapov, L. Kardonskiy, Lenya Nikitin, Z. Naryshkina, V. Orlova, Vova Semyonov, K. Slavinskiy, A. Strelnikova, V. Taube, G. Frolov, A. Chizhova.

Comedy-drama. Dimka, an energetic, mischievous kindergarten boy in Moscow, has many friends and is generally satisfied with his life. The only thing he lacks is a father. One night, Dimka dreams that his mother was unable to buy him a father because she wasted her money on ice cream. The next morning, Dimka runs away from kindergarten and sets out with his ice cream money to find a father in the city. He carefully studies the various men he sees, including department store mannequins and the statuary on buildings. Eventually he selects a young man named Andrey, who, touched by Dimka's situation, takes him for a meal and treats him to rides in an amusement park. Towards evening, Andrey takes the boy home to his mother and hurriedly tries to leave, but Dimka will not allow him to go. The adults' first meeting is awkward; they have tea together, sitting in embarrassed silence. Eventually Andrey leaves, but Dimka, a bold matchmaker, is not perturbed, excitedly anticipating the return of his new father. *Children. Bachelors. Fatherhood. Motherhood. Amusement parks. Department stores. Moscow. Dreams.*

Note: Released in the U.S.S.R. in Apr 1963 as *Ya kupil papu.*

DINAH EAST   F6.1178

Page International, Inc. *Dist* Emerson Film Enterprises. 23 Dec 1970 [Kansas City, Missouri, opening]. Sd; col (DeLuxe). 35mm. 90 min. [Also reviewed at 87 min.] *MPAA rating* X.

Prod Gene Nash, Paula Stewart. *Assoc Prod* Martin Romley. *Dir-Writ* Gene Nash. *Photog* Ross Kelsay. *Art Dir* Tom Fortner, Jerry Guild. *Set Dsgn* James McNaughton. *Set Decor* Don Betts, Ed Schmitt. *Film Ed* Anthony M. Lanza. *Mus* Gene Nash. *Mus Arr & Cond* Ernie Freeman. *Song: "Thank You, Alex"* sung by John Steele, Sondra Steele. *Sd* Frank Murphy. *Wardrobe* Waldo Angelo. *Makeup* Dodie Warren. *Hairstyles* Edith Knizan.

Cast: Jeremy Stockwell (*Dinah East*), Ultra Violet (*Daniela*), Andy Davis (*Alan Sloan*), Reid Smith (*Jeff East*), Joe Taylor (*Bobby Sloan*), Ray Foster (*Tony Locke*), Matt Bennett (*Tank Swenson*), Leland Murray (*Archibald Phipps*), Margaret Rolfe (*Mrs. Kelly*), Victoria Wales (*Janet Arnold*), Susan Romen (*Carolyn Fiske*), Kitty Carl (*Debbie Thurber*), Cal Crenshaw (*Freddie*), Steve Shaw (*Midnight Cowboy*).

Melodrama. At the age of 40, Dinah East—a legendary movie queen of the 1950's now living as a recluse—suffers a heart attack and dies while riding in her Rolls Royce. Hollywood is shocked, but the mortician attending the deceased is absolutely dumb-struck when he discovers that the former sex goddess was actually a man. Once the mortician has broken the news to the local press, the people who knew Dinah best reflect on their relationships with her. Most of them never knew that at 18 the star decided to switch sexes when a studio guard told her that the casting department was seeing only young girls. Meeting with a modicum of success as a female, Dinah decided to make the deception permanent. One of the first to befriend and help the new actress was Oscar-winning costume designer Daniela. When Dinah discovered that the older woman was a lesbian, the two made a pact of secrecy, and Daniela helped promote Dinah as a glamour girl. Tony Locke never knew the truth, however; a homosexual matinee idol, he considered it good for his image to be seen frequently in public with the beautiful Dinah. Attorney Alan Sloane knew the facts; enamored of his beautiful client, he had so persistently tried to force himself upon her that in desperation Dinah had shown him physical proof of her sex. Hardest hit by the star's death are her adopted son Jeff, who deeply loved his mother; and Tank Swenson, Dinah's loyal chauffeur. A former prizefighter and a bisexual, Tank worshiped Dinah, and his devotion and affection was often returned. Unable to reconcile himself to his loss, Tank takes his own life by walking into the Pacific Ocean. *Recluses. Undertakers. Actors. Couturiers. Lawyers. Chauffeurs. Female impersonation. Lesbianism. Male homosexuality. Adoption. Bisexuality. Suicide. Hollywood.*

Note: Location scenes filmed in California. Also known as *The Story of Dinah East.*

DINGAKA (South Africa)   F6.1179

Jamie Uys Film Productions. *Dist* Embassy Pictures. 30 Jun 1965 [New York opening]. Sd; col (Technicolor). 35mm (CinemaScope). 98 min.

Pres by Joseph E. Levine. *Prod-Dir-Writ* Jamie Uys. *Dir Photog* Manie Botha, Judex C. Viljoen. *Art Dir* Ian MacLeod, Kay Dubinski. *Film Ed* John Jympson. *Mus* Bertha Egnos, Eddie Domingo, Basil Gray. *Choreog* Sheila Wartski. *Sd Ed* Rusty Coppleman. *Prod Mgr* Ivan Hall. *Cost Dsgn* Ruth St. Moritz, Anna Richter-Visser. *Makeup* Nola Du Preez, Eric Allwright.

Cast: Stanley Baker (*Tom Davis*), Juliet Prowse (*Marion Davis*), Ken Gampu (*Ntuku Makwena*), Alfred Jabulani (*Mpudi*), John Sithebe (*witch doctor*), Paul Makgoba (*Masaba*), Siegfried Mynhardt (*judge*), Gordon Hood (*prosecutor*), Flora Motaung (*Rurari*), Bob Courtney (*prison chaplain*), George Moore (*Legal Aid Society secretary*), Hugh Rouse (*Bantu commissioner*), Simon Swindell (*doctor*), Willem Botha (*court clerk*), Sophie MqCina (*choir soloist*), Jimmy Sabe (*lead singer*), Daniel Marolen, Cocky Tlhotlhalemji (*priests*), Clement Mehlomakulu (*dancer*), Lulami Jabulani (*baby boy*), Sandy Nkomo (*prisoner*), Amigo Dira (*Eben*), Fuzi Zazayokwe (*stick fighter*), Thembi (*Oniku*), Thandi (*Letsea*).

Melodrama. Masaba, former stick fighting champion of a South African Bantu tribe, is defeated at the annual contest. He goes to the witch doctor for advice on how to win back his title and is told that he must drink a potion containing the heart of a young twin girl. Soon afterwards, one of Ntuku Makwena's twin daughters disappears, and he visits the witch doctor, who informs him that the girl was killed by Masaba. The witch doctor then places a curse on Ntuku. When Ntuku's wife goes to the top of the mountain to try to remove the curse, she slips and falls to her death. In accordance with the tribal laws of revenge, Ntuku follows Masaba to Johannesburg and tries to kill him. Arrested and awaiting trial, Ntuku learns that his defense has been assigned to Tom Davis, a member of the Legal Aid Society. Davis is annoyed at having to spend time on the case, and Ntuku refuses to help in his own defense. Disgusted by her husband's obsession with his career, Davis' wife, Marion, takes an interest in the case. Ntuku receives a mild sentence of 2 years at hard labor, but he escapes and returns to his village. There he discovers that the real murderer is the witch doctor, and he kills him, despite the belief that he will be destroyed by the gods for slaying the sacred figure. When Ntuku is not struck down, the entire village is liberated from the superstitions of the witch doctor cult, and Ntuku returns to Johannesburg with Tom and Marion

Davis, hoping to find justice. *Bantu. Witch doctors. Twins. Lawyers. Public defenders. Murder. Revenge. Prison escapes. Superstition. Contests. Curses. Trials. Johannesburg.*

Note: Released in South Africa in 1965.

IL DIO CHIAMATO DORIAN see **DORIAN GRAY**

DIO PERDONA ... IO NO see **GOD FORGIVES—I DON'T**

DIONYSUS IN '69   **F6.1180**
Performance Group. *Dist* Sigma III Corp. 22 Mar 1970 [New York opening]. Sd; b&w. 35mm. 90 min. [Also reviewed at 86 min.] *MPAA rating* X.
  A Film by Brian De Palma, Robert Fiore, Bruce Rubin. *Dir Stage Prod* Richard Schechner. *Photog* Brian De Palma, Robert Fiore. *Settings* Michael Kirby, Jerry Rojo. *Film Ed* Brian De Palma, Robert Fiore. *Sd* Bruce Rubin. *Opticals* Berkey Pathé.
  Cast—The Performance Group: William Finley *(Dionysus)*, William Shephard *(Pentheus)*, Joan MacIntosh *(Agave)*, Judith Allen, Remi Barclay, Samuel Blazer, Jason Bosseau, Cara Crosby, Richard Dia, Gwendolyn Galsworth, Rozanne Levine, Vicki May, Patrick McDermott, Margaret Ryan, Richard Schechner, Ron Schenk, Ciel Smith, Charles Strang.
  Drama. Sources: Richard Schechner, *Dionysus in '69* (New York opening: 6 Jun 1968). Euripides, *Bacchae.* Proclaiming himself the Greek god Dionysus, actor William Finley invites the audience in a Greenwich Village garage to participate in a nude orgiastic ritual. Although Pentheus, King of Thebes, denounces Dionysus, he later comes under the god's influence and joins the bacchanal. Dionysus, however, directs the king's assassination by the Bacchae. Pentheus' murder destroys Dionysus' spell, and the participants disperse as Agave mourns her son, the dead king. Dissatisfied with the play, Finley announces his presidential candidacy and is carried out onto the street. *Greeks. Royalty. Theatrical troupes. Rites and ceremonies. Spells. Orgies. Nudity. Murder. Politics. New York City—Greenwich Village. Thebes. Dionysus. Agave. Pentheus. Bacchus.*
  Note: Filmed during a performance of the play as produced in the Performing Garage in New York's Greenwich Village. Filmed in 8mm & 16mm, the film utilizes split-screen techniques.

THE DIPLOMAT'S MANSION (Japan)   **F6.1181**
Tokyo Eiga Co. *Dist* Toho Co. 27 Oct 1961 [Los Angeles opening]. Sd; col? 35mm. 109 min.
  Dir Shiro Toyoda.
  Cast: Reiko Dan *(bar girl)*, Hiroshi Akutagawa *(diplomat)*, Tsutomu Yamazaki *(his son)*, Chikage Awashima *(madam)*, Nobuko Otowa, Kyoko Kishida, Tetsuro Tamba, Nobuo Nakamura, Chisako Hara, Masao Oda, Frankie Sakai, Ichiro Arishima, Hisaya Morishige.
  Drama. An elderly aristocrat who has lost his job in the foreign service must rely for support on his son, a bartender, and on a local madam. *Aristocrats. Diplomats. Bartenders. Madams. Filial relations. Old age.*
  Note: Released in Japan in May 1961 as *Tokyo yawa.*

DIRTY DINGUS MAGEE   **F6.1182**
Metro-Goldwyn-Mayer, Inc. 18 Nov 1970 [New York opening; c23 Oct 1970; LP38249]. Sd; col (Metrocolor). 35mm (Panavision). 91 min. [Cut from 96 min.] *MPAA rating* GP.
  Prod-Dir Burt Kennedy. *Assoc Prod* Richard E. Lyons. *Screenplay* Tom Waldman, Frank Waldman, Joseph Heller. *Dir Photog* Harry Stradling, Jr. *Camera Op* Ralph Gerling. *Asst Camera* Richard Meinardus, Robert Spence. *Art Dir* George W. Davis, J. McMillan Johnson. *Set Decor* Robert R. Benton, Chuck Pierce. *Film Ed* William B. Gulick. *Mus & Mus Dir* Jeff Alexander. *Adtl Mus* Billy Strange. *Song:* "The Ballad of Dingus Magee" Mack David, Jeff Alexander. *Titl Song* Mack David. *Sung by* Mike Curb Congregation. *Sd* Hal Watkins, Bruce Wright. *Boom Op* James Utterback. *Asst Dir* Al Jennings, Lynn Guthrie, John Behm. *Unit Prod Mgr* John W. Rogers. *Script Supv* Marge Mullen. *Cost* Yvonne Wood. *Wardrobe* Lambert Marks, Elva Martien. *Makeup* Shotgun Britton. *Hairstyles* Naomi Cavin. *Sp Eff* Marcel Vercoutere. *Stunt Coörd* Jerry Gatlin. *Still Photog* Eric Carpenter. *Gaffer* George Lasher. *Prop* Bob Murdock, John Sexton. *Grip* Howard Bradner, Lloyd Isbell.
  Cast: Frank Sinatra *(Dingus Magee)*, George Kennedy *(Hoke Birdsill)*, Anne Jackson *(Belle Kops)*, Lois Nettleton *(Prudence)*, Jack Elam *(John Wesley Hardin)*, Michele Carey *(Anna Hotwater)*, John Dehner *(The General)*, Henry Jones *(Reverend Green)*, Harry Carey, [Jr.] *(Stuart)*, Paul Fix *(Chief Crazy Blanket)*, Donald Barry *(Shotgun)*, Mike Wagner *(driver)*, Terry Wilson, David Burk, David Cass, Tom Fadden *(troopers)*, Mae Old Coyote, Lillian Hogan, Florence Real Bird, Ina Bad Bear *(old crones)*, Willis Bouchey *(Ira Teasdale)*, Marya Christen *(China Poppy)*, Mina Martinez, Sheila Foster, Irene Kelly, Diane Sayer, Jean London, Gayle Rogers, Timothy Blake, Lisa Todd, Maray Ayres, Carol Anderson *(Belle's girls)*.

Western comedy. Source: David Markson, *The Ballad of Dingus Magee* (Indianapolis, 1965). Robbed by Dirty Dingus Magee, Hoke Birdsill travels to Yerkey's Hole and demands justice from Belle Kops, the town's mayor and madam. In response, the indifferent Belle appoints him sheriff. Although Birdsill repeatedly captures Magee, the bandit, assisted by his Indian mistress Anna Hotwater, escapes as often. Discovering a strongbox Magee has accidentally acquired, Birdsill steals its contents. Diverting the town by announcing a proposed gunfight with his dupe, Magee rifles Belle's bedroom. To his consternation, however, Magee discovers that Birdsill has preceded him. Appointed sheriff in Birdsill's stead, Magee searches for his fellow thief. Reunited, the two join forces and burn Belle's brothel to the ground. *Madams. Bandits. Sheriffs. Indians of North America. Mayors. Mistresses. Theft. Arson. Miscegenation. Whorehouses.*
  Note: Location scenes filmed in Arizona.

THE DIRTY DOZEN (United States/Great Britain) **F6.1183**
M. K. H. Productions-Metro-Goldwyn-Mayer, Inc. *Dist* Metro-Goldwyn-Mayer, Inc. 15 Jun 1967 [New York opening; c15 Jun 1967; LP34487]. Sd; col (Metrocolor). 35mm (see note). 149 min.
  A Kenneth Hyman Production. *Prod* Kenneth Hyman. *Assoc Prod* Raymond Anzarut. *Dir* Robert Aldrich. *Screenplay* Nunnally Johnson, Lukas Heller. *Dir Photog* Edward Scaife. *Camera Op* Alan McCabe, Tony Spratling. *Art Dir* William Hutchinson. *Main Titl Dsgn* Walter Blake. *Ed* Michael Luciano. *Mus* Frank De Vol. *Song:* "The Bramble Bush" Frank De Vol, Mack David. *Song:* "Einsam" Frank De Vol, Sibylle Siegfried. *Sd Rec* Franklin Milton, Claude Hitchcock. *Sd Ed* John Poyner. *Asst Dir* Bert Batt. *Unit Prod Mgr* Julian Mackintosh. *Cont* Angela Allen. *Makeup* Ernest Gasser, Wally Schneiderman. *Sp Eff Supv* Cliff Richardson.
  Cast: Lee Marvin *(Major Reisman)*, Ernest Borgnine *(General Worden)*, Charles Bronson *(Joseph Wladislaw)*, Jim Brown *(Robert Jefferson)*, John Cassavetes *(Victor Franko)*, Richard Jaeckel *(Sergeant Bowren)*, George Kennedy *(Maj. Max Armbruster)*, Trini Lopez *(Pedro Jiminez)*, Ralph Meeker *(Capt. Stuart Kinder)*, Robert Ryan *(Col. Everett Dasher Breed)*, Telly Savalas *(Archer Maggott)*, Donald Sutherland *(Vernon Pinkley)*, Clint Walker *(Samson Posey)*, Robert Webber *(General Denton)*, Tom Busby *(Milo Vladek)*, Ben Carruthers *(Glenn Gilpin)*, Stuart Cooper *(Roscoe Lever)*, Robert Phillips *(Corporal Morgan)*, Colin Maitland *(Seth Sawyer)*, Al Mancini *(Tassos Bravos)*, George Roubicek *(Pvt. Arthur James Gardner)*, Thick Wilson *(General Worden's aide)*, Dora Reisser *(German officer's girl)*.
  War drama. Source: E. M. Nathanson, *The Dirty Dozen* (New York, 1965). A few months before D-Day, Major Reisman, a U. S. Army officer stationed in England, is given the task of training 12 convicted GI's—murderers, rapists, thieves—for the suicidal mission of parachuting into Nazi-occupied France and blowing up a chateau housing top-ranking German officers. Although the 12 men agree to undertake the assignment in the hope of being granted pardons, their initial reaction to Reisman is one of indifference and contempt. But with Sergeant Bowren's aid, Reisman goads, browbeats, and drives the men until he earns a small measure of respect from each of them. And by standing up for his squad against the opposition of two superior officers, Colonel Breed and General Denton, Reisman eventually succeeds in forging his band of misfits into a fighting unit. To prove the worth of "The Dirty Dozen," a nickname the men acquired when they were deprived of soap and water, Reisman gains permission from General Worden to allow the men to participate in war game maneuvers. After making a fool of the pompous Colonel Breed by capturing his entire staff, the men are given the go-ahead for the dangerous mission. Once parachuted into France, they make their way to the chateau and, by various ruses and surprise attacks, gain entry. Everything goes as planned until one of the Dozen, a Bible-spouting sex degenerate, Archer Maggott, goes berserk and betrays his colleagues. He is shot down, however, as the chateau is turned into a battleground of rapid machine-gun fire and exploding grenades. The savage in-fighting ends only when gasoline-soaked grenades are thrown down ventilator shafts, blowing the chateau to bits. Only three of the 12 men—Wladislaw, Posey, and Sawyer—are still alive when it is over. Both Reisman and Sergeant Bowren are present when General Worden reveals that the ex-criminals who gave their lives are now listed as soldiers who died honorably in the line of duty. *Nazis. Criminals—Rehabilitation. Parachuting. Disguise. Sadism. Explosives. War games. World War II. France. United States Army. Germany—Army.*
  Note: Filmed in England. Print blown up to 70mm for some engagements.

THE DIRTY FIVE see **THE FILTHY FIVE**

THE DIRTY GAME (France/Italy/West Germany) **F6.1184**
Franco London Film-Fair Film-Eichberg-Film-Euro International Films. *Dist* American International Pictures. 13 Apr 1966 [Kansas City, Missouri, opening]. Sd; b&w (print by Movielab). 35mm. 91 min. [Also 87 min.]

Pres by Landau/Unger Co. An Oliver A. Unger Production. *Exec Prod* Richard Hellman. *Assoc Prod* Eugène Tucherer. *Dir* Terence Young, Christian-Jaque, Carlo Lizzani, Werner Klingler. *Screenplay* Jacques Laborie, Jacques Remy, Ennio De Concini, Christian-Jaque, Philippe Bouvard. *English Screenplay* Jo Eisinger. *Photog* Richard Angst, Pierre Petit, Erico Menczer. *Art Dir* Raymond Gabutti, Heinrich Weidemann. *Film Ed* Borys Lewin, Alan Osbiston. *Mus (see note)* Robert Mellin, Gianfranco Reverberi. *Sd* Georges Mardiguian. *Prod Mgr* Peter Hahne, Jean Mottet.

Cast: Henry Fonda *(Kourlov)*, Robert Ryan *(General Bruce)*, Vittorio Gassman *(Perego [Ferrari])*, Annie Girardot *(Nanette [Monique])*, Bourvil *(Laland [Lalande])*, Robert Hossein *(Dupont)*, Peter Van Eyck *(Berlin CIA head [Petchatkin])*, Maria Grazia Buccella *(Natalia)*, Mario Adorf *([Callagan])*, Jacques Sernas *([Glazov])*, Georges Marchal, Wolfgang Lukschy, Louis Arbessier, Jacky Blanchot, Gabriel Gobin, Helmut Wildt, Violette Marceau, Gabriella Giorgelli, Nino Crisman, Oreste Palella, Renato Terra.

Drama. The American intelligence chief in Europe, General Bruce, is ordered to meet his Russian counterpart on the East-West border in Germany to effect a prisoner exchange. En route he recalls three individual cases he supervised: The first involves an Italian scientist who has perfected a rocket fuel, which he does not want to fall into either American or Russian hands. Double agent Perego offers himself to the Russians as a kidnaping agent with a plan for removing the scientist from Italy by helicopter. Perego notifies the Italian authorities of his actions, however; and they, with the aid of American agents, are able to thwart the abduction and persuade the scientist of the good intentions of the United States. The second episode concerns an operation to prevent a Russian attack on two American submarines on maneuvers off the coast of Somaliland. A French underwater expert, Laland, defeats local enemy resistance and locates the underwater Russian base. The third incident involves an American undercover agent, Kourlov, who escapes from the Russians after 17 years of imprisonment with vital secrets intended for General Bruce. Kourlov reaches his rendezvous point a day early, and his hiding place is exposed through the treachery of Petchatkin, Berlin CIA chief. Though Kourlov is murdered, he succeeds in leaving a clue for General Bruce identifying Petchatkin as a traitor. ... As General Bruce meets with his Russian counterpart and they trade philosophical pleasantries during the exchange of prisoners, the American general comments that "War is a hell of a way to make a living." *Russians. Prisoners of war. Secret agents. Scientists. Frogmen. Escapees. Traitors. Cold war. Kidnaping. Murder. Espionage. Helicopters. Submarines. Rockets. German Democratic Republic. Somaliland. United States Army—Intelligence. United States—Central Intelligence Agency.*

Note: Filmed in West Germany, Africa, and Italy. Paris opening: Jun 1965 as *Guerre secrète*; running time: 120 min. Released in West Germany in Aug 1965 as *Spione unter sich*; running time: 113 min. Rome opening: caOct 1965 as *La guerra segreta*. Sources conflict on music credit. Only Italian sources include Euro International Films as production company. Role names in brackets refer to French release version.

THE DIRTY GIRLS   F6.1185

Charles Film Productions. *Dist* Audubon Films. 22 Jan **1965** [Los Angeles showing]. Sd; b&w. 35mm (FranScope). 82 min.

Pres by Radley Metzger. *Assoc Prod* Ava Leighton. *Dir* Radley H. Metzger. *Story-Screenplay* Peter Fernandez. *Adtl Dial* LaVerne Owens. *Photog* Roger Duculot, Hans Jura. *Mus Ed* Daniel Hart. *Prod Mgr* Osman Ragheb. *Unit Mgr* Maurice Gilli.

Cast: Reine Rohan *(Monique)*, Denyse Roland, Madeleine Constant *(Garance, see note)*, Marlene Sherter *(Nadia)*, Peter Parten *(Robert)*, Anne Stengel *(Madeleine)*, Lionel Bernier *(Michel)*, Wolfgang Petersen *(host)*, Marie Edmund *(guest)*.

Drama. Two prostitutes, one in Paris and the other in Munich, approach their livelihood from different social positions. Garance, a streetwalker on the Champs-Elysées, sets out each evening to earn her next day's living. Her first customer of the evening, Michel, is a shy young student whom she gently initiates into the world of sexual pleasure. She next encounters Antoine, a sadist; and afterwards, she entertains a regular customer, Grimaud, by donning a military uniform and disciplining him with a riding crop. Monique, a Munich call girl whose financial situation contrasts with that of Garance, receives a visit from Robert, an American businessman returning a camera borrowed by a mutual friend. Earlier, Robert had mistakenly approached Nadia, thinking that she was Monique, and an embarrassing encounter had resulted. Monique makes love to Robert in gratitude and departs to entertain at a high-society swimming pool party. She meets Armand, a movie star, and they jump into the pool together and stage a sexual exhibition for the guests. Finally, arriving home, Monique is joined by her long-awaited lover, Laurence, a woman. *Prostitutes. Students. Americans in foreign countries. Businessmen. Fetishism. Lesbianism. Masochism. Sadism. Sexual initiation. Voyeurism. Mistaken identity. Paris. Munich.*

Note: Filmed in 1963 in Paris and Munich. Also known as *D Girls* and *Dirty Girl*. Production company unconfirmed. Denyse Roland is credited with the role of Garance by film pressbook, while another source credits Madeleine Constant.

THE DIRTY GIRLS *see* **THE FLESH IS HOT**

THE DIRTY HAWK *see* **THE MASTER BEATER**

DIRTY HEROES (France/Italy/West Germany)   F6.1186

Fida Cinematografica–Productions Jacques Roitfeld–Gloria Film. *Dist* Golden Eagle Films. 11 Dec **1969** [Charlotte, North Carolina, opening]. Sd; col (Technicolor). 35mm (Techniscope). 105 min. *MPAA rating* G.

Prod Edmondo Amati. *Dir* Alberto De Martino. *Screenplay and Orig Story* Dino Verde, Vincenzo Flamini, Alberto De Martino, Alberto Verucci, Franco Silvestri, Louis Agotay. *Script Supv (see note)* Ennio De Concini. *Photog* Gianni Bergamini. *Art Dir* Nedo Azzini. *Set Decor* Pierluigi Basile. *Film Ed* Otello Colangeli. *Mus* Ennio Morricone, Bruno Nicolai. *Sd* Bruno Brunacci. *Asst Dir* Giorgio Ubaldi. *Prod Mgr* Piero Lazzari.

Cast: Frederick Stafford *(Sesamo)*, Adolfo Celi *(Rolmann)*, Daniela Bianchi *(Kristina von Keist)*, Howard Ross *(Joe)*, Curt Jurgens *(General von Keist)*, John Ireland *(Captain O'Connor)*, Michel Constantin *(Petrowsky)*, Helmut Schneider *(SS General Hassler)*, Anthony Dawson *(American colonel)*, Faida Nicols *(Magda [Marta])*, Jacques Monod *(partisan)*, Tom Felleghi *(American N. C. O.)*, Valentino Macchi.

War melodrama. As World War II nears its end, an American POW and former Chicago safecracker, Sesamo, escapes from a German prison camp in Holland with Chicago gangsters Randall and Walcott. Walcott is killed, but assisted by Petrowsky, a German soldier in league with Dutch partisans, Sesamo makes his way to Amsterdam and unveils a plot to steal German rocket installation plans from a strongroom at Wehrmacht headquarters. (What Sesamo really wants from the strongroom is a fortune in diamonds that the Nazis took from Dutch jewel merchants.) Also involved in the daring scheme are Captain O'Connor, a U. S. Air Force officer and onetime underworld colleague of Sesamo; and Rolmann, a partisan leader. To obtain the floorplans of high command headquarters, Petrowsky blackmails Kristina von Keist, the young wife of a German general, by threatening to disclose her Jewish ancestry. Though the heist is successful, Sesamo and his men are captured by Nazis, who forced the disclosure of information pertaining to the raid from Rolmann's mistress. Left with no alternative, Rolmann plans a partisan attack on the already weakened and demoralized German occupation forces. But General von Keist, unwilling to sacrifice his men, offers to return the diamonds and captives if the German troops are permitted to withdraw. To assure fulfillment of the agreement, a hostage exchange is arranged—Rolmann for Kristina—until the withdrawal is completed. Before the agreement can be fulfilled, however, General von Keist is killed as a traitor by an SS officer, General Hassler. Then O'Connor's paratroop unit arrives to rescue Sesamo's group and help the partisans defeat the Germans. After the battle, Rolmann, fatally wounded, confesses to Sesamo that he never intended to let him keep the diamonds; and to avoid prosecution by the Allies, Sesamo and his cohorts return the gems to the Dutch. After receiving 10 percent of the diamonds' value as a reward of gratitude, Sesamo turns his back on his former associates, who plan to rob a Chicago bank after the war, and seeks out the forgiving Kristina. *Safecrackers. Prisoners of war. Traitors. Nazis. Jews. Mistresses. Hostages. Gangsters. SS. Prison escapes. Resistance (political). Theft. Espionage. Blackmail. Military occupation. Paratroops. Diamonds. World War II. Netherlands. Amsterdam. United States Army. Germany—Army.*

Note: Rome opening: caJan 1968 as *Dalle ardenne all'inferno*. Paris opening: May 1968 as *La gloire des canailles*; running time: 104 min. Released in West Germany in Jul 1968 as *... und Morgen fahrt ihr zur Hölle*; running time: 106 min. Ennio De Concini's credit as script supervisor is unconfirmed. Louis Agotay is credited as coauthor of screenplay only by German sources. Renato Rossini appears under the pseudonym of Howard Ross; Antonio Margheriti as Anthony Dawson. One source credits Divina-Film as German production company in place of Gloria Film. Original running time: 120 min.

THE DIRTY OLD MAN *see* **DRACULA (THE DIRTY OLD MAN)**

DIRTY POOL   F6.1187

Dist Distribpix, Inc. ca **1970**. Sd; col. 35mm. 61 min.

Sex film. In sunny California, a couple takes a Sunday drive in the country and finds a shady spot in the woods to make love. At the same time, a wealthy married couple sunning themselves by their pool, makes love beside the pool and under the water. The first couple sees them, waits until the husband leaves, and the then forces the wife into depraved sexual acts. The husband returns, is shocked, and, attracted to the strange woman, takes her into the house and makes love with her. The others soon follow, and the foursome joins in an orgy that leads to a brutal climax of the film. *Orgies. Troilism. Swimming pools. California.*

DIRTYMOUTH　　　　　　　　　　　　　　　**F6.1188**

Superior Films. *Dist* Budco Distributing Corp., Howard Mahler Films. Sep 1970. Sd; col (Movielab). 35mm. 102 min. *MPAA rating* R.

Pres by Claude Schlanger, Herbert S. Altman. *Prod-Dir-Writ* Herbert S. Altman. *Exec Prod* Claude Schlanger. *Assoc Prod* Alfred Gilbert, Allan Altman. *Photog* Bert Spielvogel. *Film Ed* Edna Paul. *Mus* Emanuel Vardi, Lenny Hambro. *Songs Sung by* The Free Design. *Sd* Marvin Dworkin. *Makeup* John Jiras.

Cast: Bernie Travis *(Lenny Bruce)*, Courtney Sherman *(Iris McCabe)*, Wynn Irwin *(Lou Hamilton)*, Sam Teardrop *(Marlene St. Clair)*, Harry Spillman *(Lewis)*, Peter Clune *(Mr. Murdock)*, Eleanor Gould *(Mrs. McCabe)*, Bob Allen, actor *(judge in Philadelphia)*, Eugene Wood *(judge in New York)*, Chris Gampel *(defense attorney)*, John C. Becher *(Harry)*, Fred Knapp *(defense attorney in New York)*, Jim Thorne *(assistant district attorney)*, Reid Cruickshanks *(Brady)*, Frank Feda *(Ed Newton)*, Court Benson *(Johnson)*, Fuddle Bagley *(comic)*, Herb Carter *(Smith)*, Phil Carter *(Gerber)*, Horatio Fuller *(Tipstaff)*, Edward Grace *(Capote)*, Michael Zettler, Arthur French *(policemen)*, Dorothy Claire *(Mrs. McHenry)*, Alice Yourman *(Mrs. Amperian)*, Gladys Lane *(Mrs. Gerber)*, Frankie Mann, Bob Leslie *(themselves)*.

Biographical drama. A fictionalized study of the last years in the life of controversial nightclub entertainer Lenny Bruce, the film deals with his court appearances in New York, California, Pennsylvania, and Illinois on obscenity and drug charges; his increasing paranoia; and his eventual death from drug overdose. *Entertainers. Trials. Narcotics. Obscenity. Paranoia. Drug overdose. Nightclubs. New York State. California. Pennsylvania. Illinois. Lenny Bruce.*

Note: Working title: *A Tough Gig.*

THE DISCOVERY OF AMERICA　　　　　　　　**F6.1189**

Barrios Films. 4 Jun 1970 [Los Angeles opening]. Sd; col (Eastmancolor). 16mm. 83 min.

Prod-Dir Jaime Barrios.

Cast: Rolando Pena, Carmen Beuchat, Ana Maria Fuenzalida.

Experimental film. A series of home movies, dedicated to Andy Warhol, are combined to show the importance of sex. Sexual encounters are shown in basement apartments in Port Jefferson and East Hampton, New York; Red Bank and Sea Bright, New Jersey; Washington, D. C.; Wilton, Connecticut; and Manhattan. There are also scenes of a wedding in Connecticut and the landing of a sailboat at Port Jefferson. The soundtrack is largely in Spanish. *Sexuality. Home movies. Port Jefferson (New York). East Hampton (New York). Red Bank (New Jersey). Sea Bright (New Jersey). Washington (District of Columbia). Wilton (Connecticut). New York City. Andy Warhol.*

IL DISERTORE E I NOMADI *see* **THE DESERTER AND THE NOMADS**

DISK-O-TEK HOLIDAY (Great Britain)　　　　　**F6.1190**

Delmore Productions–Canterbury Productions. *Dist* Allied Artists. Jun 1966. Sd; col (Eastman Color). 35mm. 72 min.

Prod Jacques De Lane Lea. *Exec Prod* Ben Nisbet. *Prod U. S. Seq* Frank C. Slay. *Exec Prod U. S. Seq* Louis Kellman. *Dir* Douglas Hickox. *Dir U. S. Seq* Vince Scarza. *Screenplay* David Edwards. *From an Idea by* Douglas Hickox, Jacques De Lane Lea. *Photog* Martin Curtis, Stanley Pavey. *Art Dir* Peter Proud. *Film Ed* Fred Burnley. *Song:* "Tell Me When" Geoff Stephens, Les Reed. *Songs:* "Mine All Mine," "Night Time" Dave Carey. *Song:* "Hide 'n' Seek" John Baker, mus, Mike D'Abo. *Song:* "Mr. Scrooge" Tony Hiller, Shel Talmy. *Song:* "The Fox" Con Clusky, Dee Clusky, John Stokes. *Song:* "Low the Valley" Michael Carr, mus, Norman Newell. *Song:* "Teenage Valentino" Nolly Clapton, Mercy Hump. *Song:* "Leave Me Alone" Gordon Waller, Peter Asher. *Songs:* "You Were Made for Me," "Just for You," "I Wish You Everything" Mitch Murray. *Song:* "Sugar Dandy" Derek Harriott. *Song:* "The Locomotion" Gerry Goffin, Carole King. *Song:* "If I Had a Hammer" Pete Seeger. *Song:* "Don't Make Me Blue" David Foster. *Song:* "It's So Hard To Be Good" Don Spencer, mus, Mike Bradley. *Song:* "Milkman" Tony Crane, Johnny Gustafson. *Sd* Doug Turner. *Asst Dir* Roy Baird, Ted Sturgis.

With: Peter and Gordon, The Chiffons, A Band of Angels, The Bachelors, Freddy Cannon, The Vagrants, Casey Paxton, Louise Cordet, The Merseybeats, Caroline Lee, Roy Sone, Judy Jason, Johnny B. Great, The Applejacks, The Rockin' Ramrods, The Orchids, Freddie and the Dreamers, Jackie and the Raindrops, Millie Small, Al Saxon, Douglas Sheldon, Mark Wynter, The Warriors, Arnie Ginsburg, Hy Lit, Bob Foster.

Musical revue. A series of rock performances given in London and parts of the United States are introduced by American disc jockeys Arnie Ginsburg of Boston, Hy Lit of Philadelphia, and Bob Foster of Baltimore and Boston. *Disc jockeys. Entertainers. Rock and roll. Philadelphia. Boston. Baltimore. London.*

Note: Released in Great Britain in Jun 1964 as *Just for You;* running time: 64 min. Disc jockey Sam Costa introduces performers in the British version; U. S. version replaces him with Ginsberg, Lit, and Foster. Some British entertainers may have been cut and American performers added for U. S. release.

DISORDER (France/Italy)　　　　　　　　　　　**F6.1191**

Titanus–Pathé Cinéma. *Dist* Pathé Contemporary Films. 25 May 1964 [New York opening]. Sd; b&w. 35mm. 105 min.

Prod Giuseppe Bordogni. *Dir* Franco Brusati. *Screenplay* Franco Brusati, Francesco Ghedini. *French Dial* Félicien Marceau. *Photog* Leonida Barboni. *Camera* Arturo Zavattini. *Art Dir* Mario Garbuglia. *Film Ed* Ruggero Mastroianni. *Mus* Mario Nascimbene. *Sd* Giulio Tagliacozzo. *Asst Dir* Romolo Girolami. *Cost* Bice Brichetto.

Cast: Louis Jourdan *(Tom)*, Susan Strasberg *(Isabella)*, Curt Jurgens *(The Father)*, Alida Valli *(The Mother)*, Georges Wilson *(The Priest)*, Sami Frey *(Carlo)*, Renato Salvatori *(Mario)*, Jean Sorel *(Andrea)*, Antonella Lualdi *(Mali)*, Tomas Milian *(Bruno)*, Marisa Belli, Emma Baron, Adriana Asti, Lia Angeleri, Luciana Angiolillo, Inger Milton, Jole Mauro.

Drama. Returning to her family because of her industrialist father's illness, Isabella finds plans in progress for a party. Carlo, her weak brother, explains that the scheduled party will go on to appease their father's vanity, though he will not make an appearance at the affair. The man's wife, obsessed by her jealousy, gains admittance to the sickroom and is rebuffed by her husband, then rushes through the house questioning servants about a suspected mistress. Isabella, too, is rebuffed by her father when she attempts a reconciliation. When he collapses while trying to watch the party from his window, Isabella becomes hysterical. The next day the father is hospitalized, and Mario, a bartender hired for the party who had hoped to gain a position in business through the contact, goes to Milan, his ambitions dashed. While watching people entering a fashionable party, Mario meets Bruno, a boyhood friend. Impressed by Bruno's apparent wealth, Mario asks him to help his mother, who is ill in a hospital charity ward. Bruno, laughing, refuses, and Mario strikes him. Meanwhile, at the party, Andrea, whose marriage to Mali is on the rocks, tries to patch things up by seducing her in the bedroom of their host, Tom. The following day, upset because his "mistress" has left him, Tom begs Andrea and Mali to keep him company. Mali prefers Tom to Andrea, which causes Andrea to attack Tom's housemaid. Mali leaves in disgust. When Tom later asks Andrea to go because his mistress is returning, Andrea stays out of curiosity and discovers that the mistress is Bruno. Visiting his mother at the hospital, Mario talks about their situation and is overheard by a priest, who offers his help. Going to the priest's house, Mario is astonished at the behavior of the people there, and that night he discovers a wild party taking place in the attic attended by prostitutes, transvestites, and pickpockets. When he warns the priest that his charity cases are using his house as a place of assignation, the priest confesses that he has been defrocked. Mario angrily accuses him of practicing false charity. Later, Mario's mother receives a large amount of money, which will allow them to live together comfortably, from an unknown benefactor. Going to thank the priest, Mario discovers a wrecking crew at work on the priest's house. The priest has effected his own salvation by truly helping another person. *Bartenders. Industrialists. Upper classes. Idle rich. Housemaids. Mistresses. Priests. Prostitutes. Pickpockets. Filial relations. Marriage. Poverty. Vanity. Jealousy. Infidelity. Brother-sister relationship. Orgies. Seduction. Male homosexuality. Imposture. Transvestism. Charity. Hospitals. Milan.*

Note: Rome opening: Mar 1962 as *Il disordine;* running times: 105 and 97 min; Paris opening: Mar 1963 as *Le désordre;* running time: 98 min.

THE DISORDERLY ORDERLY　　　　　　　　**F6.1192**

York Pictures–Jerry Lewis Enterprises. *Dist* Paramount Pictures. 16 Dec 1964 [Seattle opening; c17 Dec 1964; LP29385]. Sd; col (Technicolor). 35mm. 90 min.

Prod Paul Jones. *Exec Prod* Jerry Lewis. *Assoc Prod* Arthur P. Schmidt. *Dir-Writ* Frank Tashlin. *Story* Norm Liebmann, Ed Haas. *Dir Photog* W. Wallace Kelley. *Camera Op* Leonard Smith. *Camera Asst* Dewey Wrigley. *Art Dir* Hal Pereira, Tambi Larsen. *Set Decor* Sam Comer, Ray Moyer. *Film Ed* John Woodcock. Russel Wiles. *Mus Score* Joseph J. Lilley. *Titl Song Sung by* Sammy Davis, Jr. *Sd* Hugo Grenzbach, Charles Grenzbach, Bud Parman, Jim Miller, Don Merritt. *Asst Dir* Ralph Axness, Bill Poole, Dale Coleman, Hal Bell. *Unit Prod Mgr* William C. Davidson. *Script Supv* Dorothy Yutzi. *Wardrobe Dsgn* Edith Head. *Wardrobe* Shirlee Strahm, Buddy Clark, Jim George. *Makeup* Bud Bashaw, Jack Stone. *Sp Eff* John P. Fulton, Paul K. Lerpae, Farciot Edouart. *Dial Coach* Marvin Weldon. *Still Photog* Sterling Smith. *Prop* Martin Pendleton, Jim Cottrell. *Grip* Ed Crowder, Robert Dabke. *Gaffer* Lorne Netten.

Cast: Jerry Lewis *(Jerome Littlefield)*, Glenda Farrell *(Dr. Jean Howard)*, Susan Oliver *(Susan Andrews)*, Everett Sloane *(Mr. Tuffington)*, Karen Sharpe *(Julie Blair)*, Kathleen Freeman *(Maggie Higgins)*, Del Moore *(Dr. Davenport)*,

Alice Pearce (*talkative patient*), Jack E. Leonard (*Fat Jack*), Barbara Nichols (*actress*), Richard Deacon (*Mr. Courtney*), Danny Costello, Mike Ross (*ambulance drivers*), Herbie Faye (*Mrs. Welles*), Frank Scannell (*Mr. McCaby*), Mike Mazurki, Murray Alper, William Wellman, Jr. (*drivers*), Benny Rubin, Milton Frome, John Macchia.

Comedy. Jerome Littlefield becomes a hospital orderly, hoping to become a doctor like his father. Afflicted with a "neurotic identification empathy" which causes him to suffer the pains of his patients, Jerome creates mayhem in his bungling attempts to help. Dr. Jean Howard, once in love with Jerome's father and now head of the hospital, is fond of him, however, and refuses to fire him. Although nurse Julie Blair is in love with Jerome, he falls in love with Susan Andrews, a young patient hospitalized after an attempted suicide. When he takes on extra duties to pay the young woman's bills, she offers him her love out of gratitude; but their first kiss is disappointing, and Jerome concludes that he must really be in love with Julie. Upon learning that the neglected Julie has run away, Jerome chases her in an ambulance. After creating an enormous traffic snarl, he wins back his true love; with his emotions properly oriented, Jerome overcomes his neurosis and makes plans to marry Julie and enter medical school. *Physicians. Orderlies (hospital). Nurses. Neurosis. Employer-employee relations. Suicide. Traffic. Hospitals. Ambulances. Chases.*

IL DISORDINE *see* **DISORDER**

IL DISPREZZO *see* **CONTEMPT**

A DISTANT TRUMPET   **F6.1193**
Warner Bros. Pictures. 27 May **1964** [New York opening; c30 May 1964; LP29439]. Sd; col (Technicolor). 35mm (Panavision). 117 min.
Prod William H. Wright. *Dir* Raoul Walsh. *Screenplay* John Twist. *Adapt* Richard Fielder, Albert Beich. *Dir Photog* William Clothier. *Art Dir* William Campbell, art dir. *Set Decor* William L. Kuehl. *Film Ed* David Wages. *Mus* Max Steiner. *Orch* Murray Cutter. *Sd* Francis E. Stahl. *Asst Dir* Russell Saunders, William Kissel. *Script Supv* Edward Hohler. *Cost* Howard Shoup. *Men's Wardrobe* Alexis Davidoff. *Women's Wardrobe* Fern Vollner. *Makeup Supv* Gordon Bau. *Hairstyles* Ann Saunders. *Supv Hairstylist* Jean Burt Reilly. *Sp Eff* Ralph Webb. *Military Cons & Adv* J. S. Peters, (Capt.). *Gaffer* Ralph Owen. *Grip* Louis Maschmeyer. *Prop* Red Turner. *Still Photog* Jack Woods, still photog.
Cast: Troy Donahue (*2d Lieut. Matthew Hazard*), Suzanne Pleshette (*Kitty Mainwaring*), Diane McBain (*Laura Greenleaf*), James Gregory (*Gen. Alexander Quait*), William Reynolds, actor (*Lieut. Theo Mainwaring*), Claude Akins (*Seeley Jones*), Kent Smith (*Secretary of War*), Judson Pratt (*Capt. Cedric Gray*), Bartlett Robinson (*Maj. Hiram Prescott*), Bobby Bare (*Cranshaw*), Larry Ward (*Sergeant Kroger*), Richard X. Slattery (*Slattery*), Mary Patton (*Jessica Prescott*), Russell Johnson (*Captain Brinker*), Lane Bradford (*Major Miller*).
Western drama. Source: Paul Horgan, *A Distant Trumpet* (New York, 1960). In 1883 U. S. Cavalry Lieut. Matt Hazard arrives at Fort Delivery on the Mexican border in Arizona to begin a new assignment and is welcomed by Kitty Mainwaring, wife of the acting commanding officer. The next day Hazard and his group are ambushed by Indians when he takes some men out to cut wood, and Hazard later rescues Kitty in a runaway wagon after her party is attacked and her driver and escort killed. A violent storm forces the two to spend the night in a cave. Back at the fort the new commanding officer, General Quait, arrives and launches a full-scale attack against the Indians. He fails to capture Indian Chief War Eagle and sends Hazard into Mexico to try to persuade War Eagle to surrender peacefully. The chief saves Hazard's life at one point and eventually agrees to peace when Hazard promises them an Arizona reservation. On their way back to Arizona, however, the Indians are met by Major Miller, who orders them to Florida. Hazard and Quait go to Washington; Hazard refuses a medal offered him; and he and Quait resign because their commitments to the Indians have not been honored. The government capitulates, and the Indians get their Arizona reservation. Quait and Hazard return to Fort Delivery, and Hazard marries Kitty, whose husband has been killed. *Indians of North America. Tribal chiefs. Duplicity. Forts. Treaties. Mexican border. Arizona. Washington (District of Columbia). Mexico. United States Army—Cavalry. Storms.*
Note: Location scenes filmed in New Mexico and Arizona.

DITES 33 *see* **THE LADY DOCTOR**

THE DIVING GIRLS' ISLAND *see* **VIOLATED PARADISE**

DIVING GIRLS OF JAPAN *see* **VIOLATED PARADISE**

DÍVKA S TŘEMI VELBLOUDY *see* **THE GIRL WITH THREE CAMELS**

DIVORCE AMERICAN STYLE   **F6.1194**
National General Productions–Tandem Enterprises. *Dist* Columbia Pictures. 21 Jun **1967** [Los Angeles opening; c1 Jul 1967; LP34891]. Sd; col (Technicolor). 35mm. 109 min.
Prod-Screenplay Norman Lear. *Dir* Bud Yorkin. *Story* Robert Kaufman. *Dir Photog* Conrad Hall. *Set Decor* Frank Tuttle. *Prod Dsgn* Edward Stephenson. *Film Ed* Ferris Webster. *Mus* Dave Grusin. *Sd Supv* Charles J. Rice. *Sd* William Randall, Jr., Jack Haynes. *Asst Dir* Rusty Meek. *Unit Prod Mgr* Howard Pine. *Cost Dsgn* Bob Mackie. *Asst Cost Dsgn* Frances Lear. *Makeup Supv* Ben Lane. *Hairstyles* Sydney Guilaroff.
Cast: Dick Van Dyke (*Richard Harmon*), Debbie Reynolds (*Barbara Harmon*), Jason Robards, [Jr.] (*Nelson Downes*), Jean Simmons (*Nancy Downes*), Van Johnson (*Al Yearling*), Joe Flynn (*Lionel Blandsforth*), Shelley Berman (*David Grieff*), Martin Gabel (*Dr. Zenwinn*), Lee Grant (*Dede Murphy*), Pat Collins (*herself*), Tom Bosley (*Farley*), Emmaline Henry (*Fern Blandsforth*), Dick Gautier (*Larry Strickland*), Tim Matthieson (*Mark*), Gary Goetzman (*Jonathan*), Eileen Brennan (*Eunice*), Shelley Morrison (*Jackie*), Bella Bruck (*Celia*), John J. Anthony (*judge*).
Domestic comedy. After 16 years of marriage, Barbara and Richard Harmon have a luxurious Los Angeles home, an expensive car, and two well-behaved but somewhat precocious sons. Despite the material success of their marriage, Barbara feels that they don't communicate and she seeks out a marriage counselor. This action, coupled with the "advice" of mutual friends, soon leads to bitter arguments that land the Harmons in a divorce court, where an embittered judge grants Barbara virtually everything, leaving Richard with $87.50 a week out of a yearly gross of $25,000. While spending a Sunday with his two boys, Richard meets Nelson Downes, a divorcé frantically trying to eliminate his own alimony payments by finding a new husband for his ex-wife, Nancy. Nelson discusses the situation with Nancy, who likes Richard, and it is agreed that if the arrangement is to be financially feasible Barbara must also have a new mate. The ideal candidate is found in bachelor Big Al Yearling, a successful used car dealer. When Barbara responds to Big Al's courtship, all the combatants (including Nelson's pregnant fiancée, Eunice) meet at a nightclub on the evening before the Harmon divorce is to be made final. During a performance by hypnotist Pat Collins, Barbara permits herself to be mesmerized. After doing an uninhibited striptease on stage, she is ordered by the hypnotist to go into the audience and kiss the man she truly loves. When she plants a resounding smack on the delighted Richard, the Harmon divorce is forgotten. As Barbara and Richard return home to resume their bickering, Nelson, never one to give up easily, desperately tries to interest Nancy in Big Al. *Marriage counsel. Judges. Used-car dealers. Bachelors. Marriage. Divorce. Alimony. Hypnotism. Striptease. Los Angeles.*

DIVORCE—ITALIAN STYLE (Italy)   **F6.1195**
Lux Film–Vides–Galatea. *Dist* Embassy Pictures. 17 Sep **1962** [New York opening]. Sd; b&w. 35mm. 104 min.
Pres by Joseph E. Levine. *Prod* Franco Cristaldi. *Dir* Pietro Germi. *Story-Screenplay* Ennio De Concini, Alfredo Giannetti, Pietro Germi. *Photog* Leonida Barboni. *Camera Op (see note)* Arturo Zavattini, Carlo Di Palma. *Asst Camera* Alfredo Palmieri, Giovanni Altinori, Giovanni Ciarlo. *Art Dir* Carlo Egidi. *Set Decor* Giovanni Checchi. *Film Ed* Roberto Cinquini. *Asst Film Ed* Sergio Montanari, Mario Morra. *Mus* Carlo Rustichelli. *Sd* Fiorenzo Magli. *Boom Op* Antonio Bramonti. *Asst Dir* Renzo Marignano. *Prod Mgr* Guglielmo Colonna. *Unit Mgr* Carlo Bartolini. *Script Girl* Myrta Corbucci. *Asst to the Dir* Enzo Battaglia. *Cost* Dina Di Bari. *Dressmaker* Elena Micheli Scardella. *Makeup* Franco Freda. *Asst Makeup* Raffaele Cristini. *Hairstyles* Anna Fabrizi.
Cast: Marcello Mastroianni (*Ferdinando Cefalù*), Daniela Rocca (*Rosalia Cefalù*), Stefania Sandrelli (*Angela*), Leopoldo Trieste (*Carmelo Patanè*), Odoardo Spadaro (*Don Gaetano*), Angela Cardile (*Agnese*), Margherita Girelli (*Sisina*), Bianca Castagnetta (*Donna Matilde*), Lando Buzzanca (*Rosario Mulè*), Pietro Tordi (*Attorney De Marzi*), Laura Tomiselli (*Aunt Fifidda*), Ugo Torrente (*Don Calogero*), Antonio Acqua (*priest*).
Comedy. Ferdinando Cefalù, an impoverished Sicilian nobleman, returns home to his once elegant family mansion. Bored to frustration by his nagging wife, Rosalia, he falls in love with his 16-year-old cousin, Angela. Since divorce is impossible under Italian law, he resigns himself to imagining different ways of doing away with his plump, mustached wife. An encounter with Angela in the garden further inflames his desire, but Angela's father disapproves of the situation and sends her away to a convent. One day Ferdinando discovers another law by which a person who commits murder in defense of his honor is subject to only a light jail sentence. Ferdinando asks Carmelo Patanè, an obscure painter and a former beau of Rosalia, to restore some frescoes in the Cefalù house in order to bring him into contact with her. Although Carmelo is timid and wary, a romance appears to be developing, but Ferdinando's plan collapses when the couple run off together, disgracing Ferdinando beyond his own expectations. He has no choice but to find the lovers and redeem his honor.

Meanwhile, Carmelo's abandoned wife has learned of the affair, and she also tracks them down and kills her husband, while Ferdinando permanently disposes of the troublesome Rosalia. Ferdinando happily receives an 18-month prison sentence, after which he quickly returns home to marry Angela. Making love on their honeymoon cruise, he is unaware that Angela is secretly planning a romance with the handsome young sailor at the helm. *Nobility. Artists. Cousins. Marriage. Murder. Law. Divorce. Infidelity. Prisons. Honeymoons. Ships. Sicily.*

Note: Location scenes filmed in Sicily. Opened in Rome in Dec 1961 as *Divorzio all'italiano;* running time: 108 min. Carlo Di Palma's participation is unconfirmed.

DIVORCE LAS VEGAS STYLE F6.1196

World Film Productions. *Dist* Fine Products. 7 Aug 1970 [Los Angeles showing]. Sd; col 35mm. 95 min.

Pres by Gerald Fine. *Prod-Dir-Writ* William White. *Assoc Prod* Carl Friedman, Antoinette Marine. *Dir Photog* Robert Caramico. *Asst Dir Photog* Jeff Kimball. *Film Ed* Andrew Herbert. *Mus* Bobby Mann, Carl Stevens. *Sd* Clark D. Will. *Prod Mgr* Chuck Alford. *Script Supv* Marlene Bucklin. *Cost* Bert Bliss. *Makeup* Rick Sagliani.

Cast: Luanne Roberts *(Sally),* John Alderman *(Jim),* Dusty Canon *(Shirley),* Dixie Donovan *(Jane),* Lois Ursone *(Betty),* Sylvana Tie *(beautician),* Rick Sagliani *(Pierre),* Marcelle Monte *(June),* Howard Payne Arnold *(Lovell),* Gesela Bernas *(new girl),* Carl Stevens, Bobby Mann *(maintenance men),* Carme *(announcer),* Sandy O'Hara *(stripper).*

Comedy-drama. Jim arrives in Las Vegas to obtain a divorce from his wife, Sally. He inadvertently checks into a hotel which caters exclusively to the needs of men waiting for divorce. Sally decides she doesn't want to lose Jim; she gets herself into shape at a beauty salon, changes her hair color, and applies for a job in the hotel as a masked masseuse. She works on Jim—unrecognized by him—and they make love. She loses the job, but wins back her husband. *Masseurs. Marriage. Divorce. Disguise. Hotels. Las Vegas.*

THE DIVORCEE F6.1197

A-A Productions. *Dist* SCA Distributors, Crest Film Distributors. 12 Sep 1969 [Champaign, Illinois, showing]. Sd; col (Eastman Color). 35mm. 90 min.

Prod-Dir-Writ A. C. Stephen. *Photog* Robert Ruben. *Art Dir* Bud Costello. *Ed* Marco Macaroni.

Cast: Marsha Jordan *(Betty Brant),* Deborah Downey, Mary Bauer, Abdull Khan, Lloyd Hudson, Bill Williams, Edie Tyson, James E. Myers, Liz Rene, Mark Delmonde.

Melodrama. Newly divorced from her roving husband, Betty Brant discovers that she is viewed by men as an easy sexual conquest. Her own lawyer takes advantage of her loneliness, and she begins to drink heavily to erase her shame. Her best friend's husband tries to seduce her; when they are discovered, she is thrown out of the house, and she resolves to start anew. A serious affair with an insurance salesman is cut short by her fear of a second marriage, and she is drawn into a life of unrestrained sexuality. Wild orgies occupy her nights, and she even finds pleasure at the hands of sadistic lovers in a sauna bath. Resolving once again to regain control, she meets John Foster Gillis, who seems to be the man she needs. Dignified and prosperous, he promises her a new life, but she discovers that he is already married, and she again turns to the bottle for solace. Invited to a party, she participates in a "psychodrama" and confesses the painful intimacies of her sordid life. Her host comforts her in the bedroom, but she awakens the next morning to find that he has taken her for a common whore, leaving a few crumpled bills behind. *Lawyers. Insurance agents. Divorce. Loneliness. Seduction. Promiscuity. Group sex. Sadomasochism. Infidelity. Alcoholism. Confession.*

Note: May also be known as *Confessions of a Divorcee.*

DIVORZIO ALL'ITALIANO see DIVORCE—ITALIAN STYLE

LA DIXIÈME VICTIME see THE 10TH VICTIM

LE 17E PARALLÈLE: LE VIETNAM EN GUERRE see 17TH PARALLEL: VIETNAM IN WAR

DJANGER "LOVE RITE OF BALI" (Reissue) F6.1198

Dist Jacon Film Distributors. 1964. Sd; b&w. 35mm. 54 min.

Note: Originally released as *Virgins of Bali;* c21 Sep 1932; MP4221.

DJÄVULENS ÖGA see THE DEVIL'S EYE

DO I BORE YOU DARLING? see DARLING, ARE YOU BORED WITH MEN?

DO ME! DO ME! DO ME! F6.1199

Mitam Productions. 11 Jul 1969 [Champaign, Illinois, showing]. Sd; col. 35mm. 75 min.

Dir Wes Ransom.

Melodrama. Mrs. Barlow inherits a house and, unable to pay the taxes, allows her friend Amy, a prostitute, to use the house to entertain customers in return for a cut of the profits. The police arrest Mrs. Barlow and, after her release from jail, she and a few friends decide to open a modeling school that will serve as a haven for married women who wish to cheat on their husbands. Angela joins the group and organizes an orgy. Her husband discovers her infidelity and is killed by one of Angela's boyfriends. The police are summoned, and Mrs. Barlow again finds herself in trouble. *Prostitutes. Housewives. Inheritance. Infidelity. Murder. Whorehouses. Orgies.*

DO NOT DISTURB F6.1200

Martin Melcher Productions–Arcola Pictures. *Dist* Twentieth Century-Fox Film Corp. 22 Dec 1965 [Los Angeles opening; c13 Dec 1965; LP32096]. Sd (Westrex); col (DeLuxe). 35mm (CinemaScope). 102 min.

An Aaron Rosenberg–Martin Melcher Production. *Prod* Aaron Rosenberg, Martin Melcher. *Assoc Prod* Barney Rosenzweig. *Dir* Ralph Levy. *Screenplay* Milt Rosen, Richard Breen. *Dir Photog* Leon Shamroy. *Art Dir* Jack Martin Smith, Robert Boyle. *Set Decor* Walter M. Scott, Jerry Wunderlich. *Main Titl* De Patie-Freleng. *Film Ed* Robert Simpson. *Mus Score & Cond* Lionel Newman. *Mus Assoc* Alexander Courage. *Titl Song* Mark Barkan, Ben Raleigh. *Song:* "Au Revoir Is Goodbye With a Smile" Robert Hilliard, Mort Garson. *Songs Sung by* Doris Day. *Orch* Mort Garson, Alexander Courage, Warren Barker. *Sd* Alfred Bruzlin, Elmer Raguse. *Asst Dir* Joseph E. Rickards. *Unit Prod Mgr* William Kaplan. *Cost Dsgn* Ray Aghayan. *Makeup* Ben Nye. *Hairstyles Supv* Margaret Donovan. *Miss Day's Hairstyles* Cheri De La Mare. *Sp Photog Eff* L. B. Abbott, Emil Kosa, Jr.

Cast: Doris Day *(Janet Harper),* Rod Taylor *(Mike Harper),* Hermione Baddeley *(Vanessa Courtwright),* Sergio Fantoni *(Paul Bellari),* Reginald Gardiner *(Simmons),* Maura McGiveney *(Claire Hackett),* Aram Katcher *(Culkos),* Leon Askin *(Langsdorf),* Lisa Pera *(Alicia),* Michael Romanoff *(delegate),* Albert Carrier *(Reynard),* Barbara Morrison *(Mrs. Ordley),* Dick Winslow *(one-man band),* Pierre Salinger *(American consul).*

Domestic comedy. Source: William Fairchild, *Some Other Love* (a play; production undetermined). Janet and Mike Harper rent a house in the English countryside from Vanessa Courtwright after Mike, an American wool company executive, moves his office to London to stimulate foreign trade. Mike spends his time in London keeping company with his assistant, Claire Hackett, and attending bachelor parties thrown by his boss, Mr. Langsdorf, while neglected Janet stays home alone. In revenge, she flirts with Paul Bellari, a handsome antique dealer whom she hires to redecorate the house. Janet and Paul fly to Paul's main office in Paris so that Janet may see an antique table. While there, they visit a bistro where Janet passes out from drinking too much wine, and when Paul takes her back to his office, they accidentally get locked in for the night. Mike hears of the trip and takes the next flight to Paris. When he finds them in the office, he fights with Paul and demands a divorce from Janet. Janet agrees, but several days later she overhears Claire Hackett discussing how much Mike loves his wife. At a cocktail party in a hotel, Janet mistakenly winds up in lecherous Mr. Langsdorf's bed, and he chases her through the hotel. Mike becomes jealous, and the two reunite. *Executives. Antique dealers. Americans in foreign countries. Infidelity. Revenge. Jealousy. Drunkenness. Employer-employee relations. Hotels. Bistros. London. Paris. Chases.*

Note: Pierre Salinger's role may have been cut from the film before release.

DO YOU KEEP A LION AT HOME? (Czechoslovakia) F6.1201

Barrandov Film Studio. *For* Československý Film. *Dist* Brandon Films. Dec 1966. Sd; col. 35mm. 81 min.

Pres by Walter Manley Enterprises. *Dir* Pavel Hobl. *Screenplay* Sheila Ochová, Bohumil Sobotka, Pavel Hobl. *Story* Sheila Ochová. *Anim* Jiří Vojta, Trmal, Novák, Vinklářek. *Camera* Jiří Vojta. *2d Camera* Ivan Wurm. *Camera Asst* Bohumil Rath. *Art Dir* Jan Brychta. *Sets* Bohumil Pokorný, Jindřich Goetz. *Film Ed* Miroslav Hájek, Jitka Šulcová. *Mus Comp* Wiliam Bukový. *Sd* Adolf Nacházel. *Sd Eff* Bohumír Brunclík. *Asst Dir* František Matoušek, Jaroslav Toms. *Head of Prod* Josef Císař. *Prod Assoc* Olga Mimrová, Miloš Rudolf, Jarka Hypiusová. *Cost* Skorepová.

Cast: Ladislav Očenášek *(Joe [Pepík]),* Josef Filip *(Johnny [Honzík]),* Olga Machoninová *(little girl),* Miloš Preininger *(father),* Dagmar Kofronová *(mother),* František Löring *(man with umbrella),* Jan Brychta *(painter),* Vendelín Šedivý *(policeman),* Arnošt Faltýnek *(museum doorman),* Jiří Valenta *(travel agency employee),* Evelyna Juhanová *(fairy),* Mirko Musil *(water fairy),* Raoul Schránil *(devil),* Gabriela Bártlová *(White Lady),* Karel Vavřík *(poster man),* Ela Šilarová, Marie Rosůlková *(ladies),* Karl Krautgartner *(sorcerer),* Jaroslav Zrotal *(general),* Pavel Hobl *(man in BMW),* Marcela Sedláčková *(French lady),* Josef Steigl *(French man),* Jaroslav Orlický *(headless man).*

Fantasy. In Prague, two little brothers, Joe and Johnny, are looking forward to a school outing when they learn that the excursion has been cancelled and their school closed for the day. Rather than return home, they decide to explore the city. First, a friendly police officer allows them to direct traffic for a few moments, and then they meet a painter who lets them experiment with his box of colors. After roller-skating through a museum, they encounter a talking dog who takes them to different places where animals speak to children. Seeking adventure, the boys visit an enchanted place and help break the evil spell a sorcerer has cast over some musicians. Finally, after winning a midget-car race, they return to their school where their father is waiting to take them home. *Brothers. Children. Police. Painters. Sorcerers. Musicians. Magic. Roller skating. Spells. Automobile racing. Museums. Prague. Dogs. Animals.*

Note: Opened in Prague in May 1964 as *Mate doma lva?*

DOBRO POZHALOVAT see **WELCOME KOSTYA!**

DOBUNEZUMI SAKUSEN see **OPERATION X**

DOBUROKU NO TATSU see **TATSU**

THE DOCK BRIEF see **TRIAL AND ERROR**

THE DOCTOR AND THE PLAYGIRL   F6.1202

First Arts Productions. *Dist* Emerson Film Enterprises. **1965.** Sd; b&w. 35mm. 80 min.

Prod-Dir-Writ William Martin. *Dir Photog* Gayne Rescher. *Film Ed* Stuart A. Hersh. *Mus* Yusho Mendel. *Asst Dir* Arthur Steckler.

Cast: Mark O'Daniels, Ann Hutchinson, Lorraine Rogers, Lon Clark, Rocky Graziano, Jake La Motta, Barney Ross, Pete Scalzo.

Melodrama. After being raped by her stepfather, a young woman becomes a New York playgirl, selling cigarettes in a nightclub. She moves in with a young male doctor, who arranges intimate sessions between young women and government officials. One of his "patients," a state department official, refuses to do special favors when threatened by the doctor. A national scandal occurs when the official attacks the playgirl. *Stepfathers. Playgirls. Cigarette girls. Physicians. Rape. Scandal. Nightclubs. New York City. United States—State Department.*

Note: Filmed in New York in 1963 as *The Dr. Ward Story.*

DOCTOR BLOOD'S COFFIN (Great Britain)   F6.1203

Caralan Productions. *Dist* United Artists. 26 Apr **1961** [Los Angeles opening]. Sd; col (Eastman Color). 35mm. 92 min.

Prod George Fowler. *Exec Prod* David E. Rose. *Dir* Sidney J. Furie. *Story-Screenplay* Jerry Juran. *Adapt* James Kelly, Peter Miller. *Photog* Stephen Dade. *Art Dir* Scott MacGregor. *Film Ed* Anthony Gibbs. *Mus Comp* Buxton Orr. *Mus Cond* Philip Martell. *Sd* Bill Salter. *Asst Dir* John Comfort. *Prod Mgr* Buddy Booth. *Sp Eff* Les Bowie, Peter Neilson.

Cast: Kieron Moore (*Dr. Peter Blood*), Hazel Court (*Linda Parker*), Ian Hunter (*Dr. Robert Blood*), Fred Johnson (*Tregaye [Morton]*), Kenneth J. Warren (*Sergeant Cook*), Andy Alston (*Beale*), Paul Stockman (*Steve Parker*), John Ronane (*Hanson*), Gerald Lawson (*Morton [Sweeting]*), Paul Hardtmuth (*professor*).

Horror film. Expelled from his studies in medical research in Vienna, Dr. Peter Blood, a frustrated biochemist, returns to the Cornish village where his father is a general practitioner. Certain that by utilizing a South American arrow tip poison he can transfer the heart of a "worthless" living person to a "worthy" corpse and restore life, Peter kidnaps several villagers and uses them as living subjects for the experiments he is conducting in an abandoned mine. He becomes attracted to his father's nurse, Linda Parker, whose husband died in an accident a year ago and who is still grieving. Eventually, Linda discovers Peter's activities and threatens to expose him, but Peter exhumes her husband's corpse and gives it the heart of a hobo he has abducted. Faced with the horrible sight of her revivified husband, Linda becomes hysterical. Peter seizes the living corpse when it attempts to strangle Linda, and the doctor and his monster become locked in a death struggle. As they destroy each other, Linda stumbles from the mine. *Physicians. Widows. Biochemists. Nurses. Revivescence. Abduction. Hysteria. Murder. Experiments. Organ transplants. Mines. Laboratories. Vienna. Cornwall (England).*

Note: Location scenes filmed in Cornwall, England. Released in Great Britain in Jan 1961. Working title: *Face of Evil.* Sources conflict in crediting the roles played by Fred Johnson and Gerald C. Lawson.

DR. BREEDLOVE see **KISS ME QUICK!**

DR. BYRD UNLOCKS RAGINA'S SECRETS see **RAGINA'S SECRETS**

DR. CADMAN'S SECRET (Reissue)   F6.1204

Bel-Air Productions. *Dist* Cari Releasing Corp. 14 Apr **1963** [New York showing]. Sd; b&w. 35mm. 81 min.

Note: Originally released as *The Black Sleep* by United Artists in 1956; c8 Jun 1956; LP6926.

DR. COPPELIUS (United States/Spain)   F6.1205

Copelia, S. A.–Coppelia Co. *Dist* Childhood Productions. 25 Dec **1968** [New York opening]. Sd; col (Eastmancolor). 35mm & 70mm (Superpanorama, see note). 97 min. *MPAA rating G.*

A Frank J. Hale Production. *Prod* Frank J. Hale. *Exec Prod* Victor Torruella. *Assoc Prod* Ted Kneeland, James Udell. *Dir-Writ* Ted Kneeland. *Scen Spanish Vers* Victor Torruella. *Photog* Cecilio Paniagua. *Art Dir* Gil Parrondo. *Dsgn Supv* Florence Lustig. *Set Decor* Roberto Carpio. *Film Ed* Juan Serra. *Mus* Clément Philibert Léo Delibes. *Adtl Film Mus* Raymond Guy Wilson. *Mus Perf* Gran Teatro del Liceo Orquesta de Barcelona. *Mus Cond* Adrián Sardó. *Choreog & Asst Choreog* Jo Anna Kneeland, Richard Dodd. *Sd* José Mane. *Prod Mgr* Ramón Plana. *Cost* Roberto Carpio, Marian Ribas. *Artistic Cons* Alicia Markova.

Cast: Walter Slezak (*Dr. Coppelius*), Claudia Corday (*Swanhilda/Coppelia*), Caj Selling (*Franz*), Eileen Elliott (*Brigitta*), Carmen Rojas (*Spanish doll*), Veronica Kusmin (*Roman doll*), Milorad Miskovitch (*Hungarian dance champion*), Luis Prendes (*The Mayor*), Marcia Bellak, Kathy Jo Brown, Clara Cravey, Kathleen Garrison, Christine Holter, Sharon Kapner (*Swanhilda's friends*), Helena Villarroya, Gran Teatro del Liceo Ballet, International Cine Ballet, Aurelio Bogado, Xenia Petrowsky.

Dance film. Based on the ballet by: Clément Philibert Léo Delibes and Charles Louis Etienne Nuitter, *Coppelia* (first performance: Paris, 1870). In the 19th century, Dr. Coppelius creates a beautiful, lifelike mechanical doll that he lovingly names Coppelia. Seeing the doll on a balcony of the doctor's house, a flirtatious village youth, Franz, becomes so enamored of it that he neglects his sweetheart, Swanhilda. Later, the jealous Swanhilda and six of her friends sneak into Coppelius' home and discover Coppelia among several other mechanical dolls. Although her friends are frightened away when Coppelius returns, Swanhilda finds a hiding place and disguises herself as the doll while the doctor is sleeping. When he is awakened by the sudden appearance of Franz, Coppelius drugs the youth and attempts to transfer his spirit of life to Coppelia. Dressed as the doll, Swanhilda dances about and deludes the doctor into believing that he has made the doll come to life. When Franz is roused from his deep sleep, however, Swanhilda reveals her true identity and runs off with her beloved, leaving behind a broken Coppelia and a disillusioned Dr. Coppelius. On the wedding day of Swanhilda and Franz, the townspeople present the doctor with a completely restored Coppelia. Forsaking his life of fantasy, Coppelius returns the love of Brigitta, the tavern maid, who has always yearned to be his wife. *Physicians. Dancers. Barmaids. Jealousy. Disguise. Duplicity. Magic. Dolls. Weddings.*

Note: Filmed in Madrid; opened there in Dec 1966 as *El fantastico mundo del Dr. Coppelius.* Shot in 70mm Superpanorama. Title is also rendered *Dr. ?? Copelius!!*

DR. CRIPPEN (Great Britain)   F6.1206

Torchlight Productions. *For* Associated British-Pathé Ltd. *Dist* Warner Bros. Pictures. 14 Feb **1964** [New York opening; c8 Feb 1964; LP29438]. Sd; b&w. 35mm. 97 min.

A John Clein Production. *Prod* John Clein. *Dir* Robert Lynn. *Screenplay-Story* Leigh Vance. *Dir Photog* Nicolas Roeg. *Camera Op* Alex Thomson. *Focus* Gordon Hayman. *Art Dir* Peter Jones. *Film Ed* Lee Doig. *Asst Film Ed* Lorna Armour. *Mus Dir* Ken Jones. *Sd Mix* Edgar Vetter. *Rec Dir* A. W. Lumkin. *Boom Op* Alan Vetter. *Sd Camera* Michael Carmody. *1st, 2d & 3d Asst Dir* Clive Freedman, Bill Cartlidge, Roger Simons. *Prod Mgr* Ronnie Bear. *Cont* Ann Besserman. *Cost* L. and H. Nathan. *Wardrobe Master* John Irwin. *Makeup* Bob Clark. *Hairstyles* Polly Young. *Grip* W. Wells.

Cast: Donald Pleasence (*Dr. Hawley Harvey Crippen*), Coral Browne (*Belle Crippen*), Samantha Eggar (*Ethel Le Neve*), Donald Wolfit (*R. D. Muir*), James Robertson-Justice (*Captain Kendall*), Geoffrey Toone (*Mr. Tobin*), Oliver Johnston (*lord chief justice*), Edward Ogden (*clerk of the court*), Elspeth March (*Mrs. Jackson*), Douglas Bradley-Smith (*Dr. Pepper*), John Arnatt (*Chief Inspector Dew*), Olga Lindo (*Clara Arditti*), Paul Carpenter (*Bruce Martin*), John Lee (*Harry*), Basil Henson (*Paul Arditti*), Betty Baskcombe (*Mrs. Stratton*), Basil Beale (*Sergeant Mitchell*), Edward Underdown (*prison governor*), Edward Cast (*Warder Harding*), Ian Whittaker, actor (*Howlett*).

Biographical drama. In 1910 Dr. Hawley Harvey Crippen, a London physician, is charged with the murder of his wife, Belle; and his beautiful typist and mistress, Ethel Le Neve, is arrested as an accessory to the crime. Both defendants plead not guilty. As the crown prosecutor, R. D. Muir, opens his case, Crippen recalls the ordeal of his marital life with Belle, an ex-music hall singer. Drunken, disreputable, and openly unfaithful, Belle tyrannized and humiliated him. With Ethel, on the other hand, Crippen shared an idyllic relationship. Belle blackmailed him into maintaining sexual relations with her after she learned of his affair with Ethel. He intended to quiet her repugnant demands by slipping her a tranquilizer but accidentally administered a fatal overdose. In his panic, he dismembered her body and buried it in the cellar, asserting that she was visiting a relative in the United States and later reporting that she had died. Ethel moved into the house, but suspicious neighbors noticed that she was wearing Belle's jewelry. Though police seemed to believe his explanation, Crippen persuaded Ethel to disguise herself as a boy, and together they fled on a steamer to Canada. Prompted by his disappearance, the police investigated further and discovered Belle's body in the cellar. On a stopover, the steamer captain saw newspaper photographs of Crippen. Later he recognized Crippen as the suspect and wired Scotland Yard. At the outcome of the trial, Ethel is acquitted but Crippen is convicted and sentenced to death. As he awaits the gallows, he continues to protest his innocence, expressing concern for Ethel and insisting that he had not meant to murder his wife but only to quiet her. *Physicians. Mistresses. Typists. Barristers. Sea captains. Singers. Murder. Infidelity. Alcoholism. Capital punishment. Disguise. Telegraph. Mutilation. Trials. Tranquilizers. Ships. London. Canada. Hawley Harvey Crippen. Ethel Le Neve. Belle Crippen. Scotland Yard.*

Note: London opening: Aug 1963; running time: 98 min.

DR. DILDOE'S SECRET F6.1207
Dist Stacey Distributors. ca **1970**. Sd; col. 16mm. 61-81 min.

Sex film. No information about the precise nature of this film has been found. *Physicians. Sexuality. Sex aids.*

DOCTOR DOLITTLE F6.1208
Apjac Productions. *Dist* Twentieth Century Fox–Film Corp. 19 Dec **1967** [New York opening; c19 Dec 1967; LP35183]. Sd (Westrex); col (De Luxe). 35mm & 70mm (Todd-AO). 152 min.

An Arthur P. Jacobs Production. *Prod* Arthur P. Jacobs. *Assoc Prod* Mort Abrahams. *Dir* Richard Fleischer. *Screenplay* Leslie Bricusse. *Dir Photog* Robert Surtees. *Camera Op* George Nogle. *Asst Camera* Emilio Calori. *Art Dir* Jack Martin Smith, Ed Graves. *Set Decor* Walter M. Scott, Stuart A. Reiss. *Prod Dsgn* Mario Chiari. *Titl & Titl Dsgn* Pacific Title, Don Record. *Film Ed* Samuel E. Beetley, Marjorie Fowler. *Mus Score & Cond* Lionel Newman, Alexander Courage. *Songs* Leslie Bricusse. *Vocal Supv* Ian Fraser. *Dance and Musical Numbers Staged by* Herbert Ross. *Sd* Douglas O. Williams, John Myers, sd, Bernard Freericks. *Sd Supv* James Corcoran, Murray Spivack. *Mus Ed* Robert Mayer. *Asst Dir* Richard Lang. *Unit Prod Mgr* William Eckhardt, Jack Stubbs. *Script Supv* June Santantonio. *Cost Dsgn* Ray Aghayan. *Wardrobe* Wesley Sherrard. *Makeup* Ben Nye, Marvin Westmore. *Hairstyles* Margaret Donovan. *Sp Photog Eff* L. B. Abbott, Art Cruickshank, Emil Kosa, Jr., Howard Lydecker. *Animals and Birds Supplied and Trained by* Jungleland of Thousand Oaks (California). *Prop* Allen Levine. *Gaffer* Earl Gilbert. *Grip* Lou Pazelli. *Animal Supv* Roy Kabat.

Cast: Rex Harrison (*Dr. John Dolittle*), Samantha Eggar (*Emma Fairfax*), Anthony Newley (*Matthew Mugg*), Richard Attenborough (*Albert Blossom*), Peter Bull (*General Bellowes*), Muriel Landers (*Mrs. Blossom*), William Dix (*Tommy Stubbins*), Geoffrey Holder (*Willie Shakespeare*), Portia Nelson (*Sarah Dolittle*), Norma Varden (*Lady Petherington*).

Musical fantasy. Based on the "Dr. Dolittle" stories by: Hugh Lofting. In the mid-19th-century English village of Puddleby-on-the-Marsh, kindly Doctor Dolittle has grown disenchanted with human beings and tends solely to the needs of animals. With the help of his parrot, Polynesia, he has mastered the dialects of some 500 animals. His only human friends are Matthew Mugg, an Irish cat food seller, and Tommy Stubbins, a local lad. The doctor's immediate concern is raising money to search for the legendary Great Pink Sea Snail. When a friend sends him the rare pushmi-pullyu (a two-headed llama), the doctor takes the animal to the rundown circus of Mr. Blossom and exhibits it for profit. At the circus he befriends Sophie, a lonely seal who is pining for her mate at the North Pole. Sympathetic to her plight, Dolittle dresses Sophie in a woman's shawl and bonnet and sets her free by tossing her into the English Channel. His act of mercy is misinterpreted, however, and he is charged with murder, and although acquitted, he is committed to an asylum. Matthew, Tommy, and the doctor's animal friends arrange for his escape, and, accompanied by pretty Emma Fairfax, they all set sail to find the Great Pink Sea Snail. They are shipwrecked during a storm at sea and cast upon a floating island ruled by a giant native called William Shakespeare the Tenth. The newcomers are blamed for a sudden spell of chilly weather and sentenced to death, but Doctor Dolittle saves the day by both curing an epidemic of colds and arranging for the giant blue whale to push the island back to its position on the African mainland. Then the Great Pink Sea Snail arrives for its annual visit, also suffering from a nasty cold. Once cured, the grateful creature offers the inside of its spacious shell to transport everyone back to England. Dolittle, however, elects to remain behind rather than risk reimprisonment. After his friends have left, and he finds himself pining for Emma, Sophie the seal pays him a visit to announce that all the animals in England are on strike because of the injustices done to him and, further, that the authorities are anxious for his return. Dolittle quickly designs a saddle for the Giant Lunar Moth and soars off in the moonlight for a speedy return to Puddleby-on-the-Marsh. *Musical*

numbers: "My Friend the Doctor" (Matthew); "The Vegetarian," "Talk to the Animals" (Dolittle); "At the Crossroads" (Emma); "I've Never Seen Anything Like It" (Albert, Dolittle, Mrs. Blossom, & Ensemble), "When I Look Into Your Eyes," "Like Animals" (Dolittle); "After Today" (Matthew); "Fabulous Places" (Emma); "I Think I Like You" (Dolittle, Emma); "Doctor Dolittle" (Matthew & Ensemble); "Something in Your Smile" (Dolittle). *Physicians. Veterinarians. Castaways. Giants. Mistaken identity. Murder. Common cold. Circus. Insane asylums. Strikes. Islands. England. English Channel. Africa. Shipwrecks. Whales. Llamas. Seals. Snails. Moths. Parrots.*

Note: Location scenes filmed in Castle Combe, England, and Santa Lucia, British West Indies.

DOCTOR FAUSTUS (Great Britain/Italy) F6.1209
Oxford University Screen Productions–Nassau Films–Venfilms. *Dist* Columbia Pictures. 6 Feb **1968** [New York opening; c1 Feb 1968; LP35620]. Sd (Westrex); col (Technicolor). 35mm. 93 min.

Prod Richard Burton, Richard McWhorter. *Dir* Richard Burton, Nevill Coghill. *Screen Adapt* Nevill Coghill. *Dir Photog* Gabor Pogany. *Camera Op* Brian West. *Art Dir* Boris Juraga. *Set Decor* Dario Simoni. *Prod Dsgn* John De Cuir. *Main Titl* National Screen Service Ltd. *Film Ed* John Shirley. *Italian Vers Ed* Carlo Fabianelli. *Mus Comp & Cond* Mario Nascimbene. *Choreog* Jacqueline Harvey. *Sd Mix* David Hildyard, John Aldred. *Sd* Aldo De Martini. *Dub Ed* Les Wiggins. *Asst Dir* Gus Agosti. *Prod Supv* Guy Luongo. *Unit Mgr* Roberto Cocco. *Cont* Elaine Schreyeck. *Tech Asst* Nicholas Young. *Prod Asst* Carlo Lastricati. *Cost Dsgn* Peter Hall. *Wardrobe* Franco Antonelli. *Elizabeth Taylor's Makeup* Frank Larue. *Richard Burton's Makeup* Ron Berkeley. *Makeup* Giannetto De Rossi. *Elizabeth Taylor's Hairdresser* Agnes Flanagan. *Hairdresser* Vasco Reggiani. *Richard Burton's and Elizabeth Taylor's Hairstyles* Alexandre of Paris. *Sp Eff* Augie Lohman, Peter Harman. *Prop* Ken Muggleston.

Cast: Richard Burton (*Doctor Faustus*), Elizabeth Taylor (*Helen of Troy*).
Cast—Members of The Oxford University Dramatic Society: Andreas Teuber (*Mephistopheles*), Ram Chopra (*Valdes*), Richard Carwardine (*Cornelius*), Patrick Barwise (*Wagner*), Michael Meneaugh (*Good Angel/bishop*), Richard Durden-Smith (*Evil Angel/knight*), David McIntosh (*Lucifer*), Jeremy Eccles (*Belzebub*), Gwydion Thomas (*Lechery/3d scholar*), Ian Marter (*emperor*), Nicholas Loukes (*Pride/Cardinal of Lorraine [see note]*), Adrian Benjamin (*pope*), Elizabeth O'Donovan (*empress*), Ambrose Coghill (*Avarice/1st professor*), Richard Heffer (*1st scholar*), Hugh Williams (*2d scholar*), Jeremy Chandler (*attendant at emperor's court*), Angus McIntosh (*Rector Magnificus*), Anthony Kaufmann (*2d professor/Envy*), Julian Wontner (*3d professor*), Richard Harrison (*4th professor*), Nevill Coghill (*5th professor*), John Sandbach (*boy-turned-into-hind*), Sebastian Walker (*idiot*), R. Peverello (*Wrath*), Maria Aitken (*Sloth*), Valerie James (*Idleness*), Bridget Coghill, Petronella Pulsford, Susan Watson (*Gluttony*), Jacqueline Harvey, Sheila Dawson, Carolyn Bennitt (*dancers*), Jane Wilford (*nun/courtlady*).

Drama. Source: Christopher Marlowe, *The Tragedy of Doctor Faustus* (1594). In 16th-century Germany, the elderly Doctor Faustus—a scholar of alchemy, astrology, and philosophy—is awarded the highest academic honors by the University of Wittenberg. Insatiable in his quest for knowledge and power, he resorts to necromancy to invoke from hell the spirit of Mephistopheles. Faustus bargains with Mephistopheles for the sale of his soul to Lucifer, provided that he will be allotted 24 years to live "in all voluptuousness" and signs the pact with his own blood. Now transformed into a young man, Faustus commands Mephistopheles to accompany him on his search for beauty and wisdom. Ever obedient, Mephistopheles shows his pupil the seven deadly sins, permits him to become invisible so that he may tease and harass a convocation of the pope and his cardinals, and escorts him through time to the court of Alexander the Great. To please three of his students, Faustus conjures up Helen of Troy and is so taken with her beauty that he beseeches Mephistopheles to let him become her lover. Though the wish is granted, Faustus can do little but contemplate his loss of heaven and his pending eternal damnation. When his time expires, Faustus follows the beckoning Helen and descends into hell. *Astrologers. Sorcerers. Philosophers. Students. Alchemy. Youth. Papacy. Invisibility. Germany. Wittenberg. Alexander the Great. Helen of Troy. The Devil. Faust. Hell. Mephistopheles. The Soul. Heaven.*

Note: Opened in London in Oct 1967. Continuity credits the roles of Ian Marter as Pride/emperor and the roles of Nicholas Loukes as Envy/Cardinal of Lorraine.

DR. FOO AND THE LOVE PIRATES *see* **THE LOVE PIRATE**

DR. FRANKENSTEIN ON CAMPUS (Canada) F6.1210
Agincourt Productions–Glen Warren Productions. *Dist* Medford Film Corp. 3 Jun **1970** [Chicago opening]. Sd; col (print by Film House). 35mm. 83 min. *MPAA rating* R.

Prod Bill Marshall. *Dir* Gilbert W. Taylor. *2d Unit Dir* Reginald Morris. *Screenplay* David Cobb, Bill Marshall, Gilbert W. Taylor. *Photog* Jackson Samuels. *Film Ed* Eric Wrate. *Mus* Paul Hoffert, Skip Prokop. *Perf by* Lighthouse. *Sd* Fred Sengmuller. *Asst Dir* Gordon Robinson. *Cost* Roger Palmer, Heather McIntosh. *Coöp* Canadian Film Development Corp.

Cast: Robin Ward *(Viktor Frankenstein)*, Kathleen Sawyer *(Susan Harris)*, Austin Willis *(Cantwell)*, Sean Sullivan *(Professor Preston)*, Ty Haller *(Tony)*, Tony Moffat-Lynch *(David)*, Stephanie Laird *(Debbie)*, Ken Hagan *(reporter)*, Alan Dean, Steffany Lind, Bill Waltho, Janine Sherman, Tony Kleiboer, Liz Rowland, Linda Rennhofer.

Horror film. Young scientist Viktor Frankenstein is dismissed from his position in a Transylvanian university and accepts an offer to continue his research in Canada. He attracts student reporter Susan Harris, who discards her boyfriend Tony to live with Frankenstein. Professor Preston, in charge of the university's computer, encourages Frankenstein to perfect an electronic system which can manipulate brain waves. Scorned by radical leader David, Frankenstein loses his job after David and three other students frame him for possession of marijuana. Seeking revenge, Frankenstein injects brain control pellets into Tony, a karate expert, and directs him to kill all those responsible for his being fired, including Dean Cantwell. Susan, who knows too much, is nearly strangled to death in a museum, but a young boy knocks the remote control box from Frankenstein. Chased by angry students, Frankenstein plunges over a bannister to his death and is revealed to have been the creation of Professor Preston. *Scientists. Researchers. Students. Reporters. Professors. Robots. Inventors. Thought control. College life. Frameup. Murder. Revenge. Computers. Marijuana. Karate. Transylvania. Chases. Frankenstein.*

Note: Filmed in Toronto. Released in Canada in 1970 as *Flick*; running time: 81 min.

DOCTOR GLAS (Denmark)   F6.1211

Laterna Film. *Dist* Twentieth Century-Fox Film Corp. 7 Apr **1969** [New York opening; c7 Apr 1969; LP38137]. Sd; b&w. 35mm. 83 min. *MPAA rating* M.

Prod Joseph Hardy, Benni Korzen. *Exec Prod* Mogens Skot-Hansen. *Assoc Prod* Charles K. Weiss. *Dir* Mai Zetterling. *Screenplay* Mai Zetterling, David Hughes. *Dir Photog* Rune Ericson. *Art Dir* Bibi Lindstrom. *Film Ed* Wic Kjellin. *Mus* Peter Willemoes, Noël Lee. *Mus Selections* Ludwig van Beethoven, Bertrand Bech, The Others. *Sd* P. O. Pettersson. *Asst Dir* Peter Hald. *Prod Supv* Carl Rald. *Prod Mgr* Morten Schyberg. *Wardrobe* Ulla Britt Söderlund. *Makeup* Lene Henriksen.

Cast: Per Oscarsson *(Dr. Glas)*, Ulf Palme *(Pastor Gregorius)*, Lone Hertz *(Helga Gregorius)*, Nils Eklund *(Markel)*, Bente Dessau *(Eva Martens)*, Lars Lunøe *(Klas Recke)*, Bendt Rothe *(Birck)*, Ingolf David *(Glas' father)*, Helle Hertz *(Anita)*, Jonas Bergström *(friend at university)*.

Drama. Source: Hjalmar Söderberg, *Doktor Glas* (1905). Dr. Glas, an elderly, nearly blind physician in Stockholm, reflects on the tragic events that influenced his lonely and empty life: *During the final years of the last century, Dr. Glas is consulted by young Helga Gregorius, who complains that the overbearing sexual demands of her husband, a middle-aged pastor, are endangering her physical and mental health. The sexually repressed young doctor, strongly attracted to Helga, begins to have erotic fantasies involving her. In spite of the knowledge that she has a secret lover, he attempts to help her by advising her husband that continued sexual intercourse is inimical to her health. This warning does not for long deter the pastor, who invokes God as his authority for continuing to exercise his "marital rights." Helga again seeks help from the doctor in avoiding her husband's excesses. Dr. Glas, whose idealistic medical ethics have in the past caused him to reject abortion and euthanasia, dreams of murdering the pastor and agonizes over his decision. He gives the pastor a drug which he knows will prove fatal, rationalizing the deed as a necessary move to save Helga's life. Afterwards he finds himself unable to distinguish his dreams and fantasy from reality.* Having grown old alone, Dr. Glas is haunted by doubts as to the motive for his crime. *Physicians. Clergymen. Medical ethics. Infidelity. Old age. Murder. Conscience. Marriage. Obsession. Inhibition. Stockholm. Fantasy.*

Note: Location scenes filmed in and around Copenhagen and Stockholm. Released in Denmark in 1968 as *Doktor Glas*; running time: 90 min.

DR. GOLDFOOT AND THE BIKINI MACHINE   F6.1212

American International Pictures. 6 Nov **1965** [Wenatchee, Washington, opening; c10 Nov 1965; LP32039]. Sd; col (Pathécolor). 35mm (Panavision). 90 min.

A James H. Nicholson-Samuel Z. Arkoff Production. *Prod* James H. Nicholson, Samuel Z. Arkoff. *Co-prod* Anthony Carras. *Dir* Norman Taurog. *Screenplay* Elwood Ullman, Robert Kaufman. *Story* James Hartford. *Dir Photog* Sam Leavitt. *Art Dir* Daniel Haller. *Set Decor* Clarence Steensen. *Main Titl Art* Clokey. *Film Ed* Ronald Sinclair, Fred Feitshans, Eve Newman. *Mus Score* Les Baxter. *Mus Supv* Al Simms. *Titl Song:* "The Bikini Machine" Guy

Hemric, Jerry Styner. *Sung by* The Supremes. *Wailing by* Al Simms. *Choreog* Jack Baker. *Sd* Vern Kramer, James Nelson, Gene Corso. *1st & 2d Asst Dir* Claude Binyon, Jr., Dick Landry. *Prod Supv* Jack Bohrer. *Script Supv* Wallace Bennett. *Cost* Richard Bruno. *Makeup* Ted Coodley. *Hairstylist* Ray Foreman. *Sp Hairstyles for Miss Hart* Jon Peters. *Sp Eff* Roger George. *Photog Eff* Butler-Glouner Inc. *Coöp* San Francisco Police Dept., Golden Gate Bridge Authorities. *Dial Coach* Michael A. Hoey. *Prop* Karl Brainard, Richard M. Rubin. *Constr Coörd* Ross Hahn.

Cast: Vincent Price *(Dr. Goldfoot)*, Frankie Avalon *(Craig Gamble)*, Dwayne Hickman *(Todd Armstrong)*, Susan Hart *(Diane)*, Jack Mullaney *(Igor)*, Fred Clark *(D. J. Pevney)*, Alberta Nelson *(Reject No. 12)*, Milton Frome *(motorcycle cop)*, Hal Riddle *(newsvendor)*, Kaye Elhardt *(girl in nightclub)*, William Baskin *(guard)*, Vince Barnett *(janitor)*, Joe Ploski *(cook)*, Sam and the Ape Men, Diane De Marco *(themselves)*, Annette Funicello, Dorothy Walley, Harvey Lembeck, Aron Kincaid *(guest stars)*, Patti Chandler, Salli Sachse, Sue Hamilton, Marianne Gaba, Issa Arnal, Pamela Rodgers, Sally Frei, Jan Watson, Mary Hughes, Luree Holmes, Laura Nicholson, China Lee, Deanna Lund, Leslie Summers, Kay Michaels, Arlene Charles *(robots)*, David Shayer, Bob Harris, Ronnie Rondell, Carey Loftin, Louis Elias, Troy Milton, Mari Ann Leslie, Ronnie Dayton, Paul Stader, Harvey Parry, Jerry Summers, Fred Stromsoe.

Comedy. Dr. Goldfoot hopes to ensnare the fortunes of the world's wealthiest men with the aid of the beautiful bikini-clad robots he manufactures in his laboratory. Diane, the prize beauty of Goldfoot's assembly line, is sent out to trap wealthy playboy Todd Armstrong, whom she succeeds in marrying and in persuading to sign over much of his wealth. Secret Intelligence Command's Craig Gamble, in love with Diane, blunders into the plot and, trying to help Armstrong, falls into Goldfoot's torture chamber, where he and Armstrong are terrorized by various devices, including a swinging pendulum. They escape, however, and are pursued by Goldfoot and his inept assistant, Igor. *Scientists. Playboys. Robots. Government agents. Imposture. Wealth. Torture. Chases.*

Note: Location scenes filmed in San Francisco, including Fisherman's Wharf. Actress Dorothy Walley is also known as Deborah Walley. Sequel: *Dr. Goldfoot and the Girl Bombs*, q. v.

DR. GOLDFOOT AND THE GIRL BOMBS (United States/Italy)   F6.1213

American International Productions-Italian International Film. *Dist* American International Pictures. Nov **1966** [c9 Nov 1966; LP33698]. Sd; col (Technicolor). 35mm. 85 min. [Copyright length: 82 min.]

Prod Fulvio Lucisano, Louis M. Heyward. *Dir* Mario Bava. *Screenplay* Louis M. Heyward, Robert Kaufman, Franco Castellano, Pipolo. *Story* James Hartford. *Photog* Antonio Rinaldi. *Mus Score* Les Baxter. *Titl Song* Guy Hemric, Jerry Styner.

Cast: Vincent Price *(Dr. Goldfoot)*, Fabian *(Bill Dexter)*, Franco Franchi *(Franco)*, Ciccio Ingrassia *(Ciccio)*, Laura Antonelli *(Rosanna)*, Moana Tahi *(Goldfoot's assistant)*, Francesco Mulè.

Farce. Backed by the power of Red China, the infamous Dr. Goldfoot has devised a plan for bringing about total war between the United States and the Soviet Union by bombing Moscow from an American plane. To do this, however, Goldfoot must eliminate nine of the ten top NATO generals and then pose as the sole survivor, America's General Willis, in order to steal a jet for the bombing mission. Goldfoot equips his renowned robot girls with proximity fuses in their navels which explode upon contact when they make love to the generals. As the assassinations near completion, an American Strategic Intelligence Command agent named Bill Dexter arrives in Rome, where Goldfoot plans to murder General Willis and then assume his identity. After recruiting the services of Franco and Ciccio, two bumbling doormen who aspire to be secret agents, Dexter successfully avoids the diversions of Rosanna, one of Goldfoot's sexiest robots. Then, upon learning that the evil doctor is jetting to Moscow, Dexter, Franco and Ciccio commandeer a hot-air carnival balloon and miraculously manage to stop Goldfoot, although he bails out just before his plane crashes. Similarly, Dexter and his two colleagues are forced to jump from the balloon. Although Dexter makes it safely back to the States, Franco and Ciccio end up in a Siberian labor camp, where Dr. Goldfoot has already established himself as the prison commandant. *Evildoers. Scientists. Spies. Soldiers. Robots. Assassination. Nuclear warfare. Impersonation. Airplanes— Jet. Balloons (ascent). Rome. Union of Soviet Socialist Republics. People's Republic of China. North Atlantic Treaty Organization.*

Note: Produced in Italy in 1966. This is a sequel to *Dr. Goldfoot and the Bikini Machine*, q. v. Film contains scenes from the original. Working title: *Dr. Goldfoot and the "S" Bomb.* Italian title: *Le spie vengono dal semifreddo.* Alternative Italian title: *I due mafiosi dell'F.B.I.*

DR. GOLDFOOT AND THE "S" BOMB *see* **DR. GOLDFOOT AND THE GIRL BOMBS**

DOCTOR, I'M COMING!   F6.1214

Dist Sack Amusement Enterprises. Nov **1970** [Los Angeles showing]. Sd; col. 35mm. 62 min.

Prod David Stefans. *Dir* Rod Killy. *Screenplay* Michael Davis, writ. *Photog* Manny White. *Mus Score* Happy Helen Hunter. *Sd* Val Earth. *Script Girl* Hortense Ragen. *Wardrobe* Doris of Mariposa. *Makeup* Sharon Gantry.

Cast: John Helmes (*Dr. Peter Phallic*), Anna Meers (*Nurse Minnie Cummings*), Dan Ivans (*Dr. Hardy Stiff*), Cece Wilson (*Myrna Brokenbridge*), Ida Blue (*Virginia Barritt*), Sara Hardt (*Elner Eager*), Chuck Arce (*Dr. Oral Ensertian*), Ben Camp (*The Government Man*).

Comedy. Dr. Peter Phallic is the director of a federally funded clinic devoted to the care and study of nymphomaniacs. He is assisted by head nurse Minnie Cummings, a former nymphomaniac who requires frequent treatment. The patients include Myrna Brokenbridge, who is drawn to Italian men, and Elner Eager, a black woman who has attempted suicide with a dildo. When a bisexual government agent investigates the unit, Minnie demonstrates her therapy on him until he cries for mercy. *Physicians. Nurses. Government agents. Italians. Negroes. Nymphomania. Suicide. Sex clinics. Sex aids.*

DOCTOR IN CLOVER *see* **CARNABY, M. D.**

DOCTOR IN DISTRESS (Great Britain)   F6.1215

Rank Organisation. *Dist* Governor Films. 7 Jul **1964** [New York opening]. Sd; col (Eastman Color). 35mm. 103 min.

A Betty E. Box–Ralph Thomas Production. *Prod* Betty E. Box. *Exec Prod* Earl St. John. *Dir* Ralph Thomas. *Screenplay* Nicholas Phipps, Ronald Scott Thorn. *Dir Photog* Ernest Steward. *Camera Op* James Bawden. *Focus* John Morgan. *Art Dir* Alex Vetchinsky. *Set Dresser* Arthur Taksen. *Ch Draughtsman* Terence Knight. *Draughtsman* Jean Peyre, Ted Ambrose. *Film Ed* Alfred Roome. *1st Asst Ed* May Dennington. *2d Asst Ed* Ian Gardiner. *Mus Comp & Cond* Norrie Paramor. *Sd Mix* Dudley Messenger. *Boom Op* J. W. N. Daniel. *Sd Camera* Otto Snel. *1st, 2d & 3d Asst Dir* Anthony Waye, Simon Relph, Bob Howard. *Prod Mgr* Charles Orme. *Cont* Gladys Goldsmith. *Prod Sec* Jean Hall. *Dress Dsgn* Yvonne Caffin. *Men's Wardrobe* Bert Simmonds. *Women's Wardrobe* Betty Knight. *Ch Makeup* W. T. Partleton. *Hairdresser* Stella Rivers. *Prop Buyer* Jim Baker. *Stills* George Courtney Ward. *Constr Mgr* Ron Udell. *Chargehand Dressing Prop* Mark Rowe. *Grip* Bill Bannister. *Ch Electrn* Bill Walpole.

Cast: Dirk Bogarde (*Dr. Simon Sparrow*), James Robertson-Justice (*Sir Lancelot Spratt*), Samantha Eggar (*Delia*), Barbara Murray (*Iris Marchant*), Mylène Demongeot (*Sonja/Helga*), Donald Houston (*Maj. Tommy Ffrench*), Jessie Evans (*Mrs. Parry [Mrs. Holly?]*), Ann Lynn (*Mrs. Whittaker*), Leo McKern (*Heilbronn*), Rodney Cardiff (*Dr. Stewart*), Dennis Price (*Dr. Blacker*), Fenella Fielding (*woman passenger*), Jill Adams (*Genevieve*), Paul Whitsun-Jones (*Grimes*), Michael Flanders (*Bradby*), Madge Ryan (*Mrs. Clapper*), Frank Finlay (*corsetier*), Amanda Barrie (*Rona*), Margaret Boyd (*Lady Willoughby*), Reginald Beckwith (*Meyer*), Bill Kerr (*Australian sailor*), Jeanette Landis (*sailor's girlfriend*), Michael Goldie (*p. t. instructor*), Ronnie Stevens (*hotel manager*), Joe Robinson (*Sonja's boyfriend*), Peter Butterworth (*ambulance driver*), Timothy Bateson (*Mr. Holly*), Derek Fowlds, Pauline Jameson, David Weston.

Comedy. Based on characters created by: Richard Gordon. Dr. Simon Sparrow and the interns and nurses of London's General Hospital are amazed when the usually gruff and eccentric head surgeon, Sir Lancelot Spratt, suddenly becomes courteous and kind. A slipped disc has caused Sir Lancelot to become a patient in his own hospital, and during the course of his treatment he has fallen in love with Iris, his physiotherapist. He seeks advice on courtship from Sparrow, who tells him to diet, visit a health clinic, and, later, be fitted for a corset. Meanwhile Sparrow becomes enamored of Delia, a patient who is both a model and aspiring actress. Sparrow has a brief affair with Sonja, a masseuse, while Delia is making a film in Rome. Sir Lancelot eventually proposes to Iris, but she gently turns him down in favor of a patient, Major Ffrench. Sir Lancelot takes comfort in the thought that his habits will not be changed, and the hospital atmosphere returns to normal as Sparrow welcomes Delia on her return. *Physicians. Hospital interns. Nurses. Nobility. Lovelorn. Physical therapists. Masseurs. Actors. Swedes. Models. Health. Courtship. Personality. Hospitals. London.*

Note: Opened in London in Jul 1963. This is the fifth film in the "Doctor" series, produced by Betty E. Box and directed by Ralph Thomas.

DOCTOR IN LOVE (Great Britain)   F6.1216

Rank Organisation. *Dist* Governor Films. 15 Nov **1961** [San Francisco opening; c22 Aug 1960; LF173]. Sd; col (Eastman Color). 35mm. 93 min.

A Betty E. Box–Ralph Thomas Production. *Prod* Betty E. Box. *Exec Prod* Earl St. John. *Dir* Ralph Thomas. *Screenplay* Nicholas Phipps. *Photog* Ernest Steward. *Camera Op* James Bawden. *Art Dir* Maurice Carter. *Set Decor* Arthur Taksen. *Film Ed* Alfred Roome. *Mus* Bruce Montgomery. *Titl Song* Ken Hare. *Sung by* Richard Allan. *Sd Ed* Don Sharpe. *Sd Rec* Dudley Messenger, Gordon K. McCallum. *Asst Dir* Stanley Hosgood. *Prod Mgr* Charles Orme. *Cont* Gladys Goldsmith. *Cost Dsgn* Yvonne Caffin. *Makeup* George Blackler. *Hairdresser* Pearl Orton.

Cast: Michael Craig (*Dr. Richard Hare*), Virginia Maskell (*Dr. Nicola [Nikki] Barrington*), Leslie Phillips (*Dr. Tony Burke*), James Robertson-Justice (*Sir Lancelot Spratt*), Carole Lesley (*Kitten Strudwick*), Nicholas Phipps (*Dr. Clive Cardew*), Reginald Beckwith (*Wildewinde*), Joan Sims (*Dawn*), Liz Fraser (*Leonora*), Ambrosine Phillpotts (*Lady Spratt*), Moira Redmond (*Sally Nightingale*), Irene Handl (*Professor MacRitchie*), Michael Ward (*Dr. Flower*), Ronnie Stevens (*Harold Green*), Nicholas Parsons (*Dr. Hinxman*), Fenella Fielding (*Mrs. Tadwich*), John Le Mesurier (*Dr. Mincing*), Esma Cannon (*physiotherapist*), Meredith Edwards (*Parker*).

Comedy. Source: Richard Gordon, *Doctor in Love* (London, 1957). Dr. Richard Hare, a trainee at St. Swithin's Hospital in London, is a patient recuperating from jaundice. Love-prone, he falls for Sally Nightingale, his night nurse; and their indiscretion causes Sally to be dismissed. Upon his release from the hospital, Hare and his equally foolhardy colleague Dr. Tony Burke sign on as dollar-a-day guinea pigs at the Foulness Anti-Cold Research Unit, but a frolic with Leonora and Dawn, two uninhibited stripteasers, terminates that means of employment. Hare then becomes an assistant to Dr. Clive Cardew, a country physician married many times. Cardew goes to America to obtain his latest divorce, leaving Hare in charge of the clinic, and Hare invites Burke to join him in the country. Burke leaves, however, after a disastrous attempt to help Wildewinde, an oddball dispenser, take the drunkenness test at the local police station. Hare then hires as his assistant Dr. Nikki Barrington, also from St. Swithin's, with whom he promptly falls in love. All goes well until Sally Nightingale becomes the new receptionist, and Nikki, jealous of Hare's ex-lovers, walks out. A short time later they are both called to St. Swithin's to remove the appendix of Sir Lancelot Spratt, Hare's old superior; and the two lovers are reconciled at the operating table. *Physicians. Nurses. Stripteasers. Pharmacists. Eccentrics. Police. Secretaries. Health. Employer-employee relations. Divorce. Drunkenness. Jealousy. Hospitals. Appendicitis. Clinics. London.*

Note: Opened in London in Jul 1960; running time: 97 min. This is the fourth in the British-made "Doctor" series.

DR. LOVE *see* **TEENIE TULIP**

DR. MASHER   F6.1217

Dist Cinex International Film Distributors, Freeway Films. ca **1969**. Sd; col (Eastmancolor). 35mm. 70 min.

Prod-Dir Alexander Maxwell. *Assoc Prod* Kenneth Foster. *Photog* Austin McKinney. *Lighting* Don Jones. *Mus* Gregory Potts. *Sd* Mike Hall.

Cast: Andrew Jurisich (*doctor*), Linda O'Bryant (*wife*), Elaine Jarrett (*voodooist*), Lynn Harris (*nymphomaniac*), Alice Friedland (*nurse*), Neola Graef (*nude dancer*), Laine Tucker (*hippie*), Margaret Kelly, Phyllis Stangel, Susan Keener, Rex Knapp, Ron Dyer, Earl D'Eon, Jennifer Holles, Robert Mead, Gerry Litimoff, Brian Forest, Brenda Verdon, Karen Thomas.

Melodrama. A doctor is obsessed with ravishing every woman he sees. Despite the availability of his buxom wife, he relentlessly searches for virgins and becomes involved with drugs, fetishism, violence, lesbianism, voodooism, exhibitionism, and hippies. *Physicians. Virginity. Hippies. Obsession. Nymphomania. Nurses. Dancers. Infidelity. Fetishism. Lesbianism. Exhibitionism. Seduction. Drugs. Voodoo.*

DR. NO (Great Britain)   F6.1218

Eon Productions. *Dist* United Artists. 8 May **1963** [Denver, Colorado, opening; c5 Oct 1962; LP24719]. Sd; col (Technicolor). 35mm. 105 min. [Copyright length: 111 min.]

Prod Harry Saltzman, Albert R. Broccoli. *Dir* Terence Young. *Screenplay* Richard Maibaum, Johanna Harwood, Berkely Mather. *Anim* Trevor Bond, Robert Ellis. *Dir Photog* Ted Moore. *Camera Op* John Winbolt. *Focus* John Shinerock. *Asst Art Dir* Syd Cain. *Ch Draughtsman* Alan Tomkins. *Prod Dsgn* Ken Adam. *Main Titl* Maurice Binder. *Film Ed* Peter Hunt. *Mus Comp* Monty Norman. *Orch* Burt Rhodes. *Mus*: "James Bond Theme" *perf by* John Barry Orchestra. *Cond* Eric Rogers. *Sd Mix* Wally Milner, John Dennis, sd. *Boom Op* Don Wortham. *Location Sd Camera Op* Stanley Samworth. *1st, 2d & 3d Asst Dir* Clive Reed, David Anderson, John Meadows. *Prod Mgr* L. C. Rudkin. *Cont* Helen Whitson. *Prod Sec* Maureen Whitty. *Wardrobe Master* John Brady. *Wardrobe Mistress* Eileen Sullivan. *Makeup* John O'Gorman. *Hairdresser* Eileen Warwick. *Sp Eff* Frank George. *Still Photog* Bert Cann. *Casting* James Liggat. *Ch Stuntman* Bob Simmons. *Chargehand Electrn* Reg Blackburn.

Cast: Sean Connery (*James Bond*), Ursula Andress (*Honey*), Joseph Wiseman (*Dr. No*), Jack Lord (*Felix Leiter*), Bernard Lee ("*M*"), Anthony

Dawson, British (*Professor Dent*), John Kitzmiller (*Quarrel*), Zena Marshall (*Miss Taro*), Eunice Gayson (*Sylvia*), Lois Maxwell (*Miss Moneypenny*), Lester Prendergast (*Puss-Feller*), Tim Moxon (*Strangways*), Margaret LeWars (*girl photographer*), Reggie Carter (*Jones*), Peter Burton (*Major Boothroyd*), William Foster-Davis (*Duff*), Louis Blaazar (*Playdell-Smith*), Michele Mok (*Sister Rose*), Dolores Keator (*Mary*).

Action melodrama. Source: Ian Fleming, *Dr. No* (London, 1958). British Secret Service Agent 007 James Bond is sent to Jamaica to investigate the murder of a fellow agent and his secretary. Upon his arrival, Bond experiences attempts on his life through an automobile crash, by means of a tarantula, and by seduction by Miss Taro. Bond, aided by the American CIA agent Felix Leiter, links the murders to Dr. No, a mad scientist operating from Crab Key; and despite the natives' fear of the key because of the legend of a fire-breathing dragon, he persuades Quarrel, a black man, to transport him there and assist him in the investigation. Landing, they encounter Honey, a blond, bikini-clad, shell-hunter; and after they are spotted by Dr. No's patrol boat, Bond persuades Honey to join them. Trying frantically to escape, they are cornered by a flamethrowing tank (the dragon of the legend), which kills Quarrel. Bond and Honey are captured and imprisoned in Dr. No's secret base, where they learn of his experiments to divert the course of rockets fired from Cape Canaveral. Bond escapes from his cell by means of a ventilator shaft and intercepts Dr. No just as he is ready to deflect another rocket. In a death struggle, Dr. No is killed, and Bond flicks every switch in the laboratory; but before the final explosion, he rescues Honey and they escape in a motor launch. *Secret agents. Scientists. Negroes. Murder. Seduction. Automobile accidents. Explosions. Tanks (armored cars). Rockets. Laboratories. Motorboats. Flamethrowers. Islands. Jamaica. Cape Canaveral. Great Britain—Intelligence service. United States—Central Intelligence Agency. James Bond. Dragons. Spiders.*

Note: Opened in London in Oct 1962.

DOCTOR NO   **F6.1219**
Dist Stacey Distributors. ca **1970**. Sd; col. 16mm. 61-81 min.

Sex film. No information about the precise nature of this film has been found. *Physicians. Sexuality.*

DOCTOR OF DOOM (Mexico)   **F6.1220**
Cinematográfica Calderón. *Dist* K. Gordon Murray Productions, Trans-International Films. ca **1965**. Sd; b&w. 35mm. 77 min.

Pres by K. Gordon Murray. *Prod* William Calderon Stell. *Prod English Vers* K. Gordon Murray. *Dir* René Cardona. *Story & Screenplay* Alfredo Salazar. *Photog* Enrique Wallace. *Art Dir* José Rodríguez Granada. *Film Ed* Jorge Bustos. *Mus* Antonio Díaz Conde. *Sd* Javier Mateos.

Cast: Lorena Velázquez, Roberto Cañedo, Armando Silvestre, Chucho Salinas, Elizabeth Campbell, Jorge Mondragón, Sonia Infante, Martha "Guera" Solis, Irma Rodríguez.

Horror film. A scientist's obsession with brain experimentation drives him to transplant a gorilla's brain in a man's head. The doctor then places an ape's brain in the head of an intelligent woman wrestler, whose death is eventually avenged by her sister, also a victim of the doctor's experiments. Other women wrestlers, assisted by several detectives, locate the doctor's residence. The doctor's laboratory and his victims are destroyed in an explosion. The fiend escapes, only to fall to his death during a struggle with a detective. *Scientists. Wrestlers. Detectives. Brain surgery. Organ transplants. Revenge. Experiments. Explosions. Apes.*

Note: Produced in Mexico in 1962 as *Las luchadoras contra el médico asesino*; running time: 90 min. William Calderon Stell is an anglicized rendering of Guillermo Calderón.

THE DOCTOR OF SEVEN DIALS *see* **CORRIDORS OF BLOOD**

THE DOCTOR SAYS (Switzerland/West Germany)   **F6.1221**
Praesens-Film–Fono-Film–CCC Filmkunst. *Dist* Royal Films International, Trans-Lux Distributing Corp. 24 Mar **1967** [Los Angeles opening]. Sd; b&w with col seq. 35mm. 87 min.

Prod Lazar Wechsler. *Dir (see note)* Aleksander Ford. *Screenplay* David Wechsler. *Story* Walter M. Diggelmann. *Photog* Eugen Shuftan. *Art Dir* Heinrich Weidemann. *Film Ed* Hermann Haller, Gisela Neumann. *Mus* Robert Blum. *Sd* Clemens Tütsch. *Dir Prod* Ruth Schoch, Heinz Götze.

Cast: Tadeusz Lomnicki (*Dr. Maurer*), Sabine Bethmann (*Mrs. Maurer*), René Deltgen (*Dr. Diener*), Dieter Borsche (*Mr. Sidler*), Margot Trooger (*Mrs. Sidler*), Peter Oehme (*president of the court*), Hermann Frick (*prosecuting counsel*), Charles Regnier (*professor*), Lutz Altschul (*defense counsel*), Margret Neuhaus, Sepp Zuger, Franz Matter, Elfriede Volker, Vera Jesse, Peter Kummer, Beate Tschudi, Ursula Heyer, Georg Wenkhaus, Gert Westphal, Fred Tanner, Gisela Glietz, Irmgard Delschneider.

Sex instruction film. A mother of three children is refused an abortion at a Zurich clinic in keeping with the prohibitions of the Swiss law known as "Paragraph 218," and she later dies after obtaining an illegal abortion. At the trial of the abortionist, a general practitioner comes into conflict with the head of the gynecological clinic over the ethics of abortion. The problem of overpopulation and various birth control methods come under discussion, and obstetrical and gynecological procedures are illustrated. The general practitioner decides to devote more time to dispensing birth control information, while the clinic doctor, who had decided to leave his job to pursue a lucrative private practice, changes his mind and remains at the clinic. *Physicians. Gynecologists. Abortion. Obstetrics. Childbirth. Birth control. Trials. Law. Medical ethics. Clinics. Zurich.*

Note: Color sequences of medical procedures were filmed at the Zurich Women's Hospital. Released in Switzerland in 1966 as *Der Arzt stellt fest ...*; running time: 82 min. Released in West Germany in Jun 1966 as *Angeklagt nach Paragraph 218*; running time: 83 min. Also known as *The Doctor Speaks Out*. U. S. press material credits F. Matter as co-director.

DR. SEX   **F6.1222**
Romike Films. *Dist* RAS International Films, Gillman Film Corp. 4 Jun **1964** [San Francisco showing]. Sd; col (Eastman Color). 35mm. [Feature length assumed.]

Pres by R-S Productions.

Sex film. Dr. Sex, a psychiatrist, discusses with his associates Dr. Diaphanous Lovejoy and Dr. Emil Schmutz his forthcoming book on sexology: *The first chapter documents the case of an associate who treats a patient who has a perplexing problem. The patient complains of being in the apartment of a disarmingly beautiful woman who saunters about nude, takes sensuous bubble baths, and engages in erotic telephone conversations before his very eyes. The patient is revealed to be a poodle. Dr. Sex's book concerns the associate's reaction to the problem: he too wants to become a poodle and be allowed access to similar voyeuristic delights.* Dr. Lovejoy suggests the second chapter: *A patient complains that he is emotionally involved with the store dummies that he dresses for a living. Dr. Lovejoy tries unsuccessfully to demonstrate that humans are not dummies, allowing her to undress her side-by-side with a dummy.* The next chapter is provided by Dr. Schmutz: *An exhibitionist becomes a striptease dancer to legitimize her desire to undress.* Dr. Sex relates the final chapter of the book: *A patient comes to him complaining that his house is populated by naked female ghosts who prevent him from relating to the real people in his house. Dr. Sex advises him to sell the house. The doctor then buys it, and he also sees the female spirits.* Dr. Schmutz begins to fear for his colleague's sanity, calls the police, and returns to keep an eye on Dr. Sex until help arrives. Dr. Sex meanwhile involves all of the "women" in an orgy. Dr. Schmutz is transformed into a poodle and joins in the fun. *Psychiatrists. Stripteasers. Police. Sex research. Nudity. Eroticism. Voyeurism. Fetishism. Exhibitionism. Metamorphosis. Dummies. Haunted houses. Orgies. Hallucinations. Ghosts. Dogs.*

DR. SHRINK   **F6.1223**
Cosmos Films. *Dist* Able Film Co. ca **1970**. Sd; col. 16mm. 45 min.

Sex film. No information about the precise nature of this film has been found. *Physicians. Sexuality.*

THE DOCTOR SPEAKS OUT *see* **THE DOCTOR SAYS**

DR. STRANGELOVE OR: HOW I LEARNED TO STOP WORRYING AND LOVE THE BOMB (Great Britain)   **F6.1224**
Hawk Films. *Dist* Columbia Pictures. 30 Jan **1964** [New York opening; c31 Dec 1963; LP26988]. Sd (Westrex); b&w. 35mm. 93 min. [Cut from 102 min.]

A Stanley Kubrick Production. *Prod-Dir* Stanley Kubrick. *Assoc Prod* Victor Lyndon. *Screenplay* Stanley Kubrick, Terry Southern, Peter George. *Dir Photog* Gilbert Taylor. *Camera Op* Kelvin Pike. *Camera Asst* Bernard Ford. *Art Dir* Peter Murton. *Prod Dsgn* Ken Adam. *Main Titl* Pablo Ferro (Ferro, Mohammed & Schwartz). *Film Ed* Anthony Harvey. *Asst Ed* Ray Lovejoy. *Assembly Ed* Geoffrey Fry. *Mus* Laurie Johnson. *Song:* "We'll Meet Again" Ross Parker, mus, Hughie Charles. *Sung by* Vera Lynn. *Sd Supv* John Cox. *Rec* Richard Bird. *Dub Mix* John Aldred. *Sd Ed* Leslie Hodgson. *Asst Dir* Eric Rattray. *Prod Mgr* Clifton Brandon. *Cont* Pamela Carlton. *Wardrobe* Bridget Sellers. *Makeup* Stuart Freeborn. *Hairdresser* Barbara Ritchie. *Sp Eff* Wally Veevers. *Traveling Matte* Vic Margutti. *Aviation Adv* John Crewdson, (Capt.). *Coöp* Solartron Electronic, Marconi's Wireless Telegraph Co., Telephone Manufacturing Co., British Oxygen Co.

Cast: Peter Sellers (*Group Capt. Lionel Mandrake/President Muffley/Dr. Strangelove*), George C. Scott (*Gen. "Buck" Turgidson*), Sterling Hayden (*Gen. Jack D. Ripper*), Keenan Wynn (*Col. "Bat" Guano*), Slim Pickens (*Maj. T. J. "King" Kong*), Peter Bull (*Ambassador de Sadesky*), Tracy Reed (*Miss Scott*), James Earl Jones (*Lieut. Lothar Zogg*), Jack Creley (*Mr. Staines*), Frank Berry (*Lieut. H. R. Dietrich*), Glenn Beck (*Lieut. W. D. Kivel*), Shane Rimmer (*Capt. G. A. "Ace" Owens*), Paul Tamarin (*Lieut. B. Goldberg*), Gordon Tanner (*General Faceman*), Robert O'Neil (*Admiral Randolph*), Roy Stephens (*Frank*), Laurence Herder, John McCarthy, actor, Hal Galili (*Burpelson* *defense team members).*

Satire. Source: Peter George, *Red Alert* (New York, 1958). Crazed by the belief that the communists are planning to conquer the free world by poisoning the water supply with fluoride, Gen. Jack D. Ripper, commanding officer of the U. S. Air Force base at Burpelson, unleashes a B-52 atomic bomb attack on Russia. Ripper prevents the countermanding of his orders through a secret code and makes himself inaccessible by sealing off the base. When President Muffley learns of the unauthorized mission, he summons his council to the War Room in the Pentagon and invites Russian Ambassador de Sadesky. Despite the hysterical advice of Gen. "Buck" Turgidson, who advocates limited nuclear war, the President orders U. S. land forces, under the command of Army Col. "Bat" Guano, to attack Burpelson. Ripper kills himself rather than face capture, but his R.A.F. aide, Group Capt. Lionel Mandrake, who has been locked in Ripper's office, works out the secret code that is instrumental in recalling the bombers. All appears safe until it is discovered that a plane commanded by a boisterous Texan, Maj. T. J. "King" Kong, did not receive the recall message. At this point, President Muffley learns from de Sadesky that the Russians have developed a "Doomsday Device" which will set off worldwide nuclear explosions if an atomic bomb is dropped anywhere over Russia. Desperate, the President turns to his physicist adviser, the paraplegic ex-Nazi, Dr. Strangelove, who calculates that humanity can survive if a selected few take to underground shelters and remain there for about 100 years. All efforts to halt the lone plane fail, and Kong wildly straddles the bomb as it plummets toward the earth. Consequently, the Doomsday Device is triggered, and atomic explosions are set off all over the world. *Psychopaths. Presidents of the United States. Russians. Diplomats. Communists. Physicists. Paraplegics. Nazis. Texans. Megalomania. Paranoia. Cold war. Poisoning. Militarism. Patriotism. Suicide. Nuclear warfare. Bombers. Atom bomb. Union of Soviet Socialist Republics. United States Air Force. United States Army. The Pentagon. Great Britain—Royal Air Force. Explosions. Doomsday.*

Note: Released in Great Britain in 1964. Other songs included on the soundtrack: "Try a Little Tenderness" and "When Johnny Comes Marching Home."

DOCTOR STUDLEY F6.1225
Munroe Productions–Janus II Productions. *For* Academy Productions. *Dist* Able Film Co. 24 Sep **1969** [New York showing]. Sd; col. 16mm. [Feature length assumed.]
Dir Richard Z. Evans.
Sex film. Dr. Veral Studley practices medicine on four women. His treatment includes breast fondling, sexual stimulation, and cunnilingus. *Physicians. Sexuality. Oral sex.*

DR. TERROR'S GALLERY OF HORRORS F6.1226
Dorad Corp.–Borealis Enterprises. *Dist* American General Pictures. **1967.** Sd; col (Technicolor, print by Pathé). 35mm (Totalvision). 84 min.
Prod David L. Hewitt, Ray Dorn. *Dir* David L. Hewitt. *Screenplay* Gary R. Heacock, David Prentiss. *Story* Russ Jones. *Photog* Austin McKinney. *Art Dir* Ray Dorn. *Film Ed* Tim Hinkle. *Makeup* Jean Lister.
Cast: Mitch Evans *(Count Alucard)*, Lon Chaney, [Jr.] *(Dr. Mendel)*, Jerry Benson *(Dr. Sedgwick)*, Ron Doyle *(Dr. Cushing)*, Vic McGee *(Amos Duncan)*, John Carradine *(warlock/narrator for "The Witch's Clock")*, Rochelle Hudson, Roger Gentry, Gray Daniels, Russ Jones, Karen Joy, Margaret Moore, Ron Brogan.
Horror film. THE WITCH'S CLOCK, which begins this 5-part horror anthology, deals with magic. In KING VAMPIRE, 19th-century London is terrorized by a blood-sucking beast, and MONSTER RAID concerns the return of a corpse from his grave. In THE SPARK OF LIFE, Dr. Mendel, assisted by colleagues Sedgwick and Cushing, brings the corpse of crazed murderer Amos Duncan back to life after being dismissed from medical college for performing similar experiments in revivification. COUNT ALUCARD pits Dracula against a werewolf. *Witches. Vampires. Monsters. Physicians. Zombies. Werewolves. Magic. Reviviscence. Murder. Experiments. London. Dracula.*
Note: Working title: *Gallery of Horrors.* Rereleased in 1968 as *The Blood Suckers.* Also known as *Return From the Past.*

DR. TERROR'S HOUSE OF HORRORS (United States/Great Britain)
F6.1227
Amicus Productions. *Dist* Paramount Pictures. Mar **1965** [c31 Dec 1964; LP29862]. Sd; col (Technicolor). 35mm (Techniscope). 98 min.
Prod Milton Subotsky, Max J. Rosenberg. *Dir* Freddie Francis. *Screenplay* Milton Subotsky. *Photog* Alan Hume. *Art Dir* William Constable. *Film Ed* Thelma Connell. *Mus* Elisabeth Lutyens. *Mus Dir* Philip Martell. *Song:* "Give Me Love" *Comp & Sung by* Kenny Lynch. *Lyr:* "Everybody's Got Love" Kenny Lynch. *Song:* "Voodoo" *Comp & Perf by* Tubby Hayes Quintet. *Mus Perf* Russell Henderson Steel Band, Roy Castle. *Choreog* Boscoe Holder. *Sd* John Cox, Buster Ambler. *Asst Dir* Bert Batt. *Wardrobe Supv* Bridget Sellers.

Makeup Roy Ashton. *Hairstyles* Frieda Steiger. *Sp Eff* Ted Samuels.
Cast: Peter Cushing *(Dr. Terror)*, Christopher Lee *(Franklyn Marsh)*, Roy Castle *(Biff Bailey)*, Donald Sutherland *(Bob Carroll)*, Neil McCallum *(Jim Dawson)*, Alan Freeman *(Bill Rogers)*, Max Adrian *(Dr. Blake)*, Edward Underdown *(Tod)*, Ursula Howells *(Dierdre Biddulph)*, Peter Madden *(Caleb)*, Katy Wild *(Valda)*, Ann Bell *(Ann Rogers)*, Sarah Nicholls *(Carol Rogers)*, Bernard Lee *(Hopkins)*, Jeremy Kemp *(Drake)*, Kenny Lynch *(Sammy Coin)*, Harold Lang *(Shine [Compère])*, Christopher Carlos *(Vrim)*, George Mossman *(pony and trap driver)*, Thomas Baptiste *(Dambala)*, Jennifer Jayne *(Nicolle)*, Michael Gough *(Eric Landor)*, Irene Richmond *(Mrs. Ellis)*, Frank Barry *(Johnny)*, Isla Blair *(girl)*, Hedger Wallace *(surgeon)*, Judy Cornwell, Laurie Leigh *(nurses)*, Al Mulock *(detective)*, Frank Forsyth *(toastmaster)*, Tauros (a dog) *(werewolf)*, James (a chimpanzee) *(an artist)*, Brian Hawkins, John Martin, Faith Kent, Kenneth Kove, Walter Sparrow, Valerie St. Clair, Russell Henderson Steel Band, Tubby Hayes Quintet.
Horror film. Dr. Sandor Schreck, known as Dr. Terror, joins five men in a train compartment and proceeds to tell each man's future with tarot cards. Architect Jim Dawson, on his way to visit his birthplace, is told that the current owner of the house, a beautiful widow named Dierdre Biddulph, will turn into a werewolf and kill him. Bill Rogers learns that a creeping vine growing on his house will engulf and destroy his family. Dr. Terror warns jazz musician Biff Bailey that the voodoo god Dambala will haunt him for performing music used in secret voodoo rites in Haiti. Bob Carroll, an American physician, hears a macabre tale in which he is persuaded by his colleague Dr. Blake to kill his new bride, Nicolle, because she is a vampire; in reality Blake, too, is a vampire, given to eliminating his competitors in the medical profession, and Carroll hangs for murder because of Blake's treachery. Art critic Franklyn Marsh, who has been skeptical of Dr. Terror's predictions, is the last to hear his future, in which the dismembered hand of an artist whom Marsh drove to suicide follows him and causes a car accident that leaves Marsh blind. As the train comes to a stop, the mysterious Dr. Terror disappears, and the five men meet their respective fates. *Fortune-tellers. Vampires. Werewolves. Architects. Musicians. Critics. Newlyweds. Widows. Physicians. Supernatural. Voodoo. Murder. Suicide. Tarot. Trains. Carnivorous plants. Automobile accidents.*
Note: Released in Great Britain in Feb 1965.

THE DR. WARD STORY *see* **THE DOCTOR AND THE PLAYGIRL**

DR. WHO AND THE DALEKS (Great Britain) F6.1228
Amicus Productions. *Dist* Continental Distributing, Inc. 11 May **1966** [Saint Louis opening]. Sd; col (Technicolor). 35mm (Techniscope). 85 min.
Prod Milton Subotsky, Max J. Rosenberg. *Exec Prod* Joe Vegoda. *Dir* Gordon Flemyng. *Screenplay* Milton Subotsky. *Photog* John Wilcox. *Art Dir* Bill Constable. *Set Decor* Scott Slimon. *Film Ed* Oswald Hafenrichter. *Mus Comp & Cond* Malcolm Lockyer. *Electronic Mus* Barry Gray. *Sd Mix* Buster Ambler. *Asst Dir* Anthony Waye. *Prod Mgr* Ted Lloyd. *Wardrobe* Jackie Cummins. *Makeup* Jill Carpenter. *Hairstyles* Henry Montsash. *Sp Eff* Ted Samuels.
Cast: Peter Cushing *(Dr. Who)*, Roy Castle *(Ian)*, Jennie Linden *(Barbara)*, Roberta Tovey *(Susan)*, Barrie Ingham *(Alydon)*, Geoffrey Toone *(Temmosus)*, Mark Petersen *(Elyon)*, John Bown *(Antodus)*, Michael Coles *(Ganatus)*, Yvonne Antrobus *(Dyoni)*.
Science fiction melodrama. Based on the BBC television serial *Dr. Who* by Terry Nation. While absentminded Dr. Who is demonstrating his latest invention, a time machine, the apparatus is accidentally set in motion, and the doctor, his two granddaughters (Barbara and Susan), and Barbara's boyfriend, Ian, all land in a petrified forest on a huge planet in the future. They are quickly captured by the Daleks, a hostile form of life encased in metal cones which protect them from the radiation caused by a massive neutron war. Also living on the planet are the Thals, friendly creatures who are able to live without the protective cones because they possess a drug which immunizes them against radioactivity. Since the Daleks desperately want the drug, they send Susan to invite the Thals to their stronghold; but when she returns, the Daleks discover that the drug is fatal to them. They decide to explode a giant neutron bomb which will increase radiation and exterminate the Thals. Dr. Who and his friends escape from their captors, warn the Thals, and help launch an attack in which the Daleks are vanquished moments before the bomb is set to explode. With the Thals free to live in peace, Dr. Who and his party return to their time machine. *Inventors. Grandfathers. Space creatures. Space travel. Radiation. Nuclear warfare. Time machines. Drugs. Imaginary planets. The Future.*
Note: Released in Great Britain in 1965; running time: 83 min. This film is followed by *Daleks—Invasion Earth 2150 A.D.,* q. v., also based on the *Dr. Who* television series.

DOCTOR, YOU'VE GOT TO BE KIDDING F6.1229
Trident Productions. *Dist* Metro-Goldwyn-Mayer, Inc. Apr **1967** [New York opening: 10 May; c31 Dec 1966; LP34093]. Sd (Westrex); col

(Metrocolor). 35mm (Panavision). 94 min.

A Mann-Laurence-Wasserman Production. *Prod* Douglas Laurence. *Dir* Peter Tewksbury. *Screenplay* Phillip Shuken. *Dir Photog* Fred Koenekamp. *Art Dir* George W. Davis, Urie McCleary. *Set Decor* Henry Grace, Charles S. Thompson. *Film Ed* Fredric Steinkamp. *Mus* Kenyon Hopkins. *Songs: "I Haven't Got Anything Better To Do," "Walk Tall Like a Man"* Paul Vance, Lee Pockriss. *Song: "Talkin' Low"* Dale Wasserman, Kenyon Hopkins. *Song: "Little Girl"* Wild Affair Trio. *Song: "All I Do Is Dream of You"* Arthur Freed, Nacio Herb Brown. *Mus Numbers Staged by* Earl Barton. *Rec Supv* Franklin Milton. *Sd* Phil Mitchell. *Asst Dir* Eric Von Stroheim, Jr. *Furs by* A. I. Lipsey. *Makeup* William Tuttle. *Hairstyles* Sydney Guilaroff.

Cast: Sandra Dee (*Heather Halloran*), George Hamilton (*Harlan Wycliff*), Celeste Holm (*Louise Halloran*), Bill Bixby (*Dick Bender*), Dick Kallman (*Pat Murad*), Mort Sahl (*Dan Ruskin*), Dwayne Hickman (*Hank Judson*), Allen Jenkins (*Joe Bonney*), Robert Gibbons (*Alex North*), Nichelle Nichols (*Jenny Ribbock*), Charlotte Considine (*Miss Reynolds*), Allison McKay (*cigarette girl*), Rica Owen Moore (*folk singer*), Wild Affair Trio (*themselves*), Med Flory, Scott White, Donald Mitchell (*policemen*).

Comedy. *Source:* Patte Wheat Mahan, *Three for a Wedding* (New York, 1965). Ever since childhood, Heather Halloran's ambitious mother, Louise, has tried to push her daughter into a stage career. But Heather is content to be a secretary with a college degree. Content, that is, until her conceited boss, Harlan Wycliff, voices his contempt for her singing and dancing talents. To the delight of her mother and three of her suitors—neighbor Dick Bender, musician Pat Murad, and would-be actor Hank Judson—Heather auditions for, and gets, a nightclub singing contract. On the day of her opening, however, she and Harlan decide they are in love and Heather fails to make her debut. The romance soon runs into trouble, and Heather once more plunges into rehearsals. Although she does make an appearance this time, she faints before singing a note. She is rushed to a hospital and discovered to be pregnant. All three of her suitors offer to become her husband, but fortunately, Harlan has a street accident and arrives at the hospital in time to marry Heather before she is wheeled into the delivery room. *Secretaries. Businessmen. Neighbors. Singers. Courtship. Ambition. Motherhood. Pregnancy. Nightclubs.*

Note: Working titles: *Three for a Wedding* and *This Way Out, Please.*

DOCTOR ZHIVAGO   F6.1230
Carlo Ponti. *Dist* Metro-Goldwyn-Mayer, Inc. 22 Dec **1965** [New York opening; c31 Dec 1965; LP33315]. *Sd* (Westrex); col (Metrocolor). 35mm (Panavision). 197 min. [Cut to 180 min.]

Prod Carlo Ponti. *Exec Prod* Arvid L. Griffen. *Dir* David Lean. *2d Unit Dir* Roy Rossotti. *Screenplay* Robert Bolt. *Dir Photog* Freddie Young. *2d Unit Photog* Manuel Berenguer. *Camera Op* Ernest Day. *Art Dir* Terence Marsh. *Asst Art Dir* Ernest Archer, Bill Hutchinson, Roy Walker. *Assoc Art Dir* Gil Parrondo. *Set Decor* Dario Simoni. *Prod Dsgn* John Box. *Film Ed* Norman Savage. *Orig Mus Comp & Cond* Maurice Jarre. *Sd Rec* Paddy Cunningham. *Sd Ed* Winston Ryder. *Re-rec* Franklin Milton, William Steinkamp. *Asst Dir* Roy Stevens, Pedro Vidal, José María Ochoa. *Prod Supv* John Palmer. *Prod Mgr* Agustin Pastor, Douglas Twiddy. *Cont* Barbara Cole. *Cost Dsgn* Phyllis Dalton. *Makeup* Mario Van Riel. *Hairstyles* Grazia De Rossi, Anna Cristofani. *Sp Eff* Eddie Fowlie. *Coöp* Iberduero S. A. Aldeadavila Dam, Spanish Railways National System, Finnish State Railways, Canadian Pacific Railway Co., C. E. A. Studios (Madrid). *Ch Elctrn* Miguel Sancho Ruiz. *Constr* Gus Walker, Fred Bennett. *Dial Coach* Hugh Miller.

Cast: Geraldine Chaplin (*Tonya Gromeko*), Julie Christie (*Lara*), Tom Courtenay (*Pasha Antipov [Strelnikoff]*), Alec Guinness (*Yevgraf Zhivago*), Siobhan McKenna (*Anna Gromeko*), Ralph Richardson (*Alexander Gromeko*), Omar Sharif (*Yuri Zhivago*), Rod Steiger (*Komarovsky*), Rita Tushingham (*girl*), Adrienne Corri (*Amelia*), Geoffrey Keen (*Professor Kurt*), Jeffrey Rockland (*Sasha*), Lucy Westmore (*Katya*), Noel Willman (*Razin*), Gérard Tichy (*Liberius*), Klaus Kinski (*Kostoyed*), Jack MacGowran (*Petya*), Maria Martin (*gentlewoman*), Tarek Sharif (*Yuri, age 8*), Mercedes Ruiz (*Tonya, age 7*), Roger Maxwell (*beef-faced soldier*), Inigo Jackson (*major*), Virgilio Teixeira (*captain*), Bernard Kay (*Bolshevik*), Erik Chitty (*old soldier*), José Nieto (*priest*), Mark Eden (*young engineer*), Emilio Carrer (*Mr. Sventytski*), Gerhard Jersch (*David*), Wolf Frees (*Comrade Yelkin*), Gwen Nelson (*Comrade Kaprugina*), José María Caffarel (*militiaman*), Brigitte Trace (*streetwalker*), Luana Alcaniz (*Mrs. Sventytski*), Lili Murati (*train jumper*), Peter Madden (*political officer*), Katherine Ellison (*raped woman*), María Vico (*demented woman*), Dodo Assad Bahador (*dragoon colonel*).

Historical drama. *Source:* Boris Leonidovich Pasternak, *Doctor Zhivago* (trans. by Max Hayward and Manya Harari; New York, 1958). Former Bolshevik Police Commissar Yevgraf Zhivago, now a general in charge of a huge Soviet dam, has traced a young girl whom he believes to be the daughter of his half brother, Yuri, and the beautiful Lara. ... The orphaned Yuri goes to live in Moscow with the family of aristocrat Alexander Gromeko. He becomes

a doctor and later marries Gromeko's daughter, Tonya. Yuri meets Lara, the daughter of dressmaker Amelia, when he helps save her life after a suicide attempt prompted by her seduction by Komarovsky, Amelia's lover. Yuri and Lara meet again at a party, where Lara vengefully shoots and wounds Komarovsky. She is taken from the party by a young political idealist, Pasha, whom she soon marries. When the Great War breaks out in 1914, Yuri goes to the front to aid the soldiers, and again encounters Lara, who has become a nurse. They fall in love, but though she has been deserted by Pasha, their relationship remains platonic. When Yuri returns to Moscow, he finds the city changed by the revolution. The Gromeko home has been taken over; the government looks with disfavor on Yuri's poetry; and he and his family, cold and starving, travel by train to their country estate in the Urals. At a library in nearby Yuriatin, Yuri again meets Lara, who is in the town to see Pasha, now known as the bandit general Strelnikov. At her apartment, Yuri and Lara make love, and their affair continues for some months. With Tonya pregnant, however, Yuri sees Lara for what he says will be the last time. On his way back to the estate, he is conscripted by the Red Army. In northern Russia, Yuri deserts the army and makes his way hundreds of miles to Yuriatin. He finds that his family has been deported to France, and he goes to Lara's apartment. Yuri and Lara are soon met by Komarovsky, who tells them that they are in danger, Yuri for his poetry and his family's associations with partisan groups in Paris, and Lara because of her associations both with Yuri and her husband. Yuri and Lara move to the estate, where they stay until they can no longer hide. (There Yuri writes a series of poems dedicated to Lara.) About to flee, Yuri changes his mind at the last moment and decides to stay in his homeland. Many years later, Yuri is helped by Yevgraf to find a job. As he travels to work on a streetcar, he sees Lara. He desperately makes his way through the crowded vehicle until he, too, is on the street, but when he tries to call to her, he collapses. Eventually, Lara is arrested, and she spends her last years in a labor camp. ... The young girl has only vague recollections of her past, and the photographs of Lara and Yuri in the latter's book of verse mean nothing to her. She leaves with her boyfriend, and, looking at her from afar, Yevgraf is certain of her identity. *Orphans. Brothers. Bolshevists. White Russians. Physicians. Aristocrats. Dressmakers. Revolutionaries. Nurses. Engineers. Idealists. Poets. Deserters—Military. Marriage. Infidelity. Class conflict. Suicide. Revenge. Starvation. Pregnancy. Deportation. Trains. Libraries. Dams. Photographs. Streetcars. Russia—History—1917–21 Revolution. World War I. Moscow. Ural Mountains.*

Note: Location scenes filmed in Spain and Finland. Blown up to 70mm for roadshow engagements.

DOCTORS FROM OH! COPENHAGEN   F6.1231
Century Cinema Corp. *Dist* Chancellor Films. ca **1970**. Sd; col. 35mm. 70 min.

Sex film. A team of psychiatrists in a Copenhagen sex clinic perform sex therapy. A young man is cured of his stutter after making love with Liz, one of the nurses. A young woman, suffering from amnesia after a brutal rape, regains her memory after treatment; nurse Liz helps her to purge her nightmare. A couple married for 3 years is treated for sexual dysfunction. The couple recreates episodes from their marriage and wedding night, and they eventually achieve marital harmony. *Psychiatrists. Nurses. Sex clinics. Rape. Amnesia. Lesbianism. Sexual dysfunction. Speech impediments. Copenhagen.*

Note: Country of origin undetermined.

THE DOG AND THE DIAMONDS (Great Britain)   F6.1232
London Independent Producers. *For* Children's Film Foundation. *Dist* Continental Distributing, Inc. 12 Apr **1962** [Maryland license]. Sd; b&w. 16mm & 35mm. 55 min.

Prod Peter Rogers. *Dir* Ralph Thomas. *Screenplay* Patricia Latham. *Story* Mary Cathcart Borer. *Photog* Gordon Lang. *Art Dir* George Provis. *Film Ed* Peter Seabourne. *Mus* Lambert Williamson.

Cast: Kathleen Harrison (*Mrs. Fossett*), George Coulouris (*Forbes*), Geoffrey Sumner (*Mr. Gayford*), Brian Oulton (*Mr. Plumpton*), Michael MacGuire, British (*Jimmy*), Robert Sandford (*Peter*), Robert Scroggins (*Ginger*), Barbara Brown (*Helen*), Molly Osborne (*Linda*), Hal Osmund, Arthur Lane, Dennis Wyndham (*crooks*).

Drama. Because pets are forbidden in their apartments, children create a zoo in the garden of an abandoned manor house which turns out to be the retreat of a trio of jewel thieves. Aided by their animals, the children apprehend the robbers. In recognition of this feat, the manor is converted into a youth center and zoo. *Children. Thieves. Heroism. Zoos. Pets.*

Note: Released in Great Britain in 1953; running time: 57 min.

DOG EAT DOG (United States/Italy/West Germany)   F6.1233
Ernst Neubach-Filmproduktion–Unione Cinematografica Internazionale–Michael Arthur Films. *Dist* Ajay Film Co. 13 Jul **1966** [New York opening]. Sd; b&w. 35mm. 84 min.

Prod Carl Szokol. *Exec Prod* Arthur Cohn. *Dir (see note)* Ray Nazarro, Albert Zugsmith. *Screenplay* Robert Hill, Michael Elkins. *Photog* Riccardo Pallottini. *Camera* Matija Brgles, Gino Conversi. *Art Dir* Wolf Witzemann. *Film Ed* Gene Ruggiero. *Mus* Carlo Savina. *Prod Mgr* Wolfgang Birk.

Cast: Cameron Mitchell *(Lylle Corbett)*, Jayne Mansfield *(Darlene)*, Elisabeth Flickenschildt *(Xenia)*, Isa Miranda *(Sandra)*, Dody Heath, Pinkas Braun, Werner Peters, Ivor Salter, Ines Taddio, Aldo Camarda.

Melodrama. Source: Robert Bloomfield, *When Strangers Meet* (New York, 1956). Gangsters Lylle Corbett and Dolph Kostis rob a bank of a million dollars, and, accompanied by Darlene, a loose woman attracted by the stolen loot, escape to an island in the Adriatic. Intent on keeping the entire sum for himself, Kostis attacks Corbett and leaves him for dead; but as he flees with Darlene to their villa hideout on a neighboring island, Corbett catches up with them and takes charge. Morelli, a shrewd hotel manager who has overheard Kostis plotting with Darlene, follows them with his sister, Sandra. Meanwhile, the robbers discover that their hiding place is inhabited by Xenia, an insane old woman, and her manservant, Jannis. Following the arrival of the second party, a number of murders are committed. Kostis is found strangled in a goldfish pond; Morelli falls from a cliff into a gasoline blaze he himself has set; and Jannis also dies. Sandra, who has taken the stolen money, pulls a gun on Corbett, whose greed has driven him mad, but they both drown in the sea. Darlene, too, dies by drowning, leaving only Xenia alive as the money floats out to sea. *Gangsters. Fugitives. Lunatics. Hotelkeepers. Domestics. Greed. Bank robberies. Murder. Brother-sister relationship. Eavesdropping. Islands. Adriatic Sea. Fires.*

Note: Filmed in Yugoslavia and Rome in 1963. Released in West Germany in Jun 1964 as *Einer frisst den anderen*; running times: 78 and 95 min. Italian title: *La morte vestita di dollari.* Prerelease source cites Michael Arthur Productions as production company and Zugsmith as director; however, notices at the time of release refer to the film as an Italian-West German co-production directed by Nazarro.

DOG STAR MAN   F6.1234

Dist Film-Makers' Cooperative, Brakhage. 22 Feb **1965** [New York opening]. Si; col with b&w seq (Eastman Color). 16mm. 78 min. [See note.]

Prod-Dir-Writ Stan Brakhage. *Photog* Stan Brakhage. *Adtl Photog* Jane Brakhage. *Film Ed* Stan Brakhage.

Cast: Stan Brakhage *(Dog Star Man)*, Jane Brakhage *(woman)*, Sirius [dog].

Experimental film. This cinematic variation on the theme of creation is composed of five parts. The Prelude, the Dog Star Man's dream, suggests the origin of man and the universe; Part I, human aspiration, as represented by a woodcutter and his dog climbing uphill in winter; Part II, birth, as embodied in the woodsman's infant and in his own infancy; Part III, generation, as evoked by the nude body of the man's wife; Part IV, life work, as illustrated by the woodsman's falls, and by his repeated attempts to demolish a whitened tree stump. *Woodsmen. Death. Parenthood. Dreams. Dogs.*

Note: *The Art of Vision*, q. v., is an elaboration of *Dog Star Man*, although it is created from exactly the same material, frame-by-frame. The prelude was first shown in New York City in early 1962; Part I premiered 18 Mar 1963; Part II 14 Dec 1964. Individual lengths: Prelude, 25 min; Part I, 30 min; Part II, 7 min; Part III, 11 min; and Part IV, 5 min. The film is composed of multiple images created by superimposing edited rolls of film over other rolls. Individual images within a roll last only a few seconds. The prelude contains two superimposed rolls; Part I, a single roll; Part II, two superimposed rolls; Part III, three superimposed rolls; Part IV, four superimposed rolls. Filmed partly in Colorado.

DOGADJAJ *see* AN EVENT

DOGGIE BAG   F6.1235

Kirt Films International-Triumph Films. *Dist* Distribpix, Inc. ca **1969**. Sd; col. 35mm. 65 min.

Prod Bob Mansy. *Dir* C. Walsh.

Cast: Janet Topaz, Margaret Leigh.

Drama. A young woman who lives in a fantasy world with her stuffed animals is suddenly introduced to sexual reality when she meets a depraved couple who teach her every way to use and abuse the human body. This woman later meets a nice young man who teaches her the beauty of true love. The woman tries to tear herself away from her sensual way of life, but she is nevertheless sucked down into depravity. *Sex deviates. Sexual initiation. Moral corruption. Toys.*

A DOG'S LIFE *see* MONDO CANE

DOJO YABURI *see* SAMURAI FROM NOWHERE

DOKTOR GLAS *see* DOCTOR GLAS

DOKURITSU GURENTAI NISHI-E *see* WESTWARD DESPERADO

DOKURITSU KIKANJUTAI IMADA SHAGEKICHU *see* OUTPOST OF HELL

IL DOLCE CORPO DI DEBORAH *see* THE SWEET BODY OF DEBORAH

LA DOLCE VITA (France/Italy)   F6.1236

Riama Film–Pathé Cinéma–Gray Films. *Dist* Astor Pictures, American International Pictures. 19 Apr **1961** [New York opening]. Sd (RCA); b&w. 35mm (Totalscope). 180 min. [See note.]

Prod Giuseppe Amato, Angelo Rizzoli. *Exec Prod* Franco Magli. *Dir* Federico Fellini. *Screenplay* Federico Fellini, Ennio Flajano, Tullio Pinelli, Brunello Rondi. *Story* Federico Fellini, Ennio Flajano, Tullio Pinelli. *Photog* Otello Martelli. *Camera Op* Arturo Zavattini, Ennio Guarnieri. *Art Dir* Piero Gherardi. *Film Ed* Leo Catozzo. *Mus* Nino Rota. *Cond* Franco Ferrara. *Soloists* I. Campanino, Adriano Celentano. *Sd* Agostino Moretti. *Asst Dir* Guidarino Guidi, Dominique Deluche, Gianfranco Mingozzi, Paolo Nuzi, Giancarlo Romani, Lilli Veenman. *Prod Mgr* Manlio M. Moretti, Nello Meniconi, Alessandro Von Norman, Mario De Biase, Mario Basile, Osvaldo De Micheli. *Cost* Piero Gherardi. *Asst Cost* Giorgio Giovannini, Lucia Mirisola, Vito Anzalone. *Makeup* Otello Fava. *Hairstyles* Renata Magnanti. *Cons Dir* Brunello Rondi.

Cast: Marcello Mastroianni *(Marcello Rubini)*, Anita Ekberg *(Sylvia)*, Anouk Aimée *(Maddalena)*, Yvonne Furneaux *(Emma)*, Magali Noël *(Fanny)*, Alain Cuny *(Steiner)*, Nadia Gray *(Nadia)*, Lex Barker *(Robert)*, Annibale Ninchi *(Marcello's father)*, Walter Santesso *(Paparazzo)*, Jacques Sernas *(matinee idol)*, Valeria Ciangottini *(Paola)*, Alan Dijon *(Frankie Stout)*, Renée Longarini *(Signora Steiner)*, Polidor *(clown)*, Giulio Questi *(Don Giulio)*, Cesarino Miceli Picardi *(irate man in nightclub)*, Adriana Moneta *(prostitute)*, Anna Maria Salerno *(her friend)*, Oscar Ghiglia, Gino Marturano *(their pimps)*, Leonardo Botta *(doctor)*, Harriet White *(Sylvia's secretary)*, Carlo Di Maggio *(producer)*, Adriano Celentano *(rock-n-roll singer)*, Gio Staiano *(effeminate male)*, Archie Savage *(Negro dancer)*, Giacomo Gabriello *(Maddalena's father)*, Giovanna, Massimo Busetti *(lying children of the miracle)*, Rina Franchetti *(their mother)*, Aurelio Nardi *(their uncle)*, Alfredo Rizzo *(TV director)*, Marianna Leibl *(Yvonne's companion)*, Iris Tree *(poetess)*, Lilly Granado *(Lucy)*, Gloria Jones *(Gloria)*, Nico Otzak *(sophisticated prostitute)*, Vadim Wolkonsky *(Prince Mascalchi)*, Audrey McDonald *(Sonia)*, Rosemary Rennel Rodd *(English medium)*, Ferdinando Brofferio *(Maddalena's lover)*, Doris Pignatelli, Princess of Monteroduni *(lady in white coat)*, Ida Galli *(debutante of the year)*, Loretta Ramaciotti *(woman in seance)*, Giulio Girola *(police commissioner)*, Mino Doro *(Nadia's lover)*, Antonio Jacono, Carlo Musto *(transvestites)*, Tito Buzzo *(muscle man)*, Sandra Lee *(Spoleto ballerina)*, Leontine Van Strein *(matinee idol's girl friend)*, Leo Coleman *(Negro dancer)*, Laura Betti *(Laura)*, Riccardo Garrone *(Riccardo, the villa owner)*, Franca Pasut *(girl covered with feathers)*, Prince Eugenio Ruspoli di Poggio Suasa *(Don Eugenio Mascalchi)*, Daniela Calvino *(Daniela)*, Enrico Glori *(Nadia's admirer)*, Enzo Cerusico, Enzo Doria, Giulio Paradisi *(photojournalists)*, Henry Thody, Donatella Della Nora, Maïté Morand, Donato Castellaneta, John Francis Lane, Concetta Ragusa, François Dieudonné, Mario Mallarno, Nadia Balabine, Umberto Felici, Maurizio Guelfi *(press conference journalists)*, Leonida Repaci, Anna Salvatore, Letizia Spadini, Margherita Russo, Winie Vagliani, Desmond O'Grady *(Steiner's other guests)*, Count Ivenda Dobrzensky *(Giovanni)*, Francesco Consalvo, Maria Teresa Vianello, Angela Giavalisco, Tiziano Cortini, Maria Mazzanti *(people at airport)*, Tomás Torres, Gloria Hendy, Noel Sheldon, April Hennessy, Angela Wilson *(people at Via Venneto)*, Giovanni Querrel, I. Campanino, Teresa Tsao, Giulio Citti *(people at nightclub)*, Lisa Schneider, Aldo Vasco, Francisco Lori, Romolo Giordani, Ada Passeri *(people in miracle sequence)*, Nina Hohenlohe, Maria Marigliano, Mario De Grenet, Franco Rossellini, Joan Antequera *(people at the castle)*, Orietta Fiume, Katherine Denise, Mario Conocchia, Umberto Orsini, Domino, Lucia Vasilico.

Drama. The citizens of Rome are startled by the sight of a huge statue of Christ being flown over the city by helicopter to the Vatican. Following in a second helicopter is Marcello Rubini, a journalist who, despite literary aspirations, earns his living writing gossip and scandal stories. In a nightclub, Marcello meets Maddalena, a jaded heiress. Together they pick up a prostitute and spend the night in the whore's room. Upon his return home at dawn, Marcello finds that his mistress, Emma, crushed by his perfidy, has attempted to poison herself. Her recovery assured, Marcello leaves Emma's side to cover the airport arrival of Sylvia Rank, a Hollywood starlet. Infatuated by the voluptuous blond actress, Marcello accompanies her on a tour of the city, following her to St. Peter's Basilica, the Baths of Caracalla, and the Trevi fountain. The escapade ends violently, however, when Sylvia's fiancé, Robert, assaults Marcello. The reporter's next assignment is to cover a purported apparition of the Blessed Virgin Mary, which two precocious children claim to have witnessed. The children's prevarication is exposed, and a sudden storm disperses the spectators. Later, Marcello's father visits him from the provinces but returns home when his son's lifestyle proves too strenuous for him. At a restaurant Marcello meets Paola, a young waitress whose provincial innocence appeals strongly to him. Marcello's assignments and adventures are punctuated by exhausting quarrels with Emma. The writer is further depressed when, following an evening of parties with aristocratic friends, he learns that Steiner, his wealthy and intellectual friend, has slain himself and his two children. Disillusioned, Marcello abandons himself to the pursuit of pleasure. The morning after an orgy at the seaside villa of the divorcée Nadia, Marcello and other guests roam through a forest to the beach, where a decomposing fish lies in the sand. As Marcello stares at its corpse, he sees Paola waving to him from across the canal; unable to understand what she is saying, he wanders off in the dawn to rejoin his friends. *Journalists. Heiresses. Prostitutes. Mistresses. Actors. Children. Waitresses. Authors. Idle rich. Jealousy. Suicide. Hoaxes. Filial relations. Murder. Moral corruption. Helicopters. Nightclubs. Orgies. Rome. Vatican. Terni. Saint Peter's Basilica. Baths of Caracalla. Trevi Fountain.*

Note: Location scenes filmed in and around Rome. Opened in Rome in Feb 1960 as *La dolce vita*; running time: 180 min; opened in Paris in May 1960 as *La douceur de vivre*; running time: 172 min. American International Pictures rereleased a dubbed version in the United States in 1966; running time: 175 min.

LE DOLCI SIGNORE see **ANYONE CAN PLAY**

DOLINA MIRA see **SERGEANT JIM**

THE DOLL (Sweden)   F6.1237
Flora Film. *Dist* Kanawha Films. 13 Jan **1964** [New York opening]. Sd; b&w. 35mm. 96 min.
Prod Lorens Marmstedt. *Dir* Arne Mattsson. *Screenplay* Eva Seeberg. *Story* Lars Forssell. *Camera* Åke Dahlquist. *Art Dir* Harald Harmland. *Film Ed* Ingemar Ejve. *Mus* Ulrik Neumann. *Sd* Nils Grening.
Cast: Per Oscarsson *(night watchman)*, Gio Petré *(The Doll)*, Tor Isedal *(barber)*, Elsa Prawitz *(landlady)*, Bengt Eklund *(caretaker)*, Malou *(young girl)*, Mimi Nelson *(The Mother)*, Rick Axberg *(young son)*, Dagmar Olsson *(charwoman)*, Agneta Prytz *(cat woman)*, Olle Grönstedt, Elisabeth Odén *(The Couple)*.
Drama. A desperately lonely, young night watchman interrupts thieves as he makes his rounds in a Stockholm shopping center. As they flee, the thieves knock over a mannequin, and the night watchman tenderly picks it up and takes it home with him, reporting it stolen. He begins to talk to the doll and brings it flowers. Eventually he falls hopelessly in love with the doll, and his yearning imagination brings it to life. Gradually the doll, the sole object of love in the young man's life, becomes more demanding and begins to dominate him. Too shy to buy her clothes, he steals a fur coat and a diamond bracelet. He neglects his job because he can't stand to be away from her. A pair of lovers in the apartment next door overhear him talking to the doll, and they steal the diamond bracelet while he is away. He protests, and the virile neighbor mocks him by caressing the doll. The night watchman shoots the intruder and then smashes the mannequin and throws the pieces into the river. When he returns to the apartment, he finds her waiting for him. *Watchmen. Neighbors. Loneliness. Insanity. Theft. Murder. Jealousy. Dummies. Stockholm. Fantasy.*
Note: Originally released in Sweden in 1962 as *Vaxdockan*.

THE DOLL HOUSE see **THE BRICK DOLLHOUSE**

THE DOLL THAT TOOK THE TOWN (Italy)   F6.1238
Peg Produzione. *Dist* Medallion Pictures. Nov **1965**. Sd; b&w. 35mm. 81 min.
Prod (see note) Lorenzo Pegoraro, Lucille Emerick. *Dir* Francesco Maselli. *Screenplay* Cesare Zavattini, Aggeo Sarioli, Francesco Maselli, Franco Bemporad. *Story* Franco Bemporad. *Photog* Armando Nannuzzi. *Film Ed* Mario Serandrei.
Cast: Virna Lisi *(Liliana)*, Haya Harareet *(Anna)*, Serge Reggiani *(Mario)*, Franco Fabrizi *(Aldo)*, Elisa Cegani, Vittorio Sanipoli, Antonio Cifariello.
Drama. Liliana, a beautiful young woman, is found unconscious, and it is generally believed that she had been robbed and assaulted. The newspapers in the city demand that the police call in a special detective squad to investigate, and Liliana becomes very popular in the course of the uproar. Receptions are held for her, and an ambitious agent helps her become a model and win a beauty contest. One of the three men arrested for the crime is the husband of Anna, a woman who refuses to believe that he is guilty. Liliana disregards all of Anna's appeals to her, and even claims to identify the man. Aldo, a photojournalist who has fallen in love with Liliana, begins to doubt her story, causing her to become perturbed. Liliana finally admits that the incident was a hoax, created purely

for publicity. *Police. Reporters. Detectives. Models. Theatrical agents. Photographers. Robbery. Hoaxes. Publicity. Beauty contests. Newspapers.*

Note: Released in Italy in 1957 as *La donna del giorno* at 90 min. Sources conflict in crediting the producer: Italian sources mention Lorenzo Pegoraro, Maryland license records list Lucille Emerick.

UN DOLLARO A TESTA see **NAVAJO JOE**

UN DOLLARO PER 7 VIGLIACCHI see **MADIGAN'S MILLIONS**

UN DOLLARO TRA I DENTI see **A STRANGER IN TOWN**

THE DOLLS see **BAMBOLE**

DOM S MEZONINOM see **HOUSE WITH AN ATTIC**

IL DOMINATORE DEI SETTE MARI see **SEVEN SEAS TO CALAIS**

DOMINIQUE   F6.1239
Dist Chancellor Films. Dec **1968**. Sd; b&w. 35mm. 64 min.
Sex film. At one of the monthly dinners of "The Daughters of Lesbos," the members listen to several narratives: Roberta tells of a man she met while intoxicated. He took advantage of her condition, drugged her with chloral hydrate, and forced her to submit to unnatural sex acts. Helga, who never has experienced sex with a man, tells of being seduced by an older woman at a summer camp. Maxine tells of a "flower child" she picked up hitchhiking, and of their lovemaking in the front seat of her car. Dominique then narrates her story: She was preparing for bed, unaware of a maintenance worker spying through her bedroom window. She stimulated herself while recalling her latest sexual experiences, and the voyeur, possessed by uncontrollable lust, came through the window and brutally raped her. The women capture the voyeur, tie him up, pull a cloth over his head, and vote to punish him. Dominique delicately arouses him by rubbing her naked body against his and then brutally castrates him with a razor-edged linoleum cutter. *Janitors. Hippies. Lesbianism. Drunkenness. Rape. Seduction. Voyeurism. Autoeroticism. Lust. Castration. Clubs. Tranquilizers.*

Note: Also known as *Daughters of Lesbos* and *Dominique in Daughters of Lesbos*.

DON-KIKHOT see **DON QUIXOTE**

DON MIKE see **CALIFORNIA**

DON QUIXOTE (U.S.S.R.)   F6.1240
Lenfilm. *Dist* Metro-Goldwyn-Mayer, Inc. 20 Jan **1961** [New York opening]. Sd; col (Sovcolor). 35mm (Sovscope). 110 min. [Also 106 min.]
Dir Grigoriy Kozintsev. *Dir English Vers* William De Lane Lea. *Screenplay* Yevgeniy Shvarts. *Photog* Andrey Moskvin. *Studio Photog* Apollinariy Dudko. *Asst Photog* Ionas Gritsyus. *Location Photog* E. Rozovskiy. *Art Dir* Yevgeniy Yeney. *Film Ed* Ye. Makhankova. *Mus* Kara Karayev. *Sd* Ilya Volk. *Asst Dir* V. Chebotaryov. *Cost & Makeup* I. Altman.
Cast: Nikolay Cherkasov *(Don Quixote)*, Yuriy Tolubeyev *(Sancho Panza)*, Serafima Birman *(housekeeper)*, L. Kasyanova *(Aldonsa)*, T. Agamirova *(Altisidora)*, Georgiy Vitsin *(Carrasco)*, B. Freyndlikh *(duke)*, L. Vertinskaya *(duchess)*, O. Vikland *(peasant girl)*, A. Beniaminov *(shepherd)*, S. Grigoryeva *(niece)*, V. Maksimov *(priest)*, V. Kolpakov *(barber)*, G. Volchek *(Maritornes)*, S. Tsomayev *(Andres)*, Vladimir Vasilyev, N. Anisimova, S. Batalova, I. Belskiy, V. Kovel, M. Korolyov, Zh. Letskiy, G. Malyshev, G. Osipenko, V. Osipov, A. Rozanov.
Voices for English Vers: Arnold Diamond *(Don Quixote)*, Howard Marion Crawford *(Sancho Panza)*, Bettina Dickson *(Altisidora)*, Peter Elliott, actor *(duke)*, Olive Gregg *(duchess)*, Robert Rietty *(Carrasco)*, Nikki Vandersil *(Aldonsa)*, Marianne Stone *(peasant girl)*.
Drama. Source: Miguel de Cervantes Saavedra, *El ingenioso hidalgo Don Quixote de la Mancha* (1605). In the 17th century, long after the age of knights in shining armor has passed, an elderly Spanish nobleman becomes so inspired by reading novels of heraldry that he resolves to become a knight-errant himself and take up arms in defense of the poor and the oppressed. He chooses Dulcinea del Toboso as the lady of his heart, and, as Don Quixote de la Mancha, he sets out with Sancho Panza, his good-natured if somewhat dimwitted and cowardly peasant squire. Don Quixote's passion for aiding humanity is interpreted as lunacy by all he meets, and he is constantly ridiculed and insulted. He mistakenly attacks wine bags, thinking them to be evil men in disguise, and he jousts with a flock of sheep. A duke summons Don Quixote to his castle to obtain amusement at the old man's expense. Altisidora, a lady-in-waiting, pretends to die of love when he spurns her in deference to his ideal lady, and he leaves, humiliated. Sancho Panza, too, is victimized when the duke makes him governor of an "island" completely surrounded by land. The two adventurers once more journey forth together, but Don Quixote's mind has been taxed by physical exhaustion and the cruelties inflicted upon him. He imagines that he tames a lion and mistakenly attacks a windmill which he

believes to be the evil enchanter Freston. Finally, he is beaten in a jousting match by a knight who in reality is an old friend who wants only to bring Don Quixote home. Once back in his own house, Don Quixote loses the will to live and lapses into a sleep of death, although an epilog asserts that his ideals will live on. *Nobility. Spanish. Peasants. Knighthood. Jousting. Don Quixote. Old age. Windmills. Age of Chivalry. Fantasy. Visions. Sheep.*

Note: Location scenes filmed in the Crimea. Released in the U.S.S.R. in 1957 as *Don-Kikhot.*

DONDI
F6.1241

Photoplay Associates. *Dist* Allied Artists. Mar **1961** [c16 Jan 1961; LP18007]. Sd; b&w. 35mm. 80 min. [Copyright length: 100 min.]

An Albert Zugsmith Production. *Prod-Writ* Albert Zugsmith, Gus Edson. *Assoc Prod* Robert Hill. *Dir* Albert Zugsmith. *Dir Photog* Carl Guthrie. *Art Dir* William Glasgow. *Set Decor* Rudy Butler. *Film Ed* Edward Curtiss. *Asst Film Ed* Jerome F. Brady. *Harmonica* Tommy Morgan. *Songs:* "Dondi," "Meadow in the Sky" Earl Schuman, Mort Garson. *Sung by* Patti Page. *Sd Ed* Del Harris, Marty Greco. *Rec Engr* Ralph Butler. *Asst Dir* William Calihan. *Asst Prod* Edward Curtiss. *Wardrobe* Roger J. Weinberg, Charles Arrico. *Makeup Artist* Stanley Campbell. *Dial Supv* Alon Cory. *Constr Supv* James West. *Prop* Ted Mossman.

Cast: David Janssen *(Dealey)*, Patti Page *(Liz)*, David Kory *(Dondi)*, Walter Winchell *(himself)*, Mickey Shaughnessy *(sergeant)*, Robert Strauss *(Sammy Boy)*, Arnold Stang *(Peewee)*, Louis Quinn *(Dimmy)*, Gale Gordon *(colonel)*, Dick Patterson *(Perky)*, Susan Kelly *(Lieutenant Calhoun)*, John Melfi *(Jo-Jo)*, Bonnie Scott *(Gladdy)*, William Wellman, Jr. *(Ted)*, Nola Thorp *(Candy)*, Joan Staley *(Sally)*.

Comedy-drama. Based on: Gus Edson and Irwin Hasen, "Dondi," a comic strip, distributed by the *Chicago Tribune–New York News* Syndicate. While stationed on the Italian border, six American soldiers befriend a 5-year-old orphan, nickname him Dondi, and make him their mascot. Their major problem becomes keeping the youngster's presence a secret from their tough top sergeant. When their outfit is transferred back to the States, little Dondi stows away on the troopship and is smuggled into New York. Before long he loses contact with his friends and has a series of adventures in Macy's department store and a run-in with a spurious blind beggar. Meanwhile, one of the G. I.'s, Dealey, and his singer-sweetheart, Liz, have launched a nationwide search for the little fellow. When the boy is finally found, he is detained by the immigration authorities for eventual deportation, but Dealey and Liz enlist the aid of columnist Walter Winchell and succeed in having Dondi declared an American citizen by act of Congress. Dealey and Liz then decide to marry and legally adopt Dondi. *Soldiers. Orphans. Italians. Stowaways. Singers. Immigrants. Columnists. Troop transports. Italy. New York City. Macy's (New York City). United States Congress.*

DONNA AND LISA
F6.1242

Dist Distribpix, Inc. 9 Apr **1969** [Champaign, Illinois, showing]. Sd; b&w. 35mm. 73 min.

Prod Leonard Kirtman, Larry Winters. *Dir-Writ* Larry Winters.

Cast: Lois Angel *(Lisa)*.

Melodrama. Lisa leaves the small midwestern town where she grew up and comes to the big city looking for fame and fortune. Lonely and destitute, she turns to Sam for companionship, finding in him a father substitute. Sam betrays Lisa's trust, however, when he arranges for her to "entertain" 10 of his friends. Lisa refuses, and she is consequently raped by each of the men. Afraid to leave Sam, who she knows is a pimp, Lisa turns to a psychiatrist for help. Sam introduces Lisa to Donna, who shrewdly recognizes that Lisa's brutal experiences with men have made her a latent lesbian. The women become lovers, and Lisa finds happiness with Donna. Lisa is still afraid to leave Sam, but she finally departs after Sam arranges for her to be whipped by a sadist with a carpet beater. Sam follows Lisa to a dark alley and stabs her to death. *Innocents. Pimps. Psychiatrists. Rape. Lesbianism. Sadism. Murder.*

LA DONNA DEI FARAONI see THE PHARAOHS' WOMAN

LA DONNA DEL GIORNO see THE DOLL THAT TOOK THE TOWN

DONNA DI VITA see LOLA

LA DONNA È DONNA see A WOMAN IS A WOMAN

LA DONNA NEL MONDO see WOMEN OF THE WORLD

LA DONNA SCIMMIA see THE APE WOMAN

DONNE ALLA FRONTIERA see THE TALL WOMEN

LE DONNE FACILI see LES BONNES FEMMES

DONNE, MITRA E DIAMANTI see MAN FROM COCODY

DONOVAN'S REEF
F6.1243

Paramount Pictures–John Ford Productions. *Dist* Paramount Pictures. 12 Jun **1963** [Philadelphia opening; c14 Jun 1963; LP25499]. Sd; col (Technicolor). 35mm. 109 min. [Copyright length: 112 min.]

A John Ford Production. *Prod-Dir* John Ford. *Screenplay* Frank Nugent, James Edward Grant. *Story* Edmund Beloin. *Photog* William Clothier. *Camera Op* Tom Morris. *Asst Camera* Robert Rhea. *2d Unit Photog* Brick Marquard. *2d Unit Camera Op* Ed Garvin. *Art Dir* Hal Pereira, Eddie Imazu. *Set Decor* Darrell Silvera. *Mus* Cyril Mockridge. *Cond* Irvin Talbot. *Orch* Leo Shuken, Jack Hayes. *Sd* Hugo Grenzbach. *Rec* Al Cuesta. *Boom Op* Bud Parman. *Asst Dir* Wingate Smith, Ed O'Fearna, Jack Barry, Dale Coleman. *Unit Prod Mgr* Don Robb. *Script Supv* Meta Stern. *Cost* Edith Head. *Wardrobe* Grace Harris, Shirlee Strahm, Frank Beetson, Sr., Frank Beetson, Jr. *Makeup* Frank Westmore, Gary Morris, William Reynolds, makeup, Web Overlander. *Hairstyles* Virginia Darcy, Naomi Cavin. *Sp Eff* Paul K. Lerpae. *Proc Photog* Farciot Edouart. *Dial Coach* Marvin Weldon. *Still Photog* G. E. Richardson. *Prop* Earl Olin, Wally Oliver. *Grip* Dominic Seminerio. *Gaffer* Chet Stafford.

Cast: John Wayne *(Michael "Guns" Donovan)*, Lee Marvin *(Aloysius "Boats" Gilhooley)*, Jack Warden *(Doc Dedham)*, Elizabeth Allen *(Amelia Dedham)*, Dick Foran *(Australian Navy officer)*, Cesar Romero *(Marquis André de Lage)*, Dorothy Lamour *(Fleur)*, Jacqueline Malouf *(Lelani)*, Mike Mazurki *(Sergeant Menkowicz)*, Marcel Dalio *(Father Cluzeot)*, Jon Fong *(Mr. Eu)*, Cherylene Lee *(Sally)*, Tim Stafford *(Luki)*, Carmen Estrabeau *(Sister Gabrielle)*, Yvonne Peattie *(Sister Matthew)*, Frank Baker *(Captain Martin)*, Patrick Wayne *(Australian Navy lieutenant)*, Edgar Buchanan *(Boston notary)*, Charles Seel *(Grand Uncle Sedley Atterbury)*, Chuck Roberson *(Festus)*, Mae Marsh, Major Sam Harris *(members of family council)*, Cliff Lyons *(officer)*.

Comedy. Based on original material by: James Albert Michener. Just off the South Sea island of Haleakoloha, World War II hero "Boats" Gilhooley jumps ship and swims ashore in search of his Navy buddy, "Guns" Donovan. Each year on their birthdays (December 7), the two men engage in a barroom brawl; this year's ritual takes place in Donovan's Reef, a tavern owned by Guns. The men nearly destroy the place before the fight is halted by island physician Doc Dedham, the third member of the naval trio. Meanwhile, Dedham's daughter, Amelia, is on her way to Haleakoloha from Boston, hoping to prevent her father, whom she has never seen, from inheriting a huge family fortune. When the three friends learn of the visit, they arrange for Guns to temporarily adopt the doctor's three halfcaste children, assuming that Amelia would never accept them as brothers and sisters, even though their late mother was an island princess. Their fears about Amelia are well-founded; although she likes the children, her relationship with Guns and Gilhooley is stormy. Island governor André de Lage attempts to court Amelia—largely for her money—but he is rebuffed. When she defeats Guns in a swimming race after a water-skiing expedition, she begins to enjoy his company. Then she learns that the children belong to her father, blames Guns for depriving them of their natural home, and walks out on him. Reconciliation attempts are interrupted when Guns and Gilhooley take on a barroom full of Australian sailors in a huge free-for-all. In the end, Amelia decides to marry Guns and remain on Haleakoloha; Gilhooley finally agrees to marry his longtime girl friend, Fleur, and a business transaction between the two brawling buddies turns the tavern into Gilhooley's Reef. *War heroes. Physicians. Halfcastes. Territorial governors. Children. Adoption. Filial relations. Duplicity. Inheritance. Water skiing. Bars. Birthdays. World War II. South Sea Islands. United States Navy. Australia—Navy.*

Note: Location scenes filmed in Kauai, Hawaii.

DON'T BOTHER TO KNOCK see WHY BOTHER TO KNOCK

DON'T CALL ME A CON MAN (Japan)
F6.1244

Toho Co. 21 Dec **1966** [Los Angeles opening]. Sd; col (Eastman Color). 35mm (Tohoscope). 109 min.

Dir Kengo Furusawa. *Screenplay* Ryozo Kasahara, Yasuo Tanami. *Photog* Tadashi Iimura.

Cast: Hitoshi Ueki *(reporter)*, Reiko Dan, Fubuki Koshiji, Kei Tani, Hajime Hana.

Crime farce. When he becomes involved with a counterfeiting ring, a reporter discovers Adolf Hitler, alive and well, commanding from the South Pacific a garrison producing missiles with which to destroy mankind. *Reporters. Counterfeiters. Megalomania. Missiles. Pacific Ocean. Adolf Hitler.*

Note: Released in Japan in 1966 as *Daiboken.*

DON'T DRINK THE WATER
F6.1245

Dist Avco Embassy Pictures. 11 Nov **1969** [New York opening]. Sd; col (Movielab). 35mm. 98 min. *MPAA rating* G.

Pres by Joseph E. Levine. A Jack Rollins–Charles H. Joffe Production. *Prod* Charles H. Joffe. *Exec Prod* Joseph E. Levine. *Assoc Prod* Jack Grossberg. *Dir*

Howard Morris. *Screenplay* R. S. Allen, Harvey Bullock. *Photog* Harvey Genkins. *Art Dir* Robert Gundlach. *Main Titl* Richard Williams. *Film Ed* Ralph Rosenblum. *Mus & Titl Song* Pat Williams. *Sd* William Roberts, sd. *Asst Dir* Louis A. Stroller. *Unit Mgr* Martin Danzig. *Cost* Gene Coffin.

Cast: Jackie Gleason *(Walter Hollander)*, Estelle Parsons *(Marion Hollander)*, Ted Bessell *(Axel Magee)*, Joan Delaney *(Susan Hollander)*, Michael Constantine *(Krojack)*, Howard St. John *(Ambassador Magee)*, Danny Meehan *(Kilroy)*, Richard Libertini *(Father Drobney)*, Pierre Olaf *(chef)*, Avery Schreiber *(sultan)*, Philip Leeds *(Sam)*, Mark Gordon *(Mirik)*, Dwayne Early *(Donald)*, Joan Murphy *(airline clerk)*, Martin Danzig *(Mishkin)*, Rene Constantineau *(organ grinder)*, Howard Morris *(getaway pilot)*.

Comedy. Source: Woody Allen, *Don't Drink the Water* (New York opening: 17 Nov 1966). Returning from a European tour, Newark caterer Walter Hollander, wife Marion, and daughter Susan, are passengers on a hijacked plane which lands in Communist Vulgaria. When the family photographs the Vulgarian airport, Krojack, the head of the Vulgarian secret police, suspects espionage and attempts to arrest them. The tourists, however, are granted asylum in the American embassy, temporarily supervised by Axel Magee, son of the ambassador. There the Hollanders meet mad Father Drobney, who for 6 years has enjoyed sanctuary within the consulate's confines. Although the United States attempts to rescue the family by repatriating Vulgarian agent Grey Fox, he commits suicide before an exchange can be negotiated. When middle-aged student agitators picket and bomb the embassy, Hollander, Marion, and Susan don the robes of a visiting sultan and his harem and rush to a rescue point. They are met by a senile American pilot who has spent 6 years awaiting the prelate's escape. Discovering room for only two on board the craft, Susan happily bids her parents farewell, and secures diplomatic immunity by marrying Magee. *Americans in foreign countries. Tourists. Caterers. Secret police. Priests. Diplomats. Hijackers. Students. Harems. Cold war. Communism. Espionage. Vacations. Demonstrations. Airfields. Sanctuaries. Bombs. Newark (New Jersey). United States—State Department. Chases.*

Note: Location scenes filmed in Miami, Florida, and Quebec, Canada.

DON'T JUST LAY THERE

F6.1246

Mattis-Pine Productions. *Dist* Fellatio Films, Able Film Co. 24 Sep **1970** [Asheville, North Carolina, opening]. Sd; col (Eastmancolor). 35mm. 80 min. [Pressbook length: 90 min.]

Exec Prod Jack E. Mattis. *Dir-Writ* Phillip Pine, dir. *Story* Kym Allison. *Cinematog* Ernie Beauchemin, Clark Johnson. *Asst Camera* Ed London. *Lighting* Dan Hall. *Orig Mus* Steve Margulies. *Orig Mus Comp, Arr & Cond* Martin Martin. *Featuring* The Humpers. *Freeway Song* Jack E. Mattis, Lilo Mattis. *Vocals by* Prickly Heat. *Sd Engr & Ed* Clark Johnson. *Script Clerk* Rick. *Grip & Standby Nurse* Ginger Hurts.

Cast: Weggener *(Sloan)*, Ron Dyer *(Rock)*, Bridget *(Billie)*, Barbara Caron *(Rusty)*, Mary Jane Shippen *(Eve)*, Fern Holbrook *(Lori)*, Jon Mattisse *(Creighton)*, Kathy Hilton *(Baller)*, Diane Lewis *(Smokey)*.

Melodrama. Billie Starr, a photographer of pornography, receives an assignment from an unknown customer to photograph an astrology-oriented sex layout at a secluded mountain cabin. Billie gathers her models and assistant for the day's outing: Eve is Billie's lesbian playmate; Sloan, Billie's assistant, is a voyeur and a drug user; and Rock is a handsome male model. Rusty, a stripper, and Lori, a black model, also come along. Billie photographs her friends engaging in various sex acts outdoors, and later the group returns to the cabin for a party. The party becomes wild and Rusty suddenly falls dead. A tape recorded message from their host, Z. Odiac, informs them that they will all die. Members of the group frantically try to escape; failing this, they indulge in frantic sex acts among themselves. *Photographers. Models. Drug addicts. Negroes. Lesbianism. Voyeurism. Group sex. Murder. Pornography. Astrology.*

DON'T JUST STAND THERE!

F6.1247

Universal Pictures. 1 May **1968** [Providence, Rhode Island, opening; c4 May 1968; LP38826]. Sd (Westrex); col (Technicolor). 35mm (Techniscope). 99 min.

Prod Stan Margulies. *Dir* Ron Winston. *Screenplay* Charles Williams. *Dir Photog* Milton Krasner. *Art Dir* Alexander Golitzen, William D. DeCinces. *Set Decor* John McCarthy, George Milo. *Film Ed* Richard Bracken. *Mus* Nick Perito. *Titl Song* Nick Perito, Ray Charles. *Sung by* Ray Charles Singers. *Mus Supv* Joseph Gershenson. *Sd* Waldon O. Watson, David H. Moriarty. *Asst Dir* Victor Vallejo, Kenny Williams. *Unit Prod Mgr* Robert E. Larson. *Gowns Dsgn* Jean Louis. *Makeup* Bud Westmore. *Hairstyles* Larry Germain.

Cast: Robert Wagner *(Lawrence Colby)*, Mary Tyler Moore *(Martine Randall)*, Glynis Johns *(Sabine Manning)*, Harvey Korman *(Merriman Dudley)*, Barbara Rhoades *(Kendall Flanagan)*, Vincent Beck *(painter)*, Joseph Perry *(Jean-Jacques)*, Stuart Margolin *(Remy)*, Emile Genest *(Henri)*, David Mauro *(Jules)*, Penny Santon *(Renee)*, Joseph Bernard *(police inspector)*, Herbert Voland *(Moffat)*, Richard Angarola *(Pascal Decaux)*, Otis Young *(Bill Elkins)*, Willie Koopman *(Gabrielle)*, Bern Hoffman, Gladys Holland.

Crime comedy. Source: Charles Williams, *The Wrong Venus* (New York, 1966). In exchange for helping writer-adventurer Lawrence Colby smuggle 300 watch parts into Paris from Switzerland, Martine Randall asks Colby to help solve a complicated situation involving her friend Sabine Manning, a well-known author of sex novels. Since Sabine is on a cruise in the Aegean Sea with her latest lover, her business manager, Merriman Dudley, had hired ghostwriter Kendall Flanagan to finish Sabine's novel, but Kendall has been kidnaped by gangsters who believe that she is Sabine. Posing as a gangster, Colby arranges to see Kendall before the ransom is paid. Kendall then uses karate to dispose of her abductors, and she and Colby flee to the woods. Colby next discovers that Kendall is wanted by the French police for the murder of a gangster whom Kendall insists was killed by French gunman Pascal Decaux. Kendall and Colby eventually make their way back to Sabine's Paris house to continue work on the novel, but Sabine returns and announces that she will no longer write about sex. Colby and Martine finally convince her, however, to complete the novel under her pen name and write scholarly works under her real name. Decaux suddenly arrives, and Colby knocks him out. In the end, the hoodlums are sent to jail, Kendall leaves for the United States, Sabine returns to the Aegean, and Colby and Martine book seats on a flight to the island of Rhodes. *Novelists. Business managers. Ghostwriters. Gangsters. French. Smuggling. Kidnaping. Mistaken identity. Imposture. Pornography. Karate. Paris.*

DON'T KNOCK THE TWIST

F6.1248

Four Leaf Productions. *Dist* Columbia Pictures. 11 Apr **1962** [New York opening; c1 Apr 1962; LP22251]. Sd (Westrex); b&w. 35mm. 87 min.

Prod Sam Katzman. *Co-prod* Kal Mann. *Dir* Oscar Rudolph. *Writ* James B. Gordon. *Dir Photog* Gordon Avil. *Camera Op* Loyal Griggs. *Asst Camera* Arnold Rich. *Art Dir* Don Ament. *Set Decor* Sidney Clifford. *Film Ed* Jerome Thoms. *Mus Supv* Fred Karger. *Titl Song* Kal Mann, Dave Appell. *Sung by* Chubby Checker. *Songs:* "The Bristol Stomp," "Do the New Continental" Kal Mann, Dave Appell. *Sung by* The Dovells. *Song:* "Let's Twist à la Paloma" Kal Mann. *Sung by* Chubby Checker. *Song:* "Little Altar Boy" Howlett Smith. *Sung by* Vic Dana. *Song:* "Yesiree" writ & sung by Linda Scott. *Song:* "Duke of Earl" Eugene Dixon, Bernice Williams, Earl Edwards. *Sung by* Gene Chandler. *Song:* "Mash Potato Time" Kal Mann, Bernie Lowe. *Song:* "Salome Twist" Robert E. Kent, Fred Karger. *Choreog* Hal Belfer. *Sd Supv* Charles J. Rice. *Sd* Josh Westmoreland. *Rec* Harold Lee. *Boom Op* Doug Grant. *Asst Dir* Sam Nelson, Norman August. *Script Supv* Sheila Lynch. *Men's Cost* Gene Martin. *Women's Cost* Edna Taylor. *Makeup* Joseph Di Bella. *Hairstyles* La Rue Matheron. *Ch Grip* Pat Sutherland. *Prop Master* Ernest Graber. *Gaffer* Howard Robertson. *Dial Dir* Tim Sullivan.

Cast: Chubby Checker *(himself)*, Gene Chandler *(The Duke of Earl)*, Vic Dana *(himself)*, Linda Scott *(herself)*, The Carroll Brothers, The Dovells *(themselves)*, Lang Jeffries *(Ted Haver)*, Mari Blanchard *(Dulcie Corbin)*, Georgine Darcy *(Madge Albright)*, Stephen Preston *(Billy Albright)*, Barbara Morrison *(Mrs. Morrison)*, Nydia Westman *(dressmaker)*, James Chandler *(Joe Albright)*, Elizabeth Harrower *(Ruth Emerson)*, Hortense Petra *(Mrs. Kay)*, Frank Albertson *(Herb Walcott)*, Viola Harris *(fashion editor)*, Peter Dawson *(Frank Emerson)*, David Landfield *(director)*, Tim Sullivan *(Mr. Fullerton)*, Ralph Montgomery *(reporter)*.

Comedy with music. New York television executive Ted Haver is ordered to put together a twist spectacular to precede a rival network's show by 2 weeks. He turns to his friend Chubby Checker, and they line up other stars including Vic Dana, Gene Chandler, Linda Scott, The Carroll Brothers, and The Dovells. While on a weekend in the country with his fiancée, Dulcie Corbin, a greedy fashion designer, Ted discovers Madge Albright twisting with her brother Billy, rehearsing for a weekly dance show they put on to raise money for an orphanage's summer camp. Disenchanted with Dulcie's mercenary attitude, Ted is attracted to Madge. When he hires Madge to do the "Salome Twist" on the spectacular, the jealous Dulcie designs an abbreviated costume for the young girl and tips off a hostile newspaper, which calls for censorship and nearly succeeds in halting the show. But Madge's followers from the Orphans' Summer Camp rally to her support, and the TV show goes on to great success. *Additional songs:* "Twistin'," "I Love To Twist," "Do the Fly With Me," "Slow Twist" (Chubby Checker); "Bo Diddley" (Carroll Brothers). *Musicians. Couturiers. Television producers. Dancers. Singers. Jealousy. Ambition. Censorship. Adolescence. Television. Rock and roll. Orphanages. New York City. Twist (dance).*

Note: This film is a sequel to *Twist Around the Clock*, q. v.

DON'T LOOK BACK

F6.1249

Leacock Pennebaker Inc. 17 May **1967** [San Francisco opening; c2 Mar 1967; MU7789]. Sd; b&w. 35mm (see note). 96 min.

A Richard Leacock—Donn Alan Pennebaker Production. *Prod* Albert Grossman, John Court. *A Film by* D. A. Pennebaker. *Photog* D. A. Pennebaker, Jones Alk, Howard Alk. *Film Ed* D. A. Pennebaker. *Songs:* "The

Times They Are A-Changin','" "Gates of Eden," "It's Alright Ma (I'm Only Bleeding),'" "The Lonesome Death of Hattie Carroll," "Don't Think Twice, It's All Right," "It's All Over Now, Baby Blue," "Subterranean Homesick Blues" comp & sung by Bob Dylan. *Songs: "Percy's Song," "Love Is Just a Four-Letter Word"* comp by Bob Dylan. *Sung by* Joan Baez. *Song: "To Sing for You"* comp & sung by Donovan. *Mus Rec* Robert Van Dyke.

With: Bob Dylan, Joan Baez, Donovan, Alan Price, Albert Grossman, Bob Neuwirth, Tito Burns, Derroll Adams, Allen Ginsberg, Horace Judson.

Documentary. The film traces folksinger Bob Dylan's concert tour of England in 1965 from his first public appearance in Sheffield to his final concert in Albert Hall. In London, Dylan's manager, Albert Grossman, has a heated argument with a hotel manager because of noise coming from Dylan's suite. Another tense moment occurs at a party attended by folksinger Joan Baez and Donovan, Dylan's British rival, when a drunken guest hurls a glass out of a window. There are also views of Dylan performing, composing, giving press interviews (in one of them he insults a reporter), negotiating contracts, and mingling with his fans. *Singers. Folk music. Sheffield (England). London. Bob Dylan. Royal Albert Hall.*

Note: Shot in 16mm.

DON'T LOOK NOW (France/Great Britain)   **F6.1250**

Les Films Corona–Lowndes Productions. *Dist* Buena Vista Distribution Co. 16 Feb **1969** [New York opening]. Sd; col (Eastman Color). 35mm (Panavision). 116 min. *MPAA rating* G.

Prod Robert Dorfmann. *Dir-Writ* Gérard Oury. *Dial* Georges Tabet, André Tabet. *Adapt* Gérard Oury, Marcel Jullian, Danièle Thompson. *Photog* Claude Renoir. *Art Dir* Jean André. *Film Ed* Albert Jurgenson. *Mus* Georges Auric. *"Symphonie Fantastique"* Hector Berlioz. *Song: "Tea for Two"* Vincent Youmans, Irving Caesar. *Sd* Antoine Bonfanti, Urbain Loiseau. *Asst Dir* Lucile Costa, Serge Vallin, Gérard Guérin, Jean-Claude Lemonnier. *Prod Mgr* Georges Valon, Pierre Saint-Blancat.

Cast: Terry-Thomas *(Reginald)*, Bourvil *(Augustin Bouvet)*, Louis de Funès *(Stanislaus Lefort)*, Claudio Brook *(Peter Cunningham)*, Marie Dubois *(Juliette)*, Benno Sterzenbach *(Colonel Achbach)*, Colette Brosset *(Madame Germaine)*, Andréa Parisy *(Sister Marie-Odile)*, Mike Marshall *(Alan MacIntosh)*, Mary Marquet *(Mother Superior)*, Pierre Bertin *(Punch and Judy operator)*, Sieghardt Rupp, Hans Meyer, Rudy Lenoir, Paul Préboist, Peter Jacob, Danièle Thompson.

War farce. "Tea for Two," a British bomber, is shot down over Nazi-occupied Paris. Before bailing out, its crew plans a reunion in the Parisian Turkish baths, where the identifying signal will be a whistled rendition of "Tea for Two." Squadron leader Reginald plunges into the seal pond of the zoo; Peter lands atop the scaffold of housepainter Augustin, splattering a Nazi below; and Alan parachutes to the roof of the Paris opera. To elude pursuing Nazis, Peter sequesters himself in the apartment of Ginette, a stranger with whom he feigns a marital dispute, while Alan represents himself as a harpist, the protege of harried Parisian conductor Stanislaus. Anticipating difficulties in attending the rendezvous, the English airmen persuade their French benefactors, Augustin and Stanislaus, to meet Reginald in the Turkish baths. There an escape to England is planned. Donning Nazi uniforms, Reginald and Augustin attend a celebration at the opera, where they discover Alan disguised as a buxom peasant girl. When the performance is interrupted by a bomb blast, Stanislaus, Augustin, Reginald, and Alan flee through the Paris sewers, with the lustful Germans, inflamed by the presumed peasant, in hot pursuit. They arrive at the train station, however, too late to accompany the departing Peter and Ginette. Aboard the train Peter is recognized as an Englishman and arrested, while Augustin and Stanislaus are captured by the border patrol. During the trio's interrogation they are rescued by Reginald and Alan, who arrive in Nazi headquarters encased in wine casks on a cart driven by Sister Marie-Odile. Having set the German wine cellar ablaze, the company departs in two gliders. Their escape is unwittingly abetted by a cross-eyed German, who shoots down the Nazi plane pursuing them. *Air pilots. Painters. Orchestra conductors. Nuns. Nazis. France—History—German occupation 1940–45. Disguise. Rescue. Zoos. Bombers. World War II. Paris. Great Britain—Royal Air Force. Germany—Army. Chases.*

Note: Location scenes filmed in Paris and Mende, France. Opened in Paris in Dec 1966 as *La grande vadrouille*; running time: 125 min. Opened in London in Jun 1968 as *Don't Look Now ... We're Being Shot At*; running time: 116 min.

DON'T LOOK NOW ... WE'RE BEING SHOT AT *see* **DON'T LOOK NOW**

DON'T MAKE WAVES   **F6.1251**

Filmways, Inc.–Reynard Productions. *Dist* Metro-Goldwyn-Mayer, Inc. 20 Jun **1967** [New York opening; c16 May 1967; LP34227]. Sd (Westrex); col (Metrocolor). 35mm (Panavision). 97 min.

A Martin Ransohoff Production. *Prod* John Calley, Martin Ransohoff. *Assoc Prod* Julian Bercovici. *Dir* Alexander Mackendrick. *Dir Skydiving Seq* Leigh Hunt. *Screenplay* Ira Wallach, George Kirgo. *Adapt* Maurice Richlin. *Dir Photog* Philip Lathrop. *Photog Skydiving Seq* Bob Buquor. *Art Dir* George W. Davis, Edward Carfagno. *Set Decor* Henry Grace, Charles S. Thompson. *Film Ed* Rita Roland, Thomas Stanford. *Mus Comp & Cond by* Vic Mizzy. *Song: "Don't Make Waves"* Jim McGuinn, Chris Hillman. *Perf by* The Byrds. *Rec Supv* Franklin Milton. *Asst Dir* Carl Beringer, Eric Von Stroheim, Jr. *Prod Mgr* Edward Woehler. *Wardrobe* Donfeld. *Makeup* William Tuttle. *Hairstyles* Sydney Guilaroff. *Tech Adv* Eduardo Tirella.

Cast: Tony Curtis *(Carlo Cofield)*, Claudia Cardinale *(Laura Califatti)*, Sharon Tate *(Malibu)*, Robert Webber *(Rod Prescott)*, Joanna Barnes *(Diane Prescott)*, David Draper *(Harry Hollard)*, Mort Sahl *(Sam Lingonberry)*, Dub Taylor *(electrician)*, Jim Backus *(himself)*, Henny Backus *(herself)*, Edgar Bergen *(Madame Lavinia)*, Ann Elder *(Millie Gunder)*, Chester Yorton *(Ted Gunder)*, Reg Lewis *(Monster)*, Marc London *(Fred Barker)*, Douglas Henderson *(Henderson)*, Sarah Selby *(Ethyl)*, Mary Grace Canfield *(seamstress)*, Julie Payne *(Helen)*, Holly Haze *(Myrna)*, Paul Barselow *(pilot)*, George Tyne, David Fresco, Gilbert Green *(newspapermen)*, Eduardo Tirella *(decorator)*.

Comedy. Source: Ira Wallach, *Muscle Beach* (Boston, 1959). When impulsive and reckless Laura Califatti totally wrecks a sports car belonging to tourist Carlo Cofield, she invites the distraught young man to spend the night on the couch of her Malibu Beach apartment. But he is thrown out by Laura's "patron," Rod Prescott, a pompous businessman who runs a swimming pool company owned by his wife. After sleeping on the beach, Carlo goes for a swim, nearly drowns, and is saved by a seductive surfer-skydiver, Malibu, who gives him mouth-to-mouth resuscitation. Captivated by the girl, Carlo decides to settle down in the area. Since he has failed to get any compensation for his sports car, he uses his knowledge of Rod's indiscreet affair with Laura to get a lucrative job as a pool salesman. Then, to further his romance with Malibu, Carlo bribes an astrologist, Madame Lavinia, into telling Malibu's body-builder boyfriend, Harry, that sex is bad for his physique. The romantic entanglements become even more involved when Rod's wife, Diane, announces that she is suing for divorce, naming Laura as corespondent. Eventually, all six participants become trapped in Carlo's cliffside house during a rainstorm. As it tips over and slides down the incline to the muddy beach below, Malibu is reunited with the muscle-bound Harry, Diane agrees to drop her divorce proceedings, and Laura and Carlo discover they are made for each other. *Tourists. Mistresses. Salesmen. Businessmen. Surfers. Skydivers. Body-builders. Astrologers. Infidelity. Divorce. Blackmail. Employment. Landslides. Swimming pools. Malibu (California). Automobile accidents.*

Note: Location scenes filmed in Southern California.

DON'T PUSH ME   **F6.1252**

Jun **1970** [Los Angeles showing]. Sd; b&w? 35mm? 65 min.

Prod Brent Brown. *Screenplay* Jack Harrell, writ, Jack Pierre.

Cast: Brian Reynolds *(David)*.

Drama. David leaves the Victorian atmosphere of his family's home in St. Louis after his father discovers that he is a homosexual. He goes to Los Angeles, where he is forced to find employment as a model through the advertisements in the *Los Angeles Free Press*. Through his jobs David gets to see many parts of the Los Angeles homosexual community. *Models. Family life. Male homosexuality. Newspapers—Underground. Saint Louis (Missouri). Los Angeles.*

DON'T RAISE THE BRIDGE, LOWER THE RIVER (Great Britain)   **F6.1253**

Walter Shenson Films. *Dist* Columbia Pictures. 19 Jun **1968** [Los Angeles opening; c31 Dec 1967; LP35730]. Sd (Westrex); col (Technicolor). 35mm. 99 min.

A Walter Shenson Production. *Prod* Walter Shenson. *Assoc Prod* Leon Becker. *Dir* Jerry Paris. *Screenplay* Max Wilk. *Dir Photog* Otto Heller. *Camera Op* Godfrey Godar. *Art Dir* John Howell. *Set Dresser* Pamela Cornell. *Film Ed* Bill Lenny. *Titl Song Lyr* Hal Shaper. *Sung by* Danny Street. *Mus Comp & Cond* David Whitaker. *Choreog* Leo Kharibian. *Sd Ed* Jeanne Henderson. *Sd Rec* Ken Ritchie, Nolan Roberts. *Asst Dir* Doug Hermes. *Prod Mgr* Basil Rayburn. *Cont* Eileen Head. *Miss Pearce's Wardrobe Dsgn* Maxine Leighton. *Wardrobe Coörd* Gabriella Falk. *Wardrobe* Jean Fairlie, Charles Guerin. *Makeup* Harry Frampton, Benny Royston, Joan Telfer.

Cast: Jerry Lewis *(George Lester)*, Terry-Thomas *(H. William Homer)*, Jacqueline Pearce *(Pamela Lester)*, Bernard Cribbins *(Fred Davies)*, Patricia Routledge *(Lucille Beatty)*, Nicholas Parsons *(Dudley Heath)*, Michael Bates *(Dr. Spink)*, Colin Gordon *(Mr. Hartford)*, John Bluthal *(Dr. Pinto)*, Sandra Caron *(Pinto's nurse)*, Margaret Nolan *(Spink's nurse)*, Pippa Benedict *(Fern Averback)*, Harold Goodwin *(Six-Eyes Wiener)*, Richard Montez *(Arab)*, Henry Soskin *(bearded Arab)*, Al Mancini *(Portuguese chauffeur)*, John Moore, actor *(Digby)*, John Barrard *(zebra man)*, Robert Lee *(Bruce)*, Francisca Tu *(Chinese telephonist)*, Colin Douglas *(barman)*, Alexandra Dane *(masseuse)*, Nike Arrighi *(Portuguese waitress)*, Tatsuo Susuki *(judo man)*, Christine Pryor *(manicurist)*, Molly Peters *(Heath's secretary)*, Jerry Paris *(baseball umpire)*.

Comedy. Source: Max Wilk, *Don't Raise the Bridge, Lower the River* (New York, 1960). After his latest get-rich-quick scheme fails, George Lester, an American living in London, is threatened with divorce by his British wife, Pamela. In a misguided attempt to demonstrate that he is willing to settle down, George converts his wife's country manor house into a Chinese discotheque while she is abroad. She returns with a pompous suitor, Dudley Heath, and demands that her home be restored, so George rekindles his friendship with H. William Homer, a notorious con man. Together, they concoct a scheme to steal Dudley's blueprints for a high-speed electronic oil drill and sell them to some Arabs. All goes well until George catches the mumps and is unable to transport the plans to Homer in Lisbon. Desperate, George devises a means of hiding the microfilmed blueprints in the teeth of unsuspecting airline steward Fred Davies. Homer contacts Lisbon dentist Dr. Pinto to extract the blueprints, but Pinto doublecrosses them. George then flies to Lisbon, followed by a suspicious Pamela. Once there, George grabs the plans and, after a series of chases, he arrives safely at the airport. Only when he is finally aboard a London-bound plane does Pamela tell George that Dudley's electronic drill is defective. Admitting defeat, George agrees to give up his wild ideas and live a peaceful life—until Homer shows up with a fool-proof, get-rich-quick idea. *Americans in foreign countries. Fortune hunters. Confidence men. Oilmen. Arabs. Airline stewards. Dentists. Divorce. Marriage. Theft. Smuggling. Perfidy. Discotheques. Microfilm. Lisbon.*

Note: Released in Great Britain in Sep 1968.

DON'T SCREAM, DORIS MAYS! *see* **DAY OF THE NIGHTMARE**

DON'T TEMPT THE DEVIL (France/Italy)   F6.1254

Méditerranée Cinéma–Flora Film–Mizar Film. *Dist* United Motion Picture Organization. 19 Apr **1964** [New York opening]. Sd; b&w. 35mm (Franscope). 106 min.

Prod Georges Cheyko. *Dir* Christian-Jaque. *Dial (see note)* Henri Jeanson, Umberto Orsini. *Adapt* Paul Andréota, Christian-Jaque, Henri Jeanson. *Photog* Armand Thirard. *Art Dir* Jean Mandaroux. *Film Ed* Jacques Desagneau. *Mus* Georges Garvarentz. *Sd* William Sivel. *Prod Mgr* Ludmilla Goulian. *Miss Vlady's Wardrobe* Jacques Helm.

Cast: Marina Vlady *(Catherine Dupré)*, Bourvil *(Magistrat Gaudet)*, Virna Lisi *(Gina Bianchi)*, Pierre Brasseur *(Cassidi)*, José-Luis de Vilallonga *(Paul Dupré)*, Umberto Orsini *(Philliet)*, Mony Dalmès *(Madame)*, Jacques Monod *(judge)*, Jacques Mauclair *(witness)*, Robert Vidalin, François Darbon, Gilbert Gil.

Crime melodrama. Source: Jean Laborde, *Les bonnes causes* (Paris, 1960). Cardiac patient Paul Dupré receives his regular injection from his nurse, Gina Bianchi, then collapses and dies. As Gina runs to telephone the doctor, Catherine, Dupré's wife, enters and attempts to seize the vial of medicine. The two women fight briefly, and the vial is crushed. Catherine summons lawyer Cassidi, friend of her late husband and her former lover. She accuses Gina of Dupré's murder, but Gina denies all guilt, including the charge that she was Dupré's mistress. Magistrate Gaudet interrogates Gina and finds circumstantial evidence against her. Laboratory tests show that the material injected—different from what Dupré should have received—was fatal. Catherine and Cassidi now resume their affair, and she confides to him that she herself contrived the murder because her husband was about to divorce her and marry Gina. Cassidi is aghast but is hopelessly in love and agrees to help her. The wily Gaudet senses that Catherine is the guilty one. He resigns from the case and with the help of lawyer Philliet works and even testifies for Gina in court, but nevertheless she is found guilty and sentenced to a jail term. After the trial, Cassidi tries to reach Catherine and learns she is having an affair with another, now that she no longer needs him. He arranges for justice to triumph, with Catherine winding up behind bars and Gina freed. *Nurses. Mistresses. Magistrates. Lawyers. Murder. Marriage. Heart disease. Circumstantial evidence. Trials. Infidelity.*

Note: Paris opening: Apr 1963 as *Les bonnes causes;* running times: 120 and 115 min. Rome opening: Aug 1963 as *Il delitto Dupré;* running time: 105 min. Some U. S. sources credit Orsini as coauthor of screenplay; French and Italian sources credit only Jeanson, Andréota, and Christian-Jaque.

DON'T TOUCH MY SISTER *see* **THE GLASS CAGE**

DON'T WORRY, WE'LL THINK OF A TITLE   F6.1255

Courageous Films–Kam Productions. *Dist* United Artists. May **1966** [c30 Mar 1966; LP32501]. Sd; b&w. 35mm. 83 min.

Prod Morey Amsterdam. *Exec Prod* Aubrey Schenck. *Assoc Prod* Hal Klein. *Dir* Harmon Jones. *Story & Screenplay* John Hart, Morey Amsterdam. *Adapt* George Schenck, William Marks. *Photog* Brick Marquard. *Art Dir* Rolland M.

Brooks, Howard Hollander. *Set Decor* Jerry Welch. *Film Ed* Robert C. Jones. *Mus* Richard La Salle. *Sd* Brad Trask, Wade Smith. *Asst Dir* Read Killgore, C. M. Florance. *Script Supv* Marge Mullen. *Wardrobe* Bob Spencer, Marge Makau. *Makeup* Gus Norin. *Hairstyles* Elaine Stone. *Sp Eff* Frank De Marco. *Prop Master* Glenn Rose. *Still Photog* Jack Harris, still photog.

Cast: Morey Amsterdam *(Charlie)*, Rose Marie *(Annie)*, Richard Deacon *(Mr. Travis/police chief)*, Tim Herbert *(Seed/Samu)*, Jackie Heller *(Mr. Big)*, Joey Adams, Andy Albin *(guys)*, Michael Ford *(Jim Holliston)*, January Jones *(Magda Anders)*, Carmen Phillips *(Olga)*, Henry Corden *(Lerowski)*, Peggy Mondo *(fat lady)*, Percy Helton *(fat man)*, LaRue Farlow *(The Lover)*, Moe Howard *(Mr. Raines)*, Yau Shan Tung *(Chinese girl)*, Arline Hunter, Annazette, Gregg Amsterdam *(students)*, Darryl Vaughan *(athlete)*, Nick Adams, Steve Allen, Cliff Arquette, Milton Berle, Carl Reiner, Irene Ryan, Danny Thomas, Forrest Tucker, Maxie Rosenbloom *(guest stars)*.

Comedy. After Charlie, a bumbling cook, and Annie, a wise-cracking waitress, lose their jobs at the Daredevil Diner, they hitchhike to Updike University to help run a bookshop inherited by their friend Magda, another former waitress at the diner. Unknown to Charlie, a group of foreign spies have mistaken him for a missing cosmonaut who has defected with invaluable spaceflight data. Before long, the bookshop is overrun with secret agents, counter-agents, security personnel attached to a space conclave, and the Updike police force. At the same time, a pair of robbers take advantage of the confusion and attempt to tunnel their way into an adjoining bank. Eventually, Charlie and Annie are captured by the master spy, Mr. Big, who turns out to be a midget. Charlie disposes of him by means of a trapdoor in the floor while Annie knocks his bodyguard unconscious. After the would-be bank robbers are apprehended and the real missing cosmonaut gives himself up, life returns to normal at the bookstore. *Booksellers. Cooks. Waitresses. Spies. Astronauts. Police. Midgets. Bodyguards. Unemployment. Mistaken identity. Bank robberies. Diners (restaurants). Bookshops.*

DON'T YOU CRY *see* **MY LOVER, MY SON**

DONZOKO *see* **THE LOWER DEPTHS**

DOOR-TO-DOOR MANIAC *see* **FIVE MINUTES TO LIVE**

DOPPELGÄNGER *see* **JOURNEY TO THE FAR SIDE OF THE SUN**

DORAN NO BETONAMU *see* **VIETNAM IN TURMOIL**

DORIAN GRAY (Italy/Liechtenstein/West Germany)   F6.1256

Sargon Film–Terra Filmkunst–Towers of London. *Dist* American International Pictures. 25 Nov **1970** [Kansas City, Missouri, opening]. Sd; col (Movielab). 35mm. 93 min. *MPAA rating* R.

Pres by Commonwealth United Entertainment Inc. *Prod* Harry Alan Towers. *Dir* Massimo Dallamano. *Screenplay* Massimo Dallamano, Marcello Coscia, Günter Ebert. *Art Dir* Maria Ambrosino. *Film Ed* Nicholas Wentworth. *Mus* Peppino De Luca, Carlo Pes.

Cast: Helmut Berger *(Dorian Gray)*, Richard Todd *(Basil Hallward)*, Herbert Lom *(Henry Wotton)*, Marie Liljedahl *(Sybil Vane)*, Margaret Lee *(Gwendolyn Wotton)*, Maria Rohm *(Alice)*, Beryl Cunningham *(Adrienne)*, Isa Miranda *(Mrs. Ruxton)*, Eleonora Rossi Drago *(Esther)*, Renato Romano *(Alan)*, Stewart Black *(James Vane)*, Francesco Tensi *(see note)*.

Drama. Inspired by: Oscar Wilde, *The Picture of Dorian Gray* (London, 1891). Dorian Gray, a student in present-day London, poses for his artist friend, Basil Hallward. Two of the artist's patrons, millionaire homosexual Henry Wotton and his lustful sister, Gwendolyn, see the portrait and are impressed with the extraordinary beauty of the young man. They later meet Dorian at a party, and, reminding him that his handsome body will wither with age, Henry persuades him to sell his soul in order to remain forever young. Dorian breaks up with his actress-fiancée, Sybil, because her performance humiliates him in front of his new friends. Upon returning home he discovers the portrait reflecting his own cruelty, and he decides to return to Sybil but learns that she has committed suicide. Taking Henry's advice, Dorian consoles himself with Gwendolyn and then becomes involved with Mrs. Ruxton, a middle-aged widow whose wealth proves substantial enough to carry him through years of debauchery. Against the pleas of Basil, Dorian has an affair with Alice, the wife of Alan, a close friend, and then blackmails Alan into helping him murder Basil. After the suicide of Alan, the still youthful Dorian admits his guilt and observes that his portrait has warped and yellowed; in his torment, he stabs the painting and writhes in pain as if he had stabbed himself. The painting takes on its original beauty as Dorian's corpse shrivels into a grotesque heap. *Students. Artists. Millionaires. Actors. Youth. Moral corruption. Male homosexuality. Brother-sister relationship. Hedonism. Narcissism. Murder. Infidelity. Suicide. Blackmail. Guilt. Portraits (paintings). London.*

Note: Released in West Germany in Oct 1970 as *Das Bildnis des Dorian Gray;* running time: 93 min; Italian title: *Il dio chiamato Dorian.* Also known in the United States as *The Secret of Dorian Gray.* Some sources erroneously credit Great Britain with production; Towers of London is based in Vaduz, Liechtenstein. Tensi's appearance in the film is noted by only one source.

DORNRÖSCHEN see **SLEEPING BEAUTY**

DOTO ICHIMAN KAIRI see **THE MAD ATLANTIC**

THE DOUBLE (Great Britain)   **F6.1257**
Merton Park Studios. *Dist* Schoenfeld Film Distributing Corp. 27 Oct **1967**. Sd; b&w. 35mm. 56 min.
Prod Jack Greenwood. *Dir* Lionel Harris. *Screenplay* Lindsay Galloway, John Roddick. *Photog* James Wilson. *Art Dir* Peter Mullins. *Film Ed* Edward Jarvis. *Mus Comp & Cond* Bernard Ebbinghouse. *Sd* Roy Norman. *Sd Rec* Sidney Rider.
Cast: Jeannette Sterke (*Mary Winston*), Alan MacNaughtan (*John Cleeve*), Robert Brown (*Richard Harrison*), Jane Griffiths (*Jane Winston*), Basil Henson (*Derreck Alwyn*), Anne Lawson (*Sally Carter*), Diane Clare (*Selena Osmonde*), Llewellyn Rees (*Bradshaw*), John Miller (*Sir Harry Osmonde*), Dorothea Rundle (*Martha Bradshaw*), Hamilton Dyce (*Detective Inspector Ames*), Henry McCarthy (*Dr. Leighton*), Tony Wall (*Logan*), Patrick Parnell (*Cooper*), Arlette Dobson (*Karen*), David Charlesworth (*Charles*), Thelma Holt (*Marie*), Brian McGrellis (*delivery boy*), Ron Eagleton (*porter*), Derek Sumner (*policeman*).
Mystery melodrama. Source: Edgar Wallace, *The Double* (London, 1928). Businessman John Cleeve is found in South Africa suffering from partial amnesia and paralyzed below the waist. Certain that he has killed his partner, Derreck Alwyn, Cleeve returns to England under the care of Mary Winston. Mary's solicitor, Richard Harrison, shows them a photograph of Alwyn, evidently still alive. As she investigates a house with a hidden safe mentioned by Cleeve, Mary senses that Harrison is allied with Alwyn. Assisted by Mary's sister, Jane, Cleeve recovers his memory and the use of his legs. Jane discovers that the supposed Alwyn is, in fact, Cleeve, who, having incapacitated his partner in Africa, has returned to England to claim Alwyn's estate. In desperation, Cleeve attempts to kill the real Alwyn by pushing his wheelchair down a flight of steps, but is himself slain in the assault. *Businessmen. Lawyers. Sisters. Imposture. Inheritance. Amnesia. Paralysis. Murder. South Africa.*
Note: Released in Great Britain in 1963.

THE DOUBLE AFFAIR see **THE SPY WITH MY FACE**

THE DOUBLE-BARRELLED DETECTIVE STORY   **F6.1258**
Saloon Co. 25 Dec **1965** [Chicago opening]. Sd; b&w (Movielab). 16mm (Scanoscope). 90 min.
A Zev Braun–Irving S. White Production. *Prod* David C. Stone. *Exec Prod* Zev Braun, Irving S. White. *Dir-Writ* Adolfas Mekas. *Sp Asst* Jonas Mekas. *Dir Photog* Graeme Ferguson. *Asst Camera* Ronald Lautore. *Unit Photog* Karl Bissinger. *Titl Song* Paul Bartel. *Ed* Adolfas Mekas. *Asst Ed* George Manasse. *Mus Comp & Cond* Meyer Kupferman. *Titl Song Sung by* Pola Chapelle. *Choreog* Leonora Hays. *Sd* William Reilly, Ralph Hotchkiss. *Re-rec* Townsend Production Service. *Prod Mgr* George Manasse, Mel Garfinkel. *Script Girl* Barbara Stone. *Prod Sec* Louise Alaimo. *Prod Foreman* Harold W. Berkebile. *Wardrobe Mistress* Cecile Verhaeghe. *Cost* Bathsheba. *Optical Eff* B. & O. Film Specialists. *Tech Cons* Ted Gaski. *Coöp* Johnstown Pennwood Players, Tamburitzans of Duquesne University, Johnstown Chamber of Commerce. *Ch Gaffer* Myron Odegaard. *Prop* Bathsheba. *Casting Cons* Terry Fay.
Cast: Hurd Hatfield (*The Father*), Greta Thyssen (*La Belle*), Jeff Siggins (*Archy*), Paul Benedict (*Wells Fargo Ferguson*), Severn Darden (*H. S. Stevens*), Ray Reinhardt (*Judge Parker*), Louis Waldon (*Shadbelly Higgins*), Robert Winston (*Sheriff Fairfax*), Ernie Austin (*Fetlock Jones*), Flora Elkins (*Amelia*), Byrne Piven (*Bill Stone*), Jerome Raphel (*Sherlock Holmes*), Sudie Bond, George Bartenieff, Ronald Demko, Ned Fay, Marcia Saintz, James Walsh, Alexandra Stone.
Mystery comedy-drama. Source: Mark Twain, *A Double Barrelled Detective Story* (New York, 1902). In Virginia in 1880 a Yankee of dubious origin marries the daughter of a distinguished plantation owner. Unbeknownst to his bride, the groom intends to revenge himself on her father, who had initially rejected his suit. To this end he subjects his wife to constant humiliation. Unwilling to break her father's heart, the bride bears his taunts stoically. Frustrated by his wife's refusal to confide these woes to her father, the husband binds the pregnant women to a roadside tree and unleashes his bloodhounds, which tear away her clothing. The next day her humiliation is common knowledge. The culprit having vanished, the victim returns to her paternal home. There she gives birth to a son, Archy. When her father dies of a broken heart, the woman moves to New England. Discovering that her son is gifted with a bloodhound's sense of smell, the woman trains him to track down his father. Upon reaching maturity, Archy undertakes this mission and travels westward. After relentlessly pursuing his presumed father, Archy discovers that he has ruined the wrong man. By accident, however, he witnesses

his true father's murder by the wronged nephew of Sherlock Holmes. *Southerners. Fathers-in-law. Fatherhood. Marriage. Revenge. Personal identity. Desertion. Murder. Virginia. Sherlock Holmes. Dogs.*

DOUBLE BUNK (Great Britain)   **F6.1259**
Fanfare Films Ltd. *For* Bryanston Films. *Dist* Showcorporation. 16 Nov **1961** [New York opening]. Sd; b&w. 35mm. 92 min.
Prod George H. Brown. *Assoc Prod* Jan Darnley-Smith. *Dir–Screenplay* C. M. Pennington-Richards. *2d Unit Dir* Douglas Hickox. *Photog* Stephen Dade. *2d Unit Photog* Geoffrey Faithfull. *Art Dir* Maurice Carter. *Set Decor* Arthur Taksen. *Film Ed* John D. Guthridge. *Mus Comp & Cond* Stanley Black. *Titl Song* Stanley Black, Jack Fishman, Mike Pratt. *Sd* Christopher Lancaster. *Sd Rec* Cecil Mason, Stephen Dalby. *Asst Dir* Jack Causey, John Meadows. *Prod Mgr* Denis Holt. *Cost* Cynthia Tingey. *Wardrobe* Harry Haynes, Tina Swanson. *Makeup* Eddie Knight. *Hairstyles* Pearl Orton.
Cast: Ian Carmichael (*Jack Goddard*), Janette Scott (*Peggy Deeley*), Sidney James (*Sid Randall*), Liz Fraser (*Sandra*), Dennis Price (*Leonard Watson*), Reginald Beckwith (*Alfred Harper*), Irene Handl (*Mrs. Harper*), Noel Purcell (*O'Malley*), Michael Shepley (*Granville-Carter*), Toby Perkins (*Pukka type*), Naunton Wayne, Bill Shine (*Thames Conservancy officers*), Miles Malleson (*Reverend Thomas*), Jacques Cey (*French official*), Hedger Wallace, Terry Scott (*policemen*), Desmond Roberts (*freighter captain*), Peter Swanwick (*freighter pilot*), Gerald Campion (*Charlie*), John Harvey (*Johnnie*), Graham Stark (*flowerman*), Tom Gill (*customs officer*), Gladys Henson (*Madame de Sola*), Willoughby Goddard (*prospective purchaser*), Marianne Stone (*his wife*).
Comedy. Newlyweds Jack and Peggy, frustrated by living in separate rooms in a boardinghouse, buy a dilapidated houseboat. At first they think that their only problems are leaks, peeling paint, and run-down equipment. They soon find, however, that Watson, a boorish yachtsman who owns the moorings, is demanding an exorbitant rental fee. After Peggy has decorated the barge with curtains and plants, Jack decides to take a trip down the Thames for a second honeymoon. Also aboard are Jack's bachelor friend, Sid, and Sid's stripteaser girl friend, Sandra. Hampered by a rusty motor, a faulty compass, and a heavy fog, the little craft crosses the English Channel and ends up in Calais, where French authorities deny the group permission to disembark because they have no passports. The sneering Watson is also there with his yacht, but he refuses to lend Jack food or fuel for the return trip. Sandra, however, distracts Watson's crew with a striptease while Jack and Sid take the necessary supplies. On the return voyage, Watson challenges Jack to a race, the stakes to be double rent or no rent for a year. Fortunately, Watson's Irish skipper, O'Malley, gets so drunk that he steers the yacht off course, and the old houseboat wins the race. *Newlyweds. Yachtsmen. Bachelors. Stripteasers. Irish. Customs officers. Navigation. Theft. Boat racing. Drunkenness. Houseboats. Yachts. Wagers. Honeymoons. Thames River. English Channel. Calais. Fog.*
Note: Locations include the Thames River. Released in Great Britain in Apr 1961.

DOUBLE DECEPTION (France)   **F6.1260**
Spéva Films–Inter Téléfilm. *Dist* United Motion Picture Organization. Jul **1963**. Sd; b&w. 35mm. 101 min.
Exec Prod Michel Safra. *Dir* Serge Friedman. *Dial* François Boyer. *Adapt* François Boyer, Bernard Revon. *Photog* Christian Matras. *Art Dir* Jean d' Eaubonne. *Film Ed* Louisette Hautecoeur. *Mus* Georges Van Parys. *Sd* Antoine Petitjean. *Prod Mgr* Henri Baum.
Cast: Jacques Riberolles (*Peter [Pierre]*), Alice Kessler (*Greta*), Ellen Kessler (*Hildegarde [Hilda]*), Jean Mercure (*Ludwig*), Daniel Sorano (*Wladimir*), Ginette Leclerc (*Odette*).
Mystery melodrama. Source: Pierre Boileau and Thomas Narcejac, *Les magiciennes* (Paris, 1957). Peter, a young pianist, returns from Paris to Munich because of the death of his father, The Great Alberto, king of magicians. At the traveling circus, he finds that his mother, Odette, has developed a severe drinking problem and wants him to stay on. He falls in love with Hildegarde, a circus illusionist, and learns that she is one of identical twins who use their resemblance to create their deceptions. (A condition of their contract is that the twins may never be seen together.) Greta, the other twin, falls in love with the pianist and becomes jealous of her sister. Later, Greta is found dead, killed by Odette, and is secretly buried to preserve the illusion that only one woman performed in their act. The pianist begins to believe that Greta isn't really dead, and, after a series of macabre events, he shoots the girl he thinks is Greta only to discover that he has actually killed Hildegarde. *Pianists. Magicians. Sisters. Twins. Magic. Murder. Alcoholism. Filial relations. Circus. Munich. Paris.*
Note: Paris opening: Aug 1960 as *Les magiciennes*; running times: 105 and 97 min. Bracketed role names refer to French release version.

THE DOUBLE-HEADED ARROW see **↔ (BACK AND FORTH)**

DOUBLE INITIATION
F6.1261

C. Tobalina Productions. *Dist* Hollywood International Film Corp. of America. 8 Apr **1970** [Los Angeles opening]. Sd; col (Eastmancolor). 35mm. 96 min. [Also reviewed at 77 and 83 min.]

Prod-Dir-Writ Carlos Tobalina. *Film Ed* Carlos Tobalina. *Theme Song:* "Whenever You're Blue" Jay Colonna, Orlin Hammitt, Carlos Tobalina.

Cast: Janet Wass *(Lisa Laine)*, Carlos Tobalina *(Carlos)*, Jeannie Anderson *(Martha)*, Maria-Pia *(Dr. Heller)*, Andy Roth *(Andy Reagan)*, Luis Vargas, Roy Donahue, Erroff Lynn, Mary Jane Carpenter, Anita De Moulin, Jane Tsentas, Joe Lazzaro.

Melodrama. Midwesterner Lisa Laine, recovering from a suicide attempt which was aborted by her roommate Martha, reveals to a Los Angeles psychiatrist, Dr. Heller, that she has been tormented since adolescence by a fear of frigidity. Attempting to overcome this problem, Lisa finally falls in love with a man, Andy Reagan, but he turns out to be a homosexual. Lisa next attempts to find love through a computer dating service. She meets Carlos, a Latin Casanova, and he uses an aphrodisiac in an attempt to seduce her. He fails, and under the influence of another aphrodisiac Lisa enjoys a lesbian experience with Martha. Now fearful of her lesbian tendencies, Lisa begins a desperate, promiscuous search for heterosexual love. At last she returns to Carlos, who manages to satisfy her sexually with the help of a neighbor, Jane. Finally, Lisa is able to accept the fact that she is a lesbian, and she returns to Martha. *Roommates. Psychiatrists. Suicide. Frigidity. Male homosexuality. Seduction. Lesbianism. Promiscuity. Troilism. Aphrodisiacs. Computer dating services. Bullfighting. Los Angeles. Tijuana (Mexico). Manuel Benítez Pérez.*

Note: Includes footage of El Cordobes in a 1969 bullfight in Tijuana.

THE DOUBLE MAN (Great Britain)
F6.1262

Albion Film Corp. *Dist* Warner Bros.–Seven Arts, Inc. 3 Apr **1968** [Portland, Oregon, opening; c31 Dec 1967; LP35828]. Sd (RCA); col (Technicolor). 35mm. 105 min.

Prod Hal E. Chester. *Dir* Franklin J. Schaffner. *Screenplay* Frank Tarloff, Alfred Hayes. *Screen Story* Frank Tarloff. *Dir Photog* Denys Coop. *Camera Op* Alan Hall, John Jordan. *Art Dir* Arthur Lawson. *Asst Art Dir* Maurice Pelling. *Set Decor* David Bill. *Main Titl* Caravel Studios, Bernard Lodge. *Film Ed* Richard Best. *Asst Film Ed* Ken Ross. *Mus Comp* Ernie Freeman. *Cond* Stanley Black. *Sd Supv* A. W. Lumkin. *Sd Mix* Anthony Wolf, Len Shilton. *Sd Ed* Charles Crafford. *Asst Dir* Ron Jackson, William P. Cartlidge. *Prod Mgr* L. C. Rudkin. *Cont* Phyllis Townshend. *Dress Dsgn* Courtney Elliott. *Wardrobe Master* Ernie Farrer. *Miss Lister's Clothes* Christian Dior. *Makeup* Richard Mills. *Hairdresser* Henry Montsash. *Coöp* Austrian State Railways, the Saint Anton and Zurs Seilbahnen. *Alexander Calder Exhibition* Brook Street Galleries (London). *Casting Dir* Robert Lennard.

Cast: Yul Brynner *(Dan Slater/Kalmar)*, Britt Ekland *(Gina Ericson)*, Clive Revill *(Frank Wheatly)*, Anton Diffring *(Colonel Berthold)*, Moira Lister *(Mrs. Carrington)*, Lloyd Nolan *(Bill Edwards)*, George Mikell *(Max Gruner)*, Brandon Brady *(Gregori)*, Julia Arnall *(Anna Wheatly)*, David Bauer *(Andrew Miller)*, Ronald Radd *(general)*, Kenneth J. Warren *(police chief)*, David Healy *(Halstead)*, Carl Jaffe *(police surgeon)*, Douglas Muir *(Wilfred)*, Frederick Schiller *(ticket seller)*, Ernst Walder *(Frischauer)*, Franklin J. Schaffner *(man at station)*.

Mystery drama. Source: Henry S. Maxfield, *Legacy of a Spy* (New York, 1958). When CIA agent Dan Slater is informed by his old friend and former CIA agent Frank Wheatly of his son's death in a skiing accident, he leaves immediately for the Austrian Alps to determine the cause of the accident. Convinced that his son's death was not accidental, Slater begins making inquiries and learns that a woman and two men were skiing in the same vicinity on the day of the accident. While conducting his investigation, Slater is followed by two East German agents, Colonel Berthold and Gregori, who have orders to capture Slater and replace him with a Soviet double. The discovery of his son's bloody skiing parka reinforces Slater's suspicions, and he continues his quest despite Washington's insistence that he return to his post. Slater finds Gina Ericson, the woman who was skiing the day his son died, and she tells him that Max Gruner was one of the men skiing that day. Taking Wheatly along, Slater drives out to Gruner's farmhouse but is greeted there by an armed Gregori. Hearing gunshot, Wheatly panics and drives off; but once his fear has subsided, he returns for Slater, unaware that the East Germans have replaced his friend with Kalmar, an enemy agent who, through plastic surgery, is an exact double for Slater. When Kalmar, posing as Slater, accuses Wheatly of framing him, Wheatly instead suggests that it was Gina who set up the confrontation with enemy agents. After brutally beating Gina, Kalmar returns to the farmhouse for Slater. Driven off for his execution, Slater bolts from the car and begins to climb the ski mountain to confront and kill his double. Wheatly intervenes, and each of the two men attempts to convince him that he is the real Slater. When the false Slater betrays himself by evincing parental concern for his dead son, Wheatly shoots him. The real Slater, Wheatly observes, has

never been capable of genuine emotion. *Government agents. Doubles. Communists. Germans. Russians. Filial relations. Friendship. Skiing. Murder. Alps. Austria. United States—Central Intelligence Agency.*

Note: Location scenes filmed in Great Britain and Austria. Released in Great Britain in 1967. Working title: *Legacy of a Spy.*

DOUBLE PLEASURE see DOUBLE YOUR PLEASURE

DOUBLE-STOP
F6.1263

Double-Stop, Ltd. *Dist* World Entertainment Corp. May **1968**. Sd; col (DeLuxe). 35mm. 95 min. [Also 100 min.]

Prod Roger I. Sindell. *Dir* Gerald Seth Sindell. *Screenplay* Roger I. Sindell, Gerald Seth Sindell. *Dir Cinematog* Flemming Olsen. *Art Dir* Frank Evans. *Film Ed* Don Stern. *Mus Comp & Cond* David H. Davis. *Comp of Harpsichord Theme* James Streem. *Sd* Thomas Peterson.

Cast: Jeremiah Sullivan *(Mike Westfall)*, Mimi Torchin *(Katherine Westfall)*, Anthony Walsh *(Don Streggor)*, Patti Fairchild *(Susan)*, Billy Kurtz *(Pablo Westfall)*, Barry Gordon *(1st art student)*, Gino Arditto *(Wilbur)*.

Drama. Mike Westfall, a cellist with the Cleveland Symphony Orchestra, his photographer wife, Katherine, and their son, Pablo, live in the fashionable Cleveland suburb of Shaker Heights. To Don Streggor, a fellow musician, his girl friend Susan, a singer, and others at an elegant cocktail party, it seems as if the Westfalls have no problems. Trouble begins to brew when Katherine, who has taken a series of photographs of the ghetto following the previous summer's riots, announces that Pablo will be bussed to a predominantly black school, arguing that he needs to experience the real world. Mike, initially against the move, relents when the first day of school arrives and takes Pablo to the waiting bus. That evening, at the opening of Katherine's photography exhibit, Susan and Don have an argument which upsets Mike so much that he leaves early. The next day Mike secretly follows the schoolbus to school and is horrified by the squalor and violence he sees there. Mike wants to remove Pablo from school, but Katherine insists that he stay. Both Katherine and Susan, who was to sing in the chorus, are absent from that evening's symphony performance. Afterwards Don says that he went to the same school Pablo attends, and he takes Mike to a bar in that neighborhood, where a hostile confrontation erupts between Don and his former acquaintances, who are black. The next day Mike, still unsure about what to do with Pablo, takes him to a rehearsal. As they arrive they notice a crowd gathered in a park across the street, and beyond that stands Don, looking disheveled. Susan has been murdered; her body lies beneath a sheet on the grass. Returning home with Pablo, Mike begins to realize the impossibility of isolating oneself from the harsh realities of life. *Musicians. Photographers. Suburbanites. Singers. Negroes. Family life. Racial integration. Urban life. Murder. Social consciousness. Ghettos. Riots. Shaker Heights (Ohio). Cleveland. Cleveland Symphony Orchestra.*

Note: Filmed on location in Cleveland.

DOUBLE SUICIDE (Japan)
F6.1264

Hyogensha–Nippon Art Theatre Guild. *Dist* Toho International, Inc. 11 Feb **1970** [Los Angeles opening]. Sd; b&w. 35mm. 104 min.

Prod Masayuki Nakajima, Masahiro Shinoda. *Dir* Masahiro Shinoda. *Screenplay* Taeko Tomioka, Masahiro Shinoda, Toru Takemitsu. *Dial* Taeko Tomioka. *Photog* Toichiro Narushima. *Art Dir* Kiyoshi Awazu. *Mus* Toru Takemitsu.

Cast: Kichiemon Nakamura *(Jihei)*, Shima Iwashita *(Koharu/Osan)*, Hosei Komatsu *(Tahei)*, Yusuke Takita *(Magoemon)*, Kamatari Fujiwara *(yamatoya owner)*, Yoshi Kato *(Gosaemon)*, Shizue Kawarazaki *(Osan's mother)*, Tokie Hidari *(Osugi)*.

Melodrama. Source: Monzaemon Chikamatsu, *Shinju ten no amijima* (a puppet play; 1720). Jihei, the married owner of a paper shop in Osaka, is in love with Koharu, a courtesan in bondage to the Kinokuniya Tea House. Unable to raise enough money to redeem himself, Jihei has vowed with Koharu to commit double suicide should another bidder succeed in buying her from her master. Jihei's elder brother, Magoemon, disguised as a samurai, visits Koharu, and she tells him that she is not eager to die with her lover. Jihei, who has eavesdropped on the conversation, unaware the samurai is indeed his brother, bursts in on the couple in a rage. Magoemon reveals his identity and reprimands Jihei for his mistreatment of Osan, his devoted wife. Jihei, shamed by his brother's lecture and infuriated at Koharu's perfidy, throws away Koharu's love letters and vows to be the faithful husband and honorable man he once was. When Jihei learns, however, that his rival, Tahei, is about to redeem Koharu, he becomes despondent. Osan, moved by her husband's sorrow and fearful for Koharu's fate, confesses to Jihei that Koharu's apparent change of heart was the result of a letter which she herself had written to the courtesan. Defending Koharu's fidelity, Osan urges Jihei to redeem Koharu and offers to sell her own clothes for the necessary money. Osan's father, enraged at his daughter's humiliation, forces her from her husband's house. Jihei, despairing at the impossibility of making his wife happy and of realizing his love with Koharu, abducts Koharu from the teahouse. After making love, they commit suicide together. *Prostitutes. Brothers. Suicide. Infidelity. Disguise. Family life. Marriage. Documentation.*

Note: Released in Japan in 1969 as *Shinju ten no amijima*; running time: 142 min.

DOUBLE TROUBLE (Japan)   F6.1265

Toho Co. Nov **1964** [Los Angeles showing]. Sd; col? 35mm. [Feature film, length unknown.]

Cast: Yumi Ito, Emi Ito, Keisuke Sonoi. Although no information on the precise nature of this film has been found, sources suggest that the story concerns a set of twins. *Twins.*

Note: Original title and release undetermined.

DOUBLE TROUBLE   F6.1266

B. C. W. *Dist* Metro-Goldwyn-Mayer, Inc. 24 May **1967** [New York opening; c31 Dec 1966; LP33848]. Sd (Westrex); col (Metrocolor). 35mm (Panavision). 92 min.

Prod Judd Bernard, Irwin Winkler. *Dir* Norman Taurog. *Screenplay* Jo Heims. *Story* Marc Brandel. *Dir Photog* Daniel L. Fapp. *Art Dir* George W. Davis, Merrill Pye. *Set Decor* Henry Grace, Hugh Hunt. *Film Ed* John McSweeney. *Mus Score* Jeff Alexander. *Song:* "Double Trouble" Doc Pomus, Mort Shuman. *Song:* "Baby, If You'll Give Me All of Your Love" Joy Byers. *Song:* "Could I Fall in Love?" Randy Starr. *Song:* "Long Legged Girl" J. Leslie McFarland, Winfield Scott. *Song:* "City By Night" Bill Giant, Florence Kaye, Bernie Baum. *Arr:* "Old MacDonald Had a Farm" Randy Starr. *Song:* "I Love Only One Girl" Sid Tepper, Roy C. Bennett. *Songs:* "There's So Much World To See," "It Won't Be Long" Sid Wayne, Ben Weisman. *Song:* "Blue River" Paul Evans, Fred Tobias. *Song:* "What Now, What Next, Where To?" Don Robertson, Hal Blair. *Song:* "Never Ending" Buddy Kaye, Philip Springer. *Songs Sung by* Elvis Presley. *Choreog* Alex Romero. *Rec Supv* Franklin Milton. *Asst Dir* Claude Binyon, Jr. *Unit Prod Mgr* Al Shenberg. *Asst to the Prod* Patricia Casey. *Cost* Don Feld. *Makeup* William Tuttle. *Hairstyles* Mary Keats. *Sp Vis Eff* J. McMillan Johnson, Carroll L. Shepphird. *Tech Adv* Col. Tom Parker.

Cast: Elvis Presley (Guy Lambert), Annette Day (Jill Conway), John Williams (Gerald Waverly), Yvonne Romain (Claire Dunham), The Wiere Brothers (themselves), Chips Rafferty (Archie Brown), Norman Rossington (Arthur Babcock), Monty Landis (Georgie), Michael Murphy (Morley), Leon Askin (Inspector De Groote), John Alderson (iceman), Stanley Adams (Captain Roach), Maurice Marsac (Frenchman), Walter Burke (mate), Helene Winston (Gerda), Monique LeMaire (desk clerk), The G Men (themselves).

Comedy-melodrama with music. While American singer Guy Lambert is performing in England, teenage heiress Jill Conway falls head-over-heels in love with him, and he also captures the attention of sophisticated Claire Dunham. In an attempt to forestall the possibility of romance, Jill's uncle and guardian, Gerald Waverly, sends her to school in Brussels, unaware that Guy has a singing engagement there. After a series of near-fatal accidents, it soon becomes apparent to Guy that someone is trying to kill Jill. Furthermore, the young couple are being closely watched by a pair of bumbling thieves who have hidden smuggled jewels in Guy's luggage. In Brussels, the Belgian police and a trio of ineffectual detectives try to help but prove to be of little use. Appointing himself as Jill's protector, Guy exposes Uncle Gerald and Claire Dunham, who is revealed to be Gerald's accomplice, as the would-be murderers who had hoped to inherit Jill's fortune. A mysterious stranger who had been trailing Guy turns out to be a Scotland Yard man, and he apprehends the jewel thieves. With all threats to their happiness removed, Jill and Guy return to England. *Singers. Americans in foreign countries. Heiresses. Uncles. Guardians. Thieves. Detectives. Adolescence. Murder. Smuggling. Jewels. England. Brussels. Scotland Yard.*

DOUBLE TROUBLE *see* SWINGIN' ALONG

DOUBLE YOUR PLEASURE   F6.1267

Dragon Films. *Dist* Able Film Co. 11 Sep **1969** [San Francisco showing]. Sd; col. 16mm. [Feature length assumed.]

Sex film. At a motel, two couples separately attempt sexual intercourse, but the newly-wed pair are unsuccessful. The women make love with each other and then decide to swap husbands, which appears to provide better sexual stimulation. *Sexuality. Mate swapping. Nudity.*

Note: Also known as *Twilight Affair* and *Double Pleasure.*

DOUCE VIOLENCE *see* SWEET ECSTASY

LA DOUCEUR DE VIVRE *see* LA DOLCE VITA

LE DOULOS *see* DOULOS—THE FINGER MAN

DOULOS—THE FINGER MAN (France/Italy)   F6.1268

Rome Paris Films—C. C. Champion. *Dist* Pathé-Contemporary Films. 2 Mar **1964** [New York opening]. Sd; b&w. 35mm. 108 min.

Prod Carlo Ponti, Georges de Beauregard. *Dir-Writ* Jean-Pierre Melville. *Photog* Nicolas Hayer. *Camera* Henri Tiquet. *Asst Camera* Andre Dubreuil, Étienne Rosenfeld. *Art Dir* Daniel Guéret. *Set Decor* Pierre Charron. *Film Ed* Monique Bonnot. *Asst Film Ed* Michèle Boehm. *Mus* Paul Misraki. *Piano Mus* Jacques Loussier. *Sd* Julien Coutellier. *Asst Sd* Victor Revelly, Jean Gaudelet. *Asst Dir* Charles Bitsch, Volker Schlöndorff. *Prod Mgr* Jean Pieuchot, Roger Scipion. *Script Girl* Elisabeth Rappeneau. *Prop* André Davalan. *Still Photog* Raymond Voinquel.

Cast: Jean-Paul Belmondo (Silien), Serge Reggiani (Maurice), Jean Desailly (Inspector Clain), Fabienne Dali (Fabienne), Michel Piccoli (Nuttheccio), Monique Hennessy (Thérèse), Carl Studer (Kern), Jacques de Léon (Armand), René Lefèvre (Gilbert), Philippe Nahon (Rémy), Aimé de March (Jean), Marcel Cuvelier (1st inspector), Jack Leonard (2d inspector), Christian Lude (doctor), Paulette Breil (Anita), Charles Bayard (old man), Daniel Crohem (Inspector Salignari), Charles Boyilland, Georges Sellier (barmen), Andres (maître d'hôtel).

Crime melodrama. Source: Pierre Lesou, *Le doulos* (Paris, 1957). Maurice Faugel, who believes he has lost his luck and courage in prison, kills Gilbert, a former friend, to avenge Gilbert's murder of Maurice's girl friend while he was in jail. Maurice escapes just as the men involved in the "Avenue Mozart" robbery arrive seeking Gilbert's services as a fence. Maurice hides at the apartment of Thérèse, his mistress, and they discuss Silien, Maurice's friend and one of the most feared men in the Paris underworld. Silien is suspected of being a "doulos," or police informer, but Maurice refuses to believe these suspicions, and he requests Silien's aid in an apparently easy burglary. Silien delivers the needed tools to Maurice and his accomplice, Rémy, and leaves to telephone Inspector Salignari of the Paris police. He then beats Thérèse into revealing the location of the burglary; subsequently, she is found dead in a smashed automobile. The two burglars are trapped by the police during the theft, and both Rémy and Salignari are killed in a gun battle. Although wounded, Maurice escapes, and, certain now that Silien is an informer, he vows revenge. Meanwhile, Inspector Clain blackmails Silien into revealing Maurice's hideout. Jailed on the charge of murdering Gilbert, Maurice hires another prisoner, Kern, to kill Silien. Meanwhile, Silien conceives a plan to free Maurice and at the same time dispose of two enemies—Nuttheccio and Armand, the "Avenue Mozart" jewel thieves. Silien, aided by Fabienne, an old girl friend who is now Nuttheccio's mistress, murders Armand and Nuttheccio and makes it look as though they killed each other in a fight over the jewels. Maurice is freed, and Silien convinces him that Thérèse was the informer. Later, remembering that Kern is to kill Silien, Maurice goes to Silien's house to stop the murder. Kern mistakes Maurice for Silien and kills him, and when Silien arrives he and Kern shoot each other in a violent gun battle. The identity of the informer dies with them. *Police. Informers. Gangsters. Mistresses. Fences (for stolen goods). Ex-convicts. Hired killers. Robbery. Murder. Blackmail. Revenge. Perfidy. Friendship. Prisons. Jewels. Paris.*

Note: Location scenes filmed in Paris. Opened in Paris in Feb 1963 as *Le doulos*. Italian title: *Lo spione.*

DOWN AMONG THE Z MEN *see* SOME KIND OF A NUT

DOWN AND DIRTY   F6.1269

Mondo Films. *Dist* Astro-Jemco Film Distributors. 17 Jan **1969** [Champaign, Illinois, showing]. Sd; col (Eastman Color). 35mm. 86 min.

Prod-Writ Jay Roberts, Edward Everett. *Assoc Prod* M. Murray. *Dir* Edward Everett. *Photog* Hal Guthu. *Set Decor* Earl Marshall. *Film Ed* Ewing Brown. *Orig Mus* Robert Phillips, mus. *Sd* Spectra Sound. *Asst Dir* Herbert Gould. *Makeup* Ray Sebastian. *Sp Eff* Ewing Brown.

Cast: Eddie Nova, Capri, Cathy Crowfoot, David Perkins, Paul Hanks, Cathy Price, Kathy Prescott, Barbara Seville, Mickey Jines, Tammy Brandon, Dene Starnes, Sheri Jackson, Ray Sebastian, Marty Lasher, Linda Styles.

Melodrama. Ed, a respectable accountant and family man, "drops out" when he discovers that his wife has been unfaithful. Abandoning his mate, home, and job, he goes to the Swingers' Club and later attends a mate-swapping party with a topless dancer from the club. He joins in the activities—drinking, nude dancing, pornographic films, and sex—until the sight of a pair of quarreling newlyweds who have just swapped mates with another couple shocks him, and he leaves. Micky, a voluptuous redhead who lives communally with a group of outcasts, introduces him to marijuana and the hippie lifestyle. One day, however, a sadist is accidentally killed while raping a virgin, and Ed realizes that he must come to grips with himself. He meets Lisa, a waitress in a coffee house, and they fall in love and marry after he rescues her from the clutches of a group of sex cultists who want her to be their "sacrificial virgin." *Accountants. Go-go dancers. Hippies. Waitresses. Newlyweds. Infidelity. Desertion. Mate swapping. Sadism. Promiscuity. Rape. Nudity. Sex exploitation films. Marijuana. Cults.*

DOWN FOR DOUBLE   F6.1270

Dist Stacey Distributors. ca **1970**. Sd; col. 16mm. 61-81 min.

Sex film. No information about the specific nature of this film has been found. *Sexuality.*

DOWNFALL *see* THE SEDUCERS

DOWNHILL RACER   F6.1271

Wildwood International, Ltd. *Dist* Paramount Pictures. 28 Oct **1969** [Reno, Nevada, opening; c29 Oct 1969; LP37272]. Sd; col (Technicolor). 35mm. 101 min. *MPAA rating* M.

Prod Richard Gregson. *Dir* Michael Ritchie. *Screenplay* James Salter. *Dir Photog* Brian Probyn. *Camera* Joe Jay Jalbert. *2d Unit Photog* Arthur Wooster, Alan Hewison, Jean-Paul Janssen, Jean-Pierre Janssen. *Photog—Colorado Locations* Gene Polito. *Adtl Photog* Tony Busbridge, Austin Parkinson, Michael Temple. *Art Dir* Ian Whittaker. *Titl Dsgn* Don Record. *Supv Ed* Nick Archer. *Ed* Richard C. Harris. *Mus* Kenyon Hopkins. *Song:* "You Got Me Climbin' up the Wall" Kenyon Hopkins. *Perf by* People. *Song:* "Moon River" Johnny Mercer, Henry Mancini. *Song:* "That Old Black Magic" Johnny Mercer, Harold Arlen. *Song:* "Olympic Hymn (Disques Erato)" Spiro Samara, Kostia Palarmas. *Sd Mix* Kevin Sutton. *Sd Rec* Elden Ruberg. *Asst Dir* Kip Gowans, Walter Coblenz, David Winbury, Graham Ford. *Prod Supv* Stanley O'Toole. *Prod Mgr* Walter Coblenz. *Location Mgr* Renate Neuchel, Robert Simmonds. *Cont* Angela Allen. *Wardrobe* Cynthia May. *Makeup* Bill Lodge. *Prop* Tony Teiger.

Cast: Robert Redford *(David Chappellet)*, Gene Hackman *(Eugene Claire)*, Camilla Sparv *(Carole Stahl)*, Joe Jay Jalbert *(Tommy Erb)*, Kenneth Kirk *(D. K. Bryan)*, Dabney Coleman *(Mayo)*, Jim McMullan *(Johnny Creech)*, Christian Doermer *(Brumm)*, Oren Stevens *(Tony Kipsmith)*, Karl Michael Vogler *(Machet)*, Rip McManus *(Bruce Devore)*, Jerry Dexter *(Ron Engel)*, Tom J. Kirk *(Stiles)*, Walter Stroud *(Mr. Chappellet)*, Carole Carle *(Lena)*, Kathleen Crowley *(American newspaperwoman)*, Rob Hutton-Potts *(Gabriel)*, Heini Schuler *(Meier)*, Peter Rohr *(Boyriven)*, Arnold Alpiger *(Hinsch)*, Eddie Waldburger *(Haas)*, Marco Walli *(Istel)*, Rudi Gertsch *(Selznick)*, James Sandoe *(spectator)*, Noam Pitlik *(TV announcer)*, Walter Gnilka *(Austrian journalist)*, Werner Heyking *(Helgerson)*, Harald Schreiber *(Oliviera)*, Harald Dietl *(journalist)*, Alexander Stampfer *(skier #16)*, Ulrike von Zerboni *(Jeanine)*, Robert Brendlin *(announcer)*, Michael Gempart *(hotel receptionist)*, Jack Ballard *(candy vendor)*.

Drama. Source: Oakley Hall, *The Downhill Racers* (New York, 1963). When one of the top American skiers on the United States team is hurt, dedicated coach Eugene Claire sends for replacements David Chappellet and D. K. Bryan. Chappellet is a loner, but he manages to stay on the team during the remainder of the European circuit, complaining all the while about his positions but producing some spectacular though inconsistent runs, even rivaling on occasion the best United States racer, Johnny Creech. Home for summer training, Chappellet leaves the team in Bend, Oregon, and hitchhikes home to Idaho Springs, Colorado, where he is no more at home than in any of the drab and anonymous hotel quarters on the tour. He is unable to communicate with his father and can show no interest in his old girl friend, Lena, whom he greets in cavalier fashion in the back seat of his father's old jalopy. Back in Europe for the season, he begins an affair with Carole Stahl, the secretary to rich ski manufacturer Machet, but is not distracted from his singular involvement with downhill racing as he wins for the United States a race that has hitherto been considered out of America's reach, and thus sharpens his rivalry with Creech. This time the American team returns home with some fulfillment of the years of hopeful promises, and Claire enthusiastically embarks upon a fundraising tour for the upcoming Olympic year. Back for his third season of major league racing, Chappellet senses the magnitude and importance of the Olympic competition as the race approaches; a quip turns into banter between him and Creech, leading to a hair-raising downhill race wherein Creech is nearly injured and Claire's patience with his prima donna rebel is worn dangerously thin. When Creech breaks his leg in the last pre-Olympic trial, Chappellet is the only American hope, but he bests all of the superior European competition with a dazzling display of downhill racing. Flush with apparent victory, his attention is called to the imposing mountain he has just conquered as word comes down that a faster run is being skied by an unknown; but a fall assures the first American gold medal in Olympic downhill racing and gives David Chappellet a precarious perch at the top of a sport in which the fastest is the best. *Skiers. Athletic coaches. Filial relations. Idaho Springs (Colorado). Austria. Switzerland. Olympic Games.*

Note: Racing footage in the film is a mixture of real races (held at Kitzbuhel, Austria, during February and March, 1969) and scenes staged by the company on location in Kitzbuhel and Wengen, Switzerland. American locations were filmed in Idaho Springs, Colorado, and around Golden, Colorado.

DRACULA HAS RISEN FROM THE GRAVE (Great Britain)   F6.1272

Hammer Film Productions. *Dist* Warner Bros.-Seven Arts, Inc. 6 Feb **1969** [Los Angeles opening]. Sd; col (Technicolor). 35mm. 92 min. *MPAA rating* G.

Prod Aida Young. *Dir* Freddie Francis. *Screenplay* John Elder. *Photog* Arthur Grant. *Camera Op* Moray Grant. *Art Dir* Bernard Robinson. *Supv Ed* James Needs. *Ed* Spencer Reeve. *Mus Comp* James Bernard. *Mus Supv* Philip Martell. *Sd Rec* Ken Rawkins. *Sd Ed* Wilfred Thompson. *Asst Dir* Dennis Robertson. *Prod Mgr* Christopher Sutton. *Cont* Doris Martin. *Wardrobe* Marion Mathie. *Makeup* Heather Nurse, Rosemarie McDonald-Peattie. *Hairstyles* Wanda Kelly. *Sp Eff* Frank George. *Matte Artist* Peter Melrose.

Cast: Christopher Lee *(Count Dracula)*, Rupert Davies *(monsignor)*, Veronica Carlson *(Maria)*, Barbara Ewing *(Zena)*, Barry Andrews *(Paul)*, Ewan Hooper *(priest)*, Michael Ripper *(Max)*, George A. Cooper *(landlord)*, Marion Mathie *(Anna)*, John D. Collins *(student)*, Chris Cunningham *(farmer)*, Norman Bacon *(boy)*, Carrie Baker *(1st victim)*.

Horror film. The fear of the vampire returns to a small village in Transylvania when the body of a young girl, with two fang marks in her neck, is found hanging in the church belfry. Some time later, a visiting monsignor finds that the terrified villagers have stopped attending church services and never venture near the castle of Count Dracula. Appalled, the monsignor forces the parish priest to accompany him while he performs an exorcism rite and hangs a crucifix on the castle door. The frightened priest flees and falls by the edge of a frozen stream. Beneath him lies the body of Dracula, who is revived by blood trickling from the wounded priest. Dracula arises, places the priest under his spell, and vows revenge on the monsignor. Upon arriving at the village where the monsignor lives with his sister-in-law Anna and her daughter Maria, the count initiates Zena, a tavern waitress, into the cult of the vampire and compels her to bring Maria to him. Zena obeys, but Maria's boyfriend, Paul, an atheist, rescues the young girl. After killing Zena for failing him, Dracula gains entry to Maria's bedroom. On his initial visit, he succeeds in leaving his fang marks on the girl's throat; his second visit, however, is thwarted when the monsignor steps forward and drives him away with a crucifix. Although the monsignor is struck down by the priest and later dies, he gives Paul instructions to combat the vampire. Finding Dracula's coffin, Paul tries to kill him but fails because he is unable to recite a Latin prayer. Then, Dracula returns for Maria and carries her off in his hearse. He orders her to remove the monsignor's crucifix from the door of the castle and hurl it down to the rocks below. Paul arrives and, during a struggle, knocks the count over the mountain wall. As Dracula is impaled on the crucifix, the repentant priest intones the requisite prayer over the vampire's body, while Paul embraces Maria and makes the sign of the cross. *Priests. Atheists. Vampires. Waitresses. Uncles. Exorcism. Revenge. Spells. Murder. Impalement. Castles. Hearses. Transylvania. Dracula.*

Note: Opened in London in Nov 1968. One of Hammer Film Productions' Dracula series.

DRACULA—PRINCE OF DARKNESS (Great Britain)   F6.1273

Seven Arts Productions-Hammer Film Productions. *Dist* Twentieth Century-Fox Film Corp. 12 Jan **1966** [Detroit opening; c30 Dec 1965; LP32699]. Sd (RCA); col (Technicolor, print by DeLuxe). 35mm (Techniscope). 90 min.

Prod Anthony Nelson Keys. *Exec Prod* Anthony Hinds. *Dir* Terence Fisher. *Screenplay* John Sansom. *Based on an Idea by* John Elder. *Dir Photog* Michael Reed. *Camera Op* Cece Cooney. *Art Dir* Don Mingaye. *Prod Dsgn* Bernard Robinson. *Supv Ed* James Needs. *Ed* Chris Barnes. *Mus Comp* James Bernard. *Mus Supv* Philip Martell. *Sd Rec* Ken Rawkins. *Sd Ed* Roy Baker. *Asst Dir* Bert Batt. *Prod Mgr* Ross MacKenzie. *Cont* Lorna Selwyn. *Wardrobe* Rosemary Burrows. *Makeup* Roy Ashton. *Hairstyles* Frieda Steiger. *Sp Eff* Bowie Films.

Cast: Christopher Lee *(Dracula)*, Barbara Shelley *(Helen Kent)*, Andrew Keir *(Father Shandor)*, Francis Matthews *(Charles Kent)*, Suzan Farmer *(Diana Kent)*, Charles Tingwell *(Alan Kent)*, Thorley Walters *(Ludwig)*, Philip Latham *(Klove)*, Walter Brown *(Brother Mark)*, George Woodbridge *(landlord)*, Jack Lambert *(Brother Peter)*, Philip Ray *(priest)*, Joyce Hemson *(mother)*, John Maxim *(coachdriver)*.

Horror film. Source: Bram Stoker, *Dracula* (London, 1899). Charles and Diana Kent, Charles's brother (Alan), and Alan's wife (Helen) vacation in the Carpathian Mountains, but they are told to stay out of the Carlsbad area, where the inhabitants are still frightened of vampires even though Dracula has been dead for 10 years. These people ignore the advice and hire a coach to take them through the area. As the coach passes Dracula's castle, however, the driver leaves them standing on the road, and he turns back. A driverless coach then takes them on to the castle, where they are persuaded by Klove, the butler, to spend the night. Later, Alan is hacked to death by Klove, and his blood drips over Dracula's ashes and causes the vampire's revivification. Dracula quickly attacks Helen and transforms her into a vampire. Charles and Diana use the protection of the cross to escape from the castle to a monastery run by sympathetic Father Shandor, one of Dracula's archenemies. Ludwig, an old man, invites Dracula and Helen to enter the monastery, and Helen tries to attack Charles but is killed when a stake is driven through her heart. Charles nearly kills Dracula, but night falls rapidly, and Dracula fights off the attacker and then retires to his coffin on the ice-covered moat. Father Shandor, recalling that vampires can be killed by running water, breaks up the ice and allows the water to flow over Dracula. *Vampires. Butlers. Priests. Murder. Impalement. Reviviscence. Vacations. Castles. Monasteries. Carpathian Mountains. Dracula.*

Note: Opened in London in Jan 1966. Working title: *Revenge of Dracula.* Sequel to *Horror of Dracula* (1958), a sequence from which is included in this film. John Elder is a pseudonym for Anthony Hinds.

DRACULA (THE DIRTY OLD MAN)   F6.1274
Vega International Pictures. *Dist* Art Films. 11 Dec **1969** [Charlotte, North Carolina, opening]. Sd; col. 35mm. 80 min.

Pres by Whit Boyd. *Prod-Dir-Writ* William Edwards. *Asst Prod* Clifton Bowen. *Camera* William Troiano. *Asst Camera* Burke Reynolds. *Art* X. O. Vangam. *Ed* Ludwig Moner. *Prod Mgr* Chuck Alford. *Script Supv* Rachel Edwards. *Makeup* Tony Tierney. *Gaffer* Gary Lawrence.

Cast: Vince Kelly *(Alucard)*, Ann Hollis *(Ann)*, Bill Whitton *(Jackal-man)*, Libby Caculus *(Joan)*, Joan Puckett *(Marge)*, Sue Allen *(Carol)*, Bob Whitton *(station attendant)*, Rebecca Reynolds *(stranded girl)*, Adrainne *(Susan)*.

Horror film. Count Dracula's lecherous descendant Alucard, taken to the United States as a small child, feeds on the blood of innocent young virgins. His servant Mike, transformed into a jackal-man, conducts the voluptuous, nude victims to Alucard's mountain lair until one day he falls in love with one of the women and challenges his master. In the fight that follows, Mike is killed, and Alucard is destroyed by sunlight. *Vampires. Monsters. Abduction. Virginity. Murder. Dracula.*

O DRAGÃO DA MALDADE CONTRA O SANTO GUERREIRO *see* ANTONIO DAS MORTES

DRAGÉES AU POIVRE *see* SWEET AND SOUR

DRAGON INN (Republic of China)   F6.1275
Union Film Co. Nov **1968** [Los Angeles showing]. Sd; col (Eastman Color). 35mm (Uniscope). [U. S. running time unknown.]

Prod Sha Yung-fong. *Dir* Hu Chin-chuan. *Photog* Hua Hui-ying. *Art Dir* Tsou Jyh-liang. *Prod Supv* Chang Tao-jan. *Prod Mgr* Yang Shih-chin. *Unit Mgr* Chang Jou-ying.

Cast: Shangkuan Ling-feng *(Chu Hui)*, Shih Cheng *(Hsiao Shao-yueh)*, Pe Ying *(Ts'ao Shao-ch'in)*, Hsu Feng *(Yu Ch'ien)*, Tsao Chien *(innkeeper Wu Ning)*, Li Chieh *(officer)*, Kao Ming *(inn manager)*, Ko Hsiao-pao *(inn servant)*, Kao Fei *(Qun Yu-chang)*, Hsieh Han *(Chu Chi)*, Han Ying-chieh *(Mao Tsung-hsien)*, Yu Chi-kung *(Yu Kuang)*, Tien Peng *(soldier)*, Miao Tien *(Pi Shao-t'ang)*, Wan Chung-shan *(Tuo La)*, Chi Wei *(Yu Mien)*, Hsu Yao-kuang, Chang Yun-wen *(chiefs)*, Lu Chin *(informer)*.

Adventure drama. In 15th-century China the eunuch Ts'ao Chi-hsiang orders Yu Ch'ien executed and his survivors sent to a Lung-men border inn used as a way station for exiled political refugees. Aiding the murder victim's family are innkeeper Wu Ning, an exiled general; Chu Chi, an old friend of Yu's; her younger sister, Chu Hui, who comes to the inn disguised as a man; and Hsiao Shao-yueh, a young man who assists Wu. After numerous battles and much swordplay, the eunuch Ts'ao Shao-chin, who feared revenge and desired the destruction of the family, is stabbed to death. *Eunuchs. Political refugees. Innkeepers. Sisters. Assassination. Disguise. Revenge. Inns. China—History—Ming Dynasty. Yu Ch'ien.*

Note: Location scenes filmed near T'ao-yuan, Taiwan; released in Taipei in Oct 1967 as *Lung-men k'o-chan;* Hong Kong running time: 106 min.

DRAGON MASTER *see* CANNON FOR CORDOBA

DRAGON SKY (France)   F6.1276
Speva Films-Ciné-Alliance-Filmsonor. *Dist* Lopert Pictures. 24 Aug **1964** [New York opening]. Sd; col (Eastmancolor). 35mm. 95 min.

Prod Michel Safra, Serge Silberman. *Dir* Marcel Camus. *Screenplay* Jacques Viot. *Adapt* Jacques Viot, Marcel Camus. *Photog* Raymond Le Moigne. *Film Ed* Andrée Feix. *Mus* Maurice Jarre. *Sd* Antoine Bonfanti. *Prod Mgr* Henri Baum.

Cast: Narie Hem *(Dara)*, Sam El *(Sok)*, Nop Nem *(Khem)*, Skarine *(Tith)*, Bopha Devi, Saky Sbong.

Drama. In Cambodia, Sok, a young and imaginative boy, leaves the Buddhist priesthood to seek a more adventurous life. Tith, a friendly fortune-teller, gives him a bird of paradise which leads him to the Royal Palace at Pnompenh. There, in an ancient temple, Sok finds Dara, a beautiful dancer in the Imperial Ballet. When she leaves the dance company to take part in ritual celebrations, Sok follows her to Angkor Wat, the city of temples, and declares his love for her. Dara is also sought by Khem, a wealthy businessman. When Khem learns of

her love for Sok, his jealousy erupts into violence, and Dara falls to her death. [According to another source, Dara commits suicide.] Sok is injured by Khem, and upon seeing the dead body of his beloved Dara, Sok also dies. The two are reunited in death, as in the legendary love story of Rama and Sita. *Fortune-tellers. Dancers. Businessmen. Jealousy. Murder. Suicide. Reincarnation. Cambodia. Pnompenh. Angkor Wat. Buddhism. Rama. Sita. Bird of paradise.*

Note: Filmed on location in Cambodia. Opened in Paris in Oct 1962 as *L'oiseau de paradis.*

THE DRAGON'S FANGS (Japan)   F6.1277
Nikkatsu Corp. *Dist* Toho Co. May **1967** [Los Angeles showing]. Sd; col? 35mm. [Feature film, length unknown.]

Cast: Hideki Takahashi, Yumiko Nogawa, Shinsuke Ashida, Jun Negami. No information about the nature of this film has been found.

Note: Original title and release undetermined.

A DRAMA OF JEALOUSY (AND OTHER THINGS) *see* THE PIZZA TRIANGLE

DRAMMA DELLA GELOSIA—TUTTI I PARTICOLARI IN CRONACA *see* THE PIZZA TRIANGLE

THE DREAD PERSUASION (Reissue)   F6.1278
Police Science Productions. *Dist* Modern Film Distributors. 10 May **1962** [New York State license]. Sd; col (Eastmancolor). 35mm. 75 min.

Note: Originally released by Harry Stern as *The Narcotic Story* in Feb 1958.

THE DREAM MAKER (Great Britain)   F6.1279
K. N. P. Productions. *For* Magna Films/British Lion Films. *Dist* Universal Pictures. 4 Mar **1964** [Los Angeles opening]. Sd; col (Eastman Color). 35mm. 86 min.

Prod Norman Williams. *Co-prod* Philip Green. *Dir* Don Sharp. *Screenplay* Leigh Vance. *Photog* Ken Hodges. *Camera Op* Ceri Davies. *Camera Focus* Ronald Anscombe. *Art Dir* Scott MacGregor. *Asst Art Dir* Brian Ackland-Snow, Freda Pearson. *Draughtsman* Terry Ackland-Snow. *Scenic Artist* Gilbert Wood. *Film Ed* John Jympson. *1st Asst Ed* Jennifer Thompson. *2d Asst Ed* Timothy Gee. *Mus Comp & Cond* Philip Green. *Lyr* Norman Newell. *Titl Song Sung by* Tommy Steele. Song: "Maximum Plus" sung by Tommy Steele, Marion Ryan. Song: "Day Without You" sung by Danny Williams. Song: "Summertime" sung by Dick Kallman, George Mitchell Show. *Choreog* Pamela Davis, Douglas Squires. *Sd Rec* Cecil Mason, Red Law. *Boom Op* Charles Wheeler, sd. *Sd Camera Op* David Hill. *Mus Ed* Ron Newill. *Dub Ed* Ted Mason. *1st, 2d & 3d Asst Dir* Colin Brewer, Gordon Gilbert, Barry Langley. *Prod Mgr* John Pellatt. *Cont* Pamela Davies. *Wardrobe Mistress* Jackie Cummins. *Makeup* Freddie Williamson. *Hairdresser* Gladys Leakey. *Prop Buyer* Ellen Parish. *Still Photog* Ricky Smith. *Casting Dir* Lionel Grose. *Electrn Gaffer* Robert Canning. *Chargehand Prop* Albert Butler.

Cast: Tommy Steele *(Billy Bowles)*, Michael Medwin *(Max Catlin)*, Angela Douglas *(Julie Singleton)*, Jean Harvey *(Delia)*, Bernard Bresslaw *(Parsons)*, Walter Hudd *(J. B. Madgeburg)*, John Tate *(Julian Singleton)*, Janet Henfrey *(April)*, Richard Goolden *(Lord Sweatstone)*, Keith Faulkner *(Mick)*, Edward Cast *(Hugh)*, Anthony Dawes *(Cyril Bong)*, Barbara Clegg *(Miss Ventnor)*, Iris Russell *(Nellie)*, Abril Ward *(Penny)*, Michael Thompson *(Pete)*, Geoffrey Chandler *(Herbert)*, Robert Dean *(Geoff Munday)*, Bill Cartwright *(head waiter)*, Bruce Beeby *(announcer)*, Gordon Waine *(stage manager)*, Marigold Russell *(pale girl)*, Gillian McCutchon *(gushing girl)*, Bryan Parker *(Archie)*, Anthony Pelly *(Norman Winten)*, John Barry, The Clyde Valley Stompers, Russ Conway, Johnny De Little, Carol Deene, Shane Fenton and the Fentones, Dick Kallman, Geoff Love, Marion Ryan, Danny Williams, George Mitchell Show, Tony Mercer, John Boulter, Dai Francis *(guest stars)*.

Musical comedy-drama. Billy Bowles is an excellent talent scout for a large record company in London's West End, but his unscrupulous boss, Max Catlin, sees that he gets little credit. Each Sunday Billy pays a visit to the Ladywick Orphanage where he was raised and where he now entertains the children by singing to them. Learning of the orphanage's need for money, Billy arranges a fundraising concert with the help of Julie, his secretary and girl friend. He plans to use singers employed by his company, and he writes to each singer, but, unknown to him, the letters are lost, and on the night of the concert there is a huge audience and no performers. Billy goes onstage to stall while Julie rounds up the singers, and his performance is a great success. The singers arrive; the benefit concert is a hit; the orphanage gets its money; the record company gets a new singing star in Billy; and Billy and Julie look forward to a happy future. *Talent scouts. Orphans. Singers. Secretaries. Rock and roll. Employer-employee relations. Orphanages. Charity. London—West End. Documentation.*

Note: Opened in London in Aug 1963 as *It's All Happening;* running time: 101 min.

A DREAM OF KINGS   F6.1280

National General Productions. *Dist* National General Pictures. 15 Dec **1969** [New York opening]. Sd (Westrex); col (Technicolor). 35mm. 107 min. *MPAA rating* R.

Prod Jules Schermer. *Assoc Prod* Harry Mark Petrakis. *Prod Assoc* James S. Elliott. *Post-Prod Supv* Jack Kirschner. *Dir* Daniel Mann. *Screenplay* Harry Mark Petrakis, Ian Hunter. *Dir Photog* Richard H. Kline. *Set Decor* William Kiernan. *Prod Dsgn* Boris Leven. *Titl* Pacific Title. *Film Ed* Walter Hannemann, Raymond Daniels. *Mus Comp & Cond* Alex North. *Sd* Bill Ford. *Mus Ed* John Mick. *Asst Dir* James Rosenberger, C. E. Dismukes, Joe Nayfack. *Exec Prod Mgr* Harry A. Caplan. *Unit Prod Mgr* Robert Goodstein. *Cost* Eric Seelig. *Makeup Supv* Charles Blackman.

Cast: Anthony Quinn (*Matsoukas*), Irene Papas (*Caliope*), Inger Stevens (*Anna*), Sam Levene (*Cicero*), Val Avery (*Fatsas*), Tamara Daykarhanova (*mother-in-law*), Peter Mamakos (*Falconis*), James Dobson (*doctor*), Zvee Scooler (*Zenoitis*), Bill Walker (*Kampana*), H. B. Haggerty (*Turk*), Alan Reed, Sr. (*Fig King*), Radames Pera (*Stavros*), Theoharis Lemonopoulos (*himself*), Stasa Damascus (*Falconis' daughter*), Katherine Theodore (*Mrs. Cournos*), James Fortunes (*Tony*), Ernest Sarracino (*Toundas*), Renata Vanni (*Mrs. Falconis*), Chris Marks (*Telecles*), Sandra Damato (*Faith*), Effie Columbus (*Hope*), Peter Kogeones (*Angelo*), Alberto Morin (*Aristotle*), Peter Xantho (*Javaras*), George Savalas (*Apollo*), Tol Avery (*Herman*), Tony Jochim (*Uncle Louie*), George Michaelides (*doctor in church*), Lisa Pera, Lisa Moore (*nurses*).

Drama. Source: Harry Mark Petrakis, *A Dream of Kings* (New York, 1966). Greco-American gambler and folk philosopher Matsoukas, a paragon of integrity, ekes out a marginal existence in Chicago. When his seven-year-old son Stavros is diagnosed as terminally ill, Matsoukas is convinced that only the sun of his native Athens can cure the boy. Pressed for air fare to Greece, Matsoukas begs from his generous friend Cicero, who dies before he can honor the request. Although they are lovers, the widow Anna, proprietress of a local bakery, denies him a loan. Desperate for money, Matsoukas loads his dice. Discovered and shamed, he permits himself to be beaten mercilessly. In his absence, his wife Caliope steals her mother's savings, enabling father and son to return to the homeland. *Greeks. Immigrants. Children. Incurable illness. Poverty. Theft. Family life. Gambling. Chicago.*

DREAM OF LOVE   F6.1281

21 Dec **1967** [New York opening]. Sd; col? 35mm? [Feature film, length unknown.]

Dir Benjamin Haymeen. No information about the precise nature of this film has been found. *Sexuality.*

DREAM OF LOVE (Japan)   F6.1282

Toho Co. 17 Jun **1970** [Los Angeles opening]. Sd; col. 35mm. [Feature film, length unknown.]

Cast: Wakako Sakai.

Drama. No information about the precise nature of this film has been found.
Note: Original title and release undetermined.

THE DREAM OF THE RED CHAMBER (Republic of China)   F6.1283

Hayien Film Studio. 25 May **1966** [New York showing]. Sd; b&w. 35mm. [Feature film, length unknown.]

Dir Wang Ping. *Mus Perf by* Yuehchu Opera Company (Shanghai).

Cast: Hsu Yu-lan, Wang Wen-chuan, Lu Jui-ying, Chin Tsai-feng, Chou Pao-kui.

Opera film. Source: Ts'ao Chan, *Hung lou mêng* (1792). Pao-yu is born into the rich and prominent Chia family, a piece of jade in his mouth. As he matures, Pao-yu is torn between his affection for his frail cousin, Tai-yu, and his attraction to Pao-ch'ai of the Hseuh family. After he loses his jade piece, his fortunes and those of his family are reversed. His father delays his departure for a post in a remote province until his son's wedding. Because of Tai-yu's ill health, the family chooses Pao-ch'ai as Pao-yu's bride without consulting him. On the wedding day Tai-yu dies, and the shocked Pao-yu sickens. Shortly thereafter his uncle is revealed to be dishonest, and the family loses position and fortune. As Pao-yu lies near death, a Buddhist monk returns the precious jade. After he awakens from a long dream, Pao-yu's life changes dramatically. He wins a literary contest, and his wife conceives a child. Pao-yu, however, disappears. His father witnesses his subsequent abduction by a Buddhist monk and Taoist priest, who return him to the great void. *Upper classes. Monks. Authors. Priests. Family life. Mysticism. Marriage—Arranged. Death. Buddhism. Pregnancy. Jade. Dreams.*

Note: Taiwanese title: *Hung lou meng.*

THE DREAM WORLD OF HARRISON MARKS *see* THE NAKED WORLD OF HARRISON MARKS

THE DREAMER (United States/Israel)   F6.1284

Toda Films–Cannon Productions. *Dist* Cannon Releasing Corp. 27 May **1970** [New York opening]. Sd; col (Movielab). 35mm. 86 min. *MPAA rating* R.

Pres by The Cannon Group. *Prod* Ami Artzi. *Exec Prod* Dennis Friedland, Christopher C. Dewey. *Asst Prod* Dassy Artzi. *Dir-Writ* Dan Wolman. *Dir Photog* Paul Glickman. *Adtl Photog* Yaacov Kallach. *Film Ed* Barry Harte Prince. *Mus* Gershon Kingsley. *Sd* Bruce Perlman, Francisco Batier. *Asst Dir* Gad Ben-Artzi, Raffi Nathan. *Prod Mgr* Abraham Berman.

Cast: Tuvia Tavi (*Eli*), Leora Rivlin (*girl*), Berta Litvina (*Rachel*), Shlomo Bar-Shavit (*manager of home*), Dvora Keidar (*mother*), Nathan Kogan (*father*), Israel Segal (*waiter*), Nathan W. Volfovitz (*Mushkin*), Bila Rabinovitz (*Litvinna*), Bronka Zaltzman, Arie Kasbiner, Esther Kadosh, Alina Starnitzka, Isaac Mandelbaum, Rodulf Henig, Abraham Markowitz, Adina Fair, Moshe Segal, Harriet Karr, Jacob Timan.

Melodrama. Eli, a handsome handyman at an old people's home in Safad, Israel, dreams of becoming an artist. In his spare time, he sketches the residents of the home. He becomes particularly fond of Rachel, an elderly woman from Kiev, and a close personal friendship develops between the two. One day, Eli meets a young girl who has come to the home to pick up the possessions of her deceased grandfather. While the two are making love in Eli's room, Rachel knocks on the door, but Eli does not answer. At first Rachel is hurt, and the other women taunt her, but she gradually comes to realize Eli's need for young company. [Other sources indicate that Eli decides that his friendship with Rachel and his responsibility to the other old people who are awaiting death are more important than the young girl.] *Handymen. Russians. Old age. Friendship. Old age homes. Drawings. Safad (Israel).*

Note: Filmed on location in Safad, Israel. Released in Israel as *Ha'timhoni.*

THE DREAMERS (Denmark)   F6.1285

Saga Film–ASA Film. *Dist* Trans–Lux Distributing Corp. Jun **1969**. Sd; b&w. 35mm. 92 min.

Dir Kirsten Stenbaek. *Screenplay* Bent Grasten, Kirsten Stenbaek. *Dir Photog* Mikael Salomon. *Film Ed* Kasper Schyberg. *Mus* Erik Moseholm. *Choreog* Vivian Bjarnov Lage. *Sd* Michael Nielsen, Leon Seibaek. *Prod Mgr* Jens Ravn, Peter Refn. *Stills* Dirk Brüel.

Cast: Sisse Reingaard (*Elise Lorentsen*), Per Bentzon (*Harald Lorentsen*), Peter Bierlich (*William*), Gertie Jung (*Isabella Torso*).

Comedy. Source: Hans Egede Schack, *Phantasterne* (Copenhagen, 1858). The marriage of Harald and Elise Lorentsen becomes a triangle when Elise and the couple's friend William fall in love. Another woman displaces Elise in William's affections, but rather than return to her husband, Elise agrees with Harald to seek an amicable divorce. *Infidelity. Divorce.*

Note: Opened in Copenhagen in May 1967 as *Fantasterne*; running time: 87 min.

DREAMS OF GLASS   F6.1286

Dist Universal Pictures. 16 Aug **1970** [New York opening]. Sd; col (DeLuxe). 35mm. 83 min. *MPAA rating* GP.

Prod-Dir-Writ Robert Clouse. *Photog* Michael Murphy, photog. *Art Dir* Ann Philip Clouse. *Film Ed* Stephen L. Lewis. *Mus* Ian Freebairn-Smith. *Lyr* W. Earl Brown. *Sd* Rod Sutton, Ken Carlson. *Opticals* Van Der Veer Photo Co.

Cast: John Denos (*Tom Parsegian*), Caroline Barrett (*Ann Murakoshi*), Joe Lo Presti (*Tom's father*), Margaret Rich (*Tom's mother*), Paul Micale (*Pucci*), Donald Elson (*Ann's father*), Pat Li (*Ann's mother*), The Smokestack Lightnin', Charles P. Thompson, Tony Benson, Miyoshi Jingu, Danny De Vito, Ken Tilles, Timothy Burns, Robert Strand.

Romantic melodrama. Tom, an unpredictable 18-year-old high school dropout, is in love with Ann, a 16-year-old Chinese girl; but Ann's conservative parents and Tom's father, a middle-aged San Pedro fisherman, both object to the relationship. Despite these objections, the couple are happy together. While walking in the local park, playing hide-and-seek and taking photographs of each other, the two are spotted by Ann's mother, who chastises Ann when she returns home. The following afternoon, Tom takes Ann to a deserted warehouse that belongs to his father, and they decide to make it their home. At Christmas, Tom gives Ann a double bed, and the couple make love. Returning home the following morning, Ann finds that her parents have reported her disappearance to the police, but she convinces them that she spent the night in the attic of her parents' home. In the meantime, Tom's father has discovered the identity of his son's lover and reprimands him severely. The couple hitchhike to the country and shock a family of tourists with their nude bathing. Upon returning to the city, they discover that their warehouse retreat has been vandalized. Ann breaks down and cries, and Tom tries to console her with a promise of marriage. *Fishermen. Chinese. Adolescence. Filial relations. Racial prejudice. Miscegenation. Christmas. San Pedro (California).*

DREAMY LOVE BED see **CANDY BABY**

DIE DREIGROSCHENOPER see **THREE PENNY OPERA**

DAS DREIMÄDERLHAUS see **THE HOUSE OF THE THREE GIRLS**

THE DRIFTER   F6.1287

Surfilms. *Dist* Film-Makers' Distribution Center. 24 May **1967** [New York opening]. Sd; b&w. 35mm. 74 min. [Original length: 85 min.]

Prod Pierre Lasry. *Dir-Writ* Alex Matter. *Photog* Stephen R. Winsten. *Mus* Ken Lauber. *Sd* Steve Harris. *Director's Cons* Jordan Leondopoulos.

Cast: John Tracy *(Alan)*, Sadja Marr *(Renee)*, Michael Fair *(Mike)*, Lew Skinner *(musician)*, Ed Randolph *(club owner)*, Paula Feiten *(waitress)*, Clair Pelly *(girl on horseback)*, Michael Onida *(ticket taker)*.

Melodrama. Lacking money or purpose, Alan, a young man, drifts around the country without establishing lasting relationships. The son of a concert pianist who apparently wishes to avoid him, Alan has made his life a stream of slight encounters. Occasionally he will accept a handout or have a tentative affair with a lonely young woman, only to move on again. One day, while walking around New York City, he meets a French singer, Renee, whom he had known previously, and follows her to Montauk Point on Long Island. Renee has a little boy who may be Alan's son. Drawn to the child, Alan experiences a brief moment during which he wants to stay. But after sobbing quietly on the beach, he leaves the young woman and her child and resumes his wandering. *Drifters. Singers. French. Children. Alienation. Fatherhood. Loneliness. New York City. Montauk Point.*

Note: Location scenes filmed in New York City and at Montauk Point, Long Island.

THE DRIFTERS see **HALLUCINATION GENERATION**

DRIVERS TO HELL see **WILD ONES ON WHEELS**

LA DROGUE DU VICE see **NIGHT OF LUST**

UN DRÔLE DE PAROISSIEN see **THANK HEAVEN FOR SMALL FAVORS**

DROP DEAD, DARLING see **ARRIVEDERCI, BABY!**

THE DROP OUTS   F6.1288

4 Apr **1969** [New York opening]. Sd; b&w? 16mm? [Feature length assumed.]No information about the precise nature of this film has been found. *Sexuality.*

DRUMS OF AFRICA   F6.1289

Metro-Goldwyn-Mayer, Inc.–Zimbalist-Krasne Productions. *Dist* Metro-Goldwyn-Mayer, Inc. 15 May **1963** [Cleveland opening; c8 Mar 1963; LP24449]. Sd (Westrex); col (Metrocolor). 35mm. 92 min.

Prod Alfred Zimbalist, Philip N. Krasne. *Dir* James B. Clark. *Screenplay* Robin Estridge. *Story* Arthur Hoerl, Robin Estridge. *Photog* Paul C. Vogel. *Art Dir* George W. Davis, Addison Hehr. *Set Decor* Henry Grace, Jack Mills. *Film Ed* Ben Lewis. *Mus Score* Johnny Mandel. *Song:* "The River Love" Russell Faith, Robert Marcucci. *Sung by* Frankie Avalon. *Rec Supv* Franklin Milton. *Asst Dir* Hank Moonjean. *Asst to the Prod* Bud Gaunt. *Makeup* William Tuttle. *Hairstyles* Mary Keats. *Sp Vis Eff* Robert R. Hoag.

Cast: Frankie Avalon *(Brian Ferrers)*, Mariette Hartley *(Ruth Knight)*, Lloyd Bochner *(David Moore)*, Torin Thatcher *(Jack Cuortemayn)*, Hari Rhodes *(Kasongo)*, George Sawaya *(Arab)*, Michael Pate *(Viledo)*, Ron Whelan *(ship captain)*, Peter Mamakos *(Chavera)*.

Adventure melodrama. In 1897 engineer David Moore is sent to Equatorial East Africa to plan a new railway route. Accompanied by young Brian Ferrers, the nephew of the railroad firm's owner, he arrives in Edwardstown. Jack Cuortemayn, an old white hunter whom he expected to lead the safari, refuses to guide them to the railroad site because of his opposition to anything that might change the Africa he loves. Cuortemayn and mission worker Ruth Knight warn Moore that he should not start his trek until a band of slavers leave the area. Moore ignores their advice, and he and Brian lose their way in the wilderness. After they are rescued by Cuortemayn and Ruth, a romance develops between Moore and the young woman. Distrustful, Cuortemayn offers to lead Moore to the railroad site if he will promise not to see Ruth again. Ruth overhears the conversation, sets off for the mission hospital, and is captured by the slavers, who take her and a group of native captives to a secret mountain hideout where they are to be sold to Arab slave traders. Moore, Cuortemayn, and Brian unite to save her; their surprise attack catches the slavers unaware; and Brian seals their fate by dynamiting them inside a cave. The safari then regroups, this time to head for the site of the proposed railroad. *Engineers. Slavers. Guides. Hunters. Missionaries. Arabs. Railroads. Safaris. Explosives. British East Africa.*

THE DRUMS OF TABU (Italy/Spain)   F6.1290

Splendor Film–F. I. S. A.–AS Films Producción. *Dist* Producers Releasing Organization. May **1967**. Sd; col (Eastman Color, print by Movielab). 35mm. 91 min.

Pres by L. M. Films, Westside International. A Sidney W. Pink Production. *Prod* Sidney Pink. *Exec Prod* José López Moreno. *Dir* Javier Setó. *Screenplay* Javier Setó, Santiago Moncada. *Photog* Modica Antonio. *Art Dir* Wolfgang Burman. *Set Decor* Pablo Gago. *Film Ed* Antonio Ramírez. *Mus* Gregorio García Segura. *Prod Mgr* Antonio López Moreno.

Cast: James Philbrook *(Bill Harrigan)*, Seyna Seyn *(Anahita)*, Frank Moran *(Yawata)*, Frank Fantasia *(Padre Lorenzo)*, Beny Deus *(Charlie)*, Chick Cicarelli *(Bruno)*, Carlo Tamberlani *(Inspector Duras)*, John Sutton *(Taaroa)*, Joseph Han *(Ling)*, Enrique Navarro, Manuel Gallardo, Renato Terra, Fernando Sánchez Polack, Barta Barri.

Adventure melodrama. On the island of Totoya in the Fiji archipelago, Korean War veteran Bill Harrigan supplies himself with whiskey by selling his boat, piece by piece. One day Anahita, a Samoan girl, is washed ashore, fleeing from Yawata, a Malayan nightclub owner who later arrives to reclaim Anahita as his slave. She stabs him and escapes with Bill to Manua, the island of her birth. En route she warns him that she is considered tabu there because of her refusal to marry Taaroa, a young man chosen for her by the high priests. Meanwhile, the wounded Yawata has instructed his men to inform the police that he was murdered by Bill and Anahita. Bill eventually is arrested, but his friends trick the authorities into sailing in the wrong direction, where they encounter Yawata returning for Anahita. In the ensuing fight between Bill and Yawata, the latter is killed by a shipboard explosion. Bill is free to begin a new life with Anahita. *Veterans. Americans in foreign countries. Samoans. Malayans. Nightclub owners. Police. Alcoholism. Social customs. Liquor. Fiji Islands. American Samoa. Ship explosions.*

Note: Location scenes filmed in Spain; working title: *Tabú (fugitivos de los mares del sur)*. Opened in Madrid in Sep 1966 as *Tabú (fugitivos de las islas del sur)*; running time: 108 min; released in Italy in 1968 as *La vergine di Samoa.* The following are credited in the United States under their anglicized names: Francisco Morán (Frank Moran), Franco Fantasia (Frank Fantasia), and Pietro Ceccarelli (Chick Cicarelli).

THE DRY BIKINI see **HER BIKINI NEVER GOT WET**

DRY SUMMER (Turkey)   F6.1291

Hitit Filim. *Dist* Manson Distributing Corp. 6 Jan **1967** [Minneapolis opening]. Sd; b&w. 35mm. 90 min.

Prod Ulvi Doğan. *Assoc Prod U. S. Vers* William Shelton. *Dir* Metin Erksan. *Assoc Dir U. S. Vers* David Durston. *Scen* Metin Erksan, İsmet Saydan, Kemal İnci. *Story* Necati Cumali. *Photog* Ali Uğur. *Film Ed* Stuart Gellman. *Mus (see note)* Yamaci, Manos Hadjidakis. *Mus Dir* Ferit Tüzün. *Mus Played by* Presidential Philharmonic Orchestra of Turkey, Ravi Shankar. *Sd Rec* Laszlo Haverland. *Optical Eff* Rodney Friedson.

Cast: Ulvi Doğan *(Hassan)*, Erol Taş *(Osman)*, Hülya Koçyiğit *(Bahar)*, Hakki Haktan, Yavuz Yalinkiliç, Zeki Tüney, Alaettin Altiok, Members of Jerusalem Theatre Arts Players, Members of Athens Hellenic Theatre, Members of Istanbul Theatre of Performing Arts.

Domestic melodrama. Osman, a selfish Turkish landowner, refuses to share his water supply with other tobacco farmers when their village is threatened with a severe drought. His younger brother, Hassan, who has recently married Bahar, disagrees with Osman's decision. Forced to guard his land from irate planters, Osman kills an intruder, but Hassan, in accordance with family deference to seniority, confesses to the crime. Hassan is imprisoned for 2 years for manslaughter, while Osman deviously attempts to win the affection of his sister-in-law. He is rejected until he convinces Bahar that Hassan has died in jail. Hassan is soon granted amnesty, however, and freed by a new political regime. Upon returning to the farm, he kills his treacherous brother and opens the floodgates to provide water for the other farmers. *Farmers. Brothers. In-laws. Newlyweds. Drought. Greed. Water rights. Manslaughter. Self-sacrifice. Infidelity. Perfidy. Fratricide.*

Note: Filmed on location in Bademler Koy. Released in Turkey in 1963 as *Susuz yaz.* Erol Taş is also known as Errol Tash, and Hülya Koçyiğit as Julie Kotch. Sources conflict in crediting music.

DRYLANDERS (Canada)   F6.1292

National Film Board of Canada. 3 Feb **1965** [Colorado Springs, Colorado, opening]. Sd; b&w. 35mm (Superscope). 69 min.

Prod Peter Jones, prod. *Assoc Prod* David Haber. *Dir* Donald Haldane. *2d Unit Dir* Kirk Jones. *Story & Screenplay* M. Charles Cohen. *Photog* Reginald Morris. *Adtl Photog* John Gunn. *Art Dir* Jack McCullagh. *Film Ed* John Kemeny, Kirk Jones. *Mus* Eldon Rathburn. *Sd* Clarke Daprato, Ron Alexander. *Cost* Yuki Yoshida. *Sp Eff* Wally Gentleman.

Cast: Frances Hyland (*Liza Greer*), James Douglas (*Dan Greer*), Lester Nixon (*Bob MacPherson*), Mary Savage (*Ada MacPherson*), William Fruet (*Colin*), Don Francks (*Russel*), Irena Mayeska (*Thora*), William Weintraub (*narrator*), Jonathon Little.

Domestic Drama. In 1907, Boer War veteran Dan Greer becomes disillusioned with his job as a clerk and leaves Montreal with his wife, Liza, and their two sons. Traveling west, they stake out a farmstead in Saskatchewan and, with the help of the MacPhersons, their Scottish neighbors, build a home. Their first harvest is destroyed by hail, but the Greers persevere and reap bumper wheat crops. However, the prosperity of the 1920's is followed by years of drought. During the Great Depression, many farmers leave the land. Dan's older son goes to the city, only to find mass unemployment. Threatened with financial ruin and near starvation, Dan dies a broken man. His widow, younger son, and daughter-in-law contemplate deserting the farm, but the drought ends and they remain to start over. *Veterans. Clerks. Homesteaders. Scotch. Neighbors. Family life. Farm life. Drought. Unemployment. Wheat. The Great Depression (1929–34). Montreal. Saskatchewan. Hailstorms.*

Note: Filmed on location in 1961 at Swift Current, Saskatchewan, Canada. Opened in Swift Current in Sep 1963. French Canadian title: *Un autre pays.*

DSCHINGIS KHAN *see* **GENGHIS KHAN**

DU BIST DIE WELT FÜR MICH *see* **YOU ARE THE WORLD FOR ME**

DU BIST MUSIK (West Germany)   **F6.1293**
CCC–Filmkunst. *Dist* Casino Films. 18 May **1962** [New York opening]. Sd; col (Eastmancolor). 35mm. 91 min.
Prod Artur Brauner. *Dir* Paul Martin. *Screenplay* Paul Martin, Tibor Yost, Janos von Vaszary. *Photog* Georg Bruckbauer. *Art Dir* Helmut Nentwig, Albrecht Hennings. *Film Ed* Jutta Hering. *Mus* Heinz Gietz, Heino Gaze. *Lyr* Kurt Feltz. *Played by* Kurt Edelhagen Orchestra. *Choreog* Billy Daniel. *Sd* Erwin Schänzle. *Prod Dir* Horst Wendlandt.
Cast: Caterina Valente (*Marina Rosario*), Paul Hubschmid (*Paul Heiden/King Otto III*), Grethe Weiser (*prime minister*), Rudolf Platte (*Financial Adviser Rudi Klemke*), Bum Krüger, Ernst Waldow, Silvio Francesco, Werner Fuetterer, Ruth Stephan, Walter Bluhm, Billy Daniel, Tommy Albertus, Robert Stevenson, actor, Gerard Nel.
Musical comedy. From a novel by: Paul H. Rameau. In Spain, after his score for a musical revue has been rejected by actress Marina Rosario, composer Paul Heiden loses consciousness in an accident. Mistaken for King Otto III, the ruler of the small municipality of Montania, Paul is taken to Otto's castle. Paul's suddenly acquired power allows him to invite Marina to perform her revue in the royal court. The real king, who has been in Egypt on an archeological expedition, returns home and discovers the deception. Paul returns to Munich, where he watches Marina perform her revue on television and declare his love for him. *Composers. Actors. Royalty. Archeologists. Doubles. Mistaken identity. Duplicity. Musical revues. Imaginary kingdoms. Spain. Munich.*

Note: Released in West Germany in Sep 1956.

DU CÔTÉ DE ROBINSON *see* **BAD COMPANY**

DU RIFIFI À PANAME *see* **THE UPPER HAND**

DU RIFIFI CHEZ LES FEMMES *see* **RIFF RAFF GIRLS**

DUBIOUS PATRIOTS *see* **THE SECRET INVASION**

THE DUBIOUS PATRIOTS *see* **YOU CAN'T WIN 'EM ALL**

IL DUCA NERO *see* **THE BLACK DUKE**

THE DUCHESS *see* **THE CHELSEA GIRLS**

I DUE COLONNELLI *see* **TWO COLONELS**

I DUE MAFIOSI DELL'F.B.I. *see* **DR. GOLDFOOT AND THE GIRL BOMBS**

DUE MARINES E UN GENERALE *see* **WAR ITALIAN STYLE**

I DUE NEMICI *see* **THE BEST OF ENEMIES**

DUE NOTTI CON CLEOPATRA *see* **TWO NIGHTS WITH CLEOPATRA**

THE DUEL (U.S.S.R.)   **F6.1294**
Mosfilm. *Dist* Artkino Pictures. 5 Sep **1964** [New York opening]. Sd; col. 35mm. 88 min. [Also reviewed at 93 min.]
Dir Tatyana Berezantseva, Lev Rudnik. *Screenplay* Tatyana Berezantseva. *Story Ed* N. Ushakova. *Photog* Antonina Egina. *Art Dir* V. Kamskiy. *Asst Art Dir* S. Dzyabura. *Film Ed* P. Chechyotkina. *Mus* V. Yurovskiy. *Cond* G. Gamburg. *Sd* V. Ladygina. *Prod Mgr* G. Lukin. *Cost* V. Nisskaya. *Makeup* Mikhail Chikiryov. *Sp Eff* B. Gorbachyov.

Cast: Lyudmila Shagalova (*Nadezhda Fyodorovna*), Oleg Strizhenov (*Layevskiy*), Vladimir Druzhnikov (*von Koren*), Aleksandr Khvylya (*Samoylenko*), L. Kadrov (*Pobedov*), G. Georgiu (*Kirilin*), Ye. Kuzmina (*Marya Konstantinovna*), L. Pirogov (*Bityugov*), Yu. Leonidov (*Achmianov*), V. Burlakova, P. Vinnik, E. Geller, A. Kuznetsov, actor 2, V. Kulik, S. Svashenko, P. Sobolevskiy, I. Fyodorova, Nina Vilvovskaya, S. Yermilov.

Drama. Source: Anton Pavlovich Chekhov, "Duel," in *Novoye vremya* (22 Oct–27 Nov 1891). Ivan Andreyevich Layevskiy serves in Yalta, leading an empty, colorless life. With his mistress Nadezhda Fyodorovna, who left her husband to join him, he dreamed of serving solemn ideals, but his idealism is a thing of the past, and love seemingly has disappeared with the passing of time. Layevskiy spends his time in card games and conversation. Nadezhda, in her own boredom, has accepted the solicitations of the vulgar Kirilin and flirts with Achmianov, the son of a wealthy local shopkeeper to whom she is in debt. The news of the death of Nadezhda's husband throws Layevskiy into confusion. With the possibility of marriage thrust upon him, Layevskiy feels repulsed by Nadezhda and their idle, dreary life. Wishing to return to St. Petersburg, he asks for a loan from his friend Dr. Samoylenko, a kind, simple-hearted man who promises to help him. Lacking his own funds, Samoylenko seeks the help of von Koren, a zoologist who boards with him. Von Koren, a socially-conscious man of affairs, holds Layevskiy in contempt, and he refuses the loan when he learns its purpose. During an evening gathering, he sends Layevskiy a derisive message, and Layevskiy becomes hysterical. An argument ensues, and von Koren accepts Layevskiy's challenge to a duel. That same evening, the jealous Achmianov informs Layevskiy of the intimate relations between Nadezhda and Kirilin. The news spreads throughout the town, but von Koren's resolve does not weaken, and he rejects Layevskiy's offer of conciliation. Layevskiy fires into the air, and a chance obstacle causes von Koren to miss his shot. Three months pass, and von Koren is preparing to leave on a trip to the Bering Straits. Samoylenko persuades him to visit Layevskiy and forgive him. Having changed greatly, Layevskiy has committed himself to working, lives frugally, and is repaying his debts. Feeling responsible toward Nadezhda, he watches over her lovingly. Von Koren, embarrassed, realizes that he was wrong in his estimation of Layevskiy. *Mistresses. Zoologists. Physicians. Alienation. Infidelity. Debt. Yalta. Duels.*

Note: Released in the U.S.S.R. in May 1961 as *Duel*; running time: 88 min.

DUEL À RIO BRAVO *see* **GUNMEN OF THE RIO GRANDE**

DUEL AT DIABLO   **F6.1295**
Rainbow Productions–Brien Productions. *Dist* United Artists. 12 May **1966** [Salt Lake City, Utah, opening; c12 May 1966; LP32947]. Sd; col (DeLuxe). 35mm. 103 min.
A Ralph Nelson–Fred Engel–Cherokee Production. *Prod* Ralph Nelson, Fred Engel. *Dir* Ralph Nelson. *Screenplay* Marvin H. Albert, Michel M. Grilikhes. *Photog* Charles F. Wheeler. *Art Dir* Alfred Ybarra. *Set Decor* Victor Gangelin. *Film Ed* Fredric Steinkamp. *Mus* Neal Hefti. *Sd* Joe Edmondson. *Mus Ed* Richard Carruth. *Asst Dir* Emmett Emerson, Philip N. Cook. *Prod Supv* J. Paul Popkin. *Asst to the Dir* Al Wyatt. *Cost* Yvonne Wood. *Makeup* Gustaf M. Norin. *Sp Eff* Roscoe Cline, Larry Hampton, George Peckham. *Head Wrangler* Bill Jones.
Cast: James Garner (*Jess Remsberg*), Sidney Poitier (*Toller*), Bibi Andersson (*Ellen Grange*), Dennis Weaver (*Willard Grange*), Bill Travers (*Lieut. Scotty McAllister*), William Redfield (*Sergeant Ferguson*), John Hoyt (*Chata*), John Crawford (*Clay Dean*), John Hubbard (*Major Novak*), Kevin Coughlin (*Norton*), Jay Ripley (*Tech*), Jeff Cooper (*Casey*), Ralph Bahnsen (*Nyles*), Bobby Crawford (*Swenson*), Richard Lapp (*Forbes*), Armand Alzamora (*Ramirez*), Alf Elson (*Colonel Foster*), Dawn Little Sky (*Chata's wife*), Eddie Little Sky (*Alchise*), Al Wyatt (*1st miner*), Bill Hart (*Corporal Harrington*), J. R. Randall (*Crowley*), John Daheim (*stableman*), Phil Schumacher (*burly soldier*), Dick Farnsworth, Joe Finnegan (*wagon drivers*).
Western melodrama. Source: Marvin H. Albert, *Apache Rising* (Greenwich, Connecticut, 1957). Scout Jess Remsberg rescues Ellen Grange, who had been a captive of the Apaches for more than a year, and takes her back to her husband at Fort Creel. When her husband denounces her for not killing herself when captured by the Apaches, Mrs. Grange rides off during the night. The next morning Lieut. Scotty McAllister and a troop of raw recruits set out for Fort Concho with Jess as scout. Jess is seeking to avenge his Comanche wife's murder by finding the unknown white man who profited from her death by selling her scalp. Also in the party are Grange, who is taking a wagonload of goods to Concho, and Toller, a Negro ex-cavalryman who now makes his living breaking in horses for the cavalry. Moving out ahead of the troop into Indian country, Jess finds Mrs. Grange in an Apache camp. As he once more carries her away, he sees that she had a child bundled in her arms. She explains that he is her half-breed son, born out of a union between herself and the Apache chief's son. Returning with Mrs. Grange to Scotty's troop, Remsberg finds they have been ambushed by Apaches; casualties are heavy and the water supply has

been destroyed. After outwitting and routing the Indians at Diablo Canyon, where there is fresh water, Remsberg rides off for reinforcements. At Fort Concho he learns that the unknown white man he is seeking is Will Grange. Riding back to Diablo, Jess joins in the savage fighting, during which Scotty is killed and Grange is captured. When reinforcements arrive and the Apaches surrender, Jeff, Toller, Mrs. Grange, and four soldiers are all that remain of the original party. Jeff goes in search of Grange and finds him strapped to a wagon wheel hung over hot coals. He is barely alive and begs Jess to shoot him. Instead, Jess hands him a pistol, and as he walks away, a shot rings loudly. *Scouts—Frontier. Negroes. Apache Indians. Comanche Indians. Horsetrainers. Racism. Torture. Kidnaping. Revenge. Murder. Motherhood. Suicide. Forts. United States—History—Indian campaigns. United States Army—Cavalry. Horses.*

Note: Filmed in Utah.

DUEL AT EZO (Japan)   F6.1296

Tokyo Eiga Co. *Dist* Toho International, Inc. 1 Jul 1970 [Los Angeles opening]. Sd; col (Eastmancolor). 35mm (Panavision). 131 min.

Exec Prod Sanezumi Fujimoto, Yorihiko Yamada. *Dir* Kengo Furusawa. *Screenplay* Ryozo Kasahara. *Story* Renzaburo Shibata. *Photog* Hiroshi Murai. *Art Dir* Motoji Kojima. *Mus* Kenjiro Hirose.

Cast: Yuzo Kayama (*Saburota Edo*), Rentaro Mikuni (*Shimbei Usa*), Shogo Shimada (*Jirozaemon Ezo*), Mitsuko Baisho (*Aka Shu*), Kunie Tanaka (*Kurobei*), Toru Abe (*ronin*), Toshio Kurosawa (*Kyuma*), Tatsuya Nakadai (*Daizennokami Honjo*).

Action melodrama. In 19th-century Japan, Shimbei, a vassal, is assigned by the Tokugawa Shogunate to a special mission in Ezo. He is joined by Saburota and six disreputable warriors who are being paid by shipping agent Echigoya to rescue the daughter of a Russian count being held prisoner in a fort by a band of Ezo natives under the leadership of Jirozaemon. Once in Ezo, the warriors learn that Echigoya had cheated Jirozaemon in an attempt to purchase guns from the Russians, and the abduction is an act of reprisal. All join forces with Jirozaemon except Shimbei, whose mission is to recover a supply of gold hidden in the fortress and bring it back to help bolster the finances of the collapsing Shogunate. In a battle between the Russian and Shogunate forces and Jirozaemon's band, Shimbei kills Jirozaemon and tries to escape on horseback. Saburota pursues him, and wins the ensuing duel as well as the love of Jirozaemon's daughter. *Merchants. Nobility. Russians. Hostages. Abduction. Perfidy. Revenge. Japan—History—Tokugawa period 1600-1867. Ezo. Duels.*

Note: Released in Japan in Feb 1970 as *Ezo yakata no ketto*.

DUEL AT GANRYU ISLAND see SAMURAI (PART III)

DUEL OF CHAMPIONS (Italy/Spain)   F6.1297

Lux Film-Tiberia Film. *Dist* Medallion Pictures. Jun 1964. Sd; col (Eastman Color). 35mm (Totalscope). 93 min.

A Terence Young Production. *Prod* Angelo Ferrara. *Dir* Terence Young, Ferdinando Baldi. *Screenplay* Carlo Lizzani, Ennio De Concini, Giuliano Montaldo. *Story* Luciano Vincenzoni. *Photog* Amerigo Gengarelli. *Art Dir* Giulio Bongini. *Film Ed* Renzo Lucidi. *Mus* Angelo Francesco Lavagnino. *Prod Mgr* Domenico Fazzari. *Cost* Mario Giorsi.

Cast: Alan Ladd (*Horatio*), Franca Bettoja (*Marcia*), Franco Fabrizi (*Curiazio*), Robert Keith (*King of Rome*), Luciano Marin (*Eli*), Jacques Sernas (*Marcus*), Andrea Aureli (*King of Alba*), Mino Doro (*Caio*), Osvaldo Ruggeri (*warrior of Alba*), Jacqueline Derval (*Horatia*), Piero Palmeri (*warrior of Alba*), Umberto Raho (*grand priest*), Alfredo Varelli (*Sabinus*), Alana Ladd (*Scilla*), Nando Angelini (*official*), Franca Pasut (*slave*).

Historical melodrama. Based on the Roman legend of the Horatii and Curiatii triplets. During the period prior to the unification of Alba and Rome, the legendary Roman hero Horatio leads his troops against the forces of Alba in the region of Tullus Hostilius. He is wounded and taken prisoner but escapes and hides in the hills. The king of Rome, believing Horatio to have died a coward's death, announces the engagement of his daughter Marcia to Horatio's brother Marcus, whom he names his heir. Both Alba and Rome are anxious to find a peaceful solution to their quarrels, and after consulting an oracle, the two kings decide that three brothers from each side should compete in a fight to the death, the winning side to dominate in the unification of the two kingdoms. Horatio comes back to Rome, but finding his name dishonored and Marcia married, he returns to the hills. On the day of the contest, however, he comes to fight alongside his two brothers. Both are killed, but Horatio continues the fight alone and kills the three Alban brothers, including Curiazio, who was the lover of Horatio's sister, Horatia. She stabs herself to death, and Horatio, now free to marry Marcia, sadly considers the cost of his victory. *Legendary characters. Soldiers. Brothers. Triplets. Brother-sister relationship. Suicide. Rome—History—Monarchy & Republic. Rome. Tullus Hostilius. Alba Longa. Duels. Horatii. Curiatii.*

Note: Rome opening in Feb 1961 as *Orazi e Curiazi*; running time: 105 min.

DUEL OF THE TITANS (Italy)   F6.1298

Titanus-Ajace Cinematografica. *Dist* Paramount Pictures. Jun 1963 [New York opening: 7 Aug; c31 Dec 1962; LP25370]. Sd; col (Eastmancolor). 35mm (CinemaScope). 90 min.

Prod Alessandro Jacovoni. *Exec Prod* Vittorio Glori Musy. *Dir-Writ* Sergio Corbucci. *2d Unit Dir* Franco Giraldi. *Screenplay* Sergio Corbucci, Luciano Martino, Sergio Leone, Sergio Prosperi, Franco Rossetti, Ennio De Concini, Duccio Tessari. *Dir Photog* Enzo Barboni, Dario Di Palma. *Art Dir* Saverio D'Eugenio. *Set Decor* Carlo Simi. *Film Ed* Gabriele Varriale. *Mus* Piero Piccioni. *Asst Dir* Guido Zurli, Mimmola Girosi. *Prod Mgr* Franco Palaggi. *Cost* Pier Luigi Pizzi.

Cast: Steve Reeves (*Romulus*), Gordon Scott (*Remus*), Virna Lisi (*Julia*), Massimo Girotti (*Tatius Titus*), Ornella Vanoni (*Tarpeia*), Jacques Sernas (*Curtius*), Franco Volpi (*Amulius*), Andrea Bosic (*Faustulus*), Laura Solari (*Rhea Silvia*), Enzo Cerusico (*Numa Pompilius*), Giuliano Dall'Ovo (*Publius*), Germano Longo (*Servius*), Franco Balducci (*Acilius*), Piero Lulli (*Sulpicius*), Gianni Glori Musy (*Fabius Celer*), Enrico Glori (*priest*), José Greci (*Estia*), Inge Nystrom (*Sira*), Mimmo Poli, Nando Angelini, Inger Milton.

Adventure melodrama. The high priestess Rhea Silvia, daughter of the murdered king of Alba Longa, bears twin sons by the god Mars and places the babies, Romulus and Remus, into the river current to prevent them from also being slain. A she-wolf finds them, nurses them, and rears them from infancy. After they reach manhood, they learn of their royal heritage, return to their homeland, and kill the usurpers to their throne. After burning the city, they lead the people beyond the mountains and swamps to a plain where they hope to build a great city. Meanwhile, bitter rivalry has sprung up between Romulus and Remus over Julia, daughter of the king of the Sabines, who has deserted her people to be with Romulus. Remus challenges his brother to a duel in which Romulus mortally wounds him. Before he dies, Remus and Romulus forgive each other their wrongdoings. Romulus, with Julia at his side, sets out to found the mighty Roman Empire. *Royalty. Usurpers. Twins. Brothers. Murder. Personal identity. Jealousy. Fratricide. Duels. Rome. Alba Longa. Romulus. Remus. Rhea Silvia. Amulius. Wolves.*

Note: Released in Italy in 1961 as *Romolo e Remo*; running time: 107 min.

DUET FOR CANNIBALS (Sweden)   F6.1299

Sandrews-Teater AB. *Dist* Grove Press. 14 Oct 1969 [New York opening]. Sd; b&w. 35mm. 105 min.

Prod Göran Lindgren. *Exec Prod* Peter Hald. *Dir-Writ* Susan Sontag. *Dir Photog* Lars Swanberg. *Camera* Hans Welin. *Film Ed* Carl-Olov Skeppstedt. *Mus From the Works of* Anton Dvořák, Gustav Mahler, Richard Wagner. *Sd* Ulf Darin. *Asst Sd* Kjell Nicklasson. *Sd Mix* Sven Fahlén. *Asst Dir* Brita Werkmäster. *Cont* Kerstin Eriksdotter. *Cost* Katerina Lindgren. *Makeup* Tina Johansson. *Prop* Katerina Lindgren. *Electrn* Ulf Björk. *English Subtitl* Susan Sontag.

Cast: Adriana Asti (*Francesca Bauer*), Lars Ekborg (*Artur Bauer*), Gösta Ekman, Jr. (*Tomas*), Agneta Ekmanner (*Ingrid*), Britta Brunius (*Mrs. Grundberg*), Stig Engström (*Lars*), Gunnar Lindqvist (*man in cafeteria*).

Drama. Artur Bauer, a middle-aged professor and ex-revolutionary leader, hires a left-wing student, Tomas, to serve as his secretary and assemble a scattered collection of papers for publication. Tomas moves into the Bauer household to facilitate his work, even though it means leaving his girl friend Ingrid. He soon becomes perplexed by the strange relationship between Bauer and his eccentric wife, Francesca, and is shocked to learn from a tape recording that the professor is suffering from a fatal disease and that he plans to murder his wife. One evening, Francesca seduces Tomas, at her husband's request. Bauer then persuades Ingrid to move into the house to protect her lover, but upon arriving, the young woman falls under the spell of the couple and enjoys the advances of both. When Tomas discovers Francesca watching Bauer make love to Ingrid, he decides that the situation has gone far enough and leaves the house, promising to return only if Ingrid is released. Bauer agrees to give Ingrid her freedom if Tomas will return to work, but Ingrid's first move upon returning to the old apartment is to take a new lover. When Tomas goes back to the Bauer household, he finds Francesca lying on the bed, apparently shot to death by the now-remorseful professor. Bauer then apparently commits suicide with the same weapon, whereupon Francesca comes back to life and joins Tomas in burning the papers. Ingrid arrives to effect a reconciliation with Tomas, and as the two young lovers drive away, they see both Bauers watching them from the window. *Professors. Secretaries. Students. Eccentrics. Employer-employee relations. Seduction. Infidelity. Incurable illness. Jealousy. Troilism. Murder. Suicide.*

Note: Released in Sweden in Sep 1969 as *Duett för kannibaler*.

DUETT FÖR KANNIBALER see **DUET FOR CANNIBALS**

DUFFY (United States/Great Britain)   F6.1300

Columbia Productions. *Dist* Columbia Pictures. 16 Sep **1968** [New York opening; c1 Oct 1968; LP36434]. Sd (Westrex); col (Technicolor). 35mm. 101 min. *MPAA rating* R.

A Martin Manulis Production. *Prod* Martin Manulis. *Assoc Prod* Harold Buck. *Dir* Robert Parrish. *2d Unit Dir* Michael Frewin. *Screenplay* Donald Cammell, Harry Joe Brown, Jr. *Story* Donald Cammell, Harry Joe Brown, Jr., Pierre La Salle. *Photog* Otto Heller. *Camera Op* Godfrey Godar. *2d Unit Camera* Egil Woxholt. *Art Dir* Philip Harrison. *Set Dresser* Patrick McLoughlin. *Titl Dsgn* Michael Graham Smith. *Film Ed* Willy Kemplen. *Mus* Ernie Freeman. *Song*: "I'm Satisfied" Cynthia Weil, Barry Mann, Ernie Freeman. *Sung by* Lou Rawls. *Sd Mix* Iain Bruce. *Dub Mix* John Aldred. *Sd Ed* Ted Mason. *Asst Dir* Peter Price. *Prod Mgr* William P. Cartlidge. *Location Prod Mgr* Ron Carr. *Cont* Joan Davis. *Cost Dsgn* Yvonne Blake. *Wardrobe Mistress* Betty Adamson. *Makeup* Harry Frampton. *Hairdresser* Maud Onslow. *Sp Eff* John Richardson, sp eff. *Aviation Adv* David Kay. *Dial Coach* Alfredo Lettieri. *Casting* Maude Spector.

Cast: James Coburn (*Duffy*), James Mason (*J. C. Calvert*), James Fox (*Stefane*), Susannah York (*Segolene*), John Alderton (*Antony*), Guy Deghy (*Captain Schoeller*), Carl Duering (*Bonivet*), Tutte Lemkow (*Spaniard*), Marne Maitland (*Abdul*), André Maranne (*Inspector Garain*), Julie Mendez (*belly dancer*), Barry Shawzin (*Bakirgian*), Steve Plytas, Peter Van Dissel.

Crime comedy. Half brothers Stefane and Antony decide to rob their father, millionaire tycoon Charles Calvert, of $2,000,000 in bank notes which he is transferring by ship from Tangiers to France. To help them carry off the heist, they recruit Duffy, an eccentric American hippie adventurer living in Tangiers. Although dubious at first, Duffy is won over by the prospect of a rich haul and by the seductive Segolene, Stefane's girl friend. Once preparations have been completed, Duffy, Segolene, and Stefane board the ship in disguises and, after a temporary delay in opening the safe, seize the loot. Duffy and Segolene dive overboard with the money and are picked up by Antony, who is waiting for them in a fishing vessel equipped with a helicopter and several fresh cadavers whose pockets have been stuffed with bank notes. Once out of sight of Calvert's ship, the trio board the helicopter and blow up the fishing boat, leaving behind nothing but floating debris and corpses. They reach their hideout on Corsica, and Antony returns to Paris while Duffy and Segolene wait for Stefane to make arrangements for exchanging the currency. Two conflicting cables, presumably from Stefane, lead Duffy to suspect a double-cross. His suspicions are confirmed when he discovers that Segolene is actually Calvert's mistress and that Calvert masterminded the whole scheme in order to keep the stolen money and at the same time collect insurance on it. Duffy quickly contacts the local chief of police and presents Calvert and Segolene with the money, which he claims to have found. The outwitted Calvert has no choice but to give Duffy a $100,000 reward. *Brothers. Millionaires. Mistresses. Eccentrics. Adventurers. Hippies. Tycoons. Americans in foreign countries. Filial relations. Fraud. Disguise. Theft. Perfidy. Helicopters. Ship explosions. Rewards. Corsica. Tangiers. Paris.*

Note: Released in Great Britain in Oct 1968. Location scenes filmed in Almeria, Spain. Working title: *Avec-Avec*.

DUGI BRODOVI see **THE LONG SHIPS**

DUNGEONS OF HORROR   F6.1301

Dist Herts-Lion International Corp. Feb **1964**. Sd; b&w. 35mm. 74 min. [Also reviewed at 80 min.]

Dir Pat Boyette. *Screenplay* Henry Garcia. *Photog* James Houston. *Art Dir* Ron Russell. *Makeup* Henry Garcia.

Cast: Russ Harvey, Helen Hogan, Bill McNulty, Maurice Harris, Ron Russell, Lee Morgan, Pat Boyette.

Horror film. During the 1870's, two survivors of a capsized boat make their way to a remote island, desolate save for a decaying castle belonging to a demented count and his leprous wife, who is also mad. The couple are imprisoned and tortured, but all are eventually doomed by the wife's dread disease. *Nobility. Insanity. Leprosy. Torture. Islands. Castles. Shipwrecks.*

Note: Also known as *Dungeon of Horror*.

THE DUNWICH HORROR   F6.1302

American International Pictures. 14 Jan **1970** [Chicago opening; c14 Jan 1970; LP38182]. Sd; col (print by Movielab). 35mm. 90 min. *MPAA rating* GP.

Prod James H. Nicholson, Samuel Z. Arkoff. *Exec Prod* Roger Corman. *Dir* Daniel Haller. *Screenplay* Curtis Lee Hanson, Henry Rosenbaum, Ronald Silkosky. *Dir Photog* Richard C. Glouner. *Camera Op* Dick Wimpy. *Camera Asst* Gene Talban. *Art Dir* Paul Sylos. *Set Decor* Ray Boltz. *Set Coörd* Ross Hahn. *Main Titl* Sandy Dvore. *Film Ed* Fred Feitshans, Jr., Christopher Holmes. *Mus* Les Baxter. *Sd* Charles Knight. *1st & 2d Asst Dir* Jack Bohrer, Lew Borzage. *Prod Mgr* Jack Bohrer. *Prod Asst* Tamara Asseyev, Beach Dickerson. *Wardrobe* Richard Bruno, Agnes Lyon. *Makeup* Jack Obringer. *Hairdresser* Faith Schmehr. *Sp Eff* Roger George. *Prop Master* Ted Berkeley. *Gaffer* Jack Spicer. *Grip* Charles Hannawalt. *Still Photog* Art Say.

Cast: Sandra Dee (*Nancy Walker*), Dean Stockwell (*Wilbur Whateley*), Ed Begley (*Dr. Henry Armitage*), Sam Jaffe (*Old Whateley*), Donna Baccala (*Elizabeth Hamilton*), Lloyd Bochner (*Dr. Cory*), Joanne Moore Jordan (*Lavinia*), Talia Coppola (*Cora*), Barboura Morris (*Mrs. Cole*), Michael Fox (*Dr. Raskin*), Jason Wingreen (*police chief*), Michael Haynes (*guard*), Beach Dickerson, Toby Russ, Jack Pierce.

Horror film. Source: H. P. Lovecraft, "The Dunwich Horror," in *Weird Tales* (Jul 1933). Nancy Walker and Elizabeth Hamilton, two students who attend Miskatonic University and work in the school library, are putting away the *Necronomicon*, a rare book on the occult, after a lecture on the supernatural given by visiting professor Dr. Henry Armitage. Dr. Armitage discovers Wilbur Whateley memorizing ritual passages from the *Necronomicon* and is at first angry, but learns that Wilbur comes from nearby Dunwich, a village having a history of evil occurrences, and that Wilbur is the great-grandson of Oliver Whateley, who was hanged by the villagers as a demon. Nancy, finding herself attracted to Wilbur, offers to drive him home when he misses his bus. Later, in the old mansion where Wilbur lives with his grandfather, Wilbur drugs Nancy and sabotages her car, thus forcing her to stay for the night. (He plans to sacrifice her in a fertility rite in the hopes of gaining for himself contact with the spiritual world.) Nancy accepts his invitation to spend the weekend there, but her absence alarms both Elizabeth and Dr. Armitage, who learn that Wilbur's mother has been living in an insane asylum since giving birth to twins—Wilbur and a boy who has never been seen. Wilbur steals the *Necronomicon* from the library, kills a guard, and takes Nancy to the "Devil's Hopyard," a rocky hillside, for the ritual. Meanwhile, Elizabeth and Dr. Armitage arrive at the Whateley house; Elizabeth opens a locked door and is immediately devoured by an invisible creature, the Dunwich Horror (Wilbur's twin). The Horror escapes and ravages the countryside, intending to kill Wilbur. Eventually, Dr. Armitage confronts Wilbur and the monster at the Devil's Hopyard, and there Armitage utters a curse which sends both Wilbur and the Dunwich Horror up in flames. *Students. Professors. Brothers. Monsters. Twins. Grandfathers. Occult. Theft. Murder. Demonology. Spiritualism. Motherhood. Insanity. Invisibility. Libraries. Drugs. Rites and ceremonies. Supernatural.*

Note: Location scenes filmed in Mendocino, California. Working title: *Dunwich*.

DUO   F6.1303

12 Jul **1969** [Portland, Oregon, opening]. Sd; col? 35mm? [Feature film, length unknown.]

Sex film. No information about the precise nature of this film has been found. *Sexuality.*

EL DUQUE NEGRO see **THE BLACK DUKE**

DURING ONE NIGHT (Great Britain)   F6.1304

Galaworldfilm Productions. *Dist* Astor Pictures. Apr **1962** [Los Angeles showing]. Sd; b&w. 35mm. 84 min.

Prod-Dir-Writ Sidney J. Furie. *Exec Prod* Kenneth Rive. *Photog* Norman Warwick. *Art Dir* John Earl. *Film Ed* Antony Gibbs. *Mus* Bill McGuffie. *Harmonica Solo* Harry Pitch. *Sd* Don Challis. *Sd Rec* Leo Wilkins, Fred Ryan. *Asst Dir* William Lang. *Prod Mgr* Fred Slark.

Cast: Don Borisenko (*David*), Susan Hampshire (*Jean*), Sean Sullivan (*major*), Joy Webster (*prostitute*), Graydon Gould (*Mike*), Tom Busby (*Sam*), Jackie Collins (*girl*), Alan Gibson (*Harry*), Colin Maitland (*gunner*), Barbara Ogilvie (*Jean's mother*), Michael Golden (*constable*), Roy Stephens (*driver*), Pamela Barney (*nurse*), Barry McClean (*tough*), John Bloomfield, Sean McCan (*MP's*).

Melodrama. A young American pilot in wartime England is shattered by the suicide of a friend who was castrated during an air raid. Obsessed by the idea that he may die in battle without having experienced sexual intercourse, the pilot goes AWOL and picks up a prostitute but is unable to respond sexually to her. Later he gets drunk and meets an equally inexperienced young woman who attempts to reassure him, but again he is incapable of response. He tries unsuccessfully to force pursuing MP's to kill him, but a chaplain intercedes and helps him talk out his difficulties. His faith in himself restored, he responds to the young woman, and they consummate their love. The pilot then leaves on his final mission, knowing that the young woman will await his return. *Air pilots. Prostitutes. Chaplains. Suicide. Castration. Impotence. Sexual initiation. Drunkenness. World War II. United States Army—Air Force. United States Army—Military Police.*

Note: Opened in London in Mar 1961; running time: 80 min. Also known as *Night of Passion*.

DUSTY BROWN see **THE ADVENTURES OF BUSTY BROWN**

DUTCHMAN (Great Britain)   **F6.1305**
   Gene Persson Enterprises–Dutchman Film Co.–Kaitlin Productions. *Dist* Gene Persson Enterprises, Continental Distributing, Inc. 28 Dec **1966** [Los Angeles opening]. Sd; b&w. 35mm. 55 min.
   Prod Gene Persson. *Assoc Prod* Hy Silverman. *Dir* Anthony Harvey. *2d Unit Dir* Edward R. Brown. *Photog* Gerry Turpin. *Art Dir* Herbert Smith, Jim Morahan. *Set Decor* Ian Whittaker. *Film Ed* Anthony Harvey. *Asst Ed* Denis Whitehouse. *Mus Comp & Cond* John Barry. *Sd Rec* George Stephenson. *Sd* John Aldred, Vivian Temple-Smith. *Asst Dir* Christopher Dryhurst. *Prod Mgr* John Comfort, Tom Blakeley. *Wardrobe* Brenda Gardner. *Makeup* Michael Morris. *Hairstyles* Ann Box.
   Cast: Shirley Knight *(Lula)*, Al Freeman, Jr. *(Clay)*, Frank Lieberman, Robert Calvert, Howard Bennett, Sandy McDonald, Dennis Alaba Peters, Keith James, Devon Hall *(subway riders)*.
   Allegory. Source: LeRoi Jones, *Dutchman* (New York opening: 24 Mar 1964). Lula, a sluttish white woman, boards a New York City subway car and sits next to Clay, a well-dressed black man who is the only other passenger. She flagrantly teases and provokes him, and by her actions and insults dares him to take advantage of her willingness to be seduced. Other passengers enter the car, however, and Clay refuses her advances. Once rejected, the woman turns on him and launches into a tirade against blacks, ridiculing them for their subservience to white men. Unable to control himself, Clay hits Lula and spits out his own deep hatred of whites. When he is finished, the woman lunges at him and stabs him to death. Some time later, after his body has been carried from the subway, Lula boards another car and steadily eyes her next black victim. *Negroes. Teases. Seduction. Racism. Murder. Subways. New York City.*
   Note: Released in Great Britain in 1967.

DVOYE see **A BALLAD OF LOVE**

THE DYNOSAURS see **FACES**

DŽINGIS-KAN see **GENGHIS KHAN**

... E DIVENNE IL PIÙ SPIETATO BANDITO DEL SUD see **A FEW BULLETS MORE**

E VENNE UN UOMO see **AND THERE CAME A MAN**

EACH MAN FOR HIMSELF see **THE RUTHLESS FOUR**

THE EAGLE AND THE HAWK see **SPREAD EAGLE**

EARLY AUTUMN (Japan)   **F6.1306**
   Toho Co. *Dist* Toho Co., New Yorker Films. Feb **1962** [Los Angeles showing]. Sd; col (Agfacolor). 35mm (Tohoscope). 103 min.
   Prod Sanezumi Fujimoto, Masakatsu Kaneko, Tadahiro Teramoto. *Dir* Yasujiro Ozu. *Screenplay* Kogo Noda, Yasujiro Ozu. *Photog* Asakazu Nakai. *Art Dir* Tomoo Shimogawara. *Mus* Toshiro Mayuzumi. *Sd* Koichi Nakagawa.
   Cast: Ganjiro Nakamura *(Manbei)*, Setsuko Hara *(Akiko)*, Yoko Tsukasa *(Noriko)*, Michiyo Aratama *(Fumiko)*, Yumi Shirakawa *(Takako)*, Reiko Dan *(Yuriko)*, Keiju Kobayashi *(Hisao)*, Akira Takarada *(Noriko's boyfriend)*, Daisuke Kato *(Yanosuke)*, Chieko Naniwa *(Tsune Sasaki)*, Haruko Togo *(Teruko)*, Haruko Sugimura, Hisaya Morishige, Chishu Ryu, Yuko Mochizuki.
   Domestic drama. Manbei Kohayagawa, who in his youth led the life of a rake, is the patriarch of a Tokyo family that includes three daughters, Fumiko, Akiko, and Noriko. Manbei has given over the daily operation of the generations-old family sake brewery to Fumiko's husband, Hisao, but business competition has forced the consideration of a merger with another concern, and Hisao will not make the decision without Manbei's participation. Meanwhile, Manbei's widowed eldest daughter, Akiko, is faced with the decision of whether to remarry with a man introduced to her by Manbei's younger brother. A prospective husband has also been selected for Noriko, but she has fallen in love with a poor schoolteacher. Fumiko discovers that her father has resumed his relationship with his former mistress, whose 21-year-old daughter Manbei believes is his own. Fumiko chides her father for his behavior, which she feels is unworthy of his age and position. One day Manbei suffers a heart attack, and the family realize how much they rely upon him. Relatives are summoned, but Manbei recovers, and there is a general feeling of relief. Confined to bed, Manbei nevertheless pays a visit to his mistress in Kyoto, suffers a relapse at her home, and dies. His family accompany his body to the crematorium and are left to face their decisions alone. *Patriarchs. Mistresses. Widows. Sisters. Schoolteachers. Family life. Filial relations. Old age. Marriage—Arranged. Heart disease. Tokyo. Kyoto.*
   Note: Released in Japan in Oct 1961 as *Kohayagawa-ke no aki*. Also known as *Last of Summer*. New York opening: 30 Nov 1970 as *The End of Summer*. Conflicting sources suggest that Haruko Togo may be the same as Haruko Sugimura.

EARLY TO BED   **F6.1307**
   Dist Stacey Distributors. ca **1970**. Sd; col. 16mm. 61-81 min.
   Sex film. No information about the precise nature of this film has been found. *Sexuality.*

EARLY WORKS (Yugoslavia)   **F6.1308**
   Avala Film–Neoplanta Film. *Dist* Grove Press. 23 Apr **1970** [New York opening]. Sd; b&w. 35mm. 87 min.
   Dir Želimir Žilnik. *Screenplay* Želimir Žilnik, Branko Vučićević. *Quotations from the works of* Karl Marx, Friedrich Engels. *Photog* Karpo Aćimović Godina. *Film Ed* Karpo Aćimović Godina.
   Cast: Milja Vujanović *(Yugoslavia)*, Bogdan Tirnanić *(Dragiša)*, Čedomir Rodović *(Kruno)*, Marko Nikolić *(Marko)*, Slobodan Aligrudić *(father)*, Želimira Žujović.
   Allegory. After burning their car, four young revolutionaries—the female Yugoslavia and her lovers, Dragiša, Kruno, and Marko—attempt to proselytize an indifferent populace. Unenthusiastic peasants rape Yugoslavia and beat her companions. Undaunted, the young people continue to agitate. The men are arrested and given haircuts by the police. Upon release the four go to work in a factory, where Yugoslavia continues a solitary protest, taunting the males with charges of political impotence. Tiring of her exhortations, Dragiša, Kruno, and Marko take Yugoslavia to an abandoned field, shoot her, and ignite the corpse with a Molotov cocktail. *Peasants. Police. Revolutionaries. Terrorism. Rape. Marxism. Factories. Molotov cocktails.*
   Note: Released in Yugoslavia in Mar 1969 as *Rani radovi*; running time: ca78 min; cut from ca94 min.

THE EARTH DIES SCREAMING (Great Britain)   **F6.1309**
   Lippert Films. *Dist* Twentieth Century–Fox Film Corp. 14 Oct **1964** [Los Angeles opening; c20 Oct 1964; LP29352]. Sd (RCA); b&w. 62 min.
   Prod Robert L. Lippert, Jack Parsons. *Dir* Terence Fisher. *Writ* Henry Cross. *Dir Photog* Arthur Lavis. *Camera Op* Len Harris. *Sd Camera Op* Jack Smart. *Art Dir* George Provis. *Supv Film Ed* Robert Winter. *Asst Ed* Clive Smith. *Mus Comp* Elisabeth Lutyens. *Mus Cond* Philip Martell. *Sd Ed* Spencer Reeve. *Sd Rec* Buster Ambler. *Asst Dir* Gordon Gilbert. *Prod Mgr* Clifton Brandon. *Cont* Renee Glynne. *Prod Sec* Angela Cockill. *Wardrobe Supv* Jean Fairlie. *Makeup* Harold Fletcher. *Hairdresser* Joyce James.
   Cast: Willard Parker *(Jeff Nolan)*, Virginia Field *(Peggy)*, Dennis Price *(Quinn Taggett)*, Vanda Godsell *(Violet)*, Thorley Walters *(Otis)*, David Spenser *(Mel)*, Anna Palk *(Lorna)*.
   Science fiction melodrama. Test pilot Jeff Nolan lands a plane after several hours aloft and finds England a grotesque panorama of death, with the population frozen into interrupted gestures, all dead by some unknown horror. Unable to elicit any shortwave response, Jeff is confronted by pistol-brandishing Quinn Taggett, who with his wife, Peggy, has survived the mysterious calamity in a hospital room. Together, the three explore the ruins and uncover two more survivors, Edgar Otis and Violet Courtland, who were saved by the purified atmosphere in a nearby chemical factory. The group is suddenly attacked by two menacing, dome-lidded robots who march relentlessly toward the earthlings, impervious to their gunfire. They all flee except Violet, who tries to communicate with the robots and is killed instantly by their touch. The survivors retreat to a hotel and are joined by Mel and his pregnant wife, Lorna. That night Violet, in a zombie-like trance, kills Quinn; her behavior leads Jeff to suspect that the menace is controlled by an outside source. He and Mel depart in search of a transmitting station, leaving Edgar with Peggy and Lorna, who delivers a healthy baby in their absence. When two robots burst into the room and menacingly approach the child, all appears lost until they suddenly collapse on the floor, inches away from their intended victims—Mel and Jeff have succeeded in destroying the transmitting station. The group is reunited, and the baby sleeps peacefully as the survivors plan to search for other survivors. *Air pilots. Robots. Space creatures. Holocausts. Childbirth. Survival. Radio. Airplanes. Hotels.*
   Note: Released in Great Britain in 1965. Henry Cross is a pseudonym for Harry Spalding.

EARTH ENTRANCED (Brazil)   **F6.1310**
   Mapa Films. *Dist* New Yorker Films. 14 May **1970** [New York opening]. Sd; b&w. 35mm. 110 min.
   Prod Zelito Viana. *Assoc Prod* Luiz Carlos Barreto, Carlos Diegues, Raymundo Vanderley. *Dir-Writ* Glauber Rocha. *Photog* Luiz Carlos Barreto. *Camera* Dib Lufti. *Asst Camera* José Ventura. *Art Dir* Paulo Gil Soares. *Film Ed* Eduardo Escorel. *Asst Film Ed* Mair Tavares. *Mus* Sergio Ricardo. "Il Guarany" Carlos Gomes. "Bachianas Brasileiras no. 3 & 6" Heitor Villa-Lobos. *Voices* Maria da Graça, Sergio Ricardo. "Otello Overture" Giuseppe Verdi. *Perf by* Edson Machado Quartet. *Sd* Aluizio Viana. *Asst Dir* Antonio Calmon, Moyses Kendler. *Prod Mgr* Agnaldo Azevedo. *Cost* Paulo Gil Soares.

Cast: Jardel Filho (Paulo Martins), José Lewgoy (Felipe Vieira), Glauce Rocha (Sara), Paulo Autran (Porfírio Diaz), Paulo Gracindo (Julio Fuentés), Danuza Leao (Silvia), Hugo Carvana (Alvaro), Zózimo Bulbul, Antonio Carnera, Emanuel Cavalcanti, Rafael de Carvalho, Mario Lago, José Marinho, Flávio Migliaccio, Francisco Milani, Paulo César Pereio, Echio Reis, Thelma Reston, Ivan de Souza, Modesto de Souza, Jofre Soares, Mauricio do Valle, Darlene Gloria, Elisabeth Gasper, Irma Alvarez, Sonia Clara, Clovis Bornay.

Drama. Paulo Martins, a journalist and poet in the South American country of Eldorado, is killed by the police as he leaves the headquarters of Felipe Vieira, the liberal governor of the province of Alecrim. As he dies, Paulo remembers his political involvements of the past years: Paulo abandons his close friend, Porfírio Diaz, a reactionary mystic, to work for the election of Vieira, the populist candidate for governor. Vieira is elected, but his peasant constituents are soon disillusioned with his neglect of reform. Paulo returns to Eldorado City in order to continue writing poetry, but his mistress Sara encourages him to reenter politics. He persuades his employer, Julio Fuentés, a wealthy industrialist with diverse interests in newspapers and television, to allow him access to the media to attack Diaz. Paulo ridicules Diaz on a television show and depicts him as a puppet for the International Exploitation Company. Vieira is now supported by the Catholic Church, but Diaz has the backing of Fuentés and the central government. Paulo unsuccessfully tries to persuade Vieira to continue in what is now a revolutionary election campaign; as Paulo leaves the Vieira headquarters, he is shot by the police. *Journalists. Poets. Mystics. Peasants. Mistresses. Industrialists. Memory. Politics. Elections. Political campaigns. Social reform. Assassination. Television. South America.*

Note: Filmed on location near Rio de Janeiro. Opened there in May 1967 as *Terra em transe.* Additional music includes "Samba of the Favela de Rio" and "Alué de candomblé of Bahía."

EARTH YEAR 2069   **F6.1311**
Dist Able Film Co. ca **1970**. Sd; col. 16mm. [Feature length assumed.]
Sex film. No information about the precise nature of this film has been found. *Sexuality. The Future.*

EAST CHINA SEA (Japan)   **F6.1312**
Imamura Productions. *Dist* Nikkatsu Corp. Apr **1969** [Los Angeles showing]. Sd; col (Fuji Color). 35mm (NikkatsuScope). 105 min.
Dir Tadahiko Isomi. *Screenplay* Shohei Imamura, Tadahiko Isomi. *Story* Shohei Imamura. *Photog* Masahisa Himeda. *Mus* Hajime Kaburagi.
Cast: Masakazu Tamura (Rokuro), Seizaburo Kawazu (Ganaha), Yukie Kagawa (Kana), Ryohei Uchida, Kin Omae, Toshinari Yamano, Takanobu Hozumi, Haruko Kato, Akemi Nara, Taiji Tonoyama, Nakajiro Tomida, Shoichi Kuwayama, Hirayoshi Aono, Shuntaro Tamamura, Yoshiyuki Nemoto, Michie Mori, Takumi Shinjo, Kanjuro Arashi, Tetsuya Watari.
Melodrama. Rokuro, a student, takes a summer job on a fishing boat. After the ship stops at Okinawa for repairs, the crew become the unwitting accomplices of Ganaha, a gangster who tricks them into disposing of a body. On a distant island, the crew are suddenly bombarded by a mysterious aircraft as they are about to complete their task. Kana, a local girl, recognizes the dead man as her cousin and fiancé, but when the men return the body to her father, he refuses to identify it. Now aware of Ganaha's insidious influence, Rokuro and his friends learn that the gangster plans to use them as targets for U. S. military bombardment. [Sources are unclear about the end of the film.] *Students. Gangsters. Cousins. Ship crews. Duplicity. Aerial bombardment. Fishing boats. Islands. Okinawa.*
Note: Released in Japan in Oct 1968 as *Higashi Shinakai.*

THE EAST IS RED (People's Republic of China)   **F6.1313**
August First Film Studio–Peking Film Studio–Central Documentary Studio. *Dist* Contemporary Films. **1968** [New York showing; c1 Sep 1967; LP36133]. Sd; col. 16mm. 130 min.
Historical drama with music. Dramatizing the People's Revolution in China in six parts, the film attacks cultural revisionism and illustrates the influence of Chairman Mao Tse-tung. SCENE 1 depicts China in 1921 when prerevolutionary feudalistic conditions prevailed. The Chinese Communist Party is born, the revolution is underway, and in SCENE 2 Chiang Kai-shek, backed by the imperialists, leads the counter-revolutionary forces. The two revolutionary forces from the Nanchung Uprising and the Harvest Uprising join forces to form the Chinese Workers' and Peasants' Red Army. The revolution effects agrarian reform as landlords are overthrown and land is redistributed. SCENE 3 depicts the installation of Mao Tse-tung as leader of the revolutionary army and the Long March through China. In SCENE 4, the Japanese imperialists occupy northern China with no resistance from the reactionaries led by Chiang Kai-shek, who is busy suppressing the communists. The communist army provides a valiant defense against the Japanese in the spirit of national liberation. In SCENE 5, the war with Japan is hardly over when Chiang Kai-shek, now supported by the United States, unleashes an all-out attack on the communists. The communists gain control, however, and SCENE 6 depicts October 1, 1949, the day Chairman Mao announces the founding of the People's Republic of China. *Peasants. Soldiers. Japanese. Revolutions. Communism. China—History—Republic 1912-49. China—History—Civil War 1945-49. China—History—Long March 1934-35. World War II. Peking. Mao Tse-tung. Chiang Kai-shek.*
Note: Released in the People's Republic of China in 1966. The first film from the People's Republic to be shown in the United States, the film records a performance staged in the Great Hall of the People in Peking to celebrate the 15th anniversary of the overthrow of the Chiang Kai-shek regime.

EAST OF KILIMANJARO (United States/Great Britain/Italy)   **F6.1314**
Dudley Pictures International–Ameurope. *Dist* Parade Releasing Organization. 30 May **1962** [Los Angeles opening]. Sd; col (Technicolor). 35mm (Vistarama). 75 min. [Also 72 min.]
Pres by Riley Jackson, Robert Patrick. *Prod* Richard Goldstone, Edoardo Capolino. *Dir* Arnold Belgard, Edoardo Capolino. *Screenplay* Arnold Belgard. *Orig Story (see note)* Richard Goldstone, Daniel Mainwaring, M. Levor. *Photog* Edwin E. Olsen, Laurie Friedman. *Film Ed* Norman Suffern. *Mus* Alberico Vitalini.
Cast: Marshall Thompson (Marsh Connors), Gaby André (Dr. Marie Avedon), Fausto Tozzi (Dr. Enrico Trino), Kris Aschan, Rolf Aschan (themselves), Mike Robotham.
Adventure melodrama. Roving camera reporter Marsh Conners is assigned to strife-torn Africa to photograph part of the Cold War. The West has sent a task force of scientists in an attempt to stamp out an epidemic affecting the cattle of the regions surrounding Mount Kilimanjaro. Conners meets and falls in love with Dr. Marie Avedon, who, along with Dr. Trino, the head bacteriologist, has convinced the Masai of the need for cattle inoculation. The authorities get white hunter Kris Aschan to pen up the big game for the tests. Various species of African wildlife are rounded up by lasso. The Masai rebel and cause a stampede when zebras, sacred to their tribe, are captured and penned up. All these animals must be captured and destroyed as a precaution. A giant vulture, shot down on a hunch, proves to be the virus carrier. Connors leaves, knowing that Marie will be happier with Dr. Trino. *Masai. Journalists. Hunters. Bacteriologists. Photographers. Cattle—Diseases. Epidemics. Stampedes. Religion. Roundups. Cold war. Tanganyika. Mount Kilimanjaro. Zebras. Cattle. Vultures.*
Note: Filmed on location in British East Africa. According to one source, filming took place in Uganda. Rome opening: Jun-Jul 1957 as *La grande caccia;* running time: 85 min. Released in Great Britain in Mar 1962 as *The Big Search;* running time: 72 min. An Italian source credits M. Levor as author of story; English language sources credit Goldstone and Mainwaring.

EAST OF SUDAN (Great Britain)   **F6.1315**
Ameran Films. *Dist* Columbia Pictures. 25 Nov **1964** [Los Angeles opening; c1 Oct 1964; LP29465]. Sd; col (Technicolor). 35mm (Techniscope). 85 min.
A Charles H. Schneer Production. *Prod-Dir* Nathan Juran. *Exec Prod* Charles H. Schneer. *Screenplay* Jud Kinberg. *Photog* Wilkie Cooper. *Camera Op* Harry Gillam. *Art Dir* Lionel Couch. *Titl Dsgn* Sam Suliman. *Film Ed* Ernest Hosler. *Mus* Laurie Johnson. *Sd Rec* George Stephenson, Red Law. *Asst Dir* Derek Parr. *Prod Mgr* Ted Wallis. *Sp Eff* Ted Samuels.
Cast: Anthony Quayle (Richard Baker), Sylvia Syms (Margaret Woodville), Derek Fowlds (Murchison), Jenny Agutter (Asua), Johnny Sekka (Kimrasi), Harold Coyne (Major Harris), Joseph Layode (Gondoko), Illario Pedro (witch doctor), Desmond Davies (aide), Derek Blomfield (2d major), Edward Ellis (Arab).
Adventure drama. In the Sudan of the 1880's, the Mahdi (Mohammed Ahmed), mystical ruler of the Moslems, rallies his forces in an effort to stamp out British influence and General "Chinese" Gordon's attempts to abolish the slave trade. When the Moslems attack Barash, a British outpost 200 miles upriver from Khartum, four people escape in a riverboat: Richard Baker, a tough, unconventional trooper; Murchison, an inexperienced, bumbling subaltern; Margaret Woodville, a prim English governess; and Asua, a young native girl in the governess' charge. Baker's unorthodox methods put him in conflict with Murchison and Miss Woodville, but after surviving numerous perils, including attacks by Moslems, slave traders, unfriendly natives, elephants, and crocodiles, the four reach safety. The mutual dislike of Baker and Miss Woodville in the meantime has given way to love. *Governesses. Muslims. Slavery. Imperialism. Riverboats. Sudan. Khartum. Charles George Gordon. Mohammed Ahmed. Great Britain—Army. Elephants. Crocodiles.*
Note: Opened in London in Aug 1964.

EAST WIND *see* **WIND FROM THE EAST**

293

THE EASTER DINNER see **THE PIGEON THAT TOOK ROME**

EASY COME, EASY GO   F6.1316

Hal Wallis Productions. *Dist* Paramount Pictures. 22 Mar **1967** [San Francisco opening; c10 Mar 1967; LP34058]. Sd; col (Technicolor). 35mm. 95 min.

A Hal B. Wallis–Joseph H. Hazen Production. *Prod* Hal B. Wallis. *Assoc Prod* Paul Nathan. *Dir* John Rich. *Writ* Allan Weiss, Anthony Lawrence. *Cinematog* William Margulies. *Underwater Photog* Michael J. Dugan. *Art Dir* Hal Pereira, Walter Tyler. *Set Decor* Robert R. Benton, Arthur Krams. *Film Ed* Archie Marshek. *Background Mus Score Comp & Cond* Joseph J. Lilley. *Vocal Accomp* The Jordanaires. *Titl Song* Sid Wayne, Ben Weisman. *Song:* "The Love Machine" Gerald Nelson, Chuck Taylor, Fred Burch. *Songs:* "Yoga Is as Yoga Goes," "Sing, You Children" Gerald Nelson, Fred Burch. *Song:* "You Gotta Stop" Bill Giant, Florence Kaye, Bernie Baum. *Song:* "I'll Take Love" Dee Fuller, Mark Barkan. *Songs Sung by* Elvis Presley. *Instrumentals:* "Freak Out," "Go-Go Jo" Lance Le Gault. *Choreog* David Winters. *Sd* John Carter, Charles Grenzbach. *Asst Dir* Robert Goodstein. *Prod Mgr* William W. Gray, Frank Caffey. *Cost* Edith Head. *Makeup* Wally Westmore. *Hairstyles* Nellie Manley. *Proc Photog* Farciot Edouart. *Sp Photog Eff* Paul K. Lerpae. *Tech Adv* Col. Tom Parker.

Cast: Elvis Presley *(Ted Jackson)*, Dodie Marshall *(Jo Symington)*, Pat Priest *(Dina Bishop)*, Pat Harrington *(Judd Whitman)*, Skip Ward *(Gil Carey)*, Sandy Kenyon *(Schwartz)*, Frank McHugh *(Captain Jack)*, Ed Griffith *(Cooper)*, Read Morgan *(Lieutenant Tompkins)*, Mickey Elley *(Lieutenant Whitehead)*, Elaine Beckett *(Vicki)*, Shari Nims *(Mary)*, Diki Lerner *(Zoltan)*, Robert Isenberg *(artist)*, Elsa Lanchester *(Madame Neherina)*, Kay York *(Tanya)*.

Comedy with music. Just before his discharge from the Navy, frogman Ted Jackson discovers what appears to be a treasure chest in the hull of a sunken brigantine off the California coast. Intrigued by the prospect of sudden wealth, he enlists the aid of his former partner, trumpet player Judd Whitman. Judd agrees to help on condition that should the salvage attempt fail, Ted will return to singing at the Easy-Go-Go discotheque. Once discharged, Ted gets the necessary equipment from Captain Jack, a nautical authority terrified of water, and also obtains the reluctant consent of Jo Symington, whose grandfather owned the sunken ship. Trouble begins when Dina Bishop, a wealthy playgirl, and her friend Gil decide to compete with Ted in diving for the treasure. Following several clashes between Ted and Gil, the two men have a decisive underwater fight, which ends in a victory for Ted. The treasure chest, however, contains copper, not gold, valued at about $4,000. After giving the proceeds to Jo (for use as a down payment on an art center she plans to start for her painter friends), Ted resumes his musical career and his romantic pursuit of Jo. *Frogmen. Trumpeters. Singers. Artists. Playgirls. Partnerships. Treasure. Discotheques. Salvage. United States Navy. California.*

Note: Location scenes filmed in southern California.

THE EASY LIFE (Italy)   F6.1317

Fair Film–Incei Film–Sancro Film. *Dist* Embassy Pictures. 22 Dec **1963** [New York opening]. Sd; b&w. 35mm. 105 min.

Pres by Joseph E. Levine. *Prod* Mario Cecchi Gori. *Dir* Dino Risi. *Screenplay* Ettore Scola, Ruggero Maccari, Dino Risi. *Photog* Alfio Contini. *Art Dir* Ugo Pericoli. *Film Ed* Maurizio Lucidi. *Mus* Riz Ortolani.

Cast: Vittorio Gassman *(Bruno Cortona)*, Jean-Louis Trintignant *(Roberto Mariani)*, Catherine Spaak *(Lilly, Bruno's daughter)*, Luciana Angiolillo *(Bruno's wife)*, Linda Sini *(Aunt Lidia)*, Corrado Olmi *(Alfredo)*, Claudio Gora *(Bibi, Lilly's fiancé)*, Franca Polesello, Edda Ferronao, Nando Angelini, Lilli Darelli, Bruno Simionato, Mila Stanic.

Drama. Bruno, a middle-aged playboy vacationing in Rome, is looking for a telephone to arrange a date. Roberto, a serious young law student, sees him and allows him to use the telephone in his apartment. After the call, Bruno invites Roberto to have a drink with him and later for a long ride in his sports car. Although he is wary of the dissolute Bruno, Roberto is attracted by his charm and carefree existence. In the course of 2 days, Roberto is exposed to Bruno's exciting friends, his teenaged daughter, and a number of beautiful women. The days are spent on the Riviera dancing, sunbathing, and sailing. Bruno succeeds in destroying Roberto's illusions and purpose in life; and the once shy and retiring young man is completely drawn into Bruno's aimless mode of living. Roberto is killed, however, as Bruno's speeding car crashes. Viewing the wreckage, Bruno finally becomes aware of the emptiness of his existence. *Law students. Playboys. Idle rich. Vacations. Moral corruption. Sports cars. Rome. Riviera. Automobile accidents.*

Note: Filmed in Rome and on the Italian Riviera. Opened in Rome in Dec 1962 as *Il sorpasso.*

EASY RIDER   F6.1318

Raybert Productions–Pando Co. *Dist* Columbia Pictures. 14 Jul **1969** [New York opening; c1 Jul 1969; LP36999]. Sd; col (Technicolor). 35mm (see note). 94 min. *MPAA rating* R.

Prod Peter Fonda. *Exec Prod* Bert Schneider. *Assoc Prod* William L. Hayward. *Dir* Dennis Hopper. *Screenplay* Peter Fonda, Dennis Hopper, Terry Southern. *Dir Photog* Laszlo Kovacs. *Asst Camera* Peter Heiser. *Art Dir* Jerry Kay. *Titl Cinefx* Film Ed* Donn Cambern. *Asst Film Ed* Stanley Siegel. *Song:* "The Pusher" Hoyt Axton. *Sung by* Steppenwolf. *Song:* "Born To Be Wild" Mars Bonfire. *Sung by* Steppenwolf. *Song:* "Wasn't Born To Follow" Gerry Goffin, Carole King. *Sung by* The Byrds. *Song:* "The Weight" Jaime Robbie Robertson. *Sung by* The Band. *Song:* "If You Want To Be a Bird" Antonia Duren. *Sung by* The Holy Modal Rounders. *Song:* "Don't Bogart That Joint" Elliot Ingber, Larry Jay Wagner. *Sung by* Fraternity of Man. *Song:* "If Six Was Nine" Jimi Hendrix. *Sung by* The Jimi Hendrix Experience. *Song:* "Let's Turkey Trot" Gerry Goffin, Jack Keller. *Sung by* Little Eva. *Song:* "Kyrie Eleison" David Axelrod. *Sung by* The Electric Prunes. *Song:* "Flash, Bam, Pow" Mike Bloomfield. *Sung by* The Electric Flag. *Song:* "It's All Right Ma (I'm Only Bleeding)" Bob Dylan. *Sung by* Roger McGuinn. *Song:* "Ballad of Easy Rider" comp & sung by* Roger McGuinn. *Sd* Ryder Sound Service. *Sd Mix* Leroy Robbins. *Sd Boom* James Contrares. *Re-rec* Producer's Sound Service. *Sd Eff* Edit-Rate Inc. *Mus Ed* Synchrofilm. *1st & 2d Asst Dir* Len Marsal, Paul Lewis. *Prod Mgr* Paul Lewis. *Script Supv* Joyce King. *Location Mgr* Tony Vorno. *Post-prod* Marilyn Schlossberg. *Makeup* Virgil Frye. *Sp Eff* Steve Karkus. *Cons* Henry Jaglom. *Stunt Gaffer* Tex Hall. *Gaffer* Richmond Aguilar. *Key Grip* Tom Ramsey. *Prop Master* Robert V. O'Neil. *Stills* Peter Sorel.

Cast—In Order of Appearance: Peter Fonda *(Wyatt)*, Dennis Hopper *(Billy)*, Antonio Mendoza *(Jesus)*, Phil Spector *(connection)*, Mac Mashourian *(bodyguard)*, Warren Finnerty *(rancher)*, Tita Colorado *(rancher's wife)*, Luke Askew *(stranger on highway)*, Luana Anders *(Lisa)*, Sabrina Scharf *(Sarah)*, Sandy Wyeth *(Joanne)*, Robert Walker, [Jr.] *(Jack)*, Robert Ball, Carmen Phillips, Ellie Walker, Michael Pataki *(mimes)*, Jack Nicholson *(George Hanson)*, George Fowler, Jr. *(guard)*, Keith Green *(sheriff)*, Hayward Robillard *(cat man)*, Arnold Hess, Jr. *(deputy)*, Buddy Causey, Jr., Duffy Lafont, Blase M. Dawson, Paul Guedry, Jr. *(customers in the cafe)*, Suzie Ramagos, Elida Ann Hebert, Rose LeBlanc, Mary Kaye Hebert, Cynthia Grezaffi, Colette Purpera *(girls in the cafe)*, Toni Basil *(Mary)*, Karen Black *(Karen)*, Lea Marmer *(madame)*, Cathi Cozzi *(dancing girl)*, Thea Salerno, Anne McClain, Beatriz Monteil, Marcia Bowman *(hookers)*, David C. Billodeau, Johnny David *(men in pickup truck)*.

Drama. At an airstrip near the California-Mexico border Wyatt and Billy, two motorcyclists, sell a large quantity of cocaine to a pusher who handles the transaction from his chauffered Rolls Royce. Once Wyatt (who is called Captain America because of the stars and stripes on his jacket and bike) has concealed the cash in his cycle's gas tank, the two young men ride off, vaguely intending to reach New Orleans in time for Mardi Gras. Unwelcome at motels because of their nonconformist appearance, they camp outdoors and smoke marijuana until they fall asleep. After stopping at a ranch where they repair their bikes and join the rancher and his Mexican wife for a meal, they pick up a hitchhiker and accompany him to the commune where he lives. Despite the friendliness of the people working the barren soil and a pleasant swim with two women, Billy becomes impatient to leave, and the two once more take to the road. Upon arriving at a Texas town, where a civic celebration is in progress, Wyatt and Billy join the procession and are jailed for "parading without a permit." Sharing their cell is alcoholic George Hanson, a civil rights lawyer who prefers sleeping off his binges in jail to facing the wrath of his wealthy father, one of the town leaders. A quick camaraderie develops among the three men; George intercedes and prevents jail officials from giving the two traditional haircuts, and he accepts their invitation to ride with them, mainly because he has always wanted to visit the House of Blue Lights in New Orleans. One night while sitting around a fire, George smokes his first joint and joyfully elucidates his theory that creatures from Venus are already living among us. The next day the three travelers stop at a small luncheonette but leave when confronted by open hostility and bigotry. That night they are attacked at their camp site by thugs who pummel George to death and leave Wyatt and Billy badly beaten. Incapable of voicing their feelings, Wyatt and Billy pay tribute to George by riding on to New Orleans and visiting the House of Blue Lights. Finding that neither the prostitutes nor the Mardi Gras festivities can overcome their moroseness, they go to a nearby cemetery to take LSD with two of the prostitutes. When the acid trip turns out to be a bad one that leaves Wyatt and Billy more despondent than before, they take to the highways again. Though Billy suggests they change direction and head for Florida, Wyatt senses the futility of continuing. The next morning they are passed on the road by two men in a pickup truck who decide to scare the two longhairs by pointing a shotgun at them. When Billy responds with a gesture of defiance, one of the men fires a shot that hits him in the stomach. After trying to reassure his dying friend,

Wyatt leaps on his cycle to ride off for help, but the truck has turned back, and this time the man with the gun takes deliberate aim and blasts Wyatt and his motorcycle off the road. *Hippies. Motorcyclists. Drug dealers. Ranchers. Mexicans. Hitchhikers. Lawyers. Prostitutes. Police. Communal living. Alcoholism. Civil rights. Bigotry. Murder. Jails. Motels. Whorehouses. Cocaine. LSD. Marijuana. Cemeteries. Mardi Gras. California. Mexican border. New Orleans. Texas.*

Note: Filmed on location between California and New Orleans, Louisiana. The LSD sequence was shot in 16mm.

EAT F6.1319
Dist Film-Makers' Cooperative. 10 Jan **1964** [New York opening]. Si; b&w. 16mm. 45 min.
Prod-Dir Andy Warhol.
Cast: Robert Indiana.
Experimental film. Photographed in closeup, a man eats a mushroom. *Mushrooms.*

EAT DRINK AND MAKE MERRIE F6.1320
Dist Crescent International Pictures. 22 May **1969** [San Francisco showing]. Sd; col. 35mm. 64 min.
Prod-Dir Whit Boyd. *Screenplay* Byron Lord. *Photog* Ludwig Moner. *Art* X. O. Vangam. *Sd* Danny Brown. *Asst Dir* Byron Lord. *Script Girl* Jeannie Hart.
Cast: Adrainne *(Renée)*, Artie Brooks *(Edward)*, Byron Lord *(Drake)*, Jimmie Raye *(Jimmy)*, Judy Farr *(Merrie)*, Chris Meyer *(Julia)*, Bunny Valenti *(Elaine)*, Jeannie Hart *(Ethel)*, Sandy Reese *(Reggie)*, Reggie Carver *(Johnny)*, Linda Lang *(Linda)*, Barbara Boiyn *(Barbara)*, Michelle Michelle *(Kathy)*.
Comedy. Merrie, a nymphomaniac, seduces every man in the family-operated boardinghouse while her younger sister Renée keeps watch. Renée soon blossoms from an awkward adolescent into a voluptuous woman who can hold her own with Merrie. The sisters join all of the boarders for a party that eventually becomes an orgy. *Sisters. Orgies. Nymphomania. Seduction. Adolescence. Boardinghouses.*
Note: Also known as *Eat, Drink, and Make Minnie*.

L'EAU À LA BOUCHE see **A GAME FOR SIX LOVERS**

THE EAVESDROPPER (United States/Argentina) F6.1321
Paul M. Heller. *Dist* Royal Films International. Sep **1966**. Sd; b&w. 35mm. 102 min.
Prod Paul M. Heller. *Exec Prod* Juan Sires. *Dir* Leopoldo Torre Nilsson. *Screenplay* Beatriz Guido, Edmundo Eichelbaum, Joe Goldberg, Leopoldo Torre Nilsson, Mabel Itzcovich. *Story* Beatriz Guido, Leopoldo Torre Nilsson. *Photog* Alberto Etchebehere. *Art Dir* Oscar Lagomarsino. *Film Ed* Jacinto Cascales. *Mus Arr & Cond* Lopez Furst. *Sd* Juan Carlos Gutiérrez, Juan Carlos Bertola.
Cast: Stathis Giallelis *(Martin Casals)*, Janet Margolin *(Inés)*, Lautaro Murúa *(Hernán Ramallo)*, Leonardo Favio *(Santos)*, Nelly Meden *(Lola)*, Ignacio de Soroa *(Ramón Casal)*, Elena Cortesina *(Mariquita)*.
Melodrama. Martin Casals is an earnest young member of a fascist organization in Buenos Aires whose major activity consists of smearing the city's political statues with tar. When the group's activities are officially supressed, Martin's uncle suggests that he hide out in an old hotel inhabited by Spanish exiles and theatrical people. To ease his loneliness, Martin persuades Inés, a childhood friend, to move in with him. In the isolation of his room, Martin overhears a troupe of Spaniards rehearsing next door and begins imagining that they are planning political activities which include the assassination of a visiting dictator whom Martin admires. When Martin sees Ramallo, the leader of the troupe, talking to some suspicious-looking men carrying parcels, his fears seem confirmed, and he persuades a fellow member of his group to report the Spaniards to the police. An investigation reveals nothing but causes the Spaniards' theater to be closed down. Upon discovering that Martin is responsible for their troubles, the actors drive him out of the hotel. *Fascists. Uncles. Spanish. Actors. Dictators. Police. Vandalism. Paranoia. Eavesdropping. Conspiracy. Assassination. Hotels. Buenos Aires.*
Note: Released in Argentina in 1964 as *El ojo de la cerradura*.

ECCO (Italy) F6.1322
Julia Film. *Dist* L. C. R. Films, Cresa Roma Films. 27 Oct **1965** [Los Angeles opening]. Sd; col (Technicolor). 35mm (Pancrorama). 100 min.
Pres by Dick Randall, Howard Smith, presenter. *Prod-Comm* Francesco Mazzei. *Exec Prod* Mario Russo. *Exec Prod for L. C. R. Films* A. J. Lech, Jr. *Dir* Gianni Proia. *Scen English Version* R. W. Cresse. *Photog* Baldi Schwarze, Emanuele DiCola. *Lighting Dir* Gianni Narzisi. *Ed* Roberto Cinquini. *American Ed* R. L. Frost. *Mus Comp & Cond* Riz Ortolani.
Cast: George Sanders *(narrator)*, Yvon Yve, Alexander, Léo Campion, Jacques Chazot, Maria Ansaldi, Laura Betti, Marcella Ruffini, Michel Simon,

Mario De Simone, Evon Evah.
Documentary. Probing cameras delve the world's incredible secrets: college students in Berlin slash each other in ritualistic duels; sleeping infants in a Japanese nursery are persuaded through hypno-pedagogy to refrain from bedwetting; karate is demonstrated in Japan; at the annual New Year's Debutante Ball at the Paris Opera, young women parade jewels valued at more than 2 billion francs, while the "clochards" hold their own celebration on the banks of the Seine; a family of French circus performers drives a motorcycle on a steel wire stretched across an Alpine village; a young man takes his vows in a Grecian monastery; an initiate is doused with chicken blood in a London black mass celebration; Rio de Janeiro holds its annual Mardi Gras carnival; tourists enjoy the performance of a tribal dance in Nairobi, while, around the corner, members of the same tribe dance the twist; guests at a hotel in the Myeri Game Reserve watch wild animals a few feet away; housewives in Reno watch a male weightlifting exhibition, while a stripper in San Francisco exhibits her strength to an all-male audience; Portuguese whalers use hand-held harpoons to hunt their quarry from small rowboats; young Swedish toughs arrive in Stockholm blinking their automobile headlights to attract interested girls; an enormous throng of near-naked youths fight to retrieve a ritual stick in the Japanese "Festival of Saidachi"; the Grand Guignol Theater in Paris, throne of blood and horror, gives its final performance; members of the "Tasses Fesses," a French society, meet to admire the female buttocks; workers at Les Halles in Paris watch an unusual nightclub act during a "cognac break"; two women's roller derby teams battle for supremacy in Los Angeles; Evon Evah, a Parisian stoic, bloodlessly pierces his body with long needles; reindeer in Lapland are herded together and castrated; lesbians perform in a Paris nightclub act; Maria Soriano, a 6-foot, 204 lb. stripper, becomes the most popular singer in Argentina; doctors in Exeter, England, artificially inseminate an infertile patient; and a woman in Rome climbs the stairway to the church of the Arachelle on her knees to ask the blessing of a child. *Students. Infants. Debutantes. Beggars. Aerialists. Housewives. Strongmen. Stripteasers. Dancers. Whalers. Juvenile delinquents. Physicians. Singers. Stoics. Rites and ceremonies. Duels. Hypnotism. Karate. Artificial insemination. Lesbianism. Witchcraft. Fetishism. Roller skating. Religion. Nightclubs. Jewels. Monasteries. Twist (dance). Mardi Gras. Festival of Saidachi. Japan. Paris. Rio de Janeiro. Nairobi. London. Portugal. Los Angeles. San Francisco. Stockholm. Argentina. Berlin. Seine River. Rome. Lapland. Greece. Reno. Exeter (England). Myeri Game Reserve. Tasses Fesses. Opera (Paris). Grand Guignol Theater (Paris). Church of the Arachelle (Rome). Animals. Whales. Reindeer.*
Note: Opened in Rome in Nov 1963 as *Mondo di notte n. 3*; running time: 110 min.

ÉCHAPPEMENT LIBRE see **BACKFIRE**

L'ÉCHELLE BLANCHE see **SECRET WORLD**

L'ÉCHIQUIER DE DIEU see **MARCO THE MAGNIFICENT**

ECHO OF TERROR see **PSYCHO A GO-GO!**

ECHOES OF SILENCE F6.1323
Dist Film-Makers' Distribution Center. 9 Feb **1965** [New York opening]. Sd; b&w. 16mm & 35mm. 74 min. [See note.]
Prod-Dir-Writ Peter Emanuel Goldman. *Photog* Peter Emanuel Goldman. *Ed* Peter Emanuel Goldman. *Mus Selections* Charles Mingus, Igor Stravinsky, Sergei Sergeevich Prokofiev, Pete Seeger. *Asst* Riva Freifeld, Michael Sheridan, Joel Boyce.
Cast: Miguel Chacour *(Miguel)*, Viraj Amonsin *(Viraj)*, Jean-François Gobbi *(Robert)*, Stasia Gelber *(Stasia)*, Astrid Spiegel *(Astrid)*, Blanche Zelinka *(Blanche)*, Jacquetta Lampson *(Jacquetta)*, Ellen Marcus, Maria Van Everett, Bill Brach, Mactavish, Irwin Shapiro, John Pope.
Drama. Miguel is an aimless and lonely young man who wanders through New York City (Pennsylvania Station, the Metropolitan Museum of Art, Times Square) searching for a young woman who would be willing to spend a few hours with him. Occasionally, such a woman does go with him to his dismal Greenwich Village apartment, but, through lack of physical desire and ineptitude the seduction usually ends in failure. Equally empty are the lives of his friends and neighbors: Astrid, a lesbian, haunts the bars on MacDougal Street; Stasia, her friend, picks up a fat out-of-towner in the hope of making a few dollars; Viraj and Robert return home after a frustrating night and begin a homosexual affair. At night these people return to the streets. With nowhere else to go, Miguel stands alone on 42d Street staring at the billboards, cluttered window displays, crowded subway entrances, sidewalk evangelists, and other faces as empty as his own. *Loneliness. Male homosexuality. Lesbianism. Seduction. Prostitution. Urban life. Bars. New York City. New York City— Greenwich Village. New York City—Times Square.*
Note: Filmed 1962-65 in 16mm. Also released in an 80-min version and in 35mm.

ECLIPSE (France/Italy) F6.1324

Interopa Film–Cineriz–Paris-Films Production. *Dist* Times Film Corp. 20 Dec **1962** [New York opening]. Sd; b&w. 35mm. 123 min.

Prod Robert Hakim, Raymond Hakim. *Dir* Michelangelo Antonioni. *Story & Screenplay* Michelangelo Antonioni, Tonino Guerra. *Screenplay Collab* Elio Bartolini, Ottiero Ottieri. *Photog* Gianni Di Venanzo. *Art Dir* Piero Poletto. *Film Ed* Eraldo Da Roma. *Mus* Giovanni Fusco. *Song*: "L'eclisse Twist" sung by Mina. *Sd* Claudio Maielli, Mario Bramonti. *Asst Dir* Franco Indovina, Gianni Arduini. *Prod Supv* Danilo Marciani. *Prod Mgr* Giorgio Baldi.

Cast: Monica Vitti (*Vittoria*), Alain Delon (*Piero*), Francisco Rabal (*Riccardo*), Lilla Brignone (*Vittoria's mother*), Louis Seigner (*Ercoli*), Rossana Rory (*Anita*), Mirella Ricciardi (*Marta*), Cyrus Elias (*drunk*).

Drama. In Rome, a young translator named Vittoria leaves her lover, Riccardo, and terminates their 4-year relationship. Following several sleepless nights, she visits her widowed mother at the stock exchange. There she meets Piero, her mother's dynamic young broker. Although they have little in common, Vittoria and Piero are nevertheless drawn to each other and fall in love. Mutually disturbed by the suspicion that their affair will not last, they attempt to push their doubts aside by making love. Vittoria visits Piero in his office, and they make plans to meet again that night and for every night thereafter—for as long as their love will endure. *Translators. Stockbrokers. Widows. Rome. La Borsa di Roma.*

Note: Filmed in Rome and Verona. Opened in Rome in Apr 1962 as *L'eclisse*; running time: 125 min; in Paris in Aug 1962 as *L'éclipse*; running time: 121 min. Cannes Film Festival (1962) length: 130 min.

L'ECLISSE *see* **ECLIPSE**

THE ECSTASIES OF WOMEN F6.1325

Dist United Pictures Organization. caApr **1969** [Chicago showing]. Sd; col (Eastmancolor). 35mm (FantaScope). 80 min.

Prod J. H. Wells. *Dir* Mark Hansen. *Dir Cinematog* Lewis. H. Gordon. *Camera Op* Eskandar Ameripoor. *Ed Supv* Sam Kopetzky. *Mus Backgrounds* Billy Allen. *Sd* Robert Casey. *Asst Dir* Richard Kanter. *Prod Mgr* Buck Buckalew. *Makeup* Helene Robbins. *Ch Electrn* Ron Forman. *Talent Coörd* Dorothy Kristman. *Props* Hollywood Designers.

Cast: Walter Camp (*Harry*), Bonnie Clark (*Summer*), Sharon Matt (*Philomena*), Jeanette Mills (*Annette*), Dee Howard (*Chris*), Vincene Wallace (*Sandy*), Antoinette Maynard (*Freddie*), Eleanor Riggs (*Kitty*), Forman Shain (*Gene*), William Vickers (*Ted*), James Brand (*Fred*).

Comedy-drama. Harry's friends throw a stag party for him at a topless go-go club on the eve of his wedding. At the party Harry recollects some of his former good times, including a number of seductions which took place on his yacht. Four of the go-go dancers accompany the bachelors from the club to the yacht, and a nightlong orgy ensues. Harry decides that marriage is not for him, and he leaves the orgy to pursue an erotic adventure with a girl he has picked up, Summer Frenzy. *Bachelors. Go-go dancers. Bridegrooms. Seduction. Orgies. Yachts. Nightclubs.*

ECSTASY OF LOVERS *see* **HONEYMOON OF TERROR**

ECSTASY ON LOVERS ISLAND *see* **HONEYMOON OF TERROR**

EDDY F6.1326

Dist Astro–Jemco Film Distributors. ca **1969**. Sd; col. 35mm. 79 min.

Melodrama. Eddy, a petty thief who steals indiscriminately and brutally exploits women, is sent to prison for raping a country girl. In prison, Eddy reflects on his past sex life while he releases his frustrations with his cellmate in homosexual encounters. When his prison term has expired Eddy leaves, intending to go straight, but his former companions threaten to castrate him unless he joins them in a burglary. Eddy goes along, is wounded, and ends up back in prison. Sex scenes include Eddy seducing the town tramp, his former schoolteacher, and a society woman. *Ex-convicts. Seduction. Rape. Male homosexuality. Burglary. Castration. Prisons.*

EDEN CRIED F6.1327

4028 Productions. *Dist* Continental Distributing, Inc., Alkoe Artists Productions. 7 Jun **1967** [Newburgh, New York, opening; c19 Jan 1966; LU3434]. Sd; col (Eastman Color). 35mm. 90 min. *MPAA rating* GP.

Prod Shael Young, Charles Ellis. *Exec Prod* Alex Kolis. *Dir-Writ* Fred Johnson, dir.

Cast: Carol Holland (*Lorraine Parker*), Tom Pace (*Skip Garroway*), Victor Izay.

Romantic melodrama. In 1955, high school students Skip Garroway and Lorraine Parker are neighbors in Malibu who enjoy beach parties, surfing, and dancing. A drag racer challenges Skip to a race one evening when Skip and Lorraine are on their way to a dance. Skip takes up the challenge, and his opponent is killed in the race. As a result of the tragedy, Skip's and Lorraine's parents try to separate the two, but they secretly continue to see each other with the help of their friends and eventually marry, to the shock and dismay of their parents. *Neighbors. Surfers. Students. High school life. Adolescence. Marriage. Automobile racing. Malibu (California). Automobile accidents.*

Note: May also be known as *In the Fall of '55 Eden Cried*. Rereleased by Alkoe Artists Productions.

EDGAR ALLAN POE'S CASTLE OF BLOOD *see* **CASTLE OF BLOOD**

EDGAR ALLAN POE'S CONQUEROR WORM *see* **CONQUEROR WORM**

EDGAR ALLAN POE'S "THE OBLONG BOX" *see* **THE OBLONG BOX**

THE EDGE F6.1328

Blue Van Films–Alpha-60. *Dist* Film-Makers' Distribution Center. 27 Mar **1968** [New York opening]. Sd; b&w. 16mm. 105 min. [Also reviewed at 100 min.]

Prod Robert Kramer, Robert Machover. *Dir-Writ* Robert Kramer. *Camera* Robert Machover. *Asst Camera* Gerald Long. *Lighting* Russell Parker, Norman Fruchter. *Film Ed* Robert Machover. *Sd* Norman Fruchter. *Asst Sd & Sd Eff Ed* Mike Robinson. *Script Girl & Prod Asst* Jane Kramer. *Pottery* Jeff Schlanger. *Darkroom Work* Ceil Coberly.

Cast: Jack Rader (*Dan*), Tom Griffin (*Tom*), Howard Loeb Babeuf (*Bill*), Jeff Weiss (*Max*), Anne Waldman Warsch (*Didi*), Sanford Cohen (*Peter*), Paul Hultberg (*Sinclair*), Catherine Merrill (*Sally*), Russell Parker (*Michael*), Gerald Long (*Gerry*), Theodora Bergery (*Anne*), Randall Conrad (*Randall*), Constance Ullman Long (*Connie*), Susan Reiner (*girl in bed*), Robert Kramer (*mental patient*).

Drama. Within a seacoast area live a group of disillusioned New Leftists in their late twenties and early thirties who were once active in civil rights, poverty, and anti-war causes, but now feel themselves drawn more and more into personal introspection. The FBI has accumulated dossiers on all of them, and they are prone to feelings of suspicion. Into this community for a brief visit comes Tom Eliot, 25 years old and filled with radical enthusiasm. Although he is a close friend of most of the members of the group, they keep from him a common secret: Dan Rainer, one of their number, plans to assassinate the President and then, because he feels justice demands "a life for a life," to commit suicide. While members of the group see Dan's plan as a senseless act and he himself recognizes its futility, it appeals to their frustration and sense of impotence. Bill Raskin, who has served a prison sentence for draft evasion, cautions against the horrors of prison. Peter Stein, once a painter but now a factory worker, becomes estranged from his wife, Didi, as a result of his inability to cope with Dan's plan; and eventually she leaves him. Sinclair Davis, who runs a nursery school, feels himself a member of an earlier generation and is unable to communicate with the younger Dan. Dan at last bids farewell to his waitress girl friend, Sally Kolka, and, carrying a gun, boards a train for Washington. His assassination attempt is foiled, however, and he is trapped by Secret Service agents. Rather than allow himself to be taken alive, he turns the gun against himself. Later, Dan's friends speculate that perhaps he was betrayed, and hospital worker Max Laing accuses ceramist Michael Warren of being an informer. Following a brief scuffle, Tom, realizing that he alone retains faith in the future, goes to Washington to retrieve Dan's body before moving to Chicago to organize student draft resistance. *Presidents of the United States. Draft dodgers. Informers. Radicalism. Assassination. Suicide. Disillusionment. Alienation. Marriage. Perfidy. Prisons. Nurseries. Trains. Vietnam War 1964–73. Washington (District of Columbia). United States Secret Service. United States—Federal Bureau of Investigation.*

Note: Filmed in New York City and New Jersey.

EEGAH! F6.1329

Fairway-International Films. 8 Jun **1962** [Atlanta showing]. Sd; col (Eastman Color). 35mm. 90 min.

Prod-Dir Nicholas Merriwether. *Screenplay* Bob Wehling. *Story* Nicholas Merriwether. *Photog* Vilis Lapenieks. *Film Ed* Don Schneider.

Cast: Arch Hall, Jr. (*Tom*), Marilyn Manning (*Roxy Miller*), Richard Kiel (*Eegah*), William Watters (*Roxy's father*), Ray Dennis Steckler.

Science fiction comedy-drama. When Roxy Miller, a teenager, runs her sports car into a giant, neither her boyfriend, Tom, nor her father believes her story. Nevertheless, they decide to investigate further and find some huge footprints, but both Roxy and her father are captured by the giant, Eegah, and brought to his cave. The cave's sulfur springs give Eegah both his great size and long life. In the cave are the mummies of Eegah's ancestors. Far from frightened, Roxy improves Eegah's appearance by shaving him, and in turn Eegah gives Roxy some trinkets. Tom finds and rescues Roxy and her father, then drives with them in his dune buggy to Palm Springs. Eegah, who has fallen in love with Roxy, follows and is shot down by the police. *Giants. Cave dwellers. Police. Adolescence. Filial relations. Springs. Sulfur. Caves. Mummies. Sports cars. Palm Springs.*

THE EERIE WORLD OF DR. JORDAN *see* SOMETHING WEIRD

EGO TRIP   F6.1330

Cosmos Films. *Dist* Able Film Co. ca **1970**. Sd; col. 16mm. [Feature length assumed.]

Sex film. Frank, a loudmouth, more than meets his match with Judy, Gayle, Teresa, and Linda. *Braggarts. Sexuality.*

EHI, AMICO ... C'È SABATA, HAI CHIUSO *see* SABATA

8 1/2 (Italy)   F6.1331

Cineriz. *Dist* Embassy Pictures. 25 Jun **1963** [New York opening]. Sd; b&w. 35mm. 135 min.

Pres by Joseph E. Levine. *Prod* Angelo Rizzoli. *Exec Prod* Clemente Fracassi. *Dir* Federico Fellini. *Screenplay* Federico Fellini, Tullio Pinelli, Ennio Flajano, Brunello Rondi. *Story* Federico Fellini, Ennio Flajano. *Photog* Gianni Di Venanzo. *Camera* Pasquale De Santis. *Asst Camera* Tazio Secchiaroli. *Art Dir* Piero Gherardi. *Asst Art Dir* Luciano Ricceri. *Film Ed* Leo Catozzo, Adrianna Olasio. *Mus* Nino Rota. *Sd* Mario Faraoni, Alberto Bartolomei. *Asst Dir* Guidarino Guidi, Lina Wertmüller. *Prod Mgr* Nello Meniconi, Alessandro Von Norman. *Asst to the Dir* Giulio Paradisi, Francesco Aluigi. *Cost* Piero Gherardi. *Makeup* Otello Fava. *Hairstyles* Renata Magnanti. *Still Photog* Paul Ronald.

Cast: Marcello Mastroianni *(Guido Anselmi)*, Claudia Cardinale *(Claudia)*, Anouk Aimée *(Luisa Anselmi)*, Sandra Milo *(Carla)*, Rossella Falk *(Rossella)*, Barbara Steele *(Gloria Morin)*, Mario Pisu *(Mezzabotta)*, Guido Alberti *(Pace, the producer)*, Madeleine Lebeau *(actress)*, Jean Rougeul *(Fabrizio Carini, the writer)*, Caterina Boratto *(fashionable woman)*, Annibale Ninchi *(Guido's father)*, Giuditta Rissone *(Guido's mother)*, Ian Dallas *(Maurice)*, Eddra Gale *(La Saraghina)*, Yvonne Casadei *(Kiki)*, Annie Gorassini *(Pace's girl friend)*, Tito Masini *(The Cardinal)*, Eugene Walter *(American journalist)*, Gilda Dahlberg *(journalist's wife)*, Hedy Vessel *(Edith)*, Nadine Sanders *(airline hostess)*, Georgia Simmons *(Guido's grandmother)*, Hazel Rogers *(Negro dancer)*, Riccardo Guglielmi *(Guido as a farm boy)*, Marco Gemini *(Guido as a schoolboy)*, Neil Robinson *(agent)*, Mino Doro *(Claudia's agent)*, Mario Tarchetti *(Claudia's press agent)*, Mary Indovino *(Maurice's partner)*, Mario Conocchia *(director)*, Cesarino Miceli Picardi *(production inspector)*, Bruno Agostini *(production secretary)*, Alberto Conocchia *(production manager)*, John Stacy *(accountant)*, Mark Herron *(Luisa's admirer)*, Elisabetta Catalano *(Luisa's sister)*, Rossella Como *(Luisa's friend)*, Francesco Rigamonti *(Enrico)*, Matilda Calnan *(older journalist)*, Alfredo de Lafeld, Sebastiano De Leandro *(cardinal's secretaries)*, Frazier Rippy *(lay secretary)*, Maria Tedeschi *(college dean)*, Maria Raimondi, Marisa Colomber *(aunts)*, Roberto Nicolosi *(doctor)*, Palma Mangini *(aging relative from the country)*, Roberta Valli *(little annoying niece)*, Eva Gioia, Dina De Santis *(two young girls in bed)*, Olimpia Cavalli *(Miss Olympia)*, Maria Antonietta Beluzzi *(screentest candidate for La Saraghina)*, Polidor *(clown in the parade)*, Elisabetta Cini, Luciana Sanseverino, Giulio Paradisi, Edward Fleming Møller, Valentina Lang, Annarosa Lattuada, Agnes Bonfanti, Flaminia Torlonia, Anna Carimini, Maria Wertmüller.

Drama. Italian film director Guido Anselmi collapses from nervous exhaustion and takes refuge at a luxurious spa. Even at the spa, however, he is badgered by the producer for whom he is committed to make a lavish science fiction film, and by actors, actresses, production personnel, and a disapproving intellectual writer. Apathetic and filled with doubts about the type of film he wants to make, Guido fantasizes about his dead parents, his early Catholic education, his schoolboy adventure watching an obese, grotesque prostitute dance on a beach and his subsequent humiliation in front of his parents and classmates, and his imaginary sexual prowess with a harem of the women he has known, whom, in his fantasy, he controls with a whip. His life is further complicated by the arrival of his giddy mistress, Carla, and his embittered wife, Luisa. One day he meets Claudia, a young actress who is the physical embodiment of the dream woman of his fantasies. When she turns out to be vain and stupid, the disillusioned Guido becomes even more paralyzed by apathy. At a press conference held on the vastly expensive rocket site constructed for his yet unformulated film, he is besieged with impossible questions and decides to abandon the film entirely; but after a final fantasy in which he commits suicide, he feels free of his doubts. A circus band of clowns arrives led by the schoolboy Guido playing a flute. They are followed by all the people Guido has known in his life; and everyone joins hands in a circle. *Motion picture directors. Motion picture producers. Motion picture crews. Actors. Catholics. Prostitutes. Mistresses. Clowns. Critics. Intellectuals. Fantasy. Memory. Childhood. Sexual initiation. Disillusionment. Suicide. Infidelity. Motion pictures. Health resorts. Harems. Press conferences. Catholic Church.*

Note: Location scenes filmed in Rome, Filacciano, and Ostia, Italy. Opened in Rome in Feb 1963 as *8 1/2 (Otto e mezzo)*; running time: 140 min. Prerelease running time: 188 min. Also known as *Federico Fellini's 8 1/2*. Actress Yvonne Casadei is also known as Jacqueline Bonbon.

EIGHT ARMS TO HOLD YOU *see* HELP!

EIGHT GIRLS *see* A MAN—EIGHT GIRLS

8 ON THE LAM   F6.1332

Bob Hope Enterprises. *Dist* United Artists. 26 Apr **1967** [New York opening; c26 Apr 1967; LP35840]. Sd; col (Deluxe). 35mm. 106 min.

Assoc Prod Bill Lawrence. *Dir* George Marshall. *Screenplay* Albert E. Lewin, Burt Styler. *Story* Bob Fisher, Arthur Marx. *Dir Photog* Alan Stensvold. *Art Dir* Walter Simonds. *Set Decor* Raymond Paul. *Film Ed* Grant Whytock. *Mus* George Romanis. *Sd* Al Overton. *Asst Dir* Frank Baur. *Prod Supv* Harold E. Knox.

Cast: Bob Hope *(Henry Dimsdale)*, Phyllis Diller *(Golda)*, Jonathan Winters *(Jasper Lynch)*, Shirley Eaton *(Ellie Barton)*, Jill St. John *(Monica Day)*, Stacey Maxwell *(Linda Dimsdale)*, Kevin Brodie *(Steve Dimsdale)*, Robert Hope *(Mike Dimsdale)*, Glenn Gilger *(Andy Dimsdale)*, Avis Hope *(Dana Dimsdale)*, Debi Storm *(Lois Dimsdale)*, Michael Freeman *(Mark Dimsdale)*, Austin Willis *(Mr. Pomeroy)*, Peter Leeds *(Marty)*.

Comedy. Henry Dimsdale, a widowed bank teller with seven children and a large dog to support, finds ten $1,000 bills in a money clip outside a supermarket. Though his combination babysitter and housekeeper, Golda, argues that the money is now his, Henry insists upon waiting 2 weeks to see whether anyone will advertise for the missing money. When no one does so, he goes on a whirlwind spending spree that includes buying an engagement ring for his fiancée, Ellie Barton. He then learns that a $50,000 shortage has been discovered at his bank, and he is the prime suspect. Quick to panic, he packs his brood into his new station wagon and heads for an Arizona hideout, while Golda tries to divert her bumbling police detective boyfriend, Jasper Lynch. While Henry and Ellie are holed up in a motel, they discover that Henry's boss, Mr. Pomeroy, is staying nearby with gold digger Monica Day. Henry begins playing detective but is interrupted by the arrival of Jasper and Golda. A mad chase on horseback and in golf carts ends with Henry being arrested just as he, Golda, and Jasper plunge into a dude ranch swimming pool. But all ends happily when two of Henry's sons place a miniature tape recorder in Mr. Pomeroy's pocket and thereby obtain enough evidence to prove the bank president guilty of embezzlement. All seven children attend the double ceremony in which their father marries Ellie and Jasper marries Golda. *Widowers. Bank clerks. Housekeepers. Babysitters. Detectives. Gold diggers. Courtship. Embezzlement. Weddings. Dude ranches. Recorders. Arizona. Chases. Dogs.*

EIGHTEEN IN THE SUN (Italy)   F6.1333

Dino De Laurentiis Cinematografica. *Dist* Goldstone Film Enterprises. 15 Dec **1964** [New York showing]. Sd; col (Eastmancolor). 35mm (see note). 85 min.

Pres by Richard G. Yates. *Prod* Isidoro Broggi, Renato Libassi. *Dir* Camillo Mastrocinque. *Screenplay* Franco Castellano, Pipolo. *Photog* Riccardo Pallottini. *Mus* Ennio Morricone. *Sd* Titra Sound Corp. *Prod Mgr* Gianni Minervini.

Cast: Catherine Spaak *(Nicole Molino)*, Lisa Gastoni *(Frances)*, Gianni Garko *(Nicola Molino)*, Spiros Focas *(Johnny)*, Fabrizio Capucci *(Matthew)*, Giampiero Littera *(Carlo)*, Stelvio Rosi *(George)*, Oliviero Prunas *(Bruno)*, Luisa Mattioli *(Jeannie)*, Franco Giacobini *(commissar)*, Gabriele Antonini *(Louie)*, Eleonora Morana *(Maggie)*, Loris Bazzocchi *(Gino)*, Paolo De Bellis.

Comedy. During the summer, the Mediterranean isle of Ischia is a popular playground for young people seeking romance and adventure. On one holiday, Nicole Molino, a young Frenchwoman, and Nicola Molino, an athletic Italian youth, are booked into the same hotel room because their names are almost identical. For economic reasons they decide to share the room. Although Nicola vows not to make improper advances toward Nicole, she nevertheless tricks him onto the terrace, locks the door, and forces him to sleep in the rain. Nicola, arrested for sunbathing in the nude, is cleared of the charge when it is revealed that Nicole reported him but had intended it to be a practical joke— and by this time the name-alikes have fallen in love. *French. Youth. Sunbathing. Nudity. Practical jokes. Islands. Hotels. Summer. Mediterranean Sea. Ischia.*

Note: Originally released in Italy in 1962 as *Diciottenni al sole*. May also be known as *Beach Party Italian Style*. Press material gives screen process as "Panoramic Wide-screen."

80 STEPS TO JONAH   F6.1334

Motion Pictures International-El Tigre Productions. *Dist* Warner Bros.-Seven Arts, Inc. 17 Nov **1969** [Boston opening; c1 Nov 1969; LP38058]. Sd; col (Technicolor). 35mm. 107 min. *MPAA rating* G.

Prod-Dir Gerd Oswald. *Exec Prod* Steve Broidy. *Screenplay* Frederic Louis Fox. *Story* Frederic Louis Fox, Gerd Oswald. *Dir Photog* Joseph La Shelle. *Art Dir* Howard Hollander. *Set Decor* Robert R. Benton, Chuck Pierce. *Film Ed* Tony Di Marco. *Mus* George Shearing. *Mus Orch & Cond* Don Vincent. *Songs:*

"*My World,*" "*If I Could Be to You,*" "*Tender Loving Care*" Wayne Newton, Don Vincent. *Song:* "*It's Such a Lonely Time of Year*" Al Gorgoni, Chip Taylor. *Rec Supv* Franklin Milton. *Mus Ed* John Caper, Jr. *Asst Dir* Gilbert Mandelik, Daisy Gerber. *Prod Supv* Eddie Saeta. *Script Supv* Cosmo Genovese. *Makeup* William Tuttle, Joe McKenney. *Hairstyles* Betty Pedretti. *Coöp* Foundation for the Junior Blind in Los Angeles. *Sculptures* Helen Walter Gerson.

Cast: Wayne Newton (*Mark Jonah Winters*), Jo Van Fleet (*Nonna*), Keenan Wynn (*Barney Glover*), Diana Ewing (*Tracy*), Slim Pickens (*Scott*), R. G. Armstrong (*Mackray*), Brandon Cruz (*Little Joe*), Erin Moran (*Kim*), Teddy Quinn (*Richard*), Michele Tobin (*Cathy*), Susan Mathews (*Velma*), Lilly Martens (*Nina*), Ira Angustain (*Pepe*), Butch Patrick (*Brian*), Dennis Cross (*Maxon*), Frank Schuller (*Whitney*), James Bacon (*hobo*), Jackie Kahane (*Jackie Kahane*), Mickey Rooney (*Wilfred Bashford*), Sal Mineo (*Jerry Taggart*), Coby Denton (*Wilks*), Joe Conley (*Jenkins*), Fred Dale, Don Familton (*sheriffs*), Holger Bendixen (*fisherman*), Lord Nelson (*Ralph*), Bertha (*a lamb*).

Melodrama. Drifter Mark Jonah Winters is arrested in Nevada after a stolen car in which he is a passenger crashes, killing hoodlum Jerry Taggart. Jonah claims that he was merely a hitchhiker but, fearing that he has no chance of establishing his innocence, he flees. Sleeping in a field, he is startled by Nina, a little blind girl. She introduces him to three other blind children, Kim, Little Joe, and Cathy, and they lead him to a camp for blind children. Here he meets Nonna, the housekeeper, and Tracy, the blind camp director. Mistaken for a handyman, Jonah wins the love of the children, for whom he feels a natural affinity as a result of his own orphaned childhood. Tracy, too, becomes attracted to Jonah, who forms his first close human attachments at the camp. Nonna recognizes Jonah's picture in a newspaper but refuses to turn him in. Meanwhile, Police Chief Barney Glover leads a determined pursuit. One night Jonah shoots a cougar that has attacked the children's pet lamb, but he accidentally wounds Kim. Relying on his army medical training, he mends Kim's broken leg. Finally, police recognize a bust of Jonah sculpted by Nonna and displayed in the Reno shop where it was taken to be fired; and Jonah is recaptured. By chance, drunkard Wilfred Bashford, who gave directions to Jonah just before he was picked up by Taggart on the night of the crash, sees Jonah at the police station and corroborates his story. Freed, Jonah returns to his friends at the camp. *Drifters. Orphans. Housekeepers. Sculptors. Police. Fugitives. Children. Blindness. Summer camps. Reno. Nevada. Automobile accidents. Sheep.*

EIKO ENO KUROHYO see **FIGHT FOR THE GLORY**

EINER FRISST DEN ANDEREN see **DOG EAT DOG**

EINER SPIELT FALSCH see **TRUNK TO CAIRO**

EL CONDOR F6.1335

National General Pictures–Carthay Continental. *Dist* National General Pictures. 19 Jun **1970** [New York opening]. Sd; col (Technicolor). 35mm. 102 min. *MPAA rating* R.

Prod Andre De Toth. *Dir* John Guillermin. *2d Unit Dir* Tap Canutt, Albert Cardiff. *Screenplay* Larry Cohen, Steven Carabatsos. *Story* Steven Carabatsos. *Photog* Henri Persin. *2d Unit Photog* Francisco Sempere. *Art Dir* Julio Molina. *Set Decor* Enrique Fernández Sagaseta. *Main Titl* Pacific Title. *Film Ed* William Ziegler, Walter Hannemann. *Mus Comp & Cond* Maurice Jarre. *Sd* Paddy Cunningham. *Asst Dir* Tony Tarruella, Russell Vreeland. *Prod Supv* Eva Monley. *Prod Mgr* Vicente Sempere, Robert Watts, Ivo Nightingale. *Sp Eff* Kit West.

Cast: Jim Brown (*Luke*), Lee Van Cleef (*Jaroo*), Patrick O'Neal (*Chavez*), Marianna Hill (*Claudine*), Iron Eyes Cody (*Santana*), Imogen Hassall (*Dolores*), Elisha Cook, Jr. (*old convict*), Gustavo Rojo (*Colonel Aguinaldo*), Florencio Amarilla (*Aguila*), Julio Peña (*General Hernandez*), Angel Del Pozo (*lieutenant*), Patricio Santiago (*Julio*), John Clarke (*prison guard captain*), Raúl Mendoza Castro (*Indian*), Rafael Albaicin (*officer*), George Ross (*guard for convicts*), Ricardo Palacios (*chief Mexican bandit*), Charles Stalnaker, Carlos Bravo, Dan Van Husen (*bandits*), Peter Lenahan, Art Larkin, Per Barclay (*convicts*).

Western melodrama. Luke, believing that a fortune in gold is hidden in the Mexican fortress of El Condor, escapes from a chain gang and joins forces with Jaroo, a con man. The two men enlist the aid of a tribe of renegade Apaches led by Santana, leading them to believe that the raid on the fortress is for food and ammunition. Chavez, the officer in charge of the fort, captures Luke and Jaroo during their first attempt, but they escape with the aid of Claudine, Chavez' wife, who has fallen in love with Luke. Later, Claudine creates a diversion by undressing in front of her bedroom window, and the raiders return and overpower the guards. Chavez manages to get away, and the raiders take control of El Condor. Santana soon discovers Jaroo's deception; and after Jaroo shoots him, the rest of the Apaches flee with the supplies and ammunition,

leaving the two bandits and Claudine in the defenseless fortress. Chavez returns with his soldiers under a flag of truce and challenges Luke to a duel, which Luke wins. The gold turns out to be only painted lead bars, however, and in a showdown, Luke kills Jaroo and remains with Claudine. *Convicts. Confidence men. Apache Indians. Mexicans. Prison escapes. Duplicity. Infidelity. Gold. Forts. Mexico. Duels.*

EL DORADO F6.1336

Laurel Productions. *Dist* Paramount Pictures. 7 Jun **1967** [Denver opening; c31 Dec 1966; LP34528]. Sd; col (Technicolor). 35mm. 126 min.

Pres by Howard Hawks. *Prod-Dir* Howard Hawks. *Assoc Prod* Paul Helmick. *Screenplay* Leigh Brackett. *Cinematog* Harold Rosson. *Art Dir* Hal Pereira, Carl Anderson. *Set Decor* Ray Moyer, Robert R. Benton. *Orig Titl Paintings* Olaf Wieghorst. *Film Ed* John Woodcock. *Mus Score & Cond* Nelson Riddle. *Titl Song* Nelson Riddle, John Gabriel. *Sung by* George Alexander. *Accomp* The Mellomen. *Orch* Gil Grau. *Sd* John Carter, Charles Grenzbach. *Asst Dir* Andrew J. Durkus, William R. Poole. *Prod Mgr* John Coonan. *Script Supv* Charlsie Bryant. *Cost* Edith Head. *Wardrobe* Forrest T. Butler, Glenita Dineen. *Makeup* Wally Westmore. *Hairstyles* Nellie Manley. *Sp Photog Eff* Paul K. Lerpae. *Proc Photog* Farciot Edouart. *Sp Eff* David Koehler. *Adv* Rodd Redwing. *Prop* Earl Olin.

Cast: John Wayne (*Cole Thornton*), Robert Mitchum (*J. P. Harrah*), James Caan (*Mississippi [Alan Bourdillon Traherne]*), Charlene Holt (*Maudie*), Arthur Hunnicutt (*Bull Harris [Bull Thomas?]*), Michele Carey (*Joey MacDonald*), R. G. Armstrong (*Kevin MacDonald*), Edward Asner (*Bart Jason*), Paul Fix (*Doc Miller*), Christopher George (*Nelse McLeod*), Marina Ghane (*Maria*), John Gabriel (*Pedro*), Robert Rothwell (*Saul MacDonald*), Robert Donner (*Milt*), Adam Roarke (*Matt MacDonald*), Chuck Courtney (*Jared MacDonald*), Victoria George (*Jared's wife*), Jim Davis (*Jason's foreman*), Anne Newman (*Saul's wife*), Diane Strom (*Matt's wife*), Johnny Crawford (*Luke MacDonald*), Olaf Wieghorst (*Swedish gunsmith*), Anthony Rogers (*Dr. Donovan*), Dean Smith (*Charlie Hagan*), Chuck Roberson.

Western drama. Source: Harry Peter M'Nab Brown, *The Stars in Their Courses* (New York, 1960). Gunfighter Cole Thornton rides into the frontier town of El Dorado and is reunited with J. P. Harrah, an old friend who is now the local sheriff. Thornton has been sent for by cattle baron Bart Jason, but he refuses to work for the man when J. P. informs him that his job will be to drive the MacDonald family off their land, which Jason needs for water. When Cole is ambushed while riding back from the Jason ranch, he wounds one of Kevin MacDonald's four sons, who shoots himself to escape the pain. Before Cole can explain the incident to MacDonald's hoydenish daughter, Joey, the young woman shoots him. The bullet lodges itself close to Cole's spine, and old "Doc" Miller feels unqualified to remove it and suggests he see a more equipped surgeon. Sometime later, at a cantina near the Mexican border, Cole strikes up a friendship with a young drifter named Mississippi. He also meets Jason's new hired gunman, Nelse McLeod, and learns that J. P. has been drunk ever since being jilted by a dancehall girl. Accompanied by Mississippi, Cole rides back to El Dorado and attempts to sober up J. P. with a liquid concoction laced with gunpowder. An effort to restore peace by jailing Jason and driving McLeod out of town is temporarily successful, but they return, capture Cole, and then trade him for Jason. As the inevitable showdown nears, Cole's right hand becomes partially paralyzed because of the bullet near his spine; and J. P. is forced to hobble around on crutches because of a leg wound. Aided by J. P.'s wizened arrow-shooting deputy, Bull Harris, and the fiery Joey, they manage to kill Jason, McLeod, and the entire gang. With peace restored, Mississippi decides to settle down with Joey; Cole resumes his longtime courtship of Maudie, El Dorado's saloon proprietress; and the now-sober J. P. basks in his renewed self respect. *Gunfighters. Sheriffs. Cattlemen. Ranchers. Physicians. Saloon keepers. Water rights. Suicide. Paralysis. Drunkenness. Mexican border.*

Note: Location scenes filmed in Arizona.

ELDRIDGE CLEAVER (Algeria) F6.1337

O. N. C. I. C. *Dist* Cinema V Distributing, Inc. 25 Aug **1970** [New York opening]. Sd; col (Eastman Color). 35mm. 75 min.

Prod-Dir-Writ William Klein. *In Collab With* Eldridge Cleaver, Robert Scheer. *Photog* William Klein. *Co-photog* Michel Brault. *Film Ed* William Klein, Jacqueline Meppiel, Valérie Mayoux. *Mus & Song:* "*The Panther Anthem*" *writ & sung by* Elaine Brown. *Sd* Antoine Bonfanti. *Prod Mgr* Majdi Abdel Madjid.

Featuring: Eldridge Cleaver, Kathleen Cleaver.

Documentary. The film consists of interviews filmed in Algeria with Eldridge Cleaver. He discusses revolutionary aims and methods of the Black Panther movement. The interviews include Mrs. Cleaver and take place in the Cleaver household and in street settings. Cleaver is shown meeting with African nationalists and visiting the North Vietnam delegation to Algeria. The film includes newsreel footage of the First Pan-African Cultural Festival and the Vietnam War. *Americans in foreign countries. Africans. Revolutionaries.*

Interviews. Black Panthers. Vietnam War 1964–73. Pan-African Cultural Festival. Democratic Republic of Vietnam. Eldridge Cleaver.

Note: Some sources credit France as country of origin. Original length: 80 min.

ELEANA   F6.1338

Dist Chancellor Films. ca **1969**. Sd; col. 35mm. 59 min.

Prod Andre Prevot. *Dir-Writ* Seemore Doules. *Dir Photog* Savas Kalogeras. *Film Ed* Seemore Doules. *Prod Supv* George Michael.

Cast: Lisa Vern, Athena Prezaki, J. Calvin Culver.

Melodrama. Walking along a deserted stretch of beach, Eleana watches while a young couple make love. Her attempts at self-arousal do not relieve the loneliness she feels since she and her lover, Mike, have separated. She visits her cousin, Laura, and while telling of her unhappiness, recalls the shock of finding Mike with another man and realizing that he is a homosexual. Laura comforts her, and their embrace leads to lovemaking. They go to a costume party (orgy), and there Eleana is attracted to a masked man. After a passionate encounter, Eleana rips the mask from her lover's face only to discover that he is Jim, Laura's husband. *Loneliness. Voyeurism. Lesbianism. Male homosexuality. Autoeroticism. Masquerades.*

Note: Country of origin undetermined.

THE ELEANOR ROOSEVELT STORY   F6.1339

Sidney Glazier Productions. *Dist* Landau Releasing Organization, Allied Artists. 8 Nov **1965** [New York opening]. Sd; b&w. 35mm. 90 min.

Pres by Landau/Unger Co. *Prod* Sidney Glazier. *Dir* Richard Kaplan. *Screenplay* Archibald MacLeish. *Stop Photog & Zoom Shots Dsgn by* Eckstein-Stone. *Film Ed* Miriam Arsham. *Mus* Ezra Laderman.

Narrators: Eric Severeid, Archibald MacLeish, Mrs. Francis Cole.

Documentary. The life of the wife and widow of President Franklin Delano Roosevelt is told through still photographs and newsreel footage. Born to a domineering mother and an alcoholic father, Eleanor Roosevelt is a shy, homely child who finds it difficult to fit into the social milieu of turn-of-the-century New York. After marriage to her fifth cousin, however, her life changes; she raises a family, contemplates the suffering undergone during the First World War, and encourages her husband, after he contracts polio and is permanently crippled, to enter politics. Eleanor Roosevelt is ever-present as her husband becomes Governor of New York and then President of the United States; after his death, she continues her active involvement in politics and the humanities—traveling the world, fighting McCarthyism, and overseeing the passage of the Declaration of Human Rights through the United Nations. *Presidents of the United States. Politics. State governors. Women in politics. McCarthyism. Humanitarianism. Civil rights. Poliomyelitis. World War I. World War II. New York State. Anna Eleanor Roosevelt. Franklin Delano Roosevelt. United Nations.*

ELECTRA (Greece)   F6.1340

Finos Films. *Dist* Lopert Pictures. 17 Dec **1962** [New York opening; c17 Dec 1962; LP25420]. Sd; b&w. 35mm. 110 min.

Prod-Dir-Writ Michael Cacoyannis. *Photog* Walter Lassally. *Camera* George Antonakis. *Art Dir* Spyros Vassilou. *Film Ed* L. Antonakis. *Mus* Mikis Theodorakis. *Sd* Mikes Damalas. *Asst Sd* Demetris Kasimatis. *Asst Dir* Vassilis Mariolis, Th. Christides. *Prod Mgr* Yannis Petropoulakis. *Script Supv* T. Vlassis. *Cost* Spyros Vassilou. *Makeup* N. Varveris.

Cast: Irene Papas *(Electra)*, Aleka Katselli *(Clytemnestra)*, Yannis Fertis *(Orestes)*, Theano Ioannidou *(chorus leader)*, Notis Peryalis *(Electra's husband)*, Takis Emmanouel *(Pylades)*, Phoebus Rhazis *(Aegisthus)*, Manos Katrakis *(The Tutor)*, Theodore Demetriou *(Agamemnon)*, Elsie Pittas *(Electra as a girl)*, Pierre Ampeles *(Orestes as a boy)*, Eleni Karpeta, Kitty Arseni, Eleni Marki, Eleni Marinou, Anna Stavridou, Rita Lagopoulou, Elli Trigonopoulou, Liza Koundouri, A. Gregoriades, D. Kallas, T. Exarchos, M. Sakellarios.

Drama. Source: Euripides, *Electra.* The Greek tragedy as adapted from Euripides' play, in which a brother and sister conspire to destroy their mother, who was partly responsible for their father's murder. *Infidelity. Human sacrifice. Murder. Revenge. Exile. Brother-sister relationship. Matricide. Trojan War. Electra. Agamemnon. Clytemnestra. Orestes. Pylades. Aegisthus. Apollo.*

Note: Filmed on location in Mycenae and Argos in 1961; original running time: 113 min.

ELECTRO-SEX   F6.1341

Dec **1970**. Sd; col. 16mm. [Feature length assumed.]

Sex film. What appear to be three women in reality are dolls created to satisfy men's sexual desires. They have sex with two men in many different ways. *Robots. Group sex. Sex aids.*

ELEKTRA (West Germany)   F6.1342

Polyphon Film & TV Productions. *Dist* Polytel International. 21 Jul **1970** [New York showing]. Sd; col. 35mm. [Feature film, length unknown.]

Prod Rolf Liebermann. *Exec Prod* Gyula Trebitsch. *Libretto* Hugo von Hofmannsthal. *Mus:* "Elektra" Richard Strauss. *Perf by* Hamburg State Philharmonic Orchestra, Hamburg State Opera Chorus. *Orch Cond by* Leopold Ludwig.

Cast: Gladys Kuchta, Regina Resnik, Ingrid Bjoner, Hans Sotin, Helmut Melchert.

Opera film. Music and libretto by Richard Strauss and Hugo von Hofmannsthal, *Elektra* (Dresden opening: 25 Jan 1909). Sophocles, *Elektra.* The Hamburg State Opera performs Richard Strauss's *Elektra. Royalty. Infidelity. Revenge. Murder. Matricide. Mycenae. Electra. Aegisthus. Clytemnestra. Orestes. Agamemnon.*

Note: Produced for West German television; original broadcast date undetermined.

AN ELEPHANT CALLED SLOWLY (Great Britain)   F6.1343

Morning Star Productions. *Dist* Continental Distributing, Inc. May **1970**. Sd; col (Eastman Color, print by Movielab). 35mm. 91 min. *MPAA rating* G.

Prod-Writ Bill Travers, James Hill. *Assoc Prod* Monty Ruben. *Dir* James Hill. *Photog* Simon Trevor. *Adtl Photog* Robert Kingston Davies. *Main Titl* Larkins Studio. *Film Ed* Andrew Borthwick. *Mus:* "A Swingin' Safari," "Market Day," "Afrikaan Beat," "Happy Trumpeter," "Tootie Flutie" Bert Kaempfert. *Adtl Mus & Mus Dir* Howard Blake. *Sd Rec* Michael Richmond. *Sd Ed* Karen Heward. *Prod Mgr* Colin Jobson.

Cast: Virginia McKenna *(Ginny)*, Bill Travers *(Bill)*, George Adamson *(himself)*, Vinay Inambar *(Mr. Mophagee)*, Joab Collins *(Henry)*, Ali Twaha *(Mutiso)*, Raffles Harman.

Adventure melodrama. Ginny and Bill arrive in Kenya to look after the home of a friend who is vacationing in Europe. They are immediately befriended by three elephants, the smallest of which they nickname Pole Pole, a Swahili word meaning "slowly." They also visit their friend George Adamson and his lions, which were featured with them in the film *Born Free.* Among the many bush animals encountered by the couple are a pair of tame rhinos. The trip is brief, and after a sad farewell to Pole Pole and the other elephants, Ginny and Bill leave Africa. *Animal life. Kenya. Elephants. Lions. Rhinoceros.*

Note: Filmed on location in Kenya and Tanzania. Released in Great Britain in 1970.

ELI KOTCH *see* **DEAD HEAT ON A MERRY-GO-ROUND**

THE ELIMINATOR *see* **DANGER ROUTE**

THE ELUSIVE CORPORAL (France)   F6.1344

Les Films du Cyclope. *Dist* Union Film Distributors, Pathé Contemporary Films. 18 Feb **1963** [New York opening]. Sd; b&w. 35mm. 108 min.

A Pathé-Cinéma Production. *Prod* J. W. Beyer. *Assoc Prod in Austria* Georges Glass. *Exec Prod* Yvonne Tourmayeff. *Dir-Dial* Jean Renoir. *Assoc Dir* Guy Lefranc. *Adapt* Jean Renoir, Guy Lefranc. *Dir Photog* Georges Leclerc. *Camera Op* Jean-Louis Picavet, Gilbert Chain, Antoine Georgakis, Robert Fraisse. *Lighting* André Moindrot. *Art Dir* Wolf Witzemann. *Stage Set* Eugène Herrly. *Film Ed* Renée Lichtig. *Asst Ed* Madeleine Lacompère. *Mus* Joseph Kosma. *Orch Cond* Serge Baudo. *Sd* Antoine Petitjean. *Asst Sd* Jacques Bissières, Gaston Demede, Jacques Gérardot. *Asst Dir* Marc Maurette, J. E. Kieffer. *Prod Mgr* René G. Vuattoux. *Script Girl* Charlotte Lefèvre-Vuattoux. *Cost* Wolf Witzemann.

Cast: Jean-Pierre Cassel *(The Corporal)*, Claude Brasseur *(Pater)*, Claude Rich *(Ballochet)*, Jean Carmet *(Emile)*, Mario David *(Caruso)*, Philippe Castelli *(electrician)*, Jacques Jouanneau *(Penche-à-Gauche)*, Conny Froboess *(Erika)*, Raymond Jourdan *(Dupieu)*, O. E. Hasse *(drunk on the train)*, Guy Bedos *(stutterer)*, Gérard Darrieu *(cross-eyed man)*, Sacha Briquet *(escaping "woman" prisoner)*, Lucien Raimbourg *(station guard)*, François Darbon *(French soldier married to German peasant)*, Elisabeth Marcus, Elisabeth Stiepl, Helmut Janatsch.

Comedy-drama. Source: Jacques Perret, *Le caporal épinglé* (Paris, 1947). In 1940, the Corporal and his friends Pater and Ballochet, prisoners of war, make an abortive escape attempt and are shipped to a detention center in Germany. Separated from Ballochet, the Corporal and Pater flee but are quickly recaptured. Peter tires of the ritual of escape and retaliation, and Penche-à-Gauche replaces him as the Corporal's partner. Again apprehended, the Corporal is reunited with Ballochet who, having misrepresented himself as a translator to his captors, has been installed in comfortable quarters and is treated with deference. The Corporal accepts his hospitality and enjoys an idyll with the daughter of a German dentist. When she confesses her admiration of his courage, the Corporal is inspired to escape. Fallen from favor with the Germans, Ballochet confesses his cowardice to the Corporal and is slain while fleeing the camp. Aided by the dentist's daughter and accompanied by Pater, the Corporal escapes from Germany by train. En route to France, the pair encounter an inebriated sympathetic German, whose interview with them is terminated by the bombing of the train. Safe in Paris, Pater and the Corporal vow to continue their resistance. *Soldiers. Prisoners of war. Germans. Prison guards. Dentists. Prison escapes. World War II. Paris. France—Army.*

Note: Location scenes filmed in and around Vienna and at Pont de Tolbiac, Paris. Opened in Paris as *Le caporal épinglé* in May 1962; running time: 115 min.

ELVIRA MADIGAN (Sweden)   F6.1345

Europa Film–Janco Films. *Dist* Cinema V Distributing, Inc. 31 Oct **1967** [New York opening]. Sd; col (Eastmancolor). 35mm. 90 min.

Dir-Writ Bo Widerberg. *Photog* Jörgen Persson. *Film Ed* Bo Widerberg. *Mus* Ulf Björlin. *Piano Concerto no. 21* Wolfgang Amadeus Mozart. *Played by* Geza Anda. *Adtl Mus From the Works of* Antonio Vivaldi. *Sd* Sven Fahlen. *Asst Dir* Kalle Boman. *Prod Mgr* Waldemar Bergendahl.

Cast: Pia Degermark *(Elvira)*, Thommy Berggren *(Sixten Sparre)*, Lennart Malmer *(friend)*, Nina Widerberg *(little girl)*, Cleo Jensen *(cook)*.

Romantic drama. Based on the ballad by: Johan Lindström Saxon, "Visan om den sköna konstberiderskan Elvira Madigans kärlek och grymma död" (1889). In the late 19th century, Sixten Sparre, a Swedish Army officer with a wife and two children, deserts his regiment and runs off with Elvira Madigan, a circus tightrope performer. Ignoring the social conventions and moral restrictions of the day, they abandon their former ways of life in the hope of finding happiness together. While picnicking in a field, Sixten shaves off his beard, and Elvira removes the gold military buttons from his jacket and replaces them with black ones from a scarecrow. They check into a small inn as husband and wife, and for a brief time, their days are filled with the simple pleasure of being in love. Eventually, however, their identity is discovered, and they are forced to flee to Denmark. There they are found by a fellow officer who tries to make Sixten return by telling him that his wife has tried to kill herself. Elvira overhears the conversation, and, believing the officer's report, she runs away. Sixten goes after her and convinces her that the suicide story is untrue; and they try to resume their idyllic life. When their money runs out, Elvira takes a job dancing at a village tavern, but Sixten becomes incensed when she shows her legs in public. A quarrel follows in which their identities are once more exposed. Now completely without funds, they must forage for food in the woods, eating berries and mushrooms. They eventually realize that life is tearing them apart. After stealing some food for a picnic lunch, they walk to a sunlit hillside to spend their last hours together. As Elvira chases a butterfly, Sixten takes his revolver and ends both their lives. *Deserters—Military. Tightrope walkers. Dancers. Fugitives. Social conformity. Infidelity. Personal identity. Poverty. Suicide. Picnics. Inns. Denmark.*

Note: Based on a true incident. Location scenes filmed in Sweden. Released in Sweden in Apr 1967. An earlier version of *Elvira Madigan*, directed by Åke Ohberb, was released in Sweden in 1943.

ELVIS—THAT'S THE WAY IT IS   F6.1346

Metro-Goldwyn-Mayer, Inc. 11 Nov **1970** [San Francisco opening; c30 Oct 1970; LP38519]. Sd; col (Metrocolor). 35mm (Panavision). 108 min. [Also 97 min.] MPAA rating G.

Prod Chief Herbert F. Solow. *Dir* Denis Sanders. *Dir Photog* Lucien Ballard. *Film Ed* Henry Berman. *Assoc Film Ed* George Folsey, Jr. *Song:* "Sweet Caroline" Neil Diamond. *Song:* "Mystery Train" Sam Phillips, Herman Parker, Jr. *Song:* "Tiger Man" J. H. Lewis, S. Burns. *Song:* "The Next Step Is Love" Paul Evans, Paul Parnes. *Song:* "Polk Salad Annie" Tony Joe White. *Song:* "Cryin' Time" Buck Owens. *Song:* "Little Sister" Doc Pomus, Mort Shuman. *Song:* "What'd I Say?" Ray Charles. *Song:* "How the Web Was Woven" David Most, Clive Westlake. *Song:* "Stranger in the Crowd" Winfield Scott. *Song:* "I Just Can't Help Believing" Barry Mann, Cynthia Weil. *Song:* "You Don't Have To Say You Love Me" Pino Donaggio, Vito Pallavicini, Vicki Wickham, Simon Napier-Bell. *Song:* "Bridge Over Troubled Water" Paul Simon. *Song:* "You've Lost That Loving Feeling" Phil Spector, Barry Mann, Cynthia Weil. *Song:* "Mary in the Morning" Mike Lendell, Johnny Cymbal. *Song:* "I've Lost You" Ken Howard, mus, Alan Blaikley. *Song:* "Patch It Up" Eddie Rabbitt, Rory Bourke. *Song:* "Love Me Tender" arr by Elvis Presley, Vera Matson, Fred Barovick. *Song:* "Heartbreak Hotel" Mae Boren Axton, Tommy Durden, Elvis Presley. *Song:* "Blue Suede Shoes" Carl Perkins. *Song:* "All Shook Up" Otis Blackwell, Elvis Presley. *Song:* "Suspicious Minds" Mark James. *Song:* "Can't Help Falling in Love" George David Weiss, Hugo Peretti, Luigi Creatore. *Song:* "Words" Barry Gibb, Maurice Gibb, Robin Gibb. *Song:* "That's All Right, Mama" Tommy Allen, mus. *Song:* "One Night With You" Dave Bartholomew, Pearl King. *Songs Sung by* Elvis Presley. *Musicians* James Burton, Charley Hodge, Ronnie Tutt, Jerry Scheff, John Wilkinson, mus. *Background Vocalists* Millie Kirkham, The Sweet Inspirations, The Imperials. *Mus Perf by* The International Hotel Orchestra. *Cond* Joe Guercio. *Sd* Larry Hadsell, Lyle Burbridge. *Asst Dir* John G. Wilson. *Unit Prod Mgr* Dale

Hutchinson. *Elvis' Wardrobe Dsgn by* Bill Belew. *Tech Adv* Col. Tom Parker. *Coörd for RCA Records* George L. Parkhill. *Tech Asst* Richard Davis, tech asst, Lamar Fike, Al Pachuki, Tom Diskin, Felton Jarvis, Bill Porter, Joe Esposito, Jim O'Brien, Sonny West.

Featuring: Elvis Presley.

Documentary. The filmed account of rock and roll giant Elvis Presley begins at the singer's headquarters on the Metro-Goldwyn-Mayer lot, as he prepares for his first concert tour since 1957 and an upcoming appearance at the "Elvis Summer Festival" in the Las Vegas International Hotel. Intercut with the musical numbers are interviews with admiring fans, who try to explain the singer's appeal and significance, and scenes of the fifth annual Elvis Presley Appreciation Society Convention in Luxembourg. The last half of the film is devoted to the Las Vegas appearance and includes shots of Presley fans Cary Grant, Juliet Prowse, Xavier Cugat, Charro, Rona Barrett, and Sammy Davis, Jr. *Singers. Rock and roll. Las Vegas. Luxembourg. California. Elvis Presley. Metro-Goldwyn-Mayer Studios. International Hotel (Las Vegas). Elvis Presley Appreciation Society.*

Note: Filmed on location in California, Luxembourg, and Las Vegas.

THE EMBALMER (Italy)   F6.1347

Gondola Film. *Dist* Europix–Consolidated Corp. 2 May **1966** [Atlanta opening]. Sd; b&w. 35mm. 83 min.

Prod Christian Marvel. *Dir-Story* Dino Tavella. *Screenplay* Dino Tavella, G. Muretta. *Photog* Mario Parapetti. *Art Dir* Giuseppe Ranieri. *Mus* Marcello Gigante. *Prod Mgr* Attilio Tosato.

Cast: Maureen Brown, Gin Mart, Elmo Caruso, Viki Castillo, Luciano Gasper, Anita Todesco, Alcide Gazzotto, Alba Brotto, Carlo Russo, Antonio Grossi, Jack Judd, Paola Vaccari, Maria Rosa Vizzina, Gaetano Dell'Era, Pietro Walter, Roberto Contero, Francesco Bagarrini.

Horror film. In Venice, a fiendish frogman emerges occasionally from the depths of one of the canals to drag a passing girl underwater to the crypt of a submerged monastery. There the fiend embalms the bodies of his victims to preserve their beauty. Three beautiful girls disappear, but police are unwilling to accept the hypothesis of a young journalist that foul play was involved. The journalist sets out to solve the mystery, offering his services as guide to a group of college tourists chaperoned by a teacher and accompanied by an archeologist. The archeologist disappears while investigating a sunken crypt beneath the group's hotel, and his body is found on the stage of a nightclub during a magic act. The chaperon, with whom the journalist has fallen in love, falls into the fiend's hands when she finds a secret passage leading to the hotel basement. The newspaperman, meanwhile, dons diving equipment and penetrates the hidden crypt; there he discovers and overpowers the madman. *Frogmen. Psychopaths. Students. Tourists. Chaperons. Schoolteachers. Journalists. Archeologists. Abduction. Embalming. Hotels. Monasteries. Tombs. Venice.*

Note: Produced in Italy in 1965 as *Il mostro di Venezia.*

THE EMBRACERS   F6.1348

Yucca Productions. *Dist* Joseph Brenner Associates. 27 May **1966**. Sd (Todd-AO); b&w. 35mm. 65 min. [Press showing length: 72 min.]

Prod-Dir-Writ Gary Graver. *Assoc Prod* Frances Graver. *Camera* John Willheim. *Orig Mus* Les McCann Ltd. *Prod Coord* Jeff Graver.

Cast: Lois Adams *(The Girl)*, Gary Graver *(The Boy)*, Billy Rhodes *(The Drunken Man)*, R. J. Gristak *(The Strange Man)*, John Romeyn *(The Boy on the Beach)*, Bert Byers, Robert Parr, Tony Tsavidis, Robert Huard *(The "Keepers")*, Murray Bolen.

Melodrama. A girl wandering along an empty stretch of California beach meets and is seduced by a young man, and she follows him back to his Hollywood apartment because she is destitute. The man's four roommates take advantage of the girl when her casual lover goes away for a week. In another part of Hollywood, a young, jobless actor who carts trash for a wealthy alcoholic meets the girl at the dump where she has gone to escape from her "keepers." The boy takes the girl to his shabby apartment where, strongly attracted to each other, they make love. A tender affair develops between them, which is marred when they encounter the four men who raped the girl. In broad daylight, they accost the lovers, push the girl into their car, assault the actor, and leave him lying in the gutter. Returning to their apartment, the four again rape the girl. A stranger picks up the dazed boy, pretending to help him. In Hollywood Hills the boy senses danger and tries to flee. The man then attempts to kill the boy by running him down with his car. The boy makes it home on foot and, disillusioned, packs his bags to leave Hollywood. The girl returns, having escaped her tormentors, and falls into the boy's arms for comfort. He is determined to go alone, however, and he drives away leaving her standing in the street. *Wanderers. Actors. Roommates. Seduction. Rape. Disillusionment. Loneliness. Poverty. Hollywood. Dumps. Beaches.*

Note: Previewed in 1963 as *The Great Dream*. Also known as *Now.*

EMIL AND THE DETECTIVES F6.1349

Walt Disney Productions. *Dist* Buena Vista Distribution Co. 16 Dec **1964** [Los Angeles opening; c15 Oct 1964; LP29234]. Sd (RCA); col (Technicolor). 35mm. 99 min.

Pres by Walt Disney. *Assoc Prod* Peter V. Herald. *Dir* Peter Tewksbury. *Screenplay* A. J. Carothers. *Dir Photog* Günter Senftleben. *Camera Op* Franz Hofer. *Art Dir* Werner Schlichting, Isabella Schlichting. *Film Ed* Thomas Stanford, Cotton Warburton. *Mus* Heinz Schreiter. *Perf by* The Berlin Symphony. *Sd* Bernard Reicherts. *Asst Dir* Brigitte Liphardt. *Prod Mgr* Paul Waldherr. *Cost* Leo Bei, Josef Wanke. *Makeup* Jupp Paschke, Joachim Schmalor.

Cast: Walter Slezak *(The Baron)*, Bryan Russell *(Emil)*, Roger Mobley *(Gustav)*, Heinz Schubert *(Grundeis)*, Peter Ehrlich *(Müller)*, Cindy Cassell *(Pony)*, Elsa Wagner *(Nana)*, Wolfgang Volz *(Stucke)*, Eva-Ingeborg Scholz *(Frau Tischbein)*, Franz Nicklisch *(desk sergeant)*, Brian Richardson *(professor)*, David Petrychka *(Dienstag)*, Robert Swann *(Hermann)*, Ann Noland *(Frieda)*, Ronnie Johnson *(Rudolf)*, Rick Johnson *(Hans)*, Paul Glawion *(traffic policeman)*, Gerhard Retschy *(Officer Kiessling)*, Viktor Hospach *(proprietor of newsstand)*, Konrad Thoms *(waiter)*, Egon Vogel *(dispatcher)*, Gert Wiedenhofen *(policeman)*, Georg Rebentisch *(bus driver)*, Rolf Rolphs *(butler)*, Roswitha Habedank *(parlor maid)*.

Crime comedy-drama. Source: Erich Kästner, *Emil und die Detektive* (Berlin, 1929). En route from Neustadt to Berlin by bus, Grundeis, a petty crook, steals the 400 marks that 10-year-old Emil Tischbein had been entrusted to deliver to his grandmother. Emil suspects Grundeis of the theft and follows him to a Berlin cafe. Emil then summons a policeman, but the shifty Grundeis, known in the underworld as The Mole, escapes to a rendezvous with The Baron, a notorious figure. Emil meanwhile enlists a band of child "detectives" led by Gustav, a street urchin, and together the boys track down Grundeis and overhear him plotting with The Baron and Müller, another accomplice, to rob a large Berlin bank by tunneling into the vault from the cellar of an adjacent bombed-out building. The boys then trail the crooks to the ruins, but Emil falls through a hole in the upper level and is captured by The Baron, who forces him to aid in blowing apart the bank vault. The Baron and Müller doublecross Grundeis and leave him sealed in the tunnel with Emil, to be obliterated by a stick of dynamite with a burning fuse just outside their grasp. Gustav arrives with reinforcements, detaches the fuse, and alerts scores of neighborhood children. The children surround The Baron and Müller, detain them until the police arrive, and receive a handsome reward. *Children. Detectives. Pickpockets. Police. Theft. Bank robberies. Perfidy. Buses. Dynamite. Neustadt an der Haardt. Berlin—West.*

Note: Filmed entirely on location in West Berlin. The story was filmed five times previously, in Germany (1932, 1954), Great Britain (1935), Japan (1956), and Brazil (1958).

EMILY *see* THE AMERICANIZATION OF EMILY

THE EMPEROR AND A GENERAL (Japan) F6.1350

Toho Co. Mar **1968** [Los Angeles showing]. Sd; b&w. 35mm (Tohoscope). 158 min.

Exec Prod Sanezumi Fujimoto, Tomoyuki Tanaka. *Dir* Kihachi Okamoto. *Screenplay* Shinobu Hashimoto. *Photog* Hiroshi Murai. *Lighting* Tsuruzo Nishikawa. *Art Dir* Iwao Akune. *Mus* Masaru Sato. *Sd Rec* Shin Tokai.

Cast: Toshiro Mifune *(War Minister Anami)*, So Yamamura *(Navy Minister)*, Chishu Ryu *(Prime Minister)*, Seiji Miyaguchi *(Foreign Minister)*, Takashi Shimura *(Information Chief)*, Toshio Kurosawa *(Major Hatanaka)*, Shogo Shimada *(Imperial Commander Mori)*, Susumu Fujita *(Colonel Haga)*, Yunosuke Ito *(Major General Nonaka)*, Daisuke Kato *(Yabe of NHK)*, Jun Tazaki *(Colonel Kosono)*, Michiyo Aratama *(Yuriko Hara)*, Nobuo Nakamura *(Lord Kido)*, Kenjiro Ishiyama *(General Tanaka)*, Keiju Kobayashi *(Chamberlain Tokugawa)*, Yuzo Kayama *(Tateno of NHK)*, Koshiro Matsumoto *(Emperor Hirohito)*, Rokko Toura, Yoshio Kosugi, Ushio Akashi, Takeshi Kato, Akihiko Hirata, Tadao Nakamaru, Ryuji Kita, Eisei Amamoto, Makoto Sato, Ichiro Nakaya, Koji Mitsui, Yoshio Tsuchiya.

Historical drama. Source: Soichi Oya, *Nihon no ichiban nagai hi* (Tokyo, 1965). Shortly after midnight on 14 August 1945 the government meets with Emperor Hirohito to discuss the acceptance of the Potsdam Declaration, which demands unconditional Japanese surrender. On 10 August it had been decided to accept the Declaration on the condition the Emperor remain on his throne. Upon receipt of the Allied reply on 12 August, however, General Anami, the War Minister, and other high-ranking officers decided to reject the Declaration with the intention of resisting the Allies to the very end. Also, a group of younger officers submitted to the War Ministry a plan to isolate the "pacifists" from the Emperor and to declare martial law in Tokyo. In the Imperial meeting of the 14th the Emperor, declaring he can no longer bear to see the Japanese people suffer, insists the Declaration be accepted and that he transmit the decision in a radio broadcast to the nation the next day. The forces opposing

surrender immediately go into action: the commander of the Imperial Guards is murdered, and the rebels occupy the palace and confine the Information Chief and his broadcasting crew to prevent the broadcast of the Emperor's speech. However, units of General Tanaka's East Army swiftly suppress the coup, and Anami commits suicide. The Emperor's speech is transmitted, and the war officially ends for Japan. *Royalty. Coups d'état. Suicide. Radio. World War II. Tokyo. Hirohito. Korechika Anami. Japan—Army. Potsdam Declaration.*

Note: Released in Japan in Sep 1967 as *Nippon no ichiban nagai hi*, or *Nihon no ichiban nagai hi*.

EMPIRE F6.1351

Dist Film-Makers' Cooperative. 6 Mar **1965** [New York opening]. Si; b&w. 16mm. ca480 min.

Prod-Dir Andy Warhol. *Co-dir* John Palmer, actor. *Camera* Jonas Mekas. *Arr by* Henry Romney.

Experimental film. A sustained long shot of the Empire State Building as seen from the Time-Life Building, held without interruption throughout the late-night hours and into the dawn that follows. *Empire State Building.*

EMPRESS WU (Hong Kong) F6.1352

Shaw Brothers (H. K.) Ltd. 15 Mar **1965** [New York opening]. Sd; col. 35mm. 120 min.

Prod Run Run Shaw, Runme Shaw. *Dir* Li Han-hsiang. *Screenplay* Wang Yueh-ting.

Cast: Li Li-hua *(Wu Tse-tien)*, Chao Lei *(Emperor Kao Tsung)*, Lo Chi *(Prince Hsuan)*, Chang Chung-wen *(Empress Wang)*, Yen Chuan *(Hsu Yiu-king)*, Lo Wei *(Pei Yen)*, Cheung Ying-tsai *(Chang Chong-chung)*, Paul Chang Chung *(Chang Yi-tse)*, Ting Ning *(Shang Kuan Wan-erh)*.

Biographical drama. Wu, a former concubine, succeeds the Emperor Kao Tsung to the throne of the T'ang dynasty. She murders many people, including her sons, to maintain her position. After a life full of court intrigue she dies, and her life is reviewed. The souls of those murdered pass before her; and she sees her successor, a prince of the dynasty. *Royalty. Assassination. China—History—T'ang Dynasty. Wu Hou. Kao Tsung.*

Note: Sources indicate Hong Kong release in 1964 as *Wu-hou*.

THE EMPTY CANVAS (France/Italy) F6.1353

C. C. Champion–Les Films Concordia–Cocinor. *Dist* Embassy Pictures. 11 Mar **1964** [Los Angeles opening]. Sd; b&w. 35mm. 118 min. [Also reviewed at 104 min.]

Pres by Joseph E. Levine. *Prod* Carlo Ponti. *Exec Prod* Joseph E. Levine. *Dir* Damiano Damiani. *Screenplay* Damiano Damiani, Tonino Guerra, Ugo Liberatore. *Dir Photog* Roberto Gerardi. *Camera* Sante Achilli. *Art Dir* Carlo Egidi. *Set Decor* Dario Micheli. *Film Ed* Renzo Lucidi. *Mus Comp & Dir* Luis Enriquez Bacalov. *Song:* "Now That You're Gone" sung by Rita Pavone. *Sd* Mario Messina. *Asst Dir* Guglielmo Giarda. *Prod Supv* Antonio Altoviti. *Prod Mgr* Carlo Lastricati. *Prod Asst* Claudio Mancini.

Cast: Bette Davis *(Dino's mother)*, Horst Buchholz *(Dino)*, Catherine Spaak *(Cecilia)*, Isa Miranda *(Cecilia's mother)*, Lea Padovani *(Balestrieri's widow)*, Daniela Rocca *(Rita [The Princess])*, Georges Wilson *(Cecilia's father)*, Leonida Repaci *(Balestrieri)*, Luigi Giuliani *(Luciani)*, Dany Paris *(nun)*, Daniela Calvino *(Emma, a prostitute)*, Micaela Dazzi *(prostitute)*, Marcella Rovena *(tenant)*, Renato Moretti, Edoardo Nevola *(waiters)*, Jole Mauro *(cashier)*, Mario Lanfranchi, actor *(detective)*.

Drama. Source: Alberto Moravia, *La noia* (Milan, 1960). Balestrieri, an aged married artist, dies while making love to Cecilia, a young model, whereupon his neighbor Dino takes the woman as his own. A failed painter dominated by his wealthy American mother, Dino attempts to overcome his ennui through ardent lovemaking with Cecilia. Dino becomes madly jealous, however, upon discovering that he shares her favors with the actor Luciani. Vainly attempting to prevent her proposed idyll in Capri with his rival, Dino proposes marriage. This failing, he invites Cecilia to his mother's palatial Roman estate, where he tries unsuccessfully to dazzle her with his wealth. As he covers Cecilia, lying naked on a bed, with banknotes, they are interrupted by his jaded mother. Realizing that he cannot possess Cecilia, the despondent Dino smashes his sportscar, a maternal birthday present, into a wall. While recuperating in a hospital, he realizes the futility of his obsession. Though Cecilia, having returned from her holiday, is ready to resume their liaison, Dino renounces his passion. *Painters. Models. Mistresses. Americans in foreign countries. Filial relations. Wealth. Jealousy. Suicide. Obsession. Rome. Automobile accidents.*

Note: Filmed in Italy. Opened in Rome in Dec 1963 as *La noia*; running time: 95 min; in Paris in Aug 1964 as *L'ennui et sa diversion, l'érotisme*; running time: 102 min.

THE EMPTY STAR (Mexico)   F6.1354

Producciones Corsa. *Dist* Azteca Films. 27 Mar **1962** [New York opening]. Sd; col (Eastmancolor). 35mm. 107 min.

Prod-Dir Emilio Gómez Muriel. *Screenplay* Julio Alejandro de Castro. *Photog* Gabriel Figueroa. *Art Dir* Jesús Bracho. *Film Ed* Jorge Bustos. *Mus Comp* Gustavo César Carrión. *Based on Themes by* Agustín Lara. *Sd (see note)* Manuel Topete, G. B. Kalee. *Gowns* Balenciaga, Jean Patou.

Cast: María Félix *(Olga Lang)*, Ignacio López Tarso *(Luis)*, Enrique Rambal *(Rodrigo)*, Carlos López Moctezuma *(Federico)*, Ramón Gay *(Raul)*, Carlos Navarro, Rita Macedo, Wolf Rubinsky, Tito Junco, José Luis Jiménez, Mauricio Garcés, Rosa Elena Durgel.

Melodrama. Source: Luis Spota, *La estrella vacia* (Mexico City, 1950). International film star Olga Lang is killed in a plane crash and some of the men she has known attempt to find a meaning in her unhappy life ... As a smalltown girl of extraordinary beauty, she pays for acting lessons by modeling in a dress shop. Her first affair is with Luis, a struggling young writer who offers her marriage. But, too ambitious to settle for domesticity, she undergoes an abortion and terminates their relationship. Luis then introduces her to the director of a theater group, an association that leads to a contract with one of Mexico's major film studios. As Luis gains fame as a novelist, Olga takes as her next lover a brutal and ruthless film tycoon, Federico. He dies of a heart attack, and Olga becomes so rich and powerful that she is able to choose the films she will make. But she meets her match in Raul, a songwriter who squanders her money on other women and mismanages her business affairs. Following a violent quarrel with Raul, who brutally beats her, Olga realizes that her life has become almost totally empty, and she decides to go to Europe and begin anew. As she boards the ill-fated plane, she is still a radiantly beautiful woman. *Mistresses. Actors. Models. Authors. Theatrical directors. Tycoons. Motion picture producers. Composers. Philanderers. Smalltown life. Abortion. Heart disease. Marriage. Ambition. Motion picture studios. Airplane accidents.*

Note: Released in Mexico in 1960 as *La estrella vacia*; running time: 105 min. A Mexican source credits Topete as sound engineer; U. S. source credits Kalee.

THE ENCHANTING SHADOW (Hong Kong)   F6.1355

Shaw Brothers (H. K.) Ltd. *Dist* Run Run Shaw. 23 Jun **1965** [New York opening]. Sd; col (Eastmancolor). 35mm. 85 min.

Prod Run Run Shaw. *Dir* Li Han-hsiang. *Screenplay* Wang Yueh-ting. *Photog* Ho Lu-ying. *Film Ed* Chan Chi-jui. *Mus* Chi Hsiang-tang.

Cast: Betty Loh Tih *(Hsiao Chien)*, Chao Lei *(Ning)*, Yang Chih-ching *(Yen)*, Marguerite Tong Jo-ching *(Lo Mu)*, Li Kuo-hua.

Fantasy. The virtuous student Ning spends the night in a temple haunted by the malevolent sorceress Lo Mu. There Ning is visited by the witch's seductive niece, the ghost Hsiao Chien, but rejects her advances and thus preserves his life. After resisting further temptations Ning vanquishes Lo Mu and revivifies Hsiao Chien by removing her body from its temple grave. *Students. Ghosts. Temptresses. Seduction. Reviviscence. Haunted houses.*

Note: Produced in Hong Kong in 1959 as *Chin nu yu hun.*

ENCRUCIJADA PARA UNA MONJA see **A NUN AT THE CROSSROADS**

END OF A PRIEST (Czechoslovakia)   F6.1356

Barrandov Film Studio. *For* Československý Film. *Dist* Grove Press. 16 Apr **1970** [New York opening]. Sd; b&w. 35mm. 82 min.

Dir Evald Schorm. *Screenplay* Evald Schorm, Josef Škvorecký. *Photog* Jaromír Šofr. *Art Dir* Jindřich Goetz. *Mus* Jan Klusák.

Cast: Vlastimil Brodský *(sexton)*, Jana Brejchová *(Majka)*, Jan Libíček *(village teacher)*, Zdena Škvorecká *(Anna)*, Jaroslav Satoranský *(Tonik)*, Vladimír Valenta *(farmer)*, Helena Růžičková *(farmer's wife)*, Josefa Pechlatová *(Granny)*, Martin Růžek *(white bishop)*, Gueye Cheick *(black bishop)*.

Comedy-drama. Source: Josef Škvorecký, *Farářův konec* (Přerov, 1969). In rural Czechoslovakia the former sexton of the Prague cathedral impersonates a priest with great success. His popularity infuriates the town's atheistic schoolmaster, a pompous Communist, who determines to undermine the false priest by surprising him in the company of Majka, the local slut. The sexton, however, is warned of the plan by his loyal disciple, the village idiot Tonik. The haystack that is to be the scene of their assignation catches fire, and a hobo hiding inside burns to death. The sexton is subsequently unmasked by two bishops. Alerted to the sexton's subversion by the schoolmaster, the police attempt to arrest him during Sunday mass. The impostor scurries to the churchtop and falls to his death. *Priests. Sextons. Atheists. Idiots. Police. Communists. Religion. Imposture. Catholic Church. Churches. Fires.*

Note: Produced in Czechoslovakia in 1969 as *Farářův konec*; Cannes Film Festival running time: 97 min.

THE END OF AUGUST AT THE HOTEL OZONE (Czechoslovakia)   F6.1357

Czechoslovak Army Film Studios. *Dist* New Line Cinema. 28 May **1967** [San Francisco opening]. Sd; b&w. 35mm. 85 min.

Dir Jan Schmidt. *Story-Screenplay* Pavel Juráček. *Photog* Jiří Macák. *Film Ed* Miroslav Hájek. *Mus* Jan Klusak. *Asst Dir* Milan Jonas.

Cast: Ondrej Jariabek *(The Old Man)*, Beta Poničanová *(The Old Woman)*, Magda Seidlerová *(Barbara)*, Hana Vítková *(Theresa)*, Jana Novaková *(Clara)*, Vanda Kalinová *(Judith)*, Natalie Maslovová *(Magdalen)*, Irina Lzicarová *(Anna)*, Jitka Horejsi *(Martha)*, Alena Lippertová *(Eva)*.

Science fiction drama. Eight young, hardened, amoral women and their protector and leader, an older woman, wander on foot and on horseback over an unnamed, rough terrain some 15 years after the end of World War III, looking for others in the hope of replenishing the human race. At a stopping place, the old woman relates to her charges a brief history of the events of the years past. Possessing few supplies—rifles, ammunition, clothing, and some canned goods—the women hunt for game, catch fish by blasting streams with hand grenades, and forage for food and provisions at previously inhabited places, destroying whatever they cannot use immediately or take with them. For sport, some of the women take pot shots at a wild dog prowling near their encampment, and they eventually kill it. They explore the ruin of a baroque palace, and there the old woman coaxes to safety one of her charges who becomes paralyzed by fear atop a high beam. After crossing some especially rough country, the group encounters a tethered cow grazing in a field. They shoot the cow, causing its owner, an old, effete man, to come running. The man, the first the younger women have ever met, is hysterical both at losing his cow and at finally seeing other people. Taking the group to his home, the Hotel Ozone, he treats them to an elegant dinner, complete with wine. An ancient phonograph plays the old man's single recording, "Škoda Lásky" ("Beer Barrel Polka"). The old woman, the guest of honor at the candlelit dinner, falls ill that night and dies. The next morning the younger women prepare to leave despite the old man's entreaties to stay, and they attempt to take with them the phonograph. They shoot the old man when he refuses to give up the phonograph and immediately afterwards set out on their uncertain journey. *Guardians. Survival. Murder. Old age. Human race. Holocausts. Hotels. The Future. Dogs. Cows.*

Note: Released in Czechoslovakia in 1967(?) as *Konec srpna v hotelu Ozon.*

THE END OF BELLE see **THE PASSION OF SLOW FIRE**

END OF DESIRE (France/Italy)   F6.1358

Agnès Delahaie Production–Nepi Film. *Dist* Continental Distributing, Inc. 9 Jul **1962** [New York opening]. Sd; col (Eastman Color). 35mm. 86 min.

Prod Agnès Delahaie, Annie Dorfmann. *Assoc Prod* Louis Wipf. *Dir* Alexandre Astruc. *Dial* Roland Laudenbach. *Adapt* Roland Laudenbach, Alexandre Astruc. *Photog* Claude Renoir. *Camera* Andréas Winding. *Asst Camera* Roger Tellier, Roger Gleize. *Art Dir* Paul Bertrand. *Asst Art Dir* Eugène Roman, Savin Couelle. *Film Ed* Claudine Bouché. *Asst Ed* Nadine Marquand. *Mus* Roman Vlad. *Sd* Antoine Archimbaud. *Sd Rec* Gabriel Salagnac. *Boom Op* Henri Richard. *Asst Dir* Claude Clément, Paul Seban. *Prod Mgr* Lucien Lippens. *Unit Mgr* René Fargeas. *Location Mgr* Roger Volper. *Script Girl* Odette Lemarchand. *Prod Sec* Monique Maraquin. *Cost* Lucilla. *Wardrobe Mistress* Paulette Ten-Have, Colette Baudot. *Makeup* Monique Archambault. *Hairstyles* Alex Archambault. *Models* Mayo. *Still Photog* André-Jacques Manson. *Prop* Daniel Laguille, Henri Berger. *English Subtitl* Herman G. Weinberg.

Cast: Maria Schell *(Jeanne Dandieu)*, Christian Marquand *(Julien de la Mare)*, Pascale Petit *(Rosalie)*, Ivan Desny *(Fourcheville)*, Antonella Lualdi *(Ghilberte Fourcheville)*, Marie-Hélène Dasté *(Madame Dandieu)*, Louis Arbessier *(Dandieu)*, Michel de Slubicki *(Paul)*, Andrée Tainsy *(Ludivine)*, Gérard Darrieu *(fisherman)*.

Melodrama. Source: Guy de Maupassant, *Une vie* (Paris, 1883). In 19th-century Normandy, Jeanne Dandieu falls in love with the debonair Julien de la Mare. Their honeymoon is happy and memorable, but it is not long before the young wife is forced to accept the fact that Julien married her to pay his debts. So strong is her love, however, that she ignores the situation. Furthermore, she must bear the knowledge that Julien has fathered a child by her maid, Rosalie. When Jeanne gives birth to a son, she is given hope that Julien will return her love, but he remains as remote and passive as ever. Eventually he takes another mistress, Ghilberte Fourcheville, the beautiful wife of a former friend. Monsieur Fourcheville is not as tolerant as the loving Jeanne, and when he catches the lovers together, he kills them both. Jeanne, her life now devoid of love and hope, must find a way to continue alone. *Chambermaids. Mistresses. Debt. Infidelity. Illegitimacy. Jealousy. Motherhood. Murder. Honeymoons. Normandy.*

Note: Filmed on location in Normandy, Brittany, and Paris. Opened in Paris in Sep 1958 as *Une vie*; running time: 100 min (alternative running time: 86

min). Opened in Rome in Feb 1959 as *Una vita*. Venice Film Festival (1958) running time: 105 min. Also known as *One Life*.

THE END OF SUMMER *see* EARLY AUTUMN

END OF THE ROAD   F6.1359

Allied Artists. 10 Feb **1970** [New York opening]. Sd; col (Eastman Color). 35mm. 111 min. *MPAA rating* X.

Prod Terry Southern, Stephen F. Kesten. *Exec Prod* Max L. Raab. *Dir* Aram Avakian. *Screenplay* Dennis McGuire, Terry Southern, Aram Avakian. *Dir Photog* Gordon Willis. *Art Dir* Robert Hamlin. *Set Decor* John Mortensen. *Prod Dsgn* Jack Wright, III. *Film Ed* Robert Q. Lovett. *Mus Supv* George Avakian. *Mus* Teo Macero. *Mus Selections* Johann Sebastian Bach, Pëtr Ilich Tchaikovsky. *Song:* "Don't Worry 'Bout Me" Rube Bloom, Ted Koehler. *Sung by* Billie Holiday. *Sd Ed* Marc Laub, Jean Bagley. *Sd Rec* Richard Vorisek, Richard Grimaglia. *Asst Dir* Alan Hopkins. *Prod Mgr* Steven Sidoot.

Cast: Stacy Keach (*Jake Horner*), Harris Yulin (*Joe Morgan*), Dorothy Tristan (*Rennie Morgan*), James Earl Jones (*Doctor D*), Grayson Hall (*Peggy Rankin*), Ray Brock (*Sniper Man/Mrs. Dockey*), James Coco (*School Man*), Oliver Clark (*Dog Man*), June Hutchinson (*Miss Banning*), Graham Jarvis (*Dr. Carter*), Maeve McGuire (*Shirley*), Joel Oppenheimer (*Chicken Man*), John Plechette (*Finkle*), Norman Simpson (*Dr. Scott*), Joel Wolfe (*ticket seller*), M. Emmet Walsh, Gail Gibson, Aram Avakian.

Comedy-drama. Source: John Barth, *The End of the Road* (Garden City, New York, 1958). English instructor and Shakespeare enthusiast Jake Horner is treated in a sanitarium run by Doctor D. Among the psychiatrist's novel methods are exposure to multi-media stimuli and the realization of fantasy. Horner, for example, observes a fellow inmate enjoying intercourse with an indignant chicken. Following his discharge, the intellectual accepts a teaching position at a local university, where he is befriended by Joe, a gun enthusiast, who promptly encourages an affair between his wife, Rennie, and colleague Horner. When Rennie becomes pregnant, however, the pedant insists on an abortion. Performed by Doctor D, its issue is tragic. Rennie suffocates, and the teacher and physician dispose of her corpse in a nearby lake. *Psychiatrists. College teachers. Housewives. Intellectuals. Physicians. Friendship. Abortion. Infidelity. Mental illness. Bestiality. Sanitariums. Guns. William Shakespeare. Fantasy. Chickens.*

THE END OF THE WORLD *see* PANIC IN YEAR ZERO!

THE ENDLESS SUMMER   F6.1360

Bruce Brown Films. *Dist* Bruce Brown Films, Cinema V Distributing, Inc. 9 Feb **1966** [Wichita, Kansas, opening]. Sd; col (Technicolor). 35mm. 95 min. [Cut to 91 min.]

Pres by Bruce Brown. *Prod-Dir-Writ* Bruce Brown. *Photog* Bruce Brown. *Asst Photog* R. Paul Allen, Bob Bagley, Paul Witzig. *Film Ed* Bruce Brown. *Mus Theme Comp & Played by* The Sandals. *Sd* Bruce Brown.

Cast—Surfers: Mike Hynson, Robert August, Sammy Lee, Butch Van Artsdalen, James Blairs, Bruce Brown.

Narrator: Bruce Brown.

Documentary. Surfers Bruce Brown, Mike Hynson, and Robert August embark on a 3-month international adventure in search of "the perfect wave." The trio's odyssey extends from the wintry beach of Malibu to the warm waters of Ghana, and includes stops in Nigeria, Australia, New Zealand, Tahiti, and Hawaii. *Surfers. Americans in foreign countries. Travel. Beaches. Ghana. Nigeria. Australia. Malibu (California). New Zealand. Tahiti. Hawaii.*

Note: Shot in 16mm.

ENDSTATION 13 SAHARA *see* STATION SIX–SAHARA

THE ENEMY *see* HELL IN THE PACIFIC

THE ENEMY, THE SEA *see* MY ENEMY, THE SEA

L'ENFANCE NUE *see* ME

L'ENFANT SAUVAGE *see* THE WILD CHILD

L'ENFER DANS LA PEAU *see* SEXUS

L'ENFER DANS LA VILLE *see* ... AND THE WILD, WILD WOMEN

ENGAGEMENT ITALIANO (France/Italy)   F6.1361

Archimede Film-France Cinéma Productions-Incom Centro Cinematografico. *Dist* Sedgeway Films. 20 Jun **1966** [New York opening]. Sd; b&w. 35mm. 85 min.

Prod Pietro Notarianni. *Dir-Screenplay-Story* Alfredo Giannetti. *Photog* Enzo Serafin. *Mus* Armando Trovajoli.

Cast: Rossano Brazzi (*Mario*), Annie Girardot (*Clara*), Tony Anthony (*Franco*), Marisa Merlini (*Regina*), Giuditta Rissone, Silla Bettini, Nino Dal Fabbro, Giorgio Tedeschi, Cesarina Gherardi, Renzo Palmer.

Comedy-drama. Mario is a 47-year-old Roman bachelor. The furrier business he inherited is competently run by the domineering Regina, his late father's mistress, who leaves him plenty of time to dally with his equally immature friends at the gymnasium and the billiard parlor. His fiancée of 5 years, Clara, patiently remains in the background. And his mother continues to humor his whims as though he were still a child. But one day one of his friends, Franco, who has been wooing Clara himself, persuades her to tell Mario that she is pregnant. At first Mario is delighted with this evidence of his virility, but when Clara presses the subject of marriage, he continues to procrastinate. Realizing how shallow and vain Mario really is, and humiliated when he slaps her in public, Clara breaks their engagement and takes up with Franco. More blows to Mario's ego follow as one by one he is deserted by his friends. As the years pass, he finds that only Regina is left to him. For years she has been waiting like a spider, and now she eagerly reaches out for him. *Playboys. Bachelors. Mistresses. Philanderers. Middle age. Filial relations. Rome.*

Note: Rome opening: Mar 1965 as *La ragazza in prestito*; running time: 95 min.

EIN ENGEL AUF ERDEN *see* ANGEL ON EARTH

L'ENNEMI PUBLIC NO. 1 *see* THE MOST WANTED MAN

L'ENNUI ET SA DIVERSION, L'ÉROTISME *see* THE EMPTY CANVAS

THE ENORMOUS MIDNIGHT   F6.1362

Junque Films. Nov **1967**. Sd; b&w. 35mm. [Feature length assumed.]

Dir William Rotsler.

Cast: Edith Bella (*university professor*), Merrill Maugham (*poet-bum*).

Melodrama. Source: Richard Ashby, *Clyde and the Nightswingers* (publication undetermined). As a means of understanding and controlling her own nymphomaniacal desires, a brilliant young university professor is making a study of a college for delinquent girls. The girls have persuaded a "poet-bum" to stay at the college so that in turn they may spend the night with him, but the exhausted poet attempts to escape. Captured, he is chained naked to a rack in the basement. The professor falls in love with the poet, and in an effort to free him, she promotes an orgy during which the poet escapes into the town and laces the water supply with LSD. As a result of contact with the contaminated water, the entire township, including personnel of a local Strategic Air Command base, engage in an orgy. *Professors. Poets. Students. Juvenile delinquents. Nymphomania. Orgies. LSD. Reformatories.*

ENOUGH ROPE (France/Italy/West Germany)   F6.1363

International Productions-Cocinor-Les Films Marceau-Sancro Film-Galatea-Corona Filmproduktion. *Dist* Artixo Productions. 29 Apr **1966** [San Francisco opening]. Sd; b&w. 35mm (Franscope). 104 min.

Pres by Artie Shaw. An Yvon Guezel Production. *Exec Prod* Yvon Guezel. *Dir* Claude Autant-Lara. *Dial* Pierre Bost. *Adapt* Jean Aurenche. *Photog* Jacques Natteau. *Art Dir* Max Douy. *Film Ed* Madeleine Gug. *Mus Comp* René Cloerec. *Mus Cond* Georges Delerue. *Sd* Gérard Brisseau. *Prod Mgr* Ralph Baum, Yves Laplanche. *Prod Supv* Alexander Grüter.

Cast: Marina Vlady (*Ellie*), Robert Hossein (*Corby*), Maurice Ronet (*Walter Saccard*), Yvonne Furneaux (*Clara Saccard*), Paulette Dubost (*Helen Kimmel*), Gert Fröbe (*Melchior Kimmel*), Harry Mayen (*Tony*), Jacques Monod (*police commissioner*), Clara Gansard.

Mystery melodrama. Source: Patricia Highsmith, *The Blunderer* (New York, 1954). In Nice architect Walter Saccard, unhappily married, is intrigued by the acquittal of Melchior Kimmel, a German bookseller accused of murdering his wife at a bus stop. After compiling relevant newspaper clippings Saccard visits the exonerated Kimmel and is convinced of the German's guilt. Saccard begs his wealthy wife, Clara, for a divorce but, mad with jealousy of his mistress Ellie, she refuses. When Clara takes a bus to visit her sick mother Saccard follows in his car. The next day her corpse is discovered in a ravine and foul play is suspected. Among those certain that Clara was not a suicide and that her husband is responsible are Kimmel, who attempts blackmail, and brutal police detective Corby, who finds the clippings. Certain that Kimmel's acquittal was a travesty of justice, Colby relentlessly stalks both architect and bookseller. Enraged because Saccard's meddling has cast doubts on his exoneration, Kimmel murders the architect. *Architects. Booksellers. Detectives. Murder. Infidelity. Blackmail. Marriage. Jealousy. Suicide. Newspapers. Nice.*

Note: Opened in Paris in Jan 1963 as *Le meurtrier*; running time: 107 min; cut from 115 min(?); in Munich in Feb 1963 as *Der Mörder*; running time: 111 min; released in Italy in 1963 as *L'omicida*. Alternative U. S. title: *The Murderer.*

ENSAYO DE UN CRIMEN *see* **THE CRIMINAL LIFE OF ARCHIBALDO DE LA CRUZ**

ENSIGN PULVER   **F6.1364**

Warner Bros. Pictures. 29 Jun **1964** [Cincinnati, Ohio, opening; c27 Jun 1964; LP29441]. Sd; col (Technicolor). 35mm (Panavision). 104 min.

Prod-Dir Joshua Logan. *Assoc Prod* Ben Kadish. *Screenplay* Joshua Logan, Peter S. Feibleman. *Photog* Charles Lawton. *Camera Op* George Nogle. *Asst Camera* Allen McKenzie. *Art Dir* Leo K. Kuter. *Asst Art Dir* Russell Menzer. *Set Decor* William Kiernan. *Film Ed* William Reynolds. *Asst Ed* Leo Shreve. *Mus* George Duning. *Sd* M. A. Merrick. *Rec* Robert J. Miller. *Boom Op* John Jensen. *Asst Dir* Daniel J. McCauley, Monty Masters, Michael Daves. *Script Supv* Marshall Wolins. *Cost* Dorothy Jeakins. *Men's Wardrobe* Bucky Rous. *Makeup Supv* Gordon Bau. *Makeup* Bill Phillips. *Hairstyles* Jean Burt Reilly. *Eff* Ralph Ayres. *Tech Dir* Carl Morrison. *Dial Supv* Joseph Curtis. *Prop Master* Archie Neel. *Gaffer* Vic Johnston. *Head Grip* Harold Noyes. *Still Photog* Ed Cronenweth.

Cast: Robert Walker, Jr. *(Ensign Pulver)*, Burl Ives *(Captain Morton)*, Walter Matthau *(Doc)*, Tommy Sands *(Bruno)*, Millie Perkins *(Scotty)*, Kay Medford *(head nurse)*, Larry Hagman *(Billings)*, Gerald S. O'Loughlin *(LaSueur)*, Sal Papa *(Gabrowski)*, Al Freeman, Jr. *(Taru)*, James Farentino *(Insigna)*, James Coco *(Skouras)*, Don Dorrell *(Payne)*, Peter L. Marshall *(Carney)*, Robert Matek *(Stretch)*, Diana Sands *(Mila)*, Joseph Marr *(Dowdy)*, Jack Nicholson *(Dolan)*.

Comedy-drama. Source: Thomas Heggen and Joshua Logan, *Mister Roberts* (New York opening: 18 Feb 1948). Thomas Heggen, *Mister Roberts* (Boston, 1946). Morale aboard a U. S. Navy cargo ship worsens when the hated Captain Morton refuses Bruno, a radio operator, permission to attend the funeral of his infant daughter. Later, Bruno tries to kill the captain, but Ensign Pulver wrests the gun from him, and the captain falls overboard during the fight. Pulver grudgingly dives in after him and maneuvers him into a life raft, but they are separated from the ship when a storm arises and presumed lost. Meanwhile, the ship's doctor institutes a new regime; he grants Bruno a shore leave, and morale picks up. On the life raft, the captain becomes ill, and as his condition worsens he becomes delerious. He reveals his past, which he believes causes his antisocial, bestial behavior, while Pulver takes notes. They land on a small island, and there Pulver, working under radioed instructions from the ship's doctor, performs an appendectomy on the captain. When they are returned to the ship, the captain becomes tyrannical again, but Pulver reveals that he knows enough about the captain's past to institute serious action against him, and he threatens to do so unless the captain has himself transferred to another ship. The captain agrees, and Pulver becomes a hero to the crew. *Blackmail. Sea rescue. Surgery. Ships. Appendicitis. Islands. United States Navy. Storms.*

Note: Location scenes filmed in Mexico City and Acapulco. Working title: *Mr. Pulver and the Captain*. Sequel to *Mister Roberts* (Warner Bros., 1955).

ENTER LAUGHING   **F6.1365**

Acre-Sajo Co. *Dist* Columbia Pictures. 31 Jul **1967** [New York opening; c1 Mar 1967; LP34731]. Sd; col (Pathé). 35mm. 112 min.

Prod Carl Reiner, Joseph Stein. *Assoc Prod* Kurt Neumann. *Dir* Carl Reiner. *Screenplay* Joseph Stein, Carl Reiner. *Dir Photog* Joseph Biroc. *Art Dir* Walter M. Simonds. *Set Decor* Morris Hoffman. *Film Ed* Charles Nelson. *Mus* Quincy Jones. *Titl Song* Quincy Jones, David Mack. *Sung by* Mel Carter. *Sd Supv* Charles J. Rice. *Sd* James Z. Flaster, Jack Haynes. *Asst Dir* Kurt Neumann. *Script Supv* Betty Levin. *Makeup Supv* Ben Lane. *Hairstyles* Virginia Jones.

Cast: Jose Ferrer *(Mr. Marlowe)*, Shelley Winters *(Mrs. Kolowitz)*, Elaine May *(Angela)*, Jack Gilford *(Mr. Foreman)*, Janet Margolin *(Wanda)*, David Opatoshu *(Mr. Kolowitz)*, Michael J. Pollard *(Marvin)*, Don Rickles *(Harry Hamburger)*, Richard Deacon *(Pike)*, Nancy Kovack *(Miss B)*, Reni Santoni *(David Kolowitz)*, Herbie Faye *(Mr. Schoenbaum)*, Rob Reiner *(Clark Baxter)*, Danny Stein *(Spencer Reynolds)*, Milton Frome *(policeman)*, Lillian Adams *(theatergoer)*, Mantan Moreland *(subway rider)*, Patrick Campbell *(butler)*, Peter Brocco *(Lawyer Peabody)*.

Comedy. Adapted from: Carl Reiner, *Enter Laughing* (New York, 1958). Joseph Stein, *Enter Laughing* (New York opening: 13 Mar 1963). In the 1930's, a teenage Bronx boy, David Kolowitz, works in Mr. Foreman's machine shop as a helper and delivery boy. Most of his time, however, is spent daydreaming of an acting career in which he imagines himself to be a latter-day Ronald Colman. His parents are unsympathetic with David's aspirations, preferring that he become a pharmacist. But, determined to be a part of the theater, David answers an ad for a job as a paying apprentice in a seedy theater troupe headed by gin-guzzling Mr. Marlowe. Mr. Marlowe's daughter and leading lady, Angela, uses her pseudo-glamour to keep David in the company when he begins to develop cold feet. By day he continues to work for Mr. Foreman, albeit aimlessly, while by night he rehearses for his first stage appearance. His girl friend, Wanda, although understanding his desire to become an actor, is jealous of both Angela and the sexy Miss B, the secretary to Harry Hamburger, to

whom David makes frequent deliveries. Meanwhile, David's parents are frantically trying to borrow money so as to induce him to withdraw from the play and begin his study of pharmacy without further delay. Nevertheless, the play does go on, with David using his new stage name of Ron Colman; and Mr. and Mrs. Kolowitz, Wanda, and David's buddy, Marvin, are all in the audience. Despite many mishaps—missed lines, missed entrances, and the stiffness of David's acting—everyone goes backstage after the performance to congratulate the new actor. And David's parents, of course, both agree that he was the best one in the show. *Errand boys. Actors. Adolescence. Family life. Alcoholism. Ambition. Jealousy. Machine shops. Theater. New York City—Bronx. Ronald Colman.*

Note: Location scenes filmed in Los Angeles and New York City.

ENTERTAINING MR. SLOANE (Great Britain)   **F6.1366**

Canterbury Films. *Dist* Continental Distributing, Inc. 27 Jul **1970** [New York opening]. Sd; col (Technicolor, print by Movielab). 35mm. 94 min.

Prod Douglas Kentish. *Dir* Douglas Hickox. *Screenplay* Clive Exton. *Dir Photog* Wolfgang Suschitzky. *Prod Dsgn* Michael Seymour. *Film Ed* John Trumper. *Mus Comp & Sung by* Georgie Fame. *Sd Ed* Alan Bell. *Sd Rec* Kevin Sutton. *Sd Re-rec* Doug Turner. *Asst Dir* Ariel Levy. *Prod Supv* Christopher Sutton. *Cost* Emma Porteous.

Cast: Beryl Reid *(Kath)*, Harry Andrews *(Ed)*, Peter McEnery *(Sloane)*, Alan Webb *(Kemp)*.

Comedy. Source: Joe Orton, *Entertaining Mr. Sloane* (London opening: 6 May 1964). Kath Kemp, a fat and "fortyish" spinster, discovers Mr. Sloane, a svelte blonde youth, sunbathing on a tombstone. She invites Sloane to lodge at her home, where he meets doddering Dadda Kemp and Kath's homosexual brother, Ed. Attracted by the youth's trim physique, middle-aged sports enthusiast Ed engages Sloane as his chauffeur and buys him an appropriate uniform, all of leather. Equally enamored, Kath seduces Sloane and is impregnated. Breaking 20 years' silence Dadda informs Ed of Sloane's perfidy and announces that the young man is the fugitive murderer of Kemp's former employer. When Sloane and Kemp are left alone, the drifter kicks the old man to death. Dadda is laid in state on the kitchen table, and the siblings agree to represent the death as accidental, on the condition that Sloane marry both. Tearing the Bible from Dadda's hand, Ed performs the service uniting Sloane and sister, and Kath reciprocates by marrying Sloane and Ed. *Lodgers. Bachelors. Chauffeurs. Male homosexuality. Brother-sister relationship. Filial relations. Jealousy. Blackmail. Murder. Marriage—Male homosexual. Cemeteries.*

Note: Opened in London in Apr 1970.

THE EPIC OF JOSIE *see* **THE BALLAD OF JOSIE**

EPILOGUE (Denmark)   **F6.1367**

Bent Christensen Filmproduktion. *Dist* Gold Star Pictures. 29 Mar **1967** [San Francisco opening]. Sd; b&w. 35mm. 93 min.

Prod Bent Christensen. *Exec Prod* Preben Philipsen. *Dir* Henning Carlsen. *Story & Screenplay* Leif Panduro. *Photog* Henning Kristiansen. *Art Dir* Steini Sveinbjørnsson. *Film Ed* Maj Soya. *Mus* Krzysztof Komeda. *Sd* Erik Jensen. *Asst Dir* Just Betzer. *Prod Mgr* Finn Aabye.

Cast: Erno Müller *(Martin)*, Maud Berthelsen *(Lis)*, Buster Larsen *(Gorm)*, Preben Neergaard *(officer)*, Jørn Jeppesen *(Fabian)*, Paul Hagen *(photographer)*, Morten Grunwald *(Ivan)*, Kirsten Rolfes, Claus Nielsen, Birger Jensen.

Drama. Martin, a middle-aged coffee planter in Kenya, returns to his native Copenhagen after a 17-year absence. He begins an affair with Lis, a pacifist half his age. Eventually Lis breaks off their relationship, unable to comprehend Martin's obsession with death and the haunting memories of his participation in the World War II resistance murder of a Nazi collaborator. Threatened by the inability of Martin to escape his past, Martin's wartime acquaintances kill him. *Planters. Pacifists. Traitors. Guilt. Obsession. Memory. Resistance (political). Murder. World War II. Kenya. Copenhagen.*

Note: Opened in Copenhagen in Sep 1963 as *Hvad med os?*; running time: 95 min.

EPISODIO DEL MARE *see* **LA TERRA TREMA**

EQUINOX   **F6.1368**

Berkshire Productions–Tonylyn Productions. *Dist* VIP Distributors. 6 May **1970** [Dallas opening; c17 Dec 1967, 11 Feb 1970; LP35244, LP37886]. Sd; col (De Luxe). 35mm (see note). 82 min. *MPAA rating* GP.

Production Credits for 1970 Vers: *Pres by* Jack H. Harris. *Prod* Jack H. Harris. *Assoc Prod* Dennis Muren. *Dir-Writ* Jack Woods. *Story* Mark Thomas McGee. *Dir Photog* Mike Hoover. *Asst Camera* Ed Begley, Jr. *Film Ed* John Joyce. *Mus Supv* John Caper, Jr. *Sd* Bradley Lane. *Prod Mgr* Sam Altonian. *Prod Asst* Bob Woods. *Script Supv* Jill Murphy. *Makeup* Robynne Hoover. *Sp Photog Eff* Dennis Muren, David Allen, sp eff, Jim Danforth. *Grip* Ben

Harwood, Jr. *Gaffer* Joel Chernoff. *Opticals* Howard A. Anderson Co.

Production Credits for Original Vers: *Prod-Dir* Dennis Muren. *Co-prod* Louis Clayton. *Co-dir & Writ* Mark Thomas McGee. *Photog* Dennis Muren. *Art Dir* Jay Greenwood. *Film Ed* Dennis Muren. *Mus* Truman Fisher. *Perf by* Hidden Valley Music Seminar. *Sd* White Productions. *Prod Staff* Alan Gould, David Stipes, Susan Turner, Bill Goodwin, Conrad Buff, Lin Kroll, Hal Roth, Chris Koppell. *Sp Photog Eff* Dennis Muren, David Allen, sp eff, Jim Danforth.

Cast—1970 Vers: Edward Connell *(Dave)*, Barbara Hewitt *(Susan)*, Frank Boers, Jr. *(Jim)*, Robin Christopher *(Vickie)*, Jack Woods *(Asmodeus)*, Jim Phillips *(reporter)*, Fritz Leiber *(Dr. Waterman)*, Patrick Burke *(Branson)*, Jim Duron *(orderly)*, Norvelle Brooks, Irving L. Lichenstein.

Adtl Cast—Original Vers: Skip Shimer, Robin Snider, Louis Clayton, Sharon Gray.

Science fiction drama. A newspaper reporter writing a story on psychiatric patient David Fielding watches him become violent after being shown a picture of his geology professor, Dr. Waterman. The reporter learns David's story from a tape recorded when the patient was admitted a year earlier. *After receiving a frantic message from Dr. Waterman, David and three friends (Susan, Jim, and Vickie) arrive at the professor's demolished mountain cabin. Notified of the professor's disappearance, forest ranger Asmodeus promises to investigate. While exploring a cave, the youths are given an ancient book by an old man; later, it is snatched away by a crazed man, revealed to be Waterman. Although the professor dies when chased by David and Jim, his corpse mysteriously vanishes when the foursome are reunited. After Susan is attacked by Asmodeus, who flees when he sees her crucifix, the youths examine the old book and learn it is an occult bible, concerned with devil worship. After rescuing the girls from an ape-like monster, Jim separates from the rest and confronts Asmodeus. The ranger reveals himself to be the Devil and demands the book, but Jim flashes an occult symbol at him and escapes. Chased by another monster through an invisible barrier to a supernatural world, Jim is mesmerized and possessed by Asmodeus. David follows and retrieves the book, but learns that the professor's translations of the bible have uncovered the secrets of the supernatural world. Asmodeus kills the girls, who are fleeing with the book, and places a death curse on David.* Neither the doctor nor the reporter believes David's story and suspect him of murdering his friends. As the reporter leaves the hospital, a supernatural being, disguised as one of David's dead friends, arrives to kill David. *Reporters. Professors. Forest rangers. Insanity. Occult. Supernatural. Murder. Curses. Castles. Caves. Monsters. The Devil.*

Note: Location scenes filmed in Big Foot Forest, Tujunga, California, and in Griffith Park, Los Angeles. In 1968 Harris bought the rights to *The Equinox,* a 71-min film registered for copyright by Berkshire Productions. Leaving intact the special effects, Harris shot additional footage—which comprised 60% of the release length—adding the character Asmodeus and rearranging some details of the story. Actors Skip Shimer and Robin Snider changed their names to Edward Connell and Robin Christopher, respectively. The original material was shot in 16mm; Harris' footage was shot in 16mm and 35mm.

ERASMUS WITH FRECKLES see **DEAR BRIGITTE**

ERCOLE AL CENTRO DELLA TERRA see **HERCULES IN THE HAUNTED WORLD**

ERCOLE ALLA CONQUISTA DI ATLANTIDE see **HERCULES AND THE CAPTIVE WOMEN**

ERCOLE CONTRO MOLOCK see **CONQUEST OF MYCENE**

ERCOLE SFIDA SANSONE see **HERCULES, SAMSON & ULYSSES**

EREKI NO WAKADAISHO see **CAMPUS A GO-GO**

ERIC SOYA'S "17" (Denmark)   F6.1369
Palladium. *Dist* Peppercorn-Wormser, Inc. 24 Jan **1967** [New York opening]. Sd; col (Eastman Color, print by Movielab). 35mm. 87 min.

Dir Annelise Meineche. *Screenplay* Bob Ramsing. *Photog* Ole Lytken. *Art Dir* Otto Lund, Herbi Gärtner. *Film Ed* Edith Schlüssel. *Mus Comp & Cond* Ole Høyer. *Titl Song Sung by* Lou Monte. *Sd* Leon Seibaek. *Asst Dir* Hass Peter Linde. *Prod Supv* Jens Ravn.

Cast: Ole Søltoft *(Jacob Petersen)*, Ghita Nørby *(Vibeke)*, Lily Broberg *(Miss Rosegod)*, Ole Monty *(Jacob's uncle)*, Bodil Steen *(Jacob's aunt)*, Hass Christensen *(Professor Petersen)*, Susanne Heinrich *(Hansigne)*, Lise Rosendahl *(Sophie)*, Hugo Herrestrup *(Knud)*, Jørgen Kiil *(Dr. Irving Mogensen [see note])*, David Ingolf *(pharmacist)*, Annie Birgit Garde *(girl on train)*, Arthur Jensen, Jytte Abildstrøm, Henry Nielsen, Valsø Holm, Jens Jensen.

Comedy-drama. Source: Carl Eric Soya, *Sytten; erindringer og refleksioner* (Copenhagen, 1953). In the summer of 1913, 17-year-old Jacob Petersen, a professor's son, feels disturbed by his awakening sexuality. He is fascinated by works of art depicting nude women, but feeling painfully inexperienced, he

avoids contact with the opposite sex, although the family maid, Sophie, is willing to initiate him into lovemaking. Jacob is invited to spend his summer holiday at his uncle's cottage in the country, and he falls in love with his beautiful cousin, Vibeke. One night when Jacob's uncle is away from home, and Vibeke's mother goes to join a family friend, Dr. Mogensen, for a rendezvous, Jacob clumsily makes love to Vibeke. After a brief period of happiness, Jacob and Vibeke are forced to separate when she returns to college. He soon embarks on an adventure with his uncle's good-natured maid, Hansigne, who takes his sexual instruction a step further. This affair comes to an abrupt conclusion when Hansigne's lover catches them in bed, and a fight ensues. However, Jacob finds his uncle's middle-aged housekeeper, Miss Rosegod, to be receptive to his attentions. By now Jacob is fully confident of his charms, and on his train trip home, he seduces an attractive fellow passenger. Sophie is waiting to greet him when he arrives at his father's home. *Housemaids. Cousins. Uncles. Aunts. Adolescence. Sexual initiation. Seduction. Manhood. Vacations.*

Note: Released in Denmark in 1965 under the title *Sytten;* running time: 89 min. Also known as *Seventeen.* Foreign sources credit actor Jørgen Kiil as the young Dr. Mogensen and David Ingolf as a pharmacist, while some U. S. sources credit Kiil as the pharmacist.

ERIK THE CONQUEROR (France/Italy)   F6.1370
Galatea–Criterion Film–Société Cinématographique Lyre. *Dist* American International Pictures. 12 Jun **1963** [Boston opening; c19 Jun 1963; LP26831]. Sd; col (Technicolor). 35mm (Dyaliscope). 90 min. [Copyright length: 81 min.]

Dir Mario Bava. *Story-Screenplay* Oreste Biancoli, Mario Bava, Piero Pierotti. *Photog* Ubaldo Terzano, Mario Bava. *Art Dir* Giorgio Giovannini. *Decor* Giuseppe Tavazzi. *Film Ed* Mario Serandrei. *Mus* Roberto Nicolosi. *Choreog* Leo Coleman. *Sd* Roberto Mattioli. *Asst Dir* Franco Prosperi. *Dir Prod* Massimo De Rita. *Cost* Tina Grani. *Makeup* Euclide Santoli.

Cast: Cameron Mitchell *(Iron)*, Giorgio Ardisson *(Erik, Duke of Helfort)*, Andrea Checchi *(Gunnar)*, Françoise Christophe *(Queen Alice)*, Ellen Kessler *(Daja)*, Alice Kessler *(Rama)*, Folco Lulli *(Aello)*, Franco Giacobini *(Rustichello)*, Joe Robinson *(Iron's rival)*, Raffaele Baldassarre *(Blak)*, Enzo Doria *(Bennet)*, Franco Ressel *(King Lotar)*, Livia Contardi *(Hadda)*, Jean-Jacques Delbo.

Adventure drama. In the 10th century, when the Vikings are defeated by the English forces, Queen Alice of Britain adopts a Viking child abandoned in battle and brings him up as Erik, Duke of Helfort. At the same time, his brother, Iron, grows up to be the Viking chieftain. The two powers clash once more, and Gunnar, Alice's ambitious counsellor, betrays her to the Vikings and in return is awarded Britain's governorship. Shipwrecked in battle, Erik is saved from slow death by Rama, twin sister of Iron's wife, Daja. He returns home to overthrow Gunnar, but the latter is guarded by Vikings. During a duel, Iron recognizes Erik by the tattoo on his chest. Gunnar kills Iron, in the hope that Erik's men will be blamed; his plans, however, are of no avail, for the Vikings unite with the British and slay Gunnar in battle. *Vikings. English. Royalty. Brothers. Sisters. Twins. Guards. Duels. Adoption. Perfidy. Shipwrecks. Tattoos. Great Britain—History—Anglo-Saxon period.*

Note: Produced in Italy in 1961 as *Gli invasori;* running time: 98 min; opened in Paris in Jul 1963 as *La ruée des Vikings;* running time: 88 min. Also known as *Fury of the Vikings.*

ERIKA/ONE   F6.1371
Century Cinema Corp. *Dist* Chancellor Films. Feb **1969**. Sd; col. 35mm. 70 min.

Dir Jerry Denby. *Screenplay* Jon Statkis. *Script* J. Glenn. *Photog* Joe Mangine. *Set Dsgn* Farley Fagg. *Film Ed* PDF Editorial. *Mus* Pov Associates. *Prod Mgr* Anthony Scaretti.

Cast: Inga Larsen *(The Model)*.

Melodrama. An ambitious young model encounters orgies, lesbianism, troilism, and other debaucheries in her climb to the top. Unfortunately, the climb leads only to her suicide. *Models. Orgies. Lesbianism. Troilism. Suicide.*

ERIKA'S HOT SUMMER   F6.1372
Dist Boxoffice International Film Distributors. Aug **1970**. Sd; col (Eastman Color). 35mm. 81 min. *MPAA rating* R.

Pres by Harry Novak. *Prod* Paul Hunt. *Cinematog* Gary Graver. *Dir* Gary Graver. *Set Dsgn* De Marco. *Film Ed (see note)* Paul Hunt, Gary Graver. *Asst Dir* George Talmage. *Location Mgr* Rocco Marchetti. *Wardrobe* Catherine Newell. *Makeup* Lucias Gerlich. *Gaffer* Walt Huang. *Key Grip* Hank Adams.

Cast: Erica Gavin *(Erika)*, Walt Phillips *(Steve)*, Merci Montello *(Sherrie)*, Julie Stone *(Lynn)*, Gary Shermack, Joseph Stark, Mary Sillmar, Gloria Jacobs, Marlene Williams, Michael Land, Sean Wilkins, Rita Spencer, Lilian Collins, Rocco Marchetti.

Melodrama. Anxious for a relationship that involves more than casual sex, Erika remains unsatisfied until she meets playboy Steve, who she believes is capable of giving her the understanding and compassion that will allow her to make love freely. Steve, who has been sexually satisfied with another woman, Sherrie, invites Erika to his apartment, but she insists that they meet on the beach. Later that night, Steve visits Sherrie again, but his thoughts return to Erika. The next day he persuades her that he, too, wants a complete relationship. Erika joyfully abandons all inhibitions with Steve, but her dreams of happiness are shattered when she is forced to recognize that Steve is still tied to Sherrie. *Playboys. Sexuality. Beaches.*

Note: Press material credits Lucias Gerlich, Paul Hunt, and Gary Graver as "makeup editors."

ERNEST HEMINGWAY'S ADVENTURES OF A YOUNG MAN *see* **HEMINGWAY'S ADVENTURES OF A YOUNG MAN**

ERNEST HEMINGWAY'S THE KILLERS *see* **THE KILLERS**

EROICA (Poland)   F6.1373

Kadr Film Unit. *For* Film Polski. *Dist* Amerpol Enterprise Films. 1 Feb **1966** [New York opening]. Sd; b&w. 35mm. 82 min.

Prod Stanisław Adler. *Dir* Andrzej Munk. *Screenplay* Jerzy Stefan Stawiński. *Photog* Jerzy Wójcik. *Art Dir* Jan Grandys. *Film Ed* Jadwiga Zaicek, Mirosława Garlicka. *Mus* Jan Krenz. *Sd* Bodhan Jankowski, Halina Paszkowska.

Cast—"Scherzo Alla Pollaca": Edward Dziewoński *(Dzidzius)*, Barbara Połomska *(Zosia)*, Leon Niemczyk *(Lieutenant Kolya)*, Ignacy Machowski *(major)*, Kazimierz Opaliński *(colonel)*.

Cast—"Ostinato Lugubre": Józef Nowak *(Kurzawa)*, Roman Kłosowski *(Szpakowski)*, Mariusz Dmochowski *(Korwin-Makowski)*, Bogumił Kobiela *(Dabecki)*, Wojciech Siemion *(Marianek)*, Kazimierz Rudzki *(Turek)*, Józef Kostecki *(Zak)*, Henryk Bąk *(Krygier)*, Tadeusz Łomnicki *(Zawistowski)*.

War drama. SCHERZO ALLA POLLACA: During the Warsaw uprising of 1944, an unscrupulous and self-centered Pole named Dzidzius ignores the chaos and bloodshed surrounding him, choosing instead to live the luxurious life of a black-marketeer. He even allows his wife to openly entertain an officer of the Hungarian Army, at that time allied with the Germans. One day, by chance he is forced to undertake a dangerous mission: informing the Warsaw underground that the Hungarians are willing to join forces if the Russians will accept them as allies. By sheer chance Dzidzius arrives safely, but the offer is rejected, and he makes his way home. His life has been changed, however; rather than remain at home in luxury, he decides to participate in the war effort. OSTINATO LUGUBRE: The Polish inmates of a Nazi prisoner-of-war camp maintain their morale by tenaciously clinging to the belief that one man, Zawistowski, managed to escape. He actually lies crouched in the roof, dying of tuberculosis. Another prisoner, Zak, is a highstrung individual, no longer able to bear the petty naggings and bickerings of his fellow prisoners. Finally, in a display of melodramatic heroism, he escapes by the only means open to him—suicide. Zawistowski eventually dies, and the men smuggle his body out of the camp in an oil burner, thereby saving face and preserving the legend of the man who escaped to his freedom. *Prisoners of war. Nazis. Wealth. Resistance (political). Prison escapes. Suicide. Concentration camps. Black market. Tuberculosis. World War II. Poland—History—Occupation 1939–45. Warsaw. Germany— Army. Hungary—Army.*

Note: Released in Poland in Jan 1958. A third episode was cut by the director before release.

EROS (Brazil)   F6.1374

Kamera Filmes-Vera Cruz Studios. *Dist* Sherpix, Inc. 5 Jul **1967** [San Francisco opening]. Sd; b&w. 35mm. 100 min. [Also 65 min.]

Prod-Dir-Writ Walter Hugo Khouri. *Photog* Rudolf Icsey. *Art Dir* Silvio Campos. *Sets* Pierino Massenzi. *Film Ed* Mauro Alice. *Mus* Rogério Duprat. *Incidental Mus Comp & Perf* Zimbo Trio.

Cast: Norma Bengell *(Mara)*, Odete Lara *(Cristina)*, Mario Benvenuti *(Luis Augusto)*, Gabriele Tinti *(Nelson)*, Marisa Woodward, Ricardo Rivas, Julia Kovach, Celia Watanabe, Anita Kennedy, Berta Waldmon, Lisa Negri, Wilfred Khouri, Darcy Cardoso, Laura Maria, The Rebels.

Melodrama. Nelson and Luis Augusto, hedonistic playboys, roam the streets of Rio de Janeiro. They meet prostitutes Mara and Cristina in an oriental bar and take them back to their hotel room. They spend the night engaging in various acts of sexual stimulation, including lesbianism, exhibitionism, and watching stag films. At dawn, the men leave the prostitutes, and the married playboy returns to his wife after making arrangements with his fellow adventurer for another evening of entertainment. *Playboys. Prostitutes. Hedonism. Eroticism. Group sex. Lesbianism. Exhibitionism. Bars. Hotels. Sex exploitation films. Rio de Janeiro.*

Note: Produced in Brazil in 1965 as *Noite vazia*. Also known as *Eros ... The Bizarre* and *Night Games*.

EROS, O BASILEUS   F6.1375

Dist Film-Makers' Cooperative. 23 Apr **1967** [New York showing]. Sd; col. 16mm. 45 min.

Prod-Dir-Writ Gregory J. Markopoulos. *Photog* Gregory J. Markopoulos. *Film Ed* Gregory J. Markopoulos.

Experimental film. The film is comprised of nine sequences, each dwelling on a single occurrence or situation. A young man representing Eros is first seen sitting contemplatively on a stool near a bare bed. He slumps and begins untying his shoe. Later he crawls to the bed. He lies on the bed, sits forlornly, half-dressed, at the foot of the bed, lies on the bed with some books and a notebook, and stretches out on the bed wearing only socks. He is blind. His hands move up the form of a dressmaker's female dummy, but as they approach the dummy's head he does not see that his hands have traveled past the headless neck toward his own head seen in the mirror behind. The young man reaches for some books (one of the authors is Paul Valéry) and a self-portrait of Corot (which reflects or suggests his own image). He temporarily withdraws into a stack of paintings, but emerges to mime Eros shooting his arrows. Near an altar-like structure, the young man sits on the floor, tries on motorcycle helmets, and strikes muscular poses, imitating the figure in Rodin's "Age of Bronze." A poster of Marlon Brando in *The Wild One* is lighted as an icon. With a muscleman pinup surmounted by a black crucifix in the background, he feels the warmth of a bare light bulb. [During the helmet and light bulb scenes, single-frame pans across the young man's body are intercut, revealing an arm lifting, a foot, the slope of a shoulder, a tapping finger, or his entire body.] *Eroticism. Male homosexuality. Blindness. Art. Dummies. Motorcycles. Paul Ambroise Valéry. Jean Baptiste Camille Corot. François Auguste René Rodin. Eros.*

Note: Filmed in New York City. Individual shots are separated by cross-fades; single-frame editing punctuates certain scenes.

EROS ... THE BIZARRE *see* **EROS**

THE EROTIC CIRCUS   F6.1376

Virumque Films. *Dist* J. E. R. Pictures. 20 Aug **1969** [Champaign, Illinois, showing]. Sd; col. 35mm. 69 min.

Dir-Writ Ron Sullivan.

Cast: Jaimy Royale *(Jaime)*, Lotta Blass *(his mother)*, Sagg Taras *(Louie)*, Mimosa Schoes *(Mary)*, Garth Maxwell *(Yenos)*, Natalie Clad *(The Girl)*.

Melodrama. Young Jaime lives on a farm with his mother and a demented caretaker. His uncle, an aging methedrine dealer, arrives at the farm with two women—one a sadist, the other a masochist. After dinner, the uncle and the masochist make love, triggering other sexual activities throughout the house. The following morning, both the sadist and the masochist are found dead, and the uncle is found murdered and castrated in a snare trap. Jaime's mother is revealed to be the murderer, and while the caretaker buries the remains of the three corpses, she plans to castrate him. *Farmers. Uncles. Caretakers. Psychopaths. Drug dealers. Filial relations. Castration. Sadism. Masochism. Murder.*

THE EROTIC EXCESS OF EVIL *see* **JUSTINE**

THE EROTIC HOUSEWIFE *see* **MARSHA, THE EROTIC HOUSEWIFE**

THE EROTIC MR. ROSE   F6.1377

Dist Emerson Film Enterprises. 18 Sep **1964** [Champaign, Illinois, showing]. Sd; b&w. 35mm. 60 min.

Dir Nicholas Millard.

Comedy. A previously innocent, elderly man becomes a woman-chaser. *Philanderers. Old age. Sexuality.*

Note: Also known as *The Conquests of Mr. Rose.*

THE EROTIC THREE *see* **SCRATCH HARRY**

THE EROTIC TOUCH OF HOT SKIN (France)   F6.1378

Les Films du Griffon–Unicité-Alcinter. *Dist* Audubon Films. 19 Nov **1965** [Philadelphia opening]. Sd; b&w. 35mm. 78 min.

Pres by Radley H. Metzger. *Dir* Max Pécas. *Screenplay* Maurice Cury, Robert Topart. *Photog* Roger Duculot. *Prod Mgr* Maurice Gilli.

Cast: Fabienne Dali *(Irene)*, Sophie Hardy *(Cloe)*, Jean Valmont *(Mark)*, François Dyrek *(fisherman)*, Amyra *(dancer)*.

Melodrama. Julian Prentice, who occupies a lavish villa on the French Riviera with his wife, Irene, is killed when he surprises Irene with her young lover, Mark. The lovers bury the body on a hill overlooking the beach and plan to report Julian as missing, but Cloe, a cousin of Irene's whom she has not seen for many years, unexpectedly arrives to spend the summer. Cloe mistakes Mark for Julian, whom she has never met, and the deception is continued. Mark finds himself attracted to Cloe, and Irene, jealous, allows herself to be seduced by a passing fisherman. One day Cloe meets Bernard, a childhood friend, and learns that Mark is an impostor. She confronts the lovers with her discovery, and they explain that Julian's death was accidental. As Cloe rushes from the house, Irene drives after her but crashes her car into a tree, killing herself, rather than run down her cousin. Bernard arrives with the police in time to prevent Mark from killing Cloe. Remaining with Bernard, Cloe attempts to forget her terrifying experience. [Also contains striptease sequences.] *Cousins. Fishermen. Murder. Seduction. Infidelity. Impersonation. Striptease. Suicide. Riviera. Automobile accidents.*

Note: Opened in Paris in Oct 1964 as *La baie du désir;* running time: ca90 min. Also advertised as *The Erotic Touch* and *Touch of Skin.*

EROTICA   **F6.1379**
Pad-Ram Enterprises. 14 Jul **1961** [Los Angeles showing; c30 Jun 1961; LP19930]. Sd; col (Eastman Color). 35mm. 60-68 min.
Prod Peter De Cenzie, Russ Meyer. *Dir* Russ Meyer.
Cast: Donna Townsend, Peggy Martin.

Sex film. A dissertation by a film editor on motion picture production is followed by six vignettes shown on a Moviola. In "Naked Innocence," a city girl enjoys the pleasures of skinny dipping in a country stream. In the second, "Beauties, Bubbles and H2O," a Brooklyn plumber discusses the many ways of bathing, illustrated by three young ladies. "The Bear and the Bare" is a humorous look at bear ranching. "Nudists on the High Seas" finds three "damsel deckhands" illustrating the fine points of sailing. "The Nymphs" contrasts the merits of bathtubs versus showers, and "The Bikini Busters" relates the history of the bathing suit from Eve in the Garden of Eden to modern times. *Motion picture editors. Nudity. Bathing customs. Eroticism. Sex exploitation films. Bathing suits. Sailors. Bears.*

EROTICA see **OF WAYWARD LOVE**

EROTIKOS see **SEX AND THE SINGLE SAILOR**

ÉROTIQUE (France)   **F6.1380**
Paris Inter Productions. *Dist* VIP Distributors, Goldstone Film Enterprises. Dec **1969** [c1 Jul 1969; LP37002]. Sd; col (Eastman Color, print by DeLuxe). 35mm. 85 min. *MPAA rating* R.
Pres by Jack H. Harris. *Prod* Joël Lifschutz. *Dir* Jean-François Davy. *Screenplay* Michel Levine, Jean-François Davy. *Photog* Daniel Lacambre. *Mus* Jack Arel.
Cast: Anna Gael (*Agnès*), Hans Meyer (*Varen*), Roland Lesaffre (*Bob*), Claude Charney (*Claude*), Robert Lombard (*Georges*), Anne Renate (*Leda [see note]*), Dominique Erlanger (*Olga*), Charles Dalin (*Francky*), Jean Droze (*Paul*), Nadia Vasil (*Solange*).

Crime melodrama. While Varen and Bob are involved in a gun battle and car chase with the Corbeaux brothers, their car catches on fire, but they escape and get a ride back to Paris with Agnès. In order to obtain money to get out of Paris and thus evade the Corbeaux, Varen and Bob agree to help Georges, a white slave trader, although Varen has misgivings about their involvement, particularly after Leda, a pretty young girl, has been lured into Georges' clutches. Varen again meets Agnès, and they spend the day together; but in the evening Varen rejoins Bob, and the two play poker at Georges' villa. The Corbeaux arrive at the villa, and one of the brothers, Francky, kills Bob, but the other brother, Paul, is killed by Varen. Wounded, he leaves the villa to find Agnès, and after she has dressed his wounds, they spend the night together. The next day, Varen telephones Georges and is tricked into leaving Agnès alone. Resisting an attempted rape, Agnès knocks out Georges, then flees panic-stricken to Normandy. There she meets a mysterious poet, Claude. Although she spends several days in Claude's dreamlike world, Agnès is determined to return to Paris and find Varen. Meanwhile, Olga, Georges' associate, has teamed up with Francky Corbeau, who has taken Georges' place in the organization, and killed Varen. Olga and Francky capture Agnès; but just as she is about to be sold into slavery, Claude arrives with the police. *Brothers. Poets. Philosophers. Gangsters. Nightclub owners. Police. Murder. Rape. White slave traffic. Poker. Paris. Normandy. Chases.*

Note: Opened in Paris in Apr 1969 as *Traquenards;* running time: 90 min; also known as *Traquenards érotiques.* Anne Renate is also credited as Renate Wolfle.

THE ERRAND BOY   **F6.1381**
Jerry Lewis Productions. *Dist* Paramount Pictures. 28 Nov **1961** [Los Angeles showing; c23 Nov 1961; LP20764]. Sd; b&w. 35mm. 92 min.
A Jerry Lewis Production. *Prod* Ernest D. Glucksman. *Assoc Prod* Arthur P. Schmidt. *Dir* Jerry Lewis. *Screenplay* Jerry Lewis, Bill Richmond. *Cinematog* W. Wallace Kelley. *Art Dir* Hal Pereira, Arthur Lonergan. *Set Decor* Sam Comer, James Payne. *Film Ed* Stanley Johnson. *Mus Scored & Cond* Walter Scharf. *Song Material* Louis Y. Brown, Bill Richmond, Jerry Lewis. *Dances Staged by* Nick Castle. *Sd* Hugo Grenzbach, Charles Grenzbach. *Asst Dir* Ralph Axness. *Unit Prod Mgr* William C. Davidson. *Cost* Edith Head. *Hairstyles* Nellie Manley.

Cast: Jerry Lewis (*Morty S. Tashman*), Brian Donlevy (*Mr. T. P.*), Dick Wesson (*The A. D.*), Howard McNear (*Dexter Sneak*), Felicia Atkins (*Serina*), Pat Dahl (*Miss Carson*), Kathleen Freeman (*Mrs. T. P.*), Mary Ritts, Paul Ritts (*themselves*), Isobel Elsom (*Irma Paramutual*), Fritz Feld (*The Foreign Director*), Iris Adrian (*The Great Actress*), Renee Taylor (*Miss Giles*), Rita Hayes (*singer*), Stanley Adams (*Grumpy*), Sig Ruman (*The Baron*), Doodles Weaver (*man on scaffold*), Kenneth MacDonald (*Fumble*), Joey Forman (*Jedson*), David Landfield (*Lance*), Del Moore (*M. C.*), Mike Mazurki (*blonde "movie siren"*), Dan Blocker, Lorne Greene, Michael Landon, Pernell Roberts (*guest stars*), Murray Alper, Phil Arnold, Richard Bakalyan, Donald Barry, Bellfontevro, John Benson, Joe Besser, Jan Bradley, Sue Casey, Connie Cezon, Harry Chesire, Booth Coleman, Theodora Davitt, Jean Engstrom, Judy Erwin, Milton Frome, Barry Gray, actor, Daryn Hinton, Bob Hopkins, Judy Howard, Robert Ivers, Hank Ladd, Frances Lax, Barry Livingston, Sally Mansfield, Mickey Manners, Quinn O'Hara, Snub Pollard, Sherwood Price, Hal Rand, Tony Regan, Caroline Richter, Sheila Rogers, Mike Ross, Benny Rubin, Frank Scannell, Jeanne Taylor, Mary Treen, Herb Vigran, William Wellman, Jr., Dick Winslow.

Farce. Determined to cut wasteful expenditures, T. P., the head of Paramutual Pictures, selects dimwitted paperhanger Morty Tashman to spy on studio employees while posing as an errand boy. Almost immediately havoc reigns as the well-meaning but disaster-prone Morty blunders through a series of calamities. He disrupts the filming of a western, accidentally becomes the escort of a voluptuous European beauty attending a Hollywood premiere, panics the studio stenographic department, and ruins a sound-recording session. Finally, he turns a birthday party for a "great star" into a total shambles by almost drowning the woman in a flood of exploding champagne. The distraught T. P. decides to fire Morty before the entire studio is destroyed. Two top directors, however, who witnessed Morty's antics at the birthday party, regard him as a potential star comedian, and T. P. is persuaded to sign him as the new reigning comic of Paramutual Pictures. *Errand boys. Spies. Actors. Motion picture directors. Motion pictures. Motion picture studios. Business management. Disguise. Birthdays. Hollywood.*

ERSTE LIEBE see **FIRST LOVE**

ESCAPE BY NIGHT (Great Britain)   **F6.1382**
Eternal Films. *Dist* Allied Artists. Aug **1964**. Sd; b&w. 35mm. 75 min.
Prod Maurice J. Wilson. *Dir* Montgomery Tully. *Screenplay* Maurice J. Wilson, Montgomery Tully. *Photog* Geoffrey Faithfull. *Camera* Alan McCabe. *Art Dir* Frank White. *Film Ed* Maurice Rootes. *Mus* John Veale. *Mus Dir* Philip Martell. *Sd Rec* David Bowen. *Asst Dir* David Tringham.
Cast: Terence Longdon (*Martin Lord*), Jennifer Jayne (*Nita Lord*), Harry Fowler (*Doug Roberts*), Peter Sallis (*Victor Lush*), Alan Wheatley (*Ronald Grey-Simmons*), Vanda Godsell (*Mrs. Grey-Simmons*), Arthur Lovegrove (*Ernie Peel*), Hilda Fenemore (*Mrs. Peel*), Mark Dignam (*Sydney Selweyn*), John Arnatt (*Inspector Croft*), Richard Carpenter (*Danny Watts*), Stanley Meadows (*George Brett*), Robert Brown (*Mawsley*), Tom Bowman (*Bart Rennison*), Ray Austin (*The Intruder*).

Melodrama. Source: Rupert Croft-Cooke, *Clash by Night* (London, 1962). A prison bus transporting six convicted men is held up by gangsters who rescue Bart Rennison, one of the prisoners. The assailants bribe Ernie Peel, the bus driver, to detour to a deserted farm, and all the occupants are locked in a barn after being warned that the roof has been sprayed with a flammable substance which will be set afire if they attempt to escape before dawn. The gangsters shoot one of the prison guards and make off with Rennison, but they are later killed when their car crashes during a police chase. The prisoners spend a tense night in the barn, and to pass the time each recalls how he became a criminal, while outside and dangerously close to the barn, merrymakers celebrate Guy Fawkes Night by igniting rockets and fireworks. Martin Lord, convicted of manslaughter because he accidentally killed an intruder who attempted to rape his wife, and petty thief Doug Roberts escape through an opening in the barn to Lord's house nearby, but they decide to return and give themselves up. In the meantime, Victor Lush, a halfwitted sex offender, sets fire to the barn. Lord and Roberts arrive in time to save all the men except Lush, who perishes in the flames. *Police. Bus drivers. Gangsters. Convicts. Thieves. Bribery. Abduction. Murder. Manslaughter. Barns. Fireworks. Guy Fawkes Day. Chases. Automobile accidents. Fires.*

Note: Released in Great Britain in 1965 as *Clash by Night.*

ESCAPE FROM BERLIN see **ESCAPE FROM EAST BERLIN**

ESCAPE FROM EAST BERLIN (United States/West Germany) **F6.1383**
Walter Wood Productions–Hans Albin-Film. *Dist* Metro-Goldwyn-Mayer, Inc. 31 Oct **1962** [Washington, D. C., opening; c8 Oct 1962; LP23348]. Sd; b&w. 35mm. 94 min. [Copyright length: 89 min.]
A Walter Wood Production. *Prod* Walter Wood. *Assoc Prod* Peter Berneis. *Dir* Robert Siodmak. *Screenplay* Gabrielle Upton, Peter Berneis, Millard

Lampell. *Story* Gabrielle Upton, Peter Berneis. *Photog* Georg Krause. *Art Dir* Ted Haworth, Dieter Bartels. *Film Ed* Maurice Wright. *Mus Comp & Cond* Hans-Martin Majewski. *Sd* Heinz Garbowski. *Asst Dir* Walter Boos. *Prod Asst* Frank Guarente. *Gen Prod Mgr* Helmut Beck. *Prod Mgr* Kurt Paetz, Thilo Theilen. *Wardrobe* Helmut Preuss, Margarete Neumann. *Makeup* Freddy Arnold, Albert Nagel. *Hairstyles* Alexa Dubrow. *Sp Eff* Augie Lohman. *Tech Adv* Erwin Becker.

Cast: Don Murray *(Kurt Schroeder)*, Christine Kaufmann *(Erika Jurgens)*, Werner Klemperer *(Brunner)*, Ingrid van Bergen *(Ingeborg Schroeder)*, Carl Schell *(Major Eckhardt)*, Edith Schultze-Westrum *(Mrs. Schroeder)*, Bruno Fritz *(Uncle Albrecht)*, Maria Tober *(Marga)*, Horst Janson *(Gunther Jurgens)*, Kai Fischer *(Heidi)*, Alfred Balthoff *(Klussendorf)*, Anita Kupsch *(Bambi)*, Kurt Waitzmann *(Professor Jurgens)*, Helma Seitz *(Frau Jurgens)*, Ronald Dehne *(Helmut)*, Arne Elsholtz *(Lemke)*, George Bastian *(Tillerman)*, Waltraut Runze-Waitzmann *(Marga Wegener)*, Bruno W. Pantel *(Moeller)*, Kate Jaenicke *(Rosa)*, Christian Bottcher *(Fritz)*.

Melodrama. Kurt Schroeder, a young chauffeur for an East German major, watches in horror as Gunther Jurgens, his closest friend, is shot down while trying to crash through the Berlin Wall in a truck. When Gunther's sister Erika also fails in an attempt to escape, Kurt rescues her and hides her in his house. Aware that his family and neighbors are also anxious to flee the Russian sector, and becoming increasingly attached to Erika, Kurt hits upon the idea of digging a tunnel from his family's home into West Berlin. One member of the group keeps watch while the others work, until one night, just before dawn, Kurt reaches the other side of the Wall. The mass escape is scheduled for the following night, but Erika's parents turn informers in the hope of winning favors from the Communists. The group learns of the betrayal from Heidi Eckhardt, the major's wife, and they make their departure ahead of schedule. As the police break into the Schroeder home, the tunnel collapses—but not before the escapees have reached the safety of West Berlin. *Chauffeurs. Escapees. Communists. Police. Family life. Death. Brother-sister relationship. Perfidy. Tunnels. Berlin—East. Berlin—West. Berlin Wall.*

Note: Filmed in West Berlin. Opened in West Berlin in Oct 1961 as *Tunnel 28.* Registered for copyright in the U. S. as *Escape From Berlin.* Based on an actual escape on 25 Jan 1962.

ESCAPE FROM HELL ISLAND *see* **THE MAN IN THE WATER**

ESCAPE FROM ZAHRAIN   **F6.1384**
Paramount Pictures. 23 May **1962** [Saint Louis opening; c31 Dec 1961; LP21933]. Sd; col (Technicolor). 35mm (Panavision). 93 min.
Prod-Dir Ronald Neame. *Assoc Prod. & 2d Unit Dir* Chico Day. *Screenplay* Robin Estridge. *Cinematog* Ellsworth Fredricks. *2d Unit Photog* Irmin Roberts. *Art Dir* Eddie Imazu, Hal Pereira. *Set Decor* Frank R. McKelvy. *Film Ed* Eda Warren. *Mus* Lyn Murray. *Sd* Gene Merritt, Charles Grenzbach. *Asst Dir* Tom Connors, Donald Roberts, John Veitch. *Unit Prod Mgr* Eric Stacey, Andrew J. Durkus, Frank Caffey. *Script Supv* Claire Behnke. *Wardrobe* Buddy Clark, Shirlee Strahm. *Makeup* Armand Del Mar, Monte Westmore. *Hairstyles* Janette Marvin. *Sp Photog Eff* John P. Fulton.

Cast: Yul Brynner *(Sharif)*, Sal Mineo *(Ahmed)*, Madlyn Rhue *(Laila)*, Jack Warden *(Huston)*, Anthony Caruso *(Tahar)*, Jay Novello *(Hassan)*, Leonard Strong *(ambulance driver)*, James Mason *(Johnson)*, Vladimir Sokoloff.

Adventure drama. Source: Michael Barrett, *Appointment in Zahrain* (London, 1960). In a strife-ridden Arab state, the fanatical followers of the revolutionary nationalist leader Sharif attack a police van transporting him to a prison for execution. Ahmed, the leader of the students' revolt, frees Sharif and three other prisoners, among them Huston, an American who has embezzled $200,000 from the Zahrain Oil Company. The fugitives capture an ambulance and, along with an Arabian nurse, Laila, flee from the city toward the border. During their trek across the desert, the convict Hassan is killed in a police trap; and the budding romance between Ahmed and Laila is cut short when the young student is shot down by a government strafing plane. Following the death of Tahar, another convict, the three lone survivors cross the frontier and reach a port on the Persian Gulf. Sharif and Laila make plans to return and continue their fight, and Huston goes in search of a ship which will take him to Cairo and his ill-gotten gains. *Revolutionaries. Arabs. Fanatics. Americans in foreign countries. Political prisoners. Students. Nurses. Fugitives. Revolts. Nationalism. Embezzlement. Ambulances. Deserts. Oil business. Middle East. Persian Gulf. Chases.*

Note: Location scenes filmed near Barstow, California.

ESCAPE LIBRE *see* **BACKFIRE**

ESCAPE TO BERLIN (United States/Switzerland/West Germany)
                                                               F6.1385
Stun-Film-Will Tremper Film. *For* Unexcelled Chemical Corp. *Dist* Herts-Lion International Corp. caNov **1962.** Sd; b&w. 35mm. 80 min.

Exec Prod? Michael K. Schwabacher. *Dir-Writ* Will Tremper. *Photog* Günter Haase, Gerd von Bonin. *Film Ed* Will Tremper. *Asst Ed* Ulivelli, Dayan. *Mus* Peter Thomas. *Asst Dir* Bob Ausböck. *Prod Mgr* Jo Sell. *Prod Supv* Heinz Karchow. *Makeup* Marian Babiuch.

Cast: Christian Doermer *(Claus Baade)*, Susanne Korda *(Doris Lange)*, Narziss Sokatscheff *(Hermann Gueden)*, Gerda Blisse, S. Kubitzky.

Drama. Claus Baade, a young communistic government worker in the German Democratic Republic is sent to a small farming village to implement the collective system. The farmers have not agreed to collectivize their lands, and one of them, Hermann Gueden, fights with Baade. Gueden decides to leave communist society and is given a ride to West Berlin by Doris Lange, a Swiss journalist. With Baade, who has fallen out of favor with the communists, the two manage to escape over the border into the free city. *Communists. Farmers. Journalists. Escapees. Political refugees. Collective farming. Village life. German Democratic Republic. Berlin—West.*

Note: Released in West Germany in Mar 1961 as *Flucht nach Berlin;* running time: 106 min (cut from 112 min). According to one U. S. source, the film was sponsored by the Unexcelled Chemical Corp. and its Swiss affiliate, Unexcelled International. Also known as *The Captives.*

ESCAPE TO EXSTACY   **F6.1386**
Dist Stacey Distributors. ca **1970.** Sd; col. 16mm. 61-81 min.
Sex film. No information about the specific nature of this film has been found. *Sexuality.*
Note: Also known as *Escape to Ecstasy.*

LES ESCLAVES EXISTENT TOUJOURS *see* **SLAVE TRADE IN THE WORLD TODAY**

ESCONDIDO *see* **A MINUTE TO PRAY, A SECOND TO DIE**

UN ESERCITO DI 5 UOMINI *see* **THE FIVE MAN ARMY**

LA ESFINGE DE CRISTAL *see* **THE GLASS SPHINX**

ESKIMAE DANCHI *see* **AN URBAN AFFAIR**

LOS ESPADACHINES DE LA REINA *see* **THE QUEEN'S SWORDSMEN**

EL ESPEJO DE LA BRUJA *see* **THE WITCH'S MIRROR**

L'ESPION *see* **THE DEFECTOR**

ESPIONS À L'AFFÛT *see* **HEAT OF MIDNIGHT**

LES ESPIONS MEURENT À BEYROUTH *see* **SECRET AGENT FIREBALL**

ESPIRITISMO *see* **SPIRITISM**

ESTAMBUL 65 *see* **THAT MAN IN ISTANBUL**

ESTATE VIOLENTA *see* **VIOLENT SUMMER**

LA ESTRELLA VACIA *see* **THE EMPTY STAR**

... ET MOURIR DE PLAISIR *see* **BLOOD AND ROSES**

ET SI ON FAISAIT L'AMOUR? *see* **LISTEN, LET'S MAKE LOVE**

L'ETÀ DEL MALESSERE *see* **LOVE PROBLEMS**

ÉTÉ VIOLENT *see* **VIOLENT SUMMER**

ETERNAL SUMMER   **F6.1387**
Viscaya Productions. caMar **1961** [Fort Lauderdale, Florida, showing]. Sd; b&w. 35mm. ca80 min.
Prod-Writ-Story J. Van Hearn. *Dir* Larry Wolk. *Lighting Dir* Bill Cabana. *Camera* Lloyd Beckworth, Max Landow. *Film Ed* Marian Kley. *Choreog* Corky Newton. *Sd Engr* David Sargeant, Grant Gravitt. *Prod Mgr* Ted Sack. *Unit Mgr* Zane Radney. *Script Supv* Marian Kley. *Still Photog* Joe Lucinian, David Holdam.

Cast: Gwen DeCastro *(Kay Holden)*, Jeff Brown *(Ed Holden)*, Ron Corsi *(Roy Gibson)*, Maggie Chamberlain *(Rose)*, Yanka Mann *(Billie)*, William Mayer *(Jack Todd)*, Dave Dundon *(Belser)*, Thora Randall *(model)*, Ed Thomas *(policeman)*.

Domestic drama. Salesman Ed Holden, his wife, Kay, and their two children live in suburban Miami. After 8 years of marriage, the couple's relationship falters. *Salesmen. Marriage. Suburban life. Miami.*
Note: Filmed in Miami.

L'ÉTERNITÉ POUR NOUS *see* **SIN ON THE BEACH**

ETERNITY OF LOVE (Japan)   F6.1388

Takarazuka Motion Picture Co. *Dist* Toho Co. Nov **1961** [Los Angeles showing]. Sd; col (Eastmancolor). 35mm (Tohoscope). 100 min.

Exec Prod Sanezumi Fujimoto, Hidehisa Suga. *Dir* Hiromichi Horikawa. *Screenplay* Zenzo Matsuyama, Toshiro Ide, Hiromichi Horikawa. *Photog* Asakazu Nakai. *Mus* Yasushi Akutagawa.

Cast: Yoko Tsukasa *(Michi)*, Tadao Takashima, Kiyoshi Kodama, Keiju Kobayashi, Hiroshi Akutagawa, Seizaburo Kawazu, Kinuyo Tanaka, Ikio Sawamura, Kenzo Tamu, Kin Sugai, Asao Koike, Chikako Hosokawa.

Melodrama. Michi, a high school student, is in love with Ishiyama, a college student boarding with her and her mother. Her romance is shattered by one of her teachers, who informs Ishiyama that Michi's father is in prison. Michi marries the teacher, who so abuses her by his cruelty that she runs away to Tokyo. There she is befriended by a Korean who gives her a job in his printing firm. Michi's husband tracks her down and abruptly destroys the peace she had achieved under the Korean's generous treatment; and her employer is forced to fire her when their friendship is misinterpreted by the other workers. Michi meets Inami, a student of progressive socialism whom the police are investigating as a possible subversive. The couple marry and live happily with a daughter born to them until Inami is arrested and drafted to serve in the waning days of World War II. He drowns when his transport is sunk, but Michi survives the bombing of Tokyo by living off the black market. One day she meets Ishiyama, the former college student and now a black marketeer, who asks her about her husband. She answers that she is waiting for him, knowing that all she has to live for now is her daughter. *Students. Koreans. Runaways. Socialists. Adolescence. Marriage. Employer-employee relations. Black market. World War II. Tokyo.*

Note: Released in Japan in 1961 as *Wakarete ikiru toki mo.*

L'ÉTOILE DU SUD see **THE SOUTHERN STAR**

UNE ÉTRANGE AVENTURE DE LEMMY CAUTION see **ALPHAVILLE**

L'ÉTRANGER see **THE STRANGER**

ETSURAKU see **THE PLEASURES OF THE FLESH**

EUGENIE ... THE STORY OF HER JOURNEY INTO PERVERSION (Great Britain/Spain/West Germany)   F6.1389

Video-Tel International Productions. *Dist* Distinction Films. 5 Aug **1970** [Los Angeles opening]. Sd; col (Technicolor). 35mm (Techniscope). 91 min. *MPAA rating* X.

Prod Harry Alan Towers. *Dir* Jess Franco. *Screenplay* Peter Welbeck. *Photog* Manuel Merino. *Mus* Bruno Nicolai.

Cast: Marie Liljedahl *(Eugenie)*, Maria Rohm *(Madame Saint-Ange)*, Jack Taylor *(Mirvel)*, Christopher Lee *(Dolmance/narrator)*, Nino Korda *(Roches)*, Herbert Fuchs *(Hardin)*, Paul Müller *(father)*, Anney Kablan *(Augustin)*, Mariá Luisa Ponte *(Mother)*, Colette Giacobino *(Colette)*, Kathy Lagarde *(maid)*, Uta Dahlberg *(mute maid [see note]).*

Melodrama. Source: Donatien Alphonse François [Marquis de] Sade, *La philosophie dans le boudoir* (Paris, 1795). Madame Marianne Saint-Ange, a wealthy disciple of the Marquis de Sade, allows herself to be seduced by the father of Eugenie, a virginal adolescent, on the condition that Eugenie spend the weekend on Marianne's island retreat. There, the young girl meets Mirvel, Marianne's stepbrother, and Augustin, a Negro servant, both of whom are Marianne's lovers. After being drugged, Eugenie is forced to participate in an orgy and is tortured by a cult of sadists led by Dolmance, preparing her for sacrifice. In the morning, Marianne insists that Eugenie merely suffered a nightmare, but Eugenie realizes the truth. When Mirvel attacks her, she stabs him. Dolmance arrives but chooses Marianne as the cultists' next victim; Eugenie then kills her and flees. Later, apparently awakening from a nightmare, Eugenie is asked by Marianne to join her for a weekend on the island. *Stepbrothers. Domestics. Negroes. Virginity. Seduction. Adolescence. Orgies. Torture. Sadism. Human sacrifice. Murder. Islands. Drugs. Cults. Donatien Alphonse François [Marquis de] Sade. Dreams.*

Note: Some location scenes filmed in Barcelona. Country of origin unconfirmed. Peter Welbeck is a pseudonym for Harry Alan Towers. Uta Dahlberg's participation in the film is unconfirmed. Also known as *Eugenie.*

EUROPA DI NOTTE see **EUROPEAN NIGHTS**

EUROPE IN THE RAW   F6.1390

Eve Productions. 28 Mar **1963** [San Francisco showing; c1 Mar 1963; LP24205]. Sd; col (Eastman Color). 35mm. 70 min. [Copyright length: 60 min.]

Prod-Dir Russ Meyer. *Narr* Franklin L. Thistle. *Photog* Russ Meyer.

With: Denise Duval, Heide Richter, Yvette Le Grand, Greta Thorwald, Abundavita, Gigi La Touche, Veronique Gabriel, Fred Owens.

Documentary. Tourist attractions, including prostitutes and striptease clubs, are surveyed in Belgium, Rotterdam, Amsterdam, Copenhagen, Stockholm, Hamburg, Berlin, Vienna, Venice, Florence, Rome, Pisa, Portofino, Rapallo, Nice, Nancy, and Paris. *Tourists. Stripteasers. Prostitution. Belgium. Rotterdam. Amsterdam. Copenhagen. Stockholm. Hamburg. Berlin. Vienna. Venice. Florence. Rome. Pisa. Portofino. Rapallo. Nice. Nancy. Paris.*

Note: Some footage included in *Mondo Topless,* q. v.

EUROPEAN DIARIES   F6.1391

Dist Film-Makers' Cooperative. 4 Sep **1966** [New York opening]. Si with sd-on-tape; col. 16mm. 60 min.

Dir Taylor Mead. *Photog* Taylor Mead. *Piano Improvisations* Taylor Mead, Jerome Hill. *Sd Ed* Jonas Mekas.

Speaking and Singing: Taylor Mead.

Film diary. A diary in single-frame shots of the filmmaker's travels through Europe. *Travel. Diaries. Europe.*

EUROPEAN NIGHTS (France/Italy)   F6.1392

Avers Film (Paris)–Avers Film (Rome). *Dist* Joseph Burstyn Releasing Corp. Apr **1963** [c1 Jan 1960; LP18881]. Sd; col (Eastman Color). 35mm. 82 min.

Prod Fabio Jegher. *Dir* Alessandro Blasetti. *Screenplay* Ennio De Concini, Alessandro Blasetti. *Candid Comment Script—English Vers* Merton Koplin. *Italian Comm* Gualtiero Jacopetti. *Photog* Gabor Pogany. *Art Dir* Flavio Mogherini. *Film Ed* Mario Serandrei. *Creative Ed Cons—English Vers* Valentine Sherry. *Mus* Carlo Savina. *Sd* Vittorio Trentino, Mario Amari. *Prod Mgr* Jean Desmouceaux.

Cast: Carmen Sevilla, Henry Salvador, Domenico Modugno, The Platters, Channing Pollock, Robert Lamouret, Colin Hicks and His Band, The Rastellis, The Charley Ballet, Orlyk Dance Group, Bandourists of the Ukraine Chorus, Princess Badia, The Archie Savage Dancers, The Togni Circus, Mac Ronay, The Tongas, The Condoras.

Cast—At the Crazy Horse Saloon: Dolly Bell, Lilli Niagara, Lady Phu Qui Cho, Crazy Horse Saloon Striptease, Les Croq' Messieurs.

Cast—At El Corral de la Moreria: Alba (entertainer), Sandoval, Carmen Casarrubios, Maria Marques.

Cast—At Le Carrousel de Paris: Coccinelle.

Cast—Candid Comment [English vers]: Henry Morgan.

Documentary. A tour of nightclub acts in major European cities begins in Paris with the belly dancing of Princess Badia. At Le Carrousel de Paris, the female impersonator Coccinelle performs. At the Crazy Horse Saloon, stripteasers Dolly Bell, Lady Phu Qui Cho, and Lilli Niagara entertain, as do The Tongas, Swiss acrobats. La Nouvelle Eve is the showplace for the Charley Ballet. The Place Pigalle hosts the Archie Savage Dancers, an American Negro jazz ballet group; comic singer Henry Salvador, who sings Brahms' "Hungarian Dance" and performs "Dans mon île" with a group of oriental dancers; and Robert Lamouret, who entertains with his duck. In London, magician Channing Pollock performs at the Pigalle Restaurant, and Colin Hicks sings rock and roll to an audience of hysterical teenagers. The Rastellis perform their musical clown act in Milan. Domenico Modugno sings in Naples, and The Platters sing in Rome. In Vienna, the Ukrainian Orlyk Dance Group and Bandourists Chorus dance and sing to the music of bandouras. At Madrid's El Corral de la Moreria, film star Carmen Sevilla joins Gypsy flamenco dancers. *Entertainers. Singers. Dancers. Magicians. Stripteasers. Clowns. Exotic dancers. Acrobats. Ventriloquism. Female impersonation. Nightclubs. Paris. London. Rome. Milan. Naples. Madrid. Vienna. Crazy Horse Saloon (Paris). Le Carrousel de Paris. Nouvelle Eve (Paris). Place Pigalle (Paris). Pigalle Restaurant (London). Corral de la Moreria (Madrid). Ducks.*

Note: Opened in Rome in Feb 1959 as *Europa di notte;* running time: ca100 min; in Paris in Sep 1959 as *Nuits d'Europe;* running time: ca100 min.

EVA (France/Italy)   F6.1393

Interopa Film–Paris-Films Production. *Dist* Times Film Corp. 28 Oct **1964** [Los Angeles opening]. Sd; b&w. 35mm. 107 min. [Also reviewed at 115 min.]

Prod Robert Hakim, Raymond Hakim. *Dir* Joseph Losey. *Screenplay* Hugo Butler, Evan Jones. *Dir Photog* Gianni Di Venanzo. *Photog* Venice Film Festival Seq Henri Decaë. *Art Dir* Richard MacDonald, Luigi Scaccianoce. *Film Ed* Reginald Beck, Franca Silvi. *Mus* Michel Legrand. *Mus Dir* Carlo Savina. *Song:* "Adam and Eve" Michel Legrand. *Sung by* Tony Middleton. *Song:* "Willow Weep for Me" Ann Ronell. *Song:* "Loveless Love" W. C. Handy. *Sung by* Billie Holiday. *Sd* Paul Boistelle, Federica Savina. *Asst Dir* Guidarino Guidi. *Prod Mgr* Danilo Marciani. *Jeanne Moreau's Cost* Pierre Cardin. *Miss Lisi's Voice Dub by* Anna Proclemer.

Cast: Jeanne Moreau *(Eva Olivier)*, Stanley Baker *(Tyvian Jones)*, Virna Lisi *(Francesca Ferrara)*, Giorgio Albertazzi *(Branco Malloni)*, James Villiers *(Arthur McCormick)*, Riccardo Garrone *(Michele)*, Lisa Gastoni *(The Redhead)*, Checco Rissone *(Pieri)*, Enzo Fiermonte *(Enzo)*, Nona Medici

(Anna Maria), Alex Revides (The Greek), John Pepper (little boy), Roberto Paoletti, Van Eicken, Evi Rigano, Ignazio Dolce, Peggy Guggenheim, Gilda Dahlberg, Joseph Losey, Vittorio De Sica.

Drama. Source: James Hadley Chase, *Eve* (London, 1945). In Venice Tyvian Jones, purported author of the autobiography of a Welsh coal miner, reaps the profits of the book's cinematic adaptation. He is, however, an impostor, the book being the work of his dead brother. Though engaged to Francesca, a screenwriter, Tyvian becomes madly infatuated with Eva, a French woman of pleasure, whom he encounters unexpectedly in his own apartment, where she and a lover have sought refuge during a storm. After ejecting her male friend, Tyvian attempts to seduce Eva, whereupon she knocks him out with an ashtray. Tyvian nevertheless follows Eva to Rome, where he woos her with promises of a Venetian holiday. During the idyll Eva demands an extravagant hotel suite, gambling stakes, and compensation for her sexual favors, humiliating him further by scorning the sum he offers her. Following the abortive weekend, Tyvian marries Francesca, only to betray her with Eva during their honeymoon. Discovering the two together, Francesca commits suicide in a speedboat. After her funeral Tyvian visits Eva. Although he intends to kill her, he can only proclaim his love. Disgusted, Eva flogs him with a riding whip and ushers him from her flat. On a Venetian holiday 2 years later, Eva encounters Tyvian, now an impecunious guide but still infatuated with her. Despite his ardent supplications, Eva shuns him. *Authors. Motion picture scriptwriters. Welsh. Brothers. Guides. Obsession. Gambling. Marriage. Suicide. Sadomasochism. Infidelity. Seduction. Imposture. Motion pictures. Prostitution. Honeymoons. Speedboats. Venice. Rome.*

Note: Filmed on location in Venice and Rome. Original running time: 155 min. Opened in Paris in Oct 1962; running time: 116 min; in Rome in Oct 1962; running time: 107 min. Originally intended for U. S. release in 1963 as *Eve.* Also known as *Eva (The Devil's Woman).*

EVA—DEN UTSTÖTTA see EVA ... WAS EVERYTHING BUT LEGAL

EVA EN LA SELVA see EVE

EVA SCONOSCIUTA see WOMEN OF THE WORLD

EVA ... WAS EVERYTHING BUT LEGAL (Sweden)   F6.1394
Swedish Filmproduction. *Dist* U-M Film Distributors. Nov **1969**. Sd; col (Eastman Color, print by Movielab). 35mm. 93 min. *MPAA rating* X.
Pres by UMC Pictures. *Prod* Stig Skoglund. *Dir-Writ* Torgny Wickman. *Photog* Max Wilén. *Mus* Mats Olsson. *English Vers* Peter Riethof.
Cast: Solveig Andersson *(Eva Blom),* Hans Wahlgren *(Lennart Svenningson),* Siw Mattson *(Maria Svenningson),* Göthe Grefbo *(Gustav Bolinder),* Barbro Hiort Af Ornäs *(Jenny Berggren),* Jan-Erik Lindqvist *(police inspector),* Arne Ragneborn *(Karlsson),* Börje Nyberg *(Mr. Somelius),* Caroline Christensen *(Mrs. Somelius),* Conny Ling *(Kenneth Somelius),* Inger Suneli *(Berit Svensson),* Marie Liljedahl *(party guest).*
Drama. The police in a Swedish village are informed that teenager Eva Blom, living with her foster parents, is having sexual intercourse with "Dirty Bertie," the local bum. The authorities look for Eva, who is with Kenneth Somelius in his father's garage. After her arrest, she tells the police, in a series of flashbacks, of the nymphomaniacal tendencies that have involved her in many affairs, including one with wealthy Gustav Bolinder, which has persisted since he seduced her 6 years earlier. Bolinder is brought to trial, and his lawyer introduces witnesses who accuse Eva of being an evil influence; but a sympathetic journalist, Lennart Svenningson, exposes his own childhood escapades in an effort to influence the court toward leniency for Eva. Realizing that the girl has only been lonely, the court's woman psychiatrist offers Eva the security of her home. *Police. Tramps. Foster parents. Lawyers. Journalists. Psychiatrists. Village life. Adolescence. Nymphomania. Seduction. Trials.*
Note: Released in Sweden in Sep 1969 as *Eva—den utstötta;* running time: 95 min. Working title: *Första stenen.* Alternative U. S. title: *Swedish and Underage.*

L'ÉVANGILE SELON SAINT-MATTHIEU see THE GOSPEL
     ACCORDING TO ST. MATTHEW

EVE (United States/Great Britain/Spain)   F6.1395
Udastex Films–Ada Films–Hispamer Films. *Dist* Commonwealth United Entertainment, Inc., Feature Film Corp. of America. Jul **1968** [New Orleans opening]. Sd; col (Eastman Color). 35mm. 97 min.
Pres by Harold Goldman Associates, Towers of London. A Sargon Etablishment Production. *Prod* Harry Alan Towers. *Dir* Jeremy Summers. *2d Unit Dir* Robert Lynn. *Screenplay* Peter Welbeck. *Photog* Manuel Merino. *Art Dir* Santiago Ontañón. *Film Ed* Allan Morrison. *Mus* Malcolm Lockyer.
Cast: Robert Walker, Jr. *(Mike Yates),* Celeste Yarnall *(Eve),* Herbert Lom *(Diego),* Fred Clark *(John Burke),* Christopher Lee *(Colonel Stuart),* Jean Caffarel *(Pepe),* Rosenda Monteros *(Conchita),* Maria Rohm *(Anna),* Ricardo Diaz *(Bruno).*

Adventure melodrama. While searching for Incan treasure, Mike, an American pilot, crashlands in the upper Amazon region of Brazil. He is rescued from savages by a white girl called Eve, who is worshiped as a goddess by the natives. When news of Mike's adventure reaches a small river port, an unscrupulous American showman, John Burke, sets out to find Eve and add her to his touring sideshow. The news also affects the plans of the villainous Diego, who has been passing off his mistress, Conchita, as the long-lost granddaughter of Colonel Stuart, a famous explorer whose son and grandchild disappeared in the jungle years before. Fearing that Eve may be the granddaughter, Diego also joins in the search. Eventually, when Mike meets Colonel Stuart, he learns that the colonel is penniless and enlists his help in finding the Incan treasure. As all the concerned parties make their way into the jungle, Eve is captured by the savages and threatened with torture because of the help she gave to a white man. Mike rescues her, and together they make their way to the cave where the treasure is hidden, unaware that Diego and Conchita have already been there and set a trap. The trap backfires, kills Diego and Conchita, and buries the treasure. Although Eve is acknowledged as the granddaughter of Colonel Stuart, she is disillusioned by what she has seen of civilization and returns to her jungle home. *Adventurers. Americans in foreign countries. Air pilots. Indians of South America. Incas. Mistresses. Grandfathers. Impersonation. Fraud. Superstition. Treasure. Jungles. Sideshows. Brazil. Amazon River. Airplane accidents.*
Note: Location scenes filmed in Brazil. Released in Spain as *Eva en la selva;* running time: 90 min; in Great Britain in 1970 as *The Face of Eve;* running time: 78 min. Peter Welbeck is a pseudonym for Harry Alan Towers, Jean Caffarel for Jose Maria Caffarel.

EVE see EVA

EVE AND THE HANDYMAN   F6.1396
Eve Productions. *Dist* Pad-Ram Enterprises. 5 May **1961** [Los Angeles showing; c1 Mar 1961; LP18686]. Sd; col (Eastman Color). 35mm. 66 min.
Prod-Dir-Writ Russ Meyer. *Photog* Russ Meyer.
Cast: Anthony-James Ryan *(The Handyman),* Eve Meyer *(Eve and other female roles).*
Comedy. This is the story of a special day in the normally uneventful life of a handyman. His foot gets stuck in a toilet in a women's restroom; a young girl disrobes behind his back as he cleans a launderette; a plunging neckline distracts him while he washes windows; his truck narrowly escapes an automobile crusher; he performs emergency tree surgery; he cannot "desecrate" a sundae because it resembles the bosom of a young woman; he gets lost and climbs what he takes to be a sign post, but the sign at the top roads "Wet Paint"; he passes an attractive hitchhiker who has stripped down to her panties and tosses her a pair of overalls; two secretaries transform their radically opposite bosoms practically before his eyes; he watches a bountiful stripper play a vigorous game of pinball and then tilts the machine as he gently tries his hand at the game; at a tennis court, he challenges a bruiser type in the company of a voluptuous young woman, but his opponent's serve breaks his racket; he shyly averts his eyes from a nude bather; and, after he observes the activities at an art school, disaster meets his attempt to paint murals. Finally, a young woman in detective's attire who has followed him throughout the day confronts him at the shack where he lives. She throws open her coat to reveal ... every conceivable kind of cleaning brush. The devoted brush saleswoman has grown fond of the handyman, however, and decides to brighten his spirits. After a night beyond his wildest hopes and dreams, there is a swagger to his walk and a new sureness with which to face the day. *Handymen. Detectives. Hitchhikers. Stripteasers. Secretaries. Saleswomen. Sexuality. Timidity. Nudity. Tennis. Laundries. Pinball machines. Art.*

EVE AND THE MERMAN   F6.1397
Caribbean Productions. *Dist* Thunderbird International Pictures. 5 Feb **1965** [Los Angeles showing]. Sd; col (Eastmancolor). 35mm. 73 min.
Prod Rod Vincent. *Dir* Chev Royton. *Cinematog* Chev Royton. *Film Ed* Louis Robert. *Mus* Carl Roth. *Sd Rec* Pierre Oden. *Prod Supv* Chev Royton. *Cont* Janine Caron. *Makeup* Heidi Baron. *Sp Eff* Emile Bordeaux. *Coöp* American Nudist Association. *Chief Electrn* Paul Rose.
Cast: Lori Dawson *(Eve),* Laura Kane *(Brenda),* Marcia LeRoux *(Suzette),* John Salvo *(merman),* Guy Lawrence *(hitchhiker),* Jackie Prince *(Linda),* Paula Guest *(Betty),* Dolores Mandel *(Dolores),* Brenda Morris *(Gail),* June Perez *(water nymph),* Christine Lee *(redhead),* Christine Paulson, Ruth Michaels, Harry Mann, John Mabbitt, Betty Meister, Miriam Roberts, Amelia Marshall, Janice London, Jane Mitchell *(bathers).*
Drama. Eve, a prudish young schoolteacher, Suzette, a dance teacher, and Brenda, a legal secretary, arrange with the director of a nudist camp to rent a house on a secluded tropical island, ignoring the camp director's warning of the mysterious disappearance of a young woman who explored one of the island's lagoons. Soon after their arrival on the island, Brenda and Suzette remove their

clothes to bask in the sun. Eve remains in the house, thinking of her sexually adventurous older sister, Linda, a figure model, as she undresses before the mirror. In the meantime, Suzette dreams of being an exotic dancer in the captivity of an Arabian harem. Eve goes off to explore, and once on the other side of the island, she removes her bikini, experiencing the pleasures of complete nudity for the first time. Soon she becomes aware of a handsome stranger watching her, and she is inexplicably drawn to him. He relates the strange story of his life as a merman and then vanishes, promising to see Eve again. Unable to tell her friends about the encounter, Eve calls her sister, but Linda has no interest in the tale of the merman, and she relates the adventures into which her buxom figure has led her. Deciding to keep the secret to herself, Eve anxiously awaits her next meeting with the merman. ... *Schoolteachers. Dance teachers. Secretaries. Sisters. Exotic dancers. Models. Mermaids and mermen. Nudism. Sunbathing. Voyeurism. Harems. Islands. Tropics. Fantasy.*

EVE WANTS TO SLEEP (Poland)   F6.1398
Syrena Film Unit. *For* Film Polski. *Dist* Harrison Pictures. 5 Jun 1961 [New York opening]. Sd; b&w. 35mm. 98 min. [Also reviewed at 93 min.]
Pres by Edward Harrison. *Prod* Wiesław Mincer. *Dir* Tadeusz Chmielewski. *Screenplay* Tadeusz Chmielewski, Andrzej Czekalski. *Photog (see note)* Stefan Matyjaszkiewicz, Josef Stawiski. *Art Dir* Roman Mann, Adam Nowakowski. *Artistic Supv* Jerzy Zarzycki. *Film Ed* Janina Niedzwiecka, Lena Deptula. *Mus* Henryk Czyż. *Sd* Stanisław Piotrowski, Wiesław Cwikliński. *English Subtitl* Noelle Gillmor.

Cast: Barbara Lass *(Eve)*, Stanisław Mikulski *(Peter)*, Ludwik Benoit *(safecracker)*, Zygmunt Zintel *(police chief)*, W. Turowski *(professor)*, Stefan Bartik *(captain)*, Roman Kłosowski *(his pupil)*, E. Wichura *(sergeant)*, B. Rachwalska *(matron)*, Jarema Stępowski *(cafe owner)*, Maria Kaniewska *(cashier)*, W. Oto-Suski *(undertaker)*, Wacław Kowalski *(arsenal supervisor)*, Stanisław Milski *(school janitor)*, Gustaw Lutkiewicz.

Farce. Sixteen-year-old Eve arrives penniless from the provinces to begin her schooling at a technical institute in a strange city where the police and the criminals cooperate. Eve comes to the city a day too early and finds the school dormitory closed. As she wanders through the streets looking for a place to sleep, she meets Lulek, a clumsy young crook who tries to sell her a gold brick. Anxious to help, Eve tries to induce an old man to buy it, but instead she is arrested by young police officer Peter, who takes her to the station house. Terrified, she attempts suicide and then locks herself in the armory and plays with hand grenades as the chief of police arrives for an inspection. A convicted safecracker is brought in to make the jail appear less empty. Eve is taken from the armory by thieves who release her while the police are hiding. Peter, whom Lulek mistakes for a master criminal, takes Eve to a women's hotel, where they create a near riot when the men in the women's rooms believe the hotel is being raided. The confusion between who is a criminal and who is a policeman is now complete as both groups compete for a jewel theft. Lulek, still believing that Peter is an archcriminal in disguise, calls for the underworld to appropriate all horses and carts and meet in the town square for a job. They are met there by the police, who also want to be in on the robbery, and the town's teamsters, who are angry about the theft of their horses and carts. While Peter is taking Eve to school, the gathering at the town square grows so explosive that even the director and technicians of the film are somersaulted out from behind the camera. *Students. Innocents. Police. Safecrackers. Thieves. Theft. Political corruption. Moral corruption. Suicide. Riots. Jails. Hotels.*

Note: Released in Poland in 1958 as *Ewa chce spać.* Only one U. S. source lists Stawiski as photographer. Barbara Lass is also known as Barbara Kwiatkowska.

AN EVENING WITH BATMAN AND ROBIN   F6.1399
Columbia Pictures. 24 Nov 1965 [Cleveland opening]. Sd; b&w. 35mm. 270 min.
Prod Rudolph Flothow. *Dir* Lambert Hillyer. *Screenplay* Victor McLeod, Leslie Swabacker, Harry Fraser. *Dir Photog* James S. Brown, Jr. *Film Ed* Dwight Caldwell, Earl Turner. *Mus* Lee Zahler. *Sd Engr* Jack Goodrich. *Asst Dir* Gene Anderson, Jr., William Austin, Charles C. Wilson.

Cast: Lewis Wilson *(Batman)*, Douglas Croft *(Robin)*, J. Carrol Naish *(Daka)*, William Austin *(Alfred)*, Shirley Patterson *(Linda)*, Charles C. Wilson *(Captain Arnold)*, Charles Middleton *(Ken Colton)*, Robert Fiske *(Foster)*, Michael Vallon *(Preston)*, Gus Glassmire *(Martin Warren)*, Eddie Parker.

Compilation film. Based on the comic characters created by: Bob Kane. Crimefighters Batman and Robin begin investigating a ring of Japanese saboteurs who plan to steal the city's radium supply. The gang kidnaps Martin Warren, the uncle of Batman's girl friend, Linda, and forces him to reveal the location of the precious element. Batman and Robin are waiting for the criminals at the radium vault; and in the ensuing fight, the "dynamic duo" capture one of the saboteurs, who reveals that the gang, led by the evil scientist Dr. Daka, intended to take the radium to their hideout, the House of the Open Door. In disguise, the dynamic duo penetrate the gang's lair and discover Linda

bound, gagged, and unconscious. Attacked by the gang, Batman and Robin escape with Linda. Dr. Daka, assisted by a group of zombies he controls by means of a magic ring, uses many traps attempting to kill the dynamic duo, but the intrepid enemies of crime escape death each time. Finally, they capture the evil doctor and force him to return Linda and Warren (who have been turned into zombies) to normal. Daka tries to flee the arriving police and falls into a pit of alligators in which he had tried to trap Batman. *Supermen. Scientists. Evildoers. Japanese. Saboteurs. Zombies. Gangs. Theft. Abduction. Disguise. Radium. Batman. Alligators.*

Note: Originally released by Columbia Pictures in 1943 as a 15-part serial. Each chapter was registered for copyright between 16 Jul and 22 Oct 1943. The chapter titles were, in order: "The Electrical Brain," "The Bat's Cave," "The Mark of the Zombies," "Slaves of the Rising Sun," "The Living Corpse," "Poison Peril," "The Phoney Doctor," "Lured by Radium," "The Sign of the Sphinx," "Flying Spies," "A Nipponese Trap," "Embers of Evil," "Eight Steps Down," "The Executioner Strikes," and "The Doom of the Rising Sun."

AN EVENING WITH THE ROYAL BALLET (Great Britain)   F6.1400
B. H. E. Productions. *Dist* Sigma III Corp. 8 Dec 1965 [New York opening]. Sd; col (Technicolor). 35mm (see note). 85 min.
Overall Production Credits: *Prod* Anthony Havelock-Allan. *Film Ed* Richard Marden, James Clark. *Sd* Edgar Vetter.
Production Credits—"La valse": *Dir* Anthony Havelock-Allan. *Photog* Geoffrey Unsworth. *Mus:* "La valse" Maurice Joseph Ravel. *Based on the Orig Choreog by* Robert Helpman, Frederick Ashton.
Production Credits—"Les Sylphides": *Dir* Anthony Asquith. *Photog* Christopher Challis. *Mus:* "Les Sylphides" Frédéric François Chopin. *Based on the Orig Choreog by* Michel Fokine.
Production Credits—"Le corsaire": *Dir* Anthony Havelock-Allan. *Photog* Geoffrey Unsworth. *Mus:* "Le corsaire" Riccardo Drigo, Léon Minkus. *Choreog* Rudolf Nureyev. *Based on the Orig Choreog by* Marius Petipa.
Production Credits—"Aurora's Wedding": *Dir* Anthony Asquith. *Photog* Geoffrey Unsworth. *Mus:* "Aurora's Wedding" from "The Sleeping Beauty" Pëtr Ilich Tchaikovsky. *Based on the Orig Choreog by* Marius Petipa.
Cast: Royal Ballet.
Featuring: Margot Fonteyn (in "Les Sylphides," "Le corsaire," and "Aurora's Wedding"), Rudolf Nureyev (in "Les Sylphides" and "Le corsaire"), David Blair, Antoinette Sibley, Brian Shaw (in "Aurora's Wedding"), Merle Park, Graham Usher ([see note]).
Dance film. The Royal Ballet is featured in four productions filmed in 1963 at the Royal Opera House, Covent Garden. The entire company dances *La valse; Les Sylphides* and *Le corsaire* include solos by Rudolf Nureyev and Margot Fonteyn, who perform a pas de deux in *Le corsaire; Aurora's Wedding* is danced by the corps de ballet and features solos by Margot Fonteyn and David Blair and a pas de deux performed by Antoinette Sibley and Brian Shaw. *Ballet. Covent Garden. "Sleeping Beauty".*
Note: Released in Great Britain in 1963. One source indicates that the production was filmed for television. *Le corsaire* was filmed in 70mm. Sources do not indicate which ballet features Merle Park and Graham Usher.

AN EVENT (Yugoslavia)   F6.1401
Jadran Film. *Dist* Continental Distributing, Inc. 16 Feb 1970 [New York opening]. Sd; col (Movielab). 35mm. 93 min.
Exec Prod Branko Lustig. *Dir* Vatroslav Mimica. *Screenplay* Željko Senečić, Vatroslav Mimica, Kruno Quien. *Dir Photog* Frano Vodopivec. *Art Dir* Željko Senečić. *Film Ed* Katja Majer. *Asst Dir* Ivana Mimica, Ljubo Šikić.
Cast: Pavle Vujisić *(grandfather)*, Serdjo Mimica *(grandson)*, Boris Dvornik *(gamekeeper)*, Fabijan Šovagović *(friend)*, Neda Spasojević *(gamekeeper's wife)*, Marina Nemet *(girl)*, Fahro Konjhodžić, Zdenka Heršak, Lena Politeo, Stevo Vujatović.
Drama. Source: Anton Pavlovich Chekhov, *Proisshestviye* (Rasskaz yamshchika) (1887). Despite the portentous baying of dogs and ominous flights of birds, a farmer and his grandson set out for the fair, where they hope to sell their horse. In the woods they are followed by a ravenous wolf, which retreats when other travelers appear. Crossing the river in a ferryboat, the pair is advised by its captain to avoid the other passengers, including a gamekeeper, his minion, and his daughter. Having sold their horse at the fair, the grandfather and his charge head homeward. As darkness falls over the forest, the two are pursued by the gamekeeper. Exhausted, the patriarch presents the purse to the boy and commands him to seek refuge. By coincidence the child enters the gamekeeper's hut, where he is eagerly received by his assailant's wife and daughter. *Children. Grandfathers. Gamekeepers. Forests. Fairs. Ferryboats. Chases. Birds. Horses. Wolves. Dogs.*
Note: Released in Yugoslavia in 1969 as *Dogadjaj.*

EVENTS F6.1402

Dist Grove Press. 12 Jun **1970** [New York opening]. Sd; col. 35mm. 84 min. *Prod-Dir-Writ* Fred Baker. *Photog* Stephen Bower, Fred Baker. *Film Ed* Bernard Hajdenberg. *Mus* Eric Gale. *Lyr* Charles Smalls. *Sd* Robert Davis. *Blowup & Opticals* Tri-Pix Film Services.

Cast: Ryan Listman (*Ryan*), Joy Wener (*Joy*), Frank Cavestani (*Frank*), Marsha Rossa (*Marsha*), Lee Roscoe (*Lee*), Greer St. John (*Greer*), Kristen Steen (*Kristen*), Myron "Butch" Ogelsby (*Butch*), Malissa Corragio (*Malissa*), Louise Violet (*Louise*), Eddie Keegan (*Eddie*), Robert Altman, actor (*Bob*).

Drama. Ryan is determined to make a film about Lenny Bruce, but to raise the necessary money and to demonstrate his talents as a filmmaker to potential producers, he must first direct a pornographic film for the commercial market. In his recruitment of actors for the project, which he organizes in Greenwich Village, he confronts a diversity of attitudes toward sex participation for financial gain. Producing the film becomes a struggle, and Ryan's girl friend Joy, who cannot accept the situation, deserts him. Other actors and friends agree to help, however, and finally shooting begins. *Actors. Filmmakers. Sex exploitation films. New York City—Greenwich Village.*

Note: Filmed in 16mm. Joy Wener is also known as Joy Bang.

EVER BEEN ON A TRIP? F6.1403

Dist Stacey Distributors. ca **1970**. Sd; col. 16mm. 61-81 min.

Sex film. No information about the precise nature of this film has been found. *Sexuality. Hallucinogens.*

EVERY BASTARD A KING (Israel) F6.1404

Every Bastard a King, Ltd. *Dist* Continental Distributing, Inc. 13 Apr **1970** [New York opening]. Sd; col (Movielab). 35mm. 93 min. *MPAA rating GP.*

Prod A. Deshe, Haym Topol. *Exec Prod* Mati Raz. *Dir* Uri Zohar. *Screenplay* Uri Zohar, Eli Tavor. *Photog* David Gurfinkel. *Camera Asst* Michael Greenblat, Menache Hova. *Sets* Zeev Lichter. *Film Ed* Anna Gurit. *Asst Ed* Orna Shick, Zmira Eilam. *Mus* Michel Colombier. *Titl Sông Sung by* Haym Topol. *Sd* Elisha Birnbaum. *Prod Asst* Asher Gat. *Makeup* Uri Gross. *Sp Eff* Yaacov Noyman. *Prod in Coöp With* Israeli Defense Forces, G. Godik, Nordisk Films. *Ch Grip* David Cordova.

Cast: Pier Angeli (*Eileen*), William Berger (*Roy Hemmings*), Oded Kotler (*Raphi Cohen*), Yehoram Gaon (*Yehoram*), Ori Levy (*foreign office man*), Reuven Morgan (*photographer*), Tami Tsifroni (*woman officer*), Moshe Yanai (*Yossi*), The Hagashash Trio, Ariela Shavid, Meir Levy, Edith Astruc, Dvora Dotan, Zecharia Manzur, Yaacov Levy, Aviva Paz, Edward Shurush, A. A. Wolf, Michael Brant, Yaacov Bukman, Nili Keinan.

War drama. Roy Hemmings, an American newspaper correspondent, is sent to Israel to report on the Arab-Israeli conflict, although he does not believe that a war will develop. Yehoram, a carefree chauffeur, escorts Roy and Eileen, his Israeli-born girl friend whom he later marries, around the countryside. Roy, who originally supported neither country, becomes sympathetic to the Israeli cause; he is impressed with the spirit of the people and especially with Raphi Cohen, a pilot who flew to Egypt to discuss a peace settlement with Nasser. Eileen, however, believes that Raphi is a fraud who is promoting the war. When war breaks out, Yehoram is ordered to report for military duty, and after rescuing a wounded soldier he becomes a hero. Although Raphi attempts to enlist, the war is over before he is admitted. Yehoram returns to his kibbutz and sees Roy walk into a field to retrieve a goat for some children and accidentally detonate a land mine. He is killed, and Eileen sadly returns to the United States with her husband's body. *Newspapermen. Americans in foreign countries. Chauffeurs. Air pilots. War heroes. Patriotism. Military draft. Kibbutzim. Mines (war explosives). Israeli-Arab War 1967. Gamal Abdel Nasser.*

Note: Released in Israel in 1968 as *Kol mamzer melech;* original running time: 120 min. Newsreel footage from the Israeli-Arab War is included.

EVERY DAY IS A HOLIDAY (Spain) F6.1405

Guión Films. *Dist* Columbia Pictures. Jul **1966**. Sd; col (Eastman Color, print by Technicolor). 35mm. 76 min.

A Manuel J. Goyanes Production. *Prod* Manuel J. Goyanes. *Exec Prod-Dir-Story* Mel Ferrer. *Screenplay* Mel Ferrer, José María Palacio. *Dir Photog* Antonio L. Ballesteros. *Art Dir* Enrique Alarcón. *Film Ed* Rosa Graceli-Salgado. *Mus* Augusto Algueró. *Songs* Augusto Algueró, José Torregrosa, Antonio Guijarro. *Choreog* José Torregrosa. *Sd* Antonio de Miguel. *Asst Dir* Manuel de la Cueva. *Prod Mgr* Samuel Menkes.

Cast: Marisol (*Chica*), Angel Peralta (*himself*), Rafael de Córdova (*dancer*), José Marco Davó (*impresario*), Pedro María Sánchez (*Manolo*), Vala Cliffton (*femme fatale*), Jesús Guzmán (*salesman*), José Sepúlveda (*gypsy*), Francisco Camoiras (*servant*), José María Labernie (*hotel employee*), Luis Barbero (*employee at bullring*), Toni Canal (*boy*), Jack Gaskins (*American father*), Juan Ramón Torremocha.

Comedy-drama with music. Chica, a young ragpicker living in Madrid with her little brother, Manolo, dresses as a boy and dreams of becoming a

rejoneador (an equestrian bullfighter). She trains her horse, Cabriola, in the traditional routines until she is ready to perform for her idol, *rejoneador* Angel Peralta. Peralta is impressed by the "boy's" skill and arranges for his manager to help Chica obtain bookings in smalltown bullrings as an equestrian comedy performer. Her appearances are highly successful, and before long she is invited to appear in the ring in Marbella. Here Chica sees Peralta with his sweetheart and reveals her sex to the manager by her fit of jealousy. At the world-famed Feria de Sevilla, Chica's bullfighting skill is recognized by the crowd, and she becomes a *rejoneador* in her own right. The manager persuades her to put on a dress for the festivities. Dressed in a gypsy costume, she sings and dances. Peralta, shocked to discover that Chica is actually a girl, lifts her up alongside him on horseback, and they ride together in the traditional parade through the streets. *Waifs. Equestrians. Entertainers. Male impersonation. Bullfighting. Brother-sister relationship. Adolescence. Jealousy. Fairs. Madrid. Marbella. Horses.*

Note: Exteriors filmed in Madrid, Marbella, and Seville. Madrid opening: Dec 1965 as *Cabriola;* running time: 90 min. Some U. S. reviews indicate ColumbiaColor print.

EVERY DAY'S A HOLIDAY *see* **SEASIDE SWINGERS**

EVERY MAN'S WOMAN *see* **A ROSE FOR EVERYONE**

EVERY SPARROW MUST FALL F6.1406

Jay Gee Productions. *Dist* Distributors Corp. of America. Nov **1964** [c27 Aug 1964; LU3336]. Sd; col (Technicolor, print by Movielab). 35mm. 82 min.

A James J. Gannon Production. *Prod* James J. Gannon. *Dir* Ronald R. Budsan. *Film Ed* Lee Jacobs. *Mus Score* Joseph A. Kroculick.

Cast: Robert Shea, Frank Salmonese.

Melodrama. Larry, a psychotic electronics engineer, invents a machine to eliminate humanity, but before he can put his plan into effect, he is poisoned by the brother of a girl whom he had driven to suicide. *Engineers. Insanity. Inventions. Suicide. Poisoning.*

EVERY THING FOR EVERYBODY *see* **EVERYTHING FOR EVERYBODY**

EVERYBODY GO HOME! (France/Italy) F6.1407

Dino De Laurentiis Cinematografica–Orsay Films. *Dist* Davis–Royal Films International. 5 Nov **1962** [New York opening]. Sd; b&w. 35mm. 115 min.

Prod Dino De Laurentiis. *Assoc Prod* Alfredo De Laurentiis. *Collab Prod* Mario Perelli. *Dir* Luigi Comencini. *Screenplay* Age & Scarpelli, Luigi Comencini, Marcello Fondato. *Story* Age & Scarpelli. *Dir Photog* Carlo Carlini, Gastone Di Giovanni. *Camera* Franco Di Giacomo. *Camera Op* Luigi Conversi. *Art Dir* Carlo Egidi. *Asst Art Dir* Ferdinando Giovannoni. *Set Decor* Riccardo Domenici. *Film Ed* Nino Baragli. *Mus Comp* Francesco Lavagnino. *Mus Cond* Franco Ferrara. *Sd* Domenico Dubbini, Umberto Picistrelli. *1st & 2d Asst Dir* Franco Montemurro, Roberto Pariante. *Unit Mgr* Giorgio Morra. *Prod Sec* Romolo Germano. *Script Girl* Annamaria Montanari. *Cost* Ugo Pericoli, Remo Palmieri. *Makeup* Giuliano Laurenti. *Hairstyles* Elda Magnanti. *Still Photog* Enrico Santelli. *Head Grip* Cesare Onorati. *Head Gaffer* Luciano Pini.

Cast: Alberto Sordi (*Alberto Innocenzi*), Martin Balsam (*Corporal Fornaciari*), Serge Reggiani (*Private Ceccarelli*), Nino Castelnuovo (*young Codegato*), Mario Feliciani (*Captain Passerin*), Didi Perego ("*available*" *girl*), Carla Gravina (*Silvia Modena*), Jole Mauro (*Maria Fornaciari*), Alex Nicol (*American paratrooper*), Eduardo De Filippo (*Innocenzi's father*), Mino Doro (*Major Nocella*), Claudio Gora (*colonel*), Vincenzo Musolino (*1st fascist*), Mac Ronay (*Evaristo Brisigoni*), Mario Frera (*2d fascist*), Silla Bettini (*Lieutenant Di Fazio*).

War comedy-drama. On 8 Sep 1943, soldiers in the Italian Army hear of an armistice and believe that the war has ended. Nevertheless, 1st Lieut. Alberto Innocenzi is ordered to round up his men and join the Italian forces. His men, with the exception of Private Ceccarelli, have other ideas, and they all desert. Although uncertain of why they are still in uniform, Innocenzi and Ceccarelli head for their assigned destination. On the road they encounter a group of partisan fighters, but Innocenzi, now determined to go home, claims that he is escorting a sick man to safety and refuses to join the patriots. Later he and Ceccarelli are joined by other soldiers, including Corporal Fornaciari, who is eventually arrested by the Italian Fascists when it becomes known that his family secretly sheltered an escaped American paratrooper. Throughout the horrible journey, they manage to retain their good spirits. When Innocenzi and Ceccarelli reach Innocenzi's home, his father tries to persuade him to join the Fascists; but, tired of warfare, he runs away. As he and Ceccarelli reach the outskirts of town, they are stopped by German soldiers and taken to work in a road gang. During a raid by partisans, Innocenzi escapes and hides in a church steeple from which point he watches the fighting and sees Ceccarelli fatally wounded. Innocenzi then realizes that he cannot escape from his responsibilities, and he joins the partisan fighters. *Fascists. Deserters—Military. Nazis. Combat zone life. Filial relations. Resistance (political). World War II. Italy—Army. Germany—Army.*

Note: Opened in Rome in Oct 1960 as *Tutti a casa*; running time: 100 min; in Paris in May 1961 as *La grande pagaille*; running time: 105 min.

EVERYBODY GOES APE   F6.1408
Dist Able Film Co. ca **1970**. Sd; col. 16mm. [Feature length assumed.]

Sex film. No information about the precise nature of this film has been found. *Sexuality.*

EVERYBODY LIKES MOUNTAIN WOMEN *see* THE UNDRESSED WEST

EVERYBODY LOVES IT   F6.1409
Dist Film World Distributors. 10 Apr **1964** [Los Angeles opening]. Sd; col. 35mm. 68 min.

Prod Edward E. Paramore, Bob Heiderich.

Comedy. A timid TV studio janitor with an urge to try his hand at acting finds a four-leaf clover and skyrockets to fame as a guest star, appearing on the stages he has formerly swept. As surgeon "Sven Crazy," he performs medical miracles that turn the hospital into a shambles. In the late, late gangster series, *The Case of the Nosey Costra,* he takes part in a fur store heist that goes awry; the gun molls pose as undraped mannequins when the police arrive, and the gangsters get away with trading stamps instead of furs. The action is frequently interrupted by commercials. In *Combat Desk Clerk,* the janitor plays Private Norbit, assigned to a special intelligence unit. Parachuted into enemy territory, he attempts to locate the hidden guns of Macaroni while he is beset on all sides by nude enemy spies. *Janitors. Actors. Surgeons. Gangsters. Police. Spies. Timidity. Nudity. Television. Robbery. Disguise. Parachuting. Combat zone life. Talismans. Television studios. Dummies. United States Army—Intelligence.*

EVERYMAN'S WOMAN *see* A ROSE FOR EVERYONE

EVERYTHING FOR EVERYBODY   F6.1410
Dist Producers Releasing International. 27 Jun **1969** [Champaign, Illinois, showing]. Sd; b&w. 35mm. 70 min.

Prod Jack Bravman. *Photog* John Amero.

Cast: Linda Boyce, Rita Gonzalez, Steve Gould.

Sex film. No information about the precise nature of this film has been found, but press material suggests that it includes scenes of lesbianism, voyeurism, and sexual intercourse. *Lesbianism. Voyeurism. Sexuality.*

Note: Also known as *Every Thing for Everybody.*

EVERYTHING'S DUCKY   F6.1411
Barbroo Enterprises. *Dist* Columbia Pictures. 8 Nov **1961** [Los Angeles opening; c15 Oct 1961; LP20694]. Sd (RCA); b&w. 35mm. 80 min.

Prod Red Doff. *Dir* Don Taylor. *Screenplay* John Fenton Murray, Benedict Freedman. *Dir Photog* Carl Guthrie. *Art Dir* Robert Peterson. *Set Decor* Darrell Silvera. *Film Ed* Richard Brockway. *Mus Scored & Cond* Bernard Green. *Songs:* "Everything's Ducky," "Moonlight Music," "Scuttlebutt Walk" Harold Spina. *Sung by* The Hi-Lo's. *Sd Supv* Charles J. Rice. *Sd* Josh Westmoreland. *Asst Dir* Jerrold Bernstein. *Asst to the Prod* Sig Frohlich. *Makeup Supv* Ben Lane.

Cast: Mickey Rooney *(Beetle McKay),* Buddy Hackett *(Admiral John Paul Jones),* Jackie Cooper *(Lieutenant Parmell),* Joanie Sommers *(Nina Lloyd),* Roland Winters *(Capt. Lewis Bollinger),* Elizabeth MacRae *(Susie Penrose),* Gene Blakely *(Lieutenant Commander Kemp),* Gordon Jones *(Chief Conroy),* Richard Deacon *(Dr. Deckham),* James Millhollin *(George Imhoff),* Jimmy Cross *(misanthropist),* Robert B. Williams *(duck hunter),* King Calder *(Frank),* Ellie Kent *(nurse),* William Hellinger *(corpsman),* Ann Morell *(WAVE),* George Sawaya *(Simmons),* Dick Winslow *(Froehlich),* Alvy Moore *(Jim Lipscott),* Harold Kennedy *(Mr. Johnson),* Walker Edmiston *(Scuttlebutt's voice).*

Comedy. While stationed at a Navy rocket-launching site, seamen Beetle McKay and Ad Jones run across a talking duck named Scuttlebutt. A Navy psychiatrist, Lieutenant Parmell, accuses them of malingering and orders them to get rid of the bird. Then it is discovered that Scuttlebutt once belonged to a pioneer rocket scientist who, before his death, taught his pet the secret of a new rocket-guidance system. Beetle and Ad are instructed to bring back Scuttlebutt, and the Navy Department assigns secretary Nina Lloyd to ingratiate herself with Beetle and make sure he recovers the duck. After a series of misadventures, a huge blunder is made when Scuttlebutt accidentally becomes one of the animals scheduled to be launched into space in a new rocket. Frantic, Beetle and Ad climb aboard the missile to rescue the bird, and all three are sent into orbit. *Sailors. Psychiatrists. Secretaries. Rocket-launching sites. Rockets. United States Navy. Ducks.*

EVIL COME, EVIL GO *see* THE YELLOW CANARY

EVIL EYE (Italy)   F6.1412
Galatea–Coronet Film. *Dist* American International Pictures. May **1964** [c20 May 1964; LP28251]. Sd; b&w. 35mm. 92 min.

Exec Prod (see note) Massimo De Rita, Ferruccio De Martino, Lionello Santi. *Assoc Prod* Salvatore Billitteri. *Dir* Mario Bava. *Story & Screenplay* Ennio De Concini, Eliana De Sabata, Franco Prosperi, Enzo Corbucci, Mino Guerrini, Mario Bava. *Dir Photog* Mario Bava. *Camera Op* Ubaldo Terzano. *Art Dir* Giorgio Giovannini. *Set Dresser* Luigi D'Andria. *Film Ed* Mario Serandrei. *Mus* Les Baxter. *Mus Coörd* Al Simms. *Mus (Orig Vers)* Roberto Nicolosi. *Sd Rec* Titra Sound Corp. *Mus Ed* Eve Newman. *Sd Ed* Al Bird, Kay Rose, Ernest Reichert. *Asst Dir* Franco Prosperi. *Prod Mgr* Paolo Mercuri. *Makeup* Euclide Santoli. *Hairdresser* Mara Rocchetti.

Cast: Leticia Roman *(Nora Dralston),* John Saxon *(Dr. Marcello Bassi),* Valentina Cortese *(Laura Terrani),* Dante Di Paolo *(Landini),* Robert Buchanan *(Doctor Alessi),* Gianni Di Benedetto *(Professor Terrani),* Jim Dolen, Virginia Doro, Chana Coubert, Peggy Nathan, Marta Melecco, Lucia Modugno, Franco Morigi, John Stacy, Milo Quesada, Tiberio Murgia, Titti Tomaino, Pini Lido, Dafydd Havard.

Mystery melodrama. While visiting her aunt in Rome, American secretary Nora Dralston finds the elderly woman suffering from a heart attack and rushes from the house to fetch Dr. Marcello Belli. She is assaulted and knocked unconscious; but a scream awakens her, and she sees what appears to be a man stabbing a woman. Nora faints, regains consciousness in a hospital, but is unable to convince Dr. Belli of the crime she witnessed. Nevertheless, he returns with her to the house of the now-deceased aunt, and they discover that it is inhabited by Dr. Terrani and his wife, Laura, and that other unsolved murders had occurred in the same area. Nora moves in with Laura, a former friend of her aunt. Dr. Terrani becomes a prime suspect, however, when Nora finds a box of newspaper clippings about the slayings. Newspaperman Landini, long interested in the case, offers to help Nora, who begins receiving mysterious telephone calls and finally a folder containing her photograph. One night, Nora finds Dr. Terrani stabbed; he tells her that Laura committed the murders and forced him to dispose of the bodies. As Laura tries to shoot Nora, the dying doctor kills Laura. *Americans in foreign countries. Secretaries. Newspapermen. Physicians. Aunts. Murder. Rome. Documentation.*

Note: Released in Italy in 1963 as *La ragazza che sapeva troppo;* running time: 92 min. Copyright claimant: Alta Vista Productions. The U. S. copyright source and most other U. S. sources credit Massimo De Rita as executive producer, Italian sources credit Ferruccio De Martino, and one British source credits Lionello Santi as executive producer and Ferruccio De Martino as producer.

EVIL GUN *see* DAY OF THE EVIL GUN

THE EVIL OF FRANKENSTEIN (Great Britain)   F6.1413
Hammer Film Productions. *Dist* Universal Pictures. 8 May **1964** [Chicago opening; c13 Jun 1964; LP37901]. Sd; col (Eastman Color). 35mm. 86 min.

Prod Anthony Hinds. *Dir* Freddie Francis. *Story-Screenplay* John Elder. *Dir Photog* John Wilcox. *Camera Op* Ronnie Maasz. *Art Dir* Don Mingaye. *Supv Ed* James Needs. *Mus Comp* Don Banks. *Mus Supv* Philip Martell. *Mus Dir* John Hollingsworth. *Sd Rec* Ken Rawkins. *Sd Ed* Roy Hyde. *Asst Dir* Bill Cartlidge, Hugh Harlow. *Prod Mgr* Don Weeks. *Cont* Pauline Harlow. *Wardrobe Mistress* Rosemary Burrows. *Makeup Artist* Roy Ashton. *Hairstyles* Frieda Steiger. *Sp Eff* Les Bowie.

Cast: Peter Cushing *(Baron Frankenstein),* Peter Woodthorpe *(Zoltan),* Duncan Lamont *(chief of police),* Sandor Eles *(Hans),* Katy Wild *(beggar girl),* David Hutcheson *(burgomaster),* James Maxwell *(priest),* Howard Goorney *(drunk),* Kiwi Kingston *(The Creature),* Caron Gardner *(burgomaster's wife),* Tony Arpino *(bodysnatcher),* Timothy Bateson *(hypnotized man),* Alister Williamson *(landlord),* Frank Forsyth *(manservant),* Kenneth Cove *(curé),* Michele Scott *(little girl),* Anthony Blackshaw *(burly constable),* David Conville *(young constable),* Derek Martin, Robert Flynn, Anthony Poole, James Garfield *(roustabouts).*

Cast—Adtl Seq: William Phipps, Steven Geray, Maria Palmer.

Horror film. Baron Frankenstein returns with his young assistant, Hans, to his ancestral castle in Karlstaad, Yugoslavia, from which he had fled years earlier after angry villagers drove Frankenstein's monster into the mountains. While following a mute beggar into a cave, the two men discover the monster, preserved in the ice of a glacier. They thaw it out and revive it electrically but learn that its brain has been damaged. The Baron persuades Zoltan, a mesmerist appearing at a local carnival, to reactivate the brain through hypnosis, but Zoltan's treatment causes the monster to obey only him. Zoltan orders the monster to steal all the gold it can find and to punish two of his enemies, but it murders the two men; the Baron, furious at the hypnotist's misuse of the creature, throws him out. Zoltan then commands the monster to kill the Baron, but it kills him instead and wanders into the mountains. The Baron is jailed, but he escapes, while Hans and a beggar girl follow the monster and bring it back to the castle. When the Baron reaches his laboratory, he finds the monster drunk on brandy and starting to drink chloroform. In the process, the monster accidentally sets the laboratory on fire; Hans and the girl escape, but Frankenstein and his creation are still inside when the entire castle explodes. *Scientists. Monsters. Hypnotists. Mutes. Beggars. Suspended animation. Brain damage. Hypnotism. Murder. Prison escapes. Castles. Caves. Yugoslavia. Fires. Explosions. Frankenstein.*

Note: Released in Great Britain in May 1964; running time: 84 min. Additional sequences filmed in the United States. Sequel to *The Curse of Frankenstein* (1957). John Elder is a pseudonym for Anthony Hinds.

THE EVIL PLEASURE F6.1414
Dist T–S Films, I. R. M. I. Films. ca **1966**. Sd; b&w. 35mm. 60 min.
Dir Jamie Delvos. *Photog* Jamie Delvos.
Cast: Marina Douget.
Drama. Max arrives in San Francisco to visit his older brother Walter, the junior partner in a booming pornography business. Walter and his prostitute girl friend, Meg, introduce Max to the world of Haight-Ashbury, populated by lesbians in search of new converts, young girls who prostitute themselves to buy drugs, sadomasochists, shoe fetishists, hippies who lose control on LSD trips, and hedonists of many descriptions. *Brothers. Pornographers. Prostitutes. Hippies. Hedonism. Lesbianism. Sadomasochism. Fetishism. Narcotics. LSD. San Francisco—Haight-Ashbury.*
Note: Also known as *Pornografi* and *Pornografi—The Evil Pleasure.*

EVIL SPELL see **WHERE THE TRUTH LIES**

EWA CHCE SPAĆ see **EVE WANTS TO SLEEP**

... EXCEPT PEOPLE GET KILLED see **MISSION BATANGAS**

EXCHANGE STUDENT F6.1415
Dist Distribpix, Inc. ca **1970**. Sd; col. 35mm. 65 min.
Sex film. A young European woman comes to America as an exchange student and arranges to live with an American couple in return for performing light housekeeping duties. She is asked for much more, however; the couple have an adventurous attitude towards sex and soon initiate her into the ways of the flesh. At first excited by their preferences, the student realizes in the midst of an orgy that these people are merely using her for their own purposes, and she violently thwarts their intentions. *Exchange students. Sexual initiation. Sexual practices. Orgies.*

EXCITED F6.1416
G. J. Productions. *Dist* Canyon Distributing Co. 13 Feb **1969** [San Francisco showing]. Sd; b&w. 35mm. 75 min.
Prod G. Ansen Courtney. *Dir-Writ* Akdov Telmig. *Camera* Len Harper. *Sd Rec* Alan Allen. *Script Girl* Penny Holmgren. *Grip* Tommy Harper.
Cast: Ellyn Donalson, Evan Richter, Kim O'Hara, Dom Michaels, Candi Carson, Fred Patini, Gerald Monsen, Faye Iveri.
Sex film. Two Los Angeles office workers, Candy and Michelle, leave work on Friday afternoon and return to their apartment. Michelle takes a bath and masturbates; Candy discovers a peeping tom watching her through the window, and she deliberately tantalizes him by performing physical exercises. Their homosexual neighbor, Richie, borrows a cup of sugar, and the women seduce him. Saturday morning, Candy and Michelle meet two hippies in the park and make love with them at a secluded spot. The hippies return home with the women, and there is an orgy. The hippies steal the women's money and leave in the middle of the night. Sunday morning, Candy and Michelle hitchhike to the park to pick up their car. They are given a lift by a movie producer who takes them to his office to do some last-minute "casting" for his new film. Outside, the women become bored, and the producer lures them to his home with the promise of parts in his next film. The producer and his crippled butler, Clifford, tie up Candy and Michelle, and the women are forced to participate in perverted acts. They escape, return to their apartment, and engage in lesbian activity. *Office clerks. Roommates. Hippies. Motion picture producers. Butlers. Voyeurism. Autoeroticism. Sadism. Male homosexuality. Lesbianism. Orgies.*

EXCITING WIVES see **THE CASE OF THE STRIPPING WIVES**

THE EXECUTIONER (Great Britain) F6.1417
Ameran Films. *Dist* Columbia Pictures. 3 Jun **1970** [Dallas opening; c1 Jun 1970; LP37953]. Sd; col (Technicolor). 35mm (Panavision). 107 min. *MPAA rating* GP.
Prod Charles H. Schneer. *Dir* Sam Wanamaker. *Screenplay* Jack Pulman. *Story* Gordon McDonell. *Dir Photog* Denys Coop. *Camera Op* Alan Hall. *Art Dir* Edward Marshall. *Film Ed* Roy Watts. *Mus & Mus Dir* Ron Goodwin. *Sd Ed* Clive Smith. *Sd Rec* Iain Bruce. *Electric Sd* P. Zinovieff. *Asst Dir* Peter Price. *Prod Mgr* John Comfort. *Cont* Barbara Rowland. *Location Mgr* Bryan

Coates. *Cost Dsgn* Yvonne Caffin. *Wardrobe Supv* Eddie Boyce. *Wardrobe Mistress* Janet Lucas. *Ch Makeup* Trevor Crole-Rees. *Casting* Miriam Brickman.
Cast: George Peppard (*John Shay*), Joan Collins (*Sarah Booth*), Judy Geeson (*Polly Bendel*), Oscar Homolka (*Racovsky*), Charles Gray (*Vaughan Jones*), Nigel Patrick (*Colonel Scott*), Keith Michell (*Adam Booth*), George Baker (*Philip Crawford*), Alexander Scourby (*Professor Parker*), Peter Bull (*Butterfield*), Ernest Clark (*Roper*), Peter Dyneley (*Balkov*), Gisela Dali (*Anna*).
Melodrama. British Intelligence agent John Shay suspects that a security leak caused the collapse of British operations in Vienna. He persuades his girl friend Polly, a secretary at Intelligence headquarters, to allow him access to secret files. The information leads Shay to suspect fellow agent Adam Booth (whose wife, Sarah, has been having an affair with him) of being a double agent for the Soviet Union. Although Shay denounces Booth, his superiors refuse to act on what they believe to be groundless charges, and Shay is suspended from his duties for obtaining the confidential files. Nevertheless, he goes to Istanbul to search for more evidence against Booth; while he is investigating, an attempt is made on his life. With conclusive information from British scientist Philip Crawford, who is also involved with Sarah, Shay then murders Booth and finds a plane ticket to Athens in his pocket. Shay boards the plane, accompanied by Sarah, who is unaware of her husband's death. In Athens, where Shay impersonates Booth, they are captured by Soviet agents and held for an exchange for Crawford. Colonel Scott, CIA agent, rescues Shay and Sarah and reveals that Booth was indeed a double agent being used by the British to transmit false information to the Russians. *Secret agents. Secretaries. Scientists. Widows. Espionage. Infidelity. Murder. Impersonation. Istanbul. Athens. Great Britain—Intelligence service. Union of Soviet Socialist Republics—Intelligence service. United States—Central Intelligence Agency.*
Note: Location scenes filmed in England and Greece. Opened in London in Jun 1970; running time: 111 min.

THE EXECUTIONERS see **HITLER'S EXECUTIONERS**

AN EXILE see **I WALK THE LINE**

THE EXILES F6.1418
Kent MacKenzie. *Dist* Pathé Contemporary Films. 7 Apr **1966** [San Francisco opening; c13 Jul 1961; LU3187]. Sd; b&w. 35mm. 72 min.
Prod-Dir-Writ Kent MacKenzie. *Photog* Erik Daarstad, Robert Kaufman, photog, John Merril. *Adtl Photog* Sven Walnum, Nicholas Clapp. *Film Ed* Kent MacKenzie, Warren Brown, Thomas Conrad, Erik Daarstad, Thomas Miller, ed, Beth Pattrick. *Mus* Anthony Hilder, The Revels, Robert Hafner, Eddie Sunrise. *Sd* Sam Farnsworth.
Cast: Yvonne Williams (*Yvonne*), Homer Nish (*Homer*), Tommy Reynolds, actor (*Tommy*).
Drama. Three American Indian youths leave their reservation to find a new life in Los Angeles. Caught between two cultures, they are unable to return to their old way of life yet unwilling to become a part of the life of the city. The youths wander about Los Angeles, drinking, playing cards, picking up girls, and getting into fights. They end up on a hilltop overlooking Los Angeles where they beat drums and try to sing and dance their old tribal songs. *Indians of North America. Youth. Social customs. Alienation. Urban life. Los Angeles.*
Note: Filmed on location in Los Angeles. Shown at the 1961 Venice Film Festival at 80 min.

THE EXOTIC ONES F6.1419
The Ormond Organization. 20 Nov **1968** [Chicago opening]. Sd; b&w? 35mm. 60 min.
Pres by June Ormond, Ron Ormond. *Prod-Dir* Ron Ormond.
Cast: Ron Ormond, June Ormond.
Melodrama. No information about the precise nature of this film has been found, but press material suggests a monster using marijuana mangles strippers in New Orleans. *Monsters. Stripteasers. Murder. Marijuana. New Orleans.*

EXPERIMENT IN TERROR F6.1420
Geoffrey–Kate Productions. *Dist* Columbia Pictures. 13 Apr **1962** [New York opening; c1 Apr 1962; LP22256]. Sd (RCA); b&w. 35mm. 123 min.
A Blake Edwards Production. *Prod-Dir* Blake Edwards. *Assoc Prod* Don Peters, prod. *Screenplay* The Gordons. *Dir Photog* Philip Lathrop. *Art Dir* Robert Peterson. *Set Decor* James M. Crowe. *Film Ed* Patrick McCormack. *Mus* Henry Mancini. *Orch* Leo Shuken, Jack Hayes. *Sd Supv* Charles J. Rice. *Sd* Lambert Day. *Asst Dir* Sam Nelson. *Script Supv* Betty Abbott. *Makeup Supv* Ben Lane.
Cast: Glenn Ford (*John Ripley*), Lee Remick (*Kelly Sherwood*), Stefanie Powers (*Toby Sherwood*), Ross Martin (*Red Lynch*), Roy Poole (*Brad*), Ned Glass (*Popcorn*), Anita Loo (*Lisa Soong*), Patricia Huston (*Nancy Ashton*), Gilbert Green (*special agent*), Clifton James (*Captain Moreno*), Al Avalon

(masher), William Bryant *(Chuck)*, Dick Crockett *(FBI agent)*, James Lanphier *(landlord)*, Warren Hsieh *(Joey Soong)*, Sidney Miller *(drunk)*, Clarence Lung *(Attorney Yung)*, Frederic Downs *(Welk)*, Sherry O'Neil *(Edna)*, Mari Lynn *(Penny)*, Harvey Evans *(Dave)*, William Sharon *(Raymond Burkhardt)*.

Crime melodrama. Source: Mildred Gordon and Gordon Gordon, *Operation Terror* (Garden City, N. Y., 1961). Late one evening, San Francisco bank teller Kelly Sherwood is seized in the garage of her home by an asthmatic stranger who warns her that unless she steals $100,000 from the bank where she works, he will kill either her or her younger sister, Toby, or both of them. Terrified, Kelly communicates with FBI agent John Ripley, who advises her to pretend to cooperate with the stranger while he and the police investigate. Official inquiries identify the man as Red Lynch, an ex-convict wanted for murder. Ripley tries to enlist the help of Lynch's current girl friend, Lisa Soong, who refuses to cooperate, because Lynch has paid heavy medical expenses for her crippled son. By tracing the purchase of a toy Lynch bought for the child, Ripley is able to discover where Lynch is holding Toby prisoner. On the day arranged for the theft, Kelly steals the $100,000 and follows Lynch's instructions by carrying the money to Candlestick Park, where a baseball game is in progress. As the game ends and Lynch tries to grab the purse from Kelly, Ripley pounces on him. Although Lynch manages to break away and fight his way through the crowd to the deserted playing field, he is shot down by Ripley as hordes of police pour down the aisles. *Ex-convicts. Bank clerks. Sisters. Orientals. Cripples. Extortion. Kidnaping. Theft. Baseball. Toys. San Francisco—Candlestick Park. San Francisco. United States—Federal Bureau of Investigation.*

Note: Filmed on location in San Francisco.

THE EXPLOITEERS see **THE PINK PUSSY (WHERE SIN LIVES)**

THE EXPLOITERS see **THE SEXPLOITERS**

EXPLORING THE KINSEY REPORTS see **1 + 1 (EXPLORING THE KINSEY REPORTS)**

EXPLOSION (Canada)   **F6.1421**
Meridian Films. *Dist* American International Pictures. Mar **1970**. Sd; col (Technicolor, print by Movielab). 35mm. 96 min. *MPAA rating* R.

Prod Julian Roffman. *Dir* Jules Bricken. *Screenplay* Jules Bricken, Alene Bricken. *Story* Jules Bricken, Robert Hartford-Davis. *Dir Photog* Joseph Brun. *Art Dir* Bruce Grimes. *Film Ed* Tony Lower. *Mus Comp & Cond* Sol Kaplan. *Orch* William McCauley. *Sd Ed* Eric Wrate. *Sd Rec* B. H. Alper, John Gusselle. *Asst Dir* Anthony Waye. *Prod Mgr* Michael Holden. *Script Girl* Pamela Walshe. *Cost* Ilse Richter. *Makeup* Phyllis Newman, makeup. *Coöp* Canadian Film Development Corp. *Prop Master* John Stooshnov. *Constr Mgr* Peter Pryor.

Cast: Don Stroud *(Richie Kovacs)*, Gordon Thomson *(Alan Evans)*, Michele Chicoine *(Doris Randolph)*, Cec Linder *(Mr. Evans)*, Richard Conte *(Dr. Philip Neal)*, Robin Ward *(Peter Evans)*, Ted Stidder *(Timms)*, Murray Matheson *(Jaguar owner)*, Ann Sears *(Jaguar owner's wife)*, Sherry Mitchell *(Susan)*, Olga Kaya *(Valerie)*, Harold Saunders *(Inspector Kelso)*.

Melodrama. Peter Evans intends to leave the United States for Canada to avoid the draft, but his father and his fiancée, Doris, persuade him to stay. Inducted into the Army, he is sent to Vietnam and killed in action. Peter's younger brother, Alan, is also approaching draft age, but he rebels against his father and blames Doris for Peter's death. Alan leaves home and meets Richie Kovacs, a hippie who agrees to go with him to Canada; they steal a car and set out for a work camp in British Columbia. Alan, who has become increasingly volatile since his brother's death, kills two policemen who attempt to prevent them from stealing gasoline. A short time later, the two fugitives decide to change cars to avoid detection. They stop at a garage where Alan kills an attendant and steals another car. Upon arriving in Vancouver, Alan and Richie learn of a public appeal made by Alan's father encouraging his son to surrender to the authorities. Richie then telephones the police and tells of their whereabouts, but Alan forces Richie to flee with him. Pursued by the police across the countryside, they are trapped, and Alan is shot while attempting to escape. *Draft dodgers. Brothers. Hippies. Police. Filial relations. Robbery. Murder. Vietnam War 1964-73. Vancouver (British Columbia).*

Note: Location scenes filmed in Vancouver, British Columbia; working title: *The Blast.* Opened in Vancouver in Jan 1970.

THE EXPLOSIVE GENERATION   **F6.1422**
Vega Productions. *Dist* United Artists. 18 Oct **1961** [Los Angeles opening; c21 Sep 1961; LP21108]. Sd; b&w. 35mm. 89 min.

Prod Stanley Colbert. *Assoc Prod* Joseph Landon, Max Barcutt. *Dir* Buzz Kulik. *Writ* Joseph Landon. *Photog* Floyd Crosby. *Film Ed* Melvin Shapiro. *Mus* Hal Borne. *Sd* William Bernds, Dean Spencer. *Asst Dir* Raoul Pagel, Lou Place. *Script Supv* Dorothy Cormack. *Wardrobe* Alexis Davidoff. *Makeup* Ted Coodley. *Hairstyles* Betty Pedretti.

Cast: William Shatner *(Peter Gifford)*, Patty McCormack *(Janet Sommers)*, Lee Kinsolving *(Dan Carlyle)*, Billy Gray *(Bobby Herman, Jr.)*, Steve Dunne *(Bobby Herman, Sr.)*, Arch Johnson *(Mr. Sommers)*, Virginia Field *(Mrs. Sommers)*, Phillip Terry *(Mr. Carlyle)*, Hanna Landy *(Mrs. Carlyle)*, Edward Platt *(Mr. Morton)*, Suzi Carnell *(Marge Ryker)*, Jocelyn Brando *(Mrs. Ryker)*, Beau Bridges *(Mark)*, Peter Virgo, Jr. *(George)*, Bruce Kerner *(Stephen)*, Peter Virgo, Sr. *(dean of men)*, Mark Lowell *(printing teacher)*, Judee Morton *(Charlene)*, Jan Norris *(Terry)*, Stafford Repp *(police captain)*, Vito Scotti *(custodian)*, Anne Dore *(The Girl)*, Michael Gibbs *(substitute teacher)*, Ronnie Kelman, Lee Harris, Jim D'Arcy.

Drama. Janet Sommers, a high school senior, is persuaded to spend the night at a rented beach house with her boyfriend, Dan Carlyle, because she is afraid of losing his affection. The next day at school, Janet suggests to Peter Gifford, the seniors' favorite teacher, that sex is the most important problem facing young people, and they ask him to give them the sex education their parents failed to provide. He suggests they write unsigned essays on the subject to read and discuss in class. The proposal causes an uproar among mothers active in the PTA, and Gifford is ordered by his principal, Mr. Morton, to destroy the papers. He is suspended when he refuses to comply. The students rally to his defense by going on a "silence strike," which reaches its peak at a basketball game; the entire gym is silent except for the sound of the ball and the referee's whistle. While the game is in progress, Janet reads her mother the paper she wrote for Gifford's class. Mrs. Sommers sees the wisdom of Gifford's efforts, and she aids in having him reinstated. The class resumes, and Gifford reads the first of the controversial papers. *Students. Schoolteachers. High school life. Sex instruction. Parenthood. Basketball. Demonstrations.*

EXPOSURE!   **F6.1423**
Lima Productions. 21 Dec **1967** [San Francisco showing]. Si; col. 16mm. 83 min.

Nudist film. Although no information about the precise nature of this film has been found, press material indicates that it is composed of five segments: "The Goddess," "Private Files of a Girl Watcher," "Splendor in the Grass," "The Magnificent Seven," and "A Midsummer Night's Dream." Press photographs suggest it contains scenes of nudism. *Nudism.*

THE EXTERMINATING ANGEL (Mexico)   **F6.1424**
Uninci, S. A.–Films 59–Gustavo Alatriste. *Dist* Altura Films International. 21 Aug **1967** [New York opening]. Sd (RCA); b&w. 35mm. 91 min.

Pres by Clem Perry. *Prod* Gustavo Alatriste. *Dir & Dial* Luis Buñuel. *Screenplay* Luis Alcoriza, Luis Buñuel. *Dir Photog* Gabriel Figueroa. *Camera* Manuel Gonzalez. *Asst Camera* Daniel López. *Art Dir* Jesús Bracho. *Main Titl* Nicolas Rueda, Jr. *Film Ed* Carlos Savage. *Asst Ed* Sigfrido García. *Mus Dir* Raúl Lavista. *Mus From the Works of* Alessandro Scarlatti, Pietro Domenico Paradisi. *Sd Supv* James L. Fields. *Sd Rec* José B. Carles. *Mus Rec* Galdino Samperio. *Asst Dir* Ignacio Villarreal. *Prod Mgr* Fidel Pizarro. *Cost* Georgette Somohano. *Makeup* Armando Meyer. *Hairdresser* Esperanza Gómez. *Sp Eff* Juan Muñoz Ravelo. *English Subtitl* Herman G. Weinberg, Juan Luis Buñuel. *Still Photog* Angel Corona.

Cast: Silvia Pinal *(Letitia, the "Walkyrie")*, Enrique Rambal *(Nobile)*, Jacqueline Andere *(Señora Alicia Roc)*, José Baviera *(Leandro)*, Augusto Benedico *(doctor)*, Luis Beristáin *(Christián)*, Antonio Bravo *(Russell)*, Claudio Brook *(major)*, César del Campo *(colonel)*, Rosa Elena Durgel *(Silvia)*, Lucy Gallardo *(Lucía Nobile)*, Enrique García Alvarez *(Señor Roc)*, Ofelia Guilmain *(Juana Avila)*, Nadia Haro Oliva *(Ana Maynar)*, Tito Junco *(Raúl)*, Javier Loyá *(Francisco Avila)*, Javier Masse *(Eduardo)*, Angel Merino *(Lucas, the waiter)*, Ofelia Montesco *(Béatriz)*, Patricia Morán *(Rita, Christián's wife)*, Patricia de Morelos *(Blanca)*, Bertha Moss *(Leonora)*, Pancho Cordova, Luis Lomeli, Guillermo Alvarez Bianchi, Elodia Hernández, Eric del Castillo, Chel López, David Hayyad Cohen, Florencio Castello.

Allegory. Source: José Bergamín, *Los náufragos de la Calle de la Providencia* (a play; production undetermined). During a formal dinner party at the home of Señor Nobile and his wife, Lucia, the servants unaccountably leave their posts until only the major-domo is left. After dinner, the guests adjourn to the music room where one of the women plays a piano sonata. Later, instead of leaving, the guests remove their jackets, loosen their gowns, and settle down for the night. By morning it is apparent that for some inexplicable reason, they are trapped in the room. Days pass, and their plight intensifies; they become quarrelsome, hostile, and hysterical. One of the guests, Russell, dies and his body is placed in a large cupboard; Béatriz and Eduardo, a young couple about to be married, lock themselves in a closet and commit suicide; a sheep is slaughtered and roasted on a fire made from floorboards; the host gives his secret supply of morphine to Leonora, whose physician, another guest, reveals to others that she is dying of cancer, but the drugs are stolen by Francisco and Juana, an incestuous brother and sister; and Ana, a practitioner of witchcraft, invokes the demons of hell while lapsing into feverish hallucinations. Eventually, Raúl suggests that Nobile is responsible for their predicament and

315

that he must be sacrificed. As Nobile offers to take his own life, Letitia sees that they are all in the same positions as when their plight began. Obeying her instructions, they retrace their conversation and movements and discover that they are free to leave the room. To celebrate their salvation, the guests attend mass at the cathedral. When the service is over, they find that they, along with the priest and the entire congregation, are once again trapped. *Domestics. Majordomos. Pianists. Physicians. Death. Infidelity. Suicide. Cancer. Theft. Incest. Brother-sister relationship. Witchcraft. Human sacrifice. Morphine. Cathedrals. Catholic Church. Sheep.*

Note: Released in Mexico in May 1962 as *El ángel exterminador*; running time: 95 min. Music also includes Gregorian chants of the *Te Deum*.

THE EXTRAORDINARY SEAMAN F6.1425

John Frankenheimer Productions–Edward Lewis Productions. *Dist* Metro-Goldwyn-Mayer, Inc. Jan 1969 [c31 Oct 1968; LP36191]. Sd; col (Metrocolor). 35mm (Panavision). 80 min. *MPAA rating* G.

Prod Edward Lewis. *Co-prod* John H. Cushingham. *Assoc Prod* Hal Dresner. *Dir* John Frankenheimer. *Screenplay* Phillip Rock, Hal Dresner. *Story* Phillip Rock. *Dir Photog* Lionel Lindon. *Camera Op* Roy Clark. *Asst Camera* Harry Young. *Art Dir* George W. Davis, Edward Carfagno. *Set Decor* Henry Grace, Hugh Hunt. *Film Ed* Fredric Steinkamp. *Asst Ed* Alex Beaton. *Orig Mus Comp & Cond* Maurice Jarre. *Rec Supv* Franklin Milton. *Rec* Tom Overton. *Boom Op* Richard Church. *Asst Dir* Enrico Isacco, Michael Glick. *Unit Prod Mgr* Russell Saunders. *Script Supv* Hazel Hall. *Location Mgr* Howard Horton. *Wardrobe* Frank Roberts. *Makeup* William Tuttle, Lewis Sweeney. *Hairstyles* Sydney Guilaroff, Betty Iverson. *Sp Vis Eff* J. McMillan Johnson, Milt Rice. *Gaffer* Bill Hannah. *Prop* Frank Agnone. *Constr Mgr* Lawrence Yzuel. *Casting* Leonard Murphy, Lee Traver.

Cast: David Niven (*Lieutenant Commander Finchhaven*), Faye Dunaway (*Jennifer Winslow*), Alan Alda (*Lieut. j.g. Morton Krim*), Mickey Rooney (*Cook 3d Class W. J. Oglethorpe*), Jack Carter (*Gunner's Mate Orville Toole*), Juano Hernandez (*Ali Shar*), Manu Tupou (*Seaman 1st Class Lightfoot Star*), Barry Kelley (*Admiral Barnwell*), Leonard O. Smith, Richard Guizon, John Cochran (*Dyaks*), Jerry Fujikawa (*Admiral Shimagoshi*).

Comedy. GRAND ALLIANCE: Four American sailors in World War II become detached from their ship in the fog and are washed up on an island somewhere in the Philippines. These men are Lieutenant Krim, an accountant with little naval experience; Oglethorpe, a cook; Toole, the gunner's mate; and able seaman Lightfoot, a fullblooded Cheyenne. They discover British Commander Finchhaven standing on the deck of an old gunboat stuck in a sandbar, wearing an immaculate white uniform and sipping a glass of whiskey. THE GATHERING STORM: The men set out to restore the old gunboat; and while exploring the island, they come across an apparently abandoned garage full of supplies. They help themselves and are shot at by Jennifer Winslow, the stranded proprietress of the garage, who agrees to give them the supplies in exchange for passage off the island. The ship, H. M.'S. *Curmudgeon*, is repaired, and they set sail. THEIR FINEST HOUR: After being bombed by the Japanese, they pick up some shipwrecked Filipinos, but through a mishap all but Finchhaven, Jennifer, and Krim drift away from the ship. All the while, Finchhaven remains on deck sipping whiskey. THE HINGE OF FATE: Finchhaven confesses that he is a ghost, restored to the ship to redeem the family honor that he lost in 1914, when he disgraced his family by getting drunk before his first battle. TRIUMPH AND TRAGEDY: Finchhaven plans to ram an approaching Japanese cruiser, which turns out to be the ship on which the peace treaty is being signed. For this new blunder, Finchhaven is condemned to wait out the new peace, piloting a fake gunboat at an amusement park until a new war provides another chance to restore his family honor. *Accountants. Cooks. Cheyenne Indians. British. Garage-keepers. Ghosts. Filipinos. Aerial bombardment. Sea rescue. Gunboats. Cruisers. Amusement parks. World War II. World War I. Philippines. Bess Wallace Truman. Dorothy Lamour. Errol Flynn. Winston Leonard Spencer Churchill. Adolf Hitler. Joseph Stalin. Douglas MacArthur. Great Britain—Royal Navy. United States Navy.*

Note: Location scenes filmed in Baha and Santa Barbara, California. Much of the film consists of newsreel footage including shots of Bess Truman, Dorothy Lamour, Errol Flynn, Winston Churchill, Adolf Hitler, Joseph Stalin, and Douglas MacArthur.

AN EYE FOR AN EYE F6.1426

Circle Productions. *Dist* Embassy Pictures. 25 May 1966 [Albuquerque, New Mexico, opening]. Sd; col (PathéColor). 35mm. 92 min.

Prod Carroll Case. *Assoc Prod* Frank Beetson, Jr. *Dir* Michael Moore. *Screenplay* Bing Russell, Sumner Williams. *Photog* Lucien Ballard. *Art Dir* Al Roelofs. *Set Decor* Chuck Pierce. *Film Ed* William Austin. *Mus* Raoul Kraushaar. *Mus Theme Whistled by* Muzzy Marcellino. *Sd* Harold Lewis. *Asst Dir* James Rosenberger. *Cost* Tony Scarano, Aida Swenson.

Cast: Robert Lansing (*Talion*), Patrick Wayne (*Benny*), Slim Pickens (*Ike Slant*), Gloria Talbott (*Bri Quince*), Paul Fix (*Quince*), Strother Martin

(*Trumbull*), Henry Wills (*Charles*), Jerry Gatlin (*Jonas*), Rance Howard (*Harry*), Clint Howard (*Jo-Hi*).

Western drama. Former bounty hunter Talion sets out to track down the men who brutally murdered his wife and son. The leader is Ike Slant, whose brother, a convicted killer, was shot down by Talion. While on the trail, Talion joins forces with Benny, a youngster who is hunting Slant for the bounty money. The two men stop at a trading post where Talion is attracted to pretty Bri Quince, but the men move on and eventually reach Slant's camp. In the ensuing gunfight, Slant's two cohorts are killed; but Talion's shooting hand is shattered, and Benny is blinded. Undaunted, the two men devise a plan whereby they work out a clock-like structure which enables Benny to fire at any given location by simply hearing a number called out to him by Talion. After months of practice, a showdown is arranged, and Slant arrives with Trumbull, his new accomplice, a grizzled derelict. When Slant reaches "3 o'clock," Talion calls out the number, and Benny fires three fatal shots; but he himself is killed by Trumbull. Talion then uses his other hand to shoot down the derelict. His mission of vengeance completed, Talion gives Bri a farewell look and leaves. *Bounty hunters. Cripples. Derelicts. Murder. Revenge. Blindness.*

EYE OF EVIL see THE 1000 EYES OF DR. MABUSE

EYE OF THE CAT F6.1427

Joseph M. Schenck Enterprises. *Dist* Universal Pictures. 18 Jun 1969 [New York opening; c2 Aug 1970; LP38883]. Sd (Westrex); col (Technicolor). 35mm. 102 min. *MPAA rating* M.

Prod Bernard Schwartz, Phillip Hazelton. *Dir* David Lowell Rich. *Screenplay* Joseph Stefano. *Dir Photog* Russell Metty, Ellsworth Fredricks. *Art Dir* Alexander Golitzen, William D. DeCinces. *Set Decor* John McCarthy, John Austin. *Main Titl* Wayne Fitzgerald, Universal Title. *Film Ed* J. Terry Williams. *Mus* Lalo Schifrin. *Mus Supv* Stanley Wilson. *Sd* Waldon O. Watson, Frank H. Wilkinson. *Asst Dir* Joseph Cavalier. *Unit Prod Mgr* Henry Kline. *Cost* Edith Head. *Makeup* Bud Westmore. *Hairstyles* Larry Germain. *Cat Trainer* Ray Berwick.

Cast: Michael Sarrazin (*Wylie*), Gayle Hunnicutt (*Kassia Lancaster*), Eleanor Parker (*Aunt Danny*), Tim Henry (*Luke*), Laurence Naismith (*Dr. Mills*), Jennifer Leak (*Poor Dear*), Linden Chiles (*Bendetto*), Mark Herron (*Bellemondo*), Annabelle Garth (*socialite*), Tullia (*The Cat*).

Melodrama. Wayward nephew Wylie's rendezvous with Poor Dear is interrupted by the appearance of Kassia Lancaster, his Aunt Danny's cosmetologist and confidante. Kassia informs the young man that Aunt Danny, dying of emphysema, is by day confined to a wheelchair, by night to an oxygen tent. Despite her condition, Aunt Danny has sequestered in her home a colony of cats, the heirs to her fortune. The cosmetologist suggests that Wylie, still uppermost in his aunt's affections, return home, displace the cats, and kill the old lady. Wylie's return is regarded with suspicion by his brother Luke, Aunt Danny's devoted attendant. The animals are removed from the house because of his ailurophobia, and Wylie is reinstated as sole heir. On the evening of the proposed murder the cats mysteriously reappear, causing the heir to faint. Beside his body Kassia and Luke reveal their liaison and discuss their plan to murder both nephew and aunt. Disconcerted by the cat colony, however, Kassia falls from a ladder and dies. Luke discovers Aunt Danny in a room where Wylie has placed her for safekeeping. As Luke and Aunt Danny confer, the composed Wylie enters and announces his departure. *Aunts. Heirs. Cosmetologists. Mistresses. Murder. Incurable illness. Cats.*

Note: Filmed on location in San Francisco; working title: *Wylie*.

EYE OF THE DEVIL (Great Britain) F6.1428

Filmways, Inc. *Dist* Metro-Goldwyn-Mayer, Inc. Sep 1967 [New York opening: 6 Dec 1967; c31 Dec 1966; LP34677]. Sd (Westrex); b&w. 35mm. 92 min.

A Martin Ransohoff Production. *Prod* Martin Ransohoff, John Calley. *Supv Prod Exec* Ben Kadish. *Dir* J. Lee Thompson. *Screenplay* Robin Estridge, Dennis Murphy. *Dir Photog* Erwin Hillier. *Camera Op* John Winbolt. *Art Dir* Elliot Scott. *Main Titl Dsgn* Maurice Binder. *Film Ed* Ernest Walter. *Mus* Gary McFarland. *Rec Supv* A. W. Watkins. *Sd Rec* Gerry Turner. *Dub Mix* J. B. Smith. *Sd Ed* Allan Sones. *Asst Dir* Basil Rayburn. *Prod Mgr* Sydney Streeter. *Cost* Julie Harris, cost. *Other Cost* John Furness.

Cast: Deborah Kerr (*Catherine de Montfaucon*), David Niven (*Philippe de Montfaucon*), Donald Pleasence (*Père Dominic*), Edward Mulhare (*Jean-Claude Ibert*), Flora Robson (*Countess Estelle*), Emlyn Williams (*Alain de Montfaucon*), Sharon Tate (*Odile*), David Hemmings (*Christian de Caray*). John Le Mesurier (*Dr. Monnet*), Suky Appleby (*Antoinette de Montfaucon*), Donald Bisset (*Rennard*), Robert Duncan (*Jacques de Montfaucon*), Michael Miller (*Grandec*), Pauline Letts.

Drama. Source: Philip Loraine, *Day of the Arrow* (New York, 1964). When Philippe de Montfaucon (the Marquis de Bellac) is informed that for the 3d successive year his vineyards near Bordeaux have failed to produce, he instructs his wife, Catherine, to remain in Paris and then leaves for his ancestral chateau. But Catherine, disturbed by his behavior, follows a few days later with their two children. Upon arriving at the chateau, she is greeted coldly by Countess Estelle, Philippe's aunt, diffidently by Père Dominic, the local priest, and disdainfully by the menacing Christian de Caray and his equally hostile sister, Odile. Informed that her husband has gone to a nearby town for the day, Catherine wanders into a chamber in the chateau and accidentally spies Philippe and 12 other men engaged in a mystic ceremonial rite. She is soon afterward terrorized in the Bellac woods by 12 hooded men, and later she learns that Philippe's father, believed dead, is actually living in a turret of the chateau. From him she hears of the dreadful fate her husband has set for himself: tradition decrees that whenever the vines fail for 3 years the head of the Montfaucon family must offer his life's blood as a sacrifice to the barren earth. Horrified, Catherine races from the chateau to summon help. But she is stopped by Père Dominic and taken back to Bellac, while Philippe and the 12 hooded horsemen ride through the village. She escapes but is too late to prevent the death ritual as Christian shoots an arrow into her husband's heart. The next day Catherine leaves with her children, vowing never to return. But she is unaware of the significant glances exchanged between Père Dominic and her young son, Jacques. The new Marquis de Bellac already knows that the ancient tradition must be carried on. *Nobility. Priests. French. Vineyardists. Human sacrifice. Rites and ceremonies. Paris. Bordeaux.*

Note: Released in Great Britain in 1968; running time: 90 min. Location scenes filmed in the Bordeaux country of France. Screen credit reads: "With grateful acknowledgment to the Baronne and the staff for the use of Château d'Hautefort." Working title: *13.*

THE EYE OF THE NEEDLE (France/Italy)   **F6.1429**
MEC Cinematografica–Agiman. *Dist* Eldorado Pictures International. 21 Jun **1965** [New York opening]. Sd; b&w. 35mm. 97 min.
Prod (see note) Aldo Calamara, Achille Filo Della Torre, Otello Cocchi. *Dir* Marcello Andrei. *Screenplay* Giuseppe Mangione, Alberto Bevilacqua, William Demby, Marcello Andrei. *Story* Giuseppe Berto, Dante Troisi. *Photog* Riccardo Pallottini. *Mus* Carlo Rustichelli.
Cast: Annette Strøyberg (*Rosaria*), Gérard Blain (*Toto*), Nino Castelnuovo (*Nicola*), Mariangela Giordano (*Carmelina*), Vittorio Gassman (*Lawyer Mazzaro*), Gino Cervi (*Lawyer D'Angelo*), Umberto Spadaro (*Don Luigino*), Ernesto Calindri (*Don Salvatore*), Ignazio Balsamo (*Don Nene*), Alfredo Varelli (*police brigadier*), Rina Franchetti (*Toto's mother [Za Rita, see note]*), Carla Calò (*Za Santa*), Leopoldo Trieste (*Don Calo*), Enrichetta Medin.
Romantic comedy-drama. Toto and Nicola, two young Sicilians, leave an exhibition of belly dancing with their passions aroused. On their way home they get caught in a rainstorm and seek shelter in an abandoned house. They find that Rosaria, a very pretty girl, has also taken shelter there and has removed her clothes to dry them. The two men deflower the virgin, in turn forcing their attentions upon her. Carmelina, Rosaria's friend, sees the men leave, and then Carmelina has to tell her that she had been raped. Following the local customs and the Sicilian code of honor, one of the pair is required to marry Rosaria, but neither wants to have his honor besmirched by marrying a woman the other has possessed. The refusal of either to marry their victim sets the various elements of Sicilian society in action to right the wrong. Rosaria's father wants to force a shotgun wedding, but the local *carabinieri* arrest the pair for their own safety. The two are put on trial for rape. Toto's father hires Mafia lawyer Mazzaro, and he and Lawyer D'Angelo each try to pin the blame on the other's client. While the trial is in progress, Toto and Rosaria find themselves falling in love, as do Nicola and Carmelina. The basis for Toto's defense is that he was provoked to commit the crime and that Rosaria did not resist. As Mazzaro says, a moving needle is hard to thread. D'Angelo, on the other hand, portrays Nicola as impotent and therefore incapable of commiting the crime. The two are acquitted; Toto and Rosaria marry with honor; and Nicola's doubts about his masculinity are relieved by his marriage to Carmelina. *Police. Lawyers. Dancers. Rape. Pride. Parenthood. Trials. Impotence. Marriage. Sexual initiation. Virginity. Sicily. Mafia.*

Note: Rome opening: Feb 1963 as *La smania addosso;* running time: 105 min? The precise functions of the three members of the production staff are undetermined. Sources vary in crediting the role played by Rina Franchetti.

THE EYES OF ANNIE JONES (United States/Great Britain)   **F6.1430**
Parroch-McCallum Productions–Associated Producers, Inc. *Dist* Twentieth Century–Fox Film Corp. Feb **1964** [New York opening: 13 May; c31 Dec 1963; LP27125]. Sd; b&w. 35mm. 73 min.
Prod Jack Parsons, Neil McCallum. *Dir* Reginald Le Borg. *Screenplay* Louis Vittes. *Story* Henry Slesar. *Dir Photog* Peter Hennessy. *Camera Op* Moray Grant. *Focus Op* Wally Byatt. *Art Dir* George Provis. *Set Dresser* Andrew Campbell. *Draughtsman* Don Picton. *Scenic Artist* Gilbert Wood. *Film Ed* Robert Winter. *1st Asst Ed* Clive Smith. *Mus Comp* Buxton Orr. *Cond* Philip Martell. *Sd Rec* Buster Ambler. *Boom Op* Peter Dukelow. *Sd Camera* Jimmy

Dooley. *1st, 2d & 3d Asst Dir* Frank Nesbitt, Stephen Victor, Ray Freeborn. *Prod Supv* Tom Lyndon-Haynes. *Cont* Joan Kirk, Lee Turner. *Wardrobe Mistress* Jean Fairlie. *Makeup* Philip Leakey. *Hairdresser* Joyce James. *Prop Buyer* Ronald Baker. *Still Photog* David James. *Grip* Tommy Miller. *Ch Electrn* Frank Robertson.
Cast: Richard Conte (*David Wheeler*), Francesca Annis (*Annie Jones*), Joyce Carey (*Aunt Helen*), Myrtle Reed (*Carol Wheeler*), Shay Gorman (*Lucas*), Victor Brooks (*Police Sergeant Henry*), Jean Lodge (*Geraldine Wheeler*), Alan Haines (*Constable Marlowe*), Mara Purcell (*orphanage matron*), Mark Dignam (*orphanage director*), Patricia McCarron (*Miss Crossley, secretary*), Max Bacon (*pub-keeper Hoskins*), Barbara Leake (*Margaret*).
Mystery melodrama. Geraldine Wheeler, a wealthy young Englishwoman, is preparing to leave her country estate for a vacation when she is murdered by Lucas, a local taxi driver with whom she has had an affair. Learning of Geraldine's disappearance, her Aunt Helen informs David, Geraldine's brother, and he arrives at the estate with his wife, Carol. The police become suspicious of Lucas, who has begun to spend large sums of money, and also question David, Geraldine's heir. Aunt Helen summons Annie Jones, a 17-year-old girl from a nearby orphanage who is believed to possess extrasensory perception. David is openly skeptical about Annie's ability to locate the missing woman, but he nevertheless responds to her obvious infatuation with him. Lucas, fearing Annie's powers to discover the truth, obtains reassurance from David, who, it is revealed, has been embezzling money from the family mills and hired Lucas to kill Geraldine. Sleepwalking, Annie walks toward the spot where Geraldine's body is buried and is stopped by David just as Lucas is about to murder her. The following day, Annie speaks in a trance in the voice of Geraldine, saying, "I go from place to place. I don't know where. They won't let me rest." Her words make no sense to her listeners, and she is returned to the orphanage. As David and Carol leave, Lucas confronts David and demands the balance of his payment for the murder. The police observe the exchange, and Lucas flees in his car and is fatally injured when it crashes. Before he dies, he confesses his guilt and implicates David. The import of Annie's message is revealed when Geraldine's body, dug up earlier by Lucas, is found in the trunk of the wrecked car. *Taxi drivers. Aunts. Police. Orphans. Hired killers. Murder. Spiritualism. Brother-sister relationship. Extrasensory perception. Somnambulism. Wealth. Embezzlement. Inheritance. Automobile accidents.*
Note: Filmed in England.

EYES OF HELL *see* **THE MASK**

EYES, THE SEA AND A BALL (Japan)   **F6.1431**
Takarazuka Motion Picture Co.–Kinoshita Productions. *Dist* Toho Co. Jun **1968** [Los Angeles showing]. Sd; col. 35mm (Tohoscope). 115 min.
Exec Prod Sanezumi Fujimoto, Keisuke Kinoshita, Masakatsu Kaneko. *Dir-Writ* Keisuke Kinoshita. *Photog* Hiroyuki Kusuda. *Mus* Chuji Kinoshita.
Cast: Yosuke Natsuki, Mayumi Ozora, Kumeko Urabe, Kamatari Fujiwara, Yoichiro Takahashi.
Drama. Toru Ieda is asked for a loan by an army friend who is burdened with debt, and after Ieda refuses, the friend commits suicide. Suffering from guilt, Ieda takes a teaching position on a remote island, where he can care for his friend's son, Kenichi. Ieda's students are the offspring of the coarse, brawling fisherman of the island, and the children care little for their studies or even sports, reflecting the contempt their ignorant parents hold for education. Ieda introduces volleyball to the children and, after an initial reluctance, the students show a great interest in and talent for the sport. Over the objections of the parents, Ieda enters the school in the island tournament. Despite their ragtag appearance and the fact that the team is comprised of both boys and girls, the Odeshima children win not only the inter-island tournament but the national tournament as well. Ieda, who had promised his fiancée he would marry her and move from the island after the team won its first game, does marry her but decides to stay on Odeshima, whose residents have gained a new sense of pride in themselves. *Schoolteachers. Fishermen. Children. Education. Suicide. Guilt. Pride. Volleyball. Fishing villages. Debt. Islands.*
Note: Released in Japan in 1967 as *Natsukashiki fue ya taiko.*

EZO YAKATA NO KETTO *see* **DUEL AT EZO**

THE F—— FIVE *see* **THE FILTHY FIVE**

"F" STREET *see* **THE GIRLS ON F—— STREET**

LA FABULEUSE AVENTURE DE MARCO POLO *see* **MARCO THE MAGNIFICENT**

THE FABULOUS BASTARD FROM CHICAGO   **F6.1432**
Walnut International Productions. *Dist* Grads Corp. caJul **1969.** Sd; col (Eastman Color; print by Berkey Pathé). 35mm. 97 min. *MPAA rating X.*

Prod Jay Fineberg. *Exec Prod* Vincent Miranda. *Assoc Prod* Jerome Knell. *Dir* Greg Corarito. *Writ* Richard Compton. *Photog* Gary Graver. *Titl* Earl Marshall. *Film Ed* Gary Graver, Ed Hunt. *Mus* Gregor Saint-Sanez. *Sd* Robert Dietz.

Cast: John Alderman *(Steve)*, Maria Lease *(Nancy)*, James Meyers *(Fats)*, Victoria Carbe *(Maria)*, Daryl Colinot *(Danny)*, Whitey Wozniak *(Mr. Thad)*, Phillip Brady *(Wes)*, Phil Marks *(Wally)*, Duke Wilmoth *(Tom)*, Bambi Allen *(Spinster O'Mally)*, Cluny Dodge *(Pearl)*, Mike Stringer *(Skinner)*, Alfred Mizracai *(Freddy, the waiter)*, Sonny Dad *(Joe, the bartender)*, Charlie Nicholson, Sian Barr, Art Shwart *(card players)*, Maria Bonner, Dorothy Barrante, Lilian Diana, Caroline Cody, Geretta Taylor, Katherine Howard, Pam Colinot *(temperance workers)*, Gary Kent, Jimmie Johnson, Pony Tobias *(unidentified roles)*, Reed Hadley *(narrator)*.

Melodrama. The year is 1927. Steve Desmond's East Side Chicago garage fronts the biggest bootleg operation in the area. Steve's rival, Fats Purcelli, attempting to muscle in on the territory, kidnaps Wally, Steve's best friend and delivery man, while Steve is enjoying himself in Maria's speakeasy. Fats then arranges for Steve's murder, sends his thugs to shoot up the garage, and sends his girl friend to seduce Steve. Steve learns from the woman that Fats has a daughter, Nancy, attending school in Miami, and he formulates a plan to kidnap the girl as the means by which to get Wally back and force Fats out of his territory. Steve flies to Miami in his private plane, meets Nancy, seduces her, and persuades her to join him on his farm in Gary, Indiana. A farmhand attacks her as she is exploring the grounds. She screams for Steve's help; he rescues her, and they fall in love. Fats arrives with his gang to reclaim his daughter. After a gun battle, Steve and Nancy fall into each other's arms, mortally wounded. *Gangsters. Bootleggers. Students. Farmhands. Murder. Seduction. Kidnaping. Business competition. Rape. Speakeasies. Chicago. Miami. Gary (Indiana). Roaring Twenties.*

Note: Also known as *The Fabulous Kid From Chicago, The Chicago Kid,* and *The Bastard Wench From Chicago.*

FABULOUS SPAIN   **F6.1433**
VPR Ltd. **1963** [Scranton, Pennsylvania, showing: 9 Nov 1964]. Sd eff & mus score; col (Technicolor). 35mm. 100-115 min.
Pres by Burton Holmes Theatre Productions. *Prod-Dir-Writ* André De La Varre, Jr. *Photog* Kurt Jetmar, Peter Baudendistel, André De La Varre, Jr. *Film Ed* André De La Varre, Jr., Pablo Zavala. *Mus Ed* André De La Varre, Jr., Music Sound Track Service.

Travelog. A travel host describes the delights of Andalusia, Seville, the Rock of Gibraltar, Tarifa, Córdoba, the Sierra Nevadas, Granada, Málaga, Costa del Sol, Almería, Barcelona, Costa Brava, the Pyrenees, San Sebastian, a bullfight in Estella, Madrid, the Escorial, Valle de los Caidos, Burgos, Avila, Toledo, the home of El Greco, Salamanca, and flamenco dancers. *Tourists. Dancers. Travel. Bullfighting. Spain. Seville. Gibraltar. Málaga (Spain). Almería. Barcelona. Pyrenees. Madrid. Toledo (Spain). El Greco.*

Note: Narration delivered live on stage.

THE FABULOUS WORLD OF JULES VERNE (Czechoslovakia)
                             F6.1434
Gottwaldov Film Studio. *For* Československý Film. *Dist* Warner Bros. Pictures. 7 Jun **1961** [Denver, Colorado, opening; c17 Jun 1960; LP25365]. Sd; b&w. 35mm. 83 min.
Pres by Joseph E. Levine. *Dir* Karel Zeman. *Screenplay* Karel Zeman, Francis Gross. *Dial* Milan Vacca. *Adapt* Jiří Brdečka. *Artist* Syd Ostrov, Joseph Zeman. *Anim* Ernest Marchand, Henry Liss, Francis Kramm. *Photog* George Taran. *Sp Eff Photog* George Taran, B. S. Piccard, Antony Hora. *Art Dir* Karel Zeman, Zep Kopal. *Film Ed* Zdenik Stehlik. *Mus* Sydney Fox. *Mus Dir* Frank Belfin. *Sd* František Strangmüller, Hanuš Silvera. *Prod Ch* Zdeněk Novák.

Cast: Louis Tock *(Simon Hart)*, Ernest Navara *(Professor Roche)*, Milo Holl *(Artigas)*, Jane Zalata *(Jana)*, Van Kissling *(Serke)*, Francis Sherr *(pirate captain)*, Hugh Downs *(prolog narrator)*.

Science fiction drama. Inspired by: Jules Verne, *Face au drapeau* (Paris, 1896). In the 19th century, Professor Roche, a scientist working on a powerful explosive, and his young assistant Simon Hart are kidnaped by pirates and taken to a volcanic island in a remote part of the Atlantic. The unsuspecting professor believes that he was captured to prevent his invention from falling into evil hands and that he is now free to work in a laboratory inside the volcano. Though Hart learns that the pirate chief, Artigas, plans to use the explosive to conquer the world, he is unable to warn the professor, who is imprisoned in an isolated hut. Aided by Jana, another captive, Hart succeeds in launching a balloon with a message to the outside world. Eventually he escapes, is picked up by a French submarine, and returns to the island in a final attempt to warn the professor. Roche has discovered the duplicity himself, however, and sets off the explosive, destroying himself, the island, and the pirates; Hart and Jana escape in a giant balloon. *Scientists. Pirates. Abduction. Duplicity. Islands. Volcanoes.*

Laboratories. Balloons (ascent). Submarines. Explosions.

Note: Released in Czechoslovakia in Jun 1958 as *Vynález zkázy*. The following are among those credited under anglicized names: Lubor Tokoš (Louis Tock), Arnošt Navrátil (Ernest Navara), Miloslav Holub (Milo Holl), Jana Zatloukalová (Jane Zalata), Václav Kyzlink (Van Kissling), František Šlégr (Francis Sherr), František Hrubín (Francis Gross), Zdeněk Liška (Sydney Fox), František Belfin (Frank Belfin), Jiří Tarantík (George Taran), Bohuslav Pikhart (B. S. Piccard), Antonín Horák (Antony Hora), Zdeněk Rozkopal (Zep Kopal), Zdeněk Stehlík (Zdenik Stehlik), Milan Vácha (Milan Vacca). The film combines live action and animation.

FACE   **F6.1435**
Dist Film-Makers' Cooperative. 8 Feb **1966** [New York opening]. Sd; b&w. 16mm. 70 min.
Prod-Dir Andy Warhol. *Prod Asst* Gerard Malanga.
Cast: Edie Sedgwick.
Film portrait. A closeup of a young woman's face.

A FACE IN THE RAIN   **F6.1436**
Embassy Pictures–Filmways, Inc.–Calvic. *Dist* Embassy Pictures. Mar **1963**. Sd; b&w. 35mm. 81 min.
Pres by Joseph E. Levine. *Prod* John Calley. *Exec Prod* Rory Calhoun, Victor Orsatti. *Dir* Irvin Kershner. *Writ for the Screen* Hugo Butler, Jean Rouverol. *Based on a Screenplay by* Guy Elmes. *Photog* Haskell Wexler. *Art Dir* Sergio Canevari. *Film Ed* Melvin Sloan. *Mus* Richard Markowitz. *Sd* Verna Fields.

Cast: Rory Calhoun *(Rand)*, Marina Berti *(Anna)*, Niall MacGinnis *(Klaus)*, Massimo Giuliani *(Paolo)*, Danny Ryais, Peter Zander.

War melodrama. Rand begins to write a letter to Anna, the Italian woman who saved his life during World War II. As he writes, Rand remembers the events of the past. *An American spy working with the underground in Nazi-occupied Pisa, he seeks refuge at the home of a contact when the Nazis discover his operation. The contact is not home, however, and Anna, the man's wife, resents Rand's presence, but her son Paolo hides him in the attic. In exchange for her husband's protection, Anna has been having an affair with Klaus, the Nazi officer who is in charge of the search for Rand. Klaus arrives to make Anna's home his headquarters for the night, and Rand is unable to escape. Because he has not captured the American and is involved with the wife of a suspected spy, Klaus is relieved of authority. Although Anna has come to love Klaus, she is unable to betray Rand, and she sends Paolo to inform the underground of the American's plight. Rand manages to escape, but the Nazis pursue Anna; she is killed by Klaus, who wishes to redeem himself with the Gestapo.* Rand, who returned safely to the United States, is unaware that he is writing to a dead woman. *Spies. Nazis. Italians. Memory. Espionage. Resistance (political). Infidelity. Murder. World War II. Pisa. United States Army—Intelligence. Gestapo. Documentation.*

Note: Filmed on location in Italy.

THE FACE OF ANOTHER (Japan)   **F6.1437**
Teshigahara Productions–Tokyo Eiga Co. *Dist* Toho International, Inc. 9 Jun **1967** [Los Angeles opening]. Sd; b&w. 35mm. 124 min.
Exec Prod Nobuyo Horiba, Kiichi Ichikawa, Tadashi Ohono. *Dir* Hiroshi Teshigahara. *Story & Screenplay* Kobo Abe. *Photog* Hiroshi Segawa. *Mus* Toru Takemitsu.

Cast: Tatsuya Nakadai *(Okuyama)*, Machiko Kyo *(his wife)*, Kyoko Kishida *(his nurse)*, Mikijiro Hira *(his doctor)*, Eiji Okada, Miki Irie, Minoru Chiaki, Etsuko Ichihara, Hideka Muranatsu, Yoshie Minami, Shinobu Itomi, Hisashi Igawa.

Drama. Okuyama, an industrialist, seriously burns his face in an explosion while inspecting his new factory; and although he is still able to see and talk, his scarred face causes him anxiety. A plastic surgeon creates a lifelike mask for him, and when Okuyama's wife passionately seduces him in his new "identity," he accuses her of adultery. She claims that she knew it was he, and she leaves him. Okuyama is arrested for attempted rape, and he kills the surgeon who he believes is responsible for his misery. *Industrialists. Surgeons. Plastic surgery. Disfiguration. Marriage. Infidelity. Jealousy. Rape. Murder. Masks. Explosions.*

Note: Released in Japan in Jul 1966 as *Tanin no kao.*

THE FACE OF EVE *see* **EVE**

FACE OF EVIL *see* **DOCTOR BLOOD'S COFFIN**

THE FACE OF FU MANCHU (Great Britain)   **F6.1438**
Hallam Productions. *Dist* Seven Arts Pictures. 13 Oct **1965** [San Francisco opening]. Sd; col (Technicolor). 35mm (Techniscope). 96 min.
Prod Oliver A. Unger, Harry Alan Towers. *Exec Prod* Oliver A. Unger. *Dir* Don Sharp. *Screenplay* Peter Welbeck. *Dir Photog* Ernest Steward. *2d Unit Camera* H. A. R. Thomson. *Camera Op* James Bawden. *Art Dir* Frank White.

Film Ed John Trumper. *Mus Comp & Cond* Christopher Whelen. *Sd Rec* Fred Hughesdon, Ken Cameron. *Asst Dir* Barrie Melrose. *Prod Supv* John Comfort. *Cont* Phyllis Townshend. *Wardrobe Supv* Dorothy Edwards. *Makeup* Gerry Fletcher. *Hairstyles* Ann Box.

Cast: Christopher Lee *(Fu Manchu)*, Nigel Green *(Nayland Smith)*, James Robertson-Justice *(Sir Charles Fortescue)*, Howard Marion-Crawford *(Dr. Petrie)*, Tsai Chin *(Lin Tang)*, Joachim Fuchsberger *(Carl Jansen)*, Karin Dor *(Maria Muller)*, Walter Rilla *(Professor Muller)*, Harry Brogan *(Professor Gaskell)*, Poulet Tu *(Lotus)*, Edwin Richfield *(Mandarin)*, Peter Mossbacher *(Hanumon)*, Archie O'Sullivan, Eric Young, Deborah Du' Lacey.

Adventure melodrama. Based on characters created by: Sax Rohmer. In London the archvillain Fu Manchu and his evil daughter, Lin Tang, kidnap Professor Muller, a German biochemist who has distilled a new, highly lethal gas from the seeds of a Tibetan poppy. In a radio broadcast, Fu Manchu announces that he intends to use the poison gas to gain world domination. The professor's daughter, Maria, informs Scotland Yard's Nayland Smith of her father's abduction, thus confirming Smith's suspicion that Fu Manchu masterminded the kidnaping, although Smith witnessed Fu Manchu's execution in China several years before. Fu Manchu kidnaps Maria to force Muller to produce more gas, whereupon Muller insists that to do so he needs some papers located in the British Museum in the possession of Professor Gaskell. Carl Jansen, Professor Muller's assistant who has also been kidnaped, escapes from his captors and warns Nayland Smith that Fu Manchu's men intend to break into the British Museum; but the papers are not found, and Fu Manchu, informed by Lin Tang that Gaskell may have the papers in his home, hypnotizes Gaskell, abducts him, and forces him to work with Muller. To show the effect of the poison gas, Fu Manchu destroys the entire village of Fleetwick with only a small quantity, but Nayland Smith stops Fu Manchu before he wreaks more destruction; he floods Fu Manchu's hideout (a tunnel under the Thames) and rescues Maria, only to learn that Fu Manchu has escaped and taken Muller hostage. Guessing that the archvillain is bound for Tibet to collect more poppyseeds, Nayland Smith lays a trap for Fu Manchu. Muller is rescued, and Fu Manchu, Lin Tang, and the rest of the gang presumably perish in an explosion. *Masterminds. Detectives. Biochemists. Germans. Capital punishment. Kidnaping. Megalomania. Murder. Hypnotism. Rescue. Lethal gas. London. Thames River. Tibet. British Museum. Scotland Yard. Chases. Documentation. Explosions. Fu Manchu.*

Note: Filmed entirely on location in and around Dublin. Released in Great Britain Oct 1965; running time: 94 min. Peter Welbeck is a pseudonym of Harry Alan Towers. *The Brides of Fu Manchu*, q. v., is a sequel to this film.

THE FACE OF SIN *see* **THE GIRL WITH HUNGRY EYES**

FACE OF TERROR (Spain)   **F6.1439**
Documento Film. *Dist* Cinema-Video International, Inc., Futuramic Releasing Organization. 3 Sep **1964** [Maryland license]. Sd; b&w. 35mm. 81 min.

Prod Gustavo Quintana. *Prod U. S. Vers* Jack Leroy Miles. *Dir* Isidoro Martínez Ferry. *Dir U. S. Vers* William J. Hole, Jr. *Screenplay U. S. Vers* Monroe Manning. *Photog* José Fernández Aguayo. *Art Dir* Sigfrido Burman. *Film Ed* José Antonio Rojo. *Mus (see note)* José Buenagu, Miguel Asins-Arbó.

Cast: Lisa Gaye *(Norma)*, Fernando Rey *(Dr. Charles Taylor)*, Virgilio Teixeira *(playboy)*, Conchita Cuetos *(Alma)*, Gerard Tichy *(sanatarium head)*, Carlos Casaravilla, Emilio Rodríguez, Angel Menéndez, Paul Pisget.

Horror film. Norma, a mental patient with a horribly disfigured face, escapes from a sanatarium and persuades Dr. Taylor, who has perfected a new system of plastic surgery, to experiment on her. After restoring her beauty, he realizes that she is a fugitive, but Norma knocks him unconscious and steals a bottle of preserving lotion, which must be applied regularly to maintain her new face. Eventually she finds work as a hotel waitress, but the manager finds out who she is and threatens to expose her. In the ensuing struggle Norma murders him, and the lotion bottle is smashed. Panic-stricken, Norma marries an admiring playboy, and they leave for a honeymoon in Paris. On the way, however, Norma's plastic face disintegrates, and the terrified husband jumps from the car. Quickly returning to Dr. Taylor's laboratory to replenish her supply of the special formula, she attacks the doctor's assistant and falls on some broken glass. The police arrive and find Norma dead on the floor; as the preservative flows from a broken vial onto her face, her beauty is restored. *Psychopaths. Physicians. Fugitives. Waitresses. Hotelkeepers. Playboys. Disfiguration. Plastic surgery. Murder. Experiments. Honeymoons.*

Note: Opened in Madrid in Oct 1962 as *La cara del terror*; running time: 83 min. Sources conflict in crediting music composer.

FACE OF THE SCREAMING WEREWOLF (Mexico)   **F6.1440**
Diana Films. *Dist* Associated Distributors Pictures. Apr **1965**. Sd; b&w. 35mm. 60 min.

Prod-Dir English Vers Jerry Warren. *Dir Spanish Vers* Gilbert Solar. *Screenplay* Gilbert Solar, Fernando de Fuentes. *Adapt* Gilbert Solar, Juan García. *Photog* Raúl Martínez Solares. *Art Dir* Jorge Fernández. *Film Ed* Carlos Savage. *Mus* Luis Hernández Bretón. *Sd* José de Pérez.

Cast: Lon Chaney, [Jr.] *(mummy/werewolf)*, Landa Varle, Raymond Gaylord, D. W. Barron, Germán "Tin Tan" Valdés, Yerye Beirute, Agustín Fernández, Consuelo Guerrero de Luna, Oscar Ortiz de Pinedo.

Horror film. A mad scientist experiments in revivification, operating on a mummy that has been in a state of suspended animation. An electrical storm provides the necessary voltage to complete the work of the scientist, and his subject is brought to life as a werewolf. The creature wreaks havoc upon a village and attacks some women before dying in a fire. *Scientists. Mummies. Werewolves. Reviviscence. Suspended animation. Experiments. Electricity. Storms. Fires.*

Note: Produced in Mexico in 1959 as *La casa del terror*; running time: 78 min. Originally released in the United States in a Spanish language version in 1960. The following are credited under anglicized names: Gilberto Martínez Solares (Gilbert Solar), Yolanda Varela (Landa Varle), and Alfredo Barrón (D. W. Barron).

THE FACE OF WAR (Japan/Sweden)   **F6.1441**
Nippon Eiga Shinsha–Minerva International Films. *Dist* Janus Films. 31 Oct **1963** [New York opening]. Sd; b&w. 35mm. 105 min.

Prod-Dir Tore Sjöberg. *Screenplay* Erik Holm, Cordella Lewis, C. D. B. Bryan, C. D. Brandt. *Film Ed* Ingemar Ejve. *Mus* Georg Riedel.

Narrator: Bryant Halliday.

Documentary. A compilation of film clips, newsreels, and still photographs describing the horrors of war and the development of weapons since World War I, culminating in the use of the atomic bomb. The film begins with the assassination of Franz Ferdinand in 1914, the event which led to World War I. Next comes a brief history of the major conflicts and war-related events from World War I to the Korean War, including the Russian Revolution (1917–21), the Sino-Japanese Conflict, the Italian invasion of Ethiopia in 1935, the Spanish Civil War, World War II (fighting in the Soviet Union, France, and Holland; the bombing of England by the Germans; and finally the dropping of atomic bombs by the United States on Hiroshima and Nagasaki), and the Korean War. The film concludes with pictures of victims of atomic radiation. *Nuclear warfare. Assassination. Radiation. Atom bomb. World War I. Russia— History—1917–21 Revolution. Sino-Japanese Conflict 1937–45. Spain— History—Civil War 1936–39. World War II. Korean War 1950–53. Ethiopia. Union of Soviet Socialist Republics. France. Netherlands. Hiroshima. Nagasaki. Franz Ferdinand. Italy—Army. Germany—Army.*

Note: Released in Sweden in 1963 as *Krigets vanvett*; also known as *Krigets ansikte*.

A FACE OF WAR   **F6.1442**
E. S. J. Productions. *For* Landau/Unger Co. *Dist* Commonwealth United Entertainment, Inc. Mar **1968** [c28 Dec 1967; LP35450]. Sd; b&w, print by Movielab. 35mm. 72 min. [Copyright length: 76 min.]

Prod-Dir Eugene S. Jones. *Photog* J. Baxter Peters, Christopher Sargent, Eugene S. Jones. *Film Ed* Jono Roberts. *Sd* Robert Peck. *Prod Mgr* Natalie R. Jones.

Documentary. Producer-director Jones and a crew of three men spent 97 days in 1966 with Mike Company, 3rd Battalion, 7th Marine Regiment. In that period more than half the company's 135 men were killed or wounded; Jones himself was wounded twice, and his first cameraman once. The film's intent is to reflect the truths of war as experienced by the foot soldier. Among the incidents depicted are a twilight ambush by the Viet Cong and a dawn raid by the Marines, the death of a village child and the birth of another, helicopter assaults and lonely patrols, the routine of life on a beleaguered hilltop outpost, and the horror of death from mines, booby traps, and enemy gunfire. *Vietcong. Combat zone life. Helicopters. Mines (war explosives). Vietnam War 1964–73. United States Marines—7th Regiment.*

Note: Filmed in Vietnam.

THE FACELESS MAN *see* **THE COUNTERFEIT KILLER**

THE FACELESS MEN *see* **INCIDENT AT PHANTOM HILL**

FACES   **F6.1443**
Maurice McEndree Productions. *Dist* Continental Distributing, Inc. 24 Nov **1968** [New York opening]. Sd; b&w (print by Movielab). 35mm. 129 min.

Prod Maurice McEndree. *Assoc Prod* Al Ruban. *Dir-Writ* John Cassavetes. *Photog* Al Ruban. *Art Dir* Phedon Papamichael. *Film Ed* Maurice McEndree, Al Ruban. *Mus Comp & Cond* Jack Ackerman. *Song:* "Never Felt Like This Before" Charles Smalls. *Sd* Don Pike. *Asst Dir* George O'Halloran. *Prod Mgr* James Joyce.

Cast: John Marley *(Richard Forst)*, Gena Rowlands *(Jeannie Rapp)*, Lynn Carlin *(Maria Forst)*, Seymour Cassel *(Chet)*, Fred Draper *(Freddie)*, Val Avery *(Jim McCarthy)*, Dorothy Gulliver *(Florence)*, Joanne Moore Jordan *(Louise)*, Darlene Conley *(Billy Mae)*, Gene Darfler *(Joe Jackson)*, Elizabeth Deering *(Stella)*, Dave Mazzie, Julie Gambol, James Bridges.

Drama. After 14 years, the childless marriage of Maria and Richard Forst has started to disintegrate. Frustrated by the approach of middle age, unable to communicate on anything more than a superficial level, and no longer comforted by their material possessions, they have begun to look elsewhere for emotional reassurance. One evening, after Maria has rejected Richard's physical advances, Richard abruptly announces that he wants a divorce and, in the presence of his wife, phones a prostitute, Jeannie Rapp, for a date. Jeannie consents, though by this time she and her friend are entertaining two out-of-town clients. Richard arrives at Jeannie's apartment, and following an ugly scene with one of the clients she gets rid of her guests and permits Richard to spend the night. Maria, meanwhile, has gone to a discotheque with three other discontented wives. Encouraged by the attentions of the fun-loving Chet, the women invite him back to Maria's home. During the party that ensues, Maria watches with mixed emotions as her friends compete for the young man's attentions, but once she is alone with Chet, she responds to his playful lovemaking. When Chet awakens the next morning, he finds Maria unconscious from an overdose of sleeping tablets. He helps her recover, then hears Richard returning home—following a pleasant breakfast with Jeannie—and impulsively leaps out of the bedroom window, hops off the first-story roof, and races across the lawn. Richard observes the escape, and now face to face with Maria, he expresses his hurt by hurling insults at her; she retaliates by flatly stating that she no longer loves him. Finally, emotionally exhausted, they sit in numbed silence on the hallway stairs. With nothing left to say to each other, they separate and walk into different parts of the house. *Businessmen. Prostitutes. Housewives. Marriage. Infidelity. Seduction. Childlessness. Middle age. Discotheques.*

Note: Filmed on location in Los Angeles in 1966. Prerelease title: *The Dynosaurs.*

FACES IN THE DARK (Great Britain)   **F6.1444**
Penington-Eady Productions. *For* Sydney Box Associates. *Dist* Schoenfeld Film Distributing Corp. 2 Sep **1964** [Fort Lee, New Jersey, opening]. Sd; b&w. 35mm. 85 min.

Prod Jon Penington. *Dir* David Eady. *Screenplay* Ephraim Kogan, John Tully. *Photog* Ken Hodges. *Camera Op* Desmond Davis. *Focus* Ken Goodman. *Art Dir* Tony Masters. *Asst Art Dir* Geoffrey Tozer. *Set Dresser* Maurice Fowler. *Draughtsman* Martin Atkinson. *Film Ed* Oswald Hafenrichter. *1st Asst Ed* Alan Corder. *Electronic Mus* Edwin Astley. *Played by* Janine de Waleyne. *Sd Rec* Red Law, Bert Ross. *Dub Ed* James Shields. *Boom Op* John Salter. *Sd Camera Op* Doug Barnett. *1st, 2d & 3d Asst Dir* Colin Brewer, Patrick Clayton, Ronald Purdie. *Prod Mgr* Patrick Marsden. *Prod Sec* Joyce Herlihy. *Cont* Yvonne Richards. *Cost Supv* Beatrice Dawson. *Wardrobe Mistress* Muriel Dickson. *Makeup* Ernest Gasser. *Hairdresser* Ann Box. *Still Photog* Ted Reed.

Cast: John Gregson *(Richard Hammond)*, Mai Zetterling *(Christiane Hammond)*, Michael Denison *(David Merton)*, John Ireland *(Max Hammond)*, Tony Wright *(Clem)*, Nanette Newman *(Janet)*, Roland Bartrop *(French doctor)*, Valerie Taylor *(Miss Hopkins)*, Colette Bartrop *(1st nun nurse)*, John Serret *(French surgeon)*, Joyce Marlow.

Crime melodrama. Source: Pierre Boileau and Thomas Narcejac, *Les visages de l'ombre* (Paris, 1953). Richard Hammond, an unscrupulous manufacturer, is blinded in a factory accident while testing a new light bulb. Although anxious to resume work, he is persuaded to vacation at his cottage in Cornwall, to which he is accompanied by Christiane, his wife; David Merton, his business associate; and Max, his playboy brother. When he discerns his name on a tombstone marking a new grave, Richard questions his sanity. Realizing that Christiane is David's mistress and that both are conspiring to kill him, Richard escapes to a hospital and learns he is actually in France. Returning home with Christiane and David the following day, Richard attempts to take his life by forcing their automobile into a river. David dies instantly. Richard swims ashore and hears his trapped wife's cries for help as she drowns. *Manufacturers. Brothers. Playboys. Mistresses. Blindness. Insanity. Infidelity. Murder. Vacations. Hospitals. Cornwall (England). France. Automobile accidents.*

Note: Released in Great Britain in 1960.

LE FACTEUR S'EN VA-T-EN GUERRE *see* **THE POSTMAN GOES TO WAR**

THE FACTS OF MURDER (Italy)   **F6.1445**
Riama Cinematografica. *Dist* Seven Arts Pictures. 30 Jun **1965** [New York opening]. Sd; b&w. 35mm. 110 min.

Prod Giuseppe Amato. *Dir* Pietro Germi. *Screenplay* Alfredo Giannetti, Pietro Germi, Ennio De Concini. *Photog* Leonida Barboni. *Art Dir* Carlo Egidi. *Film Ed* Roberto Cinquini. *Mus* Carlo Rustichelli. *Sd* Fiorenzo Magli. *Prod Mgr* Mario Silvestri.

Cast: Pietro Germi *(Insp. Ciccio Ingravallo)*, Claudia Cardinale *(Assuntina)*, Eleonora Rossi Drago *(Liliana Banducci)*, Claudio Gora *(Remo Banducci)*, Franco Fabrizi *(Valdarena)*, Nino Castelnuovo *(Diomede)*, Cristina Gajoni *(Virginia)*, Saro Urzì *(Detective Saro)*, Ildebrando Santafè *(Anzaloni)*, Gianni Glori Musy *(Retalli)*, Toni Ucci *(thief)*, Peppino De Martino *(Dr. Fumi)*, Rosolino Bua *(priest)*, Silla Bettini *(Oreste)*, Vincenzo Tocci *(Filone)*, Antonio Acqua *(The General)*, Renato Terra *(Marchetti)*, Nanda De Santis, Loretta Capitoli, Attilio Martella, Rina Mascetti, Pietro Tordi, Leandro Marini, Vittorio Scarabello, Antonio Gradoli, Maria Saccenti, April Hennessy, Vinicio Ricchi, Elsa Canevazzi, Claudia Fabiani.

Crime melodrama. Source: Carlo Emilio Gadda, *Quer pasticciaccio brutto de via Merulana* (Milan, 1957). While investigating the robbery of a wealthy homosexual, Inspector Ingravallo questions the electrician Diomede. Despite the fact that the laborer is able to establish an alibi, Ingravallo remains suspicious and counsels Diomede's fiancée, the maid Assuntina, to break the engagement. When Assuntina's employer, the wealthy socialite Liliana Banducci, is murdered, Ingravallo's suspicions are confirmed. Although he confronts other suspects, including Remo, the victim's fascist husband; Remo's mistress, Virginia; and the bogus physician Valdarena, the victim's cousin, Virginia's lover, and an infamous pimp, the detective is able to prove Diomede's guilt. *Police. Detectives. Electricians. Housemaids. Cousins. Quacks. Pimps. Fascists. Mistresses. Robbery. Murder. Infidelity. Male homosexuality.*

Note: Opened in Rome in Dec 1959 as *Un maledetto imbroglio*; running time: 115 min.

FAHRENHEIT 451 (Great Britain)   **F6.1446**
Vineyard Productions–Anglo-Enterprise Film Productions. *Dist* Universal Pictures. 14 Nov **1966** [New York opening: c4 Feb 1967: LP35389]. Sd; col (Technicolor). 35mm. 111 min.

Prod Lewis Allen. *Assoc Prod* Mickey Delamar. *Dir* François Truffaut. *Screenplay* François Truffaut, Jean-Louis Richard. *Adtl Dial* David Rudkin, Helen Scott. *Dir Photog* Nicolas Roeg. *Camera Op* Alex Thomson. *Art Dir* Syd Cain. *Prod Dsgn* Tony Walton. *Film Ed* Thom Noble. *Mus* Bernard Herrmann. *Sd* Norman Wanstall. *Sd Rec* Robert MacPhee, Gordon McCallum. *Asst Dir* Bryan Coates. *Prod Mgr* Ian Lewis. *Cost Dsgn* Tony Walton. *Assoc Cost Dsgn* Yvonne Blake. *Makeup* Basil Newall. *Sp Eff* Charles Staffell, Bowie Films.

Cast: Oskar Werner *(Montag)*, Julie Christie *(Linda/Clarisse)*, Cyril Cusack *(The Captain)*, Anton Diffring *(Fabian)*, Jeremy Spenser *(man with the apple)*, Bee Duffell *(The Book-Woman)*, Gillian Lewis *(TV announcer)*, Ann Bell *(Doris)*, Caroline Hunt *(Helen)*, Anna Palk *(Jackie)*, Roma Milne *(neighbor)*, Arthur Cox, actor, Eric Mason *(male nurses)*, Noel Davis, Donald Pickering *(TV announcers)*, Michael Mundell *(Stoneman)*, Chris Williams *(Black)*, Gillian Aldham *(judoka woman)*, Edward Kaye *(judoka man)*, Mark Lester, Kevin Elder *(small boys)*, Joan Francis *(bar telephonist)*, Tom Watson *(sergeant instructor)*.

Cast—"Book People": Alex Scott *("The Life of Henri Brulard")*, Denis Gilmore *("Martian Chronicles")*, Fred Cox *("Pride")*, Frank Cox *("Prejudice")*, Michael Balfour *(Machiavelli's "Prince")*, David Glover *("The Pickwick Papers")*, Judith Drynan *(Plato's "Dialogues")*, Yvonne Blake *("The Jewish Question")*, John Rae *("The Weir of Hermiston")*, Earl Younger *(nephew of "The Weir of Hermiston")*.

Science fiction drama. Source: Ray Bradbury, *Fahrenheit 451* (New York, 1953). In a future society all reading matter is forbidden, and the fire department must seek out citizens who disobey this edict and burn their books. Widescreen televisions in the homes and loudspeakers all over the city control the populace through propaganda. Two such citizens are Montag, a fireman whose efficiency has won him a recommendation for promotion, and his contented wife, Linda, who watches the propaganda screen all day. One day, while riding the monorail, Montag meets Clarisse, a young schoolteacher who bears a striking resemblance to his wife. Clarisse questions the reasons for book-burning and, for the first time, raises doubts in Montag's mind. Upon arriving home, Montag finds his wife unconscious from taking an overdose of sleeping pills, and after she receives a complete blood transfusion, Montag begins to change. After seeing a woman choose to die with her books, Montag starts bringing books home and secretly reading them at night. His disillusionment with society increases when Clarisse is dismissed from her job. One evening he reads from *David Copperfield* to some of Linda's guests, and their disgust makes him realize that he must leave his job. Before he has a chance to resign, however, Linda denounces him, and his last mission with the fire department turns out to be in his own home. Montag aims the flame torch at his colleagues and escapes from the city to the hideout of the "Book People," a group of outcasts who preserve books by committing them to memory. Clarisse, having fled from the firemen a few days before, is also there. Now determined that literature will not die, Montag begins memorizing the tales of Edgar Allan Poe. *Firemen. Schoolteachers. Fugitives. Propaganda. Totalitarianism. Literature. Marriage. Drug overdose. Suicide. Memory. Television. Fire departments. Edgar Allan Poe. Fires. The Future. "David Copperfield."*

Note: Location scenes filmed near London and in Châteauneuf-sur-Loire. Released in Great Britain in Nov 1966.

FAIL SAFE   **F6.1447**
Columbia Pictures. 7 Oct **1964** [New York opening; c31 Dec 1963; LP29279]. Sd; b&w. 35mm. 111 min.

A Max E. Youngstein–Sidney Lumet Production. *Prod* Max E. Youngstein. *Assoc Prod* Charles H. Maguire. *Dir* Sidney Lumet. *Screenplay* Walter Bernstein. *Dir Photog* Gerald Hirschfeld. *Camera Op* Al Taffet. *Art Dir* Albert Brenner. *Set Decor* J. C. Delaney. *Main Titl* F. Hillsberg Inc. *Film Ed* Ralph Rosenblum. *Sd Mix* William Swift. *Sd Ed* Jack Fitzstephens. *Asst Dir* Harry Falk, Jr. *Cont* Marguerite James. *Cost* Anna Hill Johnstone. *Makeup* Harry Buchman. *Sp & Anim Eff* Storyboard Inc. *Ch Electrn* Howard Fortune. *Ch Grip* Edward Knott.

Cast: Henry Fonda *(The President)*, Dan O'Herlihy *(General Black)*, Walter Matthau *(Groeteschele)*, Frank Overton *(General Bogan)*, Edward Binns *(Colonel Grady)*, Fritz Weaver *(Colonel Cascio)*, Larry Hagman *(Buck)*, William Hansen *(Secretary Swenson)*, Russell Hardie *(General Stark)*, Russell Collins *(Knapp)*, Sorrell Booke *(Congressman Raskob)*, Nancy Berg *(Ilsa Wolfe)*, John Connell *(Thomas)*, Frank Simpson *(Sullivan)*, Hildy Parks *(Betty Black)*, Janet Ward *(Mrs. Grady)*, Dom DeLuise *(Sergeant Collins)*, Dana Elcar *(Foster)*, Stuart Germain *(Mr. Cascio)*, Louise Larabee *(Mrs. Cascio)*, Frieda Altman *(Jennie)*.

Drama. Source: Eugene Burdick and Harvey Wheeler, *Fail-Safe* (New York, 1962). An emergency arises and bombers from Strategic Air Command head for the fail-safe point, but they are called back when the situation is clarified. Due to a fault in the electronic system, however, one wing of bombers passes the fail-safe point and heads for Moscow. The President and the Pentagon War Room are informed, and the President listens to the Pentagon discuss the emergency. Groeteschele, a civilian adviser, recommends that the full power of the United States be unleashed against the Soviet Union, but General Black insists that all steps must be taken to avoid world holocaust. The President, in accordance with Black's recommendation, orders the planes shot down and uses the hot line to inform the Russian leader, who is aware of the approaching bombers, that the attack is a mistake. In an effort to help destroy the deadly planes, the President orders General Bogan to release top-secret information to the Russians. One plane, piloted by Colonel Grady, manages to get through. Despite radio orders from the President to return and the pleadings of his own wife, Grady refuses to alter his course. While the President is talking to the Russian premier on the hot line, Grady releases the bombs over Moscow. To convince the Soviet Union and the rest of the world that the bombing was a gross error, the President orders the atomic destruction of New York City by U. S. planes. *Presidents of the United States. Russians. Air pilots. Cold war. Nuclear warfare. Aerial bombardment. Hot line. Moscow. Union of Soviet Socialist Republics. New York City. United States Air Force—Strategic Air Command. The Pentagon.*

A FAIRY TALE FOR ADULTS; OR THE HALF-FAST LOVER F6.1448
Dist Astro–Jemco Film Distributors. 26 Mar **1970** [Maryland license]. Sd; col. 35mm. 78 min.

Cast: Forman Shane *(Henry Wakefield/Peter)*, Phyllis Stangel.

Comedy. Homosexual fashion designer Henry Wakefield, told by doctors that he has only a month to live, summons his three female assistants to the hospital. He draws up a will leaving them his entire fortune with the provision that they never engage in heterosexual intercourse. Henry then hires a double to test their self-control. One by one, the double seduces the women, causing each to forfeit her share of the inheritance. Henry is then told by the hospital that there has been a mistake and that he is in perfect health. Happy to be alive, he joins the women and his double in an orgy. *Couturiers. Doubles. Health. Inheritance. Seduction. Male homosexuality. Wills. Orgies.*

Note: Also known as *Mixed Fruit* and *Fairy Tales for Adults.*

THE FALCON FIGHTERS (Japan)   **F6.1449**
Daiei Motion Picture Co. May **1970** [Los Angeles showing]. Sd; col (Fuji Color). 35mm (Daiei Scope). 100 min.

Dir Mitsuo Murayama. *Screenplay* Katsuya Suzaki. *Photog* Kimio Watanabe. *Art Dir* Koichi Takahashi. *Mus* Seitaro Omori. *Sp Eff* Noriaki Yuasa.

Cast: Makoto Sato *(Licut. Takeo Kato)*, Shiho Fujimura *(his wife)*, Sei Hiraizumi *(2d Lieut. Kihara)*, Kojiro Hongo *(2d Lieut. Ando)*, Jun Fujimaki *(Cho Eishun)*, Yoko Namikawa *(Keiko)*, Akio Hasegawa, Ken Utsui.

War drama. In 1929 Lieut. Takeo Kato, an instructor in the newly-formed Japanese Air Force, becomes close friends with two of his students at the Tokorozawa Flying Academy. They are 2d Lieut. Kihara, who like Kato transferred to the air force after graduating from the army academy, and Cho Eishun, a Chinese officer studying aviation in Japan. War breaks out a few years later between Japan and China. In 1937 Kato and Kihara are in northern China

when Kihara's plane is shot down by an enemy pilot (Cho Eishun). Kato challenges his old friend to an air duel and with some regret shoots him down. Kato has nightmares and continues to be troubled about his duel with Cho Eishun, and he tells his anguish to his wife, who begins to sense the impact of the incident on her husband. The Pacific war breaks out, and in May 1942 Kato's plane goes down over the Bay of Bengal. *Air pilots. Students. Chinese. Friendship. Guilt. Duels. Sino-Japanese Conflict 1937–45. World War II. Bay of Bengal. China. Japan—Air Force.*

Note: Released in Japan in 1969 as *Aa rikugun hayabusa sentotai.*

FALL GIRL *see* **LISETTE**
THE FALL GUY *see* **FALLGUY**
THE FALL OF ROME (Italy)   **F6.1450**
Atlantica Cinematografica. *Dist* Medallion Pictures. **1963**. Sd; col (Eastman Color). 35mm (Totalscope). 89 min.

Prod Marco Vicario. *Dir* Anthony Dawson. *Screenplay* Antonio Margheriti, Gianni Astolfi, Mauro Mancini. *Photog* Riccardo Pallottini. *Film Ed* Renato Cinquini. *Mus* Riz Ortolani.

Cast: Carl Möhner *(Marcus)*, Loredana Nusciak *(Svetla)*, Ida Galli *(Licia)*, Andrea Aureli *(Rako)*, Piero Palermini *(Valerio)*, Giancarlo Sbragia *(Giunio)*, Nando Tamberlani *(Matteo)*, Maria Grazia Buccella *(Xenia)*, Laura Rocca *(Madre Tullio)*, Jim Dolen *(Caius)*, Riccardo Ricci *(Tullio)*, Mimmo Maggio, Roberto Bettoni, Nando Poggi, Claudio Scarchilli, Renato Terra, Joe Pollini.

Action melodrama. With the death of Emperor Constantine, Giunio, who is attempting to seize power, arouses the Romans against the Christians. Marcus, a Christian centurion, is arrested but rescued from the gladiators' arena and given refuge in the camp of Rako, the leader of the barbarians. Giunio declares that the Christians are traitors, but Consul Caius, returning from battle, refuses to believe that Marcus has betrayed Rome. Marcus returns to Rome with Rako's daughter Svetla and wins the Christians' freedom by defeating three gladiators in the arena. Taking advantage of Caius' death at the hands of the invading barbarians, Giunio regains power and resumes persecuting the Christians. Marcus is sent to battle in the arena, but he is saved by an earthquake. Giunio is killed; the Romans are buried amid the ruins; and Marcus, preaching pacifism and tolerance, converts Svetla to his faith. [An Italian source suggests that Marcus is killed in the earthquake.] *Royalty. Centurions. Gladiators. Traitors. Christianity. Religious persecution. Religious conversion. Rome—History—Empire. Earthquakes.*

Note: Filmed in Italy in 1962 as *Il crollo di Roma.* Anthony Dawson is a pseudonym for Antonio Margheriti.

THE FALL OF THE ROMAN EMPIRE   **F6.1451**
Bronston–Roma Productions. *Dist* Paramount Pictures. 26 Mar **1964** [New York opening; c25 Mar 1964; LP28747]. Sd; col (Technicolor). 35mm (Ultra-Panavision). 188 min. [See note.]

Pres by Samuel Bronston. *Prod* Samuel Bronston. *Exec Assoc Prod* Michael Waszynski. *Assoc Prod* Jaime Prades. *Dir* Anthony Mann. *2d Unit Dir* Yakima Canutt. *Dir 2d Unit Operations* Andrew Marton. *Orig Screenplay* Ben Barzman, Basilio Franchina, Philip Yordan. *Camera* Robert Krasker. *2d Unit Photog* Cecilio Paniagua. *Set & Prod Dsgn* Veniero Colasanti, John Moore. *Film Ed* Robert Lawrence. *Asst Film Ed* Magdalena Paradell. *Mus* Dimitri Tiomkin. *Sd* David Hildyard. *Sd Rec* Gordon K. McCallum. *Sd Eff Ed* Milton Burrow. *1st & 2d Unit Asst Dir* José López Rodero, José María Ochoa. *Exec Prod Mgr* C. O. Erickson. *Cont* Elaine Schreyeck. *Wardrobe Ch* Gloria Mussetta. *Makeup* Mario Van Riel. *Hairdressing* Grazia De Rossi. *Sp Eff* Alex Weldon. *Historical Cons* Will Durant. *Dial Coach* George Tyne. *Supv Tech* Carl Gibson. *Supv Electrn* Bruno Pasqualini. *Prop Master* Stanley Detlie. *Casting* Maude Spector.

Cast: Sophia Loren *(Lucilla)*, Stephen Boyd *(Livius)*, Alec Guinness *(Marcus Aurelius)*, James Mason *(Timonides)*, Christopher Plummer *(Commodus)*, Anthony Quayle *(Verulus)*, John Ireland *(Ballomar)*, Mel Ferrer *(Cleander)*, Omar Sharif *(Sohamus)*, Eric Porter *(Julianus)*, Douglas Wilmer *(Niger)*, Peter Damon *(Claudius)*, Andrew Keir *(Polybius)*, George Murcell *(Victorinus)*, Lena von Martens *(Helva)*, Gabriella Licudi *(Tauna)*, Rafael Luis Calvo *(Lentulus)*, Norman Wooland *(Virgilianus)*, Virgilio Teixeira *(Marcellus)*, Michael Gwynn *(Cornelius)*, Guy Rolfe *(Marius)*, Finlay Currie *(Caecina)*.

Historical epic. In 180 A.D. the ailing emperor of Rome, Marcus Aurelius, confides to his daughter, Lucilla, that he has decided to relinquish his throne to his adopted son, Livius. The news is overheard by Cleander, a blind prophet close to Marcus' weak and licentious son, Commodus. After conniving with Commodus, Cleander kills Marcus with a poisoned apple, and the less ambitious Livius allows Commodus to proclaim himself emperor, much to the dismay of Lucilla. Because of her devotion to her deceased father, and, irritated with Livius for giving up the throne, she agrees to a loveless marriage to King Sohamus of Armenia in the hope it will help the Roman Empire. Despite pestilence and unrest among his citizens, Commodus continues to live a life of debauchery, banishing both Livius and the faithful Timonides, a Greek philosopher and adviser to Marcus. Nevertheless, Livius remains loyal to Commodus during an Eastern revolt in which Sohamus is killed in battle. After Livius has brought Lucilla back to Rome, Commodus becomes so enraged by Livius that he has a newly-liberated barbarian village completely destroyed; and Timonides is slain during its defense. Upon learning that Verulus, an aging gladiator, is his real father, Commodus loses his mind, proclaims himself a god, and condemns Lucilla to be burned at the stake in the arena. But Livius returns in time to kill Commodus and rescue Lucilla from the blazing pyre. As the Roman senators compete for the throne, Livius and Lucilla leave the rapidly disintegrating empire. *Royalty. Prophets. Philosophers. Greeks. Gladiators. Regicide. Filial relations. Brother-sister relationship. Marriage of convenience. Blindness. Hedonism. Insanity. Parentage. Rome—History—Empire. Armenia. Lucius Aelius Aurelius Commodus. Marcus Aurelius Antoninus.*

Note: Location scenes filmed in Spain. Also reviewed at 180 and 185 min. Copyright length: 153 min.

DER FALL X701 *see* **FROZEN ALIVE**

FALLGUY F6.1452

Harling Productions. *Dist* Fairway-International Films. May **1962.** Sd; b&w. 35mm. 64 min. [Also reviewed at 70 min.]

Prod-Dir Donn Harling. *Story-Screenplay* Richard Adams, writ, George Mitchell. *Photog* Vilis Lapenieks. *Film Ed* Ron Honthaner. *Mus Comp & Cond* Jaime Mendoza-Nava. *Asst Dir* John Dietrich. *Prod Mgr* William Redlin.

Cast: Ed Dugan (*Sonny Martin*), George Andre (*Carl Tamin*), Lou Gartner (*police chief*), Don Alderette (*Sam Johnson*), Madeline Frances (*June Johnson*), Wes Carlson, Fabian Dean.

Crime melodrama. Assisting a motorist who is the victim of an automobile accident, teenager Sonny Martin witnesses the murder of King Monarch, the city's rackets boss. Sonny seeks police protection when the syndicate tries to kill him and discovers that the police chief is a gang member trying to frame him for the gangland murder. Sonny escapes from the authorities, whereupon publisher Carl Tamin, secret leader of the gang, contracts a professional killer known as "The Indian" to eliminate Sonny, now hiding in the city slums. Sonny finally visits the home of Dr. Sam Johnson, a prominent physician, and reveals to his innocent daughter, June, that her father is a syndicate member. The two youngsters search for evidence to corroborate Sonny's story, but the racketeers close in on them. In the ensuing gunfight, Sonny and June are wounded while the gangsters kill each other. *Gangsters. Hired killers. Police. Publishers. Physicians. Murder. Adolescence. Frameup. Syndicates. Automobile accidents.*

Note: May also be known as *The Fall Guy.*

FALSE SHAME (West Germany) F6.1453

Ernst Neubach-Filmproduktion-Dieter Fritko. *Dist* Embassy Pictures. 15 Apr **1964** [New York showing]. Sd; b&w. 35mm. 85-90 min.

Prod Ernst Neubach, Dieter Fritko. *Prod Dir* Adolf Rosen. *Dir* Wolfgang Gluck. *Screenplay* Ilse Lotz-DuPont. *Based on an Idea by* Dieter Fritko. *Camera* Walter Riml. *Asst Camera* Günter Grimm, Hans Lyn. *Art Dir* Walter Renk, Heinz Gieseke. *Set Decor* Curt Stallmach. *Film Ed (see note)* Heinz Fredersdorf, Walter Friederhofer. *Asst Film Ed* Brigitte Fredersdorf. *Mus* Rudolf Perak. *Choreog* Jean Tordo. *Sd* Heinz Terworth. *Asst Dir* Ilona von Juranyi. *Prod Mgr* Hermann Hinze-Selch, Kurt Rendel. *Cost* Margot Kohlschein. *Makeup* Karl Hanoszek, Susi Krause.

Cast: Hans Söhnker (*Professor Brand*), Antje Geerk (*Monika Gruber*), Albert Rueprecht (*Martin Clair*), Friedrich Domin (*Professor Gruber*), Karin Dor (*Christa Riek*), Peter Vogel (*Peter Riek*), Evelyn Bey, Rolf Pinegger, Johanna König, Lea Krüger, Wolfgang Buttner, Joe Rive, Wolfgang Petersen, Ruth Kappelsberger, Harald Maresch, Wolfgang Schultes, Sascha Faber, F. Güntern.

Drama. Teenagers Monika and Martin make love without taking any precautions, and Monika becomes pregnant. Looking for advice and help, Monika discovers that Martin will not marry her, and her father, a college professor, sends her away. She concludes that an abortion is too dangerous, even when performed by a gynecologist, and decides to have the baby and accept her "false shame." [Portions of the film are instructional, depicting scenes of a sex education class and showing an actual childbirth.] *Professors. Adolescence. Birth control. Pregnancy. Filial relations. Abortion. Childbirth. Illegitimacy. Social conformity. Sex instruction.*

Note: Released in West Germany in Sep 1958 as *Worüber man nicht Spricht;* running time: 88 min. Sources conflict on film editor credit.

FALSE WITNESS *see* **ZIGZAG**

FALSTAFF (Spain/Switzerland) F6.1454

Internacional Films Española-Alpine Productions. *Dist* Peppercorn-Wormser, Inc., U-M Film Distributors. 19 Mar **1967** [New York opening]. Sd; b&w. 35mm. 115 min.

Pres by Harry Saltzman. *Prod* Emiliano Piedra, Angel Escolano. *Exec Prod* Alessandro Tasca. *Dir-Writ* Orson Welles. *2d Unit Dir* Jesús Franco. *Dir Photog* Edmond Richard. *Camera Op* Adolphe Charlet. *2d Unit Photog* Alejandro Ulloa, Art Dir José Antonio de la Guerra, Mariano Erdorza. *Film Ed* Fritz Muller. *Mus* Angelo Francesco Lavagnino. *Mus Cond* Pierluigi Urbini. *Mus Dir* Carlo Franci. *Sd Rec* Peter Parasheles. *Asst Dir* Antonio Fuentes, Juan Cobos. *Prod Mgr* Gustavo Quintana. *Cost Dsgn* Orson Welles. *Makeup* Francisco Puyol.

Cast: Orson Welles (*Sir John [Jack] Falstaff*), Jeanne Moreau (*Doll Tearsheet*), Margaret Rutherford (*Hostess Quickly*), John Gielgud (*King Henry IV*), Keith Baxter (*Prince Hal, later King Henry V*), Marina Vlady (*Kate Percy*), Norman Rodway (*Henry Percy, called Hotspur*), Alan Webb (*Justice Shallow*), Walter Chiari (*Mr. Silence*), Michael Aldridge (*Pistol*), Tony Beckley (*Poins*), Fernando Rey (*Worcester*), Beatrice Welles (*Falstaff's page*), Andrew Faulds (*Westmoreland*), José Nieto (*Northumberland*), Jeremy Rowe (*Prince John*), Paddy Bedford (*Bardolph*), Ralph Richardson (*narrator*), Julio Peña, Fernando Hilbeck, Andrés Meguto, Keith Pyott, Charles Farrell, British.

Historical comedy-drama. Adapted from the plays by: William Shakespeare, *Henry IV*, Parts I and II; *Henry V*; *Richard II*; *The Merry Wives of Windsor.* Raphael Holinshed, *The Chronicles of England* (London, 1577). When Henry IV assumes the throne of England, rumors are widespread that he had a hand in the elimination of Richard II, and the country divides into factions. Although a growing number of rebels rally behind the son of the Duke of Northumberland, Prince Hal ignores the threat to his father, the king, and passes his time carousing with his inseparable friend, the blustering and cheating Falstaff. Eventually, however, Prince Hal goes into battle against the rebels. But Falstaff attributes this exploit to himself; and the king, deceived by Falstaff's bragging, is convinced that his son is a coward. When the rebels are finally vanquished, Prince Hal visits the king on his deathbed and vows to reform. When King Henry dies, Prince Hal is crowned Henry V. Falstaff attends the coronation, confident that the new king will bestow a high-ranking title upon him. Instead, he is cast off. Filled with sadness at seeing his former wastrel companion transformed into a responsible ruler, Falstaff dies a lonely and embittered man. *Royalty. Wastrels. Braggarts. Duplicity. Filial relations. Great Britain—History—Lancaster/York. Henry IV (England). Richard II. Henry V (England). Falstaff.*

Note: Filmed in Barcelona, Madrid, and other Spanish locations. Released in Spain in May 1966 as *Campanadas a medianoche;* running time: 119 min. Also known as *Chimes at Midnight.* The narration is taken from the Holinshed work cited.

FAMILY DIARY (Italy) F6.1455

Titanus. *Dist* Metro-Goldwyn-Mayer, Inc. 11 Nov **1963** [New York opening; c31 Dec 1962; LP29359]. Sd; col (Technicolor). 35mm. 115 min.

Prod Goffredo Lombardo. *Dir* Valerio Zurlini. *Screenplay* Valerio Zurlini, Mario Missiroli. *Photog* Giuseppe Rotunno. *Art Dir* Flavio Mogherini. *Film Ed* Mario Serandrei. *Mus* Goffredo Petrassi. *Cost* Gaia Romanini.

Cast: Marcello Mastroianni (*Enrico*), Jacques Perrin (*Lorenzo*), Sylvie (*grandmother*), Salvo Randone (*Salocchi*), Valeria Ciangottini (*Enzina*), Serena Vergano (*hospital nun*).

Drama. Source: Vasco Pratolini, *Cronaca familiare* (Florence, 1947). In June, 1945, Enrico, a struggling journalist in Rome, receives a phone call from his newspaper office in Florence informing him of his brother Lorenzo's death. Enrico's thoughts return to the years before World War I: When their mother dies bearing Lorenzo and their father is hospitalized from war wounds, both boys are reared by their grandmother until Lorenzo is adopted by the butler of a wealthy Englishman. Enrico is raised in poverty and Lorenzo in comfort until 1935, when the brothers are reunited. Lorenzo has argued with the butler, who can no longer provide for him since his employer's death. A poor student but accustomed to a gentleman's life, Lorenzo knows no profession and is unfit for the struggle of life. Enrico tries to help him, although he has his own problems and wishes to improve himself. The brothers grow fond of each other and frequently visit their grandmother in a home for the elderly. Enrico contracts tuberculosis and is placed in a sanitarium; when he is released, he finds Lorenzo's situation unimproved. After the death of their grandmother, Enrico leaves Florence to accept a position as a journalist in Rome, while Lorenzo marries and becomes a father; but misfortunes continue to plague him. He develops an intestinal infection and enters a hospital in Rome for treatment, but his condition worsens, and Enrico moves him to a private clinic. When it becomes obvious that Lorenzo is dying, Enrico arranges to have him returned to Florence to see his wife and child once more. The next day, as Enrico is preparing to join his brother, he is informed of Lorenzo's death. *Brothers. Journalists. Grandmothers. Butlers. Death. Adoption. Old age homes. Tuberculosis. Sanitariums. Hospitals. Rome. Florence.*

Note: Opened in Rome in Sep 1962 as *Cronaca familiare;* running time: 108 min (may have been cut from 122 min).

THE FAMILY JEWELS

F6.1456

Jerry Lewis Productions–York Pictures. *Dist* Paramount Pictures. 1 Jul **1965** [Dallas opening; c16 Jun 1965; LP30969]. Sd; col (Technicolor). 35mm. 100 min.

Prod-Dir Jerry Lewis. *Assoc Prod* Arthur P. Schmidt. *Screenplay* Jerry Lewis, Bill Richmond. *Photog* W. Wallace Kelley. *Art Dir* Hal Pereira, Jack Poplin. *Set Dir* Sam Comer, Robert R. Benton. *Supv Ed* Arthur P. Schmidt. *Ed* John Woodcock. *Mus Score & Cond* Pete King. *Sd* Hugo Grenzbach, Charles Grenzbach. *Asst Dir* Ralph Axness. *Cost* Edith Head. *Sp Photog Eff* Paul K. Lerpae.

Cast: Jerry Lewis (*Willard Woodward/ Everett Peyton/ James Peyton/ Capt. Eddie Peyton/ Julius Peyton/ "Bugs" Peyton/ Skylock Peyton*), Sebastian Cabot (*Dr. Matson*), Donna Butterworth (*Donna Peyton*), Gene Baylos (*circus clown*), Milton Frome (*pilot*), Herbie Faye (*Joe*), Robert Strauss (*pool hall owner*), Jay Adler, Neil Hamilton (*attorneys*), Marjorie Bennett, Frances Lax, Ellen Corby, Renie Riano, Jesslyn Fax (*plane passengers*), Gary Lewis and the Playboys (*themselves*), Anne Baxter (*star of "Sustenance"*), John Lawrence, Francine York, John Hubbard, Mike Ross, John Macchia, Douglas Deane, Maurice Kelly.

Comedy. Donna, a precocious 9-year-old, inherits $30 million when her father dies. The will stipulates that she must choose one of her six uncles to be her new father. Accompanied by the family chauffeur, Willard, she visits each of the uncles: James, an old ferryboat captain; Everett, a circus clown; Eddie, an airline pilot; Julius, a fashion photographer; Skylock, a private investigator; and "Bugs," a gangster. All are well-meaning except Everett, who hates children, and "Bugs," who tries to kidnap Donna and hold her for ransom. None of them really appeals to her, but "Uncle Everett" turns up to claim her. Donna recognizes Willard disguised as the clown and is happy to choose him as her adopted father. *Children. Orphans. Uncles. Chauffeurs. Sea captains. Clowns. Air pilots. Photographers. Detectives. Gangsters. Inheritance. Kidnaping. Disguise. Adoption. Ferryboats. Wills.*

FAMILY ROBINSON ON THE FARM see SEX FAMILY ROBINSON ON THE FARM

THE FAMILY WAY (Great Britain)

F6.1457

Jambox. *Dist* Warner Bros.–Seven Arts, Inc. 28 Jun **1967** [New York opening]. Sd; col (Eastman Color, U. S. print by Technicolor). 35mm. 115 min.

A Boulting Brothers Production. *Prod* John Boulting. *Dir* Roy Boulting. *Screenplay* Bill Naughton. *Adapt* Roy Boulting, Jeffrey Dell. *Photog* Harry Waxman. *Art Dir* Alan Withy. *Asst Art Dir* Brian Herbert. *Film Ed* Ernest Hosler. *Mus* Paul McCartney. *Mus Supv & Arr* George Martin. *Sd* Christopher Lancaster. *Sd Rec* David Bowen, John Aldred. *Asst Dir* Peter Price. *Prod Admin* Philip Shipway. *Wardrobe* Bridget Sellers. *Makeup* Trevor Crole-Rees. *Hairstyles* Joyce James.

Cast: Hayley Mills (*Jenny Piper*), John Mills (*Ezra Fitton*), Hywel Bennett (*Arthur Fitton*), Marjorie Rhodes (*Lucy Fitton*), Avril Angers (*Liz Piper*), Liz Fraser (*Molly Thompson*), Wilfred Pickles (*Uncle Fred Piper*), John Comer (*Leslie Piper*), Barry Foster (*Joe Thompson*), Murray Head (*Geoffrey Fitton*), Colin Gordon (*Mr. Hutton*), Robin Parkinson (*Mr. Phillips*), Andrew Bradford (*Eddie*), Lesley Daine (*Dora*), Ruth Trouncer (*marriage counsellor*), Harry Locke (*Mr. Stubbs*), Maureen O'Reilly (*Miss Hunt*), Michael Cadman (*Len*), Thorley Walters (*The Vicar*), Hazel Bainbridge (*Mrs. Bell*), Ruth Gower (*Mrs. Pike*), Diana Coupland (*Mrs. Rose*), Fanny Carby (*Mrs. Stone*), Helen Booth (*Mrs. Lee*), Margaret Lacey (*Mrs. Harris*).

Domestic comedy. Source: Bill Naughton, *All in Good Time* (London opening: 6 Mar 1963). Following the wedding of young Jenny Piper and Arthur Fitton, a rowdy reception is held at a local pub where the newlyweds are subjected to much well-meaning but vulgar ribaldry. The couple returns to the Fitton home to spend their first night together before leaving for a honeymoon in Majorca, but they are followed by some of the wedding guests who keep the party going until early morning. Worse yet, when the youngsters finally are permitted to retire, their bed collapses as the result of a practical joke. The next day they discover that the travel agent who sold them their tickets to Majorca has absconded with the money, and they are stranded in rainy England. As days pass into weeks at the crowded Fitton home, the marriage remains unconsummated. The strain between the couple steadily worsens, with Arthur working nights as a cinema projectionist and Jenny spending her days behind a record counter. Not knowing where to turn, Arthur visits a marriage counsellor, but even this has a disastrous effect. The interview is overheard by a gossipy charwoman, and the young couple's unfulfilled marriage becomes a major topic of public gossip. Arthur becomes the butt of scornful jokes from his boss, Mr. Thompson, who volunteers to satisfy Jenny's marital needs. Enraged, Arthur strikes his boss and returns home to berate Jenny for disclosing their secret. As a result of the quarrel, their mutual inhibitions are dispelled, and they make love for the first time. The following day Arthur finds the courage to ask his gruff but kindly father-in-law for financial aid. The money is gladly granted, and Jenny and Arthur leave for a belated honeymoon. *Newlyweds. In-laws. Motion picture projectionists. Marriage counsel. Family life. Gossip. Inhibition. Sexual initiation. Weddings. Honeymoons. Practical jokes.*

Note: Opened in London in Dec 1966. Location scenes filmed in Bolton and elsewhere in Lancashire, England.

FANATIC see DIE! DIE! MY DARLING!

LES FANATIQUES see A BOMB FOR A DICTATOR

FANDANGO

F6.1458

Tivoli Productions. *Dist* Clover Films. 15 Jul **1970** [Washington, D. C., opening]. Sd; col (Eastmancolor). 35mm. 79 min.

Prod Henning Schellerup, Paul Hipp. *Dir-Writ* John Hayes. *Dir Photog* Paul Hipp. *Camera Op* Rick Bisman. *Mus* Mario Toscana. *Sd Rec* Sam Nesor. *Prod Mgr* Roger Gentry. *Key Grip* Ray Atkinson, grip.

Cast: James Whitworth (*Dan Murphy*), Shawn Devereaux (*Mona DeLyse*), Sebastian Gregory (*Muck Mulligan*), Jay Scott (*Billy Busby*), Marland Proctor (*Sissy Sam*), Donna Stanley (*Pauline*), Neola Graef (*Joy*), Paul Harper (*Greaser*), John Dennis, Bonnie Cooper, Miller Pettit, Frank Teichman, Wendy Sweeney, Maxine DeVille France, Jeff Latham, Jeannie Anderson, Roger Gentry, Jim Feazell, Paul Brunton, Beverly Fredericks, Gene Connor, Ray Saniger, Byron Wardlow, Jerry Seay, Earl Newell, Allison Racy Young.

Western melodrama. Dan Murphy leads a group of gold miners into the California mountains where they set up camp. The men are besieged by food shortage, bitter cold, and Muck Mulligan and his gang of outlaws. In addition, the men are anxious for female companionship, so Murphy, along with Billy Busby and Sissy Sam, visits the Fandango Saloon in a nearby town, where Murphy convinces his longtime friend, Mona DeLyse, to send some of her prostitutes to Murphy's camp. Meanwhile, Mulligan and his men are creating havoc in the town, and Murphy is injured in a gunfight with the gang. The next day Mona and three other women load their wagons and leave with the miners. During the journey, Sam's lover, Pauline, is attacked and raped by Mulligan's men. Upon arriving at the camp, the women satisfy the men's sexual needs and then prepare to return to the Fandango Saloon, but their caravan is again attacked by Mulligan. Murphy's miners come to their defense, and in the ensuing gunfight Billy is killed, and Murphy is injured. The women are captured and tortured by Mulligan, but Mona manages to shoot him. Later, Sam and Pauline are married, and Dan bids farewell to Mona, leaving her to her life of prostitution. *Gold miners. Prostitutes. Gunfighters. Rape. Murder. Torture. Saloons. California.*

FANDO AND LIS (Mexico)

F6.1459

Producciones Panic. *Dist* Cannon Releasing Corp. 2 Feb **1970** [New York opening]. Sd; b&w. 35mm. 82 min.

Pres by The Cannon Group. *Prod* Roberto Viskin, Juan López Moctezuma. *Exec Prod* Moses Rosenberg, Samuel Rosenberg. *Dir* Alexandro Jodorowsky. *Screenplay* Alexandro Jodorowsky, Fernando Arrabal. *Photog* Rafael Corkidi, Antonio Reynoso. *Film Ed* Fernando Suárez. *Mus* Pepe Avila, Hector Morelli, Mario Losua.

Cast: Sergio Klainer (*Fando*), Diana Mariscal (*Lis*), María Teresa Rivas, Tamara Garina, Juan José Arreola, Rene Rebetez, Amparo Villegas.

Fantasy. Based on the play by: Fernando Arrabal, *Fando et Lis* (Paris, 1958). Fando and Lis, a young couple, travel to the imaginary kingdom of Tar, where fantasy becomes reality and troubles supposedly disappear. Lis, a paralytic, is carried or pulled along on a cart by the impotent Fando, who alternately tortures and protects her. They remember the suffering of their early childhoods: Fando recalls his parents' deaths, and Lis remembers her terrifying experiences with some evil show people. They encounter many strange people on the way to Tar, including a group of people stuck in quicksand, a girl eating a rose, a man playing a flaming piano amidst a pile of garbage, and a man who takes blood from Lis and drinks it. They are captured by some transvestites who strip them and then dress them in each other's clothing. Later, Fando watches as several men fondle Lis. After Lis destroys Fando's only possession, his drum, he kicks her to death. He mourns her death at the funeral, and their bodies are covered with leaves as their naked spirits unite and run through the woods. [One source indicates that the mourners at the funeral devour Lis's body.] *Paralytics. Impotence. Torture. Death. Transvestism. Sadomasochism. Eroticism. Murder. Imaginary kingdoms. Funerals.*

Note: Produced in Mexico in 1968 as *Fando y Lis*; running time: 98 min.

FANDO Y LIS see FANDO AND LIS

FÄNGELSE see THE DEVIL'S WANTON

FANNY

F6.1460

Mansfield Productions. *Dist* Warner Bros. Pictures. 28 Jun **1961** [Los Angeles opening; c22 Jul 1960; LP25367]. Sd; col (Technicolor). 35mm. 133 min.

A Joshua Logan Production. *Prod-Dir* Joshua Logan. *Assoc Prod* Ben Kadish. *Screenplay* Julius J. Epstein. *Photog* Jack Cardiff. *Art Dir* Rino Mondellini. *Set Decor* Robert Turlure. *Film Ed* William Reynolds. *Mus* Harold Rome. *Mus Supv & Cond* Morris Stoloff. *Mus Adapt* Harry Sukman. *Sd* Jean Monchablon, Richard Vorisek. *Asst Dir* Michel Romanoff. *Prod Mgr* Ludmilla Goulian. *Cost* Anne-Marie Marchand. *Makeup* Michel Deruelle.

Cast: Leslie Caron (*Fanny*), Maurice Chevalier (*Panisse*), Charles Boyer (*César*), Horst Buchholz (*Marius*), Baccaloni (*Escartifique*), Georgette Anys (*Honorine*), Lionel Jeffries (*Brun*), Raymond Bussières (*The Admiral*), Victor Francen (*Louis Panisse*), Joël Flateau (*Cesario*).

Comedy-drama. Source: S. N. Behrman, Joshua Logan and Harold Rome, *Fanny* (New York opening: 4 Nov 1954). Marcel Pagnol, *Marius* (Paris opening: 9 Mar 1929). Marcel Pagnol, *Fanny* (Paris opening: 5 Dec 1931). Marcel Pagnol, *César* (a film; 1936). Fanny, the daughter of Honorine, a poor fishmonger in the port of Marseilles in the 1930's, has always loved Marius, the handsome son of César, the headstrong proprietor of a waterfront bar. Marius, however, dreams only of the sea and has secretly made arrangements to sail away on a schooner bound for the "isles beneath the wind." On the eve of his departure, he and Fanny confess their love for each other and spend the night together. When morning comes, Marius offers to remain behind, but Fanny, knowing he would never be happy on land, sends him away. A few weeks later, Fanny learns that she is carrying Marius' child, and she turns to the elderly, widowed Panisse, a wealthy sail merchant. Delighted to marry Fanny and at long last have a son to carry on the family name and business, Panisse weds the girl. One year later, Marius, after having found his cherished isles to be nothing but "volcanic ash," returns to Marseilles and tries to claim his son, Cesario. But Fanny and César explain to him that little Cesario belongs to Panisse, for it is he who has given the child the loving care that only a father can bestow. And once more Marius leaves Marseilles, this time to become a garage mechanic in a nearby town. As the years pass, little Cesario inherits his father's passion for the sea, and on his 9th birthday a friend of Marius' takes the child to visit his father. As Marius embraces his son, Fanny arrives with word that Panisse is dying. From his deathbed the old man dictates a letter to César in which he asks Marius to marry Fanny. *Fishmongers. Adventurers. Sailors. Merchants. Saloon keepers. Mechanics. Pregnancy. Marriage. Old age. Parenthood. Wills. The Sea. Marseilles. France.*

Note: Location scenes filmed in Marseilles, the Château d'If, and Notre Dame de la Garde. The following films were also based on Pagnol's trilogy: *Marius* (France, 1931), *Fanny* (France, 1932), *Cesar* (France, 1936), and *Port of Seven Seas* (U. S., 1938).

FANNY HILL (Sweden)   **F6.1461**
Minerva Film Produktion-Europa Film. *Dist* Cinemation Industries. 26 Sep 1969 [New York opening]. Sd; col (DeLuxe). 35mm. 91 min. *MPAA rating* X.
Pres by Jerry Gross, Nicholas Demetroules. *Prod* Tore Sjöberg. *Dir-Writ* Mac Ahlberg. *Photog* Jan Lindeström. *Art Dir* Rolf Boman. *Film Ed* Ingemar Ejve. *Mus* Georg Riedel. *Mus Arr & Cond* Clay Pitts. *Perf by* Oven. *Rhythm Guitar & Vocalist* Frank Thomas. *Lead Guitar & Vocalist* Richie Hitchcock. *Drummer* Bob Cohen. *Song:* "Please Touch Me" Clay Pitts. *Song:* "Sail a Boat" Clay Pitts, Don Pain. *Sung by* Richie Hitchcock. *Song:* "I Can't Get Enough of You" Clay Pitts, David Spinoza. *Song:* "Looking Back at Love" Clay Pitts, Bob Sterling. *Song:* "Gravitational Pull" Regis Mull. *Sd* Hakan Strandberg. *Prod Mgr* Waldemar Bergendahl. *Wardrobe* Gunilla Ponten. *English Vers* Titan Productions.

Cast: Diana Kjaer (*Fanny Hill*), Hans Ernback (*Roger Boman*), Keve Hjelm (*Leif Henning*), Oscar Ljung (*Otto Wilhelmson*), Tina Hedström (*Monika*), Gio Petré (*Fru Schöön*), Mona Seilitz (*Charlotte*), Astrid Bye (*Hanna*), Bo Lööf (*Will*), Gösta Prüzelius (*Skeppsredare Boman*), Hans Lindgren (*Kraftmann*), Kjell Lennartsson, Borje Nyberg, John Harryson, Jan Erik Lindqvist.

Drama. Inspired by: John Cleland, *Fanny Hill; or, Memoirs of a Woman of Pleasure* (London, 1749). Fanny Hill, an innocent country girl, meets the experienced Monika on a train to Stockholm, and they decide to share a furnished room. Fanny is hired by Monika's employer, Mrs. Schöön, whose "massage parlor" is actually a brothel catering to wealthy men. Fanny's naiveté protects her virginity until she discovers the deception, and she flees with Roger, the son of a supposedly wealthy shipowner. They fall in love, but Roger's father objects to the romance and sends him to South America. Fanny next becomes the mistress of Leif, a married businessman, and she remains happy until she finds him in bed with another woman. To avenge the insult, she seduces Leif's chauffeur, but they are discovered and turned away. Fanny then becomes devoted to Otto, a lonely retired bachelor, and they travel around Europe together. Otto dies suddenly, and Fanny learns that he has left her his considerable fortune. Now part of a new social circle in Stockholm, she throws a party and chances to meet Roger, whose father has since died. Still in love, the couple decide to marry. Roger confesses that his father was not really wealthy, but the lovers laughingly make plans to live on Fanny's fortune.

Innocents. Prostitutes. Madams. Businessmen. Chauffeurs. Mistresses. Inheritance. Wealth. Revenge. Seduction. Social classes. Whorehouses. Massage parlors. Stockholm. Fanny Hill.

Note: Released in Sweden in Eastmancolor in 1968; running time: 101 min. Filmed in Stockholm. Also known as *The Swedish Fanny Hill*.

FANNY HILL MEETS DR. EROTICO   **F6.1462**
Barry Mahon Productions. *Dist* Chancellor Films. 17 Nov 1967 [Maryland license]. Sd; col. 35mm. 78 min.
A Barry Mahon Production. *Prod-Dir* Barry Mahon. *Sd* Magno Sound.
Cast: Sue Evans (*Fanny Hill*).

Comedy-drama. After spending a year in a London brothel, Fanny Hill returns to the castle of Lady Chatterly, her former employer. The castle has since been let to a lascivious old doctor, who is trying to bring to life the man he has created. Fanny is taken back to work as a servant girl, devoting herself once again to lovemaking. Inadvertently, she triggers the electrical connections which bring the monster to life. Upon awakening, he sees Fanny and falls in love with her. Though the doctor is angry with Fanny, he cannot send her away because his monster insists on following her everywhere. She is forced to keep the monster in her bedroom. When another young maid visits Fanny's room to make lesbian advances, the monster thinks his mistress is being hurt, and he comes to her rescue. The maid's screams upset the monster, who runs berserk through the countryside and is finally cornered in a barn. When the townspeople set the barn on fire, the doctor's life work is destroyed, and Fanny must return to the road once more. *Domestics. Scientists. Prostitutes. Lesbianism. Incendiarism. Castles. England. Fanny Hill. Frankenstein.*

FANNY HILL MEETS LADY CHATTERLY   **F6.1463**
Barry Mahon Productions. *Dist* Chancellor Films. 20 Jul 1967 [San Francisco showing]. Sd; col (Eastman Color). 35mm. 71 min.
A Barry Mahon Production. *Prod* Barry Mahon. *Dir* Barry Mahon, George Matsui.

Cast: Sue Evans (*Fanny Hill*), Sally Singer (*Lady Chatterly?*), Alex Keen.
Comedy-drama. Lady Chatterly, a famous courtesan, keeps a country castle for the benefit of visiting London royalty. She is well compensated for her services as hostess to their trysts and wild orgies. Fanny Hill arrives from the country to work as a servant girl at the castle. Peter, the stableboy, introduces her to the world of sexual delights. Lady Chatterly plans a huge masquerade ball in honor of a wealthy American tobacco planter. In return for an introduction to a Hungarian princess, he plans to give Lady Chatterly and her agent, the Duke, 10,000 acres of rich, Virginia farmland. When the princess sends word at the last minute that she will be unable to attend, Lady Chatterly decides to substitute her servant girl, Fanny. Peter, excluded from Fanny's company as the two women draw closer, happens to meet the American in a tavern, and he divulges the hoax. Furious, the planter retaliates by sending Peter in his place. Well disguised, and armed with a bogus deed, Peter attends the ball. After a night of revelry with Fanny, he takes her off to London with the money the American has given her. *Domestics. Prostitutes. Royalty. British. Americans in foreign countries. Hungarians. Landed gentry. Stableboys. Sexual initiation. Imposture. Masquerades. Orgies. Wealth. Castles. England. Virginia. Fanny Hill. Lady Chatterley.*

FANNY HILL MEETS THE RED BARON   **F6.1464**
Barry Mahon Productions-RIA Films. *Dist* Chancellor Films. Sep 1968. Sd; col. 35mm. 72 min.
A John F. Rickert Production. *Prod-Dir* Barry Mahon.
Cast: Sue Evans (*Fanny Hill*).

Comedy-drama. Forced down behind British lines by engine trouble, the Red Baron camouflages his plane, switches uniforms with a dead soldier, and, posing as a Belgian, makes his way to a medical hospital. He finds the hospital staffed by a group of nurses devoted to raising the patients' morale by joining them in a variety of sexual activities. One of the nurses is Fanny Hill. Leaving the officers to their pleasures, the Baron plots to free a German prisoner of war, who is to drop an engine part for the Baron's plane at the hospital the next morning. The prisoner makes his escape during a wild can-can party given by the nurses. The Baron now has nothing to do but wait, and he joins in the festivities. Fanny's boyfriend, a young pilot, is jealous of the Baron. He has been discharged from the hospital, and he sets out to prove the Belgian an imposter. At dawn, Fanny's boyfriend flies back to the hospital to report his findings. A German plane delivers the Baron's engine part, and he gets his plane into the air once again to fight the Allied pilot. Fanny watches anxiously as her boyfriend's gun jams. The Baron, true to his code, refuses to shoot down a defenseless plane. He heads for Germany, leaving the young pilot to continue his affair with Fanny. *Nurses. Air pilots. Germans. British. Soldiers. Prisoners of war. Belgians. Imposture. Jealousy. Airplanes. Hospitals. Orgies. World War I. England. Manfred von Richthofen. Fanny Hill.*

FANNY HILL: MEMOIRS OF A WOMAN OF PLEASURE (United States/West Germany) F6.1465

Famous Players Corp.–CCC–Filmkunst. *Dist* Famous Players Corp. 10 Mar **1965** [Los Angeles opening; c1 Mar 1965; LP29863]. Sd; b&w. 35mm. 104 min.

Prod Albert Zugsmith, Artur Brauner. *Assoc Prod* Billy Frick. *Dir* Russ Meyer. *Screenplay* Robert Hill. *Dir Photog* Heinz Hölscher. *Art Dir* Paul Markwitz. *Decor Dsgn* Helmut Nentwig. *Film Ed* Alfred Srp. *Mus* Erwin Halletz. *Sd* Clemens Tutsch. *Asst Dir* Elfie Tillack. *Unit Mgr* Felix Siebenrogg. *Script Girl* Annemarie Scheu. *Prod Sec* Patricia Huston, Marianne Hennig. *Cost Dsgn* Claudia Herberg. *Wardrobe* Vera Mugge. *Makeup* Freddy Arnold. *Res* Vladek Bijak. *Dir Still Photog* Bruno Bernard.

Cast: Miriam Hopkins *(Mrs. Maude Brown)*, Leticia Roman *(Fanny Hill)*, Walter Giller *(Hemingway)*, Alex D'Arcy *(The Admiral)*, Helmut Weiss *(Mr. Dinklespieler)*, Chris Howland *(Mr. Norbert)*, Ulli Lommel *(Charles)*, Cara Garnett *(Phoebe)*, Karin Evans *(Martha)*, Syra Marty *(Hortense)*, Albert Zugsmith *(grand duke)*, Christiane Schmidtmer *(Fiona)*, Heide Hansen *(Fenella)*, Erica Ericson *(Emily)*, Patricia Huston *(Amanda)*, Marshall Raynor *(Johnny)*, Hilda Sessack *(Mrs. Snow)*, Billy Frick *(Percival)*, Jurgen Nesbach *(James)*, Herbert Knippenberg *(Mudge)*, Susanne Hsiao *(Lotus Blossom)*, Renate Hutte *(niece)*, Ellen Velero *(girl)*.

Melodrama. Source: John Cleland, *Fanny Hill; or, Memoirs of a Woman of Pleasure* (London, 1749). Fanny Hill, an innocent country girl, comes to London in 1748 to seek her fortune. Alone and jobless, Fanny is referred to Mrs. Maude Brown, the kind madam of an elite London brothel. Fanny accepts Mrs. Brown's offer to become her companion, unaware that she is to become a prostitute; for awhile Fanny is able to protect her virginity from the countless clients and relatives of Mrs. Brown. At a country outing for officers of the British Navy, Fanny meets Ensign Charles. The two take shelter in a haystack during a rainstorm, and Fanny is finally initiated into the physical act of love. Mrs. Brown refuses to have one of her girls spend time with a poor sailor and arranges to have Charles shipped out to sea, but Fanny mourns the sudden departure of her lover and continues to shun the advances of the other men. In desperation, Mrs. Brown arranges a fake marriage with Cousin Hemingway so that Fanny will finally become an active member of the house, but Charles returns in time to save her from the trap. *Madams. Prostitution. Sexual initiation. Marriage—Fake. Shanghaiing. Whorehouses. London. Great Britain—Royal Navy.*

Note: Location scenes filmed in Berlin. Released in West Germany in Sep 1964 as *Fanny Hill*; running time: 96 min. May also be known as *Romp of Fanny Hill.*

FANTASTERNE see THE DREAMERS

THE FANTASTIC PLASTIC MACHINE F6.1466

Eric Blum–Lowell Blum. *Dist* Crown International Pictures. 27 Jun **1969** [Los Angeles opening]. Sd; col (Technicolor). 35mm (Techniscope). 93 min. MPAA rating G.

Prod-Dir-Writ Eric Blum, Lowell Blum. *Dir Photog* John M. Stephens. *Adtl Photog* George Greenough, Eric Blum, Dewey Wrigley, John Kiser, Bob Linvall, Bill Kerby, Jefferson Jackson, Terry McCardle. *Main Titl* National Screen Service. *Film Ed* Albert Nalpas. *Mus Comp & Cond* Harry Betts. *Sd* Bob Linvall. *Coöp* American Team Members of Wind and Sea Surf Club.

Participants: Nat Young, Bob McTavish, George Greenough, Skip Frye, Mike Purpus, Margo Godfrey, Joey Hamasaki, Steve Bigler, Kenny Morrow, Peter Johnson, Mickey Munoz, Ed Farwell, Robert Lindkvist.

Documentary. After a controversial defeat in San Diego by Australian Nat Young, nine American surfers, members of the Wind and Sea Surf Club, go to the South Pacific and Australia for a rematch. They stop in Fiji, where they are the first surfers, and in New Zealand, which elates them. In Sydney, the Americans are disappointed to learn that neither Young nor Australia's second top surfer, Bob McTavish, will compete. The visitors are surprised, too, by a new and shorter surfboard called a "plastic machine." Invented by an American youth, George Greenough, who spends half his time in Australia, the board features a "V" bottom. Nat Young, regarded by many as the world's finest surfer, has watched surfing become the inevitable commercial success. Now, he surfs only to find himself as he communicates with nature and the sea. *Surfers. Americans in foreign countries. Fiji Islands. New Zealand. Sydney (Australia). San Diego.*

Note: Filmed in Fiji, New Zealand, Australia, Hawaii, and southern California.

FANTASTIC VOYAGE F6.1467

Twentieth Century-Fox Film Corp. 24 Aug **1966** [Los Angeles opening; c17 Aug 1966; LP33483]. Sd (Westrex); col (DeLuxe). 35mm (CinemaScope). 100 min.

Prod Saul David. *Dir* Richard Fleischer. *Screenplay* Harry Kleiner. *Adapt* David Duncan. *Story* Otto Klement, Jay Lewis Bixby. *Dir Photog* Ernest Laszlo. *Art Dir* Jack Martin Smith, Dale Hennesy. *Set Decor* Walter M. Scott, Stuart A. Reiss. *Main Titl* Richard Kuhn, National Screen Service. *Film Ed* William B. Murphy. *Mus* Leonard Rosenman. *Sd* Bernard Freericks, David Dockendorf. *Asst Dir* Ad Schaumer. *Unit Prod Mgr* Eric Stacey. *Men's Cost* Bruce Walkup, Truman Eli. *Women's Wardrobe* Ollie Hughes. *Makeup* Ben Nye. *Hairstyles* Margaret Donovan. *Sp Photog Eff* L. B. Abbott, Art Cruickshank, Emil Kosa, Jr. *Tech Adv* Fred Zendar. *Tech Adv for Flying Seq* Peter Foy. *Creative Prod Res* Harper Goff. *Casting* Marvin Schnall, Doris McHale, Michael McLean.

Cast: Stephen Boyd *(Grant)*, Raquel Welch *(Cora Peterson)*, Edmond O'Brien *(General Carter)*, Donald Pleasence *(Dr. Michaels)*, Arthur O'Connell *(Col. Donald Reid)*, William Redfield *(Capt. Bill Owens)*, Arthur Kennedy *(Dr. Duval)*, Jean Del Val *(Jan Benes)*, Barry Coe *(communications aide)*, Ken Scott *(secret service man)*, Shelby Grant *(nurse)*, James Brolin *(technician)*, Brendan Fitzgerald *(wireless operator)*.

Science fiction melodrama. In 1995 Czech scientist Jan Benes escapes from behind the Iron Curtain and is brought to the United States for interrogation. U. S. scientists are able to reduce objects, including people, to the size of bacteria, but the miniaturization can be sustained for only 60 minutes. The Czech scientist has learned the secret of prolonging the miniaturization; but before he reveals this knowledge, he sustains a severe brain injury which can be treated only from within his body. A plan is conceived whereby a crew of five will be placed in an atomic-powered submarine, miniaturized, injected into the scientist's bloodstream, and set on a course through the arteries to the brain. In addition to American secret agent Grant, the crew consists of Dr. Duval, the surgeon who will perform the operation; Cora Peterson, his assistant; Dr. Michaels, a circulatory expert; and Captain Owens, the sub's pilot. To save some of the 60 minutes, the group decides to stop the scientist's heart to allow the submarine to pass through the heart. Then Grant and the crew leave the sub, and by means of a snorkel tube attached to the patient's lungs, replenish their oxygen supply. As they near their destination, a nurse in the operating room drops a pair of surgical scissors, and the sound causes tremendous vibrations in the sub that hurl the crew from their positions. With only 6 minutes left, Dr. Michaels reveals himself to be an enemy agent intent on sabotaging the mission. The remaining crew members escape as white corpuscles envelop and digest both the submarine and Michaels. The operation is successfully performed by removing a blood clot with a laser beam, and the four survivors leave the scientist's body by swimming along the optic nerve and emerging through a tear duct. *Scientists. Czechoslovakians. Secret agents. Physicians. Surgeons. Nurses. Miniaturization. Brain surgery. Anatomy. Sabotage. Submarines. Laser. Iron Curtain. The Future.*

EL FANTASTICO MUNDO DEL DR. COPPELIUS see DR. COPPELIUS

LA FANTASTIQUE HISTOIRE VRAIE D'EDDIE CHAPMAN see TRIPLE CROSS

FANTÔMAS (France/Italy) F6.1468

P. A. C.–S. N. E. Gaumont–Fair Film–P. C. M. *Dist* Lopert Pictures. 5 Apr **1966** [New York opening]. Sd; col (Eastman Color). 35mm (Franscope). 104 min.

Prod Paul Cadéac, Alain Poiré. *Dir* André Hunebelle. *2d Unit Dir* Jacques Besnard. *Screenplay* Jean Halain, Pierre Foucaud. *Photog* Marcel Grignon. *Art Dir* Paul-Louis Boutié. *Film Ed* Jean Feyte. *Mus* Michel Magne. *Sd* René Forget. *Prod Mgr* Cyril Grize.

Cast: Jean Marais *(Fantômas/Fandor)*, Louis de Funès *(Inspector Juve)*, Mylène Demongeot *(Hélène)*, Marie-Hélène Arnaud *(Lady Beltham)*, Jacques Dynam *(Juve's assistant)*, Robert Dalban *(newspaper editor)*, Christian Toma *(chief inspector)*, Hugues Wanner, Michel Duplaix, Andrée Tainsy, Henri Attal, Pierre Collet, Rudy Lenoir, Jean Minisini, Bernard Musson, Dominique Zardi, Françoise Christophe, Jean Roger Caussimon, André Dumas, Henri Serre.

Mystery melodrama. Inspired by the "Fantômas" novels by: Marcel Allain and Pierre Souvestre. The mysterious criminal Fantômas is terrorizing all of France, much to the consternation of Police Commissioner Juve; but Fandor, a newspaper reporter, believes Fantômas is only a fiction created by the police to cover their own inability to capture real criminals. With the help of his fiancée, Hélène, a photographer, Fandor fakes a photographed interview with Fantômas. The printed story infuriates the real Fantômas, who kidnaps Fandor. The criminal, whose face is seemingly made of metal, allows Fandor 48 hours to publish a story retracting his earlier one, but in Fandor's absence, his editor prints an article under Fandor's byline that is even less palatable. Fantômas again kidnaps Fandor and, having the ability to duplicate human flesh, makes a mask of Fandor's face and uses the mask in executing a crime, thus leading the police to believe that Fantômas and Fandor are one and the same. Fantômas then commits crimes wearing a mask of Commissioner Juve's face, and the commissioner is jailed. Fantômas has also captured Hélène, but she and Fandor escape, though the police imprison Fandor along with Juve. Fantômas, disguised as a guard, frees them because he wishes to hold them while committing more crimes in their names. The two escape and with the help of the police pursue Fantômas. The criminal, however, eludes justice by escaping in a submarine. *Reporters. Photographers. Police. Editors. Kidnaping. Masks. Impersonation. Jailbreaks. Submarines.*

Note: Opened in Paris in Nov 1964 as *Fantômas* and in Rome in Sep 1967 as *Fantomas contro Scotland Yard.* Italian sources conflict in crediting the Italian production company.

FANTOMAS CONTRO SCOTLAND YARD see FANTÔMAS

FAR FROM THE MADDING CROWD (Great Britain)   F6.1469

Vic Films–Appia Films–Joseph Janni Productions. *Dist* Metro-Goldwyn-Mayer, Inc. 18 Oct **1967** [New York opening; c18 Oct 1967; LP34786]. Sd; col (Metrocolor). 35mm & 70mm (Panavision). 169 min. [See note.]

Prod Joseph Janni. *Assoc Prod* Edward Joseph. *Dir* John Schlesinger. *Screenplay* Frederic Raphael. *Dir Photog* Nicolas Roeg. *Camera Op* John Harris. *Camera Focus* Tony Richmond. *Art Dir* Roy Smith. *Set Decor* Peter James. *Prod Dsgn* Richard MacDonald. *Film Ed* Malcolm Cooke. *Mus Comp* Richard Rodney Bennett. *Mus Cond* Marcus Dods. *Sd Rec* Robin Gregory, John Aldred. *Sd Ed* Gordon Daniel, Alfred Cox. *Asst Dir* Kip Gowans, David Bracknell. *Prod Mgr* Frank Ernst. *Cont* Ann Skinner. *Cost Dsgn* Alan Barrett. *Makeup Artists* Bob Lawrence, Philip Leakey. *Hairdresser* Ivy Emmerton. *Folk Song Adv* Isla Cameron. *Camera Grip* Ted Tucker. *Casting Dir* Miriam Brickman. *Horsemaster* Max Faulkner.

Cast: Julie Christie (*Bathsheba Everdene*), Terence Stamp (*Sergeant Troy*), Peter Finch (*William Boldwood*), Alan Bates (*Gabriel Oak*), Fiona Walker (*Liddy*), Prunella Ransome (*Fanny*), Alison Leggatt (*Mrs. Hurst*), Paul Dawkins (*Henery Fray*), Julian Somers (*Jan Coggan*), John Barrett (*Joseph Poorgrass*), Freddie Jones (*Cainy Ball*), Andrew Robertson (*Andrew Randle*), Brian Rawlinson (*Matthew Moon*), Vincent Harding (*Mark Clark*), Victor Stone (*Billy Smallbury*), Owen Berry (*Old Smallbury*), Lawrence Carter (*Laban Tall*), Pauline Melville (*Mrs. Tall*), Harriet Harper (*Temperance*), Denise Coffey (*Soberness*), Margaret Lacey (*Maryann Money*), Marie Hopps (*Mrs. Coggan*), Peter Stone, actor (*Teddy Coggan*), Walter Gale (*Jacob Smallbury*), Leslie Anderson, Keith Hooper (*Boldwood's laborers*), Jonathan Newth (*gentleman at cockfight*), Derek Ware (*corporal*), John Donegal (*sailor*), Peggy Ann Clifford (*fat lady at circus*), Noel Henkel (*circus manager*), Bryan Mosley (*barker*), David Swarbrick (*fiddler at barn dance*), Julius Alba (*gentleman at party*), Frank Duncan, Hugh Walker (*farmers at corn exchange*), Michael Beint (*laborer*), John Garrie (*Pennyways*).

Drama. Source: Thomas Hardy, *Far From the Madding Crowd* (London, 1874). In England in the 1870's headstrong Bathsheba Everdene inherits her uncle's farm in Weatherbury and achieves the independence she desires. A short time later she hires a former neighbor, Gabriel Oak, to be her shepherd; a rejected suitor, Gabriel lost his own flock of sheep when one of his dogs drove them over a steep cliff. Ignoring Gabriel's love, Bathsheba impulsively sends a valentine to William Boldwood, a nearby gentleman farmer. When he misinterprets her capriciousness and proposes to her, Bathsheba promises to consider his offer. Instead, however, she becomes enamored of Frank Troy, a dashing cavalry officer. Unaware that Troy has refused to marry young Fanny Robin, a maidservant pregnant with his child, because she embarrassed him by going to the wrong church on their wedding day, Bathsheba foolishly becomes his wife. After Troy has gambled away most of Bathsheba's money and created disharmony among the farmhands, he discovers that Fanny has died in childbirth. Filled with remorse, he swears that he never loved Bathsheba, walks out on her, and disappears into the ocean. Bathsheba then promises to marry Boldwood when Troy is declared legally dead; but Troy appears at their engagement party and the nearly deranged Boldwood kills him. Shortly after Boldwood has been sent to prison, Gabriel tells Bathsheba that he is planning to emigrate to America. Realizing how much she has always needed his quiet strength and unselfish devotion, Bathsheba persuades Gabriel to remain in Weatherbury as her husband. *Farmers. Shepherds. Neighbors. Soldiers. Housemaids. Inheritance. Farm life. Courtship. Marriage. Pregnancy. Desertion. Murder. Suicide. Sheep.*

Note: Location scenes filmed in Wiltshire and Dorset, England. Released in Great Britain in 1967. For second-run engagements the distributor cut the running time to 143 min and changed the ending: early showings conclude with a shot of Bathsheba's music-box clock that Troy gave her, suggesting that in spite of her marriage to Gabriel, Troy will remain her true love; subsequent version concludes with a shot of the couple just after their marriage. Previously filmed in Great Britain in 1915 (Turner Films). Folk songs include: "Bushes and Briars," "The Bold Grenadier," "The Jolly Tinker," and "The Banks of Allan Water."

FAR FROM VIETNAM (France)   F6.1470

S. L. O. N. *Dist* New Yorker Films. 6 Jun **1968** [New York opening]. Sd; b&w with col seq. 35mm (see note). 90 min.

Organizer Jacqueline Meppiel, Andréa Haran. *Dir* Alain Resnais, William Klein, Joris Ivens, Agnès Varda, Claude Lelouch, Jean-Luc Godard. *Film Ed* Chris Marker. *Principal Collab (see note)* Michèle Ray, Roger Pic, K. S. Karol, Marceline Loridan, François Maspero, Chris Marker, Jacques Sternberg, Jean Lacouture, Willy Kurant, Jean Boffety, Jean Bosty, Kieu Tham, Denis Clairval, Ghislain Cloquet, Bernard Zitzermann, Alain Levent, Théo Robichet, Antoine Bonfanti, Harold Maury, Pierre Grunstein, Alain Franchet, Didier Beaudet, Florence Malraux, Marie-Louise Guinet, Ragnar, Jean Ravel, Roger de Monenstral, Colette Leloup, Eric Pluet, Albert Jurgenson, Ethel Blum, Michèle Bouder, Christian Quinson, Jean Larivière, Maurice Garrel, Bernard Fresson, Karen Blanguernon, Anne Bellec, Valérie Mayoux.

Film essay. For the making of this film expressing solidarity with the people of North Vietnam, six directors pooled their talents with some 150 members of the French film industry. The sequences include: footage of American bombings of North Vietnam as a narrator describes how a poor country can resist the power of a rich one; Hubert Humphrey's 1966 tour of Europe intercut with footage of anti-American demonstrations in Paris; a Loyalty Day parade in New York and May Day demonstrations on Wall Street; American TV commercials interspersed with war footage; traveling clowns in North Vietnam satirizing Lyndon Johnson and Robert McNamara; a fictional left-wing intellectual from Alain Resnais' forthcoming film (*Je t'aime, je t'aime*) trying to justify his ambivalent attitude toward U. S. intervention in Vietnam and arguing himself into silence; Ho Chi Minh declaring that his people are engaged in a patriotic war that America will lose; Jean-Luc Godard speaking of his regret that he could not get permission to enter North Vietnam and of his feelings about motion pictures and Hollywood's dominating influence; Tom Paxton singing an anti-war ballad; French reporter-photographer Michèle Ray explaining how her views changed when she spent several weeks as a prisoner of the Vietcong; General Westmoreland (shown on an out-of-focus TV screen) asserting that the war is part of a Communist conspiracy; Fidel Castro defining the reasons for the success of guerrilla warfare; Uyen, a Vietnamese woman in Paris, talking with the widow of Norman Morrison, an American Quaker who burned himself to death in front of the Pentagon as a protest against the war; and a view of the April 1967 Peace Rally in Central Park. *Filmmakers. Intellectuals. Aerial bombardment. Demonstrations. Television commercials. Vietnam War 1964–73. Democratic Republic of Vietnam. Republic of Vietnam. Hanoi. New York City. Lyndon Baines Johnson. Ho Chi Minh. Norman Morrison. Michèle Ray. Jean-Luc Godard. Fidel Castro Ruz. Tom Paxton. William Childs Westmoreland. Robert Strange McNamara. Hubert Horatio Humphrey.*

Note: Some sequences filmed in 16mm. Paris opening: Dec 1967 as *Loin du Viêtnam*; running time: 120 min. In indicating the collaborators working on the film, some sources credit Jean Bosty in place of Jean Boffety.

THE FAR HORIZONS see UNTAMED WEST

FARÁŘŮV KONEC see END OF A PRIEST

LE FARCEUR see THE JOKER

FAREWELL, DOVES (U.S.S.R.)   F6.1471

Yalta Film Studio. *Dist* Artkino Pictures. 17 Mar **1962** [New York opening]. Sd; b&w. 35mm. 82 min. [Also 94 min?]

Dir-Writ Yakov Segel. *Story* G. Bakhtiyarova, V. Pogozheva. *Photog* V. Ilyenko. *Camera* V. Kalyuta. *Art Dir* L. Georgiyev, V. Levental. *Film Ed* L. Rodionova. *Mus* M. Fradkin. *Song Lyr* M. Matusovskiy. *Cond* G. Gamburg. *Sd* V. Dmitriyev. *Asst Dir* V. Grigoryev, Ye. Fridman. *Prod Mgr* A. Yablochkin. *Cost* N. Panova.

Cast: Aleksey Loktev (*Gena*), Svetlana Savyolova (*Tanya*), Valentina Telegina (*Mariya Yefimovna*), Sergey Plotnikov (*Maksim Petrovich*), A. Nikolayeva, P. Postnikova, A. Maksimova, A. Sumarokov, V. Pridayevich, Leonid Gallis, G. Ignatyeva, S. Kramarov, P. Vesklyarov, V. Teslya, Valentin Bryleyev, Olya Narovchatova, Ye. Anufriyev, V. Savinykh, Ye. Kovalenko, V. Tvoruzhek, V. Dibrov, I. Markevich.

Comedy-drama. Gena has begun to earn his own livelihood as an apprentice gas worker in Kiev, meanwhile devoting his leisure to his childhood hobby of raising pigeons. At work he is disturbed to discover that his supervisor, Maksim Petrovich, accepts tips from clients. He reacts by rising early and completing the daily work by the time that Maksim arrives on the job, sparking a transformation in the older man's outlook. Gena's life begins to change when he falls in love with Tanya, a student nurse. Tanya is surprised to find that Gena is not a member of the Komsomol youth group but spends his free time alone. As the young people face parental misgivings over their relationship, another romance develops between Maksim Petrovich and Gena's widowed mother. Gena arranges to join Tanya at a Komsomol meeting. On the way he sees smoke pouring from a garret window and rushes to the fire, extinguishing it before the fire engines arrive. At the meeting, concern at Gena's tardiness gives way to admiration as his heroism is revealed. He begins to take an active part in the Komsomol activities and becomes engaged to Tanya. Seeing that his pigeons are old enough to fly away independently, Gena releases them from their rooftop cage. [Synopsis based on Soviet version.] *Gasmen. Widows. Students. Nurses. Adolescence. Ethics. Filial relations. Kiev. Komsomol. Fires. Pigeons.*

Note: Released in the U.S.S.R. in Mar 1961 as *Proshchayte, golubi!*; running time: 95 min.

FAREWELL, MY BELOVED (Japan)   F6.1472
Shochiku Co. *Dist* Shochiku Films of America. Oct **1969** [Los Angeles opening]. Sd; col (Eastmancolor). 35mm (Shochiku GrandScope). 93 min.

Dir Hideo Oba. *Story-Screenplay* Genyo Takahashi. *Photog* Hiroyuki Nagaoka. *Art Dir* Tadataka Yoshino. *Mus* Chuji Kinoshita.

Cast: Kazuo Funaki *(Makito)*, Mayumi Ozora *(Yuko)*, Ken Ogata *(Tadayuki)*, Nana Ozaki *(Yumiko)*.

Romantic melodrama. During the early days of World War II Makito, a young student, falls in love with Yuko, the widow of a naval officer. She is unable to return his affection, as the memory of her husband remains strong, but her younger sister, Yumiko, is attracted to Makito. Inspired by the example of Tadayuki, a naval officer and friend of Yuko's late husband, Makito enters the naval academy and is later disappointed by the news of Yuko's forthcoming marriage to Tadayuki. Shortly after the wedding Tadayuki is assigned to the Kamikaze Squadron, never to return. After the war Makito learns of the deaths of his mother and of Yumiko. He meets Yuko and informs her that Tadayuki was assigned to the Kamikaze Squadron because he had married his friend's widow. Yuko, feeling responsible for Tadayuki's death, thanks Makito for his devotion and takes her own life. *Students. Widows. Kamikazes. Military life. Suicide. Marriage. World War II. Japan—Navy.*

Note: Released in Japan in Feb 1969 as *Wakare*.

FARGO see WILD SEED

FARM DIARY   F6.1473
Dist Film-Makers' Cooperative. 11 Nov **1970** [New York opening]. Si; col. 8mm. 64 min.

Dir Gordon Ball. *Photog* Gordon Ball.

Cast: Peter Orlovsky, Candy O'Brien, Allen Ginsberg, Julius Orlovsky, Gordon Ball, Gregory Corso, Myron Wiles, Stephen Bornstein, Barbara Pionteck, Herbert Huncke, Jim Fourratt, Louis Cartwright, Ed the Hermit, Panda Manda, Any Raccoon, Bessie, Godly, Sadeyes, Papa Duck, Malcolm, Tyger, Brahma, Vishnu, Shiva, Sonja, Lygia, Cyril, Enrique, Maretta.

Documentary. A chronicle of life on the filmmaker's farm during its first 10 months. *Farm life. Rural life. Farming. Animal life.*

FARM GIRL see THE FARMER'S OTHER DAUGHTER

THE FARMER'S OTHER DAUGHTER   F6.1474
Dist United Producers Releasing Organization. 9 Jun **1965** [San Francisco opening; c9 Jun 1965; LP31250]. Sd; col. 35mm. 84 min.

Prod William Norton, Paul Leder. *Dir* John Hayes. *Screenplay* William Norton. *Camera* Paul Hipp. *Asst Camera* Arnold Baskin. *Set Dsgn* Ray Storey. *Film Ed* Bob Brebor. *Mus Comp & Cond* Victor Pierce. *Mus Coörd* Robert McCluskey. *Song:* "Ballad of Farmer Brown" Don Robertson, Jack Speirs. *Sung by* The Kentucky Colonels. *Sd* Arnold Federbush. *Sd Ed* Ron Hanthaner. *Script Girl* Barbara Bohrer. *Prod Asst* Walter V. Bodlander. *Makeup* Michael Mucsi. *Sp Eff* Carl Olson. *"American Gothic" by Grant Wood Courtesy of Art Institute of Chicago. Gaffer* Ross Kelsay. *Prop* Lee Pogoler.

Cast: Judy Pennebaker *(June)*, Bill Michael *(Jim Huckleberry)*, William Guhl *(Cyrus B. Barksnapper)*, Harry Lovejoy *(Horace Jefferson Brown)*, Jean Bennett *(Ma Jefferson Brown)*, Norman Hartweg *(Cyrus, Jr.)*, Janice Evan *(Elsie)*, Jack Barbour *(sheriff)*, Robert Adamson *(deputy)*, Joseph Sharon *(Cedric)*, Norman Fields *(government man)*, Lyle Gordon *(mayor)*, Marci Stone *(government girl)*, Clarence White, Roland White, Roger Bush, Donavan Cotton, Richard Greene, mus, Billy Ray Latham *(The Kentucky Colonels)*, Ernest Ashworth.

Rural comedy. Horace Jefferson Brown struggles to keep his farm and protect the virtue of his daughter, June. Salesman Jim Huckleberry's arrival saves Brown from the harassment of the sheriff and his deputy, and Jim is quickly taken into the family fold. June and Jim fall in love at first sight, and he easily persuades her and the other girls of the area to use his newly invented bathing suits for the 4th of July beauty contest. Meanwhile, boss Cyrus B. Barksnapper and his retarded son, Cyrus, Jr., offer to buy June for $1 million, but Horace refuses. Jim calls the Department of Agriculture in Washington, D. C., and applies for farm aid, but because of a government error, the Browns begin to receive foreign aid. That night, June and Jim sneak away to the barn to reaffirm their love. On July 4th, during a swim contest, Jim's bathing suits

disintegrate, and the townsfolk threaten him with lynching. The Barksnappers, angered over Horace's refusal to sell his daughter, call on the militia to force the Browns from their home. Horace is taken prisoner, and June, to save her father, decides to give herself to the Barksnappers. Jim escapes the mob, blows up the jail, and rescues Horace, and they rush to the Barksnappers to save June. The government aid is straightened out; the first loan check arrives; and June and Jim gain the family's approval to marry. *Farmers. Salesmen. Sheriffs. Farm life. Filial relations. Courtship. Mental retardation. Lynching. Eviction. Finance—Personal. Inventions. Loans. Fourth of July. United States—Agriculture Department.*

Note: Also known as *Farm Girl*.

FASCINATION (Reissue)   F6.1475
Allied Artists. 2 Aug **1961** [New York showing]. Sd; b&w. 35mm. 125 min.
Note: Originally released as *Love in the Afternoon* in 1957; c23 May 1957; LP8303.

THE FASCIST (Italy)   F6.1476
Dino De Laurentiis Cinematografica. *Dist* Embassy Pictures. 17 Jun **1965** [New York opening]. Sd; b&w. 35mm. 102 min.

Prod Isidoro Broggi, Renato Libassi. *Dir* Luciano Salce. *Screenplay* Luciano Salce, Pipolo, Franco Castellano. *Story* Pipolo, Franco Castellano. *Photog* Erico Menczer. *Mus* Ennio Morricone.

Cast: Ugo Tognazzi *(Primo Arcovazzi)*, Georges Wilson *(Professor Bonafè)*, Stefania Sandrelli *(Lisa)*, Mireille Granelli *(Rita)*, Gianrico Tedeschi *(Baldacci)*, Elsa Vazzoler *(Baldacci's wife)*, Franco Giacobini, Renzo Palmer, Gianni Agus, Luciano Salce.

Comedy-drama. In Italy in 1944, the Fascist High Command sends the fanatical Primo Arcovazzi to find and capture Professor Bonafè, a well-known anti-Fascist, who is hiding until the liberation of the country from the Germans. En route to Rome, the two are involved in a series of incidents, including imprisonment by the Germans, an air raid, and the loss of their clothes. When they arrive in Rome on 4 June 1944, the city is about to fall to the Americans, and a crowd of revenge-seeking citizens beat up and want to shoot Arcovazzi, who is dressed in a Fascist officer's uniform sold to him by the two teenagers responsible for stealing his own clothes. Bonafè lends Arcovazzi his civilian clothing, however, and helps him escape. *Professors. Fascism. Military occupation. World War II. Rome. Germany—Army. United States Army.*

Note: Released in Italy in 1961 as *Il federale*.

FASHION HOUSE OF DEATH see BLOOD AND BLACK LACE

THE FAST LADY (Great Britain)   F6.1477
Independent Artists. *Dist* Continental Distributing, Inc. 23 Jul **1965** [Maryland license; c24 Feb 1963; LF161]. Sd; col (Eastmancolor). 35mm. 95 min.

A Julian Wintle–Leslie Parkyn Production. *Prod* Julian Wintle, Leslie Parkyn. *Dir* Ken Annakin. *2d Unit Dir* Don Sharp. *Screenplay* Jack Davies, Henry Blyth. *Dir Photog* Reg Wyer. *Dir Photog 2d Unit* Michael Reed. *Camera Op* Dudley Lovell. *Camera Focus* Ian McMillan. *Art Dir* Harry Pottle. *Set Dresser* Peter Lamont. *Draughtsman* Eric Saw, Michael Lamont. *Film Ed* Ralph Sheldon. *1st Asst Ed* Harry Ledger. *Mus Comp & Cond* Norrie Paramor. *Sd* Lionel Selwyn. *Sd Rec* Peter Davies, John W. Mitchell. *Sd Camera Op* Michael Sale. *1st, 2d & 3d Asst Dir* Clive Reed, John Danischewsky, Eamonn Duffy. *Prod Supv* Arthur Alcott. *Location Mgr* Eddie Pike. *Cont* Joy Mercer. *Prod Sec* Jean White. *Cost Dsgn* Julie Harris, cost. *Wardrobe Mistress* Vi Murray. *Ch Makeup* Trevor Crole-Rees. *Makeup Artist* John Wilcox, makeup. *Hairdresser* Maud Onslow. *Still Photog* David James. *Constr Mgr* Charles Hammerton. *Prop Master* Fred Eames. *Prop Buyer* Harry Parr. *Grip* George Bryan. *Electrn H.O.D.* E. Gubbins.

Cast: James Robertson-Justice *(Charles Chingford)*, Stanley Baxter *(Murdoch Troon)*, Leslie Phillips *(Freddy Fox)*, Kathleen Harrison *(Mrs. Staggers)*, Julie Christie *(Claire Chingford)*, Eric Barker *(Wentworth)*, Oliver Johnston *(Bulmer)*, Allan Cuthbertson *(Bodley)*, Esma Cannon *(lady on road crossing)*, Dick Emery *(Shingler)*, Deryck Guyler *(Dr. Blake)*, Victor Brooks *(policeman)*, Terence Alexander *(police motorcyclist)*, Danny Green, Michael Balfour, Eddie Leslie *(bandits)*, Clive Dunn *(old gentleman)*, Campbell Singer *(Kingscombe)*, Trevor Reid *(examiner)*, Fred Emney, Frankie Howerd, Eddie Gray, Raymond Baxter, Graham Hill, John Bolster, John Surtees, Bill Fraser.

Comedy. Murdoch Troon, a young Scottish civil servant working in England, meets Claire Chingford, the daughter of the local Lord of the Manor and magistrate, as a result of being knocked down by her father's Rolls-Royce while on an outing with his bicycling club. Freddy Fox, a used-car dealer with whom Murdoch lodges, persuades him that Claire would be impressed if he owned a sports car. After dreaming of being a racing driver, Murdoch purchases a vintage Bentley from Freddy, who offers to teach him to drive if Murdoch will help Freddy acquire the agency for Chingford's motor business. The lesson is a disaster, and they end up in court, where the magistrate is Chingford. After a further mishap in which both Murdoch and Claire end up in the sea, Chingford forbids Murdoch to see his daughter until he has passed a driving test. While taking the test, Murdoch becomes involved in a wild chase of bank robbers; he fails the test but gets Chingford's consent to marry Claire. *Civil servants. Scotch. Used-car dealers. Bicyclists. Magistrates. Reckless driving. Bank robberies. Sports cars. Rolls-Royce automobiles. Bentley automobiles.*

Note: Opened in London in Feb 1963.

FASTER, PUSSYCAT! KILL! KILL!   F6.1478

Eve Productions. 6 Aug **1965** [Los Angeles showing; c1 Feb 1966; LP32194]. Sd; b&w. 35mm. 83 min.

Prod Russ Meyer, Eve Meyer. *Assoc Prod* Fred Owens, George Costello. *Dir* Russ Meyer. *Screenplay* Jack Moran. *Orig Story* Russ Meyer. *Photog* Walter Schenk. *Film Ed* Russ Meyer. *Mus Dir* Igo Kantor. *Mus* Paul Sawtell, Bert Shefter. *Song:* "Faster Pussycat" Paul Sawtell, Bert Shefter. *Sung by* The Bostweeds. *Sd* Charles Schelling. *Asst Dir* George Costello. *Prod Mgr* Fred Owens. *Sp Photog Eff* Orville Hallberg.

Cast: Tura Satana *(Varla)*, Haji *(Rosie)*, Lori Williams *(Billie)*, Sue Bernard *(Linda)*, Stuart Lancaster *(old man)*, Paul Trinka *(Kirk)*, Dennis Busch *(Vegetable)*, Ray Barlow *(Tommy)*, Mickey Foxx *(attendant)*.

Action melodrama. Three go-go watusi dancers set out in a racing sports car for a few days of adventure, violence, and seduction. Leading the pack is Varla, a karate expert whose lesbian lover, Rosie, is little more than an obedient slave. The third woman, Billie, is somewhat reluctant to join in the escapade and is the only one possessing any redeeming qualities. Following a water fight in a nearby lake, the women challenge a young couple, Tommy and Linda, to a "chicken race." Varla wins by resorting to unfair tactics, and when Tommy objects she breaks his back with a karate chop. Horrified, Linda faints from shock. Leaving Tommy's body behind, the women take Linda hostage and drive to a country gas station run by an old man confined to a wheelchair and his muscle-bound, dim-witted son, simply called Vegetable. Upon learning that the old man has a cache of money hidden somewhere, the women decide to find a means of getting their hands on it. While Varla and Rosie continue their snooping—and lovemaking—Billie sets out to seduce Vegetable and is aided by the voyeuristic old man, who encourages his son to rape the girl. Events come to a climax with the arrival of Kirk, the old man's other son, who hangs around for the sake of his brother's welfare. When Varla attempts to seduce him as a means of learning where the money is hidden, the jealous Rosie gets drunk and passes out. Seeking to escape from her evil companions, Billie tries to run away, but she is caught and knifed in the back by Varla. When Rosie returns to the scene of the murder to retrieve the knife, Vegetable assumes that she is responsible for Billie's death and kills her. Desperate, the old man heads back to the house in his wheelchair for his shotgun. But Varla smashes him down with her sports car and finds the cache of money, which had been hidden in the wheelchair. She then tries to kill Vegetable, but his brute strength is sufficient to hold back her surging sports car. Kirk and Linda arrive, and a death struggle ensues during which Kirk is forced to fight Varla as though combating a man. Sensing that he is losing, Linda jumps into a truck and drives it at full force into Varla. *Go-go dancers. Cripples. Brothers. Voyeurism. Drunkenness. Sadism. Rape. Mental retardation. Lesbianism. Robbery. Murder. Seduction. Filial relations. Deserts. Filling stations. Sports cars. Karate. Automobile racing.*

Note: Filmed on location in the California desert. Also known as *The Leather Girls, The Mankillers,* and *Pussycat.*

THE FASTEST GUITAR ALIVE   F6.1479

Four Leaf Productions. *Dist* Metro-Goldwyn-Mayer, Inc. Sep **1967** [New York opening: 14 Feb 1968; c31 Dec 1966; LP34169]. Sd; col (Metrocolor). 35mm. 87 min.

Prod Sam Katzman. *Assoc Prod* Jerome F. Katzman. *Dir* Michael Moore. *Writ* Robert E. Kent. *Dir Photog* W. Wallace Kelley. *Art Dir* George W. Davis, Merrill Pye. *Set Decor* Henry Grace, Joseph J. Stone. *Film Ed* Ben Lewis. *Mus Score & Cond by* Fred Karger. *Songs:* "The Fastest Guitar Alive," "Pistolero," "Good Time Party," "River," "Whirlwind," "Medicine Man," "Rollin' On" Roy Orbison, Bill Dees. *Song:* "Snuggle Huggle" Fred Karger. *Songs Sung by* Roy Orbison. *Choreog* Wilda Taylor. *Rec Supv* Franklin Milton. *Asst Dir* Donald C. Klune. *Prod Coörd* Robert Stone. *Makeup* William Tuttle. *Hairstyles* Mary Keats.

Cast: Roy Orbison *(Johnny Banner)*, Sammy Jackson *(Steve Menlo)*, Maggie Pierce *(Flo Chestnut)*, Joan Freeman *(Sue Chestnut)*, Lyle Bettger *(Charlie Mansfield)*, John Doucette *(Sheriff Max Cooper)*, Patricia Donahue *(Stella)*, Ben Cooper *(Rink)*, Ben Lessy *(Indian chief)*, Douglas Kennedy *(Joe)*, Len Hendry *(deputy)*, Iron Eyes Cody *(1st Indian)*, Sam the Sham *(1st expressman)*, Wilda Taylor *(Emily)*, Victoria Carroll *(Margie)*, Maria Korda *(Tanya)*, Poupée Gamin *(Carmen)*, Daniel M. White *([see note])*.

Comedy-drama with music. During the last months of the Civil War, Johnny Banner and Steve Menlo cross the plains in a horse-drawn medicine wagon, a cover for their actual roles as Confederate spies planning to rob a government mint. Johnny scares off a band of Indians with a rifle concealed in his guitar when the caravan is attacked. The medicine wagon is accompanied by another wagon transporting a bevy of dancing barmaids, including the Chestnut sisters, Sue and Flo, who love Johnny and Steve. Johnny's girl, unaware that his only purpose is to get information about the mint, becomes jealous when Johnny starts giving guitar lessons to the governor's daughter. Once the mint has been robbed of $150,000, the two wagons set out to deliver the gold to a Confederate general. Then word arrives that the war is over, and Johnny and Steve realize they are no longer Southern patriots but common thieves. Their efforts to return the gold to the authorities are complicated by the conniving Charlie Mansfield, a Barbary Coast spy for whom they previously worked, but the troupe finally escapes with the assistance of the Indians. In exchange for the shooting guitar, Johnny and his friends are assured of safe passage to a Union fort where they plan to surrender their bounty. *Spies. Guitarists. Indians of North America. Barmaids. Soldiers. Disguise. Theft. Firearms. Gold. United States—History— Civil War.*

Note: Daniel M. White's participation in the cast is unconfirmed.

THE FASTEST GUN *see* THE QUICK GUN

DIE FASTNACHTSBEICHTE (West Germany)   F6.1480

UFA. *Dist* Casino Films. 25 May **1962** [Chicago opening]. Sd; col. 35mm. 101 min.

Exec Prod Dietrich von Theobald. *Dir* William Dieterle. *Screenplay* Kurt Heuser. *Photog* Heinz Pehlke. *Camera Op* Wolfgang Treu. *Camera Asst* Bernhard Hellmund. *Art Dir* Emil Hasler, Walter Kutz. *Film Ed* Carl Otto Bartning. *Mus* Siegfried Franz. *Sd* Heinz Garbowski. *Asst Dir* Eberhard Itzenplitz. *Prod Asst* Wolfgang Völker. *Prod Mgr* Hans-Bolko Marcard. *Cost* Manon Hahn. *Makeup* Alois Woppmann, Ursula Mrukwa. *Prop* Helmut Deutker, Walther Rother.

Cast: Hans Söhnker *(Panezza)*, Gitty Daruga *(Viola)*, Götz George *(undetermined role)*, Friedrich Domin *(Canon Henrici)*, Berta Drews *(Frau Bäumler)*, Hilde Hildebrandt *(Madame Guttier)*, Helga Tölle *(Katharina)*, Rainer Brandt *(Ferdinand Bäumler)*, Herbert Tiede *(Merzbecher)*, Grit Böttcher, Ursula Heyer, Helga Schlack, Milena von Eckardt, Albert Bessler, Christian Wolff.

Melodrama. Source: Carl Zuckmayer, *Die Fastnachtsbeichte* (Frankfurt am Main, 1959). Mainz, 1913. Amid the carnival festivities several days before Ash Wednesday, a man, later identified as Ferdinand Bäumler, is found murdered in the cathedral. Police Detective Merzbecher investigates several persons: Panezza, the carnival prince and guilt-ridden father of the illegitimate Ferdinand; Panezza's niece Viola, who later confesses her involvement in the crime; a soldier whose uniform Ferdinand was wearing; and Katharina, the carnival princess with whom Ferdinand was hopelessly in love. A second murder occurs, but the criminals are caught on Ash Wednesday. *Detectives. Uncles. Soldiers. Murder. Guilt. Illegitimacy. Confession. Carnivals. Cathedrals. Ash Wednesday. Mainz.*

Note: Opened in Mainz in Sep 1960; running time: 101 min.

THE FAT BLACK PUSSYCAT   F6.1481

Stormco Productions–Film Programs, Inc. *Dist* Cinema Distributors of America. 6 Aug **1964** [New York State license; c31 Dec 1963; LP29333]. Sd; b&w. 35mm. 94 min. [Copyright length: 90 min.]

Prod Arnold Panken, Evelyn Storm. *Assoc Prod* Robert Steuer. *Dir-Writ* (see note) Harold Lea. *Story-Screenplay* M. A. Ripps. *Photog* John Landey, Baet Carroll. *Film Ed* Frank Forestieri. *Mus* Don Bader. *Sd Eff* Independent Productions. *Prod Mgr* Joe Catalanatto.

Cast: Frank Janus *(detective)*, Janet Damon *(Janet)*, Patricia McNair *(Mitch)*, Hugh Romney *(assistant detective)*, Lynn Gregory *(Susie)*, Dia Mitchell *(Dia)*, Barbara Wilkinson *(Claire)*.

Melodrama. The beatnik haunts of Greenwich Village are the scene of a series of sadistic murders. Five hedonistic young women meet their deaths before two police detectives discover the identity of the murderer—The Cat, a teacher who kills to quell her uncontrollable lesbian urges. *Beatniks. Detectives. Murder. Sadism. Lesbianism. Hedonism. New York City— Greenwich Village.*

Note: Written and directed by Harold Lea, according to screen credit; press material credits M. A. Ripps with story and screenplay.

THE FAT SPY   F6.1482

Phillip Productions–Magna Pictures. *Dist* Magna Pictures Distribution Corp. 11 May **1966** [Los Angeles opening]. Sd; col. 35mm. 75 min.

Prod Everett Rosenthal. *Assoc Prod* Rick Pleven. *Dir* Joseph Cates. *Screenplay* Matthew Andrews. *Photog* Joseph Brun. *Main Titl* Elinor Bunin. *Film Ed (see note)* Barry Malkin, Mort Fallick. *Mus* Al Kasha, Joel Hirschhorn, Hank Hunter. *Songs:* "Wild Way of Living," "People Sure Act Funny" Chuck Alden, Jordan Christopher. *Sd* Charles Federmack. *Asst Dir* George Goodman. *Wardrobe for Miss Mansfield* Lilli Pearlman. *Makeup* Clay Lambert.

Cast: Phyllis Diller *(Camille)*, Jack E. Leonard *(Irving/Herman)*, Brian Donlevy *(Wellington)*, Jayne Mansfield *(Junior)*, Jordan Christopher *(Frankie)*, The Wild Ones *(themselves)*, Johnny Tillotson *(Dodo)*, Lauree Berger *(Nanette)*, Lou Nelson *(sikh)*, Toni Lee Shelley *(mermaid)*, Penny Roman *(secretary)*, Adam Keefe *(special voices)*, Chuck Alden, Tommy Graves, Linda Harrison, Deborah White, Tracy Vance, Eddie Wright, Tommy Trick, Toni Turner, Jill Bleidner, Jeanette Taylor *(treasure hunters)*.

Comedy with music. On a small island near Florida, a dozen teenagers combine singing and dancing on the beach with a search for buried treasure. They do not know that Irving, "The Fat Spy," is also there seeking Ponce de León's legendary Fountain of Youth for cosmetics tycoon Wellington. When Irving fails to drive the youngsters from the island, he calls upon his brother Herman for help. Herman is madly in love with another cosmetics manufacturer, Camille, who is also searching for the precious youth fluid. And completing the group of modern-day explorers is Wellington's seductive daughter, Junior. After a series of mishaps and mixups, all concerned finally descend upon the fountain. But they are thwarted by the sudden and miraculous appearance of Ponce de León and his fiancée, who prevent their treasured secret from falling into the hands of mere mortals. *Tycoons. Brothers. Adolescence. Eternal youth. Beaches. Cosmetics. Treasure. Florida. Juan Ponce de León.*

Note: Filmed in Cape Coral, Florida. Sources conflict in crediting film editor.

FATAL DESIRE (Italy)   F6.1483

Excelsa Film. *Dist* Ultra Pictures. 9 Jan **1963** [Newark, New Jersey, opening]. Sd; b&w and col (see note). 35mm. 80 min.

Dir Carmine Gallone. *Screenplay* Mario Monicelli, Basilio Franchina, Francesco De Feo, Arthur Cohn, Carmine Gallone. *Photog* Karl Struss, Riccardo Pallottini. *Mus Cond* Oliviero De Fabritiis. *Song:* "O che bel mestiere" sung by Tito Gobbi.

Cast: Anthony Quinn *(Alfio)*, May Britt *(Santuzza)*, Umberto Spadaro *(Uncle Brasi)*, Kerima *(Lola)*, Ettore Manni *(Turiddu)*, Grazia Spadaro *(Aunt Camilla)*, Virginia Balestrieri *(Mamma Lucia)*.

Melodrama. Source: Giovanni Verga, "Cavalleria rusticana," in *Cavalleria rusticana ed altre novelle* (Milan, 1880). Pietro Mascagni, Giovanni Targioni-Tozzetti and Guido Menasci, *Cavalleria rusticana* (first performance: Rome, 17 May 1890). Turiddu returns to his Sicilian village after 5 years of military service and finds that his old sweetheart Lola is about to marry Alfio. After the marriage, Turiddu pays court to Santuzza, and gradually they seem to fall in love. Lola eventually becomes bored with the stolid Alfio and succeeds in tempting Turiddu to rekindle their love. One night, during the absence of Alfio, who is often away on business trips, Santuzza sees Turiddu enter Lola's house. The next day is Easter Sunday, and while everyone is in church, the jealous Santuzza blurts out the truth of Lola and Turiddu's betrayal to Alfio, who has just returned. Alfio challenges Turiddu to a duel, and Turiddu is killed. *Veterans. Cuckolds. Marriage. Infidelity. Jealousy. Easter. Sicily. Duels.*

Note: Released in Italy in 1953 as *Cavalleria rusticana* in Ferranicolor.

LE FATE *see* THE QUEENS

FATE IS THE HUNTER   F6.1484

Arcola Pictures. *Dist* Twentieth Century–Fox Film Corp. 30 Sep **1964** [Boston opening; c30 Sep 1964; LP28964]. Sd (Westrex); b&w. 35mm (CinemaScope). 106 min.

An Aaron Rosenberg Production. *Prod* Aaron Rosenberg. *Dir* Ralph Nelson. *Screenplay* Harold Medford. *Addl Photog* Milton Krasner. *Dir Photog* Leon Shamroy. *Art Dir* Jack Martin Smith, Hilyard Brown. *Set Decor* Walter M. Scott, Stuart A. Reiss. *Film Ed* Robert Simpson. *Mus* Jerry Goldsmith. *Titl Song* Jerry Goldsmith, Don Wolf. *Song:* "No Love, No Nothin'" Harry Warren, Leo Robin. *Sung by* Jane Russell. *Sd* Carlton W. Faulkner, Elmer Raguse. *Asst Dir* Ad Schaumer. *Prod Mgr* William Kaplan. *Cost Dsgn* Moss Mabry. *Makeup* Ben Nye. *Hairstyles* Margaret Donovan. *Sp Photog Eff* L. B. Abbott, Emil Kosa, Jr.

Cast: Glenn Ford *(Sam McBane)*, Nancy Kwan *(Sally Fraser)*, Rod Taylor *(Capt. Jack Savage)*, Suzanne Pleshette *(Martha Webster)*, Jane Russell *(herself, guest star)*, Wally Cox *(Ralph Bundy)*, Nehemiah Persoff *(Ben Sawyer)*, Mark Stevens *(Mickey Doolan)*, Max Showalter *(Dan Crawford)*, Constance Towers *(Peg Burke)*, Howard St. John *(Mark Hutchins)*, Robert J. Wilke *(Stillman)*, Bert Freed *(Dillon)*, Dort Clark *(Ted Wilson)*, Mary Wickes *(Mrs. Llewelyn)*, Robert F. Simon *(Proctor)*, Dorothy Malone *(Lisa Bond)*.

Mystery melodrama. Source: Ernest K. Gann, *Fate Is the Hunter* (New York, 1961). Continental Airlines flight 22, piloted by Capt. Jack Savage, crashes after departing Los Angeles, killing all 53 passengers and crew members except stewardess Martha Webster. Sam McBane, the airline's director of flight operations, begins an investigation of the disaster. He learns that Savage radioed shortly after takeoff that his right engine was on fire and requested

permission to land. He was told to maintain altitude on his left engine until a flight path could be cleared, but the plane crashed. McBane is baffled because the left engine's thrust should have been enough to maintain altitude. He learns from Martha, who had been in the cabin serving coffee, that soon after the right engine caught fire, a signal flashed indicating that the left engine was also aflame. Savage switched off that engine, too, and tried to land on a secluded beach but was unable to avoid crashing into an old pier. Inspecting the wreckage, McBane discovers that the left engine never caught fire, and he wonders about Martha's story. Rumors are spread that Savage was drunk before taking off, but McBane, who had served with Savage during the war, doubts this and investigates further. Sally Fraser, Savage's beneficiary in his will, insists the crash was just fate. McBane decides to reenact the fatal flight in the same kind of plane and with Martha aboard. When he cuts off the right engine, the plane lurches, causing Martha to spill the coffee she is serving. Shortly afterward, the warning light flashes, indicating that the left engine is aflame. McBane has the panel on which the coffee spilled pried up and discovers that the liquid had shorted the wires that controlled the fire signal, causing it to flash. Savage is vindicated. *Air pilots. Airline stewardesses. Investigators. Veterans. Reputation. Drunkenness. Airplanes—Jet. Airplane accidents.*

FATE OF A MAN (U.S.S.R.)   F6.1485

Mosfilm. *Dist* Lopert Pictures. 10 Jul **1961** [New York opening]. Sd; b&w. 35mm. 100 min.

Dir Sergey Bondarchuk. *Screenplay* Yuriy Lukin, Fyodor Shakhmagonov. *Story Ed* V. Leonov. *Photog* Vladimir Monakhov. *Art Dir* I. Novoderezhkin, Sergey Voronkov. *Film Ed* Tatyana Likhachyova. *Mus* Veniamin Basner. *Mus Cond* G. Gamburg. *Sd* Yuriy Mikhaylov. *Asst Dir* A. Golovanov. *Prod Mgr* G. Kuznetsov. *Cost* O. Vereyskiy. *Makeup* N. Pechentsov. *Cons* P. Lyalyakin, V. Lorents.

Cast: Sergey Bondarchuk *(Andrey Sokolov)*, Pavlik Boriskin *(Vanyushka)*, Zoya Kiriyenko *(Irina)*, Pavel Volkov *(Ivan Timofeyevich)*, Yuriy Averin *(Myuller)*, K. Alekseyev *(German major)*, P. Vinnikov, Yevgeniy Teterin, Anatoliy Chemodurov, A. Novikov, L. Borisov, V. Markin, Ye. Kudryashov, A. Kuznetsov, actor 2, V. Ivanov, Pyotr Savin, Ye. Melnikova, V. Berezko, N. Aparin, N. Pechentsov, A. Puntus, G. Shapovalov, V. Strelnikov.

War melodrama. Source: Mikhail Aleksandrovich Sholokhov, *Sudba cheloveka; rasskaz* (Moscow, 1957). While waiting with a young boy for a ferry across the Don, Andrey Sokolov relates the story of his life to a chance acquaintance: After the revolution, Sokolov, who had been a member of the Red Army, marries Irina, and they have three children. The family's happiness is interrupted by the outbreak of World War II, and Andrey is mobilized as a truckdriver. As he carries ammunition to the front lines, his truck is hit by a bomb, and he is taken prisoner. Many of his fellow prisoners succumb to Nazi atrocities, but Andrey survives by thinking of his family. He escapes and eludes his captors for 3 days, but he is hunted with dogs and finally recaptured. At another camp his defiant remarks are overheard, and he is taken before the Nazi commandant, who offers him a drink before executing him. Andrey refuses to toast the Germans and instead drinks in honor of his own death. The commandant, impressed by Andrey's drinking ability, spares him. Later Andrey is assigned as a driver to a German major. Thus provided with another escape opportunity, he delivers the major, who is carrying secret documents, to the Russian front. After a stay in a military hospital, Andrey is given leave to return to his home in Voronezh. Here he learns that his wife and two daughters have been killed and his home destroyed during a bombing raid. On V-E Day, he learns that his son, a decorated officer, has been killed at the front. Driven from Voronezh by grief, Andrey moves to Uryupinsk and works as a truckdriver. One day he meets a homeless orphan boy, Vanyushka, who wanders about the streets dressed in tatters. Andrey's heart goes out to the sad-eyed child, and he claims to be the boy's father, giving them both a reason to start life anew. *Truckdrivers. Prisoners of war. Nazis. Escapees. War heroes. Orphans. Fatherhood. Courage. War crimes. Aerial bombardment. Concentration camps. World War II. V-E Day (7 May 1945). Voronezh. Uryupinsk.*

Note: Released in the U.S.S.R. in Apr 1959 as *Sudba cheloveka.*

FATHER (Hungary)   F6.1486

Mafilm Studios. *Dist* Continental Distributing, Inc. 4 Oct **1967** [New York opening]. Sd; b&w. 35mm. 95 min.

Dir-Writ István Szabó. *Scen* János Herskó. *Dir Photog* Sándor Sára. *Asst Photog* János Kende. *Film Ed* János Rózsa. *Mus* János Gonda. *Mus Selections* Gustav Mahler. *Sd* György Pintér. *Asst Dir* László Bánk. *Prod Mgr* Tibor Hranitzky. *Cost* Erzsébet Mialkovszky.

Cast: András Bálint *(Takó)*, Miklós Gábor *(father)*, Klári Tolnay *(mother)*, Dániel Erdélyi *(Takó, as a child)*, Kati Sólyom *(Anni)*, Zsuzsa Ráthonyi *(mother, as a young woman)*, Rita Békés, Judit Halász, Anna Nagy, Zsuzsa Balogh, Judit Zsolnai, Teréz Nagy, Ila Lóth, Géza Pártos, Béla Asztalos, Géza Böszörményi, Lajos Pozsár, András Kozák, Ervin Csomák, Gyula Koltai,

György Kézdi, József Madaras, László Balogh, Ilona Petényi, László Sztanó, Mátyás Eörsi, Gabi Bertha, Károly Versits, Győző Orgon, István Raits, Gábor Algács, László Bakos, István Balogh, Elek Dániel, Gábor Erőss, Mária Egri, Róbert Földeák, Tibor Fülöp, László Haraszti, Lászlóné Haraszti, Pál Hetényi, Péter Huszti, Erzsébet Horeszku, István Kardos, Tibor Kovács Tóth, László Kurucsai, Erzsi Lados, Antal Mészáros, Gyula Nagymarosi, Jozefa Orvos-Tóth, Károlyné Öhler, János Rubleszky, Zsuzsa Pajzs, Anikó Sáfár, Ida Siménfalvy, József Szentirmai, Mátyás Vargha, Sándorné Várnagy, Klára Zakariás.

Drama. Takó is a young Hungarian boy whose father died at the end of World War II. So great is the child's tragedy that he conjures up a fantasy father who still guides him. In his own imagination, Takó becomes the son of a hero, a brave partisan who gained glory in the war. Sustained by the myth he has created, Takó establishes himself as a leader among his friends and succeeds in breaking up the courtship between his mother and a would-be suitor. When he becomes a man, Takó finds that he is able to captivate young women with stories of his father's heroism. In 1956 Takó becomes involved in the Hungarian uprising and discovers that he now has less need of his father. At this time Takó also acquires a girl friend, Anni, who is Jewish. While working together as extras at a film studio, they reenact the horror of the persecution of the Jews, and Takó experiences vicariously the pain of Anni's heritage. After resolving to learn about his own background, Takó discovers that his father was a quite ordinary man, neither hero nor partisan, but a decent, hardworking individual. Takó now understands that he must live without the myth of his father, that a man can achieve dignity only through his own strength. *War heroes. Jews. Motion picture extras. Resistance (political). Filial relations. Genocide. Hero worship. World War II. Hungary—History—Revolt 1956. Fantasy.*

Note: Released in Hungary in Dec 1966 as *Apa*.

FATHER CAME TOO (Great Britain)   **F6.1487**
Independent Artists. *Dist* Continental Distributing, Inc. 8 Feb **1966** [Maryland license; c9 Feb 1964; LF159]. Sd; col (Eastman Color). 35mm. 93 min.
Prod Julian Wintle, Leslie Parkyn. *Dir* Peter Graham Scott. *Screenplay* Jack Davies, Henry Blyth. *Photog* Reg Wyer. *Art Dir* Harry Pottle. *Film Ed* Tom Priestley. *Mus Comp & Cond* Norrie Paramor. *Sd* Lionel Selwyn. *Sd Rec* Simon Kaye. *Asst Dir* Frank Hollands. *Prod Supv* Arthur Alcott. *Prod Mgr* Geoffrey Haine.
Cast: James Robertson-Justice (*Sir Beverly Grant*), Leslie Phillips (*Roddy Chipfield*), Stanley Baxter (*Dexter Munro*), Sally Smith (*Juliet Munro*), Ronnie Barker (*Josh*), Timothy Bateson (*Wally*), Philip Locke (*Stan*), Kenneth Cope (*Ron*), Eric Barker (*bank manager*), James Villiers (*Benzil Bulstrode*), Raymond Huntley (*Mr. Wedgewood*), Geoffrey Dunn (*Mr. Trumper*), Anita Sharp Bolster (*Mrs. Trumper*), Julian Orchard (*bath salesman*), Cardew Robinson (*fire officer*), Barbara Roscoe (*Lana*), Sydney Bromley (*Lang*), Clifford Earl (*police motorcyclist*), Nicky Henson (*motorcyclist*), Arthur Mullard (*traffic warden*).
Cast—Characters in Pageant: Fred Emney (*Sir Francis Drake*), Peter Jones (*Charles II*), Terry Scott (*executioner*), Hugh Lloyd (*Mary, Queen of Scots*), Joseph Brady (*Guy Fawkes*), Vanda Hudson (*Nell Gwynne*), John Bluthal (*Robert the Bruce*), Patrick Newell (*King Harold*).
Domestic comedy. Returning from their honeymoon, newlyweds Dexter and Juliet Munro set up residence in the luxurious home of actor-manager Sir Beverly Grant, the irascible father of the bride. The couple is hopeful of obtaining their own home, and the gullible Dexter is conned by Roddy Chipfield, a real estate agent and amateur actor, into overbidding at auction for a ramshackle cottage in the country. Moving into their "desirable property," the couple is met by termites, cows in the garden, inept workmen, and the intruding Sir Beverly. Disheartened by the realization that the house needs a complete overhauling, Dexter shows Sir Beverly to the door, followed closely by the furious Juliet. Left alone in the cottage, Dexter accidentally starts a fire while trying to prepare a meal. The local fire brigade arrives too late, and the house is destroyed. Roddy Chipfield tells the distraught husband of plans to build a road through his property, thus permitting the couple to recoup their initial losses and build a new "dream house" nearby. *Newlyweds. Actors. Theatrical managers. Confidence men. Fathers-in-law. Real estate agents. Construction workers. Family life. Gullibility. Wealth. Housing. Honeymoons. Auctions. Fires. Cows.*
Note: Working titles: *And Father Came Too* and *We Want To Live Alone*. Opened in London in Feb 1964.

FATHER GOOSE   **F6.1488**
Granox Co. *Dist* Universal Pictures. 10 Dec **1964** [New York opening; c19 Dec 1964; LP35004]. Sd (Westrex); col (Technicolor). 35mm. 115 min.
Prod Robert Arthur. *In Charge of Prod* Edward Muhl. *Dir* Ralph Nelson. *Screenplay* Peter Stone, Frank Tarloff. *Dir Photog* Charles Lang, Jr. *Art Dir* Alexander Golitzen, Henry Bumstead. *Set Decor* John McCarthy, George

Milo. *Titl* Pacific Title. *Film Ed* Ted J. Kent. *Mus* Cy Coleman. *Mus Supv* Joseph Gershenson. *Song:* "Pass Me By" Cy Coleman, Caroline Leigh. *Sd* Waldon O. Watson, William Russell. *Asst Dir* Tom Shaw, James Welch. *Prod Mgr* Ernest B. Wehmeyer. *Cost* Ray Aghayan. *Makeup* Bud Westmore. *Hairstyles* Larry Germain.
Cast: Cary Grant (*Walter Eckland*), Leslie Caron (*Catherine Freneau*), Trevor Howard (*Comdr. Frank Houghton*), Jack Good (*Lieutenant Stebbins*), Verina Greenlaw (*Christine*), Pip Sparke (*Anne*), Jennifer Berrington (*Harriet*), Stephanie Berrington (*Elizabeth*), Laurelle Felsette (*Angelique*), Nicole Felsette (*Dominique*), Sharyl Locke (*Jenny*), Simon Scott (*submarine captain*), John Napier (*submarine executive*), Richard Lupino (*radioman*), Alex Finlayson (*doctor*), Peter Forster (*chaplain*), Don Spruance (*navigator*), Ken Swofford (*helmsman*).
War comedy. Source: S. H. Barnett, "A Place of Dragons" (a short story; publication undetermined). At the outbreak of World War II, American beachcomber Walter Eckland is coerced by his old friend, Australian Navy Comdr. Frank Houghton, into service as a coast-watcher on a South Pacific island. Under the code name "Mother Goose," the whiskey-loving Eckland is rewarded with a new bottle each time he spots an enemy movement. When he is ordered to rescue a spotter from another island, Eckland discovers that the man has been killed by Japanese strafers, and he finds seven stranded schoolgirls and their prim French mistress, Catherine Freneau. The two adults soon begin a contest of wills, with Catherine attempting to cure the unshaven Eckland of his drinking and use of salty language. The battle between the sexes remains a stalemate until the girls mistakenly tell Eckland that their mistress has been bitten by a poisonous snake; to ease her final hours, Eckland gets her drunk and admits that he used to be a history professor. The two discover they love each other, and they are married by radio during an air raid after it is revealed that the "snake" was actually a big stick. Houghton sends a submarine to rescue them, and a Japanese patrol boat threatens to sink it, but Eckland manages to destroy the vessel with his own launch, enabling his party of eight to be saved. *Beachcombers. Americans in foreign countries. Australians. Ground watchers (air defense). Australia—Navy. Governesses. French. Professors. Alcoholism. Radio. Aerial bombardment. Submarines. World War II. South Sea Islands. Snakes.*
Note: Locations filmed in Ocho Rios, Jamaica.

FATHER OF A SOLDIER (U.S.S.R.)   **F6.1489**
Gruziya-Film. *Dist* Artkino Pictures. 19 Feb **1966** [New York opening]. Sd; b&w. 35mm. 83 min.
Dir Rezo Chkheidze. *Screenplay (see note)* Suliko Zhgenti. *Photog* Lev Sukhov, A. Filipashvili. *Camera* L. Namgalashvili. *Art Dir* Z. Medzmariashvili, N. Kazbegi. *Film Ed* Vasiliy Dolenko. *Mus* Sulkhan Tsintsadze. *Sd* D. Lomidze. *Asst Dir* T. Mikadze. *Sp Eff* O. Magakyan, R. Vashadze.
Cast: Sergo Zakariadze (*The Father*), Vladimir Privaltsev (*Nikolay*), Keto Bochorishvili (*Arkadiy*), A. Nazarov, A. Lebedev, V. Kolokoltsev, Yu. Drozdov, I. Kosykh, Vitya Kosykh, V. Uralskiy, V. Pitsek, P. Lyubeshkin, T. Sapozhnikova, I. Barmin, I. Vykhodtseva, R. Vild An, B. Goginava, V. Zharikov, V. Kulik, G. Kobakhidze, I. Kokrashvili, I. Kvitayshvili, Yelena Maksimova, R. Muratov, V. Mizin, I. Nizharadze, L. Zgvauri, A. Startsev, F. Stepun.
War drama. Toward the end of World War II, Georgiy Makharashvili, a simple Georgian vineyardist, learns that his son Goderdzi has been wounded in battle, and he sets out on a long and arduous journey to visit the youth in an army hospital. Along the way, he grieves to see torn and mutilated the earth he loves so dearly. Upon reaching the hospital, he is bitterly disappointed to learn that his son has been returned to his tank unit. More than ever determined to see Goderdzi, Georgiy continues his journey. Finding himself in the midst of battle, he is shocked by the sight of burning fields and endless destruction; and he chooses to become a soldier despite official misgivings. As his unit attempts to recapture an enemy stronghold, his love of the land moves him to halt the destruction of German vineyards by a Soviet tank. At last, the old man hears a native folk song and recognizes the voice as Goderdzi's; but the reunion of father and son is a sad one, for Goderdzi is struck by enemy fire and dies in his father's arms. With the coming of peace, Georgiy sets out for home. [According to a conflicting source, Georgiy's move to save the vineyard occurs at the close of the film.] *Vineyardists. Peasants. War heroes. Fatherhood. Combat zone life. World War II. Germany. Georgian Soviet Socialist Republic.*
Note: Released in the U.S.S.R. in 1965 as *Otets soldata*; running time: 92 min. Some sources credit Rezo Chkheidze as co-author of screenplay.

FATHOM (Great Britain)   **F6.1490**
Twentieth Century–Fox Productions. *Dist* Twentieth Century–Fox Film Corp. 9 Aug **1967** [San Francisco opening; c2 Aug 1967; LP34617]. Sd (Westrex); col (De Luxe). 35mm (CinemaScope, see note). 99 min.
Prod John Kohn. *Assoc Prod–2d Unit Dir* Peter Medak. *Dir* Leslie H. Martinson. *Dir Parachute Seq* Ken Vos. *Screenplay* Lorenzo Semple, Jr. *Dir*

Photog Douglas Slocombe. *Photog Parachute Seq* Jacques Dubourg. *Camera Op* Chic Waterson. *Art Dir* Maurice Carter. *Asst Art Dir* Jack Maxsted. *Set Dresser* Alan Cassie. *Main Titl Seq* Maurice Binder. *Film Ed* Max Benedict. *Asst Ed* Elizabeth Thoyts. *Mus Comp & Cond* John Dankworth. *Orch* David Lindup. *Song:* "Theme From Fathom" John Dankworth. *Sd Rec* Cyril Collick, Bob Jones. *Sd Ed* Jonathan Bates. *Asst Dir* David Tringham. *Prod Supv* Clifford Parkes. *Prod Sec* Barbara Allen. *Cont* Helen Whitson. *Wardrobe Dsgn & Cons* Kiki Byrne. *Wardrobe Supv* Bridget Sellers. *Cost for Clive Revill* Henry Bardon. *Parachute Jump-Suits for Miss Welch* Michele Rosier. *Makeup* Freddie Williamson, Alan Brownie. *Hairdresser* Joan Smallwood.

Cast: Tony Franciosa *(Peter Merriweather)*, Raquel Welch *(Fathom Harvill)*, Ronald Fraser *(Colonel Campbell)*, Richard Briers *(Timothy)*, Greta Chi *(Jo-May Soon)*, Tom Adams *(Mike)*, Elizabeth Ercy *(Ulla)*, Ann Lancaster *(Mrs. Trivers)*, Tutte Lemkow *(Mehmed)*, Reg Lye *(Mr. Trivers)*, Clive Revill *(Serapkin)*.

Mystery comedy-drama. Source: Larry Forrester, *A Girl Called Fathom* (London, 1967). After winning the skydiving championship in Spain, Fathom Harvill is abducted by a man named Timothy and taken to Douglas Campbell, a Scotsman who claims to be working for NATO intelligence. He enlists her aid in outwitting two teams of foreign agents who are after the "Fire Dragon," a nuclear trigger device that was lost in the Mediterranean following the crash of a bomber plane. Representing Communist China is Serapkin, an eccentric Armenian millionaire; acting for the United States is Peter Merriweather, aided by a glamorous Oriental, Jo-May Soon. Fathom parachutes into Merriweather's villa and learns that the "Fire Dragon" is a priceless jeweled figurine stolen from a Peking museum by a Korean War deserter who is being pursued by a private detective. Although she now realizes that Merriweather and Campbell are the deserter and the private eye, she cannot determine which is which. Following an encounter with a bull in an empty arena, a harpoon attack from a hotel owner, and two knife attacks by Serapkin, Fathom discovers the "Fire Dragon" hidden in her makeup case. She decides that Campbell is the real detective and leaves with him and Timothy in their plane. Once in the air, however, the two men grab the figurine and try to force Fathom out of the plane. Merriweather arrives in his own plane and shoots Campbell as Timothy falls out of the hatchway. Using the plane's radio, Fathom makes a dinner date with Merriweather and then tosses the "Fire Dragon" out of a window; Jo-May, the only honest person involved, retrieves it. *Skydivers. Scotch. Intelligence agents. Armenians. Orientals. Deserters—Military. Detectives. Abduction. Espionage. Parachuting. Theft. Murder. Nuclear weapons. Jewels. Airplanes. Spain. Mediterranean Sea. North Atlantic Treaty Organization. Chases. Bulls.*

Note: Filmed on location in Málaga, Torremolinos, and the Costa del Sol (Spain). Released in Great Britain in 1967. May have been presented in Panavision.

FAUSSES INGÉNUES *see* **RED LIPS**

FAUST (West Germany)   **F6.1491**

Divina Film. *Dist* Walter Traut. 15 Apr **1963** [New York opening]. Sd; col. 35mm. 121 min.

Dir Peter Gorski. *Dir Supv* Gustaf Gründgens. *Photog* Günther Anders. *Art Dir* Werner Achmann. *Set Decor* Theo Otto. *Film Ed* Walter Boos. *Mus* Mark Lothar. *Sd* Werner Schlagge. *Asst Dir* Walter Boos. *Prod Dir* Ernst Steinlechner. *Cost Dsgn* Theo Otto. *Cost* Claudia Herberg.

Cast—Hamburg Deutsches Schauspielhaus: Will Quadflieg *(Faust)*, Gustaf Gründgens *(Mephisto)*, Ella Büchi *(Gretchen)*, Elisabeth Flickenschildt *(Marthe)*, Hermann Schomberg *(theater director)*, Eduard Marks *(Wagner)*, Max Eckard *(Valentin)*, Uwe Friedrichsen *(pupil)*, Heinz Reincke *(Frosch)*, Hans Irle *(Altmayer)*, F. C. Beckhaus *(Brander)*, K. H. Wüpper *(Siebel)*, Heidi Leupolt, Gustl Busch.

Drama. Source: Johann Wolfgang von Goethe, *Faust* (1808). The film records a performance of Goethe's classic German drama performed by Hamburg Deutsches Schauspielhaus and directed by Gustaf Gründgens. *Greed. Ambition. Immortality. The Soul. The Devil.*

Note: Opened in West Berlin in Dec 1960; running time: 128 min.

FBI CODE 98   **F6.1492**

Warner Bros. Pictures. 8 Apr **1964** [New York opening; c6 Jun 1964; LP29440]. Sd; b&w. 35mm. 104 min. [Copyright length: 94 min.]

Prod-Writ Stanley Niss. *Dir* Leslie H. Martinson. *Photog* Robert V. Hoffman. *Art Dir* William Campbell, art dir. *Set Decor* William Stevens. *Film Ed* Leo H. Shreve. *Mus* Max Steiner. *Sd* Stanley Jones. *Asst Dir* James T. Vaughn. *Makeup Supv* Gordon Bau. *Supv Hairstyles* Jean Burt Reilly.

Cast: Jack Kelly *(Robert P. Cannon)*, Ray Danton *(Fred Vitale)*, Andrew Duggan *(Alan W. Nichols)*, Philip Carey *(Inspector Gifford)*, William Reynolds, actor *(Special Agent Edward P. Fox)*, Peggy McCay *(Deborah Cannon)*, Kathleen Crowley *(Marian Nichols)*, Merry Anders *(Grace McLean)*, Jack Cassidy *(Walter Macklin)*, Vaughn Taylor *(Joseph Petersen)*,

Eddie Ryder *(Lloyd Kinsel)*, Ken Lynch *(SAC Gibson White)*, Charles Cooper *(Special Agent Bernard Lyons)*, Paul Comi *(Special Agent Philip Vacarro)*, Robert Hogan *(Timothy Farrell)*, Laura Shelton *(Anita Davidson)*, Robert Ridgely *(Carl Rush)*, Francis DeSales *(assistant director)*, William Quinn *(Special Agent Alan Woodward)*, Ross Elliott *(Special Agent Vernon Lockhart)*, William Woodson *(narrator)*.

Crime drama. Alan Nichols, president of an electronics firm, and two vice presidents of the company, Robert Cannon and Fred Vitale, are summoned to Cape Canaveral for the test shot of a missile which their company developed. Before they board the plane, however, Cannon's suitcase is switched for one containing a bomb. Purely by chance, Cannon opens his luggage en route and discovers the bomb, which Vitale manages to deactivate. The others all suspect Cannon's wife, and the FBI is called in to determine whether the case is one of attempted murder or attempted sabotage. Petersen, whose son had been fired by Nichols, is an electric maintenance foreman for the electronics firm, and he believes he is free from suspicion when the FBI fails to arrest him. Further investigation proves Petersen made and planted the bomb. Petersen goes to Nichols' yacht where Nichols' wife, Marian, is waiting for her lover, Walter Macklin, also a project engineer with her husband's company. Petersen tells Marian of his hatred for her husband and of his plan to take revenge by blowing up the yacht with himself and her aboard, but the FBI arrives in time to stop him. *Executives. Shop foremen. Engineers. Murder. Sabotage. Employer-employee relations. Infidelity. Revenge. Missiles. Bombs. Yachts. Cape Canaveral. United States—Federal Bureau of Investigation.*

Note: Originally produced for television. Location scenes filmed in Washington, D. C., and Quantico, Virginia.

FBI CONTRO DR. MABUSE *see* **THE RETURN OF DR. MABUSE**

FE-MAIL SPECIAL DELIVERY   **F6.1493**

Ron Lawrence Productions. *Dist* Emerson Film Enterprises. 17 Dec **1965** [Champaign, Illinois, showing]. Sd; col. 35mm. [Feature length assumed.]

Cast: Randy Glenn, Hoboken Clarke, Sandra Filer, Karen King, Sissy Simone, Nadjda Dober, Sharon Paul, Sue Layton, Deny Ladd, Candace Hayes, Denine Du Bois, Barbara Wordin.

Comedy. Meter reader Johnny is going about his work when he meets a naked woman doing her wash. She throws him down a cliff, and he ends up in a hospital bed. He takes a job as a postman and must obtain a signed receipt for a special delivery letter from a woman in a shower and from a sunbathing threesome. Johnny is also attracted to the patients and to a nurse in a doctor's office. He attempts to deliver a special delivery letter to a striptease dancer, but he is thrown out of the theater for watching her act. He returns, delivers the letter, and is again thrown out. Johnny next delivers a letter to someone in an art class, becomes involved with several nude models, and again ends up in the hospital. A kindly nurse takes pity on him. *Meter readers. Mail carriers. Stripteasers. Nurses. Models. Voyeurism. Hospitals.*

Note: Also known as *Female Special Delivery.*

THE FEAR (Greece)   **F6.1494**

Th. A. Damaskinos–V. G. Michaelides, A. E. *Dist* Trans–Lux Distributing Corp. 9 Oct **1967** [New York opening]. Sd; b&w. 35mm. 102 min.

Prod Theophanis A. Damaskinos, Viktor G. Michaelides. *Dir-Writ* Kostas Manoussakis. *Photog* Nikos Gardelis. *Film Ed* George Chaoulis. *Mus* Yannis Markopoulos.

Cast: Elli Fotiou *(Chryssa)*, Elena Nathanael *(Anna)*, Mary Chronopoulou *(Mrs. Kanalis)*, Anestis Vlachos *(Anestis Kanalis)*, Spiros Focas *(Nikos)*, Alexis Damianos *(Dimitri Kanalis)*.

Rural melodrama. A wealthy, middle-aged Greek farmer, Dimitri Kanalis, ignores his second wife and spends his time in the town gambling and chasing other women, while Anestis, the emotionally disturbed and sexually frustrated son of his first marriage, becomes interested in the family's deafmute maid, Chryssa. Anestis' stepsister, Anna, a student at the University of Athens, returns home, hoping to marry a young engineer, Nikos, whose family is hated by her father. After seeing Anna and Nikos making love, Anestis is driven to sexually assaulting and eventually killing Chryssa when she seeks to avoid him. He tries to hide Chryssa's body in the hayloft but is discovered by his stepmother, who informs the boy's father. Dimitri beats his son but decides to bury Chryssa's body in the lake and inform the police that the maid has disappeared. Because of Anna's suspicion of what must have happened, the family agree to her marriage to Nikos, but as the entire village is celebrating the wedding the body of the maid is discovered by a fisherman. *Farmers. Stepmothers. Stepsisters. Stepbrothers. Deafmutes. Engineers. Students. Gambling. Rape. Murder. Weddings. Rural life.*

Note: Released in Greece in 1966 as *Ho fovos.*

FEAR AND LOVE see **TORMENT**

FEAR NO MORE   **F6.1495**

Scaramouche Productions. *Dist* Sutton Pictures. 1 Nov **1961** [Hartford, Connecticut, opening]. Sd; b&w. 35mm. 80 min.

Prod Bernard Wiesen, Earl Durham. *Assoc Prod* Julie Gibson. *Dir* Bernard Wiesen. *Screenplay* Robert Bloomfield. *Photog* Ernest Haller. *Art Dir* Gibson Holley. *Film Ed* John Bushelman. *Mus Comp & Cond* Paul Glass. *Sd* Woodruff H. Clark. *Asst Dir* Lee Lukather. *Script Supv* Mai Mohr.

Cast: Jacques Bergerac *(Paul Colbert)*, Mala Powers *(Sharon Carlin)*, John Harding *(Milo Seymour)*, Helena Nash *(Irene Maddox)*, John Baer *(Keith Burgess)*, Ann Carroll *(Denise Colbert)*, Robert Karnes *(Joe Brady)*, Peter Brocco *(Steve Cresca)*, Peter Virgo, Jr. *(Duke Maddox)*, Gregory Irvin *(Chris Colbert)*.

Mystery melodrama. Source: Leslie Edgley, *Fear No More* (New York, 1946). Young secretary Sharon Carlin is traveling by train from Los Angeles to San Francisco on an errand for her employer Milo Seymour when she is knocked unconscious in her sleeping compartment. Upon awakening, Sharon is questioned by plainclothesman Joe Brady, who suspects her of murdering her female companion in the sleeping compartment. Joe takes Sharon into his custody, and they leave the train at the next stop; but Sharon escapes and is picked up by motorist Paul Colbert, a naturalized citizen from France, who consents to help her. Arriving home in Los Angeles, Sharon discovers the body of Keith Burgess, a drunken writer friend to whom she had lent her apartment for the weekend. Terrified, Sharon tells Paul her true identity, relates to him the recent happenings, and admits that she was a patient in a mental hospital. Though he doubts her, Paul takes her to see her employer Milo Seymour. Initially cordial, Milo denies having sent Sharon to San Francisco, and Sharon soon finds herself framed by Milo in a conspiracy. His plan was to murder his wife, blame Sharon as a homicidal maniac, and finally kill Sharon and make it appear as if she had committed suicide. Paul traces Sharon to Milo's mountain retreat, where she has been taken to be murdered, rescues her, and brings Milo and his associates to justice. *Secretaries. Detectives. French. Authors. Murder. Conspiracy. Frameup. Mental illness. Employer-employee relations. Abduction. Trains. San Francisco. Los Angeles.*

FEAR OF LOVE   **F6.1496**

Dist Distribpix, Inc. 30 Sep **1970** [Dallas opening]. Sd; col. 35mm. 70 min.

Prod-Dir-Writ Emilio Portici. *Dir Photog* Tom Barnett. *Camera Op* Carl R. Adams. *Asst Camera* Jose Prieto. *Sd Rec* Louis Arteaga. *Sd Op* Warren Sound Studios. *Prod Mgr* Chris Martell. *Asst to Prod* Gina Fellucci. *Gaffer* Gil Ward. *Ch Grip* John Roberts.

Cast: Duke Moberly, Dick Bow, Gary Cook, Richard Springer, Maxine Springer, Nicole Vadim, Lee Stevens.

Instructional film. Several married couples are assisted by a marriage counselor in solving such sexual difficulties as impotence and frigidity. Various sexual techniques are presented. *Marriage. Marriage counsel. Impotence. Frigidity. Sexual techniques.*

FEARLESS FRANK   **F6.1497**

Jericho Productions. *Dist* American International Pictures. Dec **1969** [c10 Dec 1969; LP37604]. Sd; col (print by Movielab). 35mm. 78 min. *MPAA rating* G.

Prod-Dir-Writ Philip Kaufman. *Exec Prod* Nathan Kaufman. *Cinematog* Bill Butler. *Film Ed* Aram Boyajian, Luke Bennett. *Mus Comp & Cond* Meyer Kupferman.

Cast: Jon Voight *(Frank/False Frank)*, Monique Van Vooren *(Plethora)*, Joan Darling *(Lois)*, Severn Darden *(The Good Doctor/Claude)*, Anthony Holland *(Alfred)*, Lou Gilbert *(The Boss)*, Ben Carruthers *(The Cat)*, David Steinberg *(The Rat)*, David Fisher *(Screwnose)*, Nelson Algren *(Needles)*, Ken Nordine *(The Stranger)*.

Satire. Frank, an unsophisticated young man from the country, sets out to make his fortune in the city. En route he meets The Stranger, who is going to the city to write a book. The book becomes the story of Frank's adventures. Frank meets and falls in love with Plethora, but he is killed by gangsters (Needles, The Rat, Screwnose, and The Cat) when he tries to rescue Plethora from the clutches of The Boss, whose evil influence has engulfed the city. The Good Doctor revivifies Frank and imbues him with superhuman powers. Bullet-proofed and able to fly, Frank becomes the unwitting instrument of The Good Doctor in his battle against crime and evil. The Boss, upon learning of Frank, instructs Claude, the long-lost brother of The Good Doctor, to contrive to do away with Frank. Claude creates a monster, a shabby replica of Frank, but False Frank, as he is called, is easily vanquished in a showdown with his counterpart. Eventually, Frank's personality undergoes changes—he becomes overconfident and seduces Lois, the daughter of The Good Doctor, wantonly causing her benefactor to die of a broken heart. Simultaneously, as Frank becomes more "evil," False Frank acquires nobleness. He falls in love with Plethora, turns

against his creator, and ultimately prevents Claude's planned destruction of the city. *Innocents. Strangers. Authors. Gangsters. Physicians. Scientists. Brothers. Doubles. Supermen. Monsters. Urban life. Murder. Reviviscence. Personality. Seduction.*

Note: Filmed on location in Chicago. Shown in 1967 at the Cannes Film Festival as *Frank's Greatest Adventure*; running time: 83 min.

THE FEARLESS VAMPIRE KILLERS; OR, PARDON ME BUT YOUR TEETH ARE IN MY NECK (United States/Great Britain)

F6.1498

Cadre Films–Filmways, Inc. *Dist* Metro-Goldwyn-Mayer, Inc. 13 Nov **1967** [New York opening; c31 Dec 1966; LP35102]. Sd (RCA); col (Metrocolor). 35mm (Panavision). 91 min. [See note.]

A Martin Ransohoff–Roman Polanski Production. *Prod* Gene Gutowski. *Exec Prod* Martin Ransohoff. *Dir* Roman Polanski. *Story-Screenplay* Gerard Brach, Roman Polanski. *Trans of Orig French Script* Gillian Sutro, John Sutro. *Dir Photog* Douglas Slocombe. *Camera Op* Chic Waterson. *Art Dir* Fred Carter. *Prod Dsgn* Wilfred Shingleton. *Titl Dsgn* André François. *Film Ed* Alastair McIntyre. *Mus Comp* Christopher Komeda. *Choreog* Tutte Lemkow. *Sd Rec* George Stephenson. *Sd Ed* Lionel Selwyn. *Dub Mix* Len Shilton. *Asst Dir* Roy Stevens. *Prod Mgr* David W. Orton. *Cont* Helen Whitson. *Cost Dsgn* Sophie Devine. *Makeup* Tom Smith. *Fangs* Ludwig von Krankheit. *Hairdressing* Biddy Chrystal.

Cast: Jack MacGowran *(Professor Abronsius)*, Roman Polanski *(Alfred, his assistant)*, Alfie Bass *(Shagal, an innkeeper)*, Jessie Robins *(Rebecca, his wife)*, Sharon Tate *(Sarah, their daughter)*, Ferdy Mayne *(Count von Krolock)*, Iain Quarrier *(Herbert, his son)*, Terry Downes *(Koukol, the hunchback)*, Fiona Lewis *(maid)*, Ronald Lacey *(village idiot)*, Sydney Bromley *(sleigh driver)*, Andreas Malandrinos, Otto Diamant, Matthew Walters *(woodcutters)*.

Horror comedy. Armed only with a case of crucifix stakes and a mallet, Professor Abronsius and his assistant, Alfred, arrive at a Transylvanian inn in the dead of winter to find and destroy the dreaded vampires who stalk the area. The villagers are reluctant to help, but the huge bunches of garlic hanging from every beam confirm the professor's suspicions that the town sports a resident vampire. Sarah, the innkeeper's daughter, is victimized by a vampire and abducted, but her parents refuse to help the professor track down the chief vampire. The couple pay for their uncooperativeness: the innkeeper, Yoine Shagal, is found one morning frozen stiff, with the telltale red fang marks over his arms and legs. Rebecca, Shagal's wife, cannot bring herself to save his soul by driving a stake through Shagal's heart. He is left to haunt the inn in lecherous pursuit of their maid. Alfred and Abronsius follow the crazed Shagal one night and arrive at the castle of Count von Krolock, who heads a tribe of vampires, including his homosexual son, Herbert. They find Sarah, but their efforts to save her are foiled by their own incompetence and Alfred's difficulty in discouraging the predatory and lecherous Herbert. The night of the vampires' ball arrives, but before Sarah can be presented, Abronsius and Alfred spirit her away and miraculously escape across the snowy mountains in a sleigh. As they seemingly drive to safety, however, Sarah shows her fangs and bites the enamored Alfred. The professor merrily propels the sleigh onward, unaware he is spreading the very evil he hoped to destroy. *Professors. Innkeepers. Vampires. Village life. Lechery. Male homosexuality. Abduction. Inns. Talismans. Religious objects. Castles. Balls (formal gatherings). Transylvania.*

Note: Location scenes filmed in the Dolomite Alps, Italy. Released in Great Britain in 1967 as *Dance of the Vampires*; running time: 107 min. Original length: 118 min; cut to 107 min for initial release in the United States; finally cut to ca91 min. The cuts and other changes, such as color process and redubbing, allegedly prompted Polanski to request that his name be removed from the American release version. Prerelease titles: *Your Teeth in My Neck* and *The Vampire Killers*.

FEAST OF FRIENDS   **F6.1499**

The Doors. 13 Mar **1970** [Chicago showing]. Sd; col. 16mm. 50 min.

Prod Jim Morrison, Ray Manzarek, Robbie Krieger, John Densmore. *Photog* Paul Ferrara. *Art Dir* Paul Ferrara. *Film Ed* Frank Lisciandro. Song: "The End" *lyr & sung by* Jim Morrison. *Sd* Babe Hill.

Cast: The Doors *(themselves)*.

Documentary. The Doors, a rock music group, perform their songs in concert and show the life of a rock group on a concert tour. Material in protest of the Vietnam War is inserted at several points in the film. *Musicians. Singers. Rock and roll. Vietnam War 1964–73. The Doors.*

IL FEDERALE see **THE FASCIST**

FEDERICO FELLINI'S 8 1/2 see **8 1/2**

UNE FÉE PAS COMME LES AUTRES see **THE SECRET OF MAGIC ISLAND**

FEELIN' GOOD   **F6.1500**

Pike Productions. 26 Oct **1966** [Boston opening; c26 Oct 1966; LP33594]. Sd; col (Eastmancolor). 35mm. 85 min.

Prod-Dir James A. Pike. *Screenplay* James A. Pike, Mildred Maffei. *Photog* James A. Pike. *Songs:* "*Feelin' Good,*" "*Come Back Home*" Travis Pike. *Perf by* The Montclairs. *Song:* "*Summertime*" George Gershwin. *Perf by* The Montclairs. *Songs:* "*I Beg Your Pardon,*" "*Ute Ute,*" "*Don't Hurt Me Again,*" "*It Isn't Right,*" "*The Way That I Need You,*" "*Watch Out Woman*" Travis Pike. *Perf by* Travis Pike, The Brattle Street East. *Song:* "*Ride the Rainbow*" *writ & perf by* Brenda Nichols. *Song:* "*Bad Dream*" Arthur Korb. *Background Mus Comp & Cond by* Arthur Korb.

Cast: Travis Pike (*Ted*), Patricia Ewing (*Karen*), Judi Reeve (*Judi*), Leslie Burnham (*Elaine*), Ron Stafford (*Danny*), Frank Dolan (*landlord*), Brenda Nichols, The Montclairs, The Brattle Street East.

Drama with music. Returning home following a tour of duty in Germany, Ted arrives at Logan International Airport and is greeted by his girl friend, Karen, and her friends Judi and The Brattle Street East, a rock group who welcome Ted with a song. At his homecoming party, Karen's roommate, Elaine, incurs Karen's anger by inviting Ted to try her new sportscar. They have car trouble, and by the time Ted and Elaine finally return the party has ended, and Karen angrily informs Elaine that they have been evicted. Karen refuses to see Ted, and in an effort to patch up the couple Elaine suggests to Ted that he help Karen move. The reconciled couple then goes to hear their friends, The Montclairs, compete in the Jaycees' "Battle of the Bands." To the crowd's delight, The Montclairs win first place. The next day, Ted, Karen, and Elaine and her date, Danny, go to the music and dance party on the banks of the Charles River, where they all have a good time. *Soldiers. Musicians. Roommates. Jealousy. Eviction. Bands. Contests. Boston. Charles River. Junior Chamber of Commerce (Boston). Logan International Airport.*

Note: Location scenes filmed in Boston.

FELICIA   **F6.1501**

Dist Distribpix, Inc. 18 Jul **1969** [Champaign, Illinois, showing]. Sd; b&w. 35mm. 63 min.

Prod-Dir-Writ Arlo Shiffen.

Cast: Jo Ellen (*Felicia*), Ellen Keller, Alison Page, Esther Parks.

Melodrama. Felicia, a photographer, uses her profession to attract young female models to her fashionable New York City apartment, and there, calling herself Alison to conceal her identity, she seduces and attempts to dominate sexually her models. Felicia's latest prey is a lonely midwesterner named Jo, who gradually succumbs to Felicia's advances during their first picture session, and soon consents to move in with her. Though initially aroused by Felicia's sexual quirks, Jo soon becomes frightened, but it is too late, and Felicia is leading her around by a dog leash. Felicia takes Jo to visit two male admirers who, high on liquor and marijuana, take turns tormenting Jo. In the bedroom alone with Peter, Jo responds passionately to him. Felicia is enraged and punishes her by seducing Peter herself and then forcing Jo to join them. In a fit of anger, Jo strikes at Felicia, slashes her throat, and escapes in Felicia's car. Jo's fate is sealed, however, by a female hitchhiker who robs her at knifepoint, steals the car and her clothes, and leaves Jo desolate, naked, and deranged, stumbling weakly in the snow. *Photographers. Models. Innocents. Seduction. Lesbianism. Sadomasochism. Drunkenness. Troilism. Marijuana. New York City.*

Note: There is no dialog; the characters narrate the events.

LES FÉLINS *see* **JOY HOUSE**

FELLINI SATYRICON (France/Italy)   **F6.1502**

P. E. A.–Les Productions Artistes Associés. *Dist* United Artists. 11 Mar **1970** [New York opening; c3 Sep 1969; LF59]. Sd; col (DeLuxe). 35mm (Panavision). 128 min. *MPAA rating* R.

An Alberto Grimaldi Production. *Prod* Alberto Grimaldi. *Dir* Federico Fellini. *Screenplay & Story* Federico Fellini, Bernardino Zapponi. *Screenplay Collab* Brunello Rondi. *Dir Photog* Giuseppe Rotunno. *Camera* Giuseppe Maccari. *Art Dir* Luigi Scaccianoce, Giorgio Giovannini. *Prod Dsgn* Danilo Donati. *Supv Film Ed* Enzo Ocone. *Film Ed* Ruggero Mastroianni. *Mus* Nino Rota, Ilhan Mimaroglu, Tod Dockstader, Andrew Rudin. *Sd* Oscar De Arcangelis. *Asst Dir* Maurizio Mein. *Prod Supv* Enzo Provenzale. *Prod Mgr* Roberto Cocco. *Prod Asst* Lamberto Pippia. *Cost* Danilo Donati. *Makeup* Rino Carboni. *Hairdresser* Luciano Vito. *Sp Eff* Adriano Pischiutta. *Optical Eff* Joseph Natanson. *Art History Cons* Nino Scordia. *Latin Cons* Luca Canali. *Art direction based on sketches by* Federico Fellini. *Painted Backdrops* Italo Tomassi.

Cast: Martin Potter (*Encolpius*), Hiram Keller (*Ascyltus*), Salvo Randone (*Eumolpus*), Max Born (*Giton*), Fanfulla (*Vernacchio*), Mario Romagnoli (*Trimalchio*), Capucine (*Tryphaena*), Alain Cuny (*Lichas*), Pasquale Baldassare (*Hermaphrodite*), Giuseppe Sanvitale (*Habinnas*), Hylette Adolphe (*Oriental slave girl*), Donyale Luna (*Oenothea*), Magali Noël (*Fortunata*), Gordon Mitchell (*robber*), Lucia Bosè (*suicide wife*), Joseph Wheller (*suicide husband*), Genius (*Cinedo*), Danica La Loggia (*Scintilla*), Antonia Pietrosi (*Widow of Ephesus*), Wolfgang Hillinger (*soldier at Ephesus' tomb*), Elio Gigante (*owner of Garden of Delights*), Sibilla Sedat (*nymphomaniac*), Lorenzo Piani (*nymphomaniac's husband*), Luigi Zerbinati (*nymphomaniac's slave*), Vittorio Vittori (*notary*), Carlo Giordana (*captain of Eumolpus' ship*), Marcello Di Folco (*proconsul*), Luigi Montefiori (*Minotaur*), Elisa Mainardi (*Ariadne*), Suleiman Ali Nashnush (*Tryphaena's attendant*), Luigi Battaglia (*transvestite*), Tania Duckworth (*brothel girl*), Maria De Sisti (*fat woman*), Tanya Lopert (*Caesar*), Il Moro, Elizabetta Moscatelli, Antonio Mirio.

Satire. *Source:* Petronius Arbiter, *Satyricon* (ca50–66 A.D.). In search of his lover Giton, student Encolpius visits the Roman baths. There his best friend and rival Ascyltus boasts that he has sold the youth to aged actor Vernacchio. At the theater Encolpius recovers Giton, who deserts him in favor of Ascyltus. An elderly poet, Eumolpus, invites the disconsolate Encolpius to a feast at the home of Trimalchio, a wealthy former slave and amateur poet. At the banquet, drunken Eumolpus insults the host's bad verses and is cast out, while the remaining company visits Trimalchio's newly constructed tomb. Before his sepulcher Trimalchio describes the famous perfidy of the Widow of Ephesus. Accompanied by Tryphaena, a female guest, Encolpius boards the barque of Lichas and finds the elusive Ascyltus and faithless Giton. In the midst of a celebration Giton is given in mock marriage to a little girl, Pannychina, while Lichas plans his own wedding to Encolpius. As Caesar's pleasure ship passes, however, Lichas' party witnesses the assassination of the effeminate emperor, who is battered to death by the oars of his galley slaves. The assassins then board Lichas' barque and decapitate the would-be bridegroom. Having disembarked, Encolpius and Ascyltus enter a deserted villa, where they discover the bodies of a patrician couple who have committed suicide and pursue a black female slave, with whom they spend the night. On a vacant plain a stranger solicits Ascyltus to satisfy his nymphomaniac wife. Accompanied by a bearded outlaw, the young men kidnap the pallid demigod Hermaphrodite, who dies of thirst during their desert flight. During the festival of the god Laughter Encolpius is trapped in a labyrinth and pursued by a handsome youth disguised as the Minotaur. As a reward Encolpius is presented with the voluptuous Ariadne but finds himself impotent. To no avail he visits the Garden of Delights and submits to flagellation during the Lupercalia. A priapic dwarf, however, recommends the black sorceress Oenothea, who restores the student's virility. Encolpius' consequent happiness is brief. In his presence Ascyltus dies of a mysterious wound, clawing the ground like an animal. Encolpius discovers Eumolpus' empty boat and listens to the reading of the deceased poet's will, which stipulates that his beneficiaries devour his corpse as a condition of inheritance. Encolpius bursts into laughter. *Students. Poets. Upper classes. Actors. Negroes. Dwarfs. Sorcerers. Freaks. Royalty. Hedonism. Male homosexuality. Friendship. Perfidy. Marriage. Impotence. Priapism. Nymphomania. Hermaphroditism. Assassination. Mutilation. Cannibalism. Slavery. Suicide. Marriage—Male homosexual. Flagellation. Labyrinths. Tombs. Orgies. Theater. Deserts. Ships. Lupercalia. Rome—History—Empire. The Minotaur.*

Note: Opened in Rome in Sep 1969 as *Fellini-Satyricon*; prerelease title: *Satyricon*; running time: 136 min; cut to 129 min. Paris opening: Dec 1969 as *Satyricon*; running time: ca135 min. "Genius" is the pseudonym of Eugenio Mastropietro.

FEMALE (Reissue)   **F6.1503**

Headliner Productions. 28 Jan **1966** [Maryland license]. Sd; b&w. 35mm. 58 min.

Note: Originally released in 1956 as *The Violent Years*; c8 Mar 1956; LP26971.

THE FEMALE *see* **THE FEMALE; SEVENTY TIMES SEVEN**

THE FEMALE ANIMAL (Austria/West Germany)   **F6.1504**

Schönbrunn-Film–Rex-Film. *Dist* Manhattan Films International. 17 Aug **1962** [Los Angeles opening]. Sd; b&w. 35mm. 76 min.

A Sascha-Film Production. *Dir* August Rieger. *Screenplay* Hans Maria Braun, August Rieger. *Photog* Walter Partsch, Werner Linhardt. *Mus* Hans Hagen.

Nudist film. The history of beauty is reenacted from its origins in worship of the goddess Venus to its culmination in contemporary German nudist colonies. Ancient Greek body massages, Roman thermal baths, Finnish sauna baths, and yoga exercises are also featured. *Greece—Ancient. Rome—History—Empire. Yoga. Masseurs. Rites and ceremonies. Saunas. Cults. Nudist camps. Venus.*

Note: Released in Austria and West Germany in 1955 as *Das Geheimnis der Venus*; running time: 88 min.

FEMALE ANIMAL (Italy/Spain)   **F6.1505**
Estrellus Films–Appia Industria Cinematografica. *Dist* Cinemation Industries. 23 Jan **1970** [New York opening]. Sd; col (DeLuxe). 35mm (Panavision). 92 min. *MPAA rating* X.

Pres by Jerry Gross, Nicholas Demetroules. *Prod* Antonio Benvenuti. *Dir* Juan Carlo Grinella. *Screenplay* Octavio Bellini, Marcello Lazarino. *Photog* George Zimmermann. *Film Ed* Sidney Katz, William Gaddis. *Mus* Clay Pitts.

Cast: Arlene Tiger (*Angélique*), Vassili Lambrinos (*Count DiMedici*), André Landzaat (*Alain*), Jean Avery (*Francesca*), Robert Darchi (*Rafael*), Richard Fusco (*Juan*), Harold Keith (*Marcos*), Joanne Sopko (*Carla*).

Drama. Angélique lies pensively in a hotel room after Marcos, a priest, has made love to her, left money, and departed quickly. As her cat cuddles up next to her, Angélique recalls the events leading to her present predicament. *Angélique finds life in her small fishing village unbearable. One day, while riding her bicycle, Angélique is knocked down by a car owned by Count DiMedici, a business tycoon who owns the entire island. The count offers Angélique a job as maid in his mansion, and, though aware of the count's ulterior motive, she accepts the opportunity to leave the village. Angélique becomes aware of the rivalry between the count and his jet-set son, Alain. Though Alain has a girl friend, Carla, Angélique is attracted to both father and son. She nevertheless joins Alain's crowd and samples LSD, yacht parties, and nights in discotheques. The count also takes Angélique out, and people assume that she is his mistress. When Angélique sees the count make love to his business associate, Francesca, she seduces the stableboy, who also receives the favors of the count. She learns that she is to be the prize at a roulette game between Alain and the count; and when Alain wins, he expresses a desire to marry her. Angélique returns to the mansion, where she is abused by the count and has sex with Francesca while the count secretly watches. Eager to leave the house, Angélique goes to meet Alain but finds him making love with Francesca while the count plays the piano. Realizing she has been used, Angélique flees and is approached by a man who propositions her; faced with no alternative, she accepts. Angélique now knows that she can never return to a life of poverty.* Prostitutes. Priests. Tycoons. Housemaids. Jet set. Aristocrats. Filial relations. Seduction. Male homosexuality. Sadism. Lesbianism. Voyeurism. Fishing villages. LSD. Discotheques. Roulette.

Note: Filmed in Puerto Rico. Spanish title: *La mujer del gato.*

THE FEMALE PRINCE (Hong Kong)   **F6.1506**
Shaw Brothers (H. K.) Ltd. 5 Oct **1966** [Los Angeles showing]. Sd; b&w. 35mm. 105 min.

Prod Run Run Shaw. *Dir* Chou See-loke. *Screenplay* Chang Chek.

Cast: Ivy Ling Po, Fang Yin, Li Chang, Chin Feng, Chin Han, Chiang Kuang-chao.

Drama. Despite her love for a penniless student, a young woman's father and stepmother attempt to marry her to a politician. Leaving home, she dons male attire and travels to the city, hoping to consult her brother. Instead, she becomes engaged to the emperor's daughter. Although she risks execution, her problems are happily resolved. Students. Stepmothers. Politicians. Royalty. Male impersonation. Marriage—Arranged. Disguise. Family life. Poverty.

THE FEMALE PRISONER see **LA PRISONNIÈRE**

THE FEMALE; SEVENTY TIMES SEVEN (Argentina)   **F6.1507**
Araucania Films. *Dist* Cambist Films. 19 Mar **1968** [New York opening]. Sd; b&w. 35mm. 85-92 min.

Prod Antonio P. Motti. *Dir* Leo Towers. *Screenplay* Beatriz Guido, Leopoldo Torre Nilsson. *Dir Photog* Ricardo Younis. *Set Dsgn* Oscar Lagomarsino. *Film Ed* Jacinto Cascales. *Mus* Virtu Maragno.

Cast: Isabel Sarli (*Laura [Cora]*), Francisco Rabal (*The Sheepherder [Pascual]*), Jardel Filho (*The Horse Thief [Pedro]*), Blanca Lagrotta (*The Mother*), Jacobo Finder (*The Father*), Nelly Prono (*The Duena*), Hilda Suárez, Alberto Barcel.

Melodrama. Based on two stories contained in: Dalmiro A. Sáenz, *Setenta veces siete* (Buenos Aires, 1957). Laura, a prostitute in a dilapidated bordello, angers the madam by refusing to respond to the advances of those patrons who seek her favors. Laura eventually consents to take a customer, and during the lovemaking, she silently recalls her past: Laura lives with her aged parents who keep a store in a desolate part of the Pampas. A sheepherder comes to the store, and the pliant Laura is attracted to him by his sincere expressions of loneliness and desire. She steals some provisions and rides off with him to live in his shack in the mountains. The man spends much of his time looking for a place to dig a well. A fugitive horsethief is shot down near the shack and left for dead by the posse. Laura discovers that he is alive and sends him on his way with blankets and water, but the sheepherder tracks him with the intention of killing him. Laura convinces her husband, however, that the horsethief's life should be spared so that he can help with the well. Days pass, and the men dig a deep hole. The sheepherder discovers that the horsethief has a moneybelt and

suggests to Laura that they steal the money, leave him in the well to die, and buy a farm. Laura has become attracted to the horsethief, who suggests to her in turn that they leave her husband in the well and go off together. Laura becomes numb with confusion and, unable to decide between the two men, leaves them both in the well to die. She then goes to the city where she becomes a prostitute. Prostitutes. Shepherds. Horsethieves. Marriage—Common law. Infidelity. Murder. Guilt. Whorehouses. Wells. Pampas.

Note: Also known as *The Female.* Original language title: *Setenta veces siete.* Sex exploitation scenes were added to this film after its completion by Torre Nilsson, accounting for his use of the pseudonym Leo Towers.

FEMALE SPECIAL DELIVERY see **FE-MAIL SPECIAL DELIVERY**

FEMINA RIDENS see **THE LAUGHING WOMAN**

UNE FEMME AUX ABOIS see **THE SLAVE**

UNE FEMME EST UNE FEMME see **A WOMAN IS A WOMAN**

LA FEMME INFIDÈLE (France/Italy)   **F6.1508**
Les Films La Boétie–Cinegay. *Dist* Allied Artists. 9 Nov **1969** [New York opening]. Sd; col (Eastman Color, print by DeLuxe). 35mm. 98 min. *MPAA rating* M.

Pres by Emanuel L. Wolf. *Prod* André Génovès. *Assoc Prod* Georges Casati. *Dir-Writ* Claude Chabrol. *Photog* Jean Rabier. *1st Asst Camera* Paul Bonis. *2d Asst Camera* Jeanine Rabier. *Focus* Claude Zidi. *Art Dir* Guy Littaye. *Set Decor* Raoul Guiraud. *Film Ed* Jacques Gaillard. *Asst Film Ed* Catherine Bernard. *Mus* Pierre Jansen. *Mus Cond* André Girard, Dominique Zardi. *Sd* Guy Chichignoud. *Asst Sd* Louis Devaivre. *Boom Op* Gérard Daquay. *Asst Dir* Jacques Fansten, Jean-François Détré. *Prod Mgr* Patrick Delauneux, Alain Belmondo. *Script Girl* Claudine Gaubert. *Prod Sec* Simone Allouche. *Cost Dsgn* Maurice Albray. *Wardrobe* Dolly Cousteau. *Makeup* Louis Bonnemaison. *Hairstyles* Maxime Anatole, Trieste. *Stéphane Audran's Hairstyles* Carita. *Key Grip* Roger Robert. *Ch Electrn* Gérard Gauge. *Still Photog* Helga Romanoff, Pierre Zucca.

Cast: Stéphane Audran (*Hélène Desvallées*), Michel Bouquet (*Charles Desvallées*), Maurice Ronet (*Victor Pegala*), Serge Bento (*Bignon*), Michel Duchaussoy (*Police Officer Duval*), Guy Marly (*Police Officer Gobet*), Stéphane Di Napoli (*Michel Desvallées*), Louise Chevalier (*maid*), Louise Rioton (*mother-in-law*), Henri Marteau (*Paul*), François Moro-Giaffer (*Frédéric*), Dominique Zardi (*truck driver*), Michel Charrel (*policeman*), Henri Attal (*man in cafe*), Jean-Marie Arnoux (*false witness*), Donatella Turri (*Brigitte*).

Drama. A 40-year-old insurance broker, Charles Desvallées, his wife, Hélène, and his 10-year-old son, Michel, live in luxury near Versailles. When Hélène's frequent trips to Paris arouse Charles's suspicions, he hires private detective Bignon, who later reports that Hélène is the mistress of divorced writer Victor Pegala. Charles visits and interrogates the writer. When he sees a cigarette lighter he once gave his wife in Victor's bedroom, however, Charles picks up a statuette and bludgeons the author. Charles then deftly deposits the corpse in a sack and drops it into a pond. Although baffled by her lover's absence, Hélène refuses to tell the truth to two policemen who have found her name in Victor's address book. Upon discovering an incriminating photograph of Victor in Charles's pocket, she burns it. Despite frequent police visits and the possibility that the mystery will be solved, the couple's affection grows deeper. Mistresses. Brokers. Insurance agents. Detectives. Police. Marriage. Infidelity. Murder. Photographs. Versailles. Paris.

Note: Location scenes filmed in and around Paris. Opened in Paris in Jan 1969; running time: 105 min. Date of Italian release undetermined. Also known as *Unfaithful Wife.*

UNE FEMME MARIÉE see **THE MARRIED WOMAN**

LA FEMME SPECTACLE see **NIGHT WOMEN**

LES FEMMES see **PLAYMATES**

FEMMES D'UN ÉTÉ see **LOVE ON THE RIVIERA**

LES FEMMES FLAMBOYANTES see **THE FLAMBOYANT SEX**

FEMMINA (France/Italy/West Germany)   **F6.1509**
S. N. E. Gaumont–Eichberg Film–Franca Film. *Dist* Hillgold Picture Corp. May **1968**. Sd; col (Eastman Color). 35mm. 97 min. *MPAA rating* R.

Pres by Manson Distributing Corp. A Georges Lautner Production. *Prod-Dir* Georges Lautner. *Assoc Prod* Alain Poiré. *Screenplay* Vahé Katcha. *Dial* Michel Audiard. *Adapt* Vahé Katcha, Michel Audiard, Georges Lautner. *Photog* Maurice Fellous. *Film Ed* Michèle David. *Mus* Bernard Gérard.

Cast: Mireille Darc (*Salène*), Hardy Krüger (*Carl*), Maurice Biraud (*Alfred*), Venantino Venantini (*Vladimir*), Francis Blanche (*Gedeon*), Georges Géret (*Marco*), Pepe Abed (*Grubert*), Pierre Massimi (*Le Voyou*), Margot Trooger,

Mino Doro.

Crime drama. Small-time thief Carl arrives in Beirut after narrowly eluding his archenemy Marco. Carl meets Alfred, an old friend, and joins him in a robbery scheme aimed at Grubert, a millionaire gambler. The two men devise an intricate plan to keep track of Grubert's success at the tables because Grubert always takes his winnings in cash. Carl meets Salène, a beautiful, free-spirited girl whose nickname is Sauterelle, meaning "grasshopper." Learning that Marco is on his trail again, Carl suddenly leaves Beirut to go to the country with Salène. He telephones Alfred and discovers that Marco has deferred his plan to kill Carl and, instead, will participate in the Grubert robbery. Carl plans to leave Beirut with Salène and begin his life afresh. He returns to Beirut, and one night at the casino Grubert suddenly begins to win heavily. Carl informs Alfred and Marco, who lie in wait outside, then leaves with Salène. The robbery fails as the police kill Marco and capture Alfred. *Thieves. Millionaires. Robbery. Murder. Gambling. Revenge. Perfidy. Criminals—Rehabilitation. Casinos. Beirut. Lebanon.*

Note: Filmed on location in Lebanon and Paris. Opened in Paris in Jan 1967 as *La grande sauterelle*; running time: 100 min. Released in West Germany as *Ein Mädchen wie das Meer*; length: 90 min. Also known as *Sauterelle*. Rerated by the MPAA as GP.

FEMMINE DI LUSSO *see* **LOVE, THE ITALIAN WAY**

IL FERROVIERE *see* **THE RAILROAD MAN**

FERRY CROSS THE MERSEY (Great Britain)   **F6.1510**
Subafilms. *Dist* United Artists. 19 Feb **1965** [New York opening; c6 Dec 1964; LP29675]. Sd; b&w. 35mm. 86 min.

A Brian Epstein Production. *Prod* Michael Holden. *Exec Prod* Brian Epstein. *Assoc Prod* Leigh Aman. *Dir* Jeremy Summers. *Screenplay* David Franden. *Story* Tony Warren. *Dir Photog* Gilbert Taylor. *Camera Op* Alan McCabe. *Art Dir* Tony Masters. *Set Dresser* Charles Bishop. *Film Ed* John Victor Smith. *Mus Dir* George Martin. *Songs:* "Ferry Cross the Mersey," "It's Gonna Be Alright," "Why Oh Why," "Fall in Love," "Think About Love," "This Thing Called Love," "Baby You're So Good to Me," "I'll Wait for You," "She's the Only Girl for Me" Gerry Marsden. *Sung by* Gerry and the Pacemakers. *Song:* "I Gotta Woman" Kenneth Griffiths. *Sung by* The Black Knights. *Song:* "Why Don't You Love Me" James McDermott, David Trimnell, Roy Little, Francis Gornall. *Sung by* The Blackwells. *Song:* "Shake a Tail Feather" *sung by* Earl Royce and the Olympics. *Other Songs Sung by* Cilla Black. *Sd* Kevin Sutton. *Prod Mgr* Hector Elwes. *Cont* Dee Vaughn. *Makeup* Gerry Fairbank. *Casting* John Merrick.

Cast: Gerry Marsden (*Gerry*), Fred Marsden (*Fred*), Les Chadwick (*Chad*), Les Maguire (*Les*), Julie Samuel (*Dodie*), Eric Barker (*Colonel Dawson*), Deryck Guyler (*Trasler*), George A. Cooper (*Mr. Lumsden*), Patricia Lawrence (*Miss Kneave*), Mona Washbourne (*Aunt Lil*), T. P. McKenna (*Hanson*), Mischa De La Motte (*Dawson's butler*), Margaret Nolan (*Norah*), Donald Gee, Bernard Sharpe (*art students*), Keith Smith (*Dawson's chauffeur*), Andy Ho (*Chinese restaurant manager*), Cilla Black, The Fourmost, Jimmy Savile, Earl Royce and the Olympics, The Blackwells, The Black Knights.

Comedy-drama with music. As screaming young fans jam the Manchester Airport to welcome Gerry and the Pacemakers back from an American tour, Gerry recalls the story of the group's first success: *Living with Aunt Lil at her Liverpool boardinghouse, Gerry takes the ferry across the Mersey each day to attend art school with Chad, a member of his group, while Fred and Les, the other Pacemakers, cross the river to their factory jobs. At night, the four play and sing at The Cavern, a local nightclub. Gerry's girl friend Dodie persuades Hanson, an agent, to represent the boys in a competition to select a musical act to compete in the European Beat contest. On the day of the competition, the new instruments which the agent secured for the boys are delivered to the airport by mistake and, after a wild chase, are recovered by the foursome. Gerry and the Pacemakers are driven to the competition in a funeral hearse and win the contest. They have now achieved international fame. Musicians. Aunts. Students. Factory workers. Fame. Rock and roll. Boardinghouses. Ferryboats. Contests. Liverpool. Manchester (England). Mersey River (England).*

Note: Filmed on location in and around Liverpool. Opened in London in Dec 1964; running time: 85 min.

FERRY TO HONG KONG (Great Britain)   **F6.1511**
Rank Organisation. *Dist* Twentieth Century-Fox Film Corp. 22 Feb **1961** [Saint Louis opening; c31 Dec 1959; LP18566]. Sd (Westrex); col (Eastman Color, print by DeLuxe). 35mm (CinemaScope). 103 min. [Copyright length: 111 min.]

A Lewis Gilbert Production. *Prod* George Maynard. *Exec Prod* Earl St. John. *Dir* Lewis Gilbert. *Screenplay* Vernon Harris, Lewis Gilbert. *Adtl Dial* John Mortimer. *Dir Photog* Otto Heller. *Camera Op* Harold Haysom. *Prod Dsgn* John Stoll. *Film Ed* Peter Hunt. *Mus Comp* Kenneth V. Jones. *Cond* Muir Mathieson. *Chinese Song:* "The Four Seasons" *arr by* Fook Ling Wong. *Titl*

Song Bob Sharples, Paddy Roberts. *Song:* "I Wouldn't Leave My Little Wooden Hut" Charles Collins. *Sd Rec* C. C. Stevens, Bill Daniels. *Sd Ed* Arthur Ridout, Archie Ludski. *Asst Dir* Bert Batt. *Prod Mgr* John Dark. *Cont* Gladys Goldsmith. *Makeup* Bob Lawrence. *Sp Eff* Syd Pearson. *Chinese Adv* Paula Lee Shiu. *Constr Mgr* Ron Udell.

Cast: Curt Jurgens (*Mark Conrad*), Orson Welles (*Capt. Cecil Hart*), Sylvia Syms (*Liz Ferrers*), Jeremy Spenser (*Miguel Henriques*), Noel Purcell (*Joe Skinner*), Margaret Withers (*Miss Carter*), John Wallace (*police inspector*), Roy Chiao Hung (*Johnny Sing-Up*), Shelley Shen (*Foo Soo*), Louis Seto (*Tommy Cheng*), Milton Reid (*Yen*), Ronald Decent (*Portuguese major*), Don Carlos (*archdeacon*), Nick Kendall (*2d police inspector*), Kwan Shan Lam (*1st guardian*).

Adventure melodrama. Source: Max Catto, *Ferry to Hong Kong* (London, 1957). Pompous and tyrannical Captain Hart is the skipper of the *Fa Tsan* (derisively called the "Fat Annie"), a broken-down ferryboat running between Hong Kong and Macao. One day the Hong Kong police toss aboard Mark Conrad, a drunken, cynical Austrian exile, providing him with a one-way ticket to Macao. He has been expelled following his latest brawl in a nightclub. Hart is disgusted with what he calls a "stinking piece of human refuse" but has no alternative but to take Conrad to Macao. However, the authorities there refuse to allow Conrad to come ashore, and, since he cannot return to Hong Kong, he is condemned to live permanently on the ferry. Despite Hart's opposition, Conrad finds to his surprise that he has friends: Liz Ferrers, a schoolteacher who escorts a group of children on a weekly ferry trip; and the crew, who defy their skipper by offering the exile food, drink, furniture, and friendship. Conrad begins to show that he is more than a drunken derelict. He helps rescue survivors of a blazing junk, behaves heroically when a typhoon strikes the ferry, and even takes the wheel of the vessel when Hart is incapacitated. The storm propels the ship to the China coast, and here it is boarded by pirates who terrorize the wealthier passengers. Aided by Hart and the crew, Conrad defeats the pirates and comes close to getting the storm-battered ferry back to port; but she sinks in Hong Kong harbor. As the *"Fat Annie"* goes down, Hart concedes a grudging admiration for Conrad, who has salvaged from the wreck self-respect and a future. *Derelicts. Sea captains. Austrians. Schoolteachers. Ship crews. Pirates. Cynics. Deportation. Exile. Snobbery. Heroism. Ferryboats. Hong Kong. Macao. Ship fires. Sea rescue. Typhoons.*

Note: Filmed in Hong Kong. Released in Great Britain in Aug 1959; running time: 113 min.

FESTIVAL   **F6.1512**
Patchke Productions. *Dist* Peppercorn-Wormser, Inc. 23 Oct **1967** [New York opening]. Sd; b&w (print by Movielab). 35mm (see note). 96 min.

Prod-Dir Murray Lerner. *Assoc Prod* George Pickow. *Conceived by* Murray Lerner. *Photog* Murray Lerner, Stanley Meredith, Francis Grumman, George Pickow. *Film Ed* Howard Alk. *Sd* Ben Sobin, Jack Jacobsen, Art Bloom, Mike Scott, John Gibbs. *Prod Mgr* Norman Gewirtz.

Cast: Joan Baez, Horton Barker, Fiddler Beers, Theodore Bikel, Mike Bloomfield, The Blue Ridge Mountain Dancers, Paul Butterfield Blues Band, Johnny Cash, Judy Collins, Cousin Emmy, Donovan, Bob Dylan, Mimi Fariña, Richard Fariña, The Freedom Singers, The Georgia Sea Island Singers, Ronnie Gilbert, Mrs. Ollie Gilbert, Fanny Lou Hamer, Son House, Howlin' Wolf, Mississippi John Hurt, Spider John Koerner, Jim Kweskin Jug Band, Tex Logan & the Lilly Brothers, Mel Lyman, Fred McDowell, Brownie McGhee, Pappy Clayton McMichen, Spokes Mashiyane, Moving Star Hall Singers, Odetta, The Osborne Brothers, Joe Patterson, Peter, Paul, and Mary, Almeda Riddle, Eck Robertson, The Sacred Harp Singers, Buffy Sainte-Marie, Mike Seeger, Pete Seeger, The Staple Singers, Swan Silvertones, Sonny Terry, Mrs. General Watson, Reverend Wilkins, Ed Young Fife & Drum Corps.

Documentary. During the 1960's, throngs of young people descended on the Newport (Rhode Island) Folk Festival to hear most of the top folk music singers and instrumentalists perform in a free-flowing series of concerts. As a showcase for the music and a reflection of the temper of the styles, the festival was photographed by Murray Lerner over a 4-year period (1963-66), and the footage was edited for this documentary. Between shots of the young people attentively listening (even in the rain) to their folk favorites and closeup views of the performers themselves, interviews are conducted with the singers and some of their fans in an attempt to explain the appeal of folk music. *Youth. Singers. Musicians. Folk music. Newport Folk Festival.*

Note: Filmed on location at Newport in 16mm. Also known as *Newport Festival.*

THE FESTIVAL GIRLS   **F6.1513**
United American Film Production Corp. *Dist* Olympic International Films. 22 Nov **1962** [San Francisco showing]. Sd; b&w. 35mm. 72 min. [Cut from 78 min.]

Prod Marc Frederic. *Assoc Prod* John Harris, prod. *Dir* Leigh Jason. *Screenplay* Royal Foster, Ralph Staub. *Idea by* John Harris, prod. *Photog* Erich

Küchler. *Art Dir* Ing. I. Pengow. *Film Ed* Maria Pirkmayer. *Mus* Borut Lesjak. *Sd* Franco Jurjek. *Prod Supv* Mladen Kozina. *Prod Mgr* Roman Stergel.

Cast: Alex D'Arcy *(Larry Worthington),* Barbara Valentin *(Valentine),* Scilla Gabel *(Nadia),* Alan Dijon *(Vanguard),* Eduard Linkers, Regina Seiffert, Ivan Cuk, Frank Trefalt, Demeter Bitenc, Ute Böhnig, Anita Semmler, Helga Liotta, Helma Vandenberg, Vera Pino.

Melodrama. Discovering the voluptuous, half-drowned Valentine in the water fronting his hotel, film producer Larry Worthington casts the model as the star of *Blonde Dynamite.* In return for Valentine's favors, millionaire Vanguard finances the film. At the Venice Film Festival *Blonde Dynamite* wins top honors. At the festival Nadia recognizes Vanguard as the confidence man who absconded with her fortune. Enraged by Valentine's acquisition of her jewelry, Nadia assaults the starlet and retrieves her fortune. Once more without capital, Valentine and Worthington plan another picture. *Models. Actors. Motion picture producers. Millionaires. Confidence men. Sex exploitation films. Awards. Jewels. Venice Film Festival.*

Note: Location scenes filmed in Munich in 1960. Working title: *Festival Girl.*

LA FÊTE ESPAGNOLE see **NO TIME FOR ECSTASY**

LE FEU FOLLET see **THE FIRE WITHIN**

DAS FEUERZEUG see **THE TINDER BOX**

FEVER HEAT　　　　　　　　　　　　　　　　　　　　　　　　**F6.1514**
Heartland Productions–Fever Heat, Ltd. *Dist* Paramount Pictures. 1 May **1968** [Los Angeles opening; c26 Mar 1968; LP37076]. Sd; col (Technicolor). 35mm (Techniscope). 109 min. [Copyright length: 105 min.]
Prod-Dir Russell S. Doughten, Jr.. *Assoc Prod* Dick Talarico. *Screenplay* Henry Gregor Felsen. *Photog* Gary Young, photog. *Art Dir* Ray Storey. *Film Ed* Tom Boutross. *Mus* Jaime Mendoza-Nava. *Sp Eff* Ray Dishman.

Cast: Nick Adams *(Ace Jones),* Jeannine Riley *(Sandy Richards),* Norman Alden *(Herbert Herpgrave),* Vaughn Taylor *(Toad Taplinger),* Daxson Thomas *(Ronnie Richards),* Robert Broyles *(Loren Peale),* Al Ruscio, Walt Reno, Jr., Skip Nelson, Ron Foreman, Mary Walker, Alvin Meyer, Dwayne Bacon, Arthur Greco, Sharon Baum, Robert McClelland, Art Breese, Gail Miller, Dick Davis, Lon Parsons, John Doughten, Jack Thompson.

Melodrama. Source: Angus Vicker, *Fever Heat* (New York, 1954). Banned from auto racing, former stock car driver Ace Jones stops for repairs on his truck at a garage in an Iowa town. The garage is run by Sandy Richards, the widow of another driver, with the help of Ronnie, her brother-in-law, and Toad, an elderly mechanic. Ace stays on, becomes Sandy's business partner, and gets the garage back on its feet by collecting debts owed by racers. Eventually, Ace decides to go back to racing himself, despite the fact that Herbert Herpgrave, the local track owner who loves Sandy, dislikes him intensely. When Ace and Sandy fall in love and subsequently quarrel, Toad, believing that Sandy would be more secure with Herb, tampers with Ace's car, hoping that Ace will be killed on the track. Realizing too late that he has misjudged Ace, Toad runs onto the track during the race and meets his death. In the pileup that ensues, Ace is badly crippled and two of his racing buddies are killed. Following the tragedy, Sandy decides to ignore Herb's persistent interest and stick by Ace. *Stock car drivers. Widows. Mechanics. Brothers-in-law. Automobile racing. Partnerships. Sabotage. Automobile accidents. Garages. Iowa.*

Note: Location scenes filmed in Stuart, Oskaloosa, Des Moines, and Dexter, Iowa.

A FEVER IN THE BLOOD　　　　　　　　　　　　　　　　　　**F6.1515**
Warner Bros. Pictures. 11 Jan **1961** [Chicago opening; c28 Jan 1961; LP25359]. Sd; b&w. 35mm. 117 min.
Prod Roy Huggins. *Dir* Vincent Sherman. *Screenplay* Roy Huggins, Harry Kleiner. *Photog* J. Peverell Marley. *Art Dir* Malcolm C. Bert. *Set Decor* George James Hopkins. *Film Ed* William Ziegler. *Mus* Ernest Gold. *Sd* Robert B. Lee. *Asst Dir* Sergei Petschnikoff. *Cost* Howard Shoup. *Makeup* Gordon Bau. *Hairstyles* Jean Burt Reilly.

Cast: Efrem Zimbalist, Jr. *(Judge Hoffman),* Angie Dickinson *(Cathy Simon),* Jack Kelly *(Dan Callahan),* Don Ameche *(Sen. A. S. Simon),* Ray Danton *(Marker),* Herbert Marshall *(Governor Thornwall),* Andra Martin *(Laura Mayberry),* Jesse White *(Mickey Beers),* Rhodes Reason *(Walter Thornwall),* Robert Colbert *(Thomas Morely),* Carroll O'Connor *(Matt Keenan),* Parley Baer *(Bosworth),* Saundra Edwards *(Lucy Callahan),* June Blair *(Paula Thornwall),* Nelson Leigh *(hospital doctor),* Charles Irwin *(Forst).*

Melodrama. Source: William Pearson, *A Fever in the Blood* (New York, 1959). Young Paula Thornwall is murdered in her bedroom by her gardener, who escapes undetected. Because Paula's estranged husband is the nephew of the state governor, a politically ambitious district attorney, Dan Callahan, seizes the opportunity to file a charge of murder against the nephew. Presiding at the trial is Judge Hoffman, who, like Callahan, is interested in becoming

governor. Another interested party is Sen. A. S. Simon, who believes that by becoming governor he can be assured of nomination for the Presidency. When one of Callahan's witnesses gives inadmissible evidence, the defense attorney, Marker, calls for a mistrial. Senator Simon has offered Hoffman a Federal Court judgeship for turning down just such a request, however, and the motion is denied. The trial continues, and Thornwall is found guilty. Hoffman now decides to jeopardize his career by making public Simon's bribe so that a new trial can be granted. Simon belittles the charge until he suffers a heart attack, whereupon he admits to the bribery and then dies. Though Hoffman obtains evidence of Callahan's tactics, he refuses to use it and retires from the gubernatorial race. Then the gardener confesses to the murder. Governor Thornwall and Simon's widow, Cathy, who at one time was Hoffman's mistress, seek out the judge at his mountain retreat and bring him to the nominating convention, which has reached a stalemate. Hoffman's last-minute dramatic appearance so electrifies the delegates that he is nominated by acclamation. *Gardeners. State governors. Judges. District attorneys. Politics. Bribery. Murder. Political corruption. Political conventions. Trials. Confession (law). United States Congress.*

A FEW BULLETS MORE (Italy/Spain)　　　　　　　　　　　　**F6.1516**
Aitor Films–Kinesis Films. *Dist* RAF Industries, Golden Eagle Films. 18 Dec **1968** [Charlotte, North Carolina, opening]. Sd; col (Eastman Color). 35mm (Totalvision). 85 min. *MPAA rating* G.
Prod Silvio Battistini. *Exec Prod* Ricardo Sanz. *Dir* Julio Buchs. *Screenplay* Federico de Urrutia, Julio Buchs. *Orig Story* Julio Buchs, José Mallorquí, Federico de Urrutia, Carlo Veo. *Cinematog* Miguel F. Mila. *Asst Photog* Santiago Zuazo. *Camera Op* Francisco Gomez Conde. *Art Dir* Francesco Calabrese. *Set Decor* Vazquez Brothers. *Asst Set Decor* José Antonio Hidalgo. *Set Dresser* José Luis Galicia. *Main Titl* Pablo Nuñez. *Film Ed* Magdalena Pulido. *Asst Film Ed* Cecilia Gomez. *Mus Comp & Cond* Gianni Ferrio. *Sd Engr* Antonio Alonso. *Asst Dir* Joaquin Vera, Gian Carlo Battistini. *Prod Asst* José Salcedo, Serafin García. *Script Clerk* Andres Vigh. *Wardrobe* Humberto Cornejo, Francesca Pons. *Makeup* Manolita Ponte. *Hairdresser* Ines Gonzales. *Still Photog* Julio Sanchez Caballero. *Prop* José Sánchez. *Constr* Jaime Pérez Cubero, José Luis Galicia.

Cast: Peter Lee Lawrence *(Billy Bonney),* Fausto Tozzi *(Pat Garrett),* Diane Zura *(Helen Tunstill [see note]),* Gloria Milland *(Billy's mother),* Carlos Casaravilla, Antonio Pica, Enrique Avila, Orlando Baralla, Paco Sanz, Luis Rivera, Barta Barri, Alfonso Rojas, Luis Prendes, Tomas Blanco, Luis Induni, José Canalejas.

Western melodrama. Billy Bonney kills the man who assaulted his mother and is shielded by prospector Pat Garrett, an old friend of the family. In spite of Garrett's protection, however, Billy shoots those pursuing him and flees to Mexico, where he becomes widely known as "Billy the Kid." He attempts to reform when Englishman Henry Tunstill and his daughter Helen befriend him and ask him to work on their ranch; but when Tunstill is murdered, Billy turns killer again. Governor Lew Wallace of the New Mexico Territory offers amnesty to criminals on the run, and Billy returns home to visit his dying mother. Garrett, now sheriff, tries to convince the youth to mend his ways, but Billy guns down a townsman who blames Billy for his mother's death. Once again, Billy becomes a fugitive and flees to Helen's home, where the two plan to begin a new life together in another territory. Billy manages to convince the pursuing Garrett of his sincerity, but he is ambushed by one of his old enemies. Helen accuses Garrett of the killing, which he denies, but the blame nevertheless follows him for years. *Prospectors. Outlaws. Ranchers. Territorial governors. Sheriffs. Revenge. Murder. Filial relations. Amnesty. Reputation. Mexico. New Mexico. William H. Bonney. Pat Garrett. Lew Wallace.*

Note: Released in Italy in 1967 as *... E divenne il più spietato bandito del sud;* opened in Madrid in May 1967 as *El hombre que mato a Billy el Niño;* running time: 100 min. Diane Zura is a pseudonym for Dianik Zurakowska.

LA FIANCÉE DU PIRATE see **A VERY CURIOUS GIRL**

THE FIANCES (Italy)　　　　　　　　　　　　　　　　　　　　**F6.1517**
Titanus Sicilia–Ventidue Dicembre–S. E. C. I. *Dist* Janus Films. 28 Jan **1964** [New York opening]. Sd; b&w. 35mm. 84 min.
Prod Goffredo Lombardo. *Dir-Writ* Ermanno Olmi. *Photog* Lamberto Caimi. *Art Dir* Ettore Lombardi. *Film Ed* Carla Colombo. *Mus* Gianni Ferrio. *Sd* Guido Nardone. *Prod Mgr* Attilio Tonicelli.

Cast: Carlo Cabrini *(Giovanni),* Anna Canzi *(Liliana).*

Romantic drama. Giovanni, a welder working in Milan, decides to improve his position by accepting a transfer to his company's new plant in Sicily for an 18-month period. Reluctantly he places his aging father in a rest home and leaves behind Liliana, his fiancée; their long-term relationship has become one of habit, indifference, and eventually mistrust. After a short time in Sicily, Giovanni becomes depressed by the solitude and sparse landscape and sends a postcard to Liliana. Finally able to put on paper what she was formerly unable to put into words, Liliana replies quickly, and a regular correspondence ensues between the two. The barrier that had developed dissolves, and Giovanni places a long distance telephone call to Liliana to hear the sound of her voice. They begin to look forward to a new relationship together. *Welders. Filial relations. Courtship. Loneliness. Old age homes. Milan. Sicily. Documentation.*

Note: Opened in Rome in Aug 1963 as *I fidanzati.*

FIASCO IN MILAN (France/Italy)   **F6.1518**
Titanus-Vides-S. G. C. *Dist* Avion-Trans-Universe Pictures, Jerand Film Distributors. 10 Apr **1963** [New York opening]. Sd; b&w. 35mm. 104 min.

Prod Franco Cristaldi. *Dir* Nanni Loy. *Screenplay* Age & Scarpelli, Nanni Loy. *Scen* Age & Scarpelli. *Photog* Roberto Gerardi. *Art Dir* Carlo Egidi. *Film Ed* Mario Serandrei. *Mus* Piero Umiliani.

Cast: Vittorio Gassman (*Peppe*), Renato Salvatori (*Mario Angeletti*), Vicky Ludovisi (*Floriana*), Carlo Pisacane (*Capannelle*), Claudia Cardinale (*Carmela Nicosia*), Nino Manfredi (*Ugo Nardi*), Riccardo Garrone (*The Milanese*), Tiberio Murgia (*Ferribotte*), Gianni Bonagura (*accountant*), Gastone Moschin, Mario Feliciani.

Crime comedy. A gang of petty thieves led by Peppe are recruited by a Milanese bandit to rob a suitcase filled with L90,000,000 from a soccer pool. The accountant in charge of the receipts, having fallen in love with Floriana, the Milanese's stripteaser girl friend, willingly agrees to hand over the suitcase. Peppe takes charge of the "robbery" when the Milanese is arrested on an unrelated charge. The valise is stolen during a soccer match in Milan and checked in a baggage room. The baggage claim ticket falls into the possession of Capannelle, an aging gangster who is dying of indigestion in a hospital. Peppe finally retrieves the suitcase, but he abandons it in a public park when the police, who later arrest him for jaywalking, appear to be closing in. *Thieves. Accountants. Stripteasers. Gangsters. Police. Robbery. Soccer. Hospitals. Milan.*

Note: Filmed in Italy. Opened in Rome in Dec 1959 as *Audace colpo dei soliti ignoti;* running time: 100 min; in Paris in Aug 1962 as *Hold-up à la milanaise;* running time: 97 min.

THE FICKLE FINGER OF FATE (United States/Spain)   **F6.1519**
L. M. Films-Westside International-Cinemagic, Inc. *Dist* Producers Releasing Organization. Jun **1967**. Sd; col (Eastmancolor, print by Movielab). 35mm. 91 min.

Prod Sidney W. Pink, José López Moreno. *Dir* Richard Rush. *Screenplay* Aurelio López Monis, Jim Henaghan. *Photog* Antonio Macasoli. *Set Decor* Luis Argüello. *Film Ed* John Horvath. *Mus* Gregorio García Segura.

Cast: Tab Hunter (*Jerry Parker*), Luis Prendes (*Winkle*), Gustavo Rojo (*Estrala*), Fernando Hilbeck (*Fuentes*), Ralph Browne (*Jaffe*), Pedro María Sánchez (*Paco*), Elsa Skolinstad (*Inger*), Patty Sheppard (*Pilar*), Alejandra Nilo (*María*), Andrea Lascelles (*Maika*), May Heatherly (*Jane*), Katia Losser.

Comedy. Jerry Parker, an American construction engineer, is about to leave Madrid for home, but he is detained by customs when a priceless candlestick missing from a church altar is found in his luggage. Because the incident is attributed to a baggage mixup involving a group of beauty contestants en route to Rome, the police permit Jerry to return to his hotel if he will help them expose the real thief. With the candlestick (called The Finger of Fate) placed in his room for bait, Jerry befriends the five beauty contestants and an urchin, Paco, who agrees to help him. The beauty contestants' press agent is murdered, Paco is abducted, and the candlestick inexplicably reappears on the church altar. The thief turns up at the church, and Jerry overpowers him as the police rush in. The villain is revealed to be Winkle, seemingly a tourist, who killed the press agent because he, too, attempted to get the candlestick and then abducted little Paco when the boy learned too much. Jerry now boards the next flight out of Madrid only to discover that he is on a plane headed for Rome with the beauty contestants. *Engineers. Americans in foreign countries. Press agents. Police. Theft. Murder. Abduction. Churches. Beauty contests. Madrid. Rome.*

Note: Filmed in Madrid. Opened in Madrid in Apr 1968 as *El dedo del destino;* running time: 95 min. Working title: *The Cups of San Sebastian.*

I FIDANZATI *see* **THE FIANCES**

FIDEL   **F6.1520**
Documentary Film Co. *For* National Educational Television. *Dist* Documentary Film Co., New Yorker Films. 11 Feb **1970** [San Francisco opening]. Sd; col (Eastman Color). 16mm. 96 min.

Prod-Dir-Writ Saul Landau. *Exec Prod* Alvin Duskin. *Co-dir* Irving Saraf. *Photog* Irving Saraf. *Adtl Photog* José P. Fraga. *Film Ed* Irving Saraf. *Mus* Carlos Puebla, Las Estrellas Cubanas, Joseito Fernández. *Prod Asst* Nino Serrano.

Documentary. The film, shot in Cuba from May to September of 1968, depicts Fidel Castro as a benevolent, charismatic leader, familiar with the problems of the proletariat. During a 5-day jeep trip through Oriente Province, he listens to villagers' complaints about lack of hospitals, midwives,

transportation, and roads. He also revisits his nursery school, where he recalls his first revolutionary poem. Castro candidly discusses his country's agricultural, racial, and educational problems, and comments on the psychological predisposition of the Cuban people to remain underdeveloped. Interspersed with views of Castro mingling with peasants and workers—he is seen determinedly struggling in an informal baseball game—is newsreel footage of the Cuban revolution, including scenes of the Moncada Barracks raid, the Bay of Pigs Invasion, as well as a portrait of the martyred Che Guevara. Interviews with political prisoners and expatriated Cubans seeking exile in Miami balance an essentially favorable view of the controversial man. At a factory inspection and a mass rally in Havana, Castro exhorts his people to greater revolutionary fervor. *Revolutionaries. Lower classes. Peasants. Political prisoners. Expatriates. Rural life. Social reform. Jeeps. Factories. Baseball. Cuba—History—1958 Revolution. Cuba—History—Invasion 1961. Havana. Fidel Castro Ruz. Ernesto "Che" Guevara.*

Note: Adapted from *Fidel,* a 60-min N.E.T. Special first broadcast in Apr 1969.

FIDELIO (Austria)   **F6.1521**
Akkord Film. *Dist* Brandon Films. 12 May **1961** [New York opening]. Sd; b&w. 35mm. 90 min.

Dir Walter Felsenstein. *Libretto* Walter Felsenstein, Hanns Eisler. *Photog* Nicolas Hayer, Hannes Fuchs, Viktor Meihsl, Walter Tuch. *Settings & Dsgn* Rochus Gliese, Leo Metzenbauer. *Mus* Ludwig van Beethoven. *Mus Adapt* Hanns Eisler. *Mus Dir* Erich Bertel. *Mus Perf by* Vienna Symphony Orchestra. *Cond* Fritz Lehmann. *Sung by* Vienna State Opera Chorus. *Choral Dir* Hermann Luddekke, Richard Rossmayer. *Singing Voice of Claude Nollier* Magda Laszlo. *Singing Voice of Erwin Gross* Alfred Pöll. *Singing Voice of Hannes Schiel* Heinz Rehfuss. *Spoken Voice of George Wieter* Wolfgang Hebenstreit. *Singing Voice of Michael Tellering* Kurt Equiluz. *Singing Voice of Harry Payer* Leo Heppe. *Prod Mgr* J. A. Vesely. *English Subtitl* Herman G. Weinberg.

Cast: Richard Holm (*Florestan*), Claude Nollier (*Leonore [Fidelio]*), Erwin Gross (*Don Fernando*), Hannes Schiel (*Don Pizarro*), George Wieter (*Rocco*), Sonja Schöner (*Marcellina*), Fritz Berger (*Jaquino*), Michael Tellering (*1st prisoner*), Harry Payer (*2d prisoner*).

Opera film. Source: Ludwig van Beethoven, *Fidelio* (first performance: Vienna, 20 Nov 1805). Jean Nicolas Bouilly and Pierre Gaveau, *Léonore ou l'amour conjugal* (first performance: Paris, 1798). A film adaptation of Beethoven's opera. *Spanish. Nobility. Despots. Prison wardens. Political prisoners. Imprisonment. Male impersonation. Rescue. Murder. Seville.*

Note: Filmed in Vienna in 1955.

FIDELIO (West Germany)   **F6.1522**
Polyphon Film & TV Productions. *Dist* Polytel International. 16 Jul **1970** [New York opening]. Sd; col (Eastman Color). 35mm. 119 min.

Prod Rolf Liebermann. *Exec Prod* Gyula Trebitsch. *Dir* Joachim Hess. *Orig Staging* Guenther Rennert. *Libretto* Joseph Sonnleithner, Georg Friedrich Treitschke. *Photog* Hannes Schindler. *Art Dir* Wilhelm Reinking. *Decor* Ita Maximovna. *Mus:* "Fidelio" Ludwig van Beethoven. *Mus Cond* Leopold Ludwig. *Mus Played by* Hamburg State Orchestra. *Sung by* Choir of Hamburg State Opera. *Choirmaster* Gunther Schmidt Bohlander. *Prod Supv* Rudolf Sander.

Cast: Hans Sotin (*Don Fernando*), Theo Adam (*Don Pizarro*), Richard Cassilly (*Florestan*), Anja Silja (*Leonore [Fidelio]*), Ernst Wiemann (*Rocco*), Lucia Popp (*Marcellina*), Erwin Wohlfahrt (*Jaquino*), Kurt Marschner, William Workman (*prisoners*).

Opera film. Source: Ludwig van Beethoven, *Fidelio* (first performance: Vienna, 20 Nov 1805). Jean Nicolas Bouilly and Pierre Gaveau, *Léonore ou l'amour conjugal* (first performance: Paris, 1798). A film adaptation of Beethoven's opera. *Spanish. Nobility. Despots. Prison wardens. Political prisoners. Imprisonment. Male impersonation. Murder. Rescue. Seville.*

Note: Produced for West German television in 1968.

FIELDS OF HONOR *see* **SHENANDOAH**

FIEND OF DOPE ISLAND   **F6.1523**
J. Harold Odell Productions. *Dist* Essanjay Films. Mar **1961** [Los Angeles showing]. Sd; b&w. 35mm. 76 min.

Pres by David F. Friedman, Irwin S. Joseph. A J. Harold Odell Production. *Prod* J. Harold Odell. *Exec Prod* Lawrence Rapport, David S. Odell. *Assoc Prod* Victor Carrady. *Dir-Story* Nate Watt. *Screenplay* Bruce Bennett, Mark Carabel. *Dir Photog* Gayne Rescher. *Lighting* Frank Leonetti. *Camera* Jaime Alvarez. *Asst Camera* Antonio Betancourt. *Ed* James Gaffney. *Mus* James Peterson. *Song:* "Hold Me Forever" Ken Darby. *Sd Engr* Rose Raúl Ramírez. *Sd Ed* Patrick Slattery. *Asst Dir* Robert Beche. *Prod Mgr* Harold Winston. *Makeup* Mary Mayer.

Cast: Bruce Bennett (*Charlie Davis*), Robert Bray (*David*), Tania Velia (*Glory La Verne*), Ralph Rodriguez (*Naru*), Miguel Angel Alvarez (*Captain Fred*), Edmundo Rivera Alvarez (*Paco*), Ruth Fernandez (*Tula*), Molly Odell (*Mahla*), Milton Steifel, Yvonne Peck, Tito Enriquez, Eddie Ortiz, Baby Gonzalez, Russel Torres, Amos Rivera.

Action melodrama. Charlie Davis, self-proclaimed "baron" of a Caribbean island, wields his whip freely as he exploits the natives, paying slave wages and charging inflated prices at his canteen. His illegal sidelines include growing marijuana and smuggling firearms. Charlie arranges for his chief gun runner, Captain Fred, to import an "entertainer" to the island. Lured by a $500 advance and the promise of a nightclub engagement, Glory La Verne comes to the island, but she soon becomes suspicious and discovers Charlie's illegal activities. She falls in love with David, Charlie's assistant, and the two make plans to sabotage Charlie's operation. They blow up his ammunition dump and trap Charlie in the canteen under rifle fire. Charlie escapes and radios Captain Fred for aid. As Charlie and David struggle on the dock they fall into the water, and Charlie is killed by sharks as David makes his escape. With the island freed from Charlie's tyranny, David and Glory look forward to a brighter future. *Despots. Entertainers. Gunrunners. Flagellation. Marijuana. Islands. Explosives. Firearms. Caribbean. Sharks.*

Note: Filmed in the Caribbean.

THE FIEND WITH THE ELECTRONIC BRAIN *see* **PSYCHO A GO-GO!**

THE FIENDISH GHOULS *see* **MANIA**

THE FIERCEST HEART   **F6.1524**

Twentieth Century-Fox Film Corp. 26 Apr **1961** [Detroit opening; c6 Apr 1961; LP19480]. Sd (Westrex); col (De Luxe). 35mm (CinemaScope). 91 min.

Prod-Dir George Sherman. *Screenplay* Edmund H. North. *Dir Photog* Ellis W. Carter. *Art Dir* Duncan Cramer, George Van Marter. *Set Decor* Walter M. Scott, Stuart A. Reiss. *Film Ed* Richard Billings. *Mus Comp & Cond* Irving Gertz. *Orch* Edward B. Powell. *Choreog* Roy Fitzell. *Sd* Alfred Bruzlin, Warren B. Delaplain. *Asst Dir* Jack R. Berne. *Makeup* Ben Nye. *Hairstyles* Helen Turpin.

Cast: Stuart Whitman (*Steve Bates*), Juliet Prowse (*Francina Prinsloo*), Ken Scott (*Harry Carter*), Raymond Massey (*Willem Prinsloo*), Geraldine Fitzgerald (*Tante Maria*), Rafer Johnson (*Nzobo*), Michael David (*Barent*), Eduard Franz (*Hugo Bauman*), Rachel Stephens (*Sarah*), Dennis Holmes (*Peter*), Edward Platt (*Madrigo*), Alan Caillou (*Major Adrian*), Hari Rhodes (*Hendrik*), Katherine Henryk (*Mrs. Adrian*), Oscar Beregi (*Klaas*).

Melodrama. Source: Stuart Cloete, *The Fiercest Heart* (Boston, 1960). In South Africa in 1837, three men—Steve Bates, a private in the British Army; Nzobo, his African friend; and Harry Carter, a convicted criminal—break out of a prison garrison and join a group of Boers, led by Willem Prinsloo, who are heading north to escape from British oppression. Almost immediately, Bates becomes attracted to Willem's granddaughter, Francina, and despite her engagement to a young farmer, Barent Beyer, he openly woos her. Following a Zulu raid in which Willem is wounded, Carter assaults Francina and is banished from the company. A short time later, after naming Bates as his successor, Willem dies. The wildly jealous Barent tries to kill his rival, but before he can do so he himself is killed by a Zulu spear. Meanwhile, Carter has joined forces with a brutal slave trader who, with the aid of the Zulus, plans to attack the Boers and steal their wagons. But the raid fails when Bates kills Carter in a hand-to-hand fight and Nzobo slays the Zulu chief. A few days later the Boers reach their destination, and Bates decides to become a farmer and settle down with Francina. *Boers. British. Convicts. Prison escapees. Africans. Zulus. Slavers. Jealousy. South Africa. Great Britain—Army.*

FIERY SPUR *see* **HOT SPUR**

15 FROM ROME *see* **OPIATE '67**

XV SONG TRAITS   **F6.1525**

Dist Brakhage. 3 Sep **1965** [New York opening]. Si; col. 8mm. 75 min. [Cut to 47 min.]

Dir Stan Brakhage. *Assoc* Jane Brakhage. *Photog* Stan Brakhage. *Film Ed* Stan Brakhage.

With the appearances of: Robert Kelly, Jane Brakhage, Bearthm Brakhage, Rarc Brakhage, Crystal Brakhage, Robert Creeley, Michael McClure, Myrrena Brakhage, Neowyn Brakhage, Angelo DiBenedetto, Ed Dorn, Jonas Mekas (*themselves*), Durin (*a dog*), Cheep Donkey (*a canary*).

Experimental film. A series of individual portraits of family and friends. *Family life. Friendship. Dogs. Canaries.*

Note: Also known as *Song XV*, the film is one of a series of "Songs" by Brakhage, most of which are distributed through sale only. Dedicated to Jonas Mekas.

THE FIFTH HORSEMAN IS FEAR (Czechoslovakia)   **F6.1526**

Barrandov Film Studio. For Československý Film. *Dist* Sigma III Corp. 6 May **1968** [New York opening]. Sd; b&w. 35mm. 100 min.

Pres by Carlo Ponti. *Dir-Writ* Zbyněk Brynych. *Screenplay* Zbyněk Brynych, Jan Kališ, Milan Nejedlý, Ester Krumbachová, Ota Koval. *Adapt* Věra Kalábová, Radovan Kalina. *Story* Hana Bělohradská, Zbyněk Brynych. *Photog* Jan Kališ. *Camera Op* Saša Rašilov. *Asst Camera* Rudolf Holan. *Art Dir* Milan Nejedlý. *Asst Art Dir* Jiří Hlupý. *Film Ed* Miroslav Hájek. *Asst Ed* Vilma Binterová, Jiří Sternwald. *Sd* Miloš Alster. *Asst Sd* Josef Weishaupt. *Sd Eff* Bohumír Brunclík. *Asst Dir* Ota Koval, Anna Lackovičová, Josef Krameš. *Prod Ch* Gustav Rohan. *Prod Mgr* Petr Čapek, Dana Dudová, Jan Syrový, Josef Protiva. *Tech Adv* Rudolf Iltis, Bohuslav Hodek, Miroslav Plzák. *Production Group* Šebor-Bor.

Cast: Miroslav Macháček (*Dr. Braun*), Olga Scheinpflugová (*music teacher*), Jiří Adamíra (*Mr. Vesely*), Ilja Prachař (*Šidlák*), Josef Vinklář (*Mr. Fanta*), Zdenka Procházková (*Mrs. Vesely*), Slávka Budínová (*Mrs. Wiener*), Alexandra Myšková (*singer*), Jiří Vršťala (*police inspector*), Jana Pracharová (*Šidlák's wife*), Tomáš Hádl (*Honzík*), Eva Svobodová (*porter's wife*), Karel Nováček (*Pánek*), Čestmír Řanda (*Dr. Wiener*), Iva Janžurová (*Anička*), Jana Břežková (*girl in nightclub*), Růžena Preislerová (*Löwyová*), Štěpánka Cittová (*coatroom attendant*), Ota Sattler (*musician*), František Chocholatý (*nightclub attendant*), Helena Růžičková (*masseuse*), Ivo Gübel (*chief physician*), Anny Freyová, Arnošt Vrána (*musicians*), Lída Matoušková (*nurse*), Zdeněk Hodr (*Roubíček*), Bohuslav Hodek (*Růžička*), Ladislav Potměšil (*vendor*), Helena Pejšková (*2d girl*), Eva Rohanová (*dancer*), Karel Šmíd (*deranged man*), Roman Hemala, Milan Mach, Mirko Musil, Jiří Pleskot (*husbands*), Jiří Ostermann.

Drama. Source: Hana Bělohradská, *Bez krásy, bez límce* (Prague, 1962). Dr. Braun, a Jewish physician forbidden to practice in Nazi-occupied Prague, has found a job in a warehouse. When a fellow tenant, a butcher named Šidlák, asks the doctor to remove a bullet from the wound of a political fugitive, the apathetic physician at first refuses, and although he finally agrees to perform the operation he must find morphine to keep the fugitive quiet during the night. He inquires first at the home of a Jewish doctor friend, later at a bordello maintained for German troops, where his sister works as a chambermaid, and finally at a nightclub in which everyone is trying desperately to forget the war. He eventually obtains the drug from a physician at a Jewish sanitarium. To conceal the patient from police during a search of the building, the doctor carries him up to his attic. On the following day, one of Dr. Braun's fellow tenants reports the fugitive's presence to the authorities, and all the tenants are herded into the cellar. Confronted by his "crime," the Jewish doctor freely confesses and then commits suicide by swallowing poison. When forced by the police to file past Dr. Braun's body, the guilt-ridden tenants are unable to look upon the corpse; all, that is, except for one woman who pauses to close the dead man's eyes. *Informers. Nazis. Jews. Physicians. Butchers. Fugitives. Police. Resistance (political). Military occupation. Suicide. Courage. Surgery. Whorehouses. Nightclubs. Morphine. World War II. Prague. Germany—Army.*

Note: Location scenes filmed in Prague. Opened in Prague in Feb 1965 as *... A pátý jezdec je Strach*; running time: 95 min. Additional brothel sequences which were made after the completion of the film did not appear in the Czechoslovak release version.

55 DAYS AT PEKING   **F6.1527**

Samuel Bronston Productions. *Dist* Allied Artists. 29 May **1963** [New York opening; c6 May 1963; LP27967]. Sd; col (Technicolor). 35mm & 70mm (Super Technirama 70). 150 min. [Also reviewed at 154 min.]

Prod Samuel Bronston. *Exec Assoc Prod* Michael Waszynski. *Assoc Prod* Alan Brown. *Dir* Nicholas Ray. *Dir 2d Unit Operations* Andrew Marton. *2d Unit Dir* Noel Howard. *Orig Screenplay* Philip Yordan, Bernard Gordon. *Adtl Dial* Robert Hamer. *Dir Photog* Jack Hildyard. *2d Unit Camera* Manuel Berenguer. *Set Decor* Veniero Colasanti, John Moore. *Prod Dsgn* Veniero Colasanti, John Moore. *Titl Paintings* Dong Kingman. *Film Ed* Robert Lawrence. *Asst Film Ed* Magdalena Paradell. *Mus Comp & Cond* Dimitri Tiomkin. *Song:* "So Little Time" Dimitri Tiomkin, Paul Francis Webster. *Sd Mix* David Hildyard. *Sd Eff Ed* Milton Burrow. *Re-rec* Gordon K. McCallum. *Mus Ed* Richard C. Harris. *1st & 2d Unit Asst Dir* José López Rodero, José María Ochoa. *Exec Prod Mgr* C. O. Erickson. *Cont* Lucie Lichtig. *Cost Dsgn* Veniero Colasanti, John Moore. *Wardrobe Head* Gloria Mussetta. *Makeup* Mario Van Riel. *Miss Gardner's Hairstyles* Alexandre of Paris, Grazia De Rossi. *Sp Eff* Alex Weldon. *Tech Adv* James R. Johnson, (Col.). *Casting* Maude Spector. *Prop Master* Stanley Detlie. *Supv Tech* Carl Gibson. *Supv Electrn* Bruno Pasqualini.

Cast: Charlton Heston (*Maj. Matt Lewis*), Ava Gardner (*Baroness Natalie Ivanoff*), David Niven (*Sir Arthur Robertson*), Flora Robson (*The Dowager Empress Tzü Hsi*), John Ireland (*Sergeant Harry*), Harry Andrews (*Father de Bearn*), Leo Genn (*General Jung-Lu*), Robert Helpmann (*Prince Tuan*), Ichizo

Itami (Colonel Shiba), Kurt Kasznar (Baron Sergei Ivanoff), Philippe Leroy (Julliard), Paul Lukas (Dr. Steinfeldt), Lynne Sue Moon (Teresa), Elizabeth Sellars (Lady Sarah Robertson), Massimo Serato (Garibaldi), Jacques Sernas (Major Bobrinski), Jerome Thor (Lieut. Andy Marshall), Geoffrey Bayldon (Smythe), Joseph Furst (Captain Hanselman), Walter Gotell (Captain Hoffman), Alfred Lynch (Gerald), Alfredo Mayo (Spanish minister), Martin Miller (Hugo Bergmann), Conchita Montés (Madame Gaumaire), José Nieto (Italian minister), Eric Pohlmann (Baron von Meck), Aram Stephan (Gaumaire), Robert Urquhart (Captain Hanley), Ronald Brittain (Sergeant Britten), Félix Dafauce (Dutch minister), André Esterhazy (Austrian minister), Carlos Casaravilla (Japanese minister), Fernando Sancho (Belgian minister), Michael Chow (Chiang), Mitchell Kowal (U. S. Marine), Mervyn Johns (clergyman), Nicholas Ray (American minister).

Historical epic. In June, 1900, legations in Peking representing 11 countries are threatened by the fanatical Boxers, a band of terrorists determined to drive the "foreign devils" out of China. Encouraged by Dowager Empress Tzü Hsi and her adviser, Prince Tuan, the Boxers move into the city and murder the German ambassador. Although most of the envoys vote to flee Peking, British Ambassador Sir Arthur Robertson persuades them to remain and make a stand. With only 500 military units at their disposal, the legations depend on the leadership of U. S. Marine Maj. Matt Lewis, who has prevented the deportation of Russian Baroness Natalie Ivanoff, widow of an aristocrat who committed suicide over her infidelity. Meanwhile, the empress orders the Imperial Army to aid the Boxers in their attack on the foreign powers. When their situation becomes desperate, Natalie obtains precious food and medicine by selling an emerald necklace, but she is fatally wounded while bringing the supplies into their compound. The situation appears hopeless as the Chinese launch a final assault, but on the morning of August 14th, 55 days after the initial uprising, reinforcements from all 11 nations arrive to turn back the Boxers, dethrone the empress, and topple the Manchu Dynasty. *Diplomats. Chinese. Royalty. Aristocrats. Americans in foreign countries. British. Germans. Russians. Widows. Terrorism. Imperialism. Nationalism. Assassination. Deportation. Self-sacrifice. China—History—Boxer Rebellion. Peking. Tzu Hsi. China—History—Manchu Dynasty. United States Marines.*

Note: Produced in Madrid.

50,000 B. C. (BEFORE CLOTHING)   F6.1528
Biolane Corp. *Dist* Waldorf Pictures, Sam Lake Enterprises, American Film Distributing Corp. ca **1963**. Sd; col. 35mm. 75 min.

Prod Herbert Lannard. *Dir* Warner Rose. *Mus* Martin Roman.

Cast: Charlie Robinson, Hedi Leonore, Mila Milo, The Cavegirls, Eddie Carmel, Paul Lavert and his Swinging Cavemen.

Comedy. Charlie Wishnick, an ex-burlesque comedian, receives a scolding from his prudish wife, an ex-stripper, for daring to enjoy himself at the Sewer Department Ball. He stumbles into his neighbor's time machine, which carries him back to 50,000 B. C. He is captured by a cave man, and sentenced to death by the King. The Queen intervenes to save him, but he is commanded not to touch the maiden Bubsmia, who has been promised as a sacrifice to the giant Gorax. Nevertheless, Bubsmia seduces Charlie. She is seized and sentenced to die, but charms the judge and jury, who condemn Charlie in her place. The trial recalls Charlie's vaudeville "courtroom scene." Zelda, a beautiful slave, is given the task of making Charlie's last night a happy one. Their evening together is continually interrupted, just as in Charlie's "honeymoon" vaudeville routine. As Charlie is taken to be smashed against the rocks, Gorax appears. Charlie whistles "Dixie." The hat he had rented for the Sewer Department Ball once belonged to Lincoln, and explodes at the tune. The stunned giant vanishes, and Charlie reluctantly becomes the new leader. Zelda discovers the time machine, however, and accidentally starts it. Attempting to pull her away, Charlie is caught inside. Upon his return to the modern age, he is confronted by his wife, who wants to know where he has been. Charlie struggles to restart the motor, and finally succeeds, traveling off to paradise again. *Entertainers. Cave dwellers. Stripteasers. Slavery. Seduction. Prehistory. Human sacrifice. Capital punishment. Marriage. Burlesque. Vaudeville. Time machines. Trials. Monsters. "Dixie".*

Note: Also known as *Nudes on the Rocks*.

52 MILES TO TERROR see HOT RODS TO HELL

FIGHT FOR THE GLORY (Japan)   F6.1529
Shochiku Co. *Dist* Shochiku Films of America. Apr **1970** [Los Angeles showing]. Sd; col (Eastman Color). 35mm (Shochiku GrandScope). 85 min.

Prod Kiyoshi Higuchi. *Dir* Hirokazu Ichimura. *Screenplay* Shiro Ishimori. *Photog* Masao Kosugi. *Art Dir* Chiyoo Umeda. *Film Ed* Shizu Ozaka. *Mus* Hirooki Ogawa. *Songs Sung by* Kensaku Morita, Yuuki Meguro, Mikiko Hirota.

Cast: Kensaku Morita (Goro Matsunaga), Miyoko Akaza (Misa), Yuuki Meguro (Yuji Komiwama), Chishu Ryu (Yonoshin), Shuji Sano (Professor

Kanzaki), Etsuko Ikuta (Yukiko), Yuko Enatsu (Naomi), Akuko Motoyama, Yoshiyuki Hosokawa, Taro Nanshu, Zaizu Ichiro, Akemi Kita, Mitsuko Takahashi, Miyoshi Kaneko, Jun Kashima, Nana Ozaki, Etsuko Nami, Mikiko Hirota.

Drama. Yuji, captain of the soccer team at Shinetsu University, enforces a strict training regimen for his teammates, one of whom, Goro, protests against Yuji's procedures. Meanwhile, Yuji is informed by Professor Kanzaki that he has been selected to study in Germany. Yukiko, Kanzaki's daughter, is happy for Yuji, but she realizes that they will be separated for 3 years if he accepts the offer. Yuji has his own doubts about the offer because he has promised his grandfather Yonoshin, who owns a brewery, that he will take over the business if the soccer team loses the upcoming match. Goro discovers that the team has no funds for a training camp, and he challenges Yonoshin to a fencing match on the condition that Yonoshin finance the soccer team if he loses. Goro, who is a practiced swordsman, wins the match and obtains the contribution. While practicing on the eve of the match, Yuji hurts his leg but does not reveal the injury to his teammates; during the match, however, he reinjures the leg and sends in Goro as his replacement. The opposing team wins the match, and Goro admits that Yuji had been right about his training methods. Yonoshin surprises Yuji by granting him permission to go to Germany instead of holding him to his promise, and Yuji and Yukiko part without confessing their love. *Students. Athletes. Grandfathers. Professors. Brewers. Soccer. Physical training. Fencing (sport). College life. Wagers.*

Note: Released in Japan in Dec 1969 as *Eiko eno kurohyo*.

THE FIGHTING PRINCE OF DONEGAL (Great Britain)   F6.1530
Walt Disney Productions. *Dist* Buena Vista Distribution Co. 5 Oct **1966** [Cleveland opening; c19 Aug 1966; LP32926]. Sd; col (Technicolor). 35mm. 112 min. [Copyright length: 110 min.]

Pres by Walt Disney. *Prod* Walt Disney. *Assoc Prod* Hugh Attwooll. *Co-prod* Bill Anderson, prod. *Dir* Michael O'Herlihy. *Screenplay* Robert Westerby. *Dir Photog* Arthur Ibbetson. *Camera Op* Freddie Cooper. *Art Dir* Maurice Carter. *Set Decor* David Ffolkes. *Film Ed* Peter Boita. *Mus* George Bruns. *Orch* Walter Sheets. *Sd Ed* Peter Keen. *Sd Rec* Ken Rawkins. *Sd Rec* Gordon McCallum. *Asst Dir* David Bracknell. *Prod Mgr* David Anderson. *Cont* June Faithfull. *Cost Dsgn* Anthony Mendleson. *Makeup* Harry Frampton. *Hairstyles* Eileen Warwick. *Sp Photog Eff* Peter Ellenshaw. *Casting* Maude Spector.

Cast: Peter McEnery (Hugh O'Donnell), Susan Hampshire (Kathleen MacSweeney), Tom Adams (Henry O'Neill), Gordon Jackson (Captain Leeds), Norman Wooland (Sir John Perrott), Richard Leech (Phelim O'Toole), Peter Jeffrey (troop sergeant), Marie Kean (mother), Bill Owen (1st Officer Powell), Peggy Marshall (Princess Ineen), Maurice Roëves (Martin), Donal McCann (Sean O'Toole), Fidelma Murphy (Moire), Andrew Keir (Lord MacSweeney), Maire Ni Ghrainne, Maire O'Neill (Moire's sisters), John Forbes Robertson, Patrick Holt, Robert Cawdron, Roger Croucher, Keith McConnell, Inigo Jackson, Peter Cranwell.

Costume drama. Source: Robert T. Reilly, *Red Hugh, Prince of Donegal* (Milwaukee, 1957). In 16th-century Ireland, garrisoned by British troops against the threat of Spanish invasion, the elder Prince Hugh of Donegal dies, and his son, Hugh O'Donnell, becomes head of the Donegal clan. Because of the belief that "when Hugh succeeds to Hugh, Ireland shall be free," Queen Elizabeth of England has the young prince captured and imprisoned in Dublin Castle. Aided by an Irish servant boy, Sean O'Toole, Hugh makes a bold attempt to escape but is recaptured. Lord MacSweeney and another clansman, Henry O'Neill, propose a peace treaty in return for Hugh's release. They succeed only in provoking the Irish-hating Captain Leeds; and O'Neill is thrown into the same cell with Hugh. When the two rebels eventually make good their escape, Captain Leeds seizes Donegal Castle and takes both Hugh's mother and his sweetheart, Kathleen MacSweeney, as hostages. By now all Ireland is ready to take up arms against England, and Hugh rallies the divergent clans into an army and storms Donegal Castle. The women are freed, and Captain Leeds is vanquished in a duel with Hugh. The English troops are forced to withdraw in defeat. *Irish. Royalty. Nobility. Soldiers. Hostages. Nationalism. Chauvinism. Prison escapes. Great Britain—History—Tudors. Ireland. Dublin. Donegal. Elizabeth I (England). Hugh Roe O'Donnell. Duels.*

Note: Released in Great Britain in Oct 1966; running time: 104 min.

LA FIGLIA DELLO SCEICCO see DESERT WARRIOR

IL FIGLIO DEL CAPITANO BLOOD see THE SON OF CAPTAIN BLOOD

IL FIGLIO DEL CORSARO ROSSO see SON OF THE RED CORSAIR

IL FIGLIO DI SPARTACUS see THE SLAVE

THE FILE OF THE GOLDEN GOOSE (Great Britain)   F6.1531
Theme Pictures–Caralan–Dador. *Dist* United Artists. 1 Oct **1969** [New York opening; c22 May 1969; LP37336]. Sd; col (DeLuxe). 35mm. 105 min. *MPAA rating* M.

Prod David E. Rose. *Assoc Prod* George Fowler. *Dir* Sam Wanamaker. *Screenplay* John C. Higgins, James B. Gordon. *Story* John C. Higgins. *Photog* Ken Hodges. *Art Dir* George Provis. *Film Ed* Oswald Hafenrichter. *Mus* Harry Robinson. *Mus Dir* Philip Martell. *Sd* Ken Ritchie, Nolan Roberts. *Asst Dir* Ray Frift. *Prod Mgr* Pat Green.

Cast: Yul Brynner *(Peter Novak)*, Charles Gray *(Nick Harrison, "The Owl")*, Edward Woodward *(Peter Thompson)*, John Barrie *(Sloane)*, Bernard Archard *(Collins)*, Ivor Dean *(Reynolds)*, Anthony Jacobs *(Firenzo)*, Adrienne Corri *(Tina Dell)*, Karel Stepanek *(Mueller)*, Walter Gotell *(Leeds)*, Graham Crowden *(Smythe)*, Geoffrey Reed *(Martin)*, Ken Jones, actor *(Stroud)*, Hilary Dwyer *(Anne)*, Janet Rossini *(Debbie)*, Joe Cornelius *(Grodie)*, Hugh McDermott *(Moss)*, Denis Shaw *(Vance)*, Anita Prynne *(Genevieve)*, Paddy Webster *(Mary)*, Ray Marioni *(croupier)*, Illario Pedro *(bongo player)*, Philip Anthony *(laboratory technician)*.

Crime melodrama. Peter Novak, a U. S. Treasury agent, narrowly escapes an assassination attempt in which his girl friend is killed just before he leaves for London to investigate an international counterfeit ring called the Golden Goose. He is dismayed when Scotland Yard assigns Peter Thompson to help him; Thompson is a family man, and Novak senses that he will be too cautious. Novak and Thompson work their way into the gang's confidence in Liverpool, and then the two men fake a quarrel, enabling Novak to move to the London branch of the operation run by Nick "The Owl" Harrison. In an effort to infiltrate the top of the gang, Novak supplies The Owl with new counterfeit plates to replace the gang's inferior ones. When Thompson arrives in London in an obvious position of trust with the gang, Novak suspects that he has sold out. The Owl suggests that the three of them go into business for themselves, but the gang tricks Thompson into revealing his true identity. He is murdered, and The Owl is also killed for his venture at independence. Novak is taken to a mansion where a gang member promises to turn state's evidence. Their conversation is overheard by one of the gang leaders, who kills the potential traitor but is himself killed by Novak. Although he is wounded, Novak, along with a force of men from Scotland Yard, stops the top counterfeiter (revealed to be a well-respected financier) from escaping in a helicopter. *Secret agents. Counterfeiters. Financiers. Assassination. Imposture. Organized crime. Liverpool. London. United States—Treasury Department. Scotland Yard.*

Note: Location scenes filmed in London. Released in Great Britain in Jun 1969; running time: 109 min.

FILE X FOR SEX   F6.1532
Dist Sam Lake Enterprises. 13 Dec **1967** [New York showing]. Sd; b&w. 35mm. 71 min.
A Sam Lake–C. Davis Smith Production.

Sex film. Several case histories are collected by a man engaged in a study of abnormal sexual behavior. Maria N. marries young, but her insatiable appetite for men forces the 21-year-old girl out of the rigid bounds of matrimony. Judy R. is a devoted narcissist who employs sex aids for her own gratification in front of a mirror. Charles B., a voyeur, needs visual stimulation in order to achieve an erection. Larry K. is a satyr, whose frustration forces him from girl to girl in a hopeless search for satisfaction. Young Harry M. lives by selling his body to men, while Harold J., a fetishist, exhibits a particular fondness for low-cut black leather boots. *Nymphomania. Narcissism. Voyeurism. Satyriasis. Male homosexuality. Prostitution. Fetishism. Sex aids.*

Note: May also be known as either *The Story of the Perverted* or *File X*.

FILES OF DETECTIVE X see THE SECRET FILES OF DETECTIVE "X"

LA FILLE À LA VALISE see GIRL WITH A SUITCASE

LA FILLE AUX YEUX D'OR see THE GIRL WITH THE GOLDEN EYES

LA FILLE DE FEU see FIRE IN THE FLESH

LA FILLE DE LA RIZIÈRE see RICE GIRL

UNE FILLE ET DES FUSILS see TO BE A CROOK

UNE FILLE POUR L'ÉTÉ see A MISTRESS FOR THE SUMMER

LES FILLES SÈMENT LE VENT see THE FRUIT IS RIPE

THE FILMS OF HARRY SMITH   F6.1533
·*Dist* Film-Makers' Cooperative. 15 Mar **1965** [New York opening]. Sd; b&w and col. 16mm. ca125 min.

Anthology. Included in this anthology of Smith's experimental animations are No. 1, No. 2, No. 3, No. 4, No. 5, No. 7, No. 10, No. 12, and No. 14. *Harry Smith.*

Note: Nos. 1-5, 7 and 10 were later released as *Early Abstractions*; No. 14 as *Late Superimpositions*; and No. 12 as a separate feature, q. v.

THE FILTH SHOP   F6.1534
Dist Dekko Films, American Film Distributing Corp. 9 Jul **1969** [Boston opening]. Sd; b&w. 35mm. 63 min.

Cast: Susan Sex, Lover Lee, Louise Log, Sid Burns, Looney Bear.

Crime melodrama. The film exposes a segment of the pornography industry which has become a multi-million dollar operation under the control of a powerful crime syndicate. Racketeers drug innocent women, force them into degrading and compromising situations, and take lewd photographs of them. *Racketeers. Pornography. Narcotics. Abduction. Syndicates.*

Note: Footage also included in *The Devil's Book Store*, q. v.

THE FILTHY FIVE   F6.1535
Extraordinary Films. *Dist* William Mishkin. 8 Nov **1968** [Champaign, Illinois, showing]. Sd; b&w. 35mm. 96 min.

Prod William Mishkin. *Dir* Andy Milligan. *Screenplay* Gerald Jacuzzo, Andy Milligan. *Photog* Andy Milligan.

Cast: Anne Linden *(Rita Roman)*, Matt Garth *(Johnny Longo)*, Jackie Colton *(Rose White)*, Nick Orzel *(Barney)*, Maha *(Allison)*, Gerald Jacuzzo *(Sidney Hart)*, Mark Jenkins *(Billy Delavanti)*, Maggie Rogers *(Ma Delavanti)*, Mary Carter *(Brenda Case)*, Larry Ree *(Freakout)*, Haal Borske *(Walter Cash)*, Maggie Dominic *(teeny bopper)*, Selena Robbins *(stripper)*.

Melodrama. Boxing hopeful Johnny Longo spends the night with Rose, a prostitute who has secretly used her racket connections to further his career. Johnny is up for the role of a boxer on a television series co-starring with Rita Roman, a heroin addict who was once a famous actress. Rita and Johnny meet but they quarrel continuously, ruining their rehearsals and upsetting Johnny's training schedule for an upcoming fight. Rose becomes insanely jealous, feeling that she will completely lose Johnny if he is a success on television. When she learns that Rita hates him, they plot to get him off the show. Rita throws a wild party and induces him to take LSD. Under the drug's influence, he injures himself, thereby ending his television and boxing careers and making him forever dependent upon Rose. *Boxers. Prostitutes. Actors. Drug addicts. Jealousy. Perfidy. LSD. Heroin. Television. Orgies.*

Note: Also known as *The F—— Five* and *The Filthy 5*. May also be known as *The Dirty Five*.

THE FINAL BLOW   F6.1536
Dist Stacey Distributors. ca 1970. Sd; col. 16mm. 61-81 min.
Sex film. No information about the precise nature of this film has been found. *Sexuality.*

THE FINAL WAR (Japan)   F6.1537
New Toei Co. *Dist* Sam Lake Enterprises. 3 Dec **1962** [New York State license]. Sd; b&w. 35mm (ToeiScope). 77 min.

Dir Shigeaki Hidaka. *Screenplay* Hisataka Kai. *Photog* Tadashi Arakami.

Cast: Tatsuo Umemiya, Yoshiko Mita, Yayoi Furusato, Noribumi Fujishima, Yukiko Nikaido, Michiko Hoshi.

Science fiction melodrama. A United States Air Force plane accidentally detonates a nuclear bomb over Korea. While South Korea insists that North Korea set off the explosion, the North Koreans protest U. S. violation of the 38th Parallel. In Japan, the U. S. 7th Fleet mobilizes at Yokosuko. A broadcast from Peking reports that an American U-3 jet has been shot down over the Soviet Union. As Tokyo mobilizes its civil defense units, newspaper Shigeo reports on the growing crisis, while his sweetheart, Tomoko, a nurse, prepares to care for casualties. Negotiations between the U. S. and the U.S.S.R. break down, and Moscow warns Tokyo that every Japanese airbase will be destroyed by H-bombs within minutes. At dawn, Tokyo lies in ruins, completely destroyed by nuclear weapons. Shigeo returns to the city looking for Tomoko but finds that she has been killed; he then dies from exposure to radiation. In Argentina, the only country to survive total devastation, a memorial service is held for mankind. *Reporters. Nurses. Nuclear warfare. Holocausts. Radiation. Civil defense. Tokyo. People's Democratic Republic of Korea. Republic of Korea. Union of Soviet Socialist Republics. Argentina. Peking. United States Air Force. United States Navy.*

Note: Released in Japan in Oct 1960 as *Dai Sanji Sekai Taisen—yonju-ichi jikan no kyofu*. Alternative Japanese title: *41 jikan no kyofu*. Alternative U. S. title: *World War III Breaks Out*.

FINCHÈ DURA LA TEMPESTA see TORPEDO BAY

FINDERS KEEPERS (Great Britain)   **F6.1538**

Inter-State Films. *Dist* United Artists. Mar **1967**. Sd; col (Eastman Color). 35mm. 89 min.

Prod-Story George H. Brown. *Dir* Sidney Hayers. *2d Unit Dir* Jan Darnley-Smith. *Screenplay* Michael Pertwee. *Photog* Alan Hume. *Art Dir* Jack Shampan. *Film Ed* Tristam Cones. *Mus & Lyr* The Shadows. *Mus Dir* Norrie Paramor. *Dances & Mus Numbers Created by* Hugh Lambert. *Choreog* Malcolm Clare. *Asst Dir* Stuart Freeman. *Cost* Cynthia Tingey.

Cast: Cliff Richard (*Cliff*), Bruce Welch, Hank B. Marvin, Brian Bennett, John Rostill (*themselves, The Shadows*), Robert Morley (*Colonel Roberts*), Peggy Mount (*Mrs. Bragg*), Viviane Ventura (*Emelia*), Graham Stark (*Burke*), John Le Mesurier (*Mr. X*), Robert Hutton (*commander*), Gordon Ruttan (*junior officer*), Ellen Pollock (*grandma*), Ernest Clark (*air marshall*), Burnell Tucker (*pilot*), George Roderick (*priest*), Bill Mitchell (*G.I. guard*), Ronnie Brody (*drunk*).

Comedy with music. In the Spanish resort town of San Carlos Colonel Roberts hires Cliff and The Shadows to entertain his guests, but the group arrives to find the town deserted. Burke, the colonel's assistant, explains that an American plane has lost a "Mighty Mini" bomb in the ocean, and the tourists have fled the area. Stranded, the boys make friends with Emelia, who tells them that the villagers are concerned about the fate of their annual fiesta. The colonel and Burke, in the meantime, have agreed to help a foreign power locate the bomb and, under instructions from a mysterious Mr. X, have installed microphones in all the hotel rooms. Unknown to the colonel, his gruff housekeeper, Mrs. Bragg, is sending her own messages to the British secret services. After Cliff and The Shadows have lured the Americans out of town, the real bomb is found in the kitchen of Emelia's grandmother, who has mistaken it for a gas cylinder. Cliff reports the discovery to the Americans, but his story is considered another ruse, and he and The Shadows are thrown into jail. They escape, rescue Mrs. Bragg from the colonel, and race to Emelia's grandmother's house. The bomb, however, is already in the hands of the colonel and Burke, who are driving one of the flowered parade floats. Cliff substitutes a fake bomb for the real one; and Mr. X, the colonel, and Burke abscond with the imitation. The real "Mighty Mini" is safely delivered by Cliff and his group to the police. *Tourists. Entertainers. Housekeepers. Grandmothers. Americans in foreign countries. Espionage. Electronic surveillance. Prison escapes. Resorts. Bombs. Hotels. Carnivals. Parades. Spain. Chases.*

Note: Location scenes filmed in Spain. Released in Great Britain in 1966; running time: 94 min.

FINDERS KEEPERS, LOVERS WEEPERS   **F6.1539**

Eve Productions. Oct **1968** [Los Angeles showing; c8 May 1968; LP35622]. Sd; col (Eastmancolor). 35mm. 71 min.

Prod-Dir Russ Meyer. *Exec Prod* Eve Meyer. *Assoc Prod* Anthony James Ryan. *Screenplay* Richard Zachary. *Orig Story* Russ Meyer. *Photog* Russ Meyer. *Film Ed* Russ Meyer, Richard Brummer. *Mus* Igo Kantor. *Title Song Sung by* Melvin Elling, The Casuals on the Square. *Sd* Richard Brummer. *Asst Dir* George Costello.

Cast: Anne Chapman (*Kelly*), Paul Lockwood, actor (*Paul*), Gordon Wescourt (*Ray*), Duncan McLeod (*Cal*), Robert Rudelson (*Feeny*), Lavelle Roby (*Claire*), Jan Sinclair (*Christiana*), Joey Duprez (*Joy*), Nick Wolcuff (*Nick*), Pam Collins, Vickie Roberts, John Furlong, Michael Roberts.

Drama. Paul, the owner of a Sunset Strip tavern featuring topless go-go dancers, is lured to the bordello of his longtime sexual partner Claire, unaware that she has masterminded a plan to rob his bar when it closes. Complications set in when Paul's wife Kelly tries to get revenge on her unfaithful husband by going to the club and replacing one of the go-go dancers. There she succumbs to the overtures of the bartender, Ray, who persuades her to go for a nude swim in his pool. They return to the club as the robbery is being pulled off by Claire's two thugs, Cal and Feeny. When Paul appears on the scene, the hoods tell him what has happened between his bartender and his wife and then attempt to force him into giving them the safe combination number by threatening to rape Kelly. Although bound, Paul gets loose and kills the two robbers after Claire has been slain and Ray seriously wounded with a knife. *Prostitutes. Saloon keepers. Bartenders. Go-go dancers. Infidelity. Revenge. Murder. Robbery. Whorehouses. Saloons. Los Angeles—Sunset Strip.*

A FINE MADNESS   **F6.1540**

Pan Arts Co. *Dist* Warner Bros. Pictures. 11 May **1966** [Los Angeles opening; c25 May 1966; LP32664]. Sd; col (Technicolor). 35mm. 104 min.

Prod Jerome Hellman. *Dir* Irvin Kershner. *Screenplay* Elliott Baker. *Photog* Ted McCord. *Art Dir* Jack Poplin. *Set Decor* Claude Carpenter. *Film Ed* William Ziegler. *Mus Comp & Cond* John Addison. *Sd* Everett Hughes. *Asst Dir* Russell Llewellyn. *Cost Dsgn* Ann Roth. *Makeup Supv* Gordon Bau. *Supv Hairstylist* Jean Burt Reilly.

Cast: Sean Connery (*Samson Shillitoe*), Joanne Woodward (*Rhoda Shillitoe*), Jean Seberg (*Lydia West*), Patrick O'Neal (*Dr. Oliver West*), Colleen

Dewhurst (*Dr. Vera Kropotkin*), Clive Revill (*Dr. Menken*), Werner Peters (*Dr. Vorbeck*), John Fiedler (*Daniel K. Papp*), Kay Medford (*Mrs. Fish*), Jackie Coogan (*Mr. Fitzgerald*), Zohra Lampert (*Mrs. Tupperman*), Sue Ane Langdon (*Miss Walnicki*), Sorrell Booke (*Leonard Tupperman*), Bibi Osterwald (*Mrs. Fitzgerald*), Mabel Albertson (*chairwoman*), Gerald S. O'Loughlin (*Chester Quirk*), James Millhollin (*Rollie Butter*), Jon Lormer (*Dr. Huddleson*), Harry Bellaver (*Knocker*), Ayllene Gibbons (*clubwoman*), Bernie Meyer, Richard Castellano, Renee Taylor.

Comedy-drama. Source: Elliott Baker, *A Fine Madness* (New York, 1964). Samson Shillitoe, a rebellious Greenwich Village poet, is troubled by both overdue alimony payments and Rhoda, his current wife, who does not understand poetry and seductively interferes with his work. After losing his job as a carpet cleaner by seducing an office stenographer, he grudgingly accepts a $200 offer to read poetry at a cultural luncheon. This, too, turns into a shambles when he gets drunk and insults the ladies, including Lydia West, the wife of a prominent psychiatrist. Rhoda eventually gets Samson to Dr. West's sanitarium, and he easily seduces Dr. Vera Kropotkin, before ending up in a ripple bath with Lydia. All concerned finally agree that the only solution is to perform a lobotomy on Samson, but this also fails to tame him. When Lydia tells him that she is leaving her husband and wants to go away with him, Samson invites her to share his apartment with Rhoda. Furious, Lydia leaves him. As the long-suffering Rhoda is taking Samson home, she hesitantly informs him that she is pregnant. He knocks her unconscious, then dazedly picks her up and carries her back to their apartment. *Poets. Eccentrics. Waitresses. Stenographers. Psychiatrists. Marriage. Infidelity. Drunkenness. Pregnancy. Alimony. Sanitariums. Lobotomy. New York City—Greenwich Village.*

Note: Location scenes filmed in New York City.

A FINE PAIR (Italy)   **F6.1541**

Vides. *Dist* National General Pictures. 30 May **1969** [Philadelphia opening]. Sd; col (Technicolor). 35mm (Panavision). 89 min. *MPAA rating* M.

Pres by Cinema Center Films. *Prod* Leo L. Fuchs. *Exec Prod* Franco Cristaldi. *Dir* Francesco Maselli. *Screenplay* Francesco Maselli, Luisa Montagnana, Larry Gelbart, Virgil C. Leone. *Story* Luisa Montagnana. *Photog* Alfio Contini. *Art Dir* Luciano Puccini. *Set Decor* Gabriele D'Angelo. *Film Ed* Nicoletta Nardi. *Mus Comp* Ennio Morricone. *Mus Cond* Bruno Nicolai. *Sd* Eugenio Rondani, Michael Hopkins. *Asst Dir* Serena Canevari. *Prod Mgr* Oscar Brazzi. *Cost* Enrico Sabbatini. *Makeup* Pier Antonio Mecacci, Mark Reedall. *Hairstyles* Luciano Vito.

Cast: Rock Hudson (*Capt. Mike Harmon*), Claudia Cardinale (*Esmeralda Marini*), Tomas Milian (*Roger*), Leon Askin (*Chief Wellman*), Ellen Corby (*Mrs. Walker*), Walter Giller (*Franz*), Guido Alberti (*Uncle Camillo*), Peter Dane (*Albert Kinsky*), Vittorio Campanella, Gianni Carnago, Raniero Dorascienzi, Andrea Hesterasy, Umberto Fantoni, Aldo Formisano, Adriano Fraticelli.

Comedy-drama. While living apart from his wife, New York City police detective Mike Harmon receives a surprise visit from Esmeralda Marini, the daughter of an Italian policeman who worked on a case with Mike when he was in Rome 12 years before. Esmeralda tells Mike that following the death of her father she helped an international jewel thief rob an Austrian villa in the absence of the American owners. Now repentant, Esmeralda asks Mike to help her return the gems before they are missed. Mike flies to Kitzbühel with her and tricks the local police into revealing the workings of the electronic safeguards protecting the villa. But the jewels that Esmeralda has in her possession are fakes; and, once inside the villa, she steals the genuine gems and leaves behind the imitations. Esmeralda then says that she committed a similar robbery in Rome and would also like to return those gems. Though Mike is now aware of Esmeralda's tactics, he has fallen in love with her; and, excited by her adventurous life, offers to become her partner. Ironically, Esmeralda decides that she prefers the stability of Mike's way of life to her career of professional thief. Following a quarrel, Esmeralda leaves Rome and returns to her parents' home, whereupon Mike frames her for a crime she did not commit and informs the Italian authorities that he is taking Esmeralda and some recovered jewels back to New York. Instead of catching a plane for the States, however, Mike books himself and Esmeralda on a plane bound for Beirut. Once aboard, Mike and Esmeralda discover that the Rome police have relieved them of a fortune in stolen gems. *Police. Detectives. Criminals—Rehabilitation. Americans in foreign countries. Duplicity. Theft. Frameup. Gems. New York City. Kitzbühel (Austria). Rome. Beirut.*

Note: Location scenes filmed in New York City, the Austrian Alps, and Rome. Released in Italy in 1968 as *Ruba al prossimo tuo*; running time: 115 min.

THE FINEST HOURS (Great Britain)   **F6.1542**

LeVien Films. *Dist* Columbia Pictures. 10 Nov **1964** [New York opening; c1 Oct 1964; LP29348]. Sd; b&w with col seq (Technicolor, print by Pathé). 35mm. 114 min.

Prod Jack LeVien. *Exec Prod* Arthur S. Ferriman. *Dir* Peter Baylis. *Screenplay* Victor Wolfson. *Dir Photog* Hone Glendinning. *Main Titl* Chambers & Partners. *Ed Coörd* Harry Booth. *Ed Team* Oliver Cheatle, Roger Pennington, Brian Tilling, Gerry Arbeid. *Mus* Ron Grainer. *Sd Ed* Alban Streeter. *Prod Mgr* Howard Connell. *Res Mgr* Mary Baylis. *Res Team* Sarah Erulkar, Ruth Astor, Robert Kruger.

Voices: Patrick Wymark *(Winston Churchill [see note])*, Faith Brook *(Lady Randolph)*, George Baker *(Lord Randolph)*, George Westbury *(Churchill as a boy)*, David Healy *(newsreel commentator)*, Orson Welles *(narrator)*.

Documentary. Source: Winston Churchill, *The Second World War* (London, 1948-54). This account of the life of Sir Winston Churchill covers his childhood at Woodstock, his days as a schoolboy at Harrow, his early career as a journalist, and his military adventures in Cuba, India, the Sudan, and South Africa. It traces his political career from his entry into Parliament to the beginning of World War II. The largest part of the film concentrates on his first period (1940-1945) as prime minister, with footage devoted to the battles of Dunkirk and Stalingrad, and meetings with Franklin D. Roosevelt, Field Marshal Bernard Montgomery, and Joseph Stalin. Sir Winston's second prime ministership and retirement are also highlighted; included are episodes with Queen Elizabeth II and John F. Kennedy. *Students. Journalists. Politicians. Prime ministers. World War II. Harrow. Woodstock (England). London. Cuba. India. Sudan. South Africa. Dunkirk. Stalingrad. Winston Leonard Spencer Churchill. Randolph Henry Spencer Churchill. Jennie Jerome Churchill. Franklin Delano Roosevelt. Bernard Law Montgomery. Joseph Stalin. Elizabeth II (England). John Fitzgerald Kennedy. Great Britain—Army. Great Britain—Parliament.*

Note: Released in Great Britain in 1964; running time: 116 min. The sound track features the voice of Winston Churchill for some scenes and the voice of actor Patrick Wymark for others. George Westbury is a pseudonym for Marjorie Westbury.

FINGER ON THE TRIGGER (United States/Spain)   F6.1543
Comet Pictures (Hollywood)–F. I. S. A. *Dist* Allied Artists. May **1965**. Sd; col (Technicolor). 35mm (Techniscope). 87 min.

A Sidney Pink Production. *Prod-Dir* Sidney Pink. *Exec Prod* José López Moreno. *Screenplay* Luis de los Arcos, Sidney Pink. *Photog* Antonio Macasoli, Miguel Barquero. *Art Dir* Patrick Corcoran. *Set Decor* Edward Bennett. *Film Ed* Margarita Ochoa. *Mus Comp & Cond* José Solá. *Asst Dir* Enrique Bergier, Philip Pink. *Prod Mgr* Ramón Crespo. *Wardrobe* Vicky. *Makeup* Joe Echovar. *Sp Eff* Tony Molina.

Cast: Rory Calhoun *(Larry Winton)*, James Philbrook *(Adam Hyde)*, Todd Martin *(Hillstrom)*, Silvia Solar *(Violet)*, Brud Talbot *(Fred)*, Leo Anchóriz *(Ed Bannister)*, Jorge Rigaud *(Benton)*, Eric Chapman *(McKay)*, Beny Deus *(O'Brien)*, Axel Anderson *(McNamara)*, Tito García *(Zubarri)*, Willie P. Elie *(Mike Daly)*, John Clarke *(Numitah)*, Antonio Molino Rojo *(Benham)*, Juan Antonio Peral *(Tom Sharpe)*, Germán Grech *(Delmer)*, Fernando Bilbao *(Mayer)*, Sebastian Cavalier *(Slim)*.

Western drama. At the end of the Civil War in 1865, a band of Union veterans led by Larry Winton sets out for New Mexico, where they intend to homestead. They arrive at Fort Grant, which they find under the control of diehard Confederate forces awaiting a shipment of golden horseshoes. In the ghost town of Southernville the Yankees discover the golden horseshoes. When Fort Grant and Southernville are attacked by Indians, the veterans come to the aid of their former antagonists, melting down the gold for shell casings and repulsing the attacking Indians. *Homesteaders. Veterans. Confederate veterans. Indians of North America. Forts. Gold. Ghost towns. Ammunition. United States—History—Civil War. New Mexico.*

Note: Filmed in Spain and opened in Madrid in Mar 1965 as *El dedo en el gatillo*; running time: 94 min.

FINIAN'S RAINBOW   F6.1544
Warner Bros.-Seven Arts, Inc. 9 Oct **1968** [New York opening; c1 Oct 1968; LP37259]. Sd; col (Technicolor). 35mm (Panavision, see note). 145 min.

Prod Joseph Landon. *Assoc Prod* Joel Freeman. *Dir* Francis Ford Coppola. *Screenplay* E. Y. Harburg, Fred Saidy. *Dir Photog* Philip Lathrop. *Set Decor* William L. Kuehl, Philip Abramson. *Prod Dsgn* Hilyard Brown. *Main Titl* Westheimer Co., Phill Norman. *Film Ed* Melvin Shapiro. *Asst Film Ed* Fred Talmage. *Mus Supv & Cond* Ray Heindorf. *Assoc Mus Supv* Ken Darby. *Lyr* E. Y. Harburg. *Mus* Burton Lane, *Choreog* Hermes Pan. *Sd* M. A. Merrick, Dan Wallin. *Mus Ed* Richard C. Harris. *Asst Dir* Fred Gammon, Howard Kazanjian. *Cont* Betty Levin. *Cost Dsgn* Dorothy Jeakins. *Makeup Supv* Gordon Bau. *Supv Hairstylist* Jean Burt Reilly. *Dial Supv* Ronald Colby.

Cast: Fred Astaire *(Finian McLonergan)*, Petula Clark *(Sharon McLonergan)*, Tommy Steele *(Og, the leprechaun)*, Don Francks *(Woody Mahoney)*, Keenan Wynn *(Sen. Billboard Rawkins, see note)*, Barbara Hancock *(Susan the Silent)*, Al Freeman, Jr. *(Howard)*, Ronald Colby *(Buzz Collins)*, Dolph Sweet *(sheriff)*, Wright King *(district attorney)*, Louis Silas *(Henry)*, Brenda Arnau *(sharecropper)*, Avon Long, Roy Glenn, Jester Hairston *(Passion*

Pilgrim Gospeleers).

Musical comedy. Source: E. Y. Harburg and Burton Lane, *Finian's Rainbow* (New York opening: 10 Jan 1947). Upon arriving in Rainbow Valley, Missitucky, with his daughter Sharon, Irish rascal Finian McLonergan buries a pot of stolen leprechaun gold, mistakenly believing that it will multiply because the ground is near Fort Knox. When the bigoted local senator, Billboard Rawkins, tries to foreclose on popular young Woody Mahoney's tobacco land, Finian pays the balance of Woody's debt and forever endears himself and Sharon to the sharecroppers of the valley. Woody and a fledgling black scientist, Howard, are partners in trying to develop a mint tobacco plant; but, since the leaves of their plants will not burn, Howard is helping to finance their experiments by working as a domestic for the greedy and intolerant Rawkins. Meanwhile, Og, a leprechaun, has been following the McLonergans to America to retrieve the gold; without it he is doomed to become a mortal. Eventually geologists detect the presence of Og's gold in the valley, and Rawkins renews his bid to seize Woody's land. Unaware that the pot of gold carries with it three magic wishes, Sharon wishes that Rawkins could turn black so that he would better understand the plight of the sharecroppers. When Rawkins actually does turn black, Sharon is arrested as she is about to marry Woody and sentenced to be burned as a witch. To save her, Og, who alone knows the secret of the gold pot, wishes Rawkins white again. Og, now almost totally mortal, falls in love with Woody's mute sister, Susan the Silent, and he uses the last wish to give her the power of speech. As he becomes human and the gold turns to dross, the barn fire intended for Sharon spreads to Woody's experimental laboratory and proves that the mint tobacco leaves will actually burn. Woody and Sharon are then happily wed, and the optimistic Finian leaves the valley to seek his fortune elsewhere. *Musical numbers:* "Look to the Rainbow" (Sharon, Finian, and Woody); "This Time of the Year" (Chorus); "How Are Things in Glocca Morra?" (Sharon and Finian); "If This Isn't Love" (Woody, Sharon, Finian, and Chorus); "Something Sort of Grandish" (Og and Sharon); "That Come-and-Get-It Day" (Woody, Sharon, Chorus, and Ensemble); "Old Devil Moon" (Woody and Sharon); "When the Idle Poor Become the Idle Rich" (Finian, Sharon, and Chorus); "When I'm Not Near the Girl I Love" (Og); "Rain Dance Ballet" (Susan and Chorus); "The Begat" (Rawkins and Gospeleers). *Irish. Fairies. Politicians. Farmers. Negroes. Domestics. Mutes. Geologists. Witches. Bigotry. Land rights. Immortality. Magic. Wish fulfillment. Gold. Tobacco. Weddings. Fort Knox. Fires.*

Note: Blown up to 70mm for some road-show presentations. The song "Necessity" is credited in some sources but was apparently deleted from the final print. Some sources list Keenan Wynn's role as Judge Rawkins.

FINNEGANS WAKE see PASSAGES FROM "FINNEGANS WAKE"

FINNEY   F6.1545
Bill Hare. *Dist* Gold Coast. 15 Oct **1969** [Chicago opening]. Sd; b&w with col seq. 35mm. 72 min.

Prod-Dir-Writ Bill Hare. *Photog* Jack Richards. *Film Ed* Bill Hare. *Mus* Dick Reynolds, Les Hooper. *Adtl Mus* Eli Wolf.

Cast: Robert Kilcullen *(Jim Finney)*, Bill Levinson *(Billy Freeman)*, Joan Sundstrom *(Joyce Finney)*, Anthony Mockus, Dick Stanwood, Richy Hill, Dwight Lawrence, Jerry Kaufherr.

Drama. Jim Finney, a 13-year veteran as a Chicago Bears defensive tackle, is told by the head coach that he can no longer play. Finney is offered the job of defensive coach, but he has other aspirations—he spends his time painting. He is quickly disillusioned, however, when his portrayals of football situations are spurned by his associates and by art dealers. Because Finney's failures compare unfavorably with the success of his wife, Joyce, as a singer, they eventually separate. Finney constantly relives his past glories in football; but his hopes of playing again never materialize, and at last he becomes a bartender. *Athletic coaches. Painters. Bartenders. Singers. Marriage. Football. Unemployment. Chicago Bears.*

Note: Finney's remembrances of his football career are filmed in color.

FINO A FARTI MALE see ADÉLAÏDE

FIRE IN THE FLESH (France)   F6.1546
Société Française des Films Alfred Rode. *Dist* Pacemaker Pictures. 16 Oct **1964** [Los Angeles showing]. Sd; col (Agfacolor). 35mm. 80 min.

A Gaston Hakim Production. *Prod-Dir* Alfred Rode. *Screenplay* Jean-Pierre Marchand. *Dial-Adapt* Claude Desailly, Louis Martin. *Dir Photog* Jean Isnard. *Art Dir* Claude Bouxin. *Film Ed* Paul Cayatte. *Mus* Paul Bonneau. *Sd* Georges Bouichou. *Prod Mgr* Robert Florat.

Cast: Claudine Dupuis *(Fern Heldt)*, Erno Crisa *(Larry Gordon)*, Yoko Tani *(Yulie, the captain's girl)*, Bill Marshall, actor *(Stork)*, Allan Lemarie *(Ortiz)*, Robert Dupont *(Captain Le Guen)*, Raymond Souplex *(Professor Theodore Heldt)*, Albert Dinan *(captain)*.

Romantic melodrama. Based on a short story or novel by: John D. Fellow. Professor Theodore Heldt, his young daughter, Fern, and his assistant, Larry

Gordon, are shipwrecked on an uncharted island in the South Seas while on a scientific expedition. Marooned together for 10 years, Fern and Larry fall in love and "marry" when the professor dies. Larry fears that he may lose Fern's love if they are rescued and return to civilization, and he angers Fern by failing to light a signal fire when a ship appears on the horizon. The ship, carrying a crew of international smugglers, eventually arrives in the cove. The smugglers' leader, Ortiz, and his lieutenant, Stork, decide to kill Larry and carry away the unsuspecting Fern. Larry leads them to a priceless bed of pearls, and the smugglers eventually kill each other in a gunfight provoked by greed. The ship's captain, Le Guen, fearful of an approaching typhoon, comes ashore to look for the two men, while Fern waits aboard the ship for Larry. Le Guen sees the bodies of the smugglers, and, finding no sign of Larry, sets sail, telling Fern that her "husband" has probably been killed. Fern sights Larry atop a cliff, however, and dives overboard to rejoin him on the island. *Professors. Smugglers. Sea captains. Ship crews. Marriage. Greed. Pearls. Ships. South Sea Islands. Shipwrecks. Typhoons.*

Note: Filmed in South America and on the French Riviera. Opened in Paris in Jan 1958 as *La fille de feu;* running time: 93 min. Robert Dupont is a pseudonym for Armand Mestral; Allan Lemarie for Hugo Del Carril.

THE FIRE WITHIN (France/Italy)   F6.1547
Nouvelles Editions de Films–Arco Film. *Dist* Governor Films, Gibraltar Films. 17 Feb **1964** [New York opening]. Sd; b&w. 35mm. 110 min.

Assoc Prod Alain Queffélean. *Dir-Writ* Louis Malle. *Collab Dir* Philippe Collin. *Dir Photog* Ghislain Cloquet. *Camera* Etienne Becker, Jean Chiabaut. *Art Dir* Bernard Evein. *Ch Ed* Suzanne Baron. *Ed* Monique Nanà. *Mus From "Gymnopédies" and "Gnossiennes"* Erik Satie. *Piano* Claude Helffer. *Sd Engr* Guy Villette. *Sd Mix* Jean Nény. *Asst Dir* Volker Schlöndorff. *Prod Mgr* Jean Pieuchot. *Script Girl* Elisabeth Rappeneau. *Hairstyles* Carita. *Still Photog* Georges Pierre.

Cast: Maurice Ronet *(Alain Leroy)*, Lena Skerla *(Lydia)*, Yvonne Clech *(Mademoiselle Farnoux)*, Hubert Deschamps *(d'Averseau)*, Jean-Paul Moulinot *(Dr. La Barbinais)*, Mona Dol *(Madame La Barbinais)*, Jeanne Moreau *(Jeanne)*, Alexandra Stewart *(Solange)*, Pierre Moncorbier *(Moraire)*, René Dupuy *(Charlie)*, Bernard Tiphaine *(Milou)*, Bernard Noël *(Dubourg)*, Ursula Kubler *(Fanny)*, Alain Mottet *(Urcel)*, François Gragnon *(François Minville)*, Romain Bouteille *(Jérôme Minville)*, Jacques Sereys *(Cyrille Lavaud)*, Claude Deschamps *(Maria)*, Toni Taffin *(Brancion)*, Henri Serre *(Frédéric)*, Véra Valdez, J. Wells, Claude Deleusse, Madeleine Declercq, Michèle Mahaut.

Drama. Source: Pierre Drieu La Rochelle, *Le feu follet* (Paris, 1931). Alain Leroy, a desperate 30-year-old rehabilitated alcoholic bent on suicide, is befriended by Lydia, an associate of his estranged American wife, Dorothy, now residing in New York City. After a night spent with Leroy, Lydia, concerned for his welfare, drives him to the Versailles clinic where he has been treated by Dr. La Barbinais. There he halfheartedly attempts to alleviate his ennui by smoking, doodling, clipping obituaries, perusing a photograph of Marilyn Monroe, and keeping a diary. Although Dr. La Barbinais insists that he is well and suggests that he attempt a reconciliation with Dorothy, Leroy, realizing the suggestion's futility, refuses to do so. Instead, he undertakes a Parisian holiday, during which, hoping to find a reason to continue living, he contacts former friends. Among his old acquaintances are Dubourg, now a contented bourgeois Egyptologist, married to a smug matron; Jeanne, an artist and addict; and Solange, a promiscuous socialite, married to the cooly aristocratic Cyrille. Distressed by their empty lives and unable to communicate with them, Leroy resumes his drinking. Milou, an acquaintance, takes him to the Versailles clinic, where the following morning, despite a message from Solange, Leroy packs his bags, finishes reading his book, and shoots himself. *Playboys. Artists. Aristocrats. Socialites. Drug addicts. Middle classes. Alcoholism. Suicide. Infidelity. Marriage. Sanitariums. Versailles. Paris.*

Note: Filmed on location in Paris and Versailles. Opened in Paris in Oct 1963 as *Le feu follet;* running time: 121 min. Released in Italy as *Fuoco fatuo.*

FIREBALL 500   F6.1548
American International Pictures. 7 Jun **1966** [Charlotte, North Carolina, opening]. Sd; col (Pathé Color). 35mm (Panavision). 92 min.

Prod James H. Nicholson, Samuel Z. Arkoff. *Co-prod* Burt Topper. *Assoc Prod* Gene McCabe. *Dir* William Asher. *Screenplay* William Asher, Leo Townsend. *Anim (see note)* Clokey Films. *Dir Photog* Floyd Crosby. *Camera* Harlowe Stengel, Fred Pearce. *Art Dir* Daniel Haller. *Set Decor* Harry Reif. *Film Ed* Fred Feitshans, Eve Newman. *Mus Score* Les Baxter. *Mus Supv* Al Simms. *Songs:* "Fireball 500," "Country Carnival," "Step Right Up!" "My Way That Gets Me My Way," "A Chance Like That," "Turn Around, You'll Know Where To Find Me" Guy Hemric, Jerry Styner. *Titl Song Sung by* Frankie Avalon. *Choreog* Ronnie Riordan. *Sd* Don Rush, Glenn Lambert, Jim Pilcher. *1st & 2d Asst Dir* Dale Hutchinson, Joe Nayfack. *Script Supv* Betty Crosby. *Asst to the Prod* Jack Cash. *Cost* Richard Bruno. *Makeup* Ted

Coodley. *Hairstyles* Ray Foreman. *Sp Photog Eff* Westheimer Co.. *Sp Eff* Frank DeMarco. *Proc Photog* Jacques Marquette. *Tech Adv* Jon Ward. *Still Photog* John Monte. *Key Grip* Charles Hannawalt. *Gaffer* Charles Beckett. *Constr Coörd* Ross Hahn. *Prop* Karl Brainard.

Cast: Frankie Avalon *("Fireball" Dave Owens)*, Annette Funicello *(Jane Harris)*, Fabian *(Sonny Leander Fox)*, Chill Wills *(Big Jaw Harris)*, Harvey Lembeck *(Charlie Bigg)*, Julie Parrish *(Martha Brian)*, Douglas Henderson *(Hastings)*, Baynes Barron *(Bronson)*, Sandy Reed *(race announcer)*, Mike Nader *(Joey)*, Ed Garner *(Herman)*, Vin Scully *(prolog announcer)*, Sue Hamilton *(farmer's daughter)*, Renie Riano *(Herman's wife)*, Len Lesser *(man in garage)*, Billy Beck *(jobber)*, Tex Armstrong *(Herman's friend)*, Mary Hughes, Patti Chandler, Karla Conway, Hedy Scott, Salli Sachse, Jo Collins, Maria McBane, Linda Bent *(Leander's fans)*, Don Randi Trio Plus One, Carole Lombard Singers.

Action melodrama with music. Stock car racer "Fireball" Dave Owens arrives at the racing town of Spartanburg, South Carolina, to compete against local champion Leander Fox. Dave wins both the first race and the admiration of Leander's girl friend, Jane, and Martha Brian, a wealthy woman who persuades him to drive in a cross-country night race. In fact, Dave has been tricked into transporting moonshine whiskey, and he is subsequently approached by Federal agents who threaten to send him to prison if he does not cooperate with them in breaking the illegal operation. Joey, a driver, is killed on the liquor run while attempting to avoid an onrushing car, and Dave and Leander put aside their differences to investigate the accident. Driving along the same road, they encounter the headlights of a car racing at them. By refusing to "chicken," they discover that the illusion of the other car was created by a huge mirror across the road. A trap is set which proves that Martha's partner, Charlie Bigg, was responsible for both the illegal liquor and the murder. Jealous of Dave's relationship with Martha, Charlie intended Dave as his next victim. The mystery settled, Dave goes on to win the big race, but Leander is badly burned in a racing accident. Though his career is over, Leander wins Jane as Dave and Martha go off together to continue racing around the country. *Stock car drivers. Patrons. Revenue agents. Automobile racing. Bootleggers. Fraud. Murder. Spartanburg (South Carolina). Automobile accidents.*

Note: Location scenes filmed in Charlotte, North Carolina, at the Ascot Raceway in Gardena, California, and at the Saugus Raceway in California. Animated puppet sequences appear in the prolog and the epilog.

FIREBALL JUNGLE   F6.1549
Americana Productions. Oct **1968**. Sd; col (Eastmancolor, print by Capital Film Laboratories). 35mm. 96 min.

Pres by G. B. Roberts. *Prod* G. B. Roberts. *Exec Prod* G. B. Roberts, Eli Jackson. *Dir* Jose Priete. *Screenplay* Harry Whittington. *Dir Photog* Clifford Poland. *Adtl Photog* Paul Rubenstein. *Asst Camera* Julian Wilson. *Lighting* Cecil Fernandez. *Set Dsgn* Ralph L. Brown. *Asst Film Ed* John Dalton. *Titl Song* Tiny Kennedy. *Cafe Number Sung by* Mercy Group. *Sd* Mike Chamoon. *Supv Mus Ed* Ethel Huber. *2d Asst Dir* Joseph L. Wiezcki. *Sp Eff* Doug Hobart. *Prop Master* William L. Carlton. *Head Grip* William Hunt. *Auto Stunts* Joie Chitwood. *Dog Trained by* Johnny Wells.

Cast: John Russell *(Nero Sagittarius)*, Lon Chaney, [Jr.] *(Sammy)*, Randy Kirby *(Steve Cullen)*, Alan Mixon *(Cateye Meares)*, Chuck Daniel *(Marty)*, Nancy Donohue *(Ann Tracey)*, Vicki Nunis *(Judy)*, Billy Blueriver, Tiny Kennedy, Babs Beatty, Joie Chitwood, Ed Wisner, Candy Stebbins, Andrew Martinez, Pat Rast, Sharon Cramer, James La Rue, Black Star, Bruce Atkins, Bruce Roberts, Linda Roberts, Dohle Rast, Kathy Roberts, Ronnie Bell, Bobby Rast, Edward Thompson, Herman the Wonder Dog.

Action melodrama. Gangster Nero Sagittarius hires stock car driver Cateye Meares, leader of a band of sadistic thugs, to help him gain control of several automobile racetracks. Steve Cullen, whose brother was killed in an accident caused by Cateye, races under an alias while attempting to implicate the murderer. Infuriated by Steve's skill, Cateye assaults him. After Sammy, a junkyard owner forced to fence stolen cars for Nero's syndicate, is burned alive, Steve fights Cateye in his hideout. Although badly beaten, Steve attempts to expose Cateye. During the big race, Cateye is killed in a spectacular crash while being chased by the police. *Stock car drivers. Gangsters. Brothers. Junk dealers. Fences (for stolen goods). Automobile racing. Syndicates. Automobile accidents. Chases.*

Note: Filmed in and around Tampa, Florida. Also known as *Jungle Terror.*

THE FIREBRAND   F6.1550
Associated Producers, Inc. *Dist* Twentieth Century-Fox Film Corp. 15 Aug **1962** [Portland, Oregon, opening; c7 Aug 1962; LP22827]. Sd; b&w. 35mm (CinemaScope). 63 min.

Prod-Dir Maury Dexter. *Writ* Harry Spalding. *Dir Photog* Floyd Crosby. *Set Decor* Harry Reif. *Supv Film Ed* Jodie Copelan. *Mus Comp & Cond* Richard La Salle. *Sd* William Bernds, Harry M. Leonard. *Supv Sd Ed* Jack Cornall. *Asst*

Dir Willard Kirkham. *Prod Supv* Harold E. Knox. *Script Supv* Betty Crosby. *Wardrobe* Ray Summers. *Makeup* Harry Ross. *Prop Master* Monroe Liebgold.

Cast: Kent Taylor (*Maj. Tim Bancroft*), Lisa Montell (*Clarita Vasconcelos*), Valentin De Vargas (*Joaquin Murieta*), Joe Raciti (*Jack Garcia*), Chubby Johnson (*Tampico*), Barbara Mansell (*Cassie*), Allen Jaffe (*Torres*), Troy Melton (*Walker*), Fred Krone (*Dickens*), Sid Haig (*Diego*), Felix Locher (*Ramirez*), Jerry Summers (*Rafael Vasconcelos*), Tom Daly, I. Stanford Jolley, Pat Lawless.

Historical drama. At the time of the California Gold Rush, an outlaw, Joaquin Murieta, becomes the hero of the Spanish-speaking inhabitants who are being dispossessed by the treasure-seeking hordes pouring into the West. When the brother of his sweetheart, Clarita, is wounded in a knife fight, Murieta gives his elderly captive, bounty hunter Tampico, his freedom in return for nursing the injured youth back to health. Later, after Murieta has held up a gold train guarded by the head of the California Rangers, Maj. Tim Bancroft, Bancroft forces Tampico to lead him to the outlaw camp. Murieta is absent, but several of his men, including Clarita's brother, are brutally slaughtered by the rangers. Upon hearing the news, Murieta goes berserk in a saloon and is arrested. But the deputies, unaware of the importance of their catch, release him. Murieta then rejoins his men and, after a skirmish with the rangers, subdues Bancroft, ties him to his horse, and sends him back to town. Once more at the head of his band, Murieta, with Clarita at his side, rides for Sonora. *Outlaws. Mexicans. Rangers. Bounty hunters. Gold rushes. Dispossession. Train robberies. Murder. California. Joaquín Murrieta.*

Note: Location scenes filmed in the California Sierras.

FIRECREEK　　　　　　　　　　　　　　　　　F6.1551
Warner Bros.–Seven Arts, Inc. 24 Jan **1968** [El Paso, Texas, opening; c24 Nov 1967; LP35847]. Sd; col (Technicolor). 35mm (Panavision). 104 min.

A Philip Leacock–John Mantley Production. *Prod* Philip Leacock. *Dir* Vincent McEveety. *Writ* Calvin Clements. *Dir Photog* William H. Clothier. *Art Dir* Howard Hollander. *Set Decor* William L. Kuehl. *Film Ed* William Ziegler. *Mus Comp & Cond* Alfred Newman. *Sd* Stanley Jones. *Asst Dir* Jack Cunningham. *Unit Mgr* Emmett Emerson. *Cost Dsgn* Yvonne Wood. *Makeup Supv* Gordon Bau. *Supv Hairstylist* Jean Burt Reilly. *Dial Supv* Michael Audley.

Cast: James Stewart (*Johnny Cobb*), Henry Fonda (*Larkin*), Inger Stevens (*Evelyn Pittman*), Gary Lockwood (*Earl*), Dean Jagger (*Whittier*), Ed Begley (*Preacher Broyles*), Jay C. Flippen (*Mr. Pittman*), Jack Elam (*Norman*), James Best (*Drew*), Barbara Luna (*Meli*), Jacqueline Scott (*Henrietta Cobb*), Brooke Bundy (*Leah*), J. Robert Porter (*Arthur*), Morgan Woodward (*Willard*), John Qualen (*Hall*), Louise Latham (*Dulcie*), Athena Lorde (*Mrs. Littlejohn*), Harry "Slim" Duncan (*Fyte*), Kevin Tate (*Aaron*), Christopher Shea (*Franklin*).

Western melodrama. Five freebooting adventurers from the Missouri range wars—Larkin, Earl, Drew, Norman, and Willard—enter the frontier town of Firecreek and decide to remain there until Larkin recovers from a wound. Fearing trouble, the local parttime sheriff, Johnny Cobb, leaves his nearby farm and his pregnant wife, Henrietta, to spend the night in town. While Larkin is recuperating at a boardinghouse run by Mr. Pittman, he considers the arguments against lawlessness voiced by the old man's granddaughter, Evelyn. Larkin's men, however, continue to terrorize the town and disrupt church services held by itinerant Preacher Broyles. The townspeople plead with Cobb to drive the gang out of town, but instead he tries to reason with them. His efforts prove to be futile when Arthur, a simpleminded stableboy, attempts to prevent Drew from raping an unwed Indian mother, Meli, and accidentally kills the gunman. Although Cobb jails Arthur for the boy's protection before returning to his farm to look after his wife during her labor, the gang members force the townsfolk to attend a wake for Drew and then coldbloodedly hang Arthur. Aware that Larkin and his men stayed in Firecreek because it was a town of self-defeated men who would not compete, Cobb at long last decides to stand up to the lawbreakers. Taking his gun, he kills Earl, Norman, and Willard but is, in turn, wounded by Larkin. Refusing to concede defeat, Cobb reaches for the gun which was shot out of his hand by Larkin. He is saved from certain death by Evelyn, who kills Larkin with a rifle shot. *Sheriffs. Farmers. Grandfathers. Preachers. Stableboys. Indians of North America. Frontier and pioneer life. Childbirth. Rape. Lynching. Law and order. Funerals. Gangs. Range wars. Boardinghouses. Missouri.*

Note: Location scenes filmed in Arizona and California.

THE FIREMEN'S BALL (Czechoslovakia)　　　　　F6.1552
Barrandov Film Studio. *For* Československý Film. *Dist* Cinema V Distributing, Inc. 3 Oct **1968** [New York opening]. Sd; col (Eastman Color). 35mm. 73 min.

Dir Miloš Forman. *Screenplay* Miloš Forman, Ivan Passer, Jaroslav Papoušek. *Dir Photog* Miroslav Ondříček. *Art Dir* Karel Černý. *Film Ed* Miroslav Hájek. *Mus* Karel Mareš. *Sd* Adolf Böhm. *Asst Dir* Jaroslav Papoušek. *Cost* Zdena Snajderová. *English Subtitl* Noelle Gillmor.

Cast: Václav Stöckel (*fire brigade commander*), Josef Švet (*old man*), Jan Vostrčil (*committee chairman*), Josef Kolb (*Josef*), František Debelka (*1st committee member*), Josef Šebanek (*2d committee member*), Karel Valnoha (*3d committee member*), Josef Rehorek (*4th committee member*), Marie Ježková (*Josef's wife*), Anina Lípoldová, Alena Kvetová, Mila Zelená (*beauty queen candidates*), Vratislav Čermák, Václav Novotný, František Reinstein, František Paska, Stanislav Holubec, Josef Kutalek, Ladislav Adam, Jiří Libal, Antonín Blažejovský, Stanislav Ditrich, Jarmila Kucharová, Marie Slívová, Hana Hanušová, Hana Kuberová.

Farce. The retired commander of a fire brigade is honored at a ball thrown by his former associates. Sick with cancer and 86 years old, he is to be presented with a ceremonial hatchet by the winner of the ball's beauty contest. The contestants, however, are shy as well as plain, and they huddle en masse in the lavatory, resisting the firemen's entreaties and delaying the evening's ceremonies. This impasse is broken by an alarm summoning the company to a conflagration in which an old man's home burns to the ground as the useless fire engine sinks slowly in the falling snow. The victim sits watching the conflagration in a chair, and to spare his feelings the thoughtful neighbors turn the chair away from the fire, moving it closer to the flames when he becomes chilled. To console him the firemen proffer the tickets remaining for a raffle to be conducted that evening. The gesture is in vain, however, for both tickets and prizes have been stolen in the course of the evening. Alarmed, the master of ceremonies turns out the lights, inviting the thieves to return the loot under cover of darkness. When the lights are turned on the raffle's director, alone in taking advantage of the invitation, is discovered returning a pilfered cheese. Overcome by embarrassment, the well-meaning culprit suffers a heart attack and is taken by the firemen to the conference room. In the now empty hall the patient guest of honor profusely thanks his hosts for the evening's entertainment and for what proves to be an empty hatchet case, the ceremonial gift having also been stolen. *Firemen. Balls (formal gatherings). Beauty contests. Retirement. Lotteries. Theft. Old age. Cancer. Fires.*

Note: Filmed in Czechoslovakia in 1967 as *Hoří, má panenko.*

FIRES ON THE PLAIN (Japan)　　　　　　　　　F6.1553
Daiei Motion Picture Co. *Dist* Harrison Pictures. 25 Jul **1962** [San Francisco opening]. Sd; b&w. 35mm (Daiei Scope). 105 min.

Pres by Edward Harrison. *Prod* Masaichi Nagata. *Dir* Kon Ichikawa. *Screenplay* Natto Wada. *Photog* Setsuo Kobayashi. *Art Dir* Tokuji Shibata. *Film Ed* Hiroaki Fujii, Kon Ichikawa. *Mus* Yasushi Akutagawa.

Cast: Eiji Funakoshi (*Tamura*), Osamu Takizawa (*Yasuda*), Mickey Curtis (*Nagamatsu*), Mantaro Ushio (*sergeant*), Kyu Sazanka (*army surgeon*), Yoshihiro Hamaguchi (*officer*), Asao Sano, Masaya Tsukida, Hikaru Hoshi (*soldiers*).

War drama. Source: Shohei Ooka, *Nobi* (Tokyo, 1952). Early in 1945 the retreating Japanese Army at Leyte rapidly begins to disintegrate. Rejected for being without food ration by both his squad and the hospital, the tubercular Private Tamura flees from the advancing Americans across the huge island plain toward a distant spired cross and some great columns of smoke, which could be from either Filipino guerrilla signal fires or ordinary bonfires. At a deserted native village he finds only Japanese corpses spilling from the church and wild dogs roaming the streets. After being forced to kill one of the dogs, Tamura is surprised by a couple returning for a cache of salt and panics when the woman begins screaming hysterically. He shoots her and continues firing after the escaping man. Having filled his haversack with the salt, Tamura takes to the jungle and wooded hills, where he joins three other soldiers who manage to survive by foraging for potatoes. More and more stragglers are added to the destitute group. The men get through a treacherous bog and across the main road, only to be mowed down by the waiting American tanks. Tamura escapes and hides in the hills but flees when a dying Buddhist offers him his arm to eat. Crazed with fever and exhaustion, Tamura is helped by Nagamatsu, a soldier he met earlier at the hospital, and they return to the camp he shares with his companion Yasuda. Tamura tries to eat some of the "monkey" meat they share with him, but he cannot keep it down. The men's mutual distrust grows until finally Nagamatsu ambushes, shoots, and kills Yasuda; he dismembers the body and gorges himself on the flesh. When he appears with his mouth bloody, Tamura kills him in disgust. He staggers toward one of the fires on the plain to surrender to the Americans—only to be caught in the gunfire of the farmers. *Filipinos. Guerrillas. War victims. Combat zone life. Tuberculosis. Murder. Starvation. Cannibalism. Survival. Buddhism. World War II. Leyte. United States Army. Japan—Army. Fires.*

Note: Released in Japan in 1959 as *Nobi;* running time: 104 min.

FIRST LOVE (Switzerland/West Germany)　　　　F6.1554
Franz Seitz Filmproduktion–Alfa-Film. *Dist* UMC Pictures. 7 Oct **1970** [New York opening]. Sd; col (Eastmancolor). 35mm. 90 min. *MPAA rating* R.

Pres by Sidney Glazier. *Prod* Maximilian Schell, Barry Levinson. *Dir* Maximilian Schell. *Screenplay* Maximilian Schell, John Gould. *Dir Photog*

Sven Nykvist. *Camera Crew* Dieter Lohmann, Anders Bodin, Peter Gauhe, Jorg Schmidt-Reitwein, Istvan Pazstor. *Set Dsgn* Otto Pischinger. *Film Ed* Dagmar Hirtz. *Asst Film Ed* Eva Haffenrichter. *Mus* Mark London. *Lyr* Don Black. *Sd* Paul Schöler. *Prod Mgr* Georg Focking, Dezso Jutasi. *Unit Mgr* Margarethe von Noe, Janos Krasznai. *Mgr* Viktor Rusalem. *Script Supv* Ricarda Krehl. *Asst to the Dir* Dagmar Hirtz. *Coöp* Mafilm (Hungary). *Stills* Hans Herbert Gossman, Tibor Inkey.

Cast: John Moulder-Brown *(Alexander)*, Dominique Sanda *(Sinaida)*, Maximilian Schell *(father)*, Valentina Cortese *(mother)*, Marius Goring *(Dr. Lushin)*, Dandy Nichols *(Princess Zasekina)*, Richard Warwick *(Lieutenant Belovzorov)*, Keith Bell *(Count Malevsky)*, Johannes Schaaf *(Nirmatsky)*, John Osborne *(Maidanov)*.

Drama. Source: Ivan Sergeyevich Turgenev, "Pervaya lyubov," in *Biblioteka dlya chteniya* (1860). In the days before the 1917 Revolution Alexander, a 16-year-old boy vacationing with his parents, becomes attracted to Sinaida, the 21-year-old daughter of their neighbor, Princess Zasekina, an impoverished aristocrat. Alexander is the youngest of Sinaida's many suitors. When the men play a game of chance, Alexander wins a kiss from Sinaida and falls deeply in love with her. Overwhelmed with jealousy, Alexander follows her everywhere, but she returns his affection only fleetingly. Finally, he is heartbroken and shocked when he learns that his father has been committing adultery with her. Years later, after war and revolution have swept the country, Alexander hears that Sinaida has married, and he decides to visit her. When he arrives at the house, however, he is told that she recently died in childbirth. *Aristocrats. Neighbors. Adolescence. Jealousy. Filial relations. Infidelity. Vacations. Russia—History—1917-21 Revolution.*

Note: Location scenes filmed in Hungary. Released in Switzerland and West Germany in 1970 as *Erste Liebe*.

FIRST MARINES (Reissue)   F6.1555
Paramount Pictures. *Dist* Citation Films. 31 Mar **1961** [New York opening]. Sd; col. 35mm. 95 min.

Note: Originally released in 1950 as *Tripoli* by Paramount Pictures; c1 Nov 1950; LP468.

FIRST MEN IN THE MOON (Great Britain)   F6.1556
Ameran Films. *Dist* Columbia Pictures. 20 Nov **1964** [Detroit opening; c1 Oct 1964; LP29388]. Sd (Westrex); col (Pathé). 35mm (Panavision and Dynamation). 103 min. [Copyright length: 107 min.]

A Charles H. Schneer Production. *Prod* Charles H. Schneer. *Assoc Prod* Ray Harryhausen. *Dir* Nathan Juran. *Screenplay* Nigel Kneale, Jan Read. *Dir Photog* Wilkie Cooper. *Camera Op* Harry Gillam. *Art Dir* John Blezard. *Titl Dsgn* Sam Suliman. *Film Ed* Maurice Rootes. *Mus* Laurie Johnson. *Sd Rec* Buster Ambler, Red Law. *Asst Dir* George Pollard. *Prod Mgr* Ted Wallis. *Cont* Eileen Head. *Sp Eff* Ray Harryhausen. *Tech Staff* Les Bowie, Kit West. *Tech Adv* Arthur Garratt. *Coöp* National Aeronautics and Space Administration, British Ministry of Aviation—Royal Aircraft Establishment.

Cast: Edward Judd *(Arnold Bedford)*, Lionel Jeffries *(Joseph Cavor)*, Martha Hyer *(Kate Callender)*, Erik Chitty *(Gibbs)*, Betty McDowall *(Maggie)*, Miles Malleson *(registrar)*, Laurence Herder *(Glushkov)*, Peter Finch *(bailiff's man)*, Gladys Henson *(matron)*, Marne Maitland *(Dr. Tok)*, Hugh McDermott *(Challis)*, Paul Carpenter, Huw Thomas *(announcers)*, Gordon Robinson *(U. N. Astronaut Martin)*, Sean Kelly *(U. N. Astronaut Colonel Rice)*, John Murray Scott *(U. N. Astronaut Nevsky)*.

Science fiction comedy-drama. Source: Herbert George Wells, *The First Men in the Moon* (London, 1901). The first manned United Nations space flight, with a crew of three astronauts representing the United States, England, and the Soviet Union, lands on the moon, and the crew discover the British flag with a message dated in 1899. On the earth, U. N. experts seek out aged Arnold Bedford, who claims to have made the trip to the moon 65 years earlier, and he tells them his story: *In a Kentish village in 1899, Bedford, an aspiring playwright, and his fiancée, Kate, meet Joseph Cavor, an eccentric scientist who has discovered an antigravity substance he plans to use in the construction of a spaceship for a flight to the moon. Bedford contributes money to support the project, in which he sees a possible solution to his financial difficulties, and he and Kate go along on the trip. They find the moon to be inhabited by Selenites, ant-like creatures with whom Cavor learns to communicate. The Selenites live beneath the moon's surface, surviving by filtering the sun's rays through huge crystals placed at their city's gates. After many adventures with the Selenites, Bedford becomes hostile to them and returns with Kate to the earth, while Cavor, who is fascinated with the Selenites' scientific advances, chooses to remain behind to meet their leader and further his scientific knowledge. The U. N. astronauts on the moon enter the underground city described by Bedford, but they find only mysterious ruin and decay. Bedford watches their exploration from earth on television beamed from the moon, and he recalls that Cavor had a cold, which apparently spread and caused the extinction of the Selenites.* *Playwrights. Astronauts. Scientists. Spaceship crews. Space*

creatures. Space flights. Gravitation. Finance—Personal. Television. Common cold. The Moon. The Sun. Kent (England). United Nations.

Note: Opened in London in Technicolor in Jul 1964; running time: 103 min.

FIRST SPACESHIP ON VENUS (East Germany/Poland)   F6.1557
DEFA–Iluzjon Film Unit–Film Polski–Centrala Productions. *Dist* Crown International Pictures. 31 Oct **1962** [San Diego, California, opening]. Sd; col (Agfacolor, print by Technicolor). 35mm (Totalvision). 80 min.

Exec Prod Newton P. Jacobs, Paul Schreibman, Edmund Goldman. *Exec Supv U. S. Vers* Hugo Grimaldi. *Dir* Kurt Maetzig. *Screenplay* Jan Fethke, Wolfgang Kohlhaase, Günter Reisch, Günther Rücker, Alexander Stenbock-Fermor, Kurt Maetzig. *Photog* Joachim Hasler. *Art Dir* Anatol Radzinowicz, Alfred Hirschmeier. *Film Ed* Lena Neumann. *Mus* Andrzej Markowski. *Mus U. S. Dub Vers* Gordon Zahler. *Mus Ed* Walter Greene, Joseph Von Stroheim. Ernst Kunstmann. *Sp Eff* Vera Kunstmann, Jan Olejniczak, Helmut Grewald. *Sp Photog Eff* Martin Sonnabend.

Cast: Yoko Tani *(Sumiko Ogimura)*, Oldřich Lukeš *(Harringway)*, Ignacy Machowski *(Orloff)*, Juliusz Ongewe *(Talua)*, Michal Postnikow *(Durand)*, Kurt Rackelmann *(Sikarna)*, Günther Simon *(Brinkman)*, Tang-Hua-Ta *(Tchen Yu)*, Lucyna Winnicka *(Joan Moran)*.

Science fiction drama. Source: Stanisław Lem, *Astronauci* (Warsaw, 1951). In 1985 the multinational World Federation for Space Research, numbering among its members American pilot Brinkman and nuclear physicist Harringway, Indian mathematician Sikarna, and Japanese female physician Sumiko Ogimura, participates in an expedition to Venus. Aboard the spaceship Cosmostrator I the team decodes a magnetic spool found in the Gobi desert, upon which is imprinted the Venusian plan to destroy Earth. Bombarded by meteors, the craft maneuvers for 31 days before landing. Disembarking, the scientists discover the remains of an advanced civilization destroyed by its own weapons. Before returning to Earth the crew is menaced by lava and insects and three of its members perish. *Spaceship crews. Astronauts. Scientists. Physicians. Mathematicians. Physicists. East Indians. Japanese. Space exploration. Holocausts. Meteors. Nuclear weapons. Venus (planet). Gobi. The Future.*

Note: Released in East Germany in Feb 1960 as *Der schweigende Stern*; in Poland in Mar 1960 as *Milcząca gwiazda*. Original running time: 130 min. U. S. prerelease title: *Spaceship to Venus*.

FIRST TASTE OF LOVE (France)   F6.1558
International Thanos Films. *Dist* Altura Films International. 28 Dec **1962** [New York State license]. Sd; b&w. 35mm. 80-85 min.

Prod-Dir-Writ Henry Zaphiratos. *Exec Prod* Roland Guinier du Vignaud. *Dial* Henry Zaphiratos, Bernard Chesnais, Roland Guinier du Vignaud. *Photog* Roger Duculot. *Art Dir* Roger Bar. *Film Ed* Armand Psenny. *Mus Score* Louiguy. *Sd* Séverin Frankiel. *Prod Supv* Maurice Delbez. *Prod Mgr* André Bertoux. *Tech Adv* Jacques Besnard.

Cast: Christian Pezey *(Lucien)*, Colette Descombes *(Joëlle)*, Claude Arnold *(Mireille)*, Jacques Perrin *(Philippe)*, Adrienne Servantie *(The Mother)*, Mario Pilar *(Mario)*, Corrado Guarducci *(The Producer)*, René Rozan *(The Priest)*, Michèle Dumontier *(Marianne)*, Marc Halford *(Marc)*, Marie-Thérèse Navaret *(Claire)*, Daniel Lorieux *(Jean-Loup)*, Alain Dumoulin, Colette Colas, Mathilda Sidès, Colette André, Christine Verdy, Catherine Candida, Pierre Chantarel.

Melodrama. Lucien, a modest engineering student, discovers that his steady girl friend Mireille is using him to cover up her dates with Mario, an older man. Lucien wanders about the streets of Paris and meets Joëlle, a sophisticated teenager who supports herself with a job in a sleazy nightclub. It is late when they meet, and Joëlle invites Lucien into the club and demonstrates her stripping act to her one-man audience. A feeling of rapport develops as they go from place to place seeking entertainment; in the morning the two discover they have fallen in love. Mireille learns of the romance and, on a bet, plots with Philippe and other friends to break up the affair. Neither Lucien nor Joëlle, however, succumbs to the propositions of Mireille and Philippe. Later at a nightclub, Mario gives the appearance of seducing Joëlle. Enraged, Lucien rushes at him and they fight. Lucien is reunited with Joëlle—he has learned of the complexities of love, and she has acquired from him a sense of stability. *Students. Stripteasers. Mistresses. Adolescence. Perfidy. Courtship. Wagers. Nightclubs. Paris.*

Note: Opened in Paris in Jan 1961 as *Les nymphettes*; also shown in U. S. under this title.

THE FIRST TIME   F6.1559
Mirisch-Rogallan Productions. *Dist* United Artists. Apr **1969** [New York opening: 11 Jun; c28 Mar 1969; LP36848]. Sd; col (DeLuxe). 35mm. 90 min. *MPAA rating* M.

Prod Roger Smith, Allan Carr. *Dir (see note)* James Neilson, Alex Grasshoff. *Screenplay* Jo Heims, Roger Smith. *Story* Bernard Bassey. *Photog* Ernest Laszlo. *Art Dir* Trevor Williams. *Set Dsgn* Roy Kellar. *Set Decor* David Deyell.

Film Ed Henry Molin. *Mus* Kenyon Hopkins. *Song:* "*Sweet Love in theBeginning*" Michael Clough, Michael Crowley, Kenyon Hopkins. *Sung by* MCSquared. *Sd* Al Franklin. *Asst Dir* David Salven, Newt Arnold. *Prod Mgr* John W. Rogers. *Wardrobe* Gary Waterman. *Makeup* Ken Brooke. *Hairstyles* Pat Davey.

Cast: Jacqueline Bisset (*Anna*), Wes Stern (*Kenny*), Rick Kelman (*Mike*), Wink Roberts (*Tommy*), Gerard Parkes (*Charles*), Sharon Acker (*Pamela*), Cosette Lee (*grandmother*), Vincent Marino (*Frankie*), Eric Lane (*Joe*), Sharon Masters, Rhondi Polango (*go-go girls*), Guy Sanvido (*stranger*), Murray Westgate (*customs officer*), Leslie Yeo (*bartender*), William Barringer (*elevator operator*), Gail Carrington (*blonde in hot-rod*).

Comedy-drama. With the coming of summer, three high school buddies—Kenny Leeds, Mike Decker, and Tommy Kingsley—anticipate their initiation into the pleasures of manhood. But Kenny is separated from his friends and sent to stay with his grandparents in Buffalo while his father, a widowed salesman, leaves on a business trip with his secretary-fiancée. Bored and alone in a strange city, Kenny writes his two friends letters about his adventures at "Rosie's," a fictitious brothel across the Canadian border in Niagara Falls. His lie quickly backfires, however, when Mike and Tommy, en route to summer camp, arrive in Buffalo eager for a visit to "Rosie's." While stalling for time, Kenny takes them on an aimless tour of Niagara Falls and points to a boarded-up building and pretends that the brothel must have been raided by the police. Certain there must be other such places, the boys stop at a discotheque and meet Anna, an English girl whom they mistake for a prostitute. She tells them she has lost her passport and needs help in crossing the border, so the boys smuggle her into Buffalo and bring her back to Mike and Tommy's hotel. As she sleeps in their room, they draw lots to determine who will make love to her first. Mike and Tommy precede Kenny, but both are too timid to go through with their intentions, and they decide to conceal their failure from Kenny. Before Kenny enters the room, he hears Anna talking on the telephone and learns that her married lover had decided to end their affair. Although she is at first resentful of Kenny's presence, Anna responds to the boy's awkward confusion, not unlike her own, and accepts him lovingly. The next morning, Kenny escorts Anna back to the Canadian border and discovers that she is not a call girl and that she did not make love with Mike and Tommy. Kenny asks her why she behaved differently with him, but she responds only with a smile and farewell kiss. *Prostitutes. Grandparents. English. Adolescence. Hoaxes. Sexual initiation. Mistaken identity. Whorehouses. Discotheques. Summer. Buffalo. Niagara Falls (Canada).*

Note: Filmed on location in Toronto and Niagara Falls, Canada. Working titles: *The Beginners Three, The Beginners, You Don't Need Pajamas at Rosie's, They Don't Wear Pajamas at Rosie's.* James Neilson replaced Alex Grasshoff as director after several weeks of filming.

FIRST TO FIGHT   **F6.1560**
Warner Bros. Pictures. 25 Jan **1967** [Charlotte, North Carolina, opening; c25 Feb 1967; LP36584]. Sd; col (Technicolor). 35mm (Panavision). 97 min.

Exec Prod William Conrad. *Dir* Christian Nyby. *Writ* Gene L. Coon. *Dir Photog* Harold Wellman. *Art Dir* Art Loel. *Set Decor* Hal Overell. *Film Ed* George Rohrs. *Mus* Fred Steiner. *Sd* Robert B. Lee. *Asst Dir* Victor Vallejo. *Unit Mgr* J. Russell Llewellyn. *Makeup Supv* Gordon Bau. *Supv Hairstylist* Jean Burt Reilly. *Tech Adv* Fred A. Kraus, (Maj. USMC, Ret.). *Dial Supv* Stacy Harris.

Cast: Chad Everett (*Jack Connell*), Marilyn Devin (*Peggy Sanford*), Dean Jagger (*Colonel Baseman*), Bobby Troup (*Lieutenant Overman*), Claude Akins (*Captain Mason*), Gene Hackman (*Sergeant Tweed*), James Best (*Sergeant Carnavan*), Norman Alden (*Sergeant Schmidtmer*), Bobs Watson (*Sergeant Maypole*), Ken Swofford (*O'Brien*), Ray Reese (*Hawkins*), Garry Goodgion (*Karl*), Robert Austin (*Adams*), Clint Ritchie (*Sergeant Slater*), Stephen Roberts (*President Franklin D. Roosevelt*).

War drama. After distinguishing himself in combat on Guadalcanal, Marine Sgt. Jack Connell is called back to Washington, D. C., to receive the Congressional Medal of Honor. While on a warbond selling tour, he falls in love with Peggy Sanford, a public relations woman. Peggy, whose fiancé was killed in the war, initially resists Jack's advances, but she agrees to marry him when he promises not to volunteer for active duty. For a time, Jack is content to live on an Army base with Peggy and train raw recruits for combat; but he begins to think of himself as a slacker when news comes that an old buddy has been killed on Bougainville. Sensing the change in her husband, Peggy releases him from his promise, and he accepts orders to return to the Pacific. On his first mission, he freezes under fire and becomes too terrified to fight. Gradually, however, he overcomes his fear, and once more he takes a firm command over his men and leads them in a raid against a Japanese island stronghold. *War heroes. Widows. Marriage. Combat zone life. Cowardice. World War II. United States Marines. Franklin Delano Roosevelt. "Casablanca". Medal of Honor.*

Note: Battle scenes staged at Camp Pendleton Marine Base, Oceanside, California, and in the San Fernando Valley at the Bell Ranch and Africa, U.S.A. Scenes from *Casablanca* (1942) are included in the film.

FIRST WIFE *see* **WIVES AND LOVERS**

FISHERMAN'S LUCK   **F6.1561**
Cosmos Films. *Dist* Able Film Co. ca **1970**. Sd; col. 16mm. [Feature length assumed.]

Sex film. No information about the precise nature of this film has been found. *Fishermen. Sexuality.*

FISHING, U. S. A.   **F6.1562**
Gadabout Gaddis Productions. 20 May **1969** [Lewiston, Maine, opening]. Sd; col (DeLuxe). 35mm. 110 min. *MPAA rating* G.

Cast: Vernon Gadabout Gaddis.

Documentary. Sportsman Gadabout Gaddis enjoys fresh and saltwater fishing in Maine's Kennebec River, the Okefenokee Swamp, San Diego, and the Grand Tetons, instructing the neophyte in baiting, casting, and fileting. *Sportsmen. Fishing. Kennebec River. Okefenokee Swamp. San Diego. Grand Tetons.*

FIST IN HIS POCKET (Italy)   **F6.1563**
Doria Cinematografica. *Dist* Peppercorn-Wormser, Inc. 27 May **1968** [New York opening]. Sd; b&w. 35mm. 105 min.

Prod Ezio Passadore. *Exec Prod* Enzo Dorià. *Dir-Writ* Marco Bellocchio. *Dir Photog* Alberto Marrama. *Camera Op* Giuseppe Lanci. *Asst Camera Op* Alberto Rosa. *Art Dir* Gisella Longo. *Film Ed* Aurelio Mangiarotti. *Asst Ed* Anita Cacciolati. *Mus* Ennio Morricone. *Sd* Vittorio De Sisti. *Prod Mgr* Ugo Novello. *Artistic Collab* Elda Tattoli.

Cast: Lou Castel (*Alessandro*), Paola Pitagora (*Giulia*), Marino Mase (*Augusto*), Liliana Gerace (*mother*), Pier Luigi Troglio (*Leone*), Jennie MacNeil (*Lucia*), Mauro Martini (*the boy*), Gianni Schicchi (*Tonino*), Alfredo Filippazzi (*doctor*), Gianfranco Cella (*young man at the party*), Celestina Bellocchio (*young woman at the party*), Stefania Troglio (*chambermaid*), Irene Agnelli (*Bruna*), Sandra Bergamini, Lella Bertante.

Drama. In a small villa in the mountains near Piacenza, four grown children and their blind mother suffer through a tense existence together. Augusto is engaged to Lucia and has a good job, but Alessandro, Giulia, and Leone are all epileptics entangled in a web of quarrels, helplessness, and catalepsy. Alessandro, aware that Augusto's private life is suffering because of the family's dependence on him, decides to help alleviate the problem. He tells Augusto that on their next excursion by car to their father's grave, he will drive the family off a cliff and be rid of them. Augusto, half-wishing that his brother would carry out the plan, allows him to have the car; but en route, Alessandro begins racing another car and forgets his original scheme. Some time later, however, he pushes his mother out of the car, and she falls to her death. Alessandro then decides to start a chinchilla farm with the family savings, but Augusto hopes to use the money to rent an apartment for himself and Lucia. Alessandro then murders Leone by drowning him in his bath. Giulia, who is in love with Alessandro, becomes terrified when he confesses the murder to her, and she has a cataleptic attack. She is confined to her bed, nearly paralyzed with fear. Alessandro enters her room determined to kill her but changes his mind and, instead, returns to his room, plays a succession of operatic arias on the phonograph, and undergoes severe epileptic seizures. He calls to Giulia for help, but she does not move to give him assistance. *Family life. Epilepsy. Catalepsy. Blindness. Matricide. Incest. Murder. Automobiles. Piacenza.*

Note: Opened in Rome in Mar 1966 as *I pugni in tasca.* Also known as *Fists in the Pocket.*

A FISTFUL OF DOLLARS (Italy/Spain/West Germany)   **F6.1564**
Jolly Film–Ocean Film–Constantin Film. *Dist* United Artists. 18 Jan **1967** [Los Angeles opening; c12 Sep 1964; LF5]. Sd; col (Technicolor). 35mm (Techniscope). 96 min.

Prod Arrigo Colombo, Giorgio Papi. *Dir* Sergio Leone. *Screenplay* Sergio Leone, Duccio Tessari, Victor A. Catena, Jaime Comas. *English Vers* Mark Lovell. *Story* Victor A. Catena, Sergio Leone. *Photog* Federico G. Larraya, Massimo Dallamano. *Art Dir* Carlo Simi. *Decor* Sigfrido Burman. *Titl Anim* Luigi Lardani. *Film Ed* Roberto Cinquini. *Mus* Ennio Morricone. *Sd* Elio Pacella, Edy Simson. *Asst Dir* Frank Prestland. *Prod Mgr* Franco Palaggi, Günter Raguse. *Sp Eff* John Speed.

Cast: Clint Eastwood (*Man With No Name*), Marianne Koch (*Marisol*), Gian Maria Volontè (*Ramon Rojo*), Wolfgang Lukschy (*John Baxter*), Sieghardt Rupp (*Esteban Rojo*), Antonio Prieto (*Benito Rojo*), Pepe Calvo (*Silvanito*), Margarita Lozano (*Consuela Baxter*), Daniel Martin (*Julian*), Benito Stefanelli (*Rubio*), Richard Stuyvesant (*Chico*), Bruno Carotenuto (*Antonio Baxter*), Josef Egger (*Piripero*), Carla Calo, Raf Baldassarre, Antonio Vico, Johannes Siedel.

Western melodrama. During the lawless days that followed the death of Juarez, a lone American cowboy rides into the border town of San Miguel. He learns from the saloon proprietor, Silvanito, that the town is ruled by two rival, warring clans, the Rojos and the Baxters, both of whom have amassed fortunes by dealing in contraband whiskey and rifles. Quickly sensing the opportunity to make some money, the stranger picks a fight with four of the Baxters, shoots them, and then offers his high-priced services to the Rojos. Secretly and artfully he proceeds to intensify the disputes between the two families, constantly switching his allegiance as the bloody feud gains in intensity. He even arranges for Ramon Rojo's prisoner, the beautiful Marisol, to escape and be reunited with her husband and child. But this last act drives Ramon to a frenzy, and he has the stranger brutally tortured and maimed. Aided by Silvanito, the stranger escapes to an abandoned mine. Ramon, believing that the Baxters are harboring the fugitive, sets fire to their home and kills them all. For months the stranger nurses his wounds and perfects his shooting until he is ready for the final showdown. On that day he faces Ramon and the remaining Rojos, and he outdraws all of them. Then, hard-eyed and enigmatic, he rides out of San Miguel on a mule. *Strangers. Hired killers. Gunfighters. Feuds. Murder. Torture. Bootleggers. Arson. Smuggling. Mines. Firearms. Mexican border.*

Note: Produced in Italy and Spain. Released in Italy in 1964 as *Per un pugno di dollari* at 100 min; in West Germany in 1965 as *Für eine Handvoll Dollars*; in Spain as *Por un puñado de dólares.* This is the first in a series of films directed by Sergio Leone and starring Clint Eastwood as "The Man With No Name." Screenplay appears to have been based on the Japanese film *Yojimbo* (1962), q. v., although no credit is given.

FISTFULL OF RAWHIDE   F6.1565

Rebel Arts Studio. *Dist* Gunter Productions. 1 May **1970** [Champaign, Illinois, showing]. Sd; col and b&w. 35mm. 65 min.

Dir W. G. Beggs.

Cast: Patricia Moore.

Melodrama. Danny Gorman, an itinerant cowboy, returns home unexpectedly and finds his mother making love with a woman. Danny is horrified and leaves home. Years pass, and he becomes an embittered, woman-hating outlaw. He robs a wealthy rancher and kidnaps Ruth Tilman, the rancher's sex-starved sister-in-law. Danny takes Ruth to a deserted line shack, and there he meets his partner, Lambert. Lambert attempts to kill Danny and rapes Ruth. Danny kills Lambert, Ruth comes to realize Danny's good qualities, and she initiates him into the world of love. Danny and Ruth escape from the barbaric vengeance of Ruth's brother-in-law. *Cowboys. Ranchers. Lesbianism. Misogynists. Kidnaping. Rape. Sexual initiation. Revenge.*

FISTS IN THE POCKET *see* **FIST IN HIS POCKET**

FITZWILLY   F6.1566

Mirisch Corp.–Dramatic Features. *Dist* United Artists. 20 Dec **1967** [New York opening; c20 Dec 1967; LP35104]. Sd; col (DeLuxe). 35mm (Panavision). 102 min.

A Walter Mirisch Production. *Prod* Walter Mirisch. *Assoc Prod* Irving Temaner. *Dir* Delbert Mann. *Screenplay* Isobel Lennart. *Dir Photog* Joseph Biroc. *Asst Camera* Arthur Gerstle, Eugene Lenoir. *Art Dir* Robert Boyle. *Asst Art Dir* Edwin O'Donovan. *Set Decor* Edward G. Boyle. *Film Ed* Ralph Winters. *Asst Film Ed* Marshall M. Borden. *Mus* Johnny Williams. *Song Lyr:* "Make Me Rainbows" Alan Bergman, Marilyn Bergman. *Sd Mix* Robert Martin. *Sd Ed* Robert Reich. *Mus & Eff Ed* Richard Carruth. *Re-rec* Clem Portman. *1st & 2d Asst Dir* Terry Nelson, Dennis Donnelly, Malcolm Harding. *Prod Supv* Allen K. Wood. *Prod Mgr* Patrick J. Palmer. *Script Supv* Marie Kenney. *Asst to the Prod* Jossie Ponitz. *Prod Asst* Larry DeWaay. *Cost Dsgn* Don Feld. *Men's Cost* Wes Jeffries. *Ladies' Cost* Angela Alexander. *Makeup* Tom Tuttle. *Hairdresser* Alice Monte. *Sp Eff* Norman Breedlove. *Dial Dir* Norman Stuart. *Prop Master* Sam Gordon. *Constr Coörd* William Hiney. *Casting* Lynn Stalmaster. *Key Grip* Dick Borland. *Gaffer* Babe Stafford.

Cast: Dick Van Dyke (*Fitzwilliam*), Barbara Feldon (*Juliet Nowell*), Edith Evans (*Victoria Woodworth*), John McGiver (*Albert*), Harry Townes (*Mr. Nowell*), John Fiedler (*Mr. Dunne*), Norman Fell (*Oderblatz*), Cecil Kellaway (*Buckmaster*), Stephen Strimpell (*Byron Casey*), Anne Seymour (*Grimsby*), Helen Kleeb (*Mrs. Mortimer*), Sam Waterston (*Oliver*), Paul Reed (*Prettikin*), Albert Carrier (*Pierre*), Nelson Olmsted (*Simmons*), Dennis Cooney (*Adams*), Noam Pitlik (*Charles*), Antony Eustrel (*Garland*), Laurence Naismith (*Cotty*), Karen Norris (*Kitty*), Patience Cleveland (*Dolly*), Lew Brown (*Frank*), Monroe Arnold (*Goldfarb*), Bob Williams (*Ryan*), Billy Halop (*restaurant owner*).

Comedy. Source: Poyntz Tyler, *A Garden of Cucumbers* (New York, 1960). Victoria Woodworth is a kindly elderly dowager who lives in a plush Manhattan brownstone. Although she frequently donates large sums of money to charities, the fact that she is actually penniless is concealed from her by her staff of faithful domestics. Her well-mannered but larcenous butler, Fitzwilliam (or Fitzwilly, as he is called by his friends), has been able to run Miss Vickie's

household in the black and keep ahead of her charitable contributions by organizing the other servants into a ring of smalltime crooks. One day Miss Vickie hires a part-time secretary, Juliet Nowell, to help with the dictionary she is writing for people who can't spell. Although Juliet inevitably catches on to Fitzwilly's maneuvers, she finds herself too attracted to him to notify the police. Events reach a climax when one of Miss Vickie's over-generous contributions escapes Fitzwilly's attention, and drastic measures are called for to cover the deficit. With the reluctant help of Juliet, an elaborate plan is worked out to rob Gimbel's department store on Christmas Eve. Miss Vickie's staff joins in the caper, and everything goes off on schedule, with the haul amounting to $190,000. One small hitch develops, however, when Albert, the conscience-stricken footman, confesses to the police. Since Albert refuses to name his accomplices, Miss Vickie is summoned. Unperturbed, she volunteers to write Gimbel's a check for $190,000, thereby leaving the frustrated Fitzwilly with no choice but to deposit the stolen money in Miss Vickie's bank account. But all ends happily when Miss Vickie announces that she has sold her unique dictionary, much of which is an amusing biography of her late father, to a movie producer for $500,000. *Spinsters. Philanthropists. Authors. Butlers. Domestics. Thieves. Secretaries. Theft. Conscience. Charity. Finance—Personal. Dictionaries. Christmas. New York City. Gimbel's (New York City).*

UN FIUME DI DOLLARI *see* **THE HILLS RUN RED**

FIVE BLOODY DAYS TO TOMBSTONE *see* **FIVE BLOODY GRAVES**

FIVE BLOODY GRAVES   F6.1567

Dix International Pictures. *Dist* Independent-International Pictures. Nov **1969** [New Orleans opening]. Sd; col (Technicolor). 35mm (Techniscope). 88 min. *MPAA rating* GP.

An Al Adamson Production. *Prod-Dir* Al Adamson. *Assoc Prod* John Cardos, Robert Dix. *Story & Screenplay* Robert Dix. *Dir Photog* William Zsigmond. *Titl Dsgn* Bob Lebar. *Film Ed* William Faris, Peter Perry. *Sd* Robert Dietz. *Prod Mgr* Bud Cardos. *Unit Mgr* Rick Jackson.

Cast: Robert Dix (*Ben Thompson*), Scott Brady (*Jim Wade*), Jim Davis (*Clay Bates*), John Carradine (*Boone Hawkins*), Paula Raymond (*Kansas Kelly*), John Cardos (*Joe Lightfoot/Satago*), Tara Ashton (*Althea Richards*), Kent Osborne (*Dave Miller*), Vicki Volante (*Nora Miller*), Denver Dixon (*Rawhide*), Ray Young (*Horace Wiggins*), Julie Edwards (*Lavina Wade*), Fred Meyers (*driver*), Maria Polo (*Little Fawn*), Gene Raymond (*The Voice of Death*).

Western melodrama. In the Old West, Ben Thompson, a brutal gunslinger, is known as the "Messenger of Death," and everyone he encounters is doomed. Ben spends the night with former girl friend Nora Miller, but she orders him out of the house the next morning when her husband, Dave, returns. Shortly after Ben leaves, the couple is slaughtered and scalped by a band of Yaquis led by the ruthless Satago, who had previously murdered Ben's wife. Satago is supplied with weapons by two murderous renegades, Clay Bates and Horace Wiggins. Clay rapes and kills Little Fawn, wife of Satago's half-brother Joe Lightfoot, after Satago had captured her, tied her up, tortured her, and left her in the desert to die. Meanwhile, Satago and his men overtake a wagon train in the prairie and attack its occupants—Kansas Kelly, one of the West's most notorious madams; Althea Richards and Lavina Wade, two prostitutes; Boone Hawkins, a lecherous preacher; and Jim Wade, a conniving gambler. Joined by Ben and Joe Lightfoot, the group bands together to battle the attacking Yaquis. Clay and Horace arrive at the camp and tell Joe about the vicious slaying of his wife. Joe then pursues Clay on horseback into the desert, apprehends him, and stakes him out on an anthill. Joe is then besieged by the Yaquis and left wounded and near death. Before dying, however, Joe manages to kill Clay. As the battle rages on, the members of the doomed camp are killed one by one until only Ben and Satago remain alive. Finally, in a violent fight in the rapids, Ben emerges the victor. His deadly mission accomplished, he once again rides off alone. *Gunfighters. Yaqui Indians. Madams. Prostitutes. Preachers. Gamblers. Infidelity. Torture. Rape. Murder. Massacres. Revenge. Wagon trains. Deserts.*

Note: Filmed on location in Capitol Reef, Utah. Original titles: *The Lonely Man* and *Five Bloody Days to Tombstone.*

5 CARD STUD   F6.1568

Paramount Pictures. 10 Jul **1968** [Chicago opening; c12 Jul 1968; LP36394]. Sd; col (Technicolor). 35mm. 103 min.

A Hal Wallis Production. *Prod* Hal B. Wallis. *Assoc Prod* Paul Nathan. *Dir* Henry Hathaway. *Screenplay* Marguerite Roberts. *Dir Photog* Daniel L. Fapp. *Set Decor* Ray Moyer. *Prod Dsgn* Walter Tyler. *Ed Supv* Warren Low. *Mus Comp & Cond* Maurice Jarre. *Titl Song* Maurice Jarre, Ned Washington. *Sung by* Dean Martin. *Hymn:* "Mercy's Call" W. H. Doane, F. C. Van Alstyne. *Sd Rec* Harold Lewis. *Asst Dir* Fred Gammon. *Prod Mgr* William W. Gray. *Unit Prod Mgr* Frank Beetson, Jr. *Cost* Leah Rhodes. *Makeup Artist* Del Acevedo. *Hairstyles* Carol Meikle.

Cast: Dean Martin *(Van Morgan)*, Robert Mitchum *(Reverend Rudd)*, Inger Stevens *(Lily Langford)*, Roddy McDowall *(Nick Evers)*, Katherine Justice *(Nora Evers)*, John Anderson *(Marshal Dana)*, Ruth Springford *(Mama Malone)*, Yaphet Kotto *(Little George)*, Denver Pyle *(Sig Evers)*, Bill Fletcher *(Joe Hurley)*, Whit Bissell *(Dr. Cooper)*, Ted De Corsia *(Eldon Bates)*, Don Collier *(Rowan)*, Roy Jenson *(Mace Jones)*, Boyd "Red" Morgan *(Fred Carson)*, George Rowbotham *(Stoney)*, Jerry Gatlin *(stranger)*, Robert Hoy, Louise Lorimer, Chuck Hayward.

Western melodrama. Source: Ray Gaulden, *Glory Gulch* (New York, 1967). In 1880, a stud-poker game in Rincon, Colorado, ends violently when one of the players, a stranger, is lynched for attempting to cheat. Gambler Van Morgan, who alone tried to prevent the hanging, decides to move on to Denver. After he leaves, a gold rush hits Rincon, bringing with it the self-ordained Rev. Jonathan Rudd, a fire-and-brimstone preacher, and Lily Langford, a madam with a group of lady barbers. After learning that two of the poker players have been murdered, Van returns to Rincon, despite the warning of bartender Little George that someone may be planning to kill every man who played in the game. While Van divides his time between tracking down the killer and diverting himself with both Lily and Nora Evers, two more of the game's participants are murdered. Unknown to Van, the killer is Reverend Rudd, whose brother was the lynch victim; he was supplied with the names of the other players by Nora's brother, Nick, who claims he tried to circumvent the hanging, although he actually instigated it. After killing Little George on Evers' advice, Reverend Rudd discovers that Nick was the ringleader of the lynching and that Van was also in the card game. Rudd outdraws Nick and then goes after his final victim, but the preacher is killed in the final shootout. Van leaves once more for Denver, bidding farewell to both Nora and Lily. *Gamblers. Preachers. Barbers. Madams. Prostitutes. Bartenders. Poker. Lynching. Gold rushes. Murder. Revenge. Brother-sister relationship. Colorado. Denver.*

Note: Location scenes filmed in Durango, Mexico. Copyright claimants: Paramount Pictures, Hal B. Wallis, and Joseph H. Hazen.

THE FIVE DAY LOVER (France/Italy)   F6.1569

Ariane-Filmsonor-Mondex Films-Cineriz. *Dist* Kingsley International Pictures. 13 Dec **1961** [New York opening]. Sd; b&w. 35mm. 86 min.

Prod Georges Dancigers. *Dir* Philippe de Broca. *Dial* Daniel Boulanger. *Adapt* Daniel Boulanger, Philippe de Broca. *Photog* Jean Penzer. *Art Dir* Bernard Evein. *Film Ed* Laurence Méry. *Mus* Georges Delerue. *Sd* Jean Labussière.

Cast: Jean Seberg *(Claire)*, Micheline Presle *(Madeleine)*, Jean-Pierre Cassel *(Antoine)*, François Périer *(Georges)*, Carlo Croccolo *(Mario)*, Claude Mansard *(Paulin)*, Marcella Rovena *(Madame Chanut)*, Albert Michel *(Blanchet)*, Albert Mouton *(Halavoine)*, Gib Grossac *(taxi driver)*, Jean Sylvain *(maître d'hôtel)*, Pierre Repp *(Pepere)*, Philippe de Broca.

Comedy-drama. Source: Françoise Parturier-Galichon, *L'amant de cinq jours* (Paris, 1959). Claire, a young Englishwoman, lives in Paris with her staid husband, Georges, a government archivist, and their two small children. One day, while attending a fashion show mounted by her friend Madeleine, a couturière, Claire meets a lighthearted young Frenchman, Antoine. Despite the fact that he is being kept by Madeleine, Claire responds to his advances and returns with him to his luxurious bachelor apartment. Before long she is visiting him five afternoons a week; evenings and weekends are reserved for Georges and the children. Madeleine, strong-willed and possessive, learns of the affair and decides to meet the situation directly by inviting Claire and Georges, as well as Antoine, to the same party. The desired effect is achieved when it becomes apparent that Claire is tiring of Antoine and has no intention of seeing him again. Only Georges, quiet and gentle, understands that nothing has really changed. It will not be long before Claire will once more embark on her quest for chance lovers. *English. Couturiers. Gigolos. Archivists. Marriage. Infidelity. Jealousy. Fashion shows. Paris.*

Note: Opened in Paris in Feb 1961 as *L'amant de cinq jours*; running time: 95 min. Italian title: *L'amante di cinque giorni.*

FIVE EASY PIECES   F6.1570

B. B. S. Productions. *Dist* Columbia Pictures. 12 Sep **1970** [New York opening; c1 Sep 1970; LP38186]. Sd; col (Technicolor). 35mm. 96 min. *MPAA rating* R.

Prod Bob Rafelson, Richard Wechsler. *Exec Prod* Bert Schneider. *Assoc Prod* Harold Schneider. *Dir* Bob Rafelson. *Screenplay* Adrien Joyce. *Story* Bob Rafelson, Adrien Joyce. *Dir Photog* Laszlo Kovacs. *Interior Dsgn* Toby Rafelson. *Film Ed* Christopher Holmes, Gerald Sheppard. *Asst Ed* Pete Denenberg, Harold Hazen. *Mus: Chromatic Fantasy and Fugue* Johann Sebastian Bach. *Piano Concerto in E-flat Major K.271, Fantasy in D Minor K.397* Wolfgang Amadeus Mozart. *Fantasy in F Minor opus 49, Prelude in E Minor opus 28 no. 4* Frédéric François Chopin. *Piano Solo* Pearl Kaufman. *Song:* "Stand by Your Man" Billy Sherrill, Tammy Wynette. *Song:* "D-I-V-O-R-C-E" Bobby Braddock, Claude Putman, Jr. *Song:* "When There's a Fire in

Your Heart" Merle Kilgore, Sonny Williams. *Song:* "Don't Touch Me" H. Cochran. *Sung by* Tammy Wynette. *Sd Mix* Charles Knight. *Sd Eff* Edit-Rite Inc. *Asst Dir* Sheldon Schrager. *Script Supv* Terry Terrill. *Location Mgr* Kent Remington. *Prod Coörd* Marilyn Schlossberg. *Wardrobe* Bucky Rous. *Gaffer* Richard Aguilar. *Key Grip* George Hill, Jr.. *Casting* Fred Roos. *Prop Master* Walter Starkey.

Cast: Jack Nicholson *(Robert Eroica Dupea)*, Karen Black *(Rayette Dipesto)*, Lois Smith *(Partita Dupea)*, Susan Anspach *(Catherine Van Ost)*, Billy "Green" Bush *(Elton)*, Fannie Flagg *(Stoney)*, Ralph Waite *(Carl Fidelio Dupea)*, Helena Kallianiotes *(Palm Apodaca)*, Toni Basil *(Terry Grouse)*, Sally Ann Struthers *(Betty)*, Marlena MacGuire *(Twinky)*, John Ryan *(Spicer)*, Irene Dailey *(Samia Glavia)*, Lorna Thayer *(waitress)*, Richard Stahl *(recording engineer)*, William Challee *(Nicholas Dupea)*.

Drama. Classical pianist Robert Dupea, who comes from a family of musicians, works in a California oil field. Most of his time is spent in bowling alleys, drinking beer in the trailer of his friend Elton, or with his waitress girl friend, Rayette. When he learns that she is pregnant, he quits his job and leaves for Los Angeles where his sister Partita, also a pianist, is making a recording. Partita informs him that their father has suffered two strokes and urges him to return to the family home on Puget Sound. He tells Rayette that he must go to see the old man and reluctantly agrees to take her along. On the way, they pick up Palm and Terry, two lesbians whose constant chatter about ecology increasingly annoys Robert. The four of them are thrown out of a restaurant when he becomes involved in an argument with a waitress who cannot bring his special order. Eventually, Robert reaches his destination; embarrassed by Rayette's lack of polish, he registers her in a motel and goes to visit his father, who is confined to a wheelchair and unable to speak. At dinner that night, he meets Catherine Van Ost, a young pianist engaged to his brother Carl, a violinist; in spite of personality differences, Robert and Catherine become attracted to each other and make love in her room. Meanwhile, Rayette becomes bored at the motel and comes to the Dupea estate unannounced. Her presence creates an awkward situation, but when Samia, a pompous family friend, ridicules Rayette's background, Robert is forced into a fiery defense of her. Storming from the room, he discovers his father's huge male nurse giving a massage to the semi-nude Partita; even more angered, Robert picks a senseless fight with him and is quickly knocked to the floor. After a frustrating attempt to talk with his father, Robert leaves with Rayette. Unable to function in the intellectual world of his family or in the working-class world of the oil fields, he stops at a gas station, abandons Rayette when she goes in for some coffee, and hitches a ride on a truck. *Pianists. Waitresses. Paralytics. Hitchhikers. Violinists. Nurses. Pregnancy. Family life. Strokes. Lesbianism. Infidelity. Snobbery. Oil fields. Restaurants. California. Los Angeles. Puget Sound.*

Note: Adrien Joyce is a pseudonym for Carol Eastman.

FIVE FINGER EXERCISE   F6.1571

Sonnis Corp. *Dist* Columbia Pictures. 19 Apr **1962** [New York opening; c1 Jun 1962; LP22257]. Sd (RCA); b&w. 35mm. 109 min.

Prod Frederick Brisson. *Dir* Daniel Mann. *Screenplay* Frances Goodrich, Albert Hackett. *Dir Photog* Harry Stradling. *Art Dir* Ross Bellah. *Set Decor* William Kiernan. *Film Ed* William A. Lyon. *Mus* Jerome Moross. *Sd Supv* Charles J. Rice. *Sd* James Z. Flaster. *Asst Dir* R. Robert Rosenbaum. *Miss Russell's Gowns* Orry-Kelly. *Makeup Supv* Ben Lane. *Miss Russell's Makeup* Gene Hibbs.

Cast: Rosalind Russell *(Louise Harrington)*, Jack Hawkins *(Stanley Harrington)*, Maximilian Schell *(Walter)*, Richard Beymer *(Philip Harrington)*, Annette Gorman *(Pamela Harrington)*, Lana Wood *(Mary)*, Terry Huntingdon *(Helen Hunting)*, William Quinn *(salesman)*, Kathy West *(Alice)*, Valora Noland *(girl)*, Mary Benoit *(woman)*, Jeannine Riley, Karen Parker *(girls)*, Bart Conrad *(announcer)*, Todd Armstrong *(Tony Blake, see note)*.

Domestic melodrama. Source: Peter Shaffer, *Five Finger Exercise* (London opening: 17 Jul 1958). The Harrington family is spending the summer at a beachhouse in Carmel, California. Louise Harrington is a domineering and overly culture-conscious woman who feels she has married beneath herself. Her husband, Stanley, is an intolerant, self-made furniture manufacturer who has allowed his wife complete authority in the upbringing of their two children. Young Philip, a sensitive Harvard student, is confused, semi-emasculated, and uncertain of both himself and his future. Fifteen-year-old Pamela is a frivolous child controlled by her adolescent impulses. Into their lives comes Walter, a young German whom Louise has hired as a tutor for Pamela. He has fled his home because of a brutal Nazi father; lonely, shy, and desperately in need of family love, he serves as the catalyst to unleash the hidden tensions in the family. To Stanley, Walter is one more of Louise's ridiculous affectations; to Philip, he is a much-needed friend and advisor who can save him from his mother's stifling love; to Pamela, he is a symbol of love; and to Louise, he is a potential lover. Walter's efforts to become a member of the family end in a violent domestic crisis. His attentions to Louise are misunderstood by father and son as adulterous; his "rescue" of Pamela when she swims out too far embarrasses and alienates the girl; and his confession to Louise that he regards her as a mother is met with a chilling silence. As a result he is dismissed and ordered to leave. Not knowing how he has failed to win the family's love, he attempts suicide. The drastic action awakens the Harringtons to a sudden realization of their individual selfishness and, once Walter has gone, they make an effort to repair their shattered family life. *Tutors. Manufacturers. Germans. Students. Refugees. Family life. Suicide. Infidelity. Adolescence. Snobbery. Brother-sister relationship. Summer. Carmel (California).*

Note: Armstrong's appearance in the film is unconfirmed.

FIVE FINGERS OF DEATH *see* HAND OF DEATH

5 GENTS ON THE SPOT (Japan)　　　　　　　　　　　　　**F6.1572**
Toho Co. Jan **1967** [Los Angeles showing]. Sd; col. 35mm (Tohoscope). 90 min.

Dir Shue Mitsubayashi.

Cast: Hisaya Morishige, Franky Sakai, Keiju Kobayashi, Michiyo Aratama, Yoko Tsukasa.

Comedy. No information about the precise nature of this film has been found.

Note: Released in Japan in 1966 as *Zoku shacho gyojoki.*

FIVE GENTS' TRICK BOOK (Japan)　　　　　　　　　　　**F6.1573**
Toho Co. 21 Dec **1965** [Los Angeles showing]. Sd; col (Eastmancolor). 35mm (Tohoscope). 95 min.

Prod Masumi Fujimoto. *Dir* Sayo Marubayashi. *Screenplay* Ryozo Kasahara. *Photog* Takeshi Suzuki. *Mus* Yoshiyuki Kozu.

Cast: Hisaya Morishige *(Hisataro Iwato),* Asami Kuji *(Toyoko Iwato),* Keiju Kobayashi *(Takashi Ishikawa),* Daisuke Kato *(Tyuzo Togashi),* Norihei Miki *(Benjiro Mamada),* Yoko Tsukasa *(Kyoko Ishikawa),* Franky Sakai *(Tsuyoshi Kebanai),* Junko Ikeuchi *(Chiyo Suzu),* Michiyo Aratama *(Sumiko),* Reiko Dan *(Yuriko).*

Domestic comedy. Hisataro Iwato, a business executive with an eye for women, struggles to keep his affairs a secret from his wife, Toyoko. *Businessmen. Philanderers. Infidelity. Marriage.*

Note: Released in Japan in 1965 as *Shacho ninpocho.*

FIVE GOLDEN HOURS (Great Britain/Italy)　　　　　　**F6.1574**
Avers Film (Rome)-Anglofilm-Fabio Jegher. *Dist* Columbia Pictures. 24 May **1961** [Pittsburgh opening; c1 May 1961; LP20458]. Sd; b&w. 35mm. 90 min.

Prod-Dir Mario Zampi. *Assoc Prod* Giulio Zampi. *Screenplay* Hans Wilhelm. *Scen Ed* Kathleen Connors. *Dir Photog* Christopher Challis. *Photog* Fulvio Testi. *Camera Op* Austin Dempster. *Focus* John Jordan. *Camera Grip* Jim Dawes. *Art Dir* Ivan King. *Asst Art Dir* Ted Tester. *Set Dresser* Jeff Hercombe. *Film Ed* Bill Lewthwaite. *1st Asst Ed* Alma Godfrey. *2d Asst Ed* Terry Message. *Mus Comp & Cond* Stanley Black. *Sd Rec* Cyril Swern. *Boom Op* John Streeter. *Sd Camera Op* Harold Clarke. *1st & 2d Asst Dir* Ted Sturgis, Denis Johnson, Jr. *Prod Mgr* Denis Johnson. *Cont* Lee Turner. *Prod Sec* Doris Prince. *Wardrobe Supv* Evelyn Gibbs. *Cyd Charisse's Dresses* Sartoria Sorelle Botti. *Makeup* Philip Leakey. *Hairdresser* A. G. Scott. *Still Photog* Ricky Smith. *Prop* Tommy Welsh. *Supv Electrn* R. Jeffrey.

Cast—British Version: Ernie Kovacs *(Aldo Bondi),* Cyd Charisse *(Baronessa Sandra),* George Sanders *(Mr. Bing),* Kay Hammond *(Martha),* Dennis Price *(Raphael),* Clelia Matania *(Rosalia),* John Le Mesurier *(Dr. Alfiera),* Finlay Currie *(Father Superior),* Reginald Beckwith *(Brother Geronimo),* Avice Landon *(Beatrice),* Sydney Tafler *(Alfredo),* Martin Benson *(Enrico),* Bruno Barnabe *(Cesare),* Ron Moody *(Gabrielle),* Leonard Sachs *(Mr. Morini),* Gordon Phillott *(old monk),* Georgina Cookson *(lady passenger),* Hy Hazell, Joy Shelton *(lady guests),* Marianne Stone *(Tina),* Maya Fabio *(Aldo's nurse).*

Cast (see note): Arnoldo Foà *(Enrico),* Vittorio Caprioli, Riccardo Garrone, Francesco Mulè, Franco Coop, Aldo Silvani, Franco Volpi.

Comedy. In Rome, professional mourner and pallbearer Aldo Bondi lives in style by consoling recently widowed wealthy women and then graciously accepting their expensive gifts. All goes well until he falls in love with the Baronessa Sandra, whose deceased husband has left her penniless. Eager to help, Aldo persuades three rich widows to lend him money he hopes to double on the New York Stock Exchange by taking advantage of the 5-hour time difference between New York and Rome. Though the scheme works, Sandra absconds with the money. Unable to face the duped widows, Aldo decides to do away with them, but this plan, too, is bungled, and he is forced to feign insanity to avoid imprisonment. Confined in an asylum, he meets another swindler, Mr. Bing, who is also pretending to be mad. One day, one of Aldo's widows dies and leaves him her fortune on the condition that should he regain his sanity the money is to be turned over to a monastery. By offering to split with the monastery, however, Aldo is able to keep half his inheritance and

return to Rome. Meanwhile, Mr. Bing has established contact with Sandra, just widowed for the sixth time, and, for a fee, informs her of Aldo's good fortune. Sandra ingratiates herself with Aldo and induces him to marry her—and shortly thereafter becomes a widow for the seventh time! *Widows. Nobility. Swindlers. Fraud. Insanity. Inheritance. Funerals. Stock market. Insane asylums. Monasteries. Rome. Italy. New York City.*

Note: Location scenes filmed in and around Bolzano. Opened in London in Feb 1961; in Rome in Mar 1961 as *Cinque ore in contanti.* Filmed in two versions; the second cast listing includes the Italian actors who replaced British artists in some of the minor roles for Italian release.

THE FIVE MAN ARMY (Italy)　　　　　　　　　　　　　　**F6.1575**
Tiger Film. *Dist* Metro-Goldwyn-Mayer, Inc. Feb **1970** [c31 Dec 1969; LP37774]. Sd; col (Metrocolor). 35mm. 105 min. *MPAA rating* GP.

Prod (see note) Italo Zingarelli. *Dir* Don Taylor. *Screenplay* Dario Argento, Marc Richards. *Dir Photog* Enzo Barboni. *Camera Op* Sergio Bergamini. *Art Dir* Enzo Bulgarelli. *Set Decor* Ennio Michettoni. *Film Ed* Sergio Montanari. *Mus* Ennio Morricone. *Mus Dir* Bruno Nicolai. *Sd Ed* Eraldo Giordani. *Asst Sd* Antonio Bramonti. *Asst Dir* Stefano Rolla. *Prod Mgr* Franco Palaggi, Luciano Pesciaroli. *Cost* Enzo Bulgarelli, Luciano Sagoni. *Makeup* Massimo Giustini, Sergio Petruzzelli. *Dial Dir* Raffaele Mottola.

Cast: Peter Graves *(The Dutchman),* James Daly *(Augustus),* Bud Spencer *(Mesito),* Tetsuro Tamba *(Samurai),* Nino Castelnuovo *(Luiz Dominguez),* Daniela Giordano *(Maria),* Claudio Gora *(Manuel Estaban),* Annabella Andreoli *(Perla),* Carlo Alighiero *(Gutierrez),* Jack Stuart *(Mexican officer),* Dan Sturkie, Marc Lawrence *(carnival barker [see note]).* José Torres *(Mexican spy),* Marino Masè *(train engineer).*

Western melodrama. Outlaw Luiz Dominguez travels to Texas to hire three men to help his boss, the Dutchman, steal a shipment of gold in Mexico. The three—Mesito, a Mexican of great strength; Augustus, a dynamite expert; and Samurai, a Japanese knifethrower—go to the Mexican city of Morales and rescue revolutionary Manuel Estaban from an army firing squad. Gutierrez, an ambitious and sadistic officer, captures and tortures the men, but they refuse to speak of the gold. Later, the outlaws manage to escape after destroying an ammunition dump. Using Estaban's knowledge of the train's timetable, the Dutchman and his accomplices capture the train and unhook the car containing the gold. They argue over the division of the gold until the arrival of a Mexican patrol, which the outlaws unite to defeat; the debate resumes, and the Dutchman insists that all of the gold go to the Mexican revolutionaries. At this point, Estaban and a group of revolutionaries take the gold and settle the argument. *Outlaws. Japanese. Mexicans. Revolutionaries. Train robberies. Rescue. Torture. Gold. Mexico—History—1910–17. Texas. Mexico.*

Note: Location scenes filmed in Spain. Released in Italy in 1969 as *Un esercito di 5 uomini.* Zingarelli is credited as producer and director in Italian sources. Jack Stuart is a pseudonym for Giacomo Rossi Stuart, Bud Spencer for Carlo Pedersoli. Sources conflict in crediting actor who plays the carnival barker.

FIVE MILES TO MIDNIGHT (United States/France/Italy)　**F6.1576**
Filmsonor-Dear Film-United Artists. *Dist* United Artists. 20 Feb **1963** [Chicago opening; c20 Feb 1963; LP23976]. Sd; b&w. 35mm. 110 min.

A Mercury Films Production. *Prod-Dir* Anatole Litvak. *Assoc Prod* André Smagghe. *Screenplay* Peter Viertel, Hugh Wheeler. *Dial Maurice* Druon. *Adapt* Peter Viertel. *Orig Idea* André Versini. *Dir Photog* Henri Alekan. *Camera* André Domage. *Art Dir* Alexandre Trauner. *Film Ed* Bert Bates, Ginou Dodard. *Mus* Mikis Theodorakis. *Sd Engr* Jacques Carrère. *Asst Dir* Paul Feyder. *Prod Mgr* Louis Wipf. *Cost for Miss Loren* Guy Laroche.

Cast: Sophia Loren *(Lisa Macklin),* Anthony Perkins *(Robert Macklin),* Gig Young *(David Barnes),* Jean-Pierre Aumont *(Alan Stewart),* Yolande Turner *(Barbara Ford),* Tommy Norden *(Johnny),* Mathilde Casadesus *(Madame Duval, the concierge),* Billy Kearns *(Captain Wade),* Barbara Nicot *(Mrs. Wade),* Louis Falavigna *(pharmacist),* Elina Labourdette *(Madame Lafont),* Régine *(Régine),* Pascale Roberts *(streetwalker),* Sophie Réal *(housemaid),* Jean Ozenne *(Monsieur Bagasse),* Clément Harari *(Monsieur Schmidt),* Nicolas Vogel *(Eric Ostrum),* Giselle Preville *(Mrs. Harrington),* Jean Hebey *(Nikandros),* Yves Brainville *(Monsieur Dompier),* Guy Laroche *(Guy Laroche),* Jacques Marin, Jacqueline Porel.

Melodrama. The marriage of Italian-born Lisa Macklin and her American husband, Robert, has reached an impasse because of Robert's immaturity and emotional instability. Consequently, on the day of Robert's departure from their home in Paris for Casablanca on business, Lisa tells him that she will not see him again. That night she learns that her husband's plane has crashed and all aboard are presumed dead. The following morning Robert, ragged and injured, reappears and explains that he was blown through the escape hatch just before the crash. Since no one knows he is alive, he suggests that Lisa collect the $120,000 in insurance he took out at the airport. She reluctantly agrees only when Robert intimates that he will disappear from her life once he has the money. Robert stays hidden in their apartment, while a distraught Lisa signs the necessary legal documents and, at the same time, becomes involved with David Barnes, an American newspaperman. Once she has the money, Lisa drives Robert to the Belgian border. En route, he tells her that she must stay with him always or he will turn her over to the police for insurance fraud. Desperate, she tricks him into getting out of the car and then runs him down. Shattered and driven out of her mind by the experience, she returns to the waiting David, who telephones the authorities. *Newspapermen. Americans in foreign countries. Marriage. Jealousy. Insurance. Insanity. Fraud. Murder. Paris. Airplane accidents.*

Note: Opened in Paris in Dec 1962 as *Le couteau dans la plaie;* alternative French title: *La troisième dimension.* Rome opening: Jan 1963 as *Il coltello nella piaga;* alternative Italian title: *La terza dimensione;* running time: ca115 min.

FIVE MILLION YEARS TO EARTH (Great Britain)   F6.1577
Seven Arts Productions–Hammer Film Productions. *Dist* Twentieth Century–Fox Film Corp. Mar **1968** [Los Angeles showing; c31 Dec 1967; LP35453]. Sd (RCA); col (De Luxe). 35mm. 98 min.

Prod Anthony Nelson Keys. *Dir* Roy Ward Baker. *Orig Story–Screenplay* Nigel Kneale. *Dir Photog* Arthur Grant. *Camera Op* Moray Grant. *Supv Art Dir* Bernard Robinson. *Art Dir* Ken Ryan. *Supv Ed* James Needs. *Ed* Spencer Reeve. *Mus Comp* Tristram Cary. *Mus Supv* Philip Martell. *Sd Rec* Sash Fisher. *Sd Ed* Roy Hyde. *Asst Dir* Bert Batt. *Prod Mgr* Ian Lewis. *Cont* Doreen Dearnaley. *Wardrobe Mistress* Rosemary Burrows. *Makeup* Michael Morris. *Hairstylist* Pearl Tipaldi. *Sp Eff* Bowie Films. *Casting* Irene Lamb.

Cast: James Donald *(Dr. Roney),* Andrew Keir *(Quatermass),* Barbara Shelley *(Barbara Judd),* Julian Glover *(Colonel Breen),* Duncan Lamont *(Sladden),* Bryan Marshall *(Captain Potter),* Peter Copley *(Howell),* Edwin Richfield *(minister),* Grant Taylor *(Police Sergeant Ellis),* Maurice Good *(Sergeant Cleghorn),* Robert Morris *(Watson),* Sheila Steafel *(journalist),* Hugh Futcher *(Sapper West),* Hugh Morton *(elderly journalist),* Thomas Heathcote *(vicar),* Noel Howlett *(abbey librarian),* Hugh Manning *(pub customer),* June Ellis *(blonde),* Keith Marsh *(Johnson),* James Culliford *(Corporal Gibson),* Bee Duffell *(Miss Dobson),* Roger Avon *(electrician),* Brian Peck *(technical officer),* John Graham, British *(inspector),* Charles Lamb *(newsvendor).*

Science fiction drama. Workmen building an extension to the London subway discover skulls and skeletons of what appear to have been subhuman creatures. Investigation by Dr. Roney and Barbara Judd of the Natural History Research Institute uncovers a strange missile, thought at first to be an unknown Nazi weapon of World War II. As work continues on the missile, rocket expert Professor Quatermass studies the history of the area and learns that it has always been associated with demons, dating as far back as the Roman invasion. Opening the missile, the scientists discover the bodies of locust-like creatures, which Quatermass maintains are dead Martians. Furthermore, despite the passage of millions of years, Quatermass believes that their evil force is still present. His theory is verified when a monstrous horned creature materializes above the excavation pit. This creature's sinister power is such that the mind of any human being approaching it becomes controlled and redirected by the Devil. Knowing that the future of mankind is threatened, Dr. Roney drives a large crane into the creature, causing it to disintegrate. In so doing, however, Roney sacrifices his own life. *Construction crews. Scientists. Monsters. Thought control. Self-sacrifice. Subways. Missiles. Evil spirits. London. The Devil.*

Note: Released in Great Britain in Nov 1967 as *Quatermass and the Pit.* Working title: *The Pit.* This is the third film made from the Quatermass serials written by Kneale for British television. Also released in the United States were *The Creeping Unknown* (1956) and *Enemy From Space* (1957).

THE FIVE MINUTE KISS   F6.1578
Dist I. R. M. I. Films. 23 Sep **1970** [New York opening]. Sd; col. 35mm. [Feature film, length unknown.]

Dir Otto Wilmer.

Cast: Elke Cole, Werner Anker, Donna Stanley.

Sex film. No information about the precise nature of this film has been found. *Sexuality.*

Note: Filmed on location in Berlin.

FIVE MINUTES TO LIVE   F6.1579
Somara Productions–Flower Film Productions. *Dist* Sutton Pictures, Astor Pictures, American International Pictures. 7 Dec **1961** [Dallas opening]. Sd; b&w. 35mm. 80 min.

Prod James Ellsworth. *Exec Prod* Ludlow Flower. *Assoc Prod* William Mace. *Prod Adtl Material (see note)* Robert L. Lippert. *Dir* Bill Karn. *Screenplay* Cay Forester. *Adapt* Robert L. Joseph. *Story* Palmer Thompson. *Photog* Carl Guthrie. *Art Dir* Edwin Shields. *Set Decor* Harry Reif. *Film Ed* Donald Nosseck. *Mus* Gene Kauer. *Songs:* "Five Minutes To Live," "I've

Come To Kill" *Writ & Sung by* Johnny Cash. *Guitar Solo by* Merle Travis. *Sd* William Rivol, Dale Knight. *Asst Dir* Mac V. Wright, Nathan R. Barragar. *Makeup* Armand Del Mar. *Hairstyles* Scotty Rackin.

Cast: Johnny Cash *(Johnny Cabot),* Donald Woods *(Ken Wilson),* Cay Forester *(Nancy Wilson),* Pamela Mason *(Ellen),* Midge Ware *(Doris),* Victor Tayback *(Fred Dorella),* Ronny Howard *(Bobbie Wilson),* Merle Travis *(Max),* Howard Wright *(Pop),* Norma Varden *(Priscilla).*

Crime melodrama. Johnny Cabot, a fugitive from the law, settles in the small town of Camellia Gardens with his new girl friend Doris. There underworld crook Fred Dorella approaches Johnny with a plan for a bank holdup. Johnny learns from Fred that Doris had tipped off the police in his recent brush with the law, and he kills her. The two men move quickly to put their scheme into action: after watching bank executive Ken Wilson leave his house, Johnny gains entrance by posing as a door-to-door salesman; he takes Nancy, Ken's wife, hostage while at the bank Fred demands that Ken hand over $70,000 for Nancy's release. Ken, who is planning to leave Nancy for another woman, is tempted to refuse to give the hoodlum the cash, but he relents and pays the ransom. A bank guard recognizes Fred from a wanted poster and apprehends him; the police, aided by Ken, arrive in time to save Nancy; Johnny is killed in a shootout at the Wilson home; and Ken decides to remain with his wife. *Fugitives. Bankers. Hostages. Guards. Smalltown life. Murder. Extortion. Rape. Infidelity. Imposture.*

Note: Rereleased in Nov 1966 by American International Pictures as *Door-to-Door Maniac;* running time: 74 min. Robert L. Lippert added new footage, including a rape sequence, for this version.

5 MINUTES TO LOVE see THE ROTTEN APPLE

5 SINNERS (West Germany)   F6.1580
Rex Film–Bloemer & Co. *Dist* Astor Pictures. 17 May **1961** [New York showing]. Sd; b&w. 35mm. 80 min.

Prod Ernest Müller, August Rieger. *Dir* Wolfgang Glück. *Screenplay* Peter Loos, August Rieger, Wolfgang Glück. *Photog* Walter Tuch. *Art Dir* Felix Smetana. *Film Ed* Eleonore Kunze. *Mus* Carl Niessen. *Choreog* Ernesto Bittner.

Cast: Marina Petrowa *(Magali),* Pero Alexander *(Jussuf),* Jürg Holl *(Christian "Whisky" Peters),* Marisa Mell *(Liliane),* Loni von Friedl *(Inge),* Renate Rohm *(Doris),* Aina Capell *(Gerda),* Rolf Olsen *(Police Commissioner Elam),* Gerdina Gordon *(Vera),* Raoul Letzer, Guido Wieland, Erica Schramm, Peter Preses, Heinrich Trimbur, Wolf Harnisch, Angeles Durand, Camillo Felgen, The Nielsen Brothers.

Melodrama. Five German dancing girls, stranded in a small Turkish town, are required to strip as well as dance at the Silver Moon Nightclub. Liliane, one of the women, discovers that the club is being used by Magali, the proprietress, as the center of operations for a gang of jewel thieves. During a raid, Jussuf, the bouncer, in love with Liliane, tap-dances out a warning to the police. Christian "Whisky" Peters, their undercover detective, is also in love with Liliane, and he saves her in a chase through the sewers. The proprietress shoots the bouncer before killing herself. *Dancehall girls. Stripteasers. Nightclub owners. Thieves. Detectives. Bouncers. Murder. Suicide. Sewers. Turkey. Chases.*

Note: Released in West Germany in Jun 1959 as *Das Nachtlokal zum Silbermond;* running time: 90 min. Also known as *The Sinners.*

FIVE THE HARD WAY   F6.1581
Fantascope Corp. *Dist* Crown International Pictures. May **1969**. Sd; col (Eastman Color). 35mm (Fantascope). 82 min. *MPAA rating* R.

Prod Ross Hagen. *Exec Prod* Jon Hall. *Assoc Prod* Pat Somerset, Jerry Brutsche. *Dir* Gus Trikonis. *Screenplay* Tony Houston. *Story* Larry Billman. *Dir Photog* Jon Hall. *Film Ed* Pat Somerset. *Mus* Mike Curb, Jerry Styner, Guy Hemric. *Titl Song* Jerry Styner, Guy Hemric. *Perf by* The New Life. *Sd Ed* Norman Wallerstein, Billie Owens. *Mus Ed* Ed Norton. *Asst Dir* Tony Lorea. *Prod Mgr* E. J. Lidberg. *Script Supv* Rosemary Johnston. *Stunt Coörd* Erik Cord.

Cast: Ross Hagen *(Rommel),* Diane McBain *(Rita),* Michael Pataki *(J. C.),* Claire Polan *(Paisley),* Richard Merrifield *(Luke),* Edward Parrish *(Nero),* Michael Graham *(Cooch),* Hoke Howell *(Crapout),* Robert Tessier *(Jake),* Eric Lidberg *(Tork),* Erik Cord *(Dirty John),* Toni Moss *(Lois),* Diane Tessier *(Debbie),* Joey Tessier *(Billy),* Warren Hammack, Irv Ross *(mechanics),* Tony Lorea *(announcer).*

Action melodrama. After a weekend of grueling racing, sidehacker Rommel picnics with his fiancée, Rita. Exhibition racer J. C. and his gang visit the repair shop of Rommel and his best friend, Luke, where J. C. asks Rommel to join him on the circuit and is refused. Angered, J. C. attacks members of his gang. Sidehacker Nero goes to work in the repair shop, and Paisley, J. C.'s enraged girl friend, accuses the innocent Rommel of attempted rape. J. C. and his "boys" savagely beat Rommel and rape and murder Rita. Luke pleads with Rommel to seek police assistance, but Rommel refuses, and, accompanied by Nero, recruits sidehackers Jake and Crapout to help him. Although Rommel's gang is infiltrated by Cooch, the informer is seen sneaking away to report to J. C. and beaten in retaliation. While Luke seeks the police, Rommel's gang surrounds J. C.'s hideout. Cooch tries to warn J. C., who panics and, in the confusion, shoots and kills Cooch. Fighting erupts, leaving many members of both gangs dead. J. C. brawls with the wounded Rommel, then shoots him in the back. *Motorcycle gangs. Mechanics. Motorcycle racing. Rape. Revenge. Murder.*

Note: Title later changed to *The Sidehackers;* also reviewed as *The Side-Hackers.*

FIVE WEEKS IN A BALLOON   F6.1582

Cambridge Productions. *Dist* Twentieth Century–Fox Film Corp. 10 Aug **1962** [Denver, Colorado, opening; c10 Aug 1962; LP23137]. Sd (Westrex); col (De Luxe). 35mm. (CinemaScope). 101 min.

An Irwin Allen Production. *Prod-Dir* Irwin Allen. *Screenplay* Charles Bennett, Irwin Allen, Albert Gail. *Dir Photog* Winton Hoch. *Art Dir* Jack Martin Smith, Alfred Ybarra. *Prod Illustrator* Maurice Zuberano. *Set Decor* Walter M. Scott, Stuart A. Reiss, Norman Rockett. *Main Titl* Pacific Title. *Film Ed* George Boemler. *Mus* Paul Sawtell. *Orch* Sid Cutner, Max Reese. *Titl Song* Jodi Desmond. *Sung by* The Brothers Four, Fabian. *Sd* E. Clayton Ward, Warren B. Delaplain. *Asst Dir* Ad Schaumer. *Asst to Prod* Albert Gail. *Prod Mgr* William Eckhardt. *Cost Dsgn* Paul Zastupnevich. *Makeup* Ben Nye. *Hairstyles* Helen Turpin. *Sp Photog Eff* L. B. Abbott, Emil Kosa, Jr. *Tech Adv* Donald L. Piccard.

Cast: Red Buttons (*Donald O'Shay*), Fabian (*Jacques*), Barbara Eden (*Susan Gale*), Cedric Hardwicke (*Fergusson*), Peter Lorre (*Ahmed*), Richard Haydn (*Sir Henry Vining*), Barbara Luna (*Makia*), Billy Gilbert (*sultan-auctioneer*), Herbert Marshall (*prime minister*), Reginald Owen (*consul*), Henry Daniell (*Sheik Ageiba*), Mike Mazurki (*slave captain*), Alan Caillou (*inspector*), Ben Astar (*Myanga*), Raymond Bailey (*Randolph*), Chester the Chimp ("*The Duchess*").

Fantasy-comedy. Source: Jules Verne, *Cinq semaines en ballon; Voyage de découvertes en Afrique par trois Anglais* (Paris, 1863). In 1862, Fergusson, an engineer, is commissioned by the British government to fly his latest invention, a giant balloon carrying a gondola, 4,000 miles from Zanzibar into uncharted West Africa to claim the land around the Volta River for England. Time is of the essence, since a band of international slave traders is already pushing overland to claim the territory. Fergusson is accompanied by his young assistant, Jacques. In Zanzibar they are joined by Donald O'Shay, an American playboy reporter who will write an eyewitness account of the journey, and by a runaway female slave, Makia. Sir Henry Vining, president of the Royal Geographic Institute and debunker of the invention, is sent as the Queen's envoy to accompany them. Several days later, they rescue an American mission teacher, Susan Gale, from the clutches of a bulbous, drunken sultan, and take her aboard. Also on hand is a leering, cowardly Arab slave trader, Ahmed. When the balloon is forced down by a sandstorm, all except O'Shay are captured as infidels and ordered thrown from the tallest minaret in Timbuktu; but O'Shay arrives with the balloon and plucks them to safety. When they finally reach the Volta, the balloon collapses into the river just as the slave traders are approaching. O'Shay safely plants the flag for England, and Ahmed routs the traders by stopping their leader with a well-aimed dagger. With their mission accomplished, the adventurers shake hands on a job well done. *Adventurers. Balloonists. Inventors. Reporters. Playboys. Slaves—Runaway. Slavers. Royalty. Schoolteachers. British. Arabs. Americans in foreign countries. Imperialism. Balloons (ascent). Gondolas. British West Africa. Zanzibar. Timbuktu. Volta River. Chimpanzees.*

Note: Location scenes filmed in California.

FIVE WILD GIRLS (France)   F6.1583

Les Films du Griffon–Alcinter. *Dist* American Film Distributing Corp. 12 Aug **1966** [Los Angeles showing]. Sd; b&w. 35mm. 95 min.

Assoc Prod Jacques Garcia. *Dir* Max Pécas. *Scen* Louis Soulanes. *Dial* Louis Soulanes, Maurice Cury. *Adapt* Louis Soulanes, Maurice Cury, Robert Topart, Max Pécas. *Photog* Roger Duculot. *Mus* Georges Garvarentz. *Sd* Séverin Frankiel.

Cast for French release: Marc Bonseignour, Madeleine Constant, Nicole Mérouze, Denyse Roland, Marie-France Mignal, Michel Monfort, Colette Régis, Maria Tamar.

Cast Americanized for U. S. release: Jacqueline Wolff (*Isabel*), Jeannie Peterson (*Sylvia*), Felicia Andrews (*Jenny*), Anna Marie Shaw (*Agnes*), Susann Flynn (*Gladys*), Josell Como (*Grandmother*), Fred Thompson (*Blackie*), Michael Jameson (*George*).

Melodrama. An obscure, depressed mountain village becomes the scene of a violent struggle when three sisters and their two cousins converge to claim a fortune stashed away by their grandfather before his death. The grandmother has vowed never to divulge the hiding place of the fortune. Tension mounts as two of the sisters become romantically involved with two village men, and one of the girls is raped by her sister's lover. Eventually they all learn where the treasure is buried, and they clash at the site, only to learn that their energies have been wasted. *Grandfathers. Grandmothers. Sisters. Cousins. Village life. Greed. Rape. Treasure.*

Note: Originally released in France in 1964 as *Cinq filles en furie.* Also known as *Five Wild Kids.*

FIXATION see **THE SHE MAN**

THE FIXER   F6.1584

John Frankenheimer Productions–Edward Lewis Productions. *Dist* Metro-Goldwyn-Mayer, Inc. 8 Dec **1968** [New York opening; c30 Sep 1968; LP36143]. Sd; col (Metrocolor). 35mm. 132 min. [Cut from 150 min.] *MPAA rating* M.

Prod Edward Lewis. *Assoc Prod* Enrico Isacco. *Dir* John Frankenheimer. *Screenplay* Dalton Trumbo. *Dir Photog* Marcel Grignon. *2d Unit Camera* André Domage, Iván Lakatos. *Art Dir* Béla Zeichán. *Film Ed* Henry Berman. *Mus Comp & Cond* Maurice Jarre. *Violin Solo by* Zina Schiff. *Choreog* Ágnes Roboz. *Sd Engr* Tom Overton. *Rec Supv* Franklin Milton. *Asst Dir* Gyula Kormos. *Unit Prod Mgr* Eugene Nase, Dezső Jutasi. *Prod Sec* Beatrix Varga. *Cont* Lucie Lichtig. *Cost Dsgn* Dorothy Jeakins. *Wardrobe Supv* Gladys de Segonzac. *Makeup* Kenneth Lintott. *Hairstyles* Kitty Hermann. *Coöp* Hungarofilm, Mafilm Studios. *Ch Electrn* Béla Bolykovasky. *Prop* Frank Agnone.

Cast: Alan Bates (*Yakov Bok*), Dirk Bogarde (*Bibikov*), Georgia Brown (*Marfa Golov*), Hugh Griffith (*Lebedev*), Elizabeth Hartman (*Zinaida Lebedev*), Ian Holm (*Grubeshov*), David Opatoshu (*Latke*), David Warner (*Count Odoevsky*), Carol White (*Raisl Bok*), George Murcell (*deputy warden*), Murray Melvin (*priest*), Peter Jeffrey (*Berezhinsky*), Michael Goodliffe (*Ostrovsky*), Thomas Heathcote (*Proshko*), Mike Pratt (*Father Anastasy*), Stanley Meadows (*Gronfein*), Francis De Wolff (*warden*), David Lodge (*Zhitnyak*), William Hutt (*The Tzar*), Norbert Viszlay (*Zhenia*), Roy Sone (*Akimytch*), Alfie Bass (*Potseikin*), Michael Balfour (*boatman*), Danny Green (*giggler*), Helen Dowling (*Negro page*).

Drama. Source: Bernard Malamud, *The Fixer* (New York, 1966). Yakov Bok, an educated but impoverished Jew in tzarist Russia, is deserted by Raisl, his unfaithful wife, and leaves his small farm and travels to Kiev. It is during the time of the pogroms, and Yakov poses as a gentile, taking a job as a handyman to Lebedev, an alcoholic, anti-Semitic merchant. Yakov refuses to be seduced by Lebedev's crippled daughter Zinaida, and the hysterical girl tries unsuccessfully to accuse him of rape. Despite this threat to his job, Yakov's intelligence keeps him in good standing with Lebedev, and he is promoted to factory overseer-accountant. Yakov alienates the foreman, Proshko, and is plagued by the bothersome neighborhood boys. When one of the boys is brutally murdered, the superstitious people believe the killing to be a "ritual murder" perpetrated by the Jews. Yakov, whose true background has been discovered, is arrested and treated as a convicted murderer, although no specific charges are made. His only ally is Bibikov, a government attorney who realizes the state hopes to get a confession from Yakov in order to indict the whole Jewish population. Bibikov suspects that the dead boy was slain by his mother's lover, and when he begins to probe into the case more deeply, his "suicide" is quickly arranged. As time passes, the imprisoned Yakov suffers indignities and torture but refuses to confess. Eventually, as he grows stronger in his determination, his case attracts international concern, and the tzar is forced to schedule a formal trial. Three years after his arrest, as Yakov arrives for his trial, he is acclaimed a hero by the crowd. *Jews. Handymen. Merchants. Cripples. Accountants. Shop foremen. Lawyers. Children. Anti-Semitism. Infidelity. Imposture. Alcoholism. Rape. Murder. Superstition. Ritual murder. Torture. Heroism. Pogroms. Prisons. Factories. Trials. Kiev. Nicholas II (Russia).*

Note: Location scenes filmed entirely in Budapest.

THE FLAMBOYANT SEX (Sweden)   F6.1585

Ann Burman–Anders Aspegren. *Dist* Shawn International, Inc., Albex Films, Haven International Pictures. 19 Apr **1963** [New York opening: 12 Aug]. Sd; b&w. 35mm. 76 min.

Pres by Alexander Beck. *Prod* Ann Burman, Anders Aspegren, Gustav Mandal. *Dir-Dial* Barbro Boman. *Screenplay* Peter Weiss. *Photog* Gustav Mandal. *Mus* Martial Solal. *Orch* Barel Coppet. *Sd* Herman Dahl. *Asst Dir* Staffan Lamm. *Prod Mgr* Christer Christian, Anne Marie Monfors. *Tech Asst* Bengt Tornkrantz.

Cast: Anita Lindoff (*Barbara*), Maud Elfusjö (*Lena*), Ulla Blomstrand (*Marianne*), Gösto Alm, Bernard Vincent, Alice Reichen, Bernard Fresson, Bill Hall, Katherine Kath, Regine Landeau.

Romantic melodrama. The glamour of Paris attracts Barbara, Lena and Marianne, three Swedish girls, to the city. Barbara and Lena are roommates in a run-down building. Short of funds and in debt for rent because her parents stopped her allowance when she neglected her studies, Barbara poses nude for an art class. She goes to bed with a young Frenchman who leaves her after a brief affair. Lena loses her job as a babysitter and seeks help from her friend, Marianne, who is unable to aid her. Determined to remain in Paris under any conditions, Lena accepts a job in a laundry. When she returns home in the evening she finds that Barbara has spent what little money they had on a scarf to hide a bruise on her neck that was inflicted by her lover. Furious, Lena goes for a walk, meets some jazz musicians, and goes dancing with them. This is the Paris she loves. Meanwhile, Marianne and her French lover, who have been eking out a living pasting up posters, decide to leave the city for a new life in the country. Barbara, also disillusioned, leaves Paris—as yet another Swedish girl arrives in the city of dreams. *Students. Models. Laundresses. Babysitters. Roommates. Musicians. Nudity. Seduction. Disillusionment. Urban life. Employment—Women. Cafes. Paris.*

Note: Filmed in France in 1960. Released in Sweden in 1962 as *Svenska flickor i Paris* at 78 min. Also known as *The Flamboyants* and *Les femmes flamboyantes.*

THE FLAME see **GIRLS WITHOUT ROOMS**

FLAME AND THE FIRE   F6.1586

Dist Continental Distributing, Inc. Feb **1966**. Sd; col (Eastmancolor). 35mm. 80 min.

Prod Vernon P. Becker, Mitchell R. Leiser. *Assoc Prod* Mel May. *Dir* Pierre Dominique Gaisseau. *Writ Comm* Charles Romine. *Photog* Jens Bjerre. *Adtl Photog* Jorgen Bitsch, James Bruce, Jean Fichter, Chris Hansen, Arvid Klemensen, Victor Petrashevic, Peter Rassmussen, Harald Schultz, Pierre Dominique Gaisseau. *Film Ed* Robert Farren. *Mus Comp & Cond* Michael Colicchio. *Pygmy Mus* M. Asch. *Mus Cons* Kenn Collins. *Sd* Morton Schwartz. *Sd Ed* Kenn Collins. *Location Sd* Hervé de Maigret, Carina Gaisseau. *Prod Coörd* Egon C. Nielsen.

Narrator: Pierre Dominique Gaisseau.

Documentary. Filmed in the remote jungles and outlands of Brazil, Australia, Africa, and New Guinea, this film depicts social and religious practices among little-known tribes. Foremost among these are: the Gourd Men of New Guinea, who wear gourds on their genitals as symbols of both tribal and agricultural fertility; the Kukukuku, also of New Guinea, a cannibalistic tribe who smoke-cure their dead; the Suza tribe of Brazil, whose married males wear wooden discs as large as 6 inches in diameter in their lower lips and also make a concoction similar to DDT to drug and catch fish; and the Wailbri tribe of Australia. Also shown are African Pygmies, the towering Masai, and the vanishing Auen tribe of the Kalahari Desert. *Kukukuku. Bushmen. Masai. Suza. Wailbri. Auen. Pygmies. Primitive life. Rites and ceremonies. Cannibalism. Jungles. Brazil. Australia. Africa. New Guinea. Kalahari Desert.*

FLAME IN THE STREETS (Great Britain)   F6.1587

Somerset Films–Rank Organisation. *Dist* Atlantic Pictures, National Showmanship Films. 12 Sep **1962** [New York opening]. Sd; b&w (see note). 35mm (CinemaScope). 93 min.

A Roy [Ward] Baker Production. *Prod-Dir* Roy [Ward] Baker. *Assoc Prod* Jack Hanbury. *Screenplay* Ted Willis. *Photog* Christopher Challis. *Art Dir* Alex Vetchinsky. *Film Ed* Roger Cherrill. *Mus & Mus Dir* Philip Green. *Sd* Harry Miller. *Sd Rec* Dudley Messenger, Gordon K. McCallum.

Cast: John Mills *(Jacko Palmer)*, Sylvia Syms *(Kathie Palmer)*, Brenda De Banzie *(Nell Palmer)*, Johnny Sekka *(Peter Lincoln)*, Ann Lynn *(Judy Gomez)*, Earl Cameron *(Gabriel Gomez)*, Wilfrid Brambell *(Mr. Palmer, Sr.)*, Meredith Edwards *(Harry Mitchell)*, Newton Blick *(Visser)*, Glyn Houston *(Hugh Davies)*, Michael Wynne *(Les)*, Dan Jackson *(Jubilee)*, Cyril Chamberlain *(James Dowell)*, Gretchen Franklin *(Mrs. Bingham)*, Harry Baird *(Billy)*.

Drama. Source: Ted Willis, *Hot Summer Night* (London opening: 26 Nov 1958). Jacko Palmer, a skilled craftsman in a London factory, prides himself on his fairminded attitude toward the firm's Negro employees and is their staunch defender at union meetings. Then one night he learns that his schoolmistress daughter, Kathie, plans to marry a young Jamaican, Peter Lincoln, also a schoolteacher. Jacko's wife, Nell, is violently opposed to the match, and she persuades him to call on Peter to argue him out of the marriage. But the lovers are adamant and are fully prepared to face their difficult future. Meanwhile, a disturbance is being created on the streets by some white hoodlums menacing Jamaicans. During the rioting, one of Jacko's Negro coworkers, Gabe Gomez, is pushed into a Guy Fawkes Night bonfire and badly burned. Chastened by the experience, Jacko takes Kathie and Peter home, and after a reconciliation with Nell, the family decides to face the situation together. *Factory workers. Jamaicans. Negroes. Schoolteachers. Hoodlums. Filial relations. Racial prejudice. Race relations. Miscegenation. Riots. Fires. Guy*

Fawkes Day. London.

Note: Opened in London in Jun 1961 in Eastman Color.

FLAME OVER VIETNAM (Spain/West Germany)   F6.1588

Westside International–UFA. *Dist* Producers Releasing Organization. Apr **1967**. Sd; b&w. 35mm. 88 min.

Pres by Sidney Pink. *Prod* Sidney Pink. *Dir* Joe Lacy. *Screenplay* Ralph Salvia, Joe Lacy, John Hart. *Story* Ralph Salvia. *Photog* Miguel F. Mila. *Film Ed* Félix Suárez. *Mus* Fernando García Morcillo. *Song:* "Mon amour, mon amour" Genaro Camilo Murillo. *Sung by* María Martín. *Asst Dir* Augusto Fenollar.

Cast: Elena Barrios *(Sister Paula)*, José Nieto *(Lazlo)*, Manolo Morán *(Brother Bartholomew)*, Nicolas Perchicot *(Father Elias)*, Rosita Palomar *(Selma)*, Félix Dafauce *(Ellison)*, María Martín *(Angela)*, Vicente P. Avila *(driver)*.

War drama. During the French-Indochina War, Lazlo, a wounded gunrunner, takes refuge at a Catholic mission, where he is nursed back to health by Sister Paula. Shortly after Lazlo's recovery and departure, the mission is overrun by enemy forces. Fleeing, Sister Paula and a band of orphaned children encounter Lazlo, who takes them in his ammunition truck to a railway depot. Stopped at a checkpoint on a train bound for Saigon, the children are forbidden to continue their journey because they are citizens of the state. Refusing to abandon her wards, Sister Paula accompanies them to a concentration camp. Lazlo, having chartered an airplane, bribes a guard and arranges for the release of Sister Paula and the children. Although Lazlo rescues a girl left behind in the confusion, he is killed by a sniper's bullet while attempting to lift himself aboard the plane. *Gunrunners. Nuns. Orphans. War victims. Catholics. Rescue. Self-sacrifice. Missions. Trains. Concentration camps. Airplanes. French-Indochina War 1945–54. Saigon.*

Note: West German coproduction status unconfirmed. Joe Lacy is a pseudonym for José María Elorrieta; Ralph Salvia is the anglicized name of Rafael Salvia.

THE FLAMING CITY   F6.1589

Dist Film-Makers' Cooperative. 14 Jun **1965** [New York opening]. Sd; col. 16mm. 135 min.

Dir Dick Higgins.

Drama. Although no information about the precise nature of this film has been found, sources suggest that its setting is New York, which, with its inhabitants, is either symbolically or literally destroyed. *Urban life. New York City.*

FLAMING CREATURES   F6.1590

Dist Film-Makers' Cooperative. 7 Dec **1963** [New York opening]. Sd; b&w. 16mm. 45 min.

A Film by Jack Smith.

Cast: Francis Francine, Delores Flores, Joel Markman, Shirley.

Satire. In the languid atmosphere of an orgy that has run its course, an assortment of young men and women whose gender is in many cases obscured by their costumes, lounge about in a loft decorated with drapes, cushions, and a palm tree; an atmosphere of exoticism prevails. The costumes, representative of such stereotypes as the sultry vamp, the Spanish dancer, and the vampire, are highlighted by flowers, beads, and feathers. The heavily made-up characters stare at one another, toy with each other's bodies, fondle their own sex organs, dance the fandango, embrace, rape one of their number, yelp and shriek, pose for the camera, recline on divans or the floor, and caricature various Hollywood stars. Heard on the soundtrack are bits of dialogue from Hollywood films and a selection of sentimental popular music. *Hollywood. Transvestism. Female impersonation. Orgies. Exhibitionism. Male homosexuality. Fetishism. Hedonism. Rape.*

Note: Filmed in New York City. Delores Flores is a pseudonym for Mario Montez.

FLAMING DESIRE see **THE SMALL HOURS**

FLAMING FRONTIER (West Germany/Yugoslavia)   F6.1591

Rialto Film–Jadran Film. *Dist* Warner Bros.–Seven Arts, Inc. Feb **1968** [c1 Feb 1968; LP40877]. Sd; col (Eastman Color). 35mm (Ultrascope). 93 min.

A Horst Wendlandt–Preben Philipsen Production. *Prod* Wolfgang Kühnlenz. *Exec Prod* Horst Wendlandt. *Dir* Alfred Vohrer. *Screenplay* Fred Denger. *Screenplay Collab* Johanna Sibelius, Eberhard Keindorff. *Dir Photog* Karl Löb. *Art Dir* Vladimir Tadej. *Film Ed* Hermann Haller. *Mus Comp* Martin Böttcher. *Sd* Matija Barbalić. *Asst Dir* Eva-Ruth Ebner. *Prod Supv* Erwin Gitt. *Prod Mgr* Stipe Gurdulić, Herbert Kerz, Wolfgang Hantke. *Cost* Irms Pauli. *Sp Eff* Erwin Lange.

Cast: Stewart Granger *(Old Surehand)*, Pierre Brice *(Winnetou)*, Leticia Roman *(Judith)*, Larry Pennell *(The General)*, Mario Girotti *(Toby)*, Erik Schuman *(Captain Miller)*, Wolfgang Lukschy *(Judge Edwards)*, Paddy Fox

(Jeremy Wabble), Aleksandar Gavrić, Voja Mirić, Dušan Janićijević, Dušan Antonijević, Vladimir Hedar, Hermina Pipinić, Jelena Jovanović, Bata Živojinović.

Western melodrama. Source: Karl Friedrich May, *Old Surehand* (Freiburg im Breisgau, 1894). Having searched 3 years for his brother's murderer, Western frontiersman Old Surehand rescues the surviving passengers of a mail train robbed by a gang of desperadoes led by the General. To divert attention from the holdup, the General's men slaughter buffalo in Comanche territory; and, when they slay the son of a chief, the Indians threaten war. Surehand tries to prevent an Indian uprising by visiting his blood brother, Winnetou, a young Apache chief. After the General kills a prospector and steals his map to a gold mine, the prospector's niece, Judith, and her lawyer fiancé, Toby, look for the mine. Captured by the Comanches, they are released when Surehand vows to find the chieftain's son's murderer. Old friend Jeremy Wabble tells Surehand that the General is responsible for his brother's death. Surehand escapes from a trap set by the General, then ambushes the General's men with soldiers from a nearby fort. The General flees to an abandoned mine shaft, but Surehand, assisted by Wabble, finds and kills him in a gunfight. Peace restored, Surehand gives Judith and Toby a wedding present—the missing map. *Desperadoes. Comanche Indians. Blood brothers. Apache Indians. Prospectors. Lawyers. Revenge. Murder. Frontier and pioneer life. Train robberies. Gold mines. Documentation. Winnetou. Buffalo.*

Note: Location scenes filmed in Yugoslavia. Released in West Germany in Dec 1965 as *Old Surehand, I. teil*; in Yugoslavia in 1966 as *Lavirint smrti*.

FLAMMAN *see* **GIRLS WITHOUT ROOMS**

FLAP   **F6.1592**
Warner Bros. Pictures. 19 Nov **1970** [Albuquerque, New Mexico, opening; c24 Apr 1970; LP42628]. Sd; col (Technicolor). 35mm (Panavision). 106 min. *MPAA rating GP.*

Prod Jerry Adler. *Dir* Carol Reed. *2d Unit Dir* William Kronick. *Screenplay* Clair Huffaker. *Photog* Fred Koenekamp. *Camera Op* George Nogle, Charles G. Arnold. *Asst Camera* Ron Vargas, Richard Doran, Charles Termini, Rowland S. Smith. *2d Unit Photog* Harold Wellman. *Art Dir* Mort Rabinowitz. *Set Decor* Ralph S. Hurst. *Prod Dsgn* Art Loel. *Film Ed* Frank Bracht. *Asst Ed* Roy Urbach. *Mus* Marvin Hamlisch. *Song:* "If Nobody Loves" Marvin Hamlisch, Estelle Levitt. *Sung by* Kenny Rogers and the First Edition. *Sd* Al Overton, Sr.. *Rec* George Hause. *Boom Op* Jerry Smith. *Asst Dir* Reggie Callow, Alan Callow, Jim Paisley. *Prod Supv* Milton Feldman. *Prod Mgr* Carter DeHaven, Jr.. *Script Supv* Karen Wookey. *Cost* Oscar Rodriguez, Ann Helfgott. *Wardrobe* Alex D'Alessio, Danny Chichester. *Makeup* Michael Hancock. *Hairstyles* Naomi Cavin. *Still Photog* John Monte, Bernard Abramson. *Constr Coörd* Fred Collins. *Animal Trainer* Bobby Davenport.

Cast: Anthony Quinn *(Flapping Eagle)*, Claude Akins *(Lobo Jackson)*, Tony Bill *(Eleven Snowflake)*, Victor Jory *(Wounded Bear Mr. Smith)*, Don Collier *(Mike Lyons)*, Shelley Winters *(Dorothy Bluebell)*, Susana Miranda *(Ann Looking Deer)*, Victor French *(Rafferty)*, Rodolfo Acosta *(Storekeep)*, Anthony Caruso *(Silver Dollar)*, William Mims *(Steve Gray)*, Rudy Diaz *(Larry Standing Elk)*, Pedro Regas *(She'll-Be-Back-Pretty-Soon)*, J. Edward McKinley *(Harris)*, Robert Cleaves *(Gus Kirk)*, John War Eagle *(Luke Wolf)*.

Comedy-drama. Source: Clair Huffaker, *Nobody Loves a Drunken Indian* (New York, 1967). Flap, a hard-drinking Indian who lives on an impoverished reservation in the Southwest, is in a constant state of anger over the mistreatment of his tribe. Moreover, he argues incessantly with his mistress Dorothy Bluebell, the madam of the local brothel who resents his unfaithfulness to her. Flap gets drunk one night and commandeers and destroys a bulldozer belonging to a road construction company which is encroaching on the reservation. Flap's act, intended to attract attention to the Indians' cause, results in a heated dispute between Flap and his longtime enemy, Rafferty, a halfbreed and the town's brutal police sergeant. Wounded Bear Mr. Smith, a crony of Flap's and a self-made lawyer who is an expert on Indian treaties, advises Flap that anything abandoned on an Indian reservation becomes Indian property, whereupon Flap and his friends steal a train and roll it onto the reservation, intending to claim it as Indian property. This daring act is noticed by the news services, whose representatives soon arrive at the reservation looking for Flap; but he is hiding out in the mountains, regrouping his forces for a protest march on the town. They parade down Main Street in an attempt to make people see the Indians' plight. Rafferty, in the hospital recovering from a beating he received from Flap because he maliciously caused a comrade of Flap's to suffer a fatal heart attack by cold-bloodedly shooting the man's dog, sees the protest march and from his hospital window assassinates the Indian leader as he speaks in the town square. *Indians of North America. Madams. Lawyers. Halfcastes. Police. Reporters. Alcoholism. Poverty. Theft. Publicity. Jealousy. Social reform. Assassination. Trains. Bulldozers. Heart disease. Treaties. Demonstrations.*

Note: Location scenes filmed in New Mexico. Prerelease titles: *Nobody Loves a Drunken Indian* and *Nobody Loves Flapping Eagle.*

FLAREUP   **F6.1593**
GMF Picture Corp. *Dist* Metro-Goldwyn-Mayer, Inc. 10 Nov **1969** [New York opening; c1 Oct 1969; LP37153]. Sd (Westrex); col (Metrocolor). 35mm. 98 min. *MPAA rating M.*

Prod Leon Fromkess. *Assoc Prod* Erna Lazarus. *Dir* James Neilson. *Writ* Mark Rodgers. *Photog* Andrew McIntyre. *Art Dir* Frank Sylos. *Set Decor* Ralph Sylos. *Titl Dsgn & Dir* Don Record. *Film Ed* Aaron Stell. *Mus Comp & Cond* Les Baxter. *Titl Song* Les Baxter, Lenny Adelson. *Sd* Robert Martin. *Mus Rec* Kevin Cleary. *Re-rec* Clem Portman. *Sd Eff Ed* Eugene Eliot. *Mus Ed* Carlo Lodato. *Asst Dir* Gilbert Mandelik, Jack R. Berne. *Prod Coörd* Herbert G. Luft. *Script Supv* H. Bud Otto. *Men's Cost* Frank Tauss. *Ladies' Cost* Marjorie Plecher, Gwen Fitzer. *Makeup Artists* Bob Stein, makeup, Bruce Hutchinson. *Hairstyles* Janice D. Brunson. *Dial Dir* Rita Minton. *Ch Electrn* Robert R. Farmer. *Head Grip* Lawrence Milton. *Prop Master* Irving Sindler.

Cast: Raquel Welch *(Michele)*, James Stacy *(Joe Brodnek)*, Luke Askew *(Alan Morris)*, Don Chastain *(Lieutenant Manion)*, Ron Rifkin *("Sailor")*, Jean Byron *(Jerri Benton)*, Kay Peters *(Lee)*, Pat Delany *(Iris)*, Sandra Giles *(Nikki)*, Joe Billings *(Lloyd Seibert)*, Carol-Jean Thompson *(Jackie)*, Mary Wilcox *(Tora)*, Carl Byrd *(Sergeant Newcomb)*, Steve Conte *(Lieutenant Franklin)*, Tom Fadden *(Mr. Willows)*, Michael Rougas *(Dr. Connors)*, David Moses *(technician)*, Will J. White *(Sergeant Stafford)*, Doug Rowe *(gas station attendant)*, Gordon Jump *(security guard)*, Ike Williams *(policeman)*, The Gazzari Dancers.

Melodrama. Alan Morris, distraught over the failure of his marriage, shoots his estranged wife, Nikki, a Las Vegas go-go dancer, and vows to kill Michele and Iris, Nikki's dance partners, whom he blames for his marriage breakup. He seeks out Michele and Iris as they leave the hospital where Nikki has died and runs over Iris and the police officer assigned to protect the two women. Terrified, Michele leaps into her car and flees to Los Angeles. There she finds a job at the Loser's Club and strikes up an acquaintance with Joe, the club's parking lot attendant. Alan learns of Michele's whereabouts, hitchhikes to Los Angeles, murders the man from whom he accepted the ride and steals his car, and begins stalking Michele, who, by now, has moved into Joe's apartment. After a final narrow escape in which the police arrive as Alan corners Michele at the zoo, he confronts her in Joe's apartment. His plan is to kill her after forcing her to witness Joe's murder. Minutes before Joe arrives, Michele breaks free, douses Alan with kerosene, and sets him on fire. *Go-go dancers. Psychopaths. Police. Hitchhikers. Murder. Marriage. Theft. Nightclubs. Las Vegas. Los Angeles. Chases.*

Note: Filmed largely on location in Las Vegas and Los Angeles. Also known as *Flare Up* and *Flare-Up.*

THE FLAVOR OF GREEN TEA OVER RICE *see* **TEA AND RICE**

A FLEA IN HER EAR (United States/France)   **F6.1594**
Twentieth Century-Fox Film Corp. Oct **1968** [New York opening: 27 Nov; c23 Oct 1968; LP36282]. Sd (Westrex); col (DeLuxe). 35mm (Panavision). 94 min.

A Fred Kohlmar Production. *Prod* Fred Kohlmar. *Dir* Jacques Charon. *2d Unit Dir* Noel Howard. *Screenplay* John Mortimer. *Dir Photog* Charles Lang. *Dir Photog 2d Unit* Walter Wottitz. *Camera Op* Henri Tiquet. *Art Dir* Auguste Capelier. *Set Decor* Maurice Barnathan, Pierre Charron. *Prod Dsgn* Alexander Trauner. *Film Ed* Walter Thompson. *Mus Comp* Bronislaw Kaper. *Mus Cond* Lionel Newman. *Titl Song* Bronislaw Kaper, Sammy Cahn. *Sung by* Claudine Longet. *Orch* Herbert Spencer. *Sd* Joseph de Bretagne, David Dockendorf. *Asst Dir* Paul Feyder. *Prod Mgr* Christian Ferry. *Cost* André Levasseur. *Makeup Artist for Rex Harrison* Marvin Westmore. *Makeup Artist* Alberto De Rossi. *Hairstyles for Miss Harris and Miss Roberts* Alexandre of Paris. *Hairstylists* Grazia De Rossi, Denise Lemoigne. *Sp Eff* Robert MacDonald. *Dial Coach* Frawley Becker.

Cast: Rex Harrison *(Victor Chandebisse/Poche)*, Rosemary Harris *(Gabrielle Chandebisse)*, Louis Jourdan *(Henri)*, Rachel Roberts *(Suzanne)*, John Williams *(Dr. Finache)*, Gregoire Aslan *(Max)*, Edward Hardwicke *(Pierre)*, Georges Descrières *(Don Carlos de Castilian)*, Isla Blair *(Antoinette)*, Frank Thornton *(Charles)*, Victor Sen-Yung *(Oke Saki)*, Laurence Badie *(Eugénie)*, Dominique Davray *(Olympe)*, Olivier Hussenot *(Uncle Louis)*, Estella Blain *(defendant)*, Moustache *(fat man)*, David Horne *(prosecutor)*, Roger Carel *(taxi driver)*.

Farce. Source: John Mortimer, *A Flea in Her Ear* (London opening: 1966). Georges Feydeau, *La puce à l'oreille* (Paris opening: 2 Mar 1907). Victor Chandebisse, an elegant barrister in the Paris of 1900, is shocked into impotency on his ninth wedding anniversary when his wife, Gabrielle, tells him that they "now have each other forever." Gabrielle's subsequent suspicions that her husband has been philandering are confirmed when a pair of his suspenders are returned from the Hotel Coq d'Or, a notorious house of assignation. (Actually, the suspenders were left there by Pierre, Victor's libertine nephew-assistant.) In an attempt to trap her husband, Gabrielle permits her childhood friend Suzanne, the wife of an insatiable and jealous South American, Don Carlos de Castilian, to write an anonymous note to Victor asking him to meet her at the hotel. Although intrigued, Victor passes the note on to his friend Henri Tournel, a man considered quite attractive by Gabrielle. When Don Carlos sees the note and recognizes Suzanne's handwriting, he sets out after her, with Victor in pursuit in order to warn Henri. At the hotel, which features an elaborate revolving bed designed to "defeat the forces of morality," all of the concerned parties converge in a welter of mistaken identities, flying bullets, and impending adultery, made only more confusing by Poche, a porter who looks exactly like Victor. Eventually, everyone returns unharmed to the Chandebisse home, where the real identity of Victor and Poche is determined, and Suzanne is reunited with Don Carlos. Victor and Gabrielle return to the Hotel Coq d'Or to become the first wedded couple ever to use the establishment's revolving bed. *Barristers. South Americans. Porters. Marriage. Infidelity. Friendship. Jealousy. Doubles. Hotels. Paris.*

Note: Opened in Paris in Nov 1968 as *La puce à l'oreille.* Location scenes filmed in France.

DIE FLEDERMAUS (Austria)   F6.1595

Sascha-Film. *Dist* Casino Films, United Film Enterprises. 7 Feb **1964** [New York opening]. Sd; col (Eastmancolor). 35mm. 107 min.

Prod (see note) Herbert Gruber, Karl Schwetter. *Dir-Script* Geza von Cziffra. *Dir Photog* Willy Winterstein. *Camera* Hans Jura. *Asst Camera* Helmut Bahr. *Sets* Fritz Jüptner-Jonstorff, Alexander Sawczynski. *Film Ed* Arnd Heyne. *Asst Ed* Elfriede Pröll. *Mus Adapt* Erich Becht. *Mus Dir & Lyr* Kurt Feltz. *Choreog* Willy Dirtl. *Sd* Rolf Schmidt-Gentner. *Asst Dir* Margrith Spitzer. *Prod Mgr* Fred Kollhanek, Otto Dworak, Alois Bednar. *Cost* Paul Seltenhammer, Gudrun Hildebrandt. *Wardrobe* Karl Hermann, Karl Ullmann, Trude Vogel. *Makeup* Felix Wurzel, Leo Umyssa, Stefan Kulhanek, Frieda Jungwirth. *Prop* Josef Rücker. *Still Photog* Hermann Meroth, Karlheinz Vogelmann.

Cast: Peter Alexander *(Dr. Gabriel Eisenstein)*, Marianne Koch *(Rosalinde, his wife)*, Marika Rökk *(Adele, her maid)*, Boy Gobert *(Prince Orlofsky)*, Hans Moser *(Frosch)*, Willy Millowitsch *(Frank)*, Gunther Philipp *(Pista von Bundassy)*, Oskar Sima *(Basil Arabayam)*, Susi Nicoletti *(Baroness Martens)*, Rolf Kutschera *(Alfred)*, Rudolf Carl *(Joseph)*, Carl Gernbach *(Gigerl)*, Ellen Umlauf *(young lady in prison)*, Johannes Roth *(fat vagabond)*.

With the participation of: Vienna State Opera Ballet, Vienna Volksopera Ballet, Kurt Edelhagen Orchestra.

Musical comedy. Source: Johann Strauss, *Die Fledermaus* (first performance: Vienna, 5 Apr 1874). Henri Meilhac and Ludovic Halévy, *Le réveillon* (Paris, 1874). In turn-of-the-century Vienna, the highlight of the season is the ball given by Prince Orlofsky. Pista von Bundassy, the Prince's friend, plans to use the ball to get even with his friend, the attorney Dr. Eisenstein, for a trick Eisenstein played on Bundassy at a carnival to which Bundassy came disguised as a bat. Bundassy arranges for Eisenstein to attend the prince's ball as "Marquis Renard." Bundassy and Basil Arabayam, one of Eisenstein's clients, also plan to trick the prince into selling or giving away some of his oil-rich land in Russia. To do this, they have invited "Marquise Renard" to the ball, who to Eisenstein's annoyance, turns out to be his own maid, Adele. Eisenstein's suspicious wife, Rosalinde, also attends the ball, disguised as Sonja Kowarowska, a famous Russian dancer. Rosalinde is kept busy trying to keep an eye on her husband while warding off the advances of Prince Orlofsky. The intrigues and counter-intrigues turn what started out as a harmless prank into a scandal which threatens to wreck the Eisenstein marriage. The generous Prince Orlofsky cleverly straightens things out, thereby assuring a happy ending. *Royalty. Lawyers. Housemaids. Practical jokes. Scandal. Marriage. Flirtation. Jealousy. Masquerades. Oil lands. Vienna.*

Note: Released in Austria in 1962. U.S. sources credit Herbert Gruber as producer, while sources abroad credit Karl Schwetter.

FLESH   F6.1596

Factory Films–Score Productions. *Dist* Sherpix, Inc. 26 Sep **1968** [New York opening; c26 Sep 1968; LP37571]. Sd; col (Eastmancolor). 35mm. 105 min.

An Andy Warhol Production. *Prod* Andy Warhol. *Dir-Writ* Paul Morrissey. *Photog* Paul Morrissey.

Cast: Joe Dallesandro *(Joe)*, Geraldine Smith *(Gerry)*, John Christian *(young man)*, Maurice Bardell *(artist)*, Barry Brown *(boy on street)*, Candy Darling *(blonde on sofa)*, Jackie Curtis *(redhead on sofa)*, Geri Miller *(Terry)*, Louis Waldon *(David)*, Patti D'Arbanville *(Gerry's girl friend)*.

Drama. Joe lives in the East Village with his wife and son, supporting them by working the streets of lower New York City as a hustler. A friend of Joe's wife needs $200 for an abortion, and Joe agrees to raise the money. He earns $20 for submitting to a shy homosexual and is then approached by an elderly English artist. The man takes Joe to his studio, paying him $100 to model and pose. Joe next meets other hustlers on the street, and he offers some advice on the trade. An old friend, Terry, works as a topless dancer and lives with two transvestites. Joe listens to the "women" read from a vintage movie magazine while Terry performs fellatio on him. An old acquaintance takes Joe home and tries to elicit some reassurance of his heterosexuality, but he ends up giving Joe some money. Joe finally returns home, tells his wife and her friend that he was unable to raise the needed stake, and suffers their abusive comments on his occupation. Exhausted, Joe lies down on the bed, and while the two women caress each other, he falls asleep. *Prostitutes. Artists. English. Models. Go-go dancers. Abortion. Male homosexuality. Transvestism. Prostitution. Oral sex. Lesbianism. New York City—Lower East Side.*

FLESH AND LACE   F6.1597

Longhouse Productions. *Dist* Rossmore Film Distributors, Boxoffice International Film Distributors, Amalfi Films. caDec **1965** [New York showing]. Sd; b&w. 35mm. 80 min.

A Joe Sarno Production. *Dir-Writ* Joe Sarno.

Cast: Tammy Latour *(Bev)*, Mike Higgins *(Dop)*, Jan Nash *(Joan)*, Phil Mason *(Rook)*, Judy Young.

Melodrama. Bev and Joan work together as drink hustlers in a strip club owned by Dop, a hoodlum. Joan's old boyfriend Rook returns to town to pay a gambling debt he owes Dop, and he moves into the apartment shared by the girls. Soon afterwards, Dop fires Bev, claiming she is naive, and Rook seduces her. When Joan discovers the furtive romance, she beats her rival unmercifully and throws her out of the house. Dejected, Bev remembers a toy shop where her spirits were lifted after she lost her job. She goes there again, and Julian, the amiable owner, offers her shelter. He grows to love her, but he cannot satisfy her boundless sexual desires. Reluctantly, he procures male companions for her so that he can confine her nymphomania under his protective eye. Rook, in need of money to again pay off Dop, takes Joan's gun without her knowledge and breaks into the toy store. Joan follows him to prevent him from using the gun, but it is too late. She is killed in an exchange of gunfire and Rook is mortally wounded, leaving Bev stunned but safe in Julian's arms. *Bar girls. Roommates. Hoodlums. Storekeepers. Gamblers. Pimps. Nymphomania. Infidelity. Seduction. Robbery. Debt. Nightclubs. Toys.*

Note: Also known as *Fresh & Lace* and *Fresh 'n Lacey.*

THE FLESH AND THE FIENDS *see* MANIA
THE FLESH EATERS   F6.1598

Vulcan Productions. *Dist* Cinema Distributors of America. 18 Mar **1964** [Phoenix, Arizona, opening]. Sd; b&w. 35mm. 92 min. [Cut to 88 min.]

Prod Jack Curtis, Terry Curtis, Arnold Drake. *Dir* Jack Curtis. *Screenplay* Arnold Drake. *Photog* Carson Davidson. *Film Ed* Radley Metzger, Frank Forest. *Mus* Julian Stein. *Sd Eff* Ray Benson. *Tech Cons* Evan J. Aivton.

Cast: Martin Kosleck *(Peter Bartell)*, Rita Morley *(Laura Winters)*, Byron Sanders *(Grant Murdock)*, Ray Tudor *(Omar)*, Barbara Wilkin *(Jan Letterman)*.

Horror film. A seaplane, piloted by Grant Murdock, is chartered by alcoholic film star Laura Winters and her secretary Jan Letterman. Caught in a storm, the plane is forced to crash land on an island inhabited only by marine biologist Peter Bartell. Soon, a human skeleton, recently picked clean, is washed ashore, and the group is menaced by millions of tiny, flesh-eating marine creatures. Although Bartell disavows previous knowledge of these strange animals, it is soon learned that in his laboratory he is attempting to control the organisms, increasing their size by electrical charges. The insane biologist forces Murdock, at gunpoint, to help him with a sinister plan to electrify the sea, but Laura intercedes and is shot. A beatnik known as Omar, who has shipwrecked on the island, is also murdered and devoured by the flesh eaters. Further experimentation by Bartell transforms the tiny creatures into a huge, carnivorous monster, which is destroyed by injecting Laura's blood into its one eye. [One source claims a second monster is similarly destroyed.] Bartell falls victim to his creation during the battle, but Murdock escapes to join Jan on the shore. *Air pilots. Actors. Secretaries. Marine biologists. Sea monsters. Beatniks. Alcoholism. Transmutation. Murder. Insanity. Islands. Experiments. Electricity. The Sea. Storms. Airplane accidents.*

Note: Filmed 1960-61 on location in suburban New York.

FLESH FEAST   F6.1599

Viking International Productions. *Dist* CineWorld Corp. Jul **1970**. Sd; col. 35mm. 72 min. *MPAA rating* R.

Prod Veronica Lake, Brad F. Grinter. *Dir* Brad F. Grinter. *Screenplay* Thomas Casey, Brad F. Grinter. *Photog* Thomas Casey, Andy Romanoff. *Prod Dsgn* Harry Kerwin. *Prod Mgr* Harry Kerwin. *Makeup* Doug Hobart. *Sp Eff* Doug Hobart.

Cast: Veronica Lake *(Dr. Elaine Frederick)*, Phil Philbin, Heather Hughes, Martha Mischon, Yanka Mann, Dian Wilhite, Chris Martell.

Horror film. Arriving at Miami airport, a group of South American revolutionaries, led by Carl Schumann, murder an overcurious reporter and then meet with Dr. Elaine Frederick. Recently released from a mental institution, Dr. Frederick has been experimenting with a youth restoration process in which old skin and tissue is removed by the application of a special breed of flesheating maggots. Using the basement of an old Miami Beach mansion for a laboratory, she conceals the true nature of her activities by renting rooms to nurses. Dr. Frederick is unaware, however, that Kristine, one of her new tenants, is only posing as a nurse; in reality, she is a detective working in league with the editor friend of the murdered reporter. In time, the revolutionaries bring their aged commander to the basement laboratory for treatment. With all the nurses held captive, Dr. Frederick straps the patient to an operating table, and discovers to her disbelief that the aged man before her is Adolf Hitler. Spewing invectives at him for the torture and murder of her mother years before, Dr. Frederick maniacally takes revenge by covering her agonized victim with swarms of maggots. *South Americans. Revolutionaries. Reporters. Nurses. Detectives. Physicians. Lunatics. Murder. Rejuvenation. Imposture. Torture. Revenge. Experiments. Laboratories. Miami. Miami Beach. Adolf Hitler. Maggots.*

Note: Filmed on location in Florida.

THE FLESH GAME F6.1600

J. E. R. Productions. *Dist* J. E. R. Pictures. 20 Jul **1966** [Fresno, California, showing]. Sd; b&w. 35mm. 78 min.

Prod James M. Candelle. *Dir* M. M. Mitchell.

Cast: Gloria Patrick, Laurence Pole.

Melodrama. Cindy Johnson comes to New York City and moves in with Sharon Weston, a successful prostitute married for appearances to Leslie Harris, operator of a business management firm which is actually a front for prostitution. Harris' nephew Tom Lewis, who recruits the "secretaries" Harris makes available to his business clients, seduces Cindy, and she falls in love with him. Harris throws a wild party for new client Alex Minoff, and there is an orgy. Harris perceives that Minoff and his assistant, Brennan, are vice squad detectives. Sharon and Minoff leave the party together; Harris follows them and overhears Sharon consenting to turn state's evidence in exchange for being allowed to solicit clients without police intervention. Harris kills Minoff and pistol-whips Sharon. Brennan kills Harris in Central Park, and Cindy becomes one of Tom's call girls. *Prostitutes. Pimps. Businessmen. Secretaries. Detectives. Seduction. Prostitution. Impersonation. Murder. Perfidy. Marriage of convenience. Business management. Orgies. New York City. New York City—Central Park.*

Note: Also known as *The Fresh Game* and *Fresh Games.*

THE FLESH HUSTLER F6.1601

Dist Bob Thorpe, Clamil Productions. 11 Feb **1970** [Los Angeles opening]. Sd; col. 16mm. 63 min.

Prod T. Gordon, Limp Irving. *Dir* Limp Irving.

Cast: Mark Royal, Charles Pohl, Fred Shaw, Frank Starr, J. J. Randall.

Melodrama. Bill, a male prostitute, is tired of his life and seeks refuge at the Temple of Rhu-Khan thinking it to be a religious haven. Instead the temple is dedicated to bodily pleasures, and Bill is to be its next victim. *Prostitutes. Male homosexuality. Temples.*

THE FLESH IS HOT (Japan) F6.1602

Nikkatsu Corp. *Dist* European Producers International. 13 Sep **1963** [Los Angeles showing]. Sd; b&w. 35mm (Nikkatsu Scope). 77 min.

Pres by Gaston Hakim. *Dir* Shohei Imamura. *Screenplay* Hisashi Yamanouchi. *Photog* Shinsaku Himeda. *Art Dir* Kimihiko Nakamura. *Mus* Toshiro Mayuzumi.

Cast: Hiroyuki Nagato, Jitsuko Yoshimura, Shiro Osaka, Shoichi Ozawa, Yoko Minamida, Sanae Nakahara, Masao Mishima, Tetsuro Tamba, Takeshi Kato, Mitzi Mori.

Melodrama. The Himori gang supports itself from the illegal activities that flourish around a United States naval base in post-war Japan. The authorities close down a brothel operated by the gang, and Himori devotes his resources to raising hogs for sale to the U. S. Navy, feeding the animals garbage from the naval base. Kinta, formerly a pimp, serves as manager of the farm. His girl friend, Haruko, hounds him to end his connection with the gang. Troubles begin when Hoshino, the gang's treasurer, absconds with the funds. Shortly afterwards, Haruko is the victim of a rape by American soldiers. Gunji and Daihachi, two of Himori's lieutenants, decide to steal the hogs, and Kinta agrees to assist them in the hope of obtaining money to make a new life with Haruko. They drive two trucks to the farm but find that Himori has taken the hogs himself. They overtake Himori's trucks in the midst of a bar and cabaret district, and he agrees to divide the profits with his former aides. The three men decide to rid themselves of Kinta by fingering him for a murder, but Kinta overhears their plan and opens fire with a machine gun. Mortally wounded himself, he opens the back of a truck, releasing the hogs, and crawls away to die while Haruko waits for him in vain. [Based on 108 minute version.] *Gangs. Gangsters. Pimps. Whorehouses. Rape. Theft. Murder. Perfidy. Farming. Embezzlement. United States Navy. Pigs.*

Note: Released in Japan in Jan 1961 as *Buta to gunkan*; running time: 108 min. Also known as *Hogs and Warships*. Later released as *The Dirty Girls*, cut to ca66 min.

FLESH OF MY FLESH F6.1603

Libra M Productions. *Dist* Clover Films. 2 Jul **1969** [Fresno showing]. Sd; b&w. 35mm. 70 min.

Dir Michael Macready, Robert Kelljan. *Writ* Robert Kelljan.

Melodrama. Mark feels guilty because he is sexually attracted to his sister Deena, a highly-sexed, promiscuous young woman, and he expresses his frustrations in brutal assaults on his other lovers. Mark and Deena finally have sex during one stormy night, and they both achieve total satisfaction for the first time. Stunned by the new experience, Mark tries to escape the reality of what he has done by watching an exotic dancer, but her gyrations fail to arouse him, and he realizes that he desires only Deena. Jealousy overcomes Deena when she learns of Mark's other women, and she throws herself into a sexual merry-go-round. An affair with a lesbian is followed by an experience with a married couple. Finally, after a wild orgy, Deena tearfully seeks out Mark and asks his help and forgiveness. Mark spurns her pleas, however, and violently ends her life. *Brother-sister relationship. Incest. Guilt. Jealousy. Promiscuity. Lesbianism. Seduction. Troilism. Voyeurism. Murder. Orgies.*

Note: Also known as *Little Sister.*

LA FLEUR DE L'ÂGE, OU LES ADOLESCENTES see **THE ADOLESCENTS**

LES FLEURS DU SOLEIL see **SUNFLOWER**

FLICK see **DR. FRANKENSTEIN ON CAMPUS**

FLIGHT FROM ASHIYA (United States/Japan) F6.1604

Daiei Motion Picture Co.–Harold Hecht Films. *Dist* United Artists. 25 Mar **1964** [Los Angeles opening; c20 Mar 1964; LP29365]. Sd; col (Eastman Color). 35mm (Panavision). 100 min.

Prod Harold Hecht. *Dir* Michael Anderson. *Screenplay* Elliott Arnold, Waldo Salt. *Cinematog* Joseph MacDonald, Burnett Guffey. *Art Dir* Tomoo Shimogawara. *Prod Dsgn* Eugene Lourié. *Film Ed* Gordon Pilkington. *Mus* Frank Cordell. *Sd* Masao Osumi. *Asst Dir* Milton Feldman. *Prod Mgr* Gilbert Kurland. *Sp Eff* Daiei Motion Picture Co. *Tech Adv* Eugene C. Watkins, (Maj.).

Cast: Yul Brynner (*Sgt. Mike Takashima*), Richard Widmark (*Col. Glenn Stevenson*), George Chakiris (*Lieut. John Gregg*), Suzy Parker (*Lucille Carroll*), Shirley Knight (*Caroline Gordon*), Danièle Gaubert (*Leila*), Eiko Taki (*Tomiko*), Joseph Di Reda (*Sgt. Randy Smith*), Mitsuhiro Sugiyama (*Japanese boy Charlie*), E. S. Ince (*Capt. Walter Mound*), Andrew Hughes (*Dr. Horton*).

Drama. Source: Elliott Arnold, *Flight From Ashiya* (New York, 1959). Sgt. Mike Takashima, Col. Glenn Stevenson, and Lieut. John Gregg, all members of the U. S. Air Force Rescue Service at Ashiya, Japan, set out to rescue the survivors of a Japanese ship wrecked in a still-raging storm. As they fly to the site of the wreck, each man recalls a part of his past: Gregg remembers the avalanche caused when his helicopter came too close to a mountain. The avalanche subsequently buried alive the group of people whom he was attempting to rescue. The accident has since caused him to fear flying solo. Stevenson, deeply prejudiced against the Japanese, recalls the reason for his hatred: as a civilian pilot in the Philippines prior to World War II, he met and married Caroline Gordon. She and their infant son later died in a Japanese prison camp when they were refused medical supplies which were being saved for Japanese soldiers. Takashima, half-American, half-Japanese, reminisces about his tragic love affair with Leila, an Algerian girl, during World War II. He was unable to stop the blowing up of a bridge where Leila had run to look for him after learning that his unit was being withdrawn from town. When one air rescue plane crashes while attempting to land in the treacherous seas, Stevenson refuses to jeopardize his plane for Japanese lives. At the last minute, however, he recalls Caroline's dying plea not to hate; he overcomes his prejudice and orders Takashima to parachute to the liferafts with rescue equipment. He and Gregg then land the plane at sea and rescue the survivors, but when Stevenson is injured in the landing, Gregg is forced to overcome his fear and handle the dangerous takeoff and the flight back to Ashiya. *Americans in foreign countries. Air pilots. Japanese. Halfcastes. Algerians. Sea rescue. Prejudice. Air patrol. Helicopters. World War II. Ashiya. Philippines. United States Air Force. Shipwrecks. Storms. Avalanches. Airplane accidents.*

Note: Location scenes filmed in the Japanese cities of Kyoto, Osaka, and Tachikawa. Produced in Japan in 1963 as *Ashiya Kara no Hiko.*

FLIGHT FROM MINOS   **F6.1605**
21 Dec **1967** [New York showing]. Sd; col? 35mm? [Feature film, length unknown.]

Dir Michael Sullivan, dir. No information about the precise nature of this film has been found. *Sexuality.*

FLIGHT FROM TERROR *see* **SATAN NEVER SLEEPS**

FLIGHT OF THE LOST BALLOON   **F6.1606**
W. M. J. Productions. *Dist* Woolner Bros. Pictures, American International Pictures. 8 Nov **1961** [Baltimore opening]. Sd; col (Eastman Color). 35mm (SpectraScope). 91 min.

Prod Bernard A. Woolner. *Assoc Prod-Dir-Screenplay-Story* Nathan Juran. *Exec Prod* Jacques Marquette. *Photog* Jacques Marquette. *Film Ed* Rex Lipton. *Mus* Hal Borne. *Sd* Tom Ashton. *Asst Dir* Howard Alston, Jack Bohrer. *Miniature & Proc Work* Project Unlimited.

Cast: Mala Powers *(Ellen)*, Marshall Thompson *(Dr. Joseph Faraday)*, James Lanphier *(The Hindu)*, Douglas Kennedy *(Sir Hubert)*, Robert Gillette *(Sir Adam)*, Felippe Birriel *(Golan)*, A. J. Valentine *(Giles)*, Blanquita Romero *(The Malkia)*, Jackie Donoro *(native dancer)*.

Adventure drama. In an old fortress on the Nile, a despotic Hindu is holding as his prisoner a British explorer, Sir Hubert, who has discovered the hidden tomb where Cleopatra's treasure is buried. Sir Hubert refuses to disclose the location of the jewels, and the Hindu goes to England and tricks the London Geographical Society into organizing a rescue mission. Included in the expedition is Sir Hubert's fiancée, Ellen, whom the Hindu plans to torture until Sir Hubert agrees to talk. A young explorer, Dr. Faraday, convinces the Society that the trip should be made by balloon, and he, Ellen and the Hindu set out for Egypt. After several adventures, including their temporary capture by cannibals and an attack by huge condors, the trio arrive at the Nile fortress. The Hindu has Ellen tortured on a stretching rack, but the greedy Sir Hubert still refuses to divulge his secret. They are both rescued by Faraday, but Sir Hubert dies trying to load the balloon with chests of treasure. Faraday and Ellen make their escape but are forced to jettison the gold and jewels in order to keep the balloon aloft. Ellen, however, saves one diamond for a wedding ring. *Fortune hunters. Hindus. British. Explorers. Cannibals. Abduction. Torture. Greed. Tombs. Treasure. Balloons (ascent). Nile River. Egypt. London. Cleopatra. Condors.*

Note: Location scenes filmed in Puerto Rico.

THE FLIGHT OF THE PHOENIX   **F6.1607**
Associates & Aldrich Co. *Dist* Twentieth Century-Fox Film Corp. 15 Dec **1965** [Los Angeles opening; c31 Dec 1965; LP32239]. Sd (Westrex); col (DeLuxe). 35mm. 149 min. [Copyright length: 145 min.]

Prod-Dir Robert Aldrich. *Assoc Prod* Walter Blake. *2d Unit Dir* Oscar Rudolph. *Screenplay* Lukas Heller. *Dir Photog* Joseph Biroc. *Aerial Seq* Paul Mantz. *Art Dir* William Glasgow. *Set Decor* Lucien Hafley. *Main Titl* Don Niehaus, National Screen Service. *Film Ed* Michael Luciano. *Mus* De Vol. *Orch* Al Woodbury. *Phoenix Love Theme: "Senza Fine" mus & Italian lyr* Gino Paoli. *English Lyr* Alec Wilder. *Sung by* Connie Francis. *Sd* Jack Solomon. *Asst Dir* William F. Sheehan, Cliff Coleman, Alan Callow. *Prod Mgr* Jack R. Berne. *Script Supv* Robert Gary. *Cost Dsgn* Norma Koch. *Makeup Supv* Ben Nye. *Makeup* Jack Stone, William Turner, Frank Westmore, Terry Miles, Ed Butterworth. *Sp Photog Eff* L. B. Abbott, Howard Lydecker. *Prop Master* John Orlando. *Dial Supv* Robert Sherman, Michael Audley. *Constr Coörd* John LaSalandra.

Cast: James Stewart *(Frank Towns)*, Richard Attenborough *(Lew Moran)*, Peter Finch *(Captain Harris)*, Hardy Kruger *(Heinrich Dorfmann)*, Ernest Borgnine *(Trucker Cobb)*, Ian Bannen *(Crow)*, Ronald Fraser *(Sergeant Watson)*, Christian Marquand *(Dr. Renaud)*, Dan Duryea *(Standish)*, George Kennedy *(Bellamy)*, Gabriele Tinti *(Gabriele)*, Alex Montoya *(Carlos)*, Peter Bravos *(Tasso)*, William Aldrich *(Bill)*, Barrie Chase *(Farida)*.

Drama. Source: Elleston Trevor, *The Flight of the Phoenix* (New York, 1964). Frank Towns, pilot of an oil field cargo-passenger plane, crashes in the North African desert. The crash is the fault of the alcoholic navigator, Lew Moran, who neglected to check the radio, which is now broken. Two of the men on the plane have died in the crash, and the rest are faced with death in the desert as the result of a diminishing water supply and a scarcity of food. The survivors are organized by Towns and are led by two British soldiers, Captain Harris and Sergeant Watson. Harris decides to try to get some water and leads Carlos on an expedition. They are followed by Trucker Cobb, who has suffered a mental breakdown. Only Harris returns. Heinrich Dorfmann, a German model-plane designer, comes up with a plan to remodel the double-engine plane into a salvaged single-engine model. Towns is opposed to the idea at first, but to keep their sanity all the men work on the plane. (In hallucination, they see a mirage of Farida, a dancer.) A party of Arabs meets them on the desert; but when Harris and Dr. Renaud beg them for water, the Arabs slit the two men's

throats. Finally the plane is finished, and the surviving men strap themselves to its wings as it rises out of the desert. *British. Germans. Dancers. Air pilots. Arabs. Soldiers. Survival. Radio. Murder. Deserts. Oil fields. Airplane manufacture. North Africa. Airplane accidents. Hallucinations.*

Note: Location scenes filmed near Yuma, Colorado.

THE FLIGHT OF THE SANDPIPER *see* **THE SANDPIPER**

FLIGHT THAT DISAPPEARED   **F6.1608**
Harvard Film Corp. *Dist* United Artists. 13 Sep **1961** [Los Angeles opening; c24 Aug 1961; LP21201]. Sd; b&w. 35mm. 72 min.

Prod Robert E. Kent. *Dir* Reginald Le Borg. *Screenplay* Ralph Hart, Judith Hart, Owen Harris. *Photog* Gilbert Warrenton. *Set Decor* Morris Hoffman. *Film Ed* Kenneth Crane. *Mus* Richard La Salle. *Sd* Harry Alphin, Ralph Butler. *Asst Dir* Herbert S. Greene. *Prod Mgr* Joseph Small. *Wardrobe* Sabine Manela, Jerry Bos. *Makeup* Harry Thomas. *Hairstyles* Frances Sperry. *Sp Eff* Barney Wolff.

Cast: Craig Hill *(Tom Endicott)*, Paula Raymond *(Marcia Paxton)*, Dayton Lummis *(Dr. Morris)*, Gregory Morton *(The Examiner)*, John Bryant *(Hank Norton)*, Addison Richards *(The Sage)*, Nancy Hale *(Barbara Nielsen)*, Bernadette Hale *(Joan Agnew)*, Harvey Stephens *(Walter Cooper)*, Brad Trumbull *(Jack Peters)*, Meg Wyllie *(Helen Cooper)*, Francis De Sales *(Manson)*, Carl Princi *(announcer)*, Eden Hartford *(Miss Ford)*, Ed Stoddard *(O'Connor)*, Roy Engel *(Jamison)*, Jerry James *(Ray Houser)*, Jack Mann *(Garrett)*, Stephen Ellsworth Crowley *(ATC official)*, Joe Haworth *(radio operator)*.

Science fiction melodrama. Nuclear scientists Tom Endicott, Dr. Morris, and Marcia Paxton are flying to Washington, D. C., for discussions with Pentagon officials on testing a powerful super-bomb they have developed. En route their plane suddenly soars into space at such a dizzying pace that all the passengers except the three scientists lose consciousness. When the plane stops, the trio find themselves on a cloud-shrouded plateau far beyond the earth's atmosphere. They are confronted by a mysterious figure who leads them before a jury representing the unborn generations of the future. After being accused of plotting to devastate the earth, the scientists are sentenced to remain forever suspended in time. A sage intervenes, however, to remind the jury that its decision will have no effect on the fate of mankind, since only prayer can save the human race. The three scientists are permitted to reboard the plane and miraculously land in Washington. At first the scientists believe that they have experienced a hallucination, but when they realize they are 24 hours overdue, they destroy their plans for the super-bomb and vow never to talk of their strange adventure. *Scientists. Human race. Supernatural. Religion. Space travel. Airplanes. Bombs. Nuclear warfare. Trials. Washington (District of Columbia). The Pentagon.*

FLIGHT TO FURY (United States/Philippines)   **F6.1609**
Lippert, Inc.-Filipinas Productions. *Dist* Feature Film Corp. of America. Nov **1966**. Sd; b&w. 35mm. 62 min.

Pres by Harold Goldman Associates. *Prod* Fred Roos. *Dir* Monte Hellman. *Dir Tagalog Vers* Eddie Romero. *Screenplay* Jack Nicholson. *Story* Monte Hellman, Fred Roos. *Photog* Mike Accion.

Cast: Dewey Martin *(Joe Gaines)*, Fay Spain *(Destiny Cooper)*, Jack Nicholson *(Jay Wickam)*, Jacqueline Hellman *(Gloria Walsh)*, Vic Diaz *(Lorgren)*, Joseph Estrada *(Garuda)*, John Hackett *(Al Ross)*, Juliet Prado *(Lei Ling)*, Jennings Sturgeon *(bearded man)*, Lucien Pan *(police inspector)*.

Melodrama. At a gambling casino in Southeast Asia, adventurer Joe Gaines meets Jay Wickam, an American who claims to be a tourist, and Lei Ling, whom he accompanies to her room. While Joe is momentarily absent, Lei Ling is murdered by Wickam, who has been searching her room for a cache of smuggled diamonds. After being questioned by the police, Joe boards a non-scheduled third-class airliner. Among the other passengers are Al Ross, Lei Ling's associate; Lorgren, an obese Oriental; Destiny Cooper, the latter's American mistress; and Wickam, who says he wants to share Joe's adventurous life. En route to the Philippines, the plane is forced to crash-land in the jungle. Several passengers are killed, and Ross, who is carrying the cache of diamonds, is critically wounded. Before dying, he secretly passes the gems to Joe, unaware that the real owner is Lorgren. (Ross and Lei Ling had unknowingly been working as go-betweens for Lorgren.) After Lorgren has taken the diamonds from Joe at gun point, native bandits capture the group and imprison them in a shack. Although they escape, Wickam seizes the diamonds, kills Lorgren, and shoots Destiny when she intervenes. As Wickam flees into the jungle, Joe wounds him with a pistol shot. Wickam, knowing that he is doomed, throws the diamonds into a river and then shoots himself. Joe, the last survivor, is left to await death at the hands of the bandits. *Adventurers. Americans in foreign countries. Tourists. Orientals. Mistresses. Bandits. Smuggling. Murder. Suicide. Casinos. Diamonds. Jungles. Philippines. Airplane accidents.*

Note: Filipino title: *Cordillera.*

FLIGHT TO THE STARS (U.S.S.R.)   **F6.1610**

Moscow Popular Science Studio. *Dist* Artkino Pictures. 21 Apr **1962** [New York opening]. Sd; col. 35mm. 46 min.

Dir Dmitriy Bogolepov, G. Kosenko. *Screenplay* Yevgeniy Ryabchikov. *Photog* V. Afanasyev, Dmitriy Gasyuk, Igor Kasatkin, V. Suvorov, A. Filippov, M. Beschetnov. *Mus* Mikhail Ziv. *Sd* K. Bek-Nazarov.

Documentary. A record of the second Soviet manned space flight. Included are scenes of Maj. German Stepanovich Titov in training and consulting with fellow cosmonaut Yuriy Gagarin; his flight aboard Vostok II in August 1961; Titov reciting Pushkin in a decompression chamber; and his hero's welcome in Red Square, including a meeting with Premier Nikita Khrushchev. *Astronauts. Space flights. Moscow—Red Square. German Stepanovich Titov. Nikita Sergeyevich Khrushchev. Yuriy Alekseyevich Gagarin.*

Note: Released in the U.S.S.R. in 1962 as *Snova k zvyozdam*. Released in New York as part of a program entitled *Flight to the Stars and Mountain Folk Festival.* May also be known as *Titov's Space Flight.*

THE FLIM–FLAM MAN   **F6.1611**

Lawrence Turman, Inc. *Dist* Twentieth Century-Fox Film Corp. 22 Aug **1967** [New York opening; c24 May 1967; LP34497]. Sd (Westrex); col (De Luxe). 35mm (Panavision). 104 min.

Prod Lawrence Turman. *Dir* Irvin Kershner. *2d Unit Dir* Yakima Canutt. *Screenplay* William Rose. *Dir Photog* Charles Lang. *Art Dir* Jack Martin Smith, Robert E. Smith, Lewis Creber. *Set Decor* Walter M. Scott, John Sturtevant. *Titl* Cinefx, Phill Norman. *Film Ed* Robert Swink. *Mus* Jerry Goldsmith. *Orch* Arthur Morton. *Sd* Josh Westmoreland, David Dockendorf. *Asst Dir* William Kissel. *Asst to Prod* Peter Nelson. *Unit Prod Mgr* Joseph E. Rickards. *Cost Dsgn* Dorothy Jeakins. *Makeup* Ben Nye. *Hairstyles* Margaret Donovan. *Sp Photog Eff* L. B. Abbott, Art Cruickshank, Emil Kosa, Jr.

Cast: George C. Scott (*Mordecai Jones*), Sue Lyon (*Bonnie Lee Packard*), Harry Morgan (*Sheriff Slade*), Jack Albertson (*Mr. Packard*), Alice Ghostley (*Mrs. Packard*), Albert Salmi (*Deputy Meshaw*), Slim Pickens (*Jarvis Bates*), Michael Sarrazin (*Curley Treadaway*), Strother Martin (*Lovick*), George Mitchell (*Tetter*), Woodrow Parfrey (*supermarket manager*), Jay Ose (*2d fertilizer man*), Raymond Guth (*1st fertilizer man*), Jesse L. Baker (*Doodle Powell*).

Comedy. Source: Guy Owen, *Ballad of the Flim-Flam Man* (New York, 1965). Mordecai Jones is an old-fashioned confidence man equipped with a glib tongue and a heart of pure larceny. Widely known throughout the South as the Flim-Flam Man, he is always seen carrying the beat-up satchel that contains the tools of his trade: decks of playing cards, dominoes, punchboards, play money, etc. One day he meets Curley Treadaway, a Carolina farm boy who has gone AWOL from the Army after slugging his "big-mouthed Yankee sergeant." United by a common need to survive, the two renegades join forces once Mordecai has assuaged Curley's conscience by promising to cheat only other cheaters and the greedy. Following several successful swindles, they "borrow" a car from pretty Bonnie Lee Packard, a 17-year-old with whom Curley immediately falls in love. When the police spot the stolen car and the local sheriff gives chase, Mordecai races through the town, crashing into store windows, upsetting fruit trucks, and terrifying startled citizens. Having wrecked the car, they steal a truckload of moonshine whiskey which they quickly peddle for cash and supplies. Curley, meanwhile, has been having clandestine meetings with Bonnie, who lovingly urges him to become respectable. Eventually, despite his affection for Mordecai, Curley decides to give himself up to the Army; but before he can do so he and Mordecai are captured and jailed. Curley escapes, gets some dynamite boxes, and threatens to blow up the courthouse unless Mordecai is released. Trapped, the sheriff agrees. Once Mordecai has supposedly left town, Curley reveals that his threat was just another confidence trick—he never had any dynamite. As Curley is arrested, Bonnie and her influential father promise to see that he is treated fairly. Watching from the shadows is Mordecai, who has merely walked around the corner. "Thank you son," he murmurs and then he hops a freight train slowly moving out of town. *Confidence men. Thieves. Fugitives. Sheriffs. United States Army—Desertion. Adolescence. Liquor. United States—South. Automobile accidents. Chases.*

Note: Location scenes filmed in Kentucky.

FLIPPER   **F6.1612**

Ivan Tors Films. *Dist* Metro-Goldwyn-Mayer, Inc. 29 May **1963** [Miami, Florida, opening; c19 Mar 1963; LP24116]. Sd (Westrex); col (Metrocolor). 35mm. 90 min.

Prod Ivan Tors. *Assoc Prod* Ricou Browning, Harry Redmond, Jr. *Dir* James B. Clark. *Screenplay* Arthur Weiss. *Story* Ricou Browning, Jack Cowden. *Dir Photog* Lamar Boren, Joseph Brun. *Film Ed* Warren Adams. *Mus Comp & Cond* Henry Vars. *Titl Song:* "Flipper" "By" Dunham, Henry Vars. *Sd Rec* Howard Warren. *Prod Supv* Ben Chapman. *Asst to the Prod* Robert A. Foss,

Jeb Gholson. *Adv* Robert C. Cannom, (USCG). *Coöp* Miami Seaquarium, Capt. Adelph Frohn, Marineland of the Pacific (California). *Scientific Adv* Dr. John C. Lilly. *Mitzi's owners & trainers* Milton Santini, Virginia Santini.

Cast: Chuck Connors (*Porter Ricks*), Luke Halpin (*Sandy Ricks*), Kathleen Maguire (*Martha Ricks*), Connie Scott (*Kim Parker*), Jane Rose (*Hettie White*), Joe Higgins (*L. C. Porett*), Robertson White (*Abrams*), George Applewhite (*Sheriff Rogers*), Mitzi (*Flipper, a dolphin*).

Adventure melodrama. When a plague destroys the fish in the area, Porter Ricks, a Florida Keys fisherman, searches for new grounds but is caught in a hurricane. Leaving behind his wife and 12-year-old son, Sandy, Porter goes to the mainland to have his damaged boat repaired. Sandy had promised to help repair the damage done to their house by the storm but is distracted when he finds an 8-foot wounded dolphin and tows him home. Sandy and his mother nurse the dolphin, which they call "Flipper," back to health in their fishpen, and the boy and Flipper become close friends. Porter returns, however, and orders Flipper to be returned to the ocean, annoyed because Sandy permitted his new friend to keep him from his work. The heartbroken boy releases Flipper, but the dolphin keeps returning and guides Sandy to a new fishing ground. He reports this discovery to his father, omitting any mention of Flipper. One day, while diving in the area, Sandy is attacked by sharks but is rescued by Flipper, who swims to Porter's approaching boat with the lad on his back. Porter, grateful for his son's life, permits Flipper to return to the family's lagoon where he and Sandy can romp and play together. *Fishermen. Florida Keys. Family life. Hurricanes. Pets. Dolphins. Sharks.*

Note: Filmed on location in Florida, the Bahamas, and the Virgin Islands. Producers thank the officials of New Providence Island in the Bahamas, Everglades City, and Miami for their cooperation.

FLIPPER'S NEW ADVENTURE   **F6.1613**

Ivan Tors Films. *Dist* Metro-Goldwyn-Mayer, Inc. 27 May **1964** [Miami, Florida, opening; c28 Apr 1964; LP28068]. Sd (Westrex); col (Metrocolor). 35mm. 92 min. [See note.]

An Ivan Tors Production. *Assoc Prod* Ben Chapman, Ricou Browning. *Dir* Leon Benson. *Screenplay* Art Arthur. *Story* Ivan Tors. *Based on characters created by* Ricou Browning, Jack Cowden. *Dir Photog* Lamar Boren. *Film Ed* Warren Adams, Charles Craft. *Mus Comp & Cond* Henry Vars. *Songs* "By" Dunham, Henry Vars. *Songs:* "Flipper," "Imagine" *Sung by* Chris Crosby. *Song:* "It's a Cotton Candy World" *Sung by* Jerry Wallace. *Sd Rec* Howard Warren. *Asst Dir* Edward Haldeman. *Asst to the Prod* Joseph Gannon. *Tech Adv* Robert C. Cannom, (USCG), Ric O'Feldman. *Coöp* Miami Seaquarium.

Cast: Luke Halpin (*Sandy*), Pamela Franklin (*Penny*), Helen Cherry (*Julia*), Tom Helmore (*Sir Halsey Hopewell*), Francesca Annis (*Gwen*), Brian Kelly (*Porter Ricks*), Joe Higgins (*L. C. Porett*), Lloyd Battista (*Gil*), Gordon Dilworth (*sea captain*), Courtney Brown (*convict*), William Cooley (*2d convict*), Dan Chandler (*Coast Guard commander*), Ricou Browning (*Dr. Burton*), Ric O'Feldman, Robert Baldwin (*veterinarians*), Susie (*Flipper, a dolphin*).

Adventure melodrama. When Sandy Ricks learns that he is to be deprived of his pet dolphin, Flipper, he takes a rowboat and heads for a deserted island in the Florida Keys. Flipper tows the boat to the island after Sandy collapses from exhaustion. Nearby, three escaped convicts take over Sir Halsey Hopewell's yacht, keeping Hopewell aboard but sending his wife and daughters, Penny and Gwen, to the island where Sandy is hiding. Sandy remains under cover but arranges for Flipper to toss things the Hopewells will need for survival—fish, matches, knives, flashlight, and the like—up on the beach. Meanwhile, Sandy's father has begun a search for him. Sandy reveals himself to and befriends Penny but swears her to secrecy about his presence on the island. When the convicts learn that Hopewell is an influential millionaire, they return to the island and threaten to kill his family unless he arranges for their pardon. Sandy and Flipper battle the convicts and capture two of them. The third, just before he is captured, drives a knife into Flipper during an underwater fight. Hopewell radios the authorities, and the injured Flipper is flown to Miami. There he undergoes surgery, and Sandy and his father are reunited. Flipper recovers and Mr. Ricks tells Sandy that he will be able to keep his dolphin. *Millionaires. Prison escapees. Kidnaping. Survival. Family life. Extortion. Rowboats. Yachts. Florida Keys. Miami. Dolphins.*

Note: Filmed on location in the Bahamas and Key Biscayne, Florida. Song sequences photographed at Parrot Jungle, Miami. Most sources disagree on the running time and list it variously from 92 min to 103 min. Sequel to *Flipper*, q. v.

FLITTERWOCHEN IN DER HÖLLE *see* **ISLE OF SIN**

FLOAT LIKE A BUTTERFLY, STING LIKE A BEE   **F6.1614**

Delpire Productions. *Dist* Grove Press. 21 Nov **1969** [New York opening]. Sd; b&w. 35mm. 94 min.

Prcs by Evergreen Films, Alvin Ferleger. *Prod-Dir* William Klein. *Photog* William Klein. *Film Ed* William Klein. *Mus* Mickey Baker. *Asst* Etienne Becker.

Documentary. On 25 February 1964 at Miami, Florida, Cassius Clay knocks out Sonny Liston in seven rounds to become the world's heavyweight boxing champion. "The champ of the world should be beautiful like me," Clay proclaims. "I'm king of the ring ... float like a butterfly, sting like a bee." Originally backed by a group of southern millionaires, Clay is touted by Joe Louis, Jersey Joe Walcott, Kingfish Levinsky, and Evil Eye Finkel. Malcolm X is proud of him—he has given pride to all blacks. Braggart, poet, philosopher—Clay creates a style that both fascinates and repels the public. His involvement with the Black Muslims deepens; he joins the Muslims, changing his name to Muhammad Ali. The rematch with Liston is banned in all major cities as the result of Ali's refusal to serve in the Army, and the fight takes place at Lewiston, Maine, on 26 May 1965. Ali retains the world championship, by knocking out Liston in the first round. *Prizefighters. Negroes. Fight promoters. Poets. Braggarts. Conscientious objectors. Miami. Lewiston (Maine). Muhammad Ali. Malcolm X. Sonny Liston. Joe Louis. Jersey Joe Walcott. Kingfish Levinsky. Evil Eye Finkel. Black Muslims.*

FLOATING WEEDS (Japan)   **F6.1615**
Daiei Motion Picture Co. *Dist* Altura Films International. 24 Nov **1970** [New York opening]. Sd; col (Daiei Color). 35mm. 119 min.

Dir Yasujiro Ozu. *Screenplay* Kogo Noda, Yasujiro Ozu. *Story* Yasujiro Ozu. *Photog* Kazuo Miyagawa. *Mus* Takanobu Saito.

Cast: Ganjiro Nakamura *(Komajuro)*, Haruko Sugimura *(Oyoshi)*, Hiroshi Kawaguchi *(Kiyoshi)*, Machiko Kyo *(Sumiko)*, Ayako Wakao *(Kayo)*, Koji Mitsui *(Kichinosuke)*, Mutsuko Sakura, Mantaro Ushio, Haruo Tanaka, Hitomi Nozoe, Chishu Ryu.

Melodrama. Source: Tadao Ikeda, screenplay for the film *Ukigusa monogatari*, 1934. Komajuro and his troupe of actors arrive at a small seaside town to perform traditional Japanese drama. He meets Oyoshi, his former mistress, and their illegitimate son, Kiyoshi. Neglecting his responsibility to the troupe, Komajuro spends most of his time with his son, who knows him only as an uncle. Sumiko, Komajuro's present mistress, learns of Komajuro's behavior and plots to have Kayo, a pretty young actress, seduce the son. The plan fails when Kayo and Kiyoshi fall in love, and the troupe is forced to disband in financial ruin. Nevertheless, Komajuro again abandons Oyoshi and continues his travels with Sumiko. *Actors. Mistresses. Illegitimacy. Seduction. Desertion. Theatrical troupes.*

Note: Filmed on location on the Kii Peninsula, Shijima. Released in Japan in Nov 1959 as *Ukigusa*.

FLOCKING TOGETHER *see* **THE WILD FEMALES**

FLOR DE MAYO *see* **BEYOND ALL LIMITS**

LA FLOR DEL IRUPÉ *see* **LOVE HUNGER**

FLOWER DRUM SONG   **F6.1616**
Ross Hunter Productions-Fields Productions. *Dist* Universal-International. 9 Nov **1961** [New York opening; c18 Nov 1961; LP24722]. Sd; col (Technicolor). 35mm (Panavision). 133 min.

A Ross Hunter-Joseph Fields Production. *Prod* Ross Hunter. *Dir* Henry Koster. *Screenplay* Joseph Fields. *Photog* Russell Metty. *Art Dir* Alexander Golitzen, Joseph Wright. *Set Decor* Howard Bristol. *Orig Titl Paintings* Dong Kingman. *Film Ed* Milton Carruth. *Mus Supv & Cond* Alfred Newman. *Assoc Mus Supv* Ken Darby. *Songs* Richard Rodgers, Oscar Hammerstein, II. *Choreog* Hermes Pan. *Sd* Waldon O. Watson, Joe Lapis. *Asst Dir* Phil Bowles. *Prod Mgr* Norman Deming. *Cost* Irene Sharaff. *Makeup* Bud Westmore. *Hairstyles* Larry Germain. *Tech Adv* H. K. Wong, Albert Lim.

Cast: Nancy Kwan *(Linda Low)*, James Shigeta *(Wang Ta)*, Juanita Hall *(Auntie [Madame Liang])*, Jack Soo *(Sammy Fong)*, Miyoshi Umeki *(Mei Li)*, Benson Fong *(Wang Chi-Yang)*, Reiko Sato *(Helen Chao)*, Patrick Adiarte *(Wang San)*, Kam Tong *(Dr. Li)*, Victor Sen Yung *(Frankie Wing)*, Soo Young *(Madame Fong)*, Ching Wah Lee *(professor)*, James Hong *(headwaiter)*, Spencer Chan *(Dr. Chon)*, Arthur Song *(Dr. Fong)*, Weaver Levy *(policeman)*, Herman Rudin *(holdup man)*, Cherylene Lee, Virginia Lee *(San's girlfriends)*, Virginia Grey *(TV heroine)*, Paul Sorensen *(TV sheriff)*, Ward Ramsey *(Great White Hunter)*, Laurette Luez *(Mexican girl)*, Robert Kino *(bank manager)*, Beal Wong *(tailor)*, Jon Fong *(square dance caller)*, Willard Lee, Frank Kumagai *(tradesmen)*.

Musical comedy-drama. Source: Richard Rodgers, Oscar Hammerstein, II and Joseph Fields, *Flower Drum Song* (New York opening: 1 Dec 1958). C. Y. Lee, *The Flower Drum Song* (New York, 1957). Newly arrived in San Francisco's Chinatown is Mei Li, a "picture bride" from Hong Kong who has been chosen to be the wife of Sammy Fong, a nightclub owner. Sammy,

however, is opposed to Old World marriage traditions and wants to select as his wife Linda Low, a singer and exotic dancer in his night spot. Consequently, he tries to unload Mei Li on the wealthy Wang family, who are seeking a bride for their eldest son, Wang Ta. But Ta has also been dating the wily Linda, unaware that she is merely interested in his money. At a party celebrating Ta's graduation from college and Auntie's graduation from citizenship school, the betrothal of Linda and Ta is suddenly announced, leaving Mei Li heartbroken and Sammy enraged. The latter soon has his revenge when he invites the Wangs to celebrate the Chinese New Year at his club. They abruptly call off their son's engagement when they see Linda do a spicy striptease dance. Although Ta realizes his mistake and admits his love for Mei Li, she rejects him and forces Sammy to fulfill his contractual obligations. But in the middle of the wedding ceremony, Mei Li confesses that she entered the country illegally, thereby invalidating the marriage contract. Ta happily volunteers to marry her, and Linda and Sammy decide to make it a double wedding. *Songs:* "You Are Beautiful" (Ta); "A Hundred Million Miracles" (Mei Li, Dr. Li & Chorus); "I Enjoy Being a Girl" (Linda); "I Am Going To Like It Here" (Mei Li); "Chop Suey" (Auntie, Ta, San & Chorus); "Don't Marry Me" (Sammy & Mei Li); "Grant Avenue" (Linda & Chorus); "Love, Look Away" (Helen); "Fan Tan Fanny" (Linda & Chorus); "Gliding Through My Memoree" (Frankie, Linda & Show Girls); "The Other Generation" (Wang, Auntie, San & San's girlfriends); "Sunday" (Sammy & Linda). *Chinese. Stowaways. Brides. Nightclub owners. Students. Singers. Exotic dancers. Gold diggers. Immigration. Marriage—Arranged. Wealth. Family life. Contracts. San Francisco—Chinatown.*

THE FLOWER THIEF   **F6.1617**
Dist Film-Makers' Cooperative, Film-Makers' Distribution Center, Cinema Guild. 13 Jul **1962** [New York opening]. Sd; b&w. 16mm. 70 min. [See note.]

Prod-Dir-Writ Ron Rice. *Film Ed* Ron Rice. *Mus Selections* Claude Debussy.

Cast: Taylor Mead *(flower thief)*, Philip McKenns, Ella Henry, Linda Evanoff, Turk Leclair, Dick Stevenson, Bob Kaufman, Heinz Ellsworth, Barry Clark, Mickey, Ted, Eric Nord.

Experimental film. A carefree, homosexual beatnik treks through San Francisco, carrying a flower, an American flag, and a teddy bear, seeking love and communication among people. After stealing a gardenia, he stops at a bagel shop before returning to his home, which is an abandoned powerhouse. There he discovers a man hidden in the cellar with a teddy bear. The flower thief washes the teddy bear and, on seeing a room full of people, flees from the building. Dragging his teddy bear, he climbs Telegraph Hill and, upon reaching Coit Tower at the top, coasts his wagon down the hill. He dances with a young woman in a bathing suit, destroys an old radio, accidentally sets in motion a derrick, which begins to rip up a building, and rolls a large wheel into the dilapidated wall of a ruined factory. Sleeping on the statue of a lion, the flower thief clutches its stone testicles. He enters a beatnik bar and is met with derisive mockery by the urbane poets who gather there. Once, on one of his many walks down the middle of a street, he stands behind a policeman on a main thoroughfare and directs traffic with him. Elsewhere, a group of beatniks satirize the raising of the American flag on Iwo Jima by "crucifying" the flower thief on a flagpole with a flag cravat. Finally, he picks up a young man in a penny arcade, and they wander through the amusement park, passing the merry-go-round and a display of fireworks. In the end, the two are seen walking together into the sea. *Beatniks. Thieves. Police. Male homosexuality. Flowers. Bars. Amusement parks. San Francisco. San Francisco—Telegraph Hill. Iwo Jima. "Alice in Wonderland".*

Note: Filmed on location in San Francisco, 1959–60. May have been shown originally at 48 or 59 min; 75 min and 85 min versions were subsequently released. Excerpts from *Alice in Wonderland* are read on the soundtrack. Single-frame sequences are included.

DER FLUCH DER GRÜNEN AUGEN *see* **CAVE OF THE LIVING DEAD**

FLUCHT NACH BERLIN *see* **ESCAPE TO BERLIN**

FLUCTUATIONS   **F6.1618**
Dist American Film Distributing Corp. 25 Feb **1970** [Detroit opening]. Sd; b&w. 35mm. 70 min.

Prod-Dir-Writ Leo J. Rhewdnal. *Photog* Jay Fortgang, Bruce Gordon, pseud. *Prod Asst* James Bond. *Karate Cons* Harold S. Tropp.

Cast: Sherry Martin, Larry Karto, Don Teller, Sandra Bender, Erik Carlson, Carla Pompei, Mitch Walker, Mary Drydock, Marilyn Munro, Kim Lewis.

Sex film. A series of erotic incidents take place: a heterosexual couple abduct and abuse a woman; a teenaged boy and a near-naked girl engage in a karate match that climaxes in a bathtub; and two men and a woman are whipped with the long hair of a girl friend. *Eroticism. Abduction. Adolescence. Nudity. Karate. Flagellation. Sexual practices. Bathtubs.*

Note: Leo J. Rhewdnal is a pseudonym for Joel Landwehr. All other credits are also pseudonyms.

FLUFFY
F6.1619

Scarus, Inc.-Universal Pictures. *Dist* Universal Pictures. 7 Jun **1965** [Indianapolis opening; c5 Jun 1964; LP33269]. Sd (Westrex); col (Eastman Color). 35mm. 92 min.

Prod Gordon Kay. *Dir* Earl Bellamy. *Screenplay* Samuel Roeca. *Dir Photog* Clifford Stine. *Camera Op* William Dodds. *Asst Camera* William Reisbord, James R. Connell. *Art Dir* Alexander Golitzen, Walter Simonds. *Set Decor* John McCarthy, James S. Redd. *Main Titl* Pacific Title. *Film Ed* Russell F. Schoengarth. *Asst Ed* Edward Broussard. *Mus* Irving Gertz. *Mus Supv* Joseph Gershenson. *Sd* Waldon O. Watson, Clarence Self, Russell Ashley, Roy Steele, Chick Bourland. *Asst Dir* Phil Bowles, Bob Daley. *Unit Prod Mgr* Howard Pine. *Script Supv* Cliff Bole. *Gowns* Rosemary Odell. *Wardrobe* Norman Mayreis, Dolores Sheppard. *Makeup Supv* Bud Westmore. *Makeup* Jack Freeman, Howard Smit. *Hairstyles* Larry Germain, Cheri De La Mare. *Zamba Owned and Trained by* Ralph Helfer. *Dial Coach* Herold Goodwin. *Still Photog* Robert Coburn. *Gaffer* Earl Kennedy. *Grip* Steve Rez, Sam Van Zanten. *Prop* Tony Lombardo, Charles Thomas.

Cast: Tony Randall (*Daniel Potter*), Shirley Jones (*Janice*), Edward Andrews (*Griswald*), Howard Morris (*Sweeney*), Ernest Truex (*Claridge*), Jim Backus (*sergeant*), Frank Faylen (*Catfish*), Celia Kaye (*Sally Brighton*), Dick Sargent (*Tommy*), Adam Roarke (*Bob Brighton*), Whit Bissell (*Dr. Braden*), Harriet MacGibbon (*Mrs. Claridge*), Jim Boles (*Pete*), Parley Baer (*police captain*), Connie Gilchrist (*maid*), Stuart Randall (*state trooper*), Sammee Tong (*cook*), Barry O'Hara (*fireman #2*), Sam Gilman (*policeman*), Milton Frome (*tweedy physicist*), Doodles Weaver (*yokel*), Zamba (*Fluffy, a lion*).

Comedy. Biochemist Dan Potter hurriedly leaves his post at the university when his neighbors begin to believe exaggerated reports about his mildmannered lion, Fluffy. After he is threatened by the police, he and Fluffy turn up at the Claridge Arms Hotel just as a suite is being vacated by the owner's daughter, Janice. Returning for the remainder of her belongings, Janice is horrified to find Fluffy; and after she hears a newscast giving an overstated account of the lion's antics, she calls Dan a psychopath and runs for the police. Later, Claridge meets Dan and invites him over for some venison, left over from a curtailed hunting trip. Dan shows up with Fluffy, who gnaws on the food, leaving only scraps. When the police, alerted by the neighbors' fright at the sound of Fluffy's roars, find the scraps, they assume that Fluffy has eaten Claridge. Claridge, meanwhile, has hidden in his apartment, and he takes advantage of his "death" to resume his hunting trip. At the police station, where Dan has been arrested, Fluffy's brief appearance causes havoc; and Dan, inadvertently handcuffed to Janice, escapes. They find Claridge's trailer and persuade him to tell the truth to the police and to the angered townspeople. *Biochemists. Neighbors. Police. Hunters. Hotels. Lions.*

FLY NOW, PAY LATER
F6.1620

Cinex Film Industries. 19 Mar **1969** [New York showing]. Sd; b&w. 35mm. 75 min.

Prod-Dir B. H. Dial. *Assoc Prod* Gillian Vastlake. *Writ* Gillian Vastlake, Basta Laparola. *Script* Gillian Vastlake. *Camera* B. H. Dial. *Asst Camera* Myron Mogul, IV. *Sets* Viva Lamano. *Ed* Jacques Chien-Lit. *Asst Ed* Naja Nitlodge. *Mus* A. Pismo Clamm. *Sd* Humphrey Groundloupe. *Stills* Herman Q. Muscleman.

Cast: Charlotte Rouse (*Sally*), Shep Wild (*man in snow*), O. K. Baime (*nephew*), Simone Renard (*Sandra*), Cherie Winters (*Joan*), Ronald Arunde (*Alan*), George Wilson (*Richard Fleetwood*), Judy Caine (*Beth*), Misty (*Carole*), Imano Kutt (*man with dagger*), Rip Thonger (*man with whip*), Emile Nitrate (*passive man*), Morris Towne (*Fatim*), B. S. Kroul (*Abdul*), A. Pismo Clamm (*uncle*), Myron Mogul, IV (*man in front of shop*).

Crime melodrama. Richard Fleetwood, a virile young detective, is sent to investigate the disappearance of a number of airline stewardesses flying the Morocco run. The women have fallen into the hands of an international dope ring which uses them to smuggle a vicious drug called "khelp" into New York City. The women are drugged into submission and forced to gratify the perverted desires of the gangsters. Sally, the newest victim, is forced to join Sandra, the ring leader, in lesbian lovemaking. Beth is violently slashed with a dagger by a man who finds intense pleasure in witnessing pain. Carole is forced to serve the gangsters with a whip before surrendering her body. Richard enlists the help of another stewardess, Joan, to crack the case, but the gangsters catch on to the plan. While the two spend the evening trying to decode a faked message, the gangsters make plans to eliminate the four stewardesses. Carole, given an overdose of khelp, goes berserk. Beth is drugged and placed on a couch, where two snakes poison her with their venom. Sally is stabbed with a bottle by a man who then uses her lifeless body to gratify his lust. Just as Joan is about to become the final victim, Richard bursts into the room, gunning down Sandra and her henchmen. *Airline stewardesses. Detectives. Gangsters.*

Smugglers. Drug dealers. Sadism. Murder. Lesbianism. Necrophilia. Masochism. Flagellation. Tranquilizers. Narcotics. Morocco. New York City. Snakes.

FLY, RAVEN, FLY see **THE DESERT RAVEN**

FLYING CLIPPER—TRAUMREISE UNTER WEISSEN SEGELN see **MEDITERRANEAN HOLIDAY**

THE FLYING MATCHMAKER (Israel)
F6.1621

Flying Matchmaker, Ltd. *Dist* National Showmanship Films. 14 Jan **1970** [Los Angeles opening]. Sd; col (Cineffects Color). 35mm (Totalscope). 104 min. *MPAA rating* G.

Pres by Joseph J. Macaluso. *Prod* Mordechai Navon. *Exec Prod* Melvin L. Gold. *Dir* Israel Becker. *Screenplay* Israel Becker, Alex Maimon. *English Adapt & Dial* Paulette Rubinstein. *Photog* Romolo Garroni. *Film Ed (see note)* Nelly Bogor, Nelly Gilad. *Ed English Adapt* Edward P. Bartsch. *Mus* Shaul Barzoweski. *Mus Perf by* Israel Symphony Orchestra. *Orig Lyr* Moshe Sahar. *English Lyr* Feather Schwartz. *Song:* "Have I Got a Boy for You" Paulette Rubinstein, Sherry Cloth. *Arr by* Abba Bogin. *Sung by* Jerry Jarrett. *Sd Engr* Robert Sherwood. *Asst Dir* David Perlov. *Prod Mgr* Henry Roth.

Cast: Mike Burstein (*Kouny-Lemel/Max*), Germaine Unikovsky (*Libaleh*), Rina Ganor (*Caroline*), Raphel Klatschkin (*Reb Kalman, The Matchmaker*), Shmuel Rodensky (*Pinchas'l*), Elisheva Michaeli (*Rebeka*), Aaron Meskin (*Shalmoni*), Mordecai Arnon (*Beralle*), Asher Levy (*Loksh*), Hanan Goldblatt (*professor*), Shlomo Vishinsky (*Bullfass*), Jetta Luka (*Tzipa*), Ari Kutai (*Dr. Friedberg*), Pesach Burstein (*Shiele*).

Voices for English Adapt: Mike Burstein (*Kouny-Lemel & Max*), Ken Harvey (*The Matchmaker*), Bernard Grant (*Pinchas'l*), Norman Rose (*Shalmoni*), Lillian Lux (*Rebeka*), Paulette Rubinstein (*Caroline*), Lois Brandt (*Libaleh*).

Musical comedy. Source: Abraham Goldfaden, *Der Fanatik oder di Tsvey Kuni Lemels* (a play; 1880). Reb Kalman, an enterprising matchmaker who has brought many couples together, is unable to find a husband for his own daughter Libaleh. Reb is hired by the wealthy Pinchas'l, who is anxious to find a husband for his daughter Caroline. Caroline is in love with her tutor, Max, but Pinchas'l wants her to marry someone from the upper class. Reb matches Caroline with Kouny-Lemel, a simpleton from the next village. Max, who bears a striking resemblance to Kouny-Lemel, secretly continues his courtship of Caroline. Their identities become so confused that in the end the parents allow Caroline to marry Max, and the matchmaker's daughter winds up with Kouny-Lemel. *Matchmakers. Tutors. Doubles. Halfwits. Marriage—Arranged. Courtship. Fatherhood.*

Note: Produced in Israel in 1965 and released there as *Shnei Kuni Lemel*; running time: 90 min. Sources conflict in crediting film editor.

FOG see **A STUDY IN TERROR**

FOLLOW A STAR (Great Britain)
F6.1622

Rank Organisation. *Dist* Zenith International Film Corp. 25 Apr **1961** [New York opening]. Sd; b&w. 35mm. 102 min.

A J. Arthur Rank Production. *Prod* Hugh Stewart. *Dir* Robert Asher. *Screenplay* Jack Davies, Henry Blyth, Norman Wisdom. *Photog* Jack Asher. *Camera Op* David Harcourt. *Art Dir* Maurice Carter. *Set Dresser* Vernon Dixon. *Film Ed* Roger Cherrill. *Mus* Philip Green. *Songs:* "Follow a Star," "The Square Song," "I Love You" Norman Wisdom. *Song:* "Give Me" Philip Green, Sonny Miller. *Song:* "You Deserve a Medal for That" Peter Myers, Alec Grahame. *Choreog* Eleanor Fazan. *Sd Ed* Harry Miller. *Sd Rec* C. C. Stevens, Gordon K. McCallum. *Asst Dir* Bert Batt. *Prod Mgr* Charles Orme. *Cont* Splinters Deason. *Cost Dsgn* Anthony Mendleson. *Makeup* George Blackler.

Cast: Norman Wisdom (*Norman Truscott*), June Laverick (*Judy*), Jerry Desmonde (*Vernon Carew*), Hattie Jacques (*Dymphna Dobson*), Richard Wattis (*Dr. Chatterway*), Eddie Leslie (*Harold Franklin*), John Le Mesurier (*Birkett*), Sydney Tafler (*Pendlebury*), Fenella Fielding (*Lady Finchington*), Charles Heslop (*The General*), Joe Melia (*stage manager*), Ron Moody (*violinist*).

Comedy with music. Norman Truscott, a timid suit-presser, dreams of someday becoming a popular singing star. He is so insecure, however, that he can only sing when his crippled girl friend, Judy, is on hand to play the piano for him and give him confidence. One day, fading music star Vernon Carew accidentally hears Norman sing and realizes that he has the type of voice the public wants. Carew persuades the gullible Norman, accompanied by Judy, to audition for him and secretly records the song. His agent sells the tape to a recording company as Carew's own voice, and it becomes a tremendous hit. When the record company demands another disc, Carew once more gets Norman to sing. This time, however, Judy is not there, and Norman can only croak. Carew solves the problem by forcing Norman to take a bath, on the theory that everyone sings in the bathtub. A hidden microphone records

Norman singing, and Carew has another hit record. Eventually Norman's voice coach, Dymphna Dobson, recognizes the voice of Carew's recordings as that of her pupil, and she decides to expose the fraud. While Carew is on stage at the London Palladium miming a recording of Norman's voice, she smashes the disc and brings Norman on stage. Realizing that it was his voice that made Carew famous, Norman completely captivates the audience and later finds the courage to propose to Judy. *Singers. Cripples. Pianists. Talent agents. Vocal instructors. Timidity. Self-confidence. Gullibility. Fraud. Recorders. London Palladium.*

Note: Released in Great Britain in Dec 1959; running time: 104 min.

FOLLOW ME   F6.1623

Robert E. Petersen Productions. *Dist* Cinerama Releasing Corp. 25 Apr **1969** [Hermosa Beach, California, opening; c30 Apr 1969; LP38513]. Sd; col (Eastman Color). 35mm. 79 min. *MPAA rating G.*

Pres by Robert E. Petersen. *Prod-Dir* Gene McCabe. *Exec Prod* Robert L. Dellinger. *Assoc Prod* Ric Eyrich. *Screenplay* Stanley Ralph Ross. *Photog* Mike Margulies, Jim Freeman, Greg MacGillivray. *Prod Dsgn* Ric Eyrich. *Supv Film Ed* Igo Kantor. *Film Ed* Fred Brown, Donn Cambern, Gerald Sheppard, William Martin, Almon R. Teeter. *Mus Comp & Dir* Stu Phillips. *Songs:* "Through Spray Colored Glasses," "Just Lookin' for Someone" Stu Phillips, David Gates, *Perf by* Dino, Desi & Billy. *Songs:* "Surfers 3," "Hello Linda" Stu Phillips, *Perf by* Dino, Desi & Billy. *Sd* Producers Sound Service. *Sd Eff* Edit-Rite Inc. *Post-prod Sd Ed* Synchrofilm. *Prod Mgr* Jack Dulin.

Featuring: Claude Codgen, Mary Lou McGinnis, Bob Purvey, Bonnie Hill, Andrea Kermot, Deborah Lee, Ava Zamora.

Narrator: Jerry Dexter.

Documentary. Claude Codgen, Mary Lou McGinnis, and Bob Purvey, three young surfers, set out to sample surfing conditions around the world. Their first stop is Guincho Beach, Portugal, with its cold and treacherous waves. They then travel to Morocco, Ceylon, India, Hong Kong, and Tokyo, where they surf at Summerland, an indoor pool with manmade waves. Their last stops are the legendary Waimea and Sunset Beaches of Hawaii. *Surfers. Beaches. Swimming pools. Guincho Beach (Portugal). Portugal. Ceylon. Hong Kong. Morocco. India. Tokyo. Waimea (Hawaii). Hawaii.*

Note: Filmed in Portugal, Morocco, Ceylon, India, Hong Kong, Japan, and Hawaii, in 16mm.

FOLLOW ME ... see SIX DAYS TO ETERNITY

FOLLOW ME, BOYS!   F6.1624

Walt Disney Productions. *Dist* Buena Vista Distribution Co. 1 Dec **1966** [New York opening; c24 Aug 1966; LP33001]. Sd (RCA); col (Technicolor). 35mm. 131 min. [Copyright length: 129 min.]

Pres by Walt Disney. *Prod* Walt Disney. *Co-prod* Winston Hibler. *Dir* Norman Tokar. *Screenplay* Louis Pelletier. *Dir Photog* Clifford Stine. *Art Dir* Carroll Clark, Marvin Aubrey Davis. *Set Decor* Emile Kuri, Frank R. McKelvy. *Film Ed* Robert Stafford. *Mus* George Bruns. *Orch* Walter Sheets. *Titl Song* Robert B. Sherman, Richard M. Sherman. *Sd Supv* Robert O. Cook. *Sd Mix* Robert Post. *Mus Ed* Evelyn Kennedy. *Asst Dir* Terry Morse, Jr. *Asst to the Prod* Jerome Courtland. *Cost Dsgn* Bill Thomas. *Cost* Chuck Keehne, Neva Rames. *Makeup* Pat McNalley. *Hairstyles* La Rue Matheron. *Sp Eff* Eustace Lycett. *Matte Art* Jim Fetherolf.

Cast: Fred MacMurray (*Lemuel Siddons*), Vera Miles (*Vida Downey*), Lillian Gish (*Hetty Seibert*), Charlie Ruggles (*John Everett Hughes*), Elliott Reid (*Ralph Hastings*), Kurt Russell (*Whitey*), Luana Patten (*Nora White*), Ken Murray (*Melody Murphy*), Donald May (*Edward White, Jr.*), Sean McClory (*Edward White, Sr.*), Steve Franken (*POW lieutenant*), Parley Baer (*Mayor Hi Plommer*), William Reynolds, actor (*Hoodoo Henderson as a man*), Craig Hill (*Leo as a man*), Tol Avery (*Doctor Ferris*), Willis Bouchey (*judge*), John Zaremba (*Ralph's lawyer*), Madge Blake (*Cora Anderson*), Carl Reindel (*tank captain*), Hank Brandt (*Frankie Martin as a man*), Richard Bakalyan (*umpire*), Tim McIntire (*corporal*), Willie Soo Hoo (*Quong Lee as a man*), Tony Regan (*Hetty's lawyer*), Robert B. Williams (*Artie*), Jimmy Murphy (*1st POW soldier*), Adam Williams (*POW sergeant*), Dean Moray (*Hoodoo Henderson*), Bill Booth (*Leo*), Keith Taylor (*Beefy Smith*), Rick Kelman (*Frankie Martin*), Gregg Shank (*Mickey Doyle*), Donnie Carter (*Red*), Kit Lloyd (*Oliver*), Ronnie Dapo (*Tiger*), Dennis Rush (*Jimmy*), Kevin Burchett (*Eggy*), David Bailey (*Duke*), Eddie Sallia (*Harry*), Bill "Wahoo" Mills (*David*), Warren Hsieh (*Quong Lee*), Duane Chase (*Joe*), Mike Dodge, actor (*Phil*), Greger Vigen (*Ronnie Larsen*), Michael Flatley (*scout #1, Troop #1*), Sherwood Ball (*scout #3, Troop #1*), Colyer Dupont (*scout at cliff*), Dean Bradshaw, Chris Mason, Johnny Bangert (*scouts in war games*).

Comedy. Source: MacKinlay Kantor, *God and My Country* (Cleveland, 1954). Late in the 1920's saxophone player Lem Siddons gives up his job with a broken-down traveling jazzband and settles down in the small town of Hickory. He takes a job as clerk in John Hughes's mercantile store, woos and

wins pretty Vida Downey from her fiancé, banker Ralph Hastings, and organizes a local Boy Scout troop. The only disappointment in Lem's new life is Vida's inability to bear children. Vida's love for children, however, is equal to Lem's, and she readily agrees to adopt young Whitey White, the orphaned son of the town drunkard. Lem's work with the scouts is long and rewarding as he builds his troop into one of the finest in the state. While Whitey is overseas with the Army Medical Corps in World War II, Lem uses his knowledge of law to help the town's wealthiest citizen, Hetty Seibert, against Hastings, her nephew. Lem proves that she is mentally competent in deciding to donate her valuable lake property to the scouts. When the war ends, Whitey returns home with a bride, Nora, and sets up practice as a physician. Lem continues to devote his time and energy to his beloved scouts until Whitey informs him that his heart has become too weak for such a vigorous life. As Lem reluctantly retires with the title Scoutmaster Emeritus, the entire town and most of his former scouts, including the governor, turn out to celebrate "Lem Siddons Day." *Saxophonists. Bankers. Orphans. Physicians. Aunts. Children. Marriage. Childlessness. Adoption. Smalltown life. Alcoholism. Jazzbands. Lawsuits. General stores. World War II. Boy Scouts. United States Army—Medical Service.*

FOLLOW THAT CAMEL (Great Britain)   F6.1625

Adder Productions. *Dist* Schoenfeld Film Distributing Corp. 16 Oct **1968** [Milwaukee, Wisconsin, opening; c6 Jan 1968; LF191]. Sd; col (Eastmancolor). 35mm. 95 min.

Prod Peter Rogers. *Dir* Gerald Thomas. *Screenplay* Talbot Rothwell. *Photog* Alan Hume. *Art Dir* Alex Vetchinsky. *Film Ed* Alfred Roome. *Mus* Eric Rogers. *Sd* Wally Nelson. *Sd Rec* Dudley Messenger, Ken Barker. *Asst Dir* David Bracknell. *Prod Mgr* Jack Swinburne. *Cost* Emma Selby-Walker.

Cast: Phil Silvers (*Sergeant Nocker*), Jim Dale (*Bertram Oliphant West*), Peter Butterworth (*Simpson*), Charles Hawtrey (*Captain Le Pice*), Anita Harris (*Corktip*), Kenneth Williams (*Commandant Burger*), Joan Sims (*Zigzig*), Bernard Bresslaw (*Abdul*), Angela Douglas (*Lady Jane Ponsonby*), John Bluthal (*Corporal Clotski*), Larry Taylor (*Riff*), William Hurndell (*Raff*), Gertan Klauber (*Algerian Spiv*), Peter Gilmore (*Bagshaw*), Julian Orchard (*doctor*), William Mervyn (*Ponsonby*), Julian Holloway (*ticket collector*), Vincent Ball (*ship's officer*), David Glover (*hotel manager*).

Comedy. Bertram Oliphant West—known as Bo—is unjustly accused of cheating at cricket by Bagshaw, his rival for the affections of Lady Jane Ponsonby. Accompanied by his faithful manservant Simpson, he departs England to enlist in the Foreign Legion. After reporting to Commandant Burger and Captain Le Pice at Fort Sidi Bel Abbes, they hear Sergeant Nocker relating stories of his heroic adventures on desert patrol. Bo, however, has learned from local cafe proprietress Zigzig that the sergeant actually spends his time sleeping in her back room. When Sergeant Nocker is confronted with this revealing information, their "friendship" is ensured. The three men are lured by belly dancer Corktip into capture by the unscrupulous Sheik Abdul Abulbul, who plans to capture the legion fort. Lady Jane, now aware of Bo's innocence and determined to find him, stumbles upon Abulbul, who becomes infatuated with her. Eventually the men escape, rescue Lady Jane, and secure the fort against the Arabs. Bo and Lady Jane return to England. *Valets. Arabs. Braggarts. Cafe hostesses. Exotic dancers. Sheiks. Courtship. Friendship. Cricket. Forts. Deserts. France—Army—Foreign Legion.*

Note: Opened in London in Dec 1967; running time: 95 min.

FOLLOW THAT DREAM   F6.1626

Mirisch Co. *Dist* United Artists. 11 Apr **1962** [Ocala, Florida, opening; c11 Apr 1961; LP21897]. Sd; col (De Luxe). 35mm (Panavision). 110 min.

Prod David Weisbart. *Dir* Gordon Douglas. *Screenplay* Charles Lederer. *Dir Photog* Leo Tover. *Art Dir* Malcolm C. Bert. *Set Dsgn* Gordon Gurnee. *Set Decor* Fred McLean. *Film Ed* William B. Murphy. *Mus* Hans J. Salter. *Titl Song* Fred Wise, Ben Weisman. *Song:* "What a Wonderful Life" Sid Wayne, Jerry Livingston. *Song:* "I'm Not the Marrying Kind" Mack David, Sherman Edwards. *Song:* "Sound Advice" Bill Giant, Bernie Baum, Florence Kaye. *Song:* "Angel" Sid Tepper. *Songs Sung by* Elvis Presley. *Sd* Jack Solomon, Buddy Myers, Ruth Hancock. *Mus Ed* Robert Tracy. *Asst Dir* Bert Chervin. *Prod Supv* Allen K. Wood. *Prod Mgr* Herbert E. Mendelson. *Makeup* Dan Striepeke. *Tech Adv* Col. Tom Parker.

Cast: Elvis Presley (*Toby Kwimper*), Arthur O'Connell (*Pop Kwimper*), Anne Helm (*Holly Jones*), Joanna Moore (*Alicia Claypoole*), Jack Kruschen (*Carmine*), Simon Oakland (*Nick*), Herbert Rudley (*Endicott*), Alan Hewitt (*H. Arthur King*), Howard McNear (*George*), Gavin Koon (*Eddy Bascombe*), Robin Koon (*Teddy Bascombe*), Harry Holcombe (*The Governor*), Pam Ogles (*Adriadne Pennington*), Roland Winters (*The Judge*), Frank De Kova (*Jack*), Robert Carricart (*Al*), John Duke (*Blackie*).

Comedy with music. Source: Richard Powell, *Pioneer, Go Home!* (New York, 1959). Old Pop Kwimper is a vagabond who lives on his relief checks, his son Toby's Army disability pension, and the government allowance he receives for sheltering four homeless orphans, one of whom, 19-year-old Holly, has long loved the girl-shy Toby. One day, while driving his brood through Florida, Pop runs out of gasoline, and the Kwimpers are forced to spend the night on a strip of beach just off a new highway. When Toby discovers the nearby waters are filled with giant tarpon, the family decides to homestead on the land and build a fishing dock. Their little enterprise flourishes, and since the beach is outside municipal jurisdiction, the area is soon filled with other homesteaders, including two rowdy gamblers, Nick and Carmine, whose trailer conceals a floating crap game. When the gamblers become a source of annoyance, the other settlers elect Toby sheriff of the community, and he succeeds, albeit accidentally, in driving them off. Further trouble looms when Alicia Claypoole, a state welfare worker, tries to have Pop declared unfit to care for the children. But, spurning legal counsel, the Kwimpers present their own defense and so impress the judge that he throws the case out of court. And all ends happily when Holly is at last able to convince Toby that he really does love her. *Orphans. Vagabonds. Homesteaders. Foster fathers. Sheriffs. Judges. Social workers. Timidity. Adolescence. Child welfare. Fishing. Gambling. Beaches. Trailers. Florida. Tarpon.*

Note: Location scenes filmed in Florida. Working titles: *Pioneer, Go Home!* and *What a Wonderful Life.*

FOLLOW THAT HORSE! (Great Britain)   F6.1627

Cavalcade Films. *For* Associated British Picture Corp. *Dist* Seven Arts Associated Corp. Dec **1961** [Los Angeles opening: 22 Aug 1962]. Sd; b&w. 35mm. 80 min.

Prod Thomas Clyde. *Dir* Alan Bromly. *Screenplay* Alfred Shaughnessy. *Adtl Scenes* William Douglas Home. *Adapt* Howard Mason. *Dir Photog* Norman Warwick. *Camera Op* Tony White. *Camera Focus* Maurice Arnold. *Art Dir* Harry White. *Asst Art Dir* Pamela Cornell. *Film Ed* Gerald Turney-Smith. *1st Asst Ed* Don Deacon. *2d Asst Ed* Martin Magee. *Mus* Stanley Black. *Sd* Allan Morrison. *Sd Rec* H. L. Bird, Len Shilton. *Boom Op* Don Wortham. *Sd Camera Op* Terry Sharrett. *1st, 2d & 3d Asst Dir* Frederic Goode, Michael Profit, Bill Cartlidge. *Prod Controller* Tom White. *Prod Mgr* Victor Peck. *Cont* June Randall. *Wardrobe Mistress* Eileen Sullivan. *Ch Makeup* Eric Aylott. *Ch Hairdresser* Polly Young. *Still Photog* George Higgins. *Prop Buyer* Charles Sutton. *Casting Dir* Robert Lennard. *Crowd Casting* E. Bonnichon. *Prop Master* W. Osborne.

Cast: David Tomlinson (*Dick Lanchester*), Cecil Parker (*Sir William Crane*), Richard Wattis (*Hugh Porlock*), Mary Peach (*Susan Turner*), Dora Bryan (*Miss Bradstock*), Raymond Huntley (*special branch chief*), Sam Kydd (*Farrell*), George Pravda (*Hammler*), John Welsh (*Major Turner*), Peter Copley (*Garrod*), Cyril Shaps (*Dr. Spiegel*), Victor Brooks (*Blake*), Vic Wise (*Riley*), George A. Cooper (*Rudd*), Tony Thawnton (*special branch man*), Alison Fraser (*Harriet*), Arthur Lowe (*auctioneer*), John Phillips, British (*American delegate*), Guy Deghy (*German delegate*), John Crewdson (*pilot*), John Serret, Edward Dentith, Peter Collingwood, Jonathan Clyde.

Comedy. Source: Howard Mason, *Photo Finish* (London, 1954). Assigned by the minister of atomic power to escort famed atomic physicist Dr. Spiegel to a NATO conference in London, happy-go-lucky civil servant Dick Lanchester stops to flirt with Susan Turner, daughter of a racehorse owner. Dr. Spiegel, a turncoat, sees his chance to escape the country with some secret microfilm while Dick's attention is diverted. Waiting for Spiegel are his confederates, but he mistakenly gets into the horse van being driven by Susan to the racetrack. The frightened horse rears, Spiegel drops the film in the hay, and the animal swallows it. Following the horse's victory at the races, it is put up for auction. Dick, who has since learned of Spiegel's attempted defection, is outbid by the spies because his superior refuses to give him proper authorization to purchase the horse. As the spies escape with the mare to an abandoned airfield, Dick and Susan give chase. They recover the horse, capture the spies, and eventually retrieve the film in the course of nature. *Spies. Physicists. Escorts. Civil servants. Defectors. Horseracing. Racetracks. Auctions. Airfields. Microfilm. Conferences—International. London. North Atlantic Treaty Organization. Chases. Horses.*

Note: Location scenes filmed in London. Opened in London in Jul 1960.

FOLLOW THE BOYS   F6.1628

Franmet Productions. *Dist* Metro-Goldwyn-Mayer, Inc. 27 Feb **1963** [New York opening; c5 Feb 1963; LP24162]. Sd (Westrex); col (Metrocolor). 35mm (Panavision). 95 min.

Prod–Orig Story Lawrence P. Bachmann. *Dir* Richard Thorpe. *Screenplay* David T. Chantler, David Osborn. *Dir Photog* Ted Scaife. *Art Dir* Bill Andrews. *Film Ed* John Victor Smith. *Mus Score* Ron Goodwin, Alexander Courage. *Cond* Ron Goodwin. *Song:* "Italian Lullabye" Connie Francis. *Songs:* "Follow the Boys," "Waiting for Billy," "Tonight's My Night," "Sleepyland," "Intrigue" Benny Davis, Ted Murry, Dramato Palumbo. *Songs Arr & Cond* Geoff Love. *Sung by* Connie Francis. *Sd* Rusty Coppleman. *Asst Dir* Jack Causey. *Prod Supv* Basil Somner.

Cast: Connie Francis (*Bonnie Pulaski*), Paula Prentiss (*Toni Denham*), Dany Robin (*Michele*), Russ Tamblyn (*Lieutenant Smith*), Richard Long (*Lieut. Peter Langley*), Ron Randell (*Comdr. Ben Bradville*), Roger Perry (*Radarman Bill Pulaski*), Janis Paige (*Liz Bradville*), Robert Nichols (*Hulldown*), Paul Maxwell (*C.M.A.A.*), Eric Pohlmann (*Italian farmer*), David Sumner (*Vittorio*), Sean Kelly (*duty officer*), John McClaren (*commentator*), Roger Snowdon (*Italian barman*).

Romantic comedy. Four young women pool their resources to buy a dilapidated French car and follow their husbands and boyfriends aboard the U.S.S. *Independence* from Cannes to its next port of call on the Italian Riviera. Bonnie Pulaski, a bride of only 2 hours, cannot bear to be separated from her radarman husband, Billy. Liz hopes to persuade her husband, Comdr. Ben Bradville, to take a land-based job so that they can raise a family. Wealthy Toni Denham and a French girl named Michele are both seeking Lieut. Peter Langley: Toni wants him to marry her and form a business partnership with her father, while Michele, it is revealed, is a bill collector seeking payment on a sheaf of unpaid bills. Things do not go well when the fleet followers arrive in Italy. Billy, restricted to ship, is furious with Bonnie for refusing to stay home; Ben has been given another seagoing command; and Peter rejects Toni and romances Michele. The romantic entanglements are straightened out at a grape-crushing festival when Toni falls in love with Lieutenant Smith and relinquishes Peter to Michele. All ends happily as Billy and Bonnie meet and are reconciled, and Ben decides to give up the sea to become a land-based husband. *Sailors. Brides. French. Bill collectors. Marriage. Wealth. Ships. Cannes. Italy. Riviera. United States Navy.*

Note: Location scenes filmed on the French Riviera. Dramato Palumbo is credited as co-author of songs, but music copyright listings for these songs do not include his name.

FOMA GORDEYEV see THE GORDEYEV FAMILY

THE FOOL KILLER   F6.1629

Landau Co.–Jack J. Dreyfus, Jr. *Dist* Allied Artists, Landau Releasing Organization, Jack J. Dreyfus, Jr. 28 Apr **1965** [Knoxville, Tennessee, opening]. Sd; b&w. 35mm. 99 min.

Pres by Ely Landau, Jack J. Dreyfus, Jr. An Ely Landau Production. *Prod* David Friedkin. *Exec Prod* Worthington Miner. *Assoc Prod* Harrison Starr, Alfred Markim. *Prod Assoc* Herbert R. Steinmann. *Dir* Servando Gonzalez. *Screenplay* Morton Fine, David Friedkin. *Dir Photog* Alex Phillips, Jr. *Art Dir* Rudy Sternad. *Prod Dsgn* Robert Smith. *Film Ed* (see note) Juan José Marino, Ralph Rosenblum. *Mus* Gustavo César Carrión. *Song:* "The Ballad of the Fool Killer" Mike Phillips, Tillman Franks. *Sung by* David Houston. *Sd* Richard Grimaglia. *Asst Dir* Francisco Day. *Cost* Dorothy Jeakins.

Cast: Anthony Perkins (*Milo Bogardus*), Edward Albert, Jr. (*George Mellish*), Dana Elcar (*Mr. Dodd*), Henry Hull (*Dirty Jim Jelliman*), Salome Jens (*Mrs. Dodd*), Charlotte Jones (*Mrs. Ova Fanshawe*), Arnold Moss (*Reverend Spotts*), Sindee Anne Richards (*Blessing Angelina*), Frances Garr (*old crab*), Wendell Phillips (*old man*).

Melodrama. Source: Helen Eustis, *The Fool Killer* (Garden City, New York, 1954). After the Civil War George Mellish, a 12-year-old orphan, leaves his foster home. The youth is befriended by aging reprobate Dirty Jim Jelliman, who relates to him the legend of The Fool Killer, an axe murderer. George later makes the acquaintance of Milo Bogardus, an anticlerical veteran. Unaware of Milo's profound antipathy, George persuades him to attend a revival conducted by Reverend Spotts, after which the evangelist is found hacked to death. Having moved in with the Dodds, a kindly unmarried couple, George is horrified to discover Milo lurking beside his bedroom window, hatchet in hand. George alerts Dodd and later witnesses Milo's fatal fall from the roof of the house. *Orphans. Evangelists. Veterans. Adolescence. Insanity. Murder. Mutilation. Axes. Revivals.*

Note: Location scenes filmed in Knoxville, Tennessee. Produced in 1963. Distributed in 1965 by the Landau Releasing Organization through Allied Artists. Jack Dreyfus, Jr. purchased the exclusive rights to the film, reedited it, and rereleased it in 1969. Sources conflict in crediting film editor.

FOOLS   F6.1630

Translor Productions–Tom Gries Productions. *Dist* Cinerama Releasing Corp. 23 Dec **1970** [San Francisco opening; c23 Dec 1970; LP39903]. Sd; col (Eastman Color). 35mm. 93 min.

Prod Henri Bollinger, Robert H. Yamin. *Exec Prod* Pat B. Rooney. *Dir* Tom Gries. *Screenplay* Robert Rudelson. *Dir Photog* Michel Hugo. *Camera Op* Ralph Gerling. *Asst Camera Op* Patrick J. Fennell. *Film Ed* Byron Brandt. *Asst Film Ed* Irving Rosenblum. *Mus* Shorty Rogers. *Titl Theme Song:* "Someone Who Cares" Alex Harvey. *Song:* "A Poem I Wrote for Your Hair" Paul Parrish. *Songs Sung by* Kenny Rogers and the First Edition. *Song:* "If You Love" Mimi Fariña. *Sung by* Katharine Ross, Mimi Fariña. *Songs Prod* Jimmy Bowen, Kenny Rogers. *Sd* Louis H. Yates, James T. Mansen. *Asst Dir* Clark Paylow.

Key Grip Richard D. Spah. *Gaffer* Donald M. Marshall.

Cast: Jason Robards, [Jr.] *(Matthew South)*, Katharine Ross *(Anais Appleton)*, Scott Hylands *(David Appleton)*, Roy Jenson, Mark Bramhall *(men in park)*, Marc Hannibal *(dog owner)*, Robert C. Ferro, Jr. *(private detective)*, Floy Dean, Roy Jelliffe *(restaurant couple)*, Charles B. Dorsett *(dentist)*, Laura Ash *(patient)*, Robert Rothwell, Michael Davis *(policemen)*, Vera Stough *(girl in movie)*, James Burr Johnson, Louis Picetti, Jr., Stuart P. Klitsner *(FBI men)*, Robin Menken, Christopher Pray, Jack Nance *(hippies)*, Mako *(psychiatrist)*, Mimi Fariña, Rod Arrants.

Melodrama. Matthew South, a middle-aged actor who has made his career in second-rate horror films, leaves Hollywood for San Francisco, and there he meets young Anais Appleton, who is running away from her wealthy husband, David, a lawyer. Matthew and Anais fall in love and begin living together. All goes well until a private detective hired by Anais's husband starts to interfere with their new life. Consenting to meet David, Anais tells him that she has found true love with Matthew; she returns to Matthew, but David later shoots and kills her when she attempts to avoid him. *Actors. Lawyers. Detectives. Marriage. Infidelity. Wealth. Middle age. Desertion. Jealousy. Murder. Hollywood. San Francisco.*

Note: Location scenes filmed in San Francisco.

FOOTPRINTS ON THE MOON—APOLLO 11   F6.1631
Barry Coe Productions. *Dist* Twentieth Century–Fox Film Corp. 25 Sep **1969** [Atlanta opening]. Sd; col (Technicolor). 35mm. 95 min.
  Prod Barry Coe. *Asst to the Prod* Frank Roh. *Dir* Bill Gibson. *Narr Writ* Robert S. Scott. *Moon & Space Photog* Neil Armstrong, Michael Collins, astronaut, Edwin Aldrin. *Film Ed* John F. Link, Jr. *Film Coörd* John S. Nash. *Lunar Concerto Theme* Phil Moody. *Mus Supv* Igo Kantor.
  Cast: Wernher von Braun *(narrator)*, Pierre Jalbert *(voice of Jules Verne)*.
  Documentary. This film record of the *Apollo 11* moon flight depicts the launch, the historic moon walk by Neil Armstrong and Edwin Aldrin, the ascent and docking of the *Eagle* with Michael Collins' command module, and the astronauts' safe return to earth. The narration compares the modern-day lunar voyage with that envisioned by Jules Verne. *Astronauts. Space flights. The Moon. Jules Verne. Neil Armstrong. Michael Collins. Edwin Aldrin.*
  Note: Filmed in 16mm and videotape.

FOR A FEW DOLLARS MORE (Italy/Spain/West Germany)   F6.1632
P. E. A.–Arturo Gonzales–Constantin Film. *Dist* United Artists. 10 May **1967** [Boston opening; c17 Dec 1965; LF11]. Sd; col (Technicolor). 35mm (Techniscope). 130 min.
  Prod Alberto Grimaldi. *Dir* Sergio Leone. *Screenplay* Luciano Vincenzoni, Sergio Leone. *Story* Fulvio Morsella, Sergio Leone. *Photog* Massimo Dallamano. *Art Dir* Carlo Simi. *Film Ed* Giorgio Ferralonga, Eugenio Alabiso. *Mus* Ennio Morricone. *Mus Dir* Bruno Nicolai. *Sd* Oscar De Arcangelis. *Prod Mgr* Ottavio Oppo. *Cost* Carlo Simi.
  Cast: Clint Eastwood *(The Man With No Name)*, Lee Van Cleef *(Col. Douglas Mortimer)*, Gian Maria Volontè *(Indio)*, Josef Egger *(old man over railway)*, Rosemarie Dexter *(Colonel Mortimer's sister)*, Mara Krup *(hotel manager's wife)*, Klaus Kinski *(hunchback)*, Mario Brega, Aldo Sambrell, Luigi Pistilli, Benito Stefanelli *(Indio's gang)*, Roberto Camardiel, Luis F. Rodríguez, Panos Papadopoulos, Diana Rabito, Giovanni Tarallo, Mario Meniconi, Lorenzo Robledo, Tomás Blanco, Werner Abrolat.
  Western melodrama. In the post-Civil War Southwest, two bounty hunters set out after a sadistic outlaw, Indio, for whom a $10,000 reward is offered. One of the hunters is a stranger known only as "the man with no name"; the other, Col. Douglas Mortimer, is a former Confederate Army officer whose sister committed suicide after being raped by Indio. The two men first encounter each other in El Paso and prepare for a showdown, but instead they decide to join forces in tracking down Indio and splitting the reward. To win favor with Indio, the stranger organizes a jailbreak and frees the outlaw's best friend. After joining Indio's gang, the stranger double-crosses Mortimer by persuading Indio to ride in a direction other than the one expected by Mortimer. The colonel, however, has anticipated the stranger's strategy and waits for Indio and his gang at their destination. Mortimer then proceeds to ingratiate himself with the gang leader by opening a safe stolen from the El Paso Bank. After patching up their differences, the two bounty hunters prepare to make off with the contents of the safe. But Indio captures them, and after failing to find out where they have hidden the money, he conceives a plan for eliminating both the bounty hunters and his own henchmen, thereby securing all the money for himself. He sets free Mortimer and the stranger and orders his gang to kill them. When the bloody gun battle is over, only Mortimer and the stranger are still alive. Mortimer, aided by the stranger, avenges his sister's death by killing the cowering Indio. His mission completed, Mortimer rides off, leaving the stranger to deliver all the dead bodies and collect the bounty money. *Bounty hunters. Confederate veterans. Outlaws. Strangers. Rape. Suicide. Revenge. Perfidy. Murder. Jailbreaks. Safes. El Paso.*

Note: Location scenes filmed in Spain. Released in Italy in Jan 1966 as *Per qualche dollaro in più*; in West Germany in Apr 1966 as *Für ein paar Dollar mehr*; in Spain as *La muerte tenia un precio*. This is the second in a series of three films directed by Sergio Leone and starring Clint Eastwood as "The Man With No Name." Werner Abrolat is credited in the cast only in German source.

FÖR ATT INTE TALA OM ALLA DESSA KVINNOR *see* **ALL THESE WOMEN**

FOR HE'S A JOLLY BAD FELLOW *see* **THEY ALL DIED LAUGHING**

FOR LIFE, AGAINST THE WAR   F6.1633
Dist Film-Makers' Cooperative. 26 Feb **1968** [Pittsburgh opening]. Sd & si; b&w and col. 16mm. 165 min.
  Coörd Jules Rabin. *Filmmakers* Storm De Hirsch, John Hawkins, Stan Vanderbeek, Robert Breer, Richard Preston, Lee Savage, Nina Feinberg, Ron Finne, Hannah Weiner, Manfred Kirchheimer, Peter Eliscu, Robert Fiore, Fred Wellington, Lionel Martinez, Larry Jordan, Lloyd Michael Williams, Lee Hurwitz, Tom Hurwitz, Peggy Lawson, Hilary Harris, USCO, Peter Gessner, Lewis Jacobs, Don Duga, Barbara Sultz, Stan Brakhage, Rudy Burckhardt, Maurice Amar, Richard Adams, Max Phillips, Mark Sadan, Allen Schaf, Jonas Mekas, A. M. Jimenez, Ben Van Meter, Tom Bissinger, Helen Rabin, John Willemeyer, Harry Korn, Abbott Meader, Charles Levine, Michael Snow, Stephen Sellinger, Joyce Wieland, Allan Siegel, Bob Kinney, Dave Lembert, Victor Graver, Jerry Wakefield, Walker & Henley, Karl Bissinger, Arnold Gold, Bruce Conner, Matt Hoffman. *Sponsorship* Week of the Angry Arts Against the War in Vietnam.
  Compilation film. A collection of untitled short films, each 1-3 minutes in length, which were made in 1967 in response to invitations from the "Week of the Angry Arts Against the War in Vietnam." *Demonstrations. Vietnam War 1964–73.*
  Note: Several of the filmmakers received screen credit for films which were not included in the final release version. A 38-min version including 17 of the films was subsequently released.

FOR LOVE & MONEY   F6.1634
Hollywood Cinema Associates. *Dist* Crest Film Distributors, J. E. R. Pictures. 13 Dec **1967** [New York showing]. Sd; col (Eastman Color). 35mm. 75 min.
  Prod-Dir Don Davis. *Screenplay* James Rogers, writ. *Titl Song sung by* Jose Siemans.
  Cast: Michelle Angelo, Lionel Nichols, George Caspar, Curly, Norma Mimos, Lee Margill, Janice Kelly, Miki Tani.
  Drama. Using an employment agency as a front, a ring of corporation spies employs women to steal corporate secrets, set up key executives for blackmail, and photograph them in compromising situations to ensure their not going to the police. The police are unable to solve the case until one of the victims, Don Harding, reveals under intense interrogation his story, which involves LSD, body painting, and hidden cameras and microphones. *Executives. Spies. Police. Blackmail. Sexuality. Prostitution. Body painting. Theft. Electronic surveillance. Employment—Women. Employment agencies. LSD. Photographs. Documentation.*
  Note: Also known as *For Love of Money.*

FOR LOVE OF IVY   F6.1635
Palomar Pictures International. *Dist* Cinerama Releasing Corp. 17 Jul **1968** [New York opening]. Sd; col (Perfect Color). 35mm. 102 min.
  Prod Edgar J. Scherick, Jay Weston. *Assoc Prod* Joel Glickman. *Dir* Daniel Mann. *Screenplay* Robert Alan Aurthur. *Story* Sidney Poitier. *Dir Photog* Joseph Coffey. *Camera Op* Peter Garbarini. *Lighting* Morton Novak. *Asst Art Dir* Don Swanagan. *Set Decor* Leif Pedersen. *Kings Point House Dsgn* George Nemeny. *Prod Dsgn* Peter Dohanos. *Film Ed* Patricia Jaffe. *Asst Ed* Esther Croft. *Mus* Quincy Jones. *Titl Song* Bob Russell, Quincy Jones. *Sung by* Shirley Horn. *Song: "You Put It on Me"* Maya Angelou, Quincy Jones. *Sung by* B. B. King. *Song: "My Side of the Sky"* Cashman, Pistilli & West, Quincy Jones. *Sung by* Cashman, Pistilli & West. *Sd* Charles Federmack. *Sd Eff Ed* Edward Beyer. *Mus Engr* Phillip Ramone. *Re-rec Engr* Richard Vorisek. *Asst Dir* Steve Barnett, John W. Murphy, Robert Koster. *Prod Mgr* Joel Glickman. *Unit Mgr* Alex Hapsas. *Script Supv* Judy Tucker. *Prod Sec* Connie Schoenberg. *Cost* Frank Thompson. *Makeup Artist* Scott Cunningham. *Hairdresser* William Chiarelli. *Chief Grip* Edward Engels, Sr. *Prop Master* Thomas Wright. *Casting* Jean Arley.
  Cast: Sidney Poitier *(Jack Parks)*, Abbey Lincoln *(Ivy Moore)*, Beau Bridges *(Tim Austin)*, Nan Martin *(Doris Austin)*, Lauri Peters *(Gena Austin)*, Carroll O'Connor *(Frank Austin)*, Leon Bibb *(Billy Talbot)*, Hugh Hurd *(Jerry)*, Lon Satton *(Harry)*, Stanley Greene *(Eddie)*, Paul Harris, Tony Major, Clark Morgan, Christopher St. John, Bob Carey, Marlene Clark, Laura Greene, Lani

Miyazaki, Lisa Moore, Gloria Henry, Yolande Toussaint, Gina Harding, Willis Pinkett, William Matthews, Josip Elic, The Reverend William Glenesk, Cordy Clark, Hope Stansbury, Robert Miller, Nobuko Uenishi, Kyoko Morii, Kedaki Turner, Madge West, Jerome Collamore, Anita Dangler, Peter Dohanos, Jennifer O'Neill, Robert Bannard, Sharon Henesy, Maeve McGuire, John Servetnik, Elliot Wood, Joseph Attles.

Romantic comedy. Because she wants more excitement in her life, a 27-year-old black woman, Ivy Moore, decides to leave her job as domestic to a Long Island family and go to secretarial school. When she announces her plans to her employers, the Austins, the entire family is upset at losing their maid-housekeeper-confidante of 9 years' standing. Deciding that Ivy's decision results from a lack of romance in her life, the Austins' teenaged daughter, Gena, and hippie son, Tim, decide to play matchmakers without their parents' knowledge. Tim persuades Jack Parks, a young black trucking executive, to date Ivy by threatening to expose his sideline operation—a gambling casino located inside a moving trailer truck. Afraid to lose Austin's department store contract, Jack agrees. After an awkward first date Jack and Ivy warm up to each other, but their romance cools when Ivy learns that Jack was blackmailed into dating her. Despite his aversion to marriage, Jack follows Ivy back to the Austin house and confesses his love for her, even promising to give up the gambling operation. And, as the lovers depart arm in arm, the Austins are left to face their domestic problems. *Domestics. Negroes. Suburbanites. Matchmakers. Executives. Hippies. Suburban life. Family life. Gambling. Blackmail. Adolescence. Marriage. Trucking agencies. Long Island. New York City—Harlem.*

Note: Location scenes filmed in and around New York City.

FOR LOVE OF MONEY see **FOR LOVE & MONEY**

FOR LOVE OR MONEY   F6.1636

Universal Pictures. 7 Aug **1963** [New York opening; c14 Sep 1963; LP34925]. Sd (Westrex); col (Eastman Color by Pathé). 35mm. 108 min.

Prod Robert Arthur. *In Charge of Prod* Edward Muhl. *Dir* Michael Gordon. *Screenplay* Larry Markes, Michael Morris, writ. *Dir Photog* Clifford Stine. *Camera Op* William Dodds. *Camera Asst* William Reisbord, William Egan. *Art Dir* Alexander Golitzen, Malcolm Brown. *Set Decor* Ruby Levitt. *Set Coörd* Charles Baqueta. *Main Titl* Pacific Title. *Film Ed* Alma Macrorie. *Asst Ed* Edward Broussard. *Mus* Frank De Vol. *Mus Supv* Joseph Gershenson. *Sd* Waldon O. Watson, Corson Jowett, Ed Borschell, James Rogers, James Curtis. *Asst Dir* Joseph Kenny, William S. Gilmore, Jr. *Unit Prod Mgr* Lew Leary. *Script Supv* Robert Forrest. *Gowns* Jean Louis. *Jewels* David Webb. *Wardrobe* Peter Saldutti, Rydo Loshak, Dina Joseph, Dolly Derderian, Dorothy Drake. *Makeup* Bud Westmore, Jack Freeman, Imogene Abbott, Le Vaughn Speer. *Hairstyles* Larry Germain. *Sp Eff* Whitey McMahon. *Dial Coach* Mike Ross. *Still Photog* Jack Geraghty. *Gaffer* Butch Harmon. *Grip* Walter Woodworth, Carl Johnston. *Prop* Ed Keyes, Fay Frame.

Cast: Kirk Douglas (*Deke Gentry*), Mitzi Gaynor (*Kate Brasher*), Gig Young (*Sonny Smith*), Thelma Ritter (*Chloe Brasher*), Leslie Parrish (*Jan Brasher*), Julie Newmar (*Bonnie Brasher*), William Bendix (*Joe Fogel*), Dick Sargent (*Harvey Wofford*), William Windom (*Sam Travis*), Elizabeth MacRae (*Marsha*), Willard Sage (*Orson Roark*), Ina Victor (*nurse*), Alvy Moore (*George*), Jose Gonzalez-Gonzalez (*Jaime*), Don Megowan (*Gregor*), Billy Halop (*elevator operator*), Joey Faye (*male shopper*), Theodore Marcuse (*artist*), Frank Mahony (*Red Beard*).

Romantic comedy. Chloe Brasher, a wealthy widow, hires her attorney, Deke Gentry, to act as matchmaker for her three beautiful daughters, Kate, Jan, and Bonnie. Chloe has chosen three men she considers suitable sons-in-law, and it is Deke's task to pair up the six persons. With only a minimum of effort, Deke is able to interest Bonnie, a health addict, in Harvey Wofford, an income-tax investigator. Similarly, it is not long before he has Jan, a bohemian, in the arms of Sam Travis, a prisoner-rehabilitation expert. Kate, head of a motivational research laboratory, is more difficult; for each time Deke arranges a meeting between her and Sonny Smith, playboy food magnate, Deke himself ends up spending the evening with Kate. As a result, the two fall in love; but when Kate learns of Deke's arrangement with her mother, she walks out on him. Deke persuades her to marry him, however, by offering to give up his fee. As the three couples march to the altar, Chloe reveals that she had Deke in mind for Kate all the time. *Widows. Lawyers. Matchmakers. Beatniks. Psychologists. Businessmen. Playboys. Researchers. Investigators. Motherhood. Wealth. Courtship. Criminals—Rehabilitation. Income tax. Health. Weddings.*

Note: Location scenes filmed in the San Francisco area. Working titles: *Three On a Match* and *Three Way Match*.

FOR MEN ONLY see **HOT GIRLS FOR MEN ONLY**

FOR PETE'S SAKE!   F6.1637

World-Wide Pictures. 14 Oct **1966** [Denver, Colorado, opening]. Sd; col (Eastman Color). 35mm. 90 min.

Exec Prod Frank R. Jacobson. *Dir-Writ* James F. Collier. *Photog* Richard Batcheller. *Art Dir* Theodore Holsopple. *Film Ed* Eugene Pendleton. *Mus* Ralph Carmichael. *Sd* Wallace Nogle. *Asst Dir* James Rosenberger, William Lasky. *Prod Mgr* Herbert Willis.

Cast: Billy Graham (*himself*), Robert Sampson (*gas station attendant*), Pippa Scott (*his wife*), Johnny Jensen (*their son*), Sam Groom, Al Freeman, Jr., John Milford, Irene Tedrow, Nicolas Surovy, Bob Beach, Pam McMyler, Tim O'Kelly, Danny Bravo, Terry Garr, Cynthia Hull, Connie Sawyer, Len Wayland, Dolores Quinton, Harry Lauter, Tom Peters, Stuart Nisbet, Nicholas Worth, Margaret Muse, Helyn Eby Rock, Ella Edwards.

Melodrama. A Denver gasoline station attendant, his wife, and their 10-year-old son are deeply moved after attending a Billy Graham Crusade; and they determine to lead better lives. After colliding with a gang of teenaged motorcyclists, the man is challenged to a race over mountain trails—a race symbolizing the challenge of modern youth to established religious principles. *Motorcycle gangs. Filling station attendants. Family life. Motorcycle racing. Religious conversion. Denver. Billy Graham.*

FOR SINGLE SWINGERS ONLY   F6.1638

Hollywood Cinema Associates. *Dist* Crest Film Distributors. Apr **1968**. Sd; col. 35mm. 71 min.

Prod-Dir Don Davis.

Cast: Heidi Anderson (*Gracie*), Sharon Sanford (*Gloria*), Leslie Dee, Michael Roth, Jana Lee.

Drama. Thrill-seekers Gracie and Gloria move into a singles apartment building. Gracie foolishly falls in love with David, a man she knows is depraved; while Gloria pursues her pleasures in an affair with Ruth, the apartment house manager. *Bachelors. Apartment house managers. Lesbianism.*

Note: Also known as *Single Swingers Only*.

FOR SINGLES ONLY   F6.1639

Four Leaf Productions. *Dist* Columbia Pictures. May **1968** [c1 May 1968; LP36169]. Sd; col (Pathé). 35mm. 91 min.

Prod Sam Katzman. *Assoc Prod* Jerome F. Katzman. *Dir* Arthur Dreifuss. *Screenplay* Hal Collins, Arthur Dreifuss. *Story* Arthur Hoerl, Albert Derr. *Dir Photog* John F. Warren. *Camera* Felix Barlow, Bob Wasserman. *Art Dir* George W. Davis, Leroy Coleman. *Set Decor* Henry Grace, Robert De Vestel. *Film Ed* Ben Lewis. *Asst Ed* William McMillin. *Mus Score & Cond* Fred Karger. *Titl Song* Fred Karger, Milton Berle. *Perf by* Cal Tjader Band. *Song:* "Kee Ka Roo" Walter Wanderley, Bobby Worth. *Song:* "Sensuous" Walter Wanderley, Jose Marino, Bobby Worth. *Song:* "Take a Chance With Me" Walter Wanderley, Talya Ferro. *Song:* "I'm Not Afraid" Diane Hilderbrand, Jack Keller. *Songs:* "This Town Ain't the Same Anymore," "Destination Unknown," "Why Need They Pretend?" Travis Lewis, Bommer Clarke. *Songs Perf by* Walter Wanderley Trio, Talya Ferro, Cal Tjader Band, The Lewis & Clark Expedition, The Nitty Gritty Dirt Band, The Sunshine Co., Mary Ann Mobley. *Choreog* Alex Romero. *Rec Supv* Franklin Milton. *Sd* Michael J. Clark, Bill Clark, Robert Crosby. *Asst Dir* Donald C. Klune, Read Killgore. *Unit Prod Mgr* Robert Stone. *Script Supv* Gordon Otto. *Wardrobe* Gene Murray, Dennis Fill, Margo Weintz, Trudy Gellert. *Makeup* William Tuttle, William Reynolds, makeup, Vincent Romaine. *Hairstyles* Mary Keats, Dorothy White. *Sp Eff* Edwin J. Fisher. *Still Photog* Larry Prather. *Dial Coach* Flora Duane. *Gaffer* Perry O'Brien. *Key Grip* Joe Vaughn. *Prop* Bill More, Bob Bushman.

Cast: John Saxon (*Bret Hendley*), Mary Ann Mobley (*Anne Carr*), Lana Wood (*Helen Todd*), Mark Richman (*Gerald Pryor*), Ann Elder (*Nydia Walker*), Chris Noel (*Lily*), Marty Ingels (*Archibald Baldwin*), Hortense Petra (*Miss Jenks*), Charles Robinson (*Jim Allen*), Duke Hobbie (*Bob Merrick*), Dick Castle (*singer*), Norman Wells (*clerk in bursar's office*), Norma Foster, Maria Korda, Leslie McRae, Dita Nicole (*pageant girls*), Milton Berle (*Mr. Parker*), Walter Wanderley Trio, Talya Ferro, Cal Tjader Band, The Lewis & Clark Expedition, The Nitty Gritty Dirt Band.

Comedy-drama with music. Anne Carr and Helen Todd move into the Sans Souci apartment house complex in California, which is restricted to unmarried people under 30 years of age. Mr. Parker, the social director, introduces them to their fellow residents, and soon both girls are being pursued by the men. Helen, an intellectual, is attracted to Gerald Pryor, a married man who has sneaked into the complex; while Anne is fending off many aggressive young men. Two tenants, Jim Allen and Bob Merrick, bet playboy Bret Hendley that he cannot seduce Anne within a week. He takes the wager in order to win enough money to complete his college education. After a few encounters, Bret becomes serious about Anne and rebuffs her rather than use her. Anne hears about the wager and, wanting Bret to win it for the sake of his educational expenses, pretends to have been seduced—and Jim and Bob pay. Mr. Parker, upon discovering that Anne and Bret plan to marry, gives them a party and then ousts them from the apartments. Less happily, Helen also has left the Sans Souci; after learning of Pryor's marriage, she has attempted suicide but instead has been raped by a group of waterfront thugs. She recovers and emerges as a sadder but much wiser young woman. Additional songs: "Symbol of Love," "Tight Black Gown," "The Loner." *Bachelors. Social directors. Hoodlums. Apartment house managers. Wagers. Seduction. Infidelity. Suicide. Rape. California.*

Note: Location scenes filmed in southern California.

FOR THOSE WHO THINK YOUNG   F6.1640

Schenck–Koch Enterprises. *Dist* United Artists. 3 Jun **1964** [Chicago opening; c3 Jun 1964; LP29362]. Sd; col (Technicolor). 35mm (Techniscope). 96 min.

An Aubrey Schenck–Howard W. Koch Production. *Prod* Hugh Benson. *Exec Prod* Howard W. Koch. *Dir* Leslie H. Martinson. *Screenplay* James O'Hanlon, George O'Hanlon, Dan Beaumont. *Story* Dan Beaumont. *Photog* Harold Stine. *Art Dir* Hal Pereira, Arthur Lonergan. *Set Dir* Sam Comer, James Payne. *Film Ed* Frank P. Keller. *Mus Comp & Cond* Jerry Fielding. *Titl Song* Jerry Livingston, Mack David. *Sung by* James Darren. *Choreog* Robert Tucker. *Sd* Hugo Grenzbach, John Wilkinson. *Asst Dir* Arthur Jacobson. *Makeup* Wally Westmore.

Cast: James Darren (*Gardner "Ding" Pruitt III*), Pamela Tiffin (*Sandy Palmer*), Woody Woodbury (*himself*), Paul Lynde (*Sid Hoyt*), Tina Louise (*Topaz McQueen*), Nancy Sinatra (*Karen Cross*), Bob Denver (*Kelp*), Claudia Martin (*Sue Lewis*), Robert Middleton (*Edgar J. Cronin*), Ellen McRae (*Dr. Pauline Thayer*), Jack LaRue, Allen Jenkins, Robert Armstrong (*Mr. Cronin's business associates*), Louis Quinn (*Gus Kestler*), Sammee Tong (*Sessue*), Addison Richards (*Dean Watkins*), Mousie Garner (*Mousie*), Benny Baker (*Lou*), Anna Lee (*Laura Pruitt*), George Raft, Roger Smith (*detectives*), Amedee Chabot (*beautiful beach girl*), Sheila Bromley (*Mrs. Harkness*), Alberto Morin (*butler*), Byron Kane (*reporter*).

Comedy. The favorite pastime of Oceancrest College students, aside from surfing, is going to the Silver Palms club where comedian Woody Woodbury performs. Wealthy playboy "Ding" Pruitt falls in love with Sandy Palmer, Woodbury's niece; but the romance disturbs Edgar Cronin, Ding's grandfather, who tries to have the club closed. Sociology professor Dr. Pauline Thayer also considers the Silver Palms scandalous and would like to see it made off limits to students. She changes her mind, however, after she falls in love with Woodbury. When Ding announces his intention to marry Sandy, Cronin arranges for the club to be raided by the police, but he drops the charges when he is revealed to be an ex-bootlegger; he then gives his approval to both the Silver Palms and Sandy. *Students. Entertainers. Surfers. Uncles. Grandfathers. Police. Bootleggers. Professors. College life. Nightclubs.*

Note: Location scenes filmed near Malibu Beach in California and at Occidental College in Los Angeles.

FORBID THEM NOT   F6.1641

Norman Kaplan and Associates. 19 Feb **1962** [Los Angeles opening]. Sd; b&w. 16mm. 67 min.

A Norman Kaplan Production. *Prod* Robert L. Kimble, William A. Fraker, James Robinson. *Dir-Screenplay* Robert L. Kimble. *Narr* Philip Dunne. *Photog* William A. Fraker. *Film Ed* Robert L. Kimble. *Mus* Richard Berres.

Cast: Jose Ferrer (*narrator*), Michael Cole, Jean Gale, Patti O'Neil, John Ehrin, Herb Niccolls, John Beers, Ann Dashner, Alex Gal.

Documentary. The film examines the plight of the blind, especially a 12-year-old schoolboy (Michael Cole), who becomes blind as a result of an automobile accident. Hindered in his recovery by an overprotective mother (Jean Gale) and his sister (Patti O'Neil), he is taken in by the local Foundation for the Junior Blind in Los Angeles, which assists him with rehabilitation. *Adolescence. Blindness. Family life. Schools for the Blind. Los Angeles. Automobile accidents.*

THE FORBIDDEN (France)   F6.1642

Olympic International Films. *Dist* Olympic International Films, American Film Distributing Corp. **1966**. Sd; b&w with col seq. 35mm. 66 min.

Overall Production Credits: *Prod* William Eldridge. *Dir* Benjamin Andrews.

Camera Unit No. 1: *Dir* Kasem Salhmadine. *Photog* Eldor Ishmahd. *Op* Kaldar Kashmald.

Camera Unit No. 2: *Dir* Seasu Hakasomi. *Photog* Jerome Matsumurie. *Op* Sam Tokahashi.

Camera Unit No. 3: *Dir* David Kayne. *Photog* Samual Hayatt. *Op* Lloyd Williamson.

Additional Sequences: *Prod* Bob Cresse. *Dir* Lee Frost.

Cast: Baby Bubbles.

Documentary(?). Hidden cameras explore sexual behavior throughout the world—Hollywood, Denmark, Belgium, Sweden, France, and San Francisco. Nudity, frigidity, pornography, exotic dancing, lesbianism, sadomasochism, rape, and lust all come under scrutiny. *Sexuality. Pornography. Striptease. Frigidity. Lesbianism. Sadomasochism. Rape. Hollywood. Denmark. Belgium. Sweden. San Francisco.*

Note: The film consists of footage from an unidentified French feature and additional U.S. sequences.

FORBIDDEN FLESH; AS SEEN FROM A   F6.1643
HAYLOFT IN THE HILLS

Dist Chancellor Films. Aug **1968**. Sd; col. 35mm. 69 min.

A Barry Mahon Production.

Melodrama. A salesman traveling in the Tennessee foothills obtains lodgings in the loft of a barn. The farmer's precocious daughter soon finds her way up into the hayloft along with a friend, and the weary salesman is beset by the two unrelenting country girls. He attempts to put them off by telling of his travels in the big cities of America. Elaborate and explicit accounts of go-go dancing, striptease, society orgies, and Greenwich Village lesbians, however, only further arouse the girls. At their insistence, he finally gives in, only to be discovered by the farmer's wife who is wielding a shotgun. *Traveling salesmen. Farmers. Go-go dancers. Troilism. Nymphomania. Urban life. Rural life. Lesbianism. Striptease. Orgies. Tennessee.*

FORBIDDEN LOVE AFFAIR see LOLLIPOP

FORBIDDEN PLEASURE   F6.1644

Garva Productions. *Dist* Inter-American Film Distributors. **1969**. Sd; col (Eastmancolor). 35mm. 73 min.

Melodrama. Buckley, a handsome, bearded, 40-year-old millionaire, given only a month to live, reveals the tragic news to his devoted chauffeur, Farnsworth, and gives him $30,000 to purchase, for $1,000 each, a different female companion for each of the days Buckley has left. Farnsworth seeks aid from private detective Jack Drum, who auditions the women before passing them on to Buckley. Drum quickly runs out of women willing to make love to Buckley, and the detective is forced to promise a young woman who is in love with him that he will marry her if she will spend the night with Buckley. She is told to keep the lights off and remain absolutely silent. Buckley makes love with her in the dark, but his curiosity is piqued after intercourse, and he turns on the lights to find out that he has just been with his daughter. The shock is too much for his ailing heart; he dies, and his daughter collapses in hysteria. *Millionaires. Detectives. Chauffeurs. Pimps. Prostitution. Incest. Heart disease.*

THE FORBIN PROJECT   F6.1645

Universal Pictures. 4 May **1970** [New York opening; c8 Apr 1970; LP39190]. Sd; col (Technicolor). 35mm (Panavision). 100 min. *MPAA rating* M.

Prod Stanley Chase. *Dir* Joseph Sargent. *Screenplay* James Bridges. *Dir Photog* Gene Polito. *Camera Op* Wilbur Gossman. *Art Dir* Alexander Golitzen, John J. Lloyd. *Set Decor* John McCarthy, Ruby Levitt. *Film Ed* Folmar Blangsted. *Mus* Michel Colombier. *Mus Supv* Stanley Wilson. *Sd* Waldon O. Watson, Terry Kellum, Ronald Pierce. *Asst Dir* Robin Clark. *Unit Prod Mgr* Robert E. Larson. *Script Supv* Betty Abbott. *Makeup* Bud Westmore. *Hairstyles* Larry Germain. *Sp Photog Eff* Albert Whitlock. *Sp Eff* Whitey McMahon. *Tech Adv* Jay Akerman. *Equipment Furnished by* Control Data Corp., California Computer Products. *Russian Tech Adv* Boury Booyakovitch. *Dial Coach* Bert Steinberger.

Cast: Eric Braeden (*Forbin*), Susan Clark (*Cleo*), Gordon Pinsent (*President*), William Schallert (*Grauber*), Leonid Rostoff (*1st chairman*), Georg Stanford Brown (*Fisher*), Willard Sage (*Blake*), Alex Rodine (*Kuprin*), Martin Brooks (*Johnson*), Marion Ross (*Angela*), Dolph Sweet (*missile commander*), Byron Morrow (*Secretary of State*), Lew Brown (*Peterson*), Sid McCoy (*Secretary of Defense*), Tom Basham (*Harrison*), Robert Cornthwaite, James Hong (*scientists*), Sergei Tschernisch (*translator*).

Science fiction drama. Source: D. F. Jones, *Colossus* (London, 1966). Charles Forbin, director of a U. S. defense project, announces to the world that Colossus, a computer programmed to defend the Western world, is finally operational; the self-contained system, located beneath the Rocky Mountains, will provide the ultimate nuclear deterrent to war. The computer is in operation for only a short time before it detects the presence of Guardian, a similar system located in the Soviet Union, and Colossus requests to be put in contact with his counterpart. The unwary scientists comply, and soon the two systems are communicating in computer language. American cold war strategists, fearful that secret information will be disclosed, pressure the President into severing the line of communication. The connection is then terminated by joint United States-Russian consent, but Colossus, now assuming a personality of its own, threatens retaliation unless the line is restored. Colossus and Guardian prepare to launch a missile attack upon each other's countries. At the last minute, the Americans and Russians restore communication, but not before one of the U. S. armed missiles destroys a Russian town. Forbin and his Russian counterpart, Dr. Kuprin, make plans to destroy the computers, but the plot is detected, and the computers, now working together, order Kuprin's execution. Forbin, placed under close surveillance by Colossus, continues to plan the overthrow of the computers; with his attractive chief aide, Cleo Markham, posing as his mistress, Forbin receives permission from Colossus to spend several nights alone with her. Together they attempt to overload the computer, but it learns of their plans and orders the execution of two technicians aiding in the plot. After blowing up missile sites in both the United States and Russia in retaliation for the sabotage attempt, Colossus tries to convince Forbin that they can coexist peacefully, as long as the computer is in control. *Scientists. Presidents of the United States. Defense—National. Nuclear warfare. Imposture. Sabotage. Computers. Missile sites. Rocky Mountains. Union of Soviet Socialist Republics. Explosions.*

Note: Location scenes filmed at the Lawrence Hall of Science, Berkeley, California. Working titles: *Colossus 1980* and *The Day the World Changed Hands*. Title later changed to *Colossus—The Forbin Project.*

FORCE OF IMPULSE   F6.1646

III Task Productions. *Dist* Sutton Pictures. 1 Nov **1961** [Hartford, Connecticut, opening]. Sd; b&w. 35mm. 84 min.

Prod Peter Gayle. *Co-prod* Tony Anthony. *Dir* Saul Swimmer. *Screenplay* Francis Swann. *Adapt* Richard Bernstein. *Orig Story* Saul Swimmer, Tony Anthony. *Photog* Clifford Poland. *Art Dir* Leo B. Meyer. *Film Ed* Gene Milford. *Mus Comp* Joseph Liebman. *Mus Cond* Lionel Hampton. *Songs:* "Strange Feeling," "The Blues I Got Comin' Tomorrow" Joseph Liebman, Mort Goode. *Perf by* Jack Pleis and His Orchestra.

Cast: Robert Alda *(Warren Reese)*, J. Carrol Naish *(Antonio Marino)*, Tony Anthony *(Toby Marino)*, Jeff Donnell *(Louise Reese)*, Jody McCrea *(Phil Anderson)*, Brud Talbot *(George)*, Lionel Hampton *(himself)*, Christina Crawford *(Ann)*, Kathy Barr *(Kathy)*, Teri Hope *(Bunny Reese)*, Paul Daniel *(Uncle Luigi)*.

Melodrama. Toby Marino, a 17-year-old high school football hero who delivers groceries for his father, is in love with flirtatious Bunny Reese, a wealthy 16-year-old classmate. Her parents, however, regard Toby as an unsuitable beau for their daughter and prefer Phil Anderson, a rich college graduate. Bunny invites Toby to a country club dance and taunts him by luring Phil to a secluded beach. When she returns, Toby attempts to prove that he could belong to Bunny's life by taking her on a round of the night spots, financing the date by looting his father's strongbox. They end up on the beach; but as their emotions turn to passion, Bunny breaks it off, and Toby telephones Mr. Reese to explain his daughter's absence. Furious because Bunny has been out all night, Mr. Reese calls Toby's father and demands a showdown at the football stadium. Although Mr. Reese and the two youngsters become highly emotional, the patient and understanding Mr. Marino manages to calm them down by explaining that this experience is simply the beginning of a more mature love. *Athletes. Delivery boys. Flirts. Adolescence. High school life. Filial relations. Class conflict. Theft. Football. Country clubs. Beaches. Nightclubs.*

Note: Filmed on location in and around Miami Beach.

FORCE OF THE WIND *see* WE SHALL RETURN

FOREVER MY LOVE (Austria)   F6.1647

Erma Film. *Dist* Paramount Pictures. 27 Mar **1962** [New York opening; c31 Dec 1960; LP22798]. Sd; col (Agfacolor, print by Technicolor). 35mm. 147 min. [Copyright length: 115 min.]

An Ernst Marischka Production. *Prod-Dir-Writ* Ernst Marischka. *Photog* Bruno Mondi. *Art Dir* Fritz Jüptner-Jonstorff, Alexander Sawczynski. *Film Ed* Alfred Srp. *Mus* Anton Profes. *Perf by* Vienna State Opera Choir. *Choir Dir* Rudolf Moralt. *U. S. Titl Song* Hal David, Burt Bacharach. *Sung by* Jane Morgan. *Choreog* Willy Fränzl. *Asst Dir* Rudolf Zehetgruber. *Prod Mgr* Karl Ehrlich. *Cost* Gerdago, Leo Bei.

Cast: Romy Schneider *(Princess Elisabeth [Sissi])*, Karl Boehm *(Emperor Franz Josef)*, Magda Schneider *(Duchess Ludovika)*, Vilma Degischer *(Archduchess Sophie)*, Gustav Knuth *(Duke Max of Bavaria)*, Josef Meinrad *(police major)*, Uta Franz *(Princess Helene)*, Walther Reyer *(Count Gyula Andrássy)*, Erich Nikowitz *(Archduke Franz-Karl)*, Karl Fochler *(Count Grünne)*, Peter Weck *(Archduke Karl-Ludwig)*, Hilde Wagener *(Princess Helen)*, Senta Wengraf *(Countess Bellegarde)*, Helene Lauterböck *(Countess Esterhazy)*, Klaus Knuth *(Prince Ludwig)*, Egon von Jordan *(Carlo)*, Hans Ziegler *(Privy Councillor Dr. Seeburger)*, Albert Rueprecht *(Archduke Ferdinand-Max)*, Sonja Sorell *(Henriette Mendel)*, Peter Neusser *(Count Batthyani)*, Johannes Ferigo *(Count Czaky)*, Ida Gabor *(Margit)*, Chariklia Baxevanos *(Helena)*, Oskar Wegrostek *(landlord)*, Dolores Hubert *(governess)*, Herbert Prikopa *(Italian cook)*, Walter Regelsberger *(Count Windischgraetz)*, Otto Tressler, Ivan Petrovich, Richard Eybner, Josef Egger, Hugo Gottschlich, Franca Parisi Strahl.

Historical drama. Derived from the operetta by: Fritz Kreisler, Ernst Marischka and Hubert Marischka, *Sissy* (first performance: Vienna, 23 Dec

1932). In the 1850's, Archduchess Sophie of Austria selects the Bavarian Princess Helene to wed her son, Emperor Franz Josef. But the emperor falls in love with Helene's uninhibited younger sister Elisabeth, nicknamed Sissi, whom he at first mistakes for a country girl. At a reception to announce his engagement, they meet again, and Franz Josef announces that he will marry Sissi. Following their honeymoon, Sissi takes her newly acquired responsibilities very seriously but breaks one tradition after another, violating the rigid protocol established by the archduchess. Franz Josef, however, delights in her openness and simplicity, which eventually prove instrumental in winning over the restless Hungarian nation. Hungary's Count Andrassy confesses his love for Sissi, but although she is attracted to him, she remains faithful to her husband, and they enjoy a second honeymoon in the Alps. She becomes ill with tuberculosis, however, and is sent to Spain for treatment. Under the devoted care of her mother, Duchess Ludovika, she miraculously recovers and is reunited with Franz Josef. Together they visit Italy, where they receive a hostile reception, but Sissi's wisdom and charm again convert the crowds into friends. Their mission accomplished, the royal couple returns to their native Austria. *Royalty. Sisters. Cousins. Diplomacy. Filial relations. Marriage—Arranged. Honeymoons. Tuberculosis. Hungary. Bavaria. Spain. Alps. Italy. Franz Josef. Elizabeth (Austria). Gyula Andrássy. Sophie (Archduchess of Austria). Maximilian (Duke in Bavaria). Ludovika (Duchess in Bavaria). Francis Charles (Archduke of Austria). Charles Louis (Austria 1833–96). Helene (Duchess in Bavaria). Maximilian Emperor of Mexico.*

Note: Location scenes filmed in the Alps, the French Riviera, Tirol, Schönbrunn, and elsewhere in Austria and Italy. The film is a compilation of footage from three films: *Sissi*, released in Austria in 1956 at 102 min; *Sissi—die junge Kaiserin*, released in 1957 at 106 min; and *Sissi—Schicksalsjahre einer Kaiserin*, released in 1958 at 109 min. Registered for copyright by Aspa A. G.

LA FÓRMULA SECRETA *see* THE SECRET FORMULA

FORNICON—PATTERN OF EVIL   F6.1648

Chelsea Productions. *Dist* Marvin Films. 13 Nov **1970** [Washington, D. C., opening]. Sd; col. 35mm. 72 min.

Pres by Jerald Intrator. *Prod-Dir* George Harrison Marks. *Exec Prod* Al Weiss. *Screenplay* Lawrence Sanders.

Cast: Paul Holcombe *(John Webley)*, Yvonne Paul *(Suzanne Webley)*, Cindy Neal *(Dawn Starr)*, Rena Bronson *(Madame LaBanca)*, Jutka Goz *(Gloria Andress)*, Monique Devereaux *(Greta Marr)*, Tony Barton *(William Todd)*, David London *(David Gibson)*, Howard Nelson *(Arthur Vanderhorn)*.

Melodrama. Playboy John Webley handles public relations for a London cosmetics firm run by Madame LaBanca, a bisexual. During a sales meeting at Madame LaBanca's estate, John introduces stripteaser Dawn Starr, who performs a suggestive dance indicative of the advertising campaign to be used for Formula-69, a new perfume. A competitor, trying to steal the formula and kill John, instead kills John's wife, Suzanne. Although suspected by Scotland Yard, John is released because of insufficient evidence. At a costume party at Madame LaBanca's home John, to expose his wife's murderer, suggests the guests play "Truth or Consequences." Placed on a medieval torture rack, prime suspect Greta Marr breaks down and names the killer. *Playboys. Advertising executives. Businesswomen. Stripteasers. Public relations. Business ethics. Business competition. Murder. Revenge. Torture. Bisexuality. Confession (law). Cosmetics. Masquerades. London. Scotland Yard. "Truth or Consequences".*

Note: Filmed in Great Britain. Also known as *Pattern of Evil* and *F—Pattern of Evil.*

THE FORSAKEN GARDEN *see* OF LOVE AND DESIRE

FÖRSTA STENEN *see* EVA ... WAS EVERYTHING BUT LEGAL

FORT COURAGEOUS   F6.1649

Steve Production. *Dist* Twentieth Century-Fox Film Corp. 14 Apr **1965** [New York showing; c24 Mar 1965; LP30822]. Sd; b&w. 35mm. 72 min.

Prod Hal Klein. *Dir* Lesley Selander. *Story-Screenplay* Richard Landau. *Dir Photog* Gordon Avil. *Camera Op* Edward L. Davenport. *Film Ed* John F. Schreyer. *Mus Comp & Cond* Richard La Salle. *Sd Mix* Burdick S. Trask. *Asst Dir* Joe Wonder. *Script Supv* Billy Vernon. *Cost* Patrick Cummings. *Makeup* Gustaf M. Norin. *Hairstyles* Ann Kirk. *Sp Eff* Roger George. *Photog Eff* Butler-Glouner Inc. *Prop Master* Charles Chichetti. *Key Grip* Harry Stern. *Ch Electrn* Ross Maehl.

Cast: Fred Beir *(Sergeant Lucas)*, Donald Barry *(Captain Howard)*, Hanna Landy *(woman)*, Harry Lauter *(Joe)*, Cheryl MacDonald *(daughter)*, Walter Reed, Joseph Patridge, Michael Carr, Fred Krone, George Sawaya.

Western melodrama. A relief patrol is on its way to Fort Courageous with its new commanding officer, Captain Howard, and a prisoner, Sergeant Lucas, who has just been court-martialed. As they near the fort, they come upon a roving band of Indians, and after a skirmish in which Howard is wounded, they rescue two women. Lucas assumes command of the column, and with the aid of Joe, an Indian scout, they reach the fort. Once inside, the patrol discovers that the detachment has been wiped out. The only survivor, a major, is ready for retirement and is anxious to leave for the East. The major is forced to retain command, however, when Howard dies of his wounds. He attempts to leave the fort under a truce flag but is quickly killed by Indians. Joe also is killed when he goes to scout for possible avenues of escape. Although the Indians attack again and again, they are repulsed each time by the small band of brave soldiers led by Lucas. Finally the Indians hurl the lance of gallantry over the parapet in recognition of the valiant fight put up by the few defenders. As the survivors proudly march out of the fort, they look forward to a new life in the East. *Indians of North America. Scouts—Frontier. Courts-martial. Retirement. Heroism. Forts. United States—History—Indian campaigns. United States Army—Cavalry.*

Note: Filmed in Kanab, Utah.

FORT GRAVEYARD (Japan)   **F6.1650**
Toho Co. May **1966** [Los Angeles showing]. Sd; b&w. 35mm (Tohoscope). 132 min.

Exec Prod Tomoyuki Tanaka. *Dir* Kihachi Okamoto. *Screenplay* Kihachi Okamoto, Kan Saji. *Photog* Rokuro Nishigaki. *Mus* Masaru Sato.

Cast: Toshiro Mifune (*Sergeant Kosugi*), Tatsuya Nakadai, Yunosuke Ito, Reiko Dan, Makoto Sato.

War drama. In 1945 Sergeant Kosugi, who has been decorated for valor, is sent to the Chinese front as punishment for insubordination. He falls in with a military band headed his way, to a fort where his brother is stationed. Kosugi arrives at the fort just as his brother is being executed by a firing squad for desertion. In a rage, Kosugi attacks the commanding officer and escapes a court-martial only by agreeing to attempt capture of the strategic Fort Graveyard. Kosugi, three privates released from the stockade, and the inexperienced military band manage to surprise the enemy and drive them from the fort. The Chinese, however, surround the fort, and, without food or ammunition, even Kosugi cannot hold them off. *Chinese. Brothers. Combat zone life. Capital punishment. Military bands. Forts. Sino-Japanese Conflict 1937–45. Japan—Army.*

Note: Released in Japan in 1965 as *Chi to suna*.

FORT UTAH   **F6.1651**
A. C. Lyles Productions. *Dist* Paramount Pictures. 24 May **1967** [New York opening; c10 May 1967; LP34730]. Sd; col (Technicolor). 35mm (Techniscope). 83 min.

An A. C. Lyles Production. *Prod* A. C. Lyles. *Dir* Lesley Selander. *Screenplay* Steve Fisher, Andrew Craddock. *Dir Photog* Lothrop Worth. *Art Dir* Hal Pereira, Al Roelofs. *Set Decor* Robert R. Benton, John Sturtevant. *Film Ed* John F. Schreyer. *Mus Comp* Jimmie Haskell. *Sd* John Carter, John Wilkinson. *Asst Dir* Ralph Axness. *Prod Mgr* Howard Roessel. *Makeup* Wally Westmore. *Hairstyles* Nellie Manley. *Sp Photog Eff* Paul K. Lerpae.

Cast: John Ireland (*Tom Horn*), Virginia Mayo (*Linda Lee*), Scott Brady (*Dajin*), John Russell (*Eli Jonas*), Robert Strauss (*Ben Stokes*), James Craig (*Bo Greer*), Richard Arlen (*Sam Tyler*), Jim Davis (*Scarecrow*), Donald Barry (*Harris*), Harry Lauter (*Britches*), Read Morgan (*cavalry lieutenant*), Reg Parton (*Rafe*), Eric Cody (*Shirt*).

Western melodrama. While riding through prairie country, ex-gunfighter Tom Horn meets an old friend, Indian agent Ben Stokes, and learns that the Indians have been set on the warpath by a mystery man called Dajin. The two friends spot a wagon train traveling through hostile territory without an Army escort; and while Horn joins the wagon train, Stokes heads for Fort Utah to summon troopers. Horn finds the wagon master unwilling to alarm the passengers; he remains with the group and becomes attracted to passenger Linda Lee. Stokes fails to return in 2 days, and Horn also rides off to the fort, which he finds deserted. He wanders inside and is knocked out and held prisoner along with Stokes. It is revealed that Dajin is a mutinous Army sergeant who has formed a gang of renegade troopers, murdered the fort personnel, and massacred an encampment of Indian women and children. Horn and Stokes succeed in overpowering two of the three men guarding the fort, but the third escapes to warn Dajin. Meanwhile, the Indians attack the wagon train, and the few survivors make their way to the fort. Eventually Dajin appears and begs to be saved from the marauding Indians. He is admitted but once inside attempts a double cross and is shot down. Knowing that the Indians will demand Dajin alive, Horn and Stokes strap his dead body to a saddled horse and ride through the gates of the fort with him. A volley of shots riddle Dajin's body, and, satisfied, the Indians withdraw. Horn joins the wagon train on its journey westward and anticipates a bright future with Linda Lee. *Gunfighters. Indians of North America. Indian agents. Traitors. Mutiny. Massacres. Wagon trains. Forts. United States Army—Cavalry.*

LA FORTUNA DI ESSERE DONNA *see* **WHAT A WOMAN!**

THE FORTUNE COOKIE   **F6.1652**
Phalanx Productions–Jalem Productions. *For* Mirisch Corp. *Dist* United Artists. 19 Oct **1966** [New York opening; c19 Oct 1966; LP33763]. Sd; b&w. 35mm (Panavision). 125 min.

Prod-Dir Billy Wilder. *Assoc Prod* I. A. L. Diamond, Doane Harrison. *Screenplay* Billy Wilder, I. A. L. Diamond. *Dir Photog* Joseph LaShelle. *Camera* William Lloyd Norton, Robert V. Hoffman, Elmer Fabian, Felix Barlow. *Art Dir* Robert Luthardt. *Set Decor* Edward G. Boyle. *Scenic Artist* Duncan Spencer. *Film Ed* Daniel Mandell. *Mus* Andre Previn. *Sd* Robert Martin. *Sd Ed* Wayne Fury. *Mus Ed* Richard Carruth. *Re-rec* Buddy Myers. *Asst Dir* Jack Reddish, Michael Glick. *Prod Supv* Allen K. Wood. *Prod Mgr* Patrick J. Palmer. *Unit Mgr* Nate H. Edwards. *Script Supv* Marshall Wolins. *Wardrobe* Charles Arrico, Paula Giokaris. *Makeup* Loren Cosand, Jack Petty. *Hairstyles* Alice Monte. *Sp Eff* Sass Bedig. *Prop* Frank Agnone. *Casting* Lynn Stalmaster. *Still Photog* Al St. Hilaire. *Dial Coach* Tom Miller.

Cast: Jack Lemmon (*Harry Hinkle*), Walter Matthau (*Willie Gingrich*), Ron Rich (*Luther "Boom Boom" Jackson*), Cliff Osmond (*Mr. Purkey*), Judi West (*Sandy*), Lurene Tuttle (*Mother Hinkle*), Harry Holcombe (*O'Brien*), Les Tremayne (*Thompson*), Marge Redmond (*Charlotte Gingrich*), Noam Pitlik (*Max*), Harry Davis (*Dr. Krugman*), Ann Shoemaker (*Sister Veronica*), Maryesther Denver (*ferret-faced nurse*), Lauren Gilbert (*Kincaid*), Ned Glass (*Doc Schindler*), Sig Ruman (*Professor Winterhalter*), Archie Moore (*Mr. Jackson*), Howard McNear (*Mr. Cimoli*), Bartlett Robinson, Robert Lieb, Martin Blaine, Ben Wright (*The Specialists*), William Christopher (*intern*), Dody Heath (*nun*), Herbie Faye (*Maury*), Billy Beck (*locker room assistant*), Judy Pace (*Elvira*), Helen Kleeb (*receptionist*), Lisa Jill (*Ginger*), John Todd Roberts (*Jeffrey*), Keith Jackson (*football announcer*), Herb Ellis (*TV director*), Don Reed (*newscaster*), Louise Vienna (*girl in TV commercial*), Robert DoQui (*man in bar*), Jon Silo (*tailor*).

Comedy-drama. During a Cleveland Browns–Minnesota Vikings football game in Cleveland, CBS-TV cameraman Harry Hinkle is sent sprawling when a 220-pound halfback crashes into him at the sidelines. While Harry is at the hospital for a checkup, he is visited by his brother-in-law, Willie Gingrich, a shyster lawyer who pounces upon the incident as a once-in-a-lifetime opportunity to make a million dollars by suing CBS, the Cleveland Browns, and Municipal Stadium. Harry's protests are ignored as the conniving Willie shows the weak-willed Harry how to feign all the symptoms of an injured back. Propped in a wheelchair, simulating partial paralysis and blindness, Harry, under the watchful eye of Willie, deceives a barrage of doctors and insurance investigators. The only joyful note in the masquerade for Harry is the return of his money-hungry ex-wife Sandy, who left him for a second-rate musician. Gradually, however, Harry begins to have conscience trouble as Boom Boom Jackson, the black halfback who bowled him over, becomes so despondent at the thought of having crippled a man that he insists on moving in with Harry and becoming his nurse. Meanwhile, a persistent private eye named Purkey films all of Harry's activities from a room across the street. Eventually Purkey admits to Harry and Willie that he has failed to produce evidence of a hoax and concludes with some racist remarks directed at Boom Boom, thereby provoking Harry to leap in fury from his wheelchair. Though Purkey's coup fails because he has neglected to put film in his hidden camera, Harry, who has become disgusted by Sandy's mercenary behavior, obligingly repeats his actions once the camera has been loaded. Crushed, but not defeated, Willie bellows that he and the N.A.A.C.P. will sue Purkey for his anti-Negro, anti-American remarks. *Television cameramen. Brothers-in-law. Lawyers. Physicians. Detectives. Gold diggers. Negroes. Racial prejudice. Fraud. Marriage. Football. Lawsuits. Eavesdropping. Paralysis. Blindness. Cleveland. Cleveland—Municipal Stadium. Documentation.*

Note: Location scenes filmed in Cleveland.

THE FORTUNE TELLER (Greece)   **F6.1653**
Finos Films. *Dist* Greek Motion Pictures. 20 May **1961** [New York opening]. Sd; b&w. 35mm. 90 min.

Dir-Writ Alekos Sakellarios.

Cast: Mimi Fotopoulos (*Spyros*), Georgia Vassiliadou (*Calliopi*), Smarouli Yiouli (*Kaithi*), Basil Avlonitis (*Nikitas*), Pericles Christofarides (*Mr. Giavassis*).

Comedy. Calliopi, a coffee fortune teller in Athens, needlessly complicates people's lives with her prophesies, whose damage must be corrected. Spyros, a cafe owner, has a romance with Kaithi. *Fortune-tellers. Nightclub owners. Coffee. Athens.*

Note: Released in Greece as *Kaphetzou*. Also known as *The Coffee Fortune Teller*.

FORTY ACRE FEUD   F6.1654

The Ormond Organization. *For* Atlanta Productions. *Dist* Craddock Films. 18 Aug **1965** [Knoxville, Tennessee, opening]. Sd; col. 35mm. 85 min.

Pres by Airlon Pictures. *Prod-Writ* Bill Packham. *Dir* Ron Ormond.

Cast: Ferlin Husky *(Simon Crumb)*, Minnie Pearl *(Ma Culpepper)*, Bob Corley *(Pa Culpepper)*, Claude Casey *(Uncle Foxey Calhoun)*, Jan Moore *(Nancy Calhoun)*, Del Reeves *(Del Culpepper)*, Sam Tarpley *(Postmaster Amos Quint)*, Ray Price, George Jones, Loretta Lynn, Roy Drusky, Skeeter Davis, Bill Anderson, The Willis Brothers, Hugh X. Lewis, Eddie Hill *(themselves)*.

Comedy with music. Overlooked when the Tennessee legislature reapportioned the state, the 40-acre community of Shagbottom is discovered and notified to elect a state representative. The feud between Pa Culpepper and Uncle Foxey Calhoun resurfaces, with several incidents occurring at Postmaster Amos Quint's general store between Simon Crumb and Uncle Foxey, while at the Culpepper farm Ma Culpepper is trying to persuade Pa not to run for office. Lovers Nancy Calhoun and Del Culpepper are separated by the hostilities until the Smokey Mountain Jamboree arrives to televise the election and their country music revue. *Postmasters. Rural life. Country music. State legislatures. Feuds. Elections. General stores. Tennessee.*

Note: Filmed in and around Nashville, Tennessee, in 16mm.

40 GUNS TO APACHE PASS   F6.1655

Admiral Pictures. *Dist* Columbia Pictures. May **1967** [c1 Mar 1967; LP34733]. Sd (Westrex); col (Pathé). 35mm. 95 min.

Prod Grant Whytock. *Dir* William Witney. *Writ* Willard Willingham, Mary Willingham. *Dir Photog* Jacques Marquette. *Art Dir* Paul Sylos. *Set Decor* Harry Reif. *Film Ed* Grant Whytock. *Mus* Richard LaSalle. *Sd Ed* Al Bird. *Sd* Herman Lewis. *Mus Ed* Edna Bullock. *Asst Dir* Jack R. Berne. *Prod Supv* Harold E. Knox. *Wardrobe* Joseph Dimmitt. *Makeup Supv* Ted Coodley. *Prop Master* Max Frankel.

Cast: Audie Murphy *(Captain Coburn)*, Michael Burns *(Doug)*, Kenneth Tobey *(Corporal Bodine)*, Laraine Stephens *(Ellen)*, Robert Brubaker *(Sergeant Walker)*, Michael Blodgett *(Mike)*, Michael Keep *(Cochise)*, Kay Stewart *(Kate Malone)*, Kenneth MacDonald *(Harry Malone)*, Byron Morrow *(Colonel Reed)*, Willard Willingham *(Fuller)*, Ted Gehring *(Barrett)*, James Beck *(Higgins)*.

Western melodrama. Following the Civil War, Apache chief Cochise goes on the warpath, vowing to kill every white man in Arizona. The cavalry unit at Fort Apache Wells under the unpopular command of Captain Bruce Coburn lead local homesteaders to the fort in preparation for an attack, but the men are inadequately armed. Consequently, Coburn takes some of his men, including two young homesteader brothers, Doug and Mike Malone, on a dangerous mission to meet a consignment of 40 new repeating rifles that is on its way. Along the way they fall into an ambush, and Mike is among those killed, while Doug stands paralyzed with fear. Coburn reaches his destination, but his treacherous corporal, Bodine, convinces the survivors to steal the rifles and sell them to Cochise. Facing court-martial, Coburn sets out to recover the rifles and receives unexpected aid from young Doug, who is anxious to redeem himself. Together they outwit the Apaches and return the rifles to the fort. In the climactic battle, Cochise's attack is repelled, Bodine is killed, and Doug regains his self-respect. Finally, Coburn is reunited with his sweetheart, Doug's sister Ellen. *Apache Indians. Brothers. Homesteaders. Theft. Treason. Cowardice. Firearms. Arizona. Cochise. United States Army—Cavalry. Fort Apache Wells.*

Note: Location scenes filmed in Arizona.

FORTY-NINE DAYS (U.S.S.R.)   F6.1656

Mosfilm. *Dist* Artkino Pictures. 2 Jan **1964** [New York opening]. Sd; b&w. 35mm. 80 min. [Also 84 min.]

Dir Gennadiy Gabay. *Screenplay* G. Baklanov, Yu. Bondarev, V. Tendryakov. *Story Ed* A. Repina. *Photog* Arkadiy Koltsatyy. *Camera* S. Kulish. *Art Dir* Boris Nemechek, Arnold Vaysfeld. *Film Ed* N. Anikeyeva. *Mus* Aleksey Muravlev. *Song Lyr* M. Lvovskiy. *Cond* A. Roytman. *Sd* L. Bulgakov. *1st & 2d Asst Dir* E. Khodzhikyan, Ye. Rybanets. *Prod Mgr* M. Shadur. *Cost* A. Martinson. *Makeup* T. Krylova. *Sp Eff* G. Ayzenberg, F. Krasnyy.

Cast: Vladimir Buyanovskiy *(Sergeant Rakhmatullin)*, Vitaliy Pivnenko *(Private Podgornyy)*, Vladimir Shibankov *(Private Fomin)*, G. Krasheninnikov *(Private Boykov)*, B. Gladkov, A. Zarzhitskaya, E. Knausmyuller, V. Krokhin, Yu. Levchenko, Ye. Loginov, V. Makarov, B. Oya, V. Rogov, N. Rostovikov, V. Filippov.

Drama. Soviet sailors Rakhmatullin, Podgornyy, Fomin, and Boykov are set adrift off the Siberian coast when their barge is wrecked in a storm. They endure for 49 days in the Pacific Ocean, exhibiting great courage and maintaining their dignity under hopelessly difficult circumstances. At last they are spotted by U. S. Navy pilots and rescued. *Survival. Sea rescue. Pacific Ocean. Siberia. Union of Soviet Socialist Republics—Navy. United States Navy. Storms. Shipwrecks.*

Note: Released in the U.S.S.R. in Mar 1962 as *49 dney.* Based on an actual incident of 1960 involving sailors Ivan Fedotov, Anatoliy Kryuchkovskiy, Filipp Poplavskiy, and Arkhan Ziganshin.

FORTY POUNDS OF TROUBLE   F6.1657

Curtis Enterprises. *Dist* Universal Pictures. 18 Jan **1963** [Miami, Florida, opening; c9 Feb 1962; LP32605]. Sd (Westrex); col (Eastman Color). 35mm (Panavision). 106 min.

Prod Stan Margulies. *In Charge of Prod* Edward Muhl. *Dir* Norman Jewison. *Screenplay* Marion Hargrove. *Dir Photog* Joseph MacDonald. *Camera Op* Duke Callaghan. *Asst Camera* James Saper, Bob Thomas. *Art Dir* Alexander Golitzen, Robert Clatworthy. *Set Decor* Ruby Levitt. *Set Coörd* Fred Knoth. *Film Ed* Marjorie Fowler. *Mus* Mort Lindsey. *Songs:* "If You," "What's the Scene" Mort Lindsey, Sydney Shaw. "If You" sung by Suzanne Pleshette. "What's the Scene" sung by David Allen. *Sd* Waldon O. Watson, Frank McWhorter, Don Cunliffe, Harold King, Melvin M. Metcalfe, Sr. *Asst Dir* Tom Shaw, Terry Morse, Jr., Carl Beringer. *Script Supv* John Franco. *Prod Mgr* Bob Larson. *Gowns* Rosemary Odell. *Men's Wardrobe* Peter Saldutti, Mike Tierney. *Women's Wardrobe* Olive Koenitz. *Makeup* Dan Striepeke, Emile LaVigne, Jean Mollner. *Hairstyles* Joan St. Oegger. *Coöp* Walt Disney. *Still Photog* Jack Geraghty. *Gaffer* David Curtis. *Grip* John Livesley, Dick Sutton.

Cast: Tony Curtis *(Steve McCluskey)*, Suzanne Pleshette *(Chris Lockwood)*, Phil Silvers *(Bernie Friedman)*, Claire Wilcox *(Penny Piper)*, Larry Storch *(Floyd)*, Howard Morris *(Julius)*, Edward Andrews *(Herman)*, Stubby Kaye *(Cranston)*, Warren Stevens *(Swing)*, Mary Murphy *(Liz)*, Kevin McCarthy *(Blanchard)*, Karen Steele *(Bambi)*, Tom Reese *(Bassett)*, Gregg Palmer *(Piper)*, Steve Gravers *(Daytime)*, Ford Rainey *(judge)*, Paul Comi *(Cavanaugh)*, Sharon Farrell *(Dolores)*, David Allen *(singer)*, Jack LaRue *(gambler)*.

Comedy-drama. Source: Damon Runyon, "Little Miss Marker," in *Collier's* (26 Mar 1932). Steve McCluskey, manager of a Lake Tahoe gambling casino owned by Bernie Friedman, is constantly pursued by private detectives because of his refusal to pay alimony to his ex-wife, Liz. Bernie's niece, Chris Lockwood, arrives for a singing engagement, and Steve comes to believe that she is Bernie's mistress. Then Steve is placed in charge of 6-year-old Penny Piper, whose father has left the casino to find the money to pay his gambling losses, and Steve becomes very fond of the child. A few days later, he learns that her father has died in an automobile accident. Before he breaks the news to Penny, he takes her to see Disneyland, and, so as to evade the detectives, he has Chris accompany them, giving the group a family appearance. He is spotted, however, and after a chase through the park he is caught and brought before a judge. The judge is sympathetic to Steve's story, but the juvenile authorities threaten to take Penny away from him. Steve and Chris decide to marry, adopt Penny, and spend their honeymoon at Disneyland. *Casino owners. Business managers. Detectives. Uncles. Children. Singers. Mistresses. Gamblers. Alimony. Mistaken identity. Adoption. Honeymoons. Lake Tahoe. Disneyland. Automobile accidents. Chases.*

Note: Filmed on location at Hurrah's Club at Lake Tahoe and at Disneyland. The Damon Runyon short story was filmed twice previously by Paramount Pictures as *Little Miss Marker* (1934) and *Sorrowful Jones* (1949).

47 SAMURAI see CHUSHINGURA

THE FOUNTAIN OF LOVE (Austria)   F6.1658

Intercontinental Film. *Dist* Crown International Pictures. 6 Jun **1968** [Maryland license]. Sd; col (Pathé Color). 35mm. 83 min. *MPAA rating* R.

Exec Prod Karl Spiehs. *Asst Prod* Erich Tomek. *Dir* Ernst Hofbauer. *Screenplay* Walter Schneider. *Camera* Franz Lederle. *Art Dir* Wolf Witzemann. *Ed* Grete Girinec. *Mus* Claudius Alzner. *Asst Dir* Zlata Mehlers. *Prod Mgr* Günter Eulau. *Cost* Gerdago.

Cast: Hans-Jürgen Bäumler *(Leif)*, Sieghardt Rupp *(Nils Hansen)*, Eddi Arent *(Alwin Knobbe)*, Ann Smyrner *(Stina)*, Hartmuth Hinrichs *(Carl)*, Christa Linder *(Britta)*, Christiane Rücker *(Grit)*, Marianne Schönauer *(Frau van Weyden)*, Balduin Baas *(druggist)*, Helga Marlo *(Caroline)*, Walter Buschhoff *(Wirt, the innkeeper)*, Ellen Umlauf *(teacher)*, Werner Abrolat *(John)*, Emely Reuer *(Frieda)*, Herbert Tiede *(pastor)*, Karin Field *(Victoria)*, Dimiter Panoff *(Lars Pogge)*.

Farce. The little mountain town of Jonkborn seeks a subsidy from the Austrian Bureau of Tourism. To attract tourists, Nils Hansen, the mayor of the town, hires Leif, a press agent, who publicizes the local legend of a fountain that gives sexual virility to men and beauty to women. Indeed, many of the townspeople bathe at the fountain and then enjoy the pleasures of sex. At the fountain's most potent hour, the harvest full moon, women bathe nude in its water. The minister of tourism, outraged by the publicity campaign, sends one of her subordinates, Knobbe, to investigate. The mayor, fearing the loss of the subsidy, orders a 3-day moratorium on sex, and one of the villagers dams the spring that fills the fountain. After snooping around the village, Knobbe asks the minister to come to his aid, but he is given a glass of springwater that changes his outlook. Meanwhile busloads of tourists arrive to partake of the springwater. Disappointed to find the fountain dry, they start to leave, but one of the peasants unblocks the spring and word quickly spreads. Soon the minister of tourism arrives and claims the spring for the state. The town is prosperous and everyone is happy. *Peasants. Investigators. Mayors. Tourists. Bureaucrats. Press agents. Village life. Sexuality. Nudity. Aphrodisiacs. Springs. Fountains.*

Note: Produced in Austria in 1965 as *Die Liebesquelle.*

FOUR BODIES WALLOWING IN DESIRE F6.1659
Dist Able Film Co. ca **1970**. Sd; col. 16mm. [Feature length assumed.]

Sex film. No information about the precise nature of this film has been found. *Sexuality.*

4 CLOWNS F6.1660
Robert Youngson Productions. *Dist* Twentieth Century–Fox Film Corp. Sep **1970** [c31 Dec 1969; LP39199]. Sd; b&w. 35mm. 97 min. *MPAA rating* G.

A Robert Youngson Production. *Prod-Writ* Robert Youngson. *Assoc Prod* Raymond Rohauer. *Asst Prod* Herbert Gelbspan, Alfred Dahlem. *Mus Comp & Cond* Manny Albam. *Mus Supv* Angelo Ross. *Sd Rec* Henry Markosfeld, Ross-Gaffney Inc. *Sd Eff* Alfred Dahlem. *Res Supv* Jeanne Youngson. *Coöp* Hal Roach, Hal Roach Studios, Leopold Friedman, Raymond Rohauer. *Opticals* Movielab Opticals.

Narrator: Jay Jackson.

Compilation film. Beginning with a montage of Broadway as seen in the 1920's, the film, narrated by Jay Jackson, is divided into three sections of silent film comedies. The first part is devoted to Stan Laurel and Oliver Hardy and includes scenes from: *The Hobo* (1917), *His Day Out* (1918), *No Man's Law* (1927), *Kill or Cure* (1923), *The Second Hundred Years* (1927), *Putting Pants on Phillip* (1926), *Two Tars* (1928), *Big Business* (1929), *Double Whoopee* (1929), and *Their Purple Moment* (1928). The second part of the film features Charlie Chase in scenes from: *Us* (1927), *What Price Goofy?* (1925), *Fluttering Hearts* (1927), *The Family Group* (1928), and *Limousine Love* (1928). The final sequence is devoted entirely to Buster Keaton in *Seven Chances* (1925). *Actors. Motion pictures—History. Buster Keaton. Stan Laurel. Oliver Hardy. Charlie Chase. New York City—Broadway.*

FOUR CORNERED TRIANGLE *see* **SCREAM OF THE BUTTERFLY**

4D MAN *see* **MASTER OF TERROR**

FOUR DAYS IN NOVEMBER F6.1661
Wolper Pictures. *For* United Press International. *Dist* United Artists. 6 Oct **1964** [Washington, D. C., opening; c7 Oct 1964; LP29261]. Sd; b&w. 35mm. 120 min.

Pres by David L. Wolper. *Prod-Dir* Mel Stuart. *Exec Prod* David L. Wolper. *Narr Writ* Theodore Strauss. *Film Ed* William Cartwright. *Mus* Elmer Bernstein. *Res Source* President's Commission on the Assassination of President John F. Kennedy, Military District of Washington, The Library of Congress, Dallas Police Department, Dallas Cinema Association, British Broadcasting Corp. *Coöp* Parkland Memorial Hospital (Dallas).

Narrator: Richard Basehart.

Documentary. An account of the assassination of President John F. Kennedy in Dallas, Texas, on November 22, 1963, utilizing television and newsreel clips, footage by amateurs, some stock shots, and shots of some re-created scenes. The film includes the President's and Mrs. Kennedy's activities just before and following their arrival in Dallas; the parade; the shooting, in which the President is killed and Gov. John Connally wounded; the succession to the presidency of Vice President Lyndon B. Johnson; the memorial and funeral services in Washington, D. C., and in Arlington National Cemetery; and the murder of the alleged assassin, Lee Harvey Oswald, by Jack Ruby in Dallas. In addition, the camera retraces Oswald's movements for the entire day of the crime. *Assassination. Murder. Funerals. Dallas. Washington (District of Columbia). Arlington National Cemetery. John Fitzgerald Kennedy. Lyndon Baines Johnson. Jacqueline Bouvier Kennedy. John B. Connally, Jr. Lee Harvey Oswald. Jack Ruby.*

THE FOUR DAYS OF NAPLES (United States/Italy) F6.1662
Titanus–Metro-Goldwyn-Mayer, Inc. *Dist* Metro-Goldwyn-Mayer, Inc. 19 Mar **1963** [New York opening; c31 Dec 1962; LP26212]. Sd; b&w. 35mm. 116 min.

Prod Goffredo Lombardo. *Dir* Nanni Loy. *Screenplay* Carlo Bernari, Pasquale Festa Campanile, Massimo Franciosa, Nanni Loy. *Story* Pasquale Festa Campanile, Massimo Franciosa, Nanni Loy, Vasco Pratolini. *Dir Photog* Marcello Gatti. *Camera* Giuseppe Ruzzolini. *Set Dsgn* Gianni Polidori. *Asst Set Dsgn* Andrea Crisanti, Luciano Spadoni. *Film Ed* Ruggero Mastroianni. *Mus* Carlo Rustichelli. *Sd Tech* Giovanni Rossi. *Asst to the Dir* Carlo Lastricati, Giorgio Gentili. *Prod Mgr* Giuseppe Bordogni. *Prod Supv* Anna Davini. *Sp Eff* Serse Urbisaglia.

Cast: Regina Bianchi *(Concetta Capuozzo)*, Aldo Giuffrè *(Pitrella)*, Lea Massari *(Maria)*, Jean Sorel *(Livornese)*, Franco Sportelli *(Professor Rosati)*, Charles Belmont *(sailor)*, Gian Maria Volontè *(Stimolo)*, Frank Wolff *(Salvatore)*, Luigi De Filippo *(Cicillo)*, Pupella Maggio *(Mother of Arturo)*, Georges Wilson *(reformatory director)*, Raffaele Barbato *(Ajello)*, Domenico Formato *(Gennaro Capuozzo)*, Curt Lowens *(Sakau)*, Enzo Turco *(Valente)*.

War drama. On September 8, 1943, General Badoglio of the Italian Army signs an armistice with the Allies. As the news spreads, the deliriously happy people of Naples pour out into the streets to celebrate. But their joy is short-lived; the German Wehrmacht considers the truce an act of betrayal, and Nazi forces take over all military installations. Within 4 days the occupation of the city is complete, and to show the Neapolitans who is master of the city, the German command orders the public execution of an Italian sailor named Livornese and forces the populace to kneel and applaud the killing. Furthermore, male inhabitants from 5 to 50 are rounded up for work in German labor camps. Then, on September 28th, the people of Naples revolt. Without plan, without organization, the resistance gathers force throughout the city and it is now the Germans who become the hunted. Fighting with hidden arms and makeshift weapons, the partisans build barricades in their streets, mount snipers on rooftops and in parked cars, and toss grenades at Nazi tanks. Gennaro Capuozzo, a reform school boy who dies fighting the Nazi tanks, is a particular hero. Four days later, on October 1, 1943, the Wehrmacht is forced to evacuate Naples, and Allied troops are able to enter a city that has been freed by its own people. *Nazis. Guerrillas. Neapolitans. Fascists. Sailors. War crimes. Resistance (political). World War II. Naples. Gennaro Capuozzo. Germany— Army. Italy—Army.*

Note: Released in Italy in 1962 as *Le quattro giornate di Napoli;* running time: 124 min. The cast listed above was not given screen credit.

4 FOR TEXAS F6.1663
Sam Co. *Dist* Warner Bros. Pictures. 18 Dec **1963** [Baltimore opening; c4 Jan 1964; LP29433]. Sd; col (Technicolor). 35mm. 124 min.

Prod-Dir Robert Aldrich. *Exec Prod* Howard W. Koch. *Assoc Prod* Walter Blake. *2d Unit Dir* Oscar Rudolph. *Stunt Supv* John Indrisano. *Screenplay* Teddi Sherman, Robert Aldrich. *Story* Robert Aldrich. *Photog* Ernest Laszlo. *2d Unit Photog* Carl Guthrie, Joseph Biroc, Burnett Guffey. *Camera Op* Richard Batcheller. *1st Asst Camera* Richard Johnson, photog. *Art Dir* William Glasgow. *Set Decor* Raphael Bretton. *Film Ed* Michael Luciano. *Mus* Nelson Riddle. *Orch* Gil Grau. *Sd* Jack Solomon. *Rec* Russell Ashley. *Asst Dir* Tom Connors, David Salven, William F. Sheehan. *Prod Mgr* Jack R. Berne. *Script Supv* Robert Gary. *Cost Dsgn* Norma Koch. *Cost* Joyce Rogers, Charles James. *Makeup* Robert Schiffer, Sidney Perell, Loren Cosand. *Hairstyles* Lenore Weaver, Helen Turpin. *Sp Eff* Sass Bedig. *Dial Coach* Robert Sherman. *Still Photog* Al St. Hilaire, Ted Allan. *Grip* Martin Kashuk, Harold Noyes. *Prop* John Orlando, Levi Williams. *Gaffer* Lee Wilson.

Cast: Frank Sinatra *(Zack Thomas)*, Dean Martin *(Joe Jarrett)*, Anita Ekberg *(Elya Carlson)*, Ursula Andress *(Maxine Richter)*, Charles Bronson *(Matson)*, Victor Buono *(Harvey Burden)*, Edric Connor *(Prince George)*, Nick Dennis *(Angel)*, Richard Jaeckel *(Mancini)*, Mike Mazurki *(Chad)*, Wesley Addy *(Trowbridge)*, Marjorie Bennett *(Miss Ermaline)*, Jack Elam *(Dobie)*, Fritz Feld *(maître d')*, Percy Helton *(Ansel)*, Jonathan Hole *(Renée)*, Jack Lambert *(Monk)*, Paul Langton *(Beauregard)*, Jesslyn Fax *(widow)*, Allyson Ames *(maid)*, Arthur Godfrey, The Three Stooges, Teddy Bruckner & His All-Stars *(guest stars)*.

Western comedy. Zack Thomas and Joe Jarrett separately are heading for Galveston in 1870 and witness a stagecoach attack by a gang on horseback led by Matson, a local gunslinger. After repulsing the bandits, Zack discloses a bag containing $100,000, but Joe relieves him of the money at gunpoint and proceeds to an orphanage where he was reared. He later deposits the loot in a bank run by Harvey Burden, a crook who has supported Zack in his efforts to become the town's gambling boss. Zack learns that Joe is in Galveston, and he arranges a meeting but is interrupted when Matson attempts to kill Zack. Joe wounds the bandit, thus saving his rival's life, and then goes off to see Maxine Richter, owner of a riverboat which Joe plans to refurbish as a gambling saloon. Outraged that anyone would dare to give him competition, Zack plans for his gang to take over the boat on opening night. Unknown to both men, however, Burden has decided to let the gangs destroy each other so he can move in with Matson's bandits and take control. Maxine and Elya Carlson, Zack's devoted girl friend, persuade the two gamblers to join forces. As a result of the alliance, Matson's gang is defeated, Burden is arrested, and the women get their reward at a double wedding. *Bandits. Bankers. Gamblers. Saloon keepers. Gangs. Theft. Murder. Stagecoach robberies. Perfidy. Orphanages. Riverboats. Saloons. Weddings. Casinos. Galveston.*

Note: Location scenes filmed in the Mojave Desert.

FOUR FOR THE MORGUE
F6.1664

MPA Feature Films. Nov **1962**. Sd; b&w. 35mm. 84 min.

Prod Brandon Chase. *Assoc Prod* Anthony Naylor. *Dir* John Sledge. *Screenplay* Frank Phares. *Photog* Willis Winford. *Film Ed* Edward Dutreil, Mel Wright. *Mus* Emil Ascher. *Sd* Dennis Fretwell, Chester Childs. *Asst Dir* Sam Margolis. *Prod Supv* Michael Huzsek.

Cast: Stacy Harris (*Lieut. Victor Beaujac*), Louis Sirgo (*Sgt. John Conroy*), Ginny Hostetler (*Vivian Miller*), Bill White, Clint Bolton, Nicholas Chetta, Leo Bruno, Ed Pyle, actor, Wilson Bourg, Francis Forrest, Val Winter, Pearl Nichols, Jessie Davis, Eugene Sonfield, Roy Longmire, C. Warren Kennedy.

Crime drama. New Orleans police detectives Victor Beaujac and John Conroy are working on four cases simultaneously. First, they establish the innocence of a patrolman accused of murdering a purse-snatching socialite by proving that the young, drug-addicted thief actually committed suicide. Next, after a hunter discovers the body of a murdered bank robber in a swamp, the thief's son is kidnaped by his father's killers; however, the detectives apprehend the murderers and return the boy unharmed. The third case involves a hitchhiker who murders and assumes the identity of the driver who offers him a ride, but he is caught after a gun battle with Beaujac and Conroy. Finally, unemployed taxi driver Leonard Wayne, who has reported his wife and her little dog missing, is booked for their murder after an attempts to flee. *Detectives. Thieves. Socialites. Drug addicts. Hitchhikers. Taxi drivers. Murder. Injustice. Suicide. Kidnaping. Impersonation. New Orleans. Dogs.*

Note: Filmed entirely on location in New Orleans.

THE FOUR HORSEMEN OF THE APOCALYPSE
F6.1665

Julian Blaustein Productions. *Dist* Metro-Goldwyn-Mayer, Inc. 7 Feb **1962** [Washington, D. C., opening; c31 Dec 1961; LP21323]. Sd (Westrex); col (Metrocolor). 35mm (CinemaScope). 153 min.

A Julian Blaustein Production. *Assoc Prod* Olallo Rubio, Jr. *Dir* Vincente Minnelli. *Screenplay* Robert Ardrey, John Gay. *Dir Photog* Milton Krasner. *Col Cons* Charles K. Hagedon. *Art Dir* George W. Davis, Urie McCleary, Elliot Scott. *Four Horsemen Figures Dsgn* Tony Duquette. *Set Decor* Henry Grace, Keogh Gleason. *Film Ed* Adrienne Fazan, Ben Lewis. *Montages Created by* Frank Santillo. *Mus* Andre Previn. *Choreog* Alex Romero. *Rec Supv* Franklin Milton. *Asst Dir* Eric Von Stroheim, Jr. *Cost Dsgn* René Hubert, Walter Plunkett. *Adtl Gowns for Miss Thulin* Orry-Kelly. *Makeup* Charles Parker, William Tuttle. *Hairstyles* Sydney Guilaroff. *Sp Vis Eff* A. Arnold Gillespie, Lee LeBlanc, Robert R. Hoag. *Made in Coöp With* Moctezuma Films.

Cast: Glenn Ford (*Julio Desnoyers*), Ingrid Thulin (*Marguerite Laurier*), Charles Boyer (*Marcelo Desnoyers*), Lee J. Cobb (*Julio Madariaga*), Paul Henreid (*Etienne Laurier*), Paul Lukas (*Karl von Hartrott*), Yvette Mimieux (*Chi-Chi Desnoyers*), Karlheinz Böhm (*Heinrich von Hartrott*), Harriet MacGibbon (*Doña Luisa Desnoyers*), Kathryn Givney (*Elena von Hartrott*), Marcel Hillaire (*Armand Dibie*), George Dolenz (*General von Kleig*), Stephen Bekassy (*Colonel Kleinsdorf*), Nestor Paiva (*Miguel*), Albert Rémy (*François*), Richard Franchot (*Franz von Hartrott*), Brian Avery (*Gustav von Hartrott*).

War drama. Source: Vicente Blasco Ibáñez, *Los cuatro jinetes del Apocalipsis* (Valencia, 1916). Madariaga, an 80-year-old patriarch, has built a fabulous empire on the Argentine pampas, a haven from the turmoil and tension of the 1930's. As the decade ends, however, he sees with horror that his German-fathered grandson, Heinrich, has returned from Berlin filled with fanatical Nazi ideas. The situation precipitates a violent family quarrel in which Madariaga predicts that the Four Horsemen of the Apocalypse (Conquest, War, Pestilence, and Death) will soon devastate the earth. The emotional strain proves too much for the old man, and he dies in the arms of his favorite grandson, Julio, a reckless playboy. In 1939 Julio goes to Paris with his French father, Marcelo, and is immediately drawn into the social circle of Etienne Laurier, an idealist who opposes the Nazis. Julio falls in love with Laurier's wife, Marguerite, and then becomes her lover when Laurier is sent to a concentration camp. Gradually Julio becomes involved with the French Resistance, in which his sister, Chi-Chi, is already active. Laurier is released from prison a sick and broken man, and Marguerite leaves Julio to return to her husband. Julio then becomes more and more involved in the daring raids of the French partisans against the occupying forces. Because of his family connection with two top Nazis, his Uncle Karl and cousin Heinrich, Julio is considered above suspicion by German officials, but he is unable to prevent the deaths of both Laurier and Chi-Chi. Finally, Julio decides to risk his life in a daring operation: the destruction by British bombers of the Nazi headquarters in Normandy. Since it is imperative that someone guide the planes to their target, Julio gains entry to the headquarters and accomplishes that mission. As the bombs begin falling, he is confronted by Heinrich. Knowing they are doomed, the two cousins drink a final toast to the happiness their families once shared. *Patriarchs. Playboys. Idealists. Nazism. Infidelity. Resistance (political). Family life. Aerial bombardment. Military occupation. Concentration camps. World War II.*

Argentina. Paris. Normandy.

Note: Location scenes filmed in France. This is a remake of the 1921 Metro release of the same title.

FOUR IN BED
F6.1666

Dist Able Film Co. ca **1970**. Sd; col. 16mm. [Feature length assumed.]

Sex film. No information about the precise nature of this film has been found. *Sexuality.*

FOUR KINDS OF LOVE
F6.1667

Boxoffice International Pictures. *Dist* Boxoffice International Film Distributors. Sep **1968**. Sd; b&w. 35mm. 77 min.

Prod-Dir-Writ Shannon Carse. *Photog* Dwayne Rayven. *Sd* Paul Hunt. *Mus Ed* Sam Rayven.

Cast: Kathleen Williams, Don Alman, Christine Thomas, Clint Randall, Karen Richards, James Brand, Vicky Saunders, Paul Hunt, Sheri Jackson, Hugh Hampton, Brigette Grennell, Linda Stiles, Carol Turner, Jay Edwards, Elaine Teff, Stan Logan.

Sex film. An investigation into human sexual behavior reveals four different modes of erotic involvement: sex between lovers, called "love-sex"; "money-sex," including all relationships motivated by the desire for material gain; casual or "like-sex"; and "hate-sex," which includes rape. *Sexuality. Prostitution. Rape. Sex research. Sadism.*

491 (Sweden)
F6.1668

Svensk Filmindustri. *Dist* Peppercorn-Wormser, Inc., Janus Films. 20 Dec **1967** [New York opening]. Sd; b&w (print by Movielab). 35mm. 110 min.

Prod Lars-Owe Carlberg. *Dir* Vilgot Sjöman. *Screenplay* Lars Görling. *Photog* Gunnar Fischer. *Camera* Rolf Holmqvist. *Set Dsgn* P. A. Lundgren. *Mus* Georg Riedel. *Asst Dir* Raymond Lundberg.

Cast: Lars Lind (*Krister*), Leif Nymark (*Nisse*), Stig Törnblom (*Egon*), Lars Hansson (*Pyret*), Sven Algotsson (*Jingis*), Torleif Cederstrand (*Slaktarn*), Bo Andersson (*Fisken*), Lena Nyman (*Steva*), Frank Sundström (*The Inspector*), Åke Grönberg (*The Preacher*), Mona Andersson (*Kajsa*), Jan Blomberg (*The Examiner*), Siegfried Wald, Wilhelm Fricke (*German sailors*), Erik Hell, Leif Liljeroth (*policemen*).

Melodrama. Source: Lars Görling, *491* (Stockholm, 1962). As a sociological experiment in rehabilitating young criminal offenders, a group of Stockholm juvenile delinquents are assigned to live in the home of Krister, a naive and idealistic young social worker. Except for the time spent in academic studies, the boys are free to do virtually anything they want but are required to report their activities each morning to a homosexual police inspector who exploits two of them. The violently anti-social Nisse establishes himself as leader of the group and, determined to negate Krister's continual kindness, prompts the boys to wreak havoc on the counselor's home. They break into the locked, hidden room where he keeps his piano, his heirloom furniture, and his treasured books, and they destroy what they cannot sell. One night a few of the boys, including Nisse, go in search of liquor and sneak aboard a docked German ship, where they meet a teenage prostitute, Steva. After watching a sailor brutally force her into an act of sodomy, they take her home with them. Steva stays with the boys, some of whom use her sexually, and she allows herself to be prostituted when they need money. Steva's ultimate degradation comes when she is forced to perform a sexual act with a German shepherd in front of the group. Finally shattered by the depravity surrounding him, Jingis, the youngest and shyest boy, commits suicide as Krister helplessly stands by. *Social workers. Juvenile delinquents. Sailors. Prostitutes. Police. Rape. Adolescence. Male homosexuality. Sadism. Bestiality. Criminals—Rehabilitation. Vandalism. Suicide. Stockholm.*

Note: Opened in Stockholm caJan 1964 under the title *491 (Fyrahundranittioett)*; running time: 105 min.

FOUR ON THE FLOOR
F6.1669

Actomatics Corp. *Dist* Distribpix, Inc., Nelson Fine. ca **1970**. Sd; b&w. 35mm. 70 min.

Prod-Dir Kenneth Hansen. *Orig Story* Angelique. *Photog & Lighting* Bruce Gordon, pseud. *Film Ed* Craig Stevens, ed. *Mus* KPM. *Sd* Henry Hecker. *Asst Dir* Al Hansen.

Cast: Priscilla Crisp, Red Pisces, Ron Babin, Suzzan Landow, Kim Cash, Tomba, Kamla, Camp Stevens, Frederick Douglas Roth.

Sex film. Priscilla Crisp is invited to New York City by her beau, Red Pisces, and arrives at Kennedy Airport where she is met by one of Red's friends. Installed at a nearby motel, she awaits a call from Red, who has not yet found an apartment for them. She goes to a party being given by several of Red's friends who have formed a group called "Four on the Floor"; she expects to meet Red, but finds instead an orgy in progress, and people playing a new game called "Spin the Body." The members of "Four on the Floor," Priscilla discovers, are not limited by either gender or number in their sexual couplings. The next morning she is awakened in her motel room by Red, who apologizes for his absence and makes up with her. Together they go to an afternoon party, where members of the "Four" cavort on exercise machines. The excitement of the party finally overcomes Priscilla's inhibitions, and she leaves on a hunt for more fun, with Red in hot pursuit. *Lesbianism. Sex aids. Sexual practices. Sex clubs. Orgies. Motels. New York City.*

****   **F6.1670**

Dist Andy Warhol Films, Film-Makers' Distribution Center. 15 Dec **1967**. Sd; col. 16mm. ca1500 min. [Subsequently 102 min.]

Prod-Dir Andy Warhol. *Photog* Andy Warhol. *Film Ed* Andy Warhol. *Mus* The Velvet Underground.

Cast—"International Velvet" [see note]: Alan Midgette, International Velvet.

Cast—"Alan and Dickin": Alan Midgette, Dickin.

Cast—"Imitation of Christ": Patrick Tilden *(son)*, Nico *(maid)*, Ondine *(father)*, Brigid Polk *(mother)*, Taylor Mead *(hobo)*, Tom Baker, Andrea Feldman.

Cast—"Courtroom": Ondine *(judge)*, Ivy Nicholson *(rape victim)*, Ultra Violet *(woman on judge's bench)*, Albert René Ricard *(Russian prince)*.

Cast—"Gerard Has His Hair Removed With Nair": Gerard Malanga.

Cast—"Katrina Dead": Katrina *(reclining woman)*, Albert René Ricard *(man making remarks)*, Ondine *(reclining man)*.

Cast—"Sausalito": Nico.

Cast—"Alan and Apple": Alan Midgette.

Cast—"Group One": Ingrid Superstar *(woman in kitchen)*.

Cast—"Sunset Beach on Long Island": Ondine *(man with scarf)*.

Cast—"High Ashbury": Ultra Violet, Ondine, Nico.

Cast—"Tiger Morse": Tiger Morse.

Cast—102 min version: Nico *(singer)*, Ondine *(homosexual)*, Alan Midgette, International Velvet *(lovers)*, Ivy Nicholson, Edie Sedgwick, Brigid Polk, Viva, Ingrid Superstar, Katrina, Ultra Violet, Tiger Morse.

Experimental film. INTERNATIONAL VELVET (ca30 min): In a kitchen/bathroom, a man and woman take a bath, bang utensils, whistle, drink beer, clap hands, and gaze at each other's faces. One of them washes his or her feet in the sink. ALAN AND DICKIN (ca120 min): Two men are in bed. One reads from a text dealing with LSD and Buddhism. They talk about their schoolboy past, movies, and their fondness for each other. They smoke, drink coffee, and fondle each other's hands. [Description refers to the first 30 min of the sequence.] IMITATION OF CHRIST (ca480 min): See individual entry. COURTROOM (ca30 min): In a chaotic court session, a judge presides as a young woman is apparently raped on the floor, and another woman climbs onto his bench. A crowd of people, including a Russian prince, enter and turn the courtroom into a scene of bedlam. GERARD HAS HIS HAIR REMOVED WITH NAIR (ca30 min): Four women use a depilatory to remove the hair from a young man's chest. The man is in a spotlight, surrounded by darkness; the colors of the image change constantly. The man, now without hair on his chest, poses with the four women. KATRINA DEAD (ca30 min): As a woman, apparently dead, lies on a table, people kiss her and place photographs on her body. A man makes blasphemous comments. The woman gets up from the table. A man enters and lies down in her place. SAUSALITO (ca30 min): Scenes of Sausalito, California, including boats, the docks, and streets. Eventually, the setting turns to night and boats appear silhouetted against the sky. A woman speaks poetic phrases on the soundtrack; at intervals her face is seen. A band begins to play but ceases again as lights appear in distant windows. ALAN AND APPLE (ca30 min): As a man tells of his cross-country hitchhiking journey, the colors of the image change. He eats an apple; smokes; eats a banana. In the background, a woman washes a sheet. The apple and the man's torso are seen in closeup. GROUP ONE (ca30 min): At a party, a series of discussions and arguments occur, each involving a pair of guests. An elderly woman and a young man argue on the rug. A young woman converses with a young man in the kitchen. The elderly woman stands alone in a hall. Two women discuss such topics as marriage and boyfriends. SUNSET BEACH ON LONG ISLAND (ca30 min): As a child plays in the surf, couples romp on the beach, and a man with a guitar sings about the sun and sea. A man plays with a scarf; a couple dances. There are scenes of the sand dunes and of the colors of sunset reflected in the water. HIGH ASHBURY (ca30 min): In a hippie "pad" in San Francisco, people sit on the floor, smoke marijuana, and listen to rock music. A baby is featured prominently, and his crib is seen. A person playing a wind instrument is joined by a drummer. TIGER MORSE (ca20 min): In a setting of bright lights and silver costumes, a young woman holding a silver ball talks on the subject of love. There are intermittent closeups of the ball; single-frame cuts are employed. [The 102-min version includes footage of Nico singing, a man relating a hitchhiking experience, a woman applying makeup while her boyfriend asks her pointless questions, a rape scene, a man describing a homosexual liaison, a young couple making love, a sequence featuring Tiger Morse in a silver setting, and a beach at sunset where children cavort as a man plays a guitar and sings a folksong.] *Housemaids.*

Hoboes. Judges. Hitchhikers. Hippies. Children. Sexuality. Male homosexuality. Parenthood. Rape. Death. Travel. Bathing customs. Buddhism. Religion. Motion pictures. LSD. Docks. Beaches. Marijuana. San Francisco. Sausalito. Long Island. "Imitation of Christ".

Note: Locations include New York City, Long Island, San Francisco, and Los Angeles. Shown in entirety only once; 102-min version opened in New York on 16 Dec 1967. Information on most of the segments is unobtainable; segments known by title only include: "Orion," "Emanuel," "Rolando," "Easthampton Beach," "Swimming Pool," "Sunset in California," "Philadelphia Story," "Ondine and Ingrid," "Ivy and Susan," "Ondine in Yellow Hair," "Katrina," "Barbara and Ivy," "Ondine and Edie," "Susan and David," "Nico-Katrina," "Tally and Ondine," "Ondine in Bathroom," "Susan Screen Test," and "Susan Bottomly." Two different reels, each ca30 min in length, were projected simultaneously on the screen, resulting in a superimposed image; multiple exposures also employed. The title refers to *New York Daily News* movie ratings. Also known as *Four Stars* and *The Twenty-four Hour Movie.*

THE 14 YEAR OLD GIRL   F6.1671

Dist Film-Makers' Cooperative. 3 Mar **1966** [New York opening]. Sd; b&w. 16mm. 70 min.

Prod-Dir Andy Warhol. *Writ* Ronald Tavel. *Mus Soundtrack* John Cale, Lou Reed. *Mus Perf by* The Velvet Underground. *Prod Asst* Gerard Malanga.

Cast: Mario Montez *(Hedy)*, Mary Woronov *(policewoman)*, Harvey Tavel *(judge)*, Ingrid Superstar *(saleslady)*, Ronald Tavel *(walk-on)*, Gerard Malanga, Rick Lockwood, James Claire, Randy Borscheidt, David Meyers *(husbands)*, Jack Smith *(soothsayer)*, Arnold Rockwood *(surgeon)*.

Satire. Hedy Lamarr, played by a transvestite, lies on an operating table; a surgeon and his assistants are gathered around her. A large magnifying glass in the foreground focuses on her mouth. Hedy moans and implores the doctors to make her beautiful. They continue to operate and make rude remarks about her appearance. Hedy awakens, views herself in the mirror, and comments that she looks like a 14-year-old girl. She sings a few bars of "I Feel Pretty," and reminds the doctors of her status as a movie star. Towing in hand husbands and lovers, she leaves the set of the operating room and heads into darkness, singing as the men dance a soft-shoe routine. In a department store, Hedy becomes irritated by a saleslady and threatens to have her fired. Throughout their arguments, Hedy shoplifts items from the counters. Suddenly a policewoman enters to arrest her; protesting, Hedy gives the saleslady and store manager-detective a drink of hemlock. After Hedy leaves with the policewoman, the poisoned employees writhe in death throes on the floor of the store. At her apartment, Hedy dons an exotic costume with a turban and asks for help in putting on her gloves. The policewoman searches for stolen merchandise. Hedy extols her own career as a movie star and offers a hemlock cocktail to the policewoman, but the policewoman refuses and leads Hedy away to court. On the witness stand, her first husband claims that he wanted to make her a star; the second testifies that he met her at a Schrafft's restaurant; another husband received a $500,000 divorce settlement; a fourth accuses Hedy of making pornographic films; the fifth, an Oklahoma oilman, also testifies. Hedy looks on sadly as the lone member of the courtroom audience, a soothsayer, watches through a magnifying glass. The judge hurls insulting remarks at Hedy and sentences her to death by hemlock. She is administered the hemlock and dies. The soothsayer, called to the witness stand by the judge, delivers a short eulogy. *Surgeons. Actors. Judges. Policewomen. Salesclerks. Seers. Transvestism. Plastic surgery. Motion pictures. Marriage. Shoplifting. Poisoning. Trials. Kleptomania. Sexuality. Capital punishment. Department stores. Hedy Lamarr.*

Note: A fictional account of the life of Hedy Lamarr, the film is also known as *Hedy* and *Hedy the Shoplifter.*

THE FOURTH SEX (France)   F6.1672

Les Films Univers–Condor Films. *Dist* Audubon Films. 11 Oct **1963** [Los Angeles showing]. Sd; b&w. 35mm. 82 min.

Prod (see note) José Bénazéraf, Michel Wichard. *Dir* Michel Wichard. *Dir English Vers* Radley Metzger. *Screenplay* Alfonso Gimeno. *Adapt & Dial* Jean Mitry. *English Dial* LaVerne Owens. *Photog* Marcel Combes. *Film Ed* Michel Marsac. *Mus* Louiguy. *Sd* Robert Teisseire. *Tech Supv* Jean Mitry.

Cast: Nicole Burgot *(Caroline)*, Brigitte Juslin *(Sand)*, Richard Winckler *(Michel)*, Philippe Leroy *(Paul)*, Myriam Michelsen, Jean-Pierre Posier.

Romantic melodrama. Sand, a rich though untalented young American painter in Paris, surrounds herself with a group of female friends who serve as models. At a cabaret, Sand and her group encounter a young painter, Michel, as he escorts his sister, Caroline, on a visit to Paris from the provinces. The next day, Sand invites Caroline to a party styled after a Roman orgy, during which there is a striptease exhibition, and the guests engage in unrestrained lovemaking. Afterwards, Caroline models nude for Sand, but Michel storms in and a violent fight ensues. Michel subdues Sand and they make passionate love; he then leaves abruptly. Sand, transformed by this experience, turns away her female companions and attempts to convince Michel of the change in her outlook. Though he at first hesitates to accept her love, they are at last united through the efforts of Michel's best friend, Paul. [In the original French version, Sand, suspected of lesbian tendencies, nevertheless becomes attracted to Michel, who is preoccupied with his sister's visit and ignores Sand's attentions. Paul soon assumes Michel's role as escort and falls in love with Caroline. Michel refuses to admit his love for Sand and cruelly discourages her advances. At last the proud Sand humbly confesses her love to Michel, and, convinced of her sincerity, he reciprocates.] *Americans in foreign countries. Painters. Models. Lesbianism. Bisexuality. Nudity. Brother-sister relationship. Orgies. Paris.*

Note: Opened in Paris in Mar 1962 as *Le quatrième sexe.* Radley Metzger added the Roman orgy party sequence for U. S. release. Sources conflict in crediting production company and producer. One French source credits Alfonso Gimeno as director as well as writer. Footage also included in *Dictionary of Sex,* q. v.

HO FOVOS *see* THE FEAR

THE FOX   F6.1673

Raymond Stross–Motion Pictures International. *Dist* Claridge Pictures. 7 Feb **1968** [New York opening; c29 Dec 1967; LP43778]. Sd; col (De Luxe). 35mm. 110 min. *MPAA rating R.*

Prod Raymond Stross. *Assoc Prod* Howard Koch. *Dir* Mark Rydell. *Screenplay* Lewis John Carlino, Howard Koch. *Photog* William A. Fraker. *Art Dir* Charles Bailey. *Montages & Titl* Don Record, Pacific Title. *Film Ed* Thomas Stanford. *Mus Comp & Cond* Lalo Schifrin. *Song:* "Roll Me Over" Oscar Brand. *Sung by* Anne Heywood. *Sd Des* Dollery. *Asst Dir* Burtt Harris. *Prod Supv* Arthur Broidy.

Cast: Sandy Dennis *(Jill Banford),* Keir Dullea *(Paul Grenfel),* Anne Heywood *(Ellen March),* Glyn Morris *(overseer).*

Drama. Source: David Herbert Lawrence, "The Fox," in *Dial* (May-Aug 1922). On a desolate, snowbound Canadian farm Jill Banford and Ellen March struggle to make their living by raising chickens. The more dependent and sensitive Jill tends to the kitchen chores and the bookkeeping, while the stronger and self-sufficient Ellen handles the heavier work—rebuilding broken fences, chopping wood, and stalking the red fox that raids their chicken coops. Jill seems happy with this arrangement, but Ellen is frustrated, particularly sexually, and she resorts to masturbation for satisfaction. One night a merchant seaman, Paul Grenfel, arrives to visit his grandfather, the deceased former owner of the farm. Having no other plans, Paul persuades the women to let him spend his leave with them and help with the work. Trouble develops when his obvious attraction to Ellen arouses Jill's bitter resentment. During a heated argument between the two women Paul takes a shotgun, goes out into the night, and kills the fox. Then, on the eve of his departure, he takes Ellen to an abandoned cabin, makes love to her, and urges her to go away with him. But Ellen cannot bring herself to abandon Jill. When Paul finally leaves to return to the sea, the depressed Ellen permits Jill to make love to her; and, as time passes, the women resume their former life. Ellen writes Paul, rejecting his marriage proposal. Then, while they are chopping down a dying oak, Paul suddenly returns. Taking the axe from Ellen, he warns Jill to step back lest the tree twist when it falls. But Jill petulantly ignores his advice and is killed as the giant oak crashes to the ground. Once Ellen has buried Jill and sold the farm, she goes with Paul. All that remains of the life the three persons shared is the skin of the dead fox, still hanging on the barn door where Paul nailed it. *Farmers. Seamen. Lesbianism. Farm life. Hunting. Autoeroticism. Sexuality. Jealousy. Canada. Chickens. Fox.*

Note: Locaton scenes filmed around Toronto, Canada.

THE FOX WITH NINE TAILS (Japan)   F6.1674

Japan Animated Film Co. *Dist* Daiei Motion Picture Co. Oct **1969** [Los Angeles showing]. Sd; col (Fuji Color). 35mm. 81 min.

Dir Shinichi Yagi. *Screenplay* Michio Yoshioka. *Story* Kido Okamoto. *Anim* Taku Sugiyama. *Photog* Masayoshi Kishimoto. *Art Dir* Isamu Kageyama. *Mus* Shigeru Ikeno.

Animated film. Tamamo, a beautiful girl, discovers she is really a nine-tailed fox and her purpose in life is to enslave all people to the King of Darkness. Frightened by this revelation, she flees to Kyoto, but everyone there is attracted to her beauty and, in spite of herself, she begins to carry out her destiny. She orders all statues of Buddha destroyed and an enormous statue of herself erected in their place. Tobimaru, a youth whom Tamamo has known since childhood, follows her to Kyoto and, seeing her purpose, destroys the statue. Tamamo flees to her ancestral home, but as she runs, she is turned to stone. *Idolatry. Kyoto. Fox.*

Note: Released in Japan as *Kyubi no kitsune to Tobimaru.*

FOXHOLE IN CAIRO (Great Britain)   F6.1675

Omnia Films. *Dist* Paramount Pictures. 18 Jan **1961** [Saint Louis opening; c31 Dec 1960; LP18278]. Sd; b&w. 35mm. 79 min.

Prod Steven Pallos, Donald Taylor. *Dir* John Moxey. *Screenplay* Leonard Mosley, Donald Taylor. *Dir Photog* Desmond Dickinson. *Camera Op* Jack Atchelor. *Focus Op* Ronnie Fox-Rogers. *Art Dir* John Blezard. *Draughtsman* David Catley. *Film Ed* Oswald Hafenrichter. *1st Asst Ed* Alan Corder. *2d Asst Ed* Lois Gray. *Mus* Wolfram Roehrig, Douglas Gamley, Ken Jones. *Mus for Dances* Douglas Gamley. *Dances Arr by* Patricia Kirschner. *Sd Mix* Paddy Cunningham. *Boom Op* Ken Ritchie. *Sd Camera Op* Jack Smart. *1st, 2d & 3d Asst Dir* Ted Sturgis, Derek Whitehurst, Carl Mannin. *Prod Mgr* Ben Arbeid. *Prod Sec* Cynthia Maugham. *Cont* Yvonne Richards. *Wardrobe Mistress* Freda Gibson. *Makeup* Stuart Freeborn. *Hairdresser* Barbara Barnard. *Still Photog* Eric Gray. *Prop Buyer* Harry Parr. *Ch Floor Electrn* Frank Robertson.

Cast: James Robertson-Justice *(Captain Robertson, D.S.O.),* Adrian Hoven *(John Eppler),* Niall MacGinnis *(Radek),* Peter Van Eyck *(Count Almaszy),* Robert Urquhart *(Major Wilson),* Neil McCallum *(Sandy),* Fenella Fielding *(Yvette),* Gloria Mestre *(Amina),* Albert Lieven *(Rommel),* John Westbrook *(Roger),* Lee Montague *(Aberle),* Henry Oscar *(Colonel Zeltinger),* Howard Marion Crawford *(British major),* Anthony Newlands *(SS colonel),* Richard Vernon *(general),* Michael Caine *(Weber),* Storm Durr *(Rommel's aide),* Nancy Nevinson *(Signorina Signorelli),* John Blythe *(barman),* Jerome Willis, Lane Meddick.

Melodrama. Source: Leonard Oswald Mosley, *The Cat and the Mice* (London, 1958). In 1942, Rommel halts his victorious Afrika Korps and sends German agent John Eppler and radio operator Sandy to Cairo. Their mission is to learn where the British plan to launch their counteroffensive. Eppler immediately communicates with Amina, an Egyptian cabaret dancer and his former mistress, who agrees to help him. Unknown to them, British counterespionage chief Captain Robertson has learned of Eppler's presence in Cairo and is working with the leader of Cairo's Jewish underground, Radek. Amina lures an ineffectual British officer, Major Wilson, to her houseboat and has him drugged and robbed of his briefcase containing British counteroffensive details. While Eppler and Sandy relay the information to Rommel that the battle will take place at Alam Halfa, Yvette, a member of the Jewish underground, sneaks aboard the boat and revives the unconscious Wilson. They are interrupted by Amina, who shoots Wilson but is herself stabbed to death by Yvette. Eppler arrives and is about to kill Yvette when Robertson and Radek appear and arrest Eppler. Eppler's satisfaction at having already informed Rommel that the counteroffensive will take place at Alam Halfa is short-lived. Robertson had seen to it that the plans in Wilson's briefcase were false—the real battle will take place at El Alamein. *Secret agents. Germans. Jews. Egyptians. Dancers. Espionage. Murder. Houseboats. World War II. Cairo. Erwin Rommel. Great Britain—Intelligence service. Afrika Korps. Documentation.*

Note: Opened in London in Oct 1960.

FRAGE 7 *see* QUESTION 7

LA FRANÇAISE ET L'AMOUR *see* LOVE AND THE
FRENCHWOMAN

FRANCHESCA'S SEXUAL WHIRLPOOL   F6.1676

Century Cinema Corp. *Dist* Chancellor Films. ca **1967**. Sd; col. 35mm. 60 min.

Melodrama. Franchesca prostitutes herself for men or women in order to keep her boyfriend Frankie supplied with heroin. She exhibits an utter disdain for everything her customers have to offer, except their money. When the toll becomes too much, Franchesca tries to drown herself, but she is rescued by Charlie. His tender love and encouragement help her to regain self-respect. A part of her still clings to her former ways, and she returns to Frankie, but she ultimately finds the will to reject his sordid existence forever. She leaves Frankie, the temptation of heroin, and the vicious circle of lust that brought her to death's door. *Prostitutes. Drug addicts. Suicide. Lesbianism. Heroin.*

FRANCHETTE; LES INTRIGUES   F6.1677

Dist Distribpix, Inc. 12 Dec **1969** [Champaign, Illinois, showing]. Sd; col. 35mm. 63 min.

Prod-Dir-Writ Arlo Shiffen. *Camera* Gabrial Lister. *Sd* Ron Laughlin.

Cast: Gary Michaels *(himself),* Dan Biller *(The Undercover Agent),* Kathleen Miller *(Kathy),* Nick Delgadi *(Rogers),* Angelo Marcini, Georgio Moffo *(Rogers' torpedoes),* Barbara Everest, Susan Cooper, Diane Turner.

Crime melodrama. Gary Michaels leaves New York City and becomes a beach bum in the Florida Keys, and there, to support himself, he occasionally takes tourists skindiving. Swimming alone one day, he meets Kathy, a beautiful, mysterious British woman. They fall in love and meet frequently, but Kathy's life apart from Gary remains a mystery. Gary discovers that Kathy is the mistress of Nick Rogers, a heroin dealer posing as an art collector. Rogers hires Gary to dive for him, and Gary is introduced to Kathy at Rogers' luxurious

Florida estate. Gary and Kathy continue to see each other in a nearby motel until Gary, after his first dive for Rogers, decides to report him to the authorities. Two of Rogers' "torpedoes," Angelo and Georgio, overcome Gary, shoot him full of heroin, and leave him for the narcotics squad. Dan Biller, a narcotics agent, enlists Gary's help in capturing Rogers, and with Kathy's assistance, they hope to learn where the next narcotics delivery will take place. One of Rogers' henchmen sees Kathy making love with Gary. He reports what he has seen to Rogers; Kathy is captured and tortured and raped while Rogers looks on. Rogers offers to release Kathy if Gary will make one more dive for him. Gary agrees, informs Biller, and goes out in a boat the next day with Angelo, Georgio, and Kathy. Gary kills Angelo and returns to surprise Georgio as he is molesting Kathy. He kills Georgio; Biller captures Rogers; and Gary and Kathy are reunited. *Divers. British. Mistresses. Bodyguards. Narcotics agents. Art collectors. Drug dealers. Smuggling. Rape. Murder. Sadism. Heroin. Florida Keys.*

FRANCIS OF ASSISI   F6.1678

Perseus Productions. *Dist* Twentieth Century–Fox Film Corp. 12 Jul **1961** [Chicago opening; c12 Jul 1961; LP20132]. Sd (Westrex); col (De Luxe). 35mm (CinemaScope). 106 min.

Prod Plato A. Skouras. *Dir* Michael Curtiz. *Screenplay* Eugene Vale, James Forsyth, Jack Thomas. *Dir Photog* Piero Portalupi. *Art Dir* Edward Carrere. *Set Decor* Walter M. Scott, Ferdinando Ruffo. *Film Ed* Louis R. Loeffler. *Mus Comp & Arr* Mario Nascimbene. *Mus Cond* Franco Ferrara. *Sd* Leo Wilkins. *Asst Dir* Ottavio Oppo. *Unit Mgr* Joe Popkin. *Prod Coörd* International Film Service. *Cost Dsgn* Vittorio Nino Novarese. *Wardrobe Supv* Wesley Sherrard, Annalisa Nasalli-Rocca. *Makeup* Hal Lierley. *Hairstyles* Helen Turpin. *Photog Eff* Joseph Natanson. *Tech Adv* Vincenzo Labella. *Coöp* Italian Government, Franciscan Orders, People of Assisi; Perugia; Bevagna; Rome and Oristano, Benedictines of Assisi, Superintendency of Fine Arts of Umbria.

Cast: Bradford Dillman (*Francis Bernardone*), Dolores Hart (*Clare Scefi*), Stuart Whitman (*Paolo*), Pedro Armendariz (*The Sultan*), Cecil Kellaway (*Cardinal Hugolino*), Eduard Franz (*Pietro Bernardone*), Athene Seyler (*Aunt Buona*), Finlay Currie (*Pope Innocent III*), Mervyn Johns (*Brother Juniper*), Russell Napier (*Brother Elias*), John Welsh (*Canon Cattanei*), Harold Goldblatt (*Bernard*), Edith Sharpe (*Donna Pica Bernardone*), Jack Lambert (*Scefi*), Oliver Johnston (*Father Livoni*), Malcolm Keen (*Guido*), Brendan Fitzgerald (*Enrico*), Fernando Hilbeck (*Ricardo*), Feodor Chaliapin (*Cardinal Savelli*), Odoardo Spadaro (*Gregory*), Leonardo Porzio (*Mario*), Evi Marandi (*Saracen girl*), Manuela Ballard (*Lucia*), Jole Mauro (*Elfrida*), Uti Hof (*Regina*), Nicholas Hannen (*beggar*), Paul Muller, John Karlsen, David Maunsell, Cyrus Elias, Curt Lowens, Jack Savage, Walter Maslow, Renzo Cesana (*friars*).

Biographical drama. Source: Louis De Wohl, *The Joyful Beggar* (Philadelphia, 1958). Early in the 13th century, young Francis Bernardone, the pleasure-seeking son of an Assisi cloth merchant, becomes increasingly aware of the emptiness of his life. Hoping to find some meaning for his existence, he answers the call of Pope Innocent III and joins the army being formed to liberate Sicily for King Frederick. Accompanying him is Paolo de Vandria, an impoverished nobleman and a close friend. In battle Francis hears a voice commanding him to return home. When he does so, he is branded a coward and traitor and is thrown into prison. Following his release, the Lord's voice again speaks to Francis and orders him to rebuild a church that stands in ruins outside Assisi. Enlisting the aid of farmers and workmen, he reconstructs the church and then forms a religious order, which receives the approval and blessing of the pope. Paolo, meanwhile, has fallen in love with Francis' childhood friend, Clare, the beautiful daughter of the aristocratic Scefi family. But the young girl is so moved by Francis' preachings that she renounces the worldly life and becomes a nun. Blaming Francis for her decision, Paolo, filled with bitterness and hate, rides off to the Crusades. As the Franciscan Order grows, Francis answers a plea from the pope and journeys to the Holy Land, where the crusaders are battling the sultan's forces. By offering to walk through fire to prove the strength of his faith, Francis wins the sultan's respect. He is disgusted, however, by the plunder of the crusaders, led by Paolo. Returning home, Francis is further disheartened to discover that some of the Franciscan brothers have forsaken the vow of poverty. After upbraiding his fellow monks, Francis retreats to a cave. There he resigns himself to progressive blindness and is comforted by Clare. While praying on a hillside he receives the stigmata. On his·deathbed Francis is visited by the repentant Paolo and mourned by a crowd of admirers. *Merchants. Deserters—Military. Farmers. Nuns. Nobility. Poverty. Friendship. Blindness. Stigmata. Churches. Prisons. The Crusades. Assisi. The Holy Land. Francis of Assisi. Innocent III (pope). Franciscans. Catholic Church.*

Note: Location scenes filmed in Italy and Spain.

FRANÇOISE *see* **ANATOMY OF A MARRIAGE; MY DAYS WITH JEAN-MARC**

FRANKENSTEIN CONQUERS THE WORLD (United States/Japan)
    F6.1679

Toho Co.–Henry G. Saperstein Enterprises. *Dist* American International Pictures. Jun **1966** [Chicago opening; c1 Jun 1966; LP32815]. Sd; col (Eastman Color, print by Pathé). 35mm (Tohoscope). 87 min.

Pres by James H. Nicholson, Samuel Z. Arkoff. *Prod* Tomoyuki Tanaka. *Exec Prod* Henry G. Saperstein, Reuben Bercovitch. *Dir* Inoshiro Honda. *Screenplay* Kaoru Mabuchi. *Writ From a Synopsis by* Jerry Sohl. *Based on a Story by* Reuben Bercovitch. *Camera* Hajime Koizumi. *Art Dir* Takeo Kita. *Film Ed* Ryohei Fujii. *Mus* Akira Ifukube. *Re-rec* Salvatore Billitteri. *Dir Sp Eff Photog* Eiji Tsuburaya.

Cast (see note): Nick Adams (*Dr. James Bowen*), Tadao Takashima (*scientist*), Kumi Mizuno (*woman doctor*), Yoshio Tsuchiya, Takashi Shimura, Kenchiro Kawaji, Seuko Togami.

Horror film. Toward the end of World War II, a sealed box containing the living heart of the Frankenstein monster is shipped from a Nazi laboratory in Germany to Japanese scientists at Hiroshima. As the scientists are examining the organ, the atom bomb is dropped on the city. Ten years later, an American medical scientist, Dr. James Bowen, and his Japanese assistants learn of the existence of a mysterious wild boy who subsists on wildlife. After befriending the creature and discovering that he is growing to monstrous proportions at an amazing rate, the scientists theorize that the fallout from the bomb has·brought about his birth from the Frankenstein heart. This theory is confirmed when the boy escapes his steel shackles by tearing off his hand and then quickly generating a new one. The boy grows to be almost 100 feet tall and takes refuge in the forests of Mount Fuji. Soon it is reported that a huge creature is wreaking destruction in the area, and the "Frankenstein boy" is blamed, but actually an earthquake has released a giant prehistoric reptile. As the army, police, and scientists pursue the gigantic boy, he struggles with and overcomes the reptile, but he himself perishes in another earthquake. *Scientists. Americans in foreign countries. Monsters. Mutation. Regeneration. Atom bomb. World War II. Hiroshima. Fuji. Earthquakes. Frankenstein. Reptiles.*

Note: Released in Japan in 1966 as *Furankenshutain tai Baragon;* running time; 95 min. Originally titled *Frankenstein vs. the Giant Devilfish.* Kenchiro Kawaji and Seuko Togami are listed only in non-Japanese sources. Several scenes are used in *Destroy All Monsters,* q. v.

FRANKENSTEIN CREATED WOMAN (Great Britain)   F6.1680

Seven Arts Productions–Hammer Film Productions. *Dist* Twentieth Century–Fox Film Corp. Mar **1967** [c31 Dec 1966; LP34489]. Sd (RCA); col (DeLuxe). 35mm. 92 min.

Prod Anthony Nelson Keys. *Dir* Terence Fisher. *Orig Screenplay* John Elder. *Dir Photog* Arthur Grant. *Camera Op* Moray Grant. *Art Dir* Don Mingaye. *Prod Dsgn* Bernard Robinson. *Supv Ed* James Needs, Spencer Reeve. *Mus Comp* James Bernard. *Mus Supv* Philip Martell. *Sd Rec* Ken Rawkins. *Sd Ed* Roy Hyde. *Asst Dir* Douglas Hermes. *Prod Mgr* Ian Lewis. *Cont* Eileen Head. *Wardrobe Mistress* Rosemary Burrows. *Wardrobe Master* Larry Stewart. *Makeup* George Partleton. *Hairstylist* Frieda Steiger. *Sp Eff* Les Bowie. *Casting* Irene Lamb.

Cast: Peter Cushing (*Baron Frankenstein*), Susan Denberg (*Christina*), Thorley Walters (*Dr. Hertz*), Robert Morris (*Hans*), Duncan Lamont (*prisoner*), Peter Blythe (*Anton*), Barry Warren (*Karl*), Derek Fowlds (*Johann*), Alan MacNaughtan (*Kleve*), Peter Madden (*chief of police*), Philip Ray (*mayor*), Ivan Beavis (*landlord*), Colin Jeavons (*priest*), Bartlett Mullins (*bystander*), Alec Mango (*spokesman*), Stuart Middleton (*Hans, as a boy*), John Maxim (*police sergeant*), Kevin Flood (*jailer*).

Horror film. In a 19th-century Balkan village Baron Frankenstein and Dr. Hertz conduct scientific experiments in an endeavor to transfer the souls of dead humans into other bodies. Their assistant Hans is a local boy ostracized by the villagers because his father was guillotined for murder years earlier. One night, while visiting his girl friend, Christina, a cripple with a birthmark on her otherwise pretty face, Hans is unjustly accused of murdering an innkeeper and is sentenced to the same fate that befell his father. Christina witnesses the execution of her beloved and, overcome by despair, drowns herself in a river. Frankenstein and Dr. Hertz recover both corpses and succeed in bringing Christina back to life with no sign of either her lameness or her facial blemish. And, as part of the experiment, they give her Hans's soul. As a result, the young woman is consumed with Hans's passion for revenge, and she sets out to kill the three youths responsible for the innkeeper's death. Frankenstein is unable to prevent Christina from slaying her three victims and taking her own life. *Scientists. Nobility. Cripples. Reviviscence. Village life. Murder. Injustice. Capital punishment. Suicide. Revenge. The Soul. Experiments. Birthmarks. Frankenstein. Balkans.*

Note: Released in Great Britain in 1967. John Elder is a pseudonym for Anthony Hinds.

FRANKENSTEIN MEETS THE SPACE MONSTER F6.1681

Vernon Films–Seneca Productions. *Dist* Allied Artists. 22 Sep 1965 [Ohio release; c22 Sep 1965; LP33581]. Sd; b&w. 35mm. 78 min.

Pres by Futurama Entertainment Corp. *Prod* Robert McCarty. *Exec Prod* Alan V. Iselin. *Dir* Robert Gaffney. *Screenplay* George Garrett. *Story* George Garrett, John Rodenbeck, R. H. W. Dillard. *Photog* Saul Midwall. *Film Ed* Laverne Keating.

Cast: James Karen (*Dr. Adam Steele*), David Kernan (*General Bowers*), Nancy Marshall (*Karen Grant*), Marilyn Hanold (*Princess Marcuzan*), Lou Cutell (*Nadir*), Robert Reilly (*Col. Frank Saunders/Frankenstein*).

Science fiction melodrama. Dr. Adam Steele has perfected a robot called Colonel Saunders that is so humanlike that he is able to fool the press before launching it into space. The robot is electrically damaged by a spaceship carrying invaders from another planet who plan to capture women from Earth for breeding purposes. As a result of the crash and a laser-gun attack, the robot's face is horribly disfigured, and he is transformed into a Frankenstein-type monster. The robot is traced to Puerto Rico and repaired but then captured by the invaders who also seize Dr. Steele's assistant, Karen Grant, and several other women. Meanwhile, Steele and General Bowers have prepared a large-scale attack, and once the robot has freed the women, the invading spaceship is destroyed. *Scientists. Space creatures. Abduction. Disfiguration. Robots. Laser. Puerto Rico. Frankenstein.*

Note: Exteriors filmed in Puerto Rico. Much of the film utilizes newsreel footage. May also be known as *Frankenstein Meets the Spacemen.*

FRANKENSTEIN MUST BE DESTROYED (Great Britain) F6.1682

Hammer Film Productions. *Dist* Warner Bros. Pictures. 11 Feb 1970 [Los Angeles opening]. Sd; col (Technicolor). 35mm. 97 min. *MPAA rating* GP.

Prod Anthony Nelson Keys. *Dir* Terence Fisher. *Screenplay* Bert Batt. *Story* Anthony Nelson Keys, Bert Batt. *Dir Photog* Arthur Grant. *Camera Op* Neil Binney. *Art Dir* Bernard Robinson. *Supv Film Ed* James Needs. *Film Ed* Gordon Hales. *Mus Comp* James Bernard. *Mus Dir* Philip Martell. *Sd Supv* Tony Lumkin. *Sd Rec* Ken Rawkins. *Sd Ed* Don Ranasinghe. *Asst Dir* Bert Batt. *Prod Mgr* Christopher Neame. *Cont* Doreen Dearnaley. *Wardrobe Supv* Rosemary Burrows. *Wardrobe Mistress* Lotte Slattery. *Makeup* Eddie Knight. *Hairstyles* Pat McDermott. *Sp Eff* Studio Locations Ltd. *Constr Mgr* Arthur Banks.

Cast: Peter Cushing (*Baron Frankenstein*), Simon Ward (*Karl*), Veronica Carlson (*Anna*), Thorley Walters (*Inspector Frisch*), Freddie Jones (*Dr. Richter*), Maxine Audley (*Ella Brandt*), Geoffrey Bayldon (*police doctor*), George Pravda (*Brandt*), Colette O'Neil (*madwoman*), Harold Goodwin (*burglar*), Frank Middlemas (*3d guest*), George Belbin, Norman Shelley, Michael Gover (*Anna's lodgers*), Peter Copley (*principal*), Jim Collier, British (*Dr. Heidecke*), Alan Surtees, Windsor Davies (*police sergeants*).

Horror film. Baron Frankenstein, observed performing an illegal brain transplant, flees to Altenburg where he finds a room in Anna Spengler's boardinghouse. When Frankenstein discovers that Anna's fiancé, Dr. Karl Holst, is stealing drugs from the asylum where he works, he blackmails Holst into abducting Dr. Brandt, now a patient but formerly Frankenstein's colleague and an expert on brain transplants. Brandt dies of a heart attack, however, before he can divulge his secrets. On his own, Frankenstein transplants Brandt's brain into the head of Professor Richter, a doctor at the asylum. When Brandt awakens with Richter's body and goes to Anna for help, she becomes terrified and stabs him. After Brandt staggers away, Frankenstein murders Anna and goes after Brandt, who has gone completely mad. Frankenstein finds Brandt, but the madman sets fire to his own house, destroying himself and Frankenstein. *Physicians. Scientists. Brain surgery. Organ transplants. Blackmail. Abduction. Murder. Boardinghouses. Insane asylums. Experiments. Altenburg. Fires. Frankenstein.*

Note: Opened in London in May 1969.

FRANKENSTEIN VS. THE GIANT DEVILFISH see FRANKENSTEIN CONQUERS THE WORLD

FRANKIE AND JOHNNY F6.1683

F & J Pictures. *Dist* United Artists. 31 Mar 1966 [Baton Rouge, Louisiana, opening; c31 Mar 1966; LP32331]. Sd; col (Technicolor). 35mm. 87 min.

An Edward Small Production. *Exec Prod* Edward Small. *Prod Exec* Joseph Small. *Assoc Prod* Alex Gottlieb. *Dir* Frederick De Cordova. *Screenplay* Alex Gottlieb. *Story* Nat Perrin. *Photog* James Marquette. *Art Dir* Walter Simonds. *Set Decor* Morris Hoffman. *Film Ed* Grant Whytock. *Mus & Mus Dir* Fred Karger. *Song:* "Frankie and Johnny" new words & arr Fred Karger, Alex Gottlieb, Ben Weisman. *Song:* "Chesay" Ben Weisman, Sid Wayne, Fred Karger. *Song:* "Come Along" David Hess. *Songs:* "Petunia, the Gardener's Daughter," "Beginner's Luck" Sid Tepper, Roy C. Bennett. *Song:* "What Every Woman Lives For" Doc Pomus, Mort Shuman. *Song:* "Look Out, Broadway" Fred Wise, Randy Starr. *Songs:* "Shout It Out," "Everybody Come Aboard" Bill Giant, Bernie Baum, Florence Kaye. *Song:* "Hard Luck" Ben Weisman, Sid Wayne. *Song:* "Please Don't Stop Loving Me" Joy Byers. *Songs Sung by* Elvis Presley. *Dance Dir* Earl Barton. *Sd Rec* Frank Webster, Jr.. *Sd Mix* Al Overton. *Prod Mgr* Harold E. Knox. *Fashion Coörd* Gwen Wakeling. *Makeup* Dan Greenway. *Hairstyles* Joan St. Oegger.

Cast: Elvis Presley (*Johnny*), Donna Douglas (*Frankie*), Nancy Kovack (*Nellie Bly*), Sue Ane Langdon (*Mitzi*), Anthony Eisley (*Braden*), Harry Morgan (*Cully*), Audrey Christie (*Pog*), Robert Strauss (*Blackie*), Jerome Cowan (*Wilbur*), Wilda Taylor, Larri Thomas, Dee Jay Mattis, Judy Chapman (*dancers* [see note]).

Comedy-drama with music. Frankie and Johnny, singers on Clint Braden's riverboat, are in love, but Frankie refuses to marry Johnny until he stops gambling and losing all his earnings. A gypsy fortune-teller predicts that a redheaded woman will appear and can reverse Johnny's fortune. Soon after, redheaded Nellie Bly, Clint's former girl friend, comes aboard the riverboat, and Johnny begins to win. Meanwhile, Cully, Johnny's piano-playing sidekick, writes a song, "Frankie and Johnny," that is introduced on the showboat. A music publisher hears the song, likes it, and invites Frankie and Johnny to come to New York City to perform. Hopeful that Nellie's presence will bring him luck, Johnny tries to win enough money to take him and Frankie to New York. Frankie becomes jealous of Nellie, who is only interested in marrying Clint, and breaks off with Johnny; at the same time, Clint admonishes Johnny, telling him to stay away from Nellie. At the Mardi Gras ball in New Orleans, Nellie and Frankie dress exactly alike, and Johnny, thinking he is with Nellie, gambles and wins. When Frankie unmasks, Johnny realizes that she brings him as much luck as Nellie. Clint's dim-witted bodyguard, thinking that he is looking out for his employer's interests, places real bullets in the gun Frankie uses to "shoot" Johnny in the musical number. Luckily, the bullet lodges in a charm Frankie had given Johnny, and he is unharmed. Frankie and Johnny decide to marry, as do Nellie and Clint. *Singers. Shipowners. Gypsies. Fortune-tellers. Bodyguards. Gambling. Superstition. Jealousy. Mistaken identity. Riverboats. Mardi Gras. Mississippi River. New Orleans.*

Note: Previously filmed in 1936. Some sources credit the dancers as the Earl Barton Dancers. Other songs performed: "Down by the Riverside," and "When the Saints Go Marching In."

FRANK'S GREATEST ADVENTURE see FEARLESS FRANK

FRANTIC (France) F6.1684

Nouvelles Editions de Films. *Dist* Times Film Corp. 11 Jun 1961 [New York opening]. Sd; b&w. 35mm. 90 min.

A Louis Malle Production. *Prod* Jean Thuillier. *Assoc Prod* Irénée Leriche. *Dir* Louis Malle. *Dial* Roger Nimier. *Adapt* Roger Nimier, Louis Malle. *Dir Photog* Henri Decaë. *Camera* André Villard. *Asst Camera* Jean Rabier. *Art Dir* Rino Mondellini, Jean Mandaroux. *Asst Art Dir* Pierre Guffroy. *Film Ed* Léonide Azar. *Mus* Miles Davis. *Sd Ch* Raymond Gauguier. *Rec* Claude Orhon. *Boom Op* Fernand Sartin. *Asst Dir* Alain Fraisse, François Leterrier. *Prod Mgr* Hubert Mérial. *Location Mgr* Roger Joint. *Prod Sec* André Chaussivert. *Script Girl* Francine Corteggiani. *Makeup* Boris de Fast. *Tech Cons* Jean-Paul Sassy. *Still Photog* Jean-Louis Castelli. *Prop* Jacques Martin.

Cast: Jeanne Moreau (*Florence Carala*), Maurice Ronet (*Julien Tavernier*), Georges Poujouly (*Louis*), Yori Bertin (*Véronique*), Jean Wall (*Simon Carala*), Ivan Petrovich (*Horst Bencker*), Lino Ventura (*Inspector Chérier*), Elga Andersen (*Frieda Rencker*), Félix Marten (*Subervie*), Bandeira, Hubert Deschamps, Sylvianne Aisenstein.

Drama. Source: Noël Calef, *Ascenseur pour l'échafaud* (Paris, 1956). Julien Tavernier, a former war hero, is desperately in love with Florence Carala, the wife of his ruthless employer. Together the two lovers devise a scheme whereby Julien will murder Carala and escape undetected. Late one afternoon, Julien climbs by rope from his office window to Carala's chambers on the floor above. After shooting his victim, he returns to his office and at the usual time leaves for the day, a normal departure observed by the switchboard operator. Once on the street, however, he notices that the telltale rope is still dangling from the window ledge. He rushes back to retrieve it but becomes trapped in the elevator between floors when the current is turned off for the night. Meanwhile, two thrill-happy teenagers, Louis and Véronique, have taken his sports car for a ride. After racing a German couple in a Mercedes, the two youngsters try to steal their car during a night stopover at a motel. When they are caught in the act, Louis kills the German couple with Julien's revolver. The next morning, after his release from the elevator, Julien is arrested for the murder of the German couple. Unable to produce an alibi without involving himself in Carala's death, Julien appears doomed. Florence tracks down the two teenagers and follows them to the motel, where they have left some incriminating photographs taken with Julien's camera before the murder. Awaiting them is Inspector Chérier with the incriminating evidence—pictures of Louis and Véronique with the murdered couple—and additional photographs of Florence and Julien which provide him with a motivation for the murder of Carala. *Police. Employers. War heroes. Infidelity. Murder. Theft. Adolescence. Guns. Elevators. Photographs. Motels. Sports cars.*

Note: Location scenes filmed at Le Touquet. Opened in Paris in Jan 1958 as *Ascenseur pour l'échafaud.*

THE FRATERNITY   F6.1685

12 Jun **1970** [Los Angeles showing]. Sd; col. 35mm? [Feature length assumed.]

Sex film. The secret homosexual rites of a college fraternity are depicted. *Rites and ceremonies. College life. Male homosexuality. Fraternities.*

FRAUEN, DIE DURCH DIE HÖLLE GEHEN *see* THE TALL WOMEN

FRAULEIN DOKTOR (Italy/Yugoslavia)   F6.1686

Dino De Laurentiis Cinematografica–Avala Film. *Dist* Paramount Pictures. 14 May **1969** [Los Angeles opening; c31 Dec 1968; LF36]. Sd; col (Technicolor). 35mm. 102 min. *MPAA rating M.*

Prod Dino De Laurentiis. *Dir* Alberto Lattuada. *2d Unit Dir* Leopoldo Savona. *Screenplay* Duilio Coletti, Stanley Mann, Harry A. L. Craig, Alberto Lattuada, Vittoriano Petrilli. *Story* Vittoriano Petrilli. *Dir Photog* Luigi Kuveiller. *Art Dir* Mario Chiari. *Set Decor* Enzo Eusepi. *Main Titl* Luigi Lardani. *Film Ed* Nino Baragli. *Mus* Ennio Morricone. *Mus Dir* Bruno Nicolai. *Sd Mix* Dragan Grozdanović. *Asst Dir* Marcello Aliprandi, Dušan Dimitrijević, Djordje Vujović. *Prod Supv* Alfredo Nicolai. *Prod Mgr* Bianca Lattuada, Aleksandar Krstić. *Cost* Maria De Matteis. *Military Uniforms* Enzo Bulgarelli. *Makeup* Otello Fava, Marija Kordić. *Hairstyles* Renata Magnanti, Stanislava Zarić. *Sp Eff* Dušan Piros. *Military Adv* Milutin Dimitrijević. *Dial Dir* Walter Williams.

Cast: Suzy Kendall (*Fraulein Doktor*), Kenneth More (*Colonel Foreman*), Capucine (*Dr. Saforet*), James Booth (*Meyer*), Alexander Knox (*General Peronne*), Nigel Green (*Colonel Mathesius*), Roberto Bisacco (*Hans Schell*), Malcolm Ingram (*Cartwright*), Giancarlo Giannini (*Lieut. Hans Ruppert*), Mario Novelli (*Sgt. Otto -Latemar*), Kenneth Poitevin (*2d Lieut. Ernst Weichert*), Bernard De Vries (*2d Lieutenant Wilhelm von Oberdorff*), Ralph Nossek (*lean agent*), Michael Elphick (*Tom*), Olivera Vučo (*Marchioness de Haro*), Andreina Paul (*Doña Elena de Rivas*), Silvia Monti (*Margarita*), Virginia Bell (*Doña Julia*), Colin Tapley (*General Metzler*), Gérard Herter (*Captain Munster*), Walter Williams (*General von Hindenburg*), James Mishler (*General von Ludendorff*), John Atkinson (*Major Rops*), Neale Stainton (*sergeant*), John Webb (*1st agent*), Joan Geary (*landlady*), Aca Stojković (*chemist*), Mavid Popović (*chaplain*), Janez Vrhovec (*Belgian colonel*), Bata Paskaljević, Zoran Longinović (*wounded English soldiers*), Dušan Bulajić (*Colonel Delveaux*), Miki Mićović (*Blondel*), Dušan Djurić (*aide to Ludendorff*), Maggie McGrath (*Mrs. MacPherson*), Gyorgy Nagyajtay (*Chilean ambassador*), Andreas Voutsinas.

War drama. One night during World War I a German U-boat lands three people in the Orkney Islands. When two are captured, Colonel Foreman of British intelligence tricks one of them, Meyer, into revealing that the third person landed was an infamous German spy known as Fraulein Doktor, whose mission is to kill British Field Marshal Lord Kitchener. Fraulein Doktor learns that the field marshal is aboard the H.M.S. *Hampshire*, and the Germans sink the ship, killing Kitchener and the 700 men aboard. Her mission completed, Fraulein Doktor injects herself with morphine. Meyer, meanwhile, has told Foreman about another of Fraulein Doktor's deeds: disguised as a housemaid, she won the confidence of Dr. Saforet, the French lesbian inventor of a powerful poison gas formula; murdered her; and stole the formula for the Germans. Colonel Foreman sends Meyer back to Germany as a counterspy, and Colonel Mathesius, the German spy chief, having discovered the plan, encourages Meyer to kill Fraulein Doktor. Although Meyer is attracted to the deadly spy, he carries out his assignment and returns to England. The Fraulein's "death," however, has been staged by the Germans, and she is already at work on a two-fold suicidal mission. She poses as a Spanish aristocrat and dupes the Belgian ambassador into allowing her to organize a Red Cross train to aid wounded Allies at the front; then smuggles aboard four spies to steal Allied offensive plans from a Belgian chateau. Meanwhile, Colonel Foreman has begun to suspect that Fraulein Doktor is not dead, and he takes Meyer along with him to investigate the hospital train. Though Meyer recognizes Fraulein Doktor in her nurse's uniform, he has become too infatuated to expose her, and her mission is a success. The Germans make use of the stolen plans to launch a counterattack against the Allies employing the insidious poison gas. After the German victory Colonel Foreman and Meyer arrive at a railway station where Fraulein Doktor is treating wounded soldiers. Foreman realizes that he has found the infamous spy, but he is shot dead by Meyer, who, in turn, is killed by a German patrol. Fraulein Doktor laughs maniacally and then breaks into

sobs. Meyer's death, her addiction to morphine, and her fanatical patriotism have taken a heavy toll. *Spies. Physicians. Drug addicts. Scientists. Espionage. Assassination. Lesbianism. Disguise. Gas warfare. Submarines. Trains. Morphine. World War I. Orkney Islands. England. France. Germany. Spain. Belgium. Horatio Herbert Kitchener. Great Britain—Intelligence service. Germany—Intelligence service. H. M. S. "Hampshire".*

Note: Reportedly inspired by the exploits of Anna Maria Lesser. Location scenes filmed in Yugoslavia and Hungary. Released in Yugoslavia in Feb 1969 as *Gospodjica Doktor—Špijunka bez imena.* Rome opening: 1969 as *Fräulein Doktor.* U. S. prerelease titles: *Nameless* and *The Betrayal.*

FREAKS! *see* SHE FREAK

LA FRECCIA D'ORO *see* THE GOLDEN ARROW

FREDDY UNTER FREMDEN STERNEN (West Germany)   F6.1687

Melodie Film. *Dist* Casino Films. 19 Jan **1962** [New York opening]. Sd; col (Eastmancolor). 35mm. 97 min.

Dir Wolfgang Schleif. *Screenplay* Gustav Kampendonk, Aldo von Pinelli. *Photog* Heinz Pehlke. *Art Dir* Gabriel Pellon, Peter Röhrig. *Film Ed* Hermann Ludwig. *Mus* Lothar Olias. *Sd* Eduard Kessel. *Prod Mgr* Hans Schröder. *Cost* Eva Maria Schröder. *Makeup* Friedrich Havenstein, Eva Schreckling.

Cast: Freddy Quinn (*Freddy Quinn*), Christian Machalet (*Stephan*), Vera Tschechowa, Gustav Knuth, Dieter Eppler, Ursula Krieg, Benno Sterzenbach, Hannelore Elsner, Marlies Behrens, Helga Sommerfeld, Dagmar Biener, Camilla Spira.

Musical comedy-drama. German singer Freddy Quinn travels with his stowaway orphan friend Stephan to Canada, where Freddy plans to build a home. When copper is discovered on his land, a jealous neighbor plots Freddy's destruction. Freddy's strength and singing ability, however, charm his other neighbors, friends, and five young women attracted to him. Stephan's illegal entry into the country and Freddy's love for a girl in Hamburg cause them to return home. *Singers. Orphans. Stowaways. Neighbors. Envy. Copper. Canada.*

Note: Location scenes filmed in Canada. Opened in Stuttgart in Dec 1959; running time: 100 min.

FREE GRASS   F6.1688

John Lawrence Productions. *For* Smith–Dorn Productions. *Dist* Hollywood Star Pictures. 15 Oct **1969** [Detroit opening]. Sd; col (Eastman Color). 35mm. 83 min. *MPAA rating* R.

A Maurice Smith–Ray Dorn–Lynn Steed Production. *Prod* John Lawrence. *Exec Prod* Ray Dorn. *Co-prod* Maurice Smith. *Assoc Prod* Arthur Gilbert. *Dir* Bill Brame. *Screenplay* John Lawrence, James Gordon White, Gerald Wilson, U. S. writ, Paul Stevenson. *Photog* Austin McKinney. *Mus Score* Sidewalk Productions.

Cast: Richard Beymer (*Dean*), Russ Tamblyn (*Link*), Lana Wood (*Karen*), Elizabeth Thompson (*Margo*), Warren Finnerty (*Barney*), Casey Kasem (*Phil*), Joel Dee McCrea (*agent no. 1*), Lindsay Crosby (*agent no. 2*), Dave Hull (*lieutenant*).

Melodrama. Hippies Dean and Karen fall in love; and Dean, needing money to take Karen away, agrees to help Link and his hoods smuggle marijuana across the Mexican border. Dean abandons them when they kill two narcotics agents, and he returns to Link's place to pick up Karen. There Link puts LSD in Dean's drink to make him hallucinate. Meanwhile, the rest of the gang abduct Karen in hopes of trapping Dean so that they can kill him. Dean is lured to the beach to be set afire; instead, he causes Link to go up in flames. The hoods, surrounded by police at Link's place, are killed in an exchange of gunfire. Dean rescues Karen and departs with her on his motorcycle after alerting the hippie community of the "free grass" in the hoods' car. *Hippies. Hoodlums. Narcotics agents. Police. Motorcyclists. Smuggling. Murder. Abduction. Marijuana. LSD. Mexican border. Fires. Hallucinations.*

Note: Location scenes filmed in Los Angeles. Joel Dee McCrea is also known as Jody McCrea. Title changed to *Scream Free.*

FREE LOVE CONFIDENTIAL   F6.1689

Boxoffice International Pictures. *Dist* Boxoffice International Film Distributors. 13 Nov **1967** [New York opening]. Sd; b&w. 35mm. 70 min.

Prod-Writ Sanford White. *Dir* Gordon Heller. *Camera* Manuel S. Conde. *2d Unit Camera* Ed DePriest. *Film Ed* Bob Freeman. *Mus* Miklos Rubag. *Sd Eff* Miklos Rubag. *Asst Dir* Bill Bourne. *Prod Mgr* Bethel Buckalew. *Script Supv* Lisa Bickley.

Cast: Karen Miller (*Kaye*), Yvette Corday (*Gieselle*), John Warren, actor (*Robin*), Rick Stevens, Mia Parks, Omar Legor.

Drama. Bored with their lives, Kaye, the wife of a wealthy Hollywood businessman, and her close friend Gieselle decide to answer an ad in an underground newspaper soliciting figure models with unusual talents. At Robin's photography studio, they are given some marijuana to smoke. They quickly become high and pose in a variety of provocative positions for the camera. After a final shooting session in which Robin joins them in the bedroom, the girls leave, and they suddenly realize that the photographer possesses incriminating evidence of their uninhibited activities. When they return the next day, they are met by a lesbian, Mickey, who forces them to submit to her embraces in exchange for the film's return. When she is finished with them, she demands $500 to complete the deal. Desperate, the women attempt to steal the money, and they are nearly caught by a guard. The next day, they finally meet Robin, who explains that he has no intention of blackmailing them, and he unrolls the spool of film before their eyes. *Housewives. Models. Photographers. Blackmail. Lesbianism. Theft. Marijuana. Hollywood.*

Note: Filmed in California. Conflicting sources give two variations of the director's name: Gordon Hess and Gordon Heller.

FREE, WHITE AND 21   F6.1690

Falcon International Corp. *Dist* American International Pictures. 24 Apr **1963** [Detroit opening]. Sd; b&w. 35mm. 102 min.

Dir Larry Buchanan. *Screenplay* Larry Buchanan, Hal Dwain, Cliff Pope. *Photog* Ralph K. Johnson. *Asst Camera* Laney Duck. *Art Dir* Dennis Adams. *Film Ed* Larry Buchanan. *Mus & Song:* "Hobo Twist" Joe Johnson. *Sd* Robert Redd. *Prod Asst* Betty Sooter. *Crew Ch* James Finley.

Cast: Frederick O'Neal *(Ernie Jones)*, Annalena Lund *(Greta Mae Hansen)*, George Edgley *(judge)*, George Russell *(Defense Attorney Tyler)*, John Hicks *(Prosecuting Attorney Atkins)*, Hugh Crenshaw *(assistant prosecuting attorney)*, Miles Middough, James Altgens, Bill McGee, Jonathan Ledford, Ted Mitchell, Jack Dunlop *(witnesses)*.

Melodrama. Black businessman Ernie Jones is on trial in a Texas courtroom for the alleged rape of beautiful Greta Mae Hansen, a Swede who came to Texas as a Freedom Rider. The prosecution attempts to prove that Jones, the proprietor of a hotel where Greta was forced to take lodging after her friendship with blacks made it necessary for her to leave the YWCA, assaulted and raped her after winning her confidence and offering her a job as a model. The defense admits that Jones was intimate with Greta but claims she consented to the relationship. The judge charges the jury (the theater audience), and then the verdict is announced. The jury finds for the defendant, and the lawyers wonder if justice has been done. *Swedes. Negroes. Businessmen. Freedom Riders. Hotelkeepers. Juries. Judges. Lawyers. Rape. Racial segregation. Hotels. Young Women's Christian Association. Trials. Texas.*

FREEDOM TO LOVE (West Germany)   F6.1691

Reginald Puhl Filmproduktion. *Dist* Grove Press. 26 Jun **1970** [New York opening]. Sd; col (Eastman Color). 35mm. 96 min.

Prod Reginald Puhl. *Exec Prod* Klaus Dudenhöfer, H. J. Matthies, Hans Mulder. *Dir-Writ* Phyllis Kronhausen, Eberhard Kronhausen. *Photog* Paul Grupp, Jack Linder, Dirk-Jan Biyker. *Art Dir* Dieter Bartels, Hugo Kropp, Harrie van Roy. *Film Ed* Heidi Bergthold. *Sd* Rudolph Böttger. *Synchronization* Jacqueline Porel. *Asst Dir* Dirk-Jan Biyker. *Makeup* Eleanore Krutzina.

Cast: Kess Vanderwusten *(Chuck)*, Franulka Vanderwusten *(Lucy)*, Per Massini *(Robert)*, Irene De Graaf *(Anne)*, Sacha Kraamwinkel *(Brigitte)*, Monique Kraamwinkel *(Christine)*, Margit Mecklenburg, Gaby Esche, Annemarie Graf, Simon Spies.

Interviewees: Hugh Hefner, Kenneth Tynan, John Trevelyan, Sten Hegeler, Inge Hegeler, H. H. Brydensholt, Betty Dodson, Gus Weill, Gerhard F. Kramer.

Appearing in "The Beard": Billie Dixon *(Jean Harlow)*, Richard Wright *(Billy the Kid)*.

Appearing in "Geese": Kenneth Carr *(Little Bill)*, Dan Halleck *(Hank)*, Paula Shaw *(Sandy)*, Marie Antoinette *(Deborah)*.

Appearing in "Word Play": John Fraser *(The Poet)*, Brian Phelan *(Alfred Hodge)*, Anne Fairbanks *(secretary)*.

Narrators: Phyllis Kronhausen, Eberhard Kronhausen.

Documentary. Psychotherapists Phyllis and Eberhard Kronhausen advance the view that sexual freedom benefits society and that suppression of sexuality contributes to crime, juvenile delinquency, family breakdown, and divorce. To illustrate the effects of sexual hypocrisy, the Drs. Kronhausen draw from their own case histories: a young man has sex with a willing 15-year-old and is charged with statutory rape; a college student becomes pregnant and secretly seeks an abortion; two lesbians leading productive lives are arrested after two minors accidentally witness their lovemaking; and a woman discovers that her husband has been unfaithful and threatens to divorce him, whereupon they confide in another couple and are invited to join a group sex party. These episodes are interwoven with scenes from erotic theater interviews with celebrities, censors, and psychologists concerned with erotica and documentary footage from Europe and America. Supporting the Kronhausens' conviction that sexual stimulation in art has redeeming social value. Scenes from three erotic

plays illustrate the freedom of international drama: in *The Beard*, by Michael McClure, Billy the Kid and Jean Harlow demonstrate their sexual bravado in Heaven; Gus Weill's *Geese* shows homosexual and lesbian lovemaking; a poet in *Word Play*, by John Bowen, is harassed for his frequent use of profanity and attacks the hypocrisy of his critics. Erotic art exhibitions are seen in Lund, Sweden, where children mingle among objects representing sexual obsessions, and Hamburg, where works from the Kronhausens' private collection are shown. A pornographic cartoon from the 1920's features a well-endowed character who roams the landscape having happy sexual adventures. *Psychiatrists. Psychologists. Actors. Poets. Students. Sexuality. Censorship. Law. Pornography. Erotica. Hypocrisy. Lesbianism. Male homosexuality. Juvenile delinquents. Statutory rape. Pregnancy. Abortion. Infidelity. Divorce. Group sex. Theater. Motion pictures. Art exhibits. Hamburg. Lund (Sweden). Jean Harlow. William H. Bonney.*

Note: Released in West Germany caDec 1969 as *Freiheit für die Liebe*; running time: 84 min.

FREIHEIT FÜR DIE LIEBE *see* **FREEDOM TO LOVE**

DER FREISCHÜTZ (West Germany)   F6.1692

Polyphon Film & TV Productions. *Dist* Polytel International. 18 Jul **1970** [New York opening]. Sd; col (Eastman Color). 35mm. 127 min.

Prod Rolf Liebermann. *Exec Prod* Gyula Trebitsch. *Dir* Joachim Hess. *Libretto* Johann Friedrich Kind. *Photog* Hannes Schindler. *Art Dir* Herbert Kirchhoff. *Mus:* "Der Freischütz" Carl Maria von Weber. *Mus Cond* Leopold Ludwig. *Mus Played by* Hamburg State Orchestra. *Sung by* Choir of Hamburg State Opera. *Choirmaster* Gunther Schmidt Bohlander. *Prod Supv* Rudolf Sander.

Cast: Tom Krause *(Prince Ottokar)*, Toni Blankenheim *(Kuno)*, Arlene Saunders *(Agathe)*, Edith Mathis *(Aennchen)*, Ernst Kozub *(Max)*, Gottlob Frick *(Kaspar)*, Hans Sotin *(hermit)*, Franz Grundheber *(Kilian)*, Regina Marheineke *(bridesmaid)*, Bernard Minetti *(Samiel)*.

Opera film. Source: Carl Maria von Weber and Johann Friedrich Kind, *Der Freischütz* (first performance: Berlin, 18 Jun 1821). A film adaptation of Weber's opera. *Hunters. Ghosts. Hermits. Magic. The Devil.*

Note: Produced for West German television in 1968.

EN FREMMED BANKER PÅ *see* **A STRANGER KNOCKS**

THE FRENCH GAME (France)   F6.1693

Cocinor–Les Films Marceau. *Dist* Atlantic Pictures. 20 Sep **1963** [New York opening]. Sd; b&w. 35mm. 86 min.

Pres by Wilshire International Pictures. *Assoc Prod* Claude Heymann. *Dir-Writ* Jacques Doniol-Valcroze. *Photog* Christian Matras. *Film Ed* Nadine Marquand. *Mus* Michel Legrand. *Sd* Michel Fano.

Cast: Françoise Brion *(Dominique)*, Jean-Louis Trintignant *(François)*, Raymond Gérôme *(Pierre Mallet)*, Pénélope Portrait.

Romantic comedy-drama. A young painter, François, goes for a vacation on the French Riviera with Dominique, a pretty young secretary who intends to spend the vacation with a married Chilean diplomat. The diplomat fails to appear, however, and the couple spend their time together, swimming, lazing on the beach, and sharing a bed. Although François is in love with Dominique, he is unable to alter her love for the diplomat, and their affair remains unconsummated. *Painters. Secretaries. Diplomats. Chileans. Vacations. Riviera.*

Note: Opened in Paris in Jun 1962 as *Le coeur battant*; running time: 85 min.

THE FRENCH GIRL AND THE NUDISTS *see* **KATU (THE FRENCH GIRL AND THE NUDISTS)**

A FRENCH HONEYMOON   F6.1694

European Producers International. 2 Oct **1964** [Los Angeles showing]. Sd; col. 35mm. 62 min.

Prod-Dir Gaston Hakim.

Comedy. A British playboy finally marries but discovers that his Parisian bridal suite faces an international school for strippers, whose students delight in teasing him by performing their specialties. *British. Playboys. French. Striptease. Exhibitionism. Honeymoons. Hotels. Paris.*

Note: Press material suggests film is a French production, but this is unconfirmed.

FRENCH PEEP SHOW *see* **PEEP SHOWS OF PARIS**

FRENCH POST CARDS *see* **PEEP SHOWS OF PARIS**

FRENCH WITHOUT DRESSING (Canada)   F6.1695

Independent Film Artists. *Dist* Sam Lake Enterprises. 20 Aug **1965** [Champaign, Illinois, showing]. Sd; col (Eastman Color). 35mm. 73 min.

Prod-Dir Ted Lawrence. *Assoc Prod* Jack Ennis. *Camera* Stanley Lipinski. *Camera Asst* Ed Lawrence. *Set Dsgn* Jack Reed. *Film Ed* John Cullen. *Mus*

Jean Dore. *Sd Rec* Eric Green. *Prod Mgr* Roger Carlton. *Prod Assoc* Eric Fanshaw, Roger Girard. *Script Girl* Stella Fisher. *Prod Asst* Mel Lewis. *Makeup* Peggy Stevens.

Cast: Laurie Darnell *(girl on Left Bank [card dancer])*, Patricia Knight *(masked dancer [girl camper])*, Patricia MacDonald *(girl in bath [nude in the woods])*, Sharon Lynn *(girl in hotel room)*, Amanda Keeler *(lady burglar)*, Kathy Quinn *(Egyptian belly dancer)*, Ruby "Legs" Diamond *(stripper in night club)*, Mademoiselle Jaqueline *(balloon dancer [skater])*, Laurie Lane *(artist's model)*, Jean Chevelier *(old man)*, Jean Cavall *(artist)*, Alan Stubbings *(gendarme [bell boy])*, Leigh Roy *(nobleman [hunter])*, Michael Leslie *(office manager)*, Roy Revere *(executive sales manager)*, Gerry May *(photographer)*, Ronald Fanshaw *(man in fur coat)*, Margot Stevens *(girl camper)*.

Comedy. The Way Out Electronics Company markets a new, color television set, complete with "fourth dimension," which transmits physical objects across the air and gives the viewer power over the action on the screen. The chief salesman of the company [Roy Revere] arranges a demonstration for a wealthy eccentric. As he flips the channels, the unseen eye of the camera catches the beautiful women of Paris taking off their clothes. The prospective customer gets his first demonstration of fourth dimension as the set discharges the undergarments of two young female campers who have undressed before his eyes. The customer himself uses fourth dimension to bring a young woman who is bathing out of the water. He is very impressed by the set, but he can't make a final decision. The salesman continues the demonstration, and the deal is finally concluded after a French nobleman catches a lady burglar in the act of robbing his safe. He locks her in his château and forces her to disrobe completely so that she cannot escape. The resourceful customer rescues her with the aid of fourth dimension and takes delivery of the set. *Salesmen. Campers. Burglars. Nobility. Nudity. Voyeurism. Electronic surveillance. Television. Inventions. Paris.*

Note: Ted Lawrence and Ed Lawrence are pseudonyms for Ted and Ed Leversuch.

FRENZY   F6.1696
caOct **1970**. Sd; col. 16mm. [Feature length assumed.]
Dir C. W. Feels.

Sex film. Jean has sex with two men while her friend Vicki, the girl friend of one of the men, desperately tries to gain entry into the room. The women masturbate, and Jean fantasizes a love scene in which fellatio and cunnilingus are performed. *Group sex. Oral sex. Autoeroticism. Jealousy. Fantasy.*

THE FRESH GAME *see* **THE FLESH GAME**

THE FRESHMAN *see* **BACHELOR OF HEARTS**

FREUD   F6.1697
Universal-International. 12 Dec **1962** [New York opening; c12 Dec 1962; LP25020]. Sd; b&w. 35mm. 139 min.

A John Huston Production. *Prod* Wolfgang Reinhardt. *Assoc Prod* George Golitzen. *Dir* John Huston. *Screenplay* Charles Kaufman, Wolfgang Reinhardt. *Story* Charles Kaufman. *Dir Photog* Douglas Slocombe. *Art Dir* Stephen Grimes. *Titl Backgrounds & Forward Paintings* James Leong. *Film Ed* Ralph Kemplen. *Mus* Jerry Goldsmith. *Electronic Mus Seq* Henk Badings. *Mus Supv* Joseph Gershenson. *Sd* Basil Fenton-Smith, Renato Cadueri. *Asst Dir* Ray Gosnell, Jr., Laci von Ronay. *Prod Mgr* C. O. Erickson. *Assoc to Mr. Huston* Gladys Hill. *Cost Dsgn* Doris Langley Moore. *Makeup* Robert Schiffer, Raimund Stangl. *Tech Adv* Earl A. Loomis, Jr. *Medical Cons* David Stafford-Clark.

Cast: Montgomery Clift *(Sigmund Freud)*, Susannah York *(Cecily Koertner)*, Larry Parks *(Dr. Joseph Breuer)*, Susan Kohner *(Martha Freud)*, Eric Portman *(Dr. Theodore Meynert)*, Eileen Herlie *(Frau Ida Koertner)*, Fernand Ledoux *(Professor Charcot)*, David McCallum *(Carl von Schlosser)*, Rosalie Crutchley *(Frau Freud)*, David Kossoff *(Jacob Freud)*, Joseph Fürst *(Jacob Koertner)*, Alexander Mango *(Babinsky)*, Leonard Sachs *(Brouhardier)*, Allan Cuthbertson *(Wilkie)*, Moira Redmond *(Nora Wimmer)*, Maria Perschy *(Magda)*, Elisabeth Neumann-Viertel *(Frau Bernays)*, Ursula Lyn *(Mitzi Freud)*, Victor Beaumont *(Dr. Guber)*, Manfred Andrea *(student doctor)*.

Biographical drama. In 1885, 30-year-old neurologist Dr. Sigmund Freud quarrels with his superior, Professor Theodore Meynert, over the nature of hysteria and takes a leave of absence from the Vienna General Hospital. In Paris, he studies under Professor Charcot, a pioneer in the use of hypnosis to demonstrate that disease can be mentally induced. Following his marriage to Martha Bernays, Freud becomes the protégé of Dr. Joseph Breuer, another advocate of hypnotism, and together they treat Cecily Koertner, a semi-paralyzed young woman who also suffers from insomnia and impaired vision. As a result of his sessions with both Cecily and Carl von Schlosser, a young man who assaulted his father because of an incestuous love for his mother, Freud determines that all neuroses stem from repressed sexuality. His revolutionary theory, partially based upon his own childhood recollections, offends the entire

medical profession, including Breuer. Nevertheless, Freud continues experimenting with Cecily and eventually drops hypnosis in favor of a new technique, "free association," in which he is able to analyze her dreams and interpret the meaning of chance remarks she makes during their conversations. As Cecily's mental health gradually improves, Freud develops his theory of the Oedipus complex and delivers a lecture on the subject; his colleagues react with derisive shouts, but psychoanalysis is born. *Psychiatrists. Professors. Lecturers. Psychiatry. Neurosis. Psychosomatic illness. Hypnotism. Dreams. Oedipus complex. Experiments. Vienna. Paris. Sigmund Freud. Josef Breuer. Theodor Hermann Meynert. Jean Martin Charcot.*

Note: Filmed in England. Also known as *The Secret Passion.*

FREUDUS SEXUALIS   F6.1698
William H. Starkey Associates. *Dist* Joseph Brenner Associates. 28 May **1965** [New York State license; Champaign, Illinois, showing: 23 Nov 1966]. Sd; b&w. 35mm. 73 min.

Prod George R. Merdinger. *Dir* William H. Starkey.

Cast: John Haveron, Mary Harrigan, Lisa Rolland, Hugh Warren.

Melodrama. Just out of the Army, Adam marries his childhood sweetheart Eve, and they settle down on an inherited farm. Their lovemaking fully awakens Eve's sensual nature, and the two commence a faithful and passionate marriage. Sometime later, Adam and Eve meet Seth, a wealthy neighbor, and Jezebel, who recklessly drives her sportscar around the countryside and arouses men's passions by her provocative behavior. When Adam comes upon Seth and Jezebel making love in a nearby stream, he is reminded of his affair with a French woman while he was in the Army. One day Adam is enticed by Jezebel to join her for a nude swim. Eve happens by, discovers their indiscretion, and stumbles home, pursued by Seth, who has seen all and tries unsuccessfully to seduce the grief-stricken woman. Adam soon ceases his dalliance and returns home to a brief marital fight followed by a sincere reconciliation. Seth will not be denied, however, and he waits until Eve is swimming alone in the stream and forces himself upon her. Adam interrupts the incipient rape of his wife and kills Seth with an axe. He falls horrified to his knees and looks alternately at his whimpering wife and the bloody corpse lying in the grass. *Veterans. Newlyweds. Farmers. Neighbors. Temptresses. Rural life. Nudity. Seduction. Rape. Murder.*

Note: Alternative titles: *A Man and His Woman, Man and His Woman, The Story of a Man and His Woman,* and *The Story of Man and His Woman.*

FRIDAY ON MY MIND   F6.1699
Continental Theatres. 12 Aug **1970** [Los Angeles opening]. Sd; b&w with col seq (CFI). 57 min.

Dir-Writ Wayne Schotten. *Photog* Lee Jones. *Film Ed* Wayne Schotten. *Selections from the Film Music of* Miklos Rozsa. *Sd* Andy Helman. *Asst Dir* Dean Chambers.

Cast: Michael Scott *(Randy)*, Aaron Bedford *(Ted)*, Con Covert *(Harry)*, Allen Rogers *(Ray)*, John Romero *(Phil)*, Mama Chuck *(Sandy)*, Math *(Lee)*, Andy Helman *(Billy)*.

Melodrama. Randy, who has only recently come to understand that he is a homosexual, is raped by Harry. In a Hollywood gay bar, Randy meets various homosexual types, including Lee, a hustler; Ted, an all-American boy; brokenhearted Billy; and highly effeminate Sandy. *Male homosexuality. Rape. Effeminacy. Bars. Hollywood.*

FRIEND OF THE FAMILY (France/Italy)   F6.1700
Belstar Productions–Les Films du Siècle–Ultra Film. *Dist* International Classics. 17 Nov **1965** [New York opening; c31 Dec 1964; LP32291]. Sd (Westrex); b&w. 35mm (CinemaScope). 95 min.

An André Hakim Production. *Prod* André Hakim. *Dir-Writ* Robert Thomas. *Dir Photog* Robert Lefebvre. *Sets* Max Douy. *Film Ed* Henri Taverna. *Mus* Raymond Le Sénéchal. *Mus Arr* Hubert Rostaing. *Lyr* Jean Dréjac. *Mus Cond* Jacques Météhen. *Sd Engr* Jean Rieul. *Asst Dir* Roberto Bodegas. *Prod Mgr* Léon Lanz. *Wardrobe for Danielle Darrieux & Anne Vernon* Lanvin. *Wardrobe for Sylvie Vartan* Réal. *Makeup* Alexandre Marcus, Lina Ballet. *Tech Collab* Robert Mazoyer.

Cast: Jean Marais *(Carradine)*, Danielle Darrieux *(Edith Rollo)*, Anne Vernon *(Véronique Carradine)*, Sylvie Vartan *(Alexa Rollo)*, Pierre Dux *(Léon "Patsy" Rollo)*, Jane Marken *(Berthe)*, Noël Roquevert *(Monsieur Michalon)*, Hubert Deschamps *(Adrien)*, Jacques Jouanneau *(Marcel)*, Henri Virlojeux *(Professor Richard)*, Mike Marshall *(Jean-François)*, Laurence Badie *(Jeannette)*, Daniel Ceccaldi *(Michel)*, François Charet *(Bernard)*, Julie Dassin.

Comedy-drama. Source: Marcel Achard, *Patate* (Paris opening: 23 Jan 1957). Unsuccessful toy and game inventor Léon Rollo is urged by his wife, Edith, to ask his boyhood friend Noël Carridine, a wealthy industrialist, to back his new invention. The meeting goes badly as Noël persists in calling Léon by the hated nickname "Patsy," and only the saving gestures of Edith and Véronique, Noël's wife, bring the men to an understanding. Later, Edith finds love letters belonging to her teenaged daughter, Alexa, who refuses to reveal the identity of her lover. Léon concludes that the letters were written by Noël and confronts him with the material. When Léon sees his powerful bargaining position, he decides to blackmail Noël but relents when Alexa finds a new boyfriend. The two men eventually form a smoothly operating partnership. *Inventors. Industrialists. Marriage. Partnerships. Filial relations. Adolescence. Infidelity. Documentation.*

Note: Paris opening in Oct 1964 as *Patate*; running time: 95 min. Copyright claimant: Twentieth Century-Fox Film Corp.

THE FRIENDLIEST GIRLS IN THE WORLD see COME FLY WITH ME

THE FRIENDLY KILLER (Japan)   F6.1701

Nikkatsu Corp. Mar **1970** [Los Angeles showing]. Sd; col (Fuji Color). 35mm (Nikkatsu Scope). 90 min.

Dir-Writ Teruo Ishii. *Photog* Sei Kitaizumi. *Art Dir* Takeo Kimura. *Mus* Masao Yagi.

Cast: Hiroko Ogi *(Katsumi)*, Akira Kobayashi *(Masa)*, Toru Abe *(Yasukawa)*, Tatsuya Fuji, Kokan Katsura, Yoko Yamamoto, Tomoo Koike, Shoki Fukae, Eiji Goo, Hideki Takahashi, Kiyoko Tange, Setsuko Minami, Tomoko Aki, Hatsue Tonooka, Toru Yuri, Shunji Sayama.

Crime melodrama. After her father's murder, Katsumi duplicates his dragon tattoo on her own body and assumes leadership of his gang. While Yasukawa, a rival boss, attempts to thwart Katsumi's plans, Masa, a mysterious stranger, repeatedly aids Katsumi and her men. Katsumi attempts to settle a dispute between two rival bosses, but when one of the gangsters tries to have her murdered, she kills him instead. Katsumi surrenders to the police, and, while serving a jail term, wages a campaign to improve conditions in the prison. Upon her release, she learns that Yasukawa has nearly succeeded in gaining control of her gang and territories. She demands a showdown, and the bosses acknowledge her rights. During a raid on her headquarters, Yasukawa is killed, and Masa is mortally wounded. Before he dies, Masa confesses to Katsumi that Yasukawa hired him to kill her father. *Gangsters. Hired killers. Strangers. Perfidy. Murder. Prison reform. Tattoos. Gang wars.*

Note: Released in Japan in Mar 1969 as *Noboriryu tekkahada*.

FRIENDLY NEIGHBORS   F6.1702

Dist Stacey Distributors. ca **1970**. Sd; col. 16mm. 61-81 min.

Sex film. No information about the precise nature of this film has been found. *Neighbors. Sexuality.*

FRIENDLY NEIGHBORS see THE VERY FRIENDLY NEIGHBORS

FRIENDS AND LOVERS see THE VIXENS

FRIENDS AND NEIGHBORS (Great Britain)   F6.1703

Valiant Films. *Dist* Schoenfeld Film Distributing Corp. 24 Aug **1963** [Philadelphia opening]. Sd; b&w. 35mm. 79 min.

Prod Bertram Ostrer. *Dir* Gordon Parry. *Screenplay* Val Valentine. *Adtl Dial* Talbot Rothwell. *Dir Photog* Arthur Grant. *Art Dir* Ivan King. *Film Ed* Bill Lenny. *Mus* Philip Green. *Sd* John Cox, Richard Marden. *Sd Rec* George Stephenson, Ernie Webb.

Cast: Arthur Askey *(Albert Grimshaw)*, Megs Jenkins *(Lily Grimshaw)*, Peter Illing *(Nikita)*, Tilda Thamar *(Olga)*, Reginald Beckwith *(Wilf Holmes)*, June Whitfield *(Doris Holmes)*, Danny Ross *(Sebastian Green)*, Catherine Feller *(Susan Grimshaw)*, Jess Conrad *(Buddy Fisher)*, George Wheeler *(George Cooper)*, Linda Castle *(Gloria Stockwell)*, Max Robertson *(himself)*.

Domestic comedy. Source: Austin Steele, *Friends and Neighbours* (London opening: 11 Nov 1958). In a lottery bus conductor Albert Grimshaw wins a visit from Russian social workers. An entertainment devised by his wife, Lily, bus driver Wilf Holmes, and Holmes' wife, Doris, culminates in a vodka party. Although the Russians leave the following morning, they return shortly thereafter accompanied by numerous compatriots eager to study the British proletariat. *Bus conductors. Bus drivers. Russians. Social workers. Family life. Lower classes. Lotteries.*

Note: Released in Great Britain in Dec 1959 as *Friends and Neighbours*.

FRIENDS FOR LIFE (Italy)   F6.1704

Cines. 25 Nov **1964** [Los Angeles opening]. Sd; b&w. 35mm. ca100 min.

Prod Carlo Civallero. *Dir* Franco Rossi. *Screenplay* Franco Rossi, Leo Benvenuti, Piero De Bernardi, Ugo Guerra, Giandomenico Giagni. *Story* Franco Rossi, Ottavio Alessi, Leo Benvenuti, Piero De Bernardi, Ugo Guerra. *Photog* Gabor Pogany. *Art Dir* Franco Lolli. *Film Ed* Otello Colangeli. *Mus* Nino Rota.

Cast: Geronimo Meynier *(Mario)*, Andrea Scirè *(Franco)*, Luigi Tosi, Paolo Ferrari, Dina Perbellini, Marcella Rovena, Carlo Tamberlani, Vera Carmi, Bianca Maria Bettinali.

Comedy-drama. Classmates Mario and Franco become close friends after Franco saves Mario from the shame of losing a motorscooter race he boasted he could win. The two friends keep their mutual loyalty intact throughout the usual adolescent problems, and when Franco's father, a widower, has to leave for the Middle East on business, Mario persuades Franco's father that Franco will be better off left with Mario's family. Mario wants very much to win a school sports event but is humiliated in defeat. He then accuses Franco, the victor, of being disloyal, but his charges are disregarded by his classmates because of Franco's fine reputation as a sportsman. Full of resentment, Mario offends Franco, without really meaning it, by besmirching the memory of his mother, and Franco decides to leave with his father after all. The remorseful Mario goes to the airport to beg his friend's forgiveness but arrives as the plane takes off. [A second ending was filmed, in which Mario arrives at the airport in time, and both boys pledge to remain friends for life. It has not been determined which ending was used for U. S. release.] *Students. Braggarts. Widowers. Friendship. Adolescence. Motorcycle racing. Fatherhood. Reputation. Airfields.*

Note: Opened in Rome in Oct 1955 as *Amici per la pelle*; running time: 100 min.

THE FRIGHTENED CITY (Great Britain)   F6.1705

Zodiac Productions. *Dist* Allied Artists. Jul **1962** [c13 Jul 1962; LP22249]. Sd; b&w. 35mm. 97 min.

Prod John Lemont, Leigh Vance. *Dir* John Lemont. *Screenplay* Leigh Vance. *Story* Leigh Vance, John Lemont. *Dir Photog* Desmond Dickinson. *Camera Op* Harry Gillam. *Art Dir* Maurice Carter. *Supv Ed* Bernard Gribble. *Mus Comp & Dir* Norrie Paramor. *Songs:* "Marvelous Lie." "I Laughed at Love" Norrie Paramor, Bunny Lewis. *Sd Rec* George Stephenson, Red Law. *Sd Ed* Allan Sones. *Asst Dir* Basil Rayburn. *Prod Supv* Clifton Brandon. *Cont* Lee Turner. *Wardrobe Supv* Laura Nightingale. *Makeup* Freddie Williamson. *Hairdresser* Joyce James. *Tech Adv* Sidney Careless. *Casting Dir* Lionel Grose.

Cast: Herbert Lom *(Waldo Zhernikov)*, John Gregson *(Detective Inspector Sayers)*, Sean Connery *(Paddy Damion)*, Alfred Marks *(Harry Foulcher)*, Yvonne Romain *(Anya)*, Olive McFarland *(Sadie)*, David Davies *(Alf Peters)*, Kenneth Griffith *(Wally)*, Frederick Piper *(Sergeant Ogle)*, John Stone *(hood)*, Robert Cawdron *(Nero)*, Tom Bowman *(Tanky Thomas)*, Patrick Jordan *(Frankie Farmer)*, George Pastell *(Sanchetti)*, Patrick Holt *(Superintendent Carter)*, Bruce Seton *(assistant commissioner)*, Robert Percival *(Wingrove)*, Joan Haythorne *(Miss Rush)*, Arnold Diamond *(Moffat)*, Jack Stewart, British *(Tyson)*, Douglas Robinson *(Salty Brewer)*, Marianne Stone *(barmaid)*, Neal Arden *(head waiter)*, Norrie Paramor *(pianist)*, Malcolm Clare *(choreographer)*, J. G. Devlin *(informer)*, John Witty *(TV announcer)*.

Crime melodrama. Waldo Zhernikov, an unscrupulous accountant, decides to amalgamate the six gangs operating separately in the London protection rackets. He hires Harry Foulcher, one of the gang leaders, to organize the operation and then employs Paddy Damion to collect the payoffs. Damion is a handsome gangster involved with the two female singers at Foulcher's nightclub. When Waldo becomes greedy for bigger stakes, another of the gang leaders, Alf Peters, takes his mob out of the organization. Infuriated, Waldo has Foulcher kill Peters. This act enrages Paddy, who was a friend of Peters', and he, in turn, murders Foulcher. Detective Inspector Sayers, who has been trying to break up the organization, arrives following the murder of Foulcher. Paddy agrees to testify against Waldo and thereby brings about the downfall of the crime syndicate. *Accountants. Gangsters. Racketeers. Police. Singers. Murder. Organized crime. Nightclubs. London.*

Note: Opened in London in Sep 1961.

THE FRIGID BIRD   F6.1706

Dist Stacey Distributors. ca **1970**. Sd; col. 16mm. 61-81 min.

Sex film. No information about the precise nature of the film has been found. *Sexuality. Frigidity.*

FRIGID WIFE   F6.1707

Ken Productions-Monogram Productions. *Dist* Ken Productions. 30 May **1962** [Hartford, Connecticut, opening; c25 Sep 1950, c23 Nov 1961; LP588, LP20779]. Sd; b&w. 35mm. 77 min. [Also 73 min.]

Production Credits for Prologue: *Prod-Writ* John Kenlo. *Assoc Prod* Arnold Jack Rosenthal. *Dir* Ben Parker.

Production Credits for "A Modern Marriage": A David Diamond Production. *Prod* David Diamond. *Assoc Prod* William F. Broidy. *Dir* Paul Landres. *Screenplay* Samuel Roeca, George Wallace Sayre. *Foreward* Paul Popenoe. *Photog* William Sickner. *Art Dir* David Milton. *Set Decor* Raymond G. Boltz. *Supv Film Ed* Otho Lovering. *Film Ed* Philip Cahn. *Mus & Mus Dir* Edward J. Kay. *Sd Tech* Tom Lambert. *Asst Dir* Wesley E. Barry. *Prod Supv* Allen K. Wood. *Set Cont* Ilona Vas. *Tech Supv* Paul Popenoe.

Cast—Prologue: Jeanne Neher *(Ruth Turner)*, Sondra Fisher *(Barbara Reed)*, Sid Noel *(Bill Turner)*, Bob Carr *(Larry Reed)*, Ken Elliott *(Dr. Foster)*.

Cast—"A Modern Marriage": Reed Hadley (*Dr. Donald Andrews*), Margaret Field (*Evelyn Brown*), Robert Clarke (*Bill Burke*), Nana Bryant (*Mrs. Brown*), Bert Wenland (*porter*), Christine McIntyre (*nurse*), Edward Keane (*Dr. Connors*), Charles Smith (*Jimmy Watson*), Buddy Gorman (*messenger boy*), Dick Elliott (*Mr. Burke*), Lelah Tyler (*Mrs. Burke*), Pattee Chapman (*Mary*), Buddy Swan (*Spike*), Frank Fenton (*Mr. Brown*), Sherry Jackson (*Evelyn, 5 years old*), Dian Fauntelle (*secretary's voice*), Peggy Wynne (*nurse*), Bret Hamilton (*delivery man*).

Domestic drama. Dr. Foster, a marriage counselor, gives advice to Ruth Turner, who is frigid, and to Barbara Reed, whose husband is impotent. During therapy Foster recalls the related 1950 case history of newlywed Evelyn Brown, who deserted groom Bill Burke immediately after their elopement and was seen by Dr. Donald Andrews after a suicide attempt. The child of separated parents, the bride was diagnosed as excessively dependent on her domineering hypochondriac mother. Through therapy Evelyn was enabled to break the maternal bonds and return to her husband. *Newlyweds. Psychiatrists. Hypochondriacs. Marriage counsel. Frigidity. Impotence. Desertion. Filial relations. Elopement. Separation (marital).*

Note: This film combines a 12-min prologue, *Frigid Wife* (c23 Nov 1961), and a 66-min 1950 Monogram Pictures release, *A Modern Marriage* (c25 Sep 1950). John Kenlo is the pseudonym of Julius Weinstein.

DIE FRÖHLICHE WISSENSCHAFT see **LE GAI SAVOIR**

FROM A ROMAN BALCONY (France/Italy)   **F6.1708**
Produzione Intercontinentali–Euro International Films–Transcontinental Films. *Dist* Continental Distributing, Inc. 15 Oct **1961** [New York opening]. Sd; b&w. 35mm. 84 min.
Prod Paul Graetz. *Dir* Mauro Bolognini. *Screenplay* Alberto Moravia, Pier Paolo Pasolini. *Adapt* Alberto Moravia, Pier Paolo Pasolini, Marco Visconti. *Photog* Aldo Scavarda. *Art Dir* Carlo Egidi. *Film Ed* Borys Lewin, Nino Baragli. *Mus Comp & Cond* Piero Piccioni. *Asst Dir* Luigi Bazzoni, Guy Seligman. *English Subtitl* Herman G. Weinberg.
Cast: Jean Sorel (*David*), Lea Massari (*Freya*), Jeanne Valérie (*Marina*), Rik Battaglia (*Carpiti*), Valeria Ciangottini (*Ivana*), Isabelle Corey (*Sabina*), Paolo Stoppa (*Moglie*), Marcella Valeri (*Sora Tosca*), Luigi Giacosi (*Romani*), Enrico Glori, Elvy Lissiak, Irene D'Aloisi.
Drama. Source: Alberto Moravia, *Racconti romani* (Milan, 1954). Alberto Moravia, *Nuovi racconti romani* (Milan, 1959). Early one morning David leaves his Roman tenement to look for a job so that he can marry Ivana, a young woman who has borne him a son. David visits a lawyer, Moglie, who supposedly will find him work. While in the lawyer's building, David looks into an apartment in which an unattended corpse lies in state. After taking note of an expensive ring on the dead man's hand, David enters Moglie's office. Moglie impatiently brushes him off, however, and he is once again without hope of a job. While roaming the streets, David encounters a prostitute, Marina, with whom he once had an affair. After a brief interlude of lovemaking, David accompanies Marina to her next client, who turns out to be Moglie. The two blackmail the lawyer into getting David a job as a truckdriver for the Romani oil company. Romani's mistress, Freya, is immediately attracted by David's simplicity and virility; she seduces him, but their passion is interrupted by the roar of David's abandoned truck as it crashes down a hill and bursts into flames. Once more unemployed and completely disillusioned, David heads back for Rome. He suddenly remembers the ring on the dead man's hand, goes to the empty apartment to steal it, and returns to Ivana with enough money to buy a small stall in the local market, baptize their child, and get married. *Lawyers. Prostitutes. Mistresses. Truckdrivers. Blackmail. Illegitimacy. Poverty. Unemployment. Theft. Oil business. Tenements. Corpses. Rome. Automobile accidents.*
Note: Filmed on location in Rome. Opened in Rome in Nov 1960 as *La giornata balorda*; running time: 85 min; in Paris in Jan 1961 as *Ça s'est passé à Rome*; running time: 90 min. Original running time: 102 min. Also known as *A Crazy Day*, *Love Is a Day's Work*, and *Pickup in Rome*.

FROM LADY TO TRAMP see **THE AGONY OF LOVE**

FROM NASHVILLE WITH MUSIC   **F6.1709**
John C. Bradford Productions. *Dist* Craddock Films. 8 Jul **1969** [Atlanta opening]. Sd; col. 35mm. 87 min. MPAA rating G.
Pres by John C. Bradford. *Prod-Dir* Eddie Crandall, Robert Patrick. *Dir Photog* Will Zens. *Film Ed* Will Zens. *Mus* Will Zens. *Song* "The Green Green Grass of Home" Claude Putman, Jr. *Songs* "Jody Special," "Play Off" Cousin Jody. *Song* "Hey Joe" Boudleaux Bryant. *Song* "Deep Water" Fred Rose. *Song* "White Lightning" J. P. Richardson. *Song* "Stand by Your Man" Billy Sherrill, Tammy Wynette. *Song* "Walk Through This World With Me" Sandra Seamons, Kay Savage. *Song* "Your Good Girl's Gonna Go Bad" Billy Sherrill, Glenn Sutton. *Songs* "Wild Weekend," "A Happy State of Mind" Bill Anderson. *Song* "I've Got a Tiger by the Tail" Buck Owens, Harlan Howard.

Song: "Act Naturally" Johnny Russell, Vonie Morrison. *Song:* "It's Such a Pretty World Today" Dale Noe. *Songs:* "Branded Man," "Hungry Eyes" Merle Haggard. *Song:* "Today I Started Loving You Again" Bonnie Owens, Merle Haggard. *Song:* "Lead Me On" Leon Copeland. *Song:* "Kaw Liga" Fred Rose, Hank Williams. *Song:* "Cotton Fields" arr by The Jordanaires. *Song:* "Walking in the Sunshine" Roger Miller. *Song:* "Granada" Agustin Lara. *Song:* "I'll Be a Legend in My Time" Don Gibson. *Song:* "Hello Daily News" Jim Easterby. *Song:* "Singin' the Blues" Melvin Endsley. *Song:* "Crystal Chandelier" Ted Harris. *Song:* "The Shoe Goes on the Other Foot Tonight" Buddy Mize. *Song:* "Spoke in The Wheel" Clay Boland, Bix Reichner.
Cast: Marilyn Maxwell (*Mabel*), Leo G. Carroll (*Arnold*), Gonzalez Gonzalez (*film director*), Marty Robbins, Merle Haggard, Buck Owens, Charley Pride, Tammy Wynette, Wynn Stewart, Bill Anderson, George Jones, Carl Smith, Don Gibson, Jo Ann Steele, The Jordanaires, Bonnie Owens, Big Jim Bradford, The Strangers, The Jones Boys, The Buckaroos, Cousin Jody, John C. Bradford, Susan Raye, Eddie Fukano, Buddy Alan.
Comedy with music. When their car stalls, Arnold and Mabel, a middle-aged couple on a holiday in Tennessee, meet country singer Marty Robbins, who gives them tickets for the Grand Ole Opry in Nashville. Thinking they are attending the opera, the couple are shocked at the casual attire of the audience and by the music itself. Arnold enjoys the show, however, and, eager to meet some of the singers in person, goes to watch the making of a film in which a number of the singers are appearing; but Mabel returns in disgust to New York. The couple are eventually reconciled at a party to celebrate completion of the film, and they pay a return visit to the Grand Ole Opry. *Singers. Country music. Motion pictures. Vacations. Grand Ole Opry. Tennessee. Nashville (Tennessee). New York City.*

FROM RUSSIA WITH LOVE (Great Britain)   **F6.1710**
Eon Productions–Danjaq, S. A. *Dist* United Artists. 8 Apr **1964** [New York opening; c10 Oct 1963; LP29364]. Sd; col (Technicolor). 35mm. 118 min. [Also 110 min.]
Pres by Harry Saltzman, Albert R. Broccoli. *Prod* Harry Saltzman, Albert R. Broccoli. *Dir* Terence Young. *Stunt Coörd* Peter Perkins. *Screenplay* Richard Maibaum. *Adapt* Johanna Harwood. *Dir Photog* Ted Moore. *2d Unit Photog* Robert Kindred. *Camera Op* John Winbolt. *Focus* John Shinerock. *Art Dir* Syd Cain. *Asst Art Dir* Michael White. *Set Decor* Freda Pearson. *Ch Draughtsman* Alan Tomkins. *Titl Dsgn* Robert Brownjohn, Trevor Bond. *Film Ed* Peter Hunt. *Assembly Ed* Ben Rayner. *2d Asst Ed* Stephen Warwick. *Mus Comp & Cond* John Barry. *Titl Song* Lionel Bart. *Sung by* Matt Monro. *Song:* "James Bond Theme" Monty Norman. *Sd Rec* John W. Mitchell, Colin Le Mesurier. *Dub Ed* Norman Wanstall, Harry Miller. *Boom Op* Derek Kavanagh. *Sd Camera Op* Charles Arnold. *1st & 2d Asst Dir* David Anderson, Terence Churcher, Kit Lambert. *Gen Mgr* Stanley Sopel. *Prod Mgr* Bill Hill. *Cont* Kay Mander. *Location Mgr* Frank Ernst. *Istanbul Prod Asst* Ilham Filmer. *Cost Dsgn* Jocelyn Rickards. *Wardrobe Mistress* Eileen Sullivan. *Wardrobe Master* Ernie Farrer. *Makeup* Basil Newall, Paul Rabiger. *Hairdresser* Eileen Warwick. *Sp Eff* John Stears. *Casting Dir* Weston Drury, Jr. *Prop Buyer* John Bigg. *Still Photog* Ray Hearne. *Elec Supv* Reg Blackburn. *Constr Mgr* Bill Surridge. *Chargehand Prop* P. Weymouth.
Cast: Sean Connery (*James Bond*), Daniela Bianchi (*Tatiana Romanova*), Pedro Armendariz (*Kerim Bey*), Lotte Lenya (*Rosa Klebb*), Robert Shaw (*Red Grant*), Bernard Lee ("*M*"), Eunice Gayson (*Sylvia*), Walter Gotell (*Morzeny*), Francis De Wolff (*Vavra*), George Pastell (*train conductor*), Nadja Regin (*Kerim's girl*), Lois Maxwell (*Miss Moneypenny*), Alizia Gur (*Vida*), Martine Beswick (*Zora*), Vladek Sheybal (*Kronsteen*), Leila (*belly dancer*), Hasan Ceylan (*foreign agent*), Fred Haggerty (*Krilencu*), Neville Jason (*Rolls chauffeur*), Peter Bayliss (*Benz*), Nushet Atear (*Tempo*), Peter Brayham (*Rhoda*), Desmond Llewelyn (*Boothroyd*), Jan Williams (*masseuse*), Peter Madden (*McAdams*).
Action melodrama. Source: Ian Fleming, *From Russia With Love* (London, 1957). SPECTRE, an international crime syndicate, devises a plot to discredit and kill British Secret Service Agent James Bond. Rosa Klebb, former head of the Russian secret service organization, has defected to SPECTRE, but her defection is known only to a few top men in the Soviet government. As one of the masterminds of the plot, Rosa goes to Istanbul and contacts Tatiana Romanova, a beautiful cipher clerk in the Russian embassy. She orders Tatiana to offer to help the British steal the Lektor, a valuable Russian coding machine, if James Bond will help her defect to the West. Meanwhile, a SPECTRE agent is in Istanbul with instructions to murder Bond. Russian agents are following him, too, but with the aid of Kerim Bey, a wily Turk whom he contacts upon arriving in Istanbul, Bond manages to foil several attempts on his life. Bond and Tatiana, working on plans to steal the Lektor, escape from Istanbul on the Orient Express headed for the West. SPECTRE agent Red Grant and Russian agent Benz are also on board the train and independently plan to kill Bond and steal the Lektor. Both Kerim Bey and Benz are killed; and Grant, overhearing

Bond's request for another British agent to help him, meets the designated man at the next stop, kills him, and takes his place. Grant drugs Tatiana and overpowers Bond, but Bond triumphs when an attaché case explodes, enabling the two to leave the train. Bond then forces a pursuing SPECTRE helicopter to crash and sets the sea on fire to escape from oncoming powerboats. The two arrive in the apparent safety of Venice, but Rosa Klebb enters Bond's hotel room disguised as a maid and tries to kill him with a poisonous switchblade concealed in the toe of her shoe. Tatiana, by now in love with Bond, shoots Rosa, and the Lektor is safely sent to England. Bond remains in Venice with Tatiana. *Secret agents. Russians. Defectors. Clerks. Turks. Syndicates. Espionage. Cryptography. Murder. Imposture. Disguise. Trains. Helicopters. Motorboats. London. England. Russia. Istanbul. Venice. Orient Express. Chases. Fires. Explosions. James Bond.*

Note: Some location scenes filmed in Istanbul. London opening: Oct 1963. Copyright records credit Danjaq, S. A. with production.

FROM THE INCEPTION OF HUMAN LIFE see **HELGA**

FROM THE KREMLIN TO THE COSMOS (U.S.S.R.)　　　　**F6.1711**
Moscow Popular Science Studio–Mosfilm. *Dist* Artkino Pictures. 28 Jul **1963** [New York opening]. Sd; col. 35mm. 120 min.
　　Production Credits for "Rendezvous in Space": *Dir* Dmitriy Bogolepov. *Screenplay* Yevgeniy Ryabchikov. *Photog* Dmitriy Gasyuk, Igor Kasatkin. *Camera* V. Afanasyev, M. Beschetnov, V. Golovnya, A. Kairov, R. Trishin, Z. Lalakireva, V. Sivkov. *Mus* Vladimir Rubin. *Sd* Aleksey Kulakov. *Asst Dir* I. Gostev. *Sp Eff* A. Kotov, B. Lanin.
　　Production Credits for "Inside the Kremlin": *Dir* V. Morgenshtern. *Screenplay* I. Filimonov. *Photog* Georgiy Lyakhovich. *Sd* V. Kutuzov.
　　Production Credits for "Festival of Russian Songs and Dances": *Dir-Scen* Andrey Frolov. *Photog* V. Maslennikov, V. Zakharov, photog. *Art Dir* G. Turylyov. *Sd* Ye. Kashkevich. *Prod Mgr* Ya. Svetozarov.
　　Performers featured in "Festival of Russian Songs and Dances": Russian State Folk Choir, Osipov State Russian Folk Orchestra, Fyodorova Sisters, Soviet Army Choir and Dance Ensemble, Omsk Folk Choir, Piatnitsky State Chorus and Dance Ensemble, Aleksandrov Ensemble, Beryozka Ensemble.
　　Soloists include: Mariya Mardasova, A. Ognivtsev, M. Maksakova, M. Mikhaylov, M. Selivanova, P. Kazmin, G. Babayev, V. Puchkov, G. Svetlanov, P. Peterburgskiy, V. Zhukov.
　　Compilation film. RENDEZVOUS IN SPACE: A record of the twin orbital flights of Maj. Andrian Grigoryevich Nikolayev and Lieut. Col. Pavel Romanovich Popovich aboard the spaceships *Vostok 3* and *Vostok 4* in August 1962. The cosmonauts are first seen at home before their flights. Photos taken by the men in space are included in the record of their journey. Upon their return they receive a triumphant welcome in Red Square, and Premier Khrushchev is among their wellwishers. INSIDE THE KREMLIN: A tour of the Kremlin, including a presentation on its history. FESTIVAL OF RUSSIAN SONGS AND DANCES includes performances by a number of Soviet ensembles. The finale of the compilation consists of scenes of the 1962 November 7th celebration. *Astronauts. Singers. Dancers. Space flights. Folk dancing. Moscow—Red Square. Andrian Grigoryevich Nikolayev. Pavel Romanovich Popovich. Nikita Sergeyevich Khrushchev. The Kremlin (Moscow).*

　　Note: *Rendezvous in Space,* a Moscow Popular Science Studio production of 1962, was released in the U.S.S.R. as *Zvyozdnyye bratya;* running time: ca70 min; *Inside the Kremlin,* a Moscow Popular Science Studio production of 1961, as *Iz glubiny stoletiy. Festival of Russian Songs and Dances,* a Mosfilm production, was released in Nov 1953 (in b&w?) as *Pesni rodnoy storony;* running time: 69 min.

FROM WOMAN TO WOMAN TO WOMAN　　　　　　　**F6.1712**
Dist Cinema Arts Distributing Co. **1968**. Sd; b&w. 35mm. [Feature length assumed.]
　　Pres by William Rowland.
　　Sex film. This is the story of an oversexed young man who engages in a vain, frantic search for satisfaction. *Sexuality. Satyriasis.*

FRONTEIRAS DO INFERNO see **LONESOME WOMEN**

FRONTIER ALASKA see **JONIKO AND THE KUSH TA KA**

FRONTIER HELLCAT (France/Italy/West Germany/Yugoslavia)　　　　　　　　　　　　　　　　　　　　　　　　　　**F6.1713**
Rialto Film–Atlantis Film-S. N. C.–Jadran Film. *Dist* Columbia Pictures. Mar **1966**. Sd; col (Eastmancolor). 35mm (CinemaScope). 98 min.
　　Prod Preben Philipsen. *Dir* Alfred Vohrer. *2d Unit Dir* Stipe Delić. *Screenplay* Eberhard Keindorff, Johanna Sibelius. *Photog* Karl Löb. *Art Dir* Vladimir Tadej. *Film Ed* Hermann Haller. *Mus* Martin Böttcher. *Asst Dir* Charles M. Wakefield. *Prod Supv* Horst Wendlandt. *Prod Mgr* Erwin Gitt. *Cost* Irms Pauli.

　　Cast: Stewart Granger *(Old Surehand),* Pierre Brice *(Winnetou),* Elke Sommer *(Annie),* Götz George *(Martin Baumann),* Walter Barnes *(Baumann),* Sieghardt Rupp *(Preston),* Miha Baloh *(Weller),* Renato Baldini *(Leader),* Mario Girotti *(Baker),* Louis Velle *(Gordon),* Paddy Fox *(Old Wabble),* Voja Mirić *(Steward),* Stole Arandjelović *(Milton),* Djordje Nenadović *(Miller),* Georg Mitić *(Wakadeh),* Gordana Čosić *(Wakadeh's sister),* Dušan Bulajić *(Bloomfield),* Dunja Rajter *(Betsy),* Milan Srdoč.
　　Western melodrama. Source: Karl Friedrich May, *Unter Geiern* (Radebeul-Oberlössnitz, 1914). In frontier Arizona, Old Surehand, a self-appointed lawman and blood brother of the young Apache chief Winnetou, is the sworn enemy of the Vultures, a band of outlaws disguised as Indians who terrorize prospectors and settlers. When the Vultures capture Annie, who is transporting her father's moneybelt filled with diamonds, Martin Baumann, who is in love with Annie, rescues her. Baumann mistakenly believes that the Shoshone are responsible for the slaughter of his family, and he is captured by the tribe for insulting their chief, but Old Surehand saves Baumann's life by performing feats of skill and strength. Old Surehand, Winnetou, and Baumann then hear that the wagon train in which Annie is traveling is about to be ambushed by the Vultures, and they fight off the gang until the Shoshone come to the rescue. *Blood brothers. Apache Indians. Shoshone Indians. Outlaws. Disguise. Abduction. Massacres. Frontier and pioneer life. Diamonds. Wagon trains. Arizona. Winnetou.*

　　Note: Released in West Germany in Dec 1964 as *Unter Geiern* at 102 min; in Yugoslavia in 1965 as *Medju jastrebovima;* Paris opening: Aug 1966 as *Parmi les vautours.*

FRONTIER UPRISING　　　　　　　　　　　　　　　**F6.1714**
Zenith Pictures. *Dist* United Artists. 1 Mar **1961** [Kansas City, Missouri, opening]. Sd; b&w. 35mm. 68 min.
　　Prod Robert E. Kent. *Dir* Edward L. Cahn. *Screenplay* Owen Harris. *Photog* Maury Gertsman. *Art Dir* Serge Krizman. *Set Decor* James Roach. *Film Ed* Kenneth Crane. *Mus* Paul Sawtell, Bert Shefter. *Sd* Earl Snyder. *Asst Dir* Herbert S. Greene.
　　Cast: Jim Davis *(Jim Stockton),* Nancy Hadley *(Consuela),* Ken Mayer *(Beaver),* Nestor Paiva *(Montalvo),* Don O'Kelly *(Kilpatrick),* Stuart Randall *(Ben Wright),* David Renard *(Lopez),* John Marshall, actor *(General Torena),* Eugene Iglesias *(Lieutenant Ruiz),* Herman Rudin *(Chief Taztay),* Addison Richards *(Commander Kimball),* Renata Vanni, Tudor Owen, Jan Arvan, Norman Pabst, Allan Ray, Dina Caeser, Barbara Mansell, Sid Kane.
　　Western melodrama. Source: George Bruce, "Kit Carson" (a short story; publication undetermined). Following an Indian raid in which frontier scout Jim Stockton loses a year's trapping of fur skins, he and his two friends, Beaver and Lopez, agree to lead a wagon train of settlers, accompanied by a detail of U. S. Cavalry soldiers, into Mexican-owned California. Consuela, the beautiful daughter of a pro-American Spanish nobleman, is also among the passengers, and both Stockton and Lieutenant Kilpatrick compete for her attention. All are unaware that Mexico has recently declared war on the United States, and that Mexican Gen. Rafael Torena has formed an alliance with the hostile Madoc Indians. At the California border the troops depart for Oregon, but they are trapped in a canyon by the Indians. Stockton and his two comrades blow up the blocked entrance and rescue the soldiers, who rejoin the wagon train and help fight off a savage Indian attack. Meanwhile, Consuela's father, Don Carlos Montalvo, warns the U. S. forces in Fort Monterey of a forthcoming assault. The wagon train arrives as the Mexicans reach the garrison. Sensing that the cavalry is vastly outnumbered, Stockton persuades the commander to dynamite the bastion rather than let the Mexicans gain control of it. The explosions drive the enemy away, and Stockton wins the affection of Consuela. *Trappers. Scouts—Frontier. Indians of North America. Nobility. Spanish. Frontier and pioneer life. Wagon trains. Forts. United States—History—Mexican War. United States Army—Cavalry. Mexico—Army. Explosions.*

THE FRONTIERSMAN see **BUCKSKIN**

FROZEN ALIVE (Great Britain/West Germany)　　　　**F6.1715**
Alfa-Film–Creole Films. *Dist* Magna Pictures Distribution Corp. 15 Jun **1966** [San Francisco opening]. Sd; b&w. 35mm. 80 min.
　　Prod Artur Brauner, Ronald Rietti. *Assoc Prod* Irving Dennis. *Dir* Bernard Knowles. *Screenplay* Evelyn Frazer. *Dir Photog* Robert Ziller. *Camera Op* Johannes Nowak. *Art Dir* Jürgen Kiebach. *Film Ed* Steven Collins. *Ch Sd* Gerhard Müller. *Asst Dir* Margit Rausch. *Prod Supv* Peter Hahne. *Prod Mgr* Felix Siebenrogg. *Cont* Ursula Grossman. *Cost* Vera Mugge. *Wardrobe* Charlotte Jungmann. *Makeup* Heinz Stamm. *Hairdresser* Sabine Brodt. *Still Photog* Dietrich Schnelle.
　　Cast: Mark Stevens *(Frank),* Marianne Koch *(Helen),* Delphi Lawrence *(Joan),* Joachim Hansen *(Tony),* Walter Rilla *(Sir Keith),* Wolfgang Lukschy *(Inspector Prentow),* Helmut Weiss *(Chairman),* John Longden *(Professor Hubbard),* Albert Bessler *(Martin),* Sigurd Lohde *(Dr. Merkheimer),* Wolfgang

Günther (*Sergeant Grun*).

Science fiction drama. When his marriage to an unfaithful wife breaks up, a medical scientist falls in love with the young woman with whom he is conducting experiments on the deep-freezing of human bodies. The scientist sets out to prove his theory by persuading his associate to use him as a guinea pig. While he is in a state of frozen unconsciousness, the police arrive to investigate the fatal shooting of his wife. Stunned by the news, the associate finds herself emotionally unable to continue with the experiment, but she recovers and is able to revive the scientist. His wife's lover confesses to the murder. *Scientists. Police. Infidelity. Murder. Cryogenics.*

Note: Produced in West Germany in 1964 as *Der Fall X701*; released in Great Britain in 1967 as *Frozen Alive*; running time: 63 min.

THE FROZEN DEAD (Great Britain)   F6.1716

Gold Star Productions–Seven Arts Productions. *Dist* Warner Bros.–Seven Arts, Inc. 27 Sep **1967** [Boston opening; c31 Dec 1966; LP35738]. Sd (Westrex); b&w (see note). 35mm. 95 min.

Prod-Dir-Screenplay-Orig Story Herbert J. Leder. *Exec Prod* Robert Goldstein. *Assoc Prod* Tom Sachs. *Dir Photog* Davis Boulton. *Camera Op* Ronnie Maasz. *Art Dir* Scott MacGregor. *Film Ed* Tom Simpson. *Mus Comp* Don Banks. *Mus Dir* Philip Martell. *Sd Mix* Kevin Sutton. *Sd Ed* Jim Roddan. *Asst Dir* Doug Hermes. *Cont* Doreen Soan. *Wardrobe* Mary Gibson. *Makeup* Eric Carter. *Hairdresser* Pearl Tipaldi.

Cast: Dana Andrews (*Dr. Norberg*), Anna Palk (*Jean Norberg*), Philip Gilbert (*Dr. Ted Roberts*), Kathleen Breck (*Elsa Tenney*), Karel Stepanek (*Lubeck*), Basil Henson (*Tirpitz*), Alan Tilvern (*Karl Essen*), Ann Tirard (*Mrs. Schmidt*), Edward Fox (*prisoner no. 3*), Oliver MacGreevy (*Joseph*), Tom Chatto (*Inspector Witt*), John Moore, actor (*stationmaster*), Charles Wade (*porter*).

Horror film. At the end of World War II, 1,500 of Hitler's top officials were frozen alive and hidden in caves. Former Nazis Dr. Norberg and his aide, Karl Essen, are conducting revivification experiments at a manor in the English countryside. Although they have been successful in restoring body functions, they have been unable to revive the brain. They explain to visiting ex-Wehrmacht officer General Lubeck that they need a live brain with which to experiment. Consequently, when Norberg's niece, Jean, arrives from the United States with her college friend Elsa, the sadistic Essen disposes of Elsa but keeps her decapitated head alive in a laboratory cabinet. Although Jean is told that her friend had to leave suddenly for London, the young girl is unconvinced and reveals her suspicions to Ted Roberts, an American scientist. Roberts is permitted by Norbert to view the severed head, and he agrees to keep the secret. Meanwhile, Elsa's brain is developing a telepathic rapport with Jean in order to warn her that her life is in danger. After Lubeck has concluded that Essen is a security risk and ordered him put into the deep-freeze chamber, Jean sneaks into the laboratory and discovers Elsa's head. When Lubeck aims a gun at her, Norberg intervenes on behalf of his niece. As they engage in a death struggle, Elsa's brain activates a collection of electronically-controlled dismembered arms which reach out and strangle the two ex-Nazis. *Nazis. Scientists. Uncles. Americans in foreign countries. Physicians. Reviviscence. Cryogenics. Sadism. Decapitation. Mental telepathy. Disembodiment.*

Note: Released in Great Britain in Eastmancolor in 1967.

THE FROZEN WORLD see CIVILISATION: THE SKIN OF OUR TEETH

THE FRUIT IS RIPE (France/Italy)   F6.1717

Contact Organisation–P. I. P.–Transmonde Film. *Dist* Janus Films. 20 Dec **1961** [Los Angeles showing]. Sd; b&w. 35mm. 90 min.

Prod René Thévenet. *Dir-Writ* Louis Soulanes. *Adapt & Dial* Louis Soulanes. *Dir Photog* Paul Coteret. *Camera* Roger Duculot. *Film Ed* Alice Green. *Mus* Michel Magne. *Sd* Jacques Bonpunt. *Prod Mgr* Jacques Garcia.

Cast: Scilla Gabel (*Kissa*), Françoise Saint-Laurent (*Josine*), Eva Damien (*Margo*), Philippe Leroy (*Armand*), Saro Urzi (*Buonacasa*), Michel Lemoine (*Berto*), Vittoria Prada, Sandrine, Jacques Fabbri, Philippe Mory, Françoise Dannel, Hélène Tossy, Gisèle Gallois, Elsa Kine, Janine Vila, Renée Tereusa, Roger Crouzet.

Melodrama. Each year the fruit-picking season in the lower Rhône plain attracts young women workers from the surrounding districts. Among the workers employed on the unscrupulous Buonacasa's farm are Kissa, who delights in teasing men; Margo, a tough, hardened young woman; and the tender, romantic Josine. As the hot summer sun inflames youthful passions, Kissa sets about captivating both Armand, a handsome truck driver, and the boss's insolent son, Berto, who takes pride in his American car and lords it over the workers. Meanwhile, Josine and Armand become mutually attracted. After work, Kissa shows off at the local cabaret and delights in inciting jealousy among the men. A strike among the employees adds to the turmoil. One night Berto, feverishly excited by Kissa, rapes Josine. Armand pursues Berto, who is

killed in a crash. The workers win their strike, and Kissa gives Armand up to Josine. *Farmers. Farm workers. Truckdrivers. Teases. Rape. Seduction. Automobile accidents. Summer.*

Note: Opened in Paris in Jun 1961 as *Les filles Sèment le vent*.

LA FRUSTA E IL CORPO see WHAT!

FRUSTRATED CHERIE   F6.1718

Dist Distribpix, Inc. ca **1969**. Sd; b&w. 35mm. 63 min. [Also 76 min?]

Prod Arthur Dean, Chris Keith. *Dir* Arthur Dean.

Cast: Roxanne Blak, Lynne Blak, Chris Keith.

Melodrama. The new marriage between a voluptuous young woman and a middle-aged man is not a happy one because the eccentric husband will have sexual intercourse only on those few days prescribed by his astrological guide. Sensing that her husband is impotent, the wife takes a young lover and moves in with him. Eventually she, her lover, and his sister become a sexual threesome. The deserted husband's vain attempts to persuade his wife to return to him permanently affect his psyche, and he leaves muttering the phrase, "The vile seducer has no holidays." *Newlyweds. Middle age. Impotence. Infidelity. Troilism. Lesbianism. Incest. Astrology.*

FRUSTRATIONS (France/Italy)   F6.1719

Radius Production–Pamec Cinematografica. *Dist* Audubon Films. 20 Apr **1967** [San Francisco showing]. Sd; b&w. 35mm. 89 min.

Prod-Dir Georges Combret. *Screenplay* Georges Combret, Pierre Mandru. *Photog* Pierre Lebon. *Art Dir* J.-Paul Coutan-Laboureur. *Mus* René Sylviano. *Asst Dir* J. Espiau. *Prod Mgr* Y. Crouzet.

Cast: Reine Rohan (*Marisa*), Magali Noël (*Louisa*), Paul Guers (*Jean*), Jean-Marc Tennberg (*Mario*), Evelyne Boursotti (*Edith*), Jean-Louis Tristan (*Bob?*).

Melodrama. Marisa leaves home with Jean, a playboy, in hopes of marrying him, but she discovers too late that Jean is a procurer in a white slave racket run by the couturier Mario and his wife, Louisa. Marisa finds herself a prostitute aboard a yacht. There she learns that Bob, a member of the gang, is planning an escape for Edith, one of the ring's victims, and Marisa is invited to participate. The motor boat escape attempt fails, and the gang pursues the runaways and kills Bob. The two women are sent to a "concentration" farm known as "The Hole." Jean, discovering the he loves Marisa, gets her released from the camp so that she may continue with the organization. Meanwhile, Edith is approached by Mario, and she kills him with a pitchfork. Marisa makes another escape but is pursued by Jean. Jean is killed in a crash when the police give chase, and Marisa tells the police about the organization. *Playboys. Racketeers. Couturiers. White slave traffic. Perfidy. Murder. Yachts. Chases. Automobile accidents.*

Note: Opened in Paris in Jun 1965 as *La traite des blanches*; running time: 100 min. Italian title: *La tratta delle bianche*. Also known as *Hot Frustrations*.

FU MANCHU AND THE KISS OF DEATH see KISS & KILL

FU MANCHU Y EL BESO DE LA MUERTE see KISS & KILL

FUCK see BLUE MOVIE

FUEGO (Argentina)   F6.1720

Sifa. *Dist* Haven International Pictures. 10 Oct **1969** [New York opening]. Sd; col (Eastman Color, print by Movielab). 35mm. 81 min. *MPAA rating* X.

Prod-Dir-Writ Armando Bo. *Photog* Ricardo Younis. *Mus and Songs:* "It's You," "To Remember," "Flames in Her Body" Humberto Umbriaco, Armando Bo.

Cast: Isabel Sarli (*Laura*), Armando Bo (*Carlos*), Alba Mujica (*Andrea*), Roberto Airaldi (*Dr. Zalazar*), Michael Olmos, Oscar Valicelli, Monica Grey, Marcel.

Melodrama. Although she is known by all to have a ravenous appetite for men, Laura, a voluptuous Argentine beauty, also has a taste for her middle-aged "housekeeper," Andrea. Laura falls in love with Carlos, a wealthy industrialist who asks her to marry him. She at first refuses because she knows that her excessive desires will force her to be unfaithful, but she finally agrees. Andrea is furious, but Laura assures her that they can continue as before. Soon after the wedding, Laura finds herself being unfaithful to Carlos and suffering greatly because of her inability to control her passions. One day, Carlos returns home early and finds her in bed with the telephone repairman, who tells him what everyone else in town already knows. On the advice of a doctor who diagnoses Laura's problem as a "sexual neurosis," they dismiss Andrea and go to see a specialist in New York. When Laura succumbs again, she almost commits suicide, but they decide that time alone can solve the problem, and they return home. Carlos returns from work and finds Laura in tears over having had another man. Finally he agrees with her that she is better off dead, but he is unable to pull the trigger. Laura kills herself by diving off a high cliff, and her spirit returns to comfort Carlos. Distraught at losing her, he turns the gun on himself. *Housekeepers. Industrialists. Nymphomania. Marriage. Infidelity.*

Lesbianism. Bisexuality. Suicide. Supernatural. New York City.

Note: Released in Argentina in 1968.

FUEGO see **PYRO**

LA FUGA (Italy)   **F6.1721**
Cine 3. *Dist* International Classics. 21 Mar **1966** [New York opening; c21 Mar 1966; LP34486]. Sd; b&w. 35mm. 92 min.

Prod Vittorio Glori Musy, Alberto Casati, Mario Mariani. *Dir* Paolo Spinola. *Screenplay* Sergio Amidei. *Screenplay Collab* Piero Bellanova. *Idea* Paolo Spinola, Carla Conti. *Photog* Marcello Gatti, Armando Nannuzzi. *Set Decor* Nedo Azzini. *Scenic Dsgn* Piero Gherardi. *Film Ed* Nino Baragli. *Mus* Piero Piccioni. *Song:* "Topless" sung by Peppino Di Capri. *Song:* "La tua stagione" sung by Milva. *Sd* Pietro Vesperini, Franco Bassi. *Prod Supv* Pietro Grifi. *Prod Dir* Gianni Di Stolfo. *Cost* Piero Gherardi.

Cast: Giovanna Ralli (*Piera Fabbri*), Anouk Aimée (*Luisa*), Paul Guers (*Andrea Fabbri*), Enrico Maria Salerno (*psychoanalyst*), Carol Walker (*Piera's mother*), Guido Alberti (*Piera's father*), Jone Salinas Musu (*Andrea's mother*), Maurizio Arena, Anita Sanders, Ignazio Dolce.

Drama. By all appearances, the beautiful and wealthy Piera Fabbri is happily married to a successful nuclear physicist, Andrea. Inwardly, however, she is filled with inexplicable anxieties that lead her to a psychoanalyst. Her parents have long been separated, and Piera tries to fill her empty existence by designing fabrics for her mother's textile mill. Even the birth of a son has failed to stabilize her, and she longs for the love denied her as a child. Left more and more alone because of her husband's preoccupation with his work, Piera drifts into a relationship with Luisa, an intelligent, refined interior decorator. Aware that Luisa has obvious lesbian tendencies, Piera persuades herself that at long last she has found the love she needs; but this relationship, too, ends in failure. She and her husband separate, and, following a violent quarrel with Luisa, she hysterically drives her car at breakneck speed into a truck and dies. *Housewives. Physicists. Psychiatrists. Interior decorators. Marriage. Motherhood. Lesbianism. Filial relations. Separation (marital). Suicide. Automobile accidents.*

Note: Opened in Rome in Mar 1965; running time: 95 min. Copyright claimant: 20th Century–Fox Film Corp.

FULFILLMENT, SOMETHING WORTH REMEMBERING   **F6.1722**
Charles M. Conner Productions. 1 Oct **1969** [Houston opening]. Sd; col (Eastman Color, print by Capitol Color). 35mm. 75 min. [Cut from 92 min.] MPAA rating X.

Pres by Charles M. Conner. *Prod-Dir-Writ* Charles M. Conner. *Song:* "Something Worth Remembering" sung by Michael Stoddard. *Mus Perf by* Houston Philharmonic Orchestra.

Cast: Michael Stoddard (*war hero*), Nancy Zala (*millionairess*), Carlos Garcia, Luke Leonard, Merill Graham, Cindy Shores.

Melodrama. After their adulterous spouses are killed in an automobile accident, a 24-year-old war hero marries a homely and middle-aged millionairess. During a honeymoon in Spain, the wife, dying of leukemia, kills herself. Accused of her death, the veteran donates his inheritance to charity. *Veterans. War heroes. Millionaires. Newlyweds. Marriage. Suicide. Wealth. Infidelity. Inheritance. Cancer. Honeymoons. Spain. Automobile accidents.*

Note: Location scenes filmed in Houston and other parts of Texas. Also known as *Something Worth Remembering.*

THE FULL TREATMENT see **STOP ME BEFORE I KILL!**

FUN IN ACAPULCO   **F6.1723**
Hal Wallis. *Dist* Paramount Pictures. 28 Nov **1963** [Los Angeles opening; c15 Nov 1963; LP26588]. Sd; col (Technicolor). 35mm. 100 min.

A Hal Wallis Production. *Prod* Hal Wallis. *Assoc Prod* Paul Nathan. *Dir* Richard Thorpe. *2d Unit Dir* Michael Moore. *Screenplay* Allan Weiss. *Dir Photog* Daniel L. Fapp. *2d Unit Photog* Irmin Roberts. *Col Cons* Richard Mueller. *Art Dir* Hal Pereira, Walter Tyler. *Set Decor* Sam Comer, Robert R. Benton. *Ed Supv* Warren Low. *Film Ed* Stanley Johnson. *Mus Scored & Cond* Joseph J. Lilley. *Songs Sung by* Elvis Presley. *Vocal Accompaniment* The Jordanaires, The Four Amigos. *Song:* "Fun in Acapulco" Sid Wayne, Ben Weisman. *Songs:* "Vino, Dinero y Amor," "Mexico," "The Bullfighter Was a Lady" Sid Tepper, Roy C. Bennett. *Song:* "El Toro" Bill Giant, Bernie Baum, Florence Kaye. *Song:* "Marguerita" Don Robertson. *Song:* "(There's) No Room To Rhumba (In a Sports Car)" Fred Wise, Dick Manning. *Song:* "I Think I'm Gonna Like It Here" Hal Blair, Don Robertson. *Song:* "Bossa Nova Baby" Jerry Leiber, Mike Stoller. *Song:* "You Can't Say No in Acapulco" Dee Fuller, Lee Morris, Sid Feller. *Song:* "Guadalajara" Pepe Guizar. *Mus Numbers Staged by* Charles O'Curran. *Sd Rec* Hugo Grenzbach, Charles Grenzbach. *Asst Dir* Michael Moore. *Prod Mgr* Richard Blaydon, William W. Gray. *Cost* Edith Head. *Makeup Supv* Wally Westmore. *Hairstyles* Nellie Manley. *Sp Photog Eff* Paul K. Lerpae. *Tech Adv* Col. Tom Parker.

Cast: Elvis Presley (*Mike Windgren*), Ursula Andress (*Margarita Dauphine*), Elsa Cardenas (*Dolores Gómez*), Paul Lukas (*Maxmillian*), Larry Domasin (*Raoul Almeido*), Alejandro Rey (*Moreno*), Robert Carricart (*José*), Teri Hope (*Janie Harkins*), Charles Evans (*Mr. Harkins*), Alberto Morin (*hotel manager*), Francisco Ortega (*desk clerk*), Robert De Anda (*bellboy*), Linda Rivera (*telegraph clerk*), Darlene Tompkins (*1st girl*), Linda Rand (*2d girl*), Eddie Cano, Carlos Mejia, Leon Cardenas, Fred Aguirre (*musicians*). Tom Hernandez (*photographer*), Adele Palacios (*secretary*).

Comedy-drama with music. Mike Windgren arrives in Acapulco as a sailor on a yacht. When he loses his position, Raoul, a shoeshine boy who has heard him sing, becomes his manager and gets him a job as both a fill-in singer for the temperamental featured performer at the Hilton Hotel and as siesta-time fill-in for Moreno, lifeguard at the hotel pool. Moreno also makes the 136-foot dive every evening from La Quebrada for the entertainment of spectators. Mike becomes involved with Dolores, a woman bullfighter, and Maggie, the hotel's assistant social director. Moreno is infatuated with Maggie and becomes jealous of Mike. Raoul obtains additional singing engagements for Mike in other Acapulco clubs, where he is well received. Moreno learns that Mike has been a trapezist in an American circus but developed a fear of height after an accident cost the life of his partner. The two men fight, and Moreno is injured just enough to prevent his dive at La Quebrada that night. Conquering his fear, Mike substitutes for Moreno and makes a perfect dive. With Maggie and Raoul he plans to return to his circus act in the States. *Trapezists. Singers. Sailors. Bootblacks. Children. Lifeguards. Tourists. Divers. Bullfighters. Social directors. Mexicans. Americans in foreign countries. Acrophobia. Jealousy. Nightclubs. Resorts. Hotels. Acapulco. La Quebrada.*

Note: Exteriors filmed on location in Acapulco.

THE FUN LOVERS see **SEX AND THE COLLEGE GIRL**

FUNDOSHI ISHA see **LIFE OF A COUNTRY DOCTOR**

FUNERAL IN BERLIN (Great Britain)   **F6.1724**
Lowndes Productions–Jovera, S. A. *Dist* Paramount Pictures. 22 Dec **1966** [New York opening; c21 Dec 1966; LP33768]. Sd; col (Technicolor). 35mm (Panavision). 102 min.

Pres by Harry Saltzman. *Prod* Charles Kasher. *Dir* Guy Hamilton. *2d Unit Dir* Peter Medak. *Screenplay* Evan Jones. *Lighting Camera* Otto Heller. *Camera Op* Brian Elvin. *Art Dir* Peter Murton. *Set Decor* Michael White, Vernon Dixon. *Prod Dsgn* Ken Adam. *Film Ed* John Bloom. *Mus* Konrad Elfers. *Mus Dir* Harry Rabinowitz. *Sd* Peter Davies, Ken Nightingall, Terry Sharrett. *1st Asst Dir* David Bracknell. *Prod Supv* Clifford Parkes. *Location Mgr* Frank Ernst. *Cont* Eileen Head. *Ch Makeup* Freddie Williamson. *Hairdresser* Ivy Emmerton.

Cast: Michael Caine (*Harry Palmer*), Eva Renzi (*Samantha Steel*), Paul Hubschmid (*Johnny Vulkan*), Oscar Homolka (*Colonel Stok*), Guy Doleman (*Ross*), Rachel Gurney (*Mrs. Ross*), Hugh Burden (*Hallam*), Thomas Holtzmann (*Reinhart*), Günter Meisner (*Kreutzmann*), Heinz Schubert (*Aaron Levine*), Wolfgang Völz (*Werner*), Klaus Jepsen (*Otto Rukel*), Herbert Fux (*Artur*), Rainer Brandt (*Benjamin*), Ira Hagen (*Monika*), Marthe Keller (*Brigit*).

Action melodrama. Source: Len Deighton, *Funeral in Berlin* (London, 1964). Harry Palmer, coerced into becoming a British spy, is sent to Berlin by Colonel Ross of Intelligence to arrange for the defection of Colonel Stok, the Soviet officer in charge of Berlin Wall security. The old Russian demands a foolproof method of escape, and Palmer contacts Johnny Vulkan, a fellow agent and former black market colleague who puts him in touch with Kreutzmann, a sinister professional escape artist. At the same time Palmer becomes involved with model Samantha Steel, an Israeli agent engaged in hunting Nazi war criminal Paul Louis Broum. Broum possesses documents which tell of a fortune stolen from Jews by Nazis during World War II and hidden in a Swiss bank account. Kreutzmann's plan is to arrange a funeral, hide Stok in a coffin supposedly belonging to an East German, and send it across the border. All goes as scheduled, but when the casket is opened in West Berlin, it contains the murdered body of Kreutzmann. Soon Palmer discovers that he has been double-crossed by everyone involved in the operation: the documents given to him by Ross to aid Kreutzmann are the very documents sought by Samantha's Israeli organization; Vulkan is really Broum; and Stok contrived the entire defection hoax to eliminate Kreutzmann, who posed a threat to his security arrangements. Vulkan corners Palmer in an abandoned building and forces him to hand over the documents. To protect himself from Samantha, who believes the documents are still in his possession and would kill him to obtain them, Palmer tricks Vulkan into switching topcoats. As the ex-Nazi leaves the building in Palmer's trenchcoat, the Israelis open fire. Palmer points out the documents in the dead man's pocket and strolls off. *Russians. Germans. Spies. Defectors. Escape artists. Israelis. Nazis. Models. Murder. Perfidy. Personal identity. Hoaxes. Funerals. Documentation. Berlin—East. Berlin—West. Berlin Wall. Harry Palmer.*

Note: Locations filmed in Berlin. Released in Great Britain in 1967. Most sources credit Lowndes as production company. Jovera, S. A., is copyright claimant for film.

FUNERAL PARADE OF ROSES (Japan)   F6.1725

Matsumoto Productions. Dec **1970**. Sd; b&w. 35mm. 105 min.

Prod Mitsuru Kudo. *Dir-Writ* Toshio Matsumoto. *Photog* Tatsuo Suzuki. *Art Dir* Setsu Asakura. *Film Ed* Toshie Iwasa. *Mus* Joji Yuasa. *Sd* Mikio Katayama.

Cast: Peter *(Eddie)*, Osamu Ogasawara *(Leda)*, Toyosaburo Uchiyama *(Guevara)*, Don Madrid *(Tony)*, Emiko Azuma *(Eddie's mother)*, Yoshio Tsuchiya *(Gonda)*.

Melodrama. Eddie wants to take Leda's place as the favorite of Gonda, proprietor of the Genet, a gay bar in Tokyo. All three homosexuals are troubled: Eddie is guilty of murdering his mother; Leda worries about growing old; Gonda fears that Leda will expose his drug racket to the police. Leda commits suicide, and Gonda and Eddie become lovers. Gonda learns that he is Eddie's father and fatally stabs himself, and Eddie uses the same knife to cut out his own eyes. *Nightclub owners. Male homosexuality. Matricide. Guilt. Suicide. Mutilation. Incest. Bars. Tokyo.*

Note: Original title and release date unknown.

THE FUNNIEST MAN IN THE WORLD   F6.1726

Funnyman, Inc.-Polara Organization, Inc. *Dist* Grove Press. 17 Dec **1969** [New York opening]. Sd; b&w. 35mm. 95 min. [Cut from 102 min.] *MPAA rating* GP.

Prod Vernon P. Becker, Mel May. *Assoc Prod* Mitchell R. Leiser. *Dir-Writ* Vernon P. Becker. *Art Dir* Tony Garcia. *Film Ed* William B. Dalzell. *Mus Comp* Albert Hague. *Mus Arr & Cond* Johnny Douglas. *Sd* Recording Studios Inc., Albert Gramaglia. *Sd Rec* Keith Grant. *Vis Eff* Film Formation Inc., Cinema Research Corp. *Prod Cons* John E. Allen, William K. Everson, Gerald McDonald, Edward Sutherland. *Film Restoration* Rapid Film Techniques Inc.

Narrator: Douglas Fairbanks, Jr.

Compilation film. A survey of Charles Chaplin's early career, from his impoverished childhood in London, from his beginnings as a child stage actor, through his arrival in the United States in 1910 as a vaudeville performer in Fred Karno's troupe, his discovery in 1913 by Mack Sennett, his film work for Sennett's Keystone Films and later for the Essanay and Mutual companies, his Liberty Bond campaign during World War I with Mary Pickford, Douglas Fairbanks, and Jack Dempsey, to the founding of United Artists Corp. in 1919 by Chaplin, Pickford, Fairbanks, and D. W. Griffith, prompting a studio head to remark that "the lunatics are now running the asylum." Included are clips from: *Making a Living* (1914); *Kid Auto Races at Venice* (1914); *Mabel at the Wheel* (1914); *Caught in a Cabaret* (1914); *The Masquerader* (1914); *Dough and Dynamite* (1914); *His Trysting Place* (1914); the feature-length *Tillie's Punctured Romance* (1914); *His Prehistoric Past* (1914); *His New Job* (1915); *A Night Out* (1915); *The Tramp* (1915); *Police* (1916); *The Count* (outtakes, 1916); *The Rink* (1916); *Easy Street* (1917); *The Immigrant* (1917); *The Bond* (1918); and *Triple Trouble* (1918), which includes shots from *Police*, *Work* (1915), and *Life*, a never-completed feature begun in 1915. Filmed imitations of Chaplin as well as Chaplin cartoons, comic strips, and song books attest to his universal popularity. [Foreign sources reviewing a shorter version include among the extracted films *Between Showers* and *The Rounders*, both released in 1914.] *Actors. Motion pictures—History. Music halls. World War I. Charles Chaplin. Fred Karno. Mack Sennett. Mary Pickford. Douglas Fairbanks. Jack Dempsey. David Wark Griffith. United Artists Corp.*

Note: Produced in 1966.

FUNNY GIRL   F6.1727

Rastar Productions. *Dist* Columbia Pictures. 19 Sep **1968** [New York opening; c1 Sep 1968; LP36463]. Sd; col (Technicolor). 35mm (Panavision, see note). 155 min. [Copyright length: 151 min.]

A William Wyler–Ray Stark Production. *Prod* Ray Stark. *Dir* William Wyler. *Mus Numbers Dir* Herbert Ross. *Story-Screenplay* Isobel Lennart. *Dir Photog* Harry Stradling. *Art Dir* Robert Luthardt. *Set Decor* William Kiernan. *Prod Dsgn* Gene Callahan. *Main Titl* Lepard/Neuhart. *Supv Film Ed* Robert Swink. *Film Ed* Maury Winetrobe, William Sands. *Mus Supv & Cond* Walter Scharf. *Orch* Jack Hayes, Walter Scharf, Leo Shuken, Herbert Spencer. *Songs:* "People," "Don't Rain on My Parade," "I'm the Greatest Star," "Sadie, Sadie," "His Love Makes Me Beautiful," "You Are Woman, I Am Man," "If a Girl Isn't Pretty," "The Swan," "Roller Skate Rag," "Funny Girl" Jule Styne, Bob Merrill. *Song:* "I'd Rather Be Blue" Fred Fisher, mus, Billy Rose. *Song:* "Second Hand Rose" James F. Hanley, Grant Clarke. *Song (Mus & French Lyr):* "My Man" Maurice Yvain, A. Willemetz, Jacques Charles. *English Adapt* Channing Pollock. *Vocal-Dance Arr* Betty Walberg. *Mus Ed* Ted Sebern. *Sd Supv* Charles J. Rice. *Sd* Arthur Piantadosi, Jack Solomon. *Sd Eff Ed* Joe Henrie. *Asst Dir* Jack Roe, Ray Gosnell. *Unit Prod Mgr* Paul Helmick.

Asst to the Prod David Dworski, Lorry McCauley. *Script Supv* Marshall Schlom. *Furs* Reiss & Fabrizio. *Barbra Streisand's Cost Dsgn by* Irene Sharaff. *Makeup Supv* Ben Lane. *Makeup Artist* Frank McCoy. *Hairstyles* Vivienne Walker, Virginia Darcy. *Prop* Richard M. Rubin.

Cast: Barbra Streisand *(Fanny Brice)*, Omar Sharif *(Nick Arnstein)*, Kay Medford *(Rose Brice)*, Anne Francis *(Georgia James)*, Walter Pidgeon *(Florenz Ziegfeld)*, Lee Allen *(Eddie Ryan)*, Mae Questel *(Mrs. Strakosh)*, Gerald Mohr *(Branca)*, Frank Faylen *(Keeney)*, Mittie Lawrence *(Emma)*, Gertrude Flynn *(Mrs. O'Malley)*, Penny Santon *(Mrs. Meeker)*, John Harmon *(company manager)*, Thordis Brandt, Bettina Brenna, Virginia Ann Ford, Alena Johnston, Karen Lee, Mary Jane Mangler, Inga Neilsen, Sharon Vaughn *(Ziegfeld girls)*.

Musical comedy-drama. Source: Jule Styne, Bob Merrill and Isobel Lennart, *Funny Girl* (New York opening: 26 Mar 1964). In turn-of-the-century New York, Fanny Brice, a young Jew from the Lower East Side, dreams of becoming a Broadway star, despite her unglamorous appearance. When she loses her chorus line job at Keeney's Oriental Palace, Fanny lies to enter a roller skating number and, slipping and sliding, is a comedy hit. After the performance, suave gambler Nick Arnstein visits Fanny backstage and helps get her a raise. Soon Fanny's comedy routines come to the attention of Florenz Ziegfeld, and she is hired for his Follies at the New Amsterdam Theatre. On opening night she turns the show's lavish wedding finale into a comedy by appearing as a pregnant bride. Ziegfeld's anger is placated by Fanny's success, however, and he keeps the routine and yields to her demand that she choose her own material. Also at the theater that night is Nick Arnstein, who accompanies her to a party at her mother, Rose's, beer hall and then leaves for Kentucky. One year later, while Fanny is in Baltimore on tour, she again encounters Nick. During their whirlwind affair, Nick loses a fortune on a racehorse he owns and decides to recoup his losses by gambling on an ocean liner crossing the Atlantic. As Fanny prepares to board a train for Chicago, she receives roses and a note from Nick. After phoning her resignation from the Follies to Ziegfeld, she catches a train to New York and boards a tugboat to take her to Nick's Europe-bound ship. After her marriage to Nick, the two move into a lavish manor, and Fanny gives birth to a daughter. Some time later, while Fanny is in rehearsal for a new show, Nick loses his money again and is forced to sell the house. Feeling overpowered by his wife's success, he moves back to New York City and spends more and more time gambling. As his debts mount, Fanny tries to help, but Nick bitterly rejects her offer and becomes involved in a phony bond deal. When he is exposed, he gives himself up and is sent to jail. Over a year later, he comes to Fanny's dressing room before her performance and tells her goodby. *Songs:* "I'm the Greatest Star" (Fanny); "If a Girl Isn't Pretty" (Rose & Mrs. Strakosh); "Roller Skate Rag," "I'd Rather Be Blue Over You," "His Love Makes Me Beautiful," "People" (Fanny); "You Are Woman, I Am Man" (Fanny & Nick); "Don't Rain on My Parade," "Second Hand Rose," "Sadie, Sadie," "The Swan," "Funny Girl," "My Man" (Fanny). *Jews. Entertainers. Singers. Chorus girls. Gamblers. Horsebreeders. Theatrical producers. Vaudeville. Marriage. Motherhood. Debt. Embezzlement. Filial relations. Roller skating. Beer gardens or halls. Ships. Trains. Casinos. Theatrical troupes. New York City—Lower East Side. New York City—Broadway. Baltimore. Fanny Brice. Nick Arnstein. Florenz Ziegfeld. Ziegfeld Follies.*

Note: Filmed in 35mm Panavision and blown up to 70mm for some roadshow presentations.

THE FUNNY PARISHIONER *see* THANK HEAVEN FOR SMALL FAVORS

THE FUNNY SIDE OF LIFE *see* HAROLD LLOYD'S FUNNY SIDE OF LIFE

A FUNNY THING HAPPENED ON THE WAY TO THE FORUM   F6.1728

Quadrangle Films. *Dist* United Artists. 16 Oct **1966** [New York opening; c15 Oct 1966; LP37133]. Sd; col (De Luxe). 35mm. 99 min.

A Melvin Frank Production. *Prod* Melvin Frank. *Assoc Prod* Bob McNaught. *Dir* Richard Lester. *2d Unit Dir* Bob Simmons. *Screenplay* Melvin Frank, Michael Pertwee. *Dir Photog* Nicolas Roeg. *Camera Op* Alex Thomson. *2d Unit Photog* Paul Wilson. *Exec Art Dir* Syd Cain. *Prod Dsgn* Tony Walton. *Titl* Richard Williams. *Film Ed* John Victor Smith. *Songs* Stephen Sondheim. *Mus Dir & Incidental Mus* Ken Thorne. *Mus Cond* Irwin Kostal. *Choreog* Ethel Martin, George Martin. *Sd Engr* Les Hammond. *Sd* Gerry Humphreys. *Asst Dir* José López Rodero. *Prod Mgr* Clifford Parkes. *Cost Dsgn* Tony Walton. *Makeup* Trevor Crole-Rees. *Hairstyles* Bernadette Ibbetson. *Sp Eff* Cliff Richardson.

Cast: Zero Mostel *(Pseudolus)*, Phil Silvers *(Lycus)*, Buster Keaton *(Erronius)*, Jack Gilford *(Hysterium)*, Michael Crawford *(Hero)*, Annette Andre *(Philia)*, Patricia Jessel *(Domina)*, Michael Hordern *(Senex)*, Leon Greene *(Miles Gloriosus)*, Pamela Brown *(high priestess)*, Inga Neilsen

(Gymnasia), Myrna White (Vibrata), Lucienne Bridou (Panacea), Helen Funai (Tintinabula), Jennifer Baker, Susan Baker (Geminae), Janet Webb (Fertilla), Beatrix Lehmann (Domina's mother), Alfie Bass (gatekeeper), Roy Kinnear (instructor), Frank Elliot, Bill Kerr, Jack May, Frank Thornton.

Musical comedy. Source: Burt Shevelove and Larry Gelbart, *A Funny Thing Happened on the Way to the Forum* (New York opening: 8 May 1962). In ancient Rome, Pseudolus, a lying, cheating, dishonorable slave, endlessly connives to obtain his freedom, despite the fact that his master, Senex, is tolerant of his sloppy and insubordinate conduct. When Pseudolus learns that young Hero, son of Senex, loves one of the slave girls from a house of ill repute operated by Lycus, he agrees, in exchange for his freedom, to help the somewhat stupid Hero win the maiden's love. But this girl, Philia, has already been sold to a roguish soldier, Miles Gloriosus. Pseudolus blackmails a timorous fellow slave, Hysterium, into assisting him by donning a wig and gown and impersonating the corpse of Philia, who Pseudolus claims has died of the plague. Philia, who is alive, is mistaken by Senex for his new servant, while she believes him to be her purchaser. Pseudolus, however, prevents the two from ever getting together, and when Philia's real suitor arrives, she despairs and decides to sacrifice herself at the temple. Confusion leads to pandemonium and eventually mayhem culminating in a wild chariot chase. When it is all over, Erronius, an old man who has spent years searching for his two children stolen by pirates, discovers that they are none other than Philia and Gloriosus. Hero wins Philia, and Pseudolus gains both his freedom and a buxom courtesan. *Songs*: "Comedy Tonight" (Pseudolus & Company), "Free" (Pseudolus), "Lovely" (Hero & Philia; reprise: Pseudolus & Hysterium), "Everybody Ought To Have a Maid" (Pseudolus, Lycus, Hysterium & Senex), and "Bring Me My Bride" (Miles Gloriosus). *Prostitutes. Soldiers. Pimps. Slavery. Mistaken identity. Blackmail. Female impersonation. Abduction. Plague. Whorehouses. Corpses. Chariots. Rome—History—Empire. Chases.*

Note: Produced in Spain.

FUNNYMAN   **F6.1729**
Korty Films. *Dist* New Yorker Films. Jul **1968** [Los Angeles showing]. Sd; b&w with tinted seq. 35mm. 102 min.

Prod Hugh McGraw, Stephen Schmidt. *Dir* John Korty. *Screenplay* John Korty, Peter Bonerz. *Anim* John Korty. *Photog* John Korty. *Film Ed* David Schickele. *Mus* Peter Schickele. *Sd* J. Paul Oppenheim. *Prod Asst* Michael Bortman, William Desloge, Jennifer Chinlund, Fred Padula.

Cast: Peter Bonerz (Perry), Sandra Archer (Sue), Carol Androsky (Sybil), Larry Hankin (Roger), Barbara Hiken (Molly), Gerald Hiken (Mahlon), Nancy Fish (Jan), Budd Steinhilber (Vogel), Ethel Sokolow (Vera), Marshall Efron (Sid), George Ede (advertising executive), Jane House (girl in bikini), Herb Beckman (Watson), Manuela Ruecker (Heidi), Roger Bowen (Lester), Melvin Stewart (Phil), Richard Stahl (Zach), Stephen D. Newman (Ollie), Alan Myerson (Seymour), Jerry Mander (Arnie), Lucille Bliss (girl of 1,000 voices), Ellsworth Milburn (piano player), Anne Bowen (Lester's wife), Arthur Okamura (Arthur).

Comedy-drama. Perry, a young comedian who performs with a group of San Francisco-based satirists called The Committee, is so dissatisfied with both his career and his private life that he breaks off with the troupe and ends his longstanding affair with another Committee member, Jan. Anxious to try his luck at a more ambitious profession, Perry is persuaded by his agent to work with Vogel, an offbeat gin-swilling animator, in developing insecticide commercials for a local ad agency. At first uninspired, Perry finally comes up with the slogan "*Blast* kills everything that bugs you!" and so impresses the agency's secretary that she takes him to bed. Although Perry's commercials are highly regarded, they are ultimately rejected for being too unconventional. Once again at loose ends, Perry persuades The Committee to allow him to stage an experimental one-man show for which he dreams up wild sight gags, ingenious props, and unconventional music. When the performance is only moderately successful, however, Perry is so depressed that he goes off on a vacation to a serene fishing village. There, while immersing himself in the idyllic way of life, Perry meets a Japanese-American artist and his family and, through them, Sue, a model who makes some thoughtful suggestions about his self-questioning. Returning to San Francisco with Sue, Perry vows to dedicate himself to intellectual pursuits. But when Sue accidentally hears a tape of one of his comic monologues and responds with unabashed delight, she tells him that he was best as a funnyman. Somewhat reluctantly, but with a decided sense of relief, Perry comes to the same conclusion. *Entertainers. Japanese. Models. Animators. Artists. Advertising. Vacations. Fishing villages. San Francisco. The Committee.*

Note: Filmed on location in San Francisco.

FUOCO FATUO *see* **THE FIRE WITHIN**

FÜR EIN PAAR DOLLAR MEHR *see* **FOR A FEW DOLLARS MORE**

FÜR EINE HANDVOLL DOLLARS *see* **A FISTFUL OF DOLLARS**

FURANKENSHUTAIN NO KAIJU—SANDA TAI GAILAH *see* **THE WAR OF THE GARGANTUAS**

FURANKENSHUTAIN TAI BARAGON *see* **FRANKENSTEIN CONQUERS THE WORLD**

FURESSHUMAN WAKADAISHO *see* **YOUNG GUY GRADUATES**

FURIA À BAHIA POUR OSS 117 *see* **OSS 117—MISSION FOR A KILLER**

LA FURIA DEI BARBARI *see* **FURY OF THE PAGANS**

FURIN KAZAN *see* **UNDER THE BANNER OF SAMURAI**

THE FURTHER PERILS OF LAUREL AND HARDY   **F6.1730**
Robert Youngson Productions. *Dist* Twentieth Century-Fox Film Corp. Oct **1967** [c1 Sep 1967; LP35247]. Sd; b&w. 35mm. 99 min.

Prod-Writ Robert Youngson. *Assoc Prod* Herbert Gelbspan, Alfred Dahlem. *Mus Comp & Cond* John Parker, mus. *Mus Supv* Angelo Ross. *String Quartet Mus* Lawrence Kogen. *Sd Rec* Val Peters. *Mus Rec* Harry Hirsch. *Prod Mgr* I. Hill Youngson. *Prod Asst* Richard Tonini. *Res Supv* Jeanne Youngson.

Narrator: Jay Jackson.

Compilation film. Stan Laurel and Oliver Hardy are seen in clips from films made before they became a team, Hardy in two films starring Billy West, an imitator of Chaplin, and Laurel as a brash ladykiller in Charlie Chase's *Just Rambling Along* (1918). The two actors appeared together in *Flying Elephants* and *Sugar Daddies* in 1927, but it was not until they made *Do Detectives Think?* (1927) that their famous comedy style began to emerge. Clips from the following films are included: *The Second Hundred Years* (1927), *You're Darn Tootin'* (1928), *Habeas Corpus* (1928), *That's My Wife* (1929), *Angora Love* (1929), *Should Married Men Go Home* (1928), and *Early to Bed* (1928). To further illustrate the comedy technique used by the Hal Roach Studios, the compilation also includes Charlie Chase's classic *The Way of All Pants* (1927). Other performers seen in the excerpts include Jean Harlow, Jimmy Finlayson, Snub Pollard, Bryant Washburn, Charlie Hall, Tom Kennedy, Noah Young, Charlotte Mineau, Tom Dugan, Charles Rogers, and The Original Flappers. *Actors. Motion pictures—History. Stan Laurel. Oliver Hardy.*

FURY AT SMUGGLER'S BAY (Great Britain)   **F6.1731**
Mijo Productions. *Dist* Embassy Pictures. Dec **1963**. Sd; b&w (see note). 35mm (PanaScope). 92 min.

Pres by Joseph E. Levine. *Prod-Dir-Orig Story-Screenplay* John Gilling. *Exec Prod* Joe Vegoda, Michael Green. *Assoc Prod* John Gossage. *Dir Photog* Harry Waxman. *1st Unit Camera Op* Godfrey Godar. *1st Unit Focus* Robin Vidgeon, Bernard Ford. *2d Unit Photog* Cyril Knowles. *2d Unit Camera Op* Alan Hume. *2d Unit Focus* Dennis Lewiston, Hugh Davey. *Art Dir* Duncan Sutherland. *Draughtsman* Terence Knight. *Film Ed* John Victor Smith. *1st Asst Ed* Brian Smedley-Aston. *2d Asst Ed* Gerald Kliman. *Mus Comp, Arr & Cond* Harold Geller. *Sd* Rusty Coppleman. *Sd Mix* Cecil Mason. *Boom Op* Fred Tomlin. *Sd Camera Op* Dave Goghan. *1st, 2d & 3d Asst Dir* Philip Shipway, Ted Lewis, Henry Emery. *Location Asst* Joe Levy. *2d Unit Asst Dir* Bill Snaith. *Prod Supv* Fred A. Swann. *Prod Sec* Pat Green. *1st Unit Cont* Pamela Mann, Olga Brook. *2d Unit Cont* Jane Buck. *Wardrobe Dsgn* Phyllis Dalton. *Wardrobe Mistress* Brenda Gardner. *Ch Makeup* Alex Garfath. *Makeup Artist* Len Garde. *Hairdresser* Olga Angelinetta, Jayne Seymour. *Still Photog* Charles Trigg. *Casting Dir* James Liggat. *Prod Buyer* Jimmy James.

Cast: John Fraser (Chris), Peter Cushing (Squire Trevenyan), Bernard Lee (Black John), June Thorburn (Jenny), Michèle Mercier (Louise), William Franklyn ("The Captain"), George Coulouris (François Lejeune), Liz Fraser (Betty), Miles Malleson (Duke of Avon), Katherine Kath (Maman), Jouma (Jouma), Tom Duggan ("Red Friars"), Humphrey Heathcote (Roger Treherne), Christopher Carlos (The Tiger), Maitland Moss (Tom).

Action drama. In the late 19th century the inhabitants of Tarn, a Cornish seacoast village, are terrorized by a gang of thugs who lure ships onto the rocks to be wrecked and loot them. Chris, the son of local magistrate Squire Trevenyan, discovers that Black John, a notorious rogue, is the gang's leader, but the squire is convinced that the wrecking is being done by some village fishermen who make a living by smuggling, and he sentences them to be deported. Chris is in love with Louise, the daughter of merchant François Lejeune, a French exile. Chris kills one of the gang and is sent to London. Louise summons Chris to return home, but on the way he is kidnaped and held hostage by "The Captain," a highwayman and ally of the villagers. Chris wins his abductor's friendship, and together they vow to defeat Black John and his gang. Up to this point, Squire Trevenyan has been helpless against Black John because the thug knows something damaging about the squire's past, but he finally confesses to his daughter Jenny and sends for the military. The squire and Black John are killed in the ensuing battle, but the gang is rounded up, and the sentenced villagers are returned home. Chris marries Louise and becomes the new squire; and "The Captain" is given a headstart to escape. *Fishermen. Gangs. Thieves. Magistrates. French. Merchants. Hostages. Highwaymen. Looting. Smuggling. Murder. Deportation. Kidnaping. Friendship. Marriage. Blackmail. Confession. Fishing villages. Cornwall (England). London. Shipwrecks.*

Note: Location scenes filmed in Pembrokeshire, Wales; working titles: *The Wreckers* and *Fury at Smuggler's Creek*. Released in Great Britain in Apr 1961 in Eastmancolor; running time: 97 min.

FURY OF THE PAGANS (Italy) F6.1732
Arion Film. *Dist* Columbia Pictures. May **1963** [c1 Jun 1963; LP25416]. Sd; b&w (see note). 35mm (Dyaliscope). 86 min.

Exec Prod Paolo Ricci. *Dir* Guido Malatesta. *Screenplay* Gino Mangini, Umberto Scarpelli. *Story* Gino Mangini. *Dir Photog* Vincenzo Seratrice. *Camera Op* Luigi Allegretti, Vitaliano Batalucci. *Asst Op* Camillo Bazzoni. *Art Dir* Pier Vittorio Marchi, Alfonso Russo. *Film Ed* Roberto Giandalla. *Montages* Mario Sansoni. *Orig Mus* Gian Stellari, Guido Robuschi. *Mus Arr* National Music. *Prod Dir* Michelangelo Ciafre. *Prod Asst* Giuliano Simonetti, Mario Bartolini. *Prod Inspector* Luigi Anastabi. *Makeup Artist* Antonio Giuseppi Marini. *Hairstylist* Galileo Mandini.

Cast: Edmund Purdom *(Toryok),* Rossana Podestà *(Lianora),* Livio Lorenzon *(Kovo),* Carla Calò, Daniele Vargas, Andrea Fantasia, Vittoria Feri, Ljubica Jović, Amedeo Novelli, Nikša Stefanini, Giulio Massimi, Simonetta Simeoni, Raffaella Pelloni, Luciano Marin.

Adventure melodrama. During the sixth century in the Northern Italian Alpine foothills [the Julian Alps, according to an Italian source], Kovo, the cruel chief of the village of Rutar, rapes and kills the woman betrothed to Toryok, chief of the neighboring village of Nyssia. Kovo flees, joining the Longobard hordes in their attack on Italy, and returns to Rutar 2 years later with Lianora, a lovely Veronese hostage. Toryok aids the captive in escaping before leading his men in attacking Rutar and burning the village to the ground. Kovo retaliates by leading the Longobards in an attack on Nyssia, but he is driven back. After Toryok kills Kovo in single combat and the Longobards retreat, he marries Lianora. *Soldiers. Hostages. Lombards. Rape. Murder. Military invasion. Revenge. Abduction. Incendiarism. Village life. Verona. Alps. Yugoslavia. Duels.*

Note: Released in Italy in 1960 as *La furia dei barbari.* Foreign version released in color.

FURY OF THE VIKINGS see **ERIK THE CONQUEROR**

THE FURY OF VENGEANCE see **THE DEVIL'S BEDROOM**

FUSHIN NO TAKI see **THE TIME OF RECKONING**

FUTARI NO MUSUKO see **DIFFERENT SONS**

FUTZ F6.1733
Guvnor Productions. *Dist* Commonwealth United Entertainment, Inc. 16 Nov **1969** [New York opening]. Sd; col (De Luxe). 35mm. 92 min.

Prod Alan Stroh, Ben Shapiro. *Exec Prod* Leon Mirell. *Dir* Tom O'Horgan. *Screenplay* Joseph Stefano. *Adtl Dial* Rochelle Owens. *Photog* Vilmos Zsigmond. *Prod Dsgn* Leon Ericksen. *Film Ed* Fabian Tordjinann, Stuart H. Pappé. *Mus* Tom O'Horgan. *Sd* Dean Gilmore. *Prod Mgr* Paul Lewis.

Cast: John Bakos *(Cyprus Futz),* Victor Lipari *(Brother Ned Satz),* Jerry Owen Cunliffe *(Buford),* Jeannette Ertelt *(Mother Satz),* Peter Craig *(Sheriff Tom Sluck),* Seth Allen *(Oscar Loop),* Clay Haney *(Jeffrey Weese),* Marilyn Roberts *(Mrs. Loop),* Mari-Claire Charba *(Ann Fox),* Eric Wildwoode *(Dorn),* Jane Holzer *(Emily Miller),* Fred Forrest *(Sugford),* Johnny Dodd *(Riordan),* Michael Warren Powell *(Bill Marjoram),* Rob Thirkield *(Father Satz),* Beth Porter *(Marjorie Satz),* Sally Kirkland *(Merry Lee),* Sean Shapiro *(Clay Miller).*

Rural drama. Source: Rochelle Owens, *Futz* (New York opening: 1 Mar 1967). The play *Futz* is being performed by New York's Cafe La Mama Repertory Company before a small rural audience in an open field. Cyprus Futz, a young farmer, is in love with his pig, Amanda, and rejects the advances of plump Marjorie Satz and persuades her to have sex with the pig. One day, when Futz is in the barn with his pig, he is seen by Oscar Loop, a mentally unbalanced youth with an Oedipus complex; and Loop, sexually aroused by what he has viewed, rapes and murders Ann Fox. Meanwhile, Marjorie and her family have told the townspeople of Futz's unnatural relationship with his pig, and when, after his arrest, Loop tells the townspeople the reasons for his crime, they hang Futz and slaughter his pig, after first having lynched Loop. At the close, the townspeople burn down the farm and wallow in the pig's blood. [Press material mentions scenes of nudity, masturbation, incest, transvestism, homosexuality, exhibitionism, and group sex.] *Farmers. Bestiality. Oedipus complex. Lynching. Mental retardation. Rape. Murder. Exhibitionism. Autoeroticism. Voyeurism.*

Transvestism. Male homosexuality. Incest. Group sex. Cafe La Mama Repertory Company. Pigs.

Note: Filmed on location near Stockton, California.

FUZZ F6.1734
Dist Stacey Distributors. ca **1970**. Sd; col. 16mm. 61-81 min.

Sex film. No information about the precise nature of this film has been found. *Sexuality.*

FYRAHUNDRANITTIOETT see **491**

GABRIELLE F6.1735
Lambent Productions. *Dist* Unique Film Distributors. ca **1970**. Sd; col (Eastman Color). 35mm. 65 min.

Prod Floyd Love. *Dir-Writ* Arlo Shiffen. *Camera* Gabrial Lister. *Sd* Ron Laughlin.

Cast: Dustin Farman, Bess Glove *(narration),* Elaine Trop, William Samson, Larry Taylor, Maria Streeter, Philip Donally, Natalie Fields, Celia Terry, Karen Miller, Celeste Downing, Jerry McHugh, Edward Kline.

Melodrama. Gabrielle, a mute who is unable to respond to her fiancé's sexual advances, mutilates her face after he rapes her. At the hospital, she meets Dr. Matson, who gains her confidence and convinces her to move into his home during her convalescence. She falls under his spell and joins the "family" of followers whose activities center on sexual exhibitionism and senseless murder. Convinced by Matson that she is working toward a cure, Gabrielle brutally kills a man she has never met. The doctor forces her to probe her subconscious; she recalls her traumatic adolescence and a sexual encounter with her father, a religious hypocrite. Shocked into a realization that he has used her as a tool when she finds him gratifying his desire with two of his female followers, she struggles between self-destruction and the murder of the megalomaniac doctor. *Mutes. Physicians. Psychopaths. Frigidity. Rape. Mutilation. Cults. Exhibitionism. Murder. Sadism. Incest. Fatherhood. Adolescence. Troilism. Suicide.*

LE GAI SAVOIR (France/West Germany) F6.1736
O. R. T. F.–Anouchka Films–Bavaria Atelier. *Dist* Leacock Pennebaker, Inc. Jun **1970**. Sd; col (Eastman Color). 35mm. 91 min.

Dir-Writ Jean-Luc Godard. *Dir Photog* Jean Leclerc. *Film Ed* Germaine Cohen.

Cast: Juliette Berto *(Patricia Lumumba),* Jean-Pierre Léaud *(Emile Rousseau),* Chantal Jeanson.

Allegory. Loosely based on: Jean Jacques Rousseau, *Emile; ou, de l'éducation* (Paris, 1762). At night in a darkened television studio, labor agitator Patricia, daughter of Patrice Lumumba, and university activist Emile Rousseau, a descendent of Jean Jacques, participate in a 3-year program of study and self-criticism. The first year is devoted to the compilation of sounds and images, the second to critique, and the third to creation. Through this investigation the Maoists document elitist abuse of sound and image, exposing the philosophical basis of contemporary communication. *Revolutionaries. Maoists. Labor agitators. Student activism. Propaganda. Television studios. Jean Jacques Rousseau. Patrice E. Lumumba.*

Note: Produced for French television in 1967. Shown at the 1969 Berlin Film Festival as *Die fröhliche Wissenschaft;* running time: 95 min. Included in the film is the Cuban revolutionary anthem, "Himno de 26 julio."

GAILY, GAILY F6.1737
Mirisch Productions–Cartier Productions. *Dist* United Artists. 16 Dec **1969** [New York opening; c16 Dec 1969; LP37432]. Sd; col (De Luxe). 35mm. 107 min. [Cut from 117 min.] MPAA rating M.

Prod-Dir Norman Jewison. *Assoc Prod* Hal Ashby. *Screenplay* Abram S. Ginnes. *Dir Photog* Richard Kline. *Camera Op* Marvin Gunter. *Art Dir* George Chan. *Set Decor* Edward G. Boyle, Carl Biddiscombe. *Prod Dsgn* Robert Boyle. *Film Ed* Ralph Winters. *Adtl Ed* Byron Brandt. *Mus & Instrumentals:* "Xmas Eve on Skid Row," "Gaily, Gaily," "Good Morning, Mr. Ransehoff," "The Tango I Saved for You" Henry Mancini. *Songs:* "Sentimental Dream," "There's Enough To Go Around," "Tomorrow Is My Friend" Alan Bergman, Marilyn Bergman, Henry Mancini. *Song:* "There's Enough To Go Around" *sung by* Melina Mercouri. *Song:* "Tomorrow Is My Friend" *sung by* Jimmie Rodgers. *Sd* Robert Martin. *Asst Dir* Mike Moder, Phil Parslow. *Prod Supv* Allen K. Wood. *Prod Mgr* Patrick J. Palmer. *Unit Prod Mgr* Joe Kramer. *Script Supv* Robert Forrest. *Asst to the Prod* Jerry Howard. *Location Mgr* Larry DeWaay. *Wardrobe Dsgn* Ray Aghayan. *Men's Cost* Wes Jeffries. *Women's Cost* Angela Alexander. *Head Makeup* Del Armstrong. *Hairstyles* Naomi Cavin. *Sp Eff* Sass Bedig. *Constr Coörd* William Maldonado. *Prop Master* Sam Gordon. *Key Grip* Gaylin Schultz. *Elec Gaffer* Pat Blyner. *Casting* Lynn Stalmaster.

Cast: Beau Bridges *(Ben Harvey),* Melina Mercouri *(Queen Lil),* Brian Keith *(Francis X. Sullivan),* George Kennedy *(Axel P. Johanson),* Hume Cronyn

("Honest" Tim Grogan), Margot Kidder (Adeline), Wilfrid Hyde-White (The Governor), Melodie Johnson (Lilah), Joan Huntington (Kitty), John Randolph (Father Harvey), Claudia Bryar (Mother Harvey), Eric Shea (Virgil Harvey), Merie Earle (Grandma Harvey), James V. Christy (Frankie), Charles Tyner (Dr. Lazarus), Harry Holcombe (The Stranger), Roy Poole (Dunne), Clarke Gordon (Wally Hill), Peter Brocco (Swami), Maggie Oleson (Mrs. Krump), Nikita Knatz (chauffeur), Roy Barcroft, J. S. Johnson, Tom Peters, Harvey Jason, Les Podwell, Martin Friedberg, Nora Marlowe, Don Keefer.

Comedy. Source: Ben Hecht, *Gaily, Gaily* (New York, 1963). The Galena, Illinois, Independence Day celebration in 1910 seems to young Ben Harvey an ideal time to seek out his own destiny, and with his meager savings, he sets out by train for Chicago, where he is soon pickpocketed and faints from hunger. He is rescued by Queen Lil, handsome proprietress of the Midwest's most elegant and finely furnished brothel, who takes to his innocence and installs him on the top floor of her house. Totally ignorant of the nature of his surroundings, he awakes the following morning to find Adeline, who he believes is a charming and innocent young lady, offering him a new suit of clothes. Queen Lil continues her patronage by getting Ben a job on the *Chicago Journal*, and there his resourcefulness wins over gruff but lovable Francis X. Sullivan, an admirer of the celebrated madam. Sullivan takes Ben on a drinking tour of the city's tenderloin, opening the young lad's innocent eyes to the "political realities" of life in the Windy City. Meanwhile, "reform" leader Axel P. Johanson is trying to obtain the "Big-Mitt-Ledger," a record of civic corruption compiled by local boss "Honest" Tim Grogan. During a party for Grogan at Lil's, Ben, by now realizing where he is staying, determines to devote his life to reform and inspires Adeline to similarly change her ways. She does, steals the ledger herself, and joins the Salvation Army mission. As soon as the ledger is found to be missing, Sullivan, Lil, Grogan, and Johanson are all after Ben, but it is Johanson who finds him and has his luscious ward, Lilah, seduce him in order to obtain the ledger. Ben then finds Adeline but mistakes a Salvation Army hymnal for the ledger. Pursued by Grogan and Sullivan, Ben falls from a drawbridge and drowns. But Dr. Tyner, a quack who has been experimenting with adrenalin, manages to revive Ben (who covertly attends his own funeral and witnesses his grandmother hand what she believes is the family Bible to the eulogizing preacher). The august gentleman opens the book and solemnly reads: "... And Johanson greased Judge Rafferty's palm with eight G's. ..." A mad grab ensues for what all recognize to be Grogan's ledger, which is finally entrusted to Queen Lil for safekeeping. The next morning Ben and Adeline are upstairs at Lil's as Sullivan reads from the *Chicago Journal* headline—"How I Returned From the Dead," by Ben Harvey, assisted by Francis X. Sullivan. (In an alternate ending, Sullivan instead retains the ledger and writes his own story, an exposé of "Corruption in High Places.") *Reporters. Madams. Mayors. Political campaigns. Political corruption. Funerals. Whorehouses. Epinephrine. Chicago. Galena (Illinois). Racine (Wisconsin). Salvation Army. Documentation.*

Note: Locations shot in Milwaukee, Wisconsin, and in Chicago at the Baltimore and Ohio Depot, Lincoln Park, and at the Chicago Auditorium.

GALAXIE   **F6.1738**
Dist Film-Makers' Distribution Center. 3 Sep **1966** [New York opening]. Si (see note); col. 16mm. 90 min.

Prod-Dir Gregory J. Markopoulos. *Photog* Gregory J. Markopoulos. *Film Ed* Gregory J. Markopoulos.

Subjects: Parker Tyler, Storm De Hirsch, Amy Taubin, Donald Droll, Harry Koursaros, Gordon Herzig, Ben Weber, George Kuchar, Mike Kuchar, Erick Hawkins, Louise Grady, Frances Steloff, Charles Boultenhouse, Alfonso Ossorio, Jasper Johns, Jonas Mekas, W. H. Auden, Jerome Hill, Allen Ginsberg, Peter Orlovsky, Robert Ossorio, Gregory Battcock, Hendrik Ruitenbeek, Shirley Clarke, Jan Cremer, Kenneth Kelman, Maurice Sendak, Paul Thek, Susan Sontag, Tom Chomont, Gian Carlo Menotti, Ed Emshwiller, Robert C. Scull.

Experimental film. Thirty sequential film portraits of contemporary artists, filmmakers, and writers, each about 3 minutes in length. Each segment opens with a personal-name title and closes with a period of darkness. The camera focuses almost exclusively on the heads and faces of its subjects, occasionally picking up hand or leg movements. Some sequences employ single-frame technique. *Artists. Authors. Filmmakers. Motion pictures.*

Note: Film is silent except for an electronic clang which punctuates the end of each segment.

GALIA (France/Italy)   **F6.1739**
Speva Films–Ciné-Alliance–Variety Film. *Dist* Zenith International Film Corp. 19 Dec **1966** [New York opening]. Sd; b&w. 35mm. 105 min.

Prod Michel Safra, Serge Silberman. *Dir* Georges Lautner. *Screenplay* Georges Lautner, Vahé Katcha. *Orig Story* Vahé Katcha. *Dir Photog* Maurice Fellous. *Art Dir* Jean d' Eaubonne. *Film Ed* Michèle David. *Mus* Michel Magne. *J. S. Bach Theme Sung by* The Swingle Singers. *Sd* Louis Hochet.

Cast: Mireille Darc (*Galia*), Venantino Venantini (*Greg*), Françoise Prévost (*Nicole*), Jacques Riberolles (*Wespyr*), François Chaumette (*Matik*), Edward Meeks, Philippe Castelli.

Melodrama. Galia, a beautiful and successful window decorator, lives in a penthouse apartment on the Paris Left Bank. Proud of her independence, she drifts from one love affair to another, guided only by the principle of pleasure. One night she rescues a woman from drowning in the Seine and brings her to her apartment. The woman, Nicole, reveals that she attempted suicide because of her opportunistic and unfaithful husband, Greg. Although Galia agrees to recover the suicide note Nicole left her husband, she decides to leave it in its place as a just punishment for such a man. Nicole is curious as to how the note will affect Greg, and Galia begins spying on him, which eventually leads to a meeting. Despite her awareness that he is unscrupulous, Galia cannot prevent herself from falling in love with him, and he takes her on a trip to Venice. She becomes his mistress, despite Nicole's warnings. Greg at last reveals his wife's suicide and explains that she had refused the divorce he desired. Then, one morning, Galia sees Nicole and Greg deep in conversation in a park. Later she confronts Greg, and he admits to having known all the time that his wife was alive. The reason he gives for meeting Nicole was to continue his plea for a divorce, which she refused, and he suggests that the only alternative is to arrange for her death. Shocked, but still unable to reject him, Galia returns to her apartment. She finds that Nicole has left, and sensing disaster, she telephones Greg. Nicole answers and calmly announces that she has killed Greg so that he could not ruin Galia's life as he ruined hers. *Mistresses. Hedonism. Suicide. Infidelity. Divorce. Murder. Paris. Seine River. Documentation.*

Note: Released in France in 1966. Also released as *I, and My Lovers* and *I and My Love.*

THE GALLANT ONE (United States/Peru)   **F6.1740**
Dist Gillman Film Corp. Jul **1964**. Sd; col. 35mm. 65 min.

Prod Aaron Stell, Ron Randell. *Assoc Prod* Bruce Friddle. *Dir-Writ* Aaron Stell. *Photog* J. Carlos Carbajal. *Film Ed* Milton Citron. *Mus* Eduard Ingris. *Sd* Jesús Gonzales. *Asst Dir* Luis Reatequi, Steven Campbell.

Cast: Henry Heller (*Arturo*), Gil Goluskin (*Uncle Felipe*), Laya Raki, Ricardo Bonnemaison, Jorge Montoro, Toby Fox, Fernando Samillan, Jim Parker, Harold E. Wyman, Kenny Miller, Hank Nichols.

Melodrama. Ten-year-old Arturo, a motherless Peruvian boy, moves in with his uncle Felipe when his father is unjustly imprisoned for theft. Arturo has a pet burro, which Felipe sells, using the money to buy drink and food rather than hire a lawyer for Arturo's father. Arturo finds his burro, but it is injured by a rabid puma and is put to death. A reckless truckdriver, the man responsible for his father's false arrest, nearly strikes Arturo. Eventually Arturo obtains evidence that frees his father; and his happiness is complete when the village priest presents him with another burro. *Children. Uncles. Truckdrivers. Injustice. Theft. Family life. Village life. Poverty. Reckless driving. Rabies. Donkeys. Puma.*

Note: Filmed in 1961 in Lima, Peru. National origin unconfirmed.

GALLANT REBEL (Reissue)   **F6.1741**
Paramount Pictures. *Dist* Citation Films, Paramount Pictures. 22 Nov **1961** [Columbus, Ohio, showing]. Sd; col (Technicolor). 35mm. 84 min.

Note: Originally released as *The Vanquished* by Paramount Pictures in 1953; c1 Jun 1953; LP2651.

GALLERY OF HORRORS see **DR. TERROR'S GALLERY OF HORRORS**

GAMBIT   **F6.1742**
Universal Pictures. 21 Dec **1966** [New York opening; c7 Jan 1967; LP34491]. Sd (Westrex); col (Technicolor). 35mm (Techniscope). 108 min.

Prod Leo L. Fuchs. *Dir* Ronald Neame. *Screenplay* Jack Davies, Alvin Sargent. *Story* Sidney Carroll. *Photog* Clifford Stine. *Art Dir* Alexander Golitzen, George C. Webb. *Set Decor* John McCarthy, John Austin. *Titl* Cinefx, Phill Norman. *Film Ed* Alma MacRorie. *Mus Comp & Cond* Maurice Jarre. *Mus Supv* Joseph Gershenson. *Song: "I'm Gonna Spread My Wings"* Maurice Jarre. *Sung by* Shirley MacLaine. *Choreog* Paul Godkin. *Sd* Waldon O. Watson, Melvin M. Metcalfe, Sr. *Asst Dir* Joseph Kenny. *Unit Prod Mgr* Hal Polaire. *Gowns Dsgn* Jean Louis. *Makeup* Bud Westmore. *Hairstyles for Miss MacLaine Created by* Sydney Guilaroff. *Tech Adv* Jivan R. Tabibian. *Dial Coach* Leon Charles.

Cast: Shirley MacLaine (*Nicole*), Michael Caine (*Harry*), Herbert Lom (*Shahbandar*), Roger C. Carmel (*Ram*), Arnold Moss (*Abdul*), John Abbott (*Emile*), Richard Angarola (*Colonel Salim*), Maurice Marsac (*hotel clerk*), Paul Bradley (*man in cafe*).

Crime comedy. While working in a Hong Kong nightclub, a ginger-haired Eurasian woman named Nicole Chang is approached by a cockney thief, Harry Dean, and a French sculptor, Emile Fournier. The two men plan to use her in their scheme to steal a priceless Chinese statuette, the LiSsu, from Middle

Eastern multimillionaire Ahmad Shahbandar since Nicole's appearance is remarkably similar to that of Shahbandar's late wife, whose features resembled those of the statuette. Posing as Sir Harold and Lady Dean, Harry and Nicole travel to Shahbandar's city of Dammuz, where he lives in a hotel penthouse. Although Shahbandar is immediately taken with Nicole, he quickly suspects their true purpose and substitutes a copy for the real statuette. By chance, Harry discovers the hiding place of the real statuette and removes the work, but Nicole is apprehended and told to inform him that unless the LiSsu is returned he will be killed. Harry explains to Nicole that Emile is so accomplished at duplicating art treasures that even art dealers cannot distinguish between his work and an original. After assuring Shahbandar by telegram that the real statuette remains within the penthouse, Harry makes plans to sell a copy made by Emile 2 years earlier, revealing that the "theft" was a hoax designed to facilitate the sale of the fraud. Nicole refuses to stay with Harry, however, unless he gives up his life of crime; and Harry, in a grand display of love, smashes Emile's copy of the statue. As Harry leaves with the delighted Nicole, he glances knowingly at Emile. Once alone, Emile goes to a wall closet and removes three more imitation statues. *Entertainers. Thieves. Sculptors. Art collectors. Millionaires. Eurasians. English. French. Arabs. Theft. Fraud. Hoaxes. Imposture. Hotels. Hong Kong. Middle East. Sculptures.*

THE GAMBLER WORE A GUN   F6.1743
Zenith Pictures. *Dist* United Artists. 29 Mar **1961** [Los Angeles opening]. Sd; b&w. 35mm. 67 min.
Prod Robert E. Kent. *Dir* Edward L. Cahn. *Screenplay* Owen Harris. *Story* L. L. Foreman. *Photog* Floyd Crosby. *Art Dir* Serge Krizman. *Film Ed* Kenneth Crane. *Sd* James Brock. *Asst Dir* Herbert S. Greene. *Prod Mgr* Joseph Small. *Wardrobe* Byron Munson, Sabine Manela. *Makeup* Harry Thomas. *Hairstyles* Frances Sperry.
Cast: Jim Davis (*Case Silverthorn*), Mark Allen (*Dex Harwood*), Addison Richards (*Doc Devlin*), Merry Anders (*Sharon Donovan*), Don Dorrell (*Jud Donovan*), Bob Anderson (*Tray Larkin*), Keith Richards (*Het Larkin*), John Craig (*Rebe Larkin*), Charles Cane (*Kelly Barnum*), Joe McGuinn (*Hastings*), Morgan Shaan (*Thompson*), Boyd "Red" Morgan (*Luke*), Boyd Stockman (*Dave*), Jack Kenny (*bartender*), Eden Hartford (*woman*), Brad Trumbull (*deputy*).
Western melodrama. Honest gambler Case Silverthorn purchases a ranch by mail, only to learn that the seller was lynched before the deed was recorded. Unable to take immediate possession, Case decides to help the dead man's daughter Sharon and son Jud, who have no knowledge of the transaction. While working as a card dealer in the local saloon, he discovers that his ranch is being used by saloon owner Kelly Barnum and his associates, the Larkin brothers, as a storage location for rustled cattle. The rustlers murder young Jud and try to frame Case for the killing, but town marshal Dex Hargood assists Case in trapping the villains and proving his innocence. Case then takes legal possession of the ranch and marries Sharon. *Gamblers. Rustlers. United States marshals. Lynching. Brother-sister relationship. Murder. Frameup. Ranches. Saloons. Documentation. Cattle.*
Note: Remake of a 1954 United Artists release, *The Lone Gun.*

THE GAMBLERS   F6.1744
Sidney Glazier Productions. *Dist* U-M Film Distributors. 17 Apr **1970** [Nashville, Tennessee, opening]. Sd; col (Eastmancolor). 35mm. 93 min. MPAA rating G.
Prod William A. Berns. *Exec Prod* Sidney Glazier. *Dir-Writ* Ron Winston. *Camera* Tomislav Pinter. *Art Dir* Veljko Despotović. *Film Ed* Richard Bracken. *Mus Comp & Cond* John Morris. *Prod Mgr* Stevo Petrovic.
Cast: Suzy Kendall (*Candace*), Don Gordon (*Rooney*), Pierre Olaf (*Cozzier*), Kenneth Griffith (*Broadfoot*), Stuart Margolin (*Goldy*), Richard Woo (*Koboyashi*), Massimo Serato (*Del Isolla*), Faith Domergue (*Signora Del Isolla*), Relja Bašić (*Yakov*), Anthony Chinn (*Nono*).
Comedy-drama. Source: Nikolay Vasilyevich Gogol, "Igroki," in *Sochineniya Nikolaya Gogolya; Tom Chetvyortyy* (1842). During a cruise from Trieste to Dubrovnik, professional cardsharp Rooney and his accomplice Goldy fleece a pair of professional gamblers, Broadfoot and Cozzier. The four gamblers then agree to join forces to swindle a wealthy victim in Dubrovnik, using Candace, a beautiful fellow passenger, as bait. A phony water skiing accident in Dubrovnik enables Rooney to meet their victim, the Italian aristocrat Del Isolla. Rooney and Candace begin a romantic relationship, but Rooney refuses to become too involved for fear of being distracted from the pending swindle. The entire party is invited to the Del Isolla villa where a fight is arranged between Koboyashi, Rooney's Japanese valet, and Nono, the Del Isolla houseboy, in order to warm up Del Isolla's gaming spirits; this is followed by an all-night poker game in which Del Isolla loses heavily. Del Isolla offers Rooney his IOU which Rooney intends to convert to cash in Geneva before joining his new accomplices for another swindle in Warsaw. As security, Rooney gives Broadfoot and Cozzier $50,000 in cash. At the airport, however,

Rooney meets Del Isolla and his wife and learns that they are really actors hired by Broadfoot and Cozzier in an elaborate plot to cheat him. Undaunted, Rooney finds Candace at the airport, tells her what has happened, and convinces her to stay with him. The two return to Dubrovnik empty-handed but happy. *Gamblers. Cardsharps. Swindlers. Valets. Houseboys. Actors. Aristocrats. Italians. Japanese. Fraud. Finance—Personal. Poker. Karate. Dubrovnik.*

GAMBLER'S CODE (Japan)   F6.1745
14 Dec **1966** [Los Angeles opening]. Sd; b&w. 35mm. [Feature film, length unknown.]
Cast: Hideki Takahashi, Kazuko Izumi.
Crime melodrama. No information about the precise nature of this film has been found. *Gamblers.*

THE GAMBLING SAMURAI (Japan)   F6.1746
Toho Co. 27 Sep **1966** [New York opening]. Sd; col (AgfaColor). 35mm (Tohoscope). 101 min.
Dir Senkichi Taniguchi. *Screenplay* Kaneto Shindo. *Photog* Rokuro Nishigaki.
Cast: Toshiro Mifune (*Chuji*), Michiyo Aratama, Kumi Mizuno, Daisuke Kato, Yosuke Natsuki, Kankuro Nakamura.
Action melodrama. Chuji, a gambling samurai, returns to his village after a 2-year absence to find his people living under government oppression and suffering from a year of bad crops. He is particularly angered when he hears that his sister has gone insane as a result of an assault by a magistrate; the girl eventually commits suicide and her fiancé is killed by officials. Unable to gain revenge directly, Chuji breaks into the government warehouse and distributes rice to the needy farmers. He continues to rob from the rich and give to the poor, and he and his followers hide in the forests of Mount Akagi when the government pursues him. After 3 years of scheming and waiting for the right time, he gains revenge for the deaths of his sister and her fiancé. He leaves the village, promising those who love him to return some day. *Samurai. Gamblers. Farmers. Famine. Suicide. Insanity. Murder. Revenge. Brother-sister relationship. Theft. Government—Local.*
Note: Released in Japan in 1960 as *Kunisada Chuji.*

A GAME FOR SIX LOVERS (France)   F6.1747
Films de la Pléiade. *Dist* Falcon Productions. ca2 Sep **1962** [Hartford, Connecticut, opening]. Sd; b&w. 35mm. 86 min.
Prod Dir Pierre Braunberger. *Dir-Screenplay* Jacques Doniol-Valcroze. *Photog* Roger Fellous. *Camera* Georges Pastier. *Asst Photog* Claude Zidi. *Film Ed* C. Negri, Nadine Marquand. *Mus* Serge Gainsbourg. *Sd* Michel Fano. *Asst Dir* Jean-José Richer, Luc Andrieux. *Prod Mgr* Marcel Mossoti. *Script Girl* Francine Vainer. *Makeup* Christiane Sauvage. *Administrator* Roger Fleytoux. *Still Photog* Hélène Janbrau.
Cast: Bernadette Lafont (*Prudence*), Françoise Brion (*Miléna*), Alexandra Stewart (*Fifine*), Michel Galabru (*César*), Jacques Riberolles (*Robert*), Gérard Barray (*Miguel*), Paul Guers (*Jean-Paul*), Florence Loinod (*Florence*).
Comedy-drama. Miléna, who has lived alone with her grandmother in an isolated baroque French château near the Pyrenees, becomes one of the heirs of the estate upon her grandmother's death. Her cousins Jean-Paul and Fifine, whom she has never met because of a family quarrel, are also named as heirs. The young family lawyer, Miguel, summons the brother and sister for the reading of the will, but Jean-Paul is delayed, and Fifine arrives alone. Jean-Paul's friend Robert, with whom Fifine lives, unexpectedly arrives soon afterwards, and Miléna mistakes him for her cousin. They are greatly attracted to each other, and Robert continues to assume the role of Jean-Paul in order to remain at the château. At the same time, Fifine and Miguel are drawn to each other, as are César, the butler of the château, and Prudence, the seductive new maid. The six pair off and spend the night making love. In the morning, Robert reveals his true identity, and Milena forgives him. Fifine discovers that Miguel is a philanderer and becomes hysterical, but Jean-Paul arrives in time to comfort her. *Cousins. Butlers. Housemaids. Lawyers. Heirs. Philanderers. Impersonation. Castles. Pyrenees.*
Note: Opened in Paris in Jan 1960 as *L'eau à la bouche.* May also be known as *Games for Six Lovers.*

THE GAME IS OVER (France/Italy)   F6.1748
Cocinor–Les Films Marceau–Mega Film. *Dist* Royal Films International. 9 Jan **1967** [New York opening]. Sd; col (Technicolor). 35mm (Panavision). 98 min. [Also 96 min.]
Prod-Dir Roger Vadim. *Screenplay* Jean Cau, Roger Vadim, Bernard Frechtman. *Photog* Claude Renoir. *Art Dir* Jean André. *Film Ed* Victoria Mercanton. *Mus* Jean-Pierre Bourtayre, Jean Bouchety. *Mus Adv* Jean E. Fernandez. *Vina Played by* Nageswara Rao. *Dance Mus Played by* Arthur Brown and His Orchestra. *Sd* Antoine Petitjean. *Asst Dir* Jean-Michel Lacor, Francis Girod. *Prod Mgr* Georges Valon. *Cost* Tanine Autre.

Cast: Jane Fonda *(Renée Saccard)*, Peter McEnery *(Maxime Saccard)*, Michel Piccoli *(Alexandre Saccard)*, Tina Marquand *(Anne Sernet)*, Jacques Monod *(Monsieur Sernet)*, Simone Valérie *(Madame Sernet)*, Ham Chau Luong *(Mr. Chou)*, Howard Vernon *(lawyer)*, Douglas Read *(maître d'hotel)*, Germaine Montero *(guest)*.

Drama. Source: Emile Zola, *La curée* (Paris, 1871). Following a scandal in France, industrial promoter Alexandre Saccard fled to Canada and married wealthy young Renée, who was then pregnant after an unhappy affair. Her child, however, was stillborn, and the love—if ever there was any—between the young woman and the older man soon faded. Now living in Paris, Alexandre closes his eyes to his wife's interest in other men until Maxime, his son by a former marriage, comes to live with them after completing his studies in England. Renée's interest in Maxime quickly leads to intimacy, then passion, and finally to love. Not content to be Maxime's mistress, she asks Alexandre for a divorce. Alexandre agrees, on the condition that she relinquish the fortune she brought to their marriage. Blindly in love, Renée consents to his terms and goes to Switzerland for a divorce. But while she is away, the cunning Alexandre confronts his son with two alternatives: he can either run off with the now penniless Renée or become engaged to Anne Sernet, the daughter of a banker whose friendship Alexandre wishes to cultivate. The weak-willed Maxime succumbs to his father's wishes, and Renée returns from Geneva on the night Alexandre is giving a ball to celebrate his son's engagement. As her world collapses around her, Renée contemplates suicide and throws herself into a pool. But she changes her mind and enters the ballroom dripping wet. His revenge complete, Alexandre escorts her to the gymnasium, where she sits and stares into an empty future. *Entrepreneurs. Mistresses. Marriage. Divorce. Wealth. Filial relations. Infidelity. Marriage—Arranged. Suicide. Revenge. Balls (formal gatherings). Canada. Paris. Geneva.*

Note: Opened in Paris in Jun 1966 as *La curée*; running time: 100 min.

THE GAME IS SEX   F6.1749
Cinestudio Productions–William Mishkin. *Dist* William Mishkin. Aug **1969**. Sd; b&w. 35mm. 85 min. *MPAA rating* X.

Prod-Dir Harry Wuest. *Photog* Harry Wuest. *Art Dir* Gary Martin. *Mus Ed* George Craig.

Cast: Irene Rosetti *(Irene)*, Susana March *(Nancy)*, Michael Canavan *(Andre)*, Alan Wylie *(Max)*, Joanna Morris *(Joan)*, Ken Jard *(Martin)*, Jaquelin Diann, Margaret Harel, Beverly Kolber, Andre Lessere, H. Sohl, Sasha Stevens.

Melodrama. Andre and Irene attempt to recapture the sexual excitement that has faded from their relationship by inventing erotic games. When the game of seduction proves too weak a stimulus to their jaded desire, they turn to a more violent form of make-believe. Gagged and handcuffed to the bed, Irene enjoys the beating she receives, but her pleasure turns to terror as Andre cuts away her clothing with a razor. The lovers part company, and Andre takes up with Nancy, an eager, voluptuous innocent. Soon Irene returns to become a third member of the household and is quickly seduced by Andre after visiting a group sex party. Aroused by the sound of their lovemaking, Nancy joins them in bed. The sexual threesome becomes the focus of her existence, while her partners regard the relationship as a game. Irene suggests a new version of the game of violence, which ends in tragedy. *Seduction. Eroticism. Sadomasochism. Innocents. Troilism. Group sex.*

Note: Also known as *The Game of Sex* and *The Game Is Set*. May also be the same as *The Name of the Game Is Sex*.

A GAME OF THREES   F6.1750
Dist I. R. M. I. Films. 8 Oct **1969** [New York showing]. Sd; b&w. [Feature film, length unknown.]

Dir Helmud Schuyler.

Cast: Astrid Stellar, Petya Iverson, Kristina Nylund.

Sex film. No information about the precise nature of this film has been found, but press material suggests that it contains scenes of lesbianism, oral intercourse, and rape. *Rape. Lesbianism. Oral sex.*

THE GAME PEOPLE PLAY   F6.1751
Associates Productions. *Dist* Chancellor Films. Sep **1967**. Sd; b&w. 35mm. 70 min.

Prod-Dir S. N. Johnsen. *Writ* Eugene Price. *Cinematog* Harry August. *Film Ed* A. C. Qumar. *Asst Dir* Philip Dross. *Cont* Dossie. *Stills* Bob Jardine.

Cast: Mitch McGuire, Anne Lind, Steven Harrison, Cherie Walters, Jeremy Jones, Eileen Scott, Sean Martin, Moda Bergman.

Drama. Four men play poker one night a week despite their wives' objections. The women decide to sit in on a game, and there is an orgy when one of the men suggests they play strip poker. *Marriage. Nudity. Poker. Orgies.*

Note: Also known as *Sex Is the Game People Play* and *Sex Is Games, People Play*.

GAMES   F6.1752
Universal Pictures. 17 Sep **1967** [New York opening; c4 Nov 1967; LP37793]. Sd (Westrex); col (Technicolor). 35mm (Techniscope). 100 min.

Prod George Edwards. *Assoc Prod* John Wallace Hyde. *Dir* Curtis Harrington. *Screenplay* Gene Kearney. *Story* Curtis Harrington, George Edwards. *Dir Photog* William A. Fraker. *Art Dir* Alexander Golitzen, William D. DeCinces. *Set Decor* John McCarthy, James S. Redd. *Titl Dsgn & Execution* Norbert Jobst, Pacific Title. *Film Ed* Douglas Stewart. *Mus* Samuel Matlovsky. *Mus Supv* Joseph Gershenson. *Sd* Waldon O. Watson, Robert R. Bertrand. *Asst Dir* Hal Polaire. *Unit Prod Mgr* Hal Polaire. *Makeup* Bud Westmore. *Hairstyles* Larry Germain. *Vis Cons* Morton Haack.

Cast: Simone Signoret *(Lisa Schindler)*, James Caan *(Paul Montgomery)*, Katharine Ross *(Jennifer Montgomery)*, Don Stroud *(Norman Fields)*, Kent Smith *(Harry)*, Estelle Winwood *(Miss Lillian Beattie)*, Marjorie Bennett *(Nora)*, Ian Wolfe *(Dr. Edwards)*, Antony Eustrel *(Winthrop)*, Eloise Hardt *(Celia)*, George Furth *(Terry)*, Carmen Phillips *(Holly)*, Peter Brocco *(Count)*, Florence Marly *(Baroness)*, Carl Guttenberger *(Arthur)*, Pitt Herbert *(pharmacist)*, Stuart Nisbet *(detective)*, Kendrick Huxham *(bookseller)*, Richard Guizon *(masseur)*, William O'Connell, Ena Hartman, Joanne Medley, Jeff Scott, Eddra Gale, Rachel Rosenthal, Luana Anders, Robert Aiken, Max Lewin.

Mystery drama. Manhattan socialites Paul and Jennifer Montgomery amass a vast art collection and devise novel games. In these pursuits the couple is joined by Lisa Schindler, an aging cosmetics saleswoman and amateur medium. Among the amusements contrived by Lisa is Jennifer's seduction of adolescent delivery boy Norman Fields. Surprising the pair, Paul shoots Norman. Afterwards he encases the body in plaster, adapting the corpse as an art object. When Lisa departs and Paul goes on a business trip, Jennifer is alone with the sculpture. To her horror Norman reappears and pursues her. Terrified, she shoots and kills him. Informing his distraught wife that the first murder was a hoax, Paul commits Jennifer to a mental institution. After selling the couple's art collection the socialite is joined by his accomplice Lisa, who proposes a toast to the success of their scheme. Quickly quaffing the drink, Paul falls dead at Lisa's feet. *Socialites. Art collectors. Mediums. Saleswomen. Delivery boys. Murder. Poisoning. Perfidy. Insanity. Games. Sculptures. New York City.*

THE GAMES (Great Britain)   F6.1753
Twentieth Century–Fox Film Corp. 21 Apr **1970** [Costa Mesa, California, opening; c31 Dec 1969; LP37951]. Sd (Westrex); col (De Luxe). 35mm (Panavision). 97 min. *MPAA rating* G.

A Michael Winner–Lester Linsk Production. *Prod* Lester Linsk. *Dir* Michael Winner. *Screenplay* Erich Segal. *Dir Photog* Robert Paynter. *Camera Op* Tony Troke. *Art Dir* Albert Witherick, Fred Carter, Roy Stannard. *Film Ed* Bernard Gribble. *Mus* Francis Lai. *Mus Arr* Christian Gaubert. *Dub Ed* Terry Rawlings. *Sd Rec* Brian Marshall, Hugh Strain. *Dial Ed* Russ Hill. *Asst Dir* Michael Dryhurst, Francesco Cinieri, Malcolm Stamp. *Prod Mgr* Clifton Brandon, Mario Mariani. *English Location Mgr* Michael Guest. *Location Mgr* Timothy Pitt Miller. *Cont* Pamela Carlton. *Wardrobe* Ron Beck. *Makeup* Richard Mills. *Hairdresser* Stephanie Kaye. *Tech Adv* Gordon Pirie. *Coöp* Comitato Olimpico Nazionale Italiano. *Constr Mgr* Harry Arbour.

Cast: Michael Crawford *(Harry Hayes)*, Stanley Baker *(Bill Oliver)*, Ryan O'Neal *(Scott Reynolds)*, Charles Aznavour *(Pavel Vendek)*, Jeremy Kemp *(Jim Harcourt)*, Elaine Taylor *(Christine)*, Athol Compton *(Sunny Pintubi)*, Fritz Wepper *(Kovanda)*, Kent Smith *(Kaverley)*, Sam Elliott *(Richie Robinson)*, Reg Lye *(Charlie Gilmour)*, Mona Washbourne *(Mrs. Hayes)*, Don Newsome *(Cal Wood)*, Emmy Werner *(Vera Vendek)*, Harvey Hall *(Stuart Simmonds)*, June Jago *(Mae Harcourt)*, Karel Stepanek *(Kubitsek)*, Gwendolyn Watts *(barmaid)*, John Alkin *(John)*, Rafer Johnson, Ron Pickering, Adrian Metcalfe *(commentators)*, Alexander Werner *(Juri Vendek)*, Dale Ishimoto *(Dr. Tselsura)*, Bob Cunningham *(Fred Gardner)*, Colin Jeavons *(earnest man)*, Paddy Webster *(Jocelyn)*, Tina Carter *(Miss Gibb)*, Stephanie Beacham *(Angela Simmonds)*, Basil Dignam *(Weston)*, Hugh McDermott, Warren Stanhope, Leigh Taylor-Young.

Drama. Source: Hugh Atkinson, *The Games* (London, 1967). Four long distance runners train in different parts of the world for the Olympics in Rome; all are planning to run in the gruelling 26-mile marathon. In England, milkman Harry Hayes trains under his ruthless coach, Bill Oliver, who forces Harry to give up his girl friend Christine. Yale University student Scott Reynolds uses stimulants during a race in Japan despite his heart ailment. Sunny Pintubi, an Australian aborigine under the tutelage of Charlie Gilmour, an unscrupulous promoter and gambler who wagers heavily on Sunny's races, is entered in the Olympics over the protests of the racially prejudiced Australian Olympics Committee. The Czechoslovakian champion, Col. Pavel Vendek, enters the race at the request of his government despite the fact that he is 41 years old. The big race finally takes place, but in extremely hot weather. Reynolds is overcome by the heat and stimulants and runs into a wall; Harry, fiercely driven by Oliver, collapses in exhaustion long before the finish; and Pintubi manages to beat Vendek, the sentimental favorite, and win the gold medal. *Athletes. Milkmen. Athletic coaches. Students. Gamblers. Track. Racial prejudice. Heart disease. Amphetamines. Czechoslovakia. Australia. Japan. Rome. Olympic Games.*

Note: Location scenes filmed in England, Italy, Austria, Czechoslovakia, Australia, and Japan. Opened in London in Jul 1970.

GAMES AND VARIATIONS *see* **SUGAR DADDY**

GAMES FOR SIX LOVERS *see* **A GAME FOR SIX LOVERS**

THE GAMES MEN PLAY (Argentina)   F6.1754
Tinayre-Borrás S.R.L. *Dist* Joseph Brenner Associates, Day and Day Films. 11 Jan **1968** [New Orleans opening]. Sd; b&w. 35mm. 92 min.

Prod Eduardo Borrás. *Exec Prod?* Adolfo Cabrera. *Dir* Daniel Tinayre. *Adapt* Eduardo Borrás. *Photog* Alberto Etchebehere. *Art Dir* Gori Muñoz. *Film Ed* Jorge Garate. *Mus* Lucio Milena. *English titl* Zavala Riss.

Cast: Maria Antinea *(The Wife)*, Amelia Bence *(The Prostitute)*, Elsa Daniel *(The Bride)*, Mirtha Legrand *(secretary)*, Malvina Pastorino *(teacher)*, José Cibrian *(industrialist)*, Narciso Ibañez Menta *(ventriloquist)*, Angel Magaña *(journalist)*, Luis Sandrini *(taxi driver)*, Enrique Serrano *(musician)*, Teresa Blasco *(maid)*, Guillermo Bredeston *(bridegroom)*, Diana Ingro *(model)*, Miryan de Urquijo *(lady)*, Leda Zanda *(nurse)*, Guillermo Battaglia *(doctor)*, Hector Calcano *(police commissioner)*, Homero Carpena *(manager)*, Ludio de Val *(police sergeant)*, Hector Mendez *(police inspector)*.

Comedy-drama. Source: Dante Sierra, *La Cigarra no es un bicho* (Buenos Aires, 1957). Patronizing the small, out-of-the-way hotel La Cigarra, a convenient setting for illicit sexual adventures, are six couples in search of seclusion: a middle-aged taxi driver and his wife, who seek the intimacy they are denied at home with a large family and a mother-in-law sharing the household; an industrial executive accompanied by a petulant model; a ruthless newspaper columnist and his glacial secretary-mistress; a schoolteacher and her whimsical ventriloquist boyfriend; an aging musician and his maid; and two students very much in love. The plans of the guests are disrupted when a sailor brought to the hotel by a local prostitute becomes ill with bubonic fever. As a result, all guests at the hotel are quarantined, to the amusement of the townspeople, and their predicament becomes public knowledge. As a result of their confinement, the columnist and the secretary find that their affair loses its excitement without the threat posed by his wife; the executive and the model discover that they loathe each other; the schoolteacher splits up with the ventriloquist but looks forward to an improved relationship with her students, who have been cheering her from outside the hotel; the student couple renounce the opportunity for illicit lovemaking and decide to marry; and the married couple, enjoying what is essentially their first honeymoon, rekindle their love. Only the prostitute remains unchanged, bestowing her favors on the cooks during the incarceration. The sailor is finally declared healthy and the guests leave La Cigarra, but the prostitute quickly engages a new customer and returns with him to the hotel. *Prostitutes. Industrialists. Models. Newspapermen. Secretaries. Schoolteachers. Sailors. Taxi drivers. Students. Musicians. Ventriloquism. Mistresses. Chambermaids. Infidelity. Marriage. Honeymoons. Hotels. Bubonic fever.*

Note: Released in Argentina in 1963 as *La Cigarra no es un bicho*; running time: 107 min. Spanish language version shown in the United States in 1964. English version includes additional nude footage. Also reviewed under the title translation *The Cicada Is Not an Insect*; may also be known as *The Hotel.*

GAMES OF DESIRE (France/West Germany)   F6.1755
Olympia-Film-Hans Albin-Film-C. E. C. *Dist* Victoria Films, Times Film Corp. Dec **1967** [c1 Jan 1966; LP36134]. Sd; b&w. 35mm. 90 min.

Prod Hans Albin. *Dir* Hans Albin, Peter Berneis. *Screenplay* Peter Berneis. *Camera* Klaus von Raùtenfeld. *2d Unit Photog* Hans Sachs. *Stage Set* Tibor Rednas, Max Mellin. *Film Ed* Claus von Boro. *Mus* Hermann Thieme. *Asst Dir* Madelon Truss, Pierre Léaud. *Prod Mgr* Alfred Rauschenbach.

Cast: Ingrid Thulin *(Nadine Anderson)*, Paul Hubschmid *(Eliot Anderson)*, Claudine Auger *(Elektra Tzanou)*, Nikos Kourkoulos *(Nikos Tzanou)*, Gregor von Rezzori *(Harry Dobkin)*, Bernard Verley *(Martin Troge)*, Helen Vita *(Mary Hutton)*, Helga Lerner *(Katina)*, Spyros Bakojannis, Inge Book, Eric Helgar, Cecilie Gelers.

Melodrama. Nadine Anderson, wife of Eliot Anderson, wealthy Swedish ambassador to Greece, is sexually unfulfilled because of her husband's preference for his male secretary, Martin. During the day Nadine lives as a society hostess, but at night she rents a room in the harbor area of Athens, to engage in prostitution. There she falls in love with Nikos, a dock worker, whose sister, Elektra, a stripteaser and prostitute, discovers their relationship and Nadine's identity. Elektra blackmails Nadine into hiring her as a personal maid at a high salary and during a yachting trip falls in love with Martin. Eliot becomes jealous and fires Elektra, who informs him of his wife's extra-marital

activities. Eliot agrees to allow Nadine to leave with Nikos, but Elektra exposes Nadine's true status to her brother. Enraged, Nikos hits his sister, and she accidentally falls to her death, thus destroying any chance that Nadine and Nikos will be reunited. *Secretaries. Prostitutes. Stevedores. Socialites. Domestics. Blackmail. Infidelity. Male homosexuality. Brother-sister relationship. Marriage. Waterfronts. Yachts. Sweden. Sweden—Diplomatic and consular service. Athens.*

Note: Filmed on location in Greece. Released in West Germany in Oct 1964 as *Die Lady.*

GAMETSUI YATSU *see* **THIS GREEDY OLD SKIN**

GAMLET *see* **HAMLET**

GAMMERA THE INVINCIBLE (Japan)   F6.1756
Daiei Motion Picture Co. *Dist* World Entertainment Corp. 15 Dec **1966** [New Orleans opening]. Sd; b&w. 35mm (Totalscope). 86 min.

Pres by Harris Associates. *Prod* Masaichi Nagata. *Exec Prod* Ken Barnett. *Assoc Prod* Robert Baron. *Dir* Noriaki Yuasa. *U. S. Dir* Sandy Howard. *Screenplay* Fumi Takahashi. *Adtl Dial* Richard Kraft. *From an Idea by* Yonejiro Saito. *Cinematog* Nobuo Munekawa, Julian Townsend. *U. S. Art Dir* Hank Aldrich. *Film Ed* Tatsuji Nakashizu, Ross–Gaffney Inc. *Titl Song* Wes Farrell. *Sung by* The Moons. *Asst Dir* Sid Cooperschmidt. *Sp Eff* Yonesaburo Tsukiji.

Cast: Albert Dekker *(secretary of defense)*, Brian Donlevy *(Gen. Terry Arnold)*, Diane Findlay *(WAF A/1C Susan Embers)*, John Baragrey *(Miles Standish)*, Dick O'Neill *(General O'Neill)*, Eiji Funakoshi *(Dr. Hidaka)*, Michiko Sugata *(Nobuyo)*, Harumi Kiritachi *(Kyoko)*, Jun-ichiro Yamashita *(Aoyagi)*, Yoshiro Uchida *(Toshio)*, Yoshiro Kitahara *(Sakurai)*, Jun Hamamura *(Dr. Murase)*, Mort Marshall *(Jules Manning)*, Alan Oppenheimer *(Dr. Contrare)*, Stephen Zacharias *(Senator Billings)*, Thomas J. Stubblefield *(Captain Lovel)*, Bob Carraway *(Lieutenant Simpson)*, Gene Bua *(Lieutenant Clark)*, John McCurry *(Airman First Class Hopkins)*, Walter Arnold *(American ambassador)*, Louis Zorich *(Russian ambassador)*, Robin Craven *(English ambassador)*, George Hirose *(Japanese ambassador)*.

Science fiction melodrama. An atomic bomb explodes over the Arctic, angering Gammera, a huge, fire-eating, flying turtle aroused from its prehistoric sleep. As Gammera ravages entire cities, U. S. Air Force Gen. Terry Arnold, under orders from the Secretary of Defense and the President of the United States, consults with two Japanese scientists, Drs. Hidaka and Murase, but he is informed that the monster is indestructible by modern weaponry. U. S. Senator Billings opposes Arnold's request for emergency powers, and the controversy spreads to the United Nations Security Council. General Arnold, after receiving world cooperation, utilizes Plan Z, presented by Japanese scientists, as mankind's last hope. Gammera is distracted from its destruction of Tokyo by a volcanic eruption on the nearby island of Oshima and lands in the scientists' trap. They imprison the monster in a space rocket and shoot it to Mars. *Monsters. Presidents of the United States. Scientists. Nuclear weapons. Volcanoes. Rockets. Arctic regions. Oshima. Tokyo. Mars (planet). United States Air Force. United States—Defense Department. United States Congress. United Nations. Explosions.*

Note: Released in Japan in 1965 as *Daikaiju Gamera*; running time: 88 min. Additional footage includes scenes of a U. S. Army base in Alaska, the Pentagon, and the United Nations filmed by Harris Associates for inclusion in the U. S. release version.

GANG BANG   F6.1757
Sep **1970** [Los Angeles showing]. Sd; col. 35mm? [Feature length assumed.]

Sex film. No information about the precise nature of this film has been found, but press material suggests that it involves group sex among male homosexuals. *Male homosexuality. Group sex.*

THE GANGSTER VIP (Japan)   F6.1758
Nikkatsu Corp. *Dist* Toho Co. May **1968** [Los Angeles showing]. Sd; col (Fuji Color). 35mm (Nikkatsu Scope). 94 min.

Dir Toshio Masuda. *Screenplay* Kaneo Ikegami, Reiji Kubota. *Story* Goro Fujita. *Photog* Kurataro Takamura. *Art Dir* Takeo Kimura. *Mus* Naozumi Yamamoto.

Cast: Tetsuya Watari *(Goro Fujikawa)*, Chieko Matsubara *(Yukiko Hashimoto)*, Mitsuo Hamada *(Takeo Tsujikawa)*, Tamio Kawaji *(Isamu Tsujikawa)*, Kyosuke Machida *(Katsuhiko Sugiyama)*, Kayo Matsuo *(Yumeko)*.

Crime melodrama. Goro grows up in a slum where his widowed mother works as a prostitute and his sister dies of malnutrition. Unable to enter school, he turns to petty crime but is caught and sent to jail, where he learns more effective criminal methods. Out of prison, he joins a small gang and is nearly killed by a rival group, only to be nursed back to health by his girl friend, who becomes a prostitute to pay for his medical expenses. Once healthy, he joins a larger gang, marries another woman, and has a son. His family becomes more important to him, and he decides to go straight. A fellow gangster is killed, and tradition dictates that Goro attend the funeral. Despite the suspicion over his leaving the gang that marks him as a target for other gangsters, Goro goes to the funeral, taking along a gun to protect himself. He is arrested and convicted for carrying a concealed weapon, and from his prison cell, he renews his determination that neither he nor his son will ever be involved in crime. *Gangsters. Prostitutes. Urban life. Poverty. Family life. Gangs. Slums. Prisons. Funerals.*

Note: Released in Japan in Jan 1968 as *Daikanbu.*

GANGSTER'S REVENGE (Reissue)   **F6.1759**
    Albex Films. *Dist* Beckman Film Corp. **1964.** Sd; b&w. 35mm. 65 min.
    Note: Originally released by Sterling World Distributors in 1960 as *Get Outta Town.*

DIE GANS VON SEDAN (France/West Germany)   **F6.1760**
    UFA–C. A. P. A. C. *Dist* Casino Films. 16 Nov **1962** [Chicago opening]. Sd; col (Eastmancolor). 35mm. 90 min.
    German Exec Prod Walter Ulbrich. *French Exec Prod* Paul Claudon. *Dir* Helmut Käutner. *Adapt & Dial* Jean L'Hote, Helmut Käutner. *Photog* Jacques Letellier. *Art Dir* Serge Pimenoff, Jacques Brizzio. *Film Ed* Klaus Dudenhöfer. *Mus* Bernhard Eichhorn. *Sd* Guy Rophé. *Prod Mgr* Arnold Misrach.
    Cast: Hardy Krüger *(Fritz),* Jean Richard *(Léon),* Dany Carrel *(Marguerite),* Françoise Rosay *(grandmother),* Theo Lingen *(colonel),* Lucien Nat *(captain),* Jean Verner, Emile Genevois, Robert Rollis, Fritz Tillmann, Ralf Wolter, Willy Rösner, Georg Gütlich.
    War comedy. Source: Jean L'Hote, *Un dimanche au champ d'honneur* (Paris, 1958). During the Franco-Prussian War, French soldier Léon and Prussian combatant Fritz accidentally exchange uniforms while dressing after a swim. The two later present themselves at the farm of an Alsacian peasant and her coquettish granddaughter Marguerite. Despite rivalry aroused by Marguerite, the soldiers become fast friends. When a Prussian regiment arrives they part company, after enjoying a final dip and again exchanging uniforms. *Soldiers. Flirts. Grandmothers. Prussians. Friendship. Swimming. Franco-German War 1870–71. Alsace.*
    Note: Opened in Berlin in Dec 1959; in Paris in May 1960 as *Sans tambour ni trompette.*

DIE GÄNSEMAGD *see* **THE GOOSE GIRL**

THE GAP *see* **JOE**

GARAKUTA *see* **THE RABBLE**

THE GARBAGE MAN   **F6.1761**
    Cinema Distributors of America. May **1963.** Sd; b&w with col seq (Eastman Color). 35mm. 86 min.
    Prod Robert Steuer. *Exec Prod* M. A. Ripps. *Dir-Writ* Eric Sayers.
    Cast: Toney Naylor *(garbage man),* Venita Beautrice *(dream girl),* Joseph Lincoln, "Miss" Baby Bailey.
    Comedy. A self-admitted "little man" maintains a meager existence by operating a small garbage cart drawn by a talking horse, who makes pointed comments about his master's continual harassment by the mechanized sanitation service. Later, the garbage man's dream of being surrounded by voluptuous females is realized when he meets a woman capable of helping him beat the "system" thrust upon him by the Machine Age. *Trash collectors. Wish fulfillment. Horses.*
    Note: May also be known as *The Garbage Man Cometh.*

LES GARÇONS *see* **LA NOTTE BRAVA**

THE GARNET BRACELET (U.S.S.R.)   **F6.1762**
    Mosfilm. *Dist* Artkino Pictures. 27 May **1966** [New York opening]. Sd; col (Magicolor). 35mm. 90 min.
    Dir Abram Room. *Screenplay* A. Granberg, Abram Room. *Photog* Leonid Kraynenkov. *Art Dir* O. Alikin, A. Freydin, I. Shreter. *Mus: Largo Appassionata From Sonata op. 2, no. 2* Ludwig van Beethoven. *Sd* O. Upeynik. *Asst Dir* N. Arkhangelskiy, Ye. Zilbershteyn.
    Cast: Ariadna Shengelaya *(Vera Nikolayevna),* Igor Ozerov *(Zheltkov),* O. Basilashvili *(Vasiliy Lvovich),* Vladislav Strzhelchik *(Nikolay Nikolayevich),* N. Malyavina *(Anna Nikolayevna),* Yuriy Averin *(Von Friesse),* Olga Zhizneva *(Madame Zarzhitskaya),* Leonid Gallis *(Anosov),* Zh. Terteryan *(Zhenni Reyter),* G. Gay *(A. I. Kuprin),* Stanislav Neygauz *(pianist),* David Ashkinazi *(violinist),* Pavel Massalskiy, T. Loginova, V. Rautbart, S. Karnovich-Valua, N. Latinskiy, P. Shpringfeld, Z. Chekulayeva, V. Kulik, O. Lapiado, S. Afanasyev, A. Barushnoy.
    Drama. Source: Aleksandr Ivanovich Kuprin, "Granatovyy braslet," in *Zemlya* (no. 6, 1911). In the Crimea at the turn of the century, Zheltkov, a poor clerk, falls hopelessly in love with the elegant and beautiful Princess Vera. He follows her everywhere—to concerts, to museums, and walking on the street—

and writes her letters of the most respectful devotion. Although Vera knows intuitively that these are the expressions of a true, deep feeling, she cannot regard seriously the love of a man of such a low social position. Then, on her birthday, he sends her a bracelet of garnets set in gold, which belonged to his mother and is his only possession of value. When the news of the gift leaks out to Vera's family and friends, the incident is treated with snobbish scorn. Every means is used to make the clerk feel that he has behaved in an insolent manner, and filled with remorse, he commits suicide. Upon hearing of his death, Vera ignores convention and visits his home. *Clerks. Royalty. Class conflict. Snobbery. Suicide. Jewels. Birthdays. Crimea. Documentation.*
    Note: Released in the U.S.S.R. in 1965 as *Granatovyy braslet.*

GARU THE MAD MONK *see* **GURU THE MAD MONK**

GAS-S-S-S ... OR IT MAY BECOME NECESSARY TO DESTROY THE WORLD IN ORDER TO SAVE IT!   **F6.1763**
    San Jacinto. *For* American International Pictures. *Dist* American International Pictures. Sep **1970.** Sd; col (Movielab). 35mm. 79 min. *MPAA rating* GP.
    Prod-Dir Roger Corman. *Assoc Prod-Screenplay* George Armitage. *Prod Exec* Stephanie Rothman, Charles S. Swartz. *Dir Photog* Ron Dexter. *Art Dir* David Nichols. *Set Decor* Stephen Graham. *Titl Anim* Murakami-Wolf. *Film Ed* George Van Noy. *Mus* Country Joe & the Fish. *Adtl Mus* Barry Melton. *Songs:* "I'm Looking for a World," "Please Don't Bury My Soul," "Maybe It Really Wasn't Love," "Don't Chase Me Around," "Got To Get Movin'," "This Is the Beginning" Barry Melton. *Sung by* Robert Corff. *Songs:* "Cry a Little," "Gas Man" Greg Dewey, Mark Kapner, Barry Melton, Doug Metzner. *Sung by* Johnny & the Tornados. *Songs:* "First Time, Last Time," "Today Is Where" Toni Brown. *Sung by* The Gourmet's Delight. *Songs:* "The Pueblo Pool," "Bubble Gum Girl" Barry Melton. *Sung by* Johnny & the Tornados. *Song:* "Juke Box Serenade" Greg Dewey, Mark Kapner, Barry Melton, Doug Metzner, Olsen. *Sung by* Johnny & the Tornados. *Song:* "Castles" Toni Brown, Terry Garthwaite. *Sung by* Johnny & the Tornados. *Song:* "World That We All Dreamed Of" Joe McDonald. *Sung by* Robert Corff. *Sd* James Tanenbaum. *Boom Op* Bob Easton. *Asst Dir* Robert Dijoux. *Prod Mgr* Paul Rapp. *Prod Asst* David Osterhout. *Makeup* Dean Cundy. *Grip* Mike Castle, Jim Etheridge, Gary Treadwell. *Prop Master* Peter Fain.
    Cast: Robert Corff *(Coel),* Elaine Giftos *(Cilla),* Bud Cort *(Hooper),* Talia Coppola *(Coralie),* Ben Vereen *(Carlos),* Cindy Williams *(Marissa),* Alex Wilson *(Jason),* Lou Procopio *(Marshall McLuhan),* Phil Borneo *(Quant),* Jackie Farley *(Ginny),* Country Joe McDonald *(FM Radio),* George Armitage *(Billy the Kid),* Pat Patterson *(Demeter),* Alan Braunstein *(Dr. Drake),* David Osterhout *(Texas Ranger),* Bruce Karcher *(Edgar Allan Poe),* Mike Castle *(hippie),* Jim Etheridge, Gary Treadwell *(renegade cowboys),* Peter Fain *(policeman),* Stephen Graham *(thief),* Bob Easton *(fanatic religious leader),* Country Joe & the Fish, Juretta Taylor.
    Comedy. An experimental nerve gas is accidentally released from a defense plant in Alaska, and the aging process of everyone over 25 is speeded up to such an extent that they are doomed to die within a matter of days. As alarmed reactionary elements in Dallas turn Texas into a police state, Coel and Cilla, both under 25, set out to find a new life. After their car is stolen by a modern-day Billy the Kid, they realize that many of their own generation are simply repeating the patterns and prejudices of their elders. Eventually teaming up with four other young people, they head for a hippie commune that has been set up in an old Indian pueblo in New Mexico. After stopping at a rock concert presided over by FM Radio, the group is captured by Jason and the Nomads, a fascistic football team that is planning to destroy El Paso. The group escapes and runs into the militant middle class, led by Marshall McLuhan, who accuse them of being unwashed hippy anarchists. Fleeing once again, the group finally reaches the commune. They concede that their setup is not ideal, but they recognize that it is at least a beginning. Jason and the Nomads reappear and threaten the pueblo. Despite the commune's repudiation of violence, their leader, Quant, decrees that they must defend their home. Suddenly lightning strikes, the earth opens up, and from it come many people the family met during their journey. From an Army truck, which has driven between the opposing lines of the pueblo dwellers and the Nomads, there emerges a procession of legendary youth heroes: John F. Kennedy, Martin Luther King, and Che Guevara. Edgar Allan Poe, accompanied by his raven, appears and gives his blessing, as God is heard talking with Christ about the new world. *Youth. Athletes. Fascists. Militants. Hippies. Middle classes. Doomsday. Theft. Communal living. Rock and roll. Lethal gas. Alaska. Dallas. Texas. El Paso. New Mexico. Marshall McLuhan. John Fitzgerald Kennedy. Martin Luther King, Jr. Ernesto "Che" Guevara. Edgar Allan Poe. Jesus. Lightning. Earthquakes.*
    Note: Location scenes filmed in New Mexico. Working title: *Arrowfeather.*

GASU NINGEN DAIICHIGO see **THE HUMAN VAPOR**

GATE OF FLESH (Japan)   **F6.1764**

Nikkatsu Corp. 11 Dec 1964 [Los Angeles opening]. Sd; col (Eastman Color). 35mm (Nikkatsu Scope). 90 min.

Dir Seijun Suzuki. *Screenplay* Goro Tanada. *Photog* Shigeyoshi Mine.

Cast: Yumiko Nogawa, Kayo Matsuo, Misako Tominaga, Joe Shishido, Satoko Kasai, Tomiko Ishi.

Drama. Source: Taijiro Tamura, *Nikutai no mon* (Tokyo opening: Mar 1947). In post-World War II Japan prostitutes and black marketeers organize for protection. Several of the women fall in love with Shintaro, a pimp who deals with them in his own sadistic manner. *Prostitutes. Pimps. Sadism. Black market.*

Note: Released in Japan in 1964 as *Nikutai no mon.*

GATEWAY TO GLORY (Japan)   **F6.1765**

Daiei Motion Picture Co. Jan 1970 [Los Angeles showing]. Sd; col (Eastmancolor). 35mm (Daiei Scope). 122 min.

Dir Mitsuo Murayama. *Screenplay* Ryuzo Kikushima, Yoshihiro Ishimatsu. *Photog* Akira Uehara. *Art Dir* Koichi Takahashi. *Mus* Seitaro Omori.

Cast: Kichiemon Nakamura (*Ichiro Hirata*), Shogo Shimada (*Admiral Yamamoto*), Ryunosuke Minegishi, Masayuki Mori, Sachiko Murase, Eiko Azusa, Ken Utsui, Kojiro Hongo, Jun Fujimaki.

War drama. In April 1934 Ichiro Hirata, the son of a poor farmer, enters the Naval Academy at Etajima. Annoyed by the petty rules of the Academy, Hirata concentrates instead on his studies. When the attempted coup d'état of 26 February 1936 takes place, Hirata sympathizes with the young officers who want to change the government, because he himself once wanted to be a reform politician. Hirata's mother falls ill just as the Sino-Japanese War breaks out, but he refuses to leave the Academy in a time of national emergency. Eventually he graduates at the top of his class and goes home for the first time—to visit his mother's grave. Hirata becomes a Navy pilot, participating in many battles during the Pacific war. However, in the spring of 1943, after the tide has turned against the Japanese, Hirata is assigned to escort the bomber in which Admiral Yamamoto, the Commander-in-chief of the Japanese Combined Fleet, is riding. Both planes are shot down by the Allies. *Air pilots. Students. Military life. Coups d'état. Filial relations. Sino-Japanese Conflict 1937–45. World War II. Etajima. Isoroku Yamamoto. Imperial Naval College (Japan). Japan—Navy.*

Note: Released in Japan in Jul 1969 as *Aa, Kaigun.*

A GATHERING OF EAGLES   **F6.1766**

Universal Pictures. 21 Jun 1963 [Chicago opening; c13 Jul 1963; LP33187]. Sd (Westrex); col (Eastman Color by Pathé). 35mm. 116 min.

Prod Sy Bartlett. *In Charge of Prod* Edward Muhl. *Dir* Delbert Mann. *2d Unit Dir* Robert D. Webb. *Dir of Aerial Unit* Paul Mantz. *Screenplay* Robert Pirosh. *Story* Sy Bartlett. *Dir Photog* Russell Harlan. *2d Unit Camera* Ray Fernstrom. *Camera Op* Jack Whitman. *Asst Camera* Frank Stanley, Robert Morrison. *Art Dir* Alexander Golitzen, Henry Bumstead. *Set Decor* Robert Priestley. *Set Coörd* Fred Knoth. *Main Titl* Pacific Title. *Film Ed* Russell F. Schoengarth. *Asst Ed* Robert Schulte. *Mus* Jerry Goldsmith. *Mus Supv* Joseph Gershenson. *Song:* "The SAC Song" Tom Lehrer. *Sung by* Rod Taylor. *Sd* Waldon O. Watson, Joe Lapis, John Oliver, James Alexander, Victor Goode. *Asst Dir* Joseph C. Behm, James Welch, Terry Morse, Jr., Foster Phinney. *Prod Mgr* Ernest B. Wehmeyer. *Script Supv* Teresa Brachetto. *Miss Peach's Gowns Dsgn* Irene. *Wardrobe* Seth Banks, Norman Mayreis, Olive Koenitz. *Makeup* Bud Westmore, Mark Reedall. *Hairstyles* Larry Germain, Jean Austin. *Tech Adv* Winston E. Moore, (Lieut. Col., USAF). *Dial Coach* Norman Stuart. *Still Photog* Rollie Lane. *Gaffer* Bill Neff. *Grip* Deke Smith, Jim Hilbert. *Prop* Julius Rosenkrantz, Frank Nifong.

Cast: Rock Hudson (*Col. Jim Caldwell*), Rod Taylor (*Hollis Farr*), Mary Peach (*Victoria Caldwell*), Barry Sullivan (*Colonel Fowler*), Kevin McCarthy (*General Kirby*), Henry Silva (*Colonel Garcia*), Leora Dana (*Mrs. Fowler*), Robert Lansing (*Sergeant Banning*), Richard Anderson (*Colonel Josten*), Richard Le Pore (*Sergeant Kemler*), Robert Bray (*Lieutenant Colonel Gales*), Jim Bannon (*Colonel Morse*), Nelson Leigh (*General Aymes*), Russ Bender (*Colonel Torrance*), John McKee (*Major Jarvis*), Ben Wright (*Leighton*), Dorothy Abbott (*Mrs. Josten*), John Holland (*Beresford*), John Pickard (*controller*), Ed Prentiss (*duty controller*), Ray Montgomery (*Captain Linc*), R. Wayland Williams (*Captain Hutchens*), Leif Erickson (*General Hewitt*).

Drama. When a California Air Force base fails to pass a surprise alert test ordered by the Strategic Air Command, Col. Jim Caldwell is brought in as the new base commander. After sending for his British wife, Victoria, he goes on an inspection tour of the base to learn the cause of the test failure. Upon noting that the missile squadron commander, Col. Bill Fowler, is a heavy drinker, Jim forces him into involuntary retirement, an action that irritates Fowler's friends, including Victoria, who has become close to Fowler's wife. Furthermore, Jim's devotion to his job throws Victoria more and more into the company of Hollis Farr, Jim's vice commander and Korean War buddy. Eventually Jim decides that Hollis is too busy making friends to establish any efficiency, and he recommends that Hollis be replaced. While Jim is visiting Fowler in a San Francisco hospital, another surprise alert is called; and Hollis, obliged to assume command, makes a decision that wins commendation from the SAC. The test is so favorable that Jim and Hollis are able to patch up their differences, and Victoria at last understands why Jim has been such a stern taskmaster. *Air pilots. Air traffic controllers. British. Military life. Marriage. Friendship. Alcoholism. Missiles. Hospitals. California. United States Air Force—Strategic Air Command.*

Note: Locations filmed at SAC bases and in San Francisco.

GATHERING OF EVIL   **F6.1767**

Dist Abrams & Parisi, Inc. 13 Jun 1969 [Champaign, Illinois, showing]. Sd; col (Eastmancolor). 35mm. 79 min.

A Leo–Todd Production. *Dir* Victor Bertini. *Orig Score* Irving Spice.

Cast: Anna Lindig, Morton Lewis.

Melodrama. Rhea, a beautiful woman dedicated to the gratification of her boundless sexual desires, refuses to admit defeat when her lover, successful young psychiatrist Eugene Martel, becomes engaged to another woman. To achieve her revenge, Rhea seduces him, and then hires another woman to visit his office, and strip so that she can be discovered nude in his arms by his fiancée and the clinic superintendent. Having lost both his fiancée and his position, Eugene vows revenge. His mind deranged, he tape-records the tragic story of his life, murders Rhea, and commits suicide. *Psychiatrists. Sensualists. Seduction. Revenge. Insanity. Murder. Suicide.*

EL GATO CON BOTAS see **PUSS 'N BOOTS**

IL GATTOPARDO see **THE LEOPARD**

LES GAULOISES BLEUES (France)   **F6.1768**

Les Films Treize–Ariane–Les Productions Artistes Associés. *Dist* Lopert Pictures. 12 May 1969 [New York opening; c28 Aug 1968; LF49]. Sd; col (Eastman Color). 35mm. 93 min. MPAA rating G.

Prod Alexandre Mnouchkine, Georges Dancigers, Claude Lelouch. *Dir-Writ* Michel Cournot. *Dir Photog* Alain Levent. *Camera* Armand Marco. *Asst Camera* Roger Delattre. *Art Dir* Guy Littaye, E. Freess. *Film Ed* Agnès Guillemot. *Mus from the works of* Claudio Monteverdi, Krzysztof Penderecki. *Sd* Jean Baronnet. *Sd Mix* Jacques Maumont. *Asst Dir* Philippe Fourastié. *Prod Mgr* Pierre Laurent. *Script Girl* Suzanne Schiffman. *Cost* E. Watteville, C. Maltzeff. *Makeup* Aïda Carange. *Key Grip* Roger Robert.

Cast: Annie Girardot (*The Mother*), Jean-Pierre Kalfon (*Ivan, age 30*), Nella Bielski (*Jeanne*), Bruno Crémer (*The Father*), Henri Garcin, Jean Lescot (*hunters*), Georges Demestre (*Ivan, age 6*), François Périer (*judge*), Anne Wiazemsky (*nurse*), Marcel Pagliero (*gypsy merchant*), Tsilla Chelton (*delegate*), José Varella (*lawyer*), Tanya Lopert (*Death*), Karina Gondy (*welfare agent*), Elizabeth Braconnier (*baliff-nurse*), Francis Girod, Claude Degliame, Sofie Maltzeff, Dominique Vielleville, Tania Becker, Maxmilien Decroux, Isabelle Felder, André Ancel, Jacques Baudry.

Drama. Wandering into a Paris tobacco shop for a pack of *Gauloises Bleues* cigarettes, 30-year-old Ivan meets Jeanne, a young salesgirl as lonely and impoverished as himself. After a brief courtship, Jeanne leaves her job to marry Ivan. Plagued by financial difficulties, however, the union soon becomes an unhappy one, and Ivan buys a rope in case he should want to hang himself. After committing an unspecified crime for which he is sentenced to death, Ivan is released because there is no room for him in the crowded prisons. Driven to despair, the couple decide to divorce, but Jeanne becomes pregnant. When he takes his wife to a maternity clinic, Ivan sits in the waiting room and recalls his unhappy childhood. Arrested for stealing at the age of 6, Ivan is placed in a state institution. Although his ailing mother pleads with a judge for her son's release, her request is denied because she has a criminal record. Ivan's reverie is interrupted by a nurse who informs him that his child has been born dead. *Salesclerks. Courtship. Marriage. Poverty. Capital punishment. Pregnancy. Memory. Childhood. Filial relations. Cigarstores. Prisons. Paris.*

Note: Location scenes filmed in and around Paris. Opened in Paris in Aug 1968.

GAVILAN see **BALLAD OF GAVILAN**

THE GAY BRAGGART (Japan)   **F6.1769**

Toho Co. 29 Jan 1965 [Los Angeles showing]. Sd; col. 35mm (Tohoscope). 94 min.

Dir Kengo Furusawa.

Cast: Hitoshi Ueki, Mie Hama, Mitsuko Kusabue, Kei Tani.

Comedy. Although no information about the precise nature of this film has been found, press material suggests that the story takes place during the Tokyo Olympic Games. *Braggarts. Olympic Games. Tokyo.*

Note: Released in Japan in 1964 as *Nippon ichino horafuki otoko.*

THE GAY DECEIVERS   F6.1770

Fanfare Film Productions. 9 Jul **1969** [San Francisco opening]. Sd; col (Eastman Color). 35mm. 91 min. [Also reviewed at 97 min.] *MPAA rating* R.

Pres by Joe Solomon. *Prod* Joe Solomon. *Assoc Prod* Paul Rapp. *Dir* Bruce Kessler. *Screenplay* Jerome Wish. *Story* Abe Polsky, Gil Lasky. *Dir Photog* Richard C. Glouner. *Camera Op* Don Birnkrant. *Art Dir* Archie Bacon. *Set Decor* Ray Boltz. *Film Ed* Renn Reynolds, Reg Browne. *Mus Comp & Cond* Stu Phillips. *Sd Rec* Phil Mitchell. *Asst Dir* Christopher Morgan. *Prod Supv* Peter Fain. *Script Supv* Vicky Weisbart. *Cost* Norman Saling. *Makeup* Brian Perrow. *Casting Dir* Pearl Kempton. *Prop Master* Carl Nugent. *Key Grip* John Murray. *Gaffer* Bobby Petzoldt.

Cast: Kevin Coughlin *(Danny Devlin)*, Lawrence Casey *(Elliot Crane)*, Brooke Bundy *(Karen)*, Jo Ann Harris *(Leslie Devlin)*, Michael Greer *(Malcolm)*, Sebastian Brook *(Craig)*, Jack Starrett *(Colonel Dixon)*, Richard Webb *(Mr. Devlin)*, Eloise Hardt *(Mrs. Devlin)*, Jeanne Baird *(Mrs. Conway)*, Maurishka *(Carolyn)*, Mike Kopscha *(psychiatrist)*, Joseph Tornatore *(Sergeant Kravits)*, Robert Reese *(real estate agent)*, Christopher Riordan *(Duane)*, Doug Hume *(corporal)*, David Osterhout *(Stern)*, Marilyn Wirt *(Sybil)*, Ron Gans *(Freddie)*, Rachel Romen *(Dorothy)*, Tom Grubbs *(Paul)*, Louise Williams *(Bunny)*, Randee Lynne *(Sheryl)*, Meridith Williams *(Phil)*, Harry Sodoni *(Georgette)*, Lenore Stevens *(Laverne)*, Trigg Kelly *(Jackie)*, Tony Epper *(Vince)*.

Comedy. Danny Devlin and his woman-chasing friend Elliot Crane decide to pose as homosexuals to avoid induction into the Army. As a result of interviews with Colonel Dixon and a psychiatrist, they are declared unfit. Since Danny is convinced that he and Elliot must appear to live together as homosexuals to confirm the Army's judgment, they rent a one-bedroom apartment in an area popular with the gay set. Their landlord, Malcolm, and his lover, Craig, attempt to make the "newlyweds" at home, but neither is comfortable in the new situation. When Elliot does a "campy" impersonation in the country club shower room, Danny's influential father has him fired from his job as lifeguard. Danny, meanwhile, has continued seeing his stewardess girl friend, Karen, but avoids bringing her to his new apartment. Eventually, Elliot's married and unmarried girl friends, Danny's father, and even Karen herself become convinced that the men are actually homosexual. In one final attempt to disprove the allegation, Danny's sister, Leslie, tries to get Elliot into bed with her, but the sight of a nearby Army officer renders him instantly impotent. Faced with dishonor and near ruin, the men return to Colonel Dixon and tell him that the whole situation was a ruse; but they have performed their roles too well, and the colonel refuses to allow them to enlist. The two part company, leaving Colonel Dixon free to cuddle up with his "assistant," Sergeant Kravits. *Draft dodgers. Psychiatrists. Lifeguards. Imposture. Male homosexuality. Filial relations. Brother-sister relationship. Impotence. Country clubs. United States Army.*

Note: Location scenes filmed in California.

THE GAY LIFE   F6.1771

Pyramid Productions. 21 Mar **1968** [San Francisco showing]. Sd; col. [Feature film, length unknown.]

Prod Ward McCallister. *Dir* John Foley. *Screenplay* Henry R. Beecher.

Cast: Lew Michaels *(Ace)*, William Morgan *(Cole)*, LuAnn Montague *(Bonnie)*, Barbara Nagle *(Sally)*.

Sex film. Ace and Cole invite Bonnie and Sally to their apartment, and, realizing that the women will be late, the men indulge in homosexual relations. The women finally arrive, and all four have group sex. *Male homosexuality. Group sex.*

GAY PURR-EE   F6.1772

UPA Pictures. *Dist* Warner Bros. Pictures. 7 Nov **1962** [Chicago opening; c24 Nov 1962; LP29391]. Sd; col (Technicolor). 35mm. 86 min.

Exec Prod Henry G. Saperstein. *Assoc Prod* Lee Orgel. *Dir* Abe Levitow. *Screenplay* Dorothy Jones, Chuck Jones. *Adtl Dial* Ralph Wright. *Col Stylist* Don Peters, Gloria Wood, Robert Inman, Phill Norman, Richard Kelsey. *Anim* Ben Washam, Phil Duncan, Irv Spence, Hal Ambro, Don Lusk, Ray Patterson, Hank Smith, Grant Simmons, Harvey Toombs, Volus Jones, Ken Harris, Art David, Fred Madison. *Photog* Roy Hutchcroft, Dan Miller, Jack Stevens, photog, Duane Keegan. *Art Dir* Victor Haboush. *Prod Dsgn* Robert Singer, Richard Ung, Corny Cole, Ray Aragon, Edward Levitt, Ernest Nordli. *Titl Dsgn* John Hitesman. *Supv Film Ed* Ted Baker. *Film Ed* Sam Horta, Earl Bennett. *Songs* Harold Arlen, E. Y. Harburg. *Mus Arr & Cond* Mort Lindsey. *Vocal Arr* Joseph J. Lilley. *Prod Mgr* Earl Jonas.

Voices: Judy Garland *(Mewsette)*, Robert Goulet *(Jaune-Tom)*, Red Buttons *(Robespierre)*, Hermione Gingold *(Madame Rubens-Chatte)*, Paul Frees *(Meowrice)*, Julie Bennett, Morey Amsterdam, Mel Blanc, Joan Gardner.

Animated comedy. Mewsette, a little country cat on a French farm, decides to abandon her peasant life and go to Paris. She is followed by her devoted admirer, Jaune-Tom, and his kitten companion, Robespierre. Upon arriving in Paris, Mewsette falls into the hands of the evil Meowrice who takes her to a salon run by the plump and jaded Madame Rubens-Chatte. Unaware that Meowrice is planning to groom her for marriage to a rich cat in Pittsburgh, Mewsette willingly takes beauty courses. When Jaune-Tom and Robespierre arrive in the city, Meowrice gets them drunk and has them shanghaied aboard a ship headed for Alaska. Once there, they accidentally discover gold and return to Paris laden with wealth. Mewsette, meanwhile, has learned of Meowrice's plans and tries unsuccessfully to escape. She is placed in a basket labeled for Pittsburgh, but Jaune-Tom and Robespierre come to the rescue. After disposing of the culprit, Jaune-Tom rides away with his beloved Mewsette. *Songs:* "Mewsette" (Jaune-Tom); "Roses Red–Violets Blue," "Take My Hand, Paree," "Paris Is a Lonely Town" (Mewsette); "The Horses Won't Talk," "The Money Cat" (Meowrice); "Little Drops of Rain" (Mewsette & Jaune-Tom); "Bubbles" (Jaune-Tom & Meowrice). *Innocents. Evildoers. Duplicity. Drunkenness. Shanghaiing. Wealth. Gold. Paris. Pittsburgh. Alaska. Cats.*

LE GÉANT À LA COUR DE KUBLAI KHAN *see* **SAMSON AND THE SEVEN MIRACLES OF THE WORLD**

LE GÉANT DE LA VALLÉE DES ROIS *see* **SON OF SAMSON**

DAS GEHEIMNIS DER DREI DSCHUNKEN *see* **RED-DRAGON**

DAS GEHEIMNIS DER GELBEN NARZISSEN *see* **THE DEVIL'S DAFFODIL**

DAS GEHEIMNIS DER JUNGEN WITWE *see* **A BLACK VEIL FOR LISA**

DAS GEHEIMNIS DER LEDERSCHLINGE *see* **THE MYSTERY OF THUG ISLAND**

DAS GEHEIMNIS DER SCHWARZEN HANDSCHUHE *see* **THE BIRD WITH THE CRYSTAL PLUMAGE**

DAS GEHEIMNIS DER TODESINSEL *see* **ISLAND OF THE DOOMED**

DAS GEHEIMNIS DER VENUS *see* **THE FEMALE ANIMAL**

GEHEIMNISSE IN GOLDENEN NYLONS *see* **DEAD RUN**

GELIEBTE BESTIE *see* **HIPPODROME**

GEN TO FUDO-MYOH *see* **THE YOUTH AND HIS AMULET**

LE GENDARME DE SAINT-TROPEZ *see* **THE GENDARME OF ST. TROPEZ**

THE GENDARME OF ST. TROPEZ (France/Italy)   F6.1773

S. N. C.–Franca Film. *Dist* Magna Pictures Distribution Corp. Jun **1966**. Sd; col (Eastman Color). 35mm (Dyaliscope). 93 min.

Prod René Pignères, Gérard Beytout. *Screenplay* Richard Balducci, Jacques Vilfrid, Jean Girault. *Dial* Jacques Vilfrid. *Story* Richard Balducci. *Photog* Marc Fossard. *Art Dir* Sidney Bettex. *Film Ed* Jean-Michel Gautier, Jean Feyte. *Mus* Raymond Lefèvre. *Sd* Jacques Gallois. *Asst Dir* Alain Gouze. *Prod Mgr* Pierre Cottance.

Cast: Louis de Funès *(Ludovic Cruchot)*, Geneviève Grad *(Nicole Cruchot)*, Michel Galabru *(Gerber)*, Jean Lefebvre *(Fougasse)*, Christian Marin *(Merlot)*, Daniel Cauchy *(Richard)*, Jean-Paul Bertrand *(Eddie)*, Franck Vilcour *(Jean-Luc)*, Maria Pacôme, Pierre Barouh, Claude Piéplu, Jacques Famery, Madeleine Delavaivre, Martine de Breteuil, France Rumilly, Patrice Laffont, Fernand Sardou, Gabriele Tinti, Giuseppe Porelli, Michelle Wargnier, Norma Dugo.

Comedy. Ludovic Cruchot, a strict disciplinarian who has recently been promoted to sergeant of the gendarmes, arrives with his daughter Nicole at the French resort of Saint-Tropez, where he soon finds himself dealing with the problems of tourists. He attempts to capture several elusive beach nudists, while Nicole deceives her new friends by pretending that her father is a millionaire yachtsman. She unknowingly becomes involved in the theft of a Rembrandt from the local museum, but Ludovic apprehends the crooks on their yacht and recovers the painting. *Police. Tourists. Nudity. Millionaires. Filial relations. Appearances. Robbery. Resorts. Paintings. Museums. Saint-Tropez.*

Note: Opened in Paris in Sep 1964 as *Le gendarme de Saint-Tropez*; running time: 95 min; in Rome in Apr 1965 as *Una ragazza a Saint Tropez.*

GENERATION   F6.1774

Dist Avco Embassy Pictures. 15 Dec **1969** [New York opening]. Sd; col (Technicolor). 35mm. 104 min. *MPAA rating* M.

Pres by Joseph E. Levine. A Frederick Brisson Production. *Exec Prod* Leonard Lightstone. *Dir* George Schaefer. *Screenplay* William Goodhart. *Dir Photog* Lionel Lindon. *Camera Op* George Nogle. *Set Decor* Hoyle Barrett. *Prod Dsgn* Robert E. Smith. *Film Ed* James Heckert. *Mus* Dave Grusin. *Titl Song* Dino Fekaris, Nick Zesses, Bea Verdi. *Sung by* Rare Earth. *Sd* Robert J. Miller. *Asst Dir* Fred Gammon, Fred Giles. *Prod Mgr* Ben Chapman. *Asst to the Prod* Charles Forsythe. *Cost Dsgn* Noel Taylor. *Makeup* Vincent Romaine. *Walter's Photog Display* Roddy McDowall.

Cast: David Janssen *(Jim Bolton)*, Kim Darby *(Doris Bolton Owen)*, Carl Reiner *(Stan Herman)*, Pete Duel *(Walter Owen)*, Andrew Prine *(Winn Garand)*, James Coco *(Mr. Blatto)*, Sam Waterston *(Desmond)*, David Lewis *(Arlington)*, Don Beddoe *(Gilbert)*, Jack Somack *(airline policeman)*, Lincoln Kilpatrick *(Hey Hey)*.

Comedy. Source: William Goodhart, *Generation* (New York opening: 6 Oct 1965). In her 9th month of pregnancy, Doris Bolton finally marries Walter Owen, a young anti-establishment photographer, and they return to their East Village loft. She calls her father, an advertising executive in Denver, who is so shocked by the news that he takes the next plane to New York. Outwardly a cool and sophisticated man, Jim Bolton is secretly disturbed at having sold out to institutions in which he does not believe. Although Doris assures Walter that her father is liberal, they agree not to tell him of their plan to deliver the baby at home, unaided. Jim is dismayed when he first sees their apartment and is appalled by his daughter's advanced pregnancy. He argues with Walter about their dependence on the system they decry, and Walter blurts out their plan for the natural birth. The next morning Jim seeks aid from his friend Stan, an obstetrician, and Winn, a young lawyer who once dated Doris. They feel that there is not much that can be done in the face of the parents' decision, and Jim makes a final appeal to Doris and Walter, pointing out that parents must sacrifice their own convictions for the benefit of their children. Doris replies that she doesn't want her child to feel guilty, as she always did, because Jim had sacrificed his principles for her sake. Doris goes into labor, but the delivery is not as smooth as the parents had expected. Luckily, Stan is around to help out, and as Walter and Jim fold sterilized sheets in the next room, they find themselves united by this experience. They hear a small cry from the next room and Stan announces the arrival of a boy. "Just what we need," smiles Jim, "another troublemaker!" *Newlyweds. Photographers. Fathers-in-law. Advertising executives. Physicians. Lawyers. Nonconformists. Pregnancy. Childbirth. Filial relations. Lofts. Denver. New York City—East Village.*

Note: Also known as *A Time for Giving.*

GENGHIS KHAN (United States/Great Britain/West Germany/
    Yugoslavia)   **F6.1775**
Irving Allen Ltd.-CCC-Filmkunst-Avala Film. *Dist* Columbia Pictures. 17 Jun **1965** [Dallas opening; c1 Jul 1965; LP30841]. Sd (Westrex); col (Technicolor). 35mm (Panavision). 124 min.

Prod Irving Allen. *Assoc Prod* Euan Lloyd. *Dir* Henry Levin. *2d Unit Dir* Cliff Lyons. *Action Seq* Bob Simmons. *Screenplay* Clarke Reynolds, Beverley Cross. *Story* Berkely Mather. *Dir Photog* Geoffrey Unsworth. *Camera Op* David Harcourt, Ray Parslow. *2d Unit Camera* Tony Braun. *Supv Art Ed* Maurice Carter. *Adtl Art Dir* Heinrich Weidemann, Mile Nikolić. *Set Dsgn* Toni Sarzi-Braga. *Film Ed* Geoffrey Foot. *Mus Comp* Dušan Radić. *Mus Cond* Muir Mathieson. *Sd Rec* George Stephenson, Hugh Strain. *Sd Ed* Gordon Daniel. *Asst Dir* Buddy Coleman, Bluey Hill, Frank Winterstein. *Prod Supv* William Kirby, Milenko Stanković, Peter Hahne. *Cont* Elaine Schreyeck, Rita Davison. *Cost Dsgn* Cynthia Tingey. *Wardrobe Master* Ron Beck. *Makeup* Neville Smallwood. *Hairdresser* Ivy Emmerton. *Sp Eff* Bill Warrington, David Warrington.

Cast: Stephen Boyd *(Jamuga)*, Omar Sharif *(Temujin/Genghis Khan)*, James Mason *(Kam Ling)*, Eli Wallach *(The Sha of Khwarezm)*, Françoise Dorléac *(Bortei)*, Telly Savalas *(Shan)*, Robert Morley *(The Emperor of China)*, Michael Hordern *(Geen)*, Yvonne Mitchell *(Katke)*, Woody Strode *(Sengal)*, Kenneth Cope *(Subodai)*, Roger Croucher *(Kassar)*, Don Borisenko *(Jebai)*, Patrick Holt *(Kuchluk)*, Susanne Hsiao *(Chin Yu)*, George Savalas *(Toktoa)*, Carlo Cura *(Temujin as a child)*, Gustavo Rojo *(Altan)*, Dušan Vujisić *(Ho Mun Tim)*, Jovan Tešić *(Fut Su)*, Andreja Marčić *(Chagedai)*, Thomas Margulies *(Jochi)*, Yamata Pauli, Linda Lončar *(Indian girls)*, Branislav Radović, Zvonko Jovčić *(slave dealers)*, Dominique Don, Carmen Dene, Nora Forster, Jatta Falke, Hannalore Maeusel, Yvonne Shima, May Spils, Edwina Carroll, Sally Douglas, Chieko Huber, Elke Kroger, Ursel Mumoth, Lucille Soong, Esther Anderson *(concubines)*.

Adventure melodrama. Young Prince Temujin witnesses the execution of his father, a Mongol chieftain, by the warlike Merkit Mongol leader Jamuga, who forces Temujin to wear a wooden yoke and enslaves his people. Growing to manhood, Temujin escapes into the mountains accompanied by Sengal, a Negro mute, and Geen, a wise man. He abducts Jamuga's betrothed, Princess Bortei, who becomes his devoted wife, and her brothers become his lieutenants as he

gathers an army in order someday to unite the warring Mongols. Recaptured by Jamuga, the princess is raped and branded before she is rescued by Temujin, who sets out with his forces toward China. Along the way he befriends Kam Ling, an official of the Peking court, who introduces him to the Emperor of China. The emperor imprisons the warriors in luxurious surroundings, but Temujin refuses to allow his men to grow soft. When the Merkits threaten the Great Wall, Temujin and an army of Mongols repel the invasion and capture Jamuga. The grateful emperor gives Temujin the title of Genghis Khan but refuses to permit him to leave China, fearing that he will return as an invader. Genghis Khan is warned by Kam Ling that the emperor has arranged for his assassination by Jamuga, and he escapes to spread his empire across the continent. In Persia he defeats the combined forces of the Merkits and the Shah of Khwarezm and kills Jamuga in a duel. Mortally wounded himself, Genghis Khan gives over his command to his son, having realized his dream of a united Mongol nation. *Mongols. Royalty. Tribal chiefs. Mutes. Slavery. Rape. Assassination. Abduction. Military invasion. China. Peking. Persia. Genghis Khan. Jamukha. Burte. Great Wall of China. Duels.*

Note: Location scenes filmed in Yugoslavia. Released in West Germany in both 70mm and 35mm versions in Apr 1965 as *Dschingis Khan;* running time: 128 min; in Yugoslavia in 1965 as *Džingis-Kan;* British release: Aug 1965.

THE GENTLE ART OF MURDER *see* **CRIME DOES NOT PAY**

GENTLE GIANT   **F6.1776**
Ivan Tors Films. *Dist* Paramount Pictures. 15 Nov **1967** [Portland, Oregon, opening; c4 Oct 1967; LP34927]. Sd; col (Eastmancolor). 35mm. 93 min.

Prod Ivan Tors. *Exec Prod* Stanley Colbert. *Assoc Prod* Neil Andersen. *Asst Prod* Joseph Gannon. *Dir* James Neilson. *Screenplay* Edward J. Lakso, Andy White. *Dir Photog* Howard Winner. *2d Unit Photog* Edmund Gibson. *Art Dir* Bruce Bushman. *Set Decor* Don Ivey. *Supv Film Ed* Warren Adams. *Ed* Peter Colbert. *Mus Comp & Cond* Samuel Matlovsky. *Sd* Howard Warren, John Wilkinson. *Asst Dir* Buddy Nadler. *Prod Mgr* Edward Haldeman. *Wardrobe* Peggy Kunkle. *Makeup* Guy Del Russo. *Hairstyles* Irene Aparicio. *Sp Eff* Jack Johnson. *Zoological Cons* Ralph Helfer. *Animal Seq Supv by* Africa U. S. A.

Cast: Dennis Weaver *(Tom Wedloe)*, Vera Miles *(Ellen Wedloe)*, Ralph Meeker *(Fog Hanson)*, Clint Howard *(Mark Wedloe)*, Ben *(Gentle Ben)*, Huntz Hall *(Dink Smith)*, Charles G. Martin *(Mike McDonaugh)*, Rance Howard *(Tater Coughlin)*, Frank Schuller *(Charlie Mason)*, Robertson White *(Swenson)*, Ric O'Feldman *(mate)*, James Riddle *(skipper)*, Jerry Newby *(1st townsman)*, Frank Logan *(2d townsman)*, Alfred Metz *(1st fisherman)*, Levirne DeBord *(2d fisherman)*.

Adventure drama. Source: Walt Morey, *Gentle Ben* (New York, 1965). After he befriends a bear cub on a Florida game reserve, young Mark Wedloe watches in horror as three fishermen led by Fog Hanson kill the animal's mother and take the cub captive. Despite admonitions from his parents, Tom and Ellen, Mark sneaks onto Hanson's property to feed and walk the cub, whom he names Ben. When Hanson catches the child trespassing, Mark is told never to visit Ben again, but after he overhears Hanson planning to kill the cub and sell his meat, Mark takes Ben into the wilderness to set him free. The animal refuses to leave Mark, however, and the Wedloes consent to purchase Ben from Hanson. Sentiment in the town goes against the animal, however, and the family is forced to give Ben to a zoo, but the cub breaks out of his cage while being shipped by boat and swims ashore to a wooded area. Later, Tom becomes a wildlife officer and is transferred to a new home in the Everglades. While searching for poachers, he is charged by a huge bear whom he recognizes as Ben. Fearful that the animal is wild and will have to be killed, Tom stalks it with his rifle; Mark follows and is present when his father confronts Ben. Before Tom can fire, however, a tree falls and pins him underneath. Ben follows Mark's order to push the tree away and leads them to his mate and newborn cubs he was protecting when he encountered Tom. Later, Ben occasionally finds time to visit Mark in spite of his new family responsibilities. *Fishermen. Poachers. Game wardens. Filial relations. Game preserves. Florida. Everglades. Bears. Pets.*

Note: Location scenes filmed at Palm Beach Gardens, Florida.

GENTLE PERSUASION *see* **THE ART OF GENTLE PERSUASION**

THE GENTLE RAIN (United States/Brazil)   **F6.1777**
Comet Films. *Dist* Comet Film Distributors. 10 Feb **1966** [Fort Lauderdale, Florida, opening]. Sd; col (Eastman Color). 35mm. 110 min. [Also 94 min.]

Prod-Dir Burt Balaban. *Exec Prod* Bert Caudle, Jr. *Screenplay* Robert Cream. *Photog* Mario Di Leo. *Art Dir* Carmellio Cruz. *Film Ed* Fima Noveck. *Mus* Luiz Bonfa. *Sd* Constantino Warnovski.

Cast: Christopher George *(Bill Patterson)*, Lynda Day *(Judy Reynolds)*, Fay Spain *(Nancy Masters)*, Maria Helena Dias *(Gloria)*, Lon Clark *(Harry Masters)*, Barbara Williams *(girl friend)*, Robert Assumpaco *(hotel manager)*, Herbert Moss *(Jimmy)*, Lorena *(jewelry girl)*, Nadyr Fernandes *(nightclub girl)*, Bert Caudle, Jr. *(party guest)*.

Melodrama. Wealthy, spoiled Judy Reynolds leaves New York for Rio de Janeiro when the marriage arranged for her by her parents is annulled because of her apparent frigidity. In Rio she meets architect-turned-draftsman Bill Patterson, a mute who conceals his insecurity behind a mask of open rudeness, and they become lovers. Bill explains, by gestures and pantomime, that he was once involved in an automobile accident in which his fiancée died. There was a moment when he might have pulled her to safety, but he froze and could only scream as the car exploded; this was the last sound he was to utter. Judy urges Bill to consult a psychiatrist; but he is reluctant to take this step, and Judy eventually leaves him. Once alone, Bill desperately tries to use the telephone—perhaps to call a psychiatrist, perhaps to call Judy. *Americans in foreign countries. Mutes. Architects. Frigidity. Neurosis. Marriage—Annulment. Marriage—Arranged. Rio de Janeiro. New York City. Automobile accidents.*

Note: Produced in 1965 in Brazil.

THE GENTLE SEX *see* **SIN ALLEY**

LE GENTLEMAN DE COCODY *see* **MAN FROM COCODY**

DIE GENTLEMEN BITTEN ZUR KASSE *see* **THE GREAT BRITISH TRAIN ROBBERY**

GENTLEMEN PREFER NATURE GIRLS   F6.1778

Encore Productions. *Dist* Doe-Rae Pictures, Trans-Universe Pictures. 14 Jun 1963 [Los Angeles showing]. Sd; col (Eastman Color). 35mm. 71 min.

Prod-Dir Doris Wishman. *Screenplay* Melvin Stanley. *Dir Photog* Raymond Pheelan. *Film Ed* Martin Samuels. *Sd* Titra Sound Corp. *Optical Eff* B. & O. Film Specialists.

Cast: Lon Alexion, Joan Bamford, William Mayer, Warrene Gray, Stephen Bloom, Mary Jo Walls, Norman Casserly, Craig Maudslay, Jr., Dolores K. Norris, Lee Abell, Richard Johnson, James Antonio, Sandy Sinclair, John Leonard.

Comedy-drama. Real estate agents Tom Brooks and Ann Bell keep their marriage a secret from their employer, Charles Bennett, who disapproves of marital partners working together in the same office. Bennett discovers that Tom is a member of a nudist club and summarily fires him although Tom is involved in negotiating the sale of a huge tract of land to client Al Jenkins. Nudist camp director Billy Hardy, anxious to help the couple avoid financial difficulty, offers Tom the job of temporary director while he goes on vacation. In his new capacity, Tom once again meets Al Jenkins. A devoted nudist, Jenkins hits upon a plan to overcome Bennett's objections: he agrees to close the deal if Bennett will come to his "country club," and he leads the real estate man to the nudist camp by night. In the morning, Bennett furiously insists on returning to the city. While arrangements are made, Jenkins shows him around the camp. The friendly, wholesome atmosphere impresses him, and he decides to stay for the weekend. As he is about to leave, he meets Tom and Ann and asks Tom to return to his job. The couple reveal that they are married, and Bennett decides to become a nudist. *Real estate agents. Marriage. Nudism. Employer-employee relations. Nudist camps.*

Note: Location scenes filmed at Sunny Palms Lodge, Homestead, Florida.

GEORG   F6.1779

Ariadne Productions. *Dist* Film-Makers' Cooperative, Film-Makers' Distribution Center. May 1964 [New York showing]. Sd; b&w. 16mm. 55 min.

Prod-Dir-Writ Stanton Kaye. *Camera* Detlev Wiede. *Film Ed* Stanton Kaye. *Asst Dir* Vorum Getzler, Joseph Swafford. *Sd* Fred Haines, sd.

Cast: Stanton Kaye (*Georg*), Lynn Averill (*wife*), Mark Cheka.

Drama. Georg, a German soldier in World War II who is filming a battle, finds his lost motion picture camera—still running—among the enemy dead. The events of the film are seen through this camera: Georg is the leading character in the story; he is the cinematographer who films the events as they transpire, occasionally directing on-camera; and he narrates the action. Georg's voice pleads for people to "understand." He proceeds to set up a home movie screen and show slides and movies from his boyhood: of his brother, who was injured in the war and extolled by everybody; his parents; the depressing state of the family after the war; and their emigration to the United States in 1950. In their new home in Illinois, his father constantly watches television while Georg works in a Volkswagen plant. The father dies; soon afterward Georg gets married and moves into a small trailer in a semi-arid rural location. There Georg is harassed by everyone around him for alleged acts of the past. Despite their hope to escape, the war seems to hound Georg and his wife. They discover a sinister missile site just over the hill from their trailer. One day they throw stones at one of the missiles, and soldiers chase them away. Georg's wife becomes pregnant, and they run out of money; despondent, his wife dies in childbirth. Georg longs for a time when people will be more understanding of one another, and he wonders if anyone will ever "find" him. Once again he challenges the soldiers guarding the missile site, but they shoot him down. Georg's camera, mounted on a tripod, continues to film the scene. One of the

soldiers cautiously approaches the camera, wondering what it could be, and finally realizes its harmlessness. The soldiers depart, but the camera runs on until the end. *Motion picture cameramen. Veterans. Brothers. Filial relations. Family life. Rural life. Pregnancy. Home movies. Childbirth. Automobile manufacture. Missiles. War matériel. World War II. Illinois. Germany—Army. United States Army.*

THE GEORGE RAFT STORY   F6.1780

Allied Artists. 22 Nov 1961 [Chicago opening; c22 Nov 1961; LP20719]. Sd; b&w. 35mm. 105 min.

Prod Ben Schwalb. *Dir* Joseph M. Newman. *Screenplay* Crane Wilbur. *Dir Photog* Carl Guthrie. *Art Dir* David Milton. *Set Decor* Joseph Kish. *Film Ed* George White. *Mus Comp & Cond* Jeff Alexander. *Choreog* Alex Romero. *Sd Mix* Ralph Butler. *Sd* Monty Pearce. *Mus Ed* Richard C. Harris. *Asst Dir* Lindsley Parsons, Jr. *Prod Mgr* Edward Morey, Jr. *Set Cont* Virginia Barth. *Wardrobe* Roger J. Weinberg, Norah Sharpe. *Makeup Artist* Norman Pringle. *Hairstyles* Alice Monte. *Sp Eff* Milt Olsen. *Prop* Ted Mossman. *Constr Supv* James West.

Cast: Ray Danton (*George Raft*), Jayne Mansfield (*Lisa Lang*), Julie London (*Sheila Patton*), Barrie Chase (*June*), Frank Gorshin (*Moxie Cusack*), Barbara Nichols (*Texas Guinan*), Brad Dexter (*Benny Siegel*), Robert Strauss (*Frenchie*), Herschel Bernardi (*Sam*), Margo Moore (*Ruth Harris*), Neville Brand (*Al Capone*), Joe De Santis (*Frankie Donatella*), Argentina Brunetti (*Mrs. Raft*), Pepper Davis, Tony Reese (*M. C. team*), John Bleifer (*Mr. Raft*), Jack Lambert (*Jerry Fitzpatrick*), Cecile Rogers (*Charleston dancer*), Tol Avery (*Mizner, The Wit*), Robert H. Harris (*Harvey*), Jack Albertson (*Milton*), Murvyn Vye (*Johnny*).

Biographical drama. George Raft, a product of New York City's Hell's Kitchen, breaks into show business as an exhibition dancer at the Dreamland Casino. He soon becomes friendly with bootleggers and gangsters and makes his living performing in syndicate-controlled night clubs. But he gets into trouble with the mob when he protects Ruth Harris, a cigarette girl, from the unwanted attentions of a racketeer. He then decides to go to Hollywood and try his luck at motion pictures. In 1932, he gets his big break by playing the role of a bodyguard in the film *Scarface*. As his theatrical star rises, he continues his association with well-known gangsters such as Al Capone and Benny "Bugsy" Siegel. But eventually his career fades, and he is forced to curb his big spending and give up his lavish California home. He then participates in a hotel-casino venture in Cuba. Soon after his arrival, however, the Castro revolution breaks out, and he is forced to flee. Returning to Hollywood, he makes his film comeback by once more playing a gangster—in 1959's *Some Like It Hot*. *Dancers. Bootleggers. Gangsters. Cigarette girls. Actors. Gamblers. Syndicates. Hotels. Casinos. Motion pictures. Nightclubs. New York City—Hell's Kitchen. Hollywood. Cuba—History—1958 Revolution. George Raft. Al Capone. Benny "Bugsy" Siegel. Texas Guinan. "Scarface". "Some Like It Hot".*

GEORGE'S ROOM *see* **THE CHELSEA GIRLS**

GEORGY GIRL (Great Britain)   F6.1781

Everglades Productions. *Dist* Columbia Pictures. 17 Oct 1966 [New York opening; c1 Nov 1966; LP34012]. Sd (RCA); b&w. 35mm. 100 min.

A Robert Goldston–Otto Plaschkes Production. *Prod* Robert Goldston, Otto Plaschkes. *Assoc Prod* George Pitcher. *Dir* Silvio Narizzano. *Screenplay* Margaret Forster, Peter Nichols. *Scen* Jane Buck. *Dir Photog* Ken Higgins. *Camera Op* Peter Allwork. *Art Dir* Tony Woollard. *Film Ed* John Bloom. *Song:* "Georgy Girl" Tom Springfield, Jim Dale, mus. *Sung by* The Seekers. *Mus Comp & Cond* Alexander Faris. *Cond Children's Dance Mus* Brian Hunter. *Dance & Movement for Children* Marjory Sigley. *Sd Ed* Ben Rayner. *Sd Rec* Wally Milner, Nolan Roberts. *Asst Dir* Carl Mannin. *Prod Mgr* Clive Reed. *Miss Rampling's Clothes* Mary Quant. *Makeup Artist* Harold Fletcher. *Hairdresser* Betty Glasow.

Cast: James Mason (*James*), Alan Bates (*Jos*), Lynn Redgrave (*Georgy*), Charlotte Rampling (*Meredith*), Bill Owen (*Ted*), Clare Kelly (*Doris*), Rachel Kempson (*Ellen*), Denise Coffey (*Peg*), Dorothy Alison (*health visitor*), Peggy Thorpe-Bates (*hospital sister*), Dandy Nichols (*hospital nurse*), Terence Soall (*salesman*), Jolyan Booth (*registry office clerk*).

Romantic comedy-drama. Source: Margaret Forster, *Georgy Girl* (London, 1965). Georgy Parkin is a plump and somewhat forlorn creature who partially disapproves of her parents working as servants in the palatial London home of middle-aged James Leamington and his ailing, forever-complaining wife. Resigned to her fate as one of life's misfits, Georgy shares a flat with a beautiful but cold and amoral violinist named Meredith, who regards Georgy as little more than an unobtrusive convenience who keeps the apartment neat and tidy. In return, Georgy is able to share vicariously in Meredith's numerous love affairs, particularly a long-standing affair with Jos, a madcap Cockney. One day, to her astonishment, Georgy is informed by Mr. Leamington that he would like her to become his mistress and that he has taken the trouble to have legal papers drawn up on their "agreement." Georgy, however, chooses to remain a virginal observer in her flat with Meredith, who reveals that she has become pregnant for the third time by Jos. On the previous occasions Meredith had undergone abortions, but this time Jos persuades her to marry him and have his child. Georgy is thrilled to stay on at the flat and keep house for them. While Meredith is at the hospital giving birth, Jos—first playfully, then seriously—seduces Georgy, and in the days that follow they live together idyllically. Consequently, when Meredith, who intends to put her unwanted baby up for adoption, learns of the love between Georgy and Jos, she gladly turns the infant over to them and blithely returns to her former life. For a time Georgy and Jos are happy, but Jos soon becomes restless and a little annoyed at Georgy's lavishing all of her love upon the baby. In an attempt to regain Georgy's undivided love, Jos takes her on a boat trip and clowns about pathetically in the hope they can recapture their lighthearted intimacy. Both realize, however, that something has gone out of their love, and when Jos eventually moves out, Georgy knows that the authorities will soon come and take her beloved baby away from her. All is not lost, however; for Mr. Leamington, whose wife has since died, comes to the rescue. If Georgy will marry him, he will adopt the child. Mr. Leamington thus wins his "Georgy Girl," and Georgy happily keeps her baby and prepares for a life of upper-class matrimonial comfort. *Domestics. Roommates. Violinists. Upper classes. Infants. Mistresses. Motherhood. Illegitimacy. Adoption. Marriage. London.*

Note: Opened in London in Oct 1966.

THE GERARD MALANGA STORY see THE CHELSEA GIRLS

GERONIMO   F6.1782

Levy-Gardner-Laven–Bedford Pictures. *Dist* United Artists. 28 Apr **1962** [Albuquerque, New Mexico, opening; c28 Apr 1962; LP22409]. Sd; col (Technicolor). 35mm (Panavision). 101 min.

Prod-Dir Arnold Laven. *Exec Prod* Jules Levy, Arthur Gardner. *Orig Screenplay* Pat Fielder. *Story* Pat Fielder, Arnold Laven. *Dir Photog* Alex Phillips. *Art Dir* Roberto Silva. *Set Decor* Carlos Granjean. *Film Ed* Marsh Hendry. *Mus* Hugo Friedhofer. *Cond* Herschel Burke Gilbert. *Sd* Rafael Esparza, Buddy Myers. *Asst Dir* Mario Cisneros. *Miss Devi's Wardrobe* Norma. *Makeup* Ana Guerrero. *Sp Eff* Leon Ortega. *Horses Provided by* Victor Manuel Moreno.

Cast: Chuck Connors (*Geronimo*), Kamala Devi (*Teela*), Ross Martin (*Mangus*), Pat Conway (*Maynard*), Adam West (*Delahay*), Enid Jaynes (*Huera*), Lawrence Dobkin (*General Crook*), Denver Pyle (*Senator Conrad*), Armando Silvestre (*Natchez*), John Anderson (*Burns*), Amanda Ames (*Mrs. Burns*), Mario Navarro (*Giantah*), Eduardo Noriega (*Colonel Morales*), Nancy Rodman (*Mrs. Marsh*), Joe Higgins (*Kincaide*), Robert Hughes (*corporal*), James Burk (*cavalryman*), Bill Hughes (*Indian scout*), Bravado (*El Torero, a horse*).

Western drama. Geronimo and his remaining Apache warriors, tired of warring with the governments of the United States and Mexico, surrender in 1883 to the U. S. Cavalry in return for the promise of food, shelter, and land of their own. They find instead that they are expected to live on San Carlos Reservation as humble farmers. Teela, the reservation schoolteacher, tries to persuade Geronimo to learn reading and writing, so as to share in the white man's civilization. The government representative then conspires to sell part of the Indian reservation to a cattle dealer, and Geronimo and his tribe flee to Mexico. Once there, they renew their war with the cavalry in the hope of arousing national sympathy for their cause. They make raids for food and arms and force Teela to return with them. She becomes Geronimo's wife. The tiny band continues to fight against enormous odds. Word of the injustice they have suffered finally reaches Washington, and Senator Conrad is sent to investigate the uprising. As he arrives, the Apaches are being cornered and are about to be annihilated. Conrad succeeds in convincing Geronimo that the United States Government is prepared to sign a new and more just treaty, and the Apaches again surrender. *Apache Indians. Schoolteachers. Cattlemen. Injustice. Uprisings. Racism. Land rights. Farming. Treaties. United States—History—Indian campaigns. Arizona. Mexico. Geronimo. George F. Crook. San Carlos Indian Reservation (Arizona). United States Army—Cavalry. United States Congress. Horses.*

Note: Filmed in Mexico.

GERTRUD (Denmark)   F6.1783

Palladium. *Dist* Pathé Contemporary Films. 2 Jun **1966** [New York opening]. Sd; b&w. 35mm. 115 min.

Prod Jørgen Nielsen. *Exec Prod* John Hilbard. *Assoc Prod* Jens Ravn. *Dir-Writ* Carl Th. Dreyer. *Photog* Henning Bendtsen, Arne Abrahamsen. *Art Dir* Kai Rasch. *Film Ed* Edith Schlüssel. *Mus & Soloist* Jørgen Jersild. *Songs* Grethe Risbjerg Thomsen. *Mus:* "Ich grolle nicht" Robert Schumann. *Lyr* Heinrich Heine. *Singing Voice for Nina Pens Rode* Gurli Plesners. *Sd* Knud Kristensen. *Asst Dir* Solveig Ersgaard, Jens Ravn. *Studio Mgr* Erik Overbye.

Cast: Nina Pens Rode (*Gertrud Kanning*), Bendt Rothe (*Gustav Kanning*), Ebbe Rode (*Gabriel Lidman*), Baard Owe (*Erland Jansson*), Axel Strøbye (*Axel Nygren*), Anna Malberg (*Kanning's mother*), Edouard Mielche (*The Rector Magnificus*), Vera Gebuhr (*Kanning's maid*), Karl Gustav Ahlefeldt, Lars Knutzon, William Knoblauch, Valsø Holm, Ole Sarvig.

Drama. Source: Hjalmar Söderberg, *Gertrud* (a play; 1906). Gertrud, a singer, retired from the stage when she married Gustav, a successful lawyer who is about to receive an important ministerial position in the government. Since her husband's profession detracts from the all-consuming love that she demands, Gertrud makes love with Erland, a young composer, believing that he will be the perfect lover. The next day, however, Gertrud and Gustav attend the celebration of poet Gabriel Lidman's 50th birthday, and she learns from Gabriel, a former lover, that Erland has boasted of the affair in order to advance his career. She confides to her friend Axel Nygren that she has had the misfortune to love only men who were incapable of understanding her or unwilling to give themselves completely to her. At the celebration, Gertrud is asked to perform, and accompanied by Erland, she sings "Ich grolle nicht" ("I Am Not Angry"). Shortly thereafter, she breaks with Erland, refuses to reconcile with Gustav, and turns down an opportunity to travel with Gabriel. Instead, Gertrud journeys alone to Paris to devote herself to study with Axel. Thirty years later he visits her in her hometown and gives her a copy of his new book. She returns his letters so that he may destroy them; but before he leaves, she reads to him a poem about love, written when she was only 16. *Singers. Lawyers. Composers. Poets. Marriage. Infidelity. Friendship. Birthdays. Paris.*

Note: World premiere in Paris in Dec 1964 as *Gertrud*; released in Denmark in Mar 1965.

DAS GESCHLECHT DER ENGEL see THE SEX OF ANGELS

DER GESTIEFELTE KATER see PUSS 'N BOOTS

GET 'EM ALL (Japan)   F6.1784

Toho Co. 17 Nov **1961** [Los Angeles opening]. Sd; col? 35mm. 87 min. *Dir* Eizo Sugawa.

Cast: Hiroshi Mizuhara, Akihiko Hirata, Yukiko Shimazaki, Akemi Kita, Tatsuya Nakadai, Kenzo Tamu, Seiji Miyaguchi, Tetsuro Tamba, Kyoko Kishida, Chieko Nakakita, Jerry Fujio. No information about the nature of this film has been found.

Note: Released in Japan in Nov 1960 as *Kenju yo saraba*.

GET ON WITH IT (Great Britain)   F6.1785

Bertram Ostrer Productions. *Dist* Governor Films. 3 Apr **1963** [Los Angeles opening]. Sd; b&w. 35mm. 88 min.

Prod Bertram Ostrer. *Dir* C. M. Pennington-Richards. *Screenplay* Hazel Adair, Hugh Woodhouse. *Adtl Seq* Bob Monkhouse. *Photog* Stephen Dade. *Camera Op* Jack Atchelor. *Focus* Tony Spratling. *Art Dir* Tony Masters. *Asst Art Dir* Geoffrey Tozer. *Draughtsman* Bill Alexander. *Scenic Artist* Peter Melrose. *Film Ed* Bill Lenny. *1st Asst Ed* Michael Round. *2d Asst Ed* Georgio Gomelsky. *Mus* Ken Jones. *Sd Rec* George Stephenson. *Boom Op* Jack W. Davies. *Sd Camera Op* Ernie Webb. *1st, 2d & 3d Asst Dir* Colin Brewer, Terry Lens, Michael Klaw. *Prod Mgr* Albert Becket. *Prod Sec* Jill Langley. *Cont* Pamela Carlton. *Wardrobe Mistress* Bridget Sellers. *Makeup Artist* Ernest Gasser. *Hairdresser* Barbara Barnard. *Prop Buyer* Harry Parr. *Still Photog* Laurie Ridley. *Grip* J. Vincent. *Rigger* P. Harris. *Chargehand Prop* John Hemmington. *Chargehand Electrn* Archie Dansie.

Cast: Bob Monkhouse (*David Cookson*), Kenneth Connor (*Sam Field*), Shirley Eaton (*Jill Venner*), Eric Barker (*Col. J. J. Proudfoot/The Dean*), Ronnie Stevens (*Brian Dexter*), Richard Wattis (*Macreedy*), Reginald Beckwith (*Duff*), Ian Whittaker, actor (*Fuller*), David Glover (*Bull*), David Horne (*Admiral Southbound*), Charles Hawtrey (*Roper, a chemist*), Charlotte Mitchell (*Mrs. Burke*), Richard Caldicot (*prison governor*), Cyril Chamberlain (*TV director*), Mercy Haystead (*Miss Figg*), Jeremy Hawk (*Professor Lovitt*), Michael Miles (*himself*), Sheena Marshe (*Lolita Roughage*), Patrick Holt (*news reader*), Graham Stark (*sour-faced man*), Valli Newby (*cheeky brunette*), Keith Fordyce (*himself*).

Comedy. Colonel J. J. Proudfoot, manager of Proudfoot Chemical Industries, is furious over the diminishing sales of his new toothpaste, "Dreem." Advertising executive Duff secures from his cousin, the dean of King Alfred's Dental College, the services of two recent graduates, David Cookson and Brian Dexter, to promote the sale of "Dreem." With the assistance of ex-convict Sam Field, a dental mechanic, they give free treatment to pretty factory girls, but the outraged Proudfoot threatens them with dismissal. The boys create "New Dreem," a dentifrice superior to its predecessor, which their employer thinks is a fraud. Spurred on by Jill Venner, the "Dreem" girl, Cookson poses as a U.S. senator and infiltrates a missile-launching site. He slips a tape recorded jingle advertising "New Dreem" into the satellite to replace a recorded message from the president, and the satellite is launched into a 7-year orbit. The toothpaste receives unprecedented publicity, and the colonel, delighted with its free promotion, promotes Cookson and Dexter. *Manufacturers. Deans. Dentists. Ex-convicts. Factory workers. Business management. Advertising. Publicity. Employer-employee relations. Impersonation. Toothpaste. Rocket-launching sites. Recorders.*

Note: Released in Great Britain in 1961 as *Dentist on the Job*; running time: 88 min.

GET OUTTA TOWN *see* GANGSTER'S REVENGE

GET WHAT YOU PAY FOR F6.1786

Dist Stacey Distributors. ca 1970. Sd; col. 16mm. 61-81 min.

Sex film. A director of sex films hires a nearsighted cameraman at a cheap rate to photograph his film—one that includes scenes of sadism, group sex, and lesbianism. The resulting film is disastrously out of focus. *Motion picture directors. Motion picture cameramen. Actors. Sadism. Group sex. Lesbianism. Sex exploitation films.*

Note: Also known as *You Get What You Pay For.*

GET YOURSELF A COLLEGE GIRL F6.1787

Four Leaf Productions. *Dist* Metro-Goldwyn-Mayer, Inc. 18 Dec **1964** [Charlotte, North Carolina, opening; c9 Nov 1964; LP29233]. Sd; col (Metrocolor). 35mm (Panavision). 87 min.

Prod Sam Katzman. *Dir* Sidney Miller. *Story-Screenplay* Robert E. Kent. *Photog* Fred H. Jackman. *Camera Op* Bill Ion. *Art Dir* Addison Hehr, George W. Davis. *Set Decor* Henry Grace, Jack Mills. *Film Ed* Ben Lewis. *Asst Ed* William McMillin. *Music Supv & Cond* Fred Karger. *Titl Song* Fred Karger, Sidney Miller. *Song: "The Swingin' Set"* Fred Karger, Donnie Brooks, Sidney Miller. *Choreog* Hal Belfer. *Rec Supv* Franklin Milton. *Mix* Wally Wallace. *Boom Op* Barry Thomas. *Rec* Bruce Wright. *Asst Dir* Eddie Saeta, William Lukather, Bruce Satterlee. *Prod Coörd* Robert Stone. *Script Supv* Cleo Anton. *Wardrobe* Norman Burza, Florence Hackett. *Makeup Supv* William Tuttle. *Makeup* Ron Berkeley. *Hairstyles* Sydney Guilaroff. *Sp Eff* J. E. Christensen. *Still Photog* Robert Coburn. *Gaffer* Milford Cline. *Grip* Lloyd Isbell. *Casting* Mel Ballerino.

Cast: Mary Ann Mobley *(Terry)*, Chad Everett *(Gary)*, Joan O'Brien *(Marge)*, Nancy Sinatra *(Lynne)*, Chris Noel *(Sue)*, Willard Waterman *(Sen. Hubert Morrison)*, Fabrizio Mioni *(Armand)*, James Millhollin *(Gordon)*, Paul Todd *(Ray)*, Donnie Brooks *(Donnie)*, Hortense Petra *(Donna)*, Dorothy Neumann *(Dean)*, Marti Barris *(secretary)*, Mario Costello *(bellboy)*, Dave Clark Five, The Animals, Stan Getz, Astrud Gilberto, Jimmy Smith Trio, The Standells, The Rhythm Masters, Freddie Bell, Roberta Linn, The Bell Boys *(guest stars)*.

Comedy with music. Terry, a student at a conservative girls' college, has written some sophisticated, bestselling popular songs under a pseudonym, knowing that she will be expelled if her secret is learned. Terry's extracurricular activities are discovered when her publisher, Gary, telephones her at school; and she is placed on probation until after the Christmas holidays. While spending the holidays at Sun Valley, Terry meets Gary in person. She becomes enraged and refuses his request to pose in a sheer nightgown for a painting to be used to promote her song, blaming him for her predicament. Sen. Hubert Morrison, grandson of the founder of Terry's school, arrives at Sun Valley to acquire a better understanding of youth and, coincidentally, to become acquainted with Terry's ballet teacher, Marge, also a guest at the resort. An embarrassing accident in which the senator loses his trousers on a dance floor jeopardizes his reelection; but the students, led by Gary, rally behind the senator and stage a show to regain him support. The show, featuring several popular musical groups, is a success and guarantees the senator's reelection; and Terry and Gary find they are in love. *Students. Composers. Publishers. Dance teachers. Youth. Political campaigns. Rock and roll. College life. Ski resorts. Christmas. Sun Valley. United States Congress.*

Note: Location scenes filmed in Sun Valley. Working titles: *Go-Go Set, The Swingin' Set,* and *Watusi A-Go-Go.*

GETTING INTO HEAVEN F6.1788

ExPix. 26 Feb **1970** [Maryland license]. Sd; col (Eastmancolor). 35mm. 75 min.

Prod Edward L. Montoro, James P. Somich. *Dir-Writ* Edward L. Montoro. *Photog* James P. Somich. *Re-rec* Thomas Peterson.

Cast: Marie Marceau *(Heaven)*, Jennie Lynn *(Sin)*, Miles White *(Salacity)*, Scott Cameron *(Bernie)*, Phyllis Stangel *(Karen)*.

Comedy. Three models, Heaven, Sin, and Karen, who want to break into the movies, try to convince Salacity, a lusty film producer, that they are talented, but Salacity is interested in the models only for his private pleasure. A picnic in a secluded grove gives Heaven and Sin their best chance to "persuade" Salacity to hire them, but their efforts to become starlets are in vain. Meanwhile, Heaven becomes excited by Sin, and the two models have a brief lesbian relationship. Later, Heaven's boyfriend Bernie tries to convince her to forget about getting into movies and to marry him. Heaven, however, decides

to make one last try with Salacity. The women kidnap the producer and try to exhaust him into submission and thereby get into the movies. Their marathon "love-in" leaves Salacity still willing after the three are totally exhausted. Just as Heaven finally agrees to marry Bernie, Salacity offers them roles in his new film. *Models. Motion picture producers. Lesbianism. Satyriasis. Group sex. Kidnaping. Motion pictures.*

Note: Made on location in the Sequoia National Park.

GETTING STRAIGHT F6.1789

The Organization. *Dist* Columbia Pictures. 13 May **1970** [New York opening; c1 May 1970; LP37910]. Sd; col (Eastman Color). 35mm. 124 min. *MPAA rating* R.

Prod-Dir Richard Rush. *Assoc Prod* Paul Lewis. *Screenplay* Robert Kaufman. *Dir Photog* Laszlo Kovacs. *Camera Asst* Peter Heiser. *Camera Op* Jack Courtland. *Art Dir* Sydney Z. Litwack. *Set Decor* Edward Parker. *Titl Anim* Computer Image Inc. *Film Ed* Maury Winetrobe. *Asst Film Ed* Abe Lincoln, Jr. *Mus* Ronald Stein. *Song:* "Getting Straight" Ronald Stein, Dan Peyton, Marty Kaniger, Caroline Arnell. *Songs:* "Feelings" & "Shades of Gray" Barry Mann, Cynthia Weil. *Song:* "Ain't No Way" Dan Peyton, Marty Kaniger. *Song:* "Moon Rock and Talk" Ronald Stein. *Sung by* P. K. Limited. *Song:* "I'll Build a Bridge" Jack Keller, Ernie Sheldon. *Sung by* The New Establishment. *Sd* Les Fresholtz, Chick Bourland, Arthur Piantadosi, Paul Kretchman. *Mus Ed* Else Blangsted. *Sd Eff* Edit-International. *1st & 2d Asst Dir* Sheldon Schrager, Howard W. Koch, Jr., Charles Norton. *Unit Prod Mgr* Sheldon Schrager. *Prod Asst* Sheila Scott. *Script Supv* Terry Terrill. *Wardrobe* Gene Ashman. *Makeup Supv* Leo Lotito, Ben Lane. *Hairstyles* Virginia Jones. *Sp Eff* Ira Anderson, Jr. *Gaffer* Don Carstensen. *Prop Master* Walter Starkey. *Key Grip* Carl Manoogian. *Stunt Coörd* Chuck Bail. *Still Photog* Ken Bell.

Cast: Elliott Gould *(Harry Bailey)*, Candice Bergen *(Jan)*, Robert F. Lyons *(Nick)*, Jeff Corey *(Dr. Wilhunt)*, Max Julien *(Ellis)*, Cecil Kellaway *(Dr. Kasper)*, Jon Lormer *(Vandenburg)*, Leonard Stone *(Lysander)*, William Bramley *(Wade Linden)*, Jeannie Berlin *(Judy Kramer)*, John Rubinstein *(Herbert)*, Richard Anders *(Dr. Greengrass)*, Brenda Sykes *(Luan)*, Jenny Sullivan *(Sheila)*, Gregory Sierra *(Garcia)*, Billie Bird *(landlady)*, Harrison Ford *(Jake)*, Elizabeth Lane *(Alice Linden)*, Hilarie Thompson *(Cynthia)*, Irene Tedrow *(Mrs. Stebbins)*, Joanna Serpe *(roommate)*, Scott Perry *(airline representative)*, Harry Holcombe *(Dean Chesney)*, Richard Eymann, Warren Merrill.

Comedy-drama. Source: Ken Kolb, *Getting Straight* (Philadelphia, 1967). Civil rights activist and Vietnam veteran Harry Bailey returns to college after six years to obtain a master's degree leading to a teaching certificate. Despite his conflicts with computer-oriented department chairman Wilhunt, who opposes Harry's romantic dedication to teaching, Harry is assigned to teach remedial English. Although black militant Ellis presses Harry to participate in student protests, he refuses. Among Harry's sexual partners are his students, black coeds, and his steady girl friend Jan. Upon enlisting in the marines Harry's former friend Nick reveals to Wilhunt that he has taken Harry's exams, thereby jeopardizing the graduate student's academic future. When riots break out on campus Harry is recruited as an unwilling student liaison by college president Vandenburg. He later submits to an oral examination before a professorial panel. During the test Harry disputes an examiner's homosexual interpretation of *The Great Gatsby*, in refutation dancing obscenely on the seminar table, denouncing the panel, and passionately kissing the pedant. Having thus ended his academic career, Harry rushes into the corridor, where he joins Ellis and Jan in a student riot. *Veterans. Mistresses. Professors. Militants. Students. Negroes. Student activism. College life. Miscegenation. Male homosexuality. Riots. Demonstrations. Vietnam War 1964–73. "The Great Gatsby".*

Note: Location scenes filmed at Lake Community College, Oregon.

GHARBAR *see* THE HOUSEHOLDER

THE GHASTLY ONES F6.1790

Jerome Frederick Productions. *Dist* JER Pictures. 6 Sep **1968** [Charlotte, North Carolina, opening]. Sd; col. 35mm. 81 min.

Prod Jerome Frederick. *Dir* Andy Milligan. *Screenplay* Hal Sherwood, Andy Milligan. *Photog* Andy Milligan, D. Mills. *Film Ed* Gerald Jackson.

Cast: Veronica Radbrook, Hal Belsoe, Eileen Haves, Don Williams, Maggie Rogers, Carol Vogel, Richard Ramos, Anne Linden, Fib LaBlanque, Haal Borske, Neil Flanders, Hal Sherwood.

Horror film. After their father's death, three sisters and their husbands are forced to go to a deserted island off Maine where, according to his will, they must spend time in an old mansion. They are met there by two old women and a demented hunchback. While at the mansion all three men are killed. One is found hanged; another is killed by a hooded figure who disembowels him with a butcher knife; the last is found with a pitchfork in his throat. One of the sisters is decapitated, and her head is served on a dinner platter. The two surviving sisters are cornered by the killer on a staircase. The killer, one of the old women, discloses herself to be the illegitimate half sister of their late father. She has killed everybody because she wants the estate for herself and is about to slay the two sisters with a meat ax, but the hunchback stops her. She sets him on fire, but he manages to get the ax from her and uses it to kill her as they fall downstairs. *Psychopaths. Sisters. Hunchbacks. Aunts. Wills. Murder. Decapitation. Inheritance. Illegitimacy. Islands. Maine.*

Note: Sources indicate that the film was shot in either 8 or 16mm.

GHETTO FREAKS *see* **SIGN OF AQUARIUS**

GHIDRAH, THE THREE-HEADED MONSTER (Japan)   **F6.1791**
Toho Co. *Dist* Continental Distributing, Inc. 29 Sep **1965** [Dallas opening]. Sd; col (Eastmancolor). 35mm (Tohoscope). 85 min.
    Prod Tomoyuki Tanaka. *Dir* Inoshiro Honda. *Screenplay* Shinichi Sekizawa. *Photog* Hajime Koizumi. *Art Dir* Takeo Kita. *Film Ed* Ryohei Fujii. *Mus* Akira Ifukube. *Sd Eff* Hisashi Shimonaga. *Sp Eff* Eiji Tsuburaya.
    Cast: Yosuke Natsuki *(Shindo)*, Yuriko Hoshi *(Naoko)*, Hiroshi Koizumi *(Professor Murai)*, Takashi Shimura *(Dr. Tsukamoto)*, Emi Ito, Yumi Ito *("The Peanuts," little sisters)*, Akiko Wakabayashi *(Princess Salno)*, Hisaya Ito *(Malness)*, Akihiko Hirata *(Okita)*, Kenji Sahara *(Kanamaki)*, Eiji Okada.
    Science fiction melodrama. A meteorite crashes in the mountains of Japan, and scientists rush to examine it, while the country prepares for the arrival of a foreign princess. The plane carrying Princess Salno is blown up in midair, but later she mysteriously appears in Tokyo, claiming that she has come from Mars to warn the world of danger. Naoko, a woman reporter, befriends the princess; and Naoko's brother, police detective Shindo, saves Princess Salno from assassins. Meanwhile, the meteorite bursts open; and Ghidrah, a three-headed monster, emerges and begins wreaking havoc over the countryside. In desperation officials summon the monsters Mothra, Rodan, and Godzilla to combat this new menace. After a destructive battle the three monsters defeat Ghidrah. *Monsters. Royalty. Reporters. Detectives. Assassination. Brother-sister relationship. Meteors. Tokyo. Mars (planet). Airplane accidents. Ghidrah. Mothra. Rodan. Godzilla.*
    Note: Released in Japan in 1965 as *Sandai kaiju chikyu saidai no kessen*; running time: 92 min. Also known as *The Biggest Fight on Earth* and *The Greatest Battle on Earth.*

THE GHOST (Italy)   **F6.1792**
Panda Film. *Dist* Magna Pictures Distribution Corp. 18 Feb **1965** [Dallas opening]. Sd; col (Technicolor). 35mm. 96 min.
    Prod Louis Mann. *Dir* Robert Hampton. *Screenplay* Robert Davidson, Robert Hampton. *Story* Robert Davidson. *Photog* Donald Green. *Art Dir* Samuel Fields. *Film Ed* Donna Christie. *Mus* Frank Wallace. *Prod Mgr* Lou D. Kelly. *Cost* Mary MacCharty.
    Cast: Barbara Steele *(Margaret)*, Peter Baldwin *(Dr. Charles Livingstone)*, Leonard Elliott *(Dr. Hichcock)*, Harriet White *(Catherine)*, Raoul H. Newman *(canon)*, Reginald Price Anderson *(Notary Fisher)*, Carlo Kechler *(police superintendent)*, Carol Bennet.
    Horror film. In 1910 an unfaithful wife persuades her doctor lover to inject her ailing husband with poison. Following his funeral, the husband's ghost appears before the wife to inform her where he has hidden his jewels. The wife investigates and finds the jewel box empty, and her husband's housekeeper swears the gems were taken by the doctor. Now half-crazed, the wife slashes her lover with a razor and burns his body in an incinerator. Then the husband reappears alive to explain how he and the housekeeper faked his death, but the husband accidentally drinks a glass of poison his wife had intended for herself. The doomed man crawls into a secret passage to die alone as the police arrive to drag away his raving wife. *Physicians. Housekeepers. Infidelity. Murder. Insanity. Revenge. Poisoning. Jewels. Ghosts.*
    Note: Opened in Rome in May 1963 as *Lo spettro*. Production and cast pseudonyms include: Louis Mann (Luigi Carpentieri and Ermanno Donati), Robert Hampton (Riccardo Freda), Donald Green (Raffaele Masciocchi), Samuel Fields (Mario Chiari), Donna Christie (Ornella Micheli), Frank Wallace (Franco Mannino), Lou D. Kelly (Livio Maffei), Raoul H. Newman (Umberto Raho), and Leonard G. Elliot (Elio Jotta). Sequel to *The Horrible Dr. Hichcock*, q. v.

THE GHOST AND MR. CHICKEN   **F6.1793**
Universal Pictures. 20 Jan **1966** [New Orleans opening; c2 Apr 1966; LP35375]. Sd (Westrex); col (Technicolor). 35mm (Techniscope). 90 min.
    Prod Edward J. Montagne. *Dir* Alan Rafkin. *Writ* Jim Fritzell, Everett Greenbaum. *Dir Photog* William Margulies. *Art Dir* Alexander Golitzen, George Webb. *Set Decor* John McCarthy, Oliver Emert. *Main Titl* Cinefx. *Film Ed* Sam E. Waxman. *Mus* Vic Mizzy. *Mus Supv* Joseph Gershenson. *Sd* Waldon O. Watson, Earl N. Crain, Sr. *Asst Dir* Phil Bowles, James Welch, Bill Gilmore. *Unit Prod Mgr* Wes Thompson. *Cost* Rosemary Odell. *Makeup* Bud Westmore. *Hairstyles* Larry Germain.

Cast: Don Knotts *(Luther Heggs)*, Joan Staley *(Alma)*, Liam Redmond *(Kelsey)*, Dick Sargent *(Beckett)*, Skip Homeier *(Ollie)*, Reta Shaw *(Mrs. Maxwell)*, Lurene Tuttle *(Mrs. Miller)*, Philip Ober *(Simmons)*, Harry Hickox *(Police Chief Fuller)*, Charles Lane *(Whitlow)*, Jesslyn Fax *(Mrs. Hutchinson)*, Nydia Westman *(Mrs. Cobb)*, George Chandler *(judge)*, Robert Cornthwaite *(Springer)*, Jim Begg *(Herkie)*, Sandra Gould *(Loretta Pine)*, James Millhollin *(Mr. Maxwell)*, Cliff Norton *(bailiff)*, Ellen Corby *(Miss Tremaine)*, Jim Boles *(Billy Ray)*, J. Edward McKinley *(mayor)*, Eddie Quillan *(elevator operator)*, Hope Summers *(Suzanna Blush)*, Hal Smith *(Calver Weems)*.
    Mystery comedy. Luther Heggs, a meek, timid typesetter for a smalltown newspaper, envisions himself in his daydreams as a reporter worthy of winning the love of Alma Parker. His chance comes when he writes an article on the local "haunted house," where a gruesome murder and suicide took place 20 years earlier. The newspaper piece creates such a stir that Luther's editor, George Beckett, orders him to spend a night in the old house and do a followup story. During the long vigil, the terrified Luther discovers a hidden staircase, a bloodstained organ that plays by itself, and a portrait dripping blood. When his story is published, Luther is given a town picnic in honor of his courage. Nick Simmons, a descendant of the murdered couple and the current owner of the old house, sues Luther and his paper for libel. At the trial, the judge makes the jurors and all involved parties pay a visit to the deserted mansion. Although nothing is found, Luther accidentally tricks Mr. Simmons into revealing his own guilt in the 20-year-old killings; and Luther once again becomes the town hero. *Typesetters. Reporters. Editors. Judges. Smalltown life. Murder. Ambition. Timidity. Lawsuits. Newspapers. Haunted houses. Picnics. Trials. Juries.*
    Note: Working title: *Running Scared.*

THE GHOST IN THE INVISIBLE BIKINI   **F6.1794**
American International Pictures. 6 Apr **1966** [Boston opening; c6 Apr 1966; LP32617]. Sd; col (PathéColor). 35mm (Panavision). 82 min.
    Prod James H. Nicholson, Samuel Z. Arkoff. *Co-prod* Anthony Carras. *Ghost Seq Prod* Ronald Sinclair, Carol Sinclair. *Dir* Don Weis. *Screenplay* Louis M. Heyward, Elwood Ullman. *Story* Louis M. Heyward. *Photog* Stanley Cortez. *Art Dir* Daniel Haller. *Set Decor* Clarence Steensen. *Main Titl* Butler-Glouner Inc. *Film Ed* Fred Feitshans, Eve Newman. *Mus Supv* Al Simms. *Mus Score* Les Baxter. *Songs:* "Geronimo," "Swing-A-Ma-Thing," "Don't Try To Fight It, Baby," "Stand Up and Fight," "Make the Music Pretty" Guy Hemric, Jerry Styner. *Song:* "Geronimo" sung by Nancy Sinatra. *Choreog* Jack Baker. *Sd* Wallace Nogle. *Sd Eff* Nelson-Corso. *Asst Dir* Clark Paylow. *Prod Supv* Jack Bohrer. *Prod Asst* Jack Cash. *Cost* Richard Bruno. *Makeup* Ted Coodley. *Hairstyles* Ray Foreman. *Sp Eff* Roger George. *Sp Photog Eff* Butler-Glouner Inc. *Prop* Karl Brainard, Richard M. Rubin. *Constr Coörd* Ross Hahn.
    Cast: Tommy Kirk *(Chuck Phillips)*, Deborah Walley *(Lili Morton)*, Aron Kincaid *(Bobby)*, Quinn O'Hara *(Sinistra)*, Jesse White *(J. Sinister Hulk)*, Harvey Lembeck *(Eric Von Zipper)*, Nancy Sinatra *(Vicki)*, Claudia Martin *(Lulu)*, Francis X. Bushman *(Malcolm)*, Benny Rubin *(Chicken Feather)*, Bobbi Shaw *(Princess Yolanda)*, George Barrows *(Monstro)*, Luree Holmes *(Shirl)*, Piccola Pupa *(Piccola)*, Alberta Nelson *(Alberta)*, Andy Romano *(J. D.)*, Basil Rathbone *(Reginald Ripper)*, Patsy Kelly *(Myrtle Forbush)*, Boris Karloff *(Hiram Stokely, the corpse)*, Susan Hart *(Cecily, the ghost)*, Bobby Fuller Four *(themselves)*, Ed Garner, Mary Hughes, Patti Chandler, Frank Alesia, Salli Sachse, Sue Hamilton *(boys and girls)*, Myrna Ross, Jerry Brutsche, Bob Harvey, John Macchia, Alan Fife *(The Rat Pack)*, Elena Andreas, Herb Andreas *(The Statues)*.
    Comedy. Hiram Stokely is visited in his coffin by Cecily, the ghost of his sweetheart of 30 years ago. She tells him that if he performs a good deed within 24 hours he can gain admittance into Heaven as a member in good standing and also become young again. The good deed is to prevent his scheming attorney, Reginald Ripper, from swindling Hiram's rightful heir, young Chuck Phillips, out of his inheritance. As Chuck, his fiancée, Lili Morton, and his spinster aunt Myrtle Forbush prepare for the reading of the will, Myrtle's swinging nephew Bobby arrives at the Stokely mansion to spend the weekend. Also on hand are Eric Von Zipper and his Rat Pack. Amidst all the mayhem, the villainous Ripper finds it difficult to carry out his plan for doing away with Chuck. When Ripper makes a last attempt at murder in the mansion's basement chamber of horrors, Hiram and Cecily foil the scheme, and the inheritance rightfully goes to Chuck. Having done his good deed, Hiram is given his reward, but it is more than he had bargained for; as Cecily leads him toward Heaven, he becomes 3 years old again. *Corpses. Ghosts. Lawyers. Heirs. Swindlers. Spinsters. Aunts. Murder. Inheritance. Rewards. Heaven.*
    Note: Location scenes filmed in Pasadena. Prerelease titles: *The Girl in the Invisible Bikini, Pajama Party in the Haunted House, Slumber Party in a Haunted House, Slumber Party in Horror House, Bikini Party in a Haunted House, Beach Party in a Haunted House,* and *Ghost in the Glass Bikini.*

GHOSTS—ITALIAN STYLE (France/Italy)   **F6.1795**

C. C. Champion-Les Films Concordia-Les Films Corona. *Dist* Metro-Goldwyn-Mayer, Inc. 22 Jan **1969** [New York opening; c31 Dec 1968; LP37155]. Sd; col (Technicolor). 35mm. 92 min. *MPAA rating G.*

A Carlo Ponti Production. *Prod* Carlo Ponti. *Assoc Prod* Ernest Pintoff. *Dir* Renato Castellani. *Screenplay* Renato Castellani, Adriano Baracco, Leo Benvenuti, Piero De Bernardi. *English Dial* Ernest Pintoff. *Dir Photog* Tonino Delli Colli. *Camera* Idelmo Simonelli. *Art Dir* Piero Poletto. *Interior Decor* Supermercato Mobili. *Film Ed* Iolanda Benvenuti. *Mus Comp* Luis Enriquez Bacalov. *Song:* "Vent'enni" sung by Lucio Dalla. *Sd* Carlo Palmieri, Giovanni Rosa. *Asst Dir* Mimmola Girosi. *Prod Supv* Ione Tuzi. *Prod Mgr* Giorgio Russo. *Cost Dsgn* Enrico Sabbatini. *Cost Dsgn for Miss Loren* Piero Tosi. *Makeup* Mario Van Riel. *Makeup for Miss Loren* Giuseppe Annunziata. *Hairdresser for Miss Loren* Ada Palombi. *Hairdresser* Vasco Reggiani. *Sp Eff* Tom Howard.

Cast: Sophia Loren (*Maria*), Vittorio Gassman (*Pasquale*), Mario Adorf (*Alfredo*), Aldo Giuffrè (*Raffaele*), Margaret Lee (*Sayonara*), Francesco Tensi (*Professor Santanna*), Marcello Mastroianni (*headless ghost*), Francis De Wolff, Augusta Merola, Piera Degli Esposti, Giovanni Tarallo, Nietta Zocchi, Valentino Macchi.

Comedy. Freely adapted from: Eduardo De Filippo, *Questi fantasmi!* (a play; 1946). Maria, unhappy with the life of poverty she leads with her husband, Pasquale, a luckless opera singer, seeks the help of Alfredo, the wealthy director of the orphanage in which she was raised. At the same time, the owner of a 17th-century Neapolitan palace invites Pasquale to live there rent free in the hope of dispelling rumors that the place is haunted. Without telling his wife of the ghost legend, Pasquale accepts the offer, while Alfredo, anxious to be near Maria, secretly moves into a palace room connected to the couple's apartment by a hidden staircase. After Pasquale has seen Alfredo and mistaken him for the ghost, he finds a bundle of money dropped by Alfredo and concludes that the ghost wants to help him. Hoping to turn the palace into a boardinghouse, Pasquale rents a room to a dim-witted prostitute, Sayonara. Unaware that Pasquale thinks the money was left by a ghost, Alfredo tells Maria that her husband has no objection to sharing her so long as he is well paid. Outraged, Maria makes plans to leave with Alfredo. Pasquale is enraged to discover the true source of his wealth, and Maria is shocked to discover that Pasquale was unaware of her relationship with Alfredo. She disappears, and Pasquale confesses to her murder; but, after 7 months imprisonment, he is acquitted on the grounds that his crime was motivated by honor. Returning to the palace, he finds Maria waiting. Alfredo, upon seeing what he believes to be the ghost of Maria, tearfully confesses that he was responsible for getting Pasquale fired from several jobs. Taking advantage of the situation, Maria extracts from Alfredo a large donation to her memory, and she makes him promise to marry the forlorn Sayonara. Fortified by their new wealth, Pasquale and Maria move to Scotland and take jobs as domestics for an eccentric lord who lives in a castle inhabited by a headless ghost. *Singers. Prostitutes. Ghosts. Poverty. Mistaken identity. Infidelity. Murder. Wealth. Castles. Orphanages. Haunted houses. Naples.*

Note: Released in Italy in 1967 as *Questi fantasmi*; running time: 120 min

THE GHOUL IN SCHOOL see **WEREWOLF IN A GIRLS' DORMITORY**

GIANT MONSTER see **THE NIGHT THEY KILLED RASPUTIN**

THE GIANT OF METROPOLIS (Italy)   **F6.1796**

Centro Produzione. *Dist* Seven Arts Associated Corp. 20 Nov **1963** [New York opening]. Sd; col (Eastmancolor). 35mm. 92 min.

Prod Emimmo Salvi. *Dir* Umberto Scarpelli. *Screenplay* Sabatino Ciuffini, Oreste Palella, Ambrogio Molteni, Gino Stafford, Emimmo Salvi. *Photog* Mario Sensi. *Art Dir* Giorgio Giovannini. *Film Ed* Leo Scuccuglia, Adriana Bellanti. *Mus* Armando Trovajoli. *Sd* Alessandro Sarandrea.

Cast: Gordon Mitchell (*Obro*), Roldano Lupi (*Yotar*), Bella Cortez (*Mesede*), Liana Orfei (*Queen Texen*), Furio Meniconi (*Egor*), Marietto (*Elmos*), Omero Gargano.

Science fiction melodrama. In the year 10,000 Obro and a band of men attempt to reach Metropolis, a city where science is supreme, in order to warn King Yotar that his experimenting with the secrets of nature will lead to destruction. Obro reaches Metropolis, but Yotar, determined to make his son Elmos immortal, ignores Obro's warning and subjects Obro to torture and experiments. He is rescued by Queen Texen and Princess Mesede. When Yotar's experiments finally aggravate the forces of nature to the extent of imminent destruction, the maddened king entrusts his son to Obro and Mesede, and the three escape as Metropolis and its inhabitants disappear into the sea. *Royalty. Scientists. Filial relations. Immortality. Torture. Holocausts. Experiments. The Future. Imaginary kingdoms.*

Note: Released in Italy in 1961 as *Il gigante di Metropolis*.

GIBRALTAR ADVENTURE see **THE CLUE OF THE MISSING APE**

GIDGET GOES HAWAIIAN   **F6.1797**

Jerry Bresler Productions. *Dist* Columbia Pictures. 2 Jun **1961** [Miami, Florida, opening; c1 Jun 1961; LP20450]. Sd; col (Eastman Color). 35mm. 102 min.

Prod Jerry Bresler. *Dir* Paul Wendkos. *Screenplay* Ruth Brooks Flippen. *Photog* Robert Bronner. *Art Dir* Walter Holscher. *Set Decor* Darrell Silvera. *Film Ed* William A. Lyon. *Mus* George Duning. *Orch* Arthur Morton. *Songs:* "Gidget Goes Hawaiian," "Wild About That Girl" Fred Karger, Stanley Styne. *Sung by* James Darren. *Choreog* Roland Dupree. *Sd* Charles J. Rice, Lambert Day. *Asst Dir* Jerrold Bernstein. *Makeup* Ben Lane.

Cast: James Darren (*Jeff Mather*), Michael Callan (*Eddie Horner*), Deborah Walley (*Gidget Lawrence*), Carl Reiner (*Russ Lawrence*), Peggy Cass (*Mitzi Stewart*), Eddie Foy, Jr. (*Monty Stewart*), Jeff Donnell (*Dorothy Lawrence*), Vicki Trickett (*Abby Stewart*), Joby Baker (*Judge Hamilton*), Don Edmonds (*Larry Neal*), Bart Patton (*Wally Hodges*), Jan Conaway (*Barbara Jo*), Robin Lory (*Dee Dee*), Arnold Merritt (*Clay Anderson*), Terry Huntingdon (*stewardess*), Jerardo DeCordovier (*waiter*), Vivian Marshall (*Lucy*), Guy Lee (*bellboy*), Johnny Gilbert (*Johnny Spring*), Yankee Chang (*Mr. Matsu*).

Romantic comedy. Based on the characters created by: Frederick Kohner. Gidget Lawrence has a lover's quarrel with her surfer boyfriend, Jeff Mather, when she tells him that her parents are taking her on a vacation to Waikiki Beach; instead of being miserable about the separation, he congratulates her on her good fortune. En route by plane the Lawrences become friendly with Mitzi and Monty Stewart and their spoiled teenaged daughter, Abby. Once in Hawaii, Gidget insists upon moping around despite the romantic attentions of popular TV dancer Eddie Horner, who, in turn, is being pursued by Abby. Disturbed by his daughter's lethargy, Mr. Lawrence sends for Jeff. At the same time Gidget decides to relax and enjoy both Hawaii and Eddie. Jeff arrives just in time to see Gidget kissing Eddie, and he retaliates by making a play for Abby. Further complications arise when the youngsters suspect the four parents of extramarital intrigues. All the misunderstanding is cleared up, however, and Gidget is reunited with Jeff. *Adolescence. Surfers. Dancers. Vacations. Filial relations. Jealousy. Waikiki Beach.*

Note: Location scenes filmed in Hawaii. This is a sequel to *Gidget* (Columbia, 1959).

GIDGET GOES TO ROME   **F6.1798**

Jerry Bresler Productions. *Dist* Columbia Pictures. 7 Aug **1963** [San Francisco opening; c1 Aug 1963; LP26594]. Sd (RCA); col (Eastman Color by Pathé). 35mm. 101 min.

A Jerry Bresler Production. *Prod* Jerry Bresler. *Dir* Paul Wendkos. *Screenplay* Ruth Brooks Flippen, Katherine Eunson, Dale Eunson. *Orig Story* Ruth Brooks Flippen. *Dir Photog* Enzo Barboni, Robert Bronner. *Art Dir* Toni Sarzi-Braga, Robert Peterson. *Set Decor* Ferdinando Ruffo. *Film Ed* William A. Lyon. *Mus* Johnny Williams. *Songs:* "Gegetta," "Big Italian Moon" George David Weiss, Al Kasha. *Sung by* James Darren. *Vocal Arr* Stu Phillips. *Sd Supv* Cyril Collick. *Asst Dir* Tony Brandt, Milton Feldman. *Prod Mgr* Mara Blasetti. *Cost Dsgn* Pat Barto. *Fashion Show Clothes for Jessie Royce Landis & Gidget's Sp Outfit* Sorelle Fontana (Roma). *Makeup Supv* Mel Berns. *Makeup Artist* Serafina Calef. *Hairdresser* Amalia Paoletti. *Aunt Albertina's Wigs* Aldo-Italwig (Rome).

Cast: Cindy Carol (*Gidget*), James Darren (*Jeff*), Jessie Royce Landis (*Aunt Albertina*), Cesare Danova (*Paolo Cellini*), Danielle De Metz (*Daniela Serrini*), Joby Baker (*Judge*), Trudi Ames (*Libby*), Noreen Corcoran (*Lucy*), Peter Brooks (*Clay*), Lisa Gastoni (*Anna Cellini*), Claudio Gora (*Alberto*), Don Porter (*Russ Lawrence*), Jeff Donnell (*Dorothy Lawrence*), Joe Kamel (*pinchman*), Antonio Segurini (*1st Italian boy*), Leonardo Botta (*2d Italian boy*), Umberto Raho (*Mario*), Audrey Fairfax (*contessa*), Vadim Wolkonsky (*Prince Bianchi*), Eddra Gale (*fat woman*), Irina Vasailchikoff (*lean woman*), Charles Borromel (*white-face poet*), David Maunsell (*1st listener*), Jan Commer (*2d listener*), Leon Auerbach (*East Indian yoga*), Nona Medici (*normal woman*), Matilda Calnan (*old woman*), John Stacy (*drunk butler*), Carmen Scarpitta (*1st caviar woman*), Milena Vukotic (*2d caviar woman*), Evi Marandi (*receptionist*), Mimo Billi (*Fontana doorman*), Milly Monti (*Henrietta*), Veronica Wells (*major domo dresser*), Sylvia Llore, Maya Sariole, Adria Ramaccia, Tina Lepri (*models*), Jim Dolen (*Nelson*).

Romantic comedy. Based upon the characters created by: Frederick Kohner. Leaving the surf of southern California, Gidget Lawrence goes to Rome with her boyfriend, Jeff, and their friends Libby, Lucy, Judge, and Clay. The teenagers are chaperoned by Judge's well-preserved Aunt Albertina, who leaves them on their own, much to their delight. Gidget becomes infatuated with Paolo Cellini, who introduces himself as a journalist and takes her on a tour of Rome's high spots, ostensibly for the purpose of writing an article on an American teenager's reactions to the city. Meanwhile, Jeff embarks on a romance with Daniela Serrini, a tour guide who shows him around Rome; and Gidget returns his fraternity pin. She eventually learns the truth about Paolo: he is a happily married man who undertook the chore of escorting her around the city as a favor to her father. Jeff asks Daniela to join him on the trip home, but she admits that she doesn't love him. When they finally leave for the United States, Gidget and Jeff have been reconciled, and they return home happier and somewhat wiser for their Roman holiday. *Chaperons. Aunts. Journalists. Guides. Jealousy. Adolescence. Duplicity. Vacations. Rome.*

Note: Filmed in part on location in Rome. This is the third in the series of films featuring the character Gidget.

GIFT see **VENOM**

IL GIGANTE DI METROPOLIS see **THE GIANT OF METROPOLIS**

GIGI GOES TO POT   F6.1799

Dist Chancellor Films. **1970**. Sd; col. 35mm. 71 min.
Prod-Dir Sam S. Catah. *Mus* Luristan.
Cast: Debbie Sloan (*Gigi*), Penny Lane, Art North.

Drama. Gigi Carswell, her parents, and her friend Tammy come to New York City for a holiday weekend. Gigi, angry over being separated from her hometown boyfriend, is consoled by Tammy, who makes love to her. That evening the girls tour 42d Street and see a sex exploitation film while Mr. and Mrs. Carswell attend *Oh! Calcutta!* As they leave the movie theater, Gigi and Tammy meet Rod, and they pass him off to Mr. and Mrs. Carswell as the son of a business associate—Rod's father actually is an associate of Carswell. Rod invites Gigi and Tammy to dinner, and afterwards all three smoke marijuana and make love at Rod's apartment. The Carswells return from the play and, inspired by what they have seen on stage, experiment with some new lovemaking positions; the next day they return to see another performance of *Oh! Calcutta!* The girls go to the East Village where they meet Groovy, who invites them to a "pot" party. They join in an orgy with some hippies, meet Rod and Groovy for a last rendezvous, and leave the city tired but happy. *Lesbianism. Troilism. Sex exploitation films. Marijuana. Orgies. Sexual techniques. New York City—East Village. New York City—Times Square. "Oh! Calcutta!".*

Note: Possibly the same as *Gigi Goes to Bat.*

GIGOT   F6.1800

Seven Arts Productions. *Dist* Twentieth Century–Fox Film Corp. 27 Sep **1962** [New York opening; c27 Sep 1962; LP23136]. Sd (Westrex); col (Eastman Color, prints by De Luxe). 35mm. 104 min.

Prod Kenneth Hyman. *Dir* Gene Kelly. *Screenplay* John Patrick. *Story* Jackie Gleason. *Dir Photog* Jean Bourgoin. *Camera Op* Henri Tiquet. *Art Dir* Auguste Capelier. *Artistic Cons* Alexandre Trauner. *Film Ed* Roger Dwyre. *Mus Comp* Jackie Gleason. *Mus Arr & Cond* Michel Magne. *Sd Engr* Jacques Carrère. *1st Asst Dir* Paul Feyder. *Prod Mgr* Julien Derode. *Script Supv* Lucie Lichtig. *Optical Eff* Jean Fouchet.

Cast: Jackie Gleason (*Gigot*), Katherine Kath (*Colette*), Gabrielle Dorziat (*Madame Brigitte*), Jean Lefebvre (*Gaston*), Jacques Marin (*Jean*), Albert Rémy (*Alphonse*), Yvonne Constant (*Lucille Duval*), Germaine Delbat (*Madame Greuze*), Albert Dinan (*bistro proprietor*), Diane Gardner (*Nicole*), Frank Villard (*Pierre*), Camille Guerini (*priest*), René Havard (*Albert*), Louis Falavigna (*Monsieur Duval*), Jean Michaud (*gendarme*), Richard Francoeur (*baker*), Paula Dehelly (*baker's wife*), Jacques Ary (*blade*).

Comedy. Gigot is a huge, mild-mannered mute who works as a janitor in a working-class Paris boardinghouse. Though adored by animals and children, he is badly treated by his employer and is constantly being made the butt of practical jokes. His favorite pastime is attending funerals, where he has a sense of belonging to a group. One evening Gigot finds a prostitute, Colette, and her little daughter, Nicole, and takes them to his squalid basement home. As his affection for the child grows, the mother threatens to leave; and Gigot is forced to steal money from the local bakery in order to persuade her to remain. After spending a night with her boyfriend, Colette returns home one morning and discovers that Gigot and Nicole have vanished. Assuming the mute has kidnaped the child, she arouses the neighbors; but actually Gigot is entertaining Nicole in a subcellar of his basement. The ceiling collapses, the child is injured, and Gigot carries her through the back streets to a church, where the priest summons a doctor. On the way back to his apartment to fetch a phonograph for Nicole, he is spotted by a crowd of people; they give chase, and he falls into the Seine. Seeing his cap floating in the river, the crowd believes he has drowned. Filled with remorse, they give him a lavish funeral, where the most delighted of the mourners is Gigot, who is watching from a cemetery tree. Some of the mourners spot him, however, and the chase begins again. *Mutes. Janitors. Prostitutes. Children. Friendship. Poverty. Theft. Loneliness. Motherhood. Boardinghouses. Funerals. Bakeries. Paris. Seine River. Chases.*

Note: Filmed in Paris.

GIMME SHELTER   F6.1801

Maysles Films. *Dist* Cinema V Distributing, Inc. 6 Dec **1970** [New York opening]. Sd; col 35mm. 90 min. *MPAA rating* R.

Pres by Relpic. *Exec Prod* Ronald Schneider. *Assoc Prod* Porter Bibb. *Photog* David Maysles, Albert Maysles, Charlotte Zwerin. *Photog* David Maysles, Albert Maysles, Peter Adair, Baird Bryant, Peter Churchill, Ron Dorfman, Robert Elfstrom, Elliott Erwitt, Robert Fiore, Adam Giffard, Bill Kaplan, Kevin Keating, Stephen Lighthill, George Lucas, Jim Moody, Jack Newman, Pekke Niemela, Robert Primes, Eric Saarinen, Peter Smokler, Paul Ryan, Coulter Watt, Gary Weiss, Haskell Wexler, Bill Yarrus. *Film Ed* Ellen Giffard, Joanne Burke, Robert Farren, Kent McKinney, Mirra Bank, Susan Steinberg, Janet Laurentano. *Songs:* "Jumpin' Jack Flash," "(I Can't Get No) Satisfaction," "Wild Horses," "Brown Sugar," "Honky Tonk Women," "Street Fighting Man," "Sympathy for the Devil," "Under My Thumb," "Gimme Shelter" Mick Jagger, Keith Richard. *Song:* "Love in Vain" Robert Johnson, comp. *Song:* "You Gotta Move" Fred McDowell. *Songs Sung by* The Rolling Stones. *Song:* "I've Been Loving You Too Long (To Stop Now)" Otis Redding, Jerry Butler. *Sung by* Ike and Tina Turner. *Song:* "Six Days on the Road" Earl Green, Carl Montgomery. *Sung by* The Flying Burrito Brothers. *Song:* "The Other Side of This Life" Fred Neil. *Sung by* Jefferson Airplane. *16-Track Rec at Madison Square Garden* Glyn Johns. *Sd at Altamont* Alembic Recording. *Sd Mix* Bill Blachly. *Sd* Michael Becker, John Brumbaugh, Howard Chesley, Pepper Crawford, Stanley Cronquist, Paul Deason, Tom Goodwin, Peter Pilafian, Orly Lindgren, Walter Murch, Art Rochester, Nelson Stroll, David Thompson, Alvin Tokunow. *Sp Help* Stanley Goldstein.

Featuring: Mick Jagger, Keith Richard, Mick Taylor, Charlie Watts, Bill Wyman, Ike and Tina Turner, Jefferson Airplane, The Flying Burrito Brothers, Melvin Belli, Dick Carter, Sonny Barger.

Documentary. The film is divided into two time sequences: the Rolling Stones' 1969 concert tour of the United States, and the Stones themselves watching films of the events. The scenes of the tour are interspersed with performances in Madison Square Garden, where Ike and Tina Turner are also seen, as plans for a free concert are developed. Contrasted with the scenes at the Garden is a summation of the aftermath at Altamont. At a press conference in the Rainbow Room in New York City, Mick Jagger announces that the free concert is to be held in San Francisco. Later in the tour, lawyer Melvin Belli tries to line up a site for the concert and finally acquires the Altamont Speedway, owned by Dick Carter. The scene shifts to Altamont. The Flying Burrito Brothers perform, but the Jefferson Airplane is interrupted by scuffles between the Hell's Angels (paid in beer to protect the performers and maintain order) and the crowd. Marty Balin of the Jefferson Airplane is hit, as Grace Slick's plea for peace fails to ease the violent atmosphere. That evening, the Stones appear, escorted to the stage by the Angels who clear a path with their motorcycles. As the anxious crowd of over 300,000 see the Stones begin to sing, fighting erupts, and Jagger's efforts to calm the mass prove ineffectual. After one number, a black youth in the audience is seen waving a gun and is stabbed to death by one of the Angels. The concert concludes, and a helicopter carries the Stones away from Altamont. *Musicians. Singers. Rock and roll. Manslaughter. Motion pictures. Press conferences. New York City. San Francisco. Madison Square Garden. Altamont Speedway (California). Hell's Angels.*

Note: Filmed in 16mm.

GINA (France/Mexico)   F6.1802

Dismage–Producciones Tepeyac. *Dist* Omat Films, Sutton Pictures, Pathé-America Distributing Co. 5 Apr **1961** [Chicago opening]. Sd; col (Eastman Color). 35mm. 92 min.

Pres by Lester Braunstein, Howard J. Beck. *Prod* David Mage, Oscar Dancigers. *Dir* Luis Buñuel. *Screenplay & Adapt* Luis Alcoriza, Raymond Queneau, Luis Buñuel. *Dial* Raymond Queneau, Gabriel Arout. *Photog* Jorge Stahl, Jr. *Art Dir* Edward Fitzgerald. *Film Ed* Marguerite Renoir, Alberto Valenzuela, Denise Chardein. *Mus* Paul Misraki. *Sd* José de Pérez.

Cast: Simone Signoret (*Gina*), Georges Marchal (*Chark*), Michel Piccoli (*Father Lizzardi*), Michèle Girardon (*Maria, the mute*), Charles Vanel (*Castin*), Tito Junco (*Chenko*), Luis Aceves Castañeda (*Alberto*), Jorge Martínez de Hoyos (*Captain Ferrero*), Alberto Pedret (*lieutenant*), Stefani, Marc Lambert (*workers*), Raúl Ramírez (*Alvaro*), Alicia del Lago, Francisco Reiguera.

Adventure melodrama. Source: José-André Lacour, *La mort en ce jardin* (Paris, 1954). Chark, a soldier of fortune, arrives in the South American diamond-mining village of Cacazu during a revolt by prospectors against the fascist government. After making advances toward Maria, an innocent deafmute, Chark goes to bed with Gina, a prostitute who steals his money and turns him over to the military police as a revolutionary. Eluding the authorities, Chark blows up the army ammunition dump and, in the ensuing riot, escapes to a boat on the river. There he encounters Maria and her father, Castin, an outlaw rebel; Gina; Father Lizzardi, the village priest; and Chenko, the skipper. Forced to flee the boat when Chenko betrays them, the group is led by Chark on a dangerous trek through the jungle. After days of starvation, they stumble upon the wreck of an airplane filled with provisions and jewels. Castin becomes delirious and kills Gina and Father Lizzardi before being shot by Chark, who takes Maria with him down the river on a raft salvaged from the plane. *Soldiers of fortune. Prospectors. Deafmutes. Prostitutes. Police. Outlaws. Priests. Sea captains. Revolts. Theft. Perfidy. Riots. Starvation. Murder. Fascism. Mining towns. Jungles. Airplanes. Rafts. South America. Explosions.*

Note: Filmed on location in Mexico. Opened in Paris in Sep 1956 as *La mort en ce jardin*; running time: 104 min; released in Mexico in Jun 1960 as *La muerte en este jardín*; running time: 145 min.

GINZA NO KOIBITOTACHI see **LOVERS OF GINZA**

GION MATSURI see **THE DAY THE SUN ROSE**

LA GIORNATA BALORDA see **FROM A ROMAN BALCONY**

I GIORNI DELL'IRA see **DAY OF ANGER**

GIORNI DI FUOCO see **LAST OF THE RENEGADES**

IL GIORNO DELLA CIVETTA see **MAFIA**

IL GIORNO E L'ORA see **THE DAY AND THE HOUR**

UN GIORNO IN PRETURA see **A DAY IN COURT**

I GIRASOLI see **SUNFLOWER**

A GIRL AGAINST NAPOLEON see **THE DEVIL MADE A WOMAN**

THE GIRL AND THE BUGLER (U.S.S.R.)   F6.1803
Mosfilm. *Dist* Artkino Pictures. 5 Nov **1967** [New York opening]. Sd; b&w. 35mm. 76 min.

Dir Aleksandr Mitta. *Screenplay* Aleksandr Volodin. *Photog* A. Panasyuk. *Camera* P. Lebeshev. *Art Dir* P. Kiselyov. *Mus* Veniamin Basner. *Songs From "My Fair Lady"* Alan Jay Lerner, Frederick Loewe. *Sd* S. Litvinov, Yu. Rabinovich. *Asst Dir* V. Proklov.

Cast: Lena Proklova (*Tanya*), Rolan Bykov (*The Bugler*), V. Belokurov (*Petya*), Lena Zolotukhina (*The Girl Friend*), Sergey Nikonenko, Olya Semyonova, Vitya Kosykh, Vitya Sysoyev, A. Aleynikova, L. Veytsler, V. Vladimirova, A. Denisova, Oleg Yefremov, A. Maksimova, E. Nekrasova, Lyudmila Ovchinnikova, Iya Savvina, Misha Metyolkin, Mark Bernes.

Drama. Twelve-year-old Tanya stays with neighbors in Moscow while her mother is visiting her father, who is temporarily working in a distant location. Feeling rejected by her parents, Tanya develops an infatuation with Petya, an older youth who leads a Young Pioneer group. Her infatuation finally dissolves, however, when she sees Petya ice skating with a girl his own age. Meanwhile Tanya and her girl friend seek out some of the first Pioneers to arrange a reunion. A shy older man who proves never to have been a Pioneer nevertheless attends the assembly. After the Pioneer bugler finishes playing, the older man steps onto the stage and speaks of a bugler friend who was killed during the war. He then takes the bugle from the Pioneer and plays the anthem as his friend would have played it. *Buglers. Adolescence. Moscow. Pioneer Organization (U.S.S.R.).*

Note: Released in the U.S.S.R. in 1965 as *Zvonyat, otkroyte dver.*

THE GIRL AND THE GENERAL (France/Italy)   F6.1804
C. C. Champion-Les Films Concordia. *Dist* Metro-Goldwyn-Mayer, Inc. Oct **1967** [New York opening: 6 Dec; c31 Aug 1967; LP34707]. Sd; col (Technicolor, print by Metrocolor). 35mm. 105 min. [Copyright length: 99 min.]

A Carlo Ponti Production. *Prod* Carlo Ponti. *Exec Prod* Luciano Perugia. *Dir* Pasquale Festa Campanile. *Screenplay* Luigi Malerba, Pasquale Festa Campanile. *Orig Story* Massimo Franciosa, Pasquale Festa Campanile. *Dir Photog* Ennio Guarnieri. *Camera* Arturo Zavattini. *Art Dir* Luciano Spadoni. *Set Decor* Dario Micheli. *Film Ed* Iolanda Benvenuti. *Mus* Ennio Morricone. *Asst Dir* Elvira D'Amico. *Prod Mgr* Mario De Biase. *Prod Asst* Gianna Di Michele, Antonio Mazza. *Cost Dsgn* Maria De Matteis. *Makeup* Nilo Jacoponi. *Hairstyles* Jole Cecchini.

Cast: Rod Steiger (*The General*), Virna Lisi (*Ada*), Umberto Orsini (*Private Tarasconi*), Toni Gaggia (*The Lieutenant*), Marco Mariani (*The Corporal*), Jacques Herlin (*The Veterinary*), Valentino Macchi (*soldier*).

War comedy-drama. During World War I, an Italian soldier, Tarasconi, is separated from his retreating regiment near the Italian-Austrian border. He accidentally captures a one-armed Austrian general and resolves to bring him to the Italian high command in exchange for a large reward and a medal. The general escapes from his bumbling captor but falls into the hands of a peasant girl, Ada, who agrees to share the general with Tarasconi for an even split of the reward. She later tricks the soldier, however, by taking his rifle and locking

him in a railroad car. Although Ada and the general form a grudging respect for each other, their relationship is greatly strained by days of starvation and the general's breaking his leg. They finally find a deserted farm where they can rest, and there they are fortuitously reunited with Tarasconi, who has escaped from the train. As the trek continues, the ragged trio eventually acquire a donkey, and they even get some food from Austrian soldiers when Ada offers to show them her body. Emotionally united by their misfortunes, the threesome ultimately reach a minefield, where first the donkey, then Ada and Tarasconi, are killed by explosions. The general, sick of war and grief-stricken by the deaths of his companions, surrenders to Italian forces, vowing to make sure that credit for his arrest goes to his two ill-fated captors. *Soldiers. Peasants. Prisoners of war. Bounty hunters. Austrians. Friendship. Hunger. Mines (war explosives). World War I. Donkeys.*

Note: Produced in Italy and released there in 1967 as *La ragazza e il generale*; running time: 113 min.

THE GIRL AND THE LEGEND (West Germany)   F6.1805
N. D. F. *Dist* Comet Film Distributors. May **1966**. Sd; col (Agfacolor). 35mm. 90 min.

Exec Prod Georg Richter. *Dir* Josef von Baky. *Screenplay* Emil Burri, Johannes Mario Simmel. *Photog* Günther Anders, Günter Senftleben. *Art Dir* Hein Heckroth. *Sets* Hein Heckroth, A. Windau, Walter J. Blokesch. *Film Ed* Claus von Boro. *Mus* Georg Haentzschel. *Sd* Carl Becker. *Asst Dir* Rudolf Noelte. *Prod Mgr* Karlheinz Först, Peter Hahne. *Prod Dir* Lutz Hengst. *Cost* Charlotte Flemming. *Makeup* Raimund Stangl, Anita Greil.

Cast: Romy Schneider (*Maud*), Horst Buchholz (*Tom*), Erich Ponto (*Daniel Defoe*), Magda Schneider (*mother*), Mathias Wieman (*king*), Gustav Knuth (*gangster chief*), Rudolf Vogel (*valet*), Günther Lüders (*Drinkwater*), Roland Kaiser, Wolfgang Condrus, Urs Hess (*children*), Gert Fröbe, Siegfried Lowitz, Mario Adorf, Elisabeth Flickenschildt, Joseph Offenbach, Ernst Fritz Fürbringer, Willy Leyrer, Heinrich Gretler, Karl Heinz Peters, Rudolf Rhomberg.

Drama. Source: Friedrich Forster, *Robinson soll nicht sterben* (Berlin opening: 21 Nov 1932). A confederation of rich and poor children befriend the impoverished Daniel Defoe. *Children. Authors. Wealth. Poverty. Daniel Defoe.*

Note: Released in West Germany in Feb 1957 as *Robinson soll nicht sterben*; running time: 98 min.

THE GIRL CAN'T STOP (France/Greece)   F6.1806
Les Films Marceau-Cocinor-Sport Films-Fanayotopoulos. *Dist* U. S. Films. 15 Dec **1966** [San Francisco showing]. Sd; b&w. 35mm. 87 min.

Pres by Joe Solomon. *Prod-Dir-Writ* Willy Rozier. *Adapt & Dial* Xavier Vallier, Willy Rozier. *English Vers* Peter Riethof. *Photog* Michel Rocca. *Mus by* Jean Yatove.

Cast: Maria Xenia (*Tassoula*), Georges Rivière, Claude Cerval, Jean Sobieski, Jenny Astruc, Georges Lycan, Jacques Ardennes.

Crime melodrama. Source: Thrasos Kastanakēs, *Ho Chatzē Manouēl; mythistorema* (Athens, 1956). Manuel, whose illegal business deals have lost money, follows the advice of adventurer Mourati and encourages his wife, Tassoula, to become the mistress of Georgian, nephew of a banker. Georgian embezzles money for Manuel's business but is found out by his uncle, who threatens to arrest him and Manuel. To avoid prison, Georgian and Manuel hire Mourati to murder the elderly banker. After the banker's death, the three divide Georgian's inheritance. When Tassoula discovers their guilt, she entrusts her young brother to his teacher and prepares to leave the country. Although she refuses Georgian's affections, Tassoula is raped by Mourati. She subsequently consults the teacher, and, following his advice, informs the police of the banker's murder. Exonerated at the trial, Tassoula retires to the island of Hydra, where she is visited by the teacher, who assures her a happy future. *Bankers. Schoolteachers. Mistresses. Embezzlement. Murder. Inheritance. Infidelity. Rape. Filial relations. Hydra.*

Note: Opened in Paris in Jun 1965 as *Les chiens dans la nuit*; running time: 95 min.

GIRL CRAZY see **WHEN THE BOYS MEET THE GIRLS**

GIRL FEVER   F6.1807
Y. P. Artists-Leo Film Productions. *Dist* General Screen Corp., Leo Film Distributors. Jul **1961** [c6 Sep 1960; LU3169]. Sd; col (Eastman Color by Pathé). 35mm. 72 min. [Cut from 90 min.]

Prod Sherman Price. *Dir* Yevsie Petrushansky, Sherman Price.

Cast: Count Gregory, George Camarinos, III, Choo-Choo Collins, Danielle Clary, Geraldine, Dick Richards, Edna Thayer.

Comedy with music. Broadway producer Count Gregory travels around the world to Egypt, Italy, Japan, Spain, and Paris to search for a star for his new stage musical. He meets a variety of singers and dancers who perform throughout the film. During his tour, he is taken captive by a harem. He holds up a stagecoach and runs into a den of Apaches who are meeting in an underground cafe in Paris. Finally, he returns home to America and realizes that the most talented stars are right on his stage. Among those he meets are male rock and roll singer George Camarinos, III, and female singers Choo-Choo Collins and Edna Thayer. *Theatrical producers. Americans in foreign countries. Singers. Dancers. Talent scouts. Apaches—Paris. Stagecoach robberies. Cafes. Harems. New York City—Broadway. Egypt. Italy. Japan. Spain. Paris.*

THE GIRL FRIENDS *see* LE AMICHE

THE GIRL FROM DENMARK   F6.1808
4 Jun 1970 [San Francisco opening]. Sd; col (Eastman Color). 35mm. [Feature film, length unknown.]
Sex film. No information about the precise nature of this film has been found, but press material suggests that it concerns a Dane who explores a variety of sexual activities in her desire to experience complete sexual freedom as a woman. *Danes. Sexuality. Women's rights.*
Note: May have been produced in Denmark.

GIRL FROM HONG KONG (West Germany)   F6.1809
Nero Film–Neue Deutsche Filmgesellschaft. *Dist* Comet Film Distributors. Jan 1966. Sd; col. 35mm. 95 min.
Prod Seymour Nebenzahl, Wolf Schwarz. *Dir* Franz Peter Wirth. *Screenplay* Kurt Heuser, Oliver Hassencamp. *Photog* Klaus von Rautenfeld. *Asst Camera* Rolf Kästel, Knut Seedorf. *Col Cons* Alvord Eiseman. *Art Dir* Hans Berthel, Johannes Ott. *Film Ed* Lilian Seng. *Asst Ed* Ursula Zschiesche, Thurid Söhnlein. *Mus* Michel Michelet. *Sd* Werner Schlagge. *Asst Dir* Claus von Boro, Michi Tanaka. *Prod Supv* Fritz Hoppe, Walter Zeiske. *Prod Mgr* Peter Petersen, Richard Hellman. *Mgr* Erhard Reiss. *Cost Cons* Alvord Eiseman. *Cost Dsgn* Hartmut Bake. *Wardrobe* Fritz Bergmann, Elsbeth Rohwer. *Makeup* Herbert Griesner, Gertrud Heinz-Werner. *Prop* Otto Schmidt, Wilhelm Schaumann. *Still Photog* Lilo Winterstein.
Cast: Akiko *(Anna Suh)*, Helmut Griem *(Glen Dierks)*, Carl Lange *(Hamburg innkeeper)*, Ursula Lillig *(Glen's former girl friend)*, Hanns Lothar, Peter Carsten, Carla Hagen, Eva Pflug, Klaus Kindler.
Romantic drama. Source: Heinrich Hauser, *Brackwasser* (Leipzig, 1928). In Hong Kong, German sailor Glen Dierks falls in love with Anna Suh, a Chinese dancer with a questionable past. He takes her to his home on a North Sea island, but his neighbors disapprove of her and the couple's relationship. Before their marriage, Anna Suh flees to the mainland. Glen follows her to Hamburg, where they discuss a possible future together. *Sailors. Chinese. Dancers. Miscegenation. Racial prejudice. Islands. Hong Kong. North Sea. Hamburg.*
Note: Location scenes filmed in Hong Kong and Hamburg. Opened in Hamburg in Aug 1961 as *Bis zum Ende aller Tage:* running time: 107 min.

THE GIRL FROM PUSSY CAT   F6.1810
Dist American Film Distributing Corp. Feb 1969 [New York showing]. Sd; b&w. 35mm. 70 min.
Melodrama. Bobbi, the lesbian leader of a gang of women, makes love to Darlene while Jodi visits Jean to convey the details of the plan for their first major crime, a bank robbery. Jodi, once rejected by her fiancé, now roams the streets, seeking casual sexual encounters. Jean, secretly in love with Darlene's boyfriend, Jack, tells him of Darlene's relationship with Bobbi, but although Jack is attracted to Jean, he becomes angry and upset. The next day, the four women successfully rob the bank of $250,000. They return to Bobbi's apartment, take off their clothes, and celebrate amidst the piles of bills. Several of Jodi's male friends arrive, and the orgy continues in a heterosexual vein. Darlene returns home to find Jack preparing to phone the police. Bobbi arrives, and the two women torture Jack and burn his flesh to intimidate him. Jean, fearful for Jack's life, lures the two women away by telling them that the police have been investigating. Bobbi and Darlene race back to the hideout and are killed en route in an automobile crash. Jean visits Jack's apartment in the hope that he will run away with her. He refuses but asks her to settle down with him on the raise he expects to receive for returning the stolen money. Meanwhile, Jodi continues to roam the streets in her search for men. *Gangs. Lesbianism. Bank robberies. Jealousy. Promiscuity. Torture. Criminals—Rehabilitation. Orgies. Automobile accidents.*
Note: Also known as *The Girl From P.——A.T.*

THE GIRL FROM S.I.N.   F6.1811
Bobmoral, Inc.–C. Davis Smith. *Dist* CIP Ltd. 19 May 1966 [San Francisco showing]. Sd; b&w. 35mm. 67 min.
Prod Bob Oran, Sam Stewart. *Dir-Writ* C. Davis Smith. *Film Ed* C & W Associates. *Mus* C & W Associates. *Sd* Mor-Sound. *Stills* Harry Petricek.
Cast: Joyana, Sal Rogge, Barbie Kemp, Dick Wright, Carol Evans, Jerry Merro, Lisa Ryan, Charles Little, Dolly Lee, Rick Kuhn.
Comedy-drama. Dr. Sexus, head of S.I.N., an international crime syndicate, assigns Agent 0069, Poontang Plenty, to steal a secret formula for invisibility

from Professor Drake, the scientist who developed the formula. Karen, the professor's assistant, prevents two of Sexus' men from stealing the formula: she sheds her clothes, takes one of the professor's pills to make herself invisible, and wards off the thieves. Professor Drake takes refuge in the apartment of Karen's boyfriend, Sam. There Poontang drugs Sam with an aphrodisiac and knocks him unconscious with a karate chop. She finds the professor asleep and arouses him sexually, but he takes a pill and disappears. Meanwhile, Dr. Sexus has captured Sam and Karen and is about to torture them when, suddenly, their bonds begin to loosen—the work of the invisible Professor Drake. Karen plunges a knife into Poontang, and Drake puts an end to Dr. Sexus. *Secret agents. Scientists. Gangsters. Theft. Invisibility. Seduction. Torture. Syndicates. Karate. Aphrodisiacs.*
Note: May also be known as *The Girl From the Secret Inner Network.*

THE GIRL FROM TOBACCO ROW   F6.1812
The Ormond Organization. 24 Aug 1966 [Louisville, Kentucky, opening]. Sd; col. 35mm. 87 min.
Pres by June Ormond, Ron Ormond. *Prod-Dir-Writ* Ron Ormond.
Cast: Tex Ritter, Rachel Romen, Earl Richards, Tim Ormond, Rita Faye, Ralph Emery, Johnny Russell, Martha Carson, Smiley Wilson, Kitty Wilson, Jimmy Mulcay, Mildred Mulcay.
Musical comedy. No information about the precise nature of this film has been found, but press material suggests that it concerns Nadine, a clergyman's promiscuous daughter. *Promiscuity.*
Note: Filmed in Nashville, Tennessee.

GIRL GAME (Brazil/France/Italy)   F6.1813
Ital-Victoria Film–France Cinéma Productions–Consorcio Paulista. *Dist* Cinema Distributors of America. 11 Jan 1968 [New Orleans opening]. Sd; col (Technicolor). 35mm (Dyaliscope). 90 min.
Prod Franco Cancellieri, Abilio Pereira de Almeida. *Dir* Steno. *Screenplay* Sergio Amidei, Luciano Vincenzoni. *Photog* Massimo Dallamano. *Mus* Gianni Ferrio.
Cast: Sylva Koscina *(Ines)*, Walter Chiari *(Ugo)*, Mylène Demongeot *(Zina von Raunacher)*, Paolo Ferrari *(De Fonseca)*, Gloria Paul *(Michèle)*, Claude Rich *(Buby von Raunacher)*, Raymond Bussières, Francis De Wolff, Ruggero Baldi, Franco Fabrizi.
Melodrama. The European jet set converge on the luxurious Copacabana Palace in Rio de Janeiro to celebrate the pre-Lent Carnival. The city is divided between the wealthy socialites and the swindlers and petty thieves; in the midst of the gaiety are a young woman searching for romance, a heartless playboy, and three airline stewardesses. *Socialites. Jet set. Swindlers. Playboys. Airline stewardesses. Mardi Gras. Rio de Janeiro. Copacabana Palace.*
Note: Opened in Rome in Dec 1962 as *Copacabana Palace*; running time: 100 min; in Paris in Nov 1964 under the same title; running time: 125 min. Also known as *The Saga of the Flying Hostesses.*

THE GIRL GETTERS (Great Britain)   F6.1814
Kenneth Shipman Productions. *For* Bryanston Films. *Dist* American International Pictures. 12 Apr 1966 [New York opening]. Sd; b&w (print by Movielab). 35mm. 93 min.
Pres by Landau/Unger Co. *Prod* Kenneth Shipman. *Assoc Prod* George Fowler. *Dir* Michael Winner. *Screenplay* Peter Draper. *Photog* Nicolas Roeg. *Art Dir* Geoffrey Tozer. *Film Ed* Fred Burnley. *Mus Comp & Cond* Stanley Black. *Song:* "The System" Bobby Richards, Mike Pratt. *Sung by* The Searchers. *Sd Rec* Bill Bulkley, Stephen Dalby. *Asst Dir* Peter Price. *Prod Mgr* Clifton Brandon. *Wardrobe* Bridget Sellers. *Makeup* Gerry Fletcher. *Hairstyles* Betty Glasow.
Cast: Oliver Reed *(Tinker)*, Jane Merrow *(Nicola)*, Barbara Ferris *(Suzy)*, Julia Foster *(Lorna)*, Harry Andrews *(Larsey)*, Ann Lynn *(Ella)*, Guy Doleman *(Philip)*, Andrew Ray *(Willy)*, John Porter Davison *(Grib)*, Clive Colin Bowler *(Sneakers)*, Iain Gregory *(Sammy)*, David Hemmings *(David)*, John Alderton *(Nidge)*, Jeremy Burnham *(Ivor)*, Mark Burns *(Michael)*, Derek Nimmo *(James)*, Pauline Munro *(Sylvie)*, Derek Newark *(Alfred)*, Stephanie Beaumont *(Marianne)*, Talitha Pol *(Helga)*, Dora Reisser *(Ingrid)*, Susan Burnet *(Jasmin)*, Victor Winding *(Stan Atty)*, Jennifer Tafler *(Sonia)*, Ross Parker *(Fred)*, Gwendolyn Watts.
Romantic drama. Tinker is a cynical beach photographer who has developed a foolproof system for making contacts with young women at an English seaside resort. He simply takes the picture, gets the address, and then selects the women that interest him romantically. The scheme works well until he meets Nicola, a London fashion model visiting her father at his summer home. Nicola has her own set of rules for playing the game, and, after an encounter with some of her other suitors, Tinker realizes that, although he has fallen in love with her, there is a wide gap between his rootless existence and her well-organized life. As the summer comes to an end, Nidge, one of Tinker's buddies, decides to marry his pregnant girl friend; Suzy, who had taken up with Nicola's father, is

left drunk, disillusioned, and alone; and Nicola prepares to leave for a modeling job in Rome. Tinker would like to follow her but hesitates for fear that he could not compete in a large city. Although Nicola promises to see him again, Tinker realizes that it was just a brief holiday affair for her and that she has beaten him at his own system. *Photographers. Models. Vacations. Filial relations. Pregnancy. Beaches. Resorts. Summer.*

Note: Filmed on location at Roxham. Opened in London in Sep 1964 as *The System* at 90 min. Also shown in the United States under the British title.

THE GIRL GRABBERS   F6.1815

August Films-RAF Industries. *Dist* RAF Industries. 10 Jul **1968** [Los Angeles opening]. Sd; col (Eastman Color). 35mm. 83 min.

Prod-Dir Simon Nuchtern.

Cast: Paul Cox (*Paul Desmond*), Jackie Richards (*Lynn*), Ludmilla Tchor (*Tania*), John Spence (*Nick*), Sebastian Dangerfield (*Louie*), June Francis (*Ruth*), Alaistair Burr (*Frank*), Louise Violet, Linda Boyce (*Go-go dancers*).

Melodrama. Nick and Louie force their way into a Greenwich Village apartment building, intending to loot an apartment. Instead, they rape Tania, a resident, and leave, passing her boyfriend Paul in the lobby. Paul tours the neighborhood bars, looking for the two hoodlums. Arriving at the bordello where Nick's girl friend Lynn works, he seduces her, pretending to be an old friend of Nick's, and learns that Nick works at an uptown garage that serves as a front for a dope-peddling ring. The hoods capture Paul at the garage, and the leader of the gang determines that Paul, Tania, and Lynn must die. Tania and Lynn are lured to the garage and, together with Paul, driven upstate to be executed by Nick and Louie. Lynn secretly learns of Nick's plan to also kill her, and at the crucial moment she turns on him. Nick opens fire, killing both Lynn and Louie, but Paul manages to get to the waiting car and runs over Nick. *Hoodlums. Prostitutes. Rape. Robbery. Murder. Bars. Narcotics. New York City—Greenwich Village. New York State.*

Note: Location scenes filmed in New York. Sebastian Dangerfield is also known as Stefan Peters.

GIRL HAPPY   F6.1816

Euterpe, Inc. *Dist* Metro-Goldwyn-Mayer, Inc. 14 Apr **1965** [Los Angeles opening; c24 Nov 1964; LP29360]. Sd (Westrex); col (Metrocolor). 35mm (Panavision). 96 min.

Prod Joe Pasternak. *Dir* Boris Sagal. *Screenplay* Harvey Bullock, R. S. Allen. *Dir Photog* Philip H. Lathrop. *Camera Op* William Lloyd Norton. *Asst Camera* Cliff King, Dale Varnum. *Art Dir* George W. Davis, Addison Hehr. *Set Decor* Henry Grace, Hugh Hunt. *Film Ed* Rita Roland. *Mus* George Stoll. *Titl Song* Doc Pomus, Norman Meade. *Song:* "Cross My Heart and Hope To Die" Ben Weisman, Sid Wayne. *Songs:* "Do Not Disturb," "Spring Fever," "Wolf Call" Bill Giant, Bernie Baum, Florence Kaye. *Song:* "Do the Clam" Ben Weisman, Sid Wayne, Dolores Fuller. *Songs:* "Fort Lauderdale Chamber of Commerce," "Puppet on a String" Sid Tepper, Roy C. Bennett. *Songs:* "I've Got To Find My Baby," "The Meanest Girl in Town" Joy Byers. *Song:* "Startin' Tonight" Lenore Rosenblatt, Victor Millrose. *Songs Sung by* Elvis Presley. *Vocal Backgrounds* The Jordanaires. *Choreog* David Winters. *Rec Supv* Franklin Milton. *Mix* Larry Jost. *Rec* Bruce Wright. *Boom Op* Larry Hadsell. *Asst Dir* Jack Aldworth, Wallace Jones. *Unit Prod Mgr* Al Shenberg. *Script Supv* Cleo Anton. *Wardrobe* Lambert Marks, Elva Martien. *Makeup Supv* William Tuttle. *Makeup* Ron Berkeley. *Hairstyles* Sydney Guilaroff. *Tech Adv* Col. Tom Parker. *Gaffer* Perry O'Brien. *Prop Master* Jim Luttrell.

Cast: Elvis Presley (*Rusty Wells*), Shelley Fabares (*Valerie*), Harold J. Stone (*Big Frank*), Gary Crosby (*Andy*), Joby Baker (*Wilbur*), Nita Talbot (*Sunny Daze*), Mary Ann Mobley (*Deena*), Fabrizio Mioni (*Romano*), Jimmy Hawkins (*Doc*), Jackie Coogan (*Sergeant Benson*), Peter Brooks (*Brentwood Von Durgenfeld*), John Fiedler (*Mr. Penchill*), Chris Noel (*Betsy*), Lyn Edgington (*Laurie*), Gail Gilmore (*Nancy*), Pamela Curran (*Bobbie*), Rusty Allen (*Linda*).

Comedy with music. After completing their engagement at a Chicago nightclub, Rusty Wells and his combo plan to spend Easter week in Fort Lauderdale entertaining college students. Big Frank, the owner of the nightclub, decides to waive his option to hold the group in Chicago when he learns that his daughter Valerie plans to vacation in Fort Lauderdale. He sends the group to Florida with the understanding that they keep a close watch on his daughter. While in Fort Lauderdale, Rusty and the combo find that most of their time is devoted to keeping Valerie out of trouble. To relieve the other band members of their commitment to Big Frank, Rusty offers to assume responsibility for her. The two are happy until Valerie learns of Rusty's bargain with her father, whereupon she goes on a wild drinking spree and ends up in jail. Her father posts bail for her, and soon all is forgiven as Valerie and Rusty are reunited. *Singers. Musicians. Chaperons. Students. Vacations. Filial relations. Drunkenness. Nightclubs. Jails. Easter. Chicago. Fort Lauderdale.*

THE GIRL HUNTERS (Great Britain)   F6.1817

Present Day Productions-Fellane Productions. *Dist* Colorama Features, Zodiac International Pictures. 12 Jun **1963** [Los Angeles opening]. Sd (Westrex); b&w. 35mm (Panavision). 103 min.

Prod (see note) Robert Fellows. *Assoc Prod* Charles Reynolds. *Dir* Roy Rowland. *Screenplay* Mickey Spillane, Roy Rowland, Robert Fellows. *Photog* Kenneth Talbot. *Camera Op* Alan McCabe. *Art Dir* Tony Inglis. *Film Ed* Sidney Stone. *Mus Comp & Cond* Philip Green. *Sd* Gerry Turner, Hugh Strain, Fred Turtle. *Sd Ed* Jim Roddan. *Asst Dir* George Pollard. *Prod Mgr* Denis Johnson. *Wardrobe Supv* Rene Coke. *Miss Eaton's Wardrobe* Dan Millstein. *Makeup Artist* Sydney Turner. *Hairstyles* Alice Holmes. *Fight Arr* Douglas Robinson.

Cast: Mickey Spillane (*Mike Hammer*), Shirley Eaton (*Laura Knapp*), Lloyd Nolan (*Art Rickerby*), Hy Gardner (*himself*), Scott Peters (*Pat Chambers*), Guy Kingsley Poynter (*Dr. Larry Snyder*), James Dyrenforth (*Bayliss Henry*), Charles Farrell, British (*Joe Grissi*), Kim Tracy (*nurse*), Benny Lee (*Nat Drutman*), Murray Kash (*Richie Cole*), Bill Nagy (*Georgie*), Clive Endersby (*Duck-Duck*), Richard Montez (*skinny guy*), Larry Cross (*Red Markham*), Tony Arpino (*cab driver*), Hal Galili (*bouncer*), Nelly Hanham (*landlady*), Bob Gallico (*Dr. Leo Daniels*), Michael Brennan, Howard Greene, Grant Holden (*policemen*), Francis Napier (*detective*), Larry Taylor ("*The Dragon*").

Crime melodrama. Source: Mickey Spillane, *The Girl Hunters* (New York, 1962). Private detective Mike Hammer has spent 7 years in alcoholic melancholy over the disappearance of Velda, his beloved secretary, when he is picked up out of the gutter by his former friend, New York Police Capt. Pat Chambers. The officer wants Hammer to question a dying sailor, Richie Cole. The seaman, who will talk only to Hammer, was shot with the same weapon that killed a noted U. S. senator several years earlier. Cole tells Hammer that the senator was assassinated by a communist spy ring masterminded by "The Dragon," but the private investigator refuses to relay this information to Chambers and is detained in a ward for alcoholics. After federal agent Art Rickerby explains that Cole was a fellow agent, Hammer agrees to cooperate and help bring the killer to justice. Armed with information supplied by syndicated newspaper columnist Hy Gardner, the investigator interviews Laura Knapp, the senator's flirtatious widow. Several other murders are committed, and Hammer begins to suspect Laura's complicity with the spy ring. Spurred on by the hope that Velda is still alive and imprisoned by "The Dragon," he tracks the assassin to a chicken farm, overcomes him, and nails his hands to the floor. Confronting Laura, he accuses her of conspiring with the communists to murder her husband. She fires a shotgun that Hammer secretly has rigged with a blocked barrel and kills herself. *Detectives. Secretaries. Police. Sailors. Communists. Masterminds. Government agents. Columnists. Flirts. Widows. Alcoholism. Missing persons. Murder. Assassination. Conspiracy. New York City.*

Note: Some location scenes filmed in London. Released in Great Britain in 1964; running time: 97 min. Reynolds is credited as producer in Great Britain; U. S. sources credit Fellows.

THE GIRL I ABANDONED (Japan)   F6.1818

Nikkatsu Corp. Dec **1970** [Los Angeles showing]. Sd; col (Fuji Color). 35mm (Nikkatsu Scope). 116 min.

Dir Kirio Urayama. *Screenplay* Hisashi Yamanouchi. *Story* Shusaku Endo. *Photog* Shohei Ando. *Art Dir* Yoshinaga Yokoo. *Mus* Toshiro Mayuzumi.

Cast: Choichiro Kawarazaki (*Tsutomu Yoshioka*), Toshie Kobayashi (*Mitsu*), Ruriko Asaoka (*Mariko*), Chikako Natsumi (*Shimako*), Haruko Kato, Shoichi Ozawa, Takeshi Kato, Teruko Kishi, Hideaki Ezumi, Toru Emori, Hisataka Yamane, Ryutaro Tatsumi, Kunie Origa, Hideharu Otaki, Fumie Kitahara, Tadao Nakamaru, Minako Sakaguchi, Hiroshi Shimada, Shoichi Ozawa, Sumie Sasaki, Toshio Hayano, Asao Sano, Junko Kuroda, Shigeru Tsuyuguchi, Shusaku Endo.

Drama. Tsutomu Yoshioka, an office worker, is engaged to Mariko, the niece of his company's president. Yoshioka has overcome many obstacles to reach his respectable position. While working his way through college, he met Mitsu, a country girl who worked in a factory. They had a brief but intense affair, which Yoshioka broke off when a friend advised him that Mitsu would not fit into his future plans. Shimako, who worked with Mitsu in the factory and now runs a disreputable business, meets Yoshioka at a party and tells him of Mitsu's continued hardships, including the aborted pregnancy of his child. Yoshioka is briefly concerned, but he puts Mitsu out of his mind in preparing for his wedding. Shimako arranges for the pair to meet after Yoshioka is married, and she takes photographs of the meeting, intending to blackmail Yoshioka without Mitsu's knowledge. Mitsu learns of Shimako's plans and tries to destroy the evidence. During the ensuing scuffle Mitsu falls from a window and dies. *Office clerks. Factory workers. Desertion. Blackmail. Abortion. Ambition. Photographs.*

Note: Released in Japan in Sep 1969 as *Watashi ga suteta onna.*

GIRL IN GOLD BOOTS   **F6.1819**

Ted V. Mikels Film Productions. *Dist* Geneni Film Distributing Co. 25 Apr **1968** [Houston opening]. Sd; col (Eastman Color). 35mm. 108 min.

Prod-Dir Ted V. Mikels. *Screenplay* Leighton L. Peatman, Art Names, John T. Wilson. *Dir Photog* Robert Maxwell. *Asst Camera* Jack May, photog, James M. Farquharson. *Titl* Pacific Title. *Film Ed* Leo Shreve. *Mus Score* Nicholas Carras. Songs: "Do You Want To Laugh or Cry?" "For You," "Girl in Gold Boots," "Hello, Michele," "One Good Time, One Place," comp & sung by Chris Howard. Song: "Lonesome Man" George Eddy. Song: "You Gotta Come Down" Jody Daniels, Bobby Batson. Songs Sung by Jody Daniels, Chris Howard, Larry Cartell, The Third World. Song: "Everything I Touch Turns to Gold" Denise Norwood. Song: "Cowboy Santa" Nick Busillo. Songs: "Wheels of Love," "Sin," "Minnie Shimmy" Jay Colonna, Jerry Wallace. Song: "Jimmy's Girl" Laurence Gray. Song: "Strange Things" Jay Schlessinger. Songs Sung by Larry Cartell, Joe Valino. *Harmonica* Danny Walton. *Sd Rec* John Hopkins, sd, Clark D. Will, Sam Kopetsky. *Prod Mgr* Rod Wilmoth. *Script Supv* Jim Kelly. *Wardrobe* Nora Maxwell. *Makeup* Gene Mikels. *Still Photog* James McEwen.

Cast: Jody Daniels *(Critter Jones)*, Leslie McRae *(Michele Casey)*, Tom Pace *(Buz Nichols)*, Bara Byrnes *(Joanie Nichols)*, Mark Herron *(Leo McCabe)*, William Bagdad *(Marty)*, Victor Izay *(Mr. Casey)*, Harry Lovejoy *(Harry Blatz)*, James Victor *(Joey)*, Rod Wilmoth *(officer)*, Chris Howard *(Chris)*, Mike Garrison *(gas station attendant)*, Michael Derrick *(car attendant)*, Sheila Roberts *(store clerk)*, Duke Graham, Jerry Ambler *(motorcyclists)*, Anne McAnn *(waitress)*, Genji *(cocktail waitress)*, Rafael Campos.

Melodrama with music. While traveling cross-country to visit his sister Joanie, young hood Buz Nichols picks up Michele Casey, an aspiring dancer, and draft-dodging motorcyclist Critter Jones. In Hollywood Buz introduces Casey to his sister, a go-go nightclub dancer, who arranges for Michele's audition with Leo McCabe, her drug dealing boss, who wants to replace Joanie, an addict, with fresh talent. Critter, working as a janitor at the club, learns that Buz and hoodlum Harry Blatz have killed an old man while stealing $100,000 worth of drugs from the county jail. McCabe, Buz, and Marty, bouncer at the club, threaten Critter and Michele, but Critter outfights them and calls the police. Newlyweds Critter and Michele hitchhike back to Critter's induction center so that he can report for the draft. *Hoodlums. Hitchhikers. Go-go dancers. Draft dodgers. Motorcyclists. Entertainers. Nightclub owners. Drug dealers. Drug addicts. Janitors. Bouncers. Newlyweds. Brother-sister relationship. Murder. Theft. Jails. Hollywood.*

GIRL IN HIS POCKET *see* **NUDE IN HIS POCKET**

GIRL IN ROOM 13 (United States/Brazil)   **F6.1820**

Layton Film Productions–Sinofilmes. *Dist* Astor Pictures. 28 Apr **1961** [Atlanta showing]. Sd; col (Eastman Color). 35mm. 79 min.

Prod Marc Frederic. *Assoc Prod* Michel Lebedka, Konstantin Tkaczenko. *Dir* Richard E. Cunha. *Screenplay* H. E. Barrie, Richard E. Cunha. *Photog* Konstantin Tkaczenko. *Art Dir* Pierino Massenzi. *Film Ed* Lucio Braun. *Mus* Gabriel Migliori. *Sd* Boris Silitschanu. *Asst Dir* John Herbert. *Wardrobe* Alice Pievetti. *Makeup* Flavio Torres.

Cast: Brian Donlevy *(Steve Marshall)*, Andrea Bayard *(Kitty Herman)*, Elizabeth Howard *(Elizabeth)*, Victor Merinow *(Victor Marlow)*, John Herbert *(police captain)*, Pedro Paulo Hatheyer, Carmen Marineo, Ari Ferreira, Nelson Oliver.

Melodrama. Private eye Steve Marshall is in São Paulo seeking a woman wanted in the United States for murder. At his hotel he meets another woman, Elizabeth, who suggests that the murderer is Kitty Herman, a nightclub singer. Steve visits the club and is beaten up by the owner, Victor Marlow. Steve then learns from the police that he has stumbled onto a counterfeiting ring being operated by Victor and Elizabeth. Working with both the authorities and Kitty, who admits being the woman he is seeking but claims to be innocent, Steve lays a trap for the counterfeiters. The showdown occurs at a deserted warehouse where Victor kills the doublecrossing Elizabeth and then attempts to shoot Steve. The police arrive in time to apprehend Victor and rescue Steve. Kitty is vindicated, and Steve returns to the States. *Americans in foreign countries. Detectives. Singers. Police. Murder. Counterfeiting. Perfidy. Hotels. Nightclubs. São Paulo.*

Note: Filmed in Brazil.

GIRL IN THE HEADLINES *see* **THE MODEL MURDER CASE**

THE GIRL IN THE INVISIBLE BIKINI *see* **THE GHOST IN THE INVISIBLE BIKINI**

GIRL IN THE LEATHER SUIT *see* **HELL'S BELLES**

GIRL IN TROUBLE   **F6.1821**

Vanguard Productions International. 15 Aug **1963** [Detroit opening]. Sd; b&w. 35mm. 82 min. [Also 90 min.]

A Brandon Chase Production. *Prod-Dir* Lee Beale. *Screenplay* Anthony Naylor. *Dir Photog* Leo J. Hebert. *Camera Op* George Johnson. *Art Dir* Federate Arts Studios. *Film Ed* Edmond Lacoste. *Mus Dir* George Simson. *Sd* MPA. *Asst Dir* Xavier Shapiro. *Prod Supv* William Morris. *Cost* Arthur Sherrick. *Makeup* Wilma Coleman. *Hairstyling* Maurice Charles.

Cast: Tammy Clark *(Judy Collins)*, Ray Menard *(John Watson)*, Neomie Salatich *(Mona Duvick)*, Larry Johnson, actor *("Mr. Smith")*, Martin Smith, actor *(Harry Calhoun)*, Bettina Johnson *(Loni)*, Charles Murphy *(hotel clerk)*, Jay Houck *(intern)*, L. Foster Rouse *(ambulance attendant)*, C. F. Counce *("The Mark")*, Marie Cavanaugh *(Bella)*.

Melodrama. After graduating from high school, Judy Collins decides to run away from her smalltown home and the strict discipline of her widowed father in order to experience "life" before settling down to marry her longtime boyfriend, John Watson. Judy accepts a ride to New Orleans with a stranger who attacks her along the way. They struggle, and the stranger knocks his head against a rock. Convinced that she has killed him, Judy takes his car and flees. She checks into a sleazy hotel in New Orleans but leaves when she discovers the room clerk watching her from an adjoining room. She moves into a boardinghouse and meets Mona Duvick, a good-hearted woman of dubious occupation. Judy becomes a waitress, but she quickly loses her job when she rejects the advances of the manager. With Mona's help, Judy finds work as a model in a lingerie shop run by Loni. At first Judy is embarrassed to model the scanty costumes, but she grows to enjoy the plush surroundings. She discovers too late, however, that Loni is actually a procuress. Sent to model for a client in an expensive hotel suite, Judy is raped. Mona encourages her friend to make the best of life in spite of the terrifying experience, and Judy takes a job as a dancer on Bourbon Street. John, who has never stopped searching for Judy finds her at last, and for the first time she realizes what she has become. Following an unsuccessful suicide attempt, she decides to turn herself over to the police for the murder of the motorist. John greets her at the hospital with the news that the highway attacker was only stunned, and the couple drive away to begin life together. *Runaways. Waitresses. Models. Pimps. Prostitutes. Dancers. Smalltown life. Adolescence. Rape. Murder. Voyeurism. Employer-employee relations. Suicide. Employment—Women. Boardinghouses. New Orleans.*

Note: Lee Beale is a pseudonym for Brandon Chase.

THE GIRL KILLER   **F6.1822**

Barry Mahon Productions. 5 Jul **1967** [Champaign, Illinois, showing]. Sd; b&w. 35mm. 61 min.

Melodrama. Tony is unable to endure the pressures of modern life. Laughed at by his fellow workers, cheated and betrayed by women, he can only achieve vicarious pleasure as a peeping tom. Eventually Tony becomes more brazen; he enters a woman's bedroom and strangles her with her own underwear. He goes on to commit a series of sex murders which strike terror in New York City. No one can guess the identity of the killer, until one woman manages to escape and report her attacker to the police. After a chase through the streets of Manhattan, Tony is killed. *Voyeurism. Murder. Sadism. Rape. Mental illness. New York City. Chases.*

Note: May also be known as *Sex Killer.*

GIRL MADNESS *see* **THE BEAST OF YUCCA FLATS**

GIRL MERCHANTS *see* **SELLERS OF GIRLS**

A GIRL NAMED TAMIKO   **F6.1823**

Hal Wallis Productions. *Dist* Paramount Pictures. 27 Dec **1962** [Honolulu, Hawaii, opening; c28 Dec 1962; LP23734]. Sd; col (Technicolor). 35mm (Panavision). 110 min.

Prod Hal B. Wallis, Joseph H. Hazen. *Assoc Prod* Paul Nathan. *Dir* John Sturges. *Screenplay* Edward Anhalt. *Cinematog* Charles Lang, Jr. *2d Unit Photog* W. Wallace Kelley. *Art Dir* Walter Tyler, Hal Pereira. *Set Decor* Sam Comer, Arthur Krams. *Film Ed* Warren Low. *Mus* Elmer Bernstein. *Sd* Harold Lewis, Charles Grenzbach. *Asst Dir* D. Michael Moore. *Unit Prod Mgr* Richard Blaydon. *Cost* Edith Head.

Cast: Laurence Harvey *(Ivan Kalin)*, France Nuyen *(Tamiko)*, Martha Hyer *(Fay Wilson)*, Gary Merrill *(Max Wilson)*, Michael Wilding *(Nigel Costairs)*, Miyoshi Umeki *(Eiko)*, Steve Brodie *(James Hatten)*, John Mamo *(Minya)*, Bob Okazaki *(Kimitaka)*, Richard Loo *(Otani)*, Lee Patrick *(Mary Hatten)*, Philip Ahn *(Akiba)*, David Lewis, Ray Teal.

Drama. Source: Ronald de Levington Kirkbride, *A Girl Named Tamiko* (New York, 1959). Ivan Kalin is a cynical and calculating Russo-Chinese photographer working in Tokyo. Embittered because the Japanese killed his parents, he attempts to get a visa to the United States by currying favor with Fay Wilson, a receptionist at the U. S. Embassy. Ivan begins an affair with her in the hopes of meeting Max Wilson, Fay's "protector" and a good business contact. Eiko, a bar hostess living with Ivan, realizes that she has lost him and moves in with Ivan's art dealer friend, Nigel Costairs, an expatriate from England who eventually marries Eiko. A short time later, Ivan meets Tamiko, the daughter of an old and respected Japanese family, who is the librarian at the Foreign Press Club. In the hopes of making a name for himself before reaching the United States, Ivan persuades Tamiko to introduce him to Kimitaka, a famous Japanese painter. Though forbidden to photograph the painter, he does so anyway and his photographs are a success. At the same time, Ivan finds himself falling in love with Tamiko. Fay maintains her sexual hold on him by arranging to take him to the United States, and, despite his love for Tamiko, he decides to leave Japan. Once at the airport, however, he realizes he cannot go with Fay. After making his apologies, he dashes off to find Tamiko. *Russians. Chinese. Photographers. Halfcastes. Receptionists. Philanderers. Businessmen. Art dealers. Mistresses. Expatriates. English. Barroom hostesses. Librarians. Painters. Ambition. Tokyo.*

Note: Location scenes filmed at the Toshogu Shrine at Nikko, the Todaiji Temple, Lake Biwa near Kyoto, and Tokyo.

THE GIRL OF THE MOORS (West Germany)　　　F6.1824
Real Film. *Dist* Casino Films. 26 May **1961** [New York opening]. Sd; col (Agfacolor). 35mm. 87 min.
Prod Gyula Trebitsch. *Dir* Gustav Ucicky. *Screenplay* Adolf Schütz. *Photog* Albert Benitz. *Mus* Siegfried Franz. *Prod Mgr* Werner Ludwig.
Cast: Maria Emo, Claus Holm, Wolfgang Lukschy, Werner Hinz, Horst Frank, Eva-Ingeborg Scholz, Alice Treff, Hans Nielsen, Hilde Körber, Joseph Offenbach, Berta Drews, Josef Dahmen.
Melodrama. Source: Selma Lagerlöf, "Tösen från Stormyrtorpet," in *En saga om en saga och andra sagor* (Stockholm, 1908). A maid, seduced by her employer, becomes pregnant. She tries to commit suicide, but she is saved by two woodcutters. Eventually, the employer meets a violent death, and the maid falls in love with another man and is married. *Housemaids. Employers. Woodsmen. Seduction. Pregnancy. Suicide. Marriage.*
Note: Released in West Germany in Aug 1958 as *Das Mädchen vom Moorhof.* Previously filmed in Sweden (1917, 1947), Germany (1935), and Finland (1940).

GIRL ON A CHAIN GANG　　　　　　　　　　F6.1825
Jerry Gross Productions. 21 Oct **1966** [Los Angeles showing]. Sd; b&w. 35mm. 96 min.
Pres by Jerry Gross. *Prod-Dir-Writ* Jerry Gross. *Assoc Prod* Nicholas Demetroules. *Orig Story* Don Olsen.
Cast: William Watson, Julie Ange, R. K. Charles.
Melodrama. A young woman runs afoul of the law in a small town and is put on a chain gang with 17 male convicts. *Chain gangs. Smalltown life.*

THE GIRL ON A MOTORCYCLE (France/Great Britain)　F6.1826
Mid-Atlantic Films–Arès Productions. *Dist* Claridge Pictures. 6 Nov **1968** [Los Angeles opening]. Sd; col (Technicolor). 35mm. 91 min. *MPAA rating* X.
Prod William Sassoon. *Exec Prod* Ronan O'Rahilly. *Assoc Prod* Sacha Kamenka. *Dir-Adapt* Jack Cardiff. *Screenplay* Ronald Duncan. *Thought Seq Dial* Gillian Freeman. *Photog* Jack Cardiff. *Adtl Photog* René Guissard. *Fantasy Col Cons* Laurie Atkin. *Art Dir* Russell Hagg, Jean d' Eaubonne. *Film Ed* Peter Musgrave. *Mus* Les Reed. *Mus Cond* Douglas Gamley. *Sd* Clive Smith. *Sd Rec* Robert MacPhee, John Aldred. *Asst Dir* James Hodgetts, Philippe Lefebvre. *Prod Supv* Stuart Freeman. *Prod Mgr* Paul Laffargue, Cecil Foster Kemp. *Cost* Lanvin. *Makeup* Bunty Phillips. *Stunts Arr* David Watson.
Cast: Alain Delon (*Daniel*), Marianne Faithfull (*Rebecca*), Roger Mutton (*Raymond*), Marius Goring (*Rebecca's father*), Catherine Jourdan (*Catherine*), Jean Leduc (*Jean*), Jacques Marin (*pump attendant*), André Maranne (*French superintendent*), Bari Johnson, Arnold Diamond (*French customs officers*), John G. Heller (*German customs officer*), Marika Rivera (*German waitress*), Richard Blake, Christopher Williams, Colin West, Kit Williams (*students*).
Drama. Source: André Pieyre de Mandiargues, *La motocyclette* (Paris, 1963). After 6 weeks of marriage, Rebecca awakens early one morning and slips quietly from bed without disturbing her sleeping husband, Raymond. Donning a form-fitting, fur-lined, black leather suit, Rebecca leaves her small house in the French countryside and mounts a gleaming black motorcycle. Frustrated by her conventional husband, Rebecca plans to visit Daniel, a professor at Heidelberg, and recapture the passion of their past relationship. As the sun rises, she hurtles across the countryside recalling her affair with Daniel: their initial meeting at her father's bookstore, the time Daniel first taught her to ride a motorcycle, their clandestine rendezvous at a ski resort, their sadomasochistic lovemaking, and their eventual parting when Rebecca rejected Daniel in favor of the secure life offered by Raymond. But, inevitably, Daniel has lured

Rebecca back to him by giving her a motorcycle for a wedding present. As Rebecca nears Daniel's home, her mental images of her lover, combined with her physical manipulation of her motorcycle, become increasingly erotic until, in a frenzy of passion, she loses control, sideswipes a truck, and is thrown to her death through the windshield of a passing car. *Professors. Motorcyclists. Marriage. Infidelity. Sadomasochism. Fetishism. Ski resorts. Bookshops. Motorcycles. Heidelberg. Motorcycle accidents.*
Note: Opened in Paris in Jun 1968 as *La motocyclette*; running time: ca95 min; released in Great Britain in Oct 1968 as *Girl on a Motorcycle*; running time: 91 min. Shortly after initial U. S. release, the film's MPAA rating was changed to "R" following the deletion of certain sequences; rereleased in this version in May 1970 as *Naked Under Leather.*

GIRL ON THE RUN　　　　　　　　　　　　　F6.1827
Rose Tree Productions. *Dist* Astor Pictures. Apr **1961**. Sd; b&w. 35mm. 64 min.
Prod Robert Presnell, Sr. *Dir* Joseph Lee, Arthur J. Beckhard. *Screenplay-Story* Cedric Worth, Arthur J. Beckhard. *Choreog* Dorothy Wistcott.
Cast: Richard Coogan (*Bill Martin*), Rosemary Pettit (*Janet*), Frank Albertson (*Hank, the carnival foreman*), Harry Bannister (*Clay Reeves*), Edith King (*carnival girl*), Charles Bollender (*dwarf, the carnival owner*), George Marsh (*managing editor*), Renee De Milo, Joseph Sullivan, Mike O'Dowd, John Krollers, Scott Hale.
Mystery melodrama. Newspaper reporter Bill Martin, trying to break a vice racket that is tied in with a local carnival, is suspected by the police of murdering his managing editor. Janet, Bill's trusted secretary and girl friend, helps him elude the authorities and investigate political boss Clay Reeves, whom they saw leaving the newspaper building at the time of the murder. While Bill follows Reeves, Janet takes a job at the carnival and, with the assistance of a carnival girl, attempts to uncover new information. The dwarf owner of the carnival, in order to protect his employee from being killed because she knows too much about the vice ring, turns Janet over to Reeves. The owner is subsequently shot by Reeves; but before he dies, he reveals to Bill that the dead editor was Reeves's partner in crime. *Reporters. Editors. Secretaries. Police. Racketeers. Political bosses. Carnival workers. Dwarfs. Murder. Carnivals.*

GIRL PUSHER　　　　　　　　　　　　　　　F6.1828
Mitam Productions. 27 Nov **1968** [Boston opening]. Sd; b&w. 35mm. 62 min.
Melodrama. Ben Simmons falls in love with aspiring actress Mae Miller and convinces her to move into his Hollywood apartment when her money runs out. Before long Mae announces that she is leaving to live with a film producer who has offered her a part in a picture. Ben then meets Patty and invites her home as Mae's replacement, but one day he finds her making love to his friend Dave. Ben thereupon decides to offer her sexual services to other "friends" for a price. His success leads him to engage Vera, who agrees to accommodate only those clients seeking variant forms of sex, and Sue, who later discovers she has her own clientele. At this point, Mae returns and pleads for forgiveness. Ben welcomes her back, but he goes berserk and beats her when she later informs him that she is again leaving to seek an acting break. She dies at a hospital, and Ben is arrested for murder. *Actors. Pimps. Ambition. Infidelity. Prostitution. Murder. Insanity. Hollywood.*
Note: Also known as *Girl Pushers.*

GIRL SMUGGLERS　　　　　　　　　　　　　F6.1829
Barry Mahon Productions. *Dist* Sack Amusement Enterprises. 1 Jun **1967** [New York showing]. Sd; b&w. 35mm. 63 min.
A Barry Mahon Production. *Prod-Dir* Barry Mahon.
Cast: Lucky Kargo.
Melodrama. To meet the demand in New York City for young Puerto Rican prostitutes, a gang is organized to kidnap young women in San Juan and smuggle them into the United States. The racketeers take school girls from their homes, break down their moral resistance, and place them on the streets of New York as prostitutes. Pedro, one young man, incensed at the abuse of his teenaged sister, determines to fight the gang and free her from white slavery. *Puerto Ricans. Racketeers. White slave traffic. Kidnaping. Brother-sister relationship. Adolescence. San Juan (Puerto Rico). New York City.*

THE GIRL SWAPPERS see TWO AND TWO MAKE SIX

THE GIRL, THE BODY, AND THE PILL　　　　　F6.1830
Creative Film Enterprises. *Dist* Dominant Pictures, Box Office Spectaculars. 5 Oct **1967** [New Orleans opening]. Sd; col (Eastmancolor). 35mm. 80 min. *MPAA rating* R.
Prod-Dir Herschell Gordon Lewis. *Exec Prod* Sidney J. Reich. *Screenplay* Louise Downe. *Cinematog* Roy Collodi. *Camera Op* Steve Poster. *Art Dir* Dean Alexander. *Set Dsgn* Robert Enrietto. *Ed Supv* Richard Brinkman. *Ed Asst* Robert Lewis. *Mus Dir* Larry Wellington. *Song: "The Pill"* Sheldon

Seymour. *Sd Rec* William R. Johnson. *Prod Mgr* Paul Hunter. *Crew Ch* Spyros Hortis. *2d Unit* Eskandar Ameripoor. *Ch Electrn* Cornelius Smith.

Cast: Pamela Rhea (*Marcia Barrington*), Bill Rogers (*Wesley Nichols*), Valedia Hill (*Irene Hunt*), Nancy Lee Noble (*Randy Hunt*), Otto Schlesinger (*Mr. Price*), Roy Collodi (*Pike Grover*), George Brown (*Brad Martin*), Eleanor Vaill (*Grace Nichols*), James Nelson, actor (*Ray Stanton*), Kay Ross (*Alice Nichols*), Todd Harris (*Charlie*), Sue Puccinelli (*Nancy Foster*), Pat Tenerelli (*Freddy*), Ray Sager (*Tony*), The Fly-By Nytes (*themselves*).

Melodrama. Marcia Barrington, a progressive, young high school teacher, is forced to abandon teaching sex hygiene as part of her regular curriculum when the school principal, Mr. Price, and Wesley Nichols, a powerful member of the school board, object. Marcia's students, including Wesley's daughter, Alice, ask their teacher to continue the classes outside of school. Unaware that many of the permission slips are forged, Marcia agrees, much to the disapproval of her fiancé, Brad Martin. Trouble arises when Randy, a wild youth, lies to her mother, Irene, and tells her she spent the night at Alice's house when in fact she stayed with Pike Grover and his gang. Irene visits Wesley and mentions Marcia's classes. Wesley then returns the visit under the pretext of looking at Randy's notebooks on the class, whereupon Irene and Wesley begin an affair. Wesley's guilt causes him to pressure Mr. Price into firing Marcia. Meanwhile, Alice and her boyfriend Ray Stanton break up because Ray wants to tell Wesley of their love and Alice fears that her father will disapprove. When Ray begins to date Randy, Alice makes love to Ray and then confesses to her mother. Irene discovers she is pregnant because Randy had stolen her birth control pills and replaced them with saccharine. Irene has an abortion, and Randy, fearful that her mother will die, rushes to her and asks for her forgiveness. Irene rejects Wesley, who returns to his wife. All ends well when Mr. Price reinstates Marcia, Marcia and Brad marry, and Alice and Ray decide to finish school before they marry. *Schoolteachers. School principals. Students. Gangs. Birth control. High school life. Sex instruction. Filial relations. Forgery. Infidelity. Guilt. Sexual initiation. Abortion.*

Note: Location scenes filmed in and around Chicago. Alternative title: *The Pill.*

THE GIRL WHO COULDN'T SAY NO (Italy)   F6.1831

Italnoleggio Cinematografico–Prima Cinematografica–Fulco Film. *Dist* Twentieth Century-Fox Film Corp. 5 Nov 1969 [Boston opening; c12 Nov 1969; LP43773]. Sd; col (De Luxe). 35mm (Techniscope). 83 min. *MPAA rating* GP.

Prod Luciano Perugia. *Exec Prod* Dimitri De Grunwald. *Dir* Franco Brusati. *Screenplay* Franco Brusati, Ennio De Concini. *Photog* Ennio Guarnieri. *Art Dir* Pier Luigi Pizzi. *Film Ed* Franco Arcalli. *Mus* Riz Ortolani. "*Beat Mass*" *perf by* Franco Ceccarelli. *Sd* Christopher Cruise. *Sd Rec* Doug Turner. *Prod Mgr* Mario De Biase. *Cost* Pier Luigi Pizzi.

Cast: Virna Lisi (*Yolanda*), George Segal (*Franco*), Lila Kedrova (*Yolanda's mother*), Akim Tamiroff (*Uncle Egidio*), Paola Pitagora (*widow*), Luciano Mondolfo (*professor*), Mario Brega (*cripple*), Vera Nandi (*Luisa Belli*), Richard Bill (*salesman*), Ciccio Barbi (*passenger on train*), Gianni Di Benedetto, Nora Ricci, Adriano Amidei Migliano, Germano Longo, Ugo Adinolfi, Mirella Pamphili, Felicity Mason, Jeffrey Copplestone.

Romantic drama. Franco, a career-oriented assistant surgeon, gets off his train in Rome and meets his childhood friend, Yolanda, after 15 years of separation. They fall in love, and Franco soon becomes aware of Yolanda's unpredictable and unconventional attitudes. When Yolanda literally interprets Franco's complaints about his job and releases all the animals he uses for his experiments, he is appalled. Nevertheless, they travel to Florence together, where Yolanda takes in a crippled tramp. Franco is angered and leaves her, returning to Rome to become director of a hospital. A year later, Franco and Yolanda meet again, find they are still in love, and take a vacation in the country, where they are happy until Yolanda's Dutch, guitar-playing boyfriend appears. Franco instructs his aging Uncle Egidio to tell Yolanda that he has left her. When Franco is called to Egidio's deathbed in Sweden some time later, he finds Yolanda there. Once again, Franco and Yolanda get together, and all is well until Yolanda learns that a wild trip they had—including a boat theft and a house-borrowing—was prearranged and paid for by Franco. She leaves in a rage, but they meet again, and Franco finally convinces Yolanda to marry him. At the altar, however, she refuses to take the vows, and Franco decides that he is through with her forever. Several years later, they accidentally meet at another train station; Franco is now minister of health, and Yolanda is the mother of a number of illegitimate children. Their meeting is brief, and they board different trains. *Surgeons. Eccentrics. Uncles. Tramps. Cripples. Dutch. Guitarists. Marriage. Illegitimacy. Weddings. Vacations. Trains. Hospitals. Rome. Florence. Sweden.*

Note: Filmed on location in Italy and released there in 1968 as *Tenderly*; running time: 104 min. Also known in Italy as *Il suo modo di fare.*

THE GIRL WHO KNEW TOO MUCH   F6.1832

United Pictures–Westco–Commonwealth United Productions. *Dist* Commonwealth United Entertainment, Inc. Sep 1969. Sd; col (Eastman Color). 35mm. 95 min. *MPAA rating* R.

Prod Earle Lyon. *Assoc Prod* Bill Welch. *Dir* Francis D. Lyon. *Screenplay* Charles A. Wallace. *Camera* Alan Stensvold. *Art Dir* Paul Sylos. *Film Ed* Terry O. Morse. *Mus* Joe Greene. *Sd* Bob Post. *Asst Dir* William Schwartz. *Prod Supv* Joe Wonder.

Cast: Adam West (*Johnny Cain*), Nancy Kwan (*Revel*), Robert Alda (*Allardice*), Nehemiah Persoff (*Lieutenant Crawford*), David Brian (*Had Dixon*), Buddy Greco (*Lucky*), Patricia Smith (*Tricia Grinaldi*), Weaver Levy (*Wong See*), John Napier (*Danny Deshea*), Mark Roberts (*Stephen*), Steve Peck (*Tony Grinaldi*), Diane Van Valin (*stripper*), Chick Chandler (*Hunley*), Lisa Todd (*Sugar Sweet*).

Crime Melodrama. A truck smashes into a California nightclub owned by retired CIA agent and Orient adventurer Johnny Cain, and Grinaldi, an underworld figure, is killed. Cain is pressured to find the murderer—first by Grinaldi's syndicate and then by the CIA, which enters the case because of a threat to national security. Lucky, the club's entertainer, believes that Revel, Cain's Chinese ex-mistress and secretary to the slain gangster, is involved in the affair, and he hides her at Cain's apartment. Cain learns that she is marked for murder, and he also discovers that Grinaldi planned to steal a Tibetan statue worth $500,000 to the Communists for propaganda purposes. He gains an appointment with the syndicate's second-in-command, but the man is murdered just as Cain arrives. The murderer dies in an automobile chase, and subsequently the statue is recovered. Cain confronts the chief Communist agent as the agent gives $500,000 to the two men who have inherited Grinaldi's syndicate leadership. The Communists secretly plot to take over the underworld organization in order to cripple American commerce. A bomb planted in the moneybag explodes, killing all but Cain. Allardice, now the only living member of the syndicate hierarchy, confesses to Cain that he traded the statue to the Communists in return for the murder of his superiors. Cain and Allardice are interrupted by Grinaldi's widow, Tricia, a Communist secret agent who married the gangster to further the Communist plot. She orders Allardice to kill Cain, but he shoots her instead and then falls to his death as he attempts to escape. Cain and Revel are reunited at last. *Gangsters. Adventurers. Nightclub owners. Secretaries. Secret agents. Communists. Chinese. Mistresses. Widows. Murder. Theft. Conspiracy. Defense—National. Nightclubs. Syndicates. Sculptures. California. United States—Central Intelligence Agency. Automobile accidents. Chases. Explosions.*

GIRL WITH A SUITCASE (France/Italy)   F6.1833

Titanus–S. G. C. *Dist* Ellis Films. 11 Sep 1961 [New York opening]. Sd; b&w. 35mm. 111 min.

Pres by C & D Film Associates. *Prod* Maurizio Lodi Fè. *Dir-Story* Valerio Zurlini. *Screenplay* Leo Benvenuti, Piero De Bernardi, Enrico Medioli, Giuseppe Patroni-Griffi, Valerio Zurlini, Giuseppe Bennati. *Dir Photog* Tino Santoni. *Art Dir* Flavio Mogherini. *Film Ed* Mario Serandrei. *Mus* Mario Nascimbene. *Sd* Enzo Silvestri. *Asst Dir* Mario Maffei.

Cast: Claudia Cardinale (*Aida Zepponi*), Jacques Perrin (*Lorenzo Fainardi*), Corrado Pani (*Marcello Fainardi*), Luciana Angelillo (*Aunt Marta*), Carlo Hintermann, Gian Maria Volontè (*Piero [see note]*), Riccardo Garrone (*Romolo*), Renato Baldini (*Francia*), Romolo Valli (*Father Introna*), Ciccio Barbi (*Crosia*), Nadia Bianchi (*Nuccia*), Edda Soligo (*teacher*), Elsa Albani (*Lucia*).

Melodrama. Aida, a voluptuous young singer, is having an affair with Piero, the leader of a small-time dance band. Marcello, a wealthy playboy, lures her away with the promise of a film career but then tires of her and abandons her near Parma. Close to despair, she traces him to his home, which he shares with his younger brother, 16-year-old Lorenzo, and their stern aunt. Marcello asks Lorenzo to rid him of Aida, but Lorenzo is not as callow as his brother, and he immediately sympathizes with her. He appoints himself her protector and installs her in one of the city's best hotels. The next morning he brings her new clothes, which he has bought on credit, and gives her his allowance money. The relationship between them develops into love, but the slightly older and considerably more experienced Aida realizes it could never work. Meanwhile, Aida continues to attract men who might help her in a show business career. Lorenzo's aunt learns of the affair, and Father Introna, the family priest and Lorenzo's tutor, convinces Aida that she can no longer remain in Parma. Failing to achieve a reconciliation with Piero, she decides to go away with Romolo, a musician who has offered to pay her for her companionship. Lorenzo follows her to Riccione and is brutally beaten up by Romolo. Realizing she can only bring him harm, Aida reluctantly insists that the heart-broken Lorenzo return to Parma. Before he leaves, however, he gives her an envelope filled with money. [In the original version, Aida has an illegitimate son by a man who has since died. The arrival of Lorenzo in Riccione at the conclusion of the film keeps Aida from prostituting herself in order to be able to feed the child. Aida nevertheless persuades Lorenzo to go home.] *Playboys. Band leaders. Singers. Aunts. Musicians. Brothers. Adolescence. Lovelorn. Finance—Personal. Prostitution. Illegitimacy. Parma. Riccione.*

Note: Released in Italy in 1961 as *La ragazza con la valigia* at 135 min. Paris opening on 11 May 1962 as *La fille à la valise* at 120 min. Also known as *Pleasure Girl.* Only U. S. sources credit Carlo Hintermann with the role of Piero.

GIRL WITH GREEN EYES (Great Britain) F6.1834
Woodfall Film Productions. *Dist* Lopert Pictures. 10 Aug **1964** [New York opening; c14 May 1964; LP29674]. Sd; b&w. 35mm. 91 min.

Prod Oscar Lewenstein. *Exec Prod* Tony Richardson. *Assoc Prod* Leigh Aman. *Prod Exec* Michael Holden. *Dir* Desmond Davis. *Screenplay* Edna O'Brien. *Dir Photog* Manny Wynn. *Camera Op* Denis Lewiston. *Focus Puller* Ken Goodman. *Camera Grip* Frank Boston. *Art Dir* Ted Marshall. *Asst Art Dir* Ron Benton. *Supv Ed* Anthony Gibbs. *Film Ed* Brian Smedley-Aston. *Asst Ed* Pamela Milner-Gardner. *Mus Comp & Cond* John Addison. *Sd* Derek Leather, Stephen Dalby. *Sd Rec* Robin Gregory. *Sd Ed* Don Challis. *Asst Sd Ed* Ron Pope. *Boom Op* Tom Buchanan. *1st, 2d & 3d Asst Dir* Roy Millichip, Grania O'Shannon, Michael Meighan. *Cont* Jane Buck. *Wardrobe Mistress* Barbara Gillett. *Makeup Artist* Bob Lawrence. *Hairdresser* Betty Sherriff. *Location Adv* Ralph Brinton. *Still Photog* Aubrey Dewar. *Constr Mgr* Stanley Gale. *Prod Buyer* Terry Parr. *Prop Supv* Tommy Erley. *Ch Electrn* Fred Anderson.

Cast: Peter Finch (*Eugene Gaillard*), Rita Tushingham (*Kate Brady*), Lynn Redgrave (*Baba Brenan*), Marie Kean (*Josie Hannigan*), Arthur O'Sullivan (*Mr. Brady*), Julian Glover (*Malachi Sullivan*), T. P. McKenna (*priest*), Lislott Goettinger (*Joanna*), Patrick Laffan (*Bertie Counihan*), Eileen Crowe (*Mrs. Byrne*), Kay Craig (*aunt*), Joe Lynch (*Andy Devlin*), Yolande Turner (*Mary McIntosh*), Harry Brogan (*Jack Holland*), Michael Hennessey (*Davey*), Joe O'Donnell (*Patrick Devlin*), Michael O'Briain (*Arthur*), Dave Kelly (*ticket collector*), Oliver MacGreevy (*Duggan*).

Melodrama. Source: Edna O'Brien, *The Lonely Girl* (London, 1962). Young Kate Brady leaves her father's farm in Ireland's County Clare to work in a Dublin grocery and share an apartment with Baba, a girl with whom she attended a convent school. She meets Eugene Gaillard, a writer considerably older than herself, whose wife has left him; and she is strongly attracted to him. She pursues him, and despite his reservations, he is enchanted by her. Kate goes to live with Eugene at his country house, but her conscience prevents her from having sex with him. Word of the situation reaches her father, and he forces her to return home. After being reproached by the local priest, Kate runs away back to Eugene, only to be followed by her father and a crowd of his drunken cronies, who storm the Gaillard house. They leave when Eugene and his housekeeper, who appears brandishing an ancient shotgun, threaten them. Kate's emotions finally win out over her scruples, and she surrenders to Eugene. Their relationship is uneasy because they have nothing in common but their love. Jealous of and feeling inferior to Eugene's clever friends, Kate becomes possessive. Eugene in turn becomes restless and sarcastic. They quarrel, and Kate rejoins Baba, who is leaving for London. Kate expects Eugene to follow her, but when he doesn't, she realizes that he will soon be merely a girlhood memory. *Irish. Authors. Farmers. Roommates. Youth. Filial relations. Drunkenness. Sexual initiation. Dublin. County Clare. London.*

Note: Filmed on location in and around Dublin; working title: *Once Upon a Summer.* Opened in London in May 1964.

THE GIRL WITH HUNGRY EYES F6.1835
Dist Boxoffice International Film Distributors. 25 Jan **1967** [Fresno, California, showing]. Sd; b&w. 35mm. 85 min. *MPAA rating* X.

Prod-Dir-Writ William Rotsler. *Exec Prod* Harry H. Hershey, Edward Everett.

Cast: Cathy Crowfoot (*Tigercat*), Vicky Dee (*Kitty*), Shannon Carse (*Brian*), Scott Avery (*Tom*), Oswald Fenwick (*The Man*), Pat Barrington (*The Dancer*), Frankie O'Brien, Vicky Kober, Charlotte Stewart, Sharon Smith, Billie Russell (*The Girls*).

Melodrama. While she is driving in the country with her girl friend Kitty, Tigercat, a lesbian, gives a ride to a young man having trouble with his car. Anxious to assert her independence, Kitty goes off into the woods with the man. Tigercat catches them making love, and, gripped by violent fantasies, she murders the man with a rock and forces Kitty to accompany her back to town. Their relationship becomes even more strained at an all-female birthday party, during which nude go-go dancing leads to a series of flare-ups and violent fights. Disgusted, Kitty flees the lesbian underground and returns to Brian, her former boyfriend. Tigercat hunts them down and pulls a knife on Brian; he kills her, thus freeing Kitty to begin a new life. *Lesbianism. Murder. Jealousy. Bisexuality. Nudity. Infidelity.*

Note: Also known as *The Girl With the Hungry Eyes* and *The Face of Sin.*

THE GIRL WITH THE FABULOUS BOX F6.1836
Nicena Productions. **1969**. Sd; col. 35mm. [Feature film, length unknown.]
Prod-Dir Charles Nisbet.

Satire. Attempting to prevent the success of a NASA exploration of the planet Mars, saboteurs detonate a bomb aboard the spaceship in flight. *Saboteurs. Space exploration. Spaceships. Bombs. Mars (planet). United States—National Aeronautics and Space Administration.*

THE GIRL WITH THE GOLDEN EYES (France) F6.1837
Madeleine Films. *Dist* Kingsley International Pictures, Union Film Distributors. 20 Aug **1962** [New York opening]. Sd; b&w. 35mm. 90 min.

Pres by Auerbach Film Enterprises. *Prod* Gilbert de Goldschmidt. *Dir* Jean-Gabriel Albicocco. *Screenplay* Pierre Pelegri, Jean-Gabriel Albicocco. *Dial* Pierre Pelegri, Philippe Dumarcay. *Photog* Quinto Albicocco. *Art Dir* Jacques d'Ovidio, Frédéric de Pasquale. *Film Ed* Georges Klotz. *Guitar Mus* Narciso Yepes. *Concerto Grosso, opus 60* Arcangelo Corelli. *Sd* Séverin Frankiel. *Prod Mgr* Jacques Garcia, Théo Michel.

Cast: Marie Laforêt (*girl*), Paul Guers (*Henri Marsay*), Françoise Prévost (*Eléanore [Léo] San-Réal*), Jacques Verlier (*Paul de Mannerville*), Françoise Dorléac (*Katia*), Alice Sapritch (*Madame Alberte*), Carla Marlier (*Sonia*), Frédéric de Pasquale (*Willy*), Guy Martin (*Chabert*), Philippe Moreau.

Drama. Adapted from: Honoré de Balzac, *L'histoire des Treize* (Paris, 1834-35). A hedonistic cabal of wealthy Parisian men called "The Thirteen" are devoted to helping one another attain their own selfish ends. Among them is Henri Marsay, a high-fashion photographer whose chief pastime is winning bets from the other members of his coterie by successfully seducing his attractive models. One day, quite by accident, he encounters an enchanting young woman with golden eyes. Though he eventually succeeds in adding her to his list of conquests, he is unable to learn her name or her background, nor is he able to explain the lavish apartment and wardrobe that seem to be at her disposal. Puzzled, he discusses the mysterious girl with Léo, a woman who is not only his business associate but also his close friend; then, becoming aware that Léo is the girl's benefactress and lover, Henri calls upon the thirteen for help. They discover that Léo has removed the girl to a lonely cabin in the woods, professing to help her. Henri forces Léo to accompany him to the spot, and upon their arrival, he allows Léo a few minutes alone with the girl. Following an emotional scene in which the girl confesses her love for Henri, Léo stabs her to death; and Henri catches her in his arms. *Photographers. Models. Hedonism. Seduction. Murder. Lesbianism. Wealth. Wagers. Paris.*

Note: Opened in Paris in Sep 1961 as *La fille aux yeux d'or*; running time: 95 min; cut from 105 min.

THE GIRL WITH THE MAGIC BOX F6.1838
Barry Mahon Productions. *Dist* Cinema Syndicate, Inc. 22 Apr **1965** [San Francisco showing]. Sd; col (Eastman Color). 35mm. 62 min.

A Barry Mahon Production. *Prod-Dir* Barry Mahon. *Camera* Byron Maybe. *Sd* Magno Sound. *Asst Dir* Byron Maybe. *Opticals* Eastern Effects.

Drama. Laura Eden, one of the world's most beautiful pinup photographers, is given the difficult assignment of assembling and photographing the most beautiful nude models in New York City. By telephoning friends in the business, she makes a list of the women she wants to use, but she finds that some photographers are reluctant to lend their best models. One photographer insists that Laura pose for him before he will authorize his model to work for her. Finally, Laura gathers the models together in her lavish apartment on the East River. From the moment the women take off their clothes and Laura begins to snap photos, it becomes clear that her project will be a success. *Photographers. Models. Nudity. New York City—East Side.*

Note: May also be known as *The Magic Box.*

THE GIRL WITH THREE CAMELS (Czechoslovakia) F6.1839
Barrandov Film Studio. For Československý Film. *Dist* Continental Distributing, Inc. 12 Aug **1968** [New York opening]. Sd; b&w. 35mm. 98 min.

Dir Václav Krška. *Screenplay* Miloslav Stehlík, Václav Krška. *Story* Miloslav Stehlík. *Photog* Rudolf Stahl. *Mus* Jiří Šust.

Cast: Slávka Budínová (*Bobina's mother*), Zuzana Ondrouchová (*Bobina*), Radovan Kukavský (*Alfred*), Jan Langsadl (*Josef Pepik*), Vladimír Pospíšil (*mother's 1st lover*).

Comedy-melodrama. At a dance, 17-year-old Bobina meets Josef Pepik, a young mechanic, and makes love to him on the eve of his departure for Algeria, where he has a construction job. When Bobina learns that she is pregnant, her volatile mother insists that she marry the man despite the fact that the only word that she has received from him is a postcard showing three camels beneath a blue sky. Bobina writes to him, but her letter is returned with the news that he has been killed in an accident. Bobina's mother, who is also illegitimate, takes the news as another example of the selfish way in which women are treated by men. She demands that Bobina have an abortion, but Bobina takes her mother's money and goes to a hospital to have the baby. When she returns home, she meets Alfred, her mother's latest lover, and he takes her to register the baby under Josef's name. Because of bureaucratic complications, however, they are unable to convince the authorities of the infant's paternity. Alfred eventually persuades some of Josef's friends to verify Bobina's claim, but Bobina's mother ruins the arrangement by throwing the friends out of her apartment. While Alfred, Bobina, and her mother are making tentative plans for establishing some sort of family life, Alfred's mistress of 20 years arrives to retrieve Alfred. Left alone with her illegitimate mother and her illegitimate child, Bobina thrusts the postcard in front of a portrait of her illegitimate grandmother. *Mechanics. Mistresses. Infants. Adolescence. Pregnancy. Illegitimacy. Filial relations. Parentage. Bureaucracy. Motherhood.*

Note: Released in Czechoslovakia in 1967 as *Dívka s třemi velbloudy.*

GIRLS AND THE SINGLE SAILOR see **SEX AND THE SINGLE SAILOR**

GIRLS AT SEA (Great Britain)   F6.1840

Associated British Productions. *Dist* Seven Arts Associated Corp. Feb **1962**. Sd; col (Technicolor). 35mm. 81 min.

Prod Vaughan N. Dean, Gilbert Gunn. *Dir* Gilbert Gunn. *Screenplay (see note)* T. J. Morrison, Gilbert Gunn, Walter C. Mycroft. *Photog* Erwin Hillier. *Art Dir* Peter Glazier. *Film Ed* E. B. Jarvis. *Mus* Laurie Johnson. *Sd Rec* Arthur Bradburn, Len Shilton. *Asst Dir* Jeremy Summers. *Prod Mgr* Victor Peck.

Cast: Guy Rolfe (*Capt. Alwyn Maitland*), Alan White (*The Commander*), Ronald Shiner (*Marine Ogg*), Michael Hordern (*Adm. Reginald Hewitt*), Anne Kimbell (*Mary Carlton*), Nadine Tallier (*Antoinette*), Fabia Drake (*Lady Kitty Hewitt*), Mary Steele (*Jill Eaton*), Richard Coleman (*Capt. Bobby Randall*), Lionel Jeffries (*tourist*), Ted Johnson (*The Singer*), Daniel Massey (*Flag Lieutenant Courtney*), David Lodge (*Corporal Duckett*).

Comedy. Source: Stephen King-Hall and Ian Hay, *The Middle Watch* (London opening: 12 Aug 1929). While on a visit to the French Riviera, the officers of the gunboat H.M.S. *Scotia* throw a shipboard party to celebrate the engagement of Marine Captain Randall to Jill Eaton. Upon discovering that the last shore boat is unseaworthy, Jill and her American friend Mary Carlton are forced to spend the night on the ship. Unknown to all, there is a third female aboard—Antoinette, a fiery French redhead determined to hold the wolfish Marine Ogg to his marriage proposal. Complications arise when the captain learns that Admiral Hewitt has decided to make *Scotia* his flagship and will set sail for Genoa immediately. When the admiral discovers Jill in the captain's cabin, the young woman blurts out that she married the captain that morning; unfortunately Mary tells the identical story when she is also discovered. Upon the ship's arrival in Genoa the next morning, the admiral's wife comes aboard and finds Antoinette in the captain's bath. After a round of additional misunderstandings, everyone is reconciled, except Ogg. Although he succeeds in palming Antoinette off on the ship's commander, he spots a launch approaching with another past love; and she is accompanied by her two brothers and a clergyman. *French. Americans in foreign countries. Stowaways. Philanderers. Courtship. Jealousy. Gunboats. Riviera. Genoa. Great Britain—Royal Navy.*

Note: Filmed on the Riviera. Released in Great Britain in Oct 1958; running time: 80 min. Previously filmed as *The Middle Watch* in 1930 (British International Pictures) and in 1939 under the same title (British International). Only one source credits Gunn and Mycroft with screenplay.

GIRLS COME TOO!   F6.1841

Monique Productions. *Dist* Monique Productions, Jerand Film Distributors. 12 Nov **1968** [Maryland licence]. Sd; col. 35mm. 63 min.

Cast: Morganna, Silver Dawn, Susan Moray, Billy King, Cindy Shane, Sherry Lynn, pseud, Lori Shaw, Dick Powers.

Sex film. In a Miami nudist colony, two hippie girls ride a motorcycle in the nude, and Morganna, a nightclub dancer, spends her days there lying naked in the sun. *Hippies. Dancers. Sunbathing. Nudist camps. Motorcycles. Miami.*

Note: Also known as *Girls Too.* Filmed in Miami.

GIRLS DISAPPEAR see **THE ROAD TO SHAME**

GIRLS FOR HIRE   F6.1842

Dist Stacey Distributors. ca **1970**. Sd; col. 16mm. 61-81 min.

Sex film. No information about the precise nature of this film has been found. *Prostitutes. Sexuality.*

Note: Also known as *Girl for Hire.*

GIRLS FOR MEN ONLY see **HOT GIRLS FOR MEN ONLY**

THE GIRLS FROM THUNDER STRIP   F6.1843

Borealis Enterprises. *Dist* American General Pictures. ca **1966**. Sd; col (Technicolor). 35mm (Techniscope). 82 min.

Pres by David L. Hewitt. *Prod* David L. Hewitt, Michael Mehas. *Dir* David L. Hewitt. *Screenplay* Pat Boyette.

Cast: Jody McCrea, Maray Ayres, Mick Mehas, Casey Kasem, Lindsay Crosby.

Action melodrama. Three young women in a rural area of the country are involved with moonshining, bootlegging and violence. Press material suggests the use of motorcycles and a good deal of gunfire. *Moonshiners. Bootleggers. Rural life. Motorcycle gangs.*

GIRLS! GIRLS! GIRLS!   F6.1844

Hal Wallis Productions. *Dist* Paramount Pictures. 31 Oct **1962** [Honolulu, Hawaii, opening; c31 Oct 1962; LP23321]. Sd; col (Technicolor). 35mm. 101 min. [Also 106 min.]

Prod Hal B. Wallis. *Assoc Prod* Paul Nathan. *Dir* Norman Taurog. *Screenplay* Allan Weiss, Edward Anhalt. *Orig Story* Allan Weiss. *Photog* Loyal Griggs. *Camera Op* Ken Williams. *Asst Camera* Skip Sanford, Paul Weddell. *Art Dir* Hal Pereira, Walter Tyler. *Set Decor* Sam Comer, Frank R. McKelvy. *Film Ed* Warren Low. *Mus Score & Cond* Joseph J. Lilley. *Vocal Accomp* The Jordanaires. *Song:* "Girls, Girls, Girls" Jerry Leiber, Mike Stoller. *Songs:* "Return to Sender," "We're Coming in Loaded" Otis Blackwell, Winfield Scott. *Songs:* "A Boy Like Me, a Girl Like You," "Song of the Shrimp," "Earth Boy," "The Walls Have Ears" Sid Tepper, Roy C. Bennett. *Songs:* "Thanks to the Rolling Sea," "Because of Love," "Where Do You Come From?" Ruth Batchelor, Bob Roberts. *Songs:* "We'll Be Together," "Mama" Charles O'Curran, Dudley Brooks. *Song:* "I Don't Wanna Be Tied" Bill Giant, Bernie Baum, Florence Kaye. *Song:* "I Don't Want To" Janice Torre, Fred Spielman. *Songs Sung by* Elvis Presley. *Mus Numbers Stgd by* Charles O'Curran. *Sd* Harold Lewis, Charles Grenzbach. *Rec* R. D. Cook. *Boom Op* Bill Hamilton. *Asst Dir* D. Michael Moore, James Rosenberger, Dale Coleman, Robert Goodstein. *Prod Mgr* Richard Blaydon. *Unit Prod Mgr* William W. Gray. *Script Supv* Claire Behnke. *Cost Dsgn* Edith Head. *Wardrobe* Grace Harris, John A. Anderson. *Makeup* Gary Morris. *Hairstyles* Jackie Bone. *Casting* Ed Morse. *Dial Coach* Jack Mintz. *Still Photog* Sterling Smith. *Prop* Robert McCrillis, Bernard Schoefield. *Grip* Dominic Seminerio.

Cast: Elvis Presley (*Ross Carpenter*), Stella Stevens (*Robin Gantner*), Laurel Goodwin (*Laurel Dodge*), Jeremy Slate (*Wesley Johnson*), Robert Strauss (*Sam*), Frank Puglia (*Alexander Stavros*), Guy Lee (*Chen Yung*), Benson Fong (*Kin Yung*), Beulah Quo (*Madame Yung*), Lili Valenty (*Mama Stavros*), Nestor Paiva (*Arthur Morgan*), Barbara Beall (*Leona Stavros*), Betty Beall (*Linda Stavros*), Ann McCrea (*Mrs. Morgan*), Ginny Tiu (*Mai Ling*), Elizabeth Tiu (*Tai Ling*), Alexander Tiu (*their little brother*), Gavin Gordon (*Mr. Peabody*).

Comedy-drama with music. Nightclub singer Ross Carpenter, who also skippers a charter fishing boat for Papa Stavros, dreams of someday purchasing the latter's sailboat, which Ross and his late father built. Stavros offers the prize craft for sale when he is forced to move to Arizona because of his wife's illness, and Ross is determined to earn enough money to buy it, in spite of strong objections from his girl friend, Robin Gantner, who also sings at the club. After a lovers' quarrel Ross meets and becomes attracted to wealthy Laurel Dodge. Meanwhile, the opportunistic Wesley Johnson has bought the boat and later hires Ross to skipper a fishing vessel, even though the two men's personalities conflict. Laurel, who has kept her wealth a secret, learns that Ross hopes to buy the sailboat from Johnson; she purchases it herself and offers it to Ross, but he is angered by the gesture and disappears. Laurel learns Ross has gone to an island to visit some Chinese friends and hires Johnson to take her there. En route, Johnson makes advances towards her and Ross, warned by a friend who has witnessed the scene, rushes to her rescue. The two are happily reunited, and the boat is sold back to Johnson on the condition that Ross will be able to purchase it when he can earn the money. *Boatmen. Entertainers. Playboys. Opportunists. Fishermen. Chinese. Employer-employee relations. Wealth. Fishing boats. Nightclubs. Hawaii.*

Note: Location scenes filmed in Hawaii. Copyright claimants: Hal B. Wallis and Joseph H. Hazen. Working title: *Gumbo Ya-Ya.*

GIRLS IN ARMS see **OPERATION BULLSHINE**

THE GIRLS IN 7C   F6.1845

Dist Distribpix, Inc. ca **1970**. Sd; col. 35mm. 68 min.

Sex film. An attractive young woman places a want ad for roommates, hoping to relieve her burden of loneliness and also to split the rent on her apartment. The response to her notice is immediate, and she soon shares bed and board with three other women who are promiscuous and uninhibited in their sexual lives. During an orgy, one of the women meets a former lover, and there is a wild confrontation. *Roommates. Loneliness. Lesbianism. Promiscuity. Classified advertisements. Orgies.*

GIRLS IN THE SADDLE   F6.1846

Fargo Productions. *Dist* Signature Releasing Organization. 16 Sep **1969** [Maryland license]. Sd; b&w. 35mm. 76 min.

Dir Ralph Mauro.

Cast: Sandy Baron.

Comedy. Two Hollywood screenwriters arrive at a secluded dude ranch to relax and discuss their next picture. They discover that there are a number of beautiful women at the ranch, and they decide to make a sex western as their next film. The women will do anything to get parts in the film, and the screenwriters and the women engage in a variety of sexual activities, including a striptease and lesbian embraces. *Motion picture scriptwriters. Sex exploitation films. Striptease. Lesbianism. Dude ranches.*

GIRLS OF SPIDER ISLAND *see* **IT'S HOT IN PARADISE**

GIRLS OF THE CITY *see* **ORGY GIRLS '69**

GIRLS ON A RAINY NIGHT   F6.1847

9 Apr **1970** [San Francisco showing]. Sd; col. 35mm? 90 min.
Dir Lou Green.

Sex film. No information about the precise nature of this film has been found. *Sexuality.*

THE GIRLS ON F—— STREET   F6.1848

Cameo Pictures. *Dist* Olympic International Films, Grads Corp. 10 Jun **1966** [Los Angeles showing]. Sd; b&w. 35mm. 69 min.
Prod-Dir Saul Resnick. *Photog* Saul Resnick. *Film Ed* Saul Resnick. *Film Synch* Saul Resnick. *Stills* Stan Feldstein.

Cast: Bill Arnold (narrator), Toni Lee Oliver, Ken McCormick, Nick Nickerson, Althea Curier, Kellie Everts, Barbra Norton, Eve St. Pierre, Margo Lynn Sweet, Dotty Dare, Bernice V. Philips, Bobby Carlina, Giga Patterson.

Sex film. In 1928, during the era of prohibition and the Charleston, Nick, a middle-aged sex-obsessed male in search of the bizarre, visits a burlesque house, a peep show emporium, and a "fetish house." Film contains scenes of nudity, lesbianism, fetishism, whipping, and interracial sex. *Nudity. Lesbianism. Flagellation. Striptease. Fetishism. Roaring Twenties. Prohibition. Charleston (dance).*

Note: Also known as *The Girls on F Street, Maidens of Fetish Street,* and *"F" Street.* Licensed in Maryland at 63 min.

THE GIRLS ON THE BEACH   F6.1849

Lebin Brothers Productions. *Dist* Paramount Pictures. 12 May **1965** [Saint Louis opening; c5 May 1965; LP30541]. Sd; col (Eastmancolor by Pathé). 35mm. 80 min.
Prod Harvey Jacobson. *Assoc Prod* Paul Rapp. *Exec Prod* Gene Corman. *Dir* William Witney. *Screenplay* David Malcolm. *Photog* Arch R. Dalzell. *Film Ed* Mort Tubor. *Mus* Gary Usher. *Mus Supv* Nick Venet. *Sd* John Bury. *Asst Dir* Jack Bohrer.

Cast: Martin West (Duke), Noreen Corcoran (Selma), Peter Brooks (Stu), Brian Wilson, Michael Love, Alan Jardin, Carl Wilson, Dennis Wilson (themselves, The Beach Boys), Jerry Allison, Jerry Naylor, Sonny Curtis (themselves, The Crickets), Lesley Gore (herself), Arnold Lessing (Frank), Linda Marshall (Cynthia), Steve Rogers (Brian), Anna Capri (Arlene), Aron Kincaid (Wayne), Sheila Bromley (Mrs. Winters), Mary Mitchell (Emily), Gale Gerber (Georgia), Linda Saunders (Patricia), Mary Kate Denny (Jenny), Nan Morris (1st sorority sister), Lana Wood (Bonnie), Pat Deming, Michele Corcoran, Larry Merrill (dancers), Dennis Jones, Bill Sampson (guys), Carol Jean Lewis (dancer), Joan Conrath (2d sorority sister), Rick Newton (parking lot attendant), Nancy Spry (Betty), Ron Kennedy (announcer), Bruno Ve Sota (Pops), Lynn Cartwright (waitress), Richard Miller, Leo Gordon (waiters), Helen Kay Stephens (contestant and dancer).

Comedy with music. Selma, Cynthia, and Arlene are among a group of coeds who arrive to spend the summer in the sorority beach house. They meet Duke, Brian, and Wayne and enjoy the music of Lesley Gore, The Beachboys, and The Crickets at the local nightclub. The fun is interrupted, however, when the girls learn that the sorority housemother has given all their funds to charity. With the house in danger of closing, the girls begin a series of projects to raise money, but the situation still seems hopeless until the boys boast of knowing The Beatles. Believing that The Beatles have agreed to fly from England to perform in their behalf, the girls arrange for a musical show and begin its full-scale promotion. Realizing just before the opening of the show that they have been victims of a hoax, the girls desperately attempt an impersonation of the famous British group, but the audience is not deceived. Fortunately, the audience is mollified, and the show ends as a big success. *Nightclub scenes include:* The Beachboys singing "Little Honda" and "Girls on the Beach"; The Crickets singing "La Bomba" and "Lonely Sea"; and Lesley Gore singing "I Don't Want To Be a Loser," "It's Gotta Be You," and "Leave Me Alone." *Students. Singers. Musicians. Sororities. Musical revues. Rock and roll. Hoaxes. Impersonation. Nightclubs. Beaches. The Beatles.*

Note: Working title: *Beach Girls.*

GIRLS ON THE ROCKS   F6.1850

Ocean Films. *Dist* Thunderbird International Pictures. 23 Nov **1962** [Los Angeles showing]. Sd; col (Eastman Color). 35mm. 77 min.
Prod Manuel S. Conde. *Dir* Anthony Santos.

Cast: Ivon Michel, Caesar Gary, Gigi Darlene.

Comedy. Members of an all-woman orchestra are shipwrecked on what appears to be an unknown tropical island. Thinking their rescue to be a long way off, they set out to build a shelter and bathe in the open, much to the delight of the island's only visible white male who claims to be Karzan, son of Tarzan. After rescuing the women from a band of wild natives who destroy their shelter, Karzan invites them to his adobe mansion on a ranch. It soon becomes apparent that Karzan is actually the foreman of the ranch, which is located on an island near the Florida coast, and the natives prove to be a band of Cuban dancers. When the real owner and his wife return to the ranch for their vacation, they find their foreman swinging through the trees and nude women lounging on their front lawn. *Musicians. Ranch foremen. Cubans. Dancers. Ranchers. Shipwrecks. Impersonation. Nudity. Islands. Ranches. Florida. Tarzan.*

Note: Press material claims that the film was smuggled out of Cuba.

GIRLS ON TIGER REEF *see* **NUDES ON TIGER REEF**

GIRL'S PRISON   F6.1851

Kirt Films International. *Dist* Distribpix, Inc. ca **1970**. Sd; col. 35mm. 65 min.

Melodrama. A young woman finds herself alone and broke in a strange city and resorts to prostitution. Her first customer is an under-cover policeman who reveals his identity only after she has completely incriminated herself. The woman is sent to prison and made a cellmate to a hardened prostitute, who teaches her about the lesbian warden's abnormal sex preferences. The women plan to complain about the situation in a letter to prison authorities, but are informed upon, and then subjected to bizarre sexual humiliations by the sadistic warden. *Innocents. Prostitutes. Detectives. Prison wardens. Lesbianism. Sadism. Prisons.*

GIRLS' SCHOOL SCANDAL   F6.1852

Fleetan Films. *Dist* Able Film Co. ca **1969**. Sd; col. 16mm. 55 min.
Cast: Randy Gilman, Sylvia Summers, Mavis York.

Comedy-drama. Mr. Stockwell runs Miss Grundy's exclusive boarding school with an iron hand. One day, while two innocent girls are sitting in their room discussing a history exam and wishing there were boys around, columnist Melody Antem arrives and discovers what a tyrant Stockwell really is. Masquerading as a school girl, Melody brings sex of every manner to the hallowed halls of the ancient academy. *Headmasters. Columnists. Students. Sexuality. Disguise. Adolescence. Boarding schools.*

THE GIRLS THAT DO   F6.1853

Dist Sam Lake Enterprises. **1967**. Sd; b&w. 35mm. 73 min.
A Sam Lake Production. *Prod-Dir-Writ* Sidney Knight.
Cast: Joanna Fair, Donny Lee, Judy Caine, John Acre.

Drama. Gigi and Sylvia warn their new roommate, Ruth, of the treachery of the male sex. Recalling her own unhappy experiences with men, Gigi tells of how her boyfriend tricked her into selling her body to pay his debts. Sylvia, married to a man who loved to be whipped, left him when he became a sadist. On her first job as a model, Ruth is nearly raped by a photographer, and she joins her roommates in reviling men. Gigi calls to say that she will be bringing home a man who has been pestering her. The three decide that they will take revenge on the male sex by torturing him. *Man-haters. Models. Roommates. Revenge. Sadomasochism. Torture. Prostitution. Rape.*

Note: Also released as *Some Girls Do.*

GIRLS TOO *see* **GIRLS COME TOO!**

GIRLS TOWN *see* **INNOCENT AND THE DAMNED**

GIRLS WITHOUT ROOMS (Sweden)   F6.1854

Metronome Studios. *Dist* Harry Novak and Associates. 10 May **1963** [Los Angeles showing]. Sd; b&w. 35mm. 77 min.
Prod-Dir Arne Ragneborn. *Screenplay* Gun Zacharias, Arne Ragneborn. *English Adapt* Seymour Stern. *Photog* Bengt Lindström. *Mus* Gösta Theselius.
Cast: Catrin Westerlund, Inga Gill, Marianne Löfgren, Arne Ragneborn, Lars Ekborg, Elof Ahrle.

Drama. A rebellious 17-year-old girl, nicknamed "The Flame" for her red hair, becomes a prostitute out of boredom with family life and the drudgery of a regular job. Eventually arrested by the juvenile authorities, she defends her profession and attacks the corruption and hypocrisy of society. *Juvenile delinquents. Prostitution. Hypocrisy. Adolescence.*

Note: Stockholm opening: Mar 1956 as *Flamman.* Also known as *The Flame.* Press material indicates that the film is based on case material from Stockholm's Langholmen Prison.

GIRLSAPOPPIN
F6.1855

Dist Preferred Pictures. 17 Sep **1964** [San Francisco showing]. Sd; b&w. 35mm. 60 min.

Prod Flip McWig. *Dir* Knott Good.

Cast: Chester Von Chester *(himself, a chimpanzee)*, Nina Shane, Susan Stewart, Joyce Kawamoto, Laine Carlin, Janice Carter, Dee Dee Cartier.

Action comedy. Chester von Chester, a renowned scientist who happens to be a chimpanzee, is at work on an invention that is powered by an atomic reactor. His goal is the contruction of a banana-making machine. The reactor explodes, sending Chester through the time barrier and depositing him in the Roaring Twenties. The Dinghy Detective Agency sends seven of its best men out on a search, giving them one clue to Chester's whereabouts: Chester is fond of beautiful women. The first detective looks in a harem where he disguises himself as one of the Sultan's wives. The second sleuth goes out West to check on rumors that Chester is squandering funds at the gaming tables. Chester moves on ahead of his pursuers and discovers a sextet of wood nymphs frolicking in the forests and waters. The detectives close in on the chimp, who escapes into a circus. A rampaging lion forces the detectives into an observation balloon. The balloon rises, thus allowing them to watch unnoticed as a young woman changes clothes in her boudoir. Chester solves the riddle of transporting himself back to the present and goes to work in a factory producing curvaceous women as a reminder of his adventures. *Inventors. Detectives. Nuclear energy. Time travel. Voyeurism. Nudity. Fruit. Explosions. Harems. Forests. Circus. Balloons (ascent). Roaring Twenties. Chases. Chimpanzees. Lions.*

GIRLY *see* **MUMSY, NANNY, SONNY, AND GIRLY**

GIT!
F6.1856

World-Cine Associates. *Dist* Embassy Pictures. Oct **1965**. Sd; col (Technicolor). 35mm. 92 min.

Pres by Joseph E. Levine. *Prod-Dir* Ellis Kadison. *Assoc Prod* Homer McCoy, William Schwartz. *Screenplay* Homer McCoy. *Story* Homer McCoy, Ellis Kadison. *Dir Photog* Gordon Avil. *Set Dsgn* Kenneth Tolman. *Film Ed* Donald Tait. *Mus Comp & Dir* Phillip Lambro. *Titl Song* Leon Thomas. *Song:* "No Drums, No Trumpets!" Phillip Lambro, Ellis Kadison. *Song:* "Where I Belong" *Adapt by* Llyn Paul, C. C. Jones. *Asst Dir* Joe Wonder. *Tech Dir* Ray Lawrence. *Asst to the Prod* Leo Castillo, Jeb Gholson. *Makeup* Gus Norin.

Cast: Jack Chaplian *(Deke)*, Heather North *(Elaine)*, Leslie Bradley *(Finney)*, Richard Webb *(Andrew Garrett)*, Hanna Landy *(Mrs. Finney)*, Emory Parnell *(T. C. Knox)*, Joseph Hamilton *(Jed)*, Richard Valentine *(district attorney)*, Jeff Burton *(police sergeant)*, Sherry Moreland *(Dr. Allen)*, Shug Fisher *(Sam Lewis)*, Seldom-Seen Sioux *(Rock, a dog)*.

Melodrama. Finney, a dog trainer for wealthy breeder Andrew Garrett, is preparing to shoot Rock, an English setter alleged to be an animal killer. The shooting is prevented by Deke, a 17-year-old runaway who contends that the dog would make a fine hunter. Deke is picked up by the police, but Garrett obtains custody of the youth and hires him as Finney's assistant. Deke and Garrett's 15-year-old daughter, Elaine, become friends, and they work together to train the dog. During a field trial, Rock is bitten by a rattlesnake and rushed to a veterinarian. Although Rock loses the competition, his life is saved. *Runaways. Animal trainers. Adolescence. Animal care. Snakebites. Dogs.*

GIULIETTA DEGLI SPIRITI *see* **JULIET OF THE SPIRITS**

GIULIETTA E ROMEO *see* **ROMEO AND JULIET**

GIULIO CESARE IL CONQUISTATORE DELLE GALLIE *see* **CAESAR THE CONQUEROR**

LA GIUMENTA VERDE *see* **THE GREEN MARE**

GIUSEPPE VENDUTO DAI FRATELLI *see* **THE STORY OF JOSEPH AND HIS BRETHREN**

GIVE HER THE MOON (France/Italy)
F6.1857

Les Productions Artistes Associés–P. E. A. *Dist* United Artists. 2 Oct **1970** [New York opening]. Sd; col (De Luxe). 35mm. 92 min. *MPAA rating* G.

Prod Christian Ferry. *Dir* Philippe de Broca. *Scen* Daniel Boulanger, Philippe de Broca. *Dial* Daniel Boulanger. *Dir Photog* Jean Penzer. *Camera* Jean-Paul Schwartz. *Unit Photog* Vincent Rossel. *Decor* Théo Meurisse. *Film Ed* Henri Lanoë. *Mus* Georges Delerue. *Sd Engr* Urbain Loiseau. *1st & 2d Asst Dir* Christian Fuin, Bernard Maistre. *Prod Mgr* Paul Lemaire. *Script Girl* Suzanne Durrenberger. *Prod Sec* Madeleine Billeaud. *Makeup* Jackie Reynal. *Dial Coach* Louise Vincent.

Cast: Philippe Noiret *(Gabriel)*, Bert Convy *(Broderick MacPower)*, Dorothy Marchini *(Dorothy Golden)*, Valentina Cortese *(Madeleine de Lepine)*, Fernand Gravey *(Captain Ragot)*, Marthe Keller *(Marie Panneton)*, Jean-Pierre Marielle *(Leopold Panneton)*, Didi Perego *(Aurore Panneton)*, Henri Crémieux *(postman)*, François Périer *(Jean-Jules de LePine)*.

Comedy. The idyllic life of the French village of Angevine is disrupted when inhabitant Marie Panneton, daughter of the town's strait-laced mayor-cafe owner-movie theater operator, wins the "Queen of the Sea" beauty contest, thereby attracting American Broderick MacPower. Recently deserted by his fifth wife, the millionaire has decided to marry the winner. Although Marie is in love with cellist schoolmaster Gabriel, she temporarily succumbs to the blandishments of MacPower, who to charm her moves the entire village to Bedloe's Island in New York Harbor, where it immediately becomes a tourist attraction. Nevertheless, MacPower returns the lovesick Marie to Gabriel and the homesick Angevinians to France, and plans a chain of simulated French towns. *Americans in foreign countries. Ingenues. Entrepreneurs. Millionaires. Mayors. Musicians. Schoolteachers. Tourists. Filial relations. Courtship. Urban life. Village life. Beauty contests. New York City.*

Note: Opened in Paris in Feb 1970 as *Les caprices de Marie;* running time: 90 min.

THE GIVEN WORD (Brazil)
F6.1858

Oswaldo Massaini Productions. *Dist* Lionex Films. 24 Mar **1964** [New York opening]. Sd; b&w. 35mm. 98 min.

Prod Oswaldo Massaini. *Dir-Writ* Anselmo Duarte. *Photog* Chick Fowle. *Art Dir* José Teixeira de Araújo. *Film Ed* Carlos Coimbra. *Mus* Gabriel Migliori. *Sd* Carlos Foscolo. *Asst Dir* José Teles, Ruy Rosádo. *Prod Mgr* Roberto Ribeiro. *Sp Eff* Josef Reindl. *English Subtitl* Reine Dorian.

Cast: Leonardo Vilar *(Ze)*, Gloria Menezes *(Rosa)*, Dionísio Azevedo *(Father Olavo)*, Norma Bengell *(Marli)*, Geraldo d'el Rey *(Bonitao* ["Handsome"]*)*, Roberto Ferreira *(Dédé)*, Othon Bastos *(reporter)*, Gilberto Marques *(Galego)*, Carlos Tôrres *(Monsignor)*, Antonio L. Sampaio *(Coca)*, Milton Gaúcho *(policeman)*, João Desordi *(detective)*, Irênio Simões *(editor)*, Enoch Tôrres *(inspector)*, Maria Conceiçao *(Auntie)*, Veveldo Diniz *(church clerk)*, Walter da Silveira, Napoleão Lopes Filho *(bishops)*, Copoeira Dancers of Cangiquinha.

Drama. Source: Alfredo Dias Gomes, *O pagador de promessas* (São Paulo opening: 29 Jul 1960). Ze, an honest peasant and devout Catholic, makes a vow to distribute his land and carry a heavy wooden cross on his back to the church in the neighboring village if the life of his ailing donkey is saved. When the animal recovers, Ze takes the cross and makes the arduous 30-mile pilgrimage to the Church of Santa Barbara. The local priest denies him admittance, however, because he made his vow during a voodoo ceremony. Determined to complete his mission, Ze waits patiently outside. After his wife has been seduced by Bonitao, a lecherous pimp, Ze becomes the center of attention: the town merchants exploit the event for their own mercenary ends, and newspaper reporters hail him as a communist agitator for giving away his land. Ze remains steadfast in his determination to place the cross upon the church altar. With the situation out of control, the bishop is summoned, but he is unable to persuade Ze to give up his cause. Finally, Bonitao instigates a riot during which Ze is killed. Suddenly silent, the crowd places Ze upon his cross, carries him into the church, and places the cross on the altar. *Peasants. Priests. Pimps. Reporters. Communists. Faith. Seduction. Riots. Manslaughter. Religious objects. Catholic Church. Donkeys.*

Note: Opened in São Paulo in Aug 1962 as *O pagador de promessas.*

EL GLADIADOR INVENCIBLE *see* **THE INVINCIBLE GLADIATOR**

GLADIATOR OF ROME (Italy)
F6.1859

C. I. R. A. C.–Giorgio Agliani Cinematografica. *Dist* Medallion Pictures. **1963.** Sd; col (Eastman Color). 35mm (Euroscope). 105 min.

Prod Giorgio Agliani. *Dir* Mario Costa. *Screenplay* Gian Paolo Callegari, Giuseppe Mariani. *Photog* Pierludovico Pavoni. *Art Dir* Piero Poletto. *Film Ed* Antonietta Zita. *Mus* Carlo Franci. *Cost* Giorgio Desideri.

Cast: Gordon Scott *(Marcus)*, Wandisa Guida *(Nisa)*, Roberto Risso *(Valerio)*, Ombretta Colli *(Aglae)*, Alberto Farnese *(Vezio Rufo)*, Gianni Solaro *(Macrino)*, Eleonora Vargas *(Prisca)*, Andrea Aureli *(Settimio)*, Charles Barman *(Annio)*, Miranda Campa *(Porzia)*, Mirko Ellis *(Frasto)*, Pietro De Vico *(Pompilio)*, Piero Lulli *(Astarte)*, Nando Tamberlani *(Valerio's father)*.

Action melodrama. Princess Nisa, heir to the throne in the Roman province of Cilicia, has been a slave girl in the Valeri household for 14 years. She is somewhat compensated by the love which she shares with Valerio, the Valeri son, until the emperor orders the execution of the youth's parents. Furthermore, the family's slaves are imprisoned, including Nisa and her friend Marcus, whose strength enables him to become a gladiator. Later, the emperor orders one of his henchmen to murder Nisa because she is the last survivor of the previous royal family. Since Nisa and the other slaves also face death because they are Christians, Valerio, who has avoided imprisonment, works on the outside for their escape, which is finally accomplished after Marcus bends the thick metal bars of the cell. They are recaptured and sentenced to be crucified, but a new emperor overturns the death sentence, restores Valerio and Nisa to their former positions, and frees Marcus and the other Christians. *Royalty. Gladiators.*

Slavery. Christianity. Imprisonment. Religious persecution. Capital punishment. Feats of strength. Cilicia. Rome—History—Empire.

Note: Opened in Rome in Nov 1962 as *Il gladiatore di Roma*; running time: 102 min.

IL GLADIATORE DI ROMA see **GLADIATOR OF ROME**

IL GLADIATORE INVINCIBILE see **THE INVINCIBLE GLADIATOR**

GLADIATORERNA see **THE GLADIATORS**

THE GLADIATORS (Sweden)   F6.1860
Sandrews. *Dist* New Line Cinema. 21 Dec **1970** [Yellow Springs, Ohio, opening]. Sd; col (Eastmancolor). 16mm & 35mm. 90 min.
Prod Göran Lindgren. *Exec Prod* Bo Jonsson. *Dir* Peter Watkins. *Screenplay* Nicholas Gosling, Peter Watkins. *Photog* Peter Suschitzky. *Art Dir* William Brodie. *Film Ed* Lars Hagström. *Mus:* Symphony no. 3 Gustav Mahler. *Zitar* Claes af Geijerstam. *Sd* Tage Sjöberg. *Prod Mgr* Bertil Sandgren, Jutte Ekman. *Cost* Chris Collins. *Sp Eff* Stig Lindberg.
Cast: Arthur Pentelow *(British general)*, Frederick Danner *(British staff officer)*, Hans Bendrik *(Captain Davidsson)*, Daniel Harlé *(French officer)*, Hans Berger *(West German officer)*, Rosario Gianetti *(American officer)*, Tim Yum *(Chinese staff officer)*, Kenneth Lo *(Chinese colonel)*, Björn Franzén *(Swedish colonel)*, Christer Gynge *(assistant controller)*, Jürgen Schling *(East German officer)*, Stefan Dillan *(Russian officer)*, Ugo Chiari *(Italian officer)*, Chandrakant Desai *(Indian officer)*, George Harris *(Nigerian officer)*, Jeremy Child *(B1)*, Erich Stering *(B2)*, Jean-Pierre Delamour *(B3)*, Richard Friday *(B4)*, Roy Scammel *(B5)*, J. Z. Kennedy *(B6)*, Eberhard Fehmers *(B7)*, Terry Whitmore *(B8)*, Nguyen *(B9)*, To Van Minh *(B10)*, Pik-Sen Lim *(C2)*, Michael Cheuk, Taras Lee, Eng Chee Gan, Heng Ko Lei, Henry Chan, Louis Cheng, Sik-Yng Waung, Bill Fay *(other members of Chinese team)*, Keith Bradfield *(narrator)*.
Science fiction drama. To circumvent global war the great powers devise rituals in which man's aggressive instincts are harnessed. At televised Peace Games sponsored by a spaghetti company, soldiers from many nations participate in deadly computerized war games. In Game 256, monitored by the Swedish army and supervised by a panel of international observers, an allied team of American and European contestants attempts to wrest the control room and computer from Chinese combatants. To this end the allies capture a Chinese female soldier. During a computer malfunction a British warrior falls in love with the prisoner and attempts to escape with her. Unknowingly, a radical French student, intent on sabotaging the system, reactivates the computer, and the panel executes the lovers. *British. Americans in foreign countries. Germans. Italians. French. Chinese. East Indians. Russians. Nigerians. Students. Prisoners of war. Soldiers. Revolutionaries. Traitors. War games. Capital punishment. Computers. Television. The Future.*
Note: Opened in Linköping, Sweden, in Jun 1969 as *Gladiatorerna*; running time: 105 min.

GLADIATORS SEVEN (Italy/Spain)   F6.1861
Film Columbus-Atenca Films. *Dist* Metro-Goldwyn-Mayer, Inc. 6 May **1964** [New York opening; c31 Dec 1962; LP27906]. Sd (Westrex); col (Eastmancolor). 35mm (Techniscope). 92 min.
Prod Cleto Fontini, Italo Zingarelli. *Dir* Pedro Lázaga. *Screenplay* Sandro Continenza, Bruno Corbucci, Alberto De Martino, Giovanni Grimaldi, Italo Zingarelli. *Dial* Rafael García Serrano. *Photog* Adalberto Albertini, Eloy Mella. *Art Dir* Piero Poletto, Antonio Simont. *Film Ed* Otello Colangeli. *Mus* Marcello Giombini. *Wardrobe* Mario Giorsi.
Cast: Richard Harrison *(Darius)*, Loredana Nusciak *(Aglaia)*, Livio Lorenzón *(Panurgus)*, Gerard Tichy *(Hiarba)*, Edoardo Toniolo *(Milon)*, Joseph Marco *(Xeno)*, Barta Barri *(Flaccus)*, Tony Zamperla *(Vargas)*, Franca Badeschi *(Licia)*, Enrique Avila *(Livius)*, Antonio Molino *(Macrobius)*, Tony Rubio *(Mados)*, Emily Wolkowicz *(Ismere)*.
Action melodrama. Darius, a Spartan gladiator, returns to his home with six other gladiators after winning his freedom in a fight in a Roman arena. He discovers that his father has been murdered by Hiarba, an ambitious tyrant. Hiarba has designs on Aglaia, Darius' betrothed, and has convinced her that Darius murdered her father. The seven gladiators become popular heroes, helping people resist the tyranny of Hiarba; and when the ruler sends his forces into a climactic battle with the gladiators, the seven defeat the tyrant's troops. Hiarba flees to a fortress surrounded by an army camp. He takes Aglaia along as a hostage, and she learns of Darius' innocence in her father's death. Four of the gladiators stampede a herd of bulls, demolishing the army camp. Meanwhile, Darius and the two other gladiators enter the fortress, rescue Aglaia, and kill Hiarba, thus liberating Sparta from tyranny. *Gladiators. Hostages. Soldiers. Murder. Despots. Ambition. Heroism. Arenas. Forts. Sparta. Rome—History—Empire. Stampedes. Cattle.*

Note: Filmed in Rome and Madrid in Totalscope. Released in Italy as *I sette gladiatori* in 1962; running time: 106 min. Spanish title: *Los siete espartanos.*

LE GLAIVE ET LA BALANCE see **TWO ARE GUILTY**

DAS GLAS WASSER see **A GLASS OF WATER**

THE GLASS BOTTOM BOAT   F6.1862
Arwin Productions–Reame Productions. *Dist* Metro-Goldwyn-Mayer, Inc. 9 Jun **1966** [New York opening; c4 Mar 1966; LP32330]. Sd (Westrex); col (Metrocolor). 35mm (Panavision). 110 min.
Prod Martin Melcher, Everett Freeman. *Dir* Frank Tashlin. *Screenplay* Everett Freeman. *Dir Photog* Leon Shamroy. *Art Dir* George W. Davis, Edward Carfagno. *Set Dsgn* Henry Grace, Hugh Hunt. *Film Ed* John McSweeney. *Mus* De Vol. *Song:* "The Glass Bottom Boat" Joe Lubin. *Song:* "Soft as the Starlight" Joe Lubin, Jerome Howard. *Songs Sung by* Doris Day, Arthur Godfrey. *Song:* "Que Será, Será" Jay Livingston, Ray Evans. *Sung by* Doris Day. *Rec Supv* Franklin Milton. *Asst Dir* Al Jennings. *Unit Prod Mgr* Edward Woehler. *Miss Day's Cost Dsgn* Ray Aghayan. *Makeup Supv* William Tuttle. *Makeup* Harry Maret. *Miss Day's Hairstyling* Barbara Lampson. *Sp Vis Eff* J. McMillan Johnson, Carroll L. Shepphird.
Cast: Doris Day *(Jennifer Nelson)*, Rod Taylor *(Bruce Templeton)*, Arthur Godfrey *(Axel Nordstrom)*, John McGiver *(Ralph Goodwin)*, Paul Lynde *(Homer Cripps)*, Edward Andrews *(Gen. Wallace Bleecker)*, Eric Fleming *(Edgar Hill)*, Dom De Luise *(Julius Pritter)*, Dick Martin *(Zack Molloy)*, Elisabeth Fraser *(Nina Bailey)*, George Tobias *(Mr. Fenimore)*, Alice Pearce *(Mrs. Fenimore)*, Ellen Corby *(Anna Miller)*, Dee J. Thompson *(Donna)*, Robert Vaughn *(Napoleon Solo)*.
Comedy. Jennifer Nelson, a young widow working in the public relations office of a space laboratory, meets her new boss Bruce Templeton when he accidentally catches his fishing line on a mermaid outfit she is wearing while entertaining tourists on her father's glass-bottom boat. Templeton, delighted to discover that the woman he "fished out" of Catalina Bay is working at his plant, assigns her to write a definitive biography of him while he is test-piloting a new rocket. Jenny's habit of "exercising" her dog Vladimir by telephoning him at home (he runs around the house whenever the phone rings), arouses the suspicions of CIA men. When she overhears Templeton discussing the possibility that she is a foreign spy, she makes misleading phone calls at a party at Templeton's home. Unknown to her, a secret formula has been planted in her purse, and the real espionage agent pays her a visit when she arrives home. Jenny bolts out of a window and a mad chase follows. The real culprits are apprehended, and Jenny ends up in her boss's arms. *Widows. Scientists. Air pilots. Secret agents. Employer-employee relations. Fishing. Espionage. Rockets. Telephone. Santa Catalina (California). United States—Central Intelligence Agency. Chases. Dogs.*
Note: Location scenes filmed on Catalina Island.

THE GLASS CAGE   F6.1863
Dist Futuramic Releasing Organization. 6 Feb **1964** [New York State license]. Sd; b&w. 35mm. 84 min. [See note.]
Prod Paul Lewis. *Co-prod* John Hoyt. *Dir* Antonio Santean. *Scen* John Hoyt, Antonio Santean. *Photog* Jean-Philippe Carson.
Cast: Arline Sax *(The Girl/her older sister)*, John Hoyt *(Detective Jeff Bradley)*, Elisha Cook, Robert Kelljan, King Moody.
Melodrama. A young police detective (Robert Kelljan) becomes emotionally involved in the case of a lonely young woman (Arline Sax) against the advice of his superior (John Hoyt). Arrested for shooting a prowler, the woman is absolved of guilt and released. However, the strange disappearance of her dominating older sister (Arline Sax) and her fear of her father (Elisha Cook) provoke the detective's interest. The young woman is brutally raped by a crazed beatnik artist (King Moody). Terrorized, she flees to a zoo where she falls into the bear pit. The resourceful detective arrives in the nick of time and rescues her. *Detectives. Beatniks. Sisters. Rape. Filial relations. Missing persons. Zoos. Chases. Bears.*
Note: Press material indicates that this film was also released in a 78 minute version which does not include the nude rape scene. May also be known as *Don't Touch My Sister* and *Bed of Fire.*

A GLASS OF WATER (West Germany)   F6.1864
Deutsche Film Hansa. *Dist* Casino Films. 26 Jan **1962** [Milwaukee, Wisconsin, opening]. Sd; b&w. 35mm. 84 min.
Exec Prod Georg Richter. *Dir-Writ* Helmut Käutner. *Photog* Günther Anders. *Art Dir* Herbert Kirchhoff, Albrecht Becker. *Film Ed* Klaus Dudenhöfer. *Mus* Bernhard Eichhorn, Roland Sonder-Mahnken. *Lyr* Helmut Käutner. *Sd* Werner Schlagge. *Asst Dir* Erica Balqué. *Prod Supv* Georg Mohr. *Prod Mgr* Peter Petersen, Ernsthein Kühne. *Cost* Werner Boehm.
Cast: Gustaf Gründgens *(Henry St. John, Viscount Bolingbroke)*, Liselotte Pulver *(Queen Anne)*, Hilde Krahl *(Lady Churchill, Duchess of Marlborough)*,

Sabine Sinjen (Abigail), Horst Janson (Arthur Marsham), Rudolf Forster (Marquis de Torcy), Joachim Rake (Lord Avondale), Hans Leibelt (butler), Herbert Weissbach (father confessor), Bobby Todd.

Comedy. Source: Eugène Scribe, Le verre d'eau, ou les effets et les causes (Paris opening: 17 Nov 1840). In London in 1710 the ambitious Duchess of Marlborough prevents a secret pact ending the War of Spanish Succession from reaching Queen Anne. Manipulating female jealousies, the Viscount Bolingbroke, a journalist, brings about the conflict's end. By sending the cadet Arthur Marsham to the queen's boudoir, Bolingbroke maneuvers her signature on the treaty. Discovered by the irate duchess in the queen's chambers, the cadet is ordered to marry Abigail, her majesty's attendant and his true love. Royalty. Nobility. Journalists. Cadets. Jealousy. Treaties. Spain—History— War of Succession 1701–14. London. France. Anne (England). Henry Saint John. Sarah Churchill.

Note: Opened in West Berlin in Jul 1960 as Das Glas Wasser.

THE GLASS SPHINX (Egypt/Italy/Spain)   **F6.1865**
Italian International Film–P. I. C. A. S. A.–Copro Film. Dist American International Pictures. 1968. Sd; col (Eastman Color, print by Pathé). 35mm (Techniscope). 91 min.

Prod Fulvio Lucisano. *Dir* Luigi Scattini. *Screenplay* Rafael Sánchez Campoy, Jaime Camas Gil, José Antonio Cascales. *Scen* Adalberto Albertini, Rafael Sánchez Campoy. *English Dial* Louis M. Heyward, Adriano Bolzoni. *Photog* Félix Mirón Martínez. *Art Dir* Luis Argüello. *Mus* Roberto Pregadio. *Mus English Vers* Les Baxter.

Cast: Robert Taylor (Prof. Karl Nichols), Anita Ekberg (Paulette), Gianna Serra (Jenny), Jack Stuart (Ray), Angel Del Pozo (Alex), José Truchado (Theo), Remo De Angelis (Mirko), Emad Hamdy (Fouad), Ahmed Kamis, Lidia Biondi.

Adventure melodrama. In a remote part of Egypt, Prof. Karl Nichols, a renowned archeologist, is searching for the legendary tomb of the Glass Sphinx, which is said to possess a mysterious elixir capable of sustaining life indefinitely. Nichols' niece Jenny arrives at the Cairo airport to deliver some equipment and documents to Alex, her uncle's assistant. She mistakes a stranger, Ray, for the assistant and allows him to take her to her hotel. Following the murder of one of Nichols' assistants, the equipment and documents are stolen from Jenny's room. The next day the real Alex appears and escorts Jenny to her uncle's campsite, while Ray trails closely behind. Actually, Alex and Nichols' secretary, Paulette, are in league to murder the professor once the glass sphinx is unearthed, and Ray is a Lloyd's of London agent assigned to protect Nichols' $2 million insurance policy. The tomb is found, and Nichols is knocked unconscious by Alex, but his life is spared when Paulette, who has fallen in love with the professor, intervenes. Alex and Paulette make off in a jeep loaded with treasures from the tomb. Then two of Alex's henchmen reenter the tomb to collect their share of the booty; but the sphinx suddenly shatters into thousands of pieces, killing them instantly. During a severe sandstorm, Nichols, Jenny, and Ray (who has revealed his identity) take after the escaping Alex and Paulette, only to discover upon reaching them that they have been captured by desert marauders. Alex offers to trade Paulette for his own freedom. Nichols attempts to intervene, but Paulette saves Nichols' life by stepping in the path of a sniper's bullet. Ray tracks down Alex with the aid of the Cairo police and then returns to resume his romance with Jenny. Professors. Archeologists. Uncles. Secretaries. Insurance agents. Immortality. Murder. Theft. Conspiracy. Mistaken identity. Self-sacrifice. Tombs. Potions. Treasure. Deserts. Sphinxes. Egypt. Lloyd's of London. Documentation. Sandstorms.

Note: Filmed in Egypt. Opened in Rome in Jul 1967 as La sfinge d'oro; running time: 95 min. Released in Spain as La esfinge de cristal; running time: 91 min. Alternative Italian title: Una sfinge tutta d'oro.

A GLOBAL AFFAIR   **F6.1866**
Seven Arts Productions–Hall Bartlett Productions. Dist Metro-Goldwyn-Mayer, Inc. 12 Feb 1964 [Los Angeles opening; c10 Dec 1963; LP26891]. Sd (Westrex); b&w. 35mm. 84 min.

A Hall Bartlett Production. *Prod* Hall Bartlett. *Assoc Prod* Eugene Vale. *Exec Prod* Bernard Schwartz. *Dir* Jack Arnold. *Screenplay* Arthur Marx, Bob Fisher, Charles Lederer. *Story* Eugene Vale. *Dir Photog* Joseph Ruttenberg. *Art Dir* George W. Davis. *Set Decor* Henry Grace, Charles Thompson. *Film Ed* Bud Molin. *Mus* Dominic Frontiere. *Songs:* "So Wide the World," "Fais Do Do," "A Global Affair" Dorcas Cochran, Dominic Frontiere. *Love Theme:* "So Wide the World" sung by Vic Dana. *Rec Supv* Franklin Milton. *Asst Dir* Tom Shaw, Lee Lukather. *Prod Supv* Abe Steinberg. *Wardrobe* Bill Thomas. *Makeup* William Tuttle. *Mr. Hope's Makeup* Layne Britton. *Hairstyles* Sydney Guilaroff.

Cast: Bob Hope (Frank Larrimore), Lilo Pulver (Sonya), Michele Mercier (Lisette), Elga Andersen (Yvette), Yvonne De Carlo (Dolores), Miiko Taka (Fumiko), Robert Sterling (Randy), Nehemiah Persoff (Under Secretary Segura), John McGiver (Snifter), Jacques Bergerac (Duval), Mickey

Shaughnessy (policeman), Tanya Lemani (Panja), Georgia Hayes (Jean), Edmon Ryan (Gavin), Baby Monroe (The First Citizen of the World, see note), Rafer Johnson (The Nigerian Representative), Hugh Downs (television commentator), Billy Halop, Martin Blaine, Inez Pedroza, Barbara Bouchet, Françoise Ruggieri, Reta Shaw, Voltaire Perkins.

Comedy. A baby, abandoned at United Nations Headquarters, is put in the care of Frank Larrimore, a bachelor who is in charge of the women's rights department at the U. N. His impassioned pleas for a good life for every child, delivered on his radio program, prompted the mother to leave the baby. The baby cannot be turned over to New York City authorities because the U. N. Building is international territory. Frank smuggles the child into his apartment in a dog carrier because his landlord forbids children. Frank's playboy friend Randy uses the baby as an excuse to invite a number of international beauties from the U. N. to Frank's apartment. Lisette, a U. N. guide and the woman in whom Frank is romantically interested, leaves in disgust when the gathering turns into a party. On Monday no solution is found, and Frank is forced to keep the child longer. He is quoted in the newspapers as saying the baby should go to the best nation in the world, and an international competition for the child develops. Each of the beautiful international representatives woos Frank in the hopes of winning the baby for her country. Frank finally arrives at a decision cheered by the delegates: he himself will adopt the baby, and Lisette, whom he plans to marry, will be its mother. Foundlings. Bachelors. Playboys. Guides. Diplomats. Women's rights. Adoption. Contests. New York City. United Nations.

Note: Location scenes filmed at the United Nations. According to one source, Denise and Danielle Monroe share the role of the baby. Some sources credit only Seven Arts Productions as production company.

LA GLOIRE DES CANAILLES see **DIRTY HEROES**

THE GLORY GUYS   **F6.1867**
Bristol Pictures. Dist United Artists. 22 Jun **1965** [Colorado Springs, Colorado, opening; c7 Jul 1965; LP31022]. Sd; col (DeLuxe). 35mm (Panavision). 112 min.

Prod Arnold Laven, Arthur Gardner, Jules Levy. *Dir* Arnold Laven. *Screenplay* Sam Peckinpah. *Dir Photog* James Wong Howe. *Art Dir* Roberto Silva. *Set Decor* Ray Moyer. *Prod Dsgn* Edward S. Haworth. *Titl Dsgn* Format Productions. *Film Ed* Melvin Shapiro, Ernst R. Rolf. *Mus Comp & Cond* Riz Ortolani. *Sd* Al Overton, Jr., Rafael Esparza. *Sd Eff Ed* Howard Beals. *Mus Ed* June Edgerton. *Asst Dir* Clarence Eurist. *Prod Mgr* Clarence Eurist. *Asst to the Prod* Marilyn Feibelkorn. *Prod Asst* B. C. Wylie, Jose Delfin. *Script Supv* Joseph Mazzuca. *Cost* Frank Beetson, Jr. *Makeup Artist* Donald W. Roberson. *Hairstyles* Lorraine Roberson. *Optical Eff* Westheimer Co. *Tech Adv* George Ross. *Casting* Patricia Rose. *Prop Master* Max Frankel.

Cast: Tom Tryon (Demas Harrod), Harve Presnell (Sol Rogers), Senta Berger (Lou Woodard), James Caan (Dugan), Andrew Duggan (General McCabe), Slim Pickens (Gregory), Peter Breck (Hodges), Jeanne Cooper (Mrs. McCabe), Laurel Goodwin (Beth), Adam Williams (Crain), Erik Holland (Gentry), Robert McQueeney (Marcus), Wayne Rogers (Moyan), William Meigs (Treadway), Alice Backes (Mrs. Poole), Walter Scott (Lieutenant Cook), Michael Forest (Marshall Cushman), George Ross (Hanavan), Dal McKennon (gunsmith), Stephen Chase (General Hoffman), Henry Beckman (salesman), Michael Anderson, Jr. (Martin Hale).

Western drama. Source: Hoffman Birney, The Dice of God (New York, 1956). Capt. Demas Harrod and his new recruits join the 3d Regiment of the U. S. Cavalry and find that the ambitious and opportunistic fort commander, General McCabe, is preparing to fight the combined forces of the neighboring Indian tribes. Demas has fallen in love with Lou Woodard, who lives in nearby Mule City. While visiting her one evening, he is interrupted by Sol Rogers, the regiment's chief scout, who plans to marry Lou. The two men fight and become enemies. Demas returns to the fort and is instructed to put his men through a crash training program, after which they celebrate their first leave in Mule City and run into trouble with the town marshal and his henchmen. Demas and Sol then conspire to avenge their men. At an officers' ball on the eve of the campaign, Sol realizes that Lou is in love with Demas, but Lou tells him that Demas seems to have lost interest in her. As the campaign opens, Demas becomes apprehensive when McCabe, disobeying his own orders, splits his forces, sending Demas against a band of Sioux. Demas' men suffer heavy losses, but they manage to retreat when they are joined by Sol. Demas and Sol, attempting to find water for the wounded men, are ambushed and Sol is killed. That night, after the Indians withdraw, Demas leads his reduced force to rejoin the regiment and finds that McCabe and his men, fighting the Indians on their own, have been massacred. He returns to the fort and to Lou. Scouts—Frontier. United States marshals. Sioux Indians. Ambition. Jealousy. Revenge. Massacres. Forts. United States—History—Indian campaigns. United States Army—Cavalry.

Note: Location scenes filmed in Durango, Mexico. Original title: *Dice of God.*

THE GLORY STOMPERS   F6.1868

Norman T. Herman Productions. *Dist* American International Pictures. 22 Nov **1967** [c22 Nov 1967; LP34962]. Sd; col (Pathé). 35mm (Colorscope). 85 min.

Prod John Lawrence. *Exec Prod* Maurice Smith, Arthur Gilbert. *Assoc Prod* Mike Curb, Casey Kasem, Paul Stevenson. *Dir* Anthony M. Lanza. *Writ* James Gordon White, John Lawrence. *Dir Photog* Mario Tosi. *Film Ed* Len Miller. *Mus* Sidewalk Productions, Mike Curb. *Mus Supv* Al Simms. *Sd* Arthur Names. *Asst Dir* Rudy Kaddo. *Supv* Jack Shnell. *Script Supv* Katherine De Mitt. *Makeup* Louis Lane.

Cast: Dennis Hopper *(Chino)*, Jody McCrea *(Darryl)*, Chris Noel *(Chris)*, Jock Mahoney *(Smiley)*, Saundra Gayle *(Jo Ann)*, Jim Reader *(Paul)*, Robert Tessier *(Magoo)*, Astrid Warner *(Doreen)*, Gary Wood *(Pony)*, Lindsay Crosby *(Monk)*, Casey Kasem *(Mouth)*, Al Quick, Paul Prokop, Tony Acone, Ed Cook.

Action melodrama. In an isolated wood, Chino and his rebel motorcycle gang, The Black Souls, capture Darryl, leader of a rival gang called The Glory Stompers, and Darryl's girl friend, Chris. One of the Black Souls, Magoo, attempts to rape Chris, and Chino beats up Darryl. Subsequently, the whole gang jumps Darryl, leaves him for dead, and heads for a border town to sell Chris to Mexican white slavers. In the meantime, Chino's advances toward Chris infuriate Jo Ann, his "momma." A disillusioned former Glory Stomper named Smiley, now traveling alone, happens upon the merely wounded Darryl, and together they set out to rescue Chris. En route they hear about a scheduled love-in, but upon arriving at the scene they learn that Chino and his gang have already left for the border. And so Darryl and Smiley head for the Black Souls hideout, where Chris is being guarded by Chino's admiring younger brother, Paul. Magoo, returning from the love-in alone, again tries to rape Chris. But soon Darryl, Smiley, and Chino also arrive, and a furious battle ensues. Paul is motorcycled to death by Magoo, who in turn is shot down, and Jo Ann accidentally kills Chino with a knife intended for Darryl. The bloody conflict over, Chris and Darryl are now free to go on to a better life. *Motorcycle gangs. Mexicans. Rape. White slave traffic. Gang wars. Murder. Love-ins. Mexican border.*

THE GNOME-MOBILE   F6.1869

Walt Disney Productions. *Dist* Buena Vista Distribution Co. 19 Jul **1967** [New York opening; c17 Apr 1967; LP34496]. Sd (RCA); col (Technicolor). 35mm. 90 min. [Copyright length: 85 min.]

Pres by Walt Disney. *Co-prod* James Algar. *Dir* Robert Stevenson. *2d Unit Dir* Arthur J. Vitarelli. *Screenplay* Ellis Kadison. *Dir Photog* Edward Colman. *Art Dir* Carroll Clark, William H. Tuntke. *Art Styling* Sam McKim, David Jonas. *Set Decor* Emile Kuri, Hal Gausman. *Film Ed* Norman R. Palmer. *Mus* Buddy Baker. *Orch* Wayne Robinson. *Song:* "The Gnome-Mobile Song" Robert B. Sherman, Richard M. Sherman. *Sd Supv* Robert O. Cook. *Sd Mix* Dean Thomas. *Mus Ed* Evelyn Kennedy. *Asst Dir* Paul Cameron. *Unit Mgr* Joseph L. McEveety. *Cost Dsgn* Bill Thomas. *Cost* Chuck Keehne, Neva Rames. *Makeup* Pat McNalley. *Hairstyles* La Rue Matheron. *Matte Artist* Peter Ellenshaw. *Sp Eff* Eustace Lycett, Robert A. Mattey.

Cast: Walter Brennan *(D. J. Mulrooney/Knobby)*, Matthew Garber *(Rodney Winthrop)*, Karen Dotrice *(Elizabeth Winthrop)*, Richard Deacon *(Ralph Yarby)*, Tom Lowell *(Jasper)*, Sean McClory *(Horatio Quaxton)*, Ed Wynn *(Rufus)*, Jerome Cowan *(Dr. Conrad Ramsey)*, Charles Lane *(Dr. Scroggins)*, Norman Grabowski *(male nurse)*, Gil Lamb *(gas attendant)*, Maudie Prickett *(Katie Barrett)*, Cami Sebring *(Shy Violet)*, Ellen Corby *(Etta Pettibone)*, Frank Cady *(Charlie Pettibone)*, Hal Baylor *(2d male nurse)*, Karl Held *(Paul)*, Charles Smith *(airport attendant)*, Byron Foulger *(hotel clerk)*, Susan Flannery *(airline stewardess)*, Ernestine Barrier *(Nell)*, Dee Carroll *(2d secretary)*, William Fawcett *(Gregg, the chauffeur)*, Robert S. Carson *(Twin Oaks attendant)*, Jack Davis, actor *(Manson)*, John Cliff *(night watchman)*, Mickey Martin *(bellboy)*, Mark Allen *(doorman)*, Alvy Moore *(gas station mechanic)*, Dale Van Sickel *(uniformed guard)*, Parley Baer *(voice of owl)*, Jimmy Murphy *(voice of racoon)*, Dee Carroll, Jesslyn Fax *(voices of bluejays)*, Pamela Gail *(snapdragon)*, Susan Henning, Judy Van Wormer, Dyane Robins, Toni O'Connor, Kathy Foley, Barbara Halpern, Joyce Menges, Bunny Henning, Mimi Zerbini, Kathee Francis, Pat Ann Reid, Cindy Taylor, Susan Gates, Marianna Case, Jacquelyn Mary Ray, Shawn Scott, Sandra Gimpel, Virginia Aldridge *(gnome maidens)*, Amedee Chabot, Carla Borelli, Jeanne Shipman, Nancy Gould, Karin Blake, Carol O'Kane, Pamela Howard, Carol Merrill, Jackie Andre, Brenda Power, Dorothy Duffy *(married gnomes)*.

Fantasy. Source: Upton Beall Sinclair, *The Gnomobile; a Gnice Gnew Gnarrative With Gnonsense, but Gnothing Gnaughty* (New York, 1962). Driving his vintage 1930 Rolls-Royce, D. J. Mulrooney, a California lumber tycoon, takes his visiting grandchildren, Rodney and Elizabeth Winthrop, for a picnic in a forest of redwoods. While Rodney is eating, Elizabeth wanders off

into the woods and meets Jasper, a 2-foot-high gnome, and his 943-year-old grandfather, Knobby. Against the warnings of the birds and animals, Jasper tells Elizabeth of his plight: because he cannot find a girl gnome to marry, the species is in danger of becoming extinct. Touched by his sad tale, Elizabeth gets Mulrooney to place his Rolls at the disposal of Jasper and Knobby, and they all go on a quest for other gnomes. Before they can make much progress, however, Jasper and Knobby are kidnaped by Horatio Quaxton, the crafty proprietor of the "Academy of Fantastic Freaks." And when Mulrooney orders his vice-president, Ralph Yarby, to organize a search party for the missing gnomes, the millionaire is carried off to a sanitarium. But Knobby escapes into the woods as Rodney and Elizabeth help free their grandfather and then rescue Jasper from Quaxton's clutches. After eluding attendants from the sanitarium during a wild chase over the mountains, the Rolls pulls into a glade where Knobby has contacted the gnome-king, 1100-year-old Rufus, as well as a bevy of beautiful gnome-maidens. A mating contest is held to see which one of the maidens can catch Jasper and hold on to him for a count of seven. To Jasper's delight the winner is the shy Violet. And, as Rufus marries the young couple, Mulrooney generously donates 50,000 acres of his land to the gnomes. *Tycoons. Grandfathers. Gnomes. Kidnaping. Picnics. Contests. Sanitariums. Rolls-Royce automobiles. Forests. California.*

Note: Location scenes filmed in the Santa Cruz Mountains, California.

GO-GO BIG BEAT! (Great Britain)   F6.1870

Harold Baim Productions–International Productions. *Dist* Eldorado Pictures International. Jun **1965**. Sd; col (Eastman Color). 35mm. 82 min.

Production Credits for "Swinging U. K.": *Dir* Frank Gilpin. *Photog* Harry Orchard. *Songs:* "My Boy Lollipop," "Oh Henry" sung by Millie Small. *Song:* "Love or Money" sung by The Wackers. *Songs:* "Fools Like Me," "Don't Turn Around" sung by The Merseybeats. *Songs:* "Juliet," "Running Scared" sung by The Four Pennies.

Production Credits for "U. K. Swings Again": *Dir* Frank Gilpin. *Photog* Harry Orchard. *Lyr & Arr of Song:* "Baby, Let Me Take You Home" Alan Price. *Sung by* The Animals. *Songs:* "Here I Go Again," "Baby That's All" sung by The Hollies. *Song:* "Shout" sung by Lulu and the Luvvers.

Production Credits for "Mods and Rockers": *Prod-Dir* Kenneth Hume. *Assoc Prod* Larry Parnes. *Photog* Harry Waxman. *Film Ed* Fergus McDonell. *Mus* Ian Macpherson. *Songs:* "Please, Please Me," "From Me to You," "I Wanna Be Your Man" John Lennon, Paul McCartney. *Sung by* The Cheynes. *Choreog* Peter Darrell.

Cast—"Swinging U. K.": The Cockneys, Brian Poole and the Tremeloes, Millie Small, The Wackers, The Merseybeats, The Migil Five, The Four Pennies *(themselves)*, Brian Matthew, Alan Freeman, Kent Walton *(themselves, disc jockeys)*.

Cast—"U. K. Swings Again": Brian Poole and the Tremeloes, The Swinging Blue Jeans, The Tornados, The Animals, The Hollies, The Applejacks, Lulu and the Luvvers *(themselves)*, Brian Matthew, Alan Freeman, Kent Walton *(themselves, disc jockeys)*.

Cast—"Mods and Rockers": Western Theatre Ballet Company, The Cheynes *(themselves)*.

Musical revue. In SWINGING U. K. and U. K. SWINGS AGAIN disc jockeys introduce a number of British singers and rock groups. MODS AND ROCKERS consists of two modern ballet numbers: the first features a woman and two men in a cafe; the second involves a clash between two rival London gangs, the stylish Mods and the leather-jacketed Rockers. *Singers. Disc jockeys. Rock and roll. Ballet. Gang wars. London. Mods. Rockers.*

Note: Released in Great Britain in 1964 as three shorts: *Swinging U. K.* (28 min), *U. K. Swings Again* (27 min), and *Mods and Rockers* (25 min). The first two were produced by International Productions, the last by Harold Baim Productions.

GO, GO, GO WORLD! (Italy)   F6.1871

Atlantica Cinematografica. *Dist* ABC Films. Apr **1966**. Sd; col (Technicolor). 35mm (Techniscope). 82 min.

Pres by Marco Vicario. *Prod-Screenplay* Marco Vicario. *Dir* Anthony Dawson, Renato Marvi. *English Lang Commentary* Stephen Garret, John Hart. *Photog* Giancarlo Lari, Giovanni Raffaldi, Marcello Gallinelli. *Art Dir* Francesco Longo. *Film Ed* Mario Morra. *Mus* Nino Oliviero, Bruno Nicolai.

Cast: Stephen Garret *(narrator)*.

Documentary. The oddities of human behavior are filmed throughout the world, in both "civilized" and "primitive" societies. Included are scenes of: bums sleeping on the Bowery in New York; women workers in China; a Chinese funeral; tourists cavorting in Hawaii; a fashion show and hat shop in Honolulu; a club for tall women and a height contest in Dallas; women mud wrestling in West Germany; pigs in China and England; sausage eaters in Hamburg; Hong Kong's red-light district; a meal of roast dog in Hawaii; a man taking a bubble bath; football, judo, and fashion shows in Japan; nightclubs in Hong Kong, Japan, and Cannes; unusual religious practices in southern Italy; women riding sampans in Hong Kong; wedding rituals of Borneo; a drunken performing rooster; an Indian snake charmer; producing snake anti-venin; a bar and whorehouse on wheels; a bullfight in Madrid; Pamplona bulls running through a Spanish town; trading in Chinese children; Malaysian taxi dancers; painting skulls in Borneo; a chair of nails; use of the chastity belt in Italy; bikini bathers in Cannes; a "peeping tom" striptease innovation; traffic in Rome; the Fiat factory in Italy; Fiats running on the track; and exotic eating habits in Paris. In addition, there are film clips of a variety of female impersonators, belly dancers, musclemen, strippers, prostitutes, and dancers. *Children. Taxi dancers. Exotic dancers. Tourists. Strongmen. Snake charmers. Wrestling. Prostitution. Weddings. Religion. Football. Female impersonation. Voyeurism. Funerals. Judo. Rites and ceremonies. Striptease. Bullfighting. Fashion shows. Automobile manufacture. Chastity belts. Automobile racing. Nightclubs. Whorehouses. Bars. Federal Republic of Germany. Hong Kong. Borneo. China. Malaysia. Hawaii. Spain. Paris. Cannes. New York City—Bowery. Dallas. Japan. Rome. Honolulu. Madrid. India. England. Hamburg. Bulls. Dogs. Pigs. Roosters.*

Note: Released in Italy in 1964 as *Il pelo nel mondo*, running time: 95 min. Also known as *Weird, Wicked World* and *Wicked World.*

GO GO MANIA (Great Britain)　　　　　　　　　　F6.1872
Associated British-Pathé, Ltd. *Dist* American International Pictures. 5 May **1965** [Boston opening; c5 May 1965; MP15538]. Sd; col (Technicolor). 35mm (Techniscope). 70 min.

Prod Harry Field. *Assoc Prod* Ted Bilsdon. *Dir* Frederic Goode. *Screenplay* Roger Dunton. *Photog* Geoffrey Unsworth. *Art Dir* Peter Moll. *Supv Film Ed* John Blair. *Ed* Frederick Ives. *Adtl Mus* Joan Shakespeare, John Shakespeare. *Choreog* Leo Kharibian.

Featuring: The Beatles, The Animals, Matt Monro, The Nashville Teens, Susan Maughan, The Rockin' Berries, The Honeycombs, Herman's Hermits, The Four Pennies, Peter and Gordon, The Fourmost, Sounds Incorporated, Billy Davis, Spencer Davis Group, Billy J. Kramer and the Dakotas, Tommy Quickly and the Remo Four.

Host: Jimmy Savile.

Musical revue. London disc jockey Jimmy Savile introduces 16 of England's top recording stars performing their musical specialties in stylized studio settings. Opening and closing numbers by the Beatles were filmed during an actual stage performance. *Disc jockeys. Singers. Musicians. Rock and roll.*

Note: Opened in London in Apr 1965 as *Pop Gear*; running time: 68 min.

GO-GO SET *see* **GET YOURSELF A COLLEGE GIRL**

GO NAKED IN THE WORLD　　　　　　　　　　　　F6.1873
Arcola Pictures. *Dist* Metro-Goldwyn-Mayer, Inc. 18 Jan **1961** [Minneapolis opening; c20 Dec 1960; LP18983]. Sd (Westrex); col (Metrocolor). 35mm (CinemaScope). 103 min.

Prod Aaron Rosenberg. *Dir-Screenplay* Ranald MacDougall. *Dir Photog* Milton Krasner. *Col Cons* Charles K. Hagedon. *Art Dir* George W. Davis, Edward Carfagno. *Set Decor* Henry Grace, Dick Pefferle. *Film Ed* John McSweeney, Jr. *Mus* Adolph Deutsch. *Rec Supv* Franklin Milton. *Asst Dir* William Shanks. *Cost Dsgn* Helen Rose. *Makeup* William Tuttle. *Sp Eff* Robert R. Hoag.

Cast: Gina Lollobrigida *(Giulietta Cameron)*, Anthony Franciosa *(Nick Stratton)*, Ernest Borgnine *(Pete Stratton)*, Luana Patten *(Yvonne Stratton)*, Will Kuluva *(Argus Diavolos)*, Philip Ober *(Josh Kebner)*, John Kellogg *(Cobby)*, Nancy R. Pollock *(Mary Stratton)*, Tracey Roberts *(Diana)*, Yale Wexler *(Charles Stacy)*, Rodney Bell *(Parkson)*, John Gallaudet *(Rupert)*, Chet Stratton *(Jack)*, Maggie Pierce *(girl)*, Bill Smith, juvenile *(boy)*, Jacqueline Smith *(teenager)*.

Romantic drama. Source: Tom T. Chamales, *Go Naked in the World* (New York, 1959). Following a tour of duty with the Army, wealthy Nick Stratton returns to his hometown of San Francisco. Torn between the desirability of keeping his independence and going to work for his devoted but dominating father in the construction business, he checks into a hotel to think things over for a few days. That night he meets and is immediately attracted to Giulietta (Julie) Cameron, unaware that she is a well-known and extremely high-priced prostitute. Eventually Nick's father, Pete, finds him and brings him home, but the peaceful reunion explodes into a violent argument when Pete once more tries to force his own way of life upon his son. Following the stormy session, Nick leaves home and returns to Julie, with whom he falls desperately in love. On the night of the Strattons' 30th wedding anniversary, Nick brings Julie to his parents' party and is horrified to learn that most of the men present—including his father—have had sexual relations with her. Though Nick vows never to see Julie again, he is unable to stay away, and he returns to her. Pete, however, continues to try to break up the romance, and Nick is forced to take Julie to Acapulco. Finally convinced that Nick will never be happy without Julie, Pete visits her secretly and asks her to marry Nick. Aware that her past

would always haunt their marriage, however, she pretends to be bored with the affair and sends Nick away. Once he has left, she ends her life by hurling herself into the sea. *Veterans. Prostitutes. Filial relations. Reputation. Suicide. Construction. Wealth. Wedding anniversaries. San Francisco. Acapulco.*

Note: Location scenes filmed in San Francisco and Acapulco.

GOAL! (Great Britain/Liechtenstein)　　　　　　　　F6.1874
Frigo Productions. *Dist* Royal Films International. 21 Dec **1966** [Los Angeles opening]. Sd; col (Technicolor). 35mm (Techniscope). 107 min.

Prod Octavio Senoret. *Exec Prod* Michael Sullivan. *Dir* Abidine Dino, Ross Devenish. *Comm* Brian Glanville. *Photog* Jean-Jacques Flori, David Samuelson, Harry Hart. *Photog Cons* Michael Samuelson. *Supv Film Ed* Jeanne Henderson. *Film Ed* Jack Knight, William Butler, Michael Rabiger. *Mus Comp & Cond* John Hawksworth. *Sd* Gordon Everett, Arthur Bradburn, Clive Winter, Gerry Wrexham, Bob Jones.

Narrator: Nigel Patrick.

Documentary. Coverage of the World Cup soccer series held in England in July of 1966 begins with the arrival of the players from the 16 competing nations; most of the footage centers on the four finalists—England, West Germany, Portugal, and the Soviet Union. At the early games, held in Liverpool, Middlesbrough, and Birmingham, the defending champion, Brazil, is defeated. The major part of the film is devoted to the final match at Wembley in which England emerges victorious over West Germany, and the players receive the Gold Cup from Queen Elizabeth. *Soccer. Liverpool. Middlesbrough. Birmingham (England). Wembley. Elizabeth II (England). World Cup (soccer).*

Note: Released in Great Britain in Oct 1966 as *Goal! World Cup 1966.*

GOAL! WORLD CUP 1966 *see* **GOAL!**

IL GOBBO *see* **THE HUNCHBACK OF ROME**

GOBEN NO TSUBAKI *see* **THE SCARLET CAMELLIA**

GOD FORGIVES—I DON'T (Italy/Spain)　　　　　　F6.1875
Crono Cinematografica-P. E. F. S. A. Films. *Dist* American International Pictures. May **1969** [c14 May 1969; LP37311]. Sd; col (Berkey Pathé). 35mm. 101 min. [Also 97 min.] *MPAA rating* M.

Prod Enzo D'Ambrosio. *Dir* Giuseppe Colizzi. *Story-Screenplay* Giuseppe Colizzi, Gumersindo Mollo. *Photog* Alfio Contini. *Art Dir* Gastone Carsetti, Luis Vázquez. *Film Ed* Sergio Montanari. *Mus* Angel Oliver Pina. *Asst Dir* Silvana Mangini Colizzi. *Cost* Marilu Corteny. *Sp Eff* Cataldo Galliano, Alfredo Segoviano.

Cast: Terence Hill *(Cat)*, Frank Wolff *(Bill San Antonio)*, Bud Spencer *(Earp Hargitay)*, Gina Rovere *(Rose)*, José Manuel Martín *(Bud)*, Tito García, Paco Sanz, Giovanna Lenzi, José Canalejas, Bruno Arie, Remo Capitani, Juan Olaguíbel, Rufino Inglés, Roberto Alessandri, Luis Bar Boo, Arturo Fuento, Giancarlo Bastianoni.

Western melodrama. Bill San Antonio robs a train, murders everyone aboard, and buries the money he takes. Cat, a gunfighter determined to find the money, faces San Antonio in a shootout after a crooked card game. Handed a gun filled with blanks, Cat is tricked into believing he has killed San Antonio, but he continues the search for the money. He joins forces with Earp, a brawny insurance detective, and together they find the loot and discover that San Antonio is alive. They secretly remove the money to another cache, but they are soon captured and tortured by San Antonio and his men. While San Antonio is absent on another mission, Cat and Earp surprise the guards and escape. Cat, however, is recaptured and forced to lead a guard to the cache. He kills the guard with a knife hidden near the loot and sends a messenger to San Antonio to demand a showdown. Earp arrives as Cat and San Antonio prepare to face each other. Earp is shot by San Antonio, who, in turn, is crippled by Cat. Cat has set a dynamite charge next to the cache, and San Antonio frantically tries to extinguish the fuse as he crawls toward the money. The dynamite explodes, killing San Antonio; the money, which has been removed elsewhere, remains safe. Cat and Earp, who is only wounded, ride off together to divide the money. *Robbers. Gunfighters. Detectives. Train robberies. Murder. Torture. Duplicity. Insurance. Explosives.*

Note: Released in Italy in 1967 as *Dio perdona ... io no*; running time: 109 min. Spanish title: *Tu perdonas ... yo no.* Terence Hill is a pseudonym for Mario Girotti; Bud Spencer for Carlo Pederzoli.

THE GOD GAME *see* **THE MAGUS**

THE GODDESS *see* **DEVI**

GODY MOLODYYE *see* **AGE OF YOUTH**

GODZILLA TAI MOTHRA *see* **GODZILLA VS. THE THING**

GODZILLA VS. THE THING (Japan)   **F6.1876**

Toho Co. *Dist* American International Pictures. 23 Sep **1964** [Los Angeles opening; c26 Aug 1964; LP29676]. Sd; col (Eastmancolor, print by Pathé). 35mm (Tohoscope). 90 min. [Copyright length: 98 min.]

Prod Tomoyuki Tanaka. *Dir* Inoshiro Honda. *Screenplay* Shinichi Sekizawa. *Photog* Hajime Koizumi. *Lighting* Shoshichi Kojima. *Art Dir* Takeo Kita. *Film Ed* Ryohei Fujii. *Mus* Akira Ifukube. *Sd Rec* Fumio Yanoguchi. *Sp Eff Dir* Eiji Tsuburaya. *Sp Eff Photog* Sadamasa Arikawa, Motoyoshi Tomioka. *Sp Eff Art Dir* Akira Watanabe. *Sp Eff Lighting* Kuichiro Kishida.

Cast: Akira Takarada *(Ichiro Sakai)*, Yuriko Hoshi *(Junko Nakanishi)*, Hiroshi Koizumi *(Professor Miura)*, Yu Fujiki *(Jiro Nakamura)*, Emi Ito, Yumi Ito *(The Guardians)*, Yoshifumi Tajima *(Kumayama)*, Kenji Sahara *(Banzo Torahata)*, Jun Tazaki *(newspaper editor)*, Ikio Sawamura *(priest)*, Kenzo Tadake *(mayor)*, Susumu Fujita *(public relations officer)*, Yutaka Sada *(old man)*, Yoshio Kosugi *(old man in the village)*, Yutaka Nakayama, Hiroshi Iwamoto, Koji Uno *(fishermen)*, Yasuhisa Tsutsumi *(longshoreman)*, Ren Yamamoto *(sailor)*, Haruo Nakajima *(Godzilla)*.

Science fiction drama. A gigantic egg appears on the shore as the monster Godzilla rises out of the mud in the aftermath of a typhoon off the coast of Japan. Tiny twin girls then appear, carried from their nearby radioactive atomic island by Mothra (The Thing) to retrieve their egg. Unable to persuade local promoters, who envision the egg as a major tourist attraction, to let them carry it off, the twins and Mothra return home emptyhanded. Godzilla, meanwhile, is on the rampage; and a local scientist, a photographer, and a reporter enlist the aid of Mothra, who is no match for Godzilla and soon dies. Mothra, however, has hatched the egg, and two enormous caterpillars emerge to envelop the monster in their sticky fluid. Godzilla topples from a cliff to his death in the sea below. *Monsters. Sisters. Twins. Scientists. Reporters. Photographers. Tourists. Typhoons. Eggs. Godzilla. Mothra. Caterpillars.*

Note: Released in Japan in 1964 as *Gojira tai Mosura*; running time: 94 min. Alternative Japanese title: *Godzilla tai Mothra.*

GOFORTH see **BOOM!**

GOIN' DOWN THE ROAD (Canada)   **F6.1877**

Evenden Films. *Dist* Chevron Pictures. 19 Oct **1970** [New York opening]. Sd; col (Eastmancolor, print by Movielab). 35mm. 90 min. *MPAA rating* R.

Pres by Phoenix Films, Bennet Fode. *Prod-Dir* Donald Shebib. *Screenplay* William Fruet. *Story* Donald Shebib, William Fruet. *Photog* Richard Leiterman. *Main Titl* Film Opticals. *Film Ed* Donald Shebib. *Mus* Bruce Cockburn. *Sd Rec* James McCarthy. *Sd Re-rec* Clarke Da Prato. *Coöp* Canadian Film Development Corp.

Cast: Doug McGrath *(Peter)*, Paul Bradley *(Joey)*, Jayne Eastwood *(Betty)*, Nicole Morin *(Nicole)*, Pierre LaRoche, actor *(plant foreman)*, Cayle Chernin *(Celina)*, Ted Sugar, Don Steinhouse, Ron Martin *(workers at plant)*, Sheila White *(girl in record shop)*, Dennis Bishop *(clerk in grocery store)*, Max Jones, Jack Zimmerman, Mary Black, Ivor Jackson, Ralph Stroh, Stan Ross, Stuart Marwick.

Drama. Joey and Peter, two young men from an impoverished section of Nova Scotia, travel to Toronto in search of a better life. After spending one night at the Salvation Army, they find a seedy apartment, and Joey takes a job in a bottling factory. Peter is more ambitious and seeks a job making television commercials. He is unsuccessful, however, and finally accepts a job in Joey's factory, where they spend much of their time discussing the physical attributes of Nicole, a voluptuous secretary. One night they meet waitresses Betty and Celina, but Peter is unenthusiastic about either. When Betty becomes pregnant, Joey agrees to marry her, and they move to a nicer apartment. Soon afterwards, Joey and Peter are laid off their jobs, and the three of them are forced to move to a poorer section. In dire financial straits because Betty can no longer work, Peter and Joey steal groceries from a store and assault the clerk. Upon returning home, they find all of their belongings piled in the street outside of the apartment. Joey is anxious to find Betty, but Peter persuades him to forget her so that they can continue their search for a better life in the city. *Factory workers. Secretaries. Waitresses. Pregnancy. Marriage. Unemployment. Poverty. Robbery. Eviction. Toronto. Nova Scotia. Salvation Army.*

Note: Opened in Toronto in Jul 1970; running time: 86 min. Filmed in 16mm.

GOING DOWN FOR THE 3RD TIME   **F6.1878**

Kirt Films International. *Dist* Distribpix, Inc. 5 Mar **1969** [Boston opening]. Sd; b&w. 35mm. 63 min.

Prod Leonard Kirtman. *Dir* Tommy Goetz. *Screenplay* Ron Rheego. *Photog* Leonard Kirtman. *Supv* Tommy Goetz.

Cast: Lois Lane, Rita Joyce, Mary Aster.

Melodrama. Three female spies are assigned to break up an international spy ring and liberate three of their colleagues who are being held hostages. Their plan is to seduce three men in the spy ring, each of whom has a portion of a

map showing the ring's headquarters. They locate the headquarters and join in a wild party, where normal and oral intercourse are performed, to avoid being recognized. As the party turns into an orgy, the heroines find their colleagues and, before escaping, toss a bomb into enemy headquarters. *Spies. Hostages. Espionage. Kidnaping. Seduction. Oral sex. Orgies. Bombs. Documentation.*

GOJIRA TAI MOSURA see **GODZILLA VS. THE THING**

GOJUMAN-NIN NO ISAN see **THE LEGACY OF THE 500,000**

GOLD FOR THE CAESARS (France/Italy)   **F6.1879**

Adelphia Compagnia Cinematografica–C. I. C. C. *Dist* Metro-Goldwyn-Mayer, Inc. Jun **1964** [c31 Dec 1963; LP28122]. Sd; col (Eastman Color). 35mm (CinemaScope). 86 min.

Prod Joseph Fryd. *Dir* Andre De Toth, Sabatino Ciuffini. *2d Unit Dir* Riccardo Freda. *Screenplay* Arnold Perl, Sabatino Ciuffini. *Dir Photog* Raffaele Masciocchi. *Camera* Antonio Schiavolena. *Art Dir* Ottavio Scotti. *Set Dresser* Arrigo Breschi. *Film Ed* Franco Fraticelli. *Mus Score Comp & Dir* Franco Mannino. *Sd Dir* Giovanni Rossi. *Asst Dir* Jerzy Macc. *Prod Mgr* Luciano Cattania. *Asst Prod Mgr* Paolo Gargano. *Script Girl* Anna Gruber. *Cost Dsgn* Mario Giorsi. *Makeup* Maurizio Giustini. *Hairdresser* Giancarlo Marin. *Sp Eff* Eros Bacciucchi. *Stills* Angelo Pennoni. *Fencing Master* Bruno Ukmar.

Cast: Jeffrey Hunter *(Lacer)*, Mylène Demongeot *(Penelope)*, Ron Randell *(Rufus)*, Massimo Girotti *(Maximus)*, Giulio Bosetti *(Scipio)*, Ettore Manni *(Luna)*, Georges Lycan *(Malendi)*, Furio Meniconi *(Dax)*, Jacques Stany.

Costume melodrama. Source: Florence A. Seward, *Gold for the Caesars* (Englewood Cliffs, N. J., 1961). Maximus, governor of a Roman colony in northern Spain in 96 A.D., is building roads and bridges to solidify the Roman holdings against the aggressive Celts, who are led by Malendi and his son, Luna. When the Celts start an avalanche to destroy a bridge built by Lacer, an architect-slave, they are repulsed, and Luna is captured. An emissary from the Roman emperor tells Maximus that the emperor is dying and that Maximus can become the new emperor if he has enough gold. Maximus, intending to obtain the gold in Celt-controlled Valley of the Sil, frees Luna and makes a truce with Malendi. Malendi allows a small force of Romans, supervised by Lacer and accompanied by a small force of Celts, to enter the valley to mine the gold on the condition that Maximus keep his troops away. But Maximus plans to kill Lacer after he obtains the gold because Penelope, Maximus' favorite, is in love with Lacer. She follows Lacer to warn him; Maximus breaks the truce and sends troops into the valley. The Celts attack and Lacer opens the sluice gates of the dam he had engineered to allow the mining. The Celts are drowned in the rising water while Lacer and Maximus battle atop the sluice gate. Maximus is killed, and Lacer and Penelope are given their freedom and depart for a new life in Gaul. *Architects. Royalty. Soldiers. Romans. Celts. Territorial governors. Slavery. Ambition. Jealousy. Duels. Dams. Rome—History—Empire. Spain.*

Note: Released as *Oro per i Cesari* in Italy in 1963. Released in France as *Or pour les Césars* and *L'or des Césars* in 1964; running time: 95 min.

THE GOLD GUITAR   **F6.1880**

Airlon Pictures. *Dist* Craddock Films. 10 Aug **1966** [Atlanta opening]. Sd; col. 35mm. 84 min.

Prod-Script-Story Bill Packham. *Dir* J. Hunter Todd. *Photog* Jack Steeley. *Asst Photog* Steve Fifield. *Ch Grip* John Murray. *Mus & Titl Song* Harry Middlebrooks. *Song:* "A Dollar Ain't a Dollar Anymore" Tom Glazer. *Song:* "I Can't See Me Without You" Sandra Rhodes. *Song:* "It's A Mean Ol' World" Hugh X. Lewis. *Song:* "Anywhere U.S.A." Del Reeves, Ellen Reeves. *Song:* "Alone With You" Roy Drusky, Lester Vanadore. *Song:* "One Bum Town" Hank Mills. *Song:* "7-11" Margie Bowes.

Cast: Del Reeves, Roy Drusky, Hugh X. Lewis, Margie Bowes, Skeeter Davis, Arnold Dorfman, George Ellis, Don Barber, John Fox, Mary Nell Santacroce, Bill Anderson, Eddie Hill, Bill Carlisle, Charlie Louvin.

Comedy with music. New York City gangsters attempt to steal the secret of the Nashville sound. *Gangsters. Country music.*

Note: Filmed entirely in Atlanta.

GOLD OF THE SEVEN SAINTS   **F6.1881**

Warner Bros. Pictures. 1 Feb **1961** [Los Angeles opening; c18 Feb 1961; LP25360]. Sd; b&w. 35mm (WarnerScope). 88 min.

Prod Leonard Freeman. *Dir* Gordon Douglas. *Screenplay* Leigh Brackett, Leonard Freeman. *Photog* Joseph Biroc. *Art Dir* Stanley Fleischer. *Set Decor* Fay C. Babcock. *Film Ed* Folmar Blangsted. *Mus* Howard Jackson. *Sd* Francis M. Stahl. *Asst Dir* William Kissel. *Makeup* Gordon Bau. *Hairstyles* Jean Burt Reilly.

Cast: Clint Walker *(Jim Rainbolt)*, Roger Moore *(Shaun Garrett)*, Leticia Roman *(Tita)*, Robert Middleton *(Gondora)*, Chill Wills *(Doc Gates)*, Gene Evans *(McCracken)*, Roberto Contreras *(Armanderez)*, Jack Williams *(Amos)*, Arthur Stewart *(Ricca)*.

Western drama. Source: Steve Frazee, *Desert Guns* (New York, 1957). Fur trappers Jim Rainbolt and Shaun Garrett find a fortune in gold nuggets and head across the desert for Seven Saints, Utah. A gang led by McCracken pursues them, but the two men manage to hide the gold in a cave and cover the opening with a huge boulder before being overtaken. Shaun is wounded in the resulting confrontation, but he and Jim escape when physician Doc Gates, a hard-drinking ex-gunfighter, arrives to help drive away the outlaws. Taking Doc as a new partner, the men continue their journey until they are stopped by a band of caballeros led by Gondora, an old friend of Jim's, who invites them to rest at his ranch. Also at the stopover is Tita, an Indian Gondora had cared for when she was an orphaned girl; now that she is a young woman, the bandit is willing to sell her to the highest bidder. While Jim and Gondora are rounding up some cattle, McCracken kidnaps Doc and Shaun and takes them to his mountain hideout. Doc is killed when he cannot tell where the gold is hidden, and Shaun is tortured. Jim locates his partner but is forced to divulge the hiding place to save his friend's life; in doing so, however, he topples the huge boulder onto McCracken's legs and leaves him to die. Once again the partners meet Gondora, who announces that Tita has chosen to remain with him; pushing friendship aside, the bandit demands the gold. Jim and Shaun attempt to escape, but as they navigate a dangerous river crossing, the gold is washed downstream into the rapids. The two men join Gondora in a round of hysterical laughter and ride off. *Trappers. Bandits. Gunfighters. Physicians. Indians of North America. Orphans. Partnerships. Kidnaping. Murder. Torture. Drunkenness. Gold. Caves. Ranches. Deserts. Utah.*

Note: Location scenes filmed in Utah.

DAS GOLD VON SAM COOPER *see* **THE RUTHLESS FOUR**

THE GOLDEN ARROW (Italy)   F6.1882

Titanus. *Dist* Metro-Goldwyn-Mayer, Inc. May **1964** [c31 Dec 1963; LP26845]. Sd (Westrex); col (Technicolor). 35mm (Technirama). 91 min.

Prod Goffredo Lombardo. *Dir* Antonio Margheriti. *2d Unit Dir* Ettore Fizzarotti. *Orig Screenplay* Bruno Vailati, Augusto Frassineti, Filippo Sanjust, Giorgio Prosperi, Giorgio Arlorio. *English Dial Writ & Dir* George Higgins, III. *Dir Photog* Gabor Pogany. *Photog* Giovanni Raffaldi. *Camera Op* Mario Capriotti. *Art Dir* Flavio Mogherini. *Set Decor* Massimo Tavazzi. *Film Ed* Mario Serandrei. *Mus Score* Mario Nascimbene. *Cond* Franco Ferrara. *Sd Tech* Mario Messina. *Asst Dir* Giovanni Fago. *Prod Supv* Folco Laudati. *Prod Asst* Manlio Dalla Pria. *Script Girl* Franca Franco. *Cost* Giorgio Desideri. *Makeup* Franco Di Girolamo. *Hairstyles* Anna Cristofani. *Sp Eff* Technicolor Italiana, Fernando Mazza. *Still Photog* G. B. Poletto.

Cast: Tab Hunter *(Hassan)*, Rossana Podestà *(Jamila)*, Umberto Melnati *(The Thin Genie)*, Giustino Durano *(The Absent-Minded Genie)*, Mario Feliciani *(Baktiar)*, Jose Jaspe *(Sabrath)*, Giampaolo Rosmino *(Mokbar)*, Renato Baldini *(prince of Bassora)*, Rosario Borelli *(prince of Aleppo)*, Ceco Zamurovich *(prince of Samarkland)*, Calisto Calisti *(prince of Bassora's General)*, Dominique Boschero *(queen of city of Rocky Valley)*, Abdel Moneim Ibrihim *(Captain Hamit)*, Claudio Scarchilli *(The Bandit)*, Omar Zoulfikar *(magician of Rocky Valley)*, Franco Scandurra, Gloria Milland, Renato Montalbano.

Fantasy. The benevolent Sultan of Damascus, who owns a golden arrow which, when shot, always finds its mark and returns to its owner, is assassinated at the order of Baktiar, a vizier, and the assailants escape with a child. Jamila, the Sultan's young niece, becomes ruler, but Baktiar is her advisor, and Damascus falls on evil days. When Jamila reaches marriageable age, Baktiar announces that anyone who can bend the bow and shoot the golden arrow may claim her hand and become sultan. Since no one has been able to shoot the arrow since the Sultan's murder, Baktiar is confident that all attempts will fail, thus enabling him to force Jamila to marry him. Hassan, a young thief who has come to the festivities to steal the rich gifts brought by the contenders, easily shoots the arrow. Mokbar, Jamila's trusted Elder, recognizes a birthmark on Hassan's hand as the same as that on the hand of the child abducted from the palace and declares Hassan the new Sultan, but Baktiar declares him a fraud. Hassan and his men kidnap Jamila and escape, but the golden arrow disappears. Hassan and Jamila fall in love, but Hassan is captured by Baktiar when he returns Jamila to Damascus. Three genii help him escape and promise to help him recover the arrow. They warn him that if he returns to his thieving ways, his obstacles will be greater. After a series of adventures, Hassan recovers the arrow, is sent back to Damascus on a flying carpet to defeat Baktiar, and is revealed to be the assassinated Sultan's son. Hassan is proclaimed ruler and marries Jamila. *Royalty. Thieves. Viziers. Genii. Assassination. Kidnaping. Personal identity. Archery. Magic. Marriage—Arranged. Birthmarks. Flying carpets. Damascus.*

Note: Produced in Italy in 1962 as *La freccia d'oro.*

THE GOLDEN BOX   F6.1883

Hollywood Cinema Associates. *Dist* Donald A. Davis Productions. 17 Feb **1970** [Fresno, California, showing]. Sd; col. 35mm. 79-84 min. *MPAA rating* R.

Prod-Dir Don Davis.

Cast: Marsha Jordan *(Diane)*, Ann Myers *(Donna)*, Jim Gentry *(Slade Rivers)*, Mark Edwards *(Gene Lackey)*, Steve Vincent *(The Boss)*, Bernard Bossick *(Numero Uno)*, Forman Shain *(Kirby)*, Gene Massey *(bellboy)*, Barbara O'Bryant *(girl friend in Washington)*, Mike Perry *(Charlie, the bartender)*, Frank Mills *(brother)*, Barbara Mills *(sister)*.

Drama. Hired gunmen kill a nightclub piano player and steal a music book which contains coded information on the location of a hidden treasure box. Two nightclub hostesses, both ex-mistresses of the murdered pianist, follow the hired killers from one city to another across the country, hoping to obtain the treasure for themselves. During a nude gin rummy game in New York City, they decide to seduce the bellboy in order to steal the music book; in Chicago they crack the code; and the drama ends abruptly in the canals of Venice, California. ... *Pianists. Hired killers. Nightclub hostesses. Mistresses. Murder. Theft. Seduction. Treasure. New York City. Chicago. Venice (California). Documentation.*

THE GOLDEN BREED   F6.1884

Sidewalk Productions. *Dist* Hollywood International Productions, Continental Distributing, Inc. Nov **1968** [Los Angeles showing]. Sd; col. 35mm. 88 min.

A Dale Davis Production. *Prod-Dir* Dale Davis. *Photog* Dale Davis. *Film Ed* Dale Davis. *Mus Score* Mike Curb, Jerry Styner, Harley Hatcher. *Titl Song Sung* by Mike Clifford. *Songs Perf* by The Back-Wash Rhythm Band.

Participants: Dale Davis *(narrator)*, Butch Van Artsdalen, Mickey Dora, Fred Hemings, Steve Doyle, Greg Noll, Alan Hazard, Billy Edwards, Nat Young, Jock Southerland, Joey Cabell, Ricky Grigg, Felipe Pomar *(surfers)*.

Documentary. Surfers searching for the perfect ride travel to the Hawaiian surfing resorts of Sunset Beach, Waimea Bay, Velzyland, Banzi Pipeline, Haleiwa, Pupakea, and Makaha; to Malibu, California; and to the Baja California coast of Mexico. The featured surfers include Jock Southerland from Hawaii, Joey Campbell and Ricky Grigg from California, Nat Young from Australia, and Felipe Pomar from Peru. *Surfers. Hawaii. California. Mexico.*

Note: Filmed in Hawaii, Mexico, and California.

THE GOLDEN BUDDHA (Hong Kong)   F6.1885

Shaw Brothers (H. K.) Ltd. Jan **1967** [Los Angeles showing]. Sd; 35mm. [Feature film, length unknown.]

Cast: Paul Chang Chung, Jeanette Lin Tsui, Lo Wei. No information about the precise nature of this film has been found.

GOLDEN BULLET *see* **IMPASSE**

THE GOLDEN GOOSE (East Germany)   F6.1886

DEFA. *Dist* K. Gordon Murray Productions, Trans-International Films. 8 Jan **1966** [Brooklyn, New York, opening]. Sd; col (Eastman Color). 35mm. 72 min.

Pres by K. Gordon Murray. *Prod English Vers* K. Gordon Murray.

Animated fantasy. Source: Jakob Grimm and Wilhelm Grimm, "Die goldene Gans". A film version of the fairy tale. *Cobblers. Royalty. Greed. Parades. Geese.*

Note: Released in East Germany as *Die goldene Gans;* release date undetermined.

THE GOLDEN NYMPHS *see* **HONEYMOON OF HORROR**

THE GOLDEN PLAGUE (West Germany)   F6.1887

Occident Films. *Dist* Bakros Corp. 9 Aug **1963** [New York opening]. Sd; b&w. 35mm. 95 min.

Dir John Brahm. *Screenplay* Dieter Werner.

Cast: Ivan Desny *(Sergeant Hartwig)*, Karl Boehm *(Karl Hellmer)*, Gertrud Kückelmann *(Franziska Hellmer)*, Wilfried Seyferth *(Wenzeslaw Lolowrat)*, Elise Aulinger *(Johanna)*, Heinz Hilpert *(Tonder)*, Ilse Fürstenberg *(Mrs. Foesterling)*.

Drama. A German-born American arrives in his girl friend's village at the end of World War II and finds their romance opposed by her brother, an amusement park operator and black market speculator. *Americans in foreign countries. Brother-sister relationship. Black market. Amusement parks. World War II.*

Note: Released in West Germany in 1954 as *Die goldene Pest.*

DIE GOLDENE GANS *see* **THE GOLDEN GOOSE**

DIE GOLDENE PEST see **THE GOLDEN PLAGUE**

GOLDFINGER (Great Britain)   **F6.1888**
Eon Productions–Danjaq, S. A. *Dist* United Artists. 21 Dec **1964** [New York opening; c18 Sep 1964; LP29363]. Sd; col (Technicolor). 35mm. 108 min.

Pres by Harry Saltzman, Albert R. Broccoli. *Prod* Harry Saltzman, Albert R. Broccoli. *Dir* Guy Hamilton. *Action Seq Dir* Bob Simmons. *Screenplay* Richard Maibaum, Paul Dehn. *Photog* Ted Moore. *Art Dir* Peter Murton. *Asst Art Dir* Michael White, Maurice Pelling. *Set Dresser* Freda Pearson. *Prod Dsgn* Ken Adam. *Titl Dsgn* Robert Brownjohn. *Film Ed* Peter Hunt. *Titl Song* Leslie Bricusse, Anthony Newley, John Barry. *Sung by* Shirley Bassey. *Sd* Dudley Messenger, Gordon McCallum. *Asst Dir* Frank Ernst. *Prod Mgr* L. C. Rudkin. *Makeup* Paul Rabiger, Basil Newall. *Hairdresser* Eileen Fennell. *Sp Eff* John Stears.

Cast: Sean Connery *(James Bond)*, Gert Fröbe *(Goldfinger)*, Honor Blackman *(Pussy Galore)*, Shirley Eaton *(Jill Masterson)*, Tania Mallett *(Tilly Masterson)*, Harold Sakata *(Oddjob)*, Bernard Lee *("M")*, Martin Benson *(Solo)*, Cec Linder *(Felix Leiter)*, Austin Willis *(Simmons)*, Lois Maxwell *(Miss Moneypenny)*, Bill Nagy *(Midnight)*, Alf Joint *(Capungo)*, Varley Thomas *(old lady)*, Nadja Regin *(Bonita)*, Raymond Young *(Sierra)*, Richard Vernon *(Smithers)*, Denis Cowles *(Brunskill)*, Michael Mellinger *(Kisch)*, Burt Kwouk *(Mr. Ling)*, Hal Galili *(Strap)*, Lenny Rabin *(henchman)*.

Action melodrama. Source: Ian Fleming, *Goldfinger* (London, 1959). Auric Goldfinger, one of the wealthiest and most evil men in the world, is suspected of depleting England's gold reserve through smuggling. Secret agent James Bond is assigned to investigate the matter. He meets Goldfinger at a Miami hotel and learns Goldfinger's method of cheating in high stake card games. Jill, the smuggler's secretary, views the other players' hands through a telescope and relays the information to her boss through his hearing aid. When Jill becomes attracted to Bond, Goldfinger murders her by coating her body with heavy gold paint. Bond then trails Goldfinger's Rolls Royce across Europe to his Alpine headquarters. Tilly Masterson, Jill's sister, is also trailing Goldfinger, but she is killed by Goldfinger's oriental servant, Oddjob. Bond learns that the Rolls Royce is solid gold and provides the means for smuggling, but he is captured and flown to Goldfinger's Kentucky headquarters by Pussy Galore, Goldfinger's beautiful pilot. Bond learns that Goldfinger is planning to rob Fort Knox by paralyzing the defense forces with gas sprayed from the planes of Pussy's flying circus, and then blowing up the fort with an atomic bomb borrowed from Communist China. Goldfinger proceeds with the plan, and Bond is handcuffed to the bomb; but, unknown to Goldfinger, Pussy, who has succumbed to Bond's charm, changes sides, and warns Washington. The plot is thwarted, and Bond manages to free himself from the bomb only seconds before detonation and then escapes attack from the razor-brimmed hat of Oddjob. Later, as Bond is being flown to meet the President, with Pussy aboard the Air Force jet, he is confronted by Goldfinger disguised as a U. S. general. During a fight, Goldfinger is killed when he is sucked out of the plane window; Bond and Pussy parachute to safety. *Millionaires. Secret agents. Sisters. Orientals. Air pilots. Organized crime. Gambling. Cheating. Murder. Smuggling. Conspiracy. Robbery. Disguise. Parachuting. Gold. Rolls-Royce automobiles. Airplanes. Atom bomb. London. Miami. Alps. Fort Knox. James Bond.*

Note: Location scenes filmed at Fort Knox, Kentucky, and in Miami. Opened in London in Sep 1964. Copyright claimant: Danjaq, S. A.

GOLDILOCKS AND THE THREE BARES   **F6.1889**
D & R Pictures. *Dist* Dore Productions. 6 Sep **1963** [Los Angeles showing]. Sd; col (Eastman Color). 35mm. 70 min.

Prod Thomas J. Dowd, Davis Freeman. *Dir* Lewis H. Gordon. *Camera* Marvin Lester. *Mus* Paul J. Gillette. *Sd* Davis Mason.

Cast: Vickie Miles *(Alison Edwards)*, Rex Marlow *(Eddie)*, Thomas Sweetwood *(Tommy)*, Joey Maxim *(himself, former world's light heavyweight champion)*, Netta Mallina *(Myrna)*, Craig Maudslay, Jr., Judy Parsons, Mal Arnold, Toni Toomey, Maria Stinger, Delores Mooney.

Nudist film. Singer Eddie Livingston and comedian Tommy Sweetwood work at Joey Maxim's Roaring Twenties nightclub in Miami. One day while Tommy is thumbing through a nudist magazine in a drugstore and making wisecracks, an attractive blonde stalks out of the store, followed by the apologetic Eddie. Later, while Tommy is onstage repeating a routine he worked up about the nudist magazine, Joey Maxim brings the offended blonde to a table. Eddie learns that the woman is Alison Edwards, the club's new publicist. Eddie tries to elicit the reason for Alison's indignation, but Myrna, his girl friend and agent, jealously intervenes. Eddie begins to date Alison, and Tommy dates Cynthia Martin, a photographer friend of Alison's. Both men are curious as to why their new sweethearts refuse to see them on weekends; Tommy follows the women and discovers that they spend their time at a nearby nudist camp. Eddie resents Alison's subterfuge, and he publicly embarrasses her during a radio program. Cynthia and Alison invite the boys to give nudism a

try, and Eddie and Tommy accompany the women on a fun-filled weekend at the camp. *Singers. Entertainers. Nightclub owners. Publicists. Theatrical agents. Photographers. Nudism. Jealousy. Nightclubs. Nudist camps. Miami.*

Note: Filmed in Miami; working title: *Singing in the Sun.* Also known as *(Goldilocks) Three Chicks.*

(GOLDILOCKS) THREE CHICKS see **GOLDILOCKS AND THE THREE BARES**

GOLDSTEIN   **F6.1890**
Montrose Film Productions. *Dist* Altura Films International. 7 May **1965** [New York opening]. Sd; b&w. 35mm. 85 min. [See note.]

Prod-Dir-Writ Philip Kaufman, Benjamin Manaster. *Assoc Prod* Martin Tausz, Frederick Woods. *Exec Prod* Zev Braun. *Photog* Jean-Philippe Carson. *Adtl Photog* Enrico Sarsini. *Main Titl* Michael Aloisio. *Film Ed* Adolfas Mekas. *Mus* Meyer Kupferman. *Sd* Ed Webb. *Asst Dir* Joseph Holsen. *Prod Mgr* Ronald S. Klein.

Cast: Lou Gilbert *(old man)*, Ellen Madison *(Sally)*, Thomas Erhart *(sculptor)*, Benito Carruthers *(Jay)*, Charles Fischer *(Mr. Nice)*, Severn Darden *(doctor)*, Anthony Holland *(aid)*, Nelson Algren *(himself)*, Jack Burns *(truckdriver/policeman)*, Mike Turro *(guard)*, Tony T-Ram Del *(guard's friend)*, Rudi Brandau, Viola Spolin, Del Close, Robert Ruth, Fran Collins, Eddie Goldberg, Norma Nissensen, George Rembert, Rose Kaufman, George Green.

Satire. Based on an unidentified story by: Martin Buber. Sally, living in Chicago, is pregnant and seeks an abortion. At the same time, she dismisses her boyfriend, a young sculptor who begins a search through the streets of Chicago for the prophet Elijah. An old tramp emerges from the waters of Lake Michigan, and the sculptor follows him. At one point the old man gets into the back of a delivery truck with the name "Goldstein" stamped on its side, seemingly guided by an invisible driver, and throws out some electrical and household appliances. At another point the old man is chased through a sausage factory by a guard; he is rescued by the sculptor, and the guard ends up in a meatgrinder. Later, Sally is operated on by two eccentric abortionists. Meanwhile, the sculptor has lost the old man and searches the city for him. His beatnik friend Jay tries unsuccessfully to borrow money from his wealthy father; then he steals his father's credit card and escapes, leaving the sculptor alone to continue his search for the man whom he believes to be Elijah. Novelist Nelson Algren makes an appearance, and the sculptor stops to listen to him before continuing his search. He runs from the city streets out to the lake shore to find the old man. All he finds is the tramp's hat, floating on the lake's surface. *Sculptors. Prophets. Novelists. Guards. Tramps. Beatniks. Pregnancy. Abortion. Urban life. Theft. Factories. Chicago. Lake Michigan. Elijah. Chases.*

Note: Location scenes filmed in Chicago. 1964 Cannes Film Festival running time: 115 min.

GOLIAT CONTRA LOS GIGANTES see **GOLIATH AGAINST THE GIANTS**

GOLIATH AGAINST THE GIANTS (Italy/Spain)   **F6.1891**
Cineproduzioni Associate–Procusa. *Dist* Medallion Pictures. 14 Apr **1963** [New York showing]. Sd; col (Eastman Color). 35mm (Super Totalscope). 95 min.

Prod Cesare Seccia, Manuel Pérez. *Dir* Guido Malatesta. *2d Unit Dir* Jorge Grau. *Screenplay* Gianfranco Parolini, Cesare Seccia, Giovanni Simonelli, Arpad De Riso, Sergio Sollima. *Story* Cesare Seccia. *Photog* Alejandro Ulloa. *Art Dir* Ramiro Gómez, Carlo Santonocito. *Artistic Supv* Gianfranco Parolini. *Film Ed* Mario Sansoni, Edmondo Lozzi. *Mus* Carlo Innocenzi. *Sd* Giuseppe Turcio. *Cost* Vittorio Rossi.

Cast: Brad Harris *(Goliath)*, Gloria Milland *(Elea)*, Fernando Rey *(Bokan)*, Barbara Carrol *(Daina)*, José Rubio, Lina Rosales, Carmen de Lirio, Angel Aranda, Mimmo Palmara, Fernando Sancho, Ray Martino, Ignazio Dolce, Luigi Marturano, Nello Pazzafini, Manuel Arbó, Rufino Inglés, Gianfranco Gasparri, Francisco Bernar, Angel Ortíz, Luis Marco.

Action melodrama. Goliath, engaged in battle far from his home in Beirath, learns that his throne has been usurped by Bokan, the city's governor. He sails for Beirath immediately, and after surviving a storm and defeating a sea monster, Goliath rescues Elea, a beautiful maiden sent by Bokan to kill the warrior. Instead, the two fall in love, and Elea is imprisoned for treason when she returns home. After defeating an army of Amazons en route to Beirath, Goliath kills Bokan, slays the usurper's giants, and rescues Elea. *Giants. Royalty. Amazons. Treason. Ships. Sea monsters. Storms. Goliath.*

Note: Opened in Rome in May 1961 as *Goliath contro i giganti*; in Madrid in Nov 1963 as *Goliat contra los gigantes*. May also be known as *Goliath and the Giants.*

GOLIATH AND THE GIANTS see **GOLIATH AGAINST THE GIANTS**

GOLIATH AND THE SINS OF BABYLON (Italy)   **F6.1892**

Leone Film. *Dist* American International Pictures. 11 Dec **1963** [Detroit opening]. Sd; col (Technicolor). 35mm (Techniscope). 80 min.

Prod Elio Scardamaglia. *Dir* Michele Lupo. *Screenplay* Roberto Gianviti, Francesco Scardamaglia, Lionello De Felice. *Dir Photog (see note)* Guglielmo Mancori, Mario Sbrenna. *Art Dir* Pier Vittorio Marchi. *Film Ed* Alberto Gallitti. *Mus* Francesco De Masi. *Prod Mgr* Paolo Gargano. *Makeup Supv* Amato Garbini. *Hairstyles* Amalia Paoletti.

Cast (see note): Mark Forest *(Goliath)*, Eleanora Bianchi *(Regia/Chelima)*, José Greci *(Xandros)*, Giuliano Gemma *(Alceo)*, John Chevron *(Evandro)*, Erno Crisa *(Pergaso)*, Piero Lulli *(Meneos)*, Arnaldo Fabrizio *(Morakeb)*, Mimmo Palmara, Livio Lorenzon, Jacques Herlin, Paul Müller.

Action melodrama. Pergaso, tyrannical ruler of the city of Cafaus, conquers the neighboring village of Nefer and demands 24 virgins as tribute. Goliath frees one of the young women being taken for tribute and later joins with Evandro, Xandros, and others from Nefer to rescue the women. Chelima, the mysterious woman whom Xandros loves, persuades him to take part in the annual chariot race held by Pergaso, the prize being the hand of one of his daughters. Xandros is wounded by assassins sent by Pergaso, and Goliath replaces him in the race. He wins, but Meneos, captain of the tribute ship, accuses him of treachery and tries to arrest him. Goliath escapes and joins the people of Nefer, who revolt and capture the palace at Cafaus. Xandros marries Chelima, who is actually Princess Regia of Cafaus, and the two reign over the liberated Nefer, while Goliath returns to his life in the country. *Despots. Royalty. Personal identity. Revolts. Chariots. Maciste. Goliath.*

Note: Opened in Rome in Sep 1963 as *Maciste, l'eroe più grande del mondo*. According to some foreign sources, Gemma plays the role of Xandros, Greci plays Regia/Chelima, Lorenzon plays Evandro, Lulli plays Pergaso, Herlin plays Meneos, Crisa plays Morakeb, and Palmara plays Alceo. Only U. S. press material credits Sbrenna as director of photography.

GOLIATH AND THE VAMPIRES (Italy)   **F6.1893**

Ambrosiana Cinematografica. *Dist* American International Pictures. Apr **1964** [c15 Apr 1964; LP28149]. Sd; col (Technicolor). 35mm (Totalscope, see note). 91 min.

Pres by Dino De Laurentiis. A Paolo Moffa Production. *Prod* Paolo Moffa. *Exec Prod* Dino De Laurentiis. *Dir* Giacomo Gentilomo, Sergio Corbucci. *Screenplay* Sergio Corbucci, Duccio Tessari. *Photog* Alvaro Mancori. *Art Dir* Gianni Polidori. *Film Ed* Eraldo Da Roma. *Mus* Angelo Francesco Lavagnino. *Sd* Mario Amari, Fiorenzo Magli. *Asst Dir* Guido Zurli. *Cost* Vittorio Rossi.

Cast: Gordon Scott *(Goliath)*, Gianna Maria Canale *(Astra)*, Leonora Ruffo *(Julia)*, Annabella Incontrera *(Magda)*, Rocco Vitolazzi *(Ciro)*, Jacques Sernas *(Buono)*, Mario Feliciani *(Omar)*, Van Aikens *(Amahil)*, Guido Celano *(Kobrak)*, Edy Vessel, Emma Baron, Renato Terra.

Horror film. Returning to his village, Goliath finds it destroyed by a masked band which killed all but the young women, who, along with Goliath's fiancée, Julia, have been taken to be sold as slaves. Goliath follows and, aided by Buono, a chemist, who is leader of the bluemen, frees the women, but Julia isn't among them. Buono tells Goliath that the masked men's leader is a vampire who turns men into robots and tortures his enemies. Goliath is later captured by Amazon beauty Astra, who is leading the Sultan's men; Goliath is placed in a cell, to his surprise, with Julia. They are freed when the Sultan learns that Astra is secretly in league with the vampire against him. The vampire kills the Sultan. With Julia and Buono, who knows how to return the vampire's human robots to normal, Goliath captures Astra and leaves her with Julia and Buono while he goes to find the vampire. Astra escapes and warns the vampire, and Goliath is captured by robots. The vampire assumes Goliath's identity and goes to Julia and Buono to kill them with a bomb, but Goliath escapes, assisted by the repentant Astra, and arrives in time to save his friends and kill the vampire. Astra is killed by the vampire during the battle; Buono becomes the new sultan; and Julia and Goliath return home. *Royalty. Strongmen. Amazons. Robots. Chemists. Vampires. Abduction. Slavery. Torture. Perfidy. Personal identity. Feats of strength. Maciste. Goliath.*

Note: Released in Italy in 1961 as *Maciste contro il vampiro*. At least one source lists Colorscope as the widescreen process. Copyright claimant: Alta Vista Productions.

GOLIATH CONTRO I GIGANTI see **GOLIATH AGAINST THE GIANTS**

GONE ARE THE DAYS!   **F6.1894**

Hammer Film Corp. *Dist* Hammer Brothers, Trans-Lux Distributing Corp., Futurama Entertainment Corp. 23 Sep **1963** [New York opening; c9 Aug 1963; LP40397]. Sd; b&w. 35mm. 100 min. [Also 97 min.]

Pres by Hammer Brothers. *Prod-Dir* Nicholas Webster. *Screenplay* Ossie Davis. *Photog* Boris Kaufman. *2d Unit Photog* Fred Bornet. *Prod Dsgn* Kim Swados. *Film Ed* Ralph Rosenblum. *Mus* Henry Cowen. *Choral Mus* Milton Okun. *Sd* Morgan Smith, Dick Vorisek. *Asst Dir* Edward Wells. *Wardrobe* Tauhma Seid. *Makeup* Herman Buchman. *Hairstyles* Frank Rubertone.

Cast: Ruby Dee *(Lutiebelle)*, Ossie Davis *(Purlie Victorious)*, Sorrell Booke *(Captain Cotchipee)*, Godfrey Cambridge *(Gitlow)*, Hilda Haynes *(Missy)*, Alan Alda *(Charlie Cotchipee)*, Beah Richards *(Idella)*, Charles Welch *(sheriff)*, Ralph Roberts *(deputy)*.

Satire. Source: Ossie Davis, *Purlie Victorious* (New York opening: 28 Sep 1961). After a long absence, Purlie Victorious Judson, a self-ordained preacher, returns to his hometown of Cotchipee, Georgia. He is accompanied by his disciple, Lutiebelle Gussie Mae Jenkins, a kitchen maid who figures in his scheme for buying an old barn and converting it into an integrated church. In order to raise the money needed to purchase the barn, Purlie persuades Lutiebelle to pose as his cousin Bea, who is actually deceased, to collect $500 which crusty old Captain Cotchipee, owner of the local cotton plantation, is holding in trust. Purlie and Lutiebelle share the home of Purlie's sister, Missy, and his "Uncle Tom" brother-in-law, Gitlow, who takes pride in his new position as Deputy for the Colored on the plantation. Purlie's fund-raising plan nearly succeeds, but Lutiebelle accidentally reveals her true identity to Captain Cotchipee. Determined to have his church, Purlie enlists the aid of the captain's son, Charlie, and the $500 is removed from the old man's safe. Purlie pretends to his friends that he forcibly took the money after beating the captain with his own whip, but his triumph is short-lived; Captain Cotchipee arrives on the scene and announces that he has purchased the old barn himself and plans to burn it to the ground. However, he has reckoned without Charlie, who announces that he made the purchase of the deed in Purlie's name. The news is too much for the captain, and he dies--standing upright--of a stroke. Purlie gets his church, and his first service is an integrated funeral for Captain Cotchipee. *Preachers. Planters. Domestics. Racism. Negro life. Racial integration. Fraud. Impersonation. Strokes. Filial relations. Churches. Plantations. Funerals. Georgia.*

Note: Distributed by Hammer Brothers for the opening New York City engagement and through Trans-Lux Distributing Corp. for other bookings. Rereleased in 1966 as *The Man From C.O.T.T.O.N.* by Futurama Entertainment Corp. Alternative title: *Purlie Victorious.*

GONE WITH THE WIND (Reissue)   **F6.1895**

Selznick International Pictures. *Dist* Metro-Goldwyn-Mayer, Inc. 10 Oct **1967** [New York opening]. Sd (Westrex); col (see note). 35mm & 70mm (see note). 222 min.

Note: Reissued for the sixth time; originally released by M-G-M in 1939; c31 Dec 1939; LP9390. For this release, M-G-M used an optical scanning system to blow up the original 35mm, 1.33-1 ratio image to a 70mm, 2.2-1 ratio image for roadshow release. Succeeding 35mm and 70mm prints were made from this new wide screen negative. Prints are in Metrocolor on Eastman stock; the original 3-strip Technicolor matrixes could not be used owing to shrinkage. The soundtrack was re-recorded polyphonically, and the original title music was re-performed.

A GOOD DAY FOR FIGHTING see **CUSTER OF THE WEST**

THE GOOD GUYS AND THE BAD GUYS   **F6.1896**

Ronden Productions. *Dist* Warner Bros.–Seven Arts, Inc. 7 Oct **1969** [Albuquerque, New Mexico, opening; c1 Oct 1969; LP38121]. Sd; col (Technicolor). 35mm (Panavision). 90 min. *MPAA rating* M.

A Robert Goldstein Production. *Prod-Writ* Ronald M. Cohen, Dennis Shryack. *Exec Prod* Robert Goldstein. *Assoc Prod* Stan Jolley. *Dir* Burt Kennedy. *Dir Photog* Harry Stradling, Jr. *Camera Op* Marvin Gunter. *Camera Asst* Richard Meinardus, Ralph Spence. *Helicopter Camera* Lamar Boren. *Set Decor* Ralph S. Hurst. *Prod Dsgn* Stan Jolley. *Film Ed* Howard Deane, Otho Lovering. *Mus* William Lava. *Mus Supv* Sonny Burke. *Song:* "The Ballad of Marshal Flagg" William Lava, Ned Washington. *Sung by* Glenn Yarbrough. *Sd Mix* Al Overton, Jr. *Sd Rec* Brandon Kellogg. *Boom Op* William Thompson. *Asst Dir* Richard C. Bennett, Les Gorall, Monty Masters. *Prod Mgr* William R. Finnegan. *Script Supv* Marge Mullen. *Prod Asst* Christopher Mitchum. *Location Mgr* Harry Zubrinsky. *Cost Dsgn* Yvonne Wood. *Men's Wardrobe* Robert Richards, Dominic Di Bona, Lyle Field. *Women's Wardrobe* Patricia Norris, Audrey Newell. *Makeup Supv* Gordon Bau. *Makeup Perc* Westmore. *Supv Hairstylist* Jean Burt Reilly. *Sp Eff* Horace L. Hulburd. *Gaffer* Glen Bird. *Key Grip* Louis Maschmeyer. *Prop Master* Red Turner. *Still Photog* Don Christie.

Cast: Robert Mitchum *(Marshal Jim Flagg)*, George Kennedy *(John McKay)*, David Carradine *(Waco)*, Tina Louise *(Carmel)*, Douglas Fowley *(Grundy)*, Martin Balsam *(Mayor Wilker)*, Lois Nettleton *(Mary)*, John Davis Chandler *(Deuce)*, John Carradine *(Ticker)*, Marie Windsor *(Polly)*, Dick Peabody *(Boyle)*, Kathleen Freeman *(Mrs. Stone)*, Jimmy Murphy *(Buckshot)*, Garrett Lewis *(Hawkins)*, Nick Dennis *(engineer)*, David Cargo *(newspaperman)*, Buddy Hackett.

Western comedy. Learning that his longtime antagonist, John McKay, is in the town of Progress, middle-aged Marshal Jim Flagg warns Mayor Wilker that robbery is imminent. The mayor, however, concerned with the alarm's effect on his political future, retires the marshal, promoting in his stead the incompetent deputy Boyle. Flagg conducts his own investigation; he locates the gang, but discovers that McKay is just a nominal member of the youthful band. Although Flagg is captured, the sentimental McKay refuses to allow him to be killed. Left alone by the gang, the old associates brawl. When the exhausted pair is transported to Progress by the eccentric hermit Grundy, Mayor Wilker refuses to admit McKay to the jail. Undaunted, Flagg installs the outlaw in a boardinghouse run by his lady friend, the widow Mary. Arriving in Progress, the youthful bandits promptly slay Grundy. Realizing that their object is the train, Flagg alerts the mayor. Assisted by McKay and the townspeople, he routs the gunmen. Filled with gratitude, Wilker offers Flagg his old job, but the gunfighter declines. *United States marshals. Outlaws. Mayors. Gunfighters. Hermits. Frontier and pioneer life. Friendship. Middle age. Retirement. Train robberies. Jails. Boardinghouses. Chases.*

Note: Location shooting in Chama, New Mexico.

A GOOD MAN'S HARD TO FIND *see* **A HARD MAN'S GOOD TO FIND**

GOOD MORNING *see* **OHAYO**

GOOD MORNING, AND GOODBYE!   **F6.1897**
Eve Productions. 19 Feb **1968** [New York opening; c1 Nov 1967; LP34918]. Sd; col (Eastman Color). 35mm. 80 min.

Prod-Dir-Writ Russ Meyer. *Assoc Prod* Eve Meyer. *Screenplay* John E. Moran. *Photog* Russ Meyer. *Film Ed* Russ Meyer, Richard Brummer. *Mus* Igo Kantor. *Sd* Richard Brummer, Jack Moran. *Asst Dir* George Costello. *Prod Mgr* Fred Owens.

Cast: Alaina Capri *(Angel)*, Stuart Lancaster *(Burt)*, Pat Wright *(Stone)*, Haji *(The Catalyst)*, Karen Ciral *(Lana)*, Don Johnson *(Ray)*, Tom Howland *(Herb)*, Megan Timothy *(Lottie)*, Toby Adler *(Betty)*, Sylvia Tedemar *(go-go dancer)*, Carol Peters *(nude)*.

Melodrama. Because of his age, Burt, a wealthy farmer, is unable to satisfy the prodigious sexual needs of his wife, Angel. The flamboyant affair Angel is having with Stone, a young construction worker—not to mention her wanton behavior with other men—embitters Burt and humiliates Lana, his 17-year-old daughter by a previous marriage. Lana resolves to gain revenge on her easily-cowed father by flinging herself on the good-looking Ray. But, because Ray is also intrigued by the voluptuous Angel, Lana ends up in the arms of the sex-hungry Stone. Then Burt meets a strange forest sorceress, who revives his long-dormant sexual drive. After he demonstrates his rejuvenated state to Angel, she promptly agrees to end her extramarital activities. Lana, who has been humiliated by Stone's brutal assault, comes home a reformed girl and again takes up with Ray. Stone, however, pays for his monomaniacal sexuality by being brutally beaten by the cuckolded husband of one of his earlier conquests. *Farmers. Construction workers. Sorcerers. Cuckolds. Impotence. Infidelity. Adolescence. Promiscuity.*

GOOD NEIGHBOR SAM   **F6.1898**
David Swift Productions. *Dist* Columbia Pictures. 22 Jul **1964** [New York opening; c1 Jun 1964; LP28085]. Sd (RCA); col (Eastman Color by Pathé). 35mm. 130 min.

A David Swift Production. *Prod-Dir* David Swift. *Assoc Prod* Marvin Miller. *Screenplay* Jim Fritzell, Everett Greenbaum, David Swift. *Dir Photog* Burnett Guffey. *Set Decor* Ray Moyer. *Prod Dsgn* Dale Hennesy. *Film Ed* Charles Nelson. *Mus* DeVol. *Choreog* Miriam Nelson. *Sd Supv* Charles J. Rice. *Sd* James Z. Flaster. *Asst Dir* R. Robert Rosenbaum. *Cost Dsgn* Micheline & Jacqueline. *Makeup Supv* Ben Lane. *Miss Schneider's Hairstyles* Frederic Jones.

Cast: Jack Lemmon *(Sam Bissell)*, Romy Schneider *(Janet Lagerlof)*, Dorothy Provine *(Minerva Bissell)*, Michael Connors *(Howard Ebbets)*, Edward Andrews *(Mr. Burke)*, Louis Nye *(Reinhold Shiffner)*, Robert Q. Lewis *(Earl)*, Joyce Jameson *(girl)*, Anne Seymour *(Irene)*, Charles Lane *(Jack Bailey)*, Linda Watkins *(Edna)*, Peter Hobbs *(Phil Reisner)*, Tris Coffin *(Sonny Blatchford)*, Neil Hamilton *(Larry Boling)*, Riza Royce *(Miss Halverson)*, William Forrest *(Millard Mellner)*, The Hi-Lo's *(themselves)*, Edward G. Robinson *(Simon Nurdlinger)*.

Comedy. Source: Jack Finney, *Good Neighbor Sam* (New York, 1963). Sam Bissell, a minor account executive in a San Francisco advertising agency, lives an uncomplicated suburban life with his wife, Min, and their two daughters. His wholesome approach gains him the company's top account, Nurdlinger Eggs, but his troubles begin when Janet Lagerof, Min's best friend, rents the house next door. Recently separated from her husband Howard, Janet learns that she stands to inherit $15 million from her grandfather if he believes that she is happily married. Two cousins who are second in line for the money arrive to visit, and Janet introduces Sam as her husband. The suspicious cousins hire Shiffner, a detective, to watch Janet. Sam is forced to sneak back and forth between his house and Janet's, where supposedly he is sleeping. Janet and Sam are secretly photographed together by an advertising man one day, and Janet is introduced to Mr. Nurdlinger as Sam's wife. Later, Howard arrives to attempt a reconciliation with Janet, but he is forced to pose as Min's husband. Although Howard loves Janet, she believes that he is only after her inheritance. Jealousy soon provokes friction among the four. The will is finally settled in Janet's favor, but the harried Sam has failed to check the picture of the couple to be used on the Nurdlinger billboards. The picture, a pose of himself with Janet, is captioned "Mr. and Mrs. Sam Bissell." Because Janet will lose the inheritance if she is recognized on the billboards, she and Sam stay up all night painting over their pictures on the advertisement. Min later sees a message for her that Sam has painted on one of the billboards, and they are reconciled, as are Janet and Howard; and Janet gets her inheritance. *Advertising executives. Cousins. Detectives. Neighbors. Advertising. Marriage. Suburban life. Impersonation. Greed. Jealousy. Inheritance. Billboards. San Francisco.*

Note: Filmed partly in San Francisco.

THE GOOD SOLDIER SCHWEIK (West Germany)   **F6.1899**
CCC–Filmkunst–Wienfilm. *Dist* Lionex Films. 20 Aug **1963** [New York opening]. Sd; b&w. 35mm. 98 min.

Prod Karl Ehrlich. *Exec Prod* Artur Brauner. *Dir* Axel von Ambesser. *Screenplay* Hans Jacoby. *Photog* Richard Angst. *Camera Op* Alfred Westphal. *Asst Op* Richard Reuven Rimmel. *Art Dir* Werner Schlichting, Isabella Schlichting. *Film Ed* Angelika Appel, Hermann Haller. *Mus* Bernhard Eichhorn. *Sd* Hans Riedl, Zeleniy Anton. *Asst Dir* Karl Stanzl. *Prod Supv* Wolf Brauner. *Prod Mgr* Leo Höger, Fritz Andraschko, Willy Egger. *Cost* Leo Bei. *English Subtitl* Herman G. Weinberg.

Cast: Heinz Rühmann *(Schweik)*, Ernst Stankowski *(Lieutenant Lucas)*, Ursula Borsodi *(Kathi)*, Senta Berger *(Gretl)*, Erika von Thellmann *(baroness)*, Franz Muxeneder *(Woditschka)*, Hugo Gottschlich *(Sergeant Flanderka)*, Edith Elmay, Fritz Imhoff, Franz Böheim, Karl Fochler, Hans Thimig, Erika Frey, Michael Jansich, Egon von Jordan, Lazlo Szemere, Fritz Muliar, Alma Seidler, Otto Schmöle, Jane Tilden.

Satire. Source: Jaroslav Hašek, *Osudy dobrého vojáka Švejka za světové války* (Prague, 1921–23). Schweik, an unassuming man who sells small dogs, is drafted into the German Army during World War I. Patriotic, well-intentioned, and obedient to his superiors, he manages to muddle through many scrapes, including capture by his own army and near-execution by a firing squad. *Military draft. Military life. World War I. Germany—Army.*

Note: Released in West Germany in 1960 as *Der brave Soldat Schwejk*; running time: 96 min.

THE GOOD, THE BAD AND THE BEAUTIFUL   **F6.1900**
Charles Abrams Productions. *Dist* Abrams & Parisi, Inc. Jan **1970** [periodical notice]. Sd; b&w. 35mm. 80 min.

Pres by Charles Abrams. *Prod* Charles Abrams. *Dir-Writ* Robert Canton.

Cast: Kate Wilson, Elizabeth Aubert.

Drama. A celebrated politician, whose campaign for the U. S. Senate becomes jeopardized when his wife is blackmailed by a former lover, is troubled further by his inability to resist sadomasochistic relations with his maid, who has rejected the love of an alcoholic chauffeur in order to continue whipping her employer into sexual ecstasy. *Politicians. Housemaids. Political campaigns. Blackmail. Sadomasochism. Flagellation.*

Note: May also be known as *The Candidate*.

THE GOOD, THE BAD, AND THE UGLY (Italy)   **F6.1901**
P. E. A. *Dist* United Artists. Dec **1967** [New York opening: 24 Jan 1968; c23 Dec 1966; LF21]. Sd; col (Technicolor). 35mm (Techniscope). 161 min.

Prod Alberto Grimaldi. *Dir* Sergio Leone. *Screenplay* Luciano Vincenzoni, Sergio Leone. *English Adapt* Mickey Knox. *Story* Age & Scarpelli, Sergio Leone, Luciano Vincenzoni. *Photog* Tonino Delli Colli. *Art Dir* Carlo Simi. *Titl* Ardani. *Film Ed* Nino Baragli, Eugenio Alabiso. *Mus* Ennio Morricone. *Cond* Bruno Nicolai. *Asst Dir* Giancarlo Santi. *Prod Mgr* Fernando Cinquini. *Prod Supv* Carlo Bartolini, Federico Tofi. *Cost* Carlo Simi. *Sp Eff* Eros Bacciucchi.

Cast: Clint Eastwood *(Joe)*, Eli Wallach *(Tuco)*, Lee Van Cleef *(Setenza)*, Aldo Giuffrè, Chelo Alonso, Mario Brega, Luigi Pistilli, Rada Rassimov, Enzo Petito, Claudio Scarchilli, Al Mulock, Livio Lorenzon, Antonio Casale, Sandro Scarchilli, Angelo Novi, Benito Stefanelli, Silvana Bacci, Antonio Casas, Aldo Sambrell.

Western melodrama. In the Southwest during the Civil War, a cashbox containing $200,000 is stolen and hidden in an unmarked grave. Nearby, a mysterious stranger called Joe has formed an uneasy alliance with Tuco, a Mexican outlaw. To make money, Joe turns Tuco over to a series of sheriffs, collects the bounty money, then rescues the outlaw from a hanging, and the two of them share the reward. Their scheme nearly fails because of a poor shot by Joe, and Tuco decides to betray his companion. Although Joe kills the three men commissioned by Tuco to kill him, he is nonetheless captured by Tuco and dragged through the dry heat of the desert to near death. When Joe informs Tuco that he has learned the location of the $200,000, Tuco immediately gives him water and shade before they embark on a search for the cashbox. Meanwhile, Setenza, a sadistic criminal, is conducting his own search for the cashbox and has joined the Union Army to find the soldier who knows where the money is buried. Dressed in Confederate uniforms, Tuco and Joe are captured by the Union Army and brought before Setenza. Tuco, claiming to know the location of the cashbox, is brutally beaten by Setenza until he reveals that the money is hidden in a graveyard. The three men then separately head for the graveyard, each trying to dupe the others into revealing the exact gravestone under which the cashbox is buried. In a final gunfight, Joe shoots Setenza but spares Tuco and leaves him his share of the money—all the bandit has to do for the gold coins is free himself from the rope hanging around his neck. Before he rides off, however, Joe shoots through the rope, and Tuco is left in the middle of nowhere, wealthy but without a horse. *Strangers. Mexicans. Outlaws. Hired killers. Sheriffs. Soldiers. Bounty hunters. Robbery. Lynching. Torture. Disguise. Perfidy. Greed. Deserts. Cemeteries. Gold. United States— History—Civil War.*

Note: Produced in Spain. Released in Italy in 1966 as *Il buono, il brutto, il cattivo;* running time: 180 min. This is the third in a series of three films directed by Sergio Leone and starring Clint Eastwood as "The Man With No Name."

A GOOD TIME WITH A BAD GIRL   F6.1902

Barry Mahon Productions. *Dist* Sack Amusement Enterprises. 17 Apr **1967** [San Francisco showing]. Sd; b&w. 35mm. 61 min.

A Barry Mahon Production.

Drama. Mr. Cabot, an East Coast millionaire, is forced down in Las Vegas by bad weather while flying his private jet. A man of conservative tastes, he avoids the many gaming casinos and wild bars. The only room available in his favorite motel is a plush suite with its own private swimming pool. He feels uncomfortable alone in such luxury, and he tries to convince his wife to join him for a second honeymoon. Occupied with a garden club exhibit, she refuses. Lonely and disappointed, he meets Sue, an 18-year-old nymphomaniac who has come to Las Vegas to find excitement. They make the round of nightclubs, and also of hotel rooms. Together they bathe nude in the private swimming pool, and take part in an orgy. *Millionaires. Marriage. Infidelity. Nymphomania. Orgies. Motels. Nightclubs. Las Vegas.*

Note: Also known as *A Good Time, a Bad Girl.*

GOOD TIMES   F6.1903

Motion Pictures International. *Dist* Columbia Pictures. 11 Apr **1967** [Austin, Texas, opening; c1 May 1967; LP34412]. Sd (Westrex); col (DeLuxe). 35mm. 91 min.

A Steve Broidy Production. *Prod* Lindsley Parsons. *Exec Prod* Steve Broidy. *Dir* William Friedkin. *Screenplay* Tony Barrett. *Story* Nicholas Hyams. *Dir Photog* Robert Wyckoff. *Camera* Arnold Rich. *Sp Cons on Mus Numbers* Wilmer Butler. *Art Dir* Hal Pereira, Arthur Lonergan. *Set Decor* Arthur Krams. *Film Ed* Melvin Shapiro. *Asst Film Ed* Richard Wahrman. *Neg Cutter* Helen Wright. *Mus Comp & Cond* Sonny Bono. *Mus Arr* Harold R. Battiste, Jr. *Songs:* "I Got You Babe," "It's the Little Things," "Good Times," "Trust Me," "Don't Talk to Strangers," "I'm Gonna Love You," "Just a Name" *comp & cond* Sonny Bono. *Sung by* Sonny & Cher. *Choreog* Andre Tayir. *Sd Rec* Harold Lewis. *Sd Eff* Del Harris, Carlo Lodato, Bud Parman. *Sd* Ray Cossar, Richard Spelker. *Asst Dir* David Salven, James Benjamin. *Prod Mgr* Arthur Broidy. *Script Supv* Marvin Weldon. *Cost* Leah Rhodes. *Wardrobe* Forrest T. Butler. *Makeup* Ed Butterworth. *Hairstyles* Hedvig Mjorud. *Sp Eff* Bob Peterson. *Proc Photog* Farciot Edouart. *Still Photog* George Hurrell. *Animals Trained by* Ralph Helfer, Kenneth Lee.

Cast: Sonny & Cher *(themselves),* George Sanders *(Mr. Mordicus),* Norman Alden *(Warren),* Larry Duran *(Smith),* Kelly Thordsen *(tough hombre),* Lennie Weinrib *(Leslie Garth),* Peter Robbins *(Brandon),* Edy Williams, China Lee, Diane Haggerty *(Mordicus' girls),* James Flavin *(lieutenant),* Phil Arnold *(Solly),* Hank Worden *(Kid),* Morris Buchanan *(proprietor),* Charles Smith *(telegrapher),* John Cliff *(gangster),* Herk Reardon, Bruce Tegner *(wrestlers),* Richard Collier *(peddler),* Joe Devlin *(bartender),* Mike Kopach *(deputy),* Howard Wright *(old timer).*

Comedy with music. Sonny and Cher are happily married rock and roll singing stars with millions of fans. Despite their success, Sonny longs to achieve additional fame and fortune in movies, while Cher is content with their current popularity. Film tycoon Mr. Mordicus offers to launch their career in pictures, and Sonny lapses into a series of daydreams in which he envisions himself and Cher playing various stereotyped Hollywood roles. First, he is a gun-slinging Western sheriff, and Cher is a dancehall queen. Next, he becomes Tarzan living in a treehouse with Cher as his adoring mate. Finally, he conjures up a vision

of himself as a tight-lipped private investigator, with Cher playing both a moll and a sultry singer. Sonny realizes that in all three fantasies, Mr. Mordicus appeared as a ridiculous-looking villain. Consequently, when Mordicus presents him with a stale old script, Sonny ignores the producer's threats and refuses the offer. Although he has not abandoned the idea of becoming a film star, Sonny decides to concentrate on his singing career with Cher. *Singers. Motion picture producers. Sheriffs. Dancehall girls. Detectives. Molls. Actors. Fame. Ambition. Rock and roll. Motion pictures. Hollywood. Fantasy. Tarzan.*

Note: Jungle sequences photographed at Africa, U.S.A., Inc.

GOOD TIMES, WONDERFUL TIMES (United States/Great Britain)
F6.1904

Rogosin Film Productions. *Dist* Rogosin Films, Impact Films. 18 Jul **1966** [New York opening]. Sd; b&w. 35mm. 70 min.

Prod-Dir Lionel Rogosin. *Assoc Prod* James T. Vaughn. *Screenplay* Lionel Rogosin, James T. Vaughn, Tadeusz Makarczynski. *Photog* Manny Wynn. *Film Ed* Brian Smedley-Aston. *Mus* Chatur Lal, Ram Narayan, Ian Cameron. *Sd* Stephen Dalby, John S. Smith. *Prod Mgr* Roy Millichip. *Ed & Sd Cons* Tadeusz Makarczynski.

Documentary drama. At a cocktail party in London, the guests discuss sex, religion, politics, and war. The conversation provides an opportunity for the introduction of flashbacks to the Warsaw ghetto, Nazi concentration camps, the training of the Hitler Youth, the siege of Stalingrad, and other World War II combat situations. *Nazism. Concentration camps. World War II. London. Warsaw. Hiroshima. Stalingrad. Hitler Youth.*

Note: Sources conflict in determining country of origin.

GOODBYE AGAIN (United States/France)   F6.1905

Argus Productions. *Dist* United Artists. 29 Jun **1961** [New York opening; c29 Jun 1961; LP20644]. Sd; b&w. 35mm. 120 min.

Pres by Mercury Films. An Anatole Litvak Production. *Prod-Dir* Anatole Litvak. *2d Unit Dir* André Smagghe. *Screenplay* Samuel Taylor. *Photog* Armand Thirard. *Art Dir* Alexandre Trauner. *Film Ed* Bert Bates. *Mus* Georges Auric. *Lyr* Dory Langdon. *Titl Song Sung by* Diahann Carroll. *Theme Mus Based on First and Third Symphonies* Johannes Brahms. *Sd* Jacques Carrère. *Asst Dir* Paul Feyder. *Prod Mgr* Julien Derode. *Miss Bergman's Gowns* Christian Dior. *Makeup* John O'Gorman, Georges Bouban. *Hairstyles* Joan Johnstone, Marc Blanchard.

Cast: Ingrid Bergman *(Paula Tessier),* Yves Montand *(Roger Demarest),* Anthony Perkins *(Philip Van der Besh),* Jessie Royce Landis *(Mrs. Van der Besh),* Jackie Lane *(Maisie I),* Pierre Dux *(Maitre Fleury),* Jean Clarke *(Maisie II),* Peter Bull *(client),* Michèle Mercier *(Maisie III),* Uta Taeger *(Gaby),* André Randall *(Monsieur Steiner),* David Horne *(British lawyer),* Lee Patrick *(Madame Fleury),* Colin Mann *(assistant lawyer),* Diahann Carroll *(singer),* Annie Duperoux *(Madeline Fleury),* Raymond Gérôme *(Jimmy),* Jean Hebey *(Monsieur Cherel),* Michel Garland *(young man in club),* Paul Uny *(waiter),* Alison Leggatt *(Alice).*

Romantic drama. Source: Françoise Sagan, *Aimez-vous Brahms?* (Paris, 1959). For 5 years Paula Tessier, a 40-year-old Parisian interior decorator, has been the mistress of Roger Demarest, a philandering business executive. Though well aware of his numerous affairs with other women (all of whom he calls Maisie), Paula remains faithful, hoping that eventually Roger will marry her. Then one day she meets Philip Van der Besh, the 25-year-old son of one of her wealthy American clients. When the young man becomes hopelessly enamored of her, Paula is at first embarrassed, but gradually she begins to respond to his love. Consequently, when Roger leaves on a business trip and refuses to take her along, Paula gives in to Philip's pleas and allows him to move into her apartment. Roger returns and reacts to the affair with anger, rather than show how deeply he has been hurt. He goes off with one woman after another, but he is unable to forget Paula and finally asks her to marry him. Delighted, Paula tries to break the news to Philip as gently as possible, but he runs tearfully from the apartment. Though Paula has at last become a wife, Roger continues his bachelor social life. *Businessmen. Philanderers. Interior decorators. Mistresses. Americans in foreign countries. Jealousy. Marriage. Infidelity. Paris.*

Note: Location scenes filmed in Paris. Opened in Paris in May 1961 as *Aimez-vous Brahms?* Only British sources credit France with co-production status.

GOODBYE CHARLIE   F6.1906

Venice Productions. *Dist* Twentieth Century-Fox Film Corp. 18 Nov **1964** [New York opening; c18 Nov 1964; LP29335]. Sd (Westrex); col (De Luxe). 35mm (CinemaScope). 117 min.

Prod David Weisbart. *Dir* Vincente Minnelli. *Screenplay* Harry Kurnitz. *Dir Photog* Milton Krasner. *Camera Op* Alfred Lebovitz. *Asst Camera* Al Baerthlein. *Art Dir* Jack Martin Smith, Richard Day. *Set Decor* Walter M. Scott, Keogh Gleason. *Film Ed* John W. Holmes. *Mus* Andre Previn. *Orch* Al

Woodbury. *Songs:* "Goodbye Charlie," "Seven at Once" Andre Previn, Dory Langdon. *Sung by* Jerry Wallace. *Sd* W. D. Flick, Elmer Raguse. *Rec* Bill Wells. *Boom Op* Richard Overton. *Asst Dir* David Hall, Jack Stubbs, George Light. *Script Supv* Molly Kent. *Location Mgr* Lew Tate. *Cost Dsgn* Helen Rose. *Wardrobe* Truman Eli, Mike Tierney. *Women's Wardrobe* Willie Mae Neal, Lurine Lister. *Makeup* Ben Nye. *Hairstyles for Miss Reynolds* Sydney Guilaroff. *Supv Hairstylist* Margaret Donovan. *Sp Photog Eff* L. B. Abbott, Emil Kosa, Jr. *Still Photog* Frank Powolny. *Key Grip* Jack Richter. *Gaffer* Ken Lang. *Prop* Dick Neblett, Jerome Graham.

Cast: Tony Curtis *(George Tracy)*, Debbie Reynolds *(Charlie, a female)*, Pat Boone *(Bruce Minton)*, Walter Matthau *(Sir Leopold Sartori)*, Joanna Barnes *(Janie)*, Ellen McRae *(Franny)*, Laura Devon *(Rusty)*, Martin Gabel *(Morton Craft)*, Roger C. Carmel *(inspector)*, Harry Madden *(Charlie Sorel, a male)*, Myrna Hansen *(starlet)*, Michael Romanoff *(patron)*, Michael Jackson *(himself)*, Antony Eustrel *(butler)*, Donna Michelle *(guest on yacht)*.

Comedy. Source: George Axelrod, *Goodbye Charlie* (New York opening: 16 Dec 1959). During a yachting party given by Hungarian film producer Sir Leopold Sartori, Sir Leopold finds his wife with screenwriter Charlie Sorel. Sartori shoots Sorel, whose body falls into the sea and is never recovered. When George Tracy, Charlie's best friend and executor of his will, is at Charlie's seaside home straightening out the dead man's affairs, a blonde woman appears and tells him that she is Charlie reincarnated. Charlie begins to enjoy being a woman with a man's mind. She flirts with millionaire Bruce Minton and tries to blackmail some of the wealthy married women with whom the male Charlie had been having affairs. George is appalled by Charlie's behavior but attracted to her at the same time. Sir Leopold is also attracted to Charlie, and when his wife finds Charlie in his embrace, she shoots Charlie, who once again falls into the sea. George is preparing to hush up the affair when an attractive young woman appears with a large dog, which turns out to be the third incarnation of Charlie. George and the woman are immediately attracted to each other, while the canine Charlie finds pleasure with a bottle of vodka. *Motion picture producers. Hungarians. Motion picture scriptwriters. Millionaires. Infidelity. Murder. Reincarnation. Jealousy. Blackmail. Yachts. Dogs.*

Note: Actress Ellen McRae is also known as Ellen Burstyn.

GOODBYE, COLUMBUS   **F6.1907**
Willow Tree Productions. *Dist* Paramount Pictures. 3 Apr **1969** [New York opening; c19 Mar 1969; LP36734]. Sd; col (Technicolor). 35mm. 105 min. *MPAA rating* R.

A Stanley R. Jaffe Production. *Prod* Stanley R. Jaffe. *Assoc Prod* Tony Lamarca. *Dir* Larry Peerce. *Screenplay* Arnold Schulman. *Photog* Gerald Hirschfeld. *Camera* Enrique Bravo. *Art Dir* Manny Gerard. *Film Ed* Ralph Rosenblum. *Mus* Charles Fox. *Songs:* "Goodbye, Columbus," "So Kind to You," "It's Got To Be Real" *comp & sung by* The Association. *Sd* Jack C. Jacobsen, Charles Grenzbach. *Asst Dir* Steve Barnett. *Wardrobe Dsgn* Gene Coffin. *Makeup* Andy Cianella.

Cast: Richard Benjamin *(Neil)*, Ali MacGraw *(Brenda)*, Jack Klugman *(Mr. Patimkin)*, Nan Martin *(Mrs. Patimkin)*, Michael Meyers *(Ron)*, Lori Shelle *(Julie)*, Royce Wallace *(Carlotta)*, Sylvie Straus *(Aunt Gladys)*, Kay Cummings *(Doris)*, Michael Nurie *(Don Farber)*, Betty Greyson *(Aunt Molly)*, Monroe Arnold *(Uncle Leo)*, Elaine Swain *(Sarah Ehrlich)*, Richard Wexler *(busboy)*, Rubin Schafer *(Uncle Max)*, Jacqueline Smith *(model)*, Bill Derringer *(John McKee)*, Mari Gorman *(Simp)*, Gail Ommerle *(Harriet)*, Jan Peerce, Max Peerce, Anthony McGowan, Chris Schenkel, David Benedict, Ray Baumel, Delos Smith.

Comedy-drama. Source: Philip Roth, "Goodbye, Columbus," in *Goodbye, Columbus, and Five Short Stories* (Boston, 1959). Recently discharged from the Army, and with no immediate plans for his future, college dropout Neil Klugman has moved into his Aunt Gladys' Bronx apartment and taken a job in the local library. Having been invited by his cousin Doris to spend a day at the country club to which she belongs, Neil is attracted to a vacationing Radcliffe student, Brenda Patimkin, the daughter of a nouveau riche Jewish businessman. Despite his disdain for Brenda's affluent Westchester County way of life, Neil determinedly starts dating her. Mrs. Patimkin becomes concerned about Neil's lack of ambition and concludes that he is unworthy of her daughter, but Mr. Patimkin assures his wife that Brenda will soon tire of the romance. Instead, as her summer vacation nears its end, Brenda invites Neil to spend his 2-week vacation at her home, and each night when the rest of the family is asleep Neil and Brenda make love in her room. Neil discovers that Brenda is not taking birth control pills because they make her sick, and he insists that she get fitted for a diaphragm. On the night before Brenda's return to school, her brother Ron marries his girl friend, whom he met while he was an Ohio State basketball star in Columbus. At the lavish wedding reception, a somewhat inebriated Mr. Patimkin tells Brenda how much he loves her and how much faith he has in her strong moral convictions. Once back at Radcliffe, Brenda writes to Neil and asks him to join her in Boston for a long weekend. In the

sleazy hotel room where they check in as husband and wife, Brenda tells Neil that her mother found the diaphragm in her room, shows him reproachful letters from her parents, and tells him that she can't invite him to her home again. Concluding that Brenda's guilt feelings about their affair subconsciously led her to leave the diaphragm where her mother would inevitably find it, Neil accuses Brenda of posing as someone intellectually and morally free while, in reality, she is essentially the model Jewish daughter her parents want. Disillusioned, and with nothing left to say, Neil picks up his suitcase and walks out into the street. *Jews. Nouveaux riches. Veterans. Students. Family life. Guilt. Drunkenness. Disillusionment. Birth control. Weddings. Country clubs. Hotels. Libraries. New York City. New York City—Bronx. Westchester County (New York). Radcliffe College. Ohio State University.*

Note: Location scenes filmed in New York City and nearby Westchester County.

GOODBYE GEMINI (Great Britain)   **F6.1908**
Josef Shaftel Productions. *Dist* Cinerama Releasing Corp. 23 Sep **1970** [New York opening; c6 Aug 1970; LP38515]. Sd; col (Eastman Color). 35mm. 91 min. *MPAA rating* R.

Prod Peter Snell. *Exec Prod* Josef Shaftel. *Assoc Prod* Bill Hill. *Dir* Alan Gibson. *Screenplay* Edmund Ward. *Dir Photog* Geoffrey Unsworth. *Camera Op* Peter MacDonald, Don Sharpe. *Art Dir* Fred Carter. *Set Dresser* Bryan Graves. *Prod Dsgn* Wilfred Shingleton. *Main Titl* General Screen Services. *Film Ed* Ernest Hosler. *Assembly Ed* Chris German. *Mus* Christopher Gunning. *Mus Dir* Marcus Dods. *Song:* "Tell the World We're Not In" Dennis King, Don Black. *Sung by* The Peddlers. *Songs:* "Nothing's Good and Nothing's Free," "Forget About the Day" Christopher Gunning, Peter Lee Stirling. *Sung by* Peter Lee Stirling. *Titl Song* Rick Jones, J. Alexander Ryan. *Sung by* Jackie Lee. *Sd Rec* Leslie Hammond. *Sd Ed* Don Sharpe. *Sd Re-rec* Gerry Humphreys. *Asst Dir* Anthony Waye. *Asst to the Exec Prod* Derek Horne. *Prod Mgr* Jack Causey. *Location Mgr* Jim Brennan. *Cont* Marjorie Lavelly. *Cost Dsgn* Sandy Moss. *Wardrobe Supv* Betty Adamson. *Makeup* Harry Frampton, Peter Frampton. *Hairdresser* Pat McDermott. *Casting* Irene Lamb. *Constr Mgr* Albert Blackshaw.

Cast: Judy Geeson *(Jacki)*, Martin Potter *(Julian)*, Michael Redgrave *(James Harrington-Smith)*, Alexis Kanner *(Clive Landseer)*, Mike Pratt *(Rod Barstowe)*, Marian Diamond *(Denise Pryce-Fletcher)*, Freddie Jones *(David Curry)*, Peter Jeffrey *(Detective Inspector Kingsley)*, Terry Scully *(Nigel Garfield)*, Daphne Heard *(Mrs. McLaren)*, Laurence Hardy *(minister)*, Joseph Furst *(Georgiu)*, Brian Wilde *(taxi driver)*, Ricky Renee *(Myra)*, Barry Scott *(Audrey)*, Hilda Barry *(stallholder)*, Jack Connell *(barman)*.

Melodrama. Source: Jenni Hall, *Ask Agamemnon* (London, 1964). Jacki and Julian, 20-year old twins who have been ignored by their parents, live alone in a house in London and share a very close attachment for each other. Their relationship is disturbed when they are invited to a party on a houseboat where a man named Clive pays a great deal of attention to Jacki. Julian, jealous of Clive, rejects Denise, a young woman thrust upon him as a substitute for his sister by James Harrington-Smith, a Member of Parliament. That night when Julian gets drunk, Clive escorts him to a homosexual orgy, takes photographs of him, and several days later tries to blackmail him. In desperation, Julian tricks Jacki into being an accomplice to Clive's murder. After the brutal murder, Jacki wanders aimlessly through London, suffering from shock and amnesia. The next day she finds Julian hiding from the police at the hotel where the orgy took place. She accepts his invitation to go to France, but he becomes suspicious and strangles her; he then holds her body and turns on a gas jet, waiting to die with her. *Twins. Brother-sister relationship. Incest. Jealousy. Drunkenness. Male homosexuality. Orgies. Blackmail. Perfidy. Murder. Amnesia. Suicide. Houseboats. Photographs. London. Great Britain—Parliament.*

Note: Opened in London in Aug 1970; running time: 89 min.

GOODBYE IN THE MIRROR   **F6.1909**
Bobina Productions. *Dist* Film-Makers' Cooperative, Bobina Productions. 27 May **1965** [New York opening]. Sd; b&w. 35mm & 16mm. 80 min.

Prod-Dir-Writ Storm De Hirsch. *Assoc Dir* Louis Brigante. *Dir Photog* Giorgio Turi. *Ed* Storm De Hirsch, Louis Brigante. *Mus* Norman Blagman, Jeffrey Menkes. *Italian Songs Arr & Sung by* Pola Chapelle. *Harpsichord* Steward Robb. *Sd Tech* Harlan Frost. *Tech Asst* Nathan Malkin.

Cast: Rosa Pradell *(Maria)*, Franco Volpi *(Marco)*, Diane Stainton *(Berenice)*, Barbara Apostal *(Ingrid)*, Charlotte Bradley *(Sarah)*, Federico Brook *(Federico)*, Carlo De Sanctis, Franco Morano, Giovanni Calluci, Aldo Bontempo, Angela Starone, Gino Pirelli.

Drama. Maria, a young American living and working in Rome, shares an apartment with Berenice, a young Englishwoman who aspires to a film career, and Ingrid, an introspective Swede studying voice. Maria and Berenice give private English lessons as a source of income and in order to meet Italian men; and Maria develops an intimate romance with Marco, one of the students. While Maria pursues her fascination with the surface of Roman life, Marco attempts to introduce her to life as it really is among his people. Though she continues to seek other sexual conquests, Maria strives to maintain her relationship with Marco. She creates a jealous scene with Berenice in Marco's presence when she discovers them talking together, and when she returns late one night to find that Berenice has been assaulted by one of her students, she evicts her. Maria then locks Ingrid out of the apartment one night and allows her to enter the following morning only to collect her belongings. Sarah, another American, stays briefly with Maria, and they develop a tender affection for each other, but Sarah becomes homesick and decides to return to America. With Marco away on a business trip, Maria is picked up by a stranger one evening during a walk by the Tiber River. When the man brings her home late that night, Marco is waiting for her, and Maria quickly takes leave of her escort. Marco angrily slaps Maria and tells her that he had come to ask her to marry him. Though he excuses her behavior, their relationship is again threatened when Maria presumptuously asks him whether they should return to America by boat or plane. Marco, resentful at being shipped off to another country, declares that if Maria wants to be his wife she must decide to remain in Italy with his people. She is unable to answer and Marco departs, leaving Maria, stunned, alone. *Americans in foreign countries. Expatriates. Italians. Swedes. English. Roommates. Pickups. Courtship. Jealousy. Rome. Tiber River.*

Note: Filmed on location in Rome in 16mm; New York opening in 16mm.

GOODBYE, MR. CHIPS (United States/Great Britain)   **F6.1910**
APJAC Productions. *Dist* Metro-Goldwyn-Mayer, Inc. 5 Nov 1969 [New York opening; c5 Sep 1969; LP37310]. Sd; col (Metrocolor). 35mm & 70mm (Panavision). 151 min. *MPAA rating* G.

An Arthur P. Jacobs Production. *Prod* Arthur P. Jacobs. *Assoc Prod* Mort Abrahams. *Dir* Herbert Ross. *Screenplay* Terence Rattigan. *Dir Photog* Oswald Morris. *2d Unit Photog* Brian West. *Camera Op* Jimmy Turrell. *Art Dir* Maurice Fowler. *Prod Dsgn* Ken Adam. *Film Ed* Ralph Kemplen. *Songs* Leslie Bricusse. *Mus Cond & Supv* Johnny Williams. *Dir Assoc Musical* Ian Fraser. *Assoc Choreog* Nora Kaye. *Mus Ed* William Saracino. *Rec Supv* A. W. Watkins. *Sd Rec* John Bramall. *Dub Ed* John Poyner. *Dub Mix* J. B. Smith. *Mus Rec* C. T. S. Studios (London). *Asst Dir* Dominic Fulford. *Prod Supv* David W. Orton. *Prod Mgr* Dennis Hall. *Cont* Rita Davison. *Prod Asst* Peter Perkins. *Sp Asst to Mr. Ross* Nora Kaye. *Cost Dsgn* Julie Harris, cost. *Makeup Supv* George Blackler. *Mr. O'Toole's Makeup Created by* Bill Lodge. *Hairdresser* Ivy Emmerton.

Cast: Peter O'Toole *(Arthur Chipping)*, Petula Clark *(Katherine)*, Michael Redgrave *(The Headmaster)*, George Baker *(Lord Sutterwick)*, Sian Phillips *(Ursula Mossbank)*, Michael Bryant *(Max Staefel)*, Jack Hedley *(William Baxter)*, Alison Leggatt *(headmaster's wife)*, Clinton Greyn *(Bill Calbury)*, Barbara Couper *(Mrs. Paunceforth)*, Michael Culver *(Johnny Longbridge)*, Elspeth March *(Mrs. Summersthwaite)*, Clive Morton *(General Paunceforth)*, Ronnie Stevens *(Algy)*, Mario Maranzana *(Pompeii guide)*, John Gugolka *(Sutterwick, Jr.)*, Michael Ridgeway *(David)*, Tom Owen *(Farley)*, Craig Marriott *(new boy)*, Elspet Gray *(Lady Sutterwick)*, Jeremy Lloyd *(Johnson)*, Jack May *(Price)*, Leo Britt *(elder master)*, Royston Tickner *(policeman)*, Sheila Steafel *(Tilly)*, Patricia Hayes *(Miss Honeybun)*, The Boys of Sherborne School.

Musical drama. Source: James Hilton, "Goodbye, Mr. Chips," in *British Weekly* (Dec 1933). Arthur Chipping (known as "Chips"), a shy, dedicated schoolmaster at Brookfield public school in England, looks back over the frustrations of the previous school year, recalling the hostility of his students. As vacation begins, a former pupil takes him to a London music hall, and he meets the star, exuberant singer Katherine Bridges. On a holiday exploring the Pompeiian ruins, he again meets Katherine and acts as her guide. Despite their personality differences, they fall in love and marry, taking all Brookfield by surprise upon their return. Lord Sutterwick, the school's benefactor, knows of Katherine's checkered past and threatens to have Chips removed from his position as housemaster, but he is forced to back down when Katherine invites his former mistress, Ursula Mossbank, to the Brookfield Founders' Day celebration. The couple spend the years contentedly, undaunted when Chips is passed over for the position of headmaster. In the final year of World War II, Chips succeeds to the post, but Katherine, away entertaining the troops, is killed in a German bomb attack before he can give her the news. Chips soon retires and spends his last years near Brookfield, where he remains a beloved figure. *Songs:* "Fill the World With Love" (boys' chorus), "Where Did My Childhood Go?" (Chips), "London Is London" (Katherine and chorus girls), "And the Sky Smiled" (Katherine), "Apollo" (Katherine), "When I Am Older" (the boys), "Walk Through the World" (chorus), "What Shall I Do With Today?" (Katherine), "What a Lot of Flowers" (Chips), "Schooldays" (Katherine & boys), "When I Was Younger" (Chips), "You and I" (Katherine). *Schoolteachers. Bachelors. Singers. Actors. Headmasters. Students. Patrons. Marriage. Aerial bombardment. Public schools (England). Music halls. Vacations. World War II. London. Pompeii.*

Note: Location scenes filmed at Sherborne School in Dorset, England, and in Pompeii and Paestum. Metro-Goldwyn-Mayer released a dramatic version of *Goodbye, Mr. Chips* in 1939.

GOODBYE, MOSCOW (Japan)   **F6.1911**
Toho Co. Nov **1968** [Los Angeles showing]. Sd; col (Eastmancolor). 35mm. 97 min.

Prod Masumi Fujimoto. *Dir* Hiromichi Horikawa. *Screenplay* Takeshi Tamura. *Photog* Yasumichi Fukuzawa. *Art Dir* Shinobu Muraki. *Mus* Toshiro Mayuzumi, Masao Yagi.

Cast: Yuzo Kayama *(The Promoter)*, Toshiko Morita, Shigeru Koyama, Toshio Kurosawa.

Drama. Source: Hiroyuki Itsuki, "Saraba Mosukuwa gurentai," in *Saraba Mosukuwa gurentai* (Tokyo, 1967). A jazz pianist turned promoter is financially successful but has become cynical and bored with his life. About to quit his work, he decides to travel to Moscow with one of his bands. In Russia, he befriends a youthful dissident who is also a trumpet player. Despite the disapproval of the Japanese embassy and the boy's brother, a youth leader, the promoter encourages the young musician. The youth is jailed after a fight, and the promoter, whose enthusiasm for his work had been stirred, once again finds himself alone and restless. *Russians. Brothers. Cynics. Pianists. Trumpeters. Friendship. Jazzbands. Moscow.*

Note: Location scenes filmed in Moscow and Tokyo. Released in Japan in Mar 1968 as *Saraba Mosukuwa gurentai*.

GOODBYE TO THE HILL *see* **PADDY**

THE GOOSE GIRL (West Germany)   **F6.1912**
Fritz Genschow-Film. *Dist* Childhood Productions. **1967**. Sd; col (Agfacolor). 35mm. 78 min.

Prod-Dir-Writ Fritz Genschow. *Photog* Gerhard Huttula. *Art Dir* Siegfried Kiok. *Film Ed* Erika Petrik. *Mus* Richard Stauch. *Sd* Heinz Weissert. *Cost* Grete Görlich.

Cast: Rita-Maria Nowotny, Fritz Genschow, Renée Stobrawa, Renate Fischer, Theodor Vogeler, Günter Hertel, Alexander Welbat, Wolfgang Draeger, Peter Hack.

Fantasy. Source: Jakob Grimm and Wilhelm Grimm, "Die Gänsemagd". While traveling to a distant kingdom to marry a prince, an enchanted princess loses her magic powers and is obliged to exchange identities with her evil maidservant. Arriving at their destination, the prince believes the maidservant to be his betrothed. The false princess puts the real princess to work as a goose tender and has the princess' talking horse decapitated so that it will not reveal the deception. The king learns that the goose maiden talks to the horse's head, now mounted in a gateway, discovers the false princess' treachery, and has his son marry the true princess. *Royalty. Domestics. Marriage. Magic. Imposture. Personal identity. Perfidy. Decapitation. Imaginary kingdoms. Geese. Horses.*

Note: Released in West Germany caJan 1958 as *Die Gänsemagd*.

GORATH (Japan)   **F6.1913**
Toho Co. *Dist* Brenco Pictures. 20 May **1964** [Los Angeles opening]. Sd; col (Eastmancolor). 35mm (Tohoscope). 83 min.

Pres by Edward L. Alperson, Stanley Meyer. *Exec Prod* Tomoyuki Tanaka. *Dir* Inoshiro Honda. *Screenplay* Takeshi Kimura. *Photog* Hajime Koizumi. *Mus* Kan Ishii. *Sp Eff* Eiji Tsuburaya.

Cast: Ryo Ikebe, Akihiko Hirata, Jun Tazaki, Yumi Shirakawa, Takashi Shimura, Kumi Mizuno.

Science fiction melodrama. A Japanese spaceship on its way to Saturn is diverted in order to investigate the mysterious appearance of a meteor-like body hurtling toward Earth. The crew of the ship discover that the red-hot body which they call Gorath is much larger than Earth and has 6,000 times the gravitational pull. Their ship cannot escape the strong pull of Gorath, but before it crashes it transmits enough information back to scientists in Tokyo for them to conclude that a collision between Gorath and Earth is imminent. The nations of the world cooperate to construct a rocket base in Antarctica with the hope that Earth's orbit will be altered when the rockets are detonated. A preliminary test causes an earthquake, but the damage is quickly repaired. Another launching melts the polar cap and unleashes a gigantic monster, but it is finally destroyed. On the actual launch day, Gorath appears in the skies, the moon is thrown out of orbit causing enormous tidal waves, and panic spreads over the globe. The launching is successful, however, and the collision is avoided. *Scientists. Monsters. Meteors. Earthquakes. Rockets. Spaceships. Gravitation. South Pole. Tokyo. Doomsday.*

Note: Released in Japan in 1962 as *Yosei Gorath* or *Yosei Gorasu*; running time: 89 min.

THE GORDEYEV FAMILY (U.S.S.R.)   **F6.1914**
Gorky Film Studio. *Dist* Artkino Pictures. 14 Oct **1961** [New York opening]. Sd; b&w. 35mm. 96 min.

Dir Mark Donskoy. *Screenplay* Boris Byalik, Mark Donskoy. *Story Ed* S. Rubinshteyn. *Photog* Margarita Pilikhina. *Camera* Mikhail Yakovich. *Asst Camera* Ye. Senkov. *Art Dir* Pyotr Pashkevich. *Sets* B. Duksht. *Film Ed* A. Klebanova. *Mus* Lev Shvarts. *Cond* A. Zhyuraytis. *Sd* S. Yurtsev. *1st & 2d Asst Dir* I. Magiton, Z. Genzer, L. Ostreykovskaya. *Prod Mgr* V. Rogovoy. *Cost* E. Rappoport. *Makeup* A. Smirnov, makeup. *Sp Eff* S. Ivanov.

Cast: Sergey Lukyanov (*Ignat Gordeyev*), Georgiy Yepifantsev (*Foma Gordeyev*), Pavel Tarasov (*Yakov Mayakin*), Alla Labetskaya (*Lyuba*), Marina Strizhenova (*Sasha*), Mariya Milkova (*Sofiya Pavlovna Medynskaya*), I. Sretenskiy (*Yezhov*), G. Sergeyev (*Smolin*), A. Glushchenko (*Krasnoshchyokov*), I. Gurov (*Ukhtishchev*), B. Sitko (*Knyazev*), Boris Andreyev (*Zvantsev*), A. Timontayev, A. Zhukov, A. Karpov, A. Solovyov, A. Geleva, A. Baranov, S. Troitskiy, Konstantin Nemolyayev, L. Sokolova, A. Tsinman, N. Butuzov, A. Garichev, L. Dobkevich, Ye. Pavlova, I. Nechanov.

Cast—Children: Sasha Balitskiy (*Foma*), Lyusya Nikiforova, Ira Nikiforova (*Lyuba*), Vladik Lebedev (*Smolin*), Sasha Kukareko (*Yezhov*).

Drama. Source: Maxim Gorky, *Foma Gordeyev* (St. Petersburg, 1900). At the dawn of the 20th century, Ignat Gordeyev, a self-made grain merchant trading along the Volga, hopes that his son, Foma, will follow in his footsteps, but from childhood Foma feels alienated from his surroundings. During a night of drunken revelry, Ignat dies, and thereafter Foma is schooled by his shrewd and acquisitive godfather, Mayakin, who had been his father's partner, in the law that money is power and compassion weakness. Foma finds no meaning in the accumulation of wealth, and his spirit revolts against the merchants' hypocrisy and greed. Mayakin would like Foma to marry his daughter, Lyubov, thereby merging the fortunes of the two houses, but Foma becomes involved in an affair with Sofiya Pavlovna Medynskaya, the wife of an architect. Disillusioned, he leads a life of debauchery and becomes involved with Sasha, a prostitute with whom he feels a natural kinship. At first the merchants tolerate his antics, but finally he is branded feebleminded and committed to an insane asylum when he makes public accusations against the merchants. Penniless and degraded when he is released from the asylum, Foma becomes an object of ridicule, reduced to sleeping in the dosshouse established with his father's money. *Merchants. Heirs. Godfathers. Social classes. Prostitutes. Nouveaux riches. Moral corruption. Materialism. Greed. Family life. Drunkenness. Insane asylums. Volga River.*

Note: Released in the U.S.S.R. in Nov 1959 as *Foma Gordeyev.*

GORDON IL PIRATA NERO *see* **RAGE OF THE BUCCANEERS**

GORGO (Great Britain)   F6.1915

King Brothers Productions. *Dist* Metro-Goldwyn-Mayer, Inc. 10 Feb **1961** [Philadelphia opening]. Sd; col (Technicolor). 35mm (Automation). 78 min.

Prod Wilfred Eades. *Exec Prod* Frank King, Maurice King. *Assoc Prod* James Leicester. *Dir* Eugene Lourie. *Screenplay* John Loring, Daniel Hyatt. *Orig Story* Eugene Lourie, Daniel Hyatt. *Photog* F. A. Young. *Camera Op* Jack Mills, photog. *Art Dir* Elliot Scott. *Film Ed* Eric Boyd-Perkins. *Mus* Angelo Francesco Lavagnino. *Sd* A. W. Watkins. *1st & 2d Asst Dir* Douglas Hermes, Joe Marks. *Prod Mgr* George Mills. *Prod Sec* Jean Clarkson. *Sp Photog Eff* Tom Howard. *Prop Buyer* Bryn Siddall.

Cast: Bill Travers (*Joe Ryan*), William Sylvester (*Sam Slade*), Vincent Winter (*Sean*), Bruce Seton (*Professor Flaherty*), Joseph O'Connor (*Professor Hendricks*), Martin Benson (*Dorkin*), Barry Keegan (*1st mate*), Dervis Ward (*bo'sun*), Christopher Rhodes (*McCartin*), Basil Dignam (*Admiral Brooks*), Maurice Kaufmann (*radio [television?] reporter*), Tom Duggan (*1st naval officer*), Howard Lang (*1st colonel*), Connie Tilton, David Wilding, Michael Dillon, Peter Brace, Peter Perkins (*stunt artists*).

Horror film. Following an undersea volcanic explosion off the coast of Ireland, a gigantic 65-foot monster is released from its underwater home. After terrorizing the mainland, the beast is captured in a steel net by two salvage boatmen, Joe Ryan and Sam Slade, who decide to ignore the wishes of Irish paleontologists from the University of Dublin and take the creature to London for exhibition in the Battersea Funfair. They are accompanied by a young orphan boy, Sean, whom they have befriended. Though the little boy takes pity on the curious beast, now named Gorgo, he is prevented by Joe from setting it free. Word is received that Gorgo is merely an infant and his 250-foot tall mother is heading toward London in search of her offspring. Destroyers, flamethrowers, missiles, and jet airplanes all fail to halt the monster's progress, and the terrified London populace takes flight. Big Ben, Westminster Abbey, the Houses of Parliament, the Thames' huge Tower Bridge, and Piccadilly Circus are left in ruins by the mammoth beast's rampage. Only when it reaches its infant's side does the havoc subside. Peace returns as the two creatures make their way back to the depths of the sea. *Monsters. Boatmen. Orphans. Abduction. Motherhood. Friendship. Naval bombardment. Fear. Volcanoes. Explosions. Circus. Flamethrowers. Missiles. Airplanes—Jet. London. Ireland. Thames River. The Sea. University of Dublin.*

Note: Filmed in Ireland and London. Opened in London in Oct 1961.

THE GORGON (Great Britain)   F6.1916

Hammer Film Productions. *Dist* Columbia Pictures. 17 Feb **1965** [Louisville, Kentucky, opening; c31 Dec 1964; LP31459]. Sd (RCA); col (Eastman Color by Pathé). 35mm. 83 min.

Prod Anthony Nelson Keys. *Dir* Terence Fisher. *Screenplay* John Gilling. *Orig Story* J. Llewellyn Devine. *Dir Photog* Michael Reed. *Camera Op* Cece Cooney. *Art Dir* Don Mingaye. *Prod Dsgn* Bernard Robinson. *Supv Ed* James Needs. *Ed* Eric Boyd-Perkins. *Mus Comp* James Bernard. *Mus Supv* Marcus Dods. *Sd Rec* Ken Rawkins. *Sd Ed* Roy Hyde. *Asst Dir* Bert Batt. *Prod Mgr* Don Weeks. *Cont* Pauline Harlow. *Wardrobe Mistress* Rosemary Burrows. *Makeup Artist* Roy Ashton. *Hairstyles* Frieda Steiger. *Sp Eff* Syd Pearson. *Fight Arr* Peter Diamond.

Cast: Peter Cushing (*Namaroff*), Christopher Lee (*Prof. Carl Meister*), Richard Pasco (*Paul Heitz*), Barbara Shelley (*Carla Hoffman*), Michael Goodliffe (*Professor Heitz*), Patrick Troughton (*Kanof*), Jack Watson (*Ratoff*), Jeremy Longhurst (*Bruno Heitz*), Toni Gilpin (*Sascha*), Redmond Phillips (*Hans*), Alister Williamson (*Cass*), Joyce Hemson (*Martha*), Joseph O'Connor (*coroner*), Michael Peake (*policeman*), Sally Nesbitt (*nurse*), Prudence Hyman (*chatelaine*).

Horror film. Many petrified corpses are found in the village of Vandorf in 1910. When Bruno Heitz, an artist, is found hanging from a tree following the death of his girl friend, he is assumed to be the murderer. Attempting to clear his son's name, Professor Heitz visits Vandorf, where he encounters the hostility of Police Chief Kanof, brain surgeon Namaroff, and the villagers themselves, who set his lodgings ablaze. In the ruins of Castle Borski the professor confronts Megaera, the legendary gorgon. Her gaze gradually turns him to stone, but he notifies his elder son, Paul. Accompanied by his mentor, Professor Meister, Paul arrives in Vandorf. When Namaroff refuses to see him, Meister's suspicions are aroused. Aware that Paul is attracted to Carla, Namaroff's assistant, Meister advises him to shun her. From Namaroff's papers Meister learns that Carla, an amnesiac, is the surgeon's former patient. Discovering that Paul and Carla have arranged a tryst at Castle Borski, Meister rushes to the ruins. There he and Paul slay both Namaroff and Carla, whose body had housed the gorgon. *Surgeons. Professors. Artists. Mythological characters. Monsters. Murder. Amnesia. Filial relations. Castles.*

Note: Released in Great Britain in Oct 1964.

GORILLA (Sweden)   F6.1917

Terrafilm–Alf Jörgensen. *Dist* Herts-Lion International Corp. Mar **1964**. Sd; col (EastmanColor). 35mm (AgaScope). 90 min.

Prod Lorens Marmstedt. *Dir* Lars Henrik Ottoson, Sven Nykvist. *Screenplay* Lars Henrik Ottoson. *Photog* Sven Nykvist.

Cast: Georges Galley (*game warden*), Gio Petré (*journalist*).

Adventure drama. In the Belgian Congo, a savage gorilla terrorizes a wild animal preserve and kills three women. The village witch doctor declares the terror to be the vengeance of the gods, who must be appeased by the sacrifice of the village's newest born. Antagonizing the witch doctor, the warden promises to rid the village of the beast. He is aided by a young woman journalist, who is doing a story on the natives. While overcoming many obstacles and successfully completing the hunt, they fall in love. Before she returns home, they promise to meet again. *Witch doctors. Gamekeepers. Journalists. Hunting. Superstition. Human sacrifice. Wildlife refuges. Congo. Apes.*

Note: Filmed on location in the Belgian Congo. Opened in Stockholm in Aug 1956.

GOROD BOLSHOY SUDBY *see* **INSIDE THE U.S.S.R.**

THE GOSPEL ACCORDING TO ST. MATTHEW (France/Italy)   F6.1918

Arco Film–C. C. F. Lux. *Dist* Continental Distributing, Inc. 17 Feb **1966** [New York opening]. Sd; b&w. 35mm. 136 min.

Prod Alfredo Bini. *Exec Prod* Manolo Bolognini. *Dir-Adapt* Pier Paolo Pasolini. *Photog* Tonino Delli Colli. *Camera Op* Giuseppe Ruzzolini, Victor Hugo Contino. *1st Asst Camera* G. Cianfarelli Modica. *2d Asst Camera* Sandro Ruzzolini. *Art Dir* Luigi Scaccianoce. *Film Ed* Nino Baragli. *Asst Film Ed* Andreina Casini. *Orig Mus Score* Luis Enriquez Bacalov. *Mus Selections* Johann Sebastian Bach, Sergei Sergeevich Prokofiev, Wolfgang Amadeus Mozart, Anton Webern. *Song:* "Sometimes I Feel Like a Motherless Child" sung by Odetta. *Sd* Mario Del Pezzo. *Asst Dir* Maurizio Lucidi. *Prod Mgr* Eliseo Boschi. *Script Girl* Lina D'Amico. *Prod Sec* Bruno Frascà. *Cost* Danilo Donati. *Cost Arr* Rocchetti. *Dressmaker* Piero Farani. *Makeup* Marcello Ceccarelli. *Hairstyles* Mimma Pomilia. *Dir Sp Eff* Ettore Catallucci. *Still Photog* Angelo Novi.

Cast: Enrique Irazoqui (*Jesus Christ*), Margherita Caruso (*Mary, as a girl*), Susanna Pasolini (*Mary, as a woman*), Marcello Morante (*Joseph*), Mario Socrate (*John the Baptist*), Settimo Di Porto (*Peter*), Otello Sestili (*Judas*),

Ferruccio Nuzzo (*Matthew*), Giacomo Morante (*John*), Alfonso Gatto (*Andrew*), Enzo Siciliano (*Simon*), Giorgio Agamben (*Philip*), Guido Cerretani (*Bartholomew*), Luigi Barbini (*James, son of Alpheus*), Marcello Galdini (*James, son of Zebedee*), Elio Spaziani (*Thaddeus*), Rosario Migale (*Thomas*), Rodolfo Wilcock (*Caiaphas*), Alessandro Tasca (*Pontius Pilate*), Amerigo Bevilacqua (*Herod the Great*), Francesco Leonetti (*Herod Antipas*), Franca Cupane (*Herodias*), Paola Tedesco (*Salome*), Rossana Di Rocco (*angel*), Eliseo Boschi (*Joseph of Arimathea*), Natalia Ginzburg (*Mary of Bethany*), Renato Terra (*a Pharisee*), Enrico Maria Salerno (*voice of Jesus*).

Biblical drama. In semi-documentary style, the film traces the life of Jesus Christ as told in the Gospel of St. Matthew. Highlights include: the Annunciation, the birth of Jesus in a Bethlehem stable; Herod's decree that all new-born males in Bethlehem be slaughtered; the Holy Family's flight into Egypt; Jesus' youth in Nazareth; His baptism by John the Baptist; His 40-day fast in the desert; His entry into Jerusalem; the execution of John the Baptist; the Last Supper; the betrayal by Judas; the Crucifixion; and the Resurrection. *Royalty. Jews. Christianity. Miracles. Crucifixion. The Resurrection. Bethlehem. Nazareth. Egypt. Jerusalem. Jesus. Saint Joseph. Virgin Mary. Herod Antipas. Herod the Great. Herodias. John the Baptist. Salome. Pontius Pilate. Joseph Caiaphas. Joseph of Arimathea. The Twelve Apostles. The Bible.*

Note: Filmed in southern Italy (Calabria, Lucania, and Puglia). Released in Italy in 1964 as *Il vangelo secondo Matteo*; running time: 142 min; opened in Paris in Mar 1965 as *L'évangile selon saint-Matthieu*; running time: 130 min. The word "saint" was introduced into the English title against the director's wish. The film is dedicated to the memory of Pope John XXIII. Musical selections include the Congolese *Missa Luba*, Prokofiev's "Cantata" from *Alexander Nevsky*, and Bach's *St. Matthew Passion*.

GOSPODJICA DOKTOR—ŠPIJUNKA BEZ IMENA see **FRAULEIN DOKTOR**

GÖTTERDÄMMERUNG see **THE DAMNED**

GOYOKIN (Japan)   F6.1919
Fuji Telecasting Co.–Tokyo Eiga Co. *Dist* Toho International, Inc. Sep **1969** [Los Angeles showing]. Sd; col (Eastman Color). 35mm (Panavision). 124 min.
Dir Hideo Gosha. *Screenplay* Hideo Gosha, Kei Tasaka. *Photog* Kozo Okazaki. *Art Dir* Motoji Kojima. *Mus* Masaru Sato.
Cast: Tatsuya Nakadai (*Magobei Wakizaka*), Tetsuro Tamba (*Rokugo Tatewaki*), Kinnosuke Nakamura (*Samon Fujimaki*), Isao Natsuyagi (*Kunai*), Yoko Tsukasa (*Shino*), Kunie Tanaka (*Hyosuke*), Ruriko Asaoka (*Oriha*).
Drama. In 1831 Magobei, a samurai, discovers that his brother-in-law, Rokugo, has stolen a shipload of the shogunate's gold in order to pay an oppressive tax levied by the government. Furthermore, Rokugo was forced to slaughter a village of defenseless fishermen who witnessed the theft of the bullion, thus violating the samurai code of honor. Magobei denounces his brother-in-law for sacrificing his honor for gold, and Rokugo responds by expelling him from the clan. Magobei returns to the devastated village and joins forces with a shogunate spy searching for the pirates who stole the gold. On the next moonless night, Magobei and the spy watch Rokugo misplace seashore warning lights in an attempt to wreck a shogunate ship. Magobei and Rokugo engage in a sword fight, and Rokugo is defeated. *Samurai. Brothers-in-law. Fishermen. Spies. Piracy. Massacres. Gold.*
Note: Released in Japan in May 1969.

THE GRABBERS see **THE SCAVENGERS**

THE GRADUATE   F6.1920
Lawrence Turman, Inc. *Dist* Embassy Pictures. 21 Dec **1967** [New York opening; c20 Dec 1967; LP40200]. Sd (Westrex); col (Technicolor). 35mm (Panavision). 105 min.
Pres by Joseph E. Levine. A Mike Nichols–Lawrence Turman Production. *Prod* Lawrence Turman. *Dir* Mike Nichols. *Screenplay* Calder Willingham, Buck Henry. *Dir Photog* Robert Surtees. *Camera Op* George Nogle, Al Bettcher. *Camera Asst* Emilio Calori, Jim Cowan. *Prod Dsgn* Richard Sylbert. *Asst Prod Dsgn* Joel Schiller. *Set Decor* George R. Nelson. *Sketch Artist* Harold Michelson. *Film Ed* Sam O'Steen. *Asst Film Ed* Robert Wyman. *Songs:* "Sounds of Silence," "Scarborough Fair (Canticle)," "Mrs. Robinson," "The Big, Bright Green Pleasure Machine," "April Come She Will" Paul Simon. *Sung by* Simon & Garfunkel. *Adtl Mus* Dave Grusin. *Sd* Jack Solomon. *Asst Dir* Don Kranze, Lynn Guthrie, Gene Marum. *Prod Supv* George Justin. *Script Supv* Meta Rebner. *Prod Asst* William Cannon. *Prod Sec* Joyce Lilley. *Cost* Patricia Zipprodt. *Wardrobe* Phyllis Garr, Donald J. McDonald. *Makeup* Harry Maret. *Hairdresser* Sherry Wilson. *Hairstyles* Sydney Guilaroff. *Casting Cons* Lynn Stalmaster. *Gaffer* Earl Gilbert. *Grip* Dick Borland. *Still Photog* Frank Shugrue.
Cast: Anne Bancroft (*Mrs. Robinson*), Dustin Hoffman (*Benjamin Braddock*), Katharine Ross (*Elaine Robinson*), William Daniels (*Mr.*

Braddock), Murray Hamilton (*Mr. Robinson*), Elizabeth Wilson (*Mrs. Braddock*), Brian Avery (*Carl Smith*), Walter Brooke (*Mr. McGuire*), Norman Fell (*Mr. McCleery*), Elisabeth Fraser (*lady #2*), Alice Ghostley (*Mrs. Singleman*), Buck Henry (*room clerk*), Marion Lorne (*Miss De Witt*), Harry Holcombe (*minister*), Lainie Miller (*nightclub stripper*), Eddra Gale (*woman on bus*).
Comedy-drama. Source: Charles Webb, *The Graduate* (New York, 1963). Benjamin Braddock, filled with doubts about his future, returns to his Los Angeles home after graduating from an Eastern college. His parents soon have a party so they can boast of their son's academic achievements and his bright prospects in business. Mrs. Robinson, one of the guests, persuades Ben to drive her home and there tries to seduce him, but her overtures are interrupted by the sound of her husband's car in the driveway. Blatant in her seductive maneuvers, she soon has the nervous and inexperienced Ben meeting her regularly at the Taft Hotel. As the summer passes, Benjamin becomes increasingly bored and listless; he frequently stays out overnight and returns home to loll around the pool. When his worried parents try to interest him in Elaine, Mrs. Robinson's daughter, Ben agrees to date her to avoid having the entire Robinson family invited to dinner. At first Benjamin is rude to Elaine and takes her to a striptease club, but realizing how cruel he has been, he apologizes and the two begin dating. Outraged, Mrs. Robinson demands that Ben stop seeing her daughter; instead he blurts out the truth to a shocked Elaine, who returns to college in Berkeley. Although Ben follows her and tries to persuade her to marry him, Elaine's parents intervene and encourage her to marry Carl, a student whom she has been dating. Ben returns to Los Angeles, but when Mrs. Robinson refuses to divulge any information about the wedding, he races back to Berkeley and learns that the ceremony will take place in Santa Barbara. Arriving at the church as the final vows are being spoken, he screams Elaine's name over the heads of the startled guests. Elaine sees her parents' anger toward Ben, and realizing what their influence has done, she fights off her mother and Carl and races to Ben. After locking the congregation in the church by jamming a crucifix through the door handles, the couple leap aboard a passing bus and ride away. *Youth. Students. Disillusionment. Filial relations. Seduction. Infidelity. Courtship. Weddings. Elopement. Marriage. College life. Hotels. Swimming pools. Churches. Los Angeles. Berkeley (California). Santa Barbara. University of California.*
Note: Location scenes filmed in Beverly Hills, on Sunset Strip in Los Angeles, and on the University of Southern California campus. A film clip from the ABC television series *The Newlywed Game* is used.

GRAFFITI   F6.1921
Dist AVA Distributors, Cinex Film Industries. 4 Jun **1969** [Baltimore opening]. Sd; b&w. 35mm. 72 min.
Mystery melodrama. Private detective Dan MacGlen takes a job trailing an estranged husband, but upon arriving at the man's apartment, Dan finds him murdered. The only clues are a pen and a telephone number. He takes the pen for analysis to a student criminologist, but there he interrupts a three-way orgy, and he joins in the sexual activities. Afterwards he calls the telephone number found near the dead man's body and questions the woman who answers. Dan later learns that an analysis of the pen revealed traces of plaster on the tip. Dan begins to search the city and finds suspicious notes on the wall of a men's room. The trail of clues leads him to a prostitute and to a sex deviate. He finally discovers who the murderer is—a woman who offers to satisfy his sexual demands if he will refrain from calling the police. *Detectives. Criminologists. Prostitutes. Murder. Troilism. Group sex. Bribery. Graffiti.*
Note: May include a subtitle: *The Clue to a Crime of Lust.*

GRANATOVYY BRASLET see **THE GARNET BRACELET**

THE GRAND DUKE AND MR. PIMM see **LOVE IS A BALL**

LE GRAND MEAULNES see **THE WANDERER**

THE GRAND OLYMPICS (Italy)   F6.1922
Istituto Nazionale Luce. *For* Comitato Organizzativo dei Giochi della XVII Olimpiade. *Dist* Times Film Corp. 21 Apr **1964** [New York opening]. Sd; col (Eastman Color). 35mm. 120 min.
Dir Romolo Marcellini. *Screenplay-Story* Romolo Marcellini, Nicolò Ferrari, Daniele G. Luisi. *Italian Comm* Sergio Valentini, Corrado Sofia, Donato Martucci. *Photog* Aldo Alessandri, Francesco Attenni, Libio Bartoli, Cesare Colò, Mario Damicelli, Renato Del Frate, Vittorio Della Valle, Angelo Filippini, Rino Filippini, Mario Fioretti, Angelo Jannarelli, Luigi Kuveiller, Emanuel Lomiry, Angelo Lotti, Masino Manunza, Erico Menczer, Ugo Nudi, Emanuele Piccirilli, Marco Scarpelli, Antonio Secchi, Renato Sinistri, Carlo Ventimiglia, Fausto Zuccoli. *Film Ed* Mario Serandrei, Iolanda Benvenuti, Alberto Verdejo. *Mus* Angelo Francesco Lavagnino, Armando Trovajoli. *In Charge of Prod* Franco Galliano. *Collab* Craveri, D'Amico, De Felice, Ferroni, Rino Filippini, Romolo Marcellini, Donato Martucci, Sergio Valentini, Zanetti,

Fede Arnaud, Chiecci, Daniele G. Luisi.

Documentary. A record of highlights of each day's competitions during the 17th Olympics in Rome in 1960, in which the Soviet Union's athletes won more medals than any other national group. In addition to the athletic events, including track and field contests, gymnastics, cycling, wrestling, boxing, horsemanship, weightlifting, swimming, etc., the film shows the lighting of the torch carried on foot from Mount Olympus to Rome; the parades of the athletes into the arena; Pope John's greeting to the contestants; and glimpses of Queen Frederika of Greece and her son, King Constantine II. Among the prominent athletes appearing in the film are Wilma Rudolph, Rafer Johnson, Chris von Saltza, and Abebe Bikila. *Athletes. Sports. Rome. Wilma Rudolph. Rafer Johnson. Chris Von Saltza. Abebe Bikila. John XXIII (pope). Frederika (Greece). Constantine II (Greece). Olympic Games. Olympus.*

Note: Rome opening: Jan 1961 as *La grande Olimpiade*; running time: 142 min. Some U. S. reviews indicate that an English narration was included.

GRAND PRIX   F6.1923

Joel Productions–JFP Productions–Cherokee Productions. *Dist* Metro-Goldwyn-Mayer, Inc. 21 Dec **1966** [New York opening; c31 Dec 1966; LP34163]. Sd; col (Metrocolor). 35mm & 70mm (Super Panavision). 179 min. [Copyright length: 167 min.]

A Douglas & Lewis Production. *Prod* Edward Lewis. *Dir* John Frankenheimer. *Screen Story & Screenplay* Robert Alan Aurthur. *Dir Photog* Lionel Lindon. *2d Unit Photog* John M. Stephens, Jean-Georges Fontenelle, Yann Le Masson. *Prod Dsgn* Richard Sylbert. *Vis Cons, Montages & Titl* Saul Bass. *Supv Film Ed* Fredric Steinkamp. *Film Ed* Henry Berman, Stewart Linder, Frank Santillo. *Mus Comp & Cond* Maurice Jarre. *Sd Ed* Gordon Daniel. *Sd Rec* Franklin Milton, Roy Charman. *Asst Dir* Enrico Isacco. *Unit Prod Mgr* William Kaplan. *Prod Mgr (Monaco & France)* Sacha Kamenka. *Prod Mgr (Italy)* Sam Gorodisky. *Prod Mgr (England)* Peter Crowhurst. *Cost Selected & Supv, Hairstyles & Makeup Created by* Sydney Guilaroff. *Makeup* Giuliano Laurenti, Alfio Meniconi. *Sp Eff* Milt Rice. *Racing Adv* Phil Hill, Joakim Bonnier, Richie Ginther. *Racing Seq Filmed with the Coöp of* Association Sportive de l'Automobile Club d'Auvergne "Circuit de Montagne d'Auvergne", Association Sportive de l'Automobile Club de l'Ouest "24 Heures du Mans", Automobile Club di Palermo (Sicily) "Targa Florio", Brands Hatch Circuit Limited, British Racing Drivers' Club (Silverstone), Royal Automobile Club "British Grand Prix", Comité d'Organisation du Grand Prix de Monaco "XXIVme Grand Prix de Monaco 1966", Koninklijke Nederlandsche Automobiel Club in cooperation with Nederlandse Autorensport Vereniging (Circuit Van Zandvoort) "The Dutch Grand Prix 1966", Royal Automobile Club de Belgique (Circuit de Francorchamps) "Grand Prix de Belgique 1966", Watkins Glen Grand Prix Corporation "United States Grand Prix". *Prop Master* Frank Agnone. *Racing Camera Mounts Exec by* Frick Enterprises. *Tech Cons* Carroll Shelby.

Cast: James Garner *(Pete Aron)*, Eva Marie Saint *(Louise Frederickson)*, Yves Montand *(Jean-Pierre Sarti)*, Toshiro Mifune *(Izo Yamura)*, Brian Bedford *(Scott Stoddard)*, Jessica Walter *(Pat)*, Antonio Sabato *(Nino Barlini)*, Françoise Hardy *(Lisa)*, Adolfo Celi *(Agostini Manetta)*, Claude Dauphin *(Hugo Simon)*, Enzo Fiermonte *(Guido)*, Geneviève Page *(Monique Delvaux Sarti)*, Jack Watson *(Jeff Jordan)*, Donald O'Brien *(Wallace Bennett)*, Jean Michaud *(children's father)*, Albert Remy *(surgeon)*, Rachel Kempson *(Mrs. Stoddard)*, Ralph Michael *(Mr. Stoddard)*, Alan Fordney, Anthony Marsh, Tommy Franklin *(sportscasters)*, Phil Hill *(Tim Randolph)*, Graham Hill *(Bob Turner)*, Bernard Cahier *(journalist)*, Chris Amon, Lorenzo Bandini, Jean Pierre Beltoise, Bob Bondurant, Joakim Bonnier, Jack Brabham, Ken Costello, Juan Manuel Fangio, Nino Farina, Paul Frere, Richie Ginther, Dan Gurney, Dennis Hulme, Tony Lanfranchi, Guy Ligier, Bruce McLaren, Michael Parkes, Andre Pillette, Teddy Pillette, Peter Revson, Jochen Rindt, Jim Russell, Ludovico Scarfiotti, Jo Schlesser, Skip Scott, Joe Siffert, Mike Spence *(themselves, racing drivers)*.

Action drama. Foremost among the drivers vying for fame and fortune in the 9-race competition for the World Championship of Drivers are American Pete Aron, Britisher Scott Stoddard, Corsican Jean-Pierre Sarti, and Sicilian Nino Barlini. During the first race in Monaco, a smashup hurls Aron's car into the Monte Carlo harbor and sends Stoddard crashing into a cliffside wall. Although Aron is able to swim away from his wreck, it appears unlikely that Stoddard will ever race—or walk—again; and Aron is held accountable. At a party following the event, Sarti, whose marriage has lost all of its meaning and passion, becomes attracted to Louise Frederickson, a fashion magazine editor, and the young Nino takes up with a vivacious young Frenchwoman named Lisa who follows along with him to the other races. After the French Grand Prix at Clermont-Ferrand, which Sarti wins, Aron agrees to race for a Japanese industrialist, Izo Yamura; he also begins an illicit affair with Stoddard's bored young wife, Pat. During the race in Belgium, which Aron eventually wins, Sarti's car skids on the wet track, crashes off the road, and kills two children.

The disaster has a lasting effect upon Sarti's emotional stability. Aron again wins at the German Grand Prix, but Stoddard, despite his still unhealed injuries, returns for the Dutch Grand Prix and scores an amazing victory. He repeats his triumph at Watkins Glen in the United States and again at the Mexican meet. At the British event in Brands Hatch, however, he buckles from pain and loses to Nino. By now Sarti and Louise are openly living together, but Aron and Pat have parted. At the final race in Monza, Italy, the point totals show Nino leading, one ahead of Sarti and Stoddard and two ahead of Aron. During the event Sarti dies in a terrible accident which so stuns Nino that he removes his foot from the gas pedal. Stoddard finishes a close second to Aron and also gets a second chance to save his marriage to Pat. As Aron is crowned the victor amid the throngs of cheering fans, he somehow feels strangely alone. *British. Corsicans. Sicilians. Industrialists. Fashion editors. Japanese. French. Automobile racing. Infidelity. Mexico. Monaco. Clermont-Ferrand. Belgium. Watkins Glen. Brands Hatch. Monza (Italy). Netherlands. Grand Prix (automobile race). Automobile accidents.*

Note: Filmed in Europe, England, and the United States. Presented in Cinerama; employs split screen techniques.

GRAND SLAM (Italy/Spain/West Germany)   F6.1924

Jolly Film–Coral, P. C.–Constantin Film. *Dist* Paramount Pictures. 17 Jan **1968** [Chicago opening]. Sd; col (Technicolor). 35mm (Techniscope). 121 min.

Prod Harry Colombo, George Papi. *Dir* Giuliano Montaldo. *Screenplay* Mino Roli, Marcello Fondato, Antonio de la Loma, Augusto Caminito, Marcello Coscia. *Story* Mino Roli, Augusto Caminito, Paolo Bianchini. *Photog* Antonio Macasoli. *Art Dir* Alberto Boccianti, Juan Alberto Soler. *Film Ed* Nino Baragli. *Mus Comp* Ennio Morricone. *Mus Cond* Bruno Nicolai. *Sd* Umberto Picistrelli. *Asst Dir* Mauro Sacripanti, Carlos Luiz Corito, Federico Canudas. *Prod Mgr* Franco Serino, Roberto Machado, Valentín Sallent.

Cast: Janet Leigh *(Mary Ann)*, Robert Hoffmann *(Jean-Paul Audry)*, Edward G. Robinson *(Prof. James Anders)*, Adolfo Celi *(Mark Milford)*, Klaus Kinski *(Erich Weiss)*, Georges Rigaud *(Gregg)*, Riccardo Cucciolla *(Agostino)*, Jussara *(Setuaka)*, Miguel del Castillo *(manager)*, Luciana Angiolillo, Valentino Macchi.

Crime melodrama. After 30 years of teaching at a Rio de Janeiro convent school located across from a diamond company, Prof. James Anders retires and flies to New York. He contacts an old friend, Mark Milford, now a wealthy criminal, and presents him with an elaborate plan to rob the diamond company. Milford recruits four men for the heist: Erich Weiss, a former Nazi sergeant who will supervise the operation; Gregg, one of the world's fastest safecrackers; Agostino Rossi, an electronics expert; and Jean-Paul Audry, a French gigolo who must seduce the diamond company's secretary, Mary Ann, to obtain her vault key. The men assemble in Rio and solve an unanticipated problem—a new alarm system called "Grand Slam 70." On the night of the robbery, Jean-Paul removes the key from Mary Ann's purse and passes it to his accomplices; then Gregg and Agostino, through numerous ingenious devices, break into the diamond vault. After the robbery, Jean-Paul fails to replace the key, however, and Mary Ann goes to the police. On their way to the airport the robbers are chased by the police, and Gregg is killed. Before disposing of the getaway car, Erich strangles Jean-Paul, whom he has long hated; fearing that he is next, Agostino flees but is killed by police at a fishing port. When Erich, the sole survivor, arrives at the rendezvous spot with the case of jewels, he is shot down by the waiting Milford; upon opening the case, however, Milford finds it empty. In Rome Mary Ann and Professor Anders are seated at a sidewalk cafe, congratulating themselves on their clever series of double-crosses, when they are momentarily distracted by a plane dropping leaflets. In that split second a thief rides past on a motorcycle and snatches Mary Ann's purse, unaware that he has stolen $10 million in diamonds. *Professors. Masterminds. Thieves. Safecrackers. Gigolos. Secretaries. Police. Robbery. Seduction. Murder. Perfidy. Gems. Vaults. New York City. Rio de Janeiro. Rome.*

Note: Location scenes filmed in Spain, Rome, London, New York, and Rio de Janeiro. Released in Italy in 1967 as *Ad ogni costo*; in West Germany in Jan 1968 as *Top Job* at 110 min; in Spain in 1968 as *Diamantes a go-go* at 77 min.

THE GRAND SUBSTITUTION (Hong Kong)   F6.1925

Shaw Brothers (H. K.) Ltd. *Dist* Frank Lee International. 7 Jul **1965** [San Francisco opening]. Sd; col (Eastmancolor). 35mm (Shawscope). 116 min.

Prod Run Run Shaw. *Dir* Yen Chun. *Screenplay* Chen E-hsin. *Photog* Yu Tsang-shan. *Art Dir* Chen Chin-shen, Chen Chi-jui. *Film Ed* Chiang Hsing-lung. *Mus Score* Sian Hua. *Lyr* Chen E-hsin. *Sd Rec* Wang Yung-hua. *Asst Dir* Chen You-hsin.

Cast: Li Li-hua *(Chuang Chi)*, Ivy Ling Po *(Chao Wu)*, Yen Chun *(Cheng Ying)*, Li Ting *(Po Fung)*, Chen Yen-yen *(Madam Cheng)*, Ching Miao *(Chao Tun)*, Li Yeng *(Chao Su)*, Yang Tse-ching *(Kung Sun)*, Chen You-hsin *(Chin Kung)*, Li Ying *(Tu An-chia)*, Chao Ming *(Han Chieh)*, Tung Di *(Gen. Wei Chiang)*, Tien Feng *(Chui Ying)*, Liang Ruey *(Chin Ling Kung)*, Chen Ying Chieh *(Wei Chung)*, Hsia Yi-chiu *(Chuen Lan)*.

Opera film. Emperor Ling, ruler of the State of Chin, entrusts all affairs of state to Tu An-chia, a ruthless and unscrupulous minister. During a minor disturbance, Prime Minister Chao Tun and other loyal government officials insist that the emperor dispatch the able Gen. Wei Chiang to quiet the uprising that Tu would have preferred to leave alone. Intimidated by the patriotism of the prime minister, Tu persuades the emperor to purge Chao and 300 members of Chao's clan; Chuang Chi, the emperor's sister and Chao's daughter-in-law, is the only member spared. After the massacre, Chuang gives birth to a son whose life immediately becomes endangered. To save the Chao heir, Cheng Ying, the Chaos' loyal doctor friend, substitutes his newly born son for the infant, and when Tu orders the infant brought to him, Cheng reveals the whereabouts of his own son, who is immediately killed. As a reward, Cheng asks only for the protection of the infant in his home. Tu, unaware of the deception, takes the infant and names him Cheng Wu. Fifteen years later, Cheng Ying invites Tu to his home where he is confronted by Gen. Wei Chiang, Chuang Chi, and his adopted son, who has become a fine soldier. The young man informs Tu of his origin, calls himself by his real name, Chao Wu, and avenges his family by killing Tu. Cheng Ying receives the praise of the people for his sacrifice. *Royalty. Prime ministers. Physicians. Heirs. Soldiers. Uprisings. Massacres. Self-sacrifice. Loyalty. Assassination. Personal identity. Adoption. Revenge. China.*

Note: Released in Hong Kong in 1965.

GRAND TOUR OF EASTERN EUROPE: BEHIND THE IRON CURTAIN   F6.1926

VPR Ltd. 21 Feb **1968** [Atlanta opening]. Sd eff & mus score; col (Deluxe). 35mm. 100-115 min.

Prod-Dir-Writ André De La Varre, Jr. *Photog* Kurt Jetmar, Peter Baudendistel, André De La Varre, Jr. *Film Ed* André De La Varre, Jr., Pablo Zavala. *Mus Ed* André De La Varre, Jr.

Travelog. Traveling through the Soviet Union, Hungary, Poland, and Czechoslovakia, the narrator describes Leningrad, Moscow, Sochi, the Black Sea, Georgia, the Bolshoi Opera and Ballet School, Budapest, Lake Balaton, puszta life, the Danube, Warsaw, Krakow, rural Poland, Prague, and the Bohemian forests. *Steppes. Forests. Union of Soviet Socialist Republics. Hungary. Poland. Czechoslovakia. Leningrad. Moscow. Sochi. Black Sea. Georgian Soviet Socialist Republic. Budapest. Balaton. Danube River. Warsaw. Krakow (Poland). Prague. Bohemia. Bolshoi Theater (Moscow).*

Note: Narration delivered on stage by De La Varre.

GRAND TOUR OF LONDON AND PARIS (BY DAY AND BY NIGHT)   F6.1927

VPR Ltd. 5 May **1965** [San Francisco opening]. Sd eff & mus score; col (Deluxe). 35mm. 100-115 min.

Pres by Burton Holmes Theatre Productions. *Prod-Dir-Writ* André De La Varre, Jr. *Photog* Kurt Jetmar, Peter Baudendistel, André De La Varre, Jr. *Film Ed* André De La Varre, Jr., Pablo Zavala. *Music Sound Track Service.*

Cast:

Travelog. A travel host describes the delights of Paris and London, including the following sights: the Eiffel Tower, the Seine, Notre Dame, the Latin Quarter, the Arc de Triomphe, the Champs Elysée, Montmartre, and the Metro; Houses of Parliament, Big Ben, Westminster Abbey, Buckingham Palace, the Thames, Windsor Castle, Oxford and Cambridge Universities, Stonehenge, English inns, and Piccadilly Circus. *Travel. Inns. Paris. Eiffel Tower. Seine River. Notre Dame de Paris. London. Westminster Abbey. Thames River. Windsor Castle. Oxford University. Cambridge University. Stonehenge.*

Note: Narration delivered live on stage.

GRAND TOUR '70: DESTINATION HOLY LAND   F6.1928

VPR Ltd. 21 Oct **1969** [Miami, Florida, opening]. Sd eff & mus score; col. 35mm. 100-115 min.

Prod-Dir-Writ André De La Varre, Jr. *Photog* Kurt Jetmar, Peter Baudendistel, André De La Varre, Jr. *Film Ed* André De La Varre, Jr., Pablo Zavala. *Background Theme: Violin Concerto in G Minor* Max Bruch. *Perf by* Ivry Gitlis. *Mus Ed* André De La Varre, Jr.

Travelog. Scenes of Rome, Greece, Israel, and Egypt are shown. The narrator describes the Pantheon, the Colosseum, Pope Paul celebrating mass in St. Peter's Basilica, Athens at Easter, the Acropolis, Bethlehem, Nazareth, Jerusalem, the Western Wall, Galilee, the Dead Sea, Tel Aviv, Haifa, Acre, the Nile, the Sphinx of Giza, and the Pyramids. *Easter. Rome. Greece. Israel. Egypt. Athens. Bethlehem. Nazareth. Jerusalem. Galilee. Dead Sea. Tel Aviv. Haifa. Acre. Nile River. Paul VI (pope). Pantheon (Rome). Colosseum (Rome). Saint Peter's Basilica. Acropolis. Western Wall (Jerusalem). Sphinx of Giza. Pyramids (Egypt).*

Note: Narration delivered on stage by De La Varre.

THE GRAPE DEALER'S DAUGHTER   F6.1929

Hawk Serpent Productions. *Dist* Film-Makers' Distribution Center. Jan **1970** [Los Angeles showing]. Sd; col. 16mm. 90 min.

Prod-Dir-Writ Walter Gutman. *Photog* Walter Gutman, Louis Brigante, John Delaney. *Main Titl* Noel Stevenson. *Film Ed* Louis Brigante.

Cast: Anna Norteus *(The Grape Dealer's Daughter)*, Walter Gutman *(Bacchus)*, Linda Rubera *(Juicy Lucy)*, Paul Rubera *(Juicy Lucy's lover)*, Lucinda Love *(The Mother)*, David Harting *(The Little Boy)*, Paula Tighe, Charlene Hess *(girls at fair)*, Michael Levy, Marvin Scharfstein *(boys at fair)*, Hanne Weaver, Linda Rubin, Serafina Mafia, Trudy Young, Suzanne Perry, Judy Van Hook *(themselves)*.

Film portrait. Walter Gutman photographs a number of nubile women in his search for a young female lead to play the part of the "grape dealer's daughter" to his sexagenarian Bacchus. Finally he meets Juicy Lucy, a generously-endowed woman who is wearing only a fur coat. Lucy moves sensuously on a bed as Gutman discourses on such topics as his father, founder of the first Jewish golf course in the Midwest; his Chicago background; distinctions between the sexes; American history; and female acrobats. Finally, he and his lead [Juicy Lucy?] undress and rub grapes over their bodies during an orgy scene. *Jews. Acrobats. Sexuality. Nudity. Orgies. Chicago. Bacchus.*

THE GRASSHOPPER   F6.1930

National General Pictures. 27 May **1970** [New York opening]. Sd; col (Technicolor). 35mm. 95 min. *MPAA rating* R.

Prod Jerry Belson, Garry Marshall. *Dir* Jerry Paris. *Screenplay* Jerry Belson, Garry Marshall. *Photog* Sam Leavitt. *1st Asst Camera* Frank Stanley. *2d Asst Camera* Ray Brearly. *Camera Op* James R. Connell. *Art Dir* Tambi Larsen. *Set Dsgn* Alan Boulter, Louis C. Holmes, David Haber. *Set Decor* Donald J. Sullivan. *Film Ed* Aaron Stell. *Mus Score* William Goldenberg. *Titl Song Sung by* Bob Russell. *Sd Rec* John Muchmore. *Sd Mix* John Carter. *Boom* John K. Nelson. *Asst Dir* James Rosenberger, Joe Nayfack, Francis X. Shaw, Jr. *Unit Prod Mgr* Emmett Emerson. *Script Supv* H. Bud Otto. *Miss Bisset's Wardrobe* Donfeld. *Makeup* Gustaf M. Norin. *Sp Eff* Thol O. Simonson.

Cast: Jacqueline Bisset *(Christine Adams)*, Jim Brown *(Tommy Marcott)*, Joseph Cotten *(Richard Morgan)*, Corbett Monica *(Danny Raymond)*, Ramon Bieri *(Roosevelt Dekker)*, Christopher Stone *(Jay Rigney)*, Roger Garrett *(Buck Brown)*, Stanley Adams *(Buddy Miller)*, Dick Richards *(Lou Bellman)*, Tim O'Kelly *(Eddie Molina)*, Stefanianna Christopherson *(Libby)*, Ed Flanders *(Jack Bishop)*, Wendy Farrinton *(Connie)*, Sandi Gaviola *(Kyo)*, Eris Sandy *(Vicky)*, John David Wilder *(Timmy)*, Jay Laskay *(Manny)*, Jim Smith *(Larry)*, Therese Baldwin *(Gigi)*, Chris Wong *(Billy)*, Kathalynn Turner *(Ann Marie)*, William H. Bassett *(Aaron)*, Marc Hannibal *(Marion Walters)*, David Duclon *(Miller's son)*, Jessica Myerson *(saleswoman)*.

Drama. Source: Mark McShane, *The Passing of Evil* (London, 1961). Bored, 19-year-old Christine Adams leaves her home in British Columbia and journeys to Los Angeles to join her old boyfriend, Eddie. Forced to hitchhike when her car breaks down in Utah, she is picked up by nightclub comedian Danny Raymond, who takes her to Las Vegas. In spite of her attraction to the city, Christine follows through with her original plan but soon becomes bored with the rather unexciting Eddie and her own mundane bank teller's job. She returns to Las Vegas, becomes a hotel showgirl, and meets such new friends as homosexual chorus boy Buck Brown, rock musician Jay Rigney, and Tommy Marcott, a black ex-football star who does promotional work for the same hotel. Christine and Tommy get married, but their happiness is marred by Tommy's realization that his job merely exploits his past. Christine accepts an invitation to the room of tycoon Rosie Dekker in the hopes that he can advance her husband's career. Dekker beats her brutally when she refuses his advances, and

Tommy later retaliates by assaulting Dekker on the golf course. Christine and Tommy then move to Los Angeles and look for new jobs; but Christine tires of domesticity and writes a farewell note to her husband. As she prepares to leave, Tommy is murdered by one of Dekker's associates. Afterwards Christine begins to use drugs heavily. She returns to Las Vegas, but Dekker's blackballing prevents her from finding work, and she becomes first a high-priced call girl and then mistress to millionaire Richard Morgan, who wants to marry her. She takes up with her old friend Jay and permits him to pimp for her, in hopes of earning enough money to purchase a ranch where they can live happily forever. In time, Jay absconds with their large bankroll. Now completely alone and with no hopes for the future, Christine gets stoned on marijuana and entices a skywriter to write the work "fuck" in the air. Arrested and booked by the police, Christine, now 22 years old, has the haggard, down-and-out appearance of one who has been through it all. *Hitchhikers. Entertainers. Bank clerks. Negroes. Showgirls. Musicians. Athletes. Prostitutes. Mistresses. Millionaires. Pimps. Police. Miscegenation. Male homosexuality. Revenge. Desertion. Murder. Blacklisting. Skywriting. Hotels. Golf. Marijuana. Narcotics. British Columbia. Utah. Las Vegas. Los Angeles.*

Note: Film contains location footage of Utah and Las Vegas. Working title: *Angel.*

DER GRAUSAME JOB *see* **TO COMMIT A MURDER**

THE GRAVESIDE STORY *see* **THE COMEDY OF TERRORS**

GRAZIE, ZIA (Italy)   F6.1931

Doria G. Film. *Dist* Avco Embassy Pictures. 8 Jan **1969** [New York opening]. Sd; b&w. 35mm. 93 min.

Prod Enzo Doria. *Dir* Salvatore Samperi. *Screenplay* Sergio Bazzini, Pier Giuseppe Murgia, Salvatore Samperi. *Orig Story* Salvatore Samperi. *Photog* Aldo Scavarda. *Art Dir* Giorgio Mecchia Maddalena. *Film Ed* Alessandro Giselli. *Mus Comp* Ennio Morricone. *Mus Cond* Bruno Nicolai. *Prod Mgr* Ugo Novello.

Cast: Lisa Gastoni *(Lea)*, Lou Castel *(Alvise)*, Gabriele Ferzetti *(Stefano)*, Luisa De Santis, Nicoletta Rizzi, Massimo Sarchielli, Anita Dreyer.

Drama. Alvise, the 17-year-old son of a wealthy Italian financier, has developed a psychosomatic paralysis which keeps him confined to a wheelchair. When his parents take a trip to Hong Kong, Alvise is sent to stay at the villa of his youthful Aunt Lea, a doctor who for 15 years has been the mistress of liberal journalist Stefano. Alvise's presence has a disquieting effect upon Lea, and she gradually becomes dissatisfied with her relationship with Stefano. Alvise seems obsessed with reality; he plays minature war games based on the war in Vietnam, and at the same time he withdraws into his paralysis and his comic books. He vividly remembers his aunt putting to sleep her dog, who had been run over. Quick to seize an opportunity to destroy the longstanding affair, Alvise acts so grossly that soon they are alone at the villa, even the servants having left. Lea's passion is stimulated by a series of erotic games, but Alvise always ends them by refusing to make love as he had promised. As time passes, Lea eventually breaks off her relationship with Stefano, quits her job, and lives only for her nephew. Their games have become crueler; he forces her down a well and finally almost strangles her. Lea's sexual attraction to Alvise becomes stronger, however, as she bathes him and he masturbates in front of her. Upon the return of Alvise's parents, a final game is invented—"euthanasia." By now totally subjugated to her nephew's will, Lea follows his orders and administers a fatal injection which grants him ultimate release from reality. *Physicians. Paralytics. Journalists. Aunts. Adolescence. Mercy killing. Murder. Lust. Autoeroticism. Obsession. Psychosomatic illness. Sadism. Vietnam War 1964–73.*

Note: Opened in Rome in 1968; running time; 96 min. After east and west coast premieres the film was retitled *Come Play With Me.*

THE GREAT ARMORED CAR SWINDLE (Great Britain)   F6.1932

Butcher's Film Distributors. *Dist* Falcon Pictures, Taurus Film Co. **1963** [Maryland license: 2 Mar 1964]. Sd; b&w. 35mm. 59 min.

Prod-Writ Peter Lambert. *Dir* Lance Comfort. *Photog* Basil Emmott. *Art Dir* John Earl. *Film Ed* Peter Pitt. *Mus* Albert Elms. *Sd* Michael Hart. *Sd Rec* Richard Smith. *Asst Dir* Peter Medak.

Cast: Peter Reynolds *(Eric Winlatter)*, Dermot Walsh *(Robert Wade)*, Joanna Dunham *(Cherry Winlatter)*, Lisa Gastoni *(Eva)*, Brian Cobby *(Peter de Savory)*, Jack Allen *(Ernest Winlatter)*, Geoffrey Denton *(debt collector)*, Arnold Diamond *(Telling)*, Richard Golding *(Mintos)*, John G. Heller *(Mel)*, Mercia Mansfield *(Ernest's secretary)*, Peter Walker *(Alex)*, Eric Corrie *(Wilson)*, Desmond Cullum-Jones *(Evans)*, Charles Russell *(Cappel)*, Joe Wadham *(boxer)*, Gertan Klauber *(Lofty)*, John Lawrence *(security officer)*.

Crime melodrama. Source: Laurence Meynell, *The Breaking Point* (London, 1957). The government of Lalvadore, a Middle Eastern country, to prevent a Communist coup decides to change its currency and have it printed by a reputable London company. Eric Winlatter, nephew of the firm's owner and

deep in gambling debts, is forced to become part of the Communist scheme to substitute counterfeit bills for the new money. His wife, Cherry, discovers a note from Communist agent Peter de Savory and becomes suspicious of Eric's activities. Aided and accompanied by journalist Robert Wade, Cherry learns of the plot and races to the airport where Eric will make the exchange. Although Eric has a last-minute change of heart and tries to prevent the robbery, he is killed in the ensuing fracas. As the Communist scheme is aborted, Wade restrains Cherry from running to her dead husband. *Communists. Journalists. Secret agents. Debt. Conspiracy. Counterfeiting. Theft. Imaginary republics. Coups d'état. Airfields. Middle East. London. Documentation.*

Note: Released in Great Britain in 1961 as *The Breaking Point.*

THE GREAT BANK ROBBERY   F6.1933

Warner Bros.–Seven Arts, Inc.–Malcolm Stuart Productions. *Dist* Warner Bros.–Seven Arts, Inc. 24 Jun **1969** [Houston opening; c1 Jul 1969; LP38031]. Sd; col (Technicolor). 35mm (Panavision). 98 min. *MPAA rating* M.

A Malcolm Stuart Production. *Prod* Malcolm Stuart. *Assoc Prod* Richard Freed. *Dir* Hy Averback. *2d Unit Dir* Paul Baxley. *Screenplay* William Peter Blatty. *Dir Photog* Fred Koenekamp. *2d Unit Photog* Mark Davis. *Helicopter Camera* Jack Willoughby. *Aerial Photog* Tyler Camera Systems. *Set Decor* William L. Kuehl. *Prod Dsgn* Jack Poplin. *Titl Dsgn* Don Record. *Film Ed* Gene Milford. *Mus* Nelson Riddle. *Orch* Gil Grau. *Mus Supv* Sonny Burke. *Songs:* "The Rainbow Rider," "Heaven Helps Him Who Helps Himself" Sammy Cahn, James Van Heusen. *Sung By* Zero Mostel. *Vocal Arr* Ken Darby. *Choreog* Miriam Nelson. *Sd* Everett A. Hughes. *1st & 2d Asst Dir* Jack Cunningham, Howard Kazanjian. *Prod Mgr* Ben Chapman. *2d Unit Asst Dir* Fred Gammon. *Cost* Moss Mabry. *Makeup Artist* Al Greenway. *Supv Hairstylist* Jean Burt Reilly. *Sp Eff* Ralph Webb. *Ballooning* Paul Edward Yost.

Cast: Zero Mostel *(Rev. Pious Blue)*, Kim Novak *(Lyda Kabanov)*, Clint Walker *(Ben Quick)*, Claude Akins *(Slade)*, Akim Tamiroff *(Papa Pedro)*, Larry Storch *(Juan)*, John Anderson *(Kincaid)*, Sam Jaffe *(Brother Lilac)*, Mako *(Eliot Fong)*, Elisha Cook, Jr. *(Jeb)*, Ruth Warrick *(Mrs. Applebee)*, John Fiedler *(Brother Dismas)*, John Larch *(sheriff)*, Peter Whitney *(Brother Jordan)*, Norman Alden *(The Great Gregory)*, Grady Sutton *(Reverend Sims)*, William Zuckert *(ranger commander)*, Bob Steele *(1st guard)*, Ben Aliza *(2d guard)*, Mickey Simpson *(3d guard)*, Byron Keith *(deputy)*, Kenny Endoso, Roy Ogata, George Sasaki, Yoneo Iguchi, Hiroshi Hissamuri *(Chinese laundrymen)*, Bob Mitchell Boys Choir *(church choir)*.

Western comedy. Source: Frank O'Rourke, *The Great Bank Robbery* (New York, 1969). Slade, a gunfighter, robs a Texas train of a large shipment of gold and deposits it in a bank in the town of Friendly. The vault's contents are being sought by two rival gangs. Mexican bandit Papa Pedro and his men make two fumbling attempts to rob the vault, first by rushing the bank only to be chased away by a blast of gunfire, and then by attempting to break down the door with a battering ram. The second gang is led by the Rev. Pious Blue, who has established himself as the town's preacher; his associates, who include the beautiful Lyda Kabanov, plan to tunnel into the bank and dynamite the wall on the Fourth of July, when an explosion will go unnoticed. Texas Ranger Ben Quick, with his band of five Chinese secret service agents, is also trying to tunnel into the bank, but his mission is to obtain evidence that will incriminate Kincaid, the town's crooked mayor and owner of the bank. On the Fourth of July, Reverend Blue's gang reaches the vault first. While robbing the vault they accidentally discover the evidence against Kincaid; the gang is then chased by Quick until they come to a giant balloon waiting to take them to safety. The reverend miscalculates the weight of the gold, however, and the balloon is unable to rise. To lighten the load, Lyda jumps out, permitting the reverend to escape, and she remains with her lover, Quick; and the Texas Ranger gets the evidence needed to convict Kincaid. *Gunfighters. Bandits. Mexicans. Preachers. Chinese. Mayors. Bankers. Train robberies. Bank robberies. Gold. Vaults. Dynamite. Evidence. Balloons (ascent). Fourth of July. Texas. Texas Rangers. Chases.*

THE GREAT BATTLE OF EUROPE (U.S.S.R.)   F6.1934

Central Documentary Film Studio. *Dist* Artkino Pictures. 21 Dec **1963** [New York opening]. Sd; b&w. 35mm. 63 min.

Dir Fyodor Kiselyov. *Screenplay* N. Shpikovskiy. *Art Dir* I. Nizhnik, N. Koltsov, V. Sedov. *Mus Arr* Ilya Shveytser. *Sd* I. Gunger, D. Ovsyannikov. *Coöp* State Film Archives of the U.S.S.R.

Documentary. An exposition of the Soviet role in the European theater of World War II, utilizing historical footage selected from the state film archives of the U.S.S.R. *World War II. Europe. Union of Soviet Socialist Republics—Army.*

Note: Released in the U.S.S.R. in 1961 as *Velikaya pobeda sovetskogo naroda;* running time: ca80 min.

THE GREAT BATTLE OF THE VOLGA (U.S.S.R.)   **F6.1935**
Central Documentary Film Studio. *Dist* Artkino Pictures. 18 May **1963** [New York opening]. Sd; b&w. 35mm. 75 min.

Dir Mariya Slavinskaya. *Screenplay* Yuriy Smirnitskiy. *Narr* Aleksey Surkov. *Photog* (see note) B. Vakar, M. Goldbrikh, D. Ibragimov, I. Katsman, I. Malov, V. Orlyankin, M. Poselskiy, N. Vikhiryov, I. Goldshteyn, A. Kozakov, A. Krichevskiy, Ye. Mukhin, G. Ostrovskiy, A. Sofin, B. Shadronov. *Mus* Ye. Makarov. *Mus Arr* Z. Alimova. *Mus Selections* Dmitriy Dmitriyevich Shostakovich. *Military Adv* Lieutenant-General Platonov. *Coöp* State Film Archives of the U.S.S.R.

Documentary. A documentary of the battle of Stalingrad, utilizing historical footage. *World War II. Stalingrad. Volga River. Union of Soviet Socialist Republics—Army. Germany—Army.*

Note: Released in the U.S.S.R. in 1963 as *Velikaya bitva na Volge.* May be an expansion or reworking of the 1958 Soviet release *Velikaya bitva,* directed by Mariya Slavinskaya. The documentary footage was reportedly photographed by 150 army cameramen. May also be known as *The Great Battle on the Volga.*

THE GREAT BRITISH TRAIN ROBBERY (West Germany)   **F6.1936**
Norddeutscher Rundfunk—Real Film—Stella Film. *Dist* Peppercorn-Wormser, Inc. 5 Apr **1967** [New York opening]. Sd; b&w (print by Movielab). 35mm. 104 min.

Pres by Egon Monk. *Prod* Egon Monk. *Dir* John Olden, Claus Peter Witt. *Screenplay* Henry Kolarz. *Adtl Dial* Robert Muller. *Photog* Gerald Gibbs, Frank A. Banuscher. *Art Dir* Mathias Matthies. *Film Ed* Monika Tadsen-Erfurth, Oswald Hafenrichter, Gisela Quicker. *Mus* Heinz Funk. *Sd* Horst Faahs. *Prod Supv* Oswald Hirschmann. *Police Adv* Bill Heddon.

Cast: Horst Tappert *(Michael Donegan),* Hans Cossy *(Patrick Kinsey),* Günter Neutze *(Archibald Arrow),* Karl Heinz Hess *(Geoffrey Black),* Hans Reiser *(Thomas Webster),* Rolf Nagel *(Gerald Williams),* Harry Engel *(George Slowfoot),* Wolfran Schaerf *(Andrew Elton),* Günther Tabor *(Ronald Cameron),* Franz Mosthav *(Walter Lloyd),* Wolfried Lier *(Alfred Frost),* Kurt Conradi *(Arthur Finnegan),* Horst Beck *(Twinky),* Paul Edwin Roth *(Peter Masterson),* Kai Fischer *(Inge Masterson),* Siegfried Lowitz *(Inspector MacLeod),* Lothar Grutzner *(Sergeant Robbins),* Dirk Dautzenberg *(Sergeant Davies),* Albert Hoerrmann *(Montague),* Grit Böttcher *(Jennifer Donegan),* Hannelore Schroth *(Eileen Black),* Isa Miranda *(Mona),* Sylvia Lydi *(Suzy Fast).*

Crime drama. Source: Peta Fordham, *The Robbers' Tale; The Real Story of the Great Train Robbery* (London, 1965). Hiding behind the respected guise of a London antique dealer, criminal mastermind Michael Donegan is lured into a scheme for robbing the Royal Mail Train of a fortune in banknotes. Heading a gang of 12 other seasoned professionals, Donegan, who has had wartime experience with military trains, carefully plans each detail of the crime, including the robbery of a small airport to finance the operation. Then, with everything in readiness, the men stop the mail train by triggering an electrical switch, board the locomotive, and uncouple it and the mail coach from the other cars. Once they have the banknotes, they make their way to their hideout, a farmhouse. Almost immediately they begin to argue about a method of concealment; but reaching no agreement, some of the men take their share of the loot and return to London. Scotland Yard, aided by the full cooperation of the news media, descends upon the farmhouse and discovers scores of fingerprints that lead to the arrest and conviction of 10 gang members. Donegan and two other men, however, are still at large; they are secretly meeting to plot the escapes, one by one, of their imprisoned colleagues. *Masterminds. Antique dealers. Hijackers. Disguise. Train robberies. Prison escapes. Airfields. London. Scotland Yard.*

Note: Location scenes filmed in England. Produced in three 90 min segments for West German television in 1965 as *Die Gentlemen bitten zur Kasse.* May also be known in Germany as *Der Postzug-Überfall.* Based on the robbery of the Royal Mail Train on 8 Aug 1963.

GREAT CATHERINE (Great Britain)   **F6.1937**
Keep Films. *Dist* Warner Bros.-Seven Arts, Inc. Nov **1968** [c1 Nov 1968; LP37143]. Sd (Westrex); col (Technicolor). 35mm. 99 min. *MPAA rating* G.

A Jules Buck–Peter O'Toole Production. *Prod* Jules Buck. *Prod Exec* Harry Woolveridge. *Dir* Gordon Flemyng. *Screen Adapt* Hugh Leonard. *Dir Photog* Oswald Morris. *Camera Op* Brian West. *Art Dir* Bill Hutchinson. *Scenic Artist* Ferdie Bellan. *Set Dresser* Pamela Cornell. *Prod Dsgn* John Bryan. *Film Ed* Anne V. Coates. *Asst Film Ed* Barry Peters. *Mus Comp & Cond* Dimitri Tiomkin. *Choreog* Paddy Stone. *Sd Mix* Paddy Cunningham. *Dub Ed* Don Sharpe. *Asst Dir* Peter Bolton. *Prod Mgr* Ed Harper. *Asst to the Prod* Peter Perkins. *Cont* Phyllis Crocker. *Cost Dsgn* Margaret Furse. *Wardrobe Supv* Ivy Baker. *Wardrobe Master* Ron Beck. *Mr. O'Toole's Dresser* Arthur Newman. *Makeup Supv* Bill Lodge. *Ch Hairdresser* A. G. Scott. *Sp Eff* Bowie Films. *Stills Camera* Laurie Ridley. *Casting Dir* Maude Spector. *Constr Mgr* Leon Davis.

Cast: Peter O'Toole *(Captain Edstaston),* Zero Mostel *(Patiomkin),* Jeanne Moreau *(Catherine),* Jack Hawkins *(Sir George Gorse),* Akim Tamiroff *(sergeant),* Marie Lohr *(Dowager Lady Gorse),* Marie Kean *(Princess Dashkoff),* Kenneth Griffith *(Naryshkin),* Angela Scoular *(Claire),* Kate O'Mara *(Varinka),* Lea Seidl *(grand duchess),* Oliver MacGreevy *(General Pskov),* James Mellor *(Colonel Pugachov),* Claire Gordon *(Elizabeth Vokonska),* Declan Mulholland *(Count Tokhtamysh),* Henry Woolf *(Egrebyomka),* Catherine Lancaster *(Sophia),* Alfred Ravel, Gordon Rollings *(glaziers),* Sean Barrett *(Andrei Strelkin),* Alf Joint *(Russian general),* Reuben Martin, Yuri Borienko, Rupert Evans, Milton Reid *(sergeant's henchmen),* Dinny Powell, Tom Clegg *(Patiomkin's Mongols),* Gerald Lawson, Norma Foster *(unidentified roles),* Scobie *(ambassador's dog).*

Farce. Source: George Bernard Shaw, *Great Catherine* (London opening: 18 Nov 1913). Capt. Charles Edstaston of the Light Dragoons and British Ambassador Sir George Gorse seek an audience with Catherine the Great at the Winter Palace in St. Petersburg. They find the palace in a state of total disarray: pigs and chickens run rampant while the royal protector, Prince Patiomkin, gets roaring drunk. The Prince decides that Edstaston would make an ideal lover for Catherine and forcibly carries him to the empress' bed. Attracted to the young officer, Catherine orders him to wait while she dresses. Terrified, Edstaston flees and vows to leave Russia with his fiancée, Claire, the ambassador's daughter. Before he can do so he is taken prisoner by Cossacks who return him to the palace so that he can tell Catherine of his experiences at the battle of Bunker Hill. In Catherine's bathroom, where a vast model of the battle site has been constructed, they reenact the battle until Catherine provokes Edstaston's fury by wading into her sunken tub to sink a British warship. Edstaston again flees, but he is recaptured and returned to the palace again for a grand ball. He is caught up in a troupe of whirling Russian dancers and then whisked away to a secret chamber where Catherine playfully tortures him. The indignant Claire discovers them together, and Catherine allows the young woman to lead her fiancé away after he delivers a lecture on the virtues of British domesticity. *Russians. Royalty. Diplomats. Cossacks. Dancers. Drunkenness. Sexuality. Balls (formal gatherings). United States—History—Revolution. Saint Petersburg. Bunker Hill. Catherine the Great. Grigori Aleksandrovich Potëmkin. Great Britain—Army. Winter Palace.*

Note: Opened in London in Dec 1968.

THE GREAT CHASE   **F6.1938**
Harvey Cort. *Dist* Continental Distributing, Inc. 20 Dec **1962** [New York opening]. Sd; b&w. 35mm. 77 min.

Pres by Paul Killiam, Saul J. Turell. *Prod* Harvey Cort. *Screenplay* Harvey Cort, Paul Killiam, Saul J. Turell. *Main Titl* Ted Trinkaus. *Film Ed* Harvey Cort. *Mus Comp & Played by* Larry Adler. *Mus Arr & Cond* George Bassman. *Sd* Albert Gramaglia. *Sd Eff* Val Peters.

Narrator: Frank Gallop.

Featuring: Buster Keaton, Douglas Fairbanks, Sr., Lillian Gish, Pearl White, Jetta Goudal, Marion Mack, William S. Hart, Noah Beery, Richard Barthelmess, Ruth Roland, Rod La Roque, Dorothy Bernard.

Compilation film. Portions of the following films are used to show the evolution of the chase in silent films: *The Great Train Robbery* (1903), *Desperate Encounter* (1905), *A Girl and Her Trust* (1910), *Way Down East* (1920), *The Coming of Amos* (1925), *The Mark of Zorro* (1920), *The Perils of Pauline* (1914), *Die Grüne Hölle* [1938; also known as *Kautchuk,* retitled *Jungle Treasure* for this compilation], *Tumbleweeds* (1925), and *The General* (1927). *Motion pictures—History. Chases.*

THE GREAT DREAM *see* **THE EMBRACERS**

THE GREAT ESCAPE   **F6.1939**
Mirisch Corp.-Alpha Corp. *Dist* United Artists. 3 Jul **1963** [Los Angeles opening; c27 May 1963; LP25091]. Sd; col (DeLuxe). 35mm (Panavision). 168 min.

Prod-Dir John Sturges. *Screenplay* James Clavell, W. R. Burnett. *Photog* Daniel L. Fapp. *Art Dir* Fernando Carrere. *Film Ed* Ferris Webster. *Mus* Elmer Bernstein. *Sd* Harold Lewis. *Asst Dir* Jack Reddish. *Asst to Mr. Sturges* Robert E. Relyea. *Prod Mgr* Allen K. Wood. *Script Supv* John Franco. *Wardrobe* Bert Henrikson. *Makeup* Emile Lavigne. *Tech Adv* C. Wallace Floody. *Prop* Frank Agnone.

Cast: Steve McQueen *(Hilts),* James Garner *(Hendley),* Richard Attenborough *(Bartlett),* James Donald *(Ramsey),* Charles Bronson *(Danny Velinski),* Donald Pleasence *(Blythe),* James Coburn *(Sedgwick),* David McCallum *(Ashley-Pitt),* Gordon Jackson *(MacDonald),* John Leyton *(Willie),* Angus Lennie *(Ives),* Nigel Stock *(Cavendish),* Jud Taylor *(Goff),* William Russell, British *(Sorren),* Robert Desmond *(Griffith),* Tom Adams *(Nimmo),* Lawrence Montaigne *(Haynes),* Hannes Messemer *(Von Luger),* Robert Graf *(Werner),* Harry Riebauer *(Strachwitz),* Hans Reiser *(Kuhn),* Robert Freytag *(Posen),* Heinz Weiss *(Kramer),* Til Kiwe *(Frick),* Ulrich Beiger *(Preissen),*

George Mikell (*Dietrich*), Karl Otto Alberty (*Steinach*).

War drama. Source: Paul Brickhill, *The Great Escape* (New York, 1950). In 1942, Allied officers imprisoned in a Nazi stalag plan a mammoth escape. Under the guidance of British Squadron Leader Roger Bartlett, they begin digging tunnels "Tom," "Dick," and "Harry," one of which they hope will enable 250 men to leave the camp by going under the guards. The principal conspirators are: Hilts, a brash American known as "The Cooler King" because of the amount of time he spends in solitary confinement bouncing a baseball off the prison wall; Hendley, the American in charge of scrounging supplies; Danny Velinski, the claustrophobic Pole who supervises the digging; and Blythe, the forger who makes passports and visas. Other groups are organized to supply civilian clothes, draw maps, store rations, and make compasses. Although "Tom" is discovered by the Germans during a Fourth of July celebration staged by the Americans, the men continue working on the two remaining tunnels. Eventually, everything is ready, and the prisoners escape before the Germans can be alerted. The escapees travel by foot, train, plane, and boat, and Hilts leads the Germans in a spectacular motorcycle chase before crashing into a barbwire fence. Others, such as Blythe, are killed; but a few, such as Velinski, manage to make good the escape. Angered by the effort it has taken to recapture the prisoners, the Germans execute 50 of them. Others, such as Hendley and Hilts, are returned to the camp, and the latter is seen once again with his baseball in solitary confinement. *Nazis. Prisoners of war. Prison guards. Poles. Prison escapes. Forgery. Disguise. War crimes. Tunnels. Motorcycles. Fourth of July. World War II. Germany. United States Army. Great Britain— Army. Germany—Army. Documentation.*

Note: Location scenes filmed in Germany.

GREAT EXPLORATIONS WITH JOHN GLENN—AFRICA   F6.1940

Metromedia Producers Corp. 22 Jan **1969** [Bangor, Maine, opening]. Sd; col. 35mm. 120 min. *MPAA rating* G.

Overall Production Credits: *Prod-Writ* John Peer Nugent. *Assoc Prod* William L. Young, Jr. *Dir* N. H. Cominos. *Photog* André Gunn. *Film Ed* Graham Lee Mahin, Bud Friedgen. *Asst Film Ed* Paul Schremp, Marty Spiro. *Mus Ed* Igo Kantor. *In Charge of Prod* Harvey Bernhard. *Post-prod Supv* Christina Friedgen. *Natural Resources Adv* Harold Prowse. *Coöp* Julius Nyerere, Paul Sozigwa, Tanzania Wildlife Safaris Ltd., African Wildlife Leadership Foundation, The Conservation Foundation, Tanzania National Parks Department, Tanzania Game Division. *Professional Hunter* Tom Lithgow, Harold Prowse, Keith Cormack. *Sp Drawings of Stanley's Travels by* Marvin Werlin.

Production Credits for "The Trail of Stanley and Livingstone": *Prod-Writ* John Peer Nugent. *Exec Prod* Alan Landsburg. *Assoc Prod* Joan Kaplan. *Dir* N. H. Cominos. *Photog* André Gunn. *Film Ed* Bud Friedgen. *Supv Film Ed* Lawrence E. Neiman. *Neg Cutter* Elva Fraser. *Asst Neg Cutter* Christina Friedgen. *Mus* Lyn Murray. *Mus Dir* Jack Tillar. *Sd Engr* Hans L. Koekoek, David Ronne, Bob Litt. *Sd Eff Ed* Charles Campbell, Roger Sword.

With: John Glenn, Harold Prowse, Tom Lithgow.

Narrator: Robert Colbert.

Documentary. On safari in Africa, Col. John Glenn, accompanied by natural resources specialist Harold Prowse, retraces the route taken by journalist Henry Morton Stanley in search of missionary David Livingstone in 1871. Leaving the coastal town of Bagamoyo, Glenn travels through Tanzania, exploring the various animal kingdoms and tribal domains. *Animal life. Tribal life. Safaris. Africa. Tanzania. Bagamoyo. Henry Morton Stanley. David Livingstone.*

Note: Filmed on location in Tanzania. Expanded from *The Trail of Stanley and Livingstone*, a 52-min program produced by Wolper Productions for the "Great Explorations" series; telecast on NBC on 11 Jan 1968. Also advertised as *Great Exploration With Col. John Glenn—Africa.*

THE GREAT GUNFIGHTER see GUNFIGHT AT COMANCHE CREEK

THE GREAT IMPOSTOR   F6.1941

Universal Pictures. 15 Feb **1961** [Boston opening; c18 Dec 1960; LP24330]. Sd; b&w. 35mm. 112 min.

Prod Robert Arthur. *Dir* Robert Mulligan. *Screenplay* Liam O'Brien. *Dir Photog* Robert Burks. *Art Dir* Alexander Golitzen, Henry Bumstead, Robert Luthardt. *Set Decor* Julia Heron. *Film Ed* Frederic Knudtson. *Mus* Henry Mancini. *Mus Supv* Joseph Gershenson. *Sd* Waldon O. Watson, Frank H. Wilkinson. *Asst Dir* Joseph Kenny, Charles Scott, Jr. *Unit Prod Mgr* Edward K. Dodds. *Makeup* Bud Westmore. *Hairstyles* Larry Germain. *Tech Adv* James Plomer, (Comdr. RCN).

Cast: Tony Curtis (*Ferdinand Waldo Demara, Jr.*), Karl Malden (*Father Devlin*), Edmond O'Brien (*Captain Glover*), Arthur O'Connell (*Warden Chandler*), Gary Merrill (*Pa Demara*), Joan Blackman (*Catherine Lacey*), Raymond Massey (*Abbot Donner*), Robert Middleton (*Prison Lieutenant Brown*), Jeanette Nolan (*Ma Demara*), Sue Ane Langdon (*Eulalia*), Larry

Gates (*cardinal*), Mike Kellin (*Mike Thompson*), Frank Gorshin (*Barney*), Cindi Wood (*WAC lieutenant*), Dick Sargent (*Seaman Hotchkiss*), Robert Crawford, Jr. (*Fred Demara, Jr. [as a boy]*), Doodles Weaver (*farmer*), Ward Ramsey (*Executive Officer Howard*), David White (*Dr. Hammond*), Philip Ahn (*Hun Kim*), Herbert Rudley (*senior officer*), Jerry Paris (*defense lieutenant*), Harry Carey, Jr. (*Dr. Joseph Mornay*), Willard Sage (*Lieutenant Thornton*).

Biographical drama. Source: Robert Crichton, *The Great Impostor* (New York, 1959). Arrested by state troopers on an island off the coast of Maine, Ferdinand Waldo Demara, Jr., thinks back over his life as he is taken by boat to the mainland: Frustrated by lack of formal education, young Demara hopes to attain success by deception and short cuts. His village priest, Father Devlin, tries to warn him against this attitude; but when Demara is drafted, he goes AWOL, assumes the identity of a Harvard professor, and gets a commission in the Marines. When he learns that the FBI will check his forged credentials, he fakes a suicide and disappears. He then lies his way into a Trappist order but withdraws because of the rigorous monastic discipline. He is caught by military police and is sent to a disciplinary barracks, where he quickly makes friends with the warden. Upon his release, Demara "borrows" the warden's identity and is hired by a penitentiary where J. B. Chandler is warden. Though he succeeds in taming the toughest cell block of criminals, he is once more forced to move on when a former jailmate appears and threatens to blackmail him. Demara then masquerades as a Canadian Navy doctor and falls in love with a young nurse, Catherine Lacey. They plan marriage, but his ship is sent to the Korean war zone, and Demara is forced to leave Catherine. After extracting a tooth from his commanding officer, he successfully performs 19 emergency operations, from which he receives so much publicity that he is once more exposed. He talks himself out of a court-martial, however, and goes on to become a smalltown schoolteacher. At this point in Demara's story, the boat docks, and the troopers discover that Demara has disappeared. When he learns that the State Department is looking for him and has summoned one of the troopers, the hoaxer assumes still another identity—that of the state trooper. *Schoolteachers. Priests. Professors. Trappists. Prison wardens. Nurses. Surgeons. Police. Imposture. Blackmail. Forgery. Dentists. Prisons. Korean War 1950–53. Ferdinand Waldo Demara, Jr. United States Marines. Canada— Navy. Harvard University.*

THE GREAT ONE see A NIGHT WITH THE GREAT ONE

THE GREAT RACE   F6.1942

Patricia–Jalem–Reynard Co. *Dist* Warner Bros. Pictures. 1 Jul **1965** [Los Angeles opening; c15 Jun 1965; LP32421]. Sd; col (Technicolor). 35mm (Panavision). 157 min. [See note.]

Prod Martin Jurow. *Assoc Prod* Dick Crockett. *Dir* Blake Edwards. *Screenplay* Arthur Ross. *Orig Story* Blake Edwards, Arthur Ross. *Dir Photog* Russell Harlan. *2d Unit Photog* Harold Wellman. *Set Decor* George James Hopkins. *Decor Cons* Reg Allen, Jack Stevens. *Prod Dsgn* Fernando Carrere. *Main Titl* DePatie-Freleng. *Film Ed* Ralph E. Winters. *Mus* Henry Mancini. *Song:* "He Shouldn't-a, Hadn't-a, Oughtn't-a Swang on Me" Henry Mancini, Johnny Mercer. *Sung by* Dorothy Provine. *Song:* "The Sweetheart Tree" Henry Mancini, Johnny Mercer. *Sung by* Natalie Wood. *Choreog* Hermes Pan. *Sd* M. A. Merrick. *Asst Dir* Mickey McCardle, Jack Cunningham, Dick Landry. *Unit Prod Mgr* Clem Beauchamp, Jack McEdward, Charles Hansen. *Script Supv* Betty Abbott. *Cost Dsgn* Don Feld. *Miss Wood's Clothes* Edith Head. *Makeup Supv* Gordon Bau. *Hairstyles for Miss Wood Created by* Sydney Guilaroff. *Supv Hairstylist* Jean Burt Reilly. *Sp Eff* Danny Lee. *Sp Photog Eff* Linwood Dunn, James Gordon. *Dial Supv* Ken Wales.

Cast: Jack Lemmon (*Professor Fate*), Tony Curtis (*The Great Leslie*), Natalie Wood (*Maggie DuBois*), Peter Falk (*Max*), Keenan Wynn (*Hezekiah*), Arthur O'Connell (*Henry Goodbody*), Vivian Vance (*Hester Goodbody*), Dorothy Provine (*Lily Olay*), Larry Storch (*Texas Jack*), George Macready (*General Kuhster*), Ross Martin (*Rolfe von Stuppe*), Marvin Kaplan (*Frisbee*), Hal Smith (*Major of Boracho*), Denver Pyle (*sheriff*), William Bryant, Ken Wales (*Baron's guards*), J. Edward McKinley (*chairman*), Robert S. Carson (*vice chairman*), Paul Smith, actor 1 (*1st employee*), Frank Kreig (*starter*), Charles Fredericks (*M. C.*), Clegg Hoyt (*man*), Charles Seel (*freight agent*), Joe Palma (*conductor*), Paul Bryar (*policeman*), Chester Hayes (*man in bear suit*), Chuck Hayward, Greg Benedict (*soldiers*), Ken Wales, Robert Herron (*palace guards*), William Bryant (*guard*), John Truax (*prison guard*), Johnny Silver, Hal Riddle (*bakers*).

Comedy. In 1908 in New York City, the villainous Professor Fate challenges The Great Leslie to a New York-to-Paris automobile race. Fate and his assistant Max enter their black Hannibal 8 against the white Leslie Special. At the starting line, Fate sets boobytraps for the other competitors and destroys their cars, except for Leslie's and the Stanley Steamer of Maggie DuBois, a feminist reporter for a New York newspaper. Her car breaks down, and she (with pigeons that send dispatches to New York) is picked up by Leslie and leads him to some gasoline that Professor Fate overlooked when he destroyed the supplies. They meet again in Alaska as both cars come to rest on an ice floe. They drift across the Bering Strait to Siberia; Fate then kidnaps Maggie; and both parties make their way to the Baltic republic of Carpania, ruled by Prince Hapnick (who looks exactly like Fate). Evil Baron von Stuppe uses Fate's likeness to begin a revolution. Fate escapes, however, and the race continues into France. Maggie has again joined Leslie, who proves his love for her when he stops his car a few feet from the finish line to kiss her. Fate, some distance behind, catches up with Leslie and is the first to cross the finish line; but he realizes that Leslie was the real winner. The three turn around and head back to New York. *Reporters. Royalty. Doubles. Automobile racing. Sabotage. Feminism. Kidnaping. Revolutions. Mines (war explosives). Gasoline. Ice floes. New York City. Alaska. Paris. Siberia. Bering Strait.* Stanley Steamer automobiles. Hannibal automobiles. Pigeons.

Note: Location scenes filmed in Salzburg, Vienna, and Paris. Also reviewed at 150 min and copyrighted at 180 min.

THE GREAT ST. TRINIAN'S TRAIN ROBBERY (Great Britain)
                                               F6.1943

Braywild. *Dist* British Lion Films, Gary Dartnall. 20 Dec **1967** [Washington, D. C., opening]. Sd; col (Eastman Color). 35mm. 94 min.

Prod Leslie Gilliat. *Dir* Frank Launder, Sidney Gilliat. *Screenplay* Frank Launder, Ivor Herbert. *Dir Photog* Ken Hodges. *Adtl Photog* Bert Mason. *Art Dir* Albert Witherick. *Film Ed* Geoffrey Foot. *Mus & Mus Dir* Malcolm Arnold. *Sd Rec* Cecil Mason, Bob Jones. *Asst Dir* Peter Price, Anthony Waye. *Prod Mgr* Eddie Pike. *Cost* Honoria Plesch.

Cast—The Gang: Frankie Howerd *(Alphonse Askett)*, Reg Varney *(Gilbert)*, Desmond Walter Ellis *(Leonard Edwards)*, Norman Mitchell *(William)*, Larry Martyn *(Chips)*, Cyril Chamberlain *(Maxie)*, Arthur Mullard *(Big Jim)*, Stratford Johns *(The Voice)*.

Cast—The Ministry: Raymond Huntley *(minister)*, Richard Wattis *(Bassett)*, Peter Gilmore *(Butters)*, Eric Barker *(Culpepper Brown)*, George Benson *(Gore-Blackwood)*, Michael Ripper *(liftman)*, Godfrey Winn *(Truelove)*, Lisa Lee *(Miss Brenner)*, Edwina Coven *(Dr. Judd)*.

Cast—The School: Dora Bryan *(Amber Spottiswood)*, Barbara Couper *(Mabel Radnage)*, Elspeth Duxbury *(Veronica Bledlow)*, Maggie McGrath *(Magsa O'Riley)*, Margaret Nolan *(Susie Naphill)*, Jean St. Clair *(Drunken Dolly)*, Carole Ann Ford *(Albertine)*, George Cole *(Flash Harry)*, Portland Mason *(Georgina)*, Maureen Crombie *(Marcia Askett)*.

Additional Cast: Colin Gordon *(Noakes)*, Leon Thau *(Pakistani porter)*, Meredith Edwards *(chairman)*, Jeremy Clyde *(Monty)*, Aubrey Morris *(Hutch)*, William Kendall *(Mr. Parker)*, Terry Scott.

Comedy. Inspired by the drawings of: Ronald Searle. Amber Spottiswood, headmistress of St. Trinian's School, receives a grant from her lover, the new minister of schools, to reopen her notorious school. She arranges to have Mabel Radnage, the head deputy, released from prison and then recalls the rest of the staff from temporary jobs such as stripteasing and modeling. Classes are soon underway again, to the dismay of train robbers who have stashed £2,500,000 under the school's ballroom stage. The leader of the gang, Alphonse Askett, enrolls his two daughters at St. Trinian's to aid the gang, and they decide to recover the money on parents' day. Though the gang members disguise themselves as caterers, they are discovered by both the girls and Flash Harry, the school bookie. Alphonse and his men manage to transfer the money to a stolen train and make their escape, but the schoolgirls pursue them in another train. The police soon join the chase in a third train, and the girls, having taken the money from the gang, find they must turn it over to the authorities. Using their ingenuity, the girls claim the reward money and receive medals for their good deed. *Headmistresses. Schoolteachers. Robbers. Bookies. Police. Train robberies. Disguise. Boarding schools. Trains. Rewards. Chases.*

Note: Released in Great Britain in Mar 1966; running time: 102 min. Originally released in the U. S. by Gary Dartnall, a representative of British Lion Corp. One of a series of comedies based on the drawings of Ronald Searle.

THE GREAT SIOUX MASSACRE
                                               F6.1944

F. & F. Productions. *Dist* Columbia Pictures. 16 Sep **1965** [Minot, North Dakota, opening; c1 Jun 1965; LP31607]. Sd (Westrex); col (Pathé). 35mm (Cinemascope). 91 min.

Prod Leon Fromkess. *Asst Prod* Rita Fromkess. *Dir* Sidney Salkow. *Screenplay* Fred C. Dobbs. *Story* Sidney Salkow, Marvin A. Gluck. *Dir Photog* Irving Lippman. *Art Dir* Frank Sylos. *Film Ed* William Austin. *Mus* Emil Newman, Edward B. Powell. *Sd Mix* John Bury, Samuel Goldwyn Studio Sound Dept. *Sd Eff Ed* Milton Mann. *Mus Ed* Edna Bullock. *Asst Dir* Abby Berlin. *Prod Mgr* Herbert G. Luft. *Script Supv* Duane Toler. *Wardrobe* Frank Tauss. *Makeup Artist* Beau Wilson. *Hairstyles* Doris Kurkus. *Sp Eff* Jack Erickson. *Tech Adv* Iron Eyes Cody. *Prop Master* Ted Cooper.

Cast: Joseph Cotten *(Major Reno)*, Darren McGavin *(Captain Benton)*, Philip Carey *(Col. George Armstrong Custer)*, Julie Sommars *(Caroline Reno)*,

Nancy Kovack *(Libbie Custer)*, John Matthews *(Dakota)*, Michael Pate *(Sitting Bull)*, Don Haggerty *(Sen. James Gillespie Blaine)*, Frank Ferguson *(Gen. Alfred Howe Terry)*, Stacy Harris *(Mr. Turner)*, Iron Eyes Cody *(Crazy Horse)*, House Peters, Jr. *(reporter)*, John Napier *(Tom Custer)*, William Tannen *(miner)*, Blair Davies *(presiding officer)*, Louise Serpa *(Mrs. Turner)*.

Historical drama. A United States Army disciplinary court charges Major Reno with responsibility for the slaughter at Custer's Last Stand. Captain Benton takes the stand to refute the charges against Reno and take the blame for the Sioux massacre of cavalry troops headed by Col. George Armstrong Custer. He relates the situations that led Custer and his men to slaughter on the banks of the Little Big Horn River. *Captain Benton joins Custer's staff because they both believe that the Indians should receive fair treatment from the United States Government. Soon Benton meets Major Reno's daughter Caroline, and they fall in love. Colonel Custer accuses powerful government officials in Washington, D.C., of cheating the Indians through deals with corrupt Indian agents, and, as a result, he loses his command and lives in forced retirement. Sen. James Blaine approaches Custer and offers his reinstatement and a chance to become President of the United States if he will agree to oppress the Indians. Thinking he will become a public hero, Custer, accompanied by a reporter, compromises his principles and murders Indians at every chance. Encouraged by his ambitious wife, Libbie, Custer follows orders to lead his men into a great battle against the Sioux. When he and his forces reach the Little Big Horn River, the Indian units, led by Chiefs Crazy Horse and Sitting Bull, prove stronger. The Sioux kill Custer and massacre his soldiers. After Benton finishes the story, the military board decides that nothing amiss has occurred and ends the inquiry.* Politicians. Reporters. Indian agents. Sioux Indians. Political corruption. Courts-martial. Ambition. Bribery. Massacres. United States—History—Indian campaigns. Little Big Horn. Washington (District of Columbia). George Armstrong Custer. Sitting Bull. Crazy Horse. James Gillespie Blaine. Alfred Howe Terry. Marcus A. Reno. Frederick W. Benteen. Elizabeth Bacon Custer. United States Army—Cavalry.

Note: Location scenes filmed in Tucson, Arizona. Working titles: *The Custer Massacre* and *Massacre at the Rosebud.*

THE GREAT SPY CHASE (France)
                                               F6.1945

S. N. E. Gaumont. *Dist* American International Pictures. Apr **1966** [c20 Apr 1966; LP32746]. Sd; b&w. 35mm. 84 min.

Prod-Dir Georges Lautner. *Exec Prod* Alain Poiré. *Assoc Prod* Robert Sussfeld, Jean Mottet. *Screenplay* Michel Audiard, Albert Simonin. *Dial* Michel Audiard. *Dir Photog* Maurice Fellous. *Art Dir* Jacques d' Ovidio. *Mus* Michel Magne.

Cast: Lino Ventura *(Lagneau)*, Bernard Blier *(Cafarelli)*, Francis Blanche *(Vassilieff)*, Mireille Darc *(Amaranthe)*, Charles Millot *(Muller)*, André Weber *(Rossini)*, Jess Hahn *(O'Brien)*, Jacques Balutin *(Le Douanier)*, Robert Dalban *(Le Camionneur)*, Michèle Marceau *(Rosalinde)*, Noël Roquevert.

Comedy-melodrama. Attending the funeral of a scientist who died at a French brothel are four secret agents—French, Russian, Swiss, and German— each of whom hopes to persuade the scientist's widow, Amaranthe, an ex-striptease artist, to part with her husband's plans for bacteriological and thermonuclear weapons. Also intent on obtaining the plans are a CIA agent with vast funds at his disposal and a great number of Chinese communists. The rival parties, variously disguised, descend upon Amaranthe's chateau to make overtures to the widow. The agents plot each other's demise but are forced to pool their talents to repel the onslaught of the Chinese. Eventually the French agent, Lagneau, gains the advantage by appealing to the widow's romantic nature, intimating that a marriage proposal is in the offing, although he is already married. The two sneak off to Lisbon, where the plans are held in a bank, but the other spies follow. Nevertheless, Lagneau's charms win out, and, as he boards the Paris express with Amaranthe and the documents, he happily contemplates his future as a bigamist. His wife, however, has learned of his success and awaits his arrival at the railroad station. *Scientists. Secret agents. Widows. Stripteasers. Russians. Swiss. Germans. Chinese. Americans in foreign countries. Murder. Seduction. Whorehouses. Funerals. Nuclear weapons. Castles. Lisbon. United States—Central Intelligence Agency.*

Note: Paris opening: Dec 1964 as *Les barbouzes;* running time: 115 min.

THE GREAT SPY MISSION see OPERATION CROSSBOW

GREAT TASTE see ODD TASTES

THE GREAT THAW see CIVILISATION: THE GREAT THAW

THE GREAT VAN ROBBERY (Great Britain)
                                               F6.1946

Danziger Productions. *Dist* United Artists. Feb **1963** [c5 Feb 1959; LP24338]. Sd; b&w. 35mm. 73 min.

Prod Edward J. Danziger, Harry Lee Danziger. *Dir* Max Varnel. *Story* Brian Clemens, Eldon Howard. *Photog* Nicolas Roeg. *Art Dir* Eric Blakemore. *Film Ed* Maurice Rootes. *Mus* Leon Young, Edwin Astley, Albert Elms. *Sd Rec*

Allan H. Brown.

Cast: Denis Shaw (*Caesar Smith*), Kay Callard (*Ella*), Tony Quinn (*Mercer*), Philip Saville (*Cartier*), Vera Fusek (*Mara*), Tony Doonan (*Wally*), Geoffrey Hibbert (*Venner*), Bob Simmons (*Peters*), Carl Duering (*Delgano*).

Crime drama. Scotland Yard asks INTERPOL agent Caesar Smith to investigate a large bank deposit in Rio de Janeiro, which has been found to contain some of the fortune in bank notes stolen from a Royal Mint van. Smith learns that the money has been used to buy a coffee consignment and follows the trail to Rome, Paris, and back to London, where he prevents Cartier, an apparently honest importer, from sending payment for the shipment. After Venner, the cargo's purchaser, is found murdered, Smith goes to Cartier's warehouse and finds the rest of the stolen money. A fight ensues when the importer arrives, and Ella, Cartier's girl friend, tries to run down Smith with her car; instead, the vehicle skids on some coffee beans and pins her lover to a wall. *Secret agents. Importers. Robbery. Murder. Coffee. London. Rio de Janeiro. Rome. Paris. Scotland Yard. INTERPOL. Automobile accidents.*

Note: Released in Great Britain in Feb 1959.

THE GREAT VARIETY　　　　　　　　　　　　　　F6.1947
Hollywood Mystery Films. *Dist* V. Dantini. 28 Sep **1965** [Maryland license]. Sd; b&w. 35mm. 66 min.

Narrator: V. Dantini.

Compilation film. No information about the precise nature of this film has been found, but censorship board records suggest that it is a compilation of short films.

THE GREAT WALL (Japan)　　　　　　　　　　　F6.1948
Daiei Motion Picture Co. *Dist* Magna Pictures. Sep **1965**. Sd; col (Technicolor). 35mm (Technirama). 104 min. [Cut from 120 min.]

Pres by Marshall Naify. *Prod* Masaichi Nagata. *Dir* Shigeo Tanaka. *Dir Dub Vers* Brett Morrison. *Screenplay* Fuji Yahiro. *Photog* Michio Takahashi. *Film Ed* Tatsuji Nakashizu. *Mus* Akira Ifukube.

Cast: Shintaro Katsu (*Emperor Shih Huang Ti*), Fujiko Yamamoto (*Princess Chu*), Ken Utsui (*Crown Prince Tan*), Hiroshi Kawaguchi (*Hsi Liang*), Ayako Wakao (*Chiang-nu*), Kojiro Hongo (*Li Hei*), Raizo Ichikawa (*Ching Ko*), Ganjiro Nakamura (*Hsu Fu*), Eijiro Tono (*Li Tang*), Isuzu Yamada (*dowager empress*), Ken Mitsuda (*Mencius*), Junko Kano, Kazuo Hasegawa, Machiko Kyo.

Historical epic. In 230 B. C., warrior Shih Huang Ti unifies China by conquering all the warring tribes. He builds a luxurious palace, fills it with beautiful women, and marries Princess Chu, who at first tries to kill him for ordering her father's death. Although the tyrant proposes sweeping modernization for the country, his opponents employ expert swordsman Ching Ko to assassinate him. Their plot fails, and Shih Huang Ti rousts the opposition in a chariot fight. After his wife is murdered by invading hordes from the north, the emperor orders the erection of the Great Wall to protect his country. Obsessed with this grandiose project, he brutally oppresses the enslaved laborers, among whom is Hsi Liang, a young scholar who is tortured on the day he is to wed Chiang-nu. Later, an earthquake halts construction, and in order to appease the gods, the emperor sacrifices Hsi Liang by burying him alive in the wall. Chiang-nu, denounced as a witch, is saved from execution by Li Hei, son of the emperor's favorite guard. The troubled ruler, having defied the will of the people, is killed by an assassin, and civil war again erupts throughout the country. *Despots. Royalty. Nationalism. Marriage. Assassination. Conspiracy. Slavery. Torture. Human sacrifice. Uprisings. Chariots. China. Shih Huang Ti. China—History—Ch'in Dynasty. Great Wall of China. Earthquakes.*

Note: Filmed on location in Taiwan. Released in Japan in 1962 as *Shin no shikotei* in 70mm Super Technirama; running time: 160 min.

THE GREAT WAR (France/Italy)　　　　　　　　F6.1949
Dino De Laurentiis Cinematografica–Gray Films. *Dist* Lopert Pictures. 30 Aug **1961** [New York opening; c20 Aug 1961; LP21675]. Sd; b&w. 35mm (CinemaScope). 118 min.

Pres by Dino De Laurentiis. *Prod* Dino De Laurentiis. *Dir* Mario Monicelli. *Screenplay* Age & Scarpelli, Luciano Vincenzoni, Mario Monicelli. *Story* Luciano Vincenzoni. *Photog* Giuseppe Rotunno, Roberto Gerardi. *Art Dir* Mario Garbuglia. *Film Ed* Adriana Novelli. *Mus* Nino Rota. *Mus Dir* Franco Ferrara. *Prod Mgr* Alfredo De Laurentiis, Giorgio Adriani.

Cast: Vittorio Gassman (*Giovanni Busacca*), Alberto Sordi (*Oreste Jacovacci*), Silvana Mangano (*Constantina*), Folco Lulli (*Bordin*), Bernard Blier (*Capitano Castelli*), Romolo Valli (*Tenente Gallina*), Vittorio Sanipoli (*Maggiore Venturi*), Nicola Arigliano (*Giardino*), Mario Valdemarin (*Aspirante Loquenzi*), Tiberio Mitri (*Mandich*), Livio Lorenzon (*Sergente Battiferri*), Tiberio Murgia (*Nicotra*), Carlo D'Angelo (*Capitano Ferri*), Marcello Giorda (*Il Generale*), Guido Celano (*Italian major*), Luigi Fainelli (*Giacomazzi*), Gerard Herter (*German captain*), Achille Compagnoni (*military chaplain*), Geronimo Meynier (*messenger*), Elsa Vazzoler (*Bordin's wife*),

Ferruccio Amendola (*Deconcini*).

War drama. In Italy shortly after the outbreak of World War I, Giovanni Busacca is ordered to enlist in the army in exchange for amnesty from certain criminal charges. At the enlistment center he bribes Oreste Jacovacci to obtain a deferment, but Oreste does nothing to help him. Later, the two men are sent to the front on the same troop train and forget their differences as they pool their wits to avoid arduous tasks. On the eve of a battle, the company goes AWOL, and Giovanni spends the night with a prostitute, Constantina, who steals his wallet. The next day he is forced to fight in a bloody battle that results in the capture of some Austrian installations. Sent with Oreste to obtain supplies in town, Giovanni with difficulty wrests his wallet from Constantina but realizes that he loves her. Rather than participate in the battle that is raging at their camp, the two friends admit their cowardice and spend the night in town. In the morning they find that their company has been decimated, but the townspeople, thinking that they are among the survivors, welcome them with an incongruous patriotic display. Giovanni and Oreste decide to desert rather than face more enemy gunfire, but a meeting with the wife of a comrade who has been killed in battle so moves them that they rejoin their outfit. They are sent on a special mission to deliver a message to another installation but are captured by the Austrians, who demand information about an emergency pontoon bridge the Italians are building to bring in relief troops. Giovanni, who knows where the bridge is, refuses to betray his comrades and is shot. Oreste, who does not have the information, also is killed in spite of a hysterical effort to save himself. The major, remarking on the absence of the two rascals from the next battle, assumes that they have once more managed to goldbrick their way out of combat. [Sources disagree on the precise ending of the film. According to some sources, both friends are shot when they refuse to betray their comrades.] *Prostitutes. Deserters—Military. Cowardice. Heroism. Combat zone life. Patriotism. Theft. Bribery. Bridges. World War I. Italy—Army. Austria—Army.*

Note: Opened in Rome in Oct 1959 as *La grande guerra*; running time: ca135 min.; in Paris in May 1960 as *La grande guerre*; running time: 128 min. Venice Film Festival running time: 140 min.

THE GREAT WHITE HOPE　　　　　　　　　　　F6.1950
Lawrence Turman Films. *Dist* Twentieth Century–Fox Film Corp. 11 Oct **1970** [New York opening; c11 Oct 1970; LP38328]. Sd (Westrex); col (DeLuxe). 35mm (Panavision). 103 min. *MPAA rating* GP.

A Lawrence Turman–Martin Ritt Production. *Prod* Lawrence Turman. *Dir* Martin Ritt. *Screenplay* Howard Sackler. *Dir Photog* Burnett Guffey. *Art Dir* Jack Martin Smith. *Asst Art Dir* Harry Kemm. *Set Decor* Walter M. Scott, Raphael Bretton. *Prod Dsgn* John De Cuir. *Film Ed* William Reynolds. *Mus Supv* Lionel Newman. *Song:* "Let Me Hold You in My Arms Tonight" writ & perf by Jesse Fuller. *Choreog* Donald McKayle. *Asst Dir* Jack Solomon, Ted Soderberg, Vinton Vernon. *Asst Dir & Spanish Asst Dir* Tim Zinnemann, José López Rodero. *Unit Prod Mgr* Saul Wurtzel. *Location Mgr* William Venegas. *Spanish Prod Mgr* Tadeo Villalba. *Script Supv* Marvin Weldon. *Cost Dsgn* Irene Sharaff. *Wardrobe* Mickey Sherrard, Ed Wynigear, Dorothy Drake. *Makeup Supv* Dan Striepeke. *Makeup* Ed Butterworth, Paul Stanhope. *Hairstyles* Pat Abbott, Nadine Reed. *Sp Photog Eff* L. B. Abbott, Art Cruickshank. *Tech Adv* Mushy Callahan. *Prop Master* Dennis Parrish. *Vocal Coach* Thurston Frazier. *Constr Coörd* Don Nobles. *Key Grip* Lou Pazelli. *Casting* Michael McLean.

Cast: James Earl Jones (*Jack Jefferson*), Jane Alexander (*Eleanor Bachman*), Lou Gilbert (*Goldie*), Joel Fluellen (*Tick*), Chester Morris (*Pop Weaver*), Robert Webber (*Dixon*), Marlene Warfield (*Clara*), R. G. Armstrong (*Cap'n Dan*), Hal Holbrook (*Cameron*), Beah Richards (*Mama Tiny*), Moses Gunn (*Scipio*), Lloyd Gough (*Smitty*), George Ebeling (*Fred*), Larry Pennell (*Brady*), Roy Glenn (*pastor*), Bill Walker (*deacon*), Marcel Dalio (*French promoter*), Rodolfo Acosta (*El Jefe*), Virginia Capers (*Sister Pearl*), Rockne Tarkington (*Rudy*), Oscar Beregi (*Ragosy*), Karl Otto Alberty (*Hans*), Jim Beattie (*The Kid*), Scatman Crothers (*Barker*), Manuel Padilla, Jr. (*Paco*), Basil Dignam (*English official*).

Biographical drama. Source: Howard Sackler, *The Great White Hope* (Washington, D. C., opening: 7 Dec 1967). In the first decade of the 20th century boxer Jack Jefferson beats Frank Brady in Reno and becomes the first black heavyweight champion of the world. To the consternation of his common-law wife Clara and the militant Scipio, the irrepressible fighter takes as his mistress white divorcée Eleanor Bachman. After crossing the Illinois-Wisconsin state line with Eleanor, Jefferson is arrested in a hotel, charged under the Mann Act, and sentenced to three years in the state penitentiary at Joliet. Disguised as a member of a black baseball team, however, Jefferson escapes to Canada. Accompanied by Eleanor he travels to London, where he is refused a license to fight. In Paris he beats his white opponent so badly that none will challenge him. A pariah, he journeys to Germany. In Budapest the boxer is so reduced in circumstances as to play the title role in a cabaret performance of

Uncle Tom's Cabin. Although offered a reduced sentence by a federal agent in return for throwing a fight in Havana, Jefferson refuses. He retires to Mexico, where he and Eleanor eke out a marginal existence. In desperation Eleanor begs Jefferson to accept the Havana match. The infuriated boxer berates his mistress, blaming her for their hopeless situation. Distraught, Eleanor drowns herself in a well, after which Jefferson agrees to the fixed fight. During its final rounds he rebels and attempts, too late, to win the bout. *Negroes. Prizefighters. Fugitives. Mistresses. Government agents. Militants. Racial prejudice. Race relations. Miscegenation. Political corruption. Pride. Poverty. Suicide. Marriage—Common law. The Mann Act. Cabarets. Hotels. Reno. Illinois. Wisconsin. Canada. London. Paris. Budapest. Havana. Mexico. "Uncle Tom's Cabin".*

Note: Exterior scenes filmed in Barcelona, Spain, and Globe, Arizona. Episodes are based on the careers of Jack Johnson, James Jeffries, Jess Willard, and Tommy Burns.

THE GREATEST BATTLE ON EARTH see **GHIDRAH, THE THREE-HEADED MONSTER**

THE GREATEST STORY EVER TOLD   **F6.1951**

George Stevens Productions. *Dist* United Artists. 15 Feb **1965** [New York opening; c15 Feb 1965; LP32294]. Sd; col (Technicolor). 70mm & 35mm (Ultra Panavision 70, see note). 221 min. [Cut to 183 and 141 min.]

Prod-Dir George Stevens. *Prod in Creative Assoc With* Carl Sandburg. *Exec Prod* Frank I. Davis. *Assoc Prod* George Stevens, Jr., Antonio Vellani. *2d Unit Dir* Richard Talmadge, William Hale. *Screenplay* James Lee Barrett, George Stevens. *Dir Photog* William C. Mellor, Loyal Griggs. *Col Cons* Eliot Elisofon. *Art Dir* Richard Day, William Creber. *Sets Created by* David Hall. *Set Decor* Ray Moyer, Fred MacLean, Norman Rockett. *Supv Film Ed* Harold F. Kress. *Film Ed* Argyle Nelson, Jr., Frank O'Neill. *Mus Comp & Cond* Alfred Newman. *Choral Supv* Ken Darby. *Sd* Charles Wallace. *Rec Supv* Franklin Milton, William Steinkamp. *Asst Dir* Ridgeway Callow, John Veitch. *Prod Mgr* Nathan R. Barragar, Eric Stacey. *Script Supv* John Dutton. *Cost Dsgn* Vittorio Nino Novarese. *Asst Cost Dsgn* Marjorie Best. *Makeup Creator* Del Armstrong. *Hairstyles* Carmen Dirigo. *Sp Vis Eff* J. McMillan Johnson, Clarence Slifer, A. Arnold Gillespie, Robert R. Hoag. *Res Supv* Tony Van Renterghem. *Prop Master* Sam Gordon. *Constr Supv* Jack Tait. *Casting* Lynn Stalmaster. *Prod Staff* Tom Andre, Ray Gosnell, Lee Lukather, Saul Wurtzel.

Cast: Max von Sydow *(Jesus)*, Dorothy McGuire *(Mary)*, Robert Loggia *(Joseph)*, Charlton Heston *(John the Baptist)*, Michael Anderson, Jr. *(James the Younger)*, Robert Blake *(Simon the Zealot)*, Burt Brinckerhoff *(Andrew)*, John Considine *(John)*, Jamie Farr *(Thaddaeus)*, David Hedison *(Philip)*, Peter Mann *(Nathanael)*, David McCallum *(Judas Iscariot)*, Roddy McDowall *(Matthew)*, Gary Raymond *(Peter)*, Tom Reese *(Thomas)*, David Sheiner *(James the Elder)*, Ina Balin *(Martha of Bethany)*, Janet Margolin *(Mary of Bethany)*, Michael Tolan *(Lazarus)*, Sidney Poitier *(Simon of Cyrene)*, Joanna Dunham *(Mary Magdalene)*, Carroll Baker *(Veronica)*, Pat Boone *(young man at the tomb)*, Van Heflin *(Bar Amand)*, Sal Mineo *(Uriah)*, Shelley Winters *(woman of no name [see note])*, Ed Wynn *(Old Aram)*, John Wayne *(centurion)*, Telly Savalas *(Pontius Pilate)*, Angela Lansbury *(Claudia)*, Johnny Seven *(Pilate's aide)*, Paul Stewart *(Questor)*, Harold J. Stone *(General Varus)*, Martin Landau *(Caiaphas)*, Nehemiah Persoff *(Shemiah)*, Joseph Schildkraut *(Nicodemus)*, Victor Buono *(Sorak)*, Robert Busch *(emissary)*, John Crawford *(Alexander)*, Russell Johnson *(scribe)*, John Lupton *(speaker of Capernaum)*, Abraham Sofaer *(Joseph of Arimathaea)*, Chet Stratton *(Theophilus)*, Ron Whelan *(Annas)*, Jose Ferrer *(Herod Antipas)*, Claude Rains *(Herod the Great)*, John Abbott *(Aben)*, Rodolfo Acosta *(captain of lancers)*, Michael Ansara *(Herod's commander)*, Philip Coolidge *(Chuza)*, Dal Jenkins *(Philip)*, Joseph Perry *(Archelaus)*, Marian Seldes *(Herodias)*, Donald Pleasence *(The Devil)*, Richard Conte *(Barabbas)*, Frank De Kova *(tormentor)*, Joseph Sirola *(Dumah)*, Cyril Delevanti *(Melchior)*, Mark Lenard *(Balthazar)*, Frank Silvera *(Caspar)*, The Inbal Dance Theatre of Israel.

Biblical drama. Source: Fulton Oursler, *The Greatest Story Ever Told* (New York, 1949). Henry Denker, selected writings. The life of Jesus Christ is depicted; highlights include: His birth in Bethlehem, Herod's decree ordering the slaughter of all male children in Bethlehem; the flight of the Holy Family into Egypt, Jesus' baptism by John the Baptist, the selection of the Twelve Apostles, the execution of John the Baptist, the resurrection of Lazarus from the dead, the expulsion of the moneylenders from the temple in Jerusalem, the Last Supper and subsequent betrayal by Judas, the Crucifixion, and the Resurrection. *Christianity. Infanticide. Crucifixion. The Resurrection. Miracles. Rome—History—Empire. Bethlehem. Egypt. Jerusalem. Calvary. Galilee. Jesus. Virgin Mary. Saint Joseph. John the Baptist. Mary Magdalene. Lazarus. Herod the Great. Herod Antipas. The Twelve Apostles. Pontius Pilate. Barabbas. Judas Iscariot. The Devil.*

Note: Location scenes filmed in Glen Canyon, Utah. Presented in Cinerama for roadshow engagements. For the final release version the roles of Shelley Winters and John Wayne, among others, were reduced or eliminated.

EL GRECO (France/Italy)   **F6.1952**

Produzioni Artistiche Internazionali–Arco Film–Les Films du Siècle. *Dist* Twentieth Century-Fox Film Corp. 26 Oct 1966 [Toledo, Ohio, opening; c31 Dec 1965; LP35452]. Sd (RCA); col (De Luxe). 35mm (CinemaScope). 95 min.

Prod Mel Ferrer, Alfredo Bini. *Dir* Luciano Salce. *Screenplay* Guy Elmes, Massimo Franciosa, Luigi Magni, Luciano Salce. *Story* Guy Elmes. *Photog* Leonida Barboni. *Camera Op* Giuseppe Ruzzolini. *Art Dir* Luigi Scaccianoce. *Set Dsgn* Angelo Zabón, Francesco Bronzi. *Film Ed* Fred Burnley. *Mus* Ennio Morricone. *Sd Mix* Doug Turner. *Sd Ed* Henry Richardson. *Sd* Oscar De Arcangelis, Manlio Urbani. *Asst Dir* Emilio Miraglia. *Prod Mgr* Toto Mignone. *Prod Supv* Manolo Bolognini. *Cont* Marcella Rossellini. *Cost* Danilo Donati. *Makeup* Mario Van Riel. *Hairstyles* Grazia De Rossi, Ernesta Cesetti. *Dial Dir* Fred Burnley, John Francis Lane. *Paintings From His Alicante Collection* Juan Albert Roses. *Auto Sacramental* José de Valdiviesco. *Acted by* Teatro Studio of Madrid. *Dir by* Miguel Narros.

Cast: Mel Ferrer *(El Greco)*, Rosanna Schiaffino *(Jerónima de las Cuevas)*, Adolfo Celi *(Don Miguel de las Cuevas)*, Mario Feliciani *(Cardinal Niño de Guevara)*, Franco Giacobini *(Francisco)*, Renzo Giovampietro *(Brother Félix)*, Angel Aranda *(Don Luis)*, Nino Crisman *(Don Diego de Castile)*, Gabriella Giorgelli *(María)*, Giulio Donnini *(Pignatelli)*, Fernando Rey *(King Philip II)*, Rafael Rivelles *(Marquis of Villena)*, John Karlsen *(prosecutor)*, John Francis Lane *(De Agueda)*, Rossana Martini *(Zaida)*, Maria Marchi *(Mother Superior)*, Franco Fantasia *(fencing master)*, Andrea Bosic *(prosecutor)*, Bruno Scipioni *(officer)*, Rosi Di Pietro *(Isabel)*, Giuliano Farnese *(master of arms)*, Ontanoni *(Leoni)*.

Biographical melodrama. In 1576, Domenikos Theotokopoulos, known as El Greco, arrives in Toledo to execute a commissioned altarpiece. That summer he falls in love with an aristocratic Castilian, Jerónima de las Cuevas, while painting her portrait. Though he has won the favor of both Church and State, El Greco is rejected as a suitor by Jerónima's family; moreover, she is already betrothed to a young nobleman, Don Luis. Jerónima, despite her growing love for El Greco, remains bound by her vows and kisses the painter goodby. Their farewell is witnessed by Don Luis, who has been brought to the scene by Pignatelli, an old enemy of El Greco's. After El Greco has been wounded in a duel by Don Luis, he paints a humiliating caricature of Pignatelli. The latter retaliates by planting evidence of witchcraft in the artist's home. Jerónima learns of the plot but is unable to prevent the arrest and imprisonment of her beloved. In time, El Greco's eloquent definition of his art wins him an acquittal from the Cardinal Inquisitor, and he is released. Seeking Jerónima, he learns that she died giving birth to his child. The grief-stricken painter falls into a melancholia that is destined to remain with him the rest of his life. After years of restless wandering, he begins spending more and more time at a mental institution where, by studying the faces of the inmates, he finds the inspiration for some of his greatest paintings. One day he is joined by a young apprentice—his son born of Jerónima. *Painters. Nobility. Priests. Revenge. Childbirth. Fatherhood. Witchcraft. Mental illness. Prisons. Hospitals. The Inquisition. Toledo (Spain). El Greco. Philip II (Spain). Fernando Niño de Guevara. Jerónima de las Cuebas. Duels.*

Note: Filmed in Toledo, Spain. Opened in Rome in Aug 1966; in Paris in May 1967 as *Le Greco.*

LE GRECO see **EL GRECO**

GREED IN THE SUN (France/Italy)   **F6.1953**

S. N. E. Gaumont-Trianon Productions–Ultra Film. *Dist* Metro-Goldwyn-Mayer, Inc. 18 Aug **1965** [New York opening]. Sd; b&w. 35mm (CinemaScope). 122 min.

Prod Alain Poiré. *Dir* Henri Verneuil. *Screenplay* Michel Audiard. *Adapt* Marcel Jullian, Henri Verneuil. *Photog* Marcel Grignon. *Camera* Charles-Henry Montel. *Art Dir* Robert Clavel. *Set Decor* Pierre Charron. *Film Ed* Claude Durand. *Mus* Georges Delerue. *Sd* René Longuet. *Prod Mgr* Robert Sussfeld, Irénée Leriche.

Cast: Jean-Paul Belmondo *(Rocco)*, Lino Ventura *(Hervé)*, Reginald Kernan *(Hans Steiner)*, Andréa Parisy *(Pepa)*, Gert Fröbe *(Castigliano)*, Bernard Blier *(Mitch-Mitch)*, Doudou Babet *(Khenouche)*, Pierre Mirat *(Halibi)*.

Crime melodrama. Source: Claude Veillot, *Nous n'irons pas en Nigéria* (Paris, 1962). At a trucking company in northern Africa, young Hans Steiner is assigned to drive a new truck from Morocco to Nigeria. Unknown to him and the other drivers, the truck contains guns and ammunition to be used in a border war. Rocco, a veteran driver, learns that the cargo is valuable, and with his girl friend, Pepa, he hijacks the truck and continues toward Nigeria. Meanwhile, Castigliano, the head of the company, offers Hans and Hervé, another driver, a reward to go after Rocco and Pepa. After hundreds of miles of desert roads and narrow mountain passes, Hervé and Hans finally catch up with the hijacked vehicle. Rocco's truck breaks down, however, and he forces Hervé and Hans to put the cargo in their truck. At the final destination, Rocco leaves the truck with Pepa and visits a local whorehouse; Hervé finds him there, and the two begin fighting. In the midst of the brawl, Rocco suddenly stops and bursts out laughing—Pepa has disappeared with the truck, its cargo, and the forthcoming payoff. *Truckdrivers. Hijackers. Theft. Perfidy. Trucking agencies. Whorehouses. Morocco. Nigeria. Chases.*

Note: Filmed on location in Morocco. Opened in Paris in Apr 1964 as *Cent mille dollars au soleil*; running time: 130 min; in Italy in 1965 as *Centomila dollari al sole*.

THE GREEN BERETS　　　　　　　　　　　　　　　　F6.1954

Batjac Productions. *Dist* Warner Bros.–Seven Arts, Inc. 19 Jun **1968** [New York opening; c1 Jul 1968; LP36530]. Sd; col (Technicolor). 35mm (Panavision). 141 min.

Prod Michael Wayne. *Dir* John Wayne, Ray Kellogg. *Uncredited Dir* Mervyn LeRoy. *2d Unit Dir* Cliff Lyons. *Screenplay* James Lee Barrett. *Dir Photog* Winton C. Hoch. *Set Decor* Ray Moyer. *Prod Dsgn* Walter M. Simonds. *Titl Dsgn* Wayne Fitzgerald. *Film Ed* Otho Lovering. *Mus* Miklos Rozsa. *Sd* Stanley Jones. *Asst Dir* Joe L. Cramer, Newt Arnold. *Unit Prod Mgr* Lee Lukather. *Script Supv* Crayton Smith. *Cost* Jerry Alpert. *Makeup* Dave Grayson. *Sp Eff* Sass Bedig. *Defense Dept. Project Officer* William C. Byrns, (Lieut. Col.). *Sp Forces Adv* Jerold R. Dodds, (Maj.). *Fort Benning Project Officer* August Schomburg, Jr., (Capt.). *Prop* "Red" Turner. *Construction Coörd* "Hank" Wynands.

Cast: John Wayne (*Col. Mike Kirby*), David Janssen (*George Beckworth*), Jim Hutton (*Sergeant Petersen*), Aldo Ray (*Sergeant Muldoon*), Raymond St. Jacques (*Doc McGee*), Bruce Cabot (*Colonel Morgan*), George Takei (*Captain Nim*), Luke Askew (*Sergeant Provo*), Jack Soo (*Colonel Cai*), Patrick Wayne (*Lieutenant Jamison*), Irene Tsu (*Lin*), Edward Faulkner (*Captain MacDanials*), Jason Evers (*Captain Coleman*), Mike Henry (*Sergeant Kowalski*), Craig Jue (*Hamchunk*), Chuck Roberson (*Sergeant Griffin*), Eddy Donno (*Sergeant Watson*), Rudy Robins (*Sergeant Parks*), Richard "Cactus" Pryor (*Collier*), Bach Yen (*Vietnamese singer*), Frank Koomen (*Lieutenant Sachs*), William Olds (*General Phan Son Ti*), Yodying Apibal (*ARVN soldier*), Chuck Bail (*Sergeant Lark*), Vincent Cadiente (*Viet Cong soldier*), William Shannon (*Sergeant White*).

War melodrama. Source: Robin Moore, *The Green Berets* (New York, 1965). Col. Mike Kirby of the U. S. Special Forces takes charge of a strike camp located deep in Viet Cong territory near Da Nang. On hand to report on the unit's action is George Beckworth, a liberal war correspondent whose newspaper has voiced serious misgivings about American intervention in Vietnam. Despite the best efforts of Kirby's men, assisted by South Vietnamese regulars and Montagnard tribesmen, the camp is captured by the enemy. Upon witnessing the torture of a Viet Cong infiltrator during interrogation, Beckworth protests against the Green Berets' tactics, but when he learns of Viet Cong atrocities, he changes his mind about the nature of the conflict and even joins in the fighting. Eventually, Kirby and his men are able to retake the camp after a U. S. Air Force plane has decimated the enemy ranks. Then, aided by Lin, a seductive Vietnamese model whose father was killed by the Viet Cong, Kirby and Vietnamese Colonel Cai capture a high-ranking enemy officer and lead him back to headquarters for questioning. Before the unit returns to the camp, however, Petersen is killed by a booby trap. Kirby must then explain to Hamchunk, a war orphan whom Petersen adopted, that his idol died so the children like him might live. *Guerrillas. Reporters. Communists. War victims. Orphans. Models. Montagnards (Vietnam). War crimes. Combat zone life. Torture. Mines (war explosives). Vietnam War 1964–73. Democratic Republic of Vietnam. Republic of Vietnam. Da Nang. United States Army—Special Forces. Vietcong. United States Air Force.*

Note: Location scenes filmed in Georgia and Alabama.

THE GREEN HELMET (Great Britain)　　　　　　　　F6.1955

Metro-Goldwyn-Mayer Pictures. *Dist* Metro-Goldwyn-Mayer, Inc. Apr **1961** [c31 Dec 1960; LP19328]. Sd (Westrex); b&w. 35mm. 88 min.

Prod Charles Vetter. *Dir* Michael Forlong. *Screenplay* Jon Cleary. *Dir Photog* Geoffrey Faithfull. *Camera Op* Frank Drake. *Focus* Dickie Robinson. *Camera Grip* Pat Newman. *Art Dir* Alan Withy. *Asst Art Dir* Edward Marshall. *Set Dresser* Joseph Bato. *Film Ed* Frank Clarke. *Assembly Ed* Alan Kinnock. *1st Asst Ed* Jim Atkinson. *Mus Comp & Cond* Ken Jones. *Rec Supv* A. W. Watkins. *Dub Ed* Gordon Daniel. *Sd Rec* J. B. Smith, John Bramall. *Boom Op* Bill Baldwin. *Sd Camera Op* Brian Knott. *1st, 2d & 3d Asst Dir* Stan Strangeway, Maurice Gibson, Ernie Lewis. *Prod Mgr* Al Marcus. *Prod Sec* Liz Charles-Williams. *Cont* Joan Kirk. *Cost Dsgn* Ivy Baker. *Makeup* Sydney Turner. *Hairdressing* Joan Johnstone. *Sp Eff* Tom Howard. *Tech Adv* Gordon Wilkins. *Coöp* British Racing Drivers Club, PGL Productions, Automobile Racing Club of Florida. *Still Photog* Roy Gough. *Prop Buyer* Bernard Summerfield. *Casting Dir* Irene Howard.

Cast: Bill Travers (*Greg Rafferty*), Ed Begley (*Bartell*), Sidney James (*Richie Launder*), Nancy Walters (*Diane Bartell*), Ursula Jeans (*Mrs. Rafferty*), Megs Jenkins (*Kitty Launder*), Sean Kelly (*Taz Rafferty*), Tutte Lemkow (*Carlo Zaraga*), Gordon Tanner (*Hastrow*), Ferdy Mayne (*Rossano*), Peter Collingwood (*Charlie*), Roland Curram (*George*), Diane Clare (*Pamela*), Harold Kasket (*Lupi*), Lyn Cole (*Jackie*), Glyn Houston (*pit manager*), Jack Brabham (*himself*), Roy Salvadori, Lucky Casner, John Coundley, Steve Ouvaroff, Mike Salmon (*themselves*).

Action drama. Source: Jon Cleary, *The Green Helmet* (London, 1957). Greg Rafferty, an aging English racing driver whose nerves and reputation are beginning to suffer from a series of bad crashes, agrees to race for Bartell, a wealthy American who wants to promote his brand of tires. The decision angers Greg's younger brother, Taz, who has promised their mother that he will not race until Greg has retired from the sport. At first Bartell's tires prove to be defective, and Greg is forced to use another brand to win the annual race at Sebring, Florida. Under the supervision of Greg's mechanic and navigator, Richie Launder, the tires are perfected. Greg, meanwhile, has fallen in love with Bartell's daughter, Diane, who also wants him to give up racing. On the eve of the big event at Italy's Mille Miglia, Greg and Richie make a test run in the new car Richie has designed. As they race around a bend on the 1,000-mile stretch of treacherous road, they hit a patch of oil; and Richie is killed in the subsequent crash. Without a navigator, Greg feels that he must withdraw from the race. Taz, however, offers to substitute; and Greg, feeling duty-bound to win with Richie's car, agrees to drive. He wins the race; and as he embraces Diane, he decides to retire and give Taz his chance at racing. *Mechanics. Brothers. Automobile racing. Automobile tires. Sebring (Florida). Mille Miglia. Automobile accidents.*

Note: Racing sequences staged at Silverstone (England), Sebring (Florida), the Mille Miglia (Italy), and Le Mans (France). Released in Great Britain in May 1961.

GREEN LIGHT TO JOY (Japan)　　　　　　　　　　F6.1956

Toho Co. Jan **1967** [Los Angeles showing]. Sd; b&w. 35mm (Tohoscope). 85 min.

Dir Seiji Maruyama.

Cast: Kiyoshi Atsumi, Tetsuo Ishidate, Keiko Awaji, Yuriko Hoshi, Jun Hamamura.

Drama. Although no information about the precise nature of this film has been found, press material suggests that the film concerns the relationship between a student and a laborer. *Students.*

Note: Released in Japan in 1966 as *Chichiko gusa*.

THE GREEN MARE (France/Italy)　　　　　　　　　F6.1957

S. N. E. Gaumont–S. O. P. A. C.–Zebra Film–Productions Raimbourg–Star Presse. *Dist* Zenith International Film Corp. 23 Oct **1961** [New York opening]. Sd; col (Eastmancolor). 35mm (Franscope). 93 min.

Prod-Dir Claude Autant-Lara. *Assoc Prod* Moris Ergas, Yves Laplanche. *Screenplay* Jean Aurenche, Pierre Bost. *Photog* Jacques Natteau. *Art Dir* Max Douy. *Film Ed* Madeleine Gug. *Mus* René Cloërec. *Sd* René Forget. *Cost* Rosine Delamare. *English Subtitl* Rose Sokol.

Cast: Bourvil (*Honoré Haudoin*), Sandra Milo (*Marguerite Maloret*), Francis Blanche (*Ferdinand Haudoin*), Yves Robert (*Zèphe Maloret*), Valérie Lagrange (*Juliette Haudoin*), Mireille Perrey (*Madame Haudoin, Honoré's mother*), Carette (*Philibert, the mayor*), Guy Bertil (*Toucheur*), Marie Mergey (*Adelaïde*), Nicole Mirel (*Aline*), Georges Wilson (*Honoré's father, "Old Haudoin"*), Amédée (*Ernest*), Martine Havet (*Clotilde*), Achille Zavatta (*Déodat, the mailman*), Marie Déa (*Anaïs Maloret*), Claude Sainlouis (*Noël Maloret*).

Comedy-drama. Source: Marcel Aymé, *La jument verte* (Paris, 1933). In 19th-century France, a green mare is born on the farm of Jules Haudoin, a horse dealer. The phenomenon makes the family wealthy, and when the mare dies, its portrait becomes the Haudoins' most treasured possession. Jules dies and leaves his estate to his sons, Honoré and Ferdinand. During the Franco-Prussian War, young Honoré Haudoin is betrayed to the Prussians by a neighbor, Zèphe Maloret, who has long envied the good fortune of the Haudoins. To save her son, Madame Haudoin is forced to submit to the embraces of a Prussian officer on the very bed under which young Honoré and his friend, Toucheur, are hiding. Honoré keeps his mother's rape a secret from all, including his brother, and for 15 years he waits for a chance to avenge himself on Zèphe. Finally, he hits on the plan of seducing Zèphe's daughter. Meanwhile, Ferdinand innocently promotes Zèphe for the position of mayor, and Honoré reveals to his brother the reason for his hatred. The foolish Ferdinand writes Zèphe a letter recounting the tale, and the letter gets lost. Honoré is further enraged to learn that the Malorets may know of his mother's disgrace. Fuel is added to the fire when a romance develops between Honoré's young daughter, Juliette, and Zèphe's handsome son, Noël. After considerable confusion and misunderstanding, Honoré recovers the letter and exacts his revenge by forcing Noël under the bed and "raping" the willing Madame Maloret. *Horsetraders. Brothers. Prussians. Neighbors. Rape. Wealth. Feuds. Filial relations. Revenge. Franco-German War 1870–71. Documentation. Horses.*

Note: Opened in Paris in Oct 1959 as *La jument verte*; running time: 95 min. Italian title: *La giumenta verde*. Also known as *Bedroom Vendetta*.

THE GREEN SLIME (United States/Japan)   **F6.1958**
Ram Films–Toei Co.–Southern Cross Films. *Dist* Metro-Goldwyn-Mayer, Inc. 21 May **1969** [New York opening; c1 Dec 1968; LP36590]. Sd; col (Toei Color). 35mm (Toeiscope). 90 min. *MPAA rating G.*

Prod Ivan Reiner, Walter Manley. *Assoc Prod* William Ross. *Asst Prod* Kename Ogisawa, Koji Ota. *Dir* Kinji Fukasaku. *Screenplay* Charles Sinclair, William Finger, Tom Rowe. *Story* Ivan Reiner. *Photog* Yoshikazu Yamasawa. *Lighting* Shigeru Umetani. *Art Dir* Shinichi Eno. *Set Decor* Tasaburo Matsumo. *Film Ed* Osamu Tanaka. *Mus* Charles Fox, Toshiaki Tsushima. *Sd* Yoshio Watanabe. *Asst Dir* Kazuhiko Yamaguchi. *Asst to the Prod* Michie Ross. *Script Asst* Jacqueline Vaanice, Yasuyo Yamanouchi. *Cost* Mami. *Makeup* Takeshi Ugai. *Sp Eff Dir* Akira Watanabe, Yukio Manoda. *Sp Eff* Nihon Special Effects Co.

Cast: Robert Horton *(Jack Rankin)*, Richard Jaeckel *(Vince Elliot)*, Luciana Paluzzi *(Lisa Benson)*, Bud Widom *(Jonathan Thompson)*, Ted Gunther *(Dr. Halvorsen)*, Robert Dunham *(Captain Martin)*, David Yorston *(Lieutenant Curtis)*, William Ross *(Ferguson)*, Gary Randolf *(Cordier)*, Richard Hylland *(Michael)*, Strong Ilimaiti *(doctor)*, Arthur Stark *(Barnett)*, Lynne Frederickson *(secretary)*, Tom Conrad *(Sergeant)*, David Sentman *(officer)*, Clarence Howard *(patient)*, Hans Jorgseeberger, Bob Morris, actor *(soldiers)*, Jack Morris, Carl Bengs, Tom Scott *(rocket pilots)*, Don Plante, Enver Altenbay, Gunther Greve, Eugene Vince, George Uruf *(technicians)*, Linda Hardisty, Kathy Horan, Ann Ault, Susan Skersick, Helen Kirkpatrick, Linda Miller, Patricia Elliot, Linda Malson *(nurses)*.

Science fiction film. Panic breaks out at the United Nations Space Authority when it is discovered that an asteroid has steered out of orbit and is heading for a fatal collision with Earth. Since the only way the catastrophe can be averted is to blow up the asteroid from the space station Gamma III, astronaut Jack Rankin is sent there to take charge of the mission. Although the station's commander, Vince Elliot, is a former friend of Rankin's, friction has developed between the two men because Rankin does not consider Elliot fully capable of leadership, a situation that is not helped by the fact that Elliot is now engaged to Rankin's former girl friend Lisa Benson, one of the station's doctors. Despite their hostility, the two men embark on a spaceship flight and land on the asteroid. While explosives are being set up, a scientist named Doctor Halvorsen explores a swamp filled with a jelly-like green substance that seems to be alive. After the asteroid has been destroyed and the spaceship has returned to Gamma III, Doctor Halvorsen discovers that some of the green slime that adhered to his sleeve has become activated into a blood-like substance that rapidly transforms itself into a tentacled monster capable of emitting lethal electrical shocks. When the creature kills Halvorsen, Rankin shoots it only to find that the drops of blood it emits quickly evolve into new monsters. Realizing that the more creatures they kill, the more they will create from the drops of blood, Rankin and Elliot are forced to accept the fact that Gamma III must be evacuated and blown up before the green plague spreads to Earth. Although they succeed in destroying the space station and the monsters, Elliot pays for it with his life. *Astronauts. Scientists. Physicians. Space travel. Space creatures. Jealousy. Regeneration. Self-sacrifice. Asteroids. United Nations.*

Note: Filmed in Japan. Released in Japan in Dec 1968 as *Gammo sango uchu daisakusen*; running time: 77 min. Working title: *Battle Beyond the Stars.*

THE GREEN TREE   **F6.1959**
Rol Film Co.–Salesians of Saint John Bosco. *Dist* Don Bosco Films and Filmstrips. c11 Sep **1965** [LP31659]. Sd; b&w. 16mm. 75 min.

Prod-Dir Joseph Roland. *Prod in Collab With* Joseph Perozzi. *Screenplay* Joseph Roland, Joseph Berrutti. *English Vers Writ & Dir* Ruth Zimmerman. *Photog* A. Grasso, Joseph Sacchi. *Mus* Happy Ruggero.

Cast: Robert Gho *(Mickey Magone)*, Natale Peretti *(Don Bosco)*, P. Terreno *(Theresa)*, A. Caravaggi *(Sara)*, P. Dutrelli *(Giovanni)*, V. Vaglini *(Christini)*, A. Giordenngo *(Gigio)*, Ignazio Dolce *(Ciccio)*.

Biographical drama. Source: Peter Lappin, *General Mickey* (New Rochelle, 1952). Mickey Magone's father is thrown into jail in Turin in the 1850's. Mickey becomes embittered and soon becomes the leader of a gang of boys. He is called the "general" and gets into increasing trouble. The most serious incident happens when, to test their courage, the boys hurl millstones down a hill at blindfolded figures to see if they have enough courage not to move. After incidents like this, Mickey moves into Don Bosco's Boys Town. Here he comes to know himself and with the help of Don Bosco to love God. Mickey goes back to his old home and through personal example brings peace to the gangs of boys. *Juvenile delinquents. Priests. Filial relations. Adolescence. Religion. Children's*

homes. *Turin. Saint Giovanni Bosco.*

Note: Filmed in Italy.

THE GREENGAGE SUMMER *see* **LOSS OF INNOCENCE**

GREENWICH VILLAGE STORY   **F6.1960**
Village Film Workshop. *Dist* Shawn International, Inc. 11 Jul **1963** [New York opening]. Sd; b&w. 35mm. 95 min.

Prod-Dir-Writ Jack O'Connell. *Asst Prod* Bill Montgomery. *Cinematog* Baird Bryant. *Lighting Dir* Charles Gossett. *Sets* Mildred Anderson. *Ed* Jean Bagley, Carl Lerner. *Mus* Hy Gubernick. *Sd* Lee Bost. *Asst Dir* John G. Avildsen. *Prod Mgr* Stephen R. Winsten. *Prod Coörd* Robert McCarty. *Script Girl* Kay Chapin.

Cast: Robert Hogan *(Brian)*, Melinda Plank *(Genie)*, Tani Seitz *(Anne)*, James Frawley *(Norman)*, Sunja Svendsen *(Claudine)*, James Cresson *(George)*, Aaron Banks *(Franko)*, John G. Avildsen *(Alvie)*, John Brent *(Poet)*, Charles Gossett *(judge)*, Kim McKernan *(Kimmie)*.

Melodrama. Brian, an award-winning writer who is working to complete his first novel, lives in Greenwich Village with Genie, a ballet dancer waiting for a break. Despite financial difficulties, they are happy members of the bohemian community, sharing in the hope that they will find themselves through honest self-expression. Genie hopes that they will marry; when she becomes pregnant she tries to persuade Brian without revealing her condition. He tells her that he will marry her if his novel is accepted; instead the book is greeted as immature and pretentious. Anne, a wealthy admirer, persuades Brian to join her for a weekend at her father's estate. Genie, afraid that she is losing him, visits an illegal abortionist. Brian returns home filled with remorse, but it is too late: Genie dies as a result of the operation and Brian is left heartbroken. *Dancers. Novelists. Bohemianism. Marriage. Infidelity. Abortion. New York City—Greenwich Village.*

Note: Filmed on location in Greenwich Village, film was given the pre-release title *Greenwich Village* and is also known as *Birthplace of the Hootenanny* and *They Love as They Please.*

GREETINGS   **F6.1961**
West End Films. *Dist* Sigma III Corp. 15 Dec **1968** [New York opening]. Sd; col (Eastman Color). 35mm. 88 min. *MPAA rating X.*

Prod Charles Hirsch. *Dir* Brian De Palma. *Screenplay* Charles Hirsch, Brian De Palma. *Photog* Robert Fiore. *Asst Camera* Daniel Weiss. *Titl* Chuck Shields. *Film Ed* Brian De Palma. *Asst Ed* Jeffrey Lesser. *Songs Comp & Sung by* The Children of Paradise. *Sd* Charles Pitts, Jeffrey Lesser. *Prod Mgr* George Manasse. *Cost* Chuck Shields.

Cast: Jonathan Warden *(Paul Shaw)*, Robert De Niro *(Jon Rubin)*, Gerritt Graham *(Lloyd Clay)*, Richard Hamilton *(pop artist)*, Megan McCormick *(Marina)*, Bettina Kugel *(Tina)*, Jack Cowley *(photographer)*, Jane Lee Salmons *(model)*, Ashley Oliver *(Bronx secretary)*, Melvin Margulies *("Rat" magazine vendor)*, Cynthia Peltz *(divorcee)*, Peter Maloney *(Earl Roberts)*, Ruth Alda *(Linda)*, Ted Lescault *(bookstore manager)*, Mona Feit *(mystic date)*, M. Dobish *(TV cameraman from Vietnam)*, Richard Landis *(ex-G.I. at party)*, Carol Patton *(blonde at party & park)*, Allen Garfield *(smut peddler)*, Sara-Jo Edlin *(nymphomaniac)*, Roz Kelly *(photographer)*, Ray Tuttle *(TV news correspondent)*, Tisa Chiang *(Vietnamese girl)*, Rex Marshall *(TV newscaster)*.

Farce. Three young New Yorkers—Paul Shaw, Lloyd Clay, and Jon Rubin—try to cope with contemporary society. Paul, who is obsessed with sex, gets called for a preinduction Army physical and agrees with Jon and Lloyd that the best way to beat the draft is to pose as either a homosexual or a right-wing militant or both. Lloyd, who is obsessed with various theories discrediting the Warren Commission Report on the Kennedy assassination, spends his time tracing bullet trajectories on the naked bodies of accommodating girls. Jon, a peeping tom, goes around persuading young women to disrobe under conditions ideally suited to his fixation. Awaiting his draft call, Paul goes on a series of computer dates and then makes a stag movie. Lloyd takes a brief respite from his Warren Report investigation only to get shot down while boarding a Statue of Liberty ferryboat. Eventually, it is Jon who ends up in Vietnam. As he is being interviewed in a rice paddy by a newsman, he spots a female member of the Viet Cong and cuts the interview short in an attempt to persuade the girl to remove her clothing. Back in the United States, President Johnson appears on television, to assure Americans: "We've never had it so good." *Draft dodgers. Researchers. Military draft. Voyeurism. Computer dating services. Male homosexuality. Impersonation. Nudity. Sex exploitation films. Assassination. United States Army. Vietnam War 1964–73. New York City. Vietnam. Lyndon Baines Johnson. President's Commission on the Assassination of President John F. Kennedy. Statue of Liberty.*

Note: Location scenes filmed in New York City and Secaucus, New Jersey.

GREH see **THE BEGINNING WAS SIN**

GRENOBLE (France) **F6.1962**

Les Films Treize. *Dist* United Productions of America. 25 Dec **1969** [Los Angeles opening]. Sd; col (Eastman Color). 35mm. 95 min.

Prod Georges Derocles. *Dir* Claude Lelouch, François Reichenbach. *Screenplay* Claude Lelouch, François Reichenbach, Pierre Uytterhoeven. *Photog* Willy Bogner, Jr., Jean Collomb, Guy Gilles, Jean-Paul Janssen, Pierre Willemin. *Film Ed* Claude Barrois. *Mus* Francis Lai. *Songs* Francis Lai, Pierre Barouh. *Prod Mgr* Pierre Pardon.

Documentary. The 1968 Winter Olympic Games at Grenoble, France, are shown, highlighting the performances of skier Jean-Claude Killy and skater Peggy Fleming. *Skiing. Ice skating. Grenoble. Jean-Claude Killy. Peggy Fleming. Olympic Games.*

Note: Opened in Paris in Jul 1968 as *13 jours en France*; running time: 115 min.

GREYFRIARS BOBBY (United States/Great Britain) **F6.1963**

Walt Disney Productions. *Dist* Buena Vista Distribution Co. 11 Oct **1961** [New York opening; c17 Apr 1961; LP20321]. Sd (RCA); col (Technicolor). 35mm. 91 min.

Pres by Walt Disney. *Prod* Walt Disney. *Assoc Prod* Hugh Attwooll. *Dir* Don Chaffey. *Screenplay* Robert Westerby. *Dir Photog* Paul Beeson. *2d Unit Photog* Ray Sturgess. *Camera Op* Herbert R. Smith. *Focus* Alec Mills. *2d Unit Focus* Michael Sarafian. *1st Unit Grip* M. Walters. *2d Unit Grip* W. Floyd. *Art Dir* Michael Stringer. *Set Decor* Vernon Dixon. *Scenic Artist* A. Van Montagu. *Film Ed* Peter Tanner. *1st Asst Ed* Peter Weatherley. *2d Asst Ed* Maureen Lyndon. *Mus Comp & Cond* Francis Chagrin. *Sd Rec* Norman Bolland, Red Law. *Sd Ed* Terry Poulton. *Boom Op* John Salter. *Sd Camera Op* Desmond Edwards. *Asst Dir* Dennis Bertera, Eric Rattray, Grania O'Shannon, Terence Churcher. *Prod Mgr* Peter Manley. *Prod Sec* Jean Walter. *Unit Mgr* Teresa Bolland. *Cont* Phyllis Crocker. *Asst Cont* Josie Fulford. *Cost Dsgn* Margaret Furse. *Wardrobe Master* John Briggs. *Makeup Supv* Harry Frampton. *Hairdresser* Barbara Ritchie. *Sp Photog Eff* Albert Whitlock. *Dialect Adv* John Breslin. *Still Photog* John Jay, Laurie Ridley. *Prop Buyer* Charles Townsend. *Constr Mgr* Gus Walker. *Ch Draughtsman* Norman Dorme. *Casting* Maude Spector. *Dog trainer* John Darlys.

Cast: Donald Crisp *(James [John?] Brown)*, Laurence Naismith *(Mr. Traill)*, Alex Mackenzie *(Old Jock)*, Kay Walsh *(Mrs. Brown)*, Duncan Macrae *(Constable Maclean)*, Andrew Cruickshank *(The Lord Provost)*, Gordon Jackson *(farmer)*, Rosalie Crutchley *(farmer's wife)*, Freda Jackson *(old woman caretaker)*, Moultrie Kelsall *(magistrate)*, Joyce Carey *(1st lady)*, Vincent Winter *(Tammy)*, Jameson Clark *(constable)*, Jack Lambert *(doctor)*, Joan Buck *(Ailie)*, Jennifer Nevinson *(farmer's daughter)*, Bruce Seton, Hamish Wilson, Sean Keir.

Comedy-drama. Source: Eleanor Atkinson, *Greyfriars Bobby* (New York, 1912). A hundred years ago in the Lammermuir Hills near Edinburgh, a little Skye terrier called Bobby is the devoted pet of Old Jock, a poor shepherd. When Jock loses his job because he is too old and infirm to work, he goes to Edinburgh, followed by the faithful Bobby. Before long the old man dies of pneumonia in a wretched lodging house and is laid to rest in Greyfriars' Kirkyard. Following Jock's death, Bobby spends his days begging food from Mr. Traill, the kindly owner of an eatinghouse, and playing with the local poor children. But by night the little animal avoids the crotchety caretaker of the churchyard, Mr. Brown, and keeps a vigil on Old Jock's grave. Eventually Bobby's charm wins over the caretaker and his wife, as well as most of the townspeople. Consequently, when the question of the dog's not having a license is brought to court, both Mr. Traill and Mrs. Brown insist upon paying for it. However, when the Edinburgh waifs also burst into court with the necessary funds, the Lord Provost decides that no one shall pay for the license; Bobby is to have the freedom of the city—at liberty to go where he pleases, including Old Jock's grave in Greyfriars' Kirkyard. *Shepherds. Caretakers. Old age. Loyalty. Churchyards. Edinburgh. Dogs.*

Note: Location scenes filmed in Scotland. Released in Great Britain in 1961.

IL GRIDO (United States/Italy) **F6.1964**

SPA Cinematografica-Robert Alexander Productions. *Dist* Astor Pictures. 22 Oct **1962** [New York opening]. Sd; b&w. 35mm. 115 min.

Prod Franco Cancellieri. *Dir-Story* Michelangelo Antonioni. *Screenplay-Dial* Michelangelo Antonioni, Elio Bartolini, Ennio De Concini. *Photog* Gianni Di Venanzo. *Camera Op* Erico Menczer. *Art Dir* Franco Fontana. *Film Ed* Eraldo Da Roma. *Mus* Giovanni Fusco. *Piano Played by* Lya De Barberis. *Sd* Vittorio Trentino. *Asst Dir* Luigi Vanzi. *Prod Dir* Danilo Marciani, Ralph Pinto. *Cost* Pia Marchesi.

Cast: Steve Cochran *(Aldo)*, Alida Valli *(Irma)*, Betsy Blair *(Elvia)*, Dorian Gray *(Virginia)*, Lyn Shaw *(Andreina)*, Gabriella Pallotta *(Edera)*, Mirna Girardi *(Rosina)*, Guerrino Campanili *(Virginia's father)*, Gaetano Matteucci

(Edera's fiancé), Pietro Corvelatti *(old fisherman)*, Pina Boldrini.

Drama. For 7 years, Aldo, a laborer in a sugar refinery in the town of Goriano, has been living with his mistress, Irma, and their young daughter. Word arrives that Irma's husband has died, and Aldo announces that they will marry immediately and legitimize their child. But Irma rejects him and instead chooses another man. Distraught and disillusioned, Aldo takes his daughter and sets out to find a new life. His wanderings through the Po Valley lead him to three other women: Elvia, a former girl friend, now a forlorn seamstress; Virginia, a widow who runs a roadside service station; and Andreina, a prostitute as lost and desolate as himself. After sending his daughter back to her mother, he continues his search, but, haunted by his memories of Irma, he eventually returns to Goriano. The town is about to be demolished to make way for a jet airfield, and Irma is contentedly living a new and better life. Filled with despair, Aldo climbs to the top of the refinery where he once worked. Irma follows him and sees him plunge to his death. *Laborers. Mistresses. Seamstresses. Prostitutes. Widows. Marriage—Common law. Parenthood. Illegitimacy. Suicide. Filling stations. Airfields. Sugar mills. Po River.*

Note: Filmed on location in the lower Po Valley and the Po Delta, including Occhiobello, Pontelagoscuro, Stienta, Ferrara, and Ca Venier. Opened in Rome in Nov 1957. Also known as *The Outcry*.

GRIGSBY see **THE LAST GRENADE**

GRIMACES **F6.1965**

Dist Film-Makers' Cooperative. 23 Jun **1968** [New York opening]. Sd; b&w. 16mm. 45 min.

Prod-Dir Gudmundur Gudmundsson Ferro. *Film Ed* Denise de Casabianca. *Sd* François Dufresne.

Cast: Jim Dine, Ferro, Bruno Müller, Fredric Pardo, Piqueras, Cardenas, Gregory Masurovsky, Enrico Baj, Arman, Soto, Bro, Peverelli, Barucello, Neil Williams, Ursula, Allen Jones, Takis, Aldo Mondino, Pierluca, Dova, Raymond Hains, Joe Tilson, Brian Young, Harloff, Bernard Childs, Peter Stampfli, Marcel Duchamp, Man Ray, Frank Stella, Richard Hamilton, Dick Higgins, Alfonso Ossorio, Grinberg, James Rosenquist, Kudo, Tancredi, Recalcati, Lilly Picard, Boris Lurie, Cremonini, Metcalf, Crippa, Bernard Pfriem, Clementi, Van Leyden, Margherita Russo, Consagra, Domoto, Abe, Michelangelo Pistoletto, Bona, Ikewada, Friedereich Hundertwasser, Castellani, Festa, Deschamp, Rodriguez, Edmondo Bacci, Sabine, Hulbert Dalwood, Rory McEwen, Agam, Adami, Pol Bury, Alan R. Salomon, Milvia Maglione, Samaras, Chryssa, Tim Scott, Yuen-Yuen Chinn, Bat Yosef, Del Pezzo, Mati, Ruth Francken, Edmund Alleyn, Patrick Betaudier, Sam Goodman, Robert Filliou, Kiki Kogelnik, Martial Raysse, Christo, Derek Boshier, Shirley Goldfarb, Télémaque, Robert Lebel, Le Parc, Vilfred Lam, Bill Copley, Félix Labisse, Alexandre Iolas, Scarpita, Miguel Berrocal, Jeff Nutall, Saura, Lawrence Alloway, Marta Minujin, Julian Levy, Camille Bryen, Andy Warhol, Miguel Guino, Taylor Mead, Lourdes Castro, Del Negro, CESAR, Joyce Mansour, Monory, Mel Geary, Maurice Henry, Paul de Lussanet, Arroyo, Serge Beguier, Peter Klasen, Robert Breer, Rancillac, Matta, Vostell, John Altoon, Lette Eisenhauer, Marc Brusse, Bertini, Robert Malaval, Licata, Pontus Hulten, Ted Joans, Jack Youngerman, Dado, Bernard Schultze, Degani, Carolee Schneeman, Patrick Caulfield, Georges Noel, Mark Lancaster, Tom Wesselmann, Dallegret, Laura Grisi, René de Salier, René Bertholo, Augustin Fernandez, Paul Revel, Biasi, Scanavino, Michael Farrell, Gilles Aillaud, Alain Jouffroy, Arthuro Schwarz, Alain Jacquet, Mimmo Rotella, Antonio Segui, Arnal, Domingo de la Cueva, Manina, John Chamberlain, Earle Brown, Sven Lulken, Pauline Boty, Piotr Kowalski, Marjorie Strider, Kosta Alex, Jean-Jacques Lebel, Jean Pierre Raynaud, Daniel Pommereulle, Norman Rubington, Spoerri, Claes Oldenburg, Pat Oldenburg, Hiquily, Larry Rivers, Roy Lichtenstein, Ay-o, Reinhoud, Frances Dufrene, Pierre Alechinsky, Oyvind Fahlstrom.

Satire. One after another, 173 artists, critics, and gallery owners grimace briefly; Lettriste poetry is heard on the soundtrack. *Artists. Art dealers. Critics.*

Note: Filmed 1962-67 in Europe and the United States.

EL GRITO DE LA MUERTE see **THE LIVING COFFIN**

GRITOS EN LA NOCHE see **THE AWFUL DR. ORLOF**

DAS GROSSE LIEBESSPIEL see **AND SO TO BED**

DIE GROSSE TREIBJAGD see **THE LAST MERCENARY**

THE GROUCH (Greece) **F6.1966**

Finos Films. *Dist* Greek Motion Pictures. 25 Feb **1961** [New York opening]. Sd; b&w. 35mm. 107 min.

Dir-Writ George Tzavellas.

Cast: Orestis Makris *(grouch)*, Daphne Skouras *(girl)*, Georgia Vassiliadou *(housekeeper)*, Mimi Fotopoulos *(gossip)*, Dinos Iliopoulos *(friend)*.

Drama. A grouchy old bachelor who owns a cafe suddenly finds himself caring for an abandoned infant. When the unmarried mother of the infant arrives to claim her child, the grouch protects them from the scorn of neighborhood gossip. *Bachelors. Neighbors. Illegitimacy. Gossip. Motherhood.*

Note: Released in Greece as *Ho grousouzēs.* May also be known as *The Old Grouchy.*

THE GROUP
F6.1967

Famous Artists Productions–Famartists Productions. *Dist* United Artists. 4 Mar 1966 [Detroit opening; c4 Mar 1966; LP32359]. Sd; col (De Luxe). 35mm. 150 min.

Pres by Charles K. Feldman. *Prod-Writ* Sidney Buchman. *Dir* Sidney Lumet. *Dir Photog* Boris Kaufman. *Set Decor* Jack Wright, Jr.. *Scenic Artist* Stanley Cappiello. *Prod Dsgn* Gene Callahan. *Film Ed* Ralph Rosenblum. *Mus Supv* Charles Gross. *Mus Supv in Assoc With* Score Productions. *Mus Cond* Robert de Cormier. *Sd* Dennis Maitland, Jack Fitzstephens. *Asst Dir* Dan Eriksen, Tony Belletier. *Prod Supv* Henry Spitz. *Prod Mgr* Mel Howard. *Cost Dsgn* Anna Hill Johnstone. *Makeup* Irving Buchman. *Hairstyles* Frederic Jones.

Cast—The Group: Candice Bergen (*Elinor "Lakey" Eastlake*), Joan Hackett (*Dorothy Renfrew*), Elizabeth Hartman (*Priss Hartshorn*), Shirley Knight (*Polly Andrews*), Joanna Pettet (*Kay Strong*), Mary-Robin Redd (*Pokey Prothero*), Jessica Walter (*Libby MacAusland*), Kathleen Widdoes (*Helena Davison*).

Cast—The Men: James Broderick (*Dr. James Ridgeley*), James Congdon (*Sloan Crockett*), Larry Hagman (*Harald Peterson*), Hal Holbrook (*Gus Leroy*), Richard Mulligan (*Dick Brown*).

Cast—Featuring: Robert Emhardt (*Mr. Andrews*), Carrie Nye (*Norine*), Philippa Bevans (*Mrs. Hartshorn*), Leta Bonynge (*Mrs. Prothero*), Marion Brash (*radio man's wife*), Sarah Burton (*Mrs. Davison*), Flora Campbell (*Mrs. MacAusland*), Bruno Di Cosmi (*Nils*), Leora Dana (*Mrs. Renfrew*), Bill Fletcher (*Bill*), George Gaynes (*Brook Latham*), Martha Greenhouse (*Mrs. Bergler*), Russell Hardie (*Mr. Davison*), Vincent Harding (*Mr. Eastlake*), Doreen Lang (*nurse Swenson*), Chet London (*radio man*), John O'Leary (*Putnam Blake*), Baruch Lumet (*Mr. Schneider*), Hildy Parks (*nurse Catherine*), Lidia Prochnicka (*baroness*), Polly Rowles (*Mrs. Andrews*), Douglas Rutherford (*Mr. Prothero*), Truman Smith (*Mr. Bergler*), Loretta White (*Mrs. Eastlake*), Ed Holmes (*Mr. MacAusland*), Richard Graham (*Reverend Garland*), Arthur Anderson (*Pokey's husband*), Clay Johns (*Phil*).

Drama. Source: Mary McCarthy, *The Group* (New York, 1963). During the depression of the 1930's, eight young women graduate from college and confidently face their futures. Lakey, the undisputed leader of the group, leaves for an extended stay in Europe. Dottie, a Boston Brahmin, abandons her well-ordered life to become the mistress of a Greenwich Village artist. Their affair lasts only one night, and the heartbroken Dottie returns to New England and the inevitable "proper" marriage to an Arizona business magnate. Priss, quiet and frail, is forced to give up her dream of working for President Roosevelt's poverty program when Congress declares it to be illegal. Instead, she marries an ambitious pediatrician and has two miscarriages before finally giving birth to a son. Her husband's insistence that their child be breast-fed results in a physically weak and exhausted Priss and a spoiled child. Kay, nervous and insecure, quickly marries a young playwright and helps support him by working at Macy's, but he has a weakness for liquor and other women. During a party at their apartment, when the entire group except Lakey is present, the failure of Kay's marriage, as well as her husband's career, becomes obvious. Polly, sweet and practical, takes a hospital job and has a brief, unrewarding affair with an indecisive man who cannot break the ties holding him to his estranged wife and his psychiatrist. She does, however, find happiness with a young doctor. Helena, rich, talented, and the class valedictorian, is denied her parents' permission to teach and spends her unmarried life traveling, collecting art, and giving teas. Libby, attractive and the most ambitious of the group, plunges into New York's literary set and rapidly achieves professional success but is frigid and a personal failure. Finally there is Pokey, who, after short-lived flings at flying lessons and veterinary classes, becomes an uncomplicated wife and the mother of two sets of twins. In 1939, war pressures in Europe force Lakey to return. The entire group assembles to meet her, and upon seeing her mannish baroness companion, they realize that Lakey is a lesbian. At a party celebrating Polly's engagement to her doctor, the radio announces Hitler's invasion of Holland and Belgium. Polly, worried about Kay, who has had a nervous breakdown following a violent marriage breakup, telephones her at her apartment. Hysterical, Kay has heard the newscast and, hearing what she believes to be German planes overhead, leans too far out of a window and plunges to her death. At the funeral, her arrogant husband is quietly but firmly rebuked by Lakey. *Students. Mistresses. Housewives. Artists. Businessmen. Physicians. Playwrights. Salesclerks. Nursing aids. Art collectors. Authors. Nobility. Upper classes. Wealth. Marriage. Ambition. Miscarriage. Childbirth. Alcoholism. Frigidity. Infidelity. Lesbianism. Mental illness. Suicide. Filial*

relations. Funerals. World War II. The Great Depression (1929–34). New York City. New York City—Greenwich Village. Macy's (New York City).

Note: Location scenes filmed in New York City.

GROUP ENCOUNTER *see* **SEXUAL ENCOUNTER GROUP**

GROUPIES
F6.1968

First International TV Song Festival, Inc. *Dist* Maron Films. 8 Nov 1970 [New York opening]. Sd; col (Print by Movielab). 35mm. 92 min. *MPAA rating* X.

Prod Robert Weiner. *Dir-Writ* Ron Dorfman, Peter Nevard. *Photog* Ron Dorfman. *Adtl Photog* William Markle, Michael Becker, Peter Nevard, Joshua Wallace White. *Asst Camera* Phil Roberts. *Film Ed* Ron Dorfman. *Asst Ed* Robert Lind, William Markle, Michael Becker. *Song:* "Delta Lady" Leon Russell. *Perf by* Joe Cocker and the Grease Band. *Songs:* "Good Morning Little Schoolgirl," "Help Me Baby" Sonny Boy Williamson. *Perf by* Ten Years After. *Featuring* Alvin Lee. *Song:* "Mister Sun" Charles Hall, Norman Lombardo. *Perf by* Dry Creek Road. *Song:* "Superlungs" Donovan Leitch. *Perf by* Terry Reid, Keith Webb, Peter Shelley. *Song:* "Bang Bang" Sonny Bono. *Perf by* Terry Reid, Keith Webb, Peter Shelley. *Fillmore Rehearsal Session Perf by* Spooky Tooth. *Featuring* Luther Grosvenor. *Sd Mix* Al Gramaglia. *Sd Rec* Michael Becker, William Markle. *Eight Track Location/Rec* Wally Heider, Bill Halverson. *Mus Re-rec* Alan Corbeth, Mitch Plotkin. *Mus Rec Cons* Ed Kramer. *Lighting at Fillmore West* John Groper.

With: Ten Years After, Joe Cocker and the Grease Band, Spooky Tooth, Luther Grosvenor, Terry Reid, Keith Webb, Peter Shelley, Miss Harlow, Cynthia P. Caster, Goldie Glitter, Chaz, Iris, Brenda, Diane, Lixie and Katy, Andrea Whips, Jenni Dean, Emmaretta Marks, Shelby, Miss Pamela, Joel, Donna, Nancy, Patti Cakes.

Documentary. Shot over a 9-month period in many locations across the country, including Fillmore East and Fillmore West, the film examines the lives of some young fans of rock groups, namely girls and some homosexual boys, who offer services, especially sexual favors, to popular musicians while they are on tour. Scenes backstage at concerts, in hotel rooms, and in the homes of some of the groupies are interspersed among scenes of live musical performances. The sexual aberrations of the groupies are emphasized, and the film climaxes with a visit to Miss Cynthia, whose specialty is making plaster of paris casts of the erect penes of the musicians. *Groupies. Musicians. Adolescence. Promiscuity. Rock and roll. Male homosexuality. Fillmore East (New York City). Fillmore West (San Francisco).*

Note: Filmed in 16mm. Working title: *Rock '70.*

HO GROUSOUZĒS *see* **THE GROUCH**

THE GROVE *see* **THE NAKED ZOO**

GROWN-UP CHILDREN (U.S.S.R.)
F6.1969

Mosfilm. *Dist* Artkino Pictures. 13 Apr 1963 [New York opening]. Sd; b&w. 35mm. 75 min.

Dir Villen Azarov. *Screenplay* Valentina Spirina. *Story Ed* M. Rooz. *Photog* Sergey Zaytsev, Vladimir Meybom. *Art Dir* S. Ushakov. *Film Ed* R. Novikova. *Mus* Aleksandr Flyarkovskiy. *Cond* Yu. Silantyev. *Sd* V. Sharun. *Asst Dir* Vladimir Glazkov, A. Manasarova. *Prod Mgr* V. Kantorovich. *Cost* V. Perelyotov. *Makeup* S. Kalinin. *Sp Eff* I. Felitsyn, N. Zvonaryov.

Cast: Aleksey Gribov (*Anatoliy Kuzmich Korolyov*), Zoya Fyodorova (*Tatyana Ivanovna Korolyova*), Liliya Aleshnikova (*Lyusya*), Aleksandr Demyanenko (*Igor*), Vsevolod Sanayev (*Vasiliy Vasilyevich*), A. Tutyshkin (*Boris Vladimirovich*), Grigoriy Bortnikov, N. Grabbe, Leva Rodionov, M. Khatuntseva, K. Khudyakov.

Comedy-drama. Anatoliy Kuzmich Korolyov, who has worked at a Moscow factory all his life, receives a new apartment in a new section of the city and retires. He looks forward to enjoying his leisure with his wife, Tatyana Ivanovna; to reading, visiting museums, and attending the theater. Their plans are disrupted, however, when their only daughter, Lyusya, an architect, unexpectedly marries a coworker, Igor, and makes plans to move away from home. The young couple are persuaded to share the new apartment, but though the arrangement begins comfortably, the parents find that their peace and quiet quickly evaporate in the close company of the newlyweds and their friends. Then, a new baby arrives. The young parents plan to place him in a nursery, but Anatoliy and Tatyana insist upon looking after him, considering Lyusya and Igor to be children still themselves. After a falling-out between the generations, Anatoliy and Tatyana go away for 3 weeks, forcing the young couple to manage alone with the baby and the housework. Lyusya and Igor come to understand that they have taken much for granted, but with a new appreciation of the parents' contribution comes the realization that the time has come to move out on their own. *Factory workers. Architects. Grandparents. In-laws. Newlyweds. Retirement. Filial relations. Urban life. Housing. Moscow.*

Note: Released in the U.S.S.R. in Dec 1961 as *Vzroslyye deti.*

THE GRUESOME TWOSOME　　　　**F6.1970**

Mayflower Pictures. 27 Mar **1968** [San Antonio, Texas, opening; c28 Aug 1967; LP36746]. Sd; col (Eastmancolor). 35mm. 72 min.

Prod-Dir Herschell Gordon Lewis. *Exec Prod* Fred M. Sandy. *Screenplay* Louise Downe. *Mus Supv* Larry Wellington.

Cast: Elizabeth Davis, Chris Martell, Gretchen Welles, Rodney Bedell.

Horror film. An imbecilic man scalps young women in order that his mother, a wigmaker, may work with real human hair. *Idiots. Wigmakers. Mutilation. Filial relations. Murder.*

GUDRUN *see* **SUDDENLY, A WOMAN!**

LE GUÉPARD *see* **THE LEOPARD**

LA GUERRA CONTINUA *see* **WARRIORS 5**

LA GUERRA DI TROIA *see* **THE TROJAN HORSE**

LA GUERRA SEGRETA *see* **THE DIRTY GAME**

LA GUERRE DE TROIE *see* **THE TROJAN HORSE**

LA GUERRE DES BOUTONS *see* **WAR OF THE BUTTONS**

LA GUERRE EST FINIE (France/Sweden)　　**F6.1971**

Sofracima-Europa-Film. *Dist* Brandon Films. 1 Feb **1967** [New York opening]. Sd; b&w. 35mm. 121 min.

Prod Catherine Winter, Gisèle Rebillon. *Dir* Alain Resnais. *Screenplay* Jorge Semprun. *Photog* Sacha Vierny. *Camera* Philippe Brun. *Asst Camera* Robert Alliel, Pierre Li. *Sets* Jacques Saulnier. *Film Ed* Eric Pluet. *Asst Ed* Hadassa Misrahi, Ziva Postec. *Mus* Giovanni Fusco. *Sd* Antoine Bonfanti. *Asst Sd* Robert Cambourakis, Urbain Loiseau. *Asst Dir* Jean Léon, Florence Malraux. *Prod Mgr* Alain Quefféléan. *Location Mgr* Georges Houssaye. *Prod Sec* Blanche Cochet. *Script Girl* Sylvette Baudrot. *Prod Asst* Jean Pieuchot, Louis Lliberia. *Wardrobe* Madeleine Lafon. *Miss Thulin's Clothes Dsgn* Marie-Martine. *Makeup* Alexandre Marcus, Eliane Marcus. *Prop Mgr* Charles Mérangel. *Still Photog* Nicole Lala. *Head Electrn* Yves Laurent. *Head Grip* René Pequinot. *English Subtitl* Noelle Gillmor.

Cast: Yves Montand (*Diego*), Ingrid Thulin (*Marianne*), Geneviève Bujold (*Nadine Sallanches*), Jean Dasté (*The Chief*), Jorge Semprun (*narrator*), Dominique Rozan (*Jude*), Jean-François Rémi (*Juan*), Marie Mergey (*Madame López*), Jacques Wallet (*C.R.S. policeman*), Michel Piccoli (*1st customs inspector*), Anouk Ferjac (*Madame Jude*), Roland Monod (*Antoine*), Pierre Decazes (*S.N.C.F. employee*), Paul Crauchet (*Roberto*), Claire Duhamel, Antoine Bourseiller (*travelers*), Laurence Badie (*Bernadette Pluvier*), Françoise Bertin (*Carmen*), Yvette Etiévant (*Yvette*), Jean Bouise (*Ramón*), Annie Fargue (*Agnès*), Gérard Séty (*Bill*), Catherine de Seynes (*Jeanine*), Jacques Rispal (*Manolo*), Fylgia Zadig (*woman at meeting*), Pierre Leproux (*maker of forged papers*), Roger Pelletier (*2d customs inspector*), R. J. Chauffard (*drunkard*), José-María Flotats (*Miguel*), Jean Bolo (*agent*), Pierre Barbaud (*client*), Gérard Lartigau (*head of "Revolutionary Action"*), Jean Larrouquette (*member of "Revolutionary Action"*), Martine Vatel (*student*), Laure Paillette (*old lady*), Jacques Robnard (*Pierrot*), Marcel Cuvelier (*Inspector Chardin*), Bernard Fresson (*Sarlat*), Antoine Vitez (*Air France employee*).

Drama. Diego, a revolutionary for 25 years, living in exile in Paris, is stopped and questioned by the border patrol while returning from Madrid using an assumed name and false passport. Attempting to unmask him, the police call the impostor's alleged phone number; the telephone is answered by Nadine, a student revolutionary who verifies his false identity. In Paris, Diego discovers that his contact, Juan, has already left for Spain; and he learns that comrades in Madrid have been arrested. He proposes intercepting Juan and forestalling his mission to preserve his safety, but Roberto, who arranges the trips, refuses, placing primary importance on preparations for a forthcoming general strike. Diego visits Nadine; immediately attracted, the strangers make love. Diego then returns to his devoted mistress, Marianne, a divorcée with a 12-year-old son. He is disquieted, however, by the presence of visitors. At a cell meeting the following day, Diego is prohibited from traveling to Madrid, and his friend Ramon is appointed in his stead. Furthermore, Diego's skepticism regarding the effectiveness of the general strike is attributed to his subjectivity, and he is instructed to rest and reflect upon his failings. After observing police detectives following Nadine, Diego learns that the student and her radical friends are planning to terrorize tourists in Spain and that Marianne is a sympathizer. The exhausted Diego rebukes the young revolutionaries, disavowing random violence. Diego's enforced rest is ended when Ramon dies unexpectedly. Following Diego's departure for Madrid, trouble develops, and the loyal Marianne is recruited to save him. As she boards a plane to Madrid, Marianne thinks of Diego. *Political refugees. Revolutionaries. Mistresses. Border police. Fascism. Disguise. Exile. Propaganda. Resistance (political). Strikes. Spain—*

History—Civil War 1936–39. Spain. Paris. Madrid.

Note: Filmed in Paris and other French locations. Opened in Paris in May 1966; in Stockholm in Mar 1967 as *Kriget är slut.* Also known as *The War Is Over.*

LA GUERRE INCONNUE *see* **SMASHING OF THE REICH**

GUERRE SECRÈTE *see* **THE DIRTY GAME**

GUESS WHAT!?! *see* **GUESS WHAT WE LEARNED IN SCHOOL TODAY?**

GUESS WHAT HAPPENED TO COUNT DRACULA　　**F6.1972**

Merrick International Pictures. 16 Sep **1970** [Asheville, North Carolina, opening]. Sd; col (Movielab). 35mm. 80 min. *MPAA rating* GP.

Prod Leo Rivers. *Exec Prod-Dir-Writ* Laurence Merrick. *Dir Photog* Robert Caramico. *Camera Op* Scott Davis, photog. *Art Dir* Michael Minor. *Film Ed* George Watters. *Mus Comp & Cond* Des Roberts. *Song:* "Angelica" writ & sung by Des Roberts. *Choreog* Lou Claudio. *Sd* Ted Botkin. *Asst Dir* Clancy Syrko. *Prod Mgr* Beverly Gardner. *Cont* Jim Kelly. *Wardrobe* Berman's. *Makeup* Rick Sagliani. *Hairstyles* Tom Jones, hairdresser. *Animals* Ted Derby. *Tech Asst* Magic Dungeon Academy.

Cast: Des Roberts (*Count Dracula*), Claudia Barron (*Angelica*), John Landon (*Guy*), Robert Branche (*Dr. Harris*), Frank Donato (*Imp*), Sharon Beverly (*Vamp*), Damu King (*Hunch*), Jim Settler (*Runt*), Jeff Cady (*Larry*), John King, III (*Gil*), James Young-El (*Macumba initiate*), Angela Carnon (*nurse*), Yvonne Gaudry (*gypsy*).

Horror film. Bored with his mate, Vamp, Hollywood resident Count Dracula longs for a teenaged love. Guy, a struggling actor, offers the vampire his girl friend Angelica in exchange for stardom. At a discotheque, "Dracula's Dungeon," the vampire meets the young lady and inflicts the first of three transforming bites. When she visits a doctor to complain of dizziness, the physician dismisses her complaint, jokingly suggesting that she is the victim of a vampire. Dracula then arranges to be Angelica's blind date at an orgy. While the guests are enjoying sex and marijuana, Dracula mesmerizes Angelica and bites her again. When she awakens the girl cannot stand daylight and craves raw meat. The vampire takes the adolescent to his castle and inflicts the third bite. Tormented by guilt, Guy challenges the vampire. Angelica resolves their conflict by draining the blood of her former boyfriend. Satiated, the pair prepares for an eternity together. *Actors. Vampires. Physicians. Hypnotism. Guilt. Immortality. Adolescence. Group sex. Marijuana. Castles. Discotheques. Hollywood. Dreams. Dracula.*

GUESS WHAT WE LEARNED IN SCHOOL TODAY?　　**F6.1973**

Cannon Productions–Institute for Interpersonal Relations. *Dist* William E. Heineman, Cannon Releasing Corp. 8 Jul **1970** [Minneapolis opening]. Sd; col (DeLuxe). 35mm. 90 min. *MPAA rating* R.

Prod David Gil. *Exec Prod* Dennis Friedland, Christopher C. Dewey. *Assoc Prod* James V. Clarke. *Dir* John G. Avildsen. *Screenplay* Eugene Price, John G. Avildsen. *Story* Eugene Price. *Photog* John G. Avildsen. *Titl* Zacks and Perrier. *Film Ed* John G. Avildsen. *Mus* Harper MacKay. *Titl Song* Moose Charlap, Joan Andre Gil. *Song:* "What's Happened to My Baby?" Harper MacKay. *Sung by* Sandy Stewart. *Sd Rec* Michael Scott Goldbaum. *Sd Re-rec* Jack Cooley. *Prod Mgr* Arthur Littman.

Cast: Richard Carballo (*Lieut. Roger Manley*), Devin Goldenberg (*Robbie Battle*), Zachary Haines (*Lance Battle*), Jane MacLeod (*Rita Battle*), Yvonne McCall (*Dr. Lily Whitehorn*), Rosella Olsen (*Eve Manley*), Stanton Edgehill (*Billie*), Diane Moore (*Lydia*), Larry Evers (*Al*), Iris Brooks (*Lulu*), Jean David (*Mrs. O'Reilly*), Brett Morrison, Robert Emerick (*radio voices*), Daphne Gil (*dancing girl*), George Pollack (*waiter*), Elizabeth Grusky (*Elizabeth*), Andrew Kay (*young man in pool*), Natalie Rogers, Margaret Steele (*women in pool*), Tim Lewis (*Mike Avalon*), Bradley Price (*Bradley*), Gene Price (*Marine captain*), Judy Price (*dance teacher*), Philip Price (*Philip*), Jan Saint (*mailman*), Lou Stanishia (*karate teacher*), Ches Turner (*little boy*), Sandra Wolf (*Betty*), Catherine Avildsen (*opening voice*).

Satire. Dr. Lily Whitehorn, head of the Institute for Interpersonal Relations, attempts to initiate a sex education course in the high school of a middle-class suburb, but she is thwarted by the conservative members of the community. Among the staunchest protestors are Roger Manley, a homosexual-hating vice-squad lieutenant, who believes that sex education is a communist conspiracy to undermine the moral backbone of the nation, and Lance Battle, an alcoholic, sexually impotent ex-Marine colonel, who lives in a World War II fantasy. The men's frustrated wives, however, are far more sympathetic to Dr. Whitehorn's crusade; following a morning of sipping coffee and smoking marijuana, Eve Manley asserts her own liberated sexuality by coercing Rita Battle into a lesbian affair. Later Eve volunteers herself as a sex partner for the Battles' 17-year-old son, Robbie. As Lance watches Eve and Robbie make love, he becomes so stimulated that he overcomes his impotence; and Robbie, having been initiated

435

into the pleasures of sex, turns his attention to Lydia, Dr. Whitehorn's pretty assistant. Lydia invites everyone to the institute for nude swimming, and Roger takes it upon himself to save Robbie's endangered morals. As he peeks through the trees at his uninhibited friends, Roger is horrified to find himself sexually attracted to Robbie. He rushes off to hang himself but is cut down by Billie, a black prostitute who once satisfied his sexual desires. After proving that he is not a woman but a detective in disguise, Billie arrests Roger for homosexual soliciting and dereliction of duty. Finally acknowledging that they are more in need of sex education than their children, the adults sign up for Dr. Whitehorn's course. As a final irony, Dr. Whitehorn confesses that she has no sex life but intends to remedy the situation as soon as possible. *Physicians. Veterans. Negroes. Prostitutes. Sex instruction. Suburban life. Moral corruption. Alcoholism. Impotence. Lesbianism. Adolescence. Sexual initiation. Voyeurism. Male homosexuality. Suicide. Female impersonation. Vice squads. Marijuana. Institute for Interpersonal Relations (New York).*

Note: Filmed on location in New York. Also known as *Guess What!?!* and *I Ain't No Buffalo.*

GUESS WHO'S COMING?　　　　　　　　　　F6.1974
Juniper Productions. *Dist* Imperial Pictures. 21 May **1969** [Boston opening]. Sd; b&w. 35mm. 68 min.

Prod-Writ J. Llatimer, Jai Hais. *Assoc Prod* Frieda D. Public. *Dir* Jai Hais. *Cinematog* Paul S. Pool. *Sets* A. Carpenter. *Film Ed* J. Llatimer. *Sd* Audie O'Consol. *Asst Dir* Rhoda Mandalay. *Props* Bessie Mae Mucho.

Cast: Bob O'Connell, Ellen Butler, Janine Kelly, Simone Renard, Lance Canyon, Dominique France, Gail Sedrish, Melanie Anderson, Brick Rhodes, Lorna Stewart, L. E. Laine.

Drama(?). Television commercial director Bob Rand finds that his married life has become a dull routine. His moral foundation shaken by a call to an old girl friend, he receives another blow when his boss, T. C., decides to branch into the sex exploitation field and insists that Bob direct the new productions. Bob is forced to deal with people whose sordid lives are a constant reminder of his own moral disintegration: a blonde stripper removes her clothes whenever she hears music; a shy, blushing young woman goes wild with lust for her own body; two lesbians make love whenever the desire strikes, regardless of time or place. To complicate Bob's predicament, his job is threatened by T. C.'s ambitious son Danny. Bob's first marital lapse occurs in the projection room when he joins his secretary, Milly, to screen some footage; Danny is a scheming witness. Bob joins his old girl friend Penny in a second infidelity. Danny, meanwhile, decides to usurp Bob's social life as well as his career. When Milly refuses his advances, he attempts a rape that fails when she views his naked body and bursts into laughter. Danny's film career also heads for failure. He picks up a pretty young blonde in the park and promises to put her in movies. Once inside the studio, she refuses to take off her clothes. Disgusted with himself, Bob arrives on the set to find Danny harassing his new "find." He punches the upstart in the mouth and walks out for good. His self-respect restored, Bob begins a new life with his wife. *Television directors. Television producers. Stripteasers. Actors. Marriage. Sex exploitation films. Moral corruption. Autoeroticism. Lesbianism. Infidelity. Ambition. Voyeurism. Rape. Guilt.*

GUESS WHO'S COMING TO DINNER　　　　　　　　　　F6.1975
Columbia Pictures. 11 Dec **1967** [New York opening; c31 Dec 1967; LP35733]. Sd; col (Technicolor). 35mm. 108 min.

A Stanley Kramer Production. *Prod-Dir* Stanley Kramer. *Assoc Prod* George Glass. *Screenplay* William Rose. *Dir Photog* Sam Leavitt. *Camera Op* Wilbur Gossman. *Asst Camera* Darryl Kenzel. *Set Decor* Frank Tuttle. *Set Dsgn* Gabriel Resh, Jim Bochman. *Prod Dsgn* Robert Clatworthy. *Film Ed* Robert C. Jones. *Asst Ed* Tony Friedman. *Mus* Frank De Vol. *Song:* "Glory of Love" Billy Hill. *Sung by* Jacqueline Fontaine. *Sd* Charles J. Rice, Robert Martin. *Re-rec* Clem Portman. *Boom Op* James Rogers. *Asst Dir* Ray Gosnell, Leonard Kunody. *Prod Supv* Ivan Volkman. *Script Supv* Marshall Schlom. *Wardrobe Supv* Jean Louis. *Cost* Joe King. *Women's Wardrobe* Edna Taylor. *Makeup* Ben Lane, Joseph Di Bella. *Hairstyles* Helen Hunt. *Sp Eff* Geza Gaspar. *Proc Photog* Larry Butler. *Still Photog* John Monte. *Company Grip* Martin Kashuk. *Ch Electrn* Les Everson. *Prop Master* Clarence Peet.

Cast: Spencer Tracy *(Matt Drayton)*, Sidney Poitier *(John Prentice)*, Katharine Hepburn *(Christina Drayton)*, Katharine Houghton *(Joey Drayton)*, Cecil Kellaway *(Monsignor Ryan)*, Beah Richards *(Mrs. Prentice)*, Roy Glenn *(Mr. Prentice)*, Isabell Sanford *(Tillie)*, Virginia Christine *(Hilary St. George)*, Alexandra Hay *(carhop)*, Barbara Randolph *(Dorothy)*, D'Urville Martin *(Frankie)*, Tom Heaton *(Peter)*, Grace Gaynor *(Judith)*, Skip Martin *(delivery boy)*, John Hudkins *(cab driver)*.

Comedy-drama. Among the socially prominent citizens of San Francisco are Matt Drayton, the publisher of a liberal newspaper, and his wife, Christina, the owner of a fashionable art gallery. One day their daughter, Joey, returns from a vacation in Hawaii with John Prentice, a black physician whom she has known for only 10 days but intends to marry. Because John must leave the next day

for Switzerland on behalf of the World Health Organization, Joey is determined that their wedding take place immediately, and she asks for her parents' permission. Furthermore, John secretly confides to the Draytons that he will not marry Joey without their consent. Suddenly confronted with a test of their longtime liberal beliefs, Matt and Christina find themselves unable to reach a decision. Less involved observers, however, quickly voice their opinions: Christina's business associate, Hilary St. George, is quick to reveal her bigotry; an old family friend, Monsignor Ryan, is confident that the couple will be able to overcome their obstacles; and the Draytons' shocked black maid, Tillie, berates John for his impertinence. Though Christina yields to her daughter's wishes, Matt remains undecided. The dilemma is compounded when Joey persuades John's parents to fly up from Los Angeles. Upon their arrival, Mrs. Prentice sides with Christina; but her husband is dubious about the situation and argues with his son. Mrs. Prentice appeals to Matt recalling the days when they stood on the threshold of a youthful marriage. Realizing that the decision rests with the children, he finally offers Joey and John his blessing; moved by the wisdom of Matt's words, Mr. Prentice also relents. *Publishers. Art dealers. Negroes. Physicians. Clergymen. Housemaids. Social classes. Miscegenation. Parenthood. Racial prejudice. San Francisco. United Nations—World Health Organization.*

THE GUEST (Great Britain)　　　　　　　　　　F6.1976
Caretaker Films. *Dist* Janus Films. 20 Jan **1964** [New York opening]. Sd; b&w. 35mm. 105 min.

Prod Michael Birkett. *Financial Backers* Peter Bridge, Richard Burton, Noel Coward, Peter Cadbury, Leslie Caron, Peter Hall, Charles Kasher, Harry Saltzman, Peter Sellers, Elizabeth Taylor. *Dir* Clive Donner. *Screenplay* Harold Pinter. *Photog* Nicolas Roeg. *Art Dir* Reece Pemberton. *Film Ed* Fergus McDonell. *Mus & Sd Eff* Ron Grainer. *Sd Rec* Robert Allen.

Cast: Donald Pleasence *(Davies)*, Alan Bates *(Mick)*, Robert Shaw *(Aston)*.

Drama. Source: Harold Pinter, *The Caretaker* (London opening: 27 Apr 1960). Davies, a dirty old derelict, is pitied by Aston, a softspoken man, and is invited to spend the night in a rundown London house where Aston, the only resident, occupies one room. The next morning Aston suggests that Davies remain at the house and act as caretaker. Later, while Aston is out, his sadistic brother Mick arrives and reveals that he owns the building and that Aston is a former mental patient. As time passes the derelict is bandied about by the two brothers—in favor with one brother and out of favor with the other at one moment, and just the reverse at the next moment. Though he uses his wiles to cling to his position, Davies is eventually rejected by both brothers and turned out. All three return to their former isolation. *Derelicts. Caretakers. Brothers. Eccentrics. Mental illness. Sadism. Employment. London.*

Note: Filmed entirely in a house in Hackney, London. Opened in London in Mar 1964 as *The Caretaker.*

GUESTS ARE COMING (Poland)　　　　　　　　　　F6.1977
Droga Film Unit. *For* Film Polski. *Dist* Mitchell Kowal Films. 12 May **1965** [Hartford, Connecticut, opening]. Sd; b&w. 35mm. 110 min.

Overall Production Credits: *Dir Supv* Antoni Bohdziewicz. *Dir 1st Episode* Gerard Zalewski. *Dir 2d Episode* Jan Rutkiewicz. *Dir 3d Episode* Romuald Drobaczyński. *Screenplay* Jan Józef Szczepański. *Photog* Stanisław Loth. *Mus* Stefan Kisielewski. *English Subtitl* Mitchell Kowal.

Cast—1st Episode: Paul Glass, actor *(Peter)*, Kazimierz Opaliński *(Uncle Konstanty)*, Zenon Burzyński *(son)*, Sylwia Zakrzewska *(daughter-in-law)*, Wanda Koczewska *(blonde woman)*, Maryla Butorowicz *(Madzia)*.

Cast—2d Episode: Mitchell Kowal *(Mike O'Rawiec)*, Władysław Hańcza *(village priest)*, The Gorals *(highlanders)*, Zofia Merle *(Maryna)*, Marian Jastrzebski *(Białas)*.

Cast—3d Episode: Zygmunt Zintel *(Harry Kwasnicki)*, Ryszard Pietruski *(truck driver)*.

Comedy. 1ST EPISODE: Peter, a girl-crazy American, takes time off from a business trip in Poland to visit an uncle, Konstanty, to whom his father has been sending money for maintaining an apartment. Actually Konstanty is living at a rest home and the money is being used to pay the rent for his son's and daughter-in-law's apartment. Konstanty nevertheless consents to move in with them while Peter is visiting. In so doing the old man is able to both fool the American and score a moral victory over his weak-principled son and greedy daughter-in-law. 2D EPISODE: A middle-aged widower from Indiana arrives at the Polish village of his father's birth in the hope of finding a wife. Treated like royalty, he is wined and dined by anxious mothers hopeful of marrying off a daughter to "the American millionaire." While drunk, he decides on the local barmaid and thereby ends up marrying the one girl whose charms have already been enjoyed by all the village swains. 3D EPISODE: A Chicago promoter is in Poland to dig up earth from famous battlefields to sell to Polish-Americans as authentic souvenirs. It is pointed out to him that such places are easy to find, Poland having been fought over for so long; as a result, he buys whatever dirt the eager Poles sell him and loads it aboard a ship bound for the United States.

Businessmen. Americans in foreign countries. Uncles. Widowers. Barmaids. Entrepreneurs. Houseguests. Duplicity. Ancestry. Marriage. Old age homes.

Note: Released in Poland in 1962 as *Jadą, goście, jadą* or *Jadą goście.*

GUEULE D'ANGE *see* **PLEASURES AND VICES**

THE GUIDE (United States/India) F6.1978

Stratton International, Inc.–Navketan International. *Dist* Stratton International, Inc., Goldstone Film Enterprises. 9 Feb 1965 [New York opening; c4 Dec 1964; LU3342]. Sd; col (Eastmancolor, print by Pathé). 35mm. 120 min.

Prod-Dir Tad Danielewski. *Assoc Dir* Vijay Anand. *Screenplay* Pearl S. Buck, Tad Danielewski. *Photog* Fali Mistry. *Art Dir* Ram Yedekar. *Mus* S. D. Burman. *Choreog* Hiralil. *Sd* Barot.

Cast: Dev Anand (*Raju*), Waheeda Rehman (*Rosie*), Kishore Sahu (*Marco*), Leela Chitnis (*mother*), Anwar Hussein (*Gaffur*), K. N. Singh (*Velan*), Levy Aaron (*Dilip*), Rashid Khan (*Joseph*), Dilip Dutt (*Mani*), Iftikhar (*inspector*), John Voyantiz (*British correspondent*), Krishna Dhawan (*defense lawyer*), Hazel (*Velan's sister*), Satya Dev Duby (*Velan's brother*), J. S. Kashyap (*old man*), Sheila Burghart (*TV reporter*), Jagirdar, Ullas, Praveen Paul, Purnima.

Drama. Source: R. K. Narayan, *The Guide* (New York, 1957). Raju, a brash young tour guide in an Indian village, is hired by Marco, a middle-aged archeologist, who wants to show his wife, Rosie, a former dancer, the ancient ruins. Infatuated by the woman's beauty, Raju seduces her and then offers to help her resume her dancing career. When she consents, Marco abandons her, and she becomes Raju's mistress. As she achieves fame, however, their relationship pales, and Raju is forced into the background. He is eventually jailed for forgery, and Rosie leaves him alone and penniless. After his release, he wanders into a deserted temple where his suave manner causes the naive villagers to mistake him for a spiritual leader. Raju gradually begins to live his role and even promises a miracle to end a severe drought. Rather than destroy his followers' illusions, he vows to fast until rain falls. No rain comes, and despite the pleas of the government and Rosie, Raju willingly becomes a martyr. *Guides. Dancers. Archeologists. Mistresses. Seduction. Infidelity. Mistaken identity. Imposture. Suicide. Drought. Miracles. Religion.*

Note: Location scenes filmed in New Delhi and Bombay. Produced in India in 1965. Also known as *Survival.*

A GUIDE FOR THE MARRIED MAN F6.1979

Twentieth Century-Fox Film Corp. 25 May 1967 [New York opening; c24 May 1967; LP34449]. Sd (Westrex); col (De Luxe). 35mm (Panavision). 89 min. [Copyright length: 92 min.]

Prod Frank McCarthy. *Dir* Gene Kelly. *Screenplay* Frank Tarloff. *Dir Photog* Joseph MacDonald. *Art Dir* Jack Martin Smith, William Glasgow. *Set Decor* Walter M. Scott, Raphael Bretton. *Titl* Don Record, Pacific Title. *Film Ed* Dorothy Spencer. *Mus* Johnny Williams. *Song:* "A Guide for the Married Man" Leslie Bricusse, Johnny Williams. *Sung by* The Turtles. *Orch* Herbert Spencer. *Sd* Harry M. Lindgren, David Dockendorf. *Asst Dir* Paul Helmick. *Unit Prod Mgr* Harry Caplan. *Cost Supv* Moss Mabry. *Makeup* Ben Nye. *Hairstyles* Margaret Donovan. *Sp Photog Eff* L. B. Abbott, Art Cruickshank, Emil Kosa, Jr.

Cast: Walter Matthau (*Paul Manning*), Inger Stevens (*Ruth Manning*), Sue Ane Langdon (*Mrs. Irma Johnson*), Jackie Russell (*Miss Harris*), Robert Morse (*Ed Stander*), Elaine Devry (*Jocelyn Montgomery*), Aline Towne (*mousey man's wife*), Claire Kelly (*Harriet Stander*), Eve Brent (*Joe X's blowzy blonde*), Marvin Brody (*taxi driver*), Majel Barrett (*Mrs. Fredy*), Marian Mason (*Mrs. Rance G*), Tommy Farrell (*Rance G's hanger-on*), Linda Harrison (*Miss Stardust*), Jason Wingreen (*Mr. Johnson*), Pat Becker, Fred Holliday, Robert Patten, Dee Carroll, Ray Montgomery, Jackie Joseph (*party guests*), Heather Young (*girl with megaphone*), Evelyn King (*female plaintiff*), Nancy De Carl (*woman with baby*), Warrene Ott (*woman with gun*), Michael Romanoff (*maitre d'hotel*), Karen Arthur (*lady dinner partner*), Mickey Deems (*waiter*), Damian London (*lone male diner*), Chanin Hale (*Miss Crenshaw*), Julie Tate (*woman in bed*), George Neise (*man in bed*), Tim Herbert (*shoe clerk*), Patricia Sides (*Mau Mau dancer*), Pat McCaffrie (*motel clerk*), Jimmy Cross (*Mr. Brown*), Virginia Wood (*Bubbles*), Sharyn Hillyer (*girl in bed*), Lucille Ball, Jack Benny, Polly Bergen, Joey Bishop, Sid Caesar, Art Carney, Wally Cox, Jayne Mansfield, Hal March, Louis Nye, Carl Reiner, Phil Silvers, Terry-Thomas, Ben Blue, Ann Morgan Guilbert, Jeffrey Hunter, Marty Ingels, Sam Jaffe ("*technical advisers*").

Comedy. Source: Frank Tarloff, *A Guide for the Married Man, as Told to Frank Tarloff* (Los Angeles, 1967). Paul Manning realizes to his dismay that after 12 happy years of marriage he is becoming increasingly distracted by other women. He is particularly attracted to his neighbor, Irma Johnson. To make matters worse, his philandering friend, Ed Stander, claims that to preserve a marriage, the husband should secretly indulge in a little extramarital activity. As a gesture of true camaraderie, Ed volunteers to teach Paul the finer points

of wife-cheating and illustrates his lectures with stories of friends who have had successful or unsuccessful affairs. Paul proves to be a willing and able pupil and easily manipulates his unsuspecting wife, Ruth, into suggesting that he occasionally spend a night at the steam baths. Paul then carefully selects his first target, Jocelyn Montgomery, a seductive divorcée who must also practice discretion to protect her alimony. A remote motel is chosen, and a rendezvous is arranged. But once alone in the bedroom with Jocelyn, Paul's thoughts turn to Ruth, and he shows the unbelieving Jocelyn snapshots of his family. Suddenly, police sirens and screams are heard as police raid a motel across the way. Photographers take pictures of a startled, undressed man—Ed Stander—entertaining Irma Johnson. Paul takes one quick look, leaps into his clothes, pushes Jocelyn into his car, dumps her off at a parking lot, and races home to his wife. *Philanderers. Neighbors. Vice squads. Marriage. Friendship. Infidelity. Alimony. Motels.*

Note: Location scenes filmed in and around Los Angeles.

GUILT (Sweden) F6.1980

Svensk Filmindustri. *Dist* Crown International Pictures. 10 Nov 1967 [New York opening]. Sd; b&w. 35mm. 90 min.

Dir-Writ Lars Görling. *Photog* Lars Björne. *Set Dsgn* Rolf Bowan. *Film Ed* Ulla Ryghe. *Mus* Ulf Björlin. *Sd* Lars Lalin. *Sp Eff* Evald Andersson.

Cast: Sven Bertil Taube (*Hans*), Helena Brodin (*Gunilla*), Tina Hedstrom (*Inga*), Marrit Ohlsson (*1st woman*), Inga-Lill Ahstrom (*2d woman*).

Melodrama. Late one winter night, Hans, driving with his girl friend, Gunilla, runs over a pedestrian and kills him. They leave the scene of the accident and spend the night and next day rationalizing their behavior. As they drive through the country, they talk also about their unsatisfactory physical relationship. Hans swings violently from rage at Gunilla, to blame of the dead man's carelessness, to hopelessness and exhaustion. Reluctantly, even scornfully, he accepts Gunilla's physical tenderness. Finally she can stand his guilt-ridden neuroticism no longer, and she runs away. Hans catches up with her and persuades her to come back with him. Though Hans reads the newspaper account of the accident with little visible emotion, he and Gunilla realize that the entire experience has seriously affected their relationship and altered their futures. They decide to drive home, and just as they arrive, a police car pulls up beside them. *Hit-and-run drivers. Police. Guilt. Automobile accidents.*

Note: Released in Sweden in Sep 1965 as *Tillsammans med Gunilla Måndag kväll och Tisdag.* Alternative Swedish title: *Tillsammans med Gunilla.* U. S. prerelease title: *With Gunilla Monday Evening and Tuesday.*

GUILT IS NOT MINE (Italy) F6.1981

Zeus Film–Electron Film. *Dist* Hoffberg Productions. May 1968. Sd; b&w. 35mm. 90 min.

Dir-Story Giuseppe Masini. *Screenplay* Giuseppe Masini, Siro Angeli, R. Gentili, Luigi Giacosi. *Photog* Augusto Tiezzi. *Mus* Carlo Innocenzi.

Cast: Rossano Brazzi (*Carlo Rocchi*), Gaby André (*Anna Valli*), Sergio Tofano (*Professor Valli*), Elvy Lissiak (*Barbara Soldani*), Umberto Sacripante (*Vittorio Gori*), Mino Doro, Fedele Gentile, Ubaldo Lay, Amedeo Trilli, Gianna Segale, Guido Riccioli, Nanda Primavera.

Drama. In 1889 the young physician Carlo Rocchi falls in love with Anna Valli, but her father, a professor of medicine, persuades the doctor to leave Rome. Rocchi sets up his practice in Orbetello, where he uses innovative methods to combat an outbreak of malaria. While attempting to forget Anna, the solitary physician remains indifferent to the advances of neighbor Barbara Soldani, who in a fit of jealousy suggests to the townspeople that Rocchi is responsible for deaths during the epidemic. At his trial all witnesses, including Professor Valli, decry his unorthodox techniques. Sentenced to 4 years in prison and forbidden to practice medicine, Rocchi becomes an orderly in the prison hospital. After successfully innoculating himself against malaria and thereby demonstrating the efficacy of vaccination, Rocchi is released, marries Anna, and resumes his career. *Physicians. Professors. Jealousy. Medical ethics. Epidemics. Injustice. Filial relations. Trials. Prisons. Malaria. Rome. Orbetello.*

Note: Released in Italy in 1952 as *L'ingiusta condanna.* Alternative Italian title: *Quelli che non muoiono.*

GULLIVER NO UCHU RYOKO *see* **GULLIVER'S TRAVELS BEYOND THE MOON**

GULLIVER'S TRAVELS BEYOND THE MOON (Japan) F6.1982

Toei Co. *Dist* Continental Distributing, Inc. Aug 1966. Sd; col. 35mm. 85 min.

Prod Hiroshi Okawa. *Dir* Yoshio Kuroda. *Screenplay* Shinichi Sekizawa. *Anim Dir* Hideo Furusawa. *Mus & Songs:* "I Wanna Be Like Gulliver!" "The Earth Song," "That's the Way It Goes," "Keep Your Hopes High" Milton DeLugg, Anne DeLugg.

Animated melodrama. Based on the character created by: Jonathan Swift. When a speeding car knocks a homeless waif unconscious for a few moments, the little boy has an unusual dream. *Accompanied by a colonel, a dog, and a crow, he joins old Dr. Gulliver in a rocket trip to the planet of Hope. As they are approaching the planet, magnetic rays pull them to a nearby star where they are examined by strange scientists. They also encounter a dainty princess who tells them that she, her father, and the scientists are from the planet of Hope and that they are being held captive by robots. By accident, Dr. Gulliver and the little boy discover that, in this part of space, water will disintegrate solid matter. Armed with water pistols, they destroy the robots and free the people from the planet of Hope. Regaining consciousness, the little waif sets out to face life with renewed hope. Waifs. Scientists. Royalty. Robots. Space travel. Abduction. Imaginary planets. Automobile accidents. Dreams. Dogs. Crows.*

Note: Produced in Japan in 1965 as *Gulliver no uchu ryoko.*

GUMBO YA-YA see **GIRLS! GIRLS! GIRLS!**

GUN FIGHT   F6.1983

Zenith Pictures. *Dist* United Artists. 10 May **1961** [Los Angeles opening]. Sd; b&w. 35mm. 67 min.

Prod Robert E. Kent. *Dir* Edward L. Cahn. *Screenplay* Gerald Drayson Adams, Richard Schayer. *Story* Gerald Drayson Adams. *Photog* Walter Strenge. *Art Dir* Serge Krizman. *Film Ed* Robert Carlisle. *Mus* Paul Sawtell, Bert Shefter. *Sd* John Kean. *Asst Dir* Herbert S. Greene. *Wardrobe* Einar Bourman, Sabine Manela. *Makeup* Harry Thomas. *Hairstyles* Frances Sperry.

Cast: James Brown (*Wayne Santley*), Joan Staley (*Nora Blaine*), Gregg Palmer (*Brad Santley*), Ron Soble (*Pawnee*), Ken Mayer (*Joe Emery*), Charles Cooper (*Cole Fender*), Charles Coy (*sheriff*), James Parnell (*Moose*), Connie Buck (*Coheela*), Kate Murtah (*Molly*), Andy Albin (*Jonathan*), Jon Locke (*Saunders*), Morgan Shaan (*Cory*), Monte Burkhart (*Hannah*), David Donaldson (*prospector*), John Damler (*Hank*), Robert Nash (*Vance*), Jack Kenny (*Jake*), Frank Watkins (*Roark*), Frank Eldredge (*piano player*), Gene Coogan (*Bole*), Bill Koontz (*Krag*), Boyd Stockman (*Cadiz*), Bob Woodward (*Mantz*).

Western melodrama. Wayne Santley, recently discharged from the 7th Cavalry at the time of the Indian wars, travels West to join his brother Brad on a large cattle ranch. On the stagecoach, he strikes up a romantic acquaintance with Nora Blaine, a dancehall hostess whom he rescues from the advances of gambler Cole Fender during a holdup. Wayne soon learns that his brother is a rustler and an outlaw, not a rancher. Rather than join his brother's gang, Wayne goes to work at a friend's trading post and eventually marries Nora. Pawnee, one of Brad's men, convinces him that his brother led the sheriff to their hideout. He and his men seek revenge against Wayne, but when Brad is told that Wayne was actually framed by bounty hunter Cole Fender, he repents and joins Wayne on a trapping job. Angered by Brad's desertion, Pawnee and his new gang attack the two brothers. In the ensuing gunfight, the outlaws are killed, and Brad dies at his brother's side. A short time later, a daughter is born to Nora and Wayne; they name the child Bradena, after her deceased uncle. *Brothers. Dancehall hostesses. Rustlers. Outlaws. Bounty hunters. Stagecoach robberies. Marriage. Revenge. Frameup. Ranches. Trading posts. United States Army—Cavalry.*

THE GUN HAND see **HE RIDES TALL**

THE GUN HAWK   F6.1984

Bern-Field Productions. *Dist* Allied Artists. caAug **1963** [c12 Sep 1963; LP26161]. Sd; col (De Luxe). 35mm. 92 min.

Prod Richard Bernstein. *Exec Prod* Edward Critchfield. *Assoc Prod* Leon Bleiberg, Sidney Rhueban. *Prod Assoc* Gabriel De Caesar. *Dir* Edward Ludwig. *Screenplay* Jo Heims. *Story* Richard Bernstein, Max Steeber. *Dir Photog* Paul C. Vogel. *Art Dir* Rudi Feld. *Set Decor* Clarence Steensen. *Film Ed* Rex Lipton. *Mus Comp & Cond* Jimmie Haskell. *Song:* "A Searcher for Love" Robert Marcucci, Russ Faith. *Sd Ed* Henry Adams. *Sd* Ralph Butler. *Mus Ed* George E. Marsh. *Asst Dir* Ralph Slosser, Arthur Broidy. *Prod Supv* Edward Morey, Jr.. *Asst to the Exec Prod* Ben Wurtzel. *Prod Asst* Jack Cantor, Hal Kahan, Audrey Bernstein. *Script Supv* Joan Eremin. *Wardrobe* Roger J. Weinberg. *Makeup* Beau Hickman. *Hairdresser* Alice Monte. *Constr Supv* James West. *Prop Master* Max Frankel. *Dial Coach* Don Laiffer.

Cast: Rory Calhoun (*Blaine Madden*), Rod Cameron (*Sheriff Corey*), Ruta Lee (*Marleen*), Rod Lauren (*Roan*), Morgan Woodward (*Mitchell*), Robert J. Wilke (*Johnny Flanders*), John Litel (*drunk*), Rodolfo Hoyos (*Miguel*), Lane Bradford (*Joe Sully*), Glenn Stensel (*Luke Sully*), Joan Connors (*Roan's woman*), Ron Whelan (*Blackjack*), Lee Bradley (*Pancho*), Jody Daniels, Natividad Vacio, Greg Barton, Frank Gardner, Harry Fleer.

Western melodrama. Blaine Madden, an outlaw who runs the town of Sanctuary, a haven for criminals, visits his own hometown and there comes to the aid of a young man named Roan who has been attacked by two brothers. The brothers plan to kill Madden, but the town drunkard, Madden's father, is accidentally killed instead. Against the advice of the sheriff, an old friend of his, Madden pursues the killers. He shoots them down but in turn is wounded by

the sheriff, who objects to Madden's taking the law into his own hands. Roan helps Madden get back to Sanctuary, and there the people protect him by preventing the sheriff from entering the town. Blood poisoning develops in Madden's wound. He has become fond of Roan, and, knowing he is dying and concerned lest Roan pattern his life after his own, Madden forces the young man to kill him in a gun duel. Roan is then obliged to leave Sanctuary because of an unwritten law forbidding killing among its outlaw citizens. He is taken into custody by the sheriff, who has been waiting on the town's outskirts, and is told that Madden, though an outlaw, was a good lawman because he kept Sanctuary free of crime. *Outlaws. Sheriffs. Brothers. Murder. Blood poisoning. Self-sacrifice. Friendship. Alcoholism.*

GUN RUNNER   F6.1985

Jabe Films–J. Tanenbaum Productions. *Dist* Grads Corp. **1969.** Sd; col (Eastman Color). 35mm. 76 min.

Exec Prod Charles Dickerson. *Assoc Prod* James Tanenbaum. *Dir-Writ* Richard Compton. *Camera* John Nestor, Harold Archambault. *Art Dir* Joel Sussman. *Ed* Jack Starrett. *Mus Writ & Cond* Rene DeKnight. *Nightclub Sequence Comp, Writ, & Perf by* Sallie Blair. *Sd* James Tanenbaum. *Asst Dir* Jack Pierce. *Script Supv* Francis Dole. *Key Grip* Mike Stringer. *Prop* Cameron Stuart. *Gaffer* Ted Mather.

Cast: Trent Dolan (*Terry Decker*), Victoria Carbé (*Margarete*), John Rico (*Vargas*), Beach Dickerson (*Max Keeler*), Carl Steppling, Gilda Hayworth, R. C. Adams, Geretta Taylor, Jerry Petty, Dianne Durrell, Mary Bauer, Julia Blackburn, Mary Jo Bisby, Barbara Peeters, Henry von Seyfried, Melinda Machard, Connie Nelson, Mike Stringer.

Action melodrama. Government agent Max Keeler faces pressure from Washington to crack down on a gunrunning operation headed by Manuel Vargas, who imports weapons from South America and sells them to fanatic anti-communists in Texas. Desperate, Keeler turns to drifter Terry Decker for help in infiltrating the gang. Dressed as a sailor, Decker roams the docks, visits a waterfront whorehouse, and at a seamen's bar meets Margarete, a streetwalker whose boyfriend, Morgan, is one of Vargas' henchmen. Morgan introduces Decker to Vargas, who gives him the job of inspecting a new shipment of guns. Salt Pete, Decker's government contact on the waterfront, is found stabbed beneath a pier; dying, he warns Decker that Vargas has found him out. Fired with revenge, Decker visits Margarete, who tenderly makes love to him. When the guns arrive, Decker and Morgan carry them by motorboat to the beach, and there a truck waits to speed them into distribution. Decker returns to Vargas' boat, finishes off the gunrunner and his gang, and escapes just as a bomb rips apart the boat. Exhausted, he makes his way back to the beach and finds Morgan and Margarete dead. Keeler, elated with the success of the mission, offers Decker a new assignment, but the drifter refuses and wanders off. *Drifters. Gunrunners. Government agents. Prostitutes. South Americans. Sailors. Murder. Espionage. Disguise. Revenge. Anti-communism. Texas. South America. Ship explosions.*

Note: Also known as *The Gunrunners.* John Nestor is a pseudonym for Nestor Almendros.

GUN STREET   F6.1986

Harvard Film Corp. *Dist* United Artists. 22 Nov **1961** [Los Angeles showing; c23 Nov 1961; LP21200]. Sd; b&w. 35mm. 67 min.

Prod Robert E. Kent. *Dir* Edward L. Cahn. *Screenplay* Sam C. Freedle. *Photog* Gilbert Warrenton. *Set Decor* Harry Reif. *Film Ed* Kenneth Crane. *Mus* Richard La Salle. *Asst Dir* Herbert S. Greene. *Prod Mgr* Joseph Small. *Cost* Einar Bourman, Sabine Manela. *Sp Eff* Barney Wolff.

Cast: James Brown (*Sheriff Charles Morton*), Jean Willes (*Joan Brady*), John Clarke (*Sam Freed*), Med Flory (*Willie Driscoll*), John Pickard (*Dr. Knudson*), Peggy Stewart (*Mrs. Knudson*), Sandra Stone (*Pat Bogan*), Warren Kemmerling (*Frank Bogan*), Nesdon Booth (*Mayor Phillips*), Herb Armstrong (*Jeff Baxley*), Renny McEvoy (*operator*).

Western melodrama. Frank Bogan, a convicted bank robber, escapes from prison and heads for a small western town to wreak vengeance on the people who helped imprison him. Sheriff Charles Morton and his deputy, Sam Freed, immediately alert the most likely victims—Dr. Knudson, now married to Bogan's former wife, and Jeff Baxley, who was responsible for the convict's arrest. The first indication of the fugitive's presence in the area is the brutal slaying of the doctor's pet dog. Morton then learns that Pat Bogan, sister of the hunted man, has given her brother her life savings to help him escape. Baxley is found murdered, and Morton organizes a posse to pursue the killer. After a 2-day ordeal in the desert, Morton finds his prey; but Bogan is already dead from wounds sustained in his escape from prison. *Prison escapees. Sheriffs. Physicians. Brother-sister relationship. Revenge. Bank robberies. Murder. Deserts. Posses. Dogs.*

GUNFIGHT AT ABILENE see **GUNFIGHT IN ABILENE**

GUNFIGHT AT COMANCHE CREEK　　　　　　　F6.1987

Allied Artists. caNov **1963** [c1 Jun 1963; LP26351]. Sd; col (De Luxe). 35mm (Panavision). 91 min.

Prod Ben Schwalb. *Dir* Frank McDonald. *Screenplay* Edward Bernds. *Dir Photog* Joseph Biroc. *Art Dir* Edward Jewell. *Set Decor* Clarence Steensen. *Film Ed* William Austin. *Mus* Marlin Skiles. *Sd Ed* Marty Greco. *Rec Engr* Ralph Butler. *Asst Dir* Don Torpin. *Prod Mgr* Edward Morey, Jr.. *Set Cont* Hazel Hall. *Cost Supv* Edward Armand. *Makeup Supv* Wally Westmore. *Hairstyle Supv* Nellie Manley. *Constr Supv* James West. *Prop Master* Max Frankel.

Cast: Audie Murphy (*Gifford*), Ben Cooper (*Carter*), Colleen Miller (*Abbie*), DeForest Kelley (*Troop*), Jan Merlin (*Nielson*), John Hubbard (*Marshal Shearer*), Damian O'Flynn (*Winton*), Susan Seaforth (*Janie*), Adam Williams, Mort Mills, John Milford, Michael T. Mikler, Tom Browne Henry, William Wellman, Jr., Laurie Graham, Tim Graham, Eddie Quillan.

Western melodrama. Bob Gifford of the National Detective Agency is assigned to smash a Colorado outlaw gang that operates by breaking wanted men out of jail, forcing them to be the unmasked front men in their holdups, and when the price on their heads grows high, killing them and claiming the reward money. In an effort to learn the identity of the gang's secret leader, Gifford poses as a criminal and is taken into the gang through the usual process and forced to participate in their crimes. Meanwhile, he becomes attracted to Abbie, the owner of the town's hotel-saloon. Another agent, Nielson, is assigned to follow and assist Gifford, but the outlaws eventually discover his camp, and he sacrifices himself to avoid compromising his partner. Carter, a young outlaw who wants to quit the gang and settle down, befriends Gifford and sets out to inform the local marshal of the group's activities. He fails to return, however, and Gifford realizes that the marshal himself is the leader of the gang. As Gifford is about to be killed for the reward, other National Detective Agency men come to his rescue, and, after a raging gun battle, the marshal is arrested. *Detectives. Outlaws. Bounty hunters. United States marshals. Saloon keepers. Hotelkeepers. Jailbreaks. Robbery. Murder. Imposture. Self-sacrifice. Colorado.*

Note: Working title: *The Great Gunfighter.*

GUNFIGHT IN ABILENE　　　　　　　　　　　F6.1988

Universal Pictures. May **1967** [c20 May 1967; LP36899]. Sd (Westrex); col (Technicolor). 35mm (Techniscope). 86 min.

Prod Howard Christie. *In Charge of Prod* Edward Muhl. *Dir* William Hale. *Screenplay* Berne Giler, John D. F. Black. *Dir Photog* Maury Gertsman. *Art Dir* Alexander Golitzen, William D. DeCinces. *Set Decor* John McCarthy, John Austin. *Titl Cinefx. Film Ed* Gene Palmer. *Mus* Bobby Darin. *Mus Supv* Joseph Gershenson. *Titl Song:* "Amy" *Writ & Sung by* Bobby Darin. *Orch* Shorty Rogers. *Sd* Waldon O. Watson, Frank H. Wilkinson. *Asst Dir* Joseph Kenny. *Unit Prod Mgr* William S. Gilmore, Jr. *Cost* Helen Colvig. *Makeup* Bud Westmore. *Hairstylist* Larry Germain.

Cast: Bobby Darin (*Cal Wayne*), Emily Banks (*Amy Martin*), Leslie Nielsen (*Grant Evers*), Donnelly Rhodes (*Joe Slade*), Don Galloway (*Ward Kent*), Frank McGrath (*Ned Martin*), Michael Sarrazin (*Cord Decker*), Barbara Werle (*Leann*), Johnny Seven (*Loop*), William Phipps (*Frank Norton*), William Mims (*Ed Scovie*), Robert Sorrells (*Nelson*), Don Dubbins (*Sprague*), James McCallion (*Smokey Staub*), Bryan O'Byrne (*Frobisher*).

Western melodrama. Source: Clarence Upson Young, "Gun Shy" (publication undetermined). During a Civil War battle, Confederate officer Cal Wayne mistakenly kills one of his own soldiers. When the war ends and Cal returns to his home in Abilene, he finds that the town is torn apart by the battle raging between cattlemen and farmers. Despite his reluctance to use a gun again, Cal resumes his old position as sheriff, thereby removing his double-dealing replacement, Joe Slade. To avoid further trouble, Cal decides to conceal the fact that the Confederate soldier he killed was the brother of the local cattle king, Grant Evers. Cal is also upset by the news that Amy Martin, his former fiancée who believed him to be dead, is engaged to marry Grant. The strife between the cattlemen and the farmers threatens to erupt into a range war when a young farmer, Cord Decker, is unjustly accused of cattle stealing and brutally flogged. Grant learns how his brother died and makes an attempt on Cal's life. Grant also gets into a row with Slade over the latter's refusal to leave town. The two men draw their pistols and Grant is killed. Now free of his fear of using a gun, Cal faces up to Slade and outdraws him. With peace restored, Cal resumes his courtship of Amy. *Confederate veterans. Cattlemen. Farmers. Sheriffs. Range wars. Rustling. Law and order. United States—History—Civil War. Abilene (Kansas).*

Note: Also known as *Gunfight at Abilene.*

GUNFIGHTERS OF CASA GRANDE (United States/Spain)　　F6.1989

Gregor Productions-Tecisa. *Dist* Metro-Goldwyn-Mayer, Inc. May **1965** [c31 Dec 1964; LP30049]. Sd (Westrex); col (Metrocolor). 35mm (CinemaScope). 92 min.

Prod Lester Welch. *Assoc Prod* Sam X. Abarbanel. *Dir* Roy Rowland. *Screenplay* Borden Chase, Patricia Chase, Clarke Reynolds. *Story* Borden Chase, Patricia Chase. *Dir Photog* José F. Aguayo, Manuel Merino. *Camera Op* Félix Mirón Martínez. *Art Dir* Francisco Canet. *Film Ed* George A. Lee. *Mus Comp & Cond* Johnny Douglas. *Themes:* "Ride Pistoleros," "Gunslingers of Casa Grande" Robert Mellin. *Sd Rec* Luis Rodríguez. *Sd Ed* Bill Creed. *Asst Dir* Manahen Velasco. *Prod Mgr* Miguel Proharam. *Cont* Isabel Ruiz Capillas. *Wardrobe* Flora Salamero. *Makeup* Emilio Puyol. *Hairdresser* Mercedes Guillot.

Cast: Alex Nicol (*Joe Daylight*), Jorge Mistral ("*The Traveler*"), Dick Bentley (*Doc*), Steve Rowland (*The Kid*), Phil Posner (*Henri*), Mercedes Alonso (*María*), Diana Lorys (*Gitana*), María Granada (*Pacesita*), Roberto Rey (*Don Castellar*), Aldo Sambrell (*Rojo*), Antonio Fuentes (*Carlos*), Angel Solano (*Don Ariola*), José Manuel Martín (*Don Luis*), Jim Gillen (*sheriff*), Mike Ekiss (*deputy*), Simón Arriaga (*Carvajal*), Fernando Villena (*Mario*), Emilio Rodríguez (*Francisco*), Ana María Custodio (*Señora Durano*), Mario de Barros (*Rio*), Ivan Tubau (*Pecos*), José Mayens (*Manuel*), Mike Brendel (*bartender*), María José Collado (*waitress*).

Western drama. Joe Daylight and his gang of border raiders—The Kid, Doc, and Henri—cross into Mexico, fleeing from an American posse. The plan was to meet the rest of the gang and then divide the stolen money, but Joe tells his gunfighters that instead he has used the money to buy a ranch. Some of the men protest, but they are soon brought into line and taken to the ranch by "The Traveler," a new member of the gang. The Traveler and The Kid become acquainted with María and her maid, Pacesita, and begin to enjoy living on the Casa Grande. Joe, however, is formulating a plan to rustle neighbors' cattle and drive the herd across the border, where post–Civil War beef prices insure a high profit. A temporary interruption occurs when a gang of bandits led by Rojo threatens the area, but Joe organizes the other ranchers for protection, and they succeed in chasing Rojo away. By this time conflict among Joe's men has increased, and most of them prefer to remain in Mexico. Joe responds to Doc's objections by shooting him, but Joe himself is killed by The Traveler, who has fallen in love with María. The two plan a new life together on the Casa Grande. *Americans in foreign countries. Bandits. Gangs. Rustling. Ranches. Mexico. Mexican border. Cattle.*

Note: Produced in Spain and released there in Apr 1964 as *Los pistoleros de Casa Grande*; running time: 90 min.

GUNMEN OF THE RIO GRANDE (France/Italy/Spain)　　F6.1990

Llama Films-West Film-Flora Film-Pathé Cinéma. *Dist* Allied Artists. 23 Jun **1965** [New York opening]. Sd; col (Eastman Color). 35mm (Totalscope). 86 min.

Prod Ike Zingarmann. *Dir* Tulio Demicheli. *Screenplay* Gene Luotto. *Screenplay Collab* Giovanni Simonelli, Italo Zingarelli, Natividad Zaro, Guy Lionel, Tulio Demicheli. *Story* Chen Morrison. *Photog* Guglielmo Mancori, Mario Capriotti. *Art Dir* Angelo de Amicio, Luis Argüello, A. Dea. *Mus Comp & Cond* Angelo Francesco Lavagnino. *Sd* Alessandro Sarandrea, Mario Amari. *Prod Mgr* Angel Monis.

Cast: Guy Madison (*Wyatt Earp/Laramie*), Madeleine Lebeau (*Jennie Lee*), Gérard Tichy (*Zack Williams*), Fernando Sancho (*Pancho Bogan*), Carolyn Davys (*Clementine Hewitt*), Olivier Hussenot (*judge*), Massimo Serato (*Leo*), Beny Deus, Dario Michaelis, E. Marn, H. Morrow, Xan Das Bolas, Alvaro de Luna, Juan Maján, Natividad Zaro.

Western melodrama. Wyatt Earp, posing as Laramie, a drifter, arrives in Rio Bravo to help French saloon keeper Jennie Lee prevent Zack "The Snake" Williams, who controls most of the Arizona Territory's silver mines, from usurping Clementine Hewitt's silver interests. Williams hires Mexican desperado Pancho Bogan and his bandits to stop a wagon train shipment to the Hewitt mine. Earp arouses Leo, the indifferent sheriff, to action, and they fight off the bandits. Williams, afraid that Pancho will expose him, shoots the Mexican, but in a subsequent street duel Earp kills Williams. *Drifters. Saloon keepers. Mexicans. Desperadoes. Sheriffs. Personal identity. Silver mines. Mine claims. Rio Grande. Arizona. Wyatt Earp. Duels.*

Note: Location scenes filmed in Almería, Spain. Opened in Rome in Jun 1965 as *Sfida a Rio Bravo*; running time: 100 min; in Paris in Aug 1965 as *Duel à Rio Bravo*; running time: 85 min; in Madrid in Feb 1967 as *Desafío en Río Bravo*; running time: 84 min. Alternative Spanish titles: *Jennie Lees ha una nuova pistola* and *El sheriff del O. K. Corral*. Ike Zingarmann is a pseudonym for Italo Zingarelli.

GUNN   F6.1991

Geoffrey Productions. *Dist* Paramount Pictures. 28 Jun 1967 [New York opening; c7 Jun 1967; LP34616]. Sd; col (Technicolor). 35mm. 95 min.

A Blake Edwards Production. *Prod* Owen Crump. *Assoc Prod* Ken Wales, Dick Crockett. *Dir-Story* Blake Edwards. *Screenplay* Blake Edwards, William Peter Blatty. *Cinematog* Philip Lathrop. *Art Dir* Fernando Carrère. *Set Decor* Reg Allen, Jack Stevens. *Titl* Richard Kuhn, National Screen Service. *Film Ed* Peter Zinner. *Mus* Henry Mancini. *Song:* "I Like the Look" Henry Mancini, Leslie Bricusse. *Song:* "Dreamsville" Ray Evans, Jay Livingston. *Songs Sung by* Laura Devon. *Sd* John Carter, Charles Grenzbach. *Asst Dir* Mickey McCardle. *Prod Mgr* William C. Davidson. *Unit Mgr* Jack McEdward. *Cost* Jack Bear. *Makeup* Wally Westmore. *Sp Eff* Paul K. Lerpae.

Cast: Craig Stevens (*Peter Gunn*), Laura Devon (*Edie*), Edward Asner (*Jacoby*), Sherry Jackson (*Samantha*), Helen Traubel (*Mother*), Albert Paulsen (*Fusco*), Marion Marshall (*Daisy Jane*), J. Pat O'Malley (*Tinker*), Regis Toomey ("*The Bishop*"), Dick Crockett (*Leo Gracey*), Charles Dierkop (*Lazlo Joyce*), Jerry Douglas (*Corwin*), Ken Wales (*Captain Brady*), Gary Lasdun (*Harry Ross*), George Murdock (*Archie*), Frank Kreig (*Barney*), Mikel Angel (*Rasputin*), Tom Palmer (*Priest*), Lincoln Demyan (*Julio Scarlotti*), Chanin Hale (*Scarlotti's mistress*), Ed Peck (*Lieutenant Ashford*), Jean Carson (*waitress*), Alan Oppenheimer, Wayne Heffley, Carol Wayne.

Crime melodrama. Based on the television series created by: Blake Edwards. While attending the funeral of gang czar Julio Scarlotti, private detective Peter Gunn meets the murdered gangster's likely successor, Nick Fusco. That evening Gunn visits his girl friend, Edie, who is a singer at Mother's waterfront nightclub, and learns that Fusco has upped protection rates to 50 percent of the "take." And Daisy Jane, the owner of an elegant bordello anchored in midriver, has a similar complaint; convinced that Fusco was responsible for Scarlotti's killing, she offers Gunn $10,000 to prove her theory. To assist in the investigation, Gunn pays an alcoholic hobo named Tinker to see what he can learn along the waterfront. Adding to Gunn's already complicated life are the frequent appearances of Samantha, a seductive young brunette who succeeds only in provoking Edie's jealous nature. After several attempts have been made upon Gunn's life, Tinker dies from poisoning by cleaning fluid mixed with alcohol, and Mother's place is blasted by a bomb explosion. Piecing together what clues he has, Gunn's sleuthing leads him to an address belonging to one George Gethers. While searching the mirrored apartment, he is attacked by an assailant armed with a tommy gun. Gunn shoots down his would-be assassin, but before dying, the man identifies himself as Harry Ross and gives Gunn the solution to the mystery: George Gethers is actually Daisy Jane, a transvestite who hoped to eliminate Fusco by framing him for Scarlotti's death. With the case solved, Gunn is reunited with Edie when the luscious Samantha turns out to be the gang czar's daughter who had ingratiated herself with Gunn in an effort to learn the identity of her father's murderer. *Gangsters. Detectives. Singers. Informers. Hoboes. Murder. Frameup. Transvestism. Male impersonation. Explosions. Poisoning. Whorehouses. Nightclubs. Waterfronts. Funerals.*

GUNPOINT   F6.1992

Universal Pictures. 6 Apr 1966 [Los Angeles opening; c14 May 1966; LP35475]. Sd (Westrex); col (Technicolor). 35mm. 86 min.

Prod Gordon Kay. *Dir* Earl Bellamy. *Writ* Mary Willingham, Willard Willingham. *Dir Photog* William Margulies. *Art Dir* Alexander Golitzen, Henry Bumstead. *Set Decor* John McCarthy, Oliver Emert. *Film Ed* Russell F. Schoengarth. *Mus* Hans J. Salter. *Mus Supv* Joseph Gershenson. *Sd* Waldon O. Watson, Lyle Cain. *Asst Dir* Phil Bowles, William S. Gilmore, Jr. *Unit Prod Mgr* Frank Baur. *Makeup* Bud Westmore. *Hairstylist* Larry Germain.

Cast: Audie Murphy (*Chad Lucas*), Joan Staley (*Uvalde*), Warren Stevens (*Nate Harlan*), Edgar Buchanan (*Bull*), Denver Pyle (*Cap Hold*), David Macklin (*Mark Emerson*), Nick Dennis (*Nicos*), Royal Dano (*Ode*), Kelly Thordsen (*Ab*), Morgan Woodward (*Drago*), William Bramley (*Hoag*), Robert Pine (*Mitch*), John Hoyt (*Mayor Osborne*), Ford Rainey (*Emerson*), Mike Ragan (*Zack*), Roy Barcroft (*Dr. Beardsley*).

Western melodrama. In the 1880's, Chad Lucas, sheriff of the Colorado town of Lodgepole, is shot by Cap, his deputy, as he tries to halt a train robbery in which the money the town depends on for its survival is lost. Cap, believing Chad to be dead, begins to take over the job he has coveted, but Chad recovers from his wounds and determines to retrieve the money. Going outside his jurisdiction to a New Mexico town, he finds Drago, the head of the gang that robbed the train, in a saloon owned by Nate Harlan. Drago escapes, using Uvalde, the dancehall singer, as cover. Nate, who loves Uvalde, joins the posse, unaware that Chad and Uvalde were once lovers. After the posse is depleted as a result of an Apache attack, Uvalde, released by Drago to distract the attention of the Indians, is found. Held up by three horse-hunters led by Bull, Chad and Nate escape when Drago and his men attack the camp and kill Bull. Uvalde reveals the whereabouts of the gang even though her brother is among

them. Chad and Nate overcome the gang; and Nate, realizing Uvalde's love for Chad, attempts to run off with the money but is killed by Chad. Chad and Uvalde then return to Lodgepole. *Sheriffs. Robbers. Saloon keepers. Dancehall girls. Apache Indians. Train robberies. Jealousy. Murder. Brother-sister relationship. Posses. Colorado. New Mexico.*

Note: Location scenes filmed near St. George, Utah.

THE GUNRUNNERS *see* GUN RUNNER

GUNS AT BATASI (Great Britain)   F6.1993

Twentieth Century-Fox Productions. *Dist* Twentieth Century-Fox Film Corp. 30 Sep 1964 [Denver, Colorado, opening; c3 Sep 1964; LP29235]. Sd (Westrex); b&w. 35mm (CinemaScope). 103 min.

Prod George H. Brown. *Dir* John Guillermin. *Screenplay* Robert Holles. *Adtl Material* C. M. Pennington-Richards. *Orig Adapt* Leo Marks, Marshall Pugh. *Dir Photog* Douglas Slocombe. *Camera Op* Gerry Fisher. *Art Dir* Maurice Carter. *Film Ed* Max Benedict. *Mus Comp & Cond* John Addison. *Played by* Sinfonia of London. *Sd Rec* Bill Daniels, Robert T. MacPhee. *Sd Ed* Don Deacon. *Asst Dir* Jan Darnley Smith. *Prod Mgr* David W. Orton. *Cont* Betty Harley. *Wardrobe* John McCorry. *Makeup* Stuart Freeborn. *Hairdressing* Barbara Ritchie. *Casting Dir* Stuart Lyons.

Cast: Richard Attenborough (*R. S. M. Lauderdale*), Jack Hawkins (*Col. John Deal*), Flora Robson (*Miss Barker-Wise*), John Leyton (*Pvt. Charlie Wilkes*), Mia Farrow (*Karen Eriksson*), Cecil Parker (*Sir William Fletcher*), Errol John (*Lieutenant Boniface*), Graham Stark (*Sgt. "Dodger" Brown*), Earl Cameron (*Captain Abraham*), Percy Herbert (*Col.-Sgt. Ben Parkin*), David Lodge (*Sgt. "Muscles" Dunn*), Bernard Horsfall (*Sgt. "Schoolie" Prideaux*), John Meillon (*Sgt. "Aussie" Drake ["Digger"]*), Horace James (*Corporal Abov*), Patrick Holt (*captain*), Alan Browning (*adjutant*), Richard Bidlake (*lieutenant*), Joseph Layode (*Archibong Shaw*), Ric Hutton (*Russell*), Bloke Modisane.

Melodrama. Source: Robert Holles, *The Siege of Battersea* (London, 1962). When a rebellion breaks out in the capital of the newly-independent nation of Batasi, Colonel Deal is ordered to confine all British Army personnel to quarters and to turn over his command of a mixed Anglo-African regiment to a native African officer, Captain Abraham. Colonel Deal departs for the capital, and the second-ranking African officer, Lieutenant Boniface, quickly arrests Captain Abraham and assumes command of the regiment in the name of the rebels. Stranded at the airport because of the rebellion, British Private Wilkes and a Swedish United Nations employee, Karen Eriksson, go to the all-white sergeants' mess, administered by Regimental Sergeant Major Lauderdale, a staunch old-line British career soldier. Lauderdale is serving as host to Miss Barker-Wise, a leftwing Member of Parliament on a factfinding tour. Captain Abraham escapes from his guards and, seriously injured, finds refuge in the messhall. Overriding the protests of Miss Barker-Wise, who naively champions Boniface, Lauderdale refuses to surrender Abraham to the rebel leader. Boniface threatens to destroy the mess if Lauderdale does not comply with his demand. Deal returns from the capital, and as he announces the success of the revolt and British recognition of the new government, Wilkes and Lauderdale blow up the antitank guns positioned to raze the messhall. Boniface, now a colonel, orders Lauderdale out of the country, and Lauderdale complies, looking forward to the future wherever the army may take him. *Political prisoners. Swedes. Revolutions. Colonial administration. Race relations. Military government. Great Britain—Army. Africa. Great Britain— Parliament. United Nations.*

Note: Opened in London in Sep 1964.

GUNS FOR SAN SEBASTIAN (United States/France/Italy/Mexico)   F6.1994

Cipra–Ernesto Enríquez–Filmes Cinematográfica. *Dist* Metro-Goldwyn-Mayer, Inc. 20 Mar 1968 [New York opening; c31 Jan 1968; LP35287]. Sd; col (Metrocolor). 35mm (Franscope). 111 min.

A Jacques Bar Production. *Prod* Jacques Bar. *Assoc Prod* Ernesto Enríquez. *Dir* Henri Verneuil. *Screenplay English Vers* James R. Webb. *Screenplay French, Italian & Spanish Versions* Serge Ganze, Ennio De Concini, Miguel Morayta. *Dir Photog* Armand Thirard. *Art Dir* Robert Clavel, Roberto Silva. *Film Ed* Françoise Bonnot. *Mus Score* Ennio Morricone. *Sd Engr* William R. Sivel. *Asst Dir* Claude Pinoteau, Juan Luis Buñuel. *Prod Mgr* Paul Joly. *Cost* Yvonne Wood. *Makeup & Hairdressing* Monique Archambault, Alex Archambault. *Sp Eff* Lee Zavitz. *Sp Vis Eff* J. McMillan Johnson. *Dial Coach* Walter Kelley.

Cast: Anthony Quinn (*León Alastray*), Anjanette Comer (*Kinita*), Charles Bronson (*Teclo*), Sam Jaffe (*Father Joseph*), Silvia Pinal (*Felicia*), Jorge Martínez de Hoyos (*Cayetano*), Jaime Fernández (*Golden Lance*), Rosa Furman (*Agueda*), Jorge Russek (*Pedro*), Leon Askin (*vicar general*), José Chávez (*Antonito*), Ivan Desny (*Captain Calleja*), Fernand Gravey (*governor*), Pedro Armendáriz, Jr. (*Father Lucas*), Aurora Clavel (*Magdalena*), Julio

Aldama (Diego), Ferrusquilla (Luis), Pancho Córdova (Kino), Enrique Lucero (Renaldo), Chano Urueta (Miguel), Noé Murayama (Captain López), Guillermo Hernández (Timoteo), Francisco Reiguera (bishop), Carlos Berriochoa (Pablo), Armando Acosta (Pascual), Guy Fox, Rico Lopez (villagers).

Adventure melodrama. Source: William Barby Faherty, *A Wall for San Sebastian* (Fresno, California, 1962). In mid-18th-century Mexico, rebel bandit León Alastray escapes from government troops by taking sanctuary in an old Franciscan church. When Father Joseph refuses to turn Alastray over to the authorities, the old priest is sent to the remote village of San Sebastián as punishment. Disguised in a friar's robes, Alastray joins Father Joseph in the long desert trek at the end of which they find the village deserted following a raid by marauding Yaqui Indians. After Father Joseph has been killed by a bandit, the returning villagers mistake Alastray for a priest. Teclo, a halfbreed who rides for the Yaquis, demands that the villagers give up their Christian faith or risk further Indian attacks. Though aware that Alastray is *not* a priest, a village girl, Kinita, saves him from being hanged and persuades him to become the spiritual leader of the village. Alastray helps the peasants build a dam to ensure irrigation for their crops and, knowing the Yaquis will attack again, uses his influence with the governor's wife, Felicia, who was once Alastray's mistress, to obtain guns and ammunition. When the Indians finally wage the village, they are routed by the bravely defiant peasants and Alastray's dynamiting of the dam. After Alastray has killed Teclo in hand-to-hand combat, Kinita convinces him that he must say mass for the peasants. Then, when an escort of government troops arrives with a real priest for San Sebastián, the grateful villagers help Alastray and Kinita escape. *Bandits. Franciscans. Priests. Yaqui Indians. Peasants. Halfcastes. Territorial governors. Disguise. Murder. Village life. Paganism. Ammunition. Irrigation. Christianity. Sanctuaries. Dams.*

Note: Filmed in Mexico in 1967 as *Los cañones de San Sebastián*; location scenes filmed in San Miguel de Allende and the state of Durango. Opened in Rome in 1968 as *I cannoni di San Sebastian*. Paris opening: Mar 1969 as *La bataille de San Sebastian*; running time: 120 min. Working titles: *Wall for San Sebastian* and *Miracle of San Sebastian.*

GUNS IN THE AFTERNOON see RIDE THE HIGH COUNTRY

THE GUNS OF AUGUST   F6.1995
Universal Pictures. 24 Dec **1964** [New York opening]. Sd; b&w. 35mm. 99 min.

Created and Prod by Nathan Kroll. *Exec Prod* Lawrence G. White. *Assoc Prod* Eugene Gelber. *Dir* Nathan Kroll. *Narr Writ* Arthur B. Tourtellot. *Anim* Dumont Animation Inc. *Titl* Richard Erdoes, Wango Wen. *Film Ed* Miriam Arsham. *Asst Ed* Sandra E. Robertson. *Mus Comp & Cond* Sol Kaplan. *Sd Mix* Dick Vorisek. *Sp Eff* D & G Film Effects Inc. *Stills & Maps* Herbert Matter. *European Research* William Novik.

Narrator: Fritz Weaver.

Documentary. Source: Barbara W. Tuchman, *The Guns of August* (New York, 1962). The film is a narrative of the events leading up to World War I, a study of the European royalty and statesmen involved in these events, and a chronicle of the crucial action of the war itself. The film opens with the funeral procession of England's King Edward VII on 20 May 1910 and includes portraits of many of the statesmen in attendance: Czar Nicholas of Russia, Kaiser Wilhelm of Germany, Emperor Franz Josef of Austria, King Albert of Belgium, and the Archduke Franz Ferdinand, heir apparent to the throne of Austria-Hungary. The film then deals with the gathering storm of political and royal intrigue from 1910 to the assassination of Ferdinand in Sarajevo on 28 June 1914; among those shown are Clemenceau, Poincaré, Marshal Joffre, Woodrow Wilson, Major General Ludendorff, Winston Churchill, and Rasputin. The war begins and there is fighting on two fronts. In the east, the crucial Battle of Tannenberg reveals the devastation visited upon the Russian Army by the Germans. Lenin and Trotsky appear. On the western front, the German Army marches through neutral Belgium against valiant but futile resistance, and then takes 10 French cities in 1 1/2 weeks, leaving much of France desolated. The French finally stop the German advance in the Battle of the Marne. Other action includes the Battle of Verdun, the Battle of the Somme, and the final offensive of 1918 under Ludendorff for control of Northern Europe and Scandinavia. The film also details the German Navy's submarine warfare, the American entry into the war, and the Armistice in 1918. *Military invasion. Militarism. Nationalism. Triple Alliance. Triple Entente. Funerals. Assassination. Submarines. World War I. France. Germany. Belgium. Scandinavia. Poland. Sarajevo. Edward VII (England). Nicholas II (Russia). William II (Germany). Franz Josef. Albert I (Belgium). Franz Ferdinand. Georges Clemenceau. Raymond Poincaré. Joseph Jacques Césaire Joffre. Thomas Woodrow Wilson. Erich Friedrich Wilhelm Ludendorff. Winston Leonard Spencer Churchill. Grigori Efimovich Rasputin. Nikolai Lenin. Leon Trotsky. American Expeditionary Force.*

Note: Producer Nathan Kroll used footage from government archives in Paris, London, Brussels, Berlin, and Washington, D. C.

GUNS OF DARKNESS (Great Britain)   F6.1996
Associated British Productions–Cavalcade Films. *Dist* Warner Bros. Pictures. 17 Aug **1962** [New York opening; c18 Aug 1962; LP27102]. Sd; b&w. 35mm. 103 min. [Copyright length: 95 min.]

Prod Thomas Clyde. *Exec Prod* Ben Kadish. *Dir* Anthony Asquith. *Screenplay* John Mortimer. *Dir Photog* Robert Krasker. *Camera Op* Gerry Fisher. *Art Dir* John Howell. *Film Ed* Frederick Wilson. *Mus Comp & Cond* Benjamin Frankel. *Sd* Norman Coggs, Len Shilton, Charles Crafford, A. W. Lumkin. *Boom Op* Tommy Staples. *Asst Dir* David Tomblin. *Prod Mgr* Victor Peck. *Prod Sec* Midge Warnes. *Cont* Betty Harley. *In Charge 2d Unit* Harold Haysom. *Wardrobe* Anthony Mendleson. *Wardrobe Mistress* May Walding. *Wardrobe Master* Ernie Farrer. *Makeup* Jim Hydes. *Hairdresser* Pat McDermott. *Still Photog* George Higgins. *Chargehand Prop* John Watling. *Supv Electrn* Stephen Birtles.

Cast: Leslie Caron (*Claire Jordan*), David Niven (*Tom Jordan*), David Opatoshu (*President Rivera*), James Robertson-Justice (*Hugo Bryant*), Eleanor Summerfield (*Mrs. Bastian*), Ian Hunter (*Dr. Swann*), Derek Godfrey (*Hernandez*), Richard Pearson (*Mr. Bastian*), Sandor Eles (*Lieutenant Gomez*), Steven Scott (*Gabriel*), Tutte Lemkow (*Gabriel's cousin*), Dorita Sensier (*nightclub singer*), John Carson (*1st officer*), Ali Nagi (*Indian boy*), Barry Shawzin (*General Zoreno*), Peter Allenby (*sergeant*).

Drama. Source: Francis Clifford, *Act of Mercy* (London, 1959). On New Year's Eve in the Latin American state of Tribulacion, the government of President Rivera is overthrown by revolutionary military forces. Wounded, Rivera escapes and is found the next day in a state of collapse by Tom Jordan, an immature idealist whose failure to hold a job has led to marital difficulties with his wife, Claire. Jordan decides he is morally bound to help Rivera reach the border 80 miles away, and Claire reluctantly agrees to accompany them on the journey. After a number of close calls with the police, they lose their car in a lake of quicksand and are forced to proceed by foot across rocky mountain terrain. They reach the border and are captured and taken into custody. At this point Claire tells Tom that she is pregnant. Despite his abhorrence of violence, Tom kills a guard with a corkscrew in order to get himself, Claire, and Rivera across the border. Although Rivera is beyond medical help, he dies knowing that Tom now understands it is sometimes necessary to kill in order to live. Wiser and more mature, Tom is able to effect a reconciliation with Claire. *Presidents. Idealists. Police. Guards. Revolutions. Pregnancy. Marriage. Murder. Quicksand. Latin America. Imaginary republics.*

Note: Produced in Great Britain, with location shooting in Spain. Working title: *Act of Mercy.*

THE GUNS OF NAVARONE (United States/Great Britain)   F6.1997
Open Road Films. *Dist* Columbia Pictures. 22 Jun **1961** [New York opening; cl Jul 1961; LP20445]. Sd; col (Eastman Color). 35mm (CinemaScope). 157 min.

Pres by Highroad Productions. *Exec Prod-Screenplay* Carl Foreman. *Assoc Prod* Cecil F. Ford, Leon Becker. *Dir* J. Lee Thompson. *Dir Photog* Oswald Morris. *Camera Op* Denys Coop. *Camera Asst* Ronnie Maasz. *2d Camera Asst* Michael Rutter. *Camera Grip* Albert Lott. *Dir Photog 2d Unit* John Wilcox. *Camera Op 2d Unit* Dudley Lovell. *1st Asst 2d Unit* Geoffrey Glover, Jimmy Turrell. *2d Asst 2d Unit* Douglas Milsone. *Art Dir-Prod Dsgn* Geoffrey Drake. *Asst Art Dir* Frank Willson. *Set Dresser* Maurice Fowler. *Draughtsman* Robert Cartwright. *Film Ed* Alan Osbiston. *Assoc Ed* Raymond Poulton, John Victor Smith, Oswald Hafenrichter. *1st Asst Ed* Joan Morduch. *Mus Comp & Cond* Dimitri Tiomkin. *Perf by* Sinfonia of London. *Songs Sung by* Elga Andersen. *Sd Rec* John Cox, George Stephenson. *Sd Ed* Vivian C. Greenham. *Boom Op* Jack W. Davies. *Sd Camera Op* Ernie Webb. *1st & 2d Asst Dir* Peter Yates, Roy Millichip. *Prod Mgr* Harold Buck. *Cont* Pamela Davies. *2d Unit Cont* Lee Turner. *Prod Sec* Golda Offenheim. *Wardrobe Dsgn* Olga Lehmann. *Cost* Monty Berman. *Makeup Ch* George Frost. *Makeup Artist* Wally Schneiderman. *Hairdresser* Joan Smallwood. *Sp Eff* Bill Warrington, Wally Veevers. *Tech Adv* Fritz Beyerlein, (Lieut. Gen.), D. S. T. Turnbull, (Brig. Gen.), P. F. Kertemelidis, (Lieut. Col.), P. J. Hands, (Lieut. Gen.), John Theologitis, (Comdr.), P. M. Lazaridis, (Maj.), W. D. Langham, (Maj.). *Ch Electrn* Jack Sullivan. *Carpenter* G. J. Moodey. *Prop* Bernard Murrell.

Cast: Gregory Peck (*Mallory*), David Niven (*Miller*), Anthony Quinn (*Andrea*), Stanley Baker (*Brown*), Anthony Quayle (*Franklin*), Irene Papas (*Maria*), Gia Scala (*Anna*), James Darren (*Pappadimos*), James Robertson-Justice (*Jensen/narrator*), Richard Harris (*Barnsby*), Bryan Forbes (*Cohn*), Allan Cuthbertson (*Baker*), Michael Trubshawe (*Weaver*), Percy Herbert (*Grogan*), George Mikell (*Sessler*), Walter Gotell (*Muesel*), Tutte Lemkow (*Nicholai*), Albert Lieven (*commandant*), Norman Wooland (*group captain*), Cleo Scouloudi (*bride*), Nicholas Papakonstantinou (*patrol boat captain*), Christopher Rhodes (*German gunnery officer*).

War melodrama. Source: Alistair MacLean, *Guns of Navarone* (London, 1957). In 1943, an Allied force becomes trapped on the island of Kheros in the Aegean Sea. The only possible way to evacuate the men is through a small channel dominated by two huge German guns buried deep in the solid rocks of Navarone. Because the guns are impregnable against air or sea attack, a sabotage team of six is sent to Navarone in a desperate attempt to destroy the massive weapons. Security officer Major Franklin leads the commandos, who include: Captain Mallory, a world-famous mountaineer; Corporal Miller, an explosives expert; Col. Andrea Stavros, a Greek resistance fighter; Pvt. Spyros Pappadimos, a New York–educated delinquent who was born on Navarone; and C. P. O. Brown, a veteran knife fighter. After sinking a German patrol boat, the little group loses its own vessel in a violent storm. The men reach shore with their gear, however, and succeed in scaling a sheer cliff face, the only unguarded approach to Navarone. In the ascent Franklin breaks his leg, and Mallory assumes command. The saboteurs then make contact with two resistance fighters (Spyros' sister, Maria, and a former schoolteacher, Anna, who has been shocked into dumbness by Nazi torture). Despite the aid of the two women, the commandos are captured by the Germans. Andrea tricks the Nazi guards, and the saboteurs escape in their captors' uniforms. As they approach the guns, they learn that Anna is a traitor, feigning muteness while supplying the Germans with the group's positions. Realizing she must be killed, Mallory draws his pistol, but it is Maria who fires the fatal bullet. Mallory and Miller then sneak into the fortress and set their explosives, while the others divert the attention of the Germans. Brown and Spyros are killed in the fighting, but the remainder of the group escape to the sea. At midnight British destroyers move into the channel and head for Kheros. As the giant weapons swing into action, a tremendous explosion shatters the entire cliff and the guns of Navarone crash into the sea. *Commandos. Mountaineers. Greeks. Germans. Mutes. Traitors. Nazis. Demolition. Sabotage. Military occupation. Resistance (political). Ordnance. World War II. Aegean Sea.*

Note: Location scenes filmed on the island of Rhodes.

GUNS OF THE BLACK WITCH (France/Italy)   F6.1998

Romana Film–S. N. C. *Dist* American International Pictures. caNov **1961** [c18 Nov 1961; LP21775]. Sd; col (Eastman Color, print by Pathé). 35mm (Totalscope). 81 min.

Prod Fortunato Misiano. *U. S. Vers Supv* Salvatore Billitteri. *Dir* Domenico Paolella. *U. S. Vers Dir* Lee Kresel. *Screenplay* Luciano Martino, Ugo Guerra. *Dir Photog* Carlo Bellero. *Camera Asst* Guglielmo Vincioni, Saverio Diamanti. *Set Dsgn* Alfredo Montori. *Film Ed* Lina D'Amico, Iolanda Benvenuti. *Mus* Michele Cozzoli. *Sd Supv* Umberto Lenzi, Gaetano Valle. *Prod Mgr* Nino Misiano. *Prod Asst* Diego Archimede, Pasquale Misiano. *Cost* Peruzzi. *Makeup* Massimo Giustini.

Cast: Don Megowan *(Jean)*, Silvana Pampanini *(Delores)*, Emma Danieli *(Elisa)*, Livio Lorenzon *(Guzman)*, Germano Longo *(Michel)*, Loris Gizzi *(governor)*, Philippe Hersent *(Jean's stepfather)*, Anna Alberti *(Elisa's maid)*, Corrado Annicelli, Franco Lamonte, Giovanni Baghino, Nando Angelini, Cesare Lancia, Tullio Altamura, Pasquale De Filippo, Doro Corra, Francesco De Leone.

Action drama. In the 17th century, people of a tiny Caribbean island refuse to pay tribute to their tyrannical Spanish rulers, and as a result they are attacked and massacred by the soldiers of the villainous Guzman. Two boys, Jean and Michel, escape and make their way to a pirate ship. Years later, and now officers of the *Black Witch*, they plan to overthrow the colonial government and avenge the massacre. In an unsuccessful raid, Jean is wounded, and Michel is captured. Jean is nursed back to health by Elisa, the island governor's daughter, but Michel turns traitor and joins Guzman in a plot to capture Jean and his pirates. Also in the plot is the fiery Delores, who wants revenge on Jean for having rebuffed her. But Michel, Delores, and Guzman are all killed in their effort to capture the pirates; and Jean and Elisa are free to continue their courtship. *Spanish. Despots. Escapees. Pirates. Territorial governors. Traitors. Colonial administration. Revenge. Massacres. Conspiracy. Filial relations. Islands. Ships. Caribbean.*

Note: Released in Italy in 1961 as *Il terrore dei mare*; in Paris in Aug 1962 as *La terreur des mers*; running time: 94 min. Copyright claimant: Alta Vista Productions.

GUNS OF THE MAGNIFICENT SEVEN   F6.1999

Mirisch Productions. *Dist* United Artists. 28 May **1969** [Philadelphia opening; c28 May 1969; LP37137]. Sd; col (De Luxe). 35mm (Panavision). 106 min. *MPAA rating* G.

Prod Vincent M. Fennelly. *Dir* Paul Wendkos. *Screenplay* Herman Hoffman. *Dir Photog* Antonio Macasoli. *Art Dir* José María Tapiador. *Set Decor* Rafael Salazar. *Film Ed* Walter Hannemann. *Mus Comp & Cond* Elmer Bernstein. *Sd* Roy Charman, George Rice. *Asst Dir* José María Ochoa. *Prod Supv* Robert Goodstein. *Prod Mgr* Tadeo Villalba. *Wardrobe* Eric Seelig. *Makeup* Ramon de Diego. *Hairstyles* Josefa Rubio Martos. *Sp Eff* Alex Weldon.

Cast: George Kennedy *(Chris)*, James Whitmore *(Levi Morgan)*, Monte Markham *(Keno)*, Bernie Casey *(Cassie)*, Joe Don Baker *(Slater)*, Scott Thomas *(P. J.)*, Reni Santoni *(Max)*, Michael Ansara *(Colonel Diego)*, Wende Wagner *(Tina)*, Frank Silvera *(Lobero)*, Fernando Rey *(Quintero)*, Tony Davis *(Emiliano Zapata)*, Luis Rivera *(Lieutenant Presna)*, Sancho Gracia *(Miguel)*, Jorge Rigaud *(Gabriel)*, Ramón Serrano *(Cesar)*, Vincente Sangiovanni *(Manuel)*.

Western melodrama. In 19th-century Mexico, Federales capture Quintero, the revolutionary who has attempted to rally the many disorganized groups opposing the dictatorship of President Díaz. Before going to prison, Quintero gives his lieutenant, Maximiliano O'Leary, $600 with which to continue the cause. Bandit chief Carlos Lobero demands that the money be used for guns and ammunition, but Max instead seeks the help of the legendary Chris, an American renowned for his bravery and cunning. Chris agrees to attempt a rescue of Quintero and uses $500 of Max's money to recruit five expert marksmen: the horsethief Keno; the giant Negro, Cassie; the one-armed Slater; the tubercular P. J.; and the one family man, Levi Morgan. Riding back to Mexico with Chris, the Americans become less mercenary when they observe the brutal treatment of the peasants; their journey is also marked by their encounters with a political prisoner's little boy—Emiliano Zapata—and a pretty peasant girl, Tina, who falls in love with P. J. When Lobero learns that Max did not buy guns with the $600, he refuses to allow his men to take part in Quintero's rescue. Realizing that he needs support, Chris frees a prison gang that includes Zapata's father and trains them in military tactics. Despite their superior marksmanship, Chris's men are outnumbered and their valiant effort to free Quintero appears doomed. But, at the last moment, 50 of Lobero's bandits, having slain their leader for his lack of patriotism, thunder into the prison grounds and turn the tide of battle. Of the original seven, only Chris and Levi Morgan remain; and, before riding home, they elect to donate the $600 to the peasants' cause. *Federales. Revolutionaries. Peasants. Dictators. Political prisoners. Bandits. Americans in foreign countries. Horsethieves. Negroes. Gunfighters. Amputees. Prison escapes. Patriotism. Tuberculosis. José de la Cruz Porfirio Diaz. Emiliano Zapata. Mexico.*

Note: Filmed on location in Spain. The third in a series of films following *The Magnificent Seven* (1960) and *Return of the Seven*, q. v.

GUNS OF THE TREES   F6.2000

FC Film Unit, Inc. *Dist* Emile de Antonio, Inc., Film-Makers' Cooperative. 6 Dec **1961** [New York opening]. Sd; b&w. 16mm & 35mm. 75 min. [Original running time: 85 min.]

Prod-Dir-Writ Jonas Mekas. *Asst by* Adolfas Mekas. *Co-Asst by* Sheldon Rochlin, Charles Silver. *Special Asst* Harrison Starr, Daniel Drasin. *Photog* Jonas Mekas. *Adtl Photog* Sheldon Rochlin. *Score* Lucia Dlugoszewski. *Folk Songs* Sara Wiley, Cather Wiley, Tom Sankey. *Adv* Edouard de Laurot. *Poetry Interludes Writ & Spoken by* Allen Ginsberg.

Cast: Ben Carruthers *(Ben)*, Argus Speare Juilliard *(Argus)*, Frances Stillman *(Frances)*, Adolfas Mekas *(Gregory)*, Frank Kuenstler *(Franciscan monk)*, Leonard Hicks *(social worker)*, Sudie Bond *(Frances' mother)*, Louis Brigante *(drunk man)*, Barbara Tucker *(woman with the child)*, Jewel Walker *(mime I)*, Sterling Jensen *(mime II)*, Tina Stoumen *(girl on the swing)*, Marjorie Walker *(office woman)*, George Maciunas *(man with theorbo)*, Marvin Karpatkin *(man at the desk)*, Mel Clay *(man looking for job)*, Anne Flannagan *(pregnant woman)*, Stuart Perkoff *(poetry reader)*.

Experimental film. Crucial moments in the lives of five young people living in New York's Lower East Side are depicted in fragmented "stanzas," some 1 second in length, others up to 2 minutes, separated by intervals of white space. Frances is unhappy and desperate; friends are unable to help her, and she commits suicide. Gregory, her lover, is an angry intellectual who becomes guilt-ridden over Frances' death. Frank has sought spiritual liberation as a monk; and Ben is an insurance salesman whose anguish about the world is relieved by his love for Argus, his black lover. Argus, who is pregnant, is a firm believer in the beauty and truth of life. At the beginning of the film Frances' suicide has already taken place, and the others are asking themselves why she did it. The remainder of the film deals with the events that led up to the suicide, including Frances' own activities. The other five feel a common frustration arising from their disenchantment with contemporary society—its corruption and its effect on their minds and bodies. Their quest for meaning in life underscores all their activities. They are seen in lofts, in taverns, in the streets, in suburban fields; at demonstrations and playgrounds; in a monastery garden, and on river banks. Throughout the film four choruses reappear; two figures wearing whiteface and business suits cavort in a vegetable field; air raid sirens wail periodically; unidentified voices comment on situations seen on the screen; and Allen Ginsberg reads selections of his poetry. *Monks. Insurance agents. Intellectuals. Negroes. Clowns. Urban life. Suicide. Poetry. Death. Disillusionment. Guilt. Demonstrations. Bohemianism. Pregnancy. Miscegenation. New York City—*

Lower East Side.

Note: Originally released in 16mm. Alternative title: *Guns in the Trees.*

GUNS OF WYOMING *see* **CATTLE KING**

THE GURU (United States/India)   **F6.2001**

Arcadia Films–Merchant-Ivory Productions. *Dist* Twentieth Century-Fox Film Corp. Feb **1969** [New York opening: 19 Apr; c31 Dec 1968; LP36763]. Sd (Westrex); col (DeLuxe). 35mm. 112 min. *MPAA rating* G.

An Ismail Merchant–James Ivory Production. *Prod* Ismail Merchant. *Assoc Prod* Muriel Neff, Peter Reilly. *Dir* James Ivory. *2d Unit Dir* Prayag Raaj. *Story Writ for Screen* by Ruth Prawer Jhabvala, James Ivory. *Dir Photog* Subrata Mitra. *Asst Camera* Fatik Mazumdar, Prajanan Mitra. *Art Dir* Bansi Chandragupta, Didi Contractor. *Film Ed* Prabhakar Supare. *Mus Comp & Perf* by Ustad Vilayat Khan. *Song:* "Tom's Boat Song" Ustad Imrat Hussein Khan, Ruth Prawer Jhabvala. *Song:* "Where Did You Come From?" Mark London, Don Black. *Sd Rec* Dev, Prabhat Das. *Sd Ed* Don Ranasinghe, Brian Blamey. *Asst Sd Ed* K. L. Naik, Humphrey Dixon, Shri Ghate, Chris Crane. *Asst Dir* Mohamed Shafi, Wasi Khan, Shama Habibullah. *Prod Mgr* Riaz Hafizka. *Prod Controller* Giancarlo Pettini. *Location Mgr* Rashid Abbasi. *Michael York's Cost* Gordon Deighton. *Rita Tushingham's Cost* Joanna Tyson. *Leela Naidu's Cost* Malabar. *Wardrobe* Narender Kocher. *Makeup* Toni Delaney, Nath Grover. *Coöp* Karni Singhi, Maharajah of Bikaner, Vibhti Narayansing, Maharajah of Benares. *Prop Master* Narender Kocher. *Ch Electrn* M. B. Ansari, Ranjit Biswas. *Still Photog* Douglas Webb.

Cast: Michael York (*Tom Pickle*), Rita Tushingham (*Jenny*), Utpal Dutt (*Ustad Zafar Khan*), Aparna Sen (*Ghazala*), Madhur Jaffrey (*Begum Sahiba*), Zohra Seghal (*Mustani*), Nana Palsikar (*The Guru's Guru*), Barry Foster (*Chris*), Leela Naidu (*girl at the party*), Ismail Merchant (*master of ceremonies*), Saeed Jaffrey (*Murad*), Usha Katrak (*lady reporter*), Fred Ohringer (*Howard*), Nargis Cowasji (*society hostess*), Marcus Murch (*snide guest*), Dorothy Strelsin (*tourist*), Rafi Ameer (*Arnold D'Mello*), Soni Aurora (*Miss Teen Queen*), Nadira (*courtesan*), Pincho Kapoor (*murderer*), Shri Agarwal (*doctor*), Prayag Raaj (*classical singer*).

Comedy. Tom Pickle, a popular British pop singer, comes to India to study the sitar with the famous musician Ustad Zafar Khan. Also drawn to the Ustad is Jenny, a young English hippie who is on a quest for spiritual fulfillment. Because of Tom's clamoring teenage fans and his seeming lack of respect for the guru, a series of quarrels spring up between the singer and the Ustad. Meanwhile, Jenny's obvious adoration of the Ustad angers the elder of his two wives, Begum Sahiba. When Tom takes the Ustad and Jenny to a party given in his honor by the leaders of Bombay's society, the guru becomes upset by Tom's lack of dedication and orders him to move into his household along with his other disciples. Through the intervention of Jenny, Tom stifles his annoyance and consents to the guru's wish. Following a visit to the Ustad's music school in Benares, where Tom and Jenny meet the master's second wife, Tom's London manager, Chris, arrives and tries to persuade Tom to return to England and fulfill his commitments. But Tom has succumbed to both Jenny and the tranquil Indian atmosphere. After Tom has further angered the guru by judging a local beauty contest, resulting in a near-riot by his fans, he and Jenny join the Ustad on a visit to a music festival in Bijapur. There the Ustad calls on his own guru and is rebuked for wasting his time with the two foreigners and for ruining himself as a musician. The guru then turns his back on Jenny and Tom and does not go to see Jenny even when she becomes ill. Realizing that they will always be strangers in India, Jenny and Tom effect a reconciliation with the Ustad and return to England to marry. *British. Singers. Hippies. Music teachers. Gurus. Theatrical managers. Jealousy. Polygamy. Sitarists. Bijapur. Beauty contests. Bombay. Benares.*

Note: Filmed on location in Bombay, Bikaner, and Benares.

GURU THE MAD MONK   **F6.2002**

Maipix Organization. *Dist* Nova International. 4 Dec **1970** [Buffalo, New York, opening]. Sd; col. 35mm. 62 min.

Dir Andy Milligan. *Story* M. A. Isaacs. *Photog* Andy Milligan. *Art Dir* Lillian Greneker. *Sets* James Fox, art.

Cast: Neil Flanagan (*Father Guru*), Judy Israel (*prisoner*), Paul Lieber (*jailor*), Jacqueline Webb (*vampire*), Jack Spenser (*hunchback*), Jeremy Brooks, actor (*priest*), Frank Engels (*bishop*), Julia Willis, Ron Keith.

Horror film. On the island of Mortavia in 1480, schizophrenic Father Guru is the chaplain of a Central European prison. By agreeing to rob graves for Guru, the jailor saves a beloved prisoner who has been condemned for infanticide. When Guru's bishop arrives with a replacement, the indignant priest orders their executions. Guru also murders his mistress, a lesbian vampire, and a hunchback, the pet of the reprieved prisoner. The jailor, however, hangs the priest and saves his paramour. *Priests. Chaplains. Grave robbers. Mistresses. Witches. Vampires. Hunchbacks. Capital punishment. Schizophrenia. Murder. Infanticide. Lesbianism. Islands. Prisons.*

Note: Filmed at St. Peter's Church in New York City. Also known as *Garu the Mad Monk.*

GUSARSKAYA BALLADA *see* **THE BALLAD OF A HUSSAR**

GUTTER GIRLS (Great Britain)   **F6.2003**

Animated Motion Pictures. *For* Tekli British Productions. *Dist* Topaz Film Corp. Jul **1964**. Sd; b&w. 35mm. 88 min.

Prod-Dir Robert Hartford-Davis. *Screenplay* Derek Ford, Donald Ford. *Camera Op* Denis Lewiston. *Focus* Ronnie Fox-Rogers. *Clapper/Loader* Colin Corby. *Art Dir* Bernard Sarron. *Ch Hand Set Dresser* Jimmy James. *Draughtsman* Jim Sawyer. *Ed* Teddy Darvas. *1st Asst Ed* John Poyner. *2d Asst Ed* David Woodward. *Mus Comp & Cond* Malcolm Mitchell. *Sd Mixer* Bert Ross. *Boom* Ken Reynolds. *Sd Camera* Jack Smart. *1st & 2d Asst Dir* Ross Mackenzie, Gordon Gilbert. *Prod Sec* Ann Guttridge. *Prod Asst* Derek Ford. *Sec to Mr. Hartford-Davis* Audrey Ives. *Prod Mgr* Robert Sterne. *Cont* Eileen Head. *Wardrobe Mistress* Jackie Cummins. *Makeup* Jimmy Evans. *Hairdresser* Bobbie Smith. *Stills Camera* Laurie Turner. *Prop Buyer* Sid Palmer. *Ch Hand Props* Sidney Leggett. *Grip* Albert Lott. *Ch Hand Electrn* Jack Sullivan.

Cast: Jacqueline Ellis (*Anne Mason*), Annette Whiteley (*Linda*), Georgina Patterson (*Pat*), Anne Kettle (*Sally*), Margaret Vieler (*Marsha*), Noel Dyson (*Muriel Donaghue*), Victor Brooks (*George Donaghue*), Richard Bebb (*Frank Lang*), Ann Castle (*Eileen Lang*), Douglas Sheldon (*Mike Griffin*), Lesley Dudley (*Joan*), Iain Gregory (*Kinky*), Jill Adams (*June Wilson*), John Bonney (*Paul*), Lucette Marimar (*Susie*), John Glynne Jones (*Benny Wintle*), Valli Newby (*Kim*), Norman Mitchell (*Larry*), Earle Green (*Cliff*), Harriette Johns (*Lady Gregg*), Ruth Kettlewell (*Mrs. Seymour*), Hilary Mason (*Miss Fletch*), Micheline Patton (*Mrs. Broome*), Raymond Huntley (*Harry Halburton*), Shirley Cameron (*Gloria*), Julie Martin (*Liz*), Bernadette Milnes (*Sheila*), Caron Gardner (*Carol*), Paula Gordon (*Paula*), Irene Richardson (*girl in laboratory*), Sheila Houston (*a teacher*), The Embers (*musical group*).

Melodrama. A group of teenaged girls in a boarding school proudly wear yellow teddy bear pins to show that they are not virgins. Sixteen-year-old Linda Donaghue, neglected by her parents, joins the group and becomes pregnant by one of her lovers, Kinky, a window cleaner and pop singer. June Wilson, a prostitute who holds parties for the girls in her apartment, arranges an abortion for Linda and suggests that she earn the money to pay for it by selling herself. Linda's father finds out about the planned abortion and tries to prevent it. Refusing to admit that his own neglect is linked with his daughter's condition, he blames the school's biology teacher, Anne Mason, who earlier discovered the teddy bear club and tried to discuss sex frankly with the girls. Reprimanded by the school board, Miss Mason resigns after an emotional outburst in which she insists that she was trying to help the girls. By this time, Linda has discovered that her parents are planning to send her away, and she runs away to London. *Schoolteachers. Singers. Prostitutes. Window washers. Pregnancy. Abortion. Adolescence. Parenthood. Sex instruction. Boarding schools. Sex clubs. London.*

Note: Released in Great Britain in Jul 1963 as *The Yellow Teddybears,* running time: 85 min. Also known as *The Thrill Seekers.* Working title: *The Yellow Golliwog.*

GUTTER TRASH   **F6.2004**

Extraordinary Films. *Dist* William Mishkin. 19 Jun **1969** [New York opening]. Sd; b&w. 35mm. 74 min.

Dir Andy Milligan. *Screenplay* Andy Milligan, John Borske. *Photog* Andy Milligan.

Cast: Candy Hammond (*Pussy Johnson*), Eddie Frackman (*Nick*), Patricia Dillon (*Stix*), Paul Eden (*CooCoo*), Susan Cassidy (*Minky*), Neil Flanagan (*Bunny*), David Smith (*Bill*), Suzanne Gilbert (*Sandra*), Zita Litvanas (*Louise*), Buddy Jarvis (*Marsh*), Ada McAllister (*Lorry*), Jesse Bigelow (*doctor*), Maya Reid (*Miss B.*), Anthony Moscini (*Chris*).

Melodrama. Former model Pussy Johnson, serving a 5- to 10-year sentence at a New York penitentiary, tells the prison psychiatrist of her past: *Pussy, modeling in the nude for photographer Bill Larch, seduces him, but their lovemaking is interrupted by Stix, a lesbian friend of Bill's. Pussy retires to take a nap, and Bill discourages Stix by explaining that Pussy is strictly a heterosexual. Marsh Thompson, Bill's partner, finds Pussy and forces himself on her. Bill sends Stix to Greenwich Village to buy drugs from CooCoo Corbett, a notorious pusher who keeps a "sex-slave," Minky. Stix is attracted to Minky, and she asks CooCoo to stop beating her. CooCoo offers Minky to Stix, but Stix declines to accept an unwilling lover, and she leaves after purchasing some marijuana and STP. Pussy meets and falls in love with Nick, a clean-cut young man who proposes marriage to her on the condition that she give up her involvement with Bill and his friends. Pussy refuses, and Nick leaves the country in disappointment. Bill throws a party with the drugs obtained from CooCoo, and a wild orgy ensues, complete with wife swapping, sexual* *threesomes, lesbianism, and male homosexuality. Bill's wife, Sandra, depressed by the STP and the events of the evening, sets herself on fire and burns to death. Pussy reflects on the horrible fates of all concerned, and she laments her rejection of Nick and the respectable life he could have provided. Models. Psychiatrists. Drug dealers. Photographers. Seduction. Lesbianism. Rape. Sadism. Group sex. Mate swapping. Male homosexuality. Suicide. Troilism. Prisons. Marijuana. Amphetamines. New York City—Greenwich Village.*

Note: Filmed in New York City. Also known as *Male & Female Sexualis.*

A GUY, EIGHT GALS see **A MAN—EIGHT GIRLS**

GYAKUTEN RYOKO see **TOPSY-TURVY JOURNEY**

HĒ GYMNĒ TAXIARCHIA see **THE NAKED BRIGADE**

GYPSY   F6.2005

Warner Bros. Pictures. 1 Nov **1962** [New York opening; c5 Jan 1963; LP29377]. Sd; col (Technicolor). 35mm (Technirama). 149 min. [Also reviewed at 142 min.]

A Mervyn LeRoy Production. *Prod-Dir* Mervyn LeRoy. *Screenplay* Leonard Spigelgass. *Photog* Harry Stradling, Sr. *Camera Op* Harry Stradling, Jr.. *Camera Asst* George Gall, J. B. Allen. *Art Dir* John Beckman. *Set Decor* Ralph S. Hurst. *Film Ed* Philip W. Anderson. *Asst Ed* John F. Burnett. *Mus Cond & Supv* Frank Perkins. *Songs* Jule Styne, Stephen Sondheim. *Orch* Frank Perkins, Carl Brandt. *Miss Russell's Singing Dub (see note)* Lisa Kirk. *Choreog* Robert Tucker. *Sd* M. A. Merrick, Dolph Thomas. *Boom Op* William Thompson. *Asst Dir* Gil Kissel, Greg Peters, Mecca Graham. *Unit Mgr* Floyd Joyer. *Sec to Mr. LeRoy* Ruth Bridges. *Script Supv* Erika Wernher. *Cost Dsgn for Misses Russell and Wood* Orry-Kelly. *Gen Cost Dsgn* Howard Shoup. *Asst Cost Dsgn* Bill Gaskin. *Makeup* Gordon Bau. *Miss Russell's Makeup* Gene Hibbs. *Miss Wood's Hairstyles* Sydney Guilaroff. *Hairstyles* Jean Burt Reilly. *Gaffer* Frank Flanagan. *Best Boy* William Perillard. *Ch Grip* Charles Harris. *Prop* Pat Patterson, prop.

Cast: Rosalind Russell *(Rose)*, Natalie Wood *(Louise [Gypsy])*, Karl Malden *(Herbie Sommers)*, Paul Wallace *(Tulsa No. 2)*, Betty Bruce *(Tessie Tura)*, Parley Baer *(Mr. Kringelein)*, Harry Shannon *(Grandpa)*, Suzanne Cupito ("Baby" June), Ann Jilliann ("Dainty" June), Diane Pace ("Baby" Louise), Faith Dane *(Mazeppa)*, Roxanne Arlen *(Electra)*, Jean Willes *(Betty Cratchitt)*, George Petrie *(George)*, Ben Lessy *(Mervyn Goldstone)*, Guy Raymond *(Pastey)*, Louis Quinn *(Cigar)*, James Millhollin *(Mr. Beckman)*, William Fawcett *(Mr. Willis)*, Danny Lockin *(Yonkers)*, Ian Tucker *(Angie)*, Bert Michaels *(farmboy)*, Lois Roberts *(Agnes)*, Dina Claire *(Dolores)*, Harvey Korman *(Phil)*, Jack Benny *(himself)*.

Musical comedy. Source: Arthur Laurents, *Gypsy* (New York opening: 21 May 1959). Gypsy Rose Lee, *Gypsy, a Memoir* (New York, 1957). During the 1920's in the heyday of vaudeville, Rose, an aggressive and domineering woman, vows to make stars of her two young daughters, June and Louise. Aided by Herbie Sommers, an agent who has fallen in love with her, she secures for June some bigtime circuit bookings, while the seemingly less talented Louise remains in the background. As the years pass, however, June becomes too old for her mother's childish act, and she decides to go it alone. Rose shakes off the initial hurt and concentrates on making a star performer out of Louise. But talking pictures have led to the decline of vaudeville, and bookings are scarce. Consequently, the troupe ends up at a third-rate burlesque house in Wichita. Rose is at first violently opposed to her daughter's working in such a place, but she finally acquiesces. One of the strippers is arrested for shoplifting, and the once demure, shy Louise becomes her replacement. Fame is quick to follow, and as Gypsy Rose Lee she becomes the highest paid star in burlesque. Rose still tries to run her daughter's life, but Gypsy is determined to do things her own way, and mother and daughter have a falling out. Following a violent quarrel, Rose walks onto an empty stage and cries out her frustrations to a deserted theater. After listening from the wings, Gypsy embraces her mother, and the two are reconciled. *Songs:* "Let Me Entertain You" ("Baby" June, "Dainty" June, Louise); "Some People," "Small World," "Everything's Coming Up Roses," "Rose's Turn" (Rose); "You'll Never Get Away From Me" (Rose & Herbie); "Mr. Goldstone" (Rose & chorus); "Baby June and the Newsboys" ("Baby" June); "Little Lamb" (Louise); "Dainty June and Her Farmboys" ("Dainty" June); "If Mama Was Married" (Louise & "Dainty" June); "All I Need Is the Girl" (Tulsa & Louise); "Together Wherever We Go" (Rose, Louise & Herbie); "You Gotta Have a Gimmick" (Tessie, Mazeppa & Electra). *Entertainers. Theatrical agents. Sisters. Stripteasers. Vaudeville. Filial relations. Burlesque. Wichita. Gypsy Rose Lee. Rose Hovick. June Havoc.*

Note: Lisa Kirk's voice is heard in some of Rosalind Russell's numbers.

GYPSY GIRL (Great Britain)   F6.2006

John Mills Productions. *For* Rank Organisation. *Dist* Continental Distributing, Inc. Jul **1966**. Sd; col (Eastmancolor, print by Movielab). 35mm. 102 min.

Prod Jack Hanbury. *Dir* John Mills. *Screenplay* Mary Hayley Bell, John Prebble. *Story* Mary Hayley Bell. *Photog* Arthur Ibbetson. *Art Dir* Carmen Dillon. *Set Decor* Patrick McLoughlin. *Film Ed* Gordon Hales. *Mus Comp & Cond* Malcolm Arnold. *Sd* Bill Daniels, Colin Le Mesurier. *Asst Dir* David Tringham. *Prod Mgr* Donald Toms. *Cost* Yvonne Caffin. *Makeup* Harry Frampton, Frank Turner. *Hairstyles* Ivy Emmerton.

Cast: Hayley Mills *(Brydie White)*, Ian McShane *(Roibin)*, Laurence Naismith *(Edwin Dacres)*, Geoffrey Bayldon *(Philip Moss)*, Annette Crosbie *(Mrs. White)*, Norman Bird *(Cheeseman)*, Hamilton Dyce *(Bill Slim)*, Pauline Jameson *(Mrs. Moss)*, Rachel Thomas *(grandma)*, Judith Furse *(Mrs. Rigby)*, Anne Blake *(Mrs. Potts)*, June Ellis *(Mrs. Cheeseman)*, Jack Bligh *(Fred Strong)*, Len Jones *(Dusty Miller)*, Roland Starling *(Harry)*, Jessica Hobbs *(Cathy)*, Gerald Lawson *(Jabal Jones)*, Jacqueline Pearce *(Cammellia)*, Alan Lake *(Camlo)*, Hira Talfrey *(Blossom)*, Cyril Chamberlain *(Hubberd)*, Susan Chatham *(Susie)*, Robin Crewe *(Chalky)*, Lola Payne *(Biddie)*, Nicola Street *(Nell)*, Stephen Salt *(Jakey)*, Joyce Mayhead *(Emm)*.

Drama. Seventeen-year-old Brydie White has grown up slightly retarded in a rural English village ever since one of her playmates was killed seven years earlier by a loaded shotgun left lying around by his father, Edwin Dacres. Brydie's mother ignores her responsibilities by constantly drinking gin, and Dacres disguises his guilt by blaming Brydie for the death; likewise, she is shunned by most of the villagers and can only find solace in the churchyard cemetery by the boy's grave. One day she sees a youngster burying his dead mole in the graveyard and decides to do the same with two of her recently deceased pets; soon, to the consternation of their parents, other children follow suit, and the cemetery is filled with hundreds of tiny mounds. Her newfound acquaintances include Roibin, a gypsy boy whose caravan is visiting the village. One night the disapproving Mrs. White strikes Brydie, who then runs to the graveyard and encounters the drunken Dacres. When he threatens her with a gun, Brydie runs off, falls into a nearby river, and is rescued by Roibin, who hides her in the caravan. Brydie's disappearance causes Mrs. White to die of a stroke, and the villagers believe the girl should be placed in an orphanage once she is found. The local vicar decides otherwise, however, and defies convention by permitting Brydie to leave town with the caravan. *Children. Gypsies. Clergymen. Orphans. Mental retardation. Village life. Adolescence. Filial relations. Guilt. Alcoholism. Death. Strokes. Cemeteries. Pets.*

Note: Location scenes filmed in Badminton, England. Opened in London in Jan 1966 as *Sky West and Crooked.* Working title: *Bats With Baby Faces.*

THE GYPSY MOTHS   F6.2007

Metro-Goldwyn-Mayer, Inc. 28 Aug **1969** [New York opening; c23 Jul 1969; LP37154]. Sd; col (Metrocolor). 35mm. 106 min. [See note.] *MPAA rating* M.

A John Frankenheimer–Edward Lewis Production. *Prod* Hal Landers, Bobby Roberts. *Exec Prod* Edward Lewis. *Dir* John Frankenheimer. *Screenplay* William Hanley. *Dir Photog* Philip Lathrop. *Sp Aerial Photog* Carl Boenisch. *Aerial Photog* Tyler Camera Systems. *Art Dir* George W. Davis, Cary Odell. *Set Decor* Henry Grace, Jack Mills. *Film Ed* Henry Berman. *Assoc Film Ed* Alex Beaton. *Mus* Elmer Bernstein. *Rec Supv* Franklin Milton. *Sd Engr* Tom Overton. *Asst Dir* Al Jennings. *Unit Prod Mgr* Jim Henderling. *Wardrobe Dsgn* Bill Thomas. *Makeup* William Tuttle. *Hairstyles* Sydney Guilaroff. *Sp Vis Eff* J. McMillan Johnson, Carroll L. Shepphird. *Prop Master* Frank Agnone. *Skydiving Experts* Russ Benefiel, David W. Thompson, Mike Wilts, Gerald Rouillard, Garth Taggart.

Cast: Burt Lancaster *(Mike Rettig)*, Deborah Kerr *(Elizabeth Brandon)*, Gene Hackman *(Joe Browdy)*, Scott Wilson *(Malcolm Webson)*, William Windom *(V. John Brandon)*, Bonnie Bedelia *(Annie Burke)*, Sheree North *(waitress)*, Carl Reindel *(pilot)*, Ford Rainey *(stand owner)*, John Napier *(Dick Donford)*.

Action melodrama. Source: James Drought, *The Gypsy Moths* (Norwalk, Connecticut, 1964). Professional skydivers Mike Rettig, Joe Browdy, and Malcolm Webson arrive in Kansas to perform in the small town of Bridgeville. They are invited to stay at the home of Elizabeth and John Brandon, Webson's aunt and uncle. Suffocated by her loveless, childless marriage, Elizabeth finds herself attracted to Rettig. Browdy takes up with a topless go-go dancer, and Webson begins a tenuous relationship with Annie Burke, a student boarder at the Brandon house. Later, Rettig and Elizabeth make love in the living room, while John listens silently from upstairs. On the morning of the aerial exhibition, Rettig asks Elizabeth to go away with him, but she rejects him. That afternoon, Rettig performs the dangerous "cape jump" but plummets to his death when he fails to pull the ripcord of his parachute. To pay for their friend's funeral, Browdy and Webson stage a special memorial show, and Webson insists upon attempting the cape jump for the first time. He successfully completes the stunt before a capacity crowd and leaves town, vowing never to skydive again. Browdy leaves for Hollywood to become a stuntman. *Aunts. Uncles. Go-go dancers. Students. Skydiving. Marriage. Air stunts. Loneliness.*

command of Capt. Paul Slater, is to protect the whiskey train. Slater is in love with Gearhart's daughter Louise, one of the temperance ladies. The Sioux and a Denver citizens' militia under the direction of Clayton Howell are also heading for the whiskey train. Kevin O'Flaherty and his Irish teamsters stage a slow-down strike, thus leaving the train open to attack, which comes at dawn from the Indians. Suddenly during the attack, a large sandstorm comes, totally confusing everyone. No one is hurt during the battle, and the Indians agree not to disturb the train in exchange for some whiskey. The train, now traversing territory made dangerous by quicksand, is host to a temperance meeting arranged by the ladies for the Indians, who promptly kidnap the ladies and demand whiskey as a ransom. An elaborate exchange procedure is arranged. Oracle Jones persuades Wallingham to leave immediately for Denver. He arranges for a safe journey over the quicksand by marking a trail with his underwear, but Cora and the temperance ladies move the markers. Cora causes the horses to stampede, and the barrels containing hot champagne pop their corks, simulating gunshots. The Indians form a circle with the wagons while the cavalry rides around them. Wallingham and the train follow the marked trail and end up in the quicksand, the whiskey lost. Gearhart and Cora and Slater and Louise marry, and everyone goes home, except for Wallingham and Oracle, who sit beside the quicksand waiting for the whiskey to surface. *Seers. Distillers. Editors. Sioux Indians. Irish. Temperance. Drunkenness. Strikes. Kidnaping. Weddings. Wagon trains. Liquor. Ransom. Denver. United States Army—Cavalry. Sandstorms. Quicksand.*

HALLS OF ANGER   F6.2016

Mirisch Productions. *Dist* United Artists. 25 Mar **1970** [Washington, D. C., opening; c25 Mar 1970; LP37893]. Sd; col (De Luxe). 35mm. 98 min. *MPAA rating* GP.

Prod Herbert Hirschman. *Exec Prod* Walter Mirisch. *Dir* Paul Bogart. *Screenplay* John Shaner, Al Ramrus. *Dir Photog* Burnett Guffey. *Art Dir* Addison Hehr. *Film Ed* Bud Molin. *Mus* Dave Grusin. *Song:* "Reachin' Out to You" Norman Gimbel, Dave Grusin. *Sung by* Maurice Miller. *Sd* Don Rush. *Sd Ed* Frank Warner. *Mus Ed* Richard Carruth. *Asst Dir* Victor Vallejo, Fred Brost, Joe Ellis. *Prod Supv* Edward Morey, Jr.. *Prod Mgr* Nate H. Edwards. *Script Supv* Marshall Wolins. *Tech Adv* Mike Warren.

Cast: Calvin Lockhart *(Quincy Davis)*, Janet MacLachlan *(Lorraine Nash)*, James A. Watson, Jr. *(J. T. Watson)*, Jeff Bridges *(Douglas Falk)*, Rob Reiner *(Leaky Couloris)*, Dewayne Jesse *(Lerone Johnson)*, Patricia Stich *(Sherry Vaughn)*, Roy Jenson *(Harry Greco)*, John McLiam *(Lloyd Wilkerson)*, Edward Asner *(Ernie McKay)*, Lou Frizzell *(Phil Stewart)*, Helen Kleeb *(Rita Monahan)*, Luther Whitsett *(Ivan Fowler)*, Florence St. Peter *(Miss Rowland)*, Maye Henderson *(Mrs. Taylor)*, Barry Brown, actor, Alex Clarke, Paris Earl, Randy Fredericks, Arline Hamlin, Christopher Joy, Richard Levin, Kim Manners, Linda Smith, Linda Thomas, Ta-Tanisha, Gary Tigerman, Cal Wilson, Hilly Hicks, Peggy Toy, Gilbert Green, Davis Roberts, Martin Blaine.

Melodrama. In compliance with a court order 60 white students are bused to Lafayette High School, administered by black vice-principal Quincy Davis, a former basketball star. The white presence is resented by militant blacks led by J. T. Watson, and white resentment crystallizes in the person of Leaky Couloris, a racist. While Davis interests black Lerone Johnson in reading by giving the student pornographic paperbacks, he is discouraged by the brutal beating of white athlete Douglas Falk during basketball tryouts. When Couloris and Johnson fight, both are expelled, triggering a strike by the entire student body. Informed that both offenders will be treated fairly, student leader Watson quashes the potential riot. Following this confrontation Davis persuades black teacher Lorraine Nash and white victim Falk to remain at Lafayette. *Athletes. Students. Schoolteachers. School principals. Militants. High school life. Racial integration. Busing. Student activism. Racism. Basketball. Strikes. Pornography.*

Note: Filmed partially in Los Angeles high schools.

HALLUCINATION GENERATION   F6.2017

Trans-American Films–SRS Productions. *Dist* Trans-American Films. Dec **1966** [c14 Dec 1966; LP33776]. Sd; b&w with col seq. 35mm. 90 min. [Copyright length: 86 min.]

Pres by Herbert R. Steinmann. An Edward Andrew Mann–Robert D. Weinbach Production. *Prod* Nigel Cox. *Assoc Prod* Jerome A. Siegel, Morton M. Rosenfeld. *Exec Prod* Robert D. Weinbach. *Dir-Writ* Edward Andrew Mann. *Camera* Ramon Sempere. *Film Ed* Fima Noveck. *Mus* Bernardo Segall. *Asst Dir* Antonio Chic. *Prod Mgr* Roberto Moreno. *Wardrobe* Mercedes Segura. *Makeup* Adolfo Ponte. *Sp Eff* Edward Andrew Mann, Manuel Sayans.

Cast: George Montgomery *(Eric)*, Danny Stone *(Bill)*, Renate Kasche *(Lise)*, Tom Baker *(Denny)*, Marianne Kanter *(Carol)*, Steve Rowland *(Stan)*, Claude Gersene *(Eric's boy)*.

Melodrama. Supported by an allowance from his wealthy mother, a young American named Bill arrives on Ibiza, an island off the coast of Spain, to visit his friend Denny. Denny lives with a group of young expatriates, who devote themselves to thrill-seeking and sexual promiscuity through the use of drugs, including LSD. Their acknowledged leader is an older married man, Eric, a former college art instructor, who is conducting experiments with hallucinatory drugs. Although Bill is urged to join in the experiments, he refuses, preferring instead to spend his time with Lise, a German girl whom he eventually marries. But their happiness ends abruptly when Bill's mother cuts off his allowance and Lise resents having to support her husband. Not knowing what else to do, Bill returns to the island and moves in with Eric and his family. Before long he is smoking marijuana and accumulating large gambling losses. When Eric comes up with the idea of holding up a wealthy Barcelona antique dealer, Bill rejects the plan until Eric slips him a dose of LSD. Then, while undergoing a series of fantasies, he responds to Eric's suggestions and agrees to join Denny in committing the robbery. The scheme backfires, however, when the antique dealer puts up a struggle and Denny kills him with a candlestick. Racing back to Eric's colony, Denny seeks escape from reality by taking drugs. There were witnesses to the crime, however, and before long the police trace Denny to Eric's and make an arrest. Bill, meanwhile, has made his way to a monastery high above Barcelona. Confessing to the monks, he seeks their assistance and guidance. The police are contacted and they capture the real criminal. *Americans in foreign countries. Expatriates. Art teachers. Germans. Antique dealers. Police. Hedonism. Gambling. Marriage. Robbery. Murder. Finance— Personal. Experiments. LSD. Hallucinogens. Marijuana. Monasteries. Ibiza. Barcelona.*

Note: Filmed in Spain. Working title: *The Drifters.* Prerelease title: *Hallucination.*

THE HALLUCINATORS *see* THE NAKED ZOO

HAMBURG OFF-LIMITS *see* SEVEN CONSENTING ADULTS

HAMLET   F6.2018

Electronovision Productions–American Broadcasting–Paramount Theatres, Inc.–Theatrofilm. *Dist* Warner Bros. Pictures. 23 Sep **1964** [New York opening: c23 Sep 1964; LP32355]. Sd; b&w. 35mm (Electronovision). 186 min. [See note.]

Pres by Theatrofilm. *Prod* William Sargent, Jr., Alfred W. Crown, John Heyman. *Exec Prod* Alexander H. Cohen. *Prod Assoc* Gabriel Katzka, Andre Goulston. *Electronovision Dir* Bill Colleran. *Staged by* John Gielgud. *Video* Carl Hanseman. *Electronic Film Rec* S. R. Brown. *Lighting Dir* Jim Kilgore. *Lighting* Jean Rosenthal. *Dsgn* Ben Edwards. *Film Ed* Bruce Pierce. *Audio Supv* Lionel St. Peter. *Sd Ed* James Fritch. *Asst Dir* Joel Glickman, Dan Smith. *Asst to the Prod* Gerri Gary. *Prod Supv* J. E. Kilgore. *Wardrobe* Jane Greenwood. *Makeup* Bob Philippe. *Tech Supv* Robert Ringer. *Tech Dir* Charles La Force. *Post-prod Supv* S. Richard Krown. *Tech Prod* Mark Armistead Television Inc.

Cast: Richard Burton *(Hamlet)*, Hume Cronyn *(Polonius)*, Alfred Drake *(Claudius)*, Eileen Herlie *(Gertrude)*, William Redfield *(Guildenstern)*, George Rose *(1st gravedigger)*, George Voskovec *(player king)*, Linda Marsh *(Ophelia)*, Robert Milli *(Horatio)*, John Cullum *(Laertes)*, Philip Coolidge *(Voltimand)*, Michael Ebert *(Fortinbras/Francisco)*, Dillon Evans *(Reynaldo/ Osric)*, Clement Fowler *(Rosencrantz)*, Geoff Garland *(Lucianus)*, Barnard Hughes *(priest/Marcellus)*, Hugh Alexander *(English ambassador/2d gravedigger/Cornelius)*, Frederick Young *(Bernardo)*, John Hetherington *(player prologue)*, Christopher Culkin *(player queen)*, Richard Sterne *(gentleman)*, Alex Giannini *(messenger)*, John Gielgud *(voice of The Ghost)*, Claude Harz, Gerome Ragni, Linda Seff, Carol Teitel *(lords, ladies, attendants)*.

Tragedy. Source: William Shakespeare, *Hamlet.* A film presentation of the stage production directed by John Gielgud. *Students. Royalty. Uncles. Usurpers. Death. Murder. Revenge. Friendship. Insanity. Brother-sister relationship. Filial relations. Poisoning. Regicide. Fratricide. Suicide. Incest. Castles. Theater. Skulls. Denmark. Ghosts. Visions. Duels.*

Note: Filmed in Electronovision on 30 Jun and 1 Jul 1964 during two regular performances of the play, which opened in New York 9 Apr 1964. Also reviewed at 199 and 191 min and registered for copyright at 148 min.

HAMLET (U.S.S.R.)   F6.2019

Lenfilm. *Dist* Lopert Pictures. 15 Mar **1966** [New York opening]. Sd; b&w. 35mm (Sovscope). 148 min.

Dir-Screenplay Grigoriy Kozintsev. *Photog* Ionas Gritsyus. *Camera* V. Chumak, photog, A. Chechulin. *Art Dir* Yevgeniy Yeney, G. Kropachyov. *Film Ed* Ye. Makhankova. *Mus* Dmitriy Dmitriyevich Shostakovich. *Played by* Leningrad Philharmonic Orchestra. *Mus Cond* N. Rabinovich. *Sd* B. Khutoryanskiy. *Asst Dir* I. Shapiro. *Cost* Solomon Virsaladze. *Sp Eff* A. Zavyalov, G. Senotov, B. Mikhaylov. *Sculpture* I. Zaytseva, O. Skrypko. *Fencing Master* I. Kokh.

Cast: Innokentiy Smoktunovskiy *(Hamlet, Prince of Denmark)*, Mikhail Nazvanov *(The King)*, Elza Radzin *(The Queen)*, Yuriy Tolubeyev *(Polonius)*,

Anastasiya Vertinskaya *(Ophelia)*, Vladimir Erenberg *(Horatio)*, Stepan Oleksenko *(Laertes)*, Vadim Medvedev *(Guildenstern)*, I. Dmitriyev *(Rosencrantz)*, A. Krevald *(Fortinbras)*, V. Kolpakov *(gravedigger)*, A. Chekayevskiy *(The First Player)*, R. Aren *(The Second Player)*, Yu. Berkun *(The Third Player)*, A. Lauter *(priest)*, B. Ilyasov, P. Kilgas, N. Kuzmin, B. Moreno, Andrey Popov, F. Fedorovskiy, V. Shchennikov.

Drama. Source: William Shakespeare, *Hamlet* (trans. by Boris Pasternak as *Gamlet*, prints datskiy). A screen version of *Hamlet*, performed in medieval period costume. *Students. Royalty. Uncles. Usurpers. Death. Murder. Friendship. Insanity. Filial relations. Revenge. Regicide. Incest. Poisoning. Fratricide. Suicide. Brother-sister relationship. Castles. Skulls. Theater. Denmark. Ghosts. Visions. Duels.*

Note: Released in the U.S.S.R. in 1964 as *Gamlet*; Soviet release in two parts. Filmed in whole or part on location along the Estonian seacoast.

HAMLET (West Germany)   **F6.2020**
Bavaria Atelier. *Dist* Emerson Film Enterprises. 13 Feb **1968** [Tucson, Arizona, opening]. Sd; b&w. 35mm. 120 min.
Pres by Edward Dmytryk, Sam Weiler. *Prod* Hans Gottschalk. *Dir-Adapt* Franz Peter Wirth. *English Dial Dir* Fred Brown. *Camera* Kurt Gewissen, Hermann Gruber, Rudolf H. Jakob, Boris Geriup. *Mus* Rolf Unkel. *English Dub Dir* Edward Dmytryk.
Cast: Maximilian Schell *(Hamlet)*, Hans Caninberg *(Claudius)*, Wanda Rotha *(Gertrude)*, Dunja Movar *(Ophelia)*, Franz Schafheitlin *(Polonius)*, Dieter Kirchlechner *(Laertes)*, Karl Michael Vogler *(Horatio)*, Eckard Dux *(Rosencrantz)*, Herbert Botticher *(Guildenstern)*, Karl Lieffen *(Osric)*, Rolf Boysen *(Bernardo)*, Michael Paryla *(Francisco)*, Alexander Engel *(The Ghost)*, Adolf Gerstung *(1st player)*, Paul Verhoeven *(gravedigger)*.
Tragedy. Source: William Shakespeare, *Hamlet* (trans. by August von Schlegel as *Hamlet, Prinz von Danemark*; Berlin, 1947). The film is an adaptation, substantially altered from the original, of Shakespeare's tragedy. Speeches have been deleted or delivered by different characters, and many roles have been eliminated entirely. *Students. Royalty. Uncles. Usurpers. Death. Murder. Friendship. Insanity. Filial relations. Poisoning. Revenge. Regicide. Fratricide. Suicide. Incest. Brother-sister relationship. Castles. Theater. Skulls. Denmark. Ghosts. Visions. Duels.*
Note: Produced in 1960 for West German television; running time: 130 min.

HAMLET (Great Britain)   **F6.2021**
Woodfall Films–Filmways Ltd. *Dist* Columbia Pictures. 21 Dec **1969** [New York opening; c21 Dec 1969; LP37889]. Sd; col (Technicolor). 35mm. 114 min. *MPAA rating* G.
Prod Neil Hartley. *Exec Prod* Leslie Linder, Martin Ransohoff. *Dir* Tony Richardson. *Photog* Gerry Fisher. *Dsgn* Jocelyn Herbert. *Film Ed* Charles Rees. *Mus Comp* Patrick Gowers. *Sd Ed* Don Deacon. *Sd Rec* Tony Jackson. *Sd Re-rec* Gerry Humphreys. *Asst Dir* Andrew Grieve. *Prod Supv* Gavrik Losey.
Cast: Nicol Williamson *(Hamlet)*, Anthony Hopkins *(Claudius)*, Judy Parfitt *(Gertrude)*, Mark Dignam *(Polonius)*, Marianne Faithfull *(Ophelia)*, Michael Pennington *(Laertes)*, Gordon Jackson *(Horatio)*, Ben Aris *(Rosencrantz)*, Clive Graham *(Guildenstern)*, Peter Gale *(Osric)*, John Carney *(Marcellus/player king)*, John Trenaman *(Barnardo/player/2d sailor)*, Robin Chadwick *(Francisco/courtier/player)*, Richard Everett *(player queen/courtier)*, Roger Livesey *(Lucianus/gravedigger)*, John Railton *(1st sailor/courtier)*, Roger Lloyd Pack *(Reynaldo/courtier/player)*, Michael Elphick *(captain/courtier)*, Bill Jarvis *(courtier)*, Ian Collier *(priest/courtier)*, Jennifer Tudor, Anjelica Huston *(court ladies)*, Mark Griffith *(messenger/courtier)*.
Tragedy. Source: William Shakespeare, *Hamlet*. The film is an adaptation of William Shakespeare's play, filmed on the stage of the Round House in London. The King's ghost is represented by a light rather than a special photographic effect. The original play has been drastically cut for the screen, and many supporting roles have been diminished or eliminated. *Students. Royalty. Uncles. Usurpers. Death. Murder. Friendship. Insanity. Filial relations. Poisoning. Revenge. Regicide. Fratricide. Suicide. Incest. Brother-sister relationship. Castles. Theater. Skulls. Denmark. Ghosts. Visions. Duels.*
Note: Released in Great Britain in 1970; running time: 117 min.

HAMMERHEAD (Great Britain)   **F6.2022**
Irving Allen Ltd. *Dist* Columbia Pictures. 17 Jul **1968** [Boston opening; c1 Jul 1968; LP35902]. Sd (Westrex); col (Technicolor). 35mm. 99 min.
Prod Irving Allen. *Assoc Prod* Andrew Donally. *Dir* David Miller. *Screenplay* William E. Bast, Herbert Baker. *Adapt* John Briley. *Dir Photog* Kenneth Talbot, Wilkie Cooper. *Camera Op* Cece Cooney, Ray Parslow. *Art Dir* John Howell. *Set Decor* Pamela Cornell. *Film Ed* Geoffrey Foot. *Mus Comp & Dir* David Whitaker. *Titl Song* David Whitaker, John Worsley. *Song:* "I'll Be Your Old-Fashioned Girl" David Whitaker, John Worsley, Herbert Baker. *Choreog* Ralph Tobert. *Sd Rec* Hugh Strain. *Sd Ed* Charles Crafford.

Asst Dir John O'Connor, John Danischewsky. *Prod Mgr* L. C. Rudkin. *Cont* Rita Davison. *Cost* Brian Cox. *Makeup* Alan Brownie. *Hairdresser* Ann Box. *Sp Eff* Pat Moore. *Stunt Supv* Gerry Crampton.
Cast: Vince Edwards *(Charles Hood)*, Judy Geeson *(Sue Trenton)*, Peter Vaughan *(Hammerhead)*, Diana Dors *(Kit)*, Michael Bates *(Andreas/Sir Richard)*, Beverly Adams *(Ivory)*, Patrick Cargill *(Condor)*, Patrick Holt *(Huntzinger)*, William Mervyn *(Perrin)*, Douglas Wilmer *(Vendriani)*, Tracy Reed *(Miss Hull)*, Kenneth Cope *(motorcyclist)*, Kathleen Byron *(Lady Calvert)*, Jack Woolgar *(Tookey Tate)*, Joseph Furst *(Count Ortega)*, David Prowse *(George)*, Earl Younger *(Brian)*, Romo Garrara *(Marcel)*, Maggie Wright *(Roselle)*, Veronica Carlson *(Ulla)*, Penny Brahms *(Freda)*, Sarah Harden Berg *(Kiki)*, Otto Diamant *(Joa)*, Windsor Davies *(police sergeant)*, Arthur Gomez *(cafe proprietor)*, Andreas Malandrinos *(post office guard)*.
Melodrama. Source: John Mayo, *Hammerhead* (London, 1964). American secret agent Charles Hood is instructed by Colonel Condor of British Security to trap Hammerhead, an international criminal and collector of erotic art who is suspected of wanting to steal a secret report on a nuclear defense system presented at a NATO conference in Lisbon. By offering to sell a priceless collection of pornography, Hood gets himself invited aboard Hammerhead's yacht, but his sleuthing is hampered by the attentiveness of Sue Trenton, a model and nightclub entertainer, and the seductive advances of Hammerhead's mistress, Ivory. Hood finally uncovers Hammerhead's scheme to kidnap Sir Richard Calvert, Britain's NATO delegate, and replace him at the conference with Andreas, a professional impersonator formerly employed at a nightclub owned by Kit, another of Hammerhead's mistresses. Hood and Sue are captured by Hammerhead's henchmen when the master criminal learns of Hood's true identity, but they escape from the coffin in which they were meant to be drowned. Despite Andreas' successful impersonation and the acquisition of the secret report, Hood is able to alert British Security before Hammerhead can make use of the information he has obtained. The final chase takes place as 300 hippies cavort on the rocks at Cascais Bay. Before it is over, Kit and Andreas are killed, and the vengeful Ivory harpoons Hammerhead to death. *Americans in foreign countries. Secret agents. Art collectors. Models. Entertainers. Mistresses. Hired killers. Hippies. Espionage. Theft. Kidnaping. Impersonation. Pornography. Erotica. Yachts. Lisbon. Cascais Bay. Great Britain— Intelligence service. North Atlantic Treaty Organization.*
Note: Location scenes filmed in London and Portugal. Opened in London in Nov 1968.

HAMNSTAD *see* **PORT OF CALL**

HAMP *see* **KING AND COUNTRY**

HANA TO NAMIDA TO HONOO *see* **THE PERFORMERS**

HANAOKA SEISHU NO TSUMA *see* **THE WIFE OF SEISHU HANAOKA**

THE HAND (Great Britain)   **F6.2023**
Bill and Michael Luckwell, Ltd. *Dist* American International Pictures. 22 Mar **1961** [Hartford, Connecticut, opening; c18 Dec 1960; LP20360]. Sd (RCA); b&w. 35mm. 61 min. [Copyright length: 64 min.]
A Bill Luckwell–Michael Luckwell Production. *Prod* Bill Luckwell. *Assoc Prod* D. E. A. Winn. *Dir* Henry Cass. *Screenplay-Story* Ray Cooney, Tony Hilton. *Photog* James Harvey. *Camera Op* Gus Drisse. *Art Dir* John Earl. *Film Ed* Robert Hill. *Mus Dir* Wilfred Burns. *Sd Rec* Claude Hitchcock. *Asst Dir* James Shingfield, Michael Burrage. *Prod Mgr* Clive Midwinter. *Cont* Jane Buck. *Wardrobe* Brenda Gardner. *Makeup* Jimmy Evans.
Cast: Derek Bond *(Captain Roberts/Roger Crawshaw)*, Reed De Rouen *(Pvt. Michael Brodie)*, Bryan Coleman *(Corporal Adams)*, Walter Randall *(Japanese commander)*, Tony Hilton *(Sergeant Foster)*, Harold Scott *(Charlie Taplow)*, Ray Cooney *(Detective Sergeant Pollitt)*, Gwenda Ewen *(Nurse Johns)*, Michael Moore, actor *(Dr. Metcalfe)*, Ronald Leigh-Hunt *(Inspector Munyard)*, Ronald Wilson *(doctor)*, Garard Green *(Dr. Simon Crawshaw)*, Jean Dallas *(Nurse Geiber)*, David Blake Kelly *(Marshall)*, Reginald Hearne *(Noel Brodie)*, Madeleine Burgess *(Mrs. Brodie)*, Frances Bennett *(mother)*, Susan Reid *(little girl)*, Pat Hicks *(Mrs. Adams)*, John Norman *(Peter Adams)*.
Melodrama. In World War II, a British officer, Captain Roberts, and two of his men, Adams and Brodie, are captured in Burma by the Japanese. Both Adams and Brodie endure the severance of their right hands rather than divulge secret information to the enemy, but the captain gives in, thereby saving his own hand. In contemporary London, the amputation of an alcoholic's hand and his subsequent abduction and murder are investigated by police detectives Pollitt and Munyard. Tracing the murder victim to the Allin House Nursing Home, the detectives discover that the amputation was performed by Dr. Simon Crawshaw. The surgeon, however, is murdered during the inquiry, as is Brodie, who had been hounding Roberts for his wartime capitulation. Aided by Adams and Brodie's brother Noel, the investigators pursue the murderer.

Fleeing across a railroad trestle, Roberts stumbles, and a speeding train severs his hand. *Prisoners of war. Japanese. Police. Surgeons. War crimes. Amputation. Torture. Murder. World War II. Great Britain—Army. London. Burma.*

Note: Released in Great Britain in Nov 1960; running time: 61 min.

HAND IN HAND (Great Britain)   **F6.2024**
Helen Winston Productions. *Dist* Columbia Pictures. 6 Feb **1961** [New York opening; c1 Dec 1960; LP18932]. Sd (RCA); b&w. 35mm. 75 min.

Prod Helen Winston. *Assoc Prod* Andrew Mitchell. *Dir* Philip Leacock. *Screenplay* Diana Morgan. *Adapt* Leopold Atlas. *Story* Sidney Harmon. *Scen Ed* Frederick Gotfurt. *Dir Photog* F. A. Young. *Camera Op* Tony White. *Art Dir* Ivan King. *Film Ed* Peter Tanner. *Mus Comp & Cond* Stanley Black. *Played by* The Associated British Studio Orchestra. *Rec Supv* A. W. Lumkin. *Sd Rec* H. L. Bird, Len Shilton. *Dub Ed* Terry Poulton. *Asst Dir* Doug Hermes. *Prod Mgr* Robert E. Dearing. *Cont* June Randall. *Wardrobe Mistress* Jackie Jackson. *Makeup* L. V. Clark. *Hairstyles* Polly Young. *Tech Adv* A. Katz, (Rabbi Dr.), Rev. Father Brendan-Fox. *Casting* Robert Lennard.

Cast: Loretta Parry (*Rachel Mathias*), Philip Needs (*Michael O'Malley*), John Gregson (*Father Timothy*), Sybil Thorndike (*Lady Caroline*), Finlay Currie (*Mr. Pritchard*), Derek Sydney (*Rabbi Benjamin*), Miriam Karlin (*Mrs. Mathias*), Arnold Diamond (*Mr. Mathias*), Kathleen Byron (*Mrs. O'Malley*), Barry Keegan (*Mr. O'Malley*), Martin Lawrence (*cantor*), Barbara Hicks (*Miss Roberts*), Denis Gilmore (*Tom*), Peter Pike (*Harry*), Susan Reid (*Priscilla*), Eric Francis (*newsboy*), Stratford Johns (*farmer*), Donald Tandy (*George*), Madge Ryan (*George's wife*).

Comedy-drama. Michael, a Roman Catholic, and Rachel, a Jew, 8-year-olds who attend the same school, become close friends. When Rachel learns that her family is moving away, she and Michael decide to become "blood brothers" and never let their friendship die. They start hitchhiking to London to see the queen but instead arrive at the house of Lady Caroline, who pretends to be a royal princess. Older children tell the two friends that Jews killed Jesus, and Rachel and Michael suddenly feel that a deep rift exists between them. They agree to test the strength of their bond by attending services at each other's place of worship. At first they are terrified, but when they survive the ordeal they rejoice in their new bond. Then they decide to take a trip to Africa; but their dinghy overturns, and Michael pulls Rachel ashore. Thinking that she has been killed by God as a punishment, Michael runs to his priest, Father Timothy, and sobs out his story. The priest comforts him, telling him that neither he nor Rachel has cause to be punished; though they are of different faiths, there is one God who looks after everyone. The children go to Rachel's house and meet Rabbi Benjamin, who also reassures them. Michael now realizes that both men subscribe to the same basic principles, and the two friends are once more secure in their relationship. *Jews. Catholics. Priests. Rabbis. Children. Friendship. London.*

Note: Opened in London in May 1962; running time: 80 min.

THE HAND IN THE TRAP (Argentina/Spain)   **F6.2025**
Producciones Angel-Uninci, S. A. *Dist* Angel Productions. 1 Jul **1963** [New York opening]. Sd; b&w. 35mm. 90 min.

Prod Nestor R. Gaffet. *Assoc Prod* Juan Sires. *Dir* Leopoldo Torre-Nilsson. *Screenplay* Beatriz Guido, Leopoldo Torre-Nilsson, Ricardo Luna, Ricardo Muñoz Suay. *Story* Beatriz Guido. *Photog* Alberto Etchebehere, Juan Julio Baena. *Art Dir* Oscar Lagomarsino. *Film Ed* (see note) Jorge Gárate, Pablo Gonzalez del Amo, Jacinto Cascales. *Mus* Atilio Stampone, Cristóbal Halffter. *Sd* Mario Fezia.

Cast: Elsa Daniel (*Laura Lavigne*), Francisco Rabal (*Cristóbal Achával*), Leonardo Favio (*Miguel*), María Rosa Gallo (*Inés Lavigne*), Berta Ortegosa (*Laura's mother*), Hilda Suárez (*Laura's aunt*), Enrique Vilches (*postman*), María Puchol, María del Pilar Armesto, Mirtha Dubner, Hugo Caprera, Mirko Alvarez.

Drama. Source: Beatriz Guido, *La mano en la trampa* (Buenos Aires, 1961). While on summer vacation from her convent school, Laura Lavigne stays with her mother and aunt in a small town near Buenos Aires. She inquires about noises in the upstairs portion of the house and is told that for the past 20 years the attic has been occupied by her deformed, illegitimate halfbrother. Overcome by curiosity, she sneaks up to the room and discovers that the occupant is actually Aunt Inés, who supposedly has been living in the United States. Years earlier, Inés was jilted at the altar by wealthy Cristóbal Achával; and because of family honor, she imposed a life of lonely seclusion on herself. Laura seeks out Cristóbal in an attempt to reunite him with her aunt. Although she too succumbs to his charms, she persuades him to visit the upstairs room. The sight of seeing her former lover proves too much for Inés, and she dies from shock. Shortly after the secret funeral, Laura becomes Cristóbal's mistress and goes to live with him in Buenos Aires. Alone in her room, she suddenly realizes that she has fallen into the same trap as Inés—for as long as Cristóbal wants her, she will be his prisoner. *Aunts. Mistresses. Lovelorn. Recluses. Family life.*

Desertion. Shock. Vacations. Funerals. Buenos Aires.

Note: Filmed in Argentina. Released in Argentina in 1961 and in Spain in Jun 1963 as *La mano en la trampa*. Sources conflict in crediting the film editors.

HAND OF DEATH   **F6.2026**
Associated Producers, Inc. *Dist* Twentieth Century-Fox Film Corp. Mar **1962** [c31 Dec 1961; LP21463]. Sd; b&w. 35mm (CinemaScope). 60 min.

Prod-Writ Eugene Ling. *Dir* Gene Nelson. *Dir Photog* Floyd Crosby. *Set Decor* Harry Reif. *Supv Film Ed* Jodie Copelan. *Film Ed* Carl Pierson. *Mus Comp & Cond* Sonny Burke. *Sd* Vic Appel. *Supv Sd Ed* Jack Cornall. *Asst Dir* Willard Kirkham. *Prod Supv* Harold E. Knox. *Script Supv* Winifred Gibson. *Wardrobe* John Intlekofer. *Makeup* Bob Mark. *Prop Master* Ygnacio Sepulveda.

Cast: John Agar (*Alex Marsh*), Paula Raymond (*Carol Wilson*), Steve Dunne (*Tom Holland*), Roy Gordon (*Dr. Ramsey*), John Alonzo (*Carlos*), Jack Younger, Joe Besser, Butch Patrick, Norman Burton, Fred Krone, Kevin Enright, Jack Donner, Chuck Niles, Ruth Terry, Bob Whitney.

Science fiction melodrama. Working in his isolated desert laboratory, scientist Alex Marsh accidentally discovers a gas that will paralyze the mind and render it susceptible to suggestion. Believing this discovery to be a means of averting nuclear war, Marsh continues his experiments despite the objections of his fiancée, Carol, and fellow scientist Tom Holland. Following a mishap in mixing chemicals, Marsh inadvertently kills his assistant by merely touching him. Realizing he carries the touch of destruction, he goes to ask his old friend, Dr. Ramsey, to find an antidote. En route, he accidentally kills a hitchhiker and a filling station attendant. All attempts to find a cure fail, and his hands and face become blackened and distorted. When Marsh murders Dr. Ramsey for suggesting he go to the police, Carol realizes that he is now insane, and she calls for help. As the police close in on him, Marsh escapes to the beach and drowns himself. *Scientists. Police. Hitchhikers. Filling station attendants. Lethal gas. Paralysis. Disfiguration. Manslaughter. Murder. Insanity. Suicide. Nuclear warfare. Laboratories.*

Note: Working title: *Five Fingers of Death*.

THE HAND OF NIGHT (Great Britain)   **F6.2027**
Associated British-Pathé, Ltd. *Dist* Schoenfeld Film Distributing Corp. 11 Aug **1968** [Williamsport, Pennsylvania, opening]. Sd; col (Technicolor). 35mm. 88 min.

Prod Harry Field. *Assoc Prod* Lionel Hoare. *Dir* Frederic Goode. *Screenplay* Bruce Stewart. *Photog* William Jordan. *Art Dir* Peter Moll. *Supv Ed* John Blair. *Film Ed* Frederick Ives. *Mus* John Shakespeare, Joan Shakespeare. *Choreog* Boscoe Holder. *Prod Mgr* Ron Holtzer. *Makeup* Cliff Sharpe. *Sp Eff* Biographic Cartoon Films.

Cast: William Sylvester (*Paul Carver*), Diane Clare (*Chantal*), Alizia Gur (*Marisa*), Edward Underdown (*Gunther*), Terence De Marney (*Omar*), William Dexter (*Leclerc*), Sylvia Marriott (*Mrs. Petty*), Avril Sadler (*Mrs. Carver*), Angela Lovell (*air hostess*), Maria Hallowi (*nurse*), Boscoe Holder Dancers.

Horror film. Paul Carver, obsessed with the thought that he might have been responsible for the death of his wife and children in an automobile accident, is awakened from a nightmare by a fellow airplane passenger, archeologist Gunther, who invites Carver to visit him in Morocco. He arrives at Gunther's home in the midst of a party celebrating the discovery of some ancient tombs by Gunther's assistant, Leclerc. There Carver encounters Marisa, a beautiful apparition who lures him into following her to a magnificent Moorish palace where she tries to seduce him. The next morning, Gunther and his adopted daughter, Chantal, find Carver unconscious at the site of a ruin that is haunted by a vampire who is revealed to be Marisa. Chantal tries to save Carver from the vampire's influence, but she is captured by Omar, one of Marisa's servants, and left in the desert to die. Carver must choose between Chantal and Marisa, and he decides to save Chantal, even though it means driving a stake through the heart of the vision he loves. *Archeologists. Vampires. Obsession. Filial relations. Self-sacrifice. Impalement. Airplanes. Visions. Deserts. Morocco. Dreams. Automobile accidents.*

Note: Filmed on location in North Africa. Released in Great Britain in Oct 1968; running time: 73 min. Also known as *Beast of Morocco*.

HANDLE WITH CARE   **F6.2028**
Sonac Productions. *Dist* Cinema-Video International, Inc. 6 Oct **1964** [Maryland license]. Sd; col (De Luxe). 35mm. 86 min.

Prod-Dir-Writ John K. McCarthy. *Exec Prod* E. A. Raymond. *Assoc Prod* Thomas Myers. *Dir Photog* William Troiano. *Mus Dir* Jaime Mendoza-Nava.

Cast: Georgia Carr (*Melody*), Otis Greene (*Lonesome*), Eddie Beale (*himself*), Leroy "Sloppy" Daniels (*Swami*), Ernest "Skillet" Mayhand (*Weary O'Leary*), Dave Anderson, Cathey Cooper, Carol "Lynne" Stewart.

Musical comedy. Swami, an employee at the Brass Rail, a nightclub frequented by blacks, loses several hundred dollars of the club's receipts in a holdup. Afraid to tell "Second Rate Kate," the club's owner, Swami convinces Weary, another employee, to help him return the money before Kate discovers that it is missing. They plan to steal the money from Lonesome, a young Texan newly arrived in the city, whom they mistake for a millionaire. Lonesome, an aspiring jazz pianist, is actually a man of very limited means. Unfamiliar with city life and a novice drinker, he gets drunk at the Brass Rail and falls for Melody, a singer who dislikes all musicians. The next night, Lonesome returns to the club and finds Melody talking to a drunk who is holding a canvas bag with the club's name on it. Swami spots the money bag, discovers that the drunk acquired it from a man in the alley, and persuades him to return it to the club. When the club closes for the night, a party is held in Kate's upstairs apartment. Lonesome, who has passed out after running up a sizable bill, awakens in the deserted nightclub and begins to play the piano. Kate hears Lonesome's haunting blues and offers him a job, and Melody decides that she likes him too. Songs: "Handle With Care," "Too Little and Too Late," "Sad Dreams and Bitter Teardrops." *Nightclub owners. Singers. Texans. Pianists. Millionaires. Negroes. Robbery. Drunkenness. Mistaken identity. Nightclubs.*

HANDS OF A STRANGER   F6.2029
Glenwood-Névé Productions. *Dist* Allied Artists. Mar **1962** [c27 Mar 1962; LP21679]. Sd; b&w. 35mm. 86 min.

Prod Newt Arnold, Michael Du Pont. *Asst Prod* Gerald LeGrande. *Dir-Orig Story-Screenplay* Newt Arnold. *Photog* Henry Cronjager. *Art Dir* Theodore Holsopple. *Film Ed* Bert Honey. *Mus Comp & Cond* Richard LaSalle. *Prod Mgr* Vernon Keays.

Cast: Paul Lukather *(Dr. Gil Harding)*, Joan Harvey *(Dina Paris)*, James Stapleton *(Vernon Paris)*, Irish McCalla *(Holly)*, Ted Otis *(Dr. Russ Compton)*, Michael Du Pont *(Dr. Ken Fry)*, Larry Haddon *(Police Lieutenant Syms)*, Michael Rye *(George Britton)*, Elaine Martone *(Eileen Hunter)*, George Sawaya *(cab driver)*, David Kramer *(carnival barker)*, Sally Kellerman *(Sue)*, Barry Gordon *(Skeet)*.

Horror film. The hands of pianist Vernon Paris are horribly mutilated in a taxicab accident, and Dr. Gil Harding replaces them with those of a murdered man. Dina (Vernon's sister) and George Britton (his manager) permit the transplant, believing it to be the only hope of Vernon's playing again. Though the operation is a physical success, Vernon is mentally incapable of accepting his new hands. Morose, he visits his girl friend, Eileen Hunter, and is shattered psychologically when she is repelled by his scarred wrists. Consequently, when she knocks over a candlestick and sets fire to her gown, Vernon allows her to burn to death. He visits the home of the cab driver responsible for the accident and hears his son play the piano. Vernon then tries to play, but unable to do so, he attacks the boy, who hits his head on an obstruction and dies. Now bent on total revenge, Vernon kills one of the surgeons who assisted at the transplantation and the young doctor's fiancée. Half-crazed, he goes to an empty concert hall and maniacally pounds a piano keyboard. When his sister and Dr. Harding appear, Vernon grabs the doctor and attempts to strangle him. He is prevented from committing still another murder by the timely arrival of the police. *Pianists. Taxi drivers. Surgeons. Automobile accidents. Mutilation. Transplants. Brother-sister relationship. Murder. Revenge. Insanity.*

Note: Working title: *The Answer!* Loosely based on an idea from the novel *Les mains d'Orlac* by Maurice Renard.

HANDS OF A STRANGLER see THE HANDS OF ORLAC

THE HANDS OF ORLAC (France/Great Britain)   F6.2030
Riviera International Films–Société Cinématographique des Studios de La Victorine–Pendennis Pictures. *Dist* Continental Distributing, Inc. 13 May **1964** [Detroit opening]. Sd; b&w. 35mm. 87 min. [Also 77 min?]

Production Credits for English Vers: *Prod* Steven Pallos, Donald Taylor. *Dir* Edmond T. Gréville. *Screenplay* John Baines, Edmond T. Gréville. *Dial* Donald Taylor. *Photog* Desmond Dickinson. *Camera Op* Harry Gillam. *Focus* Ronnie Fox-Rogers. *Art Dir* John Blezard. *Draughtsman* Bill Bennison. *Film Ed* Oswald Hafenrichter. *1st Asst Ed* Alan Corder. *2d Asst Ed* Lois Gray. *Mus* Claude Bolling. *Concert Mus Dir* Ilona Kabos. *Concert Mus Cond* Stanford Robinson. *Choreog* Hazel Gee. *Sd Mix* Buster Ambler. *Boom Op* Peter Dukelow. *Sd Camera Op* Jimmy Dooley. *1st, 2d & 3d Asst Dir* Basil Rabin, Timothy Burrill, Henry Emery. *Prod Mgr* Ben Arbeid. *Cont* Yvonne Richards. *Prod Sec* Cynthia Maugham. *Wardrobe* Jackie Breed. *Makeup* Stuart Freeborn. *Hairdresser* Barbara Barnard. *Still Photog* Ted Reed. *Prop Buyer* George Durant. *Ch Floor Electrn* Bert Owen.

Production Credits for French Vers: *Dial* Max Montagu. *Photog* Jacques Lemare. *Art Dir* Eugène Piérac. *Film Ed* Jean Ravel. *Sd* Robert Biart. *Asst Dir* Jacques Corbel. *Prod Mgr* Eugène Nase.

Cast: Mel Ferrer *(Steven Orlac)*, Christopher Lee *(Nero)*, Dany Carrel *(Li-lang)*, Felix Aylmer *(Dr. Cochrane)*, Basil Sydney *(Siedelman)*, Lucile Saint-Simon *(Louise Cochrane)*, Donald Wolfit, Antoine Balpêtré *(Professor Volcheff [see note])*, Anita Sharp Bolster *(Volcheff's assistant)*, Mireille Perrey

(Madame Aliberti, the landlady), Donald Pleasence *(Coates)*, Campbell Singer *(Inspector Henderson)*, Peter Reynolds *(Felix)*, Yanilou *(Emilie)*, Edouard Hemme *(Ange)*, Manning Wilson *(Jagger)*, Arnold Diamond *(dresser)*, David Peel *(pilot)*, Walter Randall *(waiter)*, Franca Bel.

Horror film. Source: Maurice Renard, *Les mains d'Orlac* (Paris, 1920). The hands of concert pianist Steven Orlac are severely burned and maimed in a Paris airplane crash, and he is taken by his fiancée, Louise Cochrane, to Professor Volcheff, a surgeon famous for his bone-grafting operations. Volcheff gives Orlac the hands of Vasseur, an accused strangler who has been guillotined. During his next piano concert, Orlac appears unable to control his hands. He becomes obsessed by the idea that his hands are now capable only of violence: his cat is found dead, and he even attempts to strangle Louise, who has become his wife. Seeking seclusion, he gives up his Monte Carlo villa and retreats to relative obscurity in Marseilles, where Nero, a second-rate music hall magician, overhears the pianist admit his fear of committing murder. Nero then forces his assistant, Li-lang, to cooperate in blackmailing Orlac by terrorizing him. Orlac returns to London with his wife and is about to strangle her when the police arrive and produce a telegram stating that the executed Frenchman was later proven innocent. His sanity restored, Orlac aids the police in apprehending Nero, who has killed Li-lang to prevent her from confessing her crime. *Pianists. Magicians. Orientals. Police. Obsession. Blackmail. Murder. Surgery. Paris. Monte Carlo. Marseilles. London. Airplane accidents. Documentation.*

Note: Location scenes filmed on the French Riviera. Opened in Paris in Apr 1961 as *Les mains d'Orlac*; running time: 105 min; released in Great Britain in Apr 1962; running time: 95 min. The role of Professor Volcheff is played by Wolfit in the English version and by Balpêtré in the French version. May also be known as *Hands of a Stranger*. Previously filmed in 1924 as *Orlac Hände* (Austria) and released in the U. S. in 1928 as *The Hands of Orlac*; also filmed in the U. S. and released in 1935 as *Mad Love*.

HANG 'EM HIGH   F6.2031
Leonard Freeman Productions–Malpaso Co. *Dist* United Artists. 31 Jul **1968** [Chicago opening; c12 Apr 1968; LP35839]. Sd; col (DeLuxe). 35mm. 114 min.

Prod Leonard Freeman. *Supv Prod* Robert Stambler. *Assoc Prod* Irving Leonard. *Dir* Ted Post. *Screenplay* Leonard Freeman, Mel Goldberg. *Cinematog* Leonard South, Richard Kline. *Art Dir* John B. Goodman. *Set Decor* Arthur Krams. *Main Titl* Pacific Title. *Film Ed* Gene Fowler, Jr. *Mus* Dominic Frontiere. *Orch* Edward B. Powell. *Mus Supv* John Caper, Jr. *Sd* Franklin Milton, Al Strasser, Jr. *Asst Dir* Richard C. Bennett, Donald C. Klune. *Prod Mgr* Frank Mayer. *Wardrobe* Gene Murray, Glen Wright, Elva Martien. *Makeup* Keester Sweeney, Irving Pringle. *Sp Eff* George Swartz.

Cast: Clint Eastwood *(Jed Cooper)*, Inger Stevens *(Rachel)*, Ed Begley *(Captain Wilson)*, Pat Hingle *(Judge Adam Fenton)*, Charles McGraw *(Sheriff Ray Calhoun)*, Ruth White *(Madame Sophie)*, Arlene Golonka *(Jennifer)*, James MacArthur *(preacher)*, Bruce Dern *(Miller)*, Alan Hale, [Jr.] *(Stone)*, James Westerfield *(prisoner)*, Dennis Hopper *(prophet)*, L. Q. Jones *(Loomis)*, Bert Freed *(hangman)*, Michael O'Sullivan *(Francis Duffy)*, Tod Andrews *(attorney)*, Rick Gates *(Ben)*, Bruce Scott *(Billy Joe)*, Roy Glenn *(guard)*, Ben Johnson, Jack Ging, Joseph Sirola, Bob Steele, Russell Thorson, Ned Romero, Jonathan Lippe, Richard Guizon, Mark Lenard, Paul Sorensen, Richard Angarola, Larry Blake, Ted Thorpe, Robert Jones, actor, Barry Cahill, John Wesley, Dennis Dengate, William Zuckert, Hal England, Robert B. Williams, Tony Di Milo.

Western melodrama. In Oklahoma in 1889 rancher Jed Cooper is hanged and left for dead by a nine-man lynch mob who believe him guilty of murder and cattle-rustling. After being saved by a passerby, Jed is exonerated and then appointed deputy marshal by Judge Adam Fenton. Jed rounds up many of the territory's toughest outlaws, but he refrains from tracking down his nine hangmen because of the judge's admonitions about taking the law into his own hands. Eventually, however, Captain Wilson, leader of the lynch mob, shoots Jed to protect his own life. Only wounded, however, Jed is nursed back to health by Rachel, a young widow who is seeking revenge against the same men who raped her after shooting down her husband. Once Jed has recovered, he pursues and kills part of Wilson's gang; the others desert Wilson, who hangs himself rather than face Jed's wrath. Aware that his vengeance has offered him no solace, Jed attempts to turn in his badge. Judge Fenton salves his conscience by releasing a prisoner who gave himself up, and Jed consents to stay on as marshal. *Ranchers. Judges. United States marshals. Outlaws. Widows. Lynching. Murder. Rustling. Revenge. Rape. Suicide. Oklahoma.*

HANG LOOSE   F6.2032
Dist Rap. 18 Feb **1970** [Los Angeles opening]. Sd; col. 35mm? [Feature film, length unknown.]

Melodrama. A drug addict supports his habit by working as a male prostitute. *Prostitutes. Drug addicts. Male homosexuality.*

THE HANG-UP
F6.2033

Dist Clover Films. 26 Nov **1969** [New York showing]. Sd; col. 35mm. 82 min.

Dir-Writ John Hayes.

Cast: Sharon Matt, Sebastian Gregory.

Drama. When Sergeant Robert Walsh, a member of the vice squad for 8 years, arrests an important political figure on a routine stakeout, he triggers an act of vengeance that changes his life. Friends of the politician, determined to get even with Walsh without using violence, know that he cannot be bribed and that he has no family to threaten. Aiming at his emotions, they arrange for Angel, a seemingly innocent and child-like girl, to enter Walsh's life, and for the first time, Walsh falls in love. Their affair is exposed, however, and he is accused of raping the 17-year-old girl in the presence of witnesses. *Politicians. Vice squads. Revenge. Statutory rape. Frameup. Reputation.*

HANG YOUR HAT ON THE WIND
F6.2034

Walt Disney Productions. *Dist* Buena Vista Distribution Co. 11 Jun **1969** [c16 May 1969; LP36993]. Sd (RCA); col (Technicolor). 35mm. 48 min. [Also 46 min.]

Prod-Dir-Story Larry Lansburgh. *Screenplay* Paul West. *Photog* Edward P. Hughes. *Film Ed* Lloyd L. Richardson. *Mus Writ & Sung by* Randy Sparks. *Mus Arr & Cond* Billy Liebert. *Sd Supv* Robert O. Cook. *Mus Ed* Rusty Jones. *Location Sd Rec* James Camery. *Prod Supv* Robert Baron. "Tom Tom" trained by Jimmy Williams. *Coöp* Navajo Nation.

Cast: Ric Natoli (*Goyo, Indian boy*), Judson Pratt (*Father O'Flaherty*), Angel Tompkins (*Fran Harper*), Edward Faulkner (*pilot*), Pete Logan (*truck driver*), Bill Cornford (*guide*), Monica Ramírez (*Tina*), Carlos Rivas (*tall bandit*), Alex Tinne (*short bandit*).

Melodrama. A van carrying a thoroughbred yearling catches fire while crossing the Arizona desert, and the driver unloads the horse. Frightened by a passing dune buggy, the horse escapes and is spotted by Goyo, a Navajo goatherd. Goyo pursues the yearling and saves him from drowning in a mudhole. He saddles the horse, names him Tom Tom, and decides to keep him. In the meantime, a search for the valuable yearling is begun by the truckdriver, assisted by helicopter pilot and cropduster Bob Davis and Father O'Flaherty, a parish priest to the Navajos. Fran Harper, the horse's owner, arrives to help in the search. Father O'Flaherty meets Goyo in the desert and advises him to return the horse to Miss Harper. Although at first he refuses to give up what he believes to be rightfully his, Goyo later relents and decides to return Tom Tom to Miss Harper. He is on his way to the parish when two Mexican bandits steal the yearling and head for Mexico. Goyo races to Father O'Flaherty and tells him of the theft. Aloft in Davis' helicopter, Goyo points out the bandits' trailer, and Davis drops a load of chemicals on the truck, thereby bringing it to a halt. Happy to have the horse back, Miss Harper rewards Goyo with a completely outfitted cow pony in return for his help in recovering her horse. *Truckdrivers. Priests. Mexicans. Goatherds. Air pilots. Navajo Indians. Posses. Theft. Deserts. Helicopters. Arizona. Horses.*

Note: Filmed on location in Monument Valley, Utah, in the Arizona desert, and at a Navajo Indian reservation in Arizona.

THE HANGING OF JAKE ELLIS
F6.2035

Great Empire Films. *Dist* Hollywood Cinemart. Feb **1969**. Sd; col (Eastman Color). 35mm. 81 min.

Prod-Dir-Writ J. Van Hearn. *Photog* John Koester. *Art Dir* Bud Costello. *Film Ed* Joe Rugero. *Mus* Elsa Singman. *Arr & Adtl Mus* Arthur Mancini. *Played by* Gerry Dykes and His Band. *Song:* "Sheriff Oh Sheriff" Elsa Singman. *Sung by* Deborah Downey. *Guitar* Craig Robertson. *Song:* "The Hanging Tree" Melvin Wilmoth, Elsa Singman. *Sung by* Charles Napier. *Song:* "The Calico Queen" Elsa Singman. *Sung by* Joe Coffey. *Sd S.* Foreman. *Asst Dir* Paul Wilmoth. *Stuntman* Melvin Wilmoth. *Stills* R. J. MacDonald.

Cast: Charles Napier (*Jake Ellis*), Deborah Downey (*Kathy Dupray*), James Lemp (*Frank Hall*), Bambi Allen (*Isabel*), Louis Ojena (*Don Avila*), Don Derby (*cattle buyer*), Rod Wilmoth (*sheriff*), Chuy Castro (*Pablo*), Sol Bar (*bartender*), Miki MacDonald (*Ellen Dupray*), Jerry Patterson (*her husband*), Larry Martinelli (*Driskill*), Don Angelo (*henchman*), Erika Andrea, Cande Thayer, Marla Marin, Maria Bonner (*cancan dancers*), Arnold Roberts, Joe Coffey, Mark Marcus.

Western melodrama. Cattle driver Jake Ellis arrives in a bawdy little cow town and finds his archenemy, Frank Hall, waiting for him. In the saloon, Jake loses his money and his horse to Isabel, a voluptuous gambler who deals from a stacked deck. The smell of food cooking over a campfire attracts impoverished Jake, and he soon finds the campsite and seduces the cook, young Kathy Dupray. After the Duprays give Jake a beating for romancing Kathy, they tell him of Frank Hall's plot to cheat them in a cattle deal. Thwarted, Hall vows to kill the entire Dupray clan. In the shootout, Kathy narrowly escapes being raped by Hall's gang, and her sister Ellen is killed. Jake is framed for her murder and sentenced to hang, but he escapes death to win both his girl and his revenge. *Cowboys. Cattlemen. Cardsharps. Dancers. Swindlers. Seduction. Fraud. Gambling. Rape. Frameup. Murder. Revenge. Capital punishment. Poker.*

Note: Also released as *The Calico Queen.*

THE HANK WILLIAMS STORY *see* YOUR CHEATIN' HEART

HANNIBAL BROOKS (Great Britain)
F6.2036

Scimitar Films. *Dist* United Artists. 2 Apr **1969** [Los Angeles opening; c13 Mar 1969; LF35]. Sd; col (De Luxe). 35mm. 101 min. *MPAA rating* M.

Prod-Dir Michael Winner. *Screenplay* Dick Clement, Ian La Frenais. *Story* Michael Winner, Tom Wright. *Photog* Robert Paynter. *2d Unit Photog* Hans Jura. *Art Dir* Jürgen Kiebach. *Set Decor* Josie MacAvin. *Prod Dsgn* John Stoll. *Film Ed* Lionel Selwyn. *Mus Comp* Francis Lai. *Mus Arr* Christian Gaubert. *Sd Rec* John Brommage, Hugh Strain. *Asst Dir* Michael Dryhurst, Udo Graf Lambsdorff. *Prod Mgr* Clifton Brandon, Laci von Ronay. *Makeup* Richard Mills. *Hairstyles* Stephanie Kaye. *Sp Eff* Erwin Lange. *Elephant Trainer* André Beilfuss. *Stunts* David Newman, stunt.

Cast: Oliver Reed (*Hannibal Brooks*), Michael J. Pollard (*Packy*), Karin Baal (*Vronia*), Wolfgang Preiss (*S. S. Colonel von Haller*), Helmut Lohner (*Willi*), James Donald (*Padre*), Peter Carsten (*Kurt*), Erik Jelde (*zoo director Stern*), Ernst Fritz Furbringer (*elephant keeper Kellerman*), Ralf Wolter (*Dr. Mendel*), Jürgen Draeger (*Sami*), Fred Haltiner (*Josef*), Maria Brockerhoff (*Anna*), Til Kiwe (*von Haller's sergeant*), Peter Bohlke (*old German captain*), Tei de Maal (*other zoo keeper*), John Alderton (*Bernard*), John Porter Davison (*Geordie*), Terence Sewards (*Twilight*), Aida (*Lucy, the elephant*).

War comedy-drama. During World War II, Brooks, a peace-loving British soldier, is captured by the Germans in Italy and placed on a prison train to Germany. On board, he meets Packy, an American prisoner of war who engineers an escape for them against Brooks's will. They are captured and taken to a prison camp outside Munich. Brooks is assigned to work at the local zoo, where he becomes attached to Lucy, a 15-year-old elephant. The elephant keeper is killed during an air raid; and Brooks is detailed to take Lucy by train to a zoo in Innsbruck, Austria. Their railroad car is commandeered by SS Col. von Haller, however, thus forcing Brooks and Lucy to make the journey by foot. Accompanying them are Willi, a friendly Austrian guard; Vronia, a Polish prisoner who is their cook; and Kurt, a disagreeable German guard who frequently gets drunk and insults both Vronia and the elephant. Brooks accidentally kills Kurt when the latter threatens to shoot Lucy; and Willi suggests they cross the Alps to the Swiss border, 60 miles away. Brooks agrees, but insists upon taking along Lucy. Brooks sets out with Lucy on the long trek across the Alps after Vronia and Willi have gone on ahead. En route, he repeatedly crosses paths with his pursuers, led by von Haller, as well as with Packy, who now leads a guerrilla band of escaped prisoners. Finally, Brooks, Packy, Vronia, and Willi all reach the border, whereupon von Haller, who is deserting as the war nears its end, tries to doublecross them to make good his own escape. During the fighting that breaks out, Vronia and Willi, who have betrayed their loyalties, are killed, but Lucy knocks down a border post and leads Brooks, Packy, and the remnants of his small army, to safety in Switzerland. *Germans. Austrians. Poles. Prisoners of war. Guerrillas. Deserters—Military. Zoo keepers. Cooks. Guards. Drunkenness. Perfidy. Loyalty. Trains. Zoos. SS. World War II. Italy. Munich. Alps. Switzerland. Germany—Army. Elephants.*

Note: Location scenes filmed in Bavaria. Opened in London in Mar 1969.

HANOI HANNA (QUEEN OF CHINA) *see* THE CHELSEA GIRLS

HANSEL AND GRETEL (West Germany)
F6.2037

Schongerfilm. *Dist* Childhood Productions. 2 Oct **1965** [Detroit opening]. Sd; col (Eastmancolor). 35mm. 52 min.

Prod Hubert Schonger. *Dir* Walter Janssen. *Screenplay* Gerhard F. Hummel. *Screenplay Adapt English Vers* Christopher Cruise. *Photog* Wolf Schwan. *Art Dir* Günther Strupp. *Mus* Giuseppe Becce. *Songs English Vers* Anne Delugg, Milton Delugg.

Cast: Paul Tripp (*narrator*), Jürgen Miksch, Mara Inken Bielenberg, Jochen Diestelmann, Ellen Frank, Barbara Gallauner, Wolfgang Eichberger.

Fantasy. Source: Jakob Grimm and Wilhelm Grimm, "Hänsel und Gretel". Hansel and Gretel live with their parents in a cottage in the woods; unable to pay the rent, the poor family is threatened with eviction by the landlord. The children decide to search for the gingerbread house, inhabited by the witch of the forest, in order to find her treasure and bring it back to their family. They find the house but are captured by the witch; she fattens Hansel, planning to bake him in her oven and eat him, and forces Gretel to work in her house. One day, Gretel pushes the witch into the oven and frees Hansel as the house burns. The children return home with the treasure of gold and jewels. *Witches. Children. Poverty. Brother-sister relationship. Treasure. Forests.*

Note: Released in West Germany in 1954 as *Hänsel und Gretel*; running time: 54 min.

HÄNSEL UND GRETEL see **HANSEL AND GRETEL**

THE HAPPENING   F6.2038

Horizon Dover, Inc. *Dist* Columbia Pictures. 22 Mar **1967** [Fort Lauderdale, Florida, opening; c1 Apr 1967; LP34168]. Sd; col (Technicolor). 35mm. 92 min. [Copyrighted at 101 min.]

Pres by Sam Spiegel. *Prod* Jud Kinberg. *Assoc Prod* Robert Manchel, David Wolfson, Howard Jaffe. *Exec Prod* Sam Spiegel. *Dir* Elliot Silverstein. *Screenplay* Frank R. Pierson, James D. Buchanan, Ronald Austin. *Story* James D. Buchanan, Ronald Austin. *Dir Photog* Philip Lathrop. *2d Unit Camera* Howard Winner. *Art Dir* Albert Brenner. *Set Decor* Don Ivey. *Prod Dsgn* Richard Day. *Main Titl* Film Effects of Hollywood. *Film Ed* Philip W. Anderson. *Mus* De Vol. *Titl Song* De Vol, Eddie Holland, Lamont Dozier, Brian Holland. *Sung by* The Supremes. *Song:* "Early in the Morning" De Vol, William Roy. *Sd* Howard Warren, Jack Haynes. *Asst Dir* Ray Gosnell, Tim Zinnemann. *Prod Mgr* Russell Saunders. *Location Mgr* Jerry Porter. *Script Supv* Charlsie Bryant. *Cost Dsgn* Gene Coffin. *Sp Wardrobe for Miss Dunaway* Jason Silverstein. *Makeup* George Fields. *Miss Hyer's Hairstyles* Sherry Wilson. *Hairstyles* Irene Aparicio. *Sp Eff* Willis Cook. *Props* Jack Johnson, prop.

Cast: Anthony Quinn (*Roc Delmonico*), George Maharis (*Taurus*), Michael Parks (*Sureshot*), Robert Walker, [Jr.] (*Herby*), Martha Hyer (*Monica*), Faye Dunaway (*Sandy*), Milton Berle (*Fred*), Oscar Homolka (*Sam*), Jack Kruschen (*inspector*), Clifton James (*O'Reilly*), Eugene Roche (*1st motorcycle officer*), James Randolph Kuhl (*Arnold*), Luke Askew (*2d motorcycle officer*).

Comedy-drama. Following a police raid of their all-night party, four young Miami beach bums set out in search of excitement. The group leader is Taurus, a part-time thief who supports himself by living off bored, wealthy Florida matrons. With him are the 25-year-old Sureshot, who exists on an allowance from his father; Herby, an ineffectual hanger-on; and Sandy, Sureshot's seductive sleeping partner from the previous night. After spotting some small boys playing with toy army weapons, they join in the neighborhood "war games" and chase one of the youngsters into his home. The child's father, former Mafia member Roc Delmonico, who is now a respectable hotel owner, mistakes them for kidnapers and offers himself as victim. The foursome, deciding to play along, take Roc to a fire-gutted mansion, where they plan to hold him for $200,000 ransom; however, Roc's wife, Monica, his business partner Fred, former Mafia associate Sam, and his mother all refuse to pay. Burdened now with a liability, Taurus decides that Roc must be killed to guarantee his silence, but in a burst of anger the kidnap victim seizes Taurus' gun and takes control. Enraged at his treatment by family and friends, Roc demands and receives $3,000,000 in blackmail payments by threatening to expose Monica's adulterous affairs, Fred's fraudulent tax returns, and various Mafia secrets. Wild with excitement, Taurus suggests that he and Roc kill the other three and split the cash, but Roc, aware that the bills are marked, sets fire to the money and walks away from his captors. *Businessmen. Beachcombers. Gigolos. Kidnaping. Family life. Revenge. Partnerships. Infidelity. Perfidy. Ransom. Miami. Mafia. Fires.*

Note: Location scenes filmed in Miami. Working titles: *Mister Innocent* and *It's What's Happening.*

HAPPENING IN AFRICA see **AFRICA EROTICA**

THE HAPPIEST MILLIONAIRE   F6.2039

Walt Disney Productions. *Dist* Buena Vista Distribution Co. 23 Jun **1967** [c22 May 1967; LP34963]. Sd; col (Technicolor). 35mm. 164 min. [See note.]

A Walt Disney Production. *Co-prod* Bill Anderson, prod. *Dir* Norman Tokar. *Screenplay* A. J. Carothers. *Dir Photog* Edward Colman. *Art Dir* Carroll Clark, John B. Mansbridge. *Set Decor* Emile Kuri, Frank R. McKelvy. *Main Titl* Alan Maley. *Film Ed* Cotton Warburton. *Mus Supv, Arr & Cond* Jack Elliott. *Songs:* "What's Wrong With That?" "Watch Your Footwork," "Valentine Candy," "I'll Always Be Irish," "Bye-Yum Pum Pum, " "Are We Dancing?" "Detroit," "There Are Those," "Let's Have a Drink on It," "It Won't Be Long 'til Christmas," "Strengthen the Dwelling," "Fortuosity" Richard M. Sherman, Robert B. Sherman. *Mus Numbers Stgd by* Marc Breaux, Dee Dee Wood. *Sd Supv* Robert O. Cook. *Sd Mix* Dean Thomas. *Mus Ed* Evelyn Kennedy. *Asst Dir* Paul Cameron. *Asst to the Prod* Tom Leetch. *Cost Dsgn* Bill Thomas. *Cost* Chuck Keehne, Neva Rames. *Makeup* Gordon Hubbard. *Hairstyles* Vivienne Zavitz. *Sp Eff* Eustace Lycett, Peter Ellenshaw.

Cast: Fred MacMurray (*Anthony J. Drexel Biddle*), Tommy Steele (*John Lawless*), Greer Garson (*Mrs. Cordelia Biddle*), Geraldine Page (*Mrs. Duke*), Gladys Cooper (*Aunt Mary Drexel*), Hermione Baddeley (*Mrs. Worth*), Lesley Ann Warren (*Cordy Biddle*), John Davidson (*Angier Buchanan Duke*), Paul Petersen (*Tony Biddle*), Eddie Hodges (*Livingston Biddle*), Joyce Bulifant (*Rosemary*), Sean McClory (*Sergeant Flanagan*), Jim McMullan (*Lieutenant Powell*), William Wellman, Jr. (*Lieutenant Grayson*), Aron Kincaid (*Walter Blakely*), Larry Merrill (*Charlie Taylor*), Frances Robinson (*Aunt Gladys*),

Norman Grabowski (*Joe Turner*), Jim Gurley (*marine lieutenant*), Joan Marshall (*maid*), George (*himself, an alligator*).

Musical comedy. Source: Kyle Crichton, *The Happiest Millionaire* (New York opening: 20 Nov 1956). Cordelia Drexel Biddle, *My Philadelphia Father* (as told to Kyle Crichton; Garden City, New York, 1955). The Philadelphia of 1916 is the home of Anthony J. Drexel Biddle, an eccentric millionaire and boxing enthusiast whose chief pastimes are raising alligators and teaching the members of his Bible class the art of self-defense, the virtues of physical fitness, and military preparedness. Newly arrived in the unorthodox household is a young Irish immigrant, John Lawless, who has hired on as the family butler. Biddle and his long-suffering but adoring wife, Cordelia, give in to straight-laced Aunt Mary Drexel's suggestion that they send their tomboyish daughter, Cordy, to a finishing school in New Jersey. Once Cordy has enrolled, she quickly falls in love with Angie Duke, the heir to a tobacco fortune, who is passionately interested in Detroit's burgeoning automobile industry. When the youngsters announce their engagement, Cordy goes to New York to be introduced to the "proper" people and taken to the right places by the socially prominent Mrs. Duke. Not to be outdone, the well-intentioned Mr. Biddle gives a large garden party in Philadelphia. But the overbearing interference of the two parents only succeeds in precipitating a series of arguments climaxed by Angie storming out of the house. Sent by Mr. Biddle to keep an eye on Angie, John Lawless trails him to an Irish pub and cleverly instigates a brawl which lands the young heir in jail. The following morning the Biddles and Mrs. Duke go to bail out Angie. Putting aside their personal grievances, Mr. Biddle and Mrs. Duke consent to the wedding and give their children their blessings. Hoisting Cordy on his shoulder, Angie declares that he and she will elope to Detroit—"the shining city where dreams are booming into gear." Biddle's time will now be devoted to training marines in hand to hand combat for World War I. *Millionaires. Eccentrics. Upper classes. Butlers. Irish. Heirs. Tomboys. Adolescence. Courtship. Family life. Physical training. Boxing. Automobile manufacture. Boarding schools. World War I. Philadelphia. New York City. Anthony J. Drexel Biddle. Cordelia Drexel Biddle. Cordelia Biddle. Mary Drexel. Angier Buchanan Duke. John Lawless. Anthony J. Drexel Biddle, Jr. Livingston Biddle. United States Marines. Alligators.*

Note: Also reviewed at 159 min, 154 min, and 141 min; copyright length: 160 min.

HAPPILY EVER AFTER see **MORE THAN A MIRACLE**

HAPPINESS see **LE BONHEUR**

HAPPINESS OF US ALONE (Japan)   F6.2040

Tokyo Eiga Co. *Dist* Toho Co. 14 Aug **1962** [Los Angeles opening]. Sd; b&w. 35mm (Tohoscope). 114 min.

Prod Sanezumi Fujimoto, Ken-ichiro Tsunoda. *Dir-Writ* Zenzo Matsuyama. *Photog* Masao Tamai. *Art Dir* Satoru Nakakao, Takeshi Kano. *Film Ed* Y. Sabura. *Mus* Hikaru Hayashi. *Sd* Kenji Nagaoka.

Cast: Hideko Takamine (*Akiko Katayama*), Keiju Kobayashi (*Michio Katayama*), Izumi Hara (*Akiko's mother*), Yoichi Numata (*Akiko's brother*), Mitsuko Kusabue (*Akiko's sister*), Yuzo Kayama (*Akira*), Kamatari Fujiwara, Chieko Nakakita, Jun Tatara, Takeshi Kato.

Domestic melodrama. Following the death of her husband in 1945, Akiko, a deafmute, returns to her mother's home. While attending the alumni meeting of her school, she meets Michio Katayama, also a deafmute, who falls in love with her. The young man persuades Akiko to marry him by convincing her that through love and understanding they can overcome their handicap. But their life is not a happy one. Their first-born dies in infancy; Akiko's hoodlum brother sells his mother's house, thereby forcing the old woman to move into Akiko's home; and the couple struggle to earn their living by shining shoes. With the birth of a second child, Akiko's mother gives her a gold ring with which to buy a sewing machine and start a little business at home. But the delinquent brother sells the machine, and Akiko runs away from home to commit suicide. Michio follows and persuades her not to give up hope. With the coming of spring, their son is graduated with honors from elementary school. On the same day Akiko is visited by an orphan, now grown to manhood, whom she rescued during a World War II air raid. Akiko realizes that, despite her handicap, she has been able to function as both wife and mother. *Widows. Deafmutes. Orphans. Family life. Poverty. Suicide. World War II.*

Note: Released in Japan in 1961 as *Namonaku mazushiku utsukushiku;* running time: 131 min.

HAPPY ALEXANDER see **VERY HAPPY ALEXANDER**

HAPPY BIRTHDAY, DAVY   F6.2041

Richard Fontaine. *Dist* Zenith Films. Mar **1970**. Sd; col. 16mm. 90 min.

Prod Richard Fontaine, Chuck Roy. *Dir* Richard Fontaine. *Screenplay* Chuck Roy. *Photog* Robert Miser. *Art Dir* George Lewis. *Film Ed* Richard Charles. *Mus* Lou Hanagan. *Sd* Tim Bartlett.

Cast: Chuck Roy *(Bob Cassidy)*, Larry Neilsen *(Davy)*, Richard Fontaine *(Balsalm)*, Judy Curtis *(Sis)*, Carl Williams, actor *(Butch)*, Jack Reed, actor *(Dick)*, Robin Roberts *(Nick)*, Joe Bell *(Joe)*, Mary Fordas, Tim Bartlett, Jerry Murray.

Drama. On his 21st birthday Davy wanders into a gay bar in Los Angeles, orders his first drink, and meets Bob Cassidy, a young businessman. Cassidy takes Davy home and leads him into his first homosexual experience. Later, Davy feels confused and guilty, but after confessing his experience to his understanding sister, he telephones Bob and makes arrangements to see him again. *Male homosexuality. Brother-sister relationship. Sexual initiation. Guilt. Bars. Los Angeles.*

Note: Location scenes filmed in Los Angeles. Original title: *I Am Curious Gay.*

THE HAPPY CLOWN see **TOBO, THE HAPPY CLOWN**

HAPPY END (Czechoslovakia)   F6.2042
Barrandov Film Studio. *For* Československý Film. *Dist* Continental Distributing, Inc. 10 Jun **1968** [New York opening]. Sd; b&w. 35mm. 73 min.

Dir Oldřich Lipský. *Screenplay* Miloš Macourek, Oldřich Lipský. *Story* Miloš Macourek. *Photog* Vladimír Novotný. *Mus* Vlastimil Hála.

Cast: Vladimír Menšík *(Bedrich)*, Jaroslava Obermayerová *(Julie)*, Josef Abrhám *(lothario)*, Bohuš Záhorský *(father-in-law)*, Stella Zázvorková *(mother-in-law)*, Helena Růžičková *(brunette)*, Josef Hlinomaz *(policeman)*.

Comedy. The severed head of Bedrich, a butcher, is returned to his body, which is standing in front of a guillotine. Bedrich then walks back into prison (which he refers to as school), but he emerges to face the outside world. He finds a suitcase on the sidewalk and takes it home. Inside are the dismembered parts of a young woman, which he reassembles. After falling in love with his creation, whom he calls Julie, he goes with her to a seaside resort. Suspecting that Julie is conducting a flirtation with a lothario, Bedrich drags him into the ocean and drowns him. Still distrusting his "wife" and depressed at her having given "unbirth" to their child (which mysteriously has shrunk in size and disappeared at the hospital), he decides to "unmarry" her. The ceremony is conducted by a priest, but Julie continues to hound him. He finally rids himself of her by throwing her into a burning building, thus permitting him to continue his romance with a dowdy, maternal brunette. *Butchers. Priests. Philanderers. Reviviscence. Murder. Capital punishment. Marriage. Infidelity. Childbirth. Prisons.*

Note: Produced in 1966 under English title. Alternative Czech title: *Šťastný konec.* All physical action and narrative in the film occurs in reverse motion.

THE HAPPY ENDING   F6.2043
Pax Enterprises. *Dist* United Artists. 21 Dec **1969** [New York opening; c16 Dec 1969; LP37434]. Sd; col (Technicolor). 35mm (Panavision). 112 min. [Prerelease length: 116 min.] *MPAA rating* M.

Prod-Dir-Writ Richard Brooks. *Dir Photog* Conrad Hall. *Film Ed* George Grenville. *Asst Ed* Murray Jordan. *Mus Comp & Cond* Michel Legrand. *Mus:* "What Are You Doing the Rest of Your Life?" Michel Legrand. *Lyr* Alan Bergman, Marilyn Bergman. *Sung by* Michael Dees, William Eaton. *Sd* William Randall, Jr.. *Sd Re-rec* Clem Portman, Harry Warren, sd. *Mus Rec* Kevin Cleary. *Sd Ed* Kay Rose. *Mus Ed* Else Blangsted. *Asst Dir* Tom Shaw. *Prod Mgr* Tom Shaw. *Script Supv* Marshall Schlom. *Prod Asst* Gene Levy. *Cost* Rita Riggs. *Makeup* Fred Blau. *Hairstyles* Sydney Guilaroff, Jan Van Uchelen. *Sp Eff* Geza Gaspar. *Optical Eff* Westheimer Co. *Ch Electrn* Harry Sundby. *Prop Master* Joe La Bella. *Key Grip* Art Brooker.

Cast: Jean Simmons *(Mary Wilson)*, John Forsythe *(Fred Wilson)*, Shirley Jones *(Flo)*, Lloyd Bridges *(Sam)*, Teresa Wright *(Mrs. Spencer)*, Dick Shawn *(Harry Bricker)*, Nanette Fabray *(Agnes)*, Robert Darin *(Franco)*, Tina Louise *(Helen Bricker)*, Kathy Fields *(Marge Wilson)*, Karen Steele *(divorcee)*, Gail Hensley *(Betty)*, Eve Brent *(Ethel)*, William O'Connell *(minister)*, Barry Cahill *(handsome man)*, Miriam Blake *(Cindy)*.

Drama. Suburban housewife Mary Wilson, who is approaching her 16th wedding anniversary, has become bored and disillusioned with her marriage. Her husband Fred, a successful Denver tax lawyer, devotes his energies to his clients. Mary's ideal of marriage has been shattered by Fred's neglect, the tedium of her daily routine, and the responsibility of bringing up a teenaged daughter. She spends most of her waking hours drinking, taking pills, and watching old films on television. To avoid a repetition of her husband's wild anniversary party of the previous year, Mary leaves home and decides to go to Nassau. En route, she meets old college friend Flo, who is on her way to Nassau to meet Sam, the latest in a series of married admirers. In Nassau, Mary is propositioned by Franco, an American who poses as Latin lover, and who intends to run off with her money. Franco drops his guise when Mary reveals that she has left home without a penny. Hurt, Mary takes a sober glance at her past: her attempted suicide over her failed marriage; the heavy drinking that began when Fred, oblivious to her needs, recommended that she take up a

pastime; the clothes-buying spree that led Fred to confiscate her credit cards; and her arrest for drunken driving. Sam finally proposes to Flo, and Fred calls Mary in Nassau to apologize. On her return to Denver, Mary is met by her maid. Instead of going home, she takes a job, rents an apartment, and enrolls in night school, where Fred meets her one night. Whatever the future may hold, their relationship will have been drastically altered. *Housewives. Lawyers. Marriage. Suburban life. Infidelity. Motherhood. Alcoholism. Reckless driving. Suicide. Wedding anniversaries. Finance—Personal. Television. Amphetamines. Denver. Nassau. "Casablanca". "Susan Lennox—Her Rise and Fall". "Father of the Bride".*

Note: Location scenes filmed in Denver and the Bahamas. Clips from *Casablanca, Susan Lennox—Her Rise and Fall,* and *Father of the Bride* appear within the film.

THE HAPPY THIEVES   F6.2044
Hillworth Productions. *Dist* United Artists. 20 Dec **1961** [Chicago opening; c12 Dec 1961; LP22354]. Sd; b&w. 35mm. 88 min.

Exec Prod James Hill, prod, Rita Hayworth. *Dir* George Marshall. *Screenplay* John Gay. *Dir Photog* Paul Beeson. *Art Dir* Ramiro Gómez. *Film Ed* Oswald Hafenrichter. *Mus Comp* Mario Nascimbene. *Sd* Sash Fisher. *Asst Dir* Ed Waller. *Miss Hayworth's Wardrobe* Pedro Rodrigues, Pierre Balmain.

Cast: Rex Harrison *(Jim Bourne)*, Rita Hayworth *(Eve Lewis)*, Joseph Wiseman *(Jean Marie Calbert)*, Grégoire Aslan *(Dr. Muñoz)*, Alida Valli *(Duchess Blanca)*, Virgilio Teixeira *(Cayetano)*, Peter Illing *(Mr. Pickett)*, Brita Ekman *(Mrs. Pickett)*, Julio Peña *(Señor Elek)*, Gérard Tichy *(Antonio)*, Lou Weber *(1st guard)*, Antonio Fuentes *(2d guard)*, George Rigaud *(inspector)*, Barta Barri *(Chern)*, Karl-Heinz Schwerdtfeger *(police official)*.

Crime comedy. Source: Richard Condon, *The Oldest Confession* (New York, 1958). Gentleman thief Jim Bourne steals a Velázquez painting, "Venus With a Mirror," from the Spanish castle of the Duchess Blanca. But as his confederate, Eve Lewis, smuggles the painting into Paris, she is outwitted by Dr. Muñoz, a fanatical art dealer and cousin of the duchess, whereupon Eve threatens to become an honest woman. Jim placates her with marriage, and they return to Madrid. There they learn that Muñoz has the Velázquez and that he also has photographs of Jim stealing it. In return for his silence, Muñoz demands that Jim steal Goya's famed "Second of May" from the Prado. Jim's artist cohort, Jean Marie Calbert, makes an exact reproduction of the painting. They plan to switch the two during the farewell performance of Cayetano, Spain's celebrated matador, who is retiring from the arena to marry the duchess. In order to create a riot and distract the Prado guards, Muñoz shoots and kills Cayetano while he is in the arena. In the ensuing panic Jim and Eve switch the two paintings, hiding the original in Jean's artist's cart. When they visit Muñoz, they find him dead, murdered by the vengeful duchess. The police arrive on the scene and hold both Jim and Jean. In exchange for the Goya, however, the police offer to release one of the two men. Jim decides that Jean will serve the 10-year manslaughter sentence; but when he realizes that Eve considers him a cad because of his decision, he himself goes to prison, knowing she will wait for him. *Gentlemen crooks. Artists. Thieves. Art dealers. Bullfighters. Nobility. Police. Guards. Theft. Smuggling. Blackmail. Forgery. Murder. Revenge. Spain. Madrid. Paris. Diego Rodríguez de Silva y Velázquez. Francisco José de Goya y Lucientes. El Prado.*

Note: Location scenes filmed in and around Madrid. Working title: *Once a Thief.* Prerelease title: *The Oldest Confession.*

HÄR HAR DU DITT LIV see **HERE'S YOUR LIFE**

HARAKIRI (Japan)   F6.2045
Shochiku Co. *Dist* Shochiku Films of America, Toho International, Inc. Dec **1963** [Los Angeles showing]. Sd; b&w. 35mm (Shochiku GrandScope). 135 min. [Also reviewed at 130 min.]

Prod Tatsuo Hosoya. *Asst Prod* Gin-ichi Kishimoto. *Dir* Masaki Kobayashi. *Screenplay* Shinobu Hashimoto. *Photog* Yoshio Miyajima. *Lighting* Shojiro Kambara. *Art Dir* Jun-ichi Ozumi, Shigemasa Toda. *Film Ed* Hisashi Sagara. *Mus* Toru Takemitsu. *Sd* Hideo Nishizaki. *Fencing Master* Seiji Iho.

Cast: Tatsuya Nakadai *(Hanshiro Tsugumo)*, Shima Iwashita *(Miho Tsugumo)*, Akira Ishihama *(Motome Chijiiwa)*, Yoshio Inaba *(Jinai Chijiiwa)*, Rentaro Mikuni *(Kageyu Saito)*, Masao Mishima *(Tango Inaba)*, Tetsuro Tamba *(Hikokuro Omodaka)*, Ichiro Nakaya *(Hayato Yazaki)*, Yoshio Aoki *(Umenosuke Kawabe)*, Jo Azumi *(Ichiro Shimmen)*, Hisashi Igawa, Shoji Kobayashi, Ryo Takeuchi *(young samurai)*, Shichisaburo Amatsu *(page)*, Kei Sato *(Masakazu Fukushima)*.

Costume drama. Source: Chohei Tsubaki, "Ibun ronin ki," in *Sandi mainichi* (24 Aug 1958). In the 17th century samurai who have been left without a livelihood as a result of the centralization of political power roam the countryside, appealing at clan estates for permission to commit harakiri, hoping that the clans will give them employment or alms rather than see them die. Hanshiro Tsugumo visits the Iyi estate in Edo and asks for such permission. As a warning Kageyu Saito, the clan's chief retainer, tells Hanshiro of Motome Chijiiwa, a young samurai who earlier came there with an identical request. To prevent the debasement of the samurai code, the young man's bluff was called and he was forced to go through the harakiri ritual, though he carried only a bamboo sword. Hanshiro, undeterred, asks in turn for each of the clan's three principal swordsmen to act as his second in the harakiri ritual, but none dares appear. Hanshiro reveals that he was Motome's guardian and father-in-law. He explains that Motome had sold his sword, desperately trying to provide for his wife and child, who have since died. In his plan for revenge Hanshiro has waylaid the three swordsmen—who were responsible for forcing Motome's suicide—and has dishonored them by cutting off their topknots. Kageyu orders his men to kill Hanshiro, but the old samurai, in a furious battle, kills and wounds many of Kageyu's men before he dies. Kageyu orders his three retainers to commit harakiri and decrees that what has occurred must remain a clan secret. *Samurai. Nobility. Fathers-in-law. Beggars. Hara-kiri. Poverty. Revenge. Edo. Japan—History—Tokugawa period 1600–1867.*

Note: Released in Japan in 1962 as *Seppuku.*

HARBOR LIGHT YOKOHAMA (Japan)   F6.2046
Shochiku Co. *Dist* Shochiku Films of America. Feb **1970** [Los Angeles showing]. Sd; col. 35mm. 91 min.

Assoc Prod Hideo Sasai, Kon Hirata. *Dir* Meijiro Umezu. *Screenplay* Isao Mori, Hisashi Aku. *Photog* Kazumi Hamazaki. *Film Ed* Teruo Nakajima. *Mus* Jun Suzuki. *Sd Rec* Meguro Studio.

Cast: Asahi Kurizuka *(Akira Taki)*, Yuki Jono *(Reiko Machida)*, Hiroshi Yamanami *(Joji)*, Ken Kuroki *(Ken)*, Ryohei Uchida *(Shuhei Isshiki)*, Ichiro Sugai *(Otaguro)*, Toru Abe *(Ichizo Uchiyama)*, Eriko Sono *(Naomi)*, Michiko Yajima *(Mina)*, Nakajiro Tomita, Hiroshi Wada, Kuniko Ogata, Akiko Nakamura, Ken Yamanouchi.

Crime melodrama. Taki flees from Japan after taking the blame for a murder committed by Joji, the brother of Reiko, the woman he loved. After 5 years, he returns to Yokohama and learns that Reiko is married to Otaguro, a financier much older than she. Taki has been given a contract by Wang, a man in Hong Kong, to murder Otaguro, who is blocking one of Wang's narcotics deals. Upon further investigation, Taki learns that mobster Uchiyama had ordered Joji to commit the murder for which Taki had been blamed and that Uchiyama had killed Taki's boss and taken over the man's position while Taki was out of the country. Reiko had married Otaguro for money to support Joji, who had promised to give up his life of crime, but instead he had used the money to buy the gold badge required of Uchiyama's henchmen. Taki manages to kill Uchiyama, but he is mortally wounded before he can see Reiko one last time. *Hired killers. Financiers. Drug dealers. Gangsters. Murder. Self-sacrifice. Brother-sister relationship. Marriage of convenience. Perfidy. Yokohama. Hong Kong.*

Note: Released in Japan in Dec 1968 as *Kiri ni musebu yoru.*

HARBOR LIGHTS   F6.2047
Associated Producers, Inc.-Cooperativa de Artes Cinematograficas, Producciones del Viejo San Juan. *Dist* Twentieth Century–Fox Film Corp. Jul **1963** [c1 May 1963; LP26211]. sd (Continental Sound Corp.); b&w. 35mm (CinemaScope). 68 min.

Prod-Dir Maury Dexter. *Assoc Prod* Frank Marrero. *Screenplay-Story* Henry Cross. *Dir Photog* John Nickolaus, Jr. *Supv Film Ed* Jodie Copelan. *Mus* Paul Sawtell, Bert Shefter. *Sd* Jack Solomon. *Sd* Harry M. Leonard. *Asst Dir* Frank Parmenter. *Prod Mgr* Axel Anderson. *Prod Supv* Frank Parmenter. *Unit Mgr* Amilcar Tirado. *Script Supv* Fare. *Makeup* Bob Mark. *Prop Master* Efrain Lopez Neris.

Cast: Kent Taylor *(Dan Crown)*, Jeff Morrow *(Cardinal)*, Miriam Colon *(Gina Rosario)*, Antonio Torres Martino *(Captain Acosta)*, Art Bedard *(Captain Aristarchus)*, Braulio Castillo *(Manolo)*, José de San Anton *(Father Riva)*, Luis Antonio Martínez *(Vallejo)*, José Manuel Caicoya *(mortician)*, Roberto Rivera Negron *(storekeeper)*, Allan Sagué *(hotel clerk)*, Victor Mojica, Alfredo Pérez, Tino García *(Cardinal's men)*, Ralph Rodriguez *(Alex Crown)*.

Action melodrama. Professional gambler Dan Crown arrives in San Juan to visit his brother Alex, only to learn from police chief Captain Acosta that Alex has been found murdered. To Acosta's questioning Dan answers that he had no knowledge of his brother's affairs. Dan then finds Gina Rosario searching his hotel room, and together they begin to investigate Alex's death. Dan receives an invitation from Cardinal, a wealthy importer who is apparently looking for something belonging to Alex. Dan learns from a priest that Alex had visited a church on the day he died. A clue in the form of a Saint Francis medal leads Dan and Gina to a church statue of Saint Francis, behind which they find a large uncut diamond Alex had smuggled to Puerto Rico. He leaves the diamond there and is followed and attacked by Cardinal's henchmen; but Gina leads the police to Cardinal, and Dan is rescued. *Gamblers. Brothers. Importers. Police. Murder. Smuggling. Diamonds. Churches. San Juan (Puerto Rico).*

Note: Filmed on location in San Juan, Puerto Rico. Henry Cross is a pseudonym of Harry Spalding.

THE HARD BUNCH *see* **HARD TRAIL**

HARD CHARGER *see* **TINY LUND: HARD CHARGER**

HARD CONTRACT   F6.2048
Marvin Schwartz Productions. *Dist* Twentieth Century–Fox Film Corp. 25 May **1969** [New York opening; c30 Apr 1969; LP36892]. Sd (Westrex); col (DeLuxe). 35mm (Panavision). 106 min. *MPAA rating* R.

Prod Marvin Schwartz. *Dir-Story-Screenplay* S. Lee Pogostin. *Dir Photog* Jack Hildyard. *Art Dir* Ed Graves. *Set Decor* James W. Payne, Fernando Gonzalez. *Film Ed* Harry Gerstad. *Mus Comp & Cond by* Alex North. *Sd* John Purchese, David Dockendorf. *Asst Dir* Julio Sempere, Kip Gowans. *Unit Prod Mgr* Eric Stacey. *Prod Mgr (Spain)* Eduardo G. Maroto. *Wardrobe* Gladys de Segonzac. *Makeup* Giuliano Laurenti. *Hairstyling* Elda Magnanti. *Sp Photog Eff* L. B. Abbott, Art Cruickshank.

Cast: James Coburn *(John Cunningham)*, Lee Remick *(Sheila)*, Lilli Palmer *(Adrianne)*, Burgess Meredith *(Ramsey)*, Patrick Magee *(Alexi)*, Sterling Hayden *(Michael Carlson)*, Claude Dauphin *(Maurice)*, Helen Cherry *(Evelyn Carlson)*, Karen Black *(Ellen)*, Sabine Sun *(Belgian prostitute)*.

Crime drama. John Cunningham, a professional assassin with the necessary emotional restraint and life-style, accepts a "hard contract" offer from business associate Ramsey Williams to kill three men in Europe. Upon arriving in Torremolinos, Spain, Cunningham meets socialite divorcée Sheila Metcalf and three of her jet set friends: Adrianne Bedford, an English aristocrat; Maurice, Adrianne's companion; and Alexi, a guilt-ridden ex-Nazi. Sheila learns that Cunningham has sex only with prostitutes. One night she poses as one, spends the night with him, and unexpectedly finds herself emotionally involved. Cunningham carries out the first part of his contract and follows Sheila and her friends to Tangiers to resume their affair. By the time he arrives in Brussels to stalk his second victim, he is beginning to change—his hand is unsteady while committing the murder, and he can no longer find gratification with a prostitute. Matters are further complicated when Ramsey informs him by phone that his final victim is Michael Carlson, a top-notch assassin of 20 years ago, now living peacefully with his family in Madrid. After asking Sheila to join him there, Cunningham accidentally meets Carlson at a Madrid hotel and senses the man's intuitive recognition of what he is. Troubled by this and by Sheila's need to believe that he is something other than a hired assassin, Cunningham is further shaken when Ramsey appears, obviously concerned over a recent telephone conversation with him. Despite his grasp of the situation, Carlson invites everyone to his ranch and, during a philosophical discussion with Cunningham, openly admits that nothing could make him kill again. Torn by his love for Sheila, his obligation to Ramsey, and his compassion for Carlson, Cunningham tries unsuccessfully to return to his emotional void by driving everyone over a cliff as he escapes. At the last moment, however, he is unable to go through with his plan, and disregarding the consequences, he runs away with Sheila. *Hired killers. Socialites. Jet set. Prostitutes. Murder. Imposture. Conscience. Torremolinos. Brussels. Tangiers. Madrid.*

Note: Filmed on location in Torremolinos, Brussels, Tangiers, and Madrid.

A HARD DAY'S NIGHT (Great Britain)   F6.2049
Proscenium Films. *Dist* United Artists. 11 Aug **1964** [New York opening; c6 Jul 1964; LP28626]. Sd; b&w. 35mm. 85 min. [Copyright length: 90 min.]

Prod Walter Shenson. *Assoc Prod* Denis O'Dell. *Dir* Richard Lester. *Orig Screenplay* Alun Owen. *Dir Photog* Gilbert Taylor. *Camera Op* Derek Browne. *Art Dir* Ray Simm. *Titl Dsgn* Robert Freeman. *Asst Ed* John Jympson, Pamela Tomling. *Mus Dir* George Martin. *Songs:* "A Hard Day's Night," "I Should Have Known Better," "I Wanna Be Your Man," "All My Loving," "If I Fell," "Can't Buy Me Love," "And I Love Her," "I'm Happy Just To Dance With You," "This Boy," "Tell Me Why," "She Loves You" John Lennon, Paul McCartney. *Song:* "Don't Bother Me" George Harrison. *Songs Sung by* The Beatles. *Sd Rec* H. L. Bird, Stephen Dalby. *Sd Ed* Gordon Daniel. *Asst Dir* John D. Merriman. *Cont* Rita Davison. *Beatles' Wardrobe* Dougie Millings & Son. *Cost Dsgn* Julie Harris, cost. *Makeup* John O'Gorman. *Hairdressing* Betty Glasow.

Cast: John Lennon *(John)*, Paul McCartney *(Paul)*, George Harrison *(George)*, Ringo Starr *(Ringo)*, Wilfrid Brambell *(Grandfather)*, Norman Rossington *(Norm)*, Victor Spinetti *(television director)*, John Junkin *(Shake)*, Deryck Guyler *(police inspector)*, Anna Quayle *(Millie)*, Kenneth Haigh *(Simon)*, Richard Vernon *(man on train)*, Michael Trubshawe *(club manager)*, Eddie Malin *(hotel waiter)*, Robin Ray *(television floor manager)*, Lionel Blair *(television choreographer)*, Alison Seebohm *(secretary)*, David Jaxon *(young boy)*, Marianne Stone *(society reporter)*, David Langton *(actor)*, Clare Kelly *(barmaid)*, Roger Avon, John Bluthal, Pattie Boyd, Margaret Nolan, Terry Hooper, Derek Nimmo, Bridget Armstrong, Rosemarie Frankland.

Comedy with music. Pursued by their zealous teenaged fans, the Beatles—Paul, John, George, and Ringo—board a London-bound train to do a television program. They are accompanied by their manager, Norm, his assistant, Shake, and Paul's cantankerous and meddlesome grandfather, whose only attribute seems to be that he is "a clean old man." On the first evening in London, after visiting a twist club, the Beatles discover that Grandfather has bribed a butler out of his dress clothes and gone to a gambling club. There they find him making quite an impression on a good-looking young woman, and despite his protests they take him back to the hotel. At the television studio on the following day, production delays enable the Beatles to wander about, and consequently they become involved in minor incidents, much to the disgruntlement of the director. Grandfather, who has been badgering Ringo about his status in the group, finally succeeds in provoking the drummer to strike out on his own. The Beatles and their managers begin to search for the missing Ringo, but Grandfather finds him in a police station and runs to tell the others. They rescue Ringo and after a wild chase return to the studio just in time for the performance. At the end of the final number, Grandfather rises through the stage floor on an elevator. The Beatles board a helicopter for their next appearance. *Musicians. Grandfathers. Talent agents. Television directors. Police. Adolescence. Rock and roll. Fame. Gambling. Disguise. Trains. Television. Clubs. Television studios. London. The Beatles. Chases.*

Note: Location scenes filmed in London. Working title: *The Beatles.* Opened in London in Jul 1964.

A HARD MAN'S GOOD TO FIND F6.2050

International Cinema. *Dist* Astro–Jemco Film Distributors. ca **1969**. Sd; col. 35mm. 72 min.

Dir Jacques Bergue.

Comedy-drama. Sam, a battle-weary American soldier, becomes separated from his unit and awakens to find himself surrounded by beautiful, nude women. Because all the men in the village have gone away to fight the Americans, the sex-starved women allow the soldier no rest until his battle fatigue pales in comparison to his new exhaustion. *Soldiers. Seduction. Lust. Battle fatigue.*

Note: Also Known as *A Good Man's Hard to Find* and *Night Shift.*

A HARD NIGHT (Great Britain) F6.2051

PRI. *Dist* Astro-Jemco Film Distributors. **1970**. Sd; b&w. 35mm. 80 min.

Drama. A man recounts his sexual adventures. Press material suggests that the film depicts the seduction of a 14-year old girl; the adventures of a woman cat-burglar; sexual intercourse with a neighbor who comes to borrow a pack of cigarettes; an exotic dancer, barebreasted and candle-lit, in a nightclub; a woman artist, her model, and their lesbian lovemaking; and acts of fetishism. *Burglars. Neighbors. Exotic dancers. Artists. Models. Seduction. Sexual practices. Lesbianism. Fetishism. Adolescence. Nightclubs.*

Note: Country of origin unconfirmed.

HARD ON THE TRAIL see HARD TRAIL

THE HARD ROAD F6.2052

Valle Film Enterprises. *Dist* Four Star Excelsior Releasing Co. May **1970**. Sd; col (Movielab). 35mm. 85 min. *MPAA rating* R.

Prod Ed De Priest. *Exec Prod* Jack Valle. *Dir* Gary Graver. *Screenplay* Richard Stetson. *Photog* Gary Graver. *Film Ed* Gary Graver. *Mus* Jaime Mendoza-Nava. *Sd* Don Jones.

Cast: Connie Nelson *(Pamela Banner)*, John Alderman *(Jimmy Devlin)*, Katherine Howard *(Jeannie)*, Gary Kent *(Leo)*, Ray Merritt *(Mr. Banner)*, Liz Renay *(Mrs. Banner)*, William Bonner *(Chad)*, Bruce Kimball *(prison guard)*, John Parker *(Max)*, Karen Lind *(Mrs. Levin)*, Issa Arnal *(social worker)*, Jay Fineberg *(landlord)*, Chuck Hutchinson *(transvestite)*, Jeff Graver *(man in alley)*, Joe Pepi, Joe Colgan *(narcotics agents)*, Alex Eliot *(bartender)*, Mike Stringer *(Muffin)*, Jean Clark *(prisoner)*, Mike Weldon *(man in motel)*, Fern Holbrook *(police worker)*, Roger Everett *(Steve Christopher)*, Jack Valle, Lewis Teague, Greg Corarito.

Melodrama. Pamela Banner leaves high school and her nagging, middle-class parents when she finds that she is pregnant. She puts the baby up for adoption and takes a job as secretary to a rock music promoter. After being introduced to marijuana by her employer, she assumes the hippie lifestyle along Sunset Strip, sharing a room with a prostitute, Jeannie, and a drug addict, Jimmy. Despite her parents' pleas for her to return home, Pamela has become too enmeshed in the culture of the area to be aware of its dangers. One night, while attending an acid party, she takes an LSD trip, suffers through it, and is killed by a motorist on a Los Angeles highway. *Students. Music producers. Secretaries. Hippies. Prostitutes. Drug addicts. Parenthood. Pregnancy. Adoption. Marijuana. LSD. Los Angeles—Sunset Strip. Hallucinations.*

Note: Also reviewed as *The Hard Row.*

THE HARD SWING F6.2053

25 Aug **1962** [New York showing]. Sd; b&w. 35mm. [Feature film, length unknown.]

Dir Michael Putnam.

Drama. As an aging stripper prepares for her act in a San Francisco burlesque hall, she reflects on the contrast between her life onstage and off. *Stripteasers. Burlesque. San Francisco.*

HARD TRAIL F6.2054

Brentwood International Productions. 12 Nov **1969** [Maryland license]. Sd; col. 35mm. 78 min.

Prod Maurice Smith. *Dir-Writ* Greg Corarito. *Dir Photog* Gary Graver. *Film Ed* Vic Davis, Ken Stewart. *Sd Mixer* William Oliver. *Script Supv* Maria Lease. *Makeup* Jerry Sousi.

Cast: Lash La Rue *(Slade)*, Donna Bradley *(Sue)*, Bob Romero *(Rafael)*, Bruce Kemp *(Ox)*, Robert Dalton *(Bixby)*, Arne Dhean *(Jaime)*, Mary Donahue *(Kathy)*, Adam Stan *(Jim Nesson)*, Greg Corarito *(Starret)*, Phil Hoover, Scott Wells, John Bloom, actor, Ron Wade, Jim Feazell, Randy Starr, Mike Armstrong, Monica Gayle, Mal Hutton, Dru Hoy, Victoria Tobian.

Western melodrama. After Jim Nesson and his wife and son are gunned down by members of the Slade gang, the villains torture and rape his daughters, Kathy and Sue, in order to force them to surrender a map showing the location of Nesson's secret mine. Starret, Kathy's fiancé, arrives on the scene in time to take revenge on the murderers, but Kathy dies in the gunfight. Burdened with guilt over Kathy's death, Starret sets out with Sue to find the mine. In the meantime, Slade dispatches more men to track them down. Ox, Nesson's partner, sets out with his "Hard Bunch" to meet Rafael, a bandido who has agreed to work the mine with his Mexicans. When the "Hard Bunch" lose their way, they rob a stagecoach and rape the female passengers. Once at their destination, they are slaughtered by the treacherous Rafael, who then rides to seize the mine for himself. After killing Slade's men with dynamite, Starret makes love with Sue. Then he takes on the Mexicans. Only the lovers survive the battle, and they head for Slade's office to settle the final score. Ignoring Slade's protests, Starret begins to tear through his desk, triggering a booby-trap that destroys friend and foe. *Mexicans. Bandits. Sisters. Murder. Rape. Torture. Revenge. Stagecoach robberies. Greed. Perfidy. Guilt. Mines. Explosives. Documentation.*

Note: Also known as *Hard on the Trail*, film was released in two versions varying in extent of sex footage included. Working title: *The Hard Bunch.*

THE HAREM BUNCH; OR WAR AND PIECE F6.2055

Pacific International Films. *Dist* Republic Amusements Corp., Clover Films. ca **1969**. Sd; col (Eastman Color). 35mm. 80 min.

Prod-Story R. W. Cresse. *Dir* Paul Hunt. *Cinematog* Ron Garcia. *Set Dsgn* Ron Garcia. *Film Ed* Abraham Posnic. *Asst Ed* Larry Markowtz. *Mus Comp & Perf by* The Toufic Barham Players. *Asst Dir* Robert Poffen Burger. *Cont* Ruby Towne. *Wardrobe* Arnie Weiss. *Makeup Artist* Dennis Marsh.

Cast: Monica Gayle *(Shwartz)*, Mitch Evans *(Irving)*, Frank Cuva *(Ali)*, Sherrie Land *(Toblosky)*, Albert James *(customer)*, Warren Ball *(Acaba)*, Leonard Goodman *(Habib)*, Barbara Caron *(Kaplan)*, Tom Counter *(Kalan)*, Bill Kersh *(beggar)*, Ron Glen *(Shamir)*, Paul Bruce *(Colonel Seigal)*, Sanford Mitchell *(messenger)*, Vick Thorne *(Hagoub)*, Leslie De Larenzo *(Hagoub's sister)*, Pam Maloney *(secretary)*, Jane Tsentas, Val Couret, Jane Dabon, Bridget Wienst Raume, Joseph Rip, Tony Ortiz.

War comedy. Ali, an Arab, and Irving, an Israeli, are partners in a men's clothing store in Tel Aviv. They tell a customer the story of how they once were bitter enemies: *In 1970, Irving, a general in the Israeli Army, tries to provoke an Arab attack that will give his army an excuse to break the cease-fire. He sends three spies behind Arab lines and gives each woman one third of a message about a bogus supply shipment. Toblosky is disguised as a jeep-driving farm girl, Shwartz as a harem girl, and Kaplan as a camel boy. Everything goes according to Irving's plan; the women are captured and imprisoned in the Arab leader's tent. The elder Arab soldiers recommend torturing the three women into disclosing their secret mission, but Ali, the American-educated son of the Arab leader, suggests using gentle persuasion on the prisoners. When he is overruled by the elders, Ali dresses up as Rudolph Valentino, bursts into the tent, and abducts the women to "safety." Taking them to an elegant hotel, Ali wines, dines, and seduces them, and they reveal their part in Irving's plan. The women are permitted to return home; a stalemate develops between the warring parties, and the cease-fire is restored. In 1982, as evidence of their continuing friendship, Irving has married Shwartz, and Ali is courting both Toblosky and Kaplan!* *Merchants. Spies. Israelis. Arabs. Friendship. Disguise. Seduction. Abduction. Israeli-Arab War 1967. Tel Aviv. Israel—Army. Documentation. Rudolph Valentino.*

Note: Also known as *The Harem Bunch; or War and Peace* and *Desert Odyssey.*

HAREM HANGUPS F6.2056

Dist Able Film Co. ca **1970**. Sd; col. 16mm. [Feature length assumed.]

Sex film. No information about the precise nature of this film has been found. *Sexuality. Harems.*

HAREM HOLIDAY *see* HARUM SCARUM

HARLOT F6.2057

Dist Film-Makers' Cooperative. 10 Jan **1965** [New York opening]. Sd; b&w. 16mm. 70 min.

Prod-Dir Andy Warhol. *Prod Asst* Gerard Malanga.

Cast: Mario Montez *(Harlot),* Philip Fagan *(adventurer),* Gerard Malanga *(man with cigarette),* Carol Koshinskie *(woman with cat),* Ronald Tavel, Harry Fainlight, Billy Linich *(voices),* White Pussy *(a cat).*

Experimental film/Satire. A tableau vivant in which Harlot, a transvestite suggestive of Jean Harlow, sits on a lounge chair. Surrounding her are a young man who holds a cigarette and stares at her, an adventurer, and a lesbian holding a white cat. Their sole activity is the consumption of bananas. Three off-camera voices recite dialog unrelated to the image on the screen. *Transvestism. Jean Harlow.*

HARLOW F6.2058

Paramount Pictures–Embassy Pictures–Prometheus Enterprises. *Dist* Paramount Pictures. 23 Jun **1965** [Chicago opening; c24 Jun 1965; LP31139]. Sd; col (Technicolor). 35mm (Panavision). 125 min.

Pres by Joseph E. Levine. *Prod* Joseph E. Levine. *Dir* Gordon Douglas. *Screenplay* John Michael Hayes. *Cinematog* Joseph Ruttenberg. *Camera Op* James Knott. *Asst Camera* Gene Liggett. *Col Cons* Richard Mueller. *Art Dir* Hal Pereira, Roland Anderson. *Set Decor* James Payne. *Film Ed* Frank Bracht, Archie Marshek. *Mus* Neal Hefti. *Song:* "Lonely Girl" Jay Livingston, Ray Evans. *Sung by* Bobby Vinton. *Sd* Stanley Jones, Charles Grenzbach. *Rec Mgr* Ashton Cossar. *Boom Op* Frank Regula. *Asst Dir* David Salven, Cliff Coleman, Tim Zinnemann. *Unit Prod Mgr* Kenneth DeLand. *Cost Supv* Edith Head. *Cost* Ruth Stella, Robert Magahay. *Makeup Supv* Wally Westmore. *Makeup* William Reynolds, makeup. *Hair Dsgn* Sydney Guilaroff. *Hairstyles* Sherry Wilson. *Prop* Robert McCrillis. *Still Photog* Art Say. *Grip* Darrell Turnmire, Douglas Cook.

Cast: Carroll Baker *(Jean Harlow),* Martin Balsam *(Everett Redman),* Red Buttons *(Arthur Landau),* Michael Connors *(Jack Harrison),* Hanna Landy *(Mrs. Arthur Landau),* Angela Lansbury *(Mama Jean Bello),* Peter Lawford *(Paul Bern),* Leslie Nielsen *(Richard Manley),* Raf Vallone *(Marino Bello),* Peter Hansen, actor *(assistant director),* Mary Murphy *(studio secretary),* Kipp Hamilton *(girl at pool),* Peter Leeds *(director of 30's).*

Biographical drama. Source: Irving Shulman, *Harlow: An Intimate Biography* (New York, 1964). Jean Harlow, an aspiring actress in Hollywood in the 1920's, supports her mother and lazy stepfather, Marino Bello, by taking bit parts in the movies. Agent Arthur Landau recognizes that the platinum blonde actress could become a new sex symbol. He gets Jean better roles, including some in slapstick comedy, until she is signed by Richard Manley, an independent producer. Jean needs more money to support her parents, and Landau tricks Manley into releasing Jean from her contract after her triumphant personal-appearance tour. She signs with Everett Redman, head of a major Hollywood studio. Though she has become Hollywood's leading sex symbol, Jean is still chaste and actually afraid of men. Both actor Jack Harrison and studio executive Paul Bern ask to marry Jean, and in an extravagant Hollywood wedding, she marries Bern but on their wedding night discovers he is impotent. After Bern commits suicide, Harlow starts drinking heavily. In her search for love she turns to Bello, Manley, and Harrison—all of whom reject her. Though she is at the height of her career, Jean starts picking up strangers in bars. Her drinking and promiscuity lead to her early death at the age of 26. *Actors. Motion picture producers. Theatrical agents. Stepfathers. Filial relations. Impotence. Suicide. Weddings. Alcoholism. Promiscuity. Hollywood. Mama Jean Bello. Marino Bello. Arthur Landau. Jean Harlow. Paul Bern.*

HARLOW F6.2058a

Electronovision Productions–Magna Pictures. *Dist* Magna Pictures Distribution Corp. 14 May **1965** [New York opening]. Sd; b&w. 35mm (Electronovision). 108 min. [Also reviewed at 120 min.]

Pres by Marshall Naify. A Bill Sargent Production. *Prod* Lee Savin. *Exec Prod* Brandon Chase. *Assoc Prod* Frank Ray. *Dir* Alex Segal. *Screenplay* Karl Tunberg. *Photog* Jim Kilgore. *Art Dir* Duncan Kramer. *Set Decor* Harry Gordon. *Mus Cond & Arr* Nelson Riddle. *Mus Comp* Nelson Riddle, Al Ham. *Songs* Marilyn Ham, Al Ham. *Sd* David Forrest. *Asst Dir* Greg Peters, John G. Wilson, Richard C. Bennett. *Prod Mgr* Edward K. Dodds. *Prod Asst* Nanette Eiland. *Cost Dsgn* Nolan Miller. *Wardrobe* Paul McArdle. *Makeup* Michael Westmore. *Hairstyles* Mary Westmoreland. *Casting* Marvin Paige, Jim Ford. *Prop* Ken Westcott.

Cast: Carol Lynley *(Jean Harlow),* Efrem Zimbalist, Jr. *(William Mansfield),* Ginger Rogers *(Mama Jean),* Barry Sullivan *(Marino Bello),* Hurd Hatfield *(Paul Bern),* Lloyd Bochner *(Marc Peters),* Hermione Baddeley *(Marie Dressler),* Audrey Totter *(Marilyn),* John Williams *(Jonathan Martin),* Audrey Christie *(Thelma),* Michael Dante *(Ed),* Jack Kruschen *(Louis B. Mayer),* Celia Lovsky *(Maria Ouspenskaya),* Robert Strauss *(Hank),* Sonny Liston *(1st fighter),* James Dobson *(counterman),* Cliff Norton *(Billy),* Paulle Clark *(waitress),* Mark Herron *(James Langley),* Jim Plunkett *(Stan Laurel),* John Fox *(Oliver Hardy),* Joel Marston *(press agent),* Christopher West *(Bern's secretary),* Fred Conte *(photographer),* Catherine Ross *(wardrobe woman),* Buddy Lewis *(Al Jolson),* Danny Francis *(casino manager),* Frank Scannell *(doctor),* Maureen Gaffney *(Miss Larsen),* Nick Dimitri *(2d fighter),* Ron Kennedy *(assistant director),* Harry Holcombe *(minister),* Lola Fisher *(nurse),* Fred Klein *(himself).*

Biographical drama. Jean Harlow, a bit player in a Laurel and Hardy film, is spotted by actor Marc Peters, who arranges a screen test for her with director Jonathan Martin. Her first picture for Martin makes her a star, despite criticism of her acting ability from popular actor William Mansfield. Harlow's mother and stepfather take advantage of their daughter's sudden fame and wealth to improve their own standard of living. Wearied by demands from her parents and the studio, Harlow seeks comfort in a marriage to producer Paul Bern, but Bern proves to be sexually impotent and Harlow's well-publicized affairs drive him to suicide. Another marriage fails to assuage Harlow's guilt over Bern's death, and, on the advice of her friend Marie Dressler, she goes East to study acting. News of her mother's illness brings her back to Hollywood, where she is welcomed by producer Louis B. Mayer, who promises to revitalize her career, and Mansfield, who is now in love with her. As her new romance blossoms, Harlow contracts a serious illness and finally dies in Mansfield's arms. *Actors. Motion picture directors. Motion picture producers. Marriage. Infidelity. Suicide. Impotence. Filial relations. Motion pictures. Hollywood. Jean Harlow. Paul Bern. Louis B. Mayer. Marie Dressler. Stan Laurel. Oliver Hardy.*

HAROLD LLOYD'S FUNNY SIDE OF LIFE F6.2059

Harold Lloyd. *Dist* Janus Films. 9 Nov **1966** [Madison, Wisconsin, opening; c1 Aug 1963; LP25723]. Sd; b&w. 35mm. 99 min.

Pres by Harold Lloyd. *Prod* Harold Lloyd. *Assoc Prod* Jack Murphy. *Narr Writ* Arthur Ross. *Prod Ed* Duncan Mansfield. *Mus* Walter Scharf. *Song:* "There Was a Boy, There Was a Girl" Ned Washington, Walter Scharf. *Sd Eff* Del Harris. *Mus Ed* Sid Sidney. *Mus Rec* Vinton Vernon. *Story Cons* Harold Lloyd, Jr.

Compilation film. A number of excerpts from Harold Lloyd's comedies of the 1920's, including *For Heaven's Sake* (1926), *Girl Shy* (1924), and *The Kid Brother* (1927), are followed by a complete version of *The Freshman* (1925). *Actors. Motion pictures—History. Harold Lloyd.*

Note: Also known as *The Funny Side of Life.*

HAROLD LLOYD'S WORLD OF COMEDY F6.2060

Harold Lloyd. *Dist* Continental Distributing, Inc. 4 Jun **1962** [New York opening; c5 Mar 1962; LP21938]. Sd; b&w. 35mm. 94 min. [Copyright length: 96 min.]

Prod Harold Lloyd. *Assoc Prod* Jack Murphy. *Narr Writ* Arthur Ross. *Prod Ed* Duncan Mansfield. *Mus* Walter Scharf. *Orch* Leo Shuken, Jack Hayes. *Sd Eff* Del Harris. *Mus Ed* Sid Sidney. *Mus Rec* Vinton Vernon. *Story Cons* Harold Lloyd, Jr.

Compilation film. Highlights from a number of Harold Lloyd's films include short sequences from *Safety Last* (1923), in which Lloyd hangs from the hands of a large clock on the side of a city building, and *The Freshman* (1925), in which he receives his chance to play football for Tate College in the last 2 minutes of an important game. In two sequences from *Hot Water* (1924) Lloyd struggles with a live turkey on a streetcar and takes his wife and in-laws for a drive in his new automobile. In *Why Worry?* (1926) Lloyd innocently becomes involved in a South American revolution. The *Girl Shy* (1924) episode is a chase sequence in which he uses an automobile, a trolley car, a motorcycle, and a wagon team to reach his beloved before she marries a bigamist. The remaining three sequences are selected from Lloyd's sound films. In *Professor Beware* (1938) Lloyd is pursued by two motorcycle policeman. Next is a scene from *Movie Crazy* (1932), in which Lloyd inadvertently wears a magician's trick coat to a formal dance. In the final episode, from *Feet First* (1930), Lloyd dangles from the side of a building and frantically tries to keep from falling by clutching at awnings, ropes, scaffolds, and window ledges. *Actors. Motion pictures—History. Harold Lloyd.*

HARPER F6.2061

Warner Bros. Pictures. 23 Feb **1966** [Los Angeles opening; c24 Jan 1966; LP32660]. Sd; col (Technicolor). 35mm (Panavision). 121 min.

A Gershwin–Kastner Production. *Prod* Jerry Gershwin, Elliott Kastner. *Dir* Jack Smight. *Screenplay* William Goldman. *Dir Photog* Conrad Hall. *Camera*

Op John R. Moore, *photog. Asst Camera* Richard Doran, Jordan Cronenweth. *Art Dir* Alfred Sweeney. *Asst Art Dir* Russell Menzer. *Set Decor* Claude Carpenter. *Film Ed* Stefan Arnsten. *Asst Ed* Don Hoskinson. *Mus* Johnny Mandel. *Song:* "Livin' Alone" Andre Previn, Dory Previn. *Sung by* Julie Harris. *Sd* Stanley Jones. *Boom Op* Frank Regula. *Asst Dir* James H. Brown, Phil Ball. *Unit Mgr* Charles Hansen. *Script Supv* Dorothy Aldrin. *Wardrobe* Sally Edwards, William Smith, cost. *Makeup Supv* Gordon Bau. *Makeup* Otis Malcolm, Gary Liddiard. *Supv Hairstyles* Jean Burt Reilly. *Hairstyles* Lenore Weaver. *Dial Supv* Bert Steinberger. *Still Photog* Bert Six. *Gaffer* Charles O'Bannon. *Grip* Kenneth Taylor, Owen Crompton. *Prop* Charles Mason, William Wainess.

Cast: Paul Newman *(Lew Harper)*, Lauren Bacall *(Mrs. Sampson)*, Julie Harris *(Betty Fraley)*, Arthur Hill *(Albert Graves)*, Janet Leigh *(Susan Harper)*, Pamela Tiffin *(Miranda Sampson)*, Robert Wagner *(Alan Taggert)*, Robert Webber *(Dwight Troy)*, Shelley Winters *(Fay Estabrook)*, Harold Gould *(Sheriff Spanner)*, Roy Jenson *(Puddler)*, Strother Martin *(Claude)*, Martin West *(deputy)*, Jacqueline DeWit *(Mrs. Kronberg)*, Eugene Iglesias *(Felix)*, Richard Carlyle *(Fred Platt)*, China Lee *(bunny dancer)*.

Mystery drama. Source: Ross MacDonald, *The Moving Target* (New York, 1949). While his estranged wife is planning divorce proceedings, private investigator Lew Harper takes on a new case on the recommendation of a long-time friend, attorney Albert Graves. Harper is asked to investigate the disappearance of the millionaire husband of Elaine Sampson, a crippled and bitter woman. At the Sampson estate, Harper also meets Elaine's spoiled stepdaughter, Miranda, and the Sampson's handsome private pilot, Alan Taggert. While searching the missing man's Los Angeles hotel suite, Harper finds a photograph of one-time starlet, Fay Estabrook. He tracks down the now plump and alcoholic Fay, gets her drunk, and takes her home. He searches her apartment and intercepts a phone call which leads him to a bar where he meets Betty Fraley, a drug-addicted singer. After being beaten up for asking too many questions, Harper visits a mountaintop site which Sampson gave to Claude, a religious fanatic. Later, Mrs. Sampson receives a ransom note, and Harper drops off the money, but Betty Fraley doublecrosses the kidnapers and intercepts the money. Harper then accuses Taggert of planning the kidnaping with Betty. Taggert draws a gun on Harper, but he is shot by Graves, who makes a timely appearance. Harper goes to Betty's apartment and finds her being tortured for the ransom money by Fay's husband, Troy, who is in league with Claude in smuggling Mexicans across the border. After killing Troy, Harper forces Betty to take him to an abandoned oil tanker where Sampson is being held prisoner. There he and Graves find the body of the murdered millionaire. Betty attempts to escape, but she is killed when her car plummets from a cliff. As they return to the Sampson estate, Grave admits that he killed Sampson because of his hatred for the man and his love for young Miranda. He draws a gun on Harper but realizes that he cannot kill his friend. *Detectives. Lawyers. Millionaires. Cripples. Air pilots. Actors. Singers. Drug addicts. Fanatics. Missing persons. Alcoholism. Kidnaping. Perfidy. Murder. Torture. Smuggling. Nightclubs. Ransom. Los Angeles. Automobile accidents.*

Note: Working title: *The Moving Target.*

HARRY FRIGG *see* **THE SECRET WAR OF HARRY FRIGG**

HARUM SCARUM   F6.2062

Four Leaf Productions. *Dist* Metro-Goldwyn-Mayer, Inc. 24 Nov **1965** [Los Angeles opening; c22 Jun 1965; LP31993]. Sd (Westrex); col (Metrocolor). 35m. 95 min. [Copyright length: 85 min.]

Prod Sam Katzman. *Dir* Gene Nelson. *Screenplay* Gerald Drayson Adams. *Dir Photog* Fred H. Jackman. *Camera Op* Joe Jackman. *Asst Camera* Bill Ion. *Art Dir* George W. Davis, H. McClure Capps. *Set Dsgn* Henry Grace, Don Greenwood, Jr. *Film Ed* Ben Lewis. *Mus Supv & Cond* Fred Karger. *Titl Song* Peter Andreoli, Vince Poncia, Jr., Jimmie Crane. *Songs:* "Golden Coins," "Go East, Young Man," "Shake That Tambourine," "Animal Instinct," "Wisdom of the Ages," "Mirage" Bill Giant, Bernie Baum, Florence Kaye. *Songs:* "Hey, Little Girl," "So Close, Yet So Far (From Paradise)" Joy Byers. *Song:* "My Desert Serenade" Stanley Jay Gelber. *Song:* "Kismet" Sid Tepper, Roy C. Bennett. *Songs Sung by* Elvis Presley. *Vocal Backgrounds* The Jordanaires. *Choreog* Earl Barton. *Rec Supv* Franklin Milton. *Sd* Charles Wallace, James Utterback, Frank Antunez, Salvador Robinson. *Asst Dir* Eddie Saeta. *Prod Coörd* Robert Stone. *Wardrobe* Beau Vandenecker, Gene Ostler, Margo Weintz. *Makeup* William Tuttle, Don Cash. *Hairstyles* Sydney Guilaroff, Jane Gorton. *Tech Adv* Col. Tom Parker. *Gaffer* George Lasher. *Grip* Hank Forrester.

Cast: Elvis Presley *(Johnny Tyronne)*, Mary Ann Mobley *(Princess Shalimar)*, Fran Jeffries *(Aishah)*, Michael Ansara *(Prince Dragna)*, Jay Novello *(Zacha)*, Philip Reed *(King Toranshah)*, Theo Marcuse *(Sinan)*, Billy Barty *(Baba)*, Dirk Harvey *(Mokar)*, Jack Costanzo *(Julna)*, Larry Chance *(Captain Herat)*, Barbara Werle *(Leilah)*, Brenda Benet *(Emerald)*, Gail Gilmore *(Sapphire)*, Wilda Taylor *(Amethyst)*, Vicki Malkin *(Sari)*, Ryck Rydon *(Mustapha)*, Richard Reeves *(scarred Bedouin)*, Joey Russo *(Yussef)*.

Comedy with music. Johnny Tyronne, an American singer, premieres his latest film in the Middle East. He meets Aishah and Prince Dragna and is invited to Lunarkand. Seduced by Aishah, Johnny is captured by a band of assassins led by Sinan. Johnny meets the Princess Shalimar, now a slave girl; and he escapes but is recaptured. Sinan wants Johnny to kill King Toranshah by using karate so that the evil Prince Dragna will get the throne. Johnny foils the plot with the help of a band of thieves led by Zacha. Johnny marries the princess and returns to Las Vegas with some of Zacha's dancing girls. *Actors. Singers. Thieves. Royalty. Conspiracy. Assassination. Motion pictures. Imaginary kingdoms. Karate. Middle East. Las Vegas.*

Note: Working title: *Harem Holiday.*

HARVEY   F6.2063

Dist Stacey Distributors. ca **1970**. Sd; col. 16mm. 61-81 min.

Sex film. No information about the precise nature of this film has been found. *Sexuality.*

HARVEY MIDDLEMAN, FIREMAN   F6.2064

Columbia Pictures. 12 Jul **1965** [New York opening; c1 Jul 1965; LP31906]. Sd; Col (Eastman Color by Pathé). 35mm. 75 min.

Prod Robert L. Lawrence. *Prod in Assoc With* Ernest Pintoff. *Assoc Prod* Robert Gaffney. *Dir-Writ* Ernest Pintoff. *Dir Photog* Karl Malkames. *Camera Op* Warren Rothenberger. *Asst Camera* Albert Kern. *Helicopter Photog* Mike Elliot. *Prod Dsgn* Gene Callahan. *Film Ed (see note)* David Donovan, Hugh A. Robertson, Jr. *Mus Comp* Ernest Pintoff. *Mus Arr & Cond* Bernard Green. *Sd Rec* Dennis Maitland. *Re-rec* Richard Vorisek. *Asst Dir* Roger Rothstein. *Script Supv* Maggie James. *Cost* Anna Hill Johnstone. *Makeup* Dick Smith. *Hairstyles* Philip Naso. *Electrn* Vincent Delaney. *Grip* Martin Nallan, Jr. *Prop* Jack Wright, III, Jack Flaherty.

Cast: Gene Troobnick *(Harvey Middleman)*, Hermione Gingold *(Mrs. Koogleman)*, Patricia Harty *(Lois)*, Arlene Golonka *(Harriet)*, Will MacKenzie *(Dinny)*, Ruth Jaroslow *(The Mother)*, Charles Durning *(Dooley)*, Peter Carew *(Barratta)*, Stanley Myron Handelman *(Mookey)*, Trudy Bordoff *(Cindy)*, Neil Rouda *(Richie)*, Gigi Chevalier *(receptionist)*, Stacy Graham *(librarian)*, Maurice Shrog *(Mr. Koogleman)*.

Comedy. Harvey Middleman, a New York City fireman, lives happily in a New Jersey suburb with his wife and two small children. Harvey likes his work and imagines that someday he will rescue a beautiful young woman from a fire. Then he rescues Lois, a model, kisses her as he resuscitates her, and falls in love. After secretly dating her several times, Harvey decides he must solve his moral dilemma by consulting a psychiatrist, Mrs. Koogleman, whose preoccupation with her own extramarital relations precludes the possibility of helping Harvey find a solution. Another fire breaks out in Lois's apartment, and Harvey's associate Dinny rescues the model while Harvey saves a cat. Lois falls in love with Dinny, and Harvey returns to his family. *Firemen. Psychiatrists. Models. Infidelity. Suburban life. New Jersey. New York City Fire Department. Fires.*

Note: Sources conflict in crediting film editor.

HARVEY SWINGS   F6.2065

Jo-Jo Productions. *Dist* Stacey Distributors. ca **1970**. Sd; col. 16mm. 74 min.

Sex film. Harvey and his wife answer a newspaper advertisement and get more than they bargained for. (Pressheet suggests scenes of female impersonation and lesbianism.) *Female impersonation. Lesbianism.*

HATACHI NO KOI *see* **LOVE AT TWENTY**

HATARI!   F6.2066

Malabar Productions. *Dist* Paramount Pictures. 20 Jun **1962** [Detroit opening; c31 Dec 1961; LP22962]. Sd; col (Technicolor). 35mm. 159 min.

Pres by Howard Hawks. *Prod-Dir* Howard Hawks. *Assoc Prod* Paul Helmick. *2d Unit Dir* Paul Helmick. *Screenplay* Leigh Brackett. *Story* Harry Kurnitz. *Dir Photog* Russell Harlan. *Assoc Photog* Joseph Brun. *Camera* Roger Monteran, Jack Whitman, Brian West. *Art Dir* Hal Pereira, Carl Anderson. *Set Decor* Sam Comer, Claude Carpenter. *Film Ed* Stuart Gilmore. *Mus Score* Henry Mancini. *Song:* "Just for Tonight" Johnny Mercer, Hoagy Carmichael. *Sd Rec* John Carter, Charles Grenzbach. *Asst Dir* Tom Connors, Russ Saunders, William R. Poole. *Prod Mgr* Don Robb. *Unit Mgr* Jim Henderling. *Cost* Edith Head. *Men's Wardrobe* Frank Beetson, Jr. *Sp Photog Eff* John P. Fulton, Dick Parker. *Tech Adv* Willie De Beer, Eric Rungren. *Coöp* Tanganyika Game Dept., Bruce G. Kinloch. *Prop Master* Earl Olin. *Animal Supv* Jan Oelofse. *Stuntman* Carey Loftin.

Cast: John Wayne *(Sean Mercer)*, Hardy Kruger *(Kurt Stahl)*, Elsa Martinelli *(Serafini "Dallas" d'Allesandro)*, Red Buttons *(Pockets)*, Gérard Blain *(Chip Maurey)*, Michèle Girardon *(Brandy)*, Bruce Cabot *(Bill "Indian" Vaughn)*, Valentin De Vargas *(Luis)*, Eduard Franz *(Dr. Sanderson)*, Jon Chevron *(Joseph)*, Queenie Leonard *(nurse)*, Emmett E. Smith *(bartender)*, Jack Williams *(man/Masai warrior/native boy)*, Henry Scott *(Sikh clerk)*, Major Sam Harris *(man in the store)*.

Adventure comedy-drama. The Momella Game Farm in Tanganyika is world-famous as a source of wild animals. When its owner is killed by a rhinoceros, his French-born daughter, Brandy, decides to carry on her father's work. Assisting her are Sean Mercer, an American game catcher embittered by a previous unhappy love affair; Kurt Stahl, a former auto racer from Germany who drives the herding jeep; Bill "Indian" Vaughn, a veteran hunter; and Pockets, a former cabbie from Brooklyn. Eventually this little group of international adventurers is joined by woman photographer Dallas and French playboy Chip Maurey, who replaces Indian when the latter is badly gored by a charging rhino. Trouble begins when Kurt and Chip compete for the attentions of Brandy, and Sean becomes infuriated by Dallas' penchant for collecting baby elephants. Gradually, however, during the many hectic safaris after wild game, the tensions are resolved. The rivalry between Kurt and Chip ends when Pockets accidentally falls from a fence and Brandy betrays her true romantic feelings by rushing up to comfort him. Following the celebration of the capture of a rhinoceros, Sean discovers that Dallas has left the farm, and he sets out to find her by using her pet baby elephants as bloodhounds. After barging through the streets, alleys, and stores of the small town of Arusha, they finally corner her in the local hotel. Sean insists upon an immediate marriage, and Dallas tearfully agrees. Their wedding night is somewhat marred, however, when Dallas' three baby elephants stampede into the bedroom. *Americans in foreign countries. Hunters. Photographers. Taxi drivers. French. Germans. Playboys. Masai. Jealousy. Courtship. Safaris. Big game. Game farms. Hotels. Arusha (Tanganyika). Tanganyika. Animals. Rhinoceros. Elephants.*

Note: Location scenes filmed at Mt. Meru, Lake Manyara, Ngorongoro Crater, Naberara, and on the Ruvu River.

THE HATE WITHIN see **STARK FEAR**

HATSUKOI JIGOKUHEN see **NANAMI: INFERNO OF FIRST LOVE**

THE HAUNTED AND THE HUNTED see **DEMENTIA 13**

THE HAUNTED HOUSE OF HORROR see **HORROR HOUSE**

THE HAUNTED PALACE　　　　　　　　　　　　　　　F6.2067
Alta Vista Productions. *Dist* American International Pictures. 28 Aug **1963** [Cincinnati, Ohio, opening; c28 Aug 1963; LP26830]. Sd; col (PathéColor). 35mm (Panavision). 85 min.
Prod-Dir Roger Corman. *Exec Prod* James H. Nicholson, Samuel Z. Arkoff. *Assoc Prod* Ronald Sinclair. *Screenplay* Charles Beaumont. *Dir Photog* Floyd Crosby. *Camera Op* Harry Underwood. *Art Dir* Daniel Haller. *Set Dresser* Harry Reif. *Titl* Armand Acosta. *Film Ed* Ronald Sinclair. *Mus* Ronald Stein. *Sd Mix* John Bury. *Asst Dir* Jack Bohrer, Paul Rapp. *Prod Mgr* Jack Bohrer. *Script Supv* Betty Crosby. *Prod Asst* Dennis Jacob. *Wardrobe Supv* Marjorie Corso. *Makeup* Ted Coodley. *Hairdresser* Lorraine Roberson. *Prop Master* Dick Rubin. *Gaffer* Harry Sundby. *Key Grip* Charles Hannawalt.
Cast: Vincent Price (*Charles Dexter Ward/Joseph Curwen*), Debra Paget (*Ann Ward*), Lon Chaney, [Jr.] (*Simon Orne*), Frank Maxwell (*Dr. Marinus Willet*), Leo Gordon (*Edgar Weeden*), Elisha Cook (*Peter Smith*), John Dierkes (*Jacob West*), Milton Parsons (*Jabez Hutchinson*), Cathy Merchant (*Hester Tillinghast*), Guy Wilkerson (*Leach*), Harry Ellerbe (*minister*), I. Stanford Jolley (*boat captain*), Darlene Lucht (*young woman victim*), Barboura Morris (*Mrs. Weeden*), Bruno Ve Sota (*bartender*).
Horror film. Source: Edgar Allan Poe, "The Haunted Palace," in *American Museum of Science* (Apr 1839). H. P. Lovecraft, "The Case of Charles Dexter Ward," in *Weird Tales* (May–Jun 1941). In 1765, several persons disappear from the New England village of Arkham. The townspeople soon discover that Squire Joseph Curwen is a warlock who with the aid of Hester Tillinghast is sacrificing village girls. Curwen is set upon by the villagers and burned alive. Through the flames, Curwen vows revenge upon the villagers and their descendants. A century later, Curwen's great-great-grandson, Charles Dexter Ward, and his wife, Ann, reopen the Curwen mansion. The villagers, who fear Curwen's curse, are openly hostile to Ward. Ward discovers mutants living near the village who, according to Dr. Marinus Willet, the only villager to befriend the Wards, are direct descendants of the villagers who burned Curwen. Ward comes under the spell of a portrait of his ancestor, whom he resembles, and is befriended by Simon Orne and Jabez Hutchinson, themselves warlocks. Together they resurrect Hester, and Curwen (in Ward's body) prepares to sacrifice Ann. Meanwhile, the villagers storm the house and burn the portrait. Ward is released from the spell, but once they are safely away from the burning mansion, the couple's features appear to undergo a change: Ward becomes Curwen and Ann becomes Hester. *Sorcerers. Physicians. Reviviscence. Mutation. Revenge. Human sacrifice. Village life. New England. Curses. Fires.*

THE HAUNTING (United States/Great Britain)　　　　F6.2068
Argyle Enterprises. *Dist* Metro-Goldwyn-Mayer, Inc. 18 Sep **1963** [New York opening; c21 Jun 1963; LP26096]. Sd (Westrex); b&w. 35mm (Panavision). 112 min.

A Robert Wise Production. *Prod-Dir* Robert Wise. *Assoc Prod* Denis Johnson. *Screenplay* Nelson Gidding. *Dir Photog* Davis Boulton. *Camera Op* Alan McCabe. *Sketch Artist* Ivor Beddoes. *Set Decor* John Jarvis. *Prod Dsgn* Elliot Scott. *Film Ed* Ernest Walter. *Mus Comp & Cond* Humphrey Searle. *Rec Supv* A. W. Watkins. *Sd Rec* Gerry Turner. *Dub Ed* Allan Sones. *Dub Mix* J. B. Smith. *Asst Dir* David Tomblin. *Cont* Hazel Swift. *Wardrobe Supv* Maude Churchill. *Claire Bloom's Clothes* Mary Quant. *Makeup* Tom Smith. *Hairdresser* Joan Johnstone. *Sp Eff* Tom Howard. *Casting Dir* Irene Howard.
Cast: Julie Harris (*Eleanor Vance*), Claire Bloom (*Theodora*), Richard Johnson (*Dr. Markway*), Russ Tamblyn (*Luke Sannerson*), Lois Maxwell (*Grace*), Rosalie Crutchley (*Mrs. Dudley*), Fay Compton (*Mrs. Sannerson*), Valentine Dyall (*Mr. Dudley*), Ronald Adam (*Eldridge Harper*), Freda Knorr (*2d Mrs. Crain*), Janet Mansell (*Abigail, 6 years*), Pamela Buckley (*1st Mrs. Crain*), Howard Lang (*Hugh Crain*), Mavis Villiers (*landlady*), Verina Greenlaw (*Dora*), Paul Maxwell (*Bud*), Diane Clare (*Carrie Fredericks*), Claude Jones (*fat man*), Susan Richards (*nurse*), Amy Dalby (*Abigail, 80 years*), Rosemary Dorken (*companion*).
Horror film. Source: Shirley Jackson, *The Haunting of Hill House* (New York, 1959). Dr. John Markway, an anthropologist with an interest in psychic research, learns that Hill House, an old mansion in New England, has a reputation for evil and supposedly is filled with supernatural powers; and he decides to conduct an experiment there. Assisting him are two women he has carefully selected: Eleanor Vance, a lonely, withdrawn woman who supposedly had a supernatural experience at the age of 10 and has devoted her life to caring for her invalid mother; and Theodora, a bohemian of lesbian leanings and remarkable extrasensory perception. Luke Sannerson, a skeptic who stands to inherit the house, accompanies them. Almost immediately the quartet are subjected to thunderous poundings, hideous screeching, and other terrifying phenomena for which Markway can find no rational explanation. Eleanor feels that the house is calling to her; and she begins to treat it as a living object. At this point Dr. Markway's skeptical wife, Grace, arrives and, defying the ghost, tries to persuade her husband to give up his experiments. Eleanor, who has fallen in love with Markway, now loses all touch with reality; and the other members of the group decide that for her own safety she must leave. As she drives away she feels a force tugging at the steering wheel; then, suddenly, Grace appears in the road, and Eleanor, in attempting to avoid hitting her, swerves off the road and is killed by crashing into the same tree under which the first mistress of Hill House died. *Anthropologists. Heirs. Cynics. Psychic phenomena. Extrasensory perception. Lesbianism. Supernatural. Fear. Haunted houses. New England. Automobile accidents.*

Note: Filmed in England; opened in London in Jan 1964.

THE HAUNTING OF CASTLE MONTEGO see **CASTLE OF EVIL**

DAS HAUS DER TAUSEND FREUDEN see **HOUSE OF A THOUSAND DOLLS**

HAUTE INFIDÉLITÉ see **HIGH INFIDELITY**

HAVE BIKINI WILL TRAVEL (Switzerland)　　　　F6.2069
Kunz Film. *Dist* Union Film Distributors. ca **1962**. Sd; col (Eastman Color). 35mm. 63 min.
Prod-Dir Werner Kunz. *English Comm* Tony Tenser. *Camera* Adolph Jenny, Werner Kunz, Edgar Reiser. *Underwater Photog* Rudolph Gygi. *Art Dir* Alexander Swiagenin. *Film Ed* Walter Kagi. *Mus* Fred Böhler.
Cast—Narrator: Guy Kingsley Poynter.
Nudist film. Bound for the nudist colony on the isle of Cavallo, Jose, Rosemary, and Anita rent a car from Henri. When Henri discovers that a part of the auto is missing, he rushes to the port of Ajaccio, where he finds his car and awaits the tourists' return. Arriving by boat at Cavallo, the trio joins the Tropical Sun Club. Among its activities are archeological expeditions, swimming, and dancing. *Tourists. Nudism. Swimming. Île de Cavallo. Ajaccio.*
Note: Original title and release undetermined. Also known as *Let's Go Native.*

HAVE FIGURE, WILL TRAVEL (Canada)　　　　　F6.2070
Green Bush Films. *Dist* Fanfare Films. 13 Mar **1963** [Chicago opening]. Sd; col (Eastman Color). 35mm. 74 min. [Also 70 min.]
Prod Philip Watson. *Dir* Alan Overton. *Photog* Stanley Lipinski. *Film Ed* Louis Klene. *Mus Comp* John Bath. *Adv* Karle Ruehle.
Cast: Susan Baxter (*Susan*), Carol MacKenzie (*Carol*), Marge Anderson (*Marge*).
Nudist film. Carol, whose widowed father has reared her very strictly, secretly visits a nudist camp with her friend Susan. When Carol's father is suddenly called away, leaving behind his 50-foot yacht, the girls plan a tour of nudist camps along the Atlantic coast, taking with them another friend, Marge, whom they hope to convert to the pleasures of nudism. After a night in Manhattan, the friends visit a nudist camp in Cape May, New Jersey. From

there they make several stops along the coast, finally arriving at a nudist camp in Florida. Camp officials welcome them and introduce them to the camp, where all three joyfully join in the nudist activities. *Nudism. Nudist camps. Yachts. New York City. Cape May (New Jersey). Florida.*

HAVE YOU HEARD OF THE SAN FRANCISCO MIME TROUPE?
F6.2071

King Screen Productions. *Dist* Film-Makers' Distribution Center. 27 Jun **1968** [New York opening]. Sd; col. 35mm. 60 min.

Prod-Dir Don Lenzer, Fred Wardenburg. *Photog* Don Lenzer. *Film Ed* Fred Wardenburg, Don Lenzer, Richard Chew. *Song:* "Old Black Joe" Stephen C. Foster. *Sd* Charles Horman.

Cast: Ronnie Davis *(himself, the director).*

Documentary. Members of the San Francisco Mime Troupe, dressed in traditional *commedia dell'arte* costumes, parade along the streets of their city one summer weekend playing instruments as they announce their upcoming free park performance. After performing an unconventional version of Molière's *The Miser*, they pass a hat to the audience. Next, the members perform *The Minstrel Show or Civil Rights in a Cracker Barrel*, in which three black and three white actors perform such songs as "Old Black Joe" within the framework of a conventional minstrel show. Later, a restroom confrontation between two blacks and a white portrays the black middle class and the white liberal. During intermission the actors go into the audience and select white women to dance with on stage. At a company meeting after the performance, director Ronnie Davis discusses the troupe's purpose and the problems of a revolutionary theater group enduring in the absence of a revolution. As a filmed record of the preceding events ends, some troupe members discuss the footage they have seen; some are despondent, others are hopeful, but all agree their work must continue. *Actors. Negroes. Theatrical directors. Mime. Race relations. Radicalism. Theatrical troupes. San Francisco. Molière. San Francisco Mime Troupe.*

HAVING A WILD WEEKEND (Great Britain)
F6.2072

Bruton Film Productions. *Dist* Warner Bros. Pictures. 28 Jul **1965** [Boston opening; c14 Aug 1965; LP32091]. Sd; b&w. 35mm. 91 min.

Prod David Deutsch. *Assoc Prod* Basil Keys. *Dir* John Boorman. *Screenplay* Peter Nichols. *Photog* Manny Wynn. *Camera Op* Freddie Cooper. *Set Dresser* Helen Thomas, Ian Whittaker. *Prod Dsgn* Tony Woollard. *Main Titl* Tony Woollard. *Film Ed* Gordon Pilkington. *Mus Dir* Dave Clark. *Songs:* "Catch Us If You Can," "Sweet Memories," "Time," "When," "I Can't Stand It" Dave Clark, Lenny Davidson. *Songs:* "On the Move," "Move On," "Ol Sol" Dave Clark, Denis Payton. *Titl Song* Dave Clark, Mike Smith. *Played by* Dave Clark Five. *Sd* Ernie Cousins. *Sd Rec* Robert Allen. *Sd Ed* Arthur Ridout. *Re-rec* Len Abbott. *Asst Dir* David Tringham. *Prod Mgr* Donald Toms. *Unit Mgr* Bruce Sharman. *Asst to the Prod* Alexander Jacobs. *Asst to the Dir* Michael Blakemore. *Cont* Ann Skinner. *Wardrobe* Brenda Dabbs, Betty Knight. *Cost* Sally Jacobs. *Makeup* Trevor Crole-Rees. *Hairdressing* Bernadette Ibbetson. *Constr Mgr* Dick Frift. *Ch Electrn* Frank Ives. *Grip* Jack Roche.

Cast: Dave Clark *(Steve),* Barbara Ferris *(Dinah),* Lenny Davidson *(Lenny),* Rick Huxley *(Rick),* Mike Smith *(Mike),* Denis Payton *(Denis),* Clive Swift *(Duffle),* Hugh Walters *(Grey),* Robin Bailey *(Guy),* Yootha Joyce *(Nan),* David De Keyser *(Zissell),* Robert Lang *(Whiting),* Michael Blakemore *(officer),* Marianne Stone *(Mrs. Stone),* Julian Holloway *(assistant director),* Susan Hanson *(Laraine),* David Lodge *(Louis),* Andrew Tyrrell *(Louis's son),* Peter Nichols *(photographer),* Edgar Harrison *(barman),* John Jones *(drinker),* Sheila Fearn *(Shirley),* Alan Lake *(cameraman),* Ronald Cunliffe *(clapper boy),* Anthony Gardner *(director),* Peter Eyre *(art director),* Ronald Lacey *(beatnik),* Michael Gwynn *(Hardingford),* Donald Morley *(barker),* Roland Arblaster.

Comedy with music. Dinah, the "Butcha Girl," and stuntmen Steve, Lenny, Rick, Mike, and Denis film television commercials for a meat-packing company. Tired of her work, Dinah convinces Steve that they should escape the studio drudgery, take the white Jaguar belonging to the film company, and travel to an island off the coast of Devon that she wants to buy. On the road to Devon they meet a group of beatniks who tell a story of a cat and a monk. Then they ride into the center of a war-games battlefield, and a stray missile demolishes the car. Guy and Nan, a wealthy, middle-aged couple, pick up the hitchhikers and invite them to the Arts Fancy Dress Ball in Bath. Meanwhile, Zissell, an advertising executive, decides to capitalize on the disappearance of Dinah and notifies newspaper columnist Whiting of his star's kidnaping. In a frantic chase, the police, Steve's friends, and the advertising agents converge upon the costume party to find Steve and Dinah there. The two dissidents flee to the ranch of Louis, former leader of a London youth club, but Louis tries to turn them in for the publicity. Disappointed in Dinah's island, the couple decide to return to Smithfield when they meet Zissell and the photographers. Dinah cooperates, but Steve refuses to play a role in the stunt being filmed and abandons the group. *Advertising executives. Stuntmen. Columnists. Police. Actors. Beatniks. Photographers. Television commercials. Meatpacking. War*

games. Kidnaping. Publicity. Islands. Masquerades. London. Devonshire (England). Jaguar automobiles. Chases.

Note: Opened in London in Jul 1965 as *Catch Us If You Can*; running time: 91 min. Former title: *The Dave Clark Five Runs Wild.*

HAWAII
F6.2073

Mirisch Corp. *Dist* United Artists. 10 Oct **1966** [New York opening; c24 Oct 1966; LP34404]. Sd; col (DeLuxe). 35mm (Panavision). 189 min.

A George Roy Hill–Walter Mirisch Production. *Prod* Walter Mirisch. *Assoc Prod* Lewis J. Rachmil. *Dir* George Roy Hill. *Prolog Seq Supv* James Blue, Daniel Vandraegen. *2d Unit Dir* Richard Talmadge. *Screenplay* Dalton Trumbo, Daniel Taradash. *Photog* Russell Harlan. *2d Unit Camera* Harold Wellman. *Prolog Seq Camera* Charles Wheeler. *Art Dir* James Sullivan. *Set Decor* Edward G. Boyle, Raymond G. Boltz. *Prod Dsgn* Cary Odell. *Film Ed* Stuart Gilmore. *Vis Eff Ed* Marshall M. Borden. *Mus* Elmer Bernstein. *Song:* "My Wishing Doll" Elmer Bernstein, Mack David. *Orch* Leo Shuken, Jack Hayes. *Choreog* Miriam Nelson. *Sd Ed* Wayne Fury. *Sd* Robert Martin, Bert Hallberg. *Re-rec* Clem Portman. *Mus Ed* Richard Carruth. *Asst Dir* Ray Gosnell. *Prod Supv* Allen K. Wood. *Prod Mgr* Robert J. Anderson, Emmett Anderson. *Script Supv* Dixie McCoy. *Cost Dsgn & Exec* Dorothy Jeakins. *Wardrobe* Eric Seelig. *Makeup* Emile LaVigne. *Hairstylist* Fae Smith. *Sp Photog Eff* Film Effects of Hollywood, Linwood Dunn, James Gordon. *Sp Eff* Paul Byrd. *Res* Lelia Alexander. *Tech Res* Lewis Teague. *Prop* Sam Gordon. *Casting* Marion Dougherty, Patricia Rose.

Cast: Julie Andrews *(Jerusha Bromley),* Max von Sydow *(Abner Hale),* Richard Harris *(Rafer Hoxworth),* Carroll O'Connor *(Charles Bromley),* Elizabeth Cole *(Abigail Bromley),* Diane Sherry *(Charity Bromley),* Heather Menzies *(Mercy Bromley),* Torin Thatcher *(Reverend Thorn),* Gene Hackman *(John Whipple),* John Cullum *(Rev. Immanuel Quigley),* Lou Antonio *(Rev. Abraham Hewlett),* Jocelyne La Garde *(Malama),* Manu Tupou *(Keoki),* Ted Nobriga *(Kelolo),* Elizabeth Logue *(Noelani),* Lokelani S. Chicarell *(Iliki),* Malcolm Atterbury *(Gideon Hale),* Dorothy Jeakins *(Hepzibah Hale),* George Rose *(Captain Janders),* Michael Constantine *(Mason),* John Harding *(Collins),* Robert Crawford, Jr. *(Cridland),* Robert Oakley *(Micah, 4 years),* Henrik von Sydow *(Micah, 7 years),* Clas S. von Sydow *(Micah, 12 years),* Bertil Werjefelt *(Micah, 18 years),* Don Doolittle.

Historical epic. Source: James Albert Michener, *Hawaii* (New York, 1959). In 1820, following his graduation from the Yale Divinity School, tall, gangling, bumbling Abner Hale volunteers to carry the word of God to the heathen natives of Hawaii. In need of a wife before he can offer himself to the service, he timorously proposes to Jerusha Bromley, a young woman in love with an adventurous sea captain, Rafer Hoxworth, from whom she has not received a letter in over three years. To Abner's astonishment, Jerusha agrees to marry him, and they soon set sail for Hawaii. After a stormy and arduous voyage, during which their tiny two-masted vessel is battered by mountainous waves off Cape Horn, Abner and Jerusha finally reach the islands, where they receive a royal welcome from the Queen, the Alii Nui, Malama. Although Jerusha easily makes friends with the natives and tries to understand their customs, the sanctimonious Abner refuses to make any concessions and rigidly imposes his will upon the pleasure-and-peace-loving Hawaiians. He orders them to destroy their pagan idols, cover their naked bodies, and abolish their ancient practice of incestuous marriage. The Alii Nui instructs her people to obey, although she herself refuses to deny the deep love she feels for her brother, Kelolo. One day a sailing ship arrives in the harbor and Jerusha suddenly finds herself face to face with Hoxworth. Although still attracted to him, she nevertheless rejects his offer of love and chooses instead to remain with Abner. Later, sailors from several ships, including Hoxworth's, set fire to Abner's church as a protest against his forbidding the native girls to mingle with seamen. Led by Abner and Jerusha, the islanders put out the fire and drive off the sailors, and peace is momentarily restored. Gradually, however, more and more white men come to the islands, commercializing and corrupting the simple way of life and leaving behind disease and unhappiness. One day the Alii Nui sends for Abner and, realizing that her death is near, sends Kelolo into exile and receives a Christian baptism; but after she has been buried in sacred ground, Kelolo removes her body and disposes of it in the traditional pagan manner. A severe measles epidemic then sweeps the islands, taking the lives of hundreds of natives, including Keoki, a native clergyman who had studied with Abner at Yale. When Abner asks Keoki's sister-wife to pray with him, she brands him as a man of hate who worships a cruel and unforgiving God. As time passes, Jerusha gives birth to three sons and never ceases in her effort to persuade Abner that he must ask for forgiveness from God for the sorrow he has brought to the islands. In 1834, Hoxworth's ship once more returns to Hawaii and on board is a prefabricated New England house he plans to present to the Hales. When he learns Jerusha has since died, he strikes Abner in a fit of rage and then, filled with regret, goes to seek help for the man he has injured. Seven more years pass, and the now old and lame Abner is informed that he has been relieved of his ministry. He sends his three sons to England for their education, choosing himself to remain in Hawaii, still hopeful of somehow bringing God's word to the islands. *Clergymen. Missionaries. Newlyweds. Americans in foreign countries. Hawaiians. Sea captains. Royalty. Sailors. Marriage. Social customs. Paganism. Christianity. Nudity. Incest. Arson. Ships. Typhoons. Churches. Epidemics. Rites and ceremonies. Hawaii. Cape Horn. England. New England. Yale University.*

Note: Location scenes filmed in Norway, New England, Tahiti, and Hawaii. Fred Zinnemann, after more than 4 years of preparation, withdrew as director before shooting began; George Roy Hill took over and, after being temporarily replaced by Arthur Hiller, finished the picture. *The Hawaiians,* which was based on another portion of Michener's novel, was released by United Artists in 1970.

HAWAII BEACH BOY see BLUE HAWAII

HAWAIIAN THIGH   F6.2074
Hollywood Industries. *Dist* Rossmore Film Distributors. 20 Aug **1965** [Los Angeles showing]. Sd; col (Eastman Color). 35mm. 65 min.
Prod-Dir Bob Felderman.
Cast: Maureen Gaffney.
Comedy. Prominent Hollywood producer Pompus J. Pumpslush invites a novice reporter to his office to promote his latest production *Hawaiian Thigh.* Unaware that Pumpslush produces "nudies," the rookie is not prepared for the reception he receives from the nude secretary, who has been instructed to impress the young man. The producer begins the interview with a preview of the film: *A group of beautiful vacationers begin a holiday in the glamour capitals of the world. After a wild send-off in Hollywood, they head for Las Vegas, where they soon run out of funds and become involved in a strip poker game. Next, they charter a yacht to Hawaii, and sunbathe on the deck while the love-starved crew looks on. Once on land, they attend a native luau and perform a hula without grass skirts. Afterwards, they happily head home.* The reporter is ecstatic. To ensure a favorable review, Pumpslush enlists the aid of the steno, who performs a wild striptease for the already-shaken reporter. *Reporters. Motion picture producers. Secretaries. Vacations. Nudity. Striptease. Poker. Sex exploitation films. Hollywood. Las Vegas. Hawaii.*
Note: Pressbook indicates that filming took place in Las Vegas, Hollywood, and Hawaii.

THE HAWAIIANS   F6.2075
Mirisch Productions. *Dist* United Artists. 17 Jun **1970** [New York opening; c24 Jun 1970; LP37995]. Sd; col (De Luxe). 35mm (Panavision). 134 min. *MPAA rating* GP.
Prod Walter Mirisch. *Assoc Prod* Robert Stambler. *Dir* Tom Gries. *Screenplay* James R. Webb. *Dir Photog* Philip Lathrop, Lucien Ballard. *Art Dir* George Chan. *Set Decor* James Berkey. *Prod Dsgn* Cary Odell. *Film Ed* Ralph Winters, Byron Brandt. *Mus* Henry Mancini. *Sd Mix* Robert Martin. *Sd Re-rec* Richard Portman. *Asst Dir* Daniel J. McCauley, Newt Arnold. *Prod Supv* Edward Morey, Jr.\ *Prod Mgr* Jim Henderling.\ *Cost Dsgn* Bill Thomas. *Sp Eff* Sass Bedig. *Stunt Coörd* Fred Zendar, Chuck Roberson.
Cast: Charlton Heston (*Whip Hoxworth*), Tina Chen (*Nyuk Tsin*), Geraldine Chaplin (*Purity Hoxworth*), John Phillip Law (*Noel Hoxworth*), Alec McCowen (*Micah Hale*), Mako (*Mun Ki*), Don Knight (*Milton Overpeck*), Miko Mayama (*Fumiko*), Virginia Lee (*Mei Li*), Tanya Chang (*Mei Li at 8*), Naomi Stevens (*Queen Liliuokalani*), Harry Townes (*American minister*), Khigh Dhiegh (*Kai Chung*), Keye Luke (*Foo Sen*), James Gregory (*Dr. Whipple, Sr.*), Lyle Bettger (*Janders*), Mary Munday (*Malama*), George Paulsin (*Noel at 15*), Jules Martin (*Noel at 8*), Winston Char (*Europe at 17*), Michael Leong (*Africa at 18*), Randy Kim (*Asia at 19*), Victor Young, actor (*America at 16*), Bill Fong (*Australia at 14*), Chris Robinson (*young Dr. Whipple*), Mark LeBuse (*Kilauea captain*), Mathew Fitzgerald (*Symes*), Bruce Wilson (*Morris*), Mailie McCauley (*Iliki*), Alan Naluai (*Kimo*), Forrest Wood (*Hewlett*), Murray Staff (*A. Whipple*), Harry Holcombe (*Fredericks*), Daniel Kaleikini, Jr. (*Lieutenant Keholo*), Galen Kam (*Jim Wu*), Herman Wedemeyer (*fire chief*), Victor Sen Yung (*Chun Fat*), Soo Young (*Mrs. Ching*), James Hong (*Ti Chong*), Elizabeth Smith (*Apikela*), Eric Lin, Moon Chu, Eddie Pang, Wayne Chow, Jeffrey Chang, Steve Choy.
Historical melodrama. Source: James Albert Michener, *Hawaii* (New York, 1959). Whip Hoxworth returns to Hawaii with a boatload of indentured Chinese laborers to find that his grandfather has died, leaving his fortune to Whip's cousin, Micah Hale. Unwilling to work for Micah, Whip establishes his own plantation with the help of the Chinese laborers, including Nyuk Tsin and Mun Ki, a couple who were brought on the boat. Milton Overpeck, an engineer, persuades Whip to drill for water, and when the well succeeds, irrigation becomes possible for the previously barren land. Whip gives Nyuk some land, and with her help, he turns the plantation into a prosperous pineapple enterprise. Purity, Whip's Hawaiian wife, is not happy, however, and leaves to rear their son Noel in native Hawaiian fashion; and Nyuk goes to a leper colony

with her husband when he develops the dread disease. Many years later, Nyuk, whose children are now embarking on prosperous careers, returns to the island and finds Whip living with a Japanese mistress. When Queen Liliuokalani, the sovereign of native Hawaiians, tries to reestablish her dominion over the island, Whip succeeds in deposing her, and Micah is appointed president of the new Republic of Hawaii. Disaster strikes again, however, as a plague hits, and the Chinese ghetto is burned to the ground to prevent the spread of infection. Whip offers to help rebuild the burned section of the city and to help restore the financially ruined Nyuk. Finally, both agree to a marriage, which they had previously opposed, between Whip's son Noel and Nyuk's daughter Mei Li. *Indentured servants. Chinese. Cousins. Engineers. Hawaiians. Japanese. Mistresses. Royalty. Irrigation. Marriage. Leprosy. Plague. Race relations. Coups d'etat. Plantations. Wells. Fruit. Ghettos. Hawaii. Lydia Kamekeha Liliuokalani. Fires.*
Note: Location scenes filmed in Hawaii. Film is a sequel to *Hawaii,* q.v.

THE HAWKS AND THE SPARROWS (Italy)   F6.2076
Arco Film. *Dist* Brandon Films. 26 Jul **1967** [New York opening]. Sd (Westrex); b&w. 35mm. 91 min.
Prod Alfredo Bini. *Dir-Writ* Pier Paolo Pasolini. *Dir Photog* Mario Bernardo, Tonino Delli Colli. *Asst Camera* Antonio Orlandini. *Camera Op* Franco Di Giacomo, Gaetano Valle. *Art Dir* Luigi Scaccianoce. *Asst Art Dir* Dante Ferretti. *Set Decor* Vittorio Biseo. *Scenic Artist* Angelo Rancati. *Film Ed* Nino Baragli. *Asst Film Ed* Rossana Maiuri. *Mus & Adapt* Ennio Morricone. *Song by* Amedo Cassola. *Sd* Pietro Ortolani. *Boom Op* Armando Bondani. *Sd Mix* Emilio Rosa. *Asst Dir* Sergio Citti. *Prod Mgr* Fernando Franchi. *Prod Supv* Gilberto Scarpellini. *Admin Supv* Vincenzo Taito. *Asst to the Dir* Carlo Morandi. *Prod Sec* Enzo Ocone. *Cost* Danilo Donati. *Asst Cost* Piero Cicoletti. *Tailoring* Piero Farani. *Footwear* Pompei. *Hairstyles* Adriana Cassini. *Hairdresser* Ditta Rocchetti. *English Subtitl* Gideon Bachmann, Herman G. Weinberg. *Key Grip* Mariano Sargenti. *Ch Electrn* Alberto Ridolfi. *Still Photog* Divo Cavicchioli. *Fauna Specialist* Pino Serpe. *Plants & Flowers* Adriano Ceccotti. *Ornithologist* Domenico Rossi.
Cast: Toto (*Innocenti Toto/Brother Ciccillo*), Ninetto Davoli (*Innocenti Ninetto/Brother Ninetto*), Femi Benussi (*Luna*), Rossana Di Rocco (*friend of Ninetto*), Lena Lin Solaro (*Urganda La Sconosciuta*), Rosina Moroni (*peasant woman*), Renato Capogna, Pietro Davoli (*medieval louts*), Gabriele Baldini (*Dante's dentist*), Riccardo Redi (*civil engineer*), Francesco Leonetti (*crow's voice*), Umberto Bevilacqua, Alfredo Leggi, Renato Montalbano, Flaminia Siciliano, Giovanni Tarallo, Vittorio Vittori, Cesare Gelli, Vittorio La Paglia, Mario Pennisi, Fides Stagni.
Allegory. While strolling down the highway of life, a man and his son encounter a talking crow who asks them where they are going and what they are doing. When they are unable to answer, the crow launches into a philosophical discourse on conflicting social and political ideologies. As the loquacious bird prattles on, the man and his son become a monk and a young friar in the year 1200. They are met by St. Francis of Assisi who asks them to decipher the language of the birds so that they can bring them God's message of love. Although the old man succeeds in talking to and apparently converting the birds, he is disheartened when a hawk swoops down and devours a sparrow. Disillusioned, he reports to St. Francis and is told—in the words of Pope Paul VI at the United Nations—that they must teach all living things to love not only their own kind but all others as well. Returning to the present, the pair continue their journey. They trespass on private land to perform an urgent personal need and become involved in a battle with the landowner; they enact the roles of both oppressor and oppressed when they threaten a starving family with eviction and then in turn are confronted by a man demanding payment of a debt; they each fulfill another need by enjoying the favors of a roadside beauty; they witness the birth of a child and also attend the funeral of Palmiro Togliatti, head of the Italian Communist Party until his death in 1963. As the persistent crow continues to elaborate on his dialectic homilies, another need arises—hunger. Winking at each other, the man and his son grab the crow and make a meal of their would-be teacher. And, as they continue down the road of life, the question posed by the crow, "Where are you going?" remains unanswered. *Wanderers. Monks. Philosophers. Christianity. Time travel. Hunger. Funerals. Francis of Assisi. Palmiro Togliatti. Paul VI (pope). Crows. Hawks. Sparrows.*
Note: Filmed on location in Tuscania, near Fiumicino, and other locations around Rome. Opened in Rome in May 1966 as *Uccellacci e uccellini*; running time: 100 min.

HE AND SHE   F6.2077
New World Studios. *Dist* Institute for Adult Education. 24 Jul **1970** [Champaign, Illinois, showing]. Sd; col. 35mm. 61-65 min.
Pres by Marv Miller, Matt Cimber. *Prod-Dir* Matt Cimber.
Sex instruction film. The film explores the relationship of a young married couple. They make love on a circular bed while scenes depicting sex foreplay and the couple's first few weeks together are intercut. Between bed sequences

they are shown playing together on a beach, taking a shower, strolling on Hollywood Boulevard, selling underground newspapers, shopping, and hitchhiking together. As the couple nears orgasm on the bed, the narrator tells of memories which supposedly flash through the mind during lovemaking: a young girl being spanked by her father, cunnilingus, fellatio, ice cream eating, bright lights, fireworks, bombs, and rockets. *Newlyweds. Marriage. Sexual techniques. Sex instruction.*

HE IS COMING   F6.2078

Cosmos Films. *Dist* Able Film Co. ca **1970**. Sd; col. 16mm. [Feature length assumed.]

Sex film. A GI returns home to find that the woman he married has lost her innocence. His homecoming results in an orgy instead of a wifely embrace. *Veterans. Housewives. Orgies.*

HE RIDES TALL   F6.2079

Gordon Kay & Associates. *Dist* Universal Pictures. 26 Feb **1964** [New York opening; c2 May 1963; LP33021]. Sd (Westrex); b&w. 35mm. 84 min.

Prod Gordon Kay. *Dir* R. G. Springsteen. *Screenplay* Charles W. Irwin, Robert Creighton Williams. *Story* Charles W. Irwin. *Dir Photog* Ellis W. Carter. *Art Dir* Paul Sylos. *Set Decor* Ray Boltz. *Film Ed* Russell F. Schoengarth. *Mus Score* Irving Gertz. *Sd* Larry Gannon. *Asst Dir* Raoul Pagel. *Prod Mgr* Jack Voglin. *Cost* Seth Banks. *Makeup* Ernie Park. *Hairstyles* Doris Durkus. *Casting Dir* Edward F. Rhine.

Cast: Tony Young (*Marshal Morg Rocklin*), Dan Duryea (*Bart Thorne*), Madlyn Rhue (*Ellie Daniels*), Jo Morrow (*Kate McCloud*), R. G. Armstrong (*Josh McCloud*), Joel Fluellen (*Dr. Sam*), Carl Reindel (*Gil*), Mickey Simpson (*Onie*), George Murdock (*Burt*), Michael Carr (*Lefty*), George Petrie (*Crowley*).

Western melodrama. On the day before he is to marry Ellie Daniels and give up his job, Marshal Morg Rocklin is forced to kill the son of old rancher Josh McCloud, who had cared for the orphaned Morg when he was a boy. Reluctantly postponing his wedding, Morg rides out to break the sad news to McCloud. En route he is ambushed by McCloud's foreman, ex-convict Bart Thorne, but manages to escape. Later, however, he is attacked by Thorne's men and knocked unconscious. Thorne then forces Dr. Sam, a Negro physician, to operate on and cripple Morg's gun hand. Unaware that Dr. Sam faked the operation, Thorne elopes with Josh's mercenary young wife, Kate, and steals the old man's money and cattle. In his flight Thorne sacrifices Kate to Indians who kill and scalp her, and he also stampedes the cattle, which trample Josh to death. Morg arrives in town and with his perfectly healed gun hand wipes out Thorne and his gang. He then throws away his gun and makes plans for a life of peace with Ellie. *United States marshals. Orphans. Ex-convicts. Ranchers. Negroes. Physicians. Indians of North America. Ranch foremen. Mutilation. Theft. Rustling. Weddings. Infidelity. Perfidy. Cattle.*

Note: Working title: *The Gun Hand.*

HE SCARED THE GIRLS OFF *see* SCARE THEIR PANTS OFF

HE, SHE OR IT! *see* LA POUPÉE

HE WHO RIDES A TIGER (Great Britain)   F6.2080

David Newman Films. *Dist* Sigma III Corp. 9 Sep **1968** [New York opening]. Sd; b&w. 35mm. 103 min.

Prod David Newman, prod. *Dir* Charles Crichton. *Story & Screenplay* Trevor Peacock. *Photog* John Kotze. *Art Dir* Richard Harrison, art, Seamus Flannery. *Film Ed* Jack Harris, John S. Smith. *Mus Comp & Cond* Alexander Faris. *Titl Song* Trevor Peacock. *Sd* Robin Gregory, Fred Hughesdon. *Asst Dir* Colin Brewer, Patrick Marsden.

Cast: Tom Bell (*Peter Rayston*), Judi Dench (*Joanne*), Paul Rogers (*Superintendent, Taylor*), Kay Walsh (*Mrs. Woodley*), Ray McAnally (*orphanage superintendent*), Jeremy Spenser (*The Panda*), Peter Madden (*Peepers Woodley*), Inigo Jackson (*Detective Sergeant Scott*), Annette Andre (*Julie*), Edina Ronay (*Anna*), Nicolette Pendrell (*Ellen*), Grant Lovatt (*Dan*), Ralph Michael (*Carter*), Frederick Piper (*Mr. Steed*), Rita Webb (*flower seller*), Robin Hughes (*Detective Sergeant Crowley*), Jimmy Gardner (*waiter*), Howard Lang (*prison governor*), Naomi Chance (*Lady Cleveland*), Pat Shakesby (*policewoman*), Harry Baird (*Stan*), Margaret Bull (*Mrs. Hutton*), Frank Sieman (*prison officer*), The Rapiers (*themselves*).

Melodrama. Upon his eighth release from prison, 30-year-old cat burglar Peter Rayston immediately resumes his former way of life, plotting and executing a series of daring thefts that satisfy his need for excitement as much as his need for the spoils that support his expensive tastes. While on his way to inspect a heavily-insured house in Surrey, he gives a lift to attractive young Joanne and cultivates her friendship when he learns she lives in a country manor. He discovers that the house is an orphanage where she teaches art in order to support her 5-year-old illegitimate son. In addition, she has a job selling encyclopedias in London. Soon Peter has become emotionally involved with

both her and her boy, Dan. Joanne eventually learns that Peter is a thief, and she breaks off their relationship though she loves him. She later reconsiders and invites Peter to a party at the orphanage; but Peter realizes that he could never change his way of life and drives off without saying goodby. As he plans his next burglary, the police follow a tip that leads them to the orphanage. Little Dan inadvertently supplies the clue to Peter's next scheduled "job," and the police arrive as the burglary is being executed. As a result, an old crony of Peter's falls to his death and a younger thief is apprehended. Though Peter flees from the scene, the police are not far behind. *Burglars. Art teachers. Children. Saleswomen. Police. Theft. Criminals—Rehabilitation. Illegitimacy. Orphanages. Surrey. London.*

Note: Opened in London in Jan 1966.

HEAD   F6.2081

Raybert Productions. *Dist* Columbia Pictures. 6 Nov **1968** [New York opening; c1 Nov 1968; LP36397]. Sd; col (Technicolor). 35mm. 86 min. *MPAA rating* G.

Prod-Writ Bob Rafelson, Jack Nicholson. *Exec Prod* Bert Schneider. *Dir* Bob Rafelson. *Dir Photog* Michel Hugo. *Art Dir* Sydney Z. Litwack. *Set Decor* Ned Parsons. *Film Ed* Mike Pozen. *Incidental Mus Comp & Cond* Ken Thorne. *Mus Coörd* Igo Kantor. *Song:* "Porpoise Song" Gerry Goffin, Carole King. *Song:* "Circle Sky" Michael Nesmith. *Songs:* "Can You Dig It," "Long Title: Do I Have To Do All This Over Again" Peter Tork. *Sung by* The Monkees. *Song:* "Daddy's Song" Nilsson. *Sung by* Davy Jones. *Song:* "As We Go Along" Carole King, Toni Stern. *Choreog* Toni Basil. *Sd Rec* Les Fresholtz. *Sd Eff* Edit-Rite Inc. *Mus Ed* Synchrofilm. *Re-rec* Producers Sound Service. *Asst Dir* Jon Andersen. *Unit Prod Mgr* Harold Schneider. *Asst to the Prod* Marilyn Schlossberg. *Cost* Gene Ashman. *Sp Eff* Geza Gaspar. *Photog Eff* Butler-Glouner Inc. *Sp Col Eff* Burton Gershfield, Bruce Lane. *Prop Master* Jack Williams.

Cast: Peter Tork, Davy Jones, Micky Dolenz, Michael Nesmith (*themselves, The Monkees*), Victor Mature (*The Big Victor*), Annette Funicello (*Minnie*), Timothy Carey (*Lord High 'n Low*), Logan Ramsey (*Officer Faye Lapid*), Abraham Sofaer (*The Swami*), Vito Scotti (*I. Vitteloni*), Charles Macaulay (*Inspector Shrink*), T. C. Jones (*Mr. and Mrs. Ace*), Charles Irving (*Mayor Feedback*), William Bagdad (*The Black Sheik*), Percy Helton (*heraldic messenger*), Sonny Liston (*extra*), Ray Nitschke (*Private One*), Carol Doda (*Sally Silicone*), Frank Zappa (*The Critic*), June Fairchild (*The Jumper*), Terry Garr (*Testy True*), I. J. Jefferson (*Lady Pleasure*).

Film clips of the following personalities: Bela Lugosi, Rona Barrett, Charles Laughton, Ronald Reagan, Rita Hayworth, Ralph Williams, Ann Miller, Chick Lambert.

Musical fantasy. After leaping off San Francisco's Golden Gate Bridge to escape from Mayor Feedback and his establishment cronies, the Monkees perform an underwater ballet. They attack a non-functioning Coca-Cola machine in the middle of a desert, pursue the Black Sheik and his Arab horsemen, and watch a World War II Italian regiment surrender to a single Allied soldier. The quartet then arrives at Columbia Pictures studios to appear in a filmed commercial, portraying dandruff in the hair of The Big Victor, a muscular movie idol of the 1940's. One of the Monkees, Davey, tries his luck in the boxing ring with a movie extra but takes a beating. Attempting to escape from the film lot, the boys wander into a Western setting, fake their way through a shoot-out, exchange insults with an overly-dramatic female impersonator, and conclude by tearing apart a studio set. As their adventures end, the Monkees are again seen free-falling from the Golden Gate Bridge. [Film contains clips from the following films: *Gilda* (1946), *Golden Boy* (1937), *City of Conquest* (1940); and footage of Vietnam War atrocities.] *Musicians. Mayors. Sheiks. Arabs. Motion picture extras. Actors. Rock and roll. Motion pictures. Underwater ballet. Television commercials. Boxing. Female impersonation. Coca-Cola. Deserts. World War II. Vietnam War 1964-73. San Francisco. Hollywood. The Monkees. Italy—Army. Golden Gate Bridge. "Gilda". "Golden Boy". "City of Conquest".*

Note: Working title: *Untitled.*

THE HEAD (West Germany)   F6.2082

Rapid Film-Prisma-Wolfgang Hartwig. *Dist* Trans-Lux Distributing Corp. 11 Oct **1961** [Los Angeles opening; c11 Oct 1961; LP21699]. Sd; b&w. 35mm. 95 min.

Prod Wolfgang Hartwig. *Assoc Prod* Otto Reinwald, Kurt Rendel. *Dir-Writ* Victor Trivas. *Story* Victor Trivas, Jacques Mage. *Dir Photog* Georg Krause. *Asst Photog* André von Piotrowski, Horst Philipp. *Art Dir* Hermann Warm, Bruno Monden. *Film Ed* Friedl Buckow-Schier. *Asst Film Ed* Heidi Rente, Eva Kohlschein. *Mus* Willy Mattes, Jacques Lasry. *Mus Cond* Erwin Lehn. *Played by* Erwin Lehn Orchestra. *Sd Structure* Lasry-Baschet. *Sd* Rudolf Kaiser. *Asst Dir* Lothar Gündisch. *Prod Mgr* Ludwig Spitaler. *Makeup* Karl Hanoszek, Susi Krause. *Sp Eff* Theo Nischwitz. *Prop* Richard Eglseder.

Cast: Horst Frank (*Dr. Ood*), Michel Simon (*Professor Abel*), Paul Dahlke (*crime commissioner*), Karin Kernke (*Irene*), Helmut Schmid (*Bert*), Christiane Maybach (*Lilly*), Dieter Eppler (*Paul*), Kurt Müller-Graf (*Dr. Burke*), Maria Stadler (*Mrs. Schneider*), Otto Storr (*bartender*), Barbara Valentin, Herb Beschanner.

Horror film. Professor Abel has created a secret formula, Serum-Z, with which he has maintained life in the severed head of a dog. He is visited by Dr. Ood, who becomes obsessed with the possibility of extending the experimentation to human subjects. Abel proposes an operation to replace his failing heart with that of a badly injured patient. Dr. Ood kills Abel's collaborator, Dr. Burke, who objects to the plan; he then decapitates Abel, and against the professor's will keeps his head alive with the help of the serum and a specially-constructed machine. Ood turns his attention to Abel's nurse, Irene, a beautiful but crippled young woman. He decides to endow her with a perfectly-formed body and searches for an appropriate subject. A stripper, Lilly, falls prey to his charm, despite the jealousy of her boyfriend, Paul. Ood lures her to the laboratory, decapitates her, and performs a successful grafting operation on Irene, who believes that the surgery is aimed at correcting her deformity. Irene becomes the object of Ood's devotion. As time passes, she finds herself strangely drawn to the nightclub where Lilly worked, and here she meets Paul. They fall in love, but he becomes suspicious when he sees her carrying Lilly's purse and forces her to reveal Dr. Ood's criminal activities. They are discovered by the warped genius, who tries to kill them, but they are saved by the intervention of the police. Ood sets the laboratory aflame and falls to his death during an attempt to escape. *Surgeons. Professors. Nurses. Cripples. Stripteasers. Police. Decapitation. Murder. Organ transplants. Insanity. Experiments. Nightclubs. Secret formulas. Fires.*

Note: Released in West Germany in Jul 1959 as *Die Nackte und der Satan*; running time: 97 min. Also known as *A Head for the Devil* and *The Screaming Head*. German sources credit only Rapid Film as production company.

A HEAD FOR THE DEVIL *see* **THE HEAD**

HEAD FOR THE HILLS *see* **SOD SISTERS**

HEAD LADY   F6.2083
B & B Productions. *Dist* FPS Ventures. 24 Apr **1968** [Minneapolis, Minnesota, showing]. Sd; col 35mm. 70 min.

Prod-Dir B. Ron Elliott. *Screenplay* Skip Pages. *Photog* James Wrong When. *Camera Op* Sy Klops. *Mus* Basso Profundo. *Sd* O. Verload. *Script Supv* Kara Kooze. *Finance* Awsome Greed.

Cast: Bermuda Schwartz, Vanessa Van Dyke, Micro Cosim, Malinda Malice, Lynn Oleum, Sarah Stunning, Ronnie Runningboard, Barrie Cobbler.

Drama. Based on two tales from: Giovanni Boccaccio, *Il decamerone*. A beautiful lesbian matron is in charge of 12 young girls in a 17th century Italian school for young noblewomen. The aging school gardener retires, and he is replaced by handsome young Mario, who pretends to be a mute. Lacking normal male companionship, the girls seduce him. The matron, busy teaching lesbianism to the girls, becomes jealous and catches a girl bathing with Mario. The girl is stripped, beaten, and sexually abused. Another girl becomes pregnant and commits suicide. An investigation by the dead girl's fiancé leads him to a beating at the hands of Mario. The matron soon finds that Mario can speak; they recognize their similarly evil natures, and begin a life together. *Gardeners. Mutes. Headmistresses. Students. Nobility. Lesbianism. Seduction. Jealousy. Pregnancy. Sadism. Suicide.*

Note: Also Known as *The Head Mistress* and *Headmistress*.

THE HEAD MISTRESS *see* **HEAD LADY**

THE HEAD OF THE FAMILY (France/Italy)   F6.2084
Ultra Film-MN Produzione Cinematografica-C. F. C.-Marianne Productions. *Dist* Allied Artists, G. G. Productions. 15 Jul **1970** [San Francisco opening]. Sd; col (Eastman Color). 35mm. 105 min. *MPAA rating* GP.

Pres by Alpha Film Associates. *Prod* Turi Vasile. *Dir* Nanni Loy. *Screenplay* Nanni Loy, Ruggero Maccari. *Story* Giorgio Arlorio, Nanni Loy, Ruggero Maccari. *Photog* Armando Nannuzzi. *Art Dir* Carlo Egidi. *Set Decor* Bruno Cesari. *Film Ed* Franco Fraticelli. *Mus Comp* Carlo Rustichelli. *Cond* Bruno Nicolai. *Prod Mgr* Danilo Nannuzzi. *Cost* Marcel Escoffier.

Cast: Leslie Caron (*Paola*), Nino Manfredi (*Marco*), Claudine Auger (*Adriana*), Ugo Tognazzi (*Romeo, the anarchist*), Evi Maltagliati (*Luisa*), Sergio Tofano (*general*), Mario Carotenuto (*Gabriele*), Elsa Vazzoler (*Carla*), Antonella Della Porta, Marisa Solinas, Adolfo Celi.

Domestic comedy-drama. In the chaos of post-World War II Rome, architecture students Paola and Marco meet, fall in love, and marry. Despite their separate convictions—he's a Communist, she's a Catholic—they plan an egalitarian marriage, in which each will pursue a career. Although they agree to wait to have children, the babies arrive. Burdened with four children, each parent blames the other. Abandoning her career after the birth of her first child,

Paola redirects her energy toward caring for others, and the couple's home becomes a haven for both relatives and friends. This, plus the permissive rearing of the children, soon takes its toll on Paola, who neglects her appearance and her husband. Marco suffers from frustrated ideals; his pragmatic friends grow rich designing buildings he despises, while he barely can pay bills from the meager salary he makes as a civil servant. In the tenth year of marriage, Marco takes a young emancipated woman, Adriana, for a mistress. Threatened, Paola resorts to womanly wiles to win back Marco. He returns to his family, attacks his career with renewed enthusiasm, and becomes a success. Paola, however, now released from the strain of 20 years of childbearing and family devotion, suffers a nervous breakdown. When Paola is sent to a nursing home, Marco, alone in the large house, realizes his wife's indispensible role in his life and that of his family. *Architects. Civil servants. Mistresses. Communists. Catholics. Marriage. Family life. Infidelity. Ambition. Mental illness. Rome.*

Note: Location scenes filmed in Rome. Opened in Rome in Jan 1968 as *Il padre di famiglia*; running time: 115 min; in Paris in May 1969 as *Jeux d'adultes*; running time: 111 min.

THE HEAD THAT WOULDN'T DIE *see* **THE BRAIN THAT WOULDN'T DIE**

A HEADFULL OF LOVE   F6.2085
Dist Distribpix, Inc. 4 Jun **1969** [Boston opening]. Sd; b&w. 35mm. 63 min.

Sex film. A previously normal young man retreats into a world of tortured fantasy after he sees his sweetheart making love with another woman. Obsessed, the man becomes a knife-wielding voyeur who entertains bizarre fantasies involving the degradation and murder of women. Among his fantasies are: "The Murderer in Lover's Lane," "The Unconscious Redhead," "The Blonde With the Banana," and "The Brunette With the Bottle." *Voyeurism. Obsession. Lesbianism. Murder. Sadism. Fantasy.*

HEADMISTRESS *see* **HEAD LADY**

THE HEART IS A LONELY HUNTER   F6.2086
Warner Bros.–Seven Arts, Inc. 31 Jul **1968** [New York opening; c10 Oct 1968; LP36781]. Sd; col (Technicolor). 35mm. 124 min.

Prod Thomas C. Ryan, Marc Merson. *Exec Prod* Joel Freeman. *Dir* Robert Ellis Miller. *Screenplay* Thomas C. Ryan. *Dir Photog* James Wong Howe. *Camera Op* Ralph Gerling. *Art Dir* LeRoy Deane. *Film Ed* John F. Burnett. *Mus* Dave Grusin. *Selections from Symphony No. 41* Wolfgang Amadeus Mozart. *Sd* Francis E. Stahl. *1st & 2d Asst Dir* Robert J. Anderson, Martin Hornstein. *Prod Mgr* Larry Kostroff. *Script Supv* Marie Kenney. *Prod Sec* Maggie Smith, sec. *Cost Dsgn* Albert Wolsky. *Makeup* Al Greenway. *Sign Lang Instr* Weston Scarsbrook. *Prop Master* Robert Eaton, Joe La Bella. *Casting* Marion Dougherty Associates. *Key Grip* Harold Noyes. *Gaffer* George Bennett.

Cast: Alan Arkin (*Singer*), Chuck McCann (*Antonapoulos*), Stacy Keach, Jr. (*Blount*), Peter Mamakos (*Spirmonedes*), John O'Leary (*Beaudine*), Sondra Locke (*Mick*), Biff McGuire (*Mr. Kelly*), Laurinda Barrett (*Mrs. Kelly*), Jackie Marlowe (*Bubber*), Robbie Barnes (*Ralph*), Wayne Smith (*Harry*), Sherri Vise (*Delores*), Richard Fingar (*Sucker*), Gavin Paulin (*Spareribs*), Percy Rodriguez (*Dr. Copeland*), Cicely Tyson (*Portia*), Johnny Popwell (*Willie*), Horace Oates, Jr. (*himself*), Don Swafford (*Dr. Gordon*), Hubert Harper (*Brannon*), Anna Lee Carroll (*Nurse Bradford*), Ronald A. Riner (*Deputy Sheriff Ivor*).

Drama. Source: Carson McCullers, *The Heart Is a Lonely Hunter* (Boston, 1940). John Singer is a deafmute who works as a silverware engraver in a small southern town. When his only companion, a retarded mute, Antonapoulos, is committed to a mental institution, Singer moves to another town in order to be near his friend. He finds work there and rents a room in the home of Mr. and Mrs. Kelly, who are having financial difficulties as a result of Mr. Kelly's recent hip injury. Because the Kellys' 14-year-old daughter, Mick, resents having to give up her room to him, Singer makes a few tentative efforts to win her friendship. He also tries to establish a rapport with Blount, a semi-alcoholic drifter, and Dr. Copeland, an embittered segregationist Negro who is secretly dying of cancer. Copeland's deepest disappointment is that his educated daughter, Portia, works as a domestic and is married to Willie Hamilton, a field hand. Following a successful attempt to win Mick's friendship by encouraging her love for classical music, Singer visits Antonapoulos, who is now suffering from a kidney infection. Although he takes his friend out for the day, Singer is more lonely than ever when he returns home. Meanwhile, Willie is jailed for defending himself against a group of white men, and subsequently he has a leg amputated after being placed in irons for trying to break jail. Feelings between Portia and her father become even more strained until Portia learns from Singer of Copeland's illness, and the two are reconciled. Mick willfully loses her virginity to Harry, the sensitive young brother of one of her classmates, when she realizes that her father's injury has permanently disabled him and she will have to leave school and go to work in order to help support the family. Profoundly disturbed by her sexual initiation, she again rejects Singer's friendship. A short time later, Singer goes to visit Antonapoulos and learns that he has been dead for several weeks. After visiting his friend's grave and saying goodby in sign language, Singer returns to his room and commits suicide. Some months thereafter, Mick brings flowers to Singer's grave and meets Dr. Copeland. As they talk, Mick explains that in a special way Singer's quiet strength has given her courage to face whatever her future may be. *Deafmutes. Engravers. Physicians. Negroes. Invalids. Domestics. Farm workers. Loneliness. Friendship. Mental retardation. Poverty. Adolescence. Music. Sexual initiation. Filial relations. Alcoholism. Racial segregation. Suicide. Death. Hospitals. Cancer. United States—South.*

Note: Filmed in Selma, Marion, Demopolis, and Birmingham, Alabama.

THE HEART OF HIROSHIMA (Japan)　　　F6.2087

Nikkatsu Corp. *Dist* Toho Co. May **1967** [Los Angeles showing]. Sd; col? 35mm. [Feature film, length unknown.]

Dir Koreyoshi Kurahara.

Cast: Tetsuya Watari, Sayuri Yoshinaga, Tomoko Hamakawa, Asao Sano. No information about the nature of this film has been found. *Hiroshima.*

Note: Released in Japan in 1966 as *Ai to shi no kiroku*.

HEAT (Argentina)　　　F6.2088

SIFA. *Dist* Unistar Films, Haven International Pictures, Marvin Films. 21 Jan **1970** [Boston opening]. Sd; b&w. 35mm. 85 min.

Pres by Jerald Intrator. *Prod-Dir-Writ* Armando Bo. *Assoc Prod* Red Evanz, Carlote Chait. *U. S. Vers Dir* Jack Curtis. *U. S. Vers Writ* Paulette Rubenstein Curtis. *Dir Photog* Julio Lavera. *Camera Op* Francis Miranda. *Film Ed* (see note) Rosa Canterbet. *Mus* Alfredo Andrés. *Sd* Juan Pool. *Asst Dir* Gilbert Sierra. *Prod Asst* Siri Suárez. *Electrn* Joe Galetini.

Cast: Isabel Sarli *(Magda)*, Armando Bo *(Juan)*, Horace Priani *(Fernando)*, Mario Casado *(Marco [Marcos])*, Anibal Pardeiro, Brenda Trillo, Marusa Coran, Paul Moret, Maruja Roig, Miguel Paparelli, Alex Castillo, Hélène Chanel, Ana Moreno, Coco Martinel *([see note])*.

Melodrama. Her boat having capsized off a rocky island, Magda collapses on the shore. In a stupor, she recalls her marriage to her wealthy cousin, Fernando, in fulfillment of the wish of her dying mother; her subsequent seduction by her former lover, the cruel gigolo Marco, whom she was unable to resist; her husband's murder of her lover; her husband's incarceration; and an unsuccessful visit to beg forgiveness of her mother-in-law. Magda is rescued by three seal hunters, two of them brothers, who are instantly inflamed by her beauty and compete for her favor. Following a fight in which the hunter Juan is victorious, his brother [the third hunter according to some sources] is killed by a stampede of seals. Fearing that Juan's jealousy will lead to further death, Magda attempts suicide. She is stopped by Juan, however, who assures her that their love is real and persuades her to remain on the island. *Cousins. Mothers-in-law. Brothers. Gigolos. Hunters. Marriage. Infidelity. Murder. Suicide. Jealousy. Islands. Storms. Shipwrecks. Seals.*

Note: Opened in Buenos Aires in Nov 1960 as ... *Y el demonio creó a los hombres*; running time: 95 min. The following are among those credited under variant names for U. S. release: Rosalino Caterbetti (Rosa Canterbet), Horacio Priani (Horace Priani), María Esther Coran (Marusa Coran), and Pablo Moran (Paul Moret). Acting credits for Castillo, Chanel, Moreno, and Martinel obtained from U. S. source only.

HEAT OF MADNESS　　　F6.2089

Cinestudio Productions. *Dist* William Mishkin. 28 Dec **1966** [Minneapolis opening]. Sd; b&w. 35mm. 82 min.

Prod-Dir Harry Wuest. *Screenplay* Eliza McCormick. *Photog* Charles Caffall. *Dsgn* Gary Martin. *Sd* Gary Harris, John Hechtman.

Cast: Kevin Scott *(John Wheelwright)*, Jennifer Llaird *(Susan Amory)*, Alan Wylie *(Bill Tucker)*, Barbara Ward *(Linda Snow)*, John Burke, actor *(Ted)*, Diana Conti *(Tracy)*, Nancy McCormick *(Nancy)*, Ann Muench *(Annie)*, Stanley Seidman *(Rudy Allen)*, Sean Spencer *(Tom)*, Jon Tolliver *(Eckhardt)*, Mark Zalk *(Dr. Ross)*.

Melodrama. John, once a promising art student, photographs calendar nudes for a living. He falls in love with Susan, an advertising agency artist, but since they can't marry on his income, he accepts a job as a photographer for a pulp magazine. Fascinated by the whippings, beatings, and knifings that his employer stages, John becomes more aggressive toward Susan, and nearly rapes her when she refuses his advances, but despite the warnings of her friends, she stands by him. When John discovers his favorite model in bed with another man, he stages a jealous rape scene that nearly becomes reality. Convinced that Susan has deserted him, he goes berserk, and, mistaking one of the models for Susan, he murders her. As Susan tries to offer help, he attacks her, and when, in self-defense, she strikes him with a whip, he begs her to continue. Realizing that John is beyond helping, Susan leaves him to his fantasy world. *Students. Artists. Photographers. Models. Sadomasochism. Rape. Murder. Flagellation. Insanity. Jealousy. Magazines (periodicals).*

Note: Filmed in and around New York City.

HEAT OF MIDNIGHT (France)　　　F6.2090

Les Films du Griffon. *Dist* Olympic International Films. 8 Dec **1966** [San Francisco showing]. Sd; b&w. 35mm. 67 min.

Prod-Dir Max Pécas. *Screenplay* Maurice Cury, Max Pécas. *Photog* Robert Lefebvre. *Film Ed* Nicole Cayatte. *Mus* Louiguy. *Sd* Séverin Frankiel. *English Vers Sd* Spectra Sound. *Asst Dir* Patrice Dubois. *Prod Mgr* Paul Cayatte.

Cast: Claudine Coster *(Fabienne)*, Jean Claudio *(Max Savelan)*, Jean Vinci *(Fred Langlois)*, Anna Gaël *(Sybil)*, Robert Lombard *(Henri)*, Dominique Santarelli, Michel Vocoret, Jean-Claude Dague.

Crime melodrama. To pay off gambling debts, Fred Langlois steals a fortune in jewels from one of the largest crime syndicates in Paris. Fabienne, Fred's ex-wife, agrees to shelter him in her country home. After learning that she is involved in a lesbian relationship with her housemate Sybil, Fred seduces Fabienne and tries to regain her love. [In the original version, Fabienne and Sybil are sisters, and no lesbian relationship is involved.] The racketeers abduct and torture Sybil in an effort to force her to divulge Fred's whereabouts. Max Savelan, a private detective, intervenes, breaks the case, exposes the syndicate and its boss, Henri, and recovers the jewels. Max makes love with Sybil, and Fred is reunited with Fabienne. *Gangsters. Thieves. Roommates. Sisters. Detectives. Lesbianism. Seduction. Abduction. Torture. Divorce. Bisexuality. Syndicates. Jewels. Paris.*

Note: Opened in Paris in Feb 1966 as *Espions à l'affût*; running time: 80 min. Also known as *Heat at Midnight*.

HEAT OF THE SUMMER (France)　　　F6.2091

Films Jacques Leitienne-K. L. F. Productions. *Dist* Ajay Film Co., Manhattan Films International. 10 Mar **1961** [Los Angeles showing]. Sd; b&w. 35mm. 83-94 min.

Prod Lola Kohn. *Dir* Louis Félix. *Script* Paule Delsol, Gilles Siry. *Dial* Paule Delsol. *Adapt* Gilles Siry. *Photog* Marcel Combes, Arthur Raimondo. *Film Ed* Linette Nicolas. *Mus* Fernand Clare. *Sd* René Renault.

Cast: Patricia Karim *(Lina)*, Yane Barry *(Magali)*, Michel Bardinet *(Robert)*, Claude Sainlouis *(Paul)*, Janine Massina *(Germaine)*.

Drama. Robert Mans, a young Parisian writer, inherits a small vineyard in Provence. The only other person on the farm is Magali, an attractive maid, who teaches him how to run the vineyard in the hopes that Robert will settle there. Robert forms a friendly, impersonal relationship with Magali, but he spends most of his time with a neighboring farmer's daughter, Lina, with whom he makes frequent visits to a deserted stretch of beach. Lina tries to persuade Robert to sell the vineyard and take her to the city, but Magali intervenes after following the lovers to the beach and engages in a wild tussle with Lina. Finally brought to his senses, Robert breaks off with Lina and decides to stay at the vineyard with Magali. *Authors. Housemaids. Neighbors. Inheritance. Jealousy. Employer-employee relations. Vineyards.*

Note: Opened in Paris in Nov 1959 as *Chaleurs d'été*; running time: 89 min.

HEAVEN & EARTH MAGIC FEATURE see NO. 12

HEAVEN ON EARTH　　　F6.2092

Dist Davis Film Distributors. 9 Feb **1966** [Waltham, Massachusetts, opening]. Sd; col. 35mm. [Feature length assumed.]

Documentary. No information about the precise nature of this film has been found, but press material suggests that it is a documentary about the Vatican and the historic visit of Pope Paul VI to the Holy Land. *Vatican. Holy Land. Paul VI (pope).*

HEAVEN SENT see THANK HEAVEN FOR SMALL FAVORS

HEAVEN WITH A GUN　　　F6.2093

King Brothers Productions. *Dist* Metro-Goldwyn-Mayer, Inc. May **1969** [New York opening: 11 Jun; c31 Jan 1969; LP36589]. Sd; col (Metrocolor). 35mm (Panavision). 101 min. *MPAA rating* M.

Prod Frank King, Maurice King. *Assoc Prod* Herman King, Red Hershon. *Dir* Lee H. Katzin. *Writ* Richard Carr. *Dir Photog* Fred Koenekamp. *Art Dir* George W. Davis, Frank Sylos. *Set Decor* Henry Grace, Don Greenwood, Jr. *Film Ed* Dann Cahn. *Mus* Johnny Mandel. Song: "A Lonely Place" Paul Francis Webster, Johnny Mandel. *Rec Supv* Franklin Milton. *Asst Dir* William P. Owens. *Unit Prod Mgr* Sam Manners. *Makeup* William Tuttle. *Hairstyles* Mary Keats.

Cast: Glenn Ford *(Jim Killian)*, Carolyn Jones *(Madge McCloud)*, Barbara Hershey *(Leloopa)*, John Anderson *(Asa Beck)*, David Carradine *(Coke Beck)*, J. D. Cannon *(Mace)*, Noah Beery *(Garvey)*, Harry Townes *(Gus Sampson)*, William Bryant *(Bart Patterson)*, Virginia Gregg *(Mrs. Patterson)*, James Griffith *(Abraham Murdock)*, Roger Perry *(Ned Hunter)*, Claude Woolman *(Gilcher)*, Ed Bakey *(Scotty Andrews)*, Barbara Babcock *(Mrs. Andrews)*, James Chandler *(Doc Foster)*, Angelique Pettyjohn *(Emily)*, Jessica James *(Jan)*, Bee Tompkins *(bar girl)*, Bill Catching *(Willy)*, Al Wyatt *(Indian)*, Ed

McCready (Charlie), Miss Eddie Crispell, Barbara Dombre (townspeople).

Western melodrama. The small western town of Vinegaroon is ruled with an iron hand by Asa Beck, a ranch owner waging a savage war against the local sheepmen. When a stranger named Jim Killian rides into town, Beck assumes that he is a gunfighter hired by the sheep herders, but Killian reveals that he is a preacher who has come to open the Mission Church of the Good Shepherd and teach the townspeople that they can live together in peace. Quick to attach herself to Killian is a young Indian named Leloopa, the daughter of a sheep herder hanged by Beck's ruthless son, Coke. After Coke has been soundly beaten by Killian for assaulting Leloopa, the young rancher is slain by one of the sheepmen. Enraged, Beck sends one of his hired killers, Mace, to burn down Killian's church. Although Killian is moved to take revenge, saloon keeper Madge McCloud uses her former friendship with Killian to dissuade him from taking up his gun. Calling together both ranchers and sheepmen, Killian delivers a sermon on peace, only to be exposed as an ex-gunslinger and convict by Mace. Then Beck makes plans to provoke a showdown with the sheepmen by driving his herd to the lake which serves as the town's only water supply. But Killian succeeds in rallying together the wives and children of both ranchers and sheepmen and persuading them to form a human shield at the lakeside. Incapable of shooting at their own families, the ranchers drop their guns and Beck is forced to admit that he has been defeated by the preacher's sermon. *Ranchers. Indians of North America. Gunfighters. Sheepmen. Preachers. Hired killers. Saloon keepers. Lynching. Arson. Range wars. Revenge. Churches.*

Note: Location scenes filmed in Arizona.

HEAVENLY BODIES   F6.2094

Eve Productions. 28 Jun **1963** [Los Angeles showing; c1 Jul 1963; LP25498]. Sd; col (Eastmancolor). 35mm. 60 min.

Prod-Dir Russ Meyer. *Photog* Russ Meyer. *Film Ed* Russ Meyer.

Cast: Ken Parker, Gaby Martine, Marian Milford, Russ Meyer, Don Cochran, Werner Kirsch, Fred Owens, Billy Newhouse, Orville Hallberg, Bill Cummings, Althea, Monica, Rochelle Kennedy, Charles Schelling, Nancy Andre, Don Goodwin, Ivana Nolte.

Documentary(?). A behind-the-scenes look at the world of figure modeling shows Hollywood "glamour" photographers at work with both professional and novice models. Ken Parker works with two models at the same time so as to afford each of them more rest, and to provoke an atmosphere of spontaneous interplay. Russ Meyer, "one of Hollywood's best known glamour photographers," leads a group of his friends, former Army Signal Corps cameramen, on an outing to demonstrate the value of the photo field trip in "glamour" photography. In the woods, models Althea and Monica pose nude for a series of nature shots. Back in Hollywood, a 21-year-old aspiring showgirl, Rochelle Kennedy, arises early for a modeling session with Charles Gilbert Schelling, who skillfully encourages her into the desired frame of mind. Russ Meyer shows his ability to elicit dynamic emotion and drive from his models. Photographer Don Goodwin demonstrates his knack for recruiting new models. He spots the striking Ivana Nolte on a Los Angeles street, convinces her of his honorable intentions, offers the promise of a profitable venture, tests her ability to pose, and puts his early appraisal of her figure to a more rigorous scrutiny. He then meets the challenge of convincing Ivana to release her inhibitions. *Photographers. Models. Motion picture cameramen. Photography. Nudity. Los Angeles. Hollywood.*

Note: Filmed in and around Los Angeles. May also be known as *Heavenly Assignment.*

HEAVENS ABOVE! (Great Britain)   F6.2095

Charter Film Productions. *For* British Lion Films. *Dist* Janus Films, Cinema V Distributing, Inc. 20 May **1963** [New York opening]. Sd; b&w. 35mm. 105min.

A Boulting Brothers Production. *Prod* Roy Boulting. *Dir* John Boulting. *Screenplay* Frank Harvey, John Boulting. *From an Idea by* Malcolm Muggeridge. *Photog* Max Greene. *Art Dir* Albert Witherick. *Film Ed* Teddy Darvas. *Mus Comp* Richard Rodney Bennett. *Mus Cond* John Hollingsworth. *Sd Rec* George Stephenson. *Asst Dir* Derek Cracknell. *Prod Mgr* Michael F. Johnson. *Asst to the Prod* Theo Richmond. *Cost* David Ffolkes. *Makeup* Stuart Freeborn, Gerry Fletcher. *Hairstyles* Barbara Ritchie.

Cast: Peter Sellers (*Rev. John Smallwood*), Cecil Parker (*Archdeacon Aspinall*), Isabel Jeans (*Lady Despard*), Eric Sykes (*Harry Smith*), Bernard Miles (*Simpson*), Brock Peters (*Matthew*), Ian Carmichael (*The Other Smallwood*), Irene Handl (*Rene Smith*), Miriam Karlin (*Winnie Smith*), Joan Miller (*Mrs. Smith-Gould*), Eric Barker (*bank manager*), Roy Kinnear (*Fred Smith*), Kenneth Griffith (*Rev. Owen Thomas*), Miles Malleson (*Rockerby*), William Hartnell (*Major Fowler*), Joan Hickson (*garrulous housewife*), Mark Eden (*Sir Geoffrey Despard*), John Comer (*butcher*), Franklyn Engelmann, Tim Brinton (*TV commentators*), Ludovic Kennedy (*Ludovic Kennedy*), Geoffrey Hibbert (*council official*), Harry Locke (*shop steward*), Nicholas Phipps (*director general*), Thorley Walters (*Tranquilax executive*), George

Woodbridge (*bishop*), Basil Dignam (*prisoner governor*), Colin Gordon (*prime minister*), Joan Heal (*disgruntled housewife*), Marjie Lawrence, Olive Sloane (*quarreling housewives*), Henry Longhurst (*deaf gentleman*), Malcolm Muggeridge (*cleric*), Conrad Phillips (*P. R. O.*), Cardew Robinson (*tramp*), Elsie Wagstaff (*lady on parish church council*), Ian Wilson (*Salvation Army major*), Josephine Woodford (*Doris Smith*), Howard Pays (*astronaut*), Drewe Henley (*Doris' boyfriend*), Billy Milton (*Fellowes*), John Harvey.

Comedy. British prison chaplain Rev. John Smallwood is mistakenly appointed vicar of a well-to-do church in Orbiston Parva, a provincial industrial town in England, instead of another Rev. John Smallwood, a fawning member of the Establishment. Smallwood shocks the wealthy parishioners, who rarely attend services, by naming as his church warden Matthew, a West Indian Negro trash collector. Next he invites to live at the vicarage the Smiths, a family of Gypsies who have been run off land they occupied belonging to the Tranquilax factory, a manufacturer of a combination sedative, stimulant, and laxative. Smallwood causes Lady Despard, the factory's dowager owner, to become ashamed of her wealth and give away her fortune; but the windfall to the townspeople, in the form of free food, angers the local shopkeepers. Further encouraged by Smallwood, Lady Despard sells her Tranquilax stock, whereupon its value plummets and unemployment threatens Orbiston Parva. Lady Despard finally comes to her senses and stops the flow of money. Smallwood is deserted by the townspeople, who, out of work, begin to riot. He escapes from the mob and is assigned to a new parish on a remote island nuclear missile site. An astronaut whom Smallwood is trying to comfort before he is launched into space taunts him about his religious beliefs; and in response Smallwood ties up the astronaut, takes his place in the rocket, and becomes known as the "bishop of outer space." *Clergymen. Negroes. West Indians. Nobility. Gypsies. Storekeepers. Astronauts. Smalltown life. Wealth. Mistaken identity. Religion. Unemployment. Charity. Patent medicines. Riots. Factories. Islands. Missiles. England.*

Note: Opened in London on 23 May 1963; running time: 118 min. Rereleased in 1965 by Cinema V Distributing, Inc.

HEDONIST HYPNOTIST   F6.2096

Dist Stacey Distributors. ca **1970**. Sd; col. 16mm. 61-81 min.

Sex film. No information about the precise nature of this film has been found. *Sexuality. Hypnotism. Hedonism.*

HEDONISTIC PLEASURES   F6.2097

Dyle IV Productions. *Dist* Canyon Distributing Co. 12 Aug **1969** [Norfolk, Virginia, opening]. Sd (Spectra Sound); col (Eastman Color). 35mm. 71 min.

Prod-Writ Ed DePriest. *Dir* Mike Weldon. *Film Ed* Ed Hunt. *Mus Score* Robin Herth.

Cast: Camille Grant (*Cathy*), Phil Walters (*Murphy*), Linda Powers (*Star*), Lisa Maria (*Lisa*), Stu Hamilton (*Barry*), Karen Wickline (*Wendy*), Mike Johns (*Lance*), Pat Neice (*Liz*).

Documentary(?). Made possible by highly sophisticated miniature cameras, this exposé of Hollywood's sexual underground deals with prostitution, sex techniques, oral sex, and group sexual encounters. Living in Hollywood there is a whole subculture of perverts, who with jaded sexual appetites, seek increasingly outrageous and bizarre means of satisfaction. *Oral sex. Prostitution. Sexual techniques. Group sex. Sexual practices. Hollywood.*

HEDY THE SHOPLIFTER see THE 14 YEAR OLD GIRL

HEIDI (Austria)   F6.2098

Sascha Film. *Dist* Warner Bros.-Seven Arts, Inc. Mar **1968**. Sd; col (Eastmancolor, print by Technicolor). 35mm. 95 min.

Prod Richard Deitsche. *Assoc Prod* Karl Schwetter. *Dir* Werner Jacobs. *Screenplay* Richard Schweizer. *Adapt* Michael Haller, writ. *Photog* Richard Angst. *Art Dir* Fritz Juptner-Jonstorff, Hans Zehetner, Hans-Gunther Malyjurek. *Film Ed* Arnd Heyne. *Mus & Titl Song* Franz Grothe. *Song:* "Echo Mountain Song" Moose Charlap. *Titl Song & Song:* "Echo Mountain Song" *English lyr* Stanley Styne. *Sd* Hans Riedl, Karl Schwarz. *Asst Dir* Margrith Spitzer. *Cost* Barbara Langbein.

Cast: Eva Maria Singhammer (*Heidi*), Gertraud Mittermayr (*Klara Sesemann*), Gustav Knuth (*grandfather*), Lotte Ledl (*Aunt Dete*), Ernst Schröder (*Herr Sesemann*), Margot Trooger (*Miss Rottenmeier*), Rolf Moebius (*Dr. Klassen*), Rudolf Vogel (*Sebastian*), Jan Koester (*Peter*), Rudolf Prack.

Drama. Source: Johanna Spyri, *Heidi* (Zurich, 1880). Heidi, an orphan, lives in the Swiss Alps with her gruff but kindly grandfather. One day Aunt Dete whisks the girl away to Frankfurt, where Heidi is hired as a companion to crippled Klara Sesemann. Despite the remonstrances of the child's governess, Miss Rottenmeier, the girls become close friends. Under Heidi's supervision Klara takes her first tentative steps. Despite her joy at Klara's probable recovery, Heidi longs for her Alpine home. When Heidi sickens, Klara's sympathetic physician, Dr. Klassen, suggests her return. Heidi is joyfully reunited with her beloved grandfather and afterwards visited by her Frankfurt friends. *Orphans. Cripples. Grandfathers. Physicians. Children. Governesses.*

Friendship. Switzerland. Alps. Frankfurt am Main.

Note: Location scenes filmed in the Swiss and German Alps and in Frankfurt. Released in Austria in 1965; running time: 103 min.

HEIGHTS OF DANGER (Great Britain)   **F6.2099**
Associated British-Pathé Ltd.—Pathé Documentary Unit. *For* Children's Film Foundation. *Dist* Continental Distributing, Inc. 5 Apr **1962** [Maryland license]. Sd; b&w. 35mm. 60 min.
Prod Howard Thomas. *Dir* Peter Bradford, dir. *Screenplay* Betty Davies. *Photog* Reg. W. Cavender. *Sets* Scott MacGregor. *Film Ed* Alex Milner-Gardner. *Mus* Doreen Carwithen.
Cast: Basil Appleby *(Mr. Burton)*, Freda Bamford *(Mrs. Burton)*, Wilfred Downing *(Wilfred Burton)*, Annette Cabot *(Annette Burton)*, Christopher Cabot *(Christopher Burton)*, Richard Goolden *(Mr. Henderson)*, Jack Melford *(Mr. Croudson)*, Roger Snowdon *(Wolfing)*, Sebastian Cabot *(Jakes)*.
Drama. Revival of business at the Burton family garage is contingent on completion of a bypass. Taking advantage of the Burtons' financial situation, the malevolent businessman Croudson attempts to buy the family out. The benign and elderly Henderson, however, takes pity on the family and pays Burton to compete in an Alpine auto race. Although Croudson's two henchmen repeatedly sabotage Burton, he wins the remunerative prize. *Businessmen. Garage-keepers. Family life. Automobile racing. Garages. Alps.*
Note: Released in Great Britain in 1953.

HEINZELMÄNNCHEN *see* **THE SHOEMAKER AND THE ELVES**

DER HEISSE TOD *see* **99 WOMEN**

HEISSER SAND AUF SYLT *see* **THE NEW LIFE STYLE**

HELDEN *see* **ARMS AND THE MAN**

HELDEN—HIMMEL UND HÖLLE *see* **THE CAVERN**

HELDINNEN (West Germany)   **F6.2100**
H. R. Sokal Film—UFA. *Dist* Casino Films. 26 May **1962** [Milwaukee, Wisconsin, opening]. Sd; col. 35mm. 97 min.
Prod H. R. Sokal. *Dir* Dietrich Haugk. *Screenplay* Charlotte Kerr. *Photog* Werner Krien. *Camera Op* Gerhard Girbig. *Camera Asst* Horst Braun. *Art Dir* Hanns Kuhnert, Wilhelm Vorwerg. *Film Ed* Claus von Boro. *Mus* Franz Grothe. *Lyr* Willy Dehmel, Charlotte Kerr, Günther Schwenn. *Choreog* Lilo Herbeth. *Sd* Hermann Dankert. *Asst Dir* Claus von Boro. *Prod Mgr* Heinz Karchow, Hans Johansen. *Wardrobe* Walter Leder, Margarete Neumann. *Cost Adv* Charlotte Flemming. *Makeup* Raimund Stangl, Charlotte Schmidt-Kersten, Ingrid Nixdorf. *Prop* Helmut Künecke, Sylvester Schimpke. *Still Photog* Leo Weisse.
Cast: Marianne Koch *(Minna von Barnhelm)*, Johanna von Koczian *(Franziska)*, Paul Hubschmid *(Major von Tellheim)*, Walter Giller *(Just)*, Günter Pfitzmann *(Werner)*, Willy Trenk-Trebitsch *(Ricaut)*, Alfred Balthoff *(innkeeper)*, Ursula Diestel, Ilse Kiewiet, Ingeborg Wellmann, Inge Wolffberg.
Musical comedy. Source: Gotthold Ephraim Lessing, *Minna von Barnhelm, oder Das Soldatenglück* (Hamburg opening: 30 Sep 1767). At the conclusion of the Seven Years' War, Major von Tellheim is suspended from the Prussian army pending an investigation into financial misconduct. While living frugally with his servant, Just, in a rustic inn, the major is sought out by his fiancée, Minna von Barnhelm, a noblewoman. In deference to her betrothed's sense of honor, which precludes continuation of the engagement during his disgrace, Minna pretends to have been ostracized by her family. Through such subterfuge Minna elicits a confession of love, while the major's timely reinstatement dissolves the barriers to their marriage. *Soldiers. Prussians. Nobility. Valets. Pride. Marriage. Inns. Seven Years' War 1756–63.*
Note: Opened in Frankfurt in Sep 1960; running time: 100 min.

HELGA (West Germany)   **F6.2101**
Rinco-Film. *Dist* American International Pictures. Aug **1968** [c8 Aug 1968; LP36077]. Sd; col (Eastmancolor by Perfect). 35mm. 87 min. [Also reviewed at 76 min.]
Prod Karl-Ludwig Ruppel. *Prod English Lang Vers* Salvatore Billitteri, Titan Productions. *Dir-Writ* Erich F. Bender. *Dir English Lang Vers* Terry Van Tell. *Cinematog* Fritz Baader, Klaus Werner. *Microcamera* Dr. Erwin Burcik. *Film Ed* Monika Pfefferle, Ilse Wüstenhöfer. *Mus* Karl Barthel. *Mus Dir* Kurt Graunke. *Soloists* Roy Etzel, Karl Barthel, Willi Muller. *Prod Mgr* Werner P. Frei. *Prod Supv* Willi Schuler. *Tech Adv* Dr. Erwin Burcik, Dr. Gerhard Döring, Dr. Wolfgang Fritsche, Dr. Christel Schultze-Rhonhof, Dr. Fritz Zimmer, Dr. Christa Topfmeier. *Diagrams* Rinco-Film. *Anatomical models* Central Health Institute—Cologne.
Cast: Ruth Gassmann *(Helga)*, Eberhard Mondry *(Helga's husband)*, Asgard Hummel, Ilse Zielstorff.
Sex instruction film. Helga, a young woman, becomes pregnant. She and her husband are instructed in the proper exercises and preparations for the birth of

their child. Physicians, nurses, and other medical personnel with the aid of diagrams and microphotographs offer Helga and her husband information on human sexuality and reproduction. Finally, the birth of Helga's son is shown in detail through the use of close-up photography. Helga is later shown nursing her baby at home. *Physicians. Nurses. Pregnancy. Childbirth. Sex instruction. Anatomy. Reproduction. Parenthood. Documentation.*
Note: Released in West Germany in 1967 with the subtitle *Vom Werden des menschlichen Lebens;* running time: 77 min. Produced under the auspices of the West German Federal Institute of Health Education. English language version, produced by Titan Productions, features a prologue. Screen credit includes the subtitle *From the Inception of Human Life.* Followed by a sequel, *Michael and Helga,* q. v.

HELGA AND MICHAEL *see* **MICHAEL AND HELGA**

HELGA UND MICHAEL *see* **MICHAEL AND HELGA**

HELL BOATS (Great Britain)   **F6.2102**
Oakmont Productions. *Dist* United Artists. Feb **1970** [c20 May 1970; LP38231]. Sd; col (Technicolor). 35mm. 95 min. *MPAA rating* GP.
Pres by Mirisch Films. *Prod* Lewis J. Rachmil. *Exec In Charge of Prod* William S. Gilmore, Jr. *Dir* Paul Wendkos. *Screenplay* Anthony Spinner, Donald Ford, Derek Ford. *Story* S. S. Schweitzer. *Dir Photog* Paul Beeson. *Camera Op* John Winbolt. *Art Dir* Tony Pratt. *Film Ed* John S. Smith. *Mus Comp* Frank Cordell. *Sd Ed* Bill Creed. *Sd Rec* Norman Bolland. *Sd Re-rec* Hugh Strain. *1st & 2d Asst Dir* Anthony Waye, Peter Carter, asst dir, Chris Kenny. *Unit Prod Mgr* Eva Monley. *Location Mgr* Ken Softley. *Wardrobe* Duncan MacPhee. *Makeup* Jill Carpenter, Eileen Fletcher. *Hairdressing* Ann Box. *Sp Eff* Ron Ballanger. *Story Cons & Tech Adv* Ian Cox, (Lieut. Comdr., Royal Navy Ret.). *Prop Man* Derek Knowler.
Cast: James Franciscus *(Lieut. Comdr. Tom Jeffords)*, Elizabeth Shepherd *(Alison Ashurst)*, Ronald Allen *(Comdr. Roger Ashurst)*, Reuven Bar-Yotam *(Yacov)*, Inigo Jackson *(Stanhope)*, Mark Hawkins *(Barlow)*, Drewe Henley *(Johnson)*, Magda Konopka *(Lucianna)*, Takis Emmanuel *(Salvatore)*, Philip Madoc *(E-boat commander)*, Sean Barrett *(Henderson)*, Andreas Malandrinos *(Benny)*.
War drama. Tom Jeffords, an American serving as a lieutenant commander in the Royal Navy in 1942, is assigned to the blockaded island of Malta and ordered to create a plan to destroy a German arsenal in Augusta, Sicily, thus allowing the British to transport supplies to their troops in North Africa. Jeffords foresees the difficult nature of the operation, and he imposes strict discipline on the men in his command, an act which incurs their enmity. Despite Jeffords' warning, three men are killed in a reconnaissance mission. Comdr. Roger Ashurst, with whose estranged wife, Alison, Jeffords has become acquainted, doubts the success of Jeffords' plan, though he volunteers to command a German E-boat, a motor torpedo boat which the Germans call a "hell boat," and pilot it through German lines. The men destroy the arsenal, and Ashurst's bravery results in his being reunited with Alison. *Military occupation. Heroism. Military invasion. Marriage. Torpedo boats. World War II. Malta. Augusta (Italy). Great Britain—Royal Navy. Germany—Navy. Explosions.*
Note: Filmed on location on Malta. Released in Great Britain caApr 1970; running time: 95 min.

HELL IN THE CITY *see* **... AND THE WILD, WILD WOMEN**

HELL IN THE PACIFIC   **F6.2103**
Selmur Pictures. *Dist* Cinerama Releasing Corp. 18 Dec **1968** [Los Angeles opening]. Sd; col (Technicolor). 35mm (Panavision). 103 min. *MPAA rating* G.
Pres by Selmur Pictures, Henry G. Saperstein. *Prod* Reuben Bercovitch. *Exec Prod* Selig J. Seligman, Henry G. Saperstein. *Dir* John Boorman. *Screenplay* Alexander Jacobs, Eric Bercovici. *Orig Story* Reuben Bercovitch. *Cinematog* Conrad Hall. *Camera Op* Jordan Cronenweth. *Lighting* Harry Sundby. *Art Dir* Tony Pratt, Masao Yamazaki. *Set Decor* Makoto Kikuchi. *Film Ed* Thomas Stanford. *Asst Ed* Neil Travis. *Mus* Lalo Schifrin. *Sd Rec* Tooru Sakata. *Sd Eff* Frank Warner. *Mus Ed* James Henrikson. *Re-rec Supv* Clem Portman. *Asst Dir* Yoichi Matsue. *Unit Prod Mgr* Lloyd Anderson, Harry F. Hogan, Isao Zeniya. *Script Supv* John Franco. *Prod Asst* B. C. Wylie. *Makeup* Shigeo Kobayashi. *Sp Eff* Joe Zomar, Kunishige Tanaka. *Tech Adv* Masaki Asukai. *Prop Master* Frank A. Wade, Kesataka Sato. *Key Grip* Art Brooker.
Cast: Lee Marvin *(American soldier)*, Toshiro Mifune *(Japanese soldier)*.
War drama. In 1944, a U. S. Marine pilot and a Japanese naval officer are simultaneously separated from their units on an uninhabited Pacific atoll. After becoming aware of each other's presence, the men stalk and threaten but do not take advantage of opportunities to kill each other. Eventually, the Japanese overpowers the American during a struggle in the jungle, brings him back to camp, and ties his arms in a yoke-like harness. Before long, however, the

American escapes, captures the Japanese, and imprisons him in a similar fashion. Like the Japanese before him, the American derives no satisfaction from holding a prisoner; he releases his opponent, and an unspoken truce gradually develops. When the Japanese attempts to build a small raft, the American is initially derisive but eventually aids in the construction. In time they set sail for a distant group of small islands and manage to reach one of them after a harrowing voyage. The island is uninhabited, but remnants from a bombed Japanese installation enable them to bathe, shave, change clothes, and get drunk on saké. Their relatively happy mood is shattered, however, when the Japanese becomes enraged by illustrations in a discarded copy of *Life* magazine showing his slain people; reverting to their hostile state, the two men go their separate ways. [Executive Producer Saperstein substituted an alternative ending on some prints in which an explosion occurs, suggesting that the two men are killed. Both versions were shown in the U. S.] *Japanese. Air pilots. Survival. Drunkenness. Rafts. World War II. South Sea Islands. United States Marines. Japan—Navy. "Life" (magazine). Explosions.*

Note: Location scenes filmed on Koror and other Palau Islands of Micronesia. Working titles: *Two Soldiers—East and West* and *The Enemy.*

HELL IS FOR HEROES
F6.2104

Paramount Pictures. 30 May **1962** [Los Angeles opening; c31 Dec 1961; LP22223]. Sd; b&w. 35mm. 90 min.

Prod Henry Blanke. *Dir* Don Siegel. *Screenplay* Robert Pirosh, Richard Carr. *Story* Robert Pirosh. *Dir Photog* Harold Lipstein. *Art Dir* Hal Pereira, Howard Richmond. *Set Decor* Sam Comer, Robert R. Benton. *Titl Backgrounds Photog* Curt Gunther, Art Say. *Film Ed* Howard Smith. *Mus* Leonard Rosenman. *Sd Rec* Philip Mitchell, John Wilkinson. *Asst Dir* William McGarry, James Rosenberger, Jack Barry. *Prod Mgr* Joseph Behm, William Mull. *Prod Supv* Frank Caffey. *Script Supv* Dorothy Yutzi. *Men's Wardrobe* Wally Harton. *Makeup Supv* Wally Westmore. *Makeup* William Morley, Bob Hickman. *Sp Photog Eff* John P. Fulton. *Sp Eff* Dick Webb, sp eff. *Tech Adv* William H. Harrigan, Jr. (Maj. USA). *Still Photog* Art Say.

Cast: Steve McQueen (*Reese*), Bobby Darin (*Private Corby*), Fess Parker (*Sergeant Pike*), Harry Guardino (*Sergeant Larkin*), Nick Adams (*Homer*), Bob Newhart (*Private Driscoll*), James Coburn (*Henshaw*), Mike Kellin (*Kolinski*), Joseph Hoover (*Captain Loomis*), Bill Mullikin (*Private Cumberly*), L. Q. Jones (*Sergeant Frazer*), Michele Montau (*Monique*), Don Haggerty (*Captain Mace*).

War drama. In autumn 1944, Reese, a sullen and rebellious American soldier, is demoted for drunkenness and sent back to his outfit, a small, battle-weary, infantry squad stationed near Germany's formidable Siegfried Line in Belgium. Reese's open resentment at being replaced as staff sergeant alienates him from his fellow GI's, despite his decoration for courage during previous combat missions. When the squad is ordered to defend a thinly wooded area facing a German pillbox, they use various ruses to convince the enemy that they are a much larger force. Although their instructions are merely to hold their position until replacements arrive, Reese realizes that they cannot long continue to fool the Germans, and he leads an unauthorized charge against the pillbox. The raid is unsuccessful and Reese is slated for court martial. But, with the coming of dawn, he unleashes a one-man assault against the stronghold and blows himself up along with the German gun crew, enabling the Allied forces to breach the hitherto impregnable Siegfried Line. *War heroes. Combat zone life. Drunkenness. Self-sacrifice. Courts-martial. World War II. Westwall. Belgium. United States Army—Infantry. Germany—Army.*

Note: Location scenes filmed in Cottonwood and Redding, California. Selections from a speech by John F. Kennedy appear on the screen as a prolog.

HELL ON WHEELS
F6.2105

Robert Patrick Productions. *Dist* Crown International Pictures. 16 Jun **1967** [Nashville, Tennessee, opening]. Sd; col (Technicolor). 35mm. 96 min.

Prod Robert Patrick. *Dir* Will Zens. *Screenplay* Wesley Cox. *Photog* Leif Rise. *Songs:* "No Tears Milady," "Fly Butterfly Fly" sung by Marty Robbins. *Adtl Songs Sung by* Connie Smith, The Stonemans. *Sd* Spectra Sound.

Cast: Marty Robbins (*Marty*), John Ashley (*Del*), Gigi Perreau (*Sue*), Robert Dornan (*Steve*), Connie Smith (*herself*), The Stonemans (*themselves*), Robert Foulk, Frank Gerstle (*moonshiners*), Christine Tabbott, Chris Eland, Eddie Crandall, Marvin Miller.

Melodrama. Stock car driver Marty gains the admiration of the crowd, while his brother Del, a mechanic, smoulders on the side lines. A third brother, Steve, a revenue agent, tries in vain to keep peace in the family. Intending to win fame for himself, Del opens his own garage, building souped-up "tankers" for moonshiners on the side. His girl friend Sue is upset but cannot stop him. Del makes a proposition to the owner of a car often beaten by Marty and is allowed to drive against his brother. Flushed with victory in a race that almost costs Marty his life, Del tries to break away from the moonshine ring, but both he and Marty are abducted by the gang. As Steve and a squad of revenue agents close in, Marty and Del escape, with the moonshiners in hot pursuit. Rounding a curve, the moonshiners' car goes out of control, and they plunge to their

deaths. Marty and Del then help Steve round up the remaining criminals. Secure in the knowledge that he is a good driver as well as mechanic, Del apologizes to Marty, and the two combine to become the most sensational team in stock car history. *Stock car drivers. Brothers. Mechanics. Revenue agents. Moonshiners. Jealousy. Automobile racing. Abduction. Garages. Chases. Automobile accidents.*

HELL TO MACAO see THE CORRUPT ONES

THE HELL WITH HEROES
F6.2106

Universal Pictures. 28 Aug **1968** [Pittsburgh opening; c5 Oct 1968; LP36905]. Sd (Westrex); col (Technicolor). 35mm (Techniscope). 102 min.

Prod Stanley Chase. *Dir* Joseph Sargent. *Screenplay* Halsted Welles, Harold Livingston. *Story* Harold Livingston. *Dir Photog* Bud Thackery. *Art Dir* Alexander Golitzen, John J. Lloyd. *Set Decor* John McCarthy, George Milo. *Film Ed* Howard Epstein. *Mus* Quincy Jones. *Song:* "Where There Is Love" Quincy Jones, Dorothy Fields. *Sung by* Sue Raney. *Mus Supv* Joseph Gershenson. *Sd* Waldon O. Watson, Lyle Cain. *Asst Dir* George Bisk. *Unit Prod Mgr* Henry Kline. *Wardrobe Dsgn* Jean Louis. *Makeup* Bud Westmore. *Hairstyles* Larry Germain. *Tech Adv* Jivan R. Tabibian. *Dial Coach* Bert Steinberger.

Cast: Rod Taylor (*Brynie MacKay*), Claudia Cardinale (*Elena*), Harry Guardino (*Lee Harris*), Kevin McCarthy (*Colonel Wilson*), Peter Deuel (*Mike Brewer*), William Marshall (*Al Poland*), Don Knight (*Pepper*), Michael Shillo (*Pol Guilbert*), Robert Yuro (*Willoughby*), Lew Brown (*Sergeant Shaeffer*), Wilhelm von Homburg (*Hans*), Tanya Lemani (*Jamila*), Mae Mercer (*chanteuse*), Emile Genest (*Inspector Bouchard*), Louis de Farra (*Pierre*), Jacqueline Bertrand (*French girl*), Ric Natoli, Tony Nassour, Ricky Namay, George Samaan, David Sindaha (*urchins*), Sid Haig (*Crespin*), Jim Creech (*1st M. P.*), Pedro Regas (*old Arab*), David Kurzon (*lookout*), Naji Gabbay (*Magid*).

Melodrama. In 1946, former Air Force pilots Brynie MacKay and Mike Brewer are operating an impoverished cargo operation out of Algeria. Embittered because the war prevented him from becoming a teacher and eager for the big money, Brynie accepts an offer from international smuggler Lee Harris to ferry Egyptian cotton to France. When Brynie learns he is flying contraband cigarettes, he extracts a larger fee from Harris, who retaliates by hiding narcotics in Brynie's plane and then reporting him to Colonel Wilson of U. S. Counterintelligence. After Brynie's payment has been confiscated and his plane impounded, he is taken to Harris' estate by the latter's mistress, Elena, the daughter of an aristocrat who has fallen on hard times. When Harris agrees to put Brynie back in business by giving him 12 more illegal cargo runs, Mike warns that they will probably both be killed after the completion of the assignment. Brynie, wanting the cash to buy his own plane, ignores the advice until Mike later tells him that he has set a trap for Harris by divulging the flight plans to Colonel Wilson. Unwilling to give up Harris' money, Brynie tries to land the plane safely away from Wilson's waiting men. Harris suspects a hijacking scheme, however, and in the ensuing struggle kills Mike before being knocked unconscious by Brynie. After landing the plane at an abandoned military air strip, Brynie informs Wilson over the phone of the whereabouts of the contraband and then escapes to North Africa with Elena. When Harris tracks them down, Brynie retaliates for Mike's murder by smashing Harris' head against a steel plate. Wilson arrives on the scene, takes Harris into custody, and announces that because of the deal he made with Mike he will not arrest Brynie. Brynie decides to return to America with Elena and become a teacher. *Air pilots. Veterans. Smugglers. Mistresses. Intelligence agents. Partnerships. Perfidy. Murder. Ambition. Narcotics. Algeria. North Africa. United States Army—Intelligence.*

Note: Location scenes filmed in Southern California. Working titles: *A Time for Heroes* and *Run Hero Run.*

THE HELLBENDERS (Italy/Spain)
F6.2107

Alba Cinematografica–TECISA. *Dist* Embassy Pictures. Jun **1967**. Sd; col (Eastman Color, print by Pathé). 35mm. 92 min.

Prod Albert Band. *Dir* Sergio Corbucci. *Screenplay* Albert Band, Ugo Liberatore. *Scen* Ugo Liberatore, José G. Maesso. *Adtl Dial U. S. Vers* Louis Garfinkle. *Story* Virgil C. Gerlach. *Photog* Enzo Barboni. *Art Dir* Jaime Pérez Cubero. *Film Ed* Nino Baragli, Alberto Gallitti. *Mus* Leo Nichols. *Trumpet Solo* Nunzio Rotondo. *Sd* Safa Palatino. *Asst Dir* Ruggero Deodato, Mario Berriatua. *Prod Mgr* Eliseo Boschi, Fernando Ocaña. *Makeup* Piero Mecacci, Francisco Puyol.

Cast: Joseph Cotten (*Jonas*), Norma Bengell (*Claire*), Julián Mateos (*Ben*), Gino Pernice (*Jeff*), Angel Aranda (*Nat*), María Martín (*Kitty*), Al Mulock (*The Beggar*), Aldo Sambrell (*Pedro*), Enio Girolami (*Fort Brent commander*), José Nieto (*sheriff*), Claudio Gora (*Reverend Pierce*), Julio Peña (*Sergeant Tolt*), Benito Stefanelli (*Slim*), Claudio Scarchilli (*Indian chief*), Alvaro de Luna, Rafael Vaquero, Ivan Scratuglia, Simón Arriaga, José Canalejas.

Western melodrama. Following the Civil War, Jonas, a former Confederate colonel, and his three sons, Ben, Jeff, and Nat, massacre a Union Army detachment in Arkansas and steal over a million dollars which the fanatical Jonas plans to use to finance renewed hostilities against the North. After concealing the cash in the coffin of a dead Confederate officer and hiring a hard-drinking woman, Kitty, to pose as the officer's bereaved widow, the four men set out for Sun Dog, the family ranch in New Mexico. En route, Kitty attempts to steal the treasure, but is caught and strangled by Jeff. Jonas quickly recruits another "widow," a dance hall hostess named Claire, and then sets out again. Attacked by Mexican bandits, the little group is rescued by Union soldiers who hang the bandits at nearby Fort Brent. Claire, in love with Ben, seizes the opportunity to thwart Jonas' plan by insisting her "husband"'s coffin be buried inside the fort. That night the enraged Jonas holds Claire as hostage and forces Ben to return to the fort and bring back the buried coffin. Although Ben succeeds, Jonas' problems continue to mount: a beggar attempts to steal the coffin and wounds Jonas before being killed himself, and Jeff's attempted rape of an Indian maiden brings forth a band of braves from her tribe demanding vengeance. When Ben offers them the coffin instead, Nat violently objects and pushes Jeff toward the Indians. In the struggle that follows, Jeff and Nat draw pistols and kill each other. Jonas, by now badly bleeding from his shoulder wound, drags the coffin away from the scene. He loses his grip and the coffin tumbles downhill to a river, breaks open, and reveals the corpse of one of the hanged Mexican bandits. In an agonizing fit of hysterical laughter, Jonas dies coughing blood. As the Indians ride off, Claire and Ben cling to each other while watching the bodies of Jonas and the bandit float downriver. *Confederate veterans. Widows. Dancehall hostesses. Mexicans. Bandits. Soldiers. Hostages. Beggars. Indians of North America. Filial relations. Robbery. Imposture. Murder. Disinterment. Rape. Massacres. Coffins. Treasure. Forts. United States—History—Reconstruction. Arkansas. New Mexico.*

Note: Location scenes filmed in Madrid, Castile, Almeria, Granada, and Anzio. Opened in Rome caApr 1967 as *I crudeli*; running time: 95 min; in Madrid in Nov 1967 as *Los despiadados*; running time: 90 min. Leo Nichols is a pseudonym for Ennio Morricone.

THE HELLCATS   F6.2108

Gemini-American Productions. *Dist* Crown International Pictures. 8 May **1968** [Los Angeles opening]. Sd; col (Eastman Color by Pathé). 35mm. 90 min.
Prod Anthony Cardoza. *Co-prod* Herman Tomlin. *Dir* Robert F. Slatzer. *Screenplay* Tony Houston, Robert F. Slatzer. *Orig Story* James Gordon White, John Zila, Jr. *Dir Photog* Gil Hubbs. *Camera* Wilson S. Hong. *Asst Camera* Paul Prince. *Art Dir* Karen Teichman. *Film Ed* Bud Hoffman. *Mus Supv* Jerry Roberts. *Songs:* "I Can't Take a Chance," "Hellcats," "Mass Confusion" *Prod* by Richard A. Podolor. *Sung by* Davy Jones and The Dolphins. *Songs:* "I'm Up," "Marionettes" *Prod* by Chance Halladay. *Sung by* Somebody's Children. *Sd* Dave Caudle, Ryder Sound Service. *Asst Dir* Tony Houston. *Script Supv* Mary T. Laub. *Wardrobe* Misty Maring.

Cast: Ross Hagen (*Monte Chapman*), Dee Duffy (*Linda*), Sharyn Kinzie (*Sheila*), Sonny West (*Snake*), Robert F. Slatzer (*Mr. Adrian*), Eric Lidberg (*Hiney*), Shannon Summers (*Rita*), Bro Beck (*David Chapman*), Diane Ryder (*Candy Cane*), Nick Raymond (*Pepper*), Richard Merrifield (*Dean*), Hildegard Wendt (*Hildy*), Tony Cardoza (*artist*), Elena Engstrom (*artist's model*), Irene Martin (*Dee, the dopehead*), Frederic Downs (*Moonfire*), Noble "Kid" Chissell (*sheriff*), Robert Strong (*deputy*), Ed Sarquist (*Zombie*), Gus Trikonis (*Scorpio*), Lydia Goya (*Betty*), Tom Hanson (*Moongoose*), Ray Cantrell (*Scab*), Joe Coffey (*Pete*), Eric Tomlin (*policeman*), Warren Hammack (*attorney*), Jack Denton (*1st detective*), Walt Swanner (*1st senator*), Bill Reese (*2d senator*).

Action melodrama. Monte Chapman vows to track down the murderer of his brother, a detective who was killed while on the trail of a female motorcycle gang known as The Hellcats. Accompanied by his brother's girl friend Linda, Monte ingratiates himself with the cycle girls and at a "freak-out love-in" learns that the Hellcats are involved with a narcotics smuggler named Mr. Adrian. Linda is invited to join the leader of the Hellcats, Sheila, and another girl, Betty, on a trip to Mexico to pick up a shipment of drugs which they will store in the headlights of their bikes. The police become suspicious and follow the trio as they return from Mexico, and Betty is killed when her cycle goes out of control. Upon delivering the dope, Sheila and Linda are held captive by Adrian for allowing themselves to be followed, and a short time later Monte is also taken prisoner. As Adrian prepares to make his getaway by boat, Monte and Linda are taken, gagged and bound, down to the docks. Sheila manages to escape and alert both the Hellcats and the police into rushing to the rescue. During the dockside melee that ensues, Adrian is killed, the narcotics ring is smashed, and Monte and Linda are reunited. *Detectives. Motorcycle gangs. Brothers. Police. Murder. Smuggling. Abduction. Orgies. Narcotics. Docks. Mexico. Motorcycle accidents.*

HELLFIGHTERS   F6.2109

Universal Pictures. 19 Dec **1968** [Houston opening; c21 Dec 1968; LP37074]. Sd (Westrex); col (Technicolor). 35mm (Panavision). 121 min. *MPAA rating G.*
Prod Robert Arthur. *Dir* Andrew V. McLaglen. *Stunt Coörd* Hal Needham. *Screenplay* Clair Huffaker. *Dir Photog* William H. Clothier. *Art Dir* Alexander Golitzen, Frank Arrigo. *Set Decor* John McCarthy, James S. Redd. *Titl* Universal Title. *Film Ed* Folmar Blangsted. *Mus Supv* Joseph Gershenson. *Mus* Leonard Rosenman. *Sd* Waldon O. Watson, Lyle Cain, Ronald Pierce. *Asst Dir* Terry Morse, Jr. *Unit Prod Mgr* Robert E. Larson. *Cost Dsgn* Edith Head. *Makeup* Bud Westmore. *Hairstyles* Larry Germain. *Matte Supv* Albert Whitlock. *Sp Eff* Fred Knoth, Whitey McMahon, Herman Townsley. *Tech Adv* "Red" Adair, "Boots" Hansen, "Coots" Matthews. *Dial Coach* Robert Forrest.

Cast: John Wayne (*Chance Buckman*), Katharine Ross (*Tish Buckman*), Jim Hutton (*Greg Parker*), Vera Miles (*Madelyn Buckman*), Jay C. Flippen (*Jack Lomax*), Bruce Cabot (*Joe Horn*), Edward Faulkner (*George Harris*), Barbara Stuart (*Irene Foster*), Edmund Hashim (*Colonel Valdez*), Valentin De Vargas (*Amal Bokru*), Frances Fong (*Madame Loo*), Alberto Morin (*General Lopez*), Alan Caillou (*Harry York*), Laraine Stephens (*Helen Meadows*), John Alderson (*Jim Hatch*), Lal Chand Mehra (*Doctor Songla*), Rudy Diaz (*Zamora*), Bebe Louie (*Gumdrop*), Chris Chandler, William Hardy, Howard Finch, Cactus Pryor, Big John Hamilton, Elizabeth Germaine.

Action melodrama. When Chance Buckman is badly injured while fighting an oil well fire, his young associate, Greg Parker, takes it upon himself to send for Chance's daughter, Tish. At the hospital where her father is under heavy sedation, Tish learns that her parents separated when she was a child because her mother, Madelyn, found it impossible to adjust to Chance's hazardous occupation. Fascinated by stories of her father's business, Tish accompanies Greg when he is called away to fight a blazing oil well in Louisiana. Upon their return Chance bellows at Greg for summoning Tish but quiets down when Greg tells him that he married Tish that morning. With the arrival of Madelyn, Chance tries to protect Greg by not sending him on dangerous missions, but his son-in-law's arguments are so strong that Chance gives him the business as a wedding present, takes a desk job in Houston, and remarries his ex-wife. Although Tish is apprehensive about Greg's work, she finds it easier to bear if she is with him on his assignments; as a result, she goes with Greg when he is called to Venezuela to extinguish a string of five oil well fires started by guerrillas. Once Greg realizes how great the danger is, he insists that Tish leave the area and fly to Caracas. She instead takes a jet to Houston and asks her mother to permit the much-needed Chance to join in the fight. Aware that Chance detests his desk job, Madelyn not only allows him to go, but she returns to Caracas with Tish. Chance and Greg snuff out the fires while their wives watch from the sidelines. Although still terrified of firefighting, Madelyn, like Tish, finds that she can stand the pressure if she is with her husband. *Firemen. Fires. Filial relations. Marriage. Divorce. Fear. Oil wells. Louisiana. Houston. Venezuela.*

THE HELLFIRE CLUB (Great Britain)   F6.2110

New World Pictures Ltd. *Dist* Embassy Pictures. Sep **1963**. Sd; b&w (see note). 35mm (Dyaliscope). 93 min.
Pres by Joseph E. Levine. *Prod-Dir* Robert S. Baker, Monty Berman. *Screenplay* Leon Griffiths, Jimmy Sangster. *Story* Jimmy Sangster. *Photog* Robert S. Baker, Monty Berman. *Camera Op* Chic Waterson. *Focus* Robin Vidgeon, Bernard Ford. *Camera Grip* Bob Dickson. *Art Dir* Ray Simm. *Set Dresser* Leonard Townsend. *Draughtsman* Terry Addison. *Film Ed* Frederick Wilson. *1st Asst Ed* Jack Knight. *Mus Comp* Clifton Parker. *Mus Cond* Muir Mathieson. *Mus Perf* by Sinfonia of London. *Sd Mix* Bill Daniels. *Sd Camera Op* Charles Arnold. *Dub Ed* Don Sharpe. *1st, 2d & 3d Asst Dir* Geoffrey Haine, Ian Goddard, Terry Clegg. *Prod Mgr* Teddy Joseph. *Prod Sec* Doris Prince. *Cont* Jane Buck. *Wardrobe Supv* Laura Nightingale. *Wardrobe Master* Ron Beck. *Makeup* Jill Carpenter. *Hairdresser* Ann Box. *Still Photog* Laurie Turner. *Prop Buyer* Margery Whittington. *Casting Dir* Betty White, casting. *Constr Mgr* Frank Trussel. *Prop Master* Harry Edgar. *Ch Electrn* Reg Blackburn.

Cast: Keith Michell (*Jason*), Kai Fischer (*Yvonne*), Adrienne Corri (*Lady Isobel*), Peter Arne (*Thomas*), David Lodge (*Timothy*), Bill Owen (*Martin*), Peter Cushing (*Merryweather*), Francis Matthews (*Sir Hugh*), Desmond Walter Ellis (*Lord Chorley*), Denis Shaw (*Sir Richard*), Tutte Lemkow (*Higgins*), Peter Howell (*Earl of Chatham*), Bernard Hunter (*Marquis de Beauville*), Michael Balfour (*John the Juggler*), Miles Malleson (*judge*), Jean Lodge (*Lady Netherden*), Andrew Faulds (*Lord Netherden*), Martin Stephens (*Jason as a boy*), Rupert Osborne (*Thomas as a boy*), Skip Martin (*Joey the Dwarf*).

Adventure melodrama. England, 1752. Young Jason accidentally blunders into an orgy being held by his father, Lord Netherden, leader of the infamous Hellfire Club, and gets a beating for his imprudence. His mother, disgusted by Lord Netherden's moral degradation, flees with the boy, but she is killed in a coach accident, leaving him to be brought up in Holland by Timothy, a family retainer. Some 15 years later, following the death of his father, Jason returns home as an acrobat in a traveling circus; but he finds that his Cousin Thomas has usurped his title and estate and has become president of the Hellfire Club. Searching for proof of his rights, Jason is aided by Merryweather, an attorney, and poses as a stable groom at his family estate, but he is discovered by Thomas and thrown into jail under sentence of death. Circus friends rescue him, however; he is reunited with his childhood sweetheart, Yvonne; and even the prime minister, who wants to disband the Hellfire Club, espouses his cause. Thomas abducts Yvonne, but Jason, disguised as a marquis, rescues her and mortally wounds Thomas. He then becomes the new Lord Netherden and marries Yvonne. *Nobility. Acrobats. Cousins. Lawyers. Prime ministers. Stableboys. Orgies. Inheritance. Disguise. Abduction. Circus. Sex clubs. Netherlands.*

Note: Released in Great Britain in Mar 1961 in Eastmancolor. Also shown in a revised, 86-min version.

THE HELLIONS (Great Britain)   F6.2111
Irving Allen Ltd. *Dist* Columbia Pictures. 14 Mar **1962** [New York opening; c1 Mar 1962; LP21506]. Sd (Westrex); col (Technicolor). 35mm (Technirama). 87 min.

An Irving Allen–Jamie Uys Production. *Prod* Harold Huth. *Exec Prod* Irving Allen, Jamie Uys. *Assoc Prod* L. C. Rudkin. *Dir* Ken Annakin. *Screenplay* Harold Swanton, Patrick Kirwan, Harold Huth. *Story* Harold Swanton. *Photog* Ted Moore. *Camera Op* John Winbolt. *Adtl Photog* Ray Parslow. *Art Dir* William Constable. *Scenic Artist* W. Simpson Robinson. *Film Ed* Bert Rule. *Mus Comp & Played by* Larry Adler. *Mus Cond* Muir Mathieson. *Orch* Sinfonia of London. *Titl Song* Larry Adler, Herbert Kretzmer. *Sung by* Marty Wilde. *Sd Rec* David Hildyard, Wally Milner. *Asst Dir* Clive Reed. *Prod Mgr* Barry Delmaine. *Cont* Marjorie Lavelly. *Makeup* Paul Rabiger.

Cast: Richard Todd (*Sam Hargis*), Anne Aubrey (*Priss Dobbs*), Jamie Uys (*Ernie Dobbs*), Marty Wilde (*John Billings*), Lionel Jeffries (*Luke Billings*), James Booth (*Jubal Billings*), Al Mulock (*Mark Billings*), Colin Blakely (*Matthew Billings*), Ronald Fraser (*Frank*), Zena Walker (*Julie Hargis*), George Moore (*Malachi*), Bill Brewer (*Mike*), Jan Bruyns (*Jan Pretorious*), Lorna Cowell (*Martha Pretorious*), Ricky Arden (*Bert*), Freddie Prozesky (*Billy Dobbs*), Patrick Mynhardt (*telegraph operator*), James Norval (*store proprietor*), Hugh Rouse (*pastor*), Leigh Crutchley (*hotel clerk*), Gert Van den Bergh (*Dr. Weiser*), Al Willox (*commercial traveler*), Gabriel Bayman (*stationmaster*), Anna Cloete (*Mrs. Archer*), Willie Herbst (*engine driver*), Hendrik Van Der Merwe (*citizen*).

Adventure drama. In 19th-century South Africa, a family of hellions—Luke Billings and sons Matthew, Mark, John, and Jubal—ride into the small town of De Wylt where Police Sergeant Sam Hargis is the sole representative of law and order. They shoot a Boer farmer, cut telegraph wires, terrorize the settlers, and humiliate Sam in front of his townsmen. Though everyone wants the outlaws driven out of town, no one is willing to join Sam in taking a stand against them. Then while Mark Billings is in the local store getting guns, he is accidentally shot and killed by Ernie Dobbs, the timid shopowner. Priss, Ernie's wife, prevents the other Billingses from discovering Mark's body by submitting to the advances of old Luke; but when Ernie learns of this sacrifice, he grabs a rifle and goes out to face Luke in the square. Sam joins him, and in the ensuing battle two more of the gang are killed. Inspired by Ernie's example, the townspeople find their courage and help rid De Wylt of the Billings family. *Brothers. Police. Boers. Farmers. Outlaws. Storekeepers. Filial relations. Courage. Self-sacrifice. South Africa.*

Note: Location scenes filmed in South Africa. Opened in London in Nov 1961; running time: 80 min.

HELLO, DOLLY!   F6.2112
Chenault Productions. *Dist* Twentieth Century-Fox Film Corp. 16 Dec **1969** [New York opening; c18 Dec 1969; LP38180]. Sd (Westrex); col (De Luxe). 35mm and 70mm (Todd-AO). 148 min. [Copyright length: 144 min.] *MPAA rating* G.

An Ernest Lehman Production. *Prod-Writ for the Screen* Ernest Lehman. *Assoc Prod* Roger Edens. *Dir* Gene Kelly. *Dir Photog* Harry Stradling. *Art Dir* Jack Martin Smith, Herman Blumenthal. *Set Decor* Walter M. Scott, George James Hopkins, Raphael Bretton. *Prod Dsgn* John De Cuir. *Film Ed* William Reynolds. *Mus Score & Cond* Lennie Hayton, Lionel Newman. *Orch* Philip J. Lang, Lennie Hayton, Herbert Spencer, Alexander Courage, Don Costa, Warren Barker, Frank Comstock, Joseph Lipman. *Choral Arr* Jack Latimer. *Songs* Jerry Herman. *Asst Choreog* Shelah Hackett. *Dance Arr* Marvin Laird. *Dances & Mus Numbers Staged by* Michael Kidd. *Sd Supv* James Corcoran. *Sd* Murray Spivack, Vinton Vernon, Jack Solomon, Douglas O. Williams. *Mus Ed* Robert Mayer, Kenneth Wannberg. *Asst Dir* Paul Helmick. *Unit Prod Mgr* Francisco Day. *Script Supv* Molly Kent. *Cost Dsgn* Irene Sharaff. *Wardrobe Supv* Courtney Halsam. *Wardrobe* Ed Wynigear, Barbara Westerland. *Makeup*

Supv Dan Striepeke. *Makeup Artist* Ed Butterworth, Dick Hamilton. *Hairstyles* Edith Lindon. *Sp Photog Eff* L. B. Abbott, Art Cruickshank, Emil Kosa, Jr. *Dial Coach* George Eckert.

Cast: Barbra Streisand (*Dolly Levi*), Walter Matthau (*Horace Vandergelder*), Michael Crawford (*Cornelius Hackl*), Louis Armstrong (*orchestra leader*), Marianne McAndrew (*Irene Molloy*), E. J. Peaker (*Minnie Fay*), Danny Lockin (*Barnaby Tucker*), Joyce Ames (*Ermengarde*), Tommy Tune (*Ambrose Kemper*), Judy Knaiz (*Gussie Granger*), David Hurst (*Rudolph Reisenweber*), Fritz Feld (*Fritz, German waiter*), Richard Collier (*Vandergelder's barber*), J. Pat O'Malley (*policeman in park*).

Musical comedy. Source: Jerry Herman and Michael Stewart, *Hello, Dolly!* (New York opening: 16 Jan 1964). Thornton Wilder, *The Matchmaker* (London opening: 4 Nov 1954). In 1890, Dolly Levi, a widowed New York City Jewish matchmaker, journeys to Yonkers, home of Horace Vandergelder, a wealthy grain merchant whom she would like to marry. Horace wants Dolly to take his niece, Ermengarde, to New York, where the girl will be protected from the attentions of Ambrose Kemper, an impoverished young artist. In addition, he reveals his intention to marry Irene Molloy, a pretty New York milliner, an announcement that inspires Dolly to devise a plan to keep Horace for herself. First, she instructs Ermengarde and Ambrose to escape to New York, hoping they will win first prize in the dance contest given at the elegant Harmonia Gardens restaurant. Upon overhearing that Cornelius and Barnaby, the destitute clerks from Horace's store, are planning to take a day off in the owner's absence, Dolly advises them to visit Irene's shop but not to reveal who has sent them. The girl-shy clerks follow her suggestion and introduce themselves as wealthy sophisticates to Irene and her assistant, Minnie Fay, but their visit is aborted when they spot Horace and Dolly about to enter. The boys hide and conceal their identity, but all marriage potential between Horace and Irene is dissolved when he discovers the two men. Pleased with the outcome of her plan, Dolly persuades Cornelius and Barnaby to take the girls to Harmonia Gardens for dinner and also arranges for Horace to be met there by a new marriage prospect, the heiress Ernestina Simple, who is, in fact, Dolly's actress friend Gussie Granger. Exquisitely coiffed and gowned, Dolly makes a dazzling entrance at the restaurant, where she charms Horace until he is about to propose to her; but he spots Ermengarde and Ambrose on the dance floor. In his hectic pursuit of the couple, Horace incites a ruckus that climaxes when he discovers his two clerks using the melee as an opportunity to sneak away from an unpaid check. He fires them, but Dolly, disgusted by Horace's lack of charity, leaves him in anger. The next morning, however, the merchant repents and gives Ermengarde and Ambrose permission to marry, promotes Cornelius and Barnaby, and finally asks Dolly to marry him, thereby making the matchmaker's scheme a total success. *Songs:* "Just Leave Everything to Me" (Dolly), "It Takes a Woman" (Horace & Chorus, Solo: Dolly), "Put On Your Sunday Clothes" (Dolly, Cornelius, Barnaby, Chorus), "Ribbons Down My Back" (Irene), "Dancing" (Dolly, Cornelius, Barnaby, Chorus), "Before the Parade Passes By" (Dolly, Chorus), "Elegance" (Cornelius, Barnaby, Irene, Minnie), "Love Is Only Love" (Dolly), "Hello, Dolly" (Dolly, Orchestra Leader, Chorus), "It Only Takes a Moment" (Cornelius, Irene), "So Long Dearie" (Dolly). *Widows. Jews. Matchmakers. Merchants. Uncles. Artists. Milliners. Heiresses. Clerks. Marriage. Employer-employee relations. Mistaken identity. Impersonation. Restaurants. Dance contests. New York City. Yonkers.*

HELLO DOWN THERE   F6.2113
Ivan Tors Films. *Dist* Paramount Pictures. Mar **1969** [New York opening: 25 Jun; c24 Nov 1968; LP36592]. Sd; col (Eastman Color). 35mm. 98 min. *MPAA rating* G.

An Ivan Tors Production. *Prod* George Sherman. *Exec Prod* Ivan Tors. *Dir* Jack Arnold. *Underwater Seq Dir* Ricou Browning. *Screenplay* John McGreevey, Frank Telford. *Story* Ivan Tors, Art Arthur. *Dir Photog* Clifford Poland. *Camera Op* James Pergola. *Asst Camera* Mike Davis. *Underwater Photog* Lamar Boren, Jordan Klein. *Art Dir* Jack Collis. *Set Decor* Don Ivey. *Film Ed* Erwin Dumbrille. *Mus and Songs:* "Hey Little Goldfish," "Glub," "Hello Down There," "I Can Love You," "Just One More Chance" Jeff Barry. *Sd Mix* Howard Warren. *1st & 2nd Asst Dir* William C. Gerrity, Nat Holt, Jr. *Prod Mgr* William P. Owens. *Script Supv* Joseph Gannon. *Makeup* Guy Del Russo. *Hairstylist* Irene Aparicio. *Coöp* Environmental Science Service Administration, Miami Seaquarium. *Gaffer* Walter Morris, Jr. *Key Grip* Perry Jones.

Cast: Tony Randall (*Fred Miller*), Janet Leigh (*Vivian Miller*), Jim Backus (*T. R. Hollister*), Roddy McDowall (*Nate Ashbury*), Ken Berry (*Mel Cheever*), Merv Griffin (*himself*), Kay Cole (*Lorrie Miller*), Gary Tigerman (*Tommie Miller*), Richard Dreyfuss (*Harold Webster*), Lou Wagner (*Marvin Webster*), Charlotte Rae (*Myrtle Ruth*), Henny Backus (*Mrs. Webster*), Bud Hoey (*Mr. Webster*), Frank Schuller (*Alan Briggs*), Lee Meredith (*Dr. Cara Wells*), Bruce Gordon (*admiral*), Harvey Lembeck (*sonarman*), Arnold Stang (*Jonah*), Pat

Henning (Reilly), Jay Laskay (Philo), Charles G. Martin (chief petty officer), Frank Logan (captain), Andy Jarrell (radio man), Lora Kaye (secretary).

Adventure comedy. Inventor Fred Miller is determined to prove to his old-fashioned boss, T. R. Hollister, the feasibility of his newly-designed undersea house, which he calls the Green Onion, by moving his family underwater for 30 days. He first overcomes his wife Vivian's fear of water and then agrees to let his teenage son and daughter, Tommie and Lorrie, bring along the rest of their rock and roll band so that they can practice; a potential contract with Nate Ashbury, boy wonder of the record industry, hangs in the balance. At first all goes well for the group as they are joined by a friendly seal, and two friendly dolphins help them ward off such dangers to underwater living as menacing sharks. Eventually, however, trouble erupts when Fred's company rival, Mel Cheever, begins construction nearby on a deep sea mining machine, and the rock music creates strange sonar blips which the Navy attributes to an enemy power. Chaos sets in when Cheever siphons a tank full of gas from Fred's house, thereby causing it to tilt and throw the electrical appliances into reverse. Cheever's experiment turns into a disaster, however, and he has to be rescued by Fred. Ashbury likes the new music created by the teenagers and signs them for the Merv Griffin television show; but in their eagerness to reach land in the family submarine they are stranded in a hurricane. Once again, Fred and the dolphins go to the rescue. All ends happily: Hollister approves the house, Merv Griffin tapes the rock group underwater, and the Navy discovers that the only thing they have to fear under the sea is the Green Onion. *Inventors. Entrepreneurs. Musicians. Family life. Underwater life. Employer-employee relations. Business competition. Adolescence. Rock and roll. Submarines. Hydrophobia. Housing. United States Navy. Dolphins. Sharks. Seals.*

Note: Filmed on location in Florida.

HELLO—GOODBYE   F6.2114

Twentieth Century-Fox Film Corp. 12 Jul **1970** [New York opening; c12 Jul 1970; LP38927]. Sd; col (DeLuxe). 35mm. 107 min. *MPAA rating* GP.

A George W. George–Frank Granat Production. *Prod* André Hakim. *Dir* Jean Negulesco. *Screenplay* Roger Marshall. *Dir Photog* Henri Decaë. *Camera Op* Charles-Henry Montel. *Asst Camera* François Lauliac. *Art Dir* Auguste Capelier. *Set Decor* Pierre Charron, Pamela Cornell. *Prod Dsgn* John Howell. *Supv Film Ed* Richard Bryan. *Asst Film Ed* Tony Price, ed, Renée Richard. *Mus* Francis Lai. *Sd Ed* Keith Palmer, Françoise Diot. *Sd Rec* Jock May, Victor Revelly, Max Olivier. *Asst Dir* Paul Feyder. *Prod Supv* William Kaplan. *Prod Mgr* Paul Joly. *Unit Mgr* Nicole Farny. *Cont* Sylvette Baudrot. *Wardrobe Dsgn* Rosine Delamare. *Wardrobe* Yves Saint-Laurent, Valentino of Rome. *Makeup for Miss Gilles* Odette Berroyer. *Makeup* Georges Bouban. *Hairdresser for Miss Gilles* Giorgio di Roma. *Sp Eff* Richard Parker. *Casting Dir* Evelyne Janic. *Prop Master* René Albouze. *Picture Car Supv* David Watson. *Still Photog* Victor Rodrigue.

Cast: Michael Crawford (Harry England), Geneviève Gilles (Dany), Curt Jurgens (Baron de Choisis), Ira Fürstenberg (Evelyne Rosson), Lon Satton (Cole), Peter Myers, actor (Bentley), Mike Marshall (Paul), Didier Haudepin (Raymond), Vivian Pickles (Joycie), Agathe Natanson (Monique), Georges Bever (hotel porter), Denise Grey (concierge), Jeffry Wickham (Dickie).

Drama. Classic car enthusiast Harry England stops his Aston Martin at a filling station on the French Riviera. There he meets Dany, an attractive aristocrat whose Rolls-Royce has broken down. In Paris they visit bistros and spend the night in a cheap hotel. When Dany suggests a visit to Marseilles, Harry insists on a trip to London, and they part company. From Cannes Harry is summoned by the Baron de Choisis and offered a job as caretaker of vintage automobiles and companion to de Choisis' 16-year-old son Raymond. Accepting, Harry discovers that the baron's wife is Dany. With the apparent approval of the baron, the two thereupon resume their affair. After taking an apartment in Marseilles, Harry begs Dany to leave her husband. When she refuses, the mechanic resigns his position, gets drunk, drives the baron's Rolls-Royce into the swimming pool, and departs. Upon later learning that the baron has left his wife for American heiress Evelyn Rosson and that Dany is sailing to America, Harry rushes to the docks of Le Havre, where he persuades the departing Dany to remain with him. *Aristocrats. Caretakers. Tutors. Heiresses. Infidelity. Marriage. Drunkenness. Filling stations. Rolls-Royce automobiles. Swimming pools. Riviera. Cannes. Paris. Le Havre.*

Note: Location scenes filmed in Cannes and on the Riviera. Working title: *Hello and Goodbye.*

HELLS ANGELS ON WHEELS   F6.2115

Fanfare Film Productions. *Dist* U. S. Films. 24 May **1967** [Wichita, Kansas, opening]. Sd; col (Eastman Color, print by Movielab). 35mm. 95 min.

Prod Joe Solomon. *Dir* Richard Rush. *Screenplay* R. Wright Campbell. *Dir Photog* Leslie Kovacs. *Asst Camera* Frank Ruttencutter. *Set Decor* Wally Moon. *Film Ed* William Martin. *Mus Score* Stu Phillips. Song: "Study in Motion No. 1" Chuck Sedacca, Stu Phillips. Sung by The Poor. *Sd Mix* LeRoy Robbins. *Boom Op* Sam Kopetzky. *1st & 2d Asst Dir* Willard Kirkham, Bruce

Satterlee. *Prod Mgr* Paul Lewis. *Script Girl* Joyce King. *Prod Sec* Sheila Scott. *Wardrobe* Roy Vanderleelie. *Makeup* Louis Lane. *Tech Adv* Sonny Barger, Tommy Thomas. *Coöp* Richmond Hell's Angels (Oakland, and Daly City, California), Nomads of Sacramento. *Still Photog* Peter Sorel. *Gaffer* Don Carstensen, James Field. *Key Grip* Bill Pecchi. *Stunt Coörd* Gary Kent.

Cast: Adam Roarke (Buddy), Jack Nicholson (Poet), Sabrina Scharf (Shill), Jana Taylor (Abigale), John Garwood (Jock), Richard Anders (Bull), I. J. Jefferson, Mimi Machu (Pearl [?]), James Oliver (Gypsy), Jack Starrett (Police Sargeant Bingham), Gary Littlejohn (Moley), Bruno Ve Sota (justice of the peace), Robert Kelljan (artist), Kathryn Harrow (Lori), Sonny Barger (himself, leader of Hell's Angels).

Action melodrama. A group of northern California motorcyclists known as the Hell's Angels roar into a town near San Francisco and terrorize a gas station owner and his patrons. That night they are joined by the gas station attendant, Poet, who has been fired from his job because he argued with a customer. After joining the Angels in a gang fight, Poet accompanies them to an amusement park and is beaten up by four sailors. In retaliation, the gang, led by Buddy, tracks down the sailors and kills one of them. Then they all go to the apartment of Buddy's girl, Shill, for a wild party. Warned by highway officer Bingham that the Angels are prime suspects in the sailor's murder, Buddy decides that they should go away for the weekend. Plans are made for two of the Angels, Gypsy and Abigale, to be married in Nevada. Following the unconventional church wedding and a battle with local thugs, the gang moves on to the "ruins," a favorite hangout, where a party is in session. During the orgy, Buddy and Poet quarrel over Shill, and a vicious fight ensues. The violence ends when Buddy crashes through a glass window and dies in the flames of his burning motorcycle. *Motorcycle gangs. Filling station attendants. Sailors. Police. Gang wars. Murder. Jealousy. Amusement parks. Weddings. Orgies. California. Nevada. Hell's Angels.*

Note: Location scenes filmed in northern California, including the San Francisco vicinity.

HELL'S ANGELS '69   F6.2116

Tracom Productions. *Dist* American International Pictures. 30 Jul **1969** [Detroit opening; c30 Jul 1969; LP37607]. Sd; col (Berkey Pathé). 35mm. 97 min. *MPAA rating* M.

Prod Tom Stern. *Exec Prod* Pat B. Rooney. *Dir* Lee Madden. *Screenplay* Don Tait. *Story* Tom Stern, Jeremy Slate. *Dir Cinematog* Paul Loman. *Film Ed* Gene Ruggiero. *Mus Score* Tony Bruno. *Mus Arr & Cond* John D'Andrea. *Sd* George Alch.

Cast: Tom Stern (Chuck), Jeremy Slate (Wes), Conny Van Dyke (Betsy), Steve Sandor (Apache), G. D. Spradlin (detective), Sonny Barger (Sonny), Terry the Tramp (Terry), Bobby Hall, Ray Renard, Michael Michaelian, Bud Ekins, Joe Hooker, Bob Harris, Ric Henry, Danielle Corn, Jerry Randall, Ed Mulder, The Oakland Hell's Angels.

Crime melodrama. Chuck and Wes, two bored New England playboys who are also half brothers, decide to amuse themselves by robbing Caesar's Palace in Las Vegas. Interested only in finding out if they can pull off the heist, they intend to mail back whatever loot they steal. Upon arriving in California, they pose as cyclists from an Eastern gang and win the admiration of the Hell's Angels by harassing an innocent highway motorist. After passing the Angels' initiation tests, Chuck and Wes are welcomed into the fold, particularly by Betsy, one of the Angels' "mamas." The boys then set the stage for their caper by talking the Angels into riding to Vegas with them. Using the unwitting Angels as a diversion, Chuck and Wes switch into college clothes and pull off the heist while the police and casino management are tangling with the gang. Quickly switching back into their cycle outfits, Chuck and Wes are about to make their getaway when they are confronted by Betsy. Aware of their masquerade and robbery, she wants a share of the loot, or Wes. Forced to comply, Chuck and Wes take Betsy along as they ride off into the desert. The police discover the ruse and inform the Angels that they have been used. Furious, the Angels pursue the trio into the desert. Chuck is cornered in a canyon by the Angels; trying to make a dangerous cycle leap, he crashes to his death. As for Wes and Betsy, the Angels drain the fuel out of their bikes and steal their water supply, leaving them to perish in the scorching desert. *Playboys. Motorcyclists. Robbery. Duplicity. Disguise. Casinos. Deserts. Las Vegas. Hell's Angels. Caesars Palace. Chases.*

Note: Filmed on location in Las Vegas and the Nevada desert.

HELL'S BELLES   F6.2117

Maury Dexter Productions. *Dist* American International Pictures. 29 Apr **1969** [New York opening; c2 Apr 1969; LP36887]. Sd; col (Berkey Pathé). 35mm. 98 min. *MPAA rating* M.

Prod-Dir Maury Dexter. *Assoc Prod* Hank Tani. *Screenplay* James Gordon White, Robert McMullen. *Photog* Kenneth Peach. *Set Decor* Harry Reif. *Film Ed* John Schreyer. *Mus* Les Baxter. *Mus Supv* Al Simms. *Sd* Brad Trask. *Asst Dir* Robert M. Jones. *Prod Mgr* Robert M. Jones. *Asst to Prod* Julie Foote.

Script Supv Marshall Schlom. *Women's Wardrobe* Sharon Thober. *Men's Wardrobe* Richard Bruno. *Makeup Artist* Paul Malcolm. *Hairstyles* Wava Green. *Sp Eff* Roger George.

Cast: Jeremy Slate *(Dan)*, Adam Roarke *(Tampa)*, Jocelyn Lane *(Cathy)*, Angelique Pettyjohn *(Cherry)*, Michael Walker *(Tony)*, Astrid Warner *(Piper)*, William Lucking *(Gippo)*, Eddie Hice *(Red Beard)*, Dick Bullock *(Meatball)*, Jerry Randall *(Crazy John)*, Jerry Brutsche *(Rabbit)*, Kristin Van Buren *(Zelda)*, Elaine Everett *(Big Sal)*, Fred Krone *(Burr)*, Ronnie Dayton *(Barney)*, Henry Kendrick *(gas station attendant)*, Frank Kennedy *(store owner)*, James Owens *(Leo)*, Larry H. Lane *(Charlie)*, Jackie Hummer *(girl friend)*, Bill Thompson *(L. G.)*, Michael Jones *(Donny)*.

Melodrama. Tony Carlyle steals the new motorcycle that Dan Holt has just won in a desert endurance race, and Tampa, a rough road character, steals the motorcycle from Tony. Dan chases Tampa and his gang into the Arizona hills, but he is outnumbered and knocked unconscious in a fight. Dan regains consciousness and discovers that Tampa has left behind Cathy, a cast-off gang girl, as a trade for the motorcycle. Dan learns from Cathy that the gang is heading for the Mexican border; in pursuit, they ride into Lawton and find that the gang has burned down a gasoline station and enraged the citizens. Escaping from Lawton, Dan and Cathy ride into the desert and soon locate the gang's temporary camp. Dan picks off the men one by one, knocking two off their motorcycles with a rope stretched across the road and throwing one into a snakepit. He takes the body of the snake-bitten man and rides defiantly with it into Tampa's camp. He offers to stop the ambush in exchange for his motorcycle, but Tampa refuses, causing his men to desert him. The two men fight it out alone with chains, and Dan breaks Tampa's shoulder and recovers his motorcycle. Cathy decides to remain with Tampa, and Dan rides for home to sell the bike and use the money to make a down payment on a small ranch. *Motorcycle gangs. Murder. Arson. Revenge. Theft. Deserts. Snakes. Arizona. Mexican border.*

Note: Location scenes filmed in Arizona. Working title: *Girl in the Leather Suit.*

HELL'S BLOODY DEVILS   F6.2118

East-West Pictures–Four Crown Productions. *Dist* Independent-International Pictures. Jan **1970.** Sd; col (De Luxe). 35mm. 92 min. *MPAA rating* GP.

An Al Adamson Production. *Prod-Dir* Al Adamson. *Exec Prod* Rex Carlton, Fred Gebhardt. *Assoc Prod* Bob Kinoshita, Jerry Evans. *Screenplay* Jerry Evans. *Dir Photog* Laszlo Kovacs, Frank Ruttencutter, Gary Graver. *Lighting* Aggie Aguilar, Brian Smith, Peter Wagner. *Titl Dsgn* Bob LeBar. *Film Ed* John Winfield. *Mus Themes* Nelson Riddle. *Mus Score* Don McGinnis. *Song:* "Faker" Nelson Riddle, John Gabriel. *Song:* "When Did the Sun Come Out?" Don McGinnis, David McKechnie. *Vocals* Debbie Stuart. *Sd Rec* Bob Dietz. *Re-Rec* Cinesound. *Sd* Peter Wagner. *Asst Dir* Mike Haggerty. *Prod Mgr* Bud Cardos. *Unit Mgr* Rick Jackson. *Script Supv* Pat Cardos, Joyce King. *Prod Cons* Samuel M. Sherman. *Still Photog* Hedy Dietz.

Cast: Broderick Crawford *(Brand)*, Scott Brady *(FBI agent)*, Kent Taylor *(Count von Delberg)*, Keith Andes *(Bremonte)*, John Carradine *(shop owner)*, John Gabriel *(Mark Adams)*, Robert Dix *(Cunk)*, Erin O'Donnell *(von Delberg's daughter)*, Vicki Volante *(Carol Bechtol)*, Anne Randall *(Amanda)*, Jack Starrett *(Rocky)*, Emily Banks *(FBI agent)*, Dan Kemp *(henchman)*, William Bonner, Jerry Mills *("Bloody Devils")*, Bambi Allen, Jill Woelfel *(pick-up girls)*, California's Hessians *(bike riders)*, Carol Brewster, Leslie McRae, Gene Shane, Arland Shubert, Alyce Andrace, Rhae Andrace, Alice Wong, Jane Wald, Richard Brander, Brand Bell, Greydon Clark, Gary Kent, Sid Lawrence, John Cardos, Kent Osborne, Sheldon Lee, Philip Difermian, Col. Harlan Sanders.

Action melodrama. To further the neo-nazi movement in America, Count von Delberg and his equally fanatical daughter have aligned themselves with a Las Vegas Mafia chief named Bremonte, as well as with the Bloody Devils, a band of California cyclists led by the sadistic Cunk. Unknown to the count, both his own party and the Mafia have been infiltrated by undercover agents: Carol Bechtol, his mistress-associate, is actually an Israeli agent searching for the Nazi colonel who executed her parents; and Mark Adams, a respected member of the Mafia underworld, is in reality an FBI agent. The count's plan is to make counterfeit money with smuggled plates from World War II and have the Mafia distribute it while the Bloody Devils eliminate interference from the authorities. While Adams is acting as the go-between among the three groups, he becomes closely involved with Carol, thereby arousing the jealous hatred of Cunk. After failing in a murderous attempt on Adams' life, Cunk and two of his sidekicks attempt to gang-rape Carol. Although she kills the bikers with an explosive device she carries, Carol meets her own end when the count, who is the sought-after Nazi colonel, discovers her spying and slashes her throat with a switchblade. Eventually, Adams and the FBI close in on the counterfeiters and wipe out almost all of the gang during a gun battle and car chase. The count

and his daughter die fiery deaths while attempting to escape in a helicopter loaded with explosives planted by Adams. *Motorcycle gangs. Mercenaries. Nazis. Mistresses. Secretaries. Secret agents. Israelis. Neo-nazism. Smuggling. Counterfeiting. Revenge. Rape. Murder. Explosives. Helicopters. Mafia. Las Vegas. Germany. United States—Federal Bureau of Investigation. Chases.*

Note: Location scenes filmed in Utah. Filmed in 1967 as *Operation M.*

HELL'S CHOSEN FEW   F6.2119

Borealis Enterprises. *Dist* Thunderbird International Pictures. 11 Jan **1968** [New Orleans opening]. Sd; col (Eastmancolor, print by Technicolor). 35mm. 92 min.

Pres by American General Pictures. *Prod-Dir* David L. Hewitt. *Assoc Prod* Titus Moody, Ewing Brown. *Screenplay* John K. McCarthy, David Prentiss. *Photog* Ewing Brown. *Mus* Charles Walden. *Sd* Jean Mainferme.

Cast: Jody Daniels *(Joe)*, Kelly Ross *(Sharon)*, Gary Kent *(Willie)*, Joe Follino *(sheriff)*, William Bonner, Vic McGee, Mick Mehas, Titus Moody, Shirley Cash, Megan Timothy.

Action melodrama. The drunken sheriff of a small, Pacific coastal town accidentally kills his daughter's boyfriend in a drunken brawl and pins the murder on Willie, an innocent member of an area motorcycle gang. Willie's brother, Joe, returns from the Marines and, with the assistance of Sharon, his brother's ex-girl friend, joins the bikers in an attempt to discover the real murderer. The sheriff's daughter commits perjury to protect her father, but she reveals to Joe what actually happened. Joe confronts the sheriff, and the latter is killed by his own gun in the fight that ensues. Willie, released from custody, rapes Sharon, but he is killed by his vengeful brother. *Sheriffs. Motorcyclists. Murder. Frameup. Filial relations. Drunkenness. Smalltown life. Perjury. Rape. Revenge. Motorcycle gangs.*

HELL'S ISLAND *see* SOUTH SEAS FURY

HELL'S PLAYGROUND   F6.2120

Dist Commercial Enterprises. ca **1967.** Sd; col. 35mm. [Feature film, length unknown.]

Prod John Baron. *Dir* Jesse Clark. *Writ* M. O'Neil.

Cast: Skip Everret, Jane Ashley, The Surftones, The Pebbles.

Action drama. No information about the precise nature of this film has been found, but press material suggests it deals with college students, hot rods, beaches, riots, and police in Fort Lauderdale. *Students. Police. Beaches. Riots. Fort Lauderdale.*

Note: May also be known as *Riot at Lauderdale.*

HELP! (Great Britain)   F6.2121

Walter Shenson Films–Subafilms. *Dist* United Artists. 9 Aug **1965** [Chicago opening; c30 Jul 1965; LP31863]. Sd; col (Eastman Color). 35mm. 90 min.

Prod Walter Shenson. *Dir* Richard Lester. *Screenplay* Marc Behm, Charles Wood. *Story* Marc Behm. *Dir Photog* David Watkin. *Camera Op* Jack Atchelor, Paul Wilson. *Col Cons* Robert Freeman. *Art Dir* Ray Simm. *Main Titl* Robert Freeman. *Film Ed* John Victor Smith. *Mus Score & Mus Dir* Ken Thorne. *Songs:* "Help!," "You're Gonna Lose That Girl," "You've Got To Hide Your Love Away," "The Night Before," "Another Girl," "Ticket To Ride" John Lennon, Paul McCartney. *Song:* "I Need You" George Harrison. *Songs Sung by* The Beatles. *Sd Rec* H. L. Bird, Stephen Dalby. *Sd Ed* Bill Blunden, Don Challis. *Mus Ed* Barry Vince. *Asst Dir* Clive Reed. *Prod Mgr* John Pellatt. *Cont* Rita Davison. *Cost Dsgn* Julie Harris, cost, Dinah Greet. *Wardrobe* Arthur Newman. *Makeup* Freddie Williamson. *Hairdresser* Betty Glasow. *Sp Eff* Cliff Richardson, Roy Whybrow.

Cast: John Lennon, Paul McCartney, Ringo Starr, George Harrison *(The Beatles)*, Leo McKern *(Clang)*, Eleanor Bron *(Ahme)*, Victor Spinetti *(Professor Foot)*, Roy Kinnear *(Algernon)*, John Bluthal *(Bhuta)*, Patrick Cargill *(superintendent)*, Alfie Bass *(doorman)*, Warren Mitchell *(Abdul)*, Peter Copley *(jeweler)*, Bruce Lacey *(Lawnmower)*, Ronnie Brody, Bob Godfrey, Louis Mansi, Rupert Evans *(priests/thugs)*, Andreas Malandrinos *(Austrian waiter)*, Golda Casimir *(cleaner in temple)*, Deborah Du' Lacey, Gai Wright, Zorenah Osborne, Eve Eden, Zienia Merton, Marie-Lise *(high priestesses)*, Durra *(belly dancer)*, Danny Almond, Edith Savile, Vera Cook, Joe Gibbons, Sue Reid, Stewart Guidotti, Wally Shufflebottom, Blake Butler, Ian Wilson, Jenny Till, Mary Ford, Jenny Landry, Glenda Warrington, Alex Macintosh, Pat Roberts, Thomas Baptiste, Dandy Nichols, Jeremy Lloyd, Gretchen Franklin.

Comedy with music. As High Priest Clang and Priestess Ahme are about to make a human sacrifice to Goddess Kaili, they notice that they cannot perform the ceremony because the red sacrificial ring is missing. In London, Ringo has received the ring from an admirer, and he wears it, unaware of any danger. When Clang and Ahme try to obtain the ring from him, Ringo finds that he is unable to take it off. After Clang and his henchman Bhuta try to murder Ringo, he goes to see Foot, a scientist, and Foot's assistant, Algernon, to have the ring removed. Foot covets the ring, which will help him control the world, and, with

Algernon, he joins the pursuit. Ahme befriends Ringo, and with the other Beatles—John, Paul, and George—they go to the Alps for a vacation. Their pursuers find them; and, following a chase in the mountains, the Beatles return to London and ask Scotland Yard for aid; then, with the British Army performing maneuvers around them on the Salisbury Plain, the Beatles record their music. After a near war between the Army and Clang's followers, the group goes to the Bahamas where they are still harried. As Ringo is about to be sacrificed, however, he learns the secret that allows the ring to slide easily off his finger. *Scientists. Musicians. Human sacrifice. Rock and roll. Religious sects. Religious objects. London. Alps. Bahamas. Salisbury Plain. The Beatles. Scotland Yard. Great Britain—Army. Chases.*

Note: Location scenes filmed in the Bahamas, Obertauern (Austria), and on the Salisbury Plain. Opened in London in Jul 1965; running time: 92 min. Working title: *Eight Arms To Hold You.*

HELP WANTED FEMALE　　　　　　　　　　　　　　F6.2122
Clover Films. 13 Sep **1968** [Champaign, Illinois, showing]. Sd; b&w. 35mm. 71 min.

Dir Harold Perkins.

Cast: Inga Olsen, Sebastian Gregory.

Drama. *Two women, Jo-Jo and Luana, will do anything for money: Jo-Jo operates a run-down karate school by day and mugs traveling salesmen by night; her friend Luana is a high-priced call girl. One night Luana is entertaining long-time customer Mr. Gregory at his home when he takes LSD, and while Luana does an erotic dance, he reveals incidents from his imaginary past: Barbara, Greg's ex-girl friend, is a sadomasochist whose perversions finally lead her to want to kill for pleasure. Greg and Barbara seek out Tina, a naive teenager who wants to become a model, induce her to model for them, and brutally kill her. That night, Greg murders Barbara when she returns home from a tryst with the next-door neighbor. Luana doesn't believe Greg's extraordinary tale until she finds what appear to be human remains in the kitchen. Terrified, she calls Jo-Jo, clouts Greg with a wooden mallet, and flees to the karate school. Jo-Jo calls the police, but Greg, having recovered from the blow on the head, arrives before the police and has a karate fight with Jo-Jo. The police arrive and issue Greg a warning when he tells them that the whole incident was a hoax. Jo-Jo meets Greg the following night and stabs him. Greg awakens screaming, and it is apparent that he has had a nightmare. He takes his cue from the dream, however, and stabs his nagging wife in order to silence her forever.* Prostitutes. Muggers. Models. Innocents. Sadomasochism. Murder. Seduction. Hoaxes. LSD. Karate. Dreams.

HEM HAYU ASAR *see* THEY WERE TEN

HEMINGWAY'S ADVENTURES OF A YOUNG MAN　　F6.2123
Jerry Wald Productions. *Dist* Twentieth Century-Fox Film Corp. 18 Jul **1962** [Chicago opening; c18 Jul 1962; LP22801]. Sd; col (De Luxe). 35mm (CinemaScope). 145 min. [Also reviewed at 140 min.]

Prod Jerry Wald. *Assoc Prod* Peter Nelson. *Dir* Martin Ritt. *Screenplay* A. E. Hotchner. *Dir Photog* Lee Garmes. *Art Dir* Jack Martin Smith, Paul Groesse. *Set Decor* Walter M. Scott, Robert Priestley. *Film Ed* Hugh S. Fowler. *Mus Comp & Cond* Franz Waxman. *Orch* Leonid Raab. *Sd* E. Clayton Ward, Warren B. Delaplain. *Asst Dir* Eli Dunn. *Cost Dsgn* Don Feld. *Makeup* Ben Nye. *Hairstyles* Helen Turpin. *Sp Photog Eff* L. B. Abbott, Emil Kosa, Jr. *Italian Seq Serviced by* International Film Service.

Cast: Richard Beymer (*Nick Adams*), Diane Baker (*Carolyn*), Corinne Calvet (*Contessa*), Fred Clark (*Mr. Turner*), Dan Dailey (*Billy Campbell*), James Dunn (*telegrapher*), Juano Hernandez (*Bugs*), Arthur Kennedy (*Dr. Adams*), Ricardo Montalban (*Major Padula*), Paul Newman ("*The Battler*"), Susan Strasberg (*Rosanna Griffi*), Jessica Tandy (*Mrs. Adams*), Eli Wallach (*John*), Edward Binns (*brakeman*), Philip Bourneuf (*Montecito*), Tullio Carminati (*Signor Griffi*), Marc Cavell (*Eddy Boulton*), Charles Fredericks (*mayor*), Simon Oakland (*Joe Boulton*), Michael J. Pollard (*George*), Whit Bissell (*Ludstrum*), Pat Hogan (*Billy Tabeshaw*).

Drama. Based on the "Nick Adams" stories by: Ernest Hemingway. *Eager to escape his weak-willed physician father and domineering mother, 19-year-old Nick Adams leaves his Michigan home in 1917 and sets out for New York to become a writer. After a few days on the road he is thrown off a freight train by a cruel brakeman and finds himself in the company of a punch-drunk ex-prizefighter, "The Battler," and his black manager, Bugs. He soon decides to wire his father for money to return home, but a philosophical telegraph operator subtly talks him out of it; instead, Nick becomes assistant to the drunken, drug-addicted Billy Campbell, who acts as a publicist for Mr. Turner, a burlesque promoter. Turner replaces Billy with Nick until the show reaches New York, where Nick tries to become a newspaperman. Rejected by a newspaper editor for lack of experience, Nick becomes a busboy at a banquet held to recruit ambulance drivers for the Italian Army in its war against Austria and Germany. Nick signs up, and later saves the life of Major Padula, his commanding officer*

in Italy; later, his own life is saved when John, an Italian-American orderly, pulls him out of a bombed trench. While convalescing, Nick falls deeply in love with his nurse, Rosanna Griffi, but she is critically wounded when the hospital is bombed; he begs a priest to marry them, and the young woman dies in his arms during the ceremony. Upon discharge, Nick receives a hero's welcome as he returns to the Michigan lake country, but his celebration is ruined by the discovery that his father committed suicide during his absence. He remains with his mother until her possessiveness becomes too much for him, and then leaves home again—this time as a man, not a boy. *Physicians. Prizefighters. Negroes. Publicists. Drug addicts. Newspapermen. Busboys. Ambulance drivers. Italians. War heroes. Nurses. Ambition. Manhood. Filial relations. Combat zone life. Aerial bombardment. Suicide. Trains. Burlesque. Hospitals. World War I. Michigan. New York City. Italy. Italy—Army.*

Note: Location scenes filmed in Wisconsin and Rome. Also known as *Adventures of a Young Man* and *Ernest Hemingway's Adventures of a Young Man.*

DER HENKER VON LONDON *see* THE MAD EXECUTIONERS

HENRY GELDZAHLER　　　　　　　　　　　　　　F6.2124
Dist Film-Makers' Cooperative. 18 Dec **1965** [New York opening]. Si; b&w. 16mm. 100 min.

Prod-Dir Andy Warhol. *Prod Asst* Gerard Malanga, Buddy Wirtschafter.

Cast: Henry Geldzahler.

Film portrait. *A man [Henry Geldzahler, curator in the Department of Contemporary Arts of the Metropolitan Museum of Art] is seen in medium closeup, smoking a cigar.* Smoking.

HENRY LIMPET *see* THE INCREDIBLE MR. LIMPET

HENRY VIII *see* ROYAL FLESH

HENRY'S NIGHT IN　　　　　　　　　　　　　　F6.2125
Dist Astro-Jemco Film Distributors. 5 Dec **1969** [Champaign, Illinois, showing]. Sd; b&w. 35mm. 75 min.

Cast: Barbara Kline, Forman Shane.

Comedy. *Henry, cowed by his shrewish wife, cannot achieve sexual satisfaction. He visits a psychiatrist, Jack, who recommends extra-marital sex as a solution. Jack has previously hypnotized two neighborhood women so that they immediately become aroused when they hear the name Jack. One day Henry buys an old trunk at an auction, and in it he finds a formula for making himself invisible. Drinking the magic potion, he repeats the name Jack to the women and finds them anxious to respond to his invisible lovemaking, while his wife, too, becomes devoted to his invisible embrace.* Psychiatrists. Impotence. Infidelity. Timidity. Hypnotism. Marriage. Auctions. Potions. Invisibility. Documentation.

HENTAI (Japan)　　　　　　　　　　　　　　　F6.2126
Dist Olympic International Films. 2 Sep **1966** [Los Angeles showing]. Sd; b&w. 35mm (Centralscope). 71 min.

Prod Nidemaru Washio. *English Vers Prod* Felix Lomax. *Dir* Takashi Shiga.

Cast: Sayuri Sakurai, Masayonshi Nagami.

Melodrama. *Kasama, a prominent Tokyo industrialist, hires young detectives Kyoto and Sugita to find his missing daughter. They learn that an unsavory circle of friends had brought the girl into contact with Takami, a powerful nightclub owner. Kyoto infiltrates Takami's organization; she submits to his embraces and is eventually delivered to a special client to be used as a subject in a series of bizarre sexual experiments. The detectives learn that Takami operates a large narcotics ring, which is headed by a mysterious masked man. Together, the men abduct, rape, and torture young women, addict them to heroin, and force them to work as prostitutes; Kasama's daughter is one of their unfortunate victims. Kyoto escapes with the help of an international narcotics agent, and while Tokyo police round up members of the gang, she joins Sugita in exposing Kasama as the mysterious head of the racket. Ruined, the industrialist learns to his horror that he [or his organization] has raped, drugged, and prostituted his own daughter.* Industrialists. Detectives. Drug dealers. Nightclub owners. Drug addicts. Missing persons. Filial relations. White slave traffic. Abduction. Rape. Sadism. Disguise. Personal identity. Incest. Heroin. Tokyo.

Note: Also known as *Abnormal.*

HER AND SHE AND HIM (France)　　　　　　　　F6.2127
Les Films du Griffon. *Dist* Audubon Films, Rochambeau Films. 7 Oct **1970** [New York opening]. Sd; col (Eastman Color). 35mm. 90 min. [Also 88 min.] *MPAA rating* X.

Pres by Radley Metzger. *Prod-Dir* Max Pecas. *Orig Story-Screenplay* Michèle Ressi. *Adapt-Dial* Max Pecas, Michèle Ressi. *Photog* Robert Lefèbvre. *Film Ed* Nicole Colombier. *Mus* Betty Hall. *Asst Dir* Yves Prigent. *Prod Mgr* Paul Cayatte.

Cast: Astrid Frank *(Greta),* Nicole Debonne *(Claude),* Yves Vincent *(Mathias),* Frédéric Sakiss *(Jean),* Bruno Balp, Kim Camba, Richard Saint-Bris, Michel Vocoret, Michel Charrel.

Drama. Greta, an innocent young Swedish guitarist, arrives in Paris without money and attempts to find work as an au pair girl or a model. Disillusioned by a series of propositions, she begins to sing at sidewalk cafes and befriends Claude, a wealthy woman with whom she establishes a lesbian relationship. Tiring of Claude's jealousy and possessiveness, Greta leaves and finds a job as a model for the famous erotic painter Mathias, a homosexual. Greta soon becomes attracted to Jean, Mathias' protégé, and she seduces him. Realizing that he is Mathias' lover, she convinces Jean to leave him. Mathias learns of the affair and tries to kill Jean; Claude, meanwhile, attempts suicide in order to regain Greta's sympathies. Both attempts fail, and Greta and Jean leave together. Five years later, happily married with a son, they watch another innocent Swedish girl arrive in Paris to seek her fortune. *Swedes. Ingenues. Guitarists. Singers. Models. Painters. Au pair girls. Lesbianism. Jealousy. Male homosexuality. Murder. Suicide. Cafes. Paris.*

Note: Opened in Paris in Mar 1970 as *Claude et Greta;* running time: 90 min. French prerelease title: *Les liaisons particulières.*

HER BIKINI NEVER GOT WET   F6.2128
Beaux Arts Films–Europa General Hemisphere. *Dist* Gaston Hakim Productions. 9 Nov **1962** [Los Angeles showing]. Sd; col (Pathé). 35mm. 74 min.

Prod-Dir-Writ Gaston Hakim. *Photog* Jean Pierre Cordero.

Cast: Brigitte Duval *(Brigitte),* Richard Essen *(Richard),* Yannick Philouze *(Jackie).*

Comedy. Richard, an American playboy, will inherit a million dollars if he can find a stuffed toy dog similar to one his father received many years before. Richard drives around the French Riviera looking for the toy, and there he meets Brigitte, an owner of a nudist camp. They fall in love, and Richard eventually finds the toy dog at the camp. It is revealed that the scheme was planned by the fathers of Richard and Brigitte so that the two young people might meet. *Playboys. Americans in foreign countries. Inheritance. Fatherhood. Nudist camps. Toys. Riviera.*

Note: Country of origin undetermined. May also be known as *The Dry Bikini.*

HER ODD TASTES   F6.2129
Hollywood Cinema Associates. *Dist* Crest Film Distributors. 5 Sep **1969** [Champaign, Illinois, showing]. Sd; col. 35mm. 72 min.

Cast: Marsha Jordan, Capri.

Drama. Christine Hunter's search for pleasure leads her to retrace the path of Charles Odman in the film *Odd Tastes,* q. v. In her travels, she encounters a group of devil worshipers and participates in their rituals. Her first stopover, Hong Kong, introduces her to some "experimentation" with erotic drugs. Moving on, she accepts the invitation of a desert sheik and experiences some of the delights of harem life. In Africa, Christine meets a youth whose unfortunate sexual experiences lead Christine into an extraordinary situation. ... *Adventuresses. Sheiks. Hedonism. Demonology. Aphrodisiacs. Rites and ceremonies. Hong Kong. Africa.*

HER "THING" ... VIBRATIONS see VIBRATIONS

HERCULE À LA CONQUÊTE DE L'ATLANTIDE see HERCULES AND THE CAPTIVE WOMEN

HERCULE CONTRE MOLOCH see CONQUEST OF MYCENE

HERCULES AGAINST THE MOON MEN (France/Italy)   F6.2130
Nike Cinematografica–Comptoir Français du Film. *Dist* Governor Films. May **1965**. Sd; col (Eastmancolor). 35mm (Cromoscope). 90 min.

Prod Luigi Mondello. *Dir* Giacomo Gentilomo. *Screenplay* Arpad De Riso, Nino Scolaro. *Story* Arpad De Riso, Nino Scolaro, Giacomo Gentilomo, Angelo Sangermano. *Photog* Oberdan Trojani. *Art Dir* Amedeo Mellone. *Mus* Carlo Franci. *Sd* Bruno Moreal. *Sp Eff* Ugo Amadoro.

Cast: Alan Steel *(Hercules),* Jany Clair *(Agar),* Anna Maria Polani *(Selena),* Nando Tamberlani, Delia D'Alberti, Jean-Pierre Honoré, Goffredo Unger.

Action melodrama. The people of Samar are held in bondage by the powers of the moon men who inhabit the interior of the Mountain of Death. Every 3 months, young men and women are sacrificed to them, and the Queen of Samar does nothing to stop this practice, since she has been promised power when the moon men complete their plans for world conquest. Patriots call on Hercules to rid the country of its oppressors, but he cannot prevent the queen from handing over her own stepsister to the moon men as a sacrificial victim. Hercules finally succeeds in gaining entrance to the Mountain of Death, freeing the stepsister, and putting an end to the terrible reign of the moon men. *Royalty. Despots. Slavery. Human sacrifice. Imaginary kingdoms. Maciste. Hercules.*

Note: Released in Italy in 1964 as *Maciste e la regina di Samar;* opened in Paris in Feb 1965 as *Maciste contre les hommes de pierre;* running time: 80 min. Alternative Italian title: *Maciste contro gli uomini della luna.*

HERCULES AND THE CAPTIVE WOMEN (France/Italy)   F6.2131
SPA Cinematografica–Comptoir Français du Film. *Dist* Woolner Bros. Pictures. 15 Apr **1963** [Honolulu, Hawaii, opening]. Sd; col (Technicolor). 35mm (Technirama (see note)). 93 min.

Prod Achille Piazzi. *Dir* Vittorio Cottafavi. *2d Unit Dir* Giorgio Cristallini. *Screenplay* Alessandro Continenza, Vittorio Cottafavi, Duccio Tessari. *Story* Archibald Zounds, Jr. *Photog* Carlo Carlini. *Film Ed* Maurizio Lucidi. *Ed U. S. Vers* Hugo Grimaldi. *Mus Comp & Cond* Gino Marinuzzi. *Mus* Armando Trovajoli. *Adtl Mus U. S. Vers* Gordon Zahler. *Choreog* Peter Van Der Sloot. *Sd* Umberto Picistrelli. *Prod Mgr* Danilo Marciani. *Cost* Vittorio Rossi.

Cast: Reg Park *(Hercules),* Fay Spain *(Antinea),* Ettore Manni *(Androcles),* Luciano Marin *(Illus),* Laura Altan, Mario Petri, Mimmo Palmara, Ivo Garrani, Mario Valdemarin, Enrico Maria Salerno, Salvatore Furnari, Maurizio Caffarelli, Gian Maria Volontè, Luciana Angiolillo, Nicola Sperli, Mino Doro.

Adventure melodrama. In ancient Greece, soothsayers intrepret strange signs in the sky to mean that a foreign civilization will conquer and enslave their country. Only Androcles, King of Thebes, sails against the enemy. He shanghais Hercules and his son Illus aboard, and while at sea, Hercules succeeds in putting down a mutiny aboard ship. During a storm, Hercules disappears in the mist, and upon reaching a strange shore, he rescues the Princess Ismene from the god Proteus. Accompanying Ismene to Atlantis, Hercules finds Androcles drugged and imprisoned by Antinea, the queen of the island who possesses the power to control men. After learning of Antinea's plan to conquer Greece and rule the world, Hercules discovers the secret of the queen's evil power from one of the high priests, but he is captured and imprisoned with his son. He manages to escape, however, and using his knowledge of the secret, he destroys Antinea and Atlantis. Before the island sinks into the sea, Hercules reaches the ship and is reunited with Illus, Ismene, and Androcles. Together they sail for Greece. *Royalty. Mythological characters. Shanghaiing. Mutiny. Megalomania. Greece—Ancient. Thebes. Storms. Hercules. Androcles. Atlantis.*

Note: Opened in Rome in Aug 1961 as *Ercole alla conquista di Atlantide;* running time: 101 min; in Paris in Feb 1962 as *Hercule à la conquête de l'Atlantide;* running time: 98 and 100 min. Originally shown in 70mm Supertechnirama.

HERCULES IN NEW YORK   F6.2132
RAF Industries. 25 Feb **1970** [Hickory, North Carolina, opening]. Sd; col (Eastmancolor). 35mm. 90 min. *MPAA rating G.*

Prod-Writ Aubrey Wisberg. *Exec Prod* Lewis G. Chapin, Jr., Murray Kaplan. *Assoc Prod* Willard W. Goodman. *Dir* Arthur A. Seidelman. *Dir Photog* Leo Lebowitz. *Film Ed* Donald P. Finamore. *Mus Comp & Cond* John Balamos. *Sd* Abe Seidman. *Asst Dir* John Quill. *Unit Location Mgr* Parnell Hall, Merve Dayan. *Wardrobe* Yvonne Stoney. *Makeup* Reg Tackley. *Prop Master* Sol Stern. *Head Grip* Charles Kolb. *Gaffer* Morton Gorowitz.

Cast: Arnold Stang *(Pretzie),* Arnold Strong *(Hercules),* Deborah Loomis *(Helen),* James Karen *(The Professor),* Ernest Graves *(Zeus),* Tanny McDonald *(Juno),* Taina Elg *(Nemesis),* Michael Lipton *(Pluto),* Howard Burstein *(Rod),* Merwin Goldsmith *(Maxie),* George Bartenieff *(Nitro),* Erica Fitz *(Venus),* Diane Goble *(Diana),* Dan Hamilton *(Mercury),* Tony Carroll *(Monstro),* Mark Tendler *(Samson),* Dennis Tinerino *(Atlas).*

Fantasy. Hercules, bored with life on Olympus, is thrust to Earth by his father, Zeus. The god is picked up by a freighter and saved from irate New York longshoremen by a diminutive stranger, Pretzie. While demonstrating feats of strength in Central Park, Hercules is befriended by a professor and his daughter, Helen. After capturing a bear that has escaped from the zoo, Hercules embarks on a career as a professional wrestler. Although Zeus orders Nemesis to take Hercules to Hades, Nemesis and Pluto rob the god of his earthly strength. Hercules and Pretzie, pursued by a gang of hoodlums, flee by chariot up Broadway. The compassionate Mercury orders Atlas and Samson to assist their fellow, while Zeus, repentant, provides the thunderbolt that subdues his son's adversaries. As Hercules returns to Olympus, Zeus contemplates visiting Earth. *Stevedores. Professors. Wrestlers. Hoodlums. Mythological characters. Rescue. Filial relations. Urban life. Freighters. Zoos. Chariots. New York City. New York City—Central Park. Chases. Hercules. Olympus. Zeus. Nemesis (goddess). Pluto (god). Mercury (god). Atlas. Samson. Bears.*

Note: Location scenes filmed in New York City.

HERCULES IN THE HAUNTED WORLD (Italy)   F6.2133
SPA Cinematografica. *Dist* Woolner Bros. Pictures. Apr **1964**. Sd; col (Technicolor). 35mm (Totalscope Super/100). 91 min. [Also reviewed at 84 and 89 min.]

Exec Prod Achille Piazzi. *Dir* Mario Bava. *Screenplay* Alessandro Continenza, Mario Bava, Franco Prosperi, Duccio Tessari. *Photog* Mario Bava. *Ch Camera* Ubaldo Terzano. *Art Dir* Franco Lolli. *Film Ed* Mario Serandrei. *Mus* Armando Trovajoli. *Sd* Luigi Puri. *Prod Mgr* Danilo Marciani. *Cost* Mario Giorsi.

Cast: Reg Park *(Hercules)*, Leonora Ruffo *(Deianira)*, Christopher Lee *(Lichas)*, Giorgio Ardisson *(Theseus)*, Franco Giacobini *(Telemachus)*, Marisa Belli, Ely Dracò, Mino Doro, Monica Neri, Ida Galli.

Adventure melodrama. The evil Lichas, Pluto's servant, kills the King of Ecalia and imprisons his daughter, Deianira, in a palace. There she succumbs to madness. Hercules, who loves Deianira, learns from Keros that the only cure for her malady is a flower which grows in Hades. Accompanied by his friend Theseus, Hercules journeys to the underworld. After overcoming numerous obstacles, he obtains the precious plant and returns to Ecalia. In thanksgiving for Deianira's recovery, Hercules builds a temple to honor Pluto, but the god destroys it because Theseus has carried off his wife, Persephone. Theseus refuses to heed Hercules' request to send her back, and the two engage in combat. Persephone intervenes and avoids further strife by returning to Pluto. Hercules abandons his plan to kill Lichas when the usurper returns to Hades. Hercules and Deianira marry, restoring peace to Ecalia. *Evildoers. Mythological characters. Murder. Insanity. Travel. Abduction. Spells. Flowers. Castles. Hercules. Hades.*

Note: Released in Italy in Dec 1961 as *Ercole al centro della terra*; running time: ca90 min.

HERCULES, SAMSON & ULYSSES (Italy)   F6.2134

I. C. D. *Dist* Metro-Goldwyn-Mayer, Inc. May **1965** [c31 Dec 1964; LP29692]. Sd (Westrex); col (Eastmancolor). 35mm. 85 min.

Prod Joseph Fryd. *Dir-Writ* Pietro Francisci. *Dir Photog* Silvano Ippoliti. *Camera* Franco Di Giacomo. *Art Dir* Giorgio Giovannini. *Set Decor* Franco Loquenzi. *Film Ed* Pietro Francisci. *Mus* Angelo Francesco Lavagnino. *Mus Cond* Carlo Savina. *Choreog* Wilbert Bradley. *Sd Engr* Antonio Bramonti. *Asst Dir* Pietro Nuccorini, Ama Rigamonti Di Cuto. *Gen Organizer* Carlo Bessi. *Cost Dsgn* Gaia Romanini. *Makeup* Euclide Santoli. *Hairstyles* Amalia Paoletti.

Cast: Kirk Morris *(Hercules)*, Richard Lloyd *(Samson)*, Liana Orfei *(Delilah)*, Enzo Cerusico *(Ulysses)*, Aldo Giuffrè *(Seren)*, Fulvia Franco, Diletta D'Andrea, Nando Angelini, Franco Fantasia, Marco Mariani, Pietro Tordi, Ugo Sasso, Alina Zalewska, Aldo Pini, Fortunato Arena, Willy Colombini, Fulvio Carrara, Stefania Sabatini, Rina Mascetti, Jole Mauro, Mario De Simone, Ettore Zamperini, Marco Wassilli, Gianni Di Benedetto, Cinzia Bruno, Loris Loddi, Walter Grant, Antonio Corevi, Vladimiro Tuikovich, Cyrus Elias.

Action melodrama. The Greek king sends Hercules and his friend Ulysses to slay a sea monster that has been plaguing the coast of Ithaca. After accomplishing this task, the heroes and their men are caught in a storm and shipwrecked near Judea. There they seek help from a tribe of Danites, who fear that the strangers may be Philistines sent to capture Samson. Hercules and Ulysses are therefore sent to the Philistine city of Gaza, where Hercules is mistaken for Samson after he kills a lion with his hands. He is then delivered to King Seren, but Hercules persuades the king to allow him to prove his identity by defeating the real Samson. The bloody battle between the two men ends in mutual respect and the decision to join forces against the Philistines. Delilah, King Seren's mistress, wins the affection of Samson and betrays him to Seren, but Hercules, Ulysses, and Samson defeat the Philistines and kill King Seren, and the Greeks sail for home. *Royalty. Greeks. Danites. Philistines. Mistresses. Mistaken identity. Perfidy. Personal identity. Sea monsters. Gaza. Judea. Greece—Ancient. Ithaca (Greece). Storms. Shipwrecks. Samson. Hercules. Delilah. Ulysses. Lions.*

Note: Opened in Rome in Mar 1964 as *Ercole sfida Sansone*; running time: 100 min or 92 min.

HERCULES VS. THE GIANT WARRIORS (France/Italy)   F6.2135

Produzione Cinematografica–Films Jacques Leitienne–Unicité. *Dist* John Alexander Film Associates. Aug **1965**. Sd; col (Eastman Color). 35mm (Cromoscope). 94 min.

Prod Alberto Chimens. *Dir* Alberto De Martino. *Screenplay* Roberto Gianviti, Alessandro Ferraù. *Photog* Pierludovico Pavoni. *Film Ed* Otello Colangeli. *Mus* Francesco De Masi. *Asst Dir* Giorgio Ubaldi. *Prod Mgr* Piero Ghioni.

Cast: Dan Vadis *(Hercules)*, Moira Orfei *(Pasiphaë)*, Pierre Cressoy *(Prince Myles)*, Marilù Tolo *(Ate)*, Piero Lulli *(Gordius)*, Enzo Fiermonte *(Eurystheus)*, Renato Rossini *(Hereus)*.

Adventure melodrama. Hercules, having agreed to restore justice to Mycenae, confronts evil Prince Myles. The villain is invested with power over giant bronze warriors by his mother Pasiphaë, a sorceress in Hades. Myles assassinates the king and abducts his cousin, Queen Ate, through whom he

plans to inherit the throne. Although Zeus temporarily removes Hercules' strength for killing Eurystheus, an innocent man framed by Myles, the god restores his powers. Hercules then saves Ate and destroys Myles, Pasiphaë, and the giant warriors. *Strongmen. Royalty. Sorcerers. Cousins. Mythological characters. Magic. Filial relations. Assassination. Abduction. Frameup. Bronze. Mycenae. Hercules. Zeus. Pasiphaë. Eurystheus. Hades.*

Note: Filmed in Italy in 1964 as *Il trionfo di Ercole*.

HERE COMES DODIE   F6.2136

MJ Productions. *Dist* MarJon Film Distributors. ca **1970**. Sd; col. 16mm. [Feature film, length unknown.]

Sex film. No information about the precise nature of this film has been found. *Sexuality.*

HERE COMES THAT NASHVILLE SOUND *see* COUNTRY BOY

HERE WE GO 'ROUND THE MULBERRY BUSH (Great Britain)
F6.2137

Giant Film Production, Ltd. *Dist* Lopert Pictures. 4 Mar **1968** [New York opening; c5 Jan 1968; LF22]. Sd; col (Technicolor, print by DeLuxe). 35mm. 96 min. [Also 114 min.]

Prod-Dir Clive Donner. *Assoc Prod–Adtl Dial* Larry Kramer. *Screenplay* Hunter Davies. *Dir Photog* Alex Thomson. *Focus* Harvey Harrison. *Art Dir* Brian Eatwell. *Asst Art Dir* Mark James, art. *Titl & Daydreams* Richard Williams Studio, Bill Rhoads. *Film Ed* Fergus McDonell. *Mus Dir* Simon Napier-Bell. *Songs:* "Taking Out Time," "Looking Back," "Every Little Thing," "Virginals Dream," "Picture of Her," "Just Like Me," "Possession" writ & perf by Spencer Davis Group. *Songs:* "Here We Go 'Round the Mulberry Bush," "Am I What I Was or Was I What I Am" Stevie Winwood. *Perf by* Stevie Winwood, Traffic. *Song:* "Utterly Simple" Dave Mason. *Perf by* Dave Mason, Traffic. *Song:* "Waltz for Caroline" Stevie Winwood. *Perf by* Spencer Davis Group. *Song:* "It's Been a Long Time" Simon Napier-Bell. *Sung by* Andy Ellison. *Sd Ed* Dino Di Campo. *Sd Rec* Robert Allen, Doug Turner. *Mus Ed* Simon Napier-Bell. *Asst Dir* Peter Price. *Prod Supv* Basil Keys. *Location Mgr* Peter Crowhurst. *Cont* Josephine Knowles. *Fashion Coörd* Sandy Moss. *Makeup* John O'Gorman. *Hairstyles* Biddy Chrystal. *Sp Fashion Coöp* Marion Foale, Sally Tuffin, Ossie Clarke, Veronica Marsh, Graziella Fontana, Clare and Deborah, Ritva, Moya. *Casting* John Merrick. *Elec Supv* David Clarke.

Cast: Barry Evans *(Jamie McGregor)*, Judy Geeson *(Mary Gloucester)*, Angela Scoular *(Caroline Beauchamp)*, Sheila White *(Paula)*, Adrienne Posta *(Linda)*, Vanessa Howard *(Audrey)*, Diane Keen *(Claire)*, Moyra Fraser *(Mrs. McGregor)*, Michael Bates *(Mr. McGregor)*, Maxine Audley *(Mrs. Beauchamp)*, Denholm Elliott *(Mr. Beauchamp)*, Christopher Timothy *(Spike)*, Nicky Henson *(Craig Foster)*, Allan Warren *(Joe McGregor)*, Roy Holder *(Arthur)*, George Layton *(Gordon)*, Gareth Robinson *(Bruce)*, Oliver Cotton *(Curtis)*, Andrew Hamilton *(Charles Beauchamp)*, Sally Avory *(Cath)*, Erika Raffael *(Ingrid)*, Cavan Kendall *(Michael the Curate)*, Trevor Jones *(Gerald)*, Gillie Austin *(Susan)*, Christopher Mitchell *(Tony)*, Pauline Challoner *(Gloria)*, Mary Griffiths, Stella Kemble *(women at chip shop)*, Angela Pleasence *(scruffy girl)*, Spencer Davis Group *(group at the church dance)*.

Comedy. Source: Hunter Davies, *Here We Go 'Round the Mulberry Bush* (London, 1965). At the age of 17, Jamie McGregor is depressed by the realization that, unlike both his friend Spike and his younger brother Joe, he is still a virgin, and he vows to experience sexual intercourse before he enters a university in the fall. Certain that the girl of his dreams, Mary Gloucester, is pure and unattainable, he decides to look elsewhere for sexual gratification. Jamie makes advances in a park to the curvaceous Linda, but he leaves her abruptly when he sees Mary waiting for a bus. He next takes up with Paula but soon learns that her flirtatious behavior is only a trap to induce him to work for a fund-raising church social. His next encounter is with aristocratic Caroline Beauchamp, who invites him to spend a weekend at her parents' country manor. Jamie's visit turns into an alcoholic orgy, but Caroline falls into a drunken stupor before he can seduce her. He returns home and attends a mattress party. There he is about to yield to the free-loving Audrey when Mary lures him away with the promise of a date. On a trip to a nearby lake, Jamie's illusions are completely shattered when he discovers that Mary is actually promiscuous. When she chides him for his romantic notions, Jamie, now disgusted, swears off women and vows to concentrate on his studies. When school ends, he meets Mary's pretty friend Claire and is thrilled to learn that he and Claire will attend the same university. *Students. Brothers. Flirts. Adolescence. Virginity. Drunkenness. Seduction. Promiscuity.*

Note: Locations scenes filmed in the London suburbs. Opened in London in Jan 1968.

HERE'S THE KNIFE, DEAR: NOW USE IT see **NIGHTMARE**

HERE'S YOUR LIFE (Sweden)   F6.2138

Svensk Filmindustri. *Dist* Brandon Films. 19 Dec **1968** [New York opening]. Sd; b&w with col seq. 35mm. 110 min.

Dir Jan Troell. *Screenplay* Jan Troell, Bengt Forslund. *Photog* Jan Troell. *Art Dir* Rolf Boman. *Film Ed* Jan Troell. *Mus* Erik Nordgren. *Sd* Leif Hansen. *Prod Mgr* Bengt Forslund.

Cast: Eddie Axberg (*Olof*), Ulla Sjöblom (*Olivia*), Gunnar Björnstrand (*Lundgren*), Per Oscarsson (*Niklas*), Ulf Palme (*Larsson*), Signe Stade (*Maria*), Allan Edwall (*August*), Anna Maria Blind (*August's wife*), Åke Fridell (*Nicke Larsson*), Holger Löwenadler (*Kristiansson*), Gudrun Brost (*Olof's stepmother*), Göran Lindberg (*Olssen*), Jan-Erik Lindqvist (*Johansson*), Max von Sydow (*Smålands-Pelle*), Stig Törnblom (*Fredrik*), Ulla Akselson (*mother*), Börje Nyberg (*foreman*), Katarina Edfeldt (*Maja*), Ulla Blomstrand (*Elfrisina*), Bengt Ekerot (*Byberg*), Bo Wahlström (*older brother*), Rick Axberg (*2d brother*), Göran Lindberg (*Olsson*), Tage Sjögren (*Lund*), Tage Jonsson (*Linus*), Birger Lensander (*manager at brickworks*), Friedrich Ochsner (*smith*), Millgård Björklund (*union member*), Bertil Linné (*Gustafsson*).

Drama. Source: Eyvind Johnson, *Romanen om Olof* (Stockholm, 1945). In 1914, fourteen-year-old Olof takes a job as a timber floater at a logging camp in Norrbotten in northern Sweden. The work is grueling, but Olof stays with it until the approach of winter forces him to find a job at a brickyard-sawmill. His disillusionment and anger upon discovering his boss's callousness toward a workman injured in an accident lead to Olof's being fired. At his next job, as a billboard sticker and candy salesman in a Boden movie theater, he meets his first girl friend, Maria; but his love for her is short-lived. Touring the summer village fairs as an assistant to Nicke, a motion picture projectionist, Olof boasts of his sexual activities, but later he reveals his inexperience by turning down a sexual invitation from Nicke's girl friend, Olivia. After hearing through a wall the sounds of Nicke and Olivia making love, Olof runs away, finds a job in a blacksmith's shop, and has his first sexual encounter when he seduces the blacksmith's daughter. Leaving her with merely a handshake, Olof takes a train out of town and arrives at a political rally. Upon returning to his job at the movie theater, he discovers that his acquired socialist leanings displease his boss, and he is fired. Retracing his steps, Olof sets up housekeeping with Olivia, but tiring of her wantonness, he soon leaves her and goes to work for a railroad. When his plans to call a strike and organize a union fail, Olof gets drunk for the first time in his life. Finally, as World War I ends, Olof looks back on his experiences, satisfied that he has become a man, and heads south in search of new adventures. *Motion picture projectionists. Blacksmiths. Socialists. Lumbering. Manhood. Seduction. Drunkenness. Motion picture theaters. Fairs. Labor unions. Strikes. World War I. Norrbotten (Sweden). Boden (Sweden).*

Note: Filmed on location in Sweden and released there in Dec 1966 as *Här har du ditt liv*; running time: 167 min.

THE HERO AS ARTIST see **CIVILISATION: THE HERO AS ARTIST**

THE HEROES see **THE INVINCIBLE SIX**

THE HEROES OF TELEMARK (Great Britain)   F6.2139

Benton Film Productions. *Dist* Columbia Pictures. 19 Jan **1966** [Chicago opening; c31 Dec 1965; LP32420]. Sd (Westrex); col (Eastman Color, print by Pathé). 35mm (Panavision). 131 min.

Prod S. Benjamin Fisz. *Dir* Anthony Mann. *2d Unit Dir* Egil Woxholt. *Screenplay* Ivan Moffat, Ben Barzman. *Dir Photog* Robert Krasker. *Camera Op* John Harris, Ronnie Maasz, John Burrows. *2d Unit Camera* Egil Woxholt. *Art Dir* Tony Masters. *Set Decor* Bob Cartwright, Ted Clements. *Film Ed* Bert Bates. *Mus Comp & Cond* Malcolm Arnold. *Sd Ed* Ted Mason. *Sd Rec* Bill Daniels, Gordon McCallum. *Asst Dir* John Quested, Derek Cracknell. *Prod Supv* George Pitcher. *Prod Mgr* Timothy Burrill. *Location Mgr* Jimmy Komisarjevsky. *Cont* Kay Mander. *Wardrobe Supv* Elsa Fennell. *Makeup* Neville Smallwood. *Hairdresser* Maud Onslow. *Sp Photog Eff* John P. Fulton. *Sp Eff* Ron Ballanger, Syd Pearson, Bill Warrington. *Stunt Adv* Gerry Crampton. *Coöp* Norsk Hydro at Rjukan. *Casting* Maude Spector.

Cast: Kirk Douglas (*Dr. Rolf Pedersen*), Richard Harris (*Knut Straud*), Ulla Jacobsson (*Anna*), Michael Redgrave (*Uncle*), David Weston (*Arne*), Sebastian Breaks (*Gunnar*), John Golightly (*Freddy*), Alan Howard (*Oli*), Patrick Jordan (*Henrik*), William Marlowe (*Claus*), Brook Williams (*Elinar*), Roy Dotrice (*Jensen*), Anton Diffring (*Major Frick*), Ralph Michael (*Nilssen*), Eric Porter (*Terboven*), Wolf Frees (*Knippelberg*), Karel Stepanek (*Hartmuller*), Gerard Heinz (*Erhardt*), Victor Beaumont (*German sergeant*), George Murcell (*sturmführer*), Mervyn Johns (*Colonel Wilkinson*), Barry Jones (*Professor Logan*), Geoffrey Keen (*General Bolt*), Robert Ayres (*General Courts*), Jennifer Hilary (*Sigrid*), Maurice Denham (*doctor at hospital*), David Davies (*Captain of "Galtesund"*), Philo Hauser (*businessman*), Faith Brook (*woman on bus*), Elvi Hale (*Mrs. Sandersen*), Russell Waters (*Mr. Sandersen*), Jan Conrad (*watchman in factory*), Alf Joint (*German guard on ferry*), Robert Bruce

(*major*), Brian Jackson (*Norwegian naval attaché*), Paul Hansard (*German official*), Annette Andre (*girl student*), Pamela Conway (*girl in darkroom*), Grace Arnold, Howard Douglas ("*Galtesund*" *passengers*), Jemma Hyde (*businessman's girl friend*), Terry Plummer, Joe Powell (*quislings*).

War melodrama. Source: Knut Haukelid, *Skis Against the Atom* (London, 1954). John Drummond, *But for These Men* (London, 1962). In Nazi-occupied Norway in 1942, underground leader Knut Straud smuggles a microfilm message from an agent in a Nazi factory hidden deep in a Norwegian valley to university Prof. Rolf Pedersen. The Nazis are producing "heavy water," an essential in the manufacture of atomic bombs, at the factory. Straud and Pedersen hijack a boat and bring the message to the Allies in England, who decide to destroy the factory. Straud and Pedersen are parachuted, along with a team of assistants, back into Norway to lay the groundwork for an attack on the factory by British commandos. The gliders carrying the commandos crash and burn, whereupon the underground team decides to try to destroy by themselves the room at the factory containing the "heavy water" machinery. They succeed, but Pedersen is subsequently wounded and captured. He escapes and rejoins Straud. The factory is back in operation, however, when the Nazis ship in duplicates of the demolished machinery. Allied bombers attack the factory but are unable to hit the high-concentration room, and the Nazis, their position discovered, decide to ship the "heavy water" to Germany under tight security. Rolf, after saving the lives of most of the innocents aboard, sinks the ferry carrying the "heavy water." The cargo is forever lost to the Nazis. *Norwegians. Nazis. Professors. Commandos. Resistance (political). Sabotage. Espionage. Military occupation. Microfilm. Factories. Atom bomb. Ferryboats. Airplanes. World War II. Norway. Germany—Army. Great Britain—Royal Air Force. Ship explosions.*

Note: Location scenes filmed in Norway and on the south coast of England at Poole and Weymouth. Opened in London in Nov 1965. Working title: *The Unknown Battle*.

HEROINA   F6.2140

Jeronimo Mitchell Melendez. *Dist* Royal Films International. 10 Nov **1965** [New York opening]. Sd; b&w. 35mm. 105 min.

Prod-Dir-Story Jeronimo Mitchell Melendez. *Exec Prod* Ben Kantrowitz. *Screenplay* Enrique de la Torre. *Dir Photog* Luis A. Maisonet. *Dir Photog 2d Unit* Orlando Jimenez. *Film Ed* Gloria A. Pineyro. *Mus Score* Charlie Palmieri. *Incidental Mus* Casa Alegre Inc. *Mus Supv* Robert W. Streinger. *Prod Mgr* Felix A. Ramírez.

Cast: Kitty de Hoyos (*Laura*), Jaime Sanchez (*Chico*), Otto Sirgo (*Marcos*), Jeddu Mascorieto (*Tito*), Marta Casanas (*The Mother*), José de San Anton (*The Father*), Nidia Caro (*Nina*), Felix Monclova (*Nick*), Freddie Baez (*addict*), Olga Guillot (*singer*), Raul Davila (*judge*), Kako y Su Combo (*orchestra*).

Melodrama. The son of well-to-do parents, Chico, a young Puerto Rican living in Spanish Harlem, becomes a heroin addict after a rivalry between him and his father for his mother's affection drives him to drugs. Following a 6-month jail term, Chico, now cured of his drug habit and working in his father's business, meets Nick, his former dealer, for a casual drink; but Chico's enraged father assumes his son has resumed drug use and again evicts him from home. Chico takes refuge with Nick and soon is helping him peddle heroin. Guilt-ridden and lonely after the death of his addict friend Tito, Chico returns to his addiction and is expelled from the drug mob. Having become involved with Laura, a prostitute, Chico is hunted by both the police and the mob. In desperation, he returns home to his father, who finally realizes his own guilt and helps protect his son. *Puerto Ricans. Drug dealers. Drug addicts. Prostitutes. Police. Filial relations. Guilt. Organized crime. Heroin. New York City—Spanish Harlem.*

Note: Filmed on location in New York City. Presented in Spanish language with English subtitles.

HERO'S ISLAND   F6.2141

Daystar Productions–Portland Productions. *Dist* United Artists. caSep **1962** [c18 Sep 1962; LP23208]. Sd; col (Technicolor). 35mm (Panavision). 94 min.

Prod-Dir-Orig Screenplay Leslie Stevens. *Assoc Prod* Elaine Michea. *Co-prod* James Mason. *Cinematog* Ted McCord. *Film Ed* Richard Brockway. *Mus* Dominic Frontiere. *Sd* Jay Ashworth. *Asst Dir* Ivan Volkman. *Prod Mgr* Edward Fitzgerald, prod mgr. *Wardrobe* Reeder Boss. *Makeup* Fred Phillips.

Cast: James Mason (*Jacob Webber*), Kate Manx (*Devon Mainwaring*), Neville Brand (*Kingstree*), Rip Torn (*Nicholas*), Warren Oates (*Wayte*), Brendan Dillon (*Thomas Mainwaring*), Robert Sampson (*Enoch*), Dean Stanton (*Dixey*), Morgan Mason (*Cullen*), Darby Hinton (*Jafar*), Robert Johnson (*Pound*), Bill Hart (*Meggett*), John Hudkins (*Bullock*).

Costume melodrama. In 1718 two former indentured servants, Devon and Thomas Mainwaring, and their children, Cullen and Jafar, settle on an island off the Carolina coast willed to them by their late master. No sooner have they established camp, than Nicholas and Enoch Gates, two brothers from an illiterate fishing family, try to drive them off the island. Although Enoch kills her husband, Devon is determined to stay. The next day Jacob Webber, a castaway, is washed ashore. Overcoming her suspicions, the young widow takes in the stranger, who reveals himself to be a pirate. Although Webber refuses at first to help fight the fishermen, he routs them all with his cutlass when the entire Gates family returns and attacks him. Nicholas Gates joins the group when he is thrown overboard for rebelling against Kingstree, a slave trader whom Enoch has hired to fight the settlers. Kingstree identifies Webber as Bluebeard's former sailmaster, and the battle becomes a personal one in which Webber kills the cutthroat. Nicholas, fascinated by Devon's ability to read, remains with her and the children to help settle the island as Webber returns to his life of piracy. *Colonists. Indentured servants. Settlers. Fishermen. Pirates. Slavers. Castaways. Survival. Inheritance. United States—History—Colonial period. Islands. Duels.*

Note: Location scenes filmed on Santa Catalina island. Also known as *The Land We Love.*

HÉROS SANS RETOUR *see* **COMMANDO**

HERRSCHER OHNE KRONE *see* **KING IN SHADOW**

HETEROSEXUAL *see* **JULIETTE DE SADE**

HEURES CHAUDES *see* **HOT HOURS**

THE HEX WITH SEX *see* **TO HEX WITH SEX**

HEY, LET'S TWIST!   F6.2142
Harry Romm Productions. *Dist* Paramount Pictures. 23 Dec **1961** [Atlanta showing; c21 Dec 1961; LP20964]. Sd; b&w. 35mm. 80 min.
Prod Harry Romm. *Assoc Prod* Martha Vera Romm. *Dir* Greg Garrison. *Screenplay* Hal Hackady. *Cinematog* George Jacobson. *Art Dir* Albert Brenner. *Supv Ed* Sidney Katz. *Mus* Henry Glover. *Songs:* "Hey, Let's Twist," "Ro-ly Po-ly" Henry Glover, Joey Dee, Morris Levy. *Song:* "I Wanna Twist" Barbara George. *Song:* "Mother Goose Twist" Evel Box. *Song:* "It's a Pity To Say Goodnight" Billy Reid. *Sd Dir* Emil Kolisch. *Asst Dir* Stanley Ackerman. *Prod Supv* Harrison Starr. *Cost Dsgn* Natalie Walker.
Cast: Joey Dee *(himself),* The Starliters *(themselves),* Teddy Randazzo *(Rickey Dee),* Kay Armen *(Angie),* Zohra Lampert *(Sharon),* Dino Di Luca *(Papa),* Richard Dickens *(Dore),* Jo-Ann Campbell *(Piper),* Peppermint Loungers *(themselves),* Allan Arbus *(The Doctor),* Hope Hampton.
Musical comedy-drama. Italian-born Papa Dinato is fulfilling a life-long ambition by putting his two sons, Joey and Rickey, through college. Consequently, when the two boys turn professional with their small combo instead of continuing their studies, Papa suffers a mild stroke and is confined to his bed. Aided by Papa's friend, the widowed Angie, Joey and Rickey take over their father's restaurant, rename it the Peppermint Lounge, and introduce the Twist there. On New Year's Eve, a society columnist (Sharon) accidentally wanders into the Lounge, takes a liking to Rickey, and soon has all of society joining the dancing teenagers. Overcome by sudden success, Rickey takes Sharon's advice and elegantly redecorates the Lounge. When he begins running the place on a "reservations only" basis, it loses its appeal and business falls off. Sharon walks out, Rickey secretly returns to college, and Joey and his girl friend, Piper, once more make the Lounge a teenage hangout. Business soars again, and all ends happily as Rickey returns and hands Papa his college diploma. *Brothers. Musicians. Widows. Columnists. Socialites. Italians. Students. Fatherhood. Adolescence. Bands. Strokes. Restaurants. Nightclubs. Rock and roll. Twist (dance). New York City. Peppermint Lounge.*

Note: Filmed at the Peppermint Lounge and elsewhere in New York City.

HEY THERE, IT'S YOGI BEAR   F6.2143
Hanna-Barbera Productions. *Dist* Columbia Pictures. 3 Jun **1964** [Salt Lake City, Utah, opening; c1 Jun 1964; LP28380]. Sd (RCA); col (Eastman Color by Pathé). 35mm. 89 min.
Prod-Dir William Hanna, Joseph Barbera. *Assoc Prod* Alex Lovy. *Screenplay* Joseph Barbera, Warren Foster, William Hanna. *Anim Dir* Charles A. Nichols. *Story Sketches* Dan Gordon. *Art Dir* Richard Bickenbach, Iwao Takamoto, William Perez, Jacques W. Rupp, Willie Ito, Tony Sgroi, Ernest Nordli, Jerry Eisenberg, Zigamond Jablecki, Bruce Bushman. *Ink & Paint Supv* Roberta Greutert. *Anim* Don Lusk, Irv Spence, George Kreisl, Ray Patterson, Jerry Hathcock, Grant Simmons, Fred Wolf, Gerry Chiniquy, Don Peterson, Ken Harris, George Goepper, Edwin Aardal, Ed Parks, Kenneth Muse, Harry Holt. *Background Dsgn* F. Montealegre, Art Lozzi, Robert Gentle, Ron Dias, Richard H. Thomas, Richard Kelsey, Fernando Arce, Don Peters, Bob Abrams, Richard Ung, Tom O'Loughlin, Bob Gribbroeck, Curtiss D. Perkins. *Photog* Frank Paiker, Norman Stainback, Roy Wade, Charles Flekal, Frank Parrish, Ted Bemiller, Bill Kotler. *Titl* Pacific Title. *Film Ed* Greg Watson, Warner Leighton, Tony Milch, Donald A. Douglas, Larry Cowan, Ken Spears. *Mus* Marty Paich. *Titl Song* David Gates. *Song:* "Ven-E, Ven-O, Ven-A" Ray

Gilbert, Doug Goodwin. *Sung by* James Darren. *Songs:* "Like I Like You," "Wet Your Whistle," "St. Louie," "Ash Can Parade" Ray Gilbert, Doug Goodwin. *Sd Rec* Buddy Myers.
Voices: Daws Butler *(Yogi Bear),* Julie Bennett *(Cindy),* Don Messick *(Boo Boo/Ranger Smith),* Mel Blanc *(Grifter),* J. Pat O'Malley *(Snively),* Hal Smith *(Corn Pone),* Jean Vanderpyl.
Animated comedy. In Jellystone National Park, the "No Feeding the Bears" signs force a showdown between Yogi Bear and Ranger Smith, causing Yogi to request a transfer to the San Diego Zoo. However, he changes his mind at the last minute, convinces another bear to go in his place, and hides in the woods with his sidekick, Boo Boo. Yogi's girl friend Cindy, unaware of the switch, tries to follow Yogi but is abducted and put on display by the Chizzling Brothers Circus. She is rescued by Yogi and Boo Boo, but the trio gets lost on the way back to Jellystone and takes refuge on top of a partially constructed building in New York City. The event is reported on the news, and Ranger Smith comes to lead the three bears back home. *Forest rangers. Abduction. National parks. Circus. New York City. Bears.*

Note: Working title: *Whistle Your Way Back Home.*

HI IN THE CELLAR *see* **UP IN THE CELLAR**

HI MO TSUKI MO *see* **THROUGH DAYS AND MONTHS**

HI, MOM!   F6.2144
West End Films. *Dist* Sigma III Corp. 27 Apr **1970** [New York opening]. Sd; col (Eastman color, print by Movielab) with b&w seq. 35mm. 87 min. *MPAA rating* R.
Prod Charles Hirsch. *Dir-Writ* Brian De Palma. *Story* Brian De Palma, Charles Hirsch. *Dir Photog* Robert Elfstrom. *Art Dir* Peter Bocour. *Film Ed* Paul Hirsch. *Mus Comp & Cond* Eric Kaz. *Lyr* John Andreolli. *Titl Song Sung* by Jeffrey Lesser. *Song:* "I'm Looking at You" sung by Boney Srabian. *Song:* "Be Black, Baby!" sung by Grady Tate. *Asst Dir* Bruce Rubin.
Cast: Robert De Niro *(Jon Rubin),* Charles Durnham *(superintendent),* Allen Garfield *(Joe Banner),* Abraham Goren *(pervert in movie theater),* Lara Parker *(Jeannie Mitchell),* Jennifer Salt *(Judy Bishop),* Gerritt Graham *(Gerrit Wood),* Nelson Peltz *(playboy),* Hector Valentin Lino, Jr., Carole Leverett *(N.I.T. Journal revolutionaries),* Ruth Bocour, Bart De Palma, Arthur Bierman *(N.I.T. Journal, at newspaper stand),* Buddy Butler, David Connell, Milton Earl Forrest, Carolyn Craven, Joyce Griffin, Kirk Kerksey *("Be Black, Baby!" troupe),* Ruth Alda, Carol Vogel, Beth Bowden, Joe Stillman, Joe Fields, Gene Elman, Paul Milvy *("Be Black, Baby!" audience),* Peter Maloney *(pharmacist),* William Daley *(co-op neighbor),* Floyd L. Peterson *(John Winnicove).*
Comedy-drama. Employed by pornographic filmmaker Joe Banner, Vietnam veteran Jon Rubin rents a room in New York's Lower East Side and trains his lens on the bedroom windows of a high rise. Among his subjects are a playboy, revolutionary Gerrit Wood, a middle class couple with two children, and a trio of single girls, including Judy Bishop, whom Rubin decides to seduce. Setting his site on her bedroom window, he proceeds to her apartment, where they begin to have sex. During their lovemaking, however, the camera tilts and fails to catch the precious moment, thereby ending Rubin's career as a photographer. Auditioning for the revue *Be Black, Baby!* the veteran wins the role of a white policeman. During the performance's filming by National Intellectual Television Journal, the actors appear in whiteface and blacken the countenances of their Caucasian audience. The cast then subjects the spectators to physical and verbal abuse. As the liberal audience expresses its approval to newsmen, the blacks, led by Wood, raid the high rise. They are repulsed by the bourgeois husband, who sprays them with machine gun fire. After marrying Judy, Rubin finds a job as an insurance salesman. Disgusted by a diet of TV dinners and tiring of his pregnant wife's demand for a yellow dishwasher, Rubin goes to the basement laundry and deposits dynamite in the washer. Interviewed by a news commentator before the devastated building, the veteran decries violence. *Pornographers. Veterans. Filmmakers. Playboys. Middle classes. Revolutionaries. Negroes. Actors. Theatrical troupes. Insurance agents. Reporters. Seduction. Disguise. Marriage. Pregnancy. Sex exploitation films. Television. Theater. New York City—Lower East Side. Documentation. Explosions.*

Note: Original title: *Son of Greetings.* "N.I.T. Journal" sequence filmed in 16mm.

THE HIDDEN ROOM OF 1,000 HORRORS *see* **THE TELL-TALE HEART**

HIDE AND SEEK (Great Britain)   F6.2145
Spectrum Films. *Dist* Universal Pictures. Feb **1964** [c2 May 1964; LP35484]. Sd (Westrex); b&w. 35mm. 90 min.
Pres by Albion Film Corp. *Exec Prod* Hal E. Chester. *Dir* Cy Endfield. *Screenplay* David Stone. *Adapt* Robert Foshko. *Story* Harold Greene. *Dir Photog* Gilbert Taylor. *Art Dir* George Provis. *Set Decor* Andrew Campbell.

Film Ed Thelma Connell. *Mus* Muir Mathieson, Gary Hughes. *Played by* Sinfonia of London. *Sd* John Cox. *Sd Rec* Cecil Mason. *Dub Ed* Ted Mason. *Asst Dir* Stuart Freeman. *Prod Mgr* John D. Merriman. *Cont* Muirne Mathieson. *Makeup* Paul Rabiger. *Hairstylist* Blanche Arden. *Sp Eff* Wally Veevers.

Cast: Ian Carmichael (*David Garrett*), Janet Munro (*Maggie*), Curt Jurgens (*Hubert Marek*), George Pravda (*Frank Melnicker*), Kieron Moore (*Paul*), Hugh Griffith (*Wilkins*), Derek Tansley (*Chambers*), James Houlihan, Leslie Crawford (*thugs*), Esma Cannon (*tea lady*), Kynaston Reeves (*hunter*), Edward Chapman (*McPherson*), Fred Peisley (*Cottrell*), Cyril Cross, Monty Warren (*agents*), John Boxer (*secretary at ministry*), Robert Moore, British (*father at wedding*), Brian Alexis (*groom*), Barbara Roscoe (*bride*), Barbara Cavan (*woman*), Bill Cartwright (*delivery man*), Sidney Vivian (*commissionaire*), Michael Segal (*train guard*), Lance Percival (*idiot*), Tommy Godfrey (*drunken songwriter*), Lynda Baron (*flying jacket*), Julian Orchard (*pompous man*), Donald Bisset (*stranger on platform*), Judy Parfitt (*chauffeur*), Cardew Robinson, Richard Butler.

Melodrama. Professor David Garrett, a British scientist, meets Frank Melnicker, an old friend from behind the Iron Curtain, at an international chess tournament. They play a game of chess, and Garrett later sees Melnicker being whisked away by two men. Garrett then realizes that during their game Melnicker secretly revealed to him an address. Garrett visits the address and meets Maggie, whose business is selling information. Maggie informs him that Melnicker operates an escape route, and she insists on taking Garrett to Melnicker's place in Yorkshire. En route, they leap off a train to avoid two thugs and are aided by Wilkins, an eccentric who lives on a barge loaded with brandy and animals. Garrett is attacked later by a stranger who seemingly falls off a cliff during the ensuing struggle. A policeman then guides Garrett to his destination, a lonely cliff-top castle where he meets Marek, the head of the communist ring, who reveals his intention to make it appear as though Garrett voluntarily defected. Both Maggie and Melnicker appear to have been involved in the plot; but Maggie, who has fallen in love with Garrett, reappears and helps Garrett outwit Marek. *Professors. Scientists. Secret agents. Hired killers. Eccentrics. Police. Communists. Defectors. Friendship. Espionage. Chess. Tournaments. Castles. Yorkshire. Iron Curtain.*

Note: Released in Great Britain in Jun 1964.

HIDE AND SEEK see THE LICKERISH QUARTET

HIER, AUJOURD'HUI ET DEMAIN see YESTERDAY, TODAY AND TOMORROW

HIGASHI KARA KITA OTOKO see THE MAN FROM THE EAST

HIGASHI SHINAKAI see EAST CHINA SEA

HIGH (Canada) F6.2146
Laurence L. Kent. *Dist* Joseph Brenner Associates. 19 Feb **1969** [San Francisco opening; c1 Jul 1967; LF19]. Sd; col & b&w. 35mm. 82 min.

Prod-Dir-Writ Laurence L. Kent. *Photog* Paul Van Der Linden. *Film Ed* Pitre Savard. *Mus & Songs* The Side Tracks. *Prod Asst* Robert Linnell.

Cast: Astri Thorvik (*Vicky*), Lanny Beckman (*Tom*), Peter Matthews, Joyce Cay, Denis Payque, Carol Epstein, Doris Cowan, Mortie Golub, Al Mayoff, Melinda McCracken, Janet Amos, Gary Eisencraft, Paul Kirby, Jack Epstein, Peter Pyper, Daphne, Sue, Kristen.

Drama. Tom, a young college dropout making his way around Canada by selling Mexican marijuana and preying upon homosexuals, meets a pretty librarian named Vicky. He gets her high on marijuana and makes love to both her and her roommate. Once Vicky has been converted to Tom's way of life, she joins him in exploiting anyone and everyone in the pursuit of pleasure. When money is low, they resort to prostitution, stealing credit cards, and even filching tips from waitresses. As their relationship grows, Vicky becomes more aggressive while Tom, having fallen in love with his "pupil," becomes more and more passive, failing even to take the initiative when they make love. Vicky is invited to take a trip to the Laurentian Mountains by one of her customers, and she brings Tom along for kicks. After she has goaded the man until he is half crazed with impotent rage, the couple murder him and prop him up against a tree while they make love in a nearby field. Eventually, Vicky tires of Tom, and she ditches him to look for a more exciting life somewhere else. *Drug dealers. Librarians. Theft. Prostitution. Murder. Marijuana. Laurentian Mountains.*

Note: Filmed in Montreal. Opened in Montreal in Oct 1968; running time: 74 min (cut from 85 min). Also known as *In.*

HIGH AND LOW (Japan) F6.2147
Toho Co.–Kurosawa Films. *Dist* Toho International, Inc., Continental Distributing, Inc. 26 Nov **1963** [New York opening]. Sd; b&w (see note). 35mm (Tohoscope). 142 min.

Prod Tomoyuki Tanaka, Ryuzo Kikushima. *Dir* Akira Kurosawa. *Screenplay* Akira Kurosawa, Hideo Oguni, Ryuzo Kikushima, Eijiro Hisaita. *Photog*

Choichi Nakai, Takao Saito. *Lighting* Ichiro Inohara. *Art Dir* Yoshiro Muraki. *Mus* Masaru Sato. *Sd Rec* Hisashi Shimonaga. *English Subtitl* Herman G. Weinberg.

Cast: Toshiro Mifune (*Kingo Gondo*), Tatsuya Nakadai (*Inspector Tokura*), Kyoko Kagawa (*Reiko, Gondo's wife*), Tatsuya Mihashi (*Kawanishi*), Yutaka Sada (*Aoki*), Kenjiro Ishiyama (*Detective Taguchi*), Tsutomu Yamazaki (*Ginji Takeuchi, the kidnaper*), Takashi Shimura (*director*), Susumu Fujita (*commissioner*), Ko Kimura (*Detective Arai*), Takeshi Kato (*Detective Nakao*), Yoshio Tsuchiya (*Detective Murata*), Hiroshi Unayama (*Detective Shimada*), Koji Mitsui (*newspaperman*).

Crime drama. Source: Ed McBain, *King's Ransom* (New York, 1959). Kingo Gondo, the nouveau riche executive director of a Yokohama shoe company, meets with three other company executives, to discuss a proposal to drastically lower the quality of the shoes they make. Gondo is opposed to the change, and he intends to prevent the move by taking over the company. Gondo mortgages his house and land to obtain the money he needs (50 million yen) to purchase company stock which, combined with the shares he already owns, will give him the controlling interest, after which Gondo will be able to dictate company policy. Shortly before the purchase is to be made, Gondo is informed that his son has been kidnaped, and a ransom of 30 million yen demanded. It is soon learned that the kidnaper has mistakenly abducted Aoki, the only son of Gondo's chauffeur. Gondo finally agrees to pay, though it means risking losing the ransom money to rescue the boy. He dutifully follows the kidnaper's instructions and boards the correct train, throwing the briefcase containing the ranson money out of a window at the right time. The boy is saved; Gondo is financially ruined; and police, who have taken photographs of the kidnaper at the time of the drop, begin to track him down. The kidnaper's two accomplices are found dead from an overdose of heroin. Finally, the kidnaper himself, a medical student who lives in a shack near Gondo's hillside house, is apprehended. He is tried, convicted, and sentenced to die. Shortly before his execution, he summons Gondo to his cell and explains that he committed the crimes out of envy of Gondo's wealth and lifestyle. *Executives. Nouveaux riches. Chauffeurs. Medical students. Children. Business ethics. Business management. Kidnaping. Parenthood. Finance—Personal. Ransom. Murder. Envy. Capital punishment. Drug overdose. Shoe manufacture. Trains. Mortgages. Yokohama.*

Note: Filmed on location in Yokohama. Released in Japan in Mar 1963 as *Tengoku to jigoku*; running time: 143 min. One scene (smoke rising from the burning briefcase) contains some color footage.

THE HIGH BRIGHT SUN see MCGUIRE, GO HOME!

THE HIGH COMMISSIONER (United States/Great Britain) F6.2148
Rank Organisation–Selmur Pictures–Rodlor, Inc. *Dist* Cinerama Releasing Corp. 25 Sep **1968** [Los Angeles opening]. Sd; col (Eastmancolor). 35mm. 93 min.

Pres by Selmur Pictures. *Prod* Betty E. Box. *Exec Prod* Selig J. Seligman. *Assoc Prod* James Ware. *Dir* Ralph Thomas. *Screenplay* Wilfred Greatorex. *Dir Photog* Ernest Steward. *Camera Op* James Bawden. *Set Dresser* Peter Young. *Prod Dsgn* Tony Woollard. *Film Ed* Ernest Hosler. *Mus Comp & Dir* Georges Delerue. *Sd Rec* Dudley Messenger, Gordon K. McCallum. *Sd Ed* Don Sharpe. *Asst Dir* Simon Relph. *Prod Mgr* Donald Toms. *Cont* Gladys Goldsmith. *Cost Coörd* Yvonne Caffin. *Makeup* W. T. Partleton, Geoffrey Rodway. *Hairdresser* Stella Rivers.

Cast: Rod Taylor (*Scobie Malone*), Christopher Plummer (*Sir James Quentin*), Lilli Palmer (*Sheila Quentin*), Camilla Sparv (*Lisa Pretorius*), Daliah Lavi (*Madame Cholon*), Franchot Tone (*Ambassador Townsend*), Clive Revill (*Joseph*), Lee Montague (*Denzil*), Calvin Lockhart (*Jamaica*), Derren Nesbitt (*Pallain*), Leo McKern (*Flannery*), Russell Napier (*Leeds*), Ken Wayne (*Ferguson*), Edric Connor (*Julius*), Alan White (*Edwards*), Peter Reynolds (*Blundell*), Burt Kwouk (*Pham Chinh*), Gerry Crampton (*rifleman*), Tony Selby, Keith Bonnard (*cameramen*), Paul Grist (*Coburn*), Charles Tingwell (*Jacaroo*).

Melodrama. Source: Jon Cleary, *The High Commissioner* (London, 1966). Scobie Malone, a detective sergeant in the bush country of Australia, is sent to London by Flannery, his ambitious supervisor, to arrest Australian High Commissioner Sir James Quentin for the murder of his first wife 25 years ago. Scobie meets Quentin in London and is impressed with his personable manner and dedication to a vital trade conference he is directing. Unperturbed by the murder charge, Quentin refuses to leave until the conference is over. Scobie moves into Quentin's house and meets Sheila, Quentin's second wife, and Lisa, his devoted secretary. When Quentin is called away to visit the ailing American ambassador, he is accompanied by Scobie, who saves him from an attempted assassination. That night, Scobie is summoned to a gambling club where he meets the beautiful Madame Cholon, spends the night with her, and is beaten by three thugs on his way home. The next day at Wimbledon, Scobie saves Quentin's life again when Pallain, a news reporter, tries to shoot him. Sheila discovers the reason for Scobie's visit and confesses that she killed Quentin's first wife, although Quentin insists that she is lying. The butler then informs Sheila that he has placed a bomb in the living room at the instruction of Madame Cholon, who is a foreign agent sent to disrupt the trade conference. To save her husband's career, Sheila takes the bomb to Madame Cholon and remains with her until it explodes. *Detectives. Australians. Diplomats. Secretaries. Butlers. Secret agents. Murder. Assassination. Self-sacrifice. Bombs. London.*

Note: Filmed on location in and around London. Opened in London in Sep 1968 as *Nobody Runs Forever*; running time: 101 min.

HIGH INFIDELITY (France/Italy) F6.2149

Documento Film–Société Productions Cinématographiques Européennes. *Dist* Magna Pictures Distribution Corp. 1 Jul **1965** [New York opening]. Sd; b&w. 35mm. 120 min.

Pres by Marshall Naify. *Prod* Gianni Hecht Lucari. *Dir for* "The Scandal" Franco Rossi. *Dir for* "Sin in the Afternoon" Elio Petri. *Dir for* "The Victim" Luciano Salce. *Dir for* "Modern People" Mario Monicelli. *Screenplay* Age & Scarpelli, Ettore Scola, Ruggero Maccari. *Photog for* "The Scandal," "Sin in the Afternoon," "The Victim" Ennio Guarnieri, Gianni Di Venanzo. *Mus* Armando Trovajoli.

Cast—"The Scandal": Nino Manfredi *(Francesco)*, Fulvia Franco *(Raffaella)*, John Phillip Law *(Ronald)*, Eleanor Beaucour, Vittorio La Paglia, Luigi Zerbinati.

Cast—"Sin in the Afternoon": Charles Aznavour *(Giulio)*, Claire Bloom *(Laura)*.

Cast—"The Victim": Monica Vitti *(Gloria)*, Jean-Pierre Cassel *(Tonino)*, Sergio Fantoni *(Paolo)*.

Cast—"Modern People": Ugo Tognazzi *(Cesare)*, Michèle Mercier *(Tebaide [Zoraïde])*, Bernard Blier *(Reguzzoni)*.

Comedy-drama. THE SCANDAL: Francesco, an unresponsive and boring husband, brings his wife Raffaella to a resort for a vacation. There, a handsome young man, Ronald, is attracted to her. Francesco, in an unusual display of vitality, becomes jealous and has a fight with Ronald. SIN IN THE AFTERNOON: Giulio, a young film producer who is unhappy over his wife's refusal to make physical contact with him, spots the stunning Laura in the street and follows her. The strangers meet and spend the night together in a motel. THE VICTIM: Paolo's wife, Gloria, while very attractive, is also very jealous. For Paolo at least, their life together becomes unbearable, and he deserts her. Gloria goes to confide in Tonino, Paolo's friend, but decides instead to take revenge on her husband by becoming Tonino's mistress. MODERN PEOPLE: Cesare, a wealthy cheese manufacturer, has considerable gambling debts. His biggest creditor, Reguzzoni, agrees to forego the debt if Cesare will allow him to sleep with his beautiful wife, Tebaide. Cesare must now persuade Tebaide to agree to this arrangement. *Mistresses. Businessmen. Motion picture producers. Marriage. Infidelity. Jealousy. Gambling. Cheese.*

Note: Opened in Rome in Jan 1964 as *Alta infedeltà* and in Paris in Jul 1964 as *Haute infidélité*. Original running time: 130 min. Italian episode titles: "Scandaloso," "Peccato nel pommeriggio," "La sospirosa," "Gente moderna"; French episode titles: "Scandaleux," "Péché dans l'après-midi," "Jalousie," "Gens modernes."

HIGH SCHOOL F6.2150

Osti Films. 14 May **1969** [Boston opening]. Sd; b&w. 16mm. 75 min.

Prod-Dir Frederick Wiseman. *Camera* Richard Leiterman. *Asst Camera* David Eames. *Film Ed* Frederick Wiseman. *Assoc Ed* Carter Howard. *Song:* "Simon Says" sung by 1910 Fruitgum Co.. *Song:* "Dock of the Bay" writ & sung by Otis Redding. *Song:* "Dangling Conversation" Paul Simon. *Sung by* Simon and Garfunkel. *Sd Rec* Frederick Wiseman.

Documentary. Education in a white, middle-class high school in suburban Philadelphia encourages conformity among its students, who are often more interested in non-academic activities than classroom work. An English instructor who reads "Casey at the Bat" to her class is no more successful at capturing her students' attention than another teacher who interprets lyrics from Simon and Garfunkel's "Dangling Conversation." Students in a girls' gym class scoot across the floor in time to the song "Simon Says," while an all-male group is told by a visiting gynecologist that extensive sex before marriage will lead to insecurity and divorce in later life. A teacher in a modeling class attempts to establish rapport with her students by giving them tips on making the best of their physical appearances. A girl is told the short dress she plans to wear to a school prom will offend the rest of the class. The faculty member in charge of discipline tells an unjustly accused boy that personal guilt is immaterial and that punishment is meant to enable a person to take orders, while a guidance counselor questions a female student's decision not to attend college. The film concludes with the reading of a letter written to the faculty by a former student who is about to be dropped behind the demilitarized zone

in Vietnam; his letter reflects the "virtues" of conformity and the importance of having respect for one's elders. *Students. Schoolteachers. Physicians. Soldiers. Suburbanites. Middle classes. Education. High school life. Sex instruction. Social conformity. Vietnam War 1964–73. Philadelphia. Documentation. "Casey at the Bat".*

Note: Filmed at Northeast High School in Philadelphia.

HIGH SCHOOL HONEYMOON (Reissue) F6.2151

Dynasty Films. *Dist* Ajay Film Co. Apr **1968**. Sd; col. 35mm. 85 min.

Note: Originally released in 1960 as *Too Soon To Love* by Universal-International; c20 Dec 1959; LP18684.

HIGH SPY see THIGH SPY

HIGH, WILD AND FREE F6.2152

Gordon Eastman. *Dist* American International Pictures. 3 Jan **1968** [Denver, Colorado, opening]. Sd; col. 35mm. 105 min.

Prod Gordon Eastman. *Photog* Gordon Eastman, Wes Marks, Lee Holen, Glen McLean, John Payne. *Mus* Jaime Mendoza-Nava. *Titl Song* Jaime Mendoza-Nava, Pear Skinner, Gordon Eastman. *Sung by* Gene Merlino.

Narrator: Gordon Eastman.

Travelog. Gordon Eastman takes his two sons on a journey to the wilds of British Columbia. It begins with 250,000 snow geese flying north for the summer. Eastman's "safari" stops at Bella Colla Valley, where Eastman fishes for the mighty steelhead, considered the world's finest trophy fish. Moving on to the most northern regions, where the Eastmans live with Indians, they trap beaver, build boats of spruce wood covered with the skins of freshly-killed moose, and travel in these craft down 200 miles of wild water. In the mountain country, Eastman's camera observes the treacherous grizzly bear leaving his winter den and the caribou and elk in their age-old battle for existence. As fall comes and the snow geese leave on their flight south, the Eastmans end their safari by hunting the largest sheep in North America, the stone sheep. *Indians of North America. Fishing. Hunting. Canoes. British Columbia. Geese. Trout. Beavers. Moose. Bears. Caribou. Elk. Sheep.*

Note: Filmed on location in British Columbia in 16mm.

A HIGH WIND IN JAMAICA (United States/Great Britain) F6.2153

Twentieth Century-Fox Film Corp. 26 May **1965** [Los Angeles opening; c25 May 1965; LP31310]. Sd (Westrex); col (DeLuxe). 35mm (CinemaScope). 104 min. [Copyright length: 135 min.]

Prod John Croydon. *Assoc Prod* Clifford Parkes, Tom Pevsner. *Dir* Alexander Mackendrick. *Screenplay* Stanley Mann, Ronald Harwood, Denis Cannan. *Dir Photog* Douglas Slocombe. *Camera Op* Chic Waterson. *2d Unit Camera* Cecil Cooney. *Supv Art Dir* John Howell, John Hoesli. *Film Ed* Derek York. *Mus Comp* Larry Adler. *Mus Cond* Philip Martell. *Titl Song* Christopher Logue, Jerry Adler. *Sung by* Mike Leroy. *Sd Ed* Matt McCarthy. *Sd Rec* H. L. Bird, Stephen Dalby. *Asst Dir* Jim Brennan, Tom Pevsner. *Cont* Helen Whitson. *Location Mgr* Bryan Coates. *Wardrobe Supv* John McCorry. *Makeup* Bill Lodge, Freddie Williamson. *Hairdressing* Daphne Martin. *Sp Eff* Bowie Films. *Dir Nautical Op* Fred Zendar.

Cast: Anthony Quinn *(Juan Chavez)*, James Coburn *(Zac)*, Dennis Price *(Mathias)*, Gert Fröbe *(Dutch captain)*, Lila Kedrova *(Rosa)*, Kenneth J. Warren *(Captain Marpole)*, Nigel Davenport *(Mr. Thornton)*, Isabel Dean *(Mrs. Thornton)*, Viviane Ventura *(Margaret Fernández)*, Benito Carruthers *(Alberto)*, Charles Hyatt, Dan Jackson, Trader Faulkner *(pirates)*, Charles Laurence *(tallyman)*, Kenji Takaki *(cook)*, Brian Phelan *(Curtis)*, Danny Williams *(Old Sam)*, Louise Bennett *(Mamie)*, Marion Ward *(Mrs. Fernández)*, Philip Madoc *(captain)*, Maude Fuller *(Josephina)*, Elsie Benjamin Barsoe *(nurse)*, Gordon Richardson *(judge)*, Deborah Baxter *(Emily)*, Martin Amis *(John Thornton)*, Karen Flack *(Laura Thornton)*, Henry Beltran *(Harry Thornton)*, Roberta Tovey *(Rachel Thornton)*, Jeffrey Chandler *(Edward Thornton)*.

Drama. Source: Richard Hughes, *A High Wind in Jamaica* (London, 1929). After a hurricane strikes Jamaica in 1870, the Thorntons are convinced that their five children—Emily, John, Rachel, Edward, and Laura—must leave for England in order to receive a proper education. Along with two Creole children, they set sail, but their ship is captured by pirates, and the children are accidentally locked in the hold where they are playing. Juan Chavez, commander of the pirate ship, becomes fond of the children (particularly Emily), but the crew believes them to be an ill omen, so Chavez sails for Tampico, hoping to leave the children with Rosa, madam of a local whorehouse. Upon arriving, however, Rosa warns Chavez that the authorities are searching for him, and after John slips and falls to his death, the pirates leave with the remaining children. When Chavez refuses to attack a Dutch vessel because the children are on board, the pirates mutiny and capture the Dutch captain. The Dutchman approaches Emily with a knife, asking her to cut his bonds, and in panic she kills him. Later, the pirates are captured by a British ship and brought to trial. Under strenuous questioning, Emily blames Chavez and his men for the accidental death of her brother and for the murder of the Dutch captain, which she herself committed. The pirates are subsequently hanged, and the children enter school. *Pirates. Madams. Children. Sailors. Dutch. Creoles. Superstition. Mutiny. Murder. Trials. Capital punishment. Injustice. Whorehouses. Jamaica. London. Tampico. Hurricanes.*

Note: Filmed in Jamaica and England. Opened in London in May 1965.

HIGH YELLOW   F6.2154

Dinero Productions. *Dist* Thunder Pictures. 4 Aug 1965 [San Antonio, Texas, opening]. Sd; b&w. 35mm. 83 min.

Exec Prod Clyde Knudson. *Dir* Larry Buchanan. *Singer of* "Going to the Go-Go" Jody Daniels.

Cast: Cynthia Hull (*Cindy*), Warren Hammack (*George*), Kay Taylor (*Judy*), Bill McGee (*Joseph*), Anne MacAdams (*Mrs. Langley*), Bob Brown (*Mr. Langley*), Bill Thurman (*Major Bates*), Jonothan Leford (*Reverend Hatfield*), Max Anderson (*officer*).

Melodrama. Source: Erskine Williams, *Diary of a Negro Maid* (publication undetermined). Cynthia Wood, a 17-year-old, light-skinned Negro housemaid who passes for white, enters the employ of rich, unhappy movie magnate Langley. Langley, a tyrant who has a loveless marriage with a hypochondriac, rules his mansion as he does his studio. His own children, however, resist him: his son, George, has been wrongly accused of homosexuality and expelled from West Point, and his teenage daughter, Judy, is wild and promiscuous. Other members of the Langley household include Major Bates, a sadistic, retired Army officer who works as a handyman and keeps his job by blackmailing Langley, and Joseph, the brooding Negro chauffeur who plans to steal the family silver and finance his own garage business. Cynthia's dreams of passing for white are destroyed by this angry, frustrated, violent household. *Motion picture producers. Housemaids. Negroes. Mulattoes. Hypochondriacs. Veterans. Handymen. Chauffeurs. Adolescence. Wealth. Male homosexuality. Reputation. Promiscuity. Blackmail. Race relations. Theft. Employment— Women. United States Military Academy.*

Note: Filmed on location at Frisco Mansion near Dallas, Texas.

HIGHWAY PICKUP (France/Italy)   F6.2155

Paris-Films Production–Interopa Fllm. *Dist* Times Film Corp. 31 Mar 1965 [New York opening; c1 Apr 1966; LF12]. Sd; b&w. 35mm. 107 min.

A Robert Hakim–Raymond Hakim Production. *Prod* Robert Hakim, Raymond Hakim. *Dir* Julien Duvivier. *Screenplay* Julien Duvivier, René Barjavel. *Dial* René Barjavel. *Photog* L. H. Burel. *Art Dir* François de Lamothe. *Film Ed* Suzanne de Troeye. *Mus* Georges Delerue. *Sd* Joseph Giaume. *Asst Dir* Tony Aboyantz. *Prod Mgr* Ralph Baum.

Cast: Robert Hossein (*Daniel Boisset*), Georges Wilson (*Thomas*), Jean Sorel (*Paul Genest*), Catherine Rouvel (*Maria*), Lucien Raimbourg (*Roux*), Nicole Berger (*Simone*), Sophie Grimaldi (*starlet*), Armand Mestral (*Corenne*), Jean-Jacques Delbo (*Joubert*), Jacques Bertrand (*Marc*), Robert Dalban (*brigadier*), Jean Lefebvre (*priest*).

Melodrama. Source: James Hadley Chase, *Come Easy—Go Easy* (London, 1960). Paul and Daniel, accomplices in a burglary, are apprehended while they are attempting to open a safe. In the struggle, Paul murders a man and escapes, but Daniel is captured by the police and convicted of the murder. Daniel escapes from prison a year later, and he is befriended by Thomas, an innkeeper who also operates a garage, and his young wife Maria, an ex-prostitute who married him for his money. Daniel and Thomas become friends, but Maria learns of Daniel's past and blackmails him into opening her husband's safe. Thomas arrives just before Daniel opens the safe. Daniel convinces Thomas that he had no interest in the money; that Maria blackmailed him into opening the safe. In an argument with her husband, Maria kills him. Daniel buries Thomas in the workshop of the gas station and is trapped into staying with Maria, but he refuses to open the safe for her. Daniel's former accomplice, Paul, arrives unexpectedly, and Maria tries to seduce him into opening the safe. He, too, refuses, but when Maria is gone, he attempts to open it for himself. Maria catches him, but he kills her after she threatens him with a shotgun. Paul attempts to escape when the police arrive, but he is captured as his automobile crashes into a gas pump. The house and filling station go up in flames, but the injured Daniel manages to escape at the last minute. *Safecrackers. Garage-keepers. Innkeepers. Prostitutes. Prison escapees. Robbery. Murder. Greed. Friendship. Blackmail. Seduction. Marriage. Automobile accidents. Safes. Filling stations. Fires.*

Note: Opened in Paris in Nov 1963 as *Chair de poule*; running time: 110 min.

LAS HIJAS DEL CID see THE SWORD OF EL CID

EL HIJO DEL CAPITÁN BLOOD see THE SON OF CAPTAIN BLOOD

EL HIJO DEL PISTOLERO see SON OF A GUNFIGHTER

HIKEN see YOUNG SWORDSMAN

HIKEN YABURI see BROKEN SWORDS

HIKINIGE see MOMENT OF TERROR

HILDUR AND THE MAGICIAN   F6.2156

Dist Canyon Cinema Cooperative. 22 Dec 1969 [New York opening]. Sd; b&w. 16mm. 95 min. [Also shown at 90 min and possibly at 70 min.]

Prod-Dir-Writ Larry Jordan. *Based on an Idea by* John Graham, Patricia Jordan. *Photog* Larry Jordan. *Set Dsgn* Roy Berger. *Film Ed* Larry Jordan. *Orig Mus* Joel Andrews, Julie Iger. *Tech Asst* Roy Berger.

Cast: John Graham (*The Magician/narrator*), Hildur Mahl (*Hildur*), Patricia Jordan (*companion*), Jim Yensan (*gnome*), Jani Novak (*driad*), Roy Berger (*wood-cutter*), Shelby Sache (*his wife*), Tres Berger (*Arabelle*), Sydney Droshin (*wicked queen*), Tito Patri (*huckster*), Cook Ruddick (*king*), Gael Knepfer (*maid*), Bunny Kirsch, Gina Batchelder, Sally Berger, Cathy Seitz, Mark Batchelder (*fairies*), Joel Andrews, Julie Iger, Avery Faulkner, Paula White (*musicians*), Sandra Della Valle.

Fantasy. In a woodland, a foolish, bungling magician prepares a potion to aid Hildur, the fairy queen, in rescuing her ward, a princess, who has been abducted by a gnome. The wicked "mortal queen" has threatened the princess with death. By an accident, the magician's potion causes Hildur to become mortal, although subliminal recollections of her mystic existence remain to haunt her. *Fairies. Gnomes. Magicians. Royalty. Wards. Abduction. Memory. Forests.*

Note: Contains animation sequences. Wardrobe and set construction created by the cast.

THE HILL (Great Britain)   F6.2157

Seven Arts Productions. *Dist* Metro-Goldwyn-Mayer, Inc., Seven Arts Associated Corp. 6 Oct 1965 [New York opening; c5 Aug 1965; LP31612]. Sd (Westrex); b&w. 35mm. 122 min.

A Kenneth Hyman Production. *Prod* Kenneth Hyman. *Assoc Prod* Raymond Anzarut. *Dir* Sidney Lumet. *Screenplay* Ray Rigby. *Dir Photog* Oswald Morris. *Camera Op* Brian West. *Art Dir* Herbert Smith. *Film Ed* Thelma Connell. *Traditional Arabic Folk Mus Arr* Cristobal Sanchez Asensio. *Song:* "Kiss Me Goodnight Sergeant Major" *Art* Noel, Don Pelosi. *Rec Supv* A. W. Watkins. *Sd Rec* David Bowen. *Dub Mix* Fred Turtle. *Sd Ed* Peter Musgrave. *Asst Dir* Frank Ernst, Pedro Vidal. *Prod Mgr* Clifton Brandon. *Cont* Lee Turner. *Wardrobe Supv* Elsa Fennell. *Makeup* George Partleton. *Tech Adv* George Montford.

Cast: Sean Connery (*Joe Roberts*), Harry Andrews (*R.S.M. Bert Wilson*), Ian Bannen (*Staff-Sgt. Charlie Harris*), Alfred Lynch (*George Stevens*), Ossie Davis (*Jacko King*), Roy Kinnear (*Monty Bartlett*), Jack Watson (*Jock McGrath*), Ian Hendry (*Sergeant Williams*), Michael Redgrave (*medical officer*), Norman Bird (*commandant*), Neil McCarthy (*Sergeant Burton*), Howard Goorney (*Walters*), Tony Caunter (*Martin*).

War drama. Source: Ray Rigby and R. S. Allen, *The Hill* (a play; production undetermined). During World War II, R.S.M. Wilson runs a British military stockade in North Africa with an iron hand. To break down the spirit of 5 new prisoners, Wilson directs Sergeant Williams, a sadistic new guard, to walk the men up and down a large man-made hill of rocks and sand with full packs on their backs until they drop from exhaustion. Jacko King, a Jamaican Negro arrested for stealing 3 quarts of Scotch from the officers' mess, receives especially harsh treatment because of the prejudice of the guards. He supports prisoner Joe Roberts, a warrant officer broken of his rank for striking a superior officer and refusing to lead his forces into battle when their ammunition was low, in his revolt against the cruel actions of the guards. When the weakest prisoner, George Stevens, guilty of going AWOL to return to his wife, dies, the prisoners threaten to revolt. At first, Stevens' death is officially recorded as an accident, but Roberts persuades the medical officer to testify to the inhumane conditions in the stockade in hopes that conditions for future military prisoners will improve. The rest of the group only want revenge against Williams; and in killing the guard they lose their opportunity to put an end to the brutal system. *Prison guards. Jamaicans. Negroes. Convicts. Physicians. Sadism. Prison revolts. Revenge. Racial prejudice. Murder. World War II. North Africa. Great Britain—Army.*

Note: Location scenes filmed in Spain. Opened in London in Jun 1965; running time: 123 min.

HILLBILLYS IN À HAUNTED HOUSE   F6.2158

Woolner Bros. Pictures. May 1967. Sd; col (Technicolor, print by DeLuxe). 35mm. 88 min. [Cut from 91 min.]

Prod Bernard A. Woolner. *Dir* Jean Yarbrough. *Screenplay* Duke Yelton. *Photog* Vaughn Wilkins. *Art Dir* Paul Sylos. *Film Ed* Roy Livingston. *Mus* Hal Borne. *Mus Dir* Igo Kantor. *Sd* Bob Post. *Prod Mgr* Jack Voglin.

Cast: Ferlin Husky (*Woody Weatherby*), Joi Lansing (*Boots Malone*), Don Bowman (*Jeepers*), John Carradine (*Dr. Himmil*), Lon Chaney, Jr. (*Maximillian*), Basil Rathbone (*Gregor*), Linda Ho (*Madame Wong*), George Barrows (*gorilla*), Molly Bee, Merle Haggard, Jim Kent, Sonny James, Marcella Wright, Richard Webb, Pat Patterson, Jay Jasin.

Comedy. En route to the Nashville Jamboree, country singers Woody Weatherby and Boots Malone and manager Jeepers are caught in a gun battle between police and foreign agents. Concerned for the health of the overworked Jeepers, the singers stop in a deserted town. When a storm breaks, they decide to spend the night in a ruined mansion. After encountering skeletons and a huge gorilla, the trio meets Madame Wong, the mastermind of an espionage ring. Wong, Gregor, and mad Dr. Himmil are using the house as a front. The mastermind and her bodyguard Maximillian steal an atomic formula from the nearby rocket base, but are pursued by Jim Meadows, an agent for M.O.T.H.E.R. (Master Organization To Halt Enemy Resistance). In the house, Woody and Jeepers enlist Jim's aid in the search for Boots, who has been abducted by the gorilla. Dr. Himmil and Gregor discover Boots and believe her to be a M.O.T.H.E.R. agent. A real ghost helps apprehend the spies, and the singers and Jeepers proceed to Nashville. *Singers. Theatrical managers. Police. Secret agents. Masterminds. Bodyguards. Ghosts. Scientists. Espionage. Insanity. Theft. Abduction. Haunted houses. Secret formulas. Country music. Nashville (Tennessee). Storms. Chases. Gorillas.*

THE HILLS RUN RED (Italy)   F6.2159

Dino De Laurentiis Cinematografica. *Dist* United Artists. 27 Sep **1967** [Los Angeles opening; c10 Feb 1967; LF75]. Sd; col (Technicolor). 35mm (Techniscope). 89 min. [Copyright length: 94 min.]

Prod Ermanno Donati, Luigi Carpentieri. *Dir* Lee W. Beaver. *Story-Screenplay* Dean Craig. *Photog* Antonio Secchi. *Art Dir* Aurelio Crugnola. *Film Ed* Ornella Micheli. *Mus* Leo Nichols. Song: "Home My Love" Leo Nichols, Audrey Nohra. *Sung by* Gino. *Cost* Elio Micheli.

Cast: Thomas Hunter (*Jerry Brewster*), Henry Silva (*Mendez*), Dan Duryea (*Getz*), Nando Gazzolo (*Ken Seagall*), Nicoletta Machiavelli (*Mary Ann*), Gianna Serra (*Hattie*), Loris Loddi (*Tim*), Geoffrey Copleston (*Horner*), Paolo Magalotti (*Stayne*), Tiberio Mitri (*Federal sergeant*), Vittorio Bonos (*1st gambler*), Mirko Valentin (*Sancho*), Guglielmo Spoletini (*Pedro*), Guido Celano (*Burger*), Mauro Mannatrizio (*soldier Mitch*), Gianluigi Crescenzi (*Carson*).

Western melodrama. At the end of the Civil War, Confederate veterans Jerry Brewster and Ken Seagall find themselves possessing an army payroll. Brewster leads pursuing troops astray while Seagall flees with the money, and Brewster is captured and sentenced to 5 years in prison. Upon his release Brewster learns that his former friend has become a wealthy and powerful landowner, despised by ranchers throughout the area. Seagall, responsible for the death of Brewster's wife, realizes that his life is in danger and sends a hired gunman, Mendez, to kill his adversary. Getz, a stranger, intervenes by rescuing Brewster while at the same time making it look as though Brewster was slain. Getz then conceives a plan for Brewster to infiltrate Seagall's band of outlaws and plot their downfall. Learning that Seagall's men are about to ride out to "punish" a rebellious town, Brewster organizes the townspeople for a defense. Brewster is wounded in the ensuing gunfight and is nursed back to health by Seagall's daughter, Mary Ann. Eventually Seagall recognizes Brewster and the battle becomes a personal one. Getz, a government agent, joins with Brewster in the final shoot-out in which Mendez, Seagall, and the unfortunate Mary Ann are killed. Brewster is reunited with his lost son; Getz appoints Brewster sheriff; and law and order is restored to the community. *Confederate veterans. Ranchers. Hired killers. Strangers. Government agents. Outlaws. Widowers. Theft. Perfidy. Wealth. Revenge. Fatherhood. Prisons.*

Note: Opened in Rome in Sep 1966 as *Un fiume di dollari*. Lee W. Beaver is a pseudonym for Carlo Lizzani; Leo Nichols for Ennio Morricone. Additional song: "I Know a Girl With Golden Hair."

HIMSELF AS HERSELF   F6.2160

Dist Film-Makers' Distribution Center. 25 Jan **1967** [New York opening]. Sd; col. 16mm. 60 min.

Prod-Dir-Writ Gregory J. Markopoulos. *Photog* Gregory J. Markopoulos. *Film Ed* Gregory J. Markopoulos. *Mus:* Selections from "Gloria" Francis Poulenc.

Cast: Gordon Baldwin (*The Young Man*).

Experimental film. Inspired by: Honoré de Balzac, "Séraphîta," in *Livre mystique* (1835). A well-heeled young man is first seen as a scientist, dressed in an evening suit, operating an electron microscope. Subsequently, he appears in ornate and elegant settings. It soon becomes apparent that there is another side to his personality, and this aspect is first seen as a figure wrapped in a blue-and-gold-embroidered sari. To this costume are added earrings, a hairpin, and a series of hand-painted fans. Despite his lush surroundings, the young man is anguished by boredom and haunted by the duality of his existence. Gold is a recurring image appearing in the forms of gold embroidery, a gilded foot, and gold ornaments on an altar. The tulip also appears in several situations. An insect moves away from pieces of a broken champagne glass. A bridal shoe on a woman's foot is inordinately large. The hero makes love to a figure whose gender is undetermined. Finally, he is intimidated by the presence of his other self following him down a staircase; when he reaches the last step, he kneels and opens his arms to receive her. In the end, he enters Trinity Church, falls at the base of the pulpit, over which a golden eagle hovers, and holds his hand clasped to his heart. *Hermaphroditism. Sexuality. Dual personality. Trinity Church (Boston).*

Note: Filmed at Trinity Church and other locations in and around Boston. Single-frame editing and superimpositions are employed. Dedicated to Emelen Etting.

HIP, HOT AND 21   F6.2161

Trans-Continental Artists. 1 Mar **1967** [Champaign, Illinois, showing]. Sd (RCA); b&w. 35mm. 78 min. [Also reviewed at 90 min.]

Prod Charles Martinez. *Dir* Dale Berry. *Orig Story* Big Daddy Epstein, III. *Photog* Carlos Martinez. *Film Ed* Jerry Moreno, Danny Moreno. *Mus* Baron von Weinberg.

Cast: Lorna Maitland (*Marla?*), Diane Darcel (*Diane*), Pat Crenshaw (*Jed McClunkey*), Metha Stanton (*Ma McClunkey*), Carol Stevens (*Michelle*), Ron Scott (*Al Hoffman*), Artie Brooks (*Earnie*), Sylvia Rundell (*Winnie*), Polly Hansen (*Hester*), Byron Tubbs (*Joe*), Gary Locke (*Tony*), Bubbles Cash (*Bubbles*), Bill Thurmond (*Lieutenant Lang*), Dale Berry (*Sergeant Hanley*), Whit Boyd (*see note*).

Melodrama. Poverty-stricken Jed McClunkey agrees to let Nick marry his stepdaughter Diane in return for a "loan" of $50 from the prospective bridegroom. Nick brings his naive country bride to live in an apartment in a southern city, and she is seduced, under the influence of alcohol, by their neighbor Marla, a bisexual narcotics-dealing prostitute. Nick, who regards his wife as a purchase, deserts her when he learns of the episode, and Diane turns for companionship to Marla. Through their association, Diane meets a number of hoodlums, degenerates, and drug addicts. Marla dies of an overdose, and Diane makes friends with Michelle, another bisexual drug pusher and prostitute. Jed comes to town to borrow money from his son-in-law, and he goes to the police when he hears of his stepdaughter's activities. They inform him that Diane is a member of a gang of dope peddlers and prostitutes being kept under surveillance. The police raid the house during an orgy, and the narcotics and sex ring is smashed in a raging gun battle. *Newlyweds. Stepfathers. Neighbors. Innocents. Police. Bisexuality. Seduction. Prostitution. Drug overdose. Drug dealers. Moral corruption. Narcotics.*

Note: Also known as *Hip, Hep and 21*. One source gives acting credit to Whit Boyd, who may be credited elsewhere under another name.

HIPNOSIS see **HYPNOSIS**

HIPPIE HOLLYWOOD: THE ACID-BLASTING FREAKS see **MONDO HOLLYWOOD**

THE HIPPIE REVOLT   F6.2162

Belish-Fremont Associates. *Dist* Headliner Productions. ca19 Dec **1967** [New York opening]. Sd; col (Technicolor). 35mm. 85 min.

Prod Art Lieberman. *Dir* Edgar Beatty. *Photog* Edgar Beatty. *Ed* Robert Springer. *Mus* Tom Bahler, John Bahler. *Mus Perf by* The Love Generation.

Documentary. Filmed during the spring and summer of 1967, this documentary looks at the hippie lifestyle in San Francisco's Haight-Ashbury district; at Strawberry Fields, a country estate; and in Los Angeles, Santa Barbara, Venice, Ojai, and Tujunga. Included in the footage are scenes of love-ins; discotheques; "crash pads"; body painting; pot and LSD use; weddings and mock funeral ceremonies; country communes; peace demonstrations; and interviews with hippies who explain their aims and philosophy. *Hippies. Love-ins. Body painting. Weddings. Funerals. Demonstrations. Communal living. Psychedelic states. Discotheques. Marijuana. LSD. San Francisco—Haight-Ashbury. Los Angeles. Santa Barbara. Venice (California). Tujunga. Ojai.*

Note: Also known as *Something's Happening*.

HIPPODROME (Austria/West Germany)   F6.2163

Sascha Film–Lux-Film (West Germany). *Dist* Continental Distributing, Inc. 12 Apr **1961** [Los Angeles opening]. Sd; col (Agfacolor). 35mm. 96 min.

Prod-Dir Arthur-Maria Rabenalt. *Exec Prod* Herbert Gruber. *Screenplay* Kurt Nachmann, H. F. Köllner. *Photog* Günther Anders. *Camera* Willy Egger, Hans Mayr. *Art Dir* Werner Schlichting, Alexander Sawczynski. *Main Titl* Rainer Fluhme, Horst Lesniczak. *Film Ed* Arnd Heyne. *Asst Film Ed* Angelika Appel. *Mus* Bert Grund. *Lyr* Walter Brandin. *Choreog* Mike De Lutry. *Sd* Kurt Schwarz. *Asst Dir* Max Diekhout. *Prod Mgr* Walter Tjaden. *Cost* Charlotte Flemming. *Makeup* Josef Schober, Leo Umyssa, Hans Nowotny. *Stunts* Theo Nischwitz.

Cast: Gerhard Riedmann (*Rudy*), Margit Nünke (*Beatrice*), Willy Birgel (*Cameron*), Mady Rahl (*Marianne*), Walter Giller (*Dody*), Massimo Giuliani (*Willi*), Gustav Knuth (*Carl de Vries*), Gretl Schörg (*Olga*), Fred Bertelmann (*John*), Sigrid Marquardt (*Anita*), Heinz Moog (*Director Lanzheim*), Ljuba Welitsch (*Mama Allison*), Leopold Hainisch (*Riley*), Emanuel Sackey, Mario Kranz, Karl Kritel, Otto Hejdusek, Hans Kurt, Berta Vitek, Josef Menschik, Charly Baumann's Tiger Group.

Melodrama. Source: Heinrich Seiler, *Männer müssen so sein* (Ebendorf, 1938). Beatrice, a young circus ballerina, is fascinated by Rudy, a handsome tiger trainer, and hopes to dance in the tiger cage while he performs his act. She gets her chance, however, only when he leaves to join another circus, and his replacement allows her to join the act. One night one of the tigers goes berserk, and Beatrice's life is saved by Cameron, the show's middle-aged sharpshooter. When the tiger act is disbanded, Beatrice agrees to become Cameron's partner. Shortly thereafter, Rudy returns, and Beatrice asks Cameron to release her from her contract. He refuses and again attempts to ruin the rival act by drugging the tigers; his plan is exposed, however, and he kills himself. Beatrice is now free to team up with Rudy. *Dancers. Animal trainers. Sharpshooters. Jealousy. Partnerships. Suicide. Circus. Tigers.*

Note: Released in West Germany in Feb 1959 as *Geliebte Bestie*; running time: 102 min; also known as *Männer müssen so sein* and *Das Mädchen im Tigerfell*.

HIRED GUN *see* **THE LAST GUNFIGHTER**

THE HIRED KILLER (France/Italy)   **F6.2164**
Cinegay–Rome Paris Films. *Dist* Paramount Pictures. 1 Mar **1967** [New York opening]. Sd; col (Technicolor). 35mm (Techniscope). 95 min.
Prod Felice Testa Gay. *Dir-Writ* Frank Shannon. *Photog* Erico Menczer. *Art Dir* Hugo Naheir. *Film Ed* Mark Sirandrews. *Mus* Robby Poitevin. *Asst Dir* Jeffrey Darcey. *Prod Mgr* Paolo Mercuri.
Cast: Robert Webber (*Clint Harris*), Franco Nero (*Tony Lobello*), Jeanne Valérie (*Mary*), José Luis de Vilallonga (*Secchy [Goldstein]*), John Hawkwood (*Andrea Ferri*), Michel Bardinet (*Barry*), Cec Linder (*Gastel*), Theodora Bergery (*Lucy*), Earl Hammond (*Frank*).

Melodrama. After killing a police informer, professional assassin Clint Harris decides to leave New York City and settle down on a farm. The syndicate that has paid him forces him into one more assignment, however: the murder of Secchy, an ex-gangster who has gone to Europe and undergone plastic surgery to escape detection. In Paris, Harris and his assistant Tony Lobello become involved with a pretty drug addict, Mary, who puts them on the trail of the man they are seeking. After tracking down and killing the victim, Harris discovers that they have murdered an impostor sent by the real Secchy. Mary is slain to prevent her from talking any further, and Secchy is shot down with his henchmen. Harris then learns that Lobello has been playing both sides and is out to murder him. When confronted, Lobello pulls a revolver on Harris, but Harris is quicker and kills Lobello. *Hired killers. Drug addicts. Americans in foreign countries. Murder. Plastic surgery. Impersonation. Perfidy. Syndicates. New York City. Paris.*

Note: Some location scenes filmed in New York City. Released in Italy in 1966 as *Tecnica di un omicidio*; running time: 105 min; opened in Paris in Feb 1967 as *Technique d'un meurtre*; running time: 100 min. Frank Shannon is a pseudonym for Franco Prosperi and Mark Sirandrews for Mario Serandrei.

HIROKU ONNADERA *see* **SECRETS OF A WOMEN'S TEMPLE**

HIS AND HIS *see* **HONEYMOON HOTEL**

HIS, HERS AND THEIRS *see* **YOURS, MINE, AND OURS**

HIS WIFE'S HABIT   **F6.2165**
Joy-Oke Productions. *Dist* Howco International. May **1970** [New Orleans showing; c15 Jul 1970; LP38788]. Sd; col (Eastman Color). 35mm. 97 min. [Also 92 min.] *MPAA rating* R.
Prod Albert J. Salzer. *Prod Adtl Seq* J. J. Milane. *Dir* Joy N. Houck, Jr. *Screenplay* Joy N. Houck, Jr., Robert A. Weaver, Albert J. Salzer. *Writ Adtl Seq* Joy N. Houck, Jr., J. J. Milane. *Story* Joy N. Houck, Sr., J. J. Milane. *Dir Photog* Robert A. Weaver. *Camera Op* Allen Roberts. *Asst Camera* James Pratt, Jr. *2d Unit Camera* G. Gibbons, Doug Sherr. *Main Titl* Consolidated Film Industries. *Film Ed* Robert A. Weaver, John H. Post. *Neg Cutter* Jack LaMantain. *Mus & Songs* Jim Helms, Gary LeMel, Norma Green. *Lauren's Theme*: "Lady in the Early Morning" sung by Gary LeMel. *Songs*: "Come on In," "Mr. Funky" sung by Sonny Geraci. *Sd Eff* Gil Marchant, Sonic Editorial Service. *Sd Rec* J. Woerter, C. Tanner. *Boom Op* Dale G. Thompson. *Asst to the Dir* Mary André. *Asst to the Prod* Susan Grapes. *Cont* Evelyn Hendricks. *Miss Darcy's Wardrobe* Carol Taylor, cost. *Wardrobe* Michael Oglesbee. *Makeup* Michael Byrd. *Hairstyles* Michael Byrd. *Photog Eff* Consolidated Film Industries. *Coöp* Richard Benson, Lete Boulion. *Casting* Albert J. Salzer. *Key Grip* Robert Perigo. *Ch Electrn* Robert Hardigan. *Prop* Nita Wilson. *Still*

Photog Allen Langhof. *Stunt Driving* Lee R. Adams, Merrill Marchadie, Doug Sherr.

Cast: Georgine Darcy (*Lauren Worthington*), Marcus J. Grapes (*Jerry*), Christa Hart (*Karen Worthington*), David Gelpi (*Danny*), Michael Anthony, U. S. actor (*Zool*), Gerald McRaney (*Terrance Bradford*), Len Swanson (*Mr. Worthington*), Cheryl Rodrigue (*Missie*), Buddy Lewis (*Paul Chase*), David Krippner (*Johnny*), Evelyn Hendricks (*party hostess*), Jed Wheeler, Michael Oglesbee (*boys—dream sequence*), Lance Gordon (*hustler*), Jim Egan (*bartender*), C. S. Fontelieu (*father—dream sequence*), Augie Lapara (*bar manager*), Michael Byrd (*car hop*), Nita Wilson (*woman at motel*), Dale G. Thompson (*man at motel*), The Armadillo (*rock band*), John Rigol (*policeman*), Waddy Jones (*Holiday Inn manager*), Ken Addington, Everett Addington, Bill Stillwell, Cathy Campbell, Renita Hamsher, Alice LeBlanc, Sandy Macera, Rita Gonsouline (*Karen's party guests*).

Domestic drama. In a New Orleans motel during Mardi Gras, Lauren Worthington, a restless housewife, leaves her sleeping husband Everett and entices Danny, a bellboy, with whom she has sex in a private suite. Their frivolity is interrupted by the sudden arrival of Paul Chase, attractive son of the apartment's tenant. Lauren meets Paul the next day at a bar, but they leave after a brief fight with the management. After dallying with Paul, Lauren meets a hustler, then returns alone to her suburban home, secretly trailed by Jerry, an enamored parking attendant. The following morning, Jerry assaults her at home, but is driven away at gunpoint. At a party that evening, Lauren seduces her daughter Karen's boyfriend, Terrance Bradford. The next night, Terrance is killed in an automobile accident, as he and Lauren are chased by the vengeful Jerry and his sadistic partner, Zool, on their motorcycles. Karen, who has since learned of her mother's many lovers, overhears Lauren being blackmailed by Jerry into meeting him at a motel. Both of the women are abducted and raped by Jerry and Zool before the police kill the men in a shootout. *Housewives. Bellboys. Police. Family life. Infidelity. Seduction. Suburban life. Revenge. Blackmail. Abduction. Rape. Motels. Bars. Motorcycles. Mardi Gras. New Orleans. Automobile accidents. Chases.*

Note: Filmed on location in New Orleans. Also known as *Women and Bloody Terror.*

HISTOIRE D'AIMER *see* **LOVE IS A FUNNY THING**

UNE HISTOIRE IMMORTELLE *see* **THE IMMORTAL STORY**

HISTOIRES EXTRAORDINAIRES *see* **SPIRITS OF THE DEAD**

HISTORIA ŻÓŁTEJ CIŻEMKI *see* **THE YELLOW SLIPPERS**

A HISTORY OF THE BLUE MOVIE   **F6.2166**
Screening Room Productions. *Dist* Sherpix, Inc. 6 Oct **1970** [Los Angeles opening]. Sd; col with b&w seq. 35mm. 140 min. [See note.]
Prod-Dir Alex DeRenzy. *Film Ed* Jack Kerpan. *Song*: "Let's Misbehave" Cole Porter. *Played by* Irving Aaronson and His Commanders. *Asst Dir* Paul Gerber.
With the Appearance of: Candy Barr, Alex DeRenzy.
Documentary. The "blue movie" is seen in historical perspective, from its beginnings as an "underground" form of entertainment viewed at stag parties and fraternity houses, through the peep show and burlesque era, to its emergence as a legitimate cinematic genre. A FREE RIDE (ca 1915): A driver has a sexual adventure with two hitchhikers in the country. ON THE BEACH (ca 1920): A man sees two women through a fence and steals their clothes. He then has intercourse with a goat through a hole in the fence, having been tricked into thinking that the animal is one of the women. Later one of the women pretends that she is pregnant and blackmails him. BURIED TREASURE (also known as EVER READY): A cartoon devoted to phallic fantasies involving humans and animals. THE JANITOR (also known as CREEPING TOM): A drunken janitor peers through the keyholes in his building and watches an artist engage in sex play with his nude models. THE NONE STORY: A nun enters a motel room, removes her habit, and erotically stimulates herself. A man who had been watching through the window confronts her, and they make love. SMART ALEC: Stripper Candy Barr makes love with an unidentified man in a Texas motel room. Following this historical overview, several of Alex deRenzy's San Francisco Screening Room Productions are presented as examples of the direction of the modern sex film industry. A nude woman frankly discusses her sexual experiences in an interview. THE MASSEUSE depicts the sexual relations between a masseuse and her client. Alex deRenzy interviews a hippie couple who have answered an advertisement in the *Berkeley Barb* soliciting models; the couple are then filmed making love. *Hitchhikers. Artists. Models. Janitors. Nuns. Motion picture producers. Hippies. Stripteasers. Masseurs. Motion pictures—History. Sex exploitation films. Sexual techniques. Bestiality. Voyeurism. Autoeroticism. Blackmail. Nudity. Beaches. Motels. Texas. San Francisco. "Berkeley Barb" Goats.*

Note: Cut to 120 or 115 min after initial release. Eliminated footage includes *Buried Treasure* and portions of the Screening Room Productions material. *The None Story* is also reviewed as *The Nun's Story*. The musical soundtrack utilizes popular songs.

HITLER F6.2167

Three Crown Productions. *Dist* Allied Artists. 21 Mar **1962** [Washington, D. C., opening; c28 Dec 1961; LP21322]. Sd; b&w. 35mm. 107 min.

Prod E. Charles Straus. *Dir* Stuart Heisler. *Writ* Sam Neuman, E. Charles Straus. *Dir Photog* Joseph Biroc. *Art Dir* William Glasgow. *Set Decor* Frank Tuttle. *Main Titl* Ben Mayer. *Film Ed* Walter Hannemann. *Mus* Hans J. Salter. *Sd* Charles Althouse, Jay Younger. *Sd Ed* Harold McGhan. *Mus Ed* Victor Lewis. *Asst Dir* Clark Paylow. *Prod Mgr* Lonnie D'Orsa. *Set Cont* Cosmo Genovese. *Wardrobe* Forrest T. Butler, Jack Bear, Olive Koenitz. *Makeup* John Holden. *Hairdresser* Agnes Flanagan. *Sp Eff* Daniel W. Hays. *Prop Master* Max Frankel.

Cast: Richard Basehart *(Adolf Hitler)*, Cordula Trantow *(Geli Raubal)*, Maria Emo *(Eva Braun)*, Martin Kosleck *(Joseph Paul Goebbels)*, John Banner *(Gregor Strasser)*, Martin Brandt *(Gen. Heinz Guderian)*, John Wengraf *(Dr. Morell)*, William Sargent *(Lieut. Col. Count von Stauffenberg)*, Narda Onyx *(Gretl Braun)*, Gregory Gay *(Field Marshal Erwin Rommel)*, Theodore Marcuse *(Julius Streicher)*, Berry Kroeger *(Ernst Roehm)*, Rick Traeger *(Heinrich Himmler)*, Lester Fletcher *(Lieut. Edmond Heines)*, Celia Lovsky *(Frau Raubal)*, John Mitchum *(Hermann Goering)*, Albert Szabo *(Emil Maurice)*, G. Stanley Jones *(Martin Bormann)*, Walter Kohler *(Gen. Alfred Jodl)*, Carl Esmond *(Field Marshal Wilhelm Keitel)*, Norbert Schiller *(Schoenberg)*, Ted Knight *(Major Buch)*, Willy Kaufman *(Wagner)*, Sirry Steffen *(Anna)*, John Siegfried *(Schmidt [Putzi])*, Otto Reichow *(SS officer)*.

Biographical drama. In the course of Adolf Hitler's rise to political power in Germany he courts his young niece, Geli Raubal, but he is rendered impotent because of her resemblance to his mother and is unable to consummate their love. When Geli realizes the truth, Hitler, overwhelmed by shame and anger, has her murdered. After becoming chancellor, Hitler arranges with Ernst Roehm the burning of the Reichstag, and he institutes his reign of terror. Roehm and his Brownshirts are purged as Hitler consolidates his power. Hitler then meets Eva Braun, who also reminds him of his mother, but she eventually succeeds in breaking down his guilt-inspired impotence and becomes his mistress. Seizing power after Hindenburg's death, Hitler and his Nazi regime sweep over Europe. When the tide is turned, however, he retires to an underground bunker, where, broken in mind and body, he is joined by Eva in a death pact. Now demented, he consents to a last-minute marriage, but at their moment of suicide he refuses to allow Eva to call herself Frau Hitler because only his mother had the right to that title. As the Allies enter Berlin, the bodies of Hitler and Eva are cremated. *Nazis. Uncles. Dictators. Mistresses. Impotence. Murder. Suicide. Marriage. Oedipus complex. World War II. Germany—History—Third Reich. Geli Raubal. Joseph Paul Goebbels. Adolf Hitler. Eva Braun. Hermann Göring. Erwin Rommel. Heinrich Himmler. Heinz Guderian. Ernst Röhm. Julius Streicher. Martin Ludwig Bormann. Alfred Jodl. Wilhelm Keitel.*

Note: Also shown as *Women of Nazi Germany*.

HITLER'S EXECUTIONERS (West Germany) F6.2168

Continent Film. *Dist* Vitalite Film Corp. 18 Jan **1961** [Los Angeles opening]. Sd; b&w. 35mm. 78 min.

Pres by Joseph Harris, Sig Shore. *Dir* Felix von Podmanitzky. *Screenplay* Joseph J. Heydecker, Johannes Leeb. *Film Ed* Felix von Podmanitzky.

English Narration: Jay Wilke.

Documentary. Based on a series of articles in the magazine *Münchener Illustrierte* by: Joseph J. Heydecker and Johannes Leeb. Beginning with the 1947 Nuremberg Trial and testimonies of such defendants as Göring, Hess, von Papen, and von Ribbentrop, the film traces the early development of the Nazi war machine in Germany. There are scenes of Hitler's rapid rise to power, his promise of a 1,000-year Reich, the African campaign, and the fighting in Holland, Poland, and France. Also shown are newsreel shots of the atrocities committed in the German concentration camps, documentation shown as evidence to the Nazi war criminals during the Nuremberg Trial, and a sequence in which 100,000 German prisoners captured at the Battle of Stalingrad are marched through the streets of Moscow. As the trial ends, newsreel footage shows two of the Nuremberg defendants being hanged. *Prisoners of war. Nazis. Genocide. International Military Tribunal. Concentration camps. Germany—History—Third Reich. Nuremberg. Moscow. Adolf Hitler. Hermann Göring. Rudolf Hess. Franz von Papen. Joachim von Ribbentrop.*

Note: Produced in West Germany in 1958 as *Der Nürnberger Prozess*; running time: 90 min. Also known as *The Executioners*.

HITOKIRI *see* TENCHU!

THE HOBO *see* HORNY HOBO

DIE HOCHZEIT DES FIGARO *see* THE MARRIAGE OF FIGARO

HOGS AND WARSHIPS *see* THE FLESH IS HOT

HOLD ON! F6.2169

Four Leaf Productions. *Dist* Metro-Goldwyn-Mayer, Inc. 30 Mar **1966** [Los Angeles opening; c31 Dec 1965; LP32079]. Sd (Westrex); col (Metrocolor). 35mm (Panavision). 85 min.

Prod Sam Katzman. *Dir* Arthur Lubin. *Screenplay* James B. Gordon. *Dir Photog* Paul C. Vogel. *Camera Op* Dick Towers. *Camera Asst* George Hollister. *Art Dir* George W. Davis, Eddie Imazu. *Set Decor* Henry Grace, Keogh Gleason. *Film Ed* Ben Lewis. *Asst Ed* Alex Beaton. *Mus Score* Fred Karger. *Songs:* "Hold On!," "A Must To Avoid" P. F. Sloan. *Song:* "Leaning on the Lamppost" Noel Tay. *Songs:* "All the Things I Do for You, Baby," "Where Were You When I Needed You?" P. F. Sloan, Steve Barri. *Songs:* "Make Me Happy," "The George and Dragon," "Got a Feeling," "We Want You, Herman," "Wild Love," "Gotta Get Away" Fred Karger, Sid Wayne, Ben Weisman. *Songs Sung by* Herman's Hermits. *Choreog* Wilda Taylor. *Rec Supv* Franklin Milton. *Sd* Lambert Day. *Rec* Bruce Wright. *Boom Op* Victor Goode. *Asst Dir* Al Shenberg, James Welch, Mickey Lewis. *Unit Prod Mgr* Robert Stone. *Asst to the Prod* Jerome F. Katzman. *Script Supv* Pearl Leiter. *Wardrobe* Gene Ostler, Vicki Nickols. *Makeup* William Tuttle, Don Donaldson. *Hairstyles* Sydney Guilaroff, Josephine Ardigo. *Sp Vis Eff* J. McMillan Johnson, Carroll L. Shepphird. *Still Photog* Ed Esterbrook. *Gaffer* Bill Shaw. *Grip* Howard Bradner, Tom Smith. *Prop* William Skammes, Jerome Graham. *Dial Coach* Vincent Chase.

Cast: Peter Noone *(Herman)*, Karl Green *(Karl)*, Keith Hopwood *(Keith)*, Derek Leckenby *(Derek)*, Barry Whitwam *(Barry)*, Shelley Fabares *(Louisa)*, Sue Ane Langdon *(Cecilie)*, Herbert Anderson *(Lindquist)*, Bernard Fox *(Dudley)*, Harry Hickox *(Grant)*, Hortense Petra *(Mrs. Page)*, Mickey Deems *(publicity man)*, Ray Kellogg, John Hart *(detectives)*, Phil Arnold *(photographer)*.

Comedy with music. When the children of American astronauts vote to name a new spaceship after Herman's Hermits, NASA assigns scholary Edward Lindquist to follow the British singing group to ascertain if they are worthy of such recognition. Included among the thousands of screaming young girls pursuing the Hermits is Cecilie Bannister, a publicity-minded movie starlet. In Los Angeles, Herman and his group slip away from the protective Lindquist for an evening of fun at an amusement park. There Herman meets attractive Louisa Page, who invites him to a lawn party her mother is giving for charity. The affair nearly turns into a riot when the Hermits begin to sing and Cecilie and a swarm of teenagers crash through the police gates. The Hermits' concert at the Rose Bowl is such a huge success that NASA decides to name a spaceship after them. *Musicians. Actors. British. Astronauts. Singers. Rock and roll. Adolescence. Riots. Charity. Amusement parks. Spaceships. Los Angeles. United States—National Aeronautics and Space Administration. Rose Bowl.*

Note: Working title: *There's No Place Like Space*.

HOLD-UP À LA MILANAISE *see* FIASCO IN MILAN

HOLIDAY IN SPAIN (Reissue) F6.2170

Holiday in Spain Co.–Michael Todd, Jr. *Dist* NT Assets Corp. 8 May **1962** [Boston opening; c21 Dec 1961; LP34094]. Sd; col. 70mm. 124 min. [Copyright length: 102 min.]

Note: Released in 1960 by Michael Todd, Jr., as *Scent of Mystery* in 70mm Smell-O-Vision. Reissue copyright claimant: Holiday in Spain Co.

DIE HÖLLE VON MACAO *see* THE CORRUPT ONES

DIE HÖLLE VON MANITOBA *see* A PLACE CALLED GLORY

HÖLLENJAGD AUF HEISSE WARE *see* SECRET AGENT SUPER DRAGON

HOLLYWOOD BLUE F6.2171

Graffitti Productions. *Dist* Blue Light Presentations, Sherpix, Inc. Nov **1970**. Sd; b&w and col. 16mm. 90 min. [Orig length: 95 min.]

Prod Bill Osco, Howard Ziehm. *Screenplay* Mike Lite, David Feller. *Photog* Howard Ziehm. *Film Ed* Mike Lite.

Cast—Interviews with: Mickey Rooney, June Wilkinson.

Documentary. A compilation of pornographic short films and erotica from past features intercut with street interviews and newsreel footage. Clips from *The Sheik*, with Rudolph Valentino; *Ecstasy*, with Hedy Lamarr; and *King Kong*, in which Kong strips Fay Wray, are juxtaposed with stag film footage. Fatima, seen both censored and uncensored, and Evelyn West, the "Hubba-Hubba" girl, are featured. A stripper, identified in the film as Marilyn Monroe, goes through her routine in a short film called *Apple Knockers and the Coke*

Bottle (also known as *A High Quality Film Presentation*). A sailor and a Marine are seen in a homosexual encounter in a park. There is newsreel footage of Ronald Reagan and Shirley Temple, and an interview with Mickey Rooney and June Wilkinson in which they talk about Jayne Mansfield. Some prints contain a bestiality sequence involving a woman and a St. Bernard. *Actors. Stripteasers. Sailors. Motion pictures—History. Sex exploitation films. Bestiality. Nudity. Male homosexuality. United States Marines. Rudolph Valentino. Hedy Lamarr. Fay Wray. Fatima. Evelyn West. Shirley Temple. Ronald Reagan. Jayne Mansfield. Marilyn Monroe. Mickey Rooney. June Wilkinson. "The Sheik". "Ecstasy". "King Kong". Dogs.*

HOLLYWOOD NUDES REPORT   F6.2172
Barry Mahon Productions. *Dist* Cinema Syndicate, Inc., Chancellor Films. 27 Dec **1963** [Los Angeles showing]. Sd; col (Eastman Color). 35mm. 64 min.
A Barry Mahon Production. *Prod-Dir* Barry Mahon. *Camera* Barry Mahon. *Film Ed* Al Ruban. *Mus* Steve Karmen. *Sd* Sande Johnsen. *Asst Dir* Al Ruban.
Cast: Chickie James, Maurice McEndree, Dorothy Proctor, Dee Lish.
Comedy. When Sloan Publications decides to make its entry into the Hollywood nude movie business, they hire an ex-combat photographer to make a film for them. Mrs. Sloan's daughter is assigned to assist the cameraman in making the transition from combat photos to pinups. The two plan to interview a number of women; they will choose the one they feel would make the most suitable lead and photograph her in the surroundings which would best display her beauty. They meet a wide variety of interesting women, including a forest ranger's daughter in the mountains, an artist living on the cliffs above Malibu Beach, and an exercise enthusiast in a gymnasium. The woman they finally select is a beautiful deafmute who feels completely at home when she is naked in front of a camera. They photograph her swimming underwater and playing chess in the nude. The completed film is a success, and the two filmmakers end their assignment by throwing a wild party for some of the friends they have made during the production. *Motion picture cameramen. Models. Deafmutes. Artists. Nudity. Sex exploitation films. Hollywood. Malibu (California).*
Note: May also be known as *Hollywood Nudes* and *Hollywood Report, or How Girls Make Nudie Movies.* Rereleased in 1967 by Chancellor Films.

HOLLYWOOD'S WORLD OF FLESH   F6.2173
Olympic International Films. 8 Nov **1963** [Los Angeles showing]. Sd; col and b&w (Eastman Color). 35mm. 72 min.
Prod Fred Nyquist. *Dir* R. L. Frost.
Cast: Baby Bubbles, Joanne Stuart.
Documentary. Hidden cameras are used in an investigation of Hollywood's world of sensuality: in a Los Angeles strip joint, prostitutes openly auction themselves to the highest bidder; beautiful nude women display themselves singly and in groups in the Santa Monica Blvd. figure model studios; guests are invited to watch as two girls bathe in the communal bath of a Japanese sex club; an interview with a prostitute is recorded; and the world of "nudie" filmmaking is explored. A producer inspects the shapes of potential cast members, and filming begins. In one sequence, a voyeur delights in watching a woman undress; at a private club, members pay $500 per year for the privilege of watching a sex circus that includes a love scene between a maid and her mistress; five hidden cameras record the activities at a producer's poolside party, which becomes an orgy as the evening progresses. *Models. Prostitutes. Actors. Motion picture producers. Photographers. Japanese. Stag shows. Prostitution. Striptease. Nudity. Voyeurism. Lesbianism. Nightclubs. Sex clubs. Sex exploitation films. Orgies. Hollywood. Los Angeles.*
Note: Also known as *World of Flesh.*

HOMBRE   F6.2174
Hombre Productions. *Dist* Twentieth Century–Fox Film Corp. 21 Mar **1967** [New York opening; c31 Dec 1966; LP34066]. Sd (Westrex); col (DeLuxe). 35mm (Panavision). 111 min.
Prod Martin Ritt, Irving Ravetch. *Dir* Martin Ritt. *2d Unit Dir* Ray Kellogg. *Screenplay* Irving Ravetch, Harriet Frank, Jr. *Dir Photog* James Wong Howe. *Camera Op* Alfred Lebowitz. *Asst Camera* Paul Waddel, Tom Kirschner. *Art Dir* Jack Martin Smith, Robert E. Smith. *Set Decor* Walter M. Scott, Raphael Bretton. *Film Ed* Frank Bracht. *Mus Comp & Cond* David Rose. *Orch* Leo Shuken, Jack Hayes. *Sd* John Carter, David Dockendorf. *Rec* Al Buffington. *Asst Dir* William McGarry, Al Murphy, Chris Seitz. *Unit Prod Mgr* Harry A. Caplan. *Script Supv* Meta Rebner. *Cost* Donfeld. *Men's Wardrobe* Bruce Walkup, John Perry. *Women's Wardrobe* Ollie Hughes. *Makeup* Ben Nye, Lynn Reynolds, Paul Stanhope, Terry Miles. *Hairstyles* Margaret Donovan, Christine Widmeyer, Virginia Darcy. *Sp Eff* Jim Halley. *Dial Coach* James Wellman. *Still Photog* James Mitchell. *Prop Master* Robert Eaton. *Key Grip* John Hennessy. *Elec Gaffer* Warren Hoag.
Cast: Paul Newman (*John Russell*), Fredric March (*Alexander Favor*), Richard Boone (*Grimes*), Diane Cilento (*Jessie Brown*), Cameron Mitchell (*Sheriff Frank Braden*), Barbara Rush (*Audra Favor*), Peter Lazer (*Billy Lee*

Blake), Margaret Blye (*Doris Lee Blake*), Martin Balsam (*Henry Mendez*), Skip Ward (*Steve Early*), Frank Silvera (*Mexican bandit*), David Canary (*Lamar Dean*), Val Avery (*Delgado*), Larry Ward (*soldier*), Linda Cordova (*Mrs. Delgado*), Pete Hernandez, Merrill C. Isbell (*Apaches*).
Western drama. Source: Elmore Leonard, *Hombre* (London, 1961). By the mid-1880's, the Apache Indians of Eastern Arizona have been relegated to living in squalor either on reservations or by themselves in the desert hills. Among the latter group is John Russell, whom they call Hombre. As a child, he was separated from his white parents, carried off by Apaches, and raised as an Indian. Upon learning that he has inherited a boardinghouse, Russell decides to trade the property for a herd of horses. Once the transaction has been settled, he leaves town on the first stagecoach. Also aboard are his friend Henry Mendez, the driver; Jessie Brown, former manager of the boardinghouse; Indian agent Alexander Favor and his young wife, Audra; a bickering young married couple, Billy Lee and Doris Blake; and Cicero Grimes, an arrogant stranger. As soon as the coach is underway, Russell is forced to sit on top because of Favor's bigoted attitude. A short time later, the coach is stopped by four gunmen, all in the employ of Grimes, who have come to rob Favor of $12,000 he has embezzled from government funds intended for Indian beef contracts. As Grimes and his henchmen make off with the money, taking Audra along as a hostage, Russell grabs a rifle and kills two of the bandits, one of whom was carrying the sack of money. After retrieving the cash, Russell leads the group to refuge in an abandoned mine cabin. The next day the outlaws appear and offer to trade Audra for the money. Russell refuses and defends his decision by reminding the others that Audra stood by as her husband let the Indians starve on dog meat while he pocketed their beef money. But when Jessie attempts to take the money to Grimes, Russell goes in her place. Gunfighting breaks out, and, although all of the bandits are killed, Russell dies saving the lives of his companions. *Apache Indians. Indian agents. Stagecoach drivers. Abduction. Racial prejudice. Stagecoach robberies. Embezzlement. Self-sacrifice. Boardinghouses. Inheritance. Arizona.*
Note: Location scenes filmed in the Coronado National Forest, Tucson, and other parts of Arizona.

EL HOMBRE DE MARRAKECH *see* **THAT MAN GEORGE**

EL HOMBRE QUE MATO A BILLY EL NIÑO *see* **A FEW BULLETS MORE**

EL HOMBRE Y EL MONSTRUO *see* **THE MAN AND THE MONSTER**

A HOME FOR TANYA (U.S.S.R.)   F6.2175
Gorky Film Studio. *Dist* Artkino Pictures. 6 Jan **1961** [Los Angeles opening]. Sd; b&w. 35mm. 97 min.
Dir Lev Kulidzhanov. *Screenplay* Budimir Metalnikov. *Story Ed* V. Pogozheva. *Photog* P. Katayev. *Art Dir* Mark Gorelik, Sergey Serebrenikov. *Film Ed* L. Zhuchkova. *Mus* Yu. Biryukov. *Cond* A. Roytman. *Sd* Anatoliy Dikan. *Asst Dir* Boris Kiselyov. *Prod Mgr* N. Petrov. *Cost* Ye. Aleksandrova. *Makeup* S. Filenova.
Cast: Vera Kuznetsova (*Natalya Avdeyevna*), Lyudmila Marchenko (*Tanya*), Nikolay Novlyanskiy (*Grandfather Avdey*), Valentin Zubkov (*Sergey Ivanovich*), Nonna Mordyukova (*Stepanida*), Lyudmila Ovchinnikova (*Nyurka*), P. Kiryutkin (*Mokeich*), Pyotr Aleynikov (*Fyodor*), Yelena Maksimova (*Makarikha*), Yu. Arkhintsev, V. Vsevolodov, Tatyana Guretskaya, G. Shapovalov, I. Kuznetsov, Ye. Melnikova.
Drama. Tanya, believed orphaned during World War II, has been raised in the comfortable urban home of Dr. Skvortsov. She receives a letter from her natural mother, who is living on a remote kolkhoz; and during her holidays, Tanya travels by train across the country to her birthplace to meet her mother. At first it is difficult for Tanya to adjust to her mother's simple existence, to country life, and to work on the kolkhoz. Gradually she comes into contact with the people of the kolkhoz and begins to understand the importance of their lives. Finally she decides to return to her birthplace after finishing her studies. Sergey Ivanovich, the kolkhoz chairman, who came from Leningrad, makes a great impression on Tanya in his concern for those in need. When Nyura, a farm girl, is accused of theft, Sergey steps in to resolve the situation happily. Tanya falls in love with him, and Sergey reacts tactfully to her youthful infatuation. Tanya learns that her father and two brothers sacrificed their lives in the war. She gains a great respect for her mother, who has triumphed over difficult circumstances, and for the people of the kolkhoz. *Orphans. Peasants. Adoption. Adolescence. Motherhood. Filial relations. Collective farming. Rural life. World War II.*
Note: Released in the U.S.S.R. in Apr 1959 as *Otchiy dom.*

HOME IS THE HERO (Ireland)   F6.2176
Emmet Dalton Productions. *Dist* Showcorporation. 25 Jan **1961** [New York opening; c21 Nov 1960; LP18336]. Sd (Westrex); b&w. 35mm. 83 min.

An Emmet Dalton Production. *Prod* Robert S. Baker, Monty Berman. *Exec Prod* Nathan Keats. *Dir* Fielder Cook. *Screenplay* Henry Keating. *Dir Photog* Stanley Pavey. *Camera Op* Ron Taylor. *Art Dir* Allan Harris. *Film Ed* John Ferris. *Mus Comp* Bruce Montgomery. *Mus Dir* Philip Martell. *Sd Rec* Liam Saurin. *Dub Mix* Wally Milner. *Asst Dir* Geoffrey Helman. *Prod Supv* Ronald Liles. *Cont* Eve Willson. *Makeup* Jill Carpenter. *Hairstyles* Mabel Ross.

Cast: Arthur Kennedy (*Willie O'Reilly*).

Cast—Abbey Theatre Players: Walter Macken (*Paddo O'Reilly*), Harry Brogan (*Dovetail*), Eileen Crowe (*Daylia O'Reilly*), Joan O'Hara (*Josie O'Reilly*), Maire O'Donnell (*Maura Green*), Marie Kean (*Bid*), Philip O'Flynn (*Trapper*), Pat Layde (*Mr. Green*), Eddie Golden (*Mr. Shannon*), John Hoey (*Finnegan*), Michael Hennessey (*Manchester Monaghan*), Michael O'Briain, Derry Power, Dermot Kelly (*men in pub*), T. P. McKenna, Eoin O'Brien (*men at dance*), Geoffrey Golden (*O'Connor*).

Drama. Source: Walter Macken, *Home Is the Hero* (New York opening: 22 Sep 1954). Paddo O'Reilly, a brutish, heavy-drinking Irishman of limited intelligence, is the delight of his cronies in the local pub but the despair of his family; his grown son, Willie, is crippled from the time, years ago, when Paddo drunkenly tossed him into the air and failed to catch him. One day, in an alcoholic rage, Paddo accidentally kills Mr. Green, the father of Willie's sweetheart, Maura. Paddo is given a 5-year prison sentence, and Willie assumes the position of head of the family by opening a shoe-repair business. Paddo's wife, Daylia, turns to drink, and his daughter, Josie, shamed by the family disgrace, takes up with a flashy local gambler. Upon his release from jail, Paddo defiantly tries to resume his paternal authority; he threatens to force Josie into giving up her boyfriend and tries to break up Willie's marriage to Maura. Only when he almost kills his old friend, Dovetail, is Paddo finally brought to his senses. *Cripples. Gamblers. Cobblers. Alcoholism. Family life. Filial relations. Fatherhood. Manslaughter. Marriage. Pubs. Prisons.*

Note: Filmed on location in Bray, County Wicklow, Ireland. Released in Dublin in Mar 1959; running time: 80 min.

HOME OF COPENHAGEN CALL GIRLS *see* **VILLA-VENNELY: HOME OF COPENHAGEN CALL GIRLS**

HOMER   **F6.2177**
Palomar Pictures International. *Dist* National General Pictures. 21 Sep **1970** [Louisville, Kentucky, opening]. Sd; col (Technicolor). 35mm. 91 min. *MPAA rating* GP.

Pres by Cinema Center Films. *Prod* Terence Dene, Steven North. *Exec Prod* Edgar J. Scherick. *Dir* John Trent. *Screenplay* Claude Harz. *Story* Claude Harz, Matt Clark. *Photog* Lazlo George. *Set Decor* Keith Barrie. *Prod Dsgn* Jack McAdams. *Film Ed* Michael Menne. *Mus & Songs* (see note) Don Scardino. *Sd* Russel Heise. *Asst Dir* Al Simonds.

Cast: Don Scardino (*Homer Edwards*), Alex Nicol (*Mr. Edwards*), Tisa Farrow (*Laurie Grainger*), Lenka Peterson (*Mrs. Edwards*), Ralph Endersby (*Hector*), Trudy Young (*Sally*), Arch McDonnell (*Mr. Grainger*), Jan Campbell (*Mrs. Grainger*), Tim Henry (*Eddie Cochran*), Murray Westgate (*Mr. Cochran*), Mona O'Hearn (*Mrs. Cochran*), Bob Warner (*sheriff*), Dennis Pendrith, Mike Ferry, Tom Harvey, Ted Gunn, Allen Doremus, Tony Parr, Frank Aldous, Debbie Turnbull, Hughie Sullivan, Larry Reynolds, Sam Turturici, Chelo Scardino.

Drama. Homer Edwards, an 18-year-old high school student in a small Wisconsin town, attempts to leave home. He waits all night on the highway trying to hitch a ride, but the sheriff brings him back to his parents' farm the next morning. His father and mother are unsympathetic with his anti-establishment attitudes, and only want Homer to cut his long hair, which he finally permits his girl friend, Laurie Grainger, to trim. Homer's friend Eddie Cochran comes home on army leave before being sent to Vietnam and begins to date Laurie; the boys' friendship is unaffected, however, as Eddie lends Homer his motorcycle for the duration of his army hitch, and Homer's rock band plays for Eddie's farewell party at the American Legion hall. Laurie loves Homer but does not begin to understand him until they talk at her house until 3:30 in the morning while her parents are at a party. When the Graingers return home, they insist that Homer spend the night, which enables Laurie to sneak into the guest room and make love with him for the first time. After Homer wrecks the family car and his father angrily puts him to work on their farm, the two are able to establish temporary communication when Mr. Edwards repairs the motorcycle and Homer rides it through the fields. Their newfound rapport lasts only until Eddie's coffin comes back from Vietnam; Homer then pickets the Veterans of Foreign Wars, sings protest songs, and finally chains himself to a post in front of the VFW hall. His humiliated father publicly slaps Homer's face and destroys the youth's record player and all his records. That night, Homer hitches a ride out of town with some hippies, and his father makes no attempt to stop him. *Students. Runaways. Sheriffs. Soldiers. Farmers. Musicians. Adolescence. Filial relations. Alienation. Smalltown life. Family life. Rock and roll. Sexual initiation. Farming. Motorcycles. Funerals. Vietnam*

War 1964–73. Wisconsin. American Legion. Veterans of Foreign Wars.

Note: Location scenes filmed in Canada. Scardino sings three songs which he composed. Other songs include "Down by the Riverside" and tunes sung by The Byrds, Led Zeppelin, and other groups.

HOMICIDAL   **F6.2178**
William Castle Productions. *Dist* Columbia Pictures. 7 Jun **1961** [Minneapolis opening; c1 Jun 1961; LP20542]. Sd; b&w. 35mm. 87 min.

Prod-Dir William Castle. *Assoc Prod* Dona Holloway. *Screenplay* Robb White. *Photog* Burnett Guffey. *Art Dir* Cary Odell. *Set Decor* Darrell Silvera. *Film Ed* Edwin Bryant. *Mus* Hugo Friedhofer. *Sd* Charles J. Rice, Lambert Day. *Asst Dir* Al Shenberg. *Makeup* Ben Lane.

Cast: Glenn Corbett (*Karl*), Patricia Breslin (*Miriam Webster*), Jean Arless (*Emily/Warren*), Eugenie Leontovich (*Helga*), Alan Bunce (*Dr. Jonas*), Richard Rust (*Jim Nesbitt*), James Westerfield (*Mr. Adrims*), Gilbert Green (*Lieutenant Miller*), Wolfe Barzell (*Olie*), Hope Summers (*Mrs. Adrims*), Teri Brooks (*Mrs. Forest*), Ralph Moody (*1st clerk*), Joe Forte (*2d clerk*), William Castle (*narrator*).

Horror film. As children, Miriam Webster and her half brother, Warren, had been cared for by Helga, a kindly nurse. The old woman is now mute and paralyzed and lives in a gloomy old mansion with a companion, Emily, Warren's alleged wife. Though Helga is threatened with murder by Emily, a homicidal maniac who has already killed the local justice of the peace, she is unable to communicate her deathly fear. Miriam and her fiance, Karl, become suspicious of Emily's strange behavior and discuss the situation with Warren. Karl decides to go to the police, and Miriam and Warren return to the old mansion, which Warren enters alone. When he fails to come out, Miriam goes in and discovers the murdered body of Helga. As she backs away in terror, she is suddenly confronted by Emily wielding a knife. Miriam watches in horror as Emily tears off her wig, thus establishing Warren and Emily as one and the same. As "Emily" raises her knife to stab Miriam, Dr. Jonas arrives unexpectedly at the house, and in the ensuing scuffle the psychotic killer is shot and killed by Miriam. Later it is revealed that following a trip to Denmark, Warren had taken on the psychopathic personality of Emily but had been forced to maintain his masculine identity in order to protect his inheritance. Both the justice of the peace and Helga were slain to keep them from exposing Warren's secret. *Psychopaths. Paraplegics. Nurses. Mutes. Brother-sister relationship. Male impersonation. Dual personality. Sex change operations. Murder. Inheritance.*

L'HOMME AUX CENT VISAGES *see* **LOVE AND LARCENY**

L'HOMME DE MARRAKECH *see* **THAT MAN GEORGE**

L'HOMME DE RIO *see* **THAT MAN FROM RIO**

UN HOMME DE TROP *see* **SHOCK TROOPS**

L'HOMME D'ISTAMBUL *see* **THAT MAN IN ISTANBUL**

L'HOMME DU MINNESOTA *see* **MINNESOTA CLAY**

UN HOMME ET UNE FEMME *see* **A MAN AND A WOMAN**

UN HOMME QUI ME PLAIT *see* **LOVE IS A FUNNY THING**

L'HOMME QUI MENT *see* **THE MAN WHO LIES**

LES HOMMES DE LAS VÉGAS *see* **THEY CAME TO ROB LAS VEGAS**

HONEY   **F6.2179**
Chellee Films–Jode Productions. *Dist* CIP Ltd. 14 Dec **1966** [Champaign, Illinois, showing]. Sd; b&w. 35mm. 57-65 min.

Prod H. K. Wilson. *Dir* Jerry Denby.

Cast: Carol Taylor, Paul Saville.

Melodrama. Honey runs away from home and meets Ray, a carnival barker who offers her a job in his "girlie revue." Honey accepts, unaware that Ray is a pimp. On the job, Honey meets Rick, a concession worker who is trying to save enough money to go back to college, and they fall in love. She shares an apartment with Doree, a lesbian. One night Benny, a psychopath, forces Honey into a room beneath the fun house and attempts to rape her. In the meantime, Ray surprises Doree in his room attempting to retrieve some compromising photos of Honey, and, as they struggle, she stabs him. Honey escapes from Benny, who catches his foot on the roller coaster track; Honey accidentally flips the starter switch, and the empty cars rush toward Benny. Rick, alerted by Doree, finds Honey, and as the lovers embrace, Doree realizes that Honey is lost to her, and she drowns herself in the ocean. *Dancers. Roommates. Psychopaths. Pimps. Runaways. Lesbianism. Suicide. Rape. Jealousy. Carnivals. Photographs.*

Note: Also known as *Honey Heat.*

HONEY HEAT *see* **HONEY**

THE HONEY POT (United States/Great Britain/Italy) F6.2180
Famous Artists Productions. *Dist* United Artists. 22 May **1967** [New York opening; c22 Mar 1967; LP34498]. Sd; col (Technicolor). 35mm. 131 min.

Pres by Charles K. Feldman. *Prod* Charles K. Feldman, Joseph L. Mankiewicz. *Dir-Screenplay* Joseph L. Mankiewicz. *Script Cont* Yvonne Axworthy. *Dir Photog* Gianni Di Venanzo. *Art Dir* Boris Juraga. *Prod Dsgn* John De Cuir. *Film Ed* David Bretherton. *Mus* John Addison. *Choreog* Lee Theodore. *Sd Mixer* David Hildyard. *Asst Dir* Gus Agosti. *Exec Prod Mgr* Attilio D'Onofrio.

Cast: Rex Harrison (*Cecil Fox*), Susan Hayward (*Mrs. Lone-Star Crockett Sheridan*), Cliff Robertson (*William McFly*), Capucine (*Princess Dominique*), Edie Adams (*Merle McGill*), Maggie Smith (*Sarah Watkins*), Adolfo Celi (*Inspector Rizzi*), Herschel Bernardi (*Oscar Ludwig*), Cy Grant (*revenue agent*), Frank Latimore (*revenue agent*), Luigi Scavran (*Massimo*), Mimmo Poli (*cook*), Antonio Corevi (*tailor*), Carlos Valles (*assistant tailor*), Hugh Manning (*Volpone*), David Dodimead (*Mosca*).

Mystery comedy-drama. Source: Frederick Knott, *Mr. Fox of Venice* (London opening: 15 Apr 1959). Thomas L. Sterling, *The Evil of the Day* (New York, 1955). Ben Jonson, *Volpone* (1605). Cecil Fox is a 20th-century millionaire living in the old world splendor of a 17th-century palazzo in Venice. After attending a performance of his favorite play, *Volpone*, he devises an intricate plan, *Volpone*-style, to trick three of his former mistresses into believing he is a dying man. Although the three women are wealthy in their own right, all of them have good reason to covet his fortune. To assist him in his scheme, Fox hires William McFly, a gigolo and a sometime actor, to act as his secretary-servant. After receiving invitations to visit Fox at his deathbed and remain for the reading of his will, the three former mistresses arrive at the villa. First there is Merle McGill, a fading Hollywood sex symbol whose career was launched by Fox; second there is Princess Dominique, who once took a cruise on Fox's yacht; and third there is Lone-Star Crockett, a Texas hypochondriac who travels with an enigmatic companion/nurse named Sarah Watkins. As Fox and McFly act out their charade, the brazen Lone-Star boldly states that she is the only one entitled to the inheritance since she has been Fox's common-law wife. That night Lone-Star is found dead from an overdose of sleeping pills. Sarah Watkins immediately suspects McFly of murder and flatly tells him so. When he locks her in her room, she escapes in a dumb-waiter, ends up in Fox's chambers and discovers the "dying man" wildly pirouetting about the room (ballet dancing is his only unfulfilled ambition). It soon becomes apparent that Fox is Lone-Star's murderer; flat broke, he had hopes of inheriting her vast fortune. Realizing his scheme has failed, Fox does a dance of death into one of the Venice canals. And it is Sarah who inherits Lone-Star's wealth—and McFly. *Millionaires. Mistresses. Actors. Gigolos. Secretaries. Royalty. Hypochondriacs. Greed. Inheritance. Suicide. Murder. Wills. Ballet. "Volpone". Venice.*

Note: Location scenes filmed in Venice. Opened in London caMay 1967; original running time: 150 min. Working title: *Anyone for Venice?* Also known as *It Comes Up Murder.*

HONEYMOON HOTEL F6.2181
Metro-Goldwyn-Mayer, Inc. 3 Jun **1964** [New York opening; c24 Feb 1964; LP28434]. Sd (Westrex); col (Metrocolor). 35mm (Panavision). 89 min.

A Pandro S. Berman Production. *Prod* Pandro S. Berman. *Assoc Prod* Kathryn Hereford. *Dir* Henry Levin. *Screenplay* R. S. Allen, Harvey Bullock. *Dir Photog* Harold Lipstein. *Art Dir* George W. Davis, Paul Groesse. *Set Decor* Henry Grace, George R. Nelson. *Film Ed* Rita Roland. *Mus Score & Cond* Walter Scharf. *Titl Song* Sammy Cahn, James Van Heusen. *Arr* Walter Scharf. *Sung by* Robert Goulet. *Song:* "I've Been Had" Sammy Cahn, James Van Heusen. *Arr* Walter Scharf. *Songs:* "Love Is Oh So Easy," "You're It" Sammy Cahn, James Van Heusen. *Arr* Sid Ramin. *Mus Numbers Stgd by* Miriam Nelson. *Rec Supv* Franklin Milton. *Asst Dir* Al Jennings. *Wardrobe Dsgn* Bill Thomas. *Makeup Supv* William Tuttle. *Hairstyles* Sydney Guilaroff. *Sp Vis Eff* J. McMillan Johnson, Robert R. Hoag.

Cast: Robert Goulet (*Ross Kingsley*), Nancy Kwan (*Lynn Hope*), Robert Morse (*Jay (Jason) Menlow*), Jill St. John (*Sherry*), Keenan Wynn (*Mr. Sampson*), Anne Helm (*Cynthia*), Elsa Lanchester (*chambermaid*), Bernard Fox (*room clerk*), Elvia Allman (*Mrs. Sampson*), Sandra Gould (*Mabel*), David Lewis (*Mr. Hampton*), Chris Noel (*Nancy Penrose*), Dale Malone (*Fatso*), Pauline Myers (*Hogan*).

Comedy with music. When Jay Menlow breaks up with his fiancée, Cynthia, just before his wedding, he decides to use his honeymoon accomodations anyway. He takes along bachelor Ross Kingsley, who was to have been his best man, and who is supposed to be representing his boss, Sampson, at a convention. Their arrival upsets the tropical hotel's management because guests are usually restricted to honeymooning couples. Ross, however, manages to date the hotel's only single girl, Lynn, the social director. Jay, on the other

hand, is bored and wants to patch up his quarrel with Cynthia, but Ross manages to intercept their calls to each other and prevent a reconciliation. Complications arise when Sampson arrives at the hotel with a beautiful girl, Sherry, followed shortly by Mrs. Sampson and then Cynthia. Lynn, thinking Sherry is Ross's girl, leaves, as does Cynthia, who thinks Sherry is with Jay. Explanations settle the situation, with Ross managing to keep his job and win back Lynn, while Jay rids himself of the domineering Cynthia and enjoys the charms of Sherry. *Bachelors. Social directors. Mistaken identity. Honeymoons. Courtship. Resorts. Marriage. Hotels.*

Note: Working title: *His and His.*

THE HONEYMOON IS OVER F6.2182
Dist Stacey Distributors. ca **1970**. Sd; col. 16mm. 61-81 min.

Sex film. No information about the precise nature of this film has been found. *Sexuality.*

THE HONEYMOON KILLERS F6.2183
Roxanne Co. *Dist* Cinerama Releasing Corp. 4 Feb **1970** [New York opening; c4 Feb 1970; LP38285]. Sd; b&w. 35mm. 107 min. *MPAA rating* R.

A Warren Steibel Production. *Prod* Warren Steibel. *Assoc Prod* Paul Asselin. *Dir-Writ* Leonard Kastle. *Dir Photog* Oliver Wood. *Film Ed* Stan Warnow, Richard Brophy. *Mus Selections* Gustav Mahler. *Sd* Fred Kamiel. *Asst to the Prod* Paul Sweeney. *Prod Mgr* Mike Haley.

Cast: Shirley Stoler (*Martha Beck*), Tony LoBianco (*Ray Fernandez*), Mary Jane Higby (*Janet Fay*), Doris Roberts (*Bunny*), Kip McArdle (*Delphine Downing*), Marilyn Chris (*Myrtle Young*), Donna Duckworth (*Mrs. Beck*), Barbara Cason (*Evelyn Long*), Ann Harris (*Doris*), Mary Breen (*Rainelle Downing*), Elsa Raven (*matron*), Mary Engel (*Lucy*), Guy Sorel (*Mr. Dranoff*), Mike Haley (*Jackson*), Diane Asselin (*Severns*), William Adams (*justice of the peace*), Eleanor Adams.

Crime melodrama. When Martha Beck, an unmarried, 200-pound nurse in a Mobile, Alabama, hospital, sends her name in to a lonely hearts club, she receives a letter from Spanish immigrant Ray Fernandez. A meeting is arranged, and Martha is immediately attracted to the suave gigolo. She persuades Ray to invite her to stay at his home in New York, where he tells her of his practice of using his appearance and charm to persuade middle-aged women to part with their money. Soon Martha, posing as Ray's sister, joins her new lover in his travels. They start by swindling Doris, a New Jersey schoolteacher, but soon Martha's jealousy causes her to add murder to their list of crimes. When Ray marries Myrtle Young, a pregnant Arkansas woman, to obtain $4,000 for legitimizing the baby, Martha gives the woman an overdose of sleeping pills. Later, in Albany, Martha bludgeons to death rich widow Janet Fay while Ray strangles her. In Grand Rapids, Michigan, they move in with Delphine Downing, an attractive widow with a 2-year-old daughter, but when Ray gets the widow pregnant, the insanely jealous Martha shoots her and drowns the child. Aware that Ray has been consistently unfaithful to her, Martha telephones the police and discloses the murders. While awaiting trial, Martha and Ray correspond with each other, still avowing their love. *Spinsters. Nurses. Spanish. Gigolos. Swindlers. Schoolteachers. Widows. Partnerships. Imposture. Jealousy. Infidelity. Marriage. Illegitimacy. Murder. Pregnancy. Confession (law). Clubs. Mobile (Alabama). New York City. Albany (New York). Grand Rapids (Michigan). Raymond Fernandez. Martha Beck.*

Note: Intended for release by American International Pictures in 1969 as *The Lonely Hearts Killers.* Working title: *Dear Martha.* Based on the lives of Raymond Fernandez and Martha Beck, who were executed for murder in 1951.

THE HONEYMOON MACHINE F6.2184
Avon Productions. *Dist* Metro-Goldwyn-Mayer, Inc. 23 Aug **1961** [New York opening; c27 Jun 1961; LP20069]. Sd (Westrex); col (Metrocolor). 35mm (CinemaScope). 88 min.

Prod Lawrence Weingarten. *Dir* Richard Thorpe. *Screenplay* George Wells. *Dir Photog* Joseph LaShelle. *Col Cons* Charles K. Hagedon. *Art Dir* George W. Davis, Preston Ames. *Set Decor* Henry Grace, Jerry Wunderlich. *Film Ed* Ben Lewis. *Mus* Leigh Harline. *Song:* "Love Is Crazy" Leigh Harline, Jack Brooks. *Rec Supv* Franklin Milton. *Asst Dir* Ronald Florance. *Cost Dsgn* Helen Rose. *Makeup* William Tuttle. *Hairstyles* Mary Keats. *Sp Visual Eff* Robert R. Hoag, Lee LeBlanc.

Cast: Steve McQueen (*Lieut. Fergie Howard*), Brigid Bazlen (*Julie Fitch*), Jim Hutton (*Jason Eldridge*), Paula Prentiss (*Pam Dunstan*), Dean Jagger (*Admiral Fitch*), Jack Weston (*Signalman Burford Taylor*), Jack Mullaney (*Ens. Beau Gilliam*), Marcel Hillaire (*casino inspector*), Ben Astar (*Russian consul*), William Lanteau (*Tommy Dane*), Ken Lynch (*Capt. James Angle*), Simon Scott (*Capt. Harvey Adam*), Norman Grabowski ("*Max's*" *operator*).

Comedy. Source: Lorenzo Semple, Jr., *The Golden Fleecing* (New York opening: 15 Oct 1959). After tracking missiles with an electronic brain (Operation Honeymoon), a U. S. battleship lays anchor off Venice. Almost immediately, young and brash Lieut. Fergie Howard hits upon the scheme of using the electronic computer to break the roulette table at the Lido casino. Aided by the reluctant Ensign Gilliam and civilian missile expert Jason Eldridge, Fergie blinker-signals all the data on the pattern of the casino game table to the ship, has the data fed into the machine, and receives back the likely winning numbers. Complications arise when Fergie falls for young Julie Fitch, who just happens to be an admiral's daughter; and Jason becomes involved with a former girl friend, a nearsighted millionairess named Pam Dunstan. The girls decide to cooperate, however, and once the plan is put into operation the boys amass a fortune. But further problems develop when the blinker communications are intercepted by Admiral Fitch and some Russians, both of whom mistakenly assume that they relate to aggressive military measures. An alcoholic signalman, Burford Taylor, stumbles upon the foursome, learns of their activities, and reveals all to the admiral. But, after a riot at the casino, Fergie talks his way out of a court-martial and even gets the admiral to accept him, albeit reluctantly, as a son-in-law. And young Jason decides that being married to a millionairess might not be so painful as he previously imagined. *Millionaires. Signalmen. Russians. Roulette. Computers. Missiles. Battleships. Casinos. Lido di Malamocco. United States Navy. Riots.*

HONEYMOON OF HORROR   F6.2185

Flamingo Productions. *Dist* Manson Distributing Corp. Sep **1964**. Sd; col (Eastmancolor). 35mm. 76-82 min.

Prod Herb Meyer. *Assoc Prod* Lucille Cohen, Martin Fried. *Dir* Irwin Meyer. *Screenplay* Alexander Panas. *Dir Photog* Clifford Poland. *Asst Camera* Edmund Gibson, Harry Walsh, Jr. *Film Ed* Tele-Visual Aids Inc. *Sd* Howard Warren. *Asst Dir* Sam Segal. *Prod Coörd* Gloria Izzo. *Makeup* Rudolph Liszt. *Hairstyles* Josephine Gibson. *Sp Eff* Jack Johnson.

Cast: Robert Parsons *(Emile Duvre)*, Abbey Heller *(Lilli Duvre)*, Alexander Panas *(Max Duvre)*, Vincent Petti *(Hajmir Dallali)*, Beverly Layne *(Helene Russel)*, Dorothy Farol *(Myra Amstadt)*, Monroe Myers *(Duane Albright)*, Michael De Beausset *(Socki Van Bridge)*, "Snuffy" Miller *(Toulouse)*, Christy Foushee *(Tutti-Frutti Johnson)*, Reuben Guberman *(Baron von Turko)*, Yanka Mann *(waitress)*.

Mystery melodrama. Lilli, the new bride of sculptor Emile Duvre, fears for her safety when, in Duvre's luxurious home, she receives threatening telephone calls and has a series of accidents. It is revealed that each of Duvre's friends has a motive for wanting the new bride dead. The mystery revolves around a collection of golden statues made by Emile. *Sculptors. Brides. Murder. Wealth. Sculptures.*

Note: Filmed in Miami; working title: *The Deadly Circle.* Also known as *Orgy of the Golden Nudes* and *The Golden Nymphs.* The sequences in Duvre's house were shot in Coconut Grove, Florida.

HONEYMOON OF TERROR   F6.2186

Dist Sonney Amusement Enterprises, Associated Film Distributors of California. 13 Jan **1961** [San Diego, California, opening]. Sd; b&w. 35mm. 62 min.

Prod Basil Bradbury, Peter Perry. *Dir* Peri.

Cast: Doug Leith *(Frank)*, Dwan Marlow *(Marion)*, Anton Van Stralen *(fiend)*, Dick Crane *(garageman)*.

Melodrama. Marion and Frank are disappointed with Las Vegas and its nightclubs on the first night of their honeymoon and decide to spend the rest of their vacation on Thunder Island. Upon arriving on the island the following day, Frank has to return to the mainland to pick up fuel for the portable stove. Marion remains behind to enjoy the swimming and sunbathing. Although a stranger attacks her, she is able to escape the would-be rapist, who has a club foot. In town, Frank hears tales of a logger known as the "Ridge Runner," who went mad, raped two women, killed a third, and has not been seen for 8 years. Frank hears some hunters tell of finding tracks on Thunder Island that might belong to the lumberjack, and he rushes back to the island, arriving to find Marion in the fiend's grasp. During the fight that ensues, Frank is knocked unconscious. As the lunatic nears Marion, she grabs his knife and fatally stabs him in the back. *Newlyweds. Cripples. Lumberjacks. Psychopaths. Rape. Murder. Honeymoons. Islands. Las Vegas.*

Note: Title changed to *Ecstasy on Lovers Island*; may also be known as *Ecstasy of Lovers.*

HONG KONG *see* **BOMBS OVER CHINA**

HONKON NO HOSHI *see* **STAR OF HONG KONG**

HONKON NO SHIROIBARA *see* **WHITE ROSE OF HONG KONG**

HONKON NO YORU *see* **A NIGHT IN HONG KONG**

HONNO *see* **LOST SEX**

HONOLULU–TOKYO–HONG KONG (Hong Kong/Japan)   F6.2187

Toho Co.–The Cathay Organization. *Dist* Toho International, Inc. Dec **1963** [Los Angeles showing]. Sd; col (Eastmancolor). 35mm (Tohoscope). 102 min.

Exec Prod Sanezumi Fujimoto, Lin Yung-tai. *Dir* Yasuki Chiba. *Screenplay* Zenzo Matsuyama. *Photog* Rokuro Nishigaki. *Mus* Hachiro Matsui.

Cast: Akira Takarada *(Yuichi Okamoto)*, Yu Ming *(Wu Ai-ling)*, Yuzo Kayama *(Jiro Okamoto)*, Yuriko Hoshi *(Teruko)*, Wang Ing *(Cheng Hao)*, Ken Uehara *(father)*, Haruko Togo *(mother)*, Choko Iida *(Granny)*, Mitsuko Kusabue.

Romantic drama. At Honolulu International Airport Yuichi Okamoto is greeted by his younger brother, Jiro, a student at the University of Hawaii. They attend a party celebrating the election of a beauty queen, Wu Ai-ling, whose photograph Jiro had entered in the contest without her knowledge. The contest prize is a 2-week trip to Tokyo and Hong Kong, and Yuichi accompanies Ai-ling back to his home in Tokyo. Despite numerous disagreements with Ai-ling, Yuichi realizes that he is falling in love with her when she becomes lost touring Tokyo and his reaction is one of frantic worry. Ai-ling phones Jiro, who tells her not to accept Yuichi's advances, as it is he who really loves her. However, Ai-ling has been told by her guardians in Hawaii that her real father affianced her to a boy in Hong Kong when she was three. Jiro flies to Tokyo but finds that Ai-ling and his brother have already departed for Hong Kong. Here Ai-ling finds her long lost sister, who is engaged to Ai-ling's betrothed. Now free to marry on her own, Ai-ling makes wedding plans with Yuichi. *Brothers. Sisters. Students. Tourists. Marriage—Arranged. Courtship. Jealousy. Travel. Parentage. Beauty contests. Honolulu. Tokyo. Hong Kong.*

Note: Released in Japan in 1963.

THE HOODLUM PRIEST   F6.2188

Murray-Wood Productions. *Dist* United Artists. 2 Apr **1961** [New York opening; c26 Feb 1961; LP20022]. Sd; b&w. 35mm. 101 min.

Prod Don Murray, Walter Wood. *Dir* Irvin Kershner. *Screenplay* Don Deer, Joseph Landon. *Dir Photog* Haskell Wexler. *Camera Op* Richard Batcheller. *Art Dir* Jack Poplin. *Set Decor* Karl Brainard. *Film Ed* Maurice Wright. *Mus Comp & Cond* Richard Markowitz. *Sd* William Bernds, Ben Winkler. *Asst Dir* George Batcheller, Ed Bernoudy. *Prod Supv* George Moskov. *Cost* Alexis Davidoff. *Makeup* Ted Coodley. *Hairstyles* Buddy Walton.

Cast: Don Murray *(Rev. Charles Dismas Clark, S. J.)*, Larry Gates *(Louis Rosen)*, Cindi Wood *(Ellen Henley)*, Keir Dullea *(Billy Lee Jackson)*, Logan Ramsey *(George Hale)*, Don Joslyn *(Pio Gentile)*, Sam Capuano *(Mario Mazziotti)*, Vincent O'Brien *(assistant district attorney)*, Alan Mack *(Judge Garrity)*, Lou Martini *(Angelo Mazziotti)*, Norman MacKaye *(Father Dunne)*, Joseph Cusanelli *(Hector Sterne)*, Bill Atwood *(Weasel)*, Roger Ray *(Detective Shattuck)*, Kelley Stephens *(Genny)*, William Wardord *(district attorney's aide)*, Ralph Peterson *(governor)*, Jack Eigen *(a prisoner)*, Walter L. Wiedmer *(Father David Michaels)*, Warren Parker *(warden)*, Joseph Hamilton *(prison chaplain)*.

Biographical melodrama. Father Charles Dismas Clark, a Jesuit priest in St. Louis, dedicates his life to the rehabilitation of delinquents and ex-convicts. By meeting them on their own terms and talking their language, he wins their confidence and their trust. He is primarily concerned with a young thief, Billy Lee Jackson, recently released from the Missouri State Penitentiary. Father Clark helps clear the boy of some trumped-up charges and then gets him an honest job with a produce market. Billy's rehabilitation is further encouraged by Ellen Henley, a young socialite with whom he falls in love. Meanwhile, aided by Louis Rosen, a successful criminal lawyer, Father Clark raises enough funds to open Halfway House, a shelter for ex-convicts readjusting to civilian life. All goes well until Billy's employer fires him for a theft he did not commit. Embittered, he and a friend, Pio, attempt to rob the produce market. They are caught by one of the owners, and he attacks Billy with a crowbar. The panic-stricken boy grabs a gun and kills him. The police chase Billy to an abandoned house, and he hides there until Father Clark persuades him to surrender. Tried and convicted of murder, he is sentenced to death. Before Billy dies in the gas chamber, Father Clark reassures him by telling him of Dismas, the thief who died on the cross, and of how Christ promised him eternal life. After the execution, Father Clark returns to Halfway House and finds his first client, Pio, drunk and repentant. *Priests. Ex-convicts. Juvenile delinquents. Police. Socialites. Lawyers. Criminals—Rehabilitation. Employer-employee relations. Revenge. Robbery. Murder. Capital punishment. Prisons. Markets. Saint Louis (Missouri). Society of Jesus. Charles Dismas Clark. Dismas.*

THE HOODLUM PRIEST (Japan)   F6.2189

Daiei Motion Picture Co. Jun **1969** [Los Angeles showing]. Sd; col. 35mm. 85 min.

Dir Kimiyoshi Yasuda.

Cast: Shintaro Katsu, Mayumi Ogawa, Kayo Sanbongi, Naoko Kubo, Mikio Narita.

Action drama. No information about the precise nature of this film has been found. *Priests.*

Note: Released in Japan in Nov 1967 as *Yakuza bozu.*

THE HOOK F6.2190

Perlberg-Seaton Productions. *Dist* Metro-Goldwyn-Mayer, Inc. 16 Jan **1963** [Washington, D. C., opening; c31 Dec 1962; LP23685]. Sd (Westrex); b&w. 35mm (Panavision). 98 min.

Prod William Perlberg. *Dir* George Seaton. *Screenplay* Henry Denker. *Dir Photog* Joseph Ruttenberg. *Camera Op* Fred Koenekamp. *Camera Asst* Bill Ion. *Art Dir* George W. Davis, Hans Peters. *Set Decor* Henry Grace, Keogh Gleason. *Film Ed* Robert J. Kern, Jr. *Mus Comp & Played by* Larry Adler. *Rec Supv* Franklin Milton. *Mix* Larry Jost. *Rec* Bernard Harlan. *Boom* Al Strasser. *Asst Dir* Donald Roberts, Ray De Camp. *Unit Mgr* William Kaplan. *Script Supv* Kathleen Fagan. *Men's wardrobe* Grady Hunt. *Makeup* William Tuttle, David Grayson. *Gaffer* George Lasher. *Prop* Dick Neblett. *Casting* Leonard Murphy.

Cast: Kirk Douglas (*Sgt. P. J. Briscoe*), Robert Walker, [Jr.] (*Pvt. O. A. Dennison*), Nick Adams (*Pvt. V. R. Hackett*), Enrique Magalona (*The Prisoner*), Nehemiah Persoff (*Captain Van Ryn*), Mark Miller (*Lieut. D. D. Troy*), John Bleifer (*steward*).

War melodrama. Source: Vahé Katcha, *L'hameçon* (Paris, 1957). While helping to load gasoline aboard a neutral freighter in the last days of the Korean War, greenhorn Private Dennison fails to notice an enemy plane, and his lieutenant is killed. As the freighter prepares to move on, Dennison rescues the wounded enemy pilot, and the man, referred to as "the gook," is taken prisoner. When Sgt. P. J. Briscoe reports by radio to South Korean headquarters, he is told that the enemy has bombed both the headquarters and a Red Cross hospital, and he is ordered to execute the prisoner. Briscoe at first objects but finally agrees rather than blacken his unblemished record. Dennison, however, pleads for the man's life and deflects Briscoe's arm when he attempts to kill him. As the hours aboard the ship become days, the prisoner becomes less an enemy and more a part of the group. When both Dennison and Briscoe's stooge, Private Hackett, refuse to carry out the execution, Briscoe decides to do the job himself; but by now, even he cannot pull the trigger. As word of an armistice arrives, the terrorized, uncomprehending prisoner escapes. Armed with a straight-edged razor, he makes his way to the hold and attempts unsuccessfully to ignite the gasoline. Just before Briscoe fells him with a fatal blow from a wrench, the man utters a word. Later, Briscoe learns the word means "I can't"—the prisoner, like his captors, has been unable to bring himself to kill. *Soldiers. Prisoners of war. Racial prejudice. Freighters. Gasoline. Korean War 1950–53.*

Note: Location scenes filmed on Santa Catalina island.

HOOK, LINE AND SINKER F6.2191

Jerry Lewis Films. *Dist* Columbia Pictures. 16 Apr **1969** [Boston opening; c1 Apr 1969; LP36821]. Sd; col (Technicolor). 35mm. 92 min. *MPAA rating* G.

A Jerry Lewis Production. *Prod* Jerry Lewis. *Assoc Prod* Joe E. Stabile. *Dir* George Marshall. *Screenplay* Rod Amateau. *Story* Rod Amateau, David Davis. *Dir Photog* W. Wallace Kelley. *Art Dir* John Beckman. *Set Decor* Frank Tuttle. *Film Ed* Russel Wiles. *Asst Ed* Joe Luciano. *Mus Comp & Cond* Dick Stabile. *Sd Supv* Charles J. Rice. *Sd* Al Overton, Sr., Arthur Piantadosi. *Asst Dir* Hal Bell. *Unit Prod Mgr* Herbert Wallerstein. *Script Supv* Hazel Hall. *Men's Wardrobe* Guy Verhille. *Makeup Supv* Ben Lane. *Makeup* Jack Stone. *Hairstyles* Virginia Jones. *Prop* Richard M. Rubin.

Cast: Jerry Lewis (*Peter Ingersoll/Fred Dobbs*), Peter Lawford (*Dr. Scott Carter*), Anne Francis (*Nancy Ingersoll*), Pedro Gonzalez-Gonzalez (*Perfecto*), Jimmy Miller (*Jimmy*), Jennifer Edwards (*Jennifer*), Eleanor Audley (*Mrs. Durham*), Henry Corden (*Kenyon Hammercher*), Phillip Pine (*head surgeon*), Felipe Turich (*foreign mortician*), Kathleen Freeman (*baby-sitter*), Sylvia Lewis (*Karlotta Hammercher*).

Comedy. As he is about to be operated on in a hospital amphitheater in Chile, a patient calling himself Fred Dobbs recalls his past life as Peter Ingersoll, a struggling California insurance salesman with a wife, Nancy, and two small children. One day, Peter's best friend, Dr. Scott Carter, informs him that he is suffering from a serious heart malfunction and has only a few months to live. When Nancy hears the sad news, she persuades Peter to go on a worldwide fishing trip, using nothing but credit cards for payment. But Peter's last fling is cut short in Portugal when Carter arrives with word that the electrocardiograph was malfunctioning and Peter's heart is healthy. Faced with $100,000 in credit card debts, Peter agrees to Carter's suggestion that he fake his death, allow Nancy to collect his insurance money, and stay in hiding until the 7-year statute of limitations has expired. Using the dead body of a Negro for a corpse, Carter signs Peter's death certificate, and Peter assumes the identity of Fred Dobbs. But Peter discovers by accident that Nancy and Carter cooked up the scheme to get rid of him, and he works out a diabolical revenge.

Switching the corpses of the Negro and a dead Southern colonel, Peter drops one of Carter's calling cards into the colonel's coffin and then takes off for Chile. After the colonel's widow finds the wrong corpse and Carter's calling card in her husband's casket, law officers appear at Peter's funeral and arrest Nancy and Carter as they are about to bury the colonel. Back in the operating room, the patient explains that he was living a perfectly happy life on a fishing boat off the coast of Chile until his chest was pierced by a swordfish. *Insurance agents. Physicians. Negroes. Heart disease. Death. Surgery. Fraud. Fishing. Personal identity. Credit. Infidelity. Insurance. Revenge. Corpses. Funerals. California. Chile. Portugal.*

Note: Location scenes filmed in San Diego, California.

THE HOOKED GENERATION F6.2192

Film Artists International. *Dist* Allied Artists. 13 Nov **1968** [San Francisco opening]. Sd; col (Eastmancolor). 35mm. 92 min. *MPAA rating* R.

Prod-Dir-Story William Grefe. *Screenplay* Quinn Morrison, Ray Preston, William Grefe. *Photog* Gregory Sandor. *Sets* William P. Kelley. *Film Ed* Julio C. Chavez. *Mus* Chris Martell. *Wardrobe* Barbara Kerwin.

Cast: Jeremy Slate (*Daisy*), Steve Alaimo (*Mark*), John Davis Chandler (*Acid*), Willie Pastrano (*Dum Dum*), Cece Stone (*Kelly*), Socrates Ballis, Walter Philbin, Milton Smith, Lee Warren, William Kerwin, Dete Parsons, Stuart Merrill, Marilyn Nordman, Curtis Perdue, Burt Huttinger, Michael De Beausset, Gay Perkins, Terry Smith, Clinton Nye, Emil Deaton, The Bangles.

Crime melodrama. Daisy, a ruthless drug dealer, and his gang, including Acid and Dum Dum, meet a boat carrying narcotics off the coast of Cuba. Instead of paying the Cubans for the shipment, the gang get them high on marijuana, kill them, take their narcotics and burn their boat. Spotting a Coast Guard cutter, Daisy has the narcotics thrown overboard in waterproof containers, but Mark and Kelly, a young couple out on a pleasure cruise, see this activity and inform the Coast Guard. Desperate, Daisy and his men kill the Coast Guardsmen and take Mark and Kelly hostage. The gang recover the narcotics but later discover that because they have been implicated in the murders they cannot sell the drugs. They move their hideout to a Seminole Indian camp where Acid rapes and then accidentally drowns an Indian girl. Sent into town for supplies, Acid stops at an addicts' hangout and is killed in a shootout with police. The FBI, tipped off by a drug dealer, pursue the gang into the Everglades. In a showdown, Dum Dum is bitten by a water moccasin and shot by FBI agents. Daisy is about to escape when Mark plunges a hypodermic needle into his neck, killing him. *Drug dealers. Drug addicts. Cubans. Seminole Indians. Murder. Abduction. Rape. Snakebites. Marijuana. Heroin. Florida Everglades. United States—Federal Bureau of Investigation. United States Coast Guard.*

Note: Location scenes filmed in the Florida Everglades. Working title: *The Pushers.*

THE HOOKERS F6.2193

Dist American Film Distributing Corp. 9 Feb **1967** [San Francisco showing]. Sd; b&w. 35mm. 70 min.

Prod-Dir Jalo Miklos Horthy. *Writ, "Callie Sue" Seq* William L. Rose. *Dir Photog* Sean O'Reilly. *Film Ed* Arno Hedlund. *Sd Rec* Norman Farren. *Asst Dir* Michael James. *Prod Mgr* Jonathon Robert. *2d Unit Mgr* Ted Bethel.

Cast—"Callie Sue": Fleurette Carter, William Reilly, Joel Carter.

Cast—"Julie": Shan Benedict, Steve Prince, Linda Lavell, Harold Heaghey.

Cast—"Barbara": Monica Lee, Lucky Kargo, Jacque Colton, Jay Martin.

Melodrama. The motives that drive three young women to prostitution are explored in three episodes: CALLIE SUE, a beautiful Negro secretary, resents being treated differently by men because of her color. One of the office executives, who is afraid to ask her out, makes blundering passes, and she recalls her youth in the South, remembering a day when two white boys tormented and raped her in a corn field. Her hatred drives her to mock the executive and to demand money for her body. JULIE, a go-go dancer, loves her employer, Mike, a pimp who promises her a show business career. At the club, a striptease fire dancer refuses the advances of one of Mike's clients; he beats the girl into submission and then takes her himself. He sends Julie to meet another client, a Broadway producer; she misunderstands and runs away when the client begins to make advances. Mike is furious, and Julie is so much in love that she agrees to become a prostitute. BARBARA, a chic, modern housewife who alleviates her boredom at the racetrack, loses a great deal of money on the horses. Unable to cajole her junior executive husband into covering her debts, she finds herself in trouble with the booking syndicate and is slapped around by one of their enforcers. She offers herself to the enforcer, and he introduces her to a profitable, exciting career in prostitution. *Secretaries. Negroes. Go-go dancers. Pimps. Housewives. Bookies. Executives. Prostitution. Racial prejudice. Rape. Gambling. Self-sacrifice. Employer-employee relations. Debt. Discotheques. Racetracks.*

HOOTENANNY HOOT F6.2194

Four Leaf Productions. *Dist* Metro-Goldwyn-Mayer, Inc. Aug **1963** [c19 Aug 1963; LP26163]. Sd (Westrex); b&w. 35mm. 91 min.

Prod Sam Katzman. *Dir* Gene Nelson. *Screenplay* James B. Gordon. *Dir Photog* Ellis W. Carter. *Art Dir* George W. Davis, Merrill Pye. *Set Decor* Henry Grace, Jerry Wunderlich. *Film Ed* Al Clark. *Mus Supv* Fred Karger. *Titl Song:* "*Hootenanny Hoot*" Sheb Wooley, Fred Karger. *Sung by* Sheb Wooley. *Choreog* Hal Belfer. *Rec Supv* Franklin Milton. *Mus Ed* Igo Kantor. *Asst Dir* Milton Feldman. *Post-prod Supv* James Nelson. *Makeup* William Tuttle. *Hairstyles* Mary Keats.

Cast: Peter Breck (*Ted Grover*), Ruta Lee (*A. G. Bannister*), Joby Baker (*Steve Laughlin*), Pamela Austin (*Billy-Jo Henley*), Bobo Lewis (*Claudia Hoffer*), Lauren Gilbert (*Howard Stauton*), Nick Novarro (*Jed Morse*), Vikki Dougan (*Vikki*), The Brothers Four, Sheb Wooley, Johnny Cash, The Gateway Trio, Judy Henske, George Hamilton, IV, Joe and Eddie, Cathie Taylor, Chris Crosby (*guest stars*).

Comedy with music. Young New York TV director Ted Grover quarrels with his ex-wife and boss, known professionally as A. G. Bannister. Although A. G., a producer, is still in love with Ted, her executive manner has driven him to break his IBS contract and head for the West Coast. En route, he is caught in traffic in Norburg, Missouri, where the college crowd is preparing for their Saturday night hootenanny. After seeing Billy-Jo Henley perform, and impressed by the enthusiasm of the crowd, Ted wires his agent, Steve Laughlin, to come to Norburg to evaluate the group for a new TV series. After notifying A. G. of Ted's whereabouts, Steve arrives, meets Billy-Jo, and falls in love with her. Ted returns to New York and sells his idea to a rival network. Their star-studded hootenanny show is highly successful on television, and A. G. (now jobless because she allowed the rival network to grab the idea) comes to congratulate Ted. They reconcile and join Billy-Jo and Steve in a happy hootenanny. *Television directors. Television producers. Singers. Musicians. Careerwomen. Marriage. Divorce. Television. Folk music. Hootenannies. New York City. Missouri.*

THE HOPELESS ONES see THE ROUND UP

HORAFUKI TAIKOKI see THE SANDAL KEEPER

HŌRÍ, MÁ PANENKO see THE FIREMEN'S BALL

THE HORIZONTAL LIEUTENANT F6.2195

Euterpe, Inc. *Dist* Metro-Goldwyn-Mayer, Inc. 18 Apr **1962** [San Francisco opening; c31 Dec 1961; LP21546]. Sd (Westrex); col (Metrocolor). 35mm (CinemaScope). 90 min.

Prod Joe Pasternak. *Dir* Richard Thorpe. *Screenplay* George Wells. *Dir Photog* Robert Bronner. *Col Cons* Charles K. Hagedon. *Art Dir* George W. Davis, Merrill Pye. *Set Decor* Henry Grace, Otto Siegel. *Film Ed* Richard Farrell. *Mus Score* George Stoll. *Titl Song* Stella Unger, George Stoll. *Sung by* The Diamonds. *Song:* "How About You?" Burton Lane, Ralph Freed. *Rec Supv* Franklin Milton. *Asst Dir* William Shanks. *Asst to the Prod* Irving Aaronson. *Makeup* William Tuttle. *Hairstyles* Mary Keats. *Sp Vis Eff* A. Arnold Gillespie, Lee LeBlanc, Robert R. Hoag.

Cast: Jim Hutton (*2d Lieut. Merle Wye*), Paula Prentiss (*Lieut. Molly Blue*), Jack Carter (*Lieut. William Monck*), Jim Backus (*Comdr. Jerry Hammerslag*), Charles McGraw (*Col. Charles Korotny*), Miyoshi Umeki (*Akiko*), Yoshido Yoda (*Sgt. Roy Tada*), Marty Ingels (*Yeoman Buckles*), Lloyd Kino (*Sgt. Jess Yomuru*), Yuki Shimoda (*Kobayashi*), Linda Wong (*Michido*), Argentina Brunetti.

Comedy. Source: Gordon Cotler, *The Bottletop Affair* (New York, 1959). Stationed in Hawaii in World War II, Merle Wye, a 2d lieutenant in Army Intelligence, becomes enamored of Molly Blue, a former schoolmate, now an Army nurse. But because of his ineptitude on the intraservice baseball team, Merle is transferred to the remote American-held island of Rotohan. His "mission" is to capture one Kobayashi, a harmless but annoying Japanese who has been stealing "vital" Army supplies (gefilte fish, soda pop, etc.). After the miserable failure of several of his schemes, Merle disguises his Oriental aide, timid Sgt. Roy Tada, as a Japanese captive and orders him to learn the identity of Kobayashi from the islanders. At this time Molly arrives at the base hospital, but she still refuses to respond to Merle's advances. One evening the islanders put on a show for the Americans, and Tada's new girl friend, Akiko, points out an acrobat as Kobayashi. Merle, however, again bungles everything, and the thief escapes. As a result, Merle is ordered transferred to an even more remote outpost. On the eve of his departure, he and Molly accidentally discover the hiding place of Kobayashi. There is a scuffle in which Merle is knocked unconscious, but Molly subdues the elusive Kobayashi. Merle receives the credit for the capture and wins both a citation and Molly. *Nurses. Japanese. Prisoners of war. Acrobats. Theft. Disguise. Baseball. Islands. World War II. Hawaii. United States Army—Intelligence.*

THE HORLA see DIARY OF A MADMAN

HORN-A-PLENTY F6.2196

Kirt Films International. *Dist* Distribpix, Inc. 18 Nov **1970** [Champaign, Illinois, showing]. Sd; col. 35mm. 70 min.

Drama. Jackie Williams, a prim young woman who lives alone in the suburbs and commutes to her job″ in the city as a market analyst, receives a gift from friend Lauri Chase that disrupts the routine of her life. The gift is a plant used in the fertility rites of a primitive South American Indian tribe, and its presence exerts a compelling influence on Jackie. She seduces Lauri's husband Roger, and then takes on both husband and wife together. Jackie later becomes involved in an orgy that includes lesbianism. Seeking desperately for sexual gratification, Jackie encounters another couple who specialize in ancient Indian positions for sexual intercourse. Jackie realizes the need to free herself from the spell of the strange plant, but she can't. *Market research analysts. Suburban life. Nymphomania. Troilism. Lesbianism. Sexual techniques. Fetishism. Plant life. Orgies. Rites and ceremonies.*

HORNETS' NEST F6.2197

Triangle Productions. *Dist* United Artists. 9 Sep **1970** [Dallas opening; c26 Aug 1970; LP38467]. Sd; col (De Luxe). 35mm. 110 min.

Pres by Stanley S. Canter. *Prod* Stanley S. Canter. *Dir* Phil Karlson. *Screenplay* S. S. Schweitzer. *Story* S. S. Schweitzer, Stanley Colbert. *Photog* Gabor Pogany. *Camera Op* Idelmo Simonelli. *Art Dir* Arrigo Equini. *Set Decor* Andrea Fantacci. *Film Ed* J. Terry Williams. *Mus & Mus Dir* Ennio Morricone. *Sd* David Hildyard. *Asst Dir* Franco Cirino. *Unit Mgr* Alfredo Chetta. *Asst to the Prod* Graham Cottle. *Prod Supv* Ottavio Oppo. *Script Supv* Francesca Roberti. *Wardrobe Coörd* Annalisa Nasalli-Rocca. *Makeup* Telemaco Tilli. *Hairstyles* Vittoria Silvi. *Sp Eff* Paul Pollard. *Dial Coach* Charles Smith, Mildred McCargar. *Constr Ch* Mario Valentini. *Gaffer* Luciano Marrocchi. *Head Grip* Franco Tocci. *Props* Marcello Medori.

Cast: Rock Hudson (*Captain Turner*), Sylva Koscina (*Bianca*), Mark Colleano (*Aldo*), Sergio Fantoni (*von Hecht*), Jacques Sernas (*Major Taussig*), Giacomo Rossi Stuart (*Schwalberg*), Mauro Gravina (*Carlo*), John Fordyce (*Dino*), Daniel Keller (*Tekko*), Daniel Dempsey (*Giorgio*), Joseph Cassuto (*Franco*), Tom Felleghi (*Colonel Jannings*), Andrea Bosic (*General von Kleber*), Bondy Esterhazy (*General Dohrmann*), Gerard Herter (*Captain Kreuger*), Hardy Stuart (*Gunther*), Marcello Turilli (*Colonel Weede*), Raphael Santos (*lieutenant with Taussig*), Viti Caronia (*lieutenant at village*), Jacques Stany (*Ehrlich*), Bruno Marco Gobbi (*Hermann*), Alain Shammas (*1st sentry*), Amos Davoli (*2d sentry*), Alessandro Jogan (*N.C.O.*), Jean Valmont (*Scarpi*), Giancarlo Prete (*Giulio*), Mino Doro (*Italian doctor*), Werner Hasselmann (*General Lewis*), Rod Dana (*U. S. colonel*), John Lemma (*jumpmaster*), Rick Petersen (*pilot*), Fabrizio Tempio, Maurizio Tempio (*Mario*), Luisa Giacinti, Anna Giacinti (*Maria*), Vincenzo Danaro (*Silvio*), Amedeo Castracane, Ronald Colombaioni, Giancarlo Colombaioni, Valerio Colombaioni, Gaetano Danaro, Luigi Criscuolo, Giuseppe Coppola, Gaetano Colisano (*gang members*).

War drama. During World War II, Captain Turner parachutes into Italy with other Army commandos to destroy a dam; the Germans are alerted, however, and shoot the men as they land. Seriously injured in the landing, Turner is the only survivor of his crew and is found by a band of renegade boys from a nearby town that has been destroyed by the German Army. Aldo, the leader of the gang, forces Bianca, an attractive German doctor, to give medical aid to Turner, and he recovers. Realizing that he cannot achieve his objective alone, he enlists the boys as his commando squad. Bianca, meanwhile, is held captive, and after she tries to attack Turner with a pair of scissors in order to escape, he throws her down and rapes her. The boys are trained to use firearms, but, prior to their mission, Aldo demands that they first launch a surprise attack on a German camp to avenge the destruction of their town. Aldo and his gang mercilessly slaughter the unprepared German soldiers, and Bianca, whose feelings for Turner have changed, also turns a gun on the Germans. With the revenge complete, Turner and his band travel to the dam and destroy it. Aldo, crazed by the killing, finds von Hecht, the local German commander, and is about to kill him when Turner intercedes and takes von Hecht prisoner. Overcome with emotion, Aldo collapses into Turner's arms. *Commandos. Italians. Physicians. Germans. Parachuting. Adolescence. Abduction. Rape. Revenge. Massacres. Dams. Explosives. World War II. Italy. United States Army. Germany—Army.*

HORNY HOBO F6.2198

Fleetan Films. *Dist* Able Film Co. 29 Oct **1969** [Los Angeles showing]. Sd; col. 16mm. ca50 min.

Sex film. While washing windows, a hobo espies two women making love. The lesbian interlude is interrupted when they discover the male onlooker, who is pulled into the bedroom. As they make love with the hobo, two other women arrive and perform cunnilingus before the husband of one of the women returns. *Hoboes. Lesbianism. Oral sex.*

Note: Also known as *The Hobo* and *Thorny Hoboes.*

HOROKI see **LONELY LANE**

HOROSCOPE (Yugoslavia)   F6.2199
Bosna Film. *Dist* Trans-National Film Corp. 29 Jun **1970** [New York showing]. Sd; b&w. 35mm. 87 min.
Pres by Laurance Joachim, Robin V. Joachim. *Dir* Boro Drašković. *Screenplay* Boro Drašković, Zuko Dzumhur. *Photog* Ognjen Milićević. *Mus* Zoran Hristić.
Cast: Milena Dravić *(girl)*, Pavle Vujisić *(stationmaster)*, Dragan Nikolić *(Vidak)*, Mihajlo Janketić *(boy)*, Josif Tatić *(buddy)*, Miloš Kandić, Dragan Zarić, Mirko Kraljev, Veljko Mandić.
Drama. At a remote railroad junction in the province of Herzegovina, bored adolescent males taunt tourists, fight with townspeople, and compete for a new blonde newspaper vendor. One of the young men, Vidak, rashly asserts that he will make love to the girl within the week, despite her indifference. After the blonde is discovered with an archeologist, she is raped by the youths. Vidak, however, abstains from participating. Pursued for a crime of which he is innocent, one of the gang is shot while attempting to catch a train. *Idlers. Archeologists. Rape. Jealousy. Adolescence. Herzegovina.*
Note: Produced in Yugoslavia in 1969 as *Horoskop.*

HOROSKOP see **HOROSCOPE**

L'HORRIBLE DR. ORLOFF see **THE AWFUL DR. ORLOF**

THE HORRIBLE DR. HICHCOCK (Italy)   F6.2200
Panda Film. *Dist* Sigma III Corp. 7 Oct **1964** [Cincinnati, Ohio, opening]. Sd; col (Technicolor). 35mm (Panoramic). 76 min.
Prod Louis Mann. *Dir* Robert Hampton. *Screenplay* Julyan Perry. *Photog* Donald Green. *Art Dir* Frank Smokecocks. *Set Dsgn* Joseph Goodman. *Film Ed* Donna Christie. *Mus* Roman Vlad. *Sd* Jackson MacGregor. *Asst Dir* John M. Farquhar. *Cost* Inoa Starly.
Cast: Robert Flemyng *(Dr. Bernard Hichcock)*, Barbara Steele *(Cynthia)*, Teresa Fitzgerald *(Margaret)*, Harriet White *(Martha)*, Montgomery Glenn *(Dr. Kurt Lowe)*, Neil Robinson, Spencer Williams, actor *(hospital assistants)*, Howard Nelson Rubien *(laboratory specialist)*, Al Christianson, Evar Simpson, Nat Harley.
Horror film. In 1885, noted London surgeon Dr. Bernard Hichcock accidentally administers an overdose of anesthetic to his wife, Margaret, during one of their sexually oriented "funeral games." Grief-stricken by her macabre death, he buries her and leaves his gloomy mansion. Twelve years later he returns with a new bride, Cynthia, and strange things occur: Martha, the housekeeper, explains that the nocturnal shrieks heard are the ravings of her mad sister whom she is harboring in the house; a skull is found on Cynthia's pillow; and a veiled woman is seen moving about the house and grounds. Learning that the veiled figure is Margaret, aged and withered from being buried alive, Hichcock once more becomes obsessed by his sexual mania and plots to murder Cynthia. She becomes suspicious, and, convinced that a glass of milk prepared for her by her husband is poisoned, she seeks the help of Dr. Lowe, her husband's assistant, who confirms her fears. Later, Hichcock attempts to drain Cynthia's blood in order to restore Margaret's youth, but Lowe comes to her rescue. In the ensuing fight a fire breaks out, consuming both Margaret and Hichcock. *Surgeons. Sex deviates. Brides. Housekeepers. Sisters. Drug overdose. Anesthetics. Death. Insanity. Obsession. Poisoning. Blood transfusion. London. Fires.*
Note: Filmed in and around Rome. Opened in Rome in Sep 1962 as *L'orribile segreto del Dr. Hichcock;* running times: 88 and 100 min. Production and cast pseudonyms include: Louis Mann (Luigi Carpentieri and Ermanno Donati), Robert Hampton (Riccardo Freda), Julyan Perry (Ernesto Gastaldi), Donald Green (Raffaele Masciocchi), Frank Smokecocks (Franco Fumagalli), Donna Christie (Ornella Micheli), and Teresa Fitzgerald (Maria Teresa Vianello). Film has a sequel, *The Ghost,* q. v.

THE HORRIBLE MILL WOMEN see **MILL OF THE STONE WOMEN**

HORROR CASTLE (Italy)   F6.2201
Gladiator Productions–Atlantica Cinematografica. *For* Walter Manley Enterprises. *Dist* Zodiac Films. 7 Apr **1965** [Los Angeles opening; c29 Sep 1964; LP33749]. Sd; col (Eastman Color). 35mm (Totalscope). 83 min.
Pres by Marco Vicario. *Prod* Marco Vicario. *Dir* Anthony Dawson. *Dir English Lang Vers* Richard McNamara. *Screenplay* Anthony Dawson, Gastad Green, Edmond T. Greville. *Photog* Riccardo Pallottini. *Art Dir* Riccardo Domenici. *Film Ed* Angel Coly. *Mus Comp & Cond* Riz Ortolani. *Sd* Albert Griffiths. *Prod Mgr* Natalino Vicario.
Cast: Rossana Podestà *(Mary)*, Georges Rivière *(Max Hunter)*, Christopher Lee *(Erich)*, Jim Dolen *(Selby)*, Anny Delli Uberti *(Marta)*, Luigi Severini

(doctor), Luciana Milone *(Trude)*, Lucile Saint-Simon, Patrick Walton, Consalvo Dell'Arti, Peter Hardy, Rex Vidor, James Borden, Bredon Brett, Robert Mayor, Carole Windsor.
Horror film. Source: Frank Bogart, *The Virgin of Nuremberg* (publication undetermined). Newlywed Max Hunter, a young German nobleman, takes his American wife, Mary, to his ancestral family castle on the Rhine. During their first night there, Mary discovers the mutilated body of a young girl inside an ancient torture device called "The Virgin of Nuremberg." The body disappears, and Max attempts to convince Mary that she has been dreaming, but the doctor who examines her finds evidence that there really was a corpse and alerts American FBI agent Selby, who has already been keeping the castle under observation. Mary's terror is compounded by the presence of Erich, the horribly scarred chauffeur-caretaker, and Marta, the housekeeper who believes the castle is inhabited by a legendary "executioner" who was put to death 300 years before. A housemaid and the butler are murdered, and Mary becomes fearful that her husband, assisted by Erich, is responsible for the heinous crimes. Max begs her to have faith in him and arranges for her to leave the castle until the mystery is solved. Before she can depart, however, more murders are committed, and Mary finds herself at the mercy of the real homicidal maniac— Max's father, an ex-Nazi who became mad after being tortured for making an attempt on Hitler's life. Selby, Max, and Erich come to Mary's rescue as the castle is destroyed by fire, and Max's crazed father dies in the flames. *Nobility. Germans. Americans in foreign countries. Caretakers. Chauffeurs. Physicians. Housekeepers. Nazis. Newlyweds. Psychopaths. Torture. Murder. Mutilation. Corpses. Castles. Rhine River. United States—Federal Bureau of Investigation. Fires.*
Note: Released in Italy in 1964 as *La vergine de Norimberga.* Rereleased Nov 1966 as *Terror Castle;* running time; 70 min. Also known as *Horror Castle (Where the Blood Flows).* Gladiator Productions is U. S. release name for Atlantica Cinematografica.

THE HORROR CHAMBER OF DR. FAUSTUS (France/Italy)   F6.2202
Champs-Elysées Productions–Lux Film. *Dist* Lopert Pictures. 28 Mar **1962** [San Francisco opening]. Sd; b&w. 35mm. 84 min. [Also reviewed at 95 min.]
Pres by William Shelton, Cameo International Pictures. *Prod* Jules Borkon. *Dir* Georges Franju. *Screenplay* Jean Redon. *Dial* Pierre Gascar. *Adapt* Georges Franju, Jean Redon, Claude Sautet, Pierre Boileau, Thomas Narcejac. *Photog* Eugen Shuftan. *Art Dir* Auguste Capelier. *Film Ed* Gilbert Natot. *Mus* Maurice Jarre. *Sd* Antoine Archimbaud. *Prod Mgr* Pierre Laurent. *Sp Eff* Henri Assola, Georges Klein.
Cast: Pierre Brasseur *(Professor Genessier)*, Alida Valli *(Louise)*, Edith Scob *(Christiane)*, François Guérin *(Jacques)*, Juliette Mayniel *(Edna Gruber)*, Béatrice Altariba *(Paulette)*, Alexandre Rignault *(Inspector Parot)*, René Génin *(bereaved father)*, Claude Brasseur, Michel Etcheverry, Yvette Etiévant, Lucien Hubert, Marcel Pérès.
Horror film. Source: Jean Redon, *Les yeux sans visage* (Paris, 1959). Professor Genessier, a prominent plastic surgeon, decides to restore the face of his daughter, Christiane, who was horribly disfigured in a car accident that he caused. Louise, his assistant, lures Parisian students whose facial features resemble Christiane's to the doctor's estate. The corpse of the first victim is discovered by the police, and Genessier identifies the body as his daughter to allay suspicion about the experiments. Another student, Edna Gruber, commits suicide after being mutilated during an unsuccessful skin graft operation. Police Inspector Parot, informed by Christiane's fiancé Jacques that he spoke with her by telephone, enlists petty thief Paulette to act as a decoy and help uncover the doctor's scheme. When Genessier is called away to an adjoining hospital, Christiane, who has gone mad, unstraps Paulette from the operating table, stabs Louise, and unleashes a kennel of dogs that viciously attack and kill her father. *Surgeons. Students. Police. Disfiguration. Plastic surgery. Filial relations. Abduction. Murder. Suicide. Mutilation. Insanity. Paris. Automobile accidents. Dogs.*
Note: Opened in Paris in Mar 1960 as *Les yeux sans visage;* running time: 88 min; in Rome in Jul 1960 as *Occhi senza volto;* running time: 88 min.

HORROR CREATURES OF THE PREHISTORIC PLANET see **HORROR OF THE BLOOD MONSTERS**

HORROR HOTEL (Great Britain)   F6.2203
Vulcan Productions, Ltd. *Dist* Trans-Lux Distributing Corp. 12 Sep **1962** [Los Angeles opening]. Sd; b&w. 35mm. 76 min.
Prod Donald Taylor. *Prod (uncredited)* Milton Subotsky. *Dir* John Moxey. *Screenplay* George Baxt. *Story* Milton Subotsky. *Photog* Desmond Dickinson. *Camera Op* Jack Atcheler. *Art Dir* John Blezard. *Film Ed* John Pomeroy. *Mus Comp & Cond* Douglas Gamley. *Dance Mus* Ken Jones. *Sd* Richard Bird. *Cont* Splinters Deason. *Wardrobe* Freda Gibson. *Makeup* George Claff. *Hairstyles* Barbara Barnard. *Sp Eff* Cliff Richardson.

Cast: Patricia Jessel *(Elizabeth Selwyn/Mrs. Newless)*, Betta St. John *(Patricia Russell)*, Christopher Lee *(Professor Driscoll)*, Dennis Lotis *(Richard Barlow)*, Venetia Stevenson *(Nan Barlow)*, Valentine Dyall *(Jethrow Keane)*, Norman MacOwan *(Reverend Russell)*, Ann Beach *(Lottie)*, Tom Naylor *(Bill Maitland)*, Fred Johnson *(elder)*.

Horror film. Nan Barlow, a student of the occult, is encouraged by her history professor, Driscoll, to visit the decaying village of Whitewood, Massachusetts. Mrs. Newless, proprietress of the Ravens Inn, is in reality Elizabeth Selwyn, a witch who was burned at the stake in 1692 but restored to life through a pact with the Devil. When Nan discovers the witch and her coven, including Professor Driscoll, performing human sacrifices on Candlemas Eve, she is killed as a sacrifice. Nan's brother Richard and her boyfriend, Bill Maitland, become worried about her absence and drive to Whitewood, arriving as Patricia Russell, granddaughter of the blind minister of Whitewood, is to be sacrificed. Bill, although fatally wounded by the witches, manages to throw the shadow of a cross over them, destroying them all, as Richard escapes with Patricia. *Students. Witches. Innkeepers. Professors. Brothers. Clergymen. Grandfathers. Occult. Reviviscence. Human sacrifice. Rites and ceremonies. Demonology. Candlemas. Massachusetts. The Devil.*

Note: Released in Great Britain in Sep 1960 as *The City of the Dead*; running time: 78 min.

HORROR HOUSE (Great Britain)   **F6.2204**

Tigon British Film Productions–American International Pictures. *Dist* American International Pictures. 15 Apr **1970** [San Diego, California, opening]. Sd; col (Eastmancolor, print by Movielab). 35mm. 79 min. *MPAA rating* GP.

Prod Louis M. Heyward. *Exec Prod* Tony Tenser. *Dir-Writ* Michael Armstrong. *Adtl Material* Peter Marcus. *Photog* Jack Atcheler. *Art Dir* Hayden Pearce. *Set Decor* Jack Holden. *Film Ed* Peter Pitt. *Mus* Reg Tilsley. *Sd Ed* Howard Lanning. *Sd Rec* Alan Kane. *Asst Dir* Nick Caris Carter. *Prod Mgr* George Mills. *Sp Eff* Arthur Beavis.

Cast: Frankie Avalon *(Chris)*, Jill Haworth *(Sheila)*, Mark Wynter *(Gary)*, Dennis Price *(Inspector Wainwright)*, George Sewell *(Kellett)*, Gina Warwick *(Sylvia)*, Richard O'Sullivan *(Peter)*, Carol Dilworth *(Dorothy)*, Julian Barnes *(Richard)*, Veronica Doran *(Madge)*, Robin Stewart *(Henry)*, Jan Holden *(Peggy)*, Clifford Earl *(police sergeant)*, Robert Raglan *(Bradley)*, Freddie Lees *(Dave)*.

Horror film. Chris, a London youth, throws a party, and Richard, one of the guests, suggests that they visit a haunted house that was the scene of several brutal murders. The group arrives at the house and attempts to conjure up ghosts by means of a seance. When this fails, they split up and explore the house. They come upon the brutally murdered body of one of their group, and Chris warns his friends not to tell the police, who already suspect them of narcotics violations. After disposing of the body, they leave the house. Wainwright, an inquisitive police inspector, begins questioning the group about their friend's disappearance, and Chris realizes that they must return to the house to search for clues. After another member of the group is found hacked to death, Chris finds himself alone with Richard, who pulls a knife and murders him only moments before the police arrive. *Police. Psychopaths. Youth. Murder. Seances. Haunted houses. London.*

Note: Location scenes filmed in London. Released in Great Britain in 1969 as *The Haunted House of Horror*; running time: 92 min. Working title: *The Dark.*

THE HORROR OF FRANKENSTEIN (Great Britain)   **F6.2205**

Hammer Film Productions–EMI Film Productions. *For* Anglo-EMI Film Distributors. *Dist* American Continental Films. 23 Dec **1970** [Chicago opening]. Sd; col (Technicolor). 35mm. 95 min. *MPAA rating* R.

Pres by Levitt-Pickman Film Corp. *Prod-Dir* Jimmy Sangster. *Screenplay* Jimmy Sangster, Jeremy Burnham. *Dir Photog* Moray Grant. *Art Dir* Scott MacGregor. *Film Ed* Chris Barnes. *Mus Comp* James Bernard. *Mus Supv* Malcolm Williamson. *Sd Ed* Terry Poulton. *Sd Rec* Claude Hitchcock. *Sd Re-rec* Bill Rowe. *Asst Dir* Derek Whitehurst. *Prod Mgr* Tom Sachs. *Makeup* Tom Smith.

Cast: Ralph Bates *(Victor Frankenstein)*, Kate O'Mara *(Alys)*, Graham James *(Wilhem)*, Veronica Carlson *(Elizabeth)*, Bernard Archard *(Elizabeth's father)*, Dennis Price *(grave robber)*, Joan Rice *(grave robber's wife)*, David Prowse *(The Monster)*.

Horror film. Based on characters created by: Mary Shelley. When Baron Frankenstein refuses to send his son Victor to Vienna University, the young man arranges for his father's death, thereby inheriting his title, castle, fortune, and housekeeper-mistress Alys. Tiring of his studies, however, Victor returns home with his best friend Wilhem and sets out to construct a human being from parts supplied by a grave robber and his wife. When Wilhem objects to the ghoulish experiments, Victor electrocutes him and immerses the corpse in a vat filled with acid. To complete his creation, Victor murders a neighboring professor. Afterwards, he offers refuge to the victim's daughter, Elizabeth, who

has loved him since childhood. His creation nearly ruined when the grave robber drops the professor's brain, Victor hurls the clumsy thief into the acid tank. A bolt of lightning from an electrical storm galvanizes the man-made being into life. Not recognizing its creator, the monster knocks Victor unconscious, escapes into the woods, and terrorizes the countryside until it is recaptured by Victor. Threatened with exposure by Alys (who is jealous of Elizabeth's presence in the castle) and by the grave robber's wife (who is searching for her missing husband), Victor uses the monster to kill the two women. Investigating the mysterious deaths and disappearances, the police arrive accompanied by a little girl, whom the monster menaced in the forest. Victor, who has hidden the creature in the empty vat, looks on in both anger and relief as the child unwittingly releases the containers that flood the tank with acid. With both his creature and the evidence of his crimes eradicated, Victor is free to continue his experiments. *Aristocrats. Students. Housekeepers. Mistresses. Grave robbers. Professors. Murder. Patricide. Castles. Experiments. Vienna. Lightning. Frankenstein.*

Note: Opened in London in Oct 1970.

THE HORROR OF IT ALL (Great Britain)   **F6.2206**

Lippert Films–Associated Producers, Inc. *Dist* Twentieth Century-Fox Film Corp. 19 Aug **1964** [Phoenix, Arizona, opening; c3 Sep 1964; LP28962]. Sd (Westrex); b&w. 35mm. 75 min.

Exec Prod Robert L. Lippert. *Assoc Prod* Margia Dean. *Dir* Terence Fisher. *Writ* Ray Russell. *Dir Photog* Arthur Lavis. *Camera Op* Len Harris. *Art Dir* Harry White. *Film Ed* Robert Winter. *Asst Ed* Clive Smith. *Mus Comp* Douglas Gamley. *Mus Cond* Philip Martell. *Titl Song Writ & Sung by* Pat Boone. *Sd Rec* Steve Stephenson. *Asst Dir* Frank Nesbitt. *Prod Mgr* Clifford Parkes. *Cont* Renee Glynne. *Prod Sec* Barbara Allen. *Wardrobe* Jean Fairlie. *Makeup* Bill Lodge. *Hairdresser* Daphne Vollmer.

Cast: Pat Boone *(Jack Robinson)*, Erica Rogers *(Cynthia Marley)*, Dennis Price *(Cornwallis Marley)*, Andree Melly *(Natalia Marley)*, Valentine Dyall *(Reginald Marley)*, Jack Bligh *(Percival Marley)*, Archie Duncan *(Muldoon Marley)*, Erik Chitty *(Grandpapa Marley)*, Oswald Laurence *(doctor)*.

Comedy-melodrama. American salesman Jack Robinson arrives unexpectedly in England to ask the parents of his fiancée, Cynthia Marley, for permission to marry their daughter. The eccentric Marleys receive Jack unenthusiastically at their ancestral mansion because Cynthia's cousin has just died. The family, which has a long history of violent death, consists of Percival, who claims to have invented electricity and the automobile; the vampirish Natalia; Reginald, the sinister head of the family; Cornwallis, a former actor; the mad Muldoon, who is kept locked in the basement; and bedridden Grandpapa. After Jack barely escapes injury in a series of accidents that kill Cornwallis and Grandpapa, he concludes that one of the Marleys is determined to become sole heir to the family fortune. Unable to contact police from the mansion, Jack is offered a ride to town in Percival's electrically-driven hearse. The car crashes on the way, and when he awakens in the hospital, Jack discovers that Cornwallis, who faked his own death, is the murderer. Later, Jack and Cynthia leave the Marley mansion to plan their marriage. *Americans in foreign countries. Heirs. Salesmen. Eccentrics. Inventors. Family life. Murder. Inheritance. Greed. Courtship. Insanity. Hearses. Hospitals. Automobile accidents.*

Note: Opened in London in Jun 1966.

THE HORROR OF PARTY BEACH   **F6.2207**

Inzom Corp. *Dist* Twentieth Century-Fox Film Corp. 1 Apr **1964** [Detroit opening; c31 Dec 1963; LP27972]. Sd; b&w. 35mm. 82 min. [Copyright length: 78 min.]

An Alan V. Iselin-Del Tenney Production. *Prod-Dir* Del Tenney. *Assoc Prod* Alan V. Iselin. *Screenplay* Richard Hilliard. *Adtl Dial* Ronald Gianettino, Lou Binder. *Photog* Richard Hilliard. *Art Dir* Robert Verberkmoss. *Film Ed* Gary Youngman. *Mus Dir* Bill Holmes. *Song:* "Elaine" Ronny Linares. *Theme Song:* "Drag" Ronny Linares, Garry Jones. *Sung by* The Del-Aires. *Songs:* "You Are Not a Summer Love," "Wigglin' n' Wobblin'" sung by The Del-Aires.

Cast: John Scott, U. S. actor *(Hank Green)*, Alice Lyon *(Elaine Gavin)*, Allen Laurel *(Dr. Gavin)*, Eulabelle Moore *(Eulabelle)*, Marilyn Clark *(Tina)*, Agustin Mayer *(Mike)*, Damon Klebroyd *(Lieutenant Wells)*, Monroe Wade *(television announcer)*, Carol Grubman, Dina Harris, Emily Laurel *(girls in car)*, Sharon Murphy, Diane Prizio *(two girls)*, The Del-Aires *(vocal group)*.

Horror film. A container holding radioactive waste material springs a leak and spills over a human skull at the bottom of the ocean, just off a beach popular with teenagers. Shortly thereafter, the skull turns into a monster and heads for the beach in search of human blood; and it is soon joined by more of its kind. The monsters murder Tina, a young girl alone on the beach, and then attack 20 girls at a seaside slumber party. Police turn to scientist Dr. Gavin for help, and, working with his daughter Elaine and her boyfriend Hank Green, Gavin discovers that sodium, an unstable metal that reacts violently to water, is the only substance capable of destroying the monsters. Elaine finds their hiding place and is nearly killed by the invaders when her father and Hank destroy them. *Scientists. Police. Filial relations. Adolescence. Skulls. Monsters. Beaches. Radiation.*

Note: Location scenes filmed in Stamford, Connecticut. Working title: *Invasion of the Zombies.*

HORROR OF THE BLOOD MONSTERS (United States/Philippines)
F6.2208

TAL Productions–Tamaraw Studios. *Dist* Independent-International Pictures. Feb **1970**. Sd; col (Movielab) with tinted b&w seq (Spectrum X). 35mm. 85 min. *MPAA rating* GP.

Prod-Dir Al Adamson. *Exec Prod* Charles McMullen, Zoe Phillips. *Assoc Prod* Ewing Brown. *2d Unit Dir* George Joseph. *Screenplay* Sue McNair. *Dir Photog* William Zsigmond, William Troiano. *Film Ed* Ewing Brown, Peter Perry. *Mus* Mike Velarde. *Orch* Restie Umali. *Sd* Jerry Hansen, Bob Dietz. *Makeup* Jean Hewitt. *Sp Eff* David L. Hewitt. *Eff Ed* Fred Badiyan. *Prod Cons* Samuel M. Sherman.

Cast: John Carradine *(Dr. Rynning)*, Robert Dix *(Colonel Manning)*, Vicki Volante *(Valerie)*, Joey Benson *(Willy)*, Jenifer Bishop *(Lian Malian)*, Bruce Powers *(Brycc)*, Fred Meyers *(Capt. Bob Scott)*, Britt Semand *(Linda)*, Theodore *(narrator)*.

Science fiction melodrama. As an inexplicable wave of vampire killings sweeps over the face of the earth, spaceship XB-13, under the supervision of Dr. Rynning, lands on a planet in an unknown solar system. Although the planet is physically similar to prehistoric Earth, its atmosphere is poisoned by "chromatic radiations" which alter the colors of the spectrum. The planet's inhabitants include giant clawed creatures, bat-like men, and two warring primitive tribes, the Tagani and the Tubatans, the latter being vampiric. By inserting a communicator into the brain of a young tribal girl, Dr. Rynning and his team are able to learn that, years before, samples of deadly blood were transported to Earth to breed new vampires. Dr. Rynning learns that a virus causes vampirism and also discovers that the infection will soon end since the planet is doomed to destruction. After the death of Captain Scott, the expedition refuels with a natural petroleum deposit and leaves the alien planet to return to Earth. *Vampires. Scientists. Spaceship crews. Space creatures. Brain surgery. Prehistory. Imaginary planets. Spaceships. Microorganisms. Radiation.*

Note: Filmed in the Philippines and Hollywood. Working titles: *Creatures of the Prehistoric Planet* and *Horror Creatures of the Prehistoric Planet.* Theodore, the narrator, is a stage name for Theodore Gottlieb.

HORROR OF THE STONE WOMEN *see* **MILL OF THE STONE WOMEN**

HORRORS OF SPIDER ISLAND *see* **IT'S HOT IN PARADISE**

HORRORS OF THE BLACK ZOO *see* **BLACK ZOO**

HORSE
F6.2209
Dist Film-Makers' Cooperative. 28 Aug **1965** [New York opening]. Sd; b&w. 16mm. 105 min. [See note.]

Prod-Dir Andy Warhol. *Writ* Ronald Tavel. *Prod Asst* Gerard Malanga, Buddy Wirtschafter.

Cast: Tosh Carillo *([The Mexican])*, Larry Latrae, Gregory Battcock, Daniel Cassidy, Jr.

Western satire. A man sits on the back of a horse as it eats a bale of hay. The Cisco Kid and the sheriff insult each other. There is a game of strip poker. The characters, who are suggestive of various western personalities, perform operatic movements to the sound of loud opera music. The horse remains unperturbed in the background. Members of the cast change places every now and then. Upon the instructions of a commentator, they pounce on the Mexican among them [The Cisco Kid?], tie him to the horse, beat him, and order him out of town. The assailants return to performing operatic movements. *Mexicans. Sheriffs. Racism. Sexuality. Opera. Poker. Cisco Kid. Horses.*

Note: The frame remains fixed throughout. A 70-min version was later released.

THE HORSE IN THE GRAY FLANNEL SUIT
F6.2210
Walt Disney Productions. *Dist* Buena Vista Distribution Co. 20 Dec **1968** [New York opening; c22 Aug 1968; LP36339]. Sd (RCA); col (Technicolor). 35mm. 113 min. *MPAA rating* G.

Prod Winston Hibler. *Dir* Norman Tokar. *2d Unit Dir* Larry Lansburgh. *Screenplay* Louis Pelletier. *Dir Photog* William Snyder. *Art Dir* Carroll Clark, John B. Mansbridge. *Set Decor* Emile Kuri, Frank R. McKelvy. *Titl* Alan Maley. *Film Ed* Robert Stafford. *Mus* George Bruns. *Orch* Walter Sheets. *Sd Supv* Robert O. Cook. *Sd Mix* Dean Thomas. *Mus Ed* Evelyn Kennedy. *Asst Dir* Christopher Hibler, Bill Poole, Richard Learman. *Unit Prod Mgr* John Bloss. *Cost Dsgn* Bill Thomas. *Cost* Chuck Keehne, Emily Sundby. *Makeup*

Otis Malcolm, Walter Schenck. *Hairstyles* La Rue Matheron, Kay Shea. *Matte Artist* Alan Maley. *Sp Eff* Tim Barr. *Gaffer* Otto Meyer.

Cast: Dean Jones *(Fred Bolton)*, Diane Baker *(Suzie Clemens)*, Lloyd Bochner *(Archer Madison)*, Fred Clark *(Tom Dugan)*, Ellen Janov *(Helen Bolton)*, Morey Amsterdam *(Charlie Blake)*, Kurt Russell *(Ronnie Gardner)*, Lurene Tuttle *(Aunt Martha)*, Alan Hewitt *(Harry Tomes)*, Federico Pinero *(Lieutenant Lorendo)*, Florence MacMichael *(Catherine)*, Joan Marshall *(Mimsey)*, Robin Eccles *(Judy Gardner)*, Adam Williams *(Sergeant Roberts)*, Norman Grabowski *(truck driver)*, Nydia Westman *(lady in elevator)*, Bill Baldwin, Sr. *(announcer)*, Albarado *(Aspercel)*, Sir Winston, Could Be *(stand-ins for Aspercel)*.

Comedy. Source: Eric Hatch, *The Year of the Horse* (New York, 1965). Madison Avenue advertising executive Fred Bolton, a Connecticut widower living beyond his means, is beset by two major problems: first, unless he comes up with a highbrow gimmick to publicize a sour-stomach remedy called Aspercel, his tyrannical boss, Tom Dugan, will fire him; second, his teenaged daughter Helen has run up a $900 bill at Suzie Clemens' riding academy. In the hope of solving both his problems at the same time, Fred gets Dugan to buy a horse, names it Aspercel, and then persuades Suzie to train Helen for all the fashionable horse shows. Helen does begin to win ribbons, but the amount of publicity is below Dugan's expectations. When Helen learns that her father's job is at stake, she falters under pressure and fails to win an important match. Suzie, however, realizes Aspercel's potential when the animal carries Fred over a 7-foot wall and tops that by out-racing a police car. Volunteering to ride Aspercel in the International Horse Show in Washington, Suzie suggests that her ex-fiancé, Archer Madison, be brought in as trainer. Suppressing his jealousy of Archer, Fred reluctantly agrees. As the result, Suzie and Aspercel win the championship, and all ends happily as Fred is rewarded with both a promotion and Suzie's love. *Advertising executives. Widowers. Riding instructors. Horsetrainers. Publicity. Ambition. Adolescence. Jealousy. Riding schools. Horseshows. Patent medicines. New York City—Madison Avenue. Connecticut. Washington (District of Columbia). Horses.*

Note: Location scenes filmed at Disney's Golden Oak Ranch near Newhall, California, and at the International Horse Show in Washington, D. C. Working title: *Year of the Horse.*

THE HORSE WITH THE FLYING TAIL
F6.2211
Walt Disney Productions. *Dist* Buena Vista Distribution Co. **1961** [c22 Dec 1960; LP18714]. Sd (RCA); col (Technicolor). 35mm. 47 min.

Pres by Walt Disney. A Walt Disney Production. *Prod-Dir* Larry Lansburgh. *Screenplay* Janet Lansburgh. *Narr Writ* Bill Bryan. *Photog* Hannes Staudinger, Werner Kurz, Robert Carmet, James Bauden, Sidney Zucker, Larry Lansburgh. *Titl Painting* Jean Bowman. *Film Ed* Warren Adams. *Mus* William Lava. *Orch* Charles Maxwell. *Sd* Glen Glenn Sound. *Mus Ed* Tom Downing.

Cast: Nautical *(himself, a horse)*, George Fenneman *(narrator)*, Dorian Williams *(English commentator)*.

Melodrama. A courageous palomino colt earns the nickname Injun Joe for his food-hunting forays into an Indian village in New Mexico. Broken and trained as a cutting horse at the age of 3, Injun Joe in turn becomes a jumper for an ex-cavalry officer, a fox hunter for a Virginia couple, and the possession of an unscrupulous horsetrainer. However, he is spotted by Bertalan de Nemethy, coach of the United States Equestrian team, and Hugh Wiley, an United States rider, who recognize Injun Joe's potential as a jumper. As a member of the United States team, Injun Joe receives a new name—Nautical—expert training, and the opportunity to compete in Europe. Nautical does well in Paris; places in the finals in Aachen, Germany; scampers in the surf of the Belgian coast; and triumphantly defeats the Spanish contender, Toscanella, for the George V Cup in London. *Equestrians. Horsetrainers. Steeplechasing. New Mexico. Virginia. Belgium. Paris. Aachen. London. Horses.*

HOSPITAL
F6.2212
Osti Films. *Dist* Zipporah Films. **1970**. Sd; b&w. 16mm. 84 min.

Prod-Dir Frederick Wiseman. *Photog* William Brayne. *Asst Photog* David Martin. *Film Ed* Frederick Wiseman, Susan Primm. *Asst Ed* Carter Stanton-Abbott. *Sd Rec* Richard Vorisek. *Prod Asst* Robbin Mason, Margot Anderson.

Documentary. At New York's Metropolitan Hospital, a female physician comforts an elderly man who is embarrassed to describe his symptoms; a diabetic decries her inability to work; a distraught daughter kisses her suffering mother, the victim of a heart attack; an ambulance driver searches for a hospital which will accept his passenger; a middle-class adolescent suffers the effects of mescaline; a Puerto Rican widower, concerned for his children, resists hospitalization; a psychiatrist advises a black homosexual on welfare payments and tries to place the youth in a private room; a nurse, caring for a 2-year-old boy, the victim of a 15-foot fall and the ward of an alcoholic grandmother, considers taking the child home with her; and, in the chapel, a Catholic priest instructs patients to consider God's greatness and man's insignificance. *Physicians. Ambulance drivers. Psychiatrists. Nurses. Children. Priests. Urban* *life. Adolescence. Old age. Heart disease. Psychedelic states. Public welfare. Filial relations. Child welfare. Male homosexuality. Mescaline. Metropolitan Hospital (New York City).*

Note: First shown on NET on 2 Feb 1970.

THE HOSTAGE F6.2213

Heartland Productions. *Dist* Crown International Pictures. 1 Nov **1966** [Des Moines, Iowa, opening]. Sd; col (Technicolor). 35mm. 84 min.

Prod-Dir Russell S. Doughten, Jr. *Screenplay* Robert Laning. *Photog* Ted V. Mikels. *Prod Dsgn* Ray Storey. *Film Ed* Gary Kurtz, Ron Honthaner. *Mus Comp & Cond* Jaime Mendoza-Nava. *Titl Song* Ronald Hanna. *Sung by* Steve Smith, mus. Sd Lee Strosnider, Marvin Walowitz. *Asst Dir* Gary Kurtz. *Prod Mgr* Gary Kurtz. *Script Girl* Bri Murphy. *Wardrobe* Marion Elmquist. *Constr* Mike McCloskey. *Constr Asst & Stuntman* Steve Karkus. *Gaffer* John Murray. *Grip* Tom Ramsey.

Cast: Don O'Kelly *(Bull)*, Dean Stanton *(Eddie)*, John Carradine *(Otis Lovelace)*, Danny Martins *(Davey Cleaves)*, Ron Hagerthy *(Steve Cleaves)*, Jenifer Lea *(Carol Cleaves)*, Ann Doran *(Miss Mabry)*, Raymond Guth *(Sam)*, Nora Marlowe *(Selma)*, Shirley O'Hara *(Mrs. Primus)*, Mike McCloskey *(bartender)*, Dick Spry *(Mr. Thomas)*, Leland Brown *(Glenn)*, Pearl Faessler.

Melodrama. Source: Henry Farrell, *The Hostage* (New York, 1959). Although Steve and Carol Cleaves are moving from the city for the benefit of their 6-year-old son, Davey, the boy is unhappy about leaving the only home he has ever known. After trying ineffectively to share his misery with Otis Lovelace, the town derelict, Davey wanders unnoticed into the moving van, unaware that the two truckdrivers, Bull, a huge, violently emotional man, and Eddie, his terrified, weak-willed partner, are murderers who killed someone the previous night. As a result, Davey finds himself locked in as the truck starts up for his new home. En route Bull and Eddie haul the murdered man into the van and then stop again at a deserted area where they bury the body. Aware now of Davey's presence, the murderers realize they have an eyewitness, whereupon Davey, keenly aware of his danger, flees to the farm house of a kindly couple, Sam and Selma. Bull tells the couple that Davey is his runaway son, and they return the boy to the killer. Meanwhile, Davey's frantic parents have called in the police, unaware that Otis, the one person who could help them, has been killed in an automobile accident. In the midst of the desperate boy-hunt, however, Eddie becomes sympathetic to Davey and, for the first time, finds sufficient courage to stand up to the demented Bull. After a near-fatal ride in the moving van on a rain-slippery highway, Eddie accomplishes his goal by delivering Davey safely to his distraught parents. *Children. Movers. Derelicts. Truckdrivers. Missing persons. Psychopaths. Police. Family life. Murder. Automobile accidents.*

Note: Filmed entirely on location near Des Moines, Iowa.

HOSTILE GUNS F6.2214

A. C. Lyles Productions. *Dist* Paramount Pictures. Dec **1967** [c21 Jun 1967; LP34995]. Sd; col (Technicolor). 35mm (Techniscope). 91 min.

An A. C. Lyles Production. *Prod* A. C. Lyles. *Dir* R. G. Springsteen. *Screenplay* Steve Fisher, Sloan Nibley. *Story* Sloan Nibley, James Edward Grant. *Dir Photog* Lothrop Worth. *Art Dir* Hal Pereira, Al Roelofs. *Set Decor* Robert R. Benton, Budd S. Friend. *Film Ed* John F. Schreyer. *Mus* Jimmie Haskell. *Sd* John Carter, John Wilkinson. *Asst Dir* Ralph Axness. *Prod Mgr* Howard Roessel. *Makeup* Wally Westmore. *Hairstyles* Nellie Manley. *Sp Photog Eff* Paul K. Lerpae. *Proc Photog* Farciot Edouart.

Cast: George Montgomery *(Gid McCool)*, Yvonne De Carlo *(Laura Manon)*, Tab Hunter *(Mike Reno)*, Brian Donlevy *(Marshal Willett)*, John Russell *(Aaron)*, Leo Gordon *(Hank Pleasant)*, Robert Emhardt *(R. C. Crawford)*, Pedro Gonzalez-Gonzalez *(Angel Dominguez)*, James Craig *(Ned Cooper)*, Richard Arlen *(Sheriff Travis)*, Emile Meyer *(Uncle Joe)*, Donald Barry *(Johnson)*, Fuzzy Knight *(Buck)*, William Fawcett *(Jensen)*, Joe Brown *(Bunco)*, Reg Parton *(Chig)*, Read Morgan *(Tubby)*, Eric Cody *(Alfie)*, Roy Jenson, Jack Catron.

Western melodrama. In the Texas of 1860, U. S. Marshal Gideon McCool is given the task of transporting four prisoners in a prison wagon across the Texas badlands to the Huntsville state penitentiary. The quartet consists of Hank Pleasant, a child-killer sentenced to hang; R. C. Crawford, an embezzling railroad commissioner; Angel Dominguez, a Mexican goat thief eager to learn a trade in prison; and Laura Manon, a dancehall entertainer who shot her unfaithful lover. With hot-tempered Mike Reno riding as his newly appointed deputy, McCool sets out on the 4-day trek, unaware that Pleasant's brother Aaron and his cousin Ned are trailing close behind waiting for the right moment to attack. While the group is camped for the night, Laura, who has kept her past romance with McCool a secret, attempts to entice Mike and pleads with him to help her escape. Their conversation is overheard by McCool, who now has no choice but to shackle Mike in the wagon with the prisoners. Then Pleasant's two relatives, plus four more of his kinfolk, attack. Realizing that McCool hasn't a chance alone, Laura confesses to Mike that she made love to him only in the hope of gaining her freedom and that she really loves McCool. Upon hearing the truth, Mike persuades McCool to release him; and together the two men shoot down their six opponents and then continue safely on the last lap of their journey. *United States marshals. Thieves. Dancehall girls. Convicts. Mexicans. Politicians. Embezzlement. Seduction. Texas. Texas State Penitentiary (Huntsville).*

Note: Location scenes filmed in the Mojave Desert, California.

THE HOT BED F6.2215

Trans American Pictures. *Dist* Crescent International Pictures, Sack Amusement Enterprises. 3 Sep **1965** [Champaign, Illinois, showing]. Sd; b&w. 35mm. 84 min. [Cut to 75 min.]

Prod Dale Berry. *Exec Prod* Carlos Martinez. *Dir* Harry Epstein. *Mus* Emilio Luna and His Orchestra, Los Pampas Trio, The Dead Beats, The Rocking R's.

Cast: Josette *(Fanny Bangs)*, Stephen Pappas *(Eddie Stud)*, DeAnna James *(Jo Ann Dykes)*, George Miden.

Melodrama. Exotic dancer Fanny Bangs is persuaded by Eddie Stud to smuggle $1 million worth of drugs into the country. The seller is also an informer, however, and alerts the border patrol. Stud is elusive, changing his apartment weekly and holding orgies in each of them. Fanny becomes involved in a triangle with Stud and Jo Ann Dykes. The fun ends when they are all arrested by the police. *Exotic dancers. Informers. Smuggling. Bisexuality. Narcotics. Orgies.*

Note: Location scenes filmed in Dallas, Houston, and Mexico City.

HOT BLOODED GALS see SOCK IT TO ME BABY

HOT BLOODED WOMAN F6.2216

Dist Crescent International Pictures. 1 Oct **1965**. Sd; b&w. 35mm. [Feature length assumed.]

Prod Whit Boyd. *Dir* Dale Berry. *Song:* "Hot Blooded Woman" Tony Harrison Trio.

Cast: Beverly Oliver, Gregg Pappas, Shirley Boyd, Bill Thurman, Bob Brown, Dale Berry.

Melodrama. Driven by a compulsion to undress in front of strange men, a young married woman falls victim to a rapist. Her husband rescues her and takes her to see a psychiatrist. She relates the history of her strange need and recalls her husband's sexual escapades. The doctor places her in a sanitarium, but she escapes, unable to bear being confined. Pursued by the police, she meets an untimely death. *Psychiatrists. Rape. Marriage. Exhibitionism. Sanitariums.*

HOT BOARDING HOUSE F6.2217

GARVA Productions. *Dist* Inter-Continental Films Distributors. Jun **1970** [periodical notice]. Sd; b&w. 35mm. [Feature film, length unknown.]

Dir Gene Shamblin. *Photog* Edward I. Miller.

Cast: Suzanne Slade, Linda Peterson, Joe Mayo, Gina Quintella, Pauline Kenny.

Drama. An emotionally troubled man suffers from nightmares in which his sexual encounters culminate in murder. A friend refers him to a "boardinghouse," where he rids himself of his nightmares by making love to one of the prostitutes. Having found peace of mind, he proposes marriage to the prostitute, and she accepts. [Included are scenes of lovemaking between a patron and two bisexual women, a bathtub party, and the seduction of a deafmute.] *Prostitutes. Deafmutes. Bisexuality. Troilism. Whorehouses. Dreams.*

HOT ENOUGH FOR JUNE see AGENT 8 3/4

HOT EROTIC DREAMS F6.2218

Lecamto Productions. *Dist* Cosmos Films. ca **1967**. Sd; b&w. 35mm. 65 min.

Prod Paul Leonardi, Phil Todaro. *Dir* Mort Shuman, photog. *Script* Nicki. *Dir Photog* Mort Shuman, photog, Douglas Scanio. *Sets* Bob Davis. *Ed* Kemper Peacock. *Mus* Al Cotton. *Script Girl* Jan Jolton.

Cast: Ann Larsen, Fred Braceman, Jeff Trainer, Tom Fredricks, Mary Olson, Linda Holmes, Bill Gilman, Laura Pinter, Carol Hertz, Richard Smith, actor.

Drama. A young model wanders into a Greenwich Village bookstore and buys a racy paperback novel. That night, she reads herself to sleep. In her dreams the book comes to life, and she finds that she has overcome her sexual inhibitions. First she is a tortured captive of Satan, next she makes love with a handsome Frenchman, and finally she engages in a lesbian love affair. The next morning, she awakens to join the bookstore owner in an erotic adventure. *Models. French. Storekeepers. Sadomasochism. Lesbianism. Bookshops. New York City—Greenwich Village. The Devil. Dreams.*

HOT FRUSTRATIONS see FRUSTRATIONS

HOT GIRLS FOR MEN ONLY (Great Britain) F6.2219

Border Films. *Dist* Paul Mart Productions, Manson Distributing Corp. Jan **1968**. Sd; col (Eastmancolor). 35mm. 61 min.

Pres by Pete Walker. *Prod-Dir-Screenplay* Pete Walker. *Dir Photog* Gerry Lewis. *1st Camera Op* Nick Ardizzoni. *Asst Camera Op* Don McMurray. *Film Ed* Sarah Ziccars, Peter Austen-Hunt. *Mus Cond & Comp* Harry South. *Sd Dir* Dal Emmanuel. *Asst Sd Dir* Byron Garvey Harris. *Mus Ed* Peter Austen-Hunt. *Prod Mgr* John Regan. *Asst to the Prod* Charles J. Nicholl. *Cost* Gerald McCann. *Makeup* Sydney Turner.

Cast: David Kernan (*Reggie Collins* [*Freddie Horne, Frederick Hall*]), Andrea Allen (*Cynthia* [*Rosalie*]), Derek Aylward (*Ronald Graham* [*Miles Fanthorpe*]), Tom Gill (*father*), Mai Bacon (*mother*), John Cazabon (*Lamphrey Gussett*), Monika Dietrich (*Janet*), Jill Field (*Gunnela*), Glyn Warship (*Rudolph*), Neville Whiting (*Claude*), Joan Ingram (*Esther*), Gladys Dawson (*Mrs. Whitely*), Apple Brook (*receptionist*).

Comedy-drama. Fired from his job as editor and chief writer on a sex magazine, Reggie Collins is interviewed by a religious publishing house at the instigation of his possessive fiancée, Cynthia. Before he can refuse the job offer, he is chauffeured by a seductive blonde to publisher Ronald Graham's country estate. There he learns that the religious magazine operation is a front for the erotic publication *For Men Only*. Residing at the estate are 40 nude models from around the world. Two motorcycle thugs hired by *Sin*, a competitive magazine, arrive to kidnap Graham's models. The hoodlums abduct 10 nude women at work on a magazine layout, molest them, and lock them in the back of a truck. Meanwhile, Cynthia arrives at the estate and, in her anger, falls into the swimming pool. Reggie finds her naked, and after an argument, the two are reconciled. On the way back to the city, the truck carrying the models breaks down, and the women escape. They chase their captors through the woods, beat them with whips, and order them about as if they were beasts of burden. Reggie and Graham, trailing the abductors' truck, meet headlong with the group of nude women at an elegant restaurant in the city. [In the British version, Reggie, at Cynthia's insistence, begins work on a men's physical culture magazine.] *Hoodlums. Editors. Publishers. Models. Pornography. Religion. Jealousy. Business competition. Nudity. Abduction. Revenge. Magazines (periodicals).*

Note: Released in Great Britain in 1967 as *I Like Birds*; running time: 43 min. Footage added for American release. Also known as *Girls for Men Only* and *For Men Only*.

HOT HANDS OF LOVE F6.2220

Dist Rossmore Film Distributors. 1 Jun **1966** [Fresno, California, showing]. Sd; b&w. 35mm. 77 min.

Pres by Harry H. Novak.

Melodrama. A gang of crazed killers terrorizes New York. These sadists, who strike only at pretty women, rob, torture, and murder their victims. Finally, the vengeful boyfriend of one of the women is able to track down the gang, and they are wiped out. *Gangs. Psychopaths. Murder. Sadism. Revenge. Torture. Robbery. New York City.*

HOT HOLLOWS *see* **PASSION IN HOT HOLLOWS**

HOT HORSE (Reissue) F6.2221

Universal–International. 24 Jul **1963** [New York opening]. Sd; b&w. 35mm (CinemaScope). 82 min.

Note: Originally released as *Once Upon a Horse* in 1958 at 85 min; c30 Jul 1958; LP12855.

HOT HOURS (France) F6.2222

K. L. F. Productions. *Dist* Raleigh Films, Joseph Brenner Associates. 11 Sep **1963** [New York State license; Champaign, Illinois, showing; 6 Nov 1964]. Sd; b&w. 35mm. 69-98 min.

Prod Lola Kohn. *Dir-Adapt* Louis Félix. *Screenplay* Gilles Siry. *Photog* Arthur Raimondo. *Film Ed* Linette Nicolas. *Mus Score* Daniel White.

Cast: Liliane Brousse (*Olivia*), Françoise Deldick (*Lise*), Claude Sainlouis (*Bruno*), Michèle Philippe (*Clémence*), Pierre Richard (*Manuel*), Liliane Sorval (*Claire* [*Aunt Irma*]), Pierre Mirat, Michel Vocoret.

Drama. Left standing at the altar, Olivia convinces her younger sister Lise that they should leave their remote village in the South of France where there are no eligible bachelors, and set out for new horizons. They go to stay with their Aunt Irma, who runs a boarding house at a small crossroad. Their beauty and exuberance causes a great stir, and Aunt Irma warns the sisters of her boarder Bruno, a devoted womanizer. Bruno quarrels with his brother and sister-in-law and quits the apartment at Aunt Irma's to be closer to his mistress, Clémence. Lise, infatuated with Bruno, tries to lure him away from Clémence, while Olivia carries on an intrigue with a married man. Pursued by Clémence's angry husband, Bruno takes refuge in Lise's room, but her hopes are disappointed when Bruno declares his love for her older sister, and he and Olivia make love. *Sisters. Mistresses. Aunts. Philanderers. Bachelors. Smalltown life. Infidelity. Marriage. Jealousy. Adolescence. Sexuality.*

Boardinghouses.

Note: Released in France in 1959 as *Heures chaudes*; running time: 90 min.

THE HOT HOUSE F6.2223

Westfilm. *Dist* Distribpix, Inc. ca **1970**. Sd; col. 35mm. 63 min.

Exec Prod H. Oscar Ward. *Dir-Writ* Al West. *Camera* Lonnie Martin. *Asst Camera* Joe Sayer. *Film Ed* Ralph Wayne. *Mus* Filmways. *Prod Asst* Luc Trudeau.

Cast: Gwen Cannon, Queen Zorr, Misty Myers, Jenny Masters, Mort Humphry, Derek Richards.

Melodrama. Ellen Bates travels from a small town in Ohio to meet her sister Sally in New York City and moves in temporarily with her and her lover Mike Davis, a free-lance writer. One night Ellen is awakened by moans of ecstasy, and she stimulates herself while watching the intense lovemaking in Mike and Sally's bedroom. The next evening, the three return home with Nora, a lesbian who, with the aid of some marijuana and at the urging of Mike and Sally, seduces Ellen. Ellen later finds herself alone in the house with Mike, and provocatively teases him, finally yielding to his brutal assault and openly declaring her love for him. When Sally returns with Dick, an old friend, the four begin to drink and take drugs. Dick makes a pass at Ellen; Mike consents to his seducing Ellen, and the young woman throws off all restraint. The aftermath of this sordid orgy finds Ellen hurt, harshly disillusioned, and contemplating suicide. *Innocents. Authors. Mistresses. Autoeroticism. Voyeurism. Lesbianism. Orgies. Drunkenness. Marijuana. New York City.*

HOT IN PARADISE *see* **IT'S HOT IN PARADISE**

HOT KISS F6.2224

Kirt Films International. *Dist* Distribpix, Inc. **1969**. Sd; col. 35mm. 62 min.

Dir Tommy Goetz. *Writ* Ron Rheego. *Asst Camera* Jack Ried. *Asst Ed* Eric Oner. *Mus* Blairs Symphony Orchestra. *Sd* Larry Parks, sd. *Rec* Fred Turner. *Asst Dir* Sam Parks. *Prod Asst* Mary Blanch. *Tech Cons* Marvin Stikes.

Crime melodrama. A small-time antique dealer's romance with a woman goes sour, and he finds himself ejected from her apartment holding a curious statuette she has given him. He puts the sculpture on display in his shop, and a strange force connected with it leads to a bizarre sequence of events: A beautiful young woman enters the shop and declares that she must own the statuette; she buys it and then is murdered after she succumbs to the dealer's sexual advances. This sex crime occurs several times with other customers until the dealer is finally caught after participating in an orgy with his former mistress and her husband. He reveals his psychotic tendency to them, and they call the police. *Antique dealers. Psychopaths. Murder. Sadism. Seduction. Orgies. Magic. Sculptures.*

HOT LEAD *see* **A TASTE OF HOT LEAD**

HOT LINE F6.2225

Kirt Films International. *Dist* Distribpix, Inc. 25 Jun **1970** [San Francisco showing]. Sd; col. 35mm. 62 min.

Dir Tommy Goetz. *Writ* Ron Rheego. *Asst Camera* Jack Ried. *Asst Ed* Eric Oner. *Mus* Blairs Symphony Orchestra. *Sd* Larry Parks, sd. *Rec* Fred Turner. *Asst Dir* Sam Parks. *Prod Asst* Mary Blanch. *Tech Cons* Marvin Stikes.

Cast: Roger Willock, Steve Mason, George Blau, Lois Lane, Rita Joyce, Mary Aster.

Drama. A typical American husband enjoys the company of both wife and mistress. He begins to suspect his mistress of two-timing him, but when he discovers that her other lover is a woman he is only slightly perturbed; he becomes irate, however, when he learns that the other woman is his wife. When he confronts them with their infidelity, the two women overcome him, tie him to a bed, and make love while lying on him. *Mistresses. Marriage. Infidelity. Lesbianism. Sadism.*

THE HOT LINE *see* **THE DAY THE HOT LINE GOT HOT**

HOT LIPS FOR HOT HEADS F6.2226

Mitam Productions. 8 Jul **1970** [Champaign, Illinois, showing]. Sd; col (Eastman Color). 35mm. 74 min.

Melodrama. A group of suburban housewives decide to relieve their boredom by pursuing extramarital sexual adventures. They begin by casually seducing unsuspecting repairmen, but they become organized after one of the women, Rita, seduces a bartender, Joe. Joe learns that Rita's friends have similar interests, and he assumes the group's direction, allowing the women to use the back room of the bar. The organization expands, and Joe convinces Rita to give an initiation party at the bar. Unbeknownst to the housewives, Joe has been catering to voyeurs, charging them to watch the group's activities through peepholes. Rita's sister-in-law, Ann, one of the group's recruits, is married to a policeman who has been staking out the bar for some time. On the night of the party, the police conduct a raid, and Ann's husband looks through a peephole just as Ann is initiated. He goes berserk with rage and murders Joe.

[Contains scenes of lesbianism.] *Bartenders. Police. Housewives. Suburbanites. Sisters-in-law. Repairmen. Infidelity. Seduction. Voyeurism. Murder. Lesbianism. Group sex. Sex clubs. Bars.*

HOT MILLIONS (Great Britain)   **F6.2227**

Metro-Goldwyn-Mayer, Inc.-Milberg Productions. *Dist* Metro-Goldwyn-Mayer, Inc. 19 Sep **1968** [New York opening; c16 Aug 1968; LP36041]. Sd; col (Metrocolor). 35mm. 105 min. [Copyright length: 107 min.]

A Mildred Freed Alberg Production. *Prod* Mildred Freed Alberg. *Dir* Eric Till. *Screenplay* Ira Wallach, Peter Ustinov. *Dir Photog* Ken Higgins. *Camera Op* Peter Allwork. *Art Dir* Bill Andrews. *Film Ed* Richard Marden. *Mus* Laurie Johnson. *Song:* "This Time" Laurie Johnson, Don Black. *Sung by* Lulu. *Rec Supv* A. W. Watkins. *Sd Rec* Gerry Turner. *Dub Mix* J. B. Smith. *Sd Ed* Allan Sones. *Asst Dir* Ted Sturgis. *Prod Mgr* Douglas Twiddy. *Cont* Joy Mercer. *Maggie Smith's Cost Dsgn by* Germinal Rangel.

Cast: Peter Ustinov *(Marcus Pendleton)*, Maggie Smith *(Patty Terwilliger)*, Karl Malden *(Carlton J. Klemper)*, Bob Newhart *(Willard C. Gnatpole)*, Robert Morley *(Caesar Smith)*, Cesar Romero *(customs inspector)*, Melinda May *(nurse)*, Ann Lancaster *(landlady)*, Frank Tragear *(bus inspector)*, Julie May *(1st charwoman)*, Margaret Courtenay *(Mrs. Hubbard)*, Elizabeth Counsell *(Miss Glyn)*, Patsy Crowther *(2d charwoman)*, Carlos Douglas *(barber)*, Lynda Baron *(Louise)*, Billy Milton *(agent)*, Peter Jones *(prison governor)*, David Bedard *(co-pilot)*, Elizabeth Hughes *(air hostess)*, Anne De Vigier *(secretary/receptionist)*, Sally Faulkner *(stewardess on Rio plane)*, Paul Farrell *(Larry)*, Wilfred Carter *(theater manager)*, Geoffrey Frederick *(customs man)*, Betty Duncan *(nun)*, Frank Singuineau *(customs man in Rio)*, Raymond Huntley *(Bayswater)*, William Mervyn *(Sir Charles Wilson)*, Kynaston Reeves *(Quayle)*, Bob Todd, British *(commissionaire)*, Anthony Sharp *(Hollis)*, Paul Dawkins *(Pritchard)*, Hugo De Vernier *(French bank official)*, Jimmy Thompson *(salesman)*, Harold Holness *(Pygny)*, William Burleigh *(page boy)*, Victor Platt *(barman)*, Penelope Jago *(ticket girl)*.

Crime comedy. Released from prison, Marcus Pendleton, an embezzler whose crime was discovered by a computer, decides to become a computer expert. He then befriends Caesar Smith, one of Britain's foremost computer authorities, and persuades him to leave the country. Equipped with Smith's identity, Pendleton is hired by Ta-Can-Co., an industrial conglomerate headed by Carlton J. Klemper; assisted by a charwoman, he programs the corporation's computer to pay large monthly checks to three nonexistent companies. Pendleton then makes secret trips to Paris, Rome, and Frankfurt to collect and cash the checks. Meanwhile, he has married his secretary, Patty Terwilliger. When Pendleton learns that he is going to become a father, he leaves Ta-Can-Co. and flees with Patty to Rio de Janeiro. Bu Klemper and his computer overseer, Willard C. Gnatpole, discover the fraud and follow the swindlers to Rio. Fortunately for Pendleton, Patty has invested some of the money and made a fortune in the stock market. After paying back the stolen money, the couple still have her funds, and Pendleton is free to fulfill his ambition of becoming an orchestra conductor—in whose orchestra Patty plays the flute. *Ex-convicts. Computer programmers. Industrialists. Swindlers. Charwomen. Secretaries. Orchestra conductors. Flutists. Embezzlement. Impersonation. Fraud. Marriage. Pregnancy. Computers. Stock market. Paris. Rome. Frankfurt am Main. Rio de Janeiro.*

Note: Opened in London in Oct 1968.

HOT MONEY GIRL (Great Britain/West Germany)   **F6.2228**

Beaconsfield Films-Sydney Box Associates-Kurt Ulrich Film-Orbit Productions. *Dist* United Producers Releasing Organization. caOct **1962**. Sd; b&w. 35mm. 81 min.

Prod John Nasht, Patrick Filmer-Sankey. *Dir* Alvin Rakoff. *Screenplay* Jack Andrews. *Story* Jeffrey Dell. *Photog* Wilkie Cooper. *Camera Op* Dudley Lovell. *Focus* Tommie Fletcher. *2d Unit Focus* R. Gibbings. *Art Dir* George Provis. *Asst Art Dir* Pamela Provis. *Film Ed* Jim Connock. *Mus* Philip Martell. *Mus from Themes by* Jeff Davis. *Adtl Mus* Don Banks. *Sd Ed* Leslie Hodgson. *Sd Rec* Syd Wiles, Fred Turtle. *Sd Camera Op* David Hill. *Asst Dir* Jimmy Komisarjevsky. *Prod Mgr* Charles Leeds. *Cont* Eve Willson. *Wardrobe Master* Jim Dunlevy. *Wardrobe Mistress* Barbara Gillett. *Makeup* George Partleton. *Hairdresser* Hilda Fox. *Prop Buyer* Frederick Hasler. *Props* Ray Rawei. *Grips* John Kirsop, John Connolly.

Cast: Willy Witte *(General von Hartmann)*, Eddie Constantine *(Larry Brennan)*, Dawn Addams *(Hedi von Hartmann)*, Gaylord Cavallaro *(Mike Jones)*, Marius Goring *(Rudi Siebert)*, Nadine Tallier *(Zizi)*, Walter Gotell *(1st inspector of Hamburg police)*, Christopher Lee *(Jaeger)*, Hubert Mittendorf *(Schneider)*, Derek Sydney *(barman)*, Penelope Horner *(bar girl)*, Tsai Chin, Diane Potter *(bar girls in fight)*, Tom Bowman *(tough)*, Steve Plytas *(station sergeant)*, Anna Turner *(maid at Billie's)*, Georgina Cookson *(Billie)*, Hutch *(piano player at Billie's)*, Susan Travers *(girl at Billie's)*, Marie Devereux *(girl with the mink)*, Thomas Gallagher *(truck driver)*, Clive Dunn *(cemetery keeper)*, Stella Bonheur *(Sister Angelica)*, Margaret Boyd *(Sister Catherine)*,

Sheldon Lawrence *(patrolling policeman)*, Egon Mohr *(2d inspector of Hamburg police)*, Walter Buhler *(uniformed policeman)*.

Melodrama. On the point of being arrested by the Gestapo, Nazi General von Hartmann, secretly working for the German resistance, asks American O.S.S. man Larry Brennan to hide his priceless family jewels at a convent in the Czechoslovakian town of Pilsen. Von Hartmann sends his daughter, Hedi, to guide Brennan to Pilsen. Unable to avoid capture any longer, the general commits suicide. After the war, Larry, now a wireless operator, finds himself in Germany again when his ship docks in Hamburg. Rudi Siebert, General von Hartmann's wartime aide, persuades Larry to undertake the recovery of the gems, now behind the Iron Curtain. Hedi has become a prostitute; she believes that Larry stole the jewels. Larry and Siebert persuade her to join them on the mission. They reach Pilsen using false passports and a stolen auto transport, but they discover that the convent has been converted into a police barracks. They break into the barracks at night, recover the strongbox, and return to West Germany. Larry and Hedi fall in love; later, the two discover that they have been doublecrossed by Siebert, who is in league with Hedi's roommate, Zizi, to steal the jewels. Siebert is murdered by Zizi and her accomplices, and Larry and Hedi are charged with the crime. Zizi attempts to make a getaway aboard the Munich Express, but Larry leaps aboard the moving train to recover the jewels. The train stops on a drawbridge, and as Larry is on the point of retrieving the strongbox, the jewels slip into the river below. Zizi and her associates are brought to justice, and Larry and Hedi find consolation in their love. *Spies. Nazis. Prostitutes. Radiomen. Americans in foreign countries. Suicide. Theft. Murder. Perfidy. Resistance (political). Jewels. Ships. Trains. World War II. Hamburg. Pilsen. United States—Office of Strategic Services. Chases.*

Note: Released in West Germany in 1959 as *Rhapsodie in Blei* and in Great Britain in 1959 as *The Treasure of San Teresa*. British working title: *Long Distance*. Apparently filmed in West Germany. One U. S. source credits the film as "An Orbit Production."

THE HOT MONTH OF AUGUST (Greece)   **F6.2229**

Danfilm. *Dist* J. E. R. Pictures. **1969**. Sd; b&w (Movielab). 35mm. 79 min.

A Viktoria-Kapsaskis Production. *Prod-Dir-Writ* Sokrates Kapsaskis. *Dir Photog* Demetris Papakonstantis. *Film Ed* Emil Habib. *Mus* Stavros Xarhakos.

Cast: Petros Fissoun, Betty Arvaniti, Yannis Fertis, Vania Aksar.

Melodrama. En route from Athens to the island of Throxsas, Jason Philippi [Philippou], although attracted to Hope Linghens, is seduced by Alexis, the unhappy wife of wealthy industrialist Yarkos [Phokas]. Arriving on Throxsas, Al Maharis [Makris], a private detective hired by Yarkos to spy on his wife, informs Yarkos of her infidelity. Maharis and Alexis, secret lovers, plot Yarkos' murder. Yarkos, overhearing their plans, kills Alexis and wounds Maharis, who collapses in the boat where he has hidden jewels stolen from Yarkos. Yarkos frames Jason, but Hope, now in love with Jason, provides him with an alibi. Maharis, discovered the following day, confesses the truth. Yarkos is apprehended, and Jason leaves prison and joins Hope. *Industrialists. Detectives. Seduction. Infidelity. Murder. Theft. Frameup. Confession (law). Islands. Jewels. Athens.*

Note: Released in Greece in 1966 as *Ho zestos mēnas Augoustos;* running time: 97 min.

HOT NIGHTS ON THE CAMPUS   **F6.2230**

Chat Productions-Tony Orlando Productions-C. Davis Smith. *Dist* CIP Ltd. 13 Jul **1966** [Champaign, Illinois, showing]. Sd; b&w. 35mm. 67 min.

A Tony Orlando Production. *Prod-Dir* Tony Orlando. *Narr* Joan Mckay, Aaron Banks. *Sd* Mor-Sound. *Prod Mgr* Gil Novak.

Cast: Gigi Darlene, Sean Martin, Alpha Centuri, Robert Pierce, Lisa Vohn, Dale Call, Justine May, Robert Parker, Judy Reinhardt, Sam Conrad, Joan Peters, Darlene Bennett, Stan Stunning, Hugh Teet, Sandee Norman.

Melodrama. Sally, an innocent college student, becomes involved with an older man. Her newly awakened sexuality leads her to join a campus sex club where she discovers an underground world of sensual abandon. Sally also becomes involved in a lesbian relationship with her roommate while at the same time keeping up her other sexual activities. When she accidentally becomes pregnant, the prospect of an abortion drives her to attempt suicide. She is saved, however, by Gig, who forgives her past and offers her true love. *Students. College life. Sexual initiation. Group sex. Lesbianism. Pregnancy. Abortion. Suicide. Sex clubs.*

Note: Also known as *Nights on the Campus.*

HOT ON SIN ISLAND *see* **IT'S HOT ON SIN ISLAND**

THE HOT PEARL SNATCH   **F6.2231**

Dist Astro Film Co., New Era Productions. ca **1966**. Sd; col (Eastman Color). 35mm. 64 min.

Cast: Pauly Dash, Jody Baby, Loralie Lee.

Melodrama. During Mardi Gras in the Virgin Islands, an old seaman in a waterfront bar attempts to pay for his drinks with pearls. The wary bartender will only accept cash, and another patron pays for the drinks. While a stripper entertains, the patron and the drunken seaman converse, and the patron learns that the old man has a map marking the most valuable pearl oyster bed in the Caribbean. The old man then tells the patron the story of the pearls: *On an island in the Caribbean, the pearls are stolen from a native tribe. The witches of the tribe place a voodoo hex on the pearls. The sailor barely escapes from the island.* All those who hear the sailor's tale become dominated by greed. The patron steals the map, and women offer their bodies in return for a share of the treasure. *Sailors. Witches. Voodoo. Greed. Theft. Prostitution. Pearls. Mardi Gras. Virgin Islands. Caribbean. Documentation.*

Note: Also known as *Hot Pearl* and *The Perilous Pearls of Pauline.*

HOT ROD ACTION   F6.2232

Robert E. Petersen Productions. *Dist* Cinerama Releasing Corp. 1 May **1969** [Charlotte, North Carolina, opening]. Sd; col (Eastmancolor). 35mm. 76 min. *MPAA rating G.*

A Robert E. Petersen Production. *Prod-Dir-Writ* Gene McCabe. *Exec Prod* Robert L. Dellinger. *Photog* Vilis Lapenieks, Mario Tosi, William Zsigmond. *Film Ed* Anthony M. Lanza. *Mus Comp & Cond* Mike Curb. *Sd Re-rec* Glen Glenn Sound. *Sd Eff* Doug Young. *Tech Adv* Dick Wells, Bob Carleton. *Coöp* Editors of Hot Rod Magazine. *Tech Supv* Ray Brock.

Cast: Keith Jackson (*narrator*), Craig Breedlove, Art Arfons (*themselves*).

Documentary. Investigating every aspect of motor racing, including car and speedboat contests, the film chronicles the Indianapolis 500, Motor Trend 500, Daytona 500, Southern 500, Winternational Drags, Indianapolis National Drags, and the World Championship Drags. Among the celebrated competitors are champions Craig Breedlove and Art Arfons. *Stock car drivers. Automobile racing. Boat racing. Racetracks. Motor Trend 500. Daytona 500. Southern 500. Winternational Drags. Indianapolis National Drags. World Championship Drags. Indianapolis 500.*

HOT ROD HULLABALOO   F6.2233

Silvercliff Pictures. *Dist* Allied Artists. 30 Nov **1966** [Albuquerque, New Mexico, opening]. Sd; b&w. 35mm. 81 min.

Prod Martin L. Low, William T. Naud. *Dir* William T. Naud. *Story & Screenplay* Stanley Schneider. *Photog* Thomas E. Spalding. *Film Ed* Frank Toth. *Mus Comp & Dir* Elliot Lawrence.

Cast: John Arnold, actor, Arlen Dean Snyder, Kendra Kerr, Ron Cummins, Val Bisoglio, Marsha Mason, William Hunter, actor, Gene Bua, Robert Paget.

Action melodrama. Despite the efforts of a citizens' group to outlaw "hot rod" and "chicken" races, a group of teenagers is preparing for the annual demolition derby. Although he knows the event can be dangerous, a young student decides to enter the race in order to win money for his college education. His chief competitor is a ruthless young driver who has already caused a death during one of the derbies. Learning the student has entered the race, the bully decides to stop him by whatever means necessary. At the preliminaries, the student's friend learns his rival is carrying a gun. Although the friend is run down at an amusement park, he gets word of the gun to the student's girl friend, and a pencil is stuffed into the gun barrel just as the race begins. Attempting to use the weapon, the rival is killed. The student goes on to win the race and the prize money. *Students. Bullies. Automobile racing. Adolescence. Demolition derbies. Guns. Amusement parks.*

Note: Location scenes filmed in and around Washington, D. C.

HOT RODS TO HELL   F6.2234

Four Leaf Productions. *Dist* Metro-Goldwyn-Mayer, Inc. ca1 Feb **1967** [Los Angeles opening; c31 Dec 1966; LP34025]. Sd (Westrex); col (Metrocolor). 35mm. 92 min. [Copyright length: 100 min.]

Prod Sam Katzman. *Dir* John Brahm. *2d Unit Dir* James Havens. *Screenplay* Robert E. Kent. *Dir Photog* Lloyd Ahern. *Art Dir* George W. Davis, Merrill Pye. *Set Decor* Henry Grace, Keogh Gleason. *Film Ed* Ben Lewis. *Mus Score & Cond* Fred Karger. *Songs* Fred Karger, Sid Wayne, Ben Weisman. *Perf by* Mickey Rooney Jr. and His Combo. *Rec Supv* Franklin Milton. *Asst Dir* Maurice Vaccarino. *Unit Prod Mgr* Robert Stone. *Asst to the Prod* Jerome F. Katzman. *Makeup* William Tuttle. *Hairstyles* Sydney Guilaroff. *Sp Visual Eff* J. McMillan Johnson, Carroll L. Shepphird.

Cast: Dana Andrews (*Tom Phillips*), Jeanne Crain (*Peg Phillips*), Mimsy Farmer (*Gloria*), Laurie Mock (*Tina Phillips*), Paul Bertoya (*Duke*), Gene Kirkwood (*Ernie*), Tim Stafford (*Jamie Phillips*), George Ives (*Lank Dailey*), Hortense Petra (*wife at picnic*), William Mims (*man at picnic*), Paul Genge (*policeman*), Peter Oliphant (*little boy*), Harry Hickox (*Bill Phillips*), Charles P. Thompson (*Charley*), Jim Hennagan (*youth*), Mickey Rooney, Jr. (*combo leader*).

Melodrama. Source: Alex Gaby, "Fifty-Two Miles to Terror," in *Saturday Evening Post* (14 Jan 1956). Because a serious automobile accident has left him with a back injury, Tom Phillips is advised by his doctor to move to a warm climate. After buying a combination motel-restaurant in the California desert, he sets out for his new home with his wife, Peg, his daughter, Tina, and his small son, Jamie. Since Tom has not yet regained his confidence behind a wheel, Peg drives the family car. As they near their destination, they are passed by three thrill-seeking teenagers—Duke, Ernie and Gloria—who toss a beer can into the Phillips' sedan. Sometime later, Tom encounters one of the boys at a filling station and threatens him with police action. As a result, the young toughs alert their friends and a number of youths soon converge on the Phillips for the remainder of their trip. Once they have reached their destination, they learn that the former owner of the motel allowed the place to be used for teenage drinking orgies. After Duke has tried to seduce Tina, Tom calls off the motel deal and heads for his brother's home, 52 miles away. They are pursued by Duke and Ernie, who are determined to prevent Tom from contacting the police. But the constant hounding eventually proves too much for Tom, and he decides to hold his ground. He parks his car, leaves the headlights on, and causes Duke's souped-up sports car to crash. Suppressing the urge to kill the two hoodlums, Tom offers them the choice of being turned over to the authorities or changing their ways. When a police car pulls up, Duke and Ernie promise to behave like sensible adults in the future. And Tom—his self-confidence restored—goes back to the motel to give his business venture another try. *Hoodlums. Police. Self-confidence. Adolescence. Motels. Deserts. Automobile accidents. California.*

Note: Location scenes filmed in Los Angeles. Formerly titled *52 Miles to Terror,* the film was originally intended to be a feature film for ABC-TV.

HOT SEX TRAMP *see* **THE MASTER BEATER**

HOT SKIN AND COLD CASH   F6.2235

Barry Mahon Productions. *Dist* Sack Amusement Enterprises. **1965** [intended release; New York showing: 27 Mar 1968]. Sd; b&w. 35mm. 63 min.

Pres by Alfred N. Sack. A Barry Mahon Production. *Prod-Dir-Screenplay* Barry Mahon. *Story* Marcus Damien. *Photog* Joe Mangine. *Ed* Philip Fitzpatrick. *Sd* Magno Sound.

Cast: Victoria Astor, Carol Davis (*Shelly [see note]*), John Connant (*Mr. Stone*), Michael Garlock (*weirdo*), Philip Fitzpatrick (*college boy*), Al Joseph (*priest*), Doug Parrish (*loudmouth*), Charles Howard.

Drama. While her husband serves a prison term, Shelly is left alone to support her baby. She launches herself as a prostitute and meets a wide variety of clients. One old man is consoled by the thought that all is for the benefit of the baby crying in the room next door. In the course of her business, Shelly encounters an impotent braggart and a beatnik who laps wine as it is poured over her breast. She provides college students with their first sexual experiences, meets her own lawyer in the course of business, and even encounters a priest. Shelly joins up with a girl friend in order to satisfy customers who enjoy group sex. Willing to satisfy any desire at a price, she discovers the diverse frustrations and needs that motivate her clients. *Braggarts. Beatniks. Students. Lawyers. Priests. Prostitution. Sexual initiation. Troilism. Employment—Women. Finance—Personal.*

Note: Also known as *Hot Skin.* One source credits Victoria Astor playing Shelly, while another lists Carol Davis; one name is a pseudonym for the other. Charles Howard is apparently a pseudonym for one of the other listed male actors.

HOT SPUR   F6.2236

Olympic International Films. *Dist* Olympic International Films, Republic Amusements Corp. 5 Jul **1968** [Los Angeles opening]. Sd; col (Eastman Color). 35mm. 91 min.

Prod-Story R. W. Cresse. *Assoc Prod* Wesdon Bishop. *Dir-Screenplay* R. L. Frost. *Main Titl* Ed Merritt Associates. *Orig Mus* Denny Martin. *Asst Dir* James E. McLarty. *Prod Mgr* Merrick Martin. *Prod Asst* Tom McFadden. *Makeup* David Holmes, actor. *Key Grip* Harry Woolman. *Sp Eff* Paul Wilmoth.

Cast: James Arena (*Jason O'Hare*), Virginia Gordon (*Susan O'Hare*), Joseph Mascolo (*Carlo*), Wes Bishop, Tom McFadden, John Alderman, Paul Frank, Monique Heguy, Angel Carter, Ellen Gaines, Paul Wilmoth, Rod Wilmoth, Sky.

Western melodrama. In 1863 in a Mexican cantina in border country, Carlo, a young Mexican, is forced to watch a group of American ranch hands, led by Wes and Jerry, humiliate and repeatedly rape his 17-year-old sister. The last man to rape her is Jason O'Hare, owner of a large Arizona cattle ranch. Carlo's sister dies as a result of the attack, and he is haunted by the thought of cowboys mounting her as they would a horse. Six years later, Carlo undertakes his revenge. He gets a job as a stableboy on O'Hare's ranch, but Susan, Jason's voluptuous wife, will not let a Mexican near her horse. She washes the horse herself, and in her clinging clothing she excites onlookers. The ranch hands then cavort with some Mexican prostitutes, arousing Jason to the point that he forces himself on his wife. Carlo watches and remembers once more his sister's cruel rape. He is thrown off the ranch that night by Tom and Wes but the next day returns to kidnap Susan. Telling her about Jason's crime, he takes her to a mine shaft in the hills, where he rapes her. Carlo deliberately has left clues leading to the mine, and Jason sends his men in pursuit. The men find Susan nude, hanging by her wrists; and Carlo manages to shoot or stab all of them but is himself wounded. Jason arrives to find all his men dead and Susan still hanging. Carlo taunts him, and in the final shootout with Jason, Carlo dies. Susan manages to cut herself free and, in blind fury, stabs Jason, mistaking him for Carlo, then turns the knife on herself. *Mexicans. Ranchers. Stableboys. Rape. Revenge. Abduction. Prejudice. Brother-sister relationship. Murder. Suicide. Mines. Mexican border. Arizona.*

Note: Also known as *The Naked Spur* and *Fiery Spur.* May also be known as *The Longest Spur.*

A HOT SUMMER GAME   F6.2237

Liberty Arts Productions. *Dist* European Producers International. 29 Oct **1965** [Los Angeles showing]. Sd; b&w. 35mm. 82 min.

Pres by Gaston Hakim. *Prod* John Robinette. A Film by James Bruner. *Screenplay* Norman Handelsman. *Photog* William Zsigmond. *Mus* Jaime Mendoza-Nava.

Cast: Valora Noland, Stuart Anderson, John Hanek. Although no information about the precise nature of this film has been found, press material suggests that it concerns sexual daliance during the summer. *Sexuality. Summer.*

Note: Also known as *It's All in the Game.*

HOT THRILLS AND WARM CHILLS   F6.2238

Trans American Pictures. *For* Mustang Producing Corp. *Dist* Trans Continental Artists, Trans American Pictures. 13 Nov **1967** [San Francisco showing]. Sd (RCA); b&w. 35mm. 80 min.

Prod Charles Martinez. *Dir* Dale Berry. *Story* Herman Eldelweis. *Photog* Carlos Martinez. *Film Ed* Charles Goldhammer. *Mus* Dario de Mexico S.A. *Unit Mgr* Herman Queer.

Cast: Rita Alexander *(Toni Montello)*, Lorna Maitland *(herself)*, Susan Branson *(Dody)*, Bubbles Cash *(Chris)*, Jean Manson *(Kitten)*, Stan Newman *(Stan)*, Lionel Day *(Lieutenant Burns)*, Dave Banchek *(Eddy)*, Dale Berry *(Chief Maloney)*, Jo Ann Dyke, Conrad Marcus, Myron Bradshaw, The Glory Roads.

Melodrama. Three women plot to steal the jeweled crown from old King Sex as he rides through the Mardi Gras parade on his float. As the crowds abandon themselves in a wild drunken orgy and prostitutes ply their trade, the women make off with the crown. The police take pursuit and engage the women in a gunfight amidst the crowded streets. [The film includes scenes of male homosexuality, rape, and a graveyard orgy.] *Police. Thieves. Rape. Male homosexuality. Orgies. Drunkenness. Cemeteries. Mardi Gras. New Orleans.*

Note: Filmed in New Orleans. Also known as *Hot Thrills.* The producer and photographer are the same person.

HOTBED OF SIN (France)   F6.2239

Société Française des Films Alfred Rode. *Dist* William Mishkin. May **1961** [New York showing]. Sd; b&w. 35mm. [U. S. running time unknown.]

Prod-Dir-Writ Alfred Rode. *Assoc Prod* Robert Florat. *Dial* Henri Decoin. *Adapt* Marcel Rivet. *Photog* Enzo Riccioni. *Camera* Léon Bellet. *Art Dir* Emile Alex. *Asst Art Dir* Jacques Delaye, Jacques Brizzio. *Set Decor* Emeric Genini. *Film Ed* André Brossier. *Asst Film Ed* Hélène Baste. *Mus* Alfred Rode, Rolf Marbot. *Lyr* André Tabet. *Sd* Joseph de Bretagne. *Sd Engr* Jacques Maumont. *Boom* Gaston Demede. *Asst Dir* Jean Bastia, Francis Dussaugey. *Prod Mgr* Fred Herold. *Unit Mgr* Maurice Percheron. *Admin* André-Léo Mellier. *Script Girl* Simone Chavaudra. *Prod Coörd* Charles Merangel. *Prod Sec* Dagmar Kleindiek. *Cost* Suzanne Revillard, Luce Scatena. *Makeup* Jean-Jacques Chanteau. *Hairstyles* Madeleine Fradel. *Still Photog* Marcel Bouguereau. *Prop* Roger Jumeau.

Cast: Claudine Dupuis *(Gina)*, Louis Seigner *(Constanza)*, Pierre-Louis *(Garnier)*, Howard Vernon *(Charles)*, Roland Leonard *(Mario)*, Junie Astor *(Julia)*, Saint-Granier *(nightclub director)*, Maurice Régamey *(Courier)*, Alfred Rode, Jane Marken, Raymonde Devarennes, Gaston Orbal, Hennery, Anouk Ferjac, Paul Demange, Marcel Pérès, Gérard Darrieu, Amédée, Mag-Avril, Robert Le Béal, Guy Darlan, Léon Pauléon, Geneviève Gérald, Adrienne Gallon, Little Bara, Julien Loisel, Fernand Squinquel, Raymond Francky, Françoise Laury, Xénia Monty.

Comedy-drama. At the Royal Montmartre, a Paris nightclub, the stars of the revue are Gina, a dancer, and Vidma Valesco's Gypsy Orchestra. Julia, the wife of Nicolas Constanza, a regular patron, is having an affair with philanderer Robert Courier. Gina's partner, Mario, is in love with her and jealous of her many admirers. Charles, the maître d'hôtel, is protective of Gina, and it is later revealed that he is her father. Mario discovers Constanza visiting Gina in her dressing room and throws him out; some time later, Constanza's dead body is found, and Garnier, a detective, initiates an investigation. Interrogations follow, and Mario is charged with the murder. Gina and the orchestra return to their

nightly act, and gaiety resumes at the Royal Montmartre. *Dancers. Entertainers. Waiters. Philanderers. Detectives. Infidelity. Jealousy. Filial relations. Murder. Orchestras. Nightclubs. Paris—Montmartre.*

Note: Opened in Paris in Jun 1951 as *Boîte de nuit*; running time: 90 min. U. S. version includes footage added by U. S. distributor.

HOTEL   F6.2240

Warner Bros. Pictures. 19 Jan **1967** [New York opening; c25 Mar 1967; LP36582]. Sd; col (Technicolor). 35mm. 124 min.

Prod-Writ for the Screen Wendell Mayes. *Dir* Richard Quine. *Dir Photog* Charles Lang. *Art Dir* Cary Odell. *Set Decor* George James Hopkins. *Film Ed* Sam O'Steen. *Orig Mus* Johnny Keating. *Sd* M. A. Merrick. *Asst Dir* Mickey McCardle. *Unit Mgr* Carter DeHaven, Jr. *Cost Dsgn* Howard Shoup. *Gowns* Edith Head. *Makeup Supv* Gordon Bau. *Supv Hairstylist* Jean Burt Reilly.

Cast: Rod Taylor *(Peter McDermott)*, Catherine Spaak *(Jeanne Rochfort)*, Karl Malden *(Keycase)*, Melvyn Douglas *(Warren Trent)*, Richard Conte *(Dupere)*, Merle Oberon *(The Duchess)*, Michael Rennie *(Duke of Lanbourne)*, Kevin McCarthy *(Curtis O'Keefe)*, Carmen McRae *(Christine)*, Alfred Ryder *(Captain Yolles)*, Roy Roberts *(Bailey)*, Al Checco *(Herbie)*, Sheila Bromley *(Mrs. Grandin)*, Harry Hickox *(Sam)*, William Lanteau *(Mason)*, Ken Lynch *(Laswell)*, Clinton Sundberg *(Morgan)*, Tol Avery *(Kilbrick)*, Davis Roberts *(Dr. Adams)*, Jack Donner *(Elliott)*, Lester Dorr *(elevator operator)*, Dee Carroll *(mother)*, Judy Norton *(daughter)*.

Melodrama. *Source:* Arthur Hailey, *Hotel* (New York, 1965). Because of financial difficulties, the elegant and respectable St. Gregory Hotel in New Orleans is in danger of falling into the hands of Curtis O'Keefe, the ruthless owner of a modernized chain of hotels. In a desperate attempt to forestall a takeover action Warren Trent, the hotel owner, a bigoted and strong-principled gentleman, takes the advice of his loyal manager, Peter McDermott, and secures union backing. O'Keefe counters by creating an incident in which a Negro couple is turned away from the hotel. Although McDermott exposes the couple as paid agitators, the union withdraws its support. Meanwhile, other crises are developing at the hotel: the Duke of Lanbourne, soon to be named British Ambassador to the United States, has killed a child in a hit-and-run accident and is being blackmailed for $25,000 by Dupere, an unscrupulous hotel detective; McDermott has become romantically involved with O'Keefe's French mistress, Jeanne; and Keycase, a thief, is attempting to burglarize as many rooms as possible. The Duke decides to turn himself over to the police, but while he is riding down in the elevator with a young mother, her daughter, and Keycase, the elevator suddenly smashes against the shaft girders. In saving the lives of the other passengers, the Duke is killed. After Keycase has been arrested, Trent turns down O'Keefe's final offer and decides to sell the St. Gregory to a real estate corporation. Jeanne leaves O'Keefe for McDermott, and Trent makes plans to open a small family inn. *Hotelkeepers. Diplomats. Nobility. British. Detectives. Mistresses. French. Thieves. Negroes. Business ethics. Hotel management. Debt. Blackmail. Manslaughter. Racial prejudice. Self-sacrifice. Hotels. Elevators. New Orleans. Labor unions.*

Note: Location scenes filmed in New Orleans.

THE HOTEL *see* THE GAMES MEN PLAY

HOTEL PARADISO (United States/Great Britain)   F6.2241

Metro-Goldwyn-Mayer, Inc.-Trianon Productions. *Dist* Metro-Goldwyn-Mayer, Inc. 14 Oct **1966** [New York opening; c25 Jul 1966; LP33303]. Sd (Westrex); col (Metrocolor). 35mm (Panavision). 100 min.

Prod-Dir Peter Glenville. *Assoc Prod* Pierre Jourdan. *Screenplay* Peter Glenville, Jean-Claude Carrière. *Dir Photog* Henri Decaë. *Gilbert Chain. Col Cons* Jacques Dupont. *Set Decor* Robert Christides. *Prod Dsgn* François de Lamothe. *Film Ed* Anne V. Coates. *Mus & Mus Dir* Laurence Rosenthal. *Sd Rec* Cyril Swern. *Sd Ed* Jonathan Bates. *Dub Mix* J. B. Smith. *Asst Dir* Georges Pellegrin. *Prod Mgr* Georges Gillet. *Unit Mgr* Philippe Modave. *Cont* Alice Ziller. *Cost Dsgn* Jacques Dupont. *Ch Makeup Artist* Louis Bonnemaison, Odette Berroyer. *Ch Hairdresser* Alex Archambault.

Cast: Gina Lollobrigida *(Marcelle Cot)*, Alec Guinness *(Benedict Boniface)*, Robert Morley *(Henri Cot)*, Peggy Mount *(Angélique Boniface)*, Douglas Byng *(Mr. Martin)*, Robertson Hare *(Duke)*, David Battley *(George)*, Ann Beach *(Victoire)*, Dario Moreno *(Turk)*, Derek Fowlds *(Maxime)*, Leonard Rossiter *(Inspector)*, Akim Tamiroff *(Anniello)*, Marie Bell *(La Grande Antoinette)*, Eddra Gale *(hotel guest)*, Candy Le Beau, Helen Mathison, Denise Powell, Melody Kaye *(Mr. Martin's daughters)*, Peter Glenville *(Georges Feydeau)*.

Farce. *Source:* Georges Feydeau and Maurice Desvallières, *L'hôtel du libre échange* (Paris opening: 5 Dec 1894; trans. by Peter Glenville as *Hotel Paradiso*; London opening: 2 May 1956). In Paris in 1910, Marcelle Cot becomes so annoyed with her neglectful husband Henri, a pompous architect, that she consents to a rendezvous with her timorous neighbor, Benedict Boniface, who has learned that his domineering wife Angélique is spending the night with her ailing sister. After dining at a cafe, Marcelle and Benedict adjourn to the Hotel Paradiso, which is also being used as a place of assignation by Monsieur Cot's nephew, Maxime, and Benedict's flirtatious maid, Victoire. Panic sets in for Marcelle and Benedict when additional arrivals include a barrister friend of Benedict's and Monsieur Cot himself, who has come to inspect the plumbing. In a series of frantic attempts to conceal their identities, Marcelle and Benedict concoct elaborate stories, flee from bedrooms to bathrooms, hide in chimneys and don disguises. The mayhem subsides when the hotel premises are raided by the police. On the next day, however, the nearsighted police inspector is unable to identify anyone; and when Maxime and Victoire openly admit to their presence in the hotel they are assumed to be the night's revelers and the affair is dropped. Peace is restored until both the Cot and Boniface households are invited to attend the opening of the new romantic play by Georges Feydeau, who also stayed at the hotel on the eventful night. Although the two principal stage characters are heavily made up and their acting larger than life, there is little doubt that they bear a remarkable resemblance to Marcelle and Benedict. *Architects. Neighbors. Housemaids. Barristers. Police. Marriage. Infidelity. Disguise. Hotels. Theater. Paris. Georges Feydeau.*

Note: Location scenes filmed in Paris.

HOTHEAD   F6.2242
Dist Cinema-Video International, Inc. Jul **1963**. Sd; b&w. 35mm. 72 min.
Prod-Writ Milton Mann. *Dir* Edward Mann.

Cast: John Delgar *(Frank)*, Robert Glenn *(Tom)*, Barbara Joyce *(Iris)*, Steve Franklin *(Bud)*, Linda Kane *(Suzie)*.

Drama. In Los Angeles, Frank, a frustrated, belligerent young man, is fired by his employer, apparently for theft but actually for incompatibility with his co-workers. At the home of his drunken aunt, Frank expresses his hatred for his long-missing father, whose neglect during Frank's childhood tainted his personality. Later, Frank joins Bud and his girl friend, Iris, for a trip to Santa Barbara. On their way to the beach, they befriend Tom, a middle-aged hobo. As they relax at a small cove, Tom is queried by Frank, who detects a similarity between his father and Tom. When Tom breaks into a nearby house, the others reluctantly join him for dancing and drinking. Aroused by Tom's advances toward Iris, Frank, having decided that Tom is in fact his father, angrily berates him. Chased to the beach, Tom is nearly killed by Frank before Bud separates the men. After Frank apologizes to Tom for his hostility, the hobo continues down the beach as the others return to the car. *Hoboes. Theft. Unemployment. Fatherhood. Personality. Desertion. Personal identity. Los Angeles.*

Note: Location scenes filmed in Los Angeles.

HOTSPRINGS HOLIDAY (Japan)   F6.2243
Geiei Productions. *Dist* Shochiku Films of America. Feb **1970** [Los Angeles showing]. Sd; b&w. 35mm. 90 min.
Prod Kunio Sawamura. *Dir* Hirokazu Ichimura. *Screenplay* Yasuo Tanami, Toshiro Hasebe. *Orig Story* Yasuo Tanami. *Photog* Masao Kosugi. *Art Dir* Chiyoo Umeda. *Mus Comp* Hirooki Ogawa.

Cast: Hiroshi Inuzuka *(Daisuke Yamato)*, Osami Nabe *(Kosuke Yamato)*, Yoshiko Kayama *(Emiko Kano)*, Hajime Hana *(chief of police)*, Kingoro Yanagiya *(Yamanouchi boss)*, Chosuke Ikariya, Chu Arai, Bo Takaki, Koji Nakamoto, Cha Kato, Michiyo Kogure, Etsuko Ikuta, Masumi Harukawa, Kumi Hayase, Norihei Miki, Akiyoshi Kitaura, Yoshijiro Uyeda, Hachiro Misumi, Koree Nakamura, Ryusuke Kita, Mitsuru Ooya, Tosen Hidari, Fukuoka Shogo, Michiko Saga, Tonpei Hidari, Taisuke Kobayashi.

Crime melodrama. Two rival groups of gangsters vie for control of a tiny port town in northern Japan. Daisuke, a member of the older of the two gangs, and Kosuke, a hoodlum in the newer gang, both fall in love with the daughter of an inn proprietor, even though she evinces more interest in improving the town than in their romantic advances. Eventually, the two hoodlums come to respect her efforts and decide to join forces in ridding the town of all gangsters. The two men succeed in restoring peace to the town and, rejected by the innkeeper's daughter, they leave town as friends. *Gangsters. Innkeepers. Gang wars. Smalltown life.*

Note: Released in Japan in 1968 as *Onsen Gerira dai shogeki.* Alternative Japanese title: *Kigeki dai shogeki.*

HOTTER AFTER DARK   F6.2244
Dist Inter-American Film Distributors. ca **1967**. Sd; b&w. [Feature film, length unknown.]

Cast: Tony Maggrore *(Mike Malone)*, Andrea Barr *(Helen)*, Gigi Martin *(Judy)*, Marcy Dome *(Nancy)*, Ami Amar *(Jo Ann)*, Dominic Peters *(Alice)*, Mayra Quintana *(Ruth)*, Mike Bergara *(Dick)*, Sonia Duval *(Maggie)*, Ali Limu *(Dr. F. Bernstein)*.

Crime melodrama. Detective Mike Malone is hired by Mrs. Star to catch her husband with his mistress. Noticing Mr. Star's resemblance to a sketch of a rapist, Malone accepts the case and hides in a closet to watch Star and his paramour make love. Afterward, Star confesses his crimes to the woman and

tries to kill her, but Malone intervenes and arrests him. In his next case, Malone is hired by Judy, a secretary to a scientist who is working on a life-prolonging formula. At the laboratory, Malone is approached by a flirtatious maid, who turns out to be a man intent on killing everyone and stealing the formula. With Judy's help, Mike captures the man. After relating these stories to his secretary, Malone takes her out for a drink and later, in his apartment, she accepts his proposal of marriage. *Detectives. Mistresses. Secretaries. Scientists. Rape. Murder. Infidelity. Disguise. Laboratories.*

HOUR OF THE GUN   F6.2245
Mirisch Corp.-Kappa Corp. *Dist* United Artists. 4 Oct **1967** [San Francisco opening; c4 Oct 1967; LP35087]. Sd; col (De Luxe). 35mm (Panavision). 101 min. [Also 90 min.]

Pres by Mirisch Corp. A John Sturges Production. *Prod-Dir* John Sturges. *Writ* Edward Anhalt. *Dir Photog* Lucien Ballard. *Camera Op* David M. Walsh. *Asst Camera* Terry Meade. *Art Dir* Alfred Ybarra. *Asst Art Dir* Harry Kemm. *Set Decor* Victor Gangelin. *Set Dsgn* Lawrence J. Cuneo. *Film Ed* Ferris Webster. *Mus* Jerry Goldsmith. *Sd* Jesús González Gancy. *Asst Dir* Thomas J. Schmidt, Robert M. Jones. *Prod Mgr* Nate H. Edwards. *Unit Mgr* Jack Lacey. *Script Supv* John Franco. *Prod Sec* Joan Arnold. *Wardrobe* Gordon Dawson. *Makeup* Charles Blackman. *Sp Eff* Sass Bedig. *Gaffer* Joe Edesa. *Key Grip* Bud Gaunt. *Prop* Joe La Bella. *Constr Coörd* William Maldonado. *Still Photog* Jack Harris, still photog.

Cast: James Garner *(Wyatt Earp)*, Jason Robards, [Jr.] *(Doc Holliday)*, Robert Ryan *(Ike Clanton)*, Albert Salmi *(Octavius Roy)*, Charles Aidman *(Horace Sullivan)*, Steve Ihnat *(Andy Warshaw)*, Michael Tolan *(Pete Spence)*, Frank Converse *(Virgil Earp)*, Sam Melville *(Morgan Earp)*, Austin Willis *(Anson Safford)*, Richard Bull *(Thomas Fitch)*, Larry Gates *(John P. Clum)*, Karl Swenson *(Dr. Goodfellow)*, Bill Fletcher *(Jimmy Ryan)*, Robert Phillips *(Frank Stilwell)*, William Schallert *(Herman Spicer)*, Jon Voight *(Curly Bill Brocius)*, Lonny Chapman *(Turkey Creek Johnson)*, Monte Markham *(Sherman McMasters)*, William Windom *(Texas Jack Vermillion)*, Edward Anhalt *(Denver doctor)*, Walter Gregg *(Billy Clanton)*, David Perna *(Frank McLowery)*, Jim Sheppard *(Tom McLowery)*, Jorge Russek *(Latigo)*.

Historical melodrama. Source: Douglas D. Martin, *The Tombstone Epitaph* (Albuquerque, 1951). In 1888, following the bloody gun battle at the O. K. Corral in Tombstone, cattle rustler Ike Clanton, the man responsible, contrives the arrest of the Earp brothers (Wyatt, Virgil, and Morgan) and their whisky-soaked, tubercular friend, Doc Holliday. The murder charge is dismissed, however, and young Virgil consents to run for city marshal; but Clanton's henchmen trap and badly wound him. Morgan is killed when he volunteers to take his crippled brother's place on the ballot. As Wyatt, accompanied by Doc, is escorting Virgil and their dead brother back to the Earp homestead in California, he receives a telegram informing him that he has been appointed Federal marshal. Doc assists in forming an authorized posse, and they set out after Clanton. On the trip, Wyatt picks off Clanton's men one by one with such coldblooded indifference that even Doc is shocked by his friend's disregard for human life. Suffering a hemorrhage, Doc is forced to admit himself to a sanitorium, but Wyatt continues on to Mexico, where Clanton is now engaged in a new cattle-rustling enterprise. Eventually Wyatt traps his prey in a small village and kills him. Having evened the score, he returns for a farewell visit with Doc. As Wyatt leaves the deathbed, he removes his gun and cartridge belt, stows them in his saddle bag, and vows never to be a lawman again. *Rustlers. United States marshals. Frameup. Alcoholism. Trials. Murder. Friendship. Revenge. Tuberculosis. Sanitariums. Tombstone (Arizona). Mexico. Wyatt Earp. John H. "Doc" Holliday. Ike Clanton.*

Note: Location scenes filmed in Mexico. Prerelease title: *The Law and Tombstone.*

HOUR OF THE WOLF (Sweden)   F6.2246
Svensk Filmindustri. *Dist* Lopert Pictures. 9 Apr **1968** [New York opening]. Sd; b&w. 35mm. 88 min.

Dir-Writ Ingmar Bergman. *Photog* Sven Nykvist. *Art Dir* Marik Vos-Lundh. *Film Ed* Ulla Ryghe. *Mus* Lars-Johan Werle. *Extract from "Die Zauberflöte" by* Wolfgang Amadeus Mozart. *Extract from an "Experiment" by* Johann Sebastian Bach. *Sd* P. O. Pettersson, Lennart Engholm. *Asst Dir* Lenn Hjörtzberg. *Prod Mgr* Lars-Owe Carlberg. *Cost* Mago. *Hairstyles* Broje Gustavsson, Kjell Gustavsson. *Sp Eff* Evald Andersson. *English Subtitl* Alan Blair.

Cast: Liv Ullmann *(Alma Borg)*, Max von Sydow *(Johan Borg)*, Erland Josephson *(Baron von Merkens)*, Gertrud Fridh *(Corinne von Merkens)*, Gudrun Brost *(The Baron's Mother)*, Georg Rydeberg *(Lindhorst)*, Ulf Johansson *(Heerbrand)*, Naima Wifstrand *(old lady with hat)*, Bertil Anderberg *(Ernst von Merkens)*, Lenn Hjörtzberg *(Kapellmeister Kreisler)*, Agda Helin *(maidservant)*, Mikael Rundqvist *(young boy)*, Mona Seilitz *(woman in mortuary)*, Folke Sundquist *(Tamino in "The Magic Flute")*, Ingrid Thulin *(Veronica Vogler)*.

Drama. While spending the summer on a desolate island with his pregnant wife, Alma, artist Johan Borg is pursued by personal furies. Unable to sleep until dawn, Johan is haunted by the memory of an androgynous youth he believes he slew and visited by disturbing apparitions, among them a figure able to walk up walls and across ceilings and a 200-year-old woman who peels off her face. Alma comes to share her husbands visions; at the direction of the fantastic crone, she reads his diary, which discloses his stormy love affair with Veronica Vogler some years earlier. During a visit to the sinister ancestral castle of the decadent Baron von Merkens, Alma is taunted by Corinne von Merkens about Johan's liaison with Veronica, and Johan becomes intoxicated. The couple returns home estranged, and Johan later shoots and wounds Alma. Returning to the castle, Johan encounters the supposed corpse of Veronica, which lies in state atop a stone slab. As he fondles the naked cadaver, it springs to life and laughs, to the amusement of von Merken's entourage. Pursued by the costumed company, Johan flees to a forest, where Alma witnesses his torture and humiliation. When Johan disappears, Alma seeks solace by narrating their saga to the spectator. *Artists. Mistresses. Nobility. Insanity. Murder. Obsession. Pregnancy. Marriage. Islands. Castles. Visions. Diaries.*

Note: Opened in Stockholm in Feb 1968 as *Vargtimmen*.

THE HOURS OF LOVE (Italy)　　　　　　　　F6.2247

Dino De Laurentiis Cinematografica. *Dist* Cinema V Distributing, Inc. 2 Sep 1965 [New York opening]. Sd; b&w. 35mm (Cinemascope). 89 min.

Prod Isidoro Broggi, Renato Libassi. *Dir* Luciano Salce. *Screenplay* Luciano Salce, Franco Castellano, Pipolo. *Story Revision & Dial* Diego Fabbri. *Story* Franco Castellano, Pipolo. *Dir Photog* Erico Menczer. *Camera* Silvio Fraschetti. *Asst Camera* Sergio Martinelli, Ferdinando Gallante. *Art Dir* Nedo Azzini. *Set Dresser* Giuseppe Ranieri. *Film Ed* Roberto Cinquini. *Mus* Luiz Bonfa. *Sd* Franco Groppioni. *Asst Dir* Emilio Miraglia. *Prod Mgr* Alessandro Von Norman. *Script Girl* Carla Fierro. *Prod Sec* Giuseppe Vinci, Nico Benetti. *Cost* Giuliano Papi. *Makeup* Giannetto De Rossi. *Hairdresser* Argentina Ferri.

Cast: Ugo Tognazzi (*Gianni*), Emmanuelle Riva (*Maretta*), Barbara Steele (*Leila*), Mara Berni (*Jolanda*), Umberto D'Orsi (*Ottavio*), Diletta D'Andrea (*Mimma*), Brunello Rondi (*Cipriani*), Renato Speziali (*psychiatrist*), Fabrizio Moroni (*Roberto*), Irene D'Aloisi, Luciano Salce.

Comedy-drama. Gianni and Maretta are lovers who believe that marriage is the natural culmination of their affair. No sooner are they married, however, than conflicts arise; their tastes prove to be far different than they had realized, and their friends continually discuss the couple's problems. For Gianni the excitement of courtship is gone, and Maretta begins to sense that she is no longer the center of her husband's attention. When Maretta is unable to become pregnant, they quarrel and Gianni moves out, taking up with an old bachelor buddy. He finds that he misses Maretta's companionship, but things are no different when he returns to her. Eventually, they decide to separate, conceding that their arrangement before marriage was best. *Newlyweds. Courtship. Marriage. Separation (marital).*

Note: Opened in Rome in Mar 1963 as *Le ore dell'amore*; running time: 100 or 105 min.

HOUSE AT THE END OF THE WORLD see DIE, MONSTER, DIE!

HOUSE AT THE END OF THE WORLD see THE TOMB OF LIGEIA

HOUSE IN NAPLES　　　　　　　　　　　　F6.2248

Beaumont Films. *Dist* Peppercorn-Wormser, Inc., U-M Film Distributors. Feb 1969. Sd; b&w. 35mm. 96 min. *MPAA rating* X.

Prod-Dir Peter Savage. *Story* Peter Rabe. *Song:* "Charley's Theme" comp & perf by Sharynne Dale.

Cast: Peter Savage (*Charles Delmont*), Jake La Motta (*Joe Senken*), Sharynne Dale (*Sherry*), Theresa Pellati (*Annette Russi*).

Melodrama. During the invasion of Italy in World War II, two American soldiers, Charles Delmont and Joe Senken, desert the Army and travel to Naples, where they set up a black market operation and are soon given the opportunity to join a lucrative narcotics smuggling syndicate. Charles becomes depressed about his former cowardice and finds in an encounter with Sherry, a prostitute, that he is impotent. Joe decides that Charles has become a liability, and Charles flees to Rome to escape threats on his life from the syndicate. There he meets and falls in love with Annette, who helps him overcome his impotence. He finally obtains a new passport and returns with Annette to Naples, but here he is trapped by assassins hired by the syndicate. He escapes, but in the meantime, believing that Charles has been murdered, Joe seduces Annette with a contrived story. Charles returns home, finds them in bed, and beats up Joe. Annette and Charles resume their relationship. *Americans in foreign countries. Deserters—Military. Prostitutes. Hired killers. Black market. Impotence. Smuggling. Syndicates. Narcotics. World War II. Naples. Rome.*

Note: Filmed in Italy.

A HOUSE IS NOT A HOME　　　　　　　　F6.2249

Embassy Pictures. 12 Aug 1964 [San Francisco opening]. Sd; b&w. 35mm. 95 min.

Pres by Joseph E. Levine. *Prod* Clarence Greene. *Dir* Russell Rouse. *Screenplay* Clarence Greene, Russell Rouse. *Photog* Harold Stine. *Camera Op* Kyme Meade. *Art Dir* Al Roelofs, Hal Pereira. *Set Decor* Sam Comer, James Roach. *Film Ed* Chester W. Schaeffer. *Mus* Joseph Weiss. *Sd Rec* Al Cuesta. *Sd* Harry M. Lindgren. *Asst Dir* William Mull, Dale Hutchinson. *Prod Mgr* Frank Caffey. *Unit Prod Mgr* Lloyd Anderson. *Script Supv* Charlsie Bryant. *Cost* Edith Head. *Makeup* Gene Hibbs. *Hairstyles* Maryce Bates. *Still Photog* Don Christie.

Cast: Shelley Winters (*Polly Adler*), Robert Taylor (*Frank Costigan*), Cesar Romero (*Lucky Luciano*), Ralph Taeger (*Casey Booth*), Kaye Ballard (*Sidonia*), Broderick Crawford (*Harrigan*), Mickey Shaughnessy (*Sgt. John Riordan*), Lisa Seagram (*Madge*), Meri Welles (*Lorraine*), Jesse White (*Rafferty*), Connie Gilchrist (*Hattie Miller*), Constance Dane (*Laura*), Allyson Ames (*Gwen*), Lewis Charles (*Angelo*), Steve Peck (*Vince*), Michael Forest (*Bernie Watson*), Stanley Adams (*Harry*), Dick Reeves (*Pete Snyder*), Roger C. Carmel (*Dixie Keeler*), J. Pat O'Malley (*Muldoon*), Alice Reinheart (*Sarah Ludwig*), Ben Astar (*Max Ludwig*), Hayden Rorke (*Bill Cameron*), Benny Rubin (*Happy Charlie*), Tom D'Andrea (*Gabe*), Gee Gee Galligan (*Dorothy*), Alex Gerry (*doctor*), Edmon Ryan (*Sam*), George Casir (*Dr. Saunders*), Charles Fredericks (*Bert*), Baynes Barron (*Matt*), Jerry James (*Tim*), Mike Ross (*dance hall manager*), Larry Barton (*bald-headed man*), Steve Carruthers (*ogle-eyed man*), Billy Beck (*goggle-eyed man*), June Gleason (*irate wife*), Wynne Brown (*secretary*), John Indrisano (*a man*), Max Power (*second man*), Sandra Scott (*scarred girl*), Roxanne Arlen (*Hattie's girl*), Wilda Taylor (*exotic dancer*), Amedee Chabot, Danica D'Hondt, Leona Gage, Sandra Grant, Diane Libby, Patricia Manning, Inga Neilsen, Francine Pyne, Astrid Schultz, Patricia Thomas, Raquel Welch, Edy Williams (*Polly's girls*).

Biographical drama. Source: Polly Adler, *A House Is Not a Home* (New York, 1953). Polish immigrant Polly Adler is taken to a dancehall by Bernie, the foreman of the sweatshop where she works. There, she meets Lorraine and Madge, two "fast" girls who give her tips on makeup and man-baiting. Later that evening Bernie rapes her, but her uncle, with whom she lives, refuses to believe it wasn't her fault and throws her out of his home. She moves into an apartment used as a front by racketeer Frank Costigan and innocently starts her career as a madam when Frank pays her for inviting her attractive girl friends to parties. As Polly becomes more successful, she moves into a plush apartment, which serves as both a bordello and an undercover meeting place for corrupt politicians, racketeers, and businessmen. Polly falls in love with Casey Booth, a musician whose career she boosts, but resolves not to see him because of her own career, of which he knows nothing. Polly is soon moved into an even plusher penthouse apartment on Park Avenue. When Casey forces Polly to see him and proposes marriage, Polly confesses her occupation. Casey walks out but later returns to say that her past is unimportant to him. Nevertheless, Polly sends him away. Meanwhile, Frank, who has become Lucky Luciano's triggerman, discovers that a shakedown of prostitutes is being conducted in Luciano's name and that a special state investigator is determined to prosecute Luciano for this. Investigating, Frank finds Luciano is innocent, and the responsible man is killed by his own brother. Later, while a party is in progress at Polly's, Casey calls Polly, making one more plea, but Polly, realizing that they could never live with her reputation, sends him out of her life forever. Sadly, she returns to the festivities, accepting her role as New York's most notorious procuress. *Madams. Racketeers. Musicians. Immigrants. Prostitutes. Politicians. Businessmen. Prostitution. Rape. Marriage. Whorehouses. Sweatshops. New York City—Park Avenue. Polly Adler. Lucky Luciano.*

THE HOUSE NEAR THE PRADO　　　　　　F6.2250

Great Empire Films. *Dist* Hollywood Cinemart. 12 Feb 1969 [Champaign, Illinois, showing]. Sd; col. 35mm. 52-75 min.

Prod-Dir-Writ J. Van Hearn.

Cast: Julia Blackburn, Marlin Marin, Marsha Jordan, Guy Anthony, Charles Napier (*see note*).

Drama. Frank Doyle, a salesman for a Los Angeles electronics company, arrives in a large South American city to discuss a million-dollar contract. A revolution is in progress, and Doyle must contact the city's police chief, Juan Valdez, and, if possible, collect money due his firm. Valdez arranges to meet Doyle at "The House Near the Prado," a luxurious bordello where Doyle enjoys himself until Valdez arrives. Several assassins invade the heavily guarded whorehouse and, during an exotic Arabian dance, attempt to kill Valdez. Angered, Valdez has all the women tied up and whipped until one of them confesses her part in the conspiracy and is put to death. Valdez is killed in an exchange of gunfire, and Doyle suddenly finds himself faced with execution by one of the scantily clad women. *Salesmen. Police. Exotic dancers. Americans in foreign countries. Revolutions. Assassination. Conspiracy. Flagellation.*

Prostitution. Murder. Whorehouses. South America.

Note: Lead actor Charles Napier may have been billed under another name.

HOUSE OF A THOUSAND DOLLS (Spain/West Germany)   **F6.2251**
Constantin Film–Hispamer Films. *Dist* American International Pictures. 8 Nov **1967** [New Orleans opening; c18 Oct 1967; LP35116]. Sd; col (Eastman Color, print by Technicolor). 35mm (Techniscope). 78 min.

A Harry Alan Towers Production. *Prod* Harry Alan Towers. *Exec Prod* Louis M. Heyward. *Dir* Jeremy Summers. *Assoc Dir* Manfred R. Köhler. *Screenplay English Vers* Peter Welbeck. *Screenplay Foreign Vers* Carmen M. Román. *Dir Photog* Manuel Merino. *Camera Op* Javier Pérez. *Art Dir* Santiago Ontañón. *Film Ed* Allan Morrison. *Asst Ed* Hermann Storr. *Mus Comp & Cond* Charles Camilleri. *Titl Song* Don Black, Mark London. *Sung by* Cliff Bennett, The Rebel Rousers. *Sd Mix* Felix Alvaro. *Boom Op* Fernando Sánchez, sd. *1st & 2d Asst Dir* Juan Estelrich, Esteban Gutiérrez. *Prod Supv* Tibor Reves. *Prod Mgr* Francisco Romero. *Cont* José Royo. *Prod Sec* Rosemary Wallace. *Wardrobe* Augustin Jiminez. *Makeup* Mariano García. *Hairdressing* Pepita Rubio.

Cast: Vincent Price *(Felix Manderville)*, Martha Hyer *(Rebecca)*, George Nader *(Stephen Armstrong)*, Ann Smyrner *(Marie Armstrong)*, Wolfgang Kieling *(Inspector Emil)*, Sancho Gracia *(Fernando)*, Maria Rohm *(Diane)*, Luis Rivera *(Paul)*, José Jaspe *(Ahmed)*, Juan Olaguibel *(Salim)*, Herbert Fux *(Abdu)*, Yelena Samarina *(Madame Viera)*, Diane Bond *(Liza)*, Andrea Lascelles, Jill Echols, Kitty Swan, Ursula Janis, Loli Muñoz, Karin Skarreso, Monique Aimé, Lara Lenti, Caroline Coon, Marisol, Sandra Petrelli, Françoise Fontages *(The Dolls)*, Milo Quesada, Fernando Cebrián, Irene G. Caba.

Melodrama. While vacationing in Tangiers, American businessman Stephen Armstrong and his Danish wife, Marie, befriend a young man, Fernando, who believes his missing fiancée, Diane, has been abducted and taken to the city's red light district. Fernando eventually learns that Diane is a captive in the House of 1,000 Dolls, a brothel run by Felix Manderville and Rebecca, illusionists who use their magic act to drug and overpower young women for an international ring of white slavers. When Fernando attempts to rescue Diane, the brothel's manageress, Madame Viera, has him killed. In an effort to uncover Fernando's murderer, Stephen misguidedly confides in Manderville. While Stephen is lured away on a false trail and involved with Moroccan Police Inspector Emil, Manderville and Rebecca abduct Marie. Her efforts to escape with Diane and Lisa, another captive, fail, but Stephen bargains for her freedom by promising Rebecca that he will help her and Manderville to obtain immunity. When Manderville wrongly suspects that Rebecca is about to betray him, however, he storms the house with his thugs; and a battle with the captives breaks out. Manderville plummets to his death in a fight with Stephen. Rebecca's pleas for immunity are ignored; Inspector Emil informs Stephen that she was actually behind the scheme. *Businessmen. Americans in foreign countries. Danes. Magicians. Madams. Police. White slave traffic. Murder. Perfidy. Abduction. Whorehouses. Vacations. Tangiers.*

Note: Location scenes filmed in Tangiers, Madrid, and Ceuta, Spain. Released in West Germany in Dec 1967 as *Das Haus der tausend Freuden;* running time: 90 min; opened in Madrid in Jun 1968 as *La casa de las mil muñecas.* Also known as *House of 1,000 Dolls.* Some sources credit Great Britain with co-production status. Peter Welbeck is a pseudonym for Harry Alan Towers.

HOUSE OF A THOUSAND DREAMS   **F6.2252**
Dist Olympic International Films. Mar **1969**. Sd; b&w. 35mm. [Feature film, length unknown.]

Prod Paul Hunt. *Screenplay* R. W. Cresse, Paul Hunt, Ron Garcia.

Cast: Tia Lake, Davis Freeman.

Drama? In Paris, wealthy people visit a house where they can buy any dream they desire. *Wealth. Paris. Fantasy.*

Note: Davis Freeman is a pseudonym for David F. Friedman.

THE HOUSE OF BRICK DOLLS *see* **THE BRICK DOLLHOUSE**

HOUSE OF CARDS   **F6.2253**
Westward Productions. *Dist* Universal Pictures. 19 Mar **1969** [Los Angeles opening; c9 Nov 1968; LP38907]. Sd (Westrex); col (Technicolor). 35mm (Techniscope). 105 min. [Cut to 87 min.] *MPAA rating* G.

Prod Dick Berg. *Dir* John Guillermin. *Screenplay (see note)* Irving Ravetch, Harriet Frank, Jr., James P. Bonner. *Photog* Piero Portalupi. *Camera (see note)* Alberto Pizzi. *Camera Op* Cesare Allione. *Art Dir* Alexander Golitzen, Frank Arrigo, Aurelio Crugnola. *Set Decor* John McCarthy, Ferdinando Ruffo. *Main Titl* Don Record, Pacific Title. *Film Ed* J. Terry Williams. *Mus* Francis Lai. *Mus Supv* Joseph Gershenson. *Titl Song* Francis Lai, Pierre Barouh. *Sd* Waldon O. Watson, Kurt Doubravsky. *Asst Dir* Tony Brandt. *Unit Prod Mgr* Fred S. Wallach. *Prod Mgr* Milton Feldman. *Asst to the Prod* David A. Hammond. *Cost* Edith Head. *Wardrobe* Itala Scandariato. *Makeup* Bud Westmore, Giuseppe Banchelli, Cesare Gambarelli. *Hairstyles for Miss Stevens* Giorgio di

Roma. *Hairstyles* Larry Germain, Vasco Reggiani. *Casting* Paolo Rolli. *London Casting* John Merrick.

Cast: George Peppard *(Reno Davis)*, Inger Stevens *(Anne de Villemont)*, Orson Welles *(Charles Leschenhaut)*, Keith Michell *(Hubert Morillon)*, Ralph Michael *(Claude de Gonde)*, Maxine Audley *(Matilde Vosiers)*, William Job *(Bernard Bourdon)*, Peter Bayliss *(Edmond Vosier)*, Patience Collier *(Gabrielle de Villemont)*, Barnaby Shaw *(Paul de Villemont)*, Ave Ninchi *(Signora Braggi)*, Renzo Palmer *(The Monk)*, Francesco Mule *(Trevi policeman)*, Rosemarie Dexter *(Daniella Braggi)*, Raoul Delfosse *(Louis Le Buc)*, Perrette Pradier *(Jeanne-Marie)*, Geneviève Cluny *(Véronique)*, James Mishler *(Jesse Hardee)*, Jean Louis *(Driot)*, Jacques Roux *(Maguy)*, Jean Hebey *(French conductor)*, Jacques Stany *(Georges)*, Paule Albert *(Sophie)*.

Mystery drama. Source: Stanley Ellin, *House of Cards* (New York, 1967). Young American Reno Davis, in Paris, is engaged by the lovely widow Anne de Villemont as a tutor for her precocious 8-year-old son, Paul, and takes up residence in a mansion already crowded by her family, servants, and other people such as psychiatrist Hubert Morillon, whose patient, the mistress of the house, drinks heavily to allay her premonition that Paul is the object of a kidnaping plot. Reno's suspicions become aroused, and after his friend Louis Le Buc is murdered and the de Villemonts disappear, he discovers their true identity as the core of a rightwing secret society bent on the overthrow of the French Government and the annexation of Algeria. Under suspicion for the murder, he finds Anne, who is being held captive, and the two flee Dijon by train for the Villa Frascati in Italy, where Paul is rumored to be held captive. There Reno uncovers an agents' list coveted by Morilion, who is in reality Sebastian de Villemont (Anne's "dead" husband who conceived his own demise at the hands of terrorists in order to return secretly to Paris as the head of the organization). In a struggle for the list, de Villemont is killed by one of his own henchmen and Reno escapes with the now legitimate widow Anne to Rome to save Paul from the designs of the organization's rival pretender to power, Charles Leschenhaut. Leschenhaut agrees to exchange the boy for Reno's list, but instead he orders Paul to avenge his father's death, for which he has claimed Reno responsible. But Paul is affected by memories of his early friendship with the American and turns the gun on Leschenhaut, who backs fearstruck through a railing and plunges to his death. *Tutors. Children. Widows. Psychiatrists. Terrorists. Murder. Kidnaping. Coups d'état. Paris. Dijon. Rome. Algeria.*

Note: Screen credits give Bonner as scriptwriter; this is a pseudonym for Ravetch and Frank. Some sources credit Pizzi with photography.

THE HOUSE OF CATS   **F6.2254**
Mitam Productions. 1 Sep **1966** [San Francisco showing]. Sd; b&w. 35mm. 63 min.

Cast: Jerry Harris, John Barry, actor *(The Pimp, see note)*, Karen Drake *(The Madam)*, Denine Martin, Angela Loring.

Melodrama. A cold, unfeeling pimp falls in love with a girl he is breaking in as a prostitute. Unwilling to marry the girl, he reluctantly turns her over to a madam, who arranges a party to initiate the girl into a life of prostitution. The girl, realizing that she is controlled by the madam, goes berserk. The madam slaps the girl and accidentally kills her. In panic, the madam calls the pimp, and he, enraged, kills the madam. The police are called, and the house is closed. *Pimps. Madams. Prostitutes. Murder. Whorehouses.*

Note: Sources conflict in crediting the actor playing the pimp; it appears that one name is a pseudonym for the other.

HOUSE OF DARK SHADOWS   **F6.2255**
Metro-Goldwyn-Mayer, Inc. 9 Sep **1970** [Detroit opening; c20 Aug 1970; LP38132]. Sd; col (Metrocolor). 35mm. 97 min. [Copyright length: 102 min.] *MPAA rating* GP.

A Dan Curtis Production. *Prod-Dir* Dan Curtis. *Assoc Prod* Trevor Williams. *Screenplay* Sam Hall, Gordon Russell. *Dir Photog* Arthur J. Ornitz. *Camera Op* Dick Mingalone. *Asst Camera* Felix Trimboli, Jamie Jacobson. *Asst Art Dir* Otis Riggs. *Set Decor* Ken Fitzpatrick. *Scenic Artist* Gene Powell, William Chaiken. *Prod Dsgn* Trevor Williams. *Titl Dsgn* Frank Hillsberg. *Film Ed* Arline Garson, Sidney Katz. *Mus Comp & Cond* Robert Cobert. *Sd* Chris Newman, Jack C. Jacobsen. *Sd Mix* Robert C. Fine. *Boom Op* Pat Suraci. *Asst Dir* William C. Gerrity, Peter Bogart. *Prod Supv* Hal Schaffel. *Asst to the Prod* George Di Cenzo. *Script Supv* Maggie James. *Wardrobe Dsgn* Ramse Mostoller. *Sp Makeup* Dick Smith. *Makeup* Robert Layden. *Hairdresser* Vern Caruso. *Casting* Linda Otto. *Stunt Coörd* Alex Stevens. *Still Photog* Charles Moore.

Cast: Jonathan Frid *(Barnabas Collins)*, Joan Bennett *(Elizabeth Collins Stoddard)*, Grayson Hall *(Dr. Julia Hoffman)*, Kathryn Leigh Scott *(Maggie Evans)*, Roger Davis *(Jeff Clark)*, Nancy Barrett *(Carolyn Stoddard)*, John Karlen *(Willie Loomis)*, Thayer David *(Prof. T. Eliot Stokes)*, Louis Edmonds *(Roger Collins)*, Donald Briscoe *(Todd Jennings)*, David Henesy *(David Collins)*, Dennis Patrick *(Sheriff George Patterson)*, Lisa Richards *(Daphne Rudd)*, Jerry Lacy *(minister)*, Barbara Cason *(Mrs. Johnson)*, Paul Michael *(old* *man*), Humbert Astredo (*Dr. Forbes*), Terry Crawford (*Todd's nurse*), Michael Stroka (*pallbearer*), Philip Larson (*deputy*).

Horror film. Based on the ABC television series *Dark Shadows*. Willie Loomis, the handyman of Collinwood, an 18th-century mansion in Maine, accidentally releases vampire Barnabas Collins from his coffin. Barnabas gains entrance to the mansion by introducing himself as a cousin from England, and Willie becomes his first victim. Carolyn Collins, the lady of the house, is Barnabas' next victim, and doctors Julia Hoffman and T. Eliot Stokes are called in to determine the cause of death. Their diagnosis of vampirism is confirmed when Carolyn returns from the dead to seek her own victims, but she is killed by a stake driven through her heart. Dr. Hoffman becomes fond of Barnabas even though she knows that he is a vampire and seeks a medical cure for him, but he soon makes both doctors his victims, along with Roger Collins, Carolyn's husband. Barnabas, enamored of Maggie Evans, a beautiful governess who reminds him of his lost love, is planning to make her his vampire bride when Jeff Clark, Maggie's fiancé, kills Barnabas with an arrow through the heart. *Vampires. Handymen. Physicians. Governesses. Reviviscence. Imposture. Murder. Coffins. Manors. Maine.*

Note: Location scenes filmed in Tarrytown, New York, and Norwalk, Connecticut. Working title: *Dark Shadows*.

THE HOUSE OF DRAGON GIRLS *see* **HOUSE OF THE RED DRAGON**

HOUSE OF DREAMS   **F6.2256**
    Robert Berry. *Dist* Alliance Theatre Corp. 11 Sep **1963** [Vincennes, Indiana, opening]. Sd; b&w. 35mm (see note). 72 min.
    Prod-Dir-Writ Robert Berry. *Camera* Robert Berry. *Film Ed* Robert Berry.
    Cast: Robert Berry.
    Horror film. No information about the precise nature of this film has been found, but press material suggests that it is a psychological chiller.
    Note: Filmed in 16mm on location in Decker, Indiana.

HOUSE OF FRIGHT (Great Britain)   **F6.2257**
    Hammer Film Productions. *Dist* American International Pictures. 3 May **1961** [Detroit opening]. Sd; col (Technicolor, print by Eastman Color). 35mm (MegaScope). 89 min. [Also 80 min.]
    Prod Michael Carreras. *Assoc Prod* Anthony Nelson Keys. *Dir* Terence Fisher. *Screenplay* Wolf Mankowitz. *Photog* Jack Asher. *Art Dir* Bernard Robinson, Don Mingaye. *Film Ed* James Needs, Eric Boyd-Perkins. *Mus & Songs* Monty Norman, David Heneker. *Mus Cond* John Hollingsworth. *Sd* Jock May. *Makeup* Roy Ashton.
    Cast: Paul Massie (*Dr. Henry Jekyll/Mr. Edward Hyde*), Dawn Addams (*Kitty Jekyll*), Christopher Lee (*Paul Allen*), David Kossoff (*Ernest Litauer*), Francis De Wolff (*inspector*), Norma Marla (*Maria*), Joy Webster, Magda Miller (*Sphinx girls*), William Kendall (*clubman*), Helen Goss (*Nannie*), Pauline Shepherd (*girl in gin shop*), Percy Cartwright (*coroner*), Joe Robinson (*Corinthian*), Arthur Lovegrove (*cabby*).
    Horror film. Source: Robert Louis Stevenson, *The Strange Case of Dr. Jekyll and Mr. Hyde* (London, 1886). In Victorian London, Dr. Henry Jekyll experiments with drugs in an attempt to separate the good and evil natures of man. One night he injects himself with his personality-changing serum, and the somber Jekyll is transformed into the debonair Mr. Hyde. He visits the Sphinx, a West End nightclub, where he encounters Jekyll's neglected wife, Kitty, dancing with his close friend, Paul Allen, an inveterate gambler. Though Jekyll tries to submerge the evil nature of Hyde, he cannot prevent himself from plotting Paul's death, and he lures his former friend into the dressing room of Maria, a snake dancer. As the terrified Paul is crushed to death by a python, the bestial Hyde assaults Kitty. Following the rape, the hysterical woman throws herself off the balcony to her death. By now the character of Hyde has taken almost complete possession of Jekyll. After murdering Maria during a moment of passion, he kills a stableboy, places his body in Jekyll's laboratory, and sets it aflame. Hyde identifies the charred body as Jekyll and convinces the police that the doctor was the deranged killer responsible for the recent deaths. At the coroner's inquest, however, the character of Jekyll emerges, and the true facts of the case are finally revealed. *Physicians. Gamblers. Dancers. Police. Coroners. Metamorphosis. Dual personality. Infidelity. Murder. Rape. Suicide. Experiments. Laboratories. Serums. Nightclubs. London—West End. Fires. Snakes.*
    Note: Released in Great Britain in Oct 1960 as *The Two Faces of Dr. Jekyll*; running time: 88 min. Also known as *Jekyll's Inferno*.

THE HOUSE OF HOOKERS   **F6.2258**
    Dist Able Film Co. ca **1970**. Sd; col. 16mm. [Feature length assumed.]
    Sex film. No information about the precise nature of this film has been found. *Sexuality. Whorehouses.*

HOUSE OF 1,000 DOLLS *see* **HOUSE OF A THOUSAND DOLLS**

HOUSE OF PAIN AND PLEASURE   **F6.2259**
    Bolo Productions. Feb **1969** [periodical notice]. Sd; col. 35mm. [Feature length assumed.]
    Dir William Rotsler.
    Cast: James Brand (*ex-con*), Bruce McQueen (*his pal*), Vincene Wallace (*coarse lesbian*), Dee Howard (*new girl*), Susan Canyon (*masochist*), Rae Torres (*2d lesbian*).
    Melodrama. While making their getaway from a diamond robbery and murder, the car of an ex-con and his pal breaks down. The two men force their way into a nearby house where four young women are living in an arrangement characterized by group sex, masochism, and lesbianism. One of the women, a coarse lesbian, has just seduced the new girl in the house. The bearded ex-con rapes the new girl at gunpoint. Another lesbian, a masochist, finds a whip for the men to apply to her, and she responds with satisfaction. The men make advances to another girl, but the coarse lesbian interferes; in retaliation, the ex-con ties her to a bed and rapes her. Eventually, the women unite and attempt to escape. In the ensuing chase, the pal is badly beaten and the ex-con is captured by the women. The coarse lesbian wants to shoot off the ex-con's genitals, but the new girl intercedes. In the following struggle, the coarse lesbian and the ex-con are killed, and the others resolve to lead better lives. *Ex-convicts. Robbers. Lesbianism. Rape. Masochism. Sadism. Seduction. Murder. Group sex. Flagellation.*
    Note: Vincene Wallace is a pseudonym for Vincene Cradduck.

HOUSE OF 7 JOYS *see* **THE WRECKING CREW**

HOUSE OF SHAME *see* **OLGA'S HOUSE OF SHAME**

THE HOUSE OF STRANGE LOVES (Japan)   **F6.2260**
    Nikkatsu Corp. *Dist* United Producers Releasing Organization. 19 Sep **1969** [Los Angeles opening]. Sd; col (Fuji Color). 35mm (Nikkatsu Scope). 83 min.
    Prod Eisei Koe. *Dir* Tan Ida. *Screenplay* Iwao Yamazaki. *Photog* Hidemitsu Iwahashi. *Art Dir* Haruyasu Kurosawa. *Mus* Seitaro Omori.
    Cast: Ryoji Hayama (*Shinzo*), Jiro Okazaki (*Takichi*), Toshie Nihonyanagi (*Hatsue*), Miki Hayashi (*Shun*), Kaoru Miya (*Toyo*), Takako Uchida (*Hatsuse*).
    Melodrama. In 18th-century Japan, many public bath attendants are young girls who have been sold into slavery. Shinzo, a government spy, uses the search for the abductors of his young neighbor, Hatsue, as a means of continuing his investigation into irregularities in the operation of the baths. Before he can reveal the identity of an important government minister behind the racket, Shinzo is thrown into prison. Hatsue has become a favorite of the shogun, and the minister moves to make her his mistress. Shinzo eventually exposes the minister, but Hatsue persuasively argues for her lover's life. Unable to bring the official to justice, Shinzo urges passage of a law forbidding mixed bathing. *Government agents. Dictators. Mistresses. Abduction. Political corruption. Slavery. Baths. Law.*
    Note: Released in Japan in Jul 1968 as *Onna ukiyoburo*.

HOUSE OF THE DAMNED   **F6.2261**
    Associated Producers, Inc. *Dist* Twentieth Century-Fox Film Corp. Mar **1963** [c15 May 1963; LP24887]. Sd; b&w. 35mm (CinemaScope). 63 min.
    Prod-Dir Maury Dexter. *Screenplay* Harry Spalding. *Dir Photog* John Nickolaus, Jr. *Set Decor* Harry Reif. *Supv Film Ed* Jodie Copelan. *Mus Comp & Cond* Henry Vars. *Sd* William Bernds, Harry M. Leonard. *Asst Dir* Harold E. Knox. *Prod Supv* Harold E. Knox. *Script Supv* Mary Chaffee. *Wardrobe* Wesley Sherrard. *Makeup* Bob Mark. *Prop Master* Jockey Liebgold.
    Cast: Ron Foster (*Scott Campbell*), Merry Anders (*Nancy Campbell*), Richard Crane (*Joseph Schiller*), Erika Peters (*Loy Schiller*), Georgia Schmidt (*Priscilla Rochester*), Dal McKennon (*Mr. Quinby*), Stacey Winters (*The Nurse*), Richard Kiel (*The Giant*), Ayllene Gibbons (*The Fat Woman*), John Gilmore (*The Legless Man*), Frieda Pushnik (*The Legless Girl*).
    Horror film. Scott Campbell, an architect, and his wife Nancy, a decorator, visit an old mansion to survey it for his lawyer friend, Joseph Schiller. The mansion, built by an eccentric millionairess who is now confined in an asylum, was last occupied by a recluse, retired circus side show operator Captain Arbuckle. After a series of strange events, Schiller's wife, Loy, disappears. Eventually, the body of the circus showman is discovered not far from Loy's apparently decapitated body. Investigation reveals a troupe of circus freaks secretly living in the castle, having stayed on after their boss's natural death. The freaks used carnival tricks to fake Loy's death so as to frighten the strangers from the castle. Loy is returned to her husband, and the freaks return to the outside world. *Architects. Freaks. Interior decorators. Millionaires. Lawyers. Recluses. Circus. Abduction. Haunted houses. Hoaxes.*

HOUSE OF THE RED DRAGON   F6.2262

Unit Ten Productions–Hollywood Productions. *Dist* Bernhard Films, Sam Lake Enterprises. 22 Oct **1969** [Champaign, Illinois, showing]. Sd; col. 35mm. 97 min.

Exec Prod Charles H. Leonard. *Dir* John Donne. *Cinematog* Lew Jennings. *Asst Dir* Jerald Cormier.

Cast: Suzie Wong, Jim White, Geraldine Kaye, Mason Bakman, Diane Hansen, Tai Hamilton, Linda Lee, Robert Long, Carol Caruso, François Duboise, George Lee, [2].

Melodrama. In the 1890's, Suzie, an 18-year-old Chinese stowaway, leaves her hiding place on a ship after it docks in San Francisco, only to find herself in the middle of the tong wars and a witness to the murder of a runaway "love-slave." She makes her escape and finds work at the Mandarin Club, owned by her distant uncle Wong, who heads the Red Dragon tong. As Wong busies himself in an attempt to seduce his niece, Police Commissioner Gordon contacts Chang, leader of the rival Black Scorpion tong, for help in averting warfare. Gordon assigns Special Agent Galen Lord to destroy the Red Dragons. When Uncle Wong discovers that his niece was a witness to the dockside murder, he sends her to his "Den of Pleasure" to be trained as a "Singsong Girl." Her teacher, Ling Chow, falls in love with her as he trains her in the art of lovemaking. Meanwhile, Chang's young bride, Heather, turns for sexual satisfaction to his "No. 1 Son." The enraged father throws Heather into his opium den where she is bound and drugged into gratifying the sexual desires of his customers. Bloody warfare erupts between the rival tongs, and Galen Lord is captured by the Red Dragons. Chang's servant Shu, also an agent, approaches the rival den as a customer in order to free Lord, but Heather (now apparently in the House of the Red Dragon) recognizes him and betrays him to Wong, who has them both tortured. As the Red Dragons celebrate the Chinese New Year, the Black Scorpions attack their house, emerging from a paper dragon. In the fighting, both Chang and Wong are killed, and Galen Lord leads police in taking control of the House of the Red Dragon. Suzie soon receives genuine immigration papers, and, with her teacher, plans to reopen the house of pleasure. *Chinese. Police. Stowaways. Uncles. Prostitution. Murder. Torture. Sadism. White slave traffic. Seduction. Infidelity. Organized crime. Whorehouses. Opium. Immigration. Chinese New Year. Gang wars. Tongs. San Francisco—Chinatown.*

Note: Also known as *The House of Dragon Girls*.

THE HOUSE OF THE SLEEPING VIRGINS (Japan)   F6.2263

Kindai Eiga Kyokai. *Dist* Shochiku Co. Mar **1969** [Los Angeles showing]. Sd; b&w. 35mm (Shochiku GrandScope). 95 min.

Dir Kozaburo Yoshimura. *Screenplay* Kaneto Shindo. *Photog* Masamichi Sato. *Art Dir* Hisatake Satsumoto. *Mus* Shigeru Ikeno.

Cast: Takahiro Tamura *(Eguchi)*, Yoshiko Kayama *(Yoshiko)*, Kikko Matsuoka *(first sweetheart)*, Sanae Nakahara *(woman in Kobe)*, Satoshi Oide *(Higuchi)*, Tetsuo Ishikawa *(Yoshida)*.

Drama. Source: Yasunari Kawabata, "Nemureru bijo," in *Nemureru bijo* (Tokyo, 1960). Eguchi, an elderly novelist, is introduced by two friends to a private clubhouse in Kamakura where young virgin girls are drugged into sleep and touched and watched by men too old to do anything else. As a regular patron of the house, Eguchi relives the memories of his youth, when a thwarted love affair led to his girl friend's suicide. At home, Yoshiko, Eguchi's daughter, is unable to choose between two suitors, Higuchi and Yoshida. But Higuchi rapes her, and she immediately decides to marry Yoshida, who accepts her in spite of her misfortune. Both of Eguchi's old friends die at the clubhouse, and as Yoshiko's wedding approaches, the writer can look forward only to a life of loneliness. *Novelists. Old age. Fatherhood. Loneliness. Courtship. Rape. Impotence. Virginity. Whorehouses. Kamakura.*

Note: Released in Japan in Feb 1968 as *Nemureru bijo*.

THE HOUSE OF THE THREE GIRLS (Austria)   F6.2264

Erma Film–Aspa Film. *Dist* Atlantic Pictures. 17 Nov **1961** [New York opening]. Sd; col (Agfacolor). 35mm. 102 min.

Prod Karl Ehrlich. *Dir-Writ* Ernst Marischka. *Photog* Bruno Mondi. *Mus Comp* Franz Peter Schubert, Anton Profes.

Cast: Karlheinz Böhm *(Franz Schubert)*, Gustav Knuth *(Christian Tschoell)*, Magda Schneider *(Frau Tschoell)*, Ewald Balser *(Ludwig van Beethoven)*, Johanna Matz *(Hanner)*, Helga Neuner *(Heider)*, Gerda Siegl *(Heder)*, Rudolf Schock *(Franz von Schober)*, Richard Romanowsky *(Diabelli)*, Helmut Lohner *(Moritz von Schwind)*, Erich Kunz *(Johann Mayrhofer)*, Albert Rueprecht *(Leopold Kupelwieser)*, Eberhard Waechter *(J. M. Vogel)*, Else Rambausek *(Mrs. Prametzberger)*, Edith Elmay *(Franzi Seidl)*, Liselotte Bav *(Therese Pichler)*, Lotte Lang *(Kathi)*.

Biographical drama. Based on the novel and operetta: Rudolf Hans Bartsch, *Schwammerl* (Leipzig, 1916). A. M. Willner, Hans Reichert and Heinrich Berté, *Das Dreimäderlhaus* (Vienna opening: 15 Jan 1916). Composer Franz Schubert falls in love with Hanner, one of three sisters, but he is too shy to

express his feelings. He asks a young baron to sing her a lieder that he has written, but Hanner falls in love with the baron. Resigned to the romance between the baron and Hanner, Schubert plays his "Ave Maria" at their wedding. Later, while composing his Eighth Symphony, Schubert hears that Beethoven has become deaf, and he leaves the symphony unfinished out of respect for his friend. *Composers. Nobility. Weddings. Franz Peter Schubert. Ludwig van Beethoven.*

Note: Filmed on location in Vienna. Produced in Austria in 1958 as *Das Dreimäderlhaus*.

HOUSE OF WOMEN   F6.2265

Warner Bros. Pictures. 11 Apr **1962** [New York opening; c15 Dec 1961; LP27115]. Sd; b&w. 35mm. 85 min.

Prod Bryan Foy. *Dir* Walter Doniger. *Writ (see note)* Crane Wilbur. *Photog* Harold Stine. *Art Dir* Leo K. Kuter. *Set Decor* John P. Austin. *Film Ed* Leo H. Shreve. *Mus* Howard Jackson. *Sd* Robert B. Lee. *Asst Dir* Russell Saunders, Al Alleborn. *Script Supv* Meta Rebner. *Wardrobe* Alexis Davidoff, Florence Hackett. *Makeup* Gordon Bau, Louis La Cava. *Hairstyles* Jean Burt Reilly, Peggy McDonald. *Still Photog* John Monte.

Cast: Shirley Knight *(Erica Hayden)*, Andrew Duggan *(Warden Cole)*, Constance Ford *(Sophie Brice)*, Barbara Nichols *(Candy Kane)*, Margaret Hayes *(Zoe Stoughton)*, Jeanne Cooper *(Helen Jennings)*, Virginia Gregg *(Mrs. Hunter)*, Patricia Huston *(Doris)*, Jason Evers *(Dr. Conrad)*, Jennifer Howard *(Addie Gates)*, Caroline Richter *(Clemens)*, Colette Jackson *(Aggie)*, Gayla Graves *(Jackie)*, Jacqueline Scott *(Mrs. Stevens)*, Paul Lambert *(Mr. Dunn)*, Carolyn Komant *(Nan)*, Virginia Capers *(Sarah)*, Drew Vigen *(Tommy)*, Laurie Sheridan *(Robin)*.

Melodrama. Despite her claims of innocence, Erica Hayden, a young expectant mother, is convicted of robbery and sentenced to 5 years in a state penitentiary for women. According to the rules of the institution, she is permitted to keep her baby with her for 3 years, whereupon the child is put up for adoption if no guardian can be found to care for the child until the mother is paroled. Erica is assigned as a maid in the private residence of the sadistic warden, Cole, who falls in love with her and begins to show greater leniency toward the inmates. Erica's parole hearing and her daughter's 3rd birthday simultaneously approach, but the welfare authorities take Robin away when Erica cannot find anyone to take care of her until her almost-certain release from prison. Cole, afraid of losing Erica, blocks her parole and orders all prison children separated from their mothers. Shortly thereafter, the son of hard-boiled Sophie Brice is killed in a fall from a prison roof. Completely berserk, Sophie incites a riot and takes a parole board member as hostage. She attempts to hurl the woman from the ledge of the roof from which her son plunged, but Erica and the prison doctor restrain her and rescue the parole board member. The incident makes newspaper headlines, resulting in the expulsion of Warden Cole and the hiring of his replacement, a woman. Erica wins her parole and is reunited with her little daughter. *Convicts. Housemaids. Children. Prison wardens. Social workers. Parole officers. Physicians. Robbery. Pregnancy. Parole. Adoption. Motherhood. Prison revolts. Prisons.*

Note: Although screenwriter Wilbur took over direction midway through production, he was denied director credit and declined co-directing credit. Working title: *Ladies of the Mob*.

THE HOUSE ON BARE MOUNTAIN   F6.2266

Olympic International Films. **1962**. Sd; col. 35mm. 62 min.

Prod Bob Cresse, David Andrew, Wesdon Bishop. *Dir* R. L. Frost. *Screenplay* Denver Scott. *Photog* Gregory Sandor. *Film Ed* Gary Lindsay. *Mus* Pierre Martel. *Sd* Bill Orovan.

Cast: Bob Cresse *(Granny Good)*, Laura Eden *(Prudence)*, Angela Webster *(Honey)*, Warren Ames *("Frankenstein")*, Jeffrey Smithers *("Count Dracula")*, Hugh Cannon *(Krakow, the werewolf)*, Laine Carlin, Letitia Cooper, Connie Hudson, Ingrid Lind, Virginia Mark, Betty Peters, Laura Sanders, Millie Stewart, Dan Hyland, William Kirk, John Nada, Roc Shannon, J. J. Watson.

Comedy. Mr. and Mrs. Baumgartner, local law enforcement officers in disguise, arrive at Granny Good's School for Good Girls on the pretext of enrolling their "daughter," Prudence. Their real purpose is to investigate suspicious activities at the school. "Granny" is actually a male bootlegger and the school a cover for a bootlegging racket. A voyeur, Granny takes many opportunities to watch the female students as they mingle in the dormitory without their clothes. She tells her chief assistant, Krakow, a 7-foot-tall wolfman, that their annual costume ball will divert attention from a large batch of liquor that is to be bottled and delivered that night. Prudence suspects Granny's ruse and goes to the basement to investigate. The party becomes a drunken brawl; the guests dance in the nude as Dracula and Frankenstein's monster join in the fun. The police arrive and pursue Granny to the basement. There she chains Prudence, the police chief, his men, and Krakow to the still, forcing them to load up the boxes for the outgoing shipment. *Bootleggers. Police. Students. Werewolves. Disguise. Female impersonation. Voyeurism.*

Nudity. Drunkenness. Boarding schools. Masquerades. Dracula. Frankenstein.

Note: Also advertised as *House on Bear Mountain* and *House on Bar Mountain.*

THE HOUSE ON BEAVER STREET F6.2267

Dist Able Film Co. ca **1970**. Sd; col. 16mm. [Feature length assumed.]

Sex film. No information about the precise nature of this film has been found. *Sexuality.*

THE HOUSE ON THE FRONT LINE (U.S.S.R.) F6.2268

Gorky Film Studio. *Dist* Artkino Pictures. 31 Aug **1963** [New York opening]. Sd; b&w. 35mm. 90 min. [Also reviewed at 105 min.]

Dir Stanislav Rostotskiy. *Screenplay* Aleksandr Galich, Stanislav Rostotskiy. *Story Ed* V. Pogozheva. *Photog* Vyacheslav Shumskiy. *Camera* Yu. Postnikov, V. Okunev. *Art Dir* Sergey Serebrenikov. *Asst Art Dir* S. Velednitskiy, E. Perelshteyn. *Film Ed* V. Mironova. *Mus* K. Molchanov. *Song Lyr* Aleksandr Galich. *Cond* E. Khachaturyan. *Sd* N. Ozornov. *Asst Dir* S. Fyodorova, P. Lyubimov. *Prod Mgr* M. Litvak. *Makeup* A. Smirnov, makeup. *Sp Eff* L. Akimov, Yu. Milovskiy. *Pyrotechnics* Vladimir Likhachyov. *Cons* M. Popov, N. Oslikovskiy.

Cast: Larisa Luzhina (*Svetlana Ivashova*), Klara Luchko (*doctor*), Vyacheslav Tikhonov (*Captain Susdalev*), Leonid Bykov (*postman*), S. Pilyavskaya, M. Strunova, L. Savchenko, Svetlana Druzhinina, Lea Chursina, Mark Troyanovskiy, V. Nevinnyy, V. Pechnikov, V. Zamanskiy, A. Romashin, A. Ignatyev, B. Vatayev, V. Pavlov, V. Denisov, G. Dunts, V. Markin, M. Zharova, Vladimir Prokofyev, P. Vinnik, S. Korenev, Yu. Fomichyov, A. Trusov, S. Kramarov, V. Savchenko, A. Safonov, K. Lipanova, A. Titov, G. Poloskov.

War melodrama. In 1941, Svetlana Ivashova leaves her home in Vladivostok to travel to a small town in the Ukraine so that she can be near her fiancé, Igor, a postal worker. Igor has already left for the front by the time she arrives, and Svetlana decides to wait for him in the now empty post office building. As the war progresses, the old building is put to many uses, and Svetlana helps in a number of capacities, gaining the admiration of all her coworkers. First, the building houses a team of correspondents who publish a newspaper for the soldiers; then, as the war moves nearer, the house becomes a field hospital and Svetlana serves as a nurse. Finally, as the Germans reach the town, Svetlana does liaison work for a Soviet infantry company, earning a medal for her exploits. As the Russians repulse the Germans the hospital returns. As the Germans are pushed further back, the surviving correspondents return, among them Susdalev, who falls in love with Svetlana and writes a story about her, inspiring the fighting men at the front. Throughout the war, Svetlana remains faithful to Igor, and at last they are reunited as he returns from the front. *Postal clerks. Nurses. Reporters. Courage. Fidelity. Postal service. Newspapers. Hospitals. World War II. Ukraine.*

Note: Released in the U.S.S.R. in May 1962 as *Na semi vetrakh*; running time: 105 min.

HOUSE ON THE SAND F6.2269

Dist Emerson Film Enterprises. Nov **1967**. Sd; b&w. 35mm. 90 min.

Prod-Dir-Writ Tony Zarindast. *Exec Prod* Robert Saidi.

Cast: Tony Zarindast, Sandra Evans, Clayton Foster, David Werthriemer.

Drama. While studying in the United States, an Iranian college exchange student falls in love with a Negro woman of mixed parentage. The white and black communities' disapproval of their relationship results in the woman's tragic death. *Iranians. Exchange students. Negroes. Racial prejudice.*

Note: Filmed ca1964.

HOUSE WITH AN ATTIC (U.S.S.R.) F6.2270

Yalta Film Studio. *Dist* Artkino Pictures. 19 Dec **1964** [New York opening]. Sd; col (Sovcolor). 35mm. 86 min.

Dir Yakov Bazelyan. *Screenplay* P. Yerofeyev. *Story Ed* V. Abyzov. *Photog* A. Rybin. *2d Camera* Ye. Davydov. *Art Dir* B. Komyakov. *Film Ed* G. Sadovnikova. *Mus* Aleksey Muravlev. *Cond* A. Roytman. *Sd* N. Sharyy. *Asst Dir* D. Kadatskiy. *Creative Supv* Sergey Gerasimov. *Prod Mgr* I. Morozov. *Cost* I. Dunayeva. *Makeup* D. Lyapich.

Cast: Sergey Yakovlev (*The Artist*), Ninel Myshkova (*Lidiya*), Lyudmila Gordeychik (*Misyus*), Olga Zhizneva (*Yekaterina Pavlovna*), Yu. Leonidov (*Belokurov*), Vera Altayskaya (*Lyubov Ivanovna*), V. Ananina (*Dasha*), Sergey Kalinin (*Belokurov's footman*), G. Smirnova, N. Oleshchenko, D. Tarasov, A. Pokorskiy.

Drama. Source: Anton Pavlovich Chekhov, "Dom s mezoninom," in *Russkaya mysl* (Apr 1896). A landscape painter from St. Petersburg spends his summer at the country estate of Belokurov. On the neighboring manor Misyus and her older sister, Lidiya, live with their mother. The artist is captivated by Misyus' youthful innocence, her spontaneity and blossoming womanhood, and they fall in love. The family is dominated by Lidiya, who teaches school and devotes herself to charitable projects for the peasants. The artist argues with Lidiya that charity will not help the peasants but instead worsen their condition; and he calls for a new order as Russia's only salvation. Lidiya detests the artist, whom she views as an idler, and she sends her sister and mother away to an aunt's house. When the artist arrives to propose to Misyus, she has already departed, and years later he remains haunted by her memory. *Artists. Landed gentry. Sisters. Peasants. Schoolteachers. Charity.*

Note: Released in the U.S.S.R. in May 1961 as *Dom s mezoninom.*

THE HOUSEHOLDER (United States/India) F6.2271

Merchant-Ivory Productions. *Dist* Royal Films International. 21 Oct **1963** [New York opening]. Sd; b&w. 35mm. 100 min.

Prod Ismail Merchant. *Dir* James Ivory. *Screenplay-Dial* Ruth Prawer Jhabvala. *Photog* Subrata Mitra. *Film Ed* Pran Mehra. *Mus Comp & Cond* Ustad Ali Akbar Khan. *Incidental Mus* Jyotirendera Moitra, Vanraj Bhatia. *Mus Rec Supv* Satyajit Ray. *Asst Dir* Prayag Raaj. *Prod Coörd* Sailen Dutta. *Wardrobe* Betina Gill. *Makeup* Nath Grover.

Cast: Shashi Kapoor (*Prem Sagar*), Leela Naidu (*Indu*), Durga Khote (*The Mother*), Hariendernath Chattopadaya (*Mr. Chadda*), Pro Sen (*Sohanlal*), Romesh Thappar (*Mr. Khanna*), Indu Lele (*Mrs. Khanna*), Achla Sachdev (*Mrs. Saigal*), Pincho Kapoor (*Mr. Saigal*), Prayag Raaj (*Raj*), Shama Beg (*Mrs. Raj*), Usha Amin (*1st lady*), Praveen Paul (*2d lady*), Pahari Snayal (*The Swami*), Jabeen Jalil (*Bobo*), Patsy Dance (*Kitty*), Walter King (*professor*), Ernest Castaldo (*Ernest*).

Comedy. Source: Ruth Prawer Jhabvala, *The Householder* (London, 1960). Prem, a young schoolteacher, helps a friend fight the depression of his recent marriage by pointing out that the responsibilities of a householder are not terribly difficult, and he relates his own first experiences. As Prem was starting his first teaching job, his marriage to Indu was arranged. Unable to cope with his job and the new responsibilities of a householder, he is terrified when he learns that Indu is pregnant. Bewildered and unhappy, he sends for his mother, but when she arrives, he finds that she does not get along with his wife. Unable to get help from his friends, he becomes involved with an American who has come to India in search of the spiritual life; next he temporarily joins a religious sect which renounces worldliness. He soon begins to realize how much he has come to love and need his wife, but upon returning home, he discovers that she has left to escape from his mother. When Indu also realizes the importance of their marriage, she returns and they trick his mother into leaving. After Prem finishes telling this story to the newlywed, he and Indu leave to go home. *Schoolteachers. Newlyweds. Mothers-in-law. Americans in foreign countries. Marriage—Arranged. Pregnancy. Filial relations. Duplicity. Religious sects.*

Note: Opened in Bombay in Jul 1964 as *Gharbar.*

HOUSEWIVES AND BARTENDERS F6.2272

Mitam Productions. 2 Oct **1968** [Champaign, Illinois, showing]. Sd; b&w. 35mm. 63 min.

Cast: Sheri, Karen Drake, Anne Shay, Capri.

Melodrama. Bartender Joey, who prefers to have affairs with married women, seduces Joan. She falls in love with him and leaves her husband, agreeing to work as a prostitute for Joey so they can get married. Joey continues to recruit for his prostitution ring, and Joan, aware that she is just being used, holds out on him. Joey beats her, sending her to the hospital, and the subsequent police investigation leads to his arrest. *Bartenders. Pimps. Prostitutes. Infidelity. Seduction.*

HOUSEWIVES ON CALL F6.2273

Mitam Productions. 18 May **1967** [San Francisco showing]. Sd; b&w. 35mm. [Feature length assumed.]

Melodrama. Jack, a photographer, and Carol run an advertisement in the newspaper in an effort to recruit housewives for part-time prostitution. Corporation executives are among the clients, and Jack takes compromising pictures to be used in an elaborate blackmail scheme. Jack eventually goes berserk and accidentally kills one of the clients. *Housewives. Executives. Photographers. Prostitution. Blackmail. Manslaughter. Insanity.*

HOW DO I LOVE THEE? F6.2274

Freeman-Enders Productions. *Dist* Cinerama Releasing Corp. 1 Oct **1970** [Los Angeles opening; c1 Oct 1970; LP43575]. Sd; col (Metrocolor). 35mm. 98 min. [Copyright length: 109 min.] *MPAA rating* GP.

Pres by ABC Pictures. *Prod* Everett Freeman, Robert Enders. *Dir* Michael Gordon. *Screenplay* Everett Freeman, Karl Tunberg. *Photog* Russell Metty. *Camera Op* Wilbur Gossman. *Camera Asst* Herb Roberts. *Art Dir* Walter M. Simonds. *Set Decor* Ned Parsons. *Film Ed* Ronald Sinclair. *Asst Ed* Jerry Irvin, Steve Cuiffo. *Mus Comp* Randy Sparks. *Mus Arr & Cond* Tim Helms. *Titl Song* Randy Sparks, Everett Freeman. *Sung by* Randy Sparks. *Rec Supv* Howard Warren. *Asst Dir* Ted Swanson, Stu Fleming. *Prod Mgr* Dave Silver. *Script Supv* Doris Grau. *Location Mgr* Burnley Johnson. *Cost* Moss Mabry. *Miss O'Hara's Makeup* Allan Snyder. *Makeup* Guy Del Russo. *Hairstyles* Irene Aparicio. *Casting* Leonard Murphy, Marion Polan. *Dial Dir* Norman Stuart.

Prop Master Sam Bergman. *Key Grip* Ken Smith. *Constr Coörd* Harold Collins. *Gaffer* Harry Sundby.

Cast: Jackie Gleason *(Stanley Waltz)*, Maureen O'Hara *(Elsie Waltz)*, Shelley Winters *(Lena Mervin)*, Rosemary Forsyth *(Marion Waltz)*, Rick Lenz *(Tom Waltz)*, Clinton Robinson *(Tom Waltz, age 11)*, James McCallion *(Pete McGurk)*, Don Sebastian *(Art Salerno)*, Jack Nagle *(Dean Bagley)*, Judy Wallace *(Mrs. Bagley)*, Don Beddoe *(Prof. Norman Littlefield)*, J. Edward McKinley *(Hugo Wellington)*, Templeton Fox *(Mrs. Wellington)*, Fritzie Burr *(Mrs. Gromulka)*, Marcia Knight *(Rachel)*, Alex Gerry *(Walter Wetzel)*, Maurice Marsac *(bishop)*, Olga Vargas *(mother superior)*, Dick Sterling *(Dr. Giroux)*, Robertson White *(Old Geezer)*, Harriet Veloshin *(Dean Bagley's secretary)*, Evelyn Turner *(French nurse)*, Ed Ross *(French dentist)*, Soroya Farah *(belly dancer)*, Frank Logan *(Frank, the bartender)*.

Comedy. Source: Peter De Vries, *Let Me Count the Ways* (Boston, 1965). Tom Waltz learns that his father, Stanley, is suffering from a mysterious malady in Lourdes. He immediately boards the next plane to France, despite the objections of his wife, Marion, who blames Tom's father for ruining his life. During the flight, Tom recalls his traumatic past: *As a child, Tom witnesses many a conflict between his atheistic father, a Polish-American furniture mover, and fundamentalist mother. After a particularly heated domestic spat, Stanley becomes infatuated with Lena, a freewheeling artist, but their "affair," a series of sexual blunders, never develops and Lena leaves town, giving Stanley a romantic poem as a farewell gift.* Tom grows up to become a philosophy teacher at the local college, and he marries Marion, a philosophy student. Stanley enters Lena's poem in a literary contest and wins the grand prize of $10,000, which he announces he will donate to Tom's department. The prize is withdrawn, however, when a live TV broadcast reveals that Stanley's "original" poem is actually an Elizabeth Barrett Browning love sonnet. Because of the scandal Tom is denied a promotion, which goes instead to Dr. Littlefield, Tom's longtime nemesis. Stumbling into church as a last resort, the anguished Stanley promises God that he will never again bother Tom if God will restore Tom's job. Upon learning that Dr. Littlefield has died and Tom has gotten the job, Stanley leaves the country in a panic. Arriving in Lourdes, Tom rushes to his ailing father's bedside and learns that Stanley holds himself responsible for Dr. Littlefield's death. Stanley makes a rapid recovery when Tom tells his father that Littlefield died before the pact with God; and he is further cheered when Marion, who has flown to Lourdes to join Tom, happily tells him he will soon be a grandfather. *Americans in foreign countries. Movers. Poles. Artists. Professors. Poets. Students. Parenthood. Marriage. Infidelity. Employer-employee relations. Religion. Plagiarism. Scandal. Atheism. Superstition. Philosophy. Contests. Television. Health. Lourdes. Elizabeth Barrett Browning.*

Note: Location scenes filmed in and around Miami.

HOW I LIVED AS EVE see KATU (THE FRENCH GIRL AND THE NUDISTS)

HOW I WON THE WAR (Great Britain)   F6.2275
Petersham Films. *Dist* United Artists. 23 Oct **1967** [San Francisco opening; c19 Oct 1967; LF17]. Sd; col (Eastmancolor). 35mm. 109 min.

Prod-Dir Richard Lester. *Assoc Prod* Denis O'Dell. *Screenplay* Charles Wood. *Lighting Camera* David Watkin. *Art Dir* Philip Harrison, John Stoll. *Film Ed* John Victor Smith. *Mus Comp & Cond* Ken Thorne. *Sd Rec* Les Hammond. *Sd* Gerry Humphreys, Don Challis, Alan Pattillo. *Asst Dir* José López Rodero. *Prod Mgr* Hubert Froelich, Roberto Roberts. *Cont* Phyllis Crocker. *Cost Dsgn* Dinah Greet. *Sp Eff* Eddie Fowlie.

Cast: Michael Crawford *(Goodbody)*, John Lennon *(Gripweed)*, Roy Kinnear *(Clapper)*, Lee Montague *(Transom)*, Jack MacGowran *(Juniper)*, Michael Hordern *(Grapple)*, Jack Hedley *(Melancholy Musketeer)*, Karl Michael Vogler *(Odlebog)*, Ronald Lacey *(Spool)*, James Cossins *(Drogue)*, Ewan Hooper *(Dooley)*, Alexander Knox *(American general)*, Robert Hardy *(British general)*, Sheila Hancock *(Mr. Clapper's friend)*, Charles Dyer *(flappy-trousered man)*, William Dysart *(paratrooper)*, Paul Daneman *(Skipper)*, Peter Graves, British *(staff officer)*, Jack May *(Toby)*, Richard Pearson *(old man at Alamein)*, Pauline Taylor *(woman in desert)*, John Ronane *(operator)*, Norman Chappell *(soldier at Alamein)*, Bryan Pringle *(reporter)*, Fanny Carby *(Mrs. Clapper)*, Dandy Nichols, Gretchen Franklin *(old ladies)*, John Junkin *(large child)*, John Trenaman *(driver)*, Mick Dillon, Kenneth Colley *(replacements)*.

Comedy-drama. Source: Patrick Ryan, *How I Won the War* (London, 1963). Lieut. Ernest Goodbody, a middle-aged veteran of World War II, smugly reminisces about his triumphs in the British Army. His warm memories are belied, however, by the realities of his disastrous military career. Goodbody's humble origins and insufficient education were inadequate preparation for leading the clumsy and irreverent Third Troop of the Fourth Musketeers. Among the motley group are Clapper, a portly inductee worried about his wife's infidelity; Gripweed, a dispirited Cockney; Juniper, a buffoon who sometimes appears in clown face; the Melancholy Musketeer, a coward; and Transom, the only regular soldier, whose valiant efforts to cover Goodbody's many mistakes

are futile. Goodbody is no better at dealing with his superiors than with his men, and he never makes sense of General Grapple's warning to beware the "wily Pathan." The troop is sent to the North African desert to set up an advance cricket pitch for VIPs, and a few of the men are killed. One by one, however, their variously colored ghosts return and continue to perform their duties. When the outfit is sent to France, and eventually to Germany, the pattern of death and the returning ghosts continues in a progressively bleaker atmosphere. Goodbody, now alone, is captured at the Rhine by Odlebog, the Nazi commandant, who is controlling the last remaining bridge and hopes to sell it to the Allies. Odlebog, who is simply obeying orders and finds the whole business of war quite inhumane, is killed beneath a tank navigated by Grapple. The present-day Goodbody, holding a lonely reunion for his men, is left to reminisce with the sole survivor, the cowardly Melancholy Musketeer. *Veterans. War heroes. Nazis. Ghosts. Military life. Combat zone life. Cowardice. Death. Cricket. Deserts. World War II. France. El Alamein. Germany. Rhine River. North Africa. Great Britain—Army.*

Note: Location scenes filmed in West Germany and Spain. Opened in London in Oct 1967. Actual footage of World War II battles is used, with each battle shown in a different color tint.

HOW MANY ROADS see THE LOST MAN

HOW MANY TIMES   F6.2276
Cine-Systems, Inc. *Dist* Distribpix, Inc. **1969**. Sd; b&w. 35mm. 64 min.

Prod-Dir-Writ Arlo Shiffen. *Camera* Gabrial Lister. *Sd* Ron Laughlin. *Prod Supv* Floyd Love.

Cast: Dustin Farman, Bess Glove *(narrators)*, John Gelgood, Enid Evans, Julia Kristi, Maureen O'Haer, Dorros Night, Morris Evans, Lawrence Oliver, Peter O'Tole, Paula Prestess, Albert Finley.

Melodrama. Rick and Angela, an extraordinary young married couple who are bored with mate swapping and orgies, decide to blackmail people into becoming their sexual slaves. Rick seduces a young woman and a freakish photographer, while Angela, not to be outdone, brings home two young men to add to their growing list of slaves. After adding another young couple to their club, Rick and Angela stage an all-night orgy. They sexually compromise the group while secretly photographing them, and later show the films to the group, demanding that they either become sexual slaves or suffer the consequences of blackmail. Seeing the films outrages the victims; they turn on Rick and Angela and torture and molest them. One angry "slave," excited by blood lust, threatens Angela with a gun and shoots her when he is taunted into insanity. *Mate swapping. Orgies. Blackmail. Infidelity. Seduction. Sadism. Murder. Motion pictures.*

HOW MUCH LOVING DOES A NORMAL COUPLE NEED?   F6.2277
Eve Productions. Jul **1967** [cl Mar 1967; LP34014]. Sd; col (Eastman Color). 35mm. 70 min.

Prod-Dir Russ Meyer. *Assoc Prod* Eve Meyer. *Orig Story & Screenplay* John E. Moran. *Photog* Wady Medawar, Jack Lucas. *Film Ed* Russ Meyer. *Mus* Igo Kantor. *Sd* Richard Brummer, Irwin Cadden. *Prod Mgr* George Costello.

Cast: Ken Swofford *(Barney Rickert)*, Alaina Capri *(Sheila Ross)*, Jack Moran *(Dewey Hoople)*, Adele Rein *(Coral Hoople)*, Andrew Hagara *(Laurence Talbot)*, Frank Bolger *(Cracker)*, Babette Bardot *(Babette)*, John Furlong *(Dr. Martin Ross)*.

Melodrama. After making off with a fortune in unclaimed stolen jewelry, ex-detective Barney Rickert arrives at a run-down Arizona dude ranch near the Colorado River. Needing a hideout, he offers to buy the place, but the owner, Dewey Hoople, refuses to sell. Determined to have privacy, Rickert bribes Cracker, an alcoholic beachcomber, to leave with the ranch's only means of transportation. Rickert then proceeds to win over the female inhabitants by seducing them one by one. Although he has little trouble succeeding with guest Sheila Ross and Hoople's voluptuous mistress, Babette, an exotic dancer, Rickert fails to conquer Hoople's teenage daughter, Coral. Furious at being rebuffed, he attempts to rape her but is prevented by a college playboy named Laurence Talbot, heir to a considerable fortune. After murdering both Cracker and Sheila, Rickert then forces Talbot and Coral to take him up the Colorado to Yuma. In the battle that ensues, Rickert is knocked overboard into the swirling waters and drowns. *Detectives. Mistresses. Exotic dancers. Ranchers. Playboys. Rape. Seduction. Murder. Theft. Jewels. Alcoholism. Dude ranches. Arizona. Colorado River.*

Note: Also known as *Conjugal Cabin*, and *Common-Law Cabin!*

HOW NOT TO ROB A DEPARTMENT STORE (France/Italy)   F6.2278
France Cinéma Productions–P. C. M. *Dist* Artixo Productions. 28 Dec **1965** [New York opening]. Sd; b&w. 35mm. 95 min.

Pres by Artie Shaw. *Prod-Dir* Pierre Grimblat. *Assoc Prod* Mario Chabert. *Adapt & Dial* Pierre Grimblat, Clarence Weff. *Dir Photog* Michel Kelber. *Camera Op* Pierre Willemin. *Asst Camera* Robert Fraisse, Jean Harnois. *Art Dir* Raymond Gabutti. *Film Ed* Robert Isnardon, Monique Isnardon. *Mus*

Georges Garvarentz. *Sd Engr* André Hervée. *Asst Dir* Michel Pézin, Francis Girod. *Prod Mgr* Julien Rivière.

Cast: Jean-Claude Brialy *(Marcel)*, Marie Laforêt *(Ida)*, Sophie Daumier *(Moune)*, Jean-Pierre Marielle *(Justin)*, Michel Serrault *(Meloune)*, Albert Remy *(Étienne)*, Daniel Ceccaldi *(Léon)*, Pierre Clementi *(Raf)*, Roland Blanche *(Curly)*, Renaud Verley *(Charles)*, Madeleine Barbulée *(Limonade)*, Robert Manuel *(Palmoni)*, René Génin *(shopkeeper)*, Gabrielle Doulcet *(his wife)*, Paul Preboist *(cousin)*, Dominique Davray *(Poulaine)*, Philippe Brizard *(Zecca)*, Jean-Pierre Rambal *(store manager)*, Roger Trapp *(brigadier)*, Bernard Fresson *(cop)*.

Crime comedy. Source: Clarence Weff, *Cent briques et des tuiles* (Paris, 1964). Marcel, a young racketeer who has to repay a poker debt within one week, contacts Étienne, a bumbling criminal, and with the assistance of Justin, Meloune, and Ida, they plan the Christmas Eve robbery of the Galeries Lafayette, Paris' largest department store. With Justin disguised as Santa Claus, they place the stolen receipts in a bag filled with toys but lose it to some juvenile delinquents. Marcel locates the teenagers at a bar and learns that the money is in the hands of Limonade, who plans to emigrate to Chile. Raf, Limonade's nephew, and Moune take the 100 million francs and flee by car, followed by the original criminals. Marcel recovers the money when Raf's automobile crashes, but Moune reports Marcel's license plate number to the authorities. At their villa hideout, the gang wash the money, which had been accidentally coated with glue, and hang it up to dry. When the police arrive in search of a runaway cow, Ida and Meloune attempt a getaway with the loot. They are given a ride to the train station by the police, and Marcel chases after them, but he is apprehended when his license is identified. Ida and Marcel are eventually captured as they board the train for Nice. *Racketeers. Juvenile delinquents. Thieves. Police. Debt. Robbery. Bars. Trains. Christmas. Paris. Galeries Lafayette (Paris). Chases. Automobile accidents. Santa Claus. Cows.*

Note: Department store scenes filmed at the Galeries Lafayette, Paris. Opened in Paris in Apr 1965 as *Cent briques et des tuiles*. Italian title: *Colpo grosso a Parigi*.

HOW NOW, SWEET EROS? see IMAGO

HOW SWEET IT IS!　　　　　　　　　　　　　　　　　　F6.2279

Cherokee Productions-National General Productions. *Dist* National General Pictures. 9 Jul **1968** [Miami Beach, Florida, opening; c10 Jul 1968; LP36053]. Sd (Westrex); col (Technicolor). 35mm (Panavision). 99 min.

Prod Garry Marshall, Jerry Belson. *Dir* Jerry Paris. *Screenplay* Garry Marshall, Jerry Belson. *Dir Photog* Lucien Ballard. *Art Dir* Arthur Lonergan. *Set Decor* James Payne, Arthur Krams, Charles S. Thompson. *Main Titl & Titl Dsgn* Pacific Title, Don Record. *Film Ed* Bud Molin. *Montage Ed* Frank Mazzola. *Mus* Pat Williams. *Orch* Nathan Van Cleave. *Songs:* "How Sweet It Is," "Montage From How Sweet It Is!" Jim Webb. *Sung by* Picardi. *Sd* John Carter. *Sd Rec* Al Cuesta. *Mus Ed* John Mick. *Asst Dir* Richard Kobritz. *Unit Prod Mgr* Maurie M. Suess. *Exec Prod Mgr* Harry A. Caplan. *Script Supv* Marge Mullen. *Post-prod Supv* Jack Kirschner. *Cost Dsgn* Helen Rose. *Men's Wardrobe* John A. Anderson. *Women's Wardrobe* Rosamonde Lytle, Sally Lister. *Makeup Supv* William Reynolds, makeup, Stan Smith. *Miss Reynolds' Hairstyles Created by* Sydney Guilaroff. *Hairstyles* Vivian Thompson. *Sp Eff* Pacific Title. *Sp Photog Eff* Norman Breedlove. *Dial Dir* Robert Hoffman. *Casting* Lynn Stalmaster.

Cast: James Garner *(Grif Henderson)*, Debbie Reynolds *(Jenny Henderson)*, Maurice Ronet *(Philippe Maspere)*, Terry-Thomas *(Gilbert Tilly)*, Paul Lynde *(The Purser)*, Marcel Dalio *(Louis)*, Gino Conforti *(Agatzi)*, Donald Losby *(Davey Henderson)*, Hilarie Thompson *(Bootsie Wax)*, Alexandra Hay *(Gloria)*, Mary Michael *(Nancy Leigh)*, Walter Brooke *(Haskell Wax)*, Elena Verdugo *(Vera Wax)*, Ann Morgan Guilbert *(Bibi)*, Patty Regan *(Midge)*, Vito Scotti *(cook)*, Christopher Ross *(Paul)*, Larry Hankin, Jerry Riggio *(policemen)*, Jack Colvin *(assistant chief)*, Leigh French *(Marie)*, Erin Moran *(little girl)*, Robert Homel *(Dubrow)*, Jon Silo *(hotel clerk)*, Don Diamond *(bartender)*, Lenny Kent *(cabbie)*, Rico Cattani, Nikita Knatz *(bouncers)*, Bella Bruck *(woman)*, Ogden Talbot, Michael French, Bert Aretsky *(customers)*, Johnny Silver *(zipper man)*.

Cast—Tour Girls: Penny Marshall, Terri Messina, Patti Braverman, Arlene Parness, Carey Lynn, Erin O'Reilly, Rori Gwynne, Julee Hunter, Peggy Babcock, Mary O'Brien, Susan Meredith, Heather Menzies.

Cast—Agatzi's Girls: Margot Nelson, Marti Litis, Myrna Ross, Jenie Jackson, Sharon Cintron, Sheila Leighton, Shiva Rozier, Barbara E. Fuller, Katherine Darc, Luana Anders, Marjorie Dayne, Margie Duncan, Jenny Fridolfs, Bea Bradley, Eve Bruce, Emese Williams, Marilyn White.

Comedy. Source: Muriel Resnik, *The Girl in the Turquoise Bikini* (New York, 1961). Jenny Henderson discovers that Davey, her son, has arranged to accompany Bootsie, his girl friend, on a European tour, and arranges to have Grif, her photographer husband, assigned to cover the tour for a magazine. Deciding that she too wants to spend the summer in Europe, Jenny makes a down payment on a Riviera villa being rented by real estate man Gilbert Tilly. Once in Europe, Grif and David set off on the photography assignment while Jenny proceeds to her villa. Upon arrival, she learns that she has been swindled: the villa's owner, wealthy playboy Philippe Maspere, is in residence. Delighted with his unexpected guest, Philippe persuades Jenny to stay on and presents her with a turquoise bikini. When Jenny visits Grif in San Remo, she is disturbed by his attentiveness to an attractive guide, Nancy Leigh, and is further irritated by his indifference toward her sharing the villa with a man. Feeling unloved and middle-aged, Jenny returns to Philippe, but any possible romance is curtailed when Grif arrives in the tour bus, catches sight of Jenny cavorting in her bikini, and belts Philippe. Later, while driving back to San Remo, Jenny and Grif are arrested for stealing the bus and are thrown into jail. Miss Leigh quickly bails out Grif, but Jenny is left in a cell with some prostitutes. When the bordello owner, Mr. Agatzi, comes to retrieve his girls, Jenny is included in the lot and taken to his brothel. Eventually, Grif and David arrive, and a fight ensues; but Jennie and Grif are reconciled. *Tourists. Photographers. Swindlers. Real estate agents. Playboys. Guides. Prostitutes. Pimps. Marriage. Parenthood. Middle age. Theft. Bathing suits. Whorehouses. Jails. Riviera. San Remo.*

Note: Location scenes filmed in southern California and Acapulco.

HOW THE WEST WAS WON　　　　　　　　　　　　　F6.2280

Metro-Goldwyn-Mayer, Inc.-Cinerama, Inc. 20 Feb **1963** [Los Angeles opening; c31 Dec 1962; LP26268]. Sd (Westrex); col (Metrocolor). 3x35mm (Cinerama). 155 min. [See note.]

Prod Bernard Smith. *Dir–"The Civil War"* John Ford. *Dir–"The Railroad"* George Marshall. *Dir–"The Rivers," "The Plains," "The Outlaws"* Henry Hathaway. *Screenplay* James R. Webb. *Dir Photog* William H. Daniels, Milton Krasner, Charles Lang, Jr., Joseph LaShelle. *2d Unit Photog* Harold E. Wellman. *Col Cons* Charles K. Hagedon. *Art Dir* George W. Davis, William Ferrari, Addison Hehr. *Set Decor* Henry Grace, Don Greenwood, Jr., Jack Mills. *Film Ed* Harold F. Kress. *Mus* Alfred Newman. *Mus Assoc* Ken Darby. *Song:* "How the West Was Won" Alfred Newman, Ken Darby. *Lyr:* "Home in the Meadow" Sammy Cahn. *Lyr:* "Raise a Ruckus," "Wait for the Hoedown," "What Was Your Name in the States?" Johnny Mercer. *Folk Singing* by Dave Guard and the Whiskeyhill Singers. *Mus Coörd* Robert Emmett Dolan. *Sd Supv* Franklin Milton. *Sd Cons* Fred Bosch, Ray Sharples. *Asst Dir* George Marshall, Jr., William McGarry, Robert Saunders, Wingate Smith, William Shanks. *Prod Supv for Cinerama* Thomas Conroy. *Cost* Walter Plunkett. *Makeup Created by* William Tuttle. *Hairstyles* Sydney Guilaroff. *Sp Vis Eff* A. Arnold Gillespie, Robert R. Hoag.

Cast: Spencer Tracy *(narrator)*, Carroll Baker *(Eve Prescott)*, Lee J. Cobb *(Lou Ramsey)*, Henry Fonda *(Jethro Stuart)*, Carolyn Jones *(Julie Rawlings)*, Karl Malden *(Zebulon Prescott)*, Gregory Peck *(Cleve Van Valen)*, George Peppard *(Zeb Rawlings)*, Robert Preston *(Roger Morgan)*, Debbie Reynolds *(Lilith Prescott)*, James Stewart *(Linus Rawlings)*, Eli Wallach *(Charlie Gant)*, John Wayne *(Gen. William T. Sherman)*, Richard Widmark *(Mike King)*, Brigid Bazlen *(Dora Hawkins)*, Walter Brennan *(Colonel Hawkins)*, David Brian *(attorney)*, Andy Devine *(Corporal Peterson)*, Raymond Massey *(Abraham Lincoln)*, Agnes Moorehead *(Rebecca Prescott)*, Harry Morgan *(Gen. Ulysses S. Grant)*, Thelma Ritter *(Agatha Clegg)*, Mickey Shaughnessy *(deputy marshal)*, Russ Tamblyn *(Reb soldier)*, Tudor Owen *(Scotsman)*, Barry Harvey, Jamie Ross *(his sons)*, Willis Bouchey *(surgeon)*, Kimm Charney *(Sam Prescott)*, Bryan Russell *(Zeke Prescott)*, Claude Johnson *(Jeremiah Rawlings)*, Jerry Holmes *(railroad clerk)*, Rudolph Acosta *(desperado)*, Chief Weasel, Red Cloud, Ben Black Elk *(Indians)*, Mark Allen *(Colin)*, Lee Van Cleef *(Marty)*, Charles Briggs *(Barker)*, Jay C. Flippen *(Huggins)*, Clinton Sundberg *(Hylan Seabury)*, James Griffith, Walter Burke *(gamblers)*, Joe Sawyer *(ship's officer)*, John Larch *(Grimes)*, Jack Pennick *(Corporal Murphy)*, Craig Duncan *(James Marshall)*.

Western epic. Based on a 7-part magazine series, "How the West Was Won," in *Life*, 6 Apr–18 May 1959. A 5-part saga beginning with THE RIVERS: In 1829, Zebulon Prescott takes his wife Rebecca and their two young sons and two daughters away from their New England farm and heads west on a raft down the Ohio River to seek new opportunities and find husbands for the girls, Eve and Lil. One night a stranger in a canoe approaches the family's campsite; at first they suspect him of being a river pirate, but he turns out to be congenial fur trapper Linus Rawlings, who impresses the Prescott boys with tall tales of legendary mountain man Jim Bridger. Eve is also taken with Linus, but the noncommittal backwoodsman leaves abruptly one morning. Linus interrupts his journey to stop at a tavern-general store operated in a cave by river pirate Colonel Hawkins, whose alluring young daughter, Dora, clubs Linus on the head and throws him into a pit in the back of the cave. Soon the Prescotts happen by and are in the midst of being robbed by the murderous Hawkins clan when Linus, who has swum outside to the river through an opening in the pit, sneaks up behind the thieves and saves the settlers with the help of some explosives. As the Prescotts continue their journey by raft, they are swept away by rapids; Zebulon and Rebecca drown; and Linus, having seen Eve survive danger twice, decides at the funeral to marry her and settle by her parents' gravesite. Lil, meanwhile, decides to go to St. Louis. THE PLAINS: Gambler Cleve Van Valen and his cronies watch Lil Prescott's dance hall act and make a wager as to how many petticoats she is wearing. Cleve goes backstage to her dressing room to obtain firsthand proof and overhears that Lil has just inherited a gold mine in California from an elderly admirer. Heavily in debt, Cleve decides to follow Lil out West in hopes of obtaining some of her revenue; along the way she falls in love with him and refuses the marriage proposal of wagon master Roger Morgan. After surviving an Indian attack, Lil and Cleve arrive in California, only to learn that the mine is worthless. The news temporarily halts Cleve's courtship, but they eventually marry after all and decide to settle in the new boomtown of San Francisco. THE CIVIL WAR: Eve, who has lost Linus to battle, watches their son, Zeb, leave home to join the Union Army. Once in combat, Zeb finds that war is not as glorious as he was led to believe, and at the Battle of Shiloh he meets a Confederate deserter who is similarly disillusioned. Together they witness an intimate conversation between Generals Sherman and Grant, in which the latter expresses concern about public criticism of his drinking. The Confederate soldier suddenly tries to assassinate the generals, and Zeb is forced to kill his new friend. After the war, he returns home to find that his mother has died; he joins the U. S. Cavalry to protect railroad workers from the Indians. THE RAILROAD: Aided by Jethro Stuart, a grizzled buffalo hunter, Zeb manages to keep peace with the Indians until ruthless foreman Mike King demands that the railroad break a treaty and take a shortcut through Indian land. Consequently, the Indians stampede the buffalo, and the animals destroy the camp, leaving several children orphaned. Angered that he has unwittingly been involved in the tragedy, Zeb resigns and goes to Arizona. THE OUTLAWS: Now a marshal in the 1880's, Zeb, his wife, Julie, and their children are visited by Lil, widowed and somewhat impoverished after a life of intermittent luxury with Cleve. Meanwhile, Zeb learns that an old enemy, Charlie Gant, is planning with his gang to rob a train carrying a gold shipment. Julie begs him not to go after Gant, but Zeb, who is anxious to send the outlaw to jail, is adamant. A furious gunfight takes place on the runaway train, during which the chains on the log car break and scatter logs across the countryside. Zeb barely escapes death, and the entire train derails, but Zeb nevertheless slays his adversary and returns to his family. *Settlers. Farmers. Sisters. Pirates. Trappers. Gamblers. Entertainers. Dancehall girls. Indians of North America. Wagon masters. Widows. Deserters—Military. Construction foremen. Hunters. United States marshals. Aunts. Outlaws. Fortune hunters. Frontier and pioneer life. Family life. Robbery. Marriage. Funerals. Inheritance. Debt. Drunkenness. Assassination. Murder. Employer-employee relations. Train robberies. Train wrecks. Rafts. Saloons. General stores. Caves. Wagers. Gold mines. Wagon trains. Boomtowns. Railroads. Treaties. Stampedes. Trains. United States—History—Civil War. Ohio River. New England. Saint Louis (Missouri). Missouri. California. San Francisco. Arizona. James Bridger. Ulysses Simpson Grant. William Tecumseh Sherman. Abraham Lincoln. United States Army—Cavalry. Explosions. Buffalo.*

Note: Location scenes filmed at Battery Rock along the Ohio River in Illinois; Courthouse Mountain in the Pinnacles National Monument, California; Chimney Rock in the Colorado Rockies; Monument Valley on the Arizona-Utah border; the countryside around Paducah, Kentucky; Custer State Park, South Dakota; and in Uncompaghre (Colorado), Tonto (Arizona) and Inyo (California-Nevada) National Forests. Opened in London 1 Nov 1962. Also reviewed at 162 and 165 min; copyright length: 149 min. The final scene in the Cinerama version, a panoramic helicopter view of modern-day America, was omitted from the film in its general release version. The non-roadshow version was released in 35mm CinemaScope.

HOW TO BE LOVED (Poland)   F6.2281

Kamera Film Unit. *For* Film Polski. *Dist* Amerpol Enterprise Films. Oct **1965** [Los Angeles showing]. Sd; b&w. 35mm. 110 min.

Prod Jozef Krawkowski. *Dir* Wojciech J. Has. *Screenplay* Kazimierz Brandys. *Photog* Stefan Matyjaszkiewicz. *Art Dir* Anatol Radzinowicz. *Film Ed* Zofia Dwornik. *Mus* Lucjan Kaszycki. *Sd* Bogdan Bienkowski.

Cast: Barbara Krafftówna (*Felicia*), Zbigniew Cybulski (*Victor*), Artur Młodnicki (*Tomasz*), Wieńczysław Gliński (*traveler*), Wiesław Gołas (*officer*), Wiesława Kwasniewska (*photographer*), Zdzisław Maklakiewicz (*reporter*), Jadwiga Krawczyk (*stewardess*), Kalina Jędrusik (*girl*), Andrzej Hrydzewicz (*soldier*), Zofia Jamry (*waitress*), Tadeusz Kalinowski (*Peters*), Irena Netto, Witold Skaruch, Tadeusz Pluciński, Alicja Bobrowska, Mieczysław Pawlikowski, W. Narowski, Krzysztof Litwin, I. Orska.

Drama. Source: Kazimierz Brandys, "Jak być kochaną" (1960). While flying to Paris for a vacation, Felicia, the popular star of a Polish radio program, is reminded of her past by the chance remark of a fellow passenger. ... In 1939 Felicia's stage debut as Ophelia is prevented by the German invasion of Warsaw, and she becomes a waitress in the cafe frequented by Victor, the actor who was to play Hamlet in the same production. One night in the cafe, Victor insults a Polish collaborator, and the man is killed by an unknown assassin as he leaves the premises. Felicia hides Victor in her apartment for 5 years and eventually falls in love with him, even though the ungrateful actor yearns only for audience adulation and does not return her affection. To protect him she permits herself to be raped by SS officers and works for a German-sponsored theatrical troupe; but Victor leaves her immediately after Warsaw is liberated, and she is banned from the stage for 5 years because of her wartime collaboration. Years later, after she achieves success in radio, Felicia again meets Victor, now an alcoholic who vehemently denies accusations of wartime cowardice. She begs him to move in with her so they can begin a new life together, but he is unable to face the future and commits suicide by jumping from a window. *Actors. Germans. Waitresses. Fugitives. Traitors. Murder. Suicide. Alcoholism. Cowardice. Rape. Airplanes. Radio. Theatrical troupes. Cafes. World War II. Warsaw. SS. "Hamlet".*

Note: Released in Poland in 1963 as *Jak być kochaną*; running time: 100 min.

HOW TO COMMIT MARRIAGE   F6.2282

Naho Productions. *Dist* Cinerama Releasing Corp. 28 May **1969** [Miami Beach, Florida, opening; c28 May 1969; LP38284]. Sd; col (Technicolor). 35mm. 98 min. *MPAA rating* M.

Prod Bill Lawrence. *Exec Prod* Bob Hope. *Dir* Norman Panama. *2d Unit Dir* Mickey Moore. *Screenplay* Ben Starr, Michael Kanin. *Dir Photog* Charles Lang. *Art Dir* Edward Engoron. *Set Decor* John Lamphear. *Titl & Montages* Wayne Fitzgerald. *Film Ed* Ronald Sinclair. *Mus Comp & Cond* Joseph J. Lilley. *Adtl Mus* The Comfortable Chair. *Choreog* Jack Baker. *Sd* Harold Lewis. *Mus Ed* Synchrofilm. *Sd Eff* Edit-Rite Inc. *Asst Dir* Arthur Jacobson. *Prod Supv* Austen Jewell. *Cost Dsgn* Nolan Miller. *Makeup* Mike Moschella, Fred Williams. *Hairstyles* Cherie. *Sp Eff* Justus Gibbs. *Casting Dir* Kerwin Coughlin. *Constr Cöord* James West.

Cast: Bob Hope (*Frank Benson*), Jackie Gleason (*Oliver Poe*), Jane Wyman (*Elaine Benson*), Maureen Arthur (*Lois Grey*), Leslie Nielsen (*Phil Fletcher*), Tina Louise (*LaVerne Baker*), Paul Stewart (*attorney*), Irwin Corey (*The Baba Ziba*), Joanna Cameron (*Nancy Benson*), Tim Matthieson (*David Poe*), The Comfortable Chair (*themselves*).

Comedy-drama. Just as real estate agent Frank Benson and his wife, Elaine, decide to divorce, their 19-year-old daughter, Nancy, announces that she and her college boyfriend, David Poe, are going to be married. David's father, Oliver, a cynical rock and roll entrepreneur, vehemently opposes the idea; consequently, when he accidentally finds a copy of the Benson's divorce settlement, Oliver turns the wedding ceremony into a shambles by branding the Bensons as hypocrites. Heartbroken, Nancy and David decide to live together and go on tour with a rock group. Since it is no longer necessary to keep up appearances, Frank moves out of his home and takes up with buxom divorcée Lois Grey, while Elaine finds solace with Phil Fletcher, who is also divorced. When Frank and Elaine learn that Nancy is pregnant and that she intends to follow the advice of Baba Ziba, a Hindu mystic, and give the child up for adoption, they arrange to adopt the baby themselves. Though Nancy and David are unaware of their child's foster parents, Oliver suspects the truth and sets out to expose the Bensons. Desperate, Frank tries to bribe Baba Ziba into persuading Nancy and David to reclaim the baby; when this venture fails, Frank dons the Indian's garments and goes on stage to plead for young people to accept responsibilities. Though Frank is unmasked, Nancy and David are convinced to take their baby back. Frank and Elaine are then reunited, and Oliver marries his longtime mistress, LaVerne. *Real estate agents. Students. Entrepreneurs. Cynics. Mystics. Hindus. Mistresses. Divorce. Marriage. Filial relations. Appearances. Pregnancy. Adoption. Impersonation. Weddings.*

Note: Location scenes filmed in Los Angeles.

HOW TO DO ANYTHING AT ALL WITH GIRLS   F6.2283

Dist Abrams & Parisi, Inc. Jun **1968**. Sd; b&w. 35mm. 80 min.

Drama. Bob, a public relations man, hires two call girls to help close a contract with a pair of important clients, entrusting his wife with the task of keeping her young sister and a college friend away from the party. To help the businessmen relax, he invites another couple, muscleman Joe and his wife. Signals immediately begin to get crossed, as the prostitutes mistake Bob for one of his clients. One call girl, an experienced Frenchwoman, leads Bob into the bedroom, while the other indulges her passion for strong bodies by joining Joe in muscle-building exercises. As Joe walks into the shower to cool off, he meets the college friend, who has arrived home early by mistake. Bob's wife, anxious to further her husband's career, allows herself to be seduced by one of the clients, while the other, a shy fellow bored and disgusted by the proceedings, is accosted by Joe's wife, who is determined to get even for her husband's attentions to the prostitute. As the client, aroused, makes his embarrassed escape, he discovers the young sister asleep in another bedroom and rapes her. The party dissolves into an impromptu body-painting session, and the young sister makes a dramatic breakaway from home. *Prostitutes. Businessmen.*

Sisters. Students. Body-builders. French. Seduction. Mistaken identity. Rape. Body painting. Public relations.

Note: Also known as *Anything With Girls.*

HOW TO LOVE A DOLL *see* **HOW TO MAKE A DOLL**

HOW TO MAKE A DIRTY MOVIE   **F6.2284**
Flectan Films. *Dist* Able Film Co. 20 Jun **1968** [San Francisco showing]. Sd; col. 16mm. 60 min.

Sex film. Newlywed Brad Murphy knocks on a neighbor's door in search of a cup of sugar. Mistaken for an actor, he is immediately ushered into the filming of a sex movie. Mrs. Murphy, wondering about Brad's long absense, goes to the neighbor's house and is introduced into the orgy. *Newlyweds. Neighbors. Sex exploitation films. Group sex.*

Note: Original title: *How To Make a Sex Movie.*

HOW TO MAKE A DOLL   **F6.2285**
Argent Film Productions. *Dist* Unusual Films International. 6 Nov **1968** [Chicago opening]. Sd; col (Eastmancolor). 35mm. 81 min.

Prod-Dir Herschell Gordon Lewis. *Exec Prod* David Chudnow. *Orig Screenplay* Bert Ray, Sheldon Seymour. *Editorial Supv* Richard Brinkman. *Camera Op* Roy Collodi. *2d Unit Camera* Eskandar Ameripoor. *Set Dsgn* Spyridon Horiatis. *Assoc Ed* Ralph Mullin. *Background Mus* Larry Wellington. *Sp Computer Sd* Sheldon Seymour. *Asst Dir* Louise Downe. *Prod Mgr* J. G. Patterson, Jr. *Crew Ch* Paul Jensen. *Asst to Prod Mgr* Steve White.

Cast: Robert Wood *(Percy Corley)*, Jim Vance *(Dr. Hamilcar West)*, Bobbi West *(Agnes Turnbull/dream girl)*, Elizabeth Davis *(Mrs. Corley)*, Geraldine Young *(Mrs. Turnbull)*, Brett Jason Merriman *(Mr. Turnbull)*, Margie Lester *(Dr. West's dream girl)*, Delores Johnson *(computer girl #1)*, Shelley Houston *(computer girl #2)*, June Marie *(computer girl #3)*, Mary Robbins *(computer girl #4)*, Paul Jensen *(computer reject)*.

Science fiction farce. Mathematics professor Percy Corley joins Dr. Hamilcar West, his superior, in perfecting a computer that creates beautiful women. Although Dr. West dies of heart failure during an orgy with his creations, he lives on in the computer's brain. Percy, whose sexual experiences with the computer-generated women give Dr. West great satisfaction, is sad because he has never shared his love with a real woman, and he provokes a battle with the electronic brain of West. Although Percy cancels West's memory bank, West creates a horde of beautiful androids who attempt to pacify Percy, who destroys them by tearing up their punch cards. Dejected, Percy, whose eyeglasses have been smashed, meets unattractive graduate student Agnes Turnbull, who is secretly in love with him, and, not able to see clearly, falls in love with her. After Percy tells her he would like a bunny as a pet, Agnes kisses him and is transformed into his computer dream "bunny." *Professors. Androids. Students. Sexuality. Transmutation. Magic. Computers. Orgies. Eyeglasses. Rabbits and hares.*

Note: Sheldon Seymour is a pseudonym of Herschell Gordon Lewis. Also advertised as *How To Love a Doll.*

HOW TO MAKE A SEX MOVIE *see* **HOW TO MAKE A DIRTY MOVIE**

HOW TO MAKE IT   **F6.2286**
Palo Alto Productions. *For* ABC Pictures. *Dist* International Film Organization. 23 May **1969** [Dallas opening]. Sd; col (DeLuxe). 35mm. ca95 min.

Pres by M. A. Ripps. A Corman Co. Production. *Prod* Gene Corman. *Assoc Prod* Charles Hannawalt. *Dir* Roger Corman. *Screenplay* Bob Barbash. *Dir Photog* Patrice Pouget. *Camera Op* Daniel Lacambre. *Set Decor* Edith Moyal. *Prod Dsgn* Sharon Compton. *Film Ed* Monte Hellman. *Mus* Les Baxter. *Song:* "What's in It for Harry?" Les Baxter, Bob Merrill. *Sd* Kenneth Osborne. *Asst Dir* Beach Dickerson, Alain Corneau, Pierre Cottrell. *Prod Mgr* Charles Sladen. *Script Supv* Frances Doel. *Wardrobe* Carolyn Diliberto. *Makeup* Nicole Barbe. *Hairstyles* Elrhodes de Paris. *Stunt Coörd* Earl Parker. *Turkish Coörd* Haldun Turkun. *Still Photog* Marie-Claude Lacambre. *Gaffer* Charles Lefebvre. *Key Grip* John Murray. *Prop* Aldo Spaperi.

Cast: Vic Morrow *(Harry Black)*, Suzanne Pleshette *(Diane Reed)*, Victor Buono *(Mosul Rashi)*, Cesar Romero *(Lieut. George Duval)*, Stanley Holloway *(Jason Carlyle)*, Charlotte Rampling *(Ruth Carlyle)*, Michael Ansara *(Maj. Miles Segora)*, Katy Fraysse *(Lisa Boulez)*, Christian Barbier *(Sulley Boulez)*, Fikret Hakan *(Inspector Devrim)*, Milton Reid *(Kemal)*, Jack Leonard *(Valdez)*, Ellen Gilbert, Tony Barnum, Joanne Clerc, Kemal Alinoren, Sait Nasifoglu, Michel Carré, Iraz Hatche, Pierre Cannon, Ali Safa, Nan Morris, Julien Faget, Memed Durdu, Horali Kalayji.

Crime melodrama. Charter airline pilot Harry Black flies Englishman Jason Carlyle to Istanbul. After Carlyle is murdered and his briefcase stolen, Harry learns that the valise contains engraving plates stolen from the British Treasury. As two rival gangs of would-be counterfeiters fight for the plates, Harry

becomes attracted to the seemingly innocent Diane Reed, and the action moves to Greece and Monte Carlo. Learning Diane is responsible for several brutal murders, Harry turns her and the missing plates over to the authorities. *Air pilots. English. Theft. Counterfeiting. Murder. Istanbul. Greece. Monte Carlo.*

Note: Location scenes filmed in Monte Carlo and Istanbul. Working title: *What's in It for Harry?*

HOW TO MURDER YOUR WIFE   **F6.2287**
Murder Inc. *Dist* United Artists. 26 Jan **1965** [New York opening; c27 Jan 1965; LP31620]. Sd; col (Technicolor). 35mm. 118 min.

Prod-Writ George Axelrod. *Exec Prod* Gordon Carroll. *Dir* Richard Quine. *Photog* Harry Stradling. *Set Decor* William Kiernan. *Prod Dsgn* Richard Sylbert. *Film Ed* David Wages. *Mus* Neal Hefti. *Choreog* Robert Sidney. *Sd* Lyle Figland, Josh Westmoreland. *Asst Dir* Carter DeHaven, Jr. *Prod Supv* Jack Fier.

Cast: Jack Lemmon *(Stanley Ford)*, Virna Lisi *(Mrs. Ford)*, Terry-Thomas *(Charles)*, Eddie Mayehoff *(Harold Lampson)*, Claire Trevor *(Edna)*, Sidney Blackmer *(Judge Blackstone)*, Max Showalter *(Tobey Rawlins)*, Jack Albertson *(Dr. Bentley)*, Alan Hewitt *(district attorney)*, Mary Wickes *(Harold's secretary)*.

Domestic comedy. Wealthy bachelor cartoonist Stanley Ford lives in a New York City apartment, his unmarried bliss protected by his English valet, Charles. After getting drunk at a stag party, however, Stanley awakens the following morning to find himself married to the girl who popped out of a cake at the party. She is an Italian who speaks little English and who was stranded in the United States after coming here to participate in a beauty contest. Stanley tries to get the marriage annulled, but Harold, his attorney, who has always wanted Stanley to wed and settle down, advises him that annulment and divorce are impossible. Mrs. Ford's "feminization" of his home and daily routine drives Stanley to distraction. Having always tried out his comic-strip situations in real life before committing them to paper, Stanley drops a dummy dressed as his wife into a foundation form at a building site; and tons of concrete are poured over the dummy. He makes this incident part of a wife-murder in his comic strip, and when Mrs. Ford sees it on his drawing board she panics and flees. Realizing at last that he loves and misses his wife, Stanley notifies the police of her disappearance; but workmen at the building site see Stanley's comic-strip account of the wife-murder and likewise notify the police. Stanley is arrested and charged with murdering his wife as depicted in the strip. At his trial Stanley delivers a tirade against marriage to the all-married male jury, convincing them that they all have wife-murder in the back of their minds, and he is acquitted. To his surprise, Mrs. Ford returns to him. *Cartoonists. Bachelors. Valets. Italians. Lawyers. English. Misogynists. Murder. Drunkenness. Marriage. Trials. New York City.*

Note: Filmed on location in New York City.

HOW TO PICK UP A GIRL *see* **SEX AND THE SINGLE SAILOR**

HOW TO SAVE A MARRIAGE—AND RUIN YOUR LIFE   **F6.2288**
Nob Hill Productions. *For* Columbia Pictures. *Dist* Columbia Pictures. 18 Jan **1968** [New York opening; c31 Dec 1967; LP35852]. Sd; col (Eastman Color by Pathé). 35mm (Panavision). 102 min.

A Stanley Shapiro Production. *Prod* Stanley Shapiro. *Dir* Fielder Cook. *Screenplay* Stanley Shapiro, Nate Monaster. *Dir Photog* Lee Garmes. *Camera Op* Ed Garvin, Bob Hosler. *Set Decor* George R. Nelson. *Prod Dsgn* Stewart Campbell. *Prod Dsgn* Robert Clatworthy. *Film Ed* Philip W. Anderson. *Mus Comp & Cond* Michel Legrand. *Song:* "The Winds of Change" Michel Legrand, Mack David. *Sung by* Ray Conniff Singers. *Sd Supv* Charles J. Rice. *Sd* William Randall, Jr., Jack Haynes, Harold Lee, Doug Grant, Louis Hogue. *Asst Dir* Ray Gosnell, Wendell Franklin. *Script Supv* Dorothy Aldrin. *Cost* Moss Mabry. *Wardrobe* Seth Banks, Morris Brown, Dina Joseph. *Makeup Supv* Ben Lane. *Makeup* Steve Lane, Hank Edds. *Body Makeup* Faye Chaney. *Hairstyles* Virginia Jones, Dorothy White. *Sp Eff* Geza Gaspar. *Prod Cons* William O'Sullivan. *Prop Master* Max Frankel. *Dial Coach* Robert Busch. *Still Photog* Al St. Hilaire. *Gaffer* Hal Franklin. *Best Boy* Frank Austin. *Grip* Walter Meins, Willard Klug.

Cast: Dean Martin *(David Sloane)*, Stella Stevens *(Carol Corman)*, Eli Wallach *(Harry Hunter)*, Anne Jackson *(Muriel Laszlo)*, Betty Field *(Thelma)*, Jack Albertson *(Mr. Slotkin)*, Katharine Bard *(Mary Hunter)*, Woodrow Parfrey *(Eddie Rankin)*, Alan Oppenheimer *(Everett Bauer)*, Shelley Morrison *(Marcia Borie)*, George Furth *(Roger)*, Monroe Arnold *(Wally Hammond)*, Claude Stroud *(Hall Satler)*.

Comedy. Bachelor attorney David Sloane attempts to save the unhappy marriage of friend Harry Hunter by making love to Harry's mistress. Assuming that Harry's mistress is his employee Carol Corman, David sets her up in an apartment and promptly proclaims her perfidy. David, however, has selected the wrong woman as the subject of his mission; Harry's real mistress is Muriel Laszlo, Carol's next door neighbor. Nevertheless, Harry, persuaded of Muriel's betrayal, attempts an abortive second honeymoon with his wife, Mary. Meanwhile, Carol and Muriel discover what has happened. Furious, they organize a union of former mistresses and persuade the repentant Harry and distressed David to accept the terms of their contract. Carol further insists that David marry her, with the prerogative of an instant divorce, a condition she elects not to honor after a night of conjugal love. *Mistresses. Bachelors. Businessmen. Neighbors. Lawyers. Marriage. Infidelity. Mistaken identity. Divorce. Jealousy. Honeymoons.*

Note: Working title: *Band of Gold.*

HOW TO SEDUCE A PLAYBOY (Austria/France/Italy)   F6.2289

Intercontinental Film-Metheus Film. *Dist* Chevron Pictures. 15 May **1968**. Sd; col (Eastmancolor by Pathé). 35mm. 94 min. [Orig length: 101 min.]

Prod Karl Spiehs. *Exec Prod U. S. Vers* Barry B. Yellen. *Assoc Prod* Antonio Morelli. *Dir* Michael Pfleghar. *Screenplay* Michael Pfleghar, Klaus Munro. *Story* Anatol Bratt. *Photog* Ernst Wild. *Art Dir* Herta Hareiter. *Film Ed* Margot von Schlieffen. *Mus* Heinz Kiessling. *Singing:* "Bel Ami au Go-Go" The Constellations. *Prod Mgr* Wolfgang Birk, Fred Kollhanek. *Cost* Helmut Holger.

Cast: Peter Alexander *(Peter Keller)*, Renato Salvatori *(Boy Schock)*, Antonella Lualdi *(Vera)*, Scilla Gabel *(Anita Biondo)*, Joachim Fuchsberger *(Sokker)*, Jocelyn Lane *(Ginette)*, Helga Anders *(Lucy)*, Linda Christian *(Lucy's mother)*, Eliane d' Almeida *(Coco)*, Christiane Rücker *(Millie)*, Joachim Teege *(Emile)*, Georg Corten *(Director Zwerch)*, Otto Ambros *(Schladitz)*, Carla Calo, Mylène Demongeot, Bernard Blier, Isarco Ravaioli *(unidentified roles, see note).*

Comedy. A giant computer used by the editors of the internationally famous men's magazine *Bel Ami* to select their "playboy of the year" spits out the name of Peter Keller, a bespectacled young accountant. Although the computer has obviously erred, senior reporter Boy Schock suggests that the magazine transform Keller into a public heart-throb and thus spare itself unfavorable publicity. Schock and Keller leave for a tour, during which the mild young man will be photographed with beautiful women around the world. Meanwhile, Vera, a rival reporter, learns of the computer's blunder and follows the pair to Paris in order to expose the fraud. En route, Keller is harassed by a number of women, all of whom compete for his renowned romantic attentions. Schock takes Keller to Tokyo, where the "playboy," mistaken for U. S. Navy aquanaut Frank Peppiat, is forced to test a new underwater rocket. His supersonic voyage ends in Rome, where he is captivated by film star Anita Biondo, who converts him into the dashing lover described by the magazine's publicity writers. When Vera finally catches up with the pair, she learns of Anita's passion for Keller and decides that perhaps his selection as "playboy of the year" was not a hoax. Vera finally lands her man, though she loses her story in the process. *Accountants. Reporters. Japanese. Actors. Playboys. Hoaxes. Publicity. Seduction. Personal identity. Computers. Magazines (periodicals). Rockets. Vienna. Paris. Tokyo. Rome. United States Navy.*

Note: Released in Austria in 1966 as *Bel Ami 2000 oder: Wie verführt man einen Playboy?*; in Italy in 1968 as *100 ragazze per un playboy*. Filmed in Vienna, Paris, Tokyo, and Rome. The final four cast members represent pre-completion credits, and their participation in the completed film is unconfirmed. Working title: *Bel Ami 66.*

HOW TO STEAL A MILLION   F6.2290

World Wide Productions. *Dist* Twentieth Century-Fox Film Corp. 13 Jul **1966** [Los Angeles opening; c3 Aug 1966; LP32998]. Sd (Westrex); col (DeLuxe). 35mm (Panavision). 127 min.

A William Wyler Production. *Prod* Fred Kohlmar. *Dir* William Wyler. *2d Unit Dir* Robert Swink. *Screenplay* Harry Kurnitz. *Dir Photog* Charles Lang. *Prod Dsgn* Alexander Trauner. *Main Titl Dsgn* Cinefx, Phill Norman. *Film Ed* Robert Swink. *Mus* Johnny Williams. *Orch* James Harbert. *Sd* Joseph de Bretagne, David Dockendorf. *Asst Dir* Paul Feyder. *Unit Prod Mgr* William Kaplan. *Prod Asst* François Moreuil, Robert Wyler. *Miss Hepburn's Clothes* Givenchy. *Makeup* Alberto De Rossi, Freddie Williamson. *Hairstyles* Alexandre of Paris. *Hairdresser* Grazia De Rossi.

Cast: Audrey Hepburn *(Nicole Bonnet)*, Peter O'Toole *(Simon Dermott)*, Eli Wallach *(David Leland)*, Hugh Griffith *(Charles Bonnet)*, Charles Boyer *(DeSolnay)*, Fernand Gravey *(Grammont)*, Marcel Dalio *(Señor Parvideo)*, Jacques Marin *(chief guard)*, Moustache *(guard)*, Roger Treville *(auctioneer)*, Eddie Malin *(insurance clerk)*, Bert Bertram *(Marcel)*.

Crime comedy. Source: George Bradshaw, "Venus Rising," in *Practise To Deceive* (London, 1962). Charles Bonnet is an incorrigible third generation art forger in Paris who dupes connoisseurs into labeling his works authentic and then sells them at elevated prices. So great is his enthusiasm for his profession that he permits his grandfather's "Cellini Venus" to be exhibited at a Paris museum. His daughter, Nicole, knows that the hoax will be discovered when government officials appraise the statue, and to protect her father, she blackmails "society" burglar Simon Dermott into helping her steal the tiny statue from the museum. Actually, Simon is a detective who specializes in

tracing stolen art objects, but, taken by Nicole's charms, he agrees to assist in the burglary. Using only a magnet, a boomerang, and their wits, Nicole and Simon remove the sculpture from its laser-protected pedestal. Simon then offers the Venus to Nicole's fiancé, American millionaire David Leland, who is so fanatic about art treasures that, in return for the statue, he agrees to give up Nicole. Futhermore, he promises Simon never to allow another person to see it. The affair settled, Simon whisks Nicole off for a honeymoon while Bonnet gleefully plans his next masterpiece. *Artists. French. Burglars. Detectives. Millionaires. Americans in foreign countries. Art collectors. Fraud. Forgery. Theft. Personal identity. Museums. Sculptures. Paris. Benvenuto Cellini.*

Note: Filmed in Paris. Working title: *How To Steal a Million Dollars and Live Happily Ever After.*

HOW TO STUFF A WILD BIKINI   F6.2291

American International Productions. *Dist* American International Pictures. 11 Aug **1965** [Los Angeles opening; c14 Jul 1965; LP31862]. Sd; col (Pathé Color). 35mm (Panavision). 93 min. [Also reviewed at 90 min.]

Prod James H. Nicholson, Samuel Z. Arkoff. *Co-prod* Anthony Carras. *Dir* William Asher. *Screenplay* William Asher, Leo Townsend. *Dir Photog* Floyd Crosby. *Art Dir* Howard Campbell. *Film Ed* Fred Feitshans, Eve Newman. *Mus Score* Les Baxter. *Mus Supv* Al Simms. *Songs* Guy Hemric, Jerry Styner. *Orch & Song:* "Give Her Lovin'" Lynn Easton. *Choreog* Jack Baker. *Sd* Don Rush. *Asst Dir* Dale Hutchinson. *Cost* Richard Bruno.

Cast: Annette Funicello *(Dee Dee)*, Dwayne Hickman *(Ricky)*, Brian Donlevy *(B. D.)*, Harvey Lembeck *(Eric Von Zipper)*, Beverly Adams *(Cassandra)*, Jody McCrea *(Bonehead)*, John Ashley *(Johnny)*, Marianne Gaba *(Animal)*, Len Lesser *(North Dakota Pete)*, Irene Tsu *(native girl)*, Arthur Julian *(Doctor Melamed)*, Bobbi Shaw *(Khola Koku)*, Frankie Avalon *(Frankie)*, Buster Keaton *(Bwana)*, The Kingsmen *(themselves)*, Alberta Nelson *(Puss)*, Andy Romano *(J. D.)*, John Macchia, Jerry Brutsche, Bob Harvey, Myrna Ross, Alan Fife *(Rat Pack)*, Alan Frohlich, Tom Quine, Hollis Morrison, Guy Boyce, Charles Reed *(ad men)*, Patti Chandler *(Patti)*, Mike Nader *(Mike)*, Luree Holmes, Jo Collins, Mary Hughes, Stephanie Nader, Jeannine White, Janice Levinson *(beach girls)*, Ed Garner, John Fain, Mickey Dora, Brian Wilson, Bruce Baker, Ned Wynn, Kerry Berry, Dick Jones, Ray Atkinson, Ronnie Dayton *(beach boys)*, Salli Sachse, Linda Bent *(Bookends)*, Marianne Gordon *(Chickie)*, Sheila Stephenson *(secretary)*, Rosemary Williams *(English girl)*, Sue Williams *(Peanuts)*, Tonia Van Deter *(Italian girl)*, Uta Stone *(German girl)*, Toni Harper *(barberette)*, Michele Barton *(manicurist)*, Victoria Carroll *(shoe shine girl)*, Mickey Rooney *(Peachy Keane)*.

Comedy with music. Frankie, away from home on Naval Reserve duty in Tahiti, calls upon Bwana, a witch doctor, to keep his girl friend Dee Dee away from male competition. Bwana sends a pelican to watch over Dee Dee, but when handsome girl-chaser Ricky starts to court Dee Dee, Bwana decides to use more powerful magic. He sends a mysterious charmer, Cassandra, to distract Ricky. Peachy Keane, an advertising man, arrives at the beach with plans to find the "Girl Next Door" for an advertising campaign and enlists the aid of Eric Von Zipper and his gang, the Rat Pack, who are preparing for an upcoming motorcycle competition. Cassandra wins the "Girl Next Door" contest; but Peachy soon discovers that she is completely uncoordinated. In a motorcycle chase, Von Zipper and his gang meet with difficulties, and Von Zipper trades in his leather jacket for a grey flannel suit. Ricky dates Cassandra, and Frankie returns to Dee Dee. *Witch doctors. Motorcycle gangs. Publicists. Temptresses. Americans in foreign countries. Magic. Beauty contests. Jealousy. Adolescence. Beaches. Tahiti. United States Navy. Pelicans.*

HOW TO SUCCEED IN BUSINESS WITHOUT REALLY TRYING
F6.2292

Mirisch Corp. *Dist* United Artists. 9 Mar **1967** [New York opening; c3 Mar 1967; LP34164]. Sd; col (De Luxe). 35mm (Panavision). 119 min.

Pres by David Swift. *Prod-Dir-Writ* David Swift. *Assoc Prod* Irving Temaner. *Visual Gags* Virgil Partch. *Dir Photog* Burnett Guffey. *Col Dsgn* Mary Blair. *Art Dir* Robert Boyle. *Set Decor* Edward G. Boyle. *Titl* Pacific Title. *Film Ed* Ralph E. Winters, Allan Jacobs. *Mus Supv & Cond* Nelson Riddle. *Mus & Lyr* Frank Loesser. *Choreog* Dale Moreda. *Sd* Robert Martin, James A. Richard. *Asst Dir* John Bloss, Michael J. Dmytryk. *Prod Supv* Allen K. Wood. *Unit Mgr* Nate H. Edwards. *Cost* Micheline. *Makeup* Robert Schiffer. *Hairstyles* Fae Smith.

Cast: Robert Morse *(J. Pierpont Finch)*, Michele Lee *(Rosemary Pilkington)*, Rudy Vallee *(J. B. Biggley)*, Anthony Teague *(Bud Frump)*, Maureen Arthur *(Hedy LaRue)*, Murray Matheson *(Benjamin Ovington)*, Kay Reynolds *(Smitty)*, Sammy Smith *(Mr. Twimble/Wally Womper)*, John Myhers *(Bratt)*, Jeff DeBenning *(Gatch)*, Ruth Kobart *(Miss Jones)*, George Fenneman *(TV announcer)*, Anne Seymour *(Mrs. Biggley)*, Erin O'Brien-Moore *(Mrs. Frump)*, Joey Faye *(taxi cab driver)*, Helen Verbit *(Finch's landlady)*, Virginia Sale *(cleaning woman)*, Al Nesor *(newspaper seller)*, Carol

Worthington (*Miss Krumholtz*), Janice Carroll (*Brenda*), Lory Patrick (*receptionist*), Pat O'Moore, Wally Strauss (*media men*), Ivan Volkman (*President of the U. S.*), David Swift (*elevator operator*), Carl Princi (*voice of the book*), Dan Tobin (*Johnson*), Robert Q. Lewis (*Tackaberry*), John Holland (*Matthews*), Paul Hartman (*Toynbee*), Justin Smith (*Jenkins*), Hy Averback (*2d executive*), Bob Sweeney (*3d executive*), Paul Bradley (*TV board member*), Tucker Smith (*junior executive*), Sheila Rogers, Don Kroll.

Musical comedy. Source: Shepherd Mead, *How To Succeed in Business Without Really Trying; the Dastard's Guide to Fame and Fortune* (New York, 1952). Abe Burrows, Jack Weinstock and Willie Gilbert, *How To Succeed in Business Without Really Trying* (New York opening: 14 Oct 1961). While on his way to work one morning, an ambitious and brash young window cleaner named J. Pierpont Finch buys a book entitled *How To Succeed in Business Without Really Trying*. Impressed by what he reads, he leaves his window washing post and enters the offices of the World Wide Wicket Company. He charms a pretty secretary, Rosemary, tricks the personnel manager into believing he is a close friend of J. B. Biggley, the pompous head of Wicket, and lands himself a job in the mailroom. Following each suggestion in the book, Finch quickly connives his way through a series of advancements and promotions until he becomes a junior executive. Finch has also won the hatred of Biggley's nephew, Bud Frump, who plots to destroy him. By supplementing the book's advice with his own methods, Finch's meteoric rise continues until he is finally made the head of advertising. Aware that his uncle detests television giveaway programs, Frump tricks Finch into suggesting a World Wide treasure hunt for shares in the Wicket Company. To Frump's consternation, however, Biggley endorses the idea when Finch nominates Hedy LaRue, Biggley's current lover, as the Treasure Girl. The idea backfires when Hedy publicly announces that the free shares are hidden in Wicket offices throughout the world; and the public quickly reduces them to shambles as they frantically search for the prizes. Finch finally admits that he is a lowly window washer who wanted to become a success. Upon hearing the confession, the chairman of the board and former window washer Wally Womper announces that he is going to retire and that Finch will be his successor. Now at the top at last, Finch admits his love for Rosemary and promises to forget about ambition. Delighted, Rosemary vows that she would love him whether he was a mailboy or President of the United States. Finch starts thinking, and a short time later he is washing the windows of the White House. *Musical numbers:* "How To Succeed in Business Without Really Trying" (Finch); "The Company Way" (Finch & Twimble); "A Secretary Is Not a Toy" (Bratt, Frump, & office staff); "Been a Long Day" (Finch, Rosemary, & Smitty/Biggley, Hedy, & Frump); "I Believe in You" (Rosemary, Finch, & executives); "Grand Old Ivy" (Finch & Biggley); "Rosemary" (Finch); "Gotta Stop That Man" (Finch & executives); "Brotherhood of Man" and reprise of "The Company Way" (Finch, Biggley, Frump, Bratt, Twimble, Miss Jones, & office staff). *Window washers. Businessmen. Secretaries. Mail clerks. Advertising executives. Uncles. Business ethics. Business management. Ambition. Television. Contests. The White House.*

Note: Dale Moreda's choreography is based upon that of Bob Fosse, who choreographed the original stage presentation. Location scenes filmed in New York City.

HOW TO SUCCEED WITH GIRLS   F6.2293

Dist United Producers Releasing Organization, Emerson Film Enterprises. c8 Aug 1964 [LP29762]. Sd; b&w with col seq. 35mm. 86 min. [Copyright length: 81 min.]

Prod Paul Leder, William Norton. *Dir* Edward A. Biery. *Screenplay* William Norton.

Cast: Marissa Mathes, Cathy Crowfoot, Ivy Gentry, Paul Leder, Clark Finney.

Comedy. Wax salesman Harvey Brubaker is shy and retiring with his beautiful wife Mary; and he falls to daydreaming fantasies in which he rescues beautiful women in distress. In one such dream, Harvey is selling wax to a wealthy sultan. Harvey recognizes his secretary among the sultan's harem girls, and he sets out to rescue them all from their evil master. While Harvey is dreaming, Pete Boswell, a footloose con artist is romancing Mrs. Brubaker. Pete drops in at the Brubaker home, reads Harvey's wife Mary some of his poetry, and seduces her. In Harvey's next fantasy, he encounters a mad scientist who is conducting experiments on a group of women, all dyed different colors. Harvey liberates the women after a struggle with the scientist, who tries unsuccessfully to turn Harvey into a monster by spraying him with a chemical. Harvey and Pete meet at a neighborhood bar and strike up a friendship. Pete boldly invites himself home to supper with Harvey; and later when Pete begins to boast about his afternoon's activities, Mary faints. The two comrades go out on the town, and soon Pete's boldness rubs off on Harvey: he returns home to his wife with greater self-confidence. *Salesmen. Royalty. Scientists. Fantasy. Self-confidence. Marriage. Infidelity. Seduction. Harems. Experiments. Wax.*

HOW TO SUCCEED WITH GIRLS *see* THE PEEPING PHANTOM

HOW TO SUCCEED WITH SEX   F6.2294

Argo Productions. *Dist* Medford Film Corp. 10 Apr **1970** [Chicago opening]. Sd; col (Movielab). 35mm. 77 min. *MPAA rating* X.

Prod Jerome F. Katzman. *Exec Prod* Sam Katzman. *Assoc Prod* Robert Stone. *Dir-Writ* Bert I. Gordon. *Photog* Michel Cetti. *Set Decor* Harry Reif. *Main Titl* Pacific Title. *Film Ed* John Bushelman. *Mus Score & Song:* "The Fairest Hands" Forest Hamilton, Sean Bonniwell. *Rec Supv* Franklin Milton. *Asst Dir* Gary Grillo. *Prod Coörd* Ruth Sinclair. *Script Supv* H. Bud Otto. *Fatherly Adv* Marty Ingels. *Prop Master* Richard Rubin. *Dial Coach* Sandra Levinbon.

Cast: Zack Taylor (*Jack*), Mary Jane Carpenter (*Sandy*), Bambi Allen (*Joan*), Victoria Bond (*Pam*), Shawn Devereaux (*Phyllis*), Luanne Roberts (*Peggy*), Keith London (*Fred*), Margaretta Ramsey (*Margaretta*), Kathy Fitzgibbon.

Comedy. Jack and Sandy are engaged to be married. Jack is trying to persuade Sandy to have premarital sex, but she insists on remaining a virgin until the wedding. On the advice of a close friend, Jack buys a book on seduction entitled *How To Succeed With Sex*. He follows the book's suggestions, including experimentation with a variety of women, but each attempt to practice the techniques on Sandy backfires. The book's final chapter advises the reader to visit a prostitute; Jack makes an appointment with an exclusive call girl and meets her in a darkened hotel room. After the session, he is surprised to find that his latest proxy is Sandy. *Bachelors. Prostitutes. Virginity. Courtship. Sex instruction. Seduction. Mistaken identity.*

Note: Working title: *Tom Cat.* Alternative title: *How To Succeed With the Opposite Sex.*

HOW TO SWING ON YOUR SPRING VACATION *see* MONDO DAYTONA

HUA MU-LAN *see* THE LADY GENERAL

HUD   F6.2295

Salem Productions–Dover Productions. *Dist* Paramount Pictures. 29 May **1963** [New York opening; c31 Dec 1962; LP25023]. Sd; b&w. 35mm (Panavision). 112 min.

Prod Martin Ritt, Irving Ravetch. *Dir* Martin Ritt. *Screenplay* Irving Ravetch, Harriet Frank, Jr. *Photog* James Wong Howe. *2d Unit Photog* Rex Wimpy. *Art Dir* Hal Pereira, Tambi Larsen. *Set Decor* Sam Comer, Robert R. Benton. *Film Ed* Frank Bracht. *Mus Score* Elmer Bernstein. *Sd Rec* John Carter, John Wilkinson. *Asst Dir* C. C. Coleman, Jr. *Unit Prod Mgr* Lloyd Anderson, Andrew J. Durkus. *Cost* Edith Head. *Makeup* Wally Westmore. *Hairstyles* Nellie Manley. *Sp Photog Eff* Paul K. Lerpae. *Process Photog* Farciot Edouart.

Cast: Paul Newman (*Hud Bannon*), Melvyn Douglas (*Homer Bannon*), Patricia Neal (*Alma*), Brandon De Wilde (*Lon Bannon*), John Ashley (*Hermy*), Whit Bissell (*Burris*), Crahan Denton (*Jesse*), Val Avery (*Jose*), Sheldon Allman (*Thompson*), Pitt Herbert (*Larker*), Peter Brooks (*George*), Curt Conway (*Truman Peters*), Yvette Vickers (*Lily Peters*), George Petrie (*Joe Scanlon*), David Kent (*Donald*), Frank Killmond (*Dumb Billy*), Carl Low (*Kirby*), Don Kennedy (*Charlie Tucker*), Robert Hinkle (*announcer*), Sharyn Hillyer (*Myra*), John Indrisano, Monty Montana (*cowboys*), Carl Saxe (*proprietor*).

Western drama. Source: Larry McMurtry, *Horseman, Pass By* (New York, 1961). Hud Bannon, the selfish, self-centered son of veteran Texas cattleman Homer Bannon, is despised by his father, a man of staunch integrity whose philosophy of life is diametrically opposed to Hud's. Homer's bitterness in part rests on his son's responsibility for an auto accident 15 years earlier that resulted in the death of Hud's older brother; the brother's orphaned son, Lon, now 17 years old, is divided between adolescent adulation of Hud and loving respect for his grandfather. Also living on the ranch is Alma, an earthy housekeeper physically attracted to Hud but unwilling to yield to his boorish advances. One of Homer Bannon's cows is found dead, apparently from hoof-and mouth disease, and Hud suggests they sell the entire herd before a government inspector can order the cattle slaughtered; but Homer refuses and agrees to have his cows killed to protect other farmers. Hud regards the decision as proof of the old man's senility and takes steps to have his father declared mentally incompetent. Hud goes on a drunk and attempts to rape Alma, but Lon interrupts him, and Alma leaves the ranch the following day. Homer is then stricken by a fatal heart attack while riding on horseback around his deserted land. After the funeral, Lon, now fully aware of his uncle's despicable nature, decides to leave and make his own way in the world. Totally alone, Hud watches the boy depart, shrugs his shoulders, and opens a can of beer. *Ranchers. Cattlemen. Orphans. Uncles. Housekeepers. Government agents. Ne'er-do-wells. Grandfathers. Filial relations. Adolescence. Ranch life. Mental incompetency. Drunkenness. Rape. Heart disease. Death. Hero worship. Ranches. Cattle—Diseases. Texas.*

Note: Location scenes filmed in Texas.

HUGS AND KISSES (Sweden)   **F6.2296**
Sandrews. *Dist* Avco Embassy Pictures. 18 Aug **1968** [New York opening]. Sd; b&w. 35mm. 93 min.
Prod Göran Lindgren. *Exec Prod* Bo Jonsson. *Dir-Screenplay* Jonas Cornell. *Photog* Lars Swanberg. *Art Dir* Walter Hirsch. *Film Ed* Ingemar Ejve. *Mus Comp* Bengt Ernryd. *Sd* Lennart Malmer. *Asst Dir* Pierre Lindstedt.
Cast: Agneta Ekmanner *(Eva)*, Sven-Bertil Taube *(Max)*, Håkan Serner *(John)*, Lena Granhagen *(Hickan)*, Rolf Larsson *(photographer)*, Ingrid Boström, Carl Johann Rönn, Peter Cornell.
Domestic comedy. John, a would-be author, is evicted by his girl friend and invited home by his old school friend Max, a successful haberdasher, on condition that he take over the domestic chores in exchange for his lodging. Though Max's wife, Eva, a fashion model, initially resents the intrusion, she finds that John's eccentric presence gives a welcome lift to her sterile marriage. Gradually, Eva becomes bored with her conventional husband and grows to resent the fun the two men share without her. Aware that he is causing problems in the household, John packs to leave, but Eva begs him to stay. Shortly thereafter, John brings home Hickan, a shrill typing instructor, so that he can have a woman of his own, and they begin to take over the apartment. Max and Eva decide that they must get rid of Hickan before John becomes too independent, and Max arranges for Eva to feign making love to John. Hickan returns home from a movie, sees Eva and John embracing, and promptly leaves, exactly as Max had planned. However, Eva resents Max's indifference and senses more warmth in John. Ignoring Eva's plea to send John packing, Max returns home a few nights later to discover them making love in earnest. Resignedly, he puts on John's old undershirt and retires into the guest room. *Authors. Storekeepers. Models. Houseguests. Domestics. Infidelity. Friendship. Marriage.*
Note: Released in Sweden in 1967 as *Puss och kram.*

HUIS CLOS see **NO EXIT**

THE HUMAN BEAST (Argentina)   **F6.2297**
Dist Ajay Film Co. 1 May **1964** [Los Angeles opening]. Sd; b&w. 35mm. 104 min.
Cast: Ana-Maria Lynch.
Melodrama(?). Source: Emile Zola, *La bête humaine* (Paris, 1890). Press material suggests that the film is based on Emile Zola's *La bête humaine,* which concerns a woman who urges her lover, a railroad engineer, to kill her husband, whom she hates. *Railroad engineers. Infidelity. Murder.*
Note: Original title: *La bestia humano.*

THE HUMAN CONDITION see **NO GREATER LOVE**

THE HUMAN CONDITION see **ROAD TO ETERNITY**

THE HUMAN CONDITION see **A SOLDIER'S PRAYER**

THE HUMAN DUPLICATORS   **F6.2298**
Hugo Grimaldi Productions. *Dist* Woolner Bros. Pictures, Allied Artists. Mar 1965 [c21 Oct 1964; LP29331]. Sd; col (Eastman Color, print by DeLuxe). 35mm. 82 min.
Prod Hugo Grimaldi, Arthur C. Pierce. *Exec Prod* Lawrence Woolner. *Assoc Prod* Jesse Corallo. *Co-prod* Donald E. Leon. *Dir* Hugo Grimaldi. *Orig Story & Screenplay* Arthur C. Pierce. *Dir Photog* Monroe Askins. *Art Dir* Paul Sylos. *Set Decor* Ray Boltz. *Film Ed* Donald Wolfe. *Mus Dir* Gordon Zahler. *Sd* Ryder Sound Service. *Sd Mix* Jean Valentino. *Asst Dir* Jesse Corallo, Harold Lewis. *Script Supv* Della Ross. *Wardrobe* Mickey Myers. *Makeup* John Chambers, Bob Mark. *Hairstyles* Kay Shea. *Sp Eff* Roger George. *Still Photog* Madison Lacy. *Gaffer* George Marqueenie. *Head Grip* John Livesley. *Prop Master* Ross Burke.
Cast: George Nader *(Glenn Martin)*, Barbara Nichols *(Gale Wilson)*, George Macready *(Professor Dornheimer)*, Dolores Faith *(Lisa)*, Richard Kiel *(Kolos)*, Richard Arlen *(National Intelligence Agency head)*, Hugh Beaumont *(Austin Welles)*, Ted Durant *(voice from outer space)*, Tommy Leonetti, Lonnie Sattin, John Indrisano.
Science fiction melodrama. Kolos, an agent from another world, is sent to Earth to create a colony of androids who will infiltrate the government and prepare for an invasion from Kolos' world. Kolos takes over the mansion of Professor Dornheimer, an electronics expert, and duplicates him and his staff with androids, sparing only the professor's blind niece, Lisa. The National Intelligence Agency assigns agent Glenn Martin to investigate thefts at research centers carried out by staff members—actually androids—who then disappeared. Martin's investigations lead him to the Dornheimer mansion where he is captured and duplicated. The android Martin is sent to throw the authorities off the trail but he arouses the suspicions of agent Gale Wilson. Although she catches him robbing a government electronics supply vault, he

escapes. The android Dornheimer rebels against Kolos, who has fallen in love with Lisa, but Kolos overcomes his opponent. Meanwhile, Lisa helps the real Martin escape and, with the help of the real Dornheimer, Martin destroys the androids with a laser beam. Kolos prepares to return to his world with a report of his failure and the inadvisability of an invasion. After restoring Lisa's eyesight, he reveals that he will be destroyed when he returns home but explains that it doesn't matter because he has discovered that he, too, is an android. *Space creatures. Androids. Professors. Uncles. Government agents. Blindness. Laser.*
Note: Location scenes filmed in Los Angeles.

THE HUMAN VAPOR (Japan)   **F6.2299**
Toho Co. *Dist* Brenco Pictures. 20 May **1964** [Los Angeles opening]. Sd; col (Eastmancolor). 35mm (Tohoscope). 79 min.
Pres by Edward L. Alperson, Stanley Meyer. *Exec Dir in Charge of Prod* Sanezumi Fujimoto. *Exec Prod* Tomoyuki Tanaka. *Dir* Inoshiro Honda. *Screenplay* Takeshi Kimura. *Photog* Hajime Koizumi. *Mus* Kunio Miyauchi. *Sp Eff* Eiji Tsuburaya.
Cast: Yoshio Tsuchiya *(Mizuno/The Vapor Man)*, Kaoru Yachigusa *(Fujichiyo, the dancer)*, Tatsuya Mihashi *(Okamoto, the detective)*, Keiko Sata *(Kyoko, the reporter)*.
Science fiction drama. In Tokyo a bank robber trying to escape the police overturns his car, but the police can find no trace of his body in the wreckage. Investigation reveals that the bank teller was strangled, although there is no trace of physical violence on his body. When a large portion of the stolen money turns up in the home of Fujichiyo, a famous dancer, she is taken into custody. Mizuno, who calls himself the Human Vapor, meets with the police; he admits that he committed the robbery out of love for Fujichiyo and that a scientist's experiments have made it possible for him to change at will into a vapor gas. Mizuno reenacts the robbery for the skeptical police and, immune to their bullets, strangles two of them. Scientists advise the police on a means of destroying the Human Vapor and, using Fujichiyo as bait, police lure him to a theater into which is piped a deadly gas. A spark ignites the gas, and the theater burns down with the Human Vapor still inside. *Scientists. Dancers. Police. Bank robberies. Transmutation. Murder. Fires. Tokyo.*
Note: Released in Japan in 1960 as *Gasu ningen daiichigo;* running time: 92 min.

THE HUMAN VOICE see **THE VOICE**

THE HUNCHBACK OF ROME (France/Italy)   **F6.2300**
Dino De Laurentiis Cinematografica–Orsay Films. *Dist* Royal Films International. Oct **1963**. Sd; b&w. 35mm. 84 min.
Prod Dino De Laurentiis. *Exec Prod* Carmine Bologna. *Assoc Prod* Domenico Bologna. *Dir* Carlo Lizzani. *Screenplay* Luciano Vincenzoni, Ugo Pirro, Carlo Lizzani, Elio Petri, Tommaso Chiaretti, Vittoriano Petrilli, Mario Socrate. *Photog* Leonida Barboni, Aldo Tonti. *2d Unit Photg* Giuseppe Aquari. *Camera Op* Michele Cristiani, Aiace Parolin. *2d Unit Camera Op* Emilio Giannini. *Art Dir* Mario Chiari. *Asst Art Dir* Pasquale Romano. *Set Dsgn* Giorgio Herman. *Film Ed* Franco Fraticelli. *Mus* Piero Piccioni. *Sd* Roy Mangano. *Sd Rec* Luigi Salvi. *Boom Op* Mario Celentano. *Sd Eff* Sergio Angeloni. *1st & 2d Asst Dir* Franco Giraldi, Guido Mazzella. *Prod Mgr* Toto Mignone, Giuseppe Barbaro. *Cont* Lina D'Amico. *Prod Sec* Enzo Cenciotti. *Cost* Piero Gherardi. *Still Photog* Alfonso Avincola. *Ch Mechanic* Salvatore Mazzini. *Ch Electrn* Enrico Bellaci.
Cast: Gérard Blain *(Alvaro Cosenza, "The Hunchback")*, Anna Maria Ferrero *(Ninetta)*, Ivo Garrani *(Moretti)*, Bernard Blier *(The Marshal)*, Pier Paolo Pasolini *(Er Monco)*, Teresa Pellati *(Fiorin Fiorello)*, Luba Bodine *(Nella)*, Enzo Cerusico *(Scheggia)*, Franco Balducci *(Pellaccia)*, Nino Castelnuovo *(Cencio)*, Roy Ciccolini *(Er Bello)*, Liuba Otasevic, Angela Luce, Piero Bugli.
War melodrama. On the outskirts of Rome in the winter of 1944, young Alvaro Cosenza, known as "The Hunchback," ruthless, deformed, and orphaned as a child, is the dominating figure in the resistance movement. He takes revenge upon Nazi collaborator Moretti by raping the traitor's daughter, Ninetta, but ironically falls in love with her. Disarmed by the resistance leaders because of his cruel, vindictive nature, The Hunchback steals weapons from a German arsenal. He is wounded and takes refuge in the reluctant Ninetta's house. He recovers and kills Moretti; later he is captured and tortured by the Fascists, but he escapes. With the liberation of Rome, the now-pregnant Ninetta, put out of her house because her father was a collaborator, loses her child by Alvaro and becomes a prostitute. Alvaro wants to aid her, but she refuses his help. The gun-happy Alvaro gathers together a gang of 150 criminals to rule over a poor suburb of Rome. He demonstrates his altruism by donating stolen merchandise to the needy, but he remains a tough outlaw. His plan to wipe out prostitution by giving money to the local whores is met with derisive laughter. Hunted by the police, Alvaro goes to Ninetta's house; and she tries

to help him escape, but they are caught in a police trap and killed. *Hunchbacks. Orphans. Traitors. Nazis. Fascists. Outlaws. Prisoners of war. Prostitutes. Gangsters. Police. Resistance (political). Revenge. Rape. Torture. Murder. Military occupation. Miscarriage. Theft. Firearms. World War II. Rome.*

Note: Location scenes filmed in and around Rome. Opened in Rome in Dec 1960 as *Il gobbo*; running time: 103 min; in Paris in Nov 1961 as *Le bossu de Rome*; running time: 90 min. Based on the exploits of the historical figure known as "Il Gobbo del Quarticciolo".

HUNG LOU MENG *see* **THE DREAM OF THE RED CHAMBER**

HUNGER (Denmark/Norway/Sweden)　　　　　　　　　**F6.2301**
Henning Carlsen–ABC-Film–Sandrews–Svensk Filmindustri. *Dist* Sigma III Corp. 12 Aug **1968** [New York opening]. Sd; b&w. 35mm. 115 min.

Prod Bertil Ohlsson. *Dir* Henning Carlsen. *Screenplay* Henning Carlsen, Peter Seeberg. *Photog* Henning Kristiansen. *Art Dir* Erik Aaes, Walther Dannerfjord. *Film Ed* Anja Breien. *Mus* Krzysztof Komeda. *Sd* Erik Jensen. *Asst Dir* Espen Thorstenson. *Prod Mgr* Jack Hald. *Cost* Ada Skolmen.

Cast: Per Oscarsson *(The Writer)*, Gunnel Lindblom *(Ylajali)*, Sigrid Horne-Rasmussen *(landlady)*, Osvald Helmuth *(pawnbroker)*, Birgitte Federspiel *(Ylajali's sister)*, Henki Kolstad *(editor)*, Sverre Hansen *(beggar)*, Egil Hjort Jensen *(man in the park)*, Per Theodor Haugen *(shop assistant)*, Lars Nordrum *("The Count")*, Roy Björnstad *(painter)*, Hans W. Petersen, Knud Rex, Wilhelm Lund, Ola B. Johannesen, Wilfred Breistrand, Else Heiberg, Veslemøy Haslund, Pål Skjönberg, Bjarne Andersen, Frimann Falck Clausen, Leif Enger, Lise Fjeldstad, Per Gjersøe, Toralf Sandø, Carsten Byhring, Carl Ottosen, Kåre Wichlund, Rolf Sand.

Drama. Source: Knut Hamsun, *Sult* (Kristiania, 1890). A young writer in late 19th-century Kristiania, unable to find a publisher for his works, takes refuge in daydreams to ease his terrible hunger pains. Having already pawned all he owns and being too proud to accept charity, he is finally reduced to chewing on discarded bones and eating scraps of paper. When he is evicted from his room for nonpayment of rent, he wanders through the streets, berating strangers for imagined insults, sleeping on park benches, and retreating further and further into hallucinations. On the strength of a promised fee for an article, he finds another room, but he is so weak from hunger that he is unable to finish his task. One night he meets a young woman, whom he had previously seen, and accompanies her to her home. Intrigued by his appearance, which she mistakenly attributes to bohemianism, she initially entices him to make love with her; then, in sudden revulsion at his condition, she spurns him. Later she sends him money, but too proud to accept what he has not earned, he throws it away. Without food, money, lodgings, warm clothing, or affection, he decides to leave the city and work as a deckhand on a ship. As the vessel sails off, he looks around expectantly, still believing in the brightness of the future. *Authors. Starvation. Poverty. Seduction. Pride. Eviction. Pawnshops. Ships. Kristiania. Hallucinations.*

Note: Norwegian and Danish title: *Sult*; Swedish title: *Svält.* Opened in Oslo, Copenhagen, and Stockholm in Aug 1966.

THE HUNGRY MAN　　　　　　　　　　　　　　　**F6.2302**
Dist Inter-Continental Films Distributors. ca **1970**. Sd; b&w. 35mm. [Feature film, length unknown.]

Crime melodrama. Al plans to marry a young, love-starved millionairess for her money. He plots with his mistress to have the woman killed. A rapist is hired to murder her, but after the crime is committed, he blackmails Al. Refusing to pay, Al is shot and killed. *Millionaires. Mistresses. Marriage. Blackmail. Murder.*

THE HUNS (France/Italy)　　　　　　　　　　　　　**F6.2303**
Comptoir Français du Film–Film Columbus. *Dist* Producers International Pictures. 14 Nov **1962** [Los Angeles opening]. Sd; col (EastmanColor). 35mm (Totalscope). 85 min.

Pres by William Hunter. *Prod* Carlo Lombardi. *Exec Prod* David Johnson. *Dir* Sergio Grieco. *Screenplay* Marcello Ciorciolini, Rate Furlan. *Story* Eric Klauss. *Dir Photog* Alfio Contini. *Art Dir* Alberto Boccianti. *Film Ed* Enzo Alfonsi. *Mus* Bruno Canfora. *Prod Mgr* Cleto Fontini, Italo Zingarelli. *Cost* Mario Giorsi.

Cast: Chelo Alonso *(Tanya)*, Jacques Sernas *(Malok)*, Folco Lulli *(Igor)*, Philippe Hersent, Ciquita Coffelli, Piero Lulli, Mario Petri, Andrea Scotti, Pietro Tordi.

Action melodrama. In the 1400's in central and southern Europe, the ferocious Tartar hordes known as Huns roam the countryside attacking villages and fighting among their own tribes. The Balas, a Tartar tribe led by Igor, destroy one village but spare the life of a young girl named Tanya and raise her as a warrior. Years later, the Balas clash with the Black Tartars, led by Malok, and Tanya and her adversary are attracted to each other. When the Black Tartars attack the Balas, they are beaten by the determined Tanya, now queen of the tribe, but she spares Malok. Assisted by Malok and his warriors, she leads

her starving tribe against the wealthy city of Kwarizim; the town is conquered but both peoples are united in a desire for peace. *Huns. Tartars. Tribal chiefs. Tribal life. Hunger. Middle Ages.*

Note: Opened in Paris in Mar 1961 as *La reine des barbares* at 87 min; in Rome in Oct 1960 as *La regina dei Tartari* at 100 min. Two U. S. sources credit Jacques Isken as producer and Roberto Paluzzi as director.

THE HUNT (Spain)　　　　　　　　　　　　　　　**F6.2304**
Elias Querejeta, P. C. *Dist* Trans–Lux Distributing Corp. 24 Apr **1967** [New York opening]. Sd; b&w. 35mm. 93 min. [Also 85 min.]

Pres by Mel Diamond, Harry Diamond, Gene Wesson. *Prod* Elias Querejeta. *Dir-Story* Carlos Saura. *Screenplay* Angelino Fons, Carlos Saura. *Photog* Luis Cuadrado. *Camera* Teodoro Escamilla. *Art Dir* Carlos Ochoa. *Film Ed* Pablo Gonzalez del Amo. *Mus* Luis de Pablo. *Asst Dir* José Luis Ruiz Marcos. *Prod Mgr* Primitivo Alvaro.

Cast: Ismael Merlo *(José)*, Alfredo Mayo *(Paco)*, José María Prada *(Luis)*, Emilio Gutiérrez Caba *(Enrique)*, Fernando Sánchez Polack *(Juan)*, Violetta García *(Nina)*, María Sánchez Arosa.

Drama. Three middle-aged men spend a day hunting rabbits on land where, years before, they fought during the Spanish Civil War. José, the organizer of the party, is an arrogant man who hopes to borrow money from Paco, a wartime comrade who has grown rich through shrewd business manipulations. The third man, Luis, is a semi-alcoholic escaping from reality through science fiction stories. Also on hand is Paco's teenaged brother-in-law, Enrique, who is anticipating the thrill of his first hunt. When José approaches Paco for a loan, Paco bluntly refuses. During the hot afternoon one of the ferrets used to rout the rabbits from their holes is shot by Paco, who detests the ferocious little animals. As the killing of the defenseless rabbits intensifies, the smoldering hatred and frustrations of the three men are triggered when Paco is killed by a blast from José's shotgun. Luis, enraged by what he believes to be premeditated murder, leaps into a jeep and drives full force at José. The latter retaliates by shooting Luis in the face, but he himself is also mortally wounded. Shocked, the unharmed Enrique stares numbly at the carnage surrounding him. *Veterans. Businessmen. Brothers-in-law. Hunting. Alcoholism. Adolescence. Murder. Loans. Spain—History—Civil War 1936–39. Rabbits and hares.*

Note: Location scenes filmed in Spain. Opened in Madrid in Nov 1966 as *La caza*; running time: 93 min.

THE HUNTERS ARE THE HUNTED *see* **HUNTING SCENES FROM BAVARIA**

THE HUNTER'S DIARY (Japan)　　　　　　　　　　**F6.2305**
Nikkatsu Corp. 11 Dec **1964** [Los Angeles opening]. Sd; b&w. 35mm (Nikkatsu Scope). 123 min.

Dir Ko Nakahira. *Screenplay* Tatsuo Asano. *Photog* Yoshihiro Yamazaki.

Cast: Noboru Nakaya, Masako Togawa, Yukiyo Toake, Kazuo Kitamura, Yoko Ozono.

Crime melodrama. Honda, who is married to a frigid wife he sees only on weekends, satisfies his overwhelming sexual appetite by systematically seducing women and recording his experiences in a notebook which he calls "The Hunter's Diary." Suddenly, each of Honda's women is found murdered and the police use his blood and semen types to arrest and convict him of the crimes. Honda's new attorney, hired to appeal the conviction, senses that the real killer, acting out of revenge, knew of Honda's rare blood type and planted the evidence at the scene of the crimes. The killer is revealed to be Honda's wife, who became enraged when she found her husband's diary, in which her name was entered first along with the notation that she was not a virgin. *Philanderers. Lawyers. Infidelity. Murder. Revenge. Frameup. Frigidity. Diaries. Evidence.*

Note: Released in Japan in 1964 as *Ryojin nikki*.

HUNTING IN SIBERIA (U.S.S.R.)　　　　　　　　　**F6.2306**
Moscow Popular Science Studio. *Dist* Artkino Pictures. 30 Jun **1962** [New York opening]. Sd; col (Sovcolor). 35mm. 60 min.

Dir Gleb Nifontov. *Screenplay* Serafima Burlyuk, Anatoliy Zhadan. *Story Ed* V. Russo. *Photog* Georgiy Kholnyy. *Camera* B. Moskalenko, K. Khabeyev. *Art Dir* G. Rozhalin, Ya. Benin. *Mus* Aleksandr Lokshin, A. Sevastyanov. *Cond* V. Smirnov. *Sd* K. Bek-Nazarov. *Asst Dir* Anatoliy Zhadan, M. Tovarnov. *Creative Supv* A. Zguridi. *Prod Mgr* Ya. Izrailev.

Cast: Ivan Savkin *(Yegorov)*, Radner Muratov *(Dudin)*, K. Albanov *(Shirvakhun)*, B. Sitko *(Zharkov)*, Ivan Koval-Samborskiy *(gloomy hunter)*, Grigoriy Mikhaylov *(Makarov)*, Konstantin Nemolyayev *(Cherepanov)*, P. Lyubeshkin *(Zotov)*, D. Netrebin *(Trofimov)*, Georgiy Millyar, V. Boriskin, Sh. Tyumenbayev, Ye. Dubasov, G. Okhrimenko.

Adventure drama. Yegorov, a young hunter who has recently completed his studies, is captivated by the romance of tiger hunting. As he embarks on work in the field, he errs through lack of patience and experience. Assigned to help capture a tiger for a zoo, he becomes frightened and shoots his quarry. As time goes on Yegorov gains experience in the wilderness and becomes familiar with the habits of the native wildlife. In the Siberian taiga, in Kazakhstan, and in the Tien Shan of Central Asia, he joins expert trappers in capturing saiga, pelicans, eagles, porcupines, and other wild animals. Yegorov becomes an experienced animal collector and at last is able to capture a tiger alive. [U. S. release version may include only Siberian footage.] *Hunters. Animal life. Education. Siberia. Kazakhstan. Tien Shan. Tigers. Antelope. Pelicans. Eagles. Porcupines.*

Note: Released in the U.S.S.R. in Jun 1959 as *Zverolovy*; running time: 82 min.

HUNTING SCENES FROM BAVARIA (West Germany)   F6.2307
Rob Houwer Film. *Dist* Radim Films. 20 May 1970 [San Francisco opening]. Sd; b&w. 35mm. 90 min.

Dir-Writ Peter Fleischmann. *Photog* Alain Derobe. *Film Ed* Barbara Mondry, Jane Seitz.

Cast: Martin Sperr *(Abram)*, Angela Winkler *(Hannelore)*, Else Quecke *(Barbara)*, Michael Strixner *(Georg)*, Maria Stadler *(butcher's wife)*, Gunja Seiser *(Maria)*, Hanna Schygulla *(Paula)*, Johann Brunner *(Hiasl)*, Renata Sandner *(Zenta)*, Erika Wackernagel *(mayor's wife)*, Hans Elwenspoek *(priest)*, Ernst Wager *(villager)*.

Drama. Source: Martin Sperr, *Jagdszenen aus Niederbayern* (Bremen opening: May 1966). Abram returns to his village after serving a term in jail for an offense involving homosexuality. Abram only wants to take up his job as a mechanic, but Hannelore, a former girl friend, wants to marry him. Hannelore claims to be pregnant by Abram, although in reality she does not know the identity of the father. When Abram gives the village idiot a ride on his bicycle, he is accused by the villagers of taking sexual liberties with the boy. Finally, Abram runs away from the village, pursued by Hannelore, whose persistence so enrages him that he strangles her. The villagers, eager to claim the reward, set out to capture him. *Ex-convicts. Mechanics. Idiots. Bounty hunters. Male homosexuality. Pregnancy. Murder. Chases.*

Note: Produced in West Germany and released there as *Jagdszenen aus Niederbayern*; running time: 85 min. Later released in the United States as *The Hunters Are the Hunted.*

HUNZA—THE HIMALAYAN SHANGRI-LA   F6.2308
International Film Enterprises. 4 Apr 1962 [Chicago opening]. Sd; col (Eastman Color). 35mm. 60 min.

Prod-Dir Zygmunt Sulistrowski. *Co-prod* Mulford J. Nobbs. *Writ* Renee Taylor. *Photog* Zygmunt Sulistrowski, Wayne Mitchell. *Film Ed* Zygmunt Sulistrowski.

Documentary. A glimpse of the Himalayan region of Hunza, whose exceptionally long-lived population appears to be untroubled by discord and illness. *Mountain life. Old age. Hunza. Himalayan Mountains.*

THE HURRICANE see VOICE OF THE HURRICANE

THE HURRICANE DRUMMER (Japan)   F6.2309
Toho Co. Oct 1967 [Los Angeles showing]. Sd; col? 35mm. [Feature film, length unknown.]

Cast: Tetsuya Watari.No information about the nature of this film has been found. *Hurricanes.*

Note: Original title and release undetermined.

HURRY SUNDOWN   F6.2310
Sigma Productions. *Dist* Paramount Pictures. 9 Feb 1967 [Los Angeles opening; c31 Dec 1966; LP34464]. Sd; col (Technicolor). 35mm (Panavision). 146 min. [See note.]

Pres by Otto Preminger. *Prod-Dir* Otto Preminger. *Screenplay* Thomas C. Ryan, Horton Foote. *Dir Photog (see note)* Milton Krasner, Loyal Griggs. *Camera Op* Duke Callaghan. *Asst Art Dir* Gordon Gurnee. *Set Decor* John Godfrey. *Architectural Supv* John Schaeffer. *Prod Dsgn* Gene Callahan. *Film Ed* Louis R. Loeffler, James Wells. *Neg Cutter* Connie Roese. *Mus* Hugo Montenegro. *Titl Song* Buddy Kaye, Hugo Montenegro. *Sung by* Robert Hooks. *Sd* Harold Lewis, Franklin Milton, Bert Hallberg, Glenn Anderson. *Sd Eff Ed* John Link, II. *Mus Ed* Richard Berres. *Asst Dir* Burtt Harris, Howard Joslin, John G. Avildsen. *Prod Mgr* Stephen F. Kesten, Eva Monley. *Exec Asst to the Prod* Nat Rudich. *Prod Sec* John Dunaway. *Script Supv* Marshall Schlom. *Cost Dsgn* Estévez. *Wardrobe* Alan Levine, Phyllis Garr, Ted Parvin. *Cost Coörd* Hope Bryce. *Makeup* Del Armstrong, Web Overlander. *Hairdressing* Frederic Jones. *Sp Eff* Willis Cook. *Ch Electrn* Joe Edesa, Homer Plannette. *Constr* Bud Pine. *Key Grip* Morris Rosen. *Dial Coach* Max Slater. *Story & Casting* Bill Barnes.

Cast: Michael Caine *(Henry Warren)*, Jane Fonda *(Julie Ann Warren)*, John Phillip Law *(Rad McDòwell)*, Diahann Carroll *(Vivian Thurlow)*, Robert Hooks *(Reeve Scott)*, Faye Dunaway *(Lou McDowell)*, Burgess Meredith *(Judge Purcell)*, Robert Reed *(Lars Finchley)*, George Kennedy *(Sheriff Coombs)*, Frank Converse *(Rev. Clem de Lavery)*, Loring Smith *(Thomas*

Elwell*)*, Beah Richards *(Rose Scott)*, Madeleine Sherwood *(Eula Purcell)*, Rex Ingram *(Professor Thurlow)*, Steve Sanders *(Charles McDowell)*, John Mark *(Colie Warren)*, Doro Merande *(Ada Hemmings)*, Luke Askew *(Dolph Higginson)*, Donna Danton *(Sukie Purcell)*, Jim Backus *(Carter Sillens)*, Peter Goff *(Lipscomb)*, William Elder *(bishop)*, Dawn Barcelona *(Ruby McDowell)*, David Sanders *(Wyatt McDowell)*, Michael Henry Roth *(Timmy McDowell)*, Gladys Newman *(Mrs. Coombs)*, Joan Parks *(Kissie)*, Robert C. Bloodwell *(Ozzie Higginson)*, Charles Keel *(Kenny)*, Gene Rutherford, Bill Hart, Dean Smith *(hunt club members)*, Kelly Ross *(Dottie)*, Ada Hall Covington *(Clara)*.

Rural melodrama. Source: K. B. Gilden, *Hurry Sundown* (New York, 1964). Following World War II, a Northern canning plant negotiates for the purchase of a large tract of uncultivated Georgia farmland, and all but two small plots are optioned from owner Julie Ann Warren and her bigoted, draft-dodging husband, Henry. The remaining land belongs to Henry's cousin, Rad McDowell, a combat veteran with a wife and family, and Reeve Scott, a young black whose mother was Julie's mammy. Neither Rad nor Reeve is interested in selling, and they form an unprecedented biracial partnership to improve their land. Henry, infuriated by this turn of events, remains determined to push through the big land deal, and when Reeve's mother dies, he tries to persuade Julie to charge Reeve with illegal ownership of his property, confident that bigoted Judge Purcell will rule against a black. Meanwhile, schoolteacher Vivian Thurlow, granddaughter of the most respected member in the local black community, finds proof in the town's official records that Reeve's land deed is legally registered. Later, Julie decides to leave Henry because of his negligent care of their retarded son and withdraws any claim to Reeve's land. In a desperate move to force the partners to sell, Henry dynamites the dam above their farms; Rad's oldest child is caught in the raging waters as the area is flooded and drowns in spite of a rescue attempt by Henry, whom the child had idolized. The tragedy unites McDowell and his wife, Lou, even more closely with Reeve and Vivian, who have fallen in love. As they set about rebuilding the farms, they are aided by neighboring blacks. *Cousins. Negroes. Veterans. Draft dodgers. Schoolteachers. Judges. Greed. Racism. Farm life. Partnerships. Race relations. Mental retardation. Filial relations. Rescue. Canneries. Land rights. Dams. Floods. Georgia. Documentation. Explosions.*

Note: Location scenes filmed in Louisiana. Also reviewed at 142 and 148 min; copyright length: 144 min. Director of photography Griggs was replaced by Krasner during filming.

HUSBANDS   F6.2311
Faces Music Inc. *Dist* Columbia Pictures. 8 Dec 1970 [New York opening; c1 Dec 1970; LP38732]. Sd; col (De Luxe). 35mm. 138 min. [See note.] *MPAA rating* GP.

Overall Production Credits: *Pres by* Al Ruban, Sam Shaw. *Prod* Al Ruban. *Assoc Prod* Sam Shaw. *Dir-Writ* John Cassavetes. *Dir Photog* Victor Kemper. *Supv Ed* Peter Tanner. *Asst Ed* Robert Heffernan, Joe Lustig. *Post Prod Ed* Jack Woods. *Prod Supv* Fred Caruso. *Prod Coörd* James Joyce.

Production Credits for New York Unit: *Camera Op* Richard Mingalone, Michael Chapman. *Asst Camera* Edde Gold. *Art Dir* René D'Auriac. *Scenic Artist* Robert Hamlin. *Sd* Dennis Maitland. *Asst Dir* Alan Hopkins. *Prod Mgr* Robert Greenhut. *Cont* Nancy Norman. *Cost Dsgn* Louis Brown. *Mr. Gazzara's Wardrobe* Lentini Creations. *Wardrobe* Edward Brennan, Joseph W. Dehn. *Makeup* Robert Laden. *Composition Artist* Edith Shaw. *Gaffer* Rich Quinlan. *Casting* All Arts. *Key Grip* Joseph Williams. *Dial Supv* Fred Draper. *Prop* Tom Saccio.

Production Credits for London Unit: *Camera Op* Geoff Glover. *Asst Camera* Edde Gold. *Mus Dir* Stanley Wilson, Jack Ackerman. *Adtl Mus* Ray Brown. *Sd* Barrie Copland. *Asst Dir* Simon Hinkley, Philip Mead. *Cont* Peggy Lashbrook. *Wardrobe* Shura Cohen, Dennis Frun. *Makeup* Tommy Manderson. *Gaffer* Len Crow. *Key Grip* Ted Tucker. *Props & Eff* Henry Newman. *Casting* Tom Busby.

Cast: Ben Gazzara *(Harry)*, Peter Falk *(Archie)*, John Cassavetes *(Gus)*, Jenny Runacre *(Mary Tynan)*, Jenny Lee Wright *(Pearl Billingham)*, Noelle Kao *(Julie)*, John Kullers *(Red)*, Meta Shaw *(Annie)*, Leola Harlow *(Leola)*, Delores Delmar *(The Countess)*, Eleanor Zee *(Mrs. Hines)*, Claire Malis *(Stuart's wife)*, Peggy Lashbrook *(Diana Mallabee)*, Eleanor Gould *("Normandy")*, Sarah Felcher *(Sarah)*, Gwen Van Dam *("Jeannie")*, John Armstrong *("Happy Birthday")*, Antoinette Kray *("Jesus Loves Me")*, Lorraine McMartin *(Annie's mother)*, Carinthia West *(Susanna)*, Edgar Franken *(Ed Weintraub)*, Joseph Boley *(minister)*, Judith Lowry *(Stuart's grandmother)*, Joe Hardy *("Shanghai Lil")*, David Rowlands *(Stuart Jackson)*, Rhonda Parker *(Margaret)*, K. C. Townsend *(barmaid)*, Anne O'Donnell, Gena Wheeler *(nurses)*, Nick Cassavetes *(Nick)*, Alexandra Cassavetes *(Xan)*, Bill Britton, Arthur Clark, Charles Gaines, Fred Draper.

Drama. Gus, Harry, and Archie, three husbands with families in suburban New York, are shaken when their best friend, Stuart Jackson, suddenly dies of a heart attack. Unable to return to work after the funeral, they spend two days playing basketball, sleeping in the subways, and going on a drinking spree until Gus, a newspaperman, and Archie, a dentist, are ready to go back to their middle-class lives. Harry has a vicious argument with his wife, however, and soon decides to go to London. He convinces the other two to fly with him, and upon arrival they check into an expensive hotel, dress in formal clothing, and visit a gambling casino. There they meet three young women whom they take back to their hotel suite; Gus pairs off with Mary Tynan, Archie stays with Julie, a Chinese woman who cannot speak English, and Harry spends the evening with Pearl Billingham, in spite of his guilt feelings about adultery. The next morning, Gus and Archie decide to return home, but they cannot convince Harry to leave with them. Instead, Harry introduces them to Diana Mallabee and two other women he is entertaining and throws a party for his departing friends. Back at the airport in New York, Gus and Archie buy gifts to placate their families and return home. *Newspapermen. Dentists. English. Chinese. Americans in foreign countries. Death. Marriage. Suburban life. Friendship. Drunkenness. Infidelity. Funerals. Casinos. New York City. London.*

Note: Location scenes filmed in London and New York City. 1970 San Francisco Film Festival running time: 154 min.

HUSH-A-BYE MURDER see **MY LOVER, MY SON**

HUSH ... HUSH, SWEET CHARLOTTE　　　　　　　　　**F6.2312**
Associates & Aldrich Co. *Dist* Twentieth Century-Fox Film Corp. 16 Dec **1964** [Los Angeles opening; c31 Dec 1964; LP29684]. Sd; b&w. 35mm. 134 min. [Copyright length: 130 min.]

Prod-Dir Robert Aldrich. *Assoc Prod* Walter Blake. *Screenplay* Henry Farrell, Lukas Heller. *Photog* Joseph Biroc. *Art Dir* William Glasgow. *Set Decor* Raphael Bretton. *Film Ed* Michael Luciano. *Mus* Frank De Vol. *Titl Song* Mack David, Frank De Vol. *Sung by* Al Martino. *Orch* Al Woodbury. *Choreog* Alex Ruiz. *Sd Mix* Herman Lewis, Bernard Freericks. *Asst Dir* William McGarry, Sam Strangis, William F. Sheehan. *Prod Supv* Jack R. Berne. *Script Supv* Robert Gary. *Cost Dsgn* Norma Koch. *Makeup* Gene Hibbs. *Prop Master* John Orlando. *Constr Coörd* John La Salandra. *Dial Supv* Robert Sherman.

Cast: Bette Davis *(Charlotte Hollis)*, Olivia De Havilland *(Miriam Deering)*, Joseph Cotten *(Dr. Drew Bayliss)*, Agnes Moorehead *(Velma Cruther)*, Cecil Kellaway *(Harry Willis)*, Victor Buono *(Big Sam Hollis)*, Mary Astor *(Mrs. Jewel Mayhew)*, William Campbell *(Paul Marchand)*, Wesley Addy *(Sheriff Luke Standish)*, Bruce Dern *(John Mayhew)*, Frank Ferguson *(editor)*, George Kennedy *(foreman)*, Dave Willock *(taxi driver)*, John Megna *(new boy)*, Michael Petit *(gang leader)*, Kelly Flynn *(2d boy)*, Percy Helton *(funeral director)*, Alida Aldrich *(young girl)*, Kelly Aldrich *(3d boy)*, William Aldrich *(boy dancer)*, Carol DeLay *(Geraldine)*, Ellen Corby, Marianne Stewart, Helen Kleeb *(town gossips)*, Lillian Randolph, Geraldine West, Mary Henderson *(cleaning women)*, Bill Walker *(chauffeur)*, Idell James *(Ginny Mae)*, Buckner All-Stars.

Horror film. Source: Henry Farrell, "Hush Now, Sweet Charlotte" (a story; publication undetermined). When the Louisiana Highway Commission decides to build a road through her property, Charlotte Hollis threatens the workmen with a shotgun. Thirty-seven years earlier Charlotte's married lover, John Mayhew, was murdered; and though the killer was never discovered, the local townspeople are convinced of Charlotte's guilt. Charlotte herself, believing that her father killed Mayhew, became a recluse, living with her housekeeper, Velma, in the deteriorating Hollis mansion. Now she seeks help in her fight against the Highway Commission from Miriam, a poor cousin who lived with the family as a girl. Upon returning, Miriam renews her relationship with Drew Bayliss, the local doctor who jilted her after the murder. The eccentric Charlotte becomes progressively wilder with Miriam's arrival—her nights haunted by mysterious piano playing of the song Mayhew wrote for her and by the appearance of Mayhew's disembodied hand and head. Velma, realizing that Miriam and Drew are trying to drive Charlotte completely mad in order to get her money, seeks help from Mr. Willis, a Lloyd's of London insurance investigator who is still interested in the Mayhew case and who has visited Mayhew's ailing widow, Jewel; but Miriam kills Velma when the housekeeper tries to remove Charlotte from the mansion for safety. Miriam and Drew trick Charlotte into shooting Drew with a gun loaded with blanks, and Miriam helps Charlotte dispose of the body in a swamp. Drew's reappearance later reduces Charlotte to whimpering insanity. Believing Charlotte completely mad and secure in her room, Miriam and Drew go into the garden to discuss what they have done. As Miriam embraces Drew, she looks up to see Charlotte, who has overheard them, push a huge stone urn from the balcony above, crushing them to death. Later, as Charlotte is taken away by the authorities, Willis hands her an envelope from the now-dead Jewel Mayhew; it contains Jewel's confession of the murder of her husband. *Recluses. Eccentrics. Housekeepers. Cousins. Physicians. Investigators. Widows. Ghosts. Infidelity. Murder. Guilt. Filial relations. Hallucinations. Mutilation. Insanity. Confession (law). Louisiana. Lloyd's of London.*

Note: Original title: *What Ever Happened to Cousin Charlotte?*

THE HUSTLER　　　　　　　　　　　　　　　　　　　　　　　　**F6.2313**
Rossen Enterprises. *Dist* Twentieth Century-Fox Film Corp. 25 Sep **1961** [New York opening; c26 Sep 1961; LP20623]. Sd (Westrex); b&w. 35mm (CinemaScope). 133 min.

A Robert Rossen Production. *Prod-Dir* Robert Rossen. *Screenplay* Sidney Carroll, Robert Rossen. *Dir Photog* Eugen Shuftan. *Camera Op* Saul Midwall. *Asst Camera* William Cronjager. *Assoc Art Dir* Albert Brenner. *Set Decor* Gene Callahan. *Prod Dsgn* Harry Horner. *Film Ed* Dede Allen. *Asst Film Ed* Richard Stone. *Mus* Kenyon Hopkins. *Louisville Mus* Dan Terry. *Sd* Jim Shields, Richard Vorisek. *Sd Ed* Edward Beyer. *Mus Ed* Angelo Ross. *Asst Dir* Charles Maguire, Don Kranze. *Unit Prod Mgr* John Graham, prod mgr. *Script Supv* Marguerite James. *Cost Dsgn* Ruth Morley. *Makeup* Robert Jiras. *Hairstyles* Donoene. *Optical Eff* Film Opticals. *Tech Adv* Willie Mosconi. *Still Photog* Muky. *Ch Electrn* David Golden. *Ch Grip* Martin Nallan, Jr.

Cast: Paul Newman *(Eddie Felson)*, Jackie Gleason *(Minnesota Fats)*, Piper Laurie *(Sarah Packard)*, George C. Scott *(Bert Gordon)*, Myron McCormick *(Charlie Burns)*, Murray Hamilton *(Findlay)*, Michael Constantine *(Big John)*, Stefan Gierasch *(Preacher)*, Clifford Pellow *(Turk)*, Jake LaMotta *(bartender)*, Gordon B. Clarke *(cashier)*, Alexander Rose *(scorekeeper)*, Carolyn Coates *(waitress)*, Carl York *(young hustler)*, Vincent Gardenia *(bartender)*, Gloria Curtis *(girl with fur coat)*, Charles Dierkop, Donald Crabtree, Brendan Fay *(poolroom hoods)*, Willie Mosconi, Don De Leo, Tom Ahearne.

Drama. Source: Walter S. Tevis, *The Hustler* (New York, 1959). Newly arrived in New York from California is "Fast" Eddie Felson, a brash pool shark who makes his living hustling in billiard parlors around the country. Taking on unwary opponents, he allows them to win until the stakes are high enough; then he makes his killing and leaves town. Eddie has come to New York with his longtime crony and manager, Charlie Burns, to challenge Minnesota Fats, the undisputed champion pool player in the country. For 36 hours the two men battle, and, at first, game after game goes to Eddie. Then, filled with too much liquor and conceit, he eventually falls apart and ends up beaten and broke. Following the bout, he wanders into an all-night coffeeshop and picks up an alcoholic, disillusioned cripple named Sarah Packard. For want of anything better to do, he moves in with her and lives a day-to-day existence by hustling in third-rate pool halls throughout the city. One night he challenges the wrong sucker, another young hustler he meets in a waterfront dive. Although Eddie wins, four hoodlums grab Eddie, throw him into the men's room, and break both his thumbs. Once recovered, Eddie aligns himself with a coldblooded gambler, Bert Gordon, who agrees to arrange bigtime matches in return for 70 percent of the winnings. Accompanied by Sarah, Eddie and Bert travel to Louisville, Kentucky, where Eddie takes on Findlay, a millionaire playboy addicted to billiards. Though the trip ends in victory for Eddie, it ends in tragedy for Sarah. Badgered by the ruthless Bert, who demands complete dominion over his client, Sarah admits defeat and slashes her wrists with a razor. Shattered by the realization that his egotism has destroyed his one chance for happiness, Eddie returns to New York and again challenges Fats. Eddie outshoots, outmaneuvers, and outthinks his opponent until Fats finally concedes defeat. Victorious, Eddie denounces Bert, refuses to give him a cut of the winnings, and walks out of the pool room. *Pool sharks. Cripples. Pickups. Gamblers. Millionaires. Suicide. Alcoholism. Billiard parlors. New York City. Louisville (Kentucky).*

Note: Filmed in New York City.

HVAD MED OS? see **EPILOGUE**

HYPNOSIS (Italy/Spain/West Germany)　　　　　　　　　**F6.2314**
International Germania Film–Domiziana Internazionale Cinematografica-Procusa. *Dist* United Film Enterprises. 19 Aug **1966** [Chicago opening]. Sd; b&w. 35mm. 86 min.

Prod Alfons Carcasina. *Dir* Eugenio Martín. *Screenplay* Giuseppe Mangione, Eugenio Martín, Gabriel Moreno Burgos, Francis Niewel, Gerhard Schmidt. *Story* Gabriel Moreno Burgos. *Photog* Francisco Sempere. *Asst Photog* Cecilio Paniagua. *Art Dir* Ramiro Gómez. *Film Ed* Antonio Gimeno, Edith von Seydewitz. *Mus (see note)* Francesco De Masi, Angelo Francesco Lavagnino, Roman Vlad. *Prod Mgr* Eduardo Lafuente.

Cast: Eleonora Rossi-Drago *(Magda Bergen)*, Jean Sorel *(Erik Stein)*, Götz George *(Chris Kronberger)*, Massimo Serato *(Georg von Cramer)*, Mara Cruz *(Carmen)*, Margot Trooger *(Katharina)*, Heinz Drache *(Insp. Herbert Kaufmann)*, Werner Peters *(police commissioner)*, Guido Celano *(Tony)*, Michael Cramer *(Pablo)*, Ana María Montaner *(Loren)*, Diana Rabito, José María Caffarel, Antonio Queipo, Antonio Casas, Hildegard Knef.

Melodrama. Fiancés Georg and Magda and their assistant Erik perform in a vaudeville act combining ventriloquism and hypnotism. Erik, jealously in love with Magda, kills Georg and frames Chris, an errand boy and petty thief, for the crime. Sought by the police, Chris goes into hiding and tries to blackmail

Erik, but Erik kills him. Erik also tries to kill Carmen, Chris's sister, when she arrives looking for her brother; but Pablo, a policeman, foils him. Magda eventually frightens Erik into confessing to the murders by tormenting him with Georg's ventriloquist dummy Grog and tape recordings of Grog's laughter. *Vaudevillians. Errand boys. Police. Ventriloquism. Hypnotism. Jealousy. Murder. Frameup. Revenge. Blackmail. Confession (law).*

Note: Released in West Germany in Jan 1963 as *Nur tote Zeugen schweigen;* running time: 86 min. Cut from 90 min. Opened in Madrid in May 1963 as *Hipnosis;* in Rome in Jun 1963 as *Ipnosi.* Sources conflict in crediting music.

HYSTERIA (Great Britain)   **F6.2315**
Hammer Film Productions. *Dist* Metro-Goldwyn-Mayer, Inc. Apr **1965** [c31 Dec 1964; LP29399]. Sd (Westrex); b&w. 35mm. 86 min.

Prod-Writ Jimmy Sangster. *Dir* Freddie Francis. *Dir Photog* John Wilcox. *Camera Op* David Harcourt. *Prod Dsgn* Edward Carrick. *Main Titl* Chambers & Partners. *Supv Ed* James Needs. *Mus Comp* Don Banks. *Mus Supv* Philip Martell. *Sd Rec* Cyril Swern. *Sd Ed* Roy Hyde. *Asst Dir* Basil Rayburn. *Prod Mgr* Don Weeks. *Cont* Yvonne Axworthy. *Wardrobe Mistress* Maude Churchill. *Makeup* Alex Garfath. *Hairstyles* Alice Holmes.

Cast: Robert Webber *(Chris Smith),* Anthony Newlands *(Dr. Keller),* Jennifer Jayne *(Gina),* Maurice Denham *(Hemmings),* Lelia Goldoni *(Denise),* Peter Woodthorpe *(Marcus Allan),* Sandra Boize *(English girl),* Sue Lloyd *(French girl),* John Arnatt, Marianne Stone, Irene Richmond, Kiwi Kingston.

Mystery melodrama. Following an automobile accident, American Chris Smith finds himself in a London hospital. Chris is informed by Dr. Keller, the physician treating him for amnesia, that his bills are being paid by an anonymous benefactor, who has made an apartment available to him. Upon release from the hospital, Chris seeks the help of Hemmings, a private investigator, and moves into the flat. To learn more about a torn photo that is his only link with the past, Chris visits the photographer, who tells him that the subject is dead, the victim of a shower murder. Warned by Dr. Keller to anticipate hallucinations, Chris hears strange voices in his flat and encounters Denise, who claims to be the widow of the man responsible for the automobile accident but bears a remarkable resemblance to the woman in the photograph. Denise plies Chris with drugs, and after one such episode, he discovers in his shower the body of a murdered woman, which later disappears. Assisted by Hemmings, Chris tricks Denise and Keller into admitting that they are the murderers, having planned to frame him for the crime, and that the victim is the physician's wife. Chris continues the romance begun in the hospital with his nurse, Gina. *Americans in foreign countries. Detectives. Nurses. Physicians. Amnesia. Murder. Frameup. Hospitals. Photographs. Drugs. London. Hallucinations. Automobile accidents.*

Note: Released in Great Britain in 1965.

I, A LOVER (Denmark/Sweden)   **F6.2316**
Novaris Film–Dansk-Svensk Film–Europa Film. *Dist* Crown International Pictures. 5 Apr **1968** [Los Angeles opening]. Sd; b&w. 35mm. 90 min.

Prod-Screenplay Peer Guldbrandsen. *Dir* Börje Nyberg. *Photog* Jan Lindeström. *Art Dir* Tage Mellerup, Poul Arnt Thomsen. *Film Ed* Edith Nisted Nielsen. *Mus* Sven Gyldmark. *Played by* Jorn Grauencards Orchestra. *Sd* Jon Branner.

Cast: Jørgen Ryg *(Peter),* Jessie Flaws *(Beatrice),* Axel Strøbye *(Ole),* Ebbe Langberg *(Isak),* Paul Hagen *(Mr. Pauce),* Dirch Passer *(Mortensen),* Kerstin Wartel *(Sigrid),* Marie Nylander *(Elizabeth),* Jeanne Darville *(Dr. Ulla Pauce),* Sigrid Horne-Rasmussen *(woman in office),* Tove Maës, Jytte Breuning, Lise Thomsen, Benny Juhlin.

Comedy. Source: Stiig Holm, *Jeg—en elsker* (Copenhagen, 1965). Disgruntled at her husband's impotence, Beatrice goes to Paris with her playboy admirer, Isak. Although at first hurt and embarrassed by his wife's departure, the husband, Peter, soon discovers that in her absence he is preoccupied with sex. Furthermore, the local women now consider his impotence a challenge to be overcome. A prostitute is the first to test herself, followed by his best friend's middle-aged wife, Sigrid, and their 16-year-old daughter, Elizabeth. Concerned about his growing sexual appetite, Peter consults a psychologist, Dr. Ulla Pauce, who also seduces him. They are joined by Sigrid and Dr. Pauce's sociologist husband. Eventually, an anonymous letter brings the wayward Beatrice home. Infuriated that her husband is impotent only with her, she is determined to win him back. Isak, hoping to dispose of Peter, finds him a job in Rome, far from Beatrice. Unbeknownst to Isak, however, Beatrice leaves with her husband. *Playboys. Psychologists. Sociologists. Prostitutes. Impotence. Infidelity. Marriage. Group sex. Rome. Paris.*

Note: Filmed in Copenhagen; released in Denmark in Apr 1966 as *Jeg—en elsker.* Swedish title: *Jag—en älskare.*

I, A MAN   **F6.2317**
Dist Factory Films, Film-Makers' Cooperative. 24 Aug **1967** [New York opening]. Sd; col (Eastman Color). 16mm. 100 min. [Also reviewed at 105 min.]

Pres by Andy Warhol. *Prod-Dir-Writ* Andy Warhol. *Photog* Andy Warhol. *Film Ed* Andy Warhol.

Cast: Tom Baker *(Tom),* Cynthia May *(girl in kitchen [first girl]),* Ivy Nicholson *(girl with television [second girl]),* Ingrid Superstar *(girl on table [third girl]),* Stephanie Graves *(girl in penthouse [fourth girl]),* Valerie Solanis *(girl on staircase [fifth girl]),* Bettina Coffin *(married girl [sixth girl]).* Ultra Violet, Nico.

Melodrama. Tom, an intense young man, goes on a 1-day odyssey in New York City to find out "what it all means." In the process he encounters six women. He has sex with the first under the bed in her apartment and romps in the nude at breakfast. The second woman, whom he brings to his apartment, feels nervous and frustrated and offers Tom no pleasure. The third lies on a table and engages in a spiritualistic ritual. She is interested in the possibility of making love with famous men of the past, notably James Dean, and expresses concern over the firmness of her breasts. The fourth woman is being kept by another man in a "mod" apartment that she detests; though she and Tom make sexual contact, she rejects his offer to move in because she suspects that his taste in furnishings is too close to that of her lover. Tom meets a lesbian on a staircase, and she ridicules him for interpreting a familiar pinch as a sign of sexual encouragement. Finally, Tom ends up at his own apartment again with a married woman who tells him at length of her arguments with her husband over the question of killing the cockroaches in their apartment. His day's experiences at an end, Tom has not discovered "what it all means." *Urban life. Prostitution. Spiritualism. Lesbianism. Infidelity. Cockroaches. New York City. James Dean.*

I, A NOBLEMAN (Denmark/Sweden)   **F6.2318**
Novaris Film–Wallius. *Dist* Producers Releasing Organization. 8 May **1968** [Bogota, New Jersey, opening]. Sd; b&w. 35mm. 90 min.

Pres by Vernon P. Becker, Mel May. *Prod* Peer Guldbrandsen, Henrik Sandberg. *Dir* Mac Ahlberg, Peer Guldbrandsen. *Screenplay* Peer Guldbrandsen. *Photog* Mac Ahlberg. *Art Dir* Kai Rasch. *Film Ed* Edith Nisted Nielsen. *Mus* Sven Gyldmark. *Mus Selections* Frédéric François Chopin, Johann Strauss. *Sd* Jon Branner.

Cast: Gabriel Axel *(Marcus Daniel Edouard Rasmussen),* Buster Larsen *(lawyer),* Karl Stegger *(Mikkelsen),* Elsa Prawitz *(Mrs. Mikkelsen),* Poul Bundgaard *(bank director),* Ove Sprogøe *(baron),* Paul Hagen *(James),* Lotte Tarp *(baroness),* John Price *(accountant),* Preben Kaas *(bookkeeper),* Jeanne Darville, Lisbeth Lindeborg, Preben Nicolaisen, Carl Ottosen, Lotte Hermann, Bjørn Puggaard-Müller, Carl Axel Elfving, Hans Brenå, Tove Maës, Lise Thomsen, Børge Møller Grimstrup, Georg Philipp, Lars Lunøe, Klaus Pagh, Hans Lindgren, Lotte Horne, Joakim Rasmussen, Jytte Breuning, Bente Juhl, Simon Rosenbaum, Ulla Johansson.

Comedy. The tastes of Marcus Daniel Edouard Rasmussen, a poor Copenhagen bookkeeper, contrast with his poverty. Despite his limited income, Marcus has regal bearing and is a multi-lingual connoisseur of the arts. When a rich relative dies, the bookkeeper expects a large inheritance but receives instead a passel of debts. Embezzling money from his firm, Marcus assumes the name de Sade and represents himself as the Marquis' wealthy descendant. Aristocratic women offer him financial gifts and expect cruel pleasures. Responding to their requests, the imposter hosts a large orgy. *Bookkeepers. Nobility. Poverty. Inheritance. Embezzlement. Imposture. Sadism. Orgies. Copenhagen. Marcus Daniel Edouard Rasmussen. Donatien Alphonse François [Marquis de] Sade.*

Note: Released in Denmark in Mar 1967 as *Jeg—en marki;* in Sweden in Oct 1967 as *Jag en markis—med uppdrag att älska.* Also known as *The Reluctant Sadist.*

I, A PUSSY   **F6.2319**
Dist Able Film Co. ca **1970.** Sd; col. 16mm. [Feature length assumed.]

Sex film. No information about the precise nature of this film has been found. *Sexuality.*

I, A WOMAN (Denmark/Sweden)   **F6.2320**
Novaris Film–Nordisk Films–Europa Film. *Dist* Audubon Films. 11 Oct **1966** [New York opening]. Sd; b&w. 35mm. 90 min.

Pres by Radley H. Metzger. *Prod* Peer Guldbrandsen. *Co-prod* Fritz Ruzicka. *Dir* Mac Ahlberg. *Screenplay* Peer Guldbrandsen. *Photog* Mac Ahlberg. *Sets* Erik Aaes. *Film Ed* Edith Nisted Nielsen. *Mus* Sven Gyldmark. *Violin Solo* Wandy Tworek. *Sd* Jon Branner, Ole Guldbrandsen.

Cast: Essy Persson *(Siv Esruth),* Jørgen Reenberg *(surgeon),* Preben Mahrt *(Heinz),* Preben Kørning *(Siv's fiancé),* Tove Maës *(Siv's mother),* Erik Hell *(Siv's father),* Bengt Brunskog *(Lars Thomsen),* Frankie Steele *(tough guy),* Ebba With.

Drama. Source: Siv Holm, *Jeg—en kvinde* (Copenhagen, 1961). Siv, a restless young nurse, revolts against her fanatically religious parents and her unworldly fiancé and allows herself to be seduced by one of the patients in the hospital where she is employed. The patient, known as a ladies' man, nevertheless falls in love with Siv and offers to divorce his wife, but Siv rejects any deeper involvement and moves to a larger city where she can enjoy greater sexual freedom. While working at another hospital, she has an affair with a sailor, Lars, but she stops seeing him when he, too, becomes enamored of her and proposes marriage. A third romantic entanglement, this time with a surgeon, ends in a similar fashion, and Siv concludes that she will never commit herself to any one man. Eventually, however, she meets her counterpart, an aggressive stranger as promiscuous as herself; and he violently makes love to her. Inexplicably drawn to the man, Siv asks to see him again, but he refuses a second meeting, maintaining that she would soon be pursuing marriage. Struck by the irony of the situation, Siv bursts into laughter. *Nurses. Sailors. Surgeons. Seduction. Promiscuity. Marriage. Religion. Hospitals.*

Note: Released in Denmark and Sweden in 1965; running time: 105 min. Produced in Denmark under the title *Jeg—en kvinde*. Swedish title: *Jag—en kvinna*. Editor Edith Nisted Nielsen is also credited as Edith Nisted.

I, A WOMAN PART II (Denmark/Sweden)   **F6.2321**
Novaris Film–Minerva Film Produktion. *Dist* Chevron Pictures. 14 Mar **1969** [New York opening]. Sd; col (Eastman Color by Movielab). 35mm. 81 min.

Prod-Writ Peer Guldbrandsen. *Dir* Mac Ahlberg. *Photog* Mac Ahlberg. *Mus* Sven Gyldmark. *Sd* Jon Branner.

Cast: Gio Petré *(Siv)*, Lars Lunøe *(Hans)*, Hjördis Petterson *(Mrs. Holm)*, Bertel Lauring *(Svendsen)*, Klaus Pagh *(Leo)*, Kate Mundt, Karl Stegger, Carl Ottosen, Bjørn Puggaard-Müller, Sigrid Horne-Rasmussen.

Melodrama. From the novel by: Siv Holm, *Jeg—en kvinde, II* (Copenhagen, 1968). Siv Holm is the wife of a cultured antique dealer named Hans who is so obsessed with his acquisitions that he cannot bring himself to sell any of them. Unable to pay the household bills, Siv seeks the help of her mother-in-law, but the older woman refuses to intercede in her son's affairs. One of Hans' other interests is photographing his wife in the nude and then, unknown to Siv, selling the pictures to Svendsen, one of his wealthy customers. One day, the voyeuristic Hans invites Svendsen to his home and informs him that, for a price, he can make love to the beautiful Siv. Following dinner, Hans sips brandy as Svendsen begins to embrace Siv passionately. Sensing that her husband is enjoying the scene, Siv gives herself to Svendsen as the bemused Hans watches. Degraded by the evening, Siv denies herself to her husband and resumes both her hospital nursing career and a former affair with a surgeon. A young woman who attempted suicide is brought to the hospital. As the woman talks about a former husband who drove her into a life of prostitution, Siv realizes that the man the woman is talking about is Hans. When Siv repeats the story to her mother-in-law, Mrs. Holm admits that her son is a monster, and she gives Siv a gun with which to kill him. Instead, Siv opens a locked chest that Hans keeps in an apartment and discovers that her husband is an unregenerate ex-Nazi. After waiting for Hans to return, Siv confronts him with what she has learned, tells him how much she loathes him, and walks out on him. *Antique dealers. Nurses. Nazis. Surgeons. Mothers-in-law. Pimps. Marriage. Voyeurism. Suicide. Prostitution. Infidelity. Finance—Personal.*

Note: Released in Denmark in 1968 as *Jeg—en kvinde, II*, and in Sweden in 1968 as *Jag en kvinna II*; running time: 89 min. Known also in the U. S. as *2*, the film is a sequel to *I, a Woman*, q. v.

I, A WOMAN PART III *see* **THE DAUGHTER; I, A WOMAN PART III**

I AIN'T NO BUFFALO *see* **GUESS WHAT WE LEARNED IN SCHOOL TODAY?**

I AM CURIOUS (BLUE) (Sweden)   **F6.2322**
Sandrews. *Dist* Grove Press. 20 May **1970** [New York opening]. Sd; b&w. 35mm. 103 min. *MPAA rating* X.

Prod Göran Lindgren. *Exec Prod* Lena Malmsjö. *Dir-Writ* Vilgot Sjöman. *Dir Revival Scene* Bertil Sandgren. *Photog* Peter Wester. *Asst Camera* Andreas Bellis. *Film Ed* Wic Kjellin, Carl-Olov Skeppstedt. *Asst Ed* Viveca Nordström. *Mus* Bengt Ernryd, Bengt Palmers. *Sd* Tage Sjöberg, Thomas Holewa. *Asst Sd* Christer Östberg. *Sd Mix* Olle Jacobsson. *Prod Mgr* Raymond Lundberg. *Prod Asst* Bengt Palmers, Rudolf Adolfsson. *Script Girl (see note)* Marianne Johnson, Kerstin Berg.

Cast: Lena Nyman *(Lena)*, Vilgot Sjöman *(Sjöman, the director)*, Börje Ahlstedt *(Börje)*, Marie Göranzon *(Marie)*, Hans Hellberg *(Hans)*, Bim Warne *(Bim)*, Gunnel Broström, Hanne Sandemose *(lesbians)*, Sonja Lindgren *(Sonja)*, Peter Lindgren *(Rune)*, Magnus Nilsson *(Magnus)*, Ulla Lyttkens *(Ulla)*, Frej Lindqvist, Gudrun Östbye, Bertil Wilkström.

Drama. Vilgot Sjöman tests actresses for the role of Madeline in a future film. In a documentary insert, actress Lena visits a sex education course in which teenaged girls conclude that sexual enjoyment is improper for females. Back at Sjöman's studio, Börje Ahlstedt is given the part of the car salesman, but he is

unable to decide if he wants it. Meanwhile, Lena converts her bedroom into a meeting place to study Sweden's political and sexual attitudes. With two friends, she conducts interviews with people on the streets of Stockholm and meets her former lover, Hans. They try to renew their relationship aboard his flagship, but he is impotent with anyone but his mistress, Bim. Sjöman enters and complains that Hans is overacting in the scene. After having sex with Börje, Lena sets out to find her mother; on the way, she preaches against the hypocrisy of religion and calls for prison reform. While interviewing teenagers at a school dance, Lena meets Sonja, a singer who has a 13-year-old illegitimate daughter. Sonja takes Lena nude swimming and camping at Strömsund Lake, but when Lena sees two lesbians having sex, she hurries back to Stockholm and stays with Hans and Bim. She overhears Hans sadistically beating Bim, and, disillusioned with the man who taught her political nonviolence, leaves the flagship. Börje and Lena learn that they have venereal disease and seek treatment at a health clinic. Sjöman interrupts the scene to explain that there is camera trouble and then announces that it is time for Lena's reunion with her mother; mother and daughter embrace. *Motion picture directors. Actors. Mistresses. Sex instruction. Adolescence. Social customs. Politics. Impotence. Illegitimacy. Lesbianism. Sadism. Filial relations. Motion pictures. Interviews. Venereal disease. Stockholm. Strömsund Lake.*

Note: Released in Stockholm in Mar 1968 as *Jag är nyfiken—blå*. Film is a followup to *I Am Curious (Yellow)*, q. v. Sources conflict in crediting script girl.

I AM CURIOUS GAY *see* **HAPPY BIRTHDAY, DAVY**

I AM CURIOUS—TAHITI   **F6.2323**
C. Tobalina Productions. *Dist* Hollywood International Film Corp. of America. 6 Nov **1970** [Los Angeles opening]. Sd; col (Eastman Color). 35mm. 65 min. [Also 70 min.]

Prod-Dir Carlos Tobalina.

Cast: William Larrabure *(Comrad Prickowsky)*, Bill Kirschner *(Professor Masturbetti)*, Maria-Pia, Leticia Young, Susane Parker, Jay Colonna.

Comedy. Maria-Pia, a Russian spy based in Los Angeles, receives a call on her automobile telephone from the Kremlin instructing her to go to Tahiti to investigate a military plot. Her contact in the Kremlin tells her to use the "transducer," a device that allows her to see and hear through walls. Maria-Pia helps Professor Masturbetti, the inventor of the device, go to Japan to obtain transistorized parts. She flies back to Tahiti and eavesdrops on various couples by using the transducer. She watches a Catholic priest seduce a nun in a monastery, a 15-year-old nymphomaniac use sex to influence her uncle, and a pair of Tahitian dancers make love. Eventually she discovers the military secrets and reports them to the Kremlin. She then returns to Tahiti to spend the rest of her life indulging in hedonistic pleasures. *Russians. Priests. Spies. Nuns. Dancers. Inventors. Uncles. Voyeurism. Nymphomania. Seduction. Incest. Monasteries. Electronic surveillance. Tahiti. Los Angeles. Japan. The Kremlin (Moscow).*

I AM CURIOUS (YELLOW) (Sweden)   **F6.2324**
Sandrews. *Dist* Grove Press. 10 Mar **1969** [New York opening]. Sd; b&w. 35mm. 120 min. *MPAA rating* X.

Prod Göran Lindgren. *Exec Prod* Lena Malmsjö. *Dir-Writ* Vilgot Sjöman. *Photog* Peter Wester. *Film Ed* Wic Kjellin. *Mus* Bengt Ernryd. *Sd* Tage Sjöberg. *Asst Dir* Bengt Palmers, Rudolf Adolfsson.

Cast: Lena Nyman *(Lena)*, Börje Ahlstedt *(Börje)*, Vilgot Sjöman *(director)*, Peter Lindgren *(Rune)*, Chris Wahlström *(Rune's friend)*, Magnus Nilsson *(Magnus)*, Marie Göranzon *(Marie)*, Ulla Lyttkens *(Ulla)*, Holger Lowenadler *(king)*, Anders Ek *(instructor)*, Öllegård Wellton *(interpreter)*, Sven Wollter *(captain)*.

Drama. While making a film, actress Lena Nyman has an affair with director Vilgot Sjöman. In the picture, Lena portrays a political activist in search of her own identity. A participant in liberal causes, she interviews people on the streets of Stockholm and asks them about Sweden's class structure, the U. S. position in Vietnam, and the teachings of Martin Luther King, Jr. At home she treats her father with contempt because of his brief dedication to Franco's Loyalists, and she turns her room into an institute filled with radical literature. In both the film and in her private life, Lena has a passionate affair with the actor, Börje. After their initial sexual encounter, Lena makes up a file on him and then has intercourse with him on a balustrade facing the Royal Palace, in the branches of trees, and in the middle of a country pond. Discovering that Börje has a mistress and a child, Lena quarrels with him and retreats to practice yoga. Though Börje follows and makes love to her, Lena flies into a rage when she learns that he is still having affairs with other women. Following a nightmare in which she guns down her former lovers and then shoots and castrates Börje, Lena hysterically destroys all the files in her room. Recognizing that her advocacy of nonviolence is hypocritical, Lena forsakes her political activities; at the same time, a radio broadcasts an announcement that the Swedish Parliament has endorsed nonviolence. In the final scene of the film,

Lena and Börje's romance ends as they are brought to a Stockholm disinfectant clinic and scrubbed. Lena terminates her liaison with the director when she sees him flirting with another actress. *Motion picture directors. Actors. Mistresses. Sexuality. Nonviolence. Radicalism. Jealousy. Hypocrisy. Castration. Filial relations. Motion pictures. Interviews. Stockholm. Martin Luther King, Jr. Dreams.*

Note: Opened in Stockholm in Oct 1967 as *Jag är nyfiken—gul;* running time: 121 min.

I AM FOR SALE F6.2325

Dist Inter-American Film Distributors. 7 May **1968** [New York showing]. Sd; b&w. 35mm. 57 min.

Cast: Andrea Barr *(Helen)*, Sunny Day *(Emma)*, Dina Diaz *(Alice)*, Chuck Trainor *(Frank)*, Pauly Dash *(John)*, Tom Martin *(sheriff)*, Ami Amar *(Judy)*, Linda Lee *(Betty)*, Mayra Quintana *(Katie)*, Sonia Duval *(Rose)*, Ali Lemu *(Bob)*.

Melodrama. Call girls relate their sexual experiences to Helen, their madam. Ex-stripper Judy goes to the apartment of a Latin man and has sex with him. There she meets a man who is revealed to be a masochistic lesbian. Alice encounters an artist, Frank, who has relations with her and paints her body. As she soaks in a bubble bath, Frank has sex with her friend Betty. After watching the couple, Alice joins them and paints their bodies. A stranger strips and beats Helen nearly to death. *Prostitutes. Madams. Artists. Prostitution. Sadomasochism. Lesbianism. Transvestism. Troilism.*

Note: Also known as *I Am for Excitement.*

I AM FURIOUS F6.2326

Dist Canyon Distributing Co. 22 May **1969** [San Francisco showing]. Sd; col. 16mm. 50 min.

Dir Alain Patrick.

Cast: Antoinette Maynard.

Sex film. A young woman fondles herself and then makes love to a visiting girl friend. The women agree to pose as nude models for the man next door for $50. Soon, they tie up their neighbor and make sexual advances towards him. They finally send him away and go back to making love to each other. *Photographers. Models. Neighbors. Autoeroticism. Lesbianism.*

Note: Also reviewed as *Je suis furieux.*

I AM SANDRA see SANDRA, THE MAKING OF A WOMAN

I AND MY LOVE see GALIA

I, AND MY LOVERS see GALIA

I BOMBED PEARL HARBOR (Japan) F6.2327

Toho Co. *Dist* Parade Releasing Organization. 29 Nov **1961** [Los Angeles opening]. Sd; col (Eastmancolor, print by Technicolor). 35mm (Tohoscope). 98 min. [Also reviewed at 91 min.]

Production Credits for Japanese Vers: *Prod* Tomoyuki Tanaka. *Dir* Shue Matsubayashi. *Screenplay* Shinobu Hashimoto, Takeo Kunihiro. *Photog* Kazuo Yamada. *Mus* Ikuma Dan. *Sp Eff Dir* Eiji Tsuburaya.

Production Credits for English Vers: *Pres by* Riley Jackson, Robert Patrick. A Hugo Grimaldi Production. *Dial* Riley Jackson, Hugo Grimaldi. *Film Ed* Hugo Grimaldi. *Mus* Gordon Zahler, Walter Greene.

Cast: Yosuke Natsuki *(Lieut. Koji Kitami)*, Toshiro Mifune *(Adm. Isoroku Yamaguchi [Yamamoto])*, Koji Tsuruta *(Lieutenant Tomonari)*, Misa Uehara *(Keiko)*, Aiko Mimasu *(Sato)*, Jun Tazaki *(captain)*, Makoto Sato *(Lieutenant Matsuura)*, Takashi Shimura *(Tosaku)*, Daisuke Kato, Akira Takarada, Hiroshi Koizumi.

War melodrama. On December 1, 1941, a Japanese fleet of 30 warships sails for Hawaii; when diplomatic negotiations in Washington fail, the task force commander, Adm. Isoroku Yamaguchi, receives orders to attack Pearl Harbor. Following the devastating aerial assault on December 7, flight navigator Koji Kitami returns to Japan and Keiko, his childhood sweetheart. Although deeply in love with the young woman, Koji fears that marriage will make him less worthy as a naval officer. During the next few months, he participates in many successful raids on U. S. and British ships and planes, but during the battle at Midway he becomes less certain of the invincibility of the Japanese fleet. While he is aboard the carrier *Hiryu*, the vessel is attacked by U. S. dive bombers and badly damaged. Officers order the ship abandoned, but rather than leave it as a prize of war, a Japanese destroyer is given instructions to sink the carrier. As the *Hiryu* goes down, Koji and others give a final salute. *Marriage. Aerial bombardment. Aircraft carriers. World War II. Pearl Harbor Attack 1941. Midway. Isoroku Yamamoto. Japan—Navy.*

Note: Released in Japan in 1960 as *Taiheiyo no arashi;* running time: 118 min. Alternative title: *The Storm Over the Pacific.*

I CALL FIRST see WHO'S THAT KNOCKING AT MY DOOR?

I CAN'T ... I CAN'T see WEDDING NIGHT

I COULD GO ON SINGING (Great Britain) F6.2328

Barbican Films. *Dist* United Artists. 20 Mar **1963** [Miami, Florida, opening; c20 Mar 1963; LP24879]. Sd; col (Technicolor). 35mm (Panavision). 99 min.

Pres by Stuart Millar, Lawrence Turman. *Prod* Lawrence Turman. *Exec Prod* Stuart Millar. *Assoc Prod* Denis Holt. *Dir* Ronald Neame. *Screenplay* Mayo Simon. *Story* Robert Dozier. *Art Dir* Wilfred Shingleton. *Set Decor* John Hoesli. *Titl* Maurice Binder. *Film Ed* John Shirley. *Mus Supv* Saul Chaplin. *Background Mus Score Comp & Cond* Mort Lindsey. *Titl Song* Harold Arlen, E. Y. Harburg. *Song:* "Hello Bluebird" Cliff Friend. *Song:* "By Myself" Arthur Schwartz, Howard Dietz. *Song:* "It Never Was You" Kurt Weill, Maxwell Anderson. *Song:* "I Am the Monarch of the Sea"* William S. Gilbert, Arthur Sullivan. *Songs Sung by* Judy Garland. *Sd* Buster Ambler, Christopher Lancaster, Red Law. *Sd Camera* Paul Wilson. *Asst Dir* Colin Brewer. *Prod Supv* Denis Holt. *Unit Mgr* John Peverall. *Asst to the Prod* Rose Tobias Shaw. *Prod Asst* Marion Rosenberg. *Cont* Pamela Davies. *Miss Garland's Cost* Edith Head. *Adtl Cost* Beatrice Dawson. *Makeup* Harold Fletcher. *Hairstyles* Pearl Tipaldi.

Cast: Judy Garland *(Jenny Bowman)*, Dirk Bogarde *(David Donne)*, Jack Klugman *(George Kogan)*, Aline MacMahon *(Ida)*, Gregory Phillips *(Matt)*, Pauline Jameson *(Miss Plimpton)*, Jeremy Burnham *(young hospital doctor)*, Russell Waters *(Reynolds)*, Gerald Sim *(assistant manager at Palladium)*, Leon Cortez *(The Busker)*.

Drama with music. While in London for an appearance at the Palladium, celebrated singing star Jenny Bowman visits British surgeon David Donne in an attempt to renew their former relationship. Years before, they had met in New York and fallen in love, but Jenny had chosen a career over marriage to David. When a son, Matt, was born, she agreed to let David take him back to England to be raised as his adopted child. Jenny begs David, now a widower, to let her see their son, and he reluctantly agrees to a single meeting. Excited by the presence of a great star and captivated by her charm, Matt defies his father's orders and allows Jenny to spend all her time with him. The boy's disobedience precipitates a bitter quarrel between David and Jenny, and Matt learns that Jenny is his mother when he overhears them arguing. Matt is then told he must choose between his parents, and when he rejects Jenny, she goes on a spree and ends up in a London hospital. David visits her and promises to take her to the only place she can find happiness; he drives her to the Palladium, and as she is swamped by admirers, Jenny admits David is right. *Singers. Surgeons. Americans in foreign countries. Widowers. Filial relations. Adoption. Illegitimacy. Drunkenness. Hospitals. London. Palladium.*

Note: Opened in London in Mar 1963. Working title: *The Lonely Stage.* Copyright claimant: Millar-Turman Productions.

I CRAVE YOUR BODY F6.2329

Dove Productions. 9 Nov **1967** [San Francisco showing]. Sd; b&w. 35mm. 87 min. [Cut to 70 min.]

Prod-Screenplay Edgar Blackland. *Exec Prod* Samuel Gough. *Dir* Abe Lutz. *Adtl Dial* Ned Craig. *Photog* William C. Wolten. *Art Dir* Lynn Phillips. *Ed* Donald Guerewitz. *Mus* Myron Paul. *Makeup* Jacques Suprenot.

Cast: Johnny Mustang *(Johnny Mustang)*, Helga Broner *(Helga Heidel)*, Dallas Kavanaugh *(Dallas Kavanaugh)*, Rena Davis *(Rena Davis)*, Helen Baker *(Helen Baker)*, Tony Bandido *(Aldo)*, Spiros Hatzes *(Stompano)*, Mosa Abdulla *(M.D.)*, Gil Cassasa *(Sammy)*, Warren Frazier *(Dominic)*.

Crime melodrama. Stompano, the sinister attorney for a notorious crime syndicate, interrupts detective Johnny Mustang and his secretary, Dallas Kavanaugh, as they make love on the office floor and hires Johnny to trail the beautiful, dangerous Rena Davis. Following a path marked by sex and violence, Johnny learns that Rena is a nymphomaniac who craves lesbian affection. He discovers that he has been used as the fall guy in an international espionage plot. He encounters Helga Heidel, a bisexual German from a Nazi Youth School, who forces him into perversion with her whip. *Detectives. Secretaries. Lawyers. Nazis. Germans. Espionage. Organized crime. Bisexuality. Nymphomania. Lesbianism. Sadism. Flagellation.*

Note: Also known as *I Crave Your ...*

I CROSSED THE COLOR LINE see THE BLACK KLANSMAN

I DEAL IN DANGER F6.2330

Rogo Productions-Twentieth Century-Fox Television. *Dist* Twentieth Century-Fox Film Corp. ca Oct **1966** [c21 Sep 1966; LP33772]. Sd (Westrex); col (DeLuxe). 35mm. 89 min.

Prod Buck Houghton. *Exec Prod* Walter Grauman. *Dir* Walter Grauman. *Screenplay* Larry Cohen. *Dir Photog* Sam Leavitt, Kurt Grigoleit. *Art Dir* Jack Martin Smith, Jack Collis, Rolf Zehetbauer. *Set Decor* Walter M. Scott, Lucien Hafley. *Film Ed* Jason Bernie, Dolf Rudeen. *Mus* Lalo Schifrin, Joseph

Mullendore. *Mus Supv* Lionel Newman. *Sd* Karsten Ullrich, Nelson-Corso. *Asst Dir* Ray Taylor, Jr., Hans Sommer, Wolfgang von Schiber. *Unit Prod Mgr* Buck Hall, Stanley Goldsmith. *Makeup* Ben Nye. *Hairstyles* Margaret Donovan. *Sp Photog Eff* Karl Baumgartner, Erwin Lange.

Cast: Robert Goulet *(David March)*, Christine Carere *(Suzanne Duchard)*, Donald Harron *(Spauling)*, Horst Frank *(Luber)*, Werner Peters *(Elm)*, Eva Pflug *(Gretchen Hoffmann)*, Christiane Schmidtmer *(Ericka von Lindendorf)*, John Van Dreelen *(von Lindendorf)*, Hans Reiser *(Richter)*, Margit Saad *(The Baroness)*, Peter Capell *(Eckhardt)*, Osman Ragheb *(Brunner)*, John Alderson *(Gorleck)*, Dieter Eppler *(Stolnitz)*, Dieter Kirchlechner *(Becker)*, Manfred Andrea *(Dr. Zimmer)*, Alexander Allerson *(Draus)*, Paul Glawion *(submarine pilot)*.

Action melodrama. During World War II, American David March, the last remaining agent of an Allied spy ring known as Blue Light, has worked his way into the higher echelons of German intelligence by posing as a Nazi sympathizer. Gestapo Captain Elm suspects March, however, and tries to trap him by taking him to neutral Lisbon to meet Guy Spauling, a British agent posing as a scientist, who claims he wants to defect to Germany. Spauling [who may be dying anyway] tries to persuade March to kill him in order to solidify March's position with the Nazis; but instead March manages to get rid of Elm, who himself is accused of being the Blue Light agent. March's assignment is to destroy the secret submarine missile manufacturing plant at Grossmünchen. Aided by Susanne Duchard, a French Allied agent posing as a collaborator, he manages to convince scientist Gretchen Hoffman of the futility of the Nazi cause and obtain her aid in blowing up the plant. March and Suzanne escape to safety, but Gretchen dies in the explosion. *Spies. Americans in foreign countries. Nazis. British. French. Scientists. Defectors. Sabotage. Self-sacrifice. Imposture. Missiles. Factories. World War II. Lisbon. Gestapo. Germany—Intelligence service. Explosions.*

Note: This film is made up of the first three segments of a television series entitled *Blue Light* which premiered on ABC-TV on 12 Jan 1966.

I DO VOODOO   F6.2331
Dist Stacey Distributors. ca **1970**. Sd; col. 16mm. 61-81 min.
Sex film. No information about the precise nature of this film has been found. *Sexuality. Voodoo.*

I EVEN MET HAPPY GYPSIES (Yugoslavia)   F6.2332
Avala Film. *Dist* Prominent Films. 6 Mar **1968** [Los Angeles opening]. Sd; col (Eastman Color). 35mm. 90 min.
Dir-Writ Aleksandar Petrović. *Photog* Tomislav Pinter. *Art Dir* Veljko Despotović. *Film Ed* Milo Mica. *Folklore Melodies Arr by* Aleksandar Petrović. *Sd* Rasa Vijić.

Cast: Bekim Fehmiu *(Bora)*, Gordana Jovanović *(Tisa)*, Bata Živojinović *(Mirta)*, Olivera Vučo *(Lence)*, Mija Aleksić *(Father Pavle)*, Etelka Filipovski *(Bora's wife)*, Milorad Jovanović *(Toni)*, Milivoje Djordjević *(Sandor)*, Rahela Ferari *(nun)*, Severin Bijelić *(religious peasant)*.

Melodrama. Bora, a gypsy goose feather merchant, is plagued by the demands of his wife and many children. In his travels Bora falls in love with Tisa, an adolescent whose lecherous stepfather, Mirta, also a feather merchant, has married her to a 12-year-old boy. Tisa runs away, and Bora finds her and takes her into his home. In time, she leaves him, and after a series of adventures she is returned to Mirta. Infuriated, Bora kills his rival. Months later, Mirta's body is found, and the police arrive to investigate, but Bora has disappeared. *Gypsies. Stepfathers. Marriage—Arranged. Marriage. Murder. Adolescence.*

Note: Filmed on location in Pannonia and Belgrade. Released in Yugoslavia in 1967 as *Skupljači perja*. Alternate Yugoslavian title: *Sreo sam čak i srećne ciganc.*

I FEEL IT COMING   F6.2333
Dist Sam Lake Enterprises. **1969**. Sd; col (Eastman Color). 35mm. 75 min.
Pres by Sam Lake. *Prod* Jean Jacques Robeau. *Dir* Sidney Knight. *Screenplay* William Ray. *Camera* Robert Morgenstern. *Ed* Sidney Knight. *Sd* Ronald Nort. *Asst Dir* Luigi D'Arc.

Cast: Sammy Cole *(Peter)*, Dandy Thomas *(Rita)*, Jean Parker, actress *(prostitute)*, David Marcus *(doctor)*, Linda Shall *(Debbie)*, Richard Zunt *(Bill)*, Cathy Neilman *(Pepper)*.

Sex film. There is a happy reunion when Peter returns home to his wife, Rita, from Vietnam, but on their first night together it becomes apparent that Peter is impotent. Rita misunderstands, and Peter leaves after an argument. He picks up a prostitute but fails again to perform, and he returns home to make up with Rita. They visit a doctor who tells Peter that he should try to forget his wartime experiences and make an effort to relax. Rita suggests a group sex experience, and calls two of their friends. They attempt to arouse Peter through striptease, lesbianism, and a variety of sexual techniques, without success. Desperate, Rita hits on the idea of relaxing Peter with some marijuana. He agrees. The young woman who makes the delivery reminds Peter of a woman he knew in Saigon.

When Rita suggests a sexual threesome, the woman refuses. They carry her struggling to the bedroom, and tie her to the bed. As Peter begins to rape her, she becomes aroused. Rita unties her, chases her out, and returns to Peter to make love at last. *Veterans. Prostitutes. Physicians. Impotence. Sexual techniques. Group sex. Striptease. Lesbianism. Rape. Troilism. Marijuana. Vietnam War 1964–73.*

Note: Also released as *Soldier's Wife.*

I HATE YOUR GUTS *see* THE INTRUDER

I LIKE BIRDS *see* HOT GIRLS FOR MEN ONLY

I LIKE MONEY (Great Britain)   F6.2334
Dimitri De Grunwald Productions. *Dist* Twentieth Century-Fox Film Corp. 18 May **1962** [New York opening; c16 Dec 1961; LP22224]. Sd (Westrex); col (Eastmancolor, print by DeLuxe). 35mm (CinemaScope). 97 min. [Also reviewed at 81 min.]
Prod-Writ Pierre Rouve. *Exec Prod* Dimitri De Grunwald. *Dir* Peter Sellers. *Dir Photog* John Wilcox. *Camera Op* Austin Dempster. *Focus* Geoff Glover, Dickie Robinson. *Art Dir* Peter Murton. *Set Dresser* Pamela Cornell. *Draughtsman* Dick Burnett, Terence Knight. *Prod Dsgn* Don Ashton. *Film Ed* Geoffrey Foot. *1st Asst Ed* Bill Blunden. *2d Asst Ed* Ralph Gruskin. *Mus Comp* Georges Van Parys. *Cond* Leighton Lucas. *Titl Song* George Martin, Herbert Kretzmer. *Sung by* Nadia Gray. *Sd Rec* Cyril Swern. *Sd Ed* Alastair McIntyre. *Rec Supv* A. W. Watkins. *Dub Mix* J. B. Smith. *Boom Op* Bill Baldwin. *Camera Op* Ron Matthews. *1st, 2d & 3d Asst Dir* Kip Gowans, Ian Goddard, Ray Freeborn. *In Charge of Prod* Roy Parkinson. *Cont* Rita Davison. *Script Assoc* Johnny Speight. *Prod Sec* Elizabeth Woodthorpe. *Wardrobe Supv* Felix Evans. *Adtl Cost* Anthony Mendleson. *Nadia Gray's Dresses* Pierre Balmain. *Makeup* Stuart Freeborn. *Hairdresser* Ann Box. *Prop Buyer* John Bigg. *Still Photog* Norman Hargood.

Cast: Peter Sellers *(Mr. Topaze)*, Nadia Gray *(Suzy Courtois)*, Herbert Lom *(Castel Benac)*, Leo McKern *(Headmaster Muche)*, Martita Hunt *(baroness)*, John Neville *(Roger de Berville)*, Billie Whitelaw *(Ernestine)*, Michael Gough *(Tamise)*, Anne Leon *(his wife)*, Joan Sims *(Colette)*, John Le Mesurier *(blackmailer)*, Pauline Shepherd *(Lilette)*, Thomas Gallagher *(policeman)*, Michael Sellers *(Gaston)*.

Comedy-drama. Source: Marcel Pagnol, *Topaze* (Paris opening: 9 Oct 1928). Mr. Topaze, a mildmannered and scrupulously honest schoolmaster in a provincial French town, plods conscientiously along, in spite of his poor pay, hoping someday to win the hand of Ernestine Muche, daughter of the school's headmaster. When he refuses to alter the poor grades of the nephew of the local baroness, he is rewarded for his integrity with a dismissal. His naive and gullible nature arouses the interest of musical comedy star Suzy Courtois, mistress of crafty city councilor Castel Benac, who promotes shady financial deals. Benac, aware that Topaze would be a perfect front, makes him a managing director and ensconces him in a lavish Paris office. All goes well until Topaze learns from his predecessor, Roger de Berville, that he is the unwitting dupe of crooks. His indignation increases when Headmaster Muche visits him and declares that he would be proud to have Topaze for a son-in-law. His illusions shattered, Topaze decides to become the biggest and best swindler of them all. He outwits Benac, takes over his empire and his chateau, and becomes a highly successful financier. *Schoolteachers. Headmasters. Nobility. Aunts. Actors. Executives. Financiers. Swindlers. Mistresses. Honesty. Courtship. Fraud. Government—Local. Gullibility. France. Paris.*

Note: Opened in London in Mar 1960 as *Mr. Topaze.* Previously filmed as *Topaze* in the United States in 1933, and in France in 1935 and 1952.

I LIVE IN FEAR (Japan)   F6.2335
Toho Co. *Dist* Brandon Films. 25 Jan **1967** [New York showing]. Sd; b&w. 35mm. 105 min.
Prod Sojiro Motoki. *Dir* Akira Kurosawa. *Screenplay* Shinobu Hashimoto, Hideo Oguni, Akira Kurosawa. *Photog* Asakazu Nakai. *Lighting* Kuichiro Kishida. *Art Dir* Yoshiro Muraki. *Mus (see note)* Fumio Hayasaka, Masaru Sato. *Sd Rec* Fumio Yanoguchi.

Cast: Toshiro Mifune *(Kiichi Nakajima)*, Eiko Miyoshi *(Toyo)*, Haruko Togo *(Yoshi)*, Takashi Shimura *(Harada)*, Masao Shimizu *(Takao Yamazaki)*, Kazuo Kato *(his son)*, Yutaka Sada *(Ichiro)*, Noriko Sengoku *(Kimie)*, Minoru Chiaki *(Jiro)*, Kyoko Aoyama *(Sue)*, Kiyomi Mizunoya *(Kiichi's 1st mistress)*, Saoko Yonemura *(her daughter)*, Akemi Negishi *(Asako Kuribayashi)*, Kichijiro Ueda *(Kuribayashi)*, Yoichi Tachikawa *(Ryoichi Suyama)*, Ken Mitsuda *(Araki)*, Toranosuke Ogawa *(Hori)*, Eijiro Tono *(old man from Brazil)*, Kamatari Fujiwara *(Okamoto)*, Nobuo Nakamura *(psychiatrist)*.

Drama. Harada, a dentist who works as a volunteer in the Domestic Relations Department of the Tokyo Family Court, becomes involved in the case of Kiichi Nakajima, a self-made industrialist who has developed an obsessive fear of the atomic dangers facing Japan. Because of Japan's history and the still present threat of atomic dust from testing in the Pacific, Kiichi decides to emigrate to Brazil. His family, however, does not share his conviction of doom; fearful that his obsession may jeopardize their financial security, they appeal to the Family Court, which declares him mentally incompetent, despite Harada's objections that Nakajima's fears are founded in reality. Powerless to act for himself, Nakajima is gripped by fear, and, after pleading with his family to leave Japan, he suffers a nervous collapse. Irrationally concluding that his family would move to South America if they were financially ruined, he burns his factory to the ground, not realizing that he is putting his employees out of work. Facing a mob of angry workers, he asks their pardon and pleads with all of them to join him in his flight to Brazil. His family finally has no choice but to have him committed to an asylum. Harada, who has become more concerned with the dangers of atomic bombs and radiation, visits him there and finds him serene and cheerful. Nakajima now believes that he is on another planet; when he sees the sun setting, he concludes that it is the earth in flames. *Dentists. Industrialists. Factory workers. Obsession. Fear. Family life. Mental illness. Arson. Atom bomb. Factories. Insane asylums. Tokyo. Brazil.*

Note: Released in Japan in Nov 1955 as *Ikimono no kiroku*; running time: 113 min. Also known as *Record of a Living Being*. Composer Hayasaka died during production, and Sato completed the musical score.

I LOVE MEXICO   F6.2336
15 Feb **1970** [Los Angeles showing]. Si; col. 35mm. ca120 min.
Pres by Explorama. *A Film by* Thayer Soule.
Travelog. A travel host describes the delights of Mexico City, Cuernavaca, Taxco, Acapulco, the top of the Popocatépetl crater, and Mayan and Toltec ruins. *Mayan Indians. Toltec Indians. Travel. Mexico. Mexico City. Cuernavaca. Taxco. Popocatépetl. Acapulco.*

Note: Narration delivered live on stage.

I LOVE MY WIFE   F6.2337
Universal Pictures. 21 Dec **1970** [New York opening; c21 Dec 1970; LP38969]. Sd; col (Technicolor). 35mm. 95 min. *MPAA rating* R.
Prod Stan Margulies. *Exec Prod* David L. Wolper. *Assoc Prod* Robert Kaufman. *Dir* Mel Stuart. *Screenplay* Robert Kaufman. *Dir Photog* Vilis Lapenieks. *Camera Op* Rex Metz. *Asst Camera* Frank Thackery, Alex Touyarot. *Art Dir* Alexander Golitzen, George C. Webb. *Set Decor* Frank McKelvy. *Set Coörd* Jason Bond. *Film Ed* David Saxon. *Asst Ed* Michael Berman. *Mus* Lalo Schifrin. *Sd* Waldon O. Watson, Robert R. Bertrand. *Rec* William Griffith. *Asst Dir* Chris Christenberry, Jack Terry. *Prod Mgr* Robert E. Larson. *Script Supv* Betty Abbott. *Cost Dsgn* Helen Colvig. *Men's Wardrobe* Peter Saldutti, Jules Melillo. *Women's Wardrobe* Joanne Haas, Carol Christie. *Makeup Artist* Mark Reedall. *Hairstyles* Gae Clark. *Gaffer* Terry White. *Casting Dir* Robert La Sanka. *Still Photog* Jack Geraghty.
Cast: Elliott Gould (*Dr. Richard Burrows*), Brenda Vaccaro (*Jody Burrows*), Angel Tompkins (*Helene Donnelly*), Dabney Coleman (*Frank Donnelly*), Leonard Stone (*Dr. Neilson*), Joan Tompkins (*Grandma Dennison*), Helen Westcott (*Mrs. Burrows*), Ivor Francis (*Dr. Korngold*), Al Checco (*Dr. Meyerberg*), Joanna Cameron (*Nurse Sharon*), Veleka Gray (*stewardess*), Damian London (*Leslie*), Tom Toner (*John Bosley*), Gloria Manon (*prostitute*), Frederic Downs (*minister*), Todd Baron (*Richard, age 12*), Laara Lacey (*woman neighbor*), Peter Stuart (*Andy, age 7*), Dawn Lyn (*Stephanie, age 5*), Heather North (*Betty*), Nikita Knatz (*art teacher*), Andy Stuart (*Andy, age 2*), Janice Pennington (*Nurse Cynthia*), Robert Kaufman (*Devil*).
Comedy-drama. Medical student Richard Burrows marries Jody Dennison, who soon becomes pregnant. When she loses interest in sex and begins to gain weight, Richard turns to the willing nurses in the hospital for sexual satisfaction. At a New Year's Eve party, Jody discovers Richard with Sharon, one of his nurse friends, and sternly rebukes him the next morning. The birth of their son does nothing to improve their relationship. Although Richard receives a prestigious position as a surgeon in a Los Angeles hospital, their marriage becomes even more strained when Jody's domineering mother moves in with them. One day at the hospital, Richard meets Helene Donnelly, a beautiful model for television commercials, who brings her husband in for treatment. They begin arranging motel meetings, and both eventually decide to divorce their spouses. Reluctant to abandon his son and newborn daughter, however, Richard makes a last effort to save his marriage; he orders his mother-in-law to leave and sends Jody to a weight reducing spa. Jody returns slim and attractive, but now she insists on the separation. After an unsuccessful attempt to renew his relationship with Helene, Richard begins a shallow existence pursuing nurses and stewardesses. *Medical students. Nurses. Surgeons. Mothers-in-law. Models. Marriage. Pregnancy. Infidelity. Family life. Separation (marital). Divorce. Hospitals. New Year's Eve. Los Angeles.*

I LOVE YOU, ALICE B. TOKLAS!   F6.2338
Warner Bros.-Seven Arts, Inc. 7 Oct **1968** [New York opening; c1 Oct 1968; LP36531]. Sd; col (Technicolor). 35mm. 94 min.

Prod Charles Maguire. *Exec Prod & Writ* Paul Mazursky, Larry Tucker. *Dir* Hy Averback. *Dir Photog* Philip Lathrop. *Set Decor* Audrey Blasdel. *Prod Dsgn* Pato Guzman. *Film Ed* Robert C. Jones. *Mus* Elmer Bernstein. *Orch* Leo Shuken, Jack Hayes. *Titl Song* Elmer Bernstein, Larry Tucker, Paul Mazursky. *Arr* Bob Thompson. *Sung by* Harper's Bizarre. *Sd* Everett A. Hughes. *Asst Dir* Jack Cunningham, Fred Giles. *Cost Dsgn* Theadora Van Runkle. *Makeup Supv* Gordon Bau. *Hairstyles Supv* Jean Burt Reilly. *Dial Supv* Bert Steinberger.
Cast: Peter Sellers (*Harold*), Jo Van Fleet (*Mother*), Leigh Taylor-Young (*Nancy*), Joyce Van Patten (*Joyce*), David Arkin (*Herbie*), Herbert Edelman (*Murray*), Salem Ludwig (*Father*), Louis Gottlieb (*guru*), Grady Sutton (*funeral director, Mr. Walsh*), Janet E. Clark (*Mrs. Foley*), Jorge Moreno (*Mr. Rodriguez*), Ed Peck (*man in dress shop*), Jack Margolis (*Big Bear*), Eddra Gale (*Love Lady*), Carol O'Leary (*Anita*), Gary Brown (*Ed Greco*), Sidney Clute (*mechanic*), Roy Glenn (*gas station attendant*), Joe Dominguez (*Grandfather Rodriguez*), William Bramley (*first patrolman*), Vince Howard (*second patrolman*), Robert Miller Driscoll (*crying hippie*), Karen Mickievic (*crying hippie's wife*).
Comedy. After constant badgering from his persistent 33-year-old secretary/ girl friend Joyce, Harold Fine, a successful Los Angeles Jewish lawyer who suffers from asthma, finally consents to set a wedding date. On that day his car gets banged up in a parking lot mishap and he borrows a psychedelically-painted station wagon from a garage. At the insistence of his mother, he agrees to attend the local butcher's funeral, and he stops by for his hippie brother Herbie, who has in tow a beautiful flower child named Nancy. A hearse drivers' strike results in Harold's loading the butcher's casket into the psychedelic wagon and delivering it—after much delay—to the cemetery. Later that day Harold encounters Nancy a second time and lets her stay the night in his apartment. By way of thanks, she uses a recipe from the *Alice B. Toklas Cook Book* and bakes him some marijuana-filled brownies which subsequently intoxicate Joyce, Harold, and his parents. Later, when Harold finds Nancy working in a dress shop, he decides he loves both her and her way of life, and he literally walks out on Joyce during their wedding ceremony. He then quits his job, lets his hair grow, and turns his apartment into a crash pad for about 40 assorted hippies. Eventually, however, as his asthma returns, he tires of communal living, as well as Nancy's attentions to others, clears out his pad, cuts his hair, and returns to Joyce. But upon entering the marriage hall where the wedding guests have assembled for the second time, Harold again balks and races from the scene. *Lawyers. Secretaries. Hippies. Brothers. Jews. Family life. Marriage. Weddings. Funerals. Social conformity. Marijuana. Asthma. Los Angeles.*

Note: Location scenes filmed at the Leo Carrillo State Beach, California.

I LOVE, YOU LOVE (France/Italy)   F6.2339
Dino De Laurentiis Cinematografica–Orsay Films. *Dist* Royal Films International. 9 Nov **1962** [New York opening]. Sd; col (Eastmancolor). 35mm (Ultrascope). 90 min.
Pres by Dino De Laurentiis. *Prod* Dino De Laurentiis. *Exec Prod* Luigi De Laurentiis. *Dir* Alessandro Blasetti. *Writ* Luigi Chiarini, Carlo Romano, Antonio Savignano. *Story Idea* Alessandro Blasetti. *Cinematog* Aldo Tonti. *Camera Op* Mario Capriotti, Luigi Kuveiller. *Camera Asst* Luciano Tonti. *Art Dir-Set Dsgn* Dario Cecchi, Mario Garbuglia. *Set Dsgn* Giorgio Mecchia Maddalena. *Film Ed* Tatiana Casini. *Mus Arr* Carlo Savina. "Hymn to Love" *sung by* Edith Piaf. *Sd* Biagio Fiorelli, Piero Capazutti, Mario Amari. *Asst Dir* Isa Baralini. *Prod Mgr* Mara Blasetti, Jean Mottet. *Prod Asst* Antonio Brandt. *Cont* Anna Gruber. *Ch Electrn* Claudio Mancini. *Ch Grip* Francesco Solitario.
The Performers: Marny Trio, Fattini, Cairoli, Don Yada's Japanese Revue, Las Hermanas Benitez, Obraszov and His Theater, Georges Lafaye, Moiseyev Ensemble, Chaz Chase, Norman Davis Dancers, Véronique, Soviet Army Choir.
Narrator: Peter L. Marshall.
Documentary. A documentary on the universality of love, compiled from shots taken of people throughout the world, features a Japanese revue, the Soviet Army Choir and the Moiseyev Ballet, a water ballet ensemble, and a puppet theater—all performing tales of love. Several nightclub acts and some newsreel footage also illustrate aspects of the themes of brotherhood, peace, and love. Young lovers walk hand in hand in Hyde Park, in the Moscow subway, along the Seine, and in the gardens of Rome, while aged couples look on and recall their own first love experiences. *Courtship. Youth. Old age. Sexuality. Nightclubs. Puppets. Ballet. Music. London—Hyde Park. Moscow. Paris. Rome. Japan.*

Note: Released in Italy in 1961 as *Io amo, tu ami*; running time: 95 min; opened in Paris in Jun 1962 as *J'aime, tu aimes*.

I, MARQUIS DE SADE   F6.2340
Eve Productions. 22 Nov **1967** [Maryland license]. Sd; b&w. 35mm. 73 min.
Prod-Dir Richard Hilliard. *Dir Photog* William Weaver, photog. *Mus Comp & Cond* Elliot Kaplan.

Cast: Sheldon Pearson *(Donald Marquis)*, Cindy Ella, Penelope, Anne Grant, Holly Saunders, Jennie Lee, Babette Bardot *(De Sade's girls)*.

Melodrama. Donald Marquis, who identifies in his fantasies with the Marquis de Sade, decides to act out his sadistic impulses. Donald becomes cruelly involved with five women: a wealthy divorcee, a man-hating sophisticate, a middle-aged woman and her young female lover, and a professional dancer and part-time prostitute. In his quest for sexual satisfaction, Donald experiences voyeurism and sadism, and he is eventually killed by one of the women. *Dancers. Lesbianism. Prostitution. Sadism. Murder. Man-haters. Voyeurism. Fantasy. Wealth. Donatien Alphonse François [Marquis de] Sade.*

Note: Also known as *I, the Marquis.*

I MARRIED TOO YOUNG see **MARRIED TOO YOUNG**

I MARRIED YOU FOR FUN (Italy) F6.2341
Fair Film. Dist Avco Embassy Pictures. 9 Jul **1969** [New York opening]. Sd; col (Eastmancolor, print by Pathé). 35mm. 100 min. *MPAA rating* X.

Pres by Joseph E. Levine. *Prod* Mario Cecchi Gori. *Dir* Luciano Salce. *Screenplay* Agenore Incrocci, Furio Scarpelli, Sandro Continenza, Natalia Ginzburg, Luciano Salce. *Orig Screenplay* Natalia Ginzburg. *Dir Photog* Carlo Di Palma. *Set Dsgn* Piero Poletto. *Set Decor* Giulio Cabras. *Film Ed* Marcello Malvestiti. *Mus* Piero Piccioni. *Sd Rec* Vittorio Massi. *Asst Dir* Marcello Pandolfi. *Prod Mgr* Pio Angeletti. *Prod Supv* Gianni Cecchin. *Cost Dsgn* Luca Sabatelli.

Cast: Monica Vitti *(Julia)*, Giorgio Albertazzi *(Peter)*, Maria Grazia Buccella *(Victoria)*, Italia Marchesini *(Peter's mother)*, Rossella Como *(Juniper)*, Michel Bardinet *(Englishman)*, Paola Corinti *(Topaz)*, Louis La Torre *(Manolo)*.

Comedy. Source: Natalia Ginzburg, *Ti ho sposato per allegria* (Turin, 1966). While her husband, Peter, attends the funeral of a friend, newlywed Julia confides the circumstances of her marriage to her assertive and inefficient maid Victoria. These include her arrival in Rome from the provinces; her brief tenure in a stationery store and her dismissal for spilling ink on a customer; her affair with the black-bearded author Manolo; her impregnation and desertion; her friendship with Manolo's slovenly wife, Topaz; her miscarriage; and her meeting with Peter at a drunken party. Ten days later they marry, moving into a hilltop apartment, the patio of which Julia furnishes with a trampoline. The day following her confession to the maid, Julia entertains Peter's mother and sister, Juniper. During an inedible meal, her mother-in-law, Julia's former customer, recognizes the bride, despite the fact that she has combed her hair in her face, donned sunglasses, and is bending her knees to conceal the effect of her miniskirt. Appalled by her son's choice of mate, Peter's pious mother decries the civil ceremony uniting the couple, accuses Julia of marrying for money, and storms out of the flat, thereby initiating a quarrel between the lovers. Asserting that she will take a lover, Julia rushes to the adjacent apartment, only to find the English tenant gone and an indecent picture of Manolo, evidently his lover, displayed prominently. Pursued by Peter, Julia jumps out the window, only to reappear seconds later. Her husband promptly joins her on the trampoline, onto which she has fallen. *Newlyweds. Housemaids. Catholics. Mothers-in-law. English. In-laws. Mistresses. Authors. Marriage. Desertion. Pregnancy. Miscarriage. Male homosexuality. Infidelity. Friendship. Trampolines. Rome.*

Note: Location scenes filmed in Rome. Opened in Rome in 1967 as *Ti ho sposato per allegria.*

I NEED F6.2342
Sebastian Films. Dist Paul Mart Productions. 28 Dec **1967** [San Francisco showing]. Sd; b&w. 35mm. 83 min.

Prod-Dir Ferdinand Sebastian. *Screenplay-Orig story* Ann Cawthorne. *Mus* The London Studio Group.

Cast: Ceci Weathers *(Ceci)*, Tom Hunter *(Alex)*, Jay Froman *(Murry)*, Sylvia Froman *(Mother)*, Tom Overton, actor *(Tom)*, Tommy Harrison *(Tommy)*, Charles Brewer *(motorcyclist)*.

Cast—The Courtroom: Casey Lynn *(doctor)*, Fred Morrow *(The Judge)*, Sharron Knox, Bill Wright, Beverly Sebastian *(jurors)*.

Cast—The Egg Cult: Ferdinand Sebastian *(leader)*, Terry Seelhurst, Helen Trogone, Suzanne DeYoung, Claire DeYoung, James Byrd, James Williams, actor.

Melodrama. Raped by her stepfather, Murry, at the age of 10, Ceci gradually becomes a nymphomaniac. At 14 she rebels against Murry's incestuous embraces and reveals his crime to a judge and jury. Two years later, her jealous mother throws her out of the house. A brief romance with Richard is followed by an affair with Benton Townsley, a married man-about-town who seeks relief from his frigid society wife. At 18 Ceci marries Alex, a has-been actor, struggling writer, and master lover who leaves, exhausted, after 3 months. Tom finally brings Ceci emotional satisfaction, but he is incapable of quenching her lust. Desperate, she becomes involved with Jeff, a well-built Negro, who leaves her equally unsatisfied. Overwhelmed by self-hatred, Ceci is driven to the brink

of insanity. *Children. Stepfathers. Authors. Actors. Negroes. Statutory rape. Incest. Nymphomania. Adolescence. Parenthood. Frigidity. Jealousy. Marriage. Insanity. Trials. Upper classes.*

Note: Also known as *I Need a Man* and *I Need a Man ... Any Man.*

I NEVER SANG FOR MY FATHER F6.2343
Jamel Productions. Dist Columbia Pictures. 18 Oct **1970** [New York opening; c1 Oct 1970; LP38185]. Sd; col (Technicolor). 35mm. 90 min. *MPAA rating* GP.

Prod-Dir Gilbert Cates. *Screenplay* Robert W. Anderson. *Dir Photog* Morris Hartzband, George Stoetzel. *Camera Op* Fred Porrett, Al Taffet. *1st Asst Camera* Felix Trimboli. *2d Asst Camera* Jamie Jacobson. *Art Dir* Hank Aldrich. *Master Scenic Artist* Sante Fiore. *Main Titl* Bert Gold. *Film Ed* Angelo Ross. *Asst Film Ed* Peet Begley. *Mus* Al Gorgoni, Barry Mann. *Song:* "Strangers" Barry Mann, Cynthia Weil. *Sung by* Roy Clark, mus. *Sd Rec* Stanley Federmack. *Sd Mix* Charles Mitteldorf, James Sabat. *Sd Re-rec* Richard Vorisek. *Boom Op* Nat Boxer. *Eff Ed* Walter Nolan. *1st & 2d Asst Dir* Stanley Panesoff, Allan Wertheim. *Prod Mgr* George Goodman. *Prod Supv* Everett Rosenthal. *Script Supv* Renata Stoia. *Unit Mgr* Phil Goldfarb. *Asst to the Prod* Peter L. Skolnik, Janise Bogard. *Prod Sec* Shirley Marcus. *Cost* Theoni V. Aldredge. *Wardrobe Mistress* Yvonne David. *Makeup* John Alese. *Hairdresser* Phil Leto. *Casting* Tom Ward Enterprise. *Gaffer* Morton Novak. *Key Grip* Robert Volpe. *Still Photog* Sam Dinin. *Orig Art* Park South Gallery.

Cast: Melvyn Douglas *(Tom Garrison)*, Gene Hackman *(Gene Garrison)*, Dorothy Stickney *(Margaret Garrison)*, Estelle Parsons *(Alice)*, Elizabeth Hubbard *(Peggy)*, Lovelady Powell *(Norma)*, Daniel Keyes *(Dr. Mayberry)*, Conrad Bain *(Reverend Pell)*, Jon Richards *(Marvin Scott)*, Nikki Counselman *(waitress)*, Carol Peterson *(1st nurse)*, Sloane Shelton *(2d nurse)*, James Karen *(old age home director)*, Gene Williams *(state hospital director)*, Jean Dexter *(hostess)*, Beverly Penberthy *(special nurse)*, Valerie Ogden *(3d nurse)*.

Drama. Source: Robert Anderson, *I Never Sang for My Father* (New York opening: 25 Jan 1968). Widowed Gene Garrison, a 40-year-old New York college professor, reluctantly tells his aging parents, Tom and Margaret, that he plans to marry Peggy, a divorced physician and mother, and move to California. Although Gene's mother is understanding, his father warns Gene that his departure will kill her. Before the marriage takes place, however, Margaret dies of a heart attack. At the funeral the professor's sister Alice, disowned by Tom for marrying a Jew, urges Gene to live his life without reference to his father's wishes. Gene introduces the old man to his fiancée, urging him to come with them to California. When Tom bitterly rejects his proposal, Gene leaves his father to die alone. *Professors. Widowers. Physicians. Filial relations. Fatherhood. Marriage. Middle age. Old age. Anti-Semitism. Brother-sister relationship. Funerals. Heart disease. New York City. California.*

Note: Filmed in New York. Working title: *Strangers.*

I PROMISE TO PAY see **PAYROLL**

I SAILED TO TAHITI WITH AN ALL GIRL CREW F6.2344
United National Pictures-National Telefilm Associates. *Dist* World Entertainment Corp. Sep **1969** [c7 Aug 1968; LP36436]. Sd; col (Deluxe). 35mm. 95 min.

Prod-Dir Richard Bare. *Screenplay* Richard Bare, Henry Irving. *Story* Richard Bare, George O'Hanlon. *Dir Photog* Leonard South, Frederic Gately. *Film Ed* John Schreyer. *Mus* Philip Springer. *Song:* "Take Me With You" Kellie Sullivan.

Cast: Gardner McKay *(Gardner)*, Fred Clark *(Fred)*, Pat Buttram *(Pat?)*, Diane McBain *(Liz)*, Richard Denning *(The Commodore)*, Edy Williams, Jeanne Ranier, Arlene Charles, Mary O'Brien, Bebe Louie, Duke Kahanamoku International Surfing Champions.

Comedy. Fred belittles the sailing abilities of his friend Gardner, and Gardner counters by betting Fred $20,000 that, using an all-female crew, he can beat him in a race to Tahiti. Gardner's crew consists of novice sailors—a murderess, a cocktail waitress, and two other women who go along for the ride—while Fred has an experienced crew. Fred bribes one of his women to sabotage Gardner's boat, and despite numerous delays owing to an island jailbreak, a mutiny, a night spent overboard, and a romantic intrigue, Gardner manages to close the gap between the rival sailing vessels; but Fred still finishes first. Fred's sabotage plan backfires, and he is forced to confess to his underhanded tactics, although he insists that he is the better sailor. Gardner challenges Fred to a rematch, this time using a crew of baboons. Fred accepts, unaware that the "baboons" Gardner intends to use are a Polynesian singing group composed of expert sailors. *Sailors. Waitresses. Polynesians. Braggarts. Singers. Ship crews. Wagers. Boat racing. Bribery. Sabotage. Jailbreaks. Mutiny. Cheating. Employment—Women. Tahiti.*

I SAW WHAT YOU DID   F6.2345

Universal Pictures. 14 May **1965** [Minneapolis opening; c7 Aug 1965; LP32633]. Sd (Westrex); b&w. 35mm. 82 min.

A William Castle Production. *Prod-Dir* William Castle. *Assoc Prod* Dona Holloway. *Screenplay* William McGivern. *Dir Photog* Joseph Biroc. *Art Dir* Alexander Golitzen, Walter M. Simonds. *Set Decor* John McCarthy, George Milo. *Film Ed* Edwin H. Bryant. *Mus Supv* Joseph Gershenson. *Mus* Van Alexander. *Sd* Waldon O. Watson, David H. Moriarty. *Asst Dir* Terry Morse, Jr. *Unit Prod Mgr* John Morrison. *Makeup* Bud Westmore. *Hairstylist* Larry Germain. *Dogs Trained by* Frank Weatherwax.

Cast: Joan Crawford *(Amy Nelson)*, John Ireland *(Steve Marak)*, Leif Erickson *(Dave Mannering)*, Sarah Lane *(Kit)*, Andi Garrett *(Libby)*, Sharyl Locke *(Tess)*, Patricia Breslin *(Ellie Mannering)*, John Archer *(John Austin)*, John Crawford *(trooper)*, Joyce Meadows *(Judith Marak)*, Douglas Evans *(Tom Ward)*, Barbara Wilkin *(Mary Ward)*.

Mystery melodrama. Source: Ursula (Reilly) Curtiss, *Out of the Dark* (New York, 1964). Dave and Ellie Mannering are preparing to leave for an overnight trip when their babysitter becomes ill. They reluctantly leave the responsibility for the house and 9-year-old Tess to her teenaged sister, Libby. Libby's friend Kit joins them, and they begin a telephone game in which they call people at random and ask silly questions. One of the numbers they find belongs to Steve Marak, whose wife, Judith, is about to leave him. Judith answers Libby's call and tries to get Steve out of the shower, but their continuing argument becomes so intense that he murders her. Steve takes the body into a wooded area and buries it. He returns to find Amy, his widowed neighbor who is in love with him, waiting at the house. Libby calls Steve again, using the name Suzette, and says, "I saw what you did, and I know who you are." Steve begins to panic and tries to counter Libby's quips with his own questions concerning a rendezvous. Amy becomes jealous while overhearing the conversation and goes into the bathroom; there she finds Judith's bloody clothes and realizes what has happened. The girls, curious to see Steve, visit him; but Amy sends them away after pocketing their automobile registration. Steve kills Amy when she tries to blackmail him into living with her; and, taking the car registration, he goes to the girls' home. Kit's father picks her up, and she eventually tells him the story. He calls the police, and they arrive at the Mannerings' home in time to shoot Steve before he strangles Libby. *Sisters. Babysitters. Neighbors. Widows. Adolescence. Practical jokes. Murder. Jealousy. Blackmail. Telephone.*

I SPIT ON YOUR GRAVE (France)   F6.2346

C. T. I.–S. I. P. R. O. *Dist* Audubon Films. 15 Aug **1962** [Providence, Rhode Island, opening]. Sd; b&w. 35mm. 100 min.

Pres by Radley H. Metzger. *Prod Dir* André Labrousse. *Dir* Michel Gast. *Supv* Ralph Habib. *Screenplay* Boris Vian, Jacques Dopagne. *English Dial* LaVerne Owens. *Photog* Marc Fossard, Paul Rodier. *Sets* Robert Bouladoux. *Film Ed* Eliane Bensdorp. *Sd* Gregory Gauguier. *Re-rec for U. S. Vers* Robert Sherwood.

Cast: Christian Marquand *(Joe Grant)*, Antonella Lualdi *(Lizabeth Shannon)*, Paul Guers *(Stan Walker)*, Renate Ewert *(Sylvia Shannon)*, Jean Sorel *(Elmer)*, Fernand Ledoux *(Chandley)*, Daniel Cauchy *(Don)*, Marina Petrowa *(Sheila)*, Jean Droze *(Ted)*, André Versini, Catherine Fontenay, Lud Germain, Gisèle Gallois, Monique Just, Marie-Blanche Vergnes, Claude Berri, Christian Boisseau.

Melodrama. Source: Boris Vian, *J'irai cracher sur vos tombes* (Paris, 1946). Joe Grant, a light-skinned Negro whose grandmother was white, moves from Memphis to a small southern town after his brother is lynched for proposing to marry an upper-class white girl. Joe passes for white and finds employment at a bookstore whose proprietor is involved with a teenage gang of motorcyclists in a blackmail photograph racket. Joe deliberately attracts the attention of many of the town's class-conscious young women, including Lizabeth Shannon, the daughter of the town's wealthiest man, and her wayward sister Sylvia. Lizabeth's fiancé, Stan Walker, returns to town and loses no time in investigating Joe's background. Joe's refusal to aid in the blackmail racket precipitates a dispute with the gang. Afterwards, he attends a party celebrating Lizabeth's engagement and seduces Sylvia. He plans to kill Lizabeth to avenge his brother's death, but because of his growing love for her, he is unable to commit the murder. Later, Lizabeth learns that Joe is a Negro, and she decides to sacrifice everything. She finds him wounded after having been beaten by the gang, and the two run off together. Stan organizes a manhunt, fabricating the story that Joe has abducted Lizabeth in order to rape her. During the pursuit, Stan is killed, and the police gun down Joe and Lizabeth as they attempt to cross the Mason-Dixon Line. [Sources vary in the details of the plot. Some sources omit mention of the motorcycle gang. In the original French version, Joe flees to Trenton after his brother's lynching and is killed with Lizabeth while trying to cross the Canadian border. Stan heads the teenage gangster group.] *Negroes. Motorcycle gangs. Gangsters. Booksellers. Upper classes. Imposture. Lynching. Miscegenation. Racism. Rape. Seduction. Blackmail. Revenge.* Murder. Memphis. United States—South.

Note: Opened in Paris in Jun 1959 as *J'irai cracher sur vos tombes*; running time: 107 min.

I THANK A FOOL (Great Britain)   F6.2347

Eaton Productions. *Dist* Metro-Goldwyn-Mayer, Inc. 12 Sep **1962** [Philadelphia opening; c15 Aug 1962; LP23204]. Sd (Westrex); col (Metrocolor). 35mm (CinemaScope). 100 min.

Prod Anatole De Grunwald. *Assoc Prod* Roy Parkinson. *Dir* Robert Stevens. *Screenplay* Karl Tunberg. *Photog* Harry Waxman. *Camera Op* Jack Lowin. *2d Unit Photog* Douglas Adamson. *Focus* Chic Anstiss. *Col Cons* Joan Bridge. *Art Dir* Sean Kenny. *Asst Art Dir* Michael Knight. *Set Dresser* Pamela Cornell. *Draughtsmen* Colin Grimes, Alan Tomkins. *Prod Dsgn* Sean Kenny. *Titl Dsgn* Chambers & Partners. *Film Ed* Frank Clarke. *1st Asst Ed* Jim Atkinson. *Assembly Ed* Philip Barnikel. *Mus Comp & Cond* Ron Goodwin. *Rec Supv* A. W. Watkins. *Sd Rec* Cyril Swern. *Sd Ed* Gordon Daniel. *Dub Mix* J. B. Smith. *Boom Op* Bill Baldwin. *Sd Camera Op* Ron Matthews. *1st, 2d & 3d Asst Dir* David Tomblin, Derek Parr, Tony Wallis. *Prod Mgr* Basil Somner. *Location Mgr* Ted Wallis. *Cont* Betty Harley. *Prod Sec* Elizabeth Woodthorpe. *Dress Dsgn* Elizabeth Haffenden. *Wardrobe Supv* Dora Lloyd. *Wardrobe Mistress* Dolly Smith. *Wardrobe Master* Charles Monet. *Makeup* Tony Sforzini. *Hairdresser* Joan Johnstone. *Sp Eff* Tom Howard. *Casting Dir* Irene Howard. *Prop Buyer* John Bigg. *Still Photog* Davis Boulton. *Rigger* T. Wilkie. *Grip* L. Kelly.

Cast: Susan Hayward *(Christine Allison)*, Peter Finch *(Stephen Dane)*, Diane Cilento *(Liane Dane)*, Cyril Cusack *(Captain Ferris)*, Kieron Moore *(Roscoe)*, Athene Seyler *(Aunt Heather)*, Richard Wattis *(Ebblington)*, Miriam Karlin *(woman in the Black Maria)*, Laurence Naismith *(O'Grady)*, Clive Morton *(judge)*, J. G. Devlin *(coroner)*, Richard Leech *(Irish doctor)*, Brenda De Banzie *(Nurse Drew)*, Marguerite Brennan *(Irish barmaid)*, Yolande Turner *(Polly)*, Judith Furse, Grace Arnold *(wardresses)*, Peter Sallis *(sleazy doctor)*, Joan Benham *(restaurant manageress)*, Joan Hickson *(landlady)*.

Drama. Source: Audrey Erskine Lindop, *I Thank a Fool* (London, 1958). After spending 2 years in prison for the mercy killing of her incurably ill lover, Canadian Dr. Christine Allison accepts employment with Stephen Dane, the prosecuting attorney at her trial. Dane explains that he wants her to look after his wife, Liane, who has been mentally unbalanced since she caused the death of her father in an automobile crash. Gradually, however, Christine begins to suspect that Dane has another reason for hiring her and is not really concerned about his wife's welfare. Her doubts increase when Liane's supposedly dead father, Captain Ferris, reappears. Determined now to help Liane, Christine takes her to her alleged lush country home in Ireland. The shock of having to admit that it is a hovel and that her father is a drunken schemer is too much for Liane, and she suffers a breakdown. On a doctor's advice, Christine gives her a sedative. When she finds Liane dead from an overdose, Christine fears that Dane arranged matters so that again she will be charged with mercy killing. But he defends her and traps Captain Ferris into admitting that he hid the empty bottle after Liane took all the pills it contained. After confessing complicity in the death of his daughter, Captain Ferris falls to his death. *Ex-convicts. Physicians. Lawyers. Canadians. Mercy killing. Filial relations. Mental illness. Perfidy. Suicide. Tranquilizers.*

Note: Location scenes filmed in Liverpool and Crookhaven, Ireland. Opened in London in Jul 1962.

I, THE BODY *see* **MORIANNA (I, THE BODY)**

I, THE MARQUIS *see* **I, MARQUIS DE SADE**

I WALK THE LINE   F6.2348

John Frankenheimer Productions–Edward Lewis Productions–Halcyon Productions–Atticus Corp. *Dist* Columbia Pictures. 12 Oct **1970** [Nashville, Tennessee, opening; c1 Oct 1970; LP38184]. Sd; col (Eastman Color). 35mm (Panavision). 95 min. *MPAA rating* GP.

An Edward Lewis Production. *Prod* Harold D. Cohen. *Exec Prod* Edward Lewis. *Dir* John Frankenheimer. *Screenplay* Alvin Sargent. *Dir Photog* David M. Walsh. *Art Dir* Albert Brenner. *Set Decor* Marvin March. *Supv Film Ed* Harold F. Kress. *Film Ed* Henry Berman. *Mus Supv* Robert Johnson. *Songs:* "I Walk the Line," "Flesh and Blood," "'Cause I Love You," "This Side of the Law," "Hungry" *writ & sung by* Johnny Cash. *Song:* "Amazing Grace" *arr* Johnny Cash. *Sd* Tom Overton, Arthur Piantadosi. *Asst Dir* Phil Parslow. *Prod Supv* Howard Pine. *Cost Dsgn* Louis Brown. *Makeup Supv* Ben Lane. *Makeup* Frank Prehoda, Jack Petty. *Prop* Anthony Bavero.

Cast: Gregory Peck *(Sheriff Henry Tawes)*, Tuesday Weld *(Alma McCain)*, Estelle Parsons *(Ellen-Haney Tawes)*, Ralph Meeker *(Carl McCain)*, Lonny Chapman *(Bascomb)*, Charles Durning *(Hunnicutt)*, Jeff Dalton *(Clay McCain)*, Freddie McCloud *(Buddy McCain)*, Jane Rose *(Elsie)*, J. C. Evans *(Grandpa Tawes)*, Margaret Ann Morris *(Sybil)*, Bill Littleton *(Pollard)*, Leo Yates *(Vogel)*, Dodo Denney *(Darlene Hunnicutt)*.

Drama. Source: Madison Jones, *An Exile* (New York, 1967). Pursuing a speeding pickup truck, Henry Tawes, middle-aged sheriff in the small town of Sutton, Tennessee, encounters adolescents Buddy and Alma McCain. Alma later appears in his office, claiming to have been stranded in town by another brother, Clay. When Tawes drives her home, she seduces him. As the sheriff is bored by his simple wife, Ellen-Haney, and Alma's moonshiner father, Carl, desires legal protection, a passionate affair ensues. The arrival of Federal agent Bascomb, however, complicates the arrangement, forcing the sheriff to demand destruction of the McCains' still. Meanwhile, sheriff's deputy Hunnicutt becomes suspicious of his supervisor. While investigating the McCains he attacks Alma and is killed by her family. Hoping to start a new life with Alma in California, the lawman disposes of the deputy's corpse in the reservoir. Upon returning, he discovers the McCains departed. Tawes successfully pursues the family, only to discover Alma unwilling to join him. Slashing Tawes with a baling hook, she leaves her wounded lover on the highway. *Sheriffs. Revenue agents. Moonshiners. Mistresses. Lower classes. Family life. Infidelity. Marriage. Murder. Brother-sister relationship. Seduction. Stills. Tennessee. Chases.*

Note: Location scenes filmed in Tennessee and northern California. Working title: *An Exile.*

I WANT MORE   F6.2349
United Road Shows. *Dist* URS Films. 24 Apr **1970** [Maryland license]. Sd; b&w. 35mm. 70 min.
Prod-Dir Jack Beap.
Cast: Sandra Olson, David Nelson, [2].
Sex film. Modern sensualists place classified advertisements in underground newspapers, seeking new thrills and heightened sexual excitement. Bill, Janet, and Gloria provide vicarious thrills for voyeuristic party-goers, performing for free when the audience is unable to pay. At one party, a deviant sends two young women into a floating coffin to make love while wax from lighted candles drips down upon them. People gather at a giant shower to drink champagne, rub one another with soap, and make love. Salty Pete, a specialty barber, shaves heart shapes in the pubic areas of his young clients. A nymphomaniac hitchhiker roams the streets of Hollywood to find four and five sexual partners at a time. Los Angeles motorcyclists indulge in unending sexual activity, making love in the kitchen sink, the bathtub, or the icebox, and riding nude through the house on their motorcycles. At a California nightclub, 24 people join together in a gigantic orgy. *Sensualists. Barbers. Motorcyclists. Hitchhikers. Sex deviates. Stag shows. Exhibitionism. Voyeurism. Troilism. Lesbianism. Group sex. Nymphomania. Newspapers—Underground. Classified advertisements. Coffins. Nightclubs. Hollywood. Los Angeles.*

Note: May also be known as *Sock It to Me With Flesh.*

I WANT YOU!   F6.2350
Chellee Films. 6 Sep **1969** [New York showing]. Sd; b&w. 35mm. 70 min.
Prod-Dir Sam S. Catah. *Script* Douglas Scanio. *Cinematog* Harry August. *Ed* The Editing Place. *Mus* Luristan. *Prod Mgr* Bob Jardine. *Stills* Kalmuk Productions.
Cast: Linda Burns (*Wanda*), Tanya (*herself*), Sophia (*herself*), Mary Scott, Helen Brown, Linda Ross, Jeri Price, Barbara Kent (*unidentified roles*), Harold Martin (*Bruce*).
Sex film. Wanda, a lesbian madam, heads a group of women who cater to the sexual desires of a jaded clientele while a hidden movie camera sets the scene for blackmail. As the camera rolls, one of the prostitutes, under the influence of drugs, eagerly offers herself to Stewart, who is desperate for love; Tanya demonstrates erotic variations to Newman, who craves interracial sex; and timid Christian finds pleasure in submitting to the powerful Sophia. Meanwhile, Wanda finds fulfillment with Barbara, her business partner, and the venture culminates in an orgy. *Madams. Prostitution. Sexual techniques. Timidity. Blackmail. Lesbianism. Orgies. Eavesdropping. Miscegenation. Narcotics.*

I WAS A MAN   F6.2351
Barry Mahon Productions. *Dist* Sack Amusement Enterprises. 2 Nov **1967** [San Francisco opening]. Sd; b&w. 35mm. 70 min.
A Barry Mahon Production. *Prod-Dir* Barry Mahon.
Cast: Ansa Kansas.
Drama. A hermaphrodite who has struggled to act the role of a man, going so far as to join the merchant marine, finds that it is hopeless to continue. He is unable to play the male role in relationships with women, and he feels the desire to dress in women's clothing. Finally, in desperation, he undergoes a sex change operation and thereafter finds happiness as a woman. *Hermaphroditism. Sex change operations. Merchant marine.*

I WAS HAPPY HERE *see* TIME LOST AND TIME REMEMBERED

I WISH I WERE IN DIXIE   F6.2352
Kirt Films International. *Dist* Distribpix, Inc. **1969**. Sd; col. 35mm. 63 min.
Prod Leonard Kirtman. *Dir-Writ* Tommy Goetz. *Mus* Cannonball Express.
Cast: Gale Jorgenson, Steve Wiston, Judith Cristy, Audray Hope.
Drama. During the Civil War, Dixie, a young and innocent Southern belle, comes North to find her lover, who has fallen into the hands of the Yankees. Dixie can't find him, however, and takes employment in a bordello, where one of her regular customers, Freddy, teaches her all about sex. *Southerners. Soldiers. Prisoners of war. Prostitutes. Whorehouses. Sexual initiation. United States—History—Civil War.*

ICE   F6.2353
Monument Film Corp.–The American Film Institute. *Dist* New Yorker Films, Film-Makers' Cooperative. 15 Oct **1970** [New York opening]. Sd; b&w. 16mm & 35mm. 132 min.
Prod David C. Stone. *Dir-Writ* Robert Kramer. *Photog* Robert Machover.
Cast: Robert Kramer (*Robert*), Tom Griffin.
Drama. In New York City sometime in the future, a radical leftist group known as the North American National Committee of International Independent Revolutionary Organizations plans means of protesting American aggression in Mexico and political repression at home. While various radical groups discuss their disunity and fear of the authorities, one radical, Robert, is attacked on the street by four men who castrate him. Ted and Jane, two other radicals, talk to the director of a radical theater about the difficulty of transporting 10 radicals from Chicago in preparation for an offensive. Later, an improvisational group from the theater participate in an encounter session during which a girl expresses her willingness to kill and die for the movement. The offensive begins with a series of terrorist activities: a sniper assassinates an official emerging from a limousine, an apartment building is taken over by radicals, and radicals set fire to an industrial complex in Texas. Ted, a narcotics user, is unable to have sex with a woman, to whom he relates sexual nightmares about his capture and torture by the police. Later, he is caught rifling files in an office and engages in a gun battle with authorities. At a country home where radicals, including one who has been shot, are hiding out, a radical argues with his parents, who own the house and want the wounded girl removed. Later, radicals wreck the house. In a phone booth, a radical talking on the phone admits that life for the revolutionaries is becoming more difficult, but he is optimistic about a spring offensive. *Revolutionaries. Police. Guerrillas. Terrorism. Sabotage. Torture. Assassination. Castration. Theater. Encounter groups. Narcotics. Texas. New York City. Mexico. The Future.*

Note: Location scenes filmed in New York City.

THE ICE HOUSE   F6.2354
C-B Productions. *Dist* Hollywood Cinemart. 9 Jul **1969** [Phoenix, Arizona, opening]. Sd; col (Eastman Color). 35mm. 85 min.
Prod Dorrell McGowan. *Assoc Prod* Carl Ryan Chandler. *Dir* Stuart E. McGowan. *Songs:* "The Ice House," "The Scrub" sung by Ray Peterson.
Cast: Sabrina (*Venus De Marco*), Robert Story (*Rick Martin*), David Story (*Fred Martin*), Scott Brady (*Lieutenant Scott*), Jim Davis (*Jake*), Kelly Ross (*Kandy Kane*), Nancy Dow (*Jan Wilson*).
Melodrama. Rick Martin, a compulsive womanizer, operates an icehouse near a large city. Fred, his twin brother, is a local sheriff. When Rick tries to seduce stripper Venus De Marco, she hits him on the head with a bottle. The blow causes him to become homicidal, and he strangles Venus and hides her body in the icehouse. Horrified, he goes to a psychiatrist for help but cannot admit his crime. Meanwhile, Fred is assigned to investigate the case. Rick, again stricken with a homicidal urge, kills Jan and dumps her body in the icehouse. He then gets drunk at the strip club and attempts to kill Kandy but is ejected from the club and makes his escape. Fred goes to the club, and Kandy tells him that her assailant is his double. He rushes to the icehouse to confront his brother, and in the struggle that follows, Fred falls and is killed. Posing as Fred, Rick resigns from the sheriff's force and returns to his icehouse, not knowing how long he can maintain his duplicity. *Stripteasers. Brothers. Twins. Sheriffs. Psychiatrists. Insanity. Murder. Drunkenness. Impersonation. Nightclubs. Icehouses.*

Note: Also known as *Love in Cold Blood* and *The Passion Pit.*

ICE STATION ZEBRA   F6.2355
Filmways, Inc. *Dist* Metro-Goldwyn-Mayer, Inc. 23 Oct **1968** [Los Angeles opening; c2 Jul 1968; LP36295]. Sd; col (Metrocolor). 35mm & 70mm (Super Panavision, see note). 152 min.
A Martin Ransohoff Production. *Prod* Martin Ransohoff, John Calley. *Assoc Prod* James C. Pratt. *Dir* John Sturges. *Screenplay* Douglas Heyes. *Screen Story* Harry Julian Fink, Jr. *Dir Photog* Daniel L. Fapp. *Adtl Arctic Photog* John M. Stephens, Nelson Tyler. *Art Dir* George W. Davis, Addison Hehr. *Set Decor* Henry Grace, Jack Mills. *Film Ed* Ferris Webster. *Mus Comp*

& Cond Michel Legrand. Rec Supv Franklin Milton. Asst Dir Thomas J. Schmidt. Unit Prod Mgr Ralph W. Nelson. Makeup William Tuttle. Sp Vis Eff J. McMillan Johnson, Carroll L. Shepphird, Clarence Slifer. Sp Eff H. E. Millar, Sr., Ralph Swartz, Earl McCoy. Optical Eff Robert R. Hoag. Tech Adv John M. Connolly, (USN Ret.). Dial Coach Norman Stuart.

Cast: Rock Hudson (Comdr. James Ferraday), Ernest Borgnine (Boris Vaslov), Patrick McGoohan (David Jones), Jim Brown (Capt. Leslie Anders), Tony Bill (Lieut. Russell Walker), Lloyd Nolan (Admiral Garvey), Alf Kjellin (Colonel Ostrovsky), Gerald S. O'Loughlin (Lieut. Comdr. Bob Raeburn), Ted Hartley (Lieut. Jonathan Hansen), Murray Rose (Lieut. George Mills), Ron Masak (Paul Zabrinczski), Sherwood Price (Lieut. Edgar Hackett), Lee Stanley (Lieutenant Mitgang), Joseph Bernard (Dr. Jack Benning), John Orchard, William O'Connell (survivors), Michael T. Mikler (Lieut. Courtney Cartwright), Jonathan Lippe (Russian aide), Ted Kristian (Wassneyer), Jim Dixon (Earl MacAuliffe), Boyd Berlind (Bruce Kentner), David Wendel (Cedric Patterson), Ronnie Rondell (Lyle Nichols), Craig Shreeve (Gafferty), Michael Grossman (Kohler), Wade Graham (Parker), Michael Rougas (Fannovich), Jed Allan (Peter Costigan), Lloyd Haynes (Webson), Buddy Garion (Edward Rawlins), T. J. Escott (Lieut. Carl Mingus), Buddy Hart (Hill), Gary Downey (Lorrison), Robert Carlson (Kelvaney), Don Newsome (Timothy Hirsch), Jim Goodwin (survivor), Bill Hillman (Phillip Munsey), Dennis Alpert (Gambetta).

Action drama. Source: Alistair MacLean, Ice Station Zebra (London, 1963). U. S. Navy Comdr. James Ferraday, stationed in Scotland, receives orders from Admiral Garvey to take his nuclear submarine to a British North Pole weather station called Ice Station Zebra. Ferraday's mission, which he does not yet know, is to recover a capsule from a grounded Russian space satellite containing reconnaissance photographs of all U. S. and Russian missile sites. Also aboard the sub are two British agents, David Jones and Boris Vaslov, the latter a communist defector, and two U. S. Marine officers, Lieut. Russell Walker and Capt. Leslie Anders. En route, the vessel is sabotaged and almost exceeds its implosion depth before the crew can repair the damage and regain normal depth. Ferraday's suspicions that Vaslov is responsible are rejected by Jones, who vouches for his associate's loyalty and, instead, accuses Anders of sabotage. Once the sub reaches Ice Station Zebra, a search party finds only fire-gutted buildings and the frozen corpses of the base personnel. As the search for the capsule begins, Ferraday learns from the sub's radar that Russian aircraft are approaching. Jones is knocked unconscious and recovers to find Anders and Vaslov fighting; assuming that Anders is the spy, Jones kills him. Later, as the capsule is recovered, Russian paratroops under the command of Colonel Ostrovsky land in the area. Vaslov now reveals his traitorous nature by attempting to hand the capsule over to the Russians, but Jones hurls Vaslov against an iceblock and strangles him. Though Ferraday is obliged to give up the capsule, he destroys it as the Russians are lifting it by recovery aircraft. With the photographs lost to both sides, Ferraday and Ostrovsky agree that the incident shall be publicized as an example of the friendly cooperation between two great nations. Russians. British. Secret agents. Communists. Defectors. Paratroops. Traitors. Reconnaissance. Espionage. Sabotage. Loyalty. Submarines. Weather stations. Photographs. Satellites. Scotland. North Pole. United States Navy. United States Marines.

Note: Road shows presented in Cinerama.

ICH BIN AUCH NUR EINE FRAU see **ONLY A WOMAN**

ICHIJOJI NO KETTO see **SAMURAI (PART II)**

I'D RATHER BE RICH   F6.2356

Ross Hunter Productions. Dist Universal Pictures. 26 Aug **1964** [Cleveland opening; c3 Oct 1964; LP32600]. Sd (Westrex); col (Eastman Color by Pathé). 35mm. 96 min.

Prod Ross Hunter. Dir Jack Smight. Screenplay Oscar Brodney, Norman Krasna, Leo Townsend. Dir Photog Russell Metty. Art Dir Alexander Golitzen, George Webb. Set Decor Howard Bristol. Main Titl Pacific Title. Film Ed Milton Carruth. Mus Percy Faith. Mus Supv Joseph Gershenson. Titl Song Richard Maltby, Jr., David Shire. Song: "Almost There" Jerry Keller, Gloria Shayne. Song: "Where Are You?" Harold Adamson, Jimmy McHugh. Song: "It Had To Be You" Gus Kahn, Isham Jones. Songs Sung by Robert Goulet, Andy Williams, Maurice Chevalier. Choreog Miriam Nelson, Hal Belfer. Sd Waldon O. Watson, Corson Jowett. Asst Dir Phil Bowles. Unit Mgr John Morrison. Gowns Dsgn Jean Louis. Makeup Bud Westmore. Hairstyles Larry Germain. Matte Artist Albert Whitlock. Dial Coach Leon Charles.

Cast: Sandra Dee (Cynthia Dulaine), Robert Goulet (Paul Benson), Andy Williams (Warren Parker), Maurice Chevalier (Philip Dulaine), Gene Raymond (Martin Wood), Charlie Ruggles (Dr. Charles Crandall), Hermione Gingold (Nurse Grimshaw), Laurie Main (Harrison), Dort Clark (Albert), Hayden Rorke (MacDougall), Rip Taylor (airline clerk), Allen Jenkins (Fred), Alex Gerry (Cartwright), Jill Jackson (Mrs. MacDougall), Milton Frome

(Max).

Comedy. Heiress Cynthia Dulaine, while in Boston with her fiancé, Warren Parker, a nightclub singer, is called home to Los Angeles to the bedside of her gravely ill grandfather, Philip Dulaine. To please her grandfather, Cynthia invites Warren to Los Angeles; but his plane is grounded by fog in Boston, and Cynthia persuades Paul Belson, a young chemical engineer who is in Los Angeles to see Philip, to pose as her fiancé. The old man likes Paul and makes a remarkable recovery, but he fakes continued illness (with the complicity of the doctor and the nurse) when he learns of Paul's imposture. Warren finally arrives, and Paul prepares to leave, but Philip, who believes that Cynthia has fallen in love with Paul, pretends to be dying, and he does so whenever Paul attempts to leave. Paul and Warren finally fight over Cynthia, and to her grandfather's delight, she discovers that she really loves Paul. Heiresses. Singers. Grandfathers. Engineers. Physicians. Nurses. Old age. Courtship. Death. Imposture. Airplanes. Boston. Los Angeles. Fog.

Note: Previously filmed as It Started With Eve (1941).

L'IDEA FISSA see **LOVE AND MARRIAGE**

IDENTIFICATION MARKS: NONE (Poland)   F6.2357

Państwowa Wyższa Szkoła Filmowa w Łodzi. For Film Polski. Dist New Yorker Films. 9 Feb **1969** [New York opening]. Sd; b&w. 35mm. 76 min.

Dir-Writ Jerzy Skolimowski. Photog Witold Mickiewicz. Art Dir Jerzy Skolimowski. Mus Krzysztof Sadowski.

Cast: Jerzy Skolimowski (Andrzej Leszczyc), Elżbieta Czyżewska (Theresa/Barbara/housewife), Tadeusz Mins (Mundzek), Andrzej Żarnecki (Raymond), Jacek Szczęk.

Drama. Andrzej Leszczyc has been dodging the draft for 3 years by pretending to be an ichthyology student at the university. Now having abandoned his thesis, he suddenly decides to enlist in the military service. At the recruiting office, he is interrogated, given medical tests, and ordered to catch a train bound for military camp that afternoon. Faced with a few hours to sort out his personal life before entering the army for 2 years, he returns to his apartment but says nothing to the woman he sometimes calls his wife. After she leaves for work, Andrzej notices that his dog is sick. At the animal clinic the dog is discovered to have hydrophobia and is put to sleep. In a cafe, an artist friend tells him of the numerous sexual encounters he has had with lonely housewives. While collecting a certificate at the university as part of his enlistment procedure, he meets a girl who has just enrolled. They talk at length, but eventually he leaves to find one of the housewives whose address was given to him by his friend. The woman is evasive, and he departs to find his wife, but nobody has heard of her at the shop where she supposedly works. He goes home, and when his wife returns, he chastises her about the true nature of her work. Rushing to the station to catch his train, he sees the girl from the university waiting for him, but there is no time for them to be together. Draft dodgers. Students. Artists. Housewives. Military draft. Perfidy. Hydrophobia. Trains. Poland—Army. Dogs.

Note: Released in Poland in 1965 as Rysopis.

THE IDIOT (Japan)   F6.2358

Shochiku Co. Dist Shochiku Films of America. 30 Apr **1963** [New York showing]. Sd; b&w. 35mm. 165 min.

Prod Takashi Koide. Dir Akira Kurosawa. Screenplay Eijiro Hisaita, Akira Kurosawa. Photog Toshio Ubukata. Camera Choichi Nakai. Art Dir So Matsuyama. Film Ed T. Saito. Mus Fumio Hayasaka.

Cast: Masayuki Mori (Kameda, the Idiot), Toshiro Mifune (Akama), Setsuko Hara (Taeko), Yoshiko Kuga (Ayako), Takashi Shimura (Ono, her father), Chieko Higashiyama (her mother), Eijiro Yanagi (Tohata), Minoru Chiaki (Kayama), Bokuzen Hidari.

Drama. Source: Fëdor Mikhailovich Dostoevski, Idiot (1868-69). Kameda, a soldier who has narrowly escaped death in a recent war, returns to Japan from Okinawa, where he has been confined to an asylum. Because he is subject to seizures of epilepsy, he is considered to be mentally ill. He becomes acquainted with Akama, a wealthy man, and they fall in love with the same woman, Taeko; in addition, Kameda is attracted to Ayako, another woman who returns his affection. Kameda soon realizes that he prefers Taeko and is disheartened to find that she is another man's mistress. He offers her money in return for her love, but she throws the money into a fire and gives herself to him. Akama learns of the affair, and he and Kameda quarrel. Realizing that he has lost Taeko, Akama stabs her, and both men go mad with grief. Veterans. Mistresses. Epilepsy. Jealousy. Murder. Insanity.

Note: Released in Japan in May 1951 as Hakuchi; running time: 166 min, cut from 265 min.

IDO ZERO DAISAKUSEN see **LATITUDE ZERO**

THE IDOL (Great Britain)   **F6.2359**
Embassy Pictures-Paramount British Pictures. *Dist* Embassy Pictures. 10 Aug **1966** [New York opening]. Sd; b&w. 35mm. 107 min.
Pres by Joseph E. Levine. *Prod* Leonard Lightstone. *Exec Prod* Joseph E. Levine. *Assoc Prod* Robert Porter. *Dir* Daniel Petrie. *Screenplay* Millard Lampell. *Orig Story* Ugo Liberatore. *Dir Photog* Ken Higgins. *Art Dir* George Provis. *Film Ed* Jack Slade. *Mus Comp & Cond* John Dankworth. *Sd* Rusty Coppleman. *Sd Rec* H. L. Bird. *Asst Dir* Bryan Coates. *Prod Mgr* Geoffrey Helman. *Cost* Yvonne Blake. *Makeup* Wally Schneiderman. *Hairdresser* Gordon Bond. *Casting Dir* Rose Tobias Shaw.
Cast: Jennifer Jones *(Carol)*, Michael Parks *(Marco)*, John Leyton *(Timothy)*, Jennifer Hilary *(Sarah)*, Guy Doleman *(Martin Livesey)*, Natasha Pyne *(Rosalind)*, Caroline Blakiston *(2d woman at party)*, Jeremy Bulloch *(Lewis)*, Fanny Carby *(barmaid)*, Vernon Dobtcheff *(man at party)*, Michael Gordon, actor *(boy)*, Gordon Gostelow *(Simon)*, Ken Haward *(policeman)*, Renee Houston *(woman at party)*, Priscilla Morgan *(Rosie)*, Edna Morris *(Mrs. Muller)*, Peter Porteous *(Tommy)*, Terry Richards, Derek Ware *(laborers)*, Jack Watson *(police inspector)*, Rita Webb *(landlady)*, Tina Williams *(Dorothea)*, Philippa Hare.
Domestic drama. In London, Marco, a young, arrogant art student from Kansas City, is friendly with Timothy, a medical student, and Sarah, his girl friend. Timothy is dominated by his beautiful mother, Carol, who is divorcing her husband. Marco tells Timothy, who he believes has a talent for art, that he is studying medicine only because his mother wishes it. Timothy makes a half-hearted attempt to free himself from his mother's domination, but she easily regains control. Marco finds a studio apartment, and Timothy pays the first 2 months' rent, planning to move in with his friend. Carol prevents the move, and Sarah, who has fallen in love with Marco, moves in instead. During a party at her weekend cottage, Carol becomes furious when she finds Marco and Sarah making love in Timothy's room, and she orders Marco from the house. Marco avoids Timothy after this incident, but he comes to Timothy's aid when the boy gets into a pub fight, and he thereby wins Carol's gratitude. Later, Marco tells Timothy that he is tired of Sarah and plans to break with her at midnight on the approaching New Year's Eve. On that evening he stops by Timothy's home to pick him up for a houseboat party they are to attend, only to learn from Carol, who is at home alone, that Timothy left earlier to warn Sarah of Marco's callous plan. Marco seduces Carol and then scornfully leaves for the party. He arrives drunk, accompanied by a streetwalker, and tells Sarah how he took Carol to bed. Timothy overhears and flees from the party, and Marco follows, trying to convince the boy he was lying. Timothy, enraged, knocks his former friend into the river. Marco drowns, and Timothy is arrested for manslaughter. *Rakes. Students. Medical students. Artists. Americans in foreign countries. Police. Filial relations. Divorce. Seduction. Drunkenness. Jealousy. Manslaughter. Houseboats. New Year's Eve. London.*
Note: Location scenes filmed in and around London. Released in Great Britain in Nov 1966; running time: 111 min.

IERI, OGGI E DOMANI *see* **YESTERDAY, TODAY AND TOMORROW**

IF.... (Great Britain)   **F6.2360**
Memorial Enterprises. *Dist* Paramount Pictures. 9 Mar **1969** [New York opening; c19 Dec 1968; LF39]. Sd; col with tinted b&w seq (Eastman Color). 35mm. 111 min. [See note.] *MPAA rating X.*
Prod Michael Medwin, Lindsay Anderson. *Exec Prod* Roy Baird. *Dir* Lindsay Anderson. *Screenplay* David Sherwin. *Orig Script:* "Crusaders" David Sherwin, John Howlett. *Dir Photog* Miroslav Ondricek. *Camera* Chris Menges. *Camera Op* Brian Harris. *Camera Asst* Michael Seresin. *Art Dir* Brian Eatwell. *Prod Dsgn* Jocelyn Herbert. *Film Ed* David Gladwell. *Asst Ed* Ian Rakoff, Michael Ellis. *Mus Comp & Cond* Marc Wilkinson. *Sanctus From the "Missa Luba"* sung by Les Troubadour du Roi Baudoin. *Sd Rec* Christian Wangler. *Dub Ed* Alan Bell. *Dub Mix* Doug Turner. *Asst Dir* John Stoneman. *Prod Mgr* Gavrik Losey. *Asst to the Prod* Neville Thompson. *Asst to the Dir* Stephen Frears, Stuart Baird. *Prod Sec* Zelda Barron. *Cont* Valerie Booth. *Wardrobe* Shura Cohen. *Makeup* Betty Blattner. *Casting Dir* Miriam Brickman. *Constr Mgr* Jack Carter, constr. *Ch Electrn* Roy Larner.
Crusaders: Malcolm McDowell *(Mick Travers)*, David Wood *(Johnny)*, Richard Warwick *(Wallace)*, Christine Noonan *(The Girl)*, Rupert Webster *(Bobby Philips)*.
Whips: Robert Swann *(Rowntree)*, Hugh Thomas *(Denson)*, Michael Cadman *(Fortinbras)*, Peter Sproule *(Barnes)*.
Staff: Peter Jeffrey *(headmaster)*, Arthur Lowe *(Mr. Kemp)*, Mona Washbourne *(matron)*, Mary MacLeod *(Mrs. Kemp)*, Geoffrey Chater *(chaplain)*, Ben Aris *(John Thomas)*, Graham Crowden *(history master)*, Charles Lloyd Pack *(classics master)*, Anthony Nicholls *(General Denson)*, Tommy Godfrey *(school porter)*, John Garrie *(music master)*.

Seniors: Guy Ross *(Stephans)*, Robin Askwith *(Keating)*, Richard Everett *(Pussy Graves)*, Philip Bagenal *(Peanuts)*, Nicholas Page *(Cox)*, Robert Yetzes *(Fisher)*, David Griffin *(Willens)*, Graham Sharman *(Van Eyssen)*, Richard Tombleson *(Baird)*.
Juniors: Richard Davies *(Machin)*, Brian Pettifer *(Biles)*, Michael Newport *(Brunning)*, Charles Sturridge *(Markland)*, Sean Bury *(Jute)*, Martin Beaumont *(Hunter)*.
Miscellaneous: Ellis Dale *(motorcycle salesman)*.
Drama. As winter term begins at the College House boarding school for boys, students settle themselves into assigned dormitory rooms. House prefects ("Whips") quickly assert their puritanical authority by subjecting the new arrivals to humiliating rituals. Although this tyrannical behavior is accepted by the administration as part of school tradition, some students refuse to yield to the system. Mick Travers, a nonconformist upperclassman, covers his wall with magazine photos and maintains that "violence and revolution are the only pure acts"; his two rebellious companions are Johnny and Wallace, the latter a superb gymnast desired by some of the school's homosexual students. During a rugby match, Mick and Johnny sneak away to town, steal a motorcycle, and spend the afternoon with a young waitress. When they return to school, the Head of House, Rowntree, punishes them for their disrespect by flogging them brutally in the gymnasium. Now provoked into open rebellion, Mick shoots and bayonets the chaplain during a field exercise, but the headmaster conceals his displeasure and offers the boys a chance to redeem themselves by clearing away junk that has accumulated under the stage of the College Hall. They find a pile of arms and ammunition in the rubble and store them until "Speech Day" arrives; then, as alumnus General Denson addresses a hall filled with faculty, students, and visiting guests, the rebels set a fire under the floor boards. As the audience pours out into the quad, Mick and his allies, including the waitress, greet them with a hail of fire from the roof; when the headmaster steps forward shouting "trust me," the girl shoots him through the head. General Denson leads a counter-attack as Mick and his friends continue firing. *Students. Nonconformists. Revolutionaries. Gymnasts. Chaplains. Waitresses. Adolescence. Hazing. Revolts. Education. Flogging. Male homosexuality. Theft. Murder. Boarding schools. Ordnance. Motorcycles. Cafes. Gymnasiums. Fires.*
Note: Location scenes filmed in Gloucestershire and London. Opened in London Dec 1968. Initially rated "X," Paramount deleted the objectionable frames, and the film was rerated "R."

IF A MAN ANSWERS   **F6.2361**
Ross Hunter Productions. *Dist* Universal International Films. 10 Oct **1962** [Chicago opening; c17 Sep 1962; LP33270]. Sd (Westrex); col (Eastman Color by Pathé). 35mm. 102 min.
Prod Ross Hunter. *In Charge of Prod* Edward Muhl. *Dir* Henry Levin. *Screenplay* Richard Morris. *Dir Photog* Russell Metty. *Art Dir* Alexander Golitzen. *Set Decor* Howard Bristol. *Main Titl* Pacific Title. *Film Ed* Milton Carruth. *Mus* Hans J. Salter. *Mus Supv* Joseph Gershenson. *Titl Song Writ & Sung by* Bobby Darin. *Song:* "Chantal Theme" writ by Bobby Darin. *Sd* Waldon O. Watson, Frank H. Wilkinson. *Asst Dir* Phil Bowles, Ernest B. Wehmeyer. *Gowns Dsgn* Jean Louis. *Jewels* David Webb. *Furs* Frank Somper. *Makeup* Bud Westmore. *Hairstyles* Larry Germain. *Dial Coach* Norman Stuart.
Cast: Sandra Dee *(Chantal Stacey)*, Bobby Darin *(Eugene Wright)*, Micheline Presle *(Maman Stacey)*, John Lund *(John Stacey)*, Cesar Romero *(Robert Swan [Adam Wright])*, Stefanie Powers *(Tina)*, Christopher Knight *(Richard)*, Ted Thorpe *(florist)*, Roger Bacon *(messenger)*, John Bleifer *(tobacconist)*, Pamela Searle *(model)*, Warrene Ott *(Rita)*, Dani Lynn *(Bunny)*, Charlene Holt *(Lisa)*, Gladys Thornton *(Boston maid)*, Gloria Comacho, Edmay Van Dyke, Rosalee Calvert *(models)*.
Comedy. Source: Winifred Wolfe, *If a Man Answers* (New York, 1961). When young Chantal Stacey, the daughter of a French mother and a Boston father, meets and falls in love with a marriage-shy commercial photographer, Eugene Wright, she successfully follows her mother's advice. After the wedding, however, Eugene starts to take Chantal for granted, and she again turns to her mother for help. This time she is instructed to train her husband as though he were a pet dog. Eugene responds well enough until he learns of the "dog theory" from Chantal's snide girl friend, Tina. He storms out of the apartment, and Chantal's mother again comes to the rescue with another marital trick: she invents a lover for Chantal, telephones her repeatedly, and then hangs up whenever Eugene answers. Eugene, however, discovers the hoax and retaliates with one of his own. He tells Chantal that her secret lover telephoned and is on his way over. The stunned Chantal is shocked when a handsome, older man appears. Eventually, he is revealed to be Eugene's father, and all ends happily as Chantal and Eugene are reunited by the news that they will soon become parents. *Photographers. French. Newlyweds. Mothers-in-law. Marriage. Jealousy. Pregnancy. Filial relations.*

IF HE HOLLERS, LET HIM GO! F6.2362

Forward Films. *Dist* Cinerama Releasing Corp. 2 Oct **1968** [Philadelphia opening; c6 Sep 1968; LP38025]. Sd; col (Eastman Color). 35mm. 111 min. [Also 106 min.] *MPAA rating* R.

Prod-Dir-Writ Charles Martin. *Assoc Prod* John W. Rogers, Harry Kaye, prod. *Dir Photog* William W. Spencer. *Camera* John Pasternak. *Camera Op* Jack Woolf. *Art Dir* James Sullivan. *Set Decor* Dick Pefferle. *Film Ed* Richard Brockway. *Asst Film Ed* Gilbert Greene. *Mus Comp & Cond* Harry Sukman. *Songs:* "A Man Has To Love," "Can't Make It With the Same Man Twice" Sammy Fain, Charles Martin. *Sung by* Barbara McNair. *Song:* "So Tired" Coleridge-Taylor Perkinson. *Sung by* Barbara McNair. *Choreog* James Hibbard. *Sd Mix* Robert Martin. *Sd Rec* Al Cuesta. *Mus Ed* Igo Kantor. *Sd Ed* John Shouse. *1st & 2d Asst Dir* Victor Vallejo, Michael Schoenbrun. *Script Supv* George Rutter. *Asst to the Prod* Fay L. McMullen. *Prod Asst* Charles Marinoff. *Wardrobe* Forrest T. Butler, Sharon E. Swenson. *Sp Eff* Justus Gibbs. *Prop Master* Bill Bates. *Casting* Marvin Paige.

Cast: Dana Wynter (*Ellen Whitlock*), Raymond St. Jacques (*James Lake*), Kevin McCarthy (*Leslie Whitlock*), Barbara McNair (*Lily*), Arthur O'Connell (*prosecutor*), John Russell (*sheriff*), Ann Prentiss (*Thelma Wilson*), Royal Dano (*Carl Blair*), Steve Sandor (*Harry*), Susan Seaforth (*Sally Blair*), James Craig (*police chief*), Don Newsome (*William Lake*), Gregg Palmer (*special officer*), James McEachin (*defense counsel*), Don Megowan (*officer*), Chet Stratton (*Jackson, the pilot*), Edward Schaaf (*Henry Wilson*), Kort Falkenberg (*gas station attendant*), Jason Johnson (*truckdriver*), Frank Gerstle (*sergeant*), James H. Drake (*deputy*), Pepper Martin (*prison guard*), E. A. Sirianni (*doctor*), Todd Martin (*officer*), Harold J. Kennedy (*judge*), Jon Lormer (*chaplain*), Ed Cook (*officer*), Mimi Gibson (*Marion*).

Crime melodrama. After breaking out of prison where he has been serving time on trumped-up charges of rape and murder, black convict James Lake encounters wealthy Leslie Whitlock, who takes him to a mansion owned by his wife, Ellen. Whitlock plans to inherit his wife's money by bribing Lake to murder her in return for $10,000 and a means of escape, but Lake, after unsuccessfully attempting to warn Ellen of the danger she faces, flees from the house. While eluding the police, Lake recalls his past affair with Lily, a beautiful nightclub singer. Realizing that his chances of reaching safety by himself are virtually impossible, Lake returns to the mansion and forces the Whitlocks to drive him through police roadblocks and hide him in their mountain cottage. After Lake has tricked Whitlock into exposing his murderous scheme, Lake and Ellen race from the cottage and make their way to the home of Lake's brother, William. There he discovers that Lily, assuming that he would be in jail for life, has married William. Nevertheless, Lily agrees to help Lake establish his innocence. With her assistance, as well as that of his other friends, Lake traces the murdered girl's stepfather, Carl Blair, to a warehouse and forces him to confess to the brutal murder. Whitlock arrives with the police, but a gunfight breaks out, and Whitlock is killed. With Blair now arrested, Ellen pledges to use her money and influence to clear Lake's name. *Negroes. Fugitives. Police. Singers. Brothers. Stepfathers. Injustice. Prison escapes. Manhunts. Rape. Murder. Bribery. Confession (law). Inheritance.*

Note: Working title: *Night Hunt.*

IF IT'S TUESDAY, THIS MUST BE BELGIUM F6.2363

Wolper Pictures. *Dist* United Artists. 24 Apr **1969** [New York opening; c24 Apr 1969; LP36904]. Sd; col (DeLuxe). 35mm. 98 min.

Pres by David L. Wolper. *Prod* Stan Margulies. *Exec Prod* David L. Wolper. *Dir* Mel Stuart. *Screenplay-Story* David Shaw. *Dir Photog* Vilis Lapenieks. *2d Unit Photog* Fritz Roland. *Art Dir* Marc Frederix. *Film Ed* David Saxon. *Mus* Walter Scharf. *Songs:* "If It's Tuesday, This Must Be Belgium," "Lord of the Reedy River" *comp & sung by* Donovan. *Sd Rec* John Pullen. *Sd* Derek Ball. *Asst Dir* Patrick O'Brien. *Supv Prod Mgr* Tom Pevsner. *Prod Mgr (Italy)* Orazio Tassara. *Prod Mgr (Switzerland)* Michel Rittener. *Prod Mgr (Germany)* Karl-Heinz Eisner. *Prod Mgr (Belgium)* Louis Pitzele. *Prod Mgr (Holland)* Wim Lindner. *Prod Mgr (England)* Jim Brennan. *Wardrobe* Ken Lewington. *Makeup* Vittorio Biseo, Ron Berkeley.

Cast: Suzanne Pleshette (*Samantha*), Ian McShane (*Charlie*), Mildred Netwick (*Jenny Grant*), Murray Hamilton (*Fred Ferguson*), Sandy Baron (*John Marino*), Michael Constantine (*Jack Harmon*), Norman Fell (*Harve Blakely*), Peggy Cass (*Edna Ferguson*), Marty Ingels (*Bert Greenfield*), Pamela Britton (*Freda*), Luke Halpin (*Bo*), Reva Rose (*Irma Blakely*), Sonia Doumen (*Miss Belgium*), Lilian Atterer (*Miss Germany*), Lucien Krier (*Miss Luxembourg*), Aubrey Morris (*Harry Dix*), Hilarie Thompson (*Shelly Ferguson*), Mario Carotenuto (*Giuseppi*), Patricia Routledge (*Mrs. Featherstone*), Marina Berti (*Gina*), Ermelinda De Felice (*Fiat driver's wife*), Paul Esser (*German sergeant*), Jenny White (*Dot*), Roger Six (*Marcel*), Frank Latimore (*George*).

Guest Stars: Ben Gazzara, John Cassavetes (*card players*), Vittorio De Sica (*shoemaker*), Donovan (*singer at youth hostel*), Anita Ekberg (*nightclub performer*), Elsa Martinelli (*woman on bridge*), Catherine Spaak (*woman posing for photographer*), Robert Vaughn (*photographer*), Senta Berger, Joan Collins, Virna Lisi.

Comedy. Under the guidance of a roguish womanizer named Charlie, a group of American tourists have assembled in London for a whirlwind 18-day bus tour of Europe. Although Charlie plans to keep his evenings free by exhausting his charges during the day, he has failed to reckon with Samantha Perkins, an indefatigable Minneapolis careerwoman who is determined to get her money's worth while trying to decide whether she should marry her conservative boyfriend George. Following a day and night in London, the travelers descend on Amsterdam, and there Edna and Fred Ferguson have trouble keeping their somewhat oversexed daughter, Shelly, away from a young hippie named Bo, and Harve Blakely loses his wife, Irma, when she climbs on the wrong bus and goes off with a group of Japanese tourists. As the sightseers are hustled through Brussels, up the Rhine by steamer, and on to Switzerland, Charlie tries to add Samantha to his list of conquests, but with little success; even when she gets drunk on spiked fondue, she remains immovable. Upon arriving in Venice, Italian-American John Marino has a disastrous encounter with his relatives and is forced to jump out of a bathroom window into a canal in order to avoid being married off to his cousin. As the tour nears its end, Charlie is at last beginning to make progress with Samantha when her boyfriend suddenly appears; but by now certain that life with George would be too dull, Samantha sends him away. Reaching their final stop at Rome, Samantha is involved in an automobile accident, and Charlie has to free her from jail. That night, the long-lost Irma, dressed in kimono and sandals, arrives at the farewell banquet and discovers her husband dancing with the entertainers; and Charlie finally succeeds in getting Samantha to make love to him. At the airport the next day when he begs her to marry him, however, she realizes that he is irresponsible. Saying "I'm a square," she bids him goodby and boards an airplane bound for the States. *Playboys. Tourists. Guides. Americans in foreign countries. Businesswomen. Japanese. Italians. Seduction. Buses. London. Amsterdam. Brussels. Rhine River. Switzerland. Venice. Rome.*

Note: Location scenes filmed in Italy, Switzerland, Germany, Belgium, Holland, and England. Inspired by a *New Yorker* cartoon and a 1966 CBS-TV News Special of the same title.

IGOROTA, THE LEGEND OF THE TREE OF LIFE (Philippines) F6.2364

Nepomuceno Productions. *Dist* Fame, Inc. 4 Sep **1970** [San Francisco opening]. Sd; col. 35mm. ca135 min.

Prod-Dir-Writ Luis Nepomuceno. *Photog* Loreto Isleta. *Film Ed* Elsa Abutal. *Mus* Tito Arevalo. *Sd Ed* Juanito Clemente.

Cast: Ric Rodrigo (*Albert*), Charito Solis (*Princess Maila*), Fred Galang.

Melodrama. Maila, princess of a primitive mountain tribe, decides to defy tradition and marry Albert, a man from a lowland tribe. At first her father refuses to allow the marriage, but when she threatens to commit suicide by cutting down her tree of life (igorota), her father relents, and the wedding ceremony is performed. The ceremonial ritual includes the slaughter of a chicken and the disemboweling of a live buffalo and a pig. Princess Maila and Albert go to live in a city, where Albert's family subjects the princess to years of humiliation. When their first child dies, the wife returns to the mountains, followed by Albert. They begin living with the mountain tribe, but he is hated by her people and eventually axed to death by one of the tribesmen. *Igorots. Royalty. Family life. Suicide. Weddings. Rites and ceremonies. Social customs. Chickens. Pigs. Buffalo.*

IKARIE XB 1 see **VOYAGE TO THE END OF THE UNIVERSE**

IKIMONO NO KIROKU see **I LIVE IN FEAR**

IL SUFFIT D'AIMER see **BERNADETTE OF LOURDES**

L'ÎLE AUX FEMMES NUES see **NAKED IN THE WIND**

L'ÎLE DU BOUT DU MONDE see **TEMPTATION**

I'LL NEVER FORGET WHAT'S 'IS NAME (Great Britain) F6.2365

Scimitar Films–Universal Pictures, Ltd. *Dist* Regional Film Distributors. 14 Apr **1968** [New York opening; c25 Jan 1967; LP38022]. Sd (Westrex); col (Technicolor). 35mm. 99 min.

Prod-Dir Michael Winner. *Screenplay* Peter Draper. *Photog* Otto Heller. *Camera Op* Godfrey Godar. *Camera Focus* John Shinerock. *Art Dir* Seamus Flannery. *Film Ed* Bernard Gribble. *Mus Comp* Francis Lai. *Mus Arr* Christian Gaubert. *Sd* Charles Poulton, Hugh Strain. *Dub Ed* Terry Rawlings. *Asst Dir* Michael Dryhurst, Michael Guest. *Prod Mgr* R. L. M. Davidson. *Location Mgr* James M. Crawford. *Location Asst* Robin Douet. *Cont* Pat Moon. *Wardrobe for Miss White* Bibas. *Makeup* Richard Mills. *Hairdresser* Stephanie Kaye. *Ch Electrn* Douglas Fenner.

Cast: Orson Welles (*Jonathan Lute*), Oliver Reed (*Andrew Quint*), Carol White (*Georgina*), Harry Andrews (*Gerald Slater*), Michael Hordern (headmaster), Wendy Craig (Louise Quint), Marianne Faithfull (Josie), Norman Rodway (Nicholas), Frank Finlay (chaplain), Harvey Hall (Maccabee), Ann Lynn (Carla), Lyn Ashley (Susannah), Veronica Clifford (Anna), Edward Fox (Walter), Stuart Cooper (Lewis Force), Roland Curram (Eldrich), Peter Graves, British (Bankman), Mark Burns (Michael Cornwall), Mark Eden (Kellaway), Josephine Rueg (Marian), Mona Chong (Vietnamese girl), Robert Mill (Galloway), Terence Sewards (Pinchin), Basil Dignam.

Comedy-drama. Carrying an ax over his shoulder, television commercials director Andrew Quint marches through the streets of London, enters his office, smashes his desk, and resigns from his job. Disenchanted with the superficiality of his work and his life, which he disspiritedly shares with his wife, Louise, and two mistresses, he decides to return to the small literary magazine which began his post-Cambridge University career. Instead of providing the refuge of a simple life, however, the magazine, edited by Quint's old friend Nicholas, proves to be just another version of modern conformity. Even an affair with Georgina, the office secretary, does not ease Quint's anxiety. After the magazine is bought by his former boss, Jonathan Lute, Quint agrees to return to the advertising organization and make one last commercial. When Georgina is killed in an automobile accident, Quint attempts to devastate the merchandizers with a bitter attack on advertising values, but even this effort backfires; the film wins first prize at an annual commercials festival. *Television directors. Editors. Secretaries. Advertising executives. Disillusionment. Advertising. Marriage. Infidelity. Magazines (periodicals). London. Cambridge (England). Automobile accidents.*

Note: Location scenes filmed in London and Cambridge. Opened in London in Dec 1967.

I'LL SAVE MY LOVE see TWO LOVES

I'LL TAKE SWEDEN   F6.2366
Superior Films. *Dist* United Artists. 2 Jun **1965** [Chicago opening; c2 Jun 1965; LP30829]. Sd; col (Technicolor). 35mm. 96 min.

An Edward Small Production. *Assoc Prod* Alex Gottlieb. *Dir* Frederick De Cordova. *Screenplay* Nat Perrin, Bob Fisher, Arthur Marx. *Story* Nat Perrin. *Dir Photog* Daniel L. Fapp. *Art Dir* Robert Peterson. *Set Decor* Frank Tuttle. *Supv Film Ed* Grant Whytock. *Mus* Jimmie Haskell. *"By"* Dunham. *Cond* Jimmie Haskell. *Songs:* "Give It to Me," "Killin' Polka," "Mad Latina," "Take It Off," "Tell Me, Tell Me" Jimmie Haskell, *"By"* Dunham. *Song:* "Watusi Jo" Jimmie Haskell, Jim Economides. *Songs:* "The Bells Keep Ringin'," "Peep Show," "There'll Be Rainbows Again" *"By"* Dunham, Bobby Beverly. *Song:* "Nothing Can Compare With You" *"By"* Dunham. *Songs:* "I'll Take Sweden," "Would Ya Like My Last Name" Kenneth Lampert, Diane Lampert.

Cast: Bob Hope (Bob Holcomb), Tuesday Weld (JoJo Holcomb), Frankie Avalon (Kenny Klinger), Dina Merrill (Karin Grandstedt), Jeremy Slate (Erik Carlson), Rosemarie Frankland (Marti), Walter Sande (Bjork), John Qualen (Olaf), Peter Bourne (Ingemar), Fay De Witt (Hilda), Alice Frost (Greta), Roy Roberts (ship's captain), Maudie Prickett (spinster), Beverly Hills (Electra), Siv Marta Åberg (Inter), The Vulcanes (musical group).

Musical comedy. Widowed oil company executive Bob Holcomb is appalled that his teenaged daughter, JoJo, plans to marry Kenny Klinger, who has just been expelled from school and spends much of his time playing the guitar. To separate them, Bob provokes a quarrel and then eagerly accepts a new assignment with his company's Stockholm office. He is relieved when JoJo becomes attracted to his handsome Swedish assistant, Erik Carlson. Meanwhile, Bob becomes romantically involved with interior designer Karin Grandstedt. Erik convinces JoJo that a "trial honeymoon" is a proper Swedish custom, and Bob in desperation sends to California for Kenny. Rebuffed in his attempt at reconciliation, Kenny finds consolation with Marti, supposedly a cousin of Erik's but actually his ex-girl friend. Pretending a business trip, Bob and Karin visit a mountain resort for a trial honeymoon of their own, and they meet the two young couples at the same hotel. Though Bob tries frantically to save his daughter from succumbing to Erik's advances, it is Kenny, warned of Erik's philandering by Marti, who saves JoJo's honor by knocking out Erik with his guitar. On their homeward-bound voyage, Bob and Karin and Kenny and JoJo have a double wedding with the ship's captain officiating. *Executives. Philanderers. Widowers. Guitarists. Interior decorators. Oil business. Adolescence. Fatherhood. Marriage—Trial. Seduction. Resorts. Hotels. Ships. Weddings. Stockholm.*

THE ILLIAC PASSION   F6.2367
Dist Film-Makers' Cooperative. 18 Apr **1968** [New York opening]. Sd; col. 16mm. 90 min.

Prod-Dir-Writ Gregory J. Markopoulos. *Photog* Gregory J. Markopoulos. *Film Ed* Gregory J. Markopoulos. *Mus Selections* Béla Bartók.

Cast: Richard Beauvais (Prometheus), David Beauvais (his conscience), Robert Alvarez (Narcissus), Taylor Mead (The Demon or Sprite), Sheila Gary (Echo), Peggy Murray (The Muse), Tom Venturi (Hyacinthus), Tally Brown

(Venus), Kenneth King (Adonis), Gerard Malanga (Ganymede), Jack Smith (Orpheus), Jan Chippman (Eurydice), Andy Warhol (Poseidon), Phillip Klass (Daedalus), Margot Brier (Pandora), Paul Swan (Zeus), Wayne Weber (Icarus), Carlos Anduze (Hades), Stella Dundas (The Moon Goddess), John Dowd (Endymion), Philip Merker (Apollo), Beverly Grant (Persephone), Clara Hoover (Io), Gregory Battcock (Phaeton), Philip Fagan (Cupid [Eros]), Gregory J. Markopoulos (The Filmmaker/Narrator).

Experimental film. Prometheus, on an odyssean journey, crosses the Brooklyn Bridge in search of the characters of his imagination. After meeting the Muse, he proceeds to the "forest." There, under an apple tree, he communes with his selves, represented by celebrated personages from the New York "underground scene" who appear as modern correlatives to the figures of Greek mythology. The filmmaker, who narrates the situations with a translation of Aeschylus' *Prometheus Bound*, finds the personalities of his characters to have a timeless universality. *Filmmakers. Mythological characters. Male homosexuality. New York City. Brooklyn Bridge. "Prometheus Bound". Prometheus.*

Note: Filmed 1964–66 on location in New York City. Employs single-frame editing and superimposed footage. Unfinished version shown in New York in Feb 1966. Working title: *The Markopoulos Passion.*

ILLUSION OF BLOOD (Japan)   F6.2368
Toho Co. *Dist* Toho Co., Frank Lee International. Mar **1966** [Los Angeles showing]. Sd; col (Eastmancolor). 35mm (Tohoscope). 107 min.

Prod Ichiro Sato. *Dir* Shiro Toyoda. *Screenplay* Toshio Yasumi. *Photog* Hiroshi Murai. *Mus* Toru Takemitsu.

Cast: Tatsuya Nakadai (Iuemon Tamiya), Mariko Okada (Oiwa), Junko Ikeuchi (Osode), Kanzaburo Nakamura (Gonbei Naosuke), Mayumi Ozora (Oume), Keiko Awaji (Omaki), Yasushi Nagata (Samon Yotsuya), Eitaro Ozawa (Kihei Ito), Masao Mishima (Takuetsu), Kanjiro Taira.

Tragedy. Based on the Kabuki play by: Namboku Tsuruya, *Tokaido Yotsuya kaidan* (1825). Samurai Iuemon Tamiya steals from the estate of his deceased master rather than accept a menial job. When his father-in-law, Samon Yotsuya, learns of the crime and demands that Iuemon's wife, Oiwa, be granted a divorce, Iuemon slays the old man in order to protect his reputation and his marriage. He helps his companion Gonbei to win the hand of Oiwa's sister by murdering her fiancé and later rescues Oume, the beautiful daughter of a wealthy lord, from a band of robbers. Determined to better himself by marrying Oume, Iuemon poisons his wife and then kills his servant, claiming that the two were secret lovers. The ghosts of the Yotsuya family [of Oiwa, according to some sources] return to haunt him, but Ieumon nevertheless weds Oume. The ghosts appear before Ieumon on his wedding night, and while in a trance he murders his bride and her father. In a desperate attempt to rid himself of the ever-present apparitions, he seeks solace in a Buddhist temple; but he can find no escape from madness and death. *Samurai. Ghosts. Sisters. Fathers-in-law. Murder. Poisoning. Insanity. Infidelity. Marriage. Ambition. Theft. Weddings.*

Note: Released in Japan in 1965 as *Yotsuya Kaidan.*

THE ILLUSTRATED MAN   F6.2369
Warner Bros.-Seven Arts, Inc.-SKM Productions. *Dist* Warner Bros.-Seven Arts, Inc. 26 Mar **1969** [New York opening; c1 Apr 1969; LP37235]. Sd; col (Technicolor). 35mm (Panavision). 103 min. *MPAA rating* M.

Prod Howard B. Kreitsek, Ted Mann. *Dir* Jack Smight. *Screenplay* Howard B. Kreitsek. *Dir Photog* Philip Lathrop. *Camera Op* George Nogle. *Art Dir* Joel Schiller. *Set Decor* Marvin March. *Film Ed* Archie Marshek. *Mus* Jerry Goldsmith. *Sd* Francis E. Stahl. *1st & 2d Asst Dir* Terry Nelson, Joe Nayfack. *Prod Mgr* Terry Nelson. *Prod Coörd* Carl Lindstrom. *Script Supv* Dorothy Aldrin. *Cost Dsgn* Anthea Sylbert. *Wardrobe* Michael Harte. *Rod Steiger's Skin Illus Dsgn* James E. Reynolds. *Makeup Supv* Gordon Bau. *Hairstyles* Ernest Adler, Lenore Weaver. *Sp Eff* Ralph Webb. *Vis Arts Cons* Richard Sylbert. *Dog Trainer* Frank Weatherwax. *Wild Animals Affection-Trained* Africa U. S. A.

Cast: Rod Steiger (Carl), Claire Bloom (Felicia), Robert Drivas (Willie), Don Dubbins (Pickard), Jason Evers (Simmons), Tim Weldon (John), Christie Matchett (Anna), Pogo (Peke, a dog).

Fantasy. Source: Ray Bradbury, "The Veldt," "The Long Rain," and "The Last Night of the World," in *The Illustrated Man* (New York, 1951). Willie, a young man hitchhiking to California in 1933, stops by a country lake and meets Carl, a former carnival roustabout who says he is looking for an old farmhouse and a mysterious woman, Felicia, whom he plans to kill. He tells Willie that 20 years ago Felicia covered his body with skin illustrations and then "went back into the future." Carl warns that if anyone looks at the one bare spot on his body, his left shoulder, that person will see his own future. Willie stares at one of the illustrations and is transported into the future in which Carl and Felicia are the parents of two precocious children, John and Anna, who have a nursery where they can electronically create any environment they wish. Disturbed that the children have chosen an African veldt inhabited by lions and vultures, Carl and Felicia order the youngsters to play in a different environment. Upon hearing the children scream, Carl and Felicia race into the nursery and are devoured by the lions. Returning to reality, Willie listens raptly to Carl's tale of how Felicia seduced him into subjecting himself to her tattoo needles. Willie then stares at another illustration and becomes, along with Carl and two other men, part of a crew of shipwrecked astronauts stranded on a small planet where it rains incessantly. While attempting to reach a sun dome, one of the other two men is shot by Carl for disobeying orders; and the second, driven mad by the driving rain, drowns himself. After Willie commits suicide, Carl, the sole survivor, reaches the sun dome and is greeted by Felicia. After the hallucination, the distraught Willie tries to leave Carl but is once more drawn into a trance by one of the illustrations. This time he is projected into the 40th century, where a world forum has decreed that the last night of the world is at hand and that all children must be given lethal sleeping tablets to spare them the ordeal. Felicia persuades Carl not to give their children the pills, but she awakens the next morning and discovers that, although the world still exists, Carl has poisoned their children. Back in the present, Willie accuses Carl of murdering his own children. Later, while Carl is sleeping, Willie gazes into the blank spot on his shoulder. Upon seeing himself being strangled by Carl, Willie picks up a rock, bashes in Carl's head, and flees in terror. The illustrated man staggers to his feet and, accompanied by his faithful dog, starts out after Willie. *Hitchhikers. Roustabouts. Children. Astronauts. Hallucinations. Parenthood. Death. Seduction. Space travel. Murder. Suicide. Doomsday. Poisoning. Infanticide. Tattoos. Nurseries. Imaginary planets. Dreams. The Future. Dogs. Lions. Vultures.*

ILS SONT NUS see **WE ARE ALL NAKED**

IM STAHLNETZ DES DR. MABUSE see **THE RETURN OF DR. MABUSE**

IMAGE see **MONDO HOLLYWOOD**

IMAGE, FLESH AND VOICE   **F6.2370**
Dist Film-Makers' Distribution Center, Grove Press, Canyon Cinema Cooperative. 21 Oct **1969** [New York opening]. Sd; b&w. 16mm & 35mm. 80 min. [Also 77 min.]
Prod-Dir-Writ Ed Emshwiller. *Photog* Ed Emshwiller. *Ed* Ed Emshwiller.
Cast: Carolyn Carlson, Emery Hermans *(dancers)*.
Experimental film. Voices, a collage from interviews and discussions, express candid feelings about relationships, love, and sex. They are counterpointed by visuals which include street scenes, faces, nude studies, silhouettes, landscapes, a party and other gatherings, semi-abstractions, and surreal sequences. Two modern dancers are featured. *Dancers. Sensualism.*

THE IMAGE OF LOVE   **F6.2371**
Raab-Stoumen Productions. *Dist* Raab-Stoumen Productions, Green Releasing Organization, Prominent Films. Dec **1964** [Los Angeles showing]. Sd; col (Eastmancolor, print by Movielab). 35mm. 90 min.
Prod-Dir-Writ Louis Clyde Stoumen. *Exec Prod* Max L. Raab. *Assoc Prod* Jack Kaufman. *Anim* Martell Photography. *Photog* Arnold Eagle. *Art Dir* Carlos Clarens. *Mus Comp & Cond* Ezra Laderman. *Titl Song* Ezra Laderman, Louis Clyde Stoumen. *Sung by* Anthony Newley. *Sd Ed* Victor Karefsky. *Vocal Sd Eff* Lucho Navarro. *Sd Rec* Charles Campbell. *Asst to the Prod* Carlos Clarens. *Prod Assoc* Angela Grieg Stoumen. *Dir Res* Carlos Clarens.
Narrator: Anthony Newley.
Additional Voices: Anthony Holland, Joan De Marrais.
Documentary. Sexual relationships are examined through painting, sculpture, and excerpts from motion pictures. *Sexuality. Motion pictures. Paintings. Sculptures.*

IMAGO   **F6.2372**
Joe Magarac, Inc. *Dist* Emerson Film Enterprises. 9 Dec **1970** [Houston opening]. Sd; col (Technicolor). 35mm. 90 min.
Prod-Dir-Writ Ned Bosnick. *Photog* Gregory Sandor. *Art Dir* Roger Collins. *Film Ed* Gary Kurtz. *Mus* Lalo Schifrin. *Perf by* Los Angeles String Quartet. *Sd* Keith Wester, Bob Dietz. *Asst Dir* Walter Robles.
Cast: Barbara Douglas *(Carole)*, Morgan Evans *(Dr. Keith)*, Victoria Wales *(Althea)*, Jenie Jackson *(Molly)*, Majila *(Barbara)*, Buddy Arett *(Dr. Dobbs)*, Peter Cord *(Peter)*, Raul Hernandez *(Reagan)*, Dick DeCoit *(Bruce)*, Robert Webb *(Dr. O'Donnell)*, Parker Herriott *(blind priest)*, Michael Rae *(Red/Keystone cop)*, Michael Loring *(Tom)*, Harvey Goldstein *(Jay)*.
Drama. Carole, a virgin, finds herself incapable of having sex with her fiancé. She goes to Keith, a psychiatrist who prescribes therapy including hypnosis and group encounter sessions. Carole becomes involved with lesbian Althea (the doctor's receptionist), tries marijuana, and experiences wild nightmares as she struggles to cope with her problems. *Psychiatrists. Virginity. Frigidity. Hypnotism. Lesbianism. Encounter groups. Marijuana. Dreams.*
Note: Working title: *How Now, Sweet Eros?*

IMITATION OF CHRIST   **F6.2373**
Dist Film-Makers' Distribution Center. 24 Jan **1970** [Los Angeles opening]. Sd; col. 16mm. 105 min. [See note.]
Prod-Dir Andy Warhol. *Film Ed* Andy Warhol.
Cast: Brigid Polk *(mother)*, Ondine *(father)*, Patrick Tilden *(son)*, Nico *(maid)*, Taylor Mead *(hobo)*, Andrea Feldman.
Satire. Suggested by the work attributed to: Thomas à Kempis, *Imitatione Christi* (ca1390-1440). A wasted young man, silent and moody, spends time with the family maid, who reads from Thomas à Kempis' *Imitation of Christ*. Meanwhile, the young man's mother and father argue in bed about their son, trying to determine what has gone wrong with him and lamenting their own state of affairs. Inter-cut are scenes of the son with a hobo, ambling through the streets of San Francisco. *Housemaids. Hoboes. Parenthood. San Francisco. "Imitation of Christ".*
Note: Filmed in New York City, Los Angeles, and San Francisco. A version running ca480 min was originally shown as part of **** *(Four Stars)*, q. v. Also reviewed at 94 min.

IMMER WENN ES NACHT WIRD see **THE LOVE FEAST**

THE IMMORAL (Sweden)   **F6.2374**
Dist Joseph Brenner Associates. 25 Dec **1965**. Sd; b&w. 35mm. 75 min.
Drama. A Swedish summer camping ground frequented by city dwellers is emptying out as the campers return to the city for another week's toil. Siri, an attractive woman left behind by her middle-aged husband for a quiet week alone, meets Usko, a handsome, young bachelor who has remained at the campsite to recover from a hangover. Unsatisfied with her drab, staid husband, Siri is drawn into a torrid affair with Usko. The intense but ill-fated affair, colored by the fear of discovery and the tragedy of deceit, comes to an abrupt finale. *Campers. Bachelors. Marriage. Infidelity.*

IMMORAL CHARGE (Great Britain)   **F6.2375**
Alva Films. *Dist* Governor Films. Mar **1962** [Los Angeles showing]. Sd; b&w. 35mm. 87 min.
Prod Mickey Delamar. *Dir* Terence Young. *Screenplay* Guy Elmes, Mickey Delamar. *Photog* Georges Perinal. *Studio Camera Op* Denys Coop. *Location Camera Op* Godfrey Godar. *Focus* Chic Anstiss. *Camera Grip* Jim Dawes. *Art Dir* Allan Harris. *Set Dresser* Freda Pearson. *Draughtsman* Don Picton. *Film Ed* Reginald Beck. *Mus* Leighton Lucas. *Songs:* "No Turning Back," "Living Doll," "Mad" Lionel Bart. *Sung by* Cliff Richard. *Song:* "Chinchilla" Randy Starr, Dick Wolf. *Sd Mix* Gerry Turner. *Sd Camera* Mickey Hickey. *Boom Op* D. Owen. *1st, 2d & 3d Asst Dir* Adrian Pryce-Jones, Peter Yates, John Stoneman. *Prod Supv* Tom Lyndon-Haynes. *Asst to the Prod* Pamela Peniakoff. *Cont* Kay Mander. *Wardrobe Master* Charles Guerin. *Wardrobe Mistress* Dulcie Midwinter. *Ch Makeup* Phil Leakey. *Hairdresser* Ivy Emmerton. *Still Photog* John Jay. *Prop Buyer* Bill Isaacs.
Cast: Anthony Quayle *(Howard Phillips)*, Sarah Churchill *(Hester Peters)*, Andrew Ray *(Larry Thompson)*, Irene Browne *(Mrs. Phillips)*, Percy Herbert *(Mrs. Thompson)*, Noel Howlett *(Mr. Peters)*, Wensley Pithey *(police sergeant)*, Leigh Madison *(Mary Williams)*, Judith Furse *(probation officer)*, Jean Cadell *(almshouse matron)*, Olive Sloane *(Mrs. Browning)*, Cliff Richard *(Curley Thompson)*, Liliane Brousse *(Michelle)*, Wilfrid Brambell *(Verger)*, George Roderick *(fishmonger)*, Wilfred Pickles *(magistrate)*.
Drama. Source: Philip King, *Serious Charge* (London opening: 17 Feb 1955). Ex-army chaplain Howard Phillips, vicar in a small English town, copes with a serious juvenile delinquency problem by developing programs for youth activities designed to keep most of the town's adolescents out of trouble. One young man, Larry Thompson, however, refuses to take any moral responsibility for the pregnancy of his girl friend; on her way home from confessing her story to Howard, she is killed in an automobile accident. Before Howard can inform Larry's family about the girl, Larry diverts their attention by falsely accusing Howard of making advances to him. Hester Peters, daughter of the former vicar, has been frustrated in her attempts to obtain Howard's love and affirms Larry's story. Howard's mother intervenes and persuades Hester to help discredit Larry, and the two women succeed in clearing Howard. *Chaplains. Clergymen. Juvenile delinquents. Adolescence. Pregnancy. Revenge. Slander. Male homosexuality. Smalltown life. Automobile accidents.*
Note: Released in Great Britain in 1959 as *Serious Charge*; running time: 99 min (cut from 105 min). Rereleased in the U. S. in 1964 as *A Touch of Hell.*

IMMORAL GIRLS OF THE NAKED WEST see **THE IMMORAL WEST—AND HOW IT WAS LOST**

THE IMMORAL MOMENT (France)   **F6.2376**
Films de la Pléiade. *Dist* Jerand Film Distributors. Apr **1967**. Sd; b&w. 35mm (Franscope). 105 min.

Prod Pierre Braunberger. *Dir-Writ* Jacques Doniol-Valcroze. *Photog* Henri Raichi. *Art Dir* Pierre Guffroy. *Film Ed* Bob Wade. *Mus* Georges Delerue. *Sd* Guy Villette.

Cast: Maurice Ronet *(Michel)*, Françoise Brion *(Elsa)*, Nicole Berger *(Eleonore)*, Sacha Pitoeff *(Malferrer)*, Michèle Grellier *(Victoire)*, François Maistre *(Patrice)*, Laurent Terzieff *(narrator)*, Florence Loinod, Gisèle Hauchecorne, Jacques Santi, Jean-Claude Darval.

Drama. Michel, a successful television producer, returns to a nightclub one afternoon to retrieve a coat he left behind. He witnesses the murder of a man who was killed because he recognized Patrice, the head of a secret political group. Interrogated by Commissioner Malferrer, Michel claims he knows nothing of the incident. Patrice, along with the police, is aware that Michel was tortured by the Germans during the Occupation and gave away information without realizing that other members of the Resistance had done the same. Patrice, who fears that Michel might now reveal the existence of the secret political group, threatens him. Despite Malferrer's pleas for cooperation, Michel maintains his silence. Although his wife, Elsa, tries to save him, Michel is killed by one of Patrice's henchmen. *Television producers. Police. Secret societies. Interrogation. Treason. Murder. France—History—German occupation 1940-45.*

Note: Opened in Paris in Jul 1962 as *La dénonciation*; running time: 108 min; also shown in the U. S. under French title. One French source credits Dyaliscope as widescreen process.

THE IMMORAL WEST—AND HOW IT WAS LOST   F6.2377

Pad-Ram Enterprises. *Dist* Pacifica Productions. 9 May **1962** [Los Angeles showing; c1 Jan 1962; LP21822]. Sd; col (Eastman Color). 35mm. 62 min.

Prod Russ Meyer, Peter De Cenzie. *Dir* Russ Meyer. *Photog* Russ Meyer. *Film Ed* Russ Meyer. *Mus* Marlin Skiles.

Cast: Julie Williams *(Goldie Nuggets)*, Jack Moran, Teri Taylor, Sammy Gilbert, Frank Bolger, Topanga Gulch Players.

Farce. The film opens with a montage of key moments in the winning of the West, including the battle of Little Big Horn and Wyatt Earp's gunfight at the O.K. Corral. A grizzled pioneer then tells the *true* story of the settlement of the West. *Snake Wolf, the epitome of evil, runs a wild town with an iron fist. A diminutive stranger rides into town on a burro, and Goldie Nuggets, Snake's woman, takes an interest in the man. Snake has the stranger bounced from a saloon, and the stranger gets mad. He reduces Snake to a state of terror, cleans up the vice-ridden town, and wins Goldie Nuggets as his woman. The old prospector finishes his story and goes off with a prostitute. Prostitutes. Gunfighters. Frontier and pioneer life. Law and order. Little Big Horn. Wyatt Earp.*

Note: Also known as *Wild Gals of the Naked West, The Naked West—And How It Was Lost, The Immoral West,* and *Immoral Girls of the Naked West.*

L'IMMORALE see THE CLIMAX

THE IMMORTAL STORY (France)   F6.2378

O. R. T. F.–Albina Films. *Dist* Fleetwood Films, Altura Films International. 11 Feb **1969** [New York opening]. Sd; col (Eastman Color). 35mm. 63 min.

Prod Micheline Rozan. *Dir-Writ* Orson Welles. *Adapt* Louise de Vilmorin. *Photog* Willy Kurant. *Asst Camera* Jean Orjollet, Jacques Assuerus. *Art Dir* André Piltant. *Film Ed* Yolande Maurette, Marcelle Pluet, Françoise Garnault, Claude Farny. *Piano Selections From the Works of* Erik Satie. *Mus Perf by* Aldo Ciccolini, Jean-Joël Barbier. *Sd* Jean Nény. *Asst Dir* Olivier Gérard, Patrice Toron, Antonio Fuentes. *Prod Mgr* Marc Maurette. *Miss Moreau's Cost* Pierre Cardin.

Cast: Orson Welles *(Mr. Clay/narrator)*, Jeanne Moreau *(Virginie Ducrot)*, Roger Coggio *(Elishama Levinsky)*, Norman Eshley *(Paul)*, Fernando Rey *(merchant)*.

Drama. Source: Karen Blixen, "Skibsdrengens fortaelling," in *Vintereventyr* (Copenhagen, 1942). Mr. Clay is an aging, wealthy merchant living on the island of Macao during the 19th century. Some time ago, Clay had driven his partner Ducrot into bankruptcy and finally suicide; he now resides alone in Ducrot's mansion. His only companion is his bookkeeper, Levinsky, a Polish emigrant whose chores include reading the account books to Mr. Clay when he cannot sleep. One night, Levinsky tries to break the routine by reading from the text of Isaiah. Clay, however, is bored by anything that is not fact, and he interrupts his clerk to relate the "true" story of a young sailor who was paid by an aging and wealthy merchant to sleep with his beautiful wife in order to provide him with an heir. The clerk tells the old man that the tale is merely a legend that is familiar to sailors in every port. Irritated, Clay resolves to turn the fiction into truth, and he orders Levinsky to find a beautiful young woman to portray his wife. Levinsky approaches Virginie Ducrot, the daughter of Clay's former partner, who eventually agrees to take part in the charade for a sum of money. Clay then finds Paul, a young Danish sailor who has been shipwrecked on an island for a year, and brings him home to play the other role.

After the sailor has dined sumptuously, he is shown to a bedroom where Virginie is waiting. All through the night Clay keeps a vigil outside the door of the bedroom where the couple are making love. In the morning when the sailor leaves, he is told that he can now tell his story around the world, and the legend will become truth. The sailor states that he has no intention of telling the story and that no one would believe him anyway. As Virginie watches the sailor depart, Mr. Clay closes his eyes and dies. *Merchants. Bookkeepers. Sailors. Danes. Partnerships. Bankruptcy. Suicide. Old age. Death. Myths. Macao. The Bible.*

Note: Location scenes filmed in Paris and Madrid. Opened in Paris in May 1968 as *Une histoire immortelle*; shown simultaneously on French television.

L'IMMORTALE see L'IMMORTELLE

L'IMMORTELLE (France/Italy/Turkey)   F6.2379

Les Films Tamara–Cocinor–Colo Films–Dino De Laurentiis Cinematografica–Hamle. *Dist* Grove Press. 19 Mar **1969** [Los Angeles opening]. Sd; b&w. 35mm. 100 min. *MPAA rating* M.

Exec Prod Michel Fano, Samy Halfon. *Dir-Story-Adapt* Alain Robbe-Grillet. *Photog* Maurice Barry. *Camera* Robert Foucard. *Art Dir* Konnell Melissos. *Film Ed* Bob Wade. *Mus* Georges Delerue, Tashin Kavalcioglu. *Sd* Jean Philippe, Jacques Maumont. *Sd Ed* Michel Fano. *Asst Dir* Jean-José Rochéa. *Prod Mgr* Emile Breysse. *Gowns* Nina Ricci.

Cast: Françoise Brion *(L, the woman)*, Jacques Doniol-Valcroze *(N, the man)*, Guido Celano *(M, the stranger)*, Catherine Carayon *(Catherine)*, Sezer Sezin *(Turkish woman)*, Ulvi Uraz *(antique dealer)*, Belkis Mutlu *(servant)*, Catherine Blisson.

Drama. On a walkway near the harbor in Istanbul, N, a young French professor, meets a mysterious Frenchwoman who refuses to divulge her real name and seems to be accompanied by a Turk (M) and two large dogs. L, as the woman becomes known, takes N on a tour of the mosques, cemeteries, and other sites and then suddenly vanishes. N frantically searches for her, making inquiries with people around town who probably know her but will not talk. Just as abruptly, however, she reappears; N sees her in the crowded city streets, followed by M and his dogs. Although L seems preoccupied, she insists that she is alone and suggests that they take a trip out of the city. As they drive through the countryside, one of M's dogs suddenly crosses the road, and L swerves to avoid hitting it. The car crashes, and L is killed. N is obsessed with her memory and again seeks to solve her mystery. His investigation proves fruitless, and he begins to doubt that she ever existed. One day he comes upon L's car, which seems to be undamaged, and buys it. Driving over the same road which he had taken with L, he swerves to avoid hitting M's other dog, crashes, and is killed. *Professors. Strangers. Death. Obsession. Memory. Istanbul. Automobile accidents. Dogs.*

Note: Filmed on location in Istanbul. Opened in Paris in Mar 1963; in Rome in Sep 1963 as *L'immortale*. Catherine Carayon is also credited as Catherine Robbe-Grillet.

IMPASSE   F6.2380

Aubrey Schenck Enterprises. *Dist* United Artists. 7 May **1969** [New York opening; c15 Jan 1969; LP37338]. Sd; col (DeLuxe). 35mm. 100 min. *MPAA rating* M.

Prod Hal Klein. *Exec Prod* Aubrey Schenck. *Dir* Richard Benedict. *Screenplay* John C. Higgins. *Photog* Mars Rasca. *Film Ed* John F. Schreyer. *Mus Comp & Cond* Philip Springer. *Song:* "Dear Sweet Miss Jones" Philip Springer, Irwin Levine. *Sd* Ben Winkler. *Asst Dir* Donald Verk. *Prod Mgr* Vicente Nayve. *Makeup* Totoy Villamin. *Hairstyles* Cecilia Abelardo. *Photog Eff* Butler-Glouner Inc.

Cast: Burt Reynolds *(Pat Morrison)*, Anne Francis *(Bobby Jones)*, Lyle Bettger *(Hansen)*, Rodolfo Acosta *(Draco)*, Jeff Corey *(Wombat)*, Clarke Gordon *(Trev Jones)*, Miko Mayama *(Mariko Riley)*, Joanne Dalsass *(Penny)*, Vic Diaz *(Jesus Jimenez Riley)*, Dely Atay-Atayan *(Pear Blossom)*, Bruno Punzalan *(Nakajima)*, Lily Campillos *(Maria Bonita)*, Shirley Gorospe *(Sherry)*, Bessie Barredo *(Kiling)*, Robert Wang *(intern)*, Eddie Nicart *(Kuli)*.

Action drama. Adventurer Pat Morrison learns that $3,000,000 in gold was hidden from the Japanese invaders of Corregidor during the early days of World War II, and he decides to go after the loot. Since the gold was buried in the labyrinths of Malinta Hill by an Army detail of four men who thought they were hiding official records, Morrison recruits the same four men for his expedition. Former officer Trev Jones is now an alcoholic who has led his daughter Bobby to believe that he is dead; Jesus Jimenez Riley is a Moro pearl diver whose wife, Mariko, steals pearls from her husband and is having an affair with Morrison; Draco is a burly Apache living in Arizona; and the bigoted Hansen is now a merchant seaman. Draco arrives from the States and joins Morrison, Riley, and Jones in breaking Hansen out of the jail where he is being held on a morals charge. As Morrison is about to put his plan into action, however, Jones is kidnaped and held by an unscrupulous blackmailer known as Wombat. Wombat informs Bobby that her father is alive and will be returned to her for a fee of $500 plus sexual favors. Morrison comes to Bobby's aid, and the two develop a mutual attraction. Once Morrison and his men have rescued Jones, they set out to recover the gold. Reenacting the parts they played in burying the gold many years ago, the four men eventually lead Morrison to the cache. Success turns to disaster, however, when Hansen and Draco come to blows and their fighting disrupts Morrison's time schedule. Hansen is killed by the Philippine guards, and the others are captured. After learning that the jealous Mariko tipped off the authorities, a handcuffed Morrison waves farewell to Bobby as she leaves to return to the United States. *Adventurers. Veterans. Moros. Apache Indians. Seamen. Filipinos. Alcoholism. Pearl diving. Infidelity. Jailbreaks. Kidnaping. Blackmail. Perfidy. Gold. Corregidor.*

Note: Filmed on location in the Philippines. Working title: *Golden Bullet.*

IMPASSE DES VERTUS see **LOVE AT NIGHT**

THE IMPERSONATOR (Great Britain)   **F6.2381**
Herald. *Dist* Continental Distributing, Inc. 16 Nov **1962** [Maryland license]. Sd; b&w. 35mm. 64 min.

Prod Anthony Perry. *Assoc Prod* Harold Orton. *Dir* Alfred Shaughnessy. *Screenplay* Alfred Shaughnessy, Kenneth Cavander. *Photog* John Coquillon. *Art Dir* Jack Maxsted. *Film Ed* John Bloom. *Mus* De Wolfe. *Sd Rec* Dudley Messenger.

Cast: John Crawford *(Jimmy Bradford)*, Jane Griffiths *(Ann Loring)*, Patricia Burke *(Mrs. Lloyd)*, John Salew *(Harry Walker)*, John Dare *(Tommy Lloyd)*, Yvonne Ball *(principal boy)*, John Arnatt *(police inspector)*, Edmund Glover.

Melodrama. Outraged by a series of attacks on single women, the townspeople of Northbridge suspect that the culprit is an American airman from the nearby base. Attempting to create good will, Sgt. Jimmy Bradford invites the Northbridge schoolchildren to the Christmas pantomime, *Mother Goose,* at the local theater, but his invitation is declined by the school board. As a courtesy, teacher Ann Loring accepts the flier's invitation to an airbase dance. When his bus breaks down, however, she goes on without him. At Mrs. Lloyd's café Bradford expels an unruly customer. In gratitude the proprietress accompanies him to the dance. While returning alone she is murdered by the ejected customer. To divert Tommy Lloyd from the search for his mother, Ann takes the boy to the pantomime, where he recognizes his mother's customer in the person of Mother Goose. Unmasked, female impersonator Walker flees, proving his guilt and exonerating the flier. No longer under suspicion, Bradford is free to declare his love for Ann. *Americans in foreign countries. Schoolteachers. Saloon keepers. Children. Sex deviates. Mime. Murder. Female impersonation. Cafes. Christmas. United States Air Force. Mother Goose.*

Note: Released in Great Britain in Jun 1961.

THE IMPORTANT MAN (Mexico)   **F6.2382**
Películas Rodríguez. *Dist* Lopert Pictures, Azteca Films. 20 Dec **1961** [San Francisco opening]. Sd; b&w. 35mm (CinemaScope). 100 min.

Prod-Dir Ismael Rodríguez. *Exec Prod* Pascual Aragones. *Screenplay* Ismael Rodríguez, Vincente Orona, Jr. *Photog* Gabriel Figueroa. *Art Dir* Edward Fitzgerald, Pablo Galvan. *Film Ed* Jorge Bustos, Pedro del Rey. *Mus* Raúl Lavista. *Sd* Manuel Topete.

Cast: Toshiro Mifune *(Animas Trujano)*, Columba Domínguez *(his wife)*, Pepito Romay *(his son)*, Flor Silvestre *(Catania)*, Antonio Aguilar *(Tadeo)*, Eduardo Fajardo, Guillermina Jiménez, Amado Zumaya, Titina Romay, Luis Aragón, José Chavez.

Drama. Source: Rogelio Barriga Rivas, *La mayordomía* (Mexico City, 1952). Animas Trujano, a Mexican peasant, has one dream in life: to be elected The Important Man, the *mayordomo* of the town at the time of its annual carnival, and thus receive the whole town's respect. In reality, he is a drunken, philandering gambler, whose wife and children must support him. Whenever Animas has money, he spends it on Catania, the town prostitute. Discovering his daughter making love with the son of the distillery owner, Animas assaults him and is sent to jail. His wife works hard to raise his bail money, but Animas is released early and wastes it all. His luck changes when he manages to sell his daughter's illegitimate baby to the distiller; with the money, he buys the election and becomes the *mayordomo.* The usual respect accorded the office does not come his way, however, so Animas again begins drinking and carousing with Catania. His wife finally becomes disgusted with him and murders the prostitute. Realizing that he has one last chance for redemption, Animas goes to confess the murder, thus sparing his wife. *Spendthrifts. Peasants. Gamblers. Prostitutes. Distillers. Drunkenness. Infidelity. Family life. Murder. Confession (law). Illegitimacy. Carnivals. Elections.*

Note: Filmed on location in Oaxaca. Produced in Mexico in 1961 as *Animas Trujano.*

IMPOSSIBLE ON SATURDAY (France/Israel)   **F6.2383**
Athos Films–Méroz Films. *Dist* Magna Pictures. 16 Feb **1966** [New York opening]. Sd; b&w. 35mm. 116 min. [Cut from 120 min.]

Pres by Marshall Naify. *Prod* Jacques Steiner. *Exec Prod* Izhak Agadati. *Dir* Alex Joffé. *Screenplay* Jean Ferry, Pierre Lévy-Corti, Shabatai-Tevet, Alex Joffé. *Story* Shabatai-Tevet, Jacques Steiner. *Photog* Jean Bourgoin. *Set Decor* Joseph Carl. *Film Ed* Eric Pluet. *Mus* Sacha Argov. *Orch Cond* Jacques Metehen. *Sd* Gérard Brisseau, Jacques LeBreton, Jacques Maumont. *Cost* Gina Rosenbach. *Sp Cost for Robert Hirsch* Maison Repetto. *Makeup* Serge Groffe. *Prop* Miquel Teitelbaum.

Cast: Robert Hirsch *(Chaim Silbershatz/Freddie/Frieda/Hans/Carlo/Zvi/Léon/McLeaf)*, Dahlia Friedland *(Debrah, Tulipman's daughter)*, Misha Asherov *(Yankel Silbershatz)*, Teddy Bilis *(Tulipman, mayor of Jerusalem)*, Geula Noni *(Aviva)*, Albert Hizkia *(Meier)*, Yona Levi *(sergeant)*, Rina Ganor, Yael Aviv, Jacob Bodo, Avner Hezkiyahu.

Fantasy. On his deathbed in a Jerusalem nursing home, 83-year-old orchestra conductor Chaim Silbershatz is visited by the ghost of his pious father, Yankel. The patriarch informs Chaim that he must atone for his sinful life by luring all his sons to Israel and marrying them to Israeli women before the Sabbath. Although he has deeded his fortune to Jerusalem, Chaim changes his will, specifying his sons as heirs contingent on their repatriation and marriage. The first to arrive in Israel is American oil magnate Freddie, Chaim's only legitimate son, who subsequently summons his siblings. These are the transvestite Hans, actually Frieda, from Hamburg; Italian bricklayer Carlo, who marries an Israeli army sergeant; married kibbutzim farmer Zvi, who declines his portion; French safecracker Léon, who enters Israel disguised as an Arab; and Scottish air pilot McLeaf. When all but Freddie marry, upon the arrival of the Sabbath the estate reverts to the city of Jerusalem. Chaim, however, having fulfilled the conditions for salvation, dies knowing his offspring are happily settled in Israel. *Patriarchs. Ghosts. Orchestra conductors. Immigrants. Brothers. Oil magnates. Construction workers. Germans. Italians. Soldiers. Farmers. Safecrackers. Arabs. Mayors. Scotch. Air pilots. Death. Jews. Inheritance. Wealth. Parenthood. Marriage. Illegitimacy. Transvestism. Kibbutzim. Jerusalem.*

Note: Filmed on location in Israel. Opened in Paris in Jan 1965 as *Pas question le samedi;* running times: 105 and 90 min. Israeli title: *Raq lo b'shabbat.*

THE IMPOSSIBLE YEARS   **F6.2384**
Marten Productions. *Dist* Metro-Goldwyn-Mayer, Inc. 5 Dec **1968** [New York opening; c10 May 1968; LP36114]. Sd; col (Metrocolor). 35mm (Panavision). 92 min. [Also 99 min.] *MPAA rating* G.

Prod Lawrence Weingarten. *Dir* Michael Gordon. *Screenplay* George Wells. *Dir Photog* William H. Daniels. *Art Dir* George W. Davis, Preston Ames. *Set Decor* Henry Grace, Hugh Hunt. *Film Ed* James E. Newcom. *Mus* Don Costa. *Titl Song* The Tokens. *Sung by* The Cowsills. *Rec Supv* Franklin Milton. *Asst Dir* Arthur Jacobson. *Unit Prod Mgr* Sergei Petschnikoff. *Makeup* William Tuttle. *Hairstyles* Sydney Guilaroff.

Cast: David Niven *(Jonathan Kingsley)*, Lola Albright *(Alice Kingsley)*, Chad Everett *(Richard Merrick)*, Ozzie Nelson *(Dr. Herbert Fleischer)*, Cristina Ferrare *(Linda Kingsley)*, Jeff Cooper *(Bartholmew Smuts)*, John Harding *(Dean Harvey Rockwell)*, Rich Chalet *(Freddie Fleischer)*, Mike McGreevey *(Andy McClaine)*, Don Beddoe *(Dr. Elliot Fish)*, Darleen Carr *(Abbey Kingsley)*, Louise Lorimer *(Mrs. Celia Fish)*, Karen Norris *(Mrs. Rockwell)*, Susan French *(Miss Hammer)*, Trudi Ames *(Francine)*, J. Edward McKinley *(Dr. Pepperell)*, Ned Wertimer *(Dr. Bodey)*.

Comedy-drama. Source: Bob Fisher and Arthur Marx, *The Impossible Years* (New York opening: 13 Oct 1965). Jonathan Kingsley, a university psychiatrist who specializes in problems of adolescence, is shocked to learn that his 17-year-old daughter, Linda, has been arrested for picketing on campus. Fearing that the incident will cost him an important appointment, he decides to put an end to his daughter's slovenly ways. He blames the boy next door for many of her problems and suggests that she enlarge her circle of friends. When she follows his advice and invites new friends to the house, the noise makes it impossible for Jonathan to work on his book. Reluctantly, he agrees to let Linda go to Catalina Island with a group of friends for a weekend. When she returns from the trip, Linda has become a sophisticated young lady. Although she finally confesses to her parents that she has secretly married, she refuses to divulge her husband's identity for fear that her parents will have the marriage annulled. Jonathan calls together several of Linda's boyfriends, and the hysterical Linda runs away, pursued by her father on a motorcycle. The chase ends on campus when Jonathan is dumped at the feet of the school board, which has just appointed him head of the new psychiatric clinic. Linda's husband is revealed to be Jonathan's colleague, Richard Merrick, and all seems to be ending happily, until Linda's younger sister runs into the house with a new boyfriend following her. *Psychiatrists. Professors. Authors. Sisters. Newlyweds. Family* life. *College life. Adolescence. Demonstrations. Elopement. Clinics. Motorcycles. Santa Catalina (California). Chases.*

THE "IMP"PROBABLE MR. WEE GEE   F6.2385
Dist American Film Distributing Corp. 22 Dec **1966** [San Francisco showing]. Sd; col. 35mm. 75 min.

Prod-Dir-Writ Sherman Price.

Cast: Dick Richards, Hella Grondahl, "Red" Kane, Sonia Silver, Ray Christian, Ines Hallendal, Mary Rooney, Roni Nins, (unidentified roles), Reuben Guberman *(Wee Gee voice)*.

Comedy. Wee Gee, a well-known photographer, searches unsuccessfully for a beautiful woman to love and control. Desperate, he falls in love with a store window dummy and follows her when she is crated and shipped to Europe. In London, he investigates a haunted house and meets a voluptuous ghost. He proceeds to Paris, and there a beautiful woman leads him afoul of the local authorities, who chase him to the top of the Eiffel Tower. Here Wee Gee and the police are stopped in their tracks by the magnificent view: a young woman takes a bath in her apartment while her beautiful female neighbors are dressing next door. *Photographers. Ghosts. Police. Fetishism. Voyeurism. Dummies. Haunted houses. London. Paris. Eiffel Tower. Chases.*

IN see HIGH

IN A SECRET GARDEN see OF LOVE AND DESIRE

IN COLD BLOOD   F6.2386
Pax Enterprises. *Dist* Columbia Pictures. 14 Dec **1967** [New York opening; c1 Feb 1968; LP35901]. Sd; b&w (print by Technicolor). 35mm (Panavision). 134 min.

Prod-Dir-Writ Richard Brooks. *Dir Photog* Conrad Hall. *Camera Op* Jordan Cronenweth. *Asst Camera* Bob Thomas, Emile Sauer. *Art Dir* Robert Boyle. *Set Decor* Jack Ahern. *Film Ed* Peter Zinner. *Asst Film Ed* Earle Herdan. *Mus* Quincy Jones. *Orch* Leo Shuken, Jack Hayes. *Sd* William Randall, Jr., Arthur Piantadosi, Dick Tyler, Jack Haynes. *Sd Eff* John Newman, Joe Henrie. *Asst Dir* Tom Shaw, Carl Beringer, John Anderson, Jr. *Script Supv* John Franco. *Wardrobe* Jack Martell. *Makeup* Gary Morris. *Sp Eff* Geza Gaspar. *Optical Eff* Pacific Title. *Coöp* Joseph Satten, The Menninger Foundation. *Ch Electrn* Harry Sundby. *Prop Master* Joe La Bella, Robert Eaton. *Grip* Art Brooker, Eugene Barragy.

Cast: Robert Blake *(Perry Smith)*, Scott Wilson *(Dick Hickock)*, John Forsythe *(Alvin Dewey)*, Paul Stewart *(reporter)*, Gerald S. O'Loughlin *(Harold Nye)*, Jeff Corey *(Dick's father)*, John Gallaudet *(Roy Church)*, James Flavin *(Clarence Duntz)*, Charles McGraw *(Perry's father)*, Jim Lantz *(Officer Rohleder)*, Will Geer *(prosecuting attorney)*, John McLiam *(Herbert Clutter)*, Ruth Storey *(Bonnie Clutter)*, Brenda C. Currin *(Nancy Clutter)*, Paul Hough *(Kenyon Clutter)*, Vaughn Taylor *("Good Samaritan")*, Duke Hobbie *(young reporter)*, Sheldon Allman *(Reverend Post)*, Sammy Thurman *(Mrs. Smith)*, Sadie Truitt, Myrtle Clare *(themselves)*, Teddy Eccles *(young hitchhiker)*, Raymond Hatton *(elderly hitchhiker)*, Mary-Linda Rapelye *(Susan Kidwell)*, Ronda Fultz *(Nancy Clutter's friend)*, Al Christy *(sheriff)*, Don Sollars *(store salesman)*, Harriet Levitt *(Mrs. Hartman)*, Stan Levitt *(insurance man)*.

Crime drama. Source: Truman Capote, *In Cold Blood* (New York, 1966). At 2:00 a.m. on November 15, 1959, in the farming town of Holcomb, Kansas, four members of the Herbert Clutter family are roused from their sleep, bound and gagged, and then brutally murdered by two assailants. The killers, Perry Smith and Dick Hickock, had first met in a state prison where the arrogant Dick picked out the quick-tempered Perry, aspirin-addicted as a result of the lingering pain of leg injuries sustained in a motorcycle accident, as the "born killer" he needed for a partner. The robbery had been planned by Dick when a former inmate told him that Mr. Clutter kept $10,000 in a safe in his home. There was no safe, however, and the killers left with only $43. As the police, led by Alvin Dewey of the Kansas Bureau of Investigation, attempt to solve the murders, the two fugitives cash a series of bad checks and make their way to Mexico, where Perry dreams of becoming a gold prospector. But the plan, like most of Perry's fantasies, comes to naught, and Dick insists that they return to the States. Confident that they have left no clues, they cash additional bad checks. Dick's prison friend has already turned informer, however, and a police dragnet has been set up. In time the two killers are apprehended in Las Vegas and subjected to intensive questioning, during which their alibis are broken by keeping them separated while they tell conflicting stories. Finally, the soles of their shoes match footprints through Mr. Clutter's blood. Swiftly brought to trial and convicted, they are sentenced to be hanged at the Kansas State Penitentiary in Lansing; following appeals and stays of execution, they go to the gallows on April 14, 1965. *Ex-convicts. Police. Informers. Fugitives. Farmers. Murder. Robbery. Capital punishment. Forgery. Prisons. Trials. Holcomb (Kansas). Las Vegas. Nevada. Missouri. Colorado. Texas. Mexico. Peter Edward Smith. Richard Eugene Hickock. Alvin Dewey. Clutter Family. Kansas Bureau of Investigation. Kansas State Penitentiary.*

Note: Filmed in Holcomb, Kansas, and on location in Missouri, Colorado, Texas, Nevada, and Mexico. Publicity material gives the following credit: "Filmed with the cooperation of the People and Law Enforcement Agencies of Kansas, Missouri, Colorado, Nevada, Texas, and Mexico."

IN DARKNESS WAITING see STRATEGY OF TERROR

IN DER HÖLLE IST NOCH PLATZ see THERE IS STILL ROOM IN HELL

IN ENEMY COUNTRY   F6.2387
Universal Pictures. 24 Jul **1968** [Kansas City, Missouri, opening; c10 Aug 1968; LP38023]. Sd (Westrex); col (Technicolor). 35mm (Techniscope). 107 min.

Prod-Dir Harry Keller. *2d Unit Dir* Joe Kane. *Screenplay* Edward Anhalt. *Story* Sy Bartlett. *Dir Photog* Loyal Griggs. *Art Dir* Alexander Golitzen, John Beckman. *Set Decor* John McCarthy, Darrell Silvera. *Main Titl* Wayne Fitzgerald. *Film Ed* Russell F. Schoengarth. *Mus Supv* Joseph Gershenson. *Sd* Waldon O. Watson, Clarence Self. *Asst Dir* Burt Astor, Skip Cosper. *Prod Mgr* Hal Polaire. *Cost Dsgn* Edith Head. *Makeup* Bud Westmore. *Hairstyles* Larry Germain. *Matte Supv* Albert Whitlock. *Dial Coach* Betty Abbott. *Stunt Coörd* David Sharpe.

Cast: Tony Franciosa *(Col. Charles Waslow-Carton)*, Anjanette Comer *(Denise Marchois)*, Guy Stockwell *(Lieut. Col. Philip Braden)*, Paul Hubschmid *(Baron Frederich von Wittenberg)*, Tom Bell *(Capt. Ian Peyton-Reid)*, Michael Constantine *(Ladislov)*, Harry Townes *(General Marchois)*, John Marley *(Rausch)*, Milton Selzer *(Josef Bartowski)*, Murray Matheson, Patric Knowles *(Gen. Lloyd Griffis [see note])*, Tige Andrews *(Nicolay)*, Emile Genest *(General Grieux)*, Lee Bergere *(Maj. Maurice Miral)*, Virginia Christine *(Frau Gulden)*, Harry Landers *(pilot)*, Jim Creech *(co-pilot)*, Gerald Michenaud *(Polish boy)*, Eugene Dynarski *(Capek)*, Ivor Barry *(Air Marshal Evelyn)*, Simon Scott *(General Jomar)*, Paul Busch *(convoy commander)*, Norbert Schiller *(Polish man)*.

War melodrama. In Paris in 1939, Col. Charles Waslow-Carton persuades Denise Marchois, a fellow member of French Intelligence, to marry Baron Frederich von Wittenberg, live with him in Germany, and pretend to defect from France. Four years later, when a newly-developed German torpedo is sinking many Allied ships, Waslow-Carton and two associates (American Air Force officer Braden and an English demolition expert, Peyton-Reid) parachute into Germany and pose as prisoners in a German labor camp near Kiel, where the torpedo factory is situated. Assisted by Ladislov, a Polish agent who is a guard at the factory, the three men determine in which plant the torpedo is assembled. Waslow-Carton goes to von Wittenberg's house disguised as an electrician and gives the information to Denise, who, in turn, transmits it to London. Peyton-Reid, escaping after Allied bombers demolish the factory, is killed by a German patrol, but Waslow-Carton and Braden successfully reach the von Wittenberg home. There Denise informs them that Polish Resistance workers are standing by to aid them in removing one of the torpedoes so that its workings may be studied in France. They steal the torpedo, but the submarine that was to transport them cannot get through, and Waslow-Carton and Braden are forced to take the torpedo to a waiting plane at a nearby airstrip. Denise tells Waslow-Carton that she intends to remain in Germany to continue her work and be with her husband, whom she now loves. The plane takes off just as a German patrol opens fire. *Spies. Nobility. Germans. Defectors. French. English. Poles. Prisoners of war. Marriage of convenience. Espionage. Imposture. Theft. Resistance (political). Torpedoes. Airplanes. Submarines. World War II. Paris. Kiel. France—Army—Intelligence service.*

Note: Sources conflict in crediting the actor who portrays Gen. Lloyd Griffis.

IN FOR LIFE   F6.2388
Dist Stacey Distributors. ca **1970**. Sd; col. 16mm. 61-81 min.

Sex film. A story about women behind bars and their resulting sexual problems. *Sexuality. Prisons.*

IN FRANKFURT SIND DIE NÄCHTE HEISS see CALL GIRLS OF FRANKFURT

IN HARM'S WAY   F6.2389
Sigma Productions. *Dist* Paramount Pictures. 6 Apr **1965** [New York opening; c7 Apr 1965; LP30826]. Sd; b&w. 35mm (Panavision). 165 min. [Copyright length: 170 min.]

Prod-Dir Otto Preminger. *Screenplay* Wendell Mayes. *Dir Photog* Loyal Griggs. *2d Unit Camera* Philip Lathrop. *Camera Op* George Nogle. *Assoc Art Dir* Al Roelofs. *Set Decor* Morris Hoffman, Richard Mansfield. *Prod Dsgn* Lyle Wheeler. *Titl* Saul Bass. *Film Ed* George Tomasini, Hugh S. Fowler. *Asst Ed* James Wells. *Neg Cutter* Connie Roese. *Mus* Jerry Goldsmith. *Sd* Harold Lewis, Charles Grenzbach. *Sd Eff Ed* Don Hall, Jr. *Mus Ed* Richard Carruth. *Asst Dir* Daniel J. McCauley, Howard Joslin, Michael Daves. *Script Supv*

Kathleen Fagan. *Exec Asst to the Prod* Nat Rudich. *Prod Mgr* Eva Monley, Henry Weinberger, Stanley Goldsmith, James E. Henderling. *Cost Coörd* Hope Bryce. *Wardrobe* Eric Seelig, Alan Levine, Gordon Dawson, Grace Harris, Gildo Scarano. *Makeup* Del Armstrong, Web Overlander, David Grayson. *Hairdressing* Frederic Jones, Naomi Cavin. *Sp Eff* Lawrence W. Butler. *Sp Photog* Farciot Edouart. *Tech Adv* Colin J. Mackenzie, (Capt. USN Ret.). *Project Officer* Blake B. Booth, (Capt. USN). *Ch Gaffer* Homer Plannette. *Constr* Elmer Rodgers. *Key Grip* Carl Gibson, Morris Rosen. *Prop Master* Wally Oliver. *Dial Coach* Max Slater. *Casting* Bill Barnes.

Cast: John Wayne *(Capt. Rockwell "Rock" Torrey)*, Kirk Douglas *(Comdr. Paul Eddington)*, Patricia Neal *(Lieut. Maggie Haynes)*, Tom Tryon *(Lieut. William "Mac" McConnel)*, Paula Prentiss *(Bev McConnel)*, Brandon De Wilde *(Ens. Jeremiah "Jere" Torrey)*, Jill Haworth *(Ens. Annalee Dorne)*, Dana Andrews *(Adm. "Blackjack" Broderick)*, Stanley Holloway *(Clayton Canfil)*, Burgess Meredith *(Comdr. Egan Powell)*, Franchot Tone *(CINCPAC I Admiral)*, Patrick O'Neal *(Comdr. Neal Owynn)*, Carroll O'Connor *(Lieutenant Commander Burke)*, Slim Pickens *(C.P.O. Culpepper)*, James Mitchum *(Ensign Griggs)*, George Kennedy *(Colonel Gregory)*, Bruce Cabot *(Quartermaster Quoddy)*, Barbara Bouchet *(Liz Eddington)*, Hugh O'Brian *(Air Force major)*, Tod Andrews *(Captain Tuthill)*, Larry Hagman *(Lieutenant j. g. Cline)*, Stewart Moss *(Ensign Balch)*, Richard Le Pore *(Lieut. j. g. Tom Agar)*, Chet Stratton *(ship's doctor)*, Soo Young *(tearful woman)*, Dort Clark *(Boston)*, Phil Mattingly *(PT boat skipper)*, Henry Fonda *(CINCPAC II Admiral)*.

War drama. Source: James Bassett, *Harm's Way* (Cleveland, 1962). Pearl Harbor, ill-prepared and unknowing, is attacked by the Japanese. Shortly afterwards, Capt. Rockwell Torrey is ordered to lead several U. S. Navy vessels against the enemy. The mission ends in disaster, and upon his return to base, Torrey is assigned to a desk job. He becomes attracted to nurse Maggie Haynes, who informs him that his son, Jere, whom he has not seen in the years since he was divorced from his wife, is an ensign on the island. Jere, an opportunistic, callow youth with only contempt for his father, has plans for obtaining an appointment on the staff of the weak and indecisive Admiral Broderick. Meanwhile, Torrey's temperamental executive officer, Eddington, has learned that his unfaithful wife was killed in a car crash during the attack. As retaliatory naval operations are being set into motion, Torrey's true value is recognized by his superiors, and he is promoted to Rear Admiral. Broderick has been unable to accomplish the spearhead mission of capturing several key islands, and Torrey is assigned to the task. Participating in the operation are Eddington, Maggie, and Jere. On Gavabutu Island, springboard for the attack, Torrey launches a successful foray, and boosts morale among his troops. He thus wins the respect of Jere, who asks to be transferred back to his PT boat. Meanwhile, Eddington, tormented by the memory of his wife's infidelity, drunkenly rapes Jere's girl friend, Annalee, at a beach party. Annalee commits suicide, and Torrey breaks the news to Jere, thereby cementing the bond between them. To redeem himself, Eddington undertakes an unauthorized "certain death" reconnaissance mission, and before he is shot down, he radios the exact size and location of the enemy force which is moving to intercept the U. S. invasion group. In the great sea battle that ensues, the American force is largely destroyed, but the Japanese retreat in confusion. Among those killed is Jere. Torrey, badly wounded, returns home to recuperate in Maggie's care. He is assured, however, that he will soon be back in action to command a new task force in the war against Japan. *Opportunists. Nurses. Military life. Filial relations. Infidelity. Rape. Drunkenness. Reconnaissance. Suicide. Cruisers. PT boats. Pearl Harbor Attack 1941. World War II. United States Navy— Women's Appointed Volunteer Emergency Service. Hawaii. United States Navy. Automobile accidents. Japan—Navy.*

Note: Produced in cooperation with the Department of Defense, including the Department of the Navy. Filmed in Hawaii, San Francisco, San Diego, and aboard U.S.S. *Braine*, U.S.S. *Capitaine*, U.S.S. *O'Bannon*, U.S.S. *Philip*, U.S.S. *Renshaw*, U.S.S. *Saint Paul*, and U.S.S. *Walker*.

IN HOT BLOOD   F6.2390

Dist American Film Distributing Corp. 5 Jun **1968** [periodical notice]. Sd; b&w. 35mm. 70 min.

Prod-Dir-Writ Leo J. Rhewdnal. *Photog* Van Enaps.

Cast: Doris Porro *(Rita)*, Ruth Colon, Yvonne Pontoon, Tom Zolfo, George Wadsworth, Gordon Spalding, Linda Brien, Mike Grey, Carole Jana, Nala Ryan, Jay Lando.

Drama. Rita, an ambitious young model, confronts some harsh realities in her attempt to achieve fame. Jaded photographers demand sexual favors in exchange for work assignments, and her competitors are not reluctant to use sex to get ahead. Rita encounters orgies, nudity, lesbianism, and the use of drugs. She is shocked by the activities of sadistic women who wear boots and whip men at their request. Her rivals engage in vicious, hair-pulling fights, and Rita is degraded when they attack her and smear her body with whipped cream.

This tale of the corruption of an innocent girl ends in bloodshed. *Models. Photographers. Ambition. Prostitution. Moral corruption. Narcotics. Sadomasochism. Nudity. Flagellation. Lesbianism. Orgies.*

Note: Leo J. Rhewdnal is a pseudonym for Joel Landwehr.

IN LIKE FLINT   F6.2391

Saul David Productions. *Dist* Twentieth Century-Fox Film Corp. 15 Mar **1967** [New York opening; c15 Mar 1967; LP34450]. Sd (Westrex); col (DeLuxe). 35mm (CinemaScope). 114 min. [Also 110 min.]

Prod Saul David. *Assoc Prod* Martin Fink. *Dir* Gordon Douglas. *Sp Action Seq Dir* Buzz Henry. *Screenplay* Hal Fimberg. *Dir Photog* William H. Daniels. *Art Dir* Jack Martin Smith, Dale Hennesy. *Set Decor* Walter M. Scott, James W. Payne. *Opening Montage & Titl* Richard Kuhn, National Screen Service. *Film Ed* Hugh S. Fowler. *Mus* Jerry Goldsmith. *Song:* "Your Zowie Face" Leslie Bricusse, Jerry Goldsmith. *Orch* Arthur Morton. *Ballet Choreog* Stefan Wenta. *Sd* Samuel F. Goode, David Dockendorf. *Asst Dir* David Hall. *Unit Prod Mgr* Eric Stacey. *Cost* Ray Aghayan. *James Coburn's Wardrobe by* Martin of California. *Makeup* Ben Nye. *Hairstyles* Margaret Donovan. *Sp Photog Eff* L. B. Abbott, Art Cruickshank, Emil Kosa, Jr. *Coöp* Ballet of Los Angeles.

Cast: James Coburn *(Derek Flint)*, Lee J. Cobb *(Cramden)*, Jean Hale *(Lisa)*, Andrew Duggan *(President/Trent)*, Anna Lee *(Elisabeth)*, Hanna Landy *(Helena)*, Totty Ames *(Simone)*, Steve Ihnat *(General Carter)*, Thomas Hasson *(Avery)*, Mary Michael *(Terry)*, Diane Bond *(Jan)*, Jacki Ray *(Denise)*, Herbert Edelman *(Russian premier)*, Yvonne Craig *(Natasha, the ballerina)*, Buzz Henry *(Austin)*, Henry Wills *(Cooper)*, John Lodge *(Russian agent)*, Mary Meade French *(Hilda)*, Erin O'Brien, Ginny Gan, Eve Bruce, Inge Jaklyn, Kay Farrington, Thordis Brandt, Inga Neilsen, Marilyn Hanold *(Amazons)*, Pat Becker, Lyzanne La Due, Nancy Stone *(lady clients at Fabulous Face)*, W. P. Lear, Sr. *(Bill Lear)*.

Action comedy. As the United States prepares its latest space launching from a remote site in the Virgin Islands, a secret society of women plans to conquer the world. Using a beauty resort called "Fabulous Face" as a front, they put their master plan into operation by abducting the President of the United States from a golf course and replacing him with a look-alike. Special Pentagon official Cramden senses a conspiracy and calls on secret agent Derek Flint for help, but Lisa, an agent for Fabulous Face, drugs Cramden and discredits him by having him photographed in bed with her. In addition, Flint's three favorite girl friends are abducted by the secret society and temporarily frozen into suspended life. After a side trip to the Soviet Union, Flint uses his innumerable gadgets to penetrate the Fabulous Face headquarters. Cramden, who attempts entry by disguising himself as a woman, is discovered and thrown into a cell with the President. Meanwhile, General Carter, a traitorous Army officer, is planning to double-cross Fabulous Face and further his own chances for world conquest by transforming the rocket into a nuclear device. However, as the rocket is prepared for blast-off, Flint and the Fabulous Face agents combine forces against their common enemy. Carter launches himself into space, intending to destroy the world, but the pursuing Flint overpowers him, thereby saving his girl friends, Cramden, the President, and the world. *Secret agents. Presidents of the United States. Doubles. Traitors. Americans in foreign countries. Conspiracy. Abduction. Perfidy. Cryogenics. Disguise. Megalomania. Rockets. Secret societies. Nuclear weapons. Beauty farms. Drugs. Union of Soviet Socialist Republics. Virgin Islands. United States Army.*

Note: Location scenes filmed in Jamaica. The film is a sequel to *Our Man Flint*, q. v.

IN PIENO SOLE see PURPLE NOON

IN SEARCH OF GREGORY (Great Britain/Italy)   F6.2392

Vic Films–Vera Film. *Dist* Universal Pictures. 6 May **1970** [New York opening; c22 Jan 1970; LF66]. Sd; col (Technicolor). 35mm. 90 min. *MPAA rating* GP.

A Joseph Janni Production. *Prod* Joseph Janni, Daniele Senatore. *Assoc Prod* Teddy Joseph. *Dir* Peter Wood, dir. *Screenplay* Tonino Guerra, Lucille Laks. *Adapt* Ken Levison. *Dir Photog* Otto Heller, Giorgio Tonti. *Camera Op* Ray Parslow. *Art Dir* Piero Poletto. *Film Ed* John Bloom. *Asst Film Ed* Lesley Walker. *Mus* Ron Grainer. *Song:* "Dreams" Ron Grainer, Don Black. *Song:* "Close" Ken Howard, mus. *Songs Sung by* Georgie Fame. *Sd Rec* Jim Willis. *Sd Ed* Chris Greenham. *Dub Mix* Gerry Humphreys. *Asst Dir* Richard Dalton, Carlo Cotti. *Prod Mgr* Carlo Lastricati. *Cont* Angela Martelli. *Wardrobe Mistress* Diane Jones. *Dress Dsgn* Gabriella Falk. *Makeup* Wally Schneiderman. *Hairdresser* Stephanie. *Casting Dir* Paolo Rolli.

Cast: Julie Christie *(Catherine)*, Michael Sarrazin *(Gregory)*, John Hurt *(Daniel)*, Paola Pitagora *(Nicole)*, Adolfo Celi *(Max)*, Roland Culver *(Wardle)*, Tony Selby *(taxi driver)*, Jimmy Lynn *(air steward)*, Violetta Chiarini *(Paquita)*, Gabriella Giorgelli *(Encarna)*, Luisa De Santis *(Giselle)*, Ernesto Pagano *(priest)*, Roderick Smith *(small boy)*, Gordon Gostelow *(old man)*.

Drama. Catherine receives an invitation to her father's fifth wedding and is persuaded to attend because of his descriptions of Gregory, an intriguing man who is also expected to be a houseguest. When Catherine arrives in Geneva, her father, his fiancée, Nicole, and Catherine's brother Daniel, tell her more about Gregory, but he never appears. Catherine imagines that he looks like the handsome autoball player whose picture she saw in the airport, and she begins to fantasize about him. When her obsessive search for Gregory proves fruitless, Catherine decides to return to Rome after the wedding, but Daniel, with whom she had an incestuous affair years before, tries unsuccessfully to persuade her not to go. At the airport, she meets the handsome autoball player, picks him up, and they go to a hotel to make love; the man later reveals that he is actually a German medical student named Gunther. Returning to the airport, Catherine calls Daniel to bid him farewell, and he tells her that Gregory just called him after returning from Rome and is looking for her. Catherine says goodbye and boards her flight without ever meeting the real Gregory, who was in the telephone booth next to her. *Athletes. Houseguests. Pickups. Family life. Incest. Brother-sister relationship. Fantasy. Weddings. Airfields. Hotels. Rome. Geneva.*

Note: Location scenes filmed in Switzerland, France, and Italy. Opened in London in Apr 1970; released in Italy in 1970 as *Alla ricerca di Gregory.*

IN SEARCH OF THE CASTAWAYS (United States/Great Britain)
             F6.2393

Walt Disney Productions. *Dist* Buena Vista Distribution Co. 21 Dec **1962** [New York opening; c16 Nov 1962; LP23343]. Sd (RCA); col (Technicolor). 35mm. 100 min.

Overall Prod Credits: *Pres by* Walt Disney. A Walt Disney Production. *Prod* Walt Disney. *Assoc Prod* Hugh Attwooll. *Dir* Robert Stevenson. *2d Unit Dir* Peter Bolton. *Screenplay* Lowell S. Hawley. *Lighting Camera* Paul Beeson. *Camera Op* David Harcourt. *Adtl Photog* Michael Reed. *Focus Puller* Alec Mills. *Supv Art Dir* Michael Stringer. *Art Dir* Ernest Archer. *Set Dresser* Vernon Dixon. *Ch Draughtsman* Norman Dorme, Terence Marsh, Roy Dorman. *Scenic Artist* A. Van Montagu, Peter Wood. *Film Ed* Gordon Stone. *Assembly Cutter* Robin Clarke. *1st Asst Ed* Barry Peters. *2d Asst Ed* Tony Hunt. *Mus Comp* William Alwyn. *Mus Dir* Muir Mathieson. *Songs* Richard M. Sherman, Robert B. Sherman. *Guitar Accomp* Michael Anderson, Jr. *Sd Ed* Peter Thornton. *Sd Rec* Dudley Messenger, Gordon McCallum. *Boom* J. W. N. Daniel. *Sd Camera* Ken Barker. *Asst Dir* Peter Bolton, David Anderson, Terence Churcher, Richard Jenkins. *Prod Mgr* Peter Manley. *Cont* Pam Carlton. *Prod Sec* Jean Walter. *Cost Dsgn* Margaret Furse. *Wardrobe Master* John Briggs. *Wardrobe Mistress* Brenda Dabbs. *Ch Makeup* Harry Frampton. *Hairdresser* Barbara Ritchie. *Sp Eff* Syd Pearson, Jim Hole, Charles Willoughby. *Constr Supv* Alec Officer. *Constr Mgr* Gus Walker, Jock Lyall. *Still Camera* Laurie Ridley. *Casting Dir* Maude Spector. *Prop Buyer* Ron Quelch. *Props Chargehand* Paddy Bennett. *Elec Supv* Harry Black. *Animals* Jimmy Chipperfield.

Prod Credits for Peter Ellenshaw Unit: *Dir* Peter Ellenshaw. *Lighting Camera* Ray Sturgess. *Camera Op* Godfrey Godar. *Focus Puller* Michael Sarafian. *Ch Draughtsman* Norman Dorme, Roy Dorman. *1st, 2d & 3d Asst Dir* Eric Rattray, Grania O'Shannon, Ron Jackson. *Unit Mgr* Clive Reed. *Cont* Kay Rawlings. *Miniatures & Sp Eff* Norman Dorme, Roy Dorman, Ted Clements. *Constr Supv* Bob Groves. *Stills* John Jay. *Props Chargehand* P. Weymouth. *Elec Supv* Reg Blackburn.

Prod Credits for Special Effects Unit: *Dir* Peter Ellenshaw. *Camera* Martin Shortall. *Matte & Sketch Artist* Alan Maley. *Matte Artist* Chris Cully. *Grip* T. Stubbs.

Cast: Maurice Chevalier *(Jacques Paganel)*, Hayley Mills *(Mary Grant)*, George Sanders *(Thomas Ayerton)*, Wilfrid Hyde-White *(Lord Glenarvan)*, Michael Anderson, Jr. *(John Glenarvan)*, Antonio Cifariello *(Thalcave)*, Keith Hamshere *(Robert Grant)*, Wilfrid Brambell *(Bill Gaye)*, Jack Gwillim *(Captain Grant)*, Ronald Fraser *(guard)*, Inia Te Wiata *(Maori chief)*, Norman Bird, Michael Wynne, Milo Sperber, Barry Keegan, George Murcell, Mark Dignam, Roger Delgado, Maxwell Shaw, Andreas Malandrinos, David Spenser.

Fantasy. Source: Jules Verne, *Les enfants du Capitaine Grant; voyage autour du monde* (Paris, 1867–68). In England in the 19th century, Professor Paganel, a whimsical French scientist, finds a floating bottle containing a note which he believes to have been written by the missing Captain Grant. Paganel and Grant's two teenaged children, Mary and Robert, approach wealthy shipping magnate Lord Glenarvan, the owner of Captain Grant's ship, and persuade him to finance a search expedition. Finally Paganel, Mary, Robert, Glenarvan, and his son John set sail for South America. In the Andes an earthquake sends them down a mountain on a glacier. A giant condor snatches up Robert, but Thalcave, an Indian chief, rescues him and later claims to know the whereabouts of Captain Grant. The group, after surviving a tidal wave and a lightning storm in their continuing search for Grant, discovers that the well-meaning Thalcave was mistaken; and they depart for Australia, where Paganel feels sure they will

find Grant. In Melbourne they are met by Thomas Ayerton, who produces evidence that Captain Grant is in New Zealand. Unaware that Ayerton is the third mate who caused a mutiny on Grant's ship, the search party once more sets sail. Ayerton, a gunrunner, causes another mutiny; he sets the group adrift, and they are captured by Maori cannibals. They escape to a volcano and evade their pursuers by starting an avalanche which triggers off an eruption. They then find Captain Grant, overcome Ayerton and his mutineers, and sail for home. *Songs:* "Merci Beaucoup" (Paganel); "Grimpons!" (Paganel & Robert); "Enjoy It" (Mary, John, Robert & Paganel); "The Castaways Theme" (Mary). *Professors. Scientists. French. Shipowners. Nobility. Maori. Gunrunners. Indians of South America. Cannibals. Missing persons. Adolescence. Brother-sister relationship. Rescue. Mutiny. Volcanoes. Ships. South America. Andes. Australia. New Zealand. Chases. Earthquakes. Glaciers. Tidal waves. Storms. Lightning. Avalanches. Condors.*

Note: Opened in London in Nov 1962. Registered for copyright as *The Search of the Castaways.*

IN THE COOL OF THE DAY   **F6.2394**

Metro-Goldwyn-Mayer, Inc.–John Houseman Productions. *Dist* Metro-Goldwyn-Mayer, Inc. 29 May **1963** [New York opening; c23 May 1963; LP25501]. Sd (Westrex); col (Metrocolor). 35mm (Panavision). 91 min. [Copyright length: 86 min.]

Prod John Houseman. *Assoc Prod* Sydney Streeter. *Dir* Robert Stevens. *Screenplay* Meade Roberts. *Dir Photog* Peter Newbrook. *2d Unit Photog* Austin Dempster. *Camera Op* Cece Cooney. *Assoc Prod Dsgn* Peter Murton, Kenneth McCallum Tait, Freda Pearson. *Prod Dsgn* Ken Adam. *Film Ed* Thomas Stanford. *Mus Comp & Cond* Francis Chagrin. *Titl Song* Manos Hadjidakis. *Greek Lyr:* "The Lemon Tree" Nikos Gatsos. *English Lyr* Liam Sullivan. *Sung by* Nat King Cole. *Rec Supv* A. W. Watkins. *Sd Rec* John Bramall. *Sd Ed* Janet Davidson. *Dub Mix* J. B. Smith. *Asst Dir* Jake Wright. *Prod Mgr* David Middlemas. *Cont* Betty Harley. *Wardrobe Supv* Ivy Baker. *Jane Fonda's Wardrobe Dsgn* Orry-Kelly. *Constance Cummings' Wardrobe Dsgn* Pierre Balmain. *Hairstyles* Olga Angelinetta. *Sp Eff* Tom Howard.

Cast: Jane Fonda *(Christine Bonner)*, Peter Finch *(Murray Logan)*, Angela Lansbury *(Sibyl Logan)*, Arthur Hill *(Sam Bonner)*, Constance Cummings *(Mrs. Gellert)*, Alexander Knox *(Frederick Bonner)*, Nigel Davenport *(Leonard)*, John Le Mesurier *(Dr. Arraman)*, Alec McCowen *(Dickie Bayliss)*, Valerie Taylor *(Lily)*, Andreas Markos *(Andreas)*, George Coulouris.

Melodrama. Source: Susan Ertz, *In the Cool of the Day* (New York, 1960). Christine Bonner, a beautiful but frail young woman, leads an unhappy married life, stifled by her adoring husband Sam's overprotectiveness. After living apart from Sam for a time Christine agrees to return to him with the understanding that she is to live an unsheltered life and have a child. Shortly thereafter she meets Murray Logan, a publisher friend of Sam's who also is unhappily married. His wife, Sibyl, blames him for an automobile accident that left her facially scarred and took the life of their son. Despite his attraction to Christine, Murray does all he can to help Sam effect a reconciliation. Sometime later the two couples decide to take a vacation in Greece. In the end Sam is forced to remain at home because of his father's illness; Murray takes Christine to see the Acropolis while Sibyl remains in her hotel room. Near the end of the trip, Sibyl runs off with a philandering Englishman, but not before informing Sam of his wife's "lurid" romance. Sam races to Greece and discovers that Christine has fallen gravely ill with pneumonia. Before dying, he makes Murray promise to visit the tiny Grecian isle they hoped to see together. *Publishers. Philanderers. English. Tourists. Marriage. Disfiguration. Infidelity. Pneumonia. Vacations. Greece. Acropolis. Automobile accidents.*

Note: Location scenes filmed in Greece.

IN THE COUNTRY   **F6.2395**

Blue Van Films. *Dist* Film-Makers' Distribution Center. ca **1967**. Sd; b&w. 16mm. 65 min.

Prod-Dir-Writ Robert Kramer. *Photog* Robert Machover. *Film Ed* Robert Machover, Robert Kramer. *Ed Room Supv* Mike Robinson. *Sd* Norman Fruchter, Robert Kramer. *Prod Asst* Mike Robinson, Pat Keen, Paul Schwartz. *Still Photog* Howard Epstein, photog.

Cast: William Devane, Catherine Merrill, Jane Kramer, Henry Heifitz, Gerald Long, Thomas Neuman.

Drama. A young couple have left the city for a life of seclusion in a country house. Formerly the man was a political activist. Having found no replacement for old associations and convictions, the couple become increasingly isolated and self-obsessed. *Rural life. Alienation.*

IN THE DOGHOUSE (Great Britain)   **F6.2396**

Rank Organisation. *Dist* Zenith International Film Corp. 13 May **1964** [Minneapolis opening]. Sd; b&w. 35mm. 84 min.

Prod Hugh Stewart. *Exec Prod* Earl St. John. *Dir* Darcy Conyers. *Screenplay* Michael Pertwee. *Photog* Alan Hume. *Camera Op* Dudley Lovell.

Focus Op Steve Claydon. *Art Dir* Maurice Carter. *Ch Draughtsman* Bert Davey. *Draughtsman* Terence Knight. *Set Dresser* Arthur Taksen. *Film Ed* Roger Cherrill. *1st Asst Ed* Jack Gardner. *2d Asst Ed* Brian Holland, ed. *Mus* Philip Green. *Titl Song* Philip Green, Sonny Miller. *Sd Mix* C. C. Stevens. *Boom Op* Gus Lloyd. *1st, 2d & 3d Asst Dir* Jimmy Komisarjevsky, Anthony Waye, Terry Clegg. *Cont* Gladys Goldsmith. *Prod Sec* Rhonda Grogan. *Dress Dsgn* Joan Ellacott. *Men's Wardrobe* John Hilling. *Makeup* George Blackler. *Hairdresser* Biddy Chrystal. *Still Photog* Norman Gryspeerdt. *Constr Mgr* Bert Jempson. *Grip* Bill Bannister. *Ch Floor Electrn* Vic Smith. *Prop* Ken Perkins, Charlie Mitchell.

Cast: Leslie Phillips (*Jimmy Fox-Upton*), Peggy Cummins (*Sally*), Hattie Jacques (*Primrose Gudgeon*), James Booth (*Bob Skeffington*), Dick Bentley (*Peddle*), Colin Gordon (*dean*), Joan Heal (*Mrs. Peddle*), Fenella Fielding (*Miss Fordyce*), Esma Cannon (*Mrs. Raikes*), Richard Goolden (*Ribart*), Joan Hickson (*Miss Gibbs*), Vida Hope (*Mrs. Crabtree*), Harry Locke (*Sid*), Kynaston Reeves (*colonel*), Peggy Thorpe-Bates (*Mrs. Muswell*), Joan Young (*middle-aged woman*), Judith Furse (*masseuse*), Philip Ray (*vicar*), Gerald Andersen (*Johnson*), Freda Bamford (*Miss Ritter*), Jacqueline Jones (*Rita*).

Comedy. Source: Alex Duncan, *It's a Vet's Life* (London, 1961). After 12 years at a London veterinary college, Jimmy Fox-Upton passes his final examinations. His rival, the unscrupulous Bob Skeffington, cheats to qualify, then sets up a shady practice in London's wealthy upper Belgravia. Bob caters to the pets of affluent owners, while Jimmy opens an animal clinic in lower Belgravia, a poor district. Jimmy chases a chimpanzee belonging to stage entertainer Sally Huxley into a ladies' Turkish bath and is fined for disorderly conduct. Later he attends to a burn the chimp has received and becomes friendly with Sally. The unsuspecting Jimmy helps Bob Skeffington and Peddle (a crooked dealer) export horses across the English Channel until he learns that the horses are going to French butchers; and with the assistance of Sally and R. S. P. C. A. Inspector Primrose Gudgeon, Jimmy exposes the racket. His rewards are Sally's affection and a telephone call, presumably from the Palace. *Veterinarians. Entertainers. Racketeers. Cheating. Wealth. Animal care. Turkish baths. London—Belgravia. English Channel. Royal Society for the Prevention of Cruelty to Animals. Animals. Chimpanzees. Horses.*

Note: Opened in London in Dec 1961; running time: 93 min. Working title: *Vet in the Doghouse.*

IN THE FALL OF '55 EDEN CRIED see EDEN CRIED

IN THE FRENCH STYLE (United States/France)   **F6.2397**
Casanna Films–Orsay Films. *Dist* Columbia Pictures. 18 Sep **1963** [New York opening; c1 Sep 1963; LP26597]. Sd (Westrex); b&w. 35mm. 106 min.

Prod Irwin Shaw, Robert Parrish. *Assoc Prod* Claude Ganz. *Dir* Robert Parrish. *Screenplay* Irwin Shaw. *Dir Photog* Michel Kelber. *Camera* Wladimir Ivanov. *Art Dir* Rino Mondellini. *Asst Art Dir* Jacques Brizzio. *Film Ed* Renée Lichtig. *Asst Ed* Françoise London. *Mus Comp* Joseph Kosma. *Cond* André Girard. *Concerto in A Minor* Robert Schumann. *Sd* Jean Monchablon. *Sd Eff Ed* Denise Baby. *Asst Dir* Michel Wyn. *Dir Prod* Ludmilla Goulian. *Prod Asst* Suzanne Wiesenfeld. *Cont* Marie-José Guissard. *Asst to the Prod* Cathy Wyler. *Miss Seberg's Wardrobe* Philippe Venet. *Makeup* Michel Deruelle, Phuong Maittret. *Coiffure* Jacques Dessange. *Coöp* Air France. *Paintings by* Jane Eakin.

Cast: Jean Seberg (*Christina James*), Stanley Baker (*Walter Beddoes*), Philippe Forquet (*Guy*), Addison Powell (*Mr. James*), Jack Hedley (*Bill*), Maurice Teynac (*baron*), James Leo Herlihy (*Dr. John Haislip*), Ann Lewis (*Guy's fiancée*), Jacques Charon (*Patrini*), Claudine Auger (*Clio*), Barbara Somers (*Madame Piguet*), Moustache (*bistro owner*).

Drama. Source: Irwin Shaw, "In the French Style," in *New Yorker* (17 Jan 1953). Irwin Shaw, "A Year To Learn the Language" (publication undetermined). In Paris to study painting, Chicago-born Christina James becomes romantically involved with a young Frenchman, Guy, who claims to be an engineering student. After 3 months of dating, they decide to consummate their love; but when they arrive in a sleazy hotel room, Guy confesses that he is only 16 and still in high school. Their affair ends, and Christina immerses herself in the life of the city and embarks upon a series of affairs. Eventually she falls in love with Walter Beddoes, a hard-drinking correspondent constantly being called away from Paris. While Walter is in Tripoli, Christina is visited by her father, a mild-mannered man who tries to persuade her to give up the life she is living and return with him to America. She refuses, preferring instead to wait for Walter's return. After several prolonged separations, she realizes that life with Walter will be an endless round of goodbys. Though still in love with him, she decides to marry a young doctor and return with him to San Francisco. Every 3 years they will be able to return to Paris for a 2-week vacation. *Students. Painters. Americans in foreign countries. Newspapermen. Physicians. Filial relations. Adolescence. Urban life. Hotels. Paris.*

Note: Opened in Paris in Mar 1964 as *À la française.* Location scenes filmed in Paris and at the Aéroport de Nice–Côte d'Azur.

IN THE HEAT OF THE NIGHT   **F6.2398**
Mirisch Corp. *Dist* United Artists. 2 Aug **1967** [New York opening; c2 Aug 1967; LP34525]. Sd; col (DeLuxe). 35mm. 109 min.

A Norman Jewison–Walter Mirisch Production. *Prod* Walter Mirisch. *Dir* Norman Jewison. *Screenplay* Stirling Silliphant. *Dir Photog* Haskell Wexler. *Art Dir* Paul Groesse. *Set Decor* Robert Priestley. *Titl* Murray Naidich. *Film Ed* Hal Ashby. *Mus Score* Quincy Jones. *Titl Song & Song:* "Foul Owl" Quincy Jones, Marilyn Bergman, Alan Bergman. *Titl Song Sung by* Ray Charles. *Sd* Walter Goss, Clem Portman, Charles Cooper, Kevin Cleary. *Asst Dir* Terry Morse, Jr., Newt Arnold. *Prod Supv* Allen K. Wood. *Prod Mgr* James E. Henderling. *Asst to the Prod* Hal Ashby. *Wardrobe* Alan Levine. *Makeup* Del Armstrong.

Cast: Sidney Poitier (*Virgil Tibbs*), Rod Steiger (*Bill Gillespie*), Warren Oates (*Sam Wood*), Lee Grant (*Mrs. Leslie Colbert*), James Patterson (*Purdy*), Quentin Dean (*Delores Purdy*), Larry Gates (*Eric Endicott*), William Schallert (*Webb Schubert*), Beah Richards (*Mrs. Bellamy [Mama Caleba]*), Scott Wilson (*Harvey Oberst*), Jack Teter (*Philip Colbert*), Matt Clark (*Packy Harrison*), Anthony James (*Ralph Henshaw*), Kermit Murdock (*H. E. Henderson*), Khalil Bezaleel (*Jess*), Peter Whitney (*George Courtney*), William Watson (*Harold Courtney*), Timothy Scott (*Shagbag Martin*), Michael Le Glaire, Larry D. Mann, Stuart Nisbet (*members of mayor's council*), Eldon Quick (*Charlie Hawthorne*), Fred Stewart (*Dr. Stuart*), Arthur Malet (*Ted Ulam*), Pete Masterson (*Arnold Fryer*), Alan Oppenheimer, Philip Garris (*two engineers*), Jester Hairston (*Henry*), Clegg Hoyt (*deputy*), Phil Adams, Nikita Knatz (*young toughs*), David Stinehart (*baggagemaster*), Buzz Barton (*conductor*).

Drama. Source: John Dudley Ball, *In the Heat of the Night* (New York, 1965). In Sparta, Mississippi, one hot September night, the murdered body of wealthy industrialist Philip Colbert is found in an alley. Hunting for suspects, the police pick up Virgil Tibbs, a well-dressed Negro, and bring him to headquarters for questioning. But, to the consternation of police chief Bill Gillespie, Tibbs turns out to be a top homicide detective from Philadelphia who has been in town visiting his mother. Ordered by his superior in Philadelphia to assist with the case, Tibbs conducts the postmortem examination and thus displays his superior knowledge of criminology. Though enraged, Gillespie reluctantly acquiesces in Tibbs's findings. As the investigation gets underway, Gillespie accuses young Harvey Oberst of the murder when he catches him with the dead man's wallet, but Tibbs quickly proves that Oberst stole the wallet after he found the body. Tibbs, for his part, is so determined to establish the guilt of Eric Endicott, an influential but insolent and bigoted conservative who opposed Colbert's progressive plans for a modern factory, that he too makes a false accusation. Gradually, as Tibbs and Gillespie combine their efforts, a grudging tolerance develops between them. After Gillespie has wrongly charged his own deputy, Sam Wood, with the murder, the local tease, Delores Purdy, is dragged into the police station by her brother, who claims that she is pregnant by Wood. Upon learning about an abortionist called Mama Caleba, Tibbs visits the woman; and he is still with her when Delores arrives, accompanied by the actual father of her child, diner counterman Ralph Henshaw. Tibbs confronts him, and Henshaw confesses that he murdered Colbert to obtain the money for Delores' abortion. With the case closed, Gillespie drives Tibbs to the railway depot. The two men shake hands in acknowledgement of the mutual respect that has grown between them. *Negroes. Police. Detectives. Industrialists. Teases. Murder. Theft. Race relations. Smalltown life. Racial prejudice. Abortion. Brother-sister relationship. Diners (restaurants). Mississippi.*

Note: Location scenes filmed in Sparta, Illinois, and in Tennessee. Sequel: *They Call Me MISTER Tibbs,* q. v.

IN THE YEAR OF THE PIG   **F6.2399**
Monday Film Production Co. *Dist* Pathé Contemporary Films, Cinetree. 26 Feb **1969** [Boston opening; c25 Oct 1968; MP25818]. Sd; b&w. 35mm (see note). 101 min.

Prod-Dir Emile De Antonio. *Exec Prod* Moxie Schell. *Assoc Prod* Terry Marrone, John Attee. *Camera* John F. Newman. *Camera in Paris* Jean Jacques Rochut. *Film Ed* Lyn Zee Klingman, Hannah Moreinis, Helen Levitt. *Mus* Steve Addiss. *Sd* Geoffrey Weinstock. *Sd in Paris* Harold Maury. *Asst Dir* Albert Maher.

Documentary. This compilation of news footage from varied sources and filmed interviews traces French involvement in Vietnam from the 1940's through the fall of Dien Bien Phu, and American support from the period of the domino theory in the 1950's to all-out American intervention in the 1960's. Included are the words of such journalists, scholars, and statesmen as David Halberstam, Arthur Schlesinger, Jr., Jean Lacouture, Paul Mus, Oliver Todd, Harrison Salisbury, David Wurfel, Roger Hilsman, and Daniel Berrigan, most of whom opposed American involvement in Southeast Asia; but the film concentrates more on the hawks, whose attitudes generally prevailed in the early days of the war. Appearing in this footage are Presidents Dwight D. Eisenhower, John F. Kennedy, and Lyndon B. Johnson; Vice President Richard M. Nixon; Senators Wayne Morse, Thruston Morton, and Joseph McCarthy; Rep. Gerald Ford; Generals Mark Clark, Curtis LeMay, Maxwell Taylor, and William Westmoreland; Col. George Patton III; former Ambassador to Vietnam Henry Cabot Lodge; Secretaries of State Dean Rusk and John Foster Dulles; United Nations Secretary-General U Thant; former Special Forces Sgt. John Towler; the State Department's Director of Vietnamese Affairs, Charlton Ogburn; ex-president of the Executive Committee of the Friends of Vietnam, Joseph Buttinger; and former member of the Expeditionary Corps in Indochina Philippe Devilers. Also featured are Ho Chi Minh, Nguyen Cao Ky, Ngo Dinh Diem, and Mrs. Ngo Dinh Nhu. *Indochina. United States Congress. United States Army. France—Army. Daniel Berrigan. Joseph Buttinger. Mark Wayne Clark. Philippe Devilers. Ngo Dinh Diem. John Foster Dulles. Dwight David Eisenhower. Gerald Rudolph Ford. David Halberstam. Roger Hilsman. Ho Chi Minh. Lyndon Baines Johnson. John Fitzgerald Kennedy. Nguyen Cao Ky. Curtis E. LeMay. Henry Cabot Lodge, II. Jean Marie Gérard Lacouture. Joseph Raymond McCarthy. Robert Strange McNamara. Wayne Lyman Morse. Thruston Ballard Morton. Paul Mus. Mme. Ngo Dinh Nhu. Richard Milhous Nixon. Charlton Ogburn, Jr. George Patton, III. Dean Rusk. Harrison Evans Salisbury. Arthur Meier Schlesinger, Jr. Maxwell Davenport Taylor. U Thant. Oliver Todd. John Towler. William Childs Westmoreland. David Wurfel.*

Note: This film contains 60% new footage filmed in 16mm.

IN TROUBLE WITH EVE (Great Britain)   F6.2400

Mancunian Film Corp. *Dist* Seymour Borde & Associates. 4 Nov **1964** [San Francisco opening]. Sd; b&w. 35mm. 64 min.

A Blakeley's Films Production. *Prod* Tom Blakeley. *Assoc Prod* John E. Blakeley. *Dir* Francis Searle. *Screen Adapt* Brock Williams. *Lighting Camera* James Harvey. *Art Dir* John Earl. *Film Ed* Eric Boyd-Perkins. *Mus* Wilfred Burns. *Asst Dir* Roger Marley. *Prod Mgr* Charles Leeds. *Cont* Leonora Hale. *Makeup* Jim Hydes.

Cast: Robert Urquhart (*Brian Maitland*), Hy Hazell (*Louise Kingston*), Garry Marsh (*Roland Axbridge*), Vera Day (*Daisy*), Sally Smith (*Eve*), Tony Quinn (*Bellchambers*), Denis Shaw (*George*), Brenda Hogan (*Angela*), Grace D. Russell (*Mrs. Mordaunt*), Iris Vandeleur (*Mrs. Biddle*), Bruce Seton (*Mr. Digby Phillpotts*), Kim Shelley (*Mrs. Digby Phillpotts*), Bill Shine (*artist*), Frank Atkinson (*taxi driver*), David Graham (*car driver*).

Comedy. Source: June Garland, *Widows Are Dangerous* (London opening: 9 Feb 1953). In the riverside village of Warlock, widow Louise Kingston converts her country cottage into a tearoom, necessitating a visit of inspection by Brian Maitland, chairman of the district council. During the inspection, an accident results in the removal of Maitland's trousers, giving rise to rumor. The arrival of Louise's daughters, unhappily married Angela and art student Eve, further scandalizes the villagers. As Police Sergeant Bellchambers is about to raid the tearoom, Eve intervenes, exonerating her mother and the mayor, who have fallen in love. *Widows. Mayors. Police. Artists. Students. Village life. Reputation. Gossip. Scandal. Filial relations. Teashops.*

Note: Opened in London in Feb 1960 as *Trouble With Eve*. Working title: *In Walked Eve.*

IN WALKED EVE see IN TROUBLE WITH EVE

INADMISSIBLE EVIDENCE (Great Britain)   F6.2401

Woodfall Films. *Dist* Paramount Pictures. 23 Jun **1968** [New York opening; c23 Jun 1968; LP36392]. Sd; b&w. 35mm. 96 min.

Prod Ronald Kinnoch. *Dir* Anthony Page. *Screenplay* John Osborne. *Dir Photog* Ken Hodges, Anthony Imi. *Art Dir* Seamus Flannery. *Film Ed* Derek York. *Mus Comp & Cond* Dudley Moore. *Songs:* "Gently," "Keep It Up" comp & sung by Dudley Moore. *Sd Rec* Kevin Sutton. *Asst Dir* Derek Whitehurst. *Cost* Anne Gainsford. *Hairstyles* Mary Bredin.

Cast: Nicol Williamson (*Bill Maitland*), Eleanor Fazan (*Anna Maitland*), Jill Bennett (*Liz*), Peter Sallis (*Hudson*), David Valla (*Jones*), Eileen Atkins (*Shirley*), Ingrid Brett (*Jane*), Gillian Hills (*Joy*), Isabel Dean (*Mrs. Garnsey*), Clare Kelly (*Mrs. Anderson*), John Normington (*Maples*), Patsy Huxter (*Hilda Maples*), Hilary Hardiman (*Wendy Watson*), John Savident (*Mr. Watson*), Rufus Dawson (*Scott*), Stephen Martin (*Peter Maitland*), Penny Bird (*Sheila*), Brian Cleaver (*clerk of court*), Martin Ryan Grace, Alan Selwyn (*plainclothesmen*), Joseph Tregonino (*caretaker*), Lindsay Anderson (*barrister*), Reg Peters (*private agent*), Ronald Clarke (*man outside strip club*), "Lee" (*striptease dancer*), Ann Lancaster (*drinking club hostess*), Ellis Dale (*clergyman*), Debbie Jacobs (*Maples' daughter*), Ellen Mann (*Hudson's secretary*), June Brown, Ishaq Bux, Norma Shebbeare, James Ottaway (*Watson's guests*), Valerie Collier (*Mrs. Anderson's mother*), Pamela Papworth.

Drama. Source: John Osborne, *Inadmissible Evidence* (London opening: 9 Sep 1964). Bill Maitland, a middle-aged London barrister, feels contempt for his mediocre life and irritation at the seeming vacuity of the people who surround him. At home he suffers the indifference of his daughter Jane and the conventionality of his son Peter. The coldness of his wife, Anna, drives him to, among other women, his mistress, Liz Eaves, who fights a losing battle against Maitland's self-torment. At the office he is taunted for his inefficiency by his co-workers, who dislike him, and for his emotional sterility by his secretary, Shirley, with whom he has had an affair. One day everything explodes at once: his wife nags him about his promiscuity, fellow attorney Hudson scorns his offer of a junior partnership, Shirley bitterly announces that she is pregnant and resigns, and Liz refuses to be neglected simply because her daughter is having a birthday party. Shackled by indecision and his own feeling of worthlessness, he becomes useless to his clients, who include Mrs. Garnsey, a distressed woman seeking a divorce, and Maples, a homosexual arrested for public indecency. Feeling increasingly trapped, Maitland leaves work and wanders through the streets of Soho. When he returns to the office, he seeks sexual solace with Joy, his mini-skirted receptionist; but they are interrupted by the unexpected arrival of his wife. Dinner with shallow friends, arguments with both his wife and mistress, and a failure to communicate with his daughter make him even more depressed. After telephoning his wife and telling her not to see him again, he smashes his office window and walks into the empty London streets. *Barristers. Mistresses. Secretaries. Receptionists. Middle age. Alienation. Neurosis. Family life. Infidelity. Pregnancy. Divorce. Male homosexuality. London—Soho.*

Note: Released in Great Britain in May 1969. Nicol Williamson sings two songs in the film: "Room 504," a pre-World War II British song, and "Moonlight Becomes You."

INCEST see WHAT NEXT?

THE INCIDENT   F6.2402

Moned Associated, Inc. *Dist* Twentieth Century-Fox Film Corp. 5 Nov **1967** [New York opening; c6 Nov 1967; LP34997]. Sd; b&w. 35mm. 107 min.

Prod Monroe Sachson, Edward Meadow. *Dir* Larry Peerce. *Screenplay* Nicholas E. Baehr. *Dir Photog* Gerald Hirschfeld. *Camera Op* Dick Kratina. *Camera Asst* Alec Hirshfeld. *Set Decor* Robert Drumheller. *Set Dresser* Fred Hempe. *Scenic Artist* Murray Stern. *Subway Car & Prod Dsgn* Manny Gerard. *Opticals & Titl* Cineffects. *Film Ed* Armond Lebowitz. *Mus Comp* Terry Knight. *Mus Score & Cond* Charles Fox. *Mus Supv* Score Productions. *Sd* Jack Jacobsen. *Sd Mixer* Richard Vorisek. *Sd Eff Ed* Erno Sethy, Gary Lebowitz. *Sd by* Reeves Recording Studios. *1st & 2d Asst Dir* Steve Barnett, Alex Hapsas. *Prod Mgr* David Golden. *Script Supv* Renata Stoia. *Asst to Prod* Jurgen Jacobsen. *Cost Dsgn* Muriel Gettinger. *Wardrobe* Jean Huljack. *Makeup* Herman Buchman. *Hairstyles* Lee Trent. *Head Projection Op* Milt Oshins. *Gaffer* Milton Moshlak. *Grip* Larry Barr. *Prop Master* Joe Caracciolo. *Constr Ch* Mickey Oates. *Stills* Sam Dinin.

Cast: Tony Musante (*Joe Ferrone*), Martin Sheen (*Artie Connors*), Beau Bridges (*Pfc Felix Teflinger*), Brock Peters (*Arnold Robinson*), Ruby Dee (*Joan Robinson*), Jack Gilford (*Sam Beckerman*), Thelma Ritter (*Bertha Beckerman*), Ed McMahon (*Bill Wilks*), Diana Van Der Vlis (*Helen Wilks*), Mike Kellin (*Harry Purvis*), Jan Sterling (*Muriel Purvis*), Gary Merrill (*Douglas McCann*), Robert Fields (*Kenneth Otis*), Robert Bannard (*Pfc Phillip Carmatti*), Victor Arnold (*Tony Goya*), Donna Mills (*Alice Keenan*), Kathleen Smith (*Wilks's daughter*), Henry Proach (*derelict*), Neal Hynes (*change booth attendant*), Ben Levi (*man who gets mugged*), Martin Meyers (*poolhall owner*), Don De Leo (*Mr. Carmatti*), Nina Hansen (*Mrs. Carmatti*), Ted Lowrie (*host*), John Servetnik (*bartender*), Ray Cole (*young man no. 1*), Barry Del Rae (*young man no. 2*), Nico Hartos (*policeman*), Maxine McCrey (*Negro woman*).

Crime melodrama. Source: Nicholas Baehr, *Ride With Terror* (a teleplay; first presented on "DuPont Show of the Week," 1 Dec 1963). During a Sunday night of drinking, two young hoodlums, Joe Ferrone and Artie Connors, mug and rob an old man in an alley and then set out in search of further kicks by boarding a Manhattan-bound subway train. During the trip that follows, the two punks trap 16 passengers in the car and, one by one, proceed to bait, taunt, and terrorize them. The victims are: Pfc Felix Teflinger, a southern soldier with a broken arm who is on leave in New York; his Army buddy, Phil Carmatti, a local Italian-American boy; high school teacher Bill Wilks and his wife, Helen, and their little daughter, returning home after visiting relatives; Tony Goya, a sexually aggressive young man, and his timorous date, Alice Keenan; Sam and Bertha Beckerman, an elderly Jewish couple concerned about their married son's selfishness; Harry and Muriel Purvis, a sexually unhappy married couple who have just been to a party; Douglas an on-the-mend alcoholic Kenneth Otis, Otis a shy homosexual attracted to McCann; Arnold Robinson, a bitterly antiwhite Negro, and his peace-loving wife, Joan; and a derelict sprawled in a drunken stupor across one of the seats. Throughout the seemingly interminable ride, not one of the passengers rises to help his beleaguered fellow riders; each individual wants only to be left alone. Eventually, however, young Teflinger can stand it no longer, and he defiantly stands up to face the two thugs. Although his arm is in a plaster cast, he turns his handicap into an advantage by using the cast to beat his two adversaries to the floor. In spite of the fact that Ferrone stabs him in the stomach, Teflinger continues to pound the young hood into senselessness until the train pulls into Grand Central Station. As the police rush aboard and drag off the two hoodlums, Carmatti helps his wounded buddy out onto the platform. And the other passengers, in an almost ashamed silence, carefully step over the drunk, now on the floor, who has slept through the whole ordeal. *Hoodlums. Soldiers. Jews. Italians. Negroes. Schoolteachers. Derelicts. Fear. Cowardice. Marriage. Drunkenness. Alcoholism. Male homosexuality. Subways. New York City.*

Note: Locations filmed in New York City.

INCIDENT AT BLOOD PASS *see* THE AMBUSH

INCIDENT AT MIDNIGHT (Great Britain) F6.2403
Merton Park Studios. *Dist* Schoenfeld Film Distributing Corp. 20 Jul **1966** [Copiague, New York, opening]. Sd; b&w. 35mm. 57 min.

Prod Jack Greenwood. *Dir* Norman Harrison. *Screenplay* Arthur La Bern. *Photog (see note)* Bert Mason, James Wilson. *Art Dir* Peter Mullins. *Film Ed* Derek Holding. *Mus* Bernard Ebbinghouse. *Sd* Sidney Rider.

Cast: Anton Diffring *(Dr. Erik Leichner)*, William Sylvester *(Vince Warren)*, Justine Lord *(Diane Graydon)*, Martin Miller *(Dr. Schroeder)*, Tony Garnett *(Brennan)*, Philip Locke *(Foster)*, Sylva Langova *(Vivienne Leichner)*, Warren Mitchell *(chemist)*, Jacqueline Jones *(Vanessa Palmer)*, Peter Howell *(Inspector Macready)*, Oliver MacGreevy *(Wilkinson)*, David Futcher *(Whitehead)*, Clifford Earl *(Sergeant)*, Geoffrey Palmer *(Dr. Tanfield)*.

Mystery melodrama. Based on a story by: Edgar Wallace. Schroeder, a surgeon who has lost his license because of his drug addiction, picks up his allotment of drugs at an all-night drugstore. There he recognizes another customer, Dr. Leichner, as a man he knew in Vienna in his younger days, a man who was then an active Nazi. Schroeder confides his belief in yet another customer, Diane Graydon. Three hoodlums led by Brennan next arrive and demand that Schroeder operate on one of them. Leichner then returns to the shop with his wife, Vivienne, and it becomes clear that he is head of a drug racket and that Vivienne is a contact for the dealers. The police, tipped off by Diane, a secret agent, break the drug ring, killing Leichner. For his part in the breakup of the ring, Schroeder hopes to regain his license. *Drug addicts. Surgeons. Nazis. Hoodlums. Drug dealers. Secret agents. Police. Surgery. Drugstores.*

Note: Opened in London in Mar 1963. Sources conflict in crediting photographer.

INCIDENT AT PHANTOM HILL F6.2404
Universal Pictures. 13 Jul **1966** [Albany, New York, opening; c6 Aug 1966; LP35394]. Sd (Westrex); col (Technicolor). 35mm (Techniscope). 88 min.

Prod-Story Harry Tatelman. *Dir* Earl Bellamy. *Screenplay* Frank Nugent, Ken Pettus. *Dir Photog* William Margulies. *Art Dir* Alexander Golitzen, Howard E. Johnson. *Set Decor* John McCarthy, Ralph Sylos. *Film Ed* Gene Milford. *Mus* Hans J. Salter. *Mus Supv* Joseph Gershenson. *Sd* Waldon O. Watson, Lyle Cain. *Asst Dir* Mike Moder. *Unit Prod Mgr* Howard Pine. *Cost* Helen Colvig. *Makeup* Bud Westmore. *Hairstyles* Larry Germain.

Cast: Robert Fuller *(Matt Martin)*, Jocelyn Lane *(Memphis)*, Dan Duryea *(Joe Barlow)*, Tom Simcox *(Adam Long)*, Linden Chiles *(Dr. Hanneford)*, Claude Akins *(Krausman)*, Noah Beery *(O'Rourke)*, Paul Fix *(General Hood)*, Denver Pyle *(1st hunter)*, William Phipps *(trader)*, Don Collier *(drum)*, Mickey Finn *(2d hunter)*.

Western drama. In 1865 near the end of the Civil War, Rebels ambush a Union convoy, steal $1 million in gold, and hide the treasure in a cave near Phantom Hill, Texas. Two Union officers, Matt Martin and Adam Long, with three enlisted men, set out to find the gold. Rebel leader Joe Barlow accompanies them; he has agreed to lead them to the treasure in exchange for his freedom. Also accompanying the search party as far as the next stagecoach stop is Memphis, a young lady of questionable reputation who is attracted to Matt. After they all survive an Indian attack, Barlow leads the group to the gold. Attempting, however, to get the money for himself, he plies the soldiers with liquor, then kills two of them. Leaving Matt, Adam, and Krausman to fend for themselves unarmed against probable Indian attack, Barlow escapes with Memphis and the gold. Outwitting the Indians, but losing Krausman, Matt and Adam retrieve their horses and pursue Barlow and Memphis. In the nick of time, Memphis throws a gun to Matt, who kills Barlow. The gold is returned to the U. S. Government. *Soldiers. Indians of North America. Prisoners of war. Robbery. Perfidy. Gold. United States—History—Civil War. Texas.*

Note: Working title: *The Faceless Men.*

INCIDENT IN AN ALLEY F6.2405
Harvard Film Corp. *Dist* United Artists. 2 May **1962** [Boston opening: c13 Jan 1962; LP21895]. Sd; b&w. 35mm. 83 min.

Prod Robert E. Kent. *Dir* Edward L. Cahn. *Screenplay* Harold Medford, Owen Harris. *Story* Rod Serling. *Photog* Gilbert Warrenton. *Set Decor* Harry Reif. *Film Ed* Robert Carlisle. *Mus* Richard La Salle. *Sd* Earl Schwartz, Stan Cooley. *Asst Dir* Herbert S. Greene, George Batcheller. *Prod Mgr* Joseph Small. *Script Supv* Bobbie Sierks. *Cost* Einar Bourman, Barbara Maxwell. *Makeup* Harry Thomas. *Hairstyles* Frances Sperry. *Casting* Ralph Acton. *Still Photog* Madison Lacy.

Cast: Chris Warfield *(Bill Joddy)*, Erin O'Donnell *(Jean Joddy)*, Harp McGuire *(Frank Frye)*, Willis Bouchey *(Captain Brady)*, Nelson Leigh *(Commissioner Bell)*, Clancy Cooper *(Sam)*, Mike Vandever *(Gussie)*, Gary Judis *(Charlie)*, James Canino *(Midge)*, Bert Michaels *(Preacher)*, Renny McEvoy *(McNulty)*, Don Keefer *(Swanson)*, Brad Trumbull *(Brannan)*, Keith Richards *(Peters)*, Warren Kemmerling *(Peterson)*, Clegg Hoyt *(manager)*, Virginia Christine *(Mrs. Connell)*, Jess Kirkpatrick *(Simpkins)*, Lia Waggner *(woman neighbor)*, Charles G. Martin *(judge)*, James Parnell *(jury foreman)*, Max Mellinger *(Mr. Blake)*, Mimi Doyle *(Mrs. Blake)*, Frank Leo *(Boo Boo)*, Lila Finn *(charwoman)*, Harlan Warde *(district attorney)*, Tom Cound *(bailiff)*, Bobby Fox *(Harvey)*.

Crime melodrama. Investigating the robbery of a music store, police officer Bill Joddy hears a woman screaming in a nearby alley. In the dim light he spots a fleeing figure and orders him to halt. When the fugitive continues running, Joddy shoots and kills him. The body is that of a 14-year-old boy who, it would appear, merely knocked down the woman in the alley. Public opinion mounts against Joddy for the "senseless killing," and he is suspended from the force pending trial for manslaughter. Though acquitted, Joddy is still considered "trigger happy" by his fellow officers. But further investigation reveals that the dead boy was in fact a member of the gang that robbed the music store. Joddy induces the young hoodlum's brother, Gussie, to admit the truth in exchange for a promise of leniency. The other gang members attempt to kill Gussie for talking, but Joddy subdues them and clears his reputation. *Police. Brothers. Juvenile delinquents. Adolescence. Manslaughter. Robbery. Trials. Music stores.*

Note: Working title: *Line of Duty.*

THE INCREDIBLE JOURNEY F6.2406
Walt Disney Productions–Cangary, Ltd. *Dist* Buena Vista Distribution Co. 20 Nov **1963** [New York opening; c20 Aug 1963; LP26979]. Sd (RCA): col (Technicolor). 35mm. 80 min.

Overall Production Credits: *Pres by* Walt Disney. A Walt Disney Production. *Co-prod* James Algar. *Dir* Fletcher Markle. *Screenplay* James Algar. *Dir Photog* Kenneth Peach. *Art Dir* Carroll Clark, John B. Mansbridge. *Set Decor* Emile Kuri, Charles S. Thompson. *Film Ed* Norman R. Palmer. *Mus* Oliver Wallace. *Orch* Walter Sheets. *Sd* Robert O. Cook. *Mus Ed* Evelyn Kennedy. *Asst Dir* Mickey McCardle. *Prod Mgr* Erwin L. Verity. *Unit Mgr* William O'Sullivan. *Cost* Chuck Keehne. *Makeup* Pat McNalley. *Animal Supv* William R. Koehler, Halleck H. Driscoll, Al Niemela.

Production Credits for Cangary, Ltd.: *Field Prod* Jack Couffer. *Photog* Jack Couffer, Lloyd Beebe.

Featuring: Muffey *(Bodger)*, Syn Cat *(Tao)*, Rink *(Luath)*, Rex Allen *(narrator)*.

The Humans in the Story: Emile Genest *(John Longridge)*, John Drainic *(Prof. Jim Hunter)*, Tommy Tweed *(The Hermit)*, Sandra Scott *(Mrs. Hunter)*, Syme Jago *(Helvi Nurmi)*, Marion Finlayson *(Elizabeth Hunter)*, Ronald Cohoon *(Peter Hunter)*, Robert Christie *(James MacKenzie)*, Beth Lockerbie *(Nell MacKenzie)*, Jan Rubes *(Carl Nurmi)*, Irena Mayeska *(Mrs. Nurmi)*, Beth Amos *(Mrs. Oakes)*, Eric Clavering *(Bert Oakes)*.

Adventure drama. Source: Sheila Burnford, *The Incredible Journey* (Boston, 1961). When the Hunter family depart from their Canadian town for a summer in England, they leave their pets—Bodger (an elderly bull terrier), Luath (a yellow Labrador retriever), and Tao (a Siamese cat)—with their friend John Longridge, who lives in Ontario 250 miles away. Toward the end of the summer, John goes off on a hunting trip, and the three homesick animals set out to find their way back to the Hunter house. During their journey across some of Canada's wildest terrain, the three participate in numerous adventures. There are an encounter with a lynx, a battle with a vicious farm dog, and a scuffle with a bear. Tao, a natural hunter, brings Bodger food after he collapses from weakness. The dogs become separated from Tao when he falls into a river and nearly drowns, but they are reunited after the cat has been rescued and nursed back to health by a little Finnish girl. Luath has a painful encounter with a porcupine, but his wounds are treated by a kindly farmer. Along the way an old hermit entertains the trio as his guests. Upon returning from England, the Hunters are informed of the disappearance of their pets. A short time later a somewhat unhappy birthday party in the Hunter garden is turned into a homecoming celebration as the three pets emerge from the woods behind the house and rush to join the family for a happy reunion. *Farmers. Hermits. Finns. Family life. Animal life. Pets. Birthdays. Canada. Ontario. Dogs. Cats. Lynx. Bears. Porcupines.*

Note: Filmed on location in Canada.

THE INCREDIBLE MR. LIMPET F6.2407

Warner Bros. Pictures. 17 Jan **1964** [Weeki Wachee Springs, Florida, opening; c28 Mar 1964; LP29436]. Sd; col (Technicolor). 35mm. 102 min. [Cut to 99 min.]

Prod Jack Rose. *Dir* Arthur Lubin. *Screenplay* Jameson Brewer, Jack Rose. *Adapt* Joe DiMona. *Photog* Harold Stine. *Camera Op* Bud Brooks. *Asst Op* Stuart Higgs. *Art Dir* LeRoy Deane. *Set Decor* William L. Kuehl. *Film Ed* Donald Tait. *Mus* Frank Perkins. *Songs:* "The Mr. Limpet March (Super Doodle Dandy)," "I Wish I Were a Fish," "Be Careful How You Wish," "Deep Rapture," "Hail To Henry Limpet" Sammy Fain, Harold Adamson. *Sd* Stanley Jones. *Asst Dir* Sergei Petschnikoff, Ira Stewart, Ed Bernoudy. *Script Supv* Jules Miliman. *Wardrobe* Robert Richards, Rose Brawd. *Makeup* Gordon Bau, Bill Phillips, Louis Phillips. *Hairstyles* Jean Burt Reilly, Lenore Weaver. *Sp Piscatorial Eff* Vladimir Tytla, Gerry Chiniquy, Hawley Pratt, Robert McKimson, Maurice Noble, Don Peters. *Gaffer* Paul Burnett. *Grip* Weldon Gilbert. *Still Photog* Sherman Clark. *Prop* Herbert Plews.

Cast: Don Knotts *(Henry Limpet)*, Carole Cook *(Bessie Limpet)*, Jack Weston *(Lieut. George Stickle)*, Andrew Duggan *(Admiral Harlock)*, Larry Keating *(Admiral Spewter)*, Elizabeth MacRae *(voice of Ladyfish)*, Paul Frees *(voice of Crusty)*, Charles Meredith *(Admiral Fourstar)*, Oscar Beregi *(Admiral Doemitz)*.

Comedy. Source: Theodore Pratt, *Mr. Limpet* (New York, 1942). Henry Limpet, a mildmannered Brooklyn bookkeeper, irritates his wife, Bessie, because his love for fish is so strong that he yearns to become one. His attempt to join the Navy fails, and matters are made worse when his best friend, George Stickle, is accepted. One day Henry, Bessie, and George go to Coney Island; Henry falls off a dock, disappears into the ocean, and miraculously is transformed into a dolphin. After making friends with a sea snail, he falls in love with Ladyfish, a female dolphin. With the outbreak of World War II, he guides the U. S. sub chasers in tracking down and sinking German U-boats, and although baffled by their success, the Navy bestows a commission upon dolphin Limpet. At the war's conclusion, he surfaces for a poignant farewell to his wife and swims off with Ladyfish. *Bookkeepers. Wish fulfillment. Transmutation. Submarines. World War II. New York City—Brooklyn. Coney Island. United States Navy. Snails. Dolphins.*

Note: Contains animation footage. Prerelease titles: *Henry Limpet, Mr. Limpet,* and *Be Careful How You Wish.*

THE INCREDIBLE SEX REVOLUTION F6.2408

Famous Players Corp. Dec **1965** [c17 Dec 1965; LP32086]. Sd; b&w. 35mm. 102 min.

Dir-Writ Albert Zugsmith.

Cast: Lee Gladden *(himself)*, Hampton Fancher *(Adam)*, Racey Tempo, Christopher Warren, Lovey Song, Ric Marlow, Alex D'Arcy.

Sex instruction film. Source: Lee Gladden, "Changing Sex Mores in Our Modern Civilization" (a report, publication undetermined). Dr. Lee Gladden explains the mental and emotional problems experienced by modern adults who take part in the sex revolution. Adam and Eve discover sex in the Garden of Eden while and Mr. and Mrs. John Smith, married but not to each other, enjoy relations in a motel room. Through a series of examples told to Dr. Gladden by his patients, the report shows that people react with emotional distress to the social disruption caused by the sexual revolution. Dr. Gladden helps Peggy, a young patient, adjust to free love, mate swapping, and other current sex practices. *Psychologists. Neurosis. Infidelity. Free love. Mate swapping. Sex research. Sexual practices. Adam and Eve.*

THE INCREDIBLY STRANGE CREATURES WHO STOPPED LIVING AND BECAME CRAZY MIXED-UP ZOMBIES
F6.2409

Morgan-Steckler Productions. *Dist* Fairway-International Films, Hollywood Star Pictures. Mar **1964** [South Bend, Indiana, showing]. Sd; col (Eastmancolor). 35mm. 82 min.

Prod-Dir Ray Dennis Steckler. *Exec Prod* George J. Morgan. *Screenplay* Gene Pollock, Robert Silliphant. *Story* E. M. Kevke. *Photog* Joseph V. Mascelli, William Zsigmond. *Art Dir* Mike Harrington, Pat Kirkwood. *Main Titl* Tom Scherman. *Film Ed* Don Schneider. *Mus* Henry Price. *Songs* Libby Quinn. *Sung by* Don Snyder, Carol Kay, Teri Randal. *Choreog* Bill Turner, choreog. Alan Smith. *Sd* Lee Strosnider, Ken Carlson. *Asst Dir* Don Russell, John McKenna. *Prod Mgr* Austin McKinney. *Makeup* Lilly. *Sp Makeup* Tom Scherman.

Cast: Cash Flagg *(Jerry)*, Brett O'Hara *(Madam Estrella)*, Carolyn Brandt *(Marge Neilson)*, Atlas King *(Harold)*, Sharon Walsh *(Angie)*, Madison Clarke *(Madison)*, Erina Enyo *(Carmelita)*, Jack Brady *(Ortega)*, Toni Camel *(Stella)*, Neil Stillman *(barker)*, Joan Howard *(Angie's mother)*, James Bowie *(nightclub emcee)*, Gene Pollock *(nightclub owner)*, Bill Ward *(dancer)*, Son Hooker *(1st policeman)*, Steve Clark *(2d policeman)*, Don Snyder, Carol Kay, Teri Randal *(singers)*, Titus Moede, Whitey Robinson, Bonnie Berkeley, Denise Lynn, Jill Carson, Patrice Michaels, Cindy Shea, Patti Crandall, Betty Downing, Pat Lynn.

Horror film. Three carnival workers, evil gypsy palmist Madam Estrella, her sister Carmelita, and their hunchbacked servant Ortega, are engaged in the business of creating carnival freaks. They hypnotize their patrons, disfigure them by throwing acid in their faces, and imprison them in cages. Marge Neilson, a dancer in a nightclub on the midway, accidentally discovers the fortune-teller's sideline and is stabbed to death by Jerry, a beatnik who has been hypnotized by Madam Estrella. Jerry then tries to strangle his girl friend Angie when he is thrown into a trance by the twirling of her umbrella, but he is prevented from doing so by the arrival of Angie's brother Madison and her mother. Estrella again hypnotizes Jerry and encages him, but this action causes the other "monsters" to riot and stampede. Jerry is shot by the police, and Estrella's activities are ended. *Gypsies. Fortune-tellers. Sisters. Dancers. Beatniks. Hunchbacks. Police. Freaks. Disfiguration. Hypnotism. Murder. Abduction. Carnivals. Umbrellas.*

Note: Exteriors filmed in Los Angeles and at an amusement park in Long Beach, California. Also billed as *The Incredibly Strange Creatures.* Rerelease title: *Teenage Psycho Meets Bloody Mary.* Actor Cash Flagg is a pseudonym for Ray Dennis Steckler.

INDAGINE SU UN CITTADINO AL DI SOPRA DI OGNI SOSPETTO *see* INVESTIGATION OF A CITIZEN ABOVE SUSPICION

INDECENT (West Germany) F6.2410

Filmaufbau–Cinelux–Film. *Dist* William Mishkin, Constitution Films. 9 Mar **1962** [New York State license]. Sd; b&w. 35mm. 90 min.

Dir Erwin Marno. *Script* Erwin Marno, Hanns Helmut Fischer. *Camera* Karl Schröder. *Sets* Hans Luigi, Gerhard Ladner. *Film Ed* Caspar van den Berg. *Mus* Fritz Schulz-Reichel. *Sd* Eduard Kessel. *Prod Mgr* Herbert Uhlich.

Cast: Peter Van Eyck *(Alexander)*, Susanne Cramer *(Karen)*, Horst Frank *(Sabri)*, Kai Fischer *(Vera)*, Helga Münster *(Sylvia)*, Eva Schreiber *(Monica)*, Helmut Schmid, Käthe Haack, Karin Maria Ostholt, Eleonore Doodt, Peter Weiss.

Drama. A group of young female dancers traveling from Marseilles to Tangiers are tricked into believing that they are scheduled to perform in an exclusive North African nightclub. Their manager is actually involved in white slave traffic, and the one woman who suspects the truth is murdered. When her body is found, the police are unsure of the cause of death, but Alexander, a German reporter who suspects murder, follows the dance troupe. In the course of his investigation, he falls in love with Karen, one of the dancers. Several of the young women are lured into prostitution and forced to perform indecent acts, but before Karen meets the same fate, Alexander resolves the case. With the aid of an undercover Interpol agent, he brings the white slave trade organization to justice. *Dancers. Reporters. Police. White slave traffic. Murder. Nightclubs. Marseilles. Tangiers. INTERPOL.*

Note: Produced in West Germany in 1958 as *Schwarze Nylons—heisse Nächte.* May also be known as *All Bad.* Shown in New York in Jan 1968 as *Waylaid Women.*

INDECENT DESIRES F6.2411

Mostest Productions. *Dist* Jerand Film Distributors. 17 Apr **1968** [Champaign, Illinois, showing]. Sd; b&w. 35mm. 72 min.

Prod-Dir Louis Silverman. *Story-Screenplay* Dawn Whitman. *Dir Photog* C. Davis Smith. *Film Ed* Dee Ess. *Sd* Titra Sound Corp. *Optical Eff* B. & O. Film Specialists.

Cast: Sharon Kent, Trom Little, Michael Lawrence, Jackie Richards.

Melodrama. Zeb, a derelict, finds a ring and a doll in a trash can and takes them home with him. One day, Zeb sees two women, Ann and Babs, in the street. Zeb follows Ann, identifying her in his mind with the castoff doll. When Zeb caresses the doll, Ann dreams that she feels his caresses and she becomes frightened. Certain that she is going mad, Ann attempts to commit suicide. Failing, she becomes a recluse. Zeb becomes angry, beats the doll, and, feeling remorse, makes love to it. Again, in a dream, Ann feels both the pain and the pleasure. Finally, Zeb sees Ann with her fiancé Tom, and he breaks the doll's neck; Ann dies of a broken neck. *Derelicts. Fetishism. Supernatural. Suicide. Sadism. Dolls. Dreams.*

INDIAN LOVE CULT   F6.2412
Feb **1970** [Los Angeles showing]. Sd; col. 16mm? [Feature length assumed.]
Cast: Cunning Offer, Little Bird, Princess Budding Flower.
Sex film. No information about the precise nature of this film has been found. *Indians of North America. Cults. Sexuality.*

INDIAN PAINT   F6.2413
Tejas Productions. *Dist* Eagle American Films, Crown International Pictures. 8 Apr **1965** [San Antonio, Texas, opening; c7 Apr 1965; LP31912]. Sd; col (Eastman Color). 35mm. 91 min.
Prod Gene Goree. *Exec Prod* Bob Callahan. *Dir-Writ* Norman Foster. *Dir Photog* Floyd Crosby. *Film Ed* Robert Crawford, Sr., George White. *Mus* Marlin Skiles. *Song:* "Song of Nishko" Norman Foster. *Sung by* Johnny Crawford. *Sd* Ted Saizis, Vincent Saizis.
Cast: Johnny Crawford (*Nishko*), Jay Silverheels (*Chief Hevatanu*), Pat Hogan (*Sutamakis*), Robert Crawford, Jr. (*Wacopi*), George J. Lewis (*Nopawallo*), Joan Hollmark (*Amatula*), Bill Blackwell (*Sutako*), Robert Crawford, Sr. (*Motopi*), Al Doney (*Lataso*), Cinda Siler (*Petala*), Suzanne Goodman (*Lataso's widow*), Marshall Jones (*Comanche leader*), Warren L. Dodge (*2d Comanche*).
Adventure drama. Source: Glenn Balch, *Indian Paint* (New York, 1942). For his future mount, 15-year-old Nishko, son of Chief Hevatanu of the Arikara tribe, selects the foal of the tribe's finest mare and a white wild stallion. In a dream Nishko has been told that his destiny is bound to that of the foal, which he names Mecapo. During training for warfare, the youth wins the prized thunder bow. Having been tricked into leaving the village, Arikara warriors return to find their tepees burned, their mounts stolen, and three maidens abducted. Pursuing a party of Snake warriors, the Arikaras retrieve their horses. Nishko fashions a travois to carry Mecapo, who is too weak to return on his own to the Arikara village. Informed that his mother, Amatula, is dying from the bite of a rattlesnake, Nishko breaks his prized bow, hoping thereby to appease the Giver of Life. When his mother's condition worsens, Nishko prepares to sacrifice the beloved Mecapo, but an emissary informs him that she has recovered. Nishko's joy at having passed the rites of tribal initiation is short-lived; a mountain lion kills the mare, and Mecapo returns to the herd of his wild sire. The herd is captured by Comanches, and Nishko, while trying to rescue Mecapo, is taken prisoner. As the white stallion leads the herd to freedom while the Comanches sleep, Nishko escapes with Mecapo. Nishko follows the horses to their winter pasture and devotes himself to regaining Mecapo's affection. Having wrenched his leg, Nishko is menaced by wolves, but Mecapo rescues him. Determined to allow the horse its freedom, Nishko prepares to return to his people. Mecapo, however, loyally follows him. *Arikara Indians. Snake Indians. Comanche Indians. Manhood. Adolescence. Filial relations. Snakebites. Rites and ceremonies. Winter. Horses. Wolves.*
Note: Filmed in and around Cleburne, Texas.

GLI INDIFFERENTI *see* TIME OF INDIFFERENCE

INDISCREET STAIRWAY   F6.2414
Dist Monique Productions, Boxoffice International Film Distributors. 16 Jul **1966** [New York showing]. Sd; b&w. 35mm. 60 min.
Dir Ren-Mart.
Comedy. The talking staircase in a French apartment building reveals the intimate lives of five of the building's tenants: two bikini-clad young women go swimming together; a muscleman who is pretending to be a painter uses a nude model; Marcy, a 15-year-old, skips school to attend a party with the milkman; and a woman whose husband is out of town showers and applies skin lotion before going to bed. *Body-builders. Models. Dance teachers. Milkmen. Nudity. Voyeurism. Adolescence.*
Note: Also known as *Up the Naughty Staircase* and *The Indiscreet Staircase.*

INFAMOUS *see* THE CHILDREN'S HOUR

L'INFERNO ADDOSSO *see* LOVE NOW ... PAY LATER

INFERNO OF FIRST LOVE *see* NANAMI: INFERNO OF FIRST LOVE

INFIDELITY AMERICAN STYLE   F6.2415
S. Catah Films. *Dist* Chancellor Films. Jan **1967**. Sd; b&w. 35mm. 75 min. [Also 59 min.]
Prod-Dir S. N. Johnsen. *Screenplay* (see note) Sean Martin, Eugene Price. *Photog* Harry August. *Mus* Luristan. *Cont* Dossie. *Tech* Philip Dross.
Cast: Cleo Nova, Brooks Cunningham.
Drama. Business executive Harold Wainwright, looking for a new vice president to fill a vacancy, invites his brightest men and their wives to a party. Several people at the party have been unfaithful, and their stories are revealed in flashback. One of the men, resentful that his wife will not compromise herself to further her husband's career, has violent fantasies in which he beats her. The

Richters remain behind after the party ends, and they swap mates with the Wainwrights. It becomes clear that Bill Richter will get the coveted promotion. *Executives. Businessmen. Employer-employee relations. Mate swapping. Ambition. Infidelity. Sadism. Fantasy.*
Note: Sources conflict in crediting writer.

INFORMATION RECEIVED (Great Britain)   F6.2416
United Co-Productions. *Dist* Universal–International Films. 22 Jun **1962** [Atlanta showing]. Sd; b&w. 35mm. 77 min.
Prod John Clein, George Maynard. *Dir* Robert Lynn. *Screenplay* Paul Ryder. *Story* Berkely Mather. *Photog* Nicolas Roeg. *Art Dir* William Hutchinson. *Film Ed* Lee Doig. *Mus Comp & Cond* Martin Slavin. *Song:* "Sabina" Martin Slavin, Abbe Gail. *Sung by* Ronnie Hall. *Sd* Bert Ross, Ted Hooker. *Asst Dir* Roy Baird. *Prod Mgr* Ronnie Bear. *Makeup* Jill Carpenter. *Hairstyles* Ann Box.
Cast: Sabina Sesselmann (*Sabina Farlow*), William Sylvester (*Rick Hogan*), Hermione Baddeley (*Maudie*), Edward Underdown (*Drake*), Robert Raglan (*Superintendent Jeffcote*), Walter Brown (*Vic Farlow*), Frank Hawkins (*Sergeant Jarvie*), David Courtney (*Mark*), Peter Allenby (*Patterson*), Bill Dancy (*Johnny Stevens*), Don Meadon (*country policeman*), Ted Bushell (*prison trustee*), Tim Brinton (*TV announcer*), Johnny Briggs (*Willis*), David Cargill (*librarian*), Larry Taylor (*Darnell*), Douglas Cameron (*Warder Benham*), David Ensor (*judge*), Tony Shepherd (*squad car policeman*).
Crime melodrama. A British gang of thieves hire an American safecracker whom they have never seen to aid them in a robbery. Upon the safecracker's arrival in London, however, the police arrest him on a previous charge and then engage Rick Hogan to take his place in prison. As expected, the thieves arrange a jailbreak and take Hogan to the hideout of Vic Farlow and his seductive wife, Sabina. The conniving woman murders her husband and implicates Hogan in the crime, but he evades capture and takes refuge with a friendly woman, Maudie. He contacts Drake, the mastermind behind the safecracking plot, but not before giving Maudie information for the police. Once the safe has been opened and valuable government files have been stolen, Drake makes plans to kill Hogan and leave the country with Sabina. But they are apprehended by Scotland Yard, and Hogan establishes his true identity. *Americans in foreign countries. Police. Safecrackers. Gangs. Masterminds. Impersonation. Theft. Murder. Frameup. Jailbreaks. London. Scotland Yard. Documentation.*
Note: Location scenes filmed in London. Released in Great Britain in Aug 1961.

THE INFORMERS *see* UNDERWORLD INFORMERS

INFRASEXUM   F6.2417
C. Tobalina Productions. *Dist* Hollywood International Film Corp. of America. 19 Jul **1969** [Los Angeles opening]. Sd; col (Eastman Color). 35mm. 96 min. [Also 85 min.] MPAA rating X.
Prod-Writ Carlos Tobalina.
Cast: Erroff Lynn (*Peter Allison*), Carlos Tobalina (*Carlos*), Marsha Jordan (*Mrs. Allison*), Maria-Pia, William Larrabure, Sharon Matt, Luis Vargas, Jay Colonna, Janet Wass, Anita De Moulin, Vincent Barbi, Joyce Wiggins, Molli Starkins, Bill Kirschner, Kate Johnson.
Drama. Having lost interest in life, sexually frustrated millionaire Peter Allison visits a psychiatrist, who advises him to get away from the depressing atmosphere of his office. He leaves his wife, visits Las Vegas, and wins a huge sum of money which he hides in the trunk of his car. Returning to Los Angeles, he meets Carlos, who introduces him to the hippie life, dominated by marijuana and drugs. He watches a psychedelic orgy and confesses to Carlos that he does not become sexually aroused. Carlos arranges meetings with a series of voluptuous women, and then sets up a lesbian exhibition, to no avail. Two hoodlums set a trap for Peter, having convinced a beautiful blonde to call and invite him for a "surprise." When Peter arrives, they rape and murder the woman and torture him in order to learn the hiding place of his money; he kills them and makes his escape. Joyce, a wealthy young woman, falls in love with Peter and invites him to her home. She becomes frenzied with desire; Carlos rushes over in a stolen police car and satisfies her. Peter renounces all sexual activity and takes up painting. His psychiatrist advises him to recreate his most enjoyable sexual experience. Carlos searches for a special woman and discovers the Charitable Sex Society. Peter fails again and returns to his art. Eventually he sells an oil painting to an art expert, who restores his self-confidence. He paints a female nude and becomes so absorbed in his creative effort that he overcomes his impotence and makes love with his model. *Millionaires. Psychiatrists. Hippies. Hoodlums. Painters. Impotence. Desertion. Gambling. Orgies. Seduction. Lesbianism. Voyeurism. Rape. Murder. Torture. Theft. Marijuana. Narcotics. Las Vegas. Los Angeles.*

INGA (United States/Sweden)   **F6.2418**
Cannon Productions–Inska Films–Omega Film. *Dist* Cinemation Industries.
20 Nov **1968** [New York opening]. Sd; b&w. 35mm. 81 min.

Pres by Jerry Gross, Nicholas Demetroules. *Prod* Donald C. Dennis. *Co-Prod* Robert Brandt. *Dir-Writ* Joseph W. Sarno. *Photog* Bruce Sparks. *Mus Comp & Cond* Clay Pitts. *Mus Perf by* The Bamboo.

Cast: Marie Liljedahl *(Inga)*, Monica Strömmerstedt *(Greta)*, Thomas Ungewitter *(Einar)*, Casten Lassen *(Karl)*, Else-Marie Brandt *(Frida)*, Sissi Kaiser *(Sigrid)*, Anne-Lise Myhrvold *(Dagmar)*, Kurt Eriksson, Rose-Marie Nilsson, Lennart Norbäck, Lotta Persson, Anders Boling, Kitty Kurkinen, Annabel Reis.

Drama. Seventeen-year-old Inga comes to live with her aunt Greta, a 35-year-old divorcee whose extravagant young lover, Karl, an aspiring writer, has consumed her financial resources. In order to enhance her income, Greta tries to persuade Inga, a bookish virgin, to become the mistress of an older neighbor, Einar. Einar's sister Sigrid, who wants to keep her brother happy, encourages the relationship, and she offers to pay Greta a monthly allowance if the scheme succeeds. Greta's plan fails, however, as Inga first turns to self-gratification and then loses her virginity to young Karl instead of to Einar. The two young people go off in a yacht given to Karl by Greta, and the conspiring aunt is left alone. *Aunts. Authors. Mistresses. Neighbors. Virginity. Gigolos. Adolescence. Greed. Infidelity. Autoeroticism. Sexual initiation. Yachts.*

Note: Released in Sweden in Apr 1968 as *Jag—en oskuld.*

L'INGIUSTA CONDANNA *see* **GUILT IS NOT MINE**

THE INHERITANCE (Japan)   **F6.2419**
Shochiku Co. *Dist* Shochiku Films of America. 24 Feb **1964** [Los Angeles opening]. Sd; b&w. 35mm (Shochiku GrandScope). 107 min.

Dir Masaki Kobayashi. *Screenplay* Koichi Inagaki. *Photog* Ko Kawamata. *Film Ed* S. Miyaki.

Cast: Keiko Kishi *(Yasuko)*, Misako Watanabe *(Senzo)*, So Yamamura *(clerk)*, Minoru Chiaki *(Marie)*, Tatsuya Nakadai, Yusuke Kawazu, Mari Yoshimura.

Drama. Industrial magnate Kawahara learns that he has cancer and will die in less than 6 months. With only his wife as legal heir to his fortune, he implores his employees to locate his three illegitimate children. One by one, the lost offspring are brought home, but none prove worthy to receive the inheritance. Rejected by his wife, he forces Yasuko, his secretary who lives in his home, to become his mistress. Before his death, Kawahara is told that Yasuko is pregnant, and he wills the inheritance to the unborn child; but it is later revealed that she has become the heiress through a clever lie. *Industrialists. Secretaries. Mistresses. Illegitimacy. Infidelity. Pregnancy. Fraud. Inheritance. Cancer.*

Note: Released in Japan in 1962 as *Karami-ai.*

THE INHERITANCE   **F6.2419a**
Mayer-Sklar Productions. *Dist* Harold Mayer. 8 Nov **1964** [New York opening; c14 May 1964; MP14411]. Sd; b&w. 16mm. 60 min.

Prod-Dir Harold Mayer. *Writ* Millard Lampell. *Camera* Edmund B. Gerard, Jesse Paley, Leonard Stark. *Film Ed* Lawrence Silk. *Mus Comp & Cond* George Kleinsinger. *Song:* "Pass It On" George Kleinsinger, Millard Lampell. *Songs Perf by* Pete Seeger, Judy Collins, Tom Paxton, Page Gaynes, Barry Kornfeld, Carla Rutolo, John R. Winn, Millard Lampell. *Sd* Al Gramaglia. *Adv* Maxwell Brandwen. *Coöp* Amalgamated Clothing Workers of America, AFL-CIO, CLC. *Cons* Sol Brandzel, Howard D. Samuel.

Narrator: Robert Ryan.

Documentary. Commemorating the fiftieth anniversary of the Amalgamated Clothing Workers of America, the film traces the growth of the American labor movement from immigrant arrival at Ellis Island through union participation in the civil rights struggle of the sixties. Focusing on the garment industry, the documentary exposes conditions in the sweatshops and ghettos of New York, Chicago, and Rochester, and depicts the police brutality accompanying protest. Among the labor martyrs eulogized are the strikers Charles Lazinskas, Samuel Kapper, Ida Brayman, and the ten Chicago Republic Steelworkers murdered while marching on Memorial Day, 1937. Union champions represented include Jane Addams of Hull House, Mrs. Raymond Robins of the Women's Trade Union League, Harold Ickes, Sidney Hillman, Clarence Darrow, Fiorello LaGuardia, and Franklin Delano Roosevelt. *Factory workers. Immigrants. Police. Civil rights. Social classes. Strikes. Demonstrations. Murder. Labor unions. Sweatshops. Ghettos. Memorial Day. Chicago. New York City—Lower East Side. Rochester (New York). Ellis Island. Jane Addams. Ida Brayman. Clarence Darrow. Sidney Hillman. Harold Ickes. Samuel Kapper. Charles Lazinskas. Fiorello LaGuardia. Mrs. Raymond Robins. Franklin Delano Roosevelt. Amalgamated Clothing Workers of America (AFL-CIO).*

Note: Copyright claimant; Amalgamated Clothing Workers of America.

THE INITIATION   **F6.2420**
Original Films. 4 Apr **1968** [Atlanta opening]. Sd; b&w. 35mm. 72 min.

Prod Tom Parker. *Assoc Prod* Sallee Parker. *Dir* William Wellburn. *Orig Screenplay* Ron Sands, Tom Parker. *Dir Photog* Robert Caramico. *Art Dir* Lafe Speirs.

Cast: Denise Lynn *(Tangi)*, Rick Strausser *(Kelly)*, Sean Ohlen *(Chuck)*, Rachel Raid *(Linda)*, Walter Willison *(Tommy)*, Lawrence Andrews *(Steve)*, Rusty Beauchane *(Ray)*, Linnell Barrett *(initiation girl)*, Sandy Baker *(Henrietta)*, Erica Gavin *(Jan)*.

Melodrama. Chuck Johnson arranges erotic happenings in the family guesthouse while his curious younger sister, Tangi, peeks through the window. Their eldest brother Kelly returns from a tour of duty in Vietnam to a homecoming planned by Chuck. The uninhibited guests enjoy a variety of erotic activities; several girls strip off each other's clothes and join the party. Tangi surprises Kelly in his room taking a "fix"; wounded in combat, he has become an addict, but he remains a hero to his sister. The following afternoon, Chuck conducts "The Initiation," an erotic beer-drinking contest. The first person to down a glass of beer removes an article of clothing from "the initiation girl." The participant who removes her last article of clothing wins the girl. Ray, a member of the orgy group, finds Tangi spying through the window and attacks her. Chuck hears her screams and comes to her aid. The fight is halted by Kelly's arrival in the custody of two narcotics agents; he was arrested while trying to buy some heroin. *Veterans. Drug addicts. Brother-sister relationship. Voyeurism. Sensualism. Drunkenness. Rape. Orgies. Contests.*

INNOCENT AND THE DAMNED (Reissue)   **F6.2421**
Loew's Inc.–Albert Zugsmith Productions. *Dist* Metro-Goldwyn-Mayer, Inc. 28 Nov **1961** [Maryland license]. Sd; b&w. 35mm. 92 min.

Note: Originally released in 1959 as *Girls' Town;* c30 Jul 1959; LP14516.

THE INNOCENTS (United States/Great Britain)   **F6.2422**
Twentieth Century–Fox Film Corp.–Achilles Film Productions. *Dist* Twentieth Century–Fox Film Corp. 25 Dec **1961** [New York opening; c15 Dec 1961; LP21039]. Sd (Westrex); b&w. 35mm (CinemaScope). 99 min.

A Jack Clayton Production. *Prod-Dir* Jack Clayton. *Exec Prod* Albert Fennell. *Screenplay* Truman Capote, William Archibald. *Script Ed* Jeanie Sims. *Adapt* John Mortimer. *Dir Photog* Freddie Francis. *Camera Op* Ron Taylor. *Camera Focus* Ronnie Maasz, Bernard Ford. *Camera Grip* Ray Jones. *Art Dir* Wilfred Shingleton. *Asst Art Dir* Martin Atkinson. *Set Dresser* Peter James. *Scenic Artist* Alan Evans. *Draughtsman* Tony Woollard, Jim Sawyer, Tony Pratt. *Film Ed* James Clark. *Asst Ed* Mary Kessell, Pamela Gardner. *Mus Comp* Georges Auric. *Cond* Lambert Williamson. *Song:* "O Willow Waly" Georges Auric, Paul Dehn. *Sd Rec* A. G. Ambler, John Cox. *Dub Ed* Peter Musgrave. *Boom Op* Ken Ritchie. *Sd Camera Op* Jimmy Dooley. *Asst Dir* Michael Birkett, Ken Softley. *Prod Mgr* James Ware. *Unit Mgr* Claude Watson. *Prod Sec* Joan Williams. *Cont* Pamela Mann. *Cost Dsgn* Motley. *Cost* Sophie Devine. *Wardrobe Mistress* Brenda Gardner. *Makeup* Harold Fletcher. *Hairdresser* Gordon Bond. *Supv Floor Electrn* Maurice Gillett. *Constr Mgr* Gus Walker. *Stills* Ted Reed.

Cast: Deborah Kerr *(Miss Giddens)*, Peter Wyngarde *(Peter Quint)*, Megs Jenkins *(Mrs. Grose)*, Michael Redgrave *(The Uncle)*, Martin Stephens *(Miles)*, Pamela Franklin *(Flora)*, Clytie Jessop *(Miss Jessel)*, Isla Cameron *(Anna)*, Eric Woodburn *(coachman)*.

Drama. Source: Henry James, *The Turn of the Screw* (New York, 1898). William Archibald, *The Innocents* (New York opening: 1 Feb 1950). Miss Giddens, a minister's daughter, is engaged in London by the master of Bly House as governess for his niece, Flora, and his nephew, Miles. She is greeted by Flora, a seemingly adorable child, and Mrs. Grose, the housekeeper. The first ominous indication that all is not as it seems is a letter from Miles' school explaining that he is being expelled for attempting to corrupt his fellow students. But when Miss Giddens meets the apparently angelic, well-mannered little boy, her anxiety disappears. As the days pass, Miss Giddens discovers that "others" are prowling about the estate—first a man, then a woman. When she describes the two people to the housekeeper, Miss Giddens is horrified to hear that she has identified a former manager, Quint, and a governess, Miss Jessel, both now deceased. Furthermore, she learns that the two "intangibles" not only had licentious relations with each other but in some horrible way perverted the children. She then realizes, or thinks she realizes, that they have returned to take possession of the children's souls. Convinced that Flora and Miles also see the haunting visions, Miss Giddens attempts to make them admit it. The employment of shock treatment for Flora only results in an hysterical outburst, and Mrs. Grose takes the child away from Bly House. Consoling herself with the thought that she has saved little Flora's soul, Miss Giddens embarks upon saving Miles. When she sees the face of Quint in the garden, Miss Giddens demands that Miles say the name of the man she is confident they both can see. The child finally screams "Quint," and then falls lifeless to the ground. Shattered, she takes the dead child in her arms and kisses him. *Governesses.*

Children. Housekeepers. Supernatural. Hysteria. Death. Brother-sister relationship. Ghosts.

Note: Opened in London in Nov 1961.

INSANE WORLD *see* **MONDO PAZZO**

THE INSECT WOMAN (Japan)   F6.2423

Nikkatsu Corp. *Dist* Jerome Balsam Films, Shochiku Films of America. 30 Jun **1964** [New York opening]. Sd; b&w. 35mm. 123 min.

Dir Shohei Imamura. *Screenplay* Keiji Hasebe, Shohei Imamura. *Planning* Yawara Otsuka, Jiro Tomoda. *Photog* Masahisa Himeda. *Art Dir* Kimihiko Nakamura. *Film Ed* Mutsuo Tanji. *Mus* Toshiro Mayuzumi. *Sd* Tsuneo Furuyama. *Asst Dir* Tadahiko Isomi. *Prod Mgr* Masanori Yamanoi.

Cast: Sachiko Hidari *(Tome)*, Jitsuko Yoshimura *(Nobuko)*, Hiroyuki Nagato *(Matsunami)*, Seizaburo Kawazu *(Karasawa)*, Kazuo Kitamura *(Chuji)*, Sumie Sasaki *(En)*, Shoichi Kuwayama *(Owagawa)*, Daizaburo Hirata *(Kamibayashi)*, Shoichi Ozawa *(Ken)*, Taiji Tonoyama *(foreman)*, Shoichi Tsuyuguchi *(Honda)*, Tanie Kitabayashi *(midwife)*, Emiko Higashi *(Kane)*, Masumi Harukawa *(Midori)*, Teruko Kishi *(Rin)*, Asao Koike *(Sawakichi)*, Emiko Aizawa *(Rui)*.

Drama. In the mountain country of Japan, Tome, a young girl, grows up in ignorance of the morals of the time. Unaware of her true father's identity, she lives with her foster father and is his bedmate until she is 20 years old. She becomes pregnant by a neighboring farmer but does not marry him; instead, she goes to work in a factory. After having an affair with the shop foreman, she becomes a housemaid for the mistress of an American soldier and derives pleasure from listening to their lovemaking. After contributing through neglect to the death of the woman's child, Tome experiences remorse. In time, however, she opens her own prostitution business and sadistically hires the woman who had been the mistress of the American soldier. Tome briefly feels love for a merchant called Karasawa, but she is disillusioned when he asks her to sleep with a client. After serving a prison term for prostitution, she returns to Tokyo. Meanwhile, Nobuko, Tome's grown daughter, learns that she is pregnant, goes to bed with Karasawa, robs him, and runs off to join her lover in the country. Tome, now old and weary, brings the girl back to the city and turns her over to Karasawa. *Foster fathers. Farmers. Housemaids. Americans in foreign countries. Merchants. Pregnancy. Illegitimacy. Prostitution. Filial relations. Factories. Tokyo.*

Note: Released in Japan in 1963 as *Nippon konchuki.* Also known as *The Insect.*

INSEL DER AMAZONEN *see* **SEVEN DARING GIRLS**

INSIDE A NUDE PARTY   F6.2424

PAD Productions. 18 Mar **1966** [San Francisco opening]. Sd; col? 35mm? [Feature film, length unknown.]

Prod Peter DeCenzie.

Sex film. No information about the precise nature of this film has been found. *Sexuality. Nudity.*

INSIDE DAISY CLOVER   F6.2425

Park Place Productions. *Dist* Warner Bros. Pictures. 22 Dec **1965** [Los Angeles opening; c31 Dec 1965; LP32144]. Sd; col (Technicolor). 35mm (Panavision). 128 min.

A Pakula-Mulligan Production. *Prod* Alan J. Pakula. *Dir* Robert Mulligan. *Screenplay* Gavin Lambert. *Dir Photog* Charles Lang. *Camera Op* George Nogle. *Asst Camera* Richard Doran, Ralph Gerling. *Asst Art Dir* Dean Tavoularis. *Set Decor* George James Hopkins. *Set Coörd* Robert Irving. *Prod Dsgn* Robert Clatworthy. *Film Ed* Aaron Stell. *Montage* John Hoffman. *Mus* Andre Previn. *Songs:* "The Circus Is a Wacky World," "A Happy Song," "You're Gonna Hear From Me" Andre Previn, Dory Previn. *Miss Wood's Voice Dubbed by* Jackie Ward. *Choreog & Asst to Choreog* Herbert Ross, Howard Jeffrey. *Sd Mix* M. A. Merrick. *Sd Rec* Russell Ashley. *Boom Op* Eugene O'Brien. *1st & 2d Asst Dir* Joseph E. Kenny, Jack Cunningham. *Prod Mgr* George Justin. *Asst to the Prod* Isabel M. Halliburton. *Script Supv* Meta Rebner. *Cost Dsgn* Bill Thomas. *Natalie Wood's Wardrobe Dsgn* Edith Head. *Ladies' Cost* Ann Landers, Rose Brandi. *Men's Wardrobe* Jack Bear. *Makeup Supv* Gordon Bau. *Makeup* Ed Butterworth, Al Greenway. *Supv Hairstyles* Jean Burt Reilly. *Miss Wood's Hairstyle Dsgn* Maryce Bates. *Still Photog* Mel Traxel. *Gaffer* Lee Wilson. *Key Grip* Louis Maschmeyer. *Prop Master* Robert Cooper.

Cast: Natalie Wood *(Daisy Clover)*, Christopher Plummer *(Raymond Swan)*, Robert Redford *(Wade Lewis)*, Roddy McDowall *(Baines)*, Ruth Gordon *(The Dealer)*, Katharine Bard *(Melora Swan)*, Peter Helm *(Milton Hopwood)*, Betty Harford *(Gloria Goslett)*, John Hale, actor *(Harry Goslett)*, Harold Gould *(cop)*, Ottola Nesmith *(old lady in hospital)*, Edna Holland *(Cynara)*.

Drama. Source: Gavin Lambert, *Inside Daisy Clover* (New York, 1963). In California in 1936, Daisy Clover, a rebellious 15-year-old, lives with her mother whom she calls "The Dealer" because of her passion for playing solitaire. Daisy, who likes to sing, makes a recording of her voice and sends it to Hollywood studio head Raymond Swan, who gives Daisy a screen test and then a contract. Daisy's sister, Gloria, connives with her husband and Swan to have "The Dealer" committed to a sanitarium and herself appointed Daisy's guardian. At Swan's party to introduce Daisy to Hollywood, she meets screen idol Wade Lewis and then spends the night with him; and she does so again after the premiere of her film. When Daisy and Wade are summoned to Swan's office to explain their behavior, Wade announces his intention to marry Daisy. They wed, but when Daisy awakens on the first morning of their honeymoon, Wade is gone. She returns to Hollywood, where Melora, Swan's wife, tells Daisy that Wade prefers men to women. Heartbroken, Daisy takes "The Dealer" out of the sanitarium and brings her to live with her at a beachhouse, but "The Dealer" dies shortly thereafter. Daisy, working on a film, has a breakdown at the studio. She becomes a recluse at her beachhouse, refusing to speak to anyone, and makes an abortive suicide attempt. She leaves the house, the gas still on and a flame under the coffee, and the house blows up as she walks down the beach. Daisy is a has-been at 17, but she has made up her mind to fight back. *Motion picture producers. Actors. Recluses. Sisters. Guardians. Adolescence. Bisexuality. Filial relations. Honeymoons. Suicide. Motion picture studios. Beaches. Sanitariums. Hollywood.*

INSIDE NORTH VIETNAM   F6.2426

Felix Greene. *For* San Francisco Chronicle/Columbia Broadcasting System. *Dist* Felix Greene, Impact Films. 10 Dec **1967** [New York opening]. Sd; col (Eastmancolor). 35mm. 85 min. [Also reviewed at 80 and 82 min.]

Prod-Dir-Screenplay Felix Greene. *Photog* Felix Greene. *Film Ed* Gordon Mueller. *Ed Cons* Lester Cole.

Narrator: Felix Greene.

Documentary. The film was made in North Vietnam from February through May of 1967 by filmmaker-writer Felix Greene, who was on assignment for CBS-TV News and *The San Francisco Chronicle.* Rather than stress the actual scenes of warfare, Greene concentrates on the personal incidents and suffering brought on by the war. The lives of the cheerful rural Vietnamese are shown: Ho Chi Minh is seen addressing some villagers; Prime Minister Pham Van Dong explains his country's position on the war; a Vietnamese colonel uses U.S. Army statistics to prove that several million U.S. men would be needed to defeat his country; Greene interviews a hospitalized U. S. pilot who urges the American people to reexamine their stance on the war; and a peasant denounces the Americans for killing his wife and child. *War victims. Interviewers. Air pilots. Prisoners of war. Peasants. Aerial bombardment. Vietnam War 1964–73. Democratic Republic of Vietnam. Hanoi. Ho Chi Minh. Pham Van Dong.*

Note: Filmed on location in the Democratic Republic of Vietnam. An air raid sequence was obtained from Japanese sources; North Vietnam provided films of the capture of the U. S. prisoner of war.

INSIDE OUT *see* **LIFE UPSIDE DOWN**

INSIDE THE U.S.S.R. (U.S.S.R.)   F6.2427

Central Documentary Film Studio–Moscow Popular Science Studio. *Dist* Artkino Pictures. 4 Nov **1961** [New York opening]. Sd; col. 35mm. 120 min.

Production Credits for "Moscow Story": *Dir* Ilya Kopalin. *Screenplay* S. Zenin, Yu. Karavkin. *Photog* Vladislav Mikosha, R. Khalushakov. *Camera* I. Bgantsev. *Song Lyr* V. Gneushev. *Mus* Aleksandr Flyarkovskiy.

Production Credits for "On Ice and Water": *Dir* Arkadiy Zenyakin. *Photog* Arkadiy Zenyakin, Vladislav Mikosha. *Film Ed* V. Plotnikova.

Production Credits for "Prokofieff—His Life and Music": *Dir* Lidiya Stepanova. *Screenplay* V. Komissarzhevskiy. *Photog* Yu. Berenshteyn. *Mus Selections From Works Including:* "War and Peace" ("Voyna i mir"), "Romeo and Juliet" ("Romeo i Dzhulyetta"), "The Ugly Duckling" ("Gadkiy utyonok"), Symphony no. 5 Sergei Sergeevich Prokofiev.

Anthology. MOSCOW STORY: A view of the city of Moscow, its inhabitants and architecture. ON ICE AND WATER: Young skaters and swimmers perform in ballet production numbers. Included are excerpts from the ice revue "Zimnyaya fantasiya" ("Winter Fantasy"). PROKOFIEFF—HIS LIFE AND MUSIC: A survey of the life and career of composer Sergey Prokofieff (Prokofiev), who is seen conducting his own works. Galina Ulanova appears in an extract from *Romeo and Juliet. Composers. Orchestra conductors. Ice skating. Swimming. Moscow. Sergei Sergeevich Prokofiev. Galina Ulanova. Underwater ballet.*

Note: *Moscow Story,* a Central Documentary Film Studio production, was released in the U.S.S.R. in 1961 as *Gorod bolshoy sudby;* running time: ca60 min; *Prokofieff—His Life and Music,* a Moscow Popular Science Studio production, in 1961 as *Kompozitor Sergey Prokofyev;* running time: ca60 min; and *On Ice and Water,* a Central Documentary Film Studio production, in 1959 as *Na ldu i na vode;* running time: ca20 min.

THE INSPECTOR see LISA

INSPECTOR CLOUSEAU (Great Britain)   **F6.2428**
Mirisch Corp. *Dist* United Artists. 29 May **1968** [Los Angeles opening; c24 May 1968; LP35869]. Sd; col (DeLuxe). 35mm (Panavision). 101 min. [See note.]

Prod Lewis J. Rachmil. *Dir* Bud Yorkin. *2d Unit Dir* Michael Frewin. *Screenplay* Tom Waldman, Frank Waldman. *Photog* Arthur Ibbetson. *2d Unit Photog* Skeets Kelly. *Art Dir* Norman Dorme. *Set Decor* Terence Morgan, Il. *Prod Dsgn* Michael Stringer. *Titl* DePatie-Freleng. *Film Ed* John Victor Smith. *Mus Comp* Ken Thorne. *Sd* A. W. Watkins, Jonathan Bates, Gerry Turner. *Asst Dir* Kip Gowans. *Prod Supv* Charles Orme. *Unit Mgr* Robert Watts. *Wardrobe* Ivy Baker, Dinah Greet. *Makeup* Ernest Kelly, Wally Schneiderman. *Hairstyles* Pearl Tipaldi. *Sp Eff* Malcolm King. *Mirisch Co. Supv* William S. Gilmore, Jr.

Cast: Alan Arkin (*Insp. Jacques Clouseau*), Delia Boccardo (*Lisa Morrel*), Frank Finlay (*Superintendent Weaver*), Patrick Cargill (*Sir Charles Braithwaite*), Beryl Reid (*Mrs. Weaver*), Barry Foster (*Addison Steele*), Clive Francis (*Clyde Hargreaves*), John Bindon (*Bull Parker*), Michael Ripper (*Frey*), Tutte Lemkow (*Frenchy LeBec*), Anthony Ainley (*Bomber LeBec*), Wallas Eaton (*Hoeffler*), David Bauer (*Geffrion*), Richard Pearson (*Shockley*), George Pravda (*Wulf*), Eric Pohlmann (*Bergesch*), Geoffrey Bayldon (*Gutch*), Arthur Lovegrove (*innkeeper*), Kathya Wyeth (*Meg*), Tracey Crisp (*Julie*), Marjie Lawrence (*Peggy*), Craig Booth (*David*), Julie Croft (*Nicole*), Robert Russell (*Stockton*), Susan Engel (*Policewoman Carmichael*), Will Stampe (*fishmonger*), Barbara Dana (*nun*).

Comedy. Based on the character created by: Blake Edwards and Maurice Richlin. Scotland Yard's Sir Charles Braithwaite discovers that the loot from the Great Train Robbery is being used to finance an even bigger caper and that one of his men may be in collusion with the robbers. He decides to call in Inspector Clouseau of Paris, despite the inspector's reputation as a bungler. Proceeding with confidence, Clouseau goes to the Wormwood Scrubs Prison barbershop to question a captured member of the gang, Addison Steele, while he is giving the warden's mincing son, Clyde, a haircut. There Clouseau is chloroformed, and Steele escapes. The next day, after being outfitted with the latest spy equipment, Clouseau visits the home of Superintendent Weaver and his amorous wife. They attend a local fair, and there Clouseau enters several contests and accidentally kills a gang member sent to murder him. The following evening, Clouseau trails the Weavers' attractive maid, Lisa, to an inn but ends up being drugged by two voluptuous women so that a plaster cast can be made of his face. Upon regaining consciousness, he pursues the two women so exuberantly that he causes a bed to collapse, thereby eliminating another gang member. Sent by Braithwaite to France, Clouseau again meets Lisa and learns that she is an INTERPOL agent also working on the case. Meanwhile, the gang, using their Clouseau masks, simultaneously have robbed 13 banks in Switzerland and hidden the money in candy wrappers loaded aboard a Rhine barge. Although Clouseau eventually kills the Scotland Yard traitor (Weaver) in a free-for-all, both he and Lisa end up on the barge as prisoners of the gang leader, the mincing Clyde. After rejecting a bribe, Clouseau inadvertently sinks the barge by burning a hole in it with his laser beam lighter. The police move in to capture the gang and recover the money, and Clouseau is decorated for his achievement. When he flies to Paris for a rendezvous with Lisa, however, he finds himself seated next to the predatory Mrs. Weaver. The indomitable Inspector Clouseau parachutes from the plane. *Police. French. Prison wardens. Housemaids. Gangs. Train robberies. Prison escapes. Bank robberies. Effeminacy. Impersonation. Lust. Fairs. Contests. Candy. Barges. Masks. Laser. Switzerland. Rhine River. Scotland Yard. INTERPOL. Inspector Clouseau.*

Note: Location scenes filmed in Europe. Released in Great Britain in 1968; running time: 96 min. U. S. copyright length: 98 min; also reviewed at 94 min; cut from 105 min (?).

INSTANT NYMPHO, OR 3 + 3 = SEX   **F6.2429**
Sep **1970** [Los Angeles showing]. Sd; col. 16mm? [Feature length assumed.]
Cast: Linda, Kim, Angela, Larry, Rob, Duke.
Sex film. No information about the precise nature of this film has been found. *Group sex.*

INTERLUDE (Great Britain)   **F6.2430**
Domino Productions. *Dist* Columbia Pictures. 2 Jul **1968** [New York opening; c1 Jun 1968; LP35848]. Sd (RCA); col (Technicolor). 35mm. 113 min.

Prod David Deutsch. *Assoc Prod* Jack Hanbury. *Dir* Kevin Billington. *Story & Screenplay* Lee Langley, Hugh Leonard. *Photog* Gerry Fisher. *Camera Op* Jimmy Turrell. *Set Decor* Peter Young. *Prod Dsgn* Tony Woollard. *Titl Topography* Tony Woollard. *Film Ed* Bert Bates. *Concert Mus Played by* Royal Philharmonic Orchestra. *Leader* John Ronane, cond. *Cond* Ernest

Fleischmann. *Mus Adv* Humphrey Burton, Ernest Fleischmann. *Orig Mus Comp & Cond* Georges Delerue. *Titl Song Sung by* Timi Yuro. *Symphony no. 5* Ludwig van Beethoven. *Symphony no. 1* Pĕtr Ilich Tchaikovsky. *Adagio in C minor* Wolfgang Amadeus Mozart. *Glass Harmonica* Bruno Hoffmann. *Flute* Gustav Scheck. *Oboe* Helmut Winschermann. *Viola* Emil Seiler. *Cello* August Wenzinger. "*Carnival Overture*" Anton Dvořák. *Symphony no. 3* Johannes Brahms. *Symphony no. 2* Sergei Rachmaninoff. *Adagio for Organ and Strings* Tommaso Albinoni. *Orch by* Remo Giazotto. *Sd Rec* Charles Poulton, Robert Allen, Jim Willis. *Re-rec* Nolan Roberts. *Sd Ed* Jim Sibley. *Asst Dir* Scott Wodehouse. *Prod Mgr* Gus Angus. *Cont* Jane Buck. *Asst to the Prod* Gerald Deutsch. *Cost Dsgn* Jocelyn Rickards. *Wardrobe* Kathleen Moore, Joanne Stewart. *Makeup* W. T. Partleton. *Hairdresser* Betty Glasow. *Casting Adv* Miriam Brickman. *Constr Mgr* Ernie Blake. *Ch Electrn* Laurie Shane. *Grip* Jack Roche.

Cast: Oskar Werner (*Stefan Zelter*), Barbara Ferris (*Sally*), Virginia Maskell (*Antonia Zelter*), Donald Sutherland (*Lawrence*), Nora Swinburne (*Mary*), Alan Webb (*Andrew*), Bernard Kay (*George Selworth*), Geraldine Sherman (*Natalie*), John Cleese (*television public relations man*), Gino Mulvazzi (*Mario*), Muguette De Braie (*Mario's wife*), Robert Lang (*Humphrey Turnbull*), Roslyn De Winter (*Humphrey's secretary*), Janet Davies (*nanny*), Sarah Jane Stratton (*Sarah Jane*), Simon Davis (*Simon*), Steve Plytas (*Frederico*), Rosalie Westwater (*hotel receptionist*), Gay Cameron (*Andrew's girl friend*), Anjula Harman (*Lawrence's pupil*), Ernest Fleischmann (*orchestra manager*), Derek Jacobi (*Paul*), Richard Pescud (*Ernest*), Humphrey Burton (*television director*).

Romantic melodrama. After a lengthy separation, two lovers who have met by accident at a party meet at the woman's old London flat and recall their brief affair: *Middle-aged, married orchestra conductor Stefan Zelter is interviewed by Sally, a young journalist. When her newspaper prints his libelous remarks the musician is sued and his performances suspended pending litigation. During his enforced holiday, Stefan and Sally fall in love. Their relationship is hampered by feelings of guilt, however. Confronted by Zelter's wife Antonia, who generously offers her husband his freedom while emphasizing his absolute absorption in music, Sally renounces the relationship. Following their chance encounter, Sally phones her new husband.* Orchestra conductors. Journalists. Mistresses. Infidelity. Guilt. Divorce. Lawsuits. Middle age. Music. London.

Note: Released in Great Britain in 1968; filmed on location in London and Rye.

INTERNATIONAL SMORGASBROAD   **F6.2431**
Barry Mahon Productions. 5 Feb **1965** [Los Angeles showing]. Sd; col (Eastman Color). 35mm. 62 min.

A Barry Mahon Production. *Prod-Dir* Barry Mahon. *Camera* Barry Mahon. *Ed* Chuck Smith. *Asst Dir* Byron Mabe. *Opticals* Eastern Effects.

Cast: Bernie Allen (*The Chef*), Cristine, Gigi, Jane, Mamie, Fanny.

Comedy. Every time gourmet chef Bernie Allen looks at food, he is inspired by visions of beautiful, nude women. Two cantaloupes, a can of sardines, and a mold of shimmering jello are among the foods which evoke mental delights. Since Bernie is a man of conscience, he tries instead to think of his librarian girl friend, or of the upcoming Sunday school picnic, but he is powerless in the face of the beautiful visions that grip his imagination as he works. *Cooks. Librarians. Nudity. Food. Fantasy.*

Note: Also known as *Smorgasbroad.*

THE INTERNS   **F6.2432**
Interns Co. *Dist* Columbia Pictures. 8 Aug **1962** [New York opening; c27 Jun 1962; LP22258]. Sd; b&w. 35mm. 120 min.

Prod Robert Cohn. *Dir* David Swift. *Screenplay* Walter Newman, David Swift. *Dir Photog* Russell Metty. *Art Dir* Don Ament. *Set Decor* Richard Mansfield. *Film Ed* Al Clark, Jerome Thoms. *Mus* Leith Stevens. *Song:* "*Bye and Bye*" *played by* Turk Murphy and His Jazz Orchestra. *Sd Supv* Charles J. Rice. *Sd* James Z. Flaster. *Asst Dir* Eddie Saeta. *Makeup* Ben Lane.

Cast: Michael Callan (*Dr. Considine*), Cliff Robertson (*Dr. John Paul Otis*), James MacArthur (*Dr. Lew Worship*), Nick Adams (*Dr. Sid Lackland*), Suzy Parker (*Lisa Cardigan*), Haya Harareet (*Mado*), Anne Helm (*Mildred*), Stefanie Powers (*Gloria*), Buddy Ebsen (*Dr. Sidney Wohl*), Telly Savalas (*Dr. Riccio*), Katharine Bard (*Nurse Flynn*), Kay Stevens (*Didi Loomis*), Gregory Morton (*Dr. Hugo Granchard*), Angela Clarke (*Mrs. Auer*), Connie Gilchrist (*Nurse Connie Dean*), Ellen Davalos (*Loara*), Charles Robinson (*Dr. Dave Simon*), Carroll Harrison (*Olga*), John Banner (*Dr. Duane*), Mari Lynn (*Samantha*), Brian G. Hutton (*Dr. Joe Parelli*), J. Edward McKinley (*Dr. Bonny*), Bobo Lewis (*Gwen*), Roger Bronte (*1st intern*), Bill Gunn (*Rosco*), William Douglas (*Dr. Apschult*), Don Edmonds (*Dr. Petchek*), Mavis Neal (*Mrs. Lawrence*), Brent Sargent (*Dr. Baker*), Mark Kantor (*Samantha's son*), Peter Brocco (*Auer*), Jud Taylor, Ira Barmak.

Melodrama. Source: Richard Frede, *The Interns* (New York, 1960). During their first year of internship at New North Hospital, a group of aspiring doctors undergo both personal and professional upheavals. John Paul Otis destroys his medical career when he falls in love with celebrated model Lisa Cardigan and tries to steal pills from the hospital in order to abort her pregnancy. His lifelong friend, Lew Worship, feels duty-bound to report the theft, and Otis is expelled. Lew, who begins internship with plans to become a surgeon, becomes dedicated to obstetrics. He falls in love with a student nurse, Gloria, and tries to persuade her to marry him and give up her dream of going abroad. Intern Considine, who is anxious to study under psychiatrist Dr. Bonny, becomes so involved in two simultaneous romances that he loses sight of his goal and suffers a nervous collapse. The interns are confronted with the ethical problems of mercy killing, and the tragic death of an incurably ill Malaysian girl inspires Dr. Sid Lackland to plan to devote his life to aiding the underprivileged in the Far East. Mado, a woman intern from behind the Iron Curtain, is so dedicated to her profession that the head surgeon, Dr. Riccio, forgets his prejudice against women doctors and makes her his assistant. At the end of the first year of internship, a party is held at a nearby bar. Here Otis, now married to Lisa and working for a drug firm, meets the group once more. He is struck by what he has lost by his one compromise of medical ethics. *Hospital interns. Physicians. Nurses. Surgeons. Models. Malaysians. Psychiatrists. Obstetrics. Abortion. Mercy killing. Medical ethics. Hospitals. Employment—Women. Incurable illness.*

Note: Location scenes filmed in Los Angeles. A sequel was released in 1964 under the title *The NEW Interns* (q.v.).

INTERPLAY   F6.2433

Success Films. *Dist* Times Film Corp. 9 Dec **1970** [New York opening]. Sd; col (Eastman Color). 35mm. 97 min. *MPAA rating X.*

Exec Prod Felix J. Bilgrey. *Dir* Albert T. Viola. *Screenplay* Harvey Flaxman. *Photog* Jack Malick. *Art Dir* Dan Gladding, Jim Porter. *Film Ed* Charles Diana. *Mus Score* James A. Burroughs. *Songs:* "Painted Ponies," "Carousel," "Magic Circle," "Silver Slippers" James A. Burroughs, V. Van Pelt. *Sung by* The Waterloo Zoo. *Asst Dir* James A. Burroughs. *Prod Mgr* Joseph Sutherin.

Cast: Zee Wilson (*Nora*), Ed Moore (*John*), Gwen Saska (*Helen*), Sam Coppola (*Mel*), Phillip R. Allen (*Eddie*), Lani Ryland (*Oriental girl*), Artie Giannini (*John's mother*). Yvonne Pontoon, Corinne Shull, Jutka Goz, Anita Ferris, Merlin Coslick, Arlene Starr, Roslyn Dickens, Ruth Reachel, Iris Acker, Ethel Hazen.

Drama. John, a successful fashion executive, lives with his wife, Nora, and their two young children on a suburban Long Island estate. Because of a childhood trauma suffered when he discovered his mother making love with two strangers, he experiences abnormal sexual drives. He asks Nora to dress as a prostitute and to caress him as if he were her child in order to arouse his desire. She acquiesces but refuses to join his encounter group for sex parties. Deprived of the true love she needs, Nora joins a theater group at John's insistence and tries to find satisfaction in acting. She joins her old friend Helen in a lesbian affair but extricates herself when Helen brings home an Oriental woman for a threesome. She devotes herself to the theater group and falls in love with the director, Mel. One day she learns that John had arranged her two affairs because he was aroused at the thought of her infidelity. Furious, she joins the sex group for a night and then walks out with the children. *Executives. Housewives. Theatrical directors. Orientals. Marriage. Oedipus complex. Suburban life. Group sex. Theater—Amateur. Lesbianism. Infidelity. Long Island.*

INTIMACY   F6.2434

Victor Stoloff. *Dist* Goldstone Film Enterprises. 20 May **1966** [Miami Beach, Florida, opening]. Sd; b&w. 35mm. 87 min.

A Victor Stoloff Production. *Prod* David Heilweil. *Dir* Victor Stoloff. *Screenplay* Eva Wolas. *Based on an Idea by* Stanley Z. Cherry. *Photog* Ted Saizis, Vincent Saizis. *Mus* Geordie Hormel. *Sd* George Blascons.

Cast: Jack Ging (*Jim Hawley*), Joan Blackman (*Barbara Nicholson*), Nancy Malone (*Virginia Hawley*), Barry Sullivan (*Walter Nicholson*), Jackie DeShannon (*Carrie Lane*).

Melodrama. Unable to obtain a government contract through bribery, Walter Nicholson, an unscrupulous businessman, attempts to blackmail Jim Hawley, an honest Washington official, by setting up a hidden motion picture camera in Hawley's hotel room. He then sends prostitute Carrie Lane to compromise Hawley. Nicholson looks at the film, discovers that his own wife is having an affair with Hawley; he suffers a heart attack and dies, unaware that Hawley had decided to award him the contract. His wife arrives at the office and finds him dead on the floor with the film still running. As she watches, she sees Hawley become reconciled with his alcoholic wife, thereby putting an end to his extra-marital romances. *Businessmen. Bureaucrats. Prostitutes. Bribery. Blackmail. Business ethics. Infidelity. Alcoholism. Eavesdropping. Hotels. Heart disease. Contracts. Cameras.*

Note: Also known as *The Deceivers.*

INTIMATE DIARY OF ARTISTS' MODELS   F6.2435

Ikay Beautiful Films. *Dist* Ikay Beautiful Films. 17 Apr **1964** [Los Angeles showing]. Sd; col. 35mm. 69 min.

Dir Larry Wolk. *Photog* Bunny Yeager. *Tech Coörd* Bunny Yeager.

Cast: Marie Perry.

Drama. A woman wins a Florida vacation in a beauty contest. Arriving there, she is determined to find a job as a model. After a photographer makes improper advances toward her, she moves in with several professional models who help her find work posing nude for photographers, artists, and a sculptor. She also visits one of the largest of the Florida artists' colonies. *Models. Photographers. Artists. Sculptors. Nudity. Beauty contests. Vacations. Art colonies. Florida.*

Note: Also known as *Diary of Artists and Models* and *Diary of a Model.* Advertised as *Artist's Models.*

INTIMATE LIGHTING (Czechoslovakia)   F6.2436

Barrandov Film Studio. *For* Československý Film. *Dist* Altura Films International, Fleetwood Films. 24 Nov **1969** [New York opening]. Sd; b&w. 35mm. 71 min.

Dir-Writ Ivan Passer. *Story & Screenplay* Jaroslav Papoušek, Václav Šašek, Ivan Passer. *Photog* Miroslav Ondříček, Josef Střecha. *Art Dir* Karel Černý. *Film Ed* Jiřina Lukešová. *Mus* Oldřich Korte, Josef Hart. *Sd* Adolf Böhm. *Asst Dir* Jiří Růžička. *In Charge of Prod* František Sandr. *Prod Asst* Ludmila Tikovská, Věra Winkelhöferová. *Film Unit* Šebor-Bor.

Cast: Věra Křesadlová (*Stepa*), Zdeněk Bezušek (*Peter*), Jan Vostrčil (*grandfather*), Vlastimila Vlková (*grandmother*), Karel Blažek (*Bambas*), Jaroslava Štědrá (*Marie*), Karel Uhlík (*pharmacist*), Miroslav Cvrk (*Kaja*), Dagmar Ředinová (*Young Marie*).

Drama. Peter, a musician, and his girl friend, Stepa, arrive in a small provincial town where Peter is scheduled to give a concert. He goes to visit Bambas, a friend from music school who now resides in the town and is director of the local music conservatory. Bambas, who has settled down to domestic life with a wife, children, and his grandparents, takes Peter to a funeral where he and his grandfather provide the music. Bambas and Peter return home for a family dinner after which they begin to rehearse for the concert, but Stepa becomes bored and disrupts the rehearsal. Later that night, Peter and Bambas share a bottle of vodka and resolve to leave the town and start their lives over again. On the road, however, they realize their mistake and drunkenly return home. The next morning, they wake up with hangovers and bid farewell over a glass of Grandmother's hardened egg nog. *Musicians. Grandparents. Family life. Friendship. Drunkenness. Funerals. Rehearsals.*

Note: Location scenes filmed in Tábor and Mirotice. Released in Czechoslovakia in Apr 1966 as *Intimní osvětlení.*

INTIMNÍ OSVĚTLENÍ *see* **INTIMATE LIGHTING**

GLI INTOCCABILI *see* **MACHINE GUN MCCAIN**

INTRAMUROS *see* **THE WALLS OF HELL**

L'INTRIGO *see* **DARK PURPOSE**

LES INTRIGUES *see* **FRANCHETTE; LES INTRIGUES**

THE INTRUDER   F6.2437

Filmgroup, Inc. *Dist* Pathé-America Distributing Co., Cinema Distributors of America. 14 May **1962** [New York opening]. Sd; b&w. 35mm. 84 min. [Also 80 min.]

A Roger Corman–Gene Corman Production. *Prod-Dir* Roger Corman. *Exec Prod* Gene Corman. *Screenplay* Charles Beaumont. *Photog* Taylor Byars. *Camera* Haskell Wexler. *Film Ed* Ronald Sinclair. *Mus* Herman Stein. *Sd* John Bury. *Asst Dir* Lou Place. *Prod Mgr* Jack Bohrer.

Cast: William Shatner (*Adam Cramer*), Frank Maxwell (*Tom McDaniel*), Beverly Lunsford (*Ella McDaniel*), Robert Emhardt (*Verne Shipman*), Jeanne Cooper (*Vi Griffin*), Leo Gordon (*Sam Griffin*), Charles Barnes (*Joey Green*), Charles Beaumont (*Dr. Harley Paton*), Katherine Smith (*Ruth McDaniel*), George Clayton Johnson (*Phil West*), William Nolan (*Bart Carey*), Phoebe Rowe (*Mrs. Lambert*), Bo Dodd (*sheriff*), Walter Kurtz (*Gramps*), Ocee Ritch (*Jack Allardyce*).

Melodrama. Source: Charles Beaumont, *The Intruder* (New York, 1959). Adam Cramer, a member of the reactionary Patrick Henry Society, arrives in a small Southern town to instigate a campaign of hatred designed to arouse white citizens into opposing integration of local schools. Full of surface charm, he ingratiates himself with the townspeople and persuades them to harass black youngsters attending the previously all-white high school; his only articulate opponent is newspaper editor Tom McDaniel, who feels bound to obey the law. Cramer makes an enemy by seducing Vi Griffin while her husband, Sam, a traveling salesman, is out of town; later, when the guilt-ridden Vi runs away, Sam senses that Cramer is responsible. Meanwhile, the town's mood becomes increasingly violent as a black minister is killed by a bomb tossed into his church; in addition, McDaniel loses an eye in a confrontation when he leads black students into school. Cramer then warns McDaniel's teenaged daughter, Ella, that he will kill her father unless she accuses a young black, Joey Green, of attempted rape. The frightened girl agrees, and a lynch-hungry mob lashes the boy to a schoolyard swing; under the prodding of Griffin, however, Ella arrives and publicly confesses her lie. Ashamed and furious at having been deceived, the crowd withdraws, leaving Cramer without support. *Negroes. Students. Editors. Traveling salesmen. Clergymen. Racism. Racial integration. Infidelity. Rape. Lynching. High school life. Blackmail. Bombs. Playgrounds. United States—South.*

Note: Filmed on location in Charleston, Missouri. Released by Cinema Distributors of America as *I Hate Your Guts.* Rereleased in 1966 as *Shame.*

LA INVASIÓN DE LOS VAMPIROS *see* **THE INVASION OF THE VAMPIRES**

INVASION EARTH 2150 A. D. *see* **DALEKS—INVASION EARTH 2150 A. D.**

INVASION FROM THE MOON *see* **MUTINY IN OUTER SPACE**

INVASION OF ASTRO-MONSTERS *see* **MONSTER ZERO**

INVASION OF THE ANIMAL PEOPLE (United States/Sweden)   **F6.2438**

Gustaf Unger Films–Fortuna Film. *Dist* A. D. P. Productions. 3 May **1962** [Hartford, Connecticut, opening]. Sd; b&w. 35mm. 55 min.

Prod Bertil Jernberg. *Prod-Dir U. S. Vers (see note)* Jerry Warren. *Dir* Virgil W. Vogel. *Screenplay* Arthur C. Pierce. *Photog* Hilding Bladh. *Art Dir* Nils Nilsson. *Mus (see note)* Allan Johannson, Harry Arnold, Arthur C. Pierce.

Cast: Robert Burton *(Dr. Frederick Wilson),* John Carradine *([see note]),* Barbara Wilson *(Diane Wilson),* Stan Gester *(Erik Engström),* Bengt Blomgren *(Col. Robert Bottiger),* Åke Grönberg *(Dr. Henrik),* Brita Borg *(singer),* Jack Haffner.

Science fiction melodrama. Diane Wilson is found by the police wandering the streets in a state of shock. After medical examiners find nothing wrong with her, Diane goes to northern Sweden to visit her American uncle, geologist Dr. Frederick Wilson. While she is there, reports are received concerning a strange meteor found in the mountains of Lapland. Forbidden to join the expedition with her uncle and his assistant Erik Engström, Diane stows away on the plane. Upon reaching the meteor, they discover that it is actually an alien spaceship surrounded by giant footprints. Erik and Diane go for help, but Diane is captured by space monsters. In an attempt to save her, Dr. Wilson and Erik start an avalanche. Frightened, the monsters release her and take off in the spaceship, narrowly escaping the avalanche. *Police. Americans in foreign countries. Uncles. Geologists. Stowaways. Space creatures. Abduction. Meteors. Spaceships. Lapland. Avalanches.*

Note: Location scenes filmed in Lapland. Produced in Sweden in 1958 as *Rymdinvasion i Lappland;* U. S. working title: *Terror in the Midnight Sun.* Original running time: 73 min. U. S. version includes footage filmed by Jerry Warren with Carradine as Dr. Wilson and Burton as Wilson's assistant. Sources conflict in crediting music. Alternative title: *Space Invasion of Lapland.*

INVASION OF THE ASTROS *see* **MONSTER ZERO**

INVASION OF THE BODY STEALERS *see* **THE BODY STEALERS**

INVASION OF THE STAR CREATURES   **F6.2439**

Alta Vista Productions. *Dist* American International Pictures. Apr **1962** [c4 Apr 1962; LP24125]. Sd; b&w. 35mm. 70 min. [See note.]

Prod Berj Hagopian. *Dir* Bruno Ve Sota. *Story–Screenplay* Jonathan Haze. *Photog* Basil Bradbury. *Art Dir* Mike McCloskey. *Film Ed* Lewis J. Guinn. *Electronic Mus* Jack Cookerly, Elliott Fisher. *Sd* James Hullerton. *Prod Mgr* Amos Powell. *Wardrobe* Dell Adams. *Makeup* Joseph Kinder.

Cast: Robert Ball *(Philbrick),* Frankie Ray *(Penn),* Gloria Victor *(Dr. Tanga),* Dolores Reed *(Professor Puna),* Mark Ferris *(Colonel Rank),* Slick Slavin, Mark Thompson, Sid Kane, Mike Del Piano, Lenore Bond, Anton Van Stralen, James Almanzar, Allen Dailey, Joseph Martin.

Science fiction comedy. Rookie soldiers Philbrick and Penn become separated from their outfit and follow some plantlike creatures into a cave, where they discover two beautiful scientists, Professor Puna and Dr. Tanga, who have come from outer space to conquer Earth. The soldiers, however, seduce their would-be conquerors with kisses, transform them into obedient mates, and take them back to camp. *Soldiers. Space creatures. Scientists. Seduction. Caves.*

Note: Also reviewed at 81 min; copyrighted at 75 min. The original title of Haze's story and screenplay was *Monsters From Nicholson Mesa.*

THE INVASION OF THE VAMPIRES (Mexico)   **F6.2440**

Tele-Talía Films. *Dist* K. Gordon Murray Productions, Trans-International Films. ca **1965.** Sd; b&w. 35mm. 92 min.

Pres by K. Gordon Murray. *Prod* Rafael Pérez Grovas. *Prod English Vers* K. Gordon Murray. *Dir-Writ* Miguel Morayta. *Photog* Raúl Martínez Solares. *Art Dir* Manuel Fontanals. *Film Ed* Gloria Schoemann. *Mus* Luis Hernández Bretón. *Sd* Jesús González Gancy.

Cast: Carlos Agosti *(Count Frankenhausen),* Rafael Etienne, Bertha Moss, Tito Junco, Erna Martha Bauman, Fernando Soto ["Mantequilla"], Enrique García Alvarez, David Reynoso, Rafael del Rio.

Horror film. In the 16th century, Dr. Ulises, a vampire expert, is convinced that Count Frankenhausen is responsible for several mysterious deaths in his village. He visits the nobleman's castle but fails to convince Brunhilda, the count's daughter, that her father is a vampire. Confronting Frankenhausen in his secret laboratory, Dr. Ulises pins the vampire, who has transformed himself into a bat, against a wall. As resurrected vampires besiege the village, Dr. Ulises destroys Frankenhausen with an injection of acid. Brunhilda is released from her father's spell, the other vampires return to their graves, and peace is restored. *Nobility. Vampires. Physicians. Murder. Filial relations. Metamorphosis. Castles. Laboratories. Spells. Bats.*

Note: Produced in Mexico in 1961 as *La invasión de los vampiros.*

INVASION OF THE ZOMBIES *see* **THE HORROR OF PARTY BEACH**

INVASION QUARTET (Great Britain)   **F6.2441**

Metro-Goldwyn-Mayer Pictures. *Dist* Metro-Goldwyn-Mayer, Inc. 27 Sep **1961** [Los Angeles opening; c7 Aug 1961; LP20356]. Sd (Westrex); b&w. 35mm (see note). 87 min.

Prod Ronald Kinnoch. *Dir* Jay Lewis. *Screenplay* Jack Trevor Story, John Briley. *Based on a Story by* Norman Collins. *Photog* Geoffrey Faithfull, Gerald Moss. *Camera Op* Frank Drake, Herbert R. Smith. *Focus* Dickie Robinson. *Camera Grip* Jim Dawes. *Art Dir* Elliot Scott. *Draughtsman* Reg Bream. *Sketch Artist* Ivor Beddoes. *Film Ed* Ernest Walter. *Assembly Ed* Peter Elliott. *1st Asst Ed* Ken Ross. *Mus Comp & Cond* Ron Goodwin. *Rec Supv* A. W. Watkins. *Sd Rec* Cyril Swern. *Dub Ed* Robert Carrick. *Dub Mix* J. B. Smith. *Boom Op* Bill Baldwin. *Sd Camera Op* Bill Robson. *Asst Dir* George Pollock, Jake Wright, Ernie Lewis. *Prod Mgr* Basil Somner. *Location Mgr* Peter Price. *Cont* Kay Rawlings. *Prod Sec* Midge Warnes. *Wardrobe Supv* Ivy Baker. *Wardrobe Mistress* Dolly Smith. *Makeup* Jim Hydes. *Hairdresser* Joan Johnstone. *Photog Eff* Tom Howard. *Prop Buyer* Bill Isaacs. *Still Photog* Davis Boulton. *Casting Dir* Irene Howard.

Cast: Bill Travers *(Maj. Freddie Oppenheimer),* Spike Milligan *(Lieut. Godfrey Pringle),* Grégoire Aslan *(Maj. Pierre Debrie),* John Le Mesurier *(The Colonel),* Thorley Walters *(Lieutenant Commander Cummings),* Maurice Denham *(Dr. Barker),* Thelma Ruby *(matron),* Millicent Martin *(Sister Kay Manning),* Cyril Luckham *(Colonel Harbottle),* William Mervyn *(leading naval officer),* John Wood *(duty officer, War Office),* Alexander Archdale *(brigadier, War Office),* Bernard Hunter *(coding officer, War Office),* Peter Swanwick *(German gun commander),* Ernst Ulman *(small German sergeant),* Eric Sykes *(German band conductor),* David Lander *(Maquis leader),* Ian Ainsley *(German officer),* Gerald Case, John Dunbar *(medical board officers),* Charles Brodie *(Maquis deputy leader),* John Crocker *(The Storeman).*

War comedy. At a military hospital near Dover in 1942, two convalescing officers, Maj. Freddie Oppenheimer, who lost a leg in combat, and Maj. Pierre Debrie, who lost a hand, judge themselves fit for active duty and devise a plan for demolishing a German gun which has been shelling the coast. Accompanied by the reluctant Lieutenant Pringle, an explosives expert with no tolerance for noise, and a veteran colonel, they leave the hospital and make their way across the English Channel in a stolen boat. Once in France, the four narrowly escape detection by German patrols and disguise themselves in stolen German uniforms. After dismantling some of the offending gun's mechanism, the invaders enlist the aid of the Germans to divert a trainload of ammunition to the gun site. Their target demolished, they make a slow escape on bicycles, but Pringle becomes separated from his comrades. As the others near the coast, members of the French underground mistake them for Germans and take them prisoner. However, with the reappearance of Pringle, whose atrocious French accent convinces the Maquis that he could only be English, the four men are permitted to return to Dover. Now hailed as heroes, they are informed by British Intelligence that another German big gun requires their immediate attention. *Maquis. Soldiers. Amputees. French. Germans. Demolition. Sabotage. Disguise. Mistaken identity. Bombardment. Hospitals. World War II. Dover. English Channel. France.*

Note: Opened in London in Oct 1961.

INVASION 1700 (France/Italy/Yugoslavia)   **F6.2442**
Europa Cinematografica–Comptoir Français du Film–Centralni Filmski Studio Košutnjak. *Dist* Medallion Pictures. Jan **1965**. Sd; col (Eastmancolor). 35mm (Euroscope). 112 min.
Dir Fernando Cerchio. *2d Unit Dir* Sergio Bergonzelli. *Screenplay* Ugo Liberatore, George St. George, Remigio Del Grosso. *Story* Ugo Liberatore. *Photog* Pier Ludovico Pavoni, Angelo Lotti. *Art Dir* Arrigo Equini. *Film Ed* Antonietta Zita. *Mus* Giovanni Fusco, Francesco De Masi. *Sd* Umberto Picistrelli. *Prod Mgr* Gianpaolo Bigazzi, Jean Maumy. *Cost* Giancarlo Bartolini Salimbeni.
Cast: Jeanne Crain *(Elena)*, John Drew Barrymore *(Bohun)*, Pierre Brice *(Col. Jan Ketusky)*, Akim Tamiroff *(Baron Zagloba)*, Elena Zareschi *(Princess Kinzevich)*, Gordon Mitchell *(Ulrich)*, Raoul Grassilli *(Basilio)*, Bruno Nessi *(Longhin)*, Eleonora Vargas *(Horpina)*, Gabriella Andreini *(Anussia)*, Nerio Bernardi *(Geremia)*, Giacomo Rossi Stuart, Ornella Vanoni, Nando Angelini, Alberto Stefanini, Milena Vukotic, Marcello Selmi, Alberto Mareschalchi, Alberto Archetti.
Historical melodrama. Source: Henryk Sienkiewicz, *Ogniem i mieczem*, in *Słowo* (1883–84). On his way to assume command of the Jurak garrison in the 17th century, Polish Col. Jan Ketusky spends the night at Rosloghi castle. There he falls in love with Elena, the ward of Princess Kinzevich, who, in return for protection, has promised Elena's hand in marriage to Bohun, the commander of the garrison at Lubin and a powerful Ukrainian ally of the Poles. Despite the engagement, Ketusky wins Elena's love and persuades the princess to agree to their marriage. Discovering her infidelity, the enraged Bohun burns the palace, kills its inhabitants, abducts Elena, and joins forces with Tartars and Ukrainians to attack the garrison commanded by Ketusky. The Polish forces, however, are victorious, and Bohun is slain. *Royalty. Wards. Tartars. Murder. Abduction. Revolts. Marriage—Arranged. Ukraine. Poland—History.*
Note: Filmed in Yugoslavia; Yugoslav co-production status uncertain. Rome opening: Aug 1962 as *Col ferro e col fuoco;* running time: ca100 min; Paris opening: May 1963 as *Par le fer et par le feu;* running time: 105 or 112 min. One source indicates 1963 U. S. release. Also known as *Daggers of Blood.*

GLI INVASORI *see* **ERIK THE CONQUEROR**

LOS INVENCIBLES *see* **THE SECRET SEVEN**

L'INVERNO TI FARÀ TORNARE *see* **THE LONG ABSENCE**

INVESTIGATION OF A CITIZEN ABOVE SUSPICION (Italy)   **F6.2443**
Vera Film. *Dist* Columbia Pictures. 20 Dec **1970** [New York opening; c1 May 1970; LP40010]. Sd; col (Technicolor). 35mm. 112 min. [Copyright length: 94 min.] *MPAA rating* R.
Prod Daniele Senatore, Marina Cicogna. *Dir* Elio Petri. *Screenplay* Ugo Pirro, Elio Petri. *Dir Photog* Luigi Kuveiller. *Camera* Ubaldo Terzano. *Asst Camera* Nino Annunziata. *Architect* Carlo Egidi. *Asst Art Dir* Egidio Spugnini. *Film Ed* Ruggero Mastroianni. *Asst Ed* Adrianna Olasio, Eddardo Romani. *Mus* Ennio Morricone. *Orch Cond* Bruno Nicolai. *Sd* Mario Bramonti. *Sd Rec* Giuseppe Muratori. *Sd Mix* Mario Amari. *1st & 2d Asst Dir* Antonio Gabrielli, Lorenzo Magnolia. *Prod Mgr* Romano Cardarelli. *Prod Supv* Hermes Gallippi, Alfredo Petri. *Prod Sec* Roberto Onorati. *Cost* Angela Sammaciccia, Mayer. *Miss Bolkan's Clothes* Tirelli of Rome. *Makeup* Franco Corridoni. *Hairdresser* Rosa Luciani. *English Titl* Sonya Mays Friedman. *Head Electrn* Sergio Coletta. *Still Photog* Mario Tursi. *Key Grip* Sergio Emidi.
Cast: Gian Maria Volontè *(police inspector)*, Florinda Bolkan *(Augusta Terzi)*, Salvo Randone *(plumber)*, Gianni Santuccio *(police commissioner)*, Arturo Dominici *(Mangani)*, Orazio Orlando *(Biglia)*, Sergio Tramonti *(Antonio Pace)*, Massimo Foschi *(Augusta's husband)*, Aldo Rendine *(homicide functionary)*, Aleka Paizi, Vittorio Duse, Pino Patti, Giuseppe Licastro, Filippo Degara, Fulvio Gramaldi, Ugo Adinolfi, Giacomo Bellini, Giuseppe Terranova, Vincenzo Falanga, Roberto Bonanni, Guido Buzzelli, Gino Usai, Franco Marletta.
Crime melodrama. While making love on a Sunday afternoon, a powerful inspector in the Rome police force slits his mistress Augusta's throat. The assassin then plants conspicuous clues and proclaims the murder in an anonymous call to headquarters. About Augusta's apartment he scatters photographs of the deceased masochistically enacting, as she did in her relationship with him, the roles of well-known homicide victims. Abundant fingerprints, bloody footprints, and a thread from the murderer's blue silk tie comprise additional, intentionally incriminating evidence. The police prefer to ignore such proofs, however, as the murderer, a rabid anti-communist, has recently been promoted from chief of the homicide section to head of the intelligence unit. They suspect instead the victim's former husband, homosexual artist Terzi, and her student lover, revolutionary chemist Antonio Pace, who witnessed the crime. Though a casual confession to a young plumber has come to naught, since the plumber, intimidated by the inspector's position,

withdraws his accusation, the inspector's written confession constrains the police commissioner to act. The commissioner proceeds to the murderer's apartment, where the waiting assassin dreams of absolute acquittal. *Police. Detectives. Plumbers. Mistresses. Students. Revolutionaries. Chemists. Artists. Murder. Sadomasochism. Anti-communism. Confession (law). Male homosexuality. Law. Photographs. Rome. Dreams. Fantasy.*
Note: Released in Italy in 1970 as *Indagine su un cittadino al di sopra di ogni sospetto;* running time: 114 min.

GLI INVINCIBILI SETTE *see* **THE SECRET SEVEN**

THE INVINCIBLE GLADIATOR (Italy/Spain)   **F6.2444**
Film Columbus–Variety Film–Atenea Films. *Dist* Seven Arts Associated Corp. Sep **1963**. Sd; col (Eastmancolor, print by Technicolor). 35mm (Techniscope). 96 min.
Prod (see note) Cleto Fontini, Italo Zingarelli, Alberto De Martino. *Dir* Antonio Momplet. *Dir English Vers* Frank Gregory. *Screenplay* Francesco De Feo, Francesco Thellung, Cleto Fontini. *Photog* Eloy Mella. *Art Dir* Santiago Ontañón. *Mus* Carlo Franci. *Sd* Alessandro Sarandrea.
Cast: Richard Harrison *(Rezius)*, Isabelle Corey *(Sira)*, Livio Lorenzon *(Itus)*, Leo Anchóriz *(Rabirius)*, José Marco Davó *(Vibius)*, Ricardo Canales, Antonio Molino, Edoardo Nevola, Jole Mauro, Giorgio Ubaldi.
Adventure drama. Rezius, a gladiator, is awarded an army command when he saves the life of Rabirius, who rules Acaste as regent in the name of the 10-year-old king, Darius. A band opposed to Rabirius, an evil monarch, is led by Princess Sira, Darius' sister. Rabirius decides to marry Sira in order to proclaim himself king. To remove all obstacles he attempts to drown Darius and Rezius, but they escape and join Sira's band. After much combat in and out of the arena, Rezius kills Rabirius, the revolt is successful, and Sira, Rezius, and the young king receive the acclaim of the populace. *Gladiators. Despots. Royalty. Marriage of convenience. Revolts. Rome—History—Empire.*
Note: Opened in Rome in Nov 1961 as *Il gladiatore invincibile;* running time: 100 min; in Madrid in Jul 1962 as *El gladiador invincible.* Credit for De Martino for producer is not confirmed.

THE INVINCIBLE SIX (United States/Iran)   **F6.2445**
Moulin Rouge Productions. *Dist* Continental Distributing, Inc. 10 Jun **1970** [Trenton, New Jersey, opening]. Sd; col (Technicolor). 35mm. 96 min. [Cut from 103 min.]
Prod Mostafa Akavan. *Assoc Prod* Morteza Akavan. *Dir* Jean Negulesco. *2d Unit Dir* Franco Prosperi. *Screenplay* Guy Elmes. *Adapt* Chester Erskine. *Photog* Piero Portalupi. *Camera* Cesare Allione. *Asst Camera* Michael Delaney. *2d Unit Photog* Sante Achilli. *Art Dir* Ivan Girard. *Set Decor* Pak Nejad. *Film Ed* Derek York. *Mus* Manos Hadjidakis. *Mus Arr* Gary Hughes. *Choreog* Rudolf Nureyev. *Sd Ed* Michael Hart, Nestor Lovera, Bahran Darai, Peter Sutton, Maurice Askew. *Asst Dir* Behi Ansary, Masud Kimiai. *Prod Mgr* Hushang Shafti, Joe Di Balsio. *2d Unit Asst Dir* Jala Mogadam, Ray Poor. *Cost Dsgn* Shai Nazemi. *Wardrobe* Kristin Anderson. *Makeup* Giannetto De Rossi, Fabrizio Sforza. *Hairstyles* Mirella Sforza. *Sp Eff* Benasseti Pasquino. *Adv* Ferreydoon Hoveyda, Monir Vakily. *Stunt Dir* Benito Stefanelli.
Cast: Stuart Whitman *(Tex)*, Elke Sommer *(Zari)*, Curt Jurgens *(The Baron)*, Ian Ogilvy *(Ronald)*, Behrooz Vosugi *(Jahan)*, Lon Sutton *(Mike)*, Isarco Ravaioli *(Giorgio)*, James Mitchum *(Nazar)*, Anoush Artin *(Captain Baruk)*, Warrene Ott *(Shirine)*, Shai Nazemi *(crown jewels guide)*, Manoocher Naderi *(mayor)*, Homayoon Bahadoran *(fake officer)*, Amir Jafari *(Darab)*, Poori Banai *(Jahan's wife)*, Iran Dafteri *(Malik's mother)*, Susan Ghasemi *(village girl)*.
Adventure drama. Source: Michael Barrett, *The Heroes of Yuka* (London, 1968). Having failed in their attempt to steal the crown jewels of Tehran, Tex and Ronald, an American and an Englishman, join fellow gang member Mike, fugitives Jahan and Giorgio, and a German aristocrat, "The Baron," in planning a new caper. Pursued into the desert by police, the sextet enters a village that has been plagued by bandit raids ever since the bandit leader, Malik, was hanged there. After offering to protect the townspeople, the thieves meet Zari, Malik's mistress, who, along with the dead leader's successor, Nazar, is after Malik's amulet, which reveals the location of hidden treasure. Following the kidnaping and torture of Ronald, Tex and his men raid and burn down the bandits' camp, but Nazar is killed and the map destroyed. Zari then decides to join Tex and the other survivors on their next adventure. *Thieves. Americans in foreign countries. English. Germans. Aristocrats. Mistresses. Fugitives. Bandits. Police. Kidnaping. Torture. Treasure. Jewels. Talismans. Documentation. Fires. Deserts. Tehran. Chases.*
Note: Produced and filmed on location in Iran. Working title: *The Heroes.*

THE INVISIBLE DR. MABUSE (West Germany)   **F6.2446**
CCC–Filmkunst. *Dist* Thunder Pictures. 28 Jul **1965** [New York opening]. Sd; b&w. 35mm. 89 min.
Pres by Robert Hartgrove. *Prod & Story Idea* Artur Brauner. *Assoc Prod* Wolf Brauner. *Dir* Harald Reinl. *Screenplay* Ladislaus Fodor. *Photog* Ernst W.

Kalinke. *Camera Crew* Everhard Dycke, Helmut Meyer. *Art Dir* Gabriel Pellon, Oskar Pietsch. *Film Ed* Hermann Haller. *Mus* Peter Sandloff. *Sd* Gerhard Müller. *Asst Dir* Carl von Barany. *Prod Mgr* Heinz Götze, Manfred Korytowski. *Cost* Irms Pauli. *Makeup* Heinz Stamm. *Sp Eff* Karl-Ludwig Ruppel.

Cast: Lex Barker *(Joe Como)*, Karin Dor *(Liane Martin)*, Siegfried Lowitz *(Inspector Brahm)*, Wolfgang Preiss *(Dr. Mabuse)*, Rudolf Fernau *(Professor Erasmus)*, Kurd Pieritz *(Dr. Bardorf)*, Walo Lüönd *(Detective Hase)*, Heinrich Gies *(optician)*, Hans Schwarz *(Max)*, Werner Peters, Martin Droste, Bobo the Clown *([see note])*, Carl de Voigt *(floor walker)*.

Horror film. New York detective Joe Como arrives in Germany to learn that fellow agent Nick Prado has been found dead in a car trunk. Continuing his ex-colleague's investigation of a phantom who is allegedly stalking the Metropol Theater, Joe questions dancer Liane Martin, who fears she is being followed by an invisible man. In a hotel room adjacent to Liane's, Joe meets Professor Erasmus, inventor of "Operation X," a secret process which renders persons and objects invisible. The professor, disfigured in an automobile accident, tells Joe that he makes himself invisible so as not to frighten his beloved Liane. Archcriminal Dr. Mabuse kidnaps Liane and demands as ransom "Operation X," which will allow him to terrorize the world. Forced to give Mabuse his secret formula, Erasmus then sacrifices his life to save Joe. Joe captures Mabuse's invisible thugs and, accompanied by the police, storms the professor's laboratory. They find Mabuse, disguised as Erasmus' assistant, Bardorf; he is insanely enraged after accidentally setting the laboratory on fire. Joe delivers Mabuse to an insane asylum and departs for America with Liane. *Detectives. Dancers. Scientists. Police. Masterminds. Murder. Invisibility. Disfiguration. Kidnaping. Self-sacrifice. Insanity. Impersonation. Hotels. Secret formulas. Laboratories. Insane asylums. Automobile accidents. Fires. Doktor Mabuse.*

Note: Released in West Germany in Mar 1962 as *Die unsichtbaren Krallen des Dr. Mabuse.* Also known as *The Invisible Horror.* One source credits Martin Droste and Bobo the Clown as role names for Werner Peters.

THE INVISIBLE HORROR *see* **THE INVISIBLE DR. MABUSE**

INVITATION TO A GUNFIGHTER   F6.2447
Kramer Co.–Larcas Productions–Hermes Productions. *Dist* United Artists. 14 Oct **1964** [Baltimore opening; c15 Oct 1964; LP29367]. Sd; col (DeLuxe). 35mm. 92 min.

A Stanley Kramer Production. *Prod-Dir* Richard Wilson. *Screenplay-Screen Story* Elizabeth Wilson, Richard Wilson. *Adapt* Alvin Sapinsley. *Story* Hal Goodman, Larry Klein. *Photog* Joseph MacDonald. *Art Dir* Robert Clatworthy. *Film Ed* Robert C. Jones. *Mus* David Raksin. *Sd* William Russell. *Asst Dir* Austen Jewell. *Prod Mgr* Ivan Volkman. *Tech Adv* Rodd Redwing.

Cast: Yul Brynner *(Jules Gaspard d'Estaing)*, Janice Rule *(Ruth Adams)*, Brad Dexter *(Kenarsie)*, Alfred Ryder *(Doc Barker)*, Mike Kellin *(Tom)*, George Segal *(Matt Weaver)*, Clifford David *(Crane Adams)*, Pat Hingle *(Sam Brewster)*, Bert Freed *(sheriff)*, Curt Conway *(McKeever)*, Clifton James *(Tuttle)*, Clarke Gordon *(Hickman)*, Arthur Peterson *(Schoop)*, Strother Martin *(Fiddler)*, Gertrude Flynn *(Widow Guthrie)*, John Alonzo *(Manuel)*, William Hickey *(Jo-Jo)*, Gerald Hiken *(Gully)*, Dal Jenkins *(dancer)*.

Western drama. Returning to Pecos, New Mexico, at the end of the Civil War, Confederate veteran Matt Weaver discovers his property appropriated and sold by banker Brewster; his former fiancée, Ruth, married to a one-armed Union soldier; and his neighbors, Yankee sympathizers, aligned against him. After Weaver shoots in self defense the new owner of his farm, Brewster hires the notorious Jules Gaspard d'Estaing to eliminate him. The gunman, an enigmatic educated mulatto, proves uncontrollable, and Brewster attempts to hire Weaver to slay d'Estaing. In the ensuing confrontation, the gunman provokes Weaver, who then slays both d'Estaing and Brewster. *Confederate veterans. Bankers. Neighbors. Amputees. Sheriffs. Hired killers. Mulattoes. Murder. Infidelity. Justifiable homicide. New Mexico.*

INVITATION TO A HANGING *see* **LAW OF THE LAWLESS**

INVITATION TO LUST   F6.2448
Daedalus Productions. *Dist* Sam Lake Enterprises. **1966.** Sd; b&w. 35mm. 72 min.

Dir-Writ Ron Wertheim. *Mus Comp & Cond* Dave Herman.

Cast: Melody Burlesen, Lisette Dark, Margie Mead.

Drama. Dr. Rachel Manheim discovers an ancient aphrodisiac which unleashes powerful lusts. She begins by experimenting with her own repressed body. The sexual appetites she arouses are boundless. Wild with desire, she uses the aphrodisiac on a sex-starved professor, and then on her beautiful lesbian secretary. Finally, in the violence of her passion, she turns a group of staid college teachers into savage orgiasts, but her own lust remains undiminished. *Professors. Secretaries. Lust. Autoeroticism. Lesbianism. Aphrodisiacs. Orgies.*

INVITATION TO MONTE CARLO (Great Britain)   F6.2449
Richmond Film Productions–Andreas Claus Schuller. 25 Mar **1961** [Chicago opening]. Sd; col (Technicolor). 35mm (Cinepanoramic). 46 min.

Prod-Dir-Writ Euan Lloyd. *Narr* Jack Davies. *Photog* John Wilcox, Tony Braun, Egil Woxholt. *Film Ed* Terry Trench. *Mus* William Hill Bowen. *Perf by* George Malachrino Orchestra. *Sd* Philip Hudsmith.

Cast: Germaine Damar *(Jacqueline)*, Gilda Emmanuelli *(Lindy)*, Katherine Page *(matron)*, Jefferson Clifford *(postman)*, Grace of Monaco, Rainier III of Monaco, Caroline Louise Marguerite of Monaco, Frank Sinatra *(themselves)*, Tosca *(himself, a cat)*.

Narrators: Leo Genn, Nicole Maurey, E. V. H. Emmett.

Travelog. Lindy, an orphan, is invited to Monaco to present Tosca, a kitten, to Princess Caroline. Jacqueline, an airline hostess, chaperons Lindy as she tours Monte Carlo. Prince Rainier III is seen skindiving, strolling at the Monaco Zoo, playing with his daughter, and escorting his wife, Princess Grace. Frank Sinatra makes a guest appearance. *Orphans. Zoos. Monaco. Monte Carlo. Cats.*

Note: Released in Great Britain in Oct 1959.

INVITATION TO MURDER (Great Britain)   F6.2450
Dist Atlantic Pictures. Nov **1962.** Sd; b&w. 35mm. 65 min.

Prod Harry Alan Towers. *Dir* Robert Lynn. *Story* Joel Murdock.

Cast: Robert Beatty *(private investigator)*, Lisa Daniely, Catherine Feller *(granddaughters [nieces?])*, Douglas Wilmer *(police inspector)*, Ernest Thesiger *(millionaire)*, Bud Knapp *(attorney)*, Denis Shaw *(millionaire's assistant)*, Guy Kingsley Poynter *(secretary)*, Olga Dickie *(nurse)*, Joan Howlett, Keith Pyott.

Melodrama. On the French Riviera, a reclusive oil millionaire bequeaths his fortune to the survivor among his potential beneficiaries. These are his granddaughters [nieces?], secretary, and attorney. Fearing for his life, the lawyer hires a private investigator. The attorney, secretary, and nurse are subsequently murdered. Rescuing one granddaughter from the magnate's assistant, the detective learns that the assassin has been hired to slay all heirs save the other granddaughter. After the millionaire dies of a heart attack, the heiress is arrested, and the fortune passes to her innocent sister. Intent on donating the money to charity, the granddaughter leaves with the detective. *Recluses. Oil magnates. Millionaires. Heirs. Grandfathers. Uncles. Secretaries. Heiresses. Sisters. Lawyers. Detectives. Nurses. Police. Murder. Duplicity. Wealth. Wills. Riviera.*

Note: Location scenes filmed on the French Riviera. Presented on British television in 1959.

INVITATION TO RUIN   F6.2451
Loric Productions. *Dist* Weisbar Co. 9 Oct **1968** [New York showing]. Sd; col (Eastman Color). 35mm. 71 min.

Prod-Dir Kurt Richter. *Exec Prod* Moe Weise. *Asst Prod* Roger Gentry. *Story-Screenplay* Max Conrad. *Dir Photog* Richard Pitstick. *Set Decor* Harry E. Grenfell. *Ed* Kurt Richter. *Sd* Soundco. *Sd Mix* Dick Damon. *Prod Mgr* Richard Thomas, prod. *Script Supv* Charlene Richter. *Wardrobe* Alma Palmer. *Makeup* Ray Sebastian. *Hairstyles* Gary Karlich. *Key Grip* James Murphy. *Still Photog* Keith Bernard.

Cast: Jim Gentry *(Jerry Slone)*, Moe Weise *(Ernie Pulaski)*, Kathleen Williams *(Allison Pulaski)*, Bobby Ross *(Elaine Conway)*, John Bliss *(Lieutenant Harris)*, Julia Blackburn *(Karen)*, James Murphy *(Mitch)*, Vincene Cradduck *(Ann)*, Bertha Bigg *(Mama Lupo)*, Bob Hunter *(Pete Mason)*, Brigitte Weiss *(Doreen)*, Tim Saverino *(Vido)*, Linda O'Bryant *(Sharon)*, Elaine Teff *(Sandra)*, Tim Wade *(Sergeant Williamson)*, Andrea Ellis *(Carol)*, Grace Landis *(Irene)*, Lurene Morris *(Gloria)*, Vicki Garson *(girl in booth)*, Ray Giffin *(boy in booth)*, Max Conrad *(unidentified role, see note)*.

Crime melodrama. Police enter the Hatbox Lounge in Los Angeles looking for the owner, Ernie Pulaski. As they question Pete, the night bartender, Pulaski enters the bar and falls over dead, a knife in his back. Pete relates the events which led to Pulaski's death: Jerry Slone, kept as a gigolo by Elaine Conway, is hired by Pulaski, a syndicate head who supplies women to buyers around the country. Jerry's duty is to seduce young women, who are then sent to Mama Lupo's castle for "conditioning." Jerry and Pulaski's daughter, Allison, begin an affair, and Jerry decides to rid himself of Elaine by turning her over to the sex ring. Pulaski orders him to bring her directly to the castle, and for the first time he becomes aware of the brutal "conditioning" process. Elaine is taken to a dungeon where she is tied to a bed and raped. Mama Lupo then interrupts the whipping of a favorite "slave" to administer heroin to Elaine and sexually abuse her. The depravity unnerves Jerry, and he makes a confession to Allison. She forgives him, but as they make love they are interrupted by Pulaski, who, in a rage, castrates Jerry and sends his daughter to the castle. There, Allison foments a rebellion. The "slaves" take their revenge on Mama Lupo and her henchmen, and Allison knifes her father in the back. *Gangsters. Pimps. Gigolos. Madams. White slave traffic. Sadism. Rape. Castration. Patricide. Seduction. Filial relations. Revenge. Bars. Heroin. Castles. Los Angeles.*

Note: Writer Max Conrad may also appear under another name in the cast listing.

IO AMO, TU AMI see **I LOVE, YOU LOVE**

IOLANTA see **YOLANTA**

THE IPCRESS FILE (Great Britain)   **F6.2452**
Steven, S. A.-Lowndes Productions. *For* Rank Organisation. *Dist* Universal Pictures. 2 Aug **1965** [New York opening; c30 Oct 1965; LP34492]. Sd (Westrex); col (Technicolor). 35mm (Techniscope). 107 min.
Pres by Rank Organisation. A Harry Saltzman Production. *Prod* Harry Saltzman. *Exec Prod* Charles Kasher. *Assoc Prod* Ronald Kinnoch. *Dir* Sidney J. Furie. *Screenplay* Bill Canaway, James Doran. *Photog* Otto Heller. *Camera Op* Brian Elvin. *Focus* John Morgan. *Art Dir* Peter Murton. *Set Dresser* Michael White. *Prod Dsgn* Ken Adam. *Film Ed* Peter Hunt. *Assembly Ed* Nicholas Steven. *Mus Comp & Cond* John Barry. *Sd Ed* Norman Wanstall, Ben Rayner. *Sd Mix* Peter Davies, Maurice Askew. *Sd Dub* Gate Recording Theatre. *Asst Dir* Fred Slark. *Prod Mgr* Denis Johnson. *Location Mgr* Ross Mackenzie. *Cont* Pat Moon. *Wardrobe Mistress* Muriel Dickson. *Makeup* Phil Leakey. *Hairstyles* Barbara Ritchie. *Casting* John Drury, Jr. *Stills* George Courtney Ward.
Cast: Michael Caine (*Harry Palmer*), Nigel Green (*Dalby*), Guy Doleman (*Ross*), Sue Lloyd (*Jean*), Gordon Jackson (*Carswell*), Aubrey Richards (*Radcliffe*), Frank Gatliff (*Bluejay*), Thomas Baptiste (*Barney*), Oliver MacGreevy (*Housemartin*), Freda Bamford (*Alice, charlady*), Pauline Winter (*charlady*), Anthony Blackshaw (*Edwards*), Barry Raymond (*Gray*), David Glover (*Chilcott-Oakes*), Stanley Meadows (*Inspector Keightley*), Peter Ashmore (*Sir Robert*), Michael Murray (*raid inspector*), Anthony Baird (*raid sergeant*), Tony Caunter (*O. N. I. man*), Charles Rea (*Taylor*), Ric Hutton (*record officer*), Douglas Blackwell (*Murray*), Richard Burrell (*operator*), Glynn Edwards (*police station sergeant*), Zsolt Vadaszffy (*prison doctor*), Joseph Behrman, Max Faulkner, Paul S. Chapman (*prison guards*).
Drama. Source: Len Deighton, *The Ipcress File* (London, 1962). After being transferred to Dalby's civil intelligence unit from Major Ross's military unit, Harry Palmer is assigned to investigate the abduction of Dr. Radcliffe, a scientist, after the murder of his bodyguard. A number of scientists have been disappearing mysteriously, then reappearing with curious "brain drains." Radcliffe is especially wanted by the intelligence authorities because of a secret file in his possession, and Palmer investigates Bluejay, a crook who deals in the sort of merchandise represented by Radcliffe. When this trail begins to fade, another clue prompts Palmer to raid a deserted London factory; and he discovers a piece of recording tape on which the perforated word "Ipcress" appears. Meanwhile, Dalby makes a deal with Bluejay to exchange the brainwashed scientist for £25,000 in cash. Then one of Dalby's unit apparently penetrates the Ipcress mystery and is strangely murdered; and when yet another civil intelligence agent is killed under circumstances implicating Palmer, Dalby suggests that Palmer go into hiding. Before he can do so, however, he is abducted and brought to the factory to be brainwashed. He escapes and calls Dalby and Ross to the factory for a disclosure. There Dalby reveals himself to be a traitor and is killed. *Intelligence agents. Scientists. Traitors. Abduction. Brainwashing. Murder. Frameup. Ransom. Recorders. London. Harry Palmer.*
Note: Location scenes filmed in London. Opened in London in Mar 1965; running time: 109 min. This is the first in a series of films based on the Harry Palmer character.

IPNOSI see **HYPNOSIS**

IREZUMI ICHIDAI see **WHITE TIGER TATOO**

IRMA LA DOUCE   **F6.2453**
Mirisch Co.-Phalanx Productions-Edward L. Alperson. *Dist* United Artists. 5 Jun **1963** [New York opening; c5 Jun 1963; LP25089]. Sd; col (Technicolor). 35mm (Panavision). 149 min. [Also rated 142 min.]
Pres by Mirisch Co., Edward L. Alperson. A Billy Wilder Production. *Prod-Dir* Billy Wilder. *Assoc Prod* I. A. L. Diamond, Doane Harrison. *Screenplay* Billy Wilder, I. A. L. Diamond. *Cinematog* Joseph La Shelle. *Art Dir* Alexander Trauner. *Set Decor* Edward G. Boyle, Maurice Barnathan. *Film Ed* Daniel Mandell. *Mus Score* Andre Previn. *Based on the Orig Stage Mus by* Marguerite Monnot. *Choreog* "Alouette" *Seq* Wally Green. *Sd* Robert Martin. *Asst Dir* Hal Polaire. *Prod Mgr* Allen K. Wood. *Wardrobe* Wes Jeffries. *Cost* Orry-Kelly. *Makeup* Emile Lavigne, Harry Ray, Frank Westmore. *Sp Eff* Milt Rice. *Tech Adv* Christian Ferry, Maurice Barnathan. *Dog Trainer* Pat La Cosa.
Cast: Jack Lemmon (*Nestor*), Shirley MacLaine (*Irma La Douce*), Lou Jacobi (*Moustache*), Bruce Yarnell (*Hippolyte*), Herschel Bernardi (*Lefevre*), Hope Holiday (*Lolita*), Joan Shawlee (*Amazon Annie*), Grace Lee Whitney (*Kiki the Cossack*), Tura Satana (*Suzette Wong*), Harriette Young (*Mimi the Maumau*), Paul Dubov (*André*), Howard McNear (*concierge*), Cliff Osmond (*police sergeant*), Diki Lerner (*JoJo*), Herb Jones (*Casablanca Charlie*), Jane

Earl, Ruth Earl (*Zebra Twins*), James Brown (*Texan customer*), Bill Bixby (*sailor*), Sheryl Deauville (*Carmen*), Lou Krugman, John Alvin (*customers*), Susan Woods (*poule with the balcony*), Billy Beck (*Officer DuPont*), Jack Sahakian (*Jack*), Don Diamond (*man with samples*), Edgar Barrier (*General Lafayette*), Richard Peel (*Englishman*), Joe Palma (*prison guard*), Shorty (*Coquette, a dog*).
Comedy. Source: Alexandre Breffort, *Irma La Douce* (Paris opening: 10 Nov 1956). Irma La Douce, a successful Parisian *poule* who plies her trade on a narrow street off Les Halles, gives all of her earnings to Hippolyte, her *mec*. Onto the scene comes a young, naive, and honest policeman, Nestor Patou, who, shocked by the open vice, conducts an unauthorized raid and arrests all the streetwalkers who frequent the bistro Chez Moustache. Unfortunately, Nestor's superior, Inspector Lefevre, is among the men arrested, and Nestor is fired from the force. He takes up with Irma, and, after a fight with Hippolyte, becomes her new *mec*. He soon falls in love with Irma and becomes jealous of her customers. With the help of Moustache, Nestor poses as a wealthy Englishman, Lord X, who claims he wants only a companion since the war has rendered him "useless." He agrees to pay Irma a huge sum for one visit a week, but in order to pay he is forced to work in the marketplace. Every morning, Nestor returns to Irma too tired to make love, and she begins to suspect that he has another lover. Irma then asks Lord X to take her to England and manages to seduce the supposedly impotent Britisher. As Irma packs to leave, Nestor decides to "murder" Lord X and dump all traces of him into the Seine. He is followed by Hippolyte, who, hearing a splash and seeing Lord X's clothes floating on the water, turns Nestor in as a murderer. Nestor is sent to prison, but when he hears that Irma is pregnant he escapes and reemerges from the Seine as Lord X, thus vindicating himself. At the church where Nestor and Irma are married, Irma collapses and has her baby. All ends well, however, when Nestor is reinstated by Inspector Lefevre; and Irma is able to contemplate a happier future. *Prostitutes. Pimps. Police. Disguise. Jealousy. Pregnancy. Bistros. Prisons. Paris. Les Halles. Seine River. Dogs.*
Note: Location scenes filmed in Paris.

IRO see **SPOILS OF THE NIGHT**

IRON ANGEL   **F6.2454**
Ken Kennedy Productions. Feb **1964**. Sd; b&w. 35mm. 84 min. [Also reviewed at 71 min.]
A Ken Kennedy Production. *Prod* Daniel P. Foley. *Dir-Writ* Ken Kennedy.
Cast: Jim Davis (*Sergeant Walsh*), Margo Woode (*Nurse Fleming*), Donald Barry, R. Wayland Williams, L. Q. Jones, Dave Barker, Joe Jenckes, John S. Hirohata.
War drama. Six men from the battered "Crazy Fox" convoy are sent to find a North Korean gun emplacement blocking the path of the convoy along a winding mountain road. Young Lieutenant Collins leads the scouting party; personal conflicts make the mission more difficult. Among the men who form the group is Sergeant Walsh, accused of breaking down under fire. Lieutenant Collins is killed in the fighting, and Walsh, who has apparently suffered another breakdown, takes command as the group sets out to find Field Hospital 101. They meet an army ambulance known as the "Iron Angel," driven by Nurse Fleming. Fresh from the States, she insists on following every rule in her regulations handbook. After a skirmish with an enemy patrol, they find a map showing a second gun emplacement directly in the path of the convoy. In a race against time, they struggle to knock out the heavily guarded gun. Hindered by Nurse Fleming's intransigence, they lose several men in the effort. *Nurses. Combat zone life. Battle fatigue. Korean War 1950–53. United States Army—Infantry. United States Army—Medical Service. Documentation.*
Note: Location scenes filmed in and around Phoenix, Arizona.

THE IRON COLLAR see **SHOWDOWN**

THE IRON KISS see **THE NAKED KISS**

THE IRON MAIDEN see **THE SWINGIN' MAIDEN**

IS PARIS BURNING? (United States/France)   **F6.2455**
Transcontinental Films-Marianne Productions. *Dist* Paramount Pictures. 10 Nov **1966** [New York opening; c10 Nov 1966; LP33770]. Sd; b&w with col seq. 35mm (Panavision). 173 min. [Copyright length: 136 min.]
Pres by Paramount Pictures, Seven Arts Productions, Ray Stark. *Prod* Paul Graetz. *Dir* René Clément. *2d Unit Dir* André Smagghe. *Screenplay (see note)* Gore Vidal, Francis Ford Coppola, Jean Aurenche, Pierre Bost, Claude Brulé. *Adtl Dial for French Scenes* Marcel Moussy. *Adtl Dial for German Scenes* Beate von Molo. *Photog* Marcel Grignon. *2d Unit Camera* Jean Tournier. *Art Dir* Willy Holt. *Set Decor* Roger Volper. *Film Ed* Robert Lawrence. *Mus Score* Maurice Jarre. *Sd* William Sivel, Antoine Petitjean. *Asst Dir* Yves Boisset, Michel Wyn. *Prod Mgr* Louis Wipf. *2d Unit Prod Mgr* Louis Daquin. *Cost* Jean Zay, Pierre Nourry. *Makeup* Michel Deruelle, Aida Carange. *Sp Eff* Robert MacDonald, Paul Pollard.

Cast: Jean-Paul Belmondo (*Morandat*), Charles Boyer (*Monod*), Leslie Caron (*Françoise Labe*), Jean-Pierre Cassel (*Lieut. Henri Karcher*), George Chakiris (*G.I. in tank*), Claude Dauphin (*Lebel*), Alain Delon (*Jacques Chaban-Delmas*), Kirk Douglas (*Gen. George Patton*), Glenn Ford (*Gen. Omar Bradley*), Gert Fröbe (*Gen. Dietrich von Choltitz*), Daniel Gélin (*Yves Bayet*), E. G. Marshall (*Intelligence Officer Powell [see note]*), Yves Montand (*Marcel Bizien*), Anthony Perkins (*Sergeant Warren*), Claude Rich (*Gen. Jacques Leclerc*), Simone Signoret (*café proprietress*), Robert Stack (*Gen. Edwin Sibert*), Jean-Louis Trintignant (*Serge*), Pierre Vaneck (*Major Roger Gallois*), Marie Versini (*Claire*), Skip Ward (*G.I. with Warren*), Orson Welles (*Consul Raoul Nordling*), Bruno Crémer (*Colonel Rol*), Suzy Delair (*a Parisienne*), Pierre Dux (*Parodi*), Billy Frick (*Hitler*), Harry Meyen (*von Arnim*), Hannes Messemer (*Jodl*), Michel Piccoli (*Pisani*), Sacha Pitoeff (*Joliot-Curie*), Wolfgang Preiss (*Ebernach*), Michel Berger (*chief of explosives*), Gehrard Borman (*von Choltitz's secretary*), Georges Claisse (*intern with Monod*), Germaine de France (*old woman*), Doc Ericson (*jeep driver*), Michel Etcheverry (*Luizet*), Pascal Fardoulis (*Gilet*), Bernard Fresson (*liaison agent*), Ernst Fritz Furbringer (*von Boineburg*), Clara Gansard (*wife of Colonel Rol*), Rol Gauffin (*Consul Nordling's secretary*), Georges Géret (*Commandant George*), Michel Gonzales (*Jacques*), Konrad Georg (*von Model*), Claus Holm (*Huhm*), Jean-Pierre Honoré (*Alain Perpezat*), Peter Jacob (*General Burgdorf*), Catherine Kamenka (*Diane*), Billy Kearns (*Patton aide*), Joëlle Latour (*Young girl with Warren*), Michel Lonsdale (*Debû-Bridel*), Roger Lumont (*"Jade Amicol"*), Maria Machado (*Stella*), Aimé de March (*Roland Pré*), Félix Marten (*Landrieu*), Paloma Matta (*The Bride*), Pierre Mirat (*café proprietor*), Harald Momm (*Colonel Jay*), Georges Montant (*doctor*), Russ Moro (*lieutenant with Warren*), Del Negro (*officer with Chaban-Delmas*), Jean Negroni (*Villon*), Alain Pommier (*Franjoux*), Georges Poujouly (*Landrieux*), Michel Puterflam (*Laffont*), Christian Rode (*Blache*), Serge Rousseau (*Colonel Fabien*), Michel Sales (*Gallois' friend*), Wolfgang Saure (*Hegel*), Georges Staquet (*Captain Dronne*), Otto Stern (*Wagenknecht*), Henia Suchar (*prefecture switchboard operator*), Toni Taffin (*Bernard Labe*), Pierre Tamin (*Maurannes*), Jean Valmont (*Bazooka*), Jo Warfield (*Major with Chaban-Delmas*), Joachim Westhoss (*German officer with Claire*), Jean-Pierre Zola (*Corporal Mayer*), Karl Otto Alberty, Albert Rémy, Joachim Hansen, Gunter Meisner, Helmut Schneider.

Historical drama. Source: Larry Collins and Dominique Lapierre, *Is Paris Burning?* (New York, 1965). In August, 1944, as Allied troops await orders to march into German-occupied Paris, Hitler assigns command of the city to Gen. Dietrich von Choltitz. The Feuhrer's orders are simple and direct—if Paris cannot be held, it is to be burned to the ground. At the same time, the French Resistance movement, which has succeeded in taking possession of two-thirds of the city, is divided over a new plan of strategy. Gen. Jacques Chaban-Delmas, a Free French follower of Charles de Gaulle, strongly opposes those Communists favoring an immediate insurrection, which he fears might turn Paris into another Warsaw. With the help of the Swedish consul, Nordling, he attempts to arrange for the release of an important political prisoner, Bernard Labe, who might succeed in forestalling the uprising; but the plan ultimately fails, and Labe is shot. Word arrives that the Allies have decided to bypass the city and push directly to the Rhine, whereupon the Free French send Major Gallois to convince the Allied High Command that at least one military unit must liberate Paris, thereby enabling Germany to save face and surrender with honor. Von Choltitz, through all of this, procrastinates and ignores Hitler's hysterical demands that the city be burned. Largely responsible for the general's hesitancy is Nordling, who appeals to both von Choltitz' reason and his vanity by pointing out that by refusing to destroy centuries of history merely to satisfy a madman, he would become known as the man who saved Paris. Consequently, the order to burn the city is never given and, on August 25th, American and French soldiers liberate Paris. As von Choltitz is taken prisoner, exultant Parisians surge through the streets to greet the return of General Charles de Gaulle. *Communists. Swedes. Diplomats. Political prisoners. Maquis. World War II. France—History—German occupation 1940-45. Paris. Dietrich von Choltitz. Jacques Chaban-Delmas. Raoul Nordling. Henri Tanguy. Roger Gallois. Adolf Hitler. Charles De Gaulle. Alexandre Parodi. Edgar Pisani. Yves Bayet. Jacques Philippe Leclerc. George Smith Patton. Omar Nelson Bradley. Edwin Sibert. Yvon Morandat. United States Army. France—Army. Germany—Army.*

Note: Opened in Paris in Oct 1966 in 70mm under the title *Paris brûle-t-il?* Initial running time: 173 min. Subsequent cuts resulted in the omission of all of E. G. Marshall's scenes. Most sources credit only Gore Vidal and Francis Ford Coppola with screenplay.

IS THIS TRIP REALLY NECESSARY?   F6.2456
Dorn-Thor Productions. *Dist* Hollywood Star Pictures. Apr **1970**. Sd; col. 35mm. 84 min. *MPAA rating* M.

Prod-Dir Ben Benoit. *Exec Prod* Ray Dorn, Lynn Steed. *Assoc Prod* Edward Edell, Jr. *Screenplay* Lee Kalcheim. *Photog* Austin McKinney. *Art Dir* Ray Markham. *Film Ed* Fred Brown. *Mus Comp* Paul Norman, Ron Blackmer, Bob Page. *Perf by* Weed's Own. *Unit Mgr* Edward Edell, Jr. *Cost* Dodie Warren. *Makeup* Dodie Warren. *Sp Eff* Robert Beck.

Cast: Marvin Miller, Peter Duryea, Carole Kane, John Carradine, Barbara Mallory, Patti Heider, Darrin Daniels, Benes Marden, Tod Spence.

Melodrama. A young man's girl friend and two other women have agreed to work for an insane director who is making an epic sex exploitation film. The young man fears for their lives and after two of the women have died under the influence of LSD, he tries to rescue the third. In the director's torture chamber, one of the actresses dies in an iron maiden. *Actors. Motion picture directors. Psychopaths. Torture. Sex exploitation films. LSD.*

Note: Working title: *Trip to Terror.*

ISABEL (Canada)   F6.2457
Quest Film Productions. *Dist* Paramount Pictures. 23 Jul **1968** [New York opening; c1 Sep 1967; LP36782]. Sd; col (Technicolor). 35mm. 108 min.

Prod-Dir-Writ Paul Almond. *Prod Assoc* Peter Carter, Joyce Kozy. *Photog* Georges Dufaux. *Typography* Malcolm Waddell. *Film Ed* George R. Appleby. *Mus* Harry Freedman. *Songs Writ & Sung by* Marc Strange. *Mus Assoc* Lowell Cross Electronic Music Studios (University of Toronto). *Sd* Russel Heise. *Sd Re-rec* Joe Grimaldi. *Prod Team* Maurice de Ermsted, Roger Cadieux, Guy Desbiens, Guy Dufaux, Rod Hayes, Arnold MacKenzie. *Cost* Roger Palmer. *Makeup* Michel Deruelle.

Cast: Geneviève Bujold (*Isabel*), Marc Strange (*Jason*), Gerard Parkes (*Uncle Matthew*), Thérèse Cadorette (*Sister Estelle*), Elton Hayes (*Eb*), Ede Kerr (*Viola*), Al Waxman (*Herb*), Ratch Wallace, Lynden Bechervaise (*Herb's friends*), Eric Clavering (*postmaster*), Rob Hayes (*fisherman*), J. Donald Dow (*storekeeper*).

Drama. Upon receiving word that her mother is gravely ill, Isabel leaves Montreal and returns to her childhood home on the rugged Gaspé of Quebec. She arrives at her family's farm to find that her mother has already died. After some hesitation, Isabel decides to remain for a time to help care for her aged Uncle Matthew, her late father's brother. Estranged from her fellow townspeople, yet haunted by memories of her strange grandfather, who was killed by a wild pig, and her brother and father, who drowned in a fishing accident, Isabel is forced to remain at the farm when she loses her Montreal job. One morning she is shocked to meet Jason, a taciturn fisherman who looks remarkably like her dead brother, and seems to be familiar with her surroundings. Although she is attracted to Jason, and he obviously harbors warmth for her, Isabel represses her emotional and sexual response to him and instead retreats more completely into the ominous house that she shares with her uncle. The oppression of ill-defined memories and spectral sounds and lights eventually proves too much for Isabel, however, and she agrees to accompany Jason to a local dance. There she is attacked in a barn by Herb, a drunken villager whom she had previously rejected, and two of his friends. But Jason saves her from the attempted rape and leads her away. Later that evening, Isabel realizes the possibility that she may be the illegitimate daughter of her uncle and mother. She rushes out of the house and down to the docks, where Jason finds her in a state of near-hysteria. As he comforts her, they begin to make love and Isabel sees images of her brother, father, and uncle merge with Jason. *Fishermen. Family life. Sexuality. Rural life. Death. Memory. Rape. Incest. Drunkenness. Illegitimacy. Uncles. Gaspé Peninsula.*

Note: Location scenes filmed in Shigawake, on the Gaspé Peninsula. Opened in Montreal in Sep 1968.

ISADORA (Great Britain)   F6.2458
Universal Pictures, Ltd. *Dist* Universal Pictures. 18 Dec **1968** [Los Angeles opening; c27 Sep 1968; LP38910]. Sd (Westrex); col (Eastman Color, print by Technicolor). 35mm. 177 min. [See note.] *MPAA rating* M.

A Robert Hakim-Raymond Hakim Production. *Prod* Robert Hakim, Raymond Hakim. *Dir* Karel Reisz. *Screenplay* Melvyn Bragg, Clive Exton. *Adtl Dial* Margaret Drabble. *Adapt* Melvyn Bragg. *Dir Photog* Larry Pizer. *Camera Op* Denis Lewiston. *Art Dir* Michael Seymour, Miso Senecic, Ralph Brinton. *Asst Art Dir* Roger King. *Set Dresser* Bryan Graves, Harry Cordwell. *Prod Dsgn* Jocelyn Herbert. *Main Titl* Barney Wan. *Film Ed* Tom Priestley. *Asst Film Ed* Philip Baker. *Orig Mus Comp & Cond* Maurice Jarre. *Mus for Dance Seq and Period Dance Mus Comp* Anthony Bowles. *Classical and Dance Mus Arr & Cond* Anthony Bowles. *Impromptu in B Flat, opus 142* Franz Peter Schubert. *"Washington Post March"* John Philip Sousa. *Waltz in A Flat, opus 42* Frédéric François Chopin. *Symphony no. 7 in A* Ludwig van Beethoven. *"Rejouissance" from Suite no. 4 in D* Johann Sebastian Bach. *Poeme opus 32 no. 1* Aleksandr Nikolaevich Scriabin. *Symphony no. 2 in B Minor* Aleksandr Porfiryevich Borodin. *"March Slav"* Pëtr Ilich Tchaikovsky. *Choreog* Litz Pisk. *Sd* Ken Ritchie, Maurice Askew. *Sd Ed* Terry Rawlings. *Dial Ed* Jim Atkinson. *Asst Dir* Claude Watson, Grania O'Shannon, Adrian Hughes. *Prod Supv* Roy

Parkinson. *Prod Mgr* Eric Rattray. *Prod Rep for Yugoslavia, Italy & France* Henri Baum. *Cont* Ann Skinner. *Prod Sec* Jean Hall. *Cost Dsgn* John Briggs, Jackie Breed. *Wardrobe* Ruth Myers. *Makeup* Wally Schneiderman. *Hairstyles* Olga Angelinetta, Biddy Chrystal. *Russian Adv* Branko Pleša. *Constr Mgr* Terry Apsey. *Casting* Miriam Brickman.

Cast: Vanessa Redgrave *(Isadora Duncan)*, John Fraser *(Roger)*, James Fox *(Gordon Craig)*, Jason Robards, [Jr.] *(Paris Singer)*, Ivan Tchenko *(Sergei Essenin)*, Vladimir Leskova *(Bugatti)*, Cynthia Harris *(Mary Desti)*, Bessie Love *(Mrs. Duncan)*, Tony Vogel *(Raymond Duncan)*, Libby Glenn *(Elizabeth Duncan)*, Ronnie Gilbert, British *(Miss Chase)*, Wallas Eaton *(Archer)*, Nicholas Pennell *(Bedford)*, John Quentin *(Pim)*, Christian Duvaleix *(Armand)*, David Healy *(Chicago theater manager)*, Lucinda Chambers *(Deirdre)*, Simon Lutton Davies *(Patrick)*, Noel Davis *(doctor)*, Ina De La Haye *(Russian teacher)*, Constantine Yranski *(Russian companion)*, Stefan Gryss *(Russian party interpreter)*, John Brandon *(Gospel Billy)*, Margaret Courtenay *(raucous woman)*, Arthur White *(hearty husband)*, Iza Teller *(Alicia)*, John Warner *(Mr. Stirling)*, Alan Gifford *(Isadora's tour manager)*, Zuleika Robson, Arnold Diamond, Anthony Gardner, Sally Travers, Mark Dignam, Robin Lloyd, Lucy Saroyan, Jan Conrad, Hal Galili, Roy Stephens, Cal McCord, Richard Marner.

Biographical drama. Source: Isadora Duncan, *My Life* (New York, 1927). Sewell Stokes, *Isadora Duncan: An Intimate Portrait* (London, 1928). In 1927, Isadora Duncan has become a legend as the innovator of modern dance, a temperamental bohemian, and an outspoken advocate of free love. Now past 40, she lives in poverty in a small hotel on the French Riviera with her companion Mary Desti and her secretary Roger, to whom she is dictating her memoirs. *As a young girl in California, Isadora first demonstrates her disdain for accepted social standards by burning her parents' marriage certificate and pledging her dedication to the pursuit of art and beauty. In 1896, she performs under the name of Peppy Dora in a rowdy music hall in Chicago and publicly embarrasses the theater manager into paying her $300 so that she can take her family to England. Modeling her free-form style of dance and costume after Greek classicism, she rapidly acquires international acclaim. In Berlin, she meets her first love, Gordon Craig, a young stage designer who promises her that together they will create a new world of theater. After bearing the already-married Craig a daughter, Isadora moves to Paris and meets Paris Singer, a millionaire who lavishes gifts upon her and later buys her an enormous estate for her to open a School for Life, where only beauty and simplicity are taught. Following the birth of a son, Isadora returns to England with Singer but becomes bored with her quiet life and enters into an affair with her pianist, Armand. A short time later, both of her children are drowned when their chauffeur-driven car plunges off a bridge into the Seine. Broken by the tragedy, Isadora leaves Singer and wanders about Europe until in 1921 she receives an offer to open a dancing school in the Soviet Union. Unaffected by the country's poverty, she develops a strong rapport with the peasantry and has a passionate affair with Sergei Essenin, a volatile poet whom she marries so that he can obtain a visa to accompany her to the United States. Essenin's outrageous behavior turns a press conference into a shambles, however, and U. S. anti-Bolshevist sentiment turns to open hostility when Isadora bares her breasts during a dance recital in Boston. Following the disintegration of her marriage, she returns to Nice to write her memoirs. Impulsively selling her possessions in order to open a new school in Paris, Isadora goes to a local cafe to celebrate and spots Bugatti, a handsome Italian whom she has been admiring for several days. She goes for a drive with him in his sports car, and as they roar along a road by the sea, Isadora's long chiffon scarf catches in the spokes of a wheel and strangles her.* Dancers. Nonconformists. Secretaries. Americans in foreign countries. Theatrical designers. Millionaires. Dance teachers. Pianists. Poets. Bolshevists. Italians. Bohemianism. Fame. Infidelity. Illegitimacy. Marriage. Immigration. Anti-communism. Exhibitionism. Music halls. Dance schools. Press conferences. Sports cars. Riviera. California. Chicago. England. Berlin. Paris. Union of Soviet Socialist Republics. Boston. Nice. Isadora Duncan. Edward Gordon Craig. Paris Singer. Sergei Essenin.

Note: Location scenes filmed in England, France, Italy, and Yugoslavia. Opened in London in Mar 1969; running time: 138 min. Withdrawn from distribution shortly after opening and cut by 20 and then 26 min. Opened in New York in 1969 as *The Loves of Isadora* at 131 min. Copyright length: 136 min.

ISHINAKA SENSEI GYOJOKI *see* **BIG WIND FROM TOKYO**

LA ISLA DE LA MUERTE *see* **ISLAND OF THE DOOMED**

THE ISLAND (Japan) **F6.2459**
Kindai Eiga Kyokai. *Dist* Zenith International Film Corp. 10 Sep 1962 [New York opening]. Sd; b&w. 35mm. 96 min.
Prod Kaneto Shindo, Eisaku Matsura. *Dir-Writ* Kaneto Shindo. *Photog* Kiyoshi Kuroda. *Film Ed* Toshio Enoki. *Mus* Hikaru Hayashi. *Sd* Kunie

Maruyama.
Cast: Nobuko Otowa *(Toyo)*, Taiji Tonoyama *(Senta)*, Shinji Tanaka *(Taro)*, Masanori Horimoto *(Jiro)*.
Domestic drama. The sole inhabitants of a small island off the coast of Japan are a farmer, his wife, and their two young sons. The arduous routine of their daily struggle for survival involves endless trips to the mainland for buckets of water which must be carried up the rocky slope of the island to water the meager crops. Each morning the mother rows her son to the school on the mainland and then returns for him in the evening. Though their life is one of endless toil, their lot is a happy one, occasionally highlighted by a festival or the sale of a large fish one of the boys has caught. Then one day the elder boy becomes ill and dies. After his funeral, the mother breaks down and, in a fit of anguish, overturns a bucket of water and uproots some of the crops. Her husband helplessly watches until her anger has subsided, then both silently return to tilling their soil. Farmers. Family life. Survival. Islands. Funerals.
Note: Released in Japan in 1961 as *Hadaka no shima*; running time: 92 min.

ISLAND OF LOVE **F6.2460**
Belgrave Enterprises. *Dist* Warner Bros. Pictures. May 1963 [c25 May 1963: LP29430]. Sd; col (Technicolor). 35mm (Panavision). 101 min.
Prod-Dir Morton DaCosta. *Screenplay* David R. Schwartz. *Story* Leo Katcher. *Photog* Harry Stradling, Sr. *Art Dir* Edward Carrere. *Set Decor* George James Hopkins. *Film Ed* William Ziegler. *Mus* George Duning. *Songs* Sammy Fain, Harold Adamson. *Orch* Arthur Morton. *Sd* Stanley Jones. *Asst Dir* Floyd Joyer. *Cost* Don Feld. *Makeup* Gordon Bau. *Hairstyles* Jean Burt Reilly.
Cast: Robert Preston *(Steve Blair)*, Tony Randall *(Paul Ferris)*, Georgia Moll *(Elena Harakas)*, Walter Matthau *(Tony Dallas)*, Betty Bruce *(Cha Cha Miller)*, Vassili Lambrinos *(Professor Pappas)*, Michael Constantine *(Andy)*, Titos Vandis *(Father Anaxagoras)*, Miranda Murat *(Mama Harakas)*, Lewis Charles *(Louie)*, Peter Mamakos *(Nick)*, Nick Dimitri, Tony Rollins, Vic Lundin, Greg Benedict *(hoods)*, Lillian Miniati *(Miranda)*.
Comedy. Con artist Steve Blair persuades Tony Dallas, a Manhattan gangster, to finance a movie about Adam and Eve by offering the female lead to Tony's stripper girl friend, Cha Cha Miller. The film is such a disaster, however, that Steve and his writer, Paul Ferris, decide to escape on a freighter to Greece. En route, Steve learns that the island of Paradeisos has lost its tourist trade because it has no apparent historical or mythological heritage. Intrigued, he hits upon the scheme of turning Paradeisos into a legendary island of love and taking a cut from all commercial enterprises. After planting Greek antiquities in the waters surrounding the island, Steve induces Paul to "recover" them, thus causing the tourist trade to increase. Steve becomes romantically involved with Elena, unaware that she is the niece of Tony Dallas. Eventually the hoax is exposed and Steve is thrown into jail, but the local priest validates Steve's claim by revealing an authentic, ancient shrine of love. At this point Tony arrives, bent on having his revenge on Steve and Paul, but when he learns Steve is planning to marry Elena, he is obliged to retreat, now that his enemy is his nephew. Confidence men. Gangsters. Motion picture producers. Stripteasers. Motion picture scriptwriters. Priests. Fraud. Tourism. Motion pictures. Islands. Freighters. Greece. Adam and Eve.
Note: Location scenes filmed in Athens and the Greek Islands of Hydra and Spetsai. Working title: *Not on Your Life*.

ISLAND OF TERROR (Great Britain) **F6.2461**
Planet Film Productions. *Dist* Universal Pictures. Feb 1967. Sd; col (Eastmancolor). 35mm. 90 min. [Also reviewed at 87 min.]
Pres by Protelco Films. *Prod* Tom Blakeley. *Exec Prod* Richard Gordon, Gerald A. Fernback. *Dir* Terence Fisher. *Screenplay* Edward Andrew Mann, Allan Ramsen. *Photog* Reg Wyer. *Art Dir* John St. John Earl. *Asst to Art Dir* Michael Albrechtsen. *Film Ed* Thelma Connell. *Mus Comp & Cond* Malcolm Lockyer. *Electronic Eff* Barry Gray. *Sd Rec* Robert MacPhee. *Asst Dir* Don Weeks. *Sp Eff* John St. John Earl.
Cast: Peter Cushing *(Dr. Stanley)*, Edward Judd *(Dr. David West)*, Carole Gray *(Toni Merrill)*, Eddie Byrne *(Dr. Landers)*, Sam Kydd *(Constable Harris)*, Niall MacGinnis *(Mr. Campbell)*, James Caffrey *(Argyle)*, Liam Gaffney *(Bellows)*, Roger Heathcott *(Dunley)*, Keith Bell *(Halsey)*, Shay Gorman *(Morton)*, Peter Forbes-Robertson *(Dr. Phillips)*, Richard Bidlake *(Carson)*, Joyce Hemson *(Mrs. Bellows)*, Edward Ogden *(helicopter pilot)*.
Science fiction drama. When several boneless human corpses are found on a small island off the coast of Ireland, Dr. Landers, the local physician, calls in scientists Dr. Stanley and Dr. West, to investigate the phenomenon. At the research laboratory they discover the formless bodies of Dr. Phillips and his assistants, who had been experimenting with a cancer cure. Examination of the doctors' notes reveals that they had developed a silicon-based form of life which feeds on bone calcium. The monsters, having tortoise-like bodies, are indestructible by firearms or dynamite; and, worse, they divide every 6 hours and will overrun the island within a week. More islanders die, including Dr.

Landers and Constable Harris. Finally the scientists develop a plan for destroying the creatures. All of the cattle on the island are injected with the isotope strontium 90. The silicates feed on the cattle and are killed by radioactive poisoning. *Scientists. Physicians. Mutation. Radiation. Monsters. Experiments. Cancer. Islands. Ireland. Cattle.*

Note: Opened in London in Jun 1966; running time: 89 min. Working titles: *The Silicates, Night of the Silicates, Night the Silicates Came, Night the Creatures Came,* and *The Creepers.*

ISLAND OF THE BLUE DOLPHINS   F6.2462

Robert B. Radnitz Productions. *Dist* Universal Pictures. 4 Jun **1964** [Dallas opening; c25 Jul 1964; LP32762]. Sd (Westrex); col (Eastman Color by Pathé). 35mm. 93 min. [Also 99 min.]

Prod Robert B. Radnitz. *In Charge of Prod* Edward Muhl. *Dir* James B. Clark. *Screenplay* Ted Sherdeman, Jane Klove. *Dir Photog* Leo Tover. *Art Dir* Alexander Golitzen, George Webb. *Set Decor* Oliver Emert. *Main Titl* Pacific Title. *Film Ed* Ted J. Kent. *Asst Ed* Fred Chulack. *Mus* Paul Sawtell. *Mus Supv* Joseph Gershenson. *Sd* Waldon O. Watson, Joe Lapis. *Asst Dir* Phil Bowles, James Welch. *Unit Prod Mgr* Terence Nelson. *Script Supv* Robert Forrest. *Cost* Rosemary Odell. *Makeup* Bud Westmore, Jack Freeman. *Hairstyles* Larry Germain. *Matte Artist* Albert Whitlock. *Coöp* Southwest Indian Museum, Santa Barbara Historical Society, Sierra Club, Millard Sheets. *"Rontu" Trained by* Frank Weatherwax. *Birds Trained by* Ray Berwick. *Still Photog* Rollie Lane.

Cast: Celia Kaye (*Karana*), Larry Domasin (*Ramo*), Ann Daniel (*Tutok*), Carlos Romero (*Chowig*), George Kennedy (*Aleut captain*), Hal Jon Norman (*Kimki*), Martin Garralaga (*priest*), Alex Montoya (*Spanish captain*), Julie Payne (*Lurai*), Junior (*Rontu, the dog*), Manchester Tribe of the Poma Nation, Kashia Tribe of the Poma Nation.

Adventure drama. Source: Scott O'Dell, *Island of the Blue Dolphins* (Boston, 1960). In 1835, a group of white hunters slay most of an Indian tribe inhabiting an island off California, forcing the survivors to flee the island. Young Karana, realizing that her 6-year-old brother, Ramo, has been left behind, returns to the island. Karana and Ramo are left alone, menaced by a pack of wild dogs. The most ferocious of the dogs kills Ramo, and Karana teaches herself archery and hunts the dog. She puts an arrow in its chest but then takes pity on the animal and nurses it back to health. She and the dog, whom she names Rontu, become fast friends. When another group of hunters come to the island, Karana hides, and although Tutok, a girl in the group, finds her and tries to befriend her, Karana refuses to trust anyone. Years pass, and Rontu dies of old age. Karana finds a puppy and names him Rontu-Aru—son of Rontu. Later, a boat carrying a missionary arrives, and this time Karana decides to trust the strangers. Taking her pets, Rontu-Aru, an otter, and some wild birds she has trained, she leaves the island. *Indians of North America. Hunters. Missionaries. Brother-sister relationship. Revenge. Survival. Islands. Archery. California. Dogs. Birds. Otter.*

Note: Filmed on location at Anchor Bay, California.

ISLAND OF THE DOOMED (Spain/West Germany)   F6.2463

Orbita Films–Tefi. *Dist* Allied Artists. Nov **1967**. Sd; col (Technicolor). 35mm (Techniscope). 88 min.

Prod George Ferrer. *Dir* Mel Welles. *Screenplay (see note)* Stephen Schmidt, writ, Ira Meltcher. *Story* Ira Meltcher, Ernst Ritter von Theumer. *Photog* Cecilio Paniagua. *Art Dir* Francisco Canet. *Film Ed* Antonio Cánovas. *Mus (see note)* Antón García Abril, Gregorio García Segura. *Asst Dir* Fanny Wessling. *Prod Mgr* Enrique Fernández Sagaseta.

Cast (see note): Cameron Mitchell (*Baron von Weser*), Elisa Montés (*Beth Christiansen*), George Martin, actor (*David Moss*), Kay Fischer (*Cora Robinson*), Ralph Naukoff (*James Robinson*), Hermann Nehlsen (*Professor Demerist*), Matilde Sampedro (*Myrtle Callahan*), Ricardo Valle (*Alfredo*), Mike Brendel (*Baldi*).

Science fiction melodrama. A group of tourists arrive to see the botanical gardens on a small island off the Italian coast. The only inhabitants of the island are the famous botanist Baron von Weser and his two faithful servants; all of the other residents fled after a series of mysterious deaths. When the car driven by the tourists' guide hits one of the baron's servants, von Weser explains that the death was due to a rare and incurable disease, not the accident. That night, the guide and Cora Robinson, one of the guests, are found murdered with all the blood drained from their bodies. Some time later a guest named David Moss discovers Baldi, the baron's mute servant, disposing of still another corpse. After beating Moss and the baron into unconsciousness, Baldi takes refuge in a chapel and is killed when the roof collapses on him. Following the deaths of several more guests, it is revealed that the baron has been experimenting with a carnivorous tree, the branches of which ensnare their victims and drain their blood. When Moss attempts to destroy the tree, the baron intervenes, but he is caught and strangled by his own creation. *Tourists. Nobility. Botanists. Domestics. Guides. Mutes. Murder. Botanical gardens. Islands. Experiments. Carnivorous plants. Automobile accidents.*

Note: Opened in Madrid in Jan 1968 as *La isla de la muerte*; in West Germany in Sep 1967 as *Das Geheimnis der Todesinsel.* Sources conflict in screenplay and music credits. The following actors appear under anglicized names: Kai Fischer (Kay Fischer), Rolf von Naukoff (Ralph Naukoff), Matilde Sampedro Muñoz (Matilde Sampedro).

ISLE OF SIN (West Germany)   F6.2464

Rapid–Film. *Dist* Manson Distributing Corp. 5 Apr **1963** [San Francisco showing]. Sd; b&w. 35mm. 74 min.

Prod Wolfgang Hartwig. *Dir-Screenplay* Johannes Kai. *Photog* Georg Krause. *Mus German Vers* Willy Mattes. *Mus English Vers* Karl Bette. *Asst Dir* Ilona von Juranyi. *Prod Mgr* Ludwig Spitaler.

Cast: Christiane Nielsen (*Martine Duval*), Erwin Strahl (*Michael Damon*), Jan Hendriks (*Mario Bertelli*), Georg Thomas (*Peter Lorenz*), Slavo Schwaiger (*Bert Frank*), Dorothee Glöcklen (*Ellen Frank*), Otto Storr (*Neils Larson*), Walter Faber (*Henry Boone*), Demeter Bitenc (*José Antonio Garcia*), Mladen Kozina, Beate Norden, Danilo Bezlay.

Melodrama. A passenger airplane bound for Venezuela waits to depart from the Mexico City airport. Among the passengers are: chorus girl Martine Duval; wealthy, middle-aged industrialist Bert Frank and his young bride, Ellen; Father Sawena, a missionary to Venezuela; Mario Bertelli, a convicted murderer being extradited to Venezuela; successful lawyer Henry Boone; newspaper reporter Michael Damon; bullfighter José Antonio Garcia; and archeologist Neils Larson. En route, a heavy storm forces the aircraft to make an emergency landing on a deserted island in the Caribbean. Father Sawena attempts to calm the survivors while Bertelli, whose police guard was killed in the crash, terrorizes them all with the policeman's gun. Bertelli strikes up a relationship with Martine, the only passenger who does not resent him. Garcia reveals that he has information that Boone, the lawyer, had committed perjury, and the latter, finding his career threatened, kills the bullfighter, intending to place the blame on Bertelli. Ellen learns that her husband, who dies from injuries he received in the crash, was involved in a financial swindle. Bertelli tries to rape Ellen, but Father Sawena intervenes. Bertelli fires at him but the bullet wounds Martine instead. Bertelli is overpowered and tied up by the men. When radio contact is made with Mexico, Boone frees Bertelli, and together they plan to kill the other survivors, although Bertelli does not intend to keep the bargain. The helicopter arrives; Boone is revealed to be Garcia's murderer; Bertelli is shot while trying to commandeer the helicopter; and the remaining survivors return to civilization. *Chorus girls. Priests. Convicts. Bullfighters. Newlyweds. Lawyers. Industrialists. Reporters. Archeologists. Extradition. Perjury. Murder. Frameup. Rape. Islands. Mexico City. Caribbean. Venezuela. Airplane accidents. Storms.*

Note: Released in West Germany in 1960 as *Flitterwochen in der Hölle*; running time: 95 min.

L'ISOLA DI ARTURO *see* ARTURO'S ISLAND

IT! (Great Britain)   F6.2465

Gold Star Productions. *For* Seven Arts Productions. *Dist* Warner Bros.–Seven Arts, Inc. 27 Sep **1967** [Boston opening; c9 Sep 1967; LP35851]. Sd (Westrex); col (Eastmancolor, print by Technicolor). 35mm. 95 min.

Prod-Dir-Orig Story-Screenplay Herbert J. Leder. *Exec Prod* Robert Goldstein. *Assoc Prod* Tom Sachs. *Dir Photog* Davis Boulton. *Camera Op* Ronnie Maasz. *Art Dir* Scott MacGregor. *Film Ed* Tom Simpson. *Mus Comp* Carlo Martelli. *Mus Dir* Philip Martell. *Sd Ed* Jim Roddan. *Sd Mix* Kevin Sutton. *1st Asst Dir* Bill Snaith. *Cont* Doreen Soan. *Wardrobe* Mary Gibson. *Makeup* Eric Carter. *Hairdresser* Mary Sturgess.

Cast: Roddy McDowall (*Arthur Pimm*), Jill Haworth (*Ellen Grove*), Paul Maxwell (*Jim Perkins*), Aubrey Richards (*Professor Weal*), Ernest Clark (*Harold Grove*), Oliver Johnston (*Trimingham*), Noel Trevarthen (*Inspector White*), Ian McCulloch (*Wayne*), Richard Goolden (*old man*), Dorothy Frere (*Miss Swanson*), Tom Chatto (*captain*), Steve Kirby (*Ellis*), Russell Napier (*boss*), Frank Sieman (*workman*), Brian Haines (*Joe Hill*), Mark Burns, Raymond Adamson (*officers*), Lindsay Campbell (*policeman*), John Baker (*guard*), Alan Sellers (*The Golem*).

Horror film. Harold Grove, a London musuem curator, is killed while examining a statue that was the sole treasure to survive a warehouse fire. Grove's mentally unbalanced assistant, Arthur Pimm, who lives alone with the decomposed corpse of his mother, becomes convinced that the statue possesses supernatural powers. Jim Perkins, an American museum representative, uncovers an inscription which suggests that the statue may be the famous 16th century Golem from Prague. Pimm, after learning the history of the Golem, removes an ancient Hebrew scroll from inside the statue and places the scroll under its tongue, thereby becoming its master. Passed over for the position of curator vacated by Grove's death, Pimm orders the Golem to murder Grove's successor and to destroy a bridge. Meanwhile, Perkins incurs Pimm's hatred by romancing his girl friend, Ellen, Grove's daughter. Inspector White of Scotland

Yard discovers the body of Pimm's mother and has Pimm committed to a prison mental hospital. But, using mental telepathy, Pimm summons the Golem to help him escape, abducts Ellen, and takes her, along with his mother's coffin, to a country mansion owned by the museum. They are followed by Inspector White, Perkins, and an Army unit equipped with a small atom bomb. Perkins rescues Ellen before the bomb explodes, destroying Pimm and the mansion. The Golem, unharmed, disappears into the sea. *Curators. Americans in foreign countries. Supernatural. Insanity. Murder. Mental telepathy. Jealousy. Museums. Corpses. Sculptures. Atom bomb. Bridges. London. Scotland Yard. The Golem.*

Note: Location scenes filmed at the Imperial War Museum, London. Released in Great Britain caJul 1967; running time: 97 min. Working title: *Curse of the Golem.*

IT ALL COMES OUT IN THE END   **F6.2466**
Dist Jo-Jo Distributors. ca **1970**. Sd; col. 16mm. 61-81 min.
   Sex film. No information about the precise nature of this film has been found. *Sexuality.*

IT BEGAN ON THE VISTULA (Great Britain)   **F6.2467**
Janusz Piekalkiewicz. *Dist* President Films. 22 Apr **1966** [Chicago opening]. Sd; b&w. 35mm. 80 min.
   Prod-Dir-Writ Janusz Piekalkiewicz. *Photog* Mathias Chromecki. *Mus* Oskar Sala.
   Documentary. This film, depicting the history of Poland between 1939 and 1945, concentrates on the effects of both the Nazi occupation and Stalin's reign of terror. Shown in detail are the signing of the Hitler-Stalin non-aggression pact, conditions at German concentration camps, the cruel methods of the Gestapo, and scenes of Siberian labor camps. *Poles. Nazis. Russians. Concentration camps. World War II. Poland—History—Occupation 1939–45. Joseph Stalin. Adolf Hitler. Gestapo.*
Note: Production began in 1961. Filmed in Polish; Polish title: *Zaczęło się nad Wisłą.* Also known as *Polish Passion* and *The Unfinished War.*

IT COMES UP MURDER see **THE HONEY POT**

IT HAPPENED AT THE WORLD'S FAIR   **F6.2468**
Ted Richmond Productions. *Dist* Metro-Goldwyn-Mayer, Inc. 3 Apr **1963** [Los Angeles opening; c31 Dec 1962; LP23743]. Sd (Westrex); col (Metrocolor). 35mm (Panavision). 105 min.
   A Ted Richmond Production. *Prod* Ted Richmond. *Dir* Norman Taurog. *Writ* Si Rose, Seaman Jacobs. *Dir Photog* Joseph Ruttenberg. *Camera Op* John Mehl. *Camera Asst* George Hollister, Bill Ion. *Art Dir* George W. Davis, Preston Ames. *Set Decor* Henry Grace, Hugh Hunt. *Film Ed* Fredric Steinkamp. *Asst Ed* Harold F. Kress, Don Guidice. *Mus Score* Leith Stevens. *Songs:* "I'm Falling in Love Tonight," "They Remind Me Too Much of You" Don Robertson. *Songs:* "Relax," "Take Me to the Fair" Sid Tepper, Roy C. Bennett. *Song:* "How Would You Like To Be" Ben Raleigh, Mark Barkan. *Song:* "Beyond the Bend" Ben Weisman, Fred Wise, Dolores Fuller. *Song:* "One Broken Heart for Sale" Otis Blackwell, Winfield Scott. *Song:* "Cotton Candy Land" Ruth Batchelor, Bob Roberts. *Song:* "A World of Our Own" Bill Giant, Bernie Baum, Florence Kaye. *Song:* "Happy Ending" Sid Wayne, Ben Weisman. *Songs Sung by* Elvis Presley. *Vocal Backgrounds* The Jordanaires, The Mellomen. *Mus Numbers Stgd by* Jack Baker. *Rec Supv* Franklin Milton. *Sd* Larry Jost, Al Strasser, Ray Bisordi, Clint Althouse. *Asst Dir* Al Jennings, Al Shenberg, Wallace Jones, Jim Myers. *Script Supv* Dorothy Aldrin. *Wardrobe* Jim Taylor, Sophia Stutz. *Makeup* William Tuttle, Roy Stork. *Hairstyles* Sydney Guilaroff, Shirley Althouse. *Tech Adv* Col. Tom Parker. *Gaffer* Milford Cline. *Prop* Jim Luttrell, Dick Hendrickson.
   Cast: Elvis Presley *(Mike Edwards),* Joan O'Brien *(Diane Warren),* Gary Lockwood *(Danny Burke),* Vicky Tiu *(Sue-Lin),* H. M. Wynant *(Vince Bradley),* Edith Atwater *(Miss Steuben),* Guy Raymond *(Barney Thatcher),* Dorothy Green *(Miss Ettinger),* Kam Tong *(Walter Ling),* Yvonne Craig *(Dorothy Johnson).*
   Comedy-drama with music. Mike and Danny, two bush pilots, are grounded when a local sheriff attaches their plane as security for unpaid bills resulting from Mike's weakness for women and Danny's for gambling. They hitch a ride to Seattle with Walter Ling, a Chinese farmer, and his young niece Sue-Lin. Upon arrival the uncle finds it impossible to take Sue-Lin to the World's Fair, and Mike volunteers to accompany her while Danny goes to search for a friend, Vince Bradley. Sue-Lin gets a stomach ache after sampling every kind of food and going on every ride. In the dispensary Mike makes a successful play for nurse Diane Warren, but during their dinner date Sue-Lin arrives and tearfully explains that she has lost her uncle. Mike takes her under his wing, but she is taken away by the Child Welfare Board, supposedly on Diane's recommendation. In reality, Danny is the informer—he wants Mike to help him pilot a plane for Vince. Mike agrees, but he learns just before takeoff that Sue-Lin has run away. He finds her at the fair and takes her to the airplane.

Meanwhile, Diane, also looking for Sue-Lin, has arrived at the runway. Mike becomes suspicious of Vince and discovers that the cargo they were to transport consists of smuggled furs. A scuffle ensues, police apprehend Vince, Mike and Diane are reconciled, Sue-Lin is reunited with her uncle, and all ends happily. *Air pilots. Sheriffs. Farmers. Chinese. Uncles. Nurses. Children. Smuggling. Airplanes. Century 21 Exposition. Seattle.*
   Note: Location scenes filmed at the Century 21 Exposition. Working title: *Take Me to the Fair.*

IT HAPPENED HERE (Great Britain)   **F6.2469**
Rath Films–Long Distance Films. *Dist* Lopert Pictures. 8 Aug **1966** [New York opening]. Sd; b&w. 35mm. 95 min.
   Prod-Dir-Writ Kevin Brownlow, Andrew Mollo. *Treatment Collab* Dinah Brooke, Jonathan Ingrams. *Orig Idea* Kevin Brownlow. *Dir Photog* Peter Suschitzky. *Adtl Photog* Kevin Brownlow. *Camera* Grant Thomson. *Art Dir* Andrew Mollo. *Adtl Art Dir* Jim Nicolson. *Film Ed* Kevin Brownlow. *Mus* Jack Beaver. *Selections from Symphony no. 9* Anton Bruckner. *Sd Ed* George Fisher, sd, Hugh Strain. *Prod Asst* Johanna Roeber, Rosemary Claxton, Alice Brooke-Howard, Graham Samuel, Prince Marshall, Pat Sullivan, Eric Mival. *Military Cons* Andrew Mollo. *Adtl Tech Adv* Guntis Zarins. *Still Photog* Rosemary Claxton.
   Cast: Pauline Murray *(Pauline),* Sebastian Shaw *(Dr. Richard Fletcher),* Fiona Leland *(Helen Fletcher),* Honor Fehrson *(Honor Hutton),* Nicholas Moore *(IA group leader Moorfield),* John Herrington *(Dr. Westerman),* Bart Allison *(Skipworth),* Stella Kemball *(Nurse Drayton),* Ralph Wilson *(Dr. Walton),* Percy Binns *(IA commandant),* Frank Bennett *(IA political leader),* Bill Thomas *(IA group leader),* Reginald Marsh *(IA medical officer),* Rex Collett *(IA NCO),* Nicolette Bernard *(IA woman commandant),* Claire Allan, Carol James *(IA girls),* Miles Halliwell *(IA political lecturer),* Ralph Wilson *(Dr. Walton),* Bertha Russell *(matron),* Peter Urbe, Graham Adam *(SS officers),* Brewster Cross *(American officer),* Colonel Pickering *(British partisan officer),* Jeremy Dacon *(British medical officer),* Werner Mallé, Peter Dineley, Alfred Ziemen *(German officers),* John Snagge, Alvar Liddell, Frank Phillips, actor, Michael Mellinger *(announcers and commentators),* Frank Gardner, Pat Kearney, Derek Milburn, Michael Passmore, Barrie Pattison, Ronald Phillips, Christopher Slaughter, Pat Sullivan, Peter Elkins, Hans Joachim Schmiedel, Klaus Umjo, Christopher Bell, actor, Norbert Dingeldein, Bob Parker, George Parker, Tony Oliver, Jim Joslyn, Rose Paddon, H. G. White, Rae Wills, Andrew Mollo, Peter Watkins, Richard Golding.
   War drama. Following the Allied defeat at Dunkirk in July 1940, Hitler's army crosses the English Channel and occupies Great Britain. Within 4 years the Nazis have crushed all opposition and transformed England into a corporate fascist state. Collaborators work with the Wehrmacht in suppressing partisan resistance stimulated by United States entry into the war. Moving to London, nurse Pauline Murray finds all welfare services under German control. In order to continue nursing, she joins the Immediate Action Organization and dons a fascist uniform. Although Hampstead friends Dr. and Helen Fletcher decry her decision, Pauline attempts to steal morphine for a wounded partisan they are harboring. Discovered, she is implicated and transferred to a country hospital. There she is ordered to give injections to Russian and Polish patients supposedly suffering from tuberculosis. Finding them dead the following day, she protests and is arrested and deported. When her train is ambushed by the English Liberation Army, the nurse is taken prisoner. Volunteering her services, Pauline cares for casualties. As the radio proclaims the imminent victory of partisan forces, the fighting intensifies. *Nazis. Nurses. Physicians. War victims. Russians. Poles. Military invasion. Military occupation. Fascism. Resistance (political). Morphine. Hospitals. World War II. London. London—Hampstead.*
   Note: Filmed on location in Salisbury, Radnorshire, Oxford, Dorset, and London. Production began in 1956. Released in London in May 1966; running time: 93 min; cut from 99 min. Some footage shot in 16mm. Musical score includes excerpts from the German march "Volk ans Gewehr."

IT HAPPENED IN ATHENS   **F6.2470**
Twentieth Century–Fox Film Corp. 14 Nov **1962** [New York opening; c27 Dec 1961; LP22225]. Sd; col (De Luxe). 35mm (CinemaScope). 92 min. [Preview length: 100 min.]
   Prod James S. Elliott. *Dir* Andrew Marton. *Writ* Laslo Vadnay. *Dir Photog* Curtis Courant. *2d Unit Camera* Basil Maros. *Art Dir* Marilena Aravantinou. *Set Decor* Aurelio Crugnola. *Supv Film Ed* Jodie Copelan. *Mus Comp & Cond* Manos Hadjidakis. *Sd* Claude Hitchcock, Derek Leather. *Asst Dir* Foster Phinney, Henry Yatrou, Nicholas Christou. *Prod Supv* Frank Parmenter. *Cost Dsgn* Adele Parmenter. *Wardrobe* Rodolfo Taddei, Wanda Antonelli. *Makeup* Marrico Spagnoli. *Hairdresser* Anna Cristofani. *Coöp* Greek Government, Greek Olympic Committee. *Dial Dir* Harriet Medin. *Prop Master* George Diamantis.

Cast: Jayne Mansfield *(Eleni Costa)*, Trax Colton *(Spiridon Loues)*, Nico Minardos *(Lieutenant Vinardos)*, Bob Mathias *(Coach Graham)*, Maria Xenia *(Christina Gratsos)*, Lili Valenty *(Mama Loues)*, Ivan Triesault *(Grandpa Loues)*, Bill Browne *(Drake)*, Brad Harris *(Garrett)*, Paris Alexander *(Nico Loues)*, Marion Silva *(Maria Loues)*, Charles Fawcett *(Ambassador Gaylord)*, Titos Vandis *(Father Loues)*, Tod Windsor *(Burke)*, Paul Muller *(priest)*, Jean Murat *(De Coubertin)*, Gustavo De Nardo *(George)*, Roger Fradet *(Dubois)*, Denton De Gray *(O'Toole)*, John Karlsen *(King of Greece)*, Ben Bennett *(Connolley)*, George Stefan *(fat man)*, George Graham *(announcer)*, Alan Caillou *(narrator)*.

Comedy-drama. In 1896 it is announced that the Olympic Games will be revived in Athens. A young shepherd, Spiridon Loues, decides to enter the 26-mile marathon. Once in Athens, he meets Christina Gratsos, a young woman from his hometown who is now the personal maid of Eleni Costa, Greece's most glamorous actress. Though he has arrived after the qualification date, Spiridon's athletic prowess so impresses Coach Graham of the American team that he is permitted to enter the contest. Eleni informs the press that she will marry the victor, confident it will be her lover, Lieutenant Vinardos. Spiridon, however, wins, and Eleni awaits him in her carriage. But he embraces Christina, and it is a defeated Vinardos who meekly comes to Eleni. *Athletes. Shepherds. Actors. Chambermaids. Athletic coaches. Mistresses. Americans in foreign countries. Olympic Games. Marriage. Greece. Athens.*

Note: Filmed on location in Greece. Actual footage from the Olympic Games is incorporated in the film.

IT HAPPENED TO JANE *see* **TWINKLE AND SHINE**

IT ONLY TAKES 5 MINUTES *see* **THE ROTTEN APPLE**

IT STARTED IN THE ALPS (Japan)   **F6.2471**
Toho Co. 21 Dec **1966** [Los Angeles opening]. Sd; col. 35mm (Tohoscope). 94 min.

Prod Sanezumi Fujimoto. *Dir* Kengo Furusawa. *Photog* Tadashi Iimura.

Cast: Yuzo Kayama *(Yuichi Tanuma)*, Yuriko Hoshi *(Sumiko)*, Kinuyo Tanaka *(Shinjiro)*, Ichiro Arishima *(Yuichi's father)*, Chōko Iida *(Yuichi's grandmother)*, Edith Hanson *(Lucienne)*, Akiko Wakabayashi, Tatsuyoshi Ebara, Machiko Naka.

Romantic comedy-drama. College student Yuichi Tanuma and his bumbling friend Shinjiro leave Japan with their professor to attend an academic conference in Geneva. While skiing in the Swiss Alps, Yuichi meets and falls in love with Sumiko, an airline stewardess on vacation. Although they are separated, their paths cross again in Vienna, Rome, and Tokyo, where Yuichi is entered in an intercollegiate ski competition. The unexpected arrival of Yuichi's French acquaintance Lucienne almost destroys his relationship with Sumiko, especially when Shinjiro inadvertently leads Sumiko to think that Yuichi has invited Lucienne to Tokyo. Yuichi and Sumiko are happily reunited in the Alps. *Students. Professors. Airline stewardesses. French. Skiing. Vacations. Contests. Geneva. Alps. Vienna. Rome. Tokyo.*

Note: Released in Japan in 1966 as *Arupusu no wakadaisho.*

IT TAKES A THIEF (Great Britain)   **F6.2472**
Alliance Productions–Alexandra Productions. *Dist* Valiant Films. Feb **1961.** Sd; b&w. 35mm. 92 min.

Pres by Joseph Harris, Sig Shore. *Prod* John Temple-Smith. *Dir–Screenplay* John Gilling. *Photog* Gordon Dines. *Art Dir* Tom Morahan, Jim Morahan. *Film Ed* Alan Osbiston, John Victor Smith. *Mus* Bill McGuffie. *Song:* "The Challenge" Bill McGuffie, Robert Halfin. *Sung by* Jayne Mansfield. *Sd* Norman Savage, Dave Goghan. *Sd Rec* Richard Smith, Wally Milner. *Prod Supv* John Pellatt.

Cast: Jayne Mansfield *(Billy Lacross)*, Anthony Quayle *(Jim Maxton)*, Carl Mohner *(Kristy)*, Peter Reynolds *(Buddy)*, John Bennett *(Spider)*, Barbara Mullen *(Ma Piper)*, Peter Pike *(Joey)*, Robert Brown *(Bob Crowther)*, Dermot Walsh *(Inspector Willis)*, Edward Judd *(Detective Sergeant Gittens)*, John Stratton *(Rick)*, Patrick Holt *(Max)*, Lorraine Clewes *(Mrs. Rick)*, Percy Herbert *(shop steward)*, Liane Marelli *(stripteaser)*, Bill McGuffie *(nightclub pianist)*, Lloyd Lamble *(Dr. Westerly)*, John Wood *(school inspector)*, Arthur Brough *(landlord)*, Wally Patch *(ticket collector)*, Bryan Pringle *(sergeant)*, Marigold Russell *(hostess)*, Victor Brooks *(foreman)*, Bill Shine *(farm laborer)*, Richard Shaw *(lorry driver)*, David Davenport *(policeman)*.

Crime melodrama. Jim Maxton, a middle-aged widower, becomes infatuated with Billy Lacross, the woman leader of a gang of crooks, and is persuaded to join them in a large-scale bullion robbery. After Jim has hidden the loot, Kristy, a gangster, informs on him, and Jim is sent to prison for 5 years. Following his release, the embittered Jim decides to live an honest life, supported by the money which is still safely hidden. Billy, meanwhile, has been supplanted as gang leader by the vicious Kristy, who is determined to wrest the money from Jim. Kristy kidnaps Joey, Jim's 6 year-old son and forces Jim to retrieve the money; but Jim discovers that the cache, hidden in a public dump, has been

destroyed in an explosion. The now-reformed Billy aids Jim and Scotland Yard in rescuing the boy and rounding up the gang. *Widowers. Informers. Gangsters. Robbery. Kidnaping. Fatherhood. Criminals—Rehabilitation. Prisons. Scotland Yard.*

Note: Released in Great Britain in May 1960 as *The Challenge*; running time: 93 min.

IT TAKES ALL KINDS (United States/Australia)   **F6.2473**
Goldsworthy Productions–Commonwealth United Productions. *Dist* Commonwealth United Entertainment, Inc. caJul **1969.** Sd; col. 35mm. 97 min.

Prod-Dir Eddie Davis. *Exec Prod* Reginald Goldsworthy. *Assoc Dir* Warwick Freeman. *Screenplay* Eddie Davis, Charles E. Savage. *Photog* Mick Bornemann. *Camera Op* Charlie Keyes. *Mus* Bob Young.

Cast: Robert Lansing *(Tony Gunther)*, Vera Miles *(Laura Ring)*, Barry Sullivan *(Orville Benton)*, Sid Melton *(Benji)*, Penny Sugg *(J. P. Duncan)*, Chris Christensen, Ted Hepple, Allen Bickford, Reg Gorman, Dennis Miller, Barry Spicer.

Action melodrama. Source: Edward D. Hoch, "A Girl Like Cathy" (a short story; publication undetermined). Tony Gunther, an American merchant seaman, decides to leave his ship when it docks in Sydney, Australia, and he is given a farewell party on the wharf. The party ends in a brawl in which a sailor named Swede is thrown overboard and Tony is knocked unconscious with a bottle. Tony awakens in the apartment of mysterious Laura Ring, who tells him that he is a suspect in Swede's murder. Laura offers him shelter in return for his help in stealing a valuable silver chalice from the Museum of Medieval Studies, and he reluctantly agrees. He removes a stained glass window to gain access to the museum, but he is unable to find the treasure. Meanwhile, Laura drives off, leaving him to escape alone. Eventually, Tony learns that Swede is alive, and that Laura's true purpose was to steal the window. He follows her to Melbourne with the police trailing close behind and learns her whereabouts with the help of a female insurance agent, J. P. Duncan, and a friendly fence, Benji. Laura hopes to sell the window to industrialist Orville Benton, who keeps valuable stolen art objects in his granary. In his efforts to retrieve the treasure, Tony is forced to confront Benton and his thugs. Meanwhile, Laura greedily attempts to take possession of Benton's collection, and she is buried beneath tons of grain. The stolen property returned, J. P. and Tony are married. *Seamen. Thieves. Insurance agents. Industrialists. Fences (for stolen goods). Americans in foreign countries. Murder. Museums. Art objects. Merchant marine. Sydney (Australia). Melbourne (Australia).*

Note: Opened in Sydney in Jun 1969.

IT WAS ALL FOR SALE *see* **IT'S ALL FOR SALE**

IT WON'T RUB OFF, BABY! *see* **SWEET LOVE, BITTER**

ITALIAN HOLIDAY   **F6.2474**
VPR Ltd. **1961.** Sd eff & mus score; col. 35mm. 100-115 min.

Pres by Burton Holmes Theatre Productions. *Prod-Dir-Writ* André De La Varre, Jr. *Photog* Kurt Jetmar, Peter Baudendistel, André De La Varre, Jr. *Film Ed* André De La Varre, Jr., Pablo Zavala. *Mus Ed* André De La Varre, Jr., Music Sound Track Service.

Travelog. Several hill towns and other obscure sites are described by a travel host during an automobile tour of the Italian countryside. *Travel. Italy.*

Note: Narration delivered live on stage.

THE ITALIAN JOB (Great Britain)   **F6.2475**
Oakhurst Productions. *Dist* Paramount Pictures. 3 Sep **1969** [Los Angeles opening; c2 Jun 1969; LP36988]. Sd; col (Eastman Color). 35mm (Panavision). 101 min.

Prod Michael Deeley. *Assoc Prod* Bob Porter. *Dir* Peter Collinson. *2d Unit Dir* Philip Wrestler. *Screenplay* Troy Kennedy Martin. *Photog* Douglas Slocombe. *2d Unit Photog* Norman Warwick. *Camera Op* Chic Waterson, Ronnie Maasz, Wally Byatt. *Art Dir* Michael Knight. *Prod Dsgn* Disley Jones. *Film Ed* John Trumper. *Mus* Quincy Jones. *Song:* "On Days Like These" Quincy Jones, Don Black. *Sung by* Matt Monro. *Song:* "Getta Bloomin' Move On!" Quincy Jones, Don Black. *Sung by* The Italian Job. *Sd Mix* John Aldred, Laurie Clarkson. *Sd* Gerry Humphreys. *Sd Camera Op* Brian Knott. *Sd Ed* Stephen Warwick. *Asst Dir* Scott Wodehouse. *Prod Mgr* Derek Kavanagh. *Dress Dsgn* Dinah Greet. *Wardrobe Supv* Dulcie Midwinter. *Wardrobe Master* Roy Ponting. *Ch Makeup Artist* Freddie Williamson. *Hairdresser* Gordon Bond. *Sp Eff* Pat Moore, Ken Morris. *Stunt Driving* L'Equipe Rémy Julienne.

Cast: Michael Caine *(Charlie Croker)*, Noel Coward *(Mr. Bridger)*, Maggie Blye *(Lorna)*, Benny Hill *(Professor Simon Peach)*, Tony Beckley *(Freddie)*, Raf Vallone *(Altabani)*, Rossano Brazzi *(Beckerman)*, Lelia Goldoni *(Madame Beckerman)*, George Innes *(Bill Bailey)*, Harry Baird *(Big William)*, Robert Powell *(Yellow)*, John Forgeham *(Frank)*, Michael Standing *(Arfur)*, Derek Ware *(Rozzer)*, Frank Jarvis *(Roger)*, Stanley Caine *(Coco)*, Irene Handl *(Miss*

Peach), John Le Mesurier *(governor)*, Fred Emney *(Brikenshaw)*, John Clive *(garage manager)*, Graham Payn *(Keats)*, Barry Cox *(Chris)*, David Salamone *(Dominic)*, Richard Essame *(Tony)*, Mario Volgoi *(Manzo)*, Renato Romano *(Cosca)*, Robert Rietty *(police chief)*, Timothy Bateson *(dentist)*, Arnold Diamond *(senior computer room official)*, Simon Dee *(shirtmaker)*, Alistair Hunter *(warder in prison cinema)*, Louis Mansi *(computer room offical)*, Franco Novelli *(Altabani's driver)*, Henry McGee *(tailor)*, Valerie Leon, Dave Kelly, Lana Gatto, John Morris, actor.

Action comedy. Charlie Croker finishes a 2-year sentence for petty theft and is released from a prison that is virtually run by Bridger, a fellow inmate and superior criminal. Lorna, Charlie's girl friend, picks him up in a stolen car and takes him to a luxurious hotel and there Charlie receives a message from Madame Beckerman, the widow of one of Charlie's associates. Beckerman has left Charlie the foolproof plans for the robbery of a shipment of gold being transported from Red China to Turin, Italy. Charlie breaks into his old prison and solicits the aid of the patriotic Bridger by suggesting to him that the gold will help the British economy. He then recruits the rest of his gang, including Professor Peach, a computer expert and inmate of a mental hospital. Despite the attempts of the Mafia, headed by the sinister Altabani, to foil the plan, which involves the use of three Mini-Coopers and the sabotaging of the computer in the Turin traffic control center to cause a massive traffic jam, the robbery is successful. The bullion is transferred to a bus headed for Switzerland via twisting mountain roads; but while Bridger and his fellow inmates celebrate the completion of the robbery, the bus skids, careens toward the precipice, and suspends teetering on a cliff. The men dare not move and upset the balance, but Charlie quickly formulates a plan to save his men, himself, and the gold. *Thieves. Widows. Professors. Robbery. Insanity. Gold. Computers. Traffic. Buses. Prisons. Turin. Switzerland. Mafia. Chases.*

Note: Location scenes filmed in Italy, England, and Switzerland. Opened in London in Jun 1969.

THE ITALIAN MOUSE see THE MAGIC WORLD OF TOPO GIGIO (THE ITALIAN MOUSE)

ITALIANI BRAVA GENTE see ITALIANO BRAVA GENTE

ITALIANO BRAVA GENTE (Italy/U.S.S.R.)   F6.2476

Galatea-Coronet Film–Mosfilm. *Dist* Embassy Pictures. 29 Oct 1965 [Los Angeles opening]. Sd; b&w. 35mm. 156 min.

Pres by Joseph E. Levine. *Prod* Lionello Santi. *Dir* Giuseppe De Santis. *2d Unit Dir* Dmitriy Vasilyev. *Screenplay* Ennio De Concini, Augusto Frassineti, Giandomenico Giagni, Sergey Smirnov, Giuseppe De Santis. *Story* Ennio De Concini, Giuseppe De Santis. *Photog* Antonio Secchi, V. Khovanskaya. *Art Dir* David Vinitskiy. *Set Decor* Ermanno Manco. *Film Ed* Mario Serandrei. *Mus* Armando Trovajoli. *Sd* V. Lagutin. *Asst Dir* Romolo Girolami, I. Bits, I. Paramonov. *Prod Mgr* Massimo De Rita. *Sp Eff* Boris Travkin, A. Rudachenko.

Cast: Arthur Kennedy *(Ferro Maria Ferri)*, Peter Falk *(medical captain)*, Tatyana Samoylova *(Sonya)*, Raffaele Pisu *(Gabrielli)*, Zhanna Prokhorenko *(Katya)*, Andrea Checchi *(Sermonti)*, Riccardo Cucciolla *(Sanna)*, Nino Vingelli *(Amalfitano)*, Lev Prygunov *(Bazzocchi)*, Grigoriy Mikhaylov *(Russian partisan)*, Gino Pernice *(Collodi)*, Valeriy Somov *(Giuliani)*, Boris Kozhukhov *(a major)*, Vincenzo Polizzi *(a Sicilian)*, S. Lukyanov *(partisan commander)*, Yuriy Nazarov *(Russian prisoner)*, Otar Koberidze *(wounded Italian)*, I. Paramonov *(German deserter)*, E. Knausmyuller *(German general)*, Ya. Yanakiyev, A. Sakhnovskiy, E. Lezhdey, D. Stolyarskaya, L. Masokha, V. Golovnenko, N. Nikitina, L. Ulyanenko, V. Berezko.

War drama. In 1942, an Italian squadron traveling by train through the Ukraine to the eastern front observes the harsh treatment suffered by Russian captives at the hands of German soldiers. An Italian offers a Russian a piece of bread, thus precipitating a fight between the Germans and Italians. Later, when a Russian town is overtaken, the Italians and Germans are unable to prevent saboteurs from destroying several buildings. The saboteurs, including a girl named Katya, are captured, and the Germans order them shot; but the Italian firing squad allows Katya to escape. Bazzocchi, a young Italian soldier, follows and tries to console the frightened girl, only to be shot down by planes. Fascist Major Ferri joins the troop, along with a compassionate Italian physician who is begged by the surrendering Russian partisans to save their wounded leader. Leaving behind a hostage, the partisans take the doctor to their camp. Although he saves the leader's life, the doctor is shot by the Germans while returning to his outfit; consequently, the hostage is also executed. Later, the Russians push back the Italians and take Ferri prisoner. During the general retreat, the Germans ride while the Italians march on foot. Ferri kills one of the Italian drivers and attempts to take over the truck, but other Italians beat him to death. A weary Italian soldier, Gabrielli, continues on alone. He comes across the frozen body of Sonya, a Russian girl whom he had met earlier, and falls to the ground to begin digging his own grave. *Germans. Prisoners of war. Saboteurs. Fascists. Physicians. Hostages. War crimes. Capital punishment.*

Resistance (political). Murder. Trains. World War II. Ukraine. Italy—Army. Germany—Army.

Note: Filmed on location in the Ukraine and on the banks of the Don River. Opened in Rome in Oct 1964 as *Italiani brava gente*; running time: 150 min. Released in the U.S.S.R. in 1965 in two parts as *Oni shli na Vostok*.

IT'S A BARE WORLD see MY BARE LADY

IT'S A BIKINI WORLD   F6.2477

Trans American Films. Apr **1967** [c19 Apr 1967; LP34370]. Sd; col (Technicolor by Pathé). 35mm (Colorscope). 86 min.

Prod Charles S. Swartz. *Dir* Stephanie Rothman. *Screenplay* Charles S. Swartz, Stephanie Rothman. *Photog* Alan Stensvold. *2d Unit Photog* Brick Marquard. *Sets* Harry Reif. *Film Ed* Leo Shreve. *Mus* Mike Curb, Bob Summers. *Mus Prod* GP IV Productions. *Sd* Wallace Nogle. *Asst Dir* Larry Johnson. *Prod Mgr* Paul Lewis.

Cast: Deborah Walley *(Delilah Dawes)*, Tommy Kirk *(Mike Samson/Herbert Samson)*, Robert Pickett *(Woody)*, Suzie Kaye *(Pebbles)*, Jack Bernardi *(Harvey Pulp)*, William O'Connell *(McSnigg)*, Sid Haig *(Daddy)*, Jim Begg *(boy)*, Lori Williams *(girl)*, Pat McGee *(Cindy)*, The Animals, The Castaways, The Toys, The Gentrys.

Comedy. Athlete Mike Samson is dismayed to overhear young Delilah Dawes refer to him as a braggart. Determined to win her approval, he decides to live a dual life by posing as Herbert Samson, Mike's shy and bespectacled brother. The deception succeeds, for Delilah responds romantically to "Herbert's" manner and polite behavior. But the situation becomes complicated when Delilah challenges Mike to participate in a series of beach sporting events. Forced to compete, Mike wins all of the contests except the last, which he allows Delilah to win. When Delilah inevitably learns of his double life, she at first refuses to listen to an explanation. But, influenced by the fact that she was allowed to win the final sporting event and convinced that Mike shows signs of improving, she changes her mind and resumes her romance with Mike/Herbert Samson. *Athletes. Braggarts. Duplicity. Contests. Beaches. Timidity.*

IT'S A MAD, MAD, MAD, MAD WORLD   F6.2478

Casey Productions. *Dist* United Artists. 7 Nov **1963** [Los Angeles opening; c7 Nov 1963; LP28452]. Sd (Westrex); col (Technicolor). 35mm & 70mm (Ultra-Panavision, see note). 192 min. [See note.]

Pres by Stanley Kramer. A Stanley Kramer Production. *Prod-Dir* Stanley Kramer. *Story & Screenplay* William Rose, Tania Rose. *Dir Photog* Ernest Laszlo. *Adtl Photog* Irmin Roberts, Hal McAlpin. *Camera Op* Charles Wheeler. *Asst Camera* Richard Johnson, photog. *Art Dir* Gordon Gurnee. *Set Decor* Joseph Kish. *Prod Dsgn* Rudolph Sternad. *Main Titl* Saul Bass. *Film Ed* Frederic Knudtson, Robert C. Jones, Gene Fowler, Jr. *Mus* Ernest Gold. *Perf by* Los Angeles Philharmonic Orchestra. *Songs:* "It's a Mad, Mad, Mad, Mad World," "Thirty One Flavors," "You Satisfy My Soul," Ernest Gold. Mack David. *Dance Seq Sung by* The Shirelles. *Played by* The Four Mads. *Sd Engr* John Kean. *Sd Ed* Walter Elliott. *Sd Dir* Gordon Sawyer. *Re-rec* Clem Portman, Roy Granville, Vinton Vernon. *Mus Ed* Art Dunham. *Asst Dir* Bert Chervin, George Batcheller, Charles Scott, Jr. *Asst to the Dir* Ivan Volkman. *Asst to Prod* Anne Kramer. *Prod Mgr* Clem Beauchamp. *Prod Coörd* Bud Pine. *Script Supv* Marshall Schlom. *Cost Supv* Joe King. *Cost Dsgn* Bill Thomas. *Makeup* George Lane, Lynn Reynolds. *Hairstyles* Connie Nichols. *Sp Eff* Danny Lee. *Photog Eff* Linwood Dunn, James Gordon, Film Effects of Hollywood. *Proc Photog* Farciot Edouart. *Stunt Supv* Carey Loftin. *Aerial Supv* Paul Mantz, Frank Tallman. *Company Grip* Morris Rosen. *Ch Gaffer* Joe Edesa. *Prop Master* Art Cole. *Casting* Stalmaster-Lister Co.

Cast: Spencer Tracy *(Capt. C. G. Culpeper)*, Milton Berle *(J. Russell Finch)*, Sid Caesar *(Melville Crump)*, Buddy Hackett *(Benjy Benjamin)*, Ethel Merman *(Mrs. Marcus)*, Mickey Rooney *(Ding Bell)*, Dick Shawn *(Sylvester Marcus)*, Phil Silvers *(Otto Meyer)*, Terry-Thomas *(J. Algernon Hawthorne)*, Jonathan Winters *(Lennie Pike)*, Edie Adams *(Monica Crump)*, Dorothy Provine *(Emmeline Finch)*, Eddie "Rochester" Anderson *(1st cab driver)*, Jim Backus *(Tyler Fitzgerald)*, Ben Blue *(airplane pilot)*, Alan Carney *(police sergeant)*, Barrie Chase *(Mrs. Haliburton)*, William Demarest *(chief of police)*, Peter Falk *(2d cab driver)*, Paul Ford *(Colonel Wilberforce)*, Leo Gorcey *(3d cab driver)*, Edward Everett Horton *(Dinckler)*, Buster Keaton *(Jimmy the Crook)*, Don Knotts *(nervous man)*, Carl Reiner *(tower control)*, The Three Stooges *(firemen)*, Joe E. Brown *(union official)*, Andy Devine *(Sheriff Mason)*, Sterling Holloway *(fire chief)*, Marvin Kaplan *(Irwin, gas station attendant)*, Arnold Stang *(Ray, gas station attendant)*, Charles Lane *(airport manager)*, Howard Da Silva *(airport officer)*, Charles McGraw *(lieutenant)*, ZaSu Pitts *(switchboard operator)*, Madlyn Rhue *(police secretary)*, Jesse White *(radio tower operator)*, Lloyd Corrigan *(mayor)*, Selma Diamond *(voice of Culpeper's wife)*, Stan Freberg *(deputy sheriff)*, Louise Glenn *(voice of Billie Sue)*, Ben Lessy *(George, the steward)*, Bobo Lewis *(pilot's wife)*, Mike Mazurki *(miner)*, Nick Stuart *(truck driver)*, Sammee Tong *(Chinese laundryman)*, Stanley Clements,

Norman Fell, Nicholas Georgiade *(detectives)*, Jimmy Durante *(Smiler Grogan)*, Allen Jenkins *(police officer)*, Harry Lauter *(radio operator)*, Doodles Weaver *(salesman)*, Tom Kennedy *(traffic cop)*, Eddie Ryder *(tower radioman)*, Don Harvey *(helicopter observer)*, Roy Engel, Paul Birch *(patrolmen)*, Don Van Sickel *(stuntman)*, Jack Benny *(man on road)*, Jerry Lewis *(mad driver)*, Chick Chandler, Barbara Pepper, Cliff Norton, Roy Roberts.

Comedy. Passengers from four vehicles rush to the scene of an accident after a fast-moving car sails off the edge of a mountain road and tumbles down a steep embankment. They include J. Russell Finch, president of the Pacific Edible Seaweed Company, who is traveling with his wife, Emmeline, and his shrewish mother-in-law, Mrs. Marcus; dentist Melville Crump and his wife, Monica; gag-writers Benjy Benjamin and Ding Bell; and furniture mover Lennie Pike. The victim, Smiler Grogan, reveals with his dying breath that he has buried $350,000 in stolen money under the "Big W" at Santa Rosita Beach State Park. Unable to determine the identity of the "Big W" or even to decide on a way to divide the cash, the greedy witnesses disperse and head for the park. Along the way, the Finch party takes on Englishman J. Algernon Hawthorne and Mrs. Marcus' beatnik son, Sylvester, and is forced to tell them of the money. The Crumps charter a dilapidated plane to give themselves a time advantage but are later delayed when they are accidentally locked in a department store basement and forced to set off an explosion to free themselves. Benjy and Ding ask drunken millionaire Tyler Fitzgerald to fly them to the site in his private plane, but he accidentally knocks himself unconscious in the cabin, and the two writers are forced to crash-land in an airport restaurant. Lennie, who has demolished a service station in his zeal to reach the park, is forced to take traveling salesman Otto Meyer into his confidence and later swears revenge when Meyer leaves him stranded on the road. Meanwhile, state police captain C. G. Culpeper, who has pursued Grogan for years, is having everyone carefully watched, patiently waiting for them to lead him to the hiding place; the captain, plagued by an unhappy family life and an inadequate pension plan, has decided to steal the money himself. The group, since joined by two taxi drivers, eventually discover four palm trees growing in the shape of a "W," and they uncover the money. Culpeper moves in to arrest the group and then tries to escape with the suitcase full of money. The men in the group pursue him in the two taxis and end up on the top of a fire escape of a condemned building where, in the confusion, the suitcase opens and scatters money to the crowd of spectators below. The fire escape comes unhinged and the fire department tries to rescue the men with a ladder truck, but the ladder topples when everyone climbs on simultaneously. The men are thrown to the ground, and all end up in the hospital—badly injured and under custody, with bankruptcy and prison sentences awaiting them. Culpeper is wondering if he will ever be able to laugh again when the despised Mrs. Marcus enters the corridor and slips on a banana peel. The downtrodden men burst into uncontrollable laughter. *Police. Businessmen. Dentists. Authors. Movers. Mothers-in-law. British. Beatniks. Traveling salesmen. Taxi drivers. Greed. Robbery. Reckless driving. Perfidy. Rescue. Family life. Drunkenness. Department stores. Filling stations. Trees. Hospitals. Fire departments. Santa Rosita Beach State Park (California). Automobile accidents. Airplane accidents. Chases. Explosions.*

Note: Presented in Cinerama. Location scenes filmed in Santa Rosita Beach State Park, California, and across highways from Colorado to San Diego. Screen credits extend thanks to the California communities of Agoura, Kernville, Long Beach, Malibu, Oxnard, Palm Desert, Palm Springs (Palos Verdes Estates), San Pedro, Santa Ana, Santa Barbara, Santa Monica, 29 Palms, Universal City, and Yucca Valley. Reviewed at running times 190–197 min; continuity lists 162 min for 70mm prints and 154 min for 35mm. The 70mm showings included 8 min of music; 16 min of intermission, considered to be part of the presentation in early engagements; and "news bulletins" on the soundtrack reporting progress in the search for the money.

IT'S A SICK, SICK, SICK WORLD   F6.2479
Dist American Film Distributing Corp. **1965** [New York showing: 14 Sep 1966]. Sd; b&w. 35mm. 70 min.
Prod Jose Scannapieco. *Assoc Prod* Fernando Serrano. *Dir* Antonio Scarpati. *Camera* Roberto Garco. *Asst Camera* Jose Gardella. *Lighting* T. A. Rosa. *Film Ed* Paul Gasparini. *Asst Ed* Lorenzo Mottoley. *Neg Cutter* Silvana Motto. *Asst Dir* Henry Sewell. *Prod Mgr* Juan Motta. *Asst to Prod* Peter Sevilla.
Narrator: John Shaffer.
Documentary? Film crews purportedly working in Rome, Paris, London, Germany, and the United States capture evidence of the search for sexual excitement: the gay night life of Paris is contrasted with the less-publicized activities of the city's prostitution district; in London, a wealthy young woman prostitutes herself because she is bored, while elsewhere a woman with an urge to travel looks for a man who is willing to pay her way. *Sexuality. Prostitution. Rome. Paris. London. Germany. New York City.*

Note: Filmed in New York City. Also known as *Sick, Sick World* and *Sick, Sick, Sick World.*

IT'S A SICK, SICK WORLD *see* **MACABRO**

IT'S A WOMAN'S WORLD (Japan)   F6.2480
Phoenix Film. *Dist* Shochiku Films of America. 8 Jan **1965** [Los Angeles showing]. Sd; col (Eastmancolor). 35mm (Shochiku GrandScope). 80 min.
Prod Yukio Taniguchi. *Dir* Taijiro Tamura. *Screenplay* Saburo Nitta. *Dir Photog* Kazutoshi Akutagawa. *Photog* Takeo Kurata. *Film Ed* Hanzaburo Kaneko. *Mus* Shoichi Makino. *Asst Dir* Satoru Kobayashi. *Prod Mgr* Toshiyuki Ike.
Commentator: Ayuro Miki.
Documentary. Women are examined in this film as objects of beauty, wonder, and mystery. Highlights include scenes of a maternity ward, women athletes, bar girls, nude waitresses, strippers, college girls in their dormitories, and a woman arriving in Japan for a legal abortion. *Women athletes. Bar girls. Waitresses. Stripteasers. Students. Nightclub hostesses. Abortion. Motherhood.*
Note: Released in Japan in Oct 1964 as *Shin onna onna onna monogatari.*

IT'S ALL FOR SALE   F6.2481
Freeway Films. *Dist* Republic Amusements Corp. 21 Mar **1969** [Champaign, Illinois, showing]. Sd; b&w. 35mm. 64-83 min.
Prod-Dir Alexander Maxwell. *Writ* Kevin Vincent. *Cinematog* Glenn Konig. *Film Ed* Edgar Smith. *Sd Rec* Mike Hall.
Cast: Albert J. Jenkins, Davee Decker, Patricia Collins, Sue Saber, Lisha Kim, Carol Turner, Karen Thomas, Barbara Aguirie, Lisa Cameron, Barbara Cory, Lola Mason, Philip Florence, Richard Hinge, Burk Katler.
Sex film. A man reads the personal advertisements in the underground newspapers and replies to some of them. He attends a swingers' party in the suburbs and visits a Los Angeles rent-a-model studio, a nudist camp, an adult book shop, and a massage parlor which features a nude Oriental masseuse. He meets people with bizarre sexual preferences: a well-muscled, homosexual masseur makes overtures to and is rejected by a male customer; two actresses become carried away during a lesbian lovemaking session; a woman shows sex aids of various sizes, shapes, and colors to a male customer; two women enjoy tying each other up in turn and fighting with whips; a model strips before a two-way mirror, thus teasing the man behind it; a Negro prostitute performs a dramatic ritual preliminary to offering herself to a customer—she makes carnal love with a python and sacrifices a chicken. *Actors. Orientals. Negroes. Suburban life. Mate swapping. Pornography. Nudity. Male homosexuality. Lesbianism. Sadomasochism. Voyeurism. Prostitution. Bestiality. Classified advertisements. Model agencies. Nudist camps. Massage parlors. Sex aids. Rites and ceremonies. Bookshops. Los Angeles. Snakes. Chickens.*
Note: Alexander Maxwell and Kevin Vincent are pseudonyms of Kevin Duffy. Also known as *It Was All for Sale.*

IT'S ALL HAPPENING *see* **THE DREAM MAKER**

IT'S ALL IN THE GAME *see* **A HOT SUMMER GAME**

IT'S HOT IN PARADISE (West Germany)   F6.2482
Rapid-Film–Intercontinental-Film. *Dist* Pacemaker Pictures. caMar **1962**. Sd; b&w. 35mm. 86 min.
A Gaston Hakim Production. *Prod* Gaston Hakim. *Dir* Fritz Böttger. *Camera* Georg Krause. *Mus* Karl Bette, Willy Mattes.
Cast: Alex D'Arcy *(Gary)*, Barbara Valentin, Harald Maresch, Helga Neuner, Helga Franck, Rainer Brandt, Dorothee Glöcklen, Eva Schauland, Gerry Sammer.
Horror film. Gary, a Hollywood talent scout, and seven showgirls, the only survivors of an airplane crash, become stranded on a remote Pacific island and find the dead body of a research scientist entangled in a huge spider's web. Gary is bitten by a giant spider and becomes a bloodthirsty monster. He terrorizes the women and brutally murders one of them. The dead scientist's two assistants, Joe and Robby, are dropped off on the island by a steamer. They find their superior's corpse and radio for help. A celebration follows, at which Robby makes love to a number of the women. He wanders off and is discovered dead. Meanwhile, Joe and the women track down the monster in the jungle, encircle him with flaming torches, and force him to his death in quicksand. Soon afterwards, a rescue ship arrives to take the survivors back to civilization. *Talent scouts. Showgirls. Monsters. Scientists. Airplane accidents. Murder. Sexuality. Corpses. Quicksand. Jungles. Islands. Pacific Ocean. Spiders.*
Note: Released in West Germany in 1960 as *Ein Toter hing im Netz*; running time: 82 min. Also known in the U. S. as *The Spider's Web* and *Girls of Spider Island.* Rereleased in Nov 1965 as *Horrors of Spider Island*; running time: 75 min. Jamie Nolan, credited as director in at least one U. S. source, is a pseudonym for Fritz Böttger. Also advertised as *Hot in Paradise.*

IT'S HOT ON SIN ISLAND   F6.2483

Dist Olympic International Films. 14 Aug **1964** [Los Angeles showing]. Sd; col (Eastman Color). 35mm. 60 min.

Prod-Dir Peter Marshall.

Cast: Pauly Dash, Dick Lynn, Cheryl Hentz.

Comedy-drama. Joey and Dick, faced with the problem of raising $12,000 to cover back payments on their newly-purchased yacht, charter the boat to five beautiful young schoolteachers. The women, after 9 months in the classroom, eagerly abandon their inhibitions as they leave Miami for an isolated island where they enjoy the pleasures of nature in the nude. Two counterfeiters arrive, hoping to escape federal authorities, and chase the naked women through the brush. The crooks capture Dick and his passengers and lock them up, bound and gagged, in a deserted house. Joey flees to Miami to pick up the original owner of the boat and returns to the island in time to capture the counterfeiters and claim the reward money. Joey and Dick pay off the mortgage on their yacht and set sail for new adventures. *Schoolteachers. Counterfeiters. Nudity. Vacations. Abduction. Finance—Personal. Yachts. Mortgages. Islands. Miami.*

Note: Filmed in the Florida Keys. Also known as *Hot on Sin Island.*

IT'S NOT MY BODY   F6.2484

Jahk Productions. *Dist* Contempo Pictures. 12 Jun **1970** [Champaign, Illinois, showing]. Sd; col. 35mm. 80 min.

Dir-Writ Ron Wertheim. *Cinematog* Joao Fernandes. *Ed* Ron Wertheim. *Mus* Dave Herman. *Sd* Charles Pitts. *Prod Mgr* Kent Bateman. *Script Cont* Victoria Bateman. *Cost* Ethel Warshovsky. *Tech Cons* Victor Petroshevic. *Grip* Joe Lewis. *Electrn* Paul Bang.

Cast: Robert Mitchel *(a man who acts)*, David Vallard *(voyeur)*, Jaqueline Friedrich *(Ann)*, Michael Castaldo *(Conrad)*, Pat Dougan *(magistratess)*, Jessica Tudor *(Delia)*, Edwin Miller *(priest)*, John Christofori, Marilyn Christofori, Laura Glenn, David Anderson, actor, Kit Chen, Robert Betwick, Susana Vaught *(jurors, agents, and gold men)*.

Drama. Delia, an efficient business executive, awakens one morning to find a group of strangers in her room. They identify themselves as members of The Court and force her to accompany them as they drive through a region beyond the boundaries of time. She sits between two golden-limbed men who flow over and into her unwilling body. They lead her to The Court; a majestically-robed woman presides at her trial, while the writhing, near-naked members of the jury hear the evidence. Witnesses from Delia's past file by to testify: a decadent sensualist with aristocratic aspirations; a bright, uninhibited young woman who offered the warmth of her body to anyone in need; and a lonely peeping tom tear away Delia's facade to reveal that she has used her body as a cruel weapon, denying the sexual desire that burned within. Delia refuses the truth. The members of The Court offer themselves to one another freely so that she may understand, but she remains blinded. Left alone to consider her crime, she meets a man who has committed the same offense. Together they find what they believe to be an escape route. Nearby, the members of The Court hover unseen, waiting for the prisoners to break through the sexual barriers that separate them. *Businesswomen. Judges. Supernatural. Trials. Sexuality. Voyeurism. Lesbianism.*

IT'S ONLY MONEY   F6.2485

York Pictures–Jerry Lewis Productions. *Dist* Paramount Pictures. 21 Nov **1962** [New York opening; c1 Nov 1962; LP23501]. Sd; b&w. 35mm. 84 min.

Prod Paul Jones. *Dir* Frank Tashlin. *Screenplay* John Fenton Murray. *Cinematog* W. Wallace Kelley. *Art Dir* Hal Pereira, Tambi Larsen. *Film Ed* Arthur P. Schmidt. *Mus* Walter Scharf. *Choreog* Bobby Van. *Sd* Gene Merritt, Charles Grenzbach. *Asst Dir* Ralph Axness. *Unit Prod Mgr* William C. Davidson. *Sp Eff* John P. Fulton, Farciot Edouart.

Cast: Jerry Lewis *(Lester March)*, Zachary Scott *(Gregory DeWitt)*, Joan O'Brien *(Wanda Paxton)*, Mae Questel *(Cecilia Albright)*, Jesse White *(Pete Flint)*, Jack Weston *(Leopold)*, Ted De Corsia *(policeman)*, Pat Dahl, Francine York *(sexy girls)*, Barbara Pepper *(fishing woman)*, Mike Ross *(policeman)*, Dick Whittinghill *(TV speaker)*, Francesca Bellini *(model on beach)*, Gary Lewis *(Lester as a boy)*, Alberto Morin, Milton Frome, Del Moore.

Comedy. Lester March, a 25-year-old orphan, works as a TV repairman but secretly longs to become a private eye. One night he and his detective friend, Pete Flint, watch a TV newscast in which spinster Cecilia Albright offers a reward for finding her long-lost nephew, the heir to a billion-dollar fortune. Lester visits the Albright mansion and is recognized as the missing heir by Cecilia's crooked lawyer, Gregory DeWitt, who plans to marry Cecilia and then murder her for her money. With the aid of Leopold, the sinister family butler, Gregory plots to kill Lester. They try to electrocute him, run him over with a car, toss him off a cliff, and poison him; but Lester fumbles safely through all the near-fatal mishaps. The first friend to suspect his true identity is the family nurse, Wanda Paxton, with whom Lester has fallen in love. Lester finally learns that he is the missing heir, and this knowledge causes Gregory and Leopold to redouble their murderous efforts. They almost succeed in trapping Lester in a

platoon of electronically-operated lawnmowers, but Pete and Wanda arrive in time to save him and apprehend the would-be killers. *Lawyers. Butlers. Orphans. Television repairmen. Detectives. Nurses. Spinsters. Heirs. Aunts. Personal identity. Murder. Rewards.*

Note: Location scenes filmed in the Malibu, California, area.

IT'S TRAD, DAD! see RING-A-DING RHYTHM

IT'S WHAT'S HAPPENING see THE HAPPENING

IT'S YOUR THING   F6.2486

Medford Film Corp.–Isley Brothers. *Dist* Medford Film Corp. 21 Aug **1970** [New York opening]. Sd; col. 35mm. 108 min. *MPAA rating* G.

Prod Ronald Isley, Rudolph Isley, O'Kelly Isley. *Dir* Mike Gargiulo. *Lighting Dsgn* Billy Knight. *Song:* "Abraham, Martin, and John" Dick Holler. *Sung by* Jackie "Moms" Mabley. *Song:* "Oh! Happy Day" sung by Edwin Hawkins Singers. *Song:* "Honky Tonk Woman" Mick Jagger, Keith Richard. *Song:* "Get Back" John Lennon, Paul McCartney. *Song:* "I Want To Take You Higher" Sylvester Stewart. *Song* "Proud Mary" John C. Fogerty. *Songs Sung by* Ike and Tina Turner. *Song:* "Family Tree" sung by Patti Austin. *Prod Supv* Betty Sperber.

Featuring: Patti Austin, Five Stair Steps and Cubie, Edwin Hawkins Singers, Isley Brothers, Jackie "Moms" Mabley, Ike and Tina Turner, Clara Ward Singers, Judy White, The Young Gents, The Brooklyn Bridge, The Winstons.

Documentary. A concert of soul music is performed at Yankee Stadium on June 21, 1969. The performers include: Patti Austin, the Five Stair Steps and Cubie, the Edwin Hawkins Singers, Jackie "Moms" Mabley, Ike and Tina Turner Revue, Clara Ward Singers, Judy White, The Young Gents, Brooklyn Bridge, and The Winstons. A riot nearly occurs during the finale when crowds rush forward to see the Isley Brothers perform. *Musicians. Singers. New York City—Yankee Stadium.*

Note: Filmed on videotape and transferred to 35mm film for theatrical release.

IVANOVO DETSTVO see MY NAME IS IVAN

IVAN'S CHILDHOOD see MY NAME IS IVAN

IZ GLUBINY STOLETIY see FROM THE KREMLIN TO THE COSMOS

J. R. see WHO'S THAT KNOCKING AT MY DOOR?

JACK AND THE BEANSTALK   F6.2487

Cinetron Corp. *Dist* R & S Film Enterprises. 10 Dec **1970** [Maryland license]. Sd; col. 35mm. 62 min. *MPAA rating* G.

Prod-Dir-Writ Barry Mahon. *Exec Prod* C. T. Robertson. *Camera & Lighting* Bill Tobin. *Asst Camera* Barry Mahon. *Scenic Dsgn* Thelma Raniero. *Film Ed* Steve Cuiffo. *Mus & Lyr* George Linsenmann, Ralph Falco. *Mus Arr* Eugene Ventresca. *Sd* Jon Williams. *Asst Sd* Mark Tannen. *Prod Mgr* Jon Williams. *Makeup* Tom Brumberger. *Cost* Peggy Praigg.

Cast: Dorothy Stokes, Mitchell Poulos, Chris Brooks, Renato Boracherro, John Loomis, Sami Sims, George Wadsworth.

Fantasy. A live action presentation of the fairy tale. *Widows. Giants. Plant life. Magic.*

JACK FROST (U.S.S.R.)   F6.2488

Gorky Film Studio. *Dist* Embassy Pictures. Sep **1966**. Sd; col (U. S. print by Pathé). 35mm. 79 min.

Dir Aleksandr Rou. *Screenplay* Mikhail Volpin, Nikolay Erdman. *Photog* Dmitriy Surenskiy. *Camera* L. Akimov. *Art Dir* Arseniy Klopotovskiy. *Asst Art Dir* Yu. Milovskiy. *Mus* Nikolay Budashkin. *Song Lyr* Mikhail Volpin. *Sd* Anatoliy Dikan. *Asst Dir* B. Kanevskiy. *Animal Trainer* G. Alekseyev, M. Simonov.

Cast: Aleksandr Khvylya *(Jack Frost [Morozko])*, Natasha Sedykh *(Nastenka)*, Eduard Izotov *(Ivan)*, Inna Churikova *(Marfushka)*, Pavel Pavlenko *(father)*, Vera Altayskaya *(stepmother)*, Georgiy Millyar *(witch)*, M. Yanshin, G. Borisova *("Old Mushrooms")*, Anatoliy Kubatskiy *(bandit chieftain)*, Valentin Bryleyev *(eligible bachelor)*, T. Pelttser *(eligible bachelor's mother)*, T. Barysheva *(matchmaker)*, V. Popova *(old woman)*, Z. Vorkul *(Ivan's mother)*, A. Zuyeva *(storyteller [Russian version])*, D. Bakhtin, V. Zhukovskiy, N. Zorina, K. Kozlenkova, M. Korabelnikova, A. Mukhin, V. Petrova, O. Peshkov, L. Potyomkin, A. Stapran, K. Starostin, A. Timontayev, T. Kharchenko, Yu. Chekulayev, A. Chumina, M. Shcherbakov, Olya Yukina, Tanya Yukina.

Fantasy. Based on the Russian fairy tale "Morozko." Beautiful Nastenka is forced to work as a scullery maid by her mean-tempered stepmother, who tyrannizes Nastenka's weak-willed father and dotes on her own ugly daughter, Marfushka. Nastenka falls in love with Ivan, a handsome, conceited young man who has set out to make his fortune in the world. To teach Ivan a lesson, Father

Mushroom endows him with the head of a bear and warns him that he will remain in this condition until he accomplishes a good deed. Nastenka's stepmother persuades the girl's father to abandon her in the forest, but kindly Jack Frost finds her and carries her back to his castle. Ivan, searching for his lost love, forces an old witch to help him. As he makes his way to Jack Frost's castle, the evil witch sends her cat to destroy Nastenka. The girl is tricked into touching Jack Frost's magic scepter, and she falls into a frozen, death-like trance. Ivan finds her apparently lifeless body and begins to weep. One of his tears falls onto Nastenka's cheek, causing her to awaken from her sleep; and Ivan regains his own handsome head. As they prepare for a lavish wedding, Nastenka's stepsister is sent into the forest in the hope that she will likewise find a handsome stranger, but she returns alone in a sled pulled by three fat pigs. Nastenka's father regains his courage and assumes control of the household. *Stepmothers. Stepsisters. Housemaids. Gnomes. Witches. Magic. Spells. Vanity. Forests. Jack Frost. Bears. Cats. Pigs.*

Note: Released in the U.S.S.R. in 1965 as *Morozko*; running time: ca90 min.

JACK JOHNSON   F6.2489

Big Fights, Inc. 25 Jul 1970 [Detroit opening; c4 Jun 1970; MP21233]. Sd; b&w. 16mm. 90 min. *MPAA rating GP.*

A Jim Jacobs Production. *Prod* Jim Jacobs. *Dir* William Cayton. *Script* Al Bodian. *Photog* Larry Garinger. *Film Ed* John Dandre. *Mus* Miles Davis. *Sd* Barney Beck, Al Schaffer.

Cast: Brock Peters *(voice of Jack Johnson)*, Kevin Kennedy *(narrator of fight sequence)*.

Documentary. Newsreel footage and still photographs chronicle the professional and personal life of black prizefighter Jack Johnson. Included are Johnson's first boxing matches at the turn of the century; his defeat of Tommy Burns to win the heavyweight championship in Australia (1908); his victory over Jim Jeffries in the "Battle of the Century" (1910); his match race with speed car driver Barney Oldfield; his much-debated loss of the heavyweight title to Jess Willard in Havana (1915); his widely-publicized marriages to three white women; his arrest and trial in Chicago for running a house of debauchery; his escape to Europe and voluntary return for imprisonment at Leavenworth; his activities in Spain during World War I, including a stint as an amateur matador in the Madrid bull ring; his trip to Russia and meeting with Rasputin on the eve of the 1917 revolution; his career in second-rate Hollywood films; his appearances in the 1930's at a Manhattan 42nd Street flea circus; and his fatal automobile crash in 1946. Also included is footage of Jack London, Nikolai Lenin, actor Victor McLaglen, Bat Masterson, fight promoter Tex Rickard, and Pancho Villa. *Prizefighters. Negroes. Bullfighters. Actors. Ex-convicts. Miscegenation. Automobile racing. Whorehouses. Flea circus. Motion pictures. World War I. Russia—History—1917-21 Revolution. Australia. Havana. Spain. Madrid. Chicago. Russia. New York City. Jack Johnson. James J. Jeffries. Jess Willard. Tommy Burns. Nikolai Lenin. Barney Oldfield. Jack London. Victor McLaglen. William Barclay Masterson. George Lewis Rickard. Francisco "Pancho" Villa. Leavenworth (U. S. penitentiary). Automobile accidents.*

JACK OF DIAMONDS (United States/West Germany)   F6.2490

Harris Associates–Bavaria Atelier. *Dist* Metro-Goldwyn-Mayer, Inc. 25 Oct 1967 [Los Angeles opening; c12 Jul 1967; LP34512]. Sd; col (Metrocolor). 35mm (Panavision). 108 min.

Prod Sandy Howard, Helmut Jedele. *Exec Prod* Lutz Hengst. *Dir* Don Taylor. *Writ* Jack DeWitt, Sandy Howard. *Adtl Dial* Robert L. Joseph. *Photog* Ernst Wild. *2d Unit Camera* Klaus von Rautenfeld. *Art Dir* Rolf Zehetbauer. *Film Ed* Hans Nikel. *Mus Comp & Cond* Peter Thomas. *Played by* Bavaria Studio Orchestra. *Adtl Compositions* Bob Harris, mus. *Rec Supv* Walter Ruhland, Hans Joachim Richter. *Asst Dir* Wolfgang Glattes. *Prod Mgr* Dieter Minx. *Cost Dsgn* Nicola Höltz. *Wardrobe* Siegfried Haubold, Irmgard Budack. *Makeup* Jonas Müller, Heidi Moser.

Cast: George Hamilton *(Jeff Hill)*, Joseph Cotten *(Ace of Diamonds)*, Marie Laforêt *(Olga)*, Maurice Evans *(Nicolai)*, Wolfgang Preiss *(Von Schenk)*, Karl Lieffen *(Helmut)*, Eduard Linkers *(Geisling)*, Alexander Hegarth *(Brugger)*, Carroll Baker, Zsa Zsa Gabor, Lilli Palmer *(themselves)*, Charles Hickman, Al Hoosman, Bob Cheslock.

Melodrama. The international jewel thief known as the Ace of Diamonds has long been in retirement, but his protégé, Jeff Hill—dubbed the Jack of Diamonds—is rapidly building a reputation equal to his mentor's. After stealing a fortune in jewels from the New York apartment of Zsa Zsa Gabor, Jeff sets out to execute a robbery aboard a luxury liner. Though he encounters another burglar in one of the staterooms, he succeeds in escaping with the gems. Then, following the theft of Carroll Baker's jewels, Jeff flies to Munich and is visited by the Ace, who tries to persuade him to quit while he is still ahead of the game. But a chance meeting with Olga leads Jeff to an introduction to the master thief of Europe, Nicolai. He learns that Olga is the burglar he encountered on the liner and agrees to join forces with her and Nicolai in removing the fabled

Zaharoff diamonds from an electronically-guarded bank vault in Paris. As the elaborate details of the crime are being worked out, Jeff cannot resist stealing the jewels of a third film star, Lilli Palmer. The Zaharoff job goes well, but, when an alarm is accidentally triggered and the police close in, the Ace appears and allows himself to be caught so that Jeff and Olga can escape. Jeff, however, refuses to accept the magnanimous gesture. A deal is negotiated with Von Schenk of the International Security Alliance whereby Jeff, Nicolai, and Olga agree to return all the jewels they have stolen—and retire from their criminal careers—in exchange for the Ace's freedom. The agreement is fulfilled, but Nicolai sheepishly admits that he has kept one small bauble for Olga's dowry. *Thieves. Actors. Police. Robbery. Bank robberies. Ocean liners. Jewels. New York City. Paris. Munich.*

Note: Location scenes filmed in New York City, Paris, Genoa, the Bavarian Alps, and Munich.

JACK THE GIANT KILLER   F6.2491

Edward Small Productions–Zenith Pictures. *Dist* United Artists. 13 Jun 1962 [Los Angeles opening; c13 Jun 1962; LP22236]. Sd; col (Technicolor). 35mm (Fantascope). 94 min.

Pres by Edward Small. An Edward Small Production. *Prod* Edward Small. *Assoc Prod* Robert E. Kent. *Dir* Nathan Juran. *Screenplay* Orville H. Hampton, Nathan Juran. *Orig Story* Orville H. Hampton. *Dir Cinematog* David S. Horsley. *Art Dir* Fernando Carrere, Frank McCoy. *Set Decor* Edward G. Boyle. *Film Ed* Grant Whytock. *Mus* Paul Sawtell, Bert Shefter. *Choreog* Jon Gregory. *Sd Mix* John Kean. *Sd Rec* Buddy Myers. *Asst Dir* Dick Moder. *Prod Mgr* Ralph Black. *Prod Supv* Ben Hersh. *Wardrobe* Bucky Rous, Sabine Manela. *Cost* David Berman. *Makeup* Charles Gemora. *Hairstyles* Louise Miehle. *Tech Dsgn & Sp Photog Eff in Fantascope* Howard A. Anderson. *Sp Photog Eff* Jim Danforth, David Pal.

Cast: Kerwin Mathews *(Jack)*, Judi Meredith *(Princess Elaine)*, Torin Thatcher *(Pendragon)*, Walter Burke *(Garna)*, Roger Mobley *(Peter)*, Barry Kelley *(Sigurd)*, Don Beddoe *(imp in bottle)*, Dayton Lummis *(King Mark)*, Anna Lee *(Lady Constance)*, Helen Wallace *(Jack's mother)*, Tudor Owen *(chancellor)*, Robert Gist *(Captain McFadden)*, Ken Mayer *(boatswain)*.

Fantasy. Pendragon, Master of Demons, is banished from ancient England and strives to regain his power by having one of his giants abduct King Mark's daughter, the Princess Elaine. She is saved by Jack, a farmer's son, who kills the giant with his ax. The grateful king appoints Jack as Elaine's protector and entrusts him to spirit her to the safety of a convent across the sea. Their ship is intercepted by Pendragon's ghouls and witches, and Elaine is captured, while Jack and 12-year-old Peter are cast overboard. They are rescued by an old Viking, Sigurd, who possesses a magic imp imprisoned in a bottle. With the help of his new friends, Jack rescues Elaine, but she has been bewitched and betrays him. Jack escapes though, and Sigurd is transformed into a dog and Peter into a chimpanzee. Jack breaks the evil spell the sorcerer has cast over the princess, but as they return to the boat Pendragon sends a two-headed giant against them. The imp calls up a many-tentacled sea monster, who kills the giant in a fierce battle, aided by Jack, the dog, and the chimpanzee. As they sail from the island together, Pendragon transforms himself into a flying dragon and attacks their small craft. Jack is carried off but slays the dragon in mid-air. As Pendragon plunges into the sea, his magic and creatures of evil die with him. The imp, who is really a leprechaun, is freed from his bottle and permitted to walk a rainbow to his home in Ireland. Jack and the princess are now free to live happily ever after. *Royalty. Vikings. Giants. Sorcerers. Sea monsters. Castles. Ships. Spells. England. Ireland. Legendary characters. Fairies. Dragons. Chimpanzees. Dogs.*

Note: Filmed partly on location at Santa Catalina Island.

JACKTOWN   F6.2492

Pictorial International Products. 1 Aug 1962 [Detroit opening]. Sd; b&w. 35mm. 62 min.

Prod-Dir-Writ William Martin. *Photog* Arthur J. Ornitz. *Art Dir* Jerry Kay. *Film Ed* Ralph Rosenblum. *Mus Comp & Cond* Aldo Provenzano. *Sd* John Feddermack. *Prod Mgr* John Haupt, Jr.

Cast: Patty McCormack *(warden's daughter)*, Richard Meade *(thief)*, Douglas Rutherford *(warden)*, Mike Tancredi, Johanna Douglas, John Anthony, actor, Gordon Grant, Alice Gordon, Harry Newman, George F. Taylor, Russ Paquette.

Melodrama. A juvenile delinquent and petty thief is caught by the police with a 15-year-old girl in the rear seat of his car and arrested for statutory rape. He feels that he has been unjustly accused since the girl had consented but had not revealed her age. Nevertheless, he is sentenced to 2 1/2 to 5 years in Southern Michigan Prison. To alleviate the tension he creates among the other convicts, he is allowed to care for the garden of the sympathetic warden and falls in love with his daughter. The warden discovers their relationship and transfers the young man to chauffeuring outside the prison. After a prison riot is quelled, a prisoner whom he is driving overpowers the guard, and the youth escapes. He goes to the warden's daughter but voluntarily returns to prison when she promises to wait for him. *Juvenile delinquents. Convicts. Prison wardens. Statutory rape. Filial relations. Prison revolts. Prison escapes.*

Note: Filmed entirely on location in Southern Michigan Prison ("Jacktown") in Jackson, Michigan. Includes newsreel footage of the 1952 riots at that institution.

JACQUES-YVES COUSTEAU'S WORLD WITHOUT SUN *see* **WORLD WITHOUT SUN**

JADĄ, GOŚCIE, JADĄ *see* **GUESTS ARE COMING**

JAG ÄR NYFIKEN—BLÅ *see* **I AM CURIOUS (BLUE)**

JAG ÄR NYFIKEN—GUL *see* **I AM CURIOUS (YELLOW)**

JAG—EN ÄLSKARE *see* **I, A LOVER**

JAG—EN KVINNA *see* **I, A WOMAN**

JAG EN KVINNA II *see* **I, A WOMAN PART II**

JAG EN MARKIS—MED UPPDRAG ATT ÄLSKA *see* **I, A NOBLEMAN**

JAG—EN OSKULD *see* **INGA**

JAGA WA HASHITTA *see* **THE CREATURE CALLED MAN**

JAGDSZENEN AUS NIEDERBAYERN *see* **HUNTING SCENES FROM BAVARIA**

J'AIME, TU AIMES *see* **I LOVE, YOU LOVE**

JAK BYĆ KOCHANĄ *see* **HOW TO BE LOVED**

JALSAGHAR *see* **THE MUSIC ROOM**

JANIE   F6.2493
Dist Cine Flicks International. ca **1970**. Sd; col (Eastmancolor). 35mm. ca80 min.

Prod-Dir Jack Bravman. *Screenplay* Mary Jane Carpenter. *Camera* Roberta Findlay. *Sd* George Holard.

Cast: Mary Jane Carpenter, Tina Grasco, William Dunnett, Jean Paila, Paul Green.

Melodrama. After making love with her father, Janie relates the day's adventures to him. *She persuades her girl friend to cut school, and they are picked up by a man in a car. Janie watches the man seduce her friend, and she kills them both. Janie later stops at a house with a pool and, confronted by the owner, kills him and takes a sunbath. She continues her drive in the stolen car, runs out of gas, and is picked up by a lesbian. After taking a hot bath at the woman's home, Janie cuts her throat. Janie returns to her father's house, kills his mistress, Roberta, and puts the body in the bathtub. Janie's father does not believe her story until he receives a call from Roberta's employers asking why she has not come to work. Janie's father finds Roberta's body and realizes that his daughter's terrible tale is true. Psychopaths. Students. Mistresses. Incest. Seduction. Murder. Lesbianism.*

JANKEN MUSUME *see* **SO YOUNG SO BRIGHT**

JASON AND THE ARGONAUTS (Great Britain)   F6.2494
Morningside Worldwide Pictures. *Dist* Columbia Pictures. 19 Jun **1963** [Boston opening; c1 May 1963; LP25630]. Sd; col (Eastman Color by Pathé). 35mm (Dynamation 90). 104 min.

Prod Charles H. Schneer. *Assoc Prod* Ray Harryhausen. *Exec Prod* John Dark. *Dir* Don Chaffey. *Screenplay* Jan Read, Beverley Cross. *Photog* Wilkie Cooper. *Camera Op* Harry Gillam. *Art Dir* Herbert Smith, Jack Maxsted, Toni Sarzi-Braga. *Prod Dsgn* Geoffrey Drake. *Titl Dsgn* James Wines. *Film Ed* Maurice Rootes. *Mus Comp & Cond* Mario Nascimbene. *Royal Philarmonic Orch Cond* Bernard Herrmann. *Sd Rec* Cyril Collick, Red Law. *Sd Ed* Alfred Cox. *Asst Dir* Dennis Bertera. *Unit Prod Mgr* Leon Lenoir. *Prod Mgr* John Dark, Jimmy Komisarjevsky, Paul Maslansky. *Cont* Phyllis Crocker. *Sp Visual Eff* Ray Harryhausen.

Cast: Todd Armstrong *(Jason)*, Nancy Kovack *(Medea)*, Gary Raymond *(Acastus)*, Laurence Naismith *(Argus)*, Niall MacGinnis *(Zeus)*, Michael Gwynn *(Hermes)*, Douglas Wilmer *(Pelias)*, Jack Gwillim *(King Aeëtes)*, Honor Blackman *(Hera)*, John Cairney *(Hylas)*, Patrick Throughton *(Phineas)*, Andrew Faulds *(Phalerus)*, Nigel Green *(Hercules)*, John Crawford *(Polydeuces)*, Douglas Robinson *(Euphemus)*, Nando Poggi *(Castor)*.

Adventure epic. On Olympus Zeus and Hera witness Pelias' murder of his half-brother, King Aeson of Thessaly, and the maturation of Aeson's son, Jason. To overcome his nephew's assertion of right to the throne, Pelias sends Jason on a treacherous journey, the quest for the Golden Fleece. Undeterred by danger, the youth immediately sets sail in the *Argo* with a crew of fast friends. En route to Colchis, site of their prize, the Argonauts surmount diverse obstacles, braving the attacks of a colossal bronze Titan, rescuing the prophet Phineas from the Harpies, and escaping death, through Hera's intervention, between the Symplegades. Despite the opposition of Colchis' King Aeëtes, to whom Jason's purpose is betrayed by Pelias' son Acastus, Jason, guided by Aeëtes' daughter Medea, kills the seven-headed Hydra guarding the Golden Fleece and vanquishes a skeletal army sown by Aeëtes from the monster's teeth. The Argonauts then return to Thessaly, bearing on board both Medea and the Golden Fleece. *Usurpers. Royalty. Ship crews. Murder. Theft. Perfidy. Ships. The Golden Fleece. Thessaly. Colchis. Pelias. Jason. Medea. Hera. Zeus. Aeëtes. Acastus. Hercules. The Argonauts.*

Note: Released in Great Britain in 1963; running time: 102 min. Filmed in Italy and Great Britain.

JAZZ ME BABY *see* **ZERO GIRLS**

JE SUIS FURIEUX *see* **I AM FURIOUS**

JE VOUS SALUE, MAFFIA *see* **HAIL! MAFIA**

JEAN-MARC *see* **ANATOMY OF A MARRIAGE; MY NIGHTS WITH FRANÇOISE**

JEG—EN ELSKER *see* **I, A LOVER**

JEG—EN KVINDE *see* **I, A WOMAN**

JEG—EN KVINDE, II *see* **I, A WOMAN PART II**

JEG—EN MARKI *see* **I, A NOBLEMAN**

JEKYLL'S INFERNO *see* **HOUSE OF FRIGHT**

JENNIE LEES HA UNA NUOVA PISTOLA *see* **GUNMEN OF THE RIO GRANDE**

JENNIE, WIFE/CHILD   F6.2495
Talent-Arts Productions-Robert Carl Cohen Productions. *Dist* Emerson Film Enterprises. Nov **1968**. Sd; b&w. 35mm. 83 min.

Prod James Enochs. *Dir* James Landis, Robert Carl Cohen. *Photog* William Zsigmond, Robert Carl Cohen. *Mus Comp* Harley Hatcher. Song: "Gonna Have a Good Time" *Sung by* Don Epperson. Song: "Peckingpaw's Theme" *Sung by* Davie Allan and the Arrows. *Other Songs Sung by* Jimmy August, Lydia Marcelle, Janine Sweet. *Sd* Robert Dietz.

Cast: Jack Lester *(Albert Peckingpaw)*, Beverly Lunsford *(Jennie)*, Jim Reader *(Mario Dingle)*, Virginia Wood *(Lulu Belle)*, Richard S. Cowl *(Dr. Hill)*.

Melodrama. Twenty-year-old Jennie marries an elderly farmer, Albert Peckingpaw. Because he cannot fulfill her desires, she attempts to seduce the naive young farmhand, Mario, who resists at first by getting drunk in town with his friend, Lulu Belle, but at last succumbs. Albert perceives what is proceeding behind his back, drugs the couple, chains them in the cellar, and, anticipating their deaths, digs their graves. As he returns to his house, however, he finds Lulu Belle standing by the barn. She seduces him, and Albert abandons his murderous plans. Mario frees himself and, unaware of the old man's change of heart, beats him until Jennie separates the two men. Filled with compassion, Jennie returns to Albert, but he gives her $2,000 and her freedom and goes off with Lulu. *Farmers. Marriage. Infidelity. Seduction. Drunkenness. Tranquilizers.*

Note: Filmed in 1965 as *Tender Grass*. Additional material filmed by Robert Carl Cohen.

JENNY   F6.2496
Palomar Pictures International. *Dist* Cinerama Releasing Corp. Jan **1970**. Sd; col (De Luxe). 35mm. 86 min. *MPAA rating* GP.

Pres by ABC Pictures. *Prod* Edgar J. Scherick. *Dir* George Bloomfield. *Screenplay* Marvin Luvat, George Bloomfield. *Story* Diana Gould. *Dir Photog* David Quaid. *Lighting* Richard Falk. *Camera Op* Richard Mingalone. *Art Dir* Trevor Williams. *Asst Art Dir* Otis Riggs. *Set Decor* John Alan Hicks. *Scenic Artist* Stanley Cappiello. *Main Titl* Arthur Eckstein. *Supv Film Ed* Patricia Jaffe. *Film Ed* Kent McKinney. *Mus Comp & Cond* Michael Small. *Mus Supv* Score Productions. *Theme Song:* "Waiting" *writ & sung by* Nilsson. *Theme Song Arr & Cond* George Tipton. Song: "Queen of Feeling" Michael Small, Michael Benedikt. *Sung by* Joe Butler. *Sd Ed* Sanford Rackow. *Sd Mix* Jim Shields. *Sd Re-rec* Richard Vorisek. *Asst Dir* Michael Hertzberg, Fred Gallo. *Prod Supv* Henry Spitz. *Asst to the Prod* Michael Haggiag. *Unit Prod Mgr* Steve Mussman. *Prod Sec* Belle Iacobellis. *Script Supv* Maggie James. *Wardrobe Dsgn* Ann Roth. *Makeup* Tom Case, John Alese. *Hairdresser* Lynn Masters, Philip Naso. *Casting* Marion Dougherty.

Cast: Marlo Thomas *(Jenny Marsh)*, Alan Alda *(Delano)*, Marian Hailey *(Kay)*, Elizabeth Wilson *(Mrs. Marsh)*, Vincent Gardenia *(Mr. Marsh)*, Stephen Strimpell *(Peter)*, Fay Bernardi *(woman in bus)*, Charlotte Rae *(Bella Star)*, Phil Bruns *(Fred)*, Estelle Winwood, Fred Willard, Michael Mislove.

Drama. Jenny Marsh, a young woman who is pregnant and unmarried, leaves her home in Connecticut for New York. There she finds a job in an antique shop filled with movie memorabilia and awaits the arrival of her baby. One afternoon she meets Delano, a filmmaker, and they become friends. Delano explains to Jenny that he is being pursued by the military draft at a critical point in his career. Having concluded that the best way to avoid the draft is to have a family, Delano suggests that they enter a marriage of convenience, thus providing Jenny's child with a father and Delano with a draft deferment. Jenny consents, and they travel to Connecticut to introduce Delano to Jenny's parents. Returning to New York, they get married, and Jenny moves into Delano's apartment. Jenny, having fallen in love with Delano, is disappointed when he continues to see his girl friend Kay, though they had arranged to have separate bedrooms and live separate lives. One night Delano gives a party, and Jenny, not wanting to smoke marijuana and feeling ignored by most of the guests, leaves the apartment. She walks into a Greenwich Village bar and meets Fred, who is attending a convention in the city. They drink together, take a walk, and end up in the lobby of a midtown hotel. Slightly drunk, Jenny falls asleep and upon awakening returns to the apartment early the next morning to find Delano angry and worried. She suddenly realizes that Delano is falling in love with her, and their marriage becomes happier. Just before the baby's birth, however, Delano learns that his request for deferment has been denied and he will be drafted. *Salesclerks. Filmmakers. Draft dodgers. Pregnancy. Military draft. Marriage of convenience. Parenthood. Marijuana. Connecticut. New York City. New York City—Greenwich Village. "A Place in the Sun".*

Note: Location scenes filmed in New York City and Tenafly, New Jersey. Working title: *And Jenny Makes Three.* Clips from *A Place in the Sun* appear in this film. Original running time: 93 min. Also reviewed at 88 min.

JENSEITS DES RHEINS see **TOMORROW IS MY TURN**

JESSE JAMES MEETS FRANKENSTEIN'S DAUGHTER   F6.2497

Circle Productions. *Dist* Embassy Pictures. 30 Mar **1966** [New Haven, Connecticut, opening]. Sd; col (Pathé Color). 35mm. 82 min.

Prod Carroll Case. *Assoc Prod* Howard W. Koch, Jr. *Dir* William Beaudine, [Sr.]. *Story & Screenplay* Carl K. Hittleman. *Dir Photog* Lothrop Worth. *Art Dir* Paul Sylos. *Set Decor* Harry Reif. *Supv Ed* William Austin. *Ed* Roy Livingston. *Mus* Raoul Kraushaar. *Sd Eff* John Hall. *Asst Dir* Max Stein. *Prod Mgr* Sam Manners. *Makeup* Ted Coodley.

Cast: John Lupton *(Jesse James)*, Cal Bolder *(Hank Tracy/Igor)*, Narda Onyx *(Maria Frankenstein)*, Steven Geray *(Rudolph Frankenstein)*, Felipe Turich *(Mañuel)*, Rosa Turich *(Nina)*, Estelita *(Juanita)*, Jim Davis *(Marshal McFee)*, Raymond Barnes *(Lonny)*, William Fawcett *(Jensen, the pharmacist)*, Page Slattery, Nestor Paiva, Dan White, Roger Creed, Fred Stromsoe, Mark Norton.

Horror film. While escaping from a posse, Jesse James and Hank Tracy, a wounded member of his gang, seek help from Juanita, a young Mexican who leads them to an ancient mission ruin inhabited by the grandchildren of the infamous Dr. Frankenstein. After sending Jesse away, ostensibly to secure medicine, Frankenstein's granddaughter Maria performs a brain transplant on Hank and transforms him into Igor, a monster similar to the one created by her grandfather. Jesse returns to the mission, and the monster, no longer recognizing his friend, knocks him unconscious; Maria then prepares to perform a similar operation on Jesse. Juanita arrives with Marshal McFee, however, and both Igor and Maria are killed. Jesse is led away by the marshal, and Juanita promises to wait for his return. *Posses. Outlaws. Mexicans. Monsters. United States marshals. Brain surgery. Organ transplants. Missions. Jesse Woodson James. Frankenstein.*

JESSICA (United States/France/Italy)   F6.2498

Dear Film–Ariane–Arts and Artists Establishment Productions. *Dist* United Artists. 28 Mar **1962** [Los Angeles opening; c28 Mar 1962; LP22237]. Sd; col (Technicolor). 35mm (Panavision). 105 min. [Also 112 min.]

A Jean Negulesco Production. *Prod-Dir* Jean Negulesco. *Adtl Dir* Oreste Palella. *Screenplay* Edith Sommer. *Screenplay Collab* Ennio De Concini. *Dir Photog* Piero Portalupi. *Art Dir* Giulio Bongini. *Film Ed* Renzo Lucidi, Marie-Sophie Dubus. *Mus Comp & Arr* Mario Nascimbene. *Songs:* "Jessica," "It Is Better To Love," "Will You Remember" Dusty Negulesco, Marguerite Monnot. *Song:* "The Vespa Song" Dusty Negulesco, Mario Nascimbene. *Sung by* Maurice Chevalier. *Sd* John Kean, Ennio Sensi. *Asst Dir* Ottavio Oppo. *Prod Supv* Nate H. Edwards. *Dir Prod* Daniele Micheletti. *Cost Dsgn* Dusty Negulesco, Annalisa Nasalli-Rocca. *Makeup* Amato Garbini. *Hairstyles* Gabriella Borzelli.

Cast: Angie Dickinson *(Jessica)*, Maurice Chevalier *(Father Antonio)*, Noël-Noël *(Old Crupi)*, Gabriele Ferzetti *(Edmondo Raumo)*, Sylva Koscina *(Nunzia Tuffi)*, Agnes Moorehead *(Maria Lombardo)*, Marcel Dalio *(Luigi Tuffi)*, Danielle De Metz *(Nicolina Lombardo)*, Antonio Cifariello *(Gianni Crupi)*, Kerima *(Virginia Toriello)*, Carlo Croccolo *(Beppi Toriello)*, Georgette Anys *(Mamma Parigi)*, Rossana Rory *(Rosa Masudino)*, Alberto Rabagliati *(Pietro Masudino)*, Angelo Galassi *(Antonio Risino)*, Marina Berti *(Filippella Risino)*, Manuela Rinaldi *(Lucia Casabranca)*, Gianni Glori Musy *(Filippo Casabranca)*, Joe Pollini *(Rosario)*.

Romantic comedy-drama. Source: Flora Sandström, *The Midwife of Pont Cléry* (New York, 1957). When her Italian-born husband is killed on their honeymoon, an American nurse named Jessica decides to remain in Sicily as a midwife in the little village of Forza d'Agro. While the beautiful girl's presence charms all the men, the women greet her with open resentment. The situation continually worsens until the women resort to the example set in ancient times by Lysistrata. If they deny themselves to their husbands, no babies will be born, and Jessica will have to leave because of lack of work. The village priest, Father Antonio, becomes greatly upset by this campaign. Then Jessica meets and falls in love with Edmondo Raumo, a wealthy *marchese* who has been living the life of a recluse since he was crippled in wartime. He allows Jessica to believe, however, that he is a poor fisherman, and when she learns the truth, she is furious with him. In retaliation, she flirts with all the men in the village and encourages their attentions. Desperate, Father Antonio persuades Raumo, the owner of Jessica's cottage, to give her notice to move. While the irate girl is packing, she is summoned to the bedside of Old Crupi, the gardener who has worked to bring Jessica and Raumo together, and who is now dying. The two are deeply affected by Old Crupi's death and the storm that follows. Raumo apologizes and asks Jessica to marry him. *Nurses. Americans in foreign countries. Widows. Midwives. Aristocrats. Recluses. Cripples. Priests. Gardeners. Village life. Jealousy. Duplicity. Flirtation. Eviction. Marriage. Forza d'Agro.*

Note: Location scenes filmed in Forza d'Agro, Sicily. Opened in Rome in Feb 1962 as *Jessica*; running time: 100 min; in Paris in Jun 1962 as *La sage-femme, le curé et le bon dieu*; running time: 90 min.

JESSICA see **MISS JESSICA IS PREGNANT**

A JEST OF GOD see **RACHEL, RACHEL**

JET STORM (Great Britain)   F6.2499

Pendennis Pictures. *For* Britannia Film Distributors/British Lion Films. *Dist* United Producers Releasing Organization. 20 Sep **1961** [Los Angeles opening; c8 Jun 1961; LP20457]. Sd (Westrex); b&w. 35mm. 91 min. [Also 88 min.]

A Steven Pallos–Cy Endfield Production. *Prod* Steven Pallos. *Dir* C. Raker Endfield. *Screenplay* C. Raker Endfield, Sigmund Miller. *Story* Sigmund Miller. *Dir Photog* Jack Hildyard. *Camera Op* Cecil Cooney. *Focus* Dennis Lewiston. *Art Dir* Scott MacGregor. *Asst Art Dir* Don Picton. *Scenic Artist* Ben Healey. *Film Ed* Oswald Hafenrichter. *Asst Ed* Kit Owens. *Mus Comp & Cond* Thomas Rajna. *Mus Adv* Ilona Kabos. *Song Comp & Sung by* Marty Wilde. *Sd Rec* Buster Ambler. *Sd Ed* James Shields. *Sd Camera* Jimmy Dooley. *Sd Boom* Peter Dukelow. *1st, 2d & 3d Asst Dir* Douglas Hermes, Patrick Clayton, Michael Stevenson. *Prod Mgr* Barry Delmaine. *Cont* Pam Carlton. *Wardrobe Supv* May Walding. *Makeup* Harry Frampton. *Hairdresser* Betty Sherriff. *Tech Adv* John Crewdson, (Capt.). *Still Photog* Ray Hearne.

Cast: Richard Attenborough *(Ernest Tilley)*, Stanley Baker *(Captain Bardow)*, Hermione Baddeley *(Mrs. Satterly)*, Bernard Braden *(Otis Randolf)*, Diane Cilento *(Angelica Como)*, Barbara Kelly *(Edwina Randolf)*, David Kossoff *(Dr. Bergstein)*, Virginia Maskell *(Pam Leyton)*, Harry Secombe *(Binky Meadows)*, Elizabeth Sellars *(Inez Barrington)*, Sybil Thorndike *(Emma Morgan)*, Mai Zetterling *(Carol Tilley)*, Marty Wilde *(Billy Forrester)*, Patrick Allen *(Mulliner)*, Paul Carpenter *(George Towers)*, Megs Jenkins *(Rose Brock)*, Jackie Lane *(Clara Forrester)*, Cec Linder *(Colonel Coe)*, Neil McCallum *("Gil" Gilbert)*, Lana Morris *(Jane Tracer)*, George Rose *(James Brock)*, Peter Bayliss *(Bentley)*, John Crewdson *(Whitman)*, Paul Eddington *(Victor Tracer)*, Glyn Houston *(Michaels)*, Peter Illing *(Gelderen)*, Jeremy Judge *(Jeremy Tracer)*, George Murcell *(Saunders)*, Alun Owen *(Green)*, Irene Prador *(Sophia Gelderen)*.

Melodrama. Ernest Tilley, a passenger on a jet bound for New York from London, is a formerly brilliant scientist who has been mentally disturbed ever since his only daughter was killed by a hit-and-run driver. Shortly after departure, Tilley rises from his seat and accuses fellow passenger James Brock of being responsible for the accident; in an emotional outburst, he accuses the entire human race of sharing the blame, then announces that he has hidden a bomb aboard the jet. The passengers panic, and Mulliner, an industrialist, plots to kill Brock in hopes of appeasing the madman. Brock, however, shatters a window in desperation and is sucked out when the decompression causes an explosion. The demented Tilley, still in need of revenge, at first refuses to reveal the bomb's hiding place but finally relents and permits its dismantling after being momentarily touched by the only child aboard. With calm restored, the jet continues toward its destination. *Scientists. Hit-and-run drivers. Children. Industrialists. Mental illness. Revenge. Airplanes—Jet. Bombs. London.*

Explosions.

Note: Opened in London in Sep 1959; running time: 99 min. Working title: *Jetstream.* Rereleased as *Killing Urge.*

JETSTREAM *see* **JET STORM**

JEU DE MASSACRE *see* **THE KILLING GAME**

UNE JEUNE FILLE, UN SEUL AMOUR *see* **MAGNIFICENT SINNER**

JEUNES FILLES EN UNIFORME *see* **MAEDCHEN IN UNIFORM**

JEUX D'ADULTES *see* **THE HEAD OF THE FAMILY**

JEUX PRÉCOCES *see* **LIPSTICK**

JIG SAW (Great Britain)   **F6.2500**
Figaro Films. *Dist* Beverly Pictures. 3 Mar 1965 [Los Angeles opening]. Sd; b&w. 35mm. 97 min.
A Val Guest Production. *Prod-Dir-Writ* Val Guest. *Assoc Prod* Frank Sherwin Green. *Photog* Arthur Grant. *Camera Op* Moray Grant. *Camera Focus* Wally Byatt, Robin Higginson. *Art Dir* Geoffrey Tozer. *Asst Art Dir* Anthony Reading. *Scenic Artist* Peter Wood. *Film Ed* Bill Lenny. *1st Asst Ed* Deveril Goodman. *Sd Mix* Norman Coggs. *Sd* Ken Cameron. *Boom Op* Tommy Staples. *Sd Camera Op* H. Raynham. *1st, 2d & 3d Asst Dir* Roy Baird, John Stoneman, Bernard Williams. *Prod Mgr* John Comfort. *Prod Sec* Shilleen O'Rourke. *Cont* Pamela Carlton. *Wardrobe Mistress* Molly Arbuthnot. *Makeup* Tony Sforzini. *Hairdresser* Polly Young. *Still Photog* Tom Edwards. *Prop Buyer* Dudley May. *Elec Chargehand* Steve Burtles. *Prop Chargehand* John Watling. *Constr Stagehand* T. Wilkie.
Cast: Jack Warner (*Detective-Inspector Fellows*), Ronald Lewis (*Detective-Sergeant Wilks*), Yolande Donlan (*Jean Sherman*), Michael Goodliffe (*Clyde Burchard*), John Le Mesurier (*Mr. Simpson*), Moira Redmond (*Joan Simpson*), Christine Bocca (*Mrs. Simpson*), Brian Oulton (*Frank Restlin*), Ray Barrett (*Sergeant Gorman*), Geoffrey Frederick (*Sergeant Unwin*), Norman Chappell (*Andy Roach*), John Barron (*Ray Tenby*), Joan Newell (*Mrs. Banks*), Peter Ashmore (*Mr. Bunnell*), Reginald Marsh (*Hilders*), Graham Payn (*Mr. Blake*), Robert Raglan (*chief constable*), John Horsley (*Superintendent Ramsey*), Gerald Campion (*Glazier*), Robert Moore, British (*Dr. MacFarlane*), Charles Houston (*garage foreman*), Timothy Bateson (*porter*), Harry Brunning (*luggage clerk*).
Mystery drama. Source: Hillary Waugh, *Sleep Long, My Love* (Garden City, New York, 1959). The office of Frank Restlin, a Brighton real estate agent, is ransacked, and Inspector Fellows and Sergeant Wilks determine from the realtor's assistant, Ray Tenby, that the leases for several properties were stolen. The policemen investigate a deserted seaside house and find the disfigured corpse of a woman. They question a prying caretaker, a hardware store owner, and Andy Roach, a grocery store watchman, whose information leads them to believe the victim might be spinster Jean Sherman. Traveling salesman Clyde Burchard is temporarily held as a suspect but released after Miss Sherman is found to be alive in Greenwich. Miss Sherman then helps Fellows determine the real identity of the dead woman and the past of the killer. The police cleverly trap their main witness, Ray Tenby, into confessing to the crime. *Real estate agents. Detectives. Traveling salesmen. Spinsters. Theft. Murder. Disfiguration. Confession (law). Corpses. Brighton (England). Greenwich (England).*
Note: Opened in London in Jun 1962; running time: 107 min.

JIGOKUHEN *see* **PORTRAIT OF HELL**

JIGSAW   **F6.2501**
Universal Pictures. 5 Jun 1968 [New York opening; c7 Sep 1968; LP38024]. Sd (Westrex); col (Technicolor). 35mm. 97 min.
Prod Ranald MacDougall. *Assoc Prod* Mort Zarcoff. *Dir* James Goldstone. *Story & Screenplay* Quentin Werty. *Dir Photog* John L. Russell. *Col Coörd* Robert Brower. *Art Dir* Howard E. Johnson. *Set Decor* John McCarthy, Hal Overell. *Main Titl* George De Lado. *Film Ed* Edward A. Biery. *Mus Score* Quincy Jones. *Mus Cond* Stanley Wilson. *Songs:* "Jigsaw," "Bullets La Verne" *perf by* Dr. West's Medicine Show and Junk Band. *Sd* Waldon O. Watson, James T. Porter, Ronald Pierce. *Asst Dir* Earl J. Bellamy. *Unit Prod Mgr* Donald Baer. *Cost* Grady Hunt. *Makeup* Bud Westmore. *Hairstyles* Larry Germain.
Cast: Harry Guardino (*Arthur Belding*), Bradford Dillman (*Jonathan Fields*), Hope Lange (*Helen Atterbury*), Pat Hingle (*Lew Haley*), Diana Hyland (*Sarah*), Victor Jory (*Dr. Edward Arkroyd*), Susan Saint James (*Ida*), Michael J. Pollard (*Dill*), Susanne Benton (*Arlene*), James Doohan (*building superintendent*), Donald Mitchell (*Peter*), Roy Jenson (*Arnie*), Ralph Maurer, Jim Creech, Kent McCord, Joan Bradley.

Crime melodrama. Source: Peter Stone, screenplay for the film *Mirage*, 1965. Walter Ericson, *Fallen Angel* (Boston, 1952). Unaware that he has accidentally dropped some LSD-filled sugar cubes into his cup of coffee, Jonathan Fields later wakes up in a strange apartment and discovers the corpse of a young woman submerged in the bathtub. Noticing dried blood on his wrist, he flees, fearing that he was responsible for the woman's death. With the assistance of private detective Arthur Belding, Fields attempts to reconstruct the previous evening's events, but a form of amnesia prevents him from remembering. Upon partially recovering his memory, however, he returns to his job as a scientist at a "think tank," where high government and military officials are evaluated by computers. There he is greeted by Lew Haley, a co-worker who is obviously eager to take over his job, and Helen Atterbury, his girl friend. Meanwhile, Belding pursues his investigation at the apartment, even though an earlier check had revealed no corpse. Hippies Dill and Arnie abduct the detective and force him to take LSD, but he escapes and recovers in the apartment of his girl friend, Sarah. Fields then takes another dose of LSD under the supervision of Belding and recalls the events of the fateful evening. His superior, Dr. Edward Arkroyd, had been having an affair with the murdered woman and was paying blackmail to Haley. Eventually, the woman threatened to talk to the police, and Haley killed her. When Arkroyd learned of the murder, he too was slain by Haley, who then planned to incriminate Fields in both crimes. Fields confronts Haley with the facts, and they engage in a fight that ends with Haley falling to his death from a window of their office building. *Detectives. Scientists. Hippies. Amnesia. Abduction. Psychedelic states. Blackmail. Murder. Frameup. LSD. Think tanks. Computers.*
Note: The film is a remake of *Mirage*, q. v. Originally made for NBC TV's World Premiere "Project 120" series. Quentin Werty is a pseudonym for producer Ranald MacDougall.

JIM THE MAN   **F6.2502**
Dist Film-Makers' Cooperative, Film-Makers' Distribution Center. 4 Feb 1967 [Los Angeles showing]. Sd; col. 16mm. 77 min.
Dir Max Katz. *Writ* Herbert Gold.
Cast: Scott Beach (*Jim Curtiss*).
Drama. Jim Curtiss, a lonely bachelor living in the city, has difficulty separating sexual fantasy from reality. Tormented by frustration, Jim attempts to fulfill a messianic mission. His experiences, however, only further alienate him. *Bachelors. Loneliness. Urban life. Sexuality. Insanity. Alienation. Fantasy.*

JINCHOGE *see* **THE DAPHNE**

JINRUIGAKU NYUMON *see* **THE AMORISTS**

J'IRAI CRACHER SUR VOS TOMBES *see* **I SPIT ON YOUR GRAVE**

JOAN OF THE ANGELS? (Poland)   **F6.2503**
Kadr Film Unit. *For* Film Polski. *Dist* Telepix Corp. 7 May 1962 [New York opening]. Sd; b&w. 35mm. 101 min.
Dir Jerzy Kawalerowicz. *Screenplay* Tadeusz Konwicki, Jerzy Kawalerowicz. *Photog* Jerzy Wójcik. *Art Dir* Roman Mann, Tadeusz Borowczyk. *Film Ed* Wiesława Otocka. Felicja Ragowska. *Mus* Adam Walaciński. *Sd Rec* Józef Bartczak, Zygmunt Nowak, Jozef Kensikowski. *Asst Dir* Maria Starzeńska, Marian Zietkiewicz, Urszula Orczykowska. *Prod Mgr* Ludwik Hager.
Cast: Lucyna Winnicka (*Mother Joan*), Mieczysław Voit (*Father Jozef Suryn/The Rabbi*), Anna Ciepielewska (*Sister Margaret*), Maria Chwalibóg (*Awdosia*), Kazimierz Fabisiak (*Father Brym*), Stanisław Jasiukiewicz (*Chrzaszczewski*), Zygmunt Zintel (*Wołodkowicz*), Franciszek Pieczka (*Odryl*), Jerzy Kaczmarek (*Kaziuk*), Jarosław Kuszewski (*Juraj*), Lech Wojciechowski, Marian Nosek, Jerzy Walden, Marian Nowak, Zygmunt Malawski, Stanisław Szymczyk.
Drama. Source: Jarosław Iwaszkiewicz, "Matka Joanna od Aniołów," in *Nowa miłość i inne opowiadania* (Warsaw, 1946). Joan of the Angels, the Mother Superior of a convent of Ursuline nuns in 17th-century Poland, is reportedly possessed by demons. The parish priest has already been burned at the stake for fathering her two children, four other priests have tried in vain to exorcise the evil spirits, and the other convent nuns (except Sister Margaret) have followed their superior's example by allowing minor demons to enter into their own bodies and souls. Now it is up to Father Jozef Suryn, a devout and humble priest, to restore Mother Joan to her former saintliness. He too fails, despite prayers, self-flagellation, and all known methods of exorcism. Frightened, he goes for advice to an elderly rabbi, who warns him that what he is combating in the convent may be only human nature. Gradually Father Suryn realizes that Mother Joan's physical needs are becoming his own, and he finds himself more and more emotionally drawn to the tormented woman. Late one night, in a desperate attempt to save her, he slays two innocent stable grooms, thereby offering his own soul to the demons that possess Mother Joan. Later he meets Sister Margaret, who has spent the night with, and then been

abandoned by, a lustful nobleman. Father Suryn orders the sobbing young woman to return to the convent and tell Mother Joan of the sacrifice he has made on her behalf. *Nuns. Priests. Rabbis. Exorcism. Sexuality. Murder. Flagellation. Self-sacrifice. Convents. Evil spirits. Ursulines. The Devil.*

Note: Released in Poland in 1961 as *Matka Joanna od Aniołów*; original running time: 125 min and 105 min. Also known as: *Mother Joan of the Angels?*

JOANNA (Great Britain)   **F6.2504**
Laughlin Films. *Dist* Twentieth Century–Fox Film Corp. 24 Nov **1968** [New York opening; c24 Nov 1968; LP36448]. Sd (Westrex); col (De Luxe). 35mm (Panavision). 107 min. *MPAA rating* R.
Prod Michael S. Laughlin. *Dir-Writ* Michael Sarne. *Dir Photog* Walter Lassally. *2d Unit Camera* David Muir. *Camera Op* Ronnie Fox Rogers. *Prod Dsgn* Michael Wield. *Film Ed* Norman Wanstall. *Mus Comp* Rod McKuen. *Arr & Cond* Arthur Greenslade. *Songs:* "Joanna," "All Catch the Sun" Rod McKuen. *Song:* "When Joanna Loved Me" Robert Wells, Jack Segal. *Arr* Wally Stott. *Arr by* Scott Walker. *Piano Arr* Ben Kendall. *Sd Rec* Delta Sound. *Dub Ed* Mike Le Mare, Jim Roddan. *Assembly Ed* Lucy O'Sullivan. *Asst Dir* Tony Kovacs. *Prod Mgr* David Anderson. *Cont* Ann Edwards. *Prod Sec* Caroline Langley. *Wardrobe Supv* Shura Cohen. *Clothes Dsgn* Sue West, Virginia Hamilton-Kearse. *Makeup Artist* Gordon Kay, makeup. *Hair* Leonard. *Constr Mgr* Bill Pearce. *Ch Electrn* Douglas Fenner. *Prop Buyer* Bill Roberts. *Prop Master* Michael Townsend. *Stills* The Swarbricks.
Cast: Genevieve Waite (*Joanna*), Christian Doermer (*Hendrik Casson*), Calvin Lockhart (*Gordon*), Donald Sutherland (*Lord Peter Sanderson*), Glenna Forster-Jones (*Beryl*), David Scheuer (*Dominic Endersley*), Marda Vanne (*Granny*), Geoffrey Morris (*father*), Michele Cooke (*Margot*), Manning Wilson (*inspector*), Clifton Jones (*black detective*), Dan Caulfield (*white detective*), Michael Chow (*Lefty*), Anthony Ainley (*Bruce*), Jane Bradbury (*Angela*), Fiona Lewis (*Miranda De Hyde*), Jayne Sofiano (*teacher*), Elizabeth MacLennan (*nurse*), Richard Hurndall (*butler*), Annette Robertson (*maid*), Jenny Hanley (*married woman*), John Gulliver (*art dealer*), Brenda Kempner (*bespectacled woman*), Peter Porteous (*taxi driver*), David Collings (*critic*), Sibylla Kay (*critic's wife*).
Comedy-drama. Joanna, a young Englishwoman, leaves her home in the provinces and goes to London to study art. She soon befriends Hendrik Casson, one of her teachers, and Beryl, a beautiful black woman who lives off wealthy men and welfare. Following a short-lived affair with Hendrik, Joanna takes up with the impoverished Dominic while Beryl becomes involved with the wealthy Lord Peter Sanderson. The quartet visit Peter's home in Morocco, and the young lord tells Joanna that he is dying of leukemia and that his illness has taught him that everyone needs to be committed to others' lives in order to fulfill his own. Peter sponsors a showing of Hendrik's paintings, but he dies shortly after the opening. Meanwhile, Dominic breaks with Joanna because of her promiscuity. Following Peter's funeral, Joanna becomes the mistress of Beryl's brother Gordon, who owns a nightclub purchased with Peter's money. Because of trouble with the protection racket, Gordon gets mixed up in a gangland vendetta in which he is beaten savagely by gangsters. In getting revenge on the gang, Gordon kills one of them. Accused of murder, he tries to escape but is apprehended, tried, and sentenced to prison. Joanna, who is carrying his child, remembers Peter's words about commitment and decides against an abortion, preferring instead to return to her father's country home and await the birth of her child. *Students. Art teachers. Negroes. Mistresses. Artists. Racketeers. Nightclub owners. Promiscuity. Cancer. Youth. Wealth. Death. Revenge. Murder. Pregnancy. Miscegenation. London. Morocco.*

Note: Produced in Great Britain in 1968; running time: 113 min, cut from 122 min. Filmed in London and Tangiers.

JOAQUÍN MURRIETA see **MURIETA**

JOE   **F6.2505**
Cannon Productions. *Dist* Cannon Releasing Corp. 15 Jul **1970** [New York opening]. Sd; col (De Luxe). 35mm. 107 min. *MPAA rating* R.
Prod David Gil. *Exec Prod* Dennis Friedland, Christopher C. Dewey. *Assoc Prod* George Manasse. *Dir* John G. Avildsen. *Screenplay* Norman Wexler. *Photog* John G. Avildsen. *1st Asst Camera* Ralph Hotchkiss. *2d Asst Camera* Stephen Bower. *Titl Art* Sal Vitale, Hugh Valentine. *Titl Dsgn* John Paratore. *Film Ed* George T. Norris. *Asst Ed* Thomas Kennedy. *Mus Comp & Cond* Bobby Scott. *Mus Supv* Gene Orloff. *Song:* "Hey Joe" Bobby Scott, Danny Meehan. *Sung by* Dean Michaels. *Song:* "You Don't Know What's Going On" *writ & sung by* Exuma. *Songs:* "Where Are You Going?" "You Can Fly" Bobby Scott. *Sung by* Jerry Butler. *Sd* Jack Cooley. *Sd Rec* Michael Scott Goldbaum. *Asst Sd Rec* Charles Hansen, sd. *Sd Eff Ed* Thomas Kennedy. *Asst Dir* Harvey Vincent, Michael Lerner. *Unit Mgr* Frank Vitale. *Post Prod Supv* William Sachs. *Script Supv* Randa Haines. *Prod Asst* Tom Feledy, Ken Robertson, Lloyd Kaufman. *Wardrobe* Andrew Kay. *Sp Eff* Louis Antzes. *Gaffer* Ralf Bode. *Still Photog* Jay Good. *Prop* Willard Bond. *Grip* Al

Sentesy.
Cast: Dennis Patrick (*Bill Compton*), Peter Boyle (*Joe Curran*), Susan Sarandon (*Melissa Compton*), Patrick McDermott (*Frank Russo*), Audrey Caire (*Joan Compton*), K. Callan (*Mary Lou Curran*), Gloria Hoye (*Janine*), Patti Caton (*Nancy*), Gary Weber (*George*), Claude Robert Simon (*Bob*), Francine Middleton (*Gail*), Bo Enivel (*Sam*), Frank Moon (*Gil Richards*), Jeanne M. Lange (*Phyllis*), Max Couper (*Ronnie*), Marlene Warfield (*Bellevue nurse*), Tim Lewis (*kid in soda shop*), Estelle Omens (*woman in bargain store*), Bob O'Connell (*man in bargain store*), Mary Case, Jenny Paine (*teeny boppers*), Reid Cruickshanks (*American bartender*), Rudy Churney (*man in bar*), Robert Emerick (*TV newscaster*), Patrick O'Neil (*bartender at Ginger Man*), Perry Gewirtz (*hippie on street*), Morty Schloss (*waiter in guitar joint*), Frank Vitale (*hippie in group*), Al Sentesy (*poster shop proprietor*).
Melodrama. After cynical drug addict Frank Russo persuades his reluctant 19-year-old girl friend, Melissa Compton, to try methadrine, she is hospitalized for an accidental overdose. When her father, Bill, a New York City advertising executive, arrives at Melissa's apartment to gather the girl's belongings, the addict taunts him. Infuriated by such callousness, Bill beats the youth to death. The dazed executive wanders into a workingman's bar and confides his crime to bigoted veteran Joe Curran. When Joe hears reports of the hippie's death on television he phones Bill his congratulations. The uneasy executive and exhilarated worker are soon socializing. Melissa, however, overhears her father describing the murder and runs away to Greenwich Village. While searching for her, Bill and Joe participate in an orgiastic pot party. Upon discovering that their wallets have been stolen, Joe forces the hosts to disclose the thieves' whereabouts. The enraged pair drive to a rural commune and slaughter its inhabitants. Too late, the executive discovers that he has shot his own daughter. *Advertising executives. Veterans. Hippies. Mistresses. Class conflict. Racial prejudice. Middle age. Adolescence. Filial relations. Murder. Communal living. Orgies. Guns. Narcotics. Marijuana. Bars. Hospitals. New York City. New York City—Greenwich Village. New York State.*

Note: Filmed on location in New York City and Rockland County, New York. Working title: *The Gap.*

JOE, EL IMPLACABLE see **NAVAJO JOE**

JOE NAVIDAD see **THE CHRISTMAS KID**

JOEN see **THE AFFAIR**

THE JOHN see **THE CHELSEA GIRLS**

JOHN AND MARY   **F6.2506**
Debrod Productions. *Dist* Twentieth Century–Fox Film Corp. 14 Dec **1969** [New York opening; c14 Dec 1969; LP37505]. Sd (Westrex); col (De Luxe). 35mm (Panavision). 92 min. *MPAA rating* R.
Prod Ben Kadish. *Dir* Peter Yates. *2d Unit Dir* Nicholas Sgarro. *Screenplay* John Mortimer. *Dir Photog* Gayne Rescher. *Asst Art Dir* Robert Wightman. *Set Decor* Philip Smith. *Prod Dsgn* John Robert Lloyd. *Film Ed* Frank P. Keller. *Mus* Quincy Jones. *Orch* Leo Shuken, Jack Hayes. *Song:* "Maybe Tomorrow" Quincy Jones. *Lyr* Alan Bergman, Marilyn Bergman. *Sd* Jack Jacobsen, David Dockendorf. *Asst Dir* Steve Barnett. *Unit Prod Mgr* David Golden. *Cost* Anthea Sylbert. *Men's Wardrobe* George Newman. *Women's Wardrobe* Marilyn Putnam. *Makeup* Irving Buchman. *Hairstyles* Robert Grimaldi. *Sp Photog Eff* L. B. Abbott, Art Cruickshank.
Cast: Dustin Hoffman (*John*), Mia Farrow (*Mary*), Michael Tolan (*James*), Sunny Griffin (*Ruth*), Stanley Beck (*Ernest*), Tyne Daly (*Hilary*), Alix Elias (*Jane*), Julie Garfield (*Fran*), Marvin Lichterman (*Dean*), Marian Mercer (*Mags Elliot*), Susan Taylor (*Minnie*), Olympia Dukakis (*John's mother*), Carl Parker (*tennis player*), Richard Clarke (*Charlie*), Cleavon Little (*film director*), Marilyn Chris (*film director's wife*), Alexander Cort (*imaginary film director*), Kristoffer Tabori (*boy scout*).
Drama. Source: Mervyn Jones, *John and Mary* (London, 1966). John, a furniture designer, and Mary, an art gallery assistant, meet at Maxwell's Plum, a New York City singles bar. Without exchanging names, they go back to John's fashionable Riverside Drive apartment and make love. Mary awakens, and while John sleeps, she looks through his book collection, at his furniture, and at a picture of his former girl friend, Ruth, a model. While Mary showers, John gets up and examines her handbag to find out who she is. Unenthusiastically, he makes breakfast for her. They engage in casual conversation while each privately sizes up the motivations of the other and recalls recent unhappy affairs. After breakfast, John plays a recording of Handel's music on his stereo system and exchanges verbal attacks with Mary. Their thoughts continue: John recalls the time that Ruth came uninvited to his apartment with all her belongings, and Mary thinks of her recent affair with James, a married politician. Mary leaves the apartment, but she forgets her keys and returns. John makes lunch for her, and during the afternoon she goes to sleep on his bed and dreams of a date with the politician in a hotel room. When she awakens,

John decides suddenly that she reminds him of his mother and asks her to go. She writes her telephone number on a mirror, but John erases it and rushes to a party given by Ruth. He quickly becomes bored with the boisterous affair and leaves to find Mary. Recalling that she lives in Murray Hill, he goes there by taxi, searching the neighborhood in vain. When he returns to his apartment, Mary is there cooking dinner. They get into bed, exchange names, and begin a relationship. *Furniture designers. Politicians. Models. Urban life. Singles bars. New York City.*

JOHN F. KENNEDY: YEARS OF LIGHTNING, DAY OF DRUMS F6.2507

United States Information Agency. *Dist* Embassy Pictures. 10 Apr **1966** [New York opening]. Sd; col (Pathé) with b&w seq. 35mm. 88 min.

Pres by The John F. Kennedy Center for the Performing Arts. *Prod* George Stevens, Jr. *Dir-Writ* Bruce Herschensohn. *Mus* Bruce Herschensohn. *Orch* William Loose, Jack Cookerly. *Sd Rec* Gordon Day. *Res* Gene Evans, ed.

Narrator: Gregory Peck.

Documentary. This compilation of film clips from John F. Kennedy's term of service of 2 years and 10 months as President of the United States is in part a memorial to the major programs he instituted. The late president's programs are presented as the six faces of the New Frontier: the Peace Corps, the Alliance for Progress, civil rights, the exploration of space, the pursuit of peace, and military preparedness. He is shown carrying his message to various countries and is heard commenting on crucial issues both here and abroad. Scenes of President Kennedy's personal efforts to implement his policies, his most famous speeches, and his family life are interwoven with footage of his funeral. The picture ends on a note of resolve that his aspirations shall one day be achieved. *Presidents of the United States. Assassination. Diplomacy. Funerals. John Fitzgerald Kennedy.*

Note: Released abroad in Nov 1964. A special act of Congress was required to permit the showing of this film in the United States. All profits were to go to the John F. Kennedy Center for the Performing Arts.

JOHN GOLDFARB, PLEASE COME HOME! F6.2508

Parker–Orchard Productions. *Dist* Twentieth Century–Fox Film Corp. 24 Mar **1965** [New York opening: c9 Nov 1964; LP29283]. Sd (Westrex); col (De Luxe). 35mm (CinemaScope). 96 min.

A Steve Parker–J. Lee Thompson Production. *Prod* Steve Parker. *Dir* J. Lee Thompson. *2d Unit Dir* Richard Talmadge. *Screenplay* William Peter Blatty. *Dir Photog* Leon Shamroy. *Art Dir* Jack Martin Smith, Dale Hennesy. *Set Decor* Walter M. Scott, Stuart A. Reiss. *Film Ed* William B. Murphy. *Mus* Johnny Williams. *Orch* Arthur Morton. *Titl Song* Johnny Williams, Don Wolf. *Sung by* Jaye P. Morgan. *Choreog* Paul Godkin. *Sd* Carlton W. Faulkner, Elmer Raguse. *Asst Dir* John Flynn, Fred Simpson. *Unit Prod Mgr* William Eckhardt. *Asst to the Prod* Alan S. Lee. *Script Supv* John Franco. *Miss MacLaine's Wardrobe Dsgn* Edith Head. *Men's Cost Dsgn* Adele Balkan. *Wardrobe* Mary Tate, Mickey Sherrard. *Makeup* Ben Nye, Frank Westmore. *Hairstyles for Miss MacLaine Created by* Sydney Guilaroff. *Supv Hairstylist* Margaret Donovan. *Sp Photog Eff* L. B. Abbott, Emil Kosa, Jr. *Dial Coach* Leon Charles. *Prop* Don Greenwood, prop. *Gaffer* Fred Hall. *Grip* Leo McCreary.

Cast: Shirley MacLaine (*Jenny Ericson*), Peter Ustinov (*King Fawz*), Richard Crenna (*John Goldfarb*), Jim Backus (*Miles Whitepaper*), Scott Brady (*Sakalakis*), Fred Clark (*Heinous Overreach*), Wilfrid Hyde-White (*Mustafa Guz*), Harry Morgan (*Deems Sarajevo*), Patrick Adiarte (*Prince Ammud*), Richard Deacon (*Maginot*), Jerome Cowan (*Brinkley*), Leon Askin (*Samir*), David Lewis (*Cronkite*), Milton Frome (*Air Force general*), Charles Lane (*editor*), Jerry Orbach (*Pinkerton*), Jackie Coogan (*Father Ryan*), Telly Savalas (*harem recruiter*), Angela Douglas (*Mandy*), Dick Wilson (*Frobish*), Nai Bonet, Sultanna (*specialty dancers*), Barbara Bouchet, Irene Tsu, Ann Morell, Shelby Grant, Eve Bruce, Gari Hardy, Jane Wald, Linda Foster.

Comedy. CIA Chief Heinous Overreach sends pilot John Goldfarb on a U-2 flight over the Soviet Union, in opposition to Secretary of Defense Maginot, who points out that "Wrong-Way" Goldfarb once ran a touchdown in the wrong direction in a college football game. Jenny Ericson, a *Strife* magazine photographer, is headed for Fawzia, an Arab kingdom, where she plans to smuggle herself into the harem of the wealthy King Fawz in order to write a story about him. Fawz is furious because his son, Prince Ammud, has returned from Notre Dame with word that he did not make the football team. The king orders a football field built for Ammud and suspends relations with the United States, thus upsetting U. S. plans to build a military base in Fawzia. Flying toward the U.S.S.R., Goldfarb is forced by mechanical troubles to crashland in Fawzia. Fawz recognizes him as the football star and gives him the choice of being turned over to the Soviets as a spy or coaching the Fawz University football team. When Goldfarb's coaching duties depress him, Fawz offers him the pick of the harem. Jenny implores him to pick her to save her from Fawz; both confess their identities and soon fall in love. Fawz tells Ambassador Brinkley that the United States can have its base if it will send a team to play

Fawz U. America dispatches the Notre Dame team with instructions to lose, but Notre Dame refuses. In the game's final moments, however, Jenny carries the ball, and because the gentlemanly Americans will not tackle her, Fawz U. wins. *Air pilots. Photographers. Arabs. Royalty. Reconnaissance. Diplomacy. Blackmail. U-2 planes. Football. Harems. Imaginary kingdoms. Union of Soviet Socialist Republics. United States—Central Intelligence Agency. United States—Defense Department. University of Notre Dame.*

JOHN LAIR'S RENFRO VALLEY BARN DANCE F6.2509

Dist Seven Arts Pictures. 20 Jul **1966** [Louisville, Kentucky, opening]. Sd; col (Eastmancolor). 35mm. 88 min.

A John Lair Production. *Prod* James F. Sullivan, Arthur W. Stanisch. *Dir* William R. Johnson. *Screenplay* John Lair, Robert Sullivan, Robert Schuler. *Mus Supv, Arr & Cond* John Lair. *Sp Songs* Ginalee Teater.

With: Red Brigham, Old Joe Clark, Russ Fisher, Joe Fisher, Farmer Sisters, Pete Stamper, Jean Gibson, Boyd Ingram, Ann Honeycutt, Al Ballinger, Roy Starkey, Pleaz W. Mobley, Aunt Mandy, Clarence Walls, Ginger Callahan (*Renfro Valley Home Folks*), B. Lucas, Sleepy Martin, Ralph Marcum, Lilly May Ledford, Buddy Durham (*Renfro Valley Fiddlers*), Don Harper (*electric guitarist*), Estil McNew and His "Kentucky Briar Hoppers" (*square dancers*).

Musical revue. The performers and citizens of Renfro Valley relate the story of their Kentucky settlement in a country music review. *Musicians. Singers. Folk music. Country music. Renfro Valley (Kentucky).*

Note: Alternative title: *Renfro Valley Barn Dance.*

JOHN OF THE FAIR (Great Britain) F6.2510

Merton Park Studios. *For* Children's Film Foundation. *Dist* Continental Distributing, Inc. 18 Apr **1962** [Maryland license]. Sd; b&w. 35mm. 63 min.

Prod Frank A. Hoare. *Dir-Writ* Michael McCarthy. *Photog* Joe Ambor. *Art Dir* George Haslam. *Film Ed* Eric Hodges. *Mus* Max Saunders. *1st Asst Dir* Fred Ruff. *Prod Mgr* M. G. Bromhead.

Cast: John Charlesworth (*John Claydon*), Arthur Young ("*Doc" Claydon*), Richard George (*William Samuels*), Michael Mulcaster (*Jasper Sly*), Hilda Barry (*Ma Miggs*), Carol Wolveridge (*Jill*), Sidney Bland (*Gilroy*), David Garth (*Sir Thomas Renton*), Fanny Wright (*Sarah Wilmott*), Tom Clegg (*Valdar*).

Adventure drama. Source: Arthur William Groom, *John of the Fair* (London, 1950). In 18th-century England, 14-year-old John Claydon assists "Doc" Claydon, a quack whom John assumes is his father, to sell Ma Miggs' herbal medicines to fairground patrons. John is abducted by his evil uncle Sir Thomas Renton, and discovers that he has inherited a title which Renton is trying to claim for himself. John's friend Jasper helps him escape. Renton's bullies, after starting a fire in which "Doc" dies, brawl with the fairground folk, led by Valdar, the strongman. Although John is brought to trial, he is vindicated when Sarah Wilmott, a fairground peddler, and the parish records prove his identity, thus enabling him to claim his title. *Quacks. Uncles. Bullies. Strongmen. Peddlers. Adolescence. Inheritance. Personal identity. Abduction. Fairs. Patent medicines. Trials. Fires.*

Note: Released in Great Britain in 1952.

JOHNNY BANCO (France/Italy/West Germany) F6.2511

Norddeutsche Filmproduktion-Chrysaor Films–Le Film d'Art Variety Film. *Dist* Ben Barry & Associates. **1969.** Sd; col (Eastmancolor). 35mm. 95 min.

Prod Gottfried Wegeleben, Paul Temps. *Dir* Yves Allégret. *Screenplay* Jean Vermorel, Yves Allégret, James Carter, Michel Audiard. *Photog* Michel Kelber. *Camera Op* Pierre Willemin. *Art Dir* Jean d' Eaubonne. *Film Ed* Henri Rust. *Mus* Michel Magne, Luigi Russeli. *Coöp* Cinecustodia (Switzerland).

Cast: Horst Buchholz (*Johnny Banco*), Sylva Koscina (*Laureen Moore*), Michel de Ré (*Orso Sebastiani*), Jean Parédès (*Anchois*), Fée Calderon (*Mignon de Brandie*), Elisabeth Wiener (*Nati*), Luciana Vincenzi (*Mary*), Friedrich Joloff (*Aristopoulos*), Romain Bouteille (*Eveillée*), Walter Giller (*Commissioner Jakubowski*), Mario Pisu.

Action melodrama. Source: Frédéric Valmain, *Le flamenco des assassins* (Paris, 1961). Adventurer Johnny Banco runs a gambling casino in Barcelona. After stealing 100 million francs from gangster Orso Sebastiani, a bogus antique dealer, Johnny flees to Monte Carlo. Followed by Orso's hired killers, Johnny, masquerading as a millionaire, entices and marries Laureen Moore, a wealthy American widow. Learning of the wedding, Orso, accompanied by Banco's mistress Nati, goes to Monte Carlo and wins back the entire fortune, compelling Johnny to contemplate killing Laureen for her inheritance. Although Orso murders Laureen, Johnny is accused of the crime. A final struggle between the two men settles the affair. *Adventurers. Gamblers. Gangsters. Antique dealers. Americans in foreign countries. Widows. Mistresses. Hired killers. Theft. Marriage. Wealth. Murder. Inheritance. Imposture. Casinos. Barcelona. Monte Carlo.*

Note: Opened in West Germany in Sep 1967 as *Jonny Banco—geliebter Taugenichts*; running time: 98 min. Opened in Paris in Mar 1968 as *Johnny Banco*; running time: 95 min; in Rome in 1968 as *Johnny Banco.*

JOHNNY CASH! THE MAN, HIS WORLD, HIS MUSIC　　F6.2512

Vérité Productions. *Dist* Continental Distributing, Inc. 28 Aug **1969** [Atlanta opening]. Sd; col (Movielab). 35mm. 94 min.

Prod Arthur Barron, Evelyn Barron. *Assoc Prod* Roy Hykin, Harry Wiland. *Dir-Writ* Robert Elfstrom. *Photog* Robert Elfstrom. *Film Ed* Lawrence Silk. *Asst Film Ed* Norman Gay. Songs: "Mister Crow," "Land of Israel," "Folsom Prison Blues," "Big River," "Cisco Clifton's Filling Station," "Five Feet High and Rising," "You Are What I Need" *comp & sung by* Johnny Cash. Songs: "Daddy Sang Bass," "Blue Suede Shoes" Carl Perkins. *Sung by* Johnny Cash. Song: "The Long Black Veil" Marijohn Wilkin, Danny Dill. *Sung by* Johnny Cash. Song: "The Great Speckle Bird" W. R. Calloway, Roy Acuff. *Sung by* Johnny Cash. Songs: "The Wall," "Busted" Harlan Howard. *Sung by* Johnny Cash. Song: "Big Foot" James R. Mundy. *Sung by* Johnny Cash. Song: "Orange Blossom Special" Erwin T. Rouse. *Sung by* Johnny Cash. Song: "The Ballad of Ira Hayes" Peter La Farge. *Sung by* Johnny Cash. Song: "Remember the Alamo" J. Bowers. *Sung by* Johnny Cash. Song: "Ring of Fire" June Carter, Merle Kilgore. *Sung by* Johnny Cash. Song: "Jackson" Billy Edd Wheeler, Gaby Rodgers. *Sung by* Johnny Cash, June Carter. Song: "The Devil To Pay" Merle Travis, L. Rusk. *Sung by* Johnny Cash, Carl Perkins. Song: "Bread and Gravy" Hoagy Carmichael. Song: "The Last Thing on My Mind" Tom Paxton. Songs: "Bank of Mariposa," "Come Away From the Roadside" *comp & sung by* Don Freed. Song: "One Too Many Mornings" Bob Dylan. *Sung by* Bob Dylan, Johnny Cash. Songs: "The Wreck of the Old 97," "She Got a Whole Lot of Motion," "Were You There When They Crucified My Lord?" Johnny Cash. *Sd* Allan Dater. *Sd Rec* Richard Vorisek.

Featuring: Johnny Cash, June Carter, Bob Dylan, Carl Perkins, The Tennessee Three, Mother Maybelle and the Carter Family, Don Freed.

Documentary. Country and Western singer Johnny Cash is featured on a concert tour with his wife, June Carter; his back-up band, the Tennessee Three; guitarist Carl Perkins; and Mother Maybelle and the Carter Family. In addition to numerous performances, Cash is seen in studio recording sessions with Perkins and also with Bob Dylan. Cash visits his boyhood home in Dyess, Arkansas, and the site of the 19th-century Indian massacre, Wounded Knee, South Dakota. One of his concert stops is a prison, where he is warmly received by the inmates. Guest artists perform "Bread and Gravy," "Fire Box," "Biscuit," "Old San Antone," "The Last Thing on My Mind," and "The Boy I Love the Best." *Singers. Country music. Prisons. Dyess (Arkansas). Wounded Knee (South Dakota). Johnny Cash.*

Note: First shown on National Educational Television on 16 Mar 1969; running time: 80 min. Also known as *Johnny Cash!*

JOHNNY COOL　　F6.2513

Chrislaw Productions. *Dist* United Artists. 30 Aug **1963** [Chicago opening; c30 Aug 1963; LP29262]. Sd; b&w. 35mm. 101 min.

Prod-Dir William Asher. *Exec Prod* Peter Lawford. *Assoc Prod* Milton Ebbins. *Screenplay* Joseph Landon. *Dir Cinematog* Sam Leavitt. *Art Dir* Frank T. Smith. *Set Decor* Budd S. Friend. *Film Ed* Otto Ludwig. *Mus Comp & Cond* Billy May. *Titl Song* "The Ballad of Johnny Cool" Sammy Cahn, James Van Heusen. *Sung by* Sammy Davis, Jr. *Sd* Philip Mitchell. *Asst Dir* Maxwell O. Henry, John Gaudioso. *Prod Supv* Stanley Scheuer. *Cost* Bob Wolfe. *Makeup* Frank La Rue. *Hairstyles* Marie Walter-Temme.

Cast: Henry Silva *(Johnny Cool [Giordano])*, Elizabeth Montgomery *(Dare Guiness)*, Richard Anderson *(correspondent)*, Jim Backus *(Louis Murphy)*, Joey Bishop *(used car salesman)*, Brad Dexter *(Lennart Crandall)*, Wanda Hendrix *(Miss Connolly)*, Hank Henry *(bus driver)*, Marc Lawrence *(Johnny Colini)*, John McGiver *(Oby Hinds)*, Gregory Morton *(Jerry March)*, Mort Sahl *(Ben Morro)*, Telly Savalas *(Mr. Santangelo)*, Joan Staley *(Suzy)*, Sammy Davis, Jr. *("Educated")*, Katharine Bard *(Mrs. Crandall)*, Steve Peck *(Kromlein)*, Douglas Henderson *(FBI man)*, Frank Albertson *(Bill)*, Mary Scott, actress *(Margaret Huntington)*, Elisha Cook, Jr. *(undertaker)*, John Dierkes *("Cripple")*, Robert Armstrong, Douglass Dumbrille *(gang members)*, Joseph Calleia *(tourist)*, George Neise.

Crime melodrama. Source: John McPartland, *The Kingdom of Johnny Cool* (New York, 1959). Colini, an exiled American gangster living in Sicily, rescues Giordano, a young Sicilian outlaw, from the police. After Giordano is groomed, polished, and renamed "Johnny Cool," Colini sends him on a vengeance mission to the United States to assassinate the men who plotted his downfall and enforced exile. Johnny arrives in New York and quickly kills several of the underworld figures on Colini's list. Meanwhile, he picks up Dare Guiness, a wealthy divorcée who becomes his accomplice, and she is severely beaten by the gangsters as a warning against the vendetta. Soon the FBI becomes involved, and when Johnny and Dare bomb the Hollywood home of gangster Lennart Crandall, the police are able to identify Dare's car. The two separate and plan to meet later, but Dare, realizing that Johnny is a vicious killer, tells his enemies where to find him. She then surrenders herself to the FBI, and

Johnny is murdered by the henchmen of one of his victims. *Gangsters. Police. Exile. Revenge. Murder. Perfidy. Bombs. Sicily. New York City. Hollywood. United States—Federal Bureau of Investigation.*

JOHNNY NOBODY (Great Britain)　　F6.2514

Viceroy Films. *Dist* Medallion Pictures. 23 Nov **1965** [New York opening]. Sd; b&w. 35mm. 88 min.

Prod John R. Sloan. *Exec Prod* Irving Allen, Albert R. Broccoli. *Dir* Nigel Patrick. *Screenplay* Patrick Kirwan. *Photog* Ted Moore. *Art Dir* Tony Inglis. *Film Ed* Geoffrey Foot. *Mus* Ron Goodwin. *Songs Sung by* Joe Lynch, Paddy MacGowan, Delia Murphy. *Sd Rec* Arthur Bradburn, Wally Milner. *Asst Dir* Ted Sturgis. *Prod Mgr* Bill Hill.

Cast: Nigel Patrick *(Father Carey)*, Yvonne Mitchell *(Miss Floyd)*, Aldo Ray *(Johnny)*, William Bendix *(Mulcahy)*, Cyril Cusack *(prosecuting counsel)*, Niall MacGinnis *(defending counsel)*, Bernie Winters *(photographer)*, Noel Purcell *(Brother Timothy)*, Eddie Byrne *(landlord)*, Jimmy O'Dea *(postman)*, John Welsh *(judge)*, Joe Lynch *(tinker/ballad singer)*, Michael Brennan *(Superintendent Lynch)*, J. G. Devlin *(caretaker)*, Christopher Casson *(Father Bernard)*, Norman Rodway *(Father Healey)*, May Craig *(tinker's mother)*, Michael O'Duffy, Dominic Behan *(ballad singers)*.

Mystery melodrama. Source: Albert Z. Carr, "The Trial of Johnny Nobody," in *Ellery Queen's Mystery Magazine* (Nov 1950). Mulcahy, a drunken, blasphemous writer living in a small Irish town, stands in front of the town church and challenges God to strike him down. He is suddenly shot and killed by a stranger who claims that an unknown force prompted him. The stranger, known only as Johnny Nobody because he claims to remember nothing before the fateful event, goes on trial in Dublin, and his deed captures public sentiment. Father Carey, a village priest called to support the defense claim that Mulcahy's death was a miracle and Johnny Nobody an instrument of heavenly vengeance, becomes suspicious of certain letters received by Johnny from a small coastal town. Meanwhile, Father Carey is hounded by a trial reporter, Miss Floyd. Traveling to the source of the mysterious letters, Father Carey discovers that Miss Floyd is Johnny's wife, and that the two killed Mulcahy because he had stolen thematic material from an unpublished book written by Johnny. Miss Floyd attempts to stop the priest from giving evidence by trumping up charges against him, but he eludes police and returns to Dublin. He arrives at the courtroom as the jury acquits Johnny, and his pleas are ignored. During a heated argument in the courtroom, however, Johnny himself blasphemes and is stricken with a fatal heart attack. *Authors. Priests. Strangers. Reporters. Atheists. Blasphemy. Drunkenness. Murder. Amnesia. Imposture. Plagiarism. Providence. Miracles. Pubs. Churches. Trials. Ireland. Dublin.*

Note: Filmed in Ireland. Opened in London in Nov 1961.

JOHNNY NORTH see THE KILLERS

JOHNNY RENO　　F6.2515

A. C. Lyles Productions. *Dist* Paramount Pictures. 9 Mar **1966** [New York opening; c31 Dec 1965; LP32242]. Sd; col (Technicolor). 35mm (Techniscope). 83 min.

Prod A. C. Lyles. *Dir* R. G. Springsteen. *Screenplay* Steve Fisher. *Story* Steve Fisher, A. C. Lyles, Andrew Craddock. *Dir Photog* Hal Stine. *Art Dir* Hal Pereira, Malcolm Brown. *Set Decor* Jerry Welch, Robert R. Benton. *Film Ed* Bernard Matis. *Mus* Jimmie Haskell. *Titl Song* Jimmie Haskell, "By" Dunham. *Sung by* Jerry Wallace. *Sd* Harold Lewis, John Wilkinson. *Asst Dir* James Rosenberger, Robert M. Jones. *Prod Mgr* Robert Goodstein. *Wardrobe* John A. Anderson, Thalia Phillips. *Makeup* Wally Westmore, Louis Haszillo. *Hairstyles* Nellie Manley.

Cast: Dana Andrews *(Johnny Reno)*, Jane Russell *(Nona Williams)*, Lon Chaney, [Jr.] *(Sheriff Hodges)*, John Agar *(Ed Tomkins)*, Lyle Bettger *(Jess Yates)*, Tom Drake *(Joe Connors)*, Richard Arlen *(Ned Duggan)*, Tracy Olsen *(Maria Yates)*, Paul Daniel *(Chief Little Bear)*, Dale Van Sickel *(Ab Connors)*, Robert Lowery *(Jake Reed)*, Reg Parton *(bartender)*, Rodd Redwing *(Indian)*, Charles Horvath *(Wooster)*, Chuck Hicks *(Bellows)*, Edmund Cobb *(townsman)*.

Western melodrama. As U. S. Marshal Johnny Reno rides toward Stone Junction, Kansas, in 1880, he becomes involved in a gunbattle with the Connors brothers, who mistakenly believe he is tracking them. Reno kills Ab Connors and captures Joe. At Stone Junction, Mayor Yates accuses Joe of having killed the son of Little Bear, an Indian chief. Reno wants Joe to have a fair trial, but Yates and the townspeople, fearing the Indians' wrath, want to lynch Joe, who claims he is innocent. Nona Williams, the saloonowner and Reno's former fiancée, helps Reno when an attempt is made to lynch Joe. When the townspeople decide to lynch Reno, Joe gives himself up on the condition that Reno be freed, but Yates doublecrosses him and plans to lynch them both. Actually, Yates had ordered his henchmen to kill Little Bear's son because the Indian was involved with Yates' daughter. Little Bear learns the truth and attacks the town. Yates is killed, and Reno and Nona ride off to start a new life together. *United States marshals. Brothers. Indians of North America. Saloon keepers. Mayors. Vigilantes. Murder. Lynching. Perfidy. Kansas.*

JOHNNY TIGER   F6.2516
Nova-Hugh Productions. *Dist* Universal Pictures. 21 Apr **1966** [Orlando, Florida, opening; c7 May 1966; LP35386]. Sd; col. 35mm. 102 min.
Prod R. John Hugh. *Exec Prod* Laird Legg, Nonus McDowell. *Dir* Paul Wendkos. *Screenplay* Paul Crabtree, R. John Hugh. *Adapt* Philip Wylie. *Orig Story:* "Tiger on the Outside" R. John Hugh. *Dir Photog* Charles Straumer. *Camera* Glenn Kirkpatrick. *2d Unit Camera* Charles O'Roark. *Lighting Cons* Wilbur Kinnett. *Art* Dick Williams. *Titl* Maury Hurt, Ed Loughlin, Bill Orr. *Ed Supv* Harry Coswick. *Asst Ed* Maurice Max. *Mus Comp & Cond* John Green. *Sd* George Yarbrough. *Mus Ed* Igo Kantor. *Asst Dir* Max Stein. *Prod Mgr* William P. Owens. *Asst to the Prod* Rod Cavin. *Script Supv* Hope McLachlin, Coswi. *Wardrobe* Lois McGee, Rebecca Cantrell. *Makeup* Guy Del Russo. *Hairdressing* Irene Aparicio. *Sp Eff* Dick Williams. *Chief Grip* Arthur Gaunt. *Wildlife Supv* Hal Granberry. *Casting Cons* Marvin Paige. *Prop* Joanna Williams.
Cast: Robert Taylor *(George Dean)*, Geraldine Brooks *(Doc Leslie Frost)*, Chad Everett *(Johnny Tiger)*, Brenda Scott *(Barbara Dean)*, Marc Lawrence *(William Billic)*, Ford Rainey *(Sam Tiger)*, Carol Seflinger *(Wendy Dean)*, Steven Wheeler *(Randy Dean)*, Pamela Melendez *(Shalonee)*, Deanna Lund *(Louisc)*.
Drama. George Dean, a widowed professor shunned by colleges because of his reputed arrogance, arrives with his three children at a Florida Indian reservation to teach the Seminoles. Appalled by the dilapidated schoolhouse, he appeals in vain to Leslie Frost, the resident health official. One day Dean's 19-year-old daughter, Barbara, is rescued from a herd of stampeding bulls by Johnny Tiger, the young grandson of the Seminole chief. Observing that the Indian children idolize Johnny, Dean asks him to encourage the youngsters to attend school. But Johnny mocks him and bitterly states that he is only a halfbreed whose mother was a barmaid. Realizing that Johnny, despite his hostility, is a man of innate intelligence, Dean urges him to attend school. Mainly because of Barbara, Johnny agrees; but the old chief, Sam Tiger, insists that Johnny abandon the white man's ways and leave the reservation. Caught in the conflict, Johnny and Barbara run off to get married. Tension between Dean and Sam mounts until a brush fire on the reservation entraps Dean's son. Risking his life, Dean races into the fire and finds the old chief holding the child protectively in a wet blanket. Badly burned, Sam Tiger asks Dean to give him back his grandson. Now tolerant of other men's beliefs, Dean accompanies Johnny to the Indian burial ground. There Johnny promises his dying grandfather to lead his people in the new ways he has learned. *Widowers. Professors. Seminole Indians. Physicians. Grandfathers. Halfcastes. Parenthood. Self-sacrifice. Marriage—Mixed. Fires. Florida. Stampedes. Bulls.*
Note: Location scenes filmed in the Florida Everglades. Working title: *The Cry of Laughing Owls.*

JOHNNY YUMA (Italy)   F6.2517
West Film-Tiger Film. *Dist* Clover Films Corp., Atlantic Pictures. Aug **1967** [Los Angeles showing]. Sd; col (Eastmancolor). 35mm. 99 min.
Pres by George Roth. *Prod* Italo Zingarelli. *Dir* Romolo Guerrieri. *Screenplay* Sauro Scavolini, George Simonelli, Fernando Di Leo, Romolo Guerrieri. *Story* Sauro Scavolini. *Photog* Mario Capriotti. *Film Ed* Sidney Klaber. *Mus* Nora Orlandi. *Titl Song* Paul Orlandi, Nora Orlandi. *Sung by* The Wilder Brothers. *Asst Dir* Jim Gregory.
Cast: Mark Damon *(Johnny Yuma)*, Lawrence Dobkin *(L. J. Carradine)*, Rosalba Neri *(Samantha Felton)*, Louis Vanner *(Pedro)*, Fidel Gonzales *(Sanchez)*, Gus Harper *(henchman)*, Leslie Daniel *(Thomas Felton)*, Gianni Solaro, Dada Gallotti, Nando Poggi, Frank Liston, Mirella Pamphili.
Western melodrama. Samantha Felton hires a killer to murder her wealthy rancher husband and then persuades L. J. Carradine, her former lover, to eliminate the only witness to the crime. Felton, however, had named his nephew, Johnny Yuma, sole heir to his fortune, and Samantha has been unable to locate the will and destroy it. Unaware of his uncle's death, Johnny meets Carradine en route to Felton's ranch. Following a shooting match in which the two men save each other's lives, they exchange holsters as a sign of mutual gratitude. Johnny, who now knows of his uncle's death, is mistaken for Carradine by Samantha's men. He is unmasked, captured, and tortured but manages to escape to the hotel in town. There he runs into Carradine, and the two men agree to a duel of honor rather than the assassination commissioned by Samantha. On the day of the duel, Samantha tries to have both men killed, but they join forces and gun down all of her henchmen, including her sadistic brother, Pedro. Before Carradine is killed by Samantha, he shoots holes in the water canteens which she has packed for her escape with the money. Later, as Johnny leaves, he discovers her sun-baked body in the desert. *Ranchers. Hired killers. Heirs. Murder. Perfidy. Mistaken identity. Torture. Wills. Deserts. Duels.*

Note: Released in Italy in 1966 as *Johnny Yuma*. Louis Vanner is a pseudonym for Luigi Vannucchi, Gus Harper for Gustavo D'Arpe, and Frank Liston for Franco Lauteri.

JOI-UCHI *see* **REBELLION**

THE JOKER (France)   F6.2518
AJYM Films. *Dist* Lopert Pictures. 7 Aug **1961** [New York opening]. Sd; b&w. 35mm. 86 min.
Exec Prod Roland Nonin. *Dir* Philippe de Broca. *Screenplay* Daniel Boulanger, Philippe de Broca. *Dial* Daniel Boulanger. *Photog* Jean Penzer. *Art Dir* Jacques Saulnier. *Film Ed* Laurence Méry. *Mus* Georges Delerue. *Sd* Jean Labussière. *Asst Dir* Georges Pellegrin.
Cast: Anouk Aimée *(Hélène Laroche)*, Jean-Pierre Cassel *(Edouard Berlon)*, Geneviève Cluny *(Pilou)*, Anne Tonietti *(Olga)*, Pierre Palau *(Uncle Théodose)*, Georges Wilson *(Guillaume Berlon)*, François Maistre *(André Laroche)*, Jean-Pierre Rambal, Liliane Patrick, Irène Chabrier.
Comedy. Life is an endless joy for madcap young Parisian Edouard Berlon. He takes pleasure from everything: animals, objects, strangers, the very air he breathes, and, most of all, the innumerable women with whom he has fallen hopelessly in love. Living with him in a charmingly unconventional house is his Uncle Théodose, an aged epicure who encourages his nephew's escapades; his brother Guillaume, a tenth-rate photographer who supports them by posing the family in tabloid representations of historic deaths; Edouard's former mistress, Pilou, who is now Guillaume's wife; a maid, Olga, who has been in the house so long that nobody knows quite how she got there; four large dogs; and Edouard's two cherubic and well-loved illegitimate children. One day Edouard again falls hopelessly in love, this time with Hélène Laroche, the beautiful, sophisticated wife of an industrialist. When she resists him, he dramatically announces that his life is over, and, mournfully playing the bassoon, he waits for death to claim him. But his charm once more proves to be effective, and Hélène decides to go away with him, much to the pleasure of Edouard's family. When she turns out to be a complaining and frigid mistress, however, the illusion of love is shattered and Edouard becomes bored. Shrugging his shoulders, he meets a young, attractive waitress, and they go off together. *Philanderers. Mistresses. Uncles. Brothers. Children. Photographers. Housemaids. Waitresses. Family life. Illegitimacy. Paris. Dogs.*
Note: Filmed in Paris; opened there in Jan 1961 as *Le farceur*; running time: 90 min.

THE JOKER IS WILD *see* **ALL THE WAY**

THE JOKERS (Great Britain)   F6.2519
Gildor Films-Scimitar Films-Adastra Films. *Dist* Universal Pictures. 15 May **1967** [New York opening]. Sd; col (Technicolor). 35mm. 94 min.
Prod Maurice Foster, Ben Arbeid. *Dir* Michael Winner. *Screenplay* Dick Clement, Ian La Frenais. *Story* Michael Winner. *Photog* Ken Hodges. *Art Dir* John Blezard. *Ed* Bernard Gribble. *Mus* Johnny Pearson. *Sd* John Purchese. *Asst Dir* Ken Softley. *Prod Supv* Fred Hymns, Patrick Marsden. *Cost* Tony Armstrong. *Makeup* Jim Hydes. *Hairstyles* Jeanette Freeman.
Cast: Michael Crawford *(Michael Tremayne)*, Oliver Reed *(David Tremayne)*, Harry Andrews *(Inspector Marryatt)*, James Donald *(Colonel Gurney-Simms)*, Daniel Massey *(Riggs)*, Michael Hordern *(Sir Matthew)*, Gabriella Licudi *(Eve)*, Lotte Tarp *(Inge)*, Frank Finlay *(harassed man)*, Warren Mitchell *(Lennie)*, Rachel Kempson *(Mrs. Tremayne)*, Peter Graves, British *(Mr. Tremayne)*, Ingrid Brett *(Sarah)*, Brian Wilde *(Sergeant Catchpole)*, Edward Fox *(Lieutenant Sprague)*, Michael Goodliffe *(Lieutenant Colonel Paling)*, William Mervyn *(Uncle Edward)*, William Kendall *(Major General Jeffcock)*, Freda Jackson *(Mrs. Pervis)*, William Devlin *(The Brigadier)*, Kenneth Colley *(De Winter, the chauffeur)*, Charlotte Curzon *(Camilla)*, Mark Burns *(Captain Browning)*, Brook Williams *(Captain Green)*, Brian Peck *(policeman)*, Basil Dignam *(bank manager)*, John Kidd *(solicitor)*, Nan Munro *(Mrs. Jeffcock)*, Nicky Henson, Eric Thompson, Peter Gilmore, Julian Holloway.
Crime comedy-drama. Architect David Tremayne and his brother Michael concoct a daring plan to "borrow" the British crown jewels from the Tower of London after Michael is expelled from military school. They prepare dated and sealed letters guaranteeing return of the jewels one week after the theft, then set their plan into motion by initiating a series of bomb scares in order to study the routine of Scotland Yard and the Army Bomb Disposal Unit. Next, they conceal a bomb in the Tower's Jewel Room, inform the police with an anonymous phone call, change into army uniforms, and join the bomb squad. Once inside, they chloroform the opposition, steal the jewels, cover themselves with fake blood, escape to a waiting ambulance, and quickly overpower the drivers. Authorities are completely baffled as the robbery becomes the talk of the nation, but David's guilt is exposed when his letter is opened the following week. Michael, however, has neglected to mail his letter, denies all knowledge of the crime, and has removed the jewels from their hiding place in David's flat.

Only David is charged and remanded into custody, but he tricks Michael into believing that Scotland Yard has found a lie in his alibi; before surrendering, however, Michael places the jewels on the Statue of Justice scales 200 feet above Old Bailey. Reunited in a prison cell, the brothers begin plans for a daring escape. *Brothers. Architects. Ambulance drivers. Hoaxes. Theft. Crown jewels (Great Britain). Ambulances. Prisons. Bombs. Scotland Yard. Great Britain—Army. Old Bailey. Tower of London. Documentation.*

Note: Filmed on location in and around London. Opened in London in Jun 1967. Only one source lists Adastra as a production company.

LE JOLI MAI (France)   **F6.2520**
Sofracima. *Dist* Pathé Contemporary Films. 9 Jun **1966** [New York opening]. Sd; b&w. 35mm. 124 min.
Prod Catherine Winter. *Dir* Chris Marker. *Screenplay* Catherine Varlin, Chris Marker. *Photog* Pierre Lhomme. *Film Ed* Eva Zora. *Mus* Michel Legrand. *Titl Song* B. Mokkoussov, Michel Legrand. *Sung by* Yves Montand. *Asst Dir* Pierre Grunstein. *Prod Mgr* André Heinrich.
Commentators: Yves Montand, Simone Signoret.
Documentary. This two-part film is set in Paris in May 1962, when anti-OAS demonstrations, the Salan trial, and strikes were rocking the French capital. The first part, "Prayer From the Top of the Eiffel Tower," consists of: interviews by the director with a suit salesman about his job and the wages he earns, the mother of nine children who is moving into a larger apartment, two youngsters eager to earn spending money, members of the stock exchange, an inventor, and a street poet proud of his poverty. Children comment on the qualities needed by an astronaut, and a supremely happy engaged couple talk about themselves. Part two, "The Return of Fantómas," alternates between public events and private discussions; reactions to the Algerian situation and the political and economic atmosphere of the country. Additionally, there are interviews with people who have become socially conscious, such as an African student who discusses French racism, a worker priest who chose the state over his church, and a woman prisoner. Finally, the film depicts the faces of Parisians whose unhappiness or anxiety is registered visually. *Africans. Children. Students. Salesmen. Poets. Inventors. Businessmen. Convicts. Priests. Politics. Racism. Strikes. Demonstrations. Algeria—History—War of Independence. Paris. Raoul Salan.*
Note: Opened in Paris in May 1963. Paris showing: 110 and 140 min; original length may have been 180 min. It appears that Simone Signoret speaks the English commentary and Yves Montand, the French.

A JOLLY BAD FELLOW see **THEY ALL DIED LAUGHING**

JONIKO AND THE KUSH TA KA   **F6.2521**
Alaska Pictures. *Dist* Alaska Pictures, American National Enterprises. 2 Apr **1969** [Wenatchee, Washington, opening]. Sd; col. 35mm. 94 min. *MPAA rating* G.
Pres by Rainbow Adventures. *Prod-Writ* Chuck D. Keen. *Dir* Ford Beebe. *Photog* Chuck D. Keen. *Film Ed* Leoncid Ortiz-Gil. *Mus* Hoyt Curtain, William Loose. *Prod Mgr* Chuck Ward. *Tlingit Culture Cons* Carl Heinmiller. *Naturalist* Bill Herd.
Cast: Tony Tucker Williams *(Joniko)*, Jimmy Cane *(grandfather)*, Richard Stitt *(father)*, Teresa Stitt *(mother)*, Charlie Paddock, Jesse Paddock *(twins)*, Penton James, Chuck Nowlin *(seal hunters)*, Sheldon Allman *(narrator)*.
Adventure drama. Joniko, a 12-year-old Alaskan, has been trained in the ways of his Tlingit tribe. When a geologist whom he has been guiding falls and injures his leg, Joniko sets out in a canoe to find his father, who departed the day before for northern seal grounds. During his journey through various animal domains, Joniko confronts grizzly bears, giant sperm whales, and an Alaskan brown bear. After entering the great sea of ice, Joniko, afraid of legendary evil demons, conquers Kush Ta Ka, the spirit of man's fear. The adolescent finds his father and returns with him to save the geologist. *Tlingit Indians. Geologists. Guides. Evil spirits. Adolescence. Tribal life. Fear. Rescue. Ice floes. Alaska. Bears. Whales.*
Note: Filmed on location in Alaska. Also known as *Joniko; Alaska Boy* and *Frontier Alaska.*

JONNY BANCO—GELIEBTER TAUGENICHTS see **JOHNNY BANCO**

JOSEPH AND HIS BRETHREN see **THE STORY OF JOSEPH AND HIS BRETHREN**

JOSEPH DESA see **THE RELUCTANT SAINT**

JOTAI see **THE CALL OF FLESH**

JOTAI see **VIXEN**

LE JOUR ET L'HEURE see **THE DAY AND THE HOUR**

LE JOURNAL D'UNE FEMME DE CHAMBRE see **DIARY OF A CHAMBERMAID**

JOURNEY BENEATH THE DESERT (France/Italy)   **F6.2522**
C. C. M.–Fidès. *Dist* Embassy Pictures. 29 Jul **1967** [New York showing]. Sd; col (Eastman Color). 35mm (Tech’nirama). 105 min.
Prod Luigi Nannerini. *Exec Prod* Nat Wachsberger. *Dir (see note)* Edgar G. Ulmer, Giuseppe Masini, Frank Borzage. *Screenplay* André Tabet, Ugo Liberatore, Remigio Del Grosso, Amedeo Nazzari. *Photog* Enzo Serafin. *Art Dir* Piero Filippone. *Prod Dsgn* Edgar G. Ulmer. *Film Ed* Renato Cinquini. *Mus* Carlo Rustichelli. *Mus Dir* Franco Ferrara. *Cost* Vittorio Rossi. *Sp Eff* Giovanni Ventimiglia.
Cast: Haya Harareet *(Antinea)*, Jean-Louis Trintignant *(Pierre)*, Rad Fulton *(Robert)*, Amedeo Nazzari *(Tamal)*, Georges Rivière *(John)*, Giulia Rubini *(Zinah)*, Gabriele Tinti *(Max)*, Gian Maria Volontè *(Tarath)*, Ignazio Dolce.
Science fiction melodrama. Source: Pierre Benoît, *L'Atlantide* (Paris, 1919). Mining engineers Pierre and Robert are surveying the Sahara in a helicopter piloted by their associate, John, when a storm forces them to crashland in an area that has been designated as a nuclear test ground. Shortly thereafter, they save the life of Tamal, a sheik who leads them into a cavern containing the lost city of Atlantis, ruled by the beautiful and ruthless Antinea. She forbids any escape attempts by her visitors, and when John tries to flee, she transforms him into a golden statue. Robert, upset by the murder of his friend, is sent to the mines and killed by Pierre, who is under Antinea's spell. Later, Zinah, a slave girl, falls in love with Pierre and helps him escape to the desert before a nuclear bomb is detonated and Atlantis destroyed. *Engineers. Air pilots. Sheiks. Royalty. Abduction. Murder. Transmutation. Spells. Helicopters. Nuclear weapons. Caves. Mines. Deserts. Sahara. Storms. Airplane accidents. Explosions. Atlantis.*
Note: Opened in Rome in May 1961 as *Antinea, l'amante della città sepolta;* running time: 100 min; in Paris in Aug 1961 as *L'Atlantide;* running time: 95 min. Borzage was replaced as director by Ulmer and Masini early in the filming. Previously filmed as *L'Atlantide* (France, 1921), *Die Herren von Atlantis* (Germany, 1932), and *Siren of Atlantis* (United States, 1948).

JOURNEY INTO NOWHERE (Great Britain)   **F6.2523**
Avon Films. *Dist* Planet Films, Globe Pictures, President Films. Dec **1963**. Sd; b&w. 35mm. 75 min.
Prod Bruce Yorke. *Exec Prod* Michael Deeley. *Dir* Denis Scully. *Photog* Vaclav Vich. *Sd Rec* Ken Cameron.
Cast: Sonja Ziemann *(Maria)*, Tony Wright *(Ricky)*, Helmut Schmid *(Joe)*.
Melodrama. Ricky, a gambler, is given 48 hours to pay off a large debt he owes to a gambling syndicate. He and Maria, an artist who has been contemplating suicide because of approaching blindness, take out a joint insurance policy with double indemnity. To collect, one must kill the other. Ironically, they fall in love, but Maria is killed in a runaway railroad car which was uncoupled by Joe, Ricky's old school friend and a syndicate thug who knows about the policy. The grief-stricken gambler collects the insurance money and pays his debt. *Gamblers. Artists. Suicide. Debt. Murder. Insurance. Blindness. Syndicates. Trains.*
Note: Released in Great Britain in Oct 1963; running time: 67 min. Filmed in South Africa. Also known as *Murder by Agreement.*

JOURNEY INTO SELF   **F6.2524**
Western Behavioral Sciences Institute–San Diego State College. *Dist* Western Behavioral Sciences Institute. Mar **1969** [Los Angeles showing]. Sd; b&w. 35mm. 47 min.
Prod Bill McGraw. *Film Ed* John Hind. *Adv* Stanley Kramer.
With: Stanley Kramer *(Intro Spoken by)*, Carl Rogers, psychologist, Richard Farson *(themselves, psychologists)*.
Documentary. Dr. Carl Rogers and Dr. Richard Farson conduct a group therapy session during which eight "normally adjusted" persons reach new levels of self-awareness through personal interaction. The participants include three businessmen, a theology student, a teacher, a school principal, and an office cashier. Attention is focused primarily on four of them: the housewife who can express affection only to her cat; a Eurasian woman who, while she perpetuates a "China doll" image, resents it and longs to be called a "broad"; the executive whose defensive belief that he does not need others masks a fear of rejection; and a black woman whose desire to comfort others is thwarted by the fear that she will be rejected because of her color. *Encounter groups. Psychologists.*
Note: Shot in 16mm.

A JOURNEY TO JERUSALEM   **F6.2525**
Filmways, Inc.–Maysles Films. *Dist* Sigma III Corp. 25 Sep **1968** [Pittsburgh opening]. Sd; col. 35mm. 84 min. [Also reviewed at 78 min.]

Prod-Dir Michael Mindlin, Jr.. *Photog* Albert Maysles, David Maysles, Richard Leacock, Stan Hirson, Joe Ryan, Sid Reichman, Bruce Martin. *Adtl Photog* F. Csaznick, R. Hirshbein. *Supv Ed* Robert Farren. *Ed* Dorothy Tod, Isaac Cohen. *Mus: Excerpts from Violin Concerto in E Minor* Felix Mendelssohn. *Violin Soloist* Isaac Stern. *Excerpts from Symphony no. 2 in C Minor ("Resurrection")* Gustav Mahler. *Vocal Soloist* Jennie Tourel, Netania Davrath. *Song: "Hatikvah"* N. N. Imber. *Mus Cond* Leonard Bernstein. *Perf by* The Israel Philharmonic, The Kol Yisrael Symphony Orchestra, Tel Aviv Philharmonic Choir. *Prod Mgr* Amatsia Hiuni. *Prod Asst* David Cordova.

Documentary. Shortly after the Six Day War Leonard Bernstein and Isaac Stern tour Jerusalem, celebrating its reunification by a concert on Mount Scopus. Among the tour's highlights are visits to a military hospital and the Western Wall. *Leonard Bernstein. Isaac Stern. Orchestra conductors. Violinists. Nationalism. Hospitals. Israeli-Arab War 1967. Israel. Jerusalem. Mount Scopus. Western Wall (Jerusalem).*

JOURNEY TO SHILOH   F6.2526

Universal Pictures. 10 May **1968** [New York showing; c6 Jul 1967; LP38820]. Sd; col (Technicolor). 35mm (Techniscope). 101 min.

Prod Howard Christie. *Assoc Prod* Frederick Shorr. *Dir* William Hale. *Screenplay* Gene L. Coon. *Dir Photog* Enzo A. Martinelli. *Camera Op* Lloyd Ward. *Asst Camera* John Hussey. *Art Dir* Alexander Golitzen, George Patrick. *Asst Art Dir* Bill Kenney, art. *Set Decor* John McCarthy, James M. Walters, Sr. *Film Ed* Edward W. Williams. *Asst Ed* Al Zuniga. *Mus* David Gates. *Mus Supv* Joseph Gershenson. *Sd* Waldon O. Watson, Lyle Cain, Don Cunliffe, Mert Strong. *Asst Dir* Jack Doran, Joe Boston. *Unit Prod Mgr* Henry Kline. *Script Supv* Diana Loomis. *Wardrobe* Edward Armand, Jack Takeuchi, Leslie Hall. *Makeup* Bud Westmore, Dick Blair, Jack Freeman. *Hairstyles* Larry Germain, Edith House. *Sp Eff* Roland Skeete. *Still Photog* Rollie Lane. *Stunt Coörd* Paul Baxley. *Animal Supv* Rusty McDonald. *Livestock* Richard Brinn.

Cast: James Caan (*Buck Burnett*), Michael Sarrazin (*Miller Nalls*), Brenda Scott (*Gabrielle DuPrey*), Don Stroud (*Todo McLean*), Paul Petersen (*J. C. Sutton*), Michael Burns (*Eubie Bell*), Michael Vincent (*Little Bit Lucket*), Harrison Ford (*Willie Bill Bearden*), John Doucette (*Gen. Braxton Bragg*), Noah Beery (*Sgt. Mercer Barnes*), Tisha Sterling (*Airybelle Sumner*), James Gammon (*Tellis Yeager*), Brian Avery (*Carter Claiborne*), Clarke Gordon (*Col. Mirabeau Cooney*), Robert Pine (*Collins*), Sean Kennedy (*Custis Claiborne*), Wesley Lau (*Colonel Boykin*), Chet Stratton (*Mr. Claiborne*), Bing Russell (*Greybeard*), Lane Bradford (*Case Pettibone*), Rex Ingram (*Jacob*), Charles Lampkin (*Edward*), Myron Healey (*Sheriff Briggs*), Eileen Wesson (*Ella Newsome*), Albert Popwell (*Samuel*).

War melodrama. Source: Will Henry, *Journey to Shiloh* (New York, 1960). Filled with dreams of glory during the Civil War, Buck Burnett and six other young men—Miller Nalls, Todo McLean, Eubie Bell, Willie Bill Bearden, Little Bit Lucket, and J. C. Sutton—leave their Texas homes to join forces with General Hood's raiders in Richmond. As they make their way eastward, they get a first-hand look at Southern prejudice and snobbery as they are turned away from the Claiborne plantation and witness the execution without trial of a runaway slave. When the youths start a barroom brawl, Buck is knocked out and a young saloon girl, Gabrielle, takes him home with her. Back on the road again, the youths are forced into service with a Pensacola brigade because of their skill with horses. No longer glory-seeking youngsters, they are shipped with thousands of others to the battle at Shiloh. During the fierce fighting, the Confederates are routed, four of the youths are killed, and Buck is wounded while trying to escape. Upon regaining consciousness in a hospital after having an arm amputated, Buck learns that Miller has deserted and is hiding in a barn. Defying orders, Buck makes his way to Miller in time to reach his dying friend. After Buck, now the sole survivor among his buddies, relates the journey to General Bragg, he is allowed to go home. *Soldiers. Bar girls. Slaves—Runaway. Amputees. Deserters—Military. Youth. Prejudice. Snobbery. Capital punishment. Combat zone life. Plantations. United States—History—Civil War. Texas. Richmond (Virginia). Shiloh (Tennessee). Braxton Bragg. Horses.*

JOURNEY TO THE BEGINNING OF TIME (Czechoslovakia)   F6.2527

Gottwaldov Film Studio–Československý Film. *Dist* New Trend Associates, Childhood Productions. 5 Nov **1966** [Boston opening; c10 Dec 1960; LP36033]. Sd; col. 35mm. 87 min.

Production Credits for U. S. Seq: *Pres by* William Cayton. *Prod-Writ* William Cayton. *Adtl Dial* Fred Ladd. *Photog* Anthony Huston. *Tech Adv* Edwin H. Colbert.

Original Production Credits: *Dir* Karel Zeman. *Screenplay* Karel Zeman, J. A. Novotný. *Photog* Václav Pazderník, Antonín Horák. *Art Dir* Karel Zeman, Zdeněk Rozkopal, Ivo Mrázek. *Film Ed* Zdeněk Stehlík. *Mus* E. F. Burian. František Strangmüller. *Prod Supv* Antonín Drvota. *Adv* Josef Augusta.

Cast—U. S. Seq: James Lukas (*Doc*), Victor Betral (*Joe ("Jo-Jo")*), Peter Hermann (*Tony*), Charles Goldsmith (*Ben*).

Original Cast: Vladimír Bejval (*Jirka*), PetrHermann (*Tonik*), Zdeněk Husták (*Jenda*), Josef Lukáš (*Petr*).

Fantasy. While visiting New York City's American Museum of Natural History, four youngsters are especially fascinated by the many exhibits devoted to the earth as it existed during prehistoric times. After seeing all the displays, the boys go rowing in the Central Park lake and discover a cavern concealed by trees and bushes. Their curiosity aroused, they row into the dark cave and enter a river that takes them back 500 million years to the beginning of time. Strange flora and fauna surround them as they encounter giant mammals similar to the ones they had seen only hours before in the museum. After numerous adventures, the boys fall asleep and awaken in the museum. *Children. Prehistory. Time travel. Caves. New York City—Central Park. American Museum of Natural History. Dreams.*

Note: Consists in large part of the 1955 Czechoslovakian release *Cesta do pravěku.* U. S. sequences filmed on location in New York City.

JOURNEY TO THE CENTER OF TIME   F6.2528

Borealis Enterprises–Dorad Corp. *Dist* American General Pictures, Western International. **1967**. Sd; col (Pathécolor). 35mm. 82 min. [Also 85 min.]

Prod David L. Hewitt, Ray Dorn. *Assoc Prod* J. Max Thornton. *Dir* David L. Hewitt. *Screenplay* David Prentiss. *Photog* Robert Caramico. *Art Dir* Edward Engoron. *Film Ed* William Wellburn. *Sd Rec* Arthur Names. *Sp Photog Eff* Modern Film Effects.

Cast: Scott Brady (*Stanton Jr.*), Anthony Eisley (*Mark Manning*), Gigi Perreau (*Karen White*), Abraham Sofaer (*Dr. von Steiner*), Austin Green (*Mr. Denning*), Poupee Gamin (*Vina*), Tracy Olsen (*Susan*), Andy Davis (*Dave*), Lyle Waggoner, Larry Evans, Jody Millhouse.

Science fiction drama. Dr. von Steiner and his assistants, Mark Manning and Karen White, demonstrate their unfinished time capsule to Stanton Jr., the heir of their research center's founder. The machine breaks down, and all are thrust into the future (6968 A.D.), to discover a totalitarian Earth under attack by alien laser beams. They escape in the capsule but are hurled back to the year 1,000,000 B.C. Their attempt to ward off an assault by a prehistoric beast results in the destruction of the ruby that provides the time capsule's power. The three men find a volcanic cave filled with precious jewels that will enable them to return to the present, but von Steiner stumbles to his death in molten lava. Stanton flees in the capsule with a fortune in gems, but not fully comprehending the controls, he is killed. With the reappearance of the machine in their situation, Mark and Karen use it to return to the present, accidentally reaching the research center a day earlier than that of their departure. Anticipating that their fate will be that of Stanton, they depart in the capsule for a timeless journey. *Scientists. Heirs. Time travel. Greed. Totalitarianism. Time machines. Laser. Jewels. Caves. Prehistory. The Future.*

JOURNEY TO THE FAR SIDE OF THE SUN (Great Britain)   F6.2529

Century 21 Pictures. *Dist* Universal Pictures. 27 Aug **1969** [Detroit opening; c1 Nov 1969; LP39049]. Sd; col (Technicolor). 35mm. 99 min. *MPAA rating* G.

A Gerry Anderson Production. *Prod-Story* Gerry Anderson, Sylvia Anderson. *Assoc Prod* Ernest Holding. *Dir* Robert Parrish. *Screenplay* Gerry Anderson, Sylvia Anderson, Donald James. *Photog* John Read. *Art Dir* Bob Bell. *Film Ed* Len Walter. *Mus Comp & Cond* Barry Gray. *Sd* John Peverill. *Sd Rec* Ken Rawkins. *Sd Re-rec* Ted Karnon. *Asst Dir* John O'Connor. *Prod Mgr* Brian Burgess. *Wardrobe* Elsa Fennell. *Makeup* Geoffrey Rodway. *Hairstyles* Barbara Ritchie. *Vis Eff Dir* Derek Meddings. *Sp Photog Eff* Harry Oakes.

Cast: Ian Hendry (*John Kane*), Roy Thinnes (*Col. Glenn Ross*), Patrick Wymark (*Jason Webb*), Lynn Loring (*Sharon Ross*), Loni von Friedl (*Lise*), Herbert Lom (*Dr. Hassler*), George Sewell (*Mark Neuman*), Franco Derosa (*Paulo Landi*), Edward Bishop (*David Poulson*), Philip Madoc, Vladek Sheybal, George Mikell.

Science fiction film. In the 21st century, Jason Webb, the director of an international scientific organization, finds evidence of a planet similar to Earth in orbit on the far side of the sun. Webb, in order to encourage U. S. politicians to provide funding for the construction of a spaceship to make the journey, discloses that Dr. Hassler, one of the scientists working on the project, is an espionage agent. The spaceship is built, and veteran astronaut Col. Glenn Ross and British astrophysicist John Kane are assigned to the crew. The two men are placed in a state of suspended animation, and the rocket is launched. In 3 weeks their ship crashes on a planet that seems to be Earth, and Kane is seriously injured. They are rescued by an unidentified spacecraft and returned to Webb's headquarters, where Kane dies of his injuries. Unable to explain to Webb why the mission lasted only half the scheduled duration, Ross realizes that everything, including newspaper print, is reversed to him; he theorizes that the new planet is an exact duplicate, a mirror-image, of Earth. Webb is convinced to finance another flight to prove the theory, but the second ship crashes into the research center, killing everyone but Webb. No one believes his story, and he is taken to a sanitarium. *Scientists. Secret agents. Astronauts. Space* *exploration. Suspended animation. Espionage. Space rescue. Spaceships. Imaginary planets. Sanitariums. The Future.*

Note: Opened in London in Oct 1969 as *Doppelgänger.*

JOURNEY TO THE SEVENTH PLANET (United States/Denmark)
F6.2530

Cinemagic, Inc.-Alta Vista Productions. *Dist* American International Pictures. Dec **1961** [c9 Dec 1961; LP21776]. Sd; col (Eastmancolor). 35mm (Techniscope). 80 min.

Prod–Dir–Orig Story Sidney Pink. *Assoc Prod* J. H. Zalabery. *Screenplay* Ib Melchior, Sidney Pink. *Camera* Aage Wiltrup. *Sp Eff Camera* Ronny Schoemmel. *Architect* Otto Lund. *Set Dressing* Helge Hansen. *Main Titl* Bent Barfod Film. *Montage Dir* Ib Melchior. *Cutter* Tove Palsbo, Thok Søndergaard. *Orig Mus Comp & Cond* Ib Glindemann. *Titl Song* Jerry Capehart, Mitchell Tableporter. *Sung by* Otto Brandenburg. *Sd* Poul Nyrup. *Asst Dir* Szasza Zalabery. *Prod Supv* Eric Moberg. *Scenemaster* Herbi Gärtner. *Wardrobe* Hanny Zalabery. *Makeup* Calma. *Sp Eff* Bent Barfod Film. *Miniatures* Krogh. *Abstracts* Børge Hamberg. *Electrn* Carlo Rasmussen, Edvard Svendsen. *Casting* William Schuller.

Cast: John Agar *(Don),* Greta Thyssen *(Greta),* Ann Smyrner *(Ingrid),* Mimi Heinrich *(Ursula),* Carl Ottosen *(Eric),* Ove Sprogøe *(Barry),* Louis Miehe-Renard *(Svend),* Peter Monch *(Karl),* Annie Birgit Garde *(Ellen),* Ulla Moritz *(Lise),* Bente Juhl *(Colleen).*

Science fiction melodrama. In 2001, after man has conquered space and discovered that no life exists on the moon, Venus, Mars, or Neptune, Earth's governing body, the United Nations, sends a five-man international expedition to explore Uranus. They land in minus 200° temperature in a beautiful but eerie land where they encounter women they knew in their past lives. Further exploration reveals that the planet is controlled by a mysterious evil Being that gives reality to all subconscious thoughts, fears, and desires: when one of the astronauts recalls his fear of rats, for instance, a huge rodent-like creature materializes. Realizing that they must destroy the Being if they are to escape from their past and return to the present, the Earthmen hunt down the creature in its hiding place in one of the caves below the surface of the planet. Since the creature can exist only in the near-normal subsurface temperature of the cave, the men destroy it by freezing it with liquid oxygen. One of the women from the past pleads to be taken back to Earth, but her image disintegrates en route. *Astronauts. Space travel. Fear. Wish fulfillment. Supernatural. Thought control. Caves. United Nations. Uranus (planet). The Future. Rats.*

Note: Filmed in Denmark.

LA JOVEN *see* **THE YOUNG ONE**

JOVITA (Poland)
F6.2531

Syrena Film Unit. *For* Film Polski. *Dist* Altura Films International. 11 Jun **1970** [New York opening]. Sd; b&w. 35mm. 95 min.

Pres by Clem Perry, Fleetwood Films. *Exec Prod* Jerzy Nitecki. *Asst Prod* Wiesław Grzelczak. *Dir* Janusz Morgenstern. *Screenplay* Tadeusz Konwicki. *Photog* Jan Laskowski. *Camera* Mieczysław Lewandowski. *Set Dsgn* Zdzisław Kielanowski. *Interiors* Anna Rachel. *Film Ed* Wiesława Otocka. *Mus Arr* Jerzy Matuszkiewicz. *"Masquerade Suite"* Aram Ilich Khachaturyan. *Perf by* Łódź Philharmonic Orchestra. *Violin Soloist* Wanda Wiłkomirska. *Sd* Jerzy Wroński. *Asst Dir* Karol Dabroqski. *Prod Mgr* Jerzy Nitecki. *Cost* Maria Karmolińska. *Makeup* Mieczysław Pośmiechowicz.

Cast: Barbara Lass *(Agnes/Jovita),* Daniel Olbrychski *(Marc Arens),* Zbigniew Cybulski *(Edouard),* Kalina Jędrusik *(Helene),* Anna Halcewicz-Pleskaczewska *(Dorota),* Ignacy Gogolewski *(Michał),* Iga Cembrzyńska *(Lola),* Anna Ciepiela *(Alina),* Ryszard Filipski *(policeman),* Aleksander Fogiel *(president),* L. Pilarska, M. Cebulski, L. Nowak, C. Kasznia.

Romantic melodrama. Source: Stanisław Dygat, *Disneyland* (Warsaw, 1965). Marc Arens, an architect and long-distance runner, sits in a concert and reminisces about an experience from his past. ... One evening at a masquerade ball, a woman dressed as an houri and calling herself Jovita repulses Marc's advances, and later she fails to keep an appointment with him. Unaccustomed to being rebuffed, Marc pursues Jovita, neglecting Agnes, a painter friend of Jovita's who loves him. At the same time, Marc has affairs with other women but becomes quarrelsome because he cannot have Jovita and provokes a fight in a restaurant. When he is in jail, he sees Agnes and learns that she is about to be married and that she is actually Jovita. *Architects. Athletes. Philanderers. Painters. Personal identity. Masquerades. Jails.*

Note: Released in Poland in 1967 as *Jowita;* running time: 97 min. Barbara Lass is also known as Barbara Kwiatkowska.

JOWITA *see* **JOVITA**

JOY HOUSE (France)
F6.2532

Cipra–Cité Films. *Dist* Metro-Goldwyn-Mayer, Inc. 28 Oct **1964** [Cincinnati, Ohio, opening; c7 Aug 1964; LP29209]. Sd; b&w. 35mm

(Franscope). 98 min.

Prod Jacques Bar. *Assoc Prod* Raymond Froment. *Dir* René Clément. *Screen Adapt* René Clément, Pascal Jardin, Charles Williams. *French Dial* Pascal Jardin. *English Dial* Charles Williams. *Dir Photog* Henri Decaë. *Camera Op* Alain Douarinou. *Art Dir* Jean André. *Asst Art Dir* Eugène Roman, Robert André. *Film Ed* Fedora Zincone. *Asst Ed* Catherine Gascuel. *Mus* Lalo Schifrin. *Sd* Antoine Bonfanti. *Asst Dir* Bernard Paul, Costa-Gavras. *Prod Supv* Léon Sanz. *Prod Mgr* Michel Choquet. *Script Girl* Yvette Vérité. *Cost for Miss Fonda & Miss Albright* Pierre Balmain. *Makeup* Aïda Carange. *Hairstyles* Jacques Dessange, Alex Archambault. *Still Photog* Victor Rodrigue.

Cast: Alain Delon *(Marc),* Jane Fonda *(Melinda),* Lola Albright *(Barbara),* Sorrell Booke *(Harry),* Carl Studer *(Loftus),* André Oumansky *(Vincent),* Arthur Howard *(Reverend Nielson),* Nick Del Negro *(Mick),* Jacques Bezard *("Napoleon"),* Berett Arcaya *(Diana),* Douking *(tramp),* Jean-Pierre Honoré *(tailor),* Marc Mazza *(Corsican),* Annette Poivre *(employee),* George Gaynes.

Action melodrama. Source: Day Keene, *Joy House* (New York, 1954). In Monte Carlo, Marc, a handsome cardsharp, escapes American gangsters who have been ordered to kill him by the boss of a New York gang because he had an affair with the boss's wife. Marc hides in a mission for the poor where Barbara, a wealthy widow, finds him and hires him as her chauffeur. At Barbara's chateau, Melinda, Barbara's niece, becomes attracted to him. Marc discovers that Barbara is hiding her lover, Vincent, in the secret rooms and passageways of the chateau. She and Vincent (a bank robber sought by the police for murdering Barbara's husband) plan to murder Marc so that Vincent may use his passport in escaping to South America. Marc and Barbara begin an affair but are discovered by Vincent, who then kills Barbara but is himself killed by the American gangsters, who mistake him for Marc. Marc and Melinda plan to dispose of the two bodies, but when Melinda learns that Marc is planning to leave without her, she tricks the police into believing Marc guilty and forces him to hide in the chateau's secret rooms. He is her prisoner, just as Vincent had been her aunt's. *Cardsharps. Gangsters. Americans in foreign countries. Hired killers. Widows. Chauffeurs. Aunts. Police. Robbers. Infidelity. Wealth. Murder. Mistaken identity. Perfidy. Missions. Monte Carlo. Riviera.*

Note: Location scenes filmed on the French Riviera. Opened in Paris in Jun 1964 as *Les félins;* running time: 110 min. Filmed mostly in English. Also known as *The Love Cage.*

JOY IN THE MORNING
F6.2533

Metro-Goldwyn-Mayer, Inc. 5 May **1965** [Chapel Hill, North Carolina, opening; c31 Dec 1964; LP29400]. Sd (Westrex); col (Metrocolor). 35mm (Panavision). 103 min.

Prod Henry T. Weinstein. *Dir* Alex Segal. *Screenplay* Sally Benson, Alfred Hayes, Norman Lessing. *Dir Photog* Ellsworth Fredricks. *Art Dir* George W. Davis, Carl Anderson. *Set Decor* Henry Grace, George R. Nelson. *Film Ed* Thomas J. McCarthy. *Mus* Bernard Herrmann. *Titl Song* Sammy Fain, Paul Francis Webster. *Sung by* Richard Chamberlain. *Rec Supv* Franklin Milton. *Asst Dir* Sheldon Schrager. *Asst to the Prod* Ira Barmak. *Cost Dsgn* Don Feld. *Makeup Supv* William Tuttle. *Hairstyles* Sydney Guilaroff. *Sp Vis Eff* J. McMillan Johnson. *Dial Supv* Frank Bessell. *Dempsey-Tunney fight ("I Can Hear It Now")* Columbia Records.

Cast: Richard Chamberlain *(Carl Brown),* Yvette Mimieux *(Annie McGairy),* Arthur Kennedy *(Patrick Brown),* Oscar Homolka *(Stan Pulaski),* Donald Davis *(Anthony Byrd),* Joan Tetzel *(Beverly Karter),* Sidney Blackmer *(Dean James Darwent),* Virginia Gregg *(Mrs. Lorgan),* Chris Noel *(Mary Ellen Kincaid),* Bartlett Robinson *(Prof. Victor Newcole),* Ellen Atterbury *(clerk),* Harvey Stephens *(Dr. Marson),* Ira Barmak *(Dr. Kirkson),* Valerie Szabo.

Romantic drama. Source: Betty Smith, *Joy in the Morning* (New York, 1963). In the late 1920's, law student Carl Brown marries Annie McGairy, despite opposition from their parents. They take up residence in a cottage near the athletic grounds of the midwestern college Carl attends. In exchange for his services as caretaker of the grounds and clubhouse, they live in the cottage rent free. To supplement their meager income, Carl takes on odd jobs, and Annie works as a babysitter for Beverly Karter, a widow who has provoked the disapproval of the town gossips by becoming the mistress of unhappily married Stan Pulaski. The goodhearted Annie also befriends another of the town's outcasts, Anthony Byrd, a homosexual florist. In an attempt to break up his son's marriage, Carl's father withdraws his financial assistance and thus forces Carl to take on a second job, as a nightwatchman. When Annie discovers that she is pregnant, she decides not to tell Carl and returns to her mother's house in an effort to relieve him of further burdens. When Carl's father discovers that his son is failing school because he is so unhappy about Annie's absence, he brings the two back together; and Annie gives birth to a son. *Law students. Mistresses. Widows. Filial relations. College life. Finance—Personal. Pregnancy. Marriage. Male homosexuality. Smalltown life. United States—Midwest.*

JOYS OF GEORGETTE F6.2534

Dist Distribpix, Inc. 24 Dec **1969** [Champaign, Illinois, showing]. Sd; col. 35mm. 64 min.

Sex film. Georgette serves as an artist's model for Derek, an insatiable hedonist, and becomes the apex of a love triangle. *Artists. Models. Troilism. Hedonism.*

THE JOYS OF JEZEBEL F6.2535

P. S. Films. 29 Jul **1970** [Champaign, Illinois, showing]. Sd; col. 35mm. 75 min.

Prod-Dir A. P. Stootsberry. *Screenplay* Maurice Smith. *Photog* Dwayne Rayven. *Asst Camera* Peter Sorel. *Lighting Dir* John Murray. *Art Dir* Earl Marshall. *Ed* Mark Perri. *Mus* Vic Lance. *Sd Mix* Bill Cooper. *Boom Op* Mike Franklin. *Asst Dir* Tony Rand. *Prod Coörd* James Brand. *Prod Mgr* Bethel Buckalew. *Script Girl* Pam Eddy. *Wardrobe* Sandy Root. *Cost* Logan Costumes. *Makeup* Ray Sebastian. *Grip & Electrn* Dick Osmun. *Prop* Jim Andrian. *Still Photog* William Rotsler.

Cast: Christine Murray *(Jezebel)*, Christopher Stone *(Lucifer)*, Johnny Rocco *(Joshua)*, Dixie Donovan *(Rachel)*, Angela Graves *(Ruth)*, Jay Edwards *(Jeremiah)*, Woody Lee *(Solomon)*, Jess White *(Goliath)*, La La *(Lust)*, Geets Romo *(Sol)*, Alice Friedland *(Sarah)*, Ron Smith *(Isaac)*, Feleshia Manning *(Esther)*, Sherise Roland *(Eve)*, Jackie Owens *(Goliath's girl)*, Bonnie Cooper *(Solomon's girl)*, Paul Austin *(donkeyman no. 1)*, Sidney Cliff *(donkeyman no. 2)*, Terry Tassione *(pit man no. 1)*, Tony Caccardo *(pit man no. 2)*, Snoopy *(pit man no. 3)*, Daniel Grant *(pit man no. 4)*, Betty Avin *(pit girl no. 1)*, Johanne Thomas *(pit girl no. 2)*, Lynne *(pit girl no. 3)*, Jeanette Mills *(pit girl no. 4)*, Monica Williams *(pit girl no. 5)*, Ruth Liben *(pit girl no. 6)*, Casey Larrain *(pit girl no. 7)*.

Biblical drama. Jezebel, beautiful and politically ambitious, is betrayed and killed by Joshua. In hell, she strikes a bargain with Lucifer, promising that she will send him the virgin Rachel if he will let her return to earth in order to avenge herself on Joshua. In the meantime, Joshua's lover, Ruth, has arranged a marriage between her unwilling sister Rachel, the virgin Jezebel promised to Lucifer, and the soldier, Jeremiah. Ruth believes that the marriage will strengthen the military alliance between Joshua and Jeremiah. Jezebel's first step in her plan of vengeance is to exchange spirits with Rachel. Jeremiah visits his bride-to-be one night and is dismayed to find that Rachel is not a virgin but an experienced temptress. Enraged, Jeremiah demands an explanation from Joshua. Joshua, in turn, confronts Ruth, accuses her of treachery, and breaks off with her. Ruth, dismayed because Joshua has scorned her, goes to Rachel for "sisterly" comfort—kisses and caresses. Together, Rachel and Ruth plan to blackmail Joshua into marrying Ruth. Rachel disguises herself as a boy and seduces Joshua, later convincing him that he has committed pederasty. Ruth arrives and exacts Joshua's promise to marry her in exchange for her silence about his misdeed. Jeremiah again visits Rachel. As he is about to deflower her, Lucifer, realizing that Jezebel has not kept her promise to send the virgin Rachel, substitutes Jezebel for Rachel and takes Rachel back to hell with him. *Temptresses. Soldiers. Virginity. Murder. Perfidy. Revenge. Marriage—Arranged. Blackmail. Seduction. Disguise. Jezebel. Joshua. Ruth. The Devil. Jeremiah. Rachel. Hell.*

Note: Also known as: *The Joy of Jesabelle* and *Jezebel.*

JUDAS CITY *see* SATAN'S BED

JUDEX (France/Italy) F6.2536

Comptoir Français du Film–Filmes Cinematografica. *Dist* Continental Distributing, Inc. 25 Apr **1966** [New York opening]. Sd; b&w. 35mm. 96 min. [Also reviewed at 91 min.]

Prod Robert de Nesle. *Dir* Georges Franju. *Dial* Francis Lacassin. *Adapt* Jacques Champreux. *Photog* Marcel Fradetal. *Art Dir* Robert Giordani. *Film Ed* Gilbert Natot. *Mus* Maurice Jarre. *Sd* Jean Labussière. *Asst Dir* Michel Worms. *Prod Mgr* Jean Maumy. *Cost* Christiane Courcelles. *English Subtitl* Herman G. Weinberg.

Cast: Channing Pollock *(Judex/Vallières)*, Francine Bergé *(Diana Monti/Marie Verdier)*, Edith Scob *(Jacqueline Favraux)*, Michel Vitold *(Favraux)*, Jacques Jouanneau *(Cocantin)*, Sylva Koscina *(Daisy)*, Théo Sarapo *(Moralès)*, Benjamin Boda *(Réglisse)*, Philippe Mareuil *(Amaury de la Rochefontaine)*, René Génin *(Pierre Kerjean)*, Jean Degrave *(notary)*, Luigi Cortese *(Pierrot)*, Roger Fradet *(Léon)*, Ketty France *(Jeanne-Marie Bontemps)*, Suzanne Gossen *(landlady)*, André Méliès *(doctor)*.

Crime melodrama. Based on a screenplay by: Arthur Bernède and Louis Feuillade, *Judex* (1916). Although warned by Judex to make retribution for dishonest dealings, banker Favraux refuses to reform and is promptly punished at a masked ball. Apparently struck dead, the banker is abducted by Judex. Informed of her father's dishonest dealings by Judex, in the guise of the banker's elderly secretary Vallières, Favraux's daughter Jacqueline renounces her inheritance. Following an abortive attempt on Jacqueline's life, governess

Diana Monti plans to procure and marry the banker. Disguised as a nun, Diana is unmasked by a young boy. When private detective Cocantin, Judex, and Jacqueline invade her hangout, Diana mistakenly stabs her lover Moralès and falls to her death. After Favraux commits suicide, Judex and Jacqueline proclaim their love. *Mistresses. Governesses. Bankers. Secretaries. Detectives. Heiresses. Inheritance. Disguise. Manslaughter. Suicide. Abduction. Filial relations. Balls (formal gatherings). Revenge.*

Note: Opened in Paris in Jan 1964; running time: 100 min. Released in Italy in 1964.

THE JUDGE AND THE SINNER (West Germany) F6.2537

Kurt Ulrich-Film. *Dist* Casino Films, Atlantic Pictures, Beaver Film Productions. 5 Jun **1964** [New York opening]. Sd; b&w. 35mm. 84 min.

Prod Kurt Ulrich. *Dir* Paul Verhoeven. *Screenplay* Hans Jacoby, Istvan Békeffi. *Camera* Erich Claunigk. *Camera Op* Gerd Neubelt. *Camera Asst* Hans Osterrieder. *Sets* Rolf Zehetbauer. *Film Ed* Hermann Haller. *Mus* Raimund Rosenberger. *Sd* Heinz Garbowski. *Asst Dir* Jochen Wiedermann. *Prod Mgr* Erwin Dräger. *Cost* Manon Hahn. *Wardrobe* Kurt Sobania, Ursula Zeller. *Makeup* Josef Coesfeld, Freddy Arnold, Herta Schwarz. *Prop* Günter Franke, Günter Beer.

Cast: Heinz Rühmann *(Judge Ferdinand Bluhme)*, Karin Baal *(Inge Schumann)*, Lola Müthel *(Elisabeth Winkler)*, Hans Nielsen *(district court president)*, Rainer Brandt *(Kurt)*, Michael Verhoeven *(Fred)*, Peter Thom *(Bill)*, Lore Schulz *(Paula Burg)*, Monika John *(Maria, maid)*, Hans Epskamp *(senate president)*, Erich Fiedler *(Vogel, salesman)*, Gerd Frickhöffer *(businessman)*, Harry Engel *(The "Black Case" Peters)*, Willi Rose *(patrol officer)*, Käthe Alving, Kunibert Gensichen, Knut Hartwig, Jan Hendriks, Hilla Hofer, Friedrich Maurer, Friedrich Siemers.

Drama. Ferdinand Bluhme, a juvenile court judge, believes that young offenders should be given a chance to reform. He puts his principles to the test on Inge Schumann, a youngster convicted of blackmail. To remove her from the unhealthy influence of her boyfriend Kurt, the leader of a teenage gang, Judge Bluhme at first sentences Inge to 8 months in prison, but he revokes the sentence when she threatens to commit suicide. He finds her a job as a waitress at the boardinghouse where he lives, although the owner, Elisabeth Winkler, objects to having a criminal in her house. At Kurt's instigation, Inge steals from a boarder, but after Judge Bluhme covers up for the theft, Inge begins to respond to his kindness and secretly falls in love with him. She finally breaks with Kurt when she learns that he is trying to blackmail Judge Bluhme by accusing the judge of having an affair with her. Judge Bluhme goes to the gang's hideout and persuades them to mend their ways and start a new life. *Juvenile delinquents. Judges. Waitresses. Blackmail. Criminals—Rehabilitation. Adolescence. Theft. Trials. Boardinghouses.*

Note: Released in Berlin in Feb 1960 as *Der Jugendrichter;* running time: 94 min.

JUDGE THE WILD QUEEN F6.2538

Crystal Productions. **1968.** Sd; b&w. 35mm. 90 min.

Exec Prod Harry E. Kerwin. *Dir* Albert J. Doucette.

Cast: Marilyn Nordman *(Teri)*, Bill Rogers *(Steve Randell)*, Gayle Aymes *(Christine)*, Mark Harris, Len Camp, Andrea Barr.

Drama. Teri wins a beauty contest and learns that contest manager Steve Randell is eager to exploit the contestants for a syndicate of ruthless entrepreneurs calling themselves a talent agency. Teri goes along with their plans and becomes a stripper, but she finds that her agent's fee allows her barely enough to survive. Although Christine, a lesbian and a hardened professional, steers Teri into more agreeable circumstances, she expects Teri's sexual favors in return. Teri becomes a success as a party girl, but Steve has fallen in love with her and now resents her activities. He punches one of Teri's wealthy clients, proposes marriage to her, and announces their joint resignation from the agency. Teri, although moved by Steve's declaration of love, nonetheless cannot suppress her excitement when she receives a telephone call with that evening's assignments. Steve sadly realizes that her degradation is irreversible. *Stripteasers. Talent agents. Racketeers. Lesbianism. Jealousy. Moral corruption. Beauty contests. Syndicates.*

JUDGMENT AT NUREMBERG F6.2539

Roxlom Films. *Dist* United Artists. 19 Dec **1961** [New York opening; c14 Dec 1961; LP21850]. Sd (Westrex); b&w. 35mm. 190 min.

Pres by Stanley Kramer. *Prod-Dir* Stanley Kramer. *Assoc Prod* Philip Langner. *Screenplay* Abby Mann. *Photog* Ernest Laszlo. *Camera Op* Charles Wheeler. *Set Decor* George Milo. *Prod Dsgn* Rudolph Sternad. *Titl* Pacific Title. *Film Ed* Frederic Knudtson. *Mus* Ernest Gold. *Song:* "Lili Marlene" Norbert Schultze, Hans Leip, Thomas Connor. *Song:* "Liebeslied" Ernest Gold, Alfred Perry. *Sd Engr* James Speak. *Sd Ed* Walter Elliott. *Mus Ed* Art Dunham. *Asst to the Dir* Ivan Volkman. *Prod Mgr* Clem Beauchamp. *Script Supv* Marshall Schlom. *Miss Dietrich's Gowns* Jean Louis. *Cost* Joe King.

Makeup Robert J. Schiffer. *Opticals* Pacific Title. *Company Grip* Morris Rosen. *Prop Master* Art Cole. *Ch Gaffer* Don Carstensen. *Casting* Stalmaster-Lister Co. *The German Crew* Richard Richtsfeld, L. Ostermeier, Lyn Hannes, Pia Arnold, Albrecht Hennings, Laci von Ronay, Hubert Karl, Egon Haedler, Frank Winterstein, Richard Eglseder, Mannelore Winterfeld.

Cast: Spencer Tracy *(Judge Dan Haywood)*, Burt Lancaster *(Ernst Janning)*, Richard Widmark *(Col. Tad Lawson)*, Marlene Dietrich *(Madame Bertholt)*, Maximilian Schell *(Hans Rolfe)*, Judy Garland *(Irene Hoffman)*, William Shatner *(Captain Byers)*, Edward Binns *(Senator Burkette)*, Kenneth MacKenna *(Judge Kenneth Norris)*, Joseph Bernard *(Maj. Abe Radnitz)*, Werner Klemperer *(Emil Hahn)*, Torben Meyer *(Werner Lammpe)*, Alan Baxter *(General Merrin)*, Virginia Christine *(Mrs. Halbestadt)*, Otto Waldis *(Pohl)*, Karl Swenson *(Dr. Geuter)*, Ray Teal *(Judge Curtiss Ives)*, Ben Wright *(Halbestadt)*, Olga Fabian *(Mrs. Lindnow)*, Martin Brandt *(Friedrich Hofstetter)*, John Wengraf *(Dr. Wieck)*, Howard Caine *(Wallner)*, Paul Busch *(Schmidt)*, Bernard Kates *(Perkins)*, Sheila Bromley *(Mrs. Ives)*, Jana Taylor *(Elsa Scheffler)*.

Drama. Source: Abby Mann, *Judgment at Nuremberg* (a teleplay; first presented on "Playhouse 90": 16 Apr 1959). In 1948 Dan Haywood, an American judge recently defeated for reelection in Maine, arrives in Nuremberg to preside over the trial of several German judges accused of destroying law and justice to support Hitler's infamous mandates which took the lives of 6 million innocent people. From the moment the prosecuting attorney, Col. Tad Lawson, makes his emotion-packed opening statements, it is obvious that he is determined to obtain the maximum punishment for the judges. The defense lawyer, Hans Rolfe, counters by charging that if these men are guilty because they upheld the laws of their country, then all of Germany must be tried. To support his accusations of inhuman actions, Lawson offers the testimony of Rudolf Petersen, a victim of sterilization who, it develops, was castrated because of mental incompetence. During the long weeks of the trial, Haywood wanders about the city trying to "understand" the German people, trying to determine if they really understood what Hitler stood for. In particular, Haywood often chats with the aristocratic Madame Bertholt, the widow of a German general executed after the earlier war crimes trials. The proceedings reach a climax when a woman named Irene Hoffman is called to the stand. When she testifies that a former friend, an aged Jew, was falsely accused of being intimate with her (thereby "polluting the Aryan race") and then executed, Rolfe tries to break down her story by frantically accusing her of distorting the truth. As the distraught woman breaks into hysterical denials, one of the accused, Ernst Janning, interrupts the hearings and asks to make a statement. Throughout the trial he has remained silent, but he now voluntarily takes the stand and admits to being guilty of both ignoring and rationalizing the inhuman Nazi acts because he felt they were for the ultimate good of the country. As Haywood and his two associate judges ponder their decisions, the news that Russia has blockaded Berlin prompts military officials to hint that lenient judgments might be wise—and expedient. But Haywood, determined to stand for "justice, truth, and the value of a single human being," refuses to compromise, and he sentences the defendants to life imprisonment. The defiant Rolfe sneers that in 5 years the convicted men will be free. *Judges. Lawyers. Widows. Nazis. Jews. Germans. War crimes. International Military Tribunal. Sterilization (sexual). Genocide. Concentration camps. World War II. Berlin Blockade 1948–49. Nuremberg. Germany—History—Third Reich.*

Note: Locations filmed in Germany. Actual footage of concentration camps is used.

JUDGMENT IN THE SUN *see* **THE OUTRAGE**

JUDITH (United States/Great Britain/Israel)   **F6.2540**
Cumulus Productions-Command. *Dist* Paramount Pictures. 20 Jan **1966** [New York opening; c31 Dec 1965; LP32135]. Sd (RCA); col (Technicolor). 35mm (Panavision). 109 min. [Copyright length: 106 min.]
Pres by Kurt Unger. *Prod* Kurt Unger. *Assoc Prod* Philip Breen. *Dir* Daniel Mann. *2d Unit Dir* Nicolas Roeg. *Screenplay* John Michael Hayes. *Orig Script* J. P. Miller. *Story* Lawrence Durrell. *Dir Photog* John Wilcox. *Adtl Photog* Nicolas Roeg. *Camera Op* Austin Dempster, Alex Thomson. *Art Dir* Tony Woollard, Tony Rimmington. *Sp Art Dir* Tony Pratt. *Set Decor* Peter Russell. *Prod Dsgn* Wilfrid Shingleton. *Film Ed* Peter Taylor. *Asst Ed* Graham Harris. *Mus Comp & Cond* Sol Kaplan. *Orch* Wally Stott. *Mus Played by* Sinfonia of London. *Sd Rec* David Hildyard, John Aldred. *Dub Ed* Archie Ludski, Janet Davidson, Stan Fiferman. *Asst Dir* Gerry O'Hara, Yoel Zilberg, Ivan Lengyel. *Prod Supv* John Coonan. *Prod Mgr* Lloyd Anderson. *Israeli Prod Mgr* Mati Raz. *Location Mgr* Geoffrey Helman, Kay Johns. *Cont* Pamela Davies. *Cost Dsgn* Yvonne Blake. *Miss Loren's Cost Dsgn* Gaia Romanini. *Ch Makeup* Wally Schneiderman. *Miss Loren's Makeup* Giuseppe Annunziata. *Miss Loren's Hairdresser* Amalia Paoletti. *Sp Eff* Cliff Richardson, Roy Whybrow. *Tech Adv* Nathan Shaham. *Constr Mgr* Peter Dukelow.

Cast—Principals: Sophia Loren *(Judith Auerbach)*, Peter Finch *(Aaron Stein)*, Jack Hawkins *(Major Lawton)*, Hans Verner *(Gen. Gustav Schiller)*, Zharira Charifai *(Dr. Rachel)*, Shraga Friedman *(Nathan)*, Andre Morell *(Chaim)*, Frank Wolff *(Eli)*, Arnoldo Foà *(interrogator)*, Joseph Gross *(Yaneck)*, Roger Beaumont *(Zeev)*, Zipora Peled *(Hannah)*, Terence Alexander *(Lieutenant Carstairs)*, Gilad Konstantiner *(Dubin)*, Daniel Ocko *(Arab guide)*, Peter Burton *(Conklin)*, John Stacy *(researcher)*, Shoshana Barnea *(Mrs. Gross)*, Alexander Yahalomi *(Zvi)*, Roland Bartrop *(Aba)*.

Cast—Members of Kibbutz Gates of Galilee: Esther Kfir, Gilad Konstantiner, Hilel Raveh, David Samadar, Aaron Shemi, Mona Silberstein, Judy Amir, Dahlia Bachboud, Eileen Benskin, Alexander Grdnovski, Judith Hirsh, Adi Kaplan, Yaacov Ben Tov, Leo Young, Chanan Avdori, Wolfe Barzell, Zmira Eilam, Rina Harareet, Geula Jeffet, Michael Kfir, Shafira Zakai, Pincus Pesso, Sam Rois, Naava Shan, Daniela Kochavi, Ben Zion Silberg, Rachel Timor, Alexander Yahalomi.

War drama. In Palestine in 1948, the last year of the British mandate and the eve of Israeli independence, leaders of the new state realize that the surrounding Arab countries will attack them as soon as British troops withdraw. Gustav Schiller, a tank expert formerly with Hitler's Afrika Korps, is helping to plan the Arab attack, but the Israelis do not know what he looks like or where in the Middle East he is to be found. Israeli intelligence learns that Schiller's former wife, Judith, is still alive in Europe. Because she was Jewish, Schiller betrayed her to the Nazis, and she and her son were sent to a concentration camp where they became separated. Judith survived, with revenge against Schiller her only purpose in life. Led by Aaron Stein, the Israelis smuggle Judith into Israel to help them identify and capture Schiller, whom they hope to force to reveal the Arab plan of attack. Through Lawton, a British major, Judith learns that Schiller is in Damascus. She goes there with a group of Israelis, and they capture him. But Judith's personal hatred overcomes her, and she shoots Schiller, thereby endangering the mission. The wounded man is taken into Palestine and nursed at a kibbutz, but, despite all threats, he refuses to talk. When the enemy attack begins, however, Schiller, fearing for his life, reveals the plan of attack to Judith. He tells her also that their son still lives and that if granted freedom he will disclose the child's whereabouts; but before he can divulge this information he is killed in an air raid. Aaron goes to the hysterical Judith and promises that they will find the child. *Jews. Germans. Nazis. Arabs. Intelligence agents. Perfidy. Motherhood. Revenge. Aerial bombardment. Kibbutzim. Concentration camps. Israeli-Arab War 1948–49. Palestine. Damascus.*

Note: Location scenes filmed in Israel in 1964. British co-production status unconfirmed.

JUDO SAGA (Japan)   **F6.2541**
Takarazuka Motion Picture Co.-Kurosawa Films. *Dist* Toho International, Inc. 27 Aug **1965** [Los Angeles opening]. Sd; b&w. 35mm. 159 min.
Dir Seiichiro Uchikawa. *Screenplay* Akira Kurosawa.
Cast: Yuzo Kayama *(Sugata Sanshiro)*, Toshiro Mifune *(Shogoro Yano)*, Eiji Okada, Tatsuo Yamazaki, Yumiko Kokonoe, Yunosuke Ito, Daisuke Kato.

Action melodrama. Source: Tsuneo Tomita, *Sugata Sanshiro* (Tokyo, 1942–44). Sugata Sanshiro, a young man troubled by personal problems, takes up judo. His teacher, Shogoro Yano, is a devout man who has aroused the enmity of the local practitioners of jujitsu, the older and more accepted of the two sports. Sugata uses his newly learned prowess to gain a measure of respect from others; however, Shogoro insists that the sport has a spiritual side, a lesson Sugata has yet to learn. Eventually, in hand-to-hand combat with the father of a young woman he loves, he comes to understand the true meaning of judo. *Judo. Jujitsu. Duels.*

Note: Released in Japan in 1965. A remake of *Sugata Sanshiro*, released in Japan in two parts in 1943 and 1945.

JUDO SHOWDOWN (Japan)   **F6.2542**
Shochiku Co. *Dist* Howard C. Brown, Shochiku Films of America. Apr **1966** [Honolulu, Hawaii, showing]. Sd; col (Eastmancolor). 35mm (GrandScope). 87 min.
Dir Masateru Nishiyama. *Screenplay* Daisei Motoyama, Narahiro Matsumura. *Photog* Shozo Honda. *Mus* Eiichi Yamada.
Cast: Toshiya Wazaki *(Sanshiro Sugata)*, Ryohei Uchida *(Daizaburo Himon)*, Shoichi Hirai *(Shogoro Yano)*, Seizaburo Kawazu *(Okakura)*, Maki Katsura *(Kaori, his daughter)*, Sanae Nakahara *(Tone)*, Shinsuke Mikimoto *(Gondo)*, Keiko Sajita, Yoko Matsuyama, Keiji Yano, Shintaro Kuraoka.

Action melodrama. Apparently based on the series of novels by: Tsuneo Tomita, *Sugata Sanshiro* (Tokyo, 1942–44). Sanshiro Sugata, a student of Kodokan judo, is on his way to Tokyo when he saves a beautiful woman from death in a dynamite explosion. The woman is Kaori, the daughter of Okakura, martial arts advisor to the Tokyo police. In Tokyo, Sanshiro enrolls in the Kodokan judo school and demonstrates his new throw. Shogoro Yano, the instructor at the school, warns Sanshiro that the throw could be lethal, especially since there is no corresponding defense. Sanshiro not only loses favor with Yano for fighting with rival jujitsu students but also with Okakura, who believes that Kodokan judo is a perverted form of jujitsu. The romance between Sanshiro and Kaori is threatened by Himon, the leading jujitsu man, who covets Okakura's position. Himon kills Okakura's first successor, but his intrigues are discovered when Okakura appoints Yano for the position. In a symbolic clash of the two schools of martial arts, Sanshiro and Himon fight a duel, and Sanshiro wins both the fight and the hand of Kaori. *Students. Jealousy. Murder. Judo. Jujitsu. Tokyo. Explosions. Duels.*

Note: Japanese title: *Yawara sempu doto no taiketsu.*

JUDY   **F6.2543**
Dist Cinex International Film Distributors, Boxoffice International Film Distributors. 1 Jul **1970** [Champaign, Illinois, showing]. Sd; col (Eastman Color). 35mm. 75 min.

Dir David W. Hanson. *Screenplay* George Mead. *Cinematog* John Hargrove. *Lighting* Lew Barstoew. *Set Dsgn* Bob Gregory. *Sd* Edward Healy. *Asst Dir* George Mead. *Prod Mgr* Abe Wienstien. *Script Girl* Sandy Ross. *Makeup* Ben Mazars. *Hairstyles* Rick W. Daly.

Cast: Dave Haller *(Gunner Sloan)*, Sandy O'Hara *(Velvet Harris)*, George Mead *(psychiatrist)*, Lee Sherry *(Regina Fairchild)*, Jay Rannie *(Fairchild)*, Garry Achzieger *(Lieutenant Thorin)*, Gary Fox *(police detective)*, Toula Flambouris *(Sylvia Silver)*, Judith Lowe *(Judy)*, Nataly Kovlev *(Judy's roommate)*, Selma Papas *(2d victim)*, Karen Beglan *(3d victim)*, Nancy Kely *(4th victim)*, Julia Willis *(5th victim)*.

Crime melodrama. A wealthy industrialist discovers that his daughter has been raped, and he turns to ex-police officer "Gunner" Sloan for confidential help. As Sloan searches for leads, he becomes involved in one torrid affair after another. He encounters an obstinate police lieutenant and a group of lesbians, and meets Judy, a seductive sensualist. Before he is through, three murders have complicated the case. With a twisted killer lurking one step ahead of him, Sloan finally brings the sordid affair to a violent conclusion. *Detectives. Police. Sensualists. Industrialists. Rape. Murder. Lesbianism. Sadism.*

JUDY'S LITTLE NO-NO   **F6.2544**
Schooner Bay Productions. 5 Nov **1969** [Mobile, Alabama, opening]. Sd; col (DeLuxe). 35mm. [Feature length assumed.]

Prod Edward Jacobs. *Dir-Writ* Sherman Price.

Cast: Elisa Ingram, John Lodge, Joe E. Ross, Zorita, Marlene.

Melodrama. Dan, skin diving off Abaco, an island in the Bahamas, saves stripper Judy after she has been thrown from a passing boat. Dan flies her to Miami to collect her clothes and back pay at Zorita's nightclub. Judy's apartment has been ransacked and her roommate bound and gagged by Cuban Castroites who were looking for a package given to Judy by her murdered refugee boyfriend. Dan and Judy return to Abaco for a night of love, and two hoods try to murder them. Handyman Woody uses his chain saw to eliminate one man and scare away the other. At Zorita's, the package containing a single jewel is missing, but belly-dancer Marlene has put the jewel in her navel. When a group of thieves try to steal it, Marlene throws it to Dan and Judy, who escape to a dog track. They contact Arturo, an anti-Castroite, and give him the jewel, but he is compromised when Judy is kidnaped. After a shoot-out, the jewel is once again restored to Arturo, and Dan and Judy fly happily back to Abaco. *Stripteasers. Cubans. Political refugees. Exotic dancers. Thieves. Murder. Kidnaping. Robbery. Airplanes. Nightclubs. Jewels. Abaco. Miami.*

Note: Also known as *Let's Do It.*

DER JUGENDRICHTER see **THE JUDGE AND THE SINNER**

JULES AND JIM (France)   **F6.2545**
Films du Carrosse–S. E. D. I. F. *Dist* Janus Films. 23 Apr **1962** [New York opening]. Sd; b&w. 35mm (Franscope). 105 min.

Dir François Truffaut. *Screenplay* François Truffaut, Jean Gruault. *Dir Photog* Raoul Coutard. *Camera Op* Claude Beausoleil. *Film Ed* Claudine Bouché. *Mus* Georges Delerue. *Song:* "Le tourbillon" Boris Bassiak. *Sung by* Jeanne Moreau. *Sd* Témoin. *Asst Dir* Georges Pellegrin, Robert Bober. *Prod Mgr* Marcel Berbert. *Cost* Fred Capel.

Cast: Jeanne Moreau *(Catherine)*, Oskar Werner *(Jules)*, Henri Serre *(Jim)*, Vanna Urbino *(Gilberte)*, Boris Bassiak *(Albert)*, Anny Nelsen *(Lucie)*, Marie Dubois *(Thérèse)*, Sabine Haudepin *(Sabine)*, Kate Noëlle *(Birgitta)*, Christiane Wagner *(Helga)*, Jean-Louis Richard, Michel Varesano *(customers in cafe)*, Danielle Bassiak *(Albert's friend)*, Pierre Fabre *(drunkard in cafe)*, Bernard Largemains *(Merlin)*, Elen Bober *(Mathilde)*, Dominique Lacarrière *(woman)*, Michel Subor *(narrator)*.

Drama. Source: Henri-Pierre Roché, *Jules et Jim* (Paris, 1953). In Montparnasse during the early 1900's, Jules, a shy, serious German, and Jim, an easygoing Frenchman, form a solid friendship, sharing a common interest in the arts, sports, and women. On a visit to a Greek island, they discover a statue with a smile that fascinates them. Shortly after their return to Paris, they

meet Catherine, a capricious and whimsical young woman whose smile reminds them of the statue. Both men fall in love with her, but Catherine marries Jules and returns with him to Germany. War breaks out, and the two friends, fighting on opposite sides, live in constant fear of shooting each other. After the armistice, Jim goes to Germany to visit Jules and Catherine and their 5-year-old daughter, Sabine. He discovers that Catherine has been having affairs with other men and has left Jules, returning after a number of months. Jules is uncertain that she will stay with him for long but remains willing to settle for the little attention his wife still shows him. In time, with Jules's assent, Catherine begins to have an affair with Jim. Though Jules gallantly offers to give Catherine a divorce, she grows dissatisfied with Jim when he fails to become pregnant. Jim returns to his mistress Gilberte in Paris, and one day meets Jules, who has returned with Catherine to live in France. The three of them have a reunion at a country restaurant, and Jim announces that he is planning to marry Gilberte. Later, Catherine asks Jim to come for a ride with her and drives away, shouting to Jules to watch closely. She goes a short distance down the road, turns onto a washed out bridge, and drives the car into the Seine. Jules makes funeral arrangements, sees the bodies of his wife and best friend cremated, and then silently leaves the cemetery. *Germans. Mistresses. Friendship. Marriage. Infidelity. Suicide. Parenthood. Sculptures. World War I. Paris— Montparnasse. Greece. Germany.*

Note: Location scenes filmed in Alsace, Paris, and Vence. Opened in Paris in Jan 1962 as *Jules et Jim*; running time: 110 min, also 105 min.

JULES ET JIM see **JULES AND JIM**

JULES VERNE'S ROCKET TO THE MOON see **THOSE FANTASTIC FLYING FOOLS**

JULIA, DU BIST ZAUBERHAFT see **ADORABLE JULIA**

JULIA UND DIE GEISTER see **JULIET OF THE SPIRITS**

JULIE IS *NO* ANGEL!   **F6.2546**
Biograph Studio Films. *Dist* Goldstone Film Enterprises. 21 Dec **1967** [San Francisco showing]. Sd; b&w. 35mm. 80 min.

Prod Frank Garto. *Dir* Larry Crane.

Cast: Sharon Kent *(Juliet Dreirmacher)*, Janet Banzet *(Thelma)*, Danny Nugent *(Jimmy Koonty)*, Harry Miller *(Bill)*, Frank Nanoia *(Hal Vern)*, Milton Levine *(Don Lewin)*, Edmund Nightwood *(Frankie)*, Luke St. Clair *(Carl Benton)*, Peter LoPicolo *(Aristotle Carnaby)*, Diana Conti *(Dora Dillon)*, Biff Williams *(man)*, Peter Bradford *(John Dixon)*, Barbara Wood *(Nina Weldon)*.

Melodrama. Juliet, a teenager, exchanges her sexual favors with the local druggist for fare to New York City when her mother, an amoral, harsh woman, throws her out for making love with her common-law husband. Julie drifts into prostitution and sleeps with various TV men—producers, directors, cameramen, agents—in hopes of finding work. She has a brief affair with commercial photographer Hal Vern. Sadist Aristotle Carnaby, a producer who promises to get her a screen test, subjects her to a whipping session with him in exchange for the favor. Upon seeing the screen test, producer John Dixon takes an interest in Julie, and she becomes his mistress. Dixon accuses Julie of an infidelity and leaves her; and she takes to the streets. She allows herself to be seduced by lesbian Nina Weldon, Dixon's casting director. Julie learns that she is pregnant and attempts suicide. Dixon visits her at the hospital and alleges that he is sterile and therefore could not be the father of Julie's child. He offers, however, to marry her and rear the child as his own, and Julie, touched by his generosity, acquiesces. *Runaways. Actors. Mistresses. Talent agents. Television producers. Television directors. Photographers. Adolescence. Filial relations. Prostitution. Jealousy. Lesbianism. Suicide. Pregnancy. Flagellation. Television.*

Note: Also known as *Julie's No Angel.*

JULIE LA ROUSSE see **JULIE THE REDHEAD**

JULIE THE REDHEAD (France)   **F6.2547**
Les Films Matignon–Films Metzger et Woog. *Dist* Shawn International, Inc., Ellis Films. 14 Oct **1963** [New York opening]. Sd; b&w. 35mm. 100 min. [Also 96 min.]

Prod Georges Glass. *Assoc Prod* Fred Genty. *Dir* Claude Boissol. *Screenplay* Paul Andréota, Claude Boissol. *Dial* Paul Andréota. *Adapt* Paul Andréota, Claude Boissol, Béatrice Rubinstein. *Photog* Roger Fellous. *Art Dir* Robert Guisgand. *Film Ed* Louis Devaivre. *Mus* René-Louis Lafforgue. *Choreog* Georges Reich. *Sd* Pierre Bertrand.

Cast: Daniel Gélin *(Edouard Lavigne/Jean Lavigne)*, Pascale Petit *(Julie)*, René-Louis Lafforgue *(Max Piccalo)*, Margo Lion *(Madame Lavigne)*, Liliane Patrick *(Tamira)*, Jocelyne Darche *(Violette)*, Gabrielle Fontan *(concierge)*, Jean Ozenne *(Uncle Roger)*, Frédéric O'Brady *(Hamib)*, Jacques Dufilho *(waiter)*, Pierre Doris *(hotel manager)*, René Blancard *(Monsieur Lavigne)*, Michel Etcheverry *(notary)*, Michel Thomas, C. Conti, Aimé de March, L.

Vivet, Alvarez et Confortes, Jean Guyon.

Comedy. In Paris in 1925, a romance between artist Edouard Lavigne and his model, Julie, is broken up by Edouard's father, who insists that his son return home and marry the heir to a nail factory. The business prospers, but Edouard secretly wishes that he had remained with Julie and pursued his artistic career, and he hopes to see his son Jean become the artist he had hoped to be. Jean, however, is interested only in the family business. Edouard dies and leaves two-thirds of his estate to "Julie the Redhead" or her children. Jean seeks out Julie in order to buy her share of the inheritance so that control of the factory will remain in the family. Julie has died, but her 22-year-old daughter, a trapezist also named Julie, is entitled to the bequest. Jean courts and marries the young woman in order to acquire her legacy. On their wedding night, Jean discovers that Julie is not the daughter of his father's mistress but rather her niece, and that her motives for marrying Jean are as mercenary as his own. After a few stormy months of marriage, however, the couple find they are indeed in love. *Artists. Mistresses. Models. Trapezists. Industrialists. Heiresses. Filial relations. Inheritance. Greed. Mistaken identity. Marriage. Factories. Wills. Paris.*

Note: Opened in Paris in Aug 1959 as *Julie la rousse*; running time: 92 min.

JULIET OF THE SPIRITS (France/Italy/West Germany)   **F6.2548**
Federiz-Francoriz-Rizzoli Films-Eichberg-Film. *Dist* Rizzoli Film Distributors. 3 Nov 1965 [New York opening.] Sd; col (Technicolor). 35mm. 148 min. [Also 137 min.]

Pres by Angelo Rizzoli. *Prod* Angelo Rizzoli. *Exec Prod* Clemente Fracassi. *Dir* Federico Fellini. *Screenplay* Federico Fellini, Tullio Pinelli, Ennio Flajano, Brunello Rondi. *Story* Federico Fellini, Tullio Pinelli. *Dir Photog* Gianni Di Venanzo. *Camera Op* Pasquale De Santis. *Art Dir* Piero Gherardi. *Set Decor* Luciano Ricceri, E. Benazzi Taglietti, Giantito Burchiellaro. *Film Ed* Ruggero Mastroianni. *Mus* Nino Rota. *Sd* Mario Faraoni, Mario Morici. *Asst Dir* Francesco Aluigi, Liliana Betti, Rosaria Zavoli. *Prod Mgr* Alessandro Von Norman. *Cost* Piero Gherardi. *Makeup* Otello Fava, Emilio Trani.

Cast: Giulietta Masina (*Giulietta*), Alba Cancellieri (*Giulietta as a child*), Mario Pisu (*Giorgio*), Caterina Boratto (*Giulietta's mother*), Luisa Della Noce (*Adele*), Sylva Koscina (*Sylva*), Sabrina Gigli, Rosella Di Sepio (*granddaughters*), Lou Gilbert (*grandfather*), Valentina Cortese (*Valentina*), Silvana Jachino (*Dolores*), Elena Fondra (*Elena*), José-Luis de Vilallonga, Cesarino Miceli Picardi (*Giorgio's friends*), Milena Vucotich, Elisabetta Gray (*Giulietta's maids*), Sandra Milo (*Susy/Iris/Fanny*), Irina Alexeieva (*Susy's grandmother*), Alessandra Mannoukine (*Susy's mother*), Gilberto Galvan (*chauffeur*), Seyna Seyn (*masseuse*), Yvonne Casadei, Hildegarde Golez, Dina De Santis (*Susy's maids*), Edoardo Torricella (*Russian teacher*), Dany Paris (*desperate friend*), Raffaele Guida (*Oriental lover*), Fred Williams, actor (*Arabian prince*), Alberto Plebani (*Lynx-Eyes*), Federico Valli, Remo Risaliti, Grillo Rufino (*Lynx-Eyes' agents*), Waleska Gert (*Bhishma*), Felice Fulchignoni (*Don Raffaele*), Asoka Rubener, Sujata Rubener, Walter Harrison (*Bhishma's helpers*), Anne Francine (*psychoanalyst*), Mario Conocchia (*family lawyer*), Friedrich Ledebur (*headmaster*), Genius (*medium*), Massimo Sarchielli (*Valentina's lover*), Giorgio Ardisson, Bob Edwards, Nadir Moretti (*models*).

Drama. Giulietta, a plain woman of 35, tries to enjoy life as best she can while living with her husband, Giorgio, who exhibits little feeling for her when he returns home late each evening to their villa near Fregene. Though she affords Giorgio the benefit of the doubt, assuming that a hard day's work and other preoccupations are responsible, she begins to harbor certain fears and a nagging mistrust. Her glamorous mother and her sisters, Adele and Sylva, frequently reproach her for the simplicity of her attitude and the lifestyle she clings to so dearly. When Giorgio brings home a group of friends to hold a seance, Giulietta finds that as one of the participants she is able to call up spirits in her that represent, on the one hand, her fears and, on the other hand, images of her childhood: her grandfather and the convent she endured. Other spirits urge her to compensate by seeking pleasure and self-gratification. Her friend Valentina coaxes her into seeing Bhishma, a mystic who corroborates all that the spirits have told her. Meanwhile, she hires a detective to follow Giorgio, and as predicted, photographs and other evidence reveal his affair with another woman. On the verge of a breakdown, Giulietta meets Susy, her neighbor whose high living and liberated friends provide the excitement and sensuality she has been seeking. But when Giorgio packs to leave for a health resort, undoubtedly with his mistress in tow, Giulietta nearly commits suicide. Instead, she comes to a realization that her fears are unwarranted, that she can survive without Giorgio, and that she has rid herself of the spirits. *Sisters. Mistresses. Mystics. Grandfathers. Detectives. Filial relations. Marriage. Fear. Infidelity. Spiritualism. Childhood. Seances. Catholic Church. Fregene (Italy).*

Note: Opened in Rome in Oct 1965 as *Giulietta degli spiriti*; running time: 120 min; in Paris as *Juliette des esprits* in Oct 1965; running time: 150 min; released in West Germany in Nov 1965 as *Julia und die Geister*; running time: 145 min.

JULIETA Y ROMEO *see* **ROMEO AND JULIET**

JULIETTE DE SADE   **F6.2549**
Inska Films. *Dist* Haven International Pictures. Dec **1969**. Sd; col (Eastmancolor). 35mm. 85 min. *MPAA rating* R.

Prod Ninki Maslansky. *Co-Prod* James Brandt, Robert Brandt. *Dir* Warren Kiefer. *Photog* Amerigo Gengarelli. *Film Ed* Edwin Picker.

Cast: Maria Pia Conte (*Juliette*), Lea Nanni (*Toni*), Christine Delit (*Clarissa*), Angela De Leo (*Angela*), John Karlsen, Jean Valmont, Linda Towne, Lars Bloch, Michel Bardinet.

Drama. Inspired by the writings of: Donatien Alphonse François [Marquis de] Sade. Sexually precocious Juliette is caught masturbating and expelled from a rural convent school. She makes her way to Rome and moves in with Toni, with whom she has a brief lesbian affair. Toni introduces Juliette to Foro, a disciple of the teachings of Marquis de Sade. Foro becomes Juliette's spiritual adviser; he buys her a car and persuades her to indulge all of her whims and desires. She has an affair with a doctor, takes a nude ride on a motorcycle, and learns to steal for thrills. Toni becomes jealous of Juliette's lover and attempts to blackmail her. Juliette sees Toni apparently drowning in the sea and does not help her. Juliette is given LSD by a hippie and has a bad trip. She discovers that Toni did not drown, but was killed later in an automobile accident. Juliette decides to leave behind her decadent life in Rome and go to Nairobi. *Roommates. Hippies. Adolescence. Hedonism. Autoeroticism. Jealousy. Nudity. Blackmail. Boarding schools. LSD. Automobile accidents. Rome. Donatien Alphonse François [Marquis de] Sade.*

Note: May also be known as *Heterosexual*. Filmed in Italy; country of origin undetermined.

JULIETTE DES ESPRITS *see* **JULIET OF THE SPIRITS**

JULIUS CAESAR (Great Britain)   **F6.2550**
Commonwealth United Productions. *Dist* American International Pictures. 22 Sep 1970 [Los Angeles opening]. Sd; col (Technicolor). 35mm (Panavision). 117 min.

Prod Peter Snell. *Exec Prod* Henry T. Weinstein, Anthony B. Unger. *Assoc Prod* James Swann. *Dir* Stuart Burge. *Screen Adapt* Robert Furnival. *Photog* Ken Higgins. *Camera Op* Roy Ford. *Art Dir* Maurice Pelling. *Prod Dsgn* Julia Trevelyan Oman. *Film Ed* Eric Boyd-Perkins. *Mus Comp & Cond* Michael J. Lewis. *Sd Rec* Paddy Cunningham. *Asst Dir* Christopher Dryhurst, Tony McWhirter, Tony Buck, Peter MacGregor Scott. *Prod Mgr* Denis Johnson, Jr. *Cost Adv* Robin Archer. *Makeup* Cliff Sharpe. *Hairstyles* Ann Fordyce.

Cast: Charlton Heston (*Marc Antony*), Jason Robards, [Jr.] (*Brutus*), John Gielgud (*Julius Caesar*), Richard Johnson (*Cassius*), Robert Vaughn (*Casca*), Richard Chamberlain (*Octavius Caesar*), Diana Rigg (*Portia*), Jill Bennett (*Calpurnia*), Christopher Lee (*Artemidorus*), Alan Browning (*Marullus*), Norman Bowler (*Titinius*), Andrew Crawford (*Volumnius*), David Dodimead (*Lepidus*), Peter Eyre (*Cinna the Poet*), Edwin Finn (*Publius*), Derek Godfrey (*Decius Brutus*), Michael Gough (*Metellus Cimber*), Paul Hardwick (*Messala*), Thomas Heathcote (*Flavius*), Ewan Hooper (*Strato*), Robert Keegan (*Lucilius*), Preston Lockwood (*Trebonius*), John Moffatt (*Popilius Lena*), Andre Morell (*Cicero*), David Neal (*Cinna the Conspirator*), Steven Pacey (*Lucius*), John Tate (*Clitus*), Damien Thomas (*Pindarus*), Laurence Harrington (*carpenter*), Ron Pember (*cobbler*), Ken Hutchinson (*1st plebian*), Michael Keating (*2d plebian*), Derek Hardwicke (*3d plebian*), Michael Wynne (*4th plebian*), David Leland (*5th plebian*), Ronald McGill (*servant to Caesar*), Linbert Spencer (*2d servant to Caesar*), Trevor Adams (*3d servant to Caesar*), Robin Chadwick (*servant to Octavius*), Christopher Cazenove (*servant to Antony*), Roy Stewart (*slave to Lepidus*), Liz Geghardt (*maid to Calpurnia*).

Tragedy. Source: William Shakespeare, *Julius Caesar*. The film, an adaptation of Shakespeare's tragedy, is prefaced by a review of Caesar's Spanish campaigns. *Ghosts. Conspiracy. Assassination. Suicide. Rome—History—Empire. Gaius Julius Caesar. Mark Antony. Marcus Junius Brutus.*

Note: Location scenes filmed in Spain. Opened in London in Jun 1970.

JUMBO   **F6.2551**
Euterpe, Inc.-Arwin Productions. *Dist* Metro-Goldwyn-Mayer, Inc. 6 Dec **1962** [New York opening; c16 Sep 1962; LP23347]. Sd (Westrex); col (Metrocolor). 35mm (Panavision). 123 min.

A Joe Pasternak Production. *Prod* Joe Pasternak, Martin Melcher. *Assoc Prod* Roger Edens. *Dir* Charles Walters. *2d Unit Dir* Busby Berkeley. *Circus Acts Coörd* Al Dobritch. *Screenplay* Sidney Sheldon. *Dir Photog* William H. Daniels. *Camera Op* Al Lane. *Camera Asst* William Johnson. *Col Cons* Charles K. Hagedon. *Art Dir* George W. Davis, Preston Ames. *Set Decor* Henry Grace, Hugh Hunt. *Film Ed* Richard Farrell. *Asst Ed* Alex Beaton. *Mus & Lyr* Richard Rodgers, Lorenz Hart. *Mus Supv & Cond* George Stoll. *Orch* Conrad Salinger, Leo Arnaud, Robert Van Eps. *Vocal Arr* Robert Tucker. *Rec Supv* Franklin

Milton. *Mix* Tom Overton. *Rec* Mike Voss. *Boom Op* Michael J. Clark, James Utterback. *Mus Ed* Ralph Ives. *Asst Dir* William Shanks, Carl Roup. *Asst to the Prod* Irving Aaronson. *Unit Mgr* David Friedman. *Script Supv* Cleo Anton. *Cost* Morton Haack. *Wardrobe* Robert Ellsworth, Beau Vanden Ecker, Elva Martien. *Makeup* William Tuttle, Jack Wilson. *Hairstyles* Sydney Guilaroff, Jane Gorton. *Sp Vis Eff* A. Arnold Gillespie, J. McMillan Johnson, Robert R. Hoag. *Still Photog* Eric Carpenter. *Electrn* Fenton Hamilton. *Grip* Lloyd Isbell. *Prop* Bob Murdock, Carl Bionde. *Casting* Leonard Murphy.

Cast: Doris Day *(Kitty Wonder)*, Stephen Boyd *(Sam Rawlins)*, Jimmy Durante *(Pop Wonder)*, Martha Raye *(Lulu)*, Dean Jagger *(John Noble)*, Joseph Waring *(Harry)*, Lynn Wood *(Tina)*, Charles Watts *(Ellis)*, James Chandler *(Parsons)*, Robert Burton *(Madison)*, Wilson Wood *(Hank)*, Norman Leavitt *(Eddie)*, Grady Sutton *(driver)*, Sydney *(Jumbo)*.

Cast—The Circus Performers: Ron Henon, The Carlisles, The Pedrolas, The Wazzans, The Hannefords, Billy Barton, Corky Cristians, Victor Julian, Richard Berg, Joe Monahan, Miss Lani, Adolph Dubsky, Pat Anthony, Janos Prohaska, The Barbettes.

Musical comedy. Source: Ben Hecht and Charles MacArthur, *Jumbo* (New York opening: 16 Nov 1935). Around 1910, Pop Wonder's circus performs throughout the Middle West. Its major asset is Jumbo, a versatile performing elephant, and its major liability is Pop's uncanny ability to lose the week's receipts at local crap games. One day Pop's daughter, Kitty, hires Sam Rawlins, a jack-of-all-circus-trades, who proves to be both an excellent performer and an able tent hand. Unknown to all, however, is the fact that Sam is the son of John Noble, a circus entrepreneur who plans to get control of the Wonder Circus—and Jumbo—by buying up all of Pop's I.O.U.'s. Despite his growing love for Kitty, Sam reluctantly carries out his father's wishes and acquires the circus from Pop. Refusing to admit defeat, Pop, Kitty, and Lulu, Pop's fiancée of 14 years, become a touring carnival. They are eventually joined by Sam, who has broken with his father and persuades them that he is interested only in getting the Wonder Circus back in business. As proof of his sincerity, he has brought with him their beloved Jumbo. By pooling their talents and efforts, the four performers make the Wonder Circus "the biggest little show in the Middle West." *Songs:* "Over and Over Again" (Kitty); "Circus on Parade" (circus performers); "Why Can't I" (Kitty & Lulu); "This Can't Be Love" (Kitty); "The Most Beautiful Girl in the World" (Sam & Pop); "My Romance," "Little Girl Blue" (Kitty); "What Is a Circus" (Sam); "Sawdust, Spangles and Dreams" (Kitty, Sam, Pop & Lulu). Entrepreneurs. Debt. Gambling. Duplicity. Filial relations. Circus. Carnivals. United States—Midwest. Elephants.

Note: Also known as *Billy Rose's Jumbo*.

LA JUMENT VERTE *see* **THE GREEN MARE**

DER JUNGE LORD *see* **THE YOUNG LORD**

EIN JUNGE SCHRIE MORD *see* **THE BOY CRIED MURDER**

DER JUNGE TÖRLESS *see* **YOUNG TORLESS**

JUNGLE ATTACK (Reissue)   F6.2552
Paramount Pictures. *Dist* Citation Films, Paramount Pictures. **1961**. Sd; col (Technicolor). 35mm. 93 min.
Note: Originally released as *Crosswinds* by Paramount Pictures in 1951; c1 Oct 1951; LP1228.

THE JUNGLE BOOK   F6.2553
Walt Disney Productions. *Dist* Buena Vista Distribution Co. 18 Oct **1967** [Los Angeles opening; c14 Sep 1967; LP34804]. Sd (RCA); col (Technicolor). 35mm. 78 min.
Pres by Walt Disney. A Walt Disney Production. *Dir* Wolfgang Reitherman. *Story* Larry Clemmons, Ralph Wright, Ken Anderson, Vance Gerry. *Dir Anim* Milt Kahl, Ollie Johnston, Frank Thomas, John Lounsbery. *Charact Anim* Hal King, Eric Cleworth, Eric Larson, Fred Hellmich, Walt Stanchfield, John Ewing, Dick Lucas. *Eff Anim* Dan MacManus. *Layout* Don Griffith, Basil Davidovich, Tom Codrick, Dale Barnhart, Sylvia Roemer. *Background Styling* Al Dempster. *Background* Bill Layne, Ralph Hulett, Art Riley, Thelma Witmer, Frank Armitage. *Film Ed* Tom Acosta, Norman Carlisle. *Mus* George Bruns. *Orch* Walter Sheets. *Songs:* "I Wanna Be Like You," "Kaa's Song," "My Own Home," "That's What Friends Are For," "Colonel Hathi's March" Robert B. Sherman, Richard M. Sherman. *Song:* "The Bare Necessities" Terry Gilkyson. *Sd* Robert O. Cook. *Mus Ed* Evelyn Kennedy. *Prod Mgr* Don Duckwall.

Voices: Phil Harris *(Baloo the Bear)*, Sebastian Cabot *(Bagheera the Panther)*, Louis Prima *(King Louie of the Apes)*, George Sanders *(Shere Khan the Tiger)*, Sterling Holloway *(Kaa the Snake)*, J. Pat O'Malley *(Colonel Hathi the Elephant)*, Bruce Reitherman *(Mowgli the Man Cub)*, Verna Felton, Clint Howard *(elephants)*, Chad Stuart, Tim Hudson *(vultures)*, John Abbott, Ben Wright *(wolves)*, Darleen Carr *(The Girl)*.

Animated musical comedy. Inspired by: Rudyard Kipling, *The Jungle Book* and other "Mowgli" stories (1893, 1894, 1895). While roaming about the jungle, the panther Bagheera finds Mowgli, an abandoned Indian boy baby, in a wrecked canoe and takes him to a wolf family to be reared as a cub. Ten years later, when it is learned that the ferocious tiger Shere Khan is returning to his hunting ground, the wolves fear for Mowgli's life and decide that for safety's sake he must return to the world of men. Bagheera agrees to escort the protesting boy through the jungle, where the two encounter many dangers. After successfully avoiding the hypnotic designs of the snake Kaa, the travelers meet Colonel Hathi's elephant herd. Exasperated by Mowgli's continual disobedience, Bagheera deserts the boy, who is then befriended by the bear Baloo, a singing, dancing jungle bum. When Mowgli is kidnaped by monkeys, Baloo persuades Bagheera to help, and the three escape just as the ape King Louie's temple crumbles. Determined to remain in the jungle, Mowgli runs away and wanders into a vultures' hangout. The birds at first tease him but later befriend the lonely boy. When Shere Khan appears, the vultures take to the trees; and Mowgli must face the tiger alone. To his surprise, he is helped by his jungle friends, and, tying a burning branch to Shere Khan's tail, Mowgli frightens the tiger away. Now nothing stands in the way of Mowgli's remaining in the jungle. A chance meeting with a young Indian girl offers a stronger attraction, however, and Bagheera and Baloo depart knowing that Mowgli will be happier with his own kind. (The voices heard in the songs are those of Louis Prima, singing "I Wanna Be Like You"; Sterling Holloway, singing "Kaa's Song"; Darleen Carr, singing "My Own Home"; Chad Stuart and Lord Tim Hudson, singing "That's What Friends Are For"; Verna Felton and Clint Howard, singing "Colonel Hathi's March"; and Phil Harris, singing "The Bare Necessities".) Children. Waifs. Nature. Jungles. India. Bears. Tigers. Snakes. Panthers. Elephants. Vultures. Wolves. Apes.

JUNGLE FIGHTERS *see* **THE LONG AND THE SHORT AND THE TALL**

JUNGLE RAMPAGE *see* **RAMPAGE**

JUNGLE STREET *see* **JUNGLE STREET GIRLS**

JUNGLE STREET GIRLS (Great Britain)   F6.2554
Theatrecraft Ltd. *Dist* Ajay Film Co., Manhattan Films International. 7 Jun **1963** [New York showing]. Sd; b&w. 35mm. 89 min.
Prod Guido Coen. *Dir* Charles Saunders. *Screenplay* Alexander Dore. *Orig Story* Guido Coen. *Photog* James Harvey. *Art Dir* Duncan Sutherland. *Film Ed* Peter Bezencenet. *Mus Comp & Dir* Harold Geller. *Lyr:* "I'm Only a Girl" Perry Ford. *Sd* Jim Sibley, Stephen Dalby.
Cast: David McCallum *(Terry Collins)*, Marion Collins *(announcer)*, Vanda Hudson *(Lucy Bell)*, Larry Burns *(barman)*, Brian Weske *(Joe Lucas)*, Joy Webster *(Rene)*, Fred Griffiths *(dealer)*, Julie Shearing *(cashier)*, Faye Craig *(native dancer)*, John Chandos *(Jacko Fielding)*, Jill Ireland *(Sue)*, Edna Doré *(Mrs. Collins)*, Thomas Gallagher *(Mr. Collins)*, Martin Sterndale *(Inspector Bowden)*, Howard Pays *(Sergeant Pelling)*, Kenneth Cope *(Johnny)*, Anne Scott *(Margot)*, Gillian Watt *(dancing girl)*, Alfred Farrell *(Mr. Burns)*, Jacqueline Jones *(Dolly)*, William Wilde *(Sid Porter)*, Meier Tzelniker *(Mr. Rose)*, Howard Douglas *(Old Bill)*, Richard McNeff *(policeman)*.

Melodrama. To have extra spending money at the nightclub Adam and Eve, Terry Collins mugs an old man and quickly spends the little money he acquires. The old man dies, the police begin to move in, and blackmailer Joe Lucas threatens to inform on Terry. Johnny, the boyfriend of beautiful stripteaser Sue, plans to help Terry rob the safe at the club. When the safe is opened, however, Terry knocks out Johnny and absconds with unwilling Sue. The police finally close in, and Terry is forced to kill an old tailor, Mr. Rose. Terry's escape is thwarted, and he is dragged away by the police while pleading for mercy. Muggers. Stripteasers. Police. Murder. Blackmail. Nightclubs. Safes.

Note: Originally released in Great Britain in Nov 1961 as *Jungle Street*; running time: 81 min.

JUNGLE TERROR *see* **FIREBALL JUNGLE**

JUST BETWEEN US   F6.2555
Pax Films. c26 Jul **1961** [LP20318]. Sd; b&w. 35mm. 84 min.
Story Charles P. Eisenmann.
Comedy-drama. A German shepherd, adopted by a 7-year-old girl, takes over her dog-sitting job for six other dogs, who run away. He runs into all sorts of adventures collecting them while he himself is pursued by two dogcatchers. Children. Dog sitters. Dogcatchers. Dogs.

JUST FOR FUN (Great Britain)   F6.2556
Amicus Productions. *Dist* Columbia Pictures. Jun **1963** [c1 Jun 1963; LP25629]. Sd (RCA); b&w. 35mm. 72 min. [Also reviewed at 84 min.]
Prod-Writ Milton Subotsky. *Dir* Gordon Flemyng. *Lighting Camera* Nicolas Roeg. *Camera Op* Alex Thomson. *Art Dir* William Constable. *Film Ed* Raymond Poulton. *Mus Supv* Franklyn Boyd. *Incidental Mus* Tony Hatch. *Sd* Stephen Dalby, Leonard Bulkley. *Dub Ed* Michael Hopkins. *Asst Dir* Ross

MacKenzie. *Prod Mgr* Ted Wallis. *Cont* Eileen Head. *Cherry Roland's Cost* Shubette of London. *Mark Wynter's Cost* John Stevens. *Makeup* Freddie Williamson. *Sp Eff* Key Sinclair.

Cast: Mark Wynter *(Mark)*, Cherry Roland *(Cherry)*, Richard Vernon *(prime minister)*, Reginald Beckwith *(opposition leader)*, John Wood *(official)*, Jeremy Lloyd *(prime minister's son)*, Harry Fowler *(interviewer)*, Edwin Richfield *(man with badge)*, Alan Freeman *(narrator)*, David Jacobs, Alan Freeman, Jimmy Savile *(disc jockeys)*, Irene Handl *(housewife)*, Hugh Lloyd *(plumber)*, Dick Emery, Mario Fabrizi, Ken Parry, Gary Hope, Douglas Ives, Ian Gray, John Martin, Jack Bentley, Frank Williams, Gordon Rollings.

Performers: Bobby Vee, The Crickets, Freddy Cannon, Johnny Tillotson, Ketty Lester, Joe Brown and the Breakaways, Karl Denver, Kenny Lynch, Jet Harris, Tony Meehan, Cloda Rodgers, Louise Cordet, Lyn Cornell, The Tornados, The Springfields, The Spotnicks, Jimmy Powell, Brian Poole and the Tremeloes, Sounds Incorporated, The Vernon Girls.

Comedy with music. With an election approaching, the two major political parties in England work desperately to capture the enthusiasm of teenagers, who have been granted the right to vote. When the prime minister cuts the quota of musical programs permitted on television, teenagers Mark and Cherry lead others youngsters in forming their own political party, which successfully utilizes popular recording artists in helping to win the election. *Songs:* "Vote for Me" (Mark Wynter); "Sweet Boy" (Cloda Rodgers); "Let Her Go" (Joe Brown and the Breakaways); "All on a Warm Summer Day" (Ketty Lester); "I Gotta Get Up Early in the Morning" (Freddy Cannon); "Touch Me" (Bobby Vee); "Crazy Crazes" (Kenny Lynch); "Kisses Can Lie" (Lyn Cornell); "Keep On Dancin' " (Brian Poole and the Tremeloes); "Lyin' to You" (Karl Denver); "Which Way the Wind Blows" (Louise Cordet); "What's the Name of the Game" (Joe Brown and the Breakaways); "I'm Happy With You" (Wynter); "Sailing on a Little Boat" (The Springfields); "Monument" (Lynch); "Just Another Girl" (The Vernon Girls); "Doing the Hully Gully" (Tony Meehan and Jet Harris); "My Bonnie Lies Over the Ocean" (The Spotnicks); "Ups and Downs of Love" (Cannon); "Judy" (Johnny Tillotson); "The Night Has a Thousand Eyes" (Vee); "My Little Girl" (The Crickets); "Just for Fun" (Wynter and Cherry Roland). *Musicians. Prime ministers. Adolescence. Political campaigns. Rock and roll. Television.*

Note: Released in Great.Britain in Apr 1963; running time: 85 min.

JUST FOR THE HELL OF IT   F6.2557

Argent Film Productions. *Dist* Unusual Films International. 6 Nov 1968 [Chicago opening]. Sd; col (Eastman Color). 35mm. 85 min.

Prod-Dir Herschell Gordon Lewis. *Exec Prod* David Chudnow. *Camera Op* Roy Collodi. *2d Unit Camera* Eskandar Ameripoor. *Set Dsgn* Robert Enrietto. *Ed Supv* Richard Brinkman. *Background Mus* Larry Wellington. *Song:* "Destruction, Inc.!" Sheldon Seymour, Robert Lewis. *Sung by* Tary Rebenar. *Sd Rec* Spyridon Horiatis.

Cast: Rodney Bedell *(Doug)*, Ray Sager *(Dexter)*, Nancy Lee Noble *(Bitsy)*, Agi Gyenes *(Jeanne)*, Steve White *(Denny)*, Ralph Mullin *(Lummox)*, Larry Williams *(Cransy)*, A. V. Dreeson *(Lieutenant Sanders)*, A. V. Dreeson, Sr. *(police chief)*, Geraldine Young, Toni Newsholme, Julia Ames, Andrea Barr *(teenyboppers)*, John Shackleford, John Chaffin *(policemen)*.

Action drama. Dexter, Denny, their girl friend Bitsy, and Lummox are members of a vicious gang bent on violence. They capriciously wreak havoc and destruction at a party and later at their restaurant hangout. The gang assaults a couple, then dope and beat up some teenaged girls. When they interrupt and fight a group of boys playing baseball, a confused old woman calls the police and says that Doug, who disapproves of the gang's antics, started the incident. While Doug is temporarily jailed, the gang threatens his girl friend, Jeanne. Bitsy calls Doug away on a ruse, and the gang brutally attacks Jeanne. Doug chases Denny and Bitsy, who escape on a motorcycle. The intervention of the police precipitates an accident, killing the couple. *Street gangs. Police. Vandalism. Adolescence. Restaurants. Drugs. Motorcycle accidents. Chases.*

Note: Sheldon Seymour is a pseudonym for Herschell Gordon Lewis.

JUST FOR YOU *see* DISK-O-TEK HOLIDAY

JUST LIKE A WOMAN (Great Britain)   F6.2558

Dormar Productions. *Dist* Emerson Film Enterprises. Feb 1968. Sd; col (Eastman Color). 35mm. 89 min.

Prod Robert Kellett. *Dir-Writ* Robert Fuest. *Dir Photog* Billy Williams. *Art Dir* Brian Eatwell. *Film Ed* Jack Slade. *Mus Comp & Cond* Kenny Napper. Kevin Sutton. *Asst Dir* Scott Wodehouse. *Cost* Caroline Mott.

Cast: Wendy Craig *(Scilla McKenzie)*, Francis Matthews *(Lewis McKenzie)*, John Wood *(John Martin)*, Dennis Price *(bathroom salesman)*, Peter Jones *(Saul Alexander)*, Miriam Karlin *(Ellen)*, Clive Dunn *(Graff Von Fischer)*, Ray Barrett *(Australian)*, Michael Brennan *(commissionaire)*, Angela Browne *(Scilla's friend)*, Sheila Steafel *(Isolde)*, Aubrey Woods *(TV floor manager)*, Barry Fantoni *(Elijah)*. Juliet Harmer *(Lewis' girl friend)*, Mark

Murphy *(singer)*.

Comedy. Vocalist Scilla McKenzie deserts her husband, Lewis, a television director, on the night before his weekly show, in which she appears, goes on the air. While Lewis, drunk, waves goodbye, Scilla moves in with John, a platonic friend, and begins to plan her new life. Scilla uses her savings to begin construction on a new house and applies her feminine wiles to thwart any substitutes Lewis chooses to sing in her place on the television show. A party at John's apartment secretly arranged by Lewis to make Scilla return to him turns, according to plan, into an orgy, and Lewis skillfully protects his wife from an attack by a drunken Australian. Reconciled, the two walk off hand in hand, leaving the party behind them. *Singers. Television directors. Australians. Marriage. Drunkenness. Orgies.*

JUST ONCE MORE (Sweden)   F6.2559

Svensk Filmindustri. *Dist* Janus Films. 7 Aug 1963 [Maryland license]. Sd; b&w. 35mm. 78 min.

Prod (see note) Gösta Ekman, Jr., David Norberg. *Dir* Gunnar Hellström. *Screenplay* Birgitta Stenberg. *Photog* Martin Bodin. *Sets* P. A. Lundgren. *Mus* Torbjörn Lundquist.

Cast: Lillevi Bergman *(Mari)*, Gösta Ekman, Jr. *(Stefan)*, Bertil Anderberg *(Natan)*, Eivor Landström *(Mari's mother)*, Sture Ericson *(Mari's father)*, Åke Fridell *(uncle)*, Åke Lagergren *(the poet)*, Torsten Wahlund *(Martin)*, Hans Wigren *(Money)*, Betty Tuven *(female supervisor)*, Nils Fritz *(manager)*, Gudrun Brost *(store owner)*, Kotti Chave *(policeman)*, Marianne Karlbeck *(policewoman)*.

Melodrama. Source: Birgitta Stenberg, *Chans* (Stockholm, 1962). Paroled from reform school, Mari, a rebellious teenager, is sent to a small town to work, but instead she returns to her home in Stockholm where she belonged to a teenage gang. She is seduced by her lecherous American uncle and runs away into the countryside where she is discovered by her parents. During her travels she meets a poet, a businessman, several truck drivers, and a group of youths out for a joy ride. Sex becomes a casual affair. Returning to Stockholm, she looks up her old boyfriend Money, but she is disappointed to find him with another girl. After a one night affair with a motorcyclist, she moves in with Natan, a drug addict and dealer, but she is followed by police, who have been keeping Natan under surveillance. Stefan, a young student, helps her escape and invites her to stay with him. Mari introduces Stefan to her mother as her fiancé, but when he leaves her alone one night, she visits Money again. When Money refuses to take her back into his gang, Mari gets drunk in desperation and returns to Natan's house. Here the police pick her up and return her to the reform school for violating her parole. *Runaways. Juvenile delinquents. Uncles. Poets. Businessmen. Truckdrivers. Motorcyclists. Drug addicts. Police. Gangs. Drug dealers. Parole. Adolescence. Drunkenness. Seduction. Reformatories. Stockholm.*

Note: Released in Sweden in 1962 as *Chans*; running time: 82 min. Maryland license records credit Gösta Ekman as producer, while a Danish source credits David Norberg with "directing production." May also be known as *Just Once More*.

JUST TO BE LOVED *see* THE NEW LIFE STYLE

JUSTICE CAIN *see* CAIN'S WAY

JUSTINE   F6.2560

Associates Productions. *Dist* Chancellor Films. May 1967. Sd; b&w. 35mm. 76 min.

Prod-Dir S. N. Johnsen. *Screenplay* Gene Price. *Cinematog* Harry August. *Asst Dir* Philip Dross. *Cont* Dossie.

Cast: Peggy Stephans *(Justine)*, Lidia Coldwell *(Juliette)*. Philip Dross *(Felipe)*.

Drama. Based on the writings of: Donatien Alphonse François [Marquis de] Sade. Sisters Justine and Juliette live in a Puerto Rican slum and survive by taking menial jobs. Justine, ambitious and jealous, is enraged by the mistaken thought that her first boyfriend Felipe has approached the innocent Juliette. Justine sells her victimized sister to a gang of hoodlums who rape her. Justine goes to New York to seek money and power. She grows wealthy as the mistress of powerful men, and she eventually returns to Puerto Rico with her latest lover. Justine is infuriated by her sister's perpetual innocence when she sees Juliette again, now with a child as a result of the rape. She again sells Juliette, this time to the syndicate run by her lover. The battle between good and evil climaxes with a violent and bloody confrontation. *Sisters. Mistresses. Racketeers. Puerto Ricans. Jealousy. Perfidy. Prostitution. Innocents. Rape. Illegitimacy. Greed. White slave traffic. Puerto Rico. New York City.*

Note: May also be known as *Justine; the Erotic Excess of Evil.*

JUSTINE   F6.2561

Berman-Century Productions. *Dist* Twentieth Century-Fox Film Corp. 6 Aug 1969 [New York opening; c6 Aug 1969; LP37418]. Sd (Westrex); col

(DeLuxe). 35mm (Panavision). 116 min. *MPAA rating* R.

A Pandro S. Berman–George Cukor Production. *Prod* Pandro S. Berman. *Assoc Prod* Kathryn Hereford. *Dir* George Cukor. *Orig Dir* (see note) Joseph Strick. *Screenplay* Lawrence B. Marcus. *Dir Photog* Leon Shamroy. *Art Dir* Jack Martin Smith, William Creber. *Asst Art Dir* Fred Harpman. *Set Decor* Walter M. Scott, Raphael Bretton. *Main Titl* National Screen Service. *Film Ed* Rita Roland. *Mus* Jerry Goldsmith. *Orch* Arthur Morton. *Choreog* Gemze de Lappe. *Sd* Bernard Freericks, David Dockendorf. *Asst Dir* Maurice Vaccarino. *Unit Prod Mgr* Saul Wurtzel, Joseph C. Behm. *Cost Dsgn* Irene Sharaff. *Makeup Supv* Dan Striepeke. *Makeup Artist* Ed Butterworth. *Hairstylist* Dorothy White. *Hairstyling Supv* Edith Lindon. *Sp Photog Eff* L. B. Abbott, Art Cruickshank. *Tech Adv* Aaron Haddad.

Cast: Anouk Aimée (*Justine*), Dirk Bogarde (*Pursewarden*), Robert Forster (*Narouz*), Anna Karina (*Melissa*), Philippe Noiret (*Pombal*), Michael York (*Darley*), John Vernon (*Nessim*), Jack Albertson (*Cohen*), Cliff Gorman (*Toto*), George Baker (*Mountolive*), Elaine Church (*Liza*), Michael Constantine (*Memlik Pasha*), Marcel Dalio (*French Consul General*), Michael Dunn (*Mnemjian*), Barry Morse (*Maskelyne*), Severn Darden (*Balthazar*), Amapola Del Vando (*Mrs. Serapamoun*), Abraham Sofaer (*proprietor*), Stanley Waxman (*Serapamoun*), De Ann Mears (*lady at ball*), Tutte Lemkow (*prisoner*).

Drama. Source: Lawrence Durrell, *The Alexandria Quartet* [*Justine, Balthazar, Mountolive,* and *Clea*] (London, 1957–60). In 1938 Justine, an enigmatic Jew in Alexandria, and her husband, Nessim Hosnani, a Coptic Christian millionaire, conspire to send arms to Palestine. Among Justine's numerous friends and lovers are Pursewarden, a British official incestuously obsessed with his blind sister, Liza; Darley, a young Irish schoolmaster; Narouz, Justine's fanatic brother-in-law; and Toto, a homosexual. Arriving in Alexandria, Darley befriends Melissa, a tubercular Greek belly dancer and the mistress of wealthy Jewish furrier Cohen, an intimate of Justine. Fearing that Melissa has revealed the conspiracy to Darley, Justine takes the Irishman as her lover. Enraged by Darley's liaison with Justine, Melissa consoles herself with Pursewarden, to whom she reveals the Hosnanis' scheme. Shocked that Justine has provided munitions for use against British forces, Darley informs his superior, Mountolive, and then commits suicide. Although the Hosnanis are placed under house arrest, Justine quickly charms her captor, the Moslem Minister of Security. *Jews. Millionaires. British. Irish. Schoolteachers. Fanatics. Greeks. Exotic dancers. Furriers. Brothers-in-law. Diplomats. Muslims. Smuggling. Infidelity. Incest. Brother-sister relationship. Blindness. Male homosexuality. Jealousy. Suicide. Tuberculosis. Ammunition. Alexandria (Egypt). Palestine.*

Note: Location scenes filmed in Tunis. Strick was replaced as director by Cukor early in the filming.

JUVENTUD A LA INTEMPERIE see **THE UNSATISFIED**

K. O. SUZETTE   **F6.2562**
Century Cinema Corp. *Dist* Distribpix, Inc. **1969**. Sd; col. 35mm. 61 min.
Cast: Suzzan Landow (*Suzette*), Linda Boyce.

Sex film. Suzette, in love with a fight-promoting racketeer, consents to destroy an aspiring prizefighter for $1,000, so that he will lose an upcoming bout with one of the racketeer's fighters. With the help of her women friends, she destroys the fighter's career by sexually exhausting him so that he is unable to box. *Prizefighters. Racketeers. Sexuality.*

DET KAERE LEGETØJ see **DANISH BLUE**

KAGI see **ODD OBSESSION**

KAGI NO KAGI see **WHAT'S UP TIGER LILY?**

KAIDAN see **KWAIDAN**

KAIJU DAISENSO see **MONSTER ZERO**

KAIJU SOSHINGEKI see **DESTROY ALL MONSTERS**

KAITEI GUNKAN see **ATRAGON**

KAITO JIBAKO see **MONSIEUR ZIVACO**

KAJA, UBIT ĆU TE see **KAYA, I'LL KILL YOU**

KALAPANA, 1964   **F6.2563**
Dist Martin Charlot. 20 May **1965** [Honolulu, Hawaii, opening]. Si with sd-on-tape; b&w. 16mm. 70 min.
Prod-Dir Martin Charlot. *Photog* Martin Charlot. *Titl Photog* Mike Ferguson. *Film Ed* Martin Charlot. *Ancient Mus* Kaupena Wong. *Sd Tech* Mike Doud, Stewart Dawson. *Tech Adv* Martin Rohde, George Tahara. *Coöp* People of Kalapana, Francis Haar, Father Joseph McGian.
Participants: Sam Komanui, Fred Punahoa, Pawao, Kapiko, Keala, Buly, Daisy, Leslie, Old Makalii, Young Makalii, Melili, Joe, John, Mr. George,

Mamo, Robert, Kimo.
Extra Voices: Richard Drake, Amalu Lee.
Documentary. Scenes of everyday life in the Hawaiian village of Kalapana, located on the slope of an active volcano, include views of fishermen casting nets on the shore; *paniolos* (Hawaiian cowboys) roping and slaughtering a bull; fishermen gathering *opihis* (shellfish) as the waves crash and recede around them; historic Hawaiian stone carvings in the lava fields; a young boy drawing pictures to show to his mother who is inside a church polishing a boar's tusk; an artist restoring a painting of a saint on the church wall; villagers weaving out of coconut fronds a small enclosure behind the church for a *luau* (traditional Hawaiian feast); children playing and swimming in a spring-fed pool; the jungle near Kalapana; two men capturing a wild pig; a *paniolo* branding a bull; the men killing and cleaning the pig and preparing it for roasting; villagers preparing the roasting pit and placing the meat to be cooked over it; people gathered around after the feast listening to Hawaiian guitar music; the aftermath of the *luau* the next morning; and finally, one villager's quietude being suddenly disturbed by the appearance of a bulldozer on his front lawn to make ready for the construction of a new road. *Village life. Fishing. Hunting. Weaving. Volcanoes. Lava. Tropics. Luaus. Sculptures. Churches. Music. Paintings. Kalapana (Hawaii). Bulls. Pigs.*

KALEIDOSCOPE (Great Britain)   **F6.2564**
Winkast Film Productions. *Dist* Warner Bros. Pictures. 22 Sep **1966** [New York opening; c26 May 1966; LP36532]. Sd; col (Technicolor). 35mm. 103 min.

Pres by Jerry Gershwin, Elliott Kastner. *Prod* Elliott Kastner. *Assoc Prod* Peter Medak. *Dir* Jack Smight. *Writ* Robert Carrington, Jane-Howard Carrington. *Dir Photog* Christopher Challis. *Camera Op* Austin Dempster. *Art Dir* Maurice Carter. *Asst Art Dir* Jack Maxsted. *Set Decor* David Ffolkes. *Main Titl Dsgn* Maurice Binder. *Film Ed* John Jympson. *Mus Comp & Cond* Stanley Myers. *Sd Rec* Dudley Messenger, Gordon K. McCallum. *Sd Ed* Rusty Coppleman. *Asst Sd Ed* Pamela Tomling. *Asst Dir* Kip Gowans. *Prod Supv* Denis Holt. *Asst to the Prod* Marion Rosenberg. *Cont* Connie Willis. *Miss Susannah York's Cost* Sally Tuffin, Marion Foale. *Mr. Beatty's Wardrobe* Anthony Sinclair. *Wardrobe* Dorothy Edwards, John Hilling. *Fashion Consult* Marit Allen. *Makeup* W. T. Partleton, Bob Lawrence. *Hairdresser* Barbara Ritchie. *Dial Coach* Alfredo Lettieri.

Cast: Warren Beatty (*Barney Lincoln*), Susannah York (*Angel McGinnis*), Clive Revill (*Inspector "Manny" McGinnis*), Eric Porter (*Harry Dominion*), Murray Melvin (*Aimes*), George Sewell (*Billy*), Stanley Meadows (*Dominion captain*), John Junkin (*Dominion porter*), Larry Taylor (*Dominion chauffeur*), Yootha Joyce (*museum receptionist*), Jane Birkin (*Exquisite Thing*), George Murcell (*Johnny*), Anthony Newlands (*Leeds*), Peter Blythe, Sean Lynch, John Bennett, Michael Balfour, José Sukhum Boonlve.

Crime comedy-drama. Barney Lincoln, a wealthy American playboy, has one exciting date in London with an attractive dress designer named Angel McGinnis and then leaves for Geneva. Once there he breaks into the Kaleidoscope card factory and etches secret marks on the printing plates used in making playing cards for all the European gambling casinos. He then goes to Monte Carlo, is reunited with Angel, and makes a fortune because of the marks on the backs of the cards. After a tour of other European casinos, where he continues to win more money, Barney returns to London with Angel. To his dismay he learns that while they were in Monte Carlo, Angel became suspicious and alerted her father Manny, a Scotland Yard detective, who now knows all about Barney's deception. Manny then reveals that in return for his freedom Barney must assist in capturing Harry Dominion, a narcotics smuggler with a weakness for poker. Accompanied by Angel, Barney sits in on a game with Dominion and wins every hand—even one played with an unmarked deck. Not accustomed to losing, Dominion uses Angel as bait to lure Barney to his country estate, where he gets back his money by force. Barney and Angel attempt to escape and are almost run down by Dominion's henchmen. But Manny and his men from Scotland Yard arrive in time to break up the dope ring and rescue Barney and Angel. *Playboys. Americans in foreign countries. Couturiers. Detectives. Gambling. Burglary. Poker. Cheating. Playing cards. Narcotics. Smuggling. Scotland Yard. Geneva. Monte Carlo. London.*

Note: Released in Great Britain in 1966; location scenes filmed in London and on the French Riviera. Rereleased in Great Britain in 1968 as *The Bank Breaker*.

KAMA SUTRA (West Germany)   **F6.2565**
Contifilm. *Dist* American International Pictures, United Producers Releasing Organization. 21 Oct **1970** [Seattle opening]. Sd; col. 35mm. 90 min. [Also reviewed at 79 min.]
Prod Richard Reuven Rimmel, Kobi Jaeger. *Dir* Kobi Jaeger. *Screenplay* George Wilson, writ, Kobi Jaeger, P. D. Shenoy. *Photog* Richard Reuven Rimmel. *Film Ed* Peter Harlos. *Mus* Irmin Schmidt. *Cost* Mani Rabadi.

Cast: Bruno Dietrich *(Mike)*, Barbara Schöne *(Anke)*, Richard Abbott *(Peter)*, Franziska Bronnen *(Helga)*, Maren Kaehler *(Carola)*, Persis Khambatta *(Nanda)*, Faryal Karim *(Asha)*, Jai Kumar *(Dlipi)*, Will Quadflieg *(narrator)*, Prem Nath.

Documentary. Source: Vātsyāyana (called Mallanāga), *Kama Sutra*. The erotic principles of the *Kama Sutra* remain universally valid, as witnessed by their successful application through the ages. Among the couples submitting to the treatise's regimen of feasts, massages, sexual games, and conversation are aristocratic Indians, young married Europeans, and members of the international set. [A 25-minute sequence depicting licentious middle-class Americans body painting, wife swapping, and taking drugs has been added to the original film, and some footage from the original has been deleted.] *East Indians. Aristocrats. Jet set. Middle classes. Sex instruction. Sexual techniques. Marriage. Body painting. Mate swapping. Food. Drugs. Games. India. "Kama Sutra."*

Note: Opened in Düsseldorf in Jun 1969 as *Kamasutra—Vollendung der Liebe* at 91 min.

KAMA SUTRA '71   F6.2566
Dist Variety Films. 21 Dec **1970** [New York opening]. Sd; col. 35mm. 76 min.

Sex film. No information about the precise nature of this film has been found, but press material indicates that the story concerns sexual techniques, with references to the *Kama Sutra*. *Sexual techniques. "Kama Sutra".*

KAMASUTRA—VOLLENDUNG DER LIEBE see KAMA SUTRA

KAMIGAMI NO FUKAKI YOKUBO see KURAGEJIMA—LEGENDS FROM A SOUTHERN ISLAND

KAMIKAZE (United States/France)   F6.2567
Le Film d'Art–Irja Film Productions–C. B. S. Europe. *Dist* Brigadier Film Associates. 2 Oct **1962** [New York opening]. Sd; b&w. 35mm. 89 min.
Prod-Dir-Writ Perry Wolff. *Film Ed* Françoise Diot, Peter Poor, Leo Zochling. *Mus* Norman Dello Joio. *Cons* James B. Faichney.
Narrators: Duncan Elliott, Jim Stephens.
Documentary. Allied and Japanese newsreel footage is used to introduce evidence that in 1941 the United States received repeated warnings that the Japanese were planning aggressive action. Following the attack on Pearl Harbor, war is declared, and Japan makes steady gains during the next 6 months. When the Americans retake bases on the Gilbert, Marshall, and Mariana Islands, however, the tide begins to turn. In a desperate attempt to regain their losses, the Japanese resort to the use of Kamikaze pilots, but the United States retaliates with the atom bomb, and Japan is forced into an unconditional surrender. *Kamikazes. Atom bomb. World War II. Pearl Harbor Attack 1941. Japan. Gilbert Islands. Marshall Islands. Mariana Islands. United States Army. United States Navy. United States Marines. Japan—Navy.*
Note: Opened in Paris in Jan 1961.

KANAŁ (Poland)   F6.2568
Kadr Film Unit. *For* Film Polski. *Dist* M. J. P. Enterprises, Kingsley-International Pictures. 9 May **1961** [New York opening]. Sd; b&w. 35mm. 96 min.
Pres by J. Jay Frankel. *Prod* Stanisław Adler. *Dir* Andrzej Wajda. *Screenplay* Jerzy Stefan Stawiński. *Photog* Jerzy Lipman. *Asst Camera* Jerzy Wójcik. *Art Dir* Roman Mann. *Asst Art Dir* Halina Krzyzanowska, Roman Wolyniec. *Film Ed* Halina Nawrocka. *Asst Ed* Aurelia Rut. *Mus* Jan Krenz. *Sd* Józef Bartczak. *Asst Dir* Kazimierz Kutz, Janusz Morgenstern, Maria Starzeńska, Anna Janeczkowa. *Cost* Jerzy Szeski.
Cast: Teresa Iżewska *(Daisy)*, Tadeusz Janczar *(Corporal Korab)*, Wieńczysław Gliński *(Lieutenant Zadra)*, Tadeusz Gwiazdowski *(Sergeant Kula)*, Stanisław Mikulski *(The Slim [Smukly])*, Władysław Sheybal *(composer)*, Emil Karewicz *(The Wise [Madry])*, Teresa Berezowska *(Halinka)*, Adam Pawlikowski *(German officer)*, Zofia Lindorf, Students of the Łódź Film School.
Drama. Source: Jerzy Stefan Stawiński, *Kanał* (Warsaw, 1956). In September of 1944, as the German Army completes the crushing of the Warsaw uprising, a tired group of Polish patriots makes its way through the rubble and ruins of the city. Zadra, their embittered commander, who knows their flight is doomed, leads them to the temporary shelter of a bombed hotel. But even in the face of death, there is still a moment for romance between Korab and Daisy, a young Resistance fighter. That night, Halinka, a young woman who acts as a messenger, has her first love affair, with a lieutenant. A composer, Michael, is on the verge of madness. The group is forced to go into the sewers in order to proceed to the center of the city. Waist-deep in the muddy, refuse-filled waters, they become separated in the maze of canals and one by one meet their inevitable end. Halinka, brutally told by the man she loves that he has a wife and children, commits suicide. Michael, by now completely insane, wanders through the passages playing the ocarina. Daisy and the wounded

Korab see the light of day at the end of a tunnel but find the exit barred with an iron grille. Meanwhile, Zadra and his sergeant make their way to an exit; but seeing none of the men behind him, the commander brands his panic-stricken sergeant a traitor and kills him. Emerging into the open air through a manhole, Zadra finds himself surrounded by a German firing squad. Silently and grimly, he descends once more into the sewers. *Composers. Resistance (political). Suicide. Murder. Insanity. Sewers. Hotels. World War II. Warsaw. Germany—Army.*
Note: Filmed on location in Warsaw. Released in Poland in Apr 1957.

KANCHENJUNGHA (India)   F6.2569
N. C. A. Productions. *Dist* Harrison Pictures. Aug **1966**. Sd; col (Eastman Color). 35mm. 102 min.
Pres by Edward Harrison. *Prod-Dir-Writ* Satyajit Ray. *Photog* Subrata Mitra. *Art Dir* Bansi Chandragupta. *Titl Paintings by* Satyajit Ray. *Film Ed* Dulal Dutta. *Mus Arr* Satyajit Ray. *Sd* Durgadas Mitra. *Prod Mgr* Anil Chowdhury.
Cast: Chhabi Biswas *(Indranath Choudhuri)*, Karuna Bannerjee *(Labanya)*, Anil Chatterjee *(Anil)*, Nilima Roy Chowdhury *(Monisha)*, Anubhe Gupta *(Anima)*, Subrata Sen Sharma *(Shankar)*, Arun Mukherjee *(Ashoke)*, N. Viswanathan *(Bannerjee)*, Pahari Sanyal *(Jagadish)*, Indrani Singh *(Tuklu)*, Vidya Singh *(Shibsankar Roy)*.
Domestic drama. Wealthy Calcutta industrialist Indranath and his family vacation in Darjeeling. Beside the great Mount Kanchenjungha they walk, converse, and drink tea. During the final afternoon of the holiday, family members voice dissatisfaction with Indranath's absolute domestic rule. His wife, Labanya, for example, disputes his choice for daughter Monisha's husband, the wealthy Bannerjee, whom the girl despises. His son Anil, meanwhile, moves fleetingly from one romantic pursuit to another. Although Indranath's son-in-law Shankar confronts his adulterous wife, Anima, the couple decides to preserve their marriage for the sake of their daughter Tuklu. In defiance of her husband, Labanya sends her brother Jagadish to tell Monisha she has the right to choose her own husband. Discouraging Bannerjee's suit, Monisha befriends Ashoke. The idealistic youth declines Indranath's offer of a position, confounding the patriarch. As Indranath expresses his confusion, the mist lifts over Kanchenjungha. *Industrialists. Upper classes. In-laws. Family life. Vacations. Infidelity. Fatherhood. Courtship. Darjeeling. Kanchenjunga. Calcutta.*
Note: Filmed on location in Darjeeling. Released in India in 1962.

KANOJO TO KARE see SHE AND HE

KAPHETZOU see THE FORTUNE TELLER

KAPITÄNLEUTNANT PRIEN—DER STIER VON SCAPA FLOW see U-47 LT. COMMANDER PRIEN

KAPO (France/Italy/Yugoslavia)   F6.2570
Vides–Zebra Film–Cineriz–Francinex–Lovćen Film. *Dist* Lionex Films, Promenade Films. 1 Jun **1964** [New York opening]. Sd; b&w. 35mm. 116 min. [Reduced to 90 min.]
Prod Moris Ergas. *Assoc Prod* Antonio Musu. *Dir* Gillo Pontecorvo. *Screenplay* Gillo Pontecorvo, Franco Solinas. *Photog* Goffredo Bellisario, Aleksandar Sekulović. *Art Dir* Piero Gherardi. *Film Ed* Roberto Cinquini. *Mus* Carlo Rustichelli. *Sd* Fausto Ancillai, Sandro Occhetti.
Cast: Susan Strasberg *(Nicole [Edith])*, Laurent Terzieff *(Sascha)*, Emmanuelle Riva *(Thérèse)*, Didi Perego *(Sofia)*, Gianni Garko *(German soldier)*, Annabella Besi, Graziella Galvani, Mira Dinulović, Dragomir Felba.
War drama. During World War II, Edith, a 14-year-old Jewish girl from Paris, is sent to a concentration camp with her family. Her parents are exterminated, but Edith escapes death when the camp doctor gives her the name and clothes of Nicole, a non-Jewish political prisoner who has died in the hospital. "Nicole" is transferred to a camp in Poland where her suffering becomes intolerable; only the friendship of Thérèse, a French partisan, keeps her from total despair. She is selected to "entertain" German soldiers, and eventually, motivated by a fear of death, she collaborates with the Nazis and becomes a "kapo," or camp guard. Her fellow prisoners grow to detest her as she becomes increasingly absorbed in the role. She falls in love with Sascha, a Russian prisoner who shares the hatred of his comrades for the brutal "kapo." The Germans cut back food rations, and Thérèse is driven to suicide. Deeply shaken, "Nicole" grows to regret her collaboration and shifts to the Russian side. As the Russian army nears the camp, she suggests a plan for a mass escape and reveals her true identity to Sascha. She falters, but at the fateful moment her love for Sascha gives her courage, and she sacrifices herself for the other prisoners. *Jews. Nazis. Russians. Germans. Prisoners of war. Traitors. Prison guards. Physicians. Personal identity. Survival. Self-sacrifice. Genocide. Prostitution. Friendship. Suicide. Concentration camps. World War II. Germany—Army. Poland.*

Note: Opened in Rome in Oct 1960 as *Kapò*; running time: ca110 min; in Paris in Apr 1961 as *Kapo*; running time: 115–120 min. Filmed in Yugoslavia and released there under the same title.

KARAMI-AI *see* **THE INHERITANCE**

KARATE, THE HAND OF DEATH F6.2571

Joel Holt. *Dist* Joseph Brenner Associates, Allied Artists. 9 Aug **1961** [Philadelphia opening]. Sd; b&w. 35mm (Hi-Fi Scope). 80 min.

Prod-Dir Joel Holt. *Assoc Prod* Margy Holt. *Story & Screenplay* David Hill, writ. *Photog* Tatsuo Namikawa. *Lighting Dir* Momomi Shima. *Titl Dsgn* Iwao Ashida. *Film Ed* Ken Tanaka. *Mus Comp & Cond* Minoru Miki. *Sd* Kunie Maruyama. *Asst Dir* Iseo Hirukawa. *Prod Mgr* Ken Noyle. *Prod Coörd* Kazuaki Iric. *Script Girl* Kazuko Iric. *Mr. Holt's Wardrobe* Andrew Pallack. *Karate Tech Dir* Hidetaka Nishiyama. *Prop Dir* Yuji Kuroda.

Cast: Joel Holt *(Matt Carver)*, Frank Blaine *(Ivan Mayberry)*, Akira Shiga *(Akira Harakawa)*, Joe Hirakawa *(Kosaka Harakawa)*, Reiko Okada *(Reiko Harakawa)*, Ken Noyle *(Rohmer)*, Fujio Ito *(Lieutenant Okada)*, Mayana *(dancer)*, Bob Markworth *(Hantaro)*, Maurice Gruel *(Maurice)*, Rie Sugiura *(nurse)*, Tony Sugahara *(waiter)*, Naboro Kudisahi *(plumber)*, Kanji Hayashi *(coin dealer)*, Tom Moore, actor *(Herr Blucher)*, Akiko Seo *(flower girl)*, Takao Minami *(little boy)*, Tadashi Yamaki *(1st thief)*, Akio Watanabe *(pickpocket)*, Shigayaoshi Kawai *(radio shop clerk)*, Yoichi Wada, Jipp Endo *(gangsters)*, Kasuo Ushida *(taxi driver)*, Taro Yamashita, Jiro Kodama, Sho Onoda *(soldiers)*, Kinji Inoue *(rag picker)*, Men of the Japan Karate Association *(karate players)*.

Action melodrama. While in Tokyo karate expert Matt Carver comes into possession of a mysterious coin and learns that it is the key to the location of a fortune in platinum smuggled from Germany. After learning that a blind man—a former Nazi official—was murdered over ownership of the coin, Matt and Ivan Mayberry, the dead man's secretary, contact nightclub owner Rohmer, who supposedly has additional information about the coin. Too late, Matt realizes he has been double-crossed by Mayberry. Beaten up by thugs, Matt narrowly escapes. Chased by Rohmer, Matt discovers the coin is a cleverly hidden wire recording, which unmasks his deceased sweetheart Toshiro's brother, Akira, as the mastermind behind the smuggling operation. Akira had killed Toshiro because she was carrying Carver's child, whose birth would have disgraced her family. The two fight, and Matt kills Akira in a savage karate duel. *Americans in foreign countries. Nazis. Secretaries. Nightclub owners. Hoodlums. Smuggling. Karate. Murder. Perfidy. Recording. Brother-sister relationship. Pregnancy. Platinum. Tokyo. Chases.*

Note: Location scenes filmed in Japan.

KÄRE JOHN *see* **DEAR JOHN**

KAREN, THE LOVEMAKER *see* **AFRICA EROTICA**

KARLA F6.2572

Bamram Films. *Dist* Craddock Films. 27 Aug **1969** [New York showing]. Sd; col. 35mm. 80 min.

Prod Peggy Steffans. *Dir-Writ* Joe Sarno. *Photog* Steve Silverman. *Mus* McKorman Productions Ltd. *Titl Song* Jim Heineman.

Cast: Suzan Thomas *(Jacqueline Windsor)*, Betty Whitman *(Lorna Tanner)*, Danielle Leman *(Karla Herrick)*, Susan Furman *(Cecil Smith)*, Rita Shea *(Doris Broun)*, Rene Howard *(Donna Smith)*, Joel Saltz *(Jeff Veltman)*, Henry Ross *(Charlie Kretscher)*, Jean Muniz *(Vera)*, Carol Ephram *(Wilma)*, Frances Goodhart *(Georgia)*, Howard Dale *(Warren)*, Stephen Price *(Pete)*.

Drama. Child psychologist Jackie Windsor and author Lorna Tanner share a large Florida house. Lorna leaves for a mysterious appointment at Karla Herrick's house, and there two naked women throw her to the floor and arouse her. A naked man then makes love to her as the two women hold her down and continue their caresses. The next morning, Lorna tells Jackie of her visits to Karla's house where women pay to be satisfied in unusual ways. Jackie, troubled and curious, visits Karla and reveals that she is a psychologist interested in the clients' reactions. She becomes Karla's assistant and watches as a woman is bound and caressed by two others. Prodded by Karla, Jackie joins the two women in satisfying the client, and Jackie soon becomes a permanent member of Karla's staff. One client, Donna, falls in love with Jackie. With the help of a boyfriend, Donna lures her to a secluded spot where they bind and make love to her. Unwilling to share Jackie with her male friend, Donna drives him away, and the two women make plans to go away together. *Psychologists. Authors. Roommates. Troilism. Group sex. Lesbianism. Sex research. Jealousy. Voyeurism. Florida.*

KATERINA IZMAILOVA (U.S.S.R.) F6.2573

Lenfilm. *Dist* Artkino Pictures. 25 Apr **1969** [New York opening]. Sd; col (Sovcolor). 35mm. 118 min.

Dir Mikhail Shapiro. *Screenplay* Dmitriy Dmitriyevich Shostakovich. *Photog* Rostislav Davydov, Vladimir Ponomaryov. *Art Dir* Yevgeniy Yeney.

Mus Comp Dmitriy Dmitriyevich Shostakovich. *Mus Cond* Konstantin Simeonov. *Mus Played by* Shevchenko Opera and Ballet Theatre Orchestra. *Sd* Ilya Volk. *Asst Dir* A. Tubenshlyak. *Prod Mgr* G. Khokhlov.

Cast: Galina Vishnevskaya *(Katerina Lvovna Izmailova [Izmaylova])*, Artyom Inozemtsev *(Sergey)*, Nikolay Boyarskiy *(Zinoviy Borisovich)*, Aleksandr Sokolov *(Boris Timofeyevich)*, R. Tkachuk *(village drunk)*, Tatyana Gavrilova *(Sonetka)*, V. Titova, L. Malinovskaya, K. Adashevskiy, I. Bogolyubov, K. Tyagunov, V. Lyubimova, A. Zhila, G. Krasulya, V. Gerasimchuk, M. Reshetin.

Voices: V. Tretyakov *(Sergey)*, V. Radziyevskiy *(Zinoviy Borisovich)*, A. Vedernikov *(Boris Timofeyevich)*, S. Strezhnev *(village drunk)*, V. Reka *(Sonetka)*, Shevchenko Opera and Ballet Theatre Chorus.

Opera film. Source: Nikolay Semyonovich Leskov, "Ledi Makbet Mtsenskogo uyezda" (1864). Dmitriy Dmitriyevich Shostakovich and A. Preys, *Katerina Izmaylova* (Leningrad opening: 22 Jan 1934). In 19th-century provincial Russia, Katerina Izmailova, the wife of a wealthy merchant, stifles in the boredom of her dull domestic routine and, in the absence of her weak-willed husband, Zinoviy, falls in love with a new farm laborer, Sergey. Her tyrannical father-in-law, Boris, learns of the affair and flogs Sergey into unconsciousness. In revenge, Katerina poisons the old man. Later, she and Sergey murder Zinoviy and hide his corpse in the basement; but the crime haunts Katerina, and the village drunk often sees her standing by the cellar door. On the day Katerina and Sergey are to be married, the drunk steals into the basement, finds Zinoviy's body, and notifies the police. Katerina is publicly beaten, and she and Sergey are sent in chains to Siberia. Despite the cruel hardship, Katerina stoically endures until Sergey tells her that he never loved her but was attracted by her wealth. Heartlessly he demands that she give him her woolen stockings and presents them to Sonetka, a younger prisoner. Taunted by Sonetka and the other convicts, Katerina is consumed by anger and grief. As the prisoners are transported across a lake by ferry, she seizes Sonetka and leaps into the water, drowning both of them. *Mistresses. Fathers-in-law. Farmhands. Convicts. Merchants. Poisoning. Wealth. Marriage. Infidelity. Flogging. Murder. Revenge. Alcoholism. Guilt. Jealousy. Suicide. Siberia.*

Note: Released in the U.S.S.R. in 1967 in 70mm; running time: ca130 min.

KATIA *see* **MAGNIFICENT SINNER**

KATOK I SKRIPKA *see* **VIOLIN AND ROLLER**

KATTORNA *see* **THE CATS**

KATU (THE FRENCH GIRL AND THE NUDISTS) (United States/Brazil) F6.2574

Dist United Producers Releasing Organization. 22 May **1964** [Maryland license]. Sd; col (Eastman Color). 35mm. 84 min.

Prod-Dir Zygmunt Sulistrowski. *Screenplay* Zygmunt Sulistrowski, Georg Lafayette. *Photog* Herbert C. Theisen. *Mus* Enrico Simonetti, Lyrio Panicali, Remo Usai.

Cast: Kitty Wolf, June Abel, Ellie Rogers, Robert Bird, Dieter K. Friedrich, Alan Kran.

Adventure drama. A group of 13 nudists from around the world go to a deserted island off the coast of Brazil. There they must live off the land for 90 days in order to win a wager that will save their nature club. Following the example of the Caiapos Indians, they build their own shelters, spear fish, and gather native fruit. The party spends its leisure time sunbathing and swimming. One of the women injures herself in a fall 3 days before their time is up. They are about to use the emergency radio and thereby lose the bet when they find that their calendar is wrong and realize that they have won. *Nudism. Survival. Fishing. Islands. Wagers. Caiapos Indians.*

Note: May also be known as *Katu (How I Lived as Eve)*.

KATZ UND MAUS *see* **CAT AND MOUSE**

KAWAITA MIZUUMI *see* **YOUTH IN FURY**

KAWANO HOTORIDE *see* **BORN IN SIN**

KAYA, I'LL KILL YOU (Yugoslavia/France) F6.2575

Jadran Film–Cinéastes Associés–Mosaic Films. *Dist* Fleetwood Films, Altura Films International. 24 Nov **1969** [New York opening]. Sd; col (Eastmancolor). 35mm. 80 min.

Pres by Clem Perry. *Prod* Branko Lustig. *Dir* Vatroslav Mimica. *Screenplay* Vatroslav Mimica, Kruno Quien. *Photog* Frano Vodopivec. *Lighting* Ivica Habazin. *Art Dir* Vladimir Tadej. *Film Ed* Joja Remenar. *Mus* Lidija Jojić. *Sd* Fedor Jeler. *Cost* Vladimir Tadej.

Cast: Zaim Muzaferija *(Kaya)*, Ugljesa Kojadinovic *(Piero)*, Antun Nalis *(Tonko)*, Jolanda Dacić *(Mare Karantanova)*, Izet Hajdarhodžić *(Ugo Bala)*, Husein Čokić *(Nikica)*.

Drama. Source: Kruno Quien, "Kaja, ubit ću te" (publication undetermined). An ancient Dalmatian coastal city has enjoyed a 300-year respite from crime.

During World War II, however, Italian occupation factionalizes the inhabitants, among them the crippled fascist convert, Piero, who delivers a death sentence to his elderly neighbor, Kaya. While soldiers wantonly vandalize buildings and statuary, the townspeople amuse themselves by killing small birds and harassing the village idiot. As Piero stalks Kaya, neighbors close their doors and windows to shut out the old man's murder. Idiots. Soldiers. Italians. Murder. Village life. Fascism. Military occupation. World War II. Dalmatia.

Note: Location scenes filmed at Trogir and Istria, Yugoslavia. Released in Yugoslavia in 1967 as Kaja, ubit ću te.

THE KEELER AFFAIR see **THE CHRISTINE KEELER AFFAIR**

KEEP ME IN see **TUCK ME IN**

KELLY'S HEROES (United States/Yugoslavia)   **F6.2576**
The Warriors Co.-Avala Film-Katzka-Loeb Productions. *Dist* Metro-Goldwyn-Mayer, Inc. 23 Jun **1970** [New York opening; c14 May 1970; LP38087]. Sd; col (Metrocolor). 35mm (Panavision). 145 min. *MPAA rating* GP.
Prod Gabriel Katzka, Sidney Beckerman. *Assoc Prod* Irving Leonard. *Dir* Brian G. Hutton. *2d Unit Dir* Andrew Marton. *Screenplay* Troy Kennedy Martin. *Dir Photog* Gabriel Figueroa. *2d Unit Photog* H. A. R. Thomson. *Camera Coörd* Dennis Fraser. *Art Dir* Jonathan Barry. *Set Decor* Mike Ford. *Prod Dsgn* Jonathan Barry. *Film Ed* John Jympson. *Orig Mus* Lalo Schifrin. *Song:* "Burning Bridges" Lalo Schifrin, Mike Curb. *Sung by* Mike Curb Congregation. *Song:* "Si tu me dis" Lalo Schifrin, Gene Lees. *Sung by* Monique Aldebert. *Song:* "Sunshine" *sung by* Hank Williams, Jr. *Sd Ed* Jonathan Bates. *Sd Rec* Cyril Swern, Harry W. Tetrick. *Asst Dir & Yugoslav Asst Dir* John C. Chulay, Stevo Petrović. *Prod Supv* Basil Somner. *Prod Mgr* Terry Lens. *Yugoslav Prod Mgr* Milenko Stanković. *Cont* Gladys Goldsmith. *Wardrobe* Anna Maria Fea. *Makeup* Trevor Crole-Rees. *Sp Eff* Karli Baumgartner. *Tech Adv* Alexander Gerry. *Stunt Coörd* Alf Joint.
Cast: Clint Eastwood (*Kelly*), Telly Savalas (*Big Joe*), Don Rickles (*Crapgame*), Donald Sutherland (*Oddball*), Carroll O'Connor (*General Colt*), Hal Buckley (*Maitland*), Stuart Margolin (*Little Joe*), Fred Pearlman (*Mitchell*), Tom Troupe (*Job*), Gavin MacLeod (*Moriarity*), Gene Collins (*Babra*), Perry Lopez (*Petchuko*), Dick Balduzzi (*Fisher*), Dean Stanton (*Willard*), Richard Davalos (*Gutkowski*), Len Lesser (*Bellamy*), Jeff Morris (*cowboy*), Michael Clark (*Grace*), George Fargo (*Penn*), Dee Pollock (*Jonesy*), Shepherd Sanders (*Turk*), Frank J. Garlotta, Sandy Kevin, Phil Adams (*tank commanders*), Read Morgan (*ADC driver*), David Hurst (*Colonel Dankhopf*), Robert McNamara (*Roach*), James McHale (*guest*), Ross Elliott (*booker*), Tom Signorelli (*Bonsor*), George Savalas (*Mulligan*), John G. Heller (*German lieutenant*), Karl Otto Alberty (*German tank commander*), Hugo De Vernier (*French mayor*), Harry Goines (*supply sergeant*), David Gross (*German captain*), Donald Waugh (*roamer*), Vincent Maracecchi (*old man in town*).
War comedy-drama. Lieutenant Kelly, an unconventional U. S. Army officer, captures a German colonel and brings him back to American headquarters for questioning. Hoping to learn the location of the German Army's supply of liquor and women, Kelly instead discovers two gold ingots hidden in the German's uniform. Further questioning reveals information concerning 14,000 more ingots worth $16 million being held in a nearby German bank. After deciding to "appropriate" the gold, Kelly and his men enlist the aid of Crapgame, the manager of the supply depot, to provide the equipment necessary for the robbery. Next, Kelly recruits Oddball, an eccentric young soldier who has stolen two Sherman tanks. Meanwhile, Field Commander General Colt, who has been listening to the radio communication setting up the operation, believes the group is on a heroic venture and sets off to join them. The unorthodox mission is finally launched, and Kelly and his men reach the bank at the cost of many German lives. A sole German remains protecting the bank, but he is persuaded to join in the robbery. Kelly's men then take the gold and leave the military victory to General Colt. Prisoners of war. Eccentrics. Traitors. Interrogation. Combat zone life. Bank robberies. Gold. Tanks (armored cars). World War II. United States Army. Germany—Army.
Note: Location scenes filmed in Yugoslavia. Working title: *The Warriors.*

KEMONOMICHI see **BEAST ALLEY**

KEMPO SAMURAI see **SAMURAI FROM NOWHERE**

KENJU YO SARABA see **GET 'EM ALL**

KENNER   **F6.2577**
M and M Productions. *Dist* Metro-Goldwyn-Mayer, Inc. 19 Mar **1969** [Washington, D. C., opening; c29 Oct 1968; LP36192]. Sd; col (Metrocolor). 35mm. 92 min. *MPAA rating* G.
Prod Mary Phillips Murray. *Dir* Steve Sekely. *Screenplay* Harold Clemins, John Loring. *Story* Mary Phillips Murray. *Dir Photog* Dieter Liphardt. *Art Dir* Ram Yedekar. *Film Ed* Richard Heermance. *Mus Score* Piero Piccioni. *Indian*

Dance Mus Comp Prem Dhawan. *Indian Dance Choreog* Sudarshan Kumar. *Rec Supv* Franklin Milton. *Asst Dir* Bluey Hill, Baba Shaikh. *Unit Prod Mgr* Somath Rangru. *Cost Dsgn* Janice Bond. *Makeup* Ruediger Von Sperle. *Hairstyles* Wilfriede Baumann. *Sp Eff* Don Courtney. *Coöp* Government of India.
Cast: Jim Brown (*Kenner*), Madlyn Rhue (*Anasuya*), Robert Coote (*Henderson*), Ricky Cordell (*Saji*), Charles Horvath (*Tom Jordan*), Prem Nath (*Sandy*), Kuljit Singh (*Young Sikh*), Sulochana (*Mother Superior*), Ursula Prince (*Sister Katherine*), Tony North (*American friend*), Ming Hung (*ring referee*), R. P. Wright (*gym owner*), Nitin Sethi (*customs officer*), Mahendra Jhaveri (*young Hindu at seaman's association*), G. S. Aasie (*shoe merchant*), Ravi Kaant (*bald disciple*), Hercules, Khalil Amir (*robed men*).
Drama. Roy Kenner, an American seafarer whose partner was murdered in Singapore, arrives in Bombay to search for the killer, dope smuggler Tom Jordan. While combing the city, Kenner is befriended by 9-year-old Saji, a native boy desperate to find his American father, unaware that the man abandoned his mother without ever marrying her. When Kenner is drugged by Jordan's associate, Henderson, and is being led to two waiting killers, Saji inadvertently causes a distraction that diverts Kenner. As a result, the narcotic has become ineffective by the time Kenner reaches his boat; and he is able to outwit Jordan, Henderson, and the two henchmen by diving overboard and remaining underwater until his would-be assassins are convinced that he has drowned. As Kenner surfaces, Saji and his mother, Anasuya, a Hindu entertainer, arrive and bring him to their house to recuperate. There, love develops between Anasuya and Kenner, while Saji gradually begins to look upon Kenner as his father. But tragedy strikes: Kenner chases Jordan through a railroad yard, and Anasuya, who has been following them, is killed by an oncoming train. After the funeral, Kenner learns that Jordan is a lover of cricket fights, and he uses Saji's pet insect to gain admittance to the secret place where the matches are held. Once they are inside, Saji is compelled to enter his cricket in a contest and then cannot bring himself to leave his pet when Kenner chases Jordan out of the place and engages him in a death struggle atop a building. When Saji's cricket is victorious, the boy runs out and discovers that Kenner has also won his battle with Jordan. At last Saji finds a father: Kenner takes the boy back to the United States with him. Seamen. Americans in foreign countries. Smugglers. Hired killers. Hindus. Entertainers. Children. Revenge. Friendship. Illegitimacy. Fatherhood. Adoption. Narcotics. Funerals. Bombay. Crickets.
Note: Filmed on location in Bombay, India. Original title: *Year of the Cricket.*

KEPT   **F6.2578**
Dist I. R. M. I. Films. **1968.** Sd; b&w. 35mm. 60 min.
Prod John Erikson. *Dir* Jan Anders.
Cast: Silvi Walter, Gary Boyd.
Sex film. No information about the precise nature of this film has been found, but press material suggests that the central character is a "kept" woman. *Mistresses. Sexuality.*

KES (Great Britain)   **F6.2579**
Woodfall Films-Kestrel Films. *Dist* United Artists. 20 Sep **1970** [New York opening; c25 Mar 1970; LF77]. Sd; col (DeLuxe). 35mm. 109 min. *MPAA rating* GP.
Prod Tony Garnett. *Dir* Kenneth Loach. *Screenplay* Barry Hines, Kenneth Loach, Tony Garnett. *Photog* Chris Menges. *Art Dir* William McCrow. *Film Ed* Roy Watts. *Mus Comp & Dir* John Cameron. *Sd Ed* Peter Pierce. *Sd Rec* Tony Jackson. *Sd Re-rec* Gerry Humphreys. *Asst Dir* Keith Evans. *Prod Supv* David Griffith. *Tech Adv* Richard Hines.
Cast: David Bradley, actor (*Billy Casper*), Lynne Perrie (*Mrs. Casper*), Freddie Fletcher (*Jud*), Colin Welland (*Mr. Farthing*), Brian Glover (*Mr. Sugden*), Bob Bowes (*Mr. Gryce*), Robert Naylor (*MacDowall*), Trevor Hasketh (*Mr. Crossley*), Geoffrey Banks (*math teacher*), Eric Bolderson (*farmer*), Zoe Sutherland (*librarian*), Joe Miller (*Mrs. Casper's friend*), Joey Kaye (*pub entertainer*), Bernard Atha (*youth employment officer*), David Glover (*Tibbutt*), Stephen Crossland, George Speed, Frank Norton (*Billy's friends*), Martin Harley (*younger boy*), Douggie Brown (*milkman*), Billy Dean (*fish and chip shop man*).
Melodrama. Source: Barry Hines, *A Kestrel for a Knave* (London, 1968). Billy Casper, a 14-year-old boy living in the industrial town of Barnsley in Yorkshire, delivers newspapers to help support his mother, who has been abandoned by Billy's father. Bored with school, he excels neither in classwork nor soccer. One day Billy discovers a kestrel's nest and takes one of the fledglings from the nest as a pet. He names the bird Kes and trains it with the aid of a book on falcons, which he shoplifted from a local store. Soon the bird has learned to return to Billy's hand on command and seize a lure in mid-air. Mr. Farthing, one of Billy's schoolteachers, asks him to tell the class a story, and as Billy relates the training of Kes, Mr. Farthing begins to realize the boy's

potential. When Billy's brutal stepbrother Jud asks him to place a bet for him at a horserace, Billy keeps the money instead and uses it to buy food for himself and Kes. The horse wins the race, and Jud, furious with Billy for not placing the bet, seeks revenge. Unable to find Billy, he takes out his revenge on Kes. Billy finds the dead bird and sadly buries him. *Newsboys. Animal trainers. Schoolteachers. Stepbrothers. Adolescence. Filial relations. Animal care. Shoplifting. Gambling. Revenge. Barnsley (England). Pets. Falcons.*

Note: Filmed entirely on location in Barnsley, England. Opened in Doncaster, England, in Mar 1970.

KETTO GANRYU JIMA *see* **SAMURAI (PART III)**

KEY CLUB WIVES   F6.2580

Mitam Productions. 4 Dec **1968** [Boston opening]. Sd; b&w. 35mm. 62 min. *Dir* (see note) Adam Clay.

Cast: Marsha Jordan, Dixie, Patti.

Melodrama. Motel operator Ann Porter and bar owner Don Mullins decide to set up a key club to satisfy sexually their clientele. The club's membership consists largely of married people seeking extramarital sexual excitement. Inhibitions are cast aside, and some unexpected results are achieved: Bob and Patti, a married couple who have independently joined the club, by chance receive matching room keys; and their encounter revitalizes their faltering marriage. Meanwhile, some of the married women discover that they are sexually attracted to other women. Ann and Don eventually throw a party for their clients. The members indulge their individual sexual preferences, and all goes well until the husband of a participant, Sharon, makes an unexpected appearance and begins to beat her. Bob tries to intervene, and he is accidentally killed by the jealous husband. The police then raid the party and break up the key club. *Marriage. Group sex. Infidelity. Murder. Lesbianism. Motels. Bars. Sex clubs.*

Note: Director credit not confirmed. May also be known as *The Wives*.

KHARTOUM (Great Britain)   F6.2581

Julian Blaustein Productions. *Dist* United Artists. 15 Jun **1966** [Minneapolis opening; c10 Jun 1966; LF8]. Sd; col (Technicolor). 35mm & 70mm (Ultra Panavision). 134 min. [Also reviewed at 128 min.]

Prod Julian Blaustein. *Dir* Basil Dearden. *2d Unit Dir* Yakima Canutt. *Dir Prolog Scenes* Eliot Elisofon. *Screenplay* Robert Ardrey. *Dir Photog* Edward Scaife. *2d Unit Photog* Harry Waxman. *Art Dir* John Howell. *Set Decor* Pamela Cornell, John Bodimeade. *Film Ed* Fergus McDonell. *Mus Comp & Cond* Frank Cordell. *Sd* Bert Ross, Laurie Clarkson, Gordon K. McCallum, Dino Di Campo. *Asst Dir* John Peverall, Bluey Hill. *Prod Supv* Charles Orme. *Wardrobe* John McCorry. *Makeup* Bill Lodge, Tom Smith. *Hairstyles* Hilda Fox. *Sp Eff* Richard Parker. *Sp Photog Eff* Cliff Culley.

Cast: Charlton Heston (*Gen. Charles Gordon*), Laurence Olivier (*The Mahdi*), Richard Johnson (*Col. J. D. H. Stewart*), Ralph Richardson (*Prime Minister Gladstone*), Alexander Knox (*Sir Evelyn Baring*), Johnny Sekka (*Khaleel*), Michael Hordern (*Lord Granville*), Zia Mohyeddin (*Zobeir Pasha*), Nigel Green (*General Wolseley*), Hugh Williams (*Lord Hartington*), Douglas Wilmer (*The Khalifa Abdullah*), Edward Underdown (*Colonel Hicks*), Alec Mango (*Bordeini Bey*), George Pastell (*Giriagis Bey*), Peter Arne (*Major Kitchener*), Alan Tilvern (*Awaan*), Michael Anthony (*Herbin*), Marne Maitland (*Sheikh Osman*), Jerome Willis (*Frank Power*), Leila (*dancer*), Ronald Leigh Hunt (*Lord Northbrook*), Ralph Michael (*Sir Charles Dilke*), Leo Genn (*narrator*).

Action epic. In 1883, 10,000 untrained British troops in Sudan are lured into the desert and slaughtered by Arab tribesmen under the leadership of the Mahdi, a religious fanatic who believes he is the "expected one of Mohammed." As a result of the massacre, Britain's Prime Minister William Gladstone reluctantly sends one of England's great military men, Gen. Charles Gordon, to Khartoum with orders to evacuate troops and civilians. Gordon, a brandy and Bible loving soldier nicknamed "Chinese" because of the 6 years he spent in the East eliminating the centuries-old slave traffic, is told that his mission must remain unofficial and that he has no authority to act in the name of the Queen. Although Gordon is hailed in Khartoum as a savior, he and his only aide, Col. J. D. H. Stewart, are unable to negotiate with the Mahdi. Instead they are told that the streets will run with blood and every man, woman, and child will die. In England, Gladstone, informed of the increasing hopelessness of the situation, orders Gordon home; but, as fanatical in his own right as the Mahdi, Gordon refuses. Following the murder of Stewart, a final confrontation takes place between the two men, and both assert that they welcome death if dying brings about the destruction of their enemy. Soon, Gordon's small army faces the onslaught of 100,000 Arabs. Khartoum falls, and Gordon is slain by a dervish's spear. His head is mounted on a pole and brought before the Mahdi. Outraged, the Mahdi screams that he forbade such an action. Some months later, the British, under the command of Major Kitchener, retake the besieged city and Gordon is honored as a national hero. *Great Britain—Army. Arabs.*

Fanatics. Heroism. Islam. Decapitation. Massacres. Great Britain—History— 19th Century. Sudan. Khartum. Charles George Gordon. Mohammed Ahmed. William Ewart Gladstone. Horatio Herbert Kitchener.

Note: Locations filmed in Egypt. Released in Great Britain in 1966; running time: 128 min. Presented for roadshow engagements in Cinerama. Also known as *Battle for Khartoum*.

KHRUSTALNYY BASHMACHOK *see* **CINDERELLA**

KHUN-E SIAAVASH *see* **SIAVASH IN PERSEPOLIS**

KID GALAHAD   F6.2582

Mirisch Co. *Dist* United Artists. 1 Aug **1962** [Atlanta opening; c1 Aug 1962; LP22408]. Sd; col (DeLuxe). 35mm. 95 min.

Prod David Weisbart. *Dir* Phil Karlson. *Screenplay* William Fay. *Cinematog* Burnett Guffey. *Art Dir* Cary Odell. *Set Decor* Edward G. Boyle. *Film Ed* Stuart Gilmore. *Mus* Jeff Alexander. *Song:* "King of the Whole Wide World" Ruth Batchelor, Bob Roberts. *Songs:* "This Is Living," "Riding the Rainbow" Fred Wise, Ben Weisman. *Songs:* "Home Is Where the Heart Is," "A Whistling Tune" Sherman Edwards, Hal David. *Song:* "I Got Lucky" Dee Fuller, Fred Wise, Ben Weisman. *Song:* "Love Is for Lovers" Ruth Batchelor, Sharon Silbert. *Songs Sung by* Elvis Presley. *Sd* Lambert Day. *Asst Dir* Jerome M. Siegel. *Prod Supv* Allen K. Wood. *Prod Mgr* Robert E. Relyea. *Wardrobe* Bert Henrikson, Irene Caine. *Makeup* Lynn Reynolds. *Hairstyles* Alice Monte. *Sp Eff* Milt Rice. *Tech Adv* Mushy Callahan.

Cast: Elvis Presley (*Walter Gulick*), Gig Young (*Willy Grogan*), Lola Albright (*Dolly Fletcher*), Joan Blackman (*Rose Grogan*), Charles Bronson (*Lew Nyack*), Ned Glass (*Lieberman*), Robert Emhardt (*Maynard*), David Lewis (*Otto Danzig*), Michael Dante (*Joie Shakes*), Judson Pratt (*Zimmerman*), George Mitchell (*Sperling*), Richard Devon (*Marvin*), Jeffrey Morris (*Ralphie*), Liam Redmond (*Father Higgins*).

Comedy-drama with music. Source: Francis Wallace, *Kid Galahad* (Boston, 1936). Following his service in the Army, Walter Gulick takes a job as a sparring partner in a Catskill training camp run by Willy Grogan and his girl friend, Dolly. Willy decides to turn Walter into a professional fighter over Dolly's objections. The lad earns the nickname "Kid Galahad" by rescuing Dolly from gangsters to whom Willy is in debt. After a series of sensational victories, Walter decides to give up boxing and settle down with Willy's sister, Rose. Upon hearing the news the gangsters warn Willy that his man must not be permitted to win his last bout, and they match him against Sugar-Boy Romero, a highly experienced fighter. Believing Willy guilty of having arranged the match for spite, Dolly walks out on him. Before the fight, Walter's trainer is offered $500 not to work in his corner. When he refuses the bribe, the hoodlums break his fingers. Walter arrives on the scene and, after a skirmish with the gangsters, goes into the ring. Despite a severe beating, he knocks out his opponent. Dolly returns to Willy, and Walter is free to marry Rose and open an auto repair shop. *Prizefighters. Fight managers. Gangsters. Athletic coaches. Mechanics. Prizefighting. Extortion. Bribery. Debt. Catskill Mountains.*

Note: Location scenes filmed in California. Previously filmed by Warner Bros. in 1937.

KID RODELO (United States/Spain)   F6.2583

Trident Films–Fénix. *Dist* Paramount Pictures. 2 Feb **1966** [Los Angeles opening; c31 Dec 1965; LP32170]. Sd; b&w. 35mm. 91 min.

Prod Jack O. Lamont, James J. Storrow, Jr. *Exec Prod* Ellis Sard. *Assoc Prod* Eduardo Manzanos, Arturo Marcos. *Dir* Richard Carlson. *Screenplay* Jack Natteford. *Spanish Script* Eduardo M. Brochero. *Story* Louis L'Amour. *Dir Photog* Manuel Merino. *Art Dir* Jaime Pérez Cubero, José Luis Galicia. *Film Ed* Allan Morrison. *Mus* Johnny Douglas. *Mus Spanish Vers* Manuel Parada. *Song:* "Love Is Trouble" Tom Glazer. *Sd* Edgar Vetter, Maurice Askew. *Prod Mgr* Victoriano G. Giraldo. *Wardrobe* Peris. *Makeup* Fernando Martínez. *Hairdresser* Maria Nieves Ruiz.

Cast: Don Murray (*Kid Rodelo*), Janet Leigh (*Nora*), Broderick Crawford (*Joe Harbin*), Richard Carlson (*Link*), José Nieto (*Thomas Reese*), Julio Peña (*Balsas*), Miguel del Castillo (*Chavas*), José Villa Sante (*Cavalry Hat*), Alfonso San Félix (*Gopher*), Emilio Rodríguez (*warden*), Fernando Hilbeck (*Perryman*), Roberto Rubenstein (*doctor*), Bill Christmas (*guard*), Alvaro de Luna, Guillermo Méndez, Mike Brendel, Juan Olaguibel.

Western melodrama. After serving a 1-year sentence in a Yuma prison because of his association with Joe Harbin, who was sentenced to life imprisonment for the murder of his partner, Kid Rodelo sets out to retrieve $50,000 in gold which Harbin hid before his capture. Meanwhile, Harbin and another convict, Thomas Reese, escape from prison and set out to reach the gold before The Kid. The Kid is picked up along the road by Link, his girl friend, Nora, and his partner, Balsas, who keep their own interest in the gold a secret. The Kid leads his three companions to the deserted town where the gold is hidden. While Nora distracts The Kid, Link and Balsas find a chest and argue over the division of its contents. The greedy Balsas shoots Link but discovers that the case contains only rocks. Harbin and Reese arrive in town with another escaped convict, Gopher, trailed by Cavalry Hat, a Yaqui Indian chief, and his tribe of bounty hunters. Balsas shoots Reese and arranges to exclude The Kid from the division of the gold, which Harbin has at last removed from its hiding place. The Kid thwarts their plan, however, and offers to lead them to the Gulf of Mexico in exchange for a share of the gold. After the Indians poison a waterhole, Gopher is killed trying to steal Harbin's water. The Kid tricks the Indians to enable the group to escape, but Harbin and Balsas decide to flee with the gold. Harbin tells Nora that The Kid has been killed, and she sets out for the Gulf with the two men. Once there, they find no boats in which to flee; and Harbin shoots Balsas in a gunfight. With the Indians following close behind, The Kid catches up with Nora and Harbin. Harbin tries to kill The Kid but is shot by Cavalry Hat. The Kid kills the Indian chief, and as the tribe carries Harbin's body away, Nora and The Kid return to civilization with the gold. *Prison escapees. Bounty hunters. Yaqui Indians. Robbers. Greed. Murder. Injustice. Perfidy. Gold. Ghost towns. Yuma (Arizona). Gulf of Mexico.*

Note: Filmed in Spain in Eastmancolor; opened in Madrid in Feb 1966; running time: 89 min.

THE KIDNAPPERS (United States/Philippines)　　　　　　**F6.2584**
Halcyon Productions-Cirio H. Santiago. *Dist* Manson Distributing Corp. Jun **1964**. Sd; b&w. 35mm. 78 min.
Dir Eddie Romero. *Screenplay* Harry Harber. *Photog* Felipe Sacdalan. *Film Ed* Joven Calub. *Mus* Ariston Avelino.
Cast: Burgess Meredith *(Louis Halliburton)*, Olivia Cenizal *(Christine Halliburton)*, William Phipps *(Jay)*, Paul Harber, Carol Varga, Amando Cortez, Zaldy Zshornack, Johnny Monteiro.
Melodrama. Louis Halliburton, an American living in the Philippines, frantic with guilt over the kidnaping of his young son, Leslie, is convinced by his Filipina wife, Christine, to enlist the aid of a former FBI agent who was once her fiancé. Jay, the kidnaper, a disgruntled American drifter, sends Halliburton from one end of Manila to the other in hopes of safely collecting his ransom, while Christine and the detective follow behind. Working with his Filipina girl friend, Jay instructs Halliburton to leave the ransom money at the railroad station. Jay then tricks his girl friend by taking the money for himself and leaving her a dummy parcel to pick up. She discovers Jay's deception and tries to stop him, but Jay runs her down in his car and flees to a warehouse, shooting and wounding the pursuing Halliburton. The police eventually corner Jay, and he falls to his death. At the same time, his dying girl friend informs Christine that her son is safe. *Detectives. Americans in foreign countries. Kidnaping. Murder. Perfidy. Ransom. Manila. United States—Federal Bureau of Investigation. Chases.*

Note: Filmed on location in Manila. Prerelease title: *Man on the Run.*

A KIEV COMEDY (U.S.S.R.)　　　　　　**F6.2585**
Dovzhenko Film Studio. *Dist* Artkino Pictures. **1963**. Sd; col. 35mm. 76 min.
Dir-Screenplay V. Ivanov, dir. *Story Ed* G. Zeldovich. *Photog* V. Ilyenko. *Art Dir* I. Yutsevich. *Film Ed* V. Bondina. *Mus* V. Gomolyaka. *Song Lyr* Ye. Kravchenko. *Cond* V. Tolba. *Sd* R. Maksimtsov. *Prod Mgr* L. Nizguretskiy. *Cost* L. Baykova. *Makeup* A. Dubchak. *Sp Eff* I. Tregubova, V. Deminskiy.
Cast: O. Borisov *(Golokhvostyy)*, M. Krinitsyna *(Pronya)*, N. Yakovchenko *(Serko)*, A. Kushnirenko *(Serchikha)*, N. Koperzhinskaya *(Sekleta)*, N. Naum *(Galya)*, A. Yurchenko *(Stepan)*, K. Yershov *(Plyashka)*, T. Litvinenko *(Khimka)*, O. Vikland *(Ninon)*, L. Alfimova, N. Antonova, A. Bykov, V. Grudynin, S. Karamash, V. Kostyrenko, N. Talyura, R. Shablovskaya, V. Shiryayev, V. Koretskiy, F. Ivanova, N. Lapshina.
Comedy. Source: Mikhaylo Petrovich Staritskiy, *Za dvoma zaytsyami* (a play; 1883). Golokhvostyy, a Kiev barber with a reputation as a fop and a dandy, loses his barbershop at cards. To remedy his finances he sets out to marry into wealth, and to this end he courts Pronya Serko, who has set her hopes on marrying a man of fashion and believes Golokhvostyy to be her dream come true. Golokhvostyy is meanwhile attracted to the modest and beautiful Galya, and he vacillates between the interests of his pocketbook and his heart. Golokhvostyy's trifling is finally his undoing, however. He is disgraced and, while making his departure, receives a sound beating. *Barbers. Fortune hunters. Courtship. Finance—Personal. Gambling. Kiev.*

Note: Released in the U.S.S.R. in Dec 1961 as *Za dvumya zaytsami.* Also known as *A Kiev Comedy; or Chasing Two Hares.*

KIGEKI DAI SHOGEKI *see* **HOTSPRINGS HOLIDAY**

KIL 1 *see* **THE SKIN GAME**

KILL (Japan)　　　　　　**F6.2586**
Toho Co. *Dist* Frank Lee International. Aug **1968** [Los Angeles showing]. Sd; b&w. 35mm (Tohoscope). 115 min.

Dir Kihachi Okamoto. *Screenplay* Akira Murao, Kihachi Okamoto. *Photog* Rokuro Nishigaki. *Art Dir* Iwao Akune. *Film Ed* Kihachi Okamoto, Yoshitami Kuroiwa. *Mus* Masaru Sato.
Cast: Tatsuya Nakadai *(Genta)*, Etsushi Takahashi *(Hanjiro)*, Shigeru Koyama *(Ayuzawa [see note])*, Eijiro Tono *(Moriuchi)*, Yuriko Hoshi *(Chino)*, Yoshio Tsuchiya *(Matsuo)*, Tadao Nakamaru *(Shoda)*, Hideo Amamoto, Nami Tamura, Ko Hashimoto, Akira Kubo.
Action drama. Source: Shugoro Yamamoto, "Torideyama no jushichinichi," in *Yamamoto Shugoro zenshu* (Tokyo, 1964). In feudal Japan, Genta, a one-time warrior who turned gambler when the samurai code forced him to kill his best friend, meets and befriends Hanjiro, a farmer's son who dreams of becoming a samurai. Meanwhile, several other samurai have banded together in a united effort to overthrow the despotic overseer of the province of Joshu. Their leader, Matsuo, tells them that he is going to present their case before the tribunal, and the men agree to hide out in a deserted fortress until a decision is made. Matsuo, however, is in league with Ayuzawa, another overseer, and the two men plan to assassinate the rebellious samurai hiding in the fortress. To accomplish this Ayuzawa dispatches a troop of archers to the fort and, for added insurance, recruits a group of farmers, including Hanjiro, to join in the assault. Genta, siding with the samurai, is captured and tortured by Matsuo's men, but he refuses to talk. Hanjiro nurses his friend back to health, and, grasping the truth of the situation, he joins Genta and the other samurai to fight against the evil Matsuo. Combining their cunning and skill with the sword, the two men help to defeat Matsuo's forces and put an end to the reign of tyranny. Once the battle is over, Genta tries to explain to Hanjiro that being a samurai does not necessarily mean being on the side of good. *Samurai. Despots. Farmers. Feudalism. Murder. Friendship. Perfidy. Gambling. Torture.*

Note: Released in Japan in Jun 1968 as *Kiru.* Actor Shigeru Koyama is also identified as Shigeru Kamiyama.

THE KILL　　　　　　**F6.2586a**
Dist Canyon Distributing Co. ca **1968**. Sd; col (Eastman Color). 35mm. 70 min.
Prod Ed DePriest. *Dir-Writ* Gary Graver. *Photog* Gary Graver. *Mus Comp & Cond* Ernest Alexander. *Sd* Hollywood Picture Recorders.
Cast: Antoinette Maynard, Walt Phillips, Sharon Wells, Natasha, Nancy McGavin, Tod Badker, Tony Brooks, Pam English, John Lee, U. S. actor, Harry Stone, Gail Lavon, Larry Vincente, April O'Connor, Shari Stevens, Bonnie Walker.
Melodrama. Antoinette hires down-and-out Private Detective Charlie Apple to find her brother Mickey after some of Mickey's associates, heroin smugglers, rape her for trying to persuade him to quit the racket. Antoinette gives Charlie a $100 retainer and seduces him. Charlie goes to Mickey's apartment and finds a dead woman there. Mickey arrives, and the two fight until Charlie is knocked out. He regains consciousness in the gangsters' warehouse and, discovering himself tied up, telephones Antoinette for help. She comes to the warehouse and frees Charlie; the gang returns; and they chase Charlie and Antoinette into a gravel pit. Antoinette is carried off while Charlie fights it out with one of the mob. Kruger, the gang leader, telephones Mickey and instructs him to kill Charlie. Mickey arranges to meet Kruger at a deserted beach where there will be a $1 million heroin delivery; he also sends Candy, his new mistress, to search Charlie's office. Charlie walks in while she is rifling his desk. He wins her confidence by making love to her, and she tells him of the beach rendezvous. Charlie goes to the beach, and there a violent showdown occurs. *Detectives. Smugglers. Drug dealers. Gangsters. Mistresses. Brother-sister relationship. Seduction. Rape. Murder. Abduction. Heroin.*

KILL A DRAGON　　　　　　**F6.2587**
Aubrey Schenck Enterprises. *Dist* United Artists. 6 Dec **1967** [New York opening; c1 Nov 1967; LP35523]. Sd; col (DeLuxe). 35mm. 91 min.
Prod Hal Klein. *Exec Prod* Aubrey Schenck. *Dir* Michael Moore. *Writ* George Schenck, William Marks. *Photog* Emmanuel Rojas. *Film Ed* John F. Schreyer. *Mus* Philip Springer, Buddy Kaye. *Sd* Ben Winkler. *Asst Dir* Robert Goodstein. *Prod Mgr* K. C. Liang. *Sp Eff* Roger George.
Cast: Jack Palance *(Rick)*, Fernando Lamas *(Patrai)*, Aldo Ray *(Vigo)*, Alizia Gur *(Tisa)*, Kam Tong *(Win Lim)*, Don Knight *(Ian)*, Hans William Lee *(Jimmie)*, Judy Dan *(Chunhyang)*.
Melodrama. A cargo junk carrying a deadly load of nitroglycerin is beached on an island near Hong Kong. The villagers claim it as their own by right of salvage, but the junk's owner, feudal baron Patrai, threatens to blow up the island if his cargo is not returned within 3 days. Despite Patrai's blockade of the harbor, village chief Win Lim manages to escape with two other villagers to enlist aid in Hong Kong. They appeal to Rick, an adventurer willing to do anything for the right price, and he agrees to help them transport the cargo to Hong Kong, both for the gold they offer and also because he is moved by the plight of the islanders, particularly a young woman named Tisa. While Patrai is kidnaping Win Lim and his companions, Rick formulates a plan to penetrate

the blockade and load the explosives onto a junk. He is assisted by karate experts Ian and Jimmie, tourist guide Vigo, and the villagers. Rick first rescues Win Lim, then outwits Patrai after having appeared to cooperate with the efforts of the unscrupulous tycoon to bribe him. Most of Patrai's henchmen are killed in a final battle, during which Rick successfully transports the explosives, but the villainous Patrai indicates that he bears the adventurer no grudge. *Tycoons. Shipowners. Adventurers. Village life. Blockades. Bribery. Kidnaping. Islands. Nitroglycerin. Salvage. Hong Kong.*

Note: Filmed in Hong Kong, Macao, and Kowloon.

KILL BABY KILL (Italy)   F6.2588

F. U. L. Film. *Dist* Europix Consolidated Corp. Oct **1966** [Pittsburgh showing]. Sd; col (EastmanColor). 35mm. 83 min.

Prod Nando Pisani, Luciano Catenacci. *Dir* Mario Bava. *Screenplay* Romano Migliorini, Roberto Natale, Mario Bava. *English Screenplay* John Hart. *Photog* Antonio Rinaldi. *Art Dir* Sandro Dell'Orco. *Film Ed* Romana Fortini. *Mus* Carlo Rustichelli. *Sd* Romano Pampaloni. *Asst Dir* Lamberto Bava. *Dub Dir* John Hart.

Cast: Erika Blanc (*Monica Schuftan*), Giacomo Rossi Stuart (*Dr. Paul Eswai*), Fabienne Dali (*Ruth*), Giana Vivaldi (*Baroness Graps*), Piero Lulli (*Police Commissioner Kroger*), Max Lawrence (*Kerl*), Micaela Esdra, Giuseppe Addobbati, Mirella Pamphili, Franca Dominici, Valeria Valeri.

Horror film. Following a series of mysterious deaths in the small Transylvanian town of Karmingan, Police Commissioner Kroger is summoned by a letter from a young girl. When he arrives the girl is already dead. While performing an autopsy, Dr. Paul Eswai and his assistant, Monica Schuftan, discover a coin embedded in the victim's heart. Confronted by the physician, the witch Ruth reveals that she has driven the coin into the victim's heart to protect her shade from further harm by the Baroness Graps, who has driven the townspeople to suicide. The sorceress also discloses the baroness' motivation, describing the death some years before of 7-year-old Melissa Graps and the villagers' lack of response to her pleas for help. Discovering that Monica, Melissa's younger sister, will be the next ignorant victim, Ruth kills the baroness, thereby destroying her evil influence. *Police. Physicians. Witches. Motherhood. Revenge. Murder. Suicide. Transylvania.*

Note: Released in Rome in Aug 1966 as *Operazione paura*; running time: 85 min.

KILL OR BE KILLED (Italy)   F6.2589

Regal Film. *Dist* Rizzoli Film Distributors, Cinemation Industries. Oct **1967**. Sd; col (Technicolor). 35mm (Techniscope). 82-92 min. [See note.]

Prod Luigi Rovere. *Dir* Amerigo Anton. *Screenplay-Story* Mario Amendola. *Photog* Aldo Giordani. *Art Dir* Saverio D'Eugenio. *Film Ed* Cleofe Conversi. *Mus* Carlo Rustichelli. *Cost* Giorgio Desideri.

Cast: Robert Mark (*Johnny Ringo/Gerry*), Elina De Witt (*Lisa Drummond*), Gordon Mitchell (*hired gunman*), Andrea Bosic, Men Fury, Tony Rogers, Fabrizio Moroni, Albert Farley, Benjamin May, Mary Land.

Western melodrama. In the West in 1885, the feud between the Griffith and Drummond families flares into renewed violence when several of the Griffiths show up at a Drummond funeral and fire shots into the coffin. A short time later, Gerry, a violin-playing stranger, arrives at the local saloon. Before long he kills one of the Griffith sons, who has forced him into a showdown. He learns that Lisa, old Drummond's daughter, is being persistently wooed by the eldest Griffith son, Chester. The sheriff discovers that Gerry is actually the renowned gunman Johnny Ringo and has him escorted out of town. But Chester and his band attack, kill the sheriff's men, and bury Ringo up to his neck in sand. With Ringo believed dead, Lisa decides to marry Chester in the hope that their union will bring peace between the two families. Secretly, however, Chester plans the marriage to seize the Drummond property. Meanwhile, Ringo, rescued by an old man, kills an outlaw hired by the Griffiths. As the wedding ceremony is being performed, Ringo arrives and demands a showdown. By the end of the gun battle, all of the Griffiths lie dead. With peace restored, Lisa and Gerry decide to make a better future in another town and leave with the sheriff's good wishes. *Strangers. Violinists. Gunfighters. Sheriffs. Outlaws. Feuds. Murder. Funerals. Saloons. Weddings.*

Note: Sources conflict as to running time. Opened in Rome in Apr 1967 as *Uccidi o muori*; running time: ca95 min. Amerigo Anton, Men Fury, Albert Farley, and Benjamin May are pseudonyms of Tanio Boccia, Furio Meniconi, Alberto Farnese, and Beniamino Maggio, respectively.

KILL OR CURE (Great Britain)   F6.2590

Metro-Goldwyn-Mayer Pictures. *Dist* Metro-Goldwyn-Mayer, Inc. 12 Nov **1962** [New York opening; c9 Oct 1962; LP23373]. Sd (Westrex); b&w. 35mm. 88 min.

Prod George H. Brown. *Exec Prod* Lawrence P. Bachmann. *Dir* George Pollock. *Orig Story & Screenplay* David Pursall, Jack Seddon. *Dir Photog* Geoffrey Faithfull. *Camera Op* Jack Lowin. *Focus Puller* Tony Busbridge.

Camera Grip Freddie Fry. *Art Dir* Harry White. *Asst Art Dir* Michael White. *Chargehand Set Dresser* A. Thatcher. *Scenic Artist* Peter Melrose. *Draughtsman* Tony Pratt. *Film Ed* Bert Rule. *1st Asst Ed* Alan Corder. *Mus Comp & Cond* Ron Goodwin. *Sd Rec* J. B. Smith, Cyril Swern. *Rec Supv* A. W. Watkins. *Dub Ed* Dino Di Campo. *Boom Op* Bill Baldwin. *Sd Camera Op* Ron Matthews. *1st, 2d & 3d Asst Dir* Jan Darnley-Smith, Ray Freeborn. *Prod Mgr* Ronnie Bear. *Cont* Betty Harley. *Prod Sec* Beryl Harvey. *Wardrobe Supv* Maude Churchill. *Cost Dsgn* Elizabeth Haffenden. *Men's Wardrobe* Bob Rayner. *Women's Wardrobe* Dolly Smith. *Makeup* Basil Newall. *Hairdressing* Joan Johnstone. *Sp Eff* Tom Howard. *Casting Dir* Irene Howard. *Still Photog* John Hardman. *Chargehand Electrn Supv* Arthur Pochetti. *Chargehand Prop* Mickey O'Toole.

Cast: Terry-Thomas (*J. Barker-Rynde*), Eric Sykes (*Rumbelow*), Dennis Price (*Dr. Crossley*), Lionel Jeffries (*Inspector Hook*), Moira Redmond (*Frances Reitman*), Katya Douglas (*Rita*), David Lodge (*Richards*), Ronnie Barker (*Burton*), Hazel Terry (*Mrs. Crossley*), Derren Nesbitt (*Roger*), Harry Locke (*Higgins*), Arthur Howard (*clerk*), Tristam Jellinek (*assistant clerk*), Peter Butterworth (*barman*), Patricia Hayes (*waitress*), Anna Russell (*Margaret Clifford*), Sidney Vivian, Julian Orchard.

Mystery comedy. Private detective J. Barker-Rynde receives a call from wealthy widow Margaret Clifford, asking him to investigate questionable occurrences at a health-cure hotel in the country. Upon arrival, he finds that his client has been murdered and her secretary, Frances Reitman, nearly killed from poisoning. Forced to pose as a guest and eat health foods in his quest for the murderer, Rynde joins forces with Rumbelow, a health instructor, in the hope that they can solve the case and split any reward money. The sleuths initially suspect the dead woman's nephew, the resort's director, and a nurse; but finally they discover that Reitman is the guilty party. With the case solved, Mrs. Clifford's will is read, revealing that all her money has been bequeathed to her dog. *Detectives. Widows. Secretaries. Aunts. Murder. Poisoning. Imposture. Greed. Health resorts. Wills. Dogs.*

Note: Opened in London in Jan 1963.

KILL THE KILLERS (Japan)   F6.2591

Daiei Motion Picture Co. Mar **1970** [Los Angeles showing]. Sd; col? 35mm. [Feature film, length unknown.]

Cast: Ryunosuke Minegishi, Osamu Sakai, Hiroko Masuda. No information about the nature of this film has been found.

Note: Original title and release undetermined.

KILL THEM ALL AND COME BACK ALONE (Italy/Spain)   F6.2592

Fida Cinematografica–Centauro Films. *Dist* Fanfare Films. May **1970**. Sd; col (Technicolor). 35mm (Techniscope). 97 min. *MPAA rating* R.

Prod Edmondo Amati. *Dir* Enzo G. Castellari. *Exec Dir* Ricardo Sanz. *Screenplay* Tito Carpi, Enzo G. Castellari, Francesco Scardamaglia, Joaquín Romero Hernández. *Story* Tito Carpi, Enzo G. Castellari. *Photog* Alejandro Ulloa. *Art Dir* Enzo Bulgarelli. *Set Decor* Jaime Pérez Cubero. *Film Ed* Tatiana Morigi Casini, María Luisa Soriano. *Mus* Francesco De Masi. *Sd* Pietro Vesperini. *Prod Mgr* Mario Mariani, Rafael Vázquez.

Cast: Chuck Connors (*Clyde*), Frank Wolff (*Captain Lynch*), Franco Citti (*Hoagy*), Leo Anchoriz (*Deker*), Ken Wood (*Kid*), Hércules Cortés (*Bogard*), Alberto Dell'Acqua (*Blade*), John Bartha, Furio Meniconi, Antonio Molino Rojo, Alfonso Rojas, Ugo Adinolfi.

Melodrama. General Hood and Captain Lynch of the Confederate Army instruct Clyde to lead his gang of outlaws against a Union arsenal and steal the gold that is concealed inside sticks of dynamite. Clyde is told by the Confederate officers that he must then kill his own men and return to Confederate headquarters alone. The outlaws manage to get the gold, but Clyde plans to hide it for himself. Before Clyde can carry out his plans, however, they all are captured by Union soldiers and taken to a prison camp run by turncoat Captain Lynch. Tortured by Lynch, who hopes to learn the whereabouts of the stolen gold, they attempt an escape. Only Clyde survives, however, and in a gunfight with Captain Lynch, Clyde kills Lynch and retrieves the gold for himself. *Soldiers. Outlaws. Perfidy. Torture. Prison escapes. Gold. Arsenals. United States—History—Civil War.*

Note: Location scenes filmed in Madrid and Almería. Released in Italy in 1968 as *Ammazzali tutti e torna solo*; in Spain in 1969 as *Matalos y vuelve*; running time: 86 min.

THE KILLERS   F6.2593

Revue Productions. *Dist* Universal Pictures. 7 Jul **1964** [New York opening; c12 Sep 1964; LP33836]. Sd (Westrex); col (Eastman Color by Pathé, print by Technicolor). 35mm. 95 min.

Prod-Dir Donald Siegel. *Screenplay* Gene L. Coon. *Ed Dept Head* David J. O'Connell. *Dir Photog* Richard L. Rawlings. *Art Dir* Frank Arrigo, George Chan. *Set Decor* John McCarthy, James S. Redd. *Film Ed* Richard Belding. *Mus Supv* Stanley Wilson. *Mus Score* Johnny Williams. *Song:* "Too Little

Time" Henry Mancini, Don Raye. *Sung by* Nancy Wilson. *Sd* David H. Moriarty. *Asst Dir* Milton Feldman. *Cost* Helen Colvig. *Makeup* Bud Westmore. *Hair Stylist* Larry Germain. *Tech Adv* Hal Brock. *Dial Coach* Scott Hale.

Cast: Lee Marvin *(Charlie)*, Angie Dickinson *(Sheila Farr)*, John Cassavetes *(Johnny North)*, Ronald Reagan *(Browning)*, Clu Gulager *(Lee)*, Claude Akins *(Earl Sylvester)*, Norman Fell *(Mickey)*, Virginia Christine *(Miss Watson)*, Don Haggerty *(mail-truck driver)*, Robert Phillips *(George)*, 'Kathleen O'Malley *(receptionist)*, Ted Jacques *(gym assistant)*, Irvin Mosley *(mail-truck guard)*, Jimmy Joyce *(salesman)*, Davis Roberts *(maitre d')*, Hal Brock *(race marshal)*, Burt Mustin *(elderly man)*, Peter Hobbs *(instructor)*, John Copage *(porter)*, Tyler McVey *(steward)*, Seymour Cassel *(postal clerk)*, Scott Hale *(hotel clerk)*.

Crime melodrama. Source: Ernest Hemingway, "The Killers," in *Men Without Women* (New York, 1927). Charlie and Lee, two hired killers, go to an institution for the blind where they shoot Johnny North, a teacher there. Curious to know why they were paid so highly to kill a man who made no resistance and suspecting that North had been involved in a million-dollar robbery some years earlier, the killers piece together his past and begin following his former associates in hopes of finding the money. They learn that North had been an ace racing driver until he had become involved with Sheila Farr, a girl kept by a middle-aged gangster named Browning, who is now masquerading as a respectable businessman. (Disillusioned when he learned of Sheila's involvement, and injured in a crash, North worked as a mechanic until Sheila found him and persuaded him to drive the car in a robbery planned by Browning. She and North had supposedly doublecrossed Browning and absconded with the money.) Charlie and Lee find Sheila and learn that she had actually doublecrossed North by leading him direct to Browning, whom she had married, and that North was shattered by her betrayal. The killers confront Browning with Sheila. Browning kills Lee and wounds Charlie, but Charlie hunts Browning down and kills both him and Sheila before dying himself as he attempts to escape with the money. *Hired killers. Schoolteachers. Gangsters. Mistresses. Mechanics. Businessmen. Murder. Robbery. Perfidy. Automobile racing. Schools for the Blind.*

Note: Hemingway's story was previously filmed by Universal Pictures in 1946. Working title: *Johnny North.* Also known as *Ernest Hemingway's The Killers.*

KILLERS THREE   F6.2594

Dee Cee Productions. *Dist* American International Pictures. Nov **1968** [New York opening: 18 Jun 1969; c13 Nov 1968; LP36459]. Sd; col (Perfect Color). 35mm. 88 min. [Copyright length: 95 min.] *MPAA rating* M.

A Dick Clark Production. *Prod* Dick Clark. *Exec Prod* Jack Bohrer. *Assoc Prod* Norman Herman. *Dir* Bruce Kessler. *Screenplay* Michael Fisher. *Story* Michael Fisher, Dick Clark. *Photog* J. Burgi Contner. *Film Ed* Renn Reynolds. *Mus* Sidewalk Productions, Mike Curb, Harley Hatcher, Jerry Styner. *Songs:* "Mama Tried" & "Killers Three" *writ & sung by* Merle Haggard. *Sd* Phil Mitchell. *Prod Mgr* Elliot Schick. *Prod Coord* Rick Jackson. *Wardrobe* Richard Bruno. *Makeup* Ted Coodley. *Prop Master* Karl Brainard. *Vehicle Crash Coörd* Larry Frank.

Cast: Robert Walker, [Jr.] *(Johnny Ward)*, Diane Varsi *(Carol Ward)*, Dick Clark *(Roger)*, Norman Alden *(Guthrie)*, Maureen Arthur *(Elvira Sweeney)*, Tony York *(J.J. Ward)*, Merle Haggard *(Charlie)*, Bonnie Owens *(singer)*, John Cardos *(Bates)*, Beach Dickerson *(Scotty)*, Jerry Petty *(R.C.)*, Clint Stringer *(Sheriff Homer Brown)*, Fairy Sykes *(Mrs. Harmon)*, William Alspaugh *(Lester Meed)*, Douglas Barger *(Felix)*, The Strangers *(singing group)*.

Crime melodrama. Johnny Ward returns to the squalor of his backwoods North Carolina home at the end of World War II and marries his sweetheart, Carol Harmon, the mother of his 5-year-old son, J.J. Johnny decides to rob his employer, a bootlegger, of $250,000 kept in a safe. To implement his plan, he enlists the aid of an Army buddy, Roger, who had demolition experience during the war, and they plan to rob the safe on the day of the town picnic, disabling the cars at the picnic to avoid pursuit. While Carol and J.J. wait in Johnny's car, the men blow up the safe; but the strongbox is thrown through the floor out of their reach. Johnny kills a Federal agent as they make their getaway, and later, while escaping from a trap, Johnny and Roger shoot down several more victims. Fearful of roadblocks, the trio leave J.J. with Carol's mother before setting out for a better life in California. Carol's patrolman brother Charlie spots them when they stop at a diner, but rather than turn in his sister he gives them 10 minutes to get away. Unaware of what has happened, Roger walks out of the men's room, fails to recognize the police officer, and kills him. Back on the run, the fugitives stop at a sawmill operated by one of Johnny's cousins and are trapped in a police ambush while trying to switch cars. Roger is killed, and Carol is mortally wounded as Johnny drives his car through a barrage of gunfire. Aware that he can never reach California, Johnny heads for home; he reaches the house and discovers that his wife has died. *Veterans. Bootleggers.*

Government agents. Police. Fugitives. Poverty. Rural life. Robbery. Employer-employee relations. Illegitimacy. Picnics. Brother-sister relationship. Murder. Safes. Explosives. Chases. North Carolina.

Note: Location scenes filmed in Ramseur, North Carolina. Film opens with 1947 newsreel.

THE KILLING GAME (France)   F6.2595

A. J. Films–Francinor–Coficitel–Les Films Modernes. *Dist* Regional Film Distributors. 26 Aug **1968** [New York opening]. Sd; col (Eastmancolor). 35mm. 94 min.

Prod René Thévenet. *Assoc Prod* Monique Natan, Louis Duchesne. *Dir-Writ* Alain Jessua. *Photog* Jacques Robin. *Art Dir* Claire Forestier. *Film Ed* Nicole Marko. *Mus* Jacques Loussier. *Titl Song Sung by* Alan Bown Group. *Sd* Antoine Bonfanti, René Longuet. *Asst Dir* Vincent Gardair. *Prod Supv* Alain Belmondo. *Comic Strips Drawn by* Guy Peellaert.

Cast: Jean-Pierre Cassel *(Pierre Meyrand)*, Claudine Auger *(Jacqueline Meyrand)*, Michel Duchaussoy *(Bob Neuman)*, Eleonore Hirt *(Madame Neuman)*, Anna Gaylor *(Lisbeth)*, Guy Saint-Jean *(Ado)*, Nancy Holloway *(Nancy)*, Regine, Oyo, Nora, Ysmane My, Roger Curel, Jean Dewever.

Drama. Writer Pierre Meyrand and his wife, Jacqueline, an illustrator, collaborate on comic strips but suffer from a lack of new ideas. They are visited by wealthy playboy Bob Neuman, who acts out their comic strip adventures. His widowed mother subsidizes his fantasies, hiring Ado, a private detective, to follow him, and paying local strippers to feign pleasure at his sadistic lovemaking. The Meyrands, without funds, accept an invitation to stay at Bob's Swiss chalet. Fascinated by Bob's mentality, Pierre and Jacqueline create a new comic strip, "The Killer of Neuchâtel," whose hero resembles Bob. The new strip is a great success and grows to include all the members of the household. Bob's mother pays Pierre twice his regular salary to remain at the chalet for her son's sake. Jacqueline, annoyed at her husband's materialism, finds herself attracted to Bob's romantic outlook, and one day, acting out another fantasy, Bob kidnaps her. Aided by Ado and by his own comic strip, Pierre rescues his wife. After trying to kill Jacqueline, Bob is finally cornered by police on the parapet of an old castle. Attempting suicide, Bob jumps but is caught in a police net and taken to a sanitarium. Some time later Bob is released, and the group settles back at the chalet to start work on a new collective comic strip. *Authors. Cartoonists. Idle rich. Playboys. Widows. Detectives. Materialism. Kidnaping. Suicide. Mental illness. Filial relations. Neuchâtel. Fantasy.*

Note: Opened in Paris in Apr 1967 as *Jeu de massacre*; running time: 90 min. Also known as *All Weekend Lovers.*

THE KILLING OF SISTER GEORGE   F6.2596

Associates & Aldrich Co. *Dist* Cinerama Releasing Corp. 16 Dec **1968** [New York opening]. Sd; col (Metrocolor). 35mm. 138 min. *MPAA rating* X.

Pres by Palomar Pictures International. *Prod-Dir* Robert Aldrich. *Assoc Prod* Walter Blake. *Screenplay* Lukas Heller. *Photog* Joseph Biroc. *2d Unit Photog* Brian West. *Camera Op* Joe Jackman, Ned Davenport. *Camera Asst* William Clark, Gary Boren. *Art Dir* William Glasgow. *Set Decor* John W. Brown. *Film Ed* Michael Luciano. *Asst Ed* Frank Urioste. *Mus* Gerald Fried. *Sd* Richard Church, George Maly, Dean Hodges, Robin Gregory. *U. S. & London Asst Dir* Daisy Gerber, Dennis Robertson. *Prod Supv* George Tobin. *Asst to the Prod* William Aldrich. *Prod Mgr* Eddie Saeta. *Script Supv* Adell Bravos. *Cost* Renie. *Wardrobe* Marie Osborne. *Makeup* Bill Turner. *Hairstyles* Jean Austin. *Prop* Ygnacio Sepulveda. *Gaffer* Bill Hannah. *Dial Coach* Robert Sherman.

Cast: Beryl Reid *(June Buckridge [Sister George])*, Susannah York *(Alice "Childie" McNaught)*, Coral Browne *(Mercy Croft)*, Ronald Fraser *(Leo Lockhart)*, Patricia Medina *(Betty Thaxter)*, Hugh Paddick *(Freddie)*, Cyril Delevanti *(Ted Baker)*, Sivi Aberg *(Diana)*, William Beckley *(floor manager)*, Elaine Church *(Marlene)*, Brendan Dillon *(Bert Turner)*, Mike Freeman *(Noel)*, Maggie Paige *(maid)*, Jack Raine *(deputy commissioner)*, Dolly Taylor *(tea lady)*, Meier Tzelniker *(Mr. Katz)*, Cicely Walper *(Mrs. Coote)*, Byron Webster *(Jack Adams)*, Rosalie Williams *(Mildred)*, Sam Kydd *(taxi driver)*.

Drama. Source: Frank Marcus, *The Killing of Sister George* (Bristol opening: 20 Apr 1965). Aging actress June Buckridge portrays nurse Sister George on a popular British soap opera. Although "George" has a lovable image on the BBC, she is actually a hard-drinking, acid-tongued lesbian who constantly quarrels with her dependent roommate and lover, 32-year-old Alice "Childie" McNaught. Fearful that her part might be written out of the series, George leaves a rehearsal, gets drunk, and terrorizes two nuns in a taxi. Acting on a complaint from the church, network executive Mercy Croft visits George's flat, insists on an apology, and hints at cast changes in the show due to a slip in the ratings. Dejected, George tells her troubles to Betty Thaxter, a sympathetic prostitute who lives next door. When she discovers that the new script only calls for her to get the flu and recover, George celebrates with Childie at a lesbian bar and flippantly invites Mrs. Croft to join them. Ignoring the club's atmosphere, the executive announces that Sister George is to be killed in a highway accident the following week. Devastated by the news, George rushes from the bar as Mrs. Croft offers Childie her protection. Once Sister George's death scene has been filmed, George is given a studio party and asked if she would like to be the voice of Clarabelle Cow on a new television series. Enraged, she storms out of the studio, returns to her flat, and discovers Mrs. Croft making love to Childie in the bedroom. After a bitter confrontation, Childie decides to move in with Mrs. Croft, and George returns to the now deserted studio, where she wrecks the sets before collapsing on a bench. Accepting her fate as Clarabelle Cow, George sits alone bellowing a pathetic "moooo." *Actors. Roommates. British. Television producers. Nuns. Prostitutes. Lesbianism. Television. Seduction. Alcoholism. Bars. London. British Broadcasting Corp.*

Note: Location scenes filmed in London.

KILLING URGE see **JET STORM**

KIMBERLEY JIM (South Africa)   F6.2597
Emil Nofal Productions–Jamie Uys Film Productions. *Dist* Embassy Pictures. 29 Apr **1965** [San Antonio, Texas, opening]. Sd; col (Agfacolor). 35mm (Scanoscope). 82 min.
Prod-Dir-Writ Emil Nofal. *Photog* Judex C. Viljoen. *Art Dir* Ian MacLeod. *Film Ed* Harry Hughes. *Mus* Billy Walker. *Choreog* Sheila Wartski. *Sd* Bonne Ter Steege. *Asst Dir* Jans Rautenbach. *Cost* Anna Richter-Visser.
Cast: Jim Reeves *(Jim Madison)*, Madeleine Usher *(Julie Patterson)*, Clive Parnell *(Gerry Bates)*, Arthur Swemmer *(Bert Patterson)*, Tromp Terre'Blanche *(Ben Vorster)*, Vonk De Ridder *(Danny Pretorious)*, Mike Holt *(Punchy)*, Dawid Van Der Walt *(Jan le Roux)*, June Neethling *(Elize)*, George Moore *(Fred Parker)*, Freddie Prozesky *(Neels le Roux)*, Don Leonard *(Rube)*, Morris Blake *(Max Bloom)*, The Blue Boys, Eddie Domingo, Webster Booth, Johan Du Plooy, Olive King, June Hern, Marie-Louise Otten, Deborah Frances, Charmain Peker, Pieter Hauptfleisch, Dick O'Shaughnessy, Ralph Loubser, Dale Swanepoel, George Lane, actor, Billy Pretorious.
Comedy-drama with music. In 1910 in South Africa's Kimberley diamond region, Americans Jim Madison and Gerry Bates earn their living by selling patent medicine and hustling the miners at poker. One of their card games nets them a partnership in Bert Patterson's diamond claim. When Jim and Gerry meet Patterson's lovely daughter, Julie, they decide to work the claim and help Patterson meet his debts. The mine continues to be unproductive, and to make matters worse saloonkeeper Ben Vorster, who owns the water rights in the region, raises his rates. Jim and Gerry earn money by putting on a musical show but lose much of it by impulsively betting on a boxing match. Their scheme to plant diamonds on the claim proves unnecessary as the mine begins to produce. Declining a partnership with Patterson, they move on, leaving Julie to her suitor. *Cardsharps. Americans in foreign countries. Miners. Saloon keepers. Partnerships. Debt. Diamond mines. Patent medicines. Water rights.*
Note: Produced in South Africa in 1963.

KIMIMO SHUSSEGA DEKIRU see **YOU CAN SUCCEED TOO**

KIN FOLK see **ALL THE LOVIN' KINFOLK**

A KIND OF LOVE see **LIKE MOTHER LIKE DAUGHTER**

A KIND OF LOVING (Great Britain)   F6.2598
Vic Films–Waterhall Productions. *Dist* Governor Films. 1 Oct **1962** [New York opening]. Sd; b&w. 35mm. 112 min.
Prod Joseph Janni. *Assoc Prod* Jack Hanbury. *Dir* John Schlesinger. *Screenplay* Willis Hall, Keith Waterhouse. *Photog* Denys Coop. *Art Dir* Ray Simm. *Set Decor* Maurice Fowler. *Film Ed* Roger Cherrill. *Mus Comp & Cond* Ron Grainer. *Sd* Don Sharpe, George Stephenson, Red Law. *Asst Dir* Frank Ernst. *Prod Mgr* Charles Hammond. *Wardrobe* Laura Nightingale. *Makeup* Bob Lawrence. *Hairstyles* Ann Box.
Cast: Alan Bates *(Vic Brown)*, June Ritchie *(Ingrid Rothwell)*, Thora Hird *(Mrs. Rothwell)*, Bert Palmer *(Mr. Brown)*, Gwen Nelson *(Mrs. Brown)*, Malcolm Patton *(Jim Brown)*, Pat Keen *(Christine)*, David Mahlowe *(David)*, Jack Smethurst *(Conroy)*, James Bolam *(Jeff)*, Michael Deacon *(Les)*, John Ronane, David Cook *(draughtsmen)*, Norman Heyes *(Laisterdyke)*, Leonard Rossiter *(Whymper)*, Fred Ferris *(Mr. Althorpe)*, Patsy Rowlands *(Dorothy)*, Annette Robertson *(Phoebe)*, Ruth Porcher *(Mrs. Keen)*, Henry Markham *(railwayman)*, Peter Madden *(registrar)*, Katherine Staff *(Mrs. Oliphant)*, Edna Ridgway *(pub pianist)*, Graham Rigby *(pub politician)*, Bud Ralston *(pub comedian)*, Bryan Mosley, Joe Gladwin *(bus conductors)*, Jerry Desmonde *(television compère)*, Reginald Green *(television competitor)*, Douglas Livingstone *(window cleaner)*.
Drama. Source: Stan Barstow, *A Kind of Loving* (London, 1960). Vic Brown, a draftsman in a Lancashire factory, becomes strongly attracted to one of the firm's typists, Ingrid Rothwell. After several dates, Ingrid allows Vic to spend the night at her home while her widowed mother is out of town. Vic now realizes that what he feels for Ingrid is almost purely physical, but Ingrid has

become more deeply involved and tries to seek assurance that she is still loved. Vic allows the affair to drop, but at a company dance Ingrid reveals that she is pregnant, and he reluctantly offers to marry her. After a brief honeymoon, they move in with Ingrid's mother, a narrow-minded and possessive woman deeply resentful of Vic. The life of the young couple becomes increasingly tense. Ingrid eventually has a miscarriage, and Vic is suddenly struck with the realization that their wedding was not necessary. Henceforth, Ingrid refuses to have sex with him. Following a drunken spree and a scene with his mother-in-law, Vic storms out of the house and turns to his happily-married sister for comfort. Instead she rebukes him for not living up to his responsibilities, and he returns to Ingrid. Now willing to look at his life in a more mature manner, he persuades her to leave her interfering mother and help him find a home of their own. Perhaps with cooperation and compromise, they will be able to attain "a kind of loving." *Draftsmen. Typists. Widows. Mothers-in-law. Pregnancy. Marriage. Miscarriage. Drunkenness. Filial relations. Brother-sister relationship. Lancashire.*
Note: Released in Great Britain in Apr 1961.

THE KINETIC ART: SERIES ONE, PROGRAM 1   F6.2599
Dist Universal Education and Visual Arts. 18 Jul **1968** [New York opening]. Sd; col and b&w. 16mm & 35mm. [Feature film, length unknown.]
Anthology. This collection of short films includes *Phenomena* (United States), *La vita* (Life in a Tin, Italy) *Il giudice* (Italy), *Happiness* (Germany), *Sophie* (France), *Rakvickarna* (Czechoslovakia), *Cruel Diagonals* (*Surove dijagonale*, Yugoslavia), *Two Grilled Fish* (Japan), *Why Did You Kiss Me Awake?* (West Germany), *Spiderelephant* (France), and *La pomme* (France).

THE KINETIC ART: SERIES ONE, PROGRAM 2   F6.2600
Dist Universal Education and Visual Arts. 19 Jul **1968** [New York opening]. Sd; col and b&w. 16mm & 35mm. [Feature film, length unknown.]
Anthology. This collection of films includes the feature, *Tonight Let's All Make Love in London* (Great Britain), q.v., and the short films, *Et Cetera* (Czechoslovakia), *Miracle* (Hungary), *Elegia* (Hungary), *What Do You Think?* (Japan), and *Paris Mai 1968* (France).

THE KINETIC ART: SERIES ONE, PROGRAM 3   F6.2601
Dist Universal Education and Visual Arts. 20 Jul **1968** [New York opening]. Sd; col and b&w. 16mm & 35mm. [Feature film, length unknown.]
Anthology. This collection of short films includes *The Last Trick of Mr. Edgar* (Czechoslovakia), *Versailles* (France), *Flower* (Japan), *Gavotte* (France), *The Magician* (Czechoslovakia), *Black, White, and Red* (West Germany), *Afterward* (*The Adventures of a Doll*, West Germany), and *Samadhi* (United States).

THE KINETIC ART: SERIES TWO, PROGRAM 1   F6.2602
Dist Universal Education and Visual Arts. 6 Mar **1970** [Pasadena, California, opening]. Sd; col and b&w. 16mm & 35mm. ca120 min.
Anthology. This collection of short films includes *Poem Field No.1* (United States), *La divina* (United States), *The Wall* (Czechoslovakia), *The Joint* (United States), *S. W. B.* (Sweet Wounded Bird, France), *Cirkusz* (Hungary), *Birthday* (Great Britain), and *Egypte, o Egypte* (France).

THE KINETIC ART: SERIES TWO, PROGRAM 2   F6.2603
Dist Universal Education and Visual Arts. 13 Mar **1970** [Pasadena, California, opening]. Sd; col and b&w. 16mm & 35mm. ca120 min.
Anthology. This collection of short films includes *Re-entry* (United States), *Unknown Reasons* (United States), *Vaucherin* (France), *Leap* (United States), *Music With Balls* (United States), *See Saw Seems* (United States), *The Room* (Japan), and *Ego* (Italy).

THE KINETIC ART: SERIES TWO, PROGRAM 3   F6.2604
Dist Universal Education and Visual Arts. 20 Mar **1970** [Pasadena, California, opening]. Sd; col and b&w. 16mm & 35mm. ca120 min.
Anthology. This collection of short films includes *Powers of Ten* (United States), *Momentum* (United States), *Historia natura* (Czechoslovakia), *Au fou* (Japan), *Arthur, Arthur* (France), and *Marie pour memoire* (France).

THE KING   F6.2605
Dist American Film Distributing Corp. 18 Dec **1968** [New York showing]. Sd; b&w. 35mm. 60 min.
Prod Wizard Glick. *Dir-Narr* Looney Bear. *Camera* Fred T. Jong.
Cast: Lisa St. Shaw *(Linda)*, King Drummond *(Mickey, "The King")*, Sandra Soft *(Joan)*, Lover Lee *(Liz)*, Montey Costello *(Renee)*.

Melodrama. "The King," a domineering lesbian, lives in New York City with her two beautiful roommates, Linda and Joan, who are pitted as rivals for her favor. To compete for the King's attentions, Linda and Joan are forced to submit to a series of humiliations. The three leave the city for a weekend at Cherry Grove on Fire Island, and there the rivalry becomes violent. *Roommates. Lesbianism. Troilism. Sadism. New York City. Fire Island.*

KING: A FILMED RECORD ... MONTGOMERY TO MEMPHIS
F6.2606

Commonwealth United Corp.-Martin Luther King Film Project. *Dist* Commonwealth United Entertainment, Inc., Maron Films. 24 Mar **1970** [c25 Feb 1970; MP20745]. Sd; b&w. 35mm. 177 min. [Copyright length: 185 min.]

Prod Ely Landau. *Assoc Prod* Richard Kaplan. *Connecting Seq Dir* Sidney Lumet, Joseph L. Mankiewicz. *Supv Film Ed* Lora Hays, John Carter, ed. *Mus* Coleridge-Taylor Perkinson.

Narrators: Paul Newman, Joanne Woodward, Ruby Dee, James Earl Jones, Clarence Williams, III, Burt Lancaster, Ben Gazzara, Charlton Heston, Harry Belafonte, Sidney Poitier.

Documentary. The film covers the public life and contribution to the civil rights movement of Martin Luther King, Jr., beginning with King's successful bus boycott in Montgomery, Alabama, in 1955-56. He is shown with the freedom riders in the early 1960's; delivering the famous "I Have a Dream" speech at the Lincoln Memorial in Washington, D. C., in 1963; and as a protagonist during the brutal confrontations in Birmingham, Alabama, and in St. Augustine, Florida. Other aspects of King's involvement included organizing the housing protests in Chicago and bringing national attention to the racial injustice in Selma, Alabama, during the voter registration marches. The highest point of acclaim for his work was in 1964 when he was awarded the Nobel Peace Prize for his courage and nonviolent principles in the fight for racial equality. In April of 1968, King's career was ended in Memphis, Tennessee, by an assassin's bullet. *Negroes. Police. Civil rights. Racial segregation. Racial prejudice. Housing. Riots. Demonstrations. Nonviolence. Assassination. Montgomery (Alabama). Washington (District of Columbia). Birmingham (Alabama). Saint Augustine. Chicago. Selma. Memphis. Martin Luther King, Jr. Nobel Prize. Lincoln Memorial (District of Columbia).*

Note: Originally shown on one night in over 500 theaters, with proceeds benefiting charity, film was released on a regular basis by Maron Films in Sep 1970.

KING AND COUNTRY (Great Britain)
F6.2607

B. H. E. Productions. *Dist* American International Pictures. 27 Jan **1966** [New York opening]. Sd; b&w (print by Movielab). 35mm. 86 min.

Pres by Landau/Unger Co. *Prod* Joseph Losey, Norman Priggen. *Exec Prod* Daniel M. Angel. *Assoc Prod* Richard Goodwin. *Dir* Joseph Losey. *Screenplay* Evan Jones. *Photog* Denys Coop. *Camera Op* Chic Waterson. *Art Dir* Peter Mullins. *Prod Dsgn* Richard MacDonald. *Film Ed* Reginald Mills. *Mus Comp & Cond* Larry Adler. *Adtl Harmonica Solo* Peter Adler. *Sd Supv* John Cox. *Sd Rec* Buster Ambler. *Sd Ed* Gerry Hambling. *Asst Dir* Scott Wodehouse. *Prod Mgr* Richard Goodwin. *Cost* Roy Ponting.

Cast: Dirk Bogarde *(Captain Hargreaves)*, Tom Courtenay *(Pvt. Arthur Hamp)*, Leo McKern *(Captain O'Sullivan)*, Barry Foster *(Lieutenant Webb)*, James Villiers *(Captain Midgley)*, Peter Copley *(colonel)*, Barry Justice *(Lieutenant Prescott)*, Vivian Matalon *(padre)*, Jeremy Spenser *(Private Sparrow)*, James Hunter, British *(Private Sykes)*, David Cook *(Private Wilson)*, Larry Taylor *(sergeant-major)*, Jonah Seymour *(Corporal Hamilton, M. P.)*, Keith Buckley *(corporal of the guard)*, Richard Arthure *(guard "Charlie")*, Derek Partridge *(captain at court martial)*, Brian Tipping *(lieutenant at court martial)*, Raymond Brody, Dan Cornwall, Terry Palmer *(soldiers in Hamp's platoon)*.

War drama. Source: John Wilson, *Hamp* (Edinburgh opening: 17 Aug 1964). James Lansdale Hodson, *Return to the Wood* (London, 1955). During World War I, Private Hamp, a young Englishman, is arrested near Calais for desertion after serving 3 years in the frontline trenches. Before his court-martial in Passchendaele, Belgium, he is questioned by the unsympathetic attorney assigned to defend him, Captain Hargreaves, who readily agrees to follow suggestions from the upper echelon that he ignore the fact that Hamp was suffering from shellshock when he deserted. Having had an unhappy youth, Hamp had enlisted in the army on a dare and had grimly accepted the deaths of his army buddies and the news of his wife's unfaithfulness until he had simply walked away from his post. After hearing all the facts, Hargreaves becomes so impressed with the private's sincerity that he delivers an impassioned plea for justice, saying that Hamp was not responsible for his actions. Nonetheless, the court finds him guilty; and Hargreaves' recommendation for leniency is denied because the battalion is moving out and military discipline must be maintained. On the eve of his execution, Hamp's fellow soldiers gather in his cell and drink stolen rum. Drunk, and dizzy from playing blindman's buff, Hamp falls into the arms of a priest and finds himself the astonished participant in last communion.

At dawn Hamp faces the firing squad, but the shots fail to kill him outright, and Hargreaves uses his revolver to put a bullet in his head. The conventional letter for soldiers killed in action is mailed to his family. *Deserters—Military. Lawyers. Priests. Combat zone life. Shell shock. Capital punishment. Drunkenness. Courts-martial. World War I. Calais. Passchendaele. Great Britain—Army.*

Note: Opened in London in Dec 1964; running time: 86 min; cut from 88 min. Working title: *Hamp.*

THE KING AND I (Reissue)
F6.2608

Twentieth Century-Fox Film Corp. 23 Mar **1961** [New York opening]. Sd; col (DeLuxe). 70mm (Grandeum 70). 133 min.

Note: Originally filmed in CinemaScope 55 but released in 35mm CinemaScope only. Released in Jun 1956; c28 Jun 1956; LP7381.

KING IN SHADOW (West Germany)
F6.2609

Bavaria Filmkunst. *Dist* Exclusive International Films. 8 May **1961** [New Haven, Connecticut, opening; c21 Dec 1959; LP21579]. Sd; col (Agfacolor). 35mm. 78 min.

Prod Georg Richter. *Dir* Harald Braun. *Screenplay* Odo Krohmann, Gerhard Menzel, Harald Braun. *English Dial* Nina Maguire. *English Adapt* William De Lane Lea. *Photog* Göran Strindberg. *Art Dir* Walter Haag. *Film Ed* Hilwa von Boro. *Mus* Werner Eisbrenner. *Sd* Hans Wunschel. *Prod Dir* Dietrich von Theobald. *Prod Mgr* Rudolf Kley. *Cost* Herbert Ploberger.

Cast: O. W. Fischer *(Friedrich Struensee)*, Horst Buchholz *(King Christian)*, Odile Versois *(Queen Mathilde)*, Günther Hadank *(state minister)*, Fritz Tillmann *(Count Rantzau)*, Elisabeth Flickenschildt *(Queen Juliane)*, Siegfried Lowitz *(Chamberlain Goldberg)*, Ingeborg Schöner *(Gertrud von Eyben)*, Wilfried-Jan Heyn *(Baron Enevied Brandt)*, Helmut Lohner *(Count Holck, chamberlain)*, Gerhard Ritter *(Dr. Berger)*, Peter Esser *(Court Chaplain Muenter)*, Horst Gnekow *(General Reventlau)*.

Historical drama. Source: Robert Neumann, *Der Favorit der Königen* (Frankfurt am Main, 1953). Friedrich Struensee, a renowned brain specialist, is summoned to Copenhagen in 1776 to give his opinion on the mental condition of 19-year-old King Christian. Struensee finds that the king is a lonely, brooding boy, whose stepmother, Queen Juliane, hopes to have him pronounced incapable of ruling Denmark so that her own son can assume the throne. Struensee, however, decrees that young Christian is sane. Through Struensee's psychological guidance, Christian is able to effect a reconciliation with his English wife, Mathilde. As a result of his efforts, Struensee becomes prime minister and the most powerful man in Denmark, until he falls in love with Mathilde. Their affair becomes a scandal in the royal palace, and Christian is persuaded to sentence them both to death. Struensee lies to save Mathilde, and she is permitted to return to England. As the bells ring to announce the death of Struensee, King Christian breaks down in a fit of madness. *Physicians. Royalty. Stepmothers. Adolescence. Insanity. Psychiatry. Infidelity. Scandal. Capital punishment. Copenhagen. Johann Friedrich von Struensee. Christian VII. Caroline Matilda.*

Note: Opened in West Berlin in Jan 1957 as *Herrscher ohne Krone*; running time: 104 min.

KING KONG ESCAPES (Japan)
F6.2610

Rankin/Bass Productions-Toho Co. *Dist* Universal Pictures. 10 Jul **1968** [New York opening; c21 Aug 1968; LP37134]. Sd; col (Eastmancolor, print by Technicolor). 35mm (Tohoscope). 96 min.

Production Credits for Japanese Version: *Prod* Tomoyuki Tanaka. *Dir* Inoshiro Honda. *Screenplay* Kaoru Mabuchi. *Photog* Hajime Koizumi. *Art Dir* Takeo Kita. *Mus* Akira Ifukube. *Dir Sp Eff Photog* Eiji Tsuburaya.

Production Credits for English Version: *Pres by* Ernest L. Scanlon. *Prod-Dir* Arthur Rankin, Jr. *Screenplay* William J. Keenan. *Sd* Glen Glenn Sound. *Post Prod Supv* Riley Jackson. *Dub Dir* Paul Frees.

Cast: Rhodes Reason *(Commander Nelson)*, Mie Hama *(Madame Piranha)*, Linda Miller *(Susan)*, Akira Takarada *(Lieut. Jiro Nomura)*, Eisei Amamoto *(Dr. Who)*.

Science fiction melodrama. Commander Nelson, the skipper of *Explorer*, a United Nations atomic submarine for research, is looking for the legendary King Kong when he surfaces his vessel at Mondo Island and goes ashore with Lieut. Joe Nomura and another expedition member, Susan. A prehistoric monster attacks Susan, whereupon King Kong appears and saves her. He takes an immediate liking to Susan and tries to prevent the party from leaving the island, but Susan persuades him to allow them to depart. Meanwhile, the evil Dr. Who, a megalomaniac, is having difficulties at his North Pole laboratory with his robot Mechani-Kong, a giant, gorilla-like robot which cannot function when exposed to the highly dangerous substance Element X. Therefore, Dr. Who and his assistant Madame Piranha (who works for an alien power) capture King Kong, as well as Nelson, Nomura, and Susan, just in case the creature needs controlling. Dr. Who hypnotizes Kong into doing his bidding, but the rays of Element X break the trance. Susan is about to be tortured for refusing to help control Kong when he escapes and heads toward Tokyo. Dr. Who sends Mechani-Kong after him, and the two creatures wage a battle atop Tokyo Tower. Madame Piranha experiences a change of heart and releases Commander Nelson, Susan, and Lieut. Nomura. Piranha then ends the fight by destroying Mechani-Kong's remote control mechanism, and Dr. Who retaliates by shooting her. Finally, King Kong kills Dr. Who and returns to his island home in the sea. *Scientists. Researchers. Sea captains. Monsters. Megalomania. Abduction. Hypnotism. Submarines. Robots. Atom bomb. North Pole. Tokyo. United Nations. Tokyo Tower. King Kong. Apes.*

Note: Produced in Japan in 1967 as *Kingu Kongu no gyakushu;* running time: 104 min. May also have been known as *King Kong no gyakushu.*

KING KONG NO GYAKUSH *see* **KING KONG ESCAPES**

KING KONG VS. GODZILLA (Japan)   F6.2611
Toho Co. *Dist* Universal-International. 26 Jun **1963** [New York opening; c2 Jul 1963; LP35483]. Sd (Westrex); col (Eastmancolor). 35mm (Tohoscope). 90 min.

Pres by John Beck. *Exec Prod* Tomoyuki Tanaka. *English Vers Prod* John Beck. *Dir* Inoshiro Honda. *English Vers Dir* Thomas Montgomery. *Screenplay* Shinichi Sekizawa. *English Vers Screenplay* Paul Mason, Bruce Howard. *Photog* Hajime Koizumi. *Ed Supv English Vers* Peter Zinner. *Mus* Akira Ifukube. *Mus Supv English Vers* Peter Zinner. *English Vers Sd Eff* William Stevenson, sd. *Dir Sp Eff* Eiji Tsuburaya.

Cast (see note): Michael Keith *(Eric Carter),* James Yagi *(Yataka Omura),* Tadao Takashima *(O. Sakurai),* Mie Hama *(Fumiko Sakurai),* Yu Fujiki *(Kinzaburo Furue),* Kenji Sahara *(Kazuo Fujita),* Ichiro Arishima *(Mr. Tako),* Harry Holcombe *(Dr. Arnold Johnson),* Tatsuo Matsumura *(Dr. Markino),* Akihiko Hirata *(Premier Shigezawa),* Akiko Wakabayashi *(Tamiye),* Senkichi Omura *(Konno).*

Science fiction melodrama. United Nations television reporter Eric Carter comments in a newscast on two items of unusual interest—first, mammoth icebergs are drifting toward Japan; second, scientists of the Pacific Pharmaceutical Company have discovered in the Solomon Islands some berries that produce a non-habit-forming narcotic. The scientists also find King Kong, who mysteriously appears during an electrical storm and kills a giant octopus. To boost a current advertising campaign, the company sends two men to capture the beast by drugging him with the narcotic. Meanwhile, the prehistoric monster Godzilla emerges from an iceberg in the Arctic Ocean, destroys a nuclear submarine, and heads toward Japan. King Kong awakens in captivity, senses the approaching enemy, and escapes from his captors. Nothing can stop the two creatures as they trample everything in their paths. They finally meet in combat atop Mount Fuji, and their battle creates an earthquake, sending them over a high cliff into the sea. Godzilla disappears, and King Kong moves on south. *Reporters. Scientists. Publicity. Ice floes. Narcotics. Monsters. Television. Storms. Submarines. Solomon Islands. Arctic Ocean. United Nations. Fuji. Earthquakes. King Kong. Godzilla. Octopi.*

Note: Released in Japan in 1962 as *King Kong tai Godzilla;* running time: 99 min. The film was reedited, and some additional scenes featuring Michael Keith, James Yagi, and Harry Holcombe were interpolated, for the English language version.

KING, MURRAY   F6.2612
Amram Nowak Associates–Leeam Lowin Productions. *Dist* EYR Programs, Iconographic. 27 Apr **1969** [New York opening]. Sd; col and b&w. 35mm. 86 min.

Prod Amram Nowak. *Dir* David Hoffman, Jonathan Gordon. *Photog* David Hoffman. *Sd* Jonathan Gordon.

Cast: Murray Ramsey King *(Murray King),* Laura Kaye *(1st girl on trip),* Gloria Riegger *(socialite),* Jackie Morris *(2d girl on trip),* Addie Pezzotta *(girl in shower),* George Koski *(masseur),* Barbara Linden, Nora Lord *(other girls),* Amram Nowak, David Hoffman, Jonathan Gordon *(themselves).*

Drama. A fictionalized account of 72 hours in the life of a successful, 46-year-old insurance salesman and former college teacher, Murray King. The picture begins as King drives his Cadillac from his expensive home on Long Island's North Shore to the estate of a client who has just signed for a $2 million life insurance policy. Following a visit to another client, King shows the filmmakers his office and talks with them about the junket he is making to Las Vegas that evening with several clients and friends. After taking two secretaries for a hamburger at a luncheonette which he patronizes because it is called "King's," he makes two business calls, then drives to the airport to meet his guests, including several attractive women. Once in Vegas, King stops briefly at an expensive restaurant and then chats with the movie-makers in his Caesars Palace hotel suite. The next morning King swims the length of a pool underwater, plays tennis with the film's producer, and invites three girls to watch him being massaged. King then argues with the filmmakers and gets them

to let him have a "shower scene" in which the most buxom of the beauties, a teacher of retarded children, soaps his back. That evening during a hotel room party, King describes a motel orgy he attended and then confesses that he made it up for the cameras. The picture ends with a dream sequence of a generously endowed woman on a sandy beach, the personification of American escapism. *Insurance agents. Secretaries. Motion picture producers. Hotels. Restaurants. Tennis. Swimming. Long Island. Las Vegas. Dreams.*

Note: Filmed in 16mm; dream sequence shot in 8mm.

KING OF AFRICA *see* **ONE STEP TO HELL**

KING OF HEARTS (France/Italy)   F6.2613
Fildebroc–Les Productions Artistes Associés–Compagnia Cinematografica Montoro. *Dist* Lopert Pictures. 19 Jun **1967** [New York opening]. Sd; col (De Luxe). 35mm (Techniscope). 102 min.

Prod-Dir Philippe de Broca. *Screenplay* Daniel Boulanger. *Based on an Idea by* Maurice Bessy. *Photog* Pierre Lhomme. *Art Dir* François de Lamothe. *Set Decor* Robert Christides. *Film Ed* Françoise Javet. *Mus* Georges Delerue. *Sd* Jacques Carrère. *Asst Dir* Marc Monnet, Renzo Cerrato, Marc Grunebaum. *Prod Mgr* Jacques Juranville. *Cost* Jacques Fonteray.

Cast: Alan Bates *(Pvt. Charles Plumpick),* Pierre Brasseur *(General Geranium),* Jean-Claude Brialy *(The Duke [Le Duc de Trèfle]),* Geneviève Bujold *(Coquelicot),* Adolfo Celi *(Col. Alexander MacBibenbrook),* Micheline Presle *(Madame Eglantine),* Françoise Christophe *(The Duchess),* Julien Guiomar *(Bishop Daisy [Monseigneur Marguerite]),* Michel Serrault *(The Crazy Barber),* Marc Dudicourt *(Lieutenant Hamburger),* Daniel Boulanger *(Col. Helmut von Krack),* Jacques Balutin *(Mac Fish),* Pierre Palau *(Alberic),* Madeleine Clervanne *(Brunehaut),* Jean Sylvain *(beadle),* Jacky Blanchot *(sailor),* Louis Jojot *(Gontrand),* Pier Paolo Capponi.

Comedy-drama. As World War I nears its end, a battalion of retreating Germans arranges for an entire French village to be blown up by placing an explosive in the town square. The charge is triggered to explode when an armored knight on the church steeple clock strikes the hour of midnight with his mace. As the villagers evacuate their town, one of them gets word of the bomb threat to a nearby Scottish regiment. A mildmannered private, Charles Plumpick, is chosen to investigate because he speaks French. By the time he arrives at the village, the only inhabitants remaining are the inmates of the insane asylum and the animals from the zoo. A harmless and carefree lot, they crown Plumpick their King of Hearts, move into the houses and shops of the town, and assume the various roles of barber, bishop, duke and duchess, bordello proprietress, etc. Ignoring Plumpick's frantic but futile search for the bomb, they devote their energies to preparing for a royal wedding between their newly-crowned king and a dainty acrobat, Coquelicot, a virgin taken from the lunatic whorehouse. Eventually a chance remark by Coquelicot leads Plumpick to the village clock, and he disconnects the bomb's detonator a few minutes before midnight. The town celebrates with the Scottish soldiers by exploding fireworks. Hearing the explosions, the Germans return to the town to investigate. Marching on opposite sides of the town square, the two forces discover each other when a lunatic throws a flower down from a balcony. Only Plumpick survives the two forces' simultaneous fire. Witnessing the senseless slaughter, the inmates voluntarily return to the relative sanity of the asylum. Though Plumpick is assigned to another unit, he does not remain with it for more than a few minutes. Discarding his uniform and equipment, he returns to the asylum, stands completely naked before a pair of startled nuns, and waits to be committed. *Scotch. Germans. Acrobats. Nuns. Virginity. Insanity. Impersonation. Village life. Insane asylums. Whorehouses. Zoos. Clocks. Bombs. Fireworks. World War I. Great Britain—Army. Germany—Army.*

Note: Paris opening: Dec 1966 as *Le roi de coeur;* running time: 110 min: Rome opening: Jul 1967 as *Tutti pazzi meno io;* running time: ca100 min. Location scenes filmed in Senlis, France.

KING OF KINGS   F6.2614
Samuel Bronston Productions. *Dist* Metro-Goldwyn-Mayer, Inc. 11 Oct **1961** [New York opening; c30 Oct 1961; LP23206]. Sd (Westrex); col (Technicolor). 35mm & 70mm (Super Technirama). 165 min. [Previewed at 168 min; copyright length: 151 min.]

Prod Samuel Bronston. *Assoc Prod* Alan Brown, Jaime Prades. *Dir* Nicholas Ray. *2d Unit Dir* Noel Howard, Sumner Williams. *Screenplay* Philip Yordan. *Narr (see note)* Ray Bradbury. *Dir Photog* Franz F. Planer, Milton Krasner. Manuel Berenguer. *Set Dsgn* Georges Wakhevitch. *Set Decor* Enrique Alarcón. *Film Ed* Harold F. Kress, Renée Lichtig. *Mus* Miklos Rozsa. *Choreog for Salome's dance* Betty Utey. *Rec Supv* Franklin Milton. *Sd Rec* Basil Fenton-Smith. *Asst Dir* Carlo Lastricati, José María Ochoa, José López Rodero. *Gen Prod Mgr* Stanley Goldsmith. *Cost Dsgn* Georges Wakhevitch. *Supv of Cost* Eric Seelig. *Makeup Created by* Mario Van Riel, Charles Parker. *Hairstyles* Anna Cristofani. *Sp Photog Eff* Lee LeBlanc. *Sp Eff* Alex Weldon. *Master of Props* Stanley Detlie. *Supv Tech* Carl Gibson. *Supv Electrn* Norton

Kurland. *Murals* Maciek Piotrowski.

Cast: Jeffrey Hunter *(Jesus Christ)*, Siobhan McKenna *(Mary, Mother of Jesus)*, Robert Ryan *(John the Baptist)*, Hurd Hatfield *(Pontius Pilate)*, Ron Randell *(Lucius, The Centurion)*, Viveca Lindfors *(Claudia)*, Rita Gam *(Herodias)*, Carmen Sevilla *(Mary Magdalene)*, Brigid Bazlen *(Salome)*, Harry Guardino *(Barabbas)*, Rip Torn *(Judas)*, Frank Thring *(Herod Antipas)*, Guy Rolfe *(Caiphas)*, Maurice Marsac *(Nicodemus)*, Grégoire Aslan *(Herod)*, Royal Dano *(Peter)*, Edric Connor *(Balthazar)*, George Couloris *(camel driver)*, Conrado San Martín *(General Pompey)*, Gérard Tichy *(Joseph)*, José Antonio *(young John)*, Luis Prendes *(The Good Thief)*, David Davies *(burly man)*, José Nieto *(Caspar)*, Ruben Rojo *(Matthew)*, Fernando Sancho *(madman)*, Michael Wager *(Thomas)*, Felix de Pomes *(Joseph of Arimathea)*, Adriano Rimoldi *(Melchior)*, Barry Keegan *(The Bad Thief)*, Rafael Luis Calvo *(Simon of Cyrene)*, Tino Barrero *(Andrew)*, Francisco Morán *(blind man)*, Orson Welles *(narrator)*.

Biblical epic. The life of Jesus Christ is depicted. Highlighted are the following events: his birth in a Bethlehem stable; the prophecies of John the Baptist and his murder; Jesus' 40-day ordeal in the desert; the selection of the Apostles; the Sermon on the Mount; Judas' betrayal of Jesus; the Passion; the Crucifixion; the Resurrection; and the Ascension. *Rome—History—Empire. Palestine. Judea. Jesus. Virgin Mary. Mary Magdalene. John the Baptist. Herod Antipas. Herod the Great. Herodias. Salome. Barabbas. Pontius Pilate. Judas Iscariot. Biblical characters. The Twelve Apostles. The Resurrection. Crucifixion. Miracles.*

Note: Filmed in Spain. Only one source credits Bradbury as author of the narration.

KING OF THE GRIZZLIES (United States/Canada)   **F6.2615**
Walt Disney Productions–Robert Lawrence Productions. *Dist* Buena Vista Distribution Co. 25 Mar **1970** [Boston opening: c12 Dec 1969; LP37662]. Sd (RCA); col (Technicolor). 35mm. 93 min. MPAA rating G.
Overall Production Credits: *Pres by* Walt Disney Productions. *Prod* Winston Hibler. *Assoc Prod* Erwin L. Verity, Robert F. Metzler. *Screenplay* Jack Speirs. *Adapt* Rod Peterson, Norman Wright, writ. *Main Titl* Jack Boyd. *Film Ed* Gregg McLaughlin. *Mus* Buddy Baker. *Orch* Franklyn Marks. *Song:* "The Campfire Is Home" Jack Speirs. *Sd* Robert O. Cook. *Mus Ed* Evelyn Kennedy. *Matte Artist* Alan Maley.
Production Credits for Robert Lawrence Productions: *Dir* Ron Kelly. *Dir Photog* Reginald Morris. *Set Decor* Wilf Culley. *Prod Asst* William Redlin, Don Hall. *Cost* Roger Palmer. *Makeup* William Morgan, makeup.
Production Credits for Cangary Ltd.: *Field Prod* Lloyd Beebe. *Wildlife and Grizzly Bear Seq Filmed by* Cangary Ltd. *Asst to Mr. Beebe* William W. Bacon, III, Terry Rowland, Marinho Correia, Bob Rowland, Al Niemela, Dell Ray. *Coöp* Stoney Indian Nation.
Cast: John Yesno *(Moki)*, Chris Wiggins *(Colonel Pierson)*, Hugh Webster *(Shorty)*, Jack Van Evera *(Slim)*, Winston Hibler *(narrator)*, Big Ted *(Wahb)*.

Drama. Source: Ernest Thompson Seton, *The Biography of a Grizzly* (New York, 1903). Moki, a Cree Indian in the late 19th-century West, works as a foreman on the ranch belonging to his former Army commanding officer, Colonel Pierson. Moki wears the sign of the tribal totem on his hand—a four-toed track, the mark of the grizzly bear. A grizzly bear invades Pierson's land and kills a steer, and Pierson shoots the bear and one of her cubs, missing the other. The surviving cub falls over a cliff and into a river and is swept downstream. Moki searches for the cub and learns that it has only four toes on one of its feet. He names it Wahb, which means four-toed grizzly, captures the bear, and sets him free on the outskirts of Pierson's land. Wahb survives and grows to maturity. At 3 years of age, Wahb appears and frightens a ranch hand, whereupon Pierson orders Moki to trap the bear; but Wahb avoids capture. Several years later, Moki encounters Wahb in the mountains. As the bear does not harm him, Moki concludes that a mystical tie binds Wahb's destiny with his own. Wahb reappears on the Pierson ranch at roundup time and stampedes the cattle. Pierson sets out to kill Wahb, but the wily bear doubles back and begins to track his pursuer. Moki attempts to warn Pierson of his danger but to no avail. Pierson meets the bear head on; his horse rears and Pierson is thrown. Wahb is about to attack Pierson when Moki intervenes and makes the Cree sign of friendship to the bear, causing him to lumber off. Pierson raises his rifle to shoot, but Moki stops him when he notices Wahb scratching a mark on a nearby tree. Moki interprets the tree-marking as a sign that the bear will never again return to Pierson's ranch. *Cree Indians. Veterans. Ranchers. Employer-employee relations. Hunting. Totems. Stampedes. Roundups. Bears.*
Note: Filmed on location in Alberta and British Columbia along the eastern approaches to the Canadian Rockies, at Moraine Lake in Banff National Park, in the Kananaskis Forest and on the Kananaskis River, at Takakkaw Falls in Yoho National Park, on Bow River, and at the Stoney Indian Reservation. Released in Canada ca 1971.

KING OF THE MOUNTAIN *see* **BEDTIME STORY**

KING OF THE ROARING 20'S—THE STORY OF ARNOLD ROTHSTEIN   **F6.2616**
Allied Artists. Jun **1961** [New York opening: 4 Oct 1961; c1 May 1961; LP19503]. Sd; b&w. 35mm. 106 min.
Prod Samuel Bischoff, David Diamond. *Dir* Joseph M. Newman. *Screenplay* Jo Swerling. *Photog* Carl Guthrie. *Art Dir* David Milton. *Set Decor* Joseph Kish. *Film Ed* George White. *Mus Comp & Cond* Franz Waxman. *Sd Mix* Ralph Butler. *Sd Ed* Charles Schelling, Marty Greco. *Mus Ed* Jill Campbell. *Asst Dir* Lindsley Parsons, Jr. *Prod Mgr* Edward Morey, Jr. *Set Cont* Billy Vernon. *Wardrobe* Roger J. Weinberg, Norah Sharpe. *Makeup Artist* Allan Snyder. *Hairstyles* Agnes Flanagan. *Sp Eff* Milt Olsen. *Prop* Ted Mossman. *Constr Supv* James West.
Cast: David Janssen *(Arnold Rothstein)*, Dianne Foster *(Carolyn Green)*, Mickey Rooney *(Johnny Burke)*, Jack Carson *("Big Tim" O'Brien)*, Diana Dors *(Madge)*, Dan O'Herlihy *(Phil Butler)*, Mickey Shaughnessy *(Jim Kelly)*, Keenan Wynn *(Tom Fowler)*, Joseph Schildkraut *(Abraham Rothstein)*, William Demarest *(Hecht)*, Murvyn Vye *(Williams)*, Regis Toomey *(Bill Baird)*, Robert Ellenstein *(Lenny)*, Teri Janssen *(Joanie)*, Jim Baird *(Arnold, as a boy)*, Tim Rooney.

Biographical drama. Source: Leo Katcher, *The Big Bankroll: The Life and Times of Arnold Rothstein* (New York, 1959). Despite a decent upbringing by devout Jewish parents, Arnold Rothstein is destined for a life of crime. A born gambler, he is always on the lookout for quick money. By the time he reaches manhood, he is well enough known in New York City to attract the attention of "Big Tim" O'Brien, a crooked politician who establishes him in a gambling house. After duping his partner, Jim Kelly, into selling his half of the business, Rothstein marries Broadway actress Carolyn Green. But domestic life has no appeal for Rothstein, and he devotes most of his time to gambling and plotting the downfall of his lifetime enemy, Phil Butler, a corrupt police official. In the end, Rothstein tricks his childhood friend, Johnny Burke, into revealing Butler's record of graft to a newspaper. Though Johnny is shot down by gunmen, Rothstein, aided by attorney Tom Fowler, succeeds in sending Butler to the chair. His underhanded and vicious tactics not only cause Carolyn to leave him, but they also arouse the wrath of the underworld. One night, while playing poker in a hotel room, Rothstein is killed by paid assassins. His last hand is the one he dreamt of all his life—a royal flush. *Politicians. Actors. Police. Lawyers. Jews. Gambling. Political corruption. Graft. Assassination. Capital punishment. Poker. New York City. Tammany Hall. Arnold Rothstein. Abraham Rothstein. Carolyn Green.*
Note: Working title: *The Big Bankroll.*

KING RAT   **F6.2617**
Coleytown Productions. *Dist* Columbia Pictures. 27 Oct **1965** [New York opening; c1 Aug 1965; LP31865]. Sd (RCA); b&w. 35mm. 134 min.
Prod James Woolf. *Assoc Prod* Marvin Miller. *Dir-Writ* Bryan Forbes. *Dir Photog* Burnett Guffey. *Camera Op* Andrew McIntyre. *Asst Camera* James Saper. *Art Dir* Robert Smith. *Set Decor* Frank Tuttle. *Film Ed* Walter Thompson. *Mus Comp & Cond* John Barry. *Sd Supv* Charles J. Rice. *Sd* James Z. Flaster, John Cox. *Rec* Harold Lee. *Boom Op* Doug Grant. *Dub Ed* Roy Baker. *Asst Dir* Russell Saunders, Bob Templeton, C. M. Florance. *Unit Mgr* Marvin Miller. *Script Girl* Marie Kenney. *Men's Cost* Ed Ware. *Makeup Supv* Ben Lane. *Makeup* Joe Dibella. *Sp Eff* John Burke. *Still Photog* Ken Bell. *Prop* Clarence Peet, Bill Kantor. *Gaffer* Seldon White. *Grip* Walter Meins, Willard Klug. *Constr Coörd* Ed Shanley.
Cast—The American Hut: George Segal *(Corporal King)*, Patrick O'Neal *(Max)*, Todd Armstrong *(Tex)*, Sammy Reese *(Kurt)*, Joseph Turkel *(Dino)*, Michael Stroka *(Miller)*, William Fawcett *(Steinmetz)*, Dick Johnson *(Pop)*.
Cast—Hut 16: James Fox *(Flight Lieutenant Marlowe)*, Denholm Elliott *(Lieut. Col. Denholm Larkin)*, Leonard Rossiter *(Major McCoy)*, John Standing *(Captain Daven)*, Hamilton Dyce *(Chaplain Drinkwater)*, Wright King *(Brough)*, John Ronane *(Captain Hawkins)*, Geoffrey Bayldon *(Squadron Leader Vexley)*, John Levingston *(Myner)*, John Barclay *(Spence)*, David Frankham *(Cox)*.
Cast—The Provost Staff: Tom Courtenay *(Lieutenant Grey)*, David Haviland *(Masters)*, Roy Dean *(Peterson)*.
Cast—The Senior Officers: John Mills *(Colonel Smedley-Taylor)*, Gerald Sim *(Colonel Jones)*, Alan Webb *(Colonel Brant)*, John Merivale *(Foster)*, John Warburton *(commandant)*.
Cast—The Hospital Staff: James Donald *(Dr. Kennedy)*, Hedley Mattingly *(Dr. Prodhomme)*, Michael Lees *(Stephens)*.
Cast—The Australians: Reg Lye *(Tinkerbell)*, John Orchard *(Private Gurble)*, Laurence Conroy *(Townsend)*, Arthur Malet *(Blakely)*, Edward Ashley *(Prouty)*, Richard Dawson *(Weaver)*.
Cast—The Japanese: Dale Ishimoto *(Yoshima)*, Teru Shimada *(Japanese general)*, Louis Neervort *(Torusumi)*.

Cast—Others: George Pelling (*Major Barry*), Anthony Faramus.

War drama. Source: James Clavell, *King Rat* (London, 1963). U. S. Corporal King is the opportunistic, cynical head of a black market operation in a Japanese prisoner of war camp on Singapore just before the end of World War II. In the camp are approximately 10,000 British, Australian, and American prisoners, most of whom outrank King, and all of whom are sick and emaciated. King maintains his own health through such methods as breeding rats and selling them as food to his fellow prisoners. He befriends British Flight Lieutenant Marlowe, who speaks Malay and thus can barter with the corrupt camp guards, and he saves Marlowe's life by paying a high price for stolen antibiotics. The provost marshal of the camp, Lieutenant Grey, King's implacable enemy, sees King's behavior as immoral and is constantly frustrated by his inability to catch King in black market deals. He is about to do so when the Japanese announce that the war is over. King and Marlowe go their separate ways, King rejecting Marlowe's offer of friendship now that the camp life ruled by King has ended. *Prisoners of war. Profiteers. Prison guards. Black market. Starvation. World War II. Singapore. United States Army. Japan—Army. Great Britain—Army. Great Britain—Royal Air Force. Australia—Army. Rats.*

Note: Filmed on location in Thousand Oaks, California.

THE KINGDOM AND THE BEAUTY (Hong Kong)   F6.2618

Shaw & Sons, Ltd. Jun **1967** [Los Angeles opening]. Sd; b&w. 35mm. [Feature film, length unknown.]

Cast: Lin Dai, Chao Lei, King Chuan, Ma Lin, Wang Yuan-lung, Yang Chih-ching, Hung Po, Mei Yueh-hua, Margaret Tu Chuan, Marguerite Tong Jo-ching, Hung Wei.No information about the precise nature of this film has been found.

Note: Produced in 1959 as *Chiang shan mei jen.*

KINGS OF THE SUN   F6.2619

Mirisch Corp. *Dist* United Artists. 18 Dec **1963** [Los Angeles opening]. Sd; col (Deluxe Color). 35mm (Panavision). 108 min.

Prod Lewis J. Rachmil. *Dir* J. Lee Thompson. *Screenplay* Elliott Arnold, James R. Webb. *Story* Elliott Arnold. *Photog* Joseph MacDonald. *Art Dir* Alfred Ybarra. *Film Ed* William Reynolds. *Mus* Elmer Bernstein. *Sd* Bert Hallberg. *Asst Dir* Tom Shaw. *Prod Supv* Allen K. Wood. *Prod Mgr* Nate H. Edwards. *Unit Mgr* Robert E. Relyea. *Cost* Norma Koch. *Makeup* Emile La Vigne. *Hairstyles* Mary Babcock. *Sp Eff* Roscoe Cline.

Cast: Yul Brynner (*Black Eagle*), George Chakiris (*Balam*), Shirley Ann Field (*Ixchel*), Richard Basehart (*Ah Min*), Brad Dexter (*Ah Haleb*), Barry Morse (*Ah Zok*), Armando Silvestre (*Isatai*), Leo Gordon (*Hunac Ceel*), Victoria Vettri (*Ixzubin*), Rudy Solari (*Pitz*), Ford Rainey (*Ixchel's father*), Angel Di Steffano (*Balam's father*), José Elías Moreno (*The Youth*).

Historical drama. Hunac Ceel's fierce warriors from the north crush the Mayan tribes of Mexico. The Mayan king is killed, his son, Balam, is chosen as successor, and the tribe runs away to the coast. Hunac Ceel follows and forces them to flee the country, and the Mayans sail to what is now North America, where they settle in hopes of establishing a new civilization. Black Eagle, head of a neighboring Indian tribe, attacks the Mayans and is wounded and taken captive in a battle with Balam. Ixchel, Balam's fianceée, nurses Black Eagle back to health; later, after Balam saves Black Eagle from being sacrificed, the two leaders become friends and decide to live together in peace. However, Hunac Ceel, intent upon destroying Mayan civilization, attacks again. This time the Mayans, with the help of Black Eagle's tribes, defeat the invaders, but Black Eagle is killed saving Balam's life. *Mayan Indians. Indians of North America. Indians of South America. Royalty. Human sacrifice. Friendship. Military invasion. Mexico. North America.*

Note: Location scenes filmed in Mazatlán and Chichén Itza.

THE KING'S PIRATE   F6.2620

Universal Pictures. Aug **1967** [c2 Sep 1967; LP36898]. Sd (Westrex); col (Technicolor). 35mm. 100 min.

Prod Robert Arthur. *Dir* Don Weis. *Screenplay* Paul Wayne, Aeneas MacKenzie, Joseph Hoffman. *Story* Aeneas MacKenzie. *Dir Photog* Clifford Stine. *Art Dir* Alexander Golitzen, George C. Webb. *Set Decor* John McCarthy, John Austin. *Titl* Pacific Title. *Film Ed* Russell F. Schoengarth. *Mus* Ralph Ferraro. *Mus Supv* Joseph Gershenson. *Sd* Waldon O. Watson, James T. Porter. *Asst Dir* Phil Bowles. *Unit Prod Mgr* Robert E. Larson. *Cost* Vittorio Nino Novarese. *Makeup* Bud Westmore. *Hairstylist* Larry Germain. *Matte Supv* Albert Whitlock. *Dial Coach* Rand Brooks. *Stunt Coörd* Ronnie Rondell.

Cast: Doug McClure (*Brian Fleming*), Jill St. John (*Jessica Stephens*), Guy Stockwell (*John Avery*), Mary Ann Mobley (*Patma*), Kurt Kasznar (*Zucco*), Richard Deacon (*Swaine*), Torin Thatcher (*Captain Cullen*), Diana Chesney (*Molvina MacGregor*), Ivor Barry (*Cloudsly*), Bill Glover (*Captain Hornsby*), Woodrow Parfrey (*Gow*), Sean McClory (*Sparkes*), Michael St. Clair (*Collins*), Emile Genest (*Captain Misson*), Ted De Corsia (*Captain McTigue*), Alex Montoya (*Caraccioli*), Tanya Lemani, Aime Luce, Robert Terhune, Chuck

Couch, Bill Couch, Loren Janes, Hank Monzello, William Snyder, actor, Rodney Hoeltzel, Danny Rees (*Zucco's troupe*).

Adventure melodrama. In 1700, when pirates are plundering merchant ships along the trade routes to India, Lieut. Brian Fleming, a British naval officer motivated by the reward money offered to check the piracy, poses as a tumbler in Zucco's acrobatic troupe in order to gain access to the buccaneers' stronghold in Madagascar. After demonstrating his courage and daring, he joins the pirates as navigator to first mate John Avery, even though the two men are competitors for the affections of Jessica, a fiery pirate girl who has inherited control of the Madagascar fortifications from her father. During their first mission together, they capture the state ship of the Emperor of India, and Brian takes as a hostage a young woman who turns out to be the Emperor's daughter, Princess Patma. When Patma is auctioned off, Brian tries to purchase her, but he is outbid by Jessica, who is determined to have Brian for herself. Eventually Avery discovers Brian's true identity and lashes him to a stake in the shark-infested surf. But Jessica rescues him as British war vessels move in to bombard the pirate fortress. When Avery attempts to escape aboard his ship, Brian and Zucco's acrobats stage a surprise attack, and Avery meets his death in a duel with Brian. Arrangements are made for Princess Patma to be safely delivered home, and Jessica, now betrothed to Brian, is granted a Royal pardon. *Pirates. British. East Indians. Acrobats. Hostages. Royalty. Imposture. Piracy. Jealousy. Slavery. Madagascar. Great Britain—Royal Navy. Duels.*

Note: Remake of *Against All Flags*, 1952.

A KING'S STORY (Great Britain)   F6.2621

LeVien Films. *Dist* Continental Distributing, Inc. 24 May **1967** [New York opening]. Sd; col with b&w seq. 35mm. 100 min.

A Jack LeVien Production. *Prod* Jack LeVien. *Assoc Prod* Arthur S. Ferriman. *Dir* Harry Booth. *Screenplay* Glyn Jones. *Narr* John Lord. *Orig Screen Treatment* Sydney Box. *Photog* Richard Bayley. *Film Ed* Alban Streeter. *Mus Comp & Cond* Ivor Slaney. *Res* Linda Metcalfe.

Voices: Orson Welles (*narrator*), Flora Robson (*Queen Mary*), Patrick Wymark (*Sir Winston Churchill*), Carleton Hobbs (*King George V*), David Warner (*Prince of Wales*).

Documentary. The film is a compilation of clips, photographs, and newsreel excerpts depicting the early life of the Duke of Windsor. The Duke provided film from his private collection and also consented to appear in sequences filmed at his country residence at Gif-sur-Yvette, near Paris. Beginning with his early childhood as the great-grandson of Queen Victoria, the young Prince of Wales is seen at school, in training for the Royal Navy, and being coached for the responsibilities and duties of his royal position. Following clips of his tours as an ambassador for Britain, and his eventual ascension to the throne as Edward VIII, there are scenes of the Duke's meeting with Mrs. Wallis Warfield Simpson, their much publicized romance, and his ultimate decision in 1936 to renounce his throne and marry her. The Duke reads his abdication speech at the conclusion of the film. *Abdication. Gif-sur-Yvette. Edward Duke of Windsor. Wallis Warfield Simpson, (Duchess of Windsor). George V (England). Mary (1867–1953). Winston Leonard Spencer Churchill.*

Note: Opened in London in May 1965; running time: 102 min.

KINGU KONGU NO GYAKUSHU *see* **KING KONG ESCAPES**

KIRI NI MUSEBU YORU *see* **HARBOR LIGHT YOKOHAMA**

KIRU *see* **KILL**

KISS   F6.2622

Dist Film-Makers' Cooperative. Jan **1964** [New York showing]. Si; b&w. 16mm. 58 min.

Prod-Dir Andy Warhol.

Cast: Naomi Levine, Ed Sanders, Rufus Collins, Gerard Malanga, Baby Jane Holzer, John Palmer, actor, Andrew Meyer, Freddie Herko, Johnny Dodd, Charlotte Gilbertson, Philip Van Rensselaet, Pierre Restaney, Marisol.

Experimental film. In brief episodes, couples are seen in closeup, kissing. Each episode ends with a flash of exposed, perforated film, indicating the end of a reel, and with a "whiteout." Couples include: Naomi Levine and Ed Sanders, Levine and Rufus Collins, Levine and Gerard Malanga, Baby Jane Holzer and John Palmer, Holzer and Malanga, and Palmer and Andrew Meyer. *Male homosexuality. Bisexuality.*

Note: The sequences involving Naomi Levine were shown in New York in Sep 1963 under the title *Andy Warhol Serial.* Other sequences were filmed subsequently. The frame remains fixed throughout each sequence.

KISS & KILL (United States/Great Britain/Spain/West Germany) F6.2623

Towers of London–Ada Films–Udastex Films–Terra Filmkunst. *Dist* Commonwealth United Entertainment, Inc. 24 Sep **1969** [Detroit opening]. Sd; col (Eastmancolor). 35mm. 92 min. *MPAA rating* M.

Pres by Commonwealth United Corp. *Prod* Harry Alan Towers. *Dir* Jess Franco. *Screenplay* Peter Welbeck. *Screenplay Collab* Manfred R. Köhler,

Manfred R. Franco. *Photog* Manuel Merino. *Art Dir* Peter Gasper, Augusto Lega. *Film Ed* Allan Morrison, Angel Serrano. *Mus* Daniel White, Gert Wilen, Hans-Martin Majewski. *Sd* Malcolm Stewart. *Prod Supv* Tibor Reves. *Prod Mgr* Juan Estelrich, Francisco Romero.

Cast: Christopher Lee (*Dr. Fu Manchu*), Richard Greene (*Nayland Smith*), Shirley Eaton (*Black Widow*), Tsai Chin (*Lin Tang*), Maria Rohm (*Ursula Wagner*), Howard Marion-Crawford (*Dr. Petrie*), Ricardo Palacios (*Sancho Lopez*), Götz George (*Carl Jansen*), Frances Kahn (*Carmen*), Loni von Friedl (*Celeste*), Isaura de Oliviera (*Yuma*), Vicente Sejournant, Marcelo Arroita.

Adventure melodrama. Based on the characters created by: Sax Rohmer. From his Brazilian underground fortress, which is protected by a group of dacoits, archvillain Fu Manchu dispatches 10 native women, each injected with a deadly snake poison, to give their kiss of death to Fu Manchu's enemies, among them some of the world's most powerful figures. Celeste goes to London to assassinate Fu Manchu's longtime rival, Inspector Nayland Smith of Scotland Yard, but she succeeds only in blinding him and is run down by a truck while attempting to flee. As Inspector Smith and his colleague, pathologist Dr. Petrie, prepare to go to South America to find a cure for Smith and to destroy Fu Manchu, the archvillain turns his attention to renegade bandit and gang leader Sancho Lopez. Fu Manchu captures him and through torture extracts the bandit's promise to kill Smith. The treacherous Fu Manchu sends Carmen, who has been injected with the snake poison, with Sancho; her instructions are to kill Sancho once he has killed Smith. Carl Jansen, an undercover agent for Smith, joins Ursula, a nurse ministering to the natives, and they rendezvous with Smith and Dr. Petrie to decide how to destroy Fu Manchu. Carl, Dr. Petrie, and Ursula set off into the jungle, leaving Smith behind. Ursula and Dr. Petrie are captured by Sancho and taken to Fu Manchu's underground headquarters, but Carmen frees them. Ursula, Dr. Petrie, and Carmen hurry back to Smith when it is learned that Carmen's blood may contain an antidote with which to cure Smith's blindness. A transfusion is effected; Smith is cured; and he and Dr. Petrie return to the underground fortress to rescue Carl, who, having rigged the fortress with dynamite charges, has been overpowered by dacoits. Smith frees Carl, and they and Petrie light the dynamite charges. A series of explosions destroys the fortress, but from the rubble comes the voice of Fu Manchu promising that the world will hear from him again. *Masterminds. Indians of South America. Detectives. Pathologists. Secret agents. Nurses. Bandits. Dacoits. Poisoning. Assassination. Blindness. Torture. Blood transfusion. Brazil. London. Scotland Yard. Explosions. Fu Manchu.*

Note: Exteriors filmed in Brazil and Madrid. Released in West Germany in Jul 1968 as *Der Todeskuss des Dr. Fu Man Chu*; running time: 82 min; in Great Britain caFeb 1969 as *The Blood of Fu Manchu*; running time: 61 min; in Spain as *Fu Manchu y el beso de la muerte*; running time: 88 min. British prerelease title: *Fu Manchu and the Kiss of Death*. Peter Welbeck is a pseudonym of Harry Alan Towers. Sources conflict in crediting music.

KISS KISS BANG BANG *see* THE BANG BANG GANG

KISS ME, BABY   F6.2624
Dist Billiken Pictures. 8 Jun **1961** [Los Angeles showing]. Sd; b&w. 35mm. 84 min.

Dir Lillian Hunt. *Photog* W. Merle Connell. *Film Ed* Phil Tucker. *Mus Dir* Richard Todd, mus. *Mus* Al Terry. *Rec* Dale Knight. *Makeup* Harry Thomas. *Mus Cons* Sanford H. Dickenson.

Cast: Taffy O'Niel, Midnight, Gina, Pat Flannery, Joy Ryder, Debbie Ray (*solo dancers*), Leon De Voe, Harry Arnie, Eddie Ware, Herbie Barris (*comedians*).

Burlesque film. No information about the precise nature of this film has been found, but press material suggests that it is a film version of a burlesque show. *Stripteasers. Entertainers. Burlesque.*

KISS ME, KISS ME, KISS ME!   F6.2625
Extraordinary Films. *Dist* William Mishkin. caJan **1968.** Sd; b&w. 35mm. 80 min.

Prod-Orig Story William Mishkin. *Dir* Andy Milligan. *Screenplay* Josef Bush. *Photog* Andy Milligan. *Titl Song* Harry Huret.

Cast: Natalie Rogers (*Jean*), Don Williams (*Stan*), Peter Ratray (*Eddie*), Joy Martin (*Ellen*), Angela Peters (*Lurlene*), Matt Baylor (*Dominic*), Gerald Jacuzzo (*Ray*), Esther Travers (*Ma*), Veronica Radburn (*Mrs. Scilletto*), Nick Orzel (*Sal*), Alan Sedan (*Lou*), Sean Martin (*Jimmy*).

Melodrama. Stan Novack, a New York City mechanic, manhandles his wife, Jean, out of exasperation when he neglects their 3-year-old son or drinks excessively. He remains ignorant of her affairs with other men. Jean seduces Stan's best friend, Eddie, and then continues to pursue him when he tries to avoid seeing her again. To insure their future meetings, Jean persuades Stan to introduce his unmarried sister, Ellen, to Eddie. The plan backfires, however, when the couple fall in love and announce their engagement. Furious, Jean arranges for Ellen to find her with Eddie in a compromising situation. Although

her scheme works, the enraged Eddie beats her up and leaves. More determined than ever to win him back, Jean abandons her young son and trails Eddie to a bar where an orgy is going on in the back room. Eddie leaves immediately, but Jean joins the lovemaking, gets drunk, and then goes to Eddie's apartment. Meanwhile, Stan learns that their little son has been killed in a fall from an open window. Grief-stricken, he tracks Jean to Eddie's apartment, storms in, and beats up Eddie. The terrified Jean runs to the rooftop to escape, and Stan follows her. Ellen arrives at the apartment to offer forgiveness to Eddie. Eddie and Ellen, fearful that Stan will murder Jean, run to the rooftop and watch as the struggling Jean and Stan topple over a ledge and plunge to their deaths. *Mechanics. Marriage. Infidelity. Promiscuity. Drunkenness. Parenthood. Orgies. New York City.*

Note: Filmed in New York City.

KISS ME MATE   F6.2626
Dist Distribpix, Inc. 17 Dec **1969** [Champaign, Illinois, showing]. Sd; col. 35mm. 63 min.

Cast: Maria Streeter.

Melodrama. Frank DeCarlo, a young writer who works in an advertising agency, cannot resist Mavis, a sex-crazed young woman, and the two are soon living together. Forced to choose between Mavis and his career as a novelist, Frank leaves Mavis in order to complete his book. Mavis transfers her affections to another playmate, and a year later Frank publishes his novel; furthermore, Frank meets Gail and believes that he is free of Mavis' influence. Then one day he sees Mavis at the marina and realizes that he still desires her. He reluctantly accepts her invitation to go on a weekend cruise with her and her spineless husband, Jerry. Frank brings Gail along, but her presence doesn't help him resist Mavis' obvious advances. The trip becomes a nightmare of lust, guilt, and passion; and it ends in tragedy when Jerry, driven insane with jealousy, murders his wife. *Authors. Mistresses. Moral corruption. Lust. Infidelity. Murder. Yachts. Advertising.*

KISS ME QUICK!   F6.2627
Fantasy Films. *Dist* G & S Productions, Rossmore Film Distributors, Boxoffice International Film Distributors. 25 Dec **1964** [Los Angeles showing]. Sd; col. 35mm. 67 min.

Dir (see note) Russ Meyer.

Cast: Frank Coe (*Sterilox/Frankenstein*), Sexton Friendly, Claudia Bauls, Jackie DeWitt, Althea Currier.

Comedy. The Grand Glon of the planet Droopiter in the distant galaxy of Buttless sends out his trusted ambassador, Sterilox, to bring back a female of the human species, since women are unknown to his planet. The visitor arrives at the castle of Dr. Breedlove, who is conducting experiments with 30 of his creations—buxom young female robots—while Dracula, Frankenstein, and The Mummy meddle in the proceedings. Sterilox acquaints himself with the female earthlings, who remove their clothes for the visitor, but he cannot single out one to take away with him. The gadget-filled castle presents a number of hazards to Sterilox, and he finally chooses a vending machine in preference to any of the women, leaving the assorted creatures at the castle to continue their adventures. *Space creatures. Scientists. Nudity. Experiments. Castles. Robots. Imaginary planets. Dracula. Frankenstein. Mummies.*

Note: Only one source credits Russ Meyer as director; the same source also credits Claudia Bauls as Claudia Banks. Sources also conflict regarding actors: one lists Jackie DeWitt, Althea Currier, and Frank Coe; others credit Sexton Friendly and Claudia Bauls. Also known as *Dr. Breedlove.*

KISS ME, STUPID   F6.2628
Phalanx Productions–Mirisch Corp.–Claude Productions. *Dist* Lopert Pictures. 16 Dec **1964** [Los Angeles opening; c22 Dec 1964; LP29547]. Sd; b&w. 35mm (Panavision). 126 min.

Prod-Dir Billy Wilder. *Assoc Prod* I. A. L. Diamond, Doane Harrison. *Screenplay* Billy Wilder, I. A. L. Diamond. *Cinematog* Joseph LaShelle. *Camera Op* Don Anderson. *Camera Asst* Bob Hosler, Jack Chandler. *Art Dir* Robert Luthardt. *Set Decor* Edward G. Boyle. *Prod Dsgn* Alexander Trauner. *Film Ed* Daniel Mandell. *Asst Ed* Dan Mandell, Jr. *Mus Score* Andre Previn. *Songs:* "Sophia," "I'm a Poached Egg," "All the Livelong Day" George Gershwin, Ira Gershwin. *Choreog* Wally Green. *Sd* Robert Martin, Wayne Fury. *Rec* Bert Hallberg. *Boom Op* W. C. Smith. *Mus Ed* Richard Carruth. *Asst Dir* C. C. Coleman, Jr., Jack Roe, Tim Zinnemann. *Prod Mgr* Allen K. Wood. *Unit Mgr* Ray Gosnell. *Script Supv* Marshall Wolins. *Cost Dsgn* Bill Thomas. *Wardrobe* Wes Jeffries, Irene Caine. *Makeup* Emile LaVigne, Loren Cosand. *Hairstyles* Alice Monte, Maudlee McDougall. *Sp Eff* Milt Rice. *Still Photog* Jack Harris, still photog. *Prop* Sam Gordon, Frank Agnone. *Grip* John Livesley. *Gaffer* Don Stott.

Cast: Dean Martin (*Dino*), Kim Novak (*Polly the Pistol*), Ray Walston (*Orville J. Spooner*), Felicia Farr (*Zelda Spooner*), Cliff Osmond (*Barney Millsap*), Barbara Pepper (*Big Bertha*), James Ward (*milkman*), Doro Merande

(Mrs. Pettibone), Howard McNear (Mr. Pettibone), Bobo Lewis (waitress), Tom Nolan (Johnny Mulligan), Alice Pearce (Mrs. Mulligan), John Fiedler (Reverend Carruthers), Arlen Stuart (Rosalie Schultz), Cliff Norton (Mack Gray), Mel Blanc (Dr. Sheldrake), Eileen O'Neill, Susan Wedell (showgirls), Bern Hoffman (bartender), Henry Gibson (Smith), Alan Dexter (Wesson), Henry Beckman (truck driver), Gene Darfler (Nevada state trooper), Sam (himself, a parakeet), Laurie Fontaine, Mary Jane Saunders, Kathy Garber.

Farce. Source: Anna Bonacci, L'ora della fantasia (Rome opening: 1945). Dino, a pop vocalist who is notorious for his heavy drinking and lecherous behavior, concludes a Las Vegas nightclub engagement and heads for Hollywood in his Italian sportscar. A detour on the highway forces him to drive through Climax, Nevada, home of amateur songwriters Barney Millsap, a gas station attendant, and music teacher Orville J. Spooner, whose wife, Zelda, is the most beautiful woman in town. Barney recognizes Dino as the famous singer, and the two composers, in hopes of interesting Dino in their songs, sabotage his car and tell him they may have to send to Milan for parts. Orville invites Dino to stay at his home, but he becomes worried about Zelda's fidelity when he hears the singer's complaint that any night without sex leaves him with a pounding headache the next morning. To satisfy Dino's libido without ruining his own marriage, Orville provokes an argument with Zelda, causing her to leave the house in tears. Orville then arranges for Polly the Pistol, a waitress and prostitute from a nearby roadhouse, to pose as his wife. The scheme works well until the insanely jealous Orville forgets the arrangement and throws Dino out for molesting his wife. Dino seeks solace at the roadhouse while Orville and Polly spend the night together. Meanwhile, Zelda, in an attempt to forget her marital problems, has gotten drunk at the same bar; and the manager, to quell the woman's raucous behavior, puts her in Polly's trailer out back. Dino finds Zelda there, mistakes her for the waitress, and easily seduces her since she has always been a fan of his. Days later, Orville and Barney hear Dino singing one of their songs on national television. As a perplexed Orville tries to determine the source of his good fortune, Zelda caresses him. *Singers. Filling station attendants. Composers. Music teachers. Waitresses. Prostitutes. Drunkenness. Lechery. Jealousy. Infidelity. Impersonation. Mistaken identity. Seduction. Nightclubs. Sports cars. Filling stations. Bars. Trailers. Television. Las Vegas. Nevada.*

Note: Location scenes filmed in Twentynine Palms, California, at the Moulin Rouge nightclub in Hollywood, and in Las Vegas.

THE KISS OF HER FLESH   F6.2629
Dist American Film Distributing Corp. **1968.** Sd; b&w. 35mm. 75 min.
Prod-Writ Julian Marsh, Anna Riva. *Dir* Julian Marsh. *Photog* Anna Riva. *Lighting* Robert Marx. *Film Ed* Anna Riva. *Sd* Robin Aden. *Grip* Chico Buck. *Still Photog* Welchie.
Cast: Artimidia Grillet, Robert Weste, Leo Heinz, Rita Vance, Susan Lund, Jane Bunce, Donna Stone.
Melodrama. After assaulting a buxom stranger on a New England beach, the assailant takes his victim home, where he tortures her with a lobster claw and electrocutes her by means of wires strung from her earrings. Learning of her death, New Yorker Maria intuits that the murderer is Richard Jennings, the assassin of her sister Claudia, and leaves for New England bent on revenge. There she enjoys an incestuous interlude with her surviving sister Dora. Disguised as a doctor, Jennings later murders Dora and her ailing friend Mona, forcing Dora to perform oral sex on his poisoned member and prescribing a lethal douche for Mona. Realizing that the physician and Jennings are one, Maria and her lover Don abduct the deviate and torture him by attaching an infernal machine onto his penis. Escaping, Jennings, armed with a machete, chases the couple onto a beach. Struggling with Don atop a radio tower, the murderer falls to his death. *Sisters. Sex deviates. Physicians. Mistresses. Torture. Murder. Incest. Lesbianism. Poisoning. Disguise. Oral sex. Sadism. Revenge. Abduction. Imposture. Beaches. New England. New York City. Chases.*
Note: Julian Marsh and Robert Weste are pseudonyms for Michael Findlay. Anna Riva is a pseudonym for Roberta Findlay.

THE KISS OF THE VAMPIRE (Great Britain)   F6.2630
Hammer Film Productions. *Dist* Universal Pictures. 11 Sep **1963** [Kansas City, Missouri, opening; c5 Oct 1962; LP32606]. Sd (RCA); col (Eastman Color). 35mm. 88 min.
Prod Anthony Hinds. *Dir* Don Sharp. *Screenplay* John Elder. *Dir Photog* Alan Hume. *Camera Op* Moray Grant. *Focus Puller* David Osborne. *Art Dir* Don Mingaye. *Asst Art Dir* Ken Ryan. *Prod Dsgn* Bernard Robinson. *Supv Ed* James Needs. *Mus Comp* James Bernard. *Mus Supv* John Hollingsworth. *Sd Rec* Ken Rawkins. *Sd Ed* James Groom. *Boom Op* Ken Nightingall. *Sd Camera Op* Al Thorne. *1st & 2d Asst Dir* Douglas Hermes, Hugh Harlow. *Prod Mgr* Don Weeks. *Cont* Pauline Wise. *Wardrobe Supv* Molly Arbuthnot. *Wardrobe Mistress* Rosemary Burrows. *Makeup Artist* Roy Ashton. *Hairstyles* Frieda Steiger. *Sp Eff* Les Bowie. *Still Photog* Curtis Reeks. *Studio Mgr* A. F. Kelly. *Constr Mgr* Arthur Banks. *Ch Electrn* Jack Curtis, electrn. *Prop Master*

Tommy Money. *Prop Buyer* Eric Hillier. *Grip* Albert Cowland.
Cast: Clifford Evans (Professor Zimmer), Noel Willman (Dr. Ravna), Edward De Souza (Gerald Harcourt), Jennifer Daniel (Marianne Harcourt), Barry Warren (Carl Ravna), Peter Madden (Bruno), Brian Oulton (1st disciple), Isobel Black (Tania), Noel Howlett (Father Xavier), Vera Cook (Anna), Jacqueline Wallis (Sabena Ravna), John Harvey (police sergeant), Stan Simmons (servant), Olga Dickie (woman at graveyard), Margaret Read (1st girl disciple), Elizabeth Valentine (2d girl disciple).
Horror film. In Bavaria in 1910, Gerald Harcourt and his bride, Marianne, run out of gasoline while touring through a forest, and Gerald sets out for help. During his absence, Marianne is terrified by the appearance of a man named Professor Zimmer who warns her that vampires inhabit an eerie chateau on the nearby mountain. After Gerald returns, they find refuge at an inn and receive a dinner invitation from Dr. Ravna, who lives at the chateau. Gerald and Marianne accept, and Dr. Ravna introduces his son Carl and daughter Sabena. After dinner, Carl plays the piano, and the music has a strange, hypnotic effect on Marianne. The next day they are invited to a masquerade ball. At the chateau, Gerald is drugged, and Marianne is put into a deep trance by Ravna, who prepares to sink his teeth into her neck. Gerald awakens but cannot find his wife and is forcibly thrown out of the castle. He enlists the aid of Professor Zimmer, and they return to the chateau where Gerald is attacked by a vampire but escapes by painting a cross on his chest with his own blood. Professor Zimmer finds Marianne, and they all rush back to the inn. The professor smears all exits to the castle with garlic, and, when he evokes a spell, hundreds of bats attack and put an end to the evil Ravna and his cult. *Newlyweds. Professors. Vampires. Honeymoons. Spells. Forests. Inns. Castles. Pianos. Bavaria. Bats.*
Note: Opened in London in Jan 1964. John Elder is a pseudonym for Anthony Hinds.

KISS-OFF   F6.2631
D-J Productions. *Dist* Canyon Distributing Co. ca **1968.** Sd; b&w. 35mm. 74 min.
Sex film. No information about the precise nature of this film has been found except that it concerns a man's futile search for sexual fulfillment. *Sexuality.*

KISS THE DEAD (West Germany)   F6.2632
Ceo Film–Sonderfilm Zwikker. *Dist* Hoffberg Productions. **1961.** Sd; b&w. 35mm. 77 min.
Dir Peter Jacob. *Screenplay* August Detleff. *Story* Rudi Beckmann. *Photog* Herbert Thallmayer. *Art Dir* Eric Hajo. *Film Ed* Lieselotte Topell. *Mus* John Paris. *Asst Dir* Osman Ragheb. *Prod Dir* Carl Opitz.
Cast: Susanne Kraetsch, Chris van Loosen, Hertha von Walther, Heinz Schorlemmer, Heliane Bei, Ric Passé, Kurt Hepperlin, Osman Ragheb, Dodo van Dören, Gerlinde Naumberg, Eric Hajo.
Melodrama. A young woman flees from East Germany only to fall into the hands of unscrupulous men who deal in narcotics and prostitution. *Political refugees. Pimps. Drug dealers. Prostitution. German Democratic Republic.*
Note: Opened in Wiesbaden in Sep 1958 as Küsse, die Töten.

KISS THE GIRLS AND MAKE THEM DIE (United States/Italy)   F6.2633
Dino De Laurentiis Cinematografica. *Dist* Columbia Pictures. 25 Jan **1967** [New York opening; c8 Nov 1966; LP33642]. Sd (Westrex); col (Technicolor). 35mm. 106 min. [Also reviewed at 101 min.]
Pres by Dino De Laurentiis. *Prod* Dino De Laurentiis. *Exec Prod* Salvatore Argento, Dino Maiuri. *Dir* (see note) Henry Levin, Dino Maiuri. *2d Unit Dir* Alberto Pieralisi, Leopoldo Savona. *Screenplay* Jack Pulman, Dino Maiuri. *Story* Dino Maiuri. *Dir Photog* Aldo Tonti. *Art Dir* Mario Garbuglia. *Asst Art Dir* Ferdinando Giovannoni. *Set Dresser* Emilio D'Andria. *Film Ed* Ralph Kemplen, Alberto Gallitti. *Asst to Film Ed* Eunice Mountjoy. *Mus & Sp Mus Eff* Mario Nascimbene. *Cond* Roberto Pregadio. *Harmonica Solo* John Sebastian. *Titl Song Lyr* Howard Greenfield. *Sung by* Lydia MacDonald. *Sd Mix* Luciano Welisch. *Sd Ed* Leslie Hodgson. *Sd Re-rec* Alberto Bartolomei. *Asst Dir* Giorgio Gentili, Gianni Cozzo. *Asst to the Dir* Ralph Serpe. *Prod Mgr* Mario Del Papa. *Script Girl* Elaine Schreyeck. *Prod Asst* Giorgio Morra. *Cost* Maria De Matteis. *Miss Provine's Cost* Piero Gherardi. *Makeup Supv* Otello Fava. *Hairdresser* Renata Magnanti. *Sp Optical Eff* Joseph Natanson. *Sp Eff* Augie Lohman. *Casting Dir* Guidarino Guidi. *Set Constr* Aldo Puccini.
Cast: Michael Connors (Kelly), Dorothy Provine (Susan Fleming), Raf Vallone (Mr. Ardonian), Terry-Thomas (Lord Aldric/James), Margaret Lee (Grace), Nicoletta Machiavelli (Sylvia), Beverly Adams (Karin), Marilù Tolo (Gioia), Seyna Seyn (Wilma Soong), Oliver MacGreevy (Ringo), Sandro Dori (Omar), Jack Gwillim (British ambassador), Andy Ho (Ling), Hans Thorner (Kruger), Nerio Bernardi (papal envoy), Michael Audley (Major Davis), Edith Peters (Maria), K. Wang (Kasai), Renato Terra, George Leech, Roland Bartrop.
Action melodrama. Assisted by an infamous Nazi doctor who conducted sterility experiments during the war, Mr. Ardonian, a mysterious industrialist

with headquarters in Rio de Janeiro, has perfected a satellite which, once in orbit, could emit ultrasonic waves capable of sterilizing mankind. After agreeing to sell his process to the Red Chinese for $500 million, Ardonian amuses himself by collecting beautiful young women and placing them in a state of suspended animation until the time when they will be needed to repopulate the earth. (Undesirable candidates are eliminated in various bizarre ways.) His activities are closely watched by both an American CIA man, Kelly, and a beautiful English secret agent, Susan Fleming, who visit an Indian village in the Brazilian jungle and discover that Ardonian's experiments have caused all sexual desire to be suppressed for more than 4 years. Susan is captured and taken to Ardonian's underwater laboratory where the madman intends to include her in his "hibernation harem." Once he has received the $500 million from the Chinese emissaries, Ardonian electrocutes them in a mass double-cross and then decides to become master of the world by sterilizing the earth's entire population. But Kelly makes his way into the undersea laboratory while Susan's chauffeur, James, goes to alert the Brazilian army. Kelly rescues Susan and knocks Ardonian into the hibernation vault just as Brazilian soldiers arrive to take charge. *Evildoers. Nazis. Physicians. Industrialists. Chinese. English. Chauffeurs. Secret agents. Sterilization (sexual). Suspended animation. Megalomania. Abduction. Perfidy. Experiments. Satellites. Jungles. Rio de Janeiro. Brazil. United States—Central Intelligence Agency. Brazil—Army.*

Note: Filmed in Rio de Janeiro. Released in Italy in 1966 as *Se tutte le donne del mondo*; running time: 105 min. Alternative Italian title: *Operazione Paradiso*. U. S. sources credit only Henry Levin as director, while foreign sources credit both Levin and Dino Maiuri.

KISS THE GIRLS AND MAKE THEM DIE! *see* **KISS THE GIRLS AND SEE THEM DIE!**

KISS THE GIRLS AND SEE THEM DIE! F6.2634
Dist Inter-American Film Distributors. ca 1968. Sd; col (Eastmancolor). 35mm. 77 min.

Crime melodrama. While attempting to rob a millionairess of her jewels, Rocky rapes and murders the socialite. Accompanied by his brother Jason, the culprit flees, later killing two pursuing policemen and holding hostage picnickers Lucy and Janet. After Rocky tries to rape Lucy, Jason ties up his impulsive brother and the women. Leaving the cave hideout, Jason arranges with Jim an escape to Mexico, unaware that Jim intends to turn him in for a reward. Breaking his bonds, Rocky again attempts to rape Lucy but is shot by Janet. Jason returns to find his brother dead and is himself killed during a police ambush. *Millionaires. Brothers. Police. Hostages. Robbery. Rape. Murder. Duplicity. Jewels. Caves. Rewards. Chases.*

Note: Also known as *Kiss the Girls and Make Them Die!*

KISS THE OTHER SHEIK (France/Italy) F6.2635
C. C. Champion–Les Films Concordia. *Dist* Metro-Goldwyn-Mayer, Inc. 29 Jul **1968** [New York opening; c1 Aug 1968; LP36132]. Sd; col (Metrocolor). 35mm (Panavision). 85 min.

A Carlo Ponti Production. *Prod* Carlo Ponti. *Dir (see note)* Luciano Salce, Eduardo De Filippo. *Story-Screenplay* Goffredo Parise, Renato Castellani, Pipolo, Luciano Salce, Eduardo De Filippo, Isabella Quarantotti. *Dir Photog* Mario Montuori, Gianni Di Venanzo. *Art Dir* Luigi Scaccianoce, Ferdinando Scarfiotti. *Film Ed* Adriana Novelli, Marcello Malvestiti. *Mus* Luis Enriquez Bacalov, Nino Rota. *Sd* Ennio Sensi, Renato Cadueri. *Prod Supv* Antonio Altoviti.

Cast: Marcello Mastroianni *(Michele)*, Pamela Tiffin *(Pepita)*, Virna Lisi *(Dorothea)*, Luciano Salce *(Arturo Rossi)*, Raimondo Vianello, Lina Valonghi, Lelio Luttazzi, Ennio Balbo, Luciano Bonanni.

Comedy. Pepita goes to police headquarters to claim her long-lost husband, Michele, a naked man suffering from amnesia. After informing the police inspector that she has not seen her husband for 2 years, she relates the facts leading to his disappearance. *Weary of his wife's canned meals, extravagant tastes, and sexual demands, Michele decides to sell Pepita to a visiting Arab chief who has a harem of blonde wives. Since the sheik already has a wife resembling Pepita, he suggests that Michele go to Morocco and peddle her to one of the other wealthy Arabs. After some difficulties, Michele finally contracts to sell his wife, but before he can conclude the deal, Pepita takes her own revenge by selling Michele to a homosexual sheik.* When Pepita has concluded her story, Michele's friend, Arturo Rossi, adds that he and his wife, Dorothea, gave refuge to Michele when he escaped from Africa; but their childish love games drove Michele to such distraction that he eventually fled. Pepita then receives custody of her husband, but the suspicious police trail her. They discover that she has sold Michele back to the homosexual Arab, but they do not know that the trunk she delivered actually contains Arturo. At last Pepita and Michele are reunited. *Police. Arabs. Sheiks. Missing persons. Amnesia. Marriage. Slavery. Revenge. Male homosexuality. Harems. Rome. Morocco.*

Note: The film consists of two of the three episodes of *Oggi, domani e dopodomani*—a Carlo Ponti production which opened in Rome in Dec 1965 and was intended for U. S. release by Embassy Pictures as *Paranoia*—and additional scenes, directed by Luciano Salce. Eduardo De Filippo, Virna Lisi, and Isabella Quarantotti had their names removed from the credits in objection to the refurbished film. Alternative title: *The Blond Wife.*

KISSES FOR MY PRESIDENT F6.2636
Pearlayne Productions. *Dist* Warner Bros. Pictures. 21 Aug **1964** [New York opening; c10 Oct 1964; LP32353]. Sd; b&w. 35mm. 113 min.

Prod-Dir Curtis Bernhardt. *Assoc Prod* Gene Taft, Steven Bernhardt. *Screenplay* Claude Binyon, Robert G. Kane. *Story* Robert G. Kane. *Dir Photog* Robert Surtees. *Camera Op* John Mehl. *Asst Camera* Emilio Calori. *Art Dir* Herman Blumenthal. *Set Decor* John P. Austin. *Film Ed* Sam O'Steen. *Asst Ed* Thomas Brown. *Mus* Bronislau Kaper. *Sd* Stanley Jones. *Boom Op* Ed Hall, sd. *Asst Dir* Arthur Lueker, Gil Kissel. *Script Supv* Erika Wernher. *Cost Dsgn* Howard Shoup. *Wardrobe* Jack Bear, Norma Brown. *Makeup Supv* Gordon Bau. *Makeup* Fred Williams, Hal Lierley. *Body Makeup* Pat O'Grady. *Supv Hairstylist* Jean Burt Reilly. *Hairstyles* Maybelle Carey, Bill Southern. *Still Photog* Bill Cary. *Prop* Levi Williams, Jack Farley. *Gaffer* Lee Wilson. *Grip* Weldon Gilbert, Frank Randall. *Constr Coörd* Paul Lunsford.

Cast: Fred MacMurray *(Thad McCloud)*, Polly Bergen *(Leslie McCloud)*, Arlene Dahl *(Doris Reid)*, Edward Andrews *(Senator Walsh)*, Eli Wallach *(Valdez)*, Donald May *(John O'Connor)*, Harry Holcombe *(Bill Richards)*, Anna Capri *(Gloria McCloud)*, Ronnie Dapo *(Peter McCloud)*, Richard St. John *(Jackson)*, Bill Walker *(Joseph)*, Adrienne Marden *(Miss Higgins)*.

Comedy. When Leslie McCloud becomes president of the United States, her husband, Thad, reluctantly gives up his successful electronics research business and finds himself at loose ends as America's "first lady." Leslie's duties allow little time for her husband and children. Their son begins developing delinquent traits and their teenaged daughter also becomes troublesome. The rowdy behavior of a visiting Latin American dictator seeking foreign aid, whom Leslie has asked Thad to escort around Washington, makes headlines and provides ammunition for Leslie's political foes, especially Senator Walsh. Doris Reid, an old girl friend of Thad's, observes the growing distance between him and Leslie and flirts with him, but he manages to elude her. When Senator Walsh questions Thad before a Senate subcommittee in an effort to defame Leslie, Thad turns the tables on him and exposes him for what he really is behind his political pretensions. Leslie is overworked, and Thad feels underprivileged, but their problems are solved when Leslie discovers she is pregnant and resigns the presidency. *Presidents of the United States. Businessmen. Latin Americans. Dictators. Family life. Scandal. Women in public office. Marriage. Pregnancy. Washington (District of Columbia). United States Congress. The White House.*

Note: Location scenes filmed in Washington, D. C.

KISSIN' COUSINS F6.2637
Four Leaf Productions. *Dist* Metro-Goldwyn-Mayer, Inc. 11 Mar **1964** [Phoenix, Arizona, opening; c14 Jan 1964; LP26892]. Sd (Westrex); col (Metrocolor). 35mm (Panavision). 96 min.

Prod Sam Katzman. *Dir* Gene Nelson. *Screenplay* Gerald Drayson Adams, Gene Nelson. *Story* Gerald Drayson Adams. *Dir Photog* Ellis W. Carter. *Art Dir* George W. Davis, Eddie Imazu. *Set Decor* Henry Grace, Budd S. Friend. *Film Ed* Ben Lewis. *Mus Supv & Cond* Fred Karger. *Background Vocals* The Jordanaires. *Songs:* "Kissin' Cousins (No. 2)," "There's Gold in the Mountains," "One Boy Two Little Girls," "Catchin' On Fast," "Tender Feeling" Bill Giant, Bernie Baum, Florence Kaye. *Song:* "Smokey Mountain Boy" Lenore Rosenblatt, Victor Millrose. *Song:* "Anyone (Could Fall in Love With You)" Bennie Benjamin, Sol Marcus, Louis A. De Jesus. *Song:* "Barefoot Ballad" Dolores Fuller, Lee Morris. *Song:* "One Is Enough" Sid Tepper, Roy C. Bennett. *Titl Song* Fred Wise, Randy Starr. *Song:* "Echoes of Love" Bob Roberts, Paddy McMains. *Song:* "(It's a) Long Lonely Highway" Doc Pomus, Mort Shuman. *Songs Sung by* Elvis Presley. *Choreog* Hal Belfer. *Rec Supv* Franklin Milton. *Sd* Josh Westmoreland. *Asst Dir* Eli Dunn, Herb Hirst, Al Murphy, Norman August. *Prod Coörd* Robert Stone. *Script Supv* Sandra Nelson. *Wardrobe* Gene Ostler, Sylvia Posner. *Makeup Supv* William Tuttle. *Hairstyles* Sydney Guilaroff, Mary Westmoreland. *Tech Adv* Col. Tom Parker. *Dial Coach* Tim Sullivan. *Still Photog* Larry Prather. *Casting* Warren Mace.

Cast: Elvis Presley *(Josh Morgan/Jodie Tatum)*, Arthur O'Connell *(Pappy Tatum)*, Glenda Farrell *(Ma Tatum)*, Jack Albertson *(Capt. Robert Salbo)*, Pamela Austin *(Selena Tatum)*, Cynthia Pepper *(Midge)*, Yvonne Craig *(Azalea Tatum)*, Donald Woods *(Gen. Alvin Donford)*, Tommy Farrell *(M. Sgt. George Bailey)*, Beverly Powers *(Trudy)*, Hortense Petra *(Dixie)*, Robert Stone *(general's aide)*.

Musical comedy. The Air Force wants to build an ICBM base atop Big Smoky Mountain in Tennessee, but each time they try to talk to Pappy Tatum, a hillbilly moonshiner who owns the land they need, he greets them with gunfire. The Air Force then sends Josh Morgan, who was born in the area, to talk with Tatum. Josh turns out to be an exact double, except for hair color, of Tatum's nephew Jodie, and it is discovered that he is their distant cousin. Josh has a hard time trying to placate Tatum while trying to cool the romantic ardor of his two daughters, Selena and Azalea, at the same time. When Tatum gets lost hunting, Josh takes out a patrol to look for him, but they are hindered by the Kittyhawks, 13 man-starved women from a nearby valley. Josh rescues Tatum, and when General Healy arrives from the Pentagon, Josh tells him that Tatum will lease the land for the base if the government will keep trespassers— including the hated "revenooers"—off his part of the land. Healy agrees. Meanwhile, Jodie has fallen in love with Midge, a WAC sent to help Josh with paperwork, and Sergeant Bailey, Josh's buddy, has fallen for Selena. Josh and Azalea also find themselves in love. *Cousins. Doubles. Revenue agents. Moonshiners. Uncles. Jealousy. Mountain life. Hunting. Missiles. Feuds. Real estate. Tennessee. Great Smoky Mountains. United States Army—Women's Army Corps. United States Air Force.*

KITAHODAKA ZESSHO see CRY OF THE MOUNTAIN

KITCHEN   F6.2638

Dist Film-Makers' Cooperative. 3 Mar **1966** [New York opening]. Sd; b&w. 16mm. 70 min.
Prod-Dir Andy Warhol. *Writ* Ronald Tavel. *Prod Asst* Gerard Malanga, Buddy Wirtschafter.
Cast: Edie Sedgwick *(mother)*, Roger Traudeau *(son)*, Albert René Ricard *(houseboy)*, David MacCabe *(photographer)*, Elecktrah, Donald Lyons.
Satire. A mother and her son are in a white kitchen. They have a lengthy conversation in which they discuss their incestuous relationship as well as other sexual and domestic affairs. The kitchen furnishings are prominent. A photographer continually enters and leaves the frame, and actors pause in their actions to pose for pictures. From time to time pages of script are handed to the actors to follow. The houseboy appears and joins in the conversation; he completes a ménage à trois with the mother and son. A portion of the dialogue is muted by the sound of an electric blender. The son murders his mother on the kitchen table. Everyone sneezes throughout the film. *Hippies. Houseboys. Photographers. Filial relations. Incest. Matricide. Sexuality.*
Note: Filmed on location in New York City. Also known as *Kitchenette.*

THE KITCHEN (Great Britain)   F6.2639

A. C. T. Films. *Dist* Kingsley International Pictures. 1 Nov **1961** [New York opening]. Sd; b&w. 35mm. 74 min.
Prod-Screenplay Sidney Cole. *Dir* James Hill. *Photog* Reginald Wyer. *Camera Op* Herbert R. Smith. *Art Dir* William Kellner. *Film Ed* Gerry Hambling. *Mus* David Lee. *Song:* "Something's Cooking" Les Vandyke. *Sung by* Adam Faith. *Sd* Claude Hitchcock. *Asst Dir* Alec Gibb. *Prod Supv* Ralph Bond. *Prod Mgr* John Workman.
Cast: Carl Mohner *(Peter)*, Mary Yeomans *(Monica)*, Brian Phelan *(Kevin)*, Tom Bell *(Paul)*, Howard Greene *(Raymond)*, Eric Pohlmann *(Mr. Marango)*, James Bolam *(Michael)*, Scot Finch *(Hans)*, Gertan Klauber *(Gaston)*, Martin Boddey *(Max)*, Sean Lynch *(Dimitri)*, Joseph Behrman *(Magi)*, George Eugeniou *(Nick)*, Frank Pettitt *(Frank)*, Charles Lloyd Pack *(chef)*, Frank Atkinson *(Alfred)*, Andreas Markos *(Mangolis)*, Jeanne Hepple *(Hattie)*, Patricia Greene *(Anne)*, Jessie Robins *(Bertha)*, Fanny Carby *(Winnie)*, Patricia Clapton *(1st jiving waitress)*, Lynn Barton *(2d jiving waitress)*, Claire Isbister *(5th waitress)*, Veronica Wells *(6th waitress)*, Gwen Nelson *(8th waitress)*, Jennifer Wallace *(9th waitress)*, Joan Geary *(14th waitress)*, Rosalind Knight *(17th waitress)*, Ida Goldapple *(19th waitress)*, Susan Field *(20th waitress)*, Nilo Christian *(21st waitress)*, Madeline Leon *(23d waitress)*, Ruth Meyers *(34th waitress)*, Andreas Constantine *(2d porter)*, Andreas Lysandrou *(1st dishwasher)*.
Drama. Source: Arnold Wesker, *The Kitchen* (London opening: 6 Sep 1959). The kitchen of a large, busy London restaurant owned by Mr. Marango is staffed with workers of many national and cultural origins—Germans, Jews, Greeks, Cypriots, Irish, and English. One particular day begins calmly with preparations for the luncheon meal, but as the rush starts and the waitresses stream in shouting orders, tension mounts and tempers explode. In the afternoon lull, Peter, the German cook, encourages his co-workers to dream of a better life beyond the kitchen. Later, as work begins on the evening repast, Peter realizes that his love affair with one of the waitresses, Monica, will never go anywhere; that she, now pregnant, has decided not to divorce her husband. Suddenly going berserk, Peter storms through the kitchen in a savage fury, smashing everything in sight. After his rampage ends, work stops as the cooks bandage Peter's bruised and bloody hands. Marango, the bewildered restaurant proprietor, stands amidst the debris and cannot understand why anyone would want to destroy his world. *Germans. Jews. Greeks. Cypriots. Irish. Restaurateurs. Waitresses. Cooks. Employer-employee relations. Divorce. Infidelity. Restaurants. London.*

Note: Opened in London in Aug 1961; running time: 74 min. Original length: 76 min.

KITTEN IN THE CAGE   F6.2640

De Lem Films–Arcturus Productions. *Dist* Boxoffice International Film Distributors. Jun **1968**. Sd; b&w. 35mm. 79 min.
Prod-Dir Richard MacLeod. *Exec Prod* George DeLemos.
Cast: Miriam Eliot *(Julie)*, John Durnham *(Ted Brown)*, June Roberts.
Melodrama. Careerwoman Julie is sent into hiding when a group of jewel thieves discover that she holds the key to the whereabouts of a cache of $1.5 million worth of stolen jewels. One morning, she awakens under confinement in a hospital, vaguely aware that she has been drugged. Under cover of darkness, she manages to make her escape. She meets Ted and falls in love, but she is forced to flee again as the hoodlums move closer. A sympathetic go-go dancer offers her refuge and draws her into a lesbian affair, but this relationship, too, is interrupted by the threat of approaching danger. Stopping at her apartment to gather her belongings, Julie is captured by the jewel thieves, who take her to their hideout and rape and torture her. Unable to hold out any longer, she reveals the location of the stolen treasure. Returning to their hideout with the booty, the thieves are surprised by Ted, who has secretly followed every move. In the gun battle that follows, all but Julie and Ted meet their deaths. With the reward they receive for the jewels, the lovers begin a new life together. *Careerwomen. Thieves. Lesbianism. Torture. Rape. Abduction. Jewels. Chases.*
Note: Also reviewed as *Kitten in a Cage.* Conflicting sources suggest the possibility that the role name of Ted Brown might be the actor's name, or a pseudonym for John Durnham.

KITTEN WITH A WHIP   F6.2641

Universal Pictures. 4 Nov **1964** [New York opening; c12 Dec 1964; LP33409]. Sd (Westrex); b&w. 35mm. 83 min.
Prod Harry Keller. *In Charge of Prod* Edward Muhl. *Dir-Writ* Douglas Heyes. *Dir Photog* Joseph Biroc. *Camera Op* Andrew McIntyre. *Asst Camera* Arthur Gerstle, Richard Vanik. *Art Dir* Alexander Golitzen, Malcolm Brown. *Set Decor* John McCarthy, John P. Austin, Oliver Emert. *Set Coörd* Fred Knoth. *Film Ed* Russell F. Schoengarth. *Asst Ed* Edward Broussard. *Mus Supv* Joseph Gershenson. *Sd* Waldon O. Watson, Frank H. Wilkinson, John Muchmore, James T. Porter, Chick Bourland, Don Nunley, sd. *Asst Dir* Terence Nelson, Terry Morse, Jr. *Script Supv* Luanna Poole. *Cost* Burton Miller. *Wardrobe* Bucky Rous, Viola Thompson. *Makeup Supv* Bud Westmore. *Makeup* Frank McCoy, Dorothy Parkinson. *Supv Hairstyles* Larry Germain. *Hairstyles* Jack Mitchell, Jean Austin. *Sp Eff* Charles Spurgeon. *Dial Coach* Robert Busch. *Still Photog* Mel Traxel. *Gaffer* Butch Harmon. *Grip* Steve Rez, Sam Van Zanten. *Prop* Ace Holmes, Charles Thomas.
Cast: Ann-Margret *(Jody Dvorak)*, John Forsythe *(David Stratton)*, Peter Brown *(Ron)*, Patricia Barry *(Vera)*, Richard Anderson *(Grant)*, James Ward *(Buck)*, Diane Sayer *(Midge)*, Ann Doran *(Mavis Varden)*, Patrick Whyte *(Philip Varden)*, Audrey Dalton *(Virginia)*, Leo Gordon *(Enders)*, Patricia Tiara *(striptease dancer)*, Nora Marlowe *(matron)*, Frances Robinson *(Martha)*, Maxine Stuart *(Peggy)*, Mildred Von Hollen *(saleslady)*, Jerry Dunphy *(newscaster)*, Doodles Weaver *(Salty Sam)*, Hal Hopper *(chauffeur)*.
Melodrama. Source: Wade Miller, *Kitten With a Whip* (Greenwich, Connecticut, 1964). After knifing a matron and setting fire to the girls' quarters of a detention home, young Jody Dvorak breaks into the house of political aspirant David Stratton, who is out for the evening while his estranged wife is in San Francisco. When David returns home and finds Jody there, she resorts to lies, threats, and deceptions to prevent him from calling the police. He gives her money for new clothes and a ticket to Los Angeles, but she returns and threatens to ruin his political career if he doesn't allow three of her friends to stay at the house. During a wild drinking party, a delinquent named Ron is slashed with a razor by Buck, a muscular beach bum, and Jody forces David to drive the injured man to a doctor in Tijuana. Jody quarrels with Buck, dumps him from the car, drops off Ron, and then makes David rent a motel room so that she can hide from her two desperate companions. David runs into some politically influential acquaintances but manages to avoid arousing their suspicions. Before he can get away from the motel, however, Buck and Ron reappear, and the former beats him into unconsciousness. Jody gets David into the car and races off as the two bullies take pursuit. Their cars crash and burst into flames, taking the lives of the three young people. While recuperating in a hospital, David learns that Jody's deathbed statement did not implicate him in any way. *Juvenile delinquents. Politicians. Prison escapees. Blackmail. Motels. Hospitals. Tijuana (Mexico). Automobile accidents. Fires.*

KLEINES ZELT UND GROSSE LIEBE see TWO IN A SLEEPING BAG

THE KNACK ... AND HOW TO GET IT (Great Britain) F6.2642

Woodfall Film Productions. *Dist* Lopert Pictures. 29 Jun **1965** [New York opening]. Sd; b&w. 35mm. 84 min.

Prod Oscar Lewenstein. *Assoc Prod* Leigh Aman, Michael Deeley. *Dir* Richard Lester. *Screenplay* Charles Wood. *Photog* David Watkin. *Art Dir* Assheton Gorton. *Titl* Robert Freeman. *Ed* Anthony Gibbs. *Mus Comp & Cond* John Barry. *Solo Jazz Organ* Alan Haven. *Sd Rec* Richard Bird. *Asst Dir* Roy Millichip. *Cost* Jocelyn Rickards. *Casting Dir* John Merrick.

Cast: Rita Tushingham *(Nancy Jones)*, Ray Brooks *(Tolen)*, Michael Crawford *(Colin)*, Donal Donnelly *(Tom)*, William Dexter *(dress shop owner)*, Charles Dyer *(man in photo booth)*, Margot Thomas *(female teacher)*, John Bluthal *(father)*, Wensley Pithey *(teacher)*, Helen Lennox *(blonde in photo booth)*, Peter Copley *(picture owner)*, Dandy Nichols *(landlady)*, Timothy Bateson *(junkman)*, George Chisholm *(porter)*, Frank Sieman *(surveyor)*, Bruce Lacey *(surveyor's assistant)*, Edgar Wreford *(man in phone booth)*, Wanda Ventham *(gym mistress)*, Gerald Toomey *(boy in classroom)*, Katherine Page *(woman in house)*, Rose Hillier *(unsuitable customer)*, Charles Wood *(soldier)*, Walter Horsbrugh *(old man)*, Julian Holloway, Vincent Harding, Kenneth Farrington, John Porter Davison *(guardsmen)*, Charlotte Rampling, Lucy Bartlett *(water skiers)*. Jacqueline Bisset.

Comedy. Source: Ann Jellicoe, *The Knack* (London opening: 27 Mar 1962). Colin, a young teacher who owns a boardinghouse in London, does not have the knack of attracting women; his tenant, Tolen, on the other hand, has so many women swarming around him that he is able to hold a reunion of girl friends at Albert Hall. Colin decides that a brass bed would improve his luck, and Tom, an artist tenant who acts as a stabilizing influence on both men, takes him to a junkyard to find one. While rolling the bed home through the streets, they come upon Nancy Jones, an innocent young woman from the provinces looking for the Y. W. C. A. The men offer to assist her, but instead she helps them push the bed, causing traffic jams and creating hysteria along the way. After reaching the house, Tolen demonstrates his amorous technique for Colin, intending for the latter to take over after Nancy becomes romantically inclined; Colin awkwardly bungles his opportunity, however, and Nancy leaves with Tolen on his motorcycle. Colin and Tom take off in pursuit and finally catch up with them in the park, where Nancy has fainted from the excitement. Despite Tolen's denials, Nancy claims to have been raped. Tolen, unnerved by the persistent accusations, loses his grip on her, enabling Colin to assert his own influence as he and Nancy become fast friends. Colin, it seems, has learned the knack at last. *Landlords. Innocents. Artists. Philanderers. Schoolteachers. Seduction. Rape. Traffic. Boardinghouses. Motorcycles. Parks. London. Royal Albert Hall. Chases.*

Note: Filmed on location in London. Opened in London in May 1965. Also known as *The Knack.*

KNIFE IN THE WATER (Poland) F6.2643

Kamera Film Unit. *For* Film Polski. *Dist* Kanawha Films. 28 Oct **1963** [New York opening]. Sd; b&w. 35mm. 94 min.

Prod Stanisław Zylewicz. *Dir* Roman Polański. *Screenplay* Jerzy Skolimowski, Jakub Goldberg, Roman Polański. *Photog* Jerzy Lipman. *Camera* Andrzej Kostenko. *Mus* Krzysztof Komeda. *Sd* Halina Paszkowska.

Cast: Leon Niemczyk *(Andrzej)*, Jolanta Umecka *(Christine [Krystyna])*, Zygmunt Malanowicz *(young man)*.

Drama. Andrzej, a successful sportswriter, and his wife, Christine, are driving to the lakes for a weekend on their yacht when they are suddenly forced to stop their car to avoid hitting a hitchhiking student. Admiring the young man's boldness, Andrzej gives him a lift and asks him to come along on the cruise. Throughout the weekend, Andrzej parades his possessions and baits the youth, who has never sailed before, mocking his clumsiness. It is apparent to Andrzej that the young man is attracted to Christine though he tries not to show it. Subsequently, a fight is started over the young man's pocket knife. The stranger is knocked overboard and vanishes. Christine and Andrzej become frightened for his safety when they remember that he cannot swim. Believing the boy drowned, Andrzej strikes out for shore to get help; and as soon as he has left the young man appears at the yacht cold and wet. Christine, angry but relieved, comforts him, and in a moment of abandon they make love. Christine drops the boy ashore and goes to find Andrzej, who has not yet reported the incident to the police. She informs him that the stranger is safe and well, but Andrzej believes she is merely trying to calm him. Then she tells him that she made love with the young man, and Andrzej must choose between his own guilt and his wife's unfaithfulness. *Egotists. Strangers. Sportswriters. Hitchhikers. Infidelity. Swimming. Guilt. Seduction. Yachts.*

Note: Released in Poland in 1962 as *Nóż w wodzie.*

KNIGHTS OF THE BLACK CROSS *see* **THE KNIGHTS OF THE TEUTONIC ORDER**

THE KNIGHTS OF THE TEUTONIC ORDER (Poland) F6.2644

Studio Film Unit. *For* Film Polski. *Dist* Amerpol Enterprise Films. Jan **1962**. Sd; col (Eastman Color). 35mm (CinemaScope). 180 min. [Also reviewed at 170 min.]

Dir Aleksander Ford. *Screenplay* Jerzy Stefan Stawiński, Aleksander Ford. *Dial* Leon Kruczkowski. *Dir Photog* Mieczysław Jahoda. *Art Dir* Roman Mann. *Film Ed* Mirosława Garlicka, Alina Faflik. *Mus* Kazimierz Serocki. *Mus Cond* Jan Krenz. *Sd Rec* Leszek Wronko, Leonard Ksiezak. *Asst Dir* Zbigniew Kuzminski, Karol Chodura, Ryszard Rydzewski. *Prod Mgr* Zygmunt Krol.

Cast: Urszula Modrzyńska *(Jagienka)*, Grażyna Staniszewska *(Danusia)*, Andrzej Szalawski *(Jurand)*, Henryk Borowski *(Siegfried de Lowe)*, Aleksander Fogiel *(Macko)*, Mieczysław Kalenik *(Zbyszko)*, Emil Karewicz *(King Jagiello)*, Tadeusz Kosudarski *(Brother Rotgier)*, Lucyna Winnicka *(Duchess of Mazovia)*, Tadeusz Białoszczyński *(Duke of Mazovia)*, Mieczysław Voit *(Kuno von Lichtenstein)*, Janusz Strachocki *(Grand Master Konrad)*, Stanisław Jasiukiewicz *(Grand Master Ulrich)*, Leon Niemczyk *(Fulko de Lorche)*, Zbigniew Skowroński *(Tolime)*, Mieczysław Stoor *(Hlawa)*, Włodzimierz Skoczylas *(Sanderus)*, Seweryn Butrym *(Count Wende)*.

Historical melodrama. Source: Henryk Sienkiewicz, *Krzyżacy* in *Tygodnik Ilustrowany* (1897–1900). In the early 15th century, the Teutonic Knights of Germany invade Poland under the guise of converting the pagan population to Christianity. As vindication for Jurand's successful defense against the invaders, the Teutons kill his wife. Shortly thereafter, Jurand's only daughter, Danusia, visits the court of Mazovia, where Zbyszko, a young member of the duchess's entourage, swears to avenge the death of Danusia's mother. When Zbyszko assaults a Teutonic emissary, the Polish king is forced to sentence him to death; in accordance with custom, however, Danusia covers Zbyszko's head with her veil at the last minute, and he is saved. Zbyszko and Danusia become engaged, but she is kidnaped by the Teutonic Knights, and Jurand is seized at the Szczytno castle, where he is tortured. After the Grand Master of the Teutonic Knights dies, his successor declares war on Poland and her other allies, including Russia and Lithuania. Meanwhile, Zbyszko conducts an extensive search for Danusia, but when at last he finds her, she has lost her sanity and dies a short time later. At the Battle of Grünwald in 1410, the Teutonic Knights' eastward expansion is finally thwarted in a major defeat, and Zbyszko returns home to Jagienka, his childhood girl friend who is now in love with him. *Teutons. Nobility. Germans. Knighthood. Christianity. Murder. Revenge. Abduction. Torture. Insanity. Military invasion. Middle Ages. Grünwald. Poland—Army.*

Note: Released in Poland in Sep 1960 as *Krzyżacy*. Also known as *Knights of the Black Cross*. Filmed in Dyaliscope.

KNIVES OF THE AVENGER (Italy) F6.2645

Sider Film. *Dist* World Entertainment Corp. 23 Oct **1968** [Boston opening]. Sd; col (Technicolor). 35mm (Techniscope). 86 min.

Prod P. Tagliaferri. *Dir* John Hold. *Screenplay* Alberto Liberati, George Simonelli, Mario Bava. *Photog* Antonio Rinaldi. *Film Ed* Othello. *Mus* Marcello Giombini. *Sd* Peter Danielson. *Asst Dir* Robert Glands.

Cast: Cameron Mitchell *(Rurik)*, Fausto Tozzi *(Aghen)*, Luciano Polletin *(Moki)*, Elisa Mitchell *(Karen)*, Jack Stewart, British *(Harald)*, Mike Moore, Renato Terra, Sergio Cortona.

Adventure melodrama. When Viking chief Harald fails to return home after 3 years at sea, his wife, Karen, consults a soothsayer. Although assured that her husband will return, Karen is warned that there are dark days ahead for the Mocar tribe—a prophecy that is fulfilled when the exiled warrior Aghen amasses a band of marauders in the hope of seizing Harald's throne. Planning to make himself the legitimate king by forcing Karen to marry him, Aghen sends two of his men to abduct her. She is rescued by a stranger from a nearby village who is careful not to reveal that his name is Rurik. Years before, after his wife and son had been beheaded by Aghen, Rurik's hatred for the Mocar people had driven him to assault Karen after her wedding. Though still determined to have revenge on Aghen, Rurik is anxious to atone for his own brutal act. Following a duel between Rurik and Aghen, from which the latter flees, Harald returns. Recognizing the man who raped his wife, Harald engages Rurik in combat, but their fighting is interrupted when it is learned that Harald's son Moki has been kidnaped by Aghen. Now united, the two men go to the child's aid, and Rurik finally slays his enemy. His vengeance complete, Rurik leaves the village. *Vikings. Royalty. Missing persons. Seers. Abduction. Decapitation. Revenge. Rape. Kidnaping. Duels.*

Note: Released in Italy in 1967 as *I coltelli del vendicatore*; also known as *Raffica di coltelli*. John Hold is a pseudonym for Mario Bava, Othello for Otello Colangeli, Elisa Mitchell for Elissa Picelli, and Jack Stewart for Giacomo Rossi Stuart.

KNOCKERS UP   F6.2646
Dist Seymour Borde & Associates. 7 Nov **1963** [San Francisco showing]. Sd; col. 35mm. 62 min.
Prod-Dir A. J. Gaylord.
Cast: Sandra Montez *(Millie the office girl)*, Sidney Saks *(Mr. Winkler)*, Althea Currier.
Comedy. Mr. Winkler, a voyeur, takes a Hindu potion that makes him invisible, and he has an office romance with his co-worker, Millie. *Voyeurism. Invisibility. Potions.*

KNOCKOUT   F6.2647
Turn of the Century Fights, Inc. *Dist* Trans-Lux Distributing Corp. 27 Oct **1965** [New York opening]. Sd; b&w. 35mm. 50 min. [Also 42 min.]
Prod-Dir William Cayton. *Asst Prod* Jim Jacobs.
Narrator: Kevin Kennedy.
Compilation film. A film record of 19 championship boxing bouts featuring the fighters listed below. *Prizefighting. Max Baer. Primo Carnera. Jack Dempsey. Luis Firpo. Sugar Ray Robinson. Jake La Motta. Max Schmeling. Joe Louis. Percy Bassett. Serraphim Ferrer. Archie Moore. Yvon Durelle. Cassius Clay. Allen Hudson. Rocky Marciano. Rex Layne. Jack Johnson. Stanley Ketchel. Floyd Patterson. Ingemar Johansson. Jean Stock. Jess Willard. Tony Zale. Rocky Graziano. Benny Leonard. Lew Tendler. Marcel Cerdan. Gene Tunney. Tom Gibbons.*
Note: This film and its sequel, *Knockout #2*, q. v., were combined to make a 110-min feature in 1969.

KNOCKOUT #2   F6.2648
Turn of the Century Fights, Inc. *Dist* Trans-Lux Distributing Corp. 2 Sep **1966** [New York opening]. Sd; b&w. 35mm. 50 min.
Prod-Dir William Cayton. *Assoc Prod* Jim Jacobs.
Narrator: Kevin Kennedy.
Compilation film. A cavalcade of 25 championship boxing bouts, beginning with Johnson's knockout of Jeffries in 1910. Other fights feature the boxers listed below. *Prizefighting. Jack Johnson. James J. Jeffries. Joe Louis. Lee Ramage. Mickey Walker. Tommy Milligan. Jake La Motta. Laurent Dauthuille. Sugar Ray Robinson. Hans Stretz. Rocky Graziano. Tony Janiro. Rocky Marciano. Rex Layne. Lee Savold. Marcel Cerdan. Dick Turpin. Sonny Liston. Wayne Bethea. Pat Valentino. Floyd Patterson. Tommy "Hurricane" Jackson. Sandy Saddler. Flash Elorde. Buddy Baer. Gene Stanton. Randy Turpin. Billy Brown. Roy Harris. Tommy Burns. Gunner Moir. Joe Becerra. Alphonse Halimi. Gus Lesnevich. Freddie Mills. Jean Stock. Primo Carnera. Vittorio Campolo. Jack Sharkey. Phil Scott. Tommy Farr. Jan Klein. Giovanni Manca. Gene Tunney. Jack Dempsey.*
Note: This film is a sequel to *Knockout*, q. v. A combined 110-min version of the two films was released in 1969.

KODAK GHOST POEMS—PART 1: THE ADVENTURES OF THE EXQUISITE CORPSE   F6.2649
Dist Film-Makers' Distribution Center, Film-Makers' Cooperative. 29 May **1968** [New York opening]. Si; col. 16mm. 50 min.
Dir Andrew Noren. *Photog* Andrew Noren.
Film diary. Composed of short segments, 1–2 1/2 minutes in length, the film spans a period of years in the life of the filmmaker. Some segments record events and occurrences in the filmmaker's daily life; others are non-representational renderings of emotions or ideas. *Filmmakers.*
Note: *Kodak Ghost Poems—Part II*, which consists of additional diary footage, was shown in New York in Oct 1971; running time: ca45 min.

KOGDA DEREVYA BYLI BOLSHIMI *see* **WHEN THE TREES WERE TALL**

KOHAYAGAWA-KE NO AKI *see* **EARLY AUTUMN**

KOJIRO (Japan)   F6.2650
Toho Co. Aug **1967** [Los Angeles showing]. Sd; col (Eastman Color). 35mm (Tohoscope). 152 min.
Assoc Prod Ken-ichiro Tsunoda. *Dir* Hiroshi Inagaki. *Screenplay* Yoshio Shirasaka, Kenro Matsuura, Hiroshi Inagaki. *Story* Genzo Murakami. *Photog* Takao Saito. *Art Dir* Hiroshi Ueda. *Mus* Goichi Sakaide.
Cast: Kikunosuke Onoe *(Kojiro Sasaki)*, Yoko Tsukasa *(Okinawa Princess)*, Mayumi Ozora *(geisha girl)*, Tatsuya Nakadai *(Musashi Miyamoto)*, Kenjiro Ishiyama *(Lord Tomita)*, Jotaro Togami *(pirate Nachimaru)*, Keiko Sawai *(kabuki dancer)*, Tatsuya Mihashi *(Jubei Minamiya)*, Yuriko Hoshi *(Tone)*, Isamu Nagato *(Shimabei)*, Yoshio Tsuchiya *(Kojiro's ancient enemy)*.
Biographical melodrama. Kojiro Sasaki, the adopted son of a medieval lord, is an ambitious young man of peasant lineage who is determined to become the most famous swordsman in Japan despite the feudal tradition which reserves such honors for born noblemen. After earning the enmity of the samurai because of his skill, he realizes that he must prove his prowess in combat. He

sets out, taking with him his foster sister. After involving himself in a feud between the Toyotomi and the Tokugawa clans, Kojiro builds a formidable reputation by cutting down many worthy opponents. Kojiro's love conquests, including the Okinawa Princess, are almost as numerous as his conquests by sword. Showered with gifts from rich men and with favors from beautiful women, Kojiro is on the threshold of achieving his lifelong dream. Only Musashi Miyamoto, the nation's legendary samurai hero, stands in his way. When Kojiro faces the invincible warrior, Kojiro is tragically defeated. *Samurai. Foster sisters. Royalty. Ambition. Feudalism. Ancestry. Fame. Kojiro Sasaki. Musashi Miyamoto.*
Note: Released in Japan in 1967 as *Sasaki Kojiro*; 165 min.

KOKKINA PHANARIA *see* **RED LANTERNS**

KOKOSEI BANCHO *see* **WAY OUT, WAY IN**

KOL MAMZER MELECH *see* **EVERY BASTARD A KING**

KOLYBELNAYA *see* **LULLABY**

KOM I MIN SÄNG *see* **TO INGRID MY LOVE, LISA**

KOMM, LIEBE MAID UND MACHE *see* **THE BRAZEN WOMEN OF BALZAC**

KOMMANDO SINAI *see* **SINAI COMMANDOS**

KOMPOZITOR SERGEY PROKOFYEV *see* **INSIDE THE U.S.S.R.**

KONA COAST   F6.2651
Pioneer Productions. *Dist* Warner Bros.–Seven Arts, Inc. May **1968** [c1 May 1968; LP36529]. Sd; col (Technicolor). 35mm. 93 min.
Prod-Dir Lamont Johnson. *Exec Prod* Richard Boone. *Screenplay* Gil Ralston. *Dir Photog* Joseph LaShelle. *Titl Dsgn* MGM Title Dept. *Film Ed* Alec McCombie. *Asst Film Ed* Richard Rabjohn. *Mus* Jack Marshall. *Sd Mix* Burdick S. Trask. *Asst Dir* Michael Glick. *Prod Mgr* William R. Finnegan. *Script Supv* Carla Coray. *Makeup* Anthony Lloyd. *Tech Adv* Jim Abernathy. *Still Photog* Bert Six. *Stunt Dir* Erwin Neal.
Cast: Richard Boone *(Sam Moran)*, Vera Miles *(Melissa Hyde)*, Joan Blondell *(Kittibelle Lightfoot)*, Chips Rafferty *(Lightfoot)*, Steve Ihnat *(Kryder)*, Kent Smith *(Akamai)*, Sam Kapu, Jr. *(Kimo)*, Gina Villines *(Mim Lowry)*, Duane Eddy *(Tigercat)*, Scott Thomas *(Tate Packer)*, Erwin Neal *(Junior Packer)*, Doris Erickson *(Doris)*, Gloria Nakea *(Dee)*, Lucky Luck *(Kunewa)*, Kaai Hayes *(butler)*, Thomas Mark *(Macklin)*, Red Kanuha *(bartender)*, Sue Paishon *(Sue)*.
Crew of Alika: Dina Kunewa *(Dina)*, Earl Perry *(Earl)*, Pocho Kanuha *(Pocho)*, Willie Erickson *(Willie)*.
Melodrama. Source: John D. MacDonald, "Kona Coast" (short story; publication undetermined). Capt. Sam Moran, skipper of a Honolulu fishing boat, receives an urgent phone call for help from his teenaged halfcaste daughter, Dee, but she is found dead on the beach before he can reach her. Sam begins making inquiries in an attempt to track down the murderer. As a result, he is beaten by the henchmen of Kryder, the playboy who introduced Dee to narcotics and then had her killed. Kryder's men burn Sam's boat, thus causing Sam's good friend Charlie Lightfoot to be severely burned while trying to save it. Sam takes the dying Lightfoot back to his Kona home and agrees to help provide additional income for his friend's sister, Kittibelle, by training her nephew Tigercat to operate Lightfoot's boat. Kittibelle needs the money to support a run-down resort she operates for the rehabilitation of alcoholics. Among Kittibelle's reformed drinkers is Melissa Hyde, an ex-marine biologist who once was Sam's girl friend. Kryder orders a big luau prepared at Kittibelle's resort and makes plans to kill Sam at the party. Meanwhile, Sam forces one of Kryder's henchmen to confess his boss's part in Dee's murder. He then pursues Kryder and his thugs at the luau and eventually shoots Kryder in the shoulder with a harpoon gun. The police arrest Kryder and his men, and Sam and Melissa decide to make a fresh start together. *Sea captains. Playboys. Hoodlums. Halfcastes. Alcoholism. Arson. Murder. Friendship. Health resorts. Luaus. Narcotics. Fishing boats. Hawaii.*
Note: Filmed on location in Hawaii.

KONEC SRPNA V HOTELU OZON *see* **THE END OF AUGUST AT THE HOTEL OZONE**

KONETS STAROY BERYOZOVKI *see* **APARTMENT IN MOSCOW**

KONGA (Great Britain)   F6.2652
Merton Park Studios. *Dist* American International Pictures. 22 Mar **1961** [Boston opening; c27 Jan 1961; LP21144]. Sd (Westrex); col (Eastman Color). 35mm (SpectaMation). 90 min.
A Herman Cohen Production. *Prod* Herman Cohen. *Assoc Prod* Jim O'Connolly. *Dir* John Lemont. *Orig Story & Screenplay* Aben Kandel, Herman Cohen. *Dir Photog* Desmond Dickinson. *Camera Op* Harry Gillam. *Art Dir*

Wilfred Arnold. *Film Ed* Jack Slade. *Mus Comp* Gerard Schürmann. *Mus Cond* Muir Mathieson. *Sd* Sidney Rider, Ronald Abbott. *Sd Eff Ed* Derek Holding. *Asst Dir* Buddy Booth. *Prod Mgr* Bill Shore. *Cont* Olga Brook. *Wardrobe* Bridget Sellers. *Makeup* Jack Craig. *Hairdresser* Daphne Vollmer.

Cast: Michael Gough (*Dr. Charles Decker*), Margo Johns (*Margaret*), Jess Conrad (*Bob Kenton*), Claire Gordon (*Sandra Banks*), Austin Trevor (*Dean Foster*), Jack Watson (*Superintendent Brown*), George Pastell (*Professor Tagore*), Vanda Godsell (*Bob's mother*), Stanley Morgan (*Inspector Lawson*), Grace Arnold (*Miss Barnesdell*), Leonard Sachs (*Bob's father*), Nicholas Bennett (*Daniel*), Kim Tracy (*Mary*), Rupert Osborne (*Eric*), Waveney Lee (*Janet*), John Welsh (*Commissioner Garland*), Sam Sylvano (*Konga, as a chimpanzee*).

Science fiction melodrama. After a year in the Ugandan jungle, botany professor Charles Decker returns to England with a revolutionary growth serum and a small chimpanzee named Konga. Decker and his assistant, Margaret, begin injecting Konga with the serum, and he grows. When the university dean reproves Decker for discussing his discovery with the press, Decker, now mad with power, hypnotizes Konga and commands him to kill the dean. In a similar fashion, Decker also disposes of a rival botanist, Professor Tagore, and Bob Kenton, the boyfriend of a pretty student, Sandra, with whom Decker has fallen in love. Eventually Margaret learns of Decker's interest in the young girl, and in a fit of jealousy she gives Konga an overdose of the serum. Konga grows to an overwhelming size, starts a fire, hurls Margaret into the flames, causes Sandra to stumble into the tentacles of a carnivorous plant, and scoops up Decker in his massive hand. Confused, baffled, and still clutching Decker, Konga staggers through the London streets, terrifying the populace. Armed troops corner the beast and bombard him with rockets and machine-gun fire. In pain and bewilderment, Konga hurls Decker at the crowd, crashes to the pavement, and shrinks to his original size as he dies. *Professors. Botanists. Deans. Students. Mental illness. Jealousy. Murder. Hypnotism. Jungles. Serums. Carnivorous plants. Uganda. London. Fires. Chimpanzees.*

Note: Released in London in Mar 1961. Copyright claimant: Alta Vista Productions.

KONKURS *see* **AUDITION**

KOŇSKÁ OPERA *see* **LEMONADE JOE**

KORT ÄR SOMMAREN *see* **SHORT IS THE SUMMER**

KOSHOKU ICHIDAI ONNA *see* **LIFE OF OHARU**

KOT I MYSZ *see* **CAT AND MOUSE**

KOTO *see* **TWIN SISTERS OF KYOTO**

KOTO NO TAIYO *see* **NO GREATER LOVE THAN THIS**

THE KOUMIKO MYSTERY (France)   **F6.2653**
Sofracima-Apec-Joudioux Films-O. R. T. F. *Dist* New Yorker Films. 6 Apr **1967** [New York opening]. Sd; col and b&w. 35mm (see note). 47 min.

Dir-Writ Chris Marker. *Mr. Marker's Asst* Koichi Yamada. *Photog* Chris Marker. *Film Ed* Chris Marker. *Mus* Toru Takemitsu.

Cast: Koumiko Muraoka (*Koumiko*).

Documentary. Koumiko, a young, French-educated, Manchurian-born Japanese, visits the 1964 Tokyo Olympics and other parts of Tokyo as she discusses her city, her country, and the Orient in general. She then responds to some questions asked by the film's director about her life expectations, the state of the world, and the possibility of lasting peace. *Japanese. Olympic Games. Tokyo. Japan.*

Note: Filmed in Tokyo during the 1964 Olympic Games as *Le mystère Koumiko*. Shot in 16mm.

KRADETSÜT NA PRASKOVI *see* **THE PEACH THIEF**

KRAKATOA, EAST OF JAVA   **F6.2654**
Security Pictures. *Dist* Cinerama Releasing Corp. 14 May **1969** [Los Angeles opening; c26 Dec 1968; LP38109]. Sd; col (Technicolor). 35mm & 70mm (see note). 148 min. [See note.] *MPAA rating* G.

Pres by American Broadcasting Companies, Cinerama Inc. *Prod* William R. Forman. *Co-prod* Lester A. Sansom. *Dir* Bernard L. Kowalski. *2d Unit Dir* Frank Kowalski. *Screenplay* Clifford Newton Gould, Bernard Gordon. *Dir Photog* Manuel Berenguer. *Underwater Photog* Egil S. Woxholt. *Camera Op* Eduardo Noé. *Asst Camera* Luis Peña, José Manuel Martínez. *2d Unit Camera Op* José Mateos, John Cabrera. *Asst Dir* Julio Molina, Luis Pérez Espinosa. *Set Decor* Antonio Mateos. *Prod Dsgn* Eugene Lourié. *Titl & Montage* Don Record, Pacific Title. *Film Ed* Maurice Rootes, Warren Low, Walter Hannemann. *Mus* Frank De Vol. *Songs:* "East of Java," "A Nice Old Fashioned Girl" Mack David. *Sd* Wally Milner, Gordon K. McCallum. *Asst Dir* José María Ochoa. *Prod Supv* Gregorio Sacristan. *Prod Mgr* José Manuel M. Herrero. *Cost* Laure de Zarate. *Wardrobe Master* Charles Simminger.

Makeup Julian Ruiz. *Hairdressing* Antonia López. *Sp Eff Dir* Eugene Lourié. *Sp Eff* Alex Weldon. *Still Photog* Antonio Luengo. *Prop Master* Julian Mateos. *Casting Dir* Lillian Kelly. *Ch Grip* Julian Fernandez. *Gaffer* Vicente Acitores.

Cast: Maximilian Schell (*Capt. Chris Hanson*), Diane Baker (*Laura Travis*), Brian Keith (*Connerly*), Barbara Werle (*Charley*), John Leyton (*Douglas Rigby*), Rossano Brazzi (*Giovanni Borghese*), Sal Mineo (*Leoncavallo Borghese*), J. D. Cannon (*Danzig*), Jacqui Chan (*Toshi*), Marc Lawrence (*Jacobs*), Geoffrey Holder (*Bazooki man*), Sumi Hari, Victoria Young, Midorri Arimoto (*Japanese divers*), Niall MacGinnis (*Henley*), Alan Hoskins (*Jan*), Robert Hall (*guard*), Peter Kowalski (*Peter*), Joseph Hann (*Kuan*).

Adventure melodrama. In 1883 the *Batavia Queen* leaves Singapore harbor. Her destination is the coast of volcanic island Krakatoa, where a ship laden with pearls has sunk. Among her passengers are Laura, widow of the lost ship's captain; Rigby, a claustrophobic diving bell pilot; the Borgheses, father and son balloonists; and Toshi, the leader of a team of Japanese diving girls. Also aboard are 30 prisoners, including the convict Danzig, who is given freedom of the deck. As the ship approaches Krakatoa, catastrophes occur in rapid succession, including accidents and natural disasters. Caught while aloft in the updraft of Krakatoa, the Borgheses save themselves by diving into the sea. Led by Danzig, the mutinous prisoners briefly control the ship. Captain Hanson retaliates by killing the convict and setting his fellows adrift in lifeboats. Upon recovering the sunken ship's safe, all are shocked to discover it empty, save for a log. Although Laura placates the passengers by assuring them that the diary specifies the treasure's location, she later reveals that she is searching for her son, left by her husband at a Catholic mission. When the *Batavia Queen* rescues the mission's staff from a sampan, the boy is among those saved. Presented by her son with the coveted pearls, Laura begins division of the treasure. However, Krakatoa erupts, causing a massive tidal wave. To escape certain destruction the ship takes to the open seas. *Sea captains. Widows. Japanese. Convicts. Balloonists. Divers. Diving. Sea rescue. Mutiny. Treasure. Safes. Volcanoes. Tidal waves. Pearls. Singapore. Krakatoa. Explosions.*

Note: Location scenes filmed in Majorca and Denia, Spain. The film was also reviewed at 127, 135 and 143 min; copyright length: 131 min. Presented in Cinerama for some roadshow presentations.

KRALJ PETROLEJA *see* **RAMPAGE AT APACHE WELLS**

THE KREMLIN LETTER   **F6.2655**
Twentieth Century-Fox Film Corp. 1 Feb **1970** [New York opening: c30 Dec 1969; LP37643]. Sd (Westrex); col (DeLuxe). 35mm (Panavision). 116 min. *MPAA rating* GP.

A John Huston-Carter De Haven, III Production. *Prod* Carter De Haven, III, Sam Wiesenthal. *Dir* John Huston. *Screenplay* John Huston, Gladys Hill. *Dir Photog* Ted Scaife. *Camera Op* Dudley Lovell. *Art Dir* Elven Webb. *Asst Art Dir* Boris Juraga. *Set Decor* Dario Simone. *Scenic Artist* Fred Tuch. *Prod Dsgn* Ted Haworth. *Film Ed* Russell Lloyd. *Mus & Mus Dir* Robert Drasnin. *Mus Comp & Cond* Toshiro Mayuzumi. *Sd Ed* Leslie Hodgson. *Sd Rec* Basil Fenton-Smith, Renato Cadueri. *Asst Dir* Gus Agosti, Carlo Cotti. *Prod Mgr* David Anderson. *Script Supv* Lucie Lichtig. *Cost Dsgn* John Furness. *Makeup Supv* George Frost. *Makeup* Amato Barbini. *Sp Eff* Augie Lohman. *Prop* Charles Torbett. *Casting Dir* Robert Lennard.

Cast: Bibi Andersson (*Erika*), Richard Boone (*Ward*), Nigel Green (*Janis*), Dean Jagger (*The Highwayman*), Lila Kedrova (*Sophie*), Michael MacLiammoir (*Sweet Alice*), Patrick O'Neal (*Rone*), Barbara Parkins (*B. A.*), Ronald Radd (*Potkin*), George Sanders (*The Warlock*), Raf Vallone (*Puppet Maker*), Max von Sydow (*Kosnov*), Orson Welles (*Bresnavitch*), Sandor Eles (*Grodin*), Niall MacGinnis (*Erector Set*), Anthony Chinn (*Kitai*), Guy Deghy (*Professor*), John Huston (*Admiral*), Fulvia Ketoff (*Sonia*), Vonetta McGee (*Negress*), Marc Lawrence (*priest*), Cyril Shaps (*police doctor*), Christopher Sandford (*Rudolph*), Hana-Maria Pravda (*Mrs. Kazar*), George Pravda (*Kazar*), Ludmilla Dudarova (*Mrs. Potkin*), Dimitri Tamarov (*Ilya*), Pehr-Olof Sirén (*receptionist*), Daniel Smid (*waiter*), Victor Beaumont (*dentist*), Stephen Zacharias (*Dittomachine*), Laura Forin (*Elena*), Saara Rannin (*Mikhail's mother*), Rune Sandlunds (*Mikhail*), Sacha Carafa (*Mrs. Grodin*).

Drama. Source: Noel Behn, *The Kremlin Letter* (New York, 1966). An American intelligence officer signs an agreement with the Soviet Union stating that both countries will attack China, and the U. S. government hastily assembles a group of espionage agents to recover the unauthorized treaty called the "Kremlin Letter." The team, under the leadership of The Highwayman, consists of Rone, a retired U. S. Navy officer; B. A., a safecracker's daughter who replaces her ailing father on the mission; Janis, a small-time pimp from a Mexican brothel; The Warlock, a transvestite found in a San Francisco gay bar; and Ward, The Highwayman's top assistant. In New York, the Americans have a lesbian seduce the daughter of U. S.-based Russian spy Potkin in order to blackmail him into turning over his Moscow apartment as a base for their operations. In Moscow, they bug the residence of Secret Police Chief Kosnov, who is married to Erika, the widow of an enemy spy; Kosnov is currently engaged in a power struggle with political leader Aleksei Bresnavitch. Meanwhile, B. A., who has become Rone's lover, is captured by Bresnavitch. When Ward temporarily leaves the country, Potkin confesses to Bresnavitch what has happened. Bresnavitch has another problem, however: Rone has discovered that he (Bresnavitch) is a traitor and that the Kremlin Letter is in Peking. Ward is also revealed to be a traitor, working for Bresnavitch. Upon his return, Ward kills Erika, who had devised a plan to sneak Rone out of Russia, and at the airport, he also murders Kosnov, an old friend who had doublecrossed him several years before. By now Rone is ready to retire, but Ward will release B. A. only if Rone will return to the United States for one more mission—to murder Potkin's wife and daughter. *Intelligence agents. Pimps. Americans in foreign countries. Spies. Traitors. Cold war. Espionage. Transvestism. Lesbianism. Seduction. Blackmail. Kidnaping. Murder. Revenge. Treaties. Electronic surveillance. San Francisco. Mexico. Union of Soviet Socialist Republics. People's Republic of China. Moscow. Union of Soviet Socialist Republics—Intelligence service.*

Note: Location scenes filmed in Rome, Mexico, New York, and Finland.

KRIEGSGERICHT *see* **COURT MARTIAL**

KRIGET ÄR SLUT *see* **LA GUERRE EST FINIE**

KRIGETS ANSIKTE *see* **THE FACE OF WAR**

KRIGETS VANVETT *see* **THE FACE OF WAR**

KRIGSFÖRBRYTARE *see* **SECRETS OF THE NAZI CRIMINALS**

KRIVI PUT *see* **THE CROOKED ROAD**

KRZYŻACY *see* **THE KNIGHTS OF THE TEUTONIC ORDER**

KUMONOSUJO *see* **THRONE OF BLOOD**

KUNGSLEDEN *see* **OBSESSION**

KUNISADA CHUJI *see* **THE GAMBLING SAMURAI**

KURAGEJIMA—LEGENDS FROM A SOUTHERN ISLAND (Japan)
                                                            F6.2656
Nikkatsu Corp. *Dist* Toho Co. 22 Jul **1970** [Los Angeles opening]. Sd; col. 35mm. 150 min. *MPAA rating* GP.

Prod Masanori Yamanoi. *Dir-Story* Shohei Imamura. *Screenplay* Shohei Imamura, Keiji Hasebe. *Photog* Masao Tochizawa. *Mus* Toshiro Mayuzumi.

Cast: Rentaro Mikuni *(brother)*, Hideko Okiyama *(retarded sister)*, Kanjuro Arashi *(patriarch)*, Yasuko Matsui *(sister)*, Kazuo Kitamura *(engineer)*, Jun Hamamura, Yoshi Kato, Choichiro Kawarazaki, Hosei Lomatsu, Taiji Tonoyama, Chikako Hosokawa, Chikage Ogi.

Domestic drama. The Futori family lives a primitive existence on Kuragejima, an island in the Pacific Ocean. The patriarch of the family, who believes that incest is permissible for the ruling family of the island, is both the father and grandfather to his late daughter's son; the son also is carrying on an incestuous relationship with one of his sisters; and another of his sisters is a retarded woman with nyphomaniac tendencies. When an engineer arrives on the island to map plans for a sugar refinery, he is seduced by the retarded sister and soon forgets his civilized past. In the end, the brother and sister are condemned for their incestuous love, and the brother is forced to dig a pit that is large enough to bury a huge stone that was washed ashore by a tidal wave. *Engineers. Incest. Filial relations. Brother-sister relationship. Nymphomania. Mental retardation. Seduction. Islands.*

Note: Released in Japan in 1968 as *Kamigami no fukaki yokubo.* Also known as *Deep Desire of Gods.*

KUREIZI OGON SAKUSEN *see* **LAS VEGAS FREE–FOR–ALL**

KUROBARA NO YAKATA *see* **BLACK ROSE**

KUROBE NO TAIYO *see* **TUNNEL TO THE SUN**

KURONEKO (Japan)   **F6.2657**
Kindai Eiga Kyokai–Nippon Eiga Shinsha. *Dist* Toho International, Inc. Jul **1968** [Los Angeles showing]. Sd; b&w. 35mm (Tohoscope). 99 min.

Prod Nichiei Shinsha. *Exec Prod* Nobuyo Horiba, Setsuo Noto, Kazuo Kuwahara. *Dir-Writ* Kaneto Shindo. *Photog* Kiyomi Kuroda. *Lighting* Shoichi Tabata. *Art Dir* Takashi Marumo. *Film Ed* Hisao Enoki. *Mus* Hikaru Hayashi. *Sd Rec* Tetsuo Ohashi. *Makeup* Shigeo Kobayashi.

Cast: Kichiemon Nakamura *(Gintoki)*, Nobuko Otowa *(mother)*, Kiwako Taichi *(daughter-in-law)*, Kei Sato *(Raiko)*, Taiji Tonoyama *(a farmer)*, Rokko Toura *(a samurai)*, Hideo Kanze *(mikado)*.

Horror film. In 12th-century Japan a woman and her 20-year-old daughter-in-law are raped and then slain by a band of samurai. Their hut is burned, and their blood attracts a black cat. Later the leader of the samurai band returns to the area and is mauled to death by a seductive woman who resembles his victim.

Another samurai band, led by Raiko, comes to the area. Gintoki, the husband of the murdered young woman and the son of the older woman, is a member of this band, and Raiko orders him to get rid of the ghosts who have been preying on the samurai. Gintoki meets the spirit of his dead wife, and she takes him back to a hut where he also sees the spirit of his dead mother. The two women vanish, but the next day the young woman returns to her husband; despite her vow to murder the samurai, she and her husband make love and remain together for 7 days. She is banished from the spirits of hell, however, in return for her husband's life. Raiko again orders Gintoki to destroy the apparitions, and the next time he encounters his mother, Gintoki severs her arm. That night, the mother returns for the arm, and the next morning Gintoki lies dead as a black cat licks his wounds. *Samurai. Ghosts. Rape. Murder. Revenge. Filial relations. Mutilation. Cats.*

Note: Released in Japan in Feb 1968 as *Yabu no naka no kuroneko.* Also known as *The Black Cat.*

KUROTOKAGE *see* **BLACK LIZARD**

KÜSSE, DIE TÖTEN *see* **KISS THE DEAD**

KUU ON VAARALLINEN *see* **PRELUDE TO ECSTASY**

KVARTERET KORPEN *see* **RAVEN'S END**

KVINNORS VÄNTAN *see* **SECRETS OF WOMEN**

KWAHERI   **F6.2658**
Afromerica Film Corp. *Dist* Unusual Films International. 9 Dec **1964** [Phoenix, Arizona, opening]. Sd; col (Eastmancolor). 35mm. 80 min.

Exec Prod David Chudnow. *Co-Prod* Thor Brooks. *Story* Michael Vittes. *Photog* Miki Carter. *Asst Camera* Peg Carter. *Film Ed* Thor Brooks. *Mus Score* Byron Ross. *Mus Supv* Lloyd Young. *Sd Eff* Gerald Wilson, sd. *Snake Handler* Alan Tarlton. *Member of Crew* Bill Daniel.

Cast: Les Tremayne *(narrator)*.

Documentary. A documentary on Africa from a sensational point of view: The large sums of money to be gained in hunting wild animals encourage Africans to engage in poaching, thereby endangering many species. Elephants are slaughtered for their tusks, rhinoceros for their horns, and antelope for meat. Hunters with another purpose undertake the dangerous mission of trapping wild animals for shipment to zoos. Others hunt poisonous snakes, which are "milked" for the manufacture of antivenin. Meanwhile, tribesmen driven further into the interior preserve ancient ways of life. Members of one tribe drink a mixture of cow's blood, urine, and ashes. A man is photographed with his 49 wives and 212 children. Pygmies, resisting the encroachments of technology, perform joyful songs and dances. On a remote island, witch doctors perform trephination without the use of antiseptic procedures or anesthetics and achieve a 96% success record. Another tribe holds an annual fertility rite in which the most beautiful female child to reach puberty is burned alive as a sacrifice. The ceremony is performed under the influence of bang, a narcotic derived from cannabis. *Pygmies. Witch doctors. Hunting. Primitive life. Polygamy. Rites and ceremonies. Human sacrifice. Poaching. Jungles. Marijuana. Big game. Trephination. Africa. Elephants. Rhinoceros. Antelope. Snakes.*

Note: Working titles: *The Witch Doctor and the Virgin* and *Vanishing Africa.*

KWAIDAN (Japan)   **F6.2659**
Bungei Production–Ninjin Club. *For* Toho Co. *Dist* Continental Distributing, Inc. 15 Jul **1965** [Los Angeles opening]. Sd; col (Eastman Color). 35mm (Tohoscope). 125 min. [See note.]

Exec Prod Shigeru Wakatsuki. *Dir* Masaki Kobayashi. *Screenplay* Yoko Mizuki. *Photog* Yoshio Miyajima. *Art Dir* Shigemasa Toda. *Mus* Toru Takemitsu. *Sd* Hideo Nishizaki.

Cast—"Black Hair": Rentaro Mikuni *(samurai)*, Michiyo Aratama *(1st wife)*, Misako Watanabe *(2d wife)*.

Cast—"The Woman of the Snow" [see note]: Keiko Kishi *(The Woman)*, Tatsuya Nakadai *(Minokichi)*, Mariko Okada.

Cast—"Hoichi, the Earless": Katsuo Nakamura *(Hoichi)*, Rentaro Mikuni *(samurai)*, Ganjiro Nakamura *(head priest)*, Takashi Shimura *(priest)*, Joichi Hayashi *(Yoshitsune)*, Tetsuro Tamba.

Cast—"In a Cup of Tea": Ganemon Nakamura *(Kannai)*, Noboru Nakaya *(Heinai)*.

Fantasy. Source: Lafcadio Hearn, "The Reconciliation," in *Shadowings* (Boston, 1900). Lafcadio Hearn, "Yuki-onna" and "The Story of Mimi-nashi-Hoichi," in *Kwaidan* (Boston, 1904). Lafcadio Hearn, "In a Cup of Tea," in *Kotto* (New York, 1902). BLACK HAIR: An impoverished samurai of Kyoto divorces his loving wife to marry the daughter of a wealthy governor. After years of tolerating the hard and selfish woman, he returns to his long neglected first wife; the next morning, he discovers that he has slept with a corpse and goes mad. THE WOMAN OF THE SNOW: Caught in a blizzard, two woodcutters seek refuge in a deserted hut. A strange woman enters the shed and kills Mosaku with her cold breath; she allows the young apprentice, Minokichi to live, as long as he tells no one what has occurred. Several years later, after marrying the beautiful O-Yuki, he relates the experience to his wife, who reveals herself to be the snow-woman. She leaves him but spares his life so that he may care for their children. HOICHI, THE EARLESS: Hoichi, a blind biwa player who works at a temple in Akamageseki, is famed for his knowledge of the ballad of the Heike clan, which was defeated in a sea battle by the Genji in 1185. One night a samurai spirit beckons Hoichi to sing before his slain infant lord at the Heike tombs. Assuming Hoichi is bewitched, Buddhist priests protect him by painting his body with scenes of the holy text, but they forget to cover his ears. Returning to find the spell on Hoichi broken, the samurai ghost cuts off the musician's ears; after recovering from his injuries, Hoichi becomes rich reciting the story of his strange adventure. IN A CUP OF TEA: Kannai, a fearless samurai, sees another warrior's face reflected in his teacup. The vision reappears in a second cup, but Kannai destroys it by drinking the tea. On guard duty that night, he meets the identical figure from the cup and thrusts his sword at him, but the intruder vanishes. The following night three samurai arrive to avenge their wounded master, Heinai, but they also vanish when attacked by Kannai. *Samurai. Woodsmen. Ghosts. Musicians. Priests. Visions. Poverty. Divorce. Insanity. Murder. Blindness. Witchcraft. Disfiguration. Revenge. Corpses. Myths. Tombs. Kyoto. Akamageseki. Blizzards.*

Note: Released in Japan in 1964 as *Kaidan*; running time: 164 min. Original segment titles: *Kurokami* (Black Hair), *Yuki-onna* (The Woman of the Snow), *Mimi-nashi-Hoichi* (Hoichi, the Earless), and *Chawan no naka* (In a Cup of Tea). Second episode was deleted from U. S. release after the Los Angeles opening.

KYOMO WARE OZORANI ARI see **TIGER FLIGHT**

KYONETSU NO KISETSU see **THE WEIRD LOVE MAKERS**

KYUBI NO KITSUNE TO TOBIMARU see **THE FOX WITH NINE TAILS**

THE L-SHAPED ROOM (Great Britain)   F6.2660
Romulus Films. *Dist* Davis-Royal Films International, Columbia Pictures. 27 May **1963** [New York opening; c31 Dec 1963; LP27120]. Sd (Westrex); b&w. 35mm. 124 min. [Copyright length: 142 min.]

Prod James Woolf, Richard Attenborough. *Assoc Prod* Jack Rix. *Dir-Writ* Bryan Forbes. *Photog* Douglas Slocombe. *Camera Op* Chic Waterson. *Camera Asst* Robin Vidgeon. *Camera Grip* Ray Jones. *Art Dir* Ray Simm. *Asst Art Dir* Martin Atkinson. *Set Dresser* Peter James. *Draughtsman* John Siddall, George Lack, Ted Ambrose. *Scenic Artist* Basil Mannin. *Film Ed* Anthony Harvey. *1st Asst Ed* Nicholas Faith. *2d Asst Ed* Eunice Mountjoy. *Mus Cond* Muir Mathieson. *Played by* Sinfonia of London. *Jazz Seq Comp* John Barry. *Piano Concerto no. 1* Johannes Brahms. *Played by* Peter Katin. *Sd Rec* George Stephenson, Red Law. *Dub Ed* Terry Rawlings. *Boom Op* Jack W. Davies. *Sd Camera Op* Ernie Webb. *1st, 2d & 3d Asst Dir* Gerry O'Hara, John Quested, Grania O'Shannon. *Cont* Penny Daniels. *Prod Sec* Ann Skinner. *Dress Dsgn* Beatrice Dawson. *Wardrobe Mistress* Laurel Staffell, May Walding. *Wardrobe Master* Ben Foster. *Makeup* Harry Frampton. *Hairdresser* Barbara Ritchie. *Casting* Jenia Reissar. *Still Photog* Laurie Ridley. *Prop* John Feehan, John Hemmington. *Prop Buyer* Percy Godbold. *Ch Electrn* Jackie Sullivan.

Cast: Leslie Caron (*Jane*), Anthony Booth (*youth in street*), Avis Bunnage (*Doris*), Patricia Phoenix (*Sonia*), Verity Edmett (*Jane II*), Tom Bell (*Toby*), Cicely Courtneidge (*Mavis*), Harry Locke (*news agent*), Ellen Dryden (*girl in news agent's*), Emlyn Williams (*Dr. Weaver*), Jenny White (*Monica*), Brock Peters (*Johnny*), Gerry Duggan (*Bert*), Joan Ingram (*woman in park*), Mark Eden (*Terry*), Stanley Morgan (*waiter in club*), Gerald Sim (*doctor in hospital*), Pamela Sholto, Ruth Burns, Diane Clare (*nurses*), Arthur White (*milkman*), Bernard Lee (*Charlie*), Nanette Newman (*girl at end*), Kay Walsh (*prostitute*).

Drama. Source: Lynne Reid Banks, *The L-Shaped Room* (London, 1960). Jane Fosset, a 27-year-old Frenchwoman, leaves her provincial home, moves to London, and spends a loveless weekend with an unemployed actor. She later discovers that she is pregnant, and she moves into a squalid L-shaped room in a Notting Hill boardinghouse and arranges to have an abortion. After one interview with a mercenary Harley Street "gynecologist," she decides to have the child. While staying at the boardinghouse, she becomes involved with a fellow lodger named Toby, an unsuccessful writer. Their affair delights most of the other tenants who have befriended her—prostitutes and actresses—but angers Toby's friend Johnny, a Negro jazz musician living in the room next to Jane's. Johnny has learned of Jane's pregnancy, and after listening to the sounds of lovemaking coming through the paper-thin walls, he tells Toby of Jane's condition. Outraged, Toby leaves, and Jane, in a moment of despair, tries to kill her baby by taking some pills given to her by Mavis, the elderly actress who

lives downstairs. But the abortion attempt fails, and Jane accepts with relief the fact that her baby will live. Although Toby returns, he is incapable of accepting a child that he has not fathered. He visits Jane when the baby is born and presents her with a copy of his first finished story, "The L-Shaped Room." After leaving the hospital to return to France, Jane leaves the story in Toby's room. A note is attached: "Darling Toby, it's a lovely story, but it hasn't got an ending. It would be marvelous with an ending." *French. Authors. Actors. Prostitutes. Negroes. Musicians. Pregnancy. Illegitimacy. Abortion. Jealousy. Boardinghouses. London—Notting Hill.*

Note: Released in Great Britain in 1962; running time: 142 min.

LABBRA ROSSE see **RED LIPS**

THE LABYRINTH OF SEX see **SESSO**

LES LACHES VIVENT D'ESPOIR see **MY BABY IS BLACK!**

LAD: A DOG   F6.2661
Vanguard Productions. *Dist* Warner Bros. Pictures. 6 Jun **1962** [Kansas City, Missouri, opening; c27 Dec 1961; LP27099]. Sd; col (Technicolor). 35mm. 98 min. [Later cut to 79 min.]

Prod Max J. Rosenberg. *Assoc Prod* Roberta Hodes. *Dir* Aram Avakian, Leslie H. Martinson. *Screenplay* Lillie Hayward, Roberta Hodes. *Photog* Bert Glennon. *Art Dir* Jack Poplin. *Set Decor* William L. Kuehl. *Film Ed* Tom McAdoo. *Mus* Heinz Roemheld. *Sd* Sid Ryan. *Asst Dir* Claude Binyon, Jr. *Script Supv* Jules Miliman. *Wardrobe* Geoffrey Alan, Ruth Hancock. *Makeup* Gordon Bau. *Hairstyles* Jean Burt Reilly. *Still Photog* Jack Woods, still photog.

Cast: Peter Breck (*Stephen Tremayne*), Peggy McCay (*Elizabeth Tremayne*), Carroll O'Connor (*Hamilcar Q. Glure*), Angela Cartwright (*Angela*), Maurice Dallimore (*Lester*), Alice Pearce (*Hilda*), Jack Daly (*The Poacher*), Charles Fredericks (*sheriff*), Tim Graham (*constable*), Lillian Buyeff (*Miss Woodward*), Lad (*himself, a dog*).

Drama. Source: Albert Payson Terhune, *Lad: A Dog* (New York, 1919). Lad is a prize-winning collie belonging to author Stephen Tremayne and his wife, Elizabeth. Jealous of the animal's fame, a wealthy neighbor, Glure, offers the use of his estate for the Hampton Dog Show and then sets up special rules to assure victory for his own English-trained collie. Glure's champion fails to complete the trials, however, and Lad wins the gold trophy. A short time later, the collie saves Glure's 8-year-old crippled daughter, Angela, from a poisonous snake. Hilda, the child's nurse, misinterprets Lad's knocking Angela over and starts beating him with her parasol. Shocked by seeing the dog unjustly punished, Angela stops the beating. Lad, bitten by the snake in the fight, slinks off into the woods. Three days later he returns after having buried himself in mud to draw the snake poison from his body. To continue the pedigree, Lady, a prize collie, is brought to the Tremaynes and the dogs are mated. Then one afternoon a vengeful poacher sets fire to the Tremayne barn. Elizabeth is hurt, and one of Lady's puppies, which has been promised to Angela, is killed. Elizabeth eventually recovers, Lad captures the poacher, and Angela is persuaded that the remaining puppy is just as lovable as the one she lost. *Authors. Children. Neighbors. Cripples. Nursemaids. Poachers. Jealousy. Revenge. Incendiarism. Pet shows. Dogs. Snakes.*

THE LADIES' MAN   F6.2662
Jerry Lewis Productions-York Pictures. *Dist* Paramount Pictures. 28 Jun **1961** [Brooklyn, New York, opening; c30 May 1961; LP19709]. Sd; col (Technicolor). 35mm. 106 min.

Prod-Dir-Screenplay Jerry Lewis. *Assoc Prod* Ernest D. Glucksman. *Adtl Material* Bill Richmond. *Cinematog* W. Wallace Kelley. *Art Dir* Hal Pereira. *Unit Art Dir* Ross Bellah. *Set Decor* Sam Comer, James Payne. *Film Ed* Stanley Johnson. *Mus* Walter Scharf. *Mus Scored & Cond* Bobby Van. *Songs* Harry Warren, Jack Brooks. *Song:* "Bang Tail" Harry James. *Played by* Harry James and His Band. *Dances Staged by* Bobby Van. *Sd* Charles Grenzbach. *Asst Dir* C. C. Coleman, Jr., Ralph Axness. *Unit Prod Mgr* William C. Davidson. *Cost* Edith Head. *Makeup* Wally Westmore. *Hairstyles* Nellie Manley. *Sp Photog Eff* John P. Fulton.

Cast: Jerry Lewis (*Herbert H. Heebert*), Helen Traubel (*Helen Welenmelon*), Pat Stanley (*Fay*), Kathleen Freeman (*Katie*), George Raft (*himself*), Harry James (*himself*), Marty Ingels (*Marty*), Buddy Lester (*Buddy*), Gloria Jean (*Gloria*), Hope Holiday (*Miss Anxious*), Jack La Lanne (*himself*), Westbrook Van Voorhis (*himself*), Sylvia Lewis (*Sylvia*), Eddie Quillan, Roscoe Ates, Jack Kruschen, Alex Gerry, Doodles Weaver, Dee Arlen, Francesca Bellini, Vicki Benet, Patricia Blair, Lillian Briggs, Bonnie Evans, Jacqueline Fontaine, Marianne Gaba, Gretchen Houser, Karyn Kupcinet, Paula Lane, Mary LaRoche, Shary Layne, Mary LeBow, Ann McCrea, Daria Massey, Fay Nuell, Madlyn Rhue, Caroline Richter, Sheila Rogers, Nancy Root, Lynn Ross, Joan Staley, Kay Tapscott, Patty Thomas, Gloria Tracey, Meri Welles, Beverly Wills.

Comedy. Herbert H. Heebert's student girl friend rejects him, and he becomes an avowed woman-hater and leaves town. Arriving in California, he takes a job as a houseboy at a large boarding hotel owned by ex-opera star Helen Welenmelon. He learns that the house is populated by 31 careerwomen and tries to quit, but Miss Welenmelon persuades him to stay on. Though most of the women think him cute but stupid, Fay, an aspiring actress, takes a genuine interest in him and helps him overcome his girl-shyness. After wrecking a television interview set up for Miss Welenmelon, Herbert gets into more trouble with some of the boarders' dates, including George Raft. On Miss Welenmelon's birthday Herbert and the women give her a surprise party, and Herbert impresses one and all with his impersonations of Chaplin, Jolson, and Groucho Marx. Just as he begins to enjoy his job, Herbert is led to believe that everyone is being nice to him only because houseboys are hard to come by. As he prepares to leave, however, the boarders persuade him that they really are fond of him. Elated, he happily drops his suitcases, hugs Fay, and decides to remain with Miss Welenmelon and all the wonderful ladies. *Houseboys. Misogynists. Singers. Actors. Careerwomen. Timidity. Impersonation. Boardinghouses. Television. California. Charles Chaplin. Al Jolson. Groucho Marx.*

LADIES OF THE MOB *see* **HOUSE OF WOMEN**

LADIES OF THE PARK *see* **LES DAMES DU BOIS DE BOULOGNE**

LADIES WHO DO (Great Britain)   F6.2663
Fanfare Films Ltd. *For* Bryanston Films. *Dist* Continental Distributing, Inc. 25 Nov 1963 [New York opening]. Sd; b&w. 35mm. 85 min.
  Prod George H. Brown. *Assoc Prod* Jan Darnley-Smith. *Dir* C. M. Pennington-Richards. *Screenplay* Michael Pertwee. *Orig Idea* John Bignell. *Photog* Geoffrey Faithfull. *Camera Op* Gerry Turpin. *Follow Focus* George Pink. *Camera Grip* Ted Tucker. *Art Dir* Harry White. *Asst Art Dir* John Siddall. *Draughtsman* David Minty. *Scenic Artist* Ben Healey. *Film Ed* Oswald Hafenrichter. *Asst Ed* David Gillard, Pepita Fairfax. *Mus Comp & Cond* Ron Goodwin. *Sd* Stephen Dalby. *Sd Mix* Leonard Bulkley. *Sd Camera Op* Dave Goghan. *Boom Op* Fred Tomlin. *Dub Ed* Alban Streeter. *1st, 2d & 3d Asst Dir* Tom Pevsner, Edward Dorian, Michael Gowans. *Prod Mgr* Sydney Streeter. *Cont* Betty Harley. *Wardrobe* Harry Haynes, Tina Swanson. *Makeup* Eddie Knight. *Hairdresser* Pat McDermott. *Casting Dir* Irene Howard. *Still Photog* John Hardman. *Prod Buyer* Roma Aplin. *Constr Mgr* Sid Payne. *Electrn* L. McKellar.
  Cast: Peggy Mount *(Mrs. Cragg)*, Robert Morley *(Colonel Whitforth)*, Harry H. Corbett *(James Ryder)*, Miriam Karlin *(Mrs. Higgins)*, Avril Elgar *(Emily Parish)*, Dandy Nichols *(Mrs. Merryweather)*, Jon Pertwee *(Mr. Tait)*, Nigel Davenport *(Mr. Strang)*, Graham Stark *(foreman)*, Ron Moody *(inspector)*, Cardew Robinson *(police driver)*, John Laurie *(Dr. MacGregor)*, Arthur Howard *(Ryder's chauffeur)*, Margaret Boyd *(Mrs. Parish)*, Joan Benham *(Miss Pensent)*, Brian Rawlinson *(compressor driver)*, Harry Fowler *(driller)*, Ed Devereaux *(Mr. Gubbins)*, Marianne Stone *(Mrs. Gubbins)*, Carol White *(Sandra)*.
  Comedy. While cleaning the London offices of real estate speculator James Ryder, Mrs. Cragg, a charwoman, finds an unsmoked cigar in the wastebasket. She wraps it in a discarded telegram and brings it home to Pitt Street to Colonel Whitforth, an out-of-luck gambler for whom she also works. He uses the valuable information in the telegram and makes a £5,000 profit on the stock exchange. Doubting his honesty, Mrs. Cragg is about to give her half of the money to Mr. Ryder when she overhears his plans to raze Pitt Street and build luxury offices there. Consequently, under the guidance of the colonel, she and three other charwomen form their own company. Though one of their numerous financial schemes almost ruins them, the ladies bring an end to the Pitt Street demolition. Forced to capitulate, Ryder is taken in as a partner, and flats are to be built instead of offices. *Charwomen. Gamblers. Businessmen. Businesswomen. Business ethics. Housing. Land speculation. Stock market. London.*
  Note: Released in Great Britain in 1963.

IL LADRO DI BAGDAD *see* **THE THIEF OF BAGHDAD**

DIE LADY *see* **GAMES OF DESIRE**

THE LADY DOCTOR (France/Italy/Spain)   F6.2664
Gallus Films–Galliera Films–Les Films Fernand Rivers–S. G. G. C.–Jolly Film–Fénix. *Dist* Governor Films. 16 Jan 1963 [New York opening]. Sd; b&w. 35mm. 103 min.
  Prod Dario Sabatello. *Dir* Camillo Mastrocinque. *Spanish Co-dir* Ana Mariscal. *Screenplay* Vittorio Metz, Marcello Marchesi, Dario Sabatello, Roberto Gianviti. *Photog* Gabor Pogany, Adalberto Albertini, Alvaro Mancori, Manuel Berenguer. *Film Ed* Roberto Cinquini, Juan Pisón. *Mus* Carlo Innocenzi. *Sd* G. Mancori. *Prod Mgr* José María Rodríguez, Franco Ferino.

  Cast: Totò *(Mike Spillone)*, Vittorio De Sica *(Marquis De Vitti)*, Abbe Lane *(Dr. Brigitte Baker)*, Darry Cowl *(a patient)*, Pierre Mondy, Teddy Reno, Germán Cobos, Agostino Salvietti, Titina De Filippo, Fulvia Franco, Tecla Scarano.
  Comedy. Lawyer Otello Bellomo meets Brigitte Baker, a Boston physician, at a medical conference in Madrid. They immediately fall in love, marry, and return to his home in Naples. There, Otello tries to please his two aunts, Ada and Ida, who have made him their sole heir, and he persuades Brigitte not to reveal her profession. Her strange hours cause the suspicious aunts to hire detective Mike Spillone to follow her, and he later reports that she has been visited by the Marquis Di Vitti. After numerous visits by him and other men, Ada and Ida finally learn the truth, and Brigitte remains beyond reproach. She adds to the family's happiness by announcing that she is pregnant. *Lawyers. Physicians. Americans in foreign countries. Aunts. Heirs. Detectives. Marriage. Personal identity. Pregnancy. Conferences—International. Madrid. Naples.*
  Note: Filmed in Spain and Italy. Opened in Rome in Dec 1957 as *Totò, Vittorio e la dottoressa*; running time: 94 min; in Madrid in Apr 1958 as *Mi mujer es doctor*; in Paris in Jul 1958 as *Dites 33*; running time: 90 min.

THE LADY GENERAL (Hong Kong)   F6.2665
Shaw Brothers (H. K.) Ltd. *Dist* Frank Lee International. 11 Feb 1965 [New York opening]. Sd; col. 35mm. 106 min.
  Prod Run Run Shaw. *Dir* Yueh Feng. *Screenplay* Ke Jui-feng.
  Cast: Ivy Ling Po *(Hua Mu-lan)*, Chin Han *(Li Kuang)*, Chen Yen Yen *(Elder Mrs. Hua)*, Yang Chi-ching *(Hua Hu)*, Chu Mu *(Hua Ming)*, Wang Lan *(Jua Mu-hui)*, Li Kun *(Chen Wei-han)*, Chiang Kuang-chao *(Chang Teh-sheng)*, Ching Miao *(Marshal Ho)*, Feng I *(Wang Kuei)*, Ho Ping *(tribal king)*, Chao Ming *(Wu Hsin-cheng)*.
  Drama with music. Hua Mu-lan, a spinning girl, has dreams of becoming a soldier, but her father forbids it, even when he is called up to fight in a war and she offers to go in his place. Her cousin helps disguise her as a young man, and they go to war together. She distinguishes herself in combat and falls in love with her tentmate Li Kuang. After the Turks are defeated with the help of Hua Mu-lan's plan, Hua Mu-lan asks to go home, as she has been wounded in the climactic battle. Later Li Kuang visits his wartime friend's family and is surprised to learn that his former tentmate is a woman. Though he must return to the army he promises to come back one day and marry her. *Weavers. Cousins. Soldiers. Turks. Male impersonation. Combat zone life.*
  Note: Shown in Hong Kong as *Hua Mu-lan*.

LADY GODIVA RIDES   F6.2666
Z. S. A. Productions–Monarex. *Dist* SCA Distributors, Crest Film Distributors. 19 Mar 1969 [Champaign, Illinois, showing]. Sd; col. 35mm (Astravision). 105 min.
  Prod-Dir A. C. Stephen. *Photog* Robert Ruben. *Mus (see note)* Peter Weiner, Jay Colonna, Robert E. Lee.
  Cast: Marsha Jordan *(Lady Godiva)*, Forman Shane *(Tom Jones)*, Deborah Downey, Elizabeth Knowles, James E. Myers, Jannie Jackson, Liz Rene, Vincent Barbi, Mary Bauer, Johnny Ellis.
  Comedy-drama. Source: A. C. Stephen, *Lady Godiva and Tom Jones* (publication undetermined). Tom Jones is discovered in Lady Godiva's bedchamber by Lord Brotherton, who attempts to kill his wife's lover and is himself accidentally shot by Her Ladyship. Condemned to death for attempted murder and adultery, Lady Godiva seduces a prison guard and escapes with the help of Tom Jones, who smuggles her onto a ship bound for San Francisco with a cargo of English maidens. A lesbian madam from London supervises the women, who have been deceived into thinking that they are to become wives for wealthy Americans. The chaperon selects five of them, including Lady Godiva, to work as "entertainers" at a saloon in Goldstone, a wild frontier mining town. Life aboard takes a hectic turn; as they cross the equator, a party for King Neptune degenerates into an orgy. When the ship docks, Lady Godiva and four other women take the stagecoach to the Goldstone Hotel, and there Kirby, the manager, reveals the true reason for their journey. Lady Godiva objects and a fist fight ensues as her identity is revealed to the chaperon. Kirby decides to keep the Lady for himself, and he is prevented from raping her by the timely arrival of Tom Jones, who informs his lover that her husband has exonerated her from all blame. The next day, there is a showdown between Tom and Kirby. Lady Godiva rides naked down the main street, distracting Kirby long enough for Tom to fire. The happy lovers prepare to return to England. *Nobility. Prostitutes. Chaperons. Sailors. English. Infidelity. Capital punishment. Seduction. Fraud. Shanghaiing. Lesbianism. Nudity. Rape. Orgies. Ships. San Francisco. London. Godiva. Tom Jones.*
  Note: Sources conflict in assigning music credit; several sources credit Weiner; one source credits Colonna and Lee. Also known as *Lady Godiva*, *Lady Godiva Reigns*, and *Lady Godiva (Loves on Two Continents)*.

LADY IN A CAGE   F6.2667

American Entertainment Corp. *Dist* Paramount Pictures. 27 May **1964** [Chicago opening; c31 Dec 1963; LP28525]. Sd; b&w. 35mm. 93 min. [Also reviewed at 100 min.]

A Luther Davis Production. *Prod-Writ* Luther Davis. *Dir* Walter Grauman. *Dir Photog* Lee Garmes. *Camera Op* Ed Garvin. *Asst Camera* Hugh Crawford. *Art Dir* Hal Pereira. *Set Decor* Joseph Kish, Sam Comer. *Prod Dsgn* Rudolph Sternad. *Titl* Tri-Arts. *Film Ed* Leon Barsha. *Mus Comp & Cond* Paul Glass. *Sd* Frank McWhorter, John Wilkinson. *Sd Rec* Al Cuesta. *Boom* Bob Simpson, sd. *Asst Dir* Howard Alston, Henry E. Brill. *Prod Mgr* Andrew J. Durkus. *Script Supv* Kay Thackary. *Wardrobe* Kathleen McCandless. *Makeup* Wally Westmore, Gene Hibbs. *Hairstyles* Jane Shugrue. *Sp Photog Eff* Paul K. Lerpae. *Still Photog* Ted Allan. *Prop* Everett Israelson, Vernon Baine. *Grip* Charles Sickler, Glenn Maschmeyer. *Gaffer* Wilbur Kinnett, Adolph Frolich, Lon Massey.

Cast: Olivia De Havilland *(Mrs. Hilyard)*, Ann Sothern *(Sade)*, Jeff Corey *(The Wino)*, James Caan *(Randall)*, Jennifer Billingsley *(Elaine)*, Rafael Campos *(Essie)*, William Swan *(Malcolm Hilyard)*, Charles Seel *(junkyard proprietor)*, Scatman Crothers *(proprietor's assistant)*.

Melodrama. Mrs. Hilyard, a wealthy widow recuperating from a broken hip, becomes trapped between floors in the cage-like elevator she has installed in her mansion. With her son Malcolm away for a summer weekend, she relies on an emergency alarm to attract attention, but the only response comes from an alcoholic derelict who ignores her pleas and steals some small items. The wino sells them to a fence, then visits his prostitute friend, Sade, attracting the attention of three young hoodlums, Randall, Elaine, and Bessie. The trio follows them back to the mansion, where they conduct an orgy, killing the wino and locking Sade in a closet. Randall then pulls himself up to the elevator and taunts Mrs. Hilyard with a note left by Malcolm threatening suicide because of her domineering manner. Shocked by the revelation, Mrs. Hilyard struggles with Randall, gouges out his eyes, and escapes to the street. The blinded assailant follows her and is run over by a passing automobile, whereupon police arrive to arrest the surviving intruders and comfort the victim. *Widows. Invalids. Prostitutes. Hoodlums. Fences (for stolen goods). Wealth. Sadism. Alcoholism. Robbery. Murder. Blindness. Motherhood. Elevators. Orgies. Automobile accidents.*

LADY IN CEMENT   F6.2668

Arcola-Millfield Productions. *Dist* Twentieth Century-Fox Film Corp. 20 Nov **1968** [New York opening; c6 Nov 1968; LP36449]. Sd (Westrex); col (DeLuxe). 35mm (Panavision). 93 min. *MPAA rating* R.

Prod Aaron Rosenberg. *Dir* Gordon Douglas. *Underwater Seq Staged by* Ricou Browning. *Screenplay* Marvin H. Albert, Jack Guss. *Dir Photog* Joseph Biroc. *Art Dir* Leroy Deane. *Set Decor* Walter M. Scott, Jerry Wunderlich. *Film Ed* Robert Simpson. *Mus Comp & Cond* Hugo Montenegro. *Orch* Billy May. *Sd* Howard Warren, David Dockendorf. *Asst Dir* Richard Lang. *Unit Prod Mgr* David Silver. *Asst to the Prod* Michael Romanoff. *Cost Dsgn* Moss Mabry. *Makeup* Dan Striepeke. *Mr. Sinatra's Makeup* Layne Britton. *Hairstyles* Edith Lindon. *Sp Photog Eff* L. B. Abbott, Art Cruickshank.

Cast: Frank Sinatra *(Tony Rome)*, Raquel Welch *(Kit Forrest)*, Richard Conte *(Lieutenant Santini)*, Martin Gabel *(Al Mungar)*, Lainie Kazan *(Maria Baretto)*, Pat Henry *(Rubin)*, Dan Blocker *(Gronsky)*, Steve Peck *(Paul Mungar)*, Virginia Wood *(Audrey)*, Richard Deacon *(Arnie Sherwin)*, Frank Raiter *(Danny Yale)*, Peter Hock *(Frenchy)*, Alex Stevens *(Shev)*, Christine Todd *(Sandra Lomax)*, Mac Robbins *(Sidney, the organizer)*, Tommy Uhlar *(The Kid, Tighe Santini)*, Ray Baumel *(Paco)*, Pauly Dash *(McComb)*, Andy Jarrell *(The Pool Boy)*, Joe E. Lewis *(himself)*.

Crime melodrama. Source: Anthony Rome, *Lady in Cement* (New York, 1960). While diving for sunken treasure off the Miami coast, private investigator Tony Rome discovers the nude corpse of a blonde whose feet have been encased in cement. Following an autopsy, which reveals that the woman was murdered with a knife, a huge ex-convict, Gronsky, hires Tony to find out if the blonde is his missing girl friend, go-go dancer Sandra Lomax. Sandra's roommate, Maria Baretto, informs Tony that Sandra was last seen at a party given by heiress Kit Forrest, but Kit, an alcoholic, claims that she was too drunk at the party to remember anything. Kit's neighbor, ex-Mafia chief Al Mungar, warns Tony to leave Kit alone. Soon afterwards, Maria is murdered, and two of Mungar's hoods make an attempt on Gronsky's life. Unperturbed, Tony continues with his sleuthing. A sketch drawn by artist Arnie Sherwin proves that the dead woman is indeed Sandra, and Tony eventually learns that Kit and Sandra clashed over Mungar's son, Paul. Maria's homosexual boss, Danny Yale, is also found murdered, and the evidence indicates that Tony is the killer. Escaping from his old friendly enemy, Police Lieutenant Santini, Tony takes refuge in Kit's home. When Kit confesses that she awoke after her party and found a paperknife in her hand and Sandra's dead body at her feet, Tony suspects that Kit may also be the victim of a frameup. After forcing Gronsky

to admit that he and Paul were partners in stealing some of the senior Mungar's robbery proceeds, Tony realizes that Paul killed Sandra to get the money Gronsky had given her. Knowing that Kit's life is now in danger, Tony and Gronsky race to the Mungar residence and save her from being knifed by Paul. With the case resolved, Tony calls in Lieutenant Santini and leaves with Kit to search for sunken treasure. *Detectives. Ex-convicts. Heiresses. Go-go dancers. Roommates. Neighbors. Hoodlums. Police. Artists. Diving. Murder. Alcoholism. Frameup. Robbery. Male homosexuality. Filial relations. Corpses. Miami. Mafia.*

Note: Filmed on location in Miami. This film is a sequel to *Tony Rome.* q.v.

THE LADY IN THE CAR WITH GLASSES AND A GUN (United States/France)   F6.2669

Lira Films–Columbia Films. *Dist* Columbia Pictures. 25 Dec **1970** [New York opening; c1 Dec 1970; LP39042]. Sd; col (Eastman Color). 35mm (Panavision). 105 min. *MPAA rating* R.

An Anatole Litvak Production. *Prod* Raymond Danon, Anatole Litvak. *Dir* Anatole Litvak. *Screenplay* Richard Harris, writ, Eleanor Perry. *Dir Photog* Claude Renoir. *Camera* Philippe Brun. *Asst Camera* Roger Tellier, René Chabal. *Art Dir* Willy Holt. *Asst Art Dir* Gérard Viard, Georges Richard. *Main Titl* Jean Fouchet. *Film Ed* Peter Thornton. *Asst Film Ed* Geneviève Billo. *Mus Comp & Cond* Michel Legrand. *Song:* "On the Road" Michel Legrand, Hal Shaper. *Sung by* Petula Clark. *Sd Ed* Barry McCormick. *Sd Rec* William Sivel. *Asst Dir* Francis Pernet, Richard Overstreet, Bernard Stora. *Prod Mgr* Marc Maurette, Claude Ganz. *Unit Mgr* René Fargeas. *Cont* Alice Ziller. *Dresses for Miss Eggar and Miss Audran* Christian Dior. *Dsgn by* Marc Bohan. *Wardrobe* Jean Zay. *Makeup* Michel Deruelle. *Hairdresser* Simone Knapp. *Casting* Margot Capelier. *Dial Coach* Frawley Becker.

Cast: Samantha Eggar *(Dany Lang)*, Oliver Reed *(Michael Caldwell)*, John McEnery *(Philippe)*, Stéphane Audran *(Anita Caldwell)*, Billie Dixon *(secretary)*, Philippe Nicaud *(highway policeman)*, Marcel Bozzufi *(Manuel)*, Jacques Fabbri *(doctor)*, Yves Pignot *(Baptistin)*, Jacques Legras *(policeman)*, Maria Mériko *(Madame Pacaud)*, André Oumansky *(Bernard Thorr)*, Martine Kelly *(Kiki)*, Robert Déac *(boy in cassis)*, Monique Mélinand *(barmaid)*, Claude Vernier *(psychiatrist)*, Lisa Jouvet, Fred Fisher *(Danish tourists)*, Raoul Delfosse, Louise Rioton *(American tourists)*, Jacqueline Porel *(2d secretary)*, Paule Noelle *(3d secretary)*, Henry Czarniak *(garage proprietor)*, Edmond Ardisson *(garage night man)*, Gilberte Géniat *(village storekeeper)*, Roger Lumont *(hotel clerk)*.

Melodrama. Source: Sébastien Japrisot, *La dame dans l'auto avec des lunettes et un fusil* (Paris, 1966). On the eve of the long Bastille Day weekend Dany Lang, a secretary at a Paris advertising agency, is asked by her supervisor, Michael Caldwell, to type something that he must take with him on a trip to Geneva. Accompanying him on the trip will be his wife, Anita, an ex-roommate of Dany's who in the past has used the secretary's apartment for adulterous affairs. Later Michael gives Dany a pay envelope and asks her to drive them in his car to the airport. On the way back to Paris Dany is caught in traffic and impulsively decides to drive to the Riviera for the weekend. Dany stops at a small cafe and is perplexed when the proprietress tries to return a coat she claims Dany left there the previous day. Her hand is injured when she is attacked in a service station rest room, and she is disturbed when strangers claim to have seen her recently. She drives on, stopping to pick up a hitchhiker, Philippe. They sleep together that night, and she confides that she fears a recent abortion has left her susceptible to memory loss. The next day Philippe steals the car just before they reach the coast, and when Dany tracks him down in Marseilles, they discover a corpse in the trunk of the car. Philippe absconds once again, whereupon Dany goes to the dead man's house in Avignon, only to find there some of her clothes and some large nude photographs of herself. She then returns to the cafe to claim the coat and finds a duplicate of her pay envelope in one of the pockets. Now totally bewildered, she goes back to the dead man's home and finds Michael waiting for her. He explains that the dead man was one of Anita's lovers, whom she murdered at his home. Michael and Anita then planted evidence to establish Dany's guilt: the house where she did the typing was actually the victim's other home; the assailant in the rest room was Michael, who deliberately injured her hand so that Anita, wearing sunglasses identical to Dany's and a bandage on her own hand, could be easily mistaken for the secretary; and Anita, using a concealed camera, had taken the nude photographs as a lark when they were roommates. Michael tells Dany he plans to kill her and make it look like suicide, but she explains that his plot is doomed to fail, for she has mailed both pay envelopes, one of which Michael had planned to destroy, to the police. *Secretaries. Advertising executives. Roommates. Hitchhikers. Infidelity. Murder. Frameup. Mistaken identity. Amnesia. Impersonation. Theft. Photographs. Automobiles. Corpses. Paris. Marseilles. Riviera. Avignon. Bastille Day.*

Note: Location scenes filmed in France. Opened in Paris in Oct 1970 as *La dame dans l'auto avec des lunettes et un fusil*; running time: 110 min.

LADY IN THE MORGUE *see* **CORPSE IN THE MORGUE**

THE LADY KILLER OF ROME (France/Italy)   **F6.2670**
Titanus–Vides–S. G. C. *Dist* Manson Distributing Corp. Aug **1965**. Sd; b&w. 35mm. 83 min.
Pres by Topaz Film Corp. *Prod* Franco Cristaldi. *Dir* Elio Petri. *Screenplay* Elio Petri, Tonino Guerra, Pasquale Festa Campanile, Massimo Franciosa. *Photog* Carlo Di Palma. *Art Dir* Renzo Vespignani. *Set Dsgn* Carlo Egidi. *Film Ed* Ruggero Mastroianni. *Mus* Piero Piccioni.
Cast: Marcello Mastroianni *(Nello Poletti)*, Micheline Presle *(Adalgisa de Matteis)*, Cristina Gajoni *(Antonella)*, Salvo Randone *(Commissioner Palumbo)*, Andrea Checchi *(Morello)*, Mac Ronay *(suicide victim)*, Max Cartier *(Adalgisa's friend)*, Giovanna Gagliardo *(Rosa)*, Enrico Maria Salerno, Bruno Scipioni, Franco Ressel, Toni Ucci, Paolo Panelli, Corrado Zingaro.
Drama. Nello Poletti has attained the ultimate of life's pleasures: a thriving antique business, fast cars, expensive clothes, and freedom from restrictions and obligations. One day, however, his former mistress Adalgisa is found murdered, and the police learn that she had established him in business and threatened to ruin him when he discarded her for the younger Antonella. Moreover, evidence given by his neighbors and friends, particularly Osvaldo Perfetti, appears to implicate him, and even the press brands him a murderer. Only Antonella maintains her belief in him. In prison Nello has time to reflect on the petty schemes and dishonesties that he has perpetrated in order to have a comfortable life. Disgusted with himself, he decides falsely to confess to the crime, but the police have already discovered that Osvaldo, rejected by Adalgisa, killed her in a fit of rage. Nello's misgivings about his behavior disappear, and he resumes his former life of pleasure, calling himself "l'assassino." *Antique dealers. Mistresses. Police. Murder. Jealousy. Circumstantial evidence. Confession (law). Rome.*
Note: Released in Rome in Apr 1961 as *L'assassino*; running time: 105 min; in France as *L'assassin*.

LADY L (United States/France/Italy)   **F6.2671**
C. C. Champion–Les Films Concordia–Metro-Goldwyn-Mayer, Inc. *Dist* Metro-Goldwyn-Mayer, Inc. 18 May **1966** [New York opening; c31 Dec 1965; LP32306]. Sd (Westrex); col (Eastman Color). 35mm (Panavision). 124 min. [Copyright length: 108 min.]
Prod Carlo Ponti. *Dir-Writ* Peter Ustinov. *Dir Photog* Henri Alekan. *Camera* Raymond Picon-Borel. *Set Dsgn* Jean d' Eaubonne, Auguste Capelier. *Set Dresser* Maurice Barnathan. *Film Ed* Roger Dwyre. *Mus Comp* Jean Françaix. *Sd Engr* William Sivel. *Asst Dir* Paul Feyder. *Prod Mgr* Pierre Laurent. *Unit Mgr* René Fargeas. *Cont Girl* Lucie Lichtig. *Cost Dsgn* Marcel Escoffier, Jacqueline Guyot. *Sp Makeup* William Tuttle. *Makeup Artist* Michel Deruelle, Giuseppe Annunziata. *Hairstyles* Alex Archambault, Amalia Paoletti. *Sp Eff* Karl Baumgartner. *Casting Dir* Margot Capelier.
Cast: Sophia Loren *(Lady L)*, Paul Newman *(Armand)*, David Niven *(Lord Lendale)*, Cecil Parker *(Sir Percy)*, Claude Dauphin *(Inspector Mercier)*, Marcel Dalio *(Sapper)*, Philippe Noiret *(Ambroise Gérôme)*, Michel Piccoli *(Lecoeur)*, Jean Wiener *(Krajewski)*, Daniel Emilfork *(Kobeleff)*, Eugene Deckers *(Koenigstein)*, Jacques Dufilho *(Beala)*, Tanya Lopert *(Agneau)*, Catherine Allégret *(Pantoufle)*, Hella Petri *(Madam)*, Peter Ustinov *(Prince Otto)*, Sacha Pitoeff *(bomb-throwing revolutionary)*, Arthur Howard *(butler)*, Roger Trapp, Jean Rupert, Joseph Dassin, Jacques Legras, Mario Feliciani, Dorothy Reynolds, Hazel Hughes, Jacques Ciron.
Comedy-drama. Source: Romain Gary, *Lady L* (Paris, 1963). Lady Lendale is celebrating her 80th birthday at her castle in Yorkshire. In reminiscing to her biographer, Sir Percy, she recalls that many years before, while known as Louise, she left her job as a laundress in Corsica for employment in a Paris brothel. There she met the one love in her life—Armand, a thief and an anarchist. Together they went to Switzerland, where Armand became involved in a plot to assassinate Prince Otto of Bavaria. While expecting Armand's child, Louise posed as a widowed countess in a hotel in Nice, where she tried to rob Lord Lendale. Though he knew all about her, Lord Lendale was so anxious to have a wife that he offered to save Armand from the police in return for Louise's hand. Since she had replaced the bomb that Armand planned to toss at Prince Otto with a dummy, Louise accepted the marriage offer. She later joined Armand in Italy and, for a while, supported his anarchist activities with her husband's money. Eventually she tired of his useless plans and went to England to assume her responsibilities as Lady Lendale. As she concludes her story, Lady L startles Sir Percy by telling him that she continues to see Armand and that all of her children are his; she married him in Switzerland, she says, and Lord Lendale consented to an arrangement whereby Armand remained both her husband and lover while posing as the family chauffeur. *Aristocrats. Authors. Thieves. Anarchists. Chauffeurs. Conspiracy. Pregnancy. Marriage.*

Imposture. Infidelity. Hotels. Whorehouses. Yorkshire. Corsica. Paris. Nice. Switzerland. Otto (Bavaria).
Note: Filmed in Paris, London, and Switzerland. Rome opening: Dec 1965; running time: 115 min; Paris opening: Dec 1965; running time: 90 min.

THE LADY OF MONZA (Italy)   **F6.2672**
Clesi Cinematografica–Finanziaria San Marco. *Dist* Tower Productions. May **1970**. Sd; col (Eastman Color, print by Movielab). 35mm. 98 min. *MPAA rating* R.
Prod Silvio Clementelli. *Dir* Eriprando Visconti. *Screenplay & Story* Eriprando Visconti, Giampiero Bona. *English Vers Dial* Edward Bond. *Photog* Luigi Kuveiller. *Art Dir* Flavio Mogherini. *Film Ed* Sergio Montanari. *Mus* Ennio Morricone. *Sd* Charles Palinieri. *Prod Mgr* Felice D'Alisera. *Cost* Danilo Donati.
Cast: Anne Heywood *(Virginia de Leyva)*, Antonio Sabato *(Gian Paolo Osio)*, Hardy Kruger *(Father Arrigone)*, Carla Gravina *(Caterina Da Meda)*, Tino Carraro *(Monsignor Barca)*, Luigi Pistilli *(Count De Fuentes)*, Margarita Lozano *(Sister Benedetta)*, Anna Maria Alegiani *(Sister Octavia)*, Giovanna Galletti *(Sister Angela)*, Caterina Boratto *(Sister Francesca)*, Angelica Ippolito *(Sister Degnamerita)*, Maria Michi *(Sister Bianca)*, Renzo Giovampietro, Laura Belli, Rita Calderoni, Pier Paolo Capponi.
Historical melodrama. Source: Mario Mazzucchelli, *La monaca di Monza (Suor Virginia Maria de Leyva)* (Milan, 1961). In Italy, early in the 17th century, Spanish soldiers attempt to plunder the property of nobleman Gian Paolo Osio. Osio kills the Spanish leader and seeks refuge with Father Arrigone, who arranges with his secret mistress, Virginia de Leyva, prioress of the Convent of Santa Margherita at Monza, for Osio's protection. Osio is immediately attracted to the prioress and attempts to rape her. Though resisting at first, Virginia yields to her repressed emotions and joins him in passionate lovemaking; then, stricken with feelings of guilt, she has Osio arrested. Later, after bearing his child, she arranges for his escape and the resumption of their affair. Once more she suspends the relationship, and Osio goes away; but upon his return, they again indulge their passion. Arrigone's jealousy is aroused, and church authorities begin to investigate the murder of a nun who had witnessed the illicit lovemaking. Osio escapes, but Virginia is tried by an ecclesiastical court in Milan. Found guilty of having had sexual relations and of being an accomplice in murder, she is sentenced to be walled up in a prison cell for life. *Spanish. Nobility. Priests. Nuns. Rape. Sexuality. Murder. Jealousy. Convents. Trials. Milan. Monza (Italy). Virginia Maria de Leyva. Gian Paolo Osio. Paolo Arrigone. Catholic Church.*
Note: Produced in Italy in 1969 and released there as *La monaca di Monza*; running time: 105 min; alternative Italian title: *Una storia lombarda*. Also known as *The Nun of Monza*.

LADY OF THE SHADOWS *see* **THE TERROR**

THE LADY ON THE TRACKS (Czechoslovakia)   **F6.2673**
Barrandov Film Studio. *For* Československý Film. *Dist* Royal Films International. 25 Nov **1968** [New York opening]. Sd; col. 35mm. 83 min. *MPAA rating* G.
Dir Ladislav Rychman. *Screenplay* Vratislav Blažek. *Photog* Josef Hanuš. *Art Dir* Olin Bosák. *Mus* Jiří Malásek, Jiří Bažant, Vlastimil Hála. *Lyr* Vratislav Blažek. *Choreog* Josef Koníček.
Cast: Jiřina Bohdalová *(Marie)*, Radoslav Brzobohatý *(Vaclav)*, František Peterka *(Bedrich)*, Libuše Geprtová *(Katerina)*, Stanislav Fišer *(Mr. Marek)*.
Musical comedy. Marie, a trolley conductress in Prague, tearfully abandons her trolley, causing a traffic jam, when she sees her husband, Vaclav, kissing a blonde at the airport terminal. She then withdraws all her bank savings, visits a fashion show and a beauty parlor, and transforms herself into a new, glamorous woman. Vaclav, meanwhile confronted by angry transport officials, guesses that Marie saw him at the terminal. When Marie arrives home with her "new look," Vaclav is alarmed at first by her expenditures, but later, after too many drinks at a company party, he becomes enamored of his beautified wife. Marie takes the drunken Vaclav to the blonde's apartment and flippantly tells her rival how Vaclav likes his food prepared. Leaving them alone, Marie watches a heftily-built man enter the blonde's apartment and then hears noises of a tremendous fight. Going on to a nightclub, Marie flirts with some customers, one of whom is a detective who books her at the police station for soliciting. Trying to explain the situation, Marie is surprised to see Vaclav, the blonde, and the hefty man, Bedrich, brought in for disturbing the peace. Seeing that Vaclav has a black eye, Marie punches Bedrich, but although Bedrich is a professional boxer, he has a gentle disposition and falls for Marie because of her spunk. Continuing to punish Vaclav, who is now doing the housework, Marie goes on a trip with Bedrich, followed by Vaclav, the blonde, and a number of new admirers. Determined to win Marie back, Vaclav takes boxing lessons and challenges Bedrich to a match. On the day of the fight the hall is filled with trolley conductresses who are hoping that Vaclav will lose because

he has been unfaithful. Vaclav is knocked out in the first round, and the spectators cheer Bedrich, while Marie jumps into the ring and raises Vaclav's arm, forgiving him. *Streetcar conductors. Boxers. Police. Jealousy. Marriage. Revenge. Infidelity. Drunkenness. Nightclubs. Prague.*

Note: Released in Czechoslovakia in 1966 as *Dáma na kolejích.*

THE LADY WITH THE DOG (U.S.S.R.) F6.2674

Lenfilm. *Dist* Artkino Pictures. 6 Nov **1962** [New York opening]. Sd; b&w. 35mm. 86 min.

Dir-Screenplay Iosif Kheyfits. *Story Ed* I. Tarsanova. *Photog* Andrey Moskvin, Dmitriy Meskhiyev. *Art Dir* B. Manevich, I. Kaplan. *Film Ed* Ye. Bazhenova. *Mus* N. Simonyan. *Sd* A. Shargorodskiy. *Asst Dir* S. Derevyanskiy. *Prod Mgr* M. Gendenshteyn. *Makeup* V. Ulyanov. *Cons* G. Byalyy, V. Glinka.

Cast: Iya Savvina (*Anna Sergeyevna*), Aleksey Batalov (*Dmitriy Gurov*), Nina Alisova (*Madame Gurov*), Pyotr Krymov (*von Didenitz*), Dmitriy Zebrov (*Frolov*), Marya Safonova (*Natasha*), Yuriy Medvedev, T. Rozanov, Yuriy Svirin, Vladimir Erenberg, G. Barysheva, K. Gun, Z. Dorogova, M. Ivanov, G. Kurovskiy, S. Mazovetskaya, A. Orlov, P. Pervushin, L. Stepanov.

Drama. Source: Anton Pavlovich Chekhov, "Dama s sobachkoy," in *Russkaya mysl* (Dec 1899). While vacationing in Yalta at the turn of the century, Dmitriy Gurov, a middle-aged banker with a family in Moscow, encounters Anna Sergeyevna, a beautiful young woman who walks her small dog along the promenade each day. Upon learning that she is the wife of a petty official and social climber and has grown tired of her husband, Dmitriy confesses that he, too, is unhappily married. What at first seems to be a casual flirtation develops into a serious affair, but the lovers nevertheless part and return to their respective homes. Once back in Moscow, Dmitriy is haunted by Anna's memory. He eventually invents an excuse to leave the city, and, in the hope of meeting her, goes to the provincial town where she lives. He meets her at the theater, and, during a moment away from her husband, Anna admits her lasting love. Later, she begins to visit Dmitriy in Moscow. Both realize that they are doomed to a life of brief secret meetings, stolen away from their families and a society whose ties they are unable, for the present, to break. However, they are hopeful that a solution will eventually be found. *Bankers. Middle classes. Civil servants. Marriage. Infidelity. Vacations. Beaches. Resorts. Yalta. Moscow. Dogs.*

Note: Released in the U.S.S.R. in Jan 1960 as *Dama s sobachkoy;* running time: 90 min.

LADYBUG LADYBUG F6.2675

Francis Productions. *Dist* United Artists. 12 Dec **1963** [Los Angeles opening; c13 Dec 1963; LP27680]. Sd; b&w. 35mm. 84 min.

Prod-Dir Frank Perry. *Assoc Prod* Stephen F. Kesten. *Screenplay* Eleanor Perry. *Story* Lois Dickert. *Dir Photog* Leonard Hirschfield. *Art Dir* Albert Brenner. *Film Ed (see note)* Armond Lebowitz, Edith Hamlin. *Mus Comp & Cond* Robert Cobert. *Sd* Stanley Kasper. *Sd Cons* Noelle Gillmor. *Asst Dir* Tony LaMarca. *Prod Mgr* Stephen R. Winsten. *Cost* Anna Hill Johnstone.

Cast—The Adults: Jane Connell (*Mrs. Maxton, the dietician*), William Daniels (*Mr. Calkins, the principal*), James Frawley (*truck driver*), Richard Hamilton (*JoAnn's father*), Kathryn Hays (*Mrs. Forbes, the secretary*), Jane Hoffman (*Mrs. Hayworth, the art teacher*), Elena Karam (*Don and Trudy's mother*), Judith Lowry (*Luke's grandmother*), Nancy Marchand (*Mrs. Andrews, the 6th grade teacher*), Estelle Parsons (*JoAnn's mother*).

Cast—The Children: Doug Chapin (*Gary*), Miles Chapin (*Joel*), Bozo Dell (*Peter*), Dianne Higgins (*Jill*), Alan Howard (*Luke*), Christopher Howard (*Steve*), David Komoroff (*Don*), Donnie Melvin (*Brian*), Susan Melvin (*Trudy*), Linda Meyer (*JoAnn*), Alice Playten (*Harriet*), Marilyn Rogers (*Sarah*), Jennifer Stone (*Pattie*).

Drama. The normal routine of a rural elementary school is suddenly disrupted when the civil defense alarm box flashes warnings that a nuclear attack is imminent. At first the principal assumes a malfunction, but after checking with the installation company and with other schools in the area, he is forced to accept the alert as a real one. The children are separated into go-home groups, and one such squad is placed under the supervision of Mrs. Andrews, the 6th-grade teacher. As fear and panic begin to register on the children's faces, she is unable to reassure them because of her own anxiety. Unaware that the alarm has been established to be false, one of the children—a 12-year-old named Harriet—invites several of her friends to share her family's bomb shelter. She and the other children enter the shelter, divide the rations, and assume various duties. A short time later, another child, Sarah, knocks on the door and asks admittance. But Harriet refuses, claiming there isn't enough food and water and that opening the door might be risking fallout contamination. Terrified, Sarah runs off to seek a hiding place. Upon reaching a dumping lot she sees a discarded icebox, climbs inside, and closes the door. An older boy, Steve, leaves the bomb shelter to search for her but runs by the box containing the rapidly suffocating child. Suddenly he spies a commercial jet and thinks it is an attacking enemy plane. Desperately clawing at the earth in a futile attempt to dig a hole, he turns toward the sky and hysterically screams "Stop! Stop! Stop!" *School principals. Schoolteachers. Children. Nuclear warfare. Civil defense. Rural life. Elementary school life. Suffocation. Fear. Bomb shelters.*

Note: Location scenes filmed at an elementary school in Gradyville, Pennsylvania, and in New York State. Story based on a true-life incident in California. One source lists Edith Hamlin as film editor, but all others give Lebowitz.

LAFAYETTE (France/Italy) F6.2676

Copernic Films–Cosmos Film. *Dist* Maco Film Corp. 10 Apr **1963** [New York opening]. Sd; col (Technicolor). 35mm & 70mm (Supertechnirama 70). 110 min.

Prod Maurice Jacquin. *Assoc Prod* Hugo Benedek. *Dir* Jean Dréville. *Screenplay* Suzanne Arduini, Jacques Sigurd, Maurice Jacquin, Jean-Bernard Luc, François Ponthier, Jean Dréville. *Dial* Jean-Bernard Luc. *Photog* Claude Renoir, Roger Hubert. *Art Dir* Maurice Colasson. *Set Decor* Maurice Colasson. *Film Ed* René Le Hénaff. *Mus* Steve Laurent, Pierre Duclos. *Sd* Norbert Gernolle. *Asst Dir* Louis A. Pascal. *Cost* Jacqueline Guyot, Françoise Tournafond, Léon Zay. *Sp Eff* Bill Warrington. *English Subtitl* John Hunter, Norbert Terry, Robert Braun.

Cast: Michel Le Royer (*Lafayette*), Jack Hawkins (*General Cornwallis*), Orson Welles (*Benjamin Franklin*), Howard St. John (*George Washington*), Vittorio De Sica (*Bancroft*), Edmund Purdom (*Silas Deane*), Pascale Audret (*Madame de Lafayette*), Jacques Castelot (*Duc d'Ayen*), Folco Lulli (*Le Boursier*), Wolfgang Preiss (*Baron Kalb*), Liselotte Pulver (*Marie Antoinette*), Albert Rémy (*Louis XVI*), Georges Rivière (*Vergennes*), Renée Saint-Cyr (*Duchesse d'Ayen*), Rosanna Schiaffino (*Comtesse de Simiane*), Henri Amilien (*Ségur*), Gilles Brissac (*Monsieur*), Roger Bontemps (*La Bergerie*), Jean-Roger Caussimon (*Maurepas*), Sylvie Coste (*Aglae*), Christian Melsen (*General Philip*), Claude Naudes (*Abbé de Cour*), Roland Rodier (*Mauroy*), René Rozan (*Lauzun*), Henri Tisot, Lois Bolton, Jean Degrave, Jean-Jacques Delbo, Michel Galabru, Jean Lanier, Anthony Stuart.

Historical drama. In 1776 when the ill-equipped American colonies are fighting for their independence against superior British forces, General Washington sends Silas Deane to France to recruit officers and soldiers sympathetic to the colonies' cause. One such soldier is the Marquis de Lafayette, a hot-blooded, 19-year-old nobleman who defies both his father-in-law and Louis XVI in order to join in the fight for freedom. While on a mission to England, Lafayette meets General Cornwallis during a fox hunt. The two men meet again later on opposite sides of an American battlefield. During the fighting, Washington becomes so impressed with the Frenchman's valor that he puts him in charge of a plan to harass Cornwallis. The strategy is successful, and the British suffer a disastrous defeat at Saratoga. As a result of the battle of Yorktown, Cornwallis is forced to surrender, and the colonies win their independence. *British. Nobility. Diplomats. Fox hunts. United States—History—Revolution. England. Saratoga (New York). Yorktown (Virginia). George Washington. Silas Deane. Marquis de Lafayette. Charles Cornwallis. Benjamin Franklin. Louis XVI (France). France—Army. Great Britain—Army.*

Note: Location scenes filmed in Yugoslavia. Opened in Paris in Feb 1962 as *La Fayette;* running time: 158 min; in Rome in Nov 1962 as *Lafayette (Una spada per due bandiere);* running time: 115 min.

LA FAYETTE see **LAFAYETTE**

IL LAGO DI SATANA see **THE SHE BEAST**

LAILA see **MAKE WAY FOR LILA**

LAILA—LIEBE UNTER DER MITTERNACHTSSONNE see **MAKE WAY FOR LILA**

THE LAKE (Japan) F6.2677

Gendai Eiga. *Dist* Shochiku Films of America. Apr **1970** [Los Angeles showing]. Sd; col? 35mm. [Feature film, length unknown.]

Assoc Prod Keinosuke Kubo. *Dir* Yoshishige Yoshida. *Screenplay* Yoshio Isihido, Yasuko Ono, Yoshishige Yoshida. *Photog* Tatsuo Suzuki. *Film Ed* Sachiko Shimizu. *Mus* Sei Ikeno.

Cast: Mariko Okada (*Miyako Mizuki*), Shinsuke Ashida (*Yuzo*), Shigeru Tsuyuguchi (*Ginpei Momoi*), Tamotsu Hayakawa (*Kitano*), Keiko Natsu (*Machie*), K. Ichikawa, Aiko Masuda, Hiroko Masuda, Sakae Umezu, Keisuke Nakai, Kazumi Higuchi, Mitsuyo Omata.

Melodrama. Source: Yasunari Kawabata, "Mizuumi," in *Shincho* (Jan-Dec 1954). Miyako Mizuki, a wife and mother, becomes romantically involved with Kitano, her interior decorator. At first a simple flirtation, the relationship soon develops into a passionate affair with secret meetings in seedy hotels. Miyako permits Kitano to take nude photographs of her as a keepsake. The negatives, however, fall into the hands of Ginpei Momoi, a teacher who has often observed the lovers in a hotel near his school. Obsessed with Miyako, Ginpei informs her that he has the negatives and arranges to meet her. Meanwhile, Miyako discovers that Kitano has another mistress to whom he is nearly engaged. Miyako and Ginpei meet, walk along the beach, and make love. Returning to her inn, Miyako finds her husband, Yuzo, waiting, Kitano having told him everything. Questioned by Yuzo about Ginpei, Miyako replies that he is dead. The couple board a train for home. ... *Interior decorators. Mistresses. Schoolteachers. Infidelity. Blackmail. Marriage. Duplicity. Nudity. Photographs. Hotels.*

Note: Released in Japan in 1966 as *Onna no mizuumi.*

LAL AGHNIHAT ELMOUTAKASRA see **THE BROKEN WINGS**

LA LAMA NEL CORPO see **THE MURDER CLINIC**

LANA TURNER see **MORE MILK EVETTE**

LANCELOT AND GUINEVERE see **SWORD OF LANCELOT**

THE LAND OF 1001 NUDES see **NAKED ISLAND: "THE LAND OF 1001 NUDES"**

THE LAND OF OZ see **THE WONDERFUL LAND OF OZ**

LAND RAIDERS   F6.2678
Morningside Pictures. *Dist* Columbia Pictures. 17 Jun **1970** [Dayton, Ohio, opening; c3 Jan 1970; LP37954]. Sd (Westrex); col (Technicolor). 35mm. 101 min. *MPAA rating* GP.
Prod Charles H. Schneer. *Assoc Prod* Roy Rowland. *Dir* Nathan Juran. *Screenplay* Ken Pettus. *Story* Ken Pettus, Jesse Lasky, Jr., Pat Silver. *Dir Photog* Wilkie Cooper. *Camera Op* Godfrey Godar. *Art Dir* José Alguer ó. *Film Ed* Archie Ludski. *Mus Comp & Cond* Bruno Nicolai. *Sd* George Stephenson. *Dub Ed* Colin Miller. *Asst Dir* José López Rodero. *Prod Supv* Luis Roberts. *Prod Mgr* Miguel Gil. *Location Mgr* D. Sempere. *Cont* Kay Rawlings. *Wardrobe Supv* Antonio Pueo. *Horsemaster* Juan Majan.
Cast: Telly Savalas (*Vince*), George Maharis (*Paul*), Arlene Dahl (*Martha*), Janet Landgard (*Kate*), Jocelyn Lane (*Luisa*), George Couloris (*Cardenas*), Guy Rolfe (*Major Tanner*), Paul Picerni (*Carney*), Phil Brown (*Mayfield*), Marcella St. Amant (*Luisa Montoya*), H. P. Picerni (*Arturo*), Robert Carricart (*Rojas*), Gustavo Rojo (*Juantez*), Fernando Rey (*priest*), Ben Tatar (*Loomis*), John Clarke (*Ace*), Charles Stalnaker (*Willis*), Susan Harvey (*Mrs. Willis*).
Western melodrama. Paul Cardenas and his brother Vince continue their long-standing feud over Paul's former girl friend whom Vince made pregnant. After the girl died mysteriously, Paul left their Arizona ranch to wander. He returns to find that Vince is trying to provoke a war with the Apaches so that property values will drop and he can buy the land cheaply. When a government Indian agent arrives, Vince has him killed with Apache arrows to prevent any peaceful settlement of Indian claims and then places a bounty on all Indian scalps. When the Apaches retaliate by attacking a wagon train, Paul arrives in time to save Kate Mayfield, daughter of the town sheriff. Vince encourages the local citizens to attack the Indian village, an act which results in the deaths of many Apache women and children, but the Apaches soon retaliate with an attack on the town. Simultaneously, Sheriff Mayfield reveals to Paul that Vince murdered the former girl friend when she threatened to name him as her baby's father. In the resulting melee, both Vince and Mayfield are killed, but Paul survives to ride out of town with his new lover, Kate. *Brothers. Apache Indians. Indian agents. Sheriffs. Feuds. Pregnancy. Land speculation. Murder. Massacres. Wagon trains. Arizona.*
Note: Filmed in Budapest and in Spain. Working title: *Day of the Landgrabber.*

THE LAND WE LOVE see **HERO'S ISLAND**

THE LANDLORD   F6.2679
Mirisch Productions–Cartier Productions. *Dist* United Artists. 20 May **1970** [New York opening; c20 May 1970; LP38466]. Sd; col (De Luxe). 35mm. 114 min. [Copyright length: 110 min.] *MPAA rating* R.
Prod Norman Jewison. *Assoc Prod* Patrick J. Palmer. *Dir* Hal Ashby. *Screenplay* Bill Gunn. *Dir Photog* Gordon Willis. *Camera Op* Michael Chapman. *Asst Camera* Tibor Sands, Sheldon Lubow. *Set Decor* John Godfrey. *Scenic Artist* Gene Powell, William Chiken. *Prod Dsgn* Robert Boyle. *Film Ed* William A. Sawyer, Edward Warschilka. *Mus & Songs* Al Kooper. *Mus Supv* Charlie Calello. *Song:* "Brand New Day" sung by The Staple Singers, Al Kooper. *Songs:* "Doing Me Dirty," "Let Me Love You" sung by Lorrane Ellison. *Song:* "A Man" sung by Al Kooper. *Song:* "God Bless the Children" Jimmy Holliday. Sung by The Staple Singers. *Sd* Chris Newman. *Sd Ed* James A. Richard, Marvin I. Kosberg. *Sd Re-rec* Richard Portman. *Sd Cons* Bill Tuck. *Asst Dir* Terence Nelson, Hal DeWindt. *Prod Supv* Edward Morey, Jr. *Location Mgr* Steven Skloot. *Script Supv* Maggie James. *Cost* Domingo Rodriguez. *Wardrobe* Pat Stuart, Yvonne Stoney. *Makeup* Mike Maggi. *Hairstyles* Harold Melvin. *Ed Cons* Don Zimmerman. *Still Photog* Josh

Weiner. *Key Grip* Robert Ward. *Gaffer* Vincent Delaney.
Cast: Beau Bridges (*Elgar Enders*), Pearl Bailey (*Marge*), Diana Sands (*Fanny*), Louis Gossett (*Copee*), Douglas Grant (*Walter Gee*), Melvin Stewart (*Professor Duboise*), Lee Grant (*Mrs. Enders*), Walter Brooke (*Mr. Enders*), Susan Anspach (*Susan*), Robert Klein (*Peter*), Will MacKenzie (*William Jr.*), Gretchen Walther (*Doris*), Stanley Greene (*Heywood*), Marki Bey (*Lanie*), Oliver Clark, Florynce Kennedy, Joe Madden, Grover Dale, Trish Van Devere, Larry Cook, Hector Elizondo, John McCurry, Lionel G. Wilson, Marlene Clark, Gloria Henry, Willis Pinkett, Hannah Battle, Michael Ferguson, Bobby V. Garvin, Richard Usher, Chelle C. Mordecai, Christopher L. Calloway, Carl Lee, Van Kirksey, Louise Stubbs, Tony Major.
Comedy-drama. Source: Kristin Hunter, *The Landlord* (New York, 1966). Elgar Enders, the son of a wealthy industrialist, buys a tenement in Brooklyn which he plans to convert into a psychedelic home for himself after evicting the present Negro tenants. Elgar's ideas are changed, however, when he becomes acquainted with the tenants, who include Marge, a fortune-teller; Professor Duboise, a black segregationist; the Copee family; and an invalid couple who live in the basement. After deciding to allow the tenants to remain, Elgar moves into the building and begins to make some improvements. Mr. and Mrs. Enders are disturbed by their son's behavior, especially when he insults Heywood, the Negro butler, for his subservience, and divulges that he is in love with Lanie, a mulatto art student. Upon returning to his tenement, he throws a party and makes love to Fanny Copee, a black woman whose husband is in jail. Months later, Fanny reports that she is pregnant, and Elgar abandons Lanie to take care of Fanny. When her husband returns from jail, he attacks Elgar with an ax but cannot bring himself to kill him; instead, he suffers a breakdown and is taken to the hospital. Fanny gives birth to the baby and tells Elgar that she plans to put the baby up for adoption so that it can be brought up as a white. Elgar takes the baby himself, packs up his belongings, and drives off to reconcile with Lanie, leaving the house to the Copee family. *Landlords. Negroes. Fortune-tellers. Professors. Invalids. Butlers. Mulattoes. Students. Eviction. Race relations. Family life. Miscegenation. Infidelity. Pregnancy. Illegitimacy. Tenements. New York City—Brooklyn.*
Note: Location scenes filmed in New York City.

THE LANDLORD see **THE LUSTY LANDLORD**

LANDRU (France/Italy)   F6.2680
Rome Paris Films–C. C. Champion. *Dist* Embassy Pictures. 9 Apr **1963** [New York opening]. Sd; col (Eastman Color). 35mm. 114 min.
Pres by Joseph E. Levine. *Prod* Carlo Ponti, Georges de Beauregard. *Dir* Claude Chabrol. *Screenplay* Françoise Sagan. *Photog* Jean Rabier. *Camera* Alain Levent. *Art Dir* Jacques Saulnier. *Film Ed* Jacques Gaillard. *Asst Film Ed* Monique Gaillard. *Mus Comp* Pierre Jansen. *Mus Cond* André Girard. *Soprano* Françoise Perret. *Sd* Julien Coutellier. *Asst Dir* Francis Cognani, Charles Bitsch, Jean Grouet. *Prod Mgr* Bruna Drigo, Jean Lavie. *Cost* Maurice Albray.
Cast: Charles Denner (*Henri-Désiré Landru*), Michèle Morgan (*Célestine Buisson*), Danielle Darrieux (*Berthe Héon*), Hildegard Neff (*Madame X*), Juliette Mayniel (*Anna Collomb*), Stéphane Audran (*Fernande Segret*), Catherine Rouvel (*Andrée Babelay*), Denise Provence (*Madame Lacoste*), Françoise Lugagne (*Madame Landru*), Mary Marquet (*Madame Guillin*), Robert Burnier (*presiding judge*), Huguette Forge (*Madame Vidal*), Jean-Louis Maury (*Commissioner Belin*), Gisèle Sandre (*Georgette*), Mario David (*prosecutor*), Claude Mansard (*defense attorney*), Sacha Briquet (*assistant prosecutor*), Serge Bento (*Maurice Landru*), Denise Lepvrier (*Catherine Landru*), Diana Lepvrier (*Landru's daughter*), Raymond Queneau (*Clemenceau*), Jean-Pierre Melville (*Mandel*), Henri Attal, Dominique Zardi (*gendarmes*).
Comedy-drama. During World War I, Henri-Désiré Landru, a furniture dealer, finds it extremely difficult to support his wife and four children. Desperate for funds, he devises a plan to murder lonely, wealthy women by placing lonelyhearts advertisements in the newspaper. His first victim is Berthe Héon, a middle-aged woman whom he takes to the opera, induces to sign over power of attorney, and then murders. The venture is so successful that he quickly eliminates 10 other victims. His infamous career ends when the armistice is declared, and he stops the killings, but he is arrested by the police when he is recognized by the sister of one of his victims. Three years after the arrest, he is brought to trial. Although he charms everyone with his offhanded dismissal of the charges against him, and although the bodies of the victims are never found, he is judged guilty. All appeals are denied, and he is condemned to death. He rejects spiritual comfort and a last meal, but he does consent to a final interview with his attorney, in which he refuses to reveal guilt or innocence. *Businessmen. Psychopaths. Lovelorn. Police. Lawyers. Finance—Personal. Murder. Capital punishment. Trials. World War I. Henri Désiré Landru. Bluebeard.*

Note: Location scenes filmed in Paris and Gambais. Opened in Paris in Jan 1963; running time: 115 min; in Rome in Mar 1963; running time: 100 min. U. S. title changed to *Bluebeard.*

LÄNGTAN *see* **NIGHT GAMES**

LAS VEGAS BY NIGHT *see* **SPREE**

LAS VEGAS, 500 MILLONES *see* **THEY CAME TO ROB LAS VEGAS**

LAS VEGAS FREE–FOR–ALL (Japan)   F6.2681
Toho Co.-Watanabe Productions. *Dist* Toho Co. Jan **1968** [Los Angeles showing]. Sd; col (Eastmancolor). 35mm (Tohoscope). 157 min. [Also 148 min.]
Exec Prod Shin Watanabe. *Dir* Takashi Tsuboshima. *Screenplay* Ryozo Kasahara, Yasuo Tanami. *Photog (see note)* Shoji Utsumi. *Mus* Yasushi Miyagawa, Tessho Hagiwara.
Cast: Hitoshi Ueki *(Shinran Machida)*, Hajime Hana *(Shigekane Itagaki)*, Kei Tani *(Kaneo Nishimoto)*, Mie Hama *(Tsukiko)*, Mari Sono *(Yuriko)*, Peggy Neal *(Mary)*, The Peanuts.
Crime farce. Shinran Machida, an inveterate gambler, is given a poker chip from a Las Vegas casino by Kid Gold, an American. Machida has the chip duplicated by the thousands and then gets himself transferred to the Los Angeles branch of his firm. Kaneo Nishimoto, a young doctor, is present when Kid Gold is fatally struck by a taxi. Before he dies, the Kid gives Nishimoto the deed to property in America the Kid claims is worth $1 million. Shigekane Itagaki, an inexperienced politician who bought his way into office, has a disagreement with his superiors and is dispatched to America for an inspection tour of sanitation facilities. The three men meet on a plane to Los Angeles, and upon arriving each receives bad news: Machida loses his job; Nishimoto's property is revealed to be an abandoned gold mine near Las Vegas; and Itagaki finds he has been linked with scandal back in Japan. The three decide to use the bogus poker chips to reap a fortune in the Las Vegas casinos, only to learn that the chips are no longer in use. Criminals hear of Nishimoto's deed and try to gain possession of it because the mine actually contains a cache of gold coins. The three Japanese find the gold first and return with it to Japan, only to learn that the treasure has been pledged to build a hospital. *Gamblers. Physicians. Politicians. Americans in foreign countries. Perfidy. Gambling. Scandal. Casinos. Gold mines. Treasure. Documentation. Automobile accidents. Los Angeles. Las Vegas.*
Note: Released in Japan in Apr 1967 as *Kureizi ogon sakusen.* Shoji Utsumi is also known as Masaharu Utsumi.

LAS VEGAS HILLBILLYS   F6.2682
Woolner Bros. Pictures. 11 May **1966** [Fresno, California, opening]. Sd; col (Eastman Color by Pathé). 35mm. 90 min.
Prod-Writ Larry E. Jackson. *Exec Prod* Bernard A. Woolner. *Dir* Arthur C. Pierce. *Song:* "Money Greases the Wheel" sung by Ferlin Husky.
Cast: Ferlin Husky *(Woody)*, Mamie Van Doren *(Boots)*, Don Bowman *(Jeepers)*, Billie Bird *(Clementine)*, Jayne Mansfield, Louis Quinn, Richard Kiel, John Harmon, Sonny James, Del Reeves, Roy Drusky, Bill Anderson, Wilma Burgess, The Duke of Paducah, Connie Smith.
Comedy with music. When he inherits a casino in Las Vegas, Woody, a stage-struck country boy, leaves his Tennessee home and sets out for the city. En route he befriends a beautiful woman (played by Jayne Mansfield) by pushing her disabled automobile to a garage. Arriving in Vegas with his buddy, Jeepers, he discovers that his casino is a rebuilt barn badly in need of repairs. The former bartender, and the singer, Boots, offer to help put the place back in shape, and Woody's Aunt Clementine shows up with her life savings. Together they plan a country music jamboree, and the beautiful woman arrives to handle the gambling casino. The show is a huge success, and the former country boy becomes a big-time entrepreneur. In addition, he and Boots fall in love. *Singers. Entrepreneurs. Country music. Casinos. Las Vegas.*
Note: Filmed in Las Vegas and Nashville, Tennessee. Working title: *Country Music, U. S. A.*

LÁSKY JEDNÉ PLAVOVLÁSKY *see* **LOVES OF A BLONDE**

LASSIE'S GREAT ADVENTURE   F6.2683
Wrather Corp. *Dist* Twentieth Century–Fox Film Corp. Aug **1963** [c14 Aug 1963; LP26266]. Sd (Westrex); col (EastmanColor, print by DeLuxe). 35mm. 103 min. [Also reviewed at 92 min.]
Pres by Jack Wrather. *Prod* Robert Golden. *Assoc Prod* Bonita Granville Wrather. *Dir* William Beaudine, Sr. *Screenplay* Monroe Manning, Charles O'Neal. *Story Ed* Maria Little. *Story* Sumner Arthur Long. *Dir Photog* Ed Fitzgerald. *Art Dir* George Troast. *Set Decor* Frank Rafferty. *Film Ed* Monica Collingwood. *Ed Admin* James Blakeley. *Sd* Wallace Nogle. *Sd Eff Ed* Bert Schoenfeld. *Mus Ed* Sid Sidney. *Asst Dir* Grayson Rogers. *Prod Supv* William Beaudine, Jr.. *Script Supv* Mercy Weireter. *Wardrobe* Walt Hoffman. *Makeup*

Don Schoenfeld. *Sp Eff* Harold Murphy. *Sp Photog Eff* Howard A. Anderson Co. *Lassie Owned & Trained by* Rudd Weatherwax. *Prop Master* Mariano Tomasino. *Dial Supv* Lloyd Nelson. *Livestock Supv* Lionel Comport. *Casting* Harvey Clermont.
Cast: June Lockhart *(Ruth Martin)*, Hugh Reilly *(Paul Martin)*, Jon Provost *(Timmy Martin)*, Robert Howard *(Sergeant Sprague)*, Will J. White *(Constable MacDonald)*, Richard Kiel *(Chinook Pete)*, Walter Stocker *(John Stanley)*, Walter Kelley *(control-tower operator)*, Patrick Waltz *(pilot)*, Leo Needham *(Ranger Henty)*, Lassie *(a dog)*, Richard Simmons, Patrick Westwood.
Adventure melodrama. Young Timmy Martin and his dog, Lassie, are carried away in a balloon used by a county fair for promotional purposes. The boy's parents, Ruth and Paul, contact John Stanley of the Civil Air Patrol, which later works in conjunction with the Canadian Mounties after it becomes apparent that wind currents have carried the balloon into the wilds of Canada. When Timmy and Lassie land in a treetop, the boy lowers himself and his dog to the ground. They make their way through the dense forest, searching for food and water. They finally reach a river despite the injury sustained by Lassie in a fight with a wild boar. After camping for the night, Timmy, helped by Lassie, builds a raft, hoping to follow the river back to civilization. They soon become separated in rapids, and Chinook Pete, a deafmute Indian, finds the exhausted Timmy on the bank. Lassie makes her way to the Indian's cabin but is chased off by Pete, who wants Timmy to remain with him as a replacement for his dead son. Lassie meets up with the Mounties and leads them to the cabin, but Pete and Timmy are gone. The boy is eventually tracked down by the Mounties and rescued by his father in a helicopter. Although Lassie disappears, the Indian, touched by the dog's loyalty, brings her back to her master. *Children. Chinook Indians. Deafmutes. Air patrol. Survival. Balloons (ascent). Forests. Helicopters. Rafts. Canada. Royal Canadian Mounted Police. Lassie. Dogs. Wild hogs.*
Note: Originally presented on CBS-TV in the *Lassie* series as a four-episode program entitled *The Journey;* registered for copyright and telecast on 17 Feb, 24 Feb, 3 Mar, 10 Mar 1963; LP31593-96.

THE LAST ADVENTURE (France/Italy)   F6.2684
S. N. C.–Compagnia Generale Finanziaria Cinematografica. *Dist* Universal Pictures. Sep **1968**. Sd; col (Eastmancolor, print by Technicolor). 35mm (Techniscope). 102 min.
Prod René Pignères, Gérard Beytout. *Dir* Robert Enrico. *Screenplay* José Giovanni, Pierre Pelegri, Robert Enrico. *Dial* José Giovanni, Pierre Pelegri. *Photog* Jean Boffety. *Art Dir* Jacques d' Ovidio. *Film Ed* Jacqueline Méppiel. *Mus* François de Roubaix. *Sd Rec* Christian Forget, Jean Nény. *Asst Dir* Serge Witta. *Prod Mgr* Paul Laffargue. *Cost* Paco Rabanne. *Sp Eff* Jean Falloux.
Cast: Alain Delon *(Manu)*, Lino Ventura *(Roland)*, Joanna Shimkus *(Letitia)*, Serge Reggiani *(The Pilot)*, Hans Meyer, Thérèse Quentin, Guy Delorme, Jean Darie, Jean Trognon, Odile Poisson, Irène Tunc, Paul Crauchet.
Crime melodrama. Source: José Giovanni, *Les aventuriers* (Paris, 1960). Manu, a stunt flyer, loses his license when he attempts a flight through the Arc de Triomphe. His friend Roland, a racing mechanic, likewise meets failure when his revolutionary racing car explodes. The two men meet Letitia, a sculptress whose first exhibition of welded metal has been a failure, and together they set off for the Congo coast to search for a downed plane with a cargo of gold and diamonds. [According to some sources they are joined by a vagrant who claims to be the plane's pilot and offers to reveal its location for a share of the treasure.] As they recover the loot, they are observed by a group of former mercenaries, who are likewise seeking the treasure. Posing as police, the mercenaries attempt to board the trio's boat, and Letitia is killed in the gunplay. Manu and Roland, who have grown to love Letitia, visit her aunt and uncle, who show them the deserted island ruin where she planned to live. The men discuss plans to use the treasure to fulfill the trio's dream of opening a restaurant on the island, but the mercenaries, who have followed them, intervene. Though the attackers are again unsuccessful in their attempt to steal the treasure, Manu is mortally wounded, and Roland is left alone. *Mechanics. Sculptors. Air pilots. Adventurers. Mercenaries. Air stunts. Automobile racing. Friendship. Treasure. Islands. Congo.*
Note: Paris opening: Apr 1967 as *Les aventuriers;* running time: 112 min. Italian title: *I tre avventurieri.*

THE LAST CHALLENGE   F6.2685
Metro-Goldwyn-Mayer, Inc. 29 Sep **1967** [Atlanta opening; c21 Mar 1967; LP34170]. Sd; col (Metrocolor). 35mm (Panavision). 96 min. [Also reviewed at 105 min.]
Prod-Dir Richard Thorpe. *Screenplay* John Sherry, Robert Emmett Ginna. *Dir Photog* Ellsworth Fredricks. *Art Dir* George W. Davis, Urie McCleary. *Set Decor* Henry Grace, Hugh Hunt. *Film Ed* Richard Farrell. *Mus* Richard Shores. *Rec Supv* Franklin Milton. *Asst Dir* Eric Von Stroheim, Jr. *Unit Prod Mgr* Marvin Stuart. *Makeup* William Tuttle. *Hairstyles* Mary Keats.

Cast: Glenn Ford (*Marshal Dan Blaine*), Angie Dickinson (*Lisa Denton*), Chad Everett (*Lot McGuire*), Gary Merrill (*Squint Calloway*), Jack Elam (*Ernest Scarnes*), Delphi Lawrence (*Marie Webster*), Royal Dano (*Pretty Horse*), Kevin Hagen (*Frank Garrison*), Florence Sundstrom (*Outdoors*), Marian Collier (*Sadie*), Robert Sorrells (*Harry Bell*), John Milford (*Turpin*), Frank McGrath (*Ballard Weeks*), Amanda Randolph (*Lisa's maid*), Bill Walker (*servant*), Letitia Paquette (*girl with Lot*), Beverly Hills (*saloon hostess*), Jack Bighead, Henry O'Brien, George Little Buffalo, Eddie Little Sky.

Western drama. Source: John Sherry, *Pistolero's Progress* (New York, 1966). In 1877, young Lot McGuire rides toward the Southwestern town of Suwora, intending to kill Marshal Dan Blaine and thereby prove himself the fastest draw in the territory. By chance, he meets and becomes friendly with his intended victim at a fishing spot outside of town but makes his intentions clear to the marshal. Blaine, a former gunfighter pacified by 10 years in prison, sees in McGuire the kind of youngster he himself once was and tries unsuccessfully to make him forget his so-called "mission." After McGuire proves his ability by outdrawing card cheat Squint Calloway, Blaine's dancehall hostess girl friend, Lisa Denton, hires gunman Ernest Scarnes to kill him. McGuire mortally wounds his would-be assassin, however, and confronts Lisa with knowledge of her treachery, although he promises not to divulge it after learning that she was only trying to protect Blaine. As the showdown nears, the desperate Lisa takes a revolver and stalks McGuire herself, but before she can shoot, Blaine stops her; aware now that a duel is inevitable, the marshal outdraws his challenger, tosses away his gun, and sadly leaves town alone. *United States marshals. Gunfighters. Ex-convicts. Hired killers. Cardsharps. Dancehall girls. Duels.*

Note: Location scenes filmed in Tucson and Palmdale, Arizona. Working title: *Pistolero*.

THE LAST CHAPTER   F6.2686

Ben-Lar Productions. 21 Feb **1966** [New York opening]. Sd; b&w. 35mm. 85 min. [Also reviewed at 90 min.]

Prod-Dir Benjamin Rothman, Lawrence Rothman. *Screenplay* S. L. Shneiderman. *Script Ed* Gene Jennings. *Scenes of Post-War Poland Filmed by* Victor Johannes. *Titl & Opticals* Eastern Effects. *Film Ed* Jacob Hameiri. *Mus* Vladimir Heifetz. *Choral Selections Sung by* Farband Culture Chorus. *Song:* "Hymn of the Jewish Partisans" Hirsch Glick. *Sd Mix* Magno Sound. *Prod Supv* Sal Termini. *Adv* Moishe Elbaum. *Historical Res* Eileen Shneiderman. *Translations* Ida Ronch. *Film Services* Termini Film Editorial Services Inc.

Narrator: Theodore Bikel.

Documentary. An old Jew who has survived the Nazi Holocaust returns to his native Poland at the end of World War II to find his way of life destroyed and over 3 million of his people murdered. The surviving Jews quickly begin to rebuild their culture; synagogues and Jewish schools are rebuilt, matzoh factories bake for Passover, and Ida Kaminska starts her Yiddish theater. This rebuilding is brought to an end on 4 July 1946 when 42 Jews are slaughtered in the town of Kielce during a Polish pogrom. Most of the remaining Jews emigrate, thus ending 1,000 years of Jewish history in Poland. The film traces Jewish history back to the beginning of the Polish state in 966. *In the town of Kazmierz on the Vistula, Jews become prominent sea captains, teachers, smiths, scholars, and even soldiers fighting for Polish independence. Warsaw, Bialystok, Krakow, and Vilna become centers of Jewish civilization, and by the 19th century two-thirds of the Jews in Poland live in the smaller shtetls (towns), wellsprings of creative force in Jewish life. Jewish culture in Poland flowers, influencing every aspect of Poland's development and providing the 20th century with great writers, such as Sholem Aleichem, I. L. Peretz, and Sholem Asch; nevertheless, Jews suffer pogroms and persecutions in Poland. During the German occupation of Poland, the Jews carry on despite their forced concentration in the Warsaw ghetto. In 1943 Hitler orders the destruction of the Jews in the Warsaw ghetto, in time for his birthday on April 20th, but the Jews rise up, and with only the crudest weapons they hold off the Germans for nearly a month, whereupon they are massacred and the ghetto destroyed. During this time the rest of the world, fully aware of the situation, refuses to criticize Hitler's act as morally outrageous or even to provide medical supplies.* The film ends with a shot of the Warsaw ghetto memorial and a statement about the indestructibility of the human spirit. *Jews. Nazis. Genocide. Holocausts. War crimes. Anti-Semitism. Pogroms. Murder. Resistance (political). Warsaw Ghetto Uprising. World War II. Poland—History. Warsaw. Kielce. Bialystok. Krakow (Poland). Vilna. Kazmierz. Adolf Hitler. Sholem Aleichem. Isaac Loeb Peretz. Sholem Asch. Ida Kaminska.*

Note: Archival footage is employed, including clips from Film Polski, such as scenes from *Kanal*, q. v. Schneiderman photographed the aftermath of the Kielce massacre.

LAST DAY OF SAMURAI (Japan)   F6.2687

Toho Co. Jan **1962** [Los Angeles showing]. Sd; col? 35mm. [Feature film, length unknown.]

Cast: Senjaku Nakamura, Chikage Ogi, Koshiro Matsumoto, Ganjiro Nakamura.

Action drama. No information about the nature of this film has been found. *Samurai.*

Note: Original title and release undetermined.

THE LAST DAY OF THE WAR (United States/Italy/Spain)   F6.2688

Prodi Cinematografica–Atlántida Films–Valencia Productions. *For* Sagittarius Productions. **1969** [c5 Jun 1970; LP38143]. Sd; col (Eastman Color). 35mm. 96 min.

Prod Sam X. Abarbanel. *Exec Prod* Henry S. White. *Dir* Juan Antonio Bardem. *Screenplay* Sam X. Abarbanel, Juan Antonio Bardem, Howard Berk. *Story* Howard Berk. *Photog* Romolo Garroni. *Art Dir* Rafael Ablanque. *Set Decor* Santiago Ontañón. *Film Ed* Margarita Ochoa. *Mus* Franco Pezzullo. *Prod Supv* José Frade. *Prod Mgr* Francisco Romero.

Cast: George Maharis (*Sgt. Chips Slater*), María Perschy (*Elena Truppe*), John Clarke (*Hobbs*), James Philbrook (*Lieutenant Poole*), Gérard Herter (*Major Skorch*), Gustavo Rojo (*Hawk*), Jack Stuart (*Kendall*), Gérard Tichy (*Bronc*), Sancho Gracia (*Martinez*), Tomás Blanco (*Martin Truppe*), Rubén Rojo (*O'Brien*), Ralph Browne (*Major Garrick*), Carl Rapp (*burgomaster*), Jorge Rigaud, Claudia Gravy, Matilde Muñoz Sampedro.

War drama. In Innsbruck at the end of World War II Sgt. Chips Slater's Intelligence and Research Platoon of the 103 Division is ordered to locate Martin Truppe, a German scientist partial to the Allies and needed for the Manhattan Project. Unknown to Slater, Major Skorch of the SS is also looking for Truppe to execute him for sabotaging Peenemünde. Elena, Truppe's daughter, is brought from the United States to help the Americans identify her father. Suffering several casualties in skirmishes with Skorch's men, they trail Skorch to a labor camp. The SS officer locates Truppe near Lake Blauberg, but an angry mob of escaped camp laborers kill Skorch. Truppe is rescued, and the I & R platoon survives the last day of the war. *Germans. Scientists. Saboteurs. Rescue. Concentration camps. World War II. Innsbruck. Austria. Peenemünde. United States Army. SS. Chases.*

Note: Location scenes filmed in and around Madrid. Released in Spain as *El último día de la guerra*; running time: 100 min. Italian title: *L'ultimo giorno della guerra.* Jack Stuart is a pseudonym for Giacomo Rossi Stuart.

THE LAST ESCAPE   F6.2689

Oakmont Productions. *Dist* United Artists. 6 May **1970** [Salt Lake City, Utah, opening; c29 Apr 1970; LP38126]. Sd; col (De Luxe). 35mm. 90 min. *MPAA rating* G.

Prod Irving Temaner. *Dir* Walter Grauman. *Screenplay* Herman Hoffman. *Story* John C. Champion, Barry Trivers. *Photog* Gernot Roll. *Art Dir* Rolf Zehetbauer. *Film Ed* Bud Molin, Peter Elliott. *Sd Ed* Frank Warner, Jim Sibley. *Sd Rec* Karsten Ullrich. *Asst Dir* Frank Guarente. *Prod Mgr* Christian Laske, Gert Stachowski. *Sp Eff* Karl Baumgartner.

Cast: Stuart Whitman (*Capt. Lee Mitchell*), John Collin (*Sgt. Harry McBee*), Martin Jarvis (*Lieut. Donald Wilcox*), Pinkas Braun (*Von Heinken*), Günter Neutze (*Major Hessel*), Margit Saad (*Karen Gerhardt*), Patrick Jordan (*Major Griggs*), Johnny Briggs (*Corporal O'Connell*), Harald Dietl (*Major Petrov*), Gerd Vespermann (*Blucher*), Andy Pap (*Curt*), Andrew Lodge (*Gregory*), David Taylor (*Morse*), Richard Abbott (*Billings*), Paul Bentley (*Jarvis*), Christian Skrobek (*Russian signal officer*), Chuck Stanford (*American lieutenant*), Frank Guarente (*American signal officer*), Michael Hinz (*junior SS officer*), Helmut Heisler.

War drama. Only Capt. Lee Mitchell, an American OSS officer, survives a German ambush. Undeterred, he resumes his mission, intent on smuggling German rocket expert Von Heinken out of Berlin. Joining a British commando unit, Mitchell wrests control from inexperienced Lieut. Donald Wilcox. While smuggling the scientist from a factory, he reluctantly accedes to Von Heinken's request that assistants and refugees accompany him. Mitchell remains suspicious of Karen Gerhardt, mistress of SS Major Hessel. He later learns, however, that her liaison was motivated by the desire to protect her young son. The downing of an Allied rescue flight convinces Mitchell that an informant is present. Von Heinken's assistant, Blucher, is subsequently unmasked and slain. Mistaking a truck containing the refugees for a German transport, a Russian tank patrol begins pursuit. Diverting the Russians, Wilcox drives his jeep over a cliff and is killed. As American forces led by Mitchell approach, rejoicing refugees stream from the truck. Realizing that these are not German troops, the Russians hold their fire. They later return the lieutenant's body to Mitchell as tribute to a fallen hero. *Commandos. War heroes. Nazis. Scientists. Refugees. Informers. Mistresses. Abduction. Rescue. Automobile accidents. Murder. Rockets. Airplanes. World War II. Germany. United States—Office of Strategic Services. Russia—Army. SS. Great Britain—Army.*

Note: Filmed on location in and around Munich. Produced in 1968.

THE LAST GAME (U.S.S.R.) F6.2690

Mosfilm. *Dist* Artkino Pictures. 24 Oct **1964** [New York opening]. Sd; b&w. 35mm. 88 min.

Dir Ye. Karelov. *Screenplay* A. Borshchagovskiy. *Story Ed* L. Nekhoroshev. *Photog* Sergey Zaytsev. *Art Dir* B. Tsaryov. *Asst Art Dir* F. Boguslavskiy. *Film Ed* K. Aleyeva. *Mus* Andrey Petrov. *Cond* A. Roytman. *Sd* R. Margacheva. *Asst Dir* R. Atamalibekov. *Prod Mgr* A. Ashkinazi. *Cons* A. Starostin. *Trainer* S. Salnikov.

Cast: Yu. Volkov, V. Kashpur, Lev Kuravlev, Yuriy Nazarov, V. Nevinnyy, Gleb Strizhenov, Gennadiy Yukhtin, A. Eybozhenko, A. Metyolkin, Ye. Paptsov *(Soviet team)*, V. Skulme, V. Tomingas, V. Lange, V. Chyornyy, M. Ogonkov, O. Savelyev, L. Novikov, B. Kvin, L. Ilyukhin, A. Zinovyev *(German team)*, I. Stravinskiy, E. Knausmyuller, T. Gurko, E. Barens, V. Markova, V. Sharykina, L. Dranovskaya, N. Abramov, I. Borisov, L. Biryulin, L. Galanov, Yu. Dmitriyev, Kolya Kozlov, Vova Kolotygin, Nikolay Novlyanskiy, Sasha Petrov, V. Pitsek, I. Pushkaryov, A. Danilova, G. Svetlani, Z. Chekulayeva.

War melodrama. Source: A. Borshchagovskiy, "Trevozhnyye oblaka" (publication undetermined). In occupied Kiev in 1942, the Nazis, endeavoring to gain a propaganda victory, arrange a soccer match between a German team and a Soviet team gathered with difficulty from among the prisoners of war. The Soviet athletes are permitted to move freely about the city; but they are confronted with a choice between defeat on the playing field or death. As the time for the match arrives, they see the people of the city gathered to watch them. Inspired by the sight of their compatriots, the Soviet athletes defeat the German team and are then led away to face a firing squad. *Nazis. Germans. Prisoners of war. War heroes. Soccer. War crimes. Military occupation. World War II. Kiev.*

Note: Wide-screen version released in the U.S.S.R. in May 1963 as *Tretiy taym*. Based on an actual World War II incident.

THE LAST GRAVE see NAVAJO RUN

THE LAST GRENADE (Great Britain) F6.2691

Josef Shaftel Productions. *Dist* Cinerama Releasing Corp. 11 Mar **1970** [Chicago opening; c6 Mar 1970; LF65]. Sd; col (Eastman Color). 35mm (Panavision). 94 min. *MPAA rating* M.

Pres by Dimitri De Grunwald. *Prod* Josef Shaftel. *Assoc Prod* Rene Dupont. *Dir* Gordon Flemyng. *Screenplay* Kenneth Ware. *Adapt* James Mitchell, writ, John Sherlock. *Photog* Alan Hume. *Camera Op* David Harcourt. *Art Dir* Tony Pratt. *Set Decor* Terence Morgan, II. *Main Titl* Ellis/Wright. *Film Ed* Ann Chegwidden, Ernest Hosler. *Mus* John Dankworth. *Sd Mix* Buster Ambler. *Sd Ed* Michael Hopkins. *Sd Re-rec* Len Shilton. *Asst Dir* Anthony Waye. *Prod Mgr* Ron Carr. *Cost Dsgn* Beatrice Dawson. *Wardrobe Supv* Roy Ponting. *Makeup Artist* Wally Schneiderman. *Hairdresser* Gordon Bond. *Sp Eff* Pat Moore.

Cast: Stanley Baker *(Maj. Harry Grigsby)*, Alex Cord *(Kip Thompson)*, Honor Blackman *(Katherine Whitely)*, Richard Attenborough *(Gen. Charles Whitely)*, Rafer Johnson *(Joe Jackson)*, Andrew Keir *(Gordon Mackenzie)*, Ray Brooks *(Lieut. David Coulson)*, Julian Glover *(Andy Royal)*, John Thaw *(Terry Mitchell)*, Philip Latham *(Adams)*, Neil Wilson *(Wilson)*, Gerald Sim *(Dr. Griffiths)*, A. J. Brown *(governor)*, Pamela Stanley *(governor's wife)*, Kenji Takaki *(Te Ching)*, Paul Dawkins *(Commissioner Doyle)*.

War melodrama. Source: John Sherlock, *The Ordeal of Major Grigsby* (London, 1964). Maj. Harry Grigsby and his band of mercenaries are fighting in the Congo when they undergo a surprise attack launched by Kip Thompson, a former colleague who is now fighting for the opposition. Grigsby's troop suffers heavy casualties, and Grigsby is forced to return to London to recuperate. There he is contacted by a government official who proposes that Grigsby go to Hong Kong to resume his battle with Thompson, now employed by the Communist Chinese. Grigsby travels to Hong Kong, where his guerrilla command is again defeated by Thompson, and Grigsby is taken captive. Although he escapes, Grigsby is hospitalized with injuries. Katherine Whitely, the wife of Grigsby's Hong Kong liaison, visits him frequently and learns that he has tuberculosis; soon she realizes that they are falling in love with each other. They agree to begin an affair after she divorces her husband, but Katherine is killed in an automobile crash engineered by Thompson. With renewed fervor, Grigsby goes after his enemy. In the final battle, Grigsby is mortally wounded, but before he dies, he tosses a hand grenade that kills Thompson. *Mercenaries. Guerrillas. Communists. Prisoners of war. Infidelity. Murder. Revenge. Hospitals. Tuberculosis. Explosives. Congo. Hong Kong. London. Great Britain—Army. Automobile accidents.*

Note: Location scenes filmed in London, Hong Kong, and Spain. Opened in London in Mar 1970. Working title: *Grigsby*.

THE LAST GUNFIGHTER (Canada) F6.2692

Dalry Productions. *Dist* Joseph Brenner Associates. Jun **1961**. Sd; b&w. 35mm. 56 min.

Prod-Dir-Writ Lindsay Shonteff. *Asst Prod* James Beggs. *Dir Photog* Herbert S. Alpert. *Sets* Edgar Keenan. *Film Ed* Lindsay Shonteff. *Mus* Fred Tudor. *Theme Song* Leslie Pouliot. *Sd* Les Hadley. *Cont* Christine Murray, cont. *Cost* Malabar Ltd. *Optical Eff* Film Opticals.

Cast: Don Borisenko, Tass Tory, Jay Shannon, Michael Zenon, Ken James, Gordon Clark, actor, James Beggs, Art Jenoff, Buddy Ferens, Jim Peddie, Ed Holmes, Bill William, James Barron, Mike Conway, Spud Abbot, Al Waxman, Bert Hilckman, Garrick Hagon.

Western melodrama. After slaying two men, a gunman waters his horse at a farm where he is offered shelter. He is subsequently hired by the local farmers to defend them from repeated onslaughts by the henchmen of a neighboring rancher. When the gunman murders the rancher's close associate, the infuriated rancher challenges him to a gunfight. As the stranger tells his mistress, a farmer's wife, that he will leave town following the confrontation, their conversation is overheard by her jealous husband. During the resulting brawl, the farmer is knocked out. Having killed the rancher in the duel, the gunman is himself shot to death by the irate farmer. *Gunfighters. Farmers. Cowboys. Ranchers. Mistresses. Murder. Infidelity. Jealousy. Revenge. Duels.*

Note: Produced in Canada in 1959. Alternative titles: *Hired Gun* and *The Devil's Spawn*. Original running time: 60 min. James Beggs is also known as Hagan Beggs.

THE LAST GUNFIGHTER see DEATH OF A GUNFIGHTER

THE LAST HERO see LONELY ARE THE BRAVE

THE LAST LADY (Japan) F6.2693

Toho Co. May **1968** [Los Angeles showing]. Sd; col? 35mm. [Feature film, length unknown.]

Cast: Michiyo Aratama, Sanae Takasugi, Sayuri Yoshinaga. No information about the nature of this film has been found.

Note: Original title and release undetermined.

THE LAST MAN ON EARTH (United States/Italy) F6.2694

La Regina Produzione–Associated Producers, Inc. *Dist* American International Pictures. 6 May **1964** [Los Angeles opening]. Sd; b&w. 35mm. 86 min.

Prod Robert L. Lippert. *Assoc Prod* Harold E. Knox. *Dir U. S. Vers* Sidney Salkow. *Dir Italian Vers* Ubaldo Ragona. *Screenplay* Logan Swanson, William P. Leicester. *Photog* Franco Delli Colli. *Art Dir* Giorgio Giovannini. *Film Ed* Gene Ruggiero. *Mus* Paul Sawtell, Bert Shefter. *Asst Dir* Carlo Grandone. *Prod Mgr* Vico Vaccaro. *Asst Prod Mgr* Lionello Maucci. *Makeup* Piero Mecacci.

Cast: Vincent Price *(Robert Morgan)*, Franca Bettoja *(Ruth)*, Emma Danieli *(Virginia)*, Giacomo Rossi Stuart *(Ben Cortman)*, Umberto Rau, Christi Courtland, Antonio Corevi, Ettore Ribotta.

Science fiction melodrama. Source: Richard Matheson, *I Am Legend* (New York, 1954). A strange plague hits the earth and turns the survivors into vampires, with the exception of Robert Morgan, a scientist who many years before contracted a fever that made him immune to the plague. Morgan's daily routine is to clear the streets of dead bodies and to seek out the vampires, who sleep by day, and drive stakes through their hearts. At night he wards off the roaming vampires with mirrors and garlic. One day he meets Ruth, a young woman who is apparently also immune, but he learns that she is one of a group of vampires who possess a serum that provides them with temporary relief from their vampirism. Morgan returns Ruth to normal by giving her a transfusion of his own blood. She informs him that members of her group are coming to destroy him, and, although he warns them that he is their only hope for a return to normalcy, they kill him. *Scientists. Vampires. Plague. Murder. Serums.*

Note: Released in Italy in 1964 as *L'ultimo uomo della terra*.

THE LAST MERCENARY (Italy/Spain/West Germany) F6.2695

Orbita Films–Roxy Film–Protor Film. *Dist* Excelsior Distributing Co. 8 Oct **1969** [San Francisco opening]. Sd; col (Technicolor). 35mm (Techniscope). 100 min. [Cut to 95 min.]

Pres by Heritage Enterprises. *Exec Prod* George Ferrer. *Dir* Dieter Müller. *Screenplay* Ricardo Ferrer Bosch, Julio Salvador. *Adtl Dial German Vers?* Manfred R. Köhler. *Story* Ricardo Ferrer Bosch. *Camera* Juan Gelpi. *Asst Camera* José Climent. *Art Dir* Luciano De Nardi. *Film Ed* Edith Schuman. *Mus* Bruno Nicolai. *Prod Mgr* Eusebio García.

Cast: Ray Danton *(Mark [Marco] Anderson)*, Pascale Petit *(Isabel)*, Georges Rigaud *(Manuel de Lagos[?])*, Carl Möhner, Günther Stoll, Salvo Basile, Vicente Roca, Irma de Santis, Tomás Torres, Piergiuseppe Sciume.

Action melodrama. Having successfully completed a Congo campaign, mercenary Mark Anderson undertakes a Brazilian assignment. Hired by entrepreneur Manuel de Lagos, Anderson circumvents saboteurs intent on possession of the capitalist's mines, famed for their ores used in the production of nuclear weapons. Through an intermediary, a former African colleague, Anderson negotiates an arms shipment from the saboteurs. When an innocent child and de Lagos are murdered, the mine owner's seductive widow, Isabel, entreats the mercenary to capitulate. Instead, Anderson arms the miners, who successfully repel the saboteurs and appropriate the mine. *Mercenaries. Entrepreneurs. Widows. Miners. Africans. Sabotage. Employer-employee relations. Nuclear weapons. Guns. Congo. Brazil.*

Note: Location scenes filmed in Barcelona. Produced in Spain in 1968 as *El mercenario*; Spanish alternative title: *El último mercenario*; running time: 100 min. Released in Italy in 1969 as *L'ultimo mercenario*; opened in Munich in Dec 1968 as *Die grosse Treibjagd*; running time: 84 min.

LAST MESSAGE FROM SAIGON *see* **OPERATION CIA**

THE LAST MOMENT   **F6.2696**
A-Y Productions. *Dist* Headliner Productions. c4 Sep **1966** [LP36597]. Sd; b&w. 16mm. 83 min.
Prod-Dir-Writ Al Yasin. *Orig Mus & Songs* George Michaelides.
Cast: Melora Conway, Nick Dimitri, Byrd Holland, Terry Olson, Stasa Damascus, Victoria Moreno, Tanya Lemani.
Melodrama. Vicky Carter, dying of leukemia, has visited Dr. Frank many times for treatments. She has been secretive about it, trying to save Bill, her husband, and her young daughter from being hurt. Bill, however, takes notice of her frequent visits to Dr. Frank. He suspects her of an adulterous affair and begins to arrange a divorce. Vicky then realizes that Bill has never loved or trusted her. At a beach party, Vicky meets Hollywood nightclub singer Anthony Adonis. Jealous of the attention Anthony gives her, Bill tells him of her "affair" with Dr. Frank. Anthony feels that he has been teased and tells Vicky that he never wants to see her again. Vicky is devastated and commits suicide by jumping off a cliff. All she leaves is a diary which tells Bill and Anthony the real reasons for her actions. *Physicians. Singers. Jealousy. Suicide. Cancer. Marriage. Infidelity. Diaries.*

LAST OF SUMMER *see* **EARLY AUTUMN**

THE LAST OF THE MOBILE HOTSHOTS   **F6.2697**
Sidney Lumet Productions. *Dist* Warner Bros.–Seven Arts, Inc. 14 Jan **1970** [New York opening; c1 Jan 1970; LP38028]. Sd; col (Technicolor). 35mm. 108 min. *MPAA rating* X.
Prod-Dir Sidney Lumet. *Assoc Prod* Jim DiGangi. *Screenplay* Gore Vidal. *Dir Photog* James Wong Howe. *Camera Op* Al Taffet. *Asst Camera* Charles Termini. *Asst Art Dir* Ben Kasazkow. *Set Decor* Leif Pedersen. *Set Dresser* Al Griswold. *Scenic Artist* Gene Rudolph. *Prod Dsgn* Gene Callahan. *Titl Dsgn* F. Hillsberg Inc. *Film Ed* Alan Heim. *Asst Film Ed* Craig McKay. *Mus* Quincy Jones. *Sd Mix* Nat Boxer. *Sd* Richard Vorisek. *Asst Dir* Burtt Harris, Bob Grand, Enid Roth. *Script Supv* B. J. Bjorkman. *Prod Sec* Arlene Albertson. *Cost* Patricia Zipprodt. *Wardrobe* Brice Sevier. *Makeup* Vince Callahan. *Hairstyles* Frederic Jones. *Sp Eff* Al Burke. *Grip* John Hennessy, Charles Kolb. *Gaffer* Warren Hoag, Richard Meyerhoff. *Prop* Bill Bates, John Martensen.
Cast: James Coburn *(Jeb Stuart Thorington)*, Lynn Redgrave *(Myrtle)*, Robert Hooks *(Chicken)*, Perry Hayes *(George)*, Reggie King *(Rube)*, Patricia Zipprodt.
Comedy. Source: Tennessee Williams, *The Seven Descents of Myrtle* (New York opening: 27 Mar 1968). Although dying of cancer and habituated to marijuana, Jeb Stuart Thorington, the last scion of a distinguished Louisiana family, searches for money to restore the family mansion, Waverly. During Happy Couple Time on Rube Benedict's television show he marries topless dancer Myrtle, the sole surviving member of an Alabama female quintet, The Mobile Hotshots. Upon arrival at the dilapidated estate the newlyweds are greeted by Rube, the black caretaker. Although Myrtle is eager to have sex with Jeb, she accepts his impotence philosophically. Jeb, however, is enraged by his affliction; he is intent on begetting a child in order to prevent his black half brother Chicken from inheriting Waverly. Anxious to repossess a covenant he has made with Chicken, Jeb instructs Myrtle to ingratiate herself with the black. Consequently, his bride bestows her sexual favors upon his brother. Armed with a pistol, Jeb surprises the lovers, but collapses from exhaustion. When Jeb orders Chicken to burn the agreement, the black reveals that he is the offspring of Jeb's mother and Rube the custodian, rather than the bastard of Jeb's father and an anonymous black woman, as was assumed. As Jeb dies of shock, the levee breaks, obliging Chicken and Myrtle to ascend to the roof of Waverly for refuge and sexual fulfillment. *Newlyweds. Brothers. Heirs. Go-go dancers. Caretakers. Mulattoes. Negroes. Inheritance. Impotence. Cancer. Illegitimacy. Marriage of convenience. Miscegenation. Television. Weddings. Marijuana. Floods. Wills. Louisiana.*
Note: Working title: *Blood Kin*. Location scenes filmed in Louisiana.

LAST OF THE RENEGADES (France/Italy/West Germany/Yugoslavia)
                                                                        F6.2698
Rialto-Film Preben Philipsen–S. N. C.–Jadran Film–Atlantis Film. *Dist* Columbia Pictures. Sep **1966**. Sd; col (Eastman Color). 35mm (CinemaScope). 93 min.
Prod Horst Wendlandt, Wolfgang Kühnlenz. *Dir* Harald Reinl. *Screenplay* Harald G. Petersson. *Photog* Ernst W. Kalinke. *Art Dir* Vladimir Tadej. *Film Ed* Hermann Haller. *Mus* Martin Böttcher. *Asst Dir* Charles M. Wakefield. *Prod Supv* Erwin Gitt. *Prod Mgr* Eberhard Junkersdorf. *Cost* Irms Pauli. *Still Photog* Gerd-Victor Krau, Lothar Winkler, Karl Reiter.
Cast: Lex Barker *(Old Shatterhand)*, Pierre Brice *(Winnetou)*, Anthony Steel *(Forrester)*, Karin Dor *(Ribanna)*, Klaus Kinski *(Luke)*. Mario Girotti *(Lieutenant Merril)*, Renato Baldini *(Col. J. F. Merril)*, Eddi Arent *(Lord Castlepool)*, Marie Noelle, Ilija Ivezić, Velimir Hitil, Mirko Boman, Rikard Brežeska.
Western melodrama. Source: Karl Friedrich May, *Winnetou, der röte Gentleman* (Freiberg im Breisgau, 1893). Apache chief Winnetou saves the life of Ribanna, the daughter of an Assiniboin chief who has declared war on the white settlers invading his tribe's hunting grounds. On his promise that he will try to keep the peace between the white men and the Indians, Winnetou intercedes on behalf of three troopers held captive by the Assiniboins, including young Lieutenant Merril, son of the local fort commander. Bud Forrester, an unscrupulous oilman, sends Luke and several other renegades to storm a Ponca settlement, after which they almost capture the lieutenant. The arrival of Old Shatterhand, Winnetou's blood brother, and his companion, Lord Castlepool, an English adventurer, prevents their abduction. Forced to burn his oil wells when Old Shatterhand arouses the oil workers against him, Forrester retaliates by kidnaping Lord Castlepool. Col. J. F. Merril acts as peacemaker, vowing to help Winnetou hunt down the perpetrators of the Ponca massacre, while his son guarantees the peace by offering to marry Ribanna. The rescue of Lord Castlepool by Winnetou and Old Shatterhand, and the uncovering of Forrester's plan to place the blame on the Indians for a recent attack of a wagon by his own men, pushes Forrester and his desperadoes to trap Lieutenant Merril, his wife, and the Indian women and children in a cave. Winnetou and his braves ride to their rescue, and peace is finally established. *Assiniboin Indians. Apache Indians. Settlers. Tribal chiefs. Peacemakers. Outlaws. Oilmen. Adventurers. Blood brothers. Desperadoes. Kidnaping. Marriage. Uprisings. Massacres. Oil wells. Fires. United States Army—Cavalry. Winnetou.*
Note: Filmed in Yugoslavia. Opened in Essen in Sep 1964 as *Winnetou— II. Teil*; running time: 94 min; in Rome caAug 1965 as *Giorni di fuoco*; in Paris in Oct 1965 as *Le trésor des montagnes bleues*. Yugoslavian title: *Vinetu II.*

THE LAST OF THE SECRET AGENTS?   **F6.2699**
Paramount Pictures. 25 May **1966** [Los Angeles opening; c16 May 1966; LP32467]. Sd; col (Technicolor). 35mm. 92 min.
Prod-Dir Norman Abbott. *Assoc Prod* Mel Tolkin. *Screenplay* Mel Tolkin. *Orig Story* Norman Abbott, Mel Tolkin. *Cinematog* Harold Stine. *Art Dir* Hal Pereira, Roland Anderson. *Set Decor* Robert R. Benton, James Payne. *Film Ed* Otho Lovering. *Mus* Pete King. *Orch* Frank Comstock. *Song:* "The Last of the Secret Agents" Lee Hazlewood. *Sung by* Nancy Sinatra. *Song:* "You Are" Neal Hefti. *Song:* "Don José Olé!" Pete King, Mel Tolkin, Norman Abbott. *Songs Sung by* Steve Rossi. *Choreog* Andre Tayir. *Sd* Harold Lewis, John Wilkinson. *1st Asst Dir* Francisco Day. *Prod Mgr* William C. Davidson. *Script Supv* Marvin Weldon. *Women's Cost Dsgn* Edith Head. *Makeup* Wally Westmore. *Hairstyling & Dressing* Nellie Manley. *Sp Photog Eff* Paul K. Lerpae. *Proc Photog* Farciot Edouart. *Prop* Martin Pendleton, Anthony Wade.
Cast: Marty Allen *(Marty Johnson)*, Steve Rossi *(Steve Donovan)*. John Williams *(J. Frederick Duval)*, Nancy Sinatra *(Micheline)*. Lou Jacobi *(Papa Leo)*, Carmen *(Baby May Zoftig)*, Theo Marcuse *(Zoltan Schubach)*. Connie Sawyer *(Florence)*, Ben Lessy *(Harry)*, Remo Pisani *(THEM # 1)*, Larry Duran *(THEM # 2)*, Thordis Brandt *(Fred Johnson)*, Wilhelm von Homburg *(GGI # 1)*, Aida Fries *(belly dancer)*, Edy Williams, Phyllis Davis *(beautiful girls)*. Don Keefer *(over-vain spy)*, Emanuel Thomas *(frogman)*, Philip Sascombe *(Englishman)*, Paul Daniel *(milkman)*, Sig Ruman *(German scientist)*. Ed Sullivan *(himself)*, Harvey Korman *(German colonel)*, Loren Ewing.
Action comedy. Marty Johnson and Steve Donovan, two American tourists in France, unwittingly become involved in the operations of THEM, an international band of art thieves headed by the diabolical Zolten Schubach. Pressed into working for GGI (Good Guys Inc.), which is the nemesis of THEM, Marty and Steve are given The Umbrella, a multi-purpose piece of spy apparatus rejected by James Bond and Derek Flint. While entertaining guests at Schubach's chateau, Marty and Steve learn that THEM is planning to steal the Venus di Milo when it is shipped to the London World's Fair. Using The Umbrella to wire their finding to GGI, the two receive orders to stay with the gang until it can be apprehended. Bedlam then follows aboard a Paris-bound

train and in a helicopter tracking the vehicle carrying the famed statue. The thieves are captured, and Marty and Steve return to the United States as heroes. But just as they are being hailed as the protectors of national treasures, helicopter cables are removing the Statue of Liberty from its foundation. *Tourists. Americans in foreign countries. Secret agents. Thieves. Conspiracy. Art. Trains. Helicopters. France. Venus di Milo. Statue of Liberty.*

THE LAST OF THE SKI BUMS　　　　　　　　　　　　F6.2700

Dick Barrymore. *Dist* U-M Film Distributors. 10 Nov **1969** [New York opening]. Sd; col (Technicolor). 35mm. 86 min. *MPAA rating* G.

Prod-Dir-Writ Dick Barrymore. *Assoc Proc* Douglas Barrymore. *Photog* Dick Barrymore. *Adtl Photog* Earl Rickers, Bill Amberg. *Mus* The Sandals. *Song:* "*Ski Bum*" Jud Strunk.

Cast: Ron Funk, Mike Zuetell, Ed Ricks *(themselves)*, Dick Barrymore *(narrator)*.

Featured Participants: Jean-Claude Killy, Heini Messner, Gerhard Nenning, Bernard Orcel, Guy Périllat, Pepi Stiegler, Robert Didier, Désiré La Croix, Eddy La Croix, Gérard Verneret, Leonard Erhardter, Herbert Jochum, Roland Couttet, Yvon Masino, Lionel Wibault, Ted Johnson, Bill Tishman, Sam Southwick, Stephen Sodat *(skiers)*, Gaston Rebuffat *(mountain climber)*.

Sports documentary. American ski bum Mike Zuetell meets veteran Ron Funk in France, and they set out together in a Volkswagen microbus to ski in the Alps. Along the way they pick up a third American, Ed Ricks. Their money soon runs out, but by employing a mathematical system developed in Zuetell's doctoral thesis on games of chance, they win a fortune at roulette in Monte Carlo. They buy a Porsche and visit the highest peaks in Europe, skiing and watching some of the world's greatest skiers. In their travels they meet famed mountain climber Gaston Rebuffat. When their money runs out again they return to Monte Carlo and sell the Porsche for capital. This time, however, they lose everything, and they set out on foot for further skiing adventures. *Skiers. Gambling. Mountain climbing. Megève (France). Val d'Isère (France). Alpe-d'Huez (France). Courchevel (France). Chamonix. Vallée Blanche (France). Zürs. Sestriere (Italy). Tasman Glacier (New Zealand). Switzerland. Monte Carlo. Gran Monte (Italy). Volkswagen automobiles. Porsche automobiles.*

Note: Filmed in Aspen, Colorado; Jackson Hole, Wyoming; Megève, Val d'Isère, Alpe-d'Huez, Courchevel, Chamonix, and Vallée Blanche, France; Zürs, Austria; Sestriere and Gran Monte, Italy; Switzerland; Monte Carlo; and the Tasman Glacier in New Zealand. Filmed in 16mm.

LAST OF THE TWO DOLLAR———　　　　　　　　　　F6.2701

Dist Chancellor Films. ca **1970**. Sd; col. 35mm. 60 min.

Sex film. A middle-aged prostitute who will do almost anything for a little money, entertains a group of men in a variety of sexual encounters. *Prostitutes. Sexual techniques. Middle age.*

LAST OF THE VIKINGS (France/Italy)　　　　　　　F6.2702

Tiberius Film-Galatea-Les Films du Cyclope-Critérion Film. *Dist* Medallion Pictures. 16 May **1962** [San Francisco opening]. Sd; col (Eastmancolor). 35mm (Dyaliscope). 102 min.

Pres by Samuel Schneider. *Prod* Roberto Capitani, Luigi Mondello. *Dir* Giacomo Gentilomo. *Screenplay* Arpad De Riso, Guido Zurli, Luigi Mondello. *Adapt* Arpad De Riso, Guido Zurli, Giacomo Gentilomo. *Photog* Enzo Serafin. *Art Dir* Saverio D'Eugenio. *Film Ed* Gino Talamo. *Mus* Roberto Nicolosi. *Cost* Tigano & Lo Faro.

Cast: Cameron Mitchell *(Harald)*, Edmund Purdom *(Sven)*, Isabelle Corey *(Hilde)*, Hélène Rémy *(Elga)*, Aldo Bufi Landi *(Londborg)*, Andrea Aureli *(Haakon)*, Giorgio Ardisson *(Guntar)*, Carla Calò *(Herta)*, Nando Tamberlani *(Gultred)*, Corrado Annicelli *(Godrun)*, Broderick Crawford *([see note])*, Andrea Checchi, Piero Lulli, Mario Feliciani, Benito Stefanelli.

Adventure melodrama. Harald, the Viking prince, returns to Viken after spending years at sea and learns that his father has been murdered by treacherous King Sven of Norway. When he also learns that Sven plans to form an alliance with the Danes by forcing his half sister, Hilde, to marry the Danish king, Harald rallies the surviving Vikings and plots his revenge. Posing as Danes, he and his men penetrate Sven's formidable fortress. A rival Viking chieftain, Haakon, exposes the deception, however, and Harald is unmasked. He manages to escape, but his younger brother Guntar is killed. After returning to the Great Viking Hall and slaying the villainous Haakon, Harald leads the attack against Sven's fortress. The king is killed, Hilde is rescued, and peace is restored to Viken. *Vikings. Royalty. Danes. Brothers. Norwegians. Revenge. Imposture. Murder.*

Note: Location scenes filmed in Norway. Opened in Rome in Mar 1961 as *L'ultimo dei Vichinghi*; running time: 100 min; in Paris in Sep 1961 as *Le dernier des Vikings*; running time: 105 min. Broderick Crawford is not credited in U. S. sources.

THE LAST OUTPOST see CAVALRY CHARGE

THE LAST REBEL (Mexico)　　　　　　　　　　　　F6.2703

Hispano Continental Films. *Dist* Sterling World Distributors. 11 Jan **1961** [Kansas City, Missouri, opening]. Sd; col (Eastman Color). 35mm. 83 min.

Prod-Dir Miguel Contreras Torres. *Screenplay* Miguel Contreras Torres, Manuel R. Ojeda. *Story* Miguel Contreras Torres. *Photog* José Ortiz Ramos. *Art Dir* Ramón Rodríguez Granada. *Film Ed* José Bustos. *Mus* Federico Ruiz. *Sd* Nicolás de la Rosa.

Cast: Carlos Thompson *(Joaquin Murrieta)*, Ariadne Welter *(Clara)*, Rodolfo Acosta *("Three Fingers" Jack)*, Charles Fawcett *(Capt. Harry Love)*, Lee Morgan *(Lang)*, Eduardo Noriega, John Kelly, Rebeca Iturbide, Carlos Múzquiz, Eduardo González Pliego, Federico Curiel, Leopoldo Ortín, Manuel Arvide, Tony Carbajal, Antonio Raxell, Claudio Brook, Bertha Lehar.

Western melodrama. In the California gold rush town of Sonora, the wife and brother of Joaquin Murrieta, a peaceful prospector, are brutally murdered by five miners. Vowing to have revenge on all gold miners, Murrieta organizes a band of outlaws and sets out on a campaign of terror. Three hundred die at the hands of his gang, and all attempts to trap him fail. It is only when the Texas Rangers, led by Capt. Harry Love, meet the outlaws in a gun battle that Murrieta is finally slain, along with his henchman "Three Fingers" Jack. Despite his murderous deeds, he is mourned by the Mexican peasants because he had often brought them generous gifts. *Prospectors. Outlaws. Peasants. Gold rushes. Murder. Revenge. Sonora (California). Texas Rangers. Joaquín Murrieta.*

Note: Produced in Mexico in 1956 as *El último rebelde*; running time: 91 min.

THE LAST SAFARI (Great Britain)　　　　　　　　F6.2704

Paramount Film Service. *Dist* Paramount Pictures. 1 Nov **1967** [Kansas City, Missouri, opening; c1 Nov 1967; LP35095]. Sd; col (Technicolor). 35mm. 110 min. [Also 115 min.]

Prod-Dir Henry Hathaway. *2d Unit Dir* Richard Talmadge. *Screenplay* John Gay. *Dir Photog* Ted Moore. *Camera Op* Robert Kindred. *2d Unit Photog* John Coquillon. *Art Dir* Maurice Fowler. *Film Ed* John Bloom. *Mus Comp & Dir* John Dankworth. *Sd* Norman Bolland, Gordon K. McCallum. *Asst Dir* Ron Carr. *Prod Mgr* Geoffrey Helman. *Wardrobe* Brian Owen-Smith. *Makeup* Neville Smallwood. *Coöp* Kenya Government, Kenya Game & Parks.

Cast: Kaz Garas *(Casey)*, Stewart Granger *(Gilchrist)*, Gabriella Licudi *(Grant)*, Johnny Sekka *(Jama)*, Liam Redmond *(Alec Beaumont)*, Eugene Deckers *(refugee leader)*, David Munya *(Chongu)*, John De Villiers *(Rich)*, Wilfred Moore *(game warden)*, Jean Parnell *(Mrs. Beaumont)*, Bill Grant, actor *(commissioner)*, John Sutton *(Harry)*, Kipkoske *(Gavai)*, Labina *(village chief)*, Masai Wakamba Tribal Dancers.

Adventure melodrama. Source: Gerald Hanley, *Gilligan's Last Elephant* (Cleveland, 1962). American playboy millionaire Casey's plans for a Kenya safari include every conceivable luxury. Disgusted, veteran safari guide Miles Gilchrist refuses to work for Casey and sets out alone on a hunt for the killer elephant that took the life of his closest friend. Learning that Miles holds himself partly to blame for his friend's death, Casey decides to follow Miles. After reproving Alec Beaumont, a profiteering white hunter who refuses to allow the halfbreed Grant (Casey's mistress) to eat at his table, Casey trails Miles and helps him save a group of whites ambushed in a Masai village. The two men gradually develop a mutual respect, and they join forces in fighting off an attacking rhino; but later, Miles loses his nerve, and he and Casey are nearly killed by a herd of charging elephants. Aware that Miles must be the one to destroy the killer elephant, Casey refuses to fire when they once again encounter the animal. Though the elephant presents a perfect target, Miles simply stands squarely before his quarry and refrains from squeezing the trigger—the return of his self-confidence is proof enough that he has regained his status. Casey bids Miles farewell and leaves Africa. The unhappy Grant, somehow at home in the rapidly changing new Africa, remains behind in the hope of finding another wealthy would-be hunter. *Americans in foreign countries. Playboys. Millionaires. Halfcastes. Mistresses. Hunters. Masai. Friendship. Self-confidence. Safaris. Kenya. Elephants. Rhinoceros.*

Note: Location scenes filmed in Kenya and East Africa. Opened in London in Dec 1967; running time: 99 min.

THE LAST SHOT YOU HEAR (Great Britain)　　　　F6.2705

Lippert Films. *Dist* Twentieth Century-Fox Film Corp. Feb **1969** [c31 Dec 1968; LP36651]. Sd; b&w. 35mm. 91 min. [Also 86 min.] *MPAA rating* R.

Prod Jack Parsons. *Exec Prod* Robert L. Lippert. *Dir* Gordon Hessler. *Screenplay* Tim Shields. *Dir Photog* David Holmes. *Camera Op* Gerry Massy-Collier. *Art Dir* Ken Ryan. *Film Ed* Robert Winter. *Asst Film Ed* Glenn Hyde. *Mus Comp* Bert Shefter. *Cond* Johnny Pearson. *Orch* Len Stevens. *Song:* "*Only Yesterday*" Jack Ackerman, Stella Stevens, Bert Shefter. *Sung by* Stella Stevens, Bill Henderson. *Sd Rec* Don Thompson. *Sd Re-rec* Doug Turner. *Asst*

Dir Ray Frift. *Prod Supv* Pat Green. *Cont* Barbara Rowland. *Wardrobe* Gloria Barnes. *Makeup* Ricky Rickerby. *Hairdresser* Henry Montsash.

Cast: Hugh Marlowe *(Dr. Charles Nordeck)*, Zena Walker *(Eileen)*, Patricia Haines *(Anne Nordeck)*, William Dysart *(Peter Marriott)*, Thorley Walters *(General Jowett)*, Joan Young *(Mrs. Jowett)*, Lionel Murton *(Rubens)*, Helen Horton *(Dodie Rubens)*, John Nettleton *(Detective Inspector Nash)*, John Wentworth *(Chambers)*, Alister Williamson *(CID officer)*, Julian Holloway *(brash young man)*, Lynley Laurence *(pretty girl)*, Daphne Barker *(woman reporter)*, James Mellor, Ian Hamilton *(reporters)*, Shaun Curry *(diver)*, Stephen Moore *(Peter's colleague)*, Job Stewart *(police officer)*, Janet Kelly *(receptionist)*.

Crime melodrama. Source: William Fairchild, *The Sound of Murder* (London opening: 5 Aug 1959). Dr. Charles Nordeck is a famous writer, lecturer, and marriage counselor whose own marriage is a failure. His wife, Anne, wants a divorce, but Nordeck refuses to grant it because of the damaging effect that it would have on his career. He is, however, tolerant of his wife's love affair with Peter Marriott, a foreign correspondent. Anne and Peter decide that their only recourse is to murder Nordeck. But a conversation concerning their plan is inadvertently recorded on a dictating machine and later discovered by Nordeck's secretary, Eileen, who is also in love with Peter. Anne arranges an alibi, and Peter goes to their home and shoots Nordeck with the doctor's own gun. Anne returns with the police and is startled to find Nordeck's body missing. Soon afterward, the police find Nordeck's personal belongings by a river and conclude that he was drowned. Later, Eileen reveals to the lovers her knowledge of their plan and agrees not to inform the police if Peter will marry her instead of Anne. Left with no real alternative, the lovers agree. Eileen and Peter prepare to leave the country together, but at the last moment she changes her mind and leaves Peter a note which contains the truth. Back at the house, Anne is terrified to confront her husband, who admits that he and Eileen planned the entire operation and loaded the gun with blanks. Nordeck threatens to use the tape recording to ensure the continuance of his marriage to Anne. He also telephones the police and informs them that he is still alive. Peter arrives, however; and having no knowledge of the phone call, decides to carry out his original plan to murder Nordeck. *Authors. Lecturers. Reporters. Secretaries. Police. Marriage counsel. Divorce. Infidelity. Murder. Blackmail. Recorders.*

Note: Released in Great Britain in Mar 1970.

THE LAST STEP DOWN　　　　　　　　　　　　　F6.2706
RAC Films. *Dist* Republic Amusements Corp. ca **1970**. Sd; col (Eastman Color). 35mm. 67 min.

Prod-Writ Phil Miller, Arthur Allen. *Assoc Prod* Russ Nannarello. *Dir* Lawrence Ramport. *Photog* Edward Claire. *Crew Supv* Russ Nannarello.

Cast: Beatrice Stolen, Olivia James, Terry Johnson, Michael Valentine.

Drama. Prostitutes Norma and Sue decide to initiate Kathy, a virgin, into prostitution. They take her to a hidden monastery where devil worshipers are holding a black mass. Kathy zealously submits to a series of sexual assaults during the black mass, in reality, an orgy. Norma and Sue force Kathy to join them in a lesbian orgy when they perceive that the bacchanal has stripped her of her inhibitions. *Prostitutes. Sexual initiation. Lesbianism. Demonology. Monasteries. Cults. Orgies.*

LAST SUMMER　　　　　　　　　　　　　　　　　F6.2707
Alsid Productions–Francis Productions. *Dist* Allied Artists. 10 Jun **1969** [New York opening]. Sd; col (Eastman Color). 35mm. 97 min. [Also reviewed at 100 min.] *MPAA rating X.*

Pres by Emanuel L. Wolf. *Prod* Alfred W. Crown, Sidney Beckerman. *Assoc Prod* Joel Glickman. *Dir* Frank Perry. *Screenplay* Eleanor Perry. *Photog* Gerald Hirschfeld. *Art Dir* Peter Dohanos. *Film Ed* Sidney Katz, Marion Kraft. *Mus* John Simon. *Sd* Charles Federmack, Nat Boxer. *Asst Dir* Terence A. Donnelly, Gene Sultan. *Prod Mgr* Phil Goldfarb. *Cost* Theoni V. Aldredge. *Animal Trainers* James Dannaldson, Mrs. James Dannaldson.

Cast: Barbara Hershey *(Sandy)*, Richard Thomas *(Peter)*, Bruce Davison *(Dan)*, Cathy Burns *(Rhoda)*, Ernesto Gonzalez *(Anibal)*, Peter Turgeon *(Mr. Caudell)*, Lou Gary, Andrew Krance, Wayne Mayer *(town hoods)*, Ralph Waite *(Peter's father)*, Conrad Bain *(Dan's father)*, Eileen Letchworth *(Dan's mother)*, Maeve McGuire *(younger woman)*, Ed Stevlingson *(Sidney)*, Glen Walker *(boy at dance)*, Lydia Wilen *(waitress)*.

Drama. Source: Evan Hunter, *Last Summer* (Garden City, New York, 1968). While spending the summer on Fire Island, Peter and Dan, two adolescent boys from upper middle-class families, meet Sandy, a young girl who has found a wounded sea gull on the beach. After the boys remove a fishhook from the bird's throat, the three youngsters become fast friends and spend all their time together—swimming, boating, smoking marijuana and cautiously experimenting with their awakening sexual impulses during visits to a movie house on the mainland. One afternoon they are joined by Rhoda, a plump 15-year-old who is anxious to make friends. When the boys discover that Sandy has brutally killed the gull for biting her, Peter begins to shift his attention to

Rhoda. Meanwhile, Sandy receives a response from a computer dating service. Finding it fun to taunt Rhoda about her inexperience with boys, Sandy gets Peter and Dan to persuade the reluctant Rhoda to take her place, and all four go to a restaurant to meet the shy Puerto Rican Anibal. To Rhoda's embarrassment, Sandy, Dan, and Peter get the man drunk and abandon him to three local bullies. Although Rhoda rebukes Peter for his behavior, she succeeds only in alienating him, and he goes off with Sandy and Dan for a picnic in the woods. Dan's plan of proving his manhood to Sandy is ruined when Rhoda tags along. Irritated by Rhoda's intrusion into their clique, Sandy removes her bikini top and dares Rhoda to do the same. Disgusted, Rhoda tries to leave, but Sandy goads the boys into holding her back. The frightened girl appeals to Peter for help, but he joins Sandy in pinning Rhoda to the ground while she is savagely raped by Dan. Following the assault, the three leave; Sandy and Dan return to the beach while Peter hesitates on a sand dune near Rhoda. *Puerto Ricans. Adolescence. Rape. Drunkenness. Wealth. Vacations. Motion picture theaters. Marijuana. Computer dating services. Summer. Fire Island. Sea gulls.*

Note: Location scenes filmed on Fire Island, and in Bay Shore, New York. X rating was changed to R after several min. were cut.

LAST SUMMER WON'T HAPPEN　　　　　　　　F6.2708
Tundra East Village Co. *Dist* Film-Makers' Cooperative, Newsreel, Leacock Pennebaker Inc. 3 Mar **1969** [New York opening]. Sd; col. 16mm. 80 min.

Prod-Dir Peter Gessner, Tom Hurwitz. *Photog* Peter Gessner. *Adtl Photog* Richard Rice. *Film Ed* Peter Gessner, Tom Hurwitz. *Mus* Country Joe & the Fish, Procol Harum. *Sd* Tom Hurwitz.

Documentary. Young people living in the East Village section of New York City are seen in the context of their rebellion against materialism, corruption, and capitalism in American society and of the transformation of this rebellion into activism. Focus is centered on the hippie movement in transition from an orientation toward "love" and "dropping out" to an increasing confrontation with the established political and social structure. Appearing in the film are runaways, drug dealers, political activists, and community figures, including Abbie Hoffman and Paul Krassner. The film concludes as co-filmmaker Peter Gessner wonders aloud what the enormous amount of energy generated by modern life will produce. *Revolutionaries. Hippies. Drug dealers. Runaways. Demonstrations. Radicalism. Urban life. New York City—East Village. Abbie Hoffman. Paul Krassner.*

THE LAST SUNSET　　　　　　　　　　　　　　F6.2709
Bryna Productions. *Dist* Universal–International. 7 Jun **1961** [Chicago opening; c10 May 1961; LP25014]. Sd; col (Eastman Color). 35mm. 112 min.

Prod Eugene Frenke, Edward Lewis. *Dir* Robert Aldrich. *Screenplay* Dalton Trumbo. *Dir Photog* Ernest Laszlo. *Art Dir* Alexander Golitzen, Alfred Sweeney. *Set Decor* Oliver Emert. *Supv Film Ed* Edward Mann. *Film Ed* Michael Luciano. *Mus* Ernest Gold. *Mus Cond* Joseph Gershenson. *Song:* "Pretty Little Girl in the Yellow Dress" Dimitri Tiomkin, Ned Washington. *Sd* Waldon O. Watson, Don Cunliffe. *Asst Dir* Tom Connors, Nate Slott. *Unit Prod Mgr* Joseph Behm. *Cost* Norma Koch. *Makeup* Bud Westmore. *Hairstyles* Larry Germain.

Cast: Rock Hudson *(Dana Stribling)*, Kirk Douglas *(Brendan O'Malley)*, Dorothy Malone *(Belle Breckenridge)*, Joseph Cotten *(John Breckenridge)*, Carol Lynley *(Missy Breckenridge)*, Neville Brand *(Frank Hobbs)*, Regis Toomey *(Milton Wing)*, Rad Fulton *(Julesburg Kid)*, Adam Williams *(Calverton)*, Jack Elam *(Ed Hobbs)*, John Shay *(Bowman)*, Margarito Luna *(José)*, José Torvay *(Rosario)*.

Western melodrama. Source: Howard Rigsby, *Sundown at Crazy Horse* (New York, 1957). American lawman Dana Stribling rides into Mexico in search of Brendan O'Malley, wanted for the murder of Dana's brother-in-law. He finds O'Malley working for John Breckenridge, a whisky-sodden cattleman readying his herd for a drive across the border to the Texas town of Crazy Horse. (O'Malley has been trying unsuccessfully to resume an affair he had 16 years before with Breckenridge's wife, Belle.) Dana, unable to serve his warrant in Mexico, signs on as a trail boss, but not before warning O'Malley that a showdown is imminent the minute they cross the border. Shortly after the trek begins, Breckenridge is killed in a barroom brawl. Dana and O'Malley take over the drive and, though still enemies, gradually develop a grudging admiration for each other. As the days pass, Belle and Dana fall in love and O'Malley is pursued by Belle's teenaged daughter, Missy. After some adventures along the way, the company arrives with the herd at the Rio Grande. Before crossing, Belle decides to celebrate. Missy dresses up in one of her mother's gowns, and O'Malley, startled by her resemblance to the Belle of 16 years ago, makes ardent love to her. Belle then confronts him with the knowledge that Missy is his daughter. Shattered by the revelation, O'Malley empties his pistol and permits Dana to kill him in their showdown. *Ranchers. Gunfighters. Cattlemen. Outlaws. Incest. Suicide. Murder. Rio Grande. Mexico. Mexican border. Cattle.*

Note: Filmed in Mexico, including exteriors in Aguascalientes.

THE LAST TIME I SAW ARCHIE   F6.2710

Mark VII Ltd.-Manzanita-Talbot Productions. *Dist* United Artists. 27 May **1961** [New York opening; c27 May 1961; LP20350]. Sd; b&w. 35mm. 98 min.

Prod-Dir Jack Webb. *Screenplay* William Bowers. *Dir Photog* Joseph MacDonald. *Art Dir* Field Gray. *Set Decor* John Sturtevant. *Film Ed* Robert Leeds. *Mus Comp & Cond* Frank Comstock. *Sd* Frank Sarver. *Asst Dir* Chico Day. *Wardrobe* Jesse Munden, Sabine Manela. *Makeup Artist* Stanley Campbell. *Hairstyles* Joan St. Oegger. *Sp Eff* A. Paul Pollard.

Cast: Robert Mitchum (*Archie Hall*), Jack Webb (*Bill Bowers*), Martha Hyer (*Peggy Kramer*), France Nuyen (*Cindy*), Joe Flynn (*Pvt. Russell Drexel*), James Lydon (*Pvt. Billy Simpson*), Del Moore (*Pvt. Frank Ostrow*), Louis Nye (*Pvt. Sam Beacham*), Richard Arlen (*Colonel Martin*), Don Knotts (*Captain Little*), Robert Strauss (*M/Sgt. Stanley Erlenheim*), Harvey Lembeck (*Sgt. Malcolm Greenbriar*), Claudia Barrett (*Lola*), Theona Bryant (*Daphne*), Elaine Davis (*Carole*), Marilyn Burtis (*Patsy Ruth*), James Mitchum (*corporal*), Gene McCarthy (*bartender*), John Nolan (*Lieutenant Oglemeyer*), Martin Dean (*first 2d lieutenant*), Bill Kilmer, Phil Gordon, Dick Cathcart (*soldiers*).

Comedy. In the waning days of World War II, a number of overaged and overweight civilian pilots are drafted into the Army Air Force to ferry aircraft and transport supplies. With the arrival of combat pilots rotated from the war zones, the older men soon find themselves with little or nothing to do. One of the group, Pvt. Archie Hall, is a born goldbrick. By swaggering around the base while jotting down notes on a clipboard, he avoids unpleasant details and convinces both officers and noncoms that he is a disguised general on a mission. Before long, he and his buddy, Pvt. Bill Bowers, are spending most of their time off the base in the company of two attractive young women, Peggy Kramer and Cindy, a Japanese-American. Eventually it becomes apparent to Archie and his buddies that Cindy, who has been giving them money, is really a spy. When it is revealed that she is exactly the opposite—a lure set to trap a real spy ring—Archie somehow manages to wangle a medal for his participation in the affair. Upon their discharge from the army, Archie and Bowers go to Hollywood and obtain jobs at a movie studio, where, as time passes, Bowers remains a scriptwriter slaving away in a small cubicle of an office. Meanwhile, Archie, still a goldbrick, succeeds in becoming head of the studio. *Air pilots. Japanese. Spies. Veterans. Motion picture scriptwriters. Motion pictures. United States Army—Air Force. World War II. Hollywood.*

Note: Location scenes filmed at Ft. MacArthur, California. Based on actual World War II experiences of screenplay writer William Bowers.

THE LAST TOMB OF LIGEIA *see* **THE TOMB OF LIGEIA**

THE LAST WOMAN OF SHANG (Hong Kong)   F6.2711

Shaw Brothers (H. K.) Ltd. *Dist* Frank Lee International. 14 Dec **1964** [New York opening]. Sd; col (Eastmancolor). 35mm (Shawscope). 107 min.

Prod Run Run Shaw. *Dir* Yueh Feng. *Screenplay* Wang Yueh-ting. *Photog* Ho Lan-shan. *Art Dir* Chen Chi-jui, Chen Chin-shen. *Film Ed* Chiang Hsing-lung. *Mus Score* Wang Fu-ling. *Lyr* Chen Di-ye. *Sd* Wang Yung-hua. *Asst Dir* Wang Shing-lei, Lim Tai-chun.

Cast: Lin Dai (*Ta Chi*), Pat Ting Hung (*Chi Yen*), Shin Yung-kyoon (*King Chou*), Ching Miao (*Duke of Sipa*), Chiang Kuang-chao (*Yiu Hun*), Yang Chih-ching (*Pei Kan*), Li Ye-chuan (*Fei Chung*), Nam Koong-woon (*Chi Fa*), Tien Feng (*Su Fu*), Chen Yung-hua (*Queen Chiang*), Fung Yee, Li Yuen-chung, Lam Way-li.

Adventure melodrama. In 12th-century B. C. China, Ta Chi seeks revenge against the cruel Emperor Chou whose constant demands for taxes have driven her father to his death. Feigning love for the emperor, Ta Chi demands that he build a tower tall enough to pluck the stars from the heavens for her. The project drains the royal treasury and causes unrest among the people. Chi Fa understands the motives behind his friend's actions, but seeing the misery they are causing, he vows to kill both Ta Chi and the emperor. Captured by the emperor, he escapes with the help of Ta Chi, whose treachery nevertheless is discovered. Chi Fa returns to the palace with a rebel army, which traps Ta Chi and the emperor in the burning tower. Ta Chi dies knowing that the emperor's downfall is complete. *Royalty. Revenge. Perfidy. Revolts. Taxes. China.*

Note: Location scenes filmed in South Korea. Produced in Hong Kong in 1962 as *Ta Chi*. Also reviewed at 109 and 147 min.

LAST YEAR AT MARIENBAD (France/Italy)   F6.2712

Terra Films–Société Nouvelle des Films Cormoran–Como Films–Précitel–Argos Films–Les Films Tamara–Cinétel–Silver Films–Cineriz. *Dist* Astor Pictures. 7 Mar **1962** [New York opening]. Sd; b&w. 35mm (Dyaliscope). 93 min. [Also reviewed at 99 min.]

Prod Pierre Courau, Raymond Froment. *Assoc Prod* Léon Sanz. *Dir* Alain Resnais. *Screenplay & Dial* Alain Robbe-Grillet. *Dir Photog* Sacha Vierny. *Camera* Philippe Brun. *Asst Op* Guy Delattre, François Lauliac. *Art Dir* Jacques Saulnier. *Set Decor* Georges Glon, André Piltant, Jean-Jacques Fabre.

Scenic Artist Charles Mérangel. *Main Titl* Jean Fouchet. *Film Ed* Henri Colpi, Jasmine Chasney. *Mus* Francis Seyrig. *Cond* André Girard. *Organist* Marie-Louise Girod. *Sd* Guy Villette. *Sd Rec* Jean-Claude Marchetti, René Renault, Jean Nény, Robert Cambourakis. *Asst to Mr. Resnais* Jean Léon. *2d Asst Dir* Volker Schlöndorff, Florence Malraux. *Prod Mgr* Michel Choquet. *Asst Prod Mgr* Jean-Jacques Lecot. *Prod Sec* Janine Thaon. *Script Girl* Sylvette Baudrot. *Cost* Bernard Evein. *Miss Seyrig's Gowns* Chanel. *Makeup* Alexandre Marcus. *English Subtitl* Noelle Gillmor. *English Intro* Alan Edwards. *Ch Electrn* Elie Fontanille. *Ch Engr* Louis Balthazard, René Stocki. *Still Photog* Georges Pierre.

Cast: Delphine Seyrig (*A/woman*), Giorgio Albertazzi (*X/stranger*), Sacha Pitoeff (*M/man/husband or lover*), Françoise Bertin, Luce Garcia-Ville, Héléna Kornel, François Spira, Karin Toeche-Mittler, Pierre Barbaud, Wilhelm von Deek, Jean Lanier, Gérard Lorin, Davide Montemuri, Gilles Quéant, Gabriel Werner.

Drama. Among the wealthy clientele at a lavish palace-spa are a man, X, a woman, A, and another man, M, who may be her husband or lover. While the other guests indulge in the games of the idle rich, X confronts A and reminds her that they met the previous year at Frederiksbad, or perhaps at Marienbad. Although the woman denies knowing him, X insists that they had an affair, that she suggested they meet this year at this hotel, and that she agreed to consider going away with him. At first the woman takes his story as a joke, but it soon becomes apparent that this is not a game. The other guests (seen only in profile), the silent string quartet, the domino games, and the performance of Ibsen's *Rosmersholm* lose their importance as the surface reality becomes lost in the private realities of the protagonists. Positive of their last meeting, X persists in his persuasion, filling the woman's mind with images that gradually become real, or seem to become real, to her. Inside the hotel, with its baroque furnishings, formal gardens, and sculpture, X and A go from one point in time to another, changing clothes and locale as X continues to try to convince A that his recollections of last year are true. Ultimately she is forced to overcome her fear and become what the stranger says she is—his lover; unquestioning, she leaves with him. *Idle rich. Memory. Resorts. Games. Marienbad. "Rosmersholm".*

Note: Location scenes filmed in Munich, including the chateaux of Nymphenburg and Schleissheim. Opened in Paris in Sep 1961 as *L'année dernière à Marienbad*; running time: 100 min; in Rome in Nov 1961 as *L'anno scorso a Marienbad*; running time: 90 min.

LATITUDE ZERO (United States/Japan)   F6.2713

Toho Co.–Don Sharp Productions. *Dist* National General Pictures. 13 May **1970** [Dallas opening; c29 Jul 1969; LF57]. Sd; col (Eastmancolor). 35mm. 99 min. [Copyright length: 106 min.] MPAA rating G.

Prod Tomoyuki Tanaka. *Dir* Ishiro Honda. *Story & Screenplay* Ted Sherdeman. *Screenplay Adv* Shinichi Sekizawa. *Photog* Taiichi Kankura. *Lighting* Kiichi Onda. *Set Decor* Takeo Kita. *Film Ed* Ume Takeda. *Mus* Akira Ifukube. *Rec* Masao Fujiyoshi. *Sd Eff* Sadamasa Nishimoto. *Mix* Hisashi Shimonaga. *Asst Dir* Seiji Tani. *Prod Mgr* Yasuaki Sakamoto. *Cost* Kiichi Ichida, Linda Glazman. *Dir Sp Eff* Eiji Tsuburaya. *Creative Adv* Warren Lewis.

Cast: Joseph Cotten (*Capt. Craig McKenzie*), Cesar Romero (*Malic*), Richard Jaeckel (*Perry Lawton*), Patricia Medina (*Lucretia*), Linda Haynes (*Dr. Anne Barton*), Akira Takarada (*Dr. Ken Tashiro*), Masumi Okada (*Dr. Jules Masson*), Hikaru Kuroki (*Kroiga*), Mari Nakayama ("*Tsuroko*" *Okada*), Tetsu Nakamura (*Pirate*), Akihiko Hirata, Kin Omae.

Science fiction melodrama. Based on the "Latitude Zero" stories by Ted Sherdeman. Oceanographer Dr. Tashiro, physicist Dr. Masson, and newspaperman Perry Lawton are exploring the ocean in a bathysphere when a volcano erupts, causing them to lose control of their vessel. The three explorers are saved by Captain McKenzie, the commander of the submarine *Alpha*, and he takes them to the undersea city of Latitude Zero, populated by scientists dedicated to the betterment of mankind. On the nearby island of Blood Rock, however, Malic the Murderer plans to kidnap Dr. Okada, who has discovered a serum to protect man against radiation. Malic succeeds in his scheme and takes Okada to Blood Rock where he hopes to learn the scientist's secret by transplanting his brain. Captain McKenzie attempts to rescue Okada but encounters a group of monsters created by Malic to defend the island. McKenzie fights off gigantic rats, a crossbreed of men and bats, and the griffin, a lion-eagle creature, before he is able to rescue Okada; Malic, meanwhile, is destroyed by one of his own hybrid monsters. Tashiro and Masson decide to remain in Latitude Zero, but Perry decides to return to land and tell the spectacular story of their voyage. *Oceanographers. Physicists. Newspapermen. Scientists. Exploration. Kidnaping. Rescue. Volcanoes. Submarines. Islands. Underwater cities. Underwater laboratories. Experiments. Serums. Monsters. Rats. Bats.*

Note: Released in Japan in 1969 as *Ido Zero daisakusen*. The participation of Don Sharp Productions is unconfirmed.

THE LAUGHING WOMAN (Italy)   **F6.2714**
   Cemo Film. *Dist* Audubon Films. 8 Apr **1970** [Washington, D. C., opening].
Sd; col (Eastman Color). 35mm. 90 min.
   Pres by Radley Metzger. *Prod* Giuseppe Zaccariello. *Dir* Piero Schivazappa.
Screenplay Piero Schivazappa, Paolo Levi, J. Mc. Lee. *Dir Photog* Sante
Achilli. *Scenic Dsgn* Francesco Cuppini. *Film Ed* Carlo Reali. *Mus* Stelvio
Cipriani. *Cost* Enrico Sabbatini.
   Cast: Philippe Leroy (*Dr. Sayer*), Dagmar Lassander (*Maria*), Maria Cumani
Quasimodo (*secretary*), Mirella Pamphili (*streetwalker*), Lorenza Guerrieri.
   Melodrama. Dr. Sayer, the director of a philanthropic foundation, spends his
weekends at his luxurious villa outside of Rome toying with sadistic fantasies.
His games are usually acted out with the help of a prostitute conversant with
his desires. When his regular prostitute becomes unavailable at the last minute,
Sayer substitutes Maria, a young journalist on his staff. After the drugged Maria
regains consciousness at his villa, Sayer realizes that he now has a real victim
on his hands. After enduring the torture, Maria realizes that Sayer's problem
is that he doubts his own virility. Maria plays up to him until Sayer confesses
that he has never really done these things before, and he begins to fall in love
with her. Finally enticing Sayer to have relations with her in a swimming pool
after a long, idyllic day together, Maria excites him to the point that he has a
heart attack and drowns. It is then revealed that Maria was in league with the
prostitute to destroy Sayer and other men. *Prostitutes. Journalists. Sadism.
Torture. Fantasy. Abduction. Seduction. Rome.*
   Note: Produced in Italy in 1969 as *Femina ridens*.

LAUGHTER IN THE DARK (France/Great Britain)   **F6.2715**
   Woodfall Films-Winkast Film Productions-Les Films Marceau. *Dist* Lopert
Pictures. 11 May **1969** [New York opening; c11 May 1969; LP40172]. Sd; col
(DeLuxe). 35mm. 101 min. *MPAA rating* X.
   Prod Neil Hartley. *Dir* Tony Richardson. *Screenplay* Edward Bond. *Dir
Photog* Dick Bush. *Art Dir* Julia Trevelyan Oman. *Set Dresser* Ian Whittaker.
Film Ed Charles Rees. *Mus* Raymond Leppard. *Sd Mix* Iain Bruce. *Asst Dir*
Andrew Grieve, Gerry Harrison, Terry Hodgkinson, Graham Cottle. *Prod Mgr*
Gavrik Losey. *Wardrobe* Eddie Boyce.
   Cast: Nicol Williamson (*Sir Edward More*), Anna Karina (*Margot*), Jean-
Claude Drouot (*Hervé Tourace*), Peter Bowles (*Paul*), Sian Phillips (*Lady
Elizabeth More*), Sebastian Breaks (*Brian*), Kate O'Toole (*Amelia More*),
Edward Gardener (*chauffeur*), Helen Booth (*maid*), Sheila Burrell (*Miss Porly*),
Willoughby Goddard (*colonel*), Basil Dignam, John Atkinson, Donald Bisset,
John Golightly (*art dealers*), Mavis Villiers (*woman at gallery*), Allison Blair
(*girl at gallery*), Diana Harris, Celia Brook (*girls at 1st party*).
   Drama. Source: Vladimir Nabokov, *Laughter in the Dark* (New York, 1938;
the author's English version of *Kamera obskura*; U.S.S.R., 1932). Sir Edward
More, a wealthy art dealer, becomes infatuated with a young cinema usherette,
Margot, and tries to initiate a discreet affair. But the young woman telephones
him at his home, visits his art gallery when his wife, Elizabeth, is there, and even
wires him a declaration of her love. After his wife has left him, taking with her
their small daughter, Edward submits to Margot, unaware that she is once more
involved sexually with her ex-lover, Hervé Tourace. As part of a plan to bilk
Edward of his fortune, Margot tells him that Hervé is a homosexual (and
therefore no threat to their love) and then persuades him to hire the younger
man as his assistant. Following the sudden death of his daughter, Edward
becomes totally dependent upon Margot and yields to her wish that they take
a holiday abroad—with Hervé as their chauffeur. Then Edward learns of her
secret affair with Hervé. He threatens to shoot Margot but is dissuaded when
she promises never to see Hervé again. But in his haste to leave with Margot,
Edward crashes his car and is left blinded by the accident. Margot now deceives
Edward into believing that Hervé has left the country and persuades Edward
that he needs a long rest; then Hervé, his presence unknown to Edward, drives
them to a secluded villa. There the lovers not only relieve Edward of his wealth
but play sadistic tricks upon him. Then Edward's brother-in-law, Paul, arrives
to learn the reason for all the exorbitant bank withdrawals. With the plot
exposed, Hervé flees as Edward asks Paul to leave him alone so that he can say
goodby to Margot in private. But when Margot returns to the villa, Edward is
waiting with a gun; as the terrified girl tries to flee, he accidentally shoots
himself dead. *Art dealers. Ushers. Brothers-in-law. Chauffeurs. Infidelity.
Sadism. Blindness. Male homosexuality. Fraud. Duplicity. Automobile
accidents.*
   Note: Filmed on location in Majorca and England. Opened in London in
Aug 1969; running time: 104 min. French title: *La chambre obscure.*

LAURA   **F6.2716**
   Dist Jo-Jo Distributors. ca **1970**. Sd; col. 16mm. 61-81 min.
   Sex film. No information about the precise nature of this film has been
found. *Sexuality.*
   Note: May be the same as *Laura in Love.*

LAURA IN LOVE   **F6.2717**
   Dist Stacey Distributors. ca **1970**. Sd; col. 16mm. 61-81 min.
   Sex film. No information about the precise nature of this film has been
found. *Sexuality.*
   Note: May be the same as *Laura.*

LAUREL AND HARDY'S LAUGHING 20'S   **F6.2718**
   Robert Youngson Productions. *Dist* Metro-Goldwyn-Mayer, Inc. Jun **1965**
[Richmond, Virginia, showing; c10 Jun 1965; LP31615]. Sd; b&w. 35mm. 90
min.
   A Robert Youngson Production. *Prod-Writ* Robert Youngson. *Assoc Prod*
Herbert Gelbspan, Alfred Dahlem. *Mus* Skeets Alquist. *Mus Cond* John
Parker, mus. *Mus Ed* Angelo Ross. *Sd* Val Peters, Ross-Gaffney Inc. *Prod Mgr*
I. Hill Youngson. *Opticals* Maurice Levy. *Res Supv* Jeanne Keyes.
   Narrator: Jay Jackson, Spec O'Donnell.
   Compilation film. The evolution of the comedy team of Stan Laurel and
Oliver Hardy is shown in a compilation of silent short films of the 1920's. The
early years in which they worked in films independently is illustrated by
Hardy's appearance in *Fattie's Fatal Fun* (1915) and Laurel's in the Hal Roach
comedy *Kill or Cure* (1923). They appeared in different scenes in *Forty-Five
Minutes From Hollywood* (1926), were casually paired in such films as *Sugar
Daddies* (1927), and co-starred in *Putting Pants on Philip* (1927). In *From Soup
to Nuts* (1928) they appeared wearing bowler hats in the characterizations that
were to become famous. Different aspects of the team's silent comedy are
explored with clips from *Wrong Again* (1929), *The Finishing Touch* (1928),
Liberty (1929), *Double Whoopee* (1929), *Leave 'Em Laughing* (1928), *You're
Darn Tootin'* (1928), *The Second Hundred Years* (1927), and *Habeas Corpus*
(1928). The work of two other Hal Roach comedians is given special attention:
Charlie Chase is featured in *Never the Dames Shall Meet* (1927) and *Snappy
Sneezer* (1929), and Max Davidson in *Call of the Cuckoo* (1927), *Pass the
Gravy* (1928), and *Dumb Daddies* (1928). The film ends with the climactic pie-
throwing sequence from Laurel and Hardy's *The Battle of the Century* (1927),
after which the two comics do their exit from *We Faw Down* [according to
cutting continuity, *We Fall Down*] (1928). *Actors. Motion pictures—History.
Stan Laurel. Oliver Hardy. Hal Roach.*

LAUTLOSE WAFFEN see **THE DEFECTOR**

LAVIRINT SMRTI see **FLAMING FRONTIER**

THE LAW (Reissue) (France/Italy)   **F6.2719**
   Ge. Si. Cinematografica-Titanus-Le Groupe des Quatre-Cité Films. *Dist*
Embassy Pictures. 22 Apr **1963** [New York opening]. Sd (Westrex); b&w.
35mm. 125 min.
   Note: Originally released as *Where the Hot Wind Blows!* in 1960 by Metro-
Goldwyn-Mayer. French title: *La loi*; Italian title: *La legge.*

LAW AND ORDER   **F6.2720**
   Osti Films. *For* Public Broadcasting Laboratory of National Educational
Television and Radio Center. *Dist* Zipporah Films. 7 Mar **1970** [Washington,
D. C., showing]. Sd; b&w. 16mm. 81 min.
   Prod-Dir-Writ Frederick Wiseman. *Photog* William Brayne. *Asst Photog*
David Martin. *Film Ed* Frederick Wiseman. *Assoc Ed* Carter Howard. *Asst Ed*
Andrea Green. *Sd Rec* Frederick Wiseman. *Prod Asst* Robbin Mason, Susan
Primm.
   Documentary. The activities of the Kansas City, Missouri, Police
Department are examined. Scenes include a confrontation in which an angry
landlady accuses a tenant of throwing a knife at her spouse and the attempt of
a black youth to take his child away from his wife. Three policemen and black
neighbors restrain a 17-year-old car thief who has wrecked three automobiles
while trying to escape. While interrogating a novice prostitute, a policeman
chokes her so violently that she is unable to answer his questions. After an
abortive attempt to rob a clothing store, three black adolescents are arrested;
one of the three is an unarmed youth who claims to be a customer. Cadets are
briefed on community relations. Irritated by an officer's refusal to help him find
a place to spend the night, a transient decries police brutality and the
Vietnamese conflict. The police remove a vomiting drunk from the sidewalk,
aid the victim of a purse snatcher, entertain a lost child at the station, and
discuss the inadequacy of their salaries. The film is concluded with Richard
Nixon's 1968 campaign promise to make American cities safe from crime.
*Police. Negroes. Landladies. Prostitutes. Children. Urban life. Race relations.
Robbery. Drunkenness. Interrogation. Adolescence. Kansas City (Missouri).
Richard Milhous Nixon. Kansas City (Missouri) Police Department.*
   Note: Filmed in Kansas City, Missouri, in 1968. First shown on NET on 2
Mar 1969.

THE LAW AND TOMBSTONE see **HOUR OF THE GUN**

LAW OF THE LAWLESS F6.2721

A. C. Lyles Productions. *Dist* Paramount Pictures. 18 Mar **1964** [Los Angeles opening; c31 Dec 1963; LP28069]. Sd; col (Technicolor). 35mm (Techniscope). 87 min.

An A. C. Lyles Production. *Prod* A. C. Lyles. *Dir* William F. Claxton. *Screenplay* Steve Fisher. *Dir Photog* Lester Shorr. *Art Dir* Hal Pereira, Al Roelofs. *Set Decor* Sam Comer, Darrell Silvera. *Film Ed* Otho Lovering. *Sd* Frank McWhorter, John Wilkinson. *Asst Dir* Harry F. Hogan. *Asst to the Prod* Pat B. Rooney. *Makeup* Wally Westmore. *Hairstyles* Nellie Manley. *Sp Photog Eff* Paul K. Lerpae. *Dial Coach* Jerry Buss.

Cast: Dale Robertson *(Judge Clem Rogers)*, Yvonne De Carlo *(Ellie Irish)*, William Bendix *(Sheriff Ed Tanner)*, Bruce Cabot *(Joe Rile)*, Barton MacLane *(Big Tom Stone)*, John Agar *(Pete Stone)*, Richard Arlen *(bartender)*, Jody McCrea *(George Stapleton)*, Kent Taylor *(Rand McDonald)*, Bill Williams *(Silas Miller)*, Rod Lauren *(Deputy Tim Ludlow)*, George Chandler *(hotel clerk)*, Lon Chaney, Jr. *(Tiny)*, Donald Barry *(Tuffy)*, Roy Jenson, Jerry Summers, Reg Parton *(Johnson brothers)*, Alex Sharp *(drifter)*, Romo Vincent, Lorraine Bendix, Joe Forte, Leigh Chapman, Dick Ryan.

Western melodrama. In Kansas in 1889, Pete Stone, son of Big Tom, who runs the state, is jailed for killing George Stapleton. Judge Clem Rogers is called to town to try Pete. His visit attracts the three Johnson brothers, whose fourth brother was sentenced to death by Rogers; a drifter with a score to settle with the judge; and Joe Rile, the murderer of Rogers' father. Rile is in town to work for Big Tom. From his cell Pete arranges for Rogers to have dinner with Ellie Irish, the saloon girl who plans to marry Pete for the sake of security. Pete plans to have his lawyer select a jury of prudes who might be influenced against the judge because of his association with a saloon girl. The Johnson brothers and the drifter try to waylay Rogers, but a deputy sheriff discovers them and kills them in a gun battle in which he himself is killed. Big Tom orders Rile to draw Rogers into a gunfight after the trial, but in a manner that will discredit the judge regardless of the outcome. The attempts to trap Rogers with Ellie fail. At the trial it is learned that Stapleton told Pete to keep away from his wife and that Pete forced him to draw and then gunned him down. Stapleton's widow testifies that she has never seen Pete before, but Ellie testifies that she saw Pete embracing the woman and was warned to keep silent. Pete is found guilty and sentenced to be hanged. Then Rile accosts Rogers, but the judge refuses to be drawn into a fight; and Rile, too, throws down his gun. Big Tom then tries to kill Rogers, but Rile disarms him. As the vindicated judge leaves town, Big Tom's orders to kill him are ignored by Big Tom's own men. *Political bosses. Judges. Brothers. Widows. Dancehall girls. Gunfighters. Sheriffs. Revenge. Murder. Jails. Trials. Kansas.*

Note: Working titles: *Invitation to a Hanging* and *The Day of the Hanging*.

LAWRENCE OF ARABIA (Great Britain) F6.2722

Horizon Pictures. *Dist* Columbia Pictures. 16 Dec **1962** [New York opening; c19 Dec 1962; LP25769]. Sd; col (Technicolor). 35mm and 70mm (Super Panavision). 222 min.

A Sam Spiegel-David Lean Production. *Prod* Sam Spiegel, David Lean. *Dir* David Lean. *2d Unit Dir* Andre Smagghe, Noel Howard. *Screenplay (see note)* Robert Bolt, Michael Wilson. *Dir Photog* F. A. Young. *2d Unit Photog* Skeets Kelly, Nicolas Roeg, Peter Newbrook. *Camera Op* Ernest Day. *Art Dir* John Stoll. *Asst Art Dir* Roy Rossotti, George Richardson, Terence Marsh, Tony Rimmington. *Set Dresser* Dario Simoni. *Prod Dsgn* John Box. *Film Ed* Anne V. Coates. *Mus Comp* Maurice Jarre. *Mus Arr* Gerard Schurmann. *Mus Coörd* Morris Stoloff. *Played by* London Philharmonic Orchestra. *Cond* Adrian Boult. *Sd* Winston Ryder, John Cox. *Sd Rec* Paddy Cunningham. *Asst Dir* Roy Stevens. *Prod Mgr* John Palmer. *Location Mgr* Douglas Twiddy. *Cont* Barbara Cole. *Cost Dsgn* Phyllis Dalton. *Wardrobe* John Wilson Apperson. *Makeup* Charles Parker. *Hairstyles* A. G. Scott. *Res* Marie Budberg. *Constr Mgr* Peter Dukelow. *Casting Dir* Maude Spector. *Prop Master* Eddie Fowlie. *Ch Electrn* Archie Dansie.

Cast: Peter O'Toole *(T. E. Lawrence)*, Alec Guinness *(Prince Faisal)*, Anthony Quinn *(Auda Abu Tayi)*, Jack Hawkins *(General Allenby)*, Jose Ferrer *(Turkish bey)*, Anthony Quayle *(Col. Harry Brighton)*, Claude Rains *(Mr. Dryden)*, Arthur Kennedy *(Jackson Bentley)*, Donald Wolfit *(General Murray)*, Omar Sharif *(Sherif Ali ibn el Kharish)*, I. S. Johar *(Gasim)*, Gamil Ratib *(Majid)*, Michel Ray *(Farraj)*, Zia Mohyeddin *(Tafas)*, John Dimech *(Daud)*, Howard Marion Crawford *(medical officer)*, Jack Gwillim *(club secretary)*, Hugh Miller *(R.A.M.C. colonel)*, Kenneth Fortescue *(Allenby's aide)*, Stuart Saunders *(regimental sergeant-major)*, Fernando Sancho *(Turkish sergeant)*, Henry Oscar *(reciter)*, Norman Rossington *(Corporal Jenkins)*, John Ruddock *(Elder Harith)*, M. Cher Kaoui, Mohammed Habachi.

Historical epic. Based on the life and writings of T. E. Lawrence. In 1916 British Intelligence supports the Arab rebellion against the Turkish-German alliance. Dryden, a civilian member of the Arab Bureau, selects Lieut. T. E. Lawrence, an enigmatic 29-year-old scholar, to evaluate the Arab revolt. Enthusiastically undertaking this assignment, the officer contacts Prince Feisal, a rebel leader, and persuades Feisal to lend him a force of 50 men. With this skeleton band, accompanied by Sherif Ali, Lawrence crosses the Nefud Desert. At the journey's end, however, Lawrence learns that one of his men is missing. Undeterred by Arab assertions that the missing man's death had been divinely decreed, Lawrence returns to the desert and rescues him, earning thereby Ali's friendship and the respect of his subordinates. At a well Lawrence is confronted by the sheikh Auda Abu Tayi, whom he persuades to join the assault on Aqaba, a Turkish port at the desert's edge. The Turks, surprised by the overland attack, are routed, and the victory revitalizes the Arab rebellion. Arab unity, however, is undermined by internecine warfare. When one of his troop slays one of Auda Abu Tayi's henchmen, Lawrence in expiation executes the murderer, who proves to be the Arab he had saved in the desert. Unnerved, Lawrence returns to Cairo. Delighted by Lawrence's military success, however, General Allenby provides him with arms and money for future victories. Lawrence launches a series of successful guerrilla raids, which, as reported by American journalist Jackson Bentley, establish his international reputation. While on a scouting mission with Ali, Lawrence is captured and tortured by the Turks. He returns to Cairo, where General Allenby persuades him to spearhead an attack on Damascus. After the battle, Lawrence leads his men in the massacre of the retreating Turks. Upon entering Damascus the British Army is met by victorious Arab forces. Lawrence relinquishes control of the city to an Arab Council, but soon factionalism threatens to destroy it. On May 19, 1935, Lawrence dies in a motorcycle crash in Dorset, England, and is commemorated in services at St. Paul's. *Soldiers. War heroes. Arabs. Bedouins. Guerrillas. Turks. Journalists. Americans in foreign countries. Revolts. Massacres. Military life. Torture. Deserts. Arabia—History—1916 Revolt. World War I. Aqaba. Cairo. Damascus. Thomas Edward Lawrence. Edmund Henry Hynman Allenby. Faisal I. Great Britain—Army. Motorcycle accidents.*

Note: Opened in London in Dec 1962. Location scenes filmed in Saudi Arabia. Michael Wilson did not receive screen credit for his work on the screenplay.

THE LAWYER F6.2723

Furie Productions. *Dist* Paramount Pictures. 4 Feb **1970** [Boston opening: c18 Aug 1969; LP37708]. Sd; col (Technicolor). 35mm. 120 min. *MPAA rating* R.

Prod Brad Dexter. *Dir* Sidney J. Furie. *Screenplay* Sidney J. Furie, Harold Buchman. *Dir Photog* Ralph Woolsey. *Art Dir* Pato Guzman. *Set Decor* Audrey Blasdel. *Film Ed* Argyle Nelson, Jr. *Asst Film Ed* Roberta Adye. *Mus* Malcolm Dodds. *Sd Rec* Glenn Anderson, John Wilkinson. *Asst Dir* Terry Morse, Jr. *Prod Mgr* Terry Morse, Jr.. *Asst to the Prod* Marlene Pivnick. *Men's Wardrobe* Ted Parvin. *Women's Wardrobe* Rita Riggs. *Hairstyles* Delyte Petty.

Cast: Barry Newman *(Tony Petrocelli)*, Harold Gould *(Eric P. Scott)*, Diana Muldaur *(Ruth Petrocelli)*, Robert Colbert *(Jack Harrison)*, Kathleen Crowley *(Alice Fiske)*, Warren Kemmerling *(Sergeant Moran)*, Booth Colman *(Judge Crawford)*, Ken Swofford *(Charlie O'Keefe)*, E. J. Andre *(F. J. Williamson)*, William Sylvester *(Paul Harrison)*, Jeff Thompson *(Andy Greer)*, Tom Harvey *(Bob Chambers)*, Ivor Barry *(Wyler)*, Melendy Britt *(Ann Greer)*, John Himes *(Myron McCauley)*, Ralph Thomas, actor *(Mike Peterson)*, Mary Wilcox *(Wilma Harrison)*, Gene O'Donnell *(Judge Swackhammer)*, Walter Mathews *(Mr. Andre)*, Ray Ballard *(Mr. Canon)*, James McEachin *(Striker)*, Robert L. Poyner *(J. C. Hornby)*.

Drama. Tony Petrocelli, an ambitious young lawyer, takes on the defense of Jack Harrison, a physician accused of murdering his wife. Jack claims that after a hard day at the hospital he fell asleep on a couch downstairs while his wife, Wilma, was having a barbecue in the backyard with several friends. Jack awakened to hear Wilma calling him. He was hit on the head and knocked unconscious when he rushed upstairs to see about her and on regaining consciousness found her dead. Believing he is innocent, Jack refuses the prosecutor's offer to allow him to plead guilty to manslaughter, and he is charged with first degree murder. The trial begins under much unfavorable publicity. Testimony is taken from an obviously prejudiced police investigator, and the local coroner is discovered to be professionally jealous of Jack. The most damaging testimony, however, comes from divorcée Alice Fiske who directly refutes Jack's own testimony by declaring that she and Jack had an extramarital affair. The jury finds Jack guilty of second degree murder, and he is sentenced to life imprisonment. Tony immediately prepares an appeal, claiming that his client did not receive a fair trial owing to prejudicial publicity. The appellate court grants a retrial, resulting in an acquittal when Tony shows that Jack's guilt was not proved beyond a reasonable doubt—Tony introduces a new witness who alleges that Wilma may have been murdered by the jealous wife of the man with whom Wilma was having an affair. *Police. Coroners. Lawyers. Physicians. Murder. Infidelity. Jealousy. Publicity. Trials.*

603

THE LAYOUT   **F6.2724**

Dist Deluxe Pictures. 1 Jan **1969**. Sd; b&w. 35mm. 79 min.

A J. Arthur Elliot Production. *Prod* J. Arthur Elliot. *Dir-Writ* Joe Sarno. *Camera* Steve Silverman. *Asst to the Prod* Peggy Steffans.

Cast: Suzan Thomas *(Pam)*, Betty Whitman *(Wendy)*, Rene Howard *(Ellen)*, Barbara Lance *(Emmy)*, Jean Muniz *(Marie)*, Howard Dale *(Robb)*.

Drama. Wendy and Pam, partners in an interior decorating enterprise, share a house. Wendy is engaged in a torrid affair with Robb Porter. Her sexual demands leave him too tired to satisfy his wife, Emmy, whose sexual appetite is also very keen. Pam, a former physiotherapist, uses an electric vibrator to satisfy her own sexual cravings. Frustrated and unhappy, Emmy visits Pam and finds the vibrator in her bedroom; Pam demonstrates its use, and the two women find intense pleasure together. Pam's niece Ellen, and a friend, Marie, visit Pam and Wendy. Returning home from a disappointing night on the town, Ellen, Marie, and Wendy eavesdrop on Emmy and Pam making love behind a closed door, and imitate what they hear. Later, after a nude romp in the swimming pool, the five women find their way to one bedroom. *Roommates. Interior decorators. Mistresses. Lesbianism. Infidelity. Group sex. Troilism. Autoeroticism. Swimming. Sex aids. Partnerships.*

LAZARILLO (Spain)   **F6.2725**

Hesperia Films. *Dist* Union Film Distributors. 4 Apr **1963** [New York opening]. Sd; b&w. 35mm. 100 min.

Pres by Myron Bresnick. *Prod* Carlos Couret. *Dir-Adapt* César Ardavín. *Photog* Manuel Berenguer. *Art Dir* Eduardo Torre de la Fuente. *Film Ed* Magdalena Pulido. Salvador Ruiz de Luna. *Mus* Emilio Lehurberg. *Prod Mgr* Luis Laso Moreno. *Cost* Humberto Cornejo. *English Subtitl* Travers Clement.

Cast: Marco Paoletti *(Lazarillo)*, Juan José Menéndez *(The Squire)*, Carlos Casaravilla *(The Blind Man)*, Memmo Carotenuto *(The Actor)*, Margarita Lozano *(Lazarillo's mother)*, Antonio Molino *(The Bailiff)*, Emilio Santiago *(Priest)*, Ana Prehan, Mary Paz Pondal, Enrique Avila, Pilar Sanclemente, Carlo Pisacane.

Drama. Based on the anonymous novel *Lazarillo de Tormes* (1554). In Spain in 1503 the impoverished and widowed mother of young Lazarillo de Tormes gives her son to a traveling blind beggar in the hope that he will take care of the child. The beggar proves to be a harsh taskmaster, however, and Lazarillo flees from him. He then aligns himself with a priest who dispenses food for the boy's soul but none for his body, and Lazarillo once more searches for a new master. Next he encounters a squire, who turns out to be just as hungry as Lazarillo. Running off again, the boy meets a troupe of theatrical players and is befriended by the chief actor, a wily character who supplements his earnings by posing as a friar and selling papal indulgences. Lazarillo becomes an accomplice, and, although sometimes troubled by his conscience, he decides that he will join the troupe and at least insure himself of a full stomach. *Children. Orphans. Beggars. Priests. Actors. Swindlers. Hunger. Poverty. Imposture. Theatrical troupes. Spain—History.*

Note: Opened in Madrid in Nov 1959 as *El Lazarillo de Tormes*; running time: 109 min.

EL LAZARILLO DE TORMES see **LAZARILLO**

THE LEAGUE OF GENTLEMEN (Great Britain)   **F6.2726**

Allied Film Makers. *Dist* Kingsley International Pictures. 24 Jan **1961** [New York opening; c18 Apr 1960; LF193]. Sd; b&w. 35mm. 114 min.

Prod Michael Relph. *Dir* Basil Dearden. *Screenplay* Bryan Forbes. *Dir Photog* Arthur Ibbetson. *Camera Op* H. A. R. Thomson. *Art Dir* Peter Proud. *Set Dresser* Arthur Taksen. *Chargehand Set Dresser* P. Weymouth. *Ch Draughtsman* Bert Davey. *Film Ed* John D. Guthridge. *1st Asst Ed* Marcel Durham. *2d Asst Ed* Vera Dover. *Mus Comp & Cond* Philip Green. *Sd Ed* Harry Miller. *Sd Rec* Geoff Daniels, Bill Daniels. *Boom Op* Harry Fairbairn. *Sd Camera Op* Roy Charman, Ted Karnon, Ken Barker. *1st, 2d & 3d Asst Dir* George Pollard, Ian Goddard, Terry Clegg. *Prod Mgr* Charles Orme. *Cont* Penny Daniels. *Prod Sec* Lorely Farley. *Dress Dsgn* Joan Ellacott. *Wardrobe* John Hilling. *Makeup* Harry Frampton. *Hairdresser* Barbara Ritchie. *Prop Buyer* Peter Pratley. *Still Photog* Ian Jeayes. *Constr Mgr* Bert Jempson. *Ch Floor Electrn* John Swan. *Grip* Fred Graver.

Cast: Jack Hawkins *(Hyde)*, Nigel Patrick *(Peter Graham Race)*, Roger Livesey *(Mycroft)*, Richard Attenborough *(Edward Lexy)*, Bryan Forbes *(Martin Porthill)*, Kieron Moore *(Stevens)*, Robert Coote *(Bunny Warren)*, Terence Alexander *(Rupert Rutland-Smith)*, Melissa Stribling *(Peggy)*, Norman Bird *(Frank Weaver)*, Nanette Newman *(Elizabeth)*, David Lodge *(C.S.M.)*, Patrick Wymark *(Wylie)*, Lydia Sherwood *(Hilda)*, Doris Hare *(Molly Weaver)*, Gerald Harper *(Captain Saunders)*, Brian Murray *(Grogan)*.

Comedy-drama. Source: John Boland, *The League of Gentlemen* (London, 1958). Resentful of his enforced retirement after 25 years of unblemished service in the British Army, ex-Lieutenant Colonel Hyde decides to apply his military talents to the subject of crime. After masterminding a daring plan for robbing a bank of £1 million, he contacts seven other discredited but experienced ex-officers—Race, Mycroft, Lexy, Porthill, Stevens, Rupert, and Weaver—and puts his scheme into action. Every phase of the operation, from removing arms and ammunition from an army supply depot to checking and rechecking getaway vehicles, is carried out with strict military precision. When all is ready, the men don gas masks, lay down a smoke screen, and enter the bank. Police radios are jammed, telephone cables disabled, and the robbery is a success. The men then return to Hyde's home to divide the bounty. Suddenly, they are interrupted by a surprise visit from Bunny Warren, a heavy-drinking army colleague of Hyde's. Through his innocent bungling, the police learn of the hideout of the "League of Gentlemen," and their brilliantly executed maneuver comes to naught. *Veterans. Police. Retirement. Drunkenness. Bank robberies. Great Britain—Army.*

Note: Opened in London in Apr 1960.

LEARN, BABY, LEARN see **THE LEARNING TREE**

THE LEARNING TREE   **F6.2727**

Winger Enterprises. *Dist* Warner Bros.–Seven Arts, Inc. 6 Aug **1969** [New York opening; c1 Sep 1969; LP37991]. Sd; col (Technicolor). 35mm Panavision. 107 min. *MPAA rating* M.

Prod-Dir-Writ Gordon Parks. *Assoc Prod* James Lydon. *Story Cons* Genevieve Young. *Dir Photog* Burnett Guffey. *Art Dir* Edward Engoron. *Set Decor* Joanne MacDougall. *Film Ed* George Rohrs. *Mus Comp* Gordon Parks. *Mus Cond & Orch* Tom McIntosh. *Mus Supv* Sonny Burke. *Titl Song* Gordon Parks. *Sung by* O. C. Smith. *Song:* "My Baby's Gone" sung by James "Jimmy" Rushing. *Sd* Robert J. Miller. *Asst Dir* Jack Aldworth, Fred Giles. *Prod Mgr* Russell Llewellyn. *Admin Asst to Mr. Parks* Suzanne Crayson. *Makeup Supv* Gordon Bau. *Hairstyles* Jean Burt Reilly. *Sp Photog Eff* Albert Whitlock.

Cast: Kyle Johnson *(Newt Winger)*, Alex Clarke *(Marcus Savage)*, Estelle Evans *(Sarah Winger)*, Dana Elcar *(Sheriff Kirky)*, Mira Waters *(Arcella Jefferson)*, Joel Fluellen *(Uncle Rob)*, Malcolm Atterbury *(Silas Newhall)*, Richard Ward *(Booker Savage)*, Russell Thorson *(Judge Cavanaugh)*, Peggy Rea *(Miss McClintock)*, Carole Lamond *(Big Mabel)*, Kevin Hagen *(Doc Cravens)*, James "Jimmy" Rushing *(Chappie Logan)*, Dub Taylor *(Spikey)*, Felix Nelson *(Jack Winger)*, George Mitchell *(Jake Kiner)*, Saundra Sharp *(Prissy)*, Stephen Perry *(Jappy)*, Don Dubbins *(Harley Davis)*, Jon Lormer *(McCormack)*, Morgan Sterne *(Mr. Hall)*, Thomas Anderson *(Pastor Broadnap)*, Philip Roye *(Pete Winger)*, Hope Summers *(Mrs. Kiner)*, Carter Vinnegar *(Seansy)*, Bobby Goss *(Skunk)*, Alfred Jones *(Cap'n Tuck)*, Zooey Hall *(Chauncey Cavanaugh)*.

Rural drama. Source: Gordon Parks, *The Learning Tree* (New York, 1963). Newt Winger, a sensitive teenaged Negro boy, lives in a small Kansas town in the mid-1920's; his mother, Sarah, is a domestic for the local circuit judge, and his father works for Jake Kiner, a kindly white rancher. When Newt is injured in a tornado, he is rescued and initiated into sex by Big Mabel, the local whore. Later, while swimming with friends, including the embittered Marcus Savage, he is forced to dive for the corpse of a frightened Negro gambler whom the bigoted Sheriff Kirky had shot in the back. After Marcus is sent to jail for brutally beating Kiner, Newt turns his attention to Arcella Johnson, a new girl in town, but he is heartbroken when her family moves away because she has become pregnant by Judge Cavanaugh's white playboy son. Soon after, while working for Mr. Kiner, Newt sees Marcus' father, Booker, and a white man, Silas Newhall, attempting to rob the rancher's liquor supply. When they are discovered and attacked by Kiner, Booker kills Kiner and flees, leaving behind the unconscious Silas. As a result, Silas is placed on trial for murder, and Newt hesitates to reveal what he knows, fearing that the white community will rise up against the blacks. Eventually, however, Newt decides to tell the truth, and Booker shoots himself upon hearing the news. By this time, Marcus is out of jail, and sets out to kill Newt, who is attending his mother's funeral. The confrontation leads to a fight, which Newt wins; he lets Marcus escape before Sheriff Kirky arrives, but Kirky follows Marcus into the woods and shoots him in the back. Newt, sickened by the hatred and violence, decides to go elsewhere to live with his aunt. *Negroes. Domestics. Ranchers. Prostitutes. Sheriffs. Rural life. Adolescence. Filial relations. Sexual initiation. Race relations. Racism. Murder. Miscegenation. Pregnancy. Robbery. Honesty. Suicide. Trials. Funerals. Kansas. Tornadoes.*

Note: Location scenes filmed in and around Fort Scott, Kansas. Also known as *Learn, Baby, Learn.*

LEATHER AND NYLON see **ACTION MAN**

THE LEATHER BOYS (Great Britain)   **F6.2728**

Raymond Stross Productions. *Dist* RLP Pictures, Allied Artists. 8 Nov **1965** [New York opening]. Sd; b&w. 35mm (Cinemascope). 108 min. [Also reviewed at 105 min.]

Pres by R. Lee Platt. A Raymond Stross Production. *Dir* Sidney J. Furie. *Screenplay* Gillian Freeman. *Photog* Gerald Gibbs. *Art Dir* Arthur Lawson.

Film Ed Reginald Beck. *Mus* Bill McGuffie. *Sd* Derek McColm. *Asst Dir* Roy Baird. *Prod Supv* Jack Swinburne.

Cast: Rita Tushingham *(Dot)*, Colin Campbell *(Reggie)*, Dudley Sutton *(Pete)*, Gladys Henson *(Gran)*, Avice Landon *(Reggie's mother)*, Lockwood West *(Reggie's father)*, Betty Marsden *(Dot's mother)*, Martin Mathews *(Uncle Arthur)*, Johnny Briggs *(boyfriend)*, James Chase *(Les)*, Geoffrey Dunn *(Mr. Lunnis)*, Dandy Nichols *(Mrs. Stanley)*, Valerie Varnam *(Brenda)*, Jill Mai Meredith *(June)*, Elizabeth Begley *(receptionist)*, Brian Phelan *(man-in-jeans)*, Oliver MacGreevy *(merchant seaman)*, Sylvia Kay *(schoolteacher)*, Sandra Caron, Tracey Rogers *(schoolgirls)*, Carmel McSharry *(bus conductress)*, Joyce Hemson *(publican's wife)*.

Drama. Source: Eliot George, *The Leather Boys* (London, 1961). Dot and Reggie are London teenagers who marry and immediately run into problems. When Dot proves to be more interested in hairstyles, movies, and comic books than in keeping house and cooking meals, Reggie spends more and more time at his motorcycle club, where he meets Pete. Soon Reggie moves to his grandmother's house and shares a room with Pete, who proves to be much more domestic than Dot. On a motorcycle race to Edinburgh, Dot and Reggie renew their affection for each other, but when Reggie returns home, he finds Dot in bed with another man. Pete tries to persuade him to go with him to New York, but in a dockside pub, Reggie discovers that Pete is a homosexual and walks away. *Motorcyclists. Marriage. Adolescence. Male homosexuality. Infidelity. Motorcycle racing. Pubs. London. Edinburgh.*

Note: Opened in London in Jan 1964. Eliot George is a pseudonym for Gillian Freeman.

THE LEATHER GIRLS *see* **FASTER, PUSSYCAT! KILL! KILL!**

DAS LEBEN MOZARTS *see* **THE LIFE OF MOZART**

LEBENSBORN *see* **ORDERED TO LOVE**

LEBENSZEICHEN *see* **SIGNS OF LIFE**

LEDA (France/Italy)   **F6.2729**
Paris-Films Production–Titanus. *Dist* Times Film Corp. 13 May **1961** [Los Angeles opening]. Sd (Western Electric); col (Eastman Color). 35mm. 101 min.
Prod Robert Hakim, Raymond Hakim. *Assoc Prod* Ralph Baum. *Dir* Claude Chabrol. *Screenplay* Paul Gégauff. *Dir Photog* Henri Decaë. *Camera* Jean Rabier. *Asst Camera* Jean-Paul Schwartz, Pierre Ginet. *Art Dir* Jacques Saulnier, Bernard Evein. *Asst Art Dir* Marc Frédérix, Georges Glon. *Set Dsgn* Maurice Bourbotte. *Film Ed* Jacques Gaillard. *Mus* Paul Misraki. *Selections from "Romeo and Juliet"* Hector Berlioz. *Selections from "Serenade in B-Flat Major"* Wolfgang Amadeus Mozart. *Sd Dir* Jean-Claude Marchetti. *Sd Rec* Maurice Rémy. *Sd Boom* Maurice Dagonneau. *Asst Dir* Philippe de Broca, Charles Bitsch. *Prod Mgr* Jean Pieuchot. *Script Girl* Jacqueline Parey. *Prod Sec* Cécile Adam. *Cost* Jeannine Germès-Vergne. *Makeup* Louis Bonnemaison. *Hairstyles* Billy Bernard. *Admin* Robert Demollière. *Still Photog* André Dino. *Location Mgr* Charles Merangel, prop.

Cast: Madeleine Robinson *(Thérèse Marcoux)*, Antonella Lualdi *(Léda)*, Jean-Paul Belmondo *(Laszlo Kovacs)*, Jacques Dacqmine *(Henri Marcoux)*, Jeanne Valérie *(Elizabeth Marcoux)*, Bernadette Lafont *(Julie)*, André Jocelyn *(Richard Marcoux)*, Mario David *(Roger, the milkman)*, Laszlo Szabo *(The Hungarian)*, Raymond Pelissier, André Dino.

Drama. Source: Stanley Ellin, *The Key to Nicholas Street* (New York, 1952). On the outskirts of Aix-en-Provence lives Henri Marcoux, a wealthy winegrower whose hatred-ridden family is held together by greed. Henri has escaped from the emptiness of his marriage by entering into an affair with Léda, a beautiful Italian artist whose home next door reflects the years she spent in Japan. Henri's conventional wife, Thérèse, is chiefly concerned with protecting the family fortune and avoiding scandal. Their young son, Richard, emasculated by his mother, has withdrawn into the world of music. Elizabeth, the daughter, finds some release from the family tensions in her love for her father's friend Laszlo, a vulgar expatriate anarchist who encourages Henri to depart with Léda. Thérèse, who finds Laszlo's presence intolerable, agrees to overlook Henri's affair with Léda if he will get rid of Laszlo. At the moment Henri decides to leave with Léda, the maid announces that she has been murdered. Suspicion falls on each member of the household, as the police ineffectually move in. Laszlo finally beats a confession from Richard, who committed the murder after he overheard a violent quarrel between his parents. Despite his mother's pleas, Richard, convinced by Laszlo, surrenders himself to the law. *Vineyardists. Mistresses. Artists. Anarchists. Family life. Murder. Insanity. Effeminacy. Infidelity. Social classes. Aix-en-Provence.*

Note: Opened in Paris in Nov 1959 as *À double tour*. Italian title: *A doppia mandata*. Title changed to *Web of Passion*. Location scenes filmed in Aix-en-Provence.

LEGACY OF A SPY *see* **THE DOUBLE MAN**

THE LEGACY OF THE 500,000 (Japan)   **F6.2730**
Mifune Productions–Toho Co. *Dist* Toho Co. Jun **1964** [Los Angeles showing]. Sd; b&w. 35mm (Tohoscope). 98 min.
Dir Toshiro Mifune. *Screenplay* Ryuzo Kikushima. *Photog* Takao Saito.

Cast: Toshiro Mifune *(Matsuo)*, Tatsuya Mihashi, Tatsuya Nakadai, Tsutomu Yamazaki.

Adventure drama. Gunji, president of a maritime trading company, learns of a treasure of 10,000 gold coins left in the Philippines by the Japanese army in the closing days of World War II. He contacts Matsuo, who knows the location of the treasure, and when the man refuses to talk, Gunji has him abducted and brought aboard a boat captained by Gunji's brother. Gunji's driver and his bodyguard complete the group, which lands secretly in the Philippines. Disguised both as Nisei serving in the U. S. Army and Chinese merchants, the men make their way to the mountainous regions of North Luzon, where the Igorots, a tribe of savage headhunters, live. The Japanese fail to find the gold. [Sources leave the conclusion of the film uncertain.] *Shipping magnates. Sea captains. Bodyguards. Chinese. Nisei. Chauffeurs. Abduction. Disguise. Treasure. Gold. Luzon. Igorots.*

Note: Released in Japan in 1963 as *Gojuman-nin no isan*.

THE LEGEND OF BLOOD MOUNTAIN   **F6.2731**
Vagabond Vultures. *Dist* Craddock Films. 29 Sep **1965** [Atlanta opening]. Sd; col. 35mm. 61 min.
Prod Don Hadley. *Exec Prod* Frank Winecoff. *Dir* Massey Cramer. *Screenplay* Massey Cramer, Don Hadley, Bob Corley. *Film Ed* Don Hadley, Massey Cramer.

Cast: George Ellis *(Bestoink Dooley)*, Zenas Sears, Glenda Brunson, Erin Fleming, Sheila Stringer.

Comedy. Bestoink Dooley, a smalltown newspaper reporter, goes in search of a story and finds pretty girls and a monster. *Reporters. Monsters. Smalltown life.*

Note: Filmed on location at Stone Mountain and Lake Spivey, Georgia.

THE LEGEND OF LOBO   **F6.2732**
Walt Disney Productions–Cangary, Ltd. *Dist* Buena Vista Distribution Co. 9 Nov **1962** [New York opening; c17 Apr 1962; LP23322]. Sd; col (Technicolor). 35mm. 67 min.
Pres by Walt Disney. A Walt Disney Production. *Co-prod* James Algar. *Field Prod for Cangary Productions* Jack Couffer. *Dir* James Algar. *Screenplay* Dwight Hauser, James Algar. *Photog* Jack Couffer, Lloyd Beebe. *Film Ed* Norman R. Palmer. *Mus* Oliver Wallace. *Orch* Walter Sheets. *Titl Song* Richard M. Sherman, Robert B. Sherman. *Sung by* Rex Allen, Sons of the Pioneers. *Sd* Robert O. Cook. *Mus Ed* Evelyn Kennedy. *Prod Mgr* Erwin L. Verity.

Narrator: Rex Allen.

Adventure melodrama. Source: Ernest Thompson-Seton, *Wild Animals I Have Known* (New York, 1959). In turn-of-the-century New Mexico, Lobo, a wolf-pup consumed by curiosity, meets an angry rattler in the course of his investigations and has to be rescued by his parents. He becomes the inseparable companion of an antelope, but when winter comes his mother and father are killed and Lobo must fend for himself. In his maturity he is the smartest, most dangerous wolf on the range, and he becomes a pack leader, taking a black female, Sombra, for his mate. Their first litter, born in a deserted Indian cliff dwelling, is accessible only by means of a tree trunk across a gorge. The reward for Lobo's capture mounts until there is a $1,000 price on his head. Relying on the devotion of wolves to their families, a professional hunter manages to snare Sombra and use her as a lure. But Lobo leads his pack to create a cattle stampede, a diversion that enables him to liberate his mate and strike out for unsettled territory. *Hunters. Animal life. Stampedes. New Mexico. Wolves. Antelope. Snakes.*

Note: Filmed entirely on location in Arizona.

THE LEGEND OF LYLAH CLARE   **F6.2733**
Associates & Aldrich Co. *Dist* Metro-Goldwyn-Mayer, Inc. 21 Aug **1968** [Los Angeles opening; c24 Jun 1968; LP35850]. Sd; col (Metrocolor). 35mm. 130 min.
Prod-Dir Robert Aldrich. *Assoc Prod* Walter Blake. *Screenplay* Hugo Butler, Jean Rouverol. *Dir Photog* Joseph Biroc. *Camera Op* Ned Davenport, Charles W. Riley. *Camera Asst* Arthur Gerstle, Gary Boren, Al Irving. *Art Dir* George W. Davis, William Glasgow. *Set Decor* Henry Grace, Keogh Gleason. *Film Ed* Michael Luciano. *Asst Ed* Frank Urioste. *Mus* De Vol. Song: "Lylah" Frank De Vol, Sibylle Siegfried. *Sung by* Sibylle Siegfried. *Rec Supv* Franklin Milton. *Sd* Phil Mitchell, Richard Church, Lee Archer. *Asst Dir* Cliff Coleman, Dennis Donnelly, Daisy Gerber. *Prod Supv* George Tobin. *Script Supv* Adell Bravos. *Location Mgr* Bob Sunderland. *Cost Dsgn* Renie. *Wardrobe* Frank Roberts, Nat Tolmach, Marie Osborne, Florence Hackett. *Makeup* William

Tuttle, Robert Schiffer. *Hairstyles* Sydney Guilaroff, Agnes Flanagan. *Sp Eff* Al Burke. *Optical Eff* Robert R. Hoag. *Dial Coach* Robert Sherman, Michael Audley. *Dog Food Commercial* Norman Tobak, The Petersen Co. *Still Photog* Ken Bell. *Grip* Richard Hager, Elbert Hunter. *Gaffer* Bill Hannah. *Constr Coörd* Jack R. Berne. *Prop Master* Hal Willis. *Stunt Coörd* John Indrisano.

Cast: Kim Novak *(Lylah Clare/Elsa Brinkmann)*, Peter Finch *(Lewis Zarkan)*, Ernest Borgnine *(Barney Sheean)*, Milton Selzer *(Bart Langner)*, Rossella Falk *(Rossella)*, Gabriele Tinti *(Paolo)*, Valentina Cortese *(Countess Bozo Bedoni)*, Jean Carroll *(Becky Langner)*, Michael Murphy *(Mark Peter Sheean)*, Lee Meriwether *(young girl)*, James Lanphier *(1st legman)*, Robert Ellenstein *(Mike)*, Nick Dennis *(Nick)*, Dave Willock *(cameraman)*, Coral Browne *(Molly Luther)*, Peter Bravos *(butler)*, Ellen Corby *(script girl)*, Michael Fox *(announcer)*, Hal Maguire *(2d legman)*, Tom Patty *(Bedoni's escort)*, Vernon Scott *(Vernon Scott)*, Queenie Smith *(hairdresser)*, Sidney Skolsky *(Sidney Skolsky)*, Barbara Ann Warkmeister, Mel Warkmeister *(aerialists)*, George Kennedy.

Melodrama. Source: Robert Thom and Edward DeBlasio, *The Legend of Lylah Clare* (a teleplay; first presented on NBC's "Dupont Show of the Week," 19 May 1963). Elsa Brinkmann, an unknown actress from Chicago, is hired by talent agent Bart Langner to star in a film biography of the late, great Hollywood star, Lylah Clare. After reluctantly agreeing to meet the young unknown, Lewis Zarkan, Lylah's director-husband, who has been inactive in films since his wife fell to her death mysteriously on their wedding night, is stunned at Elsa's uncanny resemblance to Lylah. Zarkan agrees to direct the film, and studio head Barney Sheean provides the financing. Although at first resentful of Zarkan's reworking her into an exact duplicate of the legendary Lylah, Elsa is soon drawn into recreating the old star, and even Lylah's personality begins to possess her. Eventually, Zarkan and Elsa become lovers, much to the irritation of Zarkan's housekeeper-confidante, Rossella, a drug-addicted lesbian who had been Lylah's dialogue coach. Once Elsa's transformation into Lylah is complete, she even dares to defy the powerful gossip columnist Molly Luther in a manner that would have done justice to the dead star. Elsa discovers that it is the memory of Lylah that Zarkan truly loves, and she retaliates by flagrantly carrying on a passionate affair with his handsome young gardener, Paolo. Enraged by her infidelity, Zarkan revises the ending of the film and forces Elsa to perform a dangerous stunt on a trapeze, fully aware that Elsa suffers from vertigo, just as Lylah had. As Elsa is overcome by dizziness and plummets to her death, the last moments of Lylah's life are recalled: upon discovering on their wedding night that Lylah was a lesbian, Zarkan had viciously attacked her and then permitted her to fall down a long flight of stairs. Now filled with grief at the loss of the two women he loved but destroyed, Zarkan leaves the successful premiere of his film and returns home, unaware that Rossella is waiting with a loaded gun. *Actors. Talent agents. Motion picture directors. Housekeepers. Drug addicts. Gardeners. Aerialists. Motion picture columnists. Drama coaches. Motion pictures. Impersonation. Lesbianism. Jealousy. Infidelity. Vertigo.*

THE LEGEND OF ROBIN HOOD *see* A CHALLENGE FOR ROBIN HOOD

THE LEGEND OF THE BOY AND THE EAGLE   F6.2734

Walt Disney Productions–Eagle Boy Productions. *Dist* Buena Vista Distribution Co. 21 Jun **1967** [c1 Jun 1967; LP34466]. Sd (RCA); col (Technicolor). 35mm. 48 min. [See note.]

Pres by Walt Disney. *Assoc Prod* Hamilton S. Luske, Joseph Strick. *Prod Assoc* McLaren Stewart. *Dir-Writ* Jack Couffer. *Based on a Legend Related by* White Bear Fredericks. *Photog* Jack Couffer, Ed Durden. *Film Ed* Lloyd L. Richardson, Verna Fields. *Mus* Franklyn Marks. *Orch* Walter Sheets. *Mus Ed* Rusty Jones. *Adv* White Bear Fredericks. *Coöp* Coconino National Forest. *Animal Supv* Ed Durden.

Cast: Frank De Kova *(narrator)*, Stanford Lomakema *(The Eagle Boy)*.

Legendary drama. While Hopi Indian boys in Arizona perform their traditional eagle dance, a tribal elder relates to the youngsters of the tribe the 500-year-old legend behind the ritual: *In the ancient village of Wupatki, 10-year-old Tutuvina climbs to the roof of a cliff dwelling to feed a young eagle, which someday will be sacrificed to the gods for a bountiful corn crop. Tutuvina wears a turquoise necklace, the symbol of tribal membership. The other young braves are jealous because they feel that an older boy, Crawling Wolf, should have the honor of caring for the sacred bird. Time passes, and a warm relationship grows between the boy and the eagle, which he has named Oh Mau Mana. One day the tribal dancers march to a cave where they secretly prepare for the sacrifice. Tutuvina, though aware that interfering with the ritual will defy the gods and disgrace his father, follows his heart and releases the bird, whereupon he is immediately stripped of his honored necklace and banished to the desert for 12 moons. Weary and weak, he falls prey to vultures but is saved by Oh Mau Mana. Tutuvina learns the ways of the eagle and becomes an expert hunter, but he soon becomes homesick and decides to return to his tribe.*

Though admired as a great hunter he is treated as an outcaste, but he remembers the pride of the eagle and begins an eagle dance. Grabbing Crawling Wolf's necklace, he races to the top of a cliff, spreads his arms, and soars into the air. Before their eyes he is transformed into an eagle and is joined by Oh Mau Mana. Two golden eagles are then seen perched on a ledge surveying their domain, one of them wearing a turquoise necklace. The eagle dance, the storyteller says, is performed by the Hopi boys in remembrance of brave Tutuvina. Hopi Indians. Children. Eagles. Myths. Rites and ceremonies. Hunting.

Note: Location scenes filmed in Coconino National Park, Monument Valley, Canyon de Chelly, Wupatki, National Monument, Arizona; Zuni, New Mexico, and Glen Canyon.

THE LEGEND OF THE TREE OF LIFE *see* IGOROTA, THE LEGEND OF THE TREE OF LIFE

THE LEGENDARY CHAMPIONS   F6.2735

Turn of the Century Fights, Inc. *Dist* Turn of the Century Fights, Inc., Marvin Films. 28 Oct **1968** [New York opening; c19 Dec 1967; LP19155]. Sd; b&w. 35mm. 77 min. [Copyright length: 99 min.]

A William Cayton Production. *Prod* William Cayton. *Assoc Prod* Jim Jacobs. *Dir-Writ* Harry Chapin. *Art Dir* Max Coggiola. *Supv Film Ed* Jim Jacobs. *Ed* Bernie Gagliano, Godfrey Pflager. *Mus Comp & Cond* Steve Chapin.

Narrator: Norman Rose.

Documentary. This documentary on boxing's heavyweight champions covers the years from 1882 to 1929. Highlighted are film clips of John L. Sullivan, Gentleman Jim Corbett (in scenes filmed by Thomas Edison in 1894), the first filmed title bout in 1897 (between Corbett and Bob Fitzsimmons), the 1899 fight between Jim Jeffries and Tom Sharkey, and Jack Johnson taking the title from Tommy Burns in 1907 and then losing it in the controversial 1915 fight with Jess Willard. Jack Dempsey is shown clowning with Charles Chaplin and Douglas Fairbanks, later savagely beating Willard, and ultimately losing his crown to Gene Tunney. Briefly spotlighted in the film are other prominent personalities of the times—Bat Masterson, Wyatt Earp, Carry Nation, Lillian Russell, and Theodore Roosevelt. *Prizefighters. Prizefighting. Motion pictures—History. Tommy Burns. Jim Corbett. Jack Dempsey. Bob Fitzsimmons. James J. Jeffries. Jack Johnson. Tom Sharkey. John L. Sullivan. Gene Tunney. Jess Willard. Charles Chaplin. Douglas Fairbanks. William Barclay Masterson. Wyatt Earp. Carry Nation. Lillian Russell. Theodore Roosevelt.*

LA LEGGE *see* THE LAW

LA LEGGENDA DI ENEA *see* THE AVENGER

LEHI   F6.2736

Lehi Productions. *Dist* Lehi Productions, Emerson Film Enterprises. 12 Dec **1963** [Honolulu, Hawaii, opening]. Sd; b&w. 35mm. 76 min.

Overall Production Credits: *Pres by* Ned Redding. *Prod-Dir* De Vere Baker. *Exec Prod* Emerson Yorke. *Photog* De Vere Baker. *Film Ed* Gene Blakely, ed.

Prolog Production Credits: *Dir-Writ* Emerson Yorke. *Photog* Alan Stensvold.

Participants: De Vere Baker, Larry Fogline, Dan McFarland, Edward Kekaula *(crew)*, Frank G. Baxter *(narrator)*, Tangaroa *(dog)*.

Documentary. On 5 July 1958, Capt. De Vere Baker, his three-man crew, and a dog set out from Redondo Beach, California, on the raft *Lehi IV* in Baker's fourth attempt in 10 years to prove that the Pacific Islands probably were settled by people who drifted there from surrounding continents on crafts similar to *Lehi IV*, a single-sailed vessel measuring 18 by 24 feet. Sixty-nine days later, they have survived a violent storm and are picked up by a Japanese fishing boat off the Hawaiian island Maui and towed into Lahaina. *Adventurers. Seamen. Seafaring life. Survival. Rafts. Fishing boats. Pacific Ocean. Redondo Beach. Maui. Storms. Dogs.*

Note: Filmed in 16mm. Distributed by Emerson Film Enterprises as *Voyage of the Lehi IV.*

LEJONSOMMAR *see* VIBRATION

LEMONADE JOE (Czechoslovakia)   F6.2737

Barrandov Film Studio. *For* Československý Film. *Dist* Allied Artists. 5 May **1966** [Atlanta opening]. Sd; b&w. 35mm (Cinemascope). 90 min.

Pres by Tele-Net International. *Prod* Jaroslav Jílovec. *Assoc Prod* Miloš Stejskal, Jaroslav Koucký, Renée Lavecká. *Dir* Oldřich Lipský. *Screenplay* Jiří Brdečka, Oldřich Lipský. *Story* Jiří Brdečka. *Anim Eff* Jiří Trnka, Břetislav Pojar. *Anim Eff Collab* Jiří Brdečka. *Photog* Vladimír Novotný. *2d Camera Op* Miloš Petrolín. *Asst Camera* Emil Hora, Jiří Knotek. *Art Dir* Karel Škvor, Jan Kňákal. *Film Ed* Miroslav Hájek, Jitka Šulcová. *Mus* Jan Rychlík, Vlastimil Hála. *Poems* Jiří Brdečka, Vratislav Blažek, Pavel Kopta, Jan Rychlík. *English Lyr* Sandra Markham. *Choreog* Josef Koníček. *Sd* Josef Vlček, Adolf Werner.

Sd Eff Bohumír Brunclík, Antonín Jedlička. *1st & 2d Asst Dir* Tomáš Svoboda, Marie Hejzlarová, Miloš Kohout. *Cost* Jiří Brdečka, Fernand Vácha. *Sp Eff* Vladimír Novotný, Ludvík Malý. *English Adapt* Jack Trop Films.

Cast: Karel Fiala *(Lemonade Joe)*, Miloš Kopecký *(Horace Badman)*, Květa Fialová *(Tornado Lou)*, Olga Schoberová *(Winifred Goodman)*, Rudolf Deyl *(Doug Badman)*, Bohuš Záhorský *(Goodman)*, Josef Hlinomaz *(Grimpo)*, Karel Effa *(Panjo Kid)*, Waldemar Matuška *(Banjo Kid)*, Eman Fiala *(pianist)*, Vladimír Menšík, Jiří Lír *(barmen)*, Jiří Steimar *(Kolalok)*, Jaroslav Štercl *(postmaster)*, Oldřich Lukeš *(sheriff)*, Alois Dvorský *(deaf old man)*, Miloš Nedbal *(long-haired player)*, Jaroslav Mareš *(strong gunman)*, Antonín Šura *(gunman)*, Rudolf Cortéz, Stanislav Litera *(shooters)*, Viktor Očásek *(undertaker)*, Ruda Princ *(barber)*, Miloš Vavruška, Jan Pohan *(bandits)*, Stella Zázvorková *(mother)*, Vlastimil Bedrna *(photographer)*, Lubomír Bryg *(cashier)*, Stanislaw Navrátil, Ladislav Gzela *(musicians)*, Antonín Jedlička, Jaroslav Klenot *(fighters)*, Jiří Jelínek, Jiří Schulz *(poker players)*, Jiří Lánský *(cowboy)*, Václav Štekl, Břetislav Dolejši, Karel Engel, Vladimír Erlebach, Jiří Hanzl, Václav Havelka, Gustav Jankovský, Jan Kasík, Jaroslav Mařan, R. Rademachr, Soběslav Sejk, Zdeněk Srstka, J. Šťastny, Jaroslav Tetiva, Jaroslav Tomsa, K. Vítek, Ludvík Wolf, Lubomír Záček, Yvetta Simonová, Jarmila Veselá, Karel Gott.

Western satire. From the play and novel by: Jiří Brdečka, *Limonádový Joe* (Prague, 1958). In Arizona, Lemonade Joe, a singing cowboy, rides into the Trigger Whiskey Saloon and rescues Winifred Goodman and her missionary father from a band of hard-drinking gunslingers. A teetotaler who derives his strength from Kolaloka lemonade, Joe establishes Winifred and her father as the proprietors of a rival tavern serving only soft drinks. But their competitors, Doug and Horace Badman, stage a shoot-out, kill the sheriff, and restore normal business at their saloon. After Lemonade Joe has saved Winifred from being ravaged in the cemetery by the lecherous Horace, it is disclosed that Joe is the western sales representative for Kolaloka and Son. Before he can resume his battle against the Badman brothers, he is tricked into drinking whiskey and passes out. The next day Winifred is kidnaped and carried into the desert. Joe gives chase but is once more fooled into mistaking whiskey for lemonade. While he is unconscious, his white attire is spattered with jam by the villains. Shocked by the injustice, local dancehall girl Tornado Lou kills Joe's tormentors and sets him free. The final confrontation occurs in the cemetery, where all but Joe and Winifred meet their deaths. Only then does Joe learn—by means of identical birthmarks—that the Badman brothers and Tornado Lou are his brothers and sister. Suddenly, Mr. Kolaloka (the father of the brood) appears and restores his dead offspring to life with his lemonade elixir. With peace and family unity renewed, Lemonade Joe and Winifred ride off into the sunset. *Cowboys. Gunfighters. Saloon keepers. Brothers. Dancehall girls. Filial relations. Temperance. Drunkenness. Abduction. Brother-sister relationship. Reviviscence. Saloons. Soft drinks. Cemeteries. Deserts. Birthmarks. Arizona.*

Note: Released in Czechoslovakia in Oct 1964 as *Limonádový Joe* (alternative title: *Koňská opera)*; running time: 99 min.

LENIN V POLSHE *see* **PORTRAIT OF LENIN**

LENIN W POLSCE *see* **PORTRAIT OF LENIN**

LENNY BRUCE   F6.2738
Dist Film-Makers' Distribution Center. 17 Feb **1967** [New York opening]. Sd; b&w. 16mm. 68 min.
Prod John Magnuson.
Featuring: Lenny Bruce.
Documentary. An unedited film of a San Francisco nightclub performance given by Lenny Bruce in August of 1965. He examines matters that he considers to be of greatest concern to Americans—sex, race, the bathroom, patriotism, the police, and Hollywood movies. He also discusses his famous New York State obscenity trial, in which two criminal court judges ruled that his performances were patently offensive to the average person. *Entertainers. Obscenity. Censorship. Nightclubs. San Francisco. Lenny Bruce.*
Note: Also reviewed at 60 and 65 min. May also be known as *Lenny Bruce Concert.*

LEO THE LAST (Great Britain)   F6.2739
Char-Wink-Boor Productions. *Dist* United Artists. 12 May **1970** [New York opening; c11 May 1970; LP40175]. Sd; col (De Luxe). 35mm. 104 min. *MPAA rating* R.
Prod Irwin Winkler, Robert Chartoff. *Dir* John Boorman. *Screenplay* William Stair, John Boorman. *Adtl Dial* Ram John Holder. *Dir Photog* Peter Suschitzky. *Set Decor* Peter Young. *Prod Dsgn* Tony Woollard. *Film Ed* Tom Priestley. *Mus & Songs* Fred Myrow. *Sung by* Ram John Holder, The Swingle Singers. *Sd Ed* Jim Atkinson. *Sd Rec* Ron Barron. *Asst Dir* Allan James. *Prod Mgr* James M. Crawford. *Cost* Joan Woollard. *Makeup* Alex Garfath. *Hairdresser* Colin Jamison. *Sp Eff* John Richardson, sp eff.

Cast: Marcello Mastroianni *(Leo)*, Billie Whitelaw *(Margaret)*, Calvin Lockhart *(Roscoe)*, Glenna Forster-Jones *(Salambo)*, Graham Crowden *(Max)*, Gwen Ffrangcon-Davies *(Hilda)*, David De Keyser *(David)*, Vladek Sheybal *(Laszlo)*, Keefe West *(Jasper)*, Kenneth J. Warren *(Kowalski)*, Patsy Smart *(Mrs. Kowalski)*, Ram John Holder *(Negro preacher)*, Thomas Buson *(Mr. Madi)*, Tina Solomon *(Mrs. Madi)*, Brinsley Forde *(Bip)*, Robert Redman, Malcolm Redman, Robert Kennedy *(Madi children)*, Phyllis McMahon *(blonde whore)*, Princess Patience *(Negro whore)*, Bernard Boston, Roy Stewart *(Jasper's bodyguards)*, Lucita Lijertwood *(wailing lady)*, Ishaq Bux *(supermarket manager)*, Doris Clark *(singing lady)*, Lou Gossett, Alba, Marcia Redman, Billy Russell.

Drama. Source: George Tabori, *The Prince* (a play; production undetermined). Leo, the last in the line of a deposed European monarchy, returns to London for the first time in many years. Traveling with him are his mistress, Margaret, who wants to marry him for his money, and Laszlo, the leader of a band of exiles who are still plotting to restore Leo to the throne. Although the area around his family's mansion has become a Negro ghetto, Leo is at first oblivious to everything but his hobby, ornithology. His bird-watching habits lead him to notice the plight of the poor around him. At first, Leo observes with detachment the problems of one of his black neighbors whose beautiful daughter Salambo is continually harassed by the men of the neighborhood. When a Polish shopkeeper tries to rape Salambo, her boyfriend Roscoe beats him up and is sent to jail. Salambo is then left unprotected, and Jasper, a local pimp, tries to lead her into prostitution. Leo realizes that he must protect the young girl; he becomes involved in the problems of the ghetto; and in a gesture of solidarity with the poor, he sets fire to his mansion. *Royalty. Mistresses. Negroes. Poles. Storekeepers. Pimps. Exile. Ornithology. Poverty. Rape. Ghettos. London. Fires.*
Note: Filmed in the Notting Hill Gate section of London. Released in Great Britain in 1970.

IL LEONE DI SAN MARCO *see* **THE LION OF ST. MARK**

THE LEOPARD (France/Italy)   F6.2740
Titanus–S. N. P. C.–S. G. C. *Dist* Twentieth Century-Fox Film Corp. 12 Aug **1963** [New York opening; c29 May 1963; LP26210]. Sd (Westrex); col (DeLuxe). 35mm (CinemaScope). 165 min.
Prod Goffredo Lombardo. *Exec Prod* Pietro Notarianni. *Dir-Writ* Luchino Visconti. *Screenplay* Suso Cecchi D'Amico, Pasquale Festa Campanile, Enrico Medioli, Massimo Franciosa, Luchino Visconti. *Dir Photog* Giuseppe Rotunno. *Camera Op* Nino Cristiani, Enrico Cignitti, Giuseppe Maccari. *Art Dir* Mario Garbuglia. *Asst Art Dir* Ferdinando Giovannoni. *Set Decor* Giorgio Pes, Laudomia Hercolani. *Asst Set Decor* Emilio D'Andria. *Film Ed* Mario Serandrei. *Mus Score* Nino Rota. *Perf by* Symphony Orchestra of Santa Cecilia. *Cond by* Franco Ferrara. *Unpublished Waltz by* Giuseppe Verdi. *Sd Engr* Mario Messina. *Asst Dir* Rinaldo Ricci, Albino Cocco, Francesco Massaro, Brad Fuller. *Prod Mgr* Enzo Provenzale, Giorgio Adriani. *Script Supv* Stephan Iscovescu. *Unit Mgr* Roberto Cocco, Riccardo Caneva, Gilberto Scarpellini, Gaetano Amata, Bruno Sassaroli. *Asst Unit Mgr* Umberto Sambuco, Lamberto Pippia. *Cost Dsgn* Piero Tosi. *Mr. Lancaster's and Mr. Delon's Cost Made by* Reanda. *Cost by* Sartoria Safas. *Asst Cost Dsgn* Véra Marzot, Bice Brichetto. *Makeup* Alberto De Rossi. *Wigs by* Maria Angelini, Amalia Paoletti. *Military Uniform Cons* Alessandro Gasparinetti, (Maj.). *Still Photog* G. B. Poletto. *Supv U. S. Dub Vers* Sydney Pollack.

Cast: Burt Lancaster *(Prince Don Fabrizio Salina)*, Alain Delon *(Tancredi)*, Claudia Cardinale *(Angelica Sedara/Bertiana)*, Rina Morelli *(Maria Stella)*, Paolo Stoppa *(Don Calogero Sedara)*, Romolo Valli *(Father Pirrone)*, Lucilla Morlacchi *(Concetta)*, Serge Reggiani *(Don Ciccio Tumeo)*, Ida Galli *(Carolina)*, Ottavia Piccolo *(Caterina)*, Pierre Clementi *(Francesco Paolo)*, Carlo Valenzano *(Paolo)*, Anna Maria Bottini *(Governess Mademoiselle Dombreuil)*, Mario Girotti *(Count Cayriaghi)*, Leslie French *(Cavalier Chevally)*, Olimpia Cavalli *(Mariannina)*, Marino Masè *(tutor)*, Sandra Chistolini *(youngest daughter)*, Brook Fuller *(little prince)*, Giuliano Gemma *(Garibaldino general)*, Giovanni Melisendi *(Don Onofrio Rotolo)*, Howard Nelson Rubien *(Don Diego)*, Lola Braccini *(Donna Margherita)*, Ivo Garrani *(Colonel Pallavicino)*, Vittorio Duse, Carlo Lolli, Franco Gula, Giovanni Materassi, Carmelo Artale, Anna Maria Surdo, Alina Zalewska, Winni Riva, Giuseppe Spagnitti, Rosolino Bua, Dante Posani, Stelvio Rosi, Tina Lattanzi, Marcella Rovena, Rina De Liguoro, Valerio Ruggeri, Carlo Palmucci.

Historical drama. Source: Giuseppe Tomasi di Lampedusa, *Il gattopardo* (Milan, 1958). In the spring of 1860, Italy's movement for unification reaches its peak as Garibaldi's Redshirts invade Sicily and crush the Bourbon monarchy. Plebiscites are set up in which Sicilians vote in favor of joining the rest of the peninsula in forming the United Kingdom of Italy. Most strongly affected by the political upheaval is Don Fabrizio, Prince of Salina, who realizes that the inevitable change will mean the end of the privileged class. Aware that he must endure certain changes to preserve vestiges of the dying aristocracy.

he accepts the rising middle class. Consequently, when his favorite nephew, Tancredi, falls in love with Angelica Sedara, the daughter of a wealthy bourgeois, Don Fabrizio resolves to support the match, despite the fact that Concetta, one of his three daughters, loves Tancredi. To restore wealth to the Fabrizio family and provide dowries for his other daughters, Don Fabrizio arranges for Concetta to marry Angelica's wealthy tradesman father, Don Calogero Sedara. He refuses, however, to take a senate seat in the newly-formed government, explaining that he is a man caught between the old and the new, and ill at ease in both. Tancredi introduces Angelica to Sicilian society at a lavish ball. After watching the ambitious girl relax in this new life of luxury and beauty, Don Fabrizio leaves the ball and strolls quietly in the gathering dawn—a proud but lonely figure in a changing world. *Nobility. Patriarchs. Middle classes. Uncles. Cousins. Class conflict. Courtship. Family life. Social reform. Ambition. Wealth. Finance—Personal. Military invasion. Marriage—Arranged. Italy—History—Risorgimento ca1815–70. Sicily. Giuseppe Garibaldi.*

Note: Location scenes filmed in Sicily. Opened in Paris in Jun 1963 as *Le guépard*; running time: 185 min; in Rome in Mar 1963 as *Il gattopardo*; running time: 205 min.

LESNAYA PESNYA *see* **SONG OF THE FOREST**

LET IT BE (Great Britain)   **F6.2741**
Apple Films. *Dist* United Artists. 13 May **1970** [San Francisco opening; c13 May 1970; LP37960]. Sd; col (Technicolor). 35mm (see note). 88 min. *MPAA rating* G.
Prod Neil Aspinall. *Exec Prod* The Beatles. *Dir* Michael Lindsay-Hogg. *Camera* Tony Richmond, Les Parrott, Paul Bond. *Film Ed* Tony Lenny, Graham Gilding. Songs: "Don't Let Me Down," "Maxwell's Silver Hammer," "Two of Us," "I've Got a Feeling," "Oh Darling," "One After 909," "Across the Universe," "Dig a Pony," "Long and Winding Road," "Let It Be," "Get Back" John Lennon, Paul McCartney. Songs: "Jazz Piano Song," "Octopus's Garden" Richard Starkey. Songs: "I Me Mine," "For You Blue" George Harrison. Song: "Dig It" John Lennon, Paul McCartney, Richard Starkey, George Harrison. Songs: "Besame Mucho," "You Really Got a Hold on Me," "Shake, Rattle, and Roll," "Kansas City," "Lawdy, Miss Claudy" sung by The Beatles. *Sd* Peter Sutton, Roy Mingaye, Ken Reynolds, Glyn Johns, Malcolm Evans.
Featuring: Paul McCartney, John Lennon, George Harrison, Ringo Starr, Yoko Ono, Billy Preston.
Documentary. The first part of the film shows the Beatles in rehearsal, performing and perfecting several of their songs. Next the group is seen in a recording session at Apple, their headquarters on Abbey Road in London. The final sequences include a rooftop concert by the Beatles with shots of the resulting traffic jam below and interviews with police and passersby. *Musicians. Singers. Rock and roll. Rehearsals. London. The Beatles.*
Note: Opened in London in May 1970; running time: 81 min. Filmed in 16mm. Ringo Starr is a pseudonym for Richard Starkey.

LET THERE BE BOYS   **F6.2742**
C. R. Productions. 26 Dec **1969** [trade review]. Sd; col (Ektachrome). 16mm. 123 min.
Prod Charles Robinson, prod. *Dir* Jack Pierce, dir. *Screenplay* Charles Robinson, prod, Jack Pierce, dir, Pat Rocco. *Photog* James Prestridge. *Film Ed* Pat Rocco. *Sd* Pat Rocco.
Cast: Ron Dilly, Duane Ferguson, Tim Wright, Irman Jones, Jon Christopher, Chico Rodriguez, Joe Bean, Nick Carr, Mark McKane, Brian Reynolds, Pat Rocco, Society of Pat Rocco and Enlightened Enthusiasts.
Anthology. Five films—*Lonely Hunted* (21 min), *Free Soul* (12 min), *Sunday Sundae* (20 min). *Tools of the Trade* (30 min), and *Worlds Apart* (40 min)—are packaged as a male homosexual film. The first three are basically nudist films; the fourth is a comedy; and the fifth is about a "male films" star who is followed by a devotee to a Pat Rocco film festival in San Francisco. *Actors. Male homosexuality. Film festivals. San Francisco.*

LET'S DO IT *see* **JUDY'S LITTLE NO-NO**

LET'S GO NATIVE *see* **HAVE BIKINI WILL TRAVEL**

LET'S GO WAKADAISHO *see* **LET'S GO, YOUNG GUY!**

LET'S GO, YOUNG GUY! (Japan)   **F6.2743**
Toho Co. Nov **1967** [Los Angeles showing]. Sd; col (Eastmancolor). 35mm Tohoscope. 92 min.
Exec Prod Sanezumi Fujimoto. *Dir* Katsumi Iwauchi. *Screenplay* Yasuo Tanami. *Photog* Yuzuru Aizawa. *Mus* Kenjiro Hirose.
Cast: Yuzo Kayama *(Yuichi Tanuma)*, Yuriko Hoshi, Bibari Maeda, Akira Takarada, Chen Man Ling, Hoei Tanaka, To Man Rei, Choko Iida.

Comedy-drama. Yuichi Tanuma, a popular student at Kyonan University, gets into a number of scrapes involving his old-fashioned father, his irresponsible friend, and a bevy of beautiful coeds. In Hong Kong for a soccer match, Yuichi meets a Chinese woman, much to the consternation of his Japanese girl friend, but the misunderstanding is cleared up on the soccer field. *Students. Athletes. Chinese. Fatherhood. College life. Soccer. Hong Kong.*
Note: Location scenes filmed in Hong Kong. Released in Japan in 1967 as *Let's Go wakadaisho.*

LET'S KILL UNCLE   **F6.2744**
Universal Pictures. 12 Oct **1966** [Los Angeles opening; c15 Oct 1966; LP35372]. Sd (Westrex); col (Technicolor). 35mm. 92 min.
A William Castle Production. *Prod-Dir* William Castle. *Assoc Prod* Dona Holloway. *Screenplay* Mark Rodgers. *Dir Photog* Harold Lipstein. *Art Dir* Alexander Golitzen, William D. DeCinces. *Set Decor* John McCarthy, Julia Heron. *Film Ed* Edwin H. Bryant. *Mus* Herman Stein. *Mus Supv* Joseph Gershenson. *Sd* Waldon O. Watson, Robert R. Bertrand. *Asst Dir* Carl Beringer. *Unit Prod Mgr* Howard Pine. *Makeup* Bud Westmore. *Hairstyles* Larry Germain.
Cast: Nigel Green *(Major Harrison)*, Mary Badham *(Chrissie)*, Pat Cardi *(Barnaby)*, Robert Pickering *(Travis)*, Linda Lawson *(Justine)*, Reff Sanchez *(ketchman)*, Nestor Paiva *(steward)*.
Melodrama. Source: Rohan O'Grady, *Let's Kill Uncle* (New York, 1963). Barnaby Harrison, a 12-year-old orphan who has inherited $5 million, is brought to a tropical island by Police Sgt. Jack Travis to stay with his uncle and guardian, Maj. Kevin Harrison, a former British intelligence commander who is next in line to inherit Barnaby's fortune. Chrissie, a youngster Barnaby's age, travels on the same boat to visit her attractive Aunt Justine; the only other person on the island is a legless native who lives in an abandoned hotel near a shark-infested swimming pool. One day the major hypnotizes Barnaby and tries to get him to walk off a steep cliff; but Barnaby is stopped when Justine calls to him from below. When Barnaby accuses his uncle of trying to kill him, the major cheerfully confesses, explaining that he needs the $5 million and suggesting that they make a game of his murder. Though Chrissie and Barnaby have been quarreling continuously since their arrival on the island, Chrissie, upon learning of Barnaby's dilemma, becomes his ally and suggests that they kill his uncle. But despite the aid of the shark, poisoned mushrooms, tarantulas, and fire, all murder attempts from both sides end in failure. Agreeing to end the game in a draw, the exhausted major decides to forget about the inheritance. As his uncle leaves the island, Barnaby wishes him luck. After his departure, the two children begin to argue again. *Children. Orphans. Police. Uncles. Guardians. British. Aunts. Amputees. Inheritance. Murder. Hypnotism. Poisoning. Mushrooms. Islands. Tropics. Contests. Great Britain—Intelligence service. Fires. Spiders. Sharks.*

LET'S PLAY DOCTOR   **F6.2745**
Juniper Productions. *Dist* Paul Mart Productions. 23 Oct **1964** [Los Angeles showing]. Sd; col. 35mm. 69 min.
Prod-Dir-Writ Jai Hais. *Assoc Prod* Ron Smock. *Assoc Dir* Charles Bateau. *Cinematog* Willy Arriola. *Asst Camera* Chuck Martin. *Film Ed* Willy Arriola. *Sd* Bill Frederick.
Cast: Yul Monge, L. E. Laine, Nellie Acker, Jon Raymond, Lisa Sanders, Karina, Kai Lie Cohen, Gerri Page, Eric Dinee, Marty Fuller, Derby O'Mann.
Sex film. A young physician finds that the women around him are erotic and willing. With his supply of drugs and his own sexual appetite, he finds delight in a promiscuous brunette, his over-sexed receptionist, and a happily married woman who "dreams" of lesbianism and death, of beating and crucifying her husband, and of hanging the doctor. *Physicians. Receptionists. Housewives. Promiscuity. Nymphomania. Lesbianism. Sadism. Murder. Narcotics. Hallucinations.*

LET'S TALK ABOUT WOMEN (France/Italy)   **F6.2746**
Fair Film–Les Films Concordia. *Dist* Embassy Pictures. 28 Sep **1964** [New York opening]. Sd; b&w. 35mm. 108 min.
Pres by Joseph E. Levine. *Prod* Mario Cecchi Gori. *Dir* Ettore Scola. *Story & Screenplay* Ruggero Maccari, Ettore Scola. *Photog* Sandro D'Eva. *Art Dir* Arrigo Breschi. *Film Ed* Marcello Malvestiti. *Mus Comp & Cond* Armando Trovajoli. *Titl Song Sung by* Michele. Song: "Ogni volta" C. A. Rossi, Robifer. *Sung by* Paul Anka. *Sd* Guido Ortensi, Mario Morigi. *Asst Dir* Dino De Palma, Guglielmo Ambrosi. *Prod Supv* Umberto Santoni, Antonio Sarno. *Prod Mgr* Pio Angeletti. *Cost* Ugo Pericoli.
Cast—I: Vittorio Gassman *(stranger)*, Maria Fiore *(fearful wife)*.
Cast—II: Vittorio Gassman *(practical joker)*, Donatella Mauro *(his wife)*, Mario Lucidi *(their son)*.
Cast—III: Vittorio Gassman *(client)*, Giovanna Ralli *(prostitute)*, Umberto D'Orsi *(old friend)*.

Cast—IV: Vittorio Gassman (lover), Antonella Lualdi (fiancée).

Cast—V: Vittorio Gassman (impatient lover), Sylva Koscina (reluctant girl), Edda Ferronao (willing maid).

Cast—VI: Vittorio Gassman (waiter), Heidi Stroh (pick-up).

Cast—VII: Vittorio Gassman (timid brother), Rosanna Gherardi (dishonored sister), Olga Romanelli (distraught mother), Walter Chiari (philanderer), Ivy Olsen (pick-up).

Cast—VIII: Vittorio Gassman (rag man), Eleonora Rossi-Drago (indolent lady).

Cast—IX: Vittorio Gassman (prisoner), Jeanne Valérie (his wife), Marco Tulli (other man), Attilio Dottesio (prison official).

Comedy. I. A gunslinging stranger rides up to an isolated farmhouse and encounters only one occupant, a frightened wife whose husband is momentarily absent. Fearful for the life of her husband, the woman offers herself to the stranger, unaware that he has come to the house merely to return the husband's gun. II. During the day an incorrigible practical joker torments all those he meets. By night, however, he is a tired and strait-laced husband who is something of a bore to his wife and son. III. After enjoying the services of a prostitute, a client recognizes a picture of the woman's husband as an old school chum. The husband returns home and proves to be a true friend, indeed, by refusing to let the client pay for the pleasures of the wife. IV. After enjoying an amorous interlude with a lovely woman, a pleasantly relaxed young man is loath to leave the woman's bed though she must dress for an important occasion: her wedding. V. An impatient lover has difficulty finding a trysting place which will satisfy his fastidious fiancée. While looking at an expensive motel, the lover happily encounters a flirtatious maid much less selective than the fiancée. He emerges from the motel satisfied and takes his fiancée home. VI. A night waiter gets off work after the buses have stopped running. To solve his transportation problem, he accepts offers from prostitutes who own automobiles, permits them to drive him home, and then bids them good night. VII. When his sister is "dishonored" by a philanderer, a timid young man is forced by his mother to confront the philanderer and demand retribution. Instead, he quickly forgets his mission and permits the philanderer to show him a new way of life. VIII. A rag dealer is invited to the palatial home of a jaded noblewoman, presumably to be offered a selection of rags. When he discovers that she is really offering him sex, he announces that he is interested only in material things. IX. Granted a 2-day parole to visit his "dying mother," a prisoner discovers his pass is a ruse devised by his pregnant wife to make people think that it was he who made her pregnant. Once back in jail, however, he recalls his vacation with pleasure and boasts of his wife's state of marital bliss, as the other man hovers in the background. *Gunfighters. Strangers. Housewives. Prostitutes. Chambermaids. Waiters. Philanderers. Junk dealers. Convicts. Nobility. Cuckolds. Marriage. Practical jokes. Brother-sister relationship. Seduction. Pregnancy. Infidelity. Guns. Weddings. Motels.*

Note: Released in Italy in 1964 as *Se permettete, parliamo di donne* at 110 min. Also known as *Parliamo di donne.*

LETTER FROM A NOVICE see **RITA**

LETTER FROM SIBERIA (France)   **F6.2747**

Argos Films–Procinex. *Dist* New Yorker Films. 21 May **1970** [New York opening]. Sd; col (Eastmancolor) with b&w seq. 35mm. 60 min.

Dir Chris Marker. *Anim* Arcady. *Photog* Sacha Vierny. *Film Ed* Anne Sarraute. *Mus* Pierre Barbaud. *Sp Eff* Arcady. *Res* Armand Gatti. *Expedition Organizer* André Pierrard.

Cast: Georges Rouquier (narrator).

Documentary. The film depicts Chris Marker's personal reflections of his trip to Siberia in 1957. Among other topics, Marker describes attempts to make use of the vast forests of the region by damming the rivers and building hydroelectric plants. *Forests. Dams. Electricity. Siberia.*

Note: Opened in Paris in Oct 1958 as *Lettre de Sibérie*; running time: 62 min.

THE LETTER THAT WAS NEVER SENT (U.S.S.R.)   **F6.2748**

Mosfilm. *Dist* Artkino Pictures. 17 Nov **1962** [New York opening]. Sd; col. 35mm. 98 min.

Dir Mikhail Kalatozov. *Screenplay* Grigoriy Koltunov, Valeriy Osipov, Viktor Rozov. *Story Ed* Yu. Shevkunenko. *Dir Photog* Sergey Urusevskiy. *Camera* Yu. Zubov, P. Terpsikhorov. *Art Dir* David Vinitskiy. *Film Ed* N. Anikina. *Mus* Nikolay Kryukov. *Mus Cond* A. Roytman. *Sd* Valeriy Popov. *Prod Mgr* B. Fridman. *Cost* L. Naumova. *Makeup* M. Maslova. *Cons* B. Yerofeyev, D. Ovchinnikov.

Cast: Innokentiy Smoktunovskiy (Konstantin Sabinin), Tatyana Samoylova (Tanya), Vasiliy Livanov (Andrey), Yevgeniy Urbanskiy (Sergey), G. Kozhakina (Vera).

Adventure melodrama. Source: Valeriy Osipov, "Neotpravlennoye pismo" (publication undetermined). A group of Soviet geologists are deposited by plane in Siberia to search for diamond beds. Konstantin Sabinin, the group leader, spends the bleak days and nights composing an interminable letter to his wife back home. The other members of the party include Andrey and Tanya, who are in love, and Sergey, the guide, who also falls in love with Tanya, creating tension within the group. After months of backbreaking work and fruitless searching, Tanya finds a tiny crystal. Rejoicing in their discovery, the four forget the hardships of their search. On their way home, however, they are trapped by a forest fire, and Sergey dies saving the supplies. The others resume their trek through autumn rains which turn to mud the trails that might have led them out of the forest. Andrey becomes seriously ill, and, to avoid placing an additional burden on Tanya and Sabinin, he slips away to die alone in the woods. With the coming of winter, Tanya also dies. More dead than alive, Sabinin makes his way to a river, fashions a makeshift raft, and, with a map of the diamond beds fastened to his chest, gives himself to the mercy of the current. He floats unconscious among the ice floes until at last he is spotted by helicopter and rescued. *Geologists. Guides. Survival. Heroism. Self-sacrifice. Diamonds. Forests. Rafts. Winter. Siberia. Forest fires. Documentation.*

Note: Filmed on location in Siberia. Released in the U.S.S.R. in Jun 1960 as *Neotpravlennoye pismo.* Also known as *The Unsent Letter.*

LETTERE DI UNA NOVIZIA see **RITA**

LETTRE DE SIBÉRIE see **LETTER FROM SIBERIA**

LES LIAISONS DANGEREUSES (France/Italy)   **F6.2749**

Les Films Marceau–Cocinor–Laetitia Films. *Dist* Astor Pictures. 18 Dec **1961** [New York opening]. Sd; b&w. 35mm. 106 min.

Dir Roger Vadim. *Screenplay* Roger Vailland, Roger Vadim, Claude Brulé. *Dial* Roger Vailland. *Photog* Marcel Grignon. *Art Dir* Robert Guisgand. *Film Ed* Victoria Mercanton. *Mus* Thelonius Monk, Jack Murray, mus, Barney Wilem's Orchestra, Art Blakey's Jazz Messengers. *Sd* Robert Biart. *Asst Dir* Jacques Poitrenaud. *Prod Mgr* Léopold Schlosberg.

Cast: Gérard Philipe (Valmont de Merteuil), Jeanne Moreau (Juliette de Merteuil), Jeanne Valérie (Cécile Volanges), Annette Vadim (Marianne Tourvel), Simone Renant (Madame Volanges), Jean-Louis Trintignant (Danceny), Nicolas Vogel (Court), Boris Vian (Prévan), Frédéric O'Brady, Gillian Hills.

Drama. Derived from: Pierre Ambroise François Choderlos de Laclos, *Les liaisons dangereuses* (1782). Valmont and Juliette de Merteuil are the most talked-about married couple in Paris society. Handsome, elegant, rich, and jaded, they aid and abet each other's extramarital affairs. Valmont is a compulsive seducer; his wife a cruel, intelligent woman who intrigues to have him named a representative to the United Nations. When her latest lover prematurely discards her to marry a student, Cécile, the vindictive Juliette encourages Valmont to seduce the young girl while they are vacationing at Megève. At the same time, Valmont meets Marianne, a virtuous wife and mother who resists his advances. After seducing Cécile, Valmont follows Marianne to Paris, and there she finally succumbs to his charm, choosing him over her husband and child. Ironically, Valmont finds himself emotionally involved for the first time in his life. His wife, however, forces him to discard Marianne. The loss of both husband and lover is more than Marianne can bear, and she goes insane. The situation causes a rift between Valmont and Juliette, and their strange alliance is broken. Juliette's subsequent intrigues bring about the death of Valmont at the hands of Cécile's lover, and Juliette herself is horribly disfigured by fire as she attempts to burn her husband's incriminating letters. When she attends the inquest of Valmont's death, photographers hound her and a witness hisses. *Students. Photographers. Upper classes. Marriage. Insanity. Infidelity. Murder. Seduction. Disfiguration. Paris. Megève (France). United Nations.*

Note: Opened in Paris in Sep 1959 as *Les liaisons dangereuses 1960*; running time: 108 min; in Rome in Dec 1962 as *Relazioni pericolose*; Italian co-production status unconfirmed. Also known as *Dangerous Love Affairs.*

LES LIAISONS PARTICULIÈRES see **HER AND SHE AND HIM**

LIANG SHAN-PO YÜ CHU YING-T'AI see **THE LOVE ETERNE**

THE LIARS (France)   **F6.2750**

Méditerranée Cinéma. *Dist* Shawn International, Inc., Ellis Films. Jul **1964.** Sd; b&w. 35mm. 90 min.

Prod Georges Cheyko. *Dir-Story* (see note) Edmond T. Gréville. *Adapt-Dial* Frédéric Dard, Max Montagu. *Dir Photog* Armand Thirard. *Sets* Rino Mondellini. *Film Ed* Jean Ravel. *Mus* André Hossein. *Sd* Jacques Lebreton. *Asst Dir* Jacques Corbel. *Prod Mgr* Ludmilla Goulian.

Cast: Dawn Addams (Norma O'Brien), Jean Servais (Paul Dutraz), Claude Brasseur (Dominique), Francis Blanche (Blanchin), Roland Lesaffre (Clément), Wim Patten (Hervé), Anne-Marie Bellini (Maud), Anne-Marie Coffinet (Valentine), Gaston Modot (Carloti).

Melodrama. Source: Frédéric Dard, *Cette mort dont tu parlais* (Paris, 1957). Wealthy expatriate Paul Dutraz returns to France from Africa, settles outside of Paris, and places an advertisement for a wife: "Under 40, self-sustaining." He selects Norma O'Brien, a mature, Australian actress who, like Paul, wants only to live a quiet existence and hopes to forget her first, unhappy marriage. She tells Paul of her 20-year-old son, Dominique, currently studying at the Beaux Arts in Paris, who is the object of her continual solicitude. Dominique arrives at their villa with a broken leg, and succeeding events begin to sow suspicions in Dutraz' mind. He discovers that Norma is disguising herself with stage makeup to appear older than she really is. With the help of his old friend Blanchin, he finds that Dominique's fracture is a fake. He eventually learns that Dominique is Norma's gigolo, and that the two have hatched a plot to murder him for his fortune. Blanchin, along with Dutraz' maid, Valentine, and her lover, Clément, help Paul to unravel the intrigue. Dominique dies in an auto accident, and Paul gives away his fortune and makes plans to return to Africa. At the last moment, Norma attempts suicide, and Dutraz realizes that she has grown to love him. He learns that she tried to deter Dominique from his villainous plans and forgives her; and they depart for Africa together. *Expatriates. Australians. Actors. Gigolos. Students. Fortune hunters. Wealth. Marriage. Middle age. Conspiracy. Imposture. Murder. Classified advertisements. Africa. Paris. Automobile accidents.*

Note: Opened in Paris in Oct 1961 as *Les menteurs.* Also known as *Twisted Lives.* Edmond Gréville is given story credit in U. S. pressbook, but foreign sources credit him only as director.

THE LIBERATION OF L. B. JONES   **F6.2751**
Liberation Co. *Dist* Columbia Pictures. 18 Mar **1970** [New York opening; c18 Mar 1970; LP37890]. Sd; col (Technicolor). 35mm. 102 min. [Also reviewed at 114 min.] *MPAA rating* R.

A William Wyler–Ronald Lubin Production. *Prod* Ronald Lubin. *Dir* William Wyler. *2d Unit Dir* Robert Swink. *Screenplay* Stirling Silliphant, Jesse Hill Ford. *Dir Photog* Robert Surtees. *Camera Op* William Johnson. *Camera Asst* Terry Meade. *2d Unit Photog* Jordan Cronenweth. *Set Decor* Frank Tuttle. *Prod Dsgn* Kenneth A. Reid. *Supv Film Ed* Robert Swink. *Film Ed* Carl Kress. *Asst Film Ed* Pieter Bergema. *Mus* Elmer Bernstein. *Sd* Jack Solomon, Arthur Piantadosi. *Rec* Harold Lee. *Asst Dir* Anthony Ray, M. Frankovich, Jr., Robert M. Jones. *Unit Prod Mgr* Russell Saunders. *Script Supv* Marshall Schlom. *Wardrobe* Seth Banks, Gene Ashman, Vi Alford. *Makeup Supv* Ben Lane. *Hairstyles* Virginia Jones. *Still Photog* Ken Bell.

Cast: Lee J. Cobb *(Oman Hedgepath)*, Anthony Zerbe *(Willie Joe Worth)*, Roscoe Lee Browne *(Lord Byron Jones)*, Lola Falana *(Emma Jones)*, Lee Majors *(Steve Mundine)*, Barbara Hershey *(Nella Mundine)*, Yaphet Kotto *(Sonny Boy Mosby)*, Arch Johnson *(Stanley Bumpas)*, Chill Wills *(Mr. Ike)*, Zara Cully *(Mama Lavorn)*, Fayard Nicholas *(Benny)*, Joseph Attles *(Henry)*, Lauren Jones *(Erleen)*, Dub Taylor *(mayor)*, Brenda Sykes *(Jelly)*, Larry D. Mann *(grocer)*, Ray Teal *(chief of police)*, Eve McVeagh *(Miss Griggs)*, Sonora McKeller *(Miss Ponsella)*, Robert Van Meter *(blind man)*, Jack Grinnage *(driver)*, John S. Jackson *(suspect)*.

Melodrama. Source: Jesse Hill Ford, *The Liberation of Lord Byron Jones* (Boston, 1965). Steve and Nella Mundine arrive in Somerton, Tennessee, where Steve is to join the law firm of uncle Oman Hedgepath. Arriving on the same train is Sonny Boy Mosby, a young black bent on avenging a childhood beating inflicted by white policeman Stanley Bumpas. Hedgepath is persuaded by Steve to accept the divorce suit of Lord Byron Jones, a wealthy black funeral director. Although Jones has named white policeman Willie Joe Worth as corespondent, his wife Emma contests the suit, hoping to receive a settlement sufficient to meet the needs of the child she has conceived by Worth. When Hedgepath informs the officer of the suit, he is alarmed. Fearful of scandal, Worth demands that Emma forego the contest and beats her when she refuses. After fruitlessly requesting Jones to drop the suit, Worth, assisted by officer Bumpas, arrests the undertaker. Although Jones escapes, he is pursued into a junkyard. Tired of flight, the black confronts the officers and is promptly shot and castrated. Notwithstanding the policemen's confession, Hedgepath and the town mayor decline to prosecute the murderers. Sonny Boy Mosby, however, unknowingly avenges Jones' murder by pushing Bumpas into a harvester. Despairing of southern justice, the Mundines leave town, departing on the same train as Sonny Boy Mosby. *Negroes. Police. Lawyers. Undertakers. Mistresses. Mayors. Revenge. Race relations. Miscegenation. Divorce. Infidelity. Murder. Castration. Lawsuits. Tennessee.*

Note: Filmed on location in Humboldt, Tennessee. Working title: *The Liberation of Lord Byron Jones.*

THE LIBERTINE (Italy)   **F6.2752**
Clesi Cinematografica–Finanziaria San Marco. *Dist* Audubon Films. 15 May **1969** [New York opening]. Sd; col (Eastmancolor). 35mm. 90 min.
Pres by Radley Metzger. *Prod* Silvio Clementelli. *Dir* Pasquale Festa Campanile. *Screenplay* Nicolo Ferrari, Ottavio Jemma. *Story* Nicolo Ferrari. *Dir Photog* Alfio Contini. *Art Dir* Flavio Mogherini. *Set Decor* Ennio Michettoni. *Film Ed* Sergio Montanari. *Mus* Armando Trovajoli. *Asst Dir*

Maria Teresa Girosi. *Prod Mgr* Felice D'Alisera. *Cost Dsgn* Gaia Romanini.
Cast: Catherine Spaak *(Mimi)*, Jean-Louis Trintignant *(Dr. De Marchi)*, Luigi Proietti *(Maldini)*, Luigi Pistilli *(architect)*, Renzo Montagnani *(Fabrizio)*, Nora Ricci *(Mimi's mother)*, Fabienne Dali *(Claudia)*, Paolo Stoppa *(family doctor)*, Vittorio Caprioli *(bookseller)*, Gabriele Tinti *(motorist)*, Philippe Leroy *(tennis coach)*, Frank Wolff *(dentist)*, Venantino Venantini *(plumber)*, Edda Ferronao.

Comedy-drama. Shortly after the funeral of her wealthy older husband, Mimi learns that he maintained a luxurious, secret apartment equipped for the gratification of his unusual sexual desires. In the mirrored trysting place she finds several stag movies, including one of her best friend, Claudia, and a notebook in which her husband rated his sexual partners. Her initial anger turns to curiosity, and she decides to explore the range of sexual possibilities for herself, appropriating the apartment. After broadening her knowledge by reading Krafft-Ebing's *Psychopathia Sexualis*, she systematically seduces her husband's business partner, her dentist, her tennis coach, Claudia's husband, a motorist who mistakes her for a prostitute, and a sadistic stranger. Despite the diversity of her escapades, she finds little satisfaction and succeeds only in jeopardizing her health. During a medical checkup, she sprains her ankle. A nearsighted radiologist, Dr. De Marchi, carries her, half naked, on his shoulders, thus unwittingly gratifying a fetish which gives Mimi intense pleasure. Captivated by the doctor's shyness, Mimi poses as a medical student and eventually gets him to invite her on an archeological weekend. Mimi easily seduces him, but she is shocked when he later asks her to marry her. Determined to prove her lack of moral scruples, Mimi shows De Marchi filmed records of her "experimentation," and she even disrobes in public, but she is unable to dissuade him from the idea of matrimony. As she returns to the mirrored apartment, the memories of her adventures exacerbate her desire for sexual freedom. De Marchi loses his temper, destroys the entire love nest, and implores her to settle down with him. Initially she refuses, but finally she acquiesces; and on their wedding night De Marchi assuages her guilt feelings about the fetish which gives her such pleasure and takes her for an extended erotic "pony ride." *Widows. Physicians. Seduction. Sexual practices. Sadism. Eroticism. Fetishism. Sex exploitation films.*

Note: Released in Italy in 1969 as *La matriarca.*

LICENSED TO KILL *see* **THE 2ND BEST SECRET AGENT IN THE WHOLE WIDE WORLD**

THE LICKERISH QUARTET (United States/Italy/West Germany)
                                        F6.2753
Radley Metzger–Cinemar Productions–Peter Carsten Productions. *Dist* Audubon Films. 13 Oct **1970** [New York opening]. Sd; col (Eastman Color). 35mm. 90 min. *MPAA rating* X.

A Radley Metzger Production. *Prod-Dir* Radley Metzger. *Screenplay* Michael DeForrest. *Story* Michael DeForrest, Radley Metzger. *Photog* Hans Jura. *Sets* Enrico Sabbatini. *Film Ed* Amedeo Salfa. *Mus Comp* Steven Cipriani. *Prod Mgr* Mario Mariani. *Cost* Enrico Sabbatini. *Paintings of St. Margaret* Michele Franculli.

Cast: Silvana Venturelli *(The Girl)*, Frank Wolff *(The Man)*, Erika Remberg *(The Woman)*, Paolo Turco *(The Boy)*.

Melodrama. A rich, bored couple spend an evening watching a stag movie at their Italian castle while their adolescent son, who experienced a vision of St. Margaret at the age of 3, views the scene with distaste. One night in a wall-of-death motorcycle act at a local carnival, the family encounters a woman who they believe to be the star of one of the stag films. Anxious to ascertain if they are correct, they invite the woman home, in order to watch her reactions to the films. Illusion and reality intermingle as the action on screen unfolds; and the members of the family recall past sexual traumas and project themselves into the filmed sexual encounters. The woman frees the family from their sexual problems by having sex first with the man, whose wife had believed him to be impotent; then with the couple's son; and finally with the wife. *Actors. Impotence. Adolescence. Family life. Lesbianism. Wealth. Carnivals. Sex exploitation films. Castles. Motorcycle racing. Visions. Fantasy.*

Note: Filmed at the Castle of Balsorano near Sora, Italy, and at Cinecitta studios in Rome. Pre-release title: *Hide and Seek.*

LIEBE MIT ZWANZIG *see* **LOVE AT TWENTY**

DIE LIEBESQUELLE *see* **THE FOUNTAIN OF LOVE**

LIEBESSPIELE IM SCHNEE *see* **SKI FEVER**

LT. ROBIN CRUSOE, U. S. N.   **F6.2754**
Walt Disney Productions. *Dist* Buena Vista Distribution Co. 25 Jun **1966** [c10 May 1966; LP32535]. Sd (RCA); col (Technicolor). 35mm. 110 min. [Copyright length: 114 min.]
A Walt Disney Production. *Co-prod* Bill Walsh, Ron Miller. *Dir* Byron Paul. *2d Unit Dir* Joseph L. McEveety. *Screenplay* Bill Walsh, Don DaGradi. *Story*

Retlaw Yensid. *Anim Styling* McLaren Stewart. *Anim Eff* Jack Boyd. *Dir Photog* William Snyder. *Art Dir* Carroll Clark, Carl Anderson. *Set Decor* Emile Kuri, Frank R. McKelvy. *Film Ed* Cotton Warburton. Bob Brunner. *Mus Orch* Cecil A. Crandall. *Sd Supv* Robert O. Cook. *Sd Mix* Larry Jost. *Mus Ed* Evelyn Kennedy. *Asst Dir* Tom Leetch. *Unit Mgr* Marvin Stuart. *Cost Dsgn* Bill Thomas. *Cost* Chuck Keehne, Neva Rames. *Makeup* Pat McNalley. *Hairstyles* La Rue Matheron. Peter Ellenshaw. *Sp Eff* Eustace Lycett, Robert A. Mattey. *Anim Supv* Stewart Raffill.

Cast: Dick Van Dyke *(Lt. Robin Crusoe)*, Nancy Kwan *(Wednesday)*, Akim Tamiroff *(Tanamashu)*, Arthur Malet *(umbrella man)*, Tyler McVey *(captain)*, Pete Renoudet *(pilot)*, Peter Duryea *(co-pilot)*, John Dennis *(crew chief)*, Nancy Hsueh, Victoria Young, Yvonne Ribuca, Bebe Louie, Lucia Valero *(native girls)*.

Adventure comedy. Navy pilot Lt. Robin Crusoe, on a routine flying mission, is forced to parachute into the Pacific. After drifting for days without food or water, he is washed up on a desert island. Mysterious footprints lead him to a beached Japanese World War II submarine where he discovers Floyd, an astrochimp that survived a misadventure in space. Joining forces, the pair make life more comfortable by building everything from a pagoda-style bamboo hut to a golf course. Then one day they are joined by a native girl whom Robin nicknames Wednesday. She explains that her tyrannical father, the chief on a nearby island, banished her for refusing to marry a man of his choice. Before long Wednesday is joined by other women seeking independence. Robin organizes them into an army, and when the chief and his warriors invade, the native suffragettes stage a freedom rally. Using equipment from the beached sub, Robin and Floyd make it appear that the island's stone idol is displeased with the chief and his men. As the women are celebrating their victory, Robin does a little dance with Wednesday; and when he learns that this ritual is interpreted as a marriage proposal, he and Floyd flee to the beach as a Navy helicopter comes to the rescue. The helicopter lands on a carrier to a hero's welcome. *Air pilots. Parachuting. Filial relations. Women's rights. Superstition. Rites and ceremonies. Islands. Submarines. Helicopters. Aircraft carriers. Pacific Ocean. United States Navy. Robinson Crusoe. Chimpanzees.*

Note: Location scenes filmed on the Hawaiian island of Kauai. Retlaw Yensid is a pseudonym for Walt Disney.

LIFE AT THE TOP (Great Britain)   F6.2755
Romulus Films. *Dist* Royal Films International, Columbia Pictures. 14 Dec **1965** [New York opening; c1 Dec 1965; LP33181]. Sd (Westrex); b&w. 35mm. 117 min.
Prod James Woolf. *Assoc Prod* William Kirby. *Dir* Ted Kotcheff. *Screenplay* Mordecai Richler. *Dir Photog* Oswald Morris. *Camera Op* Brian West. *Art Dir* Edward Marshall. *Set Dresser* David Ffolkes. *Film Ed* Derek York. *Mus Comp* Richard Addinsell. *Mus Cond* Marcus Dods. *Sd Rec* Norman Bolland, Bob Jones. *Dub Ed* Jonathan Bates. *Asst Dir* Kip Gowans. *Prod Mgr* Charles Blair. *Cont* Phyllis Crocker. *Cost Dsgn* Beatrice Dawson. *Wardrobe* Jackie Cummins. *Makeup Supv* George Frost. *Hairdresser* Joan Smallwood. *Casting* Jenia Reissar.

Cast: Laurence Harvey *(Joe Lampton)*, Jean Simmons *(Susan Lampton)*, Honor Blackman *(Norah Hauxley)*, Michael Craig *(Mark)*, Donald Wolfit *(Abe Brown)*, Robert Morley *(Tiffield)*, Margaret Johnston *(Sybil)*, Ambrosine Phillpotts *(Mrs. Brown)*, Allan Cuthbertson *(George Aisgill)*, Paul A. Martin *(Harry)*, Frances Cosslett *(Barbara)*, Ian Shand *(Hethersett)*, George A. Cooper *(Graffham)*, Nigel Davenport *(Mottram)*, Andrew Laurence *(McLelland)*, Geoffrey Bayldon *(industrial psychologist)*, Denis Quilley *(Ben)*, David Oxley *(Tim)*, David McKail *(Oscar)*, Paul Whitsun-Jones *(Keatley)*, Charles Lamb *(Wincastle)*, Michael Newport *(newspaper boy)*, Richard Leech *(doctor)*, Ingrid Anthofer *(stripper)*, Harry Fowler *(magic beans man)*.

Drama. Source: John Braine, *Life at the Top* (London, 1962). After 10 years of marriage to Susan, the daughter of wealthy millowner Abe Brown, Joe Lampton continues to be in disfavor because of his lower-class origins. Forced to wed Susan before she gave birth to her first child, Joe has used his ambition to raise himself to a senior position in his father-in-law's company, but his growing distress at his marriage and his seeming incompetence at his job have embittered him. His attitude remains unchanged even after he has run successfully in a local election as a Conservative. He is more concerned about losing his chance for promotion when Brown, contrary to Joe's advice, decides to merge his company with another one. Joe is also distressed because he is unable to put through his plans for slum clearance, since Brown is interested in more profitable business plans. Joe sees his private life ruined when he finds his best friend, Mark, in bed with Susan. Though she claims that she feels nothing toward Mark, Joe hurries to London to stay with his mistress, Norah Hauxley, a television announcer whom he met while running for public office. After a brief romantic fling, he becomes dissatisfied with Norah and with himself because of his lack of education and his inability to find a satisfying job. Disillusioned, he meets with Susan, who still loves him, in London; and he

decides that he will go back to Warley, where he will be made chairman of the board, succeeding Brown when he retires. *Industrialists. Opportunists. Fathers-in-law. Mistresses. Television announcers. Marriage. Ambition. Disillusionment. Lower classes. Infidelity. Elections. Mills. Slums. London. Conservative Party (United Kingdom).*

Note: Opened in London in Jan 1966. A sequel to *Room at the Top* (1959).

LIFE FOR RUTH *see* **WALK IN THE SHADOW**

LIFE IN DANGER (Great Britain)   F6.2756
Parroch Films. *Dist* Allied Artists. Feb **1964** [c1 Jan 1959; LP26800]. Sd (RCA); b&w. 35mm. 63 min.
Prod Jack Parsons. *Dir* Terry Bishop. *Orig Story & Screenplay* Malcolm Hulke, Eric Paice. *Camera Op* Gerry Massy-Collier. *Lighting Camera* Peter Hennessy. *Art Dir* Peter Proud. *Film Ed* John Trumper. *Asst Ed* Michael Pavett. *Mus Comp & Cond* William Davies. *Sd Mix* Bill Salter. *Boom Op* Gerry Humphreys. *1st, 2d & 3d Asst Dir* Jack Causey, Bob Porter, Henry Emery. *Prod Mgr* Clifford Parkes. *Cont* Phyllis Townshend. *Wardrobe* Evelyn Gibbs. *Makeup Artist* Jill Carpenter. *Hairdressing* Eileen Bates. *Stills Camera* Cyril Stanborough.

Cast: Derren Nesbitt *(The Man)*, Julie Hopkins *(Hazel Ashley)*, Howard Marion Crawford *(Major Peters)*, Victor Brooks *(Tom Baldwin)*, Jack Allen *(Jack Ashley)*, Christopher Witty *(Johnny Ashley)*, Carmel McSharry *(Mrs. Ashley)*, Mary Manson *(Jill Shadwell)*, Bruce Seton *(landlord)*, Peter Swanwick *(Dr. Nichols)*, Bryan Coleman *(Chief Constable Ryman)*, Humphrey Lestocq *(Inspector Bennet)*, Richard Pearson *(Sergeant Norris)*, Celia Hewitt *(woman at the bus stop)*, Brian Rawlinson *(male nurse)*.

Drama. Shortly after a child murderer escapes from a mental hospital, a young laborer calls at a strange house in search of water and a place to rest. There he is befriended by Hazel Ashley, an emotionally disturbed adolescent who leads him to a hayloft of a nearby barn. Hazel and the stranger talk, and she attempts unsuccessfully to persuade him to take her away from her unhappy home. Hazel's absence is noticed, and a group of townspeople led by Major Peters, a local squire, track her to the barn. The local police prevent Peters from entering the barn, and a hospital official searches the building. Hazel and the stranger hide themselves well, however, and the official can't find them. The mob disperses, and Hazel again asks the stranger to take her away with him. The townspeople find new evidence that the couple is in the barn, and they return later that night. The girl becomes terrified and rips her blouse while running from the barn. The stranger runs after her and is shot and wounded by Major Peters. A police inspector arrives on the scene and informs the mob that the escaped child murderer had been apprehended earlier that evening. *Escapees. Strangers. Vigilantes. Police. Mistaken identity. Adolescence. Mental illness. Barns.*

Note: Released in Great Britain in 1959; running time: 63 min.

LIFE IS A CIRCUS (Great Britain)   F6.2757
Vale Film Productions. *Dist* Schoenfeld Film Distributing Corp. 25 Jan **1962** [New York State license]. Sd; b&w. 35mm (CinemaScope). 84 min.
Prod E. M. Smedley-Aston. *Assoc Prod* John Pellatt. *Dir-Writ* Val Guest. *Adtl Material* John Warren, Len Heath. *Dir Photog* Arthur Graham. *Art Dir* Tony Masters. *Film Ed* Bill Lenny. *Mus* Philip Green. *Titl Song* Bernie Loren, Horace Linsley. *Song:* "For You, For You" Dave Goddard, Gene McCarthy, mus, Larry Vannata. *Sung by* Shirley Eaton, Michael Holliday. *Song:* "Underneath the Arches" Bud Flanagan. *Sung by* Bud Flanagan, Chesney Allen. *Choreog* Denys Palmer. *Sd Rec* Buster Ambler, Wally Milner.

Cast—The Crazy Gang: Bud Flanagan *(Bud)*, Jimmy Nervo *(Cecil)*, Teddy Knox *(Sebastian)*, Charlie Naughton *(Charlie)*, Jimmy Gold *(Goldie)*, Eddie Gray *(Eddie)*.

Cast: Shirley Eaton *(Shirley Winter)*, Michael Holliday *(Carl Rickenbeck)*, Lionel Jeffries *(genie)*, Eric Pohlmann *(Rickenbeck)*, Joseph Tomelty *(Joe Winter)*, Chesney Allen *(Ches)*, Fred Johnson *(Mr. Deaken)*, Harold Kasket *(Hassan)*, Maureen Moore *(Rose of Baghdad)*, Edwin Richfield *(driver)*, Peter Glaze *(1st hand)*, Sam Kydd *(removal man)*, Geoffrey Denton *(policeman)*.

Comedy. While circus owner Rickenbeck schemes to force rival Joe Winter out of business, his son, Carl, falls in love with his antagonist's daughter, Shirley. Winter is further assisted by Bud, a kindly janitor who finds a magic lamp, from which emerges a benign genie. Although distracted by a harem dancer, the genie helps save Winter's circus. *Genii. Janitors. Dancers. Circus. Business competition. Filial relations.*

Note: Location scenes filmed in Windsor and Runnymede. Working title: *Clowns in Clover.* Released in Great Britain in 1960.

LIFE LOVE DEATH (France/Italy)   F6.2758
Les Films Treize–Ariane–Les Productions Artistes Associés–P. E. A. *Dist* Lopert Pictures. 26 May **1969** [New York opening; c29 Jan 1969; LF56]. Sd; col (De Luxe) and b&w. 35mm. 115 min. *MPAA rating* R.

Prod Alexandre Mnouchkine, Georges Dancigers. *Dir* Claude Lelouch. *Screenplay* Pierre Uytterhoeven, Claude Lelouch. *Dir Photog* Jean Collomb. *Photog* Alain Dejean. *Asst Art Dir* Albert Rajau. *Film Ed* Claude Barrois. *Asst Ed* Marie-Claude Lacambre. *Mus* Francis Lai. *Orch* Christian Gaubert. *Sd Engr* Jean-Louis Ducarme. *Asst Dir* Claude Pinoteau. *Prod Mgr* Pierre Pardon. *Unit Mgr* Raymond Leplont.

Cast: Souad Amidou *(François Toledo)*, Caroline Cellier *(Caroline)*, Janine Magnan *(Jeanne)*, Marcel Bozzufi *(Inspector Marchand)*, Pierre Zimmer *(police officer)*, Lisette Bersy *(Hélène)*, Albert Naud *(defense lawyer)*, Jean-Pierre Sloan *("partie civile")*, Nathalie Durrand *(Sophie)*, Sylvia Saurel, Denyse Roland *(prostitutes)*, Claudia Morin *(girl at dance)*, Catherine Samie *(Julie)*, Rita Maiden *(prostitute in car)*, Pierre Collet *(chief executioner)*, Albert Rajau, Jacques Henry, Jean-Marc Allègre *(executioner's assistants)*, Colette Taconnat *("assistante sociale")*, Jean Collomb *(motel owner)*, Robert Hossein *(man in film)*, Annie Girardot *(woman in film)*, El Cordobés *(bullfighter in Nîmes ring)*, Jacques Portet, Yves Gabrielli, Jean-Pierre Hazi *(Police)*.

Melodrama. Paris police keep a careful watch on the activities of François Toledo, a young married factory worker with a young child, Sophie. Toledo is observed with his co-worker and mistress, Caroline, and one night, as they make love in a hotel room, they are surprised by the police and brought to the Paris detective bureau for interrogation. Confronted by the evidence against him, Toledo confesses to murder, and Caroline, stunned and tearful, leaves. When Toledo is brought to trial and convicted, both the defense and public attorneys request leniency, but he is nevertheless condemned to death. In prison, fearing to learn of the denial of his appeal (which would mean imminent execution), Toledo recalls the circumstances that led him to the present: *Despite a normal sexual relationship with his wife, Jeanne, his boredom with his home life is exaggerated by frequent quarrels with his mother-in-law, and he begins to seek out prostitutes. Unable to deal with the impotence he experiences in these situations, he grows violent. In Pigalle, he strangles a prostitute who insults him; in Nîmes, where he attends the bullfights, a frustrating encounter again leads him to murder. He meets Caroline, and through his relationship with her he overcomes his sexual problems. By this time, however, the police have published a composite drawing prepared with the help of a prostitute, and Toledo's mother-in-law has reported his resemblance to the composite.* The guillotine is assembled late one night in the prison courtyard. At dawn Toledo hears that his appeal has been denied, and he is led to execution. *Factory workers. Police. Mistresses. Lawyers. Mothers-in-law. Prostitutes. Capital punishment. Marriage. Murder. Impotence. Trials. Mental illness. Infidelity. Hotels. Prisons. Confession (law). Paris. Nîmes.*

Note: Paris opening: Jan 1969 as *La vie, l'amour, la mort*.

LIFE OF A COUNTRY DOCTOR (Japan)   **F6.2759**

Toho Co. *Dist* Toho International, Inc. May **1961** [Los Angeles showing]. Sd; b&w. 35mm (Tohoscope). 116 min. [Cut to 104 min.]

Prod Tomoyuki Tanaka. *Dir* Hiroshi Inagaki. *Screenplay* Ryuzo Kikushima. *English Adapt* Victor Suzuki. *Photog* Kazuo Yamada. *Mus* Ikuma Dan.

Cast: Hisaya Morishige *(Keisai Koyama)*, Setsuko Hara *(Iku, his wife)*, Yosuke Natsuki *(Hangoro)*, Chiemi Eri *(Osaki)*, So Yamamura *(Dr. Meikai Ikeda)*.

Historical drama. Keisai Koyama, an elderly doctor in 19th-century rural Japan, takes on a young assistant, Hangoro, who has been trained in the city in the latest techniques of medicine. Despite Hangoro's urging, Keisai continues to employ his traditional practices. When a typhus epidemic strikes the district, Keisai's resistance to change is tragically dramatized. *Physicians. Epidemics. Typhus.*

Note: Released in Japan in 1960 as *Fundoshi isha*. Alternative U. S. titles: *Life of the Country Doctor* and *The Country Doctor*.

THE LIFE OF JUANITA CASTRO   **F6.2760**

Dist Film-Makers' Cooperative. 22 Mar **1965** [New York opening]. Sd; b&w. 16mm. 70 min.

Prod-Dir Andy Warhol. *Writ* Ronald Tavel. *Photog* Andy Warhol.

Cast: Marie Menken *(Juanita)*, Elecktrah *(Raoul)*, Ronald Tavel *(stage manager)*, Mercedes Ospina *(Fidel)*, Marina Ospina *(Che)*, Waldo Díaz Balart.

Satire. Members of the cast stand or sit facing an imaginary camera throughout the film as if posing for a family portrait. In their midst, the stage manager, script in hand, gives instructions. Fidel delivers a 30-minute harangue. His sister Juanita criticizes his regime and deplores the intrusion of homosexuality into their lives. Departing from her instructions, Juanita occasionally reacts spontaneously to others' comments. *Male homosexuality. Brother-sister relationship. Juana Castro. Ernesto "Che" Guevara. Fidel Castro Ruz. Raúl Castro Ruz.*

Note: The frame remains fixed throughout.

THE LIFE OF MOZART (Austria/West Germany)   **F6.2761**

Fischer Film–Fernsehen Produktion. *Dist* Connoisseur Films. 13 Aug **1970** [New York opening]. Sd; b&w. 35mm. 140 min. [Also 145 min.]

Prod-Dir Hans Conrad Fischer. *Screenplay* Lutz Besch, Hans Conrad Fischer. *Photog* S. Alexander Moyses. *Asst Photog* Manfred Mayr. *Film Ed* Anna Höllering, Paula Dvorak. *Mus Selections* Wolfgang Amadeus Mozart. *Mus Played by* The Angelicum Orchestra, The Barchet Quintet, The Bavarian State Orchestra, The Berlin Philharmonic Orchestra, The Camerata Academica of the Salzburg Mozarteum, Chamber Orchestra of Jean-François Paillard, The Chamber Orchestra of the State High School for Music Hamburg, The Cologne Radio Symphony Orchestra, The Czech Philharmonic Orchestra, The Instrumental Ensemble Jean-Marie Leclair, The Munich Bach Orchestra, The Pro Arte Chamber Orchestra, The RIAS Symphony Orchestra, The Saxon State Orchestra, Vienna Symphony Orchestra, The Volksoper Orchestra, The Wind Ensemble of the South German Radio. *Mus Cond* Karl Böhm, Carlo Felice Cillario, Jörg Demus, Ferenc Fricsay, Wilhelm Furtwängler, Ernst Hinreiner, Eugen Jochum, Herbert von Karajan, Franz Konwitschny, Fritz Lehmann, Franz Litschauer, Jean-François Paillard, Kurt Redel, Karl Richter, Václav Smetácek, Gerhard Wimberger. *Mus Sung by* The Munich Bach Choir, The RIAS Chamber Choir, The Salzburg Radio Choir, The Salzburg Mozarteum Choir, Walter Berry, Fiorenza Cossotto, Ernst Haefliger, Richard Itzinger, Erika Köth, Friedrich Lenz, Walter Raninger, Fritz Reinharts, Lotte Schädle, Marie Stader, Fritz Wunderlich. *Organ* Wolfgang Bauer, Marie-Claire Alain, Gaston Litaize. *Clavichord & Fortepiano* Jörg Demus. *Piano* Clara Haskil. *Clarinet* Jacques Lancelot. *Harp* Lily Laskine. *Violin* David Oistrakh, Lutz Leskowitz. *Flute* Jean-Pierre Rampal. *Cembalo* Hans Schurich. *Sd* Josef Adelberger. *Prod Asst* Anke Ruppe. *Mus Adv* Hans Schurich. *English Vers* Martina Mayne, David Thomson.

Cast: Hugh Burden *(narrator)*, Salzburg Puppet Theatre.

Documentary. The life of Wolfgang Amadeus Mozart is documented with memorabilia and footage of the buildings and towns where he lived and worked. Visual material is accompanied by selections from Mozart's work. The Salzburg Puppet Theatre performs *Die Zauberflöte. Wolfgang Amadeus Mozart. "The Magic Flute".*

Note: Released in Austria and West Germany in 1967 as *Das Leben Mozarts*.

LIFE OF OHARU (Japan)   **F6.2762**

Shin Toho Co. *Dist* Toho International, Inc. 20 Apr **1964** [New York opening]. Sd; b&w. 35mm. 146 min.

Dir Kenji Mizoguchi. *Screenplay* Yoshikata Yoda, Kenji Mizoguchi. *Photog* Yoshimi Kono, Yoshimi Hirano. *Art Dir* Hiroshi Mizutani. *Mus* Ichiro Saito. *Historical Cons* Isamu Yoshi.

Cast: Kinuyo Tanaka *(Oharu)*, Toshiro Mifune *(Katsunosuke)*, Toshiko Yamane, Yuriko Hamada, Ichiro Tsugai, Masao Shimizu, Matsura Tsuke, Jukichi Uno, Takashi Shimura, Eitaro Shindo, Eijiro Yanagi, Chieko Higashiyama, Masao Mishima, Sadako Sawamura.

Drama. Source: Saikaku Ibara, *Koshuku ichidai onna* (Edo (Tokyo), 1686). Oharu, a 50-year-old prostitute in the Genroku Era of 17th-century Japan, contemplates her past in front of a Buddha image. *The youthful daughter of a samurai in the Imperial Palace of Kyoto, she falls in love with a man from a lower class. As punishment, her lover is decapitated, and her family is banished from the city. After attempting suicide, she becomes the mistress of a prince, who drives her away after she bears his son. Her father sells her to a geisha house, and she becomes a prostitute. A wealthy client buys her, but he is found to be a counterfeiter, and she ventures into prostitution again, eventually marrying a merchant. When the merchant dies, she has reached middle age and is forced once again to become a prostitute.* Having finished her contemplation before the Buddha, she is found by her son, a prince, and is offered refuge in his home. Her past has left her denigrated, however, and she leaves her son to spend the rest of her life as a beggar. *Prostitutes. Samurai. Royalty. Merchants. Beggars. Class conflict. Capital punishment. Suicide. Illegitimacy. Filial relations. Marriage. Japan—History—Genroku Era. Kyoto.*

Note: Released in Japan as *Saikaku ichidai onna* in Apr 1952; running time: 143 min. Also reviewed in Japan as *Koshoku ichidai onna*.

THE LIFE OF ST. MARIA GORETTI *see* **NO. NO. IT'S A SIN**

LIFE OF THE COUNTRY DOCTOR *see* **LIFE OF A COUNTRY DOCTOR**

LIFE UPSIDE DOWN (France)   **F6.2763**

A. J. Films. *Dist* Landau Releasing Organization, Allied Artists. 17 Aug **1965** [New York opening]. Sd; b&w. 35mm. 92 min.

Prod Michel Peynet. *Dir-Writ* Alain Jessua. *Photog* Jacques Robin. *Art Dir* Olivier Girard. *Film Ed* Nicole Marko. *Mus* Jacques Loussier. *Sd* Jean-Claude Marchetti. *Asst Dir* Christian de Chalonges. *Prod Mgr* Ginette Courtois-Doyel.

Cast: Charles Denner (*Jacques Valin*), Anna Gaylor (*Viviane*), Guy Saint-Jean (*Fernand*), Nicole Gueden (*Nicole*), Jean Yanne (*Kerbel*), Yvonne Clech (*Madame Kerbel*), Robert Bousquet (*Paul*), Françoise Moncey (*Ina*), Jean Dewever (*major*), Gilbert Meunier (*park keeper*), André Thorent (*doctor*), Bernard Sury (*inspector*), Jenny Orléans (*concierge*), Nane Germon (*mother*).

Drama. Jacques Valin works as a real estate agent and lives with Viviane, an advertising model. One day he discovers the pleasure of solitary meditation, during which he withdraws from the world around him. He begins experimenting with this technique in a variety of situations, and Viviane becomes concerned over his lack of attention. To allay her fears, Jacques proposes marriage, but he disappears from the wedding reception given by his employers and for that reason is fired. Delighted to have more free time, he continues his withdrawal, driving Viviane to attempt suicide. She recovers but leaves him when she senses his lack of real concern. Her doctor becomes interested in Jacques, and when he sees that neither Jacques' mother nor a close friend can help him, he has Jacques committed to an asylum. *Real estate agents. Models. Physicians. Meditation. Suicide. Insane asylums. Weddings.*

Note: Opened in Paris in Jun 1964 as *La vie à l'envers*. Shown at the New York Film Festival as *Inside Out*.

LIGEIA see **THE TOMB OF LIGEIA**

LIGHT BLUE see **BACHELOR OF HEARTS**

LIGHT FANTASTIC　　　　　　　　　　　　　　　F6.2764

Seneca Productions. *Dist* Embassy Pictures. caJan **1964**. Sd; b&w. 35mm. 85 min.

Pres by Joseph E. Levine. *Prod* Robert Gaffney. *Assoc Prod* Clarkson Potter. *Dir* Robert McCarty. *Screenplay* Joseph Hochstein, Robert McCarty. *Orig Story* Joseph Hochstein. *Dir Photog* J. Burgi Contner. *Camera Op* Sol Negrin. *Set Dsgn* Albert Brenner. *Set Decor* Leif Pedersen. *Titl* Everett Aison. *Film Ed* James Gaffney. *Mus Comp* Joseph Liebman. *Mus Score & Cond* Judd Woldin. *Theme Song:* "*My Secret World*" Doris Menkes, Joseph Liebman. *Sung by* Eydie Gorme. *Mus* Judd Woldin Octet. *trumpet* Buddy Yannon. *woodwinds* Buzz Brauner. *trombones* Ray Hartman, James Cleveland, Paul Faulise. *bass* Pete Rogers. *drums* Al Germansky. *Sd Engr* Frank McLaughlin. *Mus Ed* Angelo Ross. *Mus Rec* Dick Charles Studio. *Asst Dir* Ben Berk. *Prod Mgr* Lockwood Rush. *Prod Sec* Elsa Walden. *Script Girl* Anne Warren. *Clothes* De Pinna. *Eff* Ross-Gaffney Inc. *Gaffer* Dusty Wallace. *Set Constr* Mickey Bradley.

Cast: Dolores McDougal (*Beverly*), Barry Bartle (*Stephen*), Jean Shepherd (*Frank*), Lesley Woods (*Mrs. Sharpe*), Alan Bergmann (*Bill*), Cathy Sullivan, Drummond Erskine, Jane Ross, Flicka McKenna, Corrinne Orr, Nicolas Coster, Robert Mandan, Sara Berk.

Romantic melodrama. Beverly, a plain and lonely secretary in New York City, receives as a prize three free lessons at a dance studio. She makes use of them and is told by her instructor, Steve, that she has a talent for dancing. When Steve romances and flatters her into signing a long-term agreement for lessons, Beverly takes him seriously, and they begin an affair. Steve realizes that he loves Beverly, and he tries to tell her that he is not all he has pretended to be; he even offers to disregard the contract, but she refuses. He then arranges to be absent from one of the lessons, and she is shepherded through the evening by Frank, the studio manager. Frank also tells her she has a talent for dancing and uses, word for word, Steve's initial approach to her. Beverly comes to her senses and breaks with Steve, who then tries to convince her that he really loves her. They part, but Beverly is soon overcome by loneliness and returns to him. *Dance teachers. Secretaries. Loneliness. Duplicity. Lovelorn. Dance schools. Contracts. New York City.*

Note: Filmed in 1962; location scenes filmed in Manhattan. Trade screened in Oct 1962.

LIGHT IN THE PIAZZA　　　　　　　　　　　　F6.2765

Arthur Freed Productions. *Dist* Metro-Goldwyn-Mayer, Inc. 31 Jan **1962** [San Francisco opening; c31 Dec 1961; LP21324]. Sd (Westrex); col (Metrocolor). 35mm (CinemaScope). 101 min.

An Arthur Freed Production. *Dir* Guy Green. *Screenplay* Julius J. Epstein. *Dir Photog* Otto Heller. *Camera Op* Jack Lowin. *Art Dir* Frank White. *Film Ed* Frank Clarke. *Mus Comp* Mario Nascimbene. *Cond* Dock Mathieson. *Sd Rec* Cyril Swern. *Sd Ed* Robert Carrick. *Rec Supv* A. W. Watkins. *Dub Mix* J. B. Smith. *Asst Dir* Basil Rayburn. *Unit Mgr* Denis Johnson. *Asst to the Prod* Aida Young. *Cont* Kay Mander. *Wardrobe Mistress* Dolly Smith. *Miss De Havilland's Cost* Christian Dior. *Makeup* Tom Smith. *Hairstyles* Joan Johnstone. *Sp Eff* Tom Howard. *Stills Camera* Davis Boulton.

Cast: Olivia De Havilland (*Margaret Johnson*), Rossano Brazzi (*Signor Naccarelli*), Yvette Mimieux (*Clara Johnson*), George Hamilton (*Fabrizio Naccarelli*), Barry Sullivan (*Noel Johnson*), Isabel Dean (*Miss Hawtree*), Moultrie Kelsall (*The Minister*), Nancy Nevinson (*Signora Naccarelli*).

Drama. Source: Elizabeth Spencer, *The Light in the Piazza* (New York, 1960). While vacationing in Europe with her mother, 26-year-old Clara Johnson falls in love with a handsome, well-to-do young Florentine, Fabrizio Naccarelli. As Margaret Johnson watches the budding romance between her daughter and Fabrizio, she conceals the fact that Clara is a mental defective; a childhood accident has left her with the mind of a 10-year-old. When it becomes apparent that the Naccarellis would be delighted to welcome Clara into the family, Margaret (unable to tell them the truth) cables her husband, Noel, to meet her in Rome. For the brusque and unsympathetic Noel there is only one solution: Clara must return to America and be committed to a mental institution. Still uncertain, Margaret takes Clara back to Florence. Gradually she begins to feel that with the Naccarelli family Clara would somehow be safe—her every whim indulged by a devoted husband, her household needs cared for by servants, her children reared by a doting mother-in-law, and her childish nature treasured as innocence. Margaret finally decides to remain silent about Clara's condition and permit the marriage to take place. Then suddenly Signor Naccarelli asks, "Why did you not tell me?" But with relief Margaret learns that he is referring only to the fact that Clara is 3 years older than Fabrizio. The situation is quickly resolved when Clara's dowry is increased from $5,000 to $15,000. Margaret remains in Italy only long enough to see her daughter wed. As she watches the radiant Clara taking her vows, Margaret feels certain that she has done the right thing. *Italians. Americans in foreign countries. Mental retardation. Motherhood. Wealth. Marriage. Duplicity. Weddings. Dowries. Florence. Rome.*

Note: Location scenes filmed in Florence and Rome.

THE LIGHT OF EXPERIENCE see **CIVILISATION: THE LIGHT OF EXPERIENCE**

LIGHTNING BOLT (Italy/Spain)　　　　　　　　F6.2766

Seven Film–B. G. A.–Balcázar P. C. *Dist* Woolner Bros. Pictures. Aug **1967** [Los Angeles showing]. Sd; col (Technicolor). 35mm (Techniscope). 96 min.

Prod Cleto Fontini, Giuseppe De Blasio. *Exec Prod* Francisco Balcázar. *Dir* Anthony Dawson. *Screenplay* Alfonso Balcázar, José Antonio de la Loma. *Story* Alfonso Balcázar. *Photog* Riccardo Pallottini. *Art Dir* Juan Alberto Soler, Antonio Visone. *Film Ed* Otello Colangeli, Juan Luis Oliver. *Mus* Riz Ortolani. *Sd* Alessandro Sarandrea. *Asst Dir* Nino Fruscella, Louis Marin. *Prod Mgr* Louis Millozza.

Cast: Anthony Eisley (*Harry Sennet*), Wandisa Leigh (*Kary*), Folco Lulli (*Rethe*), Diana Lorys (*Capt. Patricia Flanagan*), Ursula Parker (*Luisa Rivelli*), Paco Sanz, José María Caffarel, Oreste Palella, Renato Montalbano, Luciana Petri, Tito García.

Action melodrama. When a number of U. S. moon rockets explode in midair shortly after launching from Cape Kennedy, secret agent Harry Sennet (nicknamed Goldman because of his unlimited expense account) is assigned to investigate the possibility of sabotage. Accompanied by his assistant Patricia, he goes to Miami to check on the disappearance of a prominent nuclear scientist. After almost losing his life during another disastrous launching, Harry follows some beer trucks and discovers that they contain powerful laser guns which are being used to explode the missiles. Further investigation leads him to the underground submarine base of Rethe, a madman who plans to conquer the world by means of a moon rocket equipped with a laser cannon. Once inside the base, Harry is captured and imprisoned with the missing scientist. Aided by Kary, the scientist's captive daughter, Harry escapes and triggers a massive explosion. Harry and the scientist are the sole survivors, and as they appear on the surface of the sea, a helicopter with Patricia aboard arrives to rescue them. *Secret agents. Scientists. Missing persons. Sabotage. Megalomania. Abduction. Rockets. Laser. Cape Kennedy. Miami. Explosions.*

Note: Opened in Rome in Apr 1966 as *Operazione Goldman*; running time: 96 min; in Spain in 1966 as *Operación Goldman*; running time: 100 min. Anthony Dawson is a pseudonym for Antonio Margheriti.

LIKE FATHER, LIKE SON see **THE YOUNG SINNER**

LIKE IT IS　　　　　　　　　　　　　　　　F6.2767

Lima Productions. 18 Dec **1968** [New York showing]. Sd; col. 35mm. 72 min.

Prod Chris Warfield. *Dir* William Rotsler. *Mus* Greg Porée.

Sex film. No information about the precise nature of this film has been found, but press material and photographs suggest that it contains scenes of hippie life in San Francisco—drugs, love-ins, political demonstrations, nudity, psychedelic light shows, and free love. *Hippies. Nudity. Love-ins. Demonstrations. Free love. Drugs. San Francisco.*

LIKE IT IS　　　　　　　　　　　　　　　　F6.2768

Carvel Productions. *Dist* Seymour Borde & Associates. 26 Aug **1970** [Seattle opening]. Sd; col (Technicolor). 35mm (Techniscope). ca90 min. *MPAA rating* X.

Prod-Dir Jerry Schafer. *Exec Prod* Donald B. Running. *Mus* Shorty Rogers.

Cast: James Griffith *(father)*, Karen Arthur *(stepmother)*, Belinda Palmer *(daughter)*, Jimmy Caravetta.

Melodrama. An upper-middle class girl graduates from high school but is unhappy in her suburban home. Her stepmother does not like her, especially resenting her guitar, her laziness, and the late hours she keeps. Her father loves her very much and has just given her a stuffed bear as a token of his affection. Because of her stepmother's lack of understanding the girl leaves home, taking just her guitar and bear, only to come back after her hippie boyfriend is arrested for possession of marijuana. She asks her father for bail money to get him out of jail, but he refuses. The girl leaves home again, eventually raising the money by performing in some sex exploitation films. One night the father is at a neighborhood stag party and sees his daughter in the pornographic films they are watching. He goes home and commits suicide. *Middle classes. Suburbanites. Stepmothers. Hippies. Runaways. Suburban life. Adolescence. Family life. Fatherhood. Suicide. Dolls. Marijuana. Sex exploitation films.*

LIKE MOTHER LIKE DAUGHTER   F6.2769

Rori Films–J. Tanenbaum Productions. *Dist* Grads Corp. 11 Jun **1969** [Champaign, Illinois, showing]. Sd; col (Eastman Color). 35mm. 74 min.

Prod Richard Compton. *Exec Prod* James Tanenbaum. *Dir* Robert V. O'Neil. *Screenplay* Robert V. O'Neil, Richard Compton. *Dir Photog & Camera Op* Ross Kelsay. *Asst Camera Op* Fred Miller. *Film Ed* J. Smedley Buxton. *Mus Score & Song:* "A Kind of Love" Sonny Williams, Clyde Allen. *Sd Rec* J. Sharp. *Asst Dir* Beach Dickerson. *Prod Mgr* Toby Munson. *Makeup* Ree Fox. *Gaffer* L. LePoint. *Key Grip* Mike Stringer. *Props* Ken Fix. *Stills* Cinemagraphics.

Cast: Sebastian Gregory *(Tony)*, Joann Morgan *(Jamie)*, Victoria Bond *(Kim)*, Ferell A. Garret *(San Francisco Bill)*, Vicky Todd *(Virginia)*, Helga Pferdkoph *(Stella)*, Lou Farr, Steve Jaques, Jack Rider *(bikers)*, Beach Dickerson *(Jo-Jo)*, Yvet Daux *(Bobby)*, John Rupp *(cop)*, Margo Cane *(Ivy)*, Fern Holbrook *(Lanie)*, Mel Viking *(hoodlum)*, Juli Buf *(party girl)*, Al Quick *(lead musician)*, The Warriors *(group)*, Cris Wilcott *(Tom)*, Sue Ann Kimble *(Claude)*, Les White *(Claude's friend)*, Jerry Pete *(Jerry)*, Stu Allen *(TV reporter)*, Dennis Evergreen *("Shades")*, Clinton West *("Fats")*, Nik Wice, Stanley R. Mannon, Frederick Merlyn *(gamblers)*, Ann London *(Star)*, Elane Minx *(Joy)*, Ivan Goddof *(Billy)*, Lisa Proque, Ted Kors *(couple in car)*, Sadie Johnson *("Fat Momma")*, Eddy Amter *(desk clerk)*, Gessel Kaufmann *(newspaper dealer)*, Herman F. Rodite *(bartender "princess")*, Rose Riggato *(check girl)*.

Melodrama. Tony arrives in Los Angeles after escaping from a group of New York gangsters. Tony learns that Jamie, a widow, has inherited $40,000, and he decides to swindle her of the money to pay his debts. Tony finds Jamie at a bar she runs for the local homosexuals and lesbians, and he soon seduces her. He persuades her to let him move into her large home which she shares with her attractive daughter, Kim, and a transvestite, San Francisco Bill. Tony seduces Kim, but he must share her with Virginia, another resident of the house who has been having a lesbian affair with Kim. Jamie is happy with Tony; she sets him up with a nude modeling agency and throws a party to celebrate the opening of the agency. Jamie threatens to kill Tony when she finds him making love with Kim, but he offers to leave Kim alone if Jamie will give him $5,000. Jamie gives him the money, but Tony reneges, sleeps with Kim again, and Jamie shoots him. *Widows. Inheritance. Motherhood. Male homosexuality. Lesbianism. Transvestism. Seduction. Extortion. Murder. Bars. Model agencies. Los Angeles.*

Note: Original title: *A Kind of Love*. Joann Morgan is also known as Joanne Moore Jordan.

LIKE WOW! *see* MR. PEEK-A-BOO'S PLAYMATES

LILA *see* MAKE WAY FOR LILA

LILA *see* MANTIS IN LACE

LILIES OF THE FIELD   F6.2770

Rainbow Productions. *Dist* United Artists. 25 Sep **1963** [Denver, Colorado, opening· c9 Jul, 1 Oct 1963; LP27725, LP27744]. Sd (Westrex); b&w. 35mm. 97 min. [Also 94 min.]

Prod-Dir Ralph Nelson. *Assoc Prod* J. Paul Popkin. *Screenplay* James Poe. *Dir Photog* Ernest Haller. *Titl, Opticals & Proc* CFI. *Film Ed* John McCafferty. *Mus* Jerry Goldsmith. *Vocal Arr* Jester Hairston. *Sd Engr* Carlton W. Faulkner. *Sd Eff* Del Harris. *Mus Ed* Albie Shaff. *Asst Dir* Harry R. Sherman, Joe Popkin. *Prod Coörd* Lawrence A. Hampton. *Script Supv* Stanley Scheuer. *Wardrobe* Wesley Sherrard. *Prop Master* Robert Eaton. *Head Grip* Leo McCreary. *Gaffer* Norman C. McClay.

Cast: Sidney Poitier *(Homer Smith)*, Lilia Skala·*(Mother Maria)*, Lisa Mann *(Sister Gertrude)*, Isa Crino *(Sister Agnes)*, Francesca Jarvis *(Sister Albertine)*, Pamela Branch *(Sister Elizabeth)*, Stanley Adams *(Juan)*, Dan Frazer *(Father*

Murphy), Ralph Nelson *(Mr. Ashton)*.

Comedy-drama. Source: William E. Barrett, *The Lilies of the Field* (Garden City, New York, 1962). While touring the southwestern United States, Homer Smith, a black ex-GI, encounters five nuns attempting to farm some barren Arizona land on the edge of the desert. He asks them for a day's work and learns that they are East German refugees who have come to the States to claim the farm which was willed to their Order. Homer repairs their leaky roof and performs other chores, but the Mother Superior persuades him to stay on to help clear the debris from a collapsed barn. Although he is astounded to learn that Mother Maria intends for him to erect a new chapel on the site, Homer so admires her determination that he agrees to take the job if she can provide the materials. He also goes to work for a local contractor, contributing his pay to buy food for the Order and teaches English to the nuns. When the materials run out, however, Homer leaves. He returns a few weeks later, drawn by the urge to finish the chapel, and the townspeople, ashamed of their negligence, finally join in and help Homer. The evening before the bishop is due to arrive for the dedication, Homer leaves as unceremoniously as he had arrived. *Negroes. Nuns. Refugees. Germans. Handymen. Farming. Construction. Inheritance. Churches. Arizona.*

Note: Filmed in and around Tucson, Arizona.

LILITH   F6.2771

Centaur Enterprises. *Dist* Columbia Pictures. 1 Oct **1964** [New York opening; c1 Oct 1964; LP29349]. Sd (RCA); b&w. 35mm. 114 min.

Prod-Dir-Screenplay Robert Rossen. *Asst Prod* Eleanor Wolquitt. *Dir Photog* Eugen Shuftan, Tibor Sands. *Camera Op* Joseph Coffey. *Asst Camera* Bert Siegel. *Set Decor* Gene Callahan. *Prod Dsgn* Richard Sylbert. *Titl Dsgn* Elinor Bunin. *Film Ed* Aram Avakian. *Assoc Film Ed* Hugh A. Robertson, Jr., Robert Q. Lovett. *Mus Comp & Cond* Kenyon Hopkins. *Sd* Jim Shields, Richard Vorisek. *Sd Ed* Edward Beyer. *Asst Sd Ed* Barry Malkin, Lynn Ratener. *1st & 2d Asst Dir* Larry Sturhahn, Bob Vietro, Allan Dennis. *Prod Mgr* Jim Di Gangi. *Script Supv* Dorothy Weshner Kanzer. *Cost Dsgn* Ruth Morley. *Wardrobe Woman* Flo Transfield. *Wardrobe Man* George Newman. *Makeup* Irving Buchman, Bill Herman, Robert Jiras. *Hairstyles* Frederic Jones. *Optical Eff* Film Opticals. *Still Photog* Josh Weiner. *Puppets by* The Zoo, Gene Carlough.

Cast: Warren Beatty *(Vincent Bruce)*, Jean Seberg *(Lilith Arthur)*, Peter Fonda *(Stephen Evshevsky)*, Kim Hunter *(Bea Brice)*, Anne Meacham *(Mrs. Yvonne Meaghan)*, James Patterson *(Dr. Lavrier)*, Jessica Walter *(Laura)*, Gene Hackman *(Norman)*, Robert Reilly *(Bob Clayfield)*, Rene Auberjonois *(Howie)*, Lucy Smith *(Vincent's grandmother)*, Maurice Brenner *(Mr. Gordon)*, Jeanne Barr *(Miss Glassman)*, Richard Higgs *(Mr. Palakis)*, Elizabeth Bader *(girl at the bar)*, Alice Spivak *(lonely girl)*, Walter Arnold *(lonely girl's father)*, Kathleen Phelan *(lonely girl's mother)*, Cecilia Ray *(Lilith's mother [dream])*, Gunnar Peters *(her chauffeur [dream])*, L. Jerome Offutt *(tournament judge)*, W. Jerome Offutt *(tournament announcer)*, Robert Jolivette *(older watermelon boy)*, Jason Jolivette *(younger watermelon boy)*, Jeno Mate *(assistant to Dr. Lavrier)*, Ben Carruthers *(Benito)*, Dina Paisner *(psychodrama moderator)*, Pawnee Sills *(receptionist)*, Luther Foulk, Kenneth Fuchs, Steve Dawson, Michael Paras *(doctors)*, Morton Taylor *(ambulance doctor)*, Joavan Curran, Rick Branda, Wade Taylor, Tony Lombard, David Barry, Frank Nanoia *(ambulance attendants)*, Joanne Bayes, Barbara Lowe, Patsy Klein, Gwen Van Dam, Eadie Renaud *(nurses)*, Rosalie Posner, Thom Brann, Louis Jenkins, Tracee Towers, Virginia Schneider, Robert Miller, Bruce Powers, Don Donnellan, Ken Naarden, Ron Cunningham *(occupational therapists)*, Katherine Gregg, Edith Fellows, Page Jones, Olympia Dukakis, Mildred Smith, Cynthia McAdams, Wendell Phillips, Jr., Tony Grey, Elizabeth Lawrence, Harvey Jason, Gordon Phillips, Robert Dahdah, B. J. DeSimone, Marie-Antoinette, Cornelius Frizell, Janet Banzet, Tina Rome, Thelma Ray, Katha Cale, Harry Northrup, G. K. Osborne, Charles Tyner, Sonya Zomina, Anna Van Der Heida, Jocella Jackson, Amelie Barleon, Bess Carlton, Sylvia Gassel, David Craig, Bud Truland, Ruth Baker, Ceil Ray, Jeanne DeFlorio, Joe Rankin, Paul Varro, Stuart Goodman, Billie Erlich, Peter Bosche *(patients)*.

Drama. Source: J. R. Salamanca, *Lilith* (New York, 1961). Vincent Bruce, a young Korean War veteran, returns to his Maryland hometown and begins working as an occupational therapist at a nearby mental institution for the wealthy. There he meets the beautiful Lilith Arthur, who lives in a secret world of her own creation, and he falls in love with her. They have an affair, but he soon discovers that she is also having a lesbian affair with Mrs. Meaghan, another patient, and that her pursuit of love is limitless and often dangerous. Stephen Evshevsky, another inmate who is in love with Lilith, commits suicide when she rejects him. His death destroys Lilith, severing her last connection with reality, and she retreats into complete madness. The experience also shatters Vincent, and he decides to quit the job; instead of leaving the hospital, however, he asks a doctor for help. *Veterans. Occupational therapists. Psychiatrists. Mental illness. Lesbianism. Suicide. Hospitals. Maryland.*

Note: Some location scenes filmed in Rockville, Barnesville, and Great Falls, Maryland.

LIMBO see REBEL ROUSERS

LIMONÁDOVÝ JOE see LEMONADE JOE

LINDA see A MAN—EIGHT GIRLS

LINDA AND ABILENE   F6.2772
United Pictures Organization. Sep **1969** [Chicago showing]. Sd; col (Eastman Color). 35mm. 93 min.

A Thomas J. Dowd Production. *Prod* J. H. Wells. *Dir* Mark Hansen. *Dir Cinematog* Lewis H. Gordon. *Camera Op* Eskandar Ameripoor. *Ed Supv* Richard C. Dynes. *Film Ed* Alex Ameripoor. *Mus Backgrounds* Warren Regan. *Sd Engr* Dan Krogh. *Asst Dir* John Goldman. *Prod Mgr* Buck Buckalew. *Makeup* Helene Robbins. *Ch Electrn* Larry Marcus. *Talent Coörd* Pam Eddy.

Cast: Sharon Matt (*Abilene*), Roxanne Jones (*Linda*), Kip Marsh (*Tod*), Tom Thorn (*Rawhide*), William Varris (*bartender*), Audrey Cromm (*bar girl*), Herbert Townsend (*preacher*), Bob Derne (*cowboy*).

Western melodrama. Late in the 19th century, Abilene and her brother Tod are suddenly orphaned on their western farm. In sexual frustration, Abilene begins to show her body to Tod, and both turn to autoeroticism as the outlet for their passions. One night, Abilene, frightened by thunder, cries out. Tod rushes to her bedroom to see if anything is wrong and caresses his trembling sister. The caresses become more passionate and lead to sex. The couple soon neglect their farm to pursue their passions. Tod eventually realizes that what they are doing is wrong, and he rides to town to console himself with liquor. In a saloon he confides his story to Linda, a bar girl. Rawhide, a tough cowboy, overhears, rides out to the farm, and there he ravishes the defenseless Abilene. Meanwhile, Tod and Linda are making love in town. Tod returns home the next day to find that Abilene has been raped. He rushes back to town to kill Rawhide. Linda goes to the farm that morning to see Tod, but she finds Abilene instead and attempts to comfort her. They find a mutual sex attraction and make love. Tod arrives in town, and in a gunfight with Rawhide, both men are killed. Linda and Abilene are then left in each other's arms. *Orphans. Farmers. Cowboys. Bar girls. Brother-sister relationship. Rape. Incest. Autoeroticism. Lesbianism. Revenge. Murder. Saloons.*

LINE see THE PASSIONATE DEMONS

THE LINE IS BUSY   F6.2773
Cosmos Films. *Dist* Able Film Co. ca **1970**. Sd; col. 16mm. [Feature length assumed.]

Sex film. A man finds a telephone number on a bathroom wall. He calls, and there results an exciting series of sexual adventures. *Sexuality.*

LINE OF APOGEE   F6.2774
Dist Film-Makers' Cooperative, Canyon Cinema Cooperative. 10 Apr **1968** [New York opening]. Sd; b&w with col seq. 16mm. 58 min. [See note.]

Prod-Dir-Writ Lloyd Michael Williams. *Photog* Joseph Marzano, Harold Naiderman, Lloyd Michael Williams. *Film Ed* Lloyd Michael Williams. *Orig Electronic Score* Vladimir Ussachevsky. *Electronic Sd* Sandy Fisher.

Cast: Charles Braun, Richard Denby, Beverly Baum, Anthony Coll, Anne Linden, Harold Naiderman, Lloyd Michael Williams.

Experimental film. An old astronomer, searching for the psychological influences that molded him, looks back and views himself as a young man having homosexual tendencies. His experiences are expressed in surrealistic and abstract dream passages: a blue Buddha dissolves into a gray teddy bear and begins to cry; a little girl knifes a pig and extracts a baby doll from its body; a boy buries a pile of Cheerios and urinates on the grave; 60 white gloves run across the floor; the gloves are seen floating in a pond around a large glass bowl in which a nude boy lies curled; pieces of plaster reassemble into a bust of Dante; an egg cracks, and marbles issue forth and decompose; a bridegroom at his wedding steps on an egg, and spiders rush from beneath his shoe; in bed, the man kisses his wife, and she is transformed into a succession of men, presumably his lovers; the man roams nude through a dark cave. *Astronomers. Male homosexuality. Memory. Sexuality. Childhood. Youth. Dreams.*

Note: Filmed 1964-67. The 58-min version was released by Film-Makers' Cooperative in 1968. Canyon Cinema Cooperative later released a 46-min version.

LINE OF DUTY see INCIDENT IN AN ALLEY

LIOLÀ see A VERY HANDY MAN

THE LION (Great Britain)   F6.2775
Twentieth Century-Fox Productions. *Dist* Twentieth Century-Fox Film Corp. 21 Dec **1962** [New York opening; c21 Dec 1962; LP23724]. Sd (Westrex); col (DeLuxe). 35mm (CinemaScope). 96 min.

Prod Samuel G. Engel. *Assoc Prod* Cecil F. Ford. *Dir* Jack Cardiff. *2d Unit Work* World Safari Ltd. *Screenplay* Louis Kamp, Irene Kamp. *Dir Photog* Ted Scaife. *Camera Op* Jack Atchelor. *Camera Asst-Focus* Wally Fairweather. *Art Dir* Alan Withy. *Asst Art Dir* John Hoesli. *Film Ed* Russell Lloyd. *Asst Film Ed* William Butler. *Mus Comp & Cond* Malcolm Arnold. *Sd Rec* Gordon K. McCallum. *Sd Mix* David Hildyard. *Boom Op* David Jones. *Sd Camera Op* Derek Leather. *Sd Ed* Norman Savage. *1st & 2d Asst Dir* Ted Sturgis, Carl Mannin. *Prod Mgr* David Orton. *Prod Sec* Golda Offenheim. *Cont* Connie Willis. *2d Unit Cont* Angela Martelli. *Wardrobe Master* Brian Owen-Smith. *Ch Makeup* George Frost. *Hairstyles* Joan Smallwood. *Tech Adv* Maj. W. H. M. Taberer. *Coöp* National Parks and Game Reserves in Kenya, Uganda & Tanganyika. *Animal Supv* Ralph Helfer. *Stills* Albert Clarke. *Constr Mgr* Dick Frift. *Supv Chargehand Electrn* Tom Heathcoat.

Cast: William Holden (*Robert Hayward*), Trevor Howard (*John Bullitt*), Capucine (*Christine*), Pamela Franklin (*Tina*), Makara Kwaiha Ramadhani (*Bogo*), Zakee (*Ol' Kalu*), Paul Oduor (*Oriunga*), Samuel Obiero Romboh (*Kihoro*), Christopher Agunda (*elder of Masai*), Zamba (*King, a lion*).

Adventure melodrama. Source: Joseph Kessel, *The Lion* (trans. of *Le Lion* (Paris, 1958) by Peter Green; London, 1959). Following a summons from his ex-wife, Christine, American lawyer Robert Hayward arrives at the East African game reserve supervised by John Bullitt, Christine's new husband. Christine asks Robert to help bring up their 11-year-old daughter, Tina, who accepts primitive tribal customs. (Her greatest friend is a full-grown lion she has raised from a cub.) The affection between Robert and Christine gradually rekindles, and Robert adds to the mounting tension when he violates a tribal law by saving the life of a dying chief who has been abandoned. Once recovered, the chief returns to his tribe and his son, Oriunga, who has wanted to take over the tribe and claim Tina as a wife. The chief, however, tells him that he will never be a chief until he has killed a lion. When the son chooses Tina's pet as his victim, the young girl orders the beast to kill the warrior. After the lion has fatally mauled Oriunga, Bullitt is forced to kill it. This act affects Bullitt's relationship with Tina, who now accepts Robert as her father. Facing the inevitable, Bullitt gives Christine permission to return to America with Robert and their child. *Americans in foreign countries. Lawyers. Tribal chiefs. Stepfathers. Filial relations. Adolescence. Divorce. Game preserves. East Africa. Lions.*

Note: Filmed in Kenya, Uganda, and Tanganyika. Opened in London in Aug 1962.

THE LION IN WINTER (Great Britain)   F6.2776
Haworth Productions. *Dist* Avco Embassy Pictures. 30 Oct **1968** [New York opening; c30 Oct 1968; LP40224]. Sd; col (Eastman Color). 35mm (Panavision). 134 min. [Copyright length: 137 min.]

Pres by Joseph E. Levine. A Martin Poll Production. *Prod* Martin Poll. *Exec Prod* Joseph E. Levine. *Assoc Prod* Jane C. Nusbaum. *Dir* Anthony Harvey. *Screenplay* James Goldman. *Dir Cinematog* Douglas Slocombe. *Camera Op* Chic Waterson. *Art Dir* Peter Murton. *Art Dir French Seq* Gilbert Margerie. *Set Dir* Peter James. *Film Ed* John Bloom. *Asst Ed* Lesley Walker. *Mus Comp & Cond* John Barry. *Sd* Simon Kaye, Chris Greenham. *Asst Dir* Kip Gowans, Patrick O'Brien. *Prod Supv* John Quested. *Prod Mgr* Basil Appleby. *Cost Dsgn* Margaret Furse. *Makeup* Bill Lodge. *Hairstyles* A. G. Scott. *Prop* George Ball.

Cast: Peter O'Toole (*King Henry II*), Katharine Hepburn (*Queen Eleanor of Aquitaine*), Jane Merrow (*Princess Alais*), John Castle (*Prince Geoffrey*), Timothy Dalton (*King Philip of France*), Anthony Hopkins (*Prince Richard the Lion-Hearted*), Nigel Stock (*William Marshall*), Nigel Terry (*Prince John*), Kenneth Griffith (*strolling player*), O. Z. Whitehead (*Bishop of Durham*), Kenneth Ives (*Eleanor's guard*), Henry Woolf, Karol Hagar, Mark Griffith.

Historical drama. Source: James Goldman, *The Lion in Winter* (New York opening: 3 Mar 1966). In 1183, King Henry II of England summons his estranged wife, Eleanor of Aquitaine, whom he has imprisoned for 10 years in Salisbury Tower for her part in civil wars and plots against him. Henry has called a Christmas Court at Chinon Castle to determine which of their three surviving sons—the impetuous Richard, the conniving Geoffrey, or the clumsy and insecure John—will be named successor to the crown. Also present are Henry's mistress, Princess Alais, who has been promised as wife to the new heir, and her 18-year-old brother, Philip, the king of France. Henry chooses John as successor, but Eleanor, fully aware that Henry holds all three sons in low esteem, proclaims that the throne rightfully belongs to Richard. Almost immediately, the protagonists plot to attain their own selfish ends: Eleanor offers to yield Aquitaine if Richard is named heir; Geoffrey, neglected by both parents, conspires with John and Philip to rob Richard of the throne; and Henry confesses to Alais that he intends to get his way without giving her up. It is decided that an alliance with the king of France might solve all their problems, and Eleanor sends Richard to convince Philip of the merit of their cause. The youthful king is equal to the machinations of his elders, however; confronting Henry, he exposes the homosexual bent of Richard, the treachery of Geoffrey, and the disloyalty of John. Outraged, Henry disowns his sons and demands from Eleanor an annulment of their marriage, declaring that he will marry Alais and father a new heir, but Alais insists that Henry execute his sons to protect any child she might bear. Intent on murder, Henry descends into the dungeon where his sons are imprisoned, but Eleanor has preceded him and armed the three princes to aid their escape. Although Henry raises his sword over Richard's head, he cannot bring himself to wield it. Once the others have left and Eleanor and Henry are alone, the two adversaries face the incontestable truth that the bond between them is too strong to be broken by any struggle for power. The next morning, with nothing resolved, Henry escorts Eleanor to the barge that will return her to prison; she leaves, hopeful that there will soon be a summons to appear at Chinon for an Easter Court. *Heirs. Brothers. Mistresses. French. Marriage. Filial relations. Jealousy. Imprisonment. Infidelity. Conspiracy. Male homosexuality. Swords. Christmas. Great Britain—History—Plantagenets. Henry II (England). Eleanor of Aquitaine. Philip II (France). Richard the Lion-Hearted. Geoffrey (1158–86). John (England) 1167–1216. Alais Capet. Chinon.*

Note: Location scenes filmed in Ireland, Wales, and around Tarascon, France. Opened in London in Dec 1968.

THE LION OF ST. MARK (Italy)   F6.2777

Liber Film. 18 Jul 1967 [New York showing]. Sd; col (Eastman Color). 35mm (Totalscope). 87 min. [Also reviewed at 106 min.]

Prod-Story Ottavio Poggi. *Dir* Luigi Capuano. *Dir Dub Ver* Richard McNamara. *Screenplay* Arpad De Riso, Luigi Capuano. *Photog* Alvaro Mancori. *Art Dir* Ernesto Kromberg. *Film Ed* Antonietta Zita. *Mus* Carlo Rustichelli. *Sd* Fiorenzo Magli. *Asst Dir* Gianfranco Baldanello. *Cost* Giancarlo Bartolini Salimbeni.

Cast: Gordon Scott (*Manrico Masiero*), Gianna Maria Canale (*Rosanna*), Rick Battaglia (*Dandolo*), Alberto Farnese (*Titta*), Giulio Marchetti (*Gualtiero*), Franca Bettoja (*Isabella Fieschi*).

Adventure melodrama. In early 17th-century Venice the doge arranges for his son, Manrico Masiero, to marry socially acceptable Isabella Fieschi. At the same time pirates led by Titta are plundering the city and surrounding areas, overpowering the doge's ineffective mercenary troops. After Titta's forces attack the engagement ceremony, Manrico organizes an anonymous band of concerned citizens to combat the pirates; he dons a mask and calls himself "The Lion of St. Mark" to protect his identity. Meanwhile, he becomes attracted to a pirate named Rosanna and rescues her when she is captured by the mercenaries. The grateful Rosanna nonetheless remains on the side of the pirates until she learns that the "Lion" and Manrico, her rescuer, are the same man. Following a successful routing of the pirates, Manrico's uncle adopts Rosanna, enabling her to attain the proper social standing to marry the doge's son. *Nobility. Pirates. Mercenaries. Uncles. Social classes. Marriage—Arranged. Filial relations. Disguise. Personal identity. Adoption. Rescue. Venice.*

Note: Released in Italy in 1964 as *Il leone di San Marco*.

LION OF SPARTA see **THE 300 SPARTANS**

LIONS LOVE   F6.2778

Max L. Raab. 13 Oct 1969 [New York opening]. Sd; col (Technicolor). 35mm. 115 min.

Prod-Dir-Writ Agnès Varda. *Exec Prod* Max L. Raab. *Photog* Stefan Larner. *Camera* Lee Alexander. *Art Dir* Jack Wright, III. *Film Ed* Robert Dalva. *Mus* Joseph Byrd. *Sd* George Alch, Andrew Babbish. *Prod Mgr* Jack Wright, III. *Asst to Miss Varda* Lynne Littman. *Script Cons & Historical Material* Carlos Clarens.

Cast—Leading Players: Viva, Gerome Ragni, James Rado, Shirley Clarke, Carlos Clarens, Eddie Constantine, Agnès Varda, Max Laemmle, Hal Landers, Steve Kemis, Peter Bogdanovich.

Cast—From *The Beard* by Michael McClure: Billie Dixon (*Harlow*). Richard Bright (*Billy the Kid*).

Drama. A female film director arrives in Hollywood to document the lives of three aspiring stars (two actors and an actress), who share a hilltop house. Because she cannot obtain artistic freedom from her studio, the director attempts suicide. The actors' idyll is also interrupted by the assassination of Robert Kennedy, graphically reported on their television, and by the shooting of Andy Warhol. The film is framed by scenes from Michael McClure's *The Beard. Motion picture directors. Actors. Suicide. Assassination. Television. Hollywood. Andy Warhol. Robert Francis Kennedy.*

Note: Film includes documentary footage of Robert Kennedy's assassination.

LIP SERVICE   F6.2779

Kirt Films International. *Dist* Distribpix, Inc. ca 1970. Sd; col. 35mm. 64 min.

Melodrama. A young, smalltown woman seeking thrills has her first sexual encounter with a man who gives her a lift into the city. Her experience with the man turns her into a nymphomaniac. Unable to earn money as a prostitute, the woman is caught stealing food in a grocery store and as her "punishment" is forced to participate in an orgy in the back of the store. Although she is at first willing to join the orgy, she eventually panics, runs into the street, and is struck by a car driven by the man who brought her into the city. *Hitchhikers. Sexual initiation. Nymphomania. Shoplifting. Orgies. Automobile accidents.*

LIPSTICK (France/Italy)   F6.2780

Europa Cinematografica–Explorer Film–C. F. P. C. *Dist* Medallion Pictures. Nov 1965. Sd; b&w. 35mm. 89 min.

Prod (see note) Murray J. King. *Assoc Prod* Gianni Solitro. *Dir-Story* Damiano Damiani. *Screenplay* Damiano Damiani, Cesare Zavattini. *Photog* Pier Ludovico Pavoni. *Art Dir* Sergio Baldacchini. *Film Ed* Fernando Cerchio. *Mus* Giovanni Fusco.

Cast: Laura Vivaldi (*Sylvana*), Pierre Brice (*Gino*), Georgia Moll (*Lorella*), Bella Darvi (*Nora*), Pietro Germi (*Inspector Fioresi*), Lia Angeleri, Ivano Staccioli, Nino Marchetti, Renato Mambor.

Mystery melodrama. Sylvana, a 13-year-old schoolgirl, becomes infatuated with her handsome neighbor, Gino. A prostitute is found murdered in the building where Gino lives, and the police question everyone in the neighborhood. Because Sylvana saw Gino leaving the apartment of the murdered prostitute, Gino encourages her flirtation to prevent her from destroying his alibi. Sylvana initially withholds her knowledge, but when she later learns that Gino has lied to her, she becomes disenchanted and divulges her story to the police. Taking note of Sylvana's precocity, the police disbelieve her story, attributing her accusation to vengefulness. Inspector Fioresi advises Sylvana's mother to send her to a convent-reformatory for her own protection. Ashamed and humiliated, Sylvana makes an unsuccessful suicide attempt; Fioresi is spurred to investigate Gino's past, and he uncovers the truth. As the killer prepares to marry Lorella, an heiress, he is arrested by the inspector. Sylvana is exonerated and returns to lead a normal life with her family and friends. *Neighbors. Police. Adolescence. Murder. Flirtation. Suicide. Parenthood. Reformatories.*

Note: Released in Italy in 1960 as *Il rossetto*; running time: 100 min. Opened in Paris in Mar 1962 as *Jeux précoces*; running time: 90 min. Italian alternative or working title: *La colonna infame*. Murray J. King is credited as producer by U. S. press material only.

THE LIQUIDATOR (Great Britain)   F6.2781

Metro-Goldwyn-Mayer Pictures. *Dist* Metro-Goldwyn-Mayer, Inc. 28 Oct 1966 [New York opening; c31 Dec 1965; LP33340]. Sd (Westrex); col (Metrocolor). 35mm (Panavision). 105 min.

A Leslie Elliot Production. *Prod* Jon Penington. *Assoc Prod* Harry Fine. *Exec Prod* Leslie Elliot. *Dir* Jack Cardiff. *Screenplay* Peter Yeldham. *Dir Photog* Ted Scaife. *Camera Op* Alan McCabe. *Art Dir* John Blezard. *Titl* Richard Williams Films. *Film Ed* Ernest Walter. *Mus Comp & Cond* Lalo Schifrin. *Lyr:* "The Liquidator" Peter Callander. *Sung by* Shirley Bassey. *Rec Supv* A. W. Watkins. *Sd Rec* Cyril Swern. *Dub Mix* J. B. Smith. *Sd Ed* Allan Sones. *Asst Dir* David Tomblin. *Prod Mgr* Tom Sachs. *Unit Mgr* Basil Rayburn. *Cost Dsgn* Elizabeth Haffenden, Joan Bridge.

Cast: Rod Taylor (*Boysie Oakes*), Trevor Howard (*Colonel Mostyn*), Jill St. John (*Iris MacIntosh*), Wilfrid Hyde-White (*The Chief*), David Tomlinson (*Quadrant*), Akim Tamiroff (*Sheriek*), Eric Sykes (*Griffen*), Gabriella Licudi (*Corale*), John Le Mesurier (*Chekhov*), Derek Nimmo (*Fly*), Richard Wattis (*flying instructor*), David Langton (*station commander*), Jennifer Jayne (*Janice Benedict*), Betty McDowall (*Frances Anne*), Henri Cogan (*Yakov*), Daniel Emilfork (*Gregory*), Jeremy Lloyd (*young man*), Jo Rowbottom (*Betty*), Colin Gordon (*Vicar*), Louise Dunn (*Jessie*), Scot Finch (*operations officer*), Ronald Leigh-Hunt (*Mac*), Tony Wright (*flying control*), Suzy Kendall (*Judith*).

Action melodrama. Source: John Gardner, *The Liquidator* (New York, 1964). Colonel Mostyn of British Intelligence is confronted with the task of training a private executioner who can dispose of legally untouchable but dangerous security risks. He recalls Boysie Oakes, who years before had accidentally saved his life in Paris during World War II. Unaware of his mission, Boysie, who loathes violence and becomes ill at the sight of blood, endures the rigorous training program because of the penthouse apartment, expensive wardrobe, a sports car, and female companions supplied by Mostyn. When he does learn the truth, he hires a professional killer to do any dirty work that might come up. He then defies regulations and takes Mostyn's beautiful secretary, Iris, to the French Riviera for a weekend. There he is taken prisoner by counterspies but is permitted to escape because the enemy organization plans to use him as the unwilling dupe in a plot to assassinate the Duke of Edinburgh. Boysie is informed by a courier that during a security check exercise he is to fire blank bullets at the Duke while he is inspecting an R.A.F. base. Real bullets, however, have been placed in his rifle. Although Mostyn arrives in time to prevent the disaster, the identity of the master spy remains unknown. In a moment of unusual recklessness, Boysie leaps aboard a jet bomber as it takes off with the latest anti-missile equipment. Once aboard, he overpowers the master spy, Iris, and somehow manages to bring the hijacked plane back to the base by following instructions radioed to him. *Hired killers. Secretaries. Spies. Assassination. Airplanes—Jet. Riviera. Great Britain—Intelligence service.*

Note: Released in Great Britain in Sep 1966.

LISA (United States/Great Britain)   **F6.2782**

Red Lion Productions. *Dist* Twentieth Century-Fox Film Corp. 24 May **1962** [New York opening; c24 May 1962; LP21992]. Sd (Westrex); col (DeLuxe). 35mm. (CinemaScope). 112 min.

Exec Prod Mark Robson. *Assoc Prod* Bob McNaught. *Dir* Philip Dunne. *Screenplay* Nelson Gidding. *Dir Photog* Arthur Ibbetson. *Camera Op* Paul Wilson. *Focus* Tony Spratling, Mervyn Wilson. *Art Dir* Elliot Scott. *Asst Art Dir* Maurice Pelling. *Set Dresser* John Jarvis. *Draughtsmen* Reg Bream, Tony Pratt, John Graysmark. *Film Ed* Ernest Walter. *Assembly Ed* Peter Elliott. *Asst Ed* Margaret Miller. *Mus Comp & Cond* Malcolm Arnold. *Sd Ed* Roy Baker. *Sd Rec* Gerry Turner, J. B. Smith. *Sd Camera Op* Mickey Hickey. *Boom Op* Godfrey Bowen. *1st & 2d Asst Dir* Kip Gowans, Charles Blair. *Prod Mgr* David Middlemas. *Cont* Elaine Schreyeck. *Prod Sec* Joyce Herlihy. *Wardrobe Supv* Ivy Baker. *Wardrobe Master* Brian Owen-Smith. *Makeup* John O'Gorman, Wally Schneiderman. *Hairdresser* Joan Smallwood. *Casting Dir* Nora Roberts. *Prod Buyer* Bill Isaacs. *Still Photog* Joe Pearce.

Cast: Stephen Boyd (*Peter Jongman*), Dolores Hart (*Lisa Held*), Leo McKern (*Brandt*), Hugh Griffith (*Van der Pink*), Donald Pleasence (*Sergeant Wolters*), Harry Andrews (*Ayoob*), Robert Stephens (*Dickens*), Marius Goring (*Thorens*), Finlay Currie (*De Kooi*), Harold Goldblatt (*Dr. Mitropoulous*), Neil McCallum (*Browne*), Geoffrey Keen (*Commissioner Bartels*), Jean Anderson (*Mrs. Jongman*), Michael David (*Captain Berger*), Jane Jordan Rogers (*Anaka Jongman*), Jack Gwillim (*Inspector Cobb*), Arthur Gross (*railway conductor*), Tibby Brittain (*M. P. sergeant*), Ann Dickins (*Rachael*), Vi Stephens (*barge woman*), Derek Francis (*detective inspector*), John Welsh (*agriculture officer*), Victor Brooks (*Sergeant Greninger*), Geoffrey Frederick (*soldier*), Clifford Elkin (*signaller*).

Adventure drama. Source: Jan de Hartog, *The Inspector* (New York, 1960). In 1946 Lisa Held, a survivor of the concentration camp at Auschwitz, falls into the hands of ex-Nazi Thorens, who promises to smuggle her into Palestine; actually he is a white slaver who plans to ship her to South America. She is saved when Dutch policeman Peter Jongman, who is plagued by his failure to save his fiancée from death at the hands of the Nazis, accidentally kills Thorens. Jongman then decides to atone for the past by seeing that Lisa reaches Palestine. He gets them both work on a Dutch barge owned by Captain Brandt, who takes them to Tangiers. There, a flamboyant smuggler, Van der Pink, arranges passage for them to Palestine. During Lisa's medical examination, Peter discovers that the Nazis had used her for surgical experimentation, a series of operations which have made her incapable of being a wife or mother. Peter also learns that he is wanted back in London for questioning about the death of Thorens. Since he knows the British are planning to block Lisa's illegal entry into Palestine, he makes a deal with one of their agents: if Lisa is allowed to enter the country, he will surrender himself to the British police. Once he has accomplished his mission and Lisa is delivered into the hands of the Haganah, Peter leaves to keep his rendezvous with the British authorities. *Nazis. Dutch. Police. Sea captains. Smugglers. White slave traffic. Conscience. Self-sacrifice. Manslaughter. Sterilization (sexual). Concentration camps. Barges. Palestine. Tangiers. London. Auschwitz.*

Note: Location scenes filmed in Amsterdam, London, Tangiers, and Israel. Opened in London in Jun 1962 as *The Inspector.*

LISA AND BALLERS see **THE BALLERS**

LISA, TOSCA OF ATHENS (Greece)   **F6.2783**

Delta Films (Greece). *Dist* Hellenic Films. 17 Jun **1961** [New York opening]. Sd; b&w. 35mm. 84 min.

Dir Sokrates Kapsaskis. *Screenplay* Giannis Maris. *Songs* Nana Moushouri.

Cast: Xenie Kalogeropoulos (*Lisa*), Kostas Kakavas (*Nicky*), Kostas Hadjichristos (*Bulfos*), D. Papagianopoulos (*Johnny*).

Melodrama. Lisa is vacationing in Athens to escape a loveless marriage. She eludes her parents, meets Johnny, a gentle man, and falls in love with him. She is able finally to convince her parents that she and Johnny are meant for each other. *Marriage. Infidelity. Vacations. Parenthood. Athens.*

Note: Filmed on location in and around Athens. Also known as *Lisa, the Greek Tosca.*

LISA'S FOLLY   **F6.2784**

Dist Chancellor Films. 11 Nov **1970** [Champaign, Illinois, showing]. Sd; col (Eastmancolor). 35mm. 73 min.

Crime melodrama. Cowboy and his girl friend, Chilli, arrange with Lisa and Johnny, proprietors of a model agency that is a front for prostitution, to steal $1 million from mobster Big Sal. Lisa raises some money by having sex simultaneously with a wealthy homosexual and an oversexed muscleman. She gets the keys to Big Sal's car by duping Honey, the gangster's mistress and chauffeur, and hides Cowboy in the trunk. Honey unwittingly drives Cowboy into Big Sal's well-guarded estate. Johnny joins Cowboy, and together they extort the money from Big Sal by threatening to kill Honey. Chilli and Lisa receive the loot. It is revealed that the two women are lesbians, and they doublecross their friends by absconding with the $1 million. *Hoodlums. Gangsters. Mistresses. Extortion. Male homosexuality. Troilism. Lesbianism. Perfidy. Prostitution. Model agencies.*

LISETTE   **F6.2785**

R. John Hugh. *Dist* Medallion Pictures. 25 Oct **1961** [Chicago opening]. Sd; b&w. 35mm. 83 min.

Prod-Dir-Writ R. John Hugh. *Photog* Charles O'Roark. *Mus & Song:* "Goodbye Lisette" Les Baxter. *Sung by* John Agar.

Cast: Greta Chi (*Lisette*), John Agar (*Joe McElroy*), Walter Klavun (*Amos Culpepper*), John Cestare (*Buck Culpepper*), Jim Pritchett (*Howard Shaner*), Susan Ellis (*Ruth McElroy*).

Melodrama. Newspaper editor Joe McElroy sponsors an orphan refugee from Indochina as a good-will stunt to help his father-in-law, Amos Culpepper, become senator. The "child," however, turns out to be a beautiful Eurasian woman, Lisette. Joe is immediately attracted to Lisette and makes love to her on the night that she publicly denounces the publicity scheme. In retaliation, Culpepper attempts to discredit Lisette; and Joe, ashamed of his own feelings, goes along with the plot in the hope that Lisette will leave town. Instead, she agrees to go away with Culpepper's son Buck, thinking that he plans to marry her. When she resists his drunken advances, Buck hurls her from his car and runs her down. Later, Buck surrenders to the police, while the repentant Joe hands in his resignation and returns to his wife. *Newspapermen. Fathers-in-law. Politicians. Orphans. Refugees. Eurasians. Publicity. Political campaigns. Infidelity. Murder. Drunkenness.*

Note: Location scenes filmed in Florida. Also known as *Fall Girl* and *A Crowd for Lisette.*

THE LIST OF ADRIAN MESSENGER   **F6.2786**

Joel Productions–Universal Pictures. *Dist* Universal Pictures. 29 May **1963** [New York opening; c15 Jun 1963; LP33271]. Sd (Westrex); b&w. 35mm. 98 min.

Prod Edward Lewis. *In Charge of Prod* Edward Muhl. *Dir* John Huston. *Screenplay* Anthony Veiller. *Dir Photog* Joseph MacDonald. *Dir Photog European Unit* Ted Scaife. *Art Dir* Alexander Golitzen, Stephen Grimes, George Webb. *Set Decor* Oliver Emert. *Main Titl* Pacific Title. *Film Ed* Terry O. Morse, Hugh S. Fowler. *Mus* Jerry Goldsmith. *Mus Supv* Joseph Gershenson. *Sd* Waldon O. Watson, Frank H. Wilkinson. *Asst Dir* Tom Shaw, Terry Morse, Jr. *Unit Prod Mgr* Richard McWhorter. *Assoc to Mr. Huston* Gladys Hill. *Makeup Creator* Bud Westmore. *Makeup Artist* John Chambers, Nick Marcellino, David Grayson. *Hairstyles* Larry Germain.

Cast: George C. Scott (*Anthony Gethryn*), Dana Wynter (*Lady Jocelyn Bruttenholm*), Clive Brook (*Marquis of Gleneyre*), Jacques Roux (*Raoul Le Borg*), Gladys Cooper (*Mrs. Karoudjian*), Herbert Marshall (*Sir Wilfred Lucas*), John Merivale (*Adrian Messenger*), Marcel Dalio (*Max*), Bernard Archard (*Inspector Pike*), Walter Anthony Huston (*Derek*), Roland D. Long (*Carstairs*), Anita Sharp Bolster (*shopkeeper*), Noel Purcell (*farmer*), John Huston (*huntsman*), Kirk Douglas (*George Brougham*), Tony Curtis, Burt Lancaster, Robert Mitchum, Frank Sinatra.

Mystery melodrama. Source: Philip MacDonald, *The List of Adrian Messenger* (New York, 1959). After tea at the estate of the Marquis of Gleneyre, a retired British intelligence officer, Anthony Gethryn, is given a list of 11 names by his good friend, Adrian Messenger, and asked to check the whereabouts of the people listed. Subsequently, Messenger is killed in a plane which explodes in midair, and Gethryn learns that all of the other people on the list have also met with seemingly accidental deaths. Knowing that there must be a connection in these deaths, Gethryn enlists the aid of Scotland Yard and receives valuable information from Raoul Le Borg, the sole survivor of the plane crash. Gethryn learns that the killer is a master of disguise who changes his identity for each murder. After weeks of inquiry, Gethryn has concluded that the victims were fellow POW's in Burma and that the killer was the informer who disclosed their escape plans to the enemy. This man is now becoming prominent, and he finds it necessary to remove all those who know of his unsavory past. Gethryn identifies the killer as one of the Gleneyre heirs; in fact, only a small boy is standing in his way of becoming sole owner of the estate. At a fox hunt, the killer, George Brougham, turns up without disguise, but Gethryn decides to let him make his move before arresting him. At the right moment, Gethryn closes in; and the killer dies in one of his own traps while attempting to escape. *Nobility. Prisoners of war. Informers. Heirs. Murder. Disguise. Airplanes. Fox hunts. Scotland Yard. Great Britain—Intelligence service. Explosions.*

Note: Locations filmed in Ireland.

LISTEN, LET'S MAKE LOVE (France/Italy)   **F6.2787**
P. E. A.-Les Productions Artistes Associés. *Dist* Lopert Pictures. 13 Jun **1969** [New York opening; c6 Sep 1968; LF60]. Sd; col (Technicolor, U. S. prints by DeLuxe). 35mm (Techniscope). 91 min. *MPAA rating* R.

Prod Alberto Grimaldi. *Dir* Vittorio Caprioli. *Screenplay* Vittorio Caprioli, Franca Valeri, Enrico Medioli. *Dir Photog* Pasquale De Santis. *Art Dir* Ferdinando Scarfiotti. *Set Decor* Nedo Azzini. *Film Ed* Ruggero Mastroianni. *Mus* Ennio Morricone. *Mus Dir* Bruno Nicolai. *Sd* Elio Pacella. *Asst Dir* Franco Cirino. *Prod Supv* Aldo Pomilia. *Cost* Ferdinando Scarfiotti. *Makeup* Franco Freda. *Hairstyles* Adalgisa Favella.

Cast: Pierre Clementi *(Lallo)*, Beba Loncar *(Aunt Lidia)*, Carlo Caprioli *(Uncle Carlo)*, Edwige Feuillère *(Giuditta Passani)*, Juliette Mayniel *(Gilberta)*, Tanya Lopert *(Flavia Menobo)*, Claudine Auger *(Ida Bernasconi)*, Valentina Cortese *(Lallo's mother)*, Massimo Girotti *(Tassi)*, Martine Malle *(Sveva)*, Roberto Gatto *(Ida's husband)*, Mario Meniconi *(Mr. Breuner)*, Anna Maria Covacci *(Mrs. Breuner)*, Franca Valeri *(Diraghi)*, Fabian Fabre *(Puccio Picco)*, Antonietta Fiorita *(cloakroom attendant)*, Ivan Scratuglia *(Lallo's friend)*, Ornella Polito Santoliquido *(Amparo Botti)*, Americo Tot *(Baron von Tummler)*.

Drama. Lallo, a Neapolitan youth, comes to Milan upon the death of his father, a penniless gigolo, and decides to place himself at the disposal of rich women. Since his father's wealthy longtime mistress, Giuditta, is too deep in mourning to be of help, Lallo moves in with his Aunt Lidia and Uncle Carlo and quickly latches onto Gilberta, a wealthy patroness who gives him an automobile. His Aunt Lidia's possessiveness becomes bothersome, and Lallo is relieved when she is taken abroad by her husband. Lallo moves on to the ski resort of Cortina d'Ampezzo and charms a bored socialite, ida, into paying his bills. Lallo's presence also arouses the sexual interest of Flavia, a steel heiress, and Baron von Tummler, an old homosexual, and the two compete at an auction for a pair of antique cufflinks that interests Lallo. Though the baron wins the cufflinks, Lallo chooses Flavia, but their brief affair ends after he overhears her discussing him in uncomplimentary terms with Ida. En route back to Milan Lallo unexpectedly meets his mother at a railroad station as she is on her way to remarry in Vienna. Once back at Giuditta's home, Lallo falls in love with his hostess' daughter Sveva. She breaks off her engagement and Lallo announces that he plans to marry her, but Giuditta, operating on the principle that "money marries money," dashes his hopes by telling him that Sveva is his half sister. Disillusioned, Lallo recalls the opinion of his father's friend Tassi that young men fare better if they attach themselves to homosexuals, and he accepts the lavish support of Baron von Tummler. *Neapolitans. Gigolos. Fortune hunters. Upper classes. Aunts. Mistresses. Socialites. Heiresses. Wealth. Seduction. Male homosexuality. Ski resorts. Milan. Cortina d'Ampezzo.*

Note: Locations filmed in Milan and Cortina d'Ampezzo. Released in Italy in 1968 as *Scusi, facciamo l'amore?* Paris opening: Aug 1969 as *Et si on faisait l'amour?*

LE LIT CONJUGAL *see* **THE CONJUGAL BED**

LITTLE ANGEL (Mexico)   **F6.2788**
Películas Rodríguez. *Dist* K. Gordon Murray Productions, Trans-International Films. Jan **1961**. Sd; col (Eastman Color). 35mm. 90 min.

Pres by K. Gordon Murray. *Prod* José Luis Celis. *Prod English Vers* K. Gordon Murray. *Dir* Roberto Rodríguez. *Dir English Vers* Ken Smith, dir. *Screenplay* Roberto Rodríguez, José Luis Celis, Rafael García Travesi. *Story* Roberto Rodríguez, José Luis Celis, Ricardo Garibay. *Photog* Gabriel Figueroa. *Art Dir* Salvador Lozano Mena. *Film Ed* Fernando Martínez. *Mus* Raúl Lavista. *Sd* Rafael Ruiz Esparza.

Cast: María Gracia *(Marita)*, Jorge Martínez de Hoyos *(farmhand)*, Prudencia Griffel, Emma Rodríguez, Miguel Manzano, Manuel Santoyo.

Narrator: Hugh Downs.

Drama. Marita lives on a farm with her grandmother and a youthful shepherd. Distressed because her pregnant cow cannot give milk, unhappy about her first day at school, but confident in the power of prayer, Marita converses with a statue of the Virgin Mary. The statue informs her that obedience will remove nails from the hands of Christ crucified. Cheered by this discourse, Marita returns home to find that her cow has given birth. *Grandmothers. Children. Shepherds. Farm life. Faith. Virgin Mary. Cows.*

Note: Produced in Mexico in 1957 as *La sonrisa de la Virgen.*

LITTLE BIG MAN   **F6.2789**
Hiller Productions-Stockbridge Productions. For Cinema Center Films. *Dist* National General Pictures. 14 Dec **1970** [New York opening; c9 Dec 1970; LP39207]. Sd; col (Technicolor). 35mm (Panavision). 150 min. [Copyright length: 147 min.] *MPAA rating* GP.

Prod Stuart Millar. *Assoc Prod* Gene Lasko. *Dir* Arthur Penn. *Screenplay* Calder Willingham. *Dir Photog* Harry Stradling, Jr. *Camera Op* Ralph Gerling. *Camera Asst* Richard Meinardus. *Art Dir* Angelo Graham. *Set Decor* George R. Nelson. *Prod Dsgn* Dean Tavoularis. *Main Titl* Wayne Fitzgerald. *Film Ed* Dede Allen. *Assoc Ed* Richard Marks. *Asst Ed* Stephen Rotter. *Mus* John Hammond. *Adtl Mus Arr* John Strauss. *Sd* Al Overton, Jr., Bud Alper. *Sd Eff* James A. Richard, Frank Warner. *Mus Ed* Ted Whitfield. *Sd Re-rec* Richard Portman. *Dial Ed* Marc Laub, Marvin I. Kosberg. *1st & 2nd Asst Dir* Mike Moder, Mack Harding, Jerry Preshaw. *Prod Mgr* Dick Gallegly. *Script Cont* Charlsie Bryant. *Prod Asst* Jean Sharpe. *Cost Dsgn* Dorothy Jeakins. *Wardrobe* Frank Delmar. *Mr. Hoffman's Makeup* Dick Smith. *Makeup* Terry Miles. *Hairstyles* Lynn Del Kail. *Sp Eff* Logan Frazee. *Cavalry Adv* Jerry Gatlin. *Coöp* Crow Nation, Cheyenne Nation, Stony Indians (Chippewa Nation). *Cons to the Prod* Alvin Josephy. *Still Photog* Mel Traxel. *Gaffer* Cliff Hutchinson. *Key Grip* Charles Renaud. *Prop Master* Don Nunley. *Ramrod Wrangler* Kenneth Lee. *Casting Dir* Gene Lasko. *Stunt Coord* Hal Needham.

Cast: Dustin Hoffman *(Jack Crabb)*, Faye Dunaway *(Mrs. Pendrake)*, Martin Balsam *(Allardyce T. Merriweather)*, Richard Mulligan *(Gen. George A. Custer)*, Chief Dan George *(Old Lodge Skins)*, Jeff Corey *(Wild Bill Hickok)*, Amy Eccles *(Sunshine)*, Kelly Jean Peters *(Olga)*, Carol Androsky *(Caroline)*, Robert Little Star *(Little Horse)*, Cal Bellini *(Younger Bear)*, Ruben Moreno *(Shadow That Comes in Sight)*, Steve Shemayne *(Burns Red in the Sky)*, William Hickey *(historian)*, James Anderson *(sergeant)*, Jesse Vint *(lieutenant)*, Alan Oppenheimer *(major)*, Thayer David *(Rev. Silas Pendrake)*, Philip Kenneally *(Mr. Kane)*, Jack Bannon *(captain)*, Ray Dimas *(young Jack Crabb)*, Alan Howard *(adolescent Jack Crabb)*, Jack Mullaney *(card player)*, Steve Miranda *(Younger Bear as a youth)*, Lou Cutell *(deacon)*, M. Emmet Walsh *(shotgun guard)*, Emily Cho *(Digging Bear)*, Cecelia Kootenay *(Little Elk)*, Linda Dyer *(Corn Woman)*, Dessie Bad Bear *(Buffalo Wallow woman)*, Len George *(Crow scout)*, Norman Nathan *(Pawnee)*, Helen Verbit *(Madame)*, Bert Conway *(bartender)*, Earl Rosell *(giant trooper)*, Ken Mayer *(sergeant)*, Bud Cokes *(man at bar)*, Rory O'Brien *(assassin)*, Tracy Hotchner *(flirtatious girl)*.

Western epic. Source: Thomas Berger, *Little Big Man* (New York, 1964). A historian interviews Jack Crabb, a 121-year-old man who claims to be the only white survivor of the Battle of Little Big Horn: Jack, a 10-year-old orphan lost with his sister Caroline, is found by the Cheyenne Indians. When Caroline escapes, Jack is left under the fatherly guidance of Old Lodge Skins. During adolescence, he saves the life of Younger Bear in a raid against the Pawnee Indians and is given the name Little Big Man. At the age of 16, he is about to be killed in a battle against white men when he renounces his Indian background in order to save himself. Subsequently, he is taken into the home of Rev. Silas Pendrake and his wife, who is eager to introduce Jack to the pleasures of sex. After leaving the Pendrakes, he goes into business with Allardyce T. Merriweather, a hawker of patent medicines, and later briefly becomes a gunfighter known as the "Soda Pop Kid." He becomes friends with Wild Bill Hickok, but after one of Hickok's bloody gunfights, Jack decides to settle down. Olga, a Swedish woman, becomes his bride, and Jack opens a haberdashery, but he is cheated by his partners. Following the advice of Gen. George Custer, he decides to head West to seek his fortune. During the trip, however, Olga is abducted by the Indians, and Jack searches for her, joining Custer's U. S. Cavalry unit as a scout to facilitate his search. During a savage attack on the Indian village where he once lived, Jack deserts his unit and finds an Indian woman, Sunshine, in the process of giving birth. They travel to a reservation, headed by Old Lodge Skins, now blind from a battle wound. A year later, at a reservation, Sunshine is about to give birth to Jack's child. Jack is surprised to discover that Olga and her new husband, Younger Bear, are neighbors. The morning after Jack has slept with Sunshine's three widowed sisters, Sunshine shows him his new son. But Custer suddenly strikes, and only Jack and Old Lodge Skins survive. Jack tries to take revenge on Custer and sneaks into the general's tent, but Custer's vulnerability causes Jack to falter, and he wanders off, eventually becoming an alcoholic. A brief encounter with Wild Bill helps Jack get back on his feet, but when Hickok is shot down, Jack goes off to become a hermit. Later, he meets up with Custer, who hires him as a scout. Despite Jack's advice and the opinions of the officers, Custer orders the attack on Little Big Horn; the Cheyenne massacre Custer's forces, although Jack is saved when he is recognized by Younger Bear. He is taken back to Old Lodge Skins, who is in the process of preparing for his death ritual; he takes Jack to the mountain and lies down to die, but rain begins to fall, and Old Lodge Skins realizes that his time has not yet come. The two men walk back down the mountain. Jack finishes his story, but the historian is skeptical about the accuracy of the events. *Historians. Orphans. Cheyenne Indians. Guardians. Pawnee Indians. Preachers. Gunfighters. Swedes. Scouts—Frontier. Deserters—Military. Sisters. Hermits. Brother-sister relationship. Race relations. Adolescence. Seduction. Partnerships. Marriage. Abduction.*

Childbirth. Revenge. Alcoholism. Massacres. Rites and ceremonies. Old age. Patent medicines. Haberdasheries. United States—History—Indian campaigns. Custer's Last Stand. Little Big Horn. James Butler Hickok. George Armstrong Custer. United States Army—Cavalry.

Note: Location scenes filmed in Montana, California, and Alberta, Canada.

LITTLE BOY BLUE (Mexico)   F6.2790

Dist K. Gordon Murray Productions, Trans-International Films. 12 Oct **1963** [Des Moines, Iowa, opening]. Sd; col. 35mm. 86 min.

Pres by K. Gordon Murray. *Prod English Vers* K. Gordon Murray.

Fantasy. Little Boy Blue leaves home to find his pet monkey Pancho. Although he becomes involved with thieves illegally hunting deep in the jungle, all ends happily as Little Boy Blue, his family, and Pancho are reunited. *Children. Thieves. Hunters. Jungles. Pets. Monkeys.*

LITTLE FAUSS AND BIG HALSY   F6.2791

Alfran Productions–Furie Productions. *Dist* Paramount Pictures. 21 Oct **1970** [New York opening; c6 Oct 1970; LP38419]. Sd; col (print by Movielab). 35mm (Panavision). 97 min. [Copyright length: 100 min.] *MPAA rating* R.

An Albert S. Ruddy Production. *Prod* Albert S. Ruddy. *Exec Prod* Brad Dexter. *Prod Exec* Gray Frederickson. *Dir* Sidney J. Furie. *Screenplay* Charles Eastman. *Dir Photog* Ralph Woolsey. *Camera Op* Charles W. Short. *Art Dir* Lawrence G. Paull. *Set Decor* Audrey Blasdel. *Film Ed* Argyle Nelson, Jr. *Song:* "Rollin' Free" *writ & sung by* Johnny Cash. *Song:* "Ballad of Little Fauss and Big Halsy" Carl Perkins. *Sung by* Johnny Cash. *Song:* "Wanted Man" Bob Dylan. *Sung by* Johnny Cash. *Song:* "True Love Is Greater Than Friendship" *writ & sung by* Carl Perkins. *Song:* "706 Union Avenue" Carl Perkins. *Sung by* The Tennessee Three. *Sd Ed* Keith Stafford. *Sd Rec* Glenn Anderson, Richard Portman. *1st & 2d Asst Dir* Terry Morse, Jr., Robert M. Webb, Lynn Guthrie. *Prod Mgr* Terry Morse, Jr. *Script Supv* Robert Forrest. *Prod Asst* Robert Mendelsohn, Harry Korshak. *Racing Leathers Dsgn* Pierre Cardin. *Wardrobe* Ted Parvin. *Makeup* Del Armstrong. *Tech Adv* Roxy Rockwood. *Prop Master* Ray F. Mercer, Jr. *Key Grip* Ken Adams. *Gaffer* George Holmes.

Cast: Robert Redford *(Big Halsy)*, Michael J. Pollard *(Little Fauss)*, Lauren Hutton *(Rita Nebraska)*, Noah Beery *(Sealy Fauss)*, Lucille Benson *(Mom Fauss)*, Ray Ballard *(photographer)*, Linda Gaye Scott *(Mometh)*, Erin O'Reilly *(Sylvene McFall)*, Ben Archibeck *(Rick Nifty)*, Shara St. John *(Marcy)*.

Action melodrama. Little Fauss, an amateur motorcycle racer, meets Halsy Knox, a professional racer, after a race held near Phoenix, Arizona. Fauss is attracted to Halsy's carefree lifestyle, but Fauss's father regards Halsy as a bad influence on his son and refuses to help Halsy when his truck breaks down. Later, Halsy arrives at the motorcycle repair shop where Fauss works and tricks the admiring Fauss into repairing his motorcycle free. Halsy, who has been barred from racing for drinking on the track, proposes that they form a partnership in which Halsy would race under Fauss's name with Fauss functioning as the mechanic. Despite his parents' disapproval, Fauss joins Halsy on the racing circuit. He is constantly faced with his inferiority to Halsy, both on and off the racetrack. Their partnership is finally broken when Rita Nebraska, a drop-out from a wealthy background, arrives at the racetrack and immediately attaches herself to Halsy, despite the attention Fauss pays her. After breaking his leg in a motorcycle race, Fauss returns home to his parents. Several months later, when his leg has mended, Halsy visits him and attempts to leave behind Rita, who is now pregnant, but Fauss refuses to take her. He tells Halsy that he plans to reenter the racing circuit. A short time later, the two men race against each other at the Sears Point International Raceway; Halsy's motorcycle breaks down, and as he leaves the track, he hears the announcement that Fauss has taken the lead. *Motorcyclists. Mechanics. Motorcycle racing. Filial relations. Partnerships. Pregnancy. Phoenix (Arizona). Sears Point International Raceway.*

Note: Location scenes filmed in Los Angeles, San Francisco, and Phoenix. Racing sequences filmed at Sears Point International Raceway in Sonoma, California.

LITTLE GIRLS (France)   F6.2792

Dist Olympic International Films. **1966**. Sd; b&w. 35mm. 70 min.

Prod R. W. Cresse. *Dir* Gilbert Wolmark.

Cast: Yvonne (French), Michelle, Ondine (French), Pascal, Marie.

Melodrama. Seven teenaged girls from wealthy Parisian families relieve the boredom of their lives through sexual experimentation. They try everything from lesbianism to prostitution, until their promiscuity draws them into a web of blackmail, murder, and suicide. *Paris. Promiscuity. Wealth. Adolescence. Prostitution. Lesbianism. Blackmail. Murder. Suicide.*

THE LITTLE HUMPBACKED HORSE (U.S.S.R.)   F6.2793

Central Documentary Film Studio. *Dist* Artkino Pictures. 6 Oct **1962** [New York opening]. Sd; col (Magicolor). 35mm. 82 min. [Also 85 min.]

Ballet Dir-Screenplay Aleksandr Radunskiy. *Anim* V. Krestyaninov, K. Aleksandrova, I. Znamenskiy, B. Chani. *Photog* Mikhail Silenko, Yevgeniy Yatsun. *Camera* Ye. Akkuratov, Nikolay Generalov, Ilya Gutman, L. Pankin. *Art Dir* B. Volkov. *Mus Comp* Rodion Konstantinovich Shchedrin. *Mus Cond* A. Zhyuraytis. *Mus Played by* Bolshoi Theater Orchestra. *Sd* V. Nesterov, V. Georgiyevskaya. *1st & 2d Asst Dir* Z. Tulubyeva, T. Chistyakova. *Prod Mgr* B. Chekalov.

Cast: Maya Plisetskaya *(Queen Maiden)*, Vladimir Vasilyev *(Ivan)*, Alla Shcherbinina *(The Little Humpbacked Horse)*, Aleksandr Radunskiy *(The King)*, Aleksandr Pavlinov *(Old Man)*, I. Peregudov *(Danila)*, A. Simachyov *(Gavrila)*, L. Shvachkin *(king's groom)*, Natalya Taborko *(water spirit)*, Vasya Vorokhobko *(fish)*, Georgiy Farmanyants, Gennadiy Ledyakh, Bolshoi Theater Ballet.

Dance film. Source: Rodion Konstantinovich Shchedrin, Vasiliy Ivanovich Vaynonen and Pavel Grigoryevich Malyarevskiy, *Konyok-Gorbunok* (a ballet; performed 1960). Pyotr Pavlovich Yershov, *Konyok-Gorbunok* (St. Petersburg, 1834). Ivan, a simple-minded youth, acquires two fine black steeds and a little humpbacked horse who brings good luck. Ivan's two older brothers steal the steeds and take them to the King, but, since only Ivan can control the steeds, he becomes the King's chief groom. The King falls in love with the fairytale Queen Maiden and commands Ivan on pain of death to bring her to him. With the help of the little humpbacked horse, Ivan finds the Queen Maiden, who lives beneath the sea, and captures her. Repulsed by the portly old King, she demands that a ruby ring be brought from the bottom of the sea before she will agree to the marriage. Ivan is again commanded to accomplish the task, and again his little horse helps him to succeed. The Queen Maiden finally insists that the King must bathe in boiling water before the wedding in order to become young and handsome. The King orders Ivan to test the bath, and with the help of the magic horse, he emerges extraordinarily handsome. The King dives into the water in turn and is killed. Ivan and the Queen Maiden then wed. *Brothers. Royalty. Stableboys. Magic. Youth. Jewels. The Sea. Imaginary kingdoms. Horses.*

Note: Released in the U.S.S.R. in Dec 1961 as *Skazka o Konke-Gorbunke*.

LITTLE JUNGLE BOY (Australia)   F6.2794

Mass-Brown Pictures. Dec **1969** [c18 Dec 1969; LP38134]. Sd; col (Eastman Color). 35mm. 78 min.

Pres by Golden Record Film Library. *Prod-Dir-Adapt* Mende Brown. *Dir Photog* Brendon Brown. *Mus Dir* Tommy Tycho.

Cast: Rahman Rahman, Michael Pate, Noel Ferrier, Willie Fennell, Mike Dorsey, Niki Huen, Leslie Berryman, Nicki Turner.

Adventure drama. In an animal compound in the Malayan jungle, Dr. Ben Martin and his wife, Dr. Ann Soong, nurse back to health a jungle boy wounded by the fearful Bomoh natives. Although abducted and taken to Singapore by unscrupulous reporter Tony Street, the boy escapes into the city streets. Returned by the police to the doctors, the boy is asked by a sultan to help bring penicillin to the northern part of his province, where superstitious natives suffering from a dysentery epidemic are cut off from civilization by the Bomohs. After several days' journey through the dense jungle, the boy, the sultan, and the doctors arrive in the infected kampong. Convinced of the trespassers' goodness by the boy's power over wild animals, the Bomoh medicine man allows the doctors to inject penicillin into the villagers. The natives cured, the boy returns to the jungle. *Physicians. Reporters. Police. Royalty. Medicine men. Tribal life. Abduction. Superstition. Jungles. Epidemics. Malaya. Singapore.*

Note: Filmed in Australia. Copyright title: *Momman, Little Jungle Boy*. Opened in Mt. Lawley, Australia, in May 1970.

THE LITTLE NUNS (Italy)   F6.2795

Hesperia Cinematografica. *Dist* Embassy Pictures. Sep **1965**. Sd; b&w. 35mm. 101 min.

Pres by Joseph E. Levine. *Prod* Ferruccio Brusarosco. *Assoc Prod* G. Carlo Marchetti, Mario Tugnoli. *Dir* Luciano Salce. *Story & Screenplay* Franco Castellano, Giuseppe Moccia. *Photog* Erico Menczer. *Set Decor* Aurelio Crugnola. *Film Ed* Roberto Cinquini. *Mus Comp & Cond* Ennio Morricone. *Sd* Franco Groppioni. *Asst Dir* Emilio Miraglia. *Prod Mgr* Gianni Minervini. *Cost* Giuliano Papi.

Cast: Catherine Spaak *(Sister Celeste)*, Sylva Koscina *(Elena)*, Amedeo Nazzari *(Livio Bertana)*, Didi Perego *(Mother Rachele)*, Umberto D'Orsi *(Spugna)*, Sandro Bruni *(Damiano, the orphan)*, Annie Gorassini *(Bertana's secretary)*, Alberto Bonucci *(Mr. Batistucchi)*, Lando Buzzanca.

Comedy-drama. The sound waves created by jet planes passing over the convent school of Saint Domitilla in a small Italian town are destroying the convent's ancient fresco and disturbing the children. To remedy the situation, Sister Celeste and Mother Rachele are driven to Rome by Spugna, the convent handyman, to see Livio Bertana, the general manager of the airline responsible. Damiano, an orphan from the convent, stows away in the car. The nuns give

Bertana no peace in trying to get him to change the airplane routes; they even go to his home. Elena, his mistress, is charmed by Damiano. Meanwhile, Batistucchi, an airline executive, is plotting to get Bertana's job by accusing him of mismanagement at the stockholders' meeting. To get money for the nuns to buy airline stock so that they can get into the stockholders' meeting, Spugna enters and wins a judo contest. Bertana resigns his job at the meeting, but the nuns take over the meeting, and their explanation saves Bertana's job. He agrees to change the air routes, but the nuns continue to meddle in his life until he marries Elena and adopts Damiano. Back at the convent, Sister Celeste is visited by a nun from a neighboring town who complains about jets passing over her school. Sister Celeste tells her not to worry because she has a dear friend in Rome who will remedy the situation. *Nuns. Handymen. Orphans. Executives. Mistresses. Business management. Marriage. Adoption. Judo. Convents. Airplanes—Jet. Contests. Rome.*

Note: Opened in Rome in Oct 1963 as *Le monachine;* running time: ca105 min. Giuseppe Moccia is also known as Pipolo.

THE LITTLE ONES (Great Britain)   F6.2796

Goldhawk Films. *Dist* Columbia Pictures. 15 Sep **1965** [New York opening; c7 Jul 1965; LP32275]. Sd (Westrex); b&w. 35mm. 66 min.

Prod Freddie Robertson. *Dir-Writ* Jim O'Connolly. *Dir Photog* David Holmes. *Camera Op* Norman Jones. *Art Dir* Derek Barrington. *Set Decor* Arthur Fell. *Film Ed* Henry Richardson. *Mus Arr & Cond* Malcolm Lockyer. *Beat Group Mus Played by* The Turnkeys. *Calypso Theme Mus* Freddie Robertson. *Sd* Location Sound Facilities. *Asst Dir* Bert Marotta. *Location Mgr* Ricky Coward. *Prod Controller* Bernard Coote. *Cont* Lilian Lee. *Wardrobe* Ernie Farrer. *Makeup* Harry Webber.

Cast: Carl Gonzales *(Jackie),* Kim Smith *(Ted),* Dudley Foster *(Inspector Carter),* Derek Newark *(Detective Sergeant Wilson),* Jean Marlow *(Ted's mother),* Peter Thomas, actor *(Ted's father),* Derek Francis *(Paddy),* Cyril Shaps *(child welfare officer),* John Chandos *(Lord Brantley),* Diane Aubrey *(Peggy),* George Betton, Tom Crossman, Norman Mitchell, Michael McKenzie, Anne Padwick, Bob Payne, Anthony Wager, Gillian Hayes, Harry Goodier, Valerie Jayne, Ken Jones.

Drama. Two boys, Ted, 9, and Jackie, 12, plan to run away from their homes in a London slum by stowing away on a ship bound for Jamaica. Ted is leaving home to escape his scolding parents, who forbid his friendship with the halfcaste Jackie. Jackie intends to join his Jamaican father because his mother, a white prostitute, causes him to feel that he is in the way. The boys reach Liverpool by stowing away on a furniture van traveling north. They steal a suitcase from an unlocked Rolls-Royce and sell it to a junk dealer for money to purchase food. The car's owner, shipping magnate Lord Brantley, reports the theft to police, who soon apprehend the boys. Police Inspector Carter learns of the boys' unpleasant home life, gives them a mild reprimand, and sends them home. En route they are saddened to see their ship leaving; but the welfare worker accompanying them inadvertently tells them there are plenty of ships leaving for Jamaica from their home city of London. *Children. Halfcastes. Runaways. Prostitutes. Police. Shipping magnates. Friendship. Theft. Filial relations. Racial prejudice. Slums. Ships. Liverpool. London. Jamaica.*

Note: Released in Great Britain in Jun 1965.

LITTLE RED RIDING HOOD (Mexico)   F6.2797

Películas Rodríguez. *Dist* K. Gordon Murray Productions. **1963.** Sd; col (Eastman Color). 35mm. 85 min.

Pres by K. Gordon Murray. *Prod English Vers* K. Gordon Murray. *Dir* Roberto Rodríguez. *Screenplay* Fernando Morales Ortiz, Ricardo Garibay. *Adapt* Fernando Morales Ortiz, Rafael García Travesi. *Photog* Alex Phillips. *Set Dsgn* Edward Fitzgerald. *Film Ed* José Bustos. *Mus* Sergio Guerrero. *Sd* Nicolás de la Rosa.

Cast: María Gracia, Manuel Valdés, Rafael Muñoz, Beatriz Aguirre, Guillermo Alvarez Bianchi, Prudencia Griffel, Irma Torres, Santanón.

Fantasy. Source: Charles Perrault, "Le petit Chaperon rouge," in *Recueil de pièces curieuses et nouvelles* (Paris, 1697). The Wicked Wolf and his friend Skunk prepare to trap Little Red Riding Hood into their lair by kidnaping a small boy from a village of woodcutters. Disguising himself as the Good Fairy, the Wolf deceives Red Riding Hood into thinking that she can rescue the boy. She enters the Haunted Forest but escapes from the Wolf's grasp and runs to her grandmother's house. The Wolf races ahead of her to the house and impersonates the grandmother. The trick works, but as he is about to make Red Riding Hood his victim, the woodcutters arrive and save her. The woodcutters prepare to kill the Wolf, but Red Riding Hood pleads with them not to do so. Her confidence is well placed: the Wolf is made keeper of the forest and thus becomes a useful citizen. *Woodsmen. Kidnaping. Duplicity. Impersonation. Forests. Wolves. Skunks.*

Note: Released in Mexico in 1960 as *La caperucita roja;* running time: 109 min.

LITTLE RED RIDING HOOD AND HER FRIENDS (Mexico) F6.2798

Películas Rodríguez. *Dist* K. Gordon Murray Productions. 12 Dec **1964** [Chicago showing]. Sd; col (Eastman Color). 35mm. 90 min.

Pres by K. Gordon Murray. *Prod English Vers* K. Gordon Murray. *Dir-Orig Story-Screenplay* Roberto Rodríguez. *Adapt* Roberto Rodríguez, Rafael A. Pérez. *Photog* José Ortiz Ramos. *Set Dsgn* Gunther Gerszo. *Film Ed* José Bustos. *Mus* Sergio Guerrero. *Sd* Jesús González Gancy.

Cast: Manuel Valdés *(The Wolf),* María Gracia *(Little Red Riding Hood),* Santanón *(The Fox),* Consuelo Guerrero de Luna, Alfredo Vergara, Luis Manuel Pelayo, Beatriz Aguirre, Prudencia Griffel, Eduardo Alcaraz, Guillermo Alvarez Bianchi, Armando Lujan, Enrique Edwards, Edmundo Espino, Leticia Roo, Roberto Meyer, Elvira Lodi.

Fantasy. Although no information about the precise nature of this film has been found, press material suggests that the film depicts the adventures of Little Red Riding Hood and her friends, the ferocious wolf, the wily fox, and Duce the dog, including their encounter with a band of gypsies and a visit with a fairy princess in an enchanted kingdom. *Gypsies. Royalty. Wolves. Fox. Dogs. Fairies. Imaginary kingdoms. Little Red Riding Hood.*

Note: Produced in Mexico in 1960 as *Caperucita y sus tres amigos,* the second in a series of "Caperucita" films by Películas Rodríguez. Also known as *Little Red Riding Hood and Her Three Friends.*

LITTLE RED RIDING HOOD AND THE MONSTERS (Mexico) F6.2799

Películas Rodríguez. *Dist* K. Gordon Murray Productions. 2 Feb **1965** [Maryland license]. Sd; col (Eastman Color). 35mm. 82 min.

Pres by K. Gordon Murray. *Prod English Vers* K. Gordon Murray. *Dir-Writ* Roberto Rodríguez. *Dir English Vers* Manuel San Fernando. *Story & Screenplay* Fernando Morales Ortiz, Adolfo Torres Portillo. *Adapt* Roberto Rodríguez, Sergio Magaña. *Photog* Rosalío Solano. *Set Dsgn* Roberto Silva. *Film Ed* José Bustos. *Mus* Raúl Lavista. *Songs* Fernando Morales Ortiz. *Sd* Ernesto Caballero. *English Sd Ed* J. R. Remy.

Cast: María Gracia *(Little Red Riding Hood),* José Elías Moreno, Manuel Valdés, Cesáreo Quesada, Ofelia Guilmain, Quintín Bulnes, Santanón, Magda Donato, Armando Gutiérrez.

Fantasy. In a haunted forest, Little Red Riding Hood, Tom Thumb, and their animal friends fight an evil witch and her monsters, including a vampire. *Monsters. Vampires. Witches. Little Red Riding Hood. Tom Thumb.*

Note: Produced in Mexico in 1960 as *Caperucita y Pulgarcito contra los monstruos;* running time: 90 min. Third in a series of "Caperucita" films by Películas Rodríguez.

THE LITTLE SHEPHERD OF KINGDOM COME   F6.2800

Associated Producers, Inc. *Dist* Twentieth Century–Fox Film Corp. Jan **1961** [c22 Dec 1960; LP18691]. Sd; col (De Luxe). 35mm (CinemaScope). 108 min. [Also 79 min.]

Prod Maury Dexter. *Dir* Andrew V. McLaglen. *Screenplay* Barré Lyndon. *Dir Photog* Floyd Crosby. *Art Dir* John Mansbridge. *Set Decor* Joseph Kish. *Supv Film Ed* Jodie Copelan. *Film Ed* Carl Pierson. *Mus Comp & Cond* Henry Vars. *Songs:* "When Love Is Young," "The Little Shepherd of Kingdom Come" "By" Dunham, Henry Vars. *Sung by* Jimmie Rodgers. *Sd* Charles Peck, Jack Solomon. *Asst Dir* Ira Stewart. *Prod Supv* Harold E. Knox. *Script Supv* Billy Vernon. *Wardrobe* Clark Ross. *Makeup* Jack Obringer. *Prop Master* Frank Sullivan.

Cast: Jimmie Rodgers *(Chad),* Luana Patten *(Melissa Turner),* Chill Wills *(Major Buford),* Linda Hutchins *(Margaret Dean),* Robert Dix *(Caleb Turner),* George Kennedy *(Nathan Dillon),* Kenny Miller *(Reuben),* Neil Hamilton *(General Dean),* Shirley O'Hara *(Mrs. Turner),* Lois January *(Mrs. Dean),* John Holland, Edward Faulkner, Russ Bender, Morris Ankrum, Nelson Leigh, Lane Chandler, Diana Darrin, Dan Simmons, Glen Marshall, Helen Scott, actress, Ollie O'Toole, I. Stanford Jolley, Don Giovanni, Jerry Summers, Glen Walters.

Drama. Source: John William Fox, *The Little Shepherd of Kingdom Come* (New York, 1903). Following his foster family's death during a cholera epidemic, the waif Chad is taken in by the Turners, who live in the Kentucky mountain town of Kingdom Come. Consumed by a desire to discover himself, Chad travels to Lexington, where he is befriended by Major Buford, a childless, widowed landowner. While attending college in Lexington, Chad supports himself by delivering mail. When he enlists in the Union Army, however, he alienates himself from his Confederate guardian and from his sweetheart, Margaret Dean. During the war Chad arrests Margaret's brother, Richard, and witnesses the deaths in combat of his benefactors, Caleb Turner and Major Buford. Having distinguished himself as a courier, Chad returns to Kingdom Come and Melissa Turner, his childhood sweetheart. *Kentuckians. Orphans. Landowners. Couriers. Adoption. Education. United States—History—Civil War. United States Army. Lexington (Kentucky).*

Note: Previously filmed by Goldwyn (1920) and First National (1928).

LITTLE SISTER *see* FLESH OF MY FLESH

THE LITTLE SISTER *see* MARLOWE

LITTLE WOMEN   **F6.2801**
Dist Stacey Distributors. ca **1970**. Sd; col. 16mm. 61-81 min.
Sex film. No information about the precise nature of this film has been found. *Sexuality.*

LIVE A LITTLE, LOVE A LITTLE   **F6.2802**
Metro-Goldwyn-Mayer, Inc. 23 Oct **1968** [Los Angeles opening; c2 Oct 1968; LP36082]. Sd; col (Metrocolor). 35mm (Panavision). 90 min.
A Douglas Laurence Production. *Prod* Douglas Laurence. *Dir* Norman Taurog. *Screenplay* Michael A. Hoey, Dan Greenburg. *Dir Photog* Fred Koenekamp. *Art Dir* George W. Davis, Preston Ames. *Set Decor* Henry Grace, Don Greenwood, Jr. *Film Ed* John McSweeney. *Mus Score* Billy Strange. *Song:* "A Little Less Conversation" Billy Strange, Scott Davis. *Song:* "Almost in Love" Randy Starr, Luiz Bonfa. *Song:* "Edge of Reality" Bill Giant, Bernie Baum, Florence Kaye. *Choreog* Jack Regas, Jack Baker. *Rec Supv* Franklin Milton. *Asst Dir* Al Shenberg. *Unit Prod Mgr* Lindsley Parsons, Jr. *Asst to the Prod* Michael A. Hoey. *Makeup* William Tuttle. *Hairstyles* Mary Keats.
Cast: Elvis Presley (*Greg*), Michele Carey (*Bernice*), Don Porter (*Mike Lansdown*), Rudy Vallee (*Penlow*), Dick Sargent (*Harry*), Sterling Holloway (*milkman*), Celeste Yarnall (*Ellen*), Eddie Hodges (*delivery boy*), Joan Shawlee (*Robbie's mother*), Mary Grover (*Miss Selfridge*), Emily Banks (*receptionist*), Michael Keller (*art director*), Merri Ashley, Phyllis Davis (*secretaries*), Ursula Menzel (*perfume model*), Susan Shute, Edie Baskin, Gabrielle, Ginny Kaneen, Thordis Brandt (*models*), Susan Henning (*mermaid*), Morgan Windbeil, Benjie Bancroft (*motorcycle cops*).
Comedy-drama with music. Source: Dan Greenburg, *Kiss My Firm but Pliant Lips* (New York, 1965). Greg, a freelance photographer, is chased from a California beach into the surf by a Great Dane. When Greg emerges from the freezing water, Bernice, the dog's owner, takes him to her house to dry out. As a result of the escapade, Greg develops a high fever and is obliged to stay on as a houseguest for 5 days. Greg finally returns to his own place, however, but learns from his landlady that Bernice has moved all of his things into her house. His life becomes even more complicated when he lands two jobs for the same hours in the same building. By carefully arranging his coffee breaks and lunch hours, he manages to circulate back and forth and please both bosses, the informal Mike Lansdown and the straitlaced Penlow. Though Bernice rents a house for Greg, she fakes a serious illness so that she may become his temporary tenant. Despite the girl's eccentric behavior, Greg eventually realizes that he has fallen in love with her. Disconcerted, now that their relationship has become serious, Bernice disappears; but her friend Harry leads Greg to find her on the beach, where the couple are reunited. *Photographers. Landladies. Eccentrics. Houseguests. Employer-employee relations. Beaches. California. Dogs.*

LIVE FOR LIFE (France/Italy)   **F6.2803**
Ariane–Les Productions Artistes Associés–Vides. *Dist* United Artists. 18 Dec **1967** [New York opening; c18 Dec 1967; LP36017]. Sd; col (DeLuxe). 35mm. 130 min.
Prod Alexandre Mnouchkine, Georges Dancigers. *Assoc Prod* Robert Amon. *Dir* Claude Lelouch. *Screenplay* Pierre Uytterhoeven, Claude Lelouch. *Dir Photog* Patrice Pouget. *Camera* Claude Lelouch. *Film Ed* Claude Lelouch. *Assoc Ed* Claude Barrois. *Asst Ed* Marie Claude Poyer, Thiery Derocles. *Mus* Francis Lai. *Orch* Christian Gaubert. *Song:* "Des ronds dans l'eau" Raymond Le Sénéchal, Pierre Barouh. *Sung by* Nicole Croisille, Annie Girardot. *Sd Engr* Jean Baronnet. *Admin* Janine Roualt. *Wardrobe* Yves Saint-Laurent. *Furs* Henri Stern. *Makeup* Michel Deruelle. *Hairstyles* Denise Lemoigne, Jacques Cousty. *Sp Eff* Jean Beylieu.
Cast: Yves Montand (*Robert Colomb*), Candice Bergen (*Candice*), Annie Girardot (*Catherine Colomb*), Irène Tunc (*Mireille*), Uta Taeger (*Catherine's best friend [maid]*), Jean Collomb (*waiter*), Anouk Ferjac (*Jacqueline*), Michel Parbot (*Michel*), Jacques Portet (*Candice's photographer friend*), Maurice Séveno (*himself*), Louis Lyonnet.
Drama. Because his marriage has become stagnant, Robert Colomb, a successful Parisian television news reporter, welcomes out-of-town assignments and the distraction of casual love affairs. Following a chance meeting with Candice, a 22-year-old American model, he accepts an assignment in Kenya and persuades Candice to accompany him. In Africa he films wild animals and a documentary on the training of French mercenaries. Upon his return to Paris a few weeks later, he feels conscience-bound to take his wife, Catherine, on a second honeymoon to Amsterdam. Candice follows them, and Robert, unable to resist the temptation to be with her, pretends to Catherine that he must return to Paris for 2 days because of censorship problems with his African film. In fact, he spends the time at a nearby hotel with Candice. Later, as he and

Catherine are on their way home by train, he impulsively confesses his love for Candice, and Catherine gets off the train at Brussels without saying a word. Now free to do as he chooses, Robert takes an apartment in Paris with Candice. But he can neither forget Catherine nor find fulfillment with Candice, and he accepts a dangerous assignment in Vietnam. He is taken prisoner by the Vietcong but ultimately permitted to return to France. By now Candice is back in New York attempting to resume her former life, and Catherine has become a self-sufficient careerwoman. Robert follows her to the ski resort of Alpe d'Huez, where she is vacationing with her new friends, but she discourages his hopes for a reconciliation. As he prepares to leave, however, he finds Catherine waiting for him in his car. *Reporters. Americans in foreign countries. Mercenaries. Vietcong. Careerwomen. Marriage. Infidelity. Duplicity. Television. Ski resorts. Hotels. Vacations. Trains. Paris. Kenya. Amsterdam. Vietnam. New York City. Alpe-d'Huez (France). Animals.*
Note: Opened in Paris in Sep 1967 as *Vivre pour vivre*; Italian title: *Vivere per vivere*. Sources conflict in crediting the role of actress Uta Taeger.

LIVE IT UP *see* SING AND SWING

LIVE TO LOVE *see* THE DEVIL'S HAND

LIVE YOUR OWN WAY (Japan)   **F6.2804**
Gekidan Haiyuza Shinsei Eigasha. *Dist* Shochiku Films of America. Aug **1970** [Los Angeles showing]. Sd; b&w. 35mm. 98 min.
Dir Tokihisa Morikawa. *Screenplay* Hisashi Yamanouchi. *Photog* Yoshio Miyajima. *Art Dir* Totetsu Hirakawa. *Mus* Masaru Sato.
Cast: Kunie Tanaka (*Taro*), Isao Hashimoto (*Jiro*), Kei Yamamoto (*Saburo*), Orie Sato (*Orie*), Shoji Matsuyama (*Suekichi*), Yasushi Nagata, Mie Minami, Michiko Otsuka.
Domestic melodrama. Based on the television series *Wakamono tachi*. Four sons and one daughter are left alone after their parents' death: Taro, the eldest son, a construction worker; Jiro, the second eldest son, a truckdriver; Saburo, the third son, a university student; Orie, the daughter; and Suekichi, the youngest boy, who is preparing to enter the university. Taro postpones his marriage to care for his brothers and sister and finds himself quarreling frequently with his brothers. Orie leaves home for a while, disgusted with her brothers' bickering, but she soon returns when she realizes that no one has an easy life. In the spring, Suekichi fails his entrance examination for the university, but his brothers and sister console him and determine to face the future courageously. *Orphans. Students. Brothers. Construction workers. Truckdrivers. Family life. Brother-sister relationship. Self-sacrifice.*
Note: Released in Japan in May 1969 as *Wakamono tachi*.

THE LIVELY SET   **F6.2805**
Universal Pictures. 11 Sep **1964** [Detroit opening; c24 Oct 1964; LP32603]. Sd (Westrex); col (Eastman Color). 35mm. 95 min. [Copyright length: 92 min.]
Prod William Alland. *Dir* Jack Arnold. *Screenplay* Mel Goldberg, William Wood. *Story* William Alland, Mel Goldberg. *Dir Photog* Carl Guthrie. *Camera Op* Lloyd Ward. *Asst Camera* Jacque Deerson. *Art Dir* Alexander Golitzen, Walter Simonds. *Set Decor* John McCarthy, Joe Kish. *Set Coörd* Fred Knoth. *Titl* Pacific Title. *Film Ed* Archie Marshek. *Asst Ed* Fred Chulack. *Mus* Bobby Darin. *Mus Supv* Joseph Gershenson. *Titl Song* Bobby Darin. *Sung by* James Darren. *Songs:* "If You Love Him," "Casey Wake Up" Bobby Darin. *Sung by* Joanie Sommers. *Song:* "Look at Me" Bobby Darin, Randy Newman. *Sung by* Wink Martindale. *Song:* "Boss Barracuda" Bobby Darin, Terry Melcher. *Sung by* The Surfaris. *Sd* Waldon O. Watson, Josh Westmoreland, Herb Alberty, Ora Hudson, Bob Dunning. *Asst Dir* James Welch, Carl Beringer. *Unit Prod Mgr* Frank Parmenter. *Script Supv* Cliff Bole. *Cost Dsgn* Rosemary Odell. *Wardrobe* Mike Tierney, Olive Koenitz. *Makeup* Bud Westmore, Keester Sweeney. *Hairstyles* Larry Germain, Cherie. *Sp Eff* Sass Bedig. *Tech Adv* Ron Miller, racer. *Coop for scenes in Death Valley* John Aubuchon, United States—Department of the Interior. *Gas Turbine Car* Chrysler Corp. *Sp Equipment Supplied by* Mickey Thompson Enterprises. *Dial Coach* Haile Chace. *Still Photog* James Mitchell. *Gaffer* Les Everson. *Grip* Ken Smith, Alan Hall. *Prop* Bob Bone, Curtis Baessler.
Cast: James Darren (*Casey Owens*), Pamela Tiffin (*Eadie Manning*), Doug McClure (*Chuck Manning*), Joanie Sommers (*Doreen Grey*), Marilyn Maxwell (*Marge Owens*), Charles Drake (*Paul Manning*), Peter Mann (*Stanford Rogers*), Carole Wells (*Mona*), Frances Robinson (*Celeste Manning*), Russ Conway (*Dave Moody*), Ross Elliott (*Ernie Owens*), Martin Blaine (*Professor Collins*), Greg Morris (*policeman*), Max Schumacher, Dick Whittinghill, Mickey Thompson, James Nelson, racer, Duane Carter, Billy Krause, Ron Miller, racer (*themselves, racing drivers*).
Comedy-drama with music. After 2 years in the Army, Casey Owens, who builds and drives racing cars, enrolls in college. There he meets Chuck Manning, another young man enthusiastic about cars. Casey falls in love with Eadie, Chuck's sister, and quits college to go to work in his father's garage and continue work on a gas turbine engine. He competes in races and soon becomes

something of a celebrity in racing circles. Young millionaire racing enthusiast Stanford Rogers hires Casey to build two cars for him. Scorning scientific advice, Casey refuses to conduct wind tunnel tests on the cars and, as a result, wrecks one of them when he tries to attain high speed. Rogers fires Casey; and Casey's parents, with the help of Chuck and Eadie's parents, raise enough money to buy the engine from Rogers. Heeding advice this time, Casey builds a new car around the engine, enters and wins the Tri-State Endurance Race, and with his winnings pays back the money invested in his engine. Casey marries Eadie and reenrolls in college. *Veterans. Mechanics. Students. Millionaires. Automobile racing. College life. Garages.*

Note: Location scenes filmed in Death Valley.

THE LIVER EATERS see **SPIDER BABY**

LIVING BETWEEN TWO WORLDS   F6.2806

Empire Films. Dec **1963** [Los Angeles showing]. Sd; b&w. 35mm. 78 min. [Also reviewed at 75 min.]

A Horace Jackson Production. *Prod-Writ* Horace Jackson. *Dir* Bobby Johnson. *Photog* William Zsigmond. *Set Dsgn* Carl Randell. *Film Ed* Gene Evans, ed, Frank Gardonyi. *Mus* Gordon Zahler. *Asst Dir* Ivan Dixon. *Prod Supv* DeForest Covan.

Cast: Maye Henderson (*Mom*), Anita Poree (*Bucky*), Mimi Dillard (*Helen*), Horace Jackson (*Harvey*), Irvin Mosley (*Papa*), Kyle Johnson (*Larry*), Derrick Lewis (*Norman*), Geraldine West (*Mrs. Peters*), DeForest Covan (*orderly*), Lawrence La Mar (*janitor*), Napoleon Whiting (*Reverend Williamson*), John Shaner, David Morrow.

Melodrama. Raised from birth to the ministry by his strong black mother, Harvey doubts the authenticity of his vocation and considers becoming a jazz musician. Although he is taunted for his devotion to his mother by his fiancée, Helen, the young black is strongly supported by his sister, Bucky. Following Helen's rape by two whites Harvey decides upon the ministry and is an immediate success. *Negroes. Musicians. Ministerial students. Filial relations. Negro life. Brother-sister relationship. Rape.*

THE LIVING COFFIN (Mexico)   F6.2807

Alameda Films. *Dist* K. Gordon Murray Productions, Trans-International Films. ca **1965**. Sd; col. 35mm. 72 min.

Pres by K. Gordon Murray. *Prod* César Santos Galindo. *Prod English Vers* K. Gordon Murray. *Dir* Fernando Méndez. *Story & Screenplay* Ramón Obón. *Photog* Victor Herrera. *Art Dir* Gunther Gerszo. *Film Ed* Charles Kimball. *Mus* Gustavo César Carrión. *Sd* Victor Mateos.

Cast: Gastón Santos, María Duval, Pedro d' Aguillón, Hortensia Santoveña, Guillermo Alvarez Bianchi, Antonio Raxell, Eugenia Galindo, Carlos Ancira, Quintín Bulnes, Carolina Barret.

Horror film. Afraid of being buried alive, a girl has her coffin rigged with an alarm. *Phobias. Death. Coffins.*

Note: Produced in Mexico in 1958 as *El grito de la muerte.*

THE LIVING HEAD (Mexico)   F6.2808

Cinematografica A. B. S. A. *Dist* Trans-International Films. 29 May **1968** [Maryland license]. Sd; b&w. 35mm. 75 min.

Pres by K. Gordon Murray. *Prod* Abel Salazar. *Dir* Chano Urueta. *Story-Screenplay* Federico Curiel, Adolfo Torres Portillo. *Photog (see note)* Jorge Stahl, Jr., José Ortiz Ramos. *Art Dir* Roberto Silva. *Film Ed* Alfredo Rosas Priego. *Mus* Gustavo César Carrión. *Sd* Jesús González Gancy.

Cast: Mauricio Garcés, Ana Luisa Peluffo, Germán Robles, Guillermo Cramer, Abel Salazar, Antonio Raxell.

Horror film. Acatl, chief of the Aztecs, is murdered and his head is cut off. At the same time, Xochiquetzal, his betrothed, is buried alive, along with the Grand Priest. Centuries later, archeologist Herman Mueller and his assistants Tony and Charley unearth the tomb. The mummy of Xochiquetzal disintegrates, but the heads of Acatl and the priest remain preserved. Herman takes his discoveries home to his daughter Martha, to whom he gives an Aztec ring known by legend as a ring of death. Soon afterwards, Charley becomes the victim of a human sacrifice, and the heads of Acatl and the priest return to life to place Martha under a spell. Although Martha is able to resist Acatl's orders to murder her father, her fiancé, Robert, falls under a similar spell. Eventually, however, the curse of the living head is broken. *Archeologists. Aztec Indians. Priests. Murder. Decapitation. Human sacrifice. Reviviscence. Spells. Curses. Mummies. Tombs.*

Note: Produced in Mexico in 1961 as *La cabeza viviente.* Though a Mexican source credits Stahl as photographer, a U. S. source indicates that Ramos receives screen credit.

LIVING VENUS   F6.2809

Mid-Continent Films. *Dist* Creative Services. **1961**. Sd; b&w. 35mm. 74 min.

Prod-Dir Herschell Gordon Lewis. *Prod Mgr* Preston Collins.

Cast: William Kerwin (*Jack Norwall*), Danica D'Hondt (*Peggy Brandon*), Harvey Korman (*Ken Carter*), Jeanette Leahy, Lawrence J. Aberwood, Robert Bell, Linné Ahlstrand, Billy Falbo, Bob Scobey and His Band.

Drama. Fired from his job as assistant publisher of *Newlywed Magazine*, ambitious Jack Norwall decides to organize his own girlie publication, *Pagan*. With the help of sympathetic photographer Ken Carter, Jack promotes model Peggy Brandon as the living image of Venus and a national symbol of sex appeal. Jack breaks his engagement to Diane and marries Peggy. In a fit of jealousy, Ken leaves *Pagan*. A year and a half later Jack's arrogant temperament causes his business to collapse. Peggy quits the magazine, then commits suicide when Jack informs her of his plans to divorce her. Jack, a broken man, is abandoned by those he betrayed. *Publishers. Photographers. Models. Ambition. Suicide. Perfidy. Nudity. Magazines (periodicals). Venus.*

Note: Filmed in Chicago.

LJUBAVNI SLUČAJ ILI TRAGEDIJA SLUŽBENICE P.T.T. see **LOVE AFFAIR; OR THE CASE OF THE MISSING SWITCHBOARD OPERATOR**

LOCK UP YOUR DAUGHTERS (Great Britain)   F6.2810

Domino Productions. *Dist* Columbia Pictures. 15 Oct **1969** [New York opening; c1 Sep 1969; LP37369]. Sd (RCA & Westrex); col (Technicolor). 35mm. 102 min. *MPAA rating* R.

Prod David Deutsch. *Assoc Prod* Anthony Nelson Keys. *Dir* Peter Coe, dir. *Screenplay* Keith Waterhouse, Willis Hall. *Photog* Peter Suschitzky. *Camera Op* Ron Robson. *Focus Op* Geoffrey Glover. *Set Decor* Ian Whittaker, Peter Young. *Prod Dsgn* Tony Woollard. *Film Ed* Frank Clarke. *Mus Comp & Cond* Ron Grainer. *Rec* Robert Allen. *Re-rec* Len Abbott. *Sd Ed* Mike Le Mare. *Asst Dir* Bert Batt. *Prod Mgr* Ron Jackson. *Asst to the Prod* Gerald Deutsch. *Cont* Doreen Dearnaley. *Cost Dsgn* Alan Barrett. *Wardrobe Master* Ken Lewington. *Makeup* W. T. Partleton. *Hairstyles* Anne Triebner, Susie Hill. *Casting Adv* Miriam Brickman. *Constr Mgr* Ernie Blake, Brian McCarthy. *Ch Electrn* Edward Cross. *Prop Master* Peter Spencer.

Cast: Christopher Plummer (*Lord Foppington*), Susannah York (*Hilaret*), Glynis Johns (*Mrs. Squeezum*), Ian Bannen (*Ramble*), Tom Bell (*Shaftoe*), Elaine Taylor (*Cloris*), Jim Dale (*Lusty*), Fenella Fielding (*Lady Eager*), Roy Kinnear (*Sir Tunbelly Clumsey*), Kathleen Harrison (*Lady Clumsey*), Roy Dotrice (*Master Gossip*), Peter Bayliss (*Justice Squeezum*), Georgia Brown (*Nell*), Edward Atienza (*Justice Worthy*), Peter Bull (*Bull*), Blake Butler (*Faithful*), Paul Dawkins (*Lord Eager*), Wallas Eaton (*Staff*), Fred Emney (*Earl of Ware*), Vanessa Howard (*Hoyden*), Arthur Mullard (*night watchman*), Patricia Routledge (*nurse*), Richard Wordsworth (*Coupler*), Trevor Ray (*Quill*), Michael Darbyshire (*La Verole*), Ron Pember (*Bottle*), John Morley (*nobleman*), Clive Morton (*Boswell*), Roger Hammond (*Johnsonian figure*), Tony Sympson (*clerk of the court*), Martin Crosbie, Cecil Sheehan, Tom Irwin, Danny O'Connor, Vernon Hayden, Derry Power (*constables*).

Comedy. Adapted from the plays: Bernard Miles, Laurie Johnson and Lionel Bart, *Lock Up Your Daughters* (London opening: 28 May 1959). Henry Fielding, *The Coffee House Politicians or The Justice Caught in His Own Trap* (1730). John Vanburgh, *The Relapse* (1696). Three sex-starved sailors—Shaftoe, Ramble, and Lusty—arrive in 18th-century London after a lengthy sea voyage. Shaftoe plans to elope with Hilaret, but he is mistakenly charged with rape and thrown into jail. He finds Ramble already there on the same charge after an encounter with the flirtatious Lady Eager. Hilaret attracts the attention of the lecherous Mr. Squeezum, whose wife enjoys the company of the two prisoners. Ramble, it is discovered, is the wayward husband of Hilaret's maid, Cloris. Meanwhile, Lusty is rejected by the usually available Nell in favor of wealthy Lord Foppington. In revenge, Lusty steals Lord Eager's clothes and seduces Hoyden, Foppington's fiancée, the virgin daughter of Sir Tunbelly Clumsey. Lusty persuades Bull, a worldly priest, to marry him to Hoyden; Bull earlier had agreed to marry Shaftoe and Hilaret. Lusty's maneuvers are interrupted by the unexpected arrival of Lords Eager and Foppington. After many complications and misunderstandings, however, all lovers are reunited. *Sailors. Nobility. Priests. Lust. Seduction. Rape. Revenge. Disguise. Virginity. Marriage. Jails. London.*

Note: Filmed in Ireland. Released in Great Britain in 1969.

LA LOI see **THE LAW**

LOIN DU VIÊTNAM see **FAR FROM VIETNAM**

LOLA (France/Italy)   F6.2811

Rome Paris Films–Euro International Films. *Dist* Films Around the World, Inc. 14 Oct **1962** [New York opening]. Sd; b&w. 35mm (Franscope). 90 min.

Prod Carlo Ponti, Georges de Beauregard. *Dir-Writ* Jacques Demy. *Photog* Raoul Coutard. *Art Dir* Bernard Evein. *Film Ed* Anne-Marie Cotret, Monique Teisseire. *Mus* Michel Legrand. *Mus Selections: Symphony no.* 7 Ludwig van Beethoven. "*The Well-Tempered Clavier*" Johann Sebastian Bach. *Concerto for Flute in D-major* Wolfgang Amadeus Mozart. *"Invitation to the Waltz"* Carl Maria von Weber. *Song: "Moi j'étais pour elle"* Marguerite Monnot. *Titl Song: "C'est moi, c'est Lola"* Agnès Varda. *Sung by* Anouk Aimée. *Asst Dir* Bernard Toublanc-Michel. *Prod Mgr* Bruna Drigo. *Prod Cons* Jean-Luc Godard. *English Subtitl* Rose Sokol.

Cast: Anouk Aimée *(Lola)*, Marc Michel *(Roland)*, Jacques Harden *(Michel)*, Alan Scott *(Frankie)*, Elina Labourdette *(Madame Desnoyers)*, Annie Duperoux *(Cécile)*, Margo Lion *(Michel's mother)*, Catherine Lutz *(Claire, the waitress)*, Corinne Marchand *(Daisy)*, Yvette Anziani *(Madame Frédérique)*, Gérard Delaroche *(Yvon, Lola's son)*, Jacques Goasguen *(librarian)*, Ginette Valton *(beauty shop proprietor)*, Jacques Lebreton *(bookshop owner)*, Carlo Nell *(dancing teacher)*, Dorothée Blank *(Dolly)*, Isabelle Lunghini *(Nelly)*, Annik Noël *(Ellen)*, Anne Zamire *(Maggie)*, Babette Barbin *(Minnie)*.

Romantic comedy-drama. For 7 years, Lola, a cabaret entertainer in Nantes, has been waiting for the return of her lover, Michel, who left her with a child and went out into the world to make his fortune. One day, after a brief fling with Frankie, an American sailor who reminds her of Michel, she meets Roland, a childhood friend. A dreamer unable to settle down to a job, Roland has been idling away his time in the company of a lonely widow, Madame Desnoyers, and her 14-year-old daughter, Cécile. Captivated by Lola, Roland unabashedly declares his love for her; but, true to the memory of Michel, she rejects him. Frankie, meanwhile, has also become acquainted with the romantic Cécile, and they spend an afternoon together at a local fair. Then, unexpectedly, Michel returns to Lola and her child. Wildly happy, Lola speeds off in Michel's sleek white Cadillac as a sad and forlorn Roland wanders along a riverside quay. At the same time, young Cécile runs away from home to Cherbourg, the port where Frankie's ship is harbored. *Entertainers. Widows. Americans in foreign countries. Sailors. Fidelity. Motherhood. Adolescence. Cabarets. Fairs. Nantes. Cherbourg.*

Note: Filmed on location in Nantes. Opened in Paris in Mar 1961 at 85 min; in Rome in Apr 1961 as *Donna di vita*.

LOLA MONTÈS (Reissue) (France/West Germany)　　　　**F6.2812**
Gamma Films–Florida Films–Oska Films–Union-Film. *Dist* Brandon Films. 20 Apr **1969** [New York opening]. Sd; col (Eastmancolor). 35mm (CinemaScope). 110 min.

Note: First released in the United States as *The Sins of Lola Montes* in 1959 by Transamerica Releasing Corp.; running time: 90 min. There are three versions of this film. The original opened in Paris in Dec 1955 and in Munich in Jan 1956; running time: 140 min. An altered version opened in Paris in Jan 1956; running time: 110 min. An abbreviated and reedited version opened in Paris in Feb 1967; running time: 90 min. Also known as *Lola Montez*.

LOLA'S MISTAKE (Reissue)　　　　　　　　　　　　　**F6.2813**
All God's Children Co. 2 Jun **1965** [San Francisco opening]. Sd; b&w. 35mm. 90 min.

Note: Originally released in 1960 as *This Rebel Breed* by Warner Bros. Pictures; c19 Mar 1960; LP20181.

LOLITA (United States/Great Britain)　　　　　　　　　**F6.2814**
Seven Arts Productions–A. A. Productions–Anya–Transworld Pictures. *Dist* Metro-Goldwyn-Mayer, Inc. 13 Jun **1962** [New York opening; c31 Dec 1961; LP21994]. Sd (RCA); b&w. 35mm. 152 min.

Prod James B. Harris. *Dir* Stanley Kubrick. *2d Unit Dir* Dennis Stock. *Screenplay* Vladimir Nabokov. *Dir Photog* Oswald Morris. *Camera Op* Denys Coop. *Focus* Jimmy Turrell. *Art Dir* Bill Andrews. *Assoc Art Dir* Syd Cain. *Set Dresser* Andrew Low, Peter James. *Ch Draughtsman* Frank Willson. *Scenic Artist* A. Van Montagu. *Main Titl* Chambers & Partners. *Film Ed* Anthony Harvey. *Asst Ed* W. W. Armour, Lois Gray. *Mus* Nelson Riddle. *Theme: "Lolita"* Bob Harris, mus. *Orch* Gil Grau. *Dub Ed* Winston Ryder. *Sd Rec* Len Shilton. *Sd Mix* H. L. Bird. *Boom Op* Don Wortham. *1st, 2d & 3d Asst Dir* Rene Dupont, Roy Millichip, John Danishewsky. *Prod Supv* Raymond Anzarut. *Prod Mgr* Robert Sterne. *Cont* Pamela Davies. *Prod Sec* Joan Parcell. *Wardrobe Supv* Elsa Fennell. *Wardrobe Mistress* Barbara Gillett. *Miss Winters' Cost* Gene Coffin. *Makeup* George Partleton. *Hairdresser* Betty Glasow. *Casting Dir* James Liggat. *Constr Mgr* Harry Phipps. *Prod Buyer* Terry Parr. *Still Photog* Joe Pearce. *Camera Grip* Ron Osborn. *Elec Gaffer* Wally Thompson.

Cast: James Mason *(Humbert Humbert)*, Sue Lyon *(Lolita Haze)*, Shelley Winters *(Charlotte Haze)*, Peter Sellers *(Clare Quilty)*, Marianne Stone *(Vivian Darkbloom)*, Diana Decker *(Jean Farlow)*, Jerry Stovin *(John Farlow)*, Gary Cockrell *(Dick)*, Suzanne Gibbs *(Mona Farlow)*, Roberta Shore *(Lorna)*, Eric Lane *(Roy)*, Shirley Douglas *(Mrs. Starch)*, Roland Brand *(Bill)*, Colin Maitland *(Charlie)*, Cec Linder *(physician)*, Irvin Allen *(hospital attendant)*, Lois Maxwell *(nurse Mary Lore)*, William Greene *(Swine)*, C. Denier Warren *(Potts)*, Isobel Lucas *(Haze maid)*, Maxine Holden *(hotel receptionist)*, Marion

Mathie *(Miss Lebone)*, Craig Sams *(Rex)*, John Harrison *(Tom)*, James Dyrenforth *(Beale senior)*, Terence Kilburn.

Comedy-drama. Source: Vladimir Nabokov, *Lolita* (Paris, 1955). Humbert Humbert walks into the disordered mansion of amoral television playwright Clare Quilty and shoots the drunken, mocking author. Humbert then recalls the events that began 4 years earlier: Newly arrived from England, Humbert, a staid middle-aged professor and translator of French poetry, plans to spend the summer in New Hampshire before moving on to a position as a lecturer at an Ohio college. Charlotte Haze, a sexually frustrated widow, is anxious to rent him a room in her house, but her overbearing manner nearly drives him away until he meets her precocious adolescent daughter, Lolita. The girl so arouses Humbert's passion that to be near her he marries Charlotte, meanwhile recording his impressions of mother and daughter in a diary. Charlotte's possessiveness soon awakens murderous desires in Humbert, but the problem of her presence is solved when she reads his diary and, hysterical, runs into the path of an automobile. Humbert retrieves Lolita from the summer camp where her mother had disposed of her and drives with her to Ohio, enrolling her in a private school. Lolita's interest in boys gives him no peace, however, and their relationship becomes strained as she chafes at his interference. When he discovers that Lolita has used the cover of her performance in a school play for meetings with an unknown man, Humbert takes her from school. They embark on a cross-country trip, but Humbert suspects that they are being followed. Both fall ill, and Lolita, hospitalized, disappears one night from her hospital room. Some time later, Humbert receives a letter from Lolita in which she reveals that she is married and pregnant and asks for financial help. When he visits her, she tells him that she left him for Quilty, who, in various disguises, pursued and tormented Humbert wherever he went with Lolita. Quilty abandoned the girl when she balked at becoming part of his "weird" circle, and she married a younger man. Humbert, his pride gone, begs her to come back to him, but she refuses, preferring to remain with her husband. His world at an end, Humbert gives Lolita all of his money and then goes to find Quilty. [An epilog explains that Humbert dies of a heart attack in prison.] *Professors. Television scriptwriters. Widows. Mistresses. Landladies. Obsession. Adolescence. Middle age. Murder. Motherhood. Filial relations. Jealousy. Marriage. Sexuality. Disguise. Diaries. New Hampshire. Ohio. Automobile accidents.*

Note: Filmed in part in Great Britain and in Albany, New York. Opened in London in Sep 1962.

LOLLIPOP (Brazil)　　　　　　　　　　　　　　　　　**F6.2815**
Produções Cinematográficas Herbert Richers. *Dist* Times Film Corp. 25 Mar **1966** [Fresno, California, showing]. Sd; b&w. 35mm. 89 min.

A Herbert Richers Production. *Prod* Herbert Richers. *Assoc Prod* Alexandre Horvath. *Dir-Script* J. B. Tanko. *Dir Photog* Toni Rabatoni. *Camera* Leon Varsano. *Set Dsgn* Alexandre Horvath. *Film Ed* Rafael Justo. *Mus* João Negrão. *Asst Dir* Gilvan Pereira. *Prod Mgr* Adalberto Vieira. *Makeup* Lucia Brita. *Still Photog* Nelson Di Rago.

Cast: Vera Vianna *(Lollipop)*, Jece Valadão *(Silvio)*, Maria Helena Dias *(Leticia)*, Fregolente *(Nono)*, Odilon Azevedo *(Dr. Arnaldo)*, Jorge Doria *(Dr. Bergamini)*, Nestor Montemar *(Zozimo)*, Milton Carneiro *(Dr. Vaconcelos)*, Alberico Bruno *(Father Fidelis)*, Licia Magna *(Madame Zeze)*, Tina Goncalves *(Aunt Ceci)*, Thelma Reston *(Gina)*, Rodolfo Arena *(captain)*.

Melodrama. Based on a novel by: Nelson Rodrigues, *Asfalto selvagem; livro 2: Engraçadinha, seus amôres e seus pecados depois dos 30* (Rio de Janiero, 1960). While still a child, Lollipop falls in love with her orphaned cousin Silvio, who has been raised as a member of the family by her father, Dr. Arnaldo, a highly respected government official. Years pass, and to Lollipop's dismay, Silvio becomes engaged to her cousin Leticia. During the engagement party, the enraged Lollipop seduces Silvio, and sometime later, she reveals to Leticia that she is pregnant as a result of the encounter. Leticia breaks with Silvio and urges him to marry Lollipop, but although he is unable to resist Lollipop's sensuality, he truly loves his fiancée. Dr. Arnaldo angrily forbids his daughter's marriage to Silvio and arranges to have her pregnancy aborted. Lollipop attempts to run off with Silvio, and Dr. Arnaldo is forced to disclose that Silvio is his own illegitimate son. The enormity of the incestuous sin causes Silvio to take his own life, and the guilt-ridden doctor soon follows suit, leaving Lollipop to contemplate the results of her unbridled passion. [The story is related in flashback.] *Orphans. Cousins. Incest. Suicide. Filial relations. Pregnancy. Seduction. Illegitimacy. Abortion. Guilt. Jealousy. Courtship.*

Note: Released in Brazil in 1964 as *Asfalto selvagem*. U. S. prerelease title: *Forbidden Love Affair.*

THE LOLLIPOP COVER　　　　　　　　　　　　　　　**F6.2816**
International Productions. *Dist* Continental Distributing, Inc. 17 Nov **1965** [San Francisco opening]. Sd; b&w with col seq. 35mm. 85 min. [Also reviewed at 82 min.]

Prod-Dir Everett Chambers. *Assoc Prod* Richard Chambers, Richard Rosenbloom. *Exec Prod* Robert Brandt. *Screenplay* Everett Chambers, Don Gordon. *Idea* Nancy Valentine. *Photog* Michael Murphy, photog. *Film Ed* James D. Mitchell. *Mus* Ruby Raksin. Song: *"When I See a Rainbow"* Ruby Raksin, James D. Mitchell. Song: *"If You Love Me"* Ruby Raksin. *Sung by* Sally Kellerman. *Sd* Frank Murphy.

Cast: Don Gordon (*Nick Bartaloni*), Carol Seflinger (*Felicity*), George Sawaya, Annette Valentine, Bek Nelson, David White, John Marley, Bert Remsen, Midge Ware, Cliff Carnell, Carolyn Hughes, Lee Philips.

Drama. Nick Bartaloni, a disillusioned and cynical boxer, hitchhikes to Los Angeles to recover the money his sister was holding for his retirement. (She committed suicide and gave the money to her lover, a drug addict.) On his way to the coast he meets Felicity, a nine-year-old girl abandoned by her alcoholic father, and they travel on together. Her view of the world is the opposite of Nick's; she believes in the goodness of people and when events prove too sad for her she looks at the world through translucent lollipop wrappers, which give everything a rosy hue. Nick's search for the money is unsuccessful, but his bitter outlook changes as he learns to see life through Felicity's eyes. *Boxers. Hitchhikers. Children. Innocents. Disillusionment. Fatherhood. Brother-sister relationship. Suicide. Alcoholism.*

LONDON EXPOSED see **PRIMITIVE LONDON**

LONDON IN THE RAW (Great Britain)   F6.2817
Searchlight Productions-Troubadour Films. *Dist* Olympic International Films. 23 Apr **1965** [Champaign, Illinois, showing]. Sd; col (Eastman Color). 35mm. ca76 min.
Prod-Dir-Writ Arnold Louis Miller. *Exec Prod* Michael Klinger, Tony Tenser. *Photog* Stanley A. Long. *Ed* Stephen Cross. *Mus* Synchro Recorded Music Library, Charles Brull Ltd. *Prod Mgr* Phillip Steen. *Research* Robert Gaddes.

Cast: David Gell (*narrator*).

Documentary. A tour of London reveals startling ironies: prostitutes, cleared from the streets, solicit from upper-story windows while below, an elderly street musician, whose tune is not finished by the time the client returns to the street, resists the ravages of the cold. At health and beauty clubs, women endure discomforts of every description in order to keep up appearances; a man undergoes a painful operation to graft hair onto his balding scalp. Teenagers release inhibitions at a dance club, and belly dancers entertain the "bowler hat brigade" in London's business district. Beatniks sketch a nude volunteer; a restaurant that caters to artists serves dinner while guests sketch nudes posed around the room. Lonely men allow themselves to be fleeced in clip joints; immigrant groups as a Cypriot club, a Jewish theater, and a German students' carnival night create a more joyful atmosphere. Nightclubs and striptease establishments cater to every taste; traditional entertainment is resurrected at a pub; a high-society gambling resort provides after-hours entertainment. Meanwhile, derelicts drink wood alcohol in a bombed-out cellar; drug addicts queue up at midnight outside dispensaries to collect their legal daily drug allotment; other "users" turn to the illegal drug trade in Soho. *Street musicians. Businessmen. Exotic dancers. Beatniks. Cypriots. Jews. Germans. Derelicts. Prostitution. Appearances. Nudity. Striptease. Gambling. Drug addicts. Alcoholism. Health clubs. Restaurants. Nightclubs. Clip joints. Pubs. Music halls. Theater. Law and order. London. London—Soho.*
Note: Released in Great Britain in 1964.

THE LONELINESS OF THE LONG DISTANCE RUNNER
(Great Britain)   F6.2818
Woodfall Film Productions. *For* Bryanston-Seven Arts Productions. *Dist* Continental Distributing, Inc. 8 Oct **1962** [New York opening]. Sd; b&w. 35mm. 103 min.
Prod-Dir Tony Richardson. *Assoc Prod* Michael Holden. *Prod Exec* Alan Kaplan. *Screenplay* Alan Sillitoe. *Dir Photog* Walter Lassally. *Camera Op* Desmond Davis. *Focus Puller* Manny Wynn. *Camera Grip* Frank Boston. *Art Dir* Ted Marshall. *Set Dresser* Josie Macavin. *Prod Dsgn* Ralph Brinton. *Film Ed* Anthony Gibbs. *1st Asst Ed* Brian Smedley-Aston. *2d Asst Ed* Pamela Milner-Gardner. *Mus Comp, Arr & Cond* John Addison. *Sd* Stephen Dalby. *Sd Rec* Norman Bolland. *Boom Op* Tom Buchanan. *Sd Camera Op* Derek Leather. *Dub Ed* Don Challis. *Asst Dub Ed* Karen Heward. *1st & 2d Asst Dir* Basil Rayburn, Andrew Mollo, John Danischewsky. *Prod Supv* Leigh Aman. *Asst to the Prod* Michael Holden. *Cont* Rita Davison. *Prod Sec* Jane Moscrop. *Prod Mgr* Robert Sterne. *Prod Asst* Patrick Boyle. *Wardrobe Dsgn* Sophie Harris. *Wardrobe Mistress* Brenda Dabbs. *Makeup Artist* Jimmy Evans. *Hairdresser* Bobbie Smith. *Still Photog* Aubrey Dewar. *Prop Supv* Tommy Erley. *Prop Buyer* Terry Parr. *Chargehand Electrn* Fred Anderson.
Cast: Tom Courtenay (*Colin Smith*), Michael Redgrave (*The Governor*), Avis Bunnage (*Mrs. Smith*), Peter Madden (*Mr. Smith*), James Bolam (*Mike*), Julia Foster (*Gladys*), Topsy Jane (*Audrey*), Dervis Ward (*detective*),

Raymond Dyer (*Gordon*), Alec McCowen (*Brown*), Joe Robinson (*Roach*), Philip Martin (*Stacey*), Arthur Mullard (*chief officer*), Ray Austin (*Craig*), Anthony Sagar (*Fenton*), John Thaw (*Bosworth*), Peter Kriss (*Scott*), James Cairncross (*Jones*), Peter Duguid (*doctor*), John Bull (*Ronalds*), William Ash (*Gunthorpe*), Dallas Cavell (*Lord Jaspers*), Anita Oliver (*Alice Smith*), Brian Hammond (*Johnny Smith*), Christopher Parker (*Bill Smith*), John Brooking (*Green*), Frank Finlay (*booking office clerk*), Robert Percival (*Tory politician*), Christopher Williams (*public school boy*).

Drama. Source: Alan Sillitoe, *The Loneliness of the Long Distance Runner* (London, 1959). Colin Smith, an 18-year-old from the Lancashire slums, is an aimless rebel. After robbing a bakery, he is sent to a Borstal reformatory, where he shows only contempt for the authorities, particularly the institution's governor, who stresses physical activity as a means of rehabilitating youth. One day Colin unintentionally distinguishes himself as an outstanding long distance runner, and the governor decides to train him for a forthcoming match against a prominent public school. During the lonely practice runs, Colin recalls the details of his early life: his poorly-paid laborer father who died of cancer, his ill-tempered mother who squandered her husband's insurance money on a television set and a lover, his few moments of happiness with his girl friend Audrey, and the bakery robbery. On the day of the race, Colin easily outdistances the other runners. As he approaches the finish line, however, he suddenly stops in front of the grandstand. Without revealing a sign of emotion, he waits for the other runners, and in a mock display of chivalry, he bows and gestures for them to pass. Smiling contemptuously at the stunned governor, Colin understands that he will pay dearly for his little victory; he also knows that he has refused to yield to an authority for which he has no respect. *Juvenile delinquents. Athletes. Headmasters. Adolescence. Robbery. Physical training. Track. Family life. Poverty. Cancer. Reformatories. Contests. Lancashire.*
Note: Opened in London in Sep 1962; running time: 104 min. Also known as *Rebel With a Cause.*

LONELY ARE THE BRAVE   F6.2819
Joel Productions. *For* Universal-International Films. *Dist* Universal-International Films. 24 May **1962** [Houston opening; c20 Apr 1962; LP24918]. Sd; b&w. 35mm (Panavision). 107 min.
Prod Edward Lewis. *Dir* David Miller. *Screenplay* Dalton Trumbo. *Photog* Philip Lathrop. *Photog Coörd* Tim Donahue. *Art Dir* Alexander Golitzen, Robert E. Smith. *Set Decor* George Milo. *Film Ed* Leon Barsha, Edward Mann. *Mus* Jerry Goldsmith. *Mus Supv* Joseph Gershenson. *Sd* Waldon O. Watson, Frank H. Wilkinson, Art Smith, James Alexander, James Curtis. *Asst Dir* Tom Shaw, David Silver, Ray Taylor, Jr. *Script Supv* Dick Michaels. *Wardrobe* Stanley Kufel, Peter Saldutti. *Makeup* Bud Westmore, Dave Grayson. *Hairstyles* Larry Germain. *Still Photog* Don Christie.
Cast: Kirk Douglas (*Jack Burns*), Gena Rowlands (*Jerri Bondi*), Walter Matthau (*Sheriff Johnson*), Michael Kane (*Paul Bondi*), Carroll O'Connor (*Hinton*), William Schallert (*Harry*), Karl Swenson (*Reverend Hoskins*), George Kennedy (*Gutierrez*), Dan Sheridan (*Deputy Glynn*), Bill Raisch (*One Arm*), William Mims (*1st deputy in bar*), Martin Garralaga (*old man*), Lalo Rios (*prisoner*).
Western drama. Source: Edward Abbey, *Brave Cowboy* (New York, 1956). Jack Burns, an itinerant cowboy whose individualism clashes with modern-day life, rides down from the mountains when he learns that his friend Paul Bondi has been jailed for helping illegal immigrants across the Mexican border. Hoping to help Bondi escape, Burns deliberately becomes involved in a barroom brawl and is thrown into the same jail, but Bondi prefers to serve his sentence rather than spend the rest of his life on the run. So Burns breaks out alone, gets food and ammunition from Bondi's wife, Jerri, with whom he has been romantically involved, and heads for the hills with his horse, Whisky. The local sheriff, a kindly and philosophic man, organizes a posse of seven deputies equipped with a jeep and a helicopter, while Burns, refusing to abandon his horse though he would make better time on foot, slowly climbs a steep mountainside. When the helicopter spots him, he shoots it down and heads for the Mexican border. Crossing a highway at night, Whisky balks at the oncoming traffic, and both the horse and Burns are hit by a diesel truck. The sheriff arrives, shoots the injured animal to end its misery, and quietly speaks the lonely cowboy's epitaph. *Cowboys. Sheriffs. Fugitives. Alienation. Friendship. Jailbreaks. Jails. Helicopters. Chases. Automobile accidents. Horses.*
Note: Location scenes filmed near Albuquerque, New Mexico. Working title: *The Last Hero.*

THE LONELY HEARTS KILLERS see **THE HONEYMOON KILLERS**

LONELY HOUSEWIFE   F6.2820
Janus II Productions-Academy Productions. *Dist* Stacey Distributors. **1970.** Sd; col. 16mm. 61-81 min.
Sex film. Sex-hungry housewives relieve their frustrations by seducing gasmen and repairmen. *Housewives. Gasmen. Repairmen. Seduction.*

Infidelity.

Note: Also known as *Lonely Housewives.*

LONELY LANE (Japan)   **F6.2821**

Toho Co. 18 Sep **1963** [Los Angeles showing]. Sd; b&w. 35mm (Tohoscope). 124 min.

Exec Prod Sanezumi Fujimoto, Mikio Naruse, Tadahiro Teramoto. *Dir* Mikio Naruse. *Screenplay* Toshiro Ide, Sumie Tanaka. *Photog* Jun Yasumoto. *Mus* Yuji Koseki.

Cast: Hideko Takamine *(Fumiko Hayashi)*, Kinuyo Tanaka, Daisuke Kato, Akira Takarada, Mitsuko Kusabue, Noboru Nakaya, Yoko Tsukasa.

Biographical drama. Source: Fumiko Hayashi, *Horoki* (Tokyo, 1928). Fumiko Hayashi, born in 1904 as the daughter of peddlers, lives in poverty by the roadside. Her scanty education ends at age 11 when she is obliged to help her parents on a fulltime basis. Her parents' business declines, and she takes jobs as a factory worker, waitress, and barmaid. Her experiences with men are as varied as her jobs; some men treat her with kindness, others with disdain. Through all her hardships she writes an autobiographical novel which is published in 1928 and brings her instant notoriety. Her writings appear in newspapers and magazines until her death in 1951. *Authors. Peddlers. Poverty. Employment—Women. Fumiko Hayashi.*

Note: Released in Japan in 1962 as *Horoki.* A play by Kazuo Kikuta based on Hayashi's biography may also be a source for the film.

THE LONELY MAN *see* **FIVE BLOODY GRAVES**

THE LONELY STAGE *see* **I COULD GO ON SINGING**

LONESOME COWBOYS   **F6.2822**

Dist Factory Films, Film-Makers' Cooperative, Sherpix, Inc. 20 Dec **1968** [Los Angeles opening; c20 Dec 1968; LP39041]. Sd; col (Eastmancolor). 35mm. 110 min. *MPAA rating* X.

Prod-Dir-Writ Andy Warhol. *Exec Prod* Paul Morrissey. *Photog* Paul Morrissey. *Ed* Paul Morrissey.

Cast: Viva *(Ramona Alvarez)*, Tom Hompertz *(The Drifter)*, Louis Waldon *(Mickey, the eldest brother)*, Eric Emerson *(Eric)*, Taylor Mead *(The Nurse)*, Joe Dallesandro *(Little Joe)*, Francis Francine *(The Sheriff)*, Julian Burroughs *(Julian, the brother)*, Alan Midgette *(brother).*

Western comedy-drama. The total populace living in the vicinity of a deserted Arizona town consists of a transvestite sheriff, a ranch lady known as Ramona Alvarez, her male nurse, who specializes in dancing the "Lupe Velez twist," and five "lonesome" cowboys who spend the better part of their time chatting about their hairstyles, practicing ballet on a hitching post, bedding down with each other, and discussing the loneliness that makes them love themselves more than anyone else. At the moment, however, most of the cowboys' interest centers around the young blond drifter who has recently joined their ranks and seems to be the property of their leader, Mickey. One day the cowboys ride out to Ramona's ranch, pull her from her horse, yank her clothes off, and "ravage" her in the dirt. Outraged, she confronts the sheriff, but he is too busy with other matters, particularly the perfection of his drag costume. Later, when Ramona is alone with the drifter, she seduces him while reciting a litany. When their lovemaking is finished, Ramona suggests that they die together since life can hold nothing more joyous for them. But the drifter, having been propositioned by everyone, including the usually "stoned" male nurse, rejects her offer and accepts the proposal of Mickey's younger brother Eric that they ride off on horseback together and head for California. *Cowboys. Vagabonds. Nurses. Sheriffs. Male homosexuality. Jealousy. Rape. Seduction. Transvestism. Arizona.*

Note: Filmed in 16mm. Filmed on location in Tucson, Arizona. Dialogue by the cast. Andy Warhol Films is the copyright claimant.

LONESOME WOMEN (United States/Brazil)   **F6.2823**

Sinofilmes. *Dist* John Alexander Film Associates. 30 Nov **1966** [New York opening]. Sd; col (Eastman Color). 35mm. 73 min.

Prod Michel Lebedka, Konstantin Tkaczenko. *Dir-Writ* Walter Hugo Khouri. *Photog* Konstantin Tkaczenko. *Art Dir* Pierino Massenzi. *Film Ed* Walter Hugo Khouri. *Mus* Enrico Simonetti.

Cast: Herbert Souto, Andrea Anders, Luigi Picchi, Aurora Duarte, Victor Merinow, Stanley Gavri, José Mauro, Barbara Fazio, Lola Brah, Ruth de Souza, Lyris Castellani.

Adventure melodrama. An American soldier of fortune penetrates a diamond mine despotically administered by a ruthless gang. When a miner steals a gem, the man is beaten to death before the community. Although his daughter attempts to dissuade him, a stubborn second miner purloins a diamond and subsequently suffers a fatal heart attack. Interrupting the girl's rape by a gang member, the American gives rise to the supposition that he has the gem. Abetted by the local madam, the American and the girl escape. Hoping to wrest the diamond from his possession, the gang orders its lieutenant's mistress to seduce the stranger. Infuriated by her seductive performance at a nightclub, the lieutenant rapes a woman he finds swimming nude at the beach. Discovering the missing diamond, the American confides that he has come to the mine to probe the circumstances surrounding the death of his father, a prisoner at the mine. During a confrontation with the stranger, the band's chief is shot and killed, and its lieutenant stabbed to death by a barmaid he had introduced to narcotics. *Miners. Mistresses. Soldiers of fortune. Madams. Americans in foreign countries. Barmaids. Gangs. Murder. Theft. Rape. Revenge. Filial relations. Narcotics. Diamond mines.*

Note: Filmed on location in São Paulo, Brazil. Released in Brazil in 1959 as *Fronteiras do inferno.*

THE LONG ABSENCE (France/Italy)   **F6.2824**

Société Cinématographique Lyre-Procinex-Galatea. *Dist* Commercial Pictures, Robert Hakim, Raymond Hakim. 15 Nov **1962** [New York opening]. Sd; b&w. 35mm (Dyaliscope). 85 min.

Dir Henri Colpi. *Screenplay* Marguerite Duras, Gérard Jarlot. *Story* Marguerite Duras. *Photog* Marcel Weiss. *Art Dir* Maurice Colasson. *Film Ed* Jasmine Chasney, Jacqueline Méppiel. *Mus* Georges Delerue. *Based on Themes by* Gioacchino Antonio Rossini, Gaetano Donizetti. *Sd* René Breteau, Séverin Frankiel, Jean-Claude Marchetti. *Asst Dir* Jasmine Chasney, Martin Pierre Hubrecht. *Prod Mgr* Jacques Nahum.

Cast: Alida Valli *(Thérèse Langlois)*, Georges Wilson *(tramp)*, Jacques Harden *(truckdriver)*, Diana Lepvrier *(Martine)*, Catherine Fontenay *(Alice)*, Amédée *(Marcel)*, Charles Blavette *(Fernand)*, Paul Faivre *(pensioner)*, Charles Bouillaud *(Favier)*, Pierre Parel *(manager)*, Nane Germon *(Simone)*, Pierre Mirat *(druggist)*, Jean Luisi, Corrado Guarducci *(workmen)*, Georges Bielec, Michel Risbourg *(young men)*, Clément Harari *(man at juke box).*

Drama. Sixteen years after the Germans deported her husband, Thérèse Langlois notices a tramp passing her small cafe in Paris. Certain that he is her husband, Thérèse follows him to his shack by the Seine and learns he has no memory of his life before the day he awakened in a German field. Inviting him back to her cafe, she tries to reawaken his memory by talking about her husband, but to no avail. When Thérèse notices a deep scar on the back of his head, she realizes he will never remember. Undaunted, she grasps at any slight indication that he may be her husband. As he leaves the cafe, Thérèse calls out her husband's name, Albert Langlois. The stranger stands petrified and then raises his arms like a condemned man in front of a firing squad. After waiting a moment or two, he runs into the path of a bus, picks himself up, and then continues his flight. Now certain that he is her husband, Thérèse decides she has used the wrong approach; she will find the man again and help him return to his former life. *Tramps. Missing persons. War victims. Amnesia. Deportation. Cafes. World War II. Paris.*

Note: Paris opening: May 1961 as *Une aussi longue absence;* running time: 90 min; Rome opening: Jun 1961 as *L'inverno ti farà tornare;* running time: 90 min.

THE LONG AND THE SHORT AND THE TALL (Great Britain)   **F6.2825**

Michael Balcon Productions-Associated British Productions. *Dist* Continental Distributing, Inc. Dec **1961**. Sd; b&w. 35mm. 102 min.

Prod Michael Balcon. *Exec Prod* Hal Mason. *Dir* Leslie Norman. *Screenplay* Wolf Mankowitz. *Adtl Dial* Willis Hall. *Dir Photog* Erwin Hillier. *Camera Asst-Focus* Maurice Arnold. *Camera Grip* Alf Wilkins. *Art Dir* Terence Verity, Jim Morahan. *Ch Draughtsman* Ted Tester. *Film Ed* Gordon Stone. *1st Asst Ed* Christopher Clarke. *2d Asst Ed* Barry Peters. *Mus Dir* Stanley Black. *Sd* Charles Crafford, H. L. Bird, Len Shilton. *Sd Camera Op* Terry Sharrett. *Boom Op* Don Wortham. *Rec Dir* A. W. Lumkin. *1st, 2d & 3d Asst Dir* Frederic Goode, Michael Profit, Bill Cartlidge. *Prod Mgr* Terence Verity, Victor Peck. *Prod Sec* Muirne Mathieson. *Cont* June Randall. *Wardrobe Master* Ernie Farrer. *Ch Makeup* L. V. Clark. *Ch Hairdresser* Henry Montsash. *Sp Eff* George Blackwell. *Tech Adv* Jack Hetherington. *Prop Buyer* Dudley May. *Prop Master* W. Osborne. *Still Photog* Ronnie Pilgrim. *Casting Dir* Robert Lennard. *Chargehand Electrn* Wally Thompson.

Cast: Richard Todd *(Sergeant Mitchem)*, Laurence Harvey *(Private Bamforth)*, Richard Harris *(Corporal Johnstone)*, Ronald Fraser *(Lance-Corporal MacLeish)*, John Meillon *(Private Smith)*, David McCallum *(Private Whitaker)*, John Rees *(Private Evans)*, Kenji Takaki *(Tojo).*

War drama. Source: Willis Hall, *The Long and the Short and the Tall* (London opening: 7 Jan 1959). In an Asian jungle during World War II, a seven-man British patrol led by Sergeant Mitchem captures Tojo, a Japanese scout. Mitchem wants to take Tojo to headquarters for questioning, but his men (including Corporal Johnstone, second in command) want to kill him. None of the men, however, is able to commit the deed. Private Bamforth, one of the instigators, is ordered to guard the prisoner, and soon Tojo and he become friends. A rockslide blocks the patrol's only means of escape from Japanese-held territory; desperate, and enraged by evidence of Tojo's looting, the men renew their determination to kill him, and Private Whitaker finally does. The gunfire brings nearby Japanese troops upon them, and after a brief battle only Johnstone and Whitaker are left alive to be taken as prisoners. The Japanese, finding Tojo's water bottle on Whitaker, begin to threaten him, and another situation of misunderstanding develops. *Prisoners of war. Friendship. Jungles. World War II. Japan—Army. Great Britain—Army.*

Note: Opened in London in Feb 1961; running time: 105 min. Title changed to *Jungle Fighters.*

LONG CORRIDOR see **SHOCK CORRIDOR**

THE LONG DAY'S DYING (Great Britain) **F6.2826**
Junction Films. *Dist* Paramount Pictures. 28 May **1968** [New York opening; c28 May 1968; LP36432]. Sd; col (Technicolor). 35mm (Techniscope). 93 min.
Prod Harry Fine, Peter Collinson. *Exec Prod* Michael Deeley. *Dir* Peter Collinson. *Screenplay* Charles Wood. *Adapt (see note)* Michael Deeley, Peter Yates. *Dir Photog* Brian Probyn. *Camera Op* Ernest Day. *Camera/Focus* Brian Cole. *Art Dir* Disley Jones. *Asst Art Dir* Michael Knight. *Film Ed* John Trumper. *Sd Mix* Laurie Clarkson. *Sd Boom Op* Tom Otter. *Sd Camera Op* Michael Silverlock. *1st & 2d Asst Dir* Michael Dryhurst, Michael Guest. *Prod Mgr* Ed Harper. *Cont* Ann Edwards. *Prod Sec* Vickie Emery. *Wardrobe Supv* Eddie Boyce. *Makeup* Bob Lawrence. *Dir Sp Eff* Pat Moore. *Tech Adv* John Williams, (R.S.M.).
Cast: David Hemmings *(John)*, Tom Bell *(Tom)*, Tony Beckley *(Cliff)*, Alan Dobie *(Helmut)*.
War drama. Source: Alan White, *The Long Day's Dying* (London, 1965). Three young British parachutists who are cut off from their regiment await their sergeant in a partially destroyed house. Their dissimilar personalities create frequent antagonism: John is a well-educated pacifist who nevertheless takes pride in his military skills; Tom, the oldest and most experienced of the three, cautiously follows regulations; and Cliff is a sadistic military enthusiast. Setting booby traps for the enemy, the three men capture Helmut, a German officer with a passion for efficiency, and he tricks them at a draw of straws into sparing his life and taking him with them as they search for their sergeant, whom they eventually find with his throat cut. After spending a night in a farmhouse containing a team of dead Germans, the four men confront a German search party in a woods. In the ensuing battle, Cliff is killed along with the members of the German patrol. Finally arriving within sight of the British lines, the three survivors sing British songs to show that they are friendly. However, a line of tracer bullets is fired, and Tom is mortally wounded. In a mad frenzy, the pacifist John leaps on the wounded Helmut and drives a skewer into his heart. Then, staggering back onto the field, John is also killed before the British recognize him as one of their own. *Pacifists. Prisoners of war. Germans. Combat zone life. Sadism. Great Britain—Army. Germany—Army. World War II.*
Note: Filmed on location in Chertsey, Surrey. Released in Great Britain in 1968; running time: 95 min. Peter Yates claimed adaptation credit with Michael Deeley; no screen credit given.

LONG DAY'S JOURNEY INTO NIGHT **F6.2827**
Landau Productions. *Dist* Embassy Pictures. 10 Oct **1962** [New York opening; c10 Oct 1962; LP35525]. Sd; b&w. 35mm. 174 min. [See note.]
Pres by Ely Landau, Jack J. Dreyfus, Jr. *Prod* George Justin. *Exec Prod* Ely Landau. *Dir* Sidney Lumet. *Photog* Boris Kaufman. *Art Dir* Richard Sylbert. *Film Ed* Ralph Rosenblum. *Mus Comp & Cond* Andre Previn. *In Charge of Prod* George Justin. *Cost* Motley.
Cast: Katharine Hepburn *(Mary Tyrone)*, Ralph Richardson *(James Tyrone)*, Jason Robards, Jr. *(Jamie Tyrone)*, Dean Stockwell *(Edmund Tyrone)*, Jeanne Barr *(Cathleen)*.
Drama. A screen rendering of: Eugene Gladstone O'Neill, *Long Day's Journey Into Night* (New York opening: 7 Nov 1956). On a warm day in 1912, the Tyrone family gathers at their summer home in New London, Connecticut. James, the father, is an aging popular actor whose early privations have led him to devote his career to a second-rate but commercially successful play. Mary, his convent-bred, Irish Catholic wife, has just returned from a sanitarium after supposedly being cured of drug addiction. Jamie, the eldest son, has made a half-hearted attempt to follow his father's profession but now is reduced to a life of alcoholism and cynicism. The youngest son, Edmund, a 23-year-old would-be writer, comes home penniless and ill after working as a merchant seaman. In the course of the day, Mary's fear that Edmund has tuberculosis causes her again to use morphine; and when the illness is confirmed, the family's repressed anguish, pride, and insecurity surface in bitter quarreling fueled by alcohol. The day ends as the three men sit and listen in silence as Mary lapses into her own private hell. They know that tomorrow it will all begin again. *Actors. Brothers. Irish. Catholics. Drug addicts. Seamen. Pride. Marriage. Alcoholism. Family life. Tuberculosis. New London (Connecticut).*

Note: Filmed in New York City. Also 180 and 176 min and eventually cut to 136 min for some engagements. Copyright claimant: First Co.

LONG DISTANCE see **HOT MONEY GIRL**

THE LONG DUEL (Great Britain) **F6.2828**
Rank Organisation–London Independent Producers. *Dist* Paramount Pictures. 4 Oct **1967** [Los Angeles opening; c12 Sep 1967; LP35827]. Sd; col (Technicolor). 35mm (Panavision). 115 min.
Prod-Dir Ken Annakin. *Assoc Prod* Frank Sherwin Green, Aida Young. *Co-prod* Vivian A. Cox. *Exec Prod* Sydney Box. *2d Unit Dir* Bert Batt. *Screenplay* Peter Yeldham. *Adtl Material* Geoffrey Orme. *Orig Adapt for the Screen* Ernest Borneman. *Story* Ranveer Singh. *Dir Photog* Jack Hildyard. *Camera Op* Dudley Lovell. *2d Unit Camera* John Cabrera. *Art Dir* Alex Vetchinsky. *Asst Art Dir* Ted Clements, Julio Molina. *Set Decor* Arthur Taksen. *Film Ed* Bert Bates. *Mus Comp & Cond* Patrick John Scott. *Song:* "When the World Is Ready" Patrick John Scott, Don Black. *Sung by* Vince Hill. *Choreog* Scheherazade. *Sd Rec* Dudley Messenger, Ken Barker. *Dub Ed* Jim Groom, Ted Mason. *Asst Dir* Clive Reed. *Prod Mgr* Bernard Hanson, Gregorio Sacristan. *Location Mgr* Jimmy Komisarjevsky. *Cont* Joy Mercer, Josie Fulford. *Cost Dsgn* John Furness. *Wardrobe Supv* Jackie Breed, Charles Guerin. *Makeup* Trevor Crole-Rees. *Hairdresser* Jean Bear. *Sp Eff* Dick Parker. *Indian Adv* Rafiq Anwar. *Res* Mary Bruce. *Horsemaster* Ken Buckle.
Cast: Yul Brynner *(Sultan)*, Trevor Howard *(Freddy Young)*, Harry Andrews *(Superintendent Stafford)*, Andrew Keir *(Gungaram)*, Charlotte Rampling *(Jane Stafford)*, Virginia North *(Champa)*, Laurence Naismith *(McDougal)*, Maurice Denham *(governor)*, Imogen Hassall *(Tara)*, Paul Hardwick *(Jamadar)*, Antonio Padilla Ruiz *(Munnu)*, David Sumner *(Gyan Singh)*, Rafiq Anwar *(Pahelwan)*, George Pastell *(Ram Chand)*, Shivendra Sinha *(Abdul)*, Zohra Segal *(Devi)*, Norman Florence *(Nathu)*, Kurt Christian *(Babu)*, Dino Shafeek *(Akbar)*, Terry Yorke *(Moti)*, Tommy Reeves *(sentry)*, Jimmy Lodge *(guard)*, Patrick Newell *(colonel)*, Jeremy Lloyd *(Crabbe)*, Terence Alexander *(major)*, Marianne Stone *(major's wife)*, Edward Fox *(Hardwicke)*, Bakshi Prem *(high priest)*, Toni Canal *(Kamala)*, Ramón Serrano *(Bhim)*, Ben Tatar *(Sandhu)*, Aldo Sambrell *(Prem)*, Monish Bose, Naseem Khan, Shymala Devi, Shirley Sen Suptha, Jamila Massey *(dancing girls)*.
Adventure drama. In India in the 1920's, British police officer Freddy Young strongly opposes his government's harsh treatment of local Bhantas, most recently reflected in his senior colleague Stafford's interment of the Bhantas following allegations of poaching made by a local landowner. Sultan, the Bhanta chief, engineers an escape from the fort, taking with him a small band of loyal followers and his pregnant wife. When she dies in labor on the long ride back to the hills, Sultan resolves to deliver his people from their bondage. Although the British officers regard Sultan as a dangerous criminal, Young recognizes him as a fellow idealist and an enemy to respect. Young's admiration for the chief conflicts with his assignment to capture the rebel; he even spares Sultan's life during a religious festival. While Stafford's daughter Jane is moved by Young's concern for the tribe and its leader, British authorities demand the immediate capture of Sultan. Young reluctantly agrees to bait the trap by putting Bhanta women and children on a train ostensibly bound for New Delhi. When Sultan intercepts the train, the British police are waiting for him. Many men, women, and children are killed in the ensuing battle, but Sultan and a few other survivors escape. Finally Young decides to plead with Sultan to give himself up, and the two antagonists meet for the first time. Both men begrudgingly respect each other, but Sultan refuses to surrender. Returning to the fort, Young learns that Champa, a captured Indian girl, has been tortured into betraying Sultan's location. While the British assemble to destroy the leader and his followers, Young seeks out Sultan to warn him. But he is too late: the chieftain is already mortally wounded. At their final meeting, Young agrees to raise the dying Sultan's young son as his own. *Police. Bhanta. Guerrillas. Uprisings. Colonial administration. Childbirth. Torture. Trains. India.*
Note: Location scenes filmed in Spain. Released in Great Britain in Aug 1967.

LONG JOHN SILVER see **LONG JOHN SILVER RETURNS TO TREASURE ISLAND**

LONG JOHN SILVER RETURNS TO TREASURE ISLAND (Reissue) (Australia) **F6.2829**
Treasure Island Pictures. *Dist* Childhood Productions. 6 Jan **1968** [New York opening]. Sd; col (Eastman Color). 35mm (CinemaScope). 100 min.
Note: Originally released in Feb 1955 as *Long John Silver* by Distributors Corporation of America; c21 Dec 1954; LP4657.

A LONG RIDE FROM HELL (Italy) **F6.2830**
B. R. C. Cinematografica. *Dist* Cinerama Releasing Corp. 25 Feb **1970** [New York opening]. Sd; col (Eastman Color). 35mm. 94 min. [Also reviewed at 104 min.] *MPAA rating* R.

Dir Alex Burks. *Screenplay* Roberto Natale, Steve Reeves. *Photog* Enzo Barboni. *Camera* Gaetano Valle. *Asst Camera* Fernando Gallardt, Giuseppe Buonaurio. *Set Dsgn* Gastone Carsetti. *Film Ed* Roberto Perpignani. *Mus & Theme Song*: "Go West Young Man" Carlo Savina. *Sd Engr* Dino Bronzetti. *Asst Dir* Francesco Barilli. *Prod Mgr* Paolo Frasca. *Prod Sec* Romano Raschi, Sergio Galliano. *Prod Asst* Carlo Giavagnorio. *Cost* Franco Antonelli. *Makeup* Marcello Ceccarelli. *Stunt Dir* Remo De Angelis.

Cast: Steve Reeves (*Mike Sturges*), Wayde Preston (*Mayner*), Dick Palmer (*Freeman*), Silvana Venturelli (*Ruth*), Lee Burton (*sheriff*), Ted Carter (*Shorty*), Rosalba Neri (*prostitute*), Franco Fantasia (*Roy*), Mario Maranzana (*Bobcat*), Enzo Fiermonte, Silvana Bacci, Spartaco Conversi, Ivan Scratuglia, Franco Balducci, Emma Baron, Bruno Corazzari, Sergio De Vecchi.

Western melodrama. Source: Gordon Shirreffs, *Judas Gun* (New York, 1964). When Mike Sturges and his younger brother Roy learn that their herd of prized horses has been stolen, they trail the rustlers to an old railroad station, but that night they are attacked by the thieves led by Mayner. The next morning Roy and Mike are arrested for the train robbery of a gold shipment actually committed by Mayner and his gang. Mike and Roy are imprisoned, and Roy dies as a result of prison brutality. Mike escapes, hoping to avenge himself against the thieves and clear his name. He goes to Yuma City and is befriended by a prostitute. Though prison guards and Mexican bounty hunters pursue him, Mike finds the stolen gold and waits there for Mayner. Mike singlehandedly kills the entire band in a violent battle, delivers the gold to the authorities, and is absolved of any wrongdoing. *Brothers. Rustlers. Gangs. Prison guards. Mexicans. Bounty hunters. Prostitutes. Train robberies. Frameup. Manslaughter. Revenge. Prison escapes. Gold. Horses.*

Note: Released in Italy in 1968 as *Vivo per la tua morte.* Alex Burks is a pseudonym for Camillo Bazzoni, Dick Palmer for Mimmo Palmara, Lee Burton for Guido Lollabrigida.

THE LONG RIDE HOME see A TIME FOR KILLING

THE LONG ROPE   F6.2831
Associated Producers, Inc. *Dist* Twentieth Century-Fox Film Corp. Feb **1961** [c3 Feb 1961; LP18688]. Sd; b&w. 35mm (CinemaScope). 61 min.

Prod Margia Dean. *Dir* William Witney. *Writ* Robert Hamner. *Photog* Kay Norton. *Art Dir* John Mansbridge. *Supv Film Ed* Peter Johnson. *Mus* (see note) Paul Sawtell, Bert Shefter, Frankie Ortega. *Sd* Vic Appel. *Asst Dir* Ira Stewart. *Prod Supv* Harold E. Knox. *Script Supv* Billy Vernon. *Cost* Paula Giokaris. *Makeup* Ernie Park. *Prop Master* Monroe Liebgold. *Tech Dir* Terrys L. Olender.

Cast: Hugh Marlowe (*Jonas Stone*), Alan Hale, [Jr.] (*Sheriff John Millard*), Robert J. Wilke (*Ben Matthews*), Lisa Montell (*Alicia Álvarez*), Chris Robinson (*Reb Gilroy*), Jeffrey Morris (*Will Matthews*), David Renard (*Louis Ortega*), Madeleine Holmes (*Señora Dona Vega*), John Alonzo (*Manuel Álvarez*), Jack Powers (*Luke Simms*), Kathryn Hart (*Mrs. Creech*), Jack Carlin, Scott Randall (*henchmen*), Stephen Welles (*Jim Matthews*), Linda Cordova (*Mexican waitress*), Alex Cordellis.

Western melodrama. Federal court judge Jonas Stone arrives in the frontier town of Tularosa to try Manuel Álvarez, a young Mexican storekeeper accused of murdering the brother of Ben Matthews, the local land baron. The rancher has so dominated the weak-willed sheriff that Stone is left to investigate the case on his own. Despite Ben Matthews' attempts to prevent a fair trial, and the eagerness of another brother, Will, to lynch Álvarez, Stone interrogates the "witnesses" until he finally forces a confession from the defendant's mother-in-law, Señora Dona Vega. The deranged woman had hoped to see Álvarez convicted and lynched, thereby leaving her daughter, Alicia, free to marry Matthews and regain the lands he had taken from the Vega family. Following the trial, Matthews storms from the courthouse and challenges the judge to a gun-battle. The sheriff, who has regained his courage, tries to intervene, and Matthews kills him. Aided by a young gunslinger, Reb Gilroy, Stone tricks Matthews and then arrests him for the sheriff's murder. With law and order restored, the judge leaves Tularosa to continue his circuit. *Judges. Land barons. Ranchers. Sheriffs. Brothers. Mothers-in-law. Mexicans. Storekeepers. Lynching. Murder. Law and order. Land rights. Trials. Confession (law). Tularosa (New Mexico). United States Circuit Courts.*

Note: Music credit for Frankie Ortega is unconfirmed.

THE LONG SHIPS (Great Britain/Yugoslavia)   F6.2832
Warwick Film Productions-Avala Film. *Dist* Columbia Pictures. 24 Jun **1964** [New York opening; c31 Dec 1963; LP28211]. Sd (Westrex); col (Technicolor). 35mm (Technirama 70, see note). 125 min.

Prod Irving Allen. *Assoc Prod* Denis O'Dell. *Dir* Jack Cardiff. *2d Unit Dir* Cliff Lyons. *Action Seq* Bob Simmons. *Screenplay* Berkely Mather, Beverley Cross. *Dir Photog* Christopher Challis. *2d Unit Camera* Skeets Kelly. *Camera Op* Austin Dempster, Ray Parslow. *Art Dir* Zoran Zorčić, William Constable, Vlastimir Gavrik, John Hoesli. *Prologue and Main Titl* Maurice Binder. *Film Ed* Geoffrey Foot. *Mus Comp* Dušan Radić. *Cond* Borislav Pascan. *Sd Rec* Paddy Cunningham, Hugh Strain. *Sd Ed* Gordon Daniel. *Asst Dir* Bluey Hill, Stevo Petrović. *Asst to the Prod* Paul Maslansky. *Prod Mgr* David Orton, Milenko Stanković. *Cont* Angela Allen, Eileen Head. *Cost Dsgn* Anthony Mendleson, David Ffolkes. *Wardrobe Master* Ron Beck. *Makeup Artist* Neville Smallwood. *Hairdresser* A. G. Scott. *Sp Eff* Syd Pearson, Bill Warrington. *Matte Artist* Ivor Beddoes. *Tech Adv* Erik Kiersgaard. *Mosaics* A. Benzon.

Cast: Richard Widmark (*Rolfe*), Sidney Poitier (*El Mansuh*), Rosanna Schiaffino (*Aminah*), Russ Tamblyn (*Orm*), Oscar Homolka (*Krok*), Lionel Jeffries (*Aziz*), Edward Judd (*Sven*), Beba Lončar (*Gerda*), Clifford Evans (*King Harald*), Colin Blakely (*Rhykka*), Gordon Jackson (*Vahlin*), David Lodge (*Olla*), Paul Stassino (*Raschid*), Jeanne Moody (*Ylva*), Henry Oscar (*auctioneer*).

Adventure melodrama. Source: Frans Bengtsson, *Röde Orm* (Stockholm, 1941). Rolfe, adventurer son of Krok, a Viking thane and shipbuilder, learns of the whereabouts of the long-lost Golden Bell of St. James, fashioned from gold looted by the Crusaders in Byzantium. With his younger brother, Orm, Rolfe steals a new longship built by their father for King Harald and takes as hostage the King's daughter, Princess Gerda, whom Orm loves. They set out to find the Golden Bell as the King sails in pursuit; but their ship is wrecked in a whirlpool near the hiding place of the treasure, and Rolfe and his men are captured and imprisoned by the Moorish Sheikh El Mansuh, who is also seeking the Golden Bell. Gerda is taken to El Mansuh's harem, but the Vikings escape and raid the harem before being recaptured. El Mansuh orders Rolfe's death in retaliation, but Aminah, his chief wife, persuades him that the only way to get the Golden Bell is for Rolfe and his men to take the Moors past the whirlpool in their repaired ship. Rolfe agrees, but while they are engaged in recovering the treasure, King Harald captures El Mansuh's stronghold, and in subsequent fighting both Aminah and El Mansuh die. Orm and Gerda are reunited, and King Harald, delighted to have the Golden Bell, pardons Rolfe, who sets out to interest the ruler in recovering the long-lost Three Crowns of the Saxon Kings. *Vikings. Adventurers. Brothers. Royalty. Moors. Sheiks. Filial relations. Theft. Abduction. Gold. Ships. Whirlpools. Treasure. Harems. Shipwrecks.*

Note: Filmed along the coast of Yugoslavia in Technirama 70. Released in Great Britain and Yugoslavia in 1964. Yugoslav title: *Dugi brodovi.*

LONG WAY TO OKINAWA (Japan)   F6.2833
Toho Co. Apr **1963** [Los Angeles showing]. Sd; col? 35mm. [Feature film, length unknown.]

Cast: Akira Takarada, Yuriko Hoshi, Nobuko Otowa, Keiko Awaji, Takashi Shimura. No information about the nature of this film has been found. *Okinawa.*

Note: Original title and release undetermined.

THE LONGEST DAY   F6.2834
Darryl F. Zanuck Productions. *Dist* Twentieth Century-Fox Film Corp. 4 Oct **1962** [New York opening; c4 Oct 1962; LP23378]. Sd (Westrex); b&w. 35mm (CinemaScope). 180 min.

A Darryl F. Zanuck Production. *Prod* Darryl F. Zanuck. *Assoc Prod & Coörd of Battle Episodes* Elmo Williams. *Dir American Exteriors* Andrew Marton. *Dir British Exteriors* Ken Annakin. *Dir German Episodes* Bernhard Wicki. *Dir Ste. Mere-Eglise Episodes* Gerd Oswald. *Screenplay* Cornelius Ryan. *Adtl Episodes* Romain Gary, James Jones, David Pursall, Jack Seddon. *Photog* Jean Bourgoin, Walter Wottitz, Henri Persin. *Helicopter Shots* Guy Tabary. *Art Dir* Ted Haworth, Léon Barsacq, Vincent Korda. *Set Decor* Gabriel Bechir. *Film Ed* Samuel E. Beetley. *Mus Comp & Cond* Maurice Jarre. *Theme Song* Paul Anka. *Mus Arr* Mitch Miller. *Sd* Jo de Bretagne, Jacques Maumont, William Sivel. *Asst Dir* Bernard Farrel, Tom Pevsner, Louis Pitzelé, Gerard Renateau, Henri Sokal. *Asst to the Prod* Richard D. Zanuck. *Optical Eff* Jean Fouchet. *Sp Eff* Karl Helmer, Karl Baumgartner, Augie Lohman, Robert MacDonald, Alex Weldon. *Military Cons* Gunther Blumentritt, (Gen.), James M. Gavin, (Lieut. Gen.), John Howard, (Maj.), Philippe Kieffer, (Cap. de Frégate), Pierre Koenig, (Gen. d'Armée), Helmuth Lang, (Capt.), Earl of Lovat, Frederick Morgan, (Gen.), Max Pemsel, (Lieut. Gen.), Werner Pluskat, (Maj.), Josef Priller, (Col.), Lucie Maria Rommel, Friedrich Ruge, (V. Adm.). *Tech Adv* Jean Barral, (Comdt.), Roger Bligh, (Lieut. Col.), Willard L. Bushy, (Comdr.), Hubert Deschard, (Comdt.), A. J. Hillebrand, (Lieut. Col.), James R. Johnson, (Col.), Fernand Prévost, (Cap.), E. C. Peake, (Lieut. Comdr.), Albert Saby, (Col.), Joseph B. Seay, (Col.), John Crewdson, (Capt.).

Cast—The Americans: John Wayne (*Colonel Vandervoort*), Robert Mitchum (*General Cota*), Henry Fonda (*General Roosevelt*), Robert Ryan (*General Gavin*), Rod Steiger (*commander*), Robert Wagner (*ranger*), Richard Beymer (*Schultz*), Mel Ferrer (*General Haines*), Jeffrey Hunter (*Sergeant Fuller*), Paul Anka (*ranger*), Sal Mineo (*Private Martini*), Roddy McDowall (*Private Morris*), Stuart Whitman (*Lieutenant Sheen*), Eddie Albert (*Colonel Newton*), Edmond O'Brien (*General Barton*), Fabian (*ranger*), Red Buttons (*Private Steele*), Tom Tryon (*Lieutenant Wilson*), Alexander Knox (*Gen.*

Bedell Smith), Tommy Sands (ranger), Ray Danton (Captain Frank), Henry Grace, actor (General Eisenhower), Mark Damon (Private Harris), Dewey Martin (Private Wilder, see note), Steve Forrest (Captain Harding), John Crawford (Colonel Caffey), Ron Randell (Williams), Nicholas Stuart (General Bradley), John Mellon (Rear Admiral Kirk), Fred Dürr (major of the Rangers).

Cast—The British: Richard Burton (RAF pilot), Kenneth More (Captain Maud), Peter Lawford (Lord Lovat), Richard Todd (Major Howard), Leo Genn (General Parker), John Gregson (padre), Sean Connery (Private Flanagan), Jack Hedley (briefing man), Michael Medwin (Private Watney), Norman Rossington (Private Clough), John Robinson (Admiral Ramsay), Patrick Barr (Captain Stagg), Donald Houston (RAF pilot), Trevor Reid (General Montgomery), Leslie Phillips (RAF officer), Richard Wattis, Christopher Lee.

Cast—The French: Irina Demick (Janine), Bourvil (mayor), Jean-Louis Barrault (Father Roulland), Christian Marquand (Kieffer), Arletty (Madame Barrault), Madeleine Renaud (mother superior), Georges Rivière (Sergeant Montlaur), Georges Wilson (Renaud), Jean Servais (Admiral Jaujard), Fernand Ledoux (Louis), Daniel Gélin, Françoise Rosay.

Cast—The Germans: Curt Jurgens (General Blumentritt), Werner Hinz (Marshal Rommel), Paul Hartmann (Marshal Rundstedt), Peter Van Eyck (Lieutenant Colonel Ocker), Gert Fröbe (Sergeant Kaffeeklatsch), Hans Christian Blech (Major Pluskat), Wolfgang Preiss (General Pemsel), Heinz Reincke (Colonel Priller), Richard Munch (General Marcks), Ernst Schröder (General Salmuth), Kurt Meisel (During), Wolfgang Lukschy (Gen. Alfred Jodl), Eugene Deckers.

Historical war drama. Source: Cornelius Ryan, The Longest Day: June 6, 1944 (New York, 1959). In 1944, Gen. Dwight D. Eisenhower makes the momentous decision that the combined Allied invasion of Europe will take place on the 6th of June. The decision proves to be strategically wise: the German High Command, assuming the invasion will not take place during the current inclement weather, is caught unawares; Panzer divisions are awaiting the attack at Dover, the Luftwaffe is scattered, and Hitler himself has taken a sleeping pill and left orders that he is not to be disturbed. Allied sources alert the French Resistance, who cut telegraph wires and blow up ammunition trains. Dummy parachute figures are dropped to confuse the Germans. Airborne glider infantry are landed near the key site of the Orne River Bridge. Then, at dawn, the full Allied might is unleashed as 150,000 troops, backed up by 5,000 transport and fighter vessels, storm the three major Normandy beachheads of Juno, Omaha, and Utah. Although a division of paratroopers is slaughtered when they overshoot their mark, French commandos capture the seaside town of Oistreham and American Rangers successfully scale the supposedly-impregnable cliffs of Point-du-Hoc. It is at Omaha Beach that the assault falters; held back by a seemingly impregnable cement wall, the troops are unable to advance. But Brigadier General Cota rallies his men, urges Sergeant Fuller to place a dynamite charge, and blasts a clear path from the beach. With the coming of nightfall, the Allies are firmly entrenched on European soil. Military invasion. Resistance (political). World War II. Operation Overlord. England. France. Normandy. Benjamin Vandervoort. Norman D. Cota. Theodore Roosevelt, Jr. James M. Gavin. Raymond A. Barton. John M. Steele. Dwight David Eisenhower. Walter Bedell Smith. Eugene Caffey. William Williams. Omar Nelson Bradley. Colin Maud. Earl of Lovat. John Howard. Bertram Ramsay. J. N. Stagg. Bernard Law Montgomery. Robert Jaujard. Gunther Blumentritt. Erwin Rommel. Karl Rudolf Gerd von Rundstedt. Lieutenant Colonel Ocker. Werner Pluskat. Max Pemsel. Josef Priller. Erich Marcks. Hans von Salmuth.

Note: Darryl F. Zanuck claims to have directed the American and British interiors. Dewey Martin's role was cut from the final release print.

THE LONGEST SPUR see HOT SPUR

LONGING FOR LOVE (Japan)   F6.2835
Nikkatsu Corp. 7 Oct 1966 [Los Angeles showing]. Sd; b&w (see note). 35mm (Nikkatsu Scope). 105 min.

Prod Kanou Otsuka. *Dir* Koreyoshi Kurahara. *Screenplay* Shigeya Fujita, Koreyoshi Kurahara. *Photog* Yoshio Mimiya. *Mus* Toshiro Mayuzumi.

Cast: Ruriko Asaoka (Etsuko), Nobuo Nakamura (father-in-law), Tetsuo Ishitachi (gardener), Akira Yamanouchi (second son), Chitose Kurenai (servant girl), Yuko Kusunoki, Yoko Ozono.

Melodrama. Source: Yukio Mishima, Ai no kawaki (Tokyo, 1950). Etsuko, a young widow, lives on her husband's family estate. Her father-in-law, a widower supporting his shiftless second son and his wife, continually forces his intentions on Etsuko, who puts up little resistance. Feeling lonely and trapped, she is drawn toward one of the servants, a young gardener, and her infatuation deepens until it becomes apparent to everyone but the gardener himself. When Etsuko learns that the young man has gotten a servant pregnant, she forces the mother to get rid of the child. No longer completely rational, Etsuko orders the gardener to meet her in the greenhouse, where, to shock him, she tells him of his child's death. The jealous father-in-law appears with a gun, and when the

gardener expresses relief over the outcome of the pregnancy, it is Etsuko who shoots him. Etsuko and her father-in-law secretly bury the body, and she leaves the estate, uncertain of her future. Fathers-in-law. Widows. Gardeners. Domestics. Pregnancy. Infanticide. Jealousy. Murder. Employer-employee relations.

Note: Released in Japan in Mar 1967 as Ai no kawaki. Koreyoshi Kurahara is also known as Izen Kurahara. Footage includes color frames.

LONNIE   F6.2836
Dolphin Productions. *Dist* Futuramic Releasing Organization. Dec 1963. Sd; b&w. 35mm. 76 min.

Prod Herbert Skable. *Dir* William Hale. *Screenplay* William Copeland. *Photog* Haskell Wexler. *Film Ed* Melvin Sloan. *Mus* Bob Cooper. *Titl Song Sung by* Johnny Chase.

Cast: Scott Marlowe (Lonnie), Frank Silvera (Paco), Turina Hayes (Ria), Wilton Graff (Mitchell), Michael Constantine (Gage), Joan Anderson (Lois), Arthur Storch.

Melodrama. In need of money, Lonnie rents his Cadillac to Paco, a Spanish revolutionary, and Mitchell, a jewelry store salesman, who use the car in a diamond robbery. After the heist, Lonnie discovers that Lois, his childhood sweetheart, is prostituting herself for Paco's cause. Forced to help Paco make his escape by boat, Lonnie falls in love with Ria, the motorboat owner's daughter. Chased by the gangsters, the couple hides in a vacant mansion, while Paco commits another robbery. Lonnie pretends to join Mitchell in double-crossing Paco. In a struggle with the Spaniard, Lonnie is wounded. All three men flee by car. During a scuffle, Mitchell falls to his death from the automobile. Lonnie and Paco escape through the swamp, return to town, and, disguised as musicians, elude the police. Thinking Lonnie has been killed by the gangsters, Ria shoots and kills Paco when he approaches her father's boat. Lonnie rushes aboard and the couple puts out to sea. Spanish. Revolutionaries. Gangsters. Salesmen. Prostitutes. Finance—Personal. Robbery. Perfidy. Disguise. Manslaughter. Diamonds. Motorboats. Cadillac automobiles. Swamps. Chases.

Note: Filmed in Georgia.

LOOK BEFORE YOU LAUGH see MAKE MINE A MILLION

LOOK IN ANY WINDOW   F6.2837
New Films Co. *Dist* Allied Artists. Jan 1961 [New York opening: 21 Mar; c16 Jan 1961; LP18008]. Sd; b&w. 35mm. 87 min.

Prod William Alland, Laurence E. Mascott. *Assoc Prod* Dan Gachman. *Dir* William Alland. *Writ* Laurence E. Mascott. *Camera* W. Wallace Kelley. *Art Dir* Hilyard Brown. *Film Ed* Harold Gordon. *Mus* Richard Shores. *Song:* "Look In Any Window" writ & sung by Paul Anka. *Sd Ed* Charles Schelling. *Mus Ed* Lee Osborne. *Asst Dir* Charles Bohart. *In Charge of Prod* Norman Herman. *Script Supv* Pat Miller. *Wardrobe* Byron Munson. *Swim Suits* Rose Marie Reed. *Makeup* Maurice Seiderman. *Hairdresser* Gale McGarry.

Cast: Paul Anka (Craig Fowler), Ruth Roman (Jackie Fowler), Alex Nicol (Jay Fowler), Gigi Perreau (Eileen Lowell), Carole Mathews (Betty Lowell), George Dolenz (Carlo), Jack Cassidy (Gareth Lowell), Robert Sampson (Lindstrom), Dan Grayam (Webber), Jacqueline Kruger, Norman Winston.

Melodrama. Feeling unwanted and unloved by his flirtatious mother and his weak, alcoholic father, shy teenager Craig Fowler becomes a masked prowler, finding vicarious pleasure in spying upon the private activities of neighbors in a modern suburban area. Though he is caught in the act of spying upon his next-door neighbors, the unhappily married Lowells, his identity remains unknown, and the police begin to take an active interest in the case. Following a quarrel, Craig's mother, Jackie, storms out of the house and goes off with the promiscuous Gareth Lowell. Craig then begins drinking, visits the Lowell daughter, Eileen, and attempts to seduce her. In resisting, she trips and falls through a glass-topped table, and is knocked unconscious. Panic-stricken, Craig flees from the scene. Later, at a pool party, Jay Fowler catches his wife making love to Gareth, and the resulting fight ends abruptly when the masked prowler is spotted on a patio roof. Craig attempts to get away, but he is caught by a plainclothesman. The incident has a sobering effect upon his parents, who resolve to provide a healthier home life for their son. Detectives. Neighbors. Voyeurism. Alcoholism. Adolescence. Timidity. Suburban life. Parenthood. Infidelity. Family life. Seduction.

LOOKING FOR LOVE   F6.2838
Euterpe, Inc.–Franmet Productions. *Dist* Metro-Goldwyn-Mayer, Inc. 5 Aug 1964 [Boston opening; c20 Feb 1964; LP27977]. Sd (Westrex); col (Metrocolor). 35mm (Panavision). 83 min.

Prod Joe Pasternak. *Dir* Don Weis. *Screenplay* Ruth Brooks Flippen. *Dir Photog* Milton Krasner. *Camera Op* Alfred Lebowitz. *Camera Asst* Paul Koons. *Art Dir* George W. Davis, Urie McCleary. *Set Decor* Henry Grace, Charles S. Thompson. *Film Ed* Adrienne Fazan. *Asst Ed* Rita Roland. *Mus* George Stoll. *Mus Adapt* Robert Van Eps. *Songs:* "Let's Have a Party," "When the Clock

Strikes Midnight," "Looking for Love" Hank Hunter, Stan Vincent. *Song: "Whoever You Are, I Love You"* Peter Udell, Gary Geld. *Song: "This Is My Happiest Moment"* Ted Murry, Benny Davis. *Song: "Be My Love"* Sammy Cahn, Nicholas Brodszky. *Songs Sung by* Connie Francis. *Song: "I Can't Believe That You're in Love With Me"* Jimmy McHugh, Clarence Gaskill. *Sung by* Connie Francis, Danny Thomas. *Choreog* Robert Sidney. *Rec Supv* Franklin Milton. *Sd* Conrad Kahn. *Asst Dir* William McGarry, Dale Coleman. *Unit Mgr* Eric Stacey. *Script Supv* Cleo Anton. *Cost Dsgn* Don Loper. *Wardrobe* Lambert Marks, Florence Hackett, William T. Zacha. *Makeup* William Tuttle. *Hairstyles* Sydney Guilaroff. *Sp Eff* Glen Galvin. *Still Photog* Frank Shugrue.

Cast: Connie Francis *(Libby Caruso)*, Jim Hutton *(Paul Davis)*, Susan Oliver *(Jan McNair)*, Joby Baker *(Cuz Rickover)*, Barbara Nichols *(Gaye Swinger)*, Jay C. Flippen *(Mr. Ralph Front)*, Jesse White *(Tiger Shay)*, Charles Lane *(director)*, Joan Marshall *(Miss Devine)*, Johnny Carson, George Hamilton, Yvette Mimieux, Paula Prentiss, Danny Thomas *(themselves)*, Mimi Dillard.

Comedy with music. Disappointed by her failure to break into the entertainment world, young Libby Caruso decides to look for someone to promote her invention, a clothing valet that keeps everyday clothes unwrinkled. She soon falls in love with sales-promoter Paul Davis, who arranges for her to plug the invention on Johnny Carson's television show. Libby's appearance fails to stimulate any interest in her invention, but it does start her on a singing career leading to movie stardom. Libby's growing doubtfulness about her feeling for Paul prompts her roommate, Jan, to suggest that she really loves Cuz, an old friend; Libby pursues the suggestion to success, while Paul, confused but willing, turns to Jan. *Singers. Businesswomen. Inventors. Actors. Roommates. Television. Courtship. Friendship. Johnny Carson.*

THE LOOKING GLASS WAR (Great Britain)   **F6.2839**
Frankovich Productions. *Dist* Columbia Pictures. 4 Feb **1970** [New York opening; c1 Feb 1970; LP37632]. Sd (Westrex); col (Technicolor). 35mm (Panavision). 108 min. *MPAA rating* M.
Prod John Box. *Assoc Prod* William Kirby. *Exec Prod* M. J. Frankovich. *Dir-Writ* Frank R. Pierson. *Dir Photog* Austin Dempster. *Camera Op* Paul Wilson. *Art Dir* Terence Marsh. *Asst Art Dir* Roy Walker. *Set Dresser* Henry Federer. *Film Ed* Willy Kemplen. *Asst Ed* Ray Thorne. *Mus Comp & Arr & Song: "Fly Away, Love"* Wally Stott. *Sd Rec* A. G. Ambler, John Cox. *Sd Ed* James Groom. *Asst Dir* David Tringham. *Prod Mgr* Peter Bolton. *Cont* Phyllis Crocker. *Cost Dsgn* Dinah Greet. *Wardrobe Supv* Laurel Staffell. *Makeup* Ernest Gasser. *Hairdresser* Polly Young. *Casting* Robert Lennard. *Constr Mgr* Gus Walker. *Ch Set Electrn* Maurice Gillett.

Cast: Christopher Jones *(Leiser)*, Pia Degermark *(The Girl)*, Ralph Richardson *(Leclerc)*, Anthony Hopkins *(John Avery)*, Paul Rogers *(Haldane)*, Susan George *(Susan)*, Ray McAnally *(Starr)*, Robert Urquhart *(Johnson)*, Maxine Audley *(Babs Leclerc)*, Anna Massey *(Sarah)*, Frederick Jaeger *(Captain Lansen)*, Paul Maxwell *(C.I.A. man)*, Timothy West *(Taylor)*, Vivian Pickles *(Carol)*, Peter Swanwick *(Peerson)*, Cyril Shaps *(East German detective)*, Michael Robbins *(truckdriver)*, Guy Deghy *(Fritsche)*, David Scheuer *(Russian officer)*, John Franklin *(Pine)*, Linda Hedger *(Taylor's child)*, Nicholas Stewart *(German boy)*, Ernst Walder *(radio engineer)*, Patrick Wright *(Vopo)*, Sylva Langova *(East German woman)*, Alan McClelland *(doctor)*, Angela Down *(Chelsea girl)*, Robert Wilde *(English policeman)*, Russell Lewis *(Avery's child)*.

Drama. Source: John Le Carré, *The Looking Glass War* (London, 1965). Lansen, a German airline pilot employed by the British secret service, obtains aerial photographs of Russian missile sites. In Finland, he passes the film to his British contact who is then murdered by counter-espionage agents, and the film canister falls unnoticed to the ground. Leclerc, the head of British Intelligence, recruits and hastily trains Leiser, a young Polish refugee, to enter East Germany and verify the missile sites. Dropped near the East German border, Leiser is forced to kill a guard who stops him. Unnerved by the killing, he becomes careless and remains on the radio transmitter too long, allowing the East Germans to trace his location. Close to being caught, he is picked up by a truckdriver who threatens to turn him in unless he submits to his homosexual desires; Leiser instead murders the driver and uses the vehicle to escape. He picks up a woman hitchhiker and her small son, and at a roadblock, they become embroiled in a fight with the guards but are eventually released. Arriving at a small town, Leiser rents a room and again attempts to transmit a radio message, but the Germans trace the signal, locate Leiser, and kill both him and the woman, whom they believe to be his accomplice. At the conclusion, Finn school children are seen playing with the film, destroying the results of a complicated espionage maneuver. *Air pilots. Germans. Spies. Poles. Refugees. Truckdrivers. Hitchhikers. Espionage. Murder. Cold war. Male homosexuality. Photographs. Missile sites. Radio. Finland. German Democratic Republic. Great Britain—Intelligence service.*

Note: Opened in London in Jan 1970.

LOOSE PLEASURES *see* **TIGHT SKIRTS, LOOSE PLEASURES**

LORD FARTHINGAY HOLIDAY   **F6.2840**
Dist Jo-Jo Distributors. ca **1970**. Sd; col. 16mm. 61-81 min.
Sex film. No information about the precise nature of this film has been found. *Sexuality.*

LORD JIM (United States/Great Britain)   **F6.2841**
Columbia Pictures–Keep Films. *Dist* Columbia Pictures. 25 Feb **1965** [New York opening; c1 Jul 1965; LP31136]. Sd (Westrex); col (Technicolor). 35mm & 70mm (Super Panavision). 154 min. [Copyright length: 143 min.]
A Richard Brooks Production. *Prod-Dir-Writ* Richard Brooks. *Story Ed* Arthur Knight. *Dir Photog* Freddie Young. *Camera Op* Ernest Day. *Art Dir* Bill Hutchinson, Ernest Archer. *Prod Dsgn* Geoffrey Drake. *Film Ed* Alan Osbiston. *Mus Comp* Bronislau Kaper. *Mus Cond* Muir Mathieson. *Sd Rec* Paddy Cunningham, Bob Jones. *Sd Ed* Chris Greenham. *Mus Ed* Peter Zinner. *1st & 2d Asst Dir* Roy Stevens, Michael Stevenson. *Prod Mgr* Rene Dupont. *Cont* Angela Martelli. *Wardrobe Supv* John Wilson-Apperson. *Cost Dsgn* Phyllis Dalton. *Makeup* Charles Parker. *Hairdresser* Gordon Bond. *Sp Eff* Cliff Richardson, Wally Veevers. *Adv in Oriental Mus* Mantle Hood. *Prop Master* Eddie Fowlie.

Cast: Peter O'Toole *(Lord Jim)*, James Mason *(Gentleman Brown)*, Curt Jurgens *(Cornelius)*, Eli Wallach *("The General")*, Jack Hawkins *(Marlow)*, Paul Lukas *(Stein)*, Daliah Lavi *(girl)*, Akim Tamiroff *(Schomberg)*, Ichizo Itami *(Waris)*, Tatsuo Saito *(Du-Ramin)*, Andrew Keir *(Brierly)*, Jack MacGowran *(Robinson)*, Eric Young *(Malay)*, Noel Purcell *(Captain Chester)*, Walter Gotell *(Captain of Patna)*, Rafiq Anwar *(Moslem leader)*, Marne Maitland *(elder)*, Newton Blick *(doctor)*, A. J. Brown *(magistrate)*, Christian Marquand *(French officer)*.

Drama. Source: Joseph Conrad, *Lord Jim* (London, 1900). Jim, a young British merchant seaman who has just completed his apprenticeship to become a first officer, is recuperating from a broken leg at a port in the Orient. He signs aboard the dilapidated *Patna*, but in a storm he abandons ship, leaving the passengers to drown. *Patna* survives the storm, however, and Jim is dismissed from service after an inquiry. He seeks anonymity and personal redemption in the Orient, moving to a new location each time he is recognized. When Jim extinguishes a fire on a cargo boat, the owner, Stein, becomes interested in him and sends him on an arms-delivering mission to the village of Patusan, whose natives are enslaved by a warlord whom they call "The General." Jim manages to hide the arms before being captured and tortured by the warlord. A native girl helps him escape, and he organizes a revolt, thus becoming a hero to the natives. Cornelius, The General's partner, and Schomberg, a saloon keeper, enlist the help of Gentleman Brown, a pirate. Jim and Brown meet, and Jim offers the pirate a chance to retreat; but Brown is intent on stealing the Patusan treasure. During the ensuing fight, Jim defeats his enemies, but his friend Waris, son of the native chief, is killed; Jim then sacrifices his own life to appease the chief. *Sea captains. Tribal chiefs. Warlords. Shipowners. Saloon keepers. Pirates. Conscience. Cowardice. Torture. Revolts. Self-sacrifice. Treasure. Merchant ships. Far East. Merchant marine. Shipwrecks. Storms. Fires.*

Note: Filmed in Hong Kong and Cambodia. Opened in London in Feb 1965.

LORD LOVE A DUCK   **F6.2842**
Charleston Enterprises. *Dist* United Artists. 26 Jan **1966** [Los Angeles opening; c26 Jan 1966; LP32599]. Sd; b&w. 35mm. 109 min. [Copyright length: 105 min.]
Prod-Dir George Axelrod. *Prod Exec* Jack Fier. *Screenplay* Larry H. Johnson, George Axelrod. *Photog* Daniel L. Fapp. *Art Dir* Malcolm Brown. *Set Decor* Raphael Bretton. *Main Titl* Murray Naidich. *Film Ed* William A. Lyon. *Mus* Neal Hefti. *Titl Song* Neal Hefti, Ernie Sheldon. *Sung by* The Wild Ones. *Sd* Al Overton, Lodge Cunningham. *Asst Dir* Herman Webber. *Miss Weld's Wardrobe* Jax. *Cost* Paula Giokaris. *Men's Wardrobe* Gene Martin. *Makeup* Lou Hippe. *Hairstyles* Maryce Bates. *Sp Eff* Herman Townsley.

Cast: Roddy McDowall *(Alan "Mollymauk" Musgrave)*, Tuesday Weld *(Barbara Ann Greene)*, Lola Albright *(Marie Greene)*, Martin West *(Bob Barnard)*, Ruth Gordon *(Stella Barnard)*, Harvey Korman *(Weldon Emmett)*, Sarah Marshall *(Miss Schwartz)*, Lynn Carey *(Sally Grace)*, Max Showalter *(Howard Greene)*, Donald Murphy *(Phil Neuhauser)*, Joseph Mell *(Dr. Lippman)*, Dan Frazer *(used car salesman)*, Martine Bartlett *(Inez)*, Jo Collins *(Kitten)*, Hal Baylor *(Jack)*, Laurie Mitchell *(Jack's wife)*, David Draper *(Billy Gibbons)*, Donald Foster *(Mr. Beverly)*, Judith Loomis *(Mrs. Butch Neuhauser)*, Martin Gabel *(Harry Belmont)*.

Satire. Source: Al Hine, *Lord Love a Duck* (New York, 1961). In the psychiatric ward of a prison, Alan Musgrave, who calls himself "Mollymauk" after an extinct duck-like bird, tells his story into a tape recorder. *Alan and Barbara Ann Greene are both senior transfer students at Los Angeles' new, ultra-modern Consolidated High School. Under Alan's hypnotic spell, Barbara*

Ann reveals her desire to be popular. Alan assures her that he will make her every wish come true. First, Barbara Ann wishes to join a sorority whose members must each own a designated number of cashmere sweaters, and Alan has her persuade her father to buy the sweaters. To keep Barbara Ann from failing any courses, Alan has her use her sex appeal to obtain the job of secretary to the principal. Barbara Ann then meets wealthy and handsome college senior Bob Barnard during a sex seminar at a drive-in church, and she decides to vacation at Balboa, where Bob is to be chaperon. Alan takes her to Balboa, where he sets up a possible screen test for Barbara Ann with a producer of beach-party movies. Bob, who is in love with Barbara Ann, has problems with his zany mother, so Alan installs himself in the Barnard house and takes over the management of Mrs. Barnard by introducing her to alcohol. Mrs. Barnard discovers that Marie, Barbara Ann's divorced mother, is a bar girl and tries to end the romance. Thinking that she has ruined her daughter's life and her own, Marie commits suicide. Later, Bob and Barbara Ann marry, despite Mrs. Barnard's objections. Bob, who has graduated and become a marriage counselor, disapproves of his wife's career in movies, and Alan decides to eliminate him. Bob proves almost indestructible, but by graduation time Alan has put him in a wheelchair. At Consolidated's graduation, he pursues Bob with a bulldozer, eliminating him and everyone on the speaker's platform as well. Barbara Ann goes on to Hollywood fame as the star of "Bikini Widow." In the prison, Alan tries to explain why he did it all, confessing that it might have been for love. *Students. Secretaries. Bar girls. High school life. Hypnotism. Wish fulfillment. Filial relations. Alcoholism. Suicide. Marriage counsel. Murder. Motherhood. Prisons. Sororities. Bulldozers. Motion pictures. Los Angeles. Balboa (California).*

LORD OF THE FLIES (Great Britain)   F6.2843
Allen-Hodgdon Productions–Two Arts. *Dist* Continental Distributing, Inc. 19 Aug **1963** [New York opening]. Sd; b&w. 35mm. 90 min.

A Lewis Allen–Dana Hodgdon Production. *Prod* Lewis Allen. *Exec Prod* Al Hine. *Assoc Prod* Gerald Feil. *Dir-Screenplay* Peter Brook. *Dir Photog* Tom Hollyman. *2d Camera* Gerald Feil. *Main Titl* Digby Turpin, Guy Neale, Sheila More. *Film Ed* Peter Brook, Gerald Feil, Jean-Claude Lubtchansky. *Mus* Raymond Leppard. *Sd Supv* James Townsend. *Sd Rec* Carter Harman. *Asst Dir* Toby Robertson. *Script Supv* Stella Maude.

Cast: James Aubrey *(Ralph)*, Tom Chapin *(Jack)*, Hugh Edwards *(Piggy)*, Roger Elwin *(Roger)*, Tom Gaman *(Simon)*, The Surtees Twins *(Sam & Eric)*, Roger Allen, David Brunjes, Peter Davy, Kent Fletcher, Nicholas Hammond, Christopher Harris, Alan Heaps, Burnes Hollyman, Andrew Horne, Richard Horne, Timothy Horne, Erik Jordan, Peter Ksiezopolski, Anthony McCall-Judson, Malcolm Rodker, David St. Clair, Rene Sanfiorenzo, Jr., Jeremy Scuse, John Stableford, Nicholas Valkenburg, Patrick Valkenburg, Edward Valencia, John Walsh, British, David Walsh, Jeremy Willis.

Drama. Source: William Golding, *Lord of the Flies* (London, 1954). Sometime in the future, a group of well-mannered English schoolboys are evacuated from London at the outbreak of a war. Their plane crashes en route to the South Pacific, on the shore of an uninhabited tropical island. About 35 of the boys make it to land, but there are no adult survivors and the plane wreckage is washed out to sea. Ralph, one of the older boys, is voted leader, and efforts are made to set up a society which will enable them to survive. By reflecting the sun through eyeglasses belonging to the fat and asthmatic Piggy, they start a signal fire for rescue planes. Jack, the bully of the lot, appoints himself chief hunter, and he and his aides track down and kill a wild pig, the head of which they mount on a sharpened stick as an offering to the unknown beast they believe lives on the mountain top. Actually, the "beast" is the body of a dead pilot; and what has terrified the children in the night is the fluttering of his parachute. Eventually a fight ensues between Ralph and Jack, and the latter takes his followers to another part of the island, where they paint their bodies and faces and revert to a savage, primitive life. One night, during a frenzied ritual featuring war dances and chanting, they hear a rustle in the underbrush and brutally slay the innocent Simon, who came to tell them he had learned the true identity of the beast. Now completely savage, the boys kill the helpless Piggy and then set out after Ralph, planning to offer him as a sacrifice to the beast. They chase him across the island until they come face to face with a rescue party. Confronted once more by civilization, the boys break off their pursuit and begin weeping. *Children. Bullies. Evacuation. Survival. Murder. Superstition. Hunting. Rites and ceremonies. Sea rescue. South Sea Islands. Airplane accidents. Chases. The Future. Pigs.*

Note: Filmed on location in the Caribbean on the islands of Vieques and Puerto Rico in 1961. Opened in London in Jul 1964; running time: 91 min. One source mentions picture was financed with U. S. and Puerto Rican funds.

LORNA   F6.2844
Eve Productions. 11 Sep **1964** [Los Angeles showing; c1 Feb 1964; LP26951]. Sd; b&w. 35mm. 77 min.

Prod-Dir Russ Meyer. *Screenplay* James Griffith. *Orig Story* R. Albion Meyer. *Photog* Russ Meyer. *Film Ed* Russ Meyer. *Mus Coord* Hal Hopper, James Griffith. *Titl Song* Hal Hopper. *Sung by* Bob Grabeau. *Sd* Charles Schelling.

Cast: Lorna Maitland *(Lorna)*, Mark Bradley *(fugitive)*, James Rucker *(James)*, Hal Hopper *(Luther)*, Doc Scortt *(Jonah)*, James Griffith *(prophet/narrator)*, Althea Currier, F. Rufus Owens, Franklin H. Bolger, Ken Parker.

Melodrama. Lorna has been married for 1 year to James, a poor but hard-working laborer in a salt mine. Bored with her life in a shack by a canal, Lorna takes nude swims in a nearby stream, and there she is raped by an escaped murderer. Although she resists her assailant, Lorna enjoys the experience and takes the fugitive home to continue their lovemaking. They are interrupted by James, who, having been taunted by his co-workers into a fist fight over his sexual prowess with his wife, picks a fight with the fugitive, during which both Lorna and the fugitive are accidentally killed. (The film is introduced by and ends with the appearance of a prophet, who asserts that sin requires retribution.) *Newlyweds. Miners. Fugitives. Rape. Infidelity. Jealousy.*

THE LOSERS   F6.2845
Fanfare Film Productions. 20 May **1970** [Los Angeles opening]. Sd; col (Eastman Color). 35mm. 95 min. *MPAA rating* R.

Prod Joe Solomon. *Assoc Prod* Vicente Nayve. *Dir* Jack Starrett. *Stunt Coörd* Von Deming. *Screenplay* Alan Caillou. *Photog* Nonong Rasca. *Camera Op* Ermo Santos. *Art Dir* Hernando Balon. *Main Titl* Cinefx. *Film Ed* James Moore, ed, Richard Brockway. *Mus & Mus Dir* Stu Phillips. *Sd Mix* Levy Principe. *Boom* Tinoy Corpuz. *Sd Eff* Edit-Rite Inc. *Asst Dir* Hernan Robles. *Prod Supv* Vicente Nayve. *Script Supv* Tom Moore, script supv. *Wardrobe* Vicente Cabrera. *Makeup* Ricardo Villamin. *Hairdresser* Carmelita Sioson. *Sp Eff* Roger George, Joe Zomar. *Casting Dir* Pearl Kempton. *Key Grip* Mario Carmona. *Gaffer* Julian Baltonado. *Prop Master* Eduardo Urbano.

Cast: William Smith *(Link Thomas)*, Bernie Hamilton *(Captain Jackson)*, Adam Roarke *(Duke)*, Houston Savage *(Dirty Denny)*, Eugene Cornelius *(Speed)*, Paul Koslo *(Limpy)*, John Garwood *(Sergeant Winston)*, Ana Korita *(Kim Sue)*, Lillian Margarejo *(Suriya)*, Paraluman *(Mama-san)*, Paul Nuckles *(Kowalski)*, Ronnie Ross *(Lieutenant Hayworth)*, Armando Lucero *(Screw)*, Jack Starrett *(Chet Davis)*, Fran Dinh Hy *(Charlie)*, Alan Caillou *(Albanian)*, Paquito Salcedo *(Tac Houn)*, Von Deming *(Shillick)*, Hernan Robles *(inspector)*, Monica Phillips *(Negro baby)*, Dan Kemp *(Major Thomas)*, Vic Diaz *(Diem-nuc)*.

War melodrama. To aid the escape of American presidential adviser Chet Davis, who is imprisoned by the Chinese in Cambodia, Major Thomas seeks help from his brother Link and his four motorcyclist friends—Duke, Dirty Denny, Speed, and Limpy. Two of them have other reasons for going to Vietnam: Denny to visit his old whorehouse and Duke to resume his affair with the lovely Suriya. Their motorcycles are converted into armored vehicles, and the five men prepare to leave on their mission. Duke and Suriya are ambushed and shot by Viet Cong, however, and the remaining four men enter Cambodia to find the Chinese camp. Davis, who is actually on a secret mission for the CIA, resists his rescuers and is finally forcibly taken away by Link. All the motorcyclists are killed in the getaway, and Davis returns to U. S. headquarters alone. *Motorcyclists. Prisoners of war. Chinese. Brothers. Secret agents. Vietcong. Rescue. Whorehouses. Vietnam War 1964–73. Cambodia. United States Army. United States—Central Intelligence Agency.*

Note: Filmed in the Philippines. Working title: *Nam Angels.*

LOSS OF INNOCENCE (Great Britain)   F6.2846
P. K. L. Pictures. *Dist* Columbia Pictures. 20 Sep **1961** [Los Angeles opening; c1 Sep 1961; LP20409]. Sd; col (Eastman Color by Pathé). 35mm. 99 min.

A Victor Saville–Edward Small Production. *Prod* Victor Saville. *Dir* Lewis Gilbert. *Screenplay* Howard Koch. *Photog* F. A. Young. *Camera Op* Harry Gillam. *Prod Dsgn* John Stoll. *Asst Prod Dsgn* Herbert Smith. *Titl Dsgn* Irene Haas. *Film Ed* Peter Hunt. *Mus Comp* Richard Addinsell. *Cond* Muir Mathieson. *Sd Rec* Bert Ross. *Asst Dir* Frank Ernst. *Prod Mgr* John Dark. *Cont* Shirley Barnes. *Cost Dsgn* Julie Harris, cost. *Makeup* George Partleton. *Hairdresser* Betty Glasow.

Cast: Kenneth More *(Eliot)*, Danielle Darrieux *(Madame Zizi)*, Susannah York *(Joss Grey)*, Claude Nollier *(Madame Corbet)*, Jane Asher *(Hester Grey)*, Elizabeth Dear *(Vicky Grey)*, Richard Williams, British actor *(Willmouse Grey)*, David Saire *(Paul)*, Raymond Gérôme *(Inspector Renard)*, Maurice Denham *(Uncle William Bullock)*, André Maranne *(Monsieur Dufour)*, Harold Kasket *(Monsieur Prideaux)*, Jacques Brunius *(Monsieur Foubert)*, Joy Shelton *(Mrs. Grey)*, Balbina *(Mauricette)*, Will Stampe *(Monsieur Armand)*, Jean Ozenne *(champagne director)*, Jacques Dhéry *(Bargee)*, Bessie Love, Fred Johnson *(American tourists)*.

Romantic drama. Source: Rumer Godden, *The Greengage Summer* (London, 1958). While on holiday in the champagne country of France, four

English children are stranded when their mother becomes ill and is hospitalized. The oldest child, 16-year-old Joss, takes her sisters, Hester and Vicky, and brother Willmouse, to the château-hotel on the River Marne where their mother had reservations. At first the proprietor, Madame Zizi, and the receptionist, Madame Corbet, are reluctant to take the children in, but Zizi's lover, a dashing Englishman named Eliot, insists that they be received. The next few days are filled with delight for the children as Eliot takes them sightseeing and dining. Zizi, however, resents sharing Eliot and becomes suspicious of his attentions to the rapidly-maturing Joss. One night Zizi creates a scene in the dining room by throwing a glass of champagne into Joss's face; but when Eliot follows Zizi to her bedroom, the outraged Joss gets drunk with the scullery boy, Paul, and has to be carried to her room. The next day, in a fit of adolescent jealousy, Joss sends Eliot's photograph to the Paris police, having correctly concluded that he is a wanted jewel thief. That night Paul comes into Joss's bedroom and attempts to rape her; and as Eliot, roused by the terrified girl's screams, rushes into the room, Paul falls from a window to his death. Ashamed of her actions, Joss confesses to having mailed the photograph. Though Eliot makes his escape, his concern for the children is such that he sends a wire to their uncle, summoning him to the château, thus divulging to the police his whereabouts. Before leaving the château, a much wiser Joss recalls Eliot's parting words: "Little Joss, in this summer you grew up. You've become a woman." *Children. Hotelkeepers. French. Thieves. Informers. Fugitives. Sisters. Brother-sister relationship. Adolescence. Jealousy. Rape. Drunkenness. Vacations. Photographs. Hotels. Castles. Marne River.*

Note: Location scenes filmed in the Marne River Valley of France. Opened in London in Apr 1961 as *The Greengage Summer.*

LOST BATTALION (United States/Philippines)   **F6.2847**

Alta Vista Productions–COM. *Dist* American International Pictures. 22 Nov 1961 [c4 Dec 1961; LP21927]. Sd; b&w. 35mm. 83 min.

Pres by James H. Nicholson, Samuel Z. Arkoff. *Prod-Dir* Eddie Romero. *Exec Prod* Kane W. Lynn. *Writ* Eddie Romero, César Amigo. *Photog* Felipe Sacdalan. *Asst Camera* Fredy Conde. *Art Dir* Vincente Bonus. *Film Ed* Joven Calub. *Sd Supv* Flaviano Villareal, Tommy Santos. *Rec Ed* Demetrio de Santos. *Asst Dir* José Dagumboy. *Prod Coörd* Artemio Tecson. *Asst to the Prod* Carpi Asturias. *Makeup* Remy Amazan, Victoria Manahan. *Sp Eff* Santos Hilario.

Cast: Leopoldo Salcedo (*Ramón, guerrilla leader*), Diane Jergens (*Kathy, The Girl*), Johnny Monteiro (*Bruno, bandit leader*), Joe Dennis (*Landis*), Jennings Sturgeon (*Hughes*), Joe Sison (*Pepe*), Bruce Baxter (*Jimmy*), Renato Robles (*2d guerrilla*), Rosi Acosta (*Pepe's wife*), Arsenio Alonso (*3d guerrilla*).

War melodrama. In World War II, when the Philippines are overrun by the Japanese, a Filipino guerrilla and an American major round up stranded American refugees. They then set out to a rendezvous with a submarine. As they fight their way through the jungle, they meet up with Filipino bandits. When one of the refugees, a young girl, is kidnaped by the bandit group, the guerrilla leader, Ramón, with whom she has fallen in love, rescues her but is wounded in the process. The guerrilla group is rescued by a friendly tribe of pygmies, but the bandit leader, Bruno, reappears and fights Ramón. Bruno is killed, and Ramón is fatally bitten by a cobra. He is left behind to die when the girl and the others are rescued by the submarine. *Refugees. Guerrillas. Soldiers. Bandits. Pygmies. Military occupation. Jungles. Submarines. Snakebites. World War II.*

Note: Filmed in the Philippines.

LOST COMMAND   **F6.2848**

Red Lion Productions. *Dist* Columbia Pictures. 25 May 1966 [Los Angeles opening; c1 Jul 1966; LP32836]. Sd; col (Pathé). 35mm (Panavision). 129 min. [Copyright length: 126 min.]

A Mark Robson Production. *Prod-Dir* Mark Robson. *Assoc Prod* John R. Sloan. *Screenplay* Nelson Gidding. *Dir Photog* Robert Surtees. *Adtl Photog* Jack Willoughby. *Vis* Fred Tuch. *Camera Op* Bruce Surtees. *Camera Asst* Gordon Meagher. *Art Dir* John Stoll. *Asst Art Dir* José Algueró. *Set Decor* Vernon Dixon. *Film Ed* Dorothy Spencer. *Mus* Franz Waxman. *Orch* Leonid Raab. *Sd* Wally Milner, Jack Haynes. *Sd Ed* Alfred Cox. *Boom Op* Harry Fairbairn. *Asst Dir* José Ochoa, John Quested, Jonathan Benson. *Prod Mgr* Mack Davidson. *Unit Mgr* Claud Hudson. *Location Mgr* Apolinar Rabinal. *Prod Supv* Luis Roberts. *Prod Asst* Luis Hernandez, Ramón Baíllo, Felipe Pascual. *Cont* Elaine Schreyeck. *Cost Dsgn* Tanine Autre. *Wardrobe* John Wilson Apperson, Ron Beck. *Makeup* Harold Fletcher, Francisco Puyol. *Sp Eff* Manuel Baquero, Kit West. *French Military Adv* René Lepage, (Commandant). *Spanish Military Adv* Antonio Sanz Ridruejo. *Constr Mgr* Harry Arbour. *Casting* Harvey Woods. *Prop Master* Dick Bamber. *Dialog Coach* Walter Kelley.

Cast: Anthony Quinn (*Lieutenant-Colonel Raspeguy*), Alain Delon (*Captain Esclavier*), George Segal (*Lieutenant Mahidi*), Michèle Morgan (*Countess de Clairefons*), Maurice Ronet (*Captain Boisfeuras*), Claudia Cardinale (*Aicha*), Grégoire Aslan (*Ben Saad*), Jean Servais (*General Melies*),

Maurice Sarfati (*Lieutenant Merle*), Jean-Claude Bercq (*Lieutenant Orsini*), Syl Lamont (*Sergeant Verte*), Jacques Marin (*mayor*), Jean Paul Moulinot (*De Guyot*), Andres Monreal (*Ahmed*), Gordon Heath (*Dia*). Simono (*Sapinsky*), René Havard (*Ferdinand*), Armand Mestral (*administration officer*), Burt Kwouk (*Viet officer*), Al Mulock (*Paratrooper Mugnier*), Marie Burke (*Raspeguy's mother*), Aldo Sambrell (*Ibrahim*), Jorge Rigaud (*priest*), Roberto Robles (*Manuel*), Emilio Carrer (*Mahidi's father*), Carmen Tarrazo (*Mahidi's mother*), Howard Hagen (*helicopter pilot*), Mario de Barros (*Geoffrin*), Walter Kelley (*Major M. P.*), Robert Sutton (*Yusseff*), Simon Benzaken (*Arab customer*), Hector Quiroga (*Bakhti*), Felix de Pomes (*aged speaker*).

War drama. Source: Jean Lartéguy, *Les centurions* (Paris, 1960). After the French defeat in Indochina, a paratroop unit commanded by Lieut. Col. Pierre Raspeguy returns by sea to France. One of the officers, Ben Mahidi, an Arab, leaves the transport at Algiers to visit his family. Uncertain of his own future, Raspeguy visits the Countess de Clairefons, the influential widow of one of the officers killed in action. Despite his provincialism, the countess falls in love with Raspeguy and arranges for his transfer to a crucial trouble spot in Algeria; she promises to marry him if he returns as a general. Raspeguy persuades two of him former officers, Esclavier and Boisfeuras, to help him whip his untrained regiment into a fighting unit. They learn that Ben Mahidi has joined the Algerian terrorists who are carrying on a campaign of violence against the resident French, and Raspeguy and his now well-trained regiment retaliate. Meanwhile, Esclavier has been having an affair with the beautiful Aicha, who has concealed the fact that she is Ben Mahidi's sister. Aicha takes advantage of her opportunity to divert French detonators to her brother's headquarters; but when Esclavier discovers the theft he beats her into revealing Ben Mahidi's hiding place. After promising her that her brother's life will be spared, he has Aicha sent to Paris for imprisonment. Boisfeuras storms the terrorists' stronghold and kills all of the defenders, including Ben Mahidi. Raspeguy condones the action, though Esclavier accuses him of having become a beast. Some days later, as the Countess de Clairefons proudly watches Raspeguy receiving his insignia for the rank of general, Esclavier, now in mufti, watches young Algerians scrawl *Indépendance* on barracks walls. *Paratroops. Nobility. Widows. Revolutionaries. Terrorists. Arabs. Torture. Murder. Colonial administration. Bombs. Algeria—History—War of Independence. French-Indochina War 1945–54. Algeria. France—Army.*

Note: Filmed in Spain as *The Centurions.* Prerelease title: *Not for Honor and Glory.*

THE LOST CONTINENT (Great Britain)   **F6.2849**

Hammer Film Productions–Seven Arts Productions. *Dist* Twentieth Century-Fox Film Corp. 19 Jun 1968 [New York opening; c19 Jun 1968; LP35945]. Sd (RCA); col (De Luxe). 35mm. 89 min. [Copyright length: 101 min.]

Prod Michael Carreras. *Assoc Prod* Peter Manley. *Exec Prod* Anthony Hinds. *Dir (see note)* Michael Carreras, Leslie Norman. *Screenplay* Michael Nash. *Dir Photog* Paul Beeson. *Camera Op* Russell Thomson. *Art Dir* Arthur Lawson. *Asst Art Dir* Don Picton. *Supv Ed* James Needs. *Ed* Chris Barnes. *Mus Comp* Gerard Schürmann. *Mus Supv* Philip Martell. *Songs* Roy Philips. *Sung by* The Peddlers. *Sd Ed* Roy Baker. *Sd Mix* Denis Whitlock. *Rec Supv* A. W. Lumkin. *Asst Dir* Dominic Fulford. *Prod Mgr* Peter Manley. *Cont* Doreen Soan. *Cost Dsgn* Carl Toms. *Wardrobe* Mary Gibson. *Makeup* George Partleton. *Hairdresser* Elsie Alder. *Sp Eff* Cliff Richardson. *Sp Photog Eff* Robert A. Mattey. *Cons* Arthur Hayward. *Modeller* Arthur Fehr. *Casting* Irene Lamb.

Cast: Eric Porter (*Captain Lansen*), Hildegard Knef (*Eva*), Suzanna Leigh (*Unity*), Tony Beckley (*Harry Tyler*), Nigel Stock (*Dr. Webster*), Neil McCallum (*First Officer Hemmings*), Benito Carruthers (*Ricaldi*), Jimmy Hanley (*Pat*), James Cossins (*chief*), Dana Gillespie (*Sarah*), Victor Maddern (*mate*), Reg Lye (*helmsman*), Norman Eshley (*Jonathan*), Michael Ripper (*sea lawyer*), Donald Sumpter (*Sparks*), Alf Joint (*Jason*), Charles Houston (*Braemar*), Shivendra Sinha (*Hurri Curri*), Darryl Read (*El Diablo*), Eddie Powell (*inquisitor*), Frank Hayden (*sergeant*), Mark Heath, Horace James (*customs men*).

Science fiction drama. Source: Dennis Wheatley, *Uncharted Seas* (London, 1938). Captain Lansen is sailing his old freighter from Africa to South America with a cargo of illegal explosives and a handful of motley passengers. The travelers include Dr. Webster, charged with criminal malpractice; his nymphomaniacal daughter, Unity; Eva, the ex-mistress of a recently deposed Latin American dictator; Ricaldi, an agent sent to recover money stolen by Eva; and Harry Tyler, an alcoholic piano player. When Lansen ignores his first officer's hurricane warning, his crew mutinies and abandons ship. Lansen and the passengers are also forced to take to a lifeboat, and they drift aimlessly for days. After Webster is killed by a shark and Ricaldi is carried off by an enormous octopus, the survivors come upon their ship, still in good shape though its propellers have become entangled in a morass of carnivorous seaweed. The passengers reboard the vessel and float off into another continent, where the survivors of previous wrecks have evolved a method of moving about on the deadly weed by means of gas-filled balloons. Ruling over these strange inhabitants in the manner of an evil inquisitor is El Diablo, a boy king of Spanish descent. With the aid of a friendly resident, the passengers escape death by burning the seaweed; then, having destroyed their enemies, they return to civilization. *Physicians. Seamen. Mistresses. Dictators. Secret agents. Pianists. Spanish. Filial relations. Nymphomania. Smuggling. Alcoholism. Mutiny. Freighters. Explosives. Balloons (toy). Carnivorous plants. Africa. South America. Hurricanes. Shipwrecks. Sharks. Octopi.*

Note: Opened in London in Jul 1968; running time: 98 min. Norman was replaced as director by Carreras.

LOST FLIGHT   F6.2850
Universal Pictures. **1970** [c12 Aug 1970; LP39669]. Sd; col. 35mm. 104 min. *MPAA rating* G.

Prod Paul Donnelly. *Exec Prod* Frank Price. *Dir* Leonard Horn. *Screenplay* Dean Riesner. *Dir Photog* James A. Crabe. *Col Coörd* Robert Brower. *Art Dir* Alexander Golitzen, Frank Arrigo. *Set Decor* John McCarthy, Ruby Levitt. *Main Titl* Universal Title. *Film Ed* Douglas Stewart, Jack W. Schoengarth, Larry D. Lester. *Mus* Dominic Frontiere. *Mus Supv* Stanley Wilson. *Sd* Waldon O. Watson, David H. Moriarty. *Asst Dir* George Bisk. *Unit Prod Mgr* Don Gold. *Cost* Charles Waldo. *Makeup* Bud Westmore. *Hairstyles* Larry Germain. *Optical Eff* Universal Title. *Tech Adv* J. S. Solomon. *Safety & Survival Equipment* Switlik Parachute Co.

Cast: Lloyd Bridges (*Steve Bannerman*), Anne Francis (*Gina Talbot*), Ralph Meeker (*Glenn Walkup*), Andrew Prine (*Jonesy*), Bobby Van (*Eddie Randolph*), Linden Chiles (*Allen Bedecker*), Michael Larrain (*Francis Delaney*), Billy Dee Williams (*Merle Barnaby*), Michael-James Wixted (*Charlie Burnett*), Nobu McCarthy (*Zora Lewin*), Jennifer Leak (*Beejay Caldwell*), Kasey Rogers (*Mrs. Peterson*), Connie Kreski (*Australian's wife*), Paul Comi (*Joe Turley*), Dallas Mitchell (*Dave Nathan*), Joseph Bernard (*Mr. Peterson*), William Mims (*fat man*), Edward Faulkner (*Hansen*), Georgene Barnes (*Mary Ann McGee*), Dee Carroll (*Mrs. Connors*), Albert Popwell (*black militant*), Gil Perkins (*Australian*), Robert Pearson (*hippie*), John Gilgreen (*man*), Mina Martinez (*wife*), Mike Klein (*Ed Martin*), Bob Harker (*Artie Boone*), Jeff Kennedy (*Jim Waldron*), Doug Mossman (*weather man*), Elaine Joyce (*blonde*), Paul Stader (*Patsy*), Dick Dial (*Horgan*), Carl Saxe (*Roscoe*), Denver Mattson (*Dietzig*), Howard Curtis (*Case*), Barbara Luddy (*nun*), Jack Tyree, Gary Epper (*young men*), Leslie Burt, Maggie Thrett (*girls*), Jim Malinda, Ray Ballard (*men*).

Drama. During a storm, a plane from Hawaii to Australia crashes on an uninhabited South Pacific island. Among the survivors are pugnacious pilot Steve Bannerman; Merle Barnaby, a black marine returning from combat duty in Vietnam; oil magnate Glenn Walkup, the magnate's mistress and secretary, Gina Talbot; nightclub entertainer Eddie Randolph; the lecherous bigot Jonesy; attractive Beejay Caldwell; a 10-year-old boy suffering from acute appendicitis; a pregnant woman; and a medical student. When the pilot rejects as unsafe Walkup's idea of setting out in a raft, he is brutally beaten by Walkup's henchmen. Manned by Randolph and two associates, the craft departs. A radio bulletin announces the cancellation of all rescue attempts as the barque returns, its crew half-dead. Attempting to escape Jonesy, Beejay falls from a cliff. Her panic-stricken assailant shoots Barnaby, accusing the black of Beejay's murder. Jonesy's victims recover, however, and expose him. The bigot escapes into the jungle, where he is accidentally impaled by Barnaby's animal trap. When a child is born the survivors unite to create a new society. *Air pilots. Negroes. Entertainers. Oil magnates. Medical students. Secretaries. Mistresses. Children. Survival. Racial prejudice. Lechery. Childbirth. Impalement. Airplane accidents. Appendicitis. Islands. Jungles. Vietnam War 1964–73. Pacific Ocean. United States Marines. Storms.*

Note: Location scenes filmed in Kauai, Hawaii. The film was made as a pilot for a proposed television series.

THE LOST MAN   F6.2851
Universal Pictures. 25 Jun **1969** [New York opening]. Sd; col (Technicolor). 35mm (Panavision). 113 min. [Cut from 122 min.] *MPAA rating* M.

Prod Edward Muhl, Melville Tucker. *Assoc Prod* Ernest B. Wehmeyer. *Dir-Writ* Robert Alan Aurthur. *Photog* Gerald Finnerman. *Camera Op* Herbert Pearle. *Asst Camera* Jim Sloan, Herb Roberts. *Art Dir* Alexander Golitzen, George C. Webb. *Set Decor* John McCarthy, John Austin. *Set Coörd* Virgil Clark. *Film Ed* Edward Mann. *Asst Ed* Edward Broussard. *Mus* Quincy Jones. *Mus Supv* Stanley Wilson. *Songs* Quincy Jones, Ernie Shelby, Willie Cooper. *Sd* Waldon O. Watson, William Russell, Bill Schwartz, James Alexander. *Asst Dir* Joseph Kenny, Jim Fargo. *Unit Prod Mgr* Ernest B. Wehmeyer. *Asst Unit Mgr* Skip Cosper. *Script Supv* Ray Quiroz. *Cost* Edith Head. *Wardrobe* Aida Swenson, Austin Felious, Tom Bronson, John Lemons. *Makeup* Bud Westmore, Marvin Westmore. *Hairstyles* Larry Germain, Judy Alexander.

Cast: Sidney Poitier (*Jason Higgs*), Joanna Shimkus (*Cathy Ellis*), Al Freeman, Jr. (*Dennis Laurence*), Michael Tolan (*Hamilton*), Leon Bibb (*Eddie Moxy*), Richard Dysart (*Barnes*), David Steinberg (*photographer*), Beverly Todd (*Sally*), Paul Winfield (*Orville*), Bernie Hamilton (*Reggie Page*), Richard Anthony Williams (*Ronald*), Dolph Sweet (*police captain*), Arnold Williams (*Terry*), Virginia Capers (*Theresa*), Vonetta McGee (*Diane*), Frank Marth (*Warren*), Maxine Stuart (*Miss Harrison*), George Tyne (*plainclothesman*), Paulene Myers (*Grandma*), Lee Weaver (*Willie*), Morris Erby (*Miller*), Doug Johnson (*Teddy*), Lincoln Kilpatrick (*minister*), John Daheim (*Officer Parsons*), Sonny Garrison (*Miller's assistant*).

Drama. Source: Frederick Lawrence Green, *Odd Man Out* (London, 1945). After watching police break up a nonviolent demonstration outside a factory in a large Eastern city, a group of black militants led by Jason Higgs perfect plans for robbing the same plant of its payroll to provide money for families of jailed black demonstrators. Jason, who abandoned nonviolence after 19 arrests, persuades Dennis Laurence, leader of the peaceful demonstration, to stage another protest at the same spot to divert police away from the robbery. Upon leaving Dennis's home, Jason meets Cathy Ellis, a white social worker whose obvious affection for him he ignores. On the day of the robbery, Jason and associates Eddie Moxy, Reggie Page, and Orville seize the payroll and take both the factory manager and his secretary as hostages. As they reach the getaway cars, however, the manager breaks away, and Reggie is killed in the ensuing scuffle. Jason, wounded as he shoots down his friend's assailant, flees on foot and takes refuge in a movie theater, where he meets Sally, a young black woman who takes him to her apartment for first aid. Meanwhile, Eddie and Orville go to a whorehouse and are slain trying to escape after the madam notifies the police. Sally contacts Dennis, who reluctantly agrees to help Jason get the money to his organization and make a getaway by boat. Police security prevents contact with the organization, however, and when Cathy tries to hide Jason in her home, her father, a civil rights attorney, slaps her and angrily notifies the police. Later, Hamilton, a detective, confronts Jason at the waterfront and shoots the militant after he refuses to make a deal. Jason, too weak to reach the waiting ship, has to be supported by Cathy. When police close in, making escape impossible, Cathy fires Jason's gun into the ground, drawing police gunfire that kills them both. *Negroes. Militants. Social workers. Executives. Lawyers. Fugitives. Police. Negro life. Race relations. Robbery. Filial relations. Demonstrations. Factories. Motion picture theaters. Whorehouses. Waterfronts.*

Note: Location scenes filmed in Philadelphia. Previously filmed as *Odd Man Out* (Universal–International, 1947). Pre-release title: *How Many Roads.*

LOST SEX (Japan)   F6.2852
Kindai Eiga Kyokai. *Dist* Chevron Pictures. 22 Jul **1968** [New York opening]. Sd; b&w. 35mm. 97 min.

Dir-Writ Kaneto Shindo. *Photog* Kiyomi Kuroda. *Lighting* Shiroaki Fujiyama. *Mus Comp* Hikaru Hayashi. *Sd Rec* Tetsuo Ohashi.

Cast: Hideo Kanze (*The Master*), Nobuko Otowa (*The Housemaid*), Eijiro Tono (*neighbor [writer]*), Yoshinobu Ogawa (*neighbor [son]*), Kaori Shima (*neighbor [son's wife]*).

Drama. At the beginning of each of the four seasons, a middle-aged No drama teacher retires to his mountain villa. Called "The Master" by the villagers, he lives alone and is visited only by his housekeeper, a 37-year-old war widow who comes from the village to prepare his meals. One winter day, the Master watches two newlyweds embrace in a neighboring villa, and he grows despondent. He confesses to the housekeeper that he was stationed in Hiroshima during the atomic bombing and, as a result, is impotent. A concerned nurse helped him regain his virility, and he married. He again became impotent and was divorced when he learned of an accident in which a fishing boat was covered by fallout from a nuclear test. With the coming of spring, the sympathetic housekeeper suggests that the Master observe the *Yobai*, a custom in which the young men of a village steal into the bedrooms of susceptible women to have sex. She invites him to spend the night in her cottage to witness the *Yobai*. Upon watching three would-be seducers attempt to enter his servant's home, the Master becomes stimulated, and he prevents them from entering her house. The next evening the Master disguises himself, sneaks into the housekeeper's cottage, and makes love to her. Night after night the ritual is repeated, and each night the housekeeper dreamily embraces him and utters the name "Hachibei." The Master eventually learns that there are 13 men with this name living in the village, and, castigating the housekeeper for her promiscuity, he returns to the city. The following autumn the Master returns to his villa and finds that the housekeeper has died as a result of an extra-uterine pregnancy. He also learns that she hired the local youths to observe the *Yobai* to help restore her master's virility and that her reputation in the village was spotless. Filled with remorse, the Master turns to watch the snows come to the mountains. *Drama coaches. Widows. Housekeepers. Impotence. Voyeurism. Social customs. Pregnancy. Atom bomb. Winter. Hiroshima.*

Note: Originally released in Japan in Aug 1966 as *Honno*; running time: 103 min.

LOST SOULS (Italy)   F6.2853

Oscar Film. *Dist* Ellis Films. 9 Aug **1961** [Chicago opening]. Sd; b&w. 35mm. 84 min.

Prod Federico Teti. *Dir-Writ* Adelchi Bianchi, Roberto Mauri. *Photog* Aldo Tonti.

Cast: Virna Lisi *(Anna)*, Sandra Milo *(Giulia)*, Jacques Sernas *(The Baron)*, Gabriele Tinti *(Carlo)*, Marco Guglielmi *(Toni)*, John Kitzmiller *(Luca)*, Roberto Mauri, Anna Alberti, Arturo Dominici, Gustavo De Nardo, Gennaro Sebastiani.

Crime melodrama. After escaping from a penitentiary on the island of Elba, five convicts led by The Baron enter the office of an iron mine and demand the payroll. Carlo, the mine owner's engineer son, refuses. When Carlo's sister Anna and friends Susi and Giulia come upon the criminals, Susi tries to summon help. Furious, the psychotic Negro convict Luca overpowers Susi and attempts to rape her. During their struggle Susi shoots Luca in the arm. In retaliation he murders her. Alarmed, Carlo hands over the checks, which The Baron orders his minion Toni and hostage Anna to cash. At the bank Anna endorses a check with a plea for help. As Toni returns, Luca, having slain The Baron in his absence, opens fire. Upon arrival the police discover both convicts dead and the wounded Carlo in Giulia's embrace. *Prison escapees. Engineers— Mining. Negroes. Psychopaths. Police. Robbery. Rape. Mines. Banks. Elba.*

Note: Released as *Vite perdute* in Italy in 1958; running time: 90 min.

LOST WEEKEND see **LUST WEEKEND**

THE LOST WORLD OF SINBAD see **SAMURAI PIRATE**

LOTNA (Poland)   F6.2854

Kadr Film Unit. *For* Film Polski. *Dist* Pol-Ton Films. 26 May **1966** [New York opening]. Sd; col (Agfacolor & Sepiatone). 35mm. 88 min.

Prod Stanisław Adler. *Dir* Andrzej Wajda. *Screenplay* Wojciech Żukrowski, Andrzej Wajda. *Photog* Jerzy Lipman. *Art Dir* Roman Wolyniec. *Film Ed* Janina Niedzwiecka, Lena Deptula. *Mus* Tadeusz Baird. *Played by* Warsaw National Philharmonic Orchestra. *Mus Cond* W. Rowicki. *Sd* Leszek Wronko. *Asst Dir* Janusz Morgenstern, Sylwester Checiński. *Cost* Lidia Gryś, Jan Banucha. *Makeup* Stefan Szczpański, Roman Baszkiewicz. *Military Adv* Karol Rommel.

Cast: Adam Pawlikowski *(Lieutenant Wadnicki)*, Jerzy Moes *(Ensign Grabowski)*, Jerzy Pichelski *(Captain Chodakiewicz)*, Mieczysław Łoza *(Sergeant-Major Latoń)*, Bożena Kurowska *(Ewa)*, Roman Polański, B. Dardziński, H. Dzieszyński, Wiesław Gołas, Tadeusz Kosudarski, Henryk Hunko, Artur Młodnicki, Irena Malkiewicz, Karol Rommel, T. Somogi, W. Wozniak, M. Wiśniewski.

War drama. Source: Wojciech Żukrowski, "Lotna," in *Twórczość* (no. 2, 1945). In 1939, as Nazi tanks cross the Polish border, a Polish cavalry captain acquires a beautiful white mare called Lotna from the bedridden owner of a deserted country estate. When the captain is killed, Lotna drags his body back to the remains of his regiment. Lots are drawn for the horse, and she passes into the hands of an ensign whose squadron is temporarily quartered in a village. There the ensign marries a young schoolteacher, Ewa, whom he had known in childhood. As the villagers celebrate the wedding, the depleted Polish infantry passes by in retreat. The following morning Lotna runs off, and the ensign is killed while attempting to retrieve her. A lieutenant next rides Lotna in a desperate attack against the still-advancing Germans. Following the battle, a sergeant-major finds the horse standing by the prostrate body of the lieutenant. He takes her and rides away, but he drives Lotna too hard and breaks one of her legs. The sergeant-major shoots her and buries her under a pine tree. *Schoolteachers. Weddings. World War II. Germany—Army. Poland—Army. Horses.*

Note: Released in Poland in Sep 1959.

LOUIE, THERE'S A CROWD DOWNSTAIRS! see **START THE REVOLUTION WITHOUT ME**

LOVE À LA CARTE (Italy)   F6.2855

Zebra Film. *Dist* Promenade Films. Jan **1965**. Sd; b&w. 35mm. 98 min.

Prod Moris Ergas. *Dir* Antonio Pietrangeli. *Screenplay* Ruggero Maccari, Ettore Scola, Antonio Pietrangeli, Tullio Pinelli. *Photog* Armando Nannuzzi. *Art Dir* Luigi Scaccianoce. *Film Ed* Eraldo Da Roma. *Mus* Piero Piccioni. *Sd* Pietro Ortolani. *Asst Dir* Armando Crispino, Anna Maria Leone. *Prod Mgr* Manolo Bolognini.

Cast: Simone Signoret *(Adua)*, Marcello Mastroianni *(Piero)*, Gina Rovere *(Milly)*, Sandra Milo *(Lolita)*, Emmanuelle Riva *(Marilina)*, Claudio Gora *(Ercoli)*, Ivo Garrani *(lawyer)*, Gianrico Tedeschi *(Stefano)*, Domenico Modugno.

Drama. When Rome's brothels are officially closed, four prostitutes pool their savings and buy a dilapidated restaurant. Adua, the leader, is determined to stay out of the streets. Their landlord, Ercoli, is a former client who agrees to use his name in obtaining a food license on condition that they also conduct an "upstairs business." All goes well due to the girls' personalities, excellent food, and inexpensive prices until complications arise in their personal lives. Adua imagines herself to be in love with a fast-talking auto salesman named Piero, unaware he is merely using her to further his own ambitions. Marilina brings her 4-year-old son to live above the restaurant. Milly falls in love and makes plans to settle down. Only Lolita maintains her carefree and uncomplicated existence. But with Ercoli insisting they use the upstairs, everything goes wrong. Adua discovers Piero's unfaithfulness, Marilina must return her child to his foster home, and Milly is forced to admit her former profession to her boyfriend. When the food license is revoked, the girls get even with Ercoli by destroying the restaurant. But with it go their dreams of taking their places in legitimate society. Adua's worst fears are fulfilled when she is forced out into the streets. *Prostitutes. Landlords. Restaurateurs. Salesmen. Motherhood. Whorehouses. Restaurants. Rome.*

Note: Produced in Italy and released in 1960 as *Adua e le compagne*; running time: 150 min. May also be known as *Adua and Her Friends*, or *Adua and Her Companions*.

LOVE AFFAIR; OR THE CASE OF THE MISSING SWITCHBOARD
OPERATOR (Yugoslavia)   F6.2856

Avala Film. *Dist* Brandon Films. 6 Feb **1968** [New York opening]. Sd; b&w. 35mm. 70 min.

Dir-Writ Dušan Makavejev. *Photog* Aleksandar Petković. *Art Dir* Vladislav Lazić. *Film Ed* Katarina Stojanović. *Mus* Hanns Eisler. *Sd* Dušan Aleksić. *Asst Dir* Branko Vučićević.

Cast: Eva Ras *(Isabela)*, Slobodan Aligrudić *(Ahmed)*, Ružica Sokić *(Ruza, Isabela's friend)*, Miodrag Andrić *(Mica, the postman)*, Aleksandar Kostić *(sexologist)*, Živojin Aleksić *(criminologist)*, Dragan Obradović.

Comedy-drama. The body of a pregnant young woman is discovered in a well, and the Belgrade police set out to find her murderer. (An eminent sexologist lectures on television on the history of sexual intercourse.) Isabela, a lively young switchboard operator, and Ahmed, a shy rat exterminator, fall in love and live together in tender, uncomplicated harmony. Only Isabela's occasional yearning for marriage creates any discord in their blissful love affair. (A noted criminologist speaks on the perfect crime, using the young woman's corpse to demonstrate his arguments.) While Ahmed is away on a short business trip, Isabela visits a fortune-teller, who tells her she will betray Ahmed. Isabela leaves in disbelief, but she is soon seduced by a post office Lothario. When Ahmed returns, he learns that Isabela is pregnant. She tells him that she does not want the child and, furthermore, will not be his slave, and a violent, drunken quarrel between them ensues. Bewildered and dejected by this rebellion, Ahmed goes on a drinking spree; Isabela follows him, but he rejects her. She persists in following him, and, in a senseless accident, he pushes her down a well. The body of a pregnant young woman, discovered in the well, continues to be examined carefully by the Belgrade police for clues to her murderer's identity. *Telephone operators. Police. Lecturers. Sex researchers. Exterminators. Criminologists. Fortune-tellers. Mail carriers. Murder. Infidelity. Pregnancy. Drunkenness. Sex instruction. Corpses. Wells. Television. Belgrade.*

Note: Released in Yugoslavia in 1967 as *Ljubavni slučaj ili tragedija službenice P.T.T.* at 78 min. Shown at the New York Film Festival 22 Sep 1967 as *An Affair of the Heart.*

LOVE AFTER DEATH   F6.2857

Charles Abrams Productions. *Dist* Abrams & Parisi, Inc. Nov **1968**. Sd; b&w. 35mm. 72 min.

Melodrama. Buried alive during a cataleptic seizure by his money-hungry wife and doctor, a young man emerges from the grave and sets out on a path of retribution. His mind deranged by the horrible experience, he abducts a young girl and attempts to rape her to prove his manliness, but he is unable to perform. Since rape is crucial to his plan for revenge, he tries to reassure himself. He fails again after concealing himself in the dressing room of a nightclub star, but he finally succeeds with a young woman who offers kindness and respect. In accordance with his plan, he traps the guilty couple in their love nest, murders the doctor, and rapes his wife. He chases her to the roof, strangles her before a detective can intervene, and disappears just as he is about to be arrested. *Physicians. Infidelity. Murder. Catalepsy. Revenge. Rape. Abduction. Impotence. Insanity. Greed.*

Note: Also known as *Unsatisfied Love.*

LOVE AND KISSES   F6.2858

Universal Pictures. 5 Aug **1965** [Houston opening; c9 Oct 1965; LP33027]. Sd (Westrex); col (Technicolor). 35mm. 87 min.

Prod-Dir-Writ Ozzie Nelson. *In Charge of Prod* Edward Muhl. *Dir Photog* Robert Moreno. *Camera Op* Al Cline. *Asst Camera* Michel Hugo, Ed Hearn. *Art Dir* Alexander Golitzen, Frank Arrigo. *Set Decor* John McCarthy, Julia Heron. *Main Titl* Pacific Title. *Film Ed* Newell P. Kimlin. *Mus* William Loose, Jimmie Haskell. *Mus Supv* Joseph Gershenson. *Songs:* "Love and Kisses," "Say You Love Me" Sonny Curtis. *Song:* "Come Out Dancin'" Clint Ballard, Jr., Angela Reila. *Songs Sung by* Rick Nelson. *Sd* Waldon O. Watson, Frank H. Wilkinson, William Griffith, Harold King, Neal Jack. *Asst Dir* Carl Beringer, Paul Cameron. *Unit Prod Mgr* Herman Webber. *Script Supv* Betty Levin. *Wardrobe* Seth Banks, Dolores Sheppard. *Makeup* Monte Westmore. *Hairstyles* Barbara Lampson. *Still Photog* Bill Cary. *Gaffer* Babe Stafford. *Grip* Lloyd Stafford, Eugene Barragy. *Prop* Cecil Smith, Charles Thomas.

Cast: Rick Nelson *(Buzzy Pringle)*, Jack Kelly *(Jeff Pringle)*, Kristin Nelson *(Rosemary Cotts)*, Jerry Van Dyke *(Freddy)*, Pert Kelton *(Nanny)*, Madelyn Himes *(Carol Pringle)*, Sheilah Wells *(Elizabeth Pringle)*, Howard McNear *(Mr. Frisby)*, Ivan Bonar *(Assemblyman Potter)*, Barry Livingston *(Bobby)*, Alvy Moore *(Officer Jones)*, Angelo Brovelli *(stage manager)*, Betty Rowland, Nancy Lewis, Anita Mann *(dancers)*.

Domestic comedy. Source: Anita Rowe Block, *Love and Kisses* (New York opening: 18 Dec 1963). Newly graduated from high school, Buzzy Pringle shocks his family by telling them that he has eloped with Rosemary Cotts, a high school junior. He explains that he will work at his father's business during the summer, and in the fall he will go to college and Rosemary will finish high school. Buzzy's parents, Jeff and Carol, accept the situation and offer the newlyweds a room in their house. Buzzy's sister, Elizabeth, however, is upset by the marriage of her younger brother because her own wedding, to Freddy, is only a few weeks away. Rosemary soon comes to feel that she is being treated like a baby, and she leaves to live with friends. Elizabeth and Freddy begin to quarrel, and Buzzy learns that his salary is being paid from his father's expense account. Carol blames all the troubles on Jeff, who is relegated to sleeping on the living-room couch until the problems are resolved. Buzzy finds a job at a gas line station and moves into an apartment with a forgiving Rosemary. Elizabeth and Freddy move up their wedding date, and Jeff and Carol are reconciled. *Students. Newlyweds. Adolescence. Elopement. Marriage. Parenthood. Brother-sister relationship.*

LOVE AND LARCENY (France/Italy)   F6.2859

Maxima Film–Cei Incom–S. G. C. *Dist* Major Film Distributing Corp. 2 Feb **1963** [New York opening]. Sd; b&w. 35mm (Totalscope). 94 min.

Prod Mario Cecchi Gori. *Dir* Dino Risi. *Screenplay* Sandro Continenza, Sergio Pugliese, Ettore Scola, Ruggero Maccari. *Story* Age & Scarpelli. *Photog* Massimo Dallamano. *Art Dir* Sergio Giovannini. *Film Ed* Eraldo Da Roma. *Mus* Pippo Barzizza.

Cast: Vittorio Gassman *(Gerardo)*, Anna Maria Ferrero *(Annalise)*, Dorian Gray *(Elena)*, Peppino De Filippo *(Chinotto)*, Mario Carotenuto *(Lallo Cortina)*, Alberto Bonucci *(Gloria Patri)*, Fosco Giachetti *(The General)*, Luigi Pavese *(Rebuschini)*, Linda Sini *(Laura)*, Aldo Bufi Landi *("commissioner")*, Fernando Bruni, Enrico Glori, Mario Scaccia, Mario Frera, Piera Arico, Salvatore Cafiero, Fanfulla, Armando Bandini, Dina De Santis, Walter Santesso, Ignazio Leone, Giovanni Baghino, Armando Annuale, Mimmo Poli, Enzo Petito, Pierugo Gragnani, Andrea Petricca, Enzo Cerusico, Vincenzo Talarico.

Comedy-drama. Gerardo and his wife, Annalise, are at home when they are visited by a confidence man who attempts to sell them some silver candlesticks. They agree to the purchase, but Gerardo catches him substituting a cheaper pair of candlesticks, and reveals that he himself was once a successful con man and proceeds to tell his story. An actor in a small theater, he was hired to impersonate a businessman with his colleague, Lallo, who, as it happened, absconded with the money. Gerardo was caught and sent to prison. Upon his release he went into partnership with Chinotto, whom he had met in jail. Together they tricked a shopkeeper for a pair of shoes, collected funds for a nonexistent orphanage, stole jewelry, and collected compensation from a restaurant after claiming they were served poisoned food. Meanwhile, Gerardo lost the legitimate job his girl friend Annalise had insisted he get, and as a result he lost her as well. One day he and Chinotto spotted Lallo and Elena, an assistant, stealing a ring from a jeweler. Seeking revenge on Lallo, Gerardo swept away the ring and persuaded Elena to become his new partner. Other successful tricks followed; on one occasion Gerardo impersonated Greta Garbo at a photographic session, but Annalise broke in and forced Elena to leave. Later Annalise offered to help Gerardo with a phony marriage trick, but it became apparent that Annalise had set up a legitimate marriage: hence, their current matrimonial state. The visitor to their apartment reveals that he is a policeman and has come to make an arrest. Gerardo bids farewell to Annalise, and the two men leave. Outside, however, Chinotto is waiting to drive them away. The "policeman," it appears, was a con man after all. *Confidence men. Confidence women. Actors. Convicts. Storekeepers. Police. Jewelers.*

Imposture. Theft. Extortion. Revenge. Fraud. Marriage. Employment. Jewels. Weddings. Greta Garbo.

Note: Opened in Rome in Feb 1960 as *Il mattatore* at 100 min; in Paris in May 1961 as *L'homme aux cent visages.*

LOVE AND MARRIAGE (Italy)   F6.2860

Panda Film. *Dist* Embassy Pictures. 4 Aug **1966** [New York opening]. Sd; b&w. 35mm. 106 min.

Prod Ermanno Donati, Luigi Carpentieri. *Dir* "The First Night," "Saturday, July 18" Gianni Puccini. *Dir* "One Moment Is Enough," "The Last Card" Mino Guerrini. *Story & Screenplay* Bruno Baratti, Oreste Biancoli, Eliana De Sabata, Jaja Fiastri, Mino Guerrini, Gianni Puccini, Ennio De Concini. *Photog* Luciano Trasatti, Alfio Contini, Riccardo Pallottini. *Art Dir* Aurelio Crugnola. *Film Ed* Bruna Malaguti, Mario Forges Davanzati. *Mus* Marcello Giombini. *Sd* Armando Timpani, Biagio Fiorelli. *Asst Dir* Ruggero Deodato. *Prod Mgr* Alfonso Donati, Luciano Cattania, Ennio Di Meo. *Cost* Luciana Marinucci.

Cast—"The First Night": Lando Buzzanca *(Concetto)*, Maria Grazia Buccella *(Enea)*, Umberto D'Orsi *(Roro)*, Luciana Angiolillo *(woman on yacht)*, Gianni Del Balzo *(baron)*, Amedeo Girard *(hotel clerk)*.

Cast—"One Moment Is Enough": Ingeborg Schöner *(Marina)*, Renato Tagliani *(Giancarlo)*, Sandro Moretti *(barman)*, Steve Forsyth *(young man in theater)*, Enzo Carrà *(Andrea)*, Marino Masè *(fisherman)*, Armando Tarallo *(Don Eugenio)*, Flora Volpi *(Amelia)*.

Cast—"The Last Card": Eleonora Rossi-Drago *(Elsa)*, Aldo Giuffrè *(Antonio)*, April Hennessy *(Gladys)*, June Weaver *(Ann)*, Ethel Levin *(Linda)*, Gioia Durell *(manicurist)*, Carlo Loffredo *(1st man)*, Bruno Scipioni *(2d man)*.

Cast—"Saturday, July 18": Sylva Koscina *(Diana)*, Philippe Leroy *(Mario)*.

Cast—Also Featuring: Alrise Estense, Roberto Fabbri, Nino Falanga.

Comedy. THE FIRST NIGHT: On the first day of their honeymoon in Naples, a young Sicilian couple are invited to a party aboard a yacht. Their host, a jaded aristocrat, offers to pay a million lire if the bride will spend the night with him, whereupon the husband, slightly drunk and more than slightly addled by the luxurious surroundings, persuades the wife to accept. The next morning, the couple move into an expensive hotel. But when they check out, they discover the check is no good and the husband must face going to jail unless he can explain how he earned the one million lire. ONE MOMENT IS ENOUGH: Young Giancarlo proudly boasts of his wife Marina's absolute fidelity. Secretly, however, she has been unfaithful to him countless times, despite his almost constant surveillance. When he does learn the truth, Giancarlo drags his wife into the ocean and holds her head under water until he is convinced she is dead. He then gives himself up to the police and returns with them to the scene of the crime, only to find Marina making passionate love to a fisherman who had revived her with artificial respiration. THE LAST CARD: Antonio and Elsa are happily married but dead broke because Antonio has refused to work since he gave up his career as a professional soccer player. Elsa tries to solve their financial problems by arranging for her husband to become a gigolo to American tourists, and Antonio makes an attempt to go through with the scheme. But the experience is such a nightmare that he races back to Elsa and declares that he has decided to go to work. SATURDAY, JULY 18: Each year Diana spends a month on the island of Capri even though her husband Mario can join her for only the last two weeks. On one such occasion, Mario spends the first day of his vacation boasting of his wife's beauty and fidelity. But when they are making love that night in their loudly creaking hotel bed, an indignant voice from the next room bellows: "Do we have to listen to this creaking *every* night?" *Sicilians. Newlyweds. Aristocrats. Swindlers. Fishermen. Police. Athletes. Americans in foreign countries. Gigolos. Tourists. Marriage. Prostitution. Wealth. Greed. Drunkenness. Murder. Infidelity. Finance— Personal. Honeymoons. Yachts. Hotels. Vacations. Naples. Capri.*

Note: Filmed on location in Italy. Original title: *L'idea fissa*; episode titles: "La prima notte," "Basta un attimo," "L'ultima carta," "Sabato 18 luglio." Rome opening: Nov 1964.

LOVE AND THE ANIMALS   F6.2861

Falcon International Corp. *Dist* Dal-Art Films. 17 Dec **1969** [Honolulu, Hawaii, opening]. Sd; col. 35mm. 90 min. *MPAA rating* R.

Prod Hal Dwain, Lorus J. Milne, Margery Milne, George Costello. *Exec Prod* Harold Hoffman. *Screenplay* Hal Dwain, Lorus J. Milne, Margery Milne. *Film Ed* Hal Dwain, Larry Buchanan, David Korn, Roger Carter.

Narrators: Lorus J. Milne, Margery Milne.

Documentary. Source: Lorus J. Milne and Margery Milne, *The Mating Instinct* (New York, 1968). An examination of the courtship, mating, and reproductive behavior of various animals. *Animal life. Reproduction. Courtship.*

Note: Originally titled *Sex and the Animals.* May also be known as *Love and Animals.*

LOVE AND THE FRENCHWOMAN (France)　　　　　**F6.2862**

Films Metzger et Woog–Paris Elysée Films–Unidex. *Dist* Auerbach Film Enterprises, Kingsley International Pictures. 27 Feb **1961** [New York opening]. Sd; b&w. 35mm. 143 min.

Overall Production Credits: *Orig Idea* Jacques Rémy, Robert Woog. *Anim* Jabely. *Photog* Robert Lefebvre. *Art Dir* Lucien Aguettand. *Sd* Jacques Lebreton. *Prod Mgr* Hugo Benedek. *English Commentary* Jacques Brunius.

Production Credits for "Childhood": *Dir* Henri Decoin. *Screenplay* Félicien Marceau. *Film Ed* Claude Durand. *Mus* Joseph Kosma.

Production Credits for "Adolescence": *Dir* Jean Delannoy. *Screenplay* Louise de Vilmorin, Jacques Robert. *Film Ed* Henri Taverna. *Mus* Paul Misraki.

Production Credits for "Virginity": *Dir* Michel Boisrond. *Screenplay* Annette Wademant. *Film Ed* Henri Taverna. *Mus* Jean Constantin.

Production Credits for "Marriage": *Dir-Writ* René Clair. *Film Ed* Louisette Hautecoeur. *Mus* Jacques Metehen.

Production Credits for "Adultery": *Dir* Henri Verneuil. *Screenplay* France Roche, Michel Audiard. *Film Ed* Borys Lewin. *Mus* Norbert Glanzberg.

Production Credits for "Divorce": *Dir* Christian-Jaque. *Screenplay* Charles Spaak. *Art Dir* Robert Gys, Lucien Aguettand. *Film Ed* Jacques Desagneau. *Mus* Henri Crolla.

Production Credits for "A Woman Alone": *Dir-Writ* Jean-Paul Le Chanois. *Story* Marcel Aymé. *Film Ed* Emma Le Chanois. *Mus* Georges Delerue.

Cast—"Childhood": Pierre-Jean Vaillard (*Monsieur Bazouche*), Jacqueline Porel (*Madame Bazouche*), Darry Cowl (*Dr. Dufieux*), Noël Roquevert (*Colonel Chappe*), Martine Lambert (*Gisèle*), Bibi Morat (*Jaja*), Jacques Duby (*young man*), Paulette Dubost (*Madame Tronche*), Micheline Dax (*Lulu*), Pierre Paulet (*driver*).

Cast—"Adolescence": Sophie Desmarets (*mother*), Pierre Mondy (*father*), Annie Sinigalia (*Bichette*), Roger Pierre (*Prince Charming*), François Nocher (*Jacques*), Pierre-Louis, Simone Paris.

Cast—"Virginity": Valérie Lagrange (*Ginette*), Pierre Michaël (*François*), Paul Bonifas (*father*), Nicole Chollet (*mother*).

Cast—"Marriage": Marie-José Nat (*Line*), Claude Rich (*Charles*), Yves Robert (*man with the moustache*), Liliane Patrick (*lady with cigarette*), Jacques Fabbri (*ticket collector*).

Cast—"Adultery": Dany Robin (*Nicole*), Paul Meurisse (*Jean-Claude*), Jean-Paul Belmondo (*Gil*), Alice Kessler, Ellen Kessler (*twins*), Claude Pieplu.

Cast—"Divorce": Annie Girardot (*Danielle*), François Périer (*Michel*), Denise Grey (*mother*), Jean Poiret, Michel Serrault (*lawyers*), Francis Blanche (*Marceroux*), Alfred Adam (*friend*), Georges Chamarat (*judge*).

Cast—"A Woman Alone": Martine Carol (*Eliane*), Sylvia Montfort (*Gilberte*), Robert Lamoureux (*Désiré*), Simone Renant (*lawyer*), Suzanne Nivette (*Madame Mangebois*), Paul Ville (*tribunal president*).

Comedy. CHILDHOOD: When 9-year-old Gisèle starts asking questions about the facts of life, her parents tell her that babies come from cabbages. The next day little Gisèle creates an uproar on the street when a cabbage falls from a vegetable truck. ADOLESCENCE: Bichette's first kiss is such fun that she is soon kissing all the boys at a local dance. Though her father becomes over-wrought, her mother realizes that secret kisses, hidden diaries, and dreams of Prince Charming are all parts of a young girl's growing-up. VIRGINITY: Ginette and François have been engaged for a year but are unable to marry because of financial problems. Aware of François' frustration, Ginette agrees to spend a night with him in a hotel. Once there, she is overcome by nervousness and fear. François proves to be full of tact and understanding, and he suggests they postpone consumating their love. MARRIAGE: Newlyweds Line and Charles start their honeymoon with petty quarrels about hats, relatives, and cigarettes; but by the time they reach their destination, they have started learning that marriage is a game of give and take. ADULTERY: A neglected wife, Nicole, has an affair with a young bachelor, Gil. When Nicole's husband, Jean-Claude, learns of the situation, he invites Gil to lunch and then cleverly alienates him with tales of Nicole's extravagance. Before Jean-Claude can be reconciled with his repentant wife, he is interrupted by a phone call from his mistress. DIVORCE: No longer in love but still good friends, Danielle and Michel decide to obtain a divorce. However, their hopes for a friendly parting are dashed by interfering in-laws and friends and by lengthy, unpleasant meetings with lawyers. A WOMAN ALONE: Désiré, a professional bigamist, decides to swindle a lonely woman, Eliane, out of some shares he believes she owns. But his plot fails when he falls in love with one of Eliane's roommates, Gilberte. The women expose him, and he is sent to prison. Upon his release he is met by a third lonely woman—the attractive lawyer who defended him at his trial. *Newlyweds. Bachelors. In-laws. Lawyers. Swindlers. Children. Adolescence. Parenthood. Courtship. Virginity. Sexuality. Marriage. Infidelity. Divorce. Bigamy. Hotels. Honeymoons.*

Note: Released in Paris in Sep 1960 as *La Française et l'amour* with episodes entitled: "L'enfance," "L'adolescence," "La virginité," "Le mariage," "L'adultère," "Le divorce," & "La femme seule"; running time: 137 min.

LOVE AND THE SINGLE SAILOR *see* **SEX AND THE SINGLE SAILOR**

LOVE AT NIGHT (France)　　　　　　　　　　　**F6.2863**

S. L. P. F.–Lutétia–Sonodis–Selb Films. *Dist* William Mishkin. **1961** [New York showing]. Sd; b&w. 35mm. 97 min.

Prod Georges Sénamaud. *Dir-Dial-Adapt* Pierre Méré. *Story* Jean Périne. *Photog* Joseph Brun. *Camera* René Schneider. *Asst Camera* René Castel, Guy Maria. *Film Ed* Jacques Mavel. *Asst Film Ed* Janine Verneau. *Mus* Jean Marion. *Song* René Denoncin. *Sd* Norbert Gernolle. *Rec* André Soler. *Boom Op* Urbain Loiseau. *Asst Dir* Jacques Poitrenaud, Jean-Claude Roy. *Prod Mgr* Pierre Caudrelier. *Unit Mgr* Maurice Jumeau. *Script Girl* Denise Morlot. *Wardrobe* Lily Caudrelier. *Makeup* Odette Berroyer. *Still Photog* Guy André. *Prop* Piodela.

Cast: Isabelle Pia (*Monique*), Christian Marquand (*Eugène*), Simone Paris (*Denise*), Raymond Bussières (*Gilbert*), Daniel Cauchy (*Fanfan*), Jean-Louis Le Goff, Jacqueline Carrel, Monique Clarence, Geneviève Morel, Jacques Clancy, Georges Chamarat, Gaston Rey, Emile Prudhomme, Claudy Chapeland.

Melodrama. Denise, an attractive widow, falls in love with Eugène, a man several years her junior, and supports him with her inheritance. When the money becomes scarce, Eugène prepares to leave, but Denise's 19-year-old daughter Monique returns home from a sanitarium, and Eugène tries to seduce her. He is rejected by the young woman, who decides not to reveal the incident to her mother. Meanwhile, Eugène joins Fanfan and his gang of smugglers to raise some money. One day he forces himself on Monique, and Denise arrives unexpectedly; misinterpreting what is happening, she accuses Monique of trying to take her lover away from her. Monique leaves home to live with an aunt, and although Eugène continues to stay with Denise, he loves Monique and wants to marry her. Finally, the smugglers find themselves surrounded by police and decide to let the blame fall on Eugène. Realizing his position, Eugène goes to the police, but Monique is captured by the gang, and he returns to rescue her. By the time the police arrive, Eugène has been killed by the gang. *Widows. Gigolos. Smugglers. Police. Filial relations. Infidelity. Seduction. Perfidy.*

Note: Opened in Paris in Oct 1955 as *Impasse des vertus*; running time: 98 min. Also known as *Sex at Night.*

LOVE AT TWENTY (France/Italy/Japan/Poland/West Germany) **F6.2864**

Ulysse Productions–Unitec France–Cinescolo–Toho Co.–Towa Films–Kamera Film Unit–Film Polski–Beta Film. *Dist* Embassy Pictures. 6 Feb **1963** [New York opening]. Sd; b&w. 35mm (Totalscope). 110 min. [Also 113 min.]

Overall Production Credits: *Pres by* Joseph E. Levine. *Prod* Pierre Roustang. *Film Ed* Claudine Bouché. *Linking Mus* Georges Delerue. *Sung by* Yvon Samuel, Xavier Despras. *Prod Mgr* Philippe Dussart. *Artistic Adv* Jean de Baroncelli. *Linking Still Photog* Henri Cartier-Bresson. *Still Photog Filmed by* Jean Aurel.

Production Credits for "France": *Dir-Writ* François Truffaut. *Dial* Yvon Samuel. *Dir Photog* Raoul Coutard. *Camera Op* Claude Beausoleil. *Asst Dir* Georges Pellegrin.

Production Credits for "Italy": *Dir-Writ* Renzo Rossellini. *Photog* Mario Montuori. *Asst Dir* Francesco Cinieri.

Production Credits for "Japan": *Dir-Writ* Shintaro Ishihara. *Photog* Shigeo Hayashida. *Mus* Toru Takemitsu.

Production Credits for "West Germany": *Dir-Writ* Marcel Ophüls. *Photog* Wolf Wirth.

Production Credits for "Poland": *Dir* Andrzej Wajda. *Screenplay* Jerzy Stefan Stawiński. *Photog* Jerzy Lipman. *Mus* Jerzy Matuszkiewicz. *Asst Dir* Andrzej Żuławski.

Narrator: Henri Serre.

Cast—"France": Jean-Pierre Léaud (*Antoine Doinel*), Marie-France Pisier (*Colette*), François Darbon (*Colette's father*), Rosy Varte (*Colette's mother*), Patrick Auffay (*René*), Jean-François Adam (*Albert Tazzi*).

Cast—"Italy": Eleonora Rossi-Drago (*Valentina*), Cristina Gajoni (*Christina*), Geronimo Meynier (*Leonardo*).

Cast—"Japan": Koji Furuhata (*Hiroshi*), Nami Tamura (*Fumiko*).

Cast—"West Germany": Christian Doermer (*Tonio*), Barbara Frey (*Ursula*), Vera Tschechowa, Werner Finck.

Cast—"Poland": Barbara Lass (*Basia*), Zbigniew Cybulski (*Sbyssek*), Władysław Kowalski (*Wladek*).

Drama. FRANCE: Antoine, a lover of classical music, becomes so enamored of Colette, a student he has seen at concerts, that he moves into a hotel across the street from her home. Eventually he makes her acquaintance and is invited to dinner. Although he is liked by her family, Colette goes out with another boy, leaving Antoine to watch television with her parents. ITALY: Leonardo, lover of both a young girl, Christina, and a wealthy older woman, Valentina, announces that he plans to marry Christina. Valentina flies into a rage and arranges a showdown with her rival. By depicting Leonardo as a hopeless spendthrift, Valentina is able to convince Christina that her future with Leonardo is doomed. JAPAN: Because of class differences, a maladjusted factory worker's love for a wealthy student is hopeless. Filled with despair, he murders his devoted girl friend and then kills the student. When the latter's body is not found, the young killer telephones a newspaper and confesses that he alone knows where her body is. GERMANY: While on a stopover in Munich, a magazine photographer spends a night with a young switchboard operator. When he returns after an extended absence and hears that she is pregnant, he decides to marry her. At their second meeting, he realizes that he loves her and decides to settle down with his new family. POLAND: Sbyssek, a workman, rescues a child from a pit in the zoo. Basia, a young woman who witnessed the incident, invites him to her apartment, where her friends treat him as a hero and then taunt him into a game of blindman's buff. While blindfolded, Sbyssek recalls the time during World War II when he was nearly shot by the Nazis. He becomes completely unnerved, and Basia, perplexed by his actions, leaves with her boyfriend Wladek. *Students. Factory workers. Photographers. Telephone operators. Courtship. Jealousy. Poverty. Social classes. Murder. Pregnancy. Marriage. Memory. Zoos. World War II. Munich.*

Note: Opened in Paris in Jun 1962 as *L'amour à vingt ans*; running time: 118 min. Released in Italy in 1962 as *Amore a vent'anni*; in West Germany in 1962 as *Liebe mit zwanzig*; in Poland in 1962 as *Miłość dwudziestolatków*; in Japan in 1962 as *Hatachi no koi*. The French episode is also known as "Antoine et Colette." Original running time: 123 min.

THE LOVE BLACKMAILER see ADULTEROUS AFFAIR

THE LOVE BUG
F6.2865

Walt Disney Productions. *Dist* Buena Vista Distribution Co. 13 Mar **1969** [New York opening; c3 Dec 1968; LP36528]. Sd (RCA); col (Technicolor). 35mm. 107 min. *MPAA rating* G.

Prod Bill Walsh. *Dir* Robert Stevenson. *2d Unit Dir* Arthur J. Vitarelli. *Driving Seq Supv by* Carey Loftin. *Screenplay* Bill Walsh, Don DaGradi. *Story* Gordon Buford. *Dir Photog* Edward Colman. *Art Dir* Carroll Clark, John B. Mansbridge. *Set Decor* Emile Kuri, Hal Gausman. *Film Ed* Cotton Warburton. *Mus* George Bruns. *Orch* Walter Sheets. *Sd Supv* Robert O. Cook. *Sd Mix* Dean Thomas. *Mus Ed* Evelyn Kennedy. *Asst Dir* Christopher Hibler. *Unit Mgr* Paul Cameron. *Cost Dsgn* Bill Thomas. *Cost* Chuck Keehne, Emily Sundby. *Makeup* Otis Malcolm. *Hairstylist* La Rue Matheron. *Sp Photog Eff* Eustace Lycett, Alan Maley, Peter Ellenshaw. *Sp Eff* Robert A. Mattey, Howard Jensen, Danny Lee. *Race Car Driver* Bob Bondurant, Carey Loftin.

Cast: Dean Jones *(Jim)*, Michele Lee *(Carole)*, David Tomlinson *(Thorndyke)*, Buddy Hackett *(Tennessee Steinmetz)*, Joe Flynn *(Havershaw)*, Benson Fong *(Mister Wu)*, Joe E. Ross *(detective)*, Barry Kelley *(police sergeant)*, Iris Adrian *(carhop)*, Andy Granatelli *(himself)*, Dale Van Sickel, Regina Parton, Bob Drake, Hal Brock, Rex Ramsey, Lynn Grate, Richard Warlock, Everett Creach, Bill Couch, Robert Hoy, Jack Mahoney, Richard Brill, Rudy Doucette, Jim McCullough, Glenn Wilder, Robert James, Bob Harris, Richard Geary, Jack Perkins, Ronnie Rondell, Reg Parton, Tom Bamford, Marion J. Playan, Bill Hickman, Hal Grist, Larry Schmitz, Dana Derfus, Gerald Jann, Ted Duncan, Gene Roscoe, Charles Willis, Roy Butterfield, J. J. Wilson, Bud Ekins, Gene Curtis, John Timanus, Fred Krone, Jesse Wayne, Fred Stromsoe, Kim Brewer *(The Drivers)*, Ned Glass, Gil Lamb, Nicole Jaffe, Russ Caldwell, Pete Renoudet, Alan Fordney, Gary Owens, Robert Foulk, Barry Kelley, Wally Boag, Max Balchowsky, Brian Fong, Stan Duke, Chick Hearn, Pedro Gonzalez-Gonzalez.

Comedy. Jim Douglas, a racing driver with consistently bad luck, shares a bachelor flat in a turn-of-the-century San Francisco firehouse with Tennessee Steinmetz, a guru-indoctrinated scrap metal sculptor. One day Jim is drawn into a posh automobile showroom by the attractive presence of Carole Bennett, the secretary to the showroom's stuffy manager, racing driver Peter Thorndyke. After objecting to the abusive treatment Thorndyke shows to a little white Volkswagen, Jim leaves the establishment and is followed by the grateful little car. Once a down-payment has been made on the Volkswagen, which Tennessee nicknames Herbie, Jim enters it in a race and drives to an easy win. As victory follows victory, and romance blossoms between Jim and Carole, Jim attributes his success to his own skills, but Tennessee realizes that it is Herbie who deserves the credit. Determined to get back the magical car, Thorndyke dupes Tennessee in an Irish coffee drinking bout and succeeds in getting Herbie drunk. As a result, Jim loses his next race and decides to replace Herbie with a larger model. Herbie's true worth finally becomes apparent to Jim, however; with Carole as his co-driver he competes in a race against Thorndyke. Using every trick he knows, Thorndyke almost causes Herbie to crash, but he ultimately fails when the little car literally splits in two, thus placing first and third. Their happiness complete, Jim and Carole set off on a honeymoon—with Herbie driving them to a destination of his own choosing. *Sculptors.*

Secretaries. Automobile racing. Magic. Snobbery. Cheating. Volkswagen automobiles. San Francisco.

Note: Location scenes filmed in San Francisco, on the Monterey peninsula, and at several raceways.

THE LOVE CAGE see JOY HOUSE

LOVE CAMP 7
F6.2866

Olympic International Films. *Dist* Cinex International Film Distributors, Olympic International Films, Republic Amusements Corp. **1968**. Sd; col (Eastman Color). 35mm. 95 min.

Prod-Orig Story R. W. Cresse. *Assoc Prod* Wesdon Bishop. *Dir* R. L. Frost. *Screenplay* Wesdon Bishop. *Photog* R. L. Frost. *Ed* R. L. F. Enterprises. *Asst Dir* Stefan Zema. *Prod Mgr* Paul Wilmoth. *Prod Asst* Chuck Fisher. *Uniforms & Equipment* Hollywood Military Hobbies. *Sp Eff* Harry Woolman. *Key Grip* Jay Donohue.

Cast: R. W. Cresse, Maria Lease, Dave Friedman, Patricia Roddy, Jo Ellen, Kathy Williams.

War drama. During World War II, Martha Grossman, a German-Jewish scientist who allegedly possesses information vital to the development of a turbojet engine, is held prisoner in Love Camp 7, a Nazi establishment where Jewish women are forced to become sexual playthings for Third Reich officers. Wac Lieutenants Grace Harmon and Linda Freeman volunteer to enter the camp for the purpose of memorizing the secret data, knowing that for 5 days they will be subjected to brutal and humiliating treatment by the Nazis. Linda plans to reach Martha by assaulting an officer when he tries to rape her. She finds Martha bound, amidst evidence of sadism and torture, and reveals her plans for them to escape. Meanwhile, Grace is forced to make love with a female prisoner while the voyeuristic camp commander watches. Linda and Grace, using their skills in judo and karate, go into action during an orgy staged by the Nazis. Grace is shot during the fight, but Linda and Martha escape to the waiting British airplane. *Spies. Scientists. Nazis. Hostages. Germans. Jews. Sadism. Lesbianism. Voyeurism. Torture. Rape. Murder. Concentration camps. Judo. Karate. World War II. United States Army—Women's Army Corps. Germany—History—Third Reich.*

Note: May also be known as *Love Camp.*

THE LOVE CHILD see LOVE ME ... PLEASE

LOVE CHILDREN
F6.2867

MJ Productions. *Dist* MarJon Film Distributors. ca **1970**. Sd; col. 16mm. [Feature film, length unknown.]

Sex film. No information about the precise nature of this film has been found. *Hippies. Sexuality.*

THE LOVE CHILDREN see PSYCH-OUT

THE LOVE CLINIC
F6.2868

Sebastian Films. *Dist* Boxoffice International Pictures. **1968** [c15 Jul 1968; LP37330]. Sd; col (Eastman Color). 35mm. 84 min.

Prod-Dir Ferdinand Sebastian. *Exec Prod* Beverly Sebastian. *Orig Story-Screenplay* Ann Cawthorne. *Photog* Ferdinand Sebastian.

Cast—Pretty faces: Marion Cline *(Kate Morgan)*, Judy Blye *(Marge)*, Sally Stockman *(nurse)*.

Cast—Handsome types: Jim Carlton *(Sam Morgan)*, Jerry Ballew *(Benny)*, Benny Sebastian *(Mark)*.

Cast—Noble characters: COM 9001, Rebel.

Comedy-drama. Kate Morgan, who has not been sexually satisfied after a year of marriage, visits a love clinic, and there the "computer" COM 9001 gives her lessons in sexual fulfillment. Her husband, Sam, discovers that she has enrolled in the clinic's research program. He allows her to continue her studies but becomes enraged when he finds nude photographs of her among the literature she has brought home from the clinic, and he leaves after an argument. Using binoculars, he watches Kate explore her body as she reads from a book. Embarrassed, she refuses his help in locating her erogenous zones and pledges her fidelity to the machine. Sam confronts COM 9001 and is told that he is a failure as a husband. He enters the machine with Kate for an evaluation, and they obtain a complete program for fulfillment. The schedule results only in frustration and anger. Kate, fearful that she may be at fault, joins a singles program at the clinic. Just as Kate is preparing to go into COM 9001 with a new man, Sam rushes in, destroys the machine, drags her back to their houseboat, and masterfully makes love to her. *Marriage. Sexual techniques. Autoeroticism. Sex instruction. Sexual dysfunction. Sex clinics. Computers. Houseboats. Photographs.*

LOVE, COMPUTER STYLE see THE CURIOUS FEMALE

THE LOVE CULT
F6.2869

Arcanum Productions. 10 Aug **1966** [Champaign, Illinois, showing]. Sd; b&w. 35mm. 68 min.

Dir T. A. Dee. *Story* Russel Fore.

Melodrama. "Eric the Great," a hypnotist who makes smalltown television appearances, forms an organization combining religious fervor with sex in order to defraud people of their money. He and his wife, Aggie, con and hypnotize people into contributing their money and possessions to the cult. Wealthy nymphomaniac Claire Blakesley, after attending one of his meetings, donates her country house as a temple in hopes that the hypnotist (now calling himself "Eros") will create an atmosphere in which she can practice her own sexual deviations. Eros eventually loses control of his disciples: his wife is raped and Mrs. Blakesley is murdered. Eros goes mad and the organization is dissolved. *Hypnotists. Sex deviates. Fraud. Nymphomania. Promiscuity. Rape. Murder. Insanity. Wealth. Cults. Religion.*

LOVE CYCLES (Greece)
F6.2870

Transit Film. *Dist* Europix-Consolidated Corp. Apr **1969**. Sd; b&w. 35mm. 87 min.

Pres by Dino Fazio. *Prod* Theophanis A. Damaskinos, Viktor G. Michaelides. *Dir* Georges Skalenakis. *Screenplay* Yannis Djiotis. *Photog* Andrea Anastassatos. *Mus* Yannis Markopoulos. *Prod Dir* Vion Papamichalis.

Cast: Elena Nathanael (*Elena*), Spiros Focas (*Alexander*), Theo Roubanis (*Vassilis*), Despo Diamantidou (*Marianthe*), Dimos Starenios (*teacher*), Aris Malliagross (*doctor*).

Drama. While her husband, Vassilis, is at sea, Athenian fashion model Elena stays with her insane mother, Marianthe, who still mourns the death of her son in World War II. Upon the captain's return the couple vacations at a seaside resort where Elena is irresistibly attracted to the innkeeper, Alexander. Torn by remorse, Elena confesses her infatuation to Vassilis, who beats her and returns home. No longer inhibited by his presence, the couple make love. Elena contritely returns to Athens, pursued by Alexander. Although she agrees to forsake her lover and join her husband on a cruise, Elena has relations with Alexander one final time. Arriving at the docks, she is denounced by her husband, who departs alone. *Sailors. Models. Innkeepers. Mistresses. Marriage. Infidelity. Ships. Vacations. Resorts. Athens.*

Note: Filmed in Greece in 1966 as *Dama spathi*; running time: 105 min. Also known as *Queen of Clubs*.

THE LOVE DOCTORS
F6.2871

CTG Productions. *Dist* Sigma III Corp., Unusual Films International. 12 Nov **1969** [Saint Louis opening]. Sd; col (Eastman Color). 35mm. 90 min. *MPAA rating* X.

A Byron Chudnow–Louis Garfinkle Production. *Exec Prod* David Chudnow. *Assoc Prod* Andrew Babbish. *Dir* Bon Ross. *Screenplay* Louis Garfinkle. *Dir Photog* Robert Wilson, Walter Gregg. *Film Ed* Allen Ross. *Mus* Mark David. *Sd* Bruce Bisenz. *Boom* Bruce DeMichelle. *Makeup* Guy Nicholas. *Key Grip* Larry Beckstead.

Cast: Ann Jannin (*Dr. Ballantine*), Anne Acres (*Eileen Hanson*), Winston St. Ile (*Cliff Short*), Anabelle Pope, Ann Garfield (*Jan [see note]*), Lawrence Adams (*Bill*), Ernie Palmer (*Ernie*), Lima Jaynes (*Jayne*), Joseph Berger (*Hopkins*), Frank Mahalan (*Dr. Grady*), Roberta Reeves (*Georgia*), David Martin, actor (*President Farr*), Ton D'Amico (*Denson*), Harold Oxley (*Willard*), Hank Jones (*Rex*), Richard Southern (*guard*).

Melodrama. Two doctors run a research laboratory called the Human Heterosexual Experience Lab on a California university campus. Volunteers are recruited on the basis of their problems and frustrations. A widow, Eileen, and Cliff, married to a cripple, fall in love as their sexual responses are being measured on a laboratory bed. Jayne and Ernie try to work out their own marital problems caused by her frigidity. Jan works by herself with a dildo. One of the university's regents, refused participation, tries to close down the laboratory in revenge. A hearing follows in which all the participants relate how their sex lives have been aided by their experiences, and the university president decides to allow the enterprise to continue. *Physicians. Widows. Sex research. Marriage. Frigidity. College life. Laboratories. California.*

Note: Sources conflict in crediting the role of Jan; Anabelle Pope and Ann Garfield may be the same person.

THE LOVE DOLL
F6.2872

Dist Sherpix, Inc. 19 Aug **1970** [Los Angeles opening]. Sd; col. 35mm? 63 min.

Dir L. Feder.

Comedy. When wound up by its owner, a doll comes to life as a seductive woman. *Sexuality. Metamorphosis. Dolls.*

THE LOVE ETERNE (Hong Kong)
F6.2873

Shaw Brothers (H. K.) Ltd. *Dist* Frank Lee International. 24 Jun **1964** [San Francisco opening]. Sd; col (Eastmancolor). 35mm (Shawscope). 126 min.

Prod Run Run Shaw. *Dir-Writ* Li Han-hsiang. *Photog* Ho Lan-shan. *Art Dir* Chen Chi-jui. *Mus* Chou Lan-ping. *Sd* Wang Yung-hua.

Cast: Betty Loh Tih (*Chu Ying-tai*), Ivy Ling Po (*Liang Shan-po*), Jen Chieh (*Ying Hsin*), Chen Yen Yen (*Lady Chu*), Li Kun (*Ssu Chiu*), Kao Pao-shu (*headmaster's wife*), Ching Miao (*Chu Kung-yuan*), Yang Chi-ching (*headmaster*), Au-yang Sha-fei (*Lady Liang*), Chiang Kuang-chao.

Romantic melodrama. In 4th-century China, Chu Ying-tai persuades her parents to permit her to study at the school in Hangchow. Disguised as a man she falls in love with Liang Shan-po, a fellow student, who despite her many hints never perceives her masquerade and romantic interest in him. After several years Liang Shan-po is informed of the disguise by the headmaster's wife, and he visits Chu Ying-tai, but by this time she is betrothed to another man. They part, and Liang Shan-po commits suicide. Chu Ying-tai learns of his death while preparing for her wedding, and donning mourning clothes instead of her bride's dress she visits his grave. A terrible storm breaks out, the grave opens, and she falls in. The storm abates, and Liang Shan-po and Chu Ying-tai emerge as butterflies. *Students. Lovelorn. Male impersonation. Marriage—Arranged. Suicide. Metamorphosis. Butterflies. Hangchow. Storms.*

Note: Shown in Hong Kong in 1963 as *Liang Shan-po yü Chu Ying-t'ai.*

THE LOVE EXPERTS see **THE SEXPERTS—TOUCHED BY TEMPTATION**

LOVE FACTORY (Italy)
F6.2874

Alma Film. *Dist* Seymour Borde & Associates. 1 Jan **1969** [Chicago opening]. Sd; b&w with col seq (Technicolor). 35mm. 94 min.

Pres by S. S. & B. Film Productions. *Prod* Francesco Mazzei. *Dir* Massimo Mida. *Screenplay* Bruno Baratti. *Photog* Marcello Gatti, Gianni Narzisi. *Mus* Piero Umiliani.

Cast—"White—The Unkindest Cut": Anita Ekberg (*Albachiaria*), Carlo Giuffrè (*Vitaliano*), Sandro Dori (*The Mute*), E. Caruso.

Cast—"Red—Veni, Vidi, Vici": Carlo Giuffrè (*Apollodorus*), Maria Grazia Buccella (*Poppaea*), Giancarlo Cobelli (*Nero*), Marcella Ruffini (*Sulpicia*).

Cast—"Yellow—Suicides Anonymous": Carlo Giuffrè (*Brighenti*), Agnes Spaak (*Enrichetta*), Claudia Giannotti (*Mrs. Brighenti*), Leopoldo Trieste (*unidentified role, episode uncertain*).

Cast—"Pink—The First": Carlo Giuffrè (*Johnny*), Yoko Tani (*Yoko*), Pietro Carloni, Giusi Raspani Dandolo.

Comedy. WHITE THE UNKINDEST CUT: A veterinarian becomes the lover of a woman who makes her living castrating pigs. When he leaves her waiting at the altar, she pursues him, intent on using her professional skills to avenge herself. RED VENI. VIDI. VICI: In Imperial Rome in 64 A.D., Nero's wife, Poppaea, enjoys taking milk baths with a series of lovers. Insanely jealous, Nero sets fire to Rome. YELLOW SUICIDES ANONYMOUS: A wealthy Milan industrialist is abandoned by his teenaged mistress when he loses his fortune. PINK THE FIRST: A Japanese stripper seduces a playboy at a marijuana party, and he becomes pregnant. Because of his promiscuous behavior, she refuses to believe that the baby is hers. *Veterinarians. Brides. Industrialists. Mistresses. Gold diggers. Stripteasers. Japanese. Playboys. Castration. Revenge. Bathing customs. Seduction. Infidelity. Pregnancy. Promiscuity. Jealously. Marijuana. Rome—History—Empire. Milan. Nero. Poppaea Sabina. Fires.*

Note: Released in Italy in 1965 as *Bianco, rosso, giallo, rosa*; running time: ca100 min. In the Italian version "The First" is titled "L'intrigo"; "The Unkindest Cut," "L'incastro"; and "Suicides Anonymous," "Anonima omicidi." Of the four episodes, only "Veni, Vidi, Vici" is in color. This episode was filmed on location among the landmarks of ancient Rome. Also known as *White, Red, Yellow, and Pink.*

THE LOVE FEAST (West Germany)
F6.2875

Achtmann-Filmproduktion. *Dist* Globe Pictures. 22 Jul **1966** [Los Angeles showing]. Sd; b&w. 35mm. 88 min.

Pres by Joseph Green. *Dir* Hans Dieter Bove. *Screenplay* Christoph Baal, Klaus Peter Schulze. *Camera* Erich Küchler. *Sets* Fritz Graf. *Mus* Wolfram Roehrig.

Cast: Jan Hendriks (*Bobby Elkins*), Hannelore Elsner (*Elke Gerdes*), Karin Kernke (*Karin Klausen*), Walter Wilz (*Dr. Harald Goetz*), Elisabeth Volkman (*Kitty*), Almut Berg (*Lollo*), Adeline Wagner (*Mady*), Edith Mill (*Gloria Elkins*), Gerhard Kittler (*Professor Elkins*).

Melodrama. Bobby Elkins is a playboy who belongs to a young, fast crowd; Bobby's father is an eminent physician whose second wife, young and bored with her marriage, feels rejected by Bobby. Bobby indulges in macabre pleasures with Elke, a girl of 17; he drops Elke, and she finds herself with no money and no place to go. She confides in Karin, Dr. Elkins' laboratory assistant, and Karin decides to punish Bobby. Karin accepts an invitation to one of his parties, but

Bobby ignores her to make a play for Kitty, a young starlet. Elke is arrested during a raid on prostitutes and taken to a hospital where she is found to be seriously ill. Bobby and Karin meet again, and Karin, realizing that he is lonely and ill, attempts to help him. Karin's efforts only draw her deeper into Bobby's way of life, and soon Bobby goes to another orgy. Karin tries to convince Bobby to visit Elke on her deathbed, but he refuses. As Bobby races off in his car in the opposite direction from the hospital, Dr. Goetz and the rest of Bobby's crowd give chase. Bobby's car overturns, and he is killed. *Physicians. Playboys. Prostitutes. Promiscuity. Orgies. Automobile accidents.*

Note: Released in West Germany in Dec. 1961 as *Immer wenn es Nacht wird;* running time: 95 min.

LOVE FROM PARIS   F6.2876
Dist Stacey Distributors. ca **1970**. Sd; col. 16mm. 61-81 min.
Sex film. No information about the precise nature of this film has been found. *Sexuality.*

THE LOVE GENERATION   F6.2877
Artscope, Ltd. Dec **1967**. Sd; b&w. 35mm. [Feature length assumed.]
Pres by Amin Chaudhri.
Sex film. Frankie, a Park Avenue millionaire, amuses himself by using his movie camera to record the antics of his friends. With Pussycat, his bosomy English girl friend, he visits and films boisterous parties, the auditions of willing young starlets, an orgy, and two beautiful actresses rehearsing for a sex exploitation film in which they portray lesbians. *Millionaires. Actors. English. Voyeurism. Orgies. Lesbianism. Sex exploitation films. Pornography. Home movies. Rehearsals. New York City—Park Avenue.*

THE LOVE GOD?   F6.2878
Universal Pictures. 9 Jul **1969** [Los Angeles opening; c26 Jul 1970; LP38805]. Sd (Westrex); col (Technicolor). 35mm (Techniscope). 102 min. *MPAA rating* M.
Prod Edward J. Montagne. *Assoc Prod* Billy Sands. *Dir-Writ* Nat Hiken. *Dir Photog* William Margulies. *Art Dir* Alexander Golitzen, George Patrick. *Set Decor* John McCarthy, Marvin March. *Titl & Eff* Universal Title. *Film Ed* Sam E. Waxman. *Mus Supv* Stanley Wilson. *Mus Vic* Mizzy. *Song:* "Mr. Peacock" Walter Slivinski. *Sung by* The Blossoms, Orange Colored Sky. *Song:* "Summer in the Meadow" Lyn Murray, Nat Hiken. *Choreog* Wilda Taylor. *Sd* Waldon O. Watson, Frank H. Wilkinson. *Asst Dir* Phil Bowles. *Unit Prod Mgr* Wes Thompson. *Cost Dsgn* Helen Colvig. *Makeup* Bud Westmore. *Hairstyles* Larry Germain.
Cast: Don Knotts *(Abner Audubon Peacock),* Anne Francis *(Lisa LaMonica),* Edmond O'Brien *(Osborn Tremain),* James Gregory *(Darrell Evans Hughes),* Maureen Arthur *(Eleanor Tremain),* Margaret Ann Peterson *(Rose Ellen Wilkerson),* B. S. Pully *(J. Charles Twilight),* Jesslyn Fax *(Miss Love),* Jacques Aubuchon *(Carter Fenton),* Marjorie Bennett *(Miss Pickering),* Jim Boles *(Amos Peacock),* Ruth McDevitt *(Miss Keezy),* Roy Stuart *(Joe Merkel),* Herbert Voland *(Attorney General Fred Snow),* James Westerfield *(Reverend Wilkerson),* John Hubbard *(Craig Frazier),* Bob Hastings *(Shrader),* Larry McCormick *(Rich),* Robert Lieb *(Rayfield),* Willis Bouchey *(Judge Claypool),* Herbie Faye *(Lester Timkin),* Johnny Seven *(Petey),* Joseph Perry *(Big Joe),* Jim Begg *(Hotchkiss),* Carla Borelli *(Erica Lane),* Nancy Bonniwell *(Toma),* Shelly Davis *(Ingrid),* A'Leshia Lee *(Sherry),* Terri Harper *(Delilah).*
Comedy. Having acquired the rights to Abner Audubon Peacock's financially troubled journal of ornithology, convicted pornographer Osborn Tremain promptly sends its editor on a research trip to South America and transforms the publication into a girlie magazine. When Peacock returns, he discovers himself the object of a lawsuit. Because of his attorney's eloquent defense the editor is acquitted and hailed by the press as a champion of free speech and harbinger of the sexual revolution. Actually, Peacock is a virgin, long affianced to Rose Ellen Wilkerson, the chaste daughter of a minister. Despite his inexperience, Peacock's image is embellished by liberated coeditor Lisa LaMonica, who installs the shy birdwatcher in a penthouse and equips him with an entourage of voluptuous "Pussycats." Alarmed, Rose Ellen's father insists that Peacock call a press conference to proclaim his virginity. Fearing consequent loss of circulation, the coeditor encourages the abstemious ornithologist to become intoxicated. When Peacock awakens and espies Lisa's bra hanging from the chandelier he assumes the worst. Shocked, the honorable Peacock promises to marry Lisa immediately. He insists, however, that the ambitious editor give up her job. During the ceremony Lisa gratefully defers to Rose Ellen, who takes her place at Peacock's side. *Pornographers. Editors. Clergymen. Lawyers. Freedom of the press. Ornithology. Virginity. Male chauvinism. Courtship. Magazines (periodicals). Lawsuits. Weddings. South America.*

THE LOVE GODDESSES   F6.2879
Walter Reade–Sterling, Inc. *Dist* Continental Distributing, Inc. 3 Mar **1965** [New York opening]. Sd; b&w. 35mm. 87 min. [See note.]
Pres by Walter Reade–Sterling Inc. *Prod-Writ* Saul J. Turell, Graeme Ferguson. *Film Ed* Nat Greene, Howard Kuperman. *Mus* Percy Faith. *Asst to the Prod* Edward Duffield, Janet Jacobson, Frances Morris. *Cons* William K. Everson, Paul Killiam, James A. Lebenthal. *Tech Adv* Ray Angus. *Res* Georges Labrousse, Gideon Bachmann.
Narrator: Carl King.
Compilation film. Films used to survey the history of the "love goddess" are: *Blonde Venus* (1932) and *Morocco* (1930) with Marlene Dietrich; *True Heart Susie* (1919) with Lillian Gish; *Leopard Woman* (1920) with Louise Glaum; *Cleopatra* (1917) with Theda Bara; *Intolerance* (1916) with Mae Marsh; *The Cheat* (1915) with Fannie Ward and Sessue Hayakawa; *The Sheik* (1921) with Agnes Ayres and Rudolph Valentino; *Hula* (1927) with Clara Bow; *Blood and Sand* (1922) with Nita Naldi; *Woman of the World* (1925) with Pola Negri; *The Sorrows of Satan* (1926) with Lya De Putti; *The Love of Sunya* (1927) with Gloria Swanson; *The Diary of a Lost Girl (Das Tagebuch einer Verlorenen* 1929; U. S. release uncertain) with Louise Brooks; *Ecstasy (Extase,* 1933; U. S. release: 1937) with Hedy Lamarr; *L'Atlantide* (1932; U. S. release uncertain) with Brigitte Helm; *Peter the Tramp (Luffar-Petter,* 1922; U. S. release uncertain) with Greta Garbo; *Platinum Blonde* (1931) with Jean Harlow; *Cabin in the Cotton* (1932) with Bette Davis; *Gold Diggers of 1933* (1933) with Ruby Keeler and Dick Powell; *No Man of Her Own* (1932) with Carole Lombard and Clark Gable; *Professional Sweetheart* (1933) with Ginger Rogers and Norman Foster; *Love Me Tonight* (1932) with Jeanette MacDonald, Myrna Loy, Maurice Chevalier, and Charles Ruggles; *I'm No Angel* (1933) with Mae West; *Baby Face* (1933) with Barbara Stanwyck; *Now and Forever* (1934) with Shirley Temple; *They Won't Forget* (1937) with Lana Turner; *College Swing* (1938) with Betty Grable; *Her Jungle Love* (1938) with Dorothy Lamour and Ray Milland; *Gilda* (1946) with Rita Hayworth; *A Place in the Sun* (1951) with Elizabeth Taylor and Montgomery Clift; *Some Like It Hot* (1959) with Marilyn Monroe; *It Started in Naples* (1960) with Sophia Loren and Clark Gable; *Tiger Bay* (1959) with Hayley Mills and Horst Buchholz; *Roman Holiday* (1953) with Audrey Hepburn and Gregory Peck; *Room at the Top* (1958; U. S. release: 1959) with Heather Sears and Simone Signoret; *Love Is My Profession (En cas de malheur,* 1958; U. S. release: 1959) with Brigitte Bardot; *Expresso Bongo* (1959; U. S. release: 1960) with Sylvia Syms; *The American Venus* (1926) with Esther Ralston; and *Cleopatra* (1934) with Claudette Colbert. *Actors. Motion pictures. Motion pictures—History.*
Note: Also reviewed at 76, 79, and 82 min. Film footage and stills are credited to Columbia Pictures, Editions Jean-Jacques Pauvert, the George Eastman House, the Killiam-Sterling Film Collection, the Museum of Modern Art, Paramount Pictures, the Rank Organisation, RKO Radio Pictures, Romulus Films, and United Artists.

LOVE GODDESSES OF BLOOD ISLAND *see* SIX SHES AND A HE

LOVE HAS MANY FACES   F6.2880
Jerry Bresler Productions. *Dist* Columbia Pictures. 24 Feb **1965** [New York opening; c31 Dec 1964; LP30039]. Sd (RCA); col (Eastman Color by Pathé). 35mm. 105 min. [Copyright length: 95 min.]
A Jerry Bresler Production. *Prod* Jerry Bresler. *Dir* Alexander Singer. *Screenplay* Marguerite Roberts. *Dir Photog* Joseph Ruttenberg. *Art Dir* Alfred Sweeney. *Home Furnishings Dsgn* Noldi Schreck of Mexico City. *Main Titl* DePatie-Freleng. *Film Ed* Alma Macrorie. *Mus* David Raksin. *Titl Song* Mack David, David Raksin. *Sung by* Nancy Wilson. *Sd Supv* Charles J. Rice. *Sd* Jesus Gonzalez Gancy. *Asst Dir* Dick Moder. *Prod Mgr* Joseph Behm. *Miss Turner's Wardrobe Dsgn* Edith Head. *Makeup Supv* Ben Lane. *Makeup* Del Armstrong, Del Acevedo. *Hairstyles* Naomi Cavin.
Cast: Lana Turner *(Kit Jordan),* Cliff Robertson *(Pete Jordan),* Hugh O'Brian *(Hank Walker),* Ruth Roman *(Margot Eliot),* Stefanie Powers *(Carol Lambert),* Virginia Grey *(Irene Talbot),* Ron Husmann *(Chuck Austin),* Enrique Lucero *(Lieut. Riccardo Andrade),* Carlos Montalban *(Don Julian),* Jaime Bravo *(Manuel Perez),* Fannie Schiller *(Maria),* René Dupreyon *(Ramos).*
Melodrama. Married couple Kit and Pete are questioned by the Acapulco police when the body of Billy Andrews, a beachboy, washes ashore. Kit had an affair with Billy, and Pete accuses Kit of causing Billy's suicide because she ended their affair. Pete is a former beachboy who married Kit for her money and is now having second thoughts about his way of life. When Carol Lambert, Billy's fiancée, arrives in Acapulco, Pete becomes attracted to her, and Kit, meanwhile, consoles herself with a bullfighter. At the ranch of Don Julian, where they are watching the testing of the bulls, Kit overhears Carol demand of Pete that he choose between herself and Kit. Upset, Kit rides her horse into the bullring and is gored by a bull, but Pete jumps into the ring and diverts the bull's second charge. Kit is rushed to the hospital; Carol returns to the States;

and Pete and Kit are reconciled. *Playboys. Bullfighters. Americans in foreign countries. Police. Suicide. Infidelity. Wealth. Marriage. Ranches. Acapulco. Bulls.*

Note: Filmed on location in Acapulco and Mexico City.

LOVE, HOLLYWOOD STYLE see SHANNON'S WOMEN

THE LOVE HOURS see THE LUSTING HOURS

LOVE HUNGER (Argentina)   F6.2881
Dist Cambist Films. 18 Aug **1965** [Chicago opening]. Sd; b&w with col seq (Eastman Color). 35mm. 72 min.

Prod Emilio Spitz. *Dir* Albert Dubois. *Screenplay* Albert Dubois, Albert Diego. *Dial English Vers* Jack Curtis. *Dir Photog* Juan Levaggi. *Asst Camera* Mort Segal. *Mus Comp & Cond* Ted Simon. *Dial Rec* Titra Sound Corp. *Mus Rec* Jerry Newman. *Prod Coörd* Luis Celis. *Prod Asst* Arturo Frizzera. *Makeup* Edith Bell.

Cast: Libertad Leblanc, Hector Pellegrini, Mario Hmaya, Mario Casado, Luis Alarcón, Hector Carrión, Jill Robin, George Fosati, Nancy Arnold, Steve Hollister, Amelia Folcini, Rick Angeline, Alberto Barcel, Carl Garcia.

Melodrama. After robbing a bank and killing a guard, three bandits take refuge in the shack of Pablo, an old trapper. The gang includes Robert, a gambler who despises his fellow thieves; Mex, a convicted rapist; and Joe. During an evening walk in the swamp, Robert espies a nude woman swimming. When he dives in the water, however, she vanishes. Inspired by his guests' complaints about sexual frustration, Pablo relates the legend of "The Naked Flower," according to which the only daughter of an aristocratic family was assaulted by a crazed gardener. Years later the woman marries a cavalry officer. As the couple make love outdoors the morning after their wedding, they are observed by the gardener, who has escaped from the asylum in which he has been confined. Infuriated, he kills the groom and rapes the bride. The distraught wife jumps in the swamp, but returns on moonlit nights in search of her husband. While strolling through the swamp again, Robert meets Mara, the sheltered daughter of a jealous father, and promptly has intercourse with her. When Mex attempts to steal the trio's loot, Joe shoots him to death. He then kills Mara's father and attempts to rape her. He is, however, interrupted by Robert and shot and killed by Pablo. Freed of all former ties, Robert and Mara plan a future together. *Trappers. Gamblers. Gardeners. Newlyweds. Rape. Murder. Jealousy. Swamps. Bank robberies.*

Note: Released in Argentina in 1964 as *La flor del irupé*.

LOVE IN A GOLDFISH BOWL   F6.2882
Jurow-Shepherd Productions. *Dist* Paramount Pictures. Jun **1961** [c1 Jun 1961; LP19504]. Sd; col (Technicolor). 35mm (Panavision). 88 min.

Prod Martin Jurow, Richard Shepherd. *Dir-Screenplay* Jack Sher. *Story* Irene Kamp, Jack Sher. *Dir Photog* Loyal Griggs. *Technicolor Col Cons* Richard Mueller. *Art Dir* Hal Pereira, Roland Anderson. *Set Decor* Sam Comer, Ray Moyer. *Film Ed* Terry O. Morse. *Mus Score & Cond* Jimmie Haskell. *Titl Song* Hal David, Burt Bacharach. *Sung by* Tommy Sands. *Song:* "You're Only Young Once" Russell Faith, Robert Marcucci, Peter De Angelis. *Sung by* Fabian. *Sd Rec* Frank McWhorter, John Wilkinson. *Asst Dir* Tom Shaw. *Cost Supv* Edith Head. *Makeup Supv* Wally Westmore. *Hairstyle Supv* Nellie Manley. *Sp Photog Eff* John P. Fulton. *Process Photog* Farciot Edouart. *Dial Supv* Jud Taylor.

Cast: Tommy Sands (*Gordon Slide*), Fabian (*Giuseppe ["Seppi"] La Barba*), Jan Sterling (*Sandra Slide*), Toby Michaels (*Blythe Holloway*), Edward Andrews (*Senator Clyde Holloway*), John McGiver (*Dr. Frowley*), Majel Barrett (*Alice*), Shirley O'Hara (*Clara Dumont*), Robert Patten (*Lieut. J. G. Marchon*), Phillip Baird (*Gregory*), Denny Miller (*Oscar Flegler*), Susan Silo (*Jenny*), Elizabeth MacRae (*Jackie*), Joe Hyams, Mike McKeever, Marlin McKeever, Dee J. Thompson, Tom Quinn, "Tiger".

Comedy. Gordon Slide and Blythe Holloway are juniors at a small college in southern California. Their platonic relationship is based primarily upon a common bond of parental neglect. As Easter vacation approaches, Gordon learns that his divorced mother expects him to vacation with her in Hawaii, and Blythe realizes that her father, a busy senator, wants her to join him in Denver. The two youngsters decide it would be more fun to spend the 2 weeks together, and they set themselves up at Gordon's mother's "beach pad" at Balboa. All goes well until the boat they are sailing capsizes; whereupon Blythe is rescued by an amorous Coast Guardsman named Seppi La Barba. Blythe becomes immediately attracted to the young man and suddenly finds herself playing hostess to a rowdy crowd of Coast Guardsmen and civilians. Their wild party is interrupted by the unexpected arrival of Gordon's mother and Blythe's father. Accusations follow, but eventually the parents realize how wrong their assumptions are. In the confusion, Gordon and Blythe discover that their feelings for each other are much more than platonic. Consequently, when they return to college, they begin making plans for another vacation—in a mountain hideaway in Wyoming owned by Gordon's uncle. *Students. United States Coast Guard. Italians. College life. Parenthood. Platonic love. Jealousy. Vacations. Easter. California.*

LOVE IN A HOT CLIMATE see BEAUTY AND THE BULLFIGHTER

LOVE IN CHAINS   F6.2883
Kingslie Productions. *Dist* MarJon Film Distributors. ca **1970**. Sd; col. 16mm. ca60 min.

Drama. Two young women, anxious for male companionship, consult a witch and receive a magic love potion that will render any man subservient to their desires. They lure men to their apartment and hold them captive as sex slaves. One man is captured as he is about to be married. His worried fiancée asks his best friend for help in finding him, but the friend agrees only after she consents to make love. They visit the women's apartment and are tricked into taking the potion, but all ends well as everyone joins in a group sex session. *Witches. Abduction. Group sex. Aphrodisiacs.*

LOVE IN COLD BLOOD see THE ICE HOUSE

LOVE IN 4 DIMENSIONS (France/Italy)   F6.2884
Adelphia Compagnia Cinematografica–France Cinema Productions. *Dist* Eldorado Pictures International. 21 Sep **1965** [New York opening]. Sd; b&w. 35mm. 105 min.

Overall Production Credits: *Exec Prod* Luciano Cattania. *Ed* Franco Fraticelli. *Mus* Franco Mannino. *English subtitl* Noelle Gillmor.

Production Credits for "Love and Language": *Dir-Screenplay* Massimo Mida. *Photog* Dario Di Palma.

Production Credits for "Love and Life": *Dir* Jacques Romain. *Screenplay* Bruno Baratti. *Photog* Tonino Delli Colli.

Production Credits for "Love and Art": *Dir-Screenplay* Gianni Puccini. *Photog* Carlo Di Palma.

Production Credits for "Love and Death": *Dir-Screenplay* Mino Guerrini. *Photog* Tonino Delli Colli.

Cast—"Love and Language": Carlo Giuffrè (*Gerlando, the Sicilian*), Franca Rame (*Susy*), Carlo Bagno (*Trapattoni, the taxi driver*).

Cast—"Love and Life": Sylva Koscina (*Irma, the wife*), Gastone Moschin (*The Husband*), Franca Polesello (*Rosa, the maid*), Isa Crescenzi.

Cast—"Love and Art": Philippe Leroy (*Franco Lampredi, the husband*), Elena Martini (*Livia Lampredi, his wife*), Fabrizio Capucci (*Benito Mingozzi, the typist*), Alberto Bonucci (*Pallotta, the producer*).

Cast—"Love and Death": Michèle Mercier (*Luisa*), Alberto Lionello (*Matteo*).

Comedy. LOVE AND LANGUAGE: Gerlando, a Sicilian peasant, arrives in Milan and discovers that his dialect is incomprehensible to the Milanese. He is befriended by taxicab driver Trapattoni, who takes Gerlando home and introduces him to his daughter, Susy. Gerlando stays on and falls in love with Susy, who teaches him correct Italian. They eventually marry, and Gerlando takes up his father-in-law's vocation and amuses himself by waiting at the train station for bumpkins like himself and ridiculing them for their coarse ways. LOVE AND LIFE: Irma, who has taken a lover, sets a trap for her unfaithful husband in order to win her freedom. Taking advantage of her husband's weakness for beautiful women, she engages Rosa, a voluptuous model and call girl, as a housemaid. The plan works, and Irma surprises her husband in bed with Rosa. In gratitude, she telephones Rosa the next day to offer her compliments, but it is her lover who answers. LOVE AND ART: When screenwriter Franco Lampredi cannot complete his script for film producer Pallotta, he hires a secretary to help with the work load. Livia, his wife, becomes jealous of the attractive secretary, and Pallotta sends male typist Mingozzi, who is also an aspiring screenwriter, to assist Lampredi. Soon Mingozzi is doing all the writing. Lampredi is so flattered by the producer's compliments that he overlooks the affair Mingozzi and Livia are having. LOVE AND DEATH: Visiting his wife's grave, Matteo, a middle-aged industrialist, finds a beautiful young mourner sobbing at a nearby grave. Luisa, the mourner, is disconsolate over the death of her young husband. Matteo drives her to his home, and, united by grief, they quickly become lovers. At each new embrace, her tears flow afresh, rekindling his passion. In the morning, Luisa becomes upset at a sculptor's demand for 1,000,000 *lire* to complete her husband's tomb. Matteo writes her a check for the sum and returns to Milan revitalized by a new burst of youthful energy. Unable to concentrate on his work, however, he goes to Luisa's apartment, only to find that she has moved and left no forwarding address. Matteo returns to the cemetery and sees the beautiful black-garbed figure sobbing at another new grave. As Luisa begins to faint, another middle-aged mourner leaps from his wife's grave to catch her in his arms. *Sicilians. Taxi drivers. Peasants. Industrialists. Prostitutes. Motion picture scriptwriters. Secretaries. Widows. Widowers. Wealth. Fraud. Middle age. Seduction. Infidelity. Marriage. Snobbery. Ambition. Sexuality. Cemeteries. Milan.*

Note: Produced in Italy in 1963 as *Amore in 4 dimensioni*. Opened in Paris in May 1966 as *L'amour en 4 dimensions*. Jacques Romain is a pseudonym for

Mino Guerrini. In at least one review, Elena Martini's name is rendered Lena von Martens.

LOVE IN THE AFTERNOON *see* **FASCINATION**

LOVE IN THE PACIFIC   F6.2885
International Film Enterprises. 16 Oct **1970** [Des Moines, Iowa, opening]. Sd; col (Eastmancolor). 35mm. [Feature length assumed.] *MPAA rating* GP.
Prod-Dir-Writ Zygmunt Sulistrowski. *Assoc Prod* Amcky C. C. Johnson.
Documentary. No information about the precise nature of this film has been found, but press material suggests that it includes scenes of lovemaking as practiced in Polynesia, Melanesia, Coral Sea, New Guinea, the Philippines, Taiwan, Japan, and other places in the Pacific Ocean. *Sexual practices. Polynesians. Melanesia. Coral Sea. New Guinea. Philippines. Taiwan. Japan. Pacific Ocean.*

THE LOVE-INS   F6.2886
Four Leaf Productions. *Dist* Columbia Pictures. 26 Jul **1967** [San Francisco opening; c1 Sep 1967; LP34866]. Sd; col (Pathé). 35mm. 91 min. [Copyright length: 86 min.]
Prod Sam Katzman. *Assoc Prod* Jerome F. Katzman. *Dir* Arthur Dreifuss. *Screenplay* Hal Collins, Arthur Dreifuss. *Dir Photog* John F. Warren. *Art Dir* George W. Davis, Charles K. Hagedon. *Set Decor* Henry Grace, James Berkey. *Film Ed* Ben Lewis. *Mus Scored & Cond* Fred Karger. *Choreog* Hal Belfer. *Rec Supv* Franklin Milton. *Asst Dir* Donald C. Klune. *Unit Prod Mgr* Robert Stone. *Makeup* William Tuttle. *Hairstyles* Mary Keats.
Cast: Richard Todd (*Dr. Jonathan Barnett*), James MacArthur (*Larry Osborne*), Susan Oliver (*Patricia Cross*), Mark Goddard (*Elliot*), Carol Booth (*Harriet*), Marc Cavell (*Mario*), Janee Michelle (*Lamelle*), Ronnie Eckstine (*Bobby*), Michael Evans (*Reverend Spencer*), Hortense Petra (*Mrs. Sacaccio*), James Lloyd (*Mr. Henning*), Mario Roccuzzo (*hippie on LSD*), Joe Pyne, The Chocolate Watch Band, The U. F. O.'s, The New Age (*themselves*), Donnie Brooks.
Drama. The administrators of a West Coast college expel two students, Larry Osborne and Patricia Cross, for publishing an underground avant-garde newspaper, and professor of philosophy Jonathan Barnett resigns in protest. Barnett then appears on the Joe Pyne television show, where it is revealed that in a scholarly thesis he advocated the use of LSD for religious meditation; and he becomes a hero with the hippie element in San Francisco's Haight-Ashbury district. Evicted from his apartment, he moves in with Larry and Patricia and a group of their friends. Although initially sincere in following the hippie way of life, Barnett soon takes the young people's hero worship to heart. Encouraged by a hippie opportunist, Elliot, he begins to picture himself as a "messiah" and becomes involved in a money-making scheme in which a series of admission-priced "happenings" are arranged. At one of these Patricia takes a double dose of LSD and begins to do a striptease while imagining herself to be Alice in Wonderland. After witnessing the performance, Larry quarrels with Patricia and writes a series of articles exposing the hypocrisy of Barnett's cult. Patricia also becomes disillusioned when she tells Barnett that she is pregnant and is told to have an abortion lest she destroy his public image. She attempts suicide but is saved by Larry, who then takes a gun to a mass hippie rally and kills Barnett. As the crowd threatens to retaliate with a lynching, a young hippie grabs a microphone and starts to preach love and peace. Too late Larry realizes that by killing Barnett he has created a martyr and opened the way for a new "messiah." *Students. Professors. Hippies. Opportunists. Hero worship. Abortion. Suicide. Murder. Psychedelic states. Lynching. College life. Television. Philosophy. Hypocrisy. Communal living. Newspapers—Underground. LSD. Cults. San Francisco—Haight-Ashbury. "Alice in Wonderland".*

LOVE IS A BALL   F6.2887
Gold Medal Enterprises-Oxford Productions. *Dist* United Artists. 6 Mar **1963** [Los Angeles opening; c6 Mar 1963; LP24206]. Sd; col (Technicolor). 35mm (Panavision). 111 min.
Pres by Martin Poll. *Prod* Martin Poll. *Dir* David Swift. *2d Unit Dir* Harry Caplan. *Screenplay* David Swift, Tom Waldman, Frank Waldman. *Dir Photog* Edmond Séchan. *Art Dir* Jean d' Eaubonne. *Set Decor* Fernand Bernardi. *Film Ed* Tom McAdoo, Cathy Kelber. *Mus* Michel Legrand. *Sd* Guy Rophe. *Asst Dir* Danny McCauley, Patrice Dally. *Prod Mgr* Eugène Nase. *Cost Dsgn* Frank Thompson. *Wardrobe* Gladys de Segonzac. *Makeup* Jean-Paul Ulysse. *Hairstyles* Gladys Witten.
Cast: Glenn Ford (*John Davis*), Hope Lange (*Millie Mehaffey*), Charles Boyer (*Monsieur Étienne Pimm*), Ricardo Montalban (*Gaspard*), Telly Savalas (*Dr. Gump*), Ruth McDevitt (*Mathilda*), Ulla Jacobsson (*Janine*), Georgette Anys (*Madame Gallou*), Roberto Bettoni (*milkman*), Mony Dalmès (*Madame Fernier*), Laurence Hardy (*Priory*), Jean Lemaître (*Cario*), André Luguet (*Zoltan*), Olga Valéry (*Madame Girardin*), Jean Parédès (*Freddie*), Redmond Phillips (*Stacy*), Aram Stephan (*Gallou*), Erika Soucy (*Gretl*), John Wood

(*Soames*), Jean Pierre Zola (*Mueller*).
Romantic comedy. Source: Lindsay Hardy, *The Grand Duke and Mr. Pimm* (New York, 1959). John Davis, an American adventurer at loose ends on the Riviera, agrees to work for Étienne Pimm, a professional matchmaker attempting to arrange a marriage between the impoverished Duke Gaspard and madcap American millionairess Millicent Mehaffey. While teaching the duke how to drive, ride, and play polo, Davis is also obliged to keep an eye on Millicent by becoming his chauffeur. Although Pimm succeeds in bringing his client and the heiress together, the duke falls in love with Millicent's secretary, Janine, while Millicent becomes enamored of Davis. But when Davis' part in Pimm's scheme is disclosed, the outraged Millicent denounces everyone and decides to marry fortune-hunting Freddie Paladzini. On her wedding day, however, she receives a message from Davis in the form of his chauffeur's cap. Realizing that she really does love him, she leaves the wedding and joins Davis on his tourist boat. *Matchmakers. Millionaires. Adventurers. Chauffeurs. Heiresses. Secretaries. Fortune hunters. Riviera.*
Note: Location scenes filmed on the French Riviera. Working title: *The Grand Duke and Mr. Pimm.*

LOVE IS A CAROUSEL   F6.2888
Temarro Films. *Dist* Roma Productions. c16 Nov **1970** [LU3600]. Sd; col (Eastmancolor). 35mm. 77 min. *MPAA rating* R.
Prod Roy P. Cheverton, Marvin C. Spero. *Assoc Prod* Marvin Barbach. *Dir* Roy P. Cheverton. *Screenplay* Marvin C. Spero. *Dir Photog* Roy P. Cheverton. *Camera Op* Allan Quevedo. *Art Dir* Tee Jay Johnston. *Film Ed* Cesar A. Cruz. *Mus Score* Eleanor Gary. *Songs:* "Love Is a Carousel," "End Part II," "Thought," "Some Will Come," "Yesterday's Memories," "If I Could," "Ninth Epitaph," "New York Street," "Fred's Song" comp & perf by Icarus. *Songs:* "Lucerito," "Buenos Dias," "Esta Noche," "Soñando," "Contigo," "Dos Mundos" Julio Susana. *Sd Engr* Jack Lamont, Larry Fisher. *Unit Mgr* Marvin Barbach. *Sp Lighting Eff for Psychedelic Scene* After-Image. *Portraits* Tee Jay Johnston, Julio Susana. *Still Photog* Hugh Wetzel.
Cast: Icarus (*musicians*), Eleanor Gary (*herself*), Tee Jay Johnston (*himself, an artist*), Maria Robles (*Doria*), Kay K. Kelly (*stepmother*), Anita Moran (*go-go dancer*), John Savage (*boy friend*), Ellen Marion (*Jackie, the lesbian*), Julio Susana (*himself, an artist*), Bob Moore, actor (*messenger*), Claudia Renito (*Laura*), Capt. Jack Ott (*skipper of "Shark VII"*), Bill Hewett (*crew*), Muriel Marshall (*waitress*).
Melodrama. Doria leaves home after being raped and deflowered by her stepmother's boyfriend while her stepmother drunkenly watched. She is picked up on the highway by Jackie, a lesbian whose tenderness contrasts with Doria's recent experience. Doria then meets two artists, Tee Jay and Julio, who use her as their model and introduce her to a bohemian life of parties and such drugs as marijuana and LSD. *Stepmothers. Hitchhikers. Artists. Models. Rape. Drunkenness. Sexual initiation. Lesbianism. Bohemianism. Marijuana. LSD.*
Note: The song "Guantanamera" is part of the musical score.

LOVE IS A DAY'S WORK *see* **FROM A ROMAN BALCONY**

LOVE IS A FOUR-LETTER WORD   F6.2889
Olympic International Films. **1964**. Sd; b&w. 35mm. 61 min.
Prod Bob Cresse. *Dir* R. L. Frost.
Cast: Forman Shane (*Jerry*), Dianne Michaels.
Melodrama. Jerry, a college student, feels rejected when his girl friend refuses his sexual advances. In his loneliness, he turns to fantasy and becomes a voyeur. Peering into the window of a sorority house during an initiation ceremony he is appalled by the sadistic treatment the new members receive; in Mexico, he visits an exhibition and is repelled by two women making love; he returns to find his girl friend in the arms of a woman, and his sexual frustration erupts into violence. *Students. Voyeurism. Sadism. Lesbianism. Fantasy. Loneliness. Sororities. Rites and ceremonies. Stag shows. Mexico.*
Note: Also advertised as *Love Is an Exciting Word.*

LOVE IS A FUNNY THING (France/Italy) F6.2890
Ariane-Les Films Treize-Les Productions Artistes Associés-Produzioni Associate Delphos-Majestic Films. *Dist* United Artists. 18 Mar **1970** [New York opening; c25 Feb 1970; LF69]. Sd; col (De Luxe). 35mm. 110 min. *MPAA rating* GP.
Prod Alexandre Mnouchkine, Georges Dancigers. *Exec Prod* Alexandre Mnouchkine. *Dir-Writ* Claude Lelouch. *Dial* Claude Lelouch, Pierre Uytterhoeven. *Camera* Claude Lelouch. *Lighting* Jean Collomb. *Film Ed* Claude Barrois. *Mus* Francis Lai. *Sd* Jean-Louis Ducarme. *Asst Dir* Claude Pinoteau, Robert Dijoux. *Cost* Marie Osborne.
Cast: Jean-Paul Belmondo (*Henri*), Annie Girardot (*Françoise*), Maria-Pia Conte (*Henri's wife*), Marcel Bozzufi (*Françoise's husband*), Farrah Fawcett (*Patricia*), Peter Bergman (*director*), Kaz Garas (*Paul*), Bill Quinn (*passenger*), Arturo Dominici (*customs officer*), Timothy Blake (*"The Dominos"*), Jerry Cipperley (*waiter in cafe*), Forster Hood (*Indian*), Sweet Emma (*herself*).

Simone Renant, Susan Albert.

Romantic comedy-drama. Françoise, a famous French film actress, comes to Hollywood to make a film and meets Henri, a composer who has also come from France to work on the film. The two are gradually drawn to each other but continue to telephone their spouses, who have remained abroad. Finally, they spend the night together, and in a rented convertible, they drive to Las Vegas, tour the Southwest (imagining that they are being attacked by Indians as they drive through Monument Valley), and fly to New Orleans to listen to jazz in a nightclub. Françoise calls her husband and tells him of the affair, and she and Henri decide to go their separate ways. Henri calls Françoise from New York, however, to tell her that he wants to meet her in Nice. Françoise arrives for their rendezvous, but Henri does not appear. *Actors. Composers. Tourists. Indians of North America. Infidelity. Fantasy. Motion pictures. Nightclubs. Hollywood. Las Vegas. Monument Valley. New Orleans. New York City. Nice.*

Note: Location scenes filmed in Nevada, Utah, Arizona, and Louisiana; also in Paris and Nice. Opened in Paris in Dec 1969 as *Un homme qui me plait;* running time: 115 min. Italian title: *Un tipo che mi piace.* Working titles: *Histoire d'aimer* and *Again a Love Story.*

LOVE IS A WOMAN (Great Britain)   F6.2891

Associated British–Pathé, Ltd. *Dist* Hemisphere Pictures. Jun **1967**. Sd; col (Technicolor). 35mm. 88 min.

Prod Harry Field. *Assoc Prod* Lionel Hoare. *Dir* Frederic Goode. *Story-Screenplay* Wally Bosco. *Dir Photog* William Jordan. *Underwater Photog* Stephen Halliday. *Art Dir* Peter Moll. *Film Ed* Frederick Ives. *Mus & Songs* Joan Shakespeare. *Mus Dir* John Shakespeare. Song: "Who's Foolish" sung by Anita Harris. Song: "Francesca" sung by Dennis Lotis. *Sd Rec* John Batten. *Asst Dir* Ted Morley. *Prod Mgr* Ron Holtzer.

Cast: Patsy Ann Noble (*Francesca*), Mark Burns (*Dennis*), Shaun Curry (*Joe*), William Dexter (*Malo*), Wanda Ventham (*Priscilla*), Terence De Marney (*Jacomini*), Caron Gardner (*Mary*), Mark Singleton (*Costello*), Michael Brennan (*Bonelli*), Blake Butler (*lift operator*), Dulcie Bowman (*old lady*), Anita Harris (*herself*).

Melodrama. Dennis, an undercover narcotics agent, is sent to investigate smuggling activities on a Mediterranean island; Malo and Blake, partners in a gambling casino, are his principal suspects. As Dennis arrives on the island, however, Blake is beaten by Joe and then shot by Joe's mistress, Francesca. Malo witnesses the murder and attempts to blackmail the couple. To make contact with Malo, Dennis deliberately loses money gambling and goes to Malo's apartment for a loan. As Dennis leaves the apartment, he meets Detective Costello, who insists that together they confront Malo. They return to the apartment and discover that Malo has been stabbed to death. Since the door was locked from the inside, and since Dennis was the last person to see Malo alive, he becomes the prime suspect. Priscilla, an undercover agent, arrives on the island to assist Dennis in solving Malo's murder. They immediately suspect Francesca, who has been making secret underwater excursions and receiving small packages at the apartment building she shared with Malo. On one of Francesca's trips, Dennis swims after her and narrowly escapes being struck by a spear. Having solved the mystery of Malo's death, Dennis visits Costello to demonstrate how Francesca killed Malo by firing a spear gun through her window into his and recovering the spear by means of an attached cord. Meanwhile, Francesca, who is collecting the packages of heroin from her underwater cache and, with the help of her lover, Joe, transporting them to her yacht, suddenly turns on Joe, cuts his air hose, snatches his packages, and surfaces beside her yacht—only to find a police launch with Dennis and Priscilla aboard waiting for her. *Secret agents. Detectives. Mistresses. Divers. Murder. Gambling. Blackmail. Smuggling. Frameup. Heroin. Casinos. Spear guns. Islands. Mediterranean Sea.*

Note: Location scenes filmed on Malta. Released in Great Britain in Dec 1966 as *Death Is a Woman.* Also known as *Sex Is a Woman.*

LOVE IS AN EXCITING WORD *see* LOVE IS A FOUR-LETTER WORD

LOVE IS WHERE IT'S AT   F6.2892

August Films. *Dist* American Film Distributing Corp. 2 May **1968** [New York opening]. Sd; b&w. 35mm. 70 min.

Dir-Writ Sidney Knight. *Camera* Frank Kolleogy. *Asst Camera* Morey Shadde. *Sd* Kelvin Jones. *Asst Dir* Riva Freifeld. *Prod Asst* Luigi D'Arc.

Cast: Alaistair Burr (*Phil Kane*), Greta Dare (*Sylvania Landon*), Jackie Richards (*May*), Larry Hunter (*Rick*), Louise Violet (*Jane*), DeAndrea (*Dawn*), Mary Cleave (*Lulu*), Laura Edel, Doris Poor, Sandy Kohner, Steve Allis.

Melodrama. Sylvania Landon hires New York City detective Phil Kane to find Rick, her vicious husband, who is trying to kill her. While he searches for Rick, Phil moves through some of the city's sex spots: a body-painting salon, a nightclub where he has a violent encounter with stripper Dawn, a Greenwich Village apartment inhabited by two lesbians, a hippie orgy, and finally back to Sylvania's bedroom, where he saves her from Rick's murderous intentions. Phil and Sylvania celebrate the completion of the case by making love. *Detectives. Stripteasers. Hippies. Body painting. Lesbianism. Orgies. Nightclubs. New York City. New York City—Greenwich Village.*

LOVE ITALIAN STYLE *see* LOVE, THE ITALIAN WAY

THE LOVE MACHINES *see* THE PLEASURE MACHINES

THE LOVE MAKERS *see* THE LOVEMAKERS ... CARNAL STYLE

THE LOVE MAKERS *see* LA VIACCIA

LOVE MATES (Sweden)   F6.2893

Sandrews. *Dist* Altura Films International. Sep **1967** [Los Angeles showing]. Sd; col (Eastmancolor). 35mm. 90 min.

Pres by Clem Perry. *Prod* Sven Lindberg. *Dir-Writ* Lars-Magnus Lindgren. *Photog* Rune Ericson. *Art Dir* Jan Boleslaw. *Film Ed* Lennart Wallen. *Mus* Torbjörn Lundquist, Evert Taube. *Cost* Linda (cost).

Cast: Jarl Kulle (*Jan Froman*), Christina Schollin (*Margareta Günther*), Edvin Adolphson (*Admiral Günther*), Isa Quensel (*Louise Günther*), Sigge Fürst (*Bert Hagson*), Gunnar Sjöberg (*Karl Evert Raeder*), George Fant (*Rolf*), Margit Carlqvist, Åke Claesson, Toivo Pawlo.

Comedy. Source: John Einar Åberg, *Änglar, finns dom, Pappa?* (Uppsala, 1955). Jan Froman, financially independent through a legacy from his mother, determines to succeed on his own merit. He takes a job as a bank floorwalker and plans his rise to the board of directors. Jan hopes to ingratiate himself with the influential Admiral Günther through his daughter, Margareta, also a bank employee. Jan and Margareta fall in love, and she breaks off her engagement to Rolf, a wealthy, older man. By using information he overhears at the bank, Jan shrewdly invests in the stock market and in real estate, and before long he has another fortune. He successfully placates Admiral Günther, when the older man is incensed to learn that his daughter is no longer a virgin, by pandering to his interest in ancient firearms. *Heirs. Bankers. Floorwalkers. Ambition. Virginity. Banks. Stock market. Firearms.*

Note: Released in Sweden in 1961 as *Änglar, finns dom?;* running time: 110 min.

LOVE ME LIKE I DO   F6.2894

Great Empire Films. *Dist* Hollywood Cinemart. Mar **1970**. Sd; col (Eastmancolor). 35mm. 114 min. *MPAA rating* X.

Prod-Dir-Writ J. Van Hearn. *Exec Prod* Elsa Singman. *Camera* Bob Maxwell. *Film Ed* Joe Rugero, A. D. Arnold. *Mus* Elsa Singman. *Perf by* The Mongolian Horse. *Sd* Sam Kopetzky.

Cast: Peter Carpenter (*The Husband*), Dyanne Thorne (*The Wife*), Paul Fleming (*The Other Man*), Maria De Aragon (*The Brunette*), Lynne Gordon (*The Redhead*), Richard L. Karie (*The Pilot*), Ralph J. Rose (*The Lawyer*), Arnold Roberts (*The Chief of Police*), Jacqueline Dalya (*The Lawyer's Wife*), Joey Du Prez (*go-go dancer*), Elaine Hill (*singer*), Pedro DuPuy (*male dancer*).

Comedy-drama. Keith Hunter attempts to acquire the floundering business of his competitor Bill Sloan and to seduce Bill's beautiful wife Sharon as well. At a party given by the Sloans, Bill's attention is captured by Nanette Nolan, a married woman who enjoys seducing men, while Sharon's divorced friend, Marge, arouses interest by swimming nude in the pool. Sharon tries to save her marriage by making love to her husband, but he rebuffs her, and she becomes vulnerable to Keith's attack. He nearly rapes her, but she finally surrenders to his advances. The next night Sharon makes another desperate attempt to seduce her husband, and when she fails, she reveals her infidelity with Keith. A confrontation between the two men leads to a poolside fight. Sharon goes with her children to stay with Marge, but the next morning Keith convinces her to go with him to Las Vegas. Bill, forced to surrender his car, his house, and his business, tries unsuccessfully to persuade Nanette to run off with him; then he seduces Marge, locks her in a closet, and takes away his children. Sharon's weekend with Keith is interrupted when she hears that her children have been kidnapped by their father. She returns home to find Bill staying with Nanette. Bill's temper flares when he hears Sharon discussing sex with Nanette and Marge, and he fires his gun. The police fire tear gas into the house, and Bill and Sharon are finally reconciled. *Businessmen. Business competition. Marriage. Infidelity. Kidnaping. Seduction. Rape. Swimming pools. Las Vegas.*

LOVE ME OR LEAVE   F6.2895

Cosmos Films. *Dist* Able Film Co. ca **1970**. Sd; col. 16mm. [Feature length assumed.]

Sex film. Some beautiful women who need legal counsel but are financially hard-pressed induce attorneys to provide free legal services in exchange for their favors. *Lawyers. Finance—Personal. Sexuality.*

LOVE ME ... PLEASE   F6.2896

CincCentrum, Inc. *For* Dielst. *Dist* J. E. R. Pictures. 25 Jun 1969 [Maryland license; Champaign, Illinois, showing: 27 Aug]. Sd; col. 35mm. 75-81 min.

Dir-Writ Victor Peters. *Photog* Victor Peters. *Lighting* Pierre Muller. *Ed* Elga Kaplan. *Sd* Glenn Trayce.

Cast: Linda Boyce *(Bebe)*, Shiba Stuart *(Ilona)*, Anty Linn *(3d girl)*, John Gunter *(photographer)*, Joao Felix *(first man)*, Glenn Fodor *(second man)*.

Drama. After an unsuccessful day of job hunting in New York City, Bebe allows herself to be seduced by a man who picks her up in Central Park. The man leaves her, and Bebe, lonely and depressed, visits a psychiatrist. Bebe tells him that she has always felt unloved, but he is unable to help her. She is seduced by a photographer, has a brief affair with another man, and then makes love with a woman. During this lesbian episode, Bebe recalls her past lovers and imagines that she is having an orgy with all of them. *Photographers. Psychiatrists. Seduction. Lesbianism. Loneliness. Employment—Women. Fantasy. Orgies. New York City. New York City—Central Park.*

Note: Also known as *The Love Child.*

THE LOVE MERCHANT   F6.2897

General Studios. *Dist* General Studios, Cannon Releasing Corp. 26 Sep 1966 [Maryland license]. Sd; b&w. 35mm. 80 min.

Dir-Writ Joe Sarno. *Dir Photog* Bruce Sparks. *Asst Camera* Robert Bailin. *Film Ed* George Binkey. *Mus Comp & Cond* Richard Cove. *Sd* James Lynch. *Script Supv* Bathsheba. *Asst to the Prod* Kemper Peacock. *Crew* Michael Dannenberg, George King. *Paintings* European Artists Showcase Ltd.

Cast: Loraine Claire *(Peggy Johns)*, Judson Todd *(Kendall Harvey III)*, Jim Chisholm *(Click)*, George Wolfe *(Roger Johns)*, Joanna Mills *(Bobbi)*, Patti Paget *(Polly Fields)*, Penni Peyton *(Dixie)*, Cleo Nova *(Valery)*, Francine Ashley *(Sandy)*, Michael Lawrence *(Vince)*, Annette Godette *(Hillary)*, Shep Wild *(Zug)*, Steve Barton *(Nat)*, Phil Mason *(Gig)*, Robin Marks *(go-go girl)*, Carl Olsen *(head waiter)*.

Melodrama. Newlywed Peg Johns meets millionaire playboy Kendall Harvey III through ex-school friend Bobbi Hill, a Greenwich Village painter. Kendall is introduced to Peg by Bobbi's lover Click Boyd, a pimp. Immediately attracted to Peg, Kendall offers to help the Johns when Peg's husband Roger, an advertising executive, faces financial ruin. Kendall's plan is to help land a lucrative account for Roger in exchange for having Peg stay with him for a few days. Peg consents when she notices that her husband has begun to drink heavily. She is appalled when during her stay at Kendall's she is forced to join in an orgy. Unable to shoulder the guilt, Peg confesses to her husband, who becomes angry and leaves her. Peg's opinion of Kendall changes when he declares that he has fallen in love with her, but when she arrives at Kendall's apartment, she finds him with a prostitute. Realizing that his declaration was insincere, she leaves to look for her husband and beg his forgiveness. *Painters. Pimps. Millionaires. Newlyweds. Advertising executives. Playboys. Prostitution. Infidelity. Alcoholism. Orgies. New York City—Greenwich Village.*

Note: Also known as *Love Merchants* and *Another Woman, Another Day.*

LOVE MODELS   F6.2898

Dist Stacey Distributors. ca 1970. Sd; col. 16mm. 61-81 min.

Sex film. No information about the precise nature of this film has been found. *Models. Sexuality.*

LOVE—MY WAY   F6.2899

Mitam Productions. 10 Nov 1966 [San Francisco showing]. Sd; b&w. 35mm. 63 min.

Dir Arch Hudson.

Cast: Capri *(herself/Steve's mother)*, Jerry Harris *(Steve Durand)*.

Melodrama. Steve tells a psychiatrist his life story: As a little boy, he watches his mother, a prostitute, service her customers. She discovers him and beats him with a belt. Grown older, he derives sexual pleasure as a voyeur. He is arrested for voyeurism by the police. Released from jail, he persuades two prostitutes to let him watch them make love. One of the women, Capri, will take no money from him, but she joins with him in mutual flagellation. Steve becomes overwrought and, believing Capri to be his mother, kills her. He is captured and put under the care of a psychiatrist. *Psychiatrists. Prostitutes. Voyeurism. Filial relations. Flagellation. Manslaughter.*

LOVE NOW ... PAY LATER   F6.2900

Dist William Mishkin. 10 May 1966 [Maryland license]. Sd; b&w. 35mm. 50 min.

Dir Don Rolos.

Cast: Lisa Palmer, Herman Rose.

Drama. Tom and Archie find an attaché case containing credit cards which they use to buy food and clothing for themselves. Because the case also contains papers belonging to Sir James, who is engaged in espionage, Tom and Archie are followed by three Russian spies. After becoming implicated in more frauds involving the stolen case, the pair are apprehended in San Francisco by the authorities. *Spies. Russians. Theft. Fraud. Espionage. Credit. San Francisco.*

Note: Also known as *Nudes on Credit* and *Sin Now ... Pay Later.*

LOVE NOW ... PAY LATER (Italy)   F6.2900a

Gianni Vernuccio. *Dist* William Mishkin. 29 Dec 1966 [New York opening]. Sd; b&w. 35mm. 82 min.

Prod Gianni Vernuccio, N. Negri. *Dir-Adapt* Gianni Vernuccio. *Scen* Damiano Damiani. *Dir Photog* Romolo Garroni.

Cast: Annabella Incontrera *(Micki)*, Sandro Luporini *(Marco)*, Sandro Pizzorno *(Andre [Andrea])*, Jeanine *(Gigi [Guiguitte])*, Marie Harlow, Barbara Hill, Jack Nasome, Carmen Luster, Pat Plumet, Jackie Kamen.

Melodrama. Marco, an impoverished engineering student, hides his wealthy friend Andre at his apartment in a fake kidnaping plot to obtain money from Andre's father, a furniture manufacturer. While the youths await the outcome of their ransom demand, Marco's girl friend, Micki, and her studious friend Gigi visit the apartment. Unaware of his identity, Micki falls in love with Andre, and in a jealous rage, Marco strangles his friend in the bathtub. At a party with a number of thrill-seeking friends, Marco reveals to Micki that he has killed Andre, and she agrees to help him keep the crime a secret. Meanwhile, a lawyer working for Andre's father tracks down Gigi, who in turn leads him to Marco and Micki. *Students. Lawyers. Poverty. Wealth. Friendship. Kidnaping. Jealousy. Murder. Filial relations.*

Note: Filmed in Italy in 1959; Rome opening: Mar 1961 as *L'inferno addosso*; running time: ca92 min. One source credits Eugenio Vitelli as production company. Actors credited without roles may have appeared in inserted U. S. footage; these names may also be pseudonyms. Also known as *Sin Now Pay Later.*

THE LOVE OBJECT   F6.2901

Illusions Productions. *Dist* Joseph Brenner Associates. ca 1967 [Maryland license: 7 Oct 1970]. Sd; col (Eastmancolor). 35mm. 68 min.

Prod Steven J. Bradford. *Dir* Don Schain. *Dir Photog* R. Kent Evans. *Mus Comp & Cond* Harlan Collins, Cam Shinhan. *Mus Prod* Happiness Inc. *Sd* Paul Stowe. *Script Girl* Susan Bishop. *Still Photog* Robert Putnam. *Ch Grip* Clinton R. Smith.

Cast: Kim Pope *(Sharon Austin)*, William Grannell *(bearded man)*, Kurt Howard *(young, good looking man)*, Norman Furr *(large, rough man)*, Eddye Kalish *(elderly gentleman)*, James McDonald, actor *(director)*, Juston Moyan *(agent)*, Leo Green *(professor)*.

Melodrama. Sharon Austin, an aspiring actress, arrives in New York seeking a break into the legitimate theater. Her refusals to compromise her virtue and integrity in order to make her own breaks are sustained by her relationship with a seemingly sincere young man. Unexpectedly, Sharon is abducted by three men and taken to a remote hunting lodge. Her abductors, with the complicity of Sharon's young man, use psychological and physical torture to force her into posing for pornographic pictures and compromising herself sexually. Finally, threatened with blackmail and the loss of any chance at a career, she agrees. Nude pictures of her appear in the bookstalls of New York's pornographers, and she begins sleeping with repulsive but influential men in the theater business. When Sharon appears in a small role in an off-Broadway production, her genuine talents are noticed by a prominent director. Auditioning for a role in his new play, that of a girl whose problems and conflicts are not unlike her own, Sharon gains insight into what she must do: reject the life forced on her, regardless of consequences. With a new chance in a major production and supported by a growing relationship with the director, Sharon finds that she can be both a success and be faithful to herself. *Actors. Theatrical directors. Pornographers. Nudity. Sadism. Perfidy. Blackmail. Rape. Abduction. Ambition. Photographs. New York City—Broadway.*

LOVE ON A PILLOW (France/Italy)   F6.2902

Francos Films–Incei Film. *Dist* Royal Films International. 16 Dec 1963 [New York opening]. Sd; col (Eastmancolor). 35mm (Franscope). 102 min.

A Francis Cosne Production. *Prod* Francis Cosne. *Dir* Roger Vadim. *Screenplay* Roger Vadim, Claude Choublier. *Photog* Armand Thirard. *Art Dir* Jean André. *Film Ed* Victoria Mercanton. *Mus* Michel Magne. *Sd* Robert Biart. *Prod Mgr* Paul Joly. *Wardrobe* Tanine Autre. *Makeup* Pierre Berroyer, Odette Berroyer. *English Subtitl* Herman G. Weinberg.

Cast: Brigitte Bardot *(Geneviève Le Theil)*, Robert Hossein *(Renaud Sarti)*, James Robertson-Justice *(Katov)*, Macha Méril *(Raphaele)*, Yves Barsacq *(hotel manager)*, Jacqueline Porel *(Geneviève's mother)*, Jean-Marc Bory *(Pierre)*, Christian Melsen *(police inspector)*, Michel Serrault *(Varange)*, Ursula Kubler *(nurse)*, Robert Dalban *(police sergeant)*, Jean Tuscano *(jazz musician)*, Jean-Marc Tennberg *(Coco)*.

Drama. Source: Christiane Rochefort, *Le repos du guerrier* (Paris, 1958). Geneviève Le Theil, a financially independent Parisienne, goes to Dijon to collect an inheritance. She enters the wrong hotel room and accidentally foils the suicide of a penniless alcoholic, Renaud, who has taken an overdose of sleeping pills. Renaud, rebellious and unconventional, seduces Geneviève and persuades her to take him with her to Paris, whereupon she serves ties with her mother, her friends, and her fiancé, Pierre. Renaud, who is interested mainly in liquor, sex, and reading mystery novels, continually insults and maltreats Geneviève, but out of love she accepts her degradation. Katov, a sculptor and friend of Renaud, invites the couple of to and there Renaud brashly picks up a prostitute while Geneviève is watching. As a result, Geneviève leaves him, but they are reunited when Renaud declares his love and asks her to marry him. *Heiresses. Sculptors. Prostitutes. Wealth. Suicide. Seduction. Bohemianism. Alcoholism. Hotels. Tranquilizers. Dijon. Paris. Florence.*

Note: Filmed on location in Paris and Florence. Opened in Paris in Sep 1962 as *Le repos du guerrier.* Italian title: *Il riposo del guerriero.*

LOVE ON THE RIVIERA (France/Italy) **F6.2903**
Cei-Incom–Maxima Film–Monteluce Film–Gallus Films. *Dist* Ultra Pictures. Jan **1964** [Los Angeles showing]. Sd; col (Eastman Color). 35mm (Totalscope). 88 min.
Prod Mario Cecchi Gori. *Dir* Gianni Franciolini. *Screenplay* Alberto Moravia, Alberto Sordi, Sergio Amidei, Ennio Flajano, Edoardo Anton, Rodolfo Sonego, René Barjavel, Gianni Franciolini. *Story* Alberto Moravia. *Dir Photog* Enzo Serafin. *Camera* Giuseppe Ruzzolini. *Art Dir* Giorgio Giovannini. *Film Ed* Adriana Novelli. *Mus* Piero Piccioni. *Sd Rec* Roy Mangano. *Cost* Ugo Pericoli. *Sp Eff* Goffredo Rocchetti.
Cast: Alberto Sordi *(Aristarco Bertolini),* Michèle Morgan *(Micheline),* Marcello Mastroianni *(police inspector),* Sylva Koscina *(Renata),* Gabriele Ferzetti *(Ferrari),* Dorian Gray *(Dorina),* Franca Marzi *(Clara),* Lorella De Luca *(Lina),* Franco Fabrizi *(Sandro),* Enio Girolami *(Walter),* Jorge Mistral *(beach attendant),* Dany Carrel *(Jacqueline),* Marta Marcelli *(Ada),* Anita Allan *(bather).*
Comedy-drama. (1) When a train carrying a police officer and Micheline, his beautiful prisoner, stops along the Italian Riviera, the officer decides that they should leave the train to quench their thirst. While they are bathing in the sea, their train departs, and the officer suggests that they spend the night together. He falls in love with Micheline, but the next morning he determines to take her on to prison. (2) Aristarco, a gigolo, tries to extort money from an opera diva by promising to marry her, but her mother refuses to give him any money until the ceremony actually takes place. (3) A bikini-clad gold digger sets out to extort money from wealthy men, but she falls in love with a penniless beach attendant instead. (4) A businessman plans to have his wife seduced by a millionaire playboy in the hope that the playboy will financially support a feigned business enterprise. His wife is hesitant to begin the affair, and the playboy is soon frustrated. He does, however, give the money to the husband. (5) A man tries to woo both a mother and her daughter. When he pays greater attention to the mother, the daughter becomes jealous. He borrows money from the mother, and the daughter uses that fact as an excuse to send him away. She tries to cheer up her mother by repaying the money, pretending that the man has returned it to her. *Police. Gigolos. Singers. Gold diggers. Millionaires. Businessmen. Playboys. Swindlers. Extortion. Marriage. Seduction. Jealousy. Filial relations. Riviera.*

Note: Opened in Rome in Dec 1958 as *Racconti d'estate;* running time: 113 min; in Paris in Apr 1959 as *Femmes d'un été;* running time: 100 min. Also known as *Summer Tales.*

THE LOVE PIRATE **F6.2904**
Cinetron Corp. *Dist* CineWorld Corp. 30 Jan **1970** [New York opening]. Sd; col. 35mm. 71 min.
Prod-Dir-Writ Barry Mahon.
Cast: George Matsui *(Captain Fu),* Ruth Wong *(Melodie).*
Melodrama. Captain Fu commands a junk on the China Sea, staffed by a crew of the most beautiful women in the Orient. With the help of his hunchback stooge, Captain Fu has shifted his efforts from seagoing prostitution to the even more lucrative trade of kidnaping. Though his victims are usually foreign sailors, he plans to kidnap Melodie, the daughter of a wealthy merchant, for the large ransom she will bring. Melodie receives a note saying that her lover Lin is in trouble and wants her to come immediately. She has been strictly forbidden to see Lin, but she sneaks away from the family mansion into the waiting hands of Captain Fu. Lin arrives for a secret meeting with his lover and finds that her family has just received a ransom note. Lin gets the hunchback's description from the maid, and, remembering having seen Fu when his ship was docked, he sets sail in pursuit of Fu's junk. On board the pirate ship, Melodie is forced to join in the night's carousing, until Fu drags her off to his private cabin. Lin overtakes the junk, strangles the hunchback, and makes his way to Fu's cabin. The two men fight, and Fu is killed. Lin returns home with Melodie, and her grateful father approves their marriage. *Pirates. Hunchbacks. Prostitutes. Orientals. Merchants. Sailors. Kidnaping. Filial relations. Ships. China Sea.*

Note: Filmed in Hong Kong. Working title: *Dr. Foo and the Love Pirates.*

LOVE PLAY *see* **PLAYTIME**

LOVE + FEAR = TORMENT *see* **TORMENT**

LOVE PROBLEMS (Italy) **F6.2905**
Salaria Film–Cormons Film. *Dist* RAF Industries. Apr **1970**. Sd; col (Eastman Color). 35mm. 101 min. *MPAA rating* R.
Prod Giancarlo Segarelli. *Dir* Giuliano Biagetti. *Screenplay* Dacia Maraini, Luciano Lucignani, Giuliano Biagetti. *Photog* Antonio Borghesi. *Art Dir* Franco Bottari. *Film Ed* Marcella Bevilacqua. *Mus* Stefano Rossi. *Asst Dir* Guglielmo Giarda. *Sp Eff* Pino Ferranti.
Cast: Haydée Politoff *(Enrica),* Jean Sorel *(Giorgio),* Eleonora Rossi-Drago *(countess),* Gabriele Ferzetti *(Guido),* Salvo Randone, Yorgo Voyagis, Giovanna Galletti, Edy Nogara, Gianni De Luigi, Claudio Gora.
Drama. Source: Dacia Maraini, *L'età del malessere* (Turin, 1963). Enrica, a 17-year-old computer trainee, lives in a Roman suburb with her invalid mother and drunken father. Neglected by her parents, Enrica becomes mistress to Giorgio, a selfish law student intent on marrying another woman for her money. Her mother dies, but Enrica continues her affairs with Carlo, a fellow trainee, and Guido, an adventurous lawyer. She becomes pregnant by Giorgio, who arranges an abortion through a rich and eccentric countess. Evicted from her apartment, Enrica becomes secretary to the countess. After observing the aristocrat's unhappy experiences with younger men, Enrica determines to live alone. *Computer programmers. Invalids. Mistresses. Lawyers. Eccentrics. Nobility. Secretaries. Law students. Adolescence. Drunkenness. Filial relations. Abortion. Eviction. Rome.*

Note: Produced in Italy in 1968 as *L'età del malessere.*

THE LOVE REBELLION **F6.2906**
Cannon Productions. 12 Oct **1967** [New Orleans opening]. Sd; b&w. 35mm. 77-87 min. [See note.]
Dir-Writ Joe Sarno. *Photog* Bruce Sparks. *Film Ed* Kemper Peacock. *Orig Score* Pir Marini. *Sd Engr* James Lynch. *Asst to the Dir* Gillian Mills. *Ch Electrn* Aloysius Gordon.
Cast: Ginger Stevens *(Wendy Fletcher),* Melissa Ford *(Jo Fletcher),* Alan Haff *(Hank Wiggans),* Jeremy Langham *(Bellman Carpenter),* Riley *(Bobbi Johnson),* Angelique *(Pam Carpenter),* Cleo Nova *(Nancy Lair),* Nick Dundas *(Don Halleck),* Max Sydney *(Hoag Barnes),* Nadine Stark *(Lee Doran).*
Drama. Young Wendy Fletcher accepts an invitation to a love-in from some artists who participate in group sex. The partygoers are infatuated by her innocence, and the entire group takes her to bed. She returns for more parties, but she rejects Hank, a sadistic poet; Hank then turns his fury on his mistress. He whips her and then extinguishes his smoldering cigar on her breast. The experience unnerves Wendy, who returns home to find her boyfriend, artist Bellman Carpenter, in bed with her mother. The shock sends her reeling back to Hank and his mistress, and she willingly submits to their perverted desires. Bellman, having been rejected by Mrs. Fletcher, returns, contrite, to Wendy. The two plan to escape the jaded atmosphere, but Hank and his mistress forcefully detain them. ... *Innocents. Artists. Poets. Mistresses. Moral corruption. Infidelity. Group sex. Filial relations. Sadomasochism. Love-ins.*

Note: Available in three release lengths—uncensored version: 87 min; partially edited version: 80 min; and fully edited version: 77 min.

THE LOVE ROBOTS (Japan) **F6.2907**
Dist Olympic International Films. ca **1965**. Sd; b&w. 35mm (CinemaScope). 63 min.
Prod-Dir Koji Wakamatsu.
Cast: Hidekatsu Shibata, Hideo Sakei, Tamami Wakahara.
Crime melodrama. Abducted from the streets, beautiful young women are sadistically conditioned by drugs and/or hypnotism. These "love robots" will kill or love on command and are items of sale. One victim's brother, a detective assigned to the case, is relieved of his duties, but decides to track down his sister's killers on his own. Although captured by the gangsters, the detective escapes. Later he single-handedly subdues his captors. *Detectives. Gangsters. Prostitution. Abduction. Sadism. Brainwashing. Hypnotism. Murder. Revenge. Drugs.*

Note: Original title and release undetermined. Probably altered for U. S. release.

THE LOVE ROOT *see* **MANDRAGOLA**

THE LOVE SHUFFLE *see* **THE SEX SHUFFLE**

THE LOVE STATUE **F6.2908**
Dist Vansan Productions, V & N Associates. 11 Mar **1966** [New York showing]. Sd; b&w. 35mm. 80 min.
Prod Robert A. Poore. *Exec Prod* Evander Schley, Sandy Barnett. *Dir* David Durston. *Screenplay* Richard Kent. *Story* Robert A. Poore. *Cinematog* Amin

Chaudhri. *Camera* Hiroshi Kaku. *Lighting* Ogden Lowell. *Special Photog* Jurgen. *Film Ed* David Durston. *Asst Ed* Richard Kent. *Mus Comp & Arr* Dottie Stallworth. *Mus Dir* Sandy Barnett. *Mus Ed & Sd Supv* Rudy Traylor. *Sd* Robert Van Dyke. *Mix* Bill Stoddard. *Sd Eff* Barney Beck. *Grateful Acknowledgment Is Made by the Prods* The Bitter End Club, Aldo's of Bleeker Street. *Still Photog* Martin Andrews. *Paintings Created by* Maria Sobossek.

Cast: Peter Ratray *(Tyler)*, Ondine Lise *(Lisa)*, Harvey Goldenberg *(Stan)*, Nancy Norman, actress *(The Model)*, Hisako "Choko" Tsukuba *(Mashiko)*, Coleman Younger, Cory Stevens, Liz Otto, Mario DeRosa, Lenore Rhein, Morgan Wilson, Maria Sobossek, David Roya.

Melodrama. Greenwich Village artist Tyler is unable to respond to the excessive sexual demands of his dominating mistress, Lisa. Frustrated, he turns her out and wanders into some Village bars. He meets Mashiko, a Japanese nightclub singer who takes him to a party in her apartment and gives him LSD. There he is introduced to lesbianism and voyeurism. Still under the influence of the drug, Tyler returns to his apartment, and there a statue of a woman made by his sculptor friend, Stan, seems to come to life and join him in wild lovemaking. Several days later, Lisa visits Tyler's apartment and, in a rage, destroys Tyler's paintings and Stan's sculpture. Stan arrives unexpectedly, sees what Lisa has done, and kills her. Tyler comes home, sees the dead Lisa, flees, and roams the city until he accidentally meets the model Stan used for his female statue. Through the woman, Tyler learns that Stan is a bisexual who cannot cope with his desire to be both male and female. Tyler pulls himself together and embarks on a relationship with the woman. Stan is chased to a dam site and falls to his death. *Painters. Mistresses. Sculptors. Japanese. Models. Singers. Nymphomania. Voyeurism. Lesbianism. Jealousy. Murder. Bisexuality. Insanity. LSD. Sculptures. Nightclubs. New York City— Greenwich Village. Hallucinations.*

Note: Also known as *The Statue*. Certain sequences were filmed at the Bitter End Club and Aldo's of Bleeker Street in New York City.

LOVE STORY   F6.2909
Love Story Co. *Dist* Paramount Pictures. 16 Dec **1970** [New York opening; c20 Oct 1970; LP38327]. Sd; col (print by Movielab). 35mm. 100 min. *MPAA rating* GP.

Prod Howard G. Minsky. *Exec Prod* David Golden. *Dir* Arthur Hiller. *Screenplay* Erich Segal. *Dir Photog* Dick Kratina. *Art Dir* Robert Gundlach. *Set Decor* Philip Smith. *Main Titl* National Screen Service. *Film Ed* Robert C. Jones. *Mus Score* Francis Lai. *Concerto no. 3 in D Major* Johann Sebastian Bach. *Sonata in F Major* Wolfgang Amadeus Mozart. *"Lo! A Fair Rose Is Blooming"* Michael Praetorius. *"Joy to the World"* George Frederick Handel. *Lyr* Isaac Watts. *Sd Rec* Jack C. Jacobsen, Bud Grenzbach. *Asst Dir* Peter Scoppa. *Prod Mgr* Steven Skloot, Sal Scoppa. *Cost Dsgn* Alice Manougian Martin, Pearl Somner. *Makeup* Martin Bell. *Hairstyles* William Farley. *Tech Adv for Hockey Seq* William Cleary, Robert Cleary. *Key Grip* Ed Quinn.

Cast: Ali MacGraw *(Jenny Cavilleri)*, Ryan O'Neal *(Oliver Barrett IV)*, John Marley *(Phil Cavilleri)*, Ray Milland *(Oliver Barrett III)*, Russell Nype *(Dean Thompson)*, Katharine Balfour *(Mrs. Barrett)*, Sydney Walker *(Dr. Shapeley)*, Robert Modica *(Dr. Addison)*, Walker Daniels *(Ray)*, Tom Lee Jones *(Hank)*, John Merensky *(Steve)*, Andrew Duncan *(Reverend Blauvelt)*, Bob O'Connell *(Tommy, the doorman)*, Charlotte Ford, Sudie Bond, Julie Garfield, Kevin O'Neal, Milo Boulton.

Romantic drama. Harvard student and hockey player Oliver Barrett IV visits the Radcliffe library and meets music major Jenny Cavilleri, who works in the library to help pay her tuition. Despite the fact that he is from a distinguished Boston family and she is the daughter of a poor Italian baker, they are attracted to each other. After several months together, Jenny tells Oliver that she has received a scholarship to study music in Paris; instead, of pursuing her studies, however, she accepts Oliver's proposal of marriage. Although they receive her father's blessings, Oliver's father threatens to cut him off from the family wealth. Nevertheless, the young couple is married in a simple ceremony. After graduation, Oliver applies for a grant to law school, but the dean refuses to accept Oliver's separation from his father as evidence of his need for the money. To meet the costs of school and rent, they move into a poor section of Boston, and Jenny goes to work as a schoolteacher. When Oliver finally completes law school, they move to New York City, where he enters a prestigious law firm, and they happily begin to plan a family. One day, Oliver is called into the office of Jenny's doctor, who tells him that Jenny is dying. Shocked and heartbroken, Oliver tries to hide the truth until he finds that Jenny already knows; the couple then sadly faces the inevitable prospect of death. Because he needs a great deal of money for medical expenses, Oliver is forced to visit his father and borrow $5,000, although he does not explain the reason for the loan or apologize for not communicating with him. Soon, Jenny is in the hospital and dies in Oliver's arms. As Oliver leaves, his father arrives to console him, but Oliver rejects the reconciliation, walks to Central Park, and there recalls his brief life with Jenny. *Students. Law students. Schoolteachers. Lawyers. Physicians. Italians. College*

life. *Filial relations. Social classes. Marriage. Incurable illness. Death. Hockey. Music. Hospitals. Boston. Cambridge. New York City. New York City— Central Park. Harvard University. Radcliffe College.*

Note: Location scenes filmed in Boston, Cambridge, and New York City.

LOVE—TAHITI STYLE *see* **NUDE ODYSSEY**

LOVE, THE ITALIAN WAY (Italy)   F6.2910
Italgloria–Produzione D. S.–Serena Film. *Dist* Trans-Lux Distributing Corp. 9 Nov **1964** [Maryland license]. Sd; col (Technicolor). 35mm. 90 min.

Pres by Allstar Films. A Michael Stern–Itam Production. *Prod* Dario Sabatello. *Dir* George White, pseud. *Screenplay-Orig Story* Vittorio Metz, Roberto Gianviti, Oreste Biancoli. *Photog* Tino Santoni. *Art Dir* Franco Fontana. *Song:* "Femmine di lusso" comp & sung by Domenico Modugno. *Songs:* "Te voglio stasera," "Per un attimo" Carlo Rustichelli. *Sung by* Peppino Di Capri. *Song:* "Casta diva" sung by Gina Cigna. *Cost* Elio Costanzi, Giulia Mafai.

Cast: Elke Sommer *(Greta)*, Walter Chiari *(Walter)*, Sylva Koscina *(Luciana)*, Ugo Tognazzi *(Hugo)*, Gabriele Ferzetti *(Count Luca di Sauvin [Alberto Bressan])*, Belinda Lee *(Elena [Adriana Bressan])*, Gino Cervi *(Lemeni)*, Massimo Serato *(Sicilian nobleman)*, Caprice Chantal *(Adrienne)*, Gisella Sofio *(Marilla)*, Ivan Desny *(Albert)*, Mario Scaccia *(butler)*, Malo St. George *(Indian girl)*, Gino Bartali.

Romantic comedy. Millionaire Lemeni hosts a cruise aboard his yacht along the Sicilian coast. His passengers include French industrialist Albert and his opera star wife, Adrienne; Albert's mistress, magazine editor Elena Lagarde; Adrienne's lover, Count Luca di Sauvin [according to Italian sources Alberto has hired Luca to seduce Adriana so that he can obtain a divorce]; Lemeni's son, Hugo, an ardent bicycle racing enthusiast; Luciana, a cover girl hired by Lemeni to arouse Hugo's interest in women; and Walter, a photographer employed by Lemeni. Walter's jealous fiancée, Greta, swims aboard as a stowaway when the boat leaves port. In the course of the voyage, Albert and Adrienne discover that Luca is Elena's former husband, and the divorced couple are reunited. Luciana's efforts to seduce Hugo fail, but he eventually meets Greta, and they fall in love. The confusion subsides, and before the cruise is over everyone has found romance. *Millionaires. French. Singers. Industrialists. Mistresses. Editors. Nobility. Photographers. Models. Stowaways. Marriage. Seduction. Wealth. Jealousy. Divorce. Filial relations. Bicycle racing. Yachts. Sicily. Mediterranean Sea.,*

Note: Released in Italy in Jan 1960 as *Femmine di lusso*; running time: 95 min. Also known as *Love Italian Style*. George White is a pseudonym for Giorgio Bianchi. United States and Italian sources conflict in crediting roles; role names in brackets represent Italian credit; Italian sources do not credit Ivan Desny or Caprice Chantal.

LOVE THY NEIGHBOR   F6.2911
Dist Distribpix, Inc. ca **1970**. Sd; col. 35mm. 61 min.

Drama. An attractive young couple leads a normal sex life until they move from the city into the suburbs. Their new neighborhood has a "social club" that numbers many older, sophisticated couples among its membership. Some representatives of the club call on the couple and suggestively discuss the possibilities of group sex—throwing fear into the heart of the naive wife. Her husband is more responsive, however, and the following Saturday night a drunken party takes place during which the partygoers demonstrate a persistent friendliness. The wife at first resists the advances made to her by many of the men at the party, but finally gives in to the general atmosphere of "anything goes." The frenzied activity produces a noisy furor, until neighbors call the police and the party ends abruptly. *Newlyweds. Suburbanites. Drunkenness. Mate swapping. Sex clubs.*

LOVE THY NEIGHBOR AND HIS WIFE   F6.2912
Rama Productions. *Dist* Entertainment Ventures, Inc. ca **1970**. Sd; col. 35mm. 77 min.

Prod B. Ron Elliott, L. Ray Monde. *Dir* (see note) B. Ron Elliott. *Screenplay* Virginia Vulvania. *Camera* James Wrong When. *Camera Asst* Otto Focus. *Sd* Sam Kopetsky. *Script Girl* Kara Kooze. *Wardrobe* Phunkie Attire. *Key Grip* Hal Atosis.

Cast: Mike Hunt *(Ferd)*, Ann Dee *(Andy)*, Laura Canyon *(Ruth)*, Sal Hapatika *(Bruce)*, Ronnie Runningboard *(Dan)*, Heidi Sohler *(Uschi)*, Donna M. Barr *(Linda)*, Ann Mell *(Fiona)*, Vincent Stephens *(unidentified role, see note)*.

Drama. A prominent attorney and his client bring their wives to a lakeside cottage for a weekend. The group's sexual inhibitions break down after much drinking and the screening of stag films. The two husbands exchange partners, and the wives later have sex with each other. On the other side of the lake, a lecherous, middle-aged professor has brought three of his female students to a rented cabin. Two raunchy dune buggy enthusiasts make camp near the professor's cabin, smoke marijuana, and attract the attention of the three coeds. They soon become sexually acquainted. Later, the five young people go to a nearby tavern and meet the lawyer's party. After some initial disagreement, they proceed to have an orgy. *Lawyers. Students. Professors. Mate swapping. Group sex. Lesbianism. Lechery. Drunkenness. Marijuana. Sex exploitation films.*

Note: Director B. Ron Elliott is credited by one source under the name Byron Maibe. Actor Vincent Stephens appears under an undetermined pseudonym.

LOVE UNDER THE CRUCIFIX (Japan)   F6.2913

Shochiku Co. *Dist* Shochiku Films of America. Apr **1965** [Los Angeles showing]. Sd; col (Eastmancolor). 35mm (Shochiku GrandScope). 102 min.

Prod Sennosuke Tsukimori, Shigeru Wakatsuki. *Dir* Kinuyo Tanaka. *Screenplay* Masashige Narusawa. *Photog* Yoshio Miyajima. *Art Dir* Jun-ichi Osumi. *Mus* Hikaru Hayashi.

Cast: Ineko Arima *(Gin Sama)*, Ganjiro Nakamura *(Rikyu Senno)*, Mieko Takamine *(Riki)*, Tatsuya Nakadai *(Ukon Takayama)*, Osamu Takizawa *(Hideyoshi Toyotomi)*, Yumeji Tsukioka *(Yodo Gimi)*, Koji Nanbara *(Mitsunari Ishida)*, Keiko Kishi, Manami Fuji.

Romantic melodrama. Source: Toko Kon, *O-gin Sama* (Tokyo, 1927). In 1587, Rikyu Sen, a tea master in the service of the warlord Hideyoshi Toyotomi, has a stepdaughter, Gin, who is in love with Ukon Takayama, a Christian feudal lord. Rikyu returns from an expedition to report on a proposal of marriage for Gin; Mitsunari Ishida, a warrior and friend of Hideyoshi, has informed Rikyu that Shintaro Mozuya, a wealthy merchant, desires Gin's hand. Gin is cool to the proposal, but after Ukon spurns her she gives in and marries Mozuya. Several years later an edict banning the practice of Christianity forces Ukon into hiding. Gin, whose marriage has proved to be unhappy, attends a tea ceremony held by Hideyoshi, who has become regent. Hideyoshi is attracted to Gin; noting this, Ishida and Mozuya plot to trap Ukon and hand over Gin to Hideyoshi in order to expand their influence with the regent. Using fake letters, they lure the couple to a temple, but a priest there helps Gin and Ukon escape to a nearby tea house. Ukon, whose wife has died, admits to Gin that he has always loved her. They part, promising to meet in Kaga, and Gin returns to her stepfather's home after informing Mozuya that she wants a divorce. Ishida informs Hideyoshi that Gin and Ukon have committed adultery, and the regent orders Gin to appear before him. She rejects his advances, however, even when Hideyoshi threatens her stepfather's life. That night, Rikyu insists that his stepdaughter try to join her lover, but Hideyoshi has the family's house surrounded before Gin can leave. Rather than submit, Gin writes a farewell poem and commits suicide. *Tea masters. Warlords. Stepfathers. Merchants. Marriage—Arranged. Infidelity. Perfidy. Suicide. Religious persecution. Divorce. Christianity. Poetry. Documentation.*

Note: Released in Japan in 1960 as *O-gin Sama*.

LOVE VARIATIONS (Great Britain)   F6.2914

Oppidan Film Productions. *Dist* Chevron Pictures. 7 Oct **1970** [New York opening]. Sd; col (Eastman Color). 35mm. 80 min. *MPAA rating* X.

Prod-Writ David Hamilton-Grant. *Dir* Terry Gould, dir. *Photog* Geoffrey Glover, Michael Temple. *Camera Op* Ron Robson. *Art Dir* Desmond Crowe, Tony Page. *Film Ed* Jack Knight. *Sd* Location Sound Facilities, John Hayles. *Asst Dir* Ron Jackson. *Prod Mgr* George Maynard.

Cast: Carol Jones, actress *(woman)*, Derek Stephan Tracey *(man)*, David Jackson *(doctor/narrator)*.

Sex instruction film. Source: David Hamilton-Grant, *Love Variations* (a book; publication undetermined). A couple engages in over 40 coital positions and sexual techniques. After a general practitioner discusses the reproductive organs, masturbation, and birth control, audience participants comment on the film. *Physicians. Sexual techniques. Reproduction. Autoeroticism. Birth control.*

Note: Opened in London in Jul 1970.

LOVE WITH THE PROPER STRANGER   F6.2915

Boardwalk Productions-Rona, Inc. *Dist* Paramount Pictures. Dec **1963** [c25 Dec 1963; LP26980]. Sd; b&w. 35mm. 100 min.

An Alan J. Pakula-Robert Mulligan Production. *Prod* Alan J. Pakula. *Dir* Robert Mulligan. *Screenplay* Arnold Schulman. *Dir Photog* Milton Krasner. *Camera Op* Alfred Lebowitz. *Art Dir* Hal Pereira, Roland Anderson. *Set Decor* Sam Comer, Grace Gregory. *Film Ed* Aaron Stell. *Mus Score* Elmer Bernstein. *Titl Song* Arnold Schulman, Elmer Bernstein. *Sung by* Jack Jones. *Sd* Gene Merritt. *1st & 2d Asst Dir* William McGarry, Sam Strangis. *Prod Mgr* Frank Caffey. *Asst Prod Mgr* Curtis Mick. *Unit Prod Mgr* John Coonan. *Asst to the Prod* Isabel M. Halliburton. *Script Supv* Meta Rebner. *Cost* Edith Head. *Wardrobe* Ann Landers, Jerry Alpert. *Makeup* Wally Westmore, Ed Butterworth. *Still Photog* Art Say.

Cast: Natalie Wood *(Angie Rossini)*, Steve McQueen *(Rocky Papasano)*, Edie Adams *(Barbie, Barbara of Seville)*, Herschel Bernardi *(Dominick Rossini)*, Tom Bosley *(Anthony Colombo)*, Harvey Lembeck *(Julio Rossini)*, Penny Santon *(Mama Rossini)*, Virginia Vincent *(Anna)*, Nick Alexander *(Guido Rossini)*, Augusta Ciolli *(Mrs. Papasano)*, Ann Hegira *(Beetie)*, Mario Badolati *(Elio Papasano)*, Elena Karam *(woman doctor)*, Nina Varela *(Mrs. Colombo)*, Marilyn Chris *(Gina)*, Wolfe Barzell *(The Priest)*, Keith Worthey *(Negro boy)*, Henry Howard *(Lou)*, Frank Marth *(Carlos)*, Richard Bowler *(flower vendor)*, Lennie Bremen *(truck driver)*, Nobu McCarthy *(Yuki)*, Jean Shulman *(Charlene)*, Lou Herbert *(Harold)*, M. Enserro *(Moish)*, Barney Martin *(Sidney)*, Louis Guss *(Flooey)*, Tony Mordente *(Fat)*, Val Avery *(Stein)*, Richard Mulligan *(Louie)*, Paul Price *(Klepp)*, Arlene Golonka *(Marge)*, Richard Dysart *(accountant)*, Loraine Abate *(Maria)*, Vincent Deadrick *(call boy)*, Victor Tayback *(Cye)*.

Comedy-drama. Rocky, a musician, is paged at his Manhattan union hall by Angie, with whom he spent a night at a summer hotel. She informs him that she is pregnant and asks him to recommend a doctor, whereupon he consults his current girl friend, Barbie, a stripper, but she jealously throws him out. Unaware of her pregnancy, Angie's brothers and mother want her to marry Colombo, the shy owner of a small restaurant and also of Italian extraction. Having learned of the availability of a "doctor" to solve their problem, Rocky tries to raise the necessary money, then looks up Angie at her job in Macy's and takes her to meet his unsuspecting parents, who immediately like her. However, when the two finally confront the reality of abortion, Rocky refuses to let Angie face the ordeal. Though she loves him, Angie realizes that Rocky fears marriage; and she decides to reconsider Colombo's proposal, for he has let it be known that Angie is expecting his child. Shortly thereafter, a possible reconciliation with Rocky ends in a bitter quarrel. Later, she sees him near the Macy's employees' entrance carrying a sign reading: "Better Wed Than Dead." *Musicians. Bachelors. Italians. Stripteasers. Restaurateurs. Quacks. Salesclerks. Pregnancy. Abortion. Jealousy. Filial relations. Brother-sister relationship. New York City—Lower East Side. Macy's (New York City).*

Note: Locations filmed in New York City.

THE LOVED ONE   F6.2916

Filmways, Inc. *Dist* Metro-Goldwyn-Mayer, Inc. 11 Oct **1965** [New York opening; c2 Oct 1965; LP32175]. Sd; b&w. 35mm. 116 min.

Prod John Calley, Haskell Wexler. *Exec Prod* Martin Ransohoff. *Assoc Prod* Neil Hartley. *Dir* Tony Richardson. *Screenplay* Terry Southern, Christopher Isherwood. *Dir Photog* Haskell Wexler. *Camera Op* Harlowe Stengel. *1st Asst Camera* Ralph Gerling. *2d Asst Camera* Edward Hutton. *Asst Art Dir* Sydney Z. Litwack. *Set Decor* James Payne. *Set Decor Cons* Josie Macavin. *Prod Dsgn* Rouben Ter-Arutunian. *Supv Ed* Antony Gibbs. *Ed* Brian Smedley-Aston, Hal Ashby. *Asst Ed* Stuart H. Pappé. *Mus Comp & Cond* John Addison. *Sd Ed* Stan Fiferman. *Sd Mix* Robert Post. *Boom* Gene Ashbrook. *1st & 2d Asst Dir* Kurt Neumann, Les Gorall. *Prod Mgr* Austen Jewell. *Asst to Prod* Jean Benson, Polly Hfuel. *Asst to Dir* Bud Cherry, Elizabeth Roberts. *Asst to Exec Prod* Coco Morris. *Prod Sec* Barbara Williams, prod sec. *Script Supv* Meta Rebner. *Cost Dsgn* Rouben Ter-Arutunian. *Cost* Nat Tolmach. *Men's Cost* James Kelly, cost. *Women's Cost* Marie T. Harris. *Cost Coörd* Margo Weintz. *Makeup Supv* Emile La Vigne. *Body Makeup* Bunny Armstrong. *Hairstyles* Alice Monte. *Sp Eff* Geza Gaspar. *Location Res* Harry L. Cherry. *Casting Supv* Neil Hartley. *Gaffer* Lloyd Garnell. *Head Grip* William Record. *Prop Master* Stephen Ferry, Walter Starkey. *Still Photog* Eric Carpenter. *Constr Coörd* James West.

Cast: Robert Morse *(Dennis Barlow)*, Jonathan Winters *(Wilbur Glenworthy/Harry Glenworthy)*, Anjanette Comer *(Aimee Thanatogenos)*, Rod Steiger *(Mr. Joyboy)*, Dana Andrews *(General Brinkman)*, Milton Berle *(Mr. Kenton)*, James Coburn *(immigration officer)*, John Gielgud *(Sir Francis Hinsley)*, Tab Hunter *(guide)*, Margaret Leighton *(Mrs. Kenton)*, Liberace *(Mr. Starker)*, Roddy McDowall *(D. J., Jr.)*, Robert Morley *(Sir Ambrose Abercrombie)*, Lionel Stander *(Guru Brahmin)*, Ayllene Gibbons *(Joyboy's mother)*, Bernie Kopell *(Assistant to Guru Brahmin)*, Asa Maynor *(secretary to D. J., Jr.)*, Alan Napier *(English club official)*, Martin Ransohoff *(Lorenzo Medici)*, Roxanne Arlen, Pamela Curran, Claire Kelly *(Whispering Glades hostesses)*, John Bleifer *(Mr. Bogaloff)*, Bella Bruck *(Mrs. Bogaloff)*, Ed Reimers *(Whispering Glades minister)*, Paul H. Williams *(Gunther Fry)*, "Miss Beverly Hills" *(orgy dancer)*, Chick Hearn *("Resurrection Now" TV Announcer)*, Brad Moore, Dort Clark, Robert Easton, Don Haggerty, Warren Kemmerling, Reta Shaw, Barik Trone.

Farce. Source: Evelyn Waugh, *The Loved One* (Boston, 1948). Dennis Barlow, an English poet whose speciality is plagiarism, arrives in Hollywood to stay with his uncle, Sir Francis Hinsley. Sir Francis, a long-time art director for motion picture productions is fired by his studio in an economy move and commits suicide by hanging himself. Sir Ambrose Abercrombie, leader of the British film colony, asks Dennis to arrange Sir Francis' funeral at Whispering Glades Memorial Park, the most exclusive Hollywood Cemetery. Whispering

Glades is run by the Blessed Reverend Wilbur Glenworthy. Dennis gets a job with Wilbur's twin brother, Harry, as a preacher at The Happier Hunting Grounds, a pet cemetery; and he falls in love with Aimee Thanatogenos, a Whispering Glades cosmetologist who is wooed also by Mr. Joyboy, the chief embalmer. Aimee spurns both of them because of her dismay in learning that Dennis steals his poems and her disgust for Joyboy's gluttonous mother. She is still confused about what to do after consulting the Guru Brahmin and asks the Reverend Glenworthy for advice, but she is driven to suicide by embalming herself when Glenworthy makes advances to her. He has been plotting to disinter the caskets and launch them into space, thus freeing the cemetery for valuable land use as a senior citizen's home. He had planned to initiate this program with the cooperation of Air Force General Brinkman by using the body of an astronaut. Aimee's body is substituted for the dead astronaut and lifted into space on a rocket developed by a child prodigy. Dennis goes back to England. *Gurus. British. Cosmetologists. Clergymen. Twins. Brothers. Poets. Undertakers. Motion picture art directors. Children. Death. Plagiarism. Gluttony. Motherhood. Suicide. Embalming. Disinterment. Funerals. Cemeteries. Rockets. Corpses. Hollywood. Pets.*

Note: Location scenes filmed at Greystone Mansion in Los Angeles.

THE LOVELY TOUCH see THE PSYCHO LOVER

A LOVELY WAY TO DIE   F6.2917

Universal Pictures. 12 Jul **1968** [New York opening; c19 Oct 1968; LP37189]. Sd (Westrex); col (Technicolor). 35mm (Techniscope). 103 min.

Prod Richard Lewis. *Dir* David Lowell Rich. *Screenplay* A. J. Russell. *Dir Photog* Morris Hartzband. *Art Dir* Alexander Golitzen, Willard Levitas. *Set Decor* John McCarthy, John Ward. *Scenic Artist* Edward Garzero. *Main Titl* Universal Title. *Film Ed* Sidney Katz, Gene Palmer. *Mus Supv* *Titl Song* Kenyon Hopkins, Judy Spencer. *Sung by* Jackie Wilson. *Rec Prod by* Carl Davis. *Song:* "A Lovely Way To Live" Kenyon Hopkins, Judy Spencer. *Sung by* Marge Dodson. *Sd* Waldon O. Watson, Dennis Maitland. *Asst Dir* Peter Scoppa, John Corless. *Unit Prod Mgr* Jim Di Gangi. *Script Supv* B. J. Bjorkman. *Prod Asst* Terence A. Donnelly, Leonard Jacobs. *Cost* Mary Merrill. *Makeup* Bud Westmore, Martin Bell. *Hairstyles* Larry Germain, Willis Hanchett. *Casting* Alan Shayne Associates. *Dial Coach* George Petrarca. *Gaffer* Norman Leigh. *Prop Master* Henry Brenwasser.

Cast: Kirk Douglas *(Jim Schuyler)*, Sylva Koscina *(Rena Westabrook)*, Eli Wallach *(Tennessee Fredericks)*, Kenneth Haigh *(Jonathan Fleming)*, Martyn Green *(Finchley)*, Sharon Farrell *(Carol)*, Ruth White *(cook)*, Philip Bosco *(Fuller)*, Ralph Waite *(Sean Magruder)*, Meg Myles *(Mrs. Magruder)*, William Roerick *(Loren Westabrook)*, Dana Elcar *(Layton)*, Dolph Sweet *(Haver)*, Dee Victor *(Mrs. Gordon)*, Lincoln Kilpatrick *(Daley)*, Doris Roberts *(Feeney)*, Carey Nairnes *(Harris)*, John Rogers *(Cooper)*, Gordon Peters *(Eric)*, Alex Stevens *(Lumson)*, Richard Woods, Conrad Bain *(James Lawrence)*, Robert Gerringer *(Connor)*, John Ryan *(Harry Samson)*, Sydney Walker, Jay Barney *(The Real Finchley)*, Marty Glickman *(racetrack announcer)*, Gino Piserchio *(Michel)*, Leslie Charleson *(Julie)*, Ali MacGraw *(Melody)*.

Crime melodrama. Faced with a police department investigation of his brutal methods, detective Jim Schuyler resigns and accepts a job from court lawyer Tennessee Fredericks. Schuyler's assignment is to guard Rena Westabrook, who is on trial for murdering her wealthy husband with the assistance of her lover, playboy Jonathan Fleming. Rena claims, however, that on the night of the murder, she and Jonathan attended the theater and were later seen at a bar by Sean Magruder. After fighting off an assailant and finding Magruder's dead body in his car, Schuyler forces Jonathan to confess that he had planned to blackmail Mr. Westabrook because of his tainted sexual activities but had been dissuaded by Rena. Now convinced of Rena's innocence, Schuyler sets out to find the real culprit while the trial is in progress. Schuyler discovers that the murderers are part of a gang that had disposed of Finchley, a wealthy Englishman, and substituted an imposter in a plot to steal the Finchley fortune. When Westabrook accidentally learned their secret, he was killed, and Magruder was slain because he was Rena's alibi. Once Rena is acquitted, the gang attempts to kill her as she returns home; but Schuyler commandeers a helicopter, alerts the police, and shoots down a rifleman as he is about to fire at Rena. *Detectives. Bodyguards. Widows. Playboys. English. Gangs. Police. Murder. Trials. Impersonation. Theft. Frameup. Helicopters.*

Note: Location scenes filmed in New York and New Jersey. Sources conflict in crediting actors playing the roles of James Lawrence and The Real Finchley.

THE LOVEMAKERS ... CARNAL STYLE   F6.2918

Dist Sam Lake Enterprises. caOct **1970.** Sd; col (Eastman Color). 35mm. 73 min. *MPAA rating* X.

Pres by Sam Lake. *Prod* Jean Jacques Robeau. *Dir* Sidney Knight. *Writ* Harvey Green. *Camera* Robert Morgenstern. *Film Ed* Sidney Knight. *Sd* Ronald Nort. *Asst* Jeremy Altman.

Cast: Linda Southern *(Sandra)*, Larry Hunter *(boyfriend)*, Judith James *(Nancy)*, Peter Leconte *(Charles)*, Joseph Schwartz *(Lou)*, Joel Taylor *(Bill)*, Jennie Lynn *(Louise)*, Dorothy Simmonds *(Ava)*, Daniel Harris *(Winston)*, Shelly Simmons *(Jean)*, Richard Daly *(Harry)*.

Melodrama. Sandra discovers that her boyfriend has been unfaithful, and she moves in with Nancy and Charles. Charles is a drug dealer, and the central figure in a lovemaking commune. Sandra, a shy and conservative girl, agrees to accompany Nancy and Charles the next day as an observer. She witnesses a ritual of mass lovemaking, is mesmerized by the sight, and cannot resist Charles' sexual magnetism. He seduces her. Sandra is wonderfully happy in the days that follow. The dream turns sour when Charles lends Sandra to Lou, a friend who has arrived for a visit. She submits to his embraces but feels humiliated and angry. Having decided that henceforth she will make love only with Charles, she returns home to find Nancy and Charles engaged in sex with another couple, Jean and Harry. Jean is attracted to women, and wants Sandra to join her. Charles seduces Sandra as she tries to reason with him, and then slips away, allowing Jean to indulge her passion. When Sandra realizes what has happened, she runs out hysterically; no longer able to face the degradation around her, she kills herself. *Drug dealers. Group sex. Seduction. Bisexuality. Suicide. Infidelity.*

Note: Also known as *The Love Makers.*

LOVER COME BACK   F6.2919

7 Pictures–Nob Hill Productions–Arwin Productions. *Dist* Universal-International. 20 Dec **1961** [Los Angeles opening; c18 Dec 1961; LP25071]. Sd; col (Eastman Color by Pathé). 35mm. 107 min.

Prod Stanley Shapiro, Martin Melcher. *Exec Prod* Robert Arthur. *Dir* Delbert Mann. *Screenplay* Stanley Shapiro, Paul Henning. *Photog* Arthur E. Arling. *Art Dir* Alexander Golitzen, Robert Clatworthy. *Set Decor* Oliver Emert. *Anim Titl* Pacific Title. *Film Ed* Marjorie Fowler. *Mus Supv* Joseph Gershenson. *Mus* Frank De Vol. *Song:* "Lover Come Back to Me" Alan Spilton, Frank De Vol. *Song:* "Should I Surrender" Adam Ross, William Landan. *Sd* Waldon O. Watson, Joe Lapis. *Asst Dir* Ray Gosnell, Jr., Douglas Green. *Unit Prod Mgr* Marshall Green. *Miss Day's Gowns* Irene. *Miss Day's Jewels* Laykin et Cie. *Makeup* Bud Westmore. *Hair Stylist* Larry Germain.

Cast: Rock Hudson *(Jerry Webster)*, Doris Day *(Carol Templeton)*, Tony Randall *(Peter Ramsey)*, Edie Adams *(Rebel Davis)*, Jack Oakie *(J. Paxton Miller)*, Jack Kruschen *(Dr. Linus Tyler)*, Ann B. Davis *(Millie)*, Joe Flynn *(Hadley)*, Howard St. John *(Brackett)*, Karen Norris *(Kelly)*, Jack Albertson *(Fred)*, Charles Watts *(Charlie)*, Donna Douglas *(Deborah)*, Ward Ramsey *(Hodges)*, John Litel *(board member)*.

Romantic comedy. Though they have never met, Jerry Webster and Carol Templeton, account executives with rival advertising agencies, are sworn enemies. Jerry's practice of using liquor and chorus girls to land clients galls the hard-working and conscientious Carol. When she reports him to the Advertising Council, Jerry induces Rebel Davis, a sexy nightclub performer he uses to charm his prospective clients, to testify on his behalf. As a reward for helping him win an acquittal, Jerry names Rebel the VIP girl and films a series of commercials for a nonexistent product. Unfortunately, Jerry's boss, a hopeless neurotic named Peter Ramsey who is apron-stringed to his analyst, puts the commercials on television—and VIP is launched. Frantic, Jerry engages an eccentric scientist, Dr. Linus Tyler, to invent a product that can be marketed as VIP. Carol visits Linus in an attempt to steal the account away from Jerry. When she arrives at his laboratory, she encounters Jerry, mistakes him for Linus, and announces that she will stop at nothing to get the account. Delighted by both the attractiveness of his rival and the chance to ruin her, Jerry pretends to be the scientist and allows Carol to wine and dine him. Just as he is about to complete his triumph by seducing Carol, she learns the truth. Appalled, she once more reports him to the Advertising Council, this time for advertising a nonexistent product. Jerry, however, arrives at the hearing with VIP, a mint-flavored candy he offers to one and all, including Carol. There is only one drawback: each one of Linus' wafers has the same effect as three triple martinis. The next morning, Jerry and Carol wake up in a motel with a marriage certificate hanging on the mirror. The horrified Carol has the marriage quickly annulled while Jerry flees to his firm's west coast branch. They are reunited and remarried 9 months later, however—in a hospital maternity ward. *Advertising executives. Entertainers. Scientists. Eccentrics. Psychiatrists. Advertising. Television commercials. Marriage—Annulment. Business ethics. Neurosis. Impersonation. Seduction. Candy.*

A LOVER FOR THE SUMMER see A MISTRESS FOR THE SUMMER

LOVERS AND OTHER STRANGERS   F6.2920

ABC Pictures. *Dist* Cinerama Releasing Corp. 12 Aug **1970** [New York opening]. Sd; col (Metrocolor). 35mm. 106 min. [Also reviewed at 104 min.] *MPAA rating* R.

Prod David Susskind. *Assoc Prod* Anthony Loeb. *Dir* Cy Howard. *Screenplay* Renée Taylor, Joseph Bologna, David Z. Goodman. *Photog* Andrew Laszlo. *Set Decor* John Alan Hicks. *Prod Dsgn* Ben Edwards. *Film Ed* David Bretherton, Sidney Katz. *Mus* Fred Karlin. *Lyr* Robb Wilson, Arthur James. *Songs Sung by* Country Coalition, Larry Meredith. *Sd* Jim Shields. *Asst Dir* Louis A. Stroller, Martin Danzig, William Eustace, Phil Goldfarb. *Prod Supv* Henry Spitz. *Wardrobe* Albert Wolsky.

Cast: Gig Young *(Hal Henderson)*, Bea Arthur *(Bea Vecchio)*, Bonnie Bedelia *(Susan Henderson)*, Anne Jackson *(Cathy)*, Harry Guardino *(Johnny)*, Michael Brandon *(Mike Vecchio)*, Richard Castellano *(Frank Vecchio)*, Bob Dishy *(Jerry)*, Marian Hailey *(Brenda)*, Joseph Hindy *(Richie)*, Anthony Holland *(Donaldson)*, Diane Keaton *(Joan)*, Cloris Leachman *(Bernice)*, Mort Marshall *(Father Gregory)*, Anne Meara *(Wilma)*, Bob Kaliban *(hotel clerk)*, Amy Stiller *(flower girl)*, Charlotte Jones *(Johnny's mother)*.

Domestic comedy. Source: Renée Taylor and Joseph Bologna, *Lovers and Other Strangers* (New York opening: 18 Sep 1968). Despite misgivings, Mike Vecchio and Susan Henderson, lovers for 18 months, decide to marry. Although their parents warmly applaud the decision, preparations for the wedding are punctuated by discord between married relatives. Frank Vecchio, Mike's blue-collar, Italian-American father, is shocked to learn that his childless older son, Richie, and daughter-in-law, Joan, are considering divorce. For years Hal Henderson, Susan's prosperous, Irish Catholic father, has maintained a liaison with Cathy, his wife's best friend, who now demands that he choose between them. Susan's sister, Wilma, continues to be disappointed by her husband Johnny's sexual performance and to be frustrated by his nightly absorption in television; and her constant complaining has endangered their marriage. The evening before the ceremony Mike and Susan arrange a blind date between Susan's cousin Brenda, a bridesmaid, and Mike's friend Jerry, an usher. The betrothed couple then retires to the hotel's bridal suite for a last night as lovers. Although the lecherous Jerry attempts to seduce the virginal Brenda by luring her to his apartment, her incessant chatter forestalls his lovemaking. The wedding itself catalyzes the emotions of the participants. Full of nostalgia, Frank confides in his son an early love affair; Cathy flees in tears to a rest room, where she is comforted by Hal; Brenda and Jerry make love, temporarily interrupting her prattle; Johnny performs to Wilma's satisfaction; and, the Vecchios' hopes for their reconciliation notwithstanding, Richie and Joan go their separate ways. Oblivious to the emotional chaos about them, Mike and Susan confidently begin their married life. *Brides. Bridegrooms. Cousins. Sisters. Brothers. Middle classes. Catholics. Marriage. Divorce. Seduction. Infidelity. Family life. Weddings.*

Note: Location scenes filmed around New York City.

LOVERS BY APPOINTMENT — F6.2921

Mor-Rion Films. *Dist* Producers Releasing International. Feb **1970** [periodical notice]. Sd; b&w. 35mm. 70 min.

Cast: Donny Lee, Big Bertha, Tulip Moyst, Linda Lust, Sam Bueno.

Sex film. No information about the precise nature of this film has been found, but press material and photographs suggest that it includes scenes of prostitution, lesbianism, sadism, and group sex. *Prostitution. Lesbianism. Sadism. Group sex.*

LOVERS IN LIMBO *see* **THE NAME OF THE GAME IS KILL!**

LOVERS MUST LEARN *see* **ROME ADVENTURE**

LOVERS' NET *see* **PORT OF SHAME**

LOVERS OF GINZA (Japan) — F6.2922

Toho Co. Jul **1961** [Los Angeles showing]. Sd; col? 35mm. 101 min.

Cast: Reiko Dan, Akira Takarada, Mitsuko Kusabue, Tatsuya Mihashi, Akemi Kita, Yukiko Shimazaki, Hiroshi Mizuhara, Hiroshi Koizumi, Yuzo Kayama, Haruko Togo, Choko Iida, Chisako Hara.

Romantic drama. No information about the precise nature of this film has been found. *Tokyo—Ginza District.*

Note: Released in Japan in Jan 1961 as *Ginza no koibitotachi.*

THE LOVERS OF TERUEL (France) — F6.2923

Monarch. *Dist* Continental Distributing, Inc. 14 Dec **1962** [New York opening]. Sd; col (Eastman Color). 35mm (Totalscope). 90 min.

Dir-Writ Raymond Rouleau. *Dial* René-Louis Lafforgue. *Photog* Claude Renoir. *Decor* Jacques Dupont. *Film Ed* Marinette Cadix. *Mus Comp* Mikis Theodorakis, Henri Sauguet. *Mus Cond* Kresimir Sipush. *Choreog* Milko Sparemblek. *Sd* Pierre Calvet, Julien Coutellier. *Prod Mgr* Paul Temps. *Cost* Jacques Dupont. *English Subtitl* Herman G. Weinberg, Norbert Terry.

Cast: Ludmilla Tcherina *(Isa)*, René-Louis Lafforgue *(barker)*, Milko Sparemblek *(Manuel)*, Milenko Banovitch *(Diego)*, Stevan Grebel *(Grebelito)*, Jean-Pierre Bras *(father)*, Antoine Marin *(Pablo)*, Roberto *(dwarf)*.

Dance film. Each night in public squares, a band of gypsies perform a ballet drama based on an old Spanish legend. In the dance Don Diego, the lover of

wealthy Isabelle, has been turned away by her father because he is considered unworthy, although he is given 3 years to improve his position. When the time is up and Don Diego fails to appear, Isabelle obeys her father and marries the Duke of Teruel. The day after the wedding, Don Diego reappears and, upon learning of the marriage, kills himself. Deranged by grief, Isabelle also commits suicide. Isa, the star of the dance troupe, is in the same position as the heroine of the ballet; she is pledged to marry Manuel, a man whom she does not love, while her true love, Diego, mysteriously disappeared 3 years before. Diego eventually returns, but Manuel kills him during the ballet performance. Isa then kills herself, and, true to the legend, the two lovers are buried side by side. *Gypsies. Dancers. Ballet. Myths. Marriage. Suicide. Murder. Teruel (Spain).*

Note: Opened in Paris in May 1962 as *Les amants de Teruel;* running time: 94 min.

LOVERS ON A TIGHTROPE (France) — F6.2924

Panda Films. *Dist* Interworld Film Distributors. 24 Oct **1962** [New York opening]. Sd; b&w. 35mm. 83 min.

Prod Robert Ciriez Daubigny. *Assoc Prod* Pierre Heuline. *Dir* Jean-Charles Dudrumet. *Screenplay* Roland Laudenbach, Jean-Charles Dudrumet. *Photog* Pierre Guéguen. *Art Dir* Olivier Girard. *Film Ed* Janine Verneau. *Mus* Maurice Jarre. *Sd* Paul Boistelle, Bernard Souverbie. *Asst Dir* Philippe Baraduc.

Cast: Annie Girardot *(Cora)*, François Périer *(Daniel)*, Gérard Buhr *(Henri)*, Georges Descrières *(Simon)*, Geneviève Brunet *(Isabelle)*, Hubert Deschamps *(lawyer)*, Henri Crémieux *(doctor)*, Henri Virlogeux, Piella Sorano, Michel Seldow, Pierre Moncorbier.

Melodrama. Source: Michel Lebrun, *La veuve* (Paris, 1958). Cora, the wife of a wealthy Parisian businessman, Daniel, is involved in an affair with Henri, an unscrupulous garage mechanic who has set his sights on Cora's fortune. Daniel becomes suspicious and hires a detective to investigate, but the detective is unsuccessful in pinpointing Cora's extramarital activities. Daniel overhears a telephone conversation between Cora and her lover and mistakenly believes that the man is his business partner, Simon, who is Henri's brother. Since Daniel refuses Cora a divorce, Henri persuades her to put sleeping pills into the thermos of coffee her husband will take with him on an upcoming business trip. The morning after Daniel's departure, Cora is informed that her husband has been killed in an automobile accident. Guilt-stricken, she discovers at the morgue that the man killed was actually Simon, who substituted for the suspicious Daniel at the last moment. At Simon's burial, Daniel appears, and the truth is revealed: Cora omitted the sleeping pills at the last moment, but Henri had sabotaged Daniel's car in order to guarantee the success of the plan. Daniel forgives the remorseful Cora, and they effect a somewhat uncertain reconciliation. *Paris. Garagemen. Businessmen. Detectives. Brothers. Fortune hunters. Marriage. Infidelity. Murder. Automobile accidents. Mistaken identity.*

Note: Opened in Paris in Apr 1960 under the title *La corde raide;* running time: 90 min.

LOVERS' ROCK (Republic of China) — F6.2925

Shaw Brothers (Taiwan) Ltd. 11 May **1966** [New York showing]. Sd; b&w. 35mm. [Feature film, length unknown.]

Prod Run Run Shaw. *Dir-Screenplay* Pan Lei. *Dir Photog* Hung Ching-yun. *Mus* Loh Ming Tao.

Cast: Cheng Pei-pei *(Lin Chiu-tse)*, Chiao Chuang *(Chin Yu)*, Hsang Tsung-hsin *(So Ta-kuei)*, Wen Ling *(Tseng Ah-feng)*.

Drama. So Ta-kuei, feared lost at sea, returns home to his Chinese village. On its shore stand figures of rock said to represent women who have lost their men at sea. Reunited with Lin Chiu-tse, a childhood friend just returned from the city, So Ta-kuei falls in love. His rival for Lin Chiu-tse, however, is his friend Chin Yu, a college student and mechanic. When Ta-kuei disappears in a typhoon, Lin Chiu-tse realizes she loves Chin Yu. Spurred by Lin Chiu-tse's father's insistence that his future son-in-law own his own boat, Chin Yu acquires a junk. Wedding preparations are interrupted when Ta-kuei returns home after being saved by a ship. The two men quarrel but are reconciled when Ta-kuei rescues Chin Yu from some thugs. Ta-kuei later falls in love with Tseng Ah-feng and joins his former rival in fishing expeditions. The men are lost at sea, and two new rock figures appear on the beach. *Fishermen. Students. Mechanics. In-laws. Sea rescue. Fishing boats. Fishing villages. Myths. Typhoons. Weddings. Ships.*

Note: One source gives as the film's national origin Hong Kong.

LOVES OF A BLONDE (Czechoslovakia) — F6.2926

Barrandov Film Studio. For Československý Film. *Dist* Prominent Films, CBK Film Enterprises. 26 Oct **1966** [New York opening]. Sd; b&w. 35mm. 88 min.

Dir Miloš Forman. *Screenplay* Jaroslav Papoušek, Ivan Passer, Miloš Forman, Václav Šašek. *Photog* Miroslav Ondříček. *Asst Camera* Ladislav Chroust. *Art Dir* Karel Černý. *Film Ed* Miroslav Hájek. *Mus* Evžen Illín. *Sd*

Adolf Böhm. *Asst Dir* Ivan Passer. *Prod Mgr* Rudolf Hájek. *Location Mgr* Jaroslav Solnička. *Production Group* Šebor–Bor.

Cast: Hana Brejchová *(Andula)*, Vladimír Pucholt *(Milda)*, Vladimír Menšík *(Vacovský)*, Ivan Kheil *(Maňas)*, Jiří Hrubý *(Burda)*, Milada Ježková *(Milda's mother)*, Josef Šebánek *(Milda's father)*, Marie Salačová *(Marie)*, Jana Nováková *(Jana)*, Jana Crkalová *(Jaruška)*, Zdeňka Lorencová *(Zdena)*, Táňa Zelinková *(girl with guitar)*, Jan Vostrčil *(colonel)*, Josef Kolb *(Pokorný)*, Antonín Blažejovský *(Tonda)*, M. Zedníčková *(educator)*.

Comedy-drama. Andula is a young woman who works in a shoe factory on the outskirts of Prague. Although there is an acute shortage of men in the district, Andula does have an admirer, Tonda, but his virtues fall short of the standards set by her incurably romantic ideals. One day the factory manager arranges for the army to bivouac near the town, and a dance is held to celebrate the occasion. The soldiers, however, are mostly middle-aged reservists, and the bored Andula turns her attentions toward Milda, the piano player in the dance band. Following some awkward preliminaries, Andula spends the night in Milda's room and falls in love. The next weekend she spurns Tonda and hitchhikes to Prague. She finds Milda's address and arrives unannounced at his home, where she is met by his bewildered and scandalized parents. At the time, Milda is playing for a dance and pursuing another conquest, and his parents are obliged to permit Andula to sleep on the living room sofa. When Milda finally returns, his outraged mother hustles him off to the family bed for a long—and loud—session of recriminations and moralizing. Andula listens through the door, her teary eyes expressing her disappointment. When Milda insists that he hardly knows her, that he never gave her the slightest encouragement, and that he certainly has not in any way obligated himself to her, she sadly returns to her factory dormitory. With her pride and reputation at stake and her romantic nature refusing to give in, she tells one of her girl friends about the lovely time she had with Milda and his parents at their home in Prague. *Factory workers. Pianists. Hitchhikers. Philanderers. Filial relations. Bands. Dancehalls. Prague. Czechoslovakia—Army.*

Note: Location scenes filmed in Zruč and Sázavou, Czechoslovakia. Released in Prague in Nov 1965 as *Lásky jedné plavovlásky.*

LOVES OF A PSYCHIATRIST   **F6.2927**
Mitam Productions. 5 Jun **1968** [New York showing]. Sd; b&w. 35mm. 62 min.

Cast: Karen Drake, Denine Martin.

Melodrama. An investigator interrogates two women about the illegal activities of Dr. Silo, a phony psychiatrist who takes advantage of his position to blackmail married women into gratifying his deviant sexual desires. Mrs. Stapleton tells Dr. Silo of visiting a motel with a single friend and two men they met on a plane. Both couples shared the same bed, and the women switched sexual partners. Dr. Silo threatens to inform Mrs. Stapleton's husband unless she submits to his advances. Disturbed by his first adolescent sexual experience, Silo has developed unhealthy sexual attitudes through listening to his patients recount their sexual problems. Another patient, Mrs. Voorhees, enjoys a passionate affair with Dr. Silo while her husband is away on business trips. Silo goes to Mrs. Voorhees' house and watches her niece having sex with a young neighbor. The youth becomes aware of Silo's presence and flees, mistaking him for Mr. Voorhees. Silo then tries to rape the niece, and he is discovered by Mrs. Voorhees, who knocks him out with a poker and telephones police to expose him as a fraud. *Psychiatrists. Housewives. Blackmail. Infidelity. Voyeurism. Rape. Imposture. Sexual practices. Mental illness.*

THE LOVES OF ISADORA *see* **ISADORA**

THE LOVES OF ONDINE   **F6.2928**
Dist Factory Films, Film-Makers' Cooperative. 1 Aug **1968** [New York opening]. Sd; col (Eastman Color). 16mm. 86 min.

An Andy Warhol Production. *Exec Prod* Paul Morrissey. *Dir-Writ* Andy Warhol. *Photog* Andy Warhol. *Film Ed* Andy Warhol.

Cast: Ondine *(Ondine)*, Viva *(girl in bed)*, Joe Dallesandro *("college wrestler")*, Angelina "Pepper" Davis *(girl on love seat)*, Ivy Nicholson *(girl on chair)*, Brigid Polk *(Ondine's wife)*, Bill Gary *(folk singer)*.

Satire. Ondine, a homosexual married man, makes an attempt to prove his masculinity by picking up women and persuading them to undress while being interviewed. His initial subject, who he claims is the first woman he has ever desired, sits in a love seat and occasionally giggles. She refuses to remove her clothing, and Ondine throws her out of his room. The second, whom he manages to coax into a bed in his mother's apartment, insists on being paid for each item of apparel she removes. The third, whose back hurts, sits in a chair and accuses Ondine of wanting to torture her. After he listens to a guitarist who sings folk songs by the sea, Ondine witnesses a food-and-garbage orgy among nude, Spanish-speaking participants. He goes to a party at a beach house and there he tells of being violated as a youth. Finally, he returns to his home for a lesson in Indian wrestling from a nervous "college wrestler" he has picked up.

Later, Ondine's wife barges in with friends; she sees the young man in his undershorts and accuses Ondine of indecent behavior. *Pickups. Male homosexuality. Bisexuality. Infidelity. Orgies. Folk music. Wrestling. Rape.*

Note: Filmed in New York City. Part or all of the film is contained in the full-length version of ✶✶✶✶ *(Four Stars)*, q. v.

THE LOVES OF SALAMMBO (France/Italy)   **F6.2929**
Stella Film–Fides. *Dist* Twentieth Century–Fox Film Corp. 3 Oct **1962** [Denver, Colorado, opening]. Sd; col (Deluxe). 35mm (Cinemascope). 72 min.

Dir Sergio Grieco. *Orig Adapt & Dial* André Tabet. *English Screenplay* John Blamy, Barbara Somers. *Photog* Piero Portalupi. *Film Ed* Enzo Alfonsi. *Mus* Alexandre Derevitsky.

Cast: Jeanne Valérie *(Salammbo)*, Jacques Sernas *(Mathos)*, Edmund Purdom *(Narr Havas)*, Riccardo Garrone *(Hamilcar)*, Arnoldo Foà *(Spendius)*, Charles Fawcett, Kamala Devi, Brunella Bovo.

Action melodrama. Source: Gustave Flaubert, *Salammbo* (1862). Internal strife rocks ancient Carthage as a group of mercenaries led by Mathos threaten to destroy the city if they are not paid for their services during the First Punic War. Salammbo, daughter of General Hamilcar, promises payment in jewels to Mathos, with whom she has fallen in love. Narr Havas, greedy for money and in love with Salammbo, fills the jewel chests with rocks, however, causing the angry mercenaries to again march on Carthage. They are stopped by General Hamilcar's army, Narr Havas is executed after his plot is revealed, and Salammbo and Mathos are reunited. *Mercenaries. Duplicity. Jealousy. Capital punishment. Punic wars. Carthage.*

Note: Opened in Rome in Jan 1961 as *Salambò*; running time: 100 min; in Paris in Mar 1960 as *Salammbo*; running time: 95 min (cut from 110 min).

LOVING   **F6.2930**
Columbia Pictures–Brooks Ltd. *Dist* Columbia Pictures. 4 Mar **1970** [New York opening; c4 Mar 1970; LP37949]. Sd; col (Eastman Color). 35mm. 89 min. *MPAA rating* R.

Prod-Writ Don Devlin. *Exec Prod* Raymond Wagner. *Prod Assoc* Lewis Teague. *Dir* Irvin Kershner. *Dir Photog* Gordon Willis. *Background Improvisations* Sheldon Patinkin. *Set Dresser* John Godfrey. *Prod Dsgn* Walter Scott Herndon. *Film Ed* Robert Lawrence. *Mus Comp & Cond* Bernardo Segáll. *Titl Song* Bernardo Segáll, William B. Dorsey. *Sung by* Chris Morgan. *Sd* Newton Avrutis, Nat Boxer. *Asst Dir* Ted Zachary. *Exec in Charge of Prod* Stanley Neufeld. *Prod Asst* Matthew Robbins. *Cost* Albert Wolsky. *Makeup* Joe Cranzano.

Cast: George Segal *(Brooks Wilson)*, Eva Marie Saint *(Selma Wilson)*, Sterling Hayden *(Lepridon)*, Keenan Wynn *(Edward)*, Nancie Phillips *(Nelly)*, Janis Young *(Grace)*, David Doyle *(Will)*, Paul Sparer *(Marve)*, Andrew Duncan *(Willy)*, Sherry Lansing *(Susan)*, Roland Winters *(Plommie)*, Edgar Stehli *(Mr. Kramm)*, Calvin Holt *(Danny)*, Mina Kolb *(Diane)*, Diana Douglas *(Mrs. Shavelson)*, David Ford *(Al)*, James Manis *(Charles)*, Mart Hulswit *(Ted)*, John Fink *(Brad)*, William Duffy *(Jay)*, Irving Selbst *(Benny)*, Martin Friedberg *(Roger)*, Lorraine Cullen *(Lizzie)*, Cheryl Bucher *(Hannah)*, Ed Crowley *(Mr. Shavelson)*, Roy Scheider *(Skip)*, Sab Shimono *(Byron)*, Eileen O'Neill *(Cindy)*, Diane Davies *(Barbie)*.

Comedy-drama. Source: J. M. Ryan, *Brooks Wilson, Ltd.* (New York, 1966). Freelance artist Brooks Wilson lives in Westport, Connecticut, with his wife, Selma, and their two daughters. His marriage shaky, his affair with his mistress, Grace, at a crisis point, and his job unstable, Brooks begins to crack under the pressure. On the day of his appointment with trucking magnate Lepridon, an account he badly needs, Brooks gets drunk at a private club for advertising executives and insults the club's president. In spite of himself, Brooks makes a good impression on Lepridon. At a party in the suburbs given by Grace's aunt and uncle, Brooks learns that he has won the account. He tells neither his wife, who wants to buy a new house, nor Grace, who wants him to get a divorce, and instead drunkenly succumbs to the advances of Nelly, a man-hungry neighbor. While Brooks and Nelly begin to make love in a child's playroom, party guests assemble around their host's closed-circuit television screen to watch the awkward scene. Selma makes out the blurred images as Brooks becomes aware of the camera. He runs outside, trouserless, and is beaten in the snow by the woman's husband. Left alone with his wife, who angrily thrashes him with her handbag, he tells her that he has won the Lepridon account. *Commercial artists. Mistresses. Suburbanites. Industrialists. Neighbors. Marriage. Drunkenness. Infidelity. Television. Contracts. Westport (Connecticut).*

Note: Location scenes filmed in New York city and Connecticut. Working title: *Brooks Wilson Ltd.*

LOVING COUPLES (Sweden)   **F6.2931**
Sandrews. *Dist* Prominent Films. 19 Sep **1966** [New York opening]. Sd (AGA); b&w. 35mm. 113 min.

Pres by John Nasht. *Prod* Rune Waldekranz, Göran Lindgren. *Dir* Mai Zetterling. *Screenplay* Mai Zetterling, David Hughes. *Dir Photog* Sven

Nykvist. *Camera Op* Anders Bodin. *Asst Camera Op* Peter Fischer. *Studio Photog* David Hughes. *Art Dir* Jan Boleslaw. *Film Ed* Paul Davies. *Mus* Rodger Wallis. *Choreog* Holger Rosenqvist. *Sd* P. O. Pettersson. *Boom Op* Jack Olofsson. *Sd Eff* Evald Andersson. *Sd Mix* Olle Jakobsson. *Asst Dir* Lena Malmsjö. Bertil Ohlsson. *Prod Mgr* Gösta Peterson. *Script Girl* Katherina Farago. *Cost* Birgitta Hahn. *Makeup* Gullan Westfelt. *Hairstyles* Sture Höglund, Ivar Hellqvist. *Tech Adv (Cost)* Birgitta Hahn. *Prop Master* Sven Björling.

Cast: Harriet Andersson *(Agda)*, Gunnel Lindblom *(Adèle Holström)*, Gio Petré *(Angela)*, Anita Björk *(Aunt Petra)*, Gunnar Björnstrand *(Dr. Jacob Lewin)*, Inga Landgré *(Mrs. Lewin)*, Jan Malmsjö *(Stellan von Pahlen)*, Frank Sundström *(Dir. Ola Landborg)*, Eva Dahlbeck *(Mrs. Landborg)*, Heinz Hopf *(Bernhard Landborg)*, Hans Strååt *(Thomas)*, Bengt Brunskog *(Tord Holström)*, Toivo Pawlo *(Mr. Macson)*, Margit Carlqvist *(Dora Macson)*, Jan-Erik Lindqvist *(Peter)*, Barbro Hiort af Ornäs *(Lilian)*, Märta Dorff *(Alexandra)*, Lissi Alandh *(Bell)*, Åke Grönberg *(elderly lecher in street)*, Isa Quensel *(Fredrika)*, Hans Sundberg *(organist)*, Sten Lonnert *(Kisse)*, Axel Fritz *(Per)*, Henrik Schildt *(Sam)*, Berit Gustafsson *(Henrika)*, Lars Grundtman, Lennart Grundtman *(twin brothers Nick & Nock)*, Dan Landgré *(Cecil)*, Lo Dagerman *(Angela, age 10)*, Rebecca Pawlo *(Adèle, age 10)*, Katarina Edfeldt *(Agda, age 13)*, Anja Boman *(Stanny)*, Nancy Dalunde *(Adèle's mother)*, Meta Velander *(The Woman)*, Claes Thelander *(priest)*, Kai Norström *(Daniel)*, Eva Alw *(housekeeper)*, Ulf Johansson, Börje Mellvig *(lawyers)*, Kai Reiners *(good man)*, Sonja Hjort *(patient)*, Birger Åsander *(band leader)*, Stig de la Berg *(sore loser)*, Bo Hederström, Arne Lindblad, Holger Rosenqvist, Axeline Lé Mon *(guests)*.

Drama. Source: Agnes von Krusenstjerna, *Fröknarna von Pahlen* (Stockholm, 1930-35). In 1915, three expectant mothers in a Stockholm hospital recall the moral and social changes that helped to shape their lives. *Adèle, ever resentful of being patronized by the upper classes and bitter over the loss of a childhood lover, has married a servant of the wealthy Landborg family. Agda has always been gay and irresponsible; a child of the streets, she had her first sexual experience with a lecherous old man who lured her to his apartment with a box of sweets. After that she became a promiscuous model and petty thief. And Angela has always been sensitive and aristocratic; orphaned while still a youngster, she formed a strong attachment to her Aunt Petra and later had a lesbian encounter with one of her schoolteachers. All three women are present at a summer party given by the Landborgs: Adèle as a servant, Agda to pose for Stellan, a rising young artist, and Angela as a guest. Angela falls in love with and is impregnated by Thomas, a middle-aged archeologist and the former lover of her Aunt Petra. When he subsequently abandons her, Angela joins the movement against the "double standard" and decides to bear her illegitimate child. Agda seduces the young scion of the Landborg family, Bernhard, and when it becomes known that she is carrying his child, gladly agrees to a financial arrangement and marriage to the homosexual Stellan. The still sullen and love-starved Adèle conceives out of spite and anger. In the hospital, Adèle coldly accepts Dr. Lewin's announcement that her child has been stillborn; the indifferent Agda casually has her baby while flirting outrageously with the doctor; and Angela, the only one of the three who cherishes the thought of becoming a mother, gives birth after great pain and suffering.* Thieves. Models. Aunts. Orphans. Schoolteachers. Artists. Archeologists. Physicians. Pregnancy. Class conflict. Promiscuity. Motherhood. Lesbianism. Double standard. Illegitimacy. Seduction. Male homosexuality. Stillbirth. Childbirth. Hospitals. Stockholm.

Note: Released in Sweden in Dec 1964 as *Älskande Par*; running time: 118 min.

LOVING FEELING (Great Britain)   **F6.2932**
Piccadilly Pictures. *Dist* U-M Film Distributors. Mar **1969**. Sd; col (Technicolor). 35mm (Techniscope). 82 min. *MPAA rating* X.
Prod Bachoo Sen. *Dir* Norman J. Warren. *Screenplay* Robert Hewison, Bachoo Sen, Norman J. Warren. *Photog* Peter Jessop. *Art Dir* Hayden Pearce. *Film Ed* Tristam Cones. *Mus* Patrick John Scott. *Sd Ed* Robert Peck. *Asst Dir* John Elton.
Cast: Georgina Ward *(Suzanne Day)*, Simon Brent *(Stevee Day)*, Paula Patterson *(Carol Taylor)*, John Railton *(Scott)*, Peter Dixon *(Phillip Peterson)*, Heather Kyd *(Christine)*, Carol Cunningham *(Jane)*, Sonya Benjamin *(belly dancer)*, Paul Endersby *(old man on beach)*, Françoise Pascal *(model)*, Richard Barlett *(station sound mixer)*, Allen John *(restaurant manager)*, Stanley Folb, John Aston, Mary Land, Carl Conway.
Drama. When an unsuccessful actor named Stevee Day suddenly becomes famous as a London disc jockey, his wife, Suzanne, finds herself with nothing to do other than listen to her husband's early morning show and wait for his return from the radio station. Stevee, however, spends more and more time away from home by indulging himself with the adoring young women who idolize him. Upon discovering Stevee making love to Carol Taylor, a beautiful

secretary, Suzanne turns for consolation to Scott, a longtime friend and admirer. Deciding that their marriage is over, Stevee and Suzanne meet to discuss the sale of their house. Although the reunion prompts them to try for a reconciliation, a promotional campaign at the radio station forces Stevee to spend almost all of his time with Carol. No longer able to cope with her husband's infidelity, Suzanne leaves Stevee for Scott. And, a short time later, Stevee finds himself alone as the ambitious Carol deserts him for one of the radio station's top executives. Actors. Disc jockeys. Secretaries. Infidelity. Divorce. Radio.

THE LOVING TOUCH *see* **THE PSYCHO LOVER**

THE LOW BLOW   **F6.2933**
Dist Distribpix, Inc. 16 Apr **1970** [Maryland license]. Sd; b&w. 35mm. [Feature film, length unknown.]
Cast: Minnie the Mermaid, John Kent.
Melodrama. An up-and-coming young boxer falls prey to the temptation which confronts him as a result of his success in the ring and his good looks. Press material indicates that there are included scenes of nudity, torture, and rape. Press material also claims that the film is "a true story filmed at the actual locations whenever possible. Facts and authenticity furnished by [the prizefighter's] widow and family." Prizefighters. Torture. Rape. Nudity.

THE LOWER DEPTHS (Japan)   **F6.2934**
Toho Co. *Dist* Brandon Films. 9 Feb **1962** [New York opening]. Sd; b&w. 35mm. 125 min.
Prod Sojiro Motoki, Akira Kurosawa. *Dir* Akira Kurosawa. *Screenplay (see note)* Hideo Oguni, Akira Kurosawa, Shinobu Hashimoto. *Photog (see note)* Ichio Yamazaki. *Art Dir* Yoshiro Muraki. *Mus* Masaru Sato.
Cast: Toshiro Mifune *(Sutekichi, the thief)*, Isuzu Yamada *(Osugi, the landlady)*, Ganjiro Nakamura *(Rokubei, her husband)*, Kyoko Kagawa *(Okayo, her sister)*, Bokuzen Hidari *(Kahei, the priest)*, Minoru Chiaki *(The Ex-samurai)*, Kamatari Fujiwara *(The Actor)*, Eijiro Tono *(Tomekichi, the tinker)*, Eiko Miyoshi *(Asa, his wife)*, Akemi Negishi *(Osen, the prostitute)*, Koji Mitsui *(Yoshisaburo, the gambler)*, Nijiko Kiyokawa *(Otaki)*, Haruo Tanaka *(Tatsu)*, Kichijiro Ueda *(police agent)*, Yu Fujiki.
Drama. Source: Maxim Gorky, *Na dne* (Moscow opening: Dec 1902). In 19th-century Edo near the end of the Tokugawa period, a small hostel houses an assortment of individuals, including a cynical gambler, a thief, a tinker, an ex-samurai, an alcoholic actor, and a prostitute. The landlady, Osugi, treats all of her lodgers, including a newly arrived priest, with contempt, while reserving her real passion for the thief Sutekichi rather than her husband. Sutekichi, however, loves Osugi's sister, and when the possessive landlady discovers his feelings she becomes jealous and incites him to kill her husband. Sutekichi is arrested, and with his departure Osugi goes mad with grief. The priest departs, and as the other lodgers drink saké it is discovered that the actor has hanged himself. The gambler comments, "The idiot. Just as the fun was beginning." Thieves. Landladies. Gamblers. Actors. Prostitutes. Samurai. Priests. Sisters. Jealousy. Murder. Insanity. Suicide. Roominghouses. Edo.
Note: Released in Japan in Sep 1957 as *Donzoko*; running time: 137 min. According to one source the photographer is Kazuo Yamasaki. Hashimoto's participation is unconfirmed.

LSD, I HATE YOU *see* **MOVIE STAR, AMERICAN STYLE OR; LSD, I HATE YOU**

LAS LUCHADORAS CONTRA EL MÉDICO ASESINO *see* **DOCTOR OF DOOM**

LUCI DEL VARIETÀ *see* **VARIETY LIGHTS**

THE LUCK OF GINGER COFFEY (United States/Canada)   **F6.2935**
Leon Roth-Irvin Kershner-Crawley Films. *Dist* Continental Distributing, Inc. 21 Sep **1964** [New York opening]. Sd; b&w. 35mm. 100 min.
Prod Leon Roth. *Exec Prod* F. R. Crawley. *Dir* Irvin Kershner. *Screenplay* Brian Moore. *Photog* Manny Wynn. *Art Dir* Albert Brenner. *Set Decor* Claude Bonniere. *Prod Dsgn* Harry Horner. *Film Ed* Anthony Gibbs. *Asst Ed* Margaret Chandler. *Mus Comp & Cond* Bernardo Segall. *Sd* Stanley Kasper. *Asst Dir* Martin Rich.
Cast: Robert Shaw *(Ginger Coffey)*, Mary Ure *(Vera)*, Liam Redmond *(MacGregor)*, Tom Harvey *(Joe McGlade)*, Libby McClintock *(Paulie)*, Leo Leyden *(Brott)*, Powys Thomas *(Fox)*, Tom Kneebone *(Kenny)*, Leslie Yeo *(Stan Melton)*, Vern Chapman *(Hawkins)*, Paul Guèvremont *(Marcel)*, Barry Stewart *(Clarence)*, Arch McDonnell *(O'Donnell)*, Oliva Legare *(judge)*, Jacques Godin *(policeman)*, Maurice Beaupré *(Monsieur Beaulieu)*, Sydney Brown *(Old Billy)*, Juliette Huot *(Madame Beaulieu)*, Paul Hébert *(court clerk)*, Barney McManus *(newspaper foreman)*, Clarence Goodhue *(Hickey)*.
Drama. Source: Brian Moore, *The Luck of Ginger Coffey* (Boston, 1960). Thirty-nine-year-old Ginger Coffey, unable to hold a job in his native Ireland,

emigrates to Canada with his wife, Vera, and his 14-year-old daughter, Paulie. He is no more successful there, and Vera, having saved enough money, wishes to return home. When Ginger spends the passage money, Vera takes Paulie and leaves. Paulie soon returns to live with Ginger, and he takes two jobs—newspaper proofreading at night and delivering laundry during the day—to support her. Believing that he will be promoted to a reporter's job at the newspaper, Ginger turns down a good offer at the laundry, but he is fired from the newspaper. Meanwhile, he has convinced Vera to return to him temporarily because he finds it difficult to control Paulie. Discouraged because he is not working, Ginger gets drunk and is arrested. The case is dismissed, and Vera is waiting for Ginger outside the courthouse. *Irish. Delivery men. Immigrants. Newspapermen. Family life. Unemployment. Child custody. Drunkenness.*

Note: Location scenes filmed in Montreal. Released in Canada in 1964.

LUCKY BANG BANG'S SEX CLUB INTERNATIONAL see **SEX CLUB INTERNATIONAL**

LUCKY TO BE A WOMAN see **WHAT A WOMAN!**

LUCY GALLANT see **OIL TOWN**

LUDWIG VAN BEETHOVEN (Austria/West Germany)   **F6.2936**
Fischer Film–Fernsehen Produktion. *Dist* Connoisseur Films. 15 Dec **1970** [New York opening]. Sd; col (Eastman Color). 35mm. 100 min. [Cut from 112 min.]

Prod-Dir Hans Conrad Fischer. *Screenplay* Erich Koch. *Photog* Ivan Putora. *Film Ed* Annemarie Reisetbauer. *Mus Selections* Ludwig van Beethoven. *Mus Played by* The Berlin Philharmonic Orchestra, The Concertgebouw Orchestra, Vienna Symphony Orchestra, Hamburg State Philharmonic Orchestra, The Beethoven Hall Orchestra, The Radio Prague Symphony Orchestra, The Polish Radio Orchestra, The Lower Austria Tonkünstler Orchestra, The London Wind Soloists, Jack Brymer, The Vienna Philharmonic String Quartet, The Classic Viennese Schrammel Quartet. *Trio* Wilhelm Kempff, Henryk Szeryng, Ludwig Hölscher. *Mus Cond* Karl Böhm, Miltiades Caridis, Eugen Jochum, Herbert von Karajan, Otto Klemperer, Alois Klima, Leopold Ludwig, Lorin Maazel, Krzystof Missona, Volker Wangenheim. *Mus Sung by* The Vienna Academy Choir, Theo Adam, Richard Cassilly, Anja Silja, Ernst Wiemann, Michael Schopper. *Accomp* Jörg Demus. *Piano* Wilhelm Backhaus, Friedrich Gulda. *Organ* Wolfgang von Karajan. *Choreog* Werner Ulbrich. *Sd* Helmut Schalk. *Prod Mgr* Helmut Neuper. *Mus Adv* Claus Canisus. *Research* Hans Schmidt-Isserstedt. *English Vers* David Thomson, Martina Mayne.

Cast: Felix Felton, Gabriel Woolf (narrators), Peter Arens (Egmont), The Ballet of the German Opera on the Rhine.

Documentary. The bicentennial of Beethoven's birth is celebrated by a pastiche of his works, memorabilia, footage documenting his travels, and an interview during which pianist Friedrich Gulda discusses Beethoven's piano music. *Composers. Ludwig van Beethoven.*

UN LUGAR LLAMADO "GLORY" see **A PLACE CALLED GLORY**

LULLABY (U.S.S.R.)   **F6.2937**
Moldova-Film. *Dist* Artkino Pictures. 13 May **1961** [New York opening]. Sd; b&w. 35mm. 90 min.

Dir Mikhail Kalik. *Screenplay* Avenir Zak, Isai Kuznetsov. *Photog* Vadim Derbenyov. *Camera* D. Motornyy. *Art Dir* S. Bulgakov, A. Roman. *Film Ed* Mikhail Kalik. *Mus* D. Fedov. *Song Lyr* M. Sobol, A. Konunov. *Cond* V. Dudarova. *Sd* V. Lavrik. *Asst Dir* A. Matveyev. *Artistic Supv* Sergey Yutkevich. *Prod Mgr* S. Kurbatov. *Aviation Cons* I. Avvakumov.

Cast: Nikolay Timofeyev (*Losev, The Pilot*), Viktoria Lepko (*Aurika*), Lida Pigurenko (*Aurika as a little girl*), Lyubov Chernoval (*Aurika, the archivist's daughter*), Viktor Chetverikov (*Pavel*), Yuriy Solovyov (*Sergeant Mikheyev, the orphanage director*), K. Kramarchuk (*George Nistryanu*), Shura Kuznetsov (*Niku*), Mark Troyanovskiy (*The Archivist*), V. Zamanskiy (*Andrey Petryanu*), L. Kruglyy (*Levka*), Katya Savinova (*Olga, the girl in the truck*), V. Ratomskiy (*Demushkin*), K. Polovikova (*Anfisa*), Yevgeniy Teterin (*Mikhail Yakovlevich*), Ada Voytsik (*Yekaterina Borisovna*), Tatyana Guretskaya (*Zinaida Vasilyevna*), S. Svetlichnaya (*Nata*), I. Radchenko, Ye. Shutov, Ye. Izmaylova, I. Sedykh, L. Popovchenko, N. Krasnoshchyokov, I. Kolin, N. Zaytsev, K. Kozlenkova, V. Markin, B. Sokolov, V. Shchyolokov, Vera Kuznetsova.

Drama. Many years after the end of World War II, airline pilot Dmitriy Losev finds a passport left behind by a passenger who may be his lost daughter. Losev's daughter disappeared as a newborn infant in 1941, when the hospital in which she was born was destroyed in a bombing raid and her mother was killed. Losev recalls his long and painful search for the girl. A number of orphaned babies had been evacuated by the town archivist and his daughter Aurika. Along the road, a German fighter plane attacked, killing Aurika, who shielded an infant with her body. The baby was sent to an orphanage and given the name Aurika after the young woman who saved her life. Later, she was

adopted by an old couple who were primarily interested in receiving an additional state allowance provided for her care and who engaged in profiteering. Aurika left home and went to Siberia to help settle the virgin lands. Dmitriy was unable to track her further until he found the passport. He immediately sets out for the kolkhoz listed in the travel papers. As he reaches his destination, Aurika, who has become a nurse, is driving into town with her fiancé. She insists upon stopping to help a mother with a sick child, precipitating a quarrel with her fiancé. Taking the child to seek medical help, she hails a passing car in which Losev happens to be riding; and father and daughter are reunited. *War victims. Orphans. Air pilots. Missing persons. Profiteers. Settlers. Fatherhood. Aerial bombardment. Adoption. Collective farming. Orphanages. World War II. Siberia. Documentation.*

Note: Released in the U.S.S.R. in Apr 1960 as *Kolybelnaya*; running time: 94 min. Also reviewed as *The Lullaby*.

THE LULLABY OF BARELAND   **F6.2938**
Griffith Productions. 29 Dec **1964** [New York showing]. Sd; col (Eastman Color). 35mm. 92 min.

Prod Leroy C. Griffith. *Dir* Manuel S. Conde. *Screenplay* Joe Jones. *Photog* Manuel S. Conde. *Film Ed* M. Samaniego. *Mus* Ira Sullivan. *Sd* Raul Rubio. *Asst Dir* Chester Phebus. *Script Girl* Maria D. Maury.

Cast: Virginia Bell (*Virginia Bell*), Ann Howe (*Ann Howe*), Dolores Carlos (*the wife*), Charles Aldrich (*the husband*), Bromley Kent (*the super*), Anita Adams, Maria Stinger, Phil Lane, Barbara Curtis, Al Anger, Jimmy Pinto, Carol Monroe, Dawn Meridith, Thelma Wright, Sandy Sinclair, Coffee Royal, The Beatlettes.

Sex film. A husband and wife, seeking to renew the excitement in their relationship, enjoy a weekend away from each other. A WEEKEND WITH VIRGINIA (48-24-34) BELL: the husband spends his time watching exotic dancer Virginia Bell. ANNE HOWE (46-24-34) AND THE BEATLETTES GO NUDIST: the wife goes to a nudist camp and spends her time partaking of various nudist activities. THE SUPER'S DREAM: a janitor dreams that his life is filled with beautiful women. *Exotic dancers. Janitors. Marriage. Nudism. Nudist camps. Dreams.*

Note: Nature camp sequences filmed at Coral Lake Health Resort in Dania, Florida.

LUNG-MEN K'O-CHAN see **DRAGON INN**

LUPE   **F6.2939**
Dist Film-Makers' Cooperative. 7 May **1966** [New York opening]. Sd; col. 16mm. 70 min.

Prod-Dir Andy Warhol. *Prod Asst* Gerard Malanga, Buddy Wirtschafter.

Cast: Edie Sedgwick (*Lupe*), Billy Linich (*man who gives haircut*).

Satire. A fictional account of the last night in the life of Lupe Velez. In reel one, Lupe carries flowers into a luxurious room. She sits down, drinks some wine, ambles around the room, plays with a cat, places a record on the phonograph, dances, swallows a pill, smokes, makes an effort to eat, drinks, and gets up to walk around. During the last 5 minutes of the reel, Lupe is seen lying motionless on the bathroom floor with her head on the toilet seat. In reel two, Lupe is sleeping in a bed. She awakens and makes a telephone call. A man enters and gives her a haircut. They converse inaudibly for a period of time. *Suicide. Drug overdose. Lupe Velez.*

Note: At the New York opening, reels one and two were projected simultaneously on two screens, side by side.

LUPE   **F6.2940**
Dist Film-Makers' Cooperative. 30 Jan **1967** [New York opening]. Si with sd-on-tape; col. 16mm. 60 min.

Prod-Dir José Rodriguez-Soltero.

Cast: Mario Montez (*Lupe Velez*), White Pussy (*a cat*), Medea Reid, Bill Vehr, Charles Frehse, Charles Ludlam, Charles Levine, Dorrie, Maxwell Reid, Salvador Cruz, Norman Holden.

Satire. Cast members improvise a satirical depiction of Hollywood in the thirties, focusing on the career of Lupe Velez, who is played by a transvestite. Musical numbers are included. *Actors. Transvestism. Motion pictures—History. Hollywood. Lupe Velez.*

Note: An "unedited version" of undetermined length was shown in New York in Sep 1966.

THE LURE OF THE JUNGLE see **BOY OF TWO WORLDS**

LUST AND THE FLESH   **F6.2941**
Chat Productions. *Dist* American Film Distributing Corp. 9 Apr **1965** [Champaign, Illinois, showing]. Sd; b&w. 35mm. 80 min.

A Tony Orlando–C. Davis Smith Production. *Prod-Dir-Writ* Tony Orlando. *Photog* C. Davis Smith. *Asst Camera* Tony Spalla. *Ed* C. Davis Smith. *Asst to Ed* Gertrude Cross. *Sd* Magno Sound. *Asst to Dir* Iris Hunter. *Grip* Eddie Metzie. *Still Photog* Jon Wiley.

Cast: Joe Perry *(Bob)*, Georgetta Giles *(Helen)*, Maureen Conway *(Myra)*, Louis Martini *(Mark)*, Marlene Eck *(Ilsa)*, Dorrie Michaels *(Corrina)*, Darlene Bennett, Gigi Darlene, Luke Mars, Frank Davis, actor, Lisa Vohn, Eddie Metzie.

Voices: Harold Key *(Bob)*, Joan McKay *(Helen)*, Whitney Baron *(Myra)*, John Brandt *(Mark)*, Sharon Scott *(Ilsa)*, Sandee Norman *(Corrina)*.

Melodrama. Myra, a shy and sensitive young woman, loses her virginity to a rapist on her wedding day. Afraid to tell her husband, Mark, she grows to fear all sexual contact. On an island vacation the newlyweds meet Bob, an artist who has been forced into marriage with Helen, a nymphomaniac. Myra and Bob are drawn together because of their unhappy sexual experiences while Mark, sex-starved, finds release with the insatiable Helen. Helen arranges an orgy and, to distract Myra from Bob, introduces Myra to Corrina, a lesbian. Meanwhile, Mark meets Ilsa and is invited to her cottage; and Bob, hoping to persuade Myra to go away with him, tells her that Mark is unfaithful. Myra turns instead to Corrina for comfort. The two women die tragically in a fire, and Mark comes to his senses and sets out to find true happiness with Ilsa. Bob leaves Helen, and he remains alone and disconsolate after Myra's death. *Newlyweds. Artists. Virginity. Rape. Mate swapping. Nymphomania. Lust. Frigidity. Lesbianism. Infidelity. Marriage. Fires. Orgies.*

LUST FOR ECSTASY   F6.2942
Dist George Kuchar, Mike Kuchar. 4 Mar **1964** [New York opening]. Si with Sd-on-tape; col. 8mm. 45 min.
Dir George Kuchar, Mike Kuchar. *Photog* George Kuchar, Mike Kuchar.
Satire. No information about the precise nature of this film has been found. *Sexuality.*

LUST FOR THE SUN (Switzerland)   F6.2943
Werner Kunz. *Dist* Warner Barclay Productions. 30 Jun **1961** [New York opening]. Sd; col (Eastmancolor). 35mm. 72 min.
Prod-Dir Werner Kunz.
Cast: John McClaren *(English Commentary Spoken by)*, Carole Wilson.
Nudist film. In an examination of nudism in Europe, the nudist retreat of the Duke of Bedford at Woburn Abbey is the first locale. In the next scene, Major Smith and his nephew Peter offer a ride to Anna and Ingrid, two Swedish women, and they all go to the island of Sylt in northern Germany. Peter follows the women into a nudist colony, and the major tries to retrieve him. The scene switches to Zurich, where a Swiss newlywed receives postcards from her friends Beatrice and Sylvia, who are enjoying nude sunbathing while vacationing on the Île du Levant and the Île de Cavallo. *Nudism. British. Uncles. Swedes. Hitchhikers. Newlyweds. Nudist camps. Vacations. Woburn Abbey (England). Sylt. Île du Levant. Île de Cavallo.*
Note: Produced in Switzerland in 1958. Also known as *Around the World With Nothing On.*

LUST WEEKEND   F6.2944
Evloew Productions. *Dist* Howard Farber Films, Distribpix, Inc. 15 Nov **1967**. Sd; b&w. 35mm. 70 min.
Dir Ron Sullivan.
Cast: Claire Adams, Eva Pratkowitz.
Melodrama. David and Janie, a normal, happily married young couple, are singled out and kidnaped by a sex cult led by Persephone, "The Whiplady," the secret club's most sadistic member, to participate in the group's perverted sex rites. David and Janie are at first horrified, but soon Persephone degrades them so that they slavishly respond to the unexpected desires she has awakened in them. Completely disoriented, the two choose suicide as an escape from the degradation forced upon them by the group. This double suicide reinforces Persephone's belief in moral corruptibility, and the cult walks away from the death scene, already planning for their next victims. *Kidnaping. Sexual practices. Sadomasochism. Flagellation. Suicide. Moral corruption. Cults.*
Note: Also known as *Lost Weekend.*

THE LUSTFUL TURK   F6.2945
B & B Productions. *Dist* FPS Ventures. 7 Feb **1968** [Champaign, Illinois, showing]. Sd; col (Eastman Color). 35mm. 71 min.
Prod-Dir B. Ron Elliott. *Screenplay* David F. Friedman. *Anim Seq* Rudy Escalera. *Film Ed* Bill Davies. *Orig Mus* Billy Allen. *Sd* Ryder Sound Service.
Cast: Abbe Rentz *(Emily)*, Heidi Krane *(Eliza)*, Tom Ato *(Ali, Bey of Algiers)*, Harvey Shain *(Muzra, Bey of Tunis)*, Linda Styles *(Zelia, the Greek girl)*, Felice Novid *(Honoria, the Italian girl)*, Chico Vespa *(Abadallah)*, Nancy Crandall *(Sylvia)*, Kathy Williams, Yucon Havit *(slave girls)*, Ben Cadlett *(guard)*, Woody, Chocolate, Brandy *(The Eunuchs)*.
Melodrama. Two Englishwomen, Emily Barlow and her servant Eliza Gibbs, are abducted by an Algerian pirate while en route to India and made a gift to the Bey of Algiers. Ali, the Bey, treats the women sadistically, beating and raping them. Eliza is lent to Ali's brutal friend, Muzra, but he returns her when she stabs him. Sylvia, sister of Emily's fiancé, while on a visit to southern

France, is kidnaped by Turks and given to Ali. After a month, all three women have fallen in love with the lustful pirate, but Zella, one of Ali's former concubines, castrates him and he frees the Englishwomen, realizing he can no longer provide them with pleasure. *English. Domestics. Algerians. Abduction. Sadism. Rape. Revenge. Castration. Harems. Algeria.*
Note: Based on *The Lustful Turk*; according to press material, the novel was published anonymously in London in 1828.

DIE LUSTIGEN WEIBER VON WINDSOR *see* **THE MERRY WIVES OF WINDSOR**

THE LUSTING HOURS   F6.2946
Dist American Film Distributing Corp. **1967** [New York showing: 1 Jan 1969]. Sd; b&w. 35mm. 73 min.
Prod J. Ellsworth, L. Firth. *Cinematog* Firth DeMule, J. Ellsworth. *Lighting* Maria Mateo. *Film Ed* J. Ellsworth, L. Firth. *Sd Ed* Phoebe Dinsmore. *Audio Engr* Chuck Federico. *Mus Ed* Ruth Less. *Prod Supv* J. Ellsworth, L. Firth. *Cont* Bea Arkless. *Cost* Brock Frocks. *Makeup* Joe Sabia. *Interviews by* Clarence Brown. *Res* Dick Feeler.
Cast: Anna Riva, Julian Marsh, Jean Reynolds, Vi Lean, Jim Stanton, Harrison Carrol, Kay Rice, Cindy Freemont, Don Lockwood, Lena Lamont, Fay Howard and Her Girls, Satch Gould and His Boys.
Sex film. The activities of a variety of prostitutes are shown: in a rural brothel two women viciously fight before their clients who are obviously enjoying the spectacle, while upstairs another prostitute taunts her client into raping her, and elsewhere in the house an erotic ritual turns into a full-scale orgy; in the city, Cindy, a streetwalker, is revealed privately to be a lesbian; a male hustler is seen at home being whipped by his transvestite roommate; Vi, a high-priced call girl who lives in a stylish Park Avenue apartment, visits smart supper clubs and attends an erotic performance at a private club before departing with her wealthy client; and finally, a call girl who has reached the depths of sexual depravity is shown hallucinating on a psychedelic drug. *Prostitutes. Roommates. Lesbianism. Male homosexuality. Transvestism. Rape. Whorehouses. Rites and ceremonies. Orgies. Sex shows. Clubs. Psychedelic drugs. Hallucinations. New York City—Park Avenue.*
Note: Also known as *The Love Hours* and *Wanting Hour.*

LUSTY BRAWLERS *see* **THIS MAN CAN'T DIE**

LUSTY BUSTY BROWN *see* **THE ADVENTURES OF BUSTY BROWN**

THE LUSTY LANDLORD   F6.2947
Impressive Art Productions. *Dist* Gold Star Pictures. ca **1970**. Sd; col. 16mm. 60 min.
Melodrama. Helen Dunbar rents an apartment owned by a lecherous landlord who sexually satisfies his female tenants. Among the residents is a buxom blonde housewife, who entertains the landlord during her husband's frequent business trips. Her spouse's unexpected return, however, complicates the landlord-tenant relationship. Observing the coupling, the gardener is inspired to rape a resident. Attacking his victim, the gardener finds her enthusiastically acquiescent. *Landlords. Gardeners. Housewives. Infidelity. Rape.*
Note: Also known as *The Landlord.*

LUSTY NEIGHBORS   F6.2948
Dist Stacey Distributors. ca **1970**. Sd; col. 16mm. 61-81 min.
Sex film. No information about the precise nature of this film has been found. *Neighbors. Sexuality.*

LUTRING *see* **WAKE UP AND DIE**

LUTRING ... RÉVEILLE-TOI ET MEURS *see* **WAKE UP AND DIE**

LUV   F6.2949
Manulis-Jalem Productions. *Dist* Columbia Pictures. 26 Jul **1967** [New York opening; c1 Aug 1967; LP34889]. Sd; col (Eastman Color by Pathé). 35mm (Panavision). 95 min.
A Martin Manulis Production. *Prod* Martin Manulis. *Exec Prod* Gordon Carroll. *Dir* Clive Donner. *Screenplay* Elliott Baker. *Dir Photog* Ernest Laszlo. *Set Decor* Frank Tuttle. *Prod Dsgn* Albert Brenner. *Titl Dsgn* Benjamin Jackson, Jeremy Lepard. *Film Ed* Harold F. Kress. *Mus* Gerry Mulligan. *Orch* Bill Holman. *Sd Supv* Charles J. Rice. *Sd* William Randall, Jr., Jack Haynes. *Asst Dir* David Salven. *Unit Prod Mgr* Howard Pine. *Script Supv* Betty Levin. *Cost* Donfeld. *Makeup Supv* Ben Lane. *Hairstyles* Virginia Jones. *Sp Eff* Geza Gaspar. *Dial Coach* Alan DeWitt.
Cast: Jack Lemmon *(Harry Berlin)*, Peter Falk *(Milt Manville)*, Elaine May *(Ellen Manville)*, Nina Wayne *(Linda)*, Eddie Mayehoff *(Attorney Goodhart)*, Paul Hartman *(Doyle)*, Severn Darden *(Vandergrist)*, Alan DeWitt *(Dalrymple)*.

Romantic comedy. Source: Murray Schisgal, *Luv* (New York opening: 11 Nov 1964). About to jump from New York's Manhattan Bridge, Harry Berlin is interrupted by former college classmate Milt Manville, now a Wall Street broker by day and a junk dealer by night. In return for this unsolicited favor, Milt asks Harry to rid him of his wife, Ellen, a disgruntled intellectual, so that he might marry Linda, a voluptuous gym teacher. Although at first indifferent to one another, Harry and Ellen fall in love and a divorce is quickly effected. Linda's union with Milt, however, is unsatisfactory. Having granted Ellen all his worldly possessions in his haste to have Linda, Milt finds himself the impoverished tenant of a bare apartment, his sole diversion watching Linda grow fatter and fatter. Ellen is similarly disenchanted with Harry, whose indifference to her allure surpasses that of Milt. Discovering that they are still in love, Milt and Ellen conspire to rid themselves of their new partners by introducing Harry to Linda. Having already met, neither party is impressed. Armed with Harry's old suicide note, Milt and Ellen plan his murder. While attempting to toss him from the Manhattan Bridge, Milt falls into the river, where he is joined shortly thereafter by Ellen and Harry. Passing by, Linda joins in the mutual rescue effort. As their bodies touch, Linda and Harry are magnetically attracted. *Stockbrokers. Junk dealers. Intellectuals. Schoolteachers. Medical students. Divorce. Suicide. New York City—Manhattan Bridge.*

Note: Location scenes filmed in New York City, at Niagara Falls, and in California.

LYCANTHROPUS *see* **WEREWOLF IN A GIRLS' DORMITORY**

LYDIA ATE THE APPLE *see* **PARTINGS**

LYSISTRATA   **F6.2950**
Mod Films. *Dist* Chancellor Films. 30 Oct **1968** [New York showing]. Sd; b&w. 35mm. 65 min.
Prod Frank Garto. *Dir* Jon Matt. *Screenplay* Roly Strong. *Photog* Red Del.
Melodrama. Adapted from: Aristophanes, *Lysistrata*. Hippie model Lysistrata, raped or rejected by the men in Manhattan, has become a man-hater. She forms an all-women sex club, the members of which read Aristophanes' *Lysistrata* and vow their hatred. Their plan is to tease men beyond endurance and frustrate all their attempts at sexual satisfaction. The women satisfy themselves by engaging in autoeroticism and oral intercourse. Pamela comes under Lysistrata's spell and rejects her boyfriend, Fred. For revenge, Fred spies on the secret rites in which Lysistrata demands slavish sex worship. Lysistrata becomes jealous at an orgy, and she stabs each of her disciples. Aware of Lysistrata's crime, Fred blackmails her with torture, but before the whip can be administered, she stabs herself to death. *Hippies. Models. Man-haters. Rape. Lesbianism. Autoeroticism. Oral sex. Jealousy. Murder. Sadism. Suicide. Sex clubs. Orgies. Rites and ceremonies. New York City. "Lysistrata".*

MA NUIT CHEZ MAUD *see* **MY NIGHT AT MAUD'S**

MAARAKAT ALGER *see* **THE BATTLE OF ALGIERS**

MACABRO (Italy)   **F6.2951**
Royal Film. *Dist* Trans-American Films. Jun **1966** [c15 Jun 1966; MP16162]. Sd; col (Eastman Color, print by Technicolor). 35mm. 90 min. [Copyright length: 88 min.]
Prod Guido Giambartolomei. *Dir* Romolo Marcellini. *Text* Giancarlo Del Re, Ugo Guerra. *Photog* Rino Filippini, Angelo Filippini. *Film Ed* Otello Colangeli. *Mus* Angelo Lavagnino.
Narrator: Marvin Miller.
Documentary. An exposition of curiosities of human behavior, chiefly in Italy, Scandinavia, Japan, India, Africa, and Brazil. Included are scenes depicting tribal circumcision rites; male geishas; snake eating; the mauling of children by Gypsies to make them better acrobats; the wrestling rites of Brazilian headhunters; African sorcery; "railway roulette" in Scandinavia; the quest for eternal youth; the use of burning bamboo to prevent infection of human wounds; the initiation of a Buddhist novitiate; poverty in India; gauchos in a game in which a live duck is the ball; and children hung on festival parade floats in Italy. *Gypsies. Headhunters. Geishas. Wrestlers. Physicians. Gauchos. Rites and ceremonies. Social customs. Circumcision. Japan. India. Africa. Brazil. Scandinavia. Buddhism. Snakes.*

Note: Released in Italy in 1965 as *Tabù n. 2*; running time: 85 min. U. S. prerelease title: *It's a Sick, Sick World*; also known as *Mondo Macabro*.

MACARIO (Mexico)   **F6.2952**
Clasa Films Mundiales. *Dist* Azteca Films. Mar **1961** [Los Angeles showing]. Sd; b&w. 35mm. 91 min.
Prod Armando Orive Alba. *Exec Prod* José Luis Celis. *Dir* Roberto Gavaldón. *Screenplay* Emilio Carballido, Roberto Gavaldón. *Photog* Gabriel Figueroa. *Art Dir* Manuel Fontanals. *Film Ed* Gloria Schoemann. *Mus* Raúl Lavista. *Sd* Jesús González Gancy. *Sp Eff* Juan Muñoz Ravelo.

Cast: Ignacio López Tarso (*Macario*), Pina Pellicer (*Macario's wife*), Enrique Lucero (*Death*), José Gálvez (*The Devil*), José Luis Jiménez (*God*), Mario Alberto Rodriguez (*Don Ramiro*), Sonia Infante, Eduardo Fajardo, Consuelo Frank, José Dupeyrón, Celia Tejada, Enrique García Alvarez.

Allegory. Source: B. Traven, *Macario* (Zurich, 1950). During the feast of All Souls Day, Macario, a Mexican peasant, revolts against his lifetime of poverty by vowing never to eat again until he has a whole turkey for himself. His wife steals one for him, cooks it, and tells him to eat it while his five hungry children are sleeping. His hunger stronger than his conscience, Macario goes into the woods to enjoy his feast. Two strangers representing the Devil and God, stop Macario and ask to share his food, but he refuses. He is then confronted by Death, who appears so desperate than Macario divides the turkey in order to enjoy his half undisturbed. In return Death gives the poor peasant a gourd of water which will heal the sick, but Death must give his consent in each instance; if Death appears at the head of the bed, Macario may not proceed. The liquid brings great fame and wealth to Macario until the Inquisition accuses him of being an instrument of the Devil. He is fetched from prison and given a single chance to escape death: if he can cure the Viceroy's ailing son, he will be set free. However, Death refuses to leave the head of the sick bed, and Macario is forced to flee. In his panic he runs into Death's cave where a candle burns for each human life. Macario tries to escape with his own candle, but he fails. His wife finds his body lying by a tree; in front of him is his half of the turkey. *Peasants. Poverty. Hunger. Death. Christianity. Greed. Faith cure. Caves. The Devil.*

Note: Released in Mexico in 1960.

MACBETH (United States/Great Britain)   **F6.2953**
Grand Prize Films. *Dist* Prominent Films. 20 Oct **1963** [Kansas City, Missouri, opening]. Sd; col (Technicolor). 35mm. 107 min.
Prod Phil C. Samuel. *Exec Prod* Sidney Kaufman. *Dir* George Schaefer. *Tech Dir* Anthony Squire. *Adapt* George Schaefer, Anthony Squire. *Photog* F. A. Young. *Camera Op* Jeffrey Seaholme. *Camera Focus* Ken Withers. *2d Unit Camera Op* Paul Wilson. *2d Unit Focus* Tony Spratling. *Art Dir* Edward Carrick. *Asst Art Dir* Syd Cain. *Scenic Artist* W. Simpson Robinson. *1st Draughtsman* Wallis Smith. *Film Ed* Ralph Kemplen. *1st Asst Ed* Roy Taylor. *2d Asst Ed* Eunice Mountjoy. *Mus & Orig Score* Richard Addinsell. *Mus Dir & Cond* Muir Mathieson. *Played by* Sinfonia of London. *Sd Mix* Cyril Swern. *Boom Op* John Streeter. *Sd Camera Op* Harold Clarke. *Dub Ed* Leslie Hodgson. *1st & 2d Asst Dir* Douglas Hickox, James S. Northcote, Carl Mannin. *Prod Supv* Leigh Aman. *Location Mgr* Hector Elwes. *Asst Location Mgr* Bill Stanley. *Cont* Kay Mander. *Prod Sec* Joyce Herlihy. *Sec to the Prod* Pamela Moore. *Dress Dsgn* Beatrice Dawson. *Asst Dress Dsgn* Dinah Greet. *Wardrobe Master* Larry Stewart. *Makeup Ch* Bob Lawrence. *Hairdresser Ch & Hairdresser* Iris Tilley, Daphne Vollmer. *Coöp* Joyce C. Hall, Hallmark Cards. *Still Photog* Davis Boulton. *Prop Buyer* Bill Isaacs. *Grip* L. Kelly.

Cast: Maurice Evans (*Macbeth*), Judith Anderson (*Lady Macbeth*), Michael Hordern (*Banquo*), Ian Bannen (*Macduff*), Felix Aylmer (*doctor*), Malcolm Keen (*Duncan*), Megs Jenkins (*gentlewoman*), Jeremy Brett (*Malcolm*), Barry Warren (*Donalbain*), William Hutt (*Ross*), Charles Carson (*Caithness*), Trader Faulkner (*Seyton*), George Rose (*porter*), Valerie Taylor (*1st witch*), Anita Sharp Bolster (*2d witch*), April Olrich (*3d witch*), Brewster Mason (*Angus*), Simon Lack (*Menteith*), Scot Finch (*Fleance*), Robert Brown (*bloody sergeant*), Michael Ripper (*1st murderer*), Douglas Wilmer (*2d murderer*).

Tragedy. Source: William Shakespeare, *Macbeth*. The film is a screen adaptation of William Shakespeare's play. *Scotch. Royalty. Witches. Soldiers. Regicide. Conspiracy. Murder. Insanity. Suicide. Ambition. Guilt. Castles. Scotland. Dreams.*

Note: Filmed on location in Scotland. First shown in the United States in an 80 min version on NBC's *Hallmark Hall of Fame* in 1960.

MCCORD *see* **A MINUTE TO PRAY, A SECOND TO DIE**

MCGUIRE, GO HOME! (Great Britain)   **F6.2954**
Rank Organisation. *Dist* Continental Distributing, Inc. Jul **1966**. Sd; col (Technicolor). 35mm. 101 min.
A Betty E. Box–Ralph Thomas Production. *Prod* Betty E. Box. *Exec Prod* Earl St. John. *Dir* Ralph Thomas. *Screenplay* Ian Stuart Black, Bryan Forbes. *Photog* Ernest Steward. *Art Dir* Syd Cain. *Italian Art Dir* Franco Fontana. *Film Ed* Alfred Roome. *Mus* Angelo Francesco Lavagnino. *Mus Dir* Muir Mathieson. *Sd* Don Sharpe. *Sd Rec* Peter Davies, Gordon K. McCallum. *Asst Dir* Simon Relph, Leon Lenoir. *Prod Mgr* Charles Orme. *Italian Prod Mgr* Carlo Lastricati.

Cast: Dirk Bogarde (*Major McGuire*), George Chakiris (*Haghios*), Susan Strasberg (*Juno Kozani*), Denholm Elliott (*Baker*), Grégoire Aslan (*General Skyros*), Colin Campbell (*Emile Andros*), Joseph Furst (*Dr. Andros*), Katherine Kath (*Mrs. Andros*), George Pastell (*Prinos*), Paul Stassino (*Alkis*), Nigel Stock (*Colonel Park*).

Adventure drama. Source: Ian Stuart Black, *The High Bright Sun* (London, 1962). In 1957 British intelligence officer Major McGuire is sent to Cyprus to locate General Skyros, a leader of the Cypriot terrorists. McGuire believes Skyros is hiding out at the home of Dr. Andros, a Greek Cypriot whose house guest, American archeologist Juno Kozani, professes political neutrality but also feels a certain loyalty to her hosts. One night, Juno discovers Skyros in hiding at the house, and although she promises not to reveal his whereabouts, Haghios, a fanatical student rebel, does not believe her, especially since she has become friendly with McGuire. Realizing the danger of her position, Juno decides to return to America but narrowly escapes being killed by Haghios on her way to the airport. McGuire finds Juno and hides her in his apartment while British authorities search the island for her. Although Juno refuses to reveal Skyros' whereabouts to McGuire, the two find themselves falling in love. Haghios and his men attempt to break into the apartment, but British soldiers arrive in time to save the couple. Disgraced for hiding the woman, McGuire is transferred to Greece, where he is joined by Juno. Haghios attempts once more to silence Juno, but McGuire's aide shoots him. McGuire and Juno are reunited and discover that a mysterious stranger who has been following them is a private detective gathering evidence for a divorce for McGuire's wife. *Terrorists. Archeologists. Americans in foreign countries. Fanatics. Military occupation. Murder. Cyprus—History—1955-59. Greece. Great Britain—Intelligence service. Great Britain—Army.*

Note: Location scenes filmed in Cyprus, Greece, and Italy. Opened in London in Feb 1965 as *The High Bright Sun*; running time: 114 min.

MCHALE'S NAVY
F6.2955

Universal Pictures. 10 Jul **1964** [New York opening; c22 Aug 1964; LP33410]. Sd (Westrex); col (Pathé). 35mm. 93 min.

Prod-Dir Edward J. Montagne. *In Charge of Prod* Edward Muhl. *Assoc Prod* Si Rose. *Screenplay* Frank Gill, Jr., G. Carleton Brown. *Story* Si Rose. *Dir Photog* William Margulies. *Camera Op* William Dodds. *Camera Asst* William Reisbord, William Brown. *Art Dir* Alexander Golitzen, Russell Kimball. *Set Decor* John McCarthy, James S. Redd. *Film Ed* Sam E. Waxman. *Asst Ed* Carl Vitale. *Mus* Jerry Fielding. *Sd* Waldon O. Watson, Earl N. Crain, Sr., Elmer Raguse, James T. Porter, Bruce Smith. *Asst Dir* Phil Bowles, Terry Morse, Jr. *Unit Prod Mgr* Wallace Worsley. *Script Supv* Cliff Bole. *Cost* Helen Colvig. *Wardrobe* Don Snyder, cost, Gordon Murray, Dorothy Drake. *Makeup Supv* Bud Westmore. *Makeup* Michael Westmore, Vincent Romaine. *Hairstyles* Larry Germain, Clara Holgate. *Sp Eff* Roland Skeete. *Still Photog* Frank Shugrue. *Gaffer* Irvin Malak. *Grip* Pat Warfield, Jim Hilbert. *Prop* Jack Hamilton, Pruette Romero.

Cast: Ernest Borgnine *(Lieut. Comdr. Quinton McHale)*, Tim Conway *(Ens. Charles Parker)*, Joe Flynn *(Capt. Wallace Burton Binghamton)*, Bob Hastings *(Lieut. LeRoy Carpenter)*, Gary Vinson *(Q. M. George "Christy" Christopher)*, John Wright *(Radioman Willy Moss)*, Carl Ballantine *(Torpedoman Lester Gruber)*, Billy Sands *(Motor Machinist Mate Harrison "Tinker" Bell)*, Edson Stroll *(Gunner's Mate Virgil Edwards)*, Gavin MacLeod *(Seaman Joseph "Happy" Hanes)*, Yoshio Yoda *(Takeo "Fugi" Fugiwara)*, Jean Willes *(Margo Monet)*, Claudine Longet *(Andrea Bouchard)*, George Kennedy *(Henri Le Clerc)*, Marcel Hillaire *(chef de gendarmes)*, Dale Ishimoto *(Japanese captain)*, John Mamo *(Japanese j. g.)*, Sandy Slavik *(French girl)*.

War comedy. Inspired by the ABC-TV series, *McHale's Navy*. On a South Pacific island in 1943, the crew of PT-73 tries to make money on delayed race results, but the scheme backfires, and they find themselves $2,000 in debt to a group of Marines. An attempt to win the money at a New Caledonia gambling casino fails. A fight breaks out there; and, while the crew is escaping, their boat rams a dockside warehouse, leaving them $4,000 deeper in debt. The men discover the wreck of an Australian freighter, aboard which they find the famous racehorse Silver Spots. They enter the horse in a New Caledonia race, disguising it with glued-on fur. When the fur comes off, the crew sends up a smokescreen to conceal the horse's identity. Though the horse wins, the smoke blinds the judges and prevents their making a decision. A Japanese submarine begins shelling the island, and PT-73, attempting to escape, accidentally runs the submarine aground, and captures the enemy crew. This feat causes the warehouse owner to absolve the PT-73 men of their debt, and the $2,000 reward for the return of Silver Spots allows them to discharge their debt to the Marines. But, leaving the island, PT-73 rams the warehouse again, and the crew is once more in debt. *Gambling. Horseracing. Debt. Fraud. South Sea Islands. PT boats. Submarines. Freighters. Warehouses. World War II. Pacific Ocean. New Caledonia. United States Navy. United States Marines. Japan—Navy. Horses.*

MCHALE'S NAVY JOINS THE AIR FORCE
F6.2956

Universal Pictures. 16 Jun **1965** [Providence, Rhode Island, opening; c3 Jul 1965; LP33025]. Sd (Westrex); col (Technicolor). 35mm. 90 min. [Copyright length: 93 min.]

Prod-Dir Edward J. Montagne. *In Charge of Prod* Edward Muhl. *Assoc Prod* Si Rose. *Screenplay* John Fenton Murray. *Dir Photog* Lionel Lindon. *Camera*

Op Bob Burkett. *Asst Camera* Ted Landon. *Art Dir* Alexander Golitzen, Russell Kimball. *Set Decor* John McCarthy, James S. Redd. *Main Titl* Pacific Title. *Film Ed* Sam E. Waxman. *Asst Ed* Patrick Kennedy. *Mus* Jerry Fielding. "Army Air Corps Song" Robert M. Crawford. *Sd* Waldon O. Watson, Earl N. Crain, Sr., Perry Devore, Louis Williman. *Asst Dir* George Bisk, Michael Messinger. *Unit Prod Mgr* Wes Thompson. *Script Supv* Dorothy Hughes. *Makeup* Bud Westmore, Rolf Miller. *Hairstyles* Larry Germain, Ann Ehrhart. *Sp Eff* Roland Skeete. *Still Photog* Larry Barbier. *Gaffer* William Harmon. *Grip* Ben Hawkins, Jim Hilbert. *Prop* Jack Hamilton, Jerry Josephsen.

Cast: Joe Flynn *(Capt. Wallace Burton Binghamton)*, Tim Conway *(Ens. Charles Parker)*, Bob Hastings *(Lieutenant Carpenter)*, Gary Vinson *(Christy)*, Billy Sands *(Motor Machinist Mate Harrison "Tinker" Bell)*, Edson Stroll *(Gunner's Mate Virgil Edwards)*, John Wright *(Radioman Willy Moss)*, Gavin MacLeod *(Seaman Joseph "Happy" Haines)*, Yoshio Yoda *(Fuji)*, Tom Tully *(General Harkness)*, Susan Silo *(Smitty)*, Henry Beckman *(Colonel Platt)*, Ted Bessell *(Lieut. Wilbur Harkness)*, Jean Hale *(Madge)*, Cliff Norton *(Major Grady)*, Willis Bouchey *(Admiral Doyle)*, Berkeley Harris *(Vogel)*, Jacques Aubuchon *(Dimitri)*, Len Lesser *(NKVD commissar)*, Henry Corden *(NKVD deputy)*, Jack Bernardi, Norman Leavitt, Joe Ploski, Andy Albin *(Russian seamen)*, Clay Tanner *(Lieutenant Wilson)*, Tony Franke *(Tresh)*.

Comedy. Source: William J. Lederer, "Yeoman Major," in *All the Ships at Sea* (New York, 1950). As Captain Binghamton departs for Brisbane, his torpedo boat, PT-116, springs a mysterious leak and sinks. He is forced to use PT-73, in the charge of Ensign Parker in the absence of McHale, the skipper. In Brisbane, Binghamton restricts the crew to the boat, but they are befriended by the crew of a nearby Russian merchant vessel. The Russians try to use PT-73 to smuggle Australian whiskey. In the midst of an aimless celebration in which both crews participate, two Russian NKVD officers come aboard. After mixups involving uniforms, Lieut. Wilbur Harkness, pilot son of an Army Air Force general officer, is found in a Russian outfit and is carted away as a spy. Parker, who has replaced *his* Soviet togs with the nearest uniform—Wilbur's—is forced to impersonate Wilbur and is given the rank of Army captain. Later, while in a control tower with WAC "Smitty" Smith, Parker accidentally turns on the air raid warning at the very moment a Japanese air squadron is about to make a sneak attack. For his heroism, Parker is again promoted—to Army major. When he and Binghamton are suspended in their jeep in midair by an airplane, they spot a Japanese fleet; and with an early warning, they aid an Allied victory. Parker becomes a national hero—despite the protests of Lieutenant Harkness, now released—and speeds his way to Washington to be decorated by President Roosevelt. *War heroes. Russians. Military life. Mistaken identity. Impersonation. Smuggling. Aerial bombardment. PT boats. Merchant ships. Liquor. World War II. Brisbane. United States Navy. United States Army—Air Force. NKVD. United States Army—Women's Army Corps. Japan—Navy.*

Note: This is a sequel to *McHale's Navy*, q. v.; both films were inspired by the ABC television series *McHale's Navy*.

MACHI-BUSE see THE AMBUSH

MACHINE GUN MCCAIN (Italy)
F6.2957

Euroatlantica S.p.A. *Dist* Columbia Pictures. 9 Sep **1970** [Detroit opening; c1 Sep 1970; LP38191]. Sd (Westrex); col (Technicolor). 35mm (Techniscope). 94 min. *MPAA rating* GP.

Prod Marco Vicario, Bino Cicogna. *Assoc Prod* Ascanio Cicogna. *Dir* Giuliano Montaldo. *Screenplay* Mino Roli, Giuliano Montaldo. *Story* Mino Roli. *English Adapt* Israel Horovitz. *Dir Photog* Erico Menczer. *Camera* Silvio Fraschetti. *Asst Camera* Renato Mascagni. *Art Dir* Flavio Mogherini. *Set Dsgn* Roberto Veloccia. *Set Decor* Ennio Michettoni, Emilio Baldelli. *Film Ed* Franco Fraticelli. *Mus* Ennio Morricone. *Mus Cond* Bruno Nicolai. *Song:* "The Ballad of Hank McCain" Audrey Nohra, Ennio Morricone. *Sung by* Jackie Lynton. *Sd* Luciano Welisch. *Asst Dir* Gianni Fabrizio. *Prod Mgr* Romano Cardarelli, Gray Frederickson. *Script Girl* Vittoria Vigorelli. *Prod Insp* Agostino Pane. *Prod Sec* Ennio Melonari. *Cost* Enrico Sabbatini. *Makeup* Michele Trimarchi. *Dial Coach* Neil Robinson.

Cast: John Cassavetes *(Hank McCain)*, Britt Ekland *(Irene Tucker)*, Peter Falk *(Charlie Adamo)*, Gabriele Ferzetti *(Don Francesco De Marco)*, Salvo Randone *(Don Salvatore)*, Pierluigi Aprà *(Jack McCain)*, Gena Rowlands *(Rosemary Scott)*, Florinda Bolkan *(Joni Adamo)*, Margherita Guzzinati *(Margaret De Marco)*, Stephen Zacharias *(Abe Stilberman)*, Luigi Pistilli *(Duke Mazzanga)*, James Morrison *(Joby Cuda)*, Claudio Biava *(Barclay)*, Tony Kendall *(Pete Zacari)*, Ermanno Consolazione *(Gennarino Esposito)*, Annabella Andreoli *(Assunta Esposito)*, Val Avery *(Chuck Regan)*, Dennis Sallas *(Fred Tecosky)*, Jack Ackerman *(Britten)*, Billy Lee *(Pepe)*.

Crime melodrama. Freely based on: Ovid Demaris, *Candyleg* (New York, 1961). Charlie Adamo, a West Coast Mafia boss, uses his political influence to obtain a pardon for Hank McCain, who has spent the past 12 years in prison for armed robbery. McCain's son Jack, a smalltime hoodlum working for

Adamo, recruits his father to take part in a robbery of the Royal Hotel casino in Las Vegas. Meanwhile, McCain falls in love with Irene Tucker, and they are quickly married. Belatedly, Adamo learns that the Royal is owned by one of the East Coast mob bosses and orders a halt to the plan. McCain, warned by Jack that two of Adamo's hoodlums are waiting to kill him if he refuses to cooperate, kills the thugs, but Jack dies in the gunplay. With Irene's help, McCain places bombs in various Las Vegas locations, and disguised as a fireman, he robs the hotel safe of nearly $2 million. The mob embarks on a manhunt, and Adamo is killed. Hank's former accomplice and lover, Rosemary Scott, helps the couple flee; then, threatened with torture by a Mafia hoodlum, she commits suicide to avoid betraying the couple. Nevertheless, the Mafia close in as McCain and Irene proceed to a meeting on the Long Beach, California, waterfront, on their way to Mexico. The gunmen shoot Irene, and McCain dies in a barrage of machine gun fire. *Ex-convicts. Robbery. Suicide. Murder. Filial relations. Casinos. Hotels. Bombs. Waterfronts. Las Vegas. Long Beach (California). Mafia.*

Note: Exteriors filmed in New York City, San Francisco, and Las Vegas. Released in Italy in 1968 as *Gli intoccabili*; running time: ca115 min. English language working title: *At Any Price.* Tony Kendall is a pseudonym for Luciano Stella.

MACHISMO—40 GRAVES FOR 40 GUNS   F6.2958

Pacific International Films. *Dist* Boxoffice International Film Distributors. Dec **1970**. Sd; col (Eastman Color, print by Movielab). 35mm. 95 min. *MPAA rating* R.

Pres by Harry Novak. *Prod* Ronald V. Garcia. *Exec Prod* Phillip Yankowitz, Harry Novak. *Dir* Paul Hunt. *Screenplay* Ronald Garcia, Paul Hunt. *Cinematog* Richmond Aguilar. *Camera* Richard Eisman. *Adtl Photog* Ronald Garcia. *Art Dir (see note)* Rahn Vickery, Ben Adams. *Interior Sets* Hank Adams. *Exterior Sets* Ben Adams. *Titl* Title House. *Ed* Paul Hunt, Ron Garcia, Mike Bennett. *Neg Coörd* Dwayne Rayven. *Mus Score Comp & Cond* Jack Preisner. *Songs Sung by* Chuey Franco. *Location Sd* Mike Beardsley. *Sd Boom* Neil Porter. *Sd Re-rec* Ryder Sound Service. *Asst Dir* H. P. Edwards. *Prod Mgr* Mike Bennett. *Unit Prod Asst* Bethel Buckalew. *Asst to the Prod* Toni Rodriguez. *Script Supv* Ben Michales. *Cost Supv* Sherri Tilley. *Men's Makeup Artist* Dennis Marsh. *Women's Makeup Artist* Gordon Freed. *Sp Eff* Harry Woolman. *Optical Eff* Ray Mercer and Co. *Spanish Cons* Chuey Franco. *Stunt Coörd* Randy Starr, Joseph Tornatore. *Key Grip* Paul Wilmoth. *Prop Master* Bill Rodriguez. *Set Constr* Ralph Dale.

Cast: Robert Padilla *(Hidalgo)*, Dirk Peno *(Lopez)*, Frederico Gomez *(Vicente)*, Louis Ojena *(Fernandez)*, Leslie York *(Ruby)*, Rita Rogers *(Lil)*, Stanley Adams *(Granger)*, Sue Bernard *(Julie)*, Bruce Gordon *(Burt)*, Nancy Caroline *(Louise)*, Royal Dano *(Zach)*, Chuey Franco *(Garcia)*, Jose Jasd *(Rodriguez)*, Liberty Angelo *(Dugan)*, Mike Robelo *(Captain Ramirez)*, Patti Heider *(Phyllis)*, Noble "Kid" Chissell *(Doc Peters)*, Lilyan Chauvin *(Kate)*, Sean Kenney *(Wichita)*, Joseph Tornatore *(Jake)*, Gary Kent *(Jim Harris)*, James Lemp *(Ed Harris)*, Gary Graver *(Tim Harris)*, Randy Starr *(Roper)*, Hank Adams, Vincent Barbi, Buckalew, Bartlett Carson, Thomas Duran, Frisco Estes, Silas Everett, Bob Feiner, Michael Ford, Robert Gerald, Leonard Goodman, Lou Joffred, Walter Kray, Jeff Latham, Ray Lester, Steve McKinney, Biff Maynard, Harry Novak, Richard Paradise, David Schneider, Duke Wilmoth, William Wilson, Terry Woolman *(The Harris Gang)*.

Western melodrama. Captain Ramirez of the Federales offers a group of Mexican bandits full pardon and a large reward for the murder of the Harris brothers, leaders of a band of American outlaws who ravaged the town of Tecate, murdering many citizens and stealing the pure gold cross of St. Augustine. Led by Hidalgo, the Mexicans enter Gila Bend, a decaying town used as a front by the outlaws. Young Vicente, sent disguised as a peon to scout the area, is humiliated by the racist citizenry and returns with the message that the town is populated by gringos. The next day, Julie apologizes for the town to Vicente, and Fernandez goes to spend the night with Ruby, a sympathetic bar girl. Discovering the gold cross in her room, the Mexicans plant it in the deserted main street and wait in ambush. The Harris brothers return and are quickly gunned down, but Juarez, one of Hidalgo's band, is wounded. To save him and the townspeople from the outlaws' revenge, the Mexicans remain in the town. Lil, Jim Harris' girl friend, informs Wichita, the new leader of his gang, of the identity of the attackers. Refusing his advances, she is handed over to the 40 men around the campfire. The next morning, Fernandez and Ruby bring a cannon to town from a deserted fort. With the return of the Harris gang, a bloody battle is inaugurated by a blast from the cannon. Most of the Americans are killed, but all of the Mexicans die with them. Ruby, too, lies dead when the fight is over. The racist Granger feels that a decent burial is not worth the effort and decides to throw the bodies in a ditch. *Mexicans. Federales. Outlaws. Bandits. Americans in foreign countries. Bar girls. Gangs. Brothers. Revenge. Racism. Murder. Gold. Ordnance.*

Note: Sources conflict in crediting art director.

MACHO CALLAHAN   F6.2959

Felicidad Films. *Dist* Avco Embassy Pictures. 12 Aug **1970** [Dallas opening]. Sd; col (Movielab). 35mm (Panavision). 99 min. *MPAA rating* R.

Prod Bernard L. Kowalski, Martin C. Schute. *Exec Prod* Joseph E. Levine. *Assoc Prod* Clifford Newton Gould. *Dir* Bernard L. Kowalski. *2d Unit Dir* Robert Buzz Henry. *Screenplay* Clifford Newton Gould. *Story* Richard Carr. *Dir Photog* Gerry Fisher. *Adtl Photog* Manuel Gómez Urquiza. *Art Dir* José Rodríguez Granada. *Set Decor* Ernesto Carrasco. *Prod Dsgn* Ted Marshall. *Film Ed* Frank Mazzola, Fabian Tordjinann, Jerry Taylor. *Mus* Pat Williams. *Sd* José B. Carles. *Asst Dir* Gordon Webb, Jesús Marin, Manuel Muñoz. *Asst to the Prod* Patrick O'Brien. *Cost* Barbara Rosenquest.

Cast: David Janssen *(Diego "Macho" Callahan)*, Jean Seberg *(Alexandra Mountford)*, Lee J. Cobb *(Duffy)*, James Booth *("King Harry" Wheeler)*, Pedro Armendáriz, Jr. *(Juan Fernandez)*, David Carradine *(Col. David Mountford)*, Bo Hopkins *(Yancy)*, Richard Anderson *(senior officer)*, Diane Ladd *(girl)*, Matt Clark *(jailer)*, Richard Evans *(Mulvey)*, Robert Morgan *(McIntyre)*, Anne Revere *(Crystal)*, James Gammon *(cowboy)*, Ron Soble *(2d cowboy)*, Diana Iverson *(2d girl)*, Curt Conway *(judge)*, Robert Dowdell *(blind man)*, Cyril Delevanti, William Bryant, Bucklind Beery, Mike Masters.

Western melodrama. During the Civil War, "Macho" Callahan escapes from a Confederate Army prison camp by blowing up the prison gate and sets out to find Duffy, whom he believes was responsible for his enlistment and subsequent imprisonment. In a Texas town, Callahan quarrels over a bottle of champagne with Col. David Mountford, a one-armed former Confederate officer, and kills him while Mountford's bride, Alexandra, watches helplessly from a hotel window. Vowing to avenge her husband's death, Alexandra offers a reward of $1,000 to anyone who kills Callahan. Duffy, whom Alexandra had met while traveling, agrees to help her; but Callahan recognizes Duffy as the man he is seeking, kills him, and hangs him from a windmill. Alexandra pursues Callahan alone until gambling house proprietor "King Harry" Wheeler takes up her offer. Callahan escapes, however, and again Alexandra rides after him alone. She meets Callahan with his old friend Juan Fernandez, joins them and later fails in her attempt to kill Callahan. Instead, Callahan rapes her. Eventually, Alexandra comes to understand Callahan and falls in love with him. Meanwhile, Wheeler, who has formed a group of bounty hunters to track Callahan, overtakes Callahan, Fernandez, and Alexandra and kills Fernandez. Despite Alexandra's pleas that Callahan's life be spared, one of the bounty hunters kills Callahan, and Alexandra is again left alone to grieve. *Prisoners of war. Newlyweds. Confederate veterans. Amputees. Widows. Gamblers. Bounty hunters. Prison escapes. Revenge. Murder. Rape. Texas. United States— History—Civil War. Explosions.*

Note: Location scenes filmed in Mexico.

MACISTE ALLA CORTE DEL GRAN KHAN *see* **SAMSON AND THE SEVEN MIRACLES OF THE WORLD**

MACISTE ALLA CORTE DELLO ZAR *see* **SAMSON VS. THE GIANT KING**

MACISTE ALL'INFERNO *see* **THE WITCH'S CURSE**

MACISTE CONTRE LES HOMMES DE PIERRE *see* **HERCULES AGAINST THE MOON MEN**

MACISTE CONTRO GLI UOMINI DELLA LUNA *see* **HERCULES AGAINST THE MOON MEN**

MACISTE CONTRO IL VAMPIRO *see* **GOLIATH AND THE VAMPIRES**

MACISTE E LA REGINE DI SAMAR *see* **HERCULES AGAINST THE MOON MEN**

MACISTE, L'EROE PIÙ GRANDE DEL MONDO *see* **GOLIATH AND THE SINS OF BABYLON**

MACISTE NELLA TERRA DEI CICLOPI *see* **ATLAS AGAINST THE CYCLOPS**

MACISTE NELLA VALLE DEI RE *see* **SON OF SAMSON**

MACKENNA'S GOLD   F6.2960

Highroad Productions. *Dist* Columbia Pictures. 10 May **1969** [Phoenix, Arizona, opening; c1 May 1969; LP37136]. Sd (Westrex); col (Technicolor). 35mm & 70mm (Super Panavision, see note). 128 min. *MPAA rating* M.

A Carl Foreman Production. *Prod* Carl Foreman, Dimitri Tiomkin. *Dir* J. Lee Thompson. *2d Unit Dir* Tom Shaw. *Screenplay* Carl Foreman. *Dir Photog* Joseph MacDonald. *2d Unit Photog* Harold Wellman. *Adtl Photog* John Mackey, Richard Moore, Donald Glouner, Farciot Edouart. *Art Dir* Geoffrey Drake, Cary Odell. *Set Decor* Alfred E. Spencer. *Prod Dsgn* Geoffrey Drake.

Film Ed Bill Lenny. *Assoc Film Ed* John F. Link, Jr., Raymond Poulton, Don Deacon. *1st Asst Film Ed* Lois Gray. *Mus Comp* Quincy Jones. *Orch* Leo Shuken, Jack Hayes. *Song:* "Old Turkey Buzzard" Quincy Jones, Freddy Douglass. *Sung by* José Feliciano. *Sd Supv* Derek Frye. *Unit Sd Rec* William Randall, Jr. *Stereophonic Dub* Bob Jones, John Blunt. *Sd Ed* Jeanne Henderson. *Asst Sd Ed* Peter Bond. *Asst Dir* David Salven. *Prod Mgr* Ralph Black. *Wardrobe Dsgn* Norma Koch. *Hairstyles* Virginia Jones. *Sp Vis Eff* Geoffrey Drake, John Mackey, Bob Cuff, Willis Cook, Larry Butler. *Coöp* United States Department of the Interior. *Stunt Coörd* Buzz Henry.

Cast: Gregory Peck (*Mackenna*), Omar Sharif (*Colorado*), Telly Savalas (*Sergeant Tibbs*), Camilla Sparv (*Inga*), Keenan Wynn (*Sanchez*), Julie Newmar (*Hesh-Ke*), Ted Cassidy (*Hachita*), Lee J. Cobb (*editor*), Raymond Massey (*preacher*), Burgess Meredith (*storekeeper*), Anthony Quayle (*older Englishman*), Edward G. Robinson (*Old Adams*), Eli Wallach (*Ben Baker*), Eduardo Ciannelli (*Prairie Dog*), Dick Peabody (*Avila*), Rudy Diaz (*Besh*), Robert Phillips (*Monkey*), Shelley Morrison (*Pima squaw*), J. Robert Porter (*young Englishman*), John Garfield, Jr. (*Adams' boy*), Pepe Callahan (*Laguna*), Trevor Bardette (*old man*), Madeleine Holmes (*old Apache woman*), Duke Hobbie (*lieutenant*), Victor Jory (*narrator*).

Western melodrama. Source: Will Henry, *Mackenna's Gold* (New York, 1963). In Arizona in 1874 there is a legend that the Apache gods store sacred gold in a hidden canyon. Marshal Mackenna of Hadleyburg learns the location of the canyon when he is ambushed in the desert and forced to shoot Prairie Dog, an old Apache chief. Before dying, the Indian gives Mackenna a map of the canyon but warns him that the Apache gods keep a vigil on the spot. After memorizing and burning the map, Mackenna is captured by a band of outlaws led by the ruthless Colorado, who has as his hostage Inga, a young Swedish immigrant and the daughter of the town judge. Aware that the marshal has seen the map, Colorado threatens to murder Inga unless Mackenna leads him to the canyon; Mackenna reluctantly agrees. Before long the band is joined by a group of Hadleyburg citizens who have also caught "gold fever." This group is pursued by Apache warriors who want to use the gold to fight the white man, and by a U. S. Cavalry troop tracking Colorado. The warring factions clash, and the only survivors are Mackenna, Colorado, Inga, and two renegade Apaches—the seductive Hesh-Ke and Hachita, a silent brave. They are soon joined by Cavalry Sergeant Tibbs, who has murdered his own men in order to search for the gold. As the fortune seekers make their way toward the canyon, Hesh-Ke becomes enraged by Mackenna's attentions to Inga and is killed trying to murder her rival; Hachita, believing the Apache gods are angry, kills Tibbs but in turn is slain by Colorado; and Colorado, now that he has found the treasure, engages Mackenna in a death struggle on a narrow ledge. The battle is interrupted by Apaches; their stampeding horses start an avalanche that obliterates the canyon and buries the gold. Only Mackenna, Colorado, and Inga escape. Vowing someday to find and kill Colorado, the unarmed Mackenna rides away on Sergeant Tibbs's horse, its saddlebags filled with gold. *Apache Indians. United States marshals. Outlaws. Hostages. Swedes. Immigrants. Traitors. Fortune hunters. Myths. Revenge. Murder. Greed. Jealousy. Gold. Deserts. Avalanches. Arizona. United States Army—Cavalry.*

Note: Location scenes filmed in Medford, Oregon; Kanab, Utah; and at Canyon de Chelly and Glen Canyon in Arizona. May have been shown in 70mm for some roadshow engagements.

THE MCKENZIE BREAK   F6.2961

Brighton Pictures. *Dist* United Artists. 28 Oct 1970 [New York opening; c28 Oct 1970; LP38901]. Sd; col (Deluxe). 35mm. 108 min. *MPAA rating* GP.

A Levy-Gardner-Laven Production. *Prod* Arthur Gardner, Jules Levy. *Dir* Lamont Johnson. *Screenplay* William Norton. *Dir Photog* Michael Reed. *Set Decor* Keith Liddiard. *Prod Dsgn* Frank White. *Film Ed* Tom Rolf. *Mus* Riz Ortolani. *Sd* Laurie Clarkson. *Asst Dir* Roger Good. *Prod Mgr* Geoffrey Haine. *Script Supv* Joseph Mazzuca. *Cost* Tiny Nicholls. *Makeup Artist* Alan Brownie. *Hairstyles* Ann McFayden. *Sp Eff* Thomas "Knobby" Clark.

Cast: Brian Keith (*Capt. Jack Connor*), Helmut Griem (*Schluetter*), Ian Hendry (*Major Perry*), Jack Watson (*General Kerr*), Patrick O'Connell (*Sergeant Major Cox*), Horst Janson (*Neuchl*), Alexander Allerson (*Von Sperrle*), John Abineri (*Kranz*), Constantin De Goguel (*Lieutenant Hall*), Tom Kempinski (*Schmidt*), Eric Allan (*Hochbauer*), Caroline Mortimer (*Sergeant Bell*), Mary Larkin (*Corporal Watt*), Gregg Palmer (*Berger*), Michael Sheard (*Unger*), Ingo Mogendorf (*Fullgrabe*), Franz van Norde (*Dichter*), Desmond Perry (*accomplice*), Jim Mooney (*Guard Foss*), Vernon Hayden (*Scottish dispatcher*), Maura Keely (*Scots lassie*), Noel Purcell (*ferry captain*), Paul Murphy (*Weber*), Frank Hayden (*Holtz*), Paddy Robinson (*pilot*), Robert Somerset (*guard*), Des Keogh (*guard*), Barry Cassin (*Guard Jones*), Denis Latimer (*Lieutenant Everett*), Conor Evans (*Orderly Joss*), Stephen Good (*Paisley*), Brendan Mathews (*guard*), Emmet Bergin (*Orderly Johnston*), John Kavanagh (*police inspector*), Joe Pilkington (*police communications sergeant*), Dave Kelly (*adjutant*), Mark Mulholland (*skipper*), Martin Dempsey (*colonel*),

Alec Doran (*police official*).

War melodrama. Source: Sidney Shelley, *The Bowmanville Break* (New York, 1968). Captain Connor, a tough British Army officer, is called in to quell the rebellion at Camp McKenzie, a World War II prison camp in Scotland. Connor, an Irishman who has been assigned to the camp because of his disregard for military regulations, uses fire hoses to quiet the prisoners, but he suspects that the riot was fomented by the Germans to distract attention from an escape plan. His suspicions are confirmed when Neuchl, a captured pilot, is severely beaten by his fellow prisoners and incoherently mumbles about the escape. Neuchl, ostracized by the prisoners for his homosexual tendencies, is mysteriously strangled before regaining consciousness. Schluetter, a U-boat commander who has been in contact with Berlin, arranges for the escapees to board a German U-boat. A tunnel has been dug that will allow 28 of the prisoners, all of whom are valuable submarine crewmen, to escape to the Scottish coast. Captain Connor decides to allow Schluetter and the Germans to follow through with their plan in the hope that the British will be able to capture the submarine when it picks up the men. Major Perry, the ineffectual camp commander, strongly objects, but Connor allows the prisoners to escape. Schluetter outwits Connor, however, who desperately searches for the escapees in his reconnaissance plane. At the last moment, Connor spots them as they are paddling to the waiting submarine. He radios for the British destroyer which has been placed on standby, but the ship arrives late, and only Schluetter and two of his crew are captured. Connor is left frustrated and facing disciplinary action for his abortive scheme. *Prisoners of war. Germans. Irish. Ship crews. Prison revolts. Prison escapes. Male homosexuality. Murder. Reconnaissance. Prisons. Submarines. Tunnels. World War II. Scotland. Germany—Navy. Great Britain—Army. Great Britain—Royal Navy.*

Note: Location scenes filmed in Ireland. Prerelease title: *Wolfpack.*

MCLINTOCK!   F6.2962

Batjac Productions. *Dist* United Artists. 13 Nov **1963** [New York opening; c1 Nov 1963; LP26387]. Sd (Westrex); col (Technicolor). 35mm (Panavision). 127 min.

Prod Michael Wayne. *Dir* Andrew V. McLaglen. *Screenplay* James Edward Grant. *Dir Photog* William H. Clothier. *Art Dir* Hal Pereira, Eddie Imazu. *Set Decor* Sam Comer, Darrell Silvera. *Dsgn* Richard Kuhn. *Main Titl* National Screen Service. *Film Ed* Otho Lovering, Bill Lewis. *Mus* Frank DeVol. *Mus Coörd* "By" Dunham. *Song:* "Love in the Country" "By" Dunham, Frank DeVol. *Sung by* The Limeliters. *Songs:* "Just Right for Me," "Cakewalk," "When We Dance" "By" Dunham. *Sd* Jack Solomon. *Asst Dir* Frank Parmenter. *Prod Mgr* Howard Joslin. *Prod Coörd* Robert E. Morrison. *Script Supv* Richard Chaffee. *Cost Supv* Frank Beetson, Jr. *Ladies' Cost* Ann B. Peck. *Makeup* Web Overlander. *Hairstyles* Lorraine Roberson. *Tech Adv* Cliff Lyons. *Prop* Gordon Cole, Earl Olin.

Cast: John Wayne (*George Washington McLintock*), Maureen O'Hara (*Katherine McLintock*), Patrick Wayne (*Devlin Warren*), Yvonne De Carlo (*Louise Warren*), Stefanie Powers (*Becky McLintock*), Jack Kruschen (*Birnbaum*), Chill Wills (*Drago*), Jerry Van Dyke (*Matt Douglas, Jr.*), Edgar Buchanan (*Bunny Dull*), Bruce Cabot (*Ben Sage*), Perry Lopez (*Davey Elk*), Michael Pate (*Puma*), Strother Martin (*Agard*), Gordon Jones (*Matt Douglas*), Robert Lowery (*governor*), Edward Faulkner (*Youngben Sage*), H. W. Gim (*Ching*), Aissa Wayne (*Alice Warren*), Chuck Roberson (*Sheriff Lord*), Hal Needham (*Carter*), Pedro Gonzales, Jr. (*Carlos*), Hank Worden (*Jeth*), Leo Gordon (*Jones*), Mary Patterson (*Beth*), John Hamilton (*Fauntleroy*), Ralph Volkie, Dan Borzage (*loafers*), John Stanley (*Running Buffalo*), Kari Noven (*Millie*), Mari Blanchard (*Camille*).

Western comedy. Ranchers in the southwestern town of McLintock try to force a group of homesteaders out of the area, and George Washington McLintock, ripsnorting cattle baron and the town's leading citizen, finds among them a lovely widow, Louise Warren, whom he hires as a cook. With Louise is her small daughter and her handsome son, Dev. McLintock's estranged wife, Katherine, returns from the East to insist on a divorce and to get custody of their daughter, Becky, who is returning from college. Becky finally arrives, bringing with her a Harvard boy, Matt Douglas, Jr., whose father is one of McLintock's old enemies. Young Douglas' presence leads to fisticuffs with Dev, who is also courting her. In addition to the violent arguments of Katherine and McLintock, there is more trouble when a band of Comanche Indians just released from prison arrives in town to make a final stand against the white man. Dev and Becky announce their engagement when this crisis subsides, but McLintock, roused to an exasperated fury by Katherine's jealousy and stubborness, chases her through the town and, upon catching her, gives her a solid spanking, much to the delight of the onlookers. After he tells her to go ahead and get a divorce, Katherine throws herself into his arms, and the McLintocks are together again. *Ranchers. Homesteaders. Land barons. Cattlemen. Widows. Cooks. Students. Comanche Indians. Filial relations. Marriage. Divorce. Jealousy.*

THE MCMASTERS   F6.2963

JayJen Productions. *Dist* Chevron Pictures. 7 Aug **1970** [New York opening]. Sd; col (Movielab). 35mm. 90 min. [See note.] *MPAA rating* GP.

A Dimitri De Grunwald Production. *Prod* Monroe Sachson. *Exec Prod* Dimitri De Grunwald. *Dir* Alf Kjellin. *Screenplay* Harold Jacob Smith. *Photog* Lester Shorr. *Set Decor* George R. Nelson. *Prod Dsgn* Joel Schiller. *Main Titl* Sandy Dvore. *Film Ed* Melvin Shapiro. *Mus Comp & Cond* Coleridge-Taylor Perkinson. *Sd* John V. Speak. *Asst Dir* Ray De Camp. *Prod Mgr* Harry F. Hogan. *Sp Eff* Herman Townsley, Ted Alires. *Tech Adv* Rodd Redwing.

Cast: Brock Peters (*Benjie*), Burl Ives (*Neal McMasters*), David Carradine (*White Feather*), Nancy Kwan (*Robin*), Jack Palance (*Kolby*), Dane Clark (*Spencer*), John Carradine (*preacher*), L. Q. Jones (*Russell*), R. G. Armstrong (*Watson*), Frank Raiter (*Grant*), Alan Vint (*Hank*), Marion Brash (*Mrs. Watson*), Neil Davis (*Sylvester*), Paul Eichenberg (*Jud*), Richard Alden (*Lester*), Lonnie Samuel (*Bull*), Albert Hockmeister (*sheriff*), Rev. David Strong (*Otis*), Dumas Slade (*Cullen*), Joan Howard (*Mrs. Spencer*), William Kiernan (*bartender*), José Maranio (*Indian Joe*), Leo Dillenschneider (*Watson's son*), Richard Martinez (*Black Fox*), Joseph Duran (*Black Cloud*), Bill Alexander, actor (*barber*), Frank Nanoia (*rancher*), David Welty (*Kolby's son*).

Western melodrama. Benjie returns to his hometown in the South after fighting for the North and meets with hostility from Kolby, a bigoted rancher who lost his arm while fighting for the Confederacy, and Russell, Kolby's ranch hand. Neal McMasters, a rancher who reared Benjie from childhood, offers him a half-share of his ranch. No one will work for Benjie because he is black, and McMasters is almost forced to sell Benjie's land, but Benjie's kindness to an Indian, White Feather, is reciprocated when members of his tribe arrive to help with the roundup. In further gratitude, White Feather presents Robin, his sister, to Benjie for his wife. Kolby leads some of the townsfolk in a drunken attack on McMasters and Benjie, and Robin is raped. The Indians refuse Benjie's plea for help, arguing that a black landowner is no better than the white landowners who stole their land. Despite pleas from Spencer, a liberal rancher, Kolby organizes another attack in which McMasters is killed and the house burned. Benjie is about to be hanged when the Indians launch a counterattack and kill Kolby. Benjie decides to stay on at the ranch with Robin. *Confederate veterans. Negroes. Ranchers. Amputees. Indians of North America. Race relations. Racial prejudice. Rape. Murder. Lynching. Ranch life. Miscegenation. United States—South.*

Note: Filmed in New Mexico. Also known as *The Blood Crowd*. Also shown in a 97-min version during its first New York engagement.

THE MAD ATLANTIC (Japan)   F6.2964

Mifune Productions. *Dist* Toho Co. Nov **1967** [Los Angeles showing]. Sd; b&w. 35mm (Tohoscope). 103 min.

Exec Prod Tomoyuki Tanaka, Koichi Sekizawa. *Dir* Jun Fukuda. *Screenplay* Hideo Ogawa, Shinichi Sekizawa. *Photog* Takao Saito. *Mus* Masaru Sato.

Cast: Toshiro Mifune, Makoto Sato, Mie Hama, Ryo Tamura, Tatsuya Mihashi, Tadao Nakamaru.

Drama. A Japanese fishing trawler puts into the port of Las Palmas in the Canary Islands. Owing to the trawler's having had an unsuccessful season, the captain is being supervised by an official from the company that owns the boat. The crew at first resents the presence of a stranger, but they eventually come to respect him. Just as the boat finds a large school of fish the captain receives a distress signal from a private yacht, and he is forced to decide whether to attempt the rescue and thereby lose both their nets and the fish or continue to make their first big haul. *Fishermen. Sea rescue. Fishing boats. Yachts. Atlantic Ocean. Las Palmas (Canary Islands).*

Note: Released in Japan in 1966 as *Doto ichiman kairi*.

THE MAD DOCTOR   F6.2965

Dist Stacey Distributors. ca **1970**. Sd; col. 16mm. 61-81 min.

Sex film. No information about the precise nature of this film has been found. *Physicians. Sexuality. Insanity.*

MAD DOCTOR OF BLOOD ISLAND (United States/Philippines)   F6.2966

Hemisphere Pictures. 21 May **1969** [Dayton, Ohio, opening]. Sd; col. 35mm. 86 min. *MPAA rating* M.

Prod Eddie Romero. *Exec Prod* Kane W. Lynn. *Assoc Prod* Beverly Miller. *Dir* Gerardo de Leon, Eddie Romero. *Screenplay* Reuben Candy. *Photog* Justo Paulino. *Mus* Tito Arevalo.

Cast: John Ashley (*Bill Foster*), Angelique Pettyjohn (*Sheila Willard*), Ronald Remy, Alicia Alonso, Ronaldo Valdez, Tita Muñoz, Tony Edmunds, Alfonso Carvajal, actor, Bruno Punzalan, Edward Murphy, Johnny Long, Paquito Salcedo, Felisa Salcedo, Quiel Mendoza, Ricardo Hipolito, Cenon Gonzalez, Nadja.

Horror film. Bill Foster, a young pathologist, is sent to Blood Island to investigate the discovery of a human corpse with green blood. On the boat from the mainland, he meets Sheila Willard, who is looking for her estranged father, and Carlos Lopez, who has come to take his widowed mother, Doña Anna, back to the mainland. Arriving on the island, the travelers begin to perceive trouble: Sheila's father has become a hopeless alcoholic, while Carlos' mother, Doña Anna, is now the mistress of Dr. Lorca, who holds the island in his control. A number of ghastly murders have been attributed to green, sub-human monsters. Carlos eventually discovers that the tomb of his father, Don Ramon, is empty, and Dr. Lorca admits that he used Don Ramon to experiment with a chlorophyll drug which he believed to contain the secret of youth. Don Ramon, who has been transformed into a green-blooded monster, kills Doña Anna. Dr. Lorca tries to imprison Bill and Carlos, but Don Ramon murders Dr. Lorca and sets the laboratory ablaze. Bill and Carlos, along with Sheila and her father, who has given up drinking, leave the island, believing that Don Ramon has been killed in the fire. *Pathologists. Monsters. Widows. Mistresses. Scientists. Experiments. Murder. Alcoholism. Filial relations. Immortality. Islands. Laboratories. Corpses. South Seas. Fires.*

Note: Also known as *Blood Doctor*, this film, a companion to *Brides of Blood*, q. v., has a sequel, *Beast of Blood*, q. v.

MAD DOG COLL   F6.2967

Thalia Films. *Dist* Columbia Pictures. 10 May **1961** [New York opening]. Sd; b&w. 35mm. 88 min.

Prod-Screenplay Edward Schreiber. *Dir* Burt Balaban. *Based on Material by* Leo Lieberman. *Dir Photog* Gayne Rescher. *Camera Op* Richard Miller, photog. *Art Dir* Richard Sylbert. *Set Decor* Gene Callahan. *Film Ed* Ralph Rosenblum. *Mus Comp & Cond* Stu Phillips. *Titl Song* Stu Phillips. *Lyr* Eddie D. Trush. *Sung by* Hal Waters. *Sd* Maurice Rosenblum. *Asst Dir* Arthur Steckler, Ulu Grosbard. *Prod Coörd* S. Charles Rawson. *Prod Mgr* Harrison Starr. *Script Supv* Dorothy Weshner. *Cost Dsgn* Bill Walstrom. *Makeup* Bill Herman. *Hairdresser* Ed Callaghan. *Talent Coörd* Joyce Selznick. *Ch Electrn* Richard Falk. *Ch Carpenter* Noah Bock. *Ch Grip* Larry Barr.

Cast: John Davis Chandler (*Vincent Coll*), Kay Doubleday (*Clio*), Brooke Hayward (*Elizabeth*), Neil Nephew (*Rocco*), Jerry Orbach (*Joe*), Telly Savalas (*Lieutenant Darrell*), Joy Harmon (*Caroline*), Ron Weyand (*Big Larry*), Peggy Furey (*Mother Coll*), Vincent Gardenia (*Dutch Schultz*), Gilbert Leigh (*The Official*), Stephanie King (*The Official's Wife*), Glenn Cannon (*Harry*), Tom Castronova (*Ralphie*), Gene Hackman (*cop*), Leonardo Cimino, Joe Costa, Ronald Dawson, P. Barney Goodman, James Greene, Richard Velez, Jim Lester.

Crime melodrama. In New York City in the 1920's, young Vincent Coll grows up a restless, tormented youth, the product of an unhappy home dominated by a savagely sadistic father. At the age of 17 he organizes a neighborhood gang and, by ruthless and vicious tactics, challenges the reign of New York's top mobster, Dutch Schultz, king of the bootlegging rackets. Frustrated by his unrequited love for Elizabeth, a young musician, Coll rapes her. He then takes on a nightclub stripper, Clio, as his mistress. As the years pass he becomes known as "Mad Dog" Coll, the most vicious killer in all of gangland, hated and sought by both the police and rival mobsters. Following a waterfront gang fight in which two innocent children are slain, Coll and his last remaining cohort, Joe, are forced to go into hiding. Coll, on the brink of insanity, kidnaps a member of Schultz's gang, and, under the delusion that the man is his dead father, murders him. Joe, who has fallen in love with Elizabeth, now realizes that Coll has become deranged, and he decides to tip off the police. Consequently, when Coll goes to make a phone call at a nearby drugstore, the police are waiting for him, and he is shot down in a fusillade of machine-gun fire. *Juvenile delinquents. Street gangs. Gangsters. Bootleggers. Musicians. Stripteasers. Mistresses. Police. Sadism. Filial relations. Gang wars. Rape. Murder. Insanity. Abduction. Roaring Twenties. New York City. Mad Dog Coll. Dutch Schultz.*

Note: Filmed on location in New York City.

A MAD ESCAPADE OF A PLAYBOY *see* MR. PEEK-A-BOO'S PLAYMATES

THE MAD EXECUTIONERS (West Germany)   F6.2968

CCC–Filmkunst. *Dist* Paramount Pictures. 22 Sep **1965** [New York opening]. Sd; b&w. 35mm. 92 min.

Prod Artur Brauner. *Exec Prod* Heinz Willeg. *Dir* Edwin Zbonek. *Screenplay* Robert A. Stemmle. *Photog* Richard Angst. *Art Dir* Hans Jürgen Kiebach, Ernst Schomer. *Film Ed* Walter Wischniewsky. *Mus* Raimund Rosenberger. *Sd* Erwin Schänzle. *Asst Dir* Gisela Anton. *Prod Mgr* Manfred Korytowski, Felix Siebenrogg. *Prod Dir* Heinz Götze. *Cost* Trude Ulrich.

Cast: Hansjörg Felmy (*Inspector Hillier*), Maria Perschy (*Ann*), Dieter Borsche (*Dr. MacFergusson*), Rudolf Forster (*Ann's father*), Harry Riebauer (*police surgeon*), Chris Howland (*undercover man*), Wolfgang Preiss, Rudolf

Fernau, Narziss Sokatscheff, Alexander Engel, Albert Besser, Stanislav Ledinek.

Mystery melodrama. Source: Bryan Edgar Wallace, "White Carpet" (a story; publication undetermined). A band of murderous vigilantes assume judiciary power in London; criminals who have escaped punishment in the courts are secretly tried by hooded men and executed by hanging in a public place. Inspector Hillier of Scotland Yard is assigned to the investigation, but he is anxious to solve a case involving a sex maniac who has decapitated several young women, including the inspector's sister. Ann, Hillier's fiancée, agrees to act as bait, and she is abducted by the mad surgeon, Dr. MacFergusson. Evading the police, he prepares to make Ann another victim of his gruesome experiments, but Ann escapes when the vigilantes capture MacFergusson and place him on trial. Through an undercover man, the authorities interrupt the kangaroo court and shoot the gang's leader. His hood removed, Hillier is revealed as the vengeful executioner of London. *Vigilantes. Sex deviates. Surgeons. Secret agents. Murder. Abduction. Capital punishment. Decapitation. Revenge. Kangaroo courts. London. Scotland Yard.*

Note: Released in West Germany in Nov 1963 as *Der Henker von London*; running time: 95 min.

MAD MONSTER PARTY   F6.2969
Videocraft International Productions. *Dist* Avco Embassy Pictures. 8 Mar **1969** [New York showing]. Sd; col. 35mm (Animagic). 94 min.

Pres by Joseph E. Levine. A Rankin-Bass Production. *Prod-Story* Arthur Rankin, Jr. *Exec Prod* Joseph E. Levine. *Dir* Jules Bass. *Screenplay (see note)* Len Korobkin, Harvey Kurtzman, Forrest J. Ackerman. *Puppet Dsgn* Jack Davis. *Mus & Lyr* Maury Laws, Jules Bass.

Cast—With the Talents of: Boris Karloff, Ethel Ennis, Gale Garnett, Phyllis Diller, Allen Swift.

Animated puppet film. Aging Baron Boris von Frankenstein, who lives on a Caribbean island with his monster, his wife, and his ward, Francesca, discovers the secret of total destruction, thus completing research that began with the discovery of the secret of creation. He decides to hold a convention for the world's most renowned monsters so that he may choose a successor to lead the Worldwide Organization of Monsters and to inherit his secret. The guests include Dracula, The Werewolf, the Creature From the Black Lagoon, It, Yetch (a Peter Lorre characterization), The Invisible Man (as played by Claude Rains), Dr. Jekyll and Mr. Hyde, The Mummy, Quasimodo (as played by Charles Laughton), and King Kong. Felix Flanken, Frankenstein's supposedly normal nephew, kept in ignorance of the proceedings, falls in love with Francesca, unaware that she is one of his uncle's mechanical creations. Intrigue follows intrigue as the monsters try to surpass one another to gain the prestigious position. Francesca meets with a surprise when Felix's identity is revealed. *Scientists. Monsters. Mummies. Werewolves. Robots. Conventions. Caribbean. Peter Lorre. Charles Laughton. Claude Rains. Frankenstein. The Invisible Man. Dracula. Quasimodo. King Kong. "Creature From the Black Lagoon". Dr. Jekyll and Mr. Hyde.*

Note: Produced in 1966. Ackerman does not receive screen credit. Animagic process involves stop-motion photography of stationary three-dimensional forms.

THE MAD ROOM   F6.2970
Norman Maurer Productions. *Dist* Columbia Pictures. 30 Apr **1969** [New York opening; c1 Apr 1969; LP36593]. Sd; col (Berkey Pathé). 35mm. 92 min. *MPAA rating* M.

Prod Norman Maurer. *Dir* Bernard Girard. *Screenplay* Bernard Girard, A. Z. Martin. *Dir Photog* Harry Stradling, Jr. *Art Dir* Sydney Z. Litwack. *Set Decor* Sidney Clifford. *Film Ed* Pat Somerset. *Mus* Dave Grusin. *Songs:* "Open My Eyes," "Wildwood Blues" *Writ & Sung by* Nazz. *Sd Supv* Charles J. Rice. *Sd* James Z. Flaster, Arthur Piantadosi. *Asst Dir* Rusty Meek. *Cost Dsgn* Moss Mabry. *Makeup Supv* Ben Lane. *Hairstyles* Virginia Jones.

Cast: Stella Stevens *(Ellen Hardy)*, Shelley Winters *(Mrs. Armstrong)*, Skip Ward *(Sam Aller)*, Carol Cole *(Chris)*, Severn Darden *(Nate)*, Beverly Garland *(Mrs. Racine)*, Michael Burns *(George)*, Barbara Sammeth *(Mandy)*, Lloyd Haynes *(Dr. Marion Kincaid)*, Jenifer Bishop *(Mrs. Ericson)*, Gloria Manon *(Edna)*, Lou Kane *(Armand Racine)*.

Melodrama. Source: Reginald Denham, Edward Percy, *Ladies in Retirement* (New York opening: 26 Mar 1940). Garrett Fort and Reginald Denham, screenplay for the film *Ladies in Retirement*, 1941. Ellen Hardy is the companion to Mrs. Armstrong, a wealthy widow who lives with her stepson, Sam Aller, and her maid-secretary, Chris, in a huge old mansion. Ellen and Sam are preparing to marry when Ellen learns that her teenage brother and sister, George and Mandy, are to be released from the mental institution where they have been confined; as young children, they were the prime suspects in the brutal knife slaying of their sleeping parents, but it was never determined which of the two was responsible. Claiming that the youngsters were staying with an uncle who recently died, Ellen persuades the reluctant Mrs. Armstrong to allow

them to move into the mansion. George and Mandy tell Ellen that they need a "mad room" where they can rid themselves of emotional hostilities, and Ellen secretly lets them use an attic study which Mrs. Armstrong has kept locked since her husband's death. Eventually, however, the widow learns about both the "mad room" and the children's past and demands that they leave. That night, Ellen finds Mrs. Armstrong hacked to death with one of her late husband's sabers. The children first suspect each other, but they finally realize that their sister, in her misguided attempts to shield them, committed both the present and the past murders. To cover up the crime, Ellen disposes of Mrs. Armstrong's corpse in a river and plants evidence indicating that the death was accidental. Unbeknown to Ellen, however, the family dog has carried off one of Mrs. Armstrong's severed hands. Ellen's mind totally snaps when she sees the animal carrying the hand, and Sam catches her as she is butchering the dog in the mansion basement. *Widows. Stepmothers. Secretaries. Housemaids. Murder. Mental illness. Brother-sister relationship. Wealth. Adolescence. Manors. Dogs.*

Note: Location scenes filmed in Vancouver, British Columbia. A remake of the 1941 Columbia release *Ladies in Retirement*.

MADALENA (Greece)   F6.2971
Finos Films–Th. A. Damaskinos–V. G. Michaelides, A. E. *Dist* Greek Motion Pictures. Mar **1965**. Sd; b&w. 35mm. 95 min.

Dir Dinos Dimopoulos. *Screenplay* Georges Roussos. *Photog* Walter Lassally. *Art Dir* Markos Zervas. *Mus* Manos Hadjidakis. *English Subtitl* Herman G. Weinberg.

Cast: Aliki Vouyouklaki *(Madalena)*, Dimitris Papamichael *(Giorgas)*, Pantelis Zervos *(father)*, T. Morides, Thanassis Vengos.

Comedy-drama. Madalena supports five sisters and a brother by operating her late father's ferryboat on a small Greek island. She is in love with Giorgas but refuses to admit it because he is the son of her business competitor. A kindly priest finally resolves matters by arranging marriage between Madalena and Giorgas. *Orphans. Priests. Employment—Women. Business competition. Marriage. Ferryboats. Islands.*

Note: Filmed on location in Antiparos. Produced in Greece in 1960.

THE MADAM   F6.2972
Dist Stacey Distributors. 6 Nov **1969** [San Francisco showing]. Sd; col. 16mm. 61-81 min.

Sex film. No information about the precise nature of this film has been found. *Madams. Sexuality.*

MADAME (France/Italy/Spain)   F6.2973
Ciné-Alliance–GE. SI. Cinematografica–C. C. Champion–Agata Film. *Dist* Embassy Pictures. 13 Feb **1963** [Los Angeles opening]. Sd; col (Technicolor). 35mm (Technirama). 104 min.

Pres by Joseph E. Levine. *Prod* Maleno Malenotti. *Exec Prod* Luciano Perugia. *Dir* Christian-Jaque. *Screenplay* Henri Jeanson, Ennio De Concini, Christian-Jaque, Franco Solinas, Jean Ferry. *Photog* Roberto Gerardi. *Art Dir* Jean d'Eaubonne, Mario Rappini. *Film Ed* Jacques Desagneau, Eraldo Da Roma. *Mus* Angelo Francesco Lavagnino. *Sd* Ennio Sensi. *Asst Dir* Raymond Villette, Maurizio Lucci. *Prod Mgr* Nello Meniconi. *Cost* Marcel Escoffier, Itala Scandariato.

Cast: Sophia Loren *(Catherine Hubscher [Madame])*, Robert Hossein *(Lefebvre)*, Julien Bertheau *(Napoleon Bonaparte)*, Marina Berti *(Elisa)*, Carlo Giuffrè *(Jerome)*, Gabriella Pallotta *(Heloise)*, Annalía Gadé *(Caroline)*, Laura Valenzuela *(Pauline)*, Gianrico Tedeschi *(Roquet)*, Renaud Mary *(Fouché)*, Célina Cély.

Historical comedy. Source: Emile Moreau and Victorien Sardou, *Madame Sans-Gêne* (Paris opening: 27 Oct 1893). In 1792 outspoken Parisian laundress Catherine Hubscher, who washes the shirts of young Napoleon and other soldiers fighting the Revolution, falls in love with Sergeant Lefebvre. When she is unable to obtain a pass to the front, Catherine, or "Madame Sans-Gêne," as she is known, joins a wagon of camp followers and travels to her lover; there, she and Lefebvre are captured by Austrian troops but manage to escape and blow up an enemy ammunition dump. For their valor, Napoleon, now a general, promotes Lefebvre to colonel and decorates Catherine for her bravery on the battlefield. Later, when Napoleon becomes emperor, he invites the couple, who are now married, to a palace ball in hopes of making them King and Queen of Westphalia. Catherine's lack of courtly manners creates a scandal, however, and Napoleon decides that Lefebvre will have to divorce her before he can be granted a title. Outraged, Catherine storms into the emperor's private chambers and reminds him of the days when he frequented her laundry, often unable to pay his bills. Overwhelmed by her, Napoleon concludes that it would be wiser not to separate the couple; someone else must be King of Westphalia. *Laundresses. Soldiers. Austrians. Royalty. Courage. Marriage. Ammunition. France—History—Revolution 1789–93. Paris. Napoleon I. Catherine Hubscher. François Joseph Lefebvre. Joseph Fouché.*

Note: Location scenes filmed in Caserta, Italy, and in Spain. Opened in Rome in Dec 1961 as *Madame Sans-Gêne* at 105 min; in Paris in May 1962 under the same title at 97 min; and in Madrid in Apr 1962. Previously filmed in Denmark in 1910, in France in 1911 and 1941, and in the United States in 1925. Photographed in Technirama 70.

MADAME AKI (Japan)   F6.2974

Tokyo Eiga Co. *Dist* Toho Co. 21 Nov **1963** [Los Angeles showing]. Sd; col (Eastmancolor). 35mm (Tohoscope). 114 min.

An Ichiro Sato Production. *Exec Prod* Ichiro Sato, Fumio Kinbara. *Dir* Shiro Toyoda. *Screenplay* Toshio Yazumi. *Story* Yasushi Inouye. *Photog* Kozo Okazaki. *Mus* Ikuma Dan.

Cast: Hisaya Morishige *(Katayuki)*, Fujiko Yamamoto *(Aki)*, Michiyo Aratama *(Misako)*, Tatsuya Nakadai *(Tatsumi)*, Chieko Naniwa, Hiroyuki Nagato, Mayumi Ozora.

Melodrama. Aki suspects her executive husband, Katayuki, of infidelity when he is actually carrying on a mild flirtation with Misako, the younger sister of a deceased friend. Aki meets Misako and her suspicions deepen after Katayuki admits he does like the younger woman. Convinced her husband is about to desert her, Aki takes up with Tatsumi, a young sculptor. Misako sees them together, and is only too happy to announce to Katayuki her long standing love for him. Katayuki, realizing he has a very idealistic and confused woman on his hands, refuses her advances, but he does spend a night with her as consolation. Soon, all involved parties are aware of the affairs. Misako and Tatsumi, who have come to realize that they are in love, decide to marry, leaving Katayuki and Aki to solve their own problems. *Executives. Sculptors. Idealists. Marriage. Infidelity. Flirtation.*

Note: Released in Japan in 1963 as *Yushu heiya*.

MADAME O (Japan)   F6.2975

Dist Audubon Films. ca **1970**. Sd; b&w with col seq (Eastman Color). 35mm (Colorscope). 84 min.

Prod Minoru Chiba. *Dir* Seichi Fukada.

Cast: Michiko Sakyo.

Sex film. No information about the precise nature of this film has been found. *Sexuality.*

Note: Original title and release date unknown.

MME. OLGA'S MASSAGE PARLOR   F6.2976

Dist American Film Distributing Corp. 8 Jul **1965** [San Francisco showing]. Sd; b&w. 35mm. 70 min.

Pres by Stan Borden. *Prod-Orig Idea & Story* George Weiss. *Dir* Joseph P. Mawra. *Comm* Perry Peters. *Photog* Werner Rose. *Asst Camera* Herbert Coleman. *Background Mus* Gene St. Jean. *Sd* Magno Sound.

Cast: Alice Baez *(Elaine)*, T. Wood Parker *(Nick)*, Yvonne York *(Irene)*, Anna Markus *(Laura)*, Dolly Ashton *(Evelyn)*, Gene St. Jean *(Jacques)*, Terry Candy *(Maria)*, Rosemary McGhee *(Adela)*, Vera Caw *(Cindy)*, Cathy Angel *(Leah)*, Renne Bennett *(Carmen)*, Jackie M. Iller *(Linda)*, Kathy Brandon *(Jackie)*, Geraldine Maniaci, Hilke Jessien, Robert Cohen, Irwin Gaynor *(massage parlor staff)*.

Drama. Elaine and Nick, syndicate gangsters, take over Madame Olga's health club as a front for their traffic in stolen jewels and captive, high-priced call girls. They soon establish a thriving underworld operation at the well-equipped gymnasium. In spite of Elaine's iron discipline, some of the most trusted girls keep some smuggled jewels for themselves, forcing Elaine to use the health club apparatus to conduct an inquisition and find the culprits. The mystery is soon cleared up, and the gangsters proceed with business as usual. *Gangsters. Prostitutes. Organized crime. Sadism. White slave traffic. Torture. Theft. Massage parlors. Health clubs. Jewels.*

Note: Also known as *Olga's Massage Parlor* and *Olga's Parlor.* May be same as *Massage Parlor*, shown in San Francisco 24 Feb 1966.

MADAME SANS-GÊNE see MADAME

MADAME WHITE SNAKE (Hong Kong)   F6.2977

Shaw Brothers (H. K.) Ltd. *Dist* Frank Lee International. 14 Feb **1963** [San Francisco opening]. Sd; col (Eastman Color). 35mm (Shawscope). 105 min.

Prod Run Run Shaw. *Dir* Yueh Feng. *Screenplay* Ka Jui-fan. *Photog* T. Nishimoto. *Mus* Wang Fu-ling.

Cast: Lin Dai, Chao Lei, Margaret Tu Chuan.

Fantasy. Based on the Chinese fairy tale "Pai she chuan." Pai Su-chen, a goddess who is actually a 1,000-year-old white snake, falls in love with Hsü Hsien, a drug store clerk who saved her in a previous life. In gratitude for his deed, Pai takes the form of a lovely maiden and marries him; they live in harmony until a Buddhist monk tells Hsü that his wife is a spirit and gives him three amulets. Pai overcomes the amulets' powers, but one day Hsü sees her in the form of a white snake and dies of fright. Pai revives him with a red mushroom she has obtained from the Holy Land. The monk returns and forces

Hsü to fly by magic to Mount Chin and plead with the god Fa-hai to allow the marriage of a mortal to a goddess. Fa-hai tries to kill Hsü by creating a flood, but he escapes; later Hsü dies in battle with Fa-hai and is joined in heaven by Pai. *Mythological characters. Monks. Immortality. Reincarnation. Talismans. Buddhism. Floods. Snakes.*

Note: Produced in Hong Kong as *Pai-she chuan*; running time: 124 min.

MADAME X   F6.2978

Universal Pictures-Ross Hunter Productions-Eltee Productions. *Dist* Universal Pictures. 3 Mar **1966** [Miami, Florida, opening; c2 Apr 1966; LP35373]. Sd; col (Technicolor). 35mm. 100 min.

Prod Ross Hunter. *In Charge of Prod* Edward Muhl. *Dir* David Lowell Rich. *Screenplay* Jean Holloway. *Dir Photog* Russell Metty. *Camera Op* Ed Pyle. *Asst Camera* Ledger Haddow. *Art Dir* Alexander Golitzen, George Webb. *Set Decor* Howard Bristol, John McCarthy. *Set Coörd* Jerry MacDonald. *Film Ed* Milton Carruth. *Asst Ed* Richard Bracken. *Mus* Frank Skinner. *Mus Supv* Joseph Gershenson. *Song:* "Swedish Rhapsody" Charles Wildman. *Sd* Waldon O. Watson, Clarence Self, Don Cunliffe, Victor Goode, Chick Bourland. *Asst Dir* Douglas Green, Charles Scott, Jr. *Unit Prod Mgr* John Morrison. *Gowns Dsgn* Jean Louis. *Wardrobe* Kathleen McCandless. *Makeup* Bud Westmore, Del Armstrong, Tom Tuttle, Mary Hadley. *Hairstyles* Larry Germain, Helen Young, Kay Reed. *Sp Eff* Walter Hammond. *Dial Coach* Betty Abbott. *Still Photog* Al St. Hilaire. *Prop* Tony Lombardo, Charles Chrisman. *Gaffer* Max Nippell. *Grip* Charles Cowie, Ken Smith.

Cast: Lana Turner *(Holly Parker)*, John Forsythe *(Clay Anderson)*, Ricardo Montalban *(Phil Benton)*, Burgess Meredith *(Dan Sullivan)*, John Van Dreelen *(Christian Torben)*, Virginia Grey *(Mimsy)*, Constance Bennett *(Estelle)*, Keir Dullea *(Clay, Jr.)*, Teddy Quinn *(Clay, Jr. [as a child])*, Warren Stevens *(Michael Spalding)*, Carl Benton Reid *(judge)*, Frank Maxwell *(Dr. Evans)*, Karen Verne *(Nurse Riborg)*, Joe De Santis *(Carter)*, Frank Marth *(Combs)*, Bing Russell *(Sergeant Riley)*, Teno Pollick *(Manuel Lopez)*, Jeff Burton *(Bromley)*, Jill Jackson *(police matron)*.

Melodrama. Source: Alexandre Bisson, *La Femme X* (Paris, 1909). Wealthy and politically ambitious Clay Anderson brings his bride, Holly, home to the family mansion, where she is met by Estelle, her mother-in-law. The marriage is a happy one, with Holly devoting most of her time to their son. Soon, however, Clay's ambition and frequent absences cause Holly to feel neglected, and she begins to date Phil Benton, a bachelor. Estelle, who has hired a detective to follow Holly, demands the end to the relationship; and at the time of their separation, it happens that Phil falls down the stairs in his flat and dies. Panic-stricken, Holly flees and seeks Estelle's help. Estelle then reveals that she never thought Holly good enough for her son and presents her with the alternatives: either ruin Clay's career by facing a court trial, or disappear. Holly goes abroad with a pension provided by Estelle. Falling ill in Denmark, Holly receives help from Christian Torben, a concert pianist. He falls in love with her, but Holly is unable to accept him or explain her situation and so runs away. Twenty years later, while in Mexico, Holly, now an absinthe addict, meets Dan Sullivan, a con man, who, after finding out about Holly's past, plans to blackmail the Anderson family. To prevent this crime, Holly shoots Dan and calls the police. Refusing to reveal her identity, Holly now calls herself Madame X, and upon discovering that her young lawyer is her own son, she becomes more determined than ever to keep her identity secret and readily accepts the prospect of punishment. Clay, Sr., is present at the trial and becomes suspicious of the true identity of his son's client; but Holly dies of heart failure before the verdict is rendered, knowing that she truly has a fine son. *Mothers-in-law. Politicians. Pianists. Confidence men. Lawyers. Detectives. Wealth. Ambition. Marriage. Motherhood. Infidelity. Blackmail. Murder. Personal identity. Alcoholism. Trials. Absinthe. Denmark. Mexico.*

Note: Previously filmed by Metro-Goldwyn-Mayer in 1920, 1929, and 1937.

MÄDCHEN FÜR DIE MAMBO-BAR see $100 A NIGHT

DAS MÄDCHEN IM TIGERFELL see HIPPODROME

MÄDCHEN IN UNIFORM see MAEDCHEN IN UNIFORM

DAS MÄDCHEN VOM MOORHOF see THE GIRL OF THE MOORS

EIN MÄDCHEN WIE DAS MEER see FEMMINA

THE MADDEST STORY EVER TOLD see SPIDER BABY

MADE IN ITALY (France/Italy)   F6.2979

Documento Film-Orsay Films. *Dist* Royal Films International. 30 Apr **1967** [New York opening]. Sd; col (Technicolor). 35mm (Techniscope). 101 min.

Prod Gianni Hecht Lucari. *Exec Prod* Fausto Saraceni. *Dir* Nanni Loy. *Screenplay* Ettore Scola, Ruggero Maccari, Nanni Loy. *Story* Ettore Scola, Ruggero Maccari. *Photog* Ennio Guarnieri. *Art Dir* Luciano Spadoni. *Film Ed* Ruggero Mastroianni. *Mus* Carlo Rustichelli. *Sd* Claudio Maielli. *Prod Mgr* Romano Dandi. *Cost* Pier Luigi Pizzi. *Makeup* Nilo Jacoponi.

Cast: Marina Berti (*bored diner*), Claudio Gora (*her husband*), Lionello Pio Di Savola (*another diner*), Lando Buzzanca (*Giulio*), Iolanda Modio (*Rosalia*), Walter Chiari (*Enrico*), Lea Massari (*Monica*), Virna Lisi (*Virginia*), Giulio Bosetti (*Renato*), Catherine Spaak (*Karol*), Fabrizio Moroni (*Gianremo*), Sylva Koscina (*Diana*), Jean Sorel (*Orlando*), Nino Manfredi (*Lamporecchi*), Rossella Falk (*wronged wife*), Alberto Sordi (*errant husband*), Claudie Lange (*other woman*), Anna Magnani (*Anna*), Andrea Checchi (*father*), Aldo Giuffrè, Anita Durante, Tecla Scarano, Milena Vucotich, Giampiero Albertini, Aldo Bufi-Landi, Adelmo Di Fraia, Antonio Mazza.

Comedy. Composed of 32 vignettes depicting life in modern-day Italy, the film is divided into five chapters: "Habits and Customs," "Work," "Women," "Citizens—the State—and Church," and "The Family." Linked together by scenes of four Italian laborers flying to Stockholm to look for work are incidents such as the following: Tourists in Florence are able to locate places of historical interest only by asking other tourists for directions; bored sophisticates in Rome amuse themselves by dining in the Trastevere section where they are insulted and rudely served; a young husband-to-be is relieved to learn that even though his fiancée has been involved in theft, kidnaping, and homicide, she is still a virgin; a Roman lover goes to great lengths to seduce a married woman and then finds it impossible to get rid of her; bridal gowns in a shop window are admired by a weeping nun; Virginia, a defenseless woman, describes to Renato, her former boyfriend, how she suffered at the hands of her recently deceased patron; the teenaged daughter of an ill-tempered janitor attempts to pose as a socialite; Diana, the beautiful owner of a Ferrari, allows herself to be picked up by Orlando, who is interested only in her car; impoverished villagers stare at posters urging them to "Help India"; the regally appointed offices of a financial magnate belong to a monsignor of the Catholic Church; Lamporecchi, a Roman citizen in need of an identification card, shuttles from office to office only to learn that the computers indicate that he does not exist; a young wife finds her husband in bed with another woman, and after listening to his explanations she apologizes for misunderstanding the situation; Anna, an Italian mother, shepherds her three small children, her shiftless husband, and her aged mother-in-law across three lanes of traffic to buy some ice cream and then discovers that the store is back on the other side of the highway. *Tourists. Socialites. Idle rich. Nuns. Pickups. Priests. Virginity. Seduction. Infidelity. Adolescence. Poverty. Bureaucracy. Duplicity. Family life. Employment. Airplanes. Restaurants. Automobiles. Florence. Rome. Rome—Trastevere. Stockholm. Taormina. Catania. Amalfi. Naples. Venice. Turin. Milan.*

Note: Filmed on location in Rome, Taormina, Catania, Amalfi, Naples, Venice, Turin, Milan, Florence, and Stockholm. Opened in Paris in Apr 1967 as *À l'italienne*; running time: 105 min; in Rome in Dec 1965 as *Made in Italy*; running time: 130 min. Italian chapter names: "La traversata," "Creatura indifesa," "Colpi di fulmine," "Ogni bel gioco," "Il contrattacco," "Il labirinto," "Il laureato," "Cenerentola." Additional cast members Aldo Fabrizi, Nino Castelnuovo, and Peppino De Filippo appear only in the Italian release version.

MADE IN PARIS   F6.2980

Euterpe, Inc. *Dist* Metro-Goldwyn-Mayer, Inc. 26 Jan **1966** [Chicago opening; c10 Dec 1965; LP31991]. Sd (Westrex); col (Metrocolor). 35mm (Panavision). 103 min.

Prod Joe Pasternak. *Dir* Boris Sagal. *Screenplay* Stanley Roberts. *Dir Photog* Milton Krasner. *Camera Op* Alfred Lebowitz. *Asst Camera* Paul Koons, Ed Plante. *Art Dir* George W. Davis, Preston Ames. *Set Decor* Henry Grace, Keogh Gleason. *Film Ed* William McMillin. *Mus Comp & Cond* George Stoll. *Assoc* Robert Van Eps. *Mus Played by* Mongo Santamaria and His Band. *Titl Song* Burt Bacharach, Hal David. *Sung by* Trini Lopez. *Song:* "Paris Lullaby" Sammy Fain, Paul Francis Webster. *Sung by* Ann-Margret, Louis Jourdan. *Theme:* "My True Love" Red Skelton. *Songs:* "Skol Sister," "Goof Proof" Quincy Jones. *Played by* Count Basie and His Octet. *Choreog* David Winters. *Rec Supv* Franklin Milton. *Mix* Conrad Kahn. *Rec* Hal Walker. *Boom Op* Jerry Jost. *Asst Dir* Donald C. Klune, Rowe Wallerstein. *Unit Prod Mgr* Al Shenberg. *Script Supv* Cleo Anton. *Gowns* Helen Rose. *Wardrobe* Lambert Marks, Jim Taylor, Elva Martien, Margo Weintz. *Makeup Supv* William Tuttle. *Makeup* Frank McCoy, Ron Berkeley. *Sp Hairstyles* Sydney Guilaroff. *Still Photog* Virgil Apger. *Gaffer* George Lasher. *Grip* Hank Forrester. *Casting* Mel Ballerino.

Cast: Ann-Margret (*Maggie Scott*), Louis Jourdan (*Marc Fontaine*), Richard Crenna (*Herb Stone*), Edie Adams (*Irene Chase*), Chad Everett (*Ted Barclay*), John McGiver (*Roger Barclay*), Marcel Dalio (*Georges*), Matilda Calnan (*Cecile*), Jacqueline Beer (*Denise Marton*), Marcel Hillaire (*attendant*), Michele Montau (*Elise*), Reta Shaw (*American bar singer*), Count Basie and His Octet, Mongo Santamaria and His Band (*themselves*).

Comedy-drama with music. When department store fashion buyer Irene Chase decides to get married, Mr. Barclay, owner of the store, sends Maggie Scott, her assistant, to Paris for the fashion showings. Barclay's choice surprises

Maggie because Ted, Barclay's son, has been chasing her and she has been rejecting him. In Paris, famed couturier Marc Fontaine breaks into her hotel room, believing it to be occupied by Irene, who had been a girl friend of his. They quarrel, but when Maggie is about to lose the order for Marc's collection, they make up, and Maggie becomes romantically interested in the designer. Ted, truly in love with Maggie, flies to Paris to be with her. Maggie is courted also by newspaperman Herb Stone, who takes her on a tour of nightclubs; but Maggie realizes that her involvements with Marc and Herb are only flirtatious and that she really loves Ted. She returns to America with him. *Buyers. Journalists. Couturiers. Fashion. Department stores. Nightclubs. Paris.*

MADEMOISELLE (France/Great Britain)   F6.2981

Woodfall Film Productions–Procinex. *Dist* Lopert Pictures. 1 Aug **1966** [New York opening]. Sd; b&w. 35mm (Panavision). 103 min.

Prod Oscar Lewenstein. *Assoc Prod* Neil Hartley, Claude Jaeger. *Dir* Tony Richardson. *Screenplay* Jean Genêt. *Screenplay Trans* Bernard Frechtman. *English Vers Photog* David Watkin. *French Vers Photog* Philippe Brun. *Art Dir* Jacques Saulnier. *Set Decor* Charles Mérangel. *English Vers Ed* Anthony Gibbs. *French Vers Ed* Sophie Coussein. *Sd* Peter Handford. *Sd Rec* Jean Rieul. *Asst Dir* Christian de Chalonges, Marc Grunebaum. *Prod Mgr* Marc Maurette. *Cost* Jocelyn Rickards. *Sp Eff* Daniel Braunschweig.

Cast: Jeanne Moreau (*Mademoiselle*), Ettore Manni (*Manou*), Keith Skinner (*Bruno*), Umberto Orsini (*Antonio*), Jane Berretta (*Annette*), Mony Rey (*Vievotte*), Douking (*The Priest*), Rosine Luguet (*Lisa*), Gabriel Gobin (*police sergeant*), Pierre Collet (*Marcel*), Jean Gras (*Roger*), Georges Aubert (*René*), Antoine Marin (*Armand*), Gérard Darrieu (*Boulet*), Charles Lavialle (*flood farmer*), Robert Larcebeau (*2d fire farmer*), René Hell (*peasant*), Jacques Chevalier (*3d policeman*), Claire Ifrane (*Lucie*), Denise Péronne (*Maria*), Annie Savarin (*Rose*), Valérie Girodias (*Josette*), L. Chevallier (*old peasant*), Laure Paillette (*milk woman*), Catherine Parquier (*young girl*), Jacques Monod (*mayor*), Paul Barge (*young policeman*).

Drama. The schoolmistress of a remote French farming village is a seemingly prim and introverted young spinster. Beneath her calm exterior, however, Mademoiselle is filled with suppressed sexual desires that erupt into secret acts of violence and wanton destruction. Opening floodgates to drown farm stock, setting fire to barns and homes, poisoning animals' drinking water, and smashing the nests of field birds, she takes perverse carnal pleasure in the havoc she causes. The outraged villagers, needing someone to blame for the series of disasters, turn against a lusty woodcutter, Manou, who has recently moved into the community as the leader of an Italian work crew. A widower whose 15-year-old son, Bruno, attends Mademoiselle's classes, Manou is resented by the local men because of the animal magnetism he exerts over women, a magnetism he exploits to the fullest. One day, the schoolmistress, incensed by Manou's indifference to her, lures him into a field and seduces him by crawling on her stomach and licking his hands and boots like a dog. Afterwards she returns to the village, her clothing torn and splattered with mud, and flatly states that Manou raped her. The mounting anger of the village men now bursts into frenzy, and they seek Manou out and stone him to death. Her passions momentarily sated, the schoolmistress accepts the sympathy of her neighbors, packs her few belongings, and leaves the village. Bruno alone knows her secret and the part she played in his father's death. *Schoolteachers. Italians. Spinsters. Woodsmen. Widowers. Vigilantes. Incendiarism. Sadomasochism. Seduction. Murder. Village life. Filial relations. Fires. Floods.*

Note: Filmed on location in France. Opened in Paris in Jun 1966; running time: 100 min; released in Great Britain in Jan 1967; running time: 103 min. Working title: *Summer Fires*.

MADEMOISELLE ANGE see ANGEL ON EARTH

MADIGAN   F6.2982

Universal Pictures. 29 Mar **1968** [New York opening; c1 Jun 1968; LP38827]. Sd (Westrex); col (Technicolor). 35mm (Techniscope). 101 min.

Prod Frank P. Rosenberg. *Dir* Donald Siegel. *Screenplay* Henri Simoun, Abraham Polonsky. *Dir Photog* Russell Metty. *Art Dir* Alexander Golitzen, George C. Webb. *Set Decor* John McCarthy, John Austin. *Titl Backgrounds* Graeme Ferguson. *Film Ed* Milton Shifman. *Mus* Don Costa. *Mus Supv* Joseph Gershenson. *Song:* "You Don't Know What Love Is" sung by Sheree North. *Sd* Waldon O. Watson, Lyle Cain, Ronald Pierce. *Asst Dir* Joseph Cavalier. *Unit Prod Mgr* Wes Thompson. *Makeup* Bud Westmore. *Hairstyles* Larry Germain. *Matte Supv* Albert Whitlock. *Dial Coach* Scott Hale.

Cast: Richard Widmark (*Det. Daniel Madigan*), Henry Fonda (*Commissioner Anthony X. Russell*), Inger Stevens (*Julia Madigan*), Harry Guardino (*Det. Rocco Bonaro*), James Whitmore (*Ch. Insp. Charles Kane*), Susan Clark (*Tricia Bentley*), Michael Dunn (*Midget Castiglione*), Steve Ihnat (*Barney Benesch*), Don Stroud (*Hughie*), Sheree North (*Jonesy*), Warren Stevens (*Ben Williams*), Raymond St. Jacques (*Dr. Taylor*), Bert Freed (*Ch. Det. Hap Lynch*), Harry Bellaver (*Mickey Dunn*), Frank Marth (*Lieut. James*

Price), Lloyd Gough *(Asst. Ch. Insp. Earl Griffin),* Virginia Gregg *(Esther Newman),* Tonia Machinga *(Rosita),* Rita Lynn *(Rita Bonaro),* Robert Granere *(Buster),* Henry Beckman *(Patrolman Philip Downes),* Woodrow Parfrey *(Marvin),* Dallas Mitchell *(Det. Tom Gavin),* Lloyd Haynes *(Patrolman Sam Woodley),* Ray Montgomery *(Detective O'Mara),* Seth Allen *(subway dispatcher),* Philippa Bevans *(Mrs. Hewitt),* Kay Turner *(Stella),* Diane Sayer *(Doreen),* Conrad Bain *(hotel clerk),* Ed Crowley *(man at precinct),* John McLiam *(Dunne),* William Bramley *(O'Brien),* Scott Hale *(ambulance driver).*

Crime drama. Source: Richard Dougherty, *The Commissioner* (Garden City, New York, 1962). In New York City's Spanish Harlem, police detectives Dan Madigan and Rocco Bonaro break into a sleazy apartment and arrest Barney Benesch, a hoodlum wanted for questioning by a Brooklyn precinct. Momentarily distracted by Benesch's nude girl friend, the two detectives are outwitted by Benesch, who escapes with their guns. When it is discovered that Benesch was wanted for homicide, Madigan and Bonaro are reprimanded by Police Commissioner Anthony X. Russell. Aside from this new problem, Russell is troubled by other matters: his married mistress, Tricia Bentley, has decided to end their relationship; a black minister, Dr. Taylor, is claiming that his teenaged son was subjected to brutality by racist policemen; and proof has been established that Russell's longtime friend and associate, Chief Inspector Kane, has accepted a bribe to protect a hangout for prostitutes. Irritated by the fact that Madigan and Bonaro broke the rules by working for another precinct, Russell gives the two men 72 hours to arrest Benesch. Despite the deadline, Madigan tries to spend some time with his wife, Julia, who is socially and sexually frustrated as a result of her husband's dangerous and time-consuming job. After Benesch shoots two policemen with Madigan's gun, the two detectives finally get a lead through bookie Midget Castiglione, who puts them in touch with Hughie, one of Benesch's pimps. Tracing Benesch to an apartment in Spanish Harlem, Madigan and Bonaro bring in a police cordon and order the killer to surrender. When he refuses, the two detectives rush the building and break down the door. In the exchange of gunfire, Madigan is fatally wounded before Bonaro can kill Benesch. Later, Russell tries to comfort Julia, but she accuses him of being a heartless administrator. As Russell leaves with Chief Inspector Kane, he tells him that tomorrow they will face the bribery problem together. *Detectives. Police. Hoodlums. Fugitives. Mistresses. Negroes. Clergymen. Bookies. Pimps. Widows. Manhunts. Murder. Infidelity. Racism. Police brutality. Bribery. Prostitution. Marriage. Guns. New York City— Spanish Harlem. New York City—Brooklyn.*

Note: Filmed on location in New York City and Los Angeles. Henri Simoun is a pseudonym for Howard Rodman.

MADIGAN'S MILLIONS (Italy/Spain)   F6.2983

L. M. Films–Lacy International Films–Hercules Cinematografica. *Dist* American International Pictures. 17 Dec **1969** [Detroit opening]. Sd; col (Movielab). 35mm. 77 min. *MPAA rating* G.

Pres by Westside International. *Prod* Sidney Pink. *Dir (see note)* Stanley Praeger, Giorgio Gentili, Dan Ash. *Screenplay* Jim Henaghan, José Luis Bayonas, Dan Ash. *Photog* Manuel Rojas. *Art Dir* Piero Filippone. *Film Ed* Antonio Ramírez. *Mus* Gregorio García Segura. *Prod Mgr* Angel Monis.

Cast: Dustin Hoffman *(Jason Fister),* Elsa Martinelli *(Vicky Shaw),* Cesar Romero *(Mike Madigan),* Gustavo Rojo, Franco Fabrizi, Fernando Hilbeck, Riccardo Garrone, Gérard Tichy, George Raft, Fernando Gilbert, José María Caffarel, Alfredo Mayo, Umberto Raho.

Crime comedy. Jason Fister, a U. S. Internal Revenue Service investigator, is sent to Rome to recover $1 million hidden by Mike Madigan, a gangster who was deported from the United States, fled to Rome with the million, and was murdered there by racketeers seeking the money. Rome police refuse to cooperate with Fister and threaten to arrest him if he persists in his investigation. Fister makes the acquaintance of Madigan's daughter, Vicky Shaw, who keeps secret from Fister her relationship with Madigan. (Fister believes that she was his mistress.) Vicky, who has a young child, permits Fister to sleep on her couch one night so that he might avoid his pursuers. The next morning Fister finds between the cushions a bloodstained apple with a key embedded in it, and he finds the money in Vicky's child's possession. Police apprehend the gangsters as they attempt to steal the money. After Vicky admits to Fister that she is Madigan's daughter, they decide to marry. *Gangsters. Revenue agents. Police. Deportation. Murder. Personal identity. Rome. United States—Internal Revenue Service.*

Note: Location scenes filmed in Madrid and Rome. Released in Spain in 1968 as *El millón de Madigan;* running time: 89 min; also known in Spain as *El testamento de Madigan.* Released in Italy as *Un dollaro per 7 vigliacchi.* U. S. sources credit Praeger as director; Spanish sources credit Gentili; and Italian sources credit Ash.

MADISON AVENUE   F6.2984

Twentieth Century–Fox Film Corp. 10 Jan **1962** [Los Angeles opening; c10 Dec 1961; LP21042]. Sd (Westrex); b&w. 35mm (CinemaScope). 94 min.

Prod-Dir Bruce Humberstone. *Screenplay* Norman Corwin. *Dir Photog* Charles G. Clarke. *Art Dir* Duncan Cramer, Leland Fuller. *Set Decor* Walter M. Scott, John Sturtevant. *Film Ed* Betty Steinberg. *Mus Comp & Cond* Harry Sukman. *Orch* Leo Shuken, Jack Hayes. *Song:* "Milk Song" Harry Harris. *Sd* Don McKay, Warren B. Delaplain, William Ward. *Asst Dir* Jack R. Berne, Eli Dunn, Harry M. Jones. *Script Supv* Isabel Blodgett. *Wardrobe* Truman Eli, Kathleen Dennis. *Makeup* Ben Nye. *Hairstyles* Helen Turpin. *Dial Coach* Rose Steinberg.

Cast: Dana Andrews *(Clint Lorimer),* Eleanor Parker *(Anne Tremaine),* Jeanne Crain *(Peggy Shannon),* Eddie Albert *(Harvey Ames),* Howard St. John *(J. D. Jocelyn),* Henry Daniell *(Stipe),* Kathleen Freeman *(Miss Haley),* David White *(Stevenson Brock),* Betti Andrews *(Miss Katie Olsen),* Jack Orrison *(Mayor of Bellefield),* Yvonne Peattie *(Miss Malloy),* Arline Hunter *(Miss Hom),* Doris Fesette, Michael Ford, The Sylte Sisters.

Drama. Source: Jeremy Kirk, *The Build-up Boys* (New York, 1951). Clint Lorimer, New York advertising executive, loses his job when his boss, J. D. Jocelyn, learns he is planning to steal a profitable dairy account and start his own business. Infuriated, Clint decides to have his revenge by promoting a small dairy, Cloverleaf, into a powerful force in the milk world. He persuades Peggy Shannon, a young journalist, to write about the firm; transforms Anne Tremaine, the dowdy, unsuccessful advertising executive who handles the Cloverleaf account, into an attractive and dynamic businesswoman; and inflates the ego of Harvey Ames, Cloverleaf's ineffectual president. All goes well until Peggy becomes tired of being used and writes an exposé of Clint's methods. Moreover, Anne, disillusioned about Clint's prospects as a bridegroom, spurns him. Clint then learns that a missile project he once worked on for J. D. has been reactivated, and he proves himself sufficiently clever to trick J. D. into reinstating him and to persuade Peggy to give him another chance. *Advertising executives. Journalists. Businesswomen. Employer-employee relations. Ambition. Revenge. Dairying. New York City.*

Note: Filmed in 1960.

THE MADMEN OF MANDORAS   F6.2985

San-S Productions. *Dist* Crown International Pictures. 13 Nov **1963** [San Francisco opening]. Sd; b&w. 35mm. 74 min.

Prod Carl Edwards. *Dir* David Bradley. *Screenplay* Richard Miles, Steve Bennett. *Orig Story* Steve Bennett. *Camera* Stanley Cortez. *Art Dir* Frank Sylos. *Film Ed* Leon Selditz. *Sd* Gordon Williams, Don Rogers. *Prod Mgr* Clark Paylow. *Makeup* Maurice Seiderman.

Cast: Walter Stocker *(Phil Daly),* Audrey Caire *(Kathy Daly),* Carlos Rivas *(Camine),* John Holland *(John Coleman),* Dani Lynn *(Suzanne),* Marshall Reed *(Frank Dvorak),* Nestor Paiva *(Police Chief Alaniz),* Scott Peters *(David Garrick),* Pedro Regas *(Padua),* Keith Dahle *(Tom Sharon),* Bill Freed *(Mr. H),* Hap Holmwood, Dick McHale, Chuck Beston.

Science fiction melodrama. American neurobiologist John Coleman discovers an antidote for nerve gas, and shortly afterwards, he mysteriously disappears along with one of his daughters, Suzanne. The only link with Coleman is a stranger who tried to see him shortly before his disappearance. Coleman's other daughter, Kathy, persuades her husband, Phil, to fly with her to Mandoras to look for her father when the stranger is killed and the address of a hotel on the Caribbean island of Mandoras is found in his pocket. Once on the island, they meet a native, Camine, who informs them that the island is controlled by former members of the German High Command who fled there after the collapse of the Third Reich. The Germans are led by the severed head of Adolf Hitler (which has been kept alive by means of artificial organs) and plan to conquer the world with nerve gas. Kathy disappears and Phil is arrested on a false charge of assassinating the minister of peace. He is taken to the palace of the president where he finds Coleman, both daughters, and the president being held prisoner by the Germans. Camine leads a revolt by local Mandorans, liberates the Americans, destroys the German stronghold, and kills the head of Hitler. *Biologists. Masterminds. Nazis. Americans in foreign countries. Missing persons. Exile. Assassination. Decapitation. Frameup. Filial relations. Revolts. Lethal gas. Caribbean. Adolf Hitler.*

Note: Working title: *The Return of Mr. H.*

MADRON   F6.2986

Zev Braun Productions–G. B. C.–Edric–Isracine Productions. *Dist* Four Star Excelsior Releasing Co. 16 Dec **1970** [Los Angeles opening]. Sd; col (Eastman Color). 35mm. 93 min. *MPAA rating* GP.

Prod Emanuel Henigman, Eric Weaver. *Exec Prod* Zev Braun. *Prod Exec* Alessandro Tasca. *Dir* Jerry Hopper. *Screenplay* Edward Chappell, Leo McMahon. *Story* Leo McMahon. *Photog* Marcel Grignon, Adam Greenberg. *Art Dir* Robert Ramsey. *Film Ed* Renzo Lucidi. *Mus* Riz Ortolani. *Song:* "Till Love Touches Your Life" Riz Ortolani, Arthur Hamilton. *Sung by* Richard

Williams, mus, Jan Daley. *Sd* Basil Fenton-Smith. *Asst Dir* Gus Agosti, Louis Goldman. *Prod Mgr* Mike Hartman.

Cast: Richard Boone (*Madron*), Leslie Caron (*Sister Mary*), Gabi Amrani (*Angel*), Chaim Banai (*Sam Red*), Paul Smith, actor 1 (*Gabe Price*), Aharon Ipale (*singer*), Yaakov Banai (*Sanchee*), Sami Shmueli (*Saba*), Mosko Alkalay (*Claude*), Avraham Pelta (*drygulcher*), Willy Gafni (*prospector*).

Western melodrama. After a band of Apaches massacres a wagon train of French Canadian nuns bound for Santa Fe, Sister Mary, the sole survivor, buries the dead and eventually meets up with gunslinger Madron. Impressed by her goodness, as well as by her ability to handle a gun, Madron accompanies her on the treacherous journey across the desert. Attacked by a group of Apaches led by Sam Red, Sister Mary frightens off the Indians and sews up Madron's wounds. To divert a band of outlaws, Madron tears off the front of Sister Mary's habit, then guns them down. Sister Mary wins over the survivor, Angel, by pointing a gun at him and Madron until they swear to become allies. As the trio makes its way across the desert Apaches follow. To mislead their pursuers Angel suddenly rides off. After another narrow escape from the Apaches, to comfort the distraught nun Madron makes love to her. The following morning, Sister Mary removes her coif and asks Madron to call her Antoinette. Learning of Angel's capture by the Apaches, Madron instructs Antoinette to continue to Santa Fe while he goes to Sam Red's camp to rescue their comrade. Seeing that Angel is being skinned alive, Madron shoots him to end his agony. The Apaches attack Madron, and he kills most of them, including Sam Red, before dying himself from a gunshot wound. Sister Mary hears the shots and realizes that Madron has sacrificed himself to save her, and she continues her journey. *Nuns. French Canadians. Apache Indians. Gunfighters. Massacres. Self-sacrifice. Torture. Celibacy. Wagon trains. Deserts. Santa Fe (New Mexico).*

Note: Location scenes filmed in the North Negev Desert and by the Dead Sea in Sodom, Israel.

THE MADWOMAN OF CHAILLOT (Great Britain)　　F6.2987

Commonwealth United Corp. *Dist* Warner Bros.-Seven Arts, Inc. 12 Oct **1969** [New York opening; c13 Oct 1969; LP40895]. Sd; col (Technicolor). 35mm (Panavision). 132 min. *MPAA rating* G.

Prod Ely Landau. *Exec Prod* Henry T. Weinstein. *Assoc Prod* Anthony B. Unger. *Dir* Bryan Forbes. *Dir* (see note) John Huston. *Screenplay* Edward Anhalt. *Adapt* Maurice Valency. *Photog* Claude Renoir, Burnett Guffey. *Art Dir* Georges Petitot. *Set Decor* Dario Simone. *Prod Dsgn* Ray Simm. *Titl* Robert Ellis. *Film Ed* Roger Dwyre. *Mus Comp & Cond* Michael J. Lewis. *Song:* "The Lonely Ones" Gil King, Michael J. Lewis. *Orch* Wally Stott. *Sd Ed* Janet Davidson. *Sd Rec* Bill Daniels. *Sd Re-rec* Gordon McCallum. *Asst Dir* Louis Pitzelé, Alain Bonnot. *Prod Mgr* Henri Jaquillard. *Cost* Rosine Delamare. *Makeup* Monique Archambault. *Hairstyles* Alex Archambault.

Cast: Katharine Hepburn (*Countess Aurelia*), Charles Boyer (*The Broker*), Claude Dauphin (*Dr. Jadin*), Edith Evans (*Josephine*), John Gavin (*The Reverend*), Paul Henreid (*The General*), Oscar Homolka (*The Commissar*), Margaret Leighton (*Constance*), Giulietta Masina (*Gabrielle*), Nanette Newman (*Irma*), Richard Chamberlain (*Roderick*), Yul Brynner (*The Chairman*), Donald Pleasence (*The Prospector*), Danny Kaye (*The Ragpicker*), Fernand Gravey (*police sergeant*), Gordon Heath (*folksinger*), Gerald Sim (*Julius*), Manuella Von Oppen (*newsgirl*), Gilles Segal (*deaf mute*), Gaston Palmer (*juggler*), Harriet Ariel, Catherine Berg, Henri Cogan, Christian Duvaleix, Jackie Farley, George Hilsdon, Sabine Lods, Jacques Marin, Joellina Smajda, Henri Virlojeux, Bernard Woringer.

Drama. Source: Jean Giraudoux, *La folle de Chaillot* (Paris opening: 22 Dec 1945). Countess Aurelia lives in the Chaillot district of Paris where she and her three friends, Constance, Gabrielle, and Josephine, indulge in their fantasies of life in the past. In a cafe near the countess' home, an international conspiracy is being formed by a group of financiers, military men, and a religious opportunist to drill for oil beneath the streets of Paris. Roderick, a pacifist student and the nephew of one of the conspirators, learns of their plans and tells Countess Aurelia, who at times confuses Roderick with her former lover. The countess and her friends take a dim view of this lust for money, and they formulate a plan to defeat the conspiracy. She approaches each of the conspirators and tells them that oil is beginning to seep into her cellar. A mock trial is conducted among the countess' friends; the defendants are convicted of excessive greed and condemned to death. When the conspirators arrive to inspect the oil seepage, Countess Aurelia locks them in the cellar and advises Roderick and his girl friend to take advantage of their love before it is too late. *Nobility. Eccentrics. Opportunists. Students. Fantasy. Conspiracy. Greed. Oil. Kangaroo courts. Paris.*

Note: Location scenes filmed in Paris and Nice. Opened in London in Oct 1969; running time: 145 min. Huston, the original director, was replaced by Forbes early in the filming.

MAEDCHEN IN UNIFORM (France/West Germany)　　F6.2988

Les Films Modernes-S. N. C.-CCC-Filmkunst. *Dist* Seven Arts Pictures, United Film Enterprises. Apr **1965**. Sd; b&w (see note). 35mm. 91 min.

Dir Geza Radvanyi. *Screenplay* Franz Höllering, F. D. Andam. *Camera* Werner Krien. *Asst Camera* Gerhard Krüger, Gerhard Girbig. *Decor* Emil Hasler, Walter Kutz. *Film Ed* Ira Oberberg. *Mus* Peter Sandloff. *Sd* Clemens Tütsch. *Asst Dir* Eva-Ruth Ebner. *Prod Dir* Helmut Ungerland. *Prod Mgr* Horst Götze, Heinz Springel. *Cost* Manon Hahn. *Wardrobe* Lisa Willweber, Mascha Markwordt, Anni Drkosch. *Makeup* Jupp Paschke, Anita Greil, Cilly Didzoneit, Heinz Stamm. *Prop* Kurt Lechler, Harry Freude.

Cast: Lilli Palmer (*Fräulein von Bernburg*), Romy Schneider (*Manuela von Mainhardis*), Therese Giehse (*headmistress*), Christine Kaufmann (*Mia*), Danik Patisson (*Edelgard*), Blandine Ebinger, Gina Albert, Sabine Sinjen, Marthe Mercadier, Paulette Dubost, Ginette Pigeon, Adelheid Seeck.

Drama. Source: Christa Winsloe, *Gestern und Heute* (Berlin opening: 16 Jun 1932). After the death of her mother, Manuela von Mainhardis is sent to a prestigious girls' finishing school presided over by a stern and militaristic headmistress. The only kindness Manuela receives is from Fräulein von Bernburg, a teacher who takes a special interest in Manuela and tries to help her adjust to the strict new environment. Soon Manuela's feelings for her teacher turn to devotion, and following the school play, Manuela gets drunk and confesses her love. The outburst causes her classmates to shun her, and the headmistress confines Manuela to her room while planning to expel her. When Manuela learns that Fräulein von Bernburg has decided to resign because of the trouble, Manuela tries to commit suicide. She is finally released from her room at the request of a visiting duchess who had known her mother, and the headmistress decides not to expel her. Nevertheless, Fräulein von Bernburg decides to leave the school. *Headmistresses. Students. Schoolteachers. Nobility. Adolescence. Lesbianism. Suicide. Boarding schools. Theater— Amateur.*

Note: Opened in Essen in Aug 1958 as *Mädchen in Uniform*; running time: 95 min; in Paris in Nov 1958 as *Jeunes filles en uniforme*. Filmed in Eastmancolor. Previously filmed in Germany in 1931 and released in the United States in 1932.

IL MAESTRO *see* **THE TEACHER AND THE MIRACLE**

MAEVA　　F6.2989

Umberto Bonsignori. *Dist* Cascade Films, Victoria Films, Times Film Corp. **1961**. Sd; col (Eastman Color). 35mm. 90 min. [Cut from 95 min.]

Prod-Dir Umberto Bonsignori. *Assoc Prod* Samuel Benson. *Narr* Maya Deren. *Photog* Alberto Baldecchi. *Film Ed* Umberto Bonsignori. *Mus* Teiji Ito. *Mus Supv* Sylvain & Mottet. *Songs:* "Vahine Tahiti," "Paia" *perf* by Drummers of Tahiti. *Song:* "The White Ship" sung by Augustine.

Cast: Tumata Teuiau (*Maeva*), Jean Kave (*Guido*), Oscar Spitz (*Pierre*), Poia (*girl*), Adienne de Joie (*narrator*), Lillian, Felicien.

Drama. Maeva, a beautiful Tahitian, grows up in a small fishing village where she tends the boats and nets with Kiro, a native boy. Maeva dreams of becoming his woman, but he goes away, leaving her lonely and unfulfilled. One day she is raped by a sailor, and soon after, she leaves the village to become a European painter's model. At the studio, Maeva meets Pierre, who sees her posing. Maeva seduces him, and they have a brief love affair, but he leaves her for another woman. She then begins frequenting the bars on the waterfront and having a series of reckless affairs. She meets Guido, who is kind to her at first, but like the other Europeans he soon leaves her. Realizing that she must go home, Maeva returns to her village and resumes her work with the fishing boats. At a native dance she meets Uira, who falls in love with her and asks her to be his woman. *Polynesians. Sailors. Painters. Models. Rape. Seduction. Promiscuity. Fishing villages. Tahiti.*

Note: Filmed on location in Tahiti. Also known as *Wahine, True Diary of a Wahine, True Diary of a Vahine, True Story of a Wahine, Pagan Hellcat, Maeva—Portrait of a Tahitian Girl*, and *Confessions of a Vahine*.

LA MAFFIA FAIT LA LOI *see* **MAFIA**

MAFIA (France/Italy)　　F6.2990

Panda Film-Les Films Corona. *Dist* American International Pictures. **1969**. Sd; col (Berkey-Pathé). 35mm. 98 min. *MPAA rating* M.

Prod Ermanno Donati, Luigi Carpentieri. *Exec Prod* Piero Donati. *Dir* Damiano Damiani. *Screenplay* Ugo Pirro, Damiano Damiani. *Dir Photog* Tonino Delli Colli. *Art Dir* Sergio Canevari. *Film Ed* Nino Baragli. *Mus* Giovanni Fusco. *Sd* Carlo Palmieri. *Cost* Marilu Carteny.

Cast: Claudia Cardinale (*Rosa Nicolosi*), Franco Nero (*Captain Bellodi*), Lee J. Cobb (*Don Mariano Arena*), Nehemiah Persoff (*Pizzuco*), Serge Reggiani (*Parrinieddu*), Rosanna Lopapero (*Caterina*), Gaetano Cimarosa (*Zecchinetta*).

Crime melodrama. Source: Leonardo Sciascia, *Il giorno della civetta* (Turin, 1961). While investigating the murder of a construction supplier in a Sicilian town, Captain Bellodi encounters a conspiracy of silence. Among those unwilling to testify are Rosa Nicolosi, whose husband has disappeared, and the taciturn Pizzuco, lieutenant of Don Mariano, Mafia kingpin. To discredit Rosa, the Mafia accuses her of adultery. Despite intimidation of witnesses and further murders, Bellodi learns that the crimes are related to a highway construction racket run by the Mafia. He also identifies the organization's hierarchy. Bellodi's success, however, disturbs his superiors and he is relieved of his duties. His place is taken by a less inquisitive family man. *Police. Murder. Slander. Road construction. Sicily. Mafia.*

Note: Opened in Paris in May 1969 as *La Maffia fait la loi.* Released in Italy in 1968 in Techniscope as *Il giorno della civetta;* running time: 113 min.

THE MAFIA GIRLS   F6.2991

Stage Four, Inc. *Dist* RAF Industries. 19 Oct **1969** [Tuscaloosa, Alabama, opening]. Sd; col (Eastman Color). 35mm. 74 min.

Prod Norman Senfield. *Dir* Ed Ross. *Screenplay* Bobby O'Donald. *Mus* Bobby O'Donald.

Cast: Anthony Allen *(Capozzi),* Marilyn Nordman *(Millie),* Cindy Stevens *(Rita),* Paul Stober *(Stitch),* Dolores Carlos *(Sherri),* Ruby Ross *(Jan),* Brenda Gibson *(Sonia),* Marcel De Lage *(Dubois),* Jack Spector *(Lassiter [Mr. Jeffreys?]).*

Crime melodrama. After a number of INTERPOL agents are murdered, five fellow officers, led by Agent Capozzi, disguise themselves in order to penetrate the crime syndicate responsible for the murders. They uncover the syndicate's Miami Beach organization, which blackmails politicians by setting them up with women who lure their victims into compromising situations, then secretly film their activities. After a shoot-out with police, the gang's sadistic ex-Nazi henchman, Stitch, cuts out the eye of syndicate head Jeffreys on his yacht. The leader's wife, Jan, then pushes Stitch into the ocean, where he is eaten by sharks. *Government agents. Gangsters. Politicians. Police. Murder. Disguise. Organized crime. Blackmail. Mutilation. Syndicates. Yachts. Miami Beach. INTERPOL. Mafia. Sharks.*

Note: Filmed in Miami.

MAFIOSO (Italy)   F6.2992

Compagnia Cinematografica Antonio Cervi–Dino De Laurentiis Cinematografica. *Dist* Zenith International Film Corp. 30 Jun **1964** [New York opening]. Sd; b&w. 35mm. 100 min.

Prod Antonio Cervi. *Dir* Alberto Lattuada. *Screenplay* Rafael Azcona, Marco Ferreri, Age & Scarpelli. *Story* Bruno Caruso. *Photog* Armando Nannuzzi. *Art Dir* Carlo Egidi. *Set Decor* Mario Ravasco. *Film Ed* Nino Baragli. *Mus (see note)* Piero Piccioni, Nino Rota. *Sd* Luciano Welisch. *Asst Dir* Aldo D'Angelo. *Prod Asst* Vana Caruso.

Cast: Alberto Sordi *(Antonio Badalamenti),* Norma Benguell *(Martha Badalamenti),* Cinzia Bruno *(Donatella),* Katiuscia Piretti *(Patricia),* Armando Thiné *(Dr. Zanchi),* Lilly Bistrattin *(Dr. Zanchi's secretary),* Gabriella Conti *(Rosalia Badalamenti),* Ugo Attanasio *(Don Vincenzo),* Carmelo Oliviero *(Don Liborio),* Francesco Lo Briglio *(Don Calogero),* Michèle Bally.

Crime drama. Antonio Badalamenti, supervisor in a factory in Milan, leaves with his wife and two daughters for a vacation in his native Sicily, taking along a package from his company manager to Don Vincenzo, an important man in Colanzano, Badalamenti's hometown. There is a joyous family reunion, but Badalamenti's wife is uneasy with the Sicilians. Badalamenti visits Don Vincenzo, for whom he was once an errand boy. He delivers the package and is invited on a hunting trip. When he arrives for the trip, Don Vincenzo reminds him of his indebtedness to him and asks Badalamenti to deliver a letter for him. He agrees and then is shut up in a crate and flown to the United States. Released from the crate, he finds himself among Italian-American gangsters. He delivers the letter, learns that he is selected to shoot a certain person, and is shown films to help him identify his victim. Horrified, he agrees to the murder, knowing that his wife and children will be unsafe if he refuses. Driven to a barbershop, he kills the man and then is immediately flown back to Sicily. He is repentent of his crime, but, knowing the Mafia law of "silence or death," he returns with his family to Milan and resumes his normal existence. *Factory workers. Gangsters. Vacations. Family life. Murder. Extortion. Barbershops. Sicily. Milan. New York City. Mafia.*

Note: Filmed on location in Sicily and New York City. Opened in Rome in Oct 1962 as *Il mafioso;* running time: 105 min.

THE MAGIC BOX *see* **THE GIRL WITH THE MAGIC BOX**

MAGIC BOY (Japan)   F6.2993

Toei Animation Studio Co. *For* Toei Co. *Dist* Metro-Goldwyn-Mayer, Inc. 13 Sep **1961** [Los Angeles showing; c24 Oct 1960; LP17365]. Sd; col (Magicolor). 35mm (Toeiscope). 83 min. [Also 75 min.]

Exec Prod Hiroshi Okawa. *Assoc Prod* Hideyuki Takahashi. *Dir* Akira Daikubara. *Screenplay* Dohei Muramatsu. *Orig Story* Kazuo Dan. *Anim Dir* Sanae Yamamoto. *Ch Anim* Akira Daikubara, Hideo Furusawa, Yasuji Mori,

Masao Kumagawa, Yasuo Otsuka. *Anim* Chikao Tera, Kazuko Nakamura, Shuji Konno, Masatake Kita, Daikichiro Kusube, Taku Sugiyama, Reiko Okuyama. *Art Supv* Reiji Koyama. *Photog* Seigo Otsuka, Mitsuaki Ishikawa. *Art Dir* Seigo Shindo. *Film Ed* Shintaro Miyamoto. *Mus Dir* Toru Funamura. *Titl Song* Fred Spielman, Janice Torre. *Sung by* Danny Valentino. *Arr & Cond by* Ray Ellis. *Sd Engr* Hisashi Kase. *Asst to the Prod* Teiji Yabushita.

Animated melodrama. Sasuke and his sister Oyu live in the mountains with their animal friends. Their peaceful existence is disturbed by a witch whose bandits roam the countryside, terrorizing villagers and animals. Sasuke consults Hakuunsai, a famous teacher of magic, to learn how to combat the witch's magic powers. While he is gone, Prince Sanada and his servant Miyoshi meet Oyu, and she tells them of the problems with the witch. The witch abducts Oyu, but Sasuke combines forces with the prince and the animals to rescue her and destroy the witch. *Royalty. Witches. Bandits. Brother-sister relationship. Magic. Abduction. Animals.*

Note: Released in Japan in 1960 as *Shonen Sarutobi Sasuke.*

THE MAGIC CHRISTIAN (Great Britain)   F6.2994

Grand Films. *Dist* Commonwealth United Entertainment, Inc. 11 Feb **1970** [New York opening]. Sd (RCA); col (Technicolor). 35mm. 95 min. *MPAA rating* M.

Prod Denis O'Dell. *Exec Prod* Henry T. Weinstein, Anthony B. Unger. *Dir* Joseph McGrath. *Screenplay* Terry Southern, Joseph McGrath, Peter Sellers. *Adtl Material* Graham Chapman, John Cleese. *Cartoon* Richard Williams Studio. *Dir Photog* Geoffrey Unsworth. *Camera Op* Peter MacDonald. *Art Dir* George Djurkovic. *Set Dresser* Peta Button. *Prod Dsgn* Assheton Gorton. *Film Ed* Kevin Connor. *Mus & Mus Dir* Ken Thorne. Song: "Come and Get It" Paul McCartney. Song: "Carry On to Tomorrow" sung by Tom and Pete. Song: "Rock of Ages" sung by Tom, Pete, and Mike. Song: "Something in the Air" John Keene. *Perf by* Thunderclap Newman. Song: "Mad About the Boy" Noel Coward. *Sung by* Yul Brynner. *Choreog* Lionel Blair. *Sd Ed* Brian Holland, ed. *Sd Rec* Peter Sutton. *Sd Rec-rec/Dub Mix* Gerry Humphreys. *Asst Dir* Roger Simons. *Prod Mgr* Victor Peck. *Location Mgr* David Griffith. *Cont* Margaret Unsworth. *Cost Dsgn* Vangie Harrison. *Makeup* Harry Frampton. *Hairstyles* Joyce James. *Sp Vis Eff* Wally Veevers. *Casting Dir* John Merrick. *Prop Master* Alfred Pegley.

Cast: Peter Sellers *(Sir Guy Grand),* Ringo Starr *(Youngman Grand),* Richard Attenborough *(Oxford coach),* Leonard Frey *(psychiatrist on ship),* Laurence Harvey *(Hamlet),* Christopher Lee *(Dracula),* Spike Milligan *(traffic warden),* Yul Brynner *(lady singer),* Roman Polanski *(man listening to lady singer),* Raquel Welch *(slave driver),* Isabel Jeans *(Aunt Agnes),* Caroline Blakiston *(Aunt Esther),* Wilfrid Hyde-White *(ship's captain),* Tom Boyle *("My Man Jeff"),* Terence Alexander *(mad major),* Peter Bayliss *(pompous toff),* Joan Benham *(socialite in Sotheby's),* Patrick Cargill *(auctioneer),* Graham Chapman *(Oxford stroke),* John Cleese *(director in Sotheby's),* Clive Dunn *(Sommelier),* Freddie Earlle *(Sol),* Fred Emney *(Fitzgibbon),* Kenneth Fortescue *(irate snob at Sotheby's),* Peter Graves, British *(interested Lord at ship's bar),* Patrick Holt *(Duke in Sotheby's),* David Hutcheson *(Lord Barry),* Hattie Jacques *(Ginger Horton),* John Le Mesurier *(Sir John),* Jeremy Lloyd *(Lord Hampton),* David Lodge *(ship's guide),* Victor Maddern *(hotdog vendor),* Ferdy Mayne *(Edouard),* Guy Middleton *(Duke of Mantisbriar),* Peter Myers, actor *(Lord Kilgallon),* Dennis Price *(Winthrop),* Robert Raglan *(Maltravers),* Graham Stark *(waiter),* Leon Thau *(engine room toff),* Frank Thornton *(police inspector),* Michael Trubshawe *(Sir Lionel),* Edward Underdown *(Prince Henry),* Michael Aspel, Michael Barratt, Harry Carpenter, W. Barrington Dalby, John Snagge, Alan Whicker *(television commentators).*

Comedy. Source: Terry Southern, *The Magic Christian* (New York, 1960). Sir Guy Grand, a wealthy eccentric who is disillusioned with mankind, adopts a young tramp, renames him Youngman Grand, and sets out to demonstrate to Youngman that people are easily influenced by money and will do anything to get it. First he makes a travesty of sportsmanship when he goes on a grouse hunt with a machine gun, a tank, and a flame thrower. During an evening at the theater the audience is scandalized when the actor playing Hamlet is bribed to perform a striptease. At an exclusive dinner club, Sir Guy hands out money as he repulsively stuffs food into his mouth and smears it on his face. Later, he fixes a heavyweight championship bout so that the boxers kiss each other instead of fighting. Then he bids outrageously on a piece of junk at a Sotheby's auction, causing an American couple to believe in the worth of the item and outbid him. Sir Guy plans the social event of the season, a cruise on the ocean liner *The Magic Christian.* The cruise becomes chaotic when men dressed as Dracula, King Kong, and a host of other offensive characters frighten the passengers. Believing the ship to be sinking, the passengers rush to the deck and discover that the boat never left the dock. Finally, Sir Guy prepares a vat of urine, manure, and blood for his last demonstration to Youngman. He empties a suitcase full of money into the vat; as the crowd begin diving into the foul mixture, Sir Guy and Youngman leave for the peaceful park where they first met. *Millionaires. Eccentrics. Tramps. Actors. Americans in foreign countries. Socialites. Greed. Hunting. Theater. Bribery. Gullibility. Striptease. Etiquette. Prizefighting. Disguise. Tanks (armored cars). Restaurants. Auctions. Ocean liners. "Hamlet". Dracula. King Kong.*

Note: Opened in London in Dec 1969.

MAGIC CHRISTMAS TREE   F6.2995
Holiday Pictures. 19 Dec **1964** [Seattle opening]. Sd; col. 35mm. 65 min.

Prod Diane Johnson, Chris Kroesen. *Dir* Richard C. Parish. *Screenplay* Harold Vaughn Taylor.

Cast: Chris Kroesen, Valerie Hobbs, Dick Parish, Charles Nix, Robert Maffei.

Fantasy. Three schoolboys encounter a witch. Attempting to rescue her cat, Chris, one of the students, falls from a tree and strikes his head. While unconscious, he dreams of a magical tree and ring, which endow him with supernatural strength. So empowered, he subdues an acquisitive giant, halts runaway fire engines and police cars, takes part in a chase, and saves the abducted Santa Claus. *Children. Witches. Magic. Abduction. Chases. Trees. Christmas. Santa Claus. Cats.*

Note: Filmed in and around Los Angeles.

THE MAGIC FEATURE see NO. 12

THE MAGIC FOUNTAIN   F6.2996
Allan David Productions. *Dist* Classic World Films, Davis Film Distributors. 9 Aug **1961** [Chicago opening]. Sd; col (Eastmancolor). 35mm (Ultrascope). 82 min. [See note.]

Prod-Dir Allan David. *Screenplay* John Lehmann. *Photog* Wolf Schneider. *Film Ed* Richard Hertel. *Mus Score* Jacques Belasco. *Titl Song* Steve Allen, Don George, mus. *Sd* Riva Studios. *Sp Eff* Weegee.

Cast: Peter Nestler (*Prince Alfred*), Helmo Kindermann (*Prince Frederick*), Josef Marz (*Gustavo, the dwarf*), Catherine Hansen (*Princess Kathryn*), Osman Ragheb (*Prince Hans*), Greear Wasson (*Gregory, the boy*), Erik Jelde (*King Wilhelm* [see note]), Cedric Hardwicke (*King Wilhelm/narrator*), Rolf von Nauckhoff (*Sir Phillip*), Buddy Baer (*voice of Big Benjamin*), Hans Conried (*voice of Otto the Owl*).

Fantasy. Source: Jakob Grimm and Wilhelm Grimm, "Das Wasser des Lebens". King Wilhelm's three sons, Hans, Frederick, and Alfred, seek the magic fountain, the waters of which will revive their dying father. In turn, the evil princes Hans and Frederick are turned into ravens when they tease Gregory, a dwarf who knows the fountain's secret. The fountain is in an enchanted castle guarded by Princess Kathryn. Noble Prince Alfred dispels the curse from the castle with his magic sword, but Alfred's brothers, restored at Alfred's request to human form, cast him in disrepute with the king. Nevertheless, Alfred proves himself; he regains his father's favor and marries the princess. All are reconciled. [In the second version, the villainous brothers are banished.] *Royalty. Brothers. Evildoers. Dwarfs. Magic. Reviviscence. Transmutation. Banishment. Fountains. Castles. Swords. Curses. Imaginary kingdoms. Ravens.*

Note: Filmed on location in the Black Forest, Bavaria. Erik Jelde originally portrayed King Wilhelm, but Sir Cedric Hardwicke, the narrator, replaced him in a different version released by Davis Film Distributors in May 1964; running times: 85 and 77 min.

THE MAGIC GARDEN OF STANLEY SWEETHEART   F6.2997
Metro-Goldwyn-Mayer, Inc. 26 May **1970** [New York opening; c19 May 1970; LP38088]. Sd; col (Metrocolor). 35mm. 117 min. [Copyright length: 112 min.] MPAA rating R.

Prod Martin Poll. *Assoc Prod* Robert T. Westbrook. *Dir* Leonard Horn. *Screenplay* Robert T. Westbrook. *Dir Photog* Victor Kemper. *Camera Op* Leo Lebowitz. *Set Decor* Leif Pedersen. *Prod Dsgn* Gene Callahan. *Film Ed* Nick Archer, Ted Chapman. *Mus Supv* Mike Curb. *Adtl Score & Cond* Jerry Styner. Songs: "Nobody Knows," "Sweet Gingerbread Man" Michel LeGrand, Alan Bergman, Marilyn Bergman. Song: "Nobody Knows" sung by Richie Havens. Songs: "Sweet Gingerbread Man," "Happy Together" sung by Mike Curb Congregation. Song: "Time To Make a Turn" Larry Wiegand. Sung by The Crow. Song: "Funny How It Happens" Jerry Styner. Perf by Stilroc. Songs: "Blood," "Tell Me a Story" comp & cond David Lucas. Song: "Water" David Lucas. Sung by Michael Greer. Song: "Magic Mountain" Jerry Goldsmith, War. Perf by Eric Burdon, War. Song: "Keep On Keepin' That Man" Dan Penn, Bobby Emmons. Sung by Angeline Butler. Song: "Sound of Love" Barry Gibb, Maurice Gibb, Robin Gibb. Perf by Angeline Butler. Song: "Peace on Earth" Bernie Schwartz. Perf by The Wheel. *Sd* Hal Watkins, Nat Boxer. *Mus Ed* Ed Norton. *Asst Dir* Burtt Harris. *Prod Mgr* Fred Caruso. *Asst to the Prod* Gloria Michel. *Script Supv* Roberta Hodes. *Cost Dsgn* Frank Thompson. *Makeup* Joe Cranzano. *Hairstyles* Robert Grimaldi. *Casting* Marion Dougherty, Vic Ramos.

Cast: Don Johnson (*Stanley Sweetheart*), Linda Gillin (*Shayne/Barbara*), Michael Greer (*Danny*), Dianne Hull (*Cathy*), Holly Near (*Fran*), Victoria

Racimo (*Andrea*), Brandon Maggart (*Dr. Arthur Osgood/man in café*).

Melodrama. Source: Robert T. Westbrook, *The Magic Garden of Stanley Sweetheart* (New York, 1969). Columbia University student Stanley Sweetheart meets Cathy during a language class and invites her to his apartment where she is at first shocked by his sloppiness, his antipathy towards his mother, and his pornographic underground movies. Cathy resists Stanley's initial attempt at seduction, stating that she is a virgin, but later she relents. Several days later, Cathy introduces Stanley to her plump roommate Fran, and he offers to make Fran the star of his next film. After a short filming session, Fran seduces him, and in the following weeks, Stanley is besieged by both Cathy and Fran. Seeking advice, he goes to see his hippie friend Danny, who advises him to adopt a carefree lifestyle. One evening, Danny and his bisexual friends Shayne and Andrea visit Stanley and Cathy, and they all smoke marijuana—Cathy, for the first time. A few days later, Cathy decides to leave him because his feelings for her are based only on sex. Stanley then takes Danny's advice and tries to fill the void left by Cathy with drugs and sex. At a party, he sees her, and she tells him that she has a more fulfilling relationship with Danny. Stanley then begins an affair with Shayne and Andrea, but after two weeks of group sex and drugs, Stanley realizes that neither woman can substitute for Cathy, and he decides to leave them. *Students. Motion picture directors. Hippies. Roommates. College life. Virginity. Seduction. Duplicity. Group sex. Bisexuality. Sex exploitation films. Marijuana. Drugs. New York City. Columbia University.*

Note: Filmed on location in New York City.

THE MAGIC LAND OF MOTHER GOOSE see SANTA VISITS THE MAGIC LAND OF MOTHER GOOSE

MAGIC MIRROR   F6.2998
Dist Stacey Distributors. ca 1970. Sd; col. 16mm. 61-81 min.

Sex film. No information about the precise nature of this film has been found. *Sexuality.*

MAGIC SPECTACLES   F6.2999
Dist Fairway-International Films. 23 Jun **1961** [Los Angeles showing]. Sd; col (Eastman Color). 35mm. 74 min.

Pres by Fred W. Krueger. *Prod-Writ* Arch Hall, Sr. *Dir* Bob Wehling. *Dir Photog* Vilis Lapenieks. *Film Ed* Alex Grasshoff.

Cast: Tommy Holden (*Dr. Paul Ner De Nude/Angus L. Farnsworth*), June Parr, Marilyn Brechtel (*Myra Farnsworth, see note*), Margo Mehling (*The Secretary*), Kay Cramer, Cindy Tyler, Danice Daniels, Jean Cartwright, Carla Olson (*The Go Go Go Go Girls*).

Comedy. Dr. Paul Ner De Nude, a Parisian scientist, finds an ancient Chinese formula for improving the vision of the aged and uses it to produce a pair of lenses that filter clothing from view. Centuries after Ner De Nude's death, Angus Farnsworth, a timid Hollywood advertising man finds the magic spectacles. Overwhelmed by his newfound power, he leaves his wife and drives away in his 1927 Flint automobile to become involved in a series of rare adventures in which he is able to view women in their undergarments. His fling comes to an end when his wife and the police catch up with him, and he discards the spectacles. *Scientists. Marriage. Voyeurism. Nudity. Magic. Timidity. Eyeglasses. Inventions.*

Note: Rereleased in 1964 as *Tickled Pink*. Also known as *Magical Spectacle.* Sources conflict in crediting the role of Myra Farnsworth.

THE MAGIC SWORD   F6.3000
Bert I. Gordon Productions. *Dist* United Artists. 28 Mar **1962** [Louisville, Kentucky, opening]. Sd; col (Eastman Color). 35mm. 80 min.

Prod-Dir-Story Bert I. Gordon. *Screenplay* Bernard Schoenfeld. *Photog* Paul C. Vogel. *Art Dir* Franz Bachelin. *Set Decor* George R. Nelson. *Film Ed* Harry Gerstad. *Mus* Richard Markowitz. *Sd* James Brock. *Asst Dir* Herbert E. Mendelson. *Prod Mgr* Herbert E. Mendelson. *Wardrobe* Oscar Rodriguez. *Makeup* Dan Striepeke. *Hairstyles* Lynn Burke. *Supv Sp Eff* Bert I. Gordon. *Asst Supv Sp Eff* Flora Gordon. *Sp Mechanical Eff* Milt Rice.

Cast: Basil Rathbone (*Lodac*), Estelle Winwood (*Sybil*), Gary Lockwood (*Saint George*), Anne Helm (*Princess Helene*), Liam Sullivan (*Sir Branton*), John Mauldin (*Sir Patrick*), Jacques Gallo (*Sir Dennis*), Leroy Johnson (*Sir Ulrich*), David Cross (*Sir Pedro*), Angus Duncan (*Sir James*), Taldo Kenyon (*Sir Anthony*), Maila Nurmi (*hag/intruder*), Jack Kosslyn (*ogre*), Lorrie Richards (*Anne*), Anne Graves (*Princess Laura*), Marlene Callahan (*Princess Grace*), Merritt Stone (*king*), Danielle De Metz (*French girl*), Nick Bon Tempi, Paul Bon Tempi (*Siamese twins*), Ted Finn, Angelo Rossitto (*dwarfs*), Richard Kiel (*pinhead*), Vampira.

Fantasy. When Princess Helene is abducted by the wicked magician Lodac in medieval England, George vows to rescue her. To this end the knight appeals to the witch Sybil, his stepmother, who provides him with magical sword, invincible armor, and enchanted horse. Accompanied by seven resurrected knights, George accepts the sorcerer's seven challenges. The witch, however, accidentally deprives her son of his supernatural powers, and he is captured by Lodac. After the champion's rescue by doll-sized victims of Lodac's black magic, Sybil assumes the form of a panther and kills the sorcerer. With his magic sword George slays the two-headed dragon and frees the imprisoned princess. *Royalty. Sorcerers. Witches. Stepmothers. Knighthood. Abduction. Rescue. Magic. Heroism. Metamorphosis. Reviviscence. Swords. Curses. Potions. Middle Ages. England. Saint George. Horses. Panthers. Dragons.*

Note: Working title: *St. George and the 7 Curses.*

THE MAGIC VOYAGE OF SINBAD (U.S.S.R.)   **F6.3001**

Mosfilm. *Dist* Filmgroup, Inc. caMar **1962** [Texas showing]. Sd; col. 35mm (Vistascope). 79 min.

Prod English Vers Art Diamond. *Assoc Prod English Vers* Jack Woods. *Dir* (see note) Alfred Posco. *Dir English Vers* James Landis. *Screenplay* Karl Isar. *Adapt English Vers* Francis Ford Coppola. *Photog* Frank Provor. *Camera* Konstantin Petrichenko. *Art Dir* Edward Kuman, Eva Disel. *Film Ed* George Stein. *Mus:* Selections From the Opera "Sadko" by Nikolai Andreevich Rimski-Korsakov. *Mus Arr & Supplemented by* Victor Sheblin. *Cond* G. Gamburg. *Songs English Vers* John Smich. *Vocals English Vers* Gino Marsili. *Dance Dir* Sergey Koren. *Sd* Victor Zorin. *Prod Mgr* D. Gershengorin. *Cost* O. Kruchinina. *Makeup* Jose Malar. *Sp Eff* Sidney Mulin.

Cast: Edward Stolar *(Sinbad [Sadko])*, Anna Larion *(Luberia [Lyubava])*, Maurice Troyan *(Trifon)*, Norman Malish *(Tanus [Vyshata])*, Robert Surow *(Hadabad [Ivashka])*, William Leon *(Cassim [Kuzma])*, Laurence Astan *(Prince Lal Bahari Day [maharajah])*, Irving Perev *(Abdalla [Timofey Larionovich])*, Eugene Krikol *(old merchant [Omelyan Danilovich])*, Stanley Martinson *(money lender [monk])*, Nord Fenin *(Viking leader [Varangian leader])*, Arnold Kaylor *(Neptune [tsar of the ocean])*, Olivia Viklandt *(Neptuna [tsarina of the ocean])*, Ellen Mysova *(Princess Morgiana [Princess Ilmen])*, Lucille Vertisya *(The Phoenix).*

Fantasy. Adapted from the bylina *Sadko.* Sinbad [originally the wandering minstrel Sadko] promises to aid the poverty-stricken people of Covasan [Novgorod] by finding the Phoenix, the bird of happiness. Wealthy local merchants refuse to finance his expedition, whereupon he turns for help to Princess Morgiana, a daughter of Neptune. She provides him with golden fish which enable him to finance the building of ships for the journey. Sinbad and his men visit the Vikings [Varangians], who prove hostile, and Sinbad captures their leader's white horse. In his search for the Phoenix Sinbad travels to Persia [India] and meets the evil Prince Lal Bahari Day, who challenges him to a chess game, wagering the Phoenix against the white horse. Sinbad wins but discovers that the Phoenix, endowed with the head of a beautiful woman, possesses hypnotic powers that lull men to sleep. Sinbad turns the Phoenix against the attacking armies of the vengeful prince and escapes with his men while the enemy sleeps. At sea, a storm overtakes them, and Sinbad, in an effort to calm the seas, throws himself overboard to repay the debt he owes to Neptune. At the bottom of the ocean, he is ordered to marry one of Neptune's daughters, but Princess Morgiana saves him, and he returns to Covasan. He tells the people that happiness is to be found at home. *Royalty. Vikings. Minstrels. Varangians. Poverty. Magic. Hypnotism. Self-sacrifice. Travel. Ships. Chess. India. Persia. Novgorod. Storms. Sinbad. Sadko. Imaginary kingdoms. Neptune. The Phoenix. Legendary characters. Mythological characters. Horses. Fish.*

Note: Released in the U.S.S.R. in Jan 1953 as *Sadko;* running time: 89 min. Integral Soviet version released in the U. S. in 1953 by Artkino Pictures as *Sadko.* The following are among those credited under anglicized names for English language version: Aleksandr Ptushko (Alfred Posco), K. Isayev (Karl Isar), F. Provorov (Frank Provor), Ye. Kumankov (Edward Kuman), Ye. Svidetelev (Eva Disel), V. Zorin (Victor Zorin), V. Shebalin (Victor Sheblin), S. Mukhin (Sidney Mulin), Sergey Stolyarov (Edward Stolar), Alla Larionova (Anna Larion), N. Malishyovskiy (Norman Malish), B. Surovtsev (Robert Surow), Mark Troyanovskiy (Maurice Troyan), Yu. Leonidov (William Leon), M. Astangov (Laurence Astan), O. Viklandt (Olivia Viklandt), Ye. Myshkova (Ellen Mysova), L. Vertinskaya (Lucille Vertisya), L. Fenin (Nord Fenin), S. Kayukov (Arnold Kaylor), I. Pereverzev (Irving Perev), S. Martinson (Stanley Martinson), and N. Kryuchkov (Eugene Krikol?). Mosfilm credited as Moss-Film for English language version.

THE MAGIC WEAVER (U.S.S.R.)   **F6.3002**

Gorky Film Studio. *Dist* Allied Artists. Sep **1965.** Sd; col. 35mm. 87 min.

Dir Aleksandr Rou. *Screenplay* Yevgeniy Shvarts. *Photog* Dmitriy Surenskiy. *Art Dir* Ye. Galey. *Mus* A. Volkonskiy. *Song Lyr* V. Lifshits. *Cond* A. Roytman. *Sd* Anatoliy Dikan. *Asst Dir* B. Kanevskiy. *Artistic Supv* L. Lukov. *Prod Mgr* B. Krakovskiy. *Sp Eff* L. Akimov, Arseniy Klopotovskiy, V. Nikitchenko.

Cast (see note): Mikhail Kuznetsov *(The Soldier)*, Ninel Myshkova *(Maria)*, Vitya Perevalov *(Ivanushka)*, Anatoliy Kubatskiy *(czar of the water)*, Olya Khachapuridze *(Alenushka)*, Georgiy Millyar *(Kvak)*, Vera Altayskaya *(Ttushka-Nepogodushka)*, L. Troitskiy *(Altyn Altynych)*, Aleksandr Khvylya

(Mudrets-molchalnik), N. Kondratyev, A. Alyoshin, A. Baranov, Valentin Bryleyev, N. Kuznetsov, Konstantin Nemolyayev, V. Pitsek, K. Starostin, E. Traktovenko, M. Shcherbakov.

Fantasy. Based on Russian folk tales. A good-hearted soldier happily returns homeward after many years of military service. He walks through the birch forest, meeting animal friends as he goes, and rescues a bear from a trap. The soldier meets a little boy, Ivanushka, whose mother, Maria, a weaver of marvelous skill, has been kidnaped by the czar of the water. The czar has placed Maria under lock and key and forces her to weave day and night. The soldier and Ivanushka enter the underwater kingdom; and at last, with the help of the czar's granddaughter, Alenushka, they outwit the czar and rescue Maria. *Soldiers. Children. Goblins. Weavers. Royalty. Grandfathers. Motherhood. Abduction. Magic. Forests. Imaginary kingdoms. Animals. Bears.*

Note: Released in the U.S.S.R. in Mar 1960 as *Marya-iskusnitsa;* running time: ca78 min. May also be known as *Maria, the Wonderful Weaver.* Role names for U. S. release version unavailable.

THE MAGIC WORLD OF TOPO GIGIO (THE ITALIAN MOUSE) (Italy)   **F6.3003**

Jolly Film–Cinecidi–Compagnia Perego Telecast. *Dist* Columbia Pictures. 25 Sep **1965** [Boston opening; c1 Apr 1965; LP31743]. Sd; col (Eastman Color by Pathé). 35mm. 75 min.

Prod English Vers Richard Davis. *Dir English Vers* Luca De Rico. *Dir Italian Vers* Federico Caldura. *Screenplay* Mario Faustinelli, Guido Stagnaro, Maria Perego. *Italian Vers* Federico Caldura. *Creator* Maria Perego. *Anim Topo Gigio* Maria Perego. *Anim Rosy* Annabella Spadon. *Anim Giovannino* Grazia Curti. *Other Anim* Emanuele Pagani, Emy Ricciotti. *Dir Photog* Giorgio Battilana. *Scene Photog* Renato Sardini. *Camera* Luigi Vettore. *Sets* Mario Milani. *Film Ed* Franco Alessandro. *Mus* Armando Trovajoli. *Songs:* "The Daughter of the King," "The Butterfly" Aldo Rossi. *Sd* Giuseppe Donata. *Asst Dir* Grazia Grossi. *Dir Prod* Franco Serino. *Ed Sec* Sandra Perego. *Cost* Sandro Negri. *Makeup* Giuseppe Colla. *Optical Eff Supv* Ettore Catallucci. *Dial Dir* Terry Van Tell.

Voices: Peppino Mazzulo *(Topo Gigio)*, Ermanno Roveri, Ignazio Colnaghi, Federica Milani, Armando Benetti, Ignazio Dolce, Milena Zini, Carlo Delfini.

Animated puppet film. The Italian mouse Topo Gigio builds a rocket which he hopes to fly to the moon with his friends Rosy and a cowardly worm, Giovannino. Instead, the rocket lands in an amusement park, where Topo and his friends perform for a friendly puppeteer. The audience is delighted, and the magician, whose own show is next door, loses his audience to Topo. Angered, the magician hypnotizes and kidnaps Rosy, but Topo and Giovannino find out how the magician performs his tricks and ruin them so that he makes a fool of himself. Rosy is then rescued, and the three friends escape. [An alternative ending has Topo persuading the magician to change his ways and join the puppeteer in entertaining the children.] *Puppeteers. Magicians. Hypnotism. Abduction. Rockets. Amusement parks. Puppets. Topo Gigio. Mice. Worms.*

Note: Released in Italy in Dec 1961 as *Le avventure di Topo Gigio;* running time: 85 min.

LES MAGICIENNES *see* **DOUBLE DECEPTION**

THE MAGNIFICENT CONCUBINE (Hong Kong)   **F6.3004**

Shaw Brothers (H. K.) Ltd. *Dist* Frank Lee International. 31 Jan **1964** [Honolulu, Hawaii, opening]. Sd; col. (Eastmancolor). 35mm (ShawScope). 97 min.

Prod Runme Shaw. *Exec Prod* Doven Chow. *Dir* Li Han-hsiang. *Screenplay* Wang Chih-po. *Photog* T. Nishimoto. *Film Ed* Chiang Hsing-ling. *Mus & Song* Wang Shun.

Cast: Li Li-hua *(Yang Kwei Fei)*, Yen Chuan *(Emperor Ming Huang)*, Chao Lei *(killer)*, Li Hsiang-chun *(Mei)*, Yang Chih-ching *(Yang Kuochung)*, Ku Wen-tsung, Ho Ping, Lin Ching, Weng Mu-lan, Lily Mo Chau.

Historical drama. In 8th-century China the beloved T'ang emperor Ming Huang appoints as prime minister Yang Kuochung, the corrupt brother of his favorite concubine, Yang Kwei Fei. When his concubine leaves the court because of jealousy, the emperor follows her and their affection is renewed. Yang Kuochung suppresses reports of provincial uprisings until the besieged court is forced to flee to another city. He also withholds provisions and wages from the palace guard. Disgruntled, the guard murders the rapacious official and demands the death of his sister. The concubine is found caring for the ailing emperor. In return for permission to continue her ministrations, Yang Kwei Fei promises to kill herself upon Ming Huang's recovery. The concubine honors her promise, leaving the emperor disconsolate. *Mistresses. Prime ministers. Guards. Nepotism. Political corruption. Uprisings. Suicide. Assassination. Jealousy. China—History—T'ang Dynasty. Ming Huang (Hsüan-tsung).*

Note: Produced in Hong Kong in 1962 as *Yang Kwei Fei;* running time: 103 min.

THE MAGNIFICENT CUCKOLD (France/Italy)　　　F6.3005

Sancro Film–Copernic Films. *Dist* Continental Distributing, Inc. 19 Apr **1965** [New York opening]. Sd; b&w. 35mm. 117 min.

Prod Alfonso Sansone, Henryk Chroscicki. *Dir* Antonio Pietrangeli. *Screenplay* Diego Fabbri, Ruggero Maccari, Ettore Scola, Stefano Strucchi. *Photog* Armando Nannuzzi. *Art Dir* Maurizio Chiari. *Film Ed* Eraldo Da Roma. *Mus* Armando Trovajoli. *Prod Supv* Nicolo Pomilia. *Cost* Maurizio Chiari. *Miss Cardinale's Gowns* Nina Ricci. *English Subtitl* Herman G. Weinberg.

Cast: Claudia Cardinale *(Maria Grazia Artusi)*, Ugo Tognazzi *(Andrea Artusi)*, Bernard Blier *(Corna d'Oro)*, Michèle Girardon *(Christiana)*, Salvo Randone *(Belisario)*, José-Luis de Vilallonga *(presidente)*, Gian Maria Volontè *(assessore)*, Paul Guers *(Gabriele)*, Philippe Nicaud *(doctor)*, Susy Andersen *(Wanda)*, Alfonso Sansone, Ettore Mattia *(guests)*, Brett Halsey, Jean Claudio.

Comedy. Source: Fernand Crommelynck, *Le cocu magnifique* (Paris opening: 18 Dec 1920). Andrea Artusi is a successful hat manufacturer who is proud of his popular and beautiful wife, Maria Grazia. Despite his happy home life, he is drawn into an extra-marital affair with Christiana, a respected married woman. So clever is Christiana at arranging their trysts and so cunning is she at deceiving her husband that Andrea soon begins to wonder whether Maria Grazia is similarly disloyal. Becoming increasingly suspicious, he accuses Maria Grazia of being unfaithful and demands to know the name of her secret love. Bored with his jealous rages, Maria Grazia arbitrarily identifies an antique dealer, Gabriele, as her paramour. Outraged, Andrea leaps into his car, sets out to confront the innocent Gabriele, but instead crashes into a stone wall. During his convalescence, he monitors his wife's telephone calls and thus hears her apologize to Gabriele for involving him in the deception. His confidence in Maria Grazia restored, Andrea is once more a contented husband—so content, in fact, that he is oblivious to the fact that Maria Grazia has entered into a romantic liaison with the young doctor who treated him. *Businessmen. Antique dealers. Physicians. Cuckolds. Marriage. Infidelity. Jealousy. Eavesdropping. Automobile accidents.*

Note: Opened in Rome in Nov 1964 as *Il magnifico cornuto*; running time: 123 min; in Paris in Feb 1965 as *Le cocu magnifique.*

MAGNIFICENT SINNER (France)　　　F6.3006

Speva Films. *Dist* Film–Mart, Inc. 24 Apr **1963** [New York opening]. Sd; col (Eastmancolor). 35mm. 91 min.

Prod Michel Safra. *Assoc Prod* Henri Baum. *Dir* Robert Siodmak. *Screenplay* Charles Spaak. *Dial* Georges Neveux. *Photog* Michel Kelber. *Art Dir* Jean d' Eaubonne. *Film Ed* Louisette Hautecoeur, Henri Taverna. *Mus* Joseph Kosma. *Sd Dir* Antoine Petitjean.

Cast: Romy Schneider *(Katia)*, Curt Jurgens *(Alexander II)*, Pierre Blanchar *(Koubaroff)*, Monique Mélinand *(Tsarina Maria)*, Antoine Balpêtré *(Kilbatchich)*, Françoise Brion *(Sophie)*, Jacqueline Marbaux, Alain Saury, Michel Bouquet, Bernard Dhéran, Hubert Noël, Gabrielle Dorziat, Yves Barsacq.

Historical drama. Source: Lucile Decaux, *Katia, le démon bleu du tsar Alexandre* (Paris, 1938). Katia, daughter of an impoverished nobleman, boasts to her classmates of her acquaintance with Tsar Alexander II; and when he unexpectedly visits her boarding school, he is so struck by her beauty and charm that he confirms her story. The tsarina becomes aware of the affair and permits Katia to be brought to St. Petersburg. Alexander, aware of the need for political changes, confides his aspirations for social reform to Katia; and after the tsarina dies and he and Katia marry, Alexander plans to present to Katia the proclamation of the new constitution. A few days before the coronation, however, revolutionists unaware of the impending reforms throw a bomb at the tsar's carriage, and Alexander dies in Katia's arms. *Nobility. Royalty. Revolutionaries. Infidelity. Marriage. Social reform. Assassination. Boarding schools. Saint Petersburg. Alexander II (Russia). Yekaterina Mikhaylovna Dolgorukova. Maria Fëdorovna.*

Note: Filmed in West Germany. Opened in Paris in Jan 1960 as *Katia*; running time: 93 min. Alternative title: *Une jeune fille, un seul amour.* U. S. prerelease title: *Adorable Sinner.*

THE MAGNIFICENT TRAMP (France/Italy)　　　F6.3007

Filmsonor–Intermondia Films–Cinetel–Pretoria Film–Titanus. *Dist* Cameo International Pictures. 24 Apr **1962** [New York opening]. Sd; b&w. 35mm. 76 min.

Pres by William Shelton. *Prod* Jean-Paul Guibert. *Dir* Gilles Grangier. *Screenplay* Albert Valentin, Michel Audiard, Gilles Grangier. *Scen* Albert Valentin. *Dial* Michel Audiard. *Orig Idea* Jean Moncorgé. *Dir Photog* Louis Page. *Art Dir* Jacques Colombier. *Film Ed* Jacqueline Thiédot. *Mus* Jean Prodromidès. *Ch Sd* Pierre Calvet. *Prod Mgr* Claude Hauser.

Cast: Jean Gabin *(Archimède)*, Darry Cowl *(Arsène)*, Bernard Blier *(Pichon)*, Julien Carette *(Félix)*, Paul Frankeur *(Grégoire)*, Jacqueline Maillan *(Marjorie)*, Dora Doll *(Madame Pichon)*, Noël Roquevert *(retired*

---

commandant), Albert Dinan *(restaurateur)*, Gaby Basset *(Madame Grégoire)*, Bernard Lajarrige.

Comedy-drama. Archimède is a Paris *clochard* whose peaceful abode in a large building under construction is suddenly disturbed by the din of pneumatic drills and the appearance of Félix, another *clochard*. With winter approaching, he decides that it is time to move on to more suitable quarters, such as a nice warm jail cell. After starting a riot in a local bistro, he is outraged when he receives only an 8-day sentence. Following his release, he creates several more disturbances but fails to get himself arrested. Félix then teaches him the art of stealing purebred dogs and returning them for a reward. This proves to be quite profitable until Arsène, an overenthusiastic colleague, exposes the game. Archimède decides to fulfill his dream of spending the winter on the Riviera. *Tramps. Upper classes. Theft. Rewards. Jails. Bistros. Winter. Paris. Riviera. Dogs.*

Note: Opened in Paris in Apr 1959 as *Archimède, le clochard*; running time: 86 min (cut to 79 min); in Rome in Sep 1959 as *Archimede, le clochard*; running time: ca85 min. Jean Moncorgé is the real name of Jean Gabin.

IL MAGNIFICO CORNUTO see THE MAGNIFICENT CUCKOLD

THE MAGOICHI SAGA (Japan)　　　F6.3008

Daiei Motion Picture Co. Apr **1970** [Los Angeles showing]. Sd; col (Eastmancolor). 35mm (Daiei Scope). 95 min.

Dir Kenji Misumi. *Screenplay* Ryuzo Kikushima. *Story* Ryotaro Shiba. *Photog* Kazuo Miyagawa. *Art Dir* Yoshinobu Nishioka. *Mus* Masaru Sato.

Cast: Kinnosuke Nakamura *(Magoichi Saika)*, Komaki Kurihara *(Komichi)*, Kojiro Hongo *(Priest Shinso)*, Katsuo Nakamura *(Tokichiro Kinoshita)*, Shintaro Katsu *(Lord Nobunaga Oda)*, Yoko Namikawa *(Princess Kano)*, Eiko Azusa.

Action melodrama. During a period of civil wars, Lord Nobunaga Oda gains control of nearly all Japan. Tokichiro Kinoshita, one of Lord Nobunaga's vassals, attempts to enlist the aid of Magoichi Saika and his 3,000 gunners to maintain Lord Nobunaga's control. Magoichi is in love with a woman who he thinks is Lord Nobunaga's sister and whose face he has never seen. As an inducement to Magoichi to fight on Lord Nobunaga's side, Tokichiro Kinoshita offers to Magoichi Princess Kano, a distant relative of Lord Nobunaga's, as he actually has no sisters. Believing that Princess Kano is the woman he loves, Magoichi pledges his loyalty to Lord Nobunaga, only to learn he has been tricked. In revenge, he promises his support to the enormously influential priest-warriors of Honganji Temple in overthrowing Lord Nobunaga. Ultimately Lord Nobunaga is assassinated by one of his vassals, while Magoichi finds that the woman he had sought is Komichi, sister of Shinso, one of the Honganji priests. *Nobility. Priests. Warlords. Royalty. Mercenaries. Duplicity. Revenge. Assassination. Revolts. Japan—History—Period of civil wars 1480-1568.*

Note: Released in Japan in Sep 1969 as *Shirikurae Magoichi.*

THE MAGUS (Great Britain)　　　F6.3009

Blazer Films. *Dist* Twentieth Century–Fox Film Corp. 10 Dec **1968** [New York opening; c10 Dec 1968; LP36447]. Sd (Westrex); col (DeLuxe). 35mm (Panavision). 116 min.

Prod John Kohn, Jud Kinberg. *Dir* Guy Green. *Screenplay* John Fowles. *Dir Photog* Billy Williams. *Camera Op* David Harcourt. *Art Dir* William Hutchinson. *Asst to Art Dir* Franco Fumagalli. *Prod Dsgn* Don Ashton. *Main Titl* Maurice Binder. *Film Ed* Max Benedict. *Mus Comp & Cond* John Dankworth. *Orch* David Lindup. *Sd Rec* Cyril Collick, Hugh Strain. *Dub Ed* James Shields. *Asst Dir* David Tringham. *Prod Supv* Frank Sherwin Green. *Cont* Kay Rawlings. *Cost* Anthony Mendleson. *Wardrobe* Brian Owen-Smith, Eve Faloon. *Makeup* Charles Parker, Michael Morris. *Hairdresser* Stephanie Kaye. *Constr Mgr* Dick Frift.

Cast: Michael Caine *(Nicholas Urfe)*, Anthony Quinn *(Maurice Conchis)*, Candice Bergen *(Lily)*, Anna Karina *(Anne)*, Paul Stassino *(Meli)*, Julian Glover *(Anton)*, Takis Emmanuel *(Kapetan)*, George Pastell *(Andreas, the priest)*, Daniele Noel *(Soula)*, Jerome Willis *("false" German officer)*, Ethel Farrugia *(Maria)*, Andreas Malandrinos *(goatherd)*, George Kafkaris *(2d partisan)*, Anthony Newlands *(party host)*, Stack Constantino *(3d partisan)*, Roger Lloyd Pack *(young Conchis)*, Corin Redgrave *(Captain Wimmel)*.

Drama. Source: John Fowles, *The Magus* (Boston, 1965). Nicholas Urfe leaves London to accept a teaching position at a boys' school on the Greek island of Phraxos. He recalls breaking with his mistress, Anne, a stewardess, after which he discarded her talisman, a crystal paperweight in which a flower is embedded. Upon arrival he is greeted by a fellow faculty member, who shows him to his room and informs him that his predecessor committed suicide. In the desk he finds a sheet of paper on which is inscribed the phrase "waiting room." He later finds a villa, the gate of which is similarly emblazoned. Its mysterious owner, 70-year-old Maurice Conchis, invites him to visit the next weekend. In the intervening time, Nicholas learns that the estate belongs to a

Dr. Lambros and is shown the tombstone of a man named Conchis who died in 1944. While a guest of Conchis, Nicholas stakes his life on a throw of dice but refuses to pay, thereby winning, according to Conchis' arcane logic. The host then relates the tragic story of his youthful romance with Lily, who, disappointed by Conchis' refusal to enlist at the start of World War I, died shortly thereafter. Nicholas, therefore, is puzzled to see her, apparently alive and impossibly young. By way of explanation, Conchis asserts that he is the psychiatrist, Dr. Lambros, and Lily, his patient. Lily, however, insists that she is an actress, Conchis a filmmaker, and Nicholas an ignorant participant. After an idyllic weekend with Anne in Athens, Nicholas returns to Phraxos, where he receives news of the stewardess' suicide. He is then drawn into a drama representing Conchis' dilemma during World War II, when, as mayor of his village, he was given the choice of beating three partisans to death or sacrificing 80 hostages. Thereafter, Nicholas finds himself on trial, accused by Conchis of egotism. After seeing Lily in a pornographic film, Nicholas is ordered to whip her but cannot bring himself to mete out punishment. Awakening, he is told by Conchis that he has attempted suicide, and that the game is over. Rushing to the villa, Nicholas finds it abandoned, save for the archaic statue of a goddess. Beside the sculpture is Anne's talisman; in the distance, Nicholas espies Anne herself. *Magicians. Schoolteachers. Airline stewardesses. Psychiatrists. Motion picture directors. Nazis. Hostages. Mayors. Suicide. Fantasy. Gambling. Death. Trials. Village life. Motion pictures. Sex exploitation films. Islands. Talismans. World War I. World War II. Greece. Athens.*

Note: Location scenes filmed in Spain. Opened in London in Nov 1969. Working Title: *The God Game.*

MAHANAGAR see **THE BIG CITY**

THE MAID AND THE MARTIAN see **PAJAMA PARTY**

MAID FOR MURDER (Great Britain)　　　　　　　　　**F6.3010**
Asher Brothers Productions. *For* Anglo–Amalgamated Film Distributors. *Dist* Janus Films. Mar **1963**. Sd; b&w. 35mm. 89 min.

Prod Jack Asher, Robert Asher. *Dir* Robert Asher. *Screenplay* John Waterhouse. *Dir Photog* Jack Asher. *Camera Op* Cecil Cooney. *Camera Focus* Dennis Lewiston. *Art Dir* John Stoll. *Set Dresser* Josie Macavin. *Draughtsman* John Graysmark. *Film Ed* Gerry Hambling. *1st Asst Ed* Don Ranasinghe. *2d Asst Ed* Michael Clifford. *Mus Comp & Cond* Philip Green. *Lyr* Sonny Miller. *Sd Rec* Gerry Turner. *Sd Camera Op* Mickey Hickey. *Sd Boom Op* David Bowen. *Dub Ed* James Groom. *1st, 2d & 3d Asst Dir* Gerry O'Hara, Richard Coward, Richard Gill. *Prod Supv* Fred A. Swann. *Prod Sec* Ann Guttridge. *Cont* Joan Davis. *Wardrobe Dsgn* Anthony Mendleson. *Wardrobe Mistress* Eileen Sullivan. *Makeup* Michael Morris. *Hairdresser* Pearl Orton. *Still Photog* Charles Trigg. *Prod Buyer* Bill Isaacs.

Cast: Bob Monkhouse (*Francis Oberon*), Alfred Marks (*Douglas Oberon*), Hattie Jacques (*Miss Richards*), Anna Karina (*Toni*), Dennis Lotis (*Gilbert*), Graham Stark (*Arnold*), Clive Dunn (*chemist*), Hugh Lloyd (*Macdonald*), Peter Butterworth (*doctor*), Harry Locke (*stationmaster*).

Comedy. Source: Ian Stuart Black, *We Must Kill Toni* (London opening: 29 Jun 1954). The two impoverished Oberon brothers, Francis and Douglas, learn that their grandmother has left her fortune to Toni, a cousin residing in Corsica. Expecting Toni's arrival and determined to get the money for themselves, they are relieved when a formidable visitor identifies herself as Miss Richards of *True Woman* magazine rather than the cousin they are awaiting. When Toni does arrive, she is so beautiful that, since both brothers are willing and eager to marry her, murdering her becomes the obvious alternative. Toni, however, with Miss Richards' aid, skillfully thwarts the designs of the would-be assassins. As she bids them farewell, Toni informs them that she and Gilbert, her longtime Corsican butler, will be married. *Brothers. Cousins. Reporters. Butlers. Poverty. Inheritance. Murder. Marriage.*

Note: Opened in London in Mar 1962 as *She'll Have To Go.*

THE MAID STORY (Japan)　　　　　　　　　　　　**F6.3011**
Toho Co. May **1964** [Los Angeles showing]. Sd; col? 35mm. [Feature film, length unknown.]

Cast: Hisaya Morishige, Chikage Awashima, Nobuko Otowa, Keiko Awaji. No information about the nature of this film has been found.

Note: Original title and release undetermined.

THE MAIDEN (France)　　　　　　　　　　　　　　**F6.3012**
Société Française des Films Alfred Rode. *Dist* Green-Roth Film Enterprises. 2 Aug **1961** [New York showing]. Sd; b&w. 35mm. 90 min.

Prod-Dir Alfred Rode. *Assoc Prod* Maurice Saurel. *Orig Screenplay* Jacques Companeez. *Dial* Louis Martin. *Adapt* Jacques Companeez, Louis Martin. *Dir Photog* Marc Fossard. *Camera* Michel Villet. *Art Dir* Robert Bouladoux. *Film Ed* Louisette Hautecoeur. *Mus* Roger-Roger. *Sd* Robert Teisseire. *Asst Dir* Jean Bastia. *Prod Mgr* Jean Feix. *Prod Sec* Gilberte Graillot. *Script Girl* Rosy Jegou. *Makeup* Jean-Jacques Chanteau. *Still Photog* Robert Joffré.

Cast: Claudine Dupuis (*Arlette*), Jean Gaven (*Michaud*), Dany Carrel (*Marie-Claude*), Philippe Nicaud (*Philippe*), Dora Doll (*Catherine*), Robert Berri (*Monsieur Jo*), Claude Godard (*Sonia*), Jean Tissier (*Albert*), Jacqueline Noëlle (*Bigoudi*), Jacques Morel (*Mejean*), Jean Brochard (*Alfandari*), Julien Carette, Paul Demange, Colette Brumaire, José Lopez.

Drama. Recently having been released from jail, Arlette returns to her job as a singer at the Rainbow, a nightclub in Montmartre. Once again she enters the hectic life of the "midnight dancers": afternoon rehearsals and life at the small hotel where she lives with other performers, many of whom are striptease artists. Soon, however, she becomes the unwitting object of three rival groups seeking her former lover Esposito's stolen loot. Michaud, a young police agent, poses as an underworld figure and tries to ingratiate himself with her. Marie-Claude is hired by the insurance company to join the revue at the Rainbow and becomes friends with Arlette. And Philippe is hired by an underworld gang, whose leader is the owner of the Rainbow, to pose as a wealthy man-about-town and pretend to fall in love with Arlette. Unplanned, however, is Philippe's growing attachment to Marie-Claude; he falls in love with her in earnest and decides to reform, and the victimized Arlette is poisoned by her underworld boss. *Singers. Stripteasers. Police. Insurance agents. Gangsters. Nightclub owners. Imposture. Theft. Murder. Nightclubs. Poisoning. Paris—Montmartre.*

Note: Location scenes filmed in Paris. Opened in Paris as *La môme Pigalle* in Nov 1955; running time: 100 min.

A MAIDEN FOR A PRINCE (France/Italy)　　　　　　**F6.3013**
Fair Film–Orsay Films. *Dist* Royal Films International. 18 Oct **1967** [Philadelphia opening]. Sd; col (Technicolor). 35mm (Techniscope). 92 min.

Prod Mario Cecchi Gori. *Exec Prod* Luciano Perugia. *Dir-Story* Pasquale Festa Campanile. *Screenplay* Giorgio Prosperi, Stefano Strucchi, Ugo Liberatore, Pasquale Festa Campanile. *Photog* Roberto Gerardi. *Art Dir* Pier Luigi Pizzi. *Film Ed* Otello Colangeli, Ruggero Mastroianni. *Mus* Luis Enriquez Bacalov. *Sd* Mario Faraoni, Primiano Muratori. *Asst Dir* Gabriele Palmieri. *Prod Mgr* Mario De Biase. *Cost* Pier Luigi Pizzi. *Makeup* Nilo Jacoponi, Otello Sisi. *Hairstyles* Ada Palombi.

Cast: Vittorio Gassman (*Prince Don Vincenzo Gonzaga*), Virna Lisi (*Giulia*), Philippe Leroy (*Ippolito*), Tino Buazzelli (*Duke of Mantova*), Maria Grazia Buccella (*Marchesa of Pepara*), Vittorio Caprioli (*Marchese Liginio*), Paola Borboni (*The Matron*), Anna Maria Guarnieri (*Margherita Farnese*), Giusi Raspani Dandolo (*Duchess of Mantova*), Luciano Mandolfo (*Cardinal Farnese*), Esmeralda Ruspoli (*Bianca Cappello*), Mario Scaccia (*Cardinal Gonzaga*), José Luis de Vilallonga (*Alessandro dei Medici*), Anna Maria Polani (*Eleanora dei Medici*), Claudie Lange (*Marfisa*), Alfredo Bianchini (*Cavalier Vinta*), Leopoldo Trieste (*Marchese of Pepara*), Mariangela Giordano (*lady friend of the prince*), Francesco Mulè.

Costume comedy. Based on 16th-century letters compiled by: Alberto Consiglio. In 16th-century Italy, the childless marriage of Prince Don Vincenzo Gonzaga and the Princess Margherita Farnese of Parma arouses court gossip. Defenders of the prince maintain that he is an extremely virile man burdened with a barren wife; detractors claim that his marriage has never been consummated because of his impotence. The prince's father, the Duke of Mantova, is concerned that his family will have no heir and arranges for the marriage to be annulled. To form a powerful and financially helpful alliance, the duke seeks to marry his son to Princess Eleanora dei Medici, the daughter of the wealthy rulers of Florence, but the Medici refuse to consent to the union until the prince proves his manhood. The prince angrily refuses to submit to their demand and consoles himself with his mistress and with the recently widowed Marchesa of Pepara. His father retaliates by cutting off his allowance, and the prince reluctantly agrees to a test. The Medici select a young virgin, Giulia, school her in the ways of love, and then present her to the prince. Unnerved by the presence of witnesses, the prince is unable to respond to Giulia's seduction attempts. As his time runs out, however, he overcomes his self-consciousness and establishes his manhood. Triumphant, he walks to the bedchamber window and acknowledges the cheers of the crowd below. *Royalty. Mistresses. Impotence. Marriage—Arranged. Marriage—Annulment. Seduction. Virginity. Infidelity. Florence. Parma. Mantua. Farnese Family. Gonzaga Family. The Medici.*

Note: Location scenes filmed in Caprarola, Florence, Mantua, and Urbino. Rome opening: Nov 1965 as *Una vergine per il principe*; running time: 109 min. Paris opening: May 1966 as *Une vierge pour le prince*; running time: ca100 min. Also known as *A Maiden for the Prince*; prerelease titles: *A Virgin for the Prince*, *There's Something Going On*, and *There's Something Funny Going On.*

MAIDENS OF FETISH STREET see **THE GIRLS ON F—— STREET**

MAIL ORDER BRIDE　　　　　　　　　　　　　　**F6.3014**
Metro-Goldwyn-Mayer, Inc. 11 Mar **1964** [Kansas City, Missouri, opening: c27 Nov 1963; LP26810]. Sd (Westrex); col (Metrocolor). 35mm (Panavision). 83 min.

Prod Richard E. Lyons. *Dir-Screenplay* Burt Kennedy. *Dir Photog* Paul C. Vogel. *Camera Op* Al Lane. *Art Dir* George W. Davis, Stan Jolley. *Set Decor* Henry Grace, William Calvert. *Film Ed* Frank Santillo. *Mus Comp & Cond* George Bassman. *Rec Supv* Franklin Milton. *Mix* Philip Mitchell. *Rec* Howard Voss. *Boom Op* Mal Rennings. *Asst Dir* Eli Dunn, Al Murphy, Roger Duchowny. *Script Supv* Les Hoyle. *Wardrobe* Russ Hamlin, Oral Johnson. *Makeup Supv* William Tuttle. *Makeup* Dick Hamilton. *Hairstyles* Mary Keats, Virginia Darcy. *Still Photog* Larry Prather. *Gaffer* Tom Powell. *Grip* Lloyd Isbell. *Prop* Lorne Stone.

Cast: Buddy Ebsen *(Will Lane)*, Keir Dullea *(Lee Carey)*, Lois Nettleton *(Annie Boley)*, Warren Oates *(Jace)*, Barbara Luna *(Marietta)*, Paul Fix *(Jess Linley)*, Marie Windsor *(Hanna)*, Denver Pyle *(Preacher Pope)*, Bill Smith *(Lank)*, Kathleen Freeman *(Sister Sue)*, Abigail Shelton *(young old maid)*, Jimmy Mathers *(Matt)*, Doodles Weaver *(Charlie Mary)*, Diane Sayer *(Lily)*, Ted Ryan *(bartender)*.

Western drama. Source: Van Cort, "Mail-Order Bride," in *Saturday Evening Post* (11 Aug 1951). Ex-lawman Will Lane comes to Congress, Montana, in 1890 to fulfill a promise to a dead colleague that he will look after the man's unruly son, Lee Carey. Lane has the deed to the half-built Carey ranch, which at the request of Lee's father, he is not to surrender until Lee shows some maturity. One of Lane's demands is that Lee marry, and after looking through marriage offers in a mail-order catalog, Lane visits Kansas City to interview prospects. He brings back Annie Boley, a young widow who has worked for Hanna, a saloon owner to whom Lane is attracted. Annie brings along her 6-year-old son. Over Lee's objections Lane forces the marriage, with Lee's friend Jace acting as best man. Lee reveals the situation to Annie, and she promises to pretend to be happily married. Lee, in turn, promises to support her when she eventually leaves him; until then, they will be married in name only. Lane sees through the deception and orders Annie to return east, but she refuses. Lane discovers that Jace has been stealing the ranch's cattle and orders Lee to stop seeing him. Furious with Lane, Lee rides into Congress. There Jace gets him drunk, and he agrees to steal the cattle and leave town with Jace. Upon returning to the ranch, Lee finds the new house, which he has built, in flames. He rescues Annie's son from the fire, which he discovers was set by Jace, and reveals the plan to steal the cattle to Lane. Lane disgustedly hands Lee the deed and prepares to leave, but a changed Lee asks him to help retrieve the cattle. Jace is killed in the ensuing gunfight. Lee realizes that he is in love with Annie, and they begin rebuilding the ranch. A satisfied Lane rides to Kansas City to see Hanna. *Ranchers. Widows. Heirs. Saloon keepers. Guardians. Mail-order brides. Marriage—Arranged. Rustling. Manhood. Arson. Drunkenness. Montana. Kansas City (Missouri). Documentation.*

Note: Shot on location in the High Sierra of northern California.

MAIL ORDER CONFIDENTIAL   **F6.3015**
Dekko Films–Utopia Productions. *Dist* Distribpix, Inc. 19 Jun **1968** [New York showing]. Sd; b&w. 35mm. 63 min.

Cast: Michael Courtney *(Mike Smith)*, Diana Smith, Janet Smythe, Gigi Smith.

Sex film. Mike Smith, a clean-cut, suburban family man, is a pornographer who makes films from mail-order requests. While he is photographing Jean, Mike abandons the neutral cloak of the artist and makes love with her. They are interrupted by Valda, an old friend of Mike's whose skills as an exotic dancer divert him and prompt Jean's angry departure. Mike and Valda then make love. The next day, Mike's shooting schedule includes two special requests: one to document a brutal beating, and the other to make a film showing young women performing intimacies. Mike arrives at home to find that the film about lesbians was ordered by his wife, whom he discovers viewing the film alone while stimulating herself. Mike's initial revulsion gives way to his professionalism, and he sets up his camera to photograph his wife. *Pornographers. Actors. Exotic dancers. Housewives. Infidelity. Voyeurism. Lesbianism. Sadism. Suburban life. Autoeroticism. Sex exploitation films. Mail-order business.*

THE MAIN ATTRACTION (Great Britain)   **F6.3016**
Seven Arts Productions. *Dist* Metro-Goldwyn-Mayer, Inc. 5 Jun **1963** [Denver, Colorado, opening; c31 Dec 1962; LP23744]. Sd (Westrex); col (Eastman Color). 35mm (Metroscope). 85 min. [Copyright length: 87 min.]

Prod-Writ John Patrick. *Exec Prod* Abe Steinberg. *Dir* Daniel Petrie. *Dir Photog* Geoffrey Unsworth. *Camera Op* Jack Atcheler. *Focus* John Alcott. *Art Dir* Bill Hutchinson. *Asst Art Dir* Bob Cartwright. *Set Dresser* Scott Slimon. *Scenic Artist* Gilbert Wood. *Draughtsman* Jim Sawyer. *Film Ed* Geoffrey Foot. *1st Asst Ed* Graham Shipham. *2d Asst Ed* Gerry Arbeid. *Mus Comp* Andrew Adorian. *Mus Cond* Muir Mathieson. *Titl Song* Pat Boone, Jeff Corey. *Song:* "Gondoli, Gondola" Carosone & Nisa. *Mus & Italian Lyr:* "Si, Si, Si" Domenico Modugno. *English Lyr* Abel Baer. *Song:* "Amore Baciami" C. A. Rossi. *Italian Lyr* C. C. Testoni. *English Lyr* Geoffrey Parsons, John Turner, Pat Boone. *Songs Sung by* Pat Boone. *Choreog* Lionel Blair. *Sd Mix* Buster

Ambler. *Dub Ed* Gordon Daniel. *Boom Op* Peter Dukelow. *Sd Camera Op* Jimmy Dooley. *1st, 2d & 3d Asst Dir* Frank Ernst, Terry Lens, Michael Meighan, Al Burgess. *Prod Supv* Roy Parkinson. *Prod Controller* Jack Smith, British. *Prod Sec* Jill Langley. *Cont* June Faithfull. *Wardrobe Supv* Felix Evans. *Wardrobe Master* Ben Foster. *Wardrobe Mistress* Evelyn Gibbs. *Ch Makeup* Neville Smallwood. *Ch Hairdresser* Bill Griffiths. *Dial Coach* Jeff Corey. *Prop Buyer* Sid Palmer. *Still Photog* Arthur Evans. *Casting Dir* Barry Gray, casting dir. *Chargehand Electrn* Jack Sullivan. *Chargehand Prop* Ernie Kell. *Grip* M. Walters.

Cast: Pat Boone *(Eddie)*, Nancy Kwan *(Tessa)*, Mai Zetterling *(Gina)*, Yvonne Mitchell *(Elenora)*, Kieron Moore *(Ricco)*, John Le Mesurier *(Bozo)*, Carl Duering *(bus driver)*, Warren Mitchell *(proprietor)*, Lionel Murton *(Burton)*, Golda Casimir *(peasant woman)*, Lionel Blair *(clown)*, Frank Sieman *(band announcer)*.

Drama. Eddie, a cynical American drifter, loses his singing job in a dingy Italian cafe and takes up with an older woman, Gina, who invites him to join her circus ventriloquist act. Trouble develops when Eddie becomes attracted to Tessa, the bareback rider who is the sister-in-law of Ricco, the circus owner. No longer interested in his crippled wife, Elenora, Ricco becomes jealous of Eddie's attentions to Tessa. Another problem arises when Bozo, the circus clown who is Gina's ex-husband, attacks Eddie and falls on a knife as they struggle. Believing Bozo to be dead, Eddie flees. He encounters Tessa, who has also left the circus, and the two spend the night in a deserted mountain cabin, unaware that the area has been evacuated for the dynamiting of a dangerous glacier. In the resulting avalanche, Eddie saves Tessa's life and then again flees, fearing the police. But he returns to the circus and discovers that Bozo is alive, that Ricco and Elenora are reconciled, and that Tessa truly loves him. *Drifters. Clowns. Americans in foreign countries. Singers. Cripples. Equestrians. Ventriloquism. Avalanches. Circus. Cafes. Glaciers. Italy.*

Note: Opened in London in Oct 1962; running time: 90 min.

THE MAIN CHANCE (Great Britain)   **F6.3017**
Merton Park Studios. *Dist* Embassy Pictures. Jun **1966**. Sd; b&w. 35mm. 61 min.

Prod Jack Greenwood. *Dir* John Knight. *Screenplay* Richard Harris, writ. *Photog* James Wilson. *Art Dir* Peter Mullins. *Film Ed* Derek Holding. *Mus* Bernard Ebbinghouse. *Sd* Brian Blamey. *Sd Rec* Sidney Rider, Red Law. *Asst Dir* Ted Lewis.

Cast: Grégoire Aslan *(Potter)*, Edward DeSouza *(Michael Blake)*, Tracy Reed *(Christine)*, Stanley Meadows *(Joe Hayes)*, Jack Smethurst *(Ross)*, Bernard Stone *(Miller)*, Will Stampe *(Carter)*, Julian Strange *(butler)*, Anthony Bailey *(chauffeur)*, Joyce Barbour *(Madame Rozanne)*.

Crime melodrama. Based on a novel by: Edgar Wallace. Former R.A.F. pilot Michael Blake is approached by Christine, secretary to Potter, a supposed wine importer who offers Blake a large sum of money to fly a small package from France to England. Blake refuses at first but accepts when pressure is applied, intending to double-cross Potter and keep the package's contents for himself. When the parcel is delivered, Potter finds it full of pebbles instead of the diamonds he had expected. Potter, an electronics expert, radios Blake in the plane, informing him that the double-cross had been anticipated and that a bomb is planted aboard the plane. The detonator fails to work, however: seated beside Blake in the plane is Christine, who had warned Blake about the hidden bomb before the flight. *Air pilots. Secretaries. Masterminds. Smuggling. Perfidy. Electronics. Airplanes. Diamonds. Bombs. France.*

Note: Released in Great Britain in Apr 1965.

LES MAINS D'ORLAC *see* **THE HANDS OF ORLAC**

MAJIN (Japan)   **F6.3018**
Daiei Motion Picture Co. 9 Aug **1968** [New York opening]. Sd; col (Eastman Color). 35mm (Daiei Scope). 86 min.

Prod Masaichi Nagata. *Dir* Kimiyoshi Yasuda. *Screenplay* Tetsuo Yoshida. *Photog* Fujio Morita. *Art Dir* Hisashi Okuda. *Film Ed* Hiroshi Yamada. *Mus* Akira Ifukube. *Sp Eff Dir* Yoshiyuki Kuroda.

Cast: Miwa Takada *(Kozasa Hanabusa)*, Yoshihiko Aoyama *(Tadafumi Hanabusa)*, Jun Fujimaki *(Kogenta)*, Ryutaro Gomi *(Samanosuke Odate)*, Tatsuo Endo *(Gunjuro)*.

Melodrama. During a civil war in medieval Japan the warrior god Majin is encased in a stone statue and sealed in a mountain overlooking a castle. When the local ruler and his wife are slain by the chamberlain Samanosuke, the Prince Tadafumi and Princess Kozasa escape with their servant Kogenta to the mountain. Ten years later Tadafumi and Kogenta descend into the village and learn that Samanosuke has enslaved its inhabitants. The chamberlain, however, imprisons the pair and sends his minions to destroy Majin. Overcome by grief, Kozasa prays to Majin to deliver Tadafumi and Kogenta. Touched, the god comes to life. Breaking his bonds, Majin visits the village, where he halts the execution of Tadafumi and Kogenta and destroys Samanosuke. *Warlords.*

Royalty. Slavery. Feudalism. Loyalty. Murder. Idolatry. Reviviscence. Castles.

Note: Released in Japan in Apr 1966 as *Daimajin*; running time: 84 min. Also known as *Majin, the Hideous Idol* and *The Devil Got Angry*. Rerelease title: *Majin, the Monster of Terror.*

MAJOR DUNDEE   F6.3019

Jerry Bresler Productions. *Dist* Columbia Pictures. 2 Apr **1965** [Chicago opening; c1 Apr 1965; LP30824]. Sd; col (Eastman Color by Pathé, print by Technicolor). 35mm (Panavision). 124 min. [Cut from 134 min.]

Prod Jerry Bresler. *Dir* Sam Peckinpah. *2d Unit Dir* Cliff Lyons. *Screenplay* Harry Julian Fink, Jr., Oscar Saul, Sam Peckinpah. *Story* Harry Julian Fink, Jr. *Dir Photog* Sam Leavitt. *Art Dir* Alfred Ybarra. *Film Ed* William A. Lyon, Don Starling, Howard Kunin. *Mus* Daniele Amfitheatrof. *Titl Song* Daniele Amfitheatrof, Ned Washington. *Sung by* Mitch Miller's Sing Along Gang. *Song:* "Laura Lee" Liam Sullivan, Forrest Wood. *Sd Supv* Charles J. Rice. *Sd* James Z. Flaster. *Asst Dir* Floyd Joyer, John Veitch. *Prod Mgr* Francisco Day. *Asst to the Prod* Rick Rosenberg. *Cost* Tom Dawson. *Makeup* Ben Lane, Larry Butterworth. *Sp Eff* Augie Lohman. *Prop* Joe La Bella.

Cast: Charlton Heston *(Maj. Amos Charles Dundee)*, Richard Harris *(Capt. Benjamin Tyreen)*, Jim Hutton *(Lieutenant Graham)*, James Coburn *(Samuel Potts)*, Michael Anderson, Jr. *(Tim Ryan)*, Senta Berger *(Teresa Santiago)*, Mario Adorf *(Sergeant Gomez)*, Brock Peters *(Aesop)*, Warren Oates *(O. W. Hadley)*, Ben Johnson *(Sergeant Chillum)*, R. G. Armstrong *(Reverend Dahlstrom)*, L. Q. Jones *(Arthur Hadley)*, Slim Pickens *(Wiley)*, Karl Swenson *(Captain Waller)*, Michael Pate *(Sierra Charriba)*, John Davis Chandler *(Jimmy Lee Benteen)*, Dub Taylor *(Priam)*, Albert Carrier *(Capt. Jacques Tremaine)*, Begoña Palacios *(Linda)*, Enrique Lucero *(Dr. Aguilar)*, José Carlos Ruiz *(Riago)*, Aurora Clavel *(Melinche)*, Francisco Reiguera *(old Apache)*.

Western drama. In the last months of the Civil War, a small band of Apaches led by Sierra Charriba attack a cavalry post in New Mexico, massacre almost the entire force, kidnap three children, and escape across the border to Mexico. Stationed nearby at an isolated fort is Major Dundee, warden of 400 Confederate prisoners, Union deserters, murderers, and thieves. Determined to wipe out Charriba's Apaches, Dundee augments his small force with renegades, Negro volunteers, and a group of Confederate prisoners who have been given the choice of fighting or being hanged for killing a prison guard. The Confederates are led by Capt. Benjamin Tyreen, an old enemy of Dundee's, who swears to kill him after their mission is completed. Once in Mexico, tension between the two men increases as Tyreen steps into Dundee's faltering command, and opposing loyalties to North and South divide the ranks. They free a village from occupying French soldiers, and the two leaders become rivals for the attentions of Teresa Santiago, the widow of a Mexican physician hanged by the French. Though wounded, Dundee leads his men into a last battle with Charriba's Apaches. A trap is set and the Indian chief is killed. With the mission accomplished, it now remains for Dundee and Tyreen to settle their own differences, but the remnants of the troop come across a French regiment; and in the ensuing battle Tyreen makes a daring lone charge and dies gallantly on the battlefield. The fighting ends, and Dundee and his 11 survivors head back across the river to the safety of their own country. *Apache Indians. Prisoners of war. Deserters—Military. Thieves. French. Widows. Negroes. Murder. Forts. United States—History—Civil War. Mexico—History—European intervention. New Mexico. United States Army—Cavalry.*

Note: Filmed entirely in Mexico.

A MAJORITY OF ONE   F6.3020

Warner Bros. Pictures. 11 Jan **1962** [New York opening; c15 Dec 1961; LP27096]. Sd; col (Technicolor). 35mm. 156 min.

Prod-Dir Mervyn LeRoy. *Screenplay* Leonard Spigelgass. *Photog* Harry Stradling, Sr. *Art Dir* John Beckman. *Set Decor* Ralph S. Hurst. *Film Ed* Philip W. Anderson. *Mus* Max Steiner. *Orch* Murray Cutter. *Sd* Stanley Jones. *Asst Dir* Gil Kissel. *Cost* Orry-Kelly. *Makeup* Jean Burt Reilly. *Hairstyles* Jane Shugrue. *Tech Adv* Takemo K. Shinohara.

Cast: Rosalind Russell *(Mrs. Jacoby)*, Alec Guinness *(Koichi Asano)*, Ray Danton *(Jerome Black)*, Madlyn Rhue *(Alice Black)*, Mae Questel *(Mrs. Rubin)*, Marc Marno *(Eddie)*, Gary Vinson *(Mr. McMillan)*, Sharon Hugueny *(bride)*, Frank Wilcox *(Noah Putnam)*, Francis De Sales *(American embassy representative)*, Yuki Shimoda *(Mr. Asano's secretary)*, Harriet MacGibbon *(Mrs. Putnam)*, Alan Mowbray *(Captain Norcross)*, Tsuruko Kobayashi *(Mr. Asano's daughter-in-law)*.

Comedy-drama. Source: Leonard Spigelgass, *A Majority of One* (New York opening: 16 Feb 1959). Mrs. Jacoby, a Brooklyn widow whose only son was killed by the Japanese in World War II, reluctantly agrees to accompany her daughter, Alice, and her son-in-law, Jerry Black, on a trip to Japan, where Jerry is to help negotiate a trade agreement. En route by ship, Mrs. Jacoby's resentment of the Japanese subsides when she meets Mr. Asano, a Japanese industrialist whose family was struck by tragedy during the war. Their friendship ends, however, when Jerry suspects that Mr. Asano, who is also a

negotiating member of the trade committee, is ingratiating himself with his mother-in-law for political gain. Although Mrs. Jacoby considers this suspicion unfounded, she refuses to see Mr. Asano on their last night at sea. Once in Japan, Jerry unintentionally offends Mr. Asano, and the conference meetings are terminated. Mrs. Jacoby slips away and visits Mr. Asano at his home. After a delightful evening, he agrees to resume negotiations. When things are satisfactorily settled and the three Americans are preparing to leave, Mrs. Jacoby is startled by a marriage proposal from Mr. Asano. She is also angered by the bigoted reaction of Alice and Jerry. However, her main reason for declining the offer is because she feels that both she and Mr. Asano are still tied to their memories. Months later, Mr. Asano arrives in New York as a delegate to the United Nations. He renews his acquaintance with Mrs. Jacoby, who is now happy to accept his courtship. *Widows. Industrialists. Japanese. Bigotry. Filial relations. Trade agreements. Ocean liners. World War II. Japan. New York City—Brooklyn. United Nations.*

MAKE AND BREAK *see* TELL ME LIES

MAKE LIKE A THIEF (United States/Finland)   F6.3021

V P Productions. *Dist* Emerson Film Enterprises. 8 Jun **1966** [Dallas opening]. Sd; col (Eastman Color). 35mm. 80 min.

Prod Palmer Thompson, Veikko Laihanen. *Dir* Palmer Thompson, Richard Long. *Screenplay* Palmer Thompson. *Photog* Kalle Peronkoski, Reijo Hassinen. *Art Dir* Reino Helkesalo. *Sets* Haimi Oy. *Film Ed* Kari Uusitalo. *Mus* Erkki Melakoski. *Sd* Kari Westerlund.

Cast: Richard Long *(Bart Lanigan)*, Åke Lindman *(Arvo Maki)*, Pirkko Mannola *(Marja)*, Rose-Marie Precht *(Toini)*, Juhani Kumpulainen *(Leonard Weston)*, Aulekki Tarnanen *(Helvi)*, Esko Salminen *(gunman)*, Palmer Thompson *(detective)*, Uolevi Vahteristo, Seppo Wallin, Ismo Kallio, Sylva Rossi, Sirppa Sivori-Asp, Kyosti Kayhko, Aimo Paapio, Matti Lehtela, Seija Siikamaki, Kaarina Leskinen, Kauko Kokkonen, Nils Brandt, Martti Saarikivi, Annu Aarnela, Marita Tuhkunen, Inga-Lil Helin.

Melodrama. Unjustly left to take the blame for a huge financial swindle, Bart Lanigan jumps bail, flees the United States, and follows his betrayer, Leonard Weston, to Finland. In Helsinki, a mercenary opportunist, Arvo Maki, turns him over to the police for $5,000. Lanigan manages to escape and offers Arvo a much larger fee if he will find Weston. Arvo agrees and takes Lanigan to a nightclub in which Weston has an interest. There they meet Helvi, Weston's partner, and the club's attractive vocalist, Marja. She is won over to Lanigan's side and accompanies him when he confronts Weston at his hideout. Although Arvo intends to doublecross Lanigan again, he changes his mind when he learns that Weston is solely responsible for the swindle in America. As a result, Lanigan is able to clear his name, and Marja accompanies him on his return to the United States. *Singers. Swindlers. Americans in foreign countries. Police. Perfidy. Nightclubs. Helsinki.*

Note: Filmed on location in Helsinki and opened there in Nov 1964. Working title: *Run Like a Thief.*

MAKE ME A WOMAN *see* THE SISTERS

MAKE MINE A DOUBLE (Great Britain)   F6.3022

Sydney Box Associates–Four Star Films. *Dist* Ellis Films. **1961** [New York opening: 19 Sep 1962]. Sd; b&w. 35mm. 86 min.

Pres by J. Arthur Rank. *Prod* David Henley. *Assoc Prod* Brian Rix. *Dir* Darcy Conyers. *Screenplay* John Chapman. *Photog* Ernest Steward. *Art Dir* Duncan Sutherland. *Film Ed* Sidney Stone. *Mus* Edwin Braden. *Song:* "I Want a Man" Edwin Braden, Alan Reeve-Jones. *Sd* Fred Turtle, Cyril Collick.

Cast: Brian Rix *(Aircraftsman Arthur Atwood/Wing Commander Blenkinsop)*, Cecil Parker *(Air Vice-Marshal Sir Bertram Bukpasser)*, William Hartnell *(Sergeant Bright)*, Leslie Phillips *(Squadron Leader Thomas)*, Leo Franklyn *(Sergeant Belling)*, John Welsh *(Squadron Leader Grant)*, Toby Perkins *(Flight Lieutenant Spendal)*, Liz Fraser *(Lulu)*, Vera Pearce *(Madame Grilby)*, Sarah Branch *(W.A.A.F. Hawkins)*, Oliver Johnston *(Air Commodore Turner)*, Hattie Jacques *(Ada)*, Larry Noble *(farmer)*, John Chapman *(wing commander)*, Gilbert Harrison *(corporal)*, Arnold Bell *(Wing Commander Jones)*, David Williams *(Wing Commander Priestly)*, Geoffrey Denys *(Monty's double)*, Irene Handl *(Lulu's mom)*, Charles Cameron *(General Gimble)*, Denis Shaw *(Hammerstein)*, Peter Burton *(pilot)*, Julian D'Albie, Arthur Brough, Ray Cooney, John Langham, Roland Bartrop, Julie Mendez, Harry Lane, Paul Bogdan, Victor Beaumont.

War comedy. When an unexploded buzz bomb drops on a farm in England during World War II, the military decides that the country's top secret service man, Wing Commander Blenkinsop, should go to enemy-occupied France to investigate. The authorities also agree that an exact double of Blenkinsop should be sent to North Africa to divert attention from his presence in France. The double is found in the person of Aircraftsman Arthur Atwood, an oafish latrine orderly; but on the night of their departure, their orders become mixed so that Atwood goes to France, and Blenkinsop is sent to Cairo. In attempting to escape from the enemy, Atwood inadvertently hides inside a buzz bomb about to be launched. Once in flight, he frantically pulls some wires, causing the bomb to land unexploded in England. Knighted for his act and relishing his new fame, Atwood decides to continue the impersonation while the real Blenkinsop finally gives up trying to convince people of his true identity. It happens, however, that after the war, Atwood stops at a men's washroom and discovers Blenkinsop as the attendant. Realizing it is time to end the masquerade, the two men hastily exchange clothes and resume their true identities. *Secret agents. Doubles. Orderlies (military). War heroes. Impersonation. Bombs. Great Britain—Royal Air Force. World War II. France. Cairo.*

Note: Opened in Blackpool, England, in Sep 1959 as *The Night We Dropped a Clanger.*

MAKE MINE A MILLION (Great Britain)   F6.3023

Jack Hylton Film Productions. *Dist* Schoenfeld Film Distributing Corp. 13 Jan **1965** [Springfield, Massachusetts, opening]. Sd; b&w. 35mm. 82 min.

Pres by Jack Hylton. A John Baxter Production. *Prod* John Baxter. *Assoc Prod* Barbara K. Emary. *Dir* Lance Comfort. *Screenplay* Peter Blackmore. *Adtl Comedy Scenes* Talbot Rothwell, Arthur Askey. *Story* Jack Francis. *Dir Photog* Arthur Grant. *Art Dir* Denis Wreford. *Film Ed* Peter Pitt. *Mus Dir* Stanley Black. *Sd Rec* Red Law, Buster Ambler.

Cast: Arthur Askey *(Arthur Ashton),* Sidney James *(Sid Gibson),* Dermot Walsh *(Martin Russell),* Sally Barnes *(Sally),* Olga Lindo *(Mrs. Burgess),* Bernard Cribbins *(Jack),* Bruce Seton *(Superintendent James),* Kenneth Connor *(anxious husband),* Clive Morton *(National TV director-general),* Martin Benson *(Commercial TV chairman),* Lionel Murton *(Commercial TV director),* George Margo *(assistant),* David Nettheim *(professor),* Tommy Trinder, Dickie Henderson, Evelyn Laye, Dennis Lotis, Anthea Askey, Raymond Glendenning, Patricia Bredin, Leonard Weir, Gillian Lynne, Peter Noble, Sabrina, The Television Toppers, Penge Formation Dancers *(guest stars).*

Comedy. Sid Gibson, sales promoter for Bonko detergent, persuades Arthur Ashton, a makeup man for National TV Studios, to help him promote the product by interrupting a feature program with a commercial. The resulting scandal costs Arthur his job. Sid, continuing his efforts to sell Bonko, forms a pirate station with Arthur as the director. They insert advertisements into the broadcasts of the national relays from Ascot and the Edinburgh Festival. Their "borrowed" mail van, used as a mobile transmitter, is commandeered by a gang of thieves who assume that it is filled with bullion. Hidden inside, Arthur radios the police, enabling them to pursue and capture the crooks. Sid takes advantage of Arthur's new contract with National TV to interrupt the first show with a commercial. *Cosmetologists. Television directors. Thieves. Police. Salesmanship. Advertisements. Soap. Television commercials. Television studios. Chases.*

Note: Location scenes filmed in London, Ascot, and Edinburgh. Opened in London in Feb 1959. Working title: *Look Before You Laugh.*

MAKE OUT   F6.3024

Mitam Productions. 31 Jul **1968** [Champaign, Illinois, showing]. Sd; b&w. 35mm. 63 min.

Dir Adam Clay.

Cast: Ruth, Jerry Harris.

Drama. Four young women sit in a bar and decide to enliven their evening. One girl is chosen to pick up a man at the bar. She goes with him to a motel, and steals the keys to his car. The women go on a cross-country trip trading their bodies for gas, car repairs, and food. They also become involved in an orgy. Eventually, they are tracked down, arrested, and placed on probation under the custody of their parents. *Pickups. Theft. Prostitution. Group sex. Probation. Automobiles. Bars.*

MAKE OUT MADAM   F6.3025

Mitam Productions. Sep **1970** [periodical notice]. Sd; b&w. 35mm. 64 min.

Melodrama. While waiting in a bar for her boyfriend, Lew, Lori meets Mrs. Shaw, a rich widow known as The Madam, and is invited to her home. The invitation is repeated at several subsequent meetings, and finally The Madam offers Lori money to have sex with Lew while she watches. As the couple make love, The Madam masturbates, fantasizing that Lew is her partner. After several similar encounters, The Madam asks Lori and Lew to supply her with other young couples. At a party given by the mate swapping club to which they belong, Lori and Lew recruit Tim and Sally to perform for The Madam, and eventually she hires two additional couples. One day The Madam asks Lew to perform a rape for her, and she promises to provide a woman. Believing that his partner has been similarly hired to perform in the rape scene, Lew violates her. In reality, the unsuspecting woman had been hired to participate in a lesbian act. The victim's boyfriend, who has been waiting downstairs, bursts into the room and attacks Lew. The boyfriend is accidentally killed in the

fighting, and the police apprehend The Madam and her performers. *Widows. Voyeurism. Autoeroticism. Mate swapping. Group sex. Rape. Prostitution. Bars. Sex clubs.*

MAKE OUT—SUBURBAN STYLE   F6.3026

Mitam Productions. 14 May **1969** [Champaign, Illinois, showing]. Sd; b&w. 35mm. 62 min.

Cast: Vincent Stephens.

Melodrama. A police detective learns the history of a murder from the victim's wife: Insurance adjusters Bob Smith and Tom Smalley use their positions to make sexual conquests among their company's suburbanite claimants, following in the footsteps of their boss, Jay Cramer. Bob agrees to pay the repair bill on housewife Sally Water's car if she will have sex with him, and Tom, who is new with the company, similarly adjusts a claim for another housewife, Gina. The two couples become close friends and have a group sex party. Sally's college roommate, Marilyn, asks to be included in the group's gatherings, and Bob introduces her to Jay. The six plan an orgy, but Jay is delayed, and Sally and Marilyn make love while awaiting his arrival and the beginning of the party. One afternoon, Jay intercepts a call meant for Bob and goes to a rendezvous. The woman's husband unexpectedly returns home, and in the ensuing fight the husband is killed, thus precipitating a police investigation. *Insurance agents. Police. Housewives. Roommates. Infidelity. Group sex. Lesbianism. Suburban life.*

MAKE WAY FOR LILA (Sweden/West Germany)   F6.3027

Sandrews-Rhombus Film. *Dist* Parade Pictures. 14 Jun **1962** [Dallas opening]. Sd; col (Eastmancolor). 35mm. 90 min.

Pres by Riley Jackson, Robert Patrick. *Prod* Rune Waldekranz, Georg M. Reuther. *Dir* Rolf Husberg. *Screenplay* Adolf Schütz, Rolf Husberg. *Adapt* P. Baudisch. *Photog* Sven Nykvist. *Film Ed* Lennart Wallén. *Mus* Lars-Erik Larsson. *Sd* Pelle Lonndahl.

Cast: Erika Remberg *(Lila),* Joachim Hansen *(Anders),* Birger Malmsten *(Mellet),* Edvin Adolphson *(Aslak),* Alfred Maurstad *(Jompa),* Ann-Marie Gyllen *(Inger),* Isa Quensel *(Elli),* Sif Ruud, Bengt Blomgren, Anne Blomberg, Sonja Westerberg, Bengt Eklund.

Romantic melodrama. Source: Jens Andreas Friis, *Fra Finmarken: skildringer* (Kristiania, 1881). While traveling in a sleigh during a snowstorm, a Scandinavian husband and wife are attacked and killed by wolves. Their baby girl is thrown clear and rescued by a Lapland chieftain, Aslak, and his wife, Elli. Childless for many years, the couple decide to raise the infant as their own. They name her Lila, and she is brought up according to traditional Laplander customs. Consequently, when Lila reaches maturity, she accepts the decision that she will marry the man of her father's choice, a young Laplander named Mellet. Although Mellet is humiliated when Lila beats him in the annual reindeer race, he still insists that she become his bride. Then one day she meets and falls in love with Anders, a Norwegian merchant who offers to take her away and show her the modern world. Aslak strongly objects, so Lila arranges a farewell meeting with Anders. When the jealous Mellet learns of the rendezvous, he attacks Anders and leaves him to die in a ravine. Anders recovers, however, and races on skis to Lila's wedding. Upon his arrival, Aslak finally reveals Lila's true origin, thereby freeing her to marry Anders. *Orphans. Laplanders. Norwegians. Merchants. Adoption. Social customs. Marriage— Arranged. Sledding. Jealousy. Weddings. Lapland. Blizzards. Wolves. Reindeer.*

Note: Location scenes filmed in Lapland and other areas of Sweden and Norway. Opened in Düsseldorf in Nov 1958 as *Laila—Liebe unter der Mitternachtssonne;* in Stockholm in Dec 1958 as *Laila;* original running time: 100 min. Previously filmed in Sweden and Denmark as *Lajla* or *Laila* in 1937. U. S. prerelease title: *Lila.*

EL MAL *see* RAGE

MALAGA (Great Britain)   F6.3028

Cavalcade Films-Douglas Fairbanks Ltd. *For* Associated British Picture Corp. *Dist* Warner Bros. Pictures. 22 Feb **1962** [New York opening; c24 Mar 1960; LP29393]. Sd; b&w. 35mm. 97 min.

Prod Thomas Clyde. *Dir* Laslo Benedek. *Screenplay* David Osborn, Donald Ogden Stewart. *Dir Photog* Desmond Dickinson. *Camera Op* Harry Gillam. *Focus* Peter Tabori. *Art Dir* Harry White. *Asst Art Dir* Pamela Cornell. *Film Ed* Gerald Turney-Smith. *Mus Comp & Cond* Matyas Seiber. *Sd* A. W. Lumkin, Allan Morrison, H. L. Bird, Len Shilton. *Sd Camera Op* W. Wayland. *Boom Op* Don Wortham. *1st & 2d Asst Dir* Frederic Goode, Michael Profit. *Prod Mgr* Victor Peck. *Prod Sec* Joan Parcell, June Randall. *Wardrobe Mistress* Eileen Welch. *Makeup* Jim Hydes. *Hairstyles* Eileen Warwick. *Still Photog* George Higgins. *Camera Grip* G. Kirby. *Gaffer* S. Foster.

Cast: Trevor Howard *(John Bain),* Dorothy Dandridge *(Gianna),* Edmund Purdom *(Peter Carran),* Michael Hordern *(Inspector Farrell),* Paul Stassino *(Juan Montoya),* John Bailey *(Cecil),* Alfred Burke *(Shapley),* Peter Illing *(pawnbroker)*, Barry Keegan *(Corrigan)*, Brian Worth *(airport guard)*, Thelma D'Aguiar *(Spanish woman)*, Neville Becker *(gigolo)*, Martin Boddey *(Sir John Middleburgh)*, Peter Elliott, actor *(waiter)*, Helen Goss *(Lady Middleburgh)*.

Crime melodrama. Source: Donald MacKenzie, *The Scent of Danger* (Boston, 1958). In London, John Bain and Peter Carran rob a titled celebrity of her jewels; but once the coup has been accomplished, Carran deserts his partner and heads for Spain with the loot. Bain evades the police trap laid for him by Carran and joins forces with the latter's discarded black mistress, Gianna. After learning of Carran's escape to Spain, they take pursuit despite a mutual distrust of each other. Once in Madrid, however, they discover Carran has gone to Málaga. Bain captures him there but learns that he has not yet received payment from his smuggling connections. It is decided that Gianna will travel to Gibraltar by ship and pick up the money; but soon after her departure Carran escapes from Bain, gets to the ship first, and takes Gianna prisoner. Bain then surrenders himself to the police, and Carran is trapped aboard the ship. Gianna, by now in love with Bain, offers to help him make a new beginning. *Mistresses. Negroes. Smugglers. Police. Robbery. Perfidy. Chases. Jewels. Ships. London. Madrid. Málaga (Spain).*

Note: Location scenes filmed in southern Spain. Opened in London in Jan 1960 as *Moment of Danger*; running time: 96 min. Working title: *The Takers*.

MALAMONDO (Italy)   F6.3029
Titanus. *Dist* Magna Pictures Distribution Corp. 16 Oct **1964** [San Francisco opening]. Sd; col (Eastman Color). 35mm. 80 min.

Pres by Marshall Naify. *Prod* Goffredo Lombardo. *Dir* Paolo Cavara. *English Vers Dir & Adapt* Jack Lewis. *Screenplay* Paolo Cavara, Ugo Gregoretti, Zanetti. *Comm* Guido Castaldo, Francesco Torti, Stefano Strucchi. *Photog* Ennio Guarnieri. *Mus* Ennio Morricone. *Song:* "Funny World" Ennio Morricone, Francesco Torti, Guido Castaldo. *English Lyr* Alan Brandt. *Sung by* Jane Morgan, Catherine Spaak. *Song:* "Sad Saturday Night" Ennio Morricone. *Sung by* Adriano Celentano.

Narrator: Marvin Miller.

Documentary. Twenty-three episodes show the bizarre attitudes and activities of European youth: Bertrand Russell interviews a group of English students; Italian students butcher a pig; teenagers ski nude in Switzerland; Parisian artists stage a "happening"; German youngsters visit the Dachau Museum; a student in Heidelberg has his face slashed by a barber in order to produce a scar; women in Glasgow protest free love; a female impersonator applies makeup before performing in a homosexual nightclub in Montparnasse; a rock and roll quartet improvise in a Roman piazza; students in Sweden openly contemplate suicide; parachutists in France pull the ripcord at the last possible moment during free fall and at night hold an orgy in a graveyard; French students stand on top of an ascending elevator to see who has the courage to stay the longest; English motorcyclists race on city streets with little regard for safety; students are hazed in Amsterdam; Italian teenagers hold a wild party on a beach; couples kiss in the streets on Poppy Day in Britain; men from the Royal Ballet perform; a black man and a white woman are married in Sweden; impotent young men in a Swiss clinic are served by attractive nurses who try to arouse them; and Adriano Celentano, a young Italian singing idol, sings "Sad Saturday Night." *English. Students. French. Artists. Germans. Swedes. Motorcyclists. Nurses. Singers. Youth. Skiing. Nudity. Female impersonation. Male homosexuality. Rock and roll. Suicide. Parachuting. Ballet. Miscegenation. Impotence. Nightclubs. Orgies. Elevators. Switzerland. Dachau. Heidelberg. Glasgow. Paris—Montparnasse. Sweden. Rome. France. Amsterdam. Bertrand Arthur William Russell. Royal Ballet (London). Pigs.*

Note: Released in Italy in 1964 as *I malamondo*; running time: 100 min.

LA MALDICIÓN DE LA LLORONA *see* **THE CURSE OF THE CRYING WOMAN**

LA MALDICIÓN DE LA MOMIA AZTECA *see* **THE CURSE OF THE AZTEC MUMMY**

MALE AND FEMALE *see* **MALE AND FEMALE SINCE ADAM AND EVE**

MALE & FEMALE SEXUALIS *see* **GUTTER TRASH**

MALE AND FEMALE SINCE ADAM AND EVE (Argentina)   F6.3030
Dist William Mishkin. 18 Feb **1961** [New York opening]. Sd; b&w. 35mm. 74 min.

Pres by Inc. All American Film Producers. *Prod* Alfredo Bedoya. *Dir* Carlos Rinaldi.

Cast: Carl Cores *(Robert)*, Nelly Meden *(Louise)*, Goldie Flame *(Elsa)*, Edward Cuitino *(Inspector Gomez)*, Bill Kennedy *(Adam)*, Alice Gardner *(Eve)*.

Drama. A tale of temptation through the ages: Eve offers Adam an apple from the Tree of Knowledge against the law of God. They become aware and ashamed of their nakedness and are expelled from the Garden of Eden. In the

modern age, Robert, a laborer, is unable to afford marriage to Louise, with whom he is having an affair. One night, Robert rescues Elsa from the advances of a drunk, and in appreciation she invites him to spend the night. He is infatuated with her, but the next morning she rebuffs him, explaining that she is interested only in wealthy men. Anxious to make money quickly, Robert, who has all but forgotten Louise, involves himself with a mob of gangsters. After a few months of robbery and murder, he accumulates a great sum of money and returns to Elsa but finds that he no longer loves her. He locates Louise, who has given birth to his illegitimate son, receives her forgiveness, and marries her. He tries to quit the mob by framing them, but he is killed. *Laborers. Gangsters. Wealth. Greed. Robbery. Murder. Illegitimacy. Marriage. Adam and Eve.*

Note: May also be known as *Male and Female* and *Souls of Sin*.

MALE COMPANION (France/Italy)   F6.3031
P. E. C.–Ultra Film–Les Films du Siècle. *Dist* International Classics. 14 Feb **1966** [New York opening; c31 Dec 1965; LP34465]. Sd; col (Eastmancolor, print by DeLuxe). 35mm. 92 min.

Prod & Exec Prod Julien Derode. *Dir* Philippe de Broca. *Screenplay & Dial* Henri Lanoë. *Adapt* Henri Lanoë, Philippe de Broca. *Photog* Raoul Coutard. *Art Dir* Pierre Duquesne. *Film Ed* Françoise Javet. *Mus* Georges Delerue. *Sd* Jacques Carrère. *Prod Mgr* Christian Ferry.

Cast: Jean-Pierre Cassel *(Antoine)*, Catherine Deneuve *(Isabelle)*, Jean-Pierre Marielle *(Balthazar)*, Irina Demick *(Nicole)*, Annie Girardot *(Clara)*, Sandra Milo *(Maria)*, Marcel Dalio *(Krieg von Spiel)*, Jean-Claude Brialy *(The Prince)*, André Luguet *(grandfather)*, Valérie Lagrange *(Louisette)*, Paolo Stoppa *(Professor Gaetano)*, Adolfo Celi *(Benvenuto)*, Rosemarie Dexter *(student)*, Jacques Dynam *(Isabelle's father)*, Rosy Varte *(Isabelle's mother)*, Memmo Carotenuto *(policeman)*, Giustino Durano *(baker)*, Renée Passeur, Irène Chabrier, Sacha Briquet, Darius Socratos, Hubert Deschamps, Christian Lude.

Comedy. Source: André Couteaux, *Un monsieur de compagnie* (Paris, 1961). Antoine, a young orphan who lives by the philosophy that "laziness is the mother of all virtue," spends his days with his grandfather in comfort and ease. While they are fishing one day, Antoine falls asleep. In a dream, when his grandfather dies penniless, Antoine sets out equipped only with his charm and carefree philosophy. After making friends with Balthazar, an ice cream vendor, he moves in with the vendor's girl friend, Nicole; when Nicole's affection for him becomes serious, however, Antoine sets off again. This time he ingratiates himself with an eccentric prince who is fascinated by model trains; he moves into the prince's mansion and becomes intimate with Louisette, a housemaid. Soon the impetuous Antoine leaves again, ending up in Rome in a pizzeria where he takes up with the proprietor's buxom wife, Maria. Later, he poses as the best friend of a young millionaire killed in an automobile accident, moves into the family's home, and enjoys the generous hospitality of the host and his five daughters; but when he is offered a job, Antoine vanishes. After a brief dalliance with Clara, an attractive widow, he encounters another millionaire, Von Spiel, who persuades him to write a book consisting of 200 blank pages. Antoine then falls hopelessly in love with and marries Isabelle, a simple young woman; he abandons his irresponsible ways and becomes an iron smelter, toiling endlessly in infernal heat. Antoine awakens to find himself on the quiet lake with his grandfather, who commiserates with him on the unfortunate nightmare. *Orphans. Grandfathers. Ne'er-do-wells. Royalty. Eccentrics. Housemaids. Millionaires. Widows. Infidelity. Imposture. Marriage. Rome. Dreams.*

Note: Opened in Paris in Nov 1964 as *Un monsieur de compagnie*; running time: 92 min; in Rome in Jan 1965 as *Poi ti sposerò*.

THE MALE FARM *see* **THE STUD FARM**

MALE HUNT (France/Italy)   F6.3032
Filmsonor–Procinex–Mondex Films–Euro International Films. *Dist* Pathé Contemporary Films. 19 Apr **1965** [New York opening]. Sd; b&w. 35mm. 92 min.

Prod Robert Amon, Claude Jaeger. *Dir* Edouard Molinaro. *Screenplay-Adapt* France Roche. *Idea* Yvon Guezel. *Dial* Michel Audiard. *Stories* Albert Simonin, Michel Duran. *Photog* Andréas Winding. *Art Dir* François de Lamothe. *Film Ed* Robert Isnardon. Monique Isnardon. *Mus* Michel Magne. *Greek Mus* Georges Zambetas. *Sd* Jean Rieul. *Asst Dir* Pierre Cosson.

Cast: Jean-Paul Belmondo *(Fernand)*, Jean-Claude Brialy *(Tony)*, Catherine Deneuve *(Denise)*, Françoise Dorléac *(Sandra)*, Micheline Presle *(Isabelle)*, Claude Rich *(Julien)*, Marie LaForêt *(Gisèle)*, Marie Dubois *(Sophie)*, Bernard Blier *(Monsieur Heurtin)*, Hélène Duc *(Madame Armande)*, Francis Blanche *(Papatakes)*, Michel Serrault *(Professor Lartois)*, Bernadette Lafont *(Flora)*, Mireille Darc *(Georgina)*, Patrick Thevenon, Jacques Dynam, Tanya Lopert, Jacqueline Mille, Yvon Sarray.

Comedy. On the day of his wedding, Tony, a successful Parisian commercial artist, is taken to breakfast by his best man, Julien. They encounter a waiter,

Fernand, who describes his pathetic fate as a husband. Once a carefree hoodlum, he succumbed to Sophie's charms only to end up a henpecked employee in her family's restaurant. Julien adds to the dour matrimonial picture by recounting how he falsely confessed to having an affair with his secretary, Denise, when the husband of his mistress, Isabelle, became suspicious, and how he was forced by Denise's father to marry her. Julien further persuades Tony that his fiancée hatched a plot to ensnare him. Tony reacts by abandoning his fiancée at the altar, giving her honeymoon cruise ticket to Fernand, and setting off for Greece. In the course of the trip, Fernand forms a liaison with Madame Armande, a wealthy, middle-aged woman. In Greece, Tony becomes involved with Sandra, a glamorous swindler, and agrees to marry her; he is certain, however, that the marriage will never last. *Bachelors. Waiters. Secretaries. Swindlers. Mistresses. Hoodlums. Commercial artists. Marriage. Friendship. Infidelity. Weddings. Restaurants. Paris. Greece.*

Note: Opened in Paris in Sep 1964 as *La chasse à l'homme*; running time: 95 min; released in Italy in 1965 as *Caccia al maschio*; running time: 100 min.

MALE SERVICE   F6.3033

Mitam Productions. **1966.** Sd; b&w. 35mm. 63 min.

Dir Arch Hudson.

Cast: Jerry Harris, Karen Drake, Denine Martin.

Melodrama. A male prostitute falls in love with one of his clients and asks her to marry him. She scorns him and remarks that she will not marry someone she can buy. He murders her and disposes of the body in such a way that the woman's caretaker appears to be the murderer. One of the women who frequents the house of prostitution where the man works suspects the male prostitute and tricks him into revealing his crime. *Prostitutes. Marriage. Murder. Frameup.*

MALE TECHNIQUES   F6.3034

18 Jun **1970** [San Francisco opening]. Sd; col. 35mm? [Feature length assumed.]

Sex film. Although no information on the precise nature of this film has been found, press material indicates that it concerns male homosexuality and sexual techniques. *Male homosexuality. Sexual techniques.*

UN MALEDETTO IMBROGLIO *see* **THE FACTS OF MURDER**

MALÉFICES *see* **WHERE THE TRUTH LIES**

THE MALPAS MYSTERY (Great Britain)   F6.3035

Merton Park Studios–Langton Productions. *Dist* Schoenfeld Film Distributing Corp. 21 Feb **1967** [New York opening]. Sd; b&w. 35mm. 60 min.

An Independent Artists Production. *Prod* Julian Wintle, Leslie Parkyn. *Dir* Sidney Hayers. *Screenplay* Paul Tabori, Gordon Wellesley. *Photog* Michael Reed. *Art Dir* Eric Saw. *Film Ed* Tristam Cones. *Mus* Elisabeth Lutyens. *Titl Mus* Richard Carr, mus. *Mus Dir* Muir Mathieson. *Sd Rec* Len Page, Ken Cameron. *Asst Dir* Jan Saunders.

Cast: Maureen Swanson (*Audrey Bedford*), Allan Cuthbertson (*Marshalt*), Geoffrey Keen (*Torrington*), Ronald Howard (*Dick Shannon*), Sandra Dorne (*Dora*), Alan Tilvern (*Gordon Seager*), Leslie French (*Wilkins*), Catherine Feller (*Ginette*), Richard Shaw (*Kornfeldt*), Sheila Allen (*Frau Kornfeldt*), Edward Cast (*Laker*).

Mystery melodrama. Source: Edgar Wallace, *The Face in the Night* (London, 1924). Audrey Bedford, released from prison after serving an unjust sentence, moves in with her stepsister Dora. Lacy Marshalt, Dora's criminal lover, recognizes Audrey as the lost daughter of wealthy ex-convict Torrington, whom Lacy had framed. Hoping to come into Torrington's fortune, Lacy persuades his mistress to pose as Audrey. Torrington, however, is not fooled by the fraud and recognizes his true daughter by the scar on her wrist. Audrey is employed as a typist by reclusive fellow tenant Malpas, a faceless freak. Her subsequent disappearance is noted by Scotland Yard Detective Shannon, who has been concerned for her welfare. He discovers that Marshalt is Malpas and learns that the criminal has abducted Audrey with the intention of forcibly marrying her and thereby acquiring Torrington's wealth. After Marshalt is slain Shannon reunites Audrey with her father and proposes marriage. *Ex-convicts. Freaks. Stepsisters. Mistresses. Detectives. Neighbors. Recluses. Typists. Personal identity. Frameup. Injustice. Wealth. Fatherhood. Imposture. Disguise. Marriage. Abduction. Scotland Yard.*

Note: Released in Great Britain in 1961.

THE MALTESE BIPPY   F6.3036

Freeman/Enders Productions. *Dist* Metro-Goldwyn-Mayer, Inc. 5 Jun **1969** [Los Angeles opening; c5 Jun 1969; LP36846]. Sd; col (Metrocolor). 35mm (Panavision). 92 min. *MPAA rating* G.

Prod Everett Freeman, Robert Enders. *Dir* Norman Panama. *Screenplay* Everett Freeman, Ray Singer. *Story* Everett Freeman. *Dir Photog* William H. Daniels. *Art Dir* George W. Davis, Edward Carfagno. *Set Decor* Robert R. Benton, Dick Pefferle. *Titl* Pacific Title. *Film Ed* Ronald Sinclair, Homer

Powell. *Mus Comp & Cond* Nelson Riddle. *Rec Supv* Franklin Milton. *Asst Dir* Arthur Jacobson. *Unit Prod Mgr* Kurt Neumann. *Cost* Moss Mabry. *Makeup* William Tuttle. *Hairstyles* Mary Keats. *Casting* Leonard Murphy.

Cast: Dan Rowan (*Sam Smith*), Dick Martin (*Ernest Grey*), Carol Lynley (*Robin Sherwood*), Julie Newmar (*Carlotta Ravenswood*), Mildred Natwick (*Molly Fletcher*), Fritz Weaver (*Mr. Ravenswood*), Robert Reed (*Lieut. Tim Crane*), David Hurst (*Dr. Charles Strauss*), Dana Elcar (*Sergeant Kelvaney*), Leon Askin (*Axel Kronstadt*), Alan Oppenheimer (*Adolph Springer*), Eddra Gale (*Helga*), Arthur Batanides (*Tony*), Pamela Rodgers (*Saundra*), Jenifer Bishop (*Joanna Clay*), Maudie Prickett (*Mrs. Potter*), Garry Walberg (*Harold Fenster*), Carol-Jean Thompson (*Mona*), Jerry Mann (*Wesling*).

Comedy. Sam Smith is the fast-buck producer of amateurish nudie films starring his partner Ernest Grey, a neurotic who suffers from dizzy spells and uncontrollable urges to howl like a dog. When they are forced out of their New York office for not paying rent, they move into Ernest's house on Long Island, an eerie structure located next to a cemetery where a mutilated corpse was found and a woman was attacked by a howling man. Also living at the house are Molly, Ernest's talkative housekeeper, Robin, a pretty co-ed, and Axel, an out-of-work Swedish violinist. After a doctor has voiced the opinion that Ernest's howling may be an indication that he is turning into the first all-American werewolf, Ernest is visited by his next door neighbors—the sinister Ravenswood, his voluptuous sister Carlotta, and their 200-pound housekeeper-bodyguard, Helga. Although Ernest is horrified when his neighbors say they are vampires who want him to join their pack, Sam immediately sees the commercial possibilities of using the foursome for a vaudeville act. Eventually, Ernest learns that he is not really a werewolf, but that everyone except Sam is trying to drive him away so that they can search for a giant diamond hidden in his house. Later, Sam, Ernest, and Robin, who claims she's the rightful heir to the diamond, discover that the gem is hidden in the corpse of the house's former owner. As preparations are being made to remove the diamond by surgery, all the competing villains clash with such force that Ernest's house is destroyed and a bewildering series of multiple murders eliminates everyone except Sam and Ernest. But both men are unsatisfied with the conclusion of their story, and they take turns in offering their own preferred endings. Then, hand in hand, Sam and Ernest walk off into the sunset. *Actors. Motion picture producers. Physicians. Swedes. Students. Neighbors. Bodyguards. Violinists. Werewolves. Vampires. Housekeepers. Murder. Neurosis. Diamonds. Sex exploitation films. Corpses. Cemeteries. Haunted houses. Long Island.*

Note: Working title: *The Strange Case of ...! # & %?*

MAN AGAINST MAN (Japan)   F6.3037

Toho Co. Mar **1961** [Los Angeles showing]. Sd; col (Eastmancolor). 35mm (Tohoscope). 116 min.

Dir Senkichi Taniguchi. *Screenplay* Ichiro Ikeda, Ei Ogawa. *Photog* Rokuro Nishigaki.

Cast: Toshiro Mifune, Ryo Ikebe, Takashi Shimura, Yumi Shirakawa, Akemi Kita, Yuriko Hoshi, Yuzo Kayama, Jun Tazaki, Akihiko Hirata, Yutaka Sada.

Crime drama. Kaji and Kikumori, friendly rivals in the army, go their separate ways after the war; Kaji becomes chief stevedore for a shipping firm, and Kikumori becomes manager of a nightclub. A series of suspicious accidents at the shipping firm brings Kaji to Kikumori's club to obtain information, but Kikumori does not tell his friend that he has turned away gangsters wanting him to help take over the shipping firm. The gangsters use Toshio, the son of the company's president, who is in love with Harumi, a singer in the club and also a member of the gang, to obtain control of the company's stock. Toshio discovers Harumi's treachery after his father is killed, and in a desperate move to save the company, he forces its directors to accept a highly dangerous but profitable shipment of explosives. Kikumori foils an attempt by the gang to murder him, but while he is watching Kaji and his men load the explosives, the gang leader orders him at gunpoint to explode the cargo. In the gunplay that follows, Kikumori is shot protecting Kaji, leaving his friend to fight the gang alone. *Stevedores. Nightclub managers. Gangsters. Singers. Perfidy. Murder. Self-sacrifice. Shipping companies. Explosives.*

Note: Released in Japan in 1960 as *Otoko tai otoko*.

A MAN AND A WOMAN (France)   F6.3038

Les Films Treize. *Dist* Allied Artists. 12 Jul **1966** [New York opening; c27 May 1966; LF16]. Sd; b&w, tinted sequences & col (Eastman Color). 35mm. 102 min.

Dir-Story Claude Lelouch. *Adapt & Dial* Claude Lelouch, Pierre Uytterhoeven. *Photog* Claude Lelouch. *Lighting Dir* Patrice Pouget, Jean Collomb. *Art Dir* Robert Luchaire. *Film Ed* G. Boisser, Claude Lelouch. *Mus* Francis Lai. *Lyr* Pierre Barouh. *Orch* Yvan Julien, Maurice Vander. *Song:* "Samba Saravah" Baden Powel, Vincius de Moraes. *Songs Sung by* Nicole Croisille, Jean-Claude Briodin, Pierre Barouh. *Sd* Michel Fano, Jean Baronnet. *Asst Dir* Claude Gorsky. *Prod Mgr* Roger Fleytoux.

Cast: Anouk Aimée *(Anne Gauthier),* Jean-Louis Trintignant *(Jean-Louis Duroc),* Pierre Barouh *(Pierre Gauthier),* Valérie Lagrange *(Valérie Duroc),* Simone Paris *(head mistress),* Antoine Sire *(Antoine Duroc),* Souad Amidou *(Françoise Gauthier),* Yane Barry *(Jean-Louis' mistress),* Paul Le Person *(garage man),* Henri Chemin *(driver),* Gérard Sire *(announcer).*

Romantic drama. A man and a woman, both widowed, meet while visiting their respective children at a boarding school in Deauville. The woman, Anne, misses her train, and the man, Jean-Louis, a racing car driver, offers her a ride back to Paris. During the long ride Anne speaks of her late husband, a poet, singer, and movie stunt man who was killed while making a film. Anne and Jean-Louis meet the following Sunday and take their children to lunch. They go for a sailboat ride and walk together on the wintry beach. Driving back to Paris that night, Jean-Louis talks of his own life as a racing car driver and the time 3 years earlier when he was almost killed in a crash. His wife, unable to bear the strain and shock, committed suicide. After saying goodby to Anne, Jean- Louis leaves for the races at Monte Carlo. While there, he receives a telegram from Anne telling him she loves him. Wildly elated, he drives all night and arrives in Deauville early the next morning. But when he and Anne attempt to make love, Anne, haunted by the memory of her dead husband, cannot give of herself. Believing their affair has ended, they part in silence, and Anne takes the train to Paris while Jean-Louis drives back alone. But on a sudden impulse, he drives to the station to await her arrival. She steps off the train, sees him, pauses, breaks into a smile, and races into his arms. *Widows. Widowers. Stuntmen. Parenthood. Automobile racing. Suicide. Memory. Boarding schools. Trains. Deauville. Paris. Monte Carlo. Automobile accidents.*

Note: Released in France in 1966 as *Un homme et une femme;* running time: 110 min.

A MAN AND 8 GIRLS *see* A MAN—EIGHT GIRLS

A MAN AND HIS WOMAN *see* FREUDUS SEXUALIS

MAN AND MAN   F6.3039
Signature Films, Inc. 1 Jul **1970** [Los Angeles opening]. Sd; col. 35mm? [Feature film, length unknown.]
Documentary. Fifty techniques of homosexual love are illustrated. *Male homosexuality. Sexual techniques.*

THE MAN AND THE MONSTER (Mexico)   F6.3040
Cinematográfica A. B. S. A. *Dist* K. Gordon Murray Productions, Trans-International Films. ca **1965.** Sd; b&w. 35mm. 78 min.
Pres by K. Gordon Murray. *Prod–Screenplay* Abel Salazar. *Prod English Vers* K. Gordon Murray. *Dir* Rafael Baledón. *Story* Raúl Zenteno. *Photog* Raúl Martínez Solares. *Art Dir* Javier Torres Torija. *Film Ed* Carlos Savage. *Mus* Gustavo César Carrión. *Sd* Manuel Topete.
Cast: Enrique Rambal, Abel Salazar, Martha Roth, Ofelia Guilmain, Anita Blanch, José Chavez, Carlos Suárez, Maricarmen Vela.
Horror film. Concert manager Dick Sandrow is told by famed musician Samuel Manning that his protégée, Laura, is destined to become the world's greatest pianist. Although he suspects that the musician is responsible for the death in an automobile accident of Alexandra, another pianist, Dick is unaware that Manning has sold his soul to the Devil in exchange for success. As a result of this pact, Manning is transformed into a raving monster whenever a certain tune is played on the piano. Hoping to confirm his suspicions, Dick instructs Laura to play the haunting melody. Manning, metamorphosized into the monster, attempts to attack Laura and is shot to death. *Theatrical managers. Pianists. Monsters. Metamorphosis. Automobile accidents. The Devil. The Soul.*

Note: Produced in Mexico in 1958 as *El hombre y el monstruo;* running time: 90 min.

MAN AND WIFE   F6.3041
New World Studios. *Dist* Institute for Adult Education. Aug **1969** [San Francisco showing]. Sd; col. 16mm & 35mm. 65 min.
Pres by Marv Miller, Matt Cimber.
Sex instruction film. Proceeding from the premise that the ability to perform sexual intercourse is learned rather than innate, the film offers sex instruction for modern marriages. A brief prologue provides observations on the psychology and physiology of intercourse as a means for the expression of marital love. One male and several female models [two couples, according to another source] then demonstrate 49 positions of sexual intercourse. *Sex instruction. Sexual techniques. Marriage.*

A MAN CALLED ADAM   F6.3042
Trace-Mark Productions. *Dist* Embassy Pictures. 29 Jun **1966** [Detroit opening]. Sd; b&w. 35mm. 103 min. [Also 96 min.]
Prod Ike Jones, James Waters. *Exec Prod* Joseph E. Levine. *Dir* Leo Penn. *Screenplay* Les Pine, Tina Rome. *Photog* Jack Priestley. *Art Dir* Charles Rosen. *Set Decor* Sam Robert. *Film Ed* Carl Lerner. *Mus (see note)* Benny Carter.

Songs: "All That Jazz," "Whisper to One" Benny Carter. *Song:* "Muskrat Ramble" Edward Ory, Ray Gilbert. *Mr. Davis' Trumpet Playing Dubbed by* Nat Adderly. *Sd* Dennis Maitland. *Asst Dir* Joel Glickman. *Prod Mgr* Steve Brody.
Cast: Sammy Davis, Jr. *(Adam Johnson),* Ossie Davis *(Nelson Davis),* Cicely Tyson *(Claudia Ferguson),* Louis Armstrong *(Willie "Sweet Daddy" Ferguson),* Frank Sinatra, Jr. *(Vincent),* Peter Lawford *(Manny),* Mel Torme *(himself),* Lola Falana *(Theo),* Jeanette Du Bois *(Martha),* Johnny Brown *(Les),* George Rhodes *(Leroy),* Michael Silva *(George),* Michael Lipton *(Bobby Gales),* Kai Winding, Kenneth Tobey, Gerald S. O'Loughlin, Morris Erby, Michael Gazzo, Matt Russo, Will Hussing, Ted Beniades, Roy Glenn, Donald Crabtree, Elvera Davis, Brunetta Bernstein.
Drama. Black trumpet player Adam Johnson stalks off a Cincinnati bandstand when a white patron heckles him. Returning to New York City, Adam finds that his best friend, Nelson Davis, has lent his apartment to Willie "Sweet Daddy" Ferguson and his granddaughter, Claudia, a civil rights activist. Intrigued by the young woman, Adam flirts with her but is rejected. Claudia's grandfather explains that Adam is guilt-ridden because he feels responsible for the death of his wife and child in a car accident 10 years earlier. Despite Adam's heavy drinking and bad temper, Claudia comes to understand him, and eventually she falls in love with him. In trouble because of the Cincinnati walkout, Adam is now forced to grovel before a ruthless agent, Manny, who sadistically offers him a tour of one-nighters in the segregated South. With Vincent, a young musician, as the only white member of his troupe, Adam reluctantly accepts. Claudia goes along and is happy to see that Adam is trying to control both his temper and his drinking. When Vincent is unmercifully beaten up by three white youths, Adam stands helplessly by, stunned by the injustice and violence that seem to plague his life. After Claudia has left him, Adam makes one last attempt to play his trumpet—at a casino where Willie is appearing. He begins to miss notes, collapses, and is carried offstage, where he dies. *Negroes. Booking agents. Musicians. Civil rights. Jazz. Guilt. Racial segregation. Race relations. Alcoholism. New York City. Cincinnati. United States—South.*

Note: Filmed on location in New York City. Other songs include "I Want To Be Wanted," "Playboy Theme," "Back O'Town Blues," "Someday Sweetheart."

A MAN CALLED DAGGER   F6.3043
Global Screen Associates. *Dist* Metro-Goldwyn-Mayer, Inc. Jan **1968** [c8 Nov 1967; LP34999]. Sd; col (Movielab). 35mm. 86 min.
Prod Lewis M. Horowitz. *Exec Prod* M. A. Ripps. *Assoc Prod* Ramzi Thomas. *Dir* Richard Rush. *Screenplay* James Peatman, Robert S. Weekley. *Based on an Idea by* W. L. Riffs. *Dir Photog* Leslie Kovacs. *Underwater Camera* Ray George. *Asst Camera* Emery Boos, Steve Karkus. *Art Dir* Mike McCloskey, Glenn Holse. *Film Ed* Len Miller, Tom Boutross. *Mus Comp* Steve Allen. *Adapt & Cond* Ronald Stein. *Titl Song* Buddy Kaye, Steve Allen. *Vocal:* "Don't Rock the Boat" Maureen Arthur. *Featuring* Joe Leahy Combo. *Mus Cons* Morris I. Diamond. *Sd* Lee Strosnider, Franklin Milton. *Asst Dir* Steven Bernhardt. *Script Supv* Bri Murphy. *Prod Asst* Rudy Kaddo. *Cost* Vana Carroll. *Makeup* Rafaelle Patterson. *Sp Eff* Gary Kent. *Sp Eff Ed* Paul Jasiukonis, Algis Zemaitaitis. *Gaffer* Richmond Aguilar. *Head Grip* Tom Ramsey. *Prop Master* Curt Mercer. *Still Photog* R. Charleton Wilson, Peter Sorel.
Cast: Paul Mantee *(Dick Dagger),* Terry Moore *(Harper Davis),* Jan Murray *(Rudolph Koffman),* Sue Ane Langdon *(Ingrid),* Eileen O'Neill *(Erica),* Maureen Arthur *(Joy),* Leonard Stone *(Karl Rainer),* Richard Kiel *(Otto),* Mimi Dillard *(girl in auto),* Bruno Ve Sota *(Dr. Grulik),* Margie Nelson, Lenore Waring, Diane Neff, Martha Luttrell, Virginia Wood *(Ingrid's girls).*
Action melodrama. While investigating the flow of ex-Nazi scientists into the United States, secret agent Dick Dagger is briefed by attractive fellow agent Harper Davis. She tells him that Rudolph Koffman, a former SS colonel and concentration camp commandant, owns and operates a meatpacking plant that is suspected of being a front for his neo-Nazi attempt to take over the world. Dagger visits Ingrid, Koffman's mistress who runs a beauty farm, and learns from her masseuse Joy that a young woman named Erica is being held prisoner at Koffman's plant. Unaware that Koffman is monitoring his every move, Dagger kidnaps Erica and takes her to his place. Erica, like the other girls at the beauty farm, has been brainwashed to follow Koffman's orders (transmitted by means of a small radio receiver in her teeth), and she makes an attempt on Dagger's life. Although she fails, Koffman manages to recoup by trading Erica for Harper, who has been kidnaped by Koffman. After forcing Ingrid to reveal the entrance to the secret part of the plant, Dagger enters the underground maze and rescues Joy, who is being held against her will. Koffman's guards chase and capture Dagger and Joy; but Dagger escapes from the torture chamber with the aid of a laser-beam wristwatch. In a final confrontation in a huge meatlocker, Dagger kills the cleaver-wielding Koffman and rescues the women, who now willingly cater to Dagger's whims. *Nazis. Scientists. Secret*

agents. Masterminds. Masseurs. Brainwashing. Espionage. Kidnaping. Neonazism. Beauty farms. Meatpacking. Watches. Laser. Chases.

Note: Originally intended for release by Cinema Distributors of America in Sep 1966 as *Why Spy?*

THE MAN CALLED FLINTSTONE   F6.3044

Hanna-Barbera Productions. *Dist* Columbia Pictures. 3 Aug **1966** [Indianapolis, Indiana, opening; c1 Aug 1966; LP33180]. Sd (RCA); col (Eastman Color by Pathé). 35mm. 87 min.

Prod-Dir Joseph Barbera, William Hanna. *Screenplay* Harvey Bullock, R. S. Allen. *Adtl Story Material* Joseph Barbera, William Hanna, Warren Foster, Alex Lovy. *Anim Dir* Charles A. Nichols. *Layout* Richard Bickenbach, Lance Noley, Iwao Takamoto, Jerry Eisenberg, Robert Singer, Homer Jonas, Bruce Bushman, Jack Huber, Brad Case, Walter Clinton, Steve Nakagawa. *Anim* Irv Spence, George Goepper, George Nicholas, Edward Barge, Edwin Aardal, Jerry Hathcock, Don Lusk, Kenneth Muse, Richard Lundy, Bill Keil, Ed Parks, John Sparey, Allen Wilzbach, George Kreisl, George Germanetti, Carlo Vinci, Hugh Fraser, Hicks Lokey. *Asst Anim* Sam Jaimes, Charlotte Huffine, Frank Carr, Tom Ferriter, Richard Gonzales, anim, Jack Carr, anim, Bill Nunes, Joe Roman, Grace Stanzell, Jack Kerns, John Boersema, Joan Orbison, Jack Parr, William Pratt, Jim Brummett, Rae McSpadden, Tony Love, Pat Combs, Veve Risto, Dennis Silis. *Anim Checkers* Janet Gusdavison, Marceil Ferguson, Joyce Gard, Maggie Raymond, Evelyn Sherwood, Grace McCurdy, Annie Lee Holm, Betty MacGowan, Woody Chatwood, Florence Hammontre. *Background Dsgn* F. Montcalegre, Paul Julian, Robert Gentle, Art Lozzi, Ron Dias, Tom Knowles, Fernando Arce, Rene Garcia, Richard Khim, Don Watson, Janet Brown, anim. *Lettering* Robert Schaefer. *Cell Prod* Harbard Pennington. *Ink & Paint Supv* Roberta Greutert. *Photog* Charles Flekal, Roy Wade, Gene Borghi, Bill Kotler, Norman Stainback, Dick Blundell, Frank Parrish, Hal Shiffman, John Pratt. *Art Dir* William Perez. *Ed Supv* Warner Leighton, Milton Krear, Pat Foley, Larry Cowan, Dave Horton. *Mus* Marty Paich, Ted Nichols. *Songs:* "Pensate Amore," "The Man Called Flintstone," "Team Mates," "Spy Type Guy," "The Happy Sounds of Paree," "When I'm Grown Up," "Tickle Toddle" John McCarthy, mus, Doug Goodwin. *Song:* "Pensate Amore" sung by Louis Prima. *Sd Rec* Richard Olson, Bill Getty. *Mus Ed* Tony Milch. *Prod Supv* Howard Hanson. *Tech Supv* Frank Paiker. *Asst Prod Supv* Bill Schipek. *Sp Eff* Brooke Linden.

Voices: Alan Reed, Sr. *(Fred Flintstone)*, Mel Blanc *(Barney Rubble)*, Jean Vanderpyl *(Wilma Flintstone)*, Gerry Johnson *(Betty Rubble)*, Don Messick, Janet Waldo, Paul Frees, Harvey Korman, John Stephenson, June Foray.

Animated comedy. When master spy Rock Slag is disabled by henchmen of the sinister Green Goose, head of SMIRK, the Stone Age Secret Service calls upon Fred Flintstone, who is an exact double of Rock Slag, to impersonate the agent and track down Green Goose and his seductive accomplice, Tanya. Accompanied by his wife and daughter and by Mr. and Mrs. Rubble, Fred goes on a supposed vacation trip to Paris. Tanya has moved on to Rome, however, and the two families follow. Though Fred makes contact with Tanya, she leads him into a trap, and he and Barney Rubble end up as prisoners in an abandoned amusement park that serves as headquarters for Green Goose. Both men resist torture until the real Rock Slag arrives to put an end to Green Goose's ambitious plan to conquer all of Eu-rock. Once the madman is captured, he and his coconspirators, including Tanya, are sent off into outer space in one of Green Goose's own secret missiles. With Eu-rock saved, the Flintstones and the Rubbles return to their stone age homes. *Spies. Evildoers. Secret agents. Impersonation. Conspiracy. Amusement parks. Missiles. Stone Age. Paris. Rome. Doubles.*

A MAN CALLED GANNON   F6.3045

Universal Pictures. 14 May **1969** [Kansas City, Missouri, opening; c8 Mar 1968; LP38880]. Sd (Westrex); col (Technicolor). 35mm (Techniscope). 105 min. *MPAA rating* M.

Prod Howard Christie. *Dir* James Goldstone. *Screenplay (see note)* Gene Kearney, Borden Chase, D. D. Beauchamp. *Dir Photog* William Margulies. *Camera* Allen Davey, William Brown. *Art Dir* Alexander Golitzen, Henry Bumstead. *Set Decor* John McCarthy, George Milo. *Set Coörd* Walter Woodworth. *Main Titl* Universal Title. *Asst Ed* Gene Palmer, Richard M. Sprague, Cliff Bell, Jr. *Mus* Dave Grusin. *Mus Supv* Stanley Wilson. *Song:* "A Smile, A Mem'ry and an Extra Shirt" comp & sung by Dave Grusin. *Lyr* Marilyn Bergman, Alan Bergman. *Sd* Waldon O. Watson, William Russell, Jack Bolger, William Griffith, Jack Danskin, Louis Williman. *Asst Dir* Earl J. Bellamy, Skip Cosper, James Welch. *Prod Mgr* Wallace Worsley. *Script Supv/Dial Coach* Betty Abbott. *Cost Dsgn* Helen Colvig. *Wardrobe* Ted Parvin, Tom Bronson, Joanne Haas. *Makeup* Bud Westmore, Vincent Romaine. *Hairstyles* Larry Germain, Clara Holgate. *Sp Eff* Frank Brendel. *Stunt Coörd* John Daheim. *Still Photog* Rollie Lane. *Gaffer* Eugene Woods.

Cast: Tony Franciosa *(Gannon)*, Michael Sarrazin *(Jess Washburn)*, Judi West *(Beth)*, Susan Oliver *(Matty)*, John Anderson *(Capper)*, David Sheiner

(Sheriff Polaski), James Westerfield *(Amos)*, Gavin MacLeod *(Lou)*, Eddie Firestone *(Maz)*, Ed Peck *(delivery rider)*, Harry Davis *(Harry)*, Robert Sorrells *(Goff)*, Terry Wilson *(Cass)*, Eddra Gale *(Louisa)*, Harry Basch *(Ben)*, James Callahan *(Bo)*, Cliff Potter *(Ike)*, Jason Evers *(Mills)*, Jack Perkins *(railroad lineman)*.

Western melodrama. Source: Dee Linford, *Man Without a Star* (New York, 1952). Gannon, a saddle tramp, hops aboard a freight train leaving Kansas City, and when the train stops, he rescues Jess Washburn, a young runaway tied to the tracks by an angry lineman. Gannon allows Jess to accompany him to the small town of Union Wells, where Jess becomes a willing student in the ways of the West. After Gannon has renewed his relationship with Matty, one of the local prostitutes, he and Jess sign on as hired hands for Beth, a young ranch widow. Anxious to move to the city, Beth intends to make herself wealthy in one season by bringing in 1,500 cattle and selling them before winter. The neighboring ranchers, however, are determined to stop her before the cattle destroy the grazing pastures they need for their winter cows. As the ranchers threaten to close off the grazing fields with barbwire fences, Beth pleads with Gannon to help fight the opposition. When he refuses to take her side, she seduces young Jess into helping her. Gannon tries to ward off the bloodshed by delaying the arrival of a trainload of barbwire; when this fails, he sides with the ranchers against Jess by helping put up their fences. During the showdown, Jess begs his former idol to stay out of the fighting and shoots Gannon in the arm when he refuses. Enraged, Gannon throws a rope around Jess, humiliates him by dragging him through the dirt, and then lectures him on the senselessness of gunfighting. Embarrassed and tearful, Jess watches Gannon ride away. *Drifters. Runaways. Prostitutes. Handymen. Widows. Ranchers. Rescue. Greed. Range wars. Seduction. Trains. Cattle.*

Note: Location scenes filmed in Sonora, California. The film is a remake of *Man Without a Star* (Universal, 1955). Beauchamp and Chase are the original screenplay writers; Kearney wrote the revision.

A MAN CALLED HORSE   F6.3046

Sandy Howard Productions–Cinema Center Films. *Dist* National General Pictures. 23 Apr **1970** [Sioux Falls, South Dakota, opening; c27 Mar 1970; LP38188]. Sd; col (Technicolor). 35mm (Panavision). 114 min. *MPAA rating* GP.

Prod Sandy Howard. *Assoc Prod* Frank Brill. *Dir* Elliot Silverstein. *2d Unit Dir* Yakima Canutt. *Screenplay* Jack DeWitt. *Dir Photog* Robert Hauser. *2d Unit Camera* Gabriel Torres. *Art Dir* Phil Barber. *Set Decor* Raul Serrano. *Prod Dsgn* Dennis Lynton Clark. *Titl & Optical Prod Dsgn* Jerome Rosenfeld. *Film Ed* Philip W. Anderson, Gene Fowler, Jr. *Asst Film Ed* Thomas M. Patchett, Robert Briggs. *Mus* Leonard Rosenman. *Mus Supv* Morton Stevens. *Sd* Rafael Esparza. *Supv Sd Ed* Jack Finley. *Supv Mus Ed* Gene Feldman. *Asst Dir* Terry Morse, Jr., Mario Cisneros. *Prod Mgr* Gilbert Kurland. *Unit Prod Mgr* Robert Beche. *Script Supv* Charlsie Bryant. *Prod Asst* Lynn E. D'Amato. *Cost Supv* Frank Delmar. *Cost* Jack Martell, Ted Parvin, Edward Marks. *Makeup Supv* George Lane. *Makeup Artist* Keester Sweeney, Richard Cobos. *Mr. Harris' Makeup* Frank Griffin. *Hairstyles* Agripina Lozada. *Sp Eff* Federico Farfan, Tim Smythe. *Historical Adv* Clyde D. Dollar. *Coöp* Sioux Indians of the Rosebud Reservation. *Sioux Lang Cons* Olive Pretty Bird. *Mus & Dance Cons* Lloyd One Star. *Prop Master* William Dietz. *Stunt Coörd* Terry Leonard. *Head Grip* Rafael DeLong. *Head Electrn* Don Johnson, electrn.

Cast: Richard Harris *(Lord John Morgan)*, Judith Anderson *(Buffalo Cow Head)*, Jean Gascon *(Batise)*, Manu Tupou *(Yellow Hand)*, Corinna Tsopei *(Running Deer)*, Dub Taylor *(Joe)*, William Jordan, actor *(Bent)*, James Gammon *(Ed)*, Eddie Little Sky *(Black Eagle)*, Lina Marin *(Thorn Rose)*, Tamara Garina *(Elk Woman)*, Michael Baseleon *(He-Wolf)*, Manuel Padilla *(Leaping Buck)*, Iron Eyes Cody *(medicine man, Sun Vow ritual)*, Tom Tyon, Jackson Tail, Richard Fools Bull, Ben Eagleman *(medicine men, singers)*, Terry Leonard *(Striking Bear)*, Lloyd One Star, Frank Rabbit, Jr., Justin Thin Elk, Ardene Turning Bear, Ross Kills Enemy, James Never Miss a Shot, Samuel White Horse, Lawrence Old Cross, Ben Black Bear, Bruce Pretty Bird *(warriors)*, Sioux Indians of the Rosebud Reservation.

Adventure drama. Source: Dorothy M. Johnson, "Man Called Horse," in *Collier's* (7 Jan 1950). Lord John Morgan, an aristocratic Englishman, is on a hunting expedition in the Dakotas in the early 19th century. The Sioux attack his camp and scalp his companions, but marvelling at Morgan's blonde hair, they capture him and drag him to their camp, where Chief Yellow Hand gives him to an old squaw, Buffalo Cow Head. When he is not being tortured or ridiculed, he serves as a beast of burden for the squaw. Warned by Frenchman Batise, who is also a slave to the Sioux, not to try to escape, Morgan decides to raise his status by learning the Sioux's speech and customs; later, by killing two scouts of a Shoshone war party, he proves himself to the tribe. Morgan and Running Deer, the daughter of Chief Yellow Hand, fall in love, despite Buffalo Cow Head's objections, and wish to marry; Morgan, however, must first endure the torture of the Sun Vow in which he is hung high above the ground by the skin of his chest. After performing this ritual, he and Running Deer are married. Yellow Hand is killed in a Shoshone attack, during which Morgan leads the defense of the Sioux and kills a Shoshone chief. Running Deer, who is pregnant, also dies as a result of wounds from the attack. After agreeing to become Buffalo Cow Head's son to prevent her from becoming an outcast, Morgan is named tribal chief for his bravery, but when the old woman dies, he leaves the Sioux and sadly returns to England. *English. Aristocrats. Sioux Indians. Tribal chiefs. French. Shoshone Indians. Hunting. Tribal life. Slavery. Torture. Rites and ceremonies. Miscegenation. Marriage. Courage. North Dakota. South Dakota.*

Note: Location scenes filmed in Durango, Mexico.

A MAN COULD GET KILLED F6.3047

Universal Pictures–Cherokee Productions. *Dist* Universal Pictures. 25 Mar **1966** [Miami, Florida, opening; c7 May 1966; LP35379]. Sd (Westrex); col (Technicolor). 35mm (Panavision). 97 min.

Prod Robert Arthur. *In Charge of Prod* Edward Muhl. *Assoc Prod* Ernest B. Wehmeyer. *Dir* Ronald Neame, Cliff Owen. *Screenplay* Richard Breen, T. E. B. Clarke. *Dir Photog* Gabor Pogany. *Art Dir* John De Cuir. *Set Decor* Giuseppe Chevalier. *Film Ed* Alma Macrorie. *Mus* Bert Kaempfert. *Mus Supv* Joseph Gershenson. *Sd* Waldon O. Watson, William Russell. *Asst Dir* Douglas Green, Robert Fiz. *Unit Prod Mgr* Gilbert Kurland. *Miss Dee's Wardrobe* Jean Louis. *Miss Mercouri's Wardrobe* Dimitri Kritsos. *Stunt Coörd* John Daheim.

Cast: James Garner (*William Beddoes*), Melina Mercouri (*Aurora-Celeste*), Sandra Dee (*Amy Franklin*), Tony Franciosa (*Steve-Antonio*), Robert Coote (*Hatton-Jones*), Roland Culver (*Dr. Mathieson*), Grégoire Aslan (*Florian*), Cecil Parker (*Sir Huntley Frazier*), Dulcie Gray (*Mrs. Mathieson*), Martin Benson (*Politanu*), Peter Illing (*Zarik*), Niall MacGinnis (*ship's captain*), Virgilio Teixeira (*Inspector Rodrigues*), Isabel Dean (*Miss Bannister*), Daniele Vargas (*Osman*), Nello Pazzafini (*Abdul*), George Pastell (*Lazlo*), Arnold Diamond (*Milo*), Conrad Anderson (*Heinrich*), Eric Domain (*Max*), Pasquale Carmo Fasciano, Ann Firbank (*Miss Nolan*).

Comedy. Source: David Esdaile Walker, *Diamonds for Danger* (New York, 1954). William Beddoes arrives in Lisbon to investigate financial interests for his American bank. He is mistaken by British embassy official Hatton-Jones for an agent on a secret mission concerning a fortune in missing industrial diamonds. Despite his efforts to prove his total ignorance regarding the gems, Beddoes is pursued by adventuress Aurora-Celeste, the paramour of the murdered man he supposedly is replacing, and by Steve-Antonio, a bogus Portuguese who describes himself to Beddoes as an amateur smuggler and who himself is pursued by Amy Franklin, a former acquaintance from the United States. Soon Beddoes and Aurora-Celeste are being followed by international spies, all on the trail of the hidden diamonds. After being arrested and bailed out by Hatton-Jones, Beddoes decides to ignore his amateur status and solve the mystery. Beddoes, Steve, Amy, and Aurora are invited aboard the yacht of Dr. Mathieson, an Englishman, who reveals himself to be the real thief and Hatton-Jones to be the real agent. Beddoes then engineers an escape and recovers the missing diamonds. He takes his reward money and reluctantly says goodbye to Aurora-Celeste. She, however, is fully confident that they will meet once again; she has purloined his passport. *Bankers. Americans in foreign countries. Secret agents. Adventuresses. British. Spies. Smuggling. Impersonation. Jewels. Yachts. Passports. Rewards. Lisbon. Great Britain—Diplomatic and consular service. Chases.*

Note: Location scenes filmed in Rome and Lisbon. Working title: *Welcome, Mr. Beddoes.*

A MAN—EIGHT GIRLS F6.3048

Iota Productions. *Dist* Unique Film Distributors, Astro Film Co. 4 Sep **1968** [New York showing]. Sd; col. 35mm. 69 min.

Cast: Andrea Castelmagne, Robin Burnee, Holly Saunders, Sharon Carr, Cindella, Karen Bly, Starlene, Deborah Wyler, Mendij.

Adventure melodrama. Linda, Terri, and Ann tire of their office routine and rent a boat for a weekend. Once at sea they remove their clothes and fall asleep and dream about awaking to find themselves adrift in a secluded island cove. They swim ashore and split up to explore the island. Linda and Terri are captured by five beautiful lesbian outcasts who take them to a camp where a man is caged and chained. They hurl Linda into the cage and perform a wild dance around it as the captive man rapes her. Terri and Linda are promised their freedom if Terri can arouse the exhausted man. She succeeds, and as the pair prepare to consummate their desire, Terri is pulled roughly away by the jealous leader of the gang, who whips her and then violates her with a corncob. Meanwhile, one of the gang members drinks wine from the navel of another. They force Linda to become the next object of their sex play, and she finds the experience surprisingly pleasurable. Ann eventually finds her friends, and the trio escape back to their boat with the lesbians in pursuit. *Man-haters. Lesbianism. Sadism. Flagellation. Islands. Dreams.*

Note: Also known as *A Man and 8 Girls; A Guy, Eight Gals; A Guy, 8 Girls;* and possibly as *Eight Girls.* Working title: *Linda.*

A MAN FOR ALL SEASONS (Great Britain) F6.3049

Highland Films. *Dist* Columbia Pictures. 12 Dec **1966** [New York opening; c31 Dec 1966; LP34162]. Sd; col (Technicolor). 35mm. 120 min.

A Fred Zinnemann Production. *Prod-Dir* Fred Zinnemann. *Exec Prod* William N. Graf. *2d Unit Dir* Patrick Carey. *Screenplay* Robert Bolt. *Photog* Ted Moore. *Camera Op* Robert Kindred. *Art Dir* Terence Marsh. *Asst Art Dir* Roy Walker. *Set Dresser* Josie MacAvin. *Prod Dsgn* John Box. *Film Ed* Ralph Kemplen. *Asst Ed* Marcel Durham. *Mus Comp & Cond* Georges Delerue. *Sd* Buster Ambler, Bob Jones. *Dub Ed* Harry Miller. *1st, 2d & 3d Asst Dir* Peter Bolton, Al Burgess, Bill Graf, Jr. *Prod Supv* William Kirby. *Cont* Constance Mills. *Col Cost Dsgn* Elizabeth Haffenden, Joan Bridge. *Wardrobe* Jackie Cummins. *Makeup* George Frost, Eric Allwright. *Hairdresser* Gordon Bond, Helen Bevan. *Tech Adv* Patrick McLoughlin. *Constr Mgr* Peter Dukelow. *Casting* Robert Lennard.

Cast: Paul Scofield (*Sir Thomas More*), Wendy Hiller (*Alice More*), Leo McKern (*Thomas Cromwell*), Robert Shaw (*King Henry VIII*), Orson Welles (*Cardinal Wolsey*), Susannah York (*Margaret More*), Nigel Davenport (*Duke of Norfolk*), John Hurt (*Richard Rich*), Corin Redgrave (*William Roper*), Colin Blakely (*Matthew*), Cyril Luckham (*Archbishop Cranmer*), Jack Gwillim (*chief justice*), Thomas Heathcote (*boatman*), Yootha Joyce (*Averil Machin*), Anthony Nicholls (*King's representative*), John Nettleton (*jailer*), Eira Heath (*Matthew's wife*), Molly Urquhart (*maid*), Paul Hardwick (*courtier*), Michael Latimer (*Norfolk's aide*), Philip Brack (*captain of guard*), Martin Boddey (*governor of Tower*), Eric Mason (*executioner*), Matt Zimmerman (*messenger*), Vanessa Redgrave (*Anne Boleyn*).

Historical drama. Source: Robert Bolt, *A Man for All Seasons* (London opening: 1 Jul 1960). Sir Thomas More is named to replace the fallen Cardinal Wolsey as Lord Chancellor of England. More's devotion to the Church and his deeply conscientious nature immediately bring him into conflict with young King Henry VIII. While valuing More's integrity, Henry resents More's lack of cooperation in his efforts to divorce Catherine of Aragon, who has failed to bear him an heir, and marry Anne Boleyn. Though More serves the king faithfully, he is bound by the law of the Church as the law of God. Faced with the pope's refusal to grant him a divorce, Henry makes himself the spiritual as well as political sovereign of England. The bishops of England in convocation give their consent to the act of Parliament making Henry head of the Church in England, whereupon More resigns from the king's service, hoping that he will be left to retire into private life. More voices no opinion regarding the king's actions, but his silence is taken as a personal rebuke. Henry, prodded by his ambitious advisers, particularly Thomas Cromwell, demands that More take an oath recognizing the king as head of both church and state, and when More declines he is imprisoned in the Tower of London. In time Cromwell and his opportunistic aide, Richard Rich, make false accusations against More, and he is called to answer the charge of high treason. Found guilty, he freely avows his belief that the king's actions are repugnant to the law of God. At peace, he goes to his death on the block. *Philosophers. Royalty. Nobility. Marriage. Divorce. Ambition. Church and state. Conscience. Treason. Capital punishment. Perjury. Great Britain—History—Tudors. Thomas More. Thomas Wolsey. Henry VIII (England). Catherine of Aragon. Anne Boleyn. Thomas Cromwell. Alice More. Margaret Roper. William Roper. Richard Rich. The Church. Papacy. Catholic Church. Church of England. Tower of London.*

Note: Location scenes filmed near Oxford and Southampton, England. Opened in London in Mar 1967.

THE MAN FROM BUTTON WILLOW F6.3050

Phyllis Bounds Detiege. *Dist* United Screen Arts. Jan **1965**. Sd; col (Eastman Color). 35mm. 84 min. [Cut from 87 min.]

Pres by Dale Robertson. *Prod* Phyllis Bounds Detiege. *Dir-Writ* David Detiege. *Photog* Max Morgan. *Prod Dsgn* Ernest Nordli. *Film Ed* Ted Baker, Sam Horta. *Orig Themes* George Stoll, Robert Van Eps. *Mus Cond* George Stoll. *Songs* Dale Robertson, George Bruns, Mel Henke. *Lyr* Phil Bounds. *Sung by* Dale Robertson, Howard Keel, Edgar Buchanan. *Prod Mgr* William Redlin.

Voices: Dale Robertson (*Justin Eagle*), Edgar Buchanan (*Sorry*), Barbara Jean Wong (*Stormy*), Howard Keel, Herschel Bernardi, Ross Martin, Verna Felton, Shep Menken, Pinto Colvig, Cliff Edwards, Thurl Ravenscroft, John Hiestand, Clarence Nash, Edward Platt, Buck Buchanan.

Animated western. Justin Eagle, a U. S. undercover agent in 1869, lives on a farm near the town of Button Willow with Stormy (his Chinese ward), Sorry (an old friend), and numerous animals including Rebel (his horse), Savannah (a snow-white mare), Alfy (a skunk), and Little Condor (a carrier pigeon). Justin is informed that the government is concerned about speculators headed by businessman Montgomery Blaine and his sidekick, The Whip, who are intimidating the settlers in order to acquire their land for an East-West railroad. While the friends are celebrating the birth of Rebel and Savannah's colt, Little Condor flies in and tells them that Senator Freeman, leader of the opposition to the speculators, has been kidnaped. Justin takes Rebel to the schooner in the

San Francisco Bay where the senator is being held and manages to go aboard the schooner before it sails. With the help of Andy the Swede, also a prisoner, Justin overpowers the crew and returns the schooner to port. Upon arriving in Button Willow, Justin and Rebel are warmly welcomed by their friends. *Secret agents. Chinese. Wards. Businessmen. Swedes. Farm life. Friendship. Land speculation. Kidnaping. Railroads. Schooners. San Francisco. United States Congress. Horses. Skunks. Pigeons.*

MAN FROM COCODY (France/Italy)   F6.3051

Euro France Films–S. N. E. Gaumont–P. C. M. *Dist* American International Pictures. caJul **1966**. Sd; col (Eastmancolor). 35mm (Franscope). 84 min.

Prod Roger Duchet, Alain Poiré. *Dir* Christian-Jaque. *Scen* Jean Ferry, Jacques Emmanuel, Christian-Jaque. *Story* Claude Rank. *Photog* Pierre Petit. *Film Ed* Jacques Desagneau. *Mus* Michel Magne. *Titl Song Sung by* Nancy Holloway. *Sd* Claude Durand. *Prod Mgr* Robert Sussfeld. *Sp Eff* Gil Delamare.

Cast: Jean Marais *(Jean-Luc Hervé de la Tommeraye)*, Liselotte Pulver *(Baby)*, Philippe Clay *(Renaud Lefranc)*, Nancy Holloway *(Nancy)*, Maria Grazia Buccella *(Angelina)*, Jacques Morel *(Rouffignac)*, Robert Dalban *(Pépé)*.

Adventure melodrama. When the Sons of the Panther, a secret Ivory Coast society, slay lepidopterist Dumont, police are baffled over a motive. During a subsequent investigation in Abidjan, French attaché Jean-Luc Hervé de la Tommeraye, lepidopterist Baby Sapin-Leterrier, and guide Renaud Lefranc encounter many mishaps devised by the Sons of the Panther. Despite this harassment, Baby discovers a downed airplane laden with diamonds and contacts her Parisian gang of jewel thieves. Lefranc, however, notifies the Sons of the Panther, who kidnap Baby. Rescued by Jean-Luc, Baby debates disposition of the diamonds. As the attaché argues the merits of restitution, he and Baby are abducted by helicopter and flown through the jungle dangling from a rope. The helicopter is pursued by police and finally forced down. Rouffignac, Jean-Luc's superior at the embassy, is unmasked as leader of the Sons of the Panther. Responding to Jean-Luc's supplications, Baby abandons her life of crime, instructing her minions to assist the police. *Naturalists. Butterflies. Guides. Thieves. Police. Perfidy. Abduction. Murder. Jewels. Helicopters. Secret societies. Ivory Coast. Abidjan. France—Diplomatic and consular service. Chases.*

Note: Opened in Paris in Apr 1965 as *Le gentleman de Cocody*; running time: 90 min; in Rome in Aug 1965 as *Donne, mitra e diamanti*; running time: 90 min.

THE MAN FROM C.O.T.T.O.N. see GONE ARE THE DAYS!

THE MAN FROM GALVESTON   F6.3052

Warner Bros. Pictures. 18 Dec **1963** [Seattle opening; c11 Jan 1964; LP29437]. Sd; b&w. 35mm. 57 min.

Prod Michael Meshekoff. *Exec Prod* Jack Webb. *Dir* William Conrad. *Screenplay* Dean Riesner, Michael S. Zagor. *Story* Philip Lonergan. *Photog* Bert Glennon. *Art Dir* Carl Macauley. *Set Decor* William L. Kuehl. *Film Ed* Bill Wiard. *Mus* David Buttolph. *Sd* Frank Sarver. *Asst Dir* Victor Vallejo.

Cast: Jeffrey Hunter *(Timothy Higgins)*, Preston Foster *(Judge Homer Black)*, James Coburn *(Boyd Palmer)*, Joanna Moore *(Rita Dillard)*, Edward Andrews *(Hyde)*, Kevin Hagen *(John Dillard)*, Martin West *(Stonewall Grey)*, Ed Nelson *(Cole Marteen)*, Karl Swenson *(sheriff)*, Grace Lee Whitney *(Texas Rose)*, Claude Stroud *(Harvey Sprager)*, Sherwood Price *(George Taggart)*, Arthur Malet *(Barney)*, Marjorie Bennett *(Mrs. Warren)*.

Western melodrama. Frontier lawyer Timothy Higgins arrives in Tascosa, Texas just as the circuit court is going into session. He finds that Rita Dillard, his former girl friend in Galveston, is accused of murder, and he agrees to defend her. Cole Marteen, Rita's former business associate, threatens to expose her past exploits in Galveston unless she leaves John, her husband, to go away with him. She ignores his threats, and Cole bribes Taggart to bear false witness against her at the trial. Higgins confuses Taggart on the witness stand, and Higgins' request for an adjournment is granted. Later, Taggart is found murdered, and John confesses to the crime to shield his wife. Rita did shoot at Taggart in self-defense, but Higgins proves that the fatal bullet was fired by Cole Marteen. *Lawyers. Frontier and pioneer life. Trials. Perjury. Bribery. Murder. Tascosa. Galveston.*

Note: Originally filmed as a pilot for the television series *Temple Houston*.

THE MAN FROM NOWHERE (France/Italy/Spain)   F6.3053

Leone Film–Orphée Productions–Arturo Gonzales. *Dist* G. G. Productions. 14 Nov **1968** [Houston opening]. Sd; col (Technicolor). 35mm (Techniscope). 107 min.

Pres by Nick W. Russo. *Prod* Elio Scardamaglia. *Dir* Michele Lupo. *Screenplay* Ernesto Gastaldi. *Story* Luciano Martino, Ernesto Gastaldi. *Dir Photog* Guglielmo Mancori. *Art Dir* Walter Patriarca. *Film Ed* Antonietta Zita. *Mus* Francesco De Masi. *Sd* Umberto Picistrelli. *Prod Mgr* Paolo Gargano.

Cast: Giuliano Gemma *(Arizona Colt)*, Fernando Sancho *(Gordon Watch)*, Corinne Marchand *(Jane)*, Roberto Camardiel *(Whisky)*, Rosalba Neri *(Dolores)*, Giovanni Pazzafini *(Kay)*, Pietro Tordi *(priest)*, Andrea Bosic *(Pedro)*, Gérard Lartigau *(John)*, Mirko Ellis *(sheriff)*, Gianni Solaro, Otto Rock, Renato Chiantoni, Valentino Macchi, Tom Felleghi, Emma Baron.

Western melodrama. In order to supply his outlaw band with new recruits, Gordon Watch attacks an Arizona border prison and frees the prisoners, forcing them to join his gang. Lest there be any question of the men's loyalty, Watch brands a large "S" on the arm of each escapee. Only Arizona Colt refuses to join, although he takes advantage of the jailbreak to escape to Blackstone Hill, the primary target of the marauding Watch gang. One of Watch's men murders Dolores, the promiscuous daughter of Pedro, the town's saloon keeper, and the anguished father offers a reward for the death of the killer. Arizona agrees to pursue the assailant if Pedro will add a night with his other daughter, Jane, to the reward money; and Jane accepts, but Pedro demurs. Arizona murders the killer, but he is wounded by Watch and left for dead. Whisky, an old friend, steals the bandit's loot and brings Arizona to Jane for care. Pedro joins other townspeople in forcing Arizona out of town when it becomes evident that the outlaw's wounds may not be severe enough to prevent him from claiming his reward. Immediately thereafter, Watch and his gang return to Blackstone Hill and threaten to raze the town unless the money stolen by Whisky is returned. Jane persuades Arizona to make one final stand, and he shoots the entire Watch gang in the town square. When the streets clear, Arizona promises his love to Jane and rides out of town. *Gangs. Gunfighters. Saloon keepers. Prison escapes. Loyalty. Murder. Filial relations. Extortion. Branding. Rewards. Arizona. Mexican border.*

Note: Released in Rome in Sep 1966 as *Arizona Colt*; running time: 100 min; in Paris under the same title in Sep 1967; running time: 95 min.

THE MAN FROM O. R. G. Y.   F6.3054

United Hemisphere Productions–Delta Films International. *Dist* Cinemation Industries. 3 Apr **1970** [New York opening]. Sd; col (Movielab). 35mm. 92 min. [Also reviewed at 75 min.] MPAA rating R.

Pres by Jerry Gross. *Prod* Sidney Pink. *Dir* James A. Hill. *Photog* José F. Aguayo, Jr. *Film Ed* Evan Lottman. *Mus* Charles Bernstein. *Sd* Jack Reed, sd.

Cast: Robert Walker, [Jr.] *(Steve Victor)*, Steve Rossi *(Luigi)*, Slappy White *(Vito)*, Louisa Moritz *(Gina Moretti)*, Lynn Carter *(Madam)*, Mike Dailey *(Lucky Pierre)*, Shannon O'Shea, Mimi Dillard, Mark Hannibal, Michel Stany, Mary Marx, Jan Bank.

Comedy. Source: Ted Mark, *The Man From O. R. G. Y.* (New York, 1965). Steve Victor is head of the Organization for the Rational Guidance of Youth, established to research sexual response in women. He is called upon to find three prostitutes who have inherited a uranium mine from their former madam. Each of the women is said to bear a tattoo of a gopher on her buttocks. Gina Moretti, the first heiress to be found, is apparently too wealthy to care about the inheritance. Victor discovers that he is being followed by Mafia agents Luigi and Vito, but procurer Lucky Pierre, a midget, helps Victor identify the second prostitute, who also refuses the money and then is murdered. The third heiress whom he finds is murdered in a house run by a crazy madam. Vito is also murdered, but before he dies, he kills Gina, who is revealed to be the real instigator. Lucky Pierre finally becomes the sole heir to the fortune. *Prostitutes. Madams. Midgets. Pimps. Heiresses. Sex research. Inheritance. Murder. Tattoos. Uranium. Mafia.*

Note: Filmed in Puerto Rico and New York City. Also known as *The Real Gone Girls.*

THE MAN FROM THE DINERS' CLUB   F6.3055

Dena Pictures–Ampersand Co. *Dist* Columbia Pictures. 13 Mar **1963** [Winsted, Connecticut, opening; c1 Apr 1963; LP25417]. Sd; b&w. 35mm. 96 min.

A William Bloom Production. *Dir* Frank Tashlin. *Screenplay* Bill Blatty. *Story* Bill Blatty, John Fenton Murray. *Photog* Hal Mohr. *Art Dir* Don Ament. *Set Decor* William Kiernan. *Film Ed* William A. Lyon. *Mus* Stu Phillips. *Orch* Arthur Morton. *Titl Song* Johnny Lehmann, Steve Lawrence. *Sung by* Steve Lawrence. *Sd* Lambert Day, Charles J. Rice. *Cost* Pat Barto. *Makeup* Ben Lane. *Sp Eff* Richard Albain.

Cast: Danny Kaye *(Ernie Klenk)*, Cara Williams *(Sugar Pye)*, Martha Hyer *(Lucy)*, Telly Savalas *(Foots Pulardos)*, Everett Sloane *(Martindale)*, Kay Stevens *(Bea Frampton)*, Howard Caine *(Bassanio)*, George Kennedy *(George)*, Jay Novello *(Mooseghian)*, Ann Morgan Guilbert *(Ella Trask)*, Ronald Long *(minister)*, Mark Tobin *(Quas)*, Cliff Carnell *(Buzzy)*, Edmund Williams *(Jerry Markus)*, Dean Stanton *(1st beatnik)*, Carol Dixon *(little girl)*, John Newton, actor *(father)*, Dorothy Neumann *(spinster)*.

Comedy. Mobster Foots Pulardos, who operates a health gym as a front, plans to flee to Mexico to evade government tax officials. His girl friend, Sugar Pye, suggests that he first arrange for the cremation of a man having his own peculiar identifying characteristic—feet of different sizes—and then apply for a Diners' Club card for use in paying his fare. The request for the credit card comes to the desk of Ernie Klenk, a timid clerk. Nervous about his forthcoming marriage to the boss's secretary, Lucy, Ernie inadvertently okays the application, then, discovering his mistake, rushes to the health gym to recover the club card he has issued. Foots thereupon notices that one of Ernie's feet is larger than the other and decides to burn down the gym, leaving Ernie's corpse as his own, and make his escape using Ernie's club card. By accident, Ernie becomes involved with Sugar Pye and arouses Lucy's jealousy. After arranging for Ernie's death, Foots and Sugar Pye head for the airport; but Ernie escapes and gives chase. By using a fleet of cars and messengers on bicycles, all obtained through Diners' Club cards, Ernie creates a huge traffic jam that brings Foots and Sugar Pye to a halt. As a result of his heroism, Ernie is reunited with Lucy and promoted to the detective department of his agency. *Gangsters. Clerks. Secretaries. Timidity. Arson. Taxes. Credit. Fraud. Murder. Gymnasiums. Traffic. Diners' Club. Chases.*

THE MAN FROM THE EAST (Japan)   **F6.3056**
Toho Co. Aug **1961** [Los Angeles showing]. Sd; col (Eastmancolor). 35mm (Tohoscope). 103 min.
Exec Prod Sadao Sugihara. *Dir* Umeji Inoue. *Screenplay* Katsuya Suzaki, Yoshio Hasuike. *Photog* Kozo Okazaki. *Mus* Hajime Kaburagi.
Cast: Yuzo Kayama, Yuriko Hoshi, Shiro Osaka, Makoto Sato, Jun Funato, Kazuo Yashiro, Kokinji Katsura, Shin Morikawa, Sahara Kenji, Toru Abe.
Melodrama. Kenta, a young minstrel playing in saloons, is approached by a gang of thugs, who claim he is encroaching on their territory. Although he appears strong enough to defend himself, Kenta offers no resistance when the thugs beat him. A wandering poet finds him and offers him refuge in a slum, which includes the ruins of a manufacturing firm bombed during the war. The daughter and son of the factory owner still live there, dreaming of some day rebuilding the business, but a group of gangsters also are interested in the land. The gangsters have attempted to drive off the local inhabitants, but the slum dwellers side with Michiko, the manufacturer's daughter, in resisting the mob. With Kenta's arrival, the people feel they have a champion, but he refuses to help during the next attack by the gang. Curious about Kenta's background, one of the mobsters learns he is a former prizefighter whose overwhelming strength once killed his best friend in the ring. When it is revealed that the dead fighter was also Michiko's older brother, the slum residents drive Kenta away. Kenta finds the poet in the street nearly dead from a gangster beating and becomes so enraged that he returns to help the slum people drive off the gangsters. *Minstrels. Poets. Gangsters. Prizefighters. Brother-sister relationship. Urban life. Guilt. Cowardice. Slums. Factories.*
Note: Released in Japan in 1961 as *Higashi kara kita otoko.*

MAN IN THE DARK (Great Britain)   **F6.3057**
Mancunian Film Corp. *Dist* Universal Pictures. 20 Jan **1965** [New York opening]. Sd; b&w. 35mm. 80 min.
A Blakeley's Films Production. *Prod* Tom Blakeley. *Dir* Lance Comfort. *Screenplay* James Kelly, Peter Miller. *Story* Vivian Kemble. *Dir Photog* Basil Emmott. *Camera* Ceri Davies. *Art Dir* John St. John-Earl. *Film Ed* John Trumper. *1st Asst Film Ed* Roy Taylor. *Mus Dir & Arr* Brian Fahey. *Mus Adv* Frank Patten. *Mus Theme:* "Concerto" Peter Hart. *Songs:* "Blind Corner," "Where Ya Going" Stan Butcher, Syd Cordell. *Song:* "The Princess and the Disc Jockey Bounce" Brian Fahey. *Songs Sung by* Ronnie Carroll, Barry Aldis. *Choreog* Allen Meachem. *Sd Rec* Robert MacPhee. *1st, 2d & 3d Asst Dir* John Stoneman, Stephen Christian, Tony Reed. *Prod Mgr* John Comfort. *Prod Sec* Ann Skinner. *Cont* Lorely Farley. *Wardrobe Mistress* Eve Faloon. *Makeup* George Blackler. *Hairdresser* Ann Box.
Cast: William Sylvester (*Paul Gregory*), Barbara Shelley (*Anne Gregory*), Elizabeth Shepherd (*Joan Marshall*), Alexander Davion (*Rickie Seldon*), Mark Eden (*Mike Williams*), Ronnie Carroll (*himself*), Barry Aldis (*himself*), Frank Forsyth (*police inspector*), Edward Evans (*chauffeur*), Joy Allen, Unity Grimwood, Wendy Martin (*dancers*).
Melodrama. Paul Gregory, a successful songwriter who has lofty aspirations, is blind and is unaware that his wife, Anne, is having an affair with Rickie Seldon, an artist who is painting her portrait. The two plot for Rickie to murder Paul so that Anne may inherit his money. Paul's secretary Joan, who is secretly in love with him, and his agent Mike Williams are keeping secret Anne's infidelity so as not to hurt Paul. It is revealed that Mike is Anne's real lover, and they have planned for Rickie to be discovered by the police just after he has murdered Paul. But Paul foils his wife's scheme; the plotters are arrested; and Paul leaves on a cruise with Joan. *Composers. Painters. Secretaries. Talent agents. Blindness. Infidelity. Murder. Inheritance. Perfidy.*
Note: Released in Great Britain in Sep 1964 as *Blind Corner.*

MAN IN THE MIDDLE (United States/Great Britain)   **F6.3058**
Belmont Productions-Pennebaker, Inc. *Dist* Twentieth Century-Fox Film Corp. 29 Jan **1964** [Los Angeles opening; c29 Dec 1963; LP27126]. Sd; b&w.

35mm (CinemaScope). 94 min.
A Talbot-Pennebaker Production. *Prod* Walter Seltzer. *Exec Prod* Max E. Youngstein. *Dir* Guy Hamilton. *Screenplay* Keith Waterhouse, Willis Hall. *Dir Photog* Wilkie Cooper. *Camera Op* Frank Drake. *Art Dir* John Howell. *Film Ed* John Bloom. *Theme Mus Comp* Lionel Bart. *Orch Mus Comp & Cond* John Barry. *Sd Mix* Les Hammond, Len Shilton. *Dub Ed* Matt McCarthy. *Asst Dir* Kip Gowans. *Prod Supv* David Middlemas. *Unit Prod Mgr* Joyce Herlihy. *Asst to the Prod* Jock MacGregor. *Cont* Angela Martelli. *Cost Supv* Ivy Baker. *Makeup* Sydney Turner. *Hairdresser* Olga Angelinetta. *Military Tech Adv* Myron Cochran, (M. Sgt. USAF). *Casting Dir* Harvey Woods. *Constr Mgr* Leon Davis.
Cast: Robert Mitchum (*Lieut. Col. Barney Adams*), France Nuyen (*Kate Davray*), Barry Sullivan (*General Kempton*), Trevor Howard (*Major Kensington*), Keenan Wynn (*Lieutenant Winston*), Sam Wanamaker (*Major Kaufman*), Alexander Knox (*Colonel Burton*), Gary Cockrell (*Lieutenant Morse*), Robert Nichols (*Lieutenant Bender*), Michael Goodliffe (*Colonel Shaw*), Errol John (*Sergeant Jackson*), Paul Maxwell (*Major Smith*), Lionel Murton (*Captain Gunther*), Russell Napier (*Colonel Thompson*), Jared Allen (*Captain Dwyer*), David Bauer (*Colonel Mayburt*), Edward Underdown (*Major Wyclif*), Howard Marion Crawford (*Major Poole*), Bill Mitchell (*Staff Sergeant Quinn*), Al Waxman (*Corporal Zimmerman*), Glenn Beck (*Corporal Burke*), Frank Killibrew (*Corporal Baxter*), Edward Bishop (*lieutenant at Sikri*), Terence Cooper (*Major Clement*), Graham Skidmore (*Major Hennessy*), Terry Skelton (*Colonel Burnside*), Paul Blomley (*Colonel Winovich*), Alistair Barr (*Colonel Kelly*), Brian Vaughan (*Major McCabe*), Julian Burton (*Major Cummings*).
War drama. Source: Howard Melvin Fast, *The Winston Affair* (New York, 1959). Friction develops between American and British troops stationed in India during World War II and culminates in physical outbreaks between the troops when Lieutenant Winston, an American, shoots British Staff Sergeant Quinn before 11 witnesses. American General Kempton assigns Lieut. Col. Barney Adams to defend Winston at his court-martial, assuring him that the Army Lunacy Commission has found Winston fit and sane. Adams is informed by nurse Kate Davray that Colonel Burton, who headed the lunacy commission, refused to accept the report of the hospital's psychiatric head, Dr. Kaufman, who believes Winston is a psychopath. Burton is anxious to have Winston convicted and hanged to patch the strained relations between the two forces. Adams instructs Kaufman to bring his report to the trial, but when Burton is informed of this order he transfers Kaufman to a distant hospital. Adams visits British Major Kensington; this qualified psychiatrist also considers Winston to be psychopathic but has been warned not to interfere. Kensington believes Winston killed Quinn out of a feeling of victimization because Quinn, a sergeant, had the same duties as Winston, a lieutenant. Winston, in an interview with Adams, raves that he killed Quinn for defiling the white race by consorting with a black woman. Though he despises Winston, Adams refuses to rig the trial, and he holds back his defense, waiting for Kaufman to arrive as a witness. When he learns that Kaufman has been killed in an accident on the way to the trial, Adams calls Kensington to the stand after establishing that no member of the lunacy commission is a qualified psychiatrist. As Kensington describes Winston's mental illness to the court, Winston cracks and begins raving. Adams wins his case and spends a few days of peace and happiness with nurse Davray before leaving the area. The friction between the troops is eased, and they prepare to enter battle in complete unity. *Lawyers. Nurses. Psychiatrists. Judges. Psychopaths. Murder. Insanity. Racism. Injustice. Courts-martial. World War II. India. United States Army. Great Britain—Army.*
Note: Produced in England; location scenes filmed in India. Working title: *The Winstone Affair.*

MAN IN THE MOON (Great Britain)   **F6.3059**
Excalibur Films. *For* Allied Film Makers. *Dist* Trans-Lux Distributing Corp. 12 Jun **1961** [New York opening; c2 Jun 1961; LP21700]. Sd; b&w. 35mm. 98 min.
Prod Michael Relph. *Dir* Basil Dearden. *2d Unit Dir* Norman Harrison. *Screenplay* Michael Relph, Bryan Forbes. *Dir Photog* Harry Waxman. *Camera Op* H. A. R. Thomson. *Focus* Steve Claydon. *Camera Grip* Ted Underwood. *Art Dir* Jack Maxsted. *Set Dresser* Peter Murton. *Draughtsman* Elven Webb. *Prod Dsgn* Don Ashton. *Film Ed* John D. Guthridge. *Asst Ed* Vera Dover. *Mus* Philip Green. *Sd* Norman Savage. *Sd Rec* C. C. Stevens, Bill Daniels. *Boom Op* Gus Lloyd. *Sd Camera Op* Roy Charman, Ted Karnon. *1st, 2d & 3d Asst Dir* Bert Batt, Denzil Lewis, Ronald Purdie. *Prod Mgr* Jack Swinburne. *Prod Sec* Jean Hall. *Cont* Joan Davis. *Dress Dsgn* Anthony Mendleson. *Makeup* William Partleton, John Webber. *Hairdresser* Pearl Orton. *Tech Adv* Herbert Ellis, (Comdr.). *Prop Buyer* Jim Baker. *Ch Floor Prop* Mark Rowe. *Constr Mgr* Bert Jempson. *Still Photog* Ian Jeayes. *Ch Electrn* Harry Black.
Cast: Kenneth More (*William Blood*), Shirley Ann Field (*Polly*), Norman Bird (*Herbert*), Michael Hordern (*Dr. Davidson*), John Glyn-Jones (*Dr.*

Wilmot), John Phillips, British (*Professor Stephens*), Charles Gray (*Leo*), Bernard Horsfall (*Rex*), Bruce Boa (*Roy*), Noel Purcell (*prosecutor*), Ed Devereaux (*storekeeper*), Newton Blick (*Dr. Hollis*), Richard Pearson, Lionel Gamlin (*doctors*), Russell Waters (*woomera director*), Danny Green (*lorry driver*), Jeremy Lloyd (*Jaguar driver*).

Comedy. William Blood, an extraordinarily healthy Englishman, makes his living as a human guinea pig for medical research. He loses his job, however, when his physical fitness prevents him from catching a common cold after spending the night in a meadow. Almost immediately he is recruited by Professor Davidson of the Atomic Research Center, who plans to make Blood the first man on the moon, a project that is concealed from him. When Blood emerges from tests in refrigerators, in hot boxes, on rocket sleds, and in centrifugal whirlers, Blood arouses the envy of Leo, an astronaut who had hoped to win the prize money offered to the first man to attempt a landing on the moon. This situation is remedied, however, when the scientists brainwash Leo into loving his rival. Although Blood eventually learns of the fate awaiting him, the prize money is too tempting, and he agrees to undertake the flight. His spaceship is launched from an Australian range; and the scientists are able to contact him. Unfortunately, he lands in the middle of the Australian bush country rather than on the moon. Blood then heads back to England and his Soho stripper girl friend, Sally. *Professors. Astronauts. Scientists. Stripteasers. Envy. Brainwashing. Health. Common cold. Experiments. Spaceships. The Moon. England. Australia. London—Soho.*

Note: Opened in London in Jan 1961.

THE MAN IN THE STORM (Japan)   F6.3060
Toho Co. Aug **1969** [Los Angeles showing]. Sd; b&w. 35mm. 95 min.
Exec Prod Tomoyuki Tanaka. *Dir* Senkichi Taniguchi. *Screenplay* Senkichi Taniguchi, Takero Matsuura, Takeo Murata. *Art Dir* Yasuhide Kato. *Mus* Urato Watanabe.

Cast: Toshiro Mifune (*Saburo Watari*), Kyoko Kagawa (*Akiko*), Akio Kobori (*Tsujido*), Jun Tazaki (*karate expert*), Akemi Negishi (*Okon*).

Romantic drama. During the early 20th century, Saburo Watari is on his way to his new position as judo instructor at the Shimoda Police Station when he meets Akiko, the daughter of Shimzu, the instructor Saburo is replacing. Tsujido, Shimzu's favorite pupil, becomes jealous of Saburo's romantic involvement with Akiko and unsuccessfully challenges the new instructor to a duel. Saburo is provoked into a fight with some naval officers and loses his post as a result. With the aid of an Okinawan karate expert, Tsujido once more challenges Saburo, who now accepts. Saburo wins both the duel and the right to Akiko's hand. *Schoolteachers. Jealousy. Judo. Karate. Duels. Shimoda. Japan—Navy.*

Note: Released in Japan in 1957 as *Arashi no naka no otoko*.

THE MAN IN THE WATER   F6.3061
Key West Films. *Dist* Key West Films, Crown International Pictures. Jul **1963** [Key West, Florida, showing]. Sd; b&w. 35mm. 80 min.
Prod-Writ T. L. P. Swicegood. *Co-prod* James B. Doherty. *Dir* Mark Stevens. *Dir Photog* Meredith M. Nicholson. *Camera Op* Edmund Gibson. *Film Ed* Betty Steinberg. *Mus* William Loose, Nat Aldeen. *Guitar Solo* Laurindo Almeida. *Mus Cons* Jack Tillar. *Sd* Carlton W. Faulkner, Harry M. Leonard. *Sd Eff* Leonard Corso. *Asst Dir* Harry R. Sherman. *Script Supv* Robert Gary. *Sp Eff* Thol O. Simonson.

Cast: Mark Stevens (*Captain James*), Jack Donner (*Lyle Dennison*), Linda Scott, pseud (*Linda Dennison*), David Aldrich (*Pete Sands*), Louis Oquendo (*Señor Rios*), Russell Smith, Jr. (*coast guard officer*), Mercedes Marlowe (*Mrs. Pete Sands*), Jack Clarke (*bartender at Sloppy Joe's*), Bern Martin, Alexander Panas, Edmund Reed.

Drama. Source: Robert Sheckley, *The Man in the Water* (New York, 1962). Charter boat captain James of Key West, Florida, is persuaded to help smuggle Cuban refugees seeking asylum in the United States. Among the refugees are Linda Dennison and her husband, Lyle. Drifting near the Cuban shoreline as it waits for the refugees to arrive, James's vessel is spotted by Cuban gunners. The refugees successfully board the boat, but Pete Sands, the captain's drunken crewman, is fatally wounded by a patrol boat. The U. S. authorities, alerted to James's illegal operation, impound his boat and revoke his license. Returning to Key West, James becomes attracted to Linda, enraging her jealous, psychotic husband. Lyle learns that James plans to take a cruise on his sloop while awaiting the return of his charter fishing license, and he agrees to give Linda a divorce if James will take him to Bermuda. James agrees, after some persuasion from Linda, but once at sea Lyle knocks James overboard. Lyle, however, cannot operate the boat; and James, after hovering for hours in the water nearby, boards the craft. A fight ensues; Lyle is killed; and James is picked up by a helicopter rescue unit of the U. S. Coast Guard. James returns to Linda in Key West. *Sea captains. Refugees. Cubans. Seamen. Smuggling. Jealousy. Insanity. Murder. Duplicity. Divorce. Coast patrol. Fishing boats. Helicopters. Sailboats. Cuba. Key West. United States Coast Guard.*

Note: Filmed on and around Key West. Title changed to *Escape From Hell Island* for release by Crown International Pictures. Linda Scott is a pseudonym for Ann Rouzer.

MAN MISSING *see* **YOU HAVE TO RUN FAST**

MAN OF IRON *see* **THE RAILROAD MAN**

MAN ON A MISSION   F6.3062
Mankato (Minnesota) Rotary Club. 29 Nov **1965** [Mankato, Minnesota, opening]. Sd; col. 16mm. [Feature film, length unknown]
Dir-Writ Bob Gardner. *Dir Photog* Ray Johnson.

Drama. Attempting to rescue the daughter of an East German scientist who has defected to the United States, Miles West travels to Leutenberg. *Americans in foreign countries. Scientists. Political prisoners. Defectors. German Democratic Republic.*

Note: Filmed in and around Mankato, Minnesota.

A MAN ON FIRE   F6.3063
B. P. Productions. *Dist* J. M. Nercesian Productions, Albatross Productions. 11 Aug **1967** [Maryland license]. Sd; b&w. 35mm. 67 min.
Pres by Carl Pehlman. *Prod-Dir* Carl Pehlman.

Cast: Stella DuFuay, James Byrne.

Melodrama. A peeping tom is found murdered after a series of sexual adventures. Four women are suspected of the crime. *Voyeurism. Murder.*

MAN ON THE RUN *see* **THE KIDNAPPERS**

MAN OUTSIDE   F6.3064
Dist Film-Makers' Distribution Center, Film-Makers' Cooperative. 11 Jun **1965** [New York opening]. Sd; b&w. 16mm. 120 min. [See note.]
Dir Joseph Marzano. *Orig Material* Zeno Legge, Joseph Marzano.

Cast: Barbara Ellen (*Karen*), Gordon Spencer (*Troy Dedseed*), Bhob Stewart (*Zeke Brassman*), Robert James (*Woody Hughes*), Beverly Tey (*Lucy*), Joseph Marzano.

Drama. Alienated from culture and counterculture, three youths experience a sense of loss. *Loneliness. Alienation.*

Note: Originally shown in a working version; subsequently reduced to 100 min.

THE MAN OUTSIDE (Great Britain)   F6.3065
Trio Films–Group W Films. *Dist* Allied Artists. Aug **1968**. Sd; col (Technicolor). 35mm (Techniscope). 97 min. *MPAA rating* M.
Pres by London Independent Producers. *Prod* William Gell. *Dir-Writ* Samuel Gallu. *Adtl Dial* Julian Bond, Roger Marshall. *Lighting Camera* Gilbert Taylor. *Art Dir* Peter Mullins. *Film Ed* Thom Noble. *Mus Comp & Cond* Richard Arnell. *Mus (see note)* Johnny Spence. *Sd Rec* Stephen Dalby. *Asst Dir* Ron Jackson. *Prod Mgr* Al Marcus.

Cast: Van Heflin (*Bill Maclean*), Heidelinde Weis (*Kay Sebastian*), Pinkas Braun (*Rafe Machek*), Peter Vaughan (*Nikolai Volkov*), Charles Gray (*Charles Griddon*), Paul Maxwell (*Judson Murphy*), Ronnie Barker (*George Venaxas*), Linda Marlowe (*Dorothy*), Gary Cockrell (*Brune Parry*), Bill Nagy (*Morehouse*), Larry Cross (*Austen*), Archie Duncan (*Detective Superintendent Barnes*), Willoughby Gray (*detective inspector*), Christopher Denham (*detective sergeant*), Rita Webb (*landlady*), Carole Ann Ford (*Cindy*), Carmel McSharry (*Olga*), John Sterland (*Spencer*), Alex Marchevsky (*Mikhail*), Paul Armstrong (*Gerod*), Hugh Elton (*Vadim*), Derek Baker (*Gerod's assistant*), Frank Crawshaw (*drunken hick*), Roy Sone (*Albert*), Harry Hutchinson (*caretaker*), Gabrielle Drake (*B.E.A. girl*), Carol Kingsley (*barmaid*), Martin Terry (*gambling club barman*), Anna Willoughby (*boutique attendant*), Suzanne Owens (*attendant*).

Mystery melodrama. Source: Gene Stackleborg, *Double Agent* (New York, 1959). Dismissed from the CIA for shielding a fellow agent who allegedly defected to the Russians, Bill Maclean is approached by Greek merchant George Venaxas and asked if he wants to "buy" Rafe Machek, second in command of the Russian Secret Police, who has defected and gone into hiding. Though Maclean wants nothing more to do with espionage, he has already been seen with Venaxas; and when the latter is killed by the Russian Secret Police, Nikolai Volkov, the head of that organization, demands that Maclean reveal the defector's whereabouts. The Russians frame Maclean for the murder of a nightclub hostess, and, hunted by the British police, Maclean contacts Venaxas' sister, Kay Sebastian, and learns that Machek is hiding in a deserted warehouse. Because Machek refuses to come forth without a safe conduct guarantee from the CIA, Maclean calls on his ex-supervisor Judson Murphy and asks for his assistance and $50,000 in payment for the delivery of the defector. A rightwing group headed by businessman Charles Griddon volunteers to put up the money, but the Russians kidnap Kay and threaten to torture her unless Machek is handed back to them. After taking Machek to Kay's roominghouse, Maclean brings the Russian Secret Police there, kills the guards, and then forces Volkov to order Kay's release. At that point Griddon, a double agent, arrives and attempts to kill Maclean but is shot dead by Machek. With Machek free, Maclean learns that the fellow agent he shielded was not a defector—he was drugged and kidnaped. Exonerated, Maclean is asked to resume his job at the Agency, but he refuses, claiming he has had his fill of the spy business. *Secret agents. Americans in foreign countries. Greeks. Russians. Defectors. Police. Businessmen. Espionage. Murder. Frameup. Kidnaping. London. United States—Central Intelligence Agency. NKVD.*

Note: Filmed on location in London. Opened in London in Jun 1968. One source credits Spence with music.

MAN—THE MEASURE OF ALL THINGS see CIVILISATION: MAN—THE MEASURE OF ALL THINGS

MAN-TRAP   F6.3066

Tiger Production. *Dist* Paramount Pictures. 20 Sep **1961** [Detroit opening; c14 Sep 1961; LP20354]. Sd; b&w. 35mm (Panavision). 93 min.

Prod Edmond O'Brien, Stanley Frazen. *Assoc Prod* Sam E. Waxman. *Dir* Edmond O'Brien. *Screenplay* Ed Waters. *Cinematog* Loyal Griggs. *Unit Art Dir* Al Roelofs. *Mus* Leith Stevens. *Sd* Phil Mitchell. *Asst Dir* Tom Shaw. *Unit Prod Mgr* Joseph Behm. *Cost* Edith Head.

Cast: Jeffrey Hunter (*Matt Jameson*), David Janssen (*Vince Biskay*), Stella Stevens (*Nina Jameson*), Elaine Devry (*Liz Adams*), Arthur Batanides (*Cortez*), Perry Lopez (*Puerco*), Bernard Fein (*fat man*), Virginia Gregg (*Ruth*), Mike Vandever (*Bobby-Joe*), Hugh Sanders (*E. J. Malden*), Tol Avery (*Lieutenant Heissen*), Bob Crane, Dorothy Green, Frank Albertson.

Melodrama. Source: John D. MacDonald, "Taint of the Tiger," in *Cosmopolitan* (Mar 1958). Korean War veteran Matt Jameson works in Los Angeles as an engineer for his father-in-law, E. J. Malden. His marriage to loose-moraled, alcoholic Nina is disintegrating, and there is a growing feeling of affection between himself and Malden's secretary, Liz. One day he is visited by Vince Biskay, a Marine buddy whose life Matt saved during the war. To repay Matt, Vince offers him half the reward for help in the recovery of $3.5 million stolen by enemies of a Central American dictator. When the money arrives at a San Francisco airport, they manage to make off with it, but Vince is seriously wounded in a gun battle with some Latin thugs. Going to Matt's house they hold out there until Vince recovers. Nina makes advances toward Vince; and when Matt learns that Vince has no intention of returning any of the money, he forces him to take it and get out. A short time later, the drunken Nina falls to her death from a second-story balcony during an angry encounter with Ruth, her maid. Matt finds the body, panics, and buries it in cement. Returning home, he is beaten up by the Latin thugs. The fight reopens a head injury Matt suffered in the war, and he loses his memory; but after Vince is killed in an automobile crash in Mexico and the money is found in his car, Matt gradually recalls the whole story. Nina's accidental death is verified by Ruth and Liz, and Matt is at last free to begin a new life with Liz. *Veterans. Engineers—Civil. Fathers-in-law. Secretaries. Hired killers. Housemaids. Marriage. Infidelity. Alcoholism. Robbery. Amnesia. Automobile accidents. Rewards. Airfields. Los Angeles. San Francisco.*

Note: Location scenes filmed in California. Pre-release titles: *Deadlock* and *Restless*.

THE MAN WHO CAME AT DINNER   F6.3067

Fleetan Films. *Dist* Able Film Co. ca **1969**. Sd; col. 16mm. 60 min.

Comedy-drama. George Balderson, a rich and pompous lawyer, invites Joe Rush, who is new to the firm, and his wife to dinner. Joe discovers that despite his boss's stuffy exterior, he is a swinger. George introduces his girl friend Karen as his wife and his real wife, bisexual Melinda, as his French maid. The dinner turns into a series of random couplings. *Lawyers. Housemaids. Marriage. Bisexuality.*

THE MAN WHO COULDN'T WALK (Great Britain)   F6.3068

Bill and Michael Luckwell, Ltd. *Dist* Taurus Film Co., Falcon Pictures. 8 Jan **1964** [Los Angeles opening]. Sd; b&w. 35mm. 63 min.

Prod Jock MacGregor, Umesh Mallik. *Assoc Prod* D. E. A. Winn. *Dir* Henry Cass. *Screenplay & Story* Umesh Mallik. *Photog* James Harvey. *Camera Op* Gus Drisse. *Focus Puller* Brian Cummins. *Art Dir* John Earl. *Draughtsman* Jim Morahan. *Film Ed* Robert Hill. *Mus* Wilfred Burns. *Sd Rec* John Mitchell. *Boom Op* Tom Buchanan. *Sd Camera Op* Fred Newton. *1st & 2d Asst Dir* Frank Hollands, Barrie Melrose. *Prod Mgr* Clive Midwinter. *Prod Sec* Josephine Knowles. *Cont* Splinters Deason. *Wardrobe Mistress* Brenda Gardner. *Ch Makeup* Jimmy Evans. *Hairdresser* Joyce James. *Still Photog* Norman Hargood. *Constr Mgr* Wallis Smith. *Electrn* John Richards.

Cast: Eric Pohlmann (*The Consul*), Peter Reynolds (*Keefe*), Pat Clavin (*Carol*), Reed De Rouen (*Luigi*), Bernadette Milnes (*Cora*), Richard Shaw (*Enrico*), Martin Cass (*Beppo*), Margot Van Der Burgh (*Maria*), Martin Gordon (*Lou*), Maurice Bannister (*Joey*), Endre Muller (*Johnny*), Owen Berry, John Baker (*watchmen*).

Crime melodrama. Interrupted at work, master safecracker Keefe Brand is helped out of a tight spot by Carol, who offers him a ride away from the scene of the crime. She introduces him to her crippled father, The Consul, a former Chicago gang boss and wealthy ambassador of a Central American republic. Pressed into service with the Consul's gang, Keefe helps to pull off a series of major heists. A spectacular jewel theft is planned as the biggest operation of all. The diamonds to be displayed in an international exhibition are housed in the safes of six different London jewelers; in one evening the gang will steal them all. Everything goes according to plan until the fifth theft, when police intervene and shoot Rico, one of the thieves. As they make their getaway, Keefe and Carol are captured by Luigi, a rival gang leader, and Keefe discovers that his boss is the man who murdered his father long ago in Chicago. He returns to confront the Consul, only to see him gunned down by the crazed mother of another gang member. As the police arrive, Keefe says goodby to Carol and leaves her his share of the profits. *Safecrackers. Gangsters. Diplomats. Cripples. Thieves. Police. Theft. Murder. Filial relations. Jewels. London.*

Note: Released in Great Britain in 1960. First released by Falcon Pictures; distributed through Taurus Film Co. beginning Sep 1964.

THE MAN WHO FINALLY DIED (Great Britain)   F6.3069

White Cross Productions. *Dist* Goldstone Film Enterprises. **1967**. Sd; b&w. 35mm (CinemaScope). 98 min.

Prod Norman Williams. *Dir* Quentin Lawrence. *Screenplay* Lewis Greifer, Louis Marks. *Story* Lewis Greifer. *Photog* Stephen Dade. *Art Dir* Scott MacGregor. *Film Ed* John Jympson. *Mus* Philip Green. *Harpsichord* George Malcolm. *Sd* Stephen Dalby. *Sd Rec* Bill Bulkley.

Cast: Stanley Baker (*Joe Newman*), Peter Cushing (*Dr. von Brecht*), Mai Zetterling (*Lisa*), Eric Portman (*Inspector Hofmeister*), Niall MacGinnis (*Brenner*), Nigel Green (*Hirsch*), Barbara Everest (*Martha*), Georgina Ward (*Maria*), Harold Scott (*professor*), James Ottaway (*Rahn*), Alfred Burke (*Heinrich*), Mela White (*Helga*), Maya Sorell (*Minna*).

Melodrama. After living in England since the outbreak of World War II, Joe Newman returns to the small Bavarian town of his birth to seek news of his father. There he is told that his father, now dead, had escaped from behind the Iron Curtain, taken refuge in the home of a Dr. von Brecht, and later married a woman named Lisa. The evasive attitude of all those involved, including Police Inspector Hofmeister and insurance agent Brenner, leads Joe to believe that certain facts about his father are being kept secret. He breaks into von Brecht's home and finds an old man in the attic but is clubbed from behind before he can learn the stranger's identity. When he regains consciousness, Joe sees the old man being driven away by von Brecht, Brenner, and Lisa. Joe follows them to a railway station and discovers that the man is a renowned scientist who was forced to switch places with his father just before his death. Following a battle with Brenner, Joe rescues the scientist from being abducted to the East and helps him get out of the country. *Police. Insurance agents. Scientists. Refugees. Abduction. Personal identity. World War II. Bavaria. Iron Curtain.*

Note: Opened in London in Dec 1963; running time: 100 min.

THE MAN WHO HAD POWER OVER WOMEN (Great Britain)   F6.3070

Kettledrum Productions–Rodlor, Inc. *Dist* Avco Embassy Pictures. 12 Aug **1970** [Seattle, Washington, opening]. Sd; col (Eastman Color, print by Movielab). 35mm. 89 min. *MPAA rating* R.

Pres by Joseph E. Levine. *Prod* Judd Bernard. *Exec Prod* Leonard Lightstone. *Assoc Prod* Patricia Casey. *Dir* John Krish. *Screenplay* (see note) Alan Scott, writ, Chris Bryant, Andrew Meredith. *Dir Photog* Gerry Turpin. *Art Dir* Colin Grimes. *Main Titl* David Steen. *Film Ed* Thom Noble. *Mus Comp* Johnny Mandel. *Song:* "Bend Over Backwards" Johnny Mandel, Hal David. *Sung by* Bill and Buster. *Sd* Brian Marshall. *Asst Dir* Barry Langley. *Prod Mgr* David Korda. *Cost* Brian Cox. *Makeup* George Partleton.

Cast: Rod Taylor (*Peter Reaney*), Carol White (*Jody Pringle*), James Booth (*Val Pringle*), Penelope Horner (*Angela Reaney*), Charles Korvin (*Felix*), Alexandra Stewart (*Frances*), Keith Barron (*Jake Braid*), Clive Francis (*Barry Black*), Marie-France Boyer (*Maggie*), Magali Noël (*Mrs. Franchetti*), Geraldine Moffat (*Lydia Blake*), Wendy Hamilton (*Mary Gray*), Ellis Dale (*Norman*), Philip Stone (*Angela's father*), Sara Booth (*Sarah Pringle*), Matthew Booth (*Mark Pringle*), Jimmy Jewel (*Mr. Pringle*), Patrick Durkin (*Herbie*), Virginia Clay (*Mrs. Pringle*), Diana Chance (*stripper*), Ruth Trouncer (*Mrs. Gray*), Paul Farrell (*Reaney's father*).

Comedy-drama. Source: Gordon M. Williams, *The Man Who Had Power Over Women* (London, 1967). Unhappy with both his marriage to the aristocratic, frigid Angela and his job as top public relations executive in the London talent agency promoting egotistic pop idol Barry Black, Peter Reaney turns to drinking and philandering. After he arrives home drunk one day Peter and Angela quarrel and separate. At the agency, Black is confronted by 17-year-old Mary Gray, who claims he has impregnated her. Rather than hazard their client's marriage or the notoriety of a paternity suit, the agency arranges an abortion. Indignant, Peter resigns. Following a wild party in Soho, Peter and his best friend, Val Pringle, an agency writer, return to the latter's home, where Val passes out. Peter and Val's wife, Jody, enjoy intercourse and realize their love for one another. Some time later, Jody and Peter return from a movie to discover Val in bed with Frances, Jody's glamorous friend. Although Peter intends to tell Val of his love for Jody, Val is killed in a truck accident. Badly shaken, Peter resolves to assume the care of Jody and her children. Returning to work at the agency, he learns that Mary Gray's abortion proved fatal and that the company has paid Mary's grieving mother to keep her quiet. After the inquest, Peter goes to Black's country mansion, which is surrounded by screaming adolescent fans. Peter tells the group the unflattering truth about their idol, punches Black in the nose, and, turning his back forever on his former way of life, walks away with Jody. *Public relations men. Talent agents. Executives. Singers. Marriage. Frigidity. Friendship. Infidelity. Separation (marital). Abortion. Drunkenness. Rock and roll. London. London—Soho. Automobile accidents.*

Note: Location scenes filmed in London and Paris. London opening: Oct 1970. Meredith is unconfirmed as screenwriter and may be a pseudonym for Scott and Bryant.

THE MAN WHO LIES (Czechoslovakia / France)   **F6.3071**
Como Films–C. C. F. Lux–Československý Film. *Dist* Grove Press. 13 Apr **1970** [New York opening]. Sd; b&w. 35mm. 95 min.

Prod Jan Tomaskovic. *Exec Prod* Samy Halfon. *Dir-Writ* Alain Robbe-Grillet. *Photog* Igor Luther. *Camera Asst(?)* H. Fisher. *Film Ed* Bob Wade. *Sd* Michel Fano. *Sd Engr* Raymond St. Martin. *Prod Mgr* Maurice Urbain.

Cast: Jean-Louis Trintignant *(Boris Varissa)*, Ivan Mistrík *(Jean)*, Sylvie Bréal *(Maria)*, Sylvia Turbová *(Sylvia)*, Suzana Kocuriková *(Laura)*, Dominique Prado *(Lisa)*, Jozef Króner *(Frantz)*, Július Vašek *(man)*, Catherine Robbe-Grillet.

Drama. Surrounded by German forces, Boris Varissa, impeccably attired in a business suit, flees through a forest and comes upon a gravestone bearing his name. He arrives in a town where the name of lost World War II resistance fighter Jean Robin is honored. Purporting to have fought beside Jean, Boris takes lodging at an inn where he is not recognized and is met with hostility; Boris may have betrayed Jean. He proceeds to a château where Jean's wife, sister, and father live. As the story of his relationship with Jean develops, the details are contradictory and unconvincing. Boris seduces first the maid and then Jean's sister. Jean's father dies, and a Dr. Mueller arrives to sign his death certificate; Boris had claimed to know a Dr. Mueller in the resistance but the others had believed that there was no such person in the area. Boris makes advances to Jean's wife, and his seduction is on the point of success when Jean enters and without a word shoots Boris. Jean's wife mourns the dead man, who then arises to begin telling his story again. *War heroes. Strangers. Housemaids. Maquis. Personal identity. Seduction. Mendacity. Perfidy. Castles. World War II.*

Note: Filmed on location in Czechoslovakia in 1967. Opened in Paris in Mar 1968 as *L'homme qui ment*; running time: 95–97 min.

THE MAN WHO SHOT LIBERTY VALANCE   **F6.3072**
Paramount Pictures–John Ford Productions. *Dist* Paramount Pictures. Apr **1962** [New York opening: 23 May; c13 Apr 1962; LP21681]. Sd; b&w. 35mm. 122 min.

A John Ford Production. *Prod* Willis Goldbeck. *Dir* John Ford. *Screenplay* James Warner Bellah, Willis Goldbeck. *Dir Photog* William H. Clothier. *Art Dir* Eddie Imazu, Hal Pereira. *Set Dsgn* Sam Comer, Darrell Silvera. *Film Ed* Otho Lovering. *Mus* Cyril Mockridge. "Young Mr. Lincoln" theme Alfred Newman. *Sd* Philip Mitchell. *Asst Dir* Wingate Smith. *Unit Mgr* Don Robb. *Cost* Edith Head. *Makeup* Wally Westmore.

Cast: Cleef Stewart, *(Ranse Stoddard)*, John Wayne *(Tom Doniphon)*, Vera Miles *(Hallie)*, Lee Marvin *(Liberty Valance)*, Edmond O'Brien *(Dutton Peabody)*, Andy Devine *(Link Appleyard)*, Ken Murray *(Doc Willoughby)*, Woody Strode *(Pompey)*, John Qualen *(Peter Ericson)*, Jeanette Nolan *(Nola Ericson)*, Lee Van Cleef *(Reese)*, Strother Martin *(Floyd)*, John Carradine *(Cassius Starbuckle)*, Willis Bouchey *(Jason Tully)*, Carleton Young *(Maxwell Scott)*, Denver Pyle *(Amos Carruthers)*, Robert F. Simon *(Handy Strong)*, O. Z. Whitehead *(Ben Carruthers)*, Paul Birch *(Mayor Winder)*, Joseph Hoover *(Hasbrouck)*, Jack Pennick *(bartender)*, Anna Lee *(stagecoach passenger)*, Charles Seel *(election council president)*, Shug Fisher *(drunk)*, Stuart Holmes, Dorothy Phillips, Buddy Roosevelt, Gertrude Astor, Bill Henry, Monty Montana, John B. Whiteford, Helen Gibson, Earl Hodgins, Eva Novak, Slim Talbot.

Western drama. Source: Dorothy M. Johnson, "The Man Who Shot Liberty Valance," in *Indian Country* (New York, 1953). In 1910, Sen. Ranse Stoddard and his wife, Hallie, arrive in the small town of Shinbone to attend the funeral of Tom Doniphon. A reporter questions him about his unannounced appearance, and Ranse tells about his early days as a young lawyer in Shinbone, when he opposed the ruthless rule of Liberty Valance, a notorious gunfighter. The only other two men in the town who were unafraid of the outlaw were Dutton Peabody, a drunken but courageous newspaper editor, and Tom Doniphon, a respected rancher in love with Hallie, who was then a young waitress. Valance became outraged when Ranse was elected delegate to a territorial convention and taunted him into a duel. Hallie knew that Ranse could not handle a gun and pleaded with Tom to save Ranse; but Tom, sick of Ranse's foolhardy bravery, refused. Late one night, Ranse and Valance faced each other on the darkened main street of the town. Several shots were fired, and although Ranse was wounded, Valance was the one who lay dead. Ranse became known as "the man who shot Liberty Valance" and was nominated to run for Congress. Unable to face a career built on a killing, he decided to refuse the nomination. Tom then appeared and confessed that it was he who, out of love for Hallie, fired from the shadows that night. Tom, in effect, became Ranse's conscience, the force that carried him to the U. S. Senate and a brilliant career in Washington, while Tom died a pauper. Ranse's story finished, the reporter decides not to print it because in the old West the legend had become fact. *Politicians. Reporters. Editors. Ranchers. Lawyers. Gunfighters. Outlaws. Waitresses. Reputation. Self-sacrifice. Alcoholism. Fear. Friendship. Funerals. Duels. United States Congress.*

Note: The musical score's theme was originally written by Alfred Newman for Ford's *Young Mr. Lincoln* (1939).

THE MAN WHO WAGGED HIS TAIL (Italy / Spain)   **F6.3073**
Chamartín–Falco Film. *Dist* Continental Distributing, Inc. 18 Sep **1961** [New York opening]. Sd; b&w. 35mm. 91 min.

Dir Ladislao Vajda. *Screenplay* Istvan Bekeffi. *Adapt* Istvan Bekeffi, Gian Luigi Rondi, Ugo Guerra, Ottavio Alessi, José Santugini, Ladislao Vajda. *Photog* Enrique Guerner. *Camera Op* Salvador Gil. *Art Dir* Juan Antonio Simont. *Film Ed* Juan Penas. *Mus* Bruno Canfora. *Sd* Alfonso Carvajal. *Prod Supv* Vicente Sempere, Antonio Morelli.

Cast: Peter Ustinov *(Mr. Bossi)*, Pablito Calvo *(Tonino)*, Aroldo Tieri *(Bruno)*, Silvia Marco *(Giulia)*, Maurizio Arena *(Alfonso)*, José Isbert *(Pietrino)*, Isabel de Pomés *(Paulina)*, Caligola *(dog)*, Franca Tamantini, Carlos Casaravilla, Lola Bremón, Renato Chiantoni, Juan de Landa, José Marco Davó, Enrique A. Diosdado.

Fantasy. Mr. Bossi is a mean and miserly landlord in a slum tenement in the old Italian section of Brooklyn. He drives off peddlers and bill collectors by standing behind his closed office door and barking like a ferocious dog. One day a man selling fairy tales places a curse on him and pronounces that he will turn into a dog until he finds someone to love him. Mr. Bossi is suddenly transformed into a huge, homeless mongrel, reduced to sleeping in empty lots and begging for food. The only one aware of his new identity is Bruno, his meek clerk, but he is unable to help. Eventually Mr. Bossi is befriended by Tonino, a lonely youngster who gets him bones from the local butcher. A short time later, Mr. Bossi sees Giulia, one of his tenants who is an orphan, being swindled out of her inheritance by Alfonso, a neighborhood thug. The young girl hands the money to Alfonso, but Mr. Bossi leaps up, grabs the bills, and eats them. Tonino cannot forgive his new friend for this action, and the dog is once more alone. When some roughnecks attack Tonino, however, Mr. Bossi fights them off, and the child breaks the spell by professing his love for the dog. Suddenly finding himself nude (except for a dog collar), Mr. Bossi hurries back to his office. He reimburses Giulia for her lost inheritance and gives Bruno a raise so that he and Giulia can be married; Tonino is happy to remain Mr. Bossi's friend. *Misers. Landlords. Clerks. Orphans. Swindlers. Hoodlums. Transmutation. Inheritance. Friendship. Personal identity. Tenements. Curses. New York City—Brooklyn. Dogs.*

Note: Filmed on location in Madrid and Brooklyn. Opened in Rome in Oct 1957 as *Un angelo è sceso a Brooklyn*; running time: 95 min; in Madrid in Nov 1957 as *Un angel pasó por Brooklyn*.

THE MAN WHO WALKED THROUGH THE WALL (West Germany)
     F6.3074
Pen Films. *Dist* Shawn International, Inc. 16 Oct **1964** [New York opening]. Sd; b&w. 35mm. 99 min.

Prod Kurt Ulrich. *Dir* Ladislao Vajda. *Screenplay* Istvan Békeffi, Hans Jacoby. *Photog* Bruno Mondi. *Art Dir* Rolf Zehetbauer, Gottfried Will. *Mus* Franz Grothe. *Sd* Walter Rühland. *Prod Dir* Uors van Planta.

Cast: Heinz Rühmann *(Herr Buchsbaum)*, Nicole Courcel *(Yvonne Steiner)*, Rudolf Rhomberg *(painter)*, Rudolf Vogel *(Fuchs)*, Peter Vogel *(Hirschfeld)*, Hubert von Meyerinck *(Pickler)*, Hans Leibelt *(Holtzheimer)*, Anita von Ow, Michael Burk, Hans Pössenbacher, Günter Grüwert, Max Haufler, Karl Lieffen, Richard Bohne, Elfie Pertramer, Henry Vahl, Eduard Loibner, Karl Michael Vogler, Lina Carstens, Dietrich Thoms, Fritz Eckhardt, Werner Hessenland, Georg Lehn, Ernst Fritz Fürbringer, Friedrich Domin.

Comedy. Source: Marcel Aymé, "Le passe-muraille," in *Le passe-muraille, nouvelles* (Paris, 1943). Herr Buchsbaum, a mild-mannered revenue officer whose world revolves around his stamp collecting hobby, is terrorized by a dictatorial supervisor at work. His life is further troubled when his new neighbor disturbs his peace at home by giving piano lessons. He encounters an old professor who tells him that the only thing to do when one is "up against a wall" is to walk through it. Taking the advice literally, Buchsbaum finds that he can walk through walls. Using this power, he drives his supervisor crazy and soon becomes the department head. Then he discovers that his piano-playing neighbor is an attractive widow named Yvonne Steiner, and he falls in love with her. Having no more walls to walk through, he loses his power and settles for his newfound happiness. *Revenue agents. Professors. Widows. Music teachers. Neighbors. Employer-employee relations. Timidity. Philately.*

Note: Released in West Germany in Oct 1959 as *Ein Mann geht durch die Wand.*

THE MAN WITH CONNECTIONS (France)   F6.3075
Columbia Films–Renn Productions. *Dist* Royal Films International. 21 Dec **1970** [New York opening; c1 Feb 1971; LP39226]. Sd; col (Eastman Color). 35mm. 91 min. *MPAA rating* R.
Prod-Dir-Script-Dial Claude Berri. *Dir Photog* Alain Derobe. *Camera* Jean Chiabaut, Yves Agostini. *Art Dir* Jacques d' Ovidio. *Set Dresser* Jean Marcovic. *Film Ed* Sophie Coussein. *Mus* Georges Moustaki. *Arr* Hubert Rostaing. *Sd Dir* Jean Labussière. *1st & 2d Asst Dir* Pierre Grunstein, Jérôme Kanapa, Jean-Claude Valézy. *Prod Mgr* Michelle de Broca. *Unit Mgr* Armand Tabuteau. *Cont* Claudine Gaubert. *Cost* Andrée Demarez. *Makeup* Geneviève Monteil. *Prop Master* Jacques Preisach.
Cast: Guy Bedos (*Claude Langmann*), Yves Robert (*The Father*), Rosy Varte (*The Mother*), Georges Géret (*Corsican adjutant*), Jean-Pierre Marielle (*The Lieutenant*), Zorica Lozic (*Tania*), Claude Pieplu (*The Major*), Claude Melki (*Kudierman*), Nina Demestre (*Arlette*).
Comedy. In 1955 Parisian actor Claude Langmann is drafted into the French Army and forced to leave Tania, his ballerina girl friend. Through a friend, Claude obtains a Paris assignment; but he is soon transferred to one of the provinces, and there he and his new friends are trained by a Corsican adjutant. Claude is given special privileges because he claims to have a friend who knows Brigitte Bardot. He is then assigned as a medic to Morocco, where the Arabs are rebelling against French rule. There, Claude declares all of his friends medically unfit because of various imaginary illnesses. Claude writes to Tania from Algeria to break off their affair, and he returns to Paris when he finishes his tour of duty. *Opportunists. Actors. Dancers. Corsicans. Arabs. Military draft. Revolts. Paris. French Morocco. Algeria. Brigitte Bardot. France—Army.*
Note: Location scenes filmed in Paris and Morocco. Opened in Paris in Apr 1970 as *Le pistonné;* running time: 95 min.

THE MAN WITH THE BALLOONS (France/Italy)   F6.3076
C. C. Champion–Les Films Marceau–Cocinor. *Dist* Sigma III Corp. 24 Jun **1968** [New York opening]. Sd; b&w with col seq (see note). 35mm. 85 min.
Pres by Carlo Ponti. *Dir* Marco Ferreri. *Story & Screenplay* Marco Ferreri, Rafael Azcona. *Photog* Aldo Tonti. *Art Dir* Carlo Egidi. *Mus* Teo Usuelli. *Songs:* "Where Have You Been," "Black-White" played by The Gep and Gep Combo. *Song:* "Barefoot" sung by Orietta Berti.
Cast: Marcello Mastroianni (*Mario*), Catherine Spaak (*Giovanna*), Ugo Tognazzi (*man with car*), William Berger, Sonia Romanoff, Antonio Altoviti, Igi Polidoro, Charlotte Folcher.
Comedy-drama. While working on a promotional device for his candy-manufacturing firm, Mario, a successful Milanese businessman, brings home a package of balloons. When his girl friend, Giovanna, arrives to spend the evening with him, she playfully blows up one of the balloons until it bursts. Suddenly intrigued by the idea of discovering exactly how much air a balloon will hold before it explodes, Mario ignores Giovanna's affectionate advances and rushes to seek the assistance of a poet who lives in the apartment above. This man, however, is so engrossed with four girl friends that he ridicules Mario's problem. Now in a state bordering on obsession, Mario demands that an engineer friend help solve the problem. When this effort also fails, he dejectedly wanders into a discotheque filled with huge balloons falling from the ceiling. Driven to distraction by the blare of the music and the frantic dancing of the young people, he slashes away at the balloons until he is evicted. Somewhat embarrassed, he telephones Giovanna and apologetically offers to bring back food for an intimate dinner. But during the meal he once more begins blowing up balloons, and the disgusted Giovanna walks out on him. Alone with his fixation, Mario blows up one last balloon. When it bursts, his mind snaps, and he hurls himself through a window. As an irate car owner complains about the damage the suicide has done to his parked automobile, Mario's old dog climbs to the shattered window, whimpers for a second, and then goes to eat his master's unfinished meal. *Manufacturers. Businessmen. Poets. Engineers.*

Obsession. Suicide. Balloons (toy). Discotheques. Milan. Dogs.
Note: *L'uomo dai cinque palloni* (also known as *L'uomo dai palloncini*) was produced in b&w in Italy in 1964, then cut and added to a Carlo Ponti production entitled *Oggi, domani e dopodomani,* which opened in Rome in Dec 1965 and was intended for U. S. release by Embassy Pictures as *Paranoia. The Man With the Balloons* is Marco Ferreri's reclaimed segment, released after two color sequences were added and several of the original scenes tinted. The other two segments of *Paranoia* were released by M-G-M in 1968 as *Kiss the Other Sheik,* q. v.

THE MAN WITH X-RAY EYES *see* "X"—THE MAN WITH X-RAY EYES

MAN WITHOUT A FACE *see* PYRO

MANASADEEKA *see* MNASIDIKA

THE MANCHURIAN CANDIDATE   F6.3077
M. C. Productions. *Dist* United Artists. 24 Oct **1962** [New York opening; c2 Nov 1962; LP23300]. Sd; b&w. 35mm. 126 min.
Prod George Axelrod, John Frankenheimer. *Exec Prod* Howard W. Koch. *Dir* John Frankenheimer. *Screenplay* George Axelrod. *Photog* Lionel Lindon. *Camera Op* John Mehl. *Camera Asst* Felix Barlow, Eugene Levitt. *Art Dir* Richard Sylbert. *Asst Art Dir* Phil Jeffries. *Set Decor* George R. Nelson. *Set Dsgn* Lucius Croxton, Seymour Klate, John M. Elliott, Joseph S. Toldy. *Film Ed* Ferris Webster. *Asst Ed* Carl Mahakian. *Mus Comp & Cond* David Amram. *Sd* Joe Edmondson. *Rec* Paul Wolfe. *Boom Op* William Flannery. *Asst Dir* Joseph Behm, David Salven, Read Killgore. *Prod Asst* Gene Martell. *Script Supv* Molly Kent, Grace Dubray. *Cost Dsgn* Moss Mabry. *Wardrobe* Wesley V. Jefferies, Morris Brown, Ronald Talsky, Angela Alexander, Rose Viebeck. *Makeup* Bernard Ponedel, Jack Freeman, Ron Berkeley, Dorothy Parkinson. *Hairstyles* Gene Shacove, Mary Westmoreland. *Sp Eff* Paul Pollard. *Dial Coach* Thom Conroy. *Still Photog* Bill Creamer. *Gaffer* Robert Campbell, gaffer. *Prop* Dick Borland, Gaylin Schultz, Arden Cripe, Richard M. Rubin.
Cast: Frank Sinatra (*Bennett Marco*), Laurence Harvey (*Raymond Shaw*), Janet Leigh (*Rosie*), Angela Lansbury (*Raymond's mother*), Henry Silva (*Chunjin*), James Gregory (*Sen. John Iselin*), Leslie Parrish (*Jocie Jordon*), John McGiver (*Sen. Thomas Jordon*), Khigh Dhiegh (*Yen Lo*), James Edwards (*Corporal Melvin*), Douglas Henderson (*colonel*), Albert Paulsen (*Zilkov*), Barry Kelley (*secretary of defense*), Lloyd Corrigan (*Holborn Gaines*), Madame Spivy (*Berezovo*), Joe Adams (*psychiatrist*), Whit Bissell (*medical officer*), Mimi Dillard (*Melvin's wife*), Anton Van Stralen (*officer*), John Lawrence (*Gossfeld*), Tom Lowell (*Lembeck*), Richard La Pore (*Navole*), Nicky Blair (*Silvers*), William Thourlby (*Little*), Irving Steinberg (*Freeman*), John Francis (*Haiken*), Robert Riordan (*nominee*), Reggie Nalder (*Gomel*), Robert Burton (*convention chairman*), Harry Holcombe (*general*), Nick Bolin, Miyoshi Jingu.
Melodrama. Source: Richard Condon, *The Manchurian Candidate* (New York, 1959). During the Korean War, members of a U. S. Army patrol are captured and taken to Manchuria by Chinese Communists who brainwash them into believing that Raymond Shaw, a mother-dominated sergeant, has led a successful action against the Communists. Back in the United States, Raymond is awarded the Congressional Medal of Honor on the strength of his comrades' testimony. Actually he is now a puppet of the Communists; at the sight of a Queen of Diamonds, his mind is triggered into obeying any instruction, retaining no knowledge of his subsequent actions. Meanwhile, another member of the patrol, Bennett Marco, begins having nightmares in which he vaguely recalls what happened in Korea. Suspicious, he starts an investigation and discovers Raymond's strange reaction to the playing card. Unknown to Raymond, the key Communist behind the U. S. operation is his mother, a politically ambitious woman who plans to have her son shoot the presidential nominee during a rally at Madison Square Garden, thus paving the way for her husband, Senator Iselin, the vice-presidential nominee, to take control of the government. As part of the Communist master plan, she uses the cards to force Raymond into killing both his wife, Jocie, and his father-in-law, Senator Jordan, a crusading liberal and his mother's chief political enemy. On the night of the rally, Marco confronts Raymond with a handful of the cards and tries to convince him that he no longer has control of his own mind, but Raymond follows his mother's instructions and takes a rifle to a deserted projection booth. At the last moment, however, the hypnotic spell breaks and he kills his mother and stepfather and then takes his own life. *War heroes. Veterans. Communists. Spies. Chinese. Masterminds. Politicians. Stepfathers. Fathers-in-law. Brainwashing. Hypnotism. Conspiracy. Assassination. Amnesia. Ambition. Oedipus complex. Filial relations. Matricide. Suicide. Playing cards. Political conventions. Medal of Honor. Korean War 1950–53. Manchuria. United States Army. United States Congress. Madison Square Garden. Dreams.*
Note: Location scenes filmed in and around Los Angeles and New York City.

MANDABI (France/Senegal)   F6.3078

Les Films Domirêve–Comptoir Français du Film. *Dist* Grove Press. 26 Mar 1970 [New York opening]. Sd; col (Eastman Color). 35mm. 90 min.

Exec Prod Robert de Nesle. *Assoc Prod* Jean Maumy, Paulin S. Vieyra. *Dir-Writ* Ousmane Sembene. *Story* L. S. Senghor. *Dir Photog* Paul Soulignac. *Camera* Georges Caristan. *Asst Camera* Issa Thiaw. *2d Asst Camera* Joseph Diatta. *Film Ed (see note)* Gilou Kikoine, Bernard Lefebre. *Asst Film Ed* Max Saldinger. *Sd* Henri Moline. *Boom* Mawa Guaya. *Asst Sd* El Hadj M'Bow. *Asst Dir* Ababacar Samb. *Prod Mgr* Ibrahima Barro. *Script Girl* Anne Marie Rochas. *Prod Sec* Awa Sylla. *Still Photog* Maya Bracher. *Ch Electrn* Emile Ganem. *Grip* Cherif Dia, Amate Dia.

Cast: Mamadou Gueye (*Ibrahim Dieng*), Ynousse N'Diaye (*1st wife*), Issa Niang (*2d wife*), Serigne N'Diayes (*Imam*), Serigne Sow (*Maissa*), Moustapha Touré (*shopkeeper*), Farba Sarr (*businessman*), Moudoun Faye (*mailman*), Moussa Diouf (*nephew*), Christophe M'Doulabia (*water seller*), Thérèse Bas (*Dieng's sister*), Mamadou Cisoko.

Comedy-drama. Source: Ousmane Sembene, "Le mandat," in *Vehi-ciosane; ou, Blanche-genèse; suivi du Mandat* (Paris, 1965). Ibrahim Dieng, an unemployed worker in Dakar, receives a money order from his nephew in Paris and goes to the post office to cash it, but he is told that he must have an identity card. He then goes to a police station where he is told that he cannot get an identity card without his birth certificate; at city hall he finds that he cannot get a birth certificate without a photograph. Dieng persuades another of his nephews, a water seller, to loan him the money until he can cash the money order, so the nephew gives him a check, but still without a card Dieng cannot cash it. After bribing the bank teller to cash the check, Dieng takes the balance of the money to a photographer's shop. When he returns the next day, he finds that the photographer has absconded with his money. He goes back to his nephew and asks him to cash the money order. The nephew takes the money order but returns empty-handed, explaining that his pocket has been picked. Dieng soon realizes that his nephew has cheated him, and he is now resigned to the loss of the money. *Uncles. Police. Bank clerks. Photographers. Swindlers. Unemployment. Bureaucracy. Bribery. Theft. Documentation. Loans. Dakar.*

Note: Location scenes filmed in Dakar. Opened in Paris in Nov 1968 as *Le mandat*; running time: 90 min; in Dakar in Dec 1968; running time: 105 min. Sources conflict in crediting film editor. Christophe M'Doulabia is also known as Christophe Colomb. Also known as *The Money Order*.

LE MANDAT *see* MANDABI

MANDRAGOLA (France/Italy)   F6.3079

Arco Film–C. C. F. Lux. *Dist* Europix-Consolidated Corp. 6 Jun 1966 [New York opening]. Sd; b&w. 35mm. 97 min.

Pres by Dino Fazio. *Prod* Alfredo Bini. *Dir* Alberto Lattuada. *Screenplay* Luigi Magni, Stefano Strucchi, Alberto Lattuada. *Photog* Tonino Delli Colli. *Asst Photog* Giancarlo Zagni. *Set Dsgn* Carlo Egidi. *Film Ed* Nino Baragli. *Mus* Gino Marinuzzi, Jr. *Prod Mgr* Eliseo Boschi. *Cost* Danilo Donati.

Cast: Rosanna Schiaffino (*Lucrezia*), Philippe Leroy (*Callimaco*), Jean-Claude Brialy (*Ligurio*), Totò (*Fra Timoteo*), Romolo Valli (*Nicia*), Nilla Pizzi (*Sostrata, Lucrezia's mother*), Armando Bandini (*Siro*), Pia Fioretti, Mimo Billi, Donato Castellaneta, Ugo Attanasio, Luigi Leoni, Renato Montalbano.

Costume comedy. Source: Niccolò Machiavelli, *La mandragola* (1514). In the 16th century, Callimaco, a wealthy young Florentine studying in France, hears of the celebrated beauty of Lucrezia Calfucci, the young wife of Nicia, a prominent old notary. Accompanied by his manservant, Callimaco returns to Florence to undertake the seduction of the virtuous Lucrezia. Because she has not been able to bear a child for Nicia, Lucrezia has endured a variety of torments designed to cure sterility. Callimaco connives with Ligurio, a professional parasite, on a means of executing his plan. Posing as a famed physician, Callimaco informs the foolish Nicia that his wife will bear him a child if she drinks a potion made from the mandrake root. Callimaco further explains that the first man to lie with her will die, and it is therefore imperative that a substitute lover be found. Nicia is convinced, but the chaste Lucrezia agrees only reluctantly, pressured by her mother and Fra Timoteo, a corruptible monk. Callimaco then poses as a street vagabond and allows himself to be taken by force to Lucrezia's chambers. She is repulsed by the seeming halfwit until Callimaco removes his disguise to confess his part in the conspiracy. Overcome by his passion and tenderness, Lucrezia welcomes him into her arms. Later, she informs her husband that she will require the services of her physician for a long time to come, and that Callimaco must become a permanent member of the household. *Rakes. Students. Physicians. Cuckolds. Notaries. Monks. Sterility (sexual). Seduction. Disguise. Infidelity. Duplicity. Conspiracy. Marriage. Potions. Florence.*

Note: Original Italian title: *La mandragola* (1965), running time: 100 min. English dubbed version known as *Mandragola/The Love Root* and *The Love Root*.

MANIA (Great Britain)   F6.3080

Triad Productions. *Dist* Valiant Films, Pacemaker Pictures. 24 Jan 1961 [Boston opening]. Sd; b&w. 35mm (Dyaliscope). 87 min.

Prod Robert S. Baker, Monty Berman. *Dir-Orig Story* John Gilling. *Screenplay* John Gilling, Leon Griffiths. *Photog* Monty Berman. *Art Dir* John Elphick. *Ed* Jack Slade. *Mus* Stanley Black.

Cast: Peter Cushing (*Dr. Robert Knox*), June Laverick (*Martha*), Donald Pleasence (*William Hare*), George Rose (*William Burke*), Dermot Walsh (*Doctor Mitchell*), Renee Houston (*Helen Burke*), Billie Whitelaw (*Mary Patterson*), John Cairney (*Chris Jackson*), Melvyn Hayes (*Daft Jamie*), June Powell (*Maggie O'Hara*), Geoffrey Tyrrell (*Old Davey*), Beckett Bould (*Old Angus*), George Bishop (*blind man*), Philip Leaver (*Dr. Elliott*), George Woodbridge (*Dr. Ferguson*), John Rae (*Reverend Lincoln*), Andrew Faulds (*Inspector McCulloch*), Esma Cannon (*Aggie*), Raf De La Torre (*Baxter*), Michael Balfour (*drunken sailor*), George Street (*barman*), Michael Mulcaster (*undertaker*), Jack McNaughton (*stallholder*).

Horror film. In Edinburgh during the 1820s, Dr. Robert Knox holds to the theory that nothing should stand in the way of science, not even a law stipulating that only the bodies of criminals hanged in prison may be used for medical research. Consequently, he scandalizes his more orthodox colleagues by dealing with grave robbers, in particular, two nefarious Irishmen named Burke and Hare. The two men eventually decide to obtain additional corpses by murdering unknown, drunken derelicts. But they over-reach themselves when they kill a prostitute, Mary Patterson, and her boyfriend, Chris, one of Dr. Knox's students. When the two fiends are arrested, Hare turns king's evidence to escape Burke's fate on the gallows. Upon his release, however, Hare is attacked by an angry mob who burn out his eyes as retribution for his crimes. Dr. Knox, cleared of complicity in the murders, finds himself despised by the people of Edinburgh, but he becomes a renowned lecturer. *Physicians. Prostitutes. Grave robbers. Students. Lecturers. Derelicts. Murder. Capital punishment. Revenge. Mutilation. Corpses. Edinburgh.*

Note: Released in Great Britain in Feb 1960 as *The Flesh and the Fiends*; running time: 97 min. Also known as *Psycho Killers*. Re-released by Pacemaker Pictures in Nov 1965 as *The Fiendish Ghouls*; running time: 74 min.

MANIAC (Great Britain)   F6.3081

Hammer Film Productions. *Dist* Columbia Pictures. 30 Oct 1963 [New York opening; c31 Dec 1962; LP25628]. Sd (Westrex); b&w. 35mm (Megascope). 87 min.

Prod-Writ Jimmy Sangster. *Dir* Michael Carreras. *Dir Photog* Wilkie Cooper. *Camera Op* Harry Gillam. *Focus* Tommie Fletcher, Trevor Wrenn. *Camera Grip* L. Kelly. *Art Dir* Edward Carrick. *Asst Art Dir* Jean Peyre. *Draughtsman* Fred Carter. *Scenic Artist* Felix Sergejak. *Main Titl* Chambers & Partners. *Supv Ed* James Needs. *Ed* Tom Simpson. *Mus Comp & Cond* Stanley Black. *Sd Rec* Cyril Swern. *Sd Ed* Roy Baker. *Boom Op* Bill Baldwin. *Sd Camera Op* Ron Matthews. *1st & 2d Asst Dir* Ross MacKenzie, Terry Lens. *Prod Mgr* Bill Hill. *Asst to the Prod* Ian Lewis. *Cont* Kay Rawlings. *Prod Sec* Marguerite Green. *Wardrobe Supv* Molly Arbuthnot. *Wardrobe Mistress* Jean Fairlie. *Makeup Artist* Basil Newall. *Hairdresser* Pat McDermott. *Prop Buyer* Margery Whittington. *Still Photog* James Swarbrick. *Carpenter* Tommy Westbrook. *Painter* A. Smith. *Stagehand* E. Power. *Rigger* V. Bailey. *Elec Supv* Bert Chapple. *Prop Chargehand* Tommy Ibbetson.

Cast: Kerwin Mathews (*Geoff Farrell*), Nadia Gray (*Eve Beynat*), Donald Houston (*Georges Beynat*), Liliane Brousse (*Annette Beynat*), George Pastell (*Inspector Etienne*), Arnold Diamond (*Janiello*), Norman Bird (*Salon*), Justine Lord (*Grace*), Jerold Wells (*Giles*), Leon Peers (*Blanchard*).

Crime melodrama. Innkeeper Georges Beynat is judged insane and sentenced to life imprisonment in a criminal asylum when he goes berserk and kills the man who raped his 15-year-old daughter, Annette. Four years later an American artist, Geoff Farrell, visits the small country inn operated by Annette and her attractive stepmother, Eve, in Provence, France. The older woman easily seduces Geoff, although he was interested in Annette, and involves him in a plan for helping her husband escape from the asylum. She tells Geoff that Beynat is now quite sane and that a male nurse at the asylum will help arrange the breakout. In return for his freedom, Beynat will disappear and allow Eve and Geoff to marry. On the night of the break they wait for Beynat to come over the wall. He fails to appear, and they return to their car to find him already awaiting them. After dropping him off at the Marseille docks, they find the body of a murdered man in the trunk of the car. Assuming that Beynat must still be insane and murdered the male nurse, Geoff tries, unsuccessfully, to dispose of the body. The next day he is confronted by Beynat, who ties him up and places him in an outbuilding along with the corpse of the male nurse. His plan is to burn both bodies beyond recognition, thereby leaving the police to conclude that the corpses are those of himself and the male nurse. But Geoff, aided by a handyman, escapes from the outbuilding just before the explosion. He joins Inspector Etienne in a plot for trapping Eve. It develops that the murdered man was actually Beynat, whom the male nurse, Eve's true lover, was impersonating. Eve also tries to arrange for Annette's death, but the attempt fails, and it is the male nurse who is killed as the police arrive to take Eve into custody. *Innkeepers. Artists. Americans in foreign countries. Nurses. Police. Prison escapees. Murder. Insanity. Perfidy. Rape. Fatherhood. Seduction. Insane asylums. Provence. Marseilles.*

Note: Released in Great Britain in May 1963. Filmed in La Camargue, France, and England.

MANJI *see* **PASSION**

THE MANKILLERS *see* **FASTER, PUSSYCAT! KILL! KILL!**

EIN MANN GEHT DURCH DIE WAND *see* **THE MAN WHO WALKED THROUGH THE WALL**

MÄNNER MÜSSEN SO SEIN *see* **HIPPODROME**

MÄNNISKOR MÖTS OCH LJUV MUSIK UPPSTÅR I HJÄRTAT *see* **PEOPLE MEET AND SWEET MUSIC FILLS THE HEART**

LA MANO EN LA TRAMPA *see* **THE HAND IN THE TRAP**

MANOS, THE HANDS OF FATE   F6.3082
Sun City Films. *Dist* Emerson Film Enterprises. 15 Nov 1966 [El Paso, Texas, opening]. Sd; col (Eastman Color). 35mm. 74 min.
A Film by Hal Warren.
Cast: Tom Neyman, Diane Mahree, Hal Warren, John Reynolds.
Horror film. Traveling in the desert, a family accidentally stumbles on the tomb headquarters of a cult of "night people." The family is terrorized, and a beautiful woman's face is disfigured by a burning hand as a sacrificial offering to the idol, Manos. *Disfiguration. Human sacrifice. Deserts. Cults.*
Note: Filmed in El Paso, Texas.

MAN'S FAVORITE SPORT?   F6.3083
Laurel Productions–Gibraltar Productions. *Dist* Universal Pictures. 29 Jan 1964 [Miami Beach, Florida, opening; c29 Feb 1963 (*sic*); LP32701]. Sd (Westrex); col (Technicolor). 35mm. 120 min.
Pres by Howard Hawks. *Prod-Dir* Howard Hawks. *In Charge of Prod* Edward Muhl. *Assoc Prod* Paul Helmick. *Screenplay* John Fenton Murray, Steve McNeil. *Dir Photog* Russell Harlan. *Art Dir* Alexander Golitzen, Tambi Larsen. *Set Decor* Robert Priestley. *Titl & Sp Titl Photog* Pacific Title, Don Ornitz. *Film Ed* Stuart Gilmore. *Mus* Henry Mancini. *Titl Song* Henry Mancini, Johnny Mercer. *Sd* Waldon O. Watson, Joe Lapis. *Asst Dir* Tom Connors, James Welch, David Hawks. *Unit Prod Mgr* Terence Nelson. *Script Supv* Bruce Kessler. *Cost Dsgn* Edith Head. *Men's Wardrobe* Peter Saldutti. *Makeup* Bud Westmore. *Hairstyles* Larry Germain. *Sp Mech Eff* Ben McMahon. *Tech Adv (Fishing)* Don Allen. *Tech Adv (Aquatic Seq)* Fred Zendar. *Tech Adv (Auto Seq)* Jack Poole. *Tech Adv (Sp Eff)* Dick Parker. *Tech Adv (Bear Trainer)* John Welde. *Prop Master* Julius Rosenkrantz.
Cast: Rock Hudson (*Roger Willoughby*), Paula Prentiss (*Abigail Page*), Maria Perschy (*Isolde "Easy" Mueller*), John McGiver (*William Cadwalader*), Charlene Holt (*Tex Connors*), Roscoe Karns (*Major Phipps*), James Westerfield (*policeman*), Norman Alden (*John Screaming Eagle*), Forrest Lewis (*Skaggs*), Regis Toomey (*Bagley*), Don Allen (*Tom*), Tyler McVey (*customer Bush*), Kathie Browne (*Marcia*), Med Flory (*Tucker*), Linda Foster, Paul Langton.
Comedy. Source: Pat Frank, "The Girl Who Almost Got Away" (a story; publication undetermined). Roger Willoughby, the most successful fishing equipment salesman for Abercrombie and Fitch in San Francisco, is the author of a bestselling book on fishing, although he has never fished. Abby Page, publicity agent for the Wakopoogee Lake fishing tournament, persuades Roger's boss, Mr. Cadwalader, that Roger should enter the tournament. Roger confesses to Abby that he cannot fish, but she and a friend promise to teach him. Tex, Roger's fiancée, becomes jealous of his time spent with the two women and leaves. Roger wins the tournament with the help of a bear, but, confessing that he is a phony, he forfeits the prize. Cadwalader fires him and then reconsiders when he realizes that a novice winning a tournament is better advertising for the company. Meanwhile, Roger finds Abby camping in the woods, and he climbs into her sleeping bag when a storm breaks. They fall asleep and awaken floating in the lake in the bag. Cadwalader appears in a canoe to inform Roger that he has been rehired at a higher salary, and he abandons the happy couple to find their way ashore. *Salesmen. Authors. Publicists. Fishing. Fraud. Jealousy. Employer-employee relations. Tournaments. San Francisco. Abercrombie and Fitch (San Francisco). Storms. Bears.*
Note: Location scenes filmed in San Francisco.

THE MANSTER (United States/Japan)   F6.3084
United Artists of Japan–George Breakston Enterprises. *Dist* Lopert Pictures. 28 Mar 1962 [San Francisco opening]. Sd; b&w. 35mm. 72 min.

Pres by William Shelton. A Shaw–Breakston Production. *Prod* George P. Breakston. *Assoc Prod* Robert Perkins, Ryukichi Aimono. *Dir* George P. Breakston, Kenneth Crane. *Screenplay* Walter J. Sheldon. *Photog* David Mason. *Art Dir* Nobori Miyakuni. *Film Ed* Kenneth Crane. *Mus* Hirooki Ogawa. *Sd Rec* Senri Ota.
Cast: Peter Dyneley (*Larry Stanford*), Jane Hylton (*Linda Stanford*), Satoshi Nakamura (*Dr. Suzuki*), Terri Zimmern (*Tara*), Toyoko Takechi (*Emiko*), Jerry Ito (*Superintendent Aida*), Norman Van Hawley (*Ian Matthews*), Alan Tarlton (*Jennsen*).
Science fiction melodrama. Source: George P. Breakston, "Nightmare" (publication undetermined). Larry Stanford, an American reporter in Tokyo, is assigned to interview Dr. Suzuki. Unbeknownst to the journalist, the wealthy scientist through experimentation has already rendered his wife and brother subhuman mutants. With the help of his seductive assistant Tara, Suzuki secretly injects Stanford with a serum which alters the newsman's disposition, causing him to reject family and friends. Eventually the reporter grows another head, incredibly hideous, and commits multiple murders. Enraged at his alteration, the mutant tosses Suzuki and Tara into a volcano. As he contemplates suicide, the heat from the crater splits him into two beings, one man, one monster. So separated, the journalist throws the monster in the volcano. *Monsters. Reporters. Scientists. Americans in foreign countries. Mutation. Metamorphosis. Experiments. Murder. Serums. Volcanoes. Tokyo.*
Note: Also known as *The Manster—Half Man, Half Monster.*

LE MANTEAU ROUGE *see* **THE RED CLOAK**

IL MANTELLO ROSSO *see* **THE RED CLOAK**

MANTIS IN LACE   F6.3085
Boxoffice International Pictures. *Dist* Boxoffice International Film Distributors. 19 Jun 1968 [Maryland license]. Sd; col (Eastman Color). 35mm. 80 min. *MPAA rating* R.
Pres by Harry H. Novak, Peter Perry. *Prod-Writ* Sanford White. *Exec Prod* Harry H. Novak. *Dir* William Rotsler. *Photog* Leslie Kovacs. *Lighting* Richard Aguilar. *Asst Camera* Peter Sorel. *Set Dsgn* Frank Borass. *Film Ed* Peter Perry. *Theme Song:* "Lila" Vic Lance. *Sung by* Lynn Harper. *Sd* Paul Hunt. *Boom* Rick Heenan. *Mus & Eff Ed* Frank Coe. *Prod Mgr* Bethel Buckalew. *Script Clerk* Lisa Bickley. *Makeup* Mike Weldon. *Photog Eff* Ed DePriest. *Still Photog* David Story.
Cast: Susan Stewart (*Lila*), Steve Vincent (*Sergeant Collins*), M. K. Evans (*Lieutenant Ryan*), Vic Lance (*Tiger*), Pat Barrington (*Cathy*), Janu White (*Angel*), Stuart Lancaster (*Frank*), John Caroll (*Ben*), John LaSalle (*Fred*), Hinton Pope (*Chief Barnes*), Bethel Buckalew (*bartender*), Lyn Armondo (*R. E. woman*), Norton Holper (*tenant*), Judith Crane, Cheryl Trepton (*dancers*).
Melodrama. Lila, a topless dancer in a nightclub, picks up male customers and takes them to a warehouse for strange sexual trysts in the eerie light of flickering candles. One night, Lila picks up Tiger, a young hippie who introduces her to LSD. A bunch of bananas appear to her in place of Tiger's head, and she goes berserk, stabbing him in the back with a screwdriver and scattering his mutilated remains over a vacant lot. A psychologist becomes her next victim. "Tripping" again, Lila sees him as a surgeon, poised over her with a hypodermic needle, and she stabs him with the screwdriver. Lila's next pickup, a truckdriver, accompanies her to the warehouse intent on rape. Under the influence of LSD, she murders him with a hoe and scatters his remains over the vacant lot. The police, suspecting a madman, finally trace telltale bloodstains to the warehouse. When Lila arrives with another customer, the police believe that they have found their man. Lila's latest lover carries a gun, which appears to her as a gigantic insect. As she reaches for the gun, the police shoot the innocent man. Only when Lila begins to hack his body to pieces do the police realize that she is the mass murderer. *Psychopaths. Go-go dancers. Hippies. Psychologists. Truckdrivers. Police. Pickups. Murder. Seduction. Mutilation. Insanity. Rape. Psychedelic states. LSD. Nightclubs. Hallucinations.*
Note: Re-released in Sep 1969 as *Lila*; running time: 88 min.

MANUSCRIPT FOUND IN SARAGOSSA *see* **THE SARAGOSSA MANUSCRIPT**

MÃOS SANGRENTAS *see* **THE VIOLENT AND THE DAMNED**

MARA OF THE WILDERNESS   F6.3086
Unicorn Productions, Inc. *Dist* Allied Artists. Jan 1965 [c1 Jan 1965; LP34671]. Sd; col (Eastman Color, print by DeLuxe). 35mm. 90 min.
Prod Brice Mack. *Exec Prod* Lindsley Parsons. *Dir* Frank McDonald. *Screenplay* Tom Blackburn. *Story* Rod Scott. *Photog* Robert Wyckoff. *Art Dir* Michael Haller. *Film Ed* Harold Gordon. *Mus* Harry Bluestone. *Sd* Elbert Franklin. *Asst Dir* Wilson Shyer. *Makeup* Louis La Cava.
Cast: Adam West (*Ken Williams*), Linda Saunders (*Mara Wade*), Theo Marcuse (*Jarnagan*), Denver Pyle (*Kelly*), Sean McClory (*Dr. Frank Wade*),

Eve Brent (*Mrs. Wade*), Roberto Contreras ("*Friday*"), Ed Kemmer (*1st pilot*), Stuart Walsh (*2d pilot*), Lelia Walsh (*Mara Wade, age 7*).

Adventure drama. After her parents are killed by a bear in the Alaskan wilderness, 7-year-old Mara Wade is left alone in the forest with two wolf pups. She grows into adulthood as a wild creature cared for by the fiercely protective wolves. One day she saves the life of Ken Williams, an anthropologist working for the U. S. Fish and Wildlife Service, when his arm and foot are caught in steel traps set by Jarnagan, a brutal trapper intent on capturing Mara for a freak show. While Williams is recovering from his wounds in Mara's cave, the young woman is captured by Jarnagan, but aided by her wolves, Mara escapes and goes off into the wilderness. Williams radios for help, tracks down Jarnagan, and holds him until the forest rangers arrive. He then locates the wild girl and begins teaching her the ways of civilization. *Anthropologists. Children. Trappers. Forest rangers. Indians of North America. Survival. Abduction. Alaska. United States—Fish and Wildlife Service. Wolves. Bears.*

Note: Location scenes filmed in Alaska and the Deschutes National Forest (Oregon). Working title: *Valley of the White Wolves*.

MARAT/SADE *see* **THE PERSECUTION AND ASSASSINATION OF JEAN-PAUL MARAT AS PERFORMED BY THE INMATES OF THE ASYLUM OF CHARENTON UNDER THE DIRECTION OF THE MARQUIS DE SADE**

THE MARAUDERS *see* **MERRILL'S MARAUDERS**

LA MARCA DEL MUERTO *see* **CREATURE OF THE WALKING DEAD**

MARCH OF THE SPRING HARE   **F6.3087**

Gulliver Films. *Dist* Pantages Film Co. 11 Oct **1969** [Tampa, Florida, opening]. Sd; col (print by Movielab). 35mm. 97 min. [Also 90 min.] *MPAA rating* R.

Pres by Clayton G. Pantages. *Prod* Leo Baran, Harvey Bernstein. *Dir-Writ* Jack Baran. *Photog* Bruce Sparks. *Film Ed* David Wilson. *Mus* Earth Opera. *Sd* Jeffrey Lesser.

Cast: Dan Mason (*Henry*), Harvey Marks (*Solly*), Barbara Press (*Sandy*), Theon Banos (*Rhoda*), Allen Garfield (*Martin Axborough*), Rick Wessler (*bookmaster*), Stanley Brock (*Madison*), The Pageant Players (*performers in play*).

Comedy-drama. Henry, a lowly file clerk for a New York City automobile tire collection agency, daydreams during most of his working hours about a life of Buddhist-like meditation. In his off hours, he roams through Greenwich Village with his girl friend Sandy and his carefree roommate Solly. One day, after watching a satirical play performed in Washington Square, Henry convinces Sandy to move in with him and Solly. Instead of helping carry over her things, however, he tells his problems to attractive co-worker Rhoda and ends up sharing her bed. As Sandy begins an affair with Solly, Henry tries to convince Rhoda that he (Henry) is not in love with her. Then Henry's boss, Martin Axborough, tries to instill some initiative in him by letting him make collections over the telephone. Though disillusioned at the discovery that Axborough is a swindler, Henry is consoled by a reconciliation with Sandy. Solly, sensing that three has become a crowd, moves out of the apartment. *Clerks. Roommates. Swindlers. Bill collectors. Disillusionment. Employer-employee relations. New York City. New York City—Greenwich Village.*

Note: Filmed on location in New York City. Alternative title: *Roommates*.

MARCHA O MUERE *see* **COMMANDO**

MARCHANDES D'ILLUSIONS *see* **NIGHTS OF SHAME**

MARCHANDS DE FILLES *see* **SELLERS OF GIRLS**

MARCIA O CREPA *see* **COMMANDO**

MARCO OF RIO   **F6.3088**

Bizarre Productions. *Dist* Signature, Inc., Continental Theatres. 16 Apr **1969** [Los Angeles opening]. Sd; col. 35mm (see note). 70 min.

Prod-Dir-Writ Pat Rocco. *Photog* Pat Rocco. *Film Ed* Pat Rocco. *Sd* Pat Rocco.

Cast: Marco Antonio (*The Guide*), Pat Rocco (*narrator*), Bruno Gilho, Brian Reynolds, John Helm, Erik Carlson, Cal Mason.

Sex film. Pat Rocco visits Rio de Janeiro during the annual pre-Lent Carnival, the "Farewell to the Flesh," when the entire city traditionally abandons all restraint. Accompanied by Marco Antonio, a 16-year-old homosexual guide who points out the landmarks of the city, Rocco spends much of his time observing the attractive male citizenry. Marco also displays his own nude form and relates several of his sexual adventures, including his participation in a threesome. Rocco explains that Rio is a city without inhibitions. *Guides. Tourists. Male homosexuality. Nudity. Troilism. Carnivals. Rio de Janeiro.*

Note: Filmed in Rio de Janeiro in 16mm and blown up to 35mm.

MARCO POLO (France/Italy)   **F6.3089**

Panda Film-Transfilmorsa. *Dist* American International Pictures. 4 Jul **1962** [Memphis, Tennessee, opening; c17 Aug 1962; LP23152]. Sd; col (Technicolor). 35mm (CinemaScope). 95 min. [Also reviewed at 90 min.]

Pres by James H. Nicholson, Samuel Z. Arkoff. *Prod* Ermanno Donati, Luigi Carpentieri. *Exec Prod* Piero Donati. *English Vers Supv* Lou Rusoff. *Dir* Hugo Fregonese, Piero Pierotti. *Screenplay* Piero Pierotti, Oreste Biancoli, Duccio Tessari, Antoinette Pellevant, Ennio De Concini, Eliana De Sabata. *Story* Piero Pierotti, Oreste Biancoli. *Photog* Riccardo Pallottini. *Art Dir (see note)* Aurelio Crugnola, Franco Fumagalli. *Film Ed* Ornella Micheli. *English Vers Mus* Les Baxter. *Orig Score* Angelo Lavagnino. *Sd* Leopoldo Rosi, Raffaele Del Monte. *Prod Mgr* Gianni Minervini, Lucio Orlandini. *Cost* Mario Giorsi.

Cast: Rory Calhoun (*Marco Polo*), Yoko Tani (*Princess Amuroy*), Robert Hundar (*Mongka*), Camillo Pilotto (*Great Khan*), Pierre Cressoy (*Cuday*), Michael Chow (*Ciu-Lin*), Thien-Huong (*Tai-au*), Poing Ping.

Historical adventure melodrama. En route to China in the 13th century, Marco Polo, a Venetian, saves the life of Ciu-Lin, a young Chinese who then becomes his devoted servant. Marco later rescues Princess Amuroy, daughter of the Great Khan, from bandits. Marco eventually learns that the bandits are followers of the Khan's nephew Cuday, who is in opposition to the tyrannical rule of the governing minister, Mongka. Once in Peking, Marco lands in jail but is freed by the Khan. He then meets the princess again and carries on a carefree flirtation with her. This so enrages the evil Mongka, who plans to marry Amuroy and take over the kingdom, that he arranges to have Marco killed, but Marco escapes and joins forces with Cuday. Upon meeting an old hermit who has invented gunpowder, Marco builds a special cannon which he and the rebels take to the walls of the city. Mongka and his troops are destroyed, and Peking is saved. Marco then reluctantly declines the princess' offer of marriage and continues on his journey. *Chinese. Royalty. Hermits. Despots. Bandits. Valets. Uncles. Travel. Rescue. Ambition. Jealousy. Explosives. China. Peking. Marco Polo.*

Note: Opened in Rome in Aug 1962; running time: ca100 min; in Paris in May 1963; running time: 106 min. Alternative Italian title: *L'avventura di un Italiano in Cina*. Sources conflict in crediting art director. Robert Hundar is a pseudonym for Claudio Undari.

MARCO THE MAGNIFICENT (Afghanistan/Egypt/France/Italy/ Yugoslavia)   **F6.3090**

ITTAC–S. N. C.–Prodi Cinematografica–Avala Film–Mounir Rafla–Italaf Kaboul–Cinecustodia. *Dist* Metro-Goldwyn-Mayer, Inc. Sep **1966** [New York opening: 14 Dec; c17 Jun 1966; LP33314]. Sd; col (Eastman Color). 35mm (Franscope). 100 min.

Pres by Walter Manley Enterprises. *Prod* Raoul J. Lévy. *Dir (see note)* Denys de La Patellière, Noel Howard, Christian-Jaque. *Battle Scenes* Cliff Lyons. *Screenplay & Adapt* Denys de La Patellière, Raoul J. Lévy, Jacques Rémy, Jean-Paul Rappeneau. *Dir Photog* Armand Thirard. *Camera* Wladimir Ivanov, Robert Florent. *Orig Photog* Claude Renoir. *Art Dir* Jacques Saulnier. *Film Ed (see note)* Jacqueline Thiédot, Noëlle Balenci, Albert Jurgenson. *Mus Comp* Georges Garvarentz. *Orch* Maurice J. Helison. *Orch Collab* Mario Bua. *Sd* Jean Labussière, Pierre Goumy. *Sd Mix* Jean Neny. *Asst Dir* Serge Vallin, Jean-Michel Lacor. *Prod Mgr* Georges Valon. *Asst Prod* Madeleine Billeaud, Rosalba Menichelli. *Script Girl* Colette Crochot. *Cost* Jacques Fonteray. *Sp Eff* Roscoe Cline.

Cast: Horst Buchholz (*Marco Polo*), Anthony Quinn (*Kublai Khan*), Orson Welles (*Ackermann*), Omar Sharif (*Emir Alaou*), Elsa Martinelli ("*woman with the whip*"), Akim Tamiroff ("*old man of the mountain*"), Grégoire Aslan (*Achmed Abdullah*), Robert Hossein (*Prince Nayam*), Massimo Girotti (*Marco's father, Nicolo*), Folco Lulli (*Spinello*), Lee Sue Moon (*Gogatine*), Bruno Cremer (*Guillaume de Tripolis*), Jacques Monod (*Nicolo de Vicenza*), Mića Orlović (*Marco's uncle*), Mansoureh Rihai (*Taha*), Guido Alberti (*Pope Gregory X*), Virginia Onorato.

Historical adventure melodrama. In 1271 a young Venetian, Marco Polo, answers a request of Pope Gregory X to bring the philosophy of peace to the followers of the Mongol Prince, Kublai Khan of China. Accompanied by his father, his uncle, and two Templars, Marco sets off on his mission, a journey which will take him to the Holy Land, across the mountains of Asia, and through the Gobi desert to China. En route they are captured by the cruel "old man of the mountain," who puts one of the Templars to death in an ingenious glass bell torture chamber. Only through the intervention of Sheik Emir Alaou is Marco able to regain his freedom. He reaches Samarkand, where he is reunited with his father. He then escapes an ambush by Mongolian bandits with the help of the "woman with a whip," who sacrifices her own life to save his. After crossing the Gobi desert, Marco escapes from the enemies of Kublai Khan by hiding in the river junk of Gogatine, a princess traveling to China to attend a ceremony at which a bride will be selected for Kublai Khan. Once in China,

Marco learns of the dispute between the peaceful Khan and his war-minded son, Nayam, who threatens to usurp his father's power by force. Nayam's rebel forces are quickly routed in a battle in which gunpowder is used for the first time. Marco Polo remains in China for 17 years before returning home to write a book on his travels. *Peacemakers. Mongols. Royalty. Sheiks. Knights Templars. Travel. Torture. Self-sacrifice. Filial relations. Uprisings. Murder. Inventions. Explosives. China—History—Sung Dynasty. The Holy Land. Venice. Gobi. Samarkand. Marco Polo. Gregory X (pope). Kublai Khan. Catholic Church.*

Note: Filmed in Yugoslavia, Africa, and Asia. Opened in Paris in Aug 1965 as *La fabuleuse aventure de Marco Polo*. Released in Italy in 1966 as *Le meravigliose avventure di Marco Polo*; running time: 115 min. Yugoslav title: *Marko Polo*. Working titles: *L'échiquier de Dieu* and *Lo scacchiere di Dio*. The film began production in 1963 with Christian-Jaque as director. Only one source credits Albert Jurgenson as film editor.

MARCY F6.3091
Deluxe Pictures. *Dist* Deluxe Pictures, J. E. R. Pictures. 16 Jul **1969** [Atlanta opening]. Sd; col (Eastman Color). 35mm. 95 min. [Cut to 80 min.]
A J. Arthur Elliot Production. *Prod* J. Arthur Elliot. *Dir-Writ* Joseph W. Sarno.

Cast: Artie Giannini (*Marcy Wiggins*), Sheila Britt (*June Rutland*) Nick Dundas (*Dalton Christie*), Barbara Lance (*Sharon Christie*), Aaron Green (*Norbert Justin*), Linda Boyce (*Carrie Sue Justin*), Alex Mann (*Will Diehl*).

Drama. Marcy Wiggins, a farmer, has never recovered from a high school romance she had with her neighbor, Dalton Christie, who lives on a farm with his wife, Sharon, and assistants Carrie and Norbert Justin. Sharon, jealous of Marcy, starts a rumor that Marcy is involved in a lesbian relationship with June Rutland, Marcy's employee. The rumor, circulated by Carrie Justin, sparks a series of interludes among the several people: June seduces both Will Diehl and Marcy; Carrie has sex with June; Sharon has sex with Norbert; June, Carrie, and Marcy engage in a sex trio; and Marcy and Dalton "rediscover" each other. *Farmers. Farmhands. Farm life. Jealousy. Lesbianism. Seduction. Troilism. Infidelity. Gossip.*

Note: Filmed in Summit, New York.

A MARGEM *see* **THE MARGIN**

THE MARGIN (Brazil) F6.3092
Dist Film-Makers' Distribution Center, Film-Makers' Cooperative. 4 Jul **1969** [Boston opening]. Sd; b&w. 16mm. 66 min.
Prod Ozualdo R. Candeias, Michel Saddi. *Dir-Writ-Story* Ozualdo R. Candeias. *Photog* Belarmino Mancini. *Orig Mus Comp* Luiz Chaves. *Played by* Zimbo Trio.

Cast: Mário Benvenuti, Valéria Vidal, Bentinho, Lucy Rangel, Telé, Karé, Paula Ramos, Brigitte, Ana F. Mendonça, Paulo Gaeta, Nelson Gaspari, Virgílio Sampaio, Dantas Filho, Luiz Alberto Luciano Pessoa, José Licneraki.

Melodrama. One day on the Tietê River an enormous white barge appears carrying a strange, beautiful woman. Eventually, the barge and the woman disappear, but the lives of two men and two women have been profoundly altered. Two relationships develop, and one by one the men and women involved die because of love. The barge and the woman appear again and receive them on board, sailing away quietly to an unknown place. *Death. Barges. Tietê River.*

Note: Opened in Rio de Janeiro in Nov 1967 as *A Margem*. Original gauge uncertain.

LE MARI DE LA FEMME À BARBE *see* **THE APE WOMAN**

MARIA, THE WONDERFUL WEAVER *see* **THE MAGIC WEAVER**

MARIAGE À L'ITALIENNE *see* **MARRIAGE ITALIAN STYLE**

LE MARIAGE DE FIGARO *see* **THE MARRIAGE OF FIGARO**

LA MARIÉE ÉTAIT EN NOIR *see* **THE BRIDE WORE BLACK**

MARIGOLD MAN F6.3093
Golden Age Productions. *Dist* Emerson Film Enterprises. Oct **1970**. Sd; col (Eastman Color). 35mm. 90 min.
Prod William Norton, Paul Leder. *Dir* Paul Leder. *Screenplay* William Norton. *Photog* Arch Archambault, William Lloyd Norton. *Art Dir* Kathy O'Toole. *Sd* Terry Meacham.

Cast: Greg Mullavey (*Harry*), Harry Cohn, actor (*George*), Joan Lemmo (*landlady*), Pearl Shear (*dowager*), Lew Horn (*neighbor*), Elaine Partnow (*Harry's girl friend*), James Tartan (*policeman*).

Comedy. Harry and his roommate, George, live in a shabby Hollywood apartment, existing languidly off the final payments of their unemployment insurance. Despite a 6-month lag in their rent payments and Harry's bad relations with his neighbor, their landlady does not evict them because she loves Harry, who spends his hours daydreaming about planting a 100-yard-wide row of marigolds from Los Angeles to New York for the betterment of mankind. *Roommates. Landladies. Neighbors. Unemployment. Flowers. Hollywood. Fantasy.*

MARILYN F6.3094
Twentieth Century-Fox Film Corp. 5 Jun **1963** [Boston opening; c15 May 1963; LP24885]. Sd; b&w and col (Eastman Color). 35mm (CinemaScope). 83 min.
Commentary Writ Harold Medford. *Film Ed* Pepe Torres.

Narrator: Rock Hudson.

Compilation film. These excerpts from 15 of the films Marilyn Monroe made for Twentieth Century-Fox begin with *A Ticket to Tomahawk* (1950), in which she plays one of four chorus girls. Following her famous bit role in *All About Eve* (1950), she goes on to larger roles in *Love Nest* (1951), *We're Not Married* (1952), *Don't Bother To Knock* (1952), *O. Henry's Full House* (1952), and *Monkey Business* (1952). Stardom comes with *Niagara* (1953), followed by *Gentlemen Prefer Blondes* (1953), *How To Marry a Millionaire* (1953), *River of No Return* (1954), *There's No Business Like Show Business* (1954), *The Seven Year Itch* (1955), and *Bus Stop* (1956). The film concludes with clips from her last, unfinished film, *Something's Got To Give*, in which she was to have costarred with Dean Martin. *Marilyn Monroe.*

MARINE BATTLEGROUND (United States/South Korea) F6.3095
Paul Mart Productions–Manson Distributing Corp. *Dist* Manson Distributing Corp. Feb **1966**. Sd; b&w. 35mm (CineScope). 88 min. [Original running time: 92 min.]
Pres by Edmund Goldman, Ralph Shaker. *Prod* Paul Mart, Sun ʼn. *Exec Prod* Michael F. Goldman, Ralph Shaker. *Assoc Prod* Sy De Bardas. *Dir* Man-li Lee. *Co-dir & Adapt* Milton Mann. *Screenplay* Han-chul Yu, Burton Moore, Tom Morrison. *Story* Kook-jin Jang. *Photog* William Hines, Jingmin Su. *Art Dir* Wally Moon, Sungchil Hong, Tod Jonson. *Main Titl* Robin Vaccarino. *Film Ed* Milton Mann. *Mus* Jaime Mendoza-Nava. *Sd* Austin McKinney.

Cast: Jock Mahoney (*Nick Rawlins*), Pat Yi (*Nurse Young Hi Park*), Yong-son Chon (*Young Hi as a child*), Tong-hui Chang (*squad leader*), Tae-yop Yi (*Private First Class Ku*), Pong-su Ku (*Private First Class Bong Ku*), David Lowe (*1st patient*), Lloyd Kino (*2d patient*), George Zaima.

War drama. Interviewed by newspaper correspondent Nick Rawlins, Young Hi Park, a nurse serving in an American medical unit in South Vietnam, recounts her childhood experiences in Korea. Among her memories is the communist siege of Inch'on in 1950, in which her mother was killed and Young Hi rescued and adopted by a platoon of American marines, all but two of whom were slain thereafter. Inspired by their memory, Young Hi became a nurse. *Nurses. Journalists. Americans in foreign countries. Communists. Orphans. Childhood. Rescue. Combat zone life. Memory. Hospitals. Korean War 1950–53. Vietnam War 1964–73. Inch'on. United States Marines.*

MARINES, LET'S GO! F6.3096
Twentieth Century-Fox Film Corp. 15 Aug **1961** [New York opening; c2 Aug 1961; LP20110]. Sd (Westrex); col (De Luxe). 35mm (CinemaScope). 104 min.
Prod-Dir-Story Raoul Walsh. *Screenplay* John Twist. *Dir Photog* Lucien Ballard. *Art Dir* Jack Martin Smith, Alfred Ybarra. *Titl* Pacific Title. *Film Ed* Robert Simpson. *Mus* Irving Gertz. *Orch* Edward B. Powell. *Titl Song* Mike Phillips, George Watson. *Sung by* Rex Allen. *Sd* Bernard Freericks, Warren B. Delaplain. *Asst Dir* Milton Carter. *Makeup* Ben Nye. *Hairstyles* Helen Turpin. *Adv* Jacob G. Goldberg. *Coöp* United States Marine Corps.

Cast: Tom Tryon (*Skip Roth*), David Hedison (*Dave Chatfield*), Tom Reese (*McCaffrey*), Linda Hutchins (*Grace Blake*), William Tyler (*Russ Waller*), Barbara Stuart (*Ina Baxter*), David Brandon (*Newt Levells*), Steve Baylor (*Chase*), Peter Miller, actor (*Hawkins*), Adoree Evans (*Ellen Hawkins*), Hideo Imamura (*Pete Kono*), Vince Williams (*Hank Dyer*), Fumiyo Fujimoto (*Song-Do*), Henry Okawa (*Yoshida*).

War comedy-drama. Following combat duty in Korea, a group of United States Marines are given a furlough in Japan. David Chatfield, a Boston aristocrat, says goodby to Song-Do, the native girl he plans to marry, and then joins his buddies in Yokosuka. Also in the company are Skip Roth, a shrewd fellow known as "the brain," and "Let's Go" McCaffrey, a free-wheeling, heavy-drinking soldier who resents David's upper-class background. The men have adventures in a bath house, in a night club, and with numerous American and Japanese women. McCaffrey gets into a brawl and is about to be court-martialed for the second time when an official order arrives cancelling all leaves because the Chinese forces have begun to move again. Once back in Korea, David is reunited with Song-Do; but a jealous native girl betrays them, and they are taken prisoner by the Chinese. McCaffrey and his men arrive in time to save David and Song-Do from execution. The next morning during combat, McCaffrey is severely wounded. He seeks out David, takes his hand, and dies.

Americans in foreign countries. Aristocrats. Japanese. Chinese. Military life. Combat zone life. Vacations. Drunkenness. Courage. Korean War 1950–53. Yokosuka (Japan). United States Marines. Prisoners of war.

Note: Location scenes filmed in Japan.

MARITAL FULFILLMENT   F6.3097

Scorpio Films. *Dist* Sebastian Films, All-Film Enterprises. 18 May **1970** [New York showing]. Sd; col (Eastman Color). 35mm (see note). 71 min.

Prod-Dir Ferdinand Sebastian. *Screenplay* Ann Cawthorne. *Photog* Ferdinand Sebastian. *Ed* Ferdinand Sebastian. *Mus* Anthony Mawer.

Sex instruction film. The film begins with a commentary by a medical expert explaining the importance of the knowledge of sexual techniques in a successful marriage. While the expert continues his commentary, two young couples demonstrate over 40 lovemaking positions on a revolving circular bed. Among the aspects of the marital relationship explored are: the sexual initiation of the bride on the wedding night, stimulation of the erogenous zones, techniques enabling the woman to achieve orgasm, sexual foreplay to prolong intercourse and aid in the attainment of mutual climax, and oral-genital techniques. *Sex instruction. Marriage. Sexual techniques. Eroticism. Sexual initiation. Oral sex.*

Note: Filmed in 16mm and blown up to 35mm for commercial release.

MARIZINIA (United States/Brazil)   F6.3098

International Film Enterprises. *Dist* International Film Enterprises, Diamond International Pictures, Golden Eagle Films. 4 Apr **1962** [Chicago opening]. Sd; col (Eastman Color). 35mm. 82 min.

Prod-Dir-Orig Story Zygmunt Sulistrowski. *Screenplay* Anita Manville, Austin Green. *Titl Song Sung by* Johnny Starr.

Cast: John Sutton (*John Morgan*), Gina Albert, Zygmunt Sulistrowski, Celench Costa, Eugenio Carlos.

Adventure melodrama. On the South American coast, a woman who has been saved from the sea by native fishermen is blamed by them for a sudden scarcity of fish. When the natives threaten to force her back into the sea, she escapes and joins two explorers on an expedition to the Amazon jungle. One of them saves her from drowning, and after many other adventures she pairs off with him. *Explorers. Fishermen. Superstition. Rescue. Myths. Jungles. Amazon River.*

Note: Filmed on location in Brazil. Also known as *Marizinia, the Witch Beneath the Sea,* and *The Witch Beneath the Sea.*

THE MARK (Great Britain)   F6.3099

Raymond Stross Productions. *Dist* Continental Distributing, Inc. 2 Oct **1961** [New York opening]. Sd; b&w. 35mm (CinemaScope). 127 min.

A Raymond Stross–Sidney Buchman Production. *Prod* Raymond Stross. *Dir* Guy Green. *Screenplay* Sidney Buchman, Stanley Mann. *Photog* Douglas Slocombe. *Camera Op* Chic Waterson. *Focus* Jimmy Devis, Stuart Hetherington. *Camera Grip* William Robinson. *Art Dir* Ray Simm. *Asst Art Dir* Bill Constable. *Set Dresser* Josie MacAvin. *Scenic Artist* Gilbert Wood. *Film Ed* Peter Taylor. *Asst Ed* Roy Hyde. *2d Asst Ed* Christopher Farrell. *Mus Comp* Richard Rodney Bennett. *Mus Cond* John Hollingsworth. *Sd Rec* Leo Wilkins, Red Law. *Boom Op* Tony Cripps. *Sd Camera Op* Liam Saurin. *1st, 2d & 3d Asst Dir* Michael Birkett, Jake Wright, Eamonn Duffy. *Prod Supv* Jack Rix. *Unit Mgr* John George. *Cont* Pamela Mann. *Prod Sec* Ann Skinner. *Wardrobe Mistress* Laurel Staffell. *Makeup* Charles Nash. *Prop Buyer* Maureen Roche. *Still Photog* Norman Hargood. *Still Proc* Roy Byrne.

Cast: Maria Schell (*Ruth Leighton*), Stuart Whitman (*Jim Fuller*), Rod Steiger (*Dr. Edmund McNally*), Brenda De Banzie (*Mrs. Cartwright*), Donald Houston (*Austin*), Donald Wolfit (*Mr. Clive*), Paul Rogers (*Milne*), Maurice Denham (*Arnold Cartwright*), Amanda Black (*Janie*), Marie Devereux (*Ellen*), Bill Foley (*Mr. Fuller*), Anne Monaghan (*Mrs. Fuller*), Josephine Frayne (*Patricia*), Eddie Byrne (*Acker*), Harry Baird (*Cole*), John Welsh (*1st officer*), Russell Napier (*2d officer*), Bandana Das Gupta (*Inez*).

Crime drama. Source: Charles Israel, *The Mark* (New York, 1958). The only son of a domineering, pampering mother and a weak, ineffectual father, Canadian Jim Fuller grows into manhood doubting his masculinity. After an unhappy experience with a young woman his own age, he finds himself more and more attracted to younger girls until, finally, he abducts a 10-year-old. Though he does not assault the child, he is convicted for intent to molest the girl sexually and given 3 years in a British prison, during which time he undergoes group therapy supervised by the prison psychiatrist, Dr. McNally. Following his release from prison, Jim gets a job in a public relations firm owned by Mr. Clive, the only person, other than McNally, aware of Jim's alleged crime. Under the careful scrutiny of McNally, Jim begins his rehabilitation. Slowly his self-doubt begins to disappear, particularly when he is able to have a normal relationship with Ruth, an attractive widow and Mr. Clive's secretary. Another step forward in his readjustment is the healthy attitude he has toward Ruth's 11-year-old daughter, Janie. A child is assaulted by a man resembling Jim, but his alibi proves his innocence; shortly afterwards, however, an

unscrupulous reporter, Austin, recognizes him at a carnival and publicly exposes his past. As a result, his landlady, Mrs. Cartwright, evicts him; he loses his job; and even Ruth rejects him, out of fear and panic, by refusing to let him touch Janie. Completely broken in spirit, he asks McNally to commit him to a mental institution. But through the kindly doctor's understanding and persistence, Jim decides to move to another town and make a fresh start. Ruth finds him there, apologizes for her past behavior, and begs him to give her the chance to make a new beginning. *Canadians. Psychiatrists. Criminals—Rehabilitation. Reporters. Children. Widows. Secretaries. Abduction. Child molesting. Group therapy. Public relations. Mental illness. Self-confidence. Prisons.*

Note: Location scenes filmed in Ireland. Opened in London in Jan 1961.

MARK OF THE WITCH   F6.3100

Presidio Productions. 19 Nov **1970** [San Antonio, Texas, opening]. Sd; col (Eastman Color by Pathé). 35mm. 84 min. *MPAA rating* GP

Prod Mary Davis, Tom Moore. *Exec Prod* R. B. McGowen, Jr. *Asst Prod* Patty McKiernan. *Dir* Tom Moore. *Screenplay* Mary Davis, Martha Peters. *Dir Photog* Robert E. Bethard. *Asst Camera* Manuel D'Amente. *Set Dsgn* Jim Carver. *Set Execution* Jim Marty. *Main Titl* Bob Dalzell. *Film Ed* Ken Harrison, ed. *Mus Writ & Cond* Whitey Thomas. *Perf by* Moog. *Titl Tune Writ by* Anitra Walsh. *Sung by* Trella Hart. *Sd Rec* Ken Richardson. *Asst Dir* Jim Carver. *Wardrobe* Rose Marie Powell. *Makeup* Lynn Brooks. *Casting* Barbara Claman, Pat England. *Key Grip* Don Ross, grip.

Cast: Robert Elston (*Mac Stuart*), Anitra Walsh (*Jill*), Darryl Wells (*Alan*), Marie Santell (*Margery of Jourdemain*), Barbara Brownell (*Sharon*), Jack Gardner, actor (*Harry*), Sande Drewes (*Marybeth*), Gary Brockette (*Howard*), Lori Taylor (*Alice*), John Figlmiller (*Ricky*), Lawrence DuPont (*Dr. Quimby*).

Horror film. While enrolled in a seminar treating the history of superstition, coed Jill becomes deeply involved in witchcraft. Having acquired an ancient tome at a charity book fair, the student chants its incantations during class. Unbeknownst to her classmates, Jill is now possessed by the spirit of Margery of Jourdemain, a witch hung with her lover in England in 1648. The witch reveals herself to Jill's instructor, Professor Stuart, and boyfriend, Alan, persuading the pair to teach her the ways of modern civilization. After being instructed in the proper use of the telephone, the witch leaves for the campus. There she convenes her coven, which murders lecherous student Harry and his girl friend Sharon and plans the assassination of Stuart, descendant of Margery's warlock lover. Alarmed by the slayings, the teacher subdues the witch by projecting multiple crosses on the walls of his home. However, he is unable to resist the charms of his adversary. Kissing the witch, he is transported to 17th-century England at the moment of his own execution. *Students. Professors. Witches. Sorcerers. Witchcraft. Superstition. Murder. Demonology. Ancestry. Rites and ceremonies.*

Note: Filmed in Texas.

MARKED FOR LOVE   F6.3101

Mitam Productions. 5 Oct **1967** [New Orleans opening]. Sd; b&w. 35mm. 63 min.

Dir Adam Clay.

Cast: Kitten, Capri.

Drama. Radio personality Jack interviews prostitutes, asking them to tell his audience how they began their careers. Jill, neglected by her wealthy parents, becomes promiscuous to gain attention and becomes a prostitute when her family cuts off her allowance. Jody, whose husband travels frequently, enjoys sex with other men; he finds out and divorces her, and she turns to prostitution as her means of support. Ann, whose mother was also a prostitute, pursues her occupation to support herself and her husband. Teenager Amy enjoys the money and the favors older men bestow upon her. Barbara is raped by her drunken stepfather, and she runs away and becomes a prostitute when her boyfriend rejects her. *Radio announcers. Prostitutes. Stepfathers. Prostitution. Promiscuity. Marriage. Infidelity. Divorce. Filial relations. Rape. Finance—Personal.*

Note: Also known as *Marked X for Love.*

MARKO POLO *see* **MARCO THE MAGNIFICENT**

THE MARKOPOULOS PASSION *see* **THE ILLIAC PASSION**

MARLOWE   F6.3102

Katzka-Berne Productions–Cherokee Productions–Beckerman Productions. *Dist* Metro-Goldwyn-Mayer, Inc. 22 Oct **1969** [New York opening; c27 May 1969; LP37232]. Sd; col (Metrocolor). 35mm. 95 min. [Also 100 min.] *MPAA rating* M.

Prod Gabriel Katzka, Sidney Beckerman. *Dir* Paul Bogart. *Screenplay* Stirling Silliphant. *Dir Photog* William H. Daniels. *Camera Op* William Johnson. *Asst Camera* Dominick Palmer, Harry Young. *Art Dir* George W. Davis, Addison Hehr. *Set Decor* Henry Grace, Hugh Hunt. *Film Ed* Gene

Ruggiero. *Asst Ed* Jay Humbrock, Jr. *Mus Dir* Peter Matz. *Titl Song* Peter Matz, Norman Gimbel. *Sung by* Orpheus. *Rec Supv* Franklin Milton. *Sd* Bruce Wright. *Boom Op* Clint Althouse. *Asst Dir* Bud Grace, Richard Oxford, Michael Daves. *Unit Prod Mgr* Sergei Petschnikoff. *Script Supv* Jeanne Lippman. *Location Mgr* Bob Sunderland. *Gayle Hunnicutt's Gowns & Furs* Jean Louis. *Makeup* William Tuttle, Phil Rhodes. *Hairstyles* Sydney Guilaroff, Sherry Wilson, Charles James. *Sp Vis Eff* J. McMillan Johnson, Carroll L. Shepphird. *Still Photog* Eric Carpenter. *Gaffer* George Lasher. *Prop Master* Robert Schultz. *Key Grip* Howard Bradner. *Stunt Supv* Bruce Lee.

Cast: James Garner (*Philip Marlowe*), Gayle Hunnicutt (*Mavis Wald*), Carroll O'Connor (*Lieut. Christy French*), Rita Moreno (*Dolores Gonzales*), Sharon Farrell (*Orfamay Quest*), William Daniels (*Mr. Crowell*), H. M. Wynant (*Sonny Steelgrave*), Jackie Coogan (*Grant W. Hicks*), Kenneth Tobey (*Sgt. Fred Beifus*), Bruce Lee (*Winslow Wong*), Christopher Cary (*Chuck*), George Tyne (*Oliver Hady*), Corinne Camacho (*Julie*), Paul Stevens (*Dr. Vincent Lagardie*), Roger Newman (*Orrin Quest*), Read Morgan (*Gumpshaw*), Warren Finnerty (*Haven Clausen*), Nate Esformes (*Pale Face*), Pauline Gest, Tracy Bogart.

Mystery melodrama. Source: Raymond Chandler, *The Little Sister* (Boston, 1949). Private investigator Philip Marlowe is hired by Orfamay Quest to find her missing brother Orrin. He visits a sleazy hotel and questions the owner and Grant Hicks, the current occupant of Orrin's room. Neither can provide any information, and the two men are soon found murdered with an icepick. Marlowe is knocked out but regains consciousness in time to see actress Mavis Wald flee from the hotel. He searches Hicks's body and finds a claim check for a camera shop, where he picks up some photographs of Mavis making love to notorious gangster Sonny Steelgrave. Marlowe tracks Mavis to her apartment and meets Dolores, a stripper and close friend of Mavis, but both prove uncooperative. In addition to a threat on his life made by Steelgrave and his henchman Wong, Marlowe is harassed by police Lieutenant French, who suspects him of murdering Hicks. Following a new lead, he calls on Dr. Lagardie and discovers the mortally wounded Orrin, who stabs Marlowe with an icepick before dying. After he is nursed back to health by Dolores, Marlowe tells Orfamay of her brother's death. At Dolores' request, he goes to Steelgrave's house and discovers Mavis, who is revealed to be Orfamay's sister, sitting next to Steelgrave's dead body. Marlowe, however, believes that Mavis is protecting her sister and lets her go. The following day, Mavis learns that Orfamay and Orrin planned to use the photographs to blackmail her. At the nightclub where Dolores works, Marlowe uncovers Lagardie's association with Dolores and telephones the police. Lagardie arrives before the police, shoots Dolores, and then kills himself. *Detectives. Missing persons. Actors. Gangsters. Stripteasers. Police. Physicians. Sisters. Brother-sister relationship. Murder. Blackmail. Frameup. Suicide. Hotels. Photographs. Nightclubs.*

Note: Working title: *The Little Sister.*

MARNIE F6.3103

Geoffrey Stanley, Inc. *Dist* Universal Pictures. 22 Jul **1964** [New York opening; c22 Jul 1964; LP29190]. Sd; col (Technicolor). 35mm. 110 min. [Cut from 130 min.]

Prod-Dir Alfred Hitchcock. *Screenplay* Jay Presson Allen. *Dir Photog* Robert Burks. *Camera Op* Leonard South. *Set Decor* George Milo. *Prod Dsgn* Robert Boyle. *Film Ed* George Tomasini. *Mus Comp* Bernard Herrmann. *Sd Rec* Waldon O. Watson, William Green. *Asst Dir* James H. Brown, Patricia Casey. *Unit Mgr* Hilton A. Green. *Asst to Mr. Hitchcock* Peggy Robertson. *Script Supv* Lois Thurman. *Miss Hedren's and Miss Baker's Cost Dsgn* Edith Head. *Cost Supv* Vincent Dee. *Women's Cost* Rita Riggs. *Men's Cost* James Linn. *Makeup* Jack Barron, Howard Smit, Bob Dawn. *Miss Hedren's Hairstyles Created by* Alexandre of Paris. *Hairstyles* Virginia Darcy. *Pictorial Dsgn* Albert Whitlock.

Cast: "Tippi" Hedren (*Marnie Edgar*), Sean Connery (*Mark Rutland*), Diane Baker (*Lil Mainwaring*), Martin Gabel (*Sidney Strutt*), Louise Latham (*Bernice Edgar*), Bob Sweeney (*Cousin Bob*), Milton Selzer (*man at the track*), Alan Napier (*Mr. Rutland*), Henry Backman (*1st detective*), Edith Evanson (*Rita*), Mariette Hartley (*Susan Clabon*), Bruce Dern (*sailor*), S. John Launer (*Sam Ward*), Meg Wyllie (*Mrs. Turpin*).

Drama. Source: Winston Graham, *Marnie* (London, 1961). Marnie Edgar, a young woman who loves only her crippled mother and her horse Forio, and who has a hysterical fear of thunderstorms and bright red colors, is a compulsive thief with a string of successful thefts to her credit. Her method is to obtain a secretarial position, establish a reputation for honesty, diligence, and devotion, and then loot the safe. Changing her name and appearance, Marnie finds a job with publisher Mark Rutland, who falls in love with her. Marnie panics at the thought of an entanglement and rifles the safe, only to be caught by Mark and given the choice of marrying him or going to prison. She chooses marriage, but on the honeymoon her frigidity results in Mark's forcing himself on her, then having to resuscitate her after she attempts suicide. Later, at his family estate,

Mark unsuccessfully tries amateur psychiatry on Marnie. The situation reaches its climax when one of her former victims turns up and recognizes her. The next day Marnie goes riding. The sight of a red riding coat so disturbs Marnie that she takes Forio on a wild gallop that results in the horse's death. Distraught, she goes to Mark's office but finds that she cannot bring herself to steal the money for her getaway. Mark follows her and forces her to accompany him to her mother's house in Baltimore. There, during a thunderstorm, Marnie relives the traumatic childhood experience which caused her neuroses. Her mother had been a prostitute whose leg was broken during a thunderstorm by a sailor client in the presence of young Marnie. To protect her mother, Marnie had killed the sailor with a poker blow on the head, producing a shocking flow of blood, and her mother had taken the blame for the crime. Having confronted her fears, Marnie anticipates an improved relationship with Mark. *Secretaries. Prostitutes. Publishers. Newlyweds. Cripples. Phobias. Kleptomania. Personal identity. Employer-employee relations. Frigidity. Suicide. Murder. Filial relations. Honeymoons. Baltimore. Storms. Horses.*

MAROC 7 (Great Britain) F6.3104

Cyclone Productions. *Dist* Paramount Pictures. Jan **1968** [c3 Jan 1967; LP35322]. Sd; col (Technicolor). 35mm (Panavision). 92 min.

Prod John Gale, Leslie Phillips. *Exec Prod* Martin C. Schute. *Dir* Gerry O'Hara. *2d Unit Dir* John Danischewsky. *Orig Story & Screenplay* David Osborn. *Lighting Camera* Kenneth Talbot. *Art Dir* Seamus Flannery. *Film Ed* John Jympson. *Mus Comp* Kenneth V. Jones. *Party Mus & Theme Song* Paul Ferris, Nicky Henson. *Sd Rec* Paddy Cunningham, Gerry Humphreys. *Asst Dir* David Tringham. *Prod Mgr* Roger Good. *Cont* Jane Buck. *Wardrobe* Clive of London. *Makeup* Bill Lodge. *Hairdresser* Hilda Fox. *Sp Eff* Ernie Sullivan. *Casting* Weston Drury, Jr.

Cast: Gene Barry (*Simon Grant*), Elsa Martinelli (*Claudia*), Cyd Charisse (*Louise Henderson*), Leslie Phillips (*Raymond Lowe*), Denholm Elliott (*Inspector Barrada*), Alexandra Stewart (*Michele Craig*), Eric Barker (*Professor Bannen*), Angela Douglas (*Freddie*), Tracy Reed (*Vivienne*), Maggie London (*Suzie*), Penny Riley (*Penny*), Ann Norman (*Alexa*), Lionel Blair (*hotel receptionist*), Paul Danquah (*police officer*), Tom Lee (*Abdullah*), Anne Padwick (*Consuela*), Richard Montez (*Pablo*), Roger Good (*hotel manager*), Anthony Bygraves (*young photographer*), Robert Mill (*Tony*), George Selway, Colette Wilde, Diane Bester, Michael Mundell, Vivienne Burgess, Michael Haynes, Jonathan Hanson, John Wreford, Mark Elwes, Pamela Abbott.

Crime melodrama. Louise Henderson, the editor of a top British fashion magazine, is also an international jewel thief; assisted by photographer Raymond Lowe and model Claudia, Louise uses her position, requiring frequent trips abroad, as a front for her illegal activities. When the police suspect that she is planning to steal an ancient Arabian medallion from Morocco, secret agent Simon Grant infiltrates her operation, posing as a safecracker, and coerces Louise into accepting him as a partner. The plan is for Claudia to enter Morocco wearing an imitation medallion and leave wearing the real one. Once in Morocco, Simon is instructed to cooperate with Police Chief Barrada and his assistant, Michele Craig. While the group is taking pictures for the magazine in the deserted ruins of a Berber fortress, Lowe learns Simon's true identity, and Simon is forced to kill him. After Simon has found the medallion in a grave site near the desolate fortress, Claudia takes it from him, but she is shot by Michele. By the time the police arrive, Louise, Simon, and Inspector Barrada have all been outwitted by Michele, who has disappeared with the medallion and is presumably on her way to Tahiti. *Fashion editors. Secret agents. Models. Photographers. Safecrackers. Police. Theft. Imposture. Partnerships. Murder. Jewels. Forts. Morocco.*

Note: Some location scenes filmed in Morocco in the cities of Meknes and Fez. Released in Great Britain in 1966.

MAROONED F6.3105

Frankovich Productions. *Dist* Columbia Pictures. 11 Dec **1969** [Los Angeles opening; c1 Dec 1969; LP37888]. Sd; col (Eastmancolor). 35mm (Panavision). 133 min. *MPAA rating* G.

An M.J. Frankovich-John Sturges Production. *Prod* M. J. Frankovich. *Assoc Prod* Frank Capra, Jr. *Dir* John Sturges. *2d Unit Dir* Ralph Black. *Screenplay* Mayo Simon. *Dir Photog* Daniel Fapp. *Dir Photog 2d Unit* W. Wallace Kelley. *Aerial Photog* Nelson Tyler. *Set Decor* Frank Tuttle. *Prod Dsgn* Lyle Wheeler. *Film Ed* Walter Thompson. *Sd* Les Fresholtz, Arthur Piantadosi. *Asst Dir* Daniel J. McCauley. *Exec Prod Mgr* William O'Sullivan. *Script Supv* John Franco. *Cost* Seth Banks. *Sp Vis Eff* Lawrence W. Butler, Donald Glouner, Robie Robinson. *Video Supv* Hal Landaker. *Tech Adv* Martin Caidin, George Smith. *Coöp* Philco-Ford Corp. *Dial Coach* Norman Stuart. *Photog Cons* William Widmayer.

Cast: Gregory Peck (*Charles Keith*), Richard Crenna (*Jim Pruett*), David Janssen (*Ted Dougherty*), James Franciscus (*Clayton Stone*), Gene Hackman (*Buzz Lloyd*), Lee Grant (*Celia Pruett*), Nancy Kovack (*Teresa Stone*), Mariette Hartley (*Betty Lloyd*), Scott Brady (*public affairs officer*), Craig

Huebing *(flight director)*, John Carter, actor *(flight surgeon)*, George Gaynes *(mission director)*, Tom Stewart *(Houston Cap Com)*, Frank Marth *(space systems director)*, Dennis Robertson, actor *(launch director)*, George Smith *(Cape weather officer)*, Vincent Van Lynn *(Cannon, journalist)*, Walter Brooke *(Radin, network commentator)*, Mauritz Hugo *(Hardy)*, Bill Couch *(Russian cosmonaut)*, Mary-Linda Rapelye *(Priscilla Keith)*.

Science fiction drama. Source: Martin Caidin, *Marooned* (New York, 1964). A space team consisting of pilot Buzz Lloyd, scientist Clayton Stone, and mission commander Jim Pruett tests man's endurance in outer space. Observing that the crew's efficiency has faltered after five months, Houston supervisor Charles Keith orders its return. Upon reentry, however, the ship malfunctions, leaving the astronauts with no means of reaching earth. Veteran astronaut Ted Dougherty and a presidential mandate compel the reluctant Keith to mount a rescue effort. As the astronauts' oxygen runs out, the rescue mission races against time. When the launching of Dougherty's spaceship from Cape Kennedy is delayed by a hurricane the astronauts' wives are brought to Houston for televised conversations with their husbands. During his interview Lloyd becomes hysterical, in so doing consuming additional oxygen. To compensate for this loss Keith suggests a sacrificial suicide, a possibility which the team rejects. Leaving the vehicle to correct a mechanical defect, Pruett rips his suit and floats away in space. Although the oxygen has dangerously diminished, Stone donates his supply to Lloyd, breathing the little left inside the ship's cabin. Panicking, Lloyd opens the hatch, depleting Stone's precious store. As hope dims, a Russian spaceship arrives with sufficient oxygen to maintain the American astronauts. *Spaceship crews. Astronauts. Scientists. Russians. Space rescue. Suicide. Spaceships. Oxygen. Hurricanes. Cape Kennedy. Houston. Presidents of the United States.*

Note: Location scenes filmed at Cape Kennedy and in Houston.

DER MARQUIS DE SADE see **DE SADE**

THE MARRIAGE CAME TUMBLING DOWN (France) F6.3106

Champs Elysées Productions-Isabelle Films. *Dist* Royal Films International. 5 Nov **1968** [New York opening]. Sd; col (Eastmancolor). 35mm. 88 min. *MPAA rating* G.

Prod Jules Borkon. *Dir* Jacques Poitrenaud. *Screenplay* Albert Cossery, Jacques Poitrenaud. *Photog* Jean-Marc Ripert. *Mus* Serge Gainsbourg.

Cast: Michel Simon *(Grandfather)*, Marie Dubois *(Marie)*, Yves Lefebvre *(Jacques)*, Thalie Fruges *(Agathe)*, Serge Gainsbourg *(Rémy)*, Mary Marquet *(La Duchesse)*, Jeanne Hélia.

Romantic comedy-drama. Source: Catherine Paysan, *Je m'appelle Jérico* (Paris, 1964). Marie and Jacques, whose marriage has apparently failed, take a 3-week holiday in the country with Jacques' grandfather, a retired veterinarian. Though they pretend to be happily married, Grandfather is not fooled. Marie stays at home brooding while Jacques cycles to town each day to call his mistress. One day Jacques sees a beautiful woman sunbathing and fails at first to recognize her as his wife. They begin to repair their relationship, but Marie remains skeptical of Jacques' sincerity. Grandfather meanwhile has enlisted the aid of his young neighbor Rémy, a musician, to make Jacques jealous. They all meet at the home of La Duchesse, and when Grandfather is called upon to help deliver a foal, Rémy, Marie, and Jacques look on, deeply moved. Later, Rémy advises Marie to live for herself instead of through her husband; and Grandfather recounts to Jacques how he sought pleasure outside the home but would never allow his marriage to be endangered. At a party given by La Duchesse, Jacques' mistress, whom he has begun to neglect, appears and demands that Jacques meet her the next day. Grandfather and Marie are left waiting in anticipation, but not for long, as Jacques returns shortly, having broken off his affair to be with his wife. *Grandfathers. Veterinarians. Mistresses. Neighbors. Musicians. Marriage. Infidelity. Jealousy. Horses.*

Note: Opened in Paris in Jun 1968 as *Ce sacré grand-père*; running time: 95 min.

MARRIAGE DROPOUTS F6.3107

Dist Distribpix, Inc. 12 Mar **1969** [Boston opening]. Sd; b&w. 35mm. 60 min.

Prod Leonard Kirtman. *Dir* Tommy Goetz.

Sex exploitation film. A series of marriages are probed to discover the cause of the alarmingly high divorce rate in modern society. Ted and Betty have difficulties when their son returns home and finds his mother making love to a woman. Robert and Rosie have a tempestuous sexual liaison, and they compete to top each other's perversions; Robert is finally pushed too far. Roger spies on his wife Maizie, witnessing her own self-arousal and her seduction of the paper boy. Hank and Laura: Hank cannot become aroused by his wife's impassioned overtures, and he finally succumbs to his desire for another man. *Lesbianism. Sexual practices. Autoeroticism. Marriage. Infidelity. Impotence. Male homosexuality.*

MARRIAGE ITALIAN STYLE (France/Italy) F6.3108

C. C. Champion-Les Films Concordia. *Dist* Embassy Pictures. 20 Dec **1964** [New York opening]. Sd; col (Eastmancolor). 35mm. 102 min.

Pres by Joseph E. Levine. *Prod* Carlo Ponti. *Exec Prod* Joseph E. Levine. *Dir* Vittorio De Sica. *Screenplay* Eduardo De Filippo, Renato Castellani, Tonino Guerra, Leo Benvenuti, Piero De Bernardi. *Photog* Roberto Gerardi. *Art Dir* Carlo Egidi. *Set Decor* Dario Micheli. *Film Ed* Adriana Novelli. *Mus* Armando Trovajoli. *Sd* Ennio Sensi. *Asst Dir* Luisa Alessandri, Franco Indovina. *Prod Mgr* Ione Tuzi. *Cost Dsgn* Piero Tosi, Vera Marzot, Annamode. *Makeup* Giuseppe Annunziata, Giuseppe Banchelli.

Cast: Sophia Loren *(Filomena Marturano)*, Marcello Mastroianni *(Domenico Soriano)*, Aldo Puglisi *(Alfredo)*, Tecla Scarano *(Rosalie)*, Marilù Tolo *(Diane)*, Pia Lindstrom *(cashier)*, Giovanni Ridolfi *(Umberto)*, Vito Moriconi *(Riccardo)*, Generoso Cortini *(Michele)*, Raffaello Rossi Bussola *(lawyer)*, Vincenza Di Capua *(mother)*, Vincenzo Aita *(priest)*.

Domestic comedy-drama. Source: Eduardo De Filippo, *Filumena Marturano* (Naples opening: 7 Nov 1946). Filomena Marturano meets Domenico Soriano in a Neapolitan brothel in 1943 when she is 17. She meets him again after the war, and, after a suitable courtship, he moves her into her own apartment as his exclusive mistress and, later, into his family house. For years Filomena manages Domenico's pastry shop, runs his household, and cares for his senile mother, until the woman's death. Learning that Domenico plans to marry a young girl, Filomena pretends to be dying, and Domenico, believing her, weds her. When he learns that he has been tricked, he has the marriage annulled. Filomena then informs him that her purpose was to legalize her three sons, whose existence Domenico has not suspected (she has them in foster homes). She also reveals that one is Domenico's but refuses to say which. Domenico becomes obsessed with the identification of his son and threatens Filomena to no avail until finally, after a battle with her that ends in love-making, he realizes that he loves her. In the presence of the three boys, Filomena and Domenico are married again, and after the ceremony each of the boys addresses Domenico as "Papa." He still does not know, however, which is his own. *Prostitutes. Mistresses. Businessmen. Marriage. Marriage—Annulment. Illegitimacy. Fatherhood. Whorehouses. Naples.*

Note: Location scenes filmed in Naples. Opened in Rome in Dec 1964 as *Matrimonia all'italiana*; in Paris in Dec 1964 as *Mariage à l'italienne*; running time: 100 min.

THE MARRIAGE MANUAL F6.3109

Screenpix. *Dist* ScreenCom International. 21 Feb **1970** [New York opening]. Sd; col (Eastman Color). 35mm. 65 min.

Sex instruction film. Two couples assume a variety of intercourse positions to demonstrate to married couples how they might attain sexual fulfillment. *Marriage. Sex instruction.*

THE MARRIAGE OF BALZAMINOV (U.S.S.R.) F6.3110

Mosfilm. *Dist* Artkino Pictures. 10 Jun **1966** [New York opening]. Sd; col (Moscolor). 35mm. 90 min.

Dir-Screenplay Konstantin Voinov. *Photog* G. Kupriyanov. *Art Dir* F. Yasyukevich. *Mus* Boris Chaykovskiy. *Sd* V. Krachkovskiy.

Cast: Georgiy Vitsin *(Balzaminov)*, Lyudmila Shagalova *(his mother)*, Lidiya Smirnova *(matchmaker)*, Ye. Savinova *(Matryona)*, Zhanna Prokhorenko *(Kapochka)*, Lyudmila Gurchenko *(Ustinka)*, Tamara Nosova *(Nichkina)*, Nikolay Kryuchkov *(Neuyedenov)*, Rolan Bykov *(Chebakov)*, Inna Makarova *(Anfisa)*, Nadezhda Rumyantseva *(Raisa)*, Tatyana Konyukhova *(Khimka)*, Nonna Mordyukova *(Belotelova)*, G. Shpigel, B. Baybakov, Sh. Baron, I. Bykov, A. Vlasov, V. Gerasin, G. Donyagin, S. Yefimov, V. Zavyalov, V. Kiryanov, A. Konyashin, V. Korotkov, V. Lazarev, M. Krivova, A. Larionov, Yu. Rodnoy, F. Sergeyev, M. Suvorov, V. Tatarinov.

Comedy. Source: Aleksandr Nikolayevich Ostrovskiy, *Prazdnichnyy son—do obeda* (Saint Petersburg opening: 28 Oct 1857). Aleksandr Nikolayevich Ostrovskiy, *Svoi sobaki gryzutsya, chuzhaya ne pristavay* (Moscow opening: 27 Oct 1861). Aleksandr Nikolayevich Ostrovskiy, *Za chem poydyosh, to i naydyosh (Zhenitba Balzaminova)* (Saint Petersburg opening: 1 Jan 1863). In mid-19th-century Russia, Balzaminov, a timid clerk, escapes from the drab reality of his life through wild fantasies. By closing his eyes he becomes a celebrated general, a czar, or a romantic lover galloping on a white horse to his lady love. In actuality, his quest for a wealthy and beautiful wife is filled with frustration, despite the goadings of a domineering mother and a persistent matchmaker. Each pleasing prospect for marriage eventually rejects Balzaminov as a suitor because of his bumbling and doltish ways. At last, however, Balzaminov finds a wealthy bride, though there is considerable discrepancy between the daydream and its fulfillment. Instead of a fragile young beauty, he marries Belotelova, a fat, aging widow; instead of a magnificent wedding procession, there is only a coach carrying the widow and her downtrodden husband. *Clerks. Matchmakers. Widows. Timidity. Motherhood. Obesity. Wealth. Weddings. Fantasy.*

Note: Released in the U.S.S.R. in 1965 as *Zhenitba Balzaminova*.

MARRIAGE OF CONVENIENCE (Great Britain)   F6.3111

Merton Park Studios. *Dist* Schoenfeld Film Distributing Corp. 14 Jan **1970** [New York opening]. Sd; b&w. 35mm. 58 min.

Prod Jack Greenwood. *Dir* Clive Donner. *Screenplay* Robert Stewart. *Photog* Brian Rhodes. *Art Dir* Wilfred Arnold. *Film Ed* Bernard Gribble. *Mus* Francis Chagrin. *Sd Rec* Sid Rider.

Cast: John Cairney (*Larry Wilson*), Harry H. Corbett (*Inspector Jock Bruce*), Jennifer Daniel (*Barbara Blair*), Russell Waters (*Sam Spencer*), Trevor Maskell (*Detective Sergeant Collins*), Trevor Reid (*Superintendent Carver*), John Van Eyssen (*John Mandle*), Moira Redmond (*Tina*), Patricia Burke (*woman in flat*), Alex Scott (*Vic Ellis*), Pauline Shepherd (*Evie Martin*), Duncan Burns (*garage apprentice*), Howard Goorney (*onion seller*), Alexander Archdale (*prison governor*), Leila Williams (*secretary*).

Crime melodrama. Source: Edgar Wallace, *The Three Oak Mystery* (London, 1924). Larry Wilson, in prison on a robbery charge, escapes by arranging a fake marriage with the stepdaughter of a cellmate. He soon learns that Tina, his former partner, has married John Mandle, the former Scotland Yard inspector responsible for Larry's arrest, and that they have invested the money from the robbery in a seaside resort. Inspector Jock Bruce, Mandle's old rival, follows Larry to the resort and apprehends Larry, Mandle, and Tina aboard Mandle's boat. *Prison escapees. Marriage of convenience. Perfidy. Partnerships. Resorts. Scotland Yard.*

Note: Released in Great Britain in 1961.

THE MARRIAGE OF FIGARO (France)   F6.3112

Les Productions Cinématographiques. *For* Pathé Cinéma. *Dist* Union Film Distributors. 29 Apr **1963** [New York opening]. Sd; col (Eastmancolor). 35mm. 105 min.

Prod Pierre Gérin. *Dir* Jean Meyer. *Photog* Henri Alekan. *Art Dir* Robert Clavel. *Sets* Suzanne Lalique. *Film Ed* Claude Durand. *Mus:* Selections from "*Le Nozze di Figaro*" Wolfgang Amadeus Mozart. *Songs* Pierre-Augustin Caron de Beaumarchais. *Mus Orch & Adapt* André Cadou. *Sd* Jean Rieul. *Cost* Suzanne Lalique.

Cast: Georges Descrières (*Count Almaviva*), Yvonne Gaudeau (*Countess Almaviva*), Jean Piat (*Figaro*), Micheline Boudet (*Suzanne*), Louis Seigner (*Bartholo*), Denise Gence (*Marceline*), Jean Meyer (*Bazile*), Michèle Grellier (*Chérubin*), Georges Chamarat (*Antonio*), Maurice Porterat (*Doublemain*), Georges Baconnet (*Brid'oison*), Madame Bonnefoux (*Fanchette*), Jean-Paul Roussillon (*Grippe-Soleil*), Henri Tisot (*Pédrille*), Louis Eymont (*bailiff*), Members and Students of the Comédie-Française.

Comedy. Source: Pierre-Augustin Caron de Beaumarchais, *La folle journée, ou le mariage de Figaro* (Paris opening: 27 Apr 1784). A film version of the Comédie-Française production of Beaumarchais' play. *Aristocrats. Territorial governors. Chambermaids. Valets. Housekeepers. Philanderers. Infidelity. Scandal. Impersonation. Seduction. Personal identity. Debt. Andalusia.*

Note: Paris opening: Nov 1959 as *Le mariage de Figaro.*

THE MARRIAGE OF FIGARO (West Germany)   F6.3113

Polyphon Film & TV Productions. *Dist* Polytel International. 17 Jul **1970** [New York opening]. Sd; col (Eastman Color). 35mm. 189 min.

Prod Rolf Liebermann. *Exec Prod* Gyula Trebitsch. *Dir* Joachim Hess. *Photog* Hannes Schindler. *Art Dir* Ita Maximovna. *Mus:* "*Le nozze di Figaro*" Wolfgang Amadeus Mozart. *Mus Cond* Hans Schmidt-Isserstedt. *Mus Played by* Hamburg State Orchestra. *Sung by* Choir of Hamburg State Opera. *Choirmaster* Gunther Schmidt Bohlander. *Prod Supv* Rudolf Sander.

Cast: Tom Krause (*Count Almaviva*), Arlene Saunders (*Countess*), Heinz Blankenburg (*Figaro*), Edith Mathis (*Susanna*), Elisabeth Steiner (*Cherubino*), Kurt Marschner (*Basilio*), Maria von Ilosvay (*Marzelline*), Noel Mangin (*Bartolo*), Jurgen Forster (*Don Curzio*), Karl Otto (*Antonio*), Natalie Usselmann (*Barbarina*).

Opera film. Source: Wolfgang Amadeus Mozart and Lorenzo Da Ponte, *Le nozze di Figaro* (first performance: Vienna, 1 May 1786). Pierre-Augustin Caron de Beaumarchais, *La folle journée, ou le mariage de Figaro* (Paris opening: 27 Apr 1784). The film is a cinematic adaptation of Mozart's opera. *Aristocrats. Territorial governors. Chambermaids. Valets. Housekeepers. Philanderers. Infidelity. Scandal. Impersonation. Seduction. Personal identity. Debt. Andalusia.*

Note: Produced for West German television in 1968 as *Die Hochzeit des Figaro.*

MARRIAGE ON THE ROCKS   F6.3114

A-C Productions. *Dist* Warner Bros. Pictures. 24 Sep **1965** [New York opening; c2 Oct 1965; LP32145]. Sd; col (Technicolor). 35mm (Panavision). 109 min.

A Sinatra Enterprises Production. *Prod* William H. Daniels. *Dir* Jack Donohue. *Screenplay* Cy Howard. *Photog* William H. Daniels. *Art Dir* LeRoy Deane. *Set Decor* Arthur Krams, William L. Kuehl. *Film Ed* Sam O'Steen. *Mus Comp & Cond* Nelson Riddle. *Mus Prod* Joseph C. Behm. *Song:* "There Was a Sinner Man" Trini Lopez, Bobby Weinstein, Bobby Hart, Billy Barberis, Teddy Randazzo. *Sung by* Trini Lopez. *Choreog* Jonathan Lucas. *Sd* Francis E. Stahl. *Asst Dir* Richard Lang. *Women's Cost Dsgn* Walter Plunkett. *Mr. Sinatra's Wardrobe* Carroll and Co. *Makeup Supv* Gordon Bau. *Hairstyles* Jean Burt Reilly. *Dial Supv* Thom Conroy.

Cast: Frank Sinatra (*Dan Edwards*), Deborah Kerr (*Valerie Edwards*), Dean Martin (*Ernie Brewer*), Cesar Romero (*Miguel Santos*), Hermione Baddeley (*Jeannie MacPherson*), Tony Bill (*Jim Blake*), John McGiver (*Shad Nathan*), Nancy Sinatra (*Tracy Edwards*), Davey Davison (*Lisa Sterling*), Michael Petit (*David Edwards*), Joi Lansing (*Lola*), Tara Ashton (*Bunny*), Kathleen Freeman (*Miss Blight*), Flip Mark (*Rollo*), DeForest Kelley (*Mr. Turner*), Sigrid Valdis (*Kitty*), Trini Lopez (*himself*).

Romantic comedy. Valerie Edwards, wife of advertising executive Dan Edwards, goes to lawyer Shad Nathan for a divorce on grounds of boredom after 19 years of marriage and two children, Tracy and David. On the advice of his business partner and closest friend, Ernie Brewer, Dan takes Valerie to Mexico for a second honeymoon. They stay at Miguel Santos' hotel and discover that they really want to remain married, but through a mixup Santos gets them a Mexican divorce. Dan returns to the States to take care of urgent business and sends Ernie to Mexico to tell Valerie that arrangements for their remarriage are being made. Through another mistake by Santos, Ernie and Valerie are married; and Valerie decides to teach Dan a lesson by not divorcing Ernie immediately. Ernie, a sophisticated bachelor, tries to adapt to the life of a family man, while Dan moves into Ernie's apartment and leads a carefree bachelor's existence. Life continues in this manner for a short while, but all concerned recognize the unsuitability of affairs; on Thanksgiving Day, Dan and Valerie resume their marital relationship. Valerie soon tells Dan that she is expecting another child. *Advertising executives. Hotelkeepers. Lawyers. Bachelors. Friendship. Marriage. Divorce. Honeymoons. Partnerships. Hotels. Thanksgiving Day. Mexico.*

A MARRIED COUPLE (Canada)   F6.3115

Allan King Associates. *Dist* Aquarius Films. 2 Feb **1970** [New York opening]. Sd; col (Technicolor). 16mm. 97 min.

Prod-Dir-Writ Allan King. *Assoc Prod* Gwen Iveson. *Photog* Richard Leiterman. *Dsgn Asst* Tony Hall, Bob Iveson. *Film Ed* Arla Saare. *Mus* Zalman Yanovsky, Douglas Bush. *Sd Rec* Christian Wangler. *Sd Re-rec* Ron Alexander. *Asst Dir* Richard Leiterman. *Tech Adv* Wally Gentleman, Henri Fiks, Peter Moseley.

Participants: Billy Edwards, Antoinette Edwards, Bogart Edwards (*themselves*), Merton (*their dog*).

Documentary. For more than 10 weeks, Allan King's crew filmed the life of an ordinary couple: Billy Edwards, a 42-year-old advertising executive, and his wife, Toni, a former secretary to Shelley Winters, who live in Toronto with their 3-year-old son, Bogart, and Merton, their dog. The cameras follow them in their everyday activities, which include not only tender, happy moments but also violent arguments. *Advertising executives. Children. Marriage. Family life. Toronto. Dogs.*

Note: Original running time: 112 min.

MARRIED TOO YOUNG   F6.3116

Headliner Productions. 22 May **1962** [Maryland license; c15 Sep 1961; LP21991]. Sd; b&w. 35mm. 80 min.

Dir George Moskov. *Story-Screenplay* Nathaniel Tanchuck. *Dir Photog* Ernest Haller. *Set Dir* Ted Driscoll. *Film Ed* Maurice Wright. *Orig Mus Score* Manuel Francisco. *Rec Engr* Woodruff H. Clark. *1st & 2d Asst Dir* Lindsley Parsons, Jr., George Batcheller. *Wardrobe* Forrest T. Butler. *Makeup* Fred Phillips. *Prop Master* Karl Brainard.

Cast: Harold Lloyd, Jr. (*Tommy Blaine*), Jana Lund (*Helen Newton*), Anthony Dexter (*Grimes*), Marianna Hill (*Marla*), Trudy Marshall (*Susan Newton*), Brian O'Hara (*George Newton*), Nita Loveless (*Grace Blaine*), Lincoln Demyan (*George Blaine*), David Bond (*justice of the peace*), Cedric Jordan (*Mike*), Richard Davies (*judge*), Joel Mondeaux (*Felton*), George Cisar (*Miltie*), Irene Ross (*Phyllis*), Frank Harding (*Daddy-O*), Tom Fransden (*sportscaster*).

Melodrama. After impulsively eloping, high school students Tommy Blaine and Helen Newton please their parents by participating in a small second ceremony, after which they move in with the Blaines. Despite his dream of becoming a doctor, Tommy goes to work at a garage. There he is approached by the sinister Grimes, who suggests that the youth receive stolen automobiles. Despite financial need, Tommy resists the temptation. When Helen later complains about Tommy's parents, however, he rushes to the ice cream parlor, where he fights over the desirable Marla with her boyfriend Mike and the villainous Grimes. Embarrassed by his son-in-law's behavior, Mr. Newton insists that the newlyweds move into his home and formulates rules by which

Tommy must abide. Desperate for privacy, Tommy buys a home he cannot afford. When Helen bitterly contrasts their simple wedding with the elaborate ceremony uniting Marla and Mike, Tommy accepts Grimes's offer. Riding in a contraband car, Tommy and Helen are chased and apprehended by the police. In court the judge places Tommy on probation and lectures his parents and in-laws, who join forces to send the young man to college. *Newlyweds. In-laws. Mechanics. Judges. Adolescence. Marriage. Filial relations. Finance— Personal. Elopement. Probation. Weddings. Chases.*

Note: Also known as *I Married Too Young.*

THE MARRIED WOMAN (France)   **F6.3117**
Anouchka Films-Orsay Films. *Dist* Royal Films International. 16 Aug **1965** [New York opening]. Sd; b&w. 35mm. 94 min.
Dir-Writ Jean-Luc Godard. *Photog* Raoul Coutard. *Camera* Georges Liron. *Asst Op* Jean Garcenot. *Film Ed* Agnès Guillemot, Françoise Collin. *Asst Film Ed* Andrée Chotty, Gérard Pollicand. *String quartets #7, #9, #10, #14, #15* Ludwig van Beethoven. *Song:* "Java" Claude Nougaro. *Song:* "Quand le film est triste" John D. Loudermilk, G. Aber, L. Morisse. *Sung by* Sylvie Vartan. *Sd* Antoine Bonfanti, René Levert, Jacques Maumont. *Boom Op* Robert Cambourakis. *Asst Dir* Claude Othnin-Girard, Jean-Pierre Léaud, Hélène Kalouguine. *Prod Supv* Philippe Dussart. *Prod Mgr* Maurice Urbain. *Asst Prod Mgr* Jean-Claude Durand. *Prod Sec* Jane-Marie Olivier. *Dir Sec* Patricia Finaly. *Script Girl* Suzanne Schiffman. *Asst Script* Catherine Savignac. *Cost* Laurence Clairval. *Ch Electrn* Fernand Coquet. *Ch Mech* Bernard Largemains. *Still Photog* Marilou Parolini. *Prop* Joseph Gerhardt.
Cast: Macha Méril *(Charlotte)*, Bernard Noël *(Robert, the lover)*, Philippe Leroy *(Pierre, the husband)*, Rita Maiden *(Madame Céline)*, Margaret Le Van, Véronique Duval *(girls in the swimming pool)*, ChrisTophe *(Nicolas)*, Georges Liron *(The Physician)*, Roger Leenhardt *(himself)*, Jean-Luc Godard *(narrator)*.
Drama. Charlotte, the bourgeois wife of an airplane pilot, Pierre, is preoccupied with the external manifestations of fashion and sexuality. She is having an affair with Robert, an actor to whom she has promised to make a decision about leaving her husband. She and Robert make love at his apartment. She then takes a circuitous route by car and taxi before picking up her young stepson, Nicolas, from school. She takes Nicolas to meet Pierre and his guest, Roger Leenhardt, at an airfield. After dinner husband and wife discuss life, love, and her lover and then make love. The next morning Charlotte confirms that she is 3 months pregnant. Robert telephones to arrange their afternoon meeting—he will leave soon to go on tour with his company in a production of *Bérénice.* Madame Céline, Charlotte's maid, talks of her own very satisfying sex life. Charlotte goes to a swimming pool and overhears a conversation between two teenagers about sex. She goes to the doctor for advice about her pregnancy; in the middle of a lecture about contraception and love, Charlotte tells him that she does not know who the father is. Charlotte meets Robert as planned at the Orly Airport cinema, and they go to a motel. Charlotte tells him that she cannot make the decision, and Robert says their affair is over. Charlotte seems to agree but appears to be unsure. *Housewives. Housemaids. Air pilots. Actors. Infidelity. Pregnancy. Sexuality. Marriage. Fashion. Middle classes. Paris. Roger Leenhardt. Orly Airport. "Bérénice".*
Note: Filmed on location in Paris and at Orly Airport. Opened in Paris in Dec 1964 as *Une femme mariée*; running time: 95 min. Pre-release title: *La femme mariée.*

MARRY ME! MARRY ME! (France)   **F6.3118**
Renn Productions-Parafrance Films-Madeleine Films. *Dist* Allied Artists. 7 Jul **1969** [New York opening]. Sd; col (De Luxe). 35mm. 87 min. *MPAA rating* M.
Prod-Dir-Writ Claude Berri. *Photog* Ghislain Cloquet. *Art Dir* Georges Lévy. *Film Ed* Sophie Coussein. *Mus* Emile Stern. *Sd* Jean Labussière. *Asst Dir* Pierre Grunstein, Claude Confortes. *Prod Mgr* Philippe Senné. *Cost* Paola Pilla.
Cast: Claude Berri *(Claude Avram)*, Elisabeth Wiener *(Isabelle Schmoll)*, Régine *(Marthe)*, Louisa Colpeyn *(Madame Schmoll)*, Grégoire Aslan *(Monsieur Schmoll)*, Prudence Harrington *(Helen)*, Betsy Blair *(2d English teacher)*, Gabriel Jabbour *(Monsieur Avram)*, Estera Galion *(Madame Avram)*.
Comedy-drama. Claude Avram, a Jewish encyclopedia salesman in Paris, falls in love with and impregnates Isabelle Schmoll, the daughter of a wealthy Belgian diamond merchant. Anxious to do the right thing, Claude asks for and is granted permission to marry her. It is decided that before the wedding Claude should visit Antwerp to meet the rest of Isabelle's family; before leaving, however, Claude goes for an English lesson and becomes infatuated with Helen, his beautiful tutor. Despite this new love, he dutifully goes to Belgium with Isabelle and her parents. After meeting the rest of the family, particularly Isabelle's obese sister, Marthe, Claude becomes apprehensive and, using his English lessons as an excuse, rushes back to Paris and Helen. During their idyllic weekend, Helen agrees to break her engagement to an airline pilot and marry Claude, but after Claude announces the decision to Isabelle and her

family, he learns that Helen has decided to marry the pilot instead. While the Schmoll family try to find a solution to the dilemma of their daughter's pregnancy, Claude effects a reconciliation with Isabelle, and the two are married. By the time 5 years have passed, and Isabelle is awaiting the birth of her second child, Claude realizes that he is a reasonably happy man. *Jews. Salesmen. Merchants. Belgians. Tutors. Pregnancy. Family life. Marriage. Paris. Antwerp.*
Note: Location scenes filmed in Paris and Antwerp. Opened in Paris in Sep 1968 as *Mazel tov ou le mariage*; running time: 90 min.

MARSCHIER ODER KREPIER see **COMMANDO**

MARSHA, THE EROTIC HOUSEWIFE   **F6.3119**
Hollywood Cinema Associates-Donald A. Davis Productions. 30 Jan **1970** [Maryland license]. Sd; col. 35mm. 73 min. *MPAA rating* R.
Prod-Dir Don Davis.
Cast: Marsha Jordan *(Marsha)*, Ann Myers, Christine Murray, Leslie Morgan, Ingred Hansen, Lou Brown, Mark Griffin *(unidentified roles)*, Mark Edwards *(unidentified role, see note)*.
Drama. Greg is unfaithful to his bride, Marsha, on their honeymoon. Soon thereafter, Marsha learns that Greg is involved in an affair with his secretary. She strikes out in revenge, takes a series of "vacations" in Las Vegas, and becomes involved in a number of brief affairs with casual acquaintances. She eventually comes to the conclusion that her vengeance is pointless. To preserve her marriage, she conceives a plan to lure her husband back into the marital fold, and the two are finally reconciled. *Newlyweds. Secretaries. Marriage. Infidelity. Revenge. Honeymoons. Las Vegas.*
Note: Locations filmed in Monterey, Carmel, and Big Sur, California, and Las Vegas, Nevada. Also known as *Marsha.* Actor Mark Edwards is credited by only one source and may be the same as Mark Griffin.

MARTYRS OF LOVE (Czechoslovakia)   **F6.3120**
Barrandov Film Studio. *For* Československý Film. *Dist* New Line Cinema. 25 Feb **1968** [New York opening]. Sd; b&w. 35mm. 73 min.
Prod-Dir Jan Němec. *Screenplay* Ester Krumbachová, Jan Němec. *Photog* Miroslav Ondříček. *Art Dir* Olin Bosák. *Film Ed* Miroslav Hájek. *Mus* Jan Klusák, Karel Mareš.
Cast—"The Junior Clerk's Temptation": Petr Kopriva *(junior clerk)*, Marta Kubisová *(girl)*, Jitka Cerhová *(1st girl in nightclub)*, Ivana Karbanová *(2d girl in nightclub)*, Lindsay Anderson *(himself)*.
Cast—"Anastasia's Dream": Hana Kuberová *(Anastasia)*, Karel Gott *(singer)*, Jan Klusák *(captain)*, Vladimír Preclík *(tramp)*.
Cast—"Orphan Rudolph's Adventure": Josef Koníček *(Orphan Rudolph)*, Denisa Dvořáková *(girl)*.
Comedy-drama. THE JUNIOR CLERK'S TEMPTATION: Tired by the monotony of his business and social life, a shy junior clerk decides to spend all of his savings on a night on the town. Although he goes to a movie, a dancehall, and several nightclubs, no one pays him the slightest attention. Finally, he meets a girl who suggests that she and her friends have a party in his apartment. The clerk agrees, and after the party, he is delighted to find the girl in his bed, but she is asleep before he can join her. He arrives late for work the next morning and returns to his boring life. ANASTASIA'S DREAM: While working as a maid in an elegant home, Anastasia is attracted to a handsome singer giving a recital and follows him when he leaves the house. Although the singer fails to notice her, she attracts the attention of a medical officer who invites her into his carriage and then makes immediate plans to marry her. Anastasia panics and boards a train, where she sees a guitar-playing gypsy who motions for her to approach him. Suddenly Anastasia awakens from her daydream: she is a waitress in a railway dining car. ORPHAN RUDOLPH'S ADVENTURE: Rudolph, an orphan, looks over a fence at a garden party, and the drunken guests invite him to join the festivities. Treating him as an old friend, they outfit him with a beautiful new suit, and when the party ends, Rudolph promises an attractive young girl that he will return. When he does so the next morning, there is no sign of the girl, his friends, or the garden. *Lovelorn. Clerks. Housemaids. Singers. Soldiers. Gypsies. Waitresses. Orphans. Marriage. Drunkenness. Dancehalls. Nightclubs. Trains. Gardens. Dreams.*
Note: Produced in Czechoslovakia in 1966 and released there as *Mučedníci lásky.*

MARY HAD A LITTLE ... (Great Britain)   **F6.3121**
Caralan-Dador. *Dist* Lopert Pictures, United Artists. 25 Jul **1961** [Los Angeles showing; c13 Jul 1961; LP21896]. Sd; b&w. 35mm. 83 min. [Also 79 min.]
Prod George Fowler. *Dir* Edward Buzzell. *Screenplay* Robert E. Kent, Jameson Brewer. *Adapt* Peter Miller, James Kelly. *Photog* Desmond Dickinson. *Camera Op* Dudley Lovell. *Art Dir* John Blezard, Jim Morahan. *Film Ed* Bernard Gribble. *Mus* Bruce Campbell. *Cond* Philip Martell. *Titl Song* Edward Buzzell, Bruce Campbell. *Sung by* Dick James, singer. *Prod Mgr* Buddy

Booth. *Wardrobe* Barbara Gillett. *Makeup* Gerry Fletcher. *Hairstyles* Daphne Vollmer.

Cast: Agnès Laurent (*Mary Kirk*), John Bentley (*Dr. Malcolm Nettel*), Jack Watling (*Scott Raymond*), Hazel Court (*Laurel Clive*), John Maxim (*Burly Shavely*), Rose Alba (*Duchess of Addlecombe*), Patricia Marmont (*Angie*), Noel Howlett (*Pottle*), Trevor Reid (*Dr. Liversidge*), Michael Ward (*Hunter*), Charles Saynor (*taxi driver*), Sidney Vivian (*Grimmick*), Mark Hardy (*Hawkes*), Michael Madden (*Tigg*), Margaret Bull (*1st woman*), Yvonne Ball (*2d woman*), Raymond Ray (*park keeper*), Clifford Mollison (*Watkins*), Frances Bennett (*Esther*), Vincent Harding (*Carney*), John Cazabon (*Fitchett*), Tony Thawnton (*Shakespeare*), Terry Scott (*police sergeant*), John Ronane, Stephen John (*interns*).

Comedy. Source: Arthur Herzog, Jr., Muriel Herman and Al Rosen, *Mary Had a Little——* (London opening: 27 Nov 1951). Scott Raymond, a down-and-out British stage producer, is trying to raise £5,000 to put on a new play. At his club he overhears psychiatrist Malcolm Nettel claim that he could hypnotize an expectant mother into producing a perfect baby. Seeing the chance to make some easy money, Scott needles the doctor into wagering £5,000 to back up his theory. Scott then persuades a struggling young actress, Mary Kirk, to pose as a pregnant woman and become Nettel's patient. Nettel accepts her as an ideal subject and begins his psychiatric treatment. Doctor and patient fall in love; and when Nettel is publicly ridiculed because of his theory, Mary decides to help him by actually becoming pregnant. She gets drunk, marches into Scott's flat, and demands that he have sex with her. The unexpected arrivals of both Nettel and Scott's fiancée, Laurel Clive, lead to confessions by one and all. Mary and the doctor decide to marry and start their experiment anew. *Theatrical producers. Psychiatrists. Actors. Hypnotism. Pregnancy. Wagers. Imposture.*

Note: Released in Great Britain in Sep 1961.

MARY MARY   F6.3122
Warner Bros. Pictures. 24 Oct 1963 [New York opening; c2 Nov 1963; LP29431]. Sd; col (Technicolor). 35mm. 126 min.

A Mervyn LeRoy Production. *Prod-Dir* Mervyn LeRoy. *Screenplay* Richard Breen. *Photog* Harry Stradling, Sr. *Art Dir* John Beckman. *Set Decor* Ralph S. Hurst. *Film Ed* David Wages. *Mus* Frank Perkins. *Sd* M. A. Merrick. *Asst Dir* Gil Kissel. *Cost* Travilla. *Makeup* Gordon Bau. *Hairstyles* Jean Burt Reilly.

Cast: Debbie Reynolds (*Mary McKellaway*), Barry Nelson (*Bob McKellaway*), Michael Rennie (*Dirk Winston*), Diane McBain (*Tiffany Richards*), Hiram Sherman (*Oscar Nelson*).

Comedy. Source: Jean Kerr, *Mary Mary* (New York opening: 8 Mar 1961). When book publisher Bob McKellaway is informed by his attorney, Oscar Nelson, that he will have to justify some of his income tax deductions, Bob reluctantly asks his recently divorced wife, Mary, to come to New York and help allocate the canceled checks signed during their marriage. Although Bob is apprehensive about seeing Mary again, his fiancée, Tiffany Richards, is curious to see her. Once Mary arrives, she attracts the attention of Dirk Winston, a fading Hollywood star and former war buddy of Bob's. Since Mary is unable to obtain a hotel reservation, she decides to use Bob's apartment while he and Tiffany are visiting Tiffany's parents. A blizzard forces him to return home, however, and he arrives to find Mary kissing Dirk. Because of the bad weather, Bob spends the night alone with Mary, but after a violent argument, Mary decides to go to New Orleans with Dirk. Realizing that he still loves her, Bob locks Mary in a closet to prevent her departure. Dirk leaves without her; Tiffany exits, having sensed the truth of the situation; and Bob and Mary are reunited. *Publishers. Lawyers. Actors. Divorce. Marriage. Jealousy. Income tax. New York City. Blizzards.*

MARY POPPINS   F6.3123
Walt Disney Productions. *Dist* Buena Vista Distribution Co. 26 Aug 1964 [Los Angeles opening; c18 Aug 1964; LP28936]. Sd (RCA); col (Technicolor). 35mm. 140 min.

Pres by Walt Disney. *Prod* Walt Disney. *Co-prod* Bill Walsh. *Dir* Robert Stevenson. *2d Unit Dir (Live Action)* Arthur J. Vitarelli. *Screenplay* Bill Walsh, Don DaGradi. *Anim Dir* Hamilton S. Luske. *Anim Art Dir* McLaren Stewart. *Nursery Seq Dsgn* Bill Justice, Xavier Atencio. *Anim* Milt Kahl, Ollie Johnston, John Lounsbery, Hal Ambro, Frank Thomas, Ward Kimball, Eric Larson, Cliff Nordberg, Jack Boyd. *Background* Al Dempster, Don Griffith, Art Riley, Bill Layne. *Dir Photog* Edward Colman. *Art Dir* Carroll Clark, William H. Tuntke. *Set Decor* Emile Kuri, Hal Gausman. *Film Ed* Cotton Warburton. *Songs* Richard M. Sherman, Robert B. Sherman. *Mus Supv, Arr & Cond* Irwin Kostal. *Asst to the Cond* James MacDonald. *Dance Accomp* Nat Farber. *Choreog* Marc Breaux, Dee Dee Wood. *Sd Supv* Robert O. Cook. *Sd Mix* Dean Thomas. *Mus Ed* Evelyn Kennedy. *Asst Dir* Joseph L. McEveety, Paul Feiner. *Cost & Dsgn Cons* Tony Walton. *Cost Execution* Bill Thomas. *Cost* Chuck Keehne, Gertrude Casey. *Makeup* Pat McNalley. *Hairstyles* La

Rue Matheron. *Sp Eff* Peter Ellenshaw, Eustace Lycett, Robert A. Mattey. *Cons* P. L. Travers.

Cast: Julie Andrews (*Mary Poppins*), Dick Van Dyke (*Bert/Mr. Dawes, Sr.*), David Tomlinson (*Mr. Banks*), Glynis Johns (*Mrs. Banks*), Hermione Baddeley (*Ellen*), Reta Shaw (*Mrs. Brill*), Karen Dotrice (*Jane*), Matthew Garber (*Michael*), Elsa Lanchester (*Katie Nanna*), Arthur Treacher (*constable*), Reginald Owen (*Admiral Boom*), Ed Wynn (*Uncle Albert*), Jane Darwell (*The Bird Woman*), Arthur Malet (*Mr. Dawes, Jr.*), Cyril Delevanti (*Mr. Grubbs*), Lester Matthews (*Mr. Tomes*), Clive L. Halliday (*Mr. Mousley*), Donald Barclay (*Mr. Binnacle*), Marjorie Bennett (*Miss Lark*), Alma Lawton (*Mrs. Corry*), Marjorie Eaton (*Miss Persimmon*), Doris Lloyd (*depositor*), Major Sam Harris (*citizen*), Jimmy Logan.

Musical comedy. Based on the "Mary Poppins" books by: P. L. Travers. London banker George Banks advertises for a nanny in the *Times* when his wife, a suffragette, has difficulty finding a governess firm enough to handle their children, Jane and Michael. The children also write an advertisement, but Mr. Banks throws it into the fireplace. The next morning, a number of severe-looking women apply for the job, but a strong wind blows them away; Mary Poppins glides down from the sky on her umbrella, is interviewed by Mr. Banks, and decides to give the family a trial period. She gets the children to clean up the nursery, making the task enjoyable with her magic, and then takes them for a walk. They enter a picture of the countryside that her friend Bert has chalked on the sidewalk. After having tea served by dancing penguins, they ride on a merry-go-round, leave the carousel on their horses, and trot off to a fox hunt. When rain washes the sidewalk drawing away, Mary rushes the children home. The following day, Mary takes the children and Bert to visit her Uncle Albert, whose incessant laughter causes him to float in the air; soon they are all laughing and floating on the ceiling. Mr. Banks, meanwhile, refuses to believe his children's stories and wants to fire Mary, but adopts her suggestion that he bring his children to the bank and show them how he spends his day. Michael is to open an account, but instead he attempts to retrieve his money to buy birdseed from The Bird Woman, thus creating panic in the bank. The children escape, and Bert takes them home. Mary appears; and she, Bert, and the children travel across the rooftops of London. When they return home, their gaiety spreads throughout the household, and Bert points out to Mr. Banks how damaging his severity can be. When Banks is fired from his job, he tells chairman of the board Dawes a joke he learned from Michael, then leaves to take his children to fly kites in the park. Dawes, who has not laughed in 90 years, dies laughing at the joke, and Banks is offered a position on the board. Feeling that her job is complete, Mary opens her umbrella and flies away. *Songs:* "The Perfect Nanny" (Jane & Michael); "Sister Suffragette" (Mrs. Banks & chorus); "The Life I Lead" (Mr. Banks); "A Spoonful of Sugar" (Mary); "Pavement Artist, Chim Chim Cheree" (Bert); "Jolly Holiday" (Bert & Mary); "Supercalifragilisticexpialidocious" (Mary, Bert & chorus); "Stay Awake" (Mary); "I Love To Laugh" (Uncle Albert, Mary, Bert); "Feed the Birds" (Mary & chorus); "Fidelity Fiduciary Bank" (Mr. Dawes, Sr., Mr. Banks & chorus); "Chim Chim Cheree" (Bert, Mary, Michael & Jane); "Step in Time" (Bert & chorus); "A Man Has Dreams" (Mr. Banks & Bert); "Let's Go Fly a Kite" (Mr. Banks, Bert & chorus). *English. Children. Bankers. Governesses. Suffragettes. Chimney sweeps. Uncles. Family life. Brother-sister relationship. Magic. Fantasy. Merry-go-rounds. Fox hunts. Banks. Umbrellas. Kites. London. "Times" (London). Penguins. Horses.*

MARYA-ISKUSNITSA *see* **THE MAGIC WEAVER**

MARYJANE   F6.3124
American International Pictures. 24 Jan 1968 [Kansas City, Missouri, opening; c10 Jan 1968; LP35405]. Sd; col (PathéColor). 35mm. 95 min.

A Maury Dexter Production. *Prod-Dir-Story* Maury Dexter. *Writ* Richard Gautier, Peter L. Marshall. *Dir Photog* Richard Moore. *Camera Op* Jules Brenner. *Art Dir* Paul Sylos. *Set Decor* Harry Reif. *Film Ed* Sidney Levin. *Mus Prod* Sidewalk Productions. *Mus Score* Mike Curb, Lawrence Brown. *Sd* Brad Trask. *Asst Dir* Harry M. Jones. *Prod Mgr* Harold E. Knox. *Asst to the Prod* Hank Tani. *Prod Asst* Julie Foote. *Script Supv* Bonnie Prendergast. *Men's Wardrobe* Richard Bruno. *Women's Wardrobe* Karlice Cobb. *Makeup* Bob Mark. *Hairstyles* Cheri De La Mare. *Prop Master* Ted Berkeley.

Cast: Fabian (*Phil Blake*), Diane McBain (*Ellie Holden*), Kevin Coughlin (*Jordan Bates*), Michael Margotta (*Jerry Blackburn*), Patty McCormack (*Susan Hoffman*), Russ Bender (*Harry Braxton*), Booth Colman (*Maynard Parlow*), Baynes Barron (*Police Chief Otis Mosley*), Henry Hunter (*Mayor Arthur Ford*), Phil Vandervort (*Herbie Mueller*), Ivan Bonar (*Roger Campbell*), Robert Lipton (*Dick Marsh*), Byron Morrow (*judge*), Ward Ramsey (*Mr. Blackburn*), Frank Alesia, Tom Nolan (*Frenchy [see note]*), Bruce Mars (*Toby*), Steve Cory (*Chuck Poe*), Harold Ayer (*minister*), Linda Cooper (*Linda*), Ronnie Dayton (*George*), Terry Garr (*Terri*), Jo Ann Harris (*Jo Ann*), Hilarie Thompson (*Hilarie*), David Meo (*Ben*), Wayne Heffley (*ice cream company manager*), Dodie Warren (*Angela*), Carl Gottlieb (*Larry Kane*), Peter Madsen (*Kirby*).

Garry Marshall (service station attendant), Joe E. Ross (Mr. Reardon), Floyd Mutrux (Ollie), Helen Steusloff (waitress), Perry Cook (shop owner), Linda Sue Risk (little girl).

Melodrama. In a smalltown high school, a clique led by Jordan Bates gets together regularly to smoke marijuana. The town's civic leaders are alarmed at the increasing use of marijuana among the young but flounder in their attempts to curtail the illegal activity. Phil Blake, an art teacher who opposes spying on the students, admits that he once tried marijuana. He tries to gain the confidence of Jerry Blackburn, a sensitive art student who has become sick from smoking a marijuana cigarette given to him by the clique he desperately wants to join. Phil's efforts to reach Jerry fail, however, and the next night the boy "borrows" Phil's car to attend a "Maryjane" party. The gathering is interrupted by the police, and Jordan, in his haste, dumps a package of marijuana in Phil's car before Jerry returns it to the teacher's house. Phil is arrested on charges of marijuana possession but is bailed out of jail by Ellie Holden, a teacher to whom he is attracted. He learns that Jordan is involved in selling marijuana, but his attempt to talk to the youth results in a scuffle. Jordan sends Jerry to deliver a package of fake "Acapulco Gold" to a group of young toughs. Phil learns of the fraud and sets out to rescue Jerry. Halted by police, he rushes to borrow Ellie's car and discovers that it is she who has been supplying marijuana to Jordan and the other teenagers. Phil forces Jordan to accompany him to the mansion where the thugs have beaten Jerry. Phil rescues Jerry, leaving Jordan to face the wrath of the gang he tried to cheat. *Students. Art teachers. Police. Schoolteachers. Drug dealers. Gangs. High school life. Smalltown life. Theft. Perfidy. Marijuana.*

Note: Most sources credit Tom Nolan with the role of Frenchy; Frank Alesia receives screen credit.

MAS ALLA DE LAS MONTAÑAS see **THE DESPERATE ONES**

LA MASCARA DE SCARAMOUCHE see **THE ADVENTURES OF SCARAMOUCHE**

LA MASCHERA DEL DEMONIO see **BLACK SUNDAY**

MASCULIN FÉMININ see **MASCULINE FEMININE**

MASCULINE FEMININE (France/Sweden) F6.3125
Anouchka Films–Argos Films–Svensk Filmindustri–Sandrews. *Dist* Royal Films International. 19 Sep **1966** [New York opening]. Sd; b&w. 35mm. 103 min.
Dir-Writ Jean-Luc Godard. *Photog* Willy Kurant. *Film Ed* Marguerite Renoir, Agnès Guillemot. *Mus* Jean-Jacques Debout, Francis Lai. *Sd* René Levert. *Prod Mgr* Philippe Dussart. *1st Asst* Bernard Toublanc-Michel. *2d Asst* Jacques Barratier. *Asst* Pascal Aubier, Penni Jacques.
Cast: Jean-Pierre Léaud (Paul), Chantal Goya (Madeleine), Marlène Jobert (Elisabeth), Michel Debord (Robert), Catherine Duport (Catherine), Eva-Britt Strandberg (Lavinia), Birger Malmsten (actor), Elsa Leroy (Miss 19 of "Mademoiselle Age Tendre"), Françoise Hardy (woman with American officer), Chantal Darget (woman on metro), Brigitte Bardot, Antoine Bourseiller (themselves).
Comedy-drama. Source: Guy de Maupassant, "La femme de Paul," in *La Maison Tellier* (Paris, 1881). Guy de Maupassant, "Le signe," in *Gil Blas* (17 Apr 1886). Following his discharge from the army, a young French Marxist named Paul becomes an interrogator for a public opinion poll concerned primarily with the attitudes and opinions of the country's youth. After casually watching a woman murder her husband on a Paris street, Paul strikes up an acquaintance with a singer, Madeleine, who openly admits to using sex to further her career. He moves in with her and her two roommates, Elisabeth and Catherine, and becomes involved in the web of their relationship. Paul joins their get-togethers at coffee shops, discotheques, cafes, and the cinema, where they see a Swedish erotic film [made by Godard]. Their conversations include discussions of birth control, James Bond, military and civil authority, sexual perversion, and communism versus democracy. One day he watches a demonstration against U. S. involvement in Vietnam in which President Johnson is compared to Hitler and a young radical burns himself to death screaming "Give us TV and cars but spare us liberty." Paul is still undecided about his future when his mother dies and leaves him a considerable amount of money which he uses to buy a small, unfinished building. One day, while inspecting it, he falls—or perhaps jumps—to his death, leaving behind a pregnant Madeleine. *Veterans. Pollsters. Singers. Roommates. Youth. Murder. Urban life. Marxism. Politics. Demonstrations. Inheritance. Suicide. Birth control. Pregnancy. Motion pictures. Vietnam War 1964–73. Paris. Lyndon Baines Johnson. James Bond.*
Note: Released in France in 1966 as *Masculin féminin*; running time: 110 min; in Sweden in 1966 as *Maskulinum-Femininum*. Filmed on location in Paris.

M*A*S*H F6.3126
Aspen Productions. *Dist* Twentieth Century-Fox Film Corp. 25 Jan **1970** [New York opening; c30 Dec 1969; LP37644]. Sd (Westrex); col (DeLuxe). 35mm (Panavision). 116 min. *MPAA rating* R.
An Ingo Preminger Production. *Prod* Ingo Preminger. *Assoc Prod* Leon Ericksen. *Dir* Robert Altman. *Screenplay* Ring Lardner, Jr. *Dir Photog* Harold Stine. *Art Dir* Jack Martin Smith, Arthur Lonergan. *Set Decor* Walter M. Scott, Stuart A. Reiss. *Main Titl* Pacific Title. *Film Ed* Danford B. Greene. *Mus* Johnny Mandel. *Orch* Herbert Spencer. *Titl Song:* "Suicide Is Painless" Mike Altman, Johnny Mandel. *Sd* Bernard Freericks, John Stack. *Asst Dir* Ray Taylor, Jr. *Asst to the Prod* Ross Levy. *Unit Prod Mgr* Norman Cook. *Makeup Supv* Dan Striepeke. *Makeup Artist* Lester Berns. *Hairstyles* Edith Lindon. *Sp Photog Eff* L. B. Abbott, Art Cruickshank. *Medical Adv* David Sachs.
Cast: Donald Sutherland (Hawkeye Pierce), Elliott Gould (Trapper John McIntyre), Tom Skerritt (Duke Forrest), Sally Kellerman (Maj. Hot Lips O'Houlihan), Robert Duvall (Maj. Frank Burns), Jo Ann Pflug (Lieutenant Dish), Rene Auberjonois (Dago Red), Roger Bowen (Col. Henry Blake), Gary Burghoff (Radar O'Reilly), David Arkin (Sergeant Major Vollmer), Fred Williamson (Spearchucker Jones), Michael Murphy (Me Lay), Kim Atwood (Ho-jon), Tim Brown (Corporal Judson), Indus Arthur (Lieutenant Leslie), John Schuck (Painless Pole), Ken Prymus (Private First Class Seidman), Dawn Damon (Captain Scorch), Carl Gottlieb (Ugly John), Tamara Horrocks (Captain Knocko), G. Wood (General Hammond), Bobby Troup (Sergeant Gorman), Bud Cort (Private Boone), Danny Goldman (Captain Murrhardt), Corey Fischer (Captain Bandini), J. B. Douglas (Colonel Douglas), Yoko Young (Japanese servant), Ben Davidson, Fran Tarkenton, Howard Williams, Jack Concannon, John Myers, Tom Woodeschick, Tommy Brown, Buck Buchanan, Nolan Smith (football players).
War comedy. Source: Richard Hooker, *MASH* (New York, 1968). During the Korean War, U. S. Army surgeons Hawkeye Pierce and Duke Forrest steal a jeep to take them to their new assignment with the Mobile Army Surgical Hospital. Though close to the combat zone, the camp is peaceful except for disorders caused by the two surgeons' inability to get along with the pious Maj. Frank Burns. The tension increases with the arrival of "chest cutter" Trapper John McIntyre, who attacks Burns when he blames a young male nurse for a patient's death. Major O'Houlihan, a stunning blonde woman, arrives to take charge of the nurses and forms a professional alliance with Burns to compel the unruly surgeons to accept military discipline. Their relationship quickly becomes intimate, and Radar O'Reilly, a crony of the surgeons, places a microphone in Burns's tent and broadcasts the sound of their lovemaking. By the next morning, Major O'Houlihan is nicknamed Hot Lips; Major Burns suffers a breakdown and is led away in a straightjacket. Painless Pole, the hospital's dentist and a notorious lover, becomes temporarily impotent and threatens suicide after diagnosing himself a latent homosexual. The staff arranges a "Last Supper" in which Painless is given a suicide pill (actually a tranquilizer). Hawkeye then persuades Lieutenant Dish, a married nurse with whom he has been having an affair, to have sex with Painless, thus enabling the dentist to regain his potency. Later the men decide to find out if Hot Lips is a natural blonde; they rig the shower so that one of its walls collapses while she is bathing, thereby exposing her to the gathered onlookers. When Trapper John is called to Japan to perform an operation on a congressman's son, he takes along Hawkeye as his assistant; after the operation, the surgeons make a side trip to play golf. They return to the MASH unit as General Hammond arrives to investigate Major O'Houlihan's complaints. Hawkeye brags about the unit's football ability, whereupon the general challenges them to a game with a wager of $5,000. Through devious tactics, including the use of a professional player and a sedative, the MASH unit wins the game and the money. Soon afterward, Hawkeye and Duke receive their orders to return home. *Surgeons. Nurses. Dentists. Combat zone life. Theft. Mental illness. Impotence. Suicide. Male homosexuality. Infidelity. Cheating. Hospitals. Practical jokes. Golf. Tranquilizers. Football. Wagers. Korean War 1950–53. Korea. Japan. United States Army—Mobile Army Surgical Hospital. United States Army—Women's Army Corps.*

THE MASK (United States/Canada) F6.3127
Taylor-Roffman Productions. *For* Beaver-Champion Attractions. *Dist* Warner Bros. Pictures, New Line Cinema, Trans-International Films. 27 Oct **1961** [New York opening; c11 Nov 1961; LP27111]. Sd; b&w. 35mm [Depth-dimension, see note]. 83 min. [Cut from 95 min.]
Prod-Dir Julian Roffman. *Assoc Prod* Frank Taubes, Sandy Haber. *Assoc to the Prod* Jean Lenauer, Yvonne Taylor. *Screenplay* Frank Taubes, Sandy Haber. *Scen for Dream Seq* Slavko Vorkapich. *Photog* Herbert S. Alpert. *Depth-Dimensional Photog Supv* Charles W. Smith. *Sp Eff Photog, Depth-Dimensional Seq* James Gordon. *Art Dir* David S. Ballou, Hugo Wuchtrich. *Film Ed* Stephen Timar, Robert Schulte. *Mus* Louis Applebaum. *Choreog* Don Gillies. *Sd* Willard Goodman, Richard Vorisek. *Prod Mgr* William P. Owens.

Sp Eff & Depth-Dimensional Seq Herman Townsley.

Cast: Paul Stevens (*Dr. Allan Barnes*), Claudette Nevins (*Pamela Albright*), Bill Walker (*Lieutenant Martin*), Anne Collings (*Jill Goodrich*), Martin Lavut (*Michael Radin*), Leo Leyden (*Dr. Soames*), Eleanor Beecroft (*Mrs. Kelly*), William Brydon (*Anderson*), Norman Ettlinger (*Professor Quincy*), Stephen Appleby (*museum guide*), Ray Lawlor (*lab technician*), Jim Moran (*himself*), Nancy Island (*girl who is killed*), Rudi Linschoten (*Dr. Barnes' alter ego*), Paul Nevins (*The Demon of the Mask*).

Horror film. Psychiatrist Allan Barnes is visited by archeologist Michael Radin, who claims he is under the evil spell of a ritual mask he unearthed in the ruins of an ancient city. The mask forces him to commit murder. Barnes expresses skepticism, and the highly emotional Radin rushes from the office, returns to his room, and, after mailing the mask to Barnes, commits suicide. Upon receiving the package, the curious doctor dons the mask and experiences eerie and frightening hallucinations. Though shaken by the experience, he informs his fiancée, Pamela Albright, that he plans to continue experimenting with the unearthly object. Thinking of his safety, Pamela takes the mask to a museum, but Barnes breaks in at night and steals it. After two more experiences with the mask, he suddenly becomes obsessed with the desire to murder his pretty receptionist, Jill Goodrich. But as he tries to strangle her, she gashes his face and escapes into the night. Returning to Pamela, Barnes forces her to put on the mask, and he becomes enraged and tries to choke her when she experiences no reaction. The police arrive in time to rescue her. Restored to its place in the museum, the mask seems to attract another young man, a museum visitor. *Archeologists. Psychiatrists. Professors. Suicide. Hallucinations. Supernatural. Ritual murder. Masks. Museums.*

Note: Released in Canada in 1961. Also known as *Eyes of Hell.* Approximately 15 minutes of the film uses Depth-Dimension, a 3-D process developed by Britain's National Research Development Corp. Viewers are given a mask to put on whenever a character in film does the same. The film also contains a prologue, in which publicist Jim Moran explains the powers attributed to ancient masks.

MASKULINUM-FEMININUM *see* **MASCULINE FEMININE**

THE MASQUE OF THE RED DEATH (United States/Great Britain)
                                                              F6.3128
Alta Vista Productions–Anglo Amalgamated Productions. *Dist* American International Pictures. 24 Jun **1964** [Los Angeles opening; c24 Jun 1964; LP28693]. Sd (RCA); col (Pathécolor, print by Technicolor). 35mm (Panavision). 90 min.

Pres by James H. Nicholson, Samuel Z. Arkoff. *Prod-Dir* Roger Corman. *Assoc Prod* George Willoughby. *Screenplay* Charles Beaumont, R. Wright Campbell. *Dir Photog* Nicolas Roeg. *Camera Op* Alex Thomson. *Art Dir* Robert Jones. *Set Dresser* Colin Southcott. *Prod Dsgn* Daniel Haller. *Titl Dsgn* James Baker. *Film Ed* Ann Chegwidden. *Mus Comp & Cond* David Lee. *Choreog* Jack Carter, choreog. *Sd* Len Abbott, Richard Bird. *Dub Ed* Allan Morrison. *Asst Dir* Peter Price. *Cont* Joan Davis. *Cost Supv* Laura Nightingale. *Makeup* George Partleton. *Hairstyles* Elsie Alder. *Sp Eff* George Blackwell. *Constr Mgr* Dick Frift. *Casting Dir* G. B. Walker.

Cast: Vincent Price (*Prince Prospero*), Hazel Court (*Juliana*), Jane Asher (*Francesca*), David Weston (*Gino*), Patrick Magee (*Alfredo*), Nigel Green (*Ludovico*), Skip Martin (*Hop Toad*), John Westbrook (*man in red*), Gaye Brown (*Señora Escobar*), Julian Burton (*Señor Veronese*), Doreen Dawn (*Anna-Marie*), Paul Whitsun-Jones (*Scarlatti*), Jean Lodge (*Scarlatti's wife*), Verina Greenlaw (*Esmeralda*), Brian Hewlett (*Lampredi*), Harvey Hall (*Clistor*), Robert Brown (*guard*), David Davies, Sarah Brackett.

Horror film. Source: Edgar Allan Poe, "The Masque of the Red Death," in *Graham's Magazine* (May 1842). Edgar Allan Poe, "Hop-frog, or the Eight Chained Orang-outangs," in *Flag of Our Union* (17 Mar 1849). In 12th-century Italy Prospero, a Satan-worshiping prince, jails two peasants, Gino and Ludovico, for defying his authority to tax citizens. Francesca, Ludovico's daughter and Gino's fiancée, pleads for their lives, and the intrigued Prospero agrees to spare whichever one she chooses. Later, the prince sees evidence of the Red Death plague in the village and orders all houses in the infected area burned. The disease obliges Prospero to retreat to his castle, and he forces Francesca to accompany him, intending to dress her in courtly attire and have her watch him indulge in sadistic pleasures as part of her instruction in diabolism. Juliana, the prince's mistress, is jealous of Francesca but aids her attempt to help Gino and Ludovico escape. The plot is foiled, however, and at one of the events preceding Prospero's annual masked ball, the prince orders the men to cut themselves with five knives, one of which is poisoned. Ludovico is impaled on Prospero's sword when he attempts to kill the prince with one of the weapons, and Gino is banished to the burning village, promising to return. Juliana, meanwhile, sacrifices herself to Satan while Prospero watches unperturbed. On his way back to town, Gino meets a strange figure in red, who takes him back to the castle and instructs him to wait outside for Francesca.

As the mysterious intruder enters the ball, Prospero and his guests die of the Red Death, but Gino and Francesca are permitted to survive. *Royalty. Peasants. Mistresses. Demonology. Death. Sadism. Jealousy. Self-sacrifice. Plague. Castles. Masquerades. Taxes. Swords. Middle Ages. Italy. Fires.*

Note: Opened in London in Jun 1964; running time: 84 min.

MASQUERADE (Great Britain)   **F6.3129**
Novus Films. *Dist* United Artists. 28 Apr **1965** [New York opening; c28 Apr 1965; LP30761]. Sd; col (Eastmancolor). 35mm. 101 min.

Prod Michael Relph. *Dir* Basil Dearden. *Screenplay* Michael Relph, William Goldman. *Photog* Otto Heller. *Art Dir* Jack Stephens. *Prod Dsgn* Don Ashton. *Film Ed* John D. Guthridge. *Mus Comp & Cond* Philip Green. *Titl Song* Norman Newell. *Sung By* Danny Williams. *Sd* C. C. Stevens, Gordon K. McCallum. *Asst Dir* John Peverall. *Prod Supv* Jack Rix. *Cost Dsgn* Beatrice Dawson. *Makeup* Harry Frampton.

Cast: Cliff Robertson (*David Frazer*), Jack Hawkins (*Colonel Drexel*), Marisa Mell (*Sophie*), Michel Piccoli (*Sarrassin*), Bill Fraser (*Dunwoody*), Christopher Witty (*Prince Jamil*), Tutte Lemkow (*Paviot*), Keith Pyott (*Gustave*), José Burgos (*El Mono*), Charles Gray (*Benson*), John Le Mesurier (*Sir Robert*), Roger Delgado (*Ahmed Ben Fa'id*), Jerold Wells (*Brindle*), Felix Aylmer (*Henrickson*), Denis Bernard (*King Ahmed*), Ernest Clark (*minister*), David Nettheim (*photographer*), Anthony Singleton (*photographer's assistant*), Norman Fisher (*bishop*), Eric Blyth (*general*), James Mossman (*himself*).

Adventure comedy. Source: Victor Canning, *Castle Minerva* (London, 1955). Vital oil-concession talks between Britain and the Middle Eastern state of Ramaut have broken down, and the Foreign Office sends for Colonel Drexel, wartime liberator of Ramaut. Drexel's assignment is to kidnap the young heir to the throne, Prince Jamil, and keep him hidden until he ascends the throne and signs an agreement favorable to the British. Despite official objections, Drexel insists on hiring a wartime comrade, David Frazer, as his assistant. A daring soldier of fortune, Frazer follows his instructions and goes to a villa in Spain to be met by Drexel and the prince. Shortly after encountering the beautiful Sophie and her suspicious-looking companions, Frazer is knocked unconscious and Prince Jamil disappears. British officials suspect Frazer of duplicity, but Drexel staunchly defends him. Frazer soon learns, however, that Drexel is behind the kidnaping and plans to sell the prince back to his uncle. When Frazer confronts him with his knowledge of the facts, Drexel offers to include Frazer in the arrangement, but Frazer refuses the offer. Drexel then departs with the prince and is pursued by Frazer. They cross a canyon by means of a rope-suspension bridge; the bridge collapses; and Frazer saves both Drexel and Prince Jamil from death. British authorities watching the scene from a helicopter assume that both men have done their jobs well. The prince is restored to his throne, Drexel is awarded a commendation and a lucrative oil company job, and Frazer receives a modest check. *Heirs. Royalty. Government agents. Soldiers of fortune. Oil. Kidnaping. Duplicity. Bridges. Helicopters. Middle East. Spain. Great Britain—Foreign Office.*

Note: Location scenes filmed in Spain and the Middle East. Working title: *The Shabby Tiger.* Opened in London in Apr 1965; running time: 102 min. Also known as *Operation Masquerade.*

MASSACRE AT THE ROSEBUD *see* **THE GREAT SIOUX MASSACRE**

MASSACRE DE PLAISIR *see* **MASSACRE OF PLEASURE**

MASSACRE OF PLEASURE (Luxembourg)   **F6.3130**
Kaldea Films–C. T. A. *Dist* Olympic International Films. **1966.** Sd; b&w. 35mm. 67 min. [Cut from 91 min.]

Prod R. W. Cresse. *Dir* Jean-Loup Grosdard. *English Vers Dir* James E. McClarty. *Screenplay* Chris Pentel. *Photog* Jean-Jacques Renon.

Cast: Pierre Cabanne, José Diaz, Joël Barbouth, Jean Dumaine, Béatrice Cenci, Jean-Pierre Pontier, Willy Braque, Gaston Meunier, Valentine Pratz, Nicole Karen.

Crime melodrama. A Parisian crime syndicate led by Captain Jo barters women for narcotics, compelling its victims to submit to sadistic sexual practices. The gangsters torture and murder those who refuse to cooperate. Some of the women, forced to choose between submission and death, find pleasure in their degradation. Police detective Jean-Pierre infiltrates the syndicate and, posing as a sailor, traps Captain Jo. *Gangsters. Police. White slave traffic. Sadomasochism. Torture. Murder. Imposture. Syndicates. Narcotics. Paris.*

Note: Filmed in France as *Massacre pour une orgie.* Alternative U. S. title: *Massacre de plaisir.*

MASSACRE POUR UNE ORGIE *see* **MASSACRE OF PLEASURE**

THE MASTER BEATER　　　　　　　　　　　　**F6.3131**

Art-Gems, Inc. *Dist* Cinex Film Industries. 31 Jul **1969** [Maryland license]. Sd; b&w. 35mm. 73 min.

Prod Joc Bikini. *Exec Prod* Lou Campa. *Dir-Screenplay* Charles Carmello. *Asst Dir* Paul Moran.

Cast: John Lee, U. S. actor *(Hawk)*, Stephanie Bae *(Elaine)*, John Savage *(Rocco)*, Ilia *(Lez)*, Marty *(Les)*, Mike Scott, actor, Aaron Kaplan *(detectives)*, John Hunt *(Zappo)*, Kim Lazarus *(barmaid)*, Donald Barfield, Ed Geschrandtner *(hippies)*, Geri Gross *(Geri)*, Lou Campa *(Lou)*, Donna Lamb *(Sherry)*, Sherry, Ursula *(models)*, Bob Niles *(male model)*, Bo Bo *(auto wrecker)*, Harold Baad *(lover)*, Bella Bottle *(Judy)*, James C. Graves *(Flipper)*, Zita Rehorn.

Melodrama. Hawk, a brutal sadist, derives his pleasure from the pain and degradation he inflicts upon others. Skilled at exploiting human weakness, he forces men to sell their wives into white slavery for a bag full of a white, powdered drug. No woman can resist his overpowering evil. He inflicts the most terrible pain upon his slaves and leaves them begging for more. He takes the women he loves into his private world of tenderness and pain; but a violent death awaits those who incur his wrath. *Drug dealers. Sadomasochism. Murder. White slave traffic. Narcotics.*

Note: Formerly *The Dirty Hawk*; also known as *Hot Sex Tramp*.

MASTER OF HORROR (Argentina)　　　　　　**F6.3132**

Gates-Torres Productions–Vicente Marco Productions. *For* Argentina Sono Film. *Dist* U. S. Films, Jack H. Harris Enterprises. 16 Jun **1965** [Norfolk, Virginia, opening; c1 Oct 1964; LP36953]. Sd; b&w (see note). 35mm. 61 min. *MPAA rating* GP.

Pres by Jack H. Harris. *Prod* Nicolas Carreras. *Exec Prod* Rickey Torres, James C. Gates. *Exec Prod U. S. Vers* Jack H. Harris. *Dir* Enrique Carreras. *Screenplay* Luis Penafiel. *Screenplay Asst* Rodolfo M. Taboada. *Photog* Américo Hoss. *Art Dir* Mario Vanarelli. *Film Ed* José Gallego. *Mus* Victor Schlichter. *Prod Coörd* Henning Bystron.

Cast: Narciso Ibañez Menta, Carlos Estrada, Inéz Moreno, Narciso Ibañez Serrador, Mercedes Carreras, Lilian Valmar.

Horror film. Source: Edgar Allan Poe, "The Facts in M. Valdemar's Case," in *American Whig Review* (Dec 1845). Edgar Allan Poe, "The Cask of Amontillado," in *Godey's Magazine and Lady's Book* (Nov 1846). One stormy night a bored French maid reads two tales by Edgar Allan Poe. In "The Strange Case of Mr. Valdemar" Dr. Ekstrom hypnotizes a consumptive at the moment of death, thereby preserving him. Incredulous physicians Chambers and McCaffrey, however, force the hypnotist to break the trance, after which Valdemar's corpse quickly decomposes. In "The Cask of Amontillado" Burgundian dilettante Samivet drowns his unfaithful wife in a vat of wine, having encased her lover Maurice behind an adjacent wall. Shrugging off the stories, the housemaid enters the kitchen and faints at the sight of a mouse. *French. Housemaids. Physicians. Death. Hypnotism. Murder. Jealousy. Torture. Infidelity. Tuberculosis. Corpses. Burgundy. Edgar Allan Poe. Storms. Mice.*

Note: Produced in Argentina in color in 1960 and released there as *Obras maestras del terror*; running time: 115 min. A third segment, based on Poe's "The Tell-Tale Heart," was deleted from the English version. Copyrighted as *The Master of Horror*.

MASTER OF TERROR (Reissue)　　　　　　　**F6.3133**

Fairview Productions. *Dist* U. S. Films. 16 Jun **1965** [Norfolk, Virginia, opening]. Sd; col (Deluxe). 35mm. 85 min.

Note: Originally released as *4D Man* in 1959 by Universal-International; c25 Aug 1959; LP18563.

MASTER OF THE WORLD　　　　　　　　　　**F6.3134**

Alta Vista Productions. *Dist* American International Pictures. 31 May **1961** [Los Angeles opening; c30 May 1961; LP21145]. Sd; col (Magna Color, print by Pathé). 35mm. 104 min. [Also 100 min.]

Pres by James H. Nicholson, Samuel Z. Arkoff. A Roger Corman Production. *Prod* James H. Nicholson. *Exec Prod* Samuel Z. Arkoff. *Assoc Prod* Bartlett A. Carre, Daniel Haller. *Co-prod* Anthony Carras. *Dir* William Witney. *Screenplay* Richard Matheson. *Dir Photog* Gilbert Warrenton. *Aerial Photog* Kay Norton. *Art Dir* Daniel Haller. *Set Decor* Harry Reif. *Prod Dsgn* Daniel Haller. *Film Ed* Anthony Carras. *Mus Comp & Cond* Les Baxter. *Mus Coörd* Al Simms. *Orch* Albert Harris. *Titl Song* Les Baxter, Lenny Addelson. *Sung by* Darrye Stevens. *Sd* Carl Zint, Bill Warmarth, Vinton Vernon, Jerry Alexander. *Sd Ed* Al Bird. *Mus Ed* Eve Newman. *Asst Dir* Robert Agnew. *Prod Mgr* Bartlett A. Carre. *Prod Asst* Jack Cash. *Wardrobe* Marjorie Corso. *Makeup* Fred Phillips. *Photog Eff* Butler-Glouner Inc., Ray Mercer. *Sp Eff* Tim Barr, Wah Chang, Gene Warren. *Sp Prop & Eff* Pat Dinga. *Sp Col Proc* Modern Film Effects. *Prop Master* Dick Cugen.

Cast: Vincent Price *(Robur)*, Charles Bronson *(Strock)*, Henry Hull *(Prudent)*, Mary Webster *(Dorothy)*, David Frankham *(Philip)*, Richard Harrison *(Alistair)*, Vito Scotti *(Topage)*, Wally Campo *(Turner)*, Steve Masino *(Weaver)*, Ken Terrell *(Shanks)*, Peter Besbas *(Wilson)*.

Science fiction farce. Source: Jules Verne, *Maître du monde* (Paris, 1904). Jules Verne, *Robur-le-conquérant* (Paris, 1886). In the 19th century government agent Strock is ordered to sail in a balloon over a Pennsylvania crater to investigate a series of mysterious eruptions. Accompanying him are a munitions maker, Prudent, with his daughter, Dorothy, and her fiancé, Philip. Their balloon is shot down over the crater, and they become the prisoners of Robur, an inventor who has built a fantastic flying ship, *Albatross*, which he plans to use to destroy all instruments of war, thereby bringing lasting peace to the world. With his prisoners aboard, Robur proceeds on his mission across the world, bombing London, the English navy yards, and the armies of Austria and Egypt. Realizing that Robur is mad, Strock determines to destroy *Albatross*, at the risk of death to all aboard. When the flying ship lands for repairs at a Mediterranean island, the prisoners escape; and with ammunition taken from the ship's armory, Strock sets off an explosion that sends *Albatross*, Robur, and the crew to the bottom of the sea. *Government agents. Inventors. Pacifists. Fanatics. Aeronautics. Aerial bombardment. Balloons (ascent). Ammunition. Dirigibles. Islands. Egypt. Pennsylvania. Mediterranean Sea. London.*

Note: Included in the film is newsreel footage of early attempts by man to fly.

THE MASTER PIECE　　　　　　　　　　　　**F6.3135**

MOD Ventures. *Dist* Entertainment Ventures, Inc. 4 Mar **1970** [Champaign, Illinois, showing]. Sd; col. 35mm. 65 min.

Prod-Writ Tom Alderman, David Presnell. *Dir* Lee Van Horn. *Photog* Gil Hubbs. *Asst Camera* Tony Fisher. *Art Dir* David Presnell. *Film Ed* Clip Fabre. *Sd Art* Names. *Asst Dir* Michael Gary, Ram Stewart. *Asst to the Prod* Geoffrey Fernage. *Key Grip* Larry La Point. *Gaffer* Pat Kirkwood.

Cast: Lisa Grant *(Norma Sands)*, Lawrence Adams *(Ramon Wellman)*, Kay Mills *(Janet)*, Forman Shain *(Robert Sinclair)*, Larry Gardner *(Harry)*, Roxanne West *(Maria)*, Cecil Reddick.

Melodrama. Film star Norma Sands meets and desires ambitious young director Ramon Wellman, who enjoys the company of hopeful starlets and films his own bedroom exploits. Norma and Ramon begin an affair which culminates when Ramon is assigned to direct Norma in a film. Ramon moves on to greater exploits; breaking with Norma, he begins an affair with Janet, another featured player. Jilted, Norma tries to coerce Ramon into returning to her, but he refuses and blackmails her with his privately made sex films of her. Norma retaliates by murdering Ramon and Janet while they are in bed together. *Actors. Motion picture directors. Blackmail. Murder. Revenge. Sex exploitation films. Motion pictures.*

Note: Also known as *The Masterpiece*.

MASTER SPY (Great Britain)　　　　　　　　**F6.3136**

Eternal Films. *Dist* Allied Artists. 19 Aug **1964** [New York opening]. Sd; b&w. 35mm. 71 min.

Prod Maurice J. Wilson. *Dir* Montgomery Tully. *Screenplay* Maurice J. Wilson, Montgomery Tully. *Photog* Geoffrey Faithfull. *Camera Op* Chic Anstiss. *Art Dir* Harry White. *Film Ed* Eric Boyd-Perkins. *Mus* Ken Thorne. *Mus Dir* Philip Martell. *Sd Rec* John Bramall. *Asst Dir* David Tringham. *Prod Mgr* Frederick Gunn.

Cast: Stephen Murray *(Boris Turganev)*, June Thorburn *(Leila)*, Alan Wheatley *(Paul Skelton)*, John Carson *(Richard Colman)*, John Brown, British *(John Baxter)*, Jack Watson *(Captain Foster)*, Ernest Clark *(Dr. Pembury)*, Peter Gilmore *(Tom Masters)*, Marne Maitland *(Dr. Asafu)*, Ellen Pollock *(Dr. Morrell)*, Hugh Morton *(Sir Gilbert Saunders)*, Basil Dignam *(Richard Horton)*, Victor Beaumont *(Petrov)*, Derek Francis *(police inspector)*, Hamilton Dyce *(airport controller)*.

Melodrama. Source: Gerald Anstruther and Paul White, "They Also Serve" (a story; publication undetermined). Boris Turganev, a Russian physicist attending a conference in England, requests and is granted political asylum there. He is permitted to continue his research at Barfield, a British nuclear experimental laboratory, where he passes secret files to Paul Skelton, a wealthy local landowner. Leila, Turganev's assistant, has a narrow escape when she discovers that he and Skelton are spies, although Turganev is actually working for British Intelligence and is feeding false information to the traitorous Skelton. It is arranged for Turganev to be caught spying, stand trial, and be condemned in order to allay suspicion. A prison escape is engineered so that he can return to his own country and continue his espionage work there for the British government. *Defectors. Russians. Physicists. Landed gentry. Traitors. Espionage. Conferences—International. Laboratories. Prison escapes.*

Note: Released in Great Britain in May 1963; running time: 74 min.

THE MASTERPIECE see **THE MASTER PIECE**

MATA HARI, AGENT H-21 (France/Italy)   F6.3137

Filmel–Films du Carrosse–Simar–Films–Fida Cinematografica. *Dist* Magna Pictures Distribution Corp. Jan **1967**. Sd; b&w. 35mm. 106 min.

Prod Eugène Lépicier. *Dir* Jean-Louis Richard. *Screenplay* Jean-Louis Richard, François Truffaut. *Dial* François Truffaut. *Photog* Michel Kelber. *Art Dir* Claude Pignot. *Film Ed* Kenout Peltier. *Mus* Georges Delerue. *Sd* André Hervée. *Asst Dir* Christian de Chalonges. *Prod Mgr* Georges Casati. *Cost* Pierre Cardin.

Cast: Jeanne Moreau (*Mata Hari*), Jean-Louis Trintignant (*Capt. François Lassalle*), Claude Rich (*Julien, the chauffeur*), Frank Villard (*Colonel Pelletier*), Albert Rémy (*Adam Zelle*), Georges Riquier (*Ludovic*), Henri Garcin (*Gaston*), Hella Petri (*Baronne du Maine*), Marie Dubois (*soldier's fiancée*), Nicole Desailly (*Mata Hari's maid*), Carla Marlier (*chambermaid*), Jean-Marie Drot (*German spy chief*), Marcel Berbert (*plainclothesman following Mata Hari*), Georges Géret, Charles Denner.

Biographical drama. Paris, 1917. German spy Mata Hari (née Margaretha Geertruida Zelle in Holland), posing as a Javanese dancer, is ordered by Ludovic to seduce French Capt. François Lassalle, thereby enabling another spy to steal secret documents. Although successful, she falls in love with the officer. Later, during a similar mission, Mata Hari is observed by François making love to Colonel Pelletier. Abandoned by François, Mata Hari flees to Spain, but she later returns to France to follow François to the front. They are reunited, but the next morning François is killed by a German patrol. In Paris Mata Hari is betrayed to the French by her German commanders. Arrested and convicted of espionage, she is shot outside the Château de Vincennes. *Soldiers. Germans. Dutch. Exotic dancers. Espionage. Disguise. Seduction. Capital punishment. World War I. Paris. Spain. Margaretha Geertruida Zelle. Château de Vincennes.*

Note: Opened in Paris in Jan 1965 as *Mata-Hari agent H-21*; running time: 95 min; in Rome in Feb 1965 as *Mata Hari, agente segreto H 21*; running time: 100 min.

MATALOS Y VUELVE see **KILL THEM ALL AND COME BACK ALONE**

HA'MATARAH TIRAN see **SINAI COMMANDOS**

MATCHLESS (Italy)   F6.3138

Dino De Laurentiis Cinematografica. *Dist* United Artists. 27 Sep **1967** [Los Angeles opening; c15 Sep 1967; LP39823]. Sd; col (Technicolor, print by DeLuxe). 35mm. 104 min.

A Dino De Laurentiis Production. *Prod* Ermanno Donati, Luigi Carpentieri. *Dir* Alberto Lattuada. *Screenplay* Alberto Lattuada, Dean Craig, Luigi Malerba, Jack Pulman. *Story* Ermanno Donati. *Photog* Sandro D'Eva. *Art Dir* Enzo Del Prato. *Set Decor* Gisella Longo. *Film Ed* Franco Fraticelli. *Mus* Ennio Morricone, Piero Piccioni, Gino Marinuzzi, Jr.. *Cond* Bruno Nicolai. *Sd* Luciano Welisch. *Asst Dir* Antonio Brandt. *Prod Mgr* Piero Donati. *Cost* Piero Tosi, Cesare Rovatti. *Miss Fürstenberg's Cost* Forquet. *Sp Eff* Guy Delecluse.

Cast: Patrick O'Neal (*Perry "Matchless" Liston*), Ira von Fürstenberg (*Arabella*), Donald Pleasence (*Andreanu*), Henry Silva (*Hank Norris*), Nicoletta Machiavelli (*Tipsy*), Howard St. John (*General Shapiro*), Sorrell Booke (*Colonel Coolpepper*), Tiziano Cortini (*Hogdon*), Valery Inkijinoff (*hypnotizer*), Andy Ho (*O-Chin*), Elizabeth Wu (*O-Lan*), M. Mishiku (*Li-Huang*), Jacques Herlin (*O-Chin's doctor*), Giulio Donnini (*professor*), Lewis Jordan, Ennio Antonelli, Alfredo Martinelli.

Action melodrama. Mistaken for a spy by the Communist Chinese, New York journalist Perry "Matchless" Liston is tortured to obtain information about a lethal chemical substance. An elderly Oriental with whom he shares a cell gives Liston a ring that, when rubbed, makes him invisible for a short period of time. With the ring's help, he escapes from a Chinese firing squad but lands in the U. S. military's torture chamber for his presumed knowledge about the same chemical. He reluctantly agrees to assist U. S. intelligence forces in recovering the formula as well as samples of the substance held by Andreanu, a sinister international gangster. Aided by agent Arabella, whom he meets in London, Liston plots to get the material out of a Munich bank, but he encounters competition from foreign agent Tipsy and American traitor Hank Norris. Eventually Liston succeeds in extracting the formula and samples by employing the magical ring. Not trusting even the U. S. military with the dangerous information, Liston throws everything into the harbor at Hamburg. Unknown to Arabella, however, Liston keeps the magic ring. *Americans in foreign countries. Journalists. Communists. Chinese. Gangsters. Foreign agents. Traitors. Mistaken identity. Torture. Invisibility. Espionage. Bank robberies. Secret formulas. Hamburg. Munich. New York City. London. United States Army—Intelligence.*

Note: Location scenes filmed in Rome, Munich, and Hamburg. Opened in Rome in Sep 1967 under the English title; running time: 105 min. Dean Craig is a pseudonym for Mario Pierotti.

MATE DOMA LVA? see **DO YOU KEEP A LION AT HOME?**

MATINEE COWBOY see **THE SIDEWALK COWBOY**

MATINEE WIVES   F6.3139

Gentlemen II Productions. *Dist* Sack Amusement Enterprises. 25 Nov **1970** [Champaign, Illinois, showing]. Sd; col. 35mm. 93 min.

Prod (see note) Robert Warner, Robert Leigh. *Exec Prod* Anthony B. DeMaret. *Dir* Ken Stewart. *Screenplay* Robert Cole. *Dir Photog* Andy Remlap. *Camera* Ernie Chapman. *2d Unit Camera* Troy Remington. *Ed* James Walters. *Mus* Oliver Howard. *Sd Rec* Joe Pierce. *Asst Dir* Fred Husenbak. *Prod Mgr* Robert Leigh. *Makeup* Allyn Snitzill. *Hairstyles* Lynn Tarbitt. *Key Grip* Robert Rubio. *Gaffer* Richard Alliston.

Cast: Stephen Treadwell (*Paul Devlin*), Barbara Caron (*Linda Devlin*), Robert Cole (*Tom Chandler*), Allessanora (*Pat Chandler*), Mark Edwards (*Dr. Milton Arnold/Ken McCord*), Jeanne Henderson, actress (*Betty Morgan*), Christine Murray (*Kay Gavin*), Denny Lynn (*cocktail waitress/go-go dancer*).

Comedy-drama. Paul Devlin and Tom Chandler are real estate brokers whose quest for financial success has made them oblivious to the sexual needs of their wives. Both men, however, brag to each other of their sexual prowess, and particularly of their sexual relationships with their wives. The frustrated wives join a group of prominent housewives in the employ of Kay Gavin, an ex-hooker who is now a madam. While the husbands attempt to seduce their female clients, their wives spend the afternoons working as prostitutes. After exhausting a client who claims that he can simultaneously satisfy them both, the two women turn to each other for sexual fulfillment. One day the husbands ask Kay Gavin to supply them with women, and each unknowingly receives the other's wife. In two adjoining motel rooms, both couples find total sexual satisfaction. Complications arise when the proud husbands decide to meet socially in the company of their wives. *Madams. Real estate agents. Housewives. Braggarts. Prostitution. Mate swapping. Marriage. Infidelity. Lesbianism. Seduction. Troilism. Motels.*

Note: One source credits Robert Warner as producer, writer, and star, while pressbook credits Robert Leigh as producer and Robert Cole as writer and actor; the three are one and the same.

MATING MODERN STYLE see **WHAT A WOMAN!**

THE MATING OF THE SABINE WOMEN see **THE SHAME OF THE SABINE WOMEN**

MATKA JOANNA OD ANIOŁÓW see **JOAN OF THE ANGELS?**

LA MATRIARCA see **THE LIBERTINE**

MATRIMONIA ALL'ITALIANA see **MARRIAGE ITALIAN STYLE**

IL MATTATORE see **LOVE AND LARCENY**

A MATTER OF CONVICTION see **THE YOUNG SAVAGES**

A MATTER OF DAYS (Czechoslovakia/France)   F6.3140

Telcia Films–Barrandov Film Studio–Československý Film. *Dist* Royal Films International. 19 May **1969** [New York opening]. Sd; col. 35mm. 106 min. [Also reviewed at 96 min.] *MPAA rating* R.

Prod-Dir Yves Ciampi. *Assoc Prod* Jacques Simonnet. *Screenplay* Yves Ciampi, Rodolphe M. Arlaud, Vladimír Kalina, Alena Vostrá. *Story* Yves Ciampi. *Photog* Vladimír Novotný, Claude Saunier. *Art Dir* Jan Zázvorka. *Art Dir of Stage Sets* Gabriel Paris. *Set Decor* Karel Lukáš, Jacques Preisach. *Film Ed* Georges Alépée. *Mus* Svata Havelka, Jean-Jacques Debout, Christian Gaubert. *Sd* Jacques Lebreton, Josef Vlček. *Prod Mgr* Zdeněk Oves. *Cost* La Gaminerie. *Makeup* V. Hamr, Chantal Godaert.

Cast: Thalie Frugès (*Françoise*), Vít Olmer (*Pavel*), Philippe Baronnet (*Jean-Louis*), Jana Šulcová (*Vladena*), Milan Mach (*The Father*), Michel Ducrocq (*Philippe*), Josef Čáp (*Stašek*), Valérie Vienne (*Maite*), Radúz Chmelík (*conservative professor*), Ota Ornest (*Kotas*), Petr Svojtka (*Kotalik*), Danièle Garnier (*Virginie*), Pascal Fardoulis (*elder student*), Alexandre Klimenko (*director*), Jean-Pierre Marichal (*Gruber*), Jeanne Heuclin (*cook*), Dorothée Blank (*concubine*), Shoshana Seguev (*goddess*), Ladislav Janský (*Honza*), Lenka Termer (*Radka*), Hana Brejchová (*Kueta*), Karel Pavlík (*policeman*).

Drama. Françoise, a French sociology student and political activist, arrives at the university in Prague where she has won a graduate study scholarship for the 1967-68 academic year, and she falls in love with Pavel, a young professor of French who is also a political activist. Françoise, however, is already married to Jean-Louis, a drama student whom she met while studying at Nanterre. When Pavel learns of Françoise's marriage, he reacts with bitterness. Françoise returns to Paris for the Christmas holidays and asks Jean-Louis for a divorce; deeply hurt, Jean-Louis refuses to grant Françoise her freedom. Back in Prague, she discovers that her relationship with Pavel has become strained. Interpreting his support for the new Dubček regime as a sign that he supports the bóurgeois society which she opposes, Françoise telephones Jean-Louis in Paris, hoping for a reconciliation, but instead he offers to give her the divorce. Having attained fame as an actor, he wishes to enjoy his new success without the obligations of marriage. In May, Françoise learns of the student revolt in Paris and decides that she can no longer remain in Prague while her friends at home are fighting. Now it is Pavel who cannot comprehend Françoise's emotions over her homeland. Realizing the extent of their differences, Françoise leaves Pavel and returns alone to Paris. *Students. Professors. Actors. Student activism. Demonstrations. Infidelity. Duplicity. Divorce. France—History— Demonstrations May 1968. Prague. Paris. Nanterre. Karlova Universita (Prague).*

Note: Location scenes filmed in Nanterre, Paris and Prague. Opened in Paris in Apr 1969 as *À quelques jours près.*

A MATTER OF INNOCENCE (Great Britain)   **F6.3141**
Mariana Productions–Universal Pictures, Ltd. *Dist* Universal Pictures. 19 Jan **1968** [Miami, Florida, opening; c2 Mar 1967; LP38774]. Sd (Westrex); col (Technicolor). 35mm (Techniscope). 102 min.

A George W. George–Frank Granat Production. *Prod* George W. George, Frank Granat. *Assoc Prod* Sydney Streeter. *Dir* Guy Green. *Screenplay* Keith Waterhouse, Willis Hall. *Dir Photog* Arthur Ibbetson. *2d Unit Camera* H. A. R. Thomson. *Camera Op* Ron Robson. *Art Dir* Peter Mullins. *Main Titl* Maurice Binder. *Film Ed* Frank Clarke. *Mus Comp & Cond* Michel Legrand. *Song:* "Pretty Polly" Michel Legrand, Don Black. *Sung by* Matt Monro. *Sd Rec* C. C. Stevens, Gordon K. McCallum. *Sd Ed* Harry Miller, Gerry Hambling. *Sd Len* Shilton. *Asst Dir* David Tringham. *Prod Mgr* Terry Lens. *Prod Sec* Janet Turner. *Cont* Kay Rawlings. *Cost Dsgn* Anthony Mendleson. *Wardrobe* Dorothy Edwards, Ernie Farrer. *Makeup* Trevor Crole-Rees. *Hairstyles* Bernadette Ibbetson.

Cast: Hayley Mills *(Polly Barlow)*, Trevor Howard *(Robert Hook)*, Shashi Kapoor *(Amaz)*, Brenda De Banzie *(Mrs. Innes-Hook)*, Dick Patterson *(Rick Preston)*, Kalen Liu *(Lorelei)*, Patricia Routledge *(Miss Gudgeon)*, Peter Bayliss *(Critch)*, Dorothy Alison *(Mrs. Barlow)*, David Prosser *(Ambrose)*, Toni Murphy *(lady tourist)*, Eric Young *(Lim Kee)*, Sarah Abdullah *(bad girl)*, Anthony Chin *(Japanese proprietor)*, S. Y. Han *(occultists)*, Colonel Fairbanks *(minister)*, Fred Bryant, Lorne Polanski, Peter Martin, Paul Fagg *(sailors)*, Edward Johnson *(Gunther)*, Ong Ah Lock *(Noughts & Crosses boy)*, Palham Groom, Norman Grant *(planters)*, Peter Honri *(cabin steward)*.

Romantic comedy-drama. Source: Noel Coward, "Pretty Polly Barlow," in *Pretty Polly Barlow and Other Stories* (London, 1964). Homely, bespectacled Polly Barlow leaves her mother's bakery shop in England to go on a world cruise as a traveling companion for her rich and vulgar aunt, Mrs. Innes-Hook. Polly's uncle, Robert Hook, is supposed to meet them in Singapore, but he becomes too occupied with his Chinese mistress and sends an Eurasian guide, Amaz, to show them the sights of the city. After devouring a huge meal, Mrs. Innes-Hook drowns in the hotel swimming pool, leaving the 21-year-old Polly in possession of the dead woman's jewelry and money. Under the guidance of Amaz, Polly buys new clothes and contact lenses, which improve her plain appearance considerably—to the amazement of Robert, who arrives for Mrs. Innes-Hook's funeral. Later, Rick Preston, another tourist, begins to court her, and Polly then realizes that she has become an attractive young woman. Although aware that Amaz is a gigolo who would never consider marriage, Polly does not discourage his advances, but eventually she decides that it is time to fly back to England. As she prepares to sail for Hong Kong, Polly receives a talking parrot as a farewell present from Amaz. *Aunts. Uncles. Chinese. Mistresses. Eurasians. Tourists. Guides. Gigolos. Bakeries. Inheritance. Funerals. Singapore. Parrots.*

Note: Location scenes filmed in Singapore. Released in Great Britain Nov 1967 as *Pretty Polly.*

A MATTER OF MORALS (United States/Sweden)   **F6.3142**
Fortress Productions. *Dist* United Artists. 31 May **1961** [New York opening]. Sd; b&w. 35mm (AgaScope). 90 min.

Prod Steven Hopkins, John D. Hess. *Admin Prod* Tom Younger. *Dir* John Cromwell. *Screenplay* John D. Hess. *Photog* Sven Nykvist. *Sets* Bibi Lindström. *Film Ed* Eric Norden. *Mus Comp* Dag Wiren. *Mus Cond* Torbjörn Lundquist. *Prod Mgr* Gösta Peterson.

Cast: Patrick O'Neal *(Alan Kennebeck)*, Maj-Britt Nilsson *(Anita Anderson)*, Mogen Wieth *(Erik Walderman)*, Eva Dahlbeck *(Eva Walderman)*, Claes Thelander *(Bjornson)*, Lennart Lindberg *(Sven Arborg)*, Vernon Young *(Henderson)*, Gösta Cederlund *(Eklund)*, Hampe Faustman *(Kronstad)*.

Crime drama. Alan Kennebeck, a banker from Milwaukee, arrives in Stockholm to verify the final details of a $1 million loan from his bank to a Swedish factory. One of the conditions of the loan is an insurance policy on the life of the factory owner, Eklund, who has been away from Sweden for many years. Kennebeck is met by factory manager Erik Walderman, who has been

embezzling from the company. During the investigation, Kennebeck falls in love with Anita, Walderman's sister-in-law, and asks her to marry him. Though she discourages his attentions, Kennebeck goes home, divorces his wife, and returns to Stockholm. When Anita rejects him, he joins forces with Walderman and, as proof of his intentions, makes him the beneficiary of Eklund's insurance policy. Matters come to a climax when Eklund unexpectedly returns. Walderman persuades Kennebeck that they must murder Eklund, but before they can complete their plans, Eklund commits suicide. To insure payment of the policy money, Walderman orders Kennebeck to make the death look like murder. The police suddenly arrive, and Kennebeck becomes the victim of his own plot. He escapes long enough to kill Walderman, but he is then apprehended. *Americans in foreign countries. Bankers. Manufacturers. Embezzlement. Infidelity. Murder. Suicide. Loans. Insurance. Stockholm.*

Note: Filmed on location in Stockholm. Released in Sweden in Mar 1960 as *De sista stegen*; running time: 98 min.

A MATTER OF RESISTANCE *see* **LA VIE DE CHÂTEAU**

A MATTER OF WHO (Great Britain)   **F6.3143**
Foray Films. *Dist* Herts-Lion International Corp. 24 Jul **1962** [New York opening]. Sd; b&w. 35mm. 90 min.

Prod Walter Shenson, Milton Holmes. *Dir* Don Chaffey. *Screenplay* Milton Holmes. *Adapt* Patricia Lee. *Story* Patricia Lee, Paul Dickson. *Photog* Erwin Hillier. *Art Dir* Elliot Scott. *Film Ed* Frank Clarke. *Mus* Edwin Astley. *Titl Song* Bob Russell. *Sung by* Roy Castle. *Played by* John Barry Seven. *Sd* A. W. Watkins, Gordon Daniel. *Sd Rec* Norman Coggs, J. B. Smith. *Asst Dir* Dennis Bertera. *Prod Mgr* Denis Johnson. *Sp Eff* Tom Howard.

Cast: Terry-Thomas *(Archibald Bannister)*, Alex Nicol *(Edward Kennedy)*, Sonja Ziemann *(Michèle Cooper)*, Richard Briers *(Jamieson)*, Clive Morton *(Hatfield)*, Vincent Ball *(Doctor Blake)*, Honor Blackman *(Sister Bryan)*, Cyril Wheeler *(Steven Cooper)*, Carol White *(Beryl)*, Jacqueline Jones *(Miss Forsythe)*, Guy Deghy *(Nick Ivanovitch)*, Martin Benson *(Rahman)*, Bruce Beeby *(Captain Brook)*, Geoffrey Keen *(Foster)*, Eduard Linkers *(Linkers)*, Andrew Faulds *(Ralph)*, Barbara Hicks *(Margery)*, Michael Ripper *(skipper)*, George Cormack *(Henry)*, Julie Alexander, Chulam Mohammed, Roland Branel, Meekah.

Mystery comedy-drama. Archibald Bannister, a "germ detective" for WHO (World Health Organization), detains oilman Steven Cooper for observation at the London airport to diagnose a disease contracted by Cooper. Accompanying Cooper is his bride of two weeks, Michèle. Also at the airport is Edward Kennedy, Cooper's American partner, who is puzzled by the negative report Cooper submitted on oil-drilling tests carried out in the Middle East. Later, at a party given by unscrupulous oil tycoon Nick Ivanovitch, Kennedy is snubbed by his host after requesting more funds for additional drilling. The party is interrupted by Bannister, who announces that Cooper has smallpox and that all the guests must be vaccinated. Back at WHO headquarters, Bannister finds reports of two other smallpox cases. After questioning Michèle about Cooper's activities, he becomes convinced that all three cases are somehow related. He and Kennedy join forces to solve the mystery which leads them to an Alpine village. Here they discover that a missing document belonging to Cooper is the carrier of smallpox. With this new information, Kennedy unmasks Ivanovitch as the brains behind an oil swindle. Following Cooper's death, Kennedy and Michèle decide to form a professional—and romantic—alliance. *Detectives. Oilmen. Newlyweds. Americans in foreign countries. Tycoons. Swindlers. Smallpox. Partnerships. Airfields. London. Middle East. Alps. United Nations—World Health Organization. Documentation.*

Note: Location scenes filmed in the Austrian Alps. Released in Great Britain in 1961; running time: 92 min.

LES MAUVAIS COUPS *see* **NAKED AUTUMN**

LES MAUVAISES FRÉQUENTATIONS *see* **BAD COMPANY**

MAX-OUT   **F6.3144**
Robert Kaylor Productions. 17 Feb **1970** [New York showing]. Sd; b&w. 16mm. 45 min.

Prod Phoebe Kaylor. *Dir* Robert Kaylor. *Story Outline* Mel Rivers, Kenneth Jackson. *Camera* Robert Kaylor. *Asst Camera* Doug Barton. *Lighting* Mel Rivers. *Sd* Kenneth Jackson. *Coöp* The Fortune Society.

Cast: Mel Rivers, Joe Rizzo, Charles McGregor, Amy Macri, Joe Senatore, Annette Cerutti, Kenneth Jackson, Isidore Zimmerman, Doug Barton, Eddie Davis, U. S. actor, James Childs, James Hayes, Joe Sanchez.

Drama. Upon his release from jail in New York City, a young black man faces a society in which the odds are stacked against him. He purchases a subway token and is left with a nickel to his name. At a blood bank he receives $6 for a pint of his blood, the only source of income he now has. Having no place to sleep, he goes to a bar and finds a homosexual who takes him home and offers the use of his apartment. The homosexual treats him "just like a wife," but when his benefactor goes to work, the ex-convict starts to gather together the clothes he plans to take when he leaves. Returning to his old neighborhood, he finds a furnished room and a "connection" who will buy the clothes he is about to steal. The next morning, after spending one more night at the homosexual's apartment, he brings a full suitcase to his connection. To rid his mind of his homosexual experience, he picks up a woman in a bar, but while in bed with her he passes out. He awakens to find the woman and his money gone. He looks for jobs but is continually turned down. Though he finally obtains a painting job through a friend, his bigoted employer tricks him out of his day's wages, and he loses the rest of his money in a crap game on the street. He returns to his furnished room alone and angry. *Ex-convicts. Negroes. Racial prejudice. Male homosexuality. Theft. Loneliness. Criminals—Rehabilitation. Blood banks. Bars. New York City. The Fortune Society.*

Note: Filmed in New York City. Most of the cast and crew were members of the Fortune Society, an organization of ex-convicts whose aim is to inform the public about prison conditions. The dialogue was improvised by the cast.

MAXIME (France) F6.3145

Films Raoul Ploquin–Cocinor. *Dist* Interworld Film Distributors. 24 Oct **1962** [New York opening]. Sd (Western Electric); b&w. 35mm. 94 min.

Prod Raoul Ploquin. *Assoc Prod* Jean Mottet. *Dir* Henri Verneuil. *Scen & Adapt* Albert Valentin, Henri Verneuil, Henri Jeanson. *Dial* Henri Jeanson. *Photog* Christian Matras. *Camera* Gilbert Chain. *Asst Op* Ernest Bourreaud. *Art Dir* Robert Clavel. *Film Ed* Gabriel Rongier. *Mus* Georges Van Parys. *Ch Sd* Antoine Petitjean. *Sd Rec* Jean-Claude Dubois. *Boom* Gaston Ancessi. *Asst Dir* Michel Wyn, Jean Becker. *Script Girl* Lucile Costa. *Prod Mgr* Jacques Serres. *Location Mgr* Gabriel Bechir. *Prod Sec* Laquerrière. *Cost* Rosine Delamare, Blanche Van Parys. *Makeup* Jean-Paul Ulysse. *Hairstyles* Simone Knapp. *Still Photog* Marcel Bouguereau.

Cast: Charles Boyer *(Maxime)*, Michèle Morgan *(Jacqueline Monneron)*, Arletty *(Gazelle)*, Félix Marten *(Hubert Treffujean)*, Jacques Dufilho *(Flick)*, Micheline Luccioni *(Liliane)*, Jane Marken, Meg Lemonnier, André Brunot, Jean-Marie Proslier, Yvonne Constant, Geneviève Morel, Odette Barancay, Van Doude, Fernand Fabre, Lud Germain, Richard Larke, Liliane Patrick.

Romantic melodrama. Source: Henri Duvernois, *Maxime* (Paris, 1929). In turn-of-the-century Paris, Maxime, an aging, impoverished, yet charming aristocrat, exists by arranging romantic rendezvous for Hubert Treffujean, a boorish and drunken millionaire. Hubert has become enamored of the beautiful Jacqueline Monneron, but the young woman, familiar with his behavior, refuses to meet him. Instead, she falls in love with the debonair Maxime. As their love affair progresses, Maxime finds it increasingly difficult to live up to his man-about-town reputation and to match Jacqueline's high scale of living. Then one day Jacqueline surprises him at his home and discovers his poverty. Although touched, she realizes that he can never provide her with the brilliant life she has always known, and her passion turns to compassion. Hubert, meanwhile, has modeled himself after Maxime and become a sober and pleasant young man. Consequently, when Jacqueline eventually does meet him, she decides in favor of wealth and youth. After challenging his patron to a duel in an effort to salvage his dignity, Maxime faces a lonely future. *Idle rich. Playboys. Patrons. Aristocrats. Poverty. Middle age. Wealth. Drunkenness. Paris. Duels.*

Note: Location scenes filmed in Paris. Opened in Paris in Nov 1958; running time: 124 min.

MAYA F6.3146

King Brothers Productions. *Dist* Metro-Goldwyn-Mayer, Inc. 22 Jun **1966** [New York opening; c31 Dec 1965; LP32541]. Sd (Westrex); col (Technicolor). 35mm (Panavision). 91 min.

Prod Frank King, Maurice King. *Assoc Prod* Herman King, Mary Phillips Murray. *Dir* John Berry. *Screenplay* John Fante. *Adapt* Gilbert Wright. *Dir Photog* Gunter Senftleben. *Art Dir* Edward S. Haworth, Ram Yedekar. *Film Ed* Richard Heermance. *Asst Film Ed* Don Guidice. *Mus Comp & Cond* Riz Ortolani. *Rec Supv* Franklin Milton. *Rec* Pandurang Boloor. *Asst Dir* Bluey Hill. *Unit Prod Mgr* Clarence Eurist. *Prod Asst* Baba Shaikh, Chimankant Gandhi. *Cont* Trudy von Trotha. *Makeup* Reudiger von Sperl. *Sp Eff* Milt Rice. *Still Photog* Gunvant R. Patel, B. S. Achar.

Cast: Clint Walker *(Hugh Bowen)*, Jay North *(Terry Bowen)*, I. S. Johar *(One-Eye)*, Sajid Kahn *(Raji)*, Jairaj *(Gammu Ghat)*, Sonia Sahni *(Sheela)*, Ullas *(village spokesman)*, Nana Palsikar *(Raji's father)*, Uma Rao *(One-Eye's daughter)*, Madhusdan Pathak *(stationmaster)*.

Adventure drama. Source: Jalal Din and Lois Roth, "The Wild Elephant" (a story; publication undetermined). After the death of his mother, 13-year-old Terry journeys from Wyoming to India to join his father, Hugh Bowen, a big-game hunter whom the boy idolizes. Arriving a day earlier than expected, Terry walks to his father's house and is disappointed to find him reserved in his behavior. He then learns that his father has lost his courage after an almost fatal clawing by a tiger. Terry is further disillusioned when his father, in fear, shoots a cheetah the boy was trying to tame. Terry runs away and meets Raji, an Indian

boy whose father's dying wish was for the boy to deliver a sacred white elephant, the calf of the mammoth elephant Maya, to a distant temple in the jungle. Terry persuades Raji to carry out his father's desire and accompanies him on the long trip. The boys are menaced by tigers and by the evil One-Eye, a man who wants to steal the valuable white elephant. With the help of Terry's father, who regains his courage, the boys safely accomplish their mission. *Americans in foreign countries. Hunters. Adolescence. Filial relations. Courage. Friendship. Jungles. India. Big game. Tigers. Elephants. Cheetahs.*

Note: Filmed on location in India.

MAYERLING (France/Great Britain) F6.3147

Les Films Corona–Winchester Film Productions. *Dist* Metro-Goldwyn-Mayer, Inc. 13 Feb **1969** [New York opening; c31 Dec 1968; LP36546]. Sd; col (Technicolor). 35mm (Panavision). 140 min.

Prod Robert Dorfmann. *Exec Prod* Eugène Tucherer, Marcel Hellman. *Assoc Prod* Maurice Jacquin. *Dir-Writ* Terence Young. *Dir* "Giselle" Claude Giraud. *Adtl Dial* Denis Cannan, Joseph Kessel. *Photog* Henri Alekan. *Art Dir* Maurice Colasson, Roman Toman. *Prod Dsgn* Georges Wakhevitch. *Film Ed* Ben Rayner. *Mus Score* Francis Lai. *Theme* Aram Ilich Khachaturyan. *Sd* Jacques Carrère, Jo de Bretagne. *Asst Dir* Christian Roaux. *Prod Mgr* Georges Valon, Hugo Benedek. *Cost* Marcel Escoffier.

Cast: Omar Sharif *(Crown Prince Rudolf)*, Catherine Deneuve *(Baroness Maria Vetsera)*, James Mason *(Emperor Franz Josef)*, Ava Gardner *(Empress Elizabeth)*, James Robertson-Justice *(Edward, Prince of Wales)*, Geneviève Page *(Countess Larisch)*, Ivan Desny *(Count Josef Hoyos)*, Andréa Parisy *(Crown Princess Stephanie)*, Fabienne Dali *(Mizzi Kaspar)*, Maurice Teynac *(Moritz Azeps)*, Moustache *(Bratfisch)*, Bernard Lajarrige *(Loschek)*, Véronique Vendell *(Lisl Stockau)*, Charles Millot *(Count Taafe)*, Roger Pigaut *(Count Karolyi)*, Mony Dalmès *(Baroness Helen Vetsera)*, Lyne Chardonnet *(Hannah Vetsera)*, Irene von Meyendorff *(Countess Stockau)*, Jean-Claude Bercq *(Michael of Braganza)*, Jacques Berthier *(Prince John Salvator)*, Howard Vernon *(Prince Montenuevo)*, Jean-Michel Rouzière *(police superintendent)*, Roger Lumont *(Inspector Losch)*, Jacqueline Lavielle *(Marinka)*, Jacques Dorfmann *(rioting student)*, Anthony Stuart *(head gardener)*, Pierre Vernet *(court tailor)*, Richard Larke *(McTavish)*, Fred Vellaca *(Lawson)*.

With: Grand Ballet Classique de France *(performing "Giselle")*, Liane Dayde, James Urbain, Genia Melikova, Michel Nunes *(principal dancers)*.

Historical drama. Based on historical documentation and: Claude Anet, *Mayerling* (Paris, 1931). Michael Arnold, *The Archduke* (New York, 1967). In Vienna in 1888, Crown Prince Rudolf, the heir apparent to the Hapsburg Empire, is frustrated by both his political and domestic life. Sympathetic to the cause of the progressives pressing for a more democratic government, as well as for the independence of Hungary, he defies his father, the Emperor Franz Josef, by participating in student demonstrations. Furthermore, the failure of Rudolf's politically arranged marriage to the Crown Princess Stephanie of Belgium has driven him to morphine and public debauchery, highlighted by his flagrant affair with a somewhat infamous actress named Mizzi Kaspar. Then one day he meets the beautiful, 17-year-old Baroness Maria Vetsera, whose nouveau riche family is not accepted at court. Shortly after his mother, the Empress Elizabeth, returns from abroad—with Edward, the Prince of Wales, in tow—Rudolf persuades his cousin, Countess Larisch, to arrange a clandestine meeting between him and Maria. Surprised at finding himself in love, Rudolf makes no secret of his feelings, and the affair quickly creates a court scandal. Franz Josef sends Rudolf on a tour of inspection, and Maria is virtually banished to Venice, whereupon Rudolf counters by first appealing to the Vatican for an annulment of his marriage and then seeking sanctuary for him and Maria in France. When both requests are denied, the Empress advises her son to take Maria to Mayerling, the royal hunting lodge secluded in the Vienna woods. While they are there, word arrives that the Hungarian uprising has been suppressed and Rudolf's complicity in it has been discovered by his father. Realizing that any chance for happiness has been destroyed, the lovers form a suicide pact. And, at dawn, on January 30, 1889, Rudolf takes a revolver, shoots the sleeping Maria, and then turns the gun on himself. *Actors. Nouveaux riches. Royalty. Filial relations. Marriage—Arranged. Infidelity. Scandal. Politics. Marriage—Annulment. Uprisings. Suicide. Morphine. Vienna. Austria. Franz Josef. Rudolf (Austria). Elizabeth (Austria). Maria Vetsera. Mizzi Kaspar. "Giselle".*

Note: Released in Great Britain in 1968; opened in Paris in Dec 1968; location scenes filmed in Austria. Remake of the 1936 French film of the same title, released in the United States by Pax Films.

MAYHEM *see* **SCREAM, BABY, SCREAM**

MAYYA PLISETSKAYA *see* **PLISETSKAYA DANCES**

MAZEL TOV OU LE MARIAGE see **MARRY ME! MARRY ME!**

ME (France)   **F6.3148**

Athos Films–Parc Film–Stéphan Films–Renn Productions–Films du Carrosse. *Dist* Altura Films International. 2 Mar **1970** [New York opening]. Sd; col (Eastman Color). 35mm. 83 min.

Pres by Clem Perry, Fleetwood Films. *Prod* François Truffaut, Claude Berri, Mag Bodard, Guy Benier. *Dir-Writ* Maurice Pialat. *Adapt* Arlette Langman. *Dir Photog* Claude Beausoleil. *Sd* Henri Moline. *English Titl* Gwendolyn Wright.

Cast: Michel Terrazon (*François*), Marie-Louise Thierry (*Madame Minguet*), René Thierry (*Minguet*), Marie Marc (*Mémé*), Henri Puff (*Raoul*), Pierette Deplanque (*Josette*), Linda Gutemberg (*Simone*), Raoul Billerey (*Roby*), Maurice Coussoneau (*Letillon*).

Drama. François, a 10-year-old whose mother has abandoned him, is a ward of the state. The authorities place him in a foster home, but François does not adapt easily to his new surroundings. Because of his moodiness, his foster parents return him to the orphanage. François is next placed with the Minguets, an elderly couple whose own children have grown up and left home. François has trouble getting along with Raoul, an older boy who is also a foster child in the home of the affectionate Minguets. François grows fond of the Minguets, particularly of Madame Minguet's aged mother, Mémé. Mémé dies and François deeply suffers her loss. In spite of the Minguets' loving care, François remains troubled. He drops a cat down a stairwell to prove that the animal will land on its feet, and then tries to nurse it back to health. He causes a severe accident by throwing bars from a bridge and as a result is sent to a special school. All is not lost, however, for François knows that upon his release he can return to the Minguets. *Juvenile delinquents. Foster parents. Foster brothers. Childhood. Family life. Death. Desertion. Orphanages.*

Note: Opened in Paris in Jan 1969 as *L'enfance nue*; running time: 90 min. Shown as *Naked Childhood* at the 1968 New York Film Festival.

ME AND MY BROTHER   **F6.3149**

Two Faces Co. *Dist* New Yorker Films. 2 Feb **1969** [New York opening]. Sd; col & b&w. 35mm. 91 min.

Prod Helen Silverstein. *Dir* Robert Frank. *Screenplay* Sam Shepard, Robert Frank. *Photog* Robert Frank. *Film Ed* Robert Frank, Helen Silverstein, Lynn Ratener, Bob Easton, ed.

Cast: Julius Orlovsky (*himself*), Joseph Chaikin (*Julius Orlovsky*), John Coe (*psychiatrist*), Allen Ginsberg, Peter Orlovsky (*themselves*), Virginia Kiser (*social worker*), Nancy Fish (*herself*), Cynthia McAdams (*actress*), Roscoe Lee Browne (*photographer*), Seth Allen, Maria Tucci, Jack Greenbaum, Christopher Walken, Beth Porter, Fred Ainsworth, Richard Orzel, Philippe La Prelle, Otis Young, Gregory Corso, Sully Boyar, Joel Press, Louis Waldon.

Documentary drama. In New York City in 1965, Julius Orlovsky, a catatonic schizophrenic, is released from a mental institution in the care of his nonconformist brother Peter. Recruited for a film about homosexuality and psychopathology, Julius remains silent and withdrawn, unable, or unwilling, to respond to the questions put to him by Peter, by a psychiatrist, or by poet Allen Ginsberg, who lives with the two brothers. Julius accompanies Peter and Allen on a poetry-reading tour of Kansas. As a result of his reticence, Julius is replaced in the film by actor Joseph Chaikin. Aside from depicting Julius' life, the film incorporates experiences of other people directly or indirectly associated with Julius. Julius disappears during a visit to San Francisco; he gets lost and is returned to a mental institution. Though electric shock treatment and Thorazine do not fully restore Julius to reality, they partially restore his speech, and he is again released in Peter's care. When asked about his reaction to the movie camera, Julius hesitatingly replies, "It's a reflection ... of the real truth." *Brothers. Mutes. Nonconformists. Psychiatrists. Filmmakers. Actors. Poets. Catalepsy. Schizophrenia. Motion pictures. Male homosexuality. Hospitals. Tranquilizers. Shock therapy. New York City. San Francisco. Kansas. Julius Orlovsky.*

Note: Production on the film began in 1965.

ME, NATALIE   **F6.3150**

Nob Hill Productions–Cinema Center Films. *Dist* National General Pictures. 13 Jul **1969** [New York opening; c6 Jun 1969; LP39149]. Sd; col (DeLuxe). 35mm. 111 min. *MPAA rating* M.

Prod Stanley Shapiro. *Assoc Prod* Kurt Neumann. *Dir* Fred Coe. *Screenplay* A. Martin Zweiback. *Story* Stanley Shapiro. *Dir Photog* Arthur J. Ornitz. *Art Dir* George Jenkins. *Film Ed* Sheila Bakerman, Jack McSweeney. *Mus* Henry Mancini. *Titl Song* Henry Mancini, Rod McKuen. *Sd Mix* Dennis Maitland. *Asst Dir* Michael Hertzberg. *Prod Mgr* Roger Rothstein. *Makeup Artist* Dick Smith.

Cast: Patty Duke (*Natalie Miller*), James Farentino (*David Harris*), Martin Balsa.n (*Uncle Harold*), Elsa Lanchester (*Miss Dennison*), Salome Jens (*Shirley Norton*), Nancy Marchand (*Mrs. Miller*), Phil Sterling (*Mr. Miller*),

Deborah Winters (*Betty Simon*), Ronald Hale (*Stanley Dexter*), Bob Balaban (*Morris*), Matthew Cowles (*Harvey Belman*), Ann Thomas (*Mrs. Schroder*), Al Pacino (*Tony*), Catherine Burns (*Hester*), Robyn Morgan (*Natalie, age 7*), Daniel Keyes (*surviving brother*), Peter Turgeon (*attorney*), Milt Kamen (*plastic surgeon*), Ross Charap (*Arnold*), Dorothea Duckworth (*Mrs. Simon*), Milo Boulton (*Mr. Simon*), Dennis Allen (*Max*), Robert Frink (*Freddie*), Melinda Blachley (*Betty Simon, age 10*).

Comedy. On the night of the senior prom Natalie Miller, a homely Brooklyn adolescent, tells her parents that she must meet her date, a medical student, at the Staten Island Ferry. At the docks she surveys disembarking passengers, half hoping her imaginary escort will step ashore. Later, when supportive Uncle Harold, a retired Navy pharmacist, marries buxom Shirley Norton, Natalie's self-confidence is shattered. Although she enrolls in college, she is expelled for political activism. Desperate for their daughter's future, her parents bribe an aspirant optometrist to date Natalie. Discovering her parents' investment, Natalie buys a Honda, rents a Greenwich Village apartment operated by eccentric Miss Dennison, and gets a job as a waitress at the Topless-Bottomless Club. While riding to her flat in the dumbwaiter, Natalie attracts the attention of David Harris, an artist and architect, and they become lovers. Invited to popular Betty Simon's wedding, Natalie is delighted to discover her classmate pregnant and the unsuspecting groom abysmally ugly. Drunk with pleasure, she rushes to Harris' apartment and jumps in his bed, unexpectedly disturbing his wife. Horrified by the realization that her lover is a married man, Natalie confronts the architect. Although Harris suggests that he divorce his wife and live with Natalie, the young woman rejects such dependence and returns home. *Students. Pharmacists. Uncles. Landladies. Waitresses. Artists. Adolescence. Filial relations. Courtship. Self-confidence. Infidelity. Motorcycles. Weddings. Ferryboats. New York City—Greenwich Village. New York City—Brooklyn. New York City—Staten Island.*

Note: Filmed on location in New York City.

MEANWHILE, BACK AT THE RANCH see **THE BALLAD OF JOSIE**

MEANWHILE, FAR FROM THE FRONT see **THE SECRET WAR OF HARRY FRIGG**

MEAT/RACK   **F6.3151**

Dist Sherpix, Inc. Apr **1970**. Sd; b&w with col seq (Eastmancolor). 35mm. 71 min.

Prod Les Natali, Michael Thomas. *Exec Prod* Louis K. Sher. *Asst Prod* Robert Jenson. *Dir* Michael Thomas. *Screenplay* Joel Ensana. *Photog* Michael Thomas. *Film Ed* Michael Thomas. *Mus* Donald Skinner. *Sd* Carl Harrison. *Makeup* Robert Jenson.

Cast: David Calder (*J.C.*), Donna Troy (*Jean*), Jan Stratton (*mother*), Bob Romero (*father*), Steve Ferris (*Ken*), Ronald Ebbert (*J.C. as a child*), Alan Dye (*preacher*), Rodney Wheelock (*photographer*), Anne Muckerman (*housewife*), "Frog" (*fat man*), Roland Trupp (*man on beach*), Pat Monclair, Bambi Wayne (*transvestites*), Terry Sullivan (*driver at accident*), Gary Stevens (*go-go boy*), Philip Castle (*man in bar*), Nadine Davis (*prostitute in park*).

Drama. J.C. is a young male hustler in San Francisco. He often recalls his unhappy youth as the son of a loose-moraled mother, and he feels alienated from straight life, seeking solace in darkened movie houses where he often picks up customers. J.C. sells his body to men, but he occasionally makes love with women. While staying in a cheap hotel, J.C. intervenes when he sees a photographer attacking his nude model, Jean. Jean flees with J.C., and the two become lovers. J.C. and Jean are forced to make love in a stag film when they are blackmailed by a pair of transvestites who know that J.C. beat up the photographer. They decide to leave for Seattle, and J.C. picks up a masochist in order to get money for the trip. Jean surprises J.C. with the man and she flees, distraught, only to be run down by a car. J.C. returns to the streets. *Prostitutes. Photographers. Models. Male homosexuality. Bisexuality. Blackmail. Transvestism. Masochism. Sex exploitation films. San Francisco. Automobile accidents.*

Note: Produced in San Francisco. Also known as *Street/Rack*; may also be known as *Meat Rack*. Filmed in 16mm and blown up to 35mm for theatrical release.

MED MORD I BAGAGET see **NO TIME TO KILL**

MEDITERRANEAN HOLIDAY (West Germany)   **F6.3152**

M. C. S.-Film. *Dist* Continental Distributing, Inc. 5 Mar **1964** [Plainfield, New Jersey, opening]. Sd; col (Technicolor). 70mm (Wonderama, see note). 158 min.

Prod Georg M. Reuther. *Assoc Prod* Claus Hardt, Juan Hutchison. *Dir* Hermann Leitner, Rudolf Nussgruber. *Screenplay* Gerd Nickstadt, Arthur Elliott, Hans Dieter Bove. *English Narr Writ* William Lovelock. *Photog* Siegfried Hold, Heinz Hölscher, Tony Braun, Klaus König, Bernhard Stebich. *Aerial Photog* Heinrich Schafer, Heinz Hölscher. *Film Ed* Karl Aulitzky.

Harold J. Dennis, Harold McKenzie, Edward P. Campbell. *Mus Comp & Dir* Riz Ortolani. *Songs* Burl Ives. *Songs:* "Wherever You May Go," "Have Faith," "Sing Sagapo" George David Weiss, Riz Ortolani. *Sung by* Katyna Ranieri. *Sd* Jean Neny, Hans Joachim Richter, Hans von Hoesslin. *Asst Dir* Don José. *Prod Supv* Rudolf M. Travnicek. *Prod Mgr* Richard Oehlers, Peter Homfeld.

Cast —Participants: Captain Skoglund, Florian Bauer, Michael Hornung, Günther Metz, Christoph Gerhard, Udo Janson, Erich Moritz, Jürgen Richter *(cadets)*, Burl Ives *(narrator)*.

Travelog. Twenty teenage cadets in the Swedish merchant marine take a Mediterranean training cruise aboard the *Flying Clipper*, a three-masted topsail schooner designed in America and built in England. Chosen from among a hundred applicants, the cadets, led by Captain Skoglund and officers of the *Flying Clipper*, visit some of the Mediterranean ports they will later revisit as officers in the Swedish merchant marine. From Göteborg they sail to Nazare, a Portuguese fishing village, to take on fresh water, then to Lisbon where they visit an 18th century man-of-war which has been converted to an orphanage for sons of men lost at sea. From there, the *Flying Clipper* enters the Mediterranean through the Strait of Gibraltar en route to the Adriatic and Dubrovnik. Leaving Yugoslavia, the group visits several ports in Egypt, among them Port Said at the entrance to the Suez Canal. As the *Flying Clipper* maneuvers through the Canal, accompanied by a desert patrol mounted on camels, three of the boys and a newspaper reporter leave in a small boat for a trip along the Nile. They see the Theban ruins at Karnak, the temple of Amenhotep III at Luxor, the mausoleum of Aga Khan at Aswan, and the temple of Ramses II at Abu Simbel. Before joining the rest of the crew, they visit Tutankhamen's tomb in the Valley of the Kings. After touring the city of Cairo and visiting the Sphinx and Cheops' pyramid at Giza, they sail to Beirut and see the temple at Baalbek, then inland to the ski country near the cedars of Lebanon. After a thrilling bus ride down the Damascus highway, the group heads for Turkey to see the camel fights at Antalya, the Anatolian flatlands at Goreme, and the colorful attractions of Istanbul. The cruise is delayed when one of the cadets has an appendicitis attack. He is taken by helicopter to the U.S.S. *Shangri-La* for an emergency operation. The schooner wends its way into the Aegean, passing the legendary Greek islands Santorin, Mykonos, and Kalymnos. En route to Rhodes, the *Shangri-La* returns the cadet, recovered, to his shipmates. After a short stay on Rhodes they sail to Athens, where they meet King Constantine and visit the Acropolis. On a tour by plane they see Delphi, Olympia, and Meteora before the *Flying Clipper* sets sail for Naples and Capri. After a quick stop in Monaco to meet Prince Rainier and Princess Grace and witness the Grand Prix de Monaco, the crew of the *Flying Clipper* heads for the last country on its voyage, Spain. They see the "Guardia de Barcelona," world-famous horseback riders, the Alhambra in Granada, and finally in Seville they join in the celebration of the Feria and attend a bullfight at the Plaza de Toros. *Swedes. Cadets. Sea captains. Tourists. Travel. Skiing. Bullfighting. Schooners. Merchant marine. Tombs. Pyramids (Egypt). Appendicitis. Mediterranean Sea. Adriatic Sea. Göteborg. Nazare. Lisbon. Strait of Gibraltar. Dubrovnik. Port Said. Suez Canal. Nile River. Karnak. Luxor. Aswan. Abu Simbel. Cairo. Giza. Beirut. Lebanon. Syria. Antalya. Goreme. Istanbul. Santorin. Mykonos. Kalymnos. Rhodes. Athens. Naples. Capri. Monaco. Barcelona. Granada. Seville. Delphi. Olympia. Meteora. Acropolis. Sphinx of Giza. Thebes. Constantine II (Greece). Rainier III of Monaco. Grace of Monaco. United States Navy. Camels. Horses.*

Note: Released in West Germany in Dec 1962 as *Flying Clipper—Traumreise unter weissen Segeln*; running time: 154 min. Produced in Modern Cinema System 70mm; presented in the U. S. in Wonderama; shown in Cinerama for key engagements; in subsequent bookings released in 35mm CinemaScope. A U. S. source credits editors Dennis, McKenzie, and Campbell as photographers of a prolog included in the U. S. version.

MEDIUM COOL   F6.3153

H & J Pictures. *Dist* Paramount Pictures. 27 Aug **1969** [New York opening; c4 Aug 1969; LP37075]. Sd; col (Technicolor). 35mm. 110 min. *MPAA rating* X.

Prod Jerrold Wexler, Haskell Wexler. *Exec Prod* Tully Friedman. *Assoc Prod* Michael Philip Butler, Steven North. *Dir-Writ* Haskell Wexler. *Dir Photog* Haskell Wexler. *Camera Op* Mike Margulies. *Camera Asst* Ron Vargas. *Art Dir* Leon Ericksen. *Titl* James Talbot. *Film Ed* Verna Fields. *Asst Ed* Marcia Griffin. *Ed Cons* Paul Golding. *Mus Score* Mike Bloomfield. *Incidental Mus* The Mothers of Invention. *Song:* "Merry-Go-Round" Wild Man Fisher. *Sd Mix* Chris Newman. *Sd Ed* Kay Rose. *Asst Dir* Wendell Franklin. *Prod Asst* William Schwartz. *Asst to the Prod* Jonathan Haze. *Script Supv* Meta Rebner. *Chicago Cons* Studs Terkel. *Gaffer* Tom Ryan.

Cast: Robert Forster *(John Cassellis)*, Verna Bloom *(Eileen Horton)*, Peter Bonerz *(Gus)*, Marianna Hill *(Ruth)*, Harold Blankenship *(Harold Horton)*, Sid McCoy *(Frank Baker)*, Christine Bergstrom *(Dede)*, Robert McAndrew *(Pennybaker)*, William Sickingen *(News Director Karlin)*, Beverly Younger

(rich lady), Marrian Walters *(social worker)*, Edward Croke *(plainclothesman)*, Sandra Ann Roberts *(blonde in car)*, Doug Kimball *(newscaster)*, Janet Langhart *(maid)*, Peter Boyle *(gun clinic manager)*, Georgia Tadda *(secretary)*, Charles Geary *(Buddy, Harold's father)*, Jeff Donaldson, Richard Abrams, Felton Perry, Val Grey, Bill Sharp, Robert Paige, Walter Bradford, Russell Davis, Livingston Lewis, Barbara Jones, John S. Jackson *(black militants)*, Simone Zorn, Madeleine Marcou, Mickey Pallas, Lynn Erlich, Lester Brownlee, Morris Bleckman, Wally Wright, Sam Ventura, George Boulet *(reporters & photographers)*, James Jacobs, Spence Jackson, Dorien Suhr, Kenneth Whitener, Connie Fleischauer, Mary Smith, Nancy Lee Noble *(Kennedy students)*, Linda Handelman, Moira Friedman, Kathryn Schubert, Barbara Brydenthal, Elizabeth Moisant, Rose Bormacher *(gun clinic ladies)*, Roger Phillips, Robert Blankenship, China Lee, Sirri Murad.

Drama. Loosely based on the novel: Jack Couffer, *The Concrete Wilderness* (New York, 1967). John Cassellis, a news cameraman for a Chicago television station, and his soundman, Gus, cover a wide spectrum of events, including the assassination of Robert Kennedy and Resurrection City in Washington, D. C. John's attitude is cool and dispassionate; he films the victim of a car crash before calling an ambulance and encounters hostility and accusations of social irresponsibility when covering a human interest story in a black neighborhood. He has a run-in with 13-year-old Harold, whom he suspects of breaking into his car. Fleeing the parking lot, Harold drops a carrying case containing a pet pigeon. Once John realizes that the boy was not trying to rob him, he returns the case to the slum tenement where Harold lives with his mother, Eileen, a welfare recipient who moved from her West Virginia home when her husband was sent to Vietnam. Meanwhile, tension mounts in the city: war protestors plan to demonstrate during the 1968 Democratic National Convention, and Chicago's police force and the Illinois National Guard prepare for a confrontation. Criticized by his superiors for shooting too much film and outraged at his television station's surrender of his footage to the FBI, John creates a row and is fired. During this period of inactivity, he devotes most of his time to Eileen and Harold, thereby ending his long affair with Ruth, a nurse. As the political convention begins, John gets a free-lance assignment to cover the event. On the eve of the first session at the International Amphitheatre, Harold becomes so upset at seeing his mother and John embracing that he runs away from home. Eileen searches for him in Grant Park and is caught in a violent clash between demonstrators and police. Finding her in the midst of armed National Guardsmen and exploding tear gas bombs, John takes her to his car and drives her around the city, unaware that Harold has returned home. Distracted by the day's events, John loses control of the car and smashes into a tree, killing Eileen and seriously injuring himself. A passing motorist stops for a moment to photograph the accident and then drives on. *Television cameramen. Negroes. Widows. Police. Nurses. Militants. Social consciousness. Urban life. Demonstrations. Public welfare. Adolescence. Motherhood. Assassination. Television. Pets. Slums. Vietnam War 1964–73. Democratic National Convention 1968. Chicago. Washington (District of Columbia). Robert Francis Kennedy. National Guard. Automobile accidents. Pigeons.*

Note: Filmed entirely on location in Kentucky, Minnesota, Chicago, and Washington, D. C. Working title: *Concrete Wilderness*.

MEDJU JASTREBOVIMA see FRONTIER HELLCAT

MEET ME IN MOSCOW (U.S.S.R.)   F6.3154

Mosfilm. *Dist* Accord International Corp., Cinemasters International, Ltd. 2 May **1966** [New York opening]. Sd; b&w. 35mm. 73 min.

Pres by J. Jay Frankel. *Dir* Georgiy Daneliya. *Screenplay* Gennadiy Shpalikov. *Story Ed* I. Sergiyevskaya. *Photog* Vadim Yusov. *Art Dir* A. Myagkov. *Film Ed* L. Lysenkova. *Mus* Andrey Petrov. *Sd* S. Minervin. *Asst Dir* M. Chernova. *Prod Mgr* Yu. Rogozovskiy. *Cost* D. Ozerova. *Makeup* T. Panteleyeva, A. Demidov. *Sp Eff* B. Pluzhnikov, A. Rudachenko.

Cast: Nikita Mikhalkov *(Kolka)*, Aleksey Loktev *(Volodya)*, Galina Polskikh *(Alena)*, Yevgeniy Steblov *(Sasha)*, V. Basov *(floor polisher)*, Rolan Bykov *(man in park)*, A. Aleynikova, V. Ananina, S. Besedina, V. Vasilyeva, N. Vinogradova, N. Likhobabina, Ye. Melnikova, I. Miroshnichenko, A. Pavlova, A. Rumyantseva, Irina Skobtseva, L. Sokolova, D. Stolyarskaya, I. Titova, V. Babenko, B. Balakin, B. Bityukov, A. Bogolyubov, V. Volkov, G. Guskov, P. Dolzhanov, L. Durov, Ye. Kazakov, Uno Masaaki, K. Novikov, A. Smirnov, V. Sorokovov, V. Shilov, V. Shkurkin, V. Shurupov, G. Yalovich.

Comedy. Volodya, a construction engineer with an interest in writing, stops in Moscow for 24 hours en route back to his job in the Kamchatka region of Siberia. He makes friends with Kolka, a subway worker, and Kolka's friend Sasha. After a night on the job, Kolka accompanies Sasha to the military induction office so that Sasha can obtain a last-minute postponement of his induction in order to be married. Kolka then sets out with Volodya to meet Voronin, a well-known writer who has written Volodya a letter complimenting his newly-published story. Later, Kolka and Volodya both become attracted to Alena, a salesgirl in the record section of a department store, and they become rivals. In Gorky Park, Kolka and Volodya pursue a pickpocket, and at the police station Volodya is accused of being the criminal. However, Alena's resourcefulness is responsible for the capture of the true culprit. The three friends go to Sasha's home for his wedding party but find him in despair, having quarreled with his new bride. She has returned to her mother's home, but Kolka arranges a reconciliation. Finally, Volodya leaves to begin his journey homeward, and Kolka and Alena accompany him to the subway. *Tourists. Engineers—Civil. Authors. Salesclerks. Pickpockets. Friendship. Youth. Military draft. Mistaken identity. Weddings. Moscow. Moscow—Gorky Park. Siberia.*

Note: Released in the U.S.S.R. in Apr 1964 as *Ya shagayu po Moskve*; running time: 77 min.

MEET MISS MARPLE *see* **MURDER SHE SAID**

MEET THE SEX   F6.3155
Dist American Film Distributing Corp. 23 Apr **1969** [New York showing]. Sd; b&w. 35mm. 63 min.

Melodrama(?). Press material suggests that the film contains scenes of body painting, lesbianism, and male homosexuality among young people. *Youth. Male homosexuality. Lesbianism. Body painting.*

Note: Also known as *Meet the Set*. May also be known as *Meet the Nude Set*. Footage also included in *The Devil's Book Store*, q. v.

MEETING ON 69TH STREET   F6.3156
Lecamto Productions. *Dist* Cosmos Films. 4 Jun **1969** [Boston opening]. Sd; b&w. 35mm. 65 min.
Prod Phil Todaro, Paul Leonardi. *Dir* Kemper Peacock. *Screenplay* Joe Bates.
Cast: Rita Marsh, Marlene Carol, Rock Grande, Bill Tillman, Art Yates, III, Carol Tames, Vera Lane.
Drama. Three young women search for a house in which to establish themselves as prostitutes. They find a dilapidated two-story flat on 69th Street, not far from a naval base. The women work assiduously to remodel the bedrooms and then send out invitations to a housewarming. Three curious sailors decide to visit the house while on furlough. For three days the men indulge every desire, and the residents call in additional women to help meet their demands. *Prostitutes. Sailors. Group sex. Whorehouses.*
Note: Rita Marsh is also known as Zita Marlowe, and Marlene Carol as Carol Morley.

MEGLIO VEDOVA *see* **BETTER A WIDOW**

MEIN KAMPF (Sweden)   F6.3157
Minerva International Films. *Dist* Columbia Pictures. 21 Apr **1961** [New York opening; c1 May 1961; LP20500]. Sd; b&w. 35mm. 119 min.
Prod Töre Sjöberg. *Dir-Writ* Erwin Leiser, Ingemar Ejve, Töre Sjöberg. *Film Ed* Ingemar Ejve. *Mus* Marton Lorand.
English Vers Narrator: Claude Stephenson.
Documentary. Using films from the Nazi files, footage from other sources, and still photographs, the rise and fall of the Third Reich is documented. Seen are Hitler's early years in Vienna, his arrest after the unsuccessful revolt in Munich in 1923, and the prison where he wrote his autobiography *Mein Kampf*; the rise of Nazi power in politically divided Germany; the plunging of Europe into war; atrocities against the Jews, particularly in the Warsaw ghetto and in concentration camps; the trial of German military officers after their attempt to assassinate Hitler; and the eventual defeat of Germany by the Allies. Some of the persons whose activities are portrayed include: Von Hindenburg, Liebknecht, Göring, Goebbels, and Hess. Other themes or events include: post-World War I Germany, the Treaty of Versailles, the Reichstag fire, Nazi rallies at Nuremberg, the annexation of Austria, and the post-World War II International Military Tribunal at Nuremberg. *Nazis. Jews. Genocide. Conspiracy. Assassination. Assassination. Concentration camps. World War II. Germany—History—Third Reich. Nuremberg Rallies. Versailles Treaty (1919). Vienna. Austria. Warsaw. Munich. Adolf Hitler. Hermann Göring. Joseph Paul Goebbels. Rudolf Hess. Paul von Hindenburg. Wilhelm Liebknecht. International Military Tribunal. Documentation. "Mein Kampf".*
Note: Released in Sweden in May 1960 as *Den blodiga tiden*.

MEIN KAMPF II *see* **SECRETS OF THE NAZI CRIMINALS**

DIE MEISTERSINGER VON NÜRNBERG (West Germany)   F6.3158
Polyphon Film & TV Productions. *Dist* Polytel International. 15 Jul **1970** [New York showing]. Sd; col. 35mm. 251 min.
Prod Rolf Liebermann. *Exec Prod* Gyula Trebitsch. *Dir* Leopold Lindtberg. *Libretto* Richard Wagner. *Photog* Joachim Hess. *Mus:* "Die Meistersinger von Nürnberg" Richard Wagner. *Mus Played by* Hamburg State Philharmonic Orchestra. *Orch Cond by* Leopold Ludwig. *Mus Sung by* Hamburg State Opera Chorus.

Cast: Giorgio Tozzi (*Hans Sachs*), Richard Cassilly (*Walther von Stolzing*), Arlene Saunders (*Eva*), Toni Blankenheim (*Sixtus Beckmesser*), Ursula Boese (*Magdalena*), Ernst Wiemann, Gerhard Unger.
Opera film. Source: Richard Wagner, *Die Meistersinger von Nürnberg* (first performance: Munich, 21 Jun 1868). A film of the Hamburg Opera's performance of Richard Wagner's *Die Meistersinger von Nürnberg*. *Singers. Cobblers. Poets. Jealousy. Knighthood. Elopement. Marriage—Arranged. Nuremberg. Hans Sachs.*
Note: Produced for West German television; original broadcast date undetermined.

MELISSA: THE TOTAL FEMALE   F6.3159
Dist Canyon Distributing Co. Aug **1970** [periodical notice]. Sd; col (Eastmancolor). 35mm. 60 min.
Prod John Philips, David Aston. *Dir* Arthur Penton. *Screenplay* William Shwartz. *Story* Bruce Fine. *Ed* Ed Lyons. *Mus* Jacob Casarini. *Sd* Hollywood Picture Recorders. *Sp Eff* Canspex.
Cast: Nancy Gresham (*Melissa*), Paul Crowther (*Fred*), Sarah Neri (*Susan Holt*), Peter Harding (*Al*), Stephanie D'Arcy (*Gail*), Angel Crellin, George McCarthy, Felice Thompson, Kathy Burns, Bruce Fine, Carole Murphy, Ireen Mayes (*models*).
Drama. Melissa believes that her fiancé, Fred, is a producer of television commercials, but Fred is actually a producer of pornographic films. Although Fred remains chaste with Melissa, he freely indulges in sex with his actresses. Susan Holt, one of his favorites, overhears Fred talking on the telephone to Melissa while directing a group sex orgy. Feeling sorry for the deceived Melissa, Susan calls her and tells her of Fred's other life. Melissa, shattered by the news, telephones the police to report Fred's activities. The police arrive during an orgy and arrest Fred and his actors. [Press photographs suggest that the film also contains scenes of lesbianism and fellatio.] *Actors. Motion picture producers. Revenge. Lesbianism. Duplicity. Infidelity. Oral sex. Sex exploitation films. Orgies.*

MELLEM VENNER *see* **DAYS OF SIN AND NIGHTS OF NYMPHOMANIA**

MÉLODIE EN SOUS-SOL *see* **ANY NUMBER CAN WIN**

MEMENTO MEI   F6.3160
Dist Martin Charlot. **1963** [Honolulu, Hawaii, showing]. Si; b&w with col seq. 16mm. 70 min.
Prod-Dir Martin Charlot. *Photog* Martin Charlot. *Film Ed* Martin Charlot.
Cast: Patrick Silva (*Pat*), Don Tescher (*doctor*), Edward Mulvaney (*old man*), Cecilia Souza (*girl*), Robert D. Browne, Edward Stasack (*men*), Richard Drake (*masked man/giant*), Juliette May Fraser (*old lady*), David Asherman (*hunchback*), Cor Mulder (*barber*), Wright Esser (*artist*), Jean Charlot (*client*).
Fantasy. A hospitalized old man sitting in a wheelchair remembers a time ca1900: Pat, a young man, runs along a hill holding hands with a girl friend. She runs ahead as he pauses to rest; chasing after her, he climbs a cliff, at the top of which sit two men in whiteface and a third whose face is encased in a white mask. When Pat is unable to pull away the mask, he tries to smash it with a rock. He falls through the mask, through space, into the yard of a dilapidated old house. Stumbling through the creaky interior, he confronts a hooded figure holding a watch. Outside the house the girl waits with her back turned, but as Pat approaches her she turns and is seen to be a hag. Running through the forest, Pat is thrown to the ground by a bearded giant carrying a staff; and a hunchback joyfully dances. The giant releases Pat and the three walk through the forest. At a stream, the giant and hunchback force Pat underwater; but the young man floats downstream, and the giant and hunchback, after chasing him, disappear into the forest. Pat's beard grows as he floats, and he awakens at the edge of the stream. A grinning barber shaves off his beard with two strokes, then swipes at Pat. As the young man leaps up, his forehead is cut. Alone in the forest, Pat pulls out a 3-leaved fern from the site of his wound and bandages his head. He sees an old factory; the girl is walking up its outside staircase. Rushing into the building, he once again confronts the old woman, who laughs at him. He claws at her and they struggle, but she vanishes. Pat finds himself in an artist's studio. A stuffy client sits in a chair as the artist frenetically paints an "action" portrait. The client, furious at the result, jumps through the canvas. Pat's face becomes an abstraction. The old man in the wheelchair moves painfully, then settles back: Pat runs up the hill and walks off with the girl. *Giants. Hunchbacks. Barbers. Painters. Memory. Youth. Old age. Death. Hospitals. Forests.*
Note: Filmed on location in Hawaii.

MEN OF THE TENTH *see* **THE RED, WHITE AND BLACK**

MENNESKER MØDES OG SØD MUSIK OPSTÅR I HJERTET see
PEOPLE MEET AND SWEET MUSIC FILLS THE HEART

MENSCHEN IM NETZ see UNWILLING AGENT

LES MENTEURS see THE LIARS

LA MENTIROSA see SIX DAYS A WEEK

LE MÉPRIS see CONTEMPT

LE MERAVIGLIE DI ALADINO see THE WONDERS OF ALADDIN

LE MERAVIGLIOSE AVVENTURE DI MARCO POLO see MARCO
THE MAGNIFICENT

LE MERCENAIRE see SWORDSMAN OF SIENA

THE MERCENARIES see DARK OF THE SUN

EL MERCENARIO see THE LAST MERCENARY

IL MERCENARIO see THE MERCENARY

IL MERCENARIO see SWORDSMAN OF SIENA

LOS MERCENARIOS see REVOLT OF THE MERCENARIES

THE MERCENARY (Italy/Spain)   **F6.3161**
P. E. A.–Produzioni Associate Delphos–Profilms 21. *Dist* United Artists. 6
Mar **1970** [New York opening; c20 Dec 1968; LF62]. Sd; col (Technicolor).
35mm (Techniscope). 105 min. *MPAA rating* GP.
   Pres by Alberto Grimaldi. *Prod* Alberto Grimaldi. *Assoc Prod* Salvatore
Alabiso. *Dir* Sergio Corbucci. *Screenplay* Luciano Vincenzoni, Sergio Spina,
Sergio Corbucci. *Story* Franco Solinas, Giorgio Arlorio. *Dir Photog* Alejandro
Ulloa. *Camera Op* Sergio Bergamini, Hans Burman. *Asst Camera Op* Isidro
Muro, Julio M. Leyva. *Art Dir* Luis Vázquez, Piero Filippone. *Film Ed* Eugenio
Alabiso. *Ed Supv* Enzo Ocone. *Mus* Ennio Morricone, Bruno Nicolai. *Sd* Carlo
Diotallevi, Alfredo Polo. *Asst Dir* Ricardo Huertas, Filiberto Fiaschi. *Prod Mgr*
Manuel Castedo, Francesco Merli. *Unit Mgr* Pietro Nofri. *Prod Sec* Orlando
Pierfederici, Serafin García, José N. de la Rosa. *Script Girl* Franca Invernizzi.
Cost Dsgn Jurgen Henze. *Makeup* Raoul Ranieri, Alejandro Millon.
Hairdresser Giuseppina Bovino. *Sp Eff* Manuel Baquero, C. Battistelli. *Set
Photog* Antonio Benetti. *Master of Arms* Remo De Angelis.
   Cast: Franco Nero (*Bill Douglas*), Tony Musante (*Eufemio*), Jack Palance
(*Ricciolo*), Giovanna Ralli (*Columba*), Eduardo Fajardo (*Alfonso Garcia*),
Bruno Corazzari (*Studs*), Remo De Angelis (*Hudo*), Joe Camel (*Larkin*),
Franco Giacobini (*Pepote*), Vicente Roca (*Elias Garcia*), José Riesgo (*2d
Mexican*), Angel Ortiz (*3d Mexican*), Fernando Villena (*sergeant*), Tito García
(*vigilante*), Juan Cazalilla (*mayor*), Guillermo Mendez
(*captain*), José Zalde (*innkeeper*), Alvaro de Luna (*Ramón*), José Antonio
López (*Juan*), Milo Quesada (*Marco*), Raf Baldassarre (*Mateo*), José Canalejas
(*Pablo*), Simón Arriaga (*Simon*), Paco Nieto (*Antonio*), José Ma Aguinaco
(*Ramirez*), Franco Ressel, Ugo Adinolfi.
   Melodrama. Bill Douglas, a mercenary during the Mexican Revolution, is
hired by mine owner Garcia to escort his silver across the border into Texas.
When Bill arrives at the mine, he discovers that the workers, led by Eufemio,
have taken over, and they hire Bill to help them fight the Federales. The
Mexican soldiers arrive to recover the mine, and Bill slaughters them with his
machine gun. Ricciolo, another mercenary, thinks that Bill has a hidden cache
of silver and captures him, but Eufemio and his men rescue him, leaving
Ricciolo naked in the desert. Eufemio and Bill then form a partnership in which
they travel around the country robbing banks and freeing peasants from the
Federales. During one of their missions, Eufemio meets and soon marries a
young woman named Columba, under whose influence he becomes dedicated
to the revolution. Meanwhile, Bill has become wealthy from the robberies, and
Eufemio and Columba decide to expropriate Bill's money for the revolution and
throw him in jail. Garcia and the Mexican soldiers, tipped off by Ricciolo,
attack and defeat the revolutionaries, but Eufemio and Bill escape separately.
Some months later, Bill recognizes Eufemio working as a rodeo clown; Ricciolo
also appears, swearing revenge on Eufemio. Bill sets up a duel between the two
men, and Ricciolo is killed. Afterwards, Bill tells Eufemio that he is going to
turn him in for the bounty money, but the Federales again attack and capture
them both. A band of revolutionaries, led by Columba, rescue them, and after
one last fight, the two men go their separate ways. *Mercenaries. Miners.
Mexicans. Federales. Peasants. Revolutionaries. Clowns. Bounty hunters.
Partnerships. Bank robberies. Revenge. Silver mines. Deserts. Rodeos. Duels.
Mexico—History—1910–17. Mexico. Mexican border. Texas. Mexico—Army.*
   Note: Released in Italy in 1968 as *Il mercenario*; in Spain in 1970 as *Salario
para matar*; running time: 111 min.

THE MERMAID (Hong Kong)   **F6.3162**
   Shaw Brothers (H. K.) Ltd. *Dist* Frank Lee International. 21 Jan **1966** [New
York opening]. Sd; col (Eastman Color). 35mm (Shawscope). 99 min.
   Prod Runme Shaw. *Dir* Kao Li. *Screenplay* Chang Chien. *Photog* Tung
Shao-yung. *Art Dir* Chen Chi-jui. *Set Dsgn* Chen Chin-shen. *Film Ed* Chiang
Hsing-lung. *Mus* Wang Fu-ling. *Lyr* Chang Chien. *Sd Rec* Wang Yung-hua.
Asst Dir Yueh Cheng-chun. *Makeup* Fong Yuen.
   Cast: Ivy Ling Po (*Chang Chen*), Li Ching (*Fairy Marina/Peony Chin*),
Ching Miao (*Lord Pao*), Au-yang Sha-fei (*Madam Wang*), Yang Tse-ching
(*Chin*), Chiang Kuang-chao (*turtle-fairy*), Tung Di (*lobster-fairy*), Li Yuen-
chung (*sorcerer*), Yeh Ching, Feng I, Yueh Hua.
   Operetta film. Chang has been betrothed since birth to Peony Chin,
daughter of the prime minister. When the couple are of marriageable age, Chin
decides that his daughter can make a better match than the poverty-stricken
orphan Chang, and he demands that the student pass the imperial exams. Chang
goes to Chin's lakeside hut, where he studies and pines for Peony. The fairy
Marina, an immortal 1,000-year-old carp, takes pity on Chang. Each night she
takes the form of Peony Chin and visits Chang. When Chang approaches the
real Peony, she turns him over to her father. Although Chin banishes Chang,
his fairy lover brings him home. The pair are caught dancing by Chin, who
summons Lord Pao to decide who is his real daughter. The fairy, however,
duplicates the lord. Chin then commands a wicked sorcerer to fight against the
couple. An underwater battle rages between Marina and her friends and the evil
forces of Chin. The Goddess of Mercy intervenes, offering Marina mortal
human form, which she accepts in order to wed Chang. *Prime ministers.
Orphans. Students. Fairies. Mermaids and mermen. Doubles. Sorcerers.
Marriage—Arranged. Poverty. Immortality. Metamorphosis. Filial relations.
Fish.*
   Note: Original release undetermined.

THE MERMAIDS OF TIBURON   **F6.3163**
   Aquarex–Pacifica Films. *Dist* Art Films International, Filmgroup, Inc. 13
Jun **1962** [Los Angeles opening; c16 Jun 1962; LP31626]. Sd; col (Eastman
Color). 35mm (AquaScope). 76 min.
   A John Lamb Production. *Prod-Dir-Writ* John Lamb. *Assoc Prod* Ronald
Graham. *Prin Photog* John Lamb. *Dial Photog* Hal McAlpin, Brydon Baker.
Ed Bert Honey. *Mus* Richard La Salle. *Sd Eff Ed* Del Harris. *Mus Ed* Lloyd
Young.
   Cast: Diane Webber (*The Mermaid Queen*), George Rowe (*Dr. Samuel
Jamison*), Timothy Carey (*Milo Sangster*), Jose Gonzalez-Gonzalez (*Pepe
Gallardo*), John Mylong (*Ernst Steinhauer*), Gil Baretto (*Señor Barquero*),
Vicki Kantenwine, Nani Morissey, Judy Edwards, Jean Carroll, Diana Cook,
Karen Goodman, Nancy Burns (*mermaids*).
   Melodrama. Upon receiving reports that strange unclassified creatures,
possibly mermaids, have been observed in the coastal waters off Tiburon Island,
marine biologist Samuel Jamison agrees to co-finance an expedition to the
island. His partner, Ernst Steinhauer, is a pearl trader who claims there is a rich
supply of fire pearls to be found at Tiburon. When Steinhauer disappears,
Jamison makes the trip alone, unaware that Milo Sangster, a fellow passenger
on the chartered boat, is a ruthless adventurer who has murdered Steinhauer
in the hope of getting the fire pearls for himself. Once at the desolate island,
Jamison encounters a mermaid queen who leads him to an underwater cave
filled with fire pearls. Sangster also locates the cave, but mermaids put him
under their spell and lure him to his death. Jamison tries to find the mermaid
queen to persuade her to return to civilization with him. The mermaid, realizing
that she could never leave her world beneath the sea, hides from view until he
reboards his ship and pulls anchor. As the vessel leaves the island, the mermaid
surfaces, sadly watches it depart, and then disappears from sight. *Biologists.
Adventurers. Pearls. Mermaids and mermen. Murder. Tiburon Island.*
   Note: Location scenes filmed in La Paz, Mexico; the Caribbean; the Red Sea;
and on Santa Catalina. Re-released with alterations in 1964 as *The Aqua Sex*,
q. v.

MERRILL'S MARAUDERS   **F6.3164**
   United States Productions. *Dist* Warner Bros. Pictures. 13 Jun **1962** [New
York opening; c7 Jul 1962; LP24662]. Sd; col (Technicolor). 35mm
(CinemaScope). 98 min.
   Prod Milton Sperling. *Dir* Samuel Fuller. *Screenplay* Milton Sperling,
Samuel Fuller. *Dir Photog* William Clothier. *2d Unit Photog* Higino J.
Fallorina. *Film Ed* Folmar Blangsted. *Mus* Howard Jackson. *Sd* Francis M.
Stahl. *Asst Dir* William Kissel. *Prod Supv* William J. Magginetti. *Makeup*
Gordon Bau. *Sp Eff* Ralph Ayres. *Tech Adv* Samuel Wilson, (Lieut. Col.).
   Cast: Jeff Chandler (*Brig. Gen. Frank Merrill*), Ty Hardin (*Lieut. Lee
Stockton*), Peter Brown (*Bullseye*), Andrew Duggan (*Maj. George "Doc"
Nemeny*), Will Hutchins (*Chowhound*), Claude Akins (*Sergeant Kolowicz*),
Luz Valdez (*Burmese girl*), John Hoyt (*Gen. Joseph W. Stilwell*), Charles
Briggs (*Muley*), Chuck Roberson, Chuck Hayward (*officers*), Jack Williams

(medic), Chuck Hicks *(Corporal Doskis)*, Vaughan Wilson *(Lieutenant Colonel Bannister)*, Pancho Magalona *(Taggy)*.

War drama. Source: Charlton Ogburn, Jr., *The Marauders* (New York, 1959). In 1944, Brig. Gen. Frank Merrill's 5307th Composite Unit, known as Merrill's Marauders, is deep behind Japanese lines in the dense Burma jungle. Even though the 3,000 men suffer from exhaustion, illness, and starvation, they are ordered to capture a gun emplacement, an enemy arsenal, and a railway yard. Merrill realizes that his men cannot be an effective fighting force without rest, but he also knows that they must make the 500-mile trek to Myitkyina to prevent Japanese and German armies from merging in India. Following an enemy raid, however, the Marauders are virtually walking dead men, physically and mentally incapable of launching a new attack, and Merrill himself collapses from a heart seizure. He arises from the stretcher, however, and urges the men to keep moving. They watch in silence as he staggers among them and falls unconscious, until Lieut. Lee Stockton, inspired by Merrill's indomitable spirit, rallies the men for one last campaign and drives them forward. When Merrill regains consciousness, fresh troops and supplies are landing on the Myitkyina airfield, which has been liberated by the Marauders. *Combat zone life. Courage. Heart disease. Jungles. World War II. Burma. Myitkyina (Burma). Frank Merrill. Joseph W. Stilwell. United States Army—Infantry. Japan—Army.*

Note: Location scenes filmed in the Philippines. Working title: *The Marauders.*

THE MERRY WIVES OF WINDSOR (Austria)   **F6.3165**
Wien Film. *Dist* Sigma III Corp. 16 Feb **1966** [Washington, D. C., opening]. Sd; col (Technicolor). 35mm. 97 min.
Prod-Screenplay-English Adapt Norman Foster. *Dir* George Tressler. *Photog* Hannes Staudinger. *Camera Op* Robert Hofer, Sepp Riff. *Camera Asst* Konrad Bruckner. *Art Dir* Hugo Halbig. *Stage Dsgn* Gerd Krauss. *Film Ed* Paula Dvorak. *Asst Film Ed* Lisl Köberl. *Mus* Otto Nicolai. *Perf by* The Zagreb Symphony Orchestra. *Cond* Milan Horvath. *Choreog* Rosella Hightower. *Sd Rec* Wolleitner. *Asst Dir* Auguste Bruenjes-Goldschwendt. *Prod Dir* Robert Russ. *Prod Mgr* Peter Müller, Günter Köpf. *Cost* Helga Pinnow. *Wardrobe* Hans Nowotny. *Makeup* Arthur Schramm. *Hairstyles* Margarete Pitter. *Mus Cons* Kurt Rapf. *Gaffer* Karl Weber. *Prop* Hermann Voigtländer, Julius Hubl.
Cast: Norman Foster *(Sir John Falstaff)*, Colette Boky *(Frau Fluth [Mistress Ford])*, Igor Gorin *(Herr Fluth [Mr. Ford])*, Mildred Miler *(Frau Reich [Mistress Page])*, Edmond Hurshell *(Herr Reich [Master Page])*, Lucia Popp *(Anna [Mistress Ann])*, Ernst Shütz *(Fenton)*, John Gittings *(Cajus)*, Marshall Raynor *(Spärlich)*, Rosella Hightower *(ballerina)*.
Opera film. Source: Otto Nicolai, *Die lustigen Weiber von Windsor* (Berlin opening: 9 Mar 1849). William Shakespeare, *The Merry Wives of Windsor.* The aging and corpulent Sir John Falstaff, trying to prove that he is still a ladies' man, sends identical love letters to Frau Fluth and Frau Reich. When the husbands discover the letters, Herr Fluth is suspicious of Falstaff, but Herr Reich is more concerned that his daughter Anna marry Spärlich, his favorite of her many suitors. The wives, with no intention of being seduced by Falstaff, hide him in a laundry basket when Herr Fluth arrives and then dump him into a pond. The jealous Herr Fluth, intent on catching his wife with Falstaff, goes to a nearby town when he pays Falstaff to meet once again with her. On his next visit, Falstaff narrowly escapes, disguised in an old woman's clothes. After the husbands learn of their wives' pranks, the four set out to play a final trick on Falstaff; dressed as fairies and hobgoblins, the group lures Falstaff into the forest and frightens him. Anna then arrives, having just married Fenton, her favorite suitor, and everyone celebrates the marriage. *Philanderers. Infidelity. Duplicity. Filial relations. Disguise. Marriage. Documentation. Practical jokes.*
Note: Released in Austria in 1965 as *Die lustigen Weiber von Windsor.*

MES FEMMES AMÉRICAINES *see* **RUN FOR YOUR WIFE**

MESDAMES ET MESSIEURS *see* **THE BIRDS, THE BEES, AND THE ITALIANS**

MESMERIZED MAIDENS   **F6.3166**
Dist Able Film Co. ca **1970**. Sd; col. 16mm. [Feature length assumed.]
Sex film. No information about the precise nature of this film has been found. *Sexuality.*

LA MÉTAMORPHOSE DES CLOPORTES *see* **CLOPORTES**

METEMPSYCO *see* **TOMB OF TORTURE**

MEURTRE EN 45 TOURS *see* **MURDER AT 45 R. P. M.**

LE MEURTRIER *see* **ENOUGH ROPE**

MGM'S BIG PARADE OF COMEDY   **F6.3167**
Robert Youngson Productions. *Dist* Metro-Goldwyn-Mayer, Inc. 3 Sep **1964** [New York opening; c31 Dec 1963; LP28884]. Sd; b&w. 35mm. 90 min. [Also reviewed at 109 min.]

Prod-Writ Robert Youngson. *Assoc Prod* Alfred Dahlem. *Titl & Eff Dsgn* Robert Youngson. *Mus* Bernard Green. *Songs:* "Jean, Oh Jean," "Marie," "Big Parade of Comedy March" Bernard Green, Robert Youngson. *Prod Mgr* I. Hill Youngson. *Res Supv* Jeanne Keyes.
Narrator: Les Tremayne.
Compilation film. This collection of scenes from comedy films produced by Metro-Goldwyn-Mayer from 1925 through 1948 opens with a few shots from nickelodeon days and proceeds to publicity scenes of silent stars (John Gilbert, Leatrice Joy, Douglas Fairbanks, Sr.) on the M-G-M lot. Following are film clips from *The Sporting Venus* (1925), with Lew Cody and Josephine Crowell; *Pretty Ladies* (1925) and *The Boob* (1926), featuring two early screen appearances of Joan Crawford; *The Red Mill* (1927), with Marion Davies and Owen Moore; *China Bound* (1929), with Karl Dane and George K. Arthur; *Detectives* (1928), with Arthur and Marceline Day; *The Cameraman* (1928), with Day and Buster Keaton; *Hollywood Party* (1934), with Jimmy Durante and Lupe Velez; *Reducing* (1931), with Marie Dressler and Anita Page; *Tugboat Annie* (1933), with Dressler and Wallace Beery; and seven Jean Harlow vehicles: *Hold Your Man* (1933), with Clark Gable; *Bombshell* (1933), with Franchot Tone and Lee Tracy; *The Girl From Missouri* (1934), with Lionel Barrymore; *Suzy* (1936), with Cary Grant and Lewis Stone; *Personal Property* (1937), with Robert Taylor; *Libeled Lady* (1936), with Spencer Tracy; *Dinner at Eight* (1933), with Beery, Barrymore, and Dressler. Also: *The Gay Bride* (1934), with Carole Lombard, ZaSu Pitts, Chester Morris, and Nat Pendleton; a Three Stooges short, featuring Ted Healy; *David Copperfield* (1935), with W. C. Fields and Freddie Bartholomew; another scene from *Hollywood Party*, featuring Stan Laurel & Oliver Hardy and Velez; *Bonnie Scotland* (1935), with Laurel & Hardy and Jimmy Finlayson; *Too Hot To Handle* (1938), with Gable and Leo Carrillo; *The Philadelphia Story* (1940), with Grant and Hepburn; three Robert Benchley shorts: *That Inferior Feeling* (1939), *How To Read* (1938), and *A Night at the Movies* (1937); *The Thin Man* (1934) and *After the Thin Man* (1936), with William Powell, Myrna Loy, and Asta; *Love Crazy* (1940), with Powell and Gail Patrick; *Rio Rita* (1941), with Bud Abbott & Lou Costello; *Meet the People* (1944), with Lucille Ball and Bert Lahr; *A Southern Yankee* (1948), with Red Skelton, John Ireland, and Brian Donlevy; *Ninotchka* (1939), with Greta Garbo, Melvyn Douglas, and George Tobias; *Two-Faced Woman* (1941), with Garbo and Douglas; *Go West* (1940), with Groucho, Chico, and Harpo Marx, plus John Carroll and Diana Lewis; and clips from some Pete Smith shorts, featuring Dave O'Brien. The film also includes footage of Charles Chaplin, Marion Davies, and William Haines taken inside a theater lobby. *Actors. Motion pictures—History.*
Note: Also known as *The Big Parade of Comedy.*

MI MUJER ES DOCTOR *see* **THE LADY DOCTOR**

LA MIA DROGA SI CHIAMA JULIE *see* **MISSISSIPPI MERMAID**

MIAMI RENDEZVOUS *see* **PASSION HOLIDAY**

MICHAEL AND HELGA (West Germany)   **F6.3168**
Cämmerer Film. *Dist* American International Pictures. Apr **1969** [c5 Mar 1969; LP37220]. Sd; col (Pathé). 35mm. 87 min.
Pres by Dr. Roland Cämmerer. *Prod* Dr. Roland Cämmerer. *Dir* Erich F. Bender. *Screenplay* Erich F. Bender, Dr. Roland Cämmerer, Klaus E. R. von Schwarze. *Cinematog* Fritz Baader, Erdmann Beyer. *Microphotog* Dr. Erwin Burcik, B. Rosner. *Film Ed* Malva Stohr, Ilse Wüstenhöfer. *Mus* Karl Barthel. *Prod Mgr* Werner Fischer. *Tech Adv* Dr. Gerhard Döring, Dr. Fritz Zimmer, Dr. Waldemar Mehring, Dr. Christel Schultze-Rhonhof, Klaus E. R. von Schwarze, Dr. Wolfgang Wickler, Dr. Erwin Burcik.
Cast: Ruth Gassmann *(Helga)*, Felix Franchy *(Michael)*, Hildegard Linden *(doctor)*, Elfi Rueter *(young mother)*, Christian Margulies *(Christian)*, Christian Fredersdorf *(father, 1st family)*, Ursula Mellin *(mother, 1st family)*, Jochel Piel *(father, 2d family)*, Lisa Ravel *(mother, 2d family)*, Sonja Lindorf, Elke Hart, Sabine Dall, Claus Hoeft, Peter Bach, Ulla Best.
Sex instruction film. Following the birth of their first child, which is shown through close-up photography, a young couple, Michael and Helga, enroll in child care classes. They learn that an Oedipus complex can be avoided if both parents love the baby equally; that it is natural for infants to explore their sexual organs; and that masturbation is a normal reaction to puberty. Since Michael and Helga are also concerned with their own sexual happiness and hygiene, they listen to a physician lecture on the necessity for birth control, the different sexual responses of men and women, marital counseling, and the human anatomy. The doctor also speaks on the legalization of abortion and demonstrates the use of contraceptives. The research findings of Kinsey and Masters and Johnson serve as the basis for a discussion of the need for sexual foreplay, the most effective techniques in intercourse, and the stages leading to orgasm and postlude. At last Michael and Helga experience the fulfillment of their own sexual relationship, freed of neurotic impediments to enjoyment. *Physicians. Infants. Sex instruction. Abortion. Childbirth. Parenthood. Sexual*

techniques. Birth control. Marriage. Marriage counsel. Anatomy. Alfred Charles Kinsey. Documentation. William Howell Masters. Virginia Eshelman Johnson.

Note: Released in West Germany in Nov 1968 as *Helga und Michael;* running time: 99 min. This film is a sequel to *Helga,* q. v. May also be known as *Helga and Michael.*

MICHELENE AND THE DEVICE   F6.3169

Harob Film Productions. 4 Dec **1968** [New York showing]. Sd; b&w. 35mm. 68 min.

Prod-Dir R. Jack Roberts. *Screenplay* Carl Johnston. *Dir Photog* James Lewis. *Song:* "*Take Me*" Bennie Martini.

Cast: Renay Claire *(Michelene),* Rhonda Taylor, Barbara West, Don Howard, Christan Dee.

Sex film. No information about the precise nature of this film has been found, but press material suggests that it includes scenes of lesbianism and women using sex aids. *Lesbianism. Sex aids.*

Note: Also known as *Michelene.*

MICHELLE (France)   F6.3170

Paris Inter Productions. *Dist* Audubon Films. **1970.** Sd; b&w. 35mm. 87 min.

Dir-Writ Henry Jacques. *Screenplay* Claude Sandron. *Dial* Henry Jacques. *Adapt* Henry Jacques. *Photog* Jean-Michel Boussaguet. *Film Ed* Charles Nobel. *Mus* Armand Seggian. *Asst Dir* Louis Duchesne. *Prod Mgr* Joël Lifschutz.

Cast: Linda Veras, Agnès Datin, Karine Ker, Sylvain Corthay, Jean-Louis Tristan, Pascal Ogé, Kim Camba, Sandrine.

Crime melodrama. After hiding a suitcase containing stolen goods, Michelle is arrested. She escapes, nevertheless, with her supposed friend, Cora. The painter Pascal drives the pair to a villa. Despite Cora's objections, Michelle invites Pascal to stay. Unbeknownst to Michelle, Cora and her accomplice Kelly covet the suitcase. Michelle also does not know that Kelly has murdered her partner, Bastien. When Kelly attempts to torture Michelle, however, Cora intervenes and accidentally shoots herself. Michelle and her lover Pascal flee to a house near Paris, where they are discovered by Kelly and his new associate, a stripteaser, who also uncover a cache of gold coins. The police arrive and arrest the culprits. Softened by her love for Pascal, Michelle cooperates with them. Although she is sentenced to prison, Pascal proposes to Michelle and promises to wait for her. *Thieves. Painters. Fugitives. Stripteasers. Criminals—Rehabilitation. Paris.*

Note: Opened in Paris in May 1967 as *Sexy Gang;* running time: 90 min. Original title: *Adorables canailles.*

MICKEY ONE   F6.3171

Florin-Tatira Productions. *Dist* Columbia Pictures. 27 Oct **1965** [Chicago opening; c1 Jul 1965; LP31864]. Sd (Westrex); b&w. 35mm. 93 min.

Prod-Dir Arthur Penn. *Assoc Prod* Harrison Starr. *Asst Prod* Gene Lasko. *Screenplay* Alan M. Surgal. *Dir Photog* Ghislain Cloquet. *Camera Op* Lutz Hapke. *Asst Art Dir* William Crawford, art. *Prod Dsgn* George Jenkins. *Film Ed* Aram Avakian. *Assembly Ed* Robert Q. Lovett. *Asst Ed* Marc Laub. *Mus Supv & Cond* Jack Shaindlin. *Mus Comp* Eddie Sauter. *Mus Improvisations* Stan Getz. *Sd Mix* Walter Goss. *Sd Eff Ed* Edward Beyer, Hugh A. Robertson, Jr. *Asst Dir* Russell Saunders, Jim Henderling. *Unit Supv* William T. Schneider. *Asst Prod Mgr* John G. Avildsen. *Prod Aid* Jill Jakes. *Script Supv* Roberta Hodes. *Cost Dsgn* Domingo Rodriguez. *Wardrobe* Marie Sorg. *Makeup* Robert Jiras. *Ch Grip* Morris Rosen. *Prop Master* Thomas Wright. *Gaffer* William Steube. *Dial Coach/Casting Dir* Gene Lasko. *Still Photog* Harry Postal.

Cast: Warren Beatty *(Mickey One),* Alexandra Stewart *(Jenny),* Hurd Hatfield *(Castle),* Franchot Tone *(Ruby Lopp),* Teddy Hart *(Berson),* Jeff Corey *(Fryer),* Kamatari Fujiwara *(The Artist),* Donna Michelle *(The Girl),* Ralph Foody *(police captain),* Norman Gottschalk *(The Evangelist),* Dick Lucas, actor *(employment agent),* Jack Goodman *(cafeteria manager),* Jeri Jensen *(Helen),* Charlene Lee *(The Singer),* Benny Dunn *(nightclub comic),* Denise Darnell *(stripper),* Dick Baker *(boss at Shaley's),* Helen Witkowski *(landlady),* William Koza, David Crane *(art gallery patrons),* Mike Fish *(Italian restaurant owner),* Greg Louis, Gus Christy *(bartenders),* David Eisen *(desk clerk),* Robert Sickinger *(policeman),* Lew Prentiss *(Kismet boss),* Grace Colette *(b-girl),* Boris Gregurevitch *(Kismet comic),* James Middleton, actor *(Iggie),* Dink Freeman *(Xanadu M. C.).*

Drama. A nightclub comedian in Detroit lives extravagantly and accumulates a number of large gambling debts. Certain that the underworld syndicate that controls his debts and the clubs where he works is going to punish him, he flees, eventually winding up on the west side of Chicago. He uses a social security card with the name Miklos Wunejeva to obtain a restaurant job hauling garbage. Wanting to resume his career, he contacts an agent, Berson, who books him at the posh Club Xanadu, owned by Ed Castle. Meanwhile, Mickey's landlady attempts to evict him and move another tenant, Jenny, into

his apartment. Mickey refuses to leave, and he and Jenny fall in love. One night, they watch an artist, whom Mickey has seen around town, unveil a kinetic sculpture which goes out of control, explodes, and burns down. Mickey is wary of the Xanadu booking, fearful that Castle may know his enemies in the syndicate. Mickey is persuaded by Castle to audition for a man connected with clubs in the midwest, but, fearful that the man might be a mobster and unable to perform without an audience, Mickey cuts his performance short. Determined to contact someone in the syndicate, Mickey searches for the mob-run crap game, but he is beaten in a brawl involving costumed doormen from various clubs. After he discovers that Berson has disappeared, he decides to keep his commitment to Castle and begins his first show at the club. *Artists. Entertainers. Landladies. Theatrical agents. Nightclub owners. Gambling. Debt. Fear. Syndicates. Nightclubs. Chicago.*

Note: Filmed on location in Chicago.

MID-DAY MISTRESS   F6.3172

Camelot Pictures. *Dist* Distribpix, Inc. 16 Oct **1968** [Boston opening]. Sd; b&w. 35mm. 74 min.

Prod Henrik Emyl. *Dir* Rolf Emyl. *Screenplay* Nils Emyl. *Mus* Sly and the Family Stone.

Cast: Tekla Anderson *(Lauri Blaine),* Stan Howard *(Harry),* Sam Stewart *(Groovy),* Lino Desmond *(Rico),* Alou Mitsou.

Melodrama. Lauri Blaine, a call girl on New York's East Side, refuses the offer of a client who promises to leave his wife and children for her. She then tells him her story: *New to the glamorous New York hip scene, Lauri falls in love with Groovy, a Greenwich Village legendary character who, though older than many of the street people, has won their love and affection. Groovy is supported by a sister who lives with a film director in the south of France, and he uses his generous allowance from her to buy marijuana and LSD and distributes them gratis to his friends. Rico, a Mafia drug dealer in the Village, notes a decline in business and sends two of his thugs to "persuade" Groovy to stop giving away drugs. They rape Lauri and accidentally kill Groovy. Fearing detection, Rico has his mistress Monique befriend Lauri in order to find out from her whether she can identify her assailants. When Monique fails, Rico courts Lauri and makes her his mistress. Defiant, Monique reveals to Lauri that Rico is responsible for Groovy's death. While Lauri tells her story, a paralyzed man sits in a wheelchair on the terrace—it is Rico. Dependent on Lauri's earnings, Rico pays mute witness to the parade of men she entertains in a sordid act of self-degradation; thus, she exacts her retribution for Groovy's death.* Prostitutes. Drug dealers. Hippies. Mistresses. Paraplegics. Murder. Rape. Revenge. Marijuana. LSD. Mafia. New York City—East Side. New York City—Greenwich Village.*

Note: May also be known as *The Businessman's Lunch, Mid-Day Miss.*

MIDARE-GUMO *see* **TWO IN THE SHADOW**

MIDARERU *see* **YEARNING**

MIDAS RUN   F6.3173

Motion Pictures International–Selmur Pictures. *Dist* Cinerama Releasing Corp. 30 Apr **1969** [Chicago opening]. Sd; col. 35mm. 106 min. *MPAA rating* M.

A Raymond Stross Production. *Prod* Raymond Stross. *Exec Prod* Selig J. Seligman. *Dir* Alf Kjellin. *Screenplay* James D. Buchanan, Ronald Austin, Berne Giler. *Story* Berne Giler. *Dir Cinematog* Ken Higgins. *Camera Op* Peter Allwork. *Art Dir* Arthur Lawson, Ezio Cescotti. *Set Decor* Massimo Tavazzi. *Paintings* Oliver Foss. *Film Ed* Fredric Steinkamp. *Asst Ed* Claudio Cutry, Wanda Boileau. *Mus* Elmer Bernstein. *Titl Song* Don Black, Elmer Bernstein. *Sung by* Anne Heywood. *Sd Engr* Ben Winkler. *Sd Ed* Vernon Messenger. *Asst Dir* Luciano Sacripanti, Luciano Palermo. *Prod Supv* Leon Chooluck. *Unit Mgr* Armando Govoni. *Prod Asst* Maria Luisa Alcaraz. *Script Supv* Karen Wookey. *Wardrobe* Franco Antonelli. *Makeup* Pino Capogrosso. *Hairstyles* Mirella Ginnoto.

Cast: Richard Crenna *(Mike Warden),* Anne Heywood *(Sylvia Giroux),* Fred Astaire *(John Pedley),* Roddy McDowall *(Wister),* Ralph Richardson *(Henshaw),* Cesar Romero *(Dodero),* Adolfo Celi *(Aldo Ferranti),* Maurice Denham *(Crittenden),* John LeMesurier *(Wells),* Aldo Bufi-Landi *(carabiniere),* Fred Astaire, Jr. *(co-pilot),* Jacques Sernas *(Giroux),* Karl Otto Alberty *(Dietrich),* George Hartman *(Pfeiffer),* Caroline De Fonseca *(Mrs. Pfeiffer),* Stanley Baugh *(pilot),* Bruce Beeby *(Gordon),* Robert Henderson *(The Dean).*

Crime comedy-drama. Veteran British secret service officer John Pedley, irritated that he has never been knighted, decides to hijack a government shipment of $15 million in gold ingots being flown from Zurich to Tanzania via Italy. He contacts an American acquaintance, writer Mike Warden, who has recently lost his university position because of his pacifist political views, and lures him to Venice on the pretense of introducing him to an interested publisher; instead, Mike is introduced to Sylvia Giroux, Pedley's accomplice, and persuaded to help organize the heist. While Pedley directs the operation from London, Sylvia and Mike make the necessary arrangements in Italy: a Messerschmidt piloted by a former Luftwaffe officer will shoot down the plane carrying the gold, and ex-Fascist general Aldo Ferranti will sell the ingots after they have been smuggled to him. Pedley, who is ordered aboard the plane at the last minute by his superior, instructs the pilot to land the passengers safely when the Messerschmidt attacks. As the gold is carried away in three trucks, Pedley, whose motive for the hijacking is to capture Ferranti and thus prove his worth, quickly engineers the capture of two of the vehicles. Sylvia and Mike are arrested by Italian police as they escape in the third truck, but Pedley intervenes, claiming that Mike is his agent. After the two thieves exchange a package of ingots in return for half the compensation Pedley will receive from an insurance firm, the agent is finally invited to be knighted by the queen. Sylvia and Mike then make marriage plans. *British. Hijackers. Americans in foreign countries. Professors. Authors. Pacifists. Fascists. Italians. Air pilots. Germans. Police. Knighthood. Conspiracy. Perfidy. Gold. Airplanes. London. Zurich. Italy. Great Britain—Intelligence service.*

Note: Location scenes filmed in London, Rome, Venice, and Milan.

MIDNIGHT COWBOY   F6.3174

Jerome Hellman Productions. *Dist* United Artists. 25 May 1969 [New York opening; c26 May 1969; LP37236]. Sd; col (De Luxe). 35mm. 113 min. [Pre-release length: 119 min.] *MPAA rating X.*

A Jerome Hellman–John Schlesinger Production. *Prod* Jerome Hellman. *Assoc Prod* Kenneth Utt. *Dir* John Schlesinger. *2d Unit Dir* Burtt Harris. *Screenplay* Waldo Salt. *Dir Photog* Adam Holender. *Camera Op* Dick Kratina. *Set Decor* Philip Smith. *Master Scenic Artist* Edward Garzero. *Prod Dsgn* John Robert Lloyd. *Titl & Graphic Eff* Pablo Ferro. *Film Ed* Hugh A. Robertson, Jr. *Asst Ed* Edward Rothkowitz, Leonard Saltzberg, Richard Cirincione. *Mus Supv* John Barry. *Mus Prod* Toxey French. *Song:* "Everybody's Talking" Fred Neil. *Arr & Cond* George Tipton. *Sung by* Nilsson. *Songs:* "A Famous Myth," "Tears and Joys" Jeffrey Comanor. *Sung by* The Groop. *Song:* "He Quit Me" Warren W. Zevon. *Arr & Cond* Garry Sherman. *Sung by* Lesley Miller. *Song:* "Crossroads of the Stepping Stones" Michal Shapiro, Stan Bronstein. *Sung by* Elephants Memory. *Song:* "Jungle Jim at the Zoo" Richard Sussman, Richard Frank, mus, Stan Bronstein. *Prod* Wes Farrell. *Sung by* Elephants Memory. *Song:* "Old Man Willow" Richard Sussman, Michal Shapiro, Myron Yules, Stan Bronstein. *Prod* Wes Farrell. *Sung by* Elephants Memory. *Electronic Mus* Sear Electronic Music Production. *Harmonica* Jean "Toots" Theilemans. *Sd* Abe Seidman. *Sd Ed* Jack Fitzstephens, Vincent Connelly. *Sd Mix* Dick Vorisek. *Prod Mgr* Hal Schaffel. *Asst Prod Mgr* Fred Caruso. *Cont* Nicholas Sgarro. *Asst to the Dir* Michael Childers. *Cost Dsgn* Ann Roth. *Wardrobe Supv* Max Solomon. *Makeup Cons* Dick Smith. *Makeup* Irving Buchman. *Hairdressing* Robert Grimaldi. *Sp Lighting Eff* Joshua Light Show. *Creative Cons* Jim Clark. *Casting* Marion Dougherty Associates. *Ch Electrn* Willie Meyerhoff, Norman Leigh. *Key Grip* Mike Mahony. *Constr Grip* William J. Gerrity. *Head Carpenter* Ed Swanson.

Cast: Dustin Hoffman (*Ratso Rizzo*), Jon Voight (*Joe Buck*), Sylvia Miles (*Cass*), John McGiver (*Mr. O'Daniel*), Brenda Vaccaro (*Shirley*), Barnard Hughes (*Towny*).

Cast—Texas: Ruth White (*Sally Buck*), Jennifer Salt (*Crazy Annie*), Gil Rankin (*Woodsy Niles*), Gary Owens, T. Tom Marlow (*Little Joe*), George Eppersen (*Ralph*), Al Scott (*cafeteria manager*), Linda Davis (*mother on the bus*), J. T. Masters (*old cowhand*), Arlene Reeder (*old lady*).

Cast—New York: Georgann Johnson (*rich lady*), Jonathan Kramer (*Jackie*), Anthony Holland (*TV Bishop*), Bob Balaban (*young student*), Jan Tice (*freaked-out lady*), Paul Benjamin (*bartender*), Peter Scalia, Vito Siracusa (*vegetable grocers*), Peter Zamaglias (*hat shop owner*), Arthur Anderson (*hotel clerk*), Tina Scala, Alma Felix (*laundromat ladies*), Richard Clarke (*escort service man*), Ann Thomas (*frantic lady*).

Cast—Party: Viva (*Gretel McAlbertson*), Gastone Rossilli (*Hansel McAlbertson*), Ultra Violet, Paul Jabara, International Velvet, William Dorr, Cecelia Lipson, Taylor Mead, Paul Morrissey, Paul Jasmin (*guests*).

Cast—Florida: Joan Murphy (*waitress*), Al Stetson, actor (*bus driver*).

Drama. Source: James Leo Herlihy, *Midnight Cowboy* (New York, 1965). Restless and dissatisfied with his life as a dishwasher in a small Texas town, young Joe Buck outfits himself in a flashy cowboy outfit and heads for New York City, confident that his fortune will be made by selling himself to wealthy, sex-starved Manhattan women. While traveling by bus, he recalls some of the events of his childhood—the father who abandoned his wayward mother, the endless stream of men who visited his frisky grandmother Sally, and a series of sexual encounters during adolescence, including a gang rape of both Joe and his girl friend Annie. After checking into a seedy Manhattan hotel, Joe takes to the streets and eventually picks up Cass, a rich, coarse, middle-aged blonde. Although they make love in her East Side apartment, Joe not only fails to collect a fee but ends up giving her $20 for cab fare. Later, at a cheap Broadway

bar, Joe meets Ratso Rizzo, a crippled, tubercular petty thief and con artist who volunteers to work as his pimp and manager. Although the two misfits have a falling out when Ratso sends Joe to the sleazy room of Mr. O'Daniel, a homosexual religious fanatic, they patch up their differences and agree to share Ratso's dismally cold room in a condemned building. Almost in spite of themselves, their mutual loneliness leads to genuine friendship as Ratso shares with Joe his fantasy of someday living a life of luxury in Miami Beach. Economically, their partnership meets with little success, since Joe's typical "conquests" turn out to be as unprofitable as his encounter with a timid student to whom he gives himself in a 42nd street theater balcony, only to discover that the boy cannot pay. Things pick up a little when Joe meets Shirley, a chic swinger at an underground party in Greenwich Village, and earns $20 for spending a wild night with her. By now, however, winter has taken its toll on Ratso, and he can no longer walk. Determined to get the bus fare to take his friend to Florida, Joe brutally beats up an aging homosexual in a hotel room and steals his money. Ratso manages to stumble onto the bus, but he dies as they reach Miami. Facing an uncertain future, Joe Buck puts his arm around the dead body of the only true friend he ever had. *Dishwashers. Texans. Confidence men. Pimps. Cripples. Loneliness. Prostitution. Male homosexuality. Childhood. Adolescence. Rape. Friendship. Death. Theft. Urban life. Family life. Finance—Personal. Buses. Hotels. Bars. Slums. Tuberculosis. Winter. New York City—Greenwich Village. New York City—East Side. New York City—Times Square. Texas. Miami.*

Note: Location scenes filmed in New York City, Texas, and Florida.

MIDNIGHT COWGIRL   F6.3175

Nov 1970 [periodical notice]. Sd; col. 16mm. [Feature film, length unknown.]

Dir Gene Fizz.

Sex film. Buxom Diane enjoys masturbation, intercourse, and cunnilingus with several men and two lesbians before trying to settle down with a kind and wealthy man. *Group sex. Autoeroticism. Lesbianism. Oral sex.*

Note: Original title: *They Came Together.*

THE MIDNIGHT GRADUATE   F6.3176

Venus International Productions. *Dist* Grads Corp. 13 Nov 1970 [Philadelphia opening]. Sd; col (Eastman Color). 35mm. 70 min.

Prod-Dir Don Brown. *Photog* Don Brown. *Mus* Jaime Mendoza-Nava.

Cast: Uschi Digart (*Jackie*).

Drama. In Los Angeles, Jackie learns that her father, whom she thought to have died many years earlier, has recently passed away in Mexico. To inherit his fortune, Jackie agrees to perform certain sex acts stipulated in his will. Traveling through Mexico, Texas, and the American Southwest, Jackie has several lesbian encounters and also enjoys heterosexual relationships. *Heiresses. Bisexuality. Lesbianism. Wills. Los Angeles. Mexico. Texas.*

Note: Location scenes filmed in Los Angeles, the San Fernando Valley, and in Mexico. Filmed in 16mm.

THE MIDNIGHT JOGGER   F6.3177

Fleetan Films. *Dist* Able Film Co. Aug 1970 [periodical notice]. Sd; col. 16mm. [Feature length assumed.]

Sex film. A jogger makes love with four women, with one interlude involving the smearing of fruit on one woman's body, with the fruit juices then being licked off. He apparently returns home to his wife, who refuses to make love with him, opting for self-stimulation in front of a mirror. *Sexuality. Autoeroticism. Fruit.*

A MIDSUMMER NIGHT'S DREAM (Czechoslovakia)   F6.3178

Československý Film. *Dist* Showcorporation. 19 Dec 1961 [New York opening]. Sd; col (Eastmancolor). 35mm (CinemaScope). 74 min.

Prod-Dir-Scen Jiří Trnka. *English Adapt & Dir* Howard Sackler. *Scen Collab* Jiří Brdečka. *Anim* Jan Karpaš, Stanislav Látal, Vlasta Jurajdová, Břetislav Pojar, Jan Adam, Bohumil Šrámek. *Camera* Jiří Vojta. *Art Dir* Jiří Trnka. *Film Ed* Hana Walachová. *Mus Comp & Cond* Václav Trojan. *Sd* Emanuel Formánek, Josef Vlček, Emil Poledník. *Studio Ch* Jiří Vaněk. *Prod mgr* Jaroslav Možíš. *Adv* Břetislav Hodek. *English Vers Dial Supv* Len Appelson.

Narrator: Richard Burton.

Cast—Voices: Tom Criddle (*Lysander*), Ann Bell (*Hermia*), Michael Meacham (*Demetrius*), John Warner (*Egeus*), Barbara Leigh-Hunt (*Helena*), Hugh Manning (*Theseus*), Joss Ackland (*Quince*), Alec McCowen (*Bottom*), Stephen Moore (*Flute*), Barbara Jefford (*Titania*), Jack Gwillim (*Oberon*), Roger Shepherd (*Puck*), Laura Graham (*Hippolyta*).

Puppet film. Source: William Shakespeare, *A Midsummer Night's Dream.* A puppet performance of Shakespeare's comedy, beginning with a reading of his Sonnet XV. *Royalty. Fairies. Weavers. Magic. Mistaken identity. Metamorphosis. Sleep. Weddings. Theater—Amateur. Forests. Flowers. Spells. Dreams. Donkeys.*

Note: Released in Czechoslovakia in 1959 as *Sen Noci Svatojanské;* running time: 80 min. Original version contains no dialog.

A MIDSUMMER NIGHT'S DREAM   F6.3179

Oberon Productions. *Dist* Columbia Pictures, Showcorporation. 17 Apr **1967** [New York showing]. Sd; col (Eastmancolor by Pathé). 35mm (Panavision). 93 min.

Released in Assoc With City Center of Music and Drama Inc., McCall's *Magazine. Prod* Richard Davis. *Dir* Dan Eriksen. *Prod Conceived by* George Balanchine. *Dir Photog* Arthur J. Ornitz. *Art Dir* Albert Brenner. *Prod Dsgn* Howard Bay. *Main Titl* Henry Wolf. *Film Ed* Armond Lebowitz. *Mus:* "*A Midsummer Night's Dream*" Felix Mendelssohn. *Cond* Robert Irving. *Perf by* Orchestra of the New York City Ballet. *Choreog* George Balanchine. *Cost* Karinska.

Cast: Suzanne Farrell *(Titania),* Edward Villella *(Oberon),* Arthur Mitchell *(Puck),* Mimi Paul *(Helena),* Nicholas Magallanes *(Lysander),* Patricia McBride *(Hermia),* Roland Vazquez *(Demetrius),* Francisco Moncion *(Theseus),* Gloria Govrin *(Hippolyta),* Richard Rapp *(Bottom),* Jacques D'Amboise *(court danseur),* Allegra Kent *(court danseuse),* The New York City Ballet, Children of the School of American Ballet.

Dance film. Source: William Shakespeare, *A Midsummer Night's Dream.* George Balanchine, *A Midsummer Night's Dream* (New York opening: 17 Jan 1962). The film is a screen version of Balanchine's New York City Ballet production. *Royalty. Fairies. Weavers. Magic. Mistaken identity. Metamorphosis. Sleep. Weddings. Theater—Amateur. Forests. Flowers. Spells. Dreams. Donkeys.*

Note: The opening date is a special benefit showing, released by Columbia Pictures in association with the City Center of Music and Drama, Inc. The film was subsequently released by Showcorporation with the sponsorship of McCall's Magazine.

THE MIDWIFE (Greece)   F6.3180

Finos Films. *Dist* Greek Motion Pictures. 27 Feb **1961** [Maryland license]. Sd; b&w. 35mm. 80 min.

Dir-Writ Alekos Sakellarios.

Cast: Orestis Makris *(Dr. Lycourgos),* Georgia Vassiliadou *(The Midwife),* Xenie Kalogeropoulos *(Kathy Lycourgos),* Dimitris Papamichael *(Dimitrios),* Eleni Zaferiou *(Mrs. Lycourgos).*

Comedy-drama. Retired Dr. Lycourgos and a rustic midwife are rivals. Their conflicts are resolved, however, when the physician's daughter Kathy falls in love with the midwife's son. *Physicians. Midwives. Rural life. Jealousy.*

THE MIGHTY GORGA   F6.3181

Borealis Enterprises. *Dist* American General Pictures, Western International. **1969.** Sd; col (DeLuxe). 35mm. 83 min.

Prod Robert V. O'Neil, David L. Hewitt. *Dir* David L. Hewitt. *Screenplay* Jean Hewitt, David Prentiss. *Photog* Gary Cramer. *Mus* Charles Walden. *Sd* Mike Beardsley. *Prod Mgr* Dale Sillcorn.

Cast: Anthony Eisley *(Mark Remington),* Megan Timothy *(April Adams),* Kent Taylor *(Bwana Jack),* Scott Brady *(Morgan),* Lee Parrish *(George),* Bruce Kemp *(witch doctor),* Sheldon Lee *(Kabula).*

Melodrama. To save his insolvent circus, entrepreneur Mark Remington travels in search of the legendary Gorga, a 50-ton gorilla. Arriving in Africa, the American finds his contact, Bwana Jack, missing. After placating Jack's greedy associate Morgan, Remington, accompanied by Jack's daughter, April Adams, and foreman, George, sets out through the jungle. Deserted by native guides, the company encounters dinosaurs and Gorga, and is abducted by a hostile tribe. Their sacrifice, along with that of Jack, discovered to be a fellow prisoner, is interrupted by the reappearance of the gorilla. Fleeing their captors the four seek shelter in a cave, where they unearth a treasure and are menaced by a prehistoric beast. Upon emerging from the cave, George is slain by Morgan, who is himself killed by Gorga. Laden with treasure, the trio returns home. *Guides. Americans in foreign countries. Entrepreneurs. Bankruptcy. Missing persons. Greed. Abduction. Human sacrifice. Murder. Jungles. Caves. Treasure. Circus. Monsters. Africa. Apes. Dinosaurs.*

THE MIGHTY JUNGLE (United States/Mexico)   F6.3182

Robert Patrick Productions–México Films. *Dist* Parade Releasing Organization. 7 Oct **1964** [Denver opening]. Sd; col (Technicolor). 35mm. 88 min.

Pres by Robert Patrick. A Robert Patrick Production. *Amazonia Unit Dir* David DaLie. *Dir-Writ (see note)* Ismael Rodríguez. *African Unit Dir & Narr* Arnold Belgard. *Story* Arnold Belgard, David DaLie. *Amazonia Unit Photog* Augustín Martínez Solares. *African Unit Photog* Laurie Friedman. *Art Dir* Edward Fitzgerald. *Film Ed* Norman Suffern, Erma Levin. *Ed (see note)* Fernando Martínez. *Mus* Les Baxter. *Sd & Mus Eff* John Bushelman, Ving Hershon. *Sd Rec* Richard Pitstick. *Sd (see note)* Jesús González Gancy. *Asst Dir* Mario Leoria.

Cast: Marshall Thompson *(Marsh Conners),* David DaLie *(Dave Reardon),* Antonio Gutiérrez *(Tony),* Rosenda Monteros *(Orica),* Andrés Soler, José Jasso, José Chávez.

Narrator: Lou Krugman.

Adventure drama. Adventurers Marsh Conners and Dave Reardon accept different assignments—Dave in Amazonia and Marsh in the Congo. The South American expedition meets disaster; Dave, the sole survivor, barely escapes an anaconda. The Marsh expedition proves successful; he joins a tribe of Pygmies on an elephant hunt, braves the Congo River rapids, and visits an elephant training school. Meanwhile, Dave hires a guide, Tony, and together they watch fights between a wild hog and a snake, a tarantula and a scorpion, and two iguanas. Tony's wife, Orica, tries to kill Dave, but fails in her attempt to prevent her husband and the explorer from venturing deeper into the jungle. Dave is killed by a crocodile while saving the guide's life. *Explorers. Adventurers. Pygmies. Guides. Exploration. Survival. Hunting. Self-sacrifice. Amazonia. Congo. Congo River. Elephants. Wild hogs. Snakes. Spiders. Scorpions. Lizards. Crocodiles.*

Note: Location scenes filmed in the Congo and Amazonia. Amazonia sequences derived from a 1959 Mexican film, *La ciudad sagrada.* Credits for original film include production company: México Films; director-writer: Rodríguez; photographer: Martínez Solares; art director: Fitzgerald; editor: Martínez; sound: González Gancy; DaLie is credited only as an actor.

MIGHTY URSUS (Italy/Spain)   F6.3183

Cine Italia–Atenea Films. *Dist* United Artists. 11 Apr **1962** [Los Angeles opening; c5 Apr 1962; LP22316]. Sd; col (Eastman Color). 35mm (Totalscope). 92 min.

Dir Carlo Campogalliani. *Screenplay* Giuliano Carmineo, Giuseppe Mangione, Sergio Sollima. *Story* Giuseppe Mangione. *Photog* Eloy Mella. *Art Dir* Antonio Simont. *Mus* Roman Vlad.

Cast: Ed Fury *(Ursus),* Luis Prendes *(Setas),* Moira Orfei *(Attea),* Cristina Gajoni *(Magali),* Mary Marlon *(Doreide),* Mario Scaccia, Roberto Camardiel, Rafael Luis Calvo, Mariangela Giordano, Soledad Miranda.

Costume melodrama. Upon his return from the wars, the mighty Ursus learns that his betrothed, Attea, has been abducted and carried away to a distant island ruled by pagan priests. When he sets out to find her, he is accompanied by a blind slave girl, Doreide, who believes Attea was kidnaped by Ursus former friend, Setas. En route to the island, Ursus is captured by Setas but breaks his bonds and continues on the journey. He encounters a courtesan, Magali, who offers to guide him and Doreide across a desert leading to the island. When Ursus refuses Magali's favors, she sets a trap for him with the help of Setas, but she is killed. Once on the island, Ursus discovers that Attea, now under the power of Setas, is the island's evil priestess. Failing to arouse Ursus' former love, she throws him into an arena with a giant bull, but he slays the beast and starts an island revolt against the rule of the priests. Both Attea and Setas are killed; Ursus sails away with Doreide, whose sight has been restored by a violent shock. *Priests. Prostitutes. Abduction. Paganism. Slavery. Blindness. Revolts. Islands. Deserts. Ursus. Bulls.*

Note: Opened in Rome as *Ursus* in Mar 1961; running time: 95 min; in Madrid in Apr 1961 under the same title. Originally released in Ferraniacolor. Mary Marlon is a pseudonym for María Luisa Merlo.

THE MIGHTY WARRIOR see THE TROJAN HORSE

THE MIKADO (Great Britain)   F6.3184

B. H. E. Productions. *Dist* Warner Bros. Pictures. 15 Mar **1967** [New York opening; c8 Mar 1967; LP37992]. Sd; col (Technicolor). 35mm. 125 min.

Prod Anthony Havelock-Allan, John Brabourne. *Assoc Prod* Richard Goodwin. *Dir* Stuart Burge. *Libretto* William S. Gilbert. *Dir Photog* Gerry Fisher. *Camera* Austin Dempster, Paul Wilson, George Minassian. *Art Dir* Peter Howitt. *Stage Setting* Disley Jones. *Film Ed* Alma Godfrey. *Asst Ed* Roger Spottiswoode. *Mus* Arthur Sullivan. *Perf by* D'Oyly Carte Opera Company. *Perf by* City of Birmingham Symphony Orchestra. *Mus Cond* Isidore Godfrey. *Sd Rec* Edgar Vetter. *Sd* Anthony Pullen. *Prod Mgr* Roy Stevens. *Cost* Betty Harley. *Cost* Charles Ricketts, Disley Jones. *Makeup* Colin Garde, Tony Sforzini. *Hairstyles* Hilda Fox, Hazel Catmull.

D'Oyly Carte Opera Company: Donald Adams *(The Mikado),* Philip Potter *(Nanki-Poo),* John Reed *(Ko-Ko),* Kenneth Sandford *(Pooh-Bah),* Thomas Lawlor *(Pish-Tush),* George Cook *(Go-To),* Valerie Masterson *(Yum-Yum),* Peggy Ann Jones *(Pitti-Sing),* Pauline Wales *(Peep-Bo),* Christene Palmer *(Katisha),* Katherine Dyson, Abby Hadfield, Susan Maisey, Marian Martin, Alison Parker, Vera Ryan, Anna Vincent, Mercia Glossop, Beti Lloyd-Jones, Jennifer Marks, Norma Millar, Abigail Ryan, Anne Sessions *(ladies' chorus),* Glyn Adams, John Hugill, Gordon Mackenzie, Ralph Mason, Clifford Parkes, actor, David Rayson, Howard Williamson, Neville Grave, Peter Lodwick, James Marsland, Alfred Oldridge, Anthony Raffell, John Webley *(men's chorus).*

Operetta film. Source: W. S. Gilbert and Arthur Sullivan, *The Mikado* (first performance: London, 14 Mar 1885). In ancient Japan, young Nanki-Poo, the son of the Mikado, runs away from home rather than marry the elderly woman his father has chosen for him. Disguised as a wandering minstrel, he arrives at Titipu and learns that his beloved Yum-Yum is to be wed to her guardian, Ko-Ko, the newly-appointed Lord High Executioner. When the Mikado decrees that an execution must take place within a month, Nanki-Poo agrees to be the victim if he will be permitted to marry Yum-Yum first and thus have one month of happiness before yielding Yum-Yum to Ko-Ko. Complications arise, however, because of a law stating that when a man is beheaded his wife must be buried with him. The dilemma is settled by forging a death certificate for Nanki-Poo and presenting it to the Mikado. Upon learning that the executed man was his only son, the Mikado demands that Nanki-Poo be brought back to life; Nanki-Poo stipulates that he will return to life only if he is permitted to have Yum-Yum for his wife. The Mikado consents and all ends happily, except for Ko-Ko, who is obliged to marry the mean-tempered woman intended for Nanki-Poo. *Royalty. Runaways. Minstrels. Executioners. Filial relations. Marriage—Arranged. Disguise. Capital punishment. Reviviscence. Marriage. Japan.*

Note: Filmed at the Savoy Theatre, London. Released in Great Britain in Apr 1967; running time: 122 min.

MIKRES APHRODITES see **YOUNG APHRODITES**

MILCZĄCA GWIAZDA see **FIRST SPACESHIP ON VENUS**

THE MILKY WAY (France/Italy)   **F6.3185**
Greenwich Film Production–Fraia Film. *Dist* U-M Film Distributors. Dec **1969** [Los Angeles showing]. Sd; col (Eastman Color). 35mm. 105 min.
Prod Serge Silberman. *Assoc Prod* Ulrich Pickard. *Dir* Luis Buñuel. *Screenplay-Dial-Adapt* Luis Buñuel, Jean-Claude Carrière. *Dir Photog* Christian Matras. *1st Asst* Ernest Bourreaud. *2d Asst Camera* Paul Cost. *Focus* Bernard Noisette. *Art Dir* Pierre Guffroy. *Asst Art Dir* Pierre Cadiou. *Film Ed* Louisette Hautecoeur. *Mus* Luis Buñuel. *Sd* Jacques Gallois. *Sd Ed* Dominique Amy. *Asst Dir* Pierre Lary, Patrick Saglio. *Prod Mgr* Jean Lara. *Asst Prod Mgr* Michel Breuil. *Location Mgr* Claude Sune. *Script Girl* Suzanne Durrenberger. *Prod Sec* Odette Darrigol. *Cost Created by* Jacqueline Guyot. *Cost* Jacqueline Moreau, Françoise Tournafond. *Wigs* Jean Pipard. *Makeup* Jacqueline Pipard. *Duel Dir by* Claude Carliez. *Prod Admin* Jacqueline Dudilleux. *Still Photog* Jean Distinghin.
Cast: Paul Frankeur *(Pierre)*, Laurent Terzieff *(Jean)*, Alain Cuny *(man with the cape)*, Edith Scob *(Virgin Mary)*, Bernard Verley *(Jesus)*, François Maistre *(French priest)*, Claude Cerval *(brigadier)*, Muni *(mother superior)*, Julien Bertheau *(maître d'hotel)*, Ellen Bahl *(Madame Garnier)*, Michel Piccoli *(The Marquis)*, Agnès Capri *(Lamartine Institution directress)*, Michel Etcheverry *(The Inquisitor)*, Pierre Clementi *(The Devil [Angel of Death])*, Georges Marchal *(The Jesuit)*, Jean Piat *(The Jansenist)*, Denis Manuel *(Rodolphe)*, Daniel Pilon *(François)*, Claudio Brook *(bishop)*, Julien Guiomar *(Spanish priest)*, Marcel Pérès *(Spanish innkeeper)*, Delphine Seyrig *(prostitute)*, Jean-Claude Carrière *(Priscillian)*, Christine Simon *(Thérèse)*, Augusta Carrière *(Sister Françoise)*, Jean-Daniel Ehrmann *(condemned man)*, Pierre Lary *(young monk)*, Bernard Musson *(French innkeeper)*, Michel Dacquin *(Monsieur Garnier)*, Gabriel Gobin *(father)*, Pierre Maguelon *(civil guard corporal)*, Marius Laurey *(blind man)*, Jean Clarieux *(Apostle Peter)*, Christian Van Cau *(Apostle Andrew)*, Claudine Berg *(mother)*, Rita Maiden, Béatrice Constantini *(Priscillian's daughters)*, Claude Jetter *(virgin in Spanish inn)*, Jacqueline Rouillard *(restaurant maid)*, José Bergosa *(Priscillian's first deacon)*, Douking *(shepherd)*, Jean-Louis Broust, Stéphane Bouy, Michel Creton, Raoul Delfosse, Jean Dhermay, Pascal Fardoulis, Paul Pavel, Douglas Read, Jacques Rispal, César Torres.
Religious drama. Two tramps, Pierre and Jean, on a road near Paris en route to the Spanish shrine of Santiago de Compostela, are approached by a stranger cloaked in black who tells them to father a prostitute's children. Pierre and Jean continue on their journey, encountering various scenes from the history of heretical doctrines pertaining to the six divine mysteries of Catholicism: Christ's dual nature as God and man; the Holy Trinity; free will; the origin of evil; the Immaculate Conception; and the Eucharist. At an inn, the tramps witness an army officer and a priest arguing the question of transsubstantiation as they eat dinner. Their host, indicating a paté, voices the heresy that "Christ is in the host as the hare is in the paté." The priest suddenly becomes convinced of the truth of the heresy, flings his coffee at the army officer, and is led back to the insane asylum from whence he escaped. That night in the woods, Pierre and Jean meet Priscillian, Bishop of Avila, a Latin-speaking shepherd who dispassionately conducts an orgy among his followers to mortify the flesh. The following day, at a swank restaurant in Tours, the maître d'hotel discusses Christ's dual nature with the staff, serves two diners, and shoos away the tramps. In a dungeon, the Marquis de Sade speaks his philosophy from *Justine*

to a pious young girl he has shackled to the floor; and at the wedding at Cana, Christ is seen as a man like any other. The tramps beg food at a picnic at the Lamartine Institution near Bordeaux. Here a young girls' catechism class mounts a stage to declare all heretics anathema; the scene is interrupted by Jean's vision of a pope being executed by anarchists. In an Inquisition setting, a heretic is led away to be burned, and a young priest who questions the purpose of such punishment is told by the Inquisitor that the burnings serve a secular function. Further on, Jean wishes the death of a motorist who has passed them by. An accident quickly brings him his wish; and at the scene the two friends talk with the Devil, who expresses the belief that the damned one day may be saved. A Jansenist nun of the Convulsionist sect has herself crucified while the count who is the convent's benefactor stands by. Afterwards the Jansenist count meets a Jesuit, and they argue theology as they duel and then walk off as friends. As Pierre and Jean reach Burgos, they meet two Protestant students who dispute the doctrine of the Trinity at the disinterment of a heretic bishop. The students flee from the Inquisition into the woods, and the Virgin Mary appears to one of them. At an inn a priest and two police officers sample a ham prepared by the innkeeper. The Protestant student describes to the priest the Virgin's miraculous appearance, but the priest dismisses it as an everyday occurrence. The priest regales the group with the story of a trustworthy Carmelite nun who left the key to her convent's coffer at the foot of the Virgin's statue as she ran away to live with a lover and returned to the fold years later to find that the Virgin had assumed her form to accomplish her tasks over the years. The innkeeper insists that the students occupy separate rooms and warns them to open their doors to no one. The priest asks admittance, and when he is refused, he sits outside their doors to discuss the mystery of the Virgin and the Immaculate Conception. Meanwhile, a pure young woman and a man appear in the students' rooms. The tramps steal away from the inn by night with the innkeeper's ham and reach Santiago de Compostela. They consort with a prostitute who wants them to father her children, fulfilling the prophecy of the start of their journey. The prostitute tells them that the shrine is now empty since the remains in the crypt were discovered to be those of Priscillian rather than of St. James. Christ appears elsewhere in the woods with his disciples. He tells them that he has come not to bring peace but a sword. He restores sight to two blind men, but as they follow him they come to a small ditch which hinders their crossing as if they were sightless. *Tramps. Pilgrims. Priests. Soldiers. Students. Anarchists. Nuns. Prostitutes. Theology. Heresy. Asceticism. Insanity. Blindness. Inns. Latin language. Orgies. Restaurants. The Inquisition. The Reformation. The Counter-Reformation. Santiago de Compostela. Tours (France). Burgos. Donatien Alphonse François (Marquis de) Sade. Priscillian. The Church. Catholic Church. Society of Jesus. Duels. Automobile accidents. Miracles. Fantasy. Jesus. Virgin Mary. The Devil. The Twelve Apostles.*
Note: Paris opening: Mar 1969 as *La voie lactée*; running time: 100 min. Released in Italy in 1969 as *La via lattea*.

MILL OF THE STONE WOMEN (France/Italy)   **F6.3186**
Wanguard Film–Faro Film–Explorer Film–C. E. C. *Dist* Parade Pictures. 23 Jan **1963** [Phoenix, Arizona, opening]. Sd; col (Eastmancolor, print by Technicolor). 35mm (Dyaliscope). 94 min.
Pres by Riley Jackson, Robert Patrick. *Prod* Gianpaolo Bigazzi. *Assoc Prod* Lucien Vittet. *Dir* Giorgio Ferroni. *Screenplay* Remigio Del Grosso, Ugo Liberatore, Giorgio Stegani, Giorgio Ferroni. *Story* Giorgio Ferroni, Remigio Del Grosso. *Photog* Pierludovico Pavoni. *Art Dir* Arrigo Equini. *Film Ed* Antonietta Zita. *Mus* Carlo Innocenzi.
Cast: Pierre Brice *(Hans)*, Scilla Gabel *(Helfy)*, Dany Carrel *(Liselotte)*, Wolfgang Preiss *(Professor Wahl)*, Herbert Boehme *(Bohlem)*, Marco Guglielmi *(Raab)*, Liana Orfei, Olga Solbelli.
Horror film. Based on an unidentified short story in "Flemish Tales" by: Peter Van Weigen. In 1912 Hans, an art student in Amsterdam, is doing research on an 18th-century windmill-driven carousel of statues of famous women in death poses. He meets Professor Wahl, who owns the mill, and his daughter Helfy, who suffers from a strange illness. When the girl dies and later reappears alive, Hans fears that he is going crazy; then he discovers that the statues are actually petrified corpses of women whose blood the professor has drained to continually revivify his daughter. Hans rescues his own girl friend from the macabre operation and flees from the mill as it bursts into flames, killing both the professor and his daughter. *Students. Professors. Filial relations. Reviviscence. Windmills. Sculptures. Corpses. Amsterdam.*
Note: Location scenes filmed in Holland. Opened in Rome in Oct 1960 as *Il mulino delle donne di pietra*; in Paris in Sep 1962 as *Le moulin des supplices*; running time: 91 min. Also known as *Horror of the Stone Women* and *The Horrible Mill Women*.

LES MILLE ET UNE NUITS *see* **THE WONDERS OF ALADDIN**

MILLION DOLLAR MANHUNT (Great Britain)   F6.3187
Butcher's Film Distributors. *Dist* Anglo Amalgamated Film Distributors. Feb **1962**. Sd; b&w. 35mm. 67 min.
   Prod William G. Chalmers. *Dir-Writ* Maclean Rogers. *Photog* Ernest Palmer. *Art Dir* John Stoll. *Film Ed* Peter Mayhew. *Mus* Wilfred Burns.
   Cast: Richard Denning *(Keen)*, Carole Mathews *(Hedy)*, Ronald Adam *(Scammel/Dumetrius)*, Danny Green *(Yottie)*, Brian Worth *(Ridgeway)*, Jan Holden *(Sally)*, Hugh Moxey *(Sergeant Coutts)*, Elwyn Brook-Jones *(Mitchell)*, Peter Swanwick *(Bonnet)*.
   Crime melodrama. Source: Al Bocca, *Requiem for a Redhead* (London, 1953). An international gang of criminals arrives in London to search for $12 million in counterfeit money printed by the Germans during World War II and stolen before the Allies had reached Berlin. Keen, an intelligence agent assigned to the case, falls in love with one of the suspects, Hedy, a German cabaret singer and gang member. Dumetrius, the gang's leader, is impersonating Scammel, a British staff officer recently murdered in Berlin. Attempting to recover the counterfeit currency, Dumetrius resorts to murder, alienating Hedy, who henceforth assists Keen. The intelligence agent sets a trap baited with incriminating photographs of Dumetrius in Berlin and confronts the gang in a warehouse. After murdering Hedy, Dumetrius falls to his death during a scuffle with Keen. *Intelligence agents. Singers. Gangs. Germans. Counterfeiting. Imposture. Murder. Photographs. Cabarets. World War II. Berlin. London. Great Britain—Army.*
   Note: Released in Great Britain in 1956 as *Assignment Redhead;* running time: 79 min.

THE MILLION EYES OF SU-MURU (Great Britain)   F6.3188
Sumuru Films. *Dist* American International Pictures. 17 May **1967** [Baltimore opening; c17 May 1967; LP35115]. Sd; col (Technicolor). 35mm (Techniscope). 95 min. [See note.]
   Prod Harry Alan Towers. *Dir* Lindsay Shonteff. *Screenplay* Kevin Kavanagh. *Story* Peter Welbeck. *Photog* John Kotze. *Art Dir* Scott MacGregor. *Film Ed* Allan Morrison. *Mus Comp & Cond* Johnny Scott. *Sd* Brian Marshall. *Asst Dir* Anthony Waye. *Prod Mgr* Terry Bourke.
   Cast: Frankie Avalon *(Tommy Carter)*, George Nader *(Nick West)*, Shirley Eaton *(Su-Muru)*, Wilfrid Hyde-White *(Colonel Baisbrook)*, Klaus Kinski *(President Boong)*, Patti Chandler *(Louise)*, Salli Sachse *(Mikki)*, Ursula Rank *(Erna)*, Christa Nell *(Zoe)*, Maria Rohm *(Helga)*, Paul Chang *(Inspector Koo)*, Essie Huang *(Kitty)*, Jon Fong *(Colonel Medika)*, Denise Davreux, Mary Cheng, Jill Hamilton, Lisa Gray, Christine Lok, Margaret Cheung, Louise Lee *(The Su-Muru Guard)*.
   Action melodrama. Based on books and characters created by: Sax Rohmer. The security chief of the small Asian country of Sinonesia is murdered in Italy, and Colonel Baisbrook of British Intelligence persuades Tommy Carter and Nick West, two Americans, to assist in the investigation. They discover that behind the killing is a world-wide organization of women plotting the enslavement of mankind. Led by the beautiful and sadistic Su-Muru, the women plan to assassinate Sinonesia's President Boong. After finding a dead woman in Nick's hotel bed, the two men, suspecting a frameup, flee to Hong Kong to warn President Boong. Su-Muru's assistants follow them, however, and Nick is abducted and taken to the organization's island headquarters. Forced into cooperating, Nick poses as Boong's new security chief and introduces the president to Helga, one of Su-Muru's executives, whose job is to carry out the assassination. Helga has a change of heart, however, and another woman uses the deadly gun which turns the victim into stone. Once it is learned that the dead man is Boong's double, Helga appeals to Tommy for help, while Nick is taken back to Su-Muru's torture chambers. Tommy and Helga win the aid of the Hong Kong police against Su-Muru's army. During the ensuing battle, Tommy rescues Nick just before Su-Muru's island is destroyed by a huge explosion. Colonel Baisbrook congratulates the men on their accomplishment and reveals that Tommy is actually a British secret agent. *Americans in foreign countries. Man-haters. Doubles. Police. Secret agents. Assassination. Sadism. Conspiracy. Frameup. Abduction. Torture. Imposture. Islands. Asia. Italy. Hong Kong. Great Britain—Intelligence service. Explosions.*
   Note: Location scenes filmed in Hong Kong. Released in Great Britain in Nov 1967 as *Sumuru;* running time: 84 min (cut from 95 min). Copyright length: 77 min; also reviewed at 71 and 86 min. Peter Welbeck is a pseudonym for Harry Alan Towers.

MILLIONAIRE'S WOMEN   F6.3189
15 May **1969** [San Francisco showing]. Sd; col. 35mm. 80 min.
   Sex film. Wealthy Beverly Hills housewives, bored with their lives, go to a club run by a drug dealer, get high, and have sex with the men there. Their husbands, who spend their free time playing cards, learn of their wives' activities, crash the club, and elect to stay and join in the fun instead of fighting

their rivals. *Housewives. Drug dealers. Infidelity. Wealth. Narcotics. Nightclubs. Los Angeles—Beverly Hills.*
   Note: Also known as *Millionaire Women.*

THE MILLIONAIRESS (Great Britain)   F6.3190
Anatole de Grunwald, Ltd. *Dist* Twentieth Century–Fox Film Corp. 9 Feb **1961** [New York opening; c26 Dec 1960; LP18565]. Sd (Westrex); col (Eastman Color, print by Deluxe). 35mm (CinemaScope). 90 min.
   A Dimitri De Grunwald Production. *Prod* Pierre Rouve. *Exec Prod* Dimitri De Grunwald. *Dir* Anthony Asquith. *Screenplay* Wolf Mankowitz. *Adapt* Riccardo Aragno. *Dir Photog* Jack Hildyard. *Camera Op* Gerry Fisher. *Focus* Chic Anstiss. *Art Dir* Harry White. *Set Dresser* Pamela Cornell. *Draughtsman* Bill Alexander. *Prod Dsgn* Paul Sheriff. *Film Ed* Anthony Harvey. *1st Asst Ed* Andy Michallidis. *2d Asst Ed* Julian Mackintosh. *Mus Comp* Georges Van Parys. *Cond* Leighton Lucas. *Rec Supv* A. W. Watkins. *Sd Rec* Gerry Turner. *Sd Ed* Alastair McIntyre. *Dub Mix* J. B. Smith. *Boom Op* David Bowen. *Sd Camera Op* Mickey Hickey. *1st & 2d Asst Dir* Frank Hollands, Ted Wallis. *Prod Admin* Leonard Urry. *In Charge of Prod* Roy Parkinson. *Cont* June Faithfull. *Prod Sec* Elizabeth Woodthorpe. *Wardrobe Supv* Felix Evans. *Dresses* Pierre Balmain. *Makeup* Dave Aylott. *Hairdresser* Sarah Beber. *Portraits by* Olga Lehmann. *Prop Buyer* Fred Lacey. *Still Photog* Norman Hargood.
   Cast: Sophia Loren *(Epifania Parerga)*, Peter Sellers *(Dr. Achmed el Kabir/ Parerga)*, Alastair Sim *(Julius Sagamore)*, Vittorio De Sica *(Joe)*, Dennis Price *(Dr. Adrian Bond)*, Gary Raymond *(Alastair)*, Alfie Bass *(fish curer)*, Miriam Karlin *(Mrs. Joe)*, Noel Purcell *(professor)*, Virginia Vernon *(Polly Smith)*, Graham Stark *(butler)*, Diana Coupland *(nurse)*, Pauline Jameson *(Muriel Pilkington)*, Eleanor Summerfield *(Mrs. Willoughby)*, Willoughby Goddard *(president)*, Basil Hoskins, Gordon Sterne *(secretaries)*, Tempe Adam *(Gloria)*, Wally Patch *(whelk seller)*, Charles Hill *(Corelli)*, Davy Kaye *(Tommy True)*.
   Comedy. Source: George Bernard Shaw, *The Millionairess* (Vienna opening: 5 Jan 1937). Heiress Epifania Parerga, the richest woman in the world, longs for a happy marriage. After an unfortunate marriage to the handsome but unfaithful Alastair, Epifania seeks help from Sagamore, her shrewd solicitor, who recommends that she see a psychiatrist, Adrian. The latter makes a bid for her hand, but when he criticizes her father, the brief romance ends abruptly. After making a token suicide attempt, Epifania meets an Indian doctor, Kabir, who runs an inadequately equipped clinic for the poor. When he seems indifferent to her beauty and wealth, Epifania vows to make him change his mind and marry her. On her orders, buildings are destroyed around Kabir's clinic, and she builds a huge modern one nearby. Terrified of being submerged by this woman of strong will, Kabir struggles to rid himself of her. He insists on a test of her resourcefulness: she is to make a living on her own for 3 months; she agrees on condition that Kabir triple a certain sum of money through his own exertions in the same period of time. Epifania succeeds in proving herself, but the doctor deliberately loses the money and announces that they can never marry. Heartbroken, Epifania decides to enter a Tibetan monastery; but Kabir weakens, and the lovers are reconciled. *Heiresses. Psychiatrists. Millionaires. Italians. East Indians. Physicians. Marriage. Suicide. Clinics. Monasteries.*
   Note: Opened in London in Oct 1960.

EL MILLÓN DE MADIGAN *see* **MADIGAN'S MILLIONS**

MIŁOŚĆ DWUDZIESTOLATKÓW *see* **LOVE AT TWENTY**

MIMI LA DOUCE   F6.3191
Fearless Productions. Dec **1968** [San Francisco showing]. Si?; col. 16mm? [Feature film, length unknown.]
   Sex film. Four lesbians engage in group sex with each other, including oral sex. *Lesbianism. Group sex. Oral sex.*

MIN VÄN BALTHAZAR *see* **AU HASARD, BALTHAZAR**

MINAMI NO SHIMA NI YUKI GA FURA *see* **SNOW IN THE SOUTH SEAS**

THE MIND BENDERS (Great Britain)   F6.3192
Novus Productions. *For* Anglo-Amalgamated Film Distributors. *Dist* American International Pictures. 1 May **1963** [New York opening]. Sd; b&w. 35mm. 99 min.
   A Michael Relph–Basil Dearden Production. *Prod* Michael Relph. *Dir* Basil Dearden. *Screenplay* James Kennaway. *Photog* Denys Coop. *Camera Op* Eric Besche. *Camera Focus* Neil Binney. *Art Dir* Jim Morahan. *Film Ed* John D. Guthridge. *Mus Comp* Georges Auric. *Mus Cond* Muir Mathieson. *Played by* Sinfonia of London. *Sd* Gordon K. McCallum. *Sd Ed* William Butler. *Sd Mix* Robert T. MacPhee. *Sd Rec* Vivian Temple-Smith. *Boom Op* Roy Charman. *1st, 2d & 3d Asst Dir* Basil Rayburn, Simon Relph, Stephen Christian. *Prod Mgr* Charles Orme. *Asst to the Prod* John L. Hargreaves. *Prod Sec* Jean Hall. *Cont* Sue Dyson. *Cost Dsgn* Anthony Mendleson. *Makeup* Harry Frampton.

Hairdresser Pearl Orton. *Still Photog* George Courtney Ward. *Constr Mgr* Bill Surridge. *Grip* George Beavis.

Cast: Dirk Bogarde *(Dr. Henry Longman)*, Mary Ure *(Oonagh Longman)*, John Clements *(Major Hall)*, Michael Bryant *(Dr. Tate)*, Wendy Craig *(Annabelle)*, Harold Goldblatt *(Professor Sharpey)*, Geoffrey Keen *(Calder)*, Terry Palmer *(Norman)*, Norman Bird *(Aubrey)*, Roger Delgado *(Dr. Jean Bonvoulois)*, Edward Fox *(Stewart)*, Terence Alexander *(coach)*, Georgina Moon *(Persephone)*, Teresa Van Hoorn *(Penny)*, Timothy Beaton *(Paul)*, Christopher Ellis *(Peers)*, Edward Palmer *(porter)*, Elizabeth Counsell *(girl student on station)*, Anthony Singleton *(student on station)*, Pauline Winter *(mother)*, Philip Ray *(father)*, Rene Setan *(1st Indian student)*, Ashik Devello *(2d Indian student)*, Robin Hawdon *(student in Oxford)*, Terence Edmond *(1st student at party)*, Ian Dewar *(crowd ringleader)*.

Science fiction drama. Following the suicide of Professor Sharpey, a scientist involved in an experiment sponsored by the British space agency to test an individual's reaction when he is deprived of essential sense stimuli, military security officer Major Hall presents Calder, the director of the laboratory where Sharpey worked, with evidence that the dead man was a traitor. Hall then visits Sharpey's associate, Dr. Longman, at Oxford University to continue his investigation. Longman angrily defends his colleague and claims that the experiment was responsible for the alleged security violations and the events leading up to Sharpey's suicide. He contends that Sharpey, the experiment's primary subject, was not a traitor but was brainwashed to give away the secrets. Determined to prove his belief, Longman submits himself to the experiment, is immersed in a tank of warm water for several hours, and emerges in a state of nervous collapse. Dr. Tate, an associate, and Major Hall, to help Longman prove his theory, attempt to undermine Longman's love for his wife, Oonagh, by brainwashing him and tape recording the session. Only after the apparent failure of the experiment does Longman begin to show signs that the experiment actually succeeded. He is indifferent when Oonagh announces that she is pregnant; their relationship becomes progressively uneasy; and Longman becomes infatuated with Annabelle, a "college widow." Major Hall becomes concerned over Longman's behavior and vainly attempts to undo the damage by playing for Longman the recording he and Tate made of the brainwashing session; but Longman remains unaffected and departs with Annabelle for her houseboat. Oonagh, in the last month of her pregnancy, takes a fall and begins labor; and the birth of his child brings Longman back to his senses. *Professors. Scientists. Government agents. Investigators. Suicide. Treason. Brainwashing. Sense perception. Marriage. Infidelity. Pregnancy. Childbirth. Experiments. Laboratories. Recorders. Oxford University.*

Note: Opened in London in Feb 1963; running time: 113 min.

MIND BLOWERS   F6.3193

Janus II Productions–Academy Productions. *Dist* Stacey Distributors. **1970.** Sd; col. 16mm. ca60 min.

Drama. Siamese twin sisters are separated surgically at birth, but mental transferrence begins unexpectedly to occur. As they grow up, their paths through life diverge sharply; one chooses a solitary life as a prim schoolteacher, the other becomes a sexual adventuress. Suddenly, their dreams become filled with terror: the swinger is struck by shame and a sense of degradation, while the schoolmistress vicariously experiences disturbing sexual fantasies. *Twins. Sisters. Schoolteachers. Promiscuity. Eroticism. Personal identity. Dreams.*

Note: Also known as *Mindblowers* and *Mind Blower*.

THE MIND BLOWERS   F6.3194

Dist Cosmos Films. 5 Sep **1968** [San Francisco showing]. Sd; b&w. 35mm. 70 min.

Pres by Hal Friend. A Guy King Production. *Prod* Guy King. *Dir-Script* Harlan Renvok. *Sp Scenes Dir* Douglas Scanio. *Dir Photog* Hal Kay. *Asst Photog* Steve Bowser. *Ed* Harlan Renvok. *Mus Associated. Makeup* Heleene. *Stills* Bob Davis.

Cast: Ingrid Superstar, Chris Markson, Hal Friend, Red Lion, Phil Cross, Eric Emerson, Ryder Guthrie, Ellen Butler, Marc Sylvan, Tanus Root, Nanook North, Kristen Steen, Lily Lemis.

Comedy-drama. Psychiatrist Wolfgang Gotterdam investigates the workings of the brain. He discovers that if the brain waves of an animal engaged in a particular activity are recorded, the playback of that recording through the animal's brain will stimulate a repetition of that activity. The professor decides to experiment on humans, and he selects as subjects a prostitute, a virtuous young woman, a male homosexual, and a lusty young sailor. Unaware that his mischievous assistant has mislabeled the recordings, the professor plays back the wrong messages into the subjects' brains—the sailor's recording is exchanged with the homosexual's and the prostitute's with that taken from the chaste subject. *Psychiatrists. Prostitutes. Sailors. Researchers. Male homosexuality. Chastity. Experiments. Practical jokes. Sexuality.*

THE MIND OF MR. SOAMES (Great Britain)   F6.3195

Amicus Productions. *Dist* Columbia Pictures. 23 Sep **1970** [Dallas opening: c1 Sep 1970; LP38168]. Sd; col (Eastman Color, print by Movielab). 35mm. 95 min. *MPAA rating* GP.

Prod Max J. Rosenberg, Milton Subotsky. *Dir* Alan Cooke. *Screenplay* John Hale, Edward Simpson. *Lighting Camera* Billy Williams. *Camera Op* David Harcourt. *Art Dir* Don Mingaye. *Set Dresser* Andrew Low. *Prod Dsgn* Bill Constable. *Film Ed* Bill Blunden. *Mus Comp & Cond* Michael Dress. *Perf by* John Williams and the Vesuvius Ensemble. *Dub Ed* Ian Fuller. *Sd Mix* John Aldred. *Dub Mix* Nolan Roberts. *Asst Dir* Jake Wright. *Prod Mgr* Teresa Bolland. *Cont* Kay Rawlings. *Wardrobe* Evelyn Gibbs. *Makeup* Jill Carpenter. *Hairdresser* Gordon Bond. *Constr Mgr* Bill Waldron.

Cast: Terence Stamp *(John Soames)*, Robert Vaughn *(Dr. Michael Bergen)*, Nigel Davenport *(Dr. Maitland)*, Donal Donnelly *(Dr. Joe Allen)*, Christian Roberts *(Thomas Fleming)*, Vickery Turner *(Naomi)*, Scott Forbes *(Richard Bannerman)*, Judy Parfitt *(Jenny Bannerman)*, Norman Jones, actor *(Davis)*, Dan Jackson *(Nicholls)*, Joe McPartland *(Inspector Moore)*, Pamela Moiseiwitsch *(girl on train)*, Eric Brooks *(TV floor manager)*, Billy Cornelius *(Sergeant Clifford)*, Jon Croft *(guard)*, Esmond Webb *(ticket seller)*, Bill Pilkington *(pub owner)*, Kate Binchy *(barmaid)*, Joe Gladwin *(old man in car)*, Tony Caunter *(schoolteacher)*.

Melodrama. Source: Charles Eric Maine, *The Mind of Mr. Soames* (London, 1961). John Soames, a victim of congenital brain damage, has been in a coma for 30 years. Dr. Michael Bergen, an American neurosurgeon, operates on him and brings him to consciousness, whereupon Soames undergoes a highly accelerated educational program administered by Dr. Maitland, head of the neurophysical institute. With television director Thomas Fleming monitoring Soames's every movement with his cameras, Bergen argues that Maitland is trying to accomplish too much too fast and allows the patient to have a brief, unauthorized encounter with the outside world. Maitland locates Soames, however, and brings him back to the hospital, but the frustrated man escapes. Shortly thereafter, Soames is struck by drunk driver Richard Bannerman, who takes him home, where his sympathetic wife, Jenny, learns the victim's true identity and decides to return him to the hospital. He again escapes, this time on a train to London. Tracked to a barn by the doctors, Soames is finally persuaded to give himself up, but the clamor of newsmen frightens him, and he stabs Bergen with a pitchfork. In the ambulance returning him to the hospital, Soames indicates that he may begin to trust Bergen's associate, Dr. Joe Allen. *Surgeons. Physicians. Escapees. Television directors. Television cameramen. Brain damage. Brain surgery. Mental retardation. Education. Hospitals. Trains. London. Automobile accidents.*

Note: Opened in London in Nov 1970; running time: 98 min.

MINGUS   F6.3196

Inlet Films. *Dist* Film-Makers' Distribution Center. 16 May **1968** [New York opening]. Sd; b&w. 16mm. 60 min.

Prod-Dir Thomas Reichman. *Assoc Prod* William O'Boyle. *Photog* Lee Osborne, photog, Michael Wadley. *Adtl Photog* Edward Barnett, Aries Di Mertzis. *Main Titl* Steve Weiss. *Film Ed* Richard Clarke, ed, Mars Potamkin, Thomas Reichman. *Song:* "All the Things You Are" Jerome Kern, Oscar Hammerstein, II. *Song:* "Take the A Train" Billy Strayhorn. *Song:* "Secret Love" Sammy Fain, Paul Francis Webster. *Sd* Jim McBride, Jeff Strickler. *Still Photog* Charles Stewart, Robert Parent.

Cast: Charles Mingus, Carolyn Mingus.

Musicians: Charles McPherson *(Alto)*, Lonnie Hillyer *(Trumpet)*, Walter Bishop *(Piano)*, John Gillmore *(Tenor)*, Danny Richmond *(Drums)*, Charles Mingus *(Bass & Piano)*.

Documentary. This portrait of jazz bassist/composer Charles Mingus focuses on the night he and his 5-year-old daughter Carolyn are to be evicted from his loft studio for nonpayment of rent. (Mingus considers his eviction in November of 1966 as the last stop on a downward trend from the pinnacle of his acclaimed concert at the 1964 Monterey Jazz Festival; in the interim he started his own record company and suffered both financial and personal setbacks. At the time of the film Mingus is composing several scores for the Boston Ballet and asserts that he will never again appear in nightclubs.) In the loft, the unseen director asks Mingus questions about his life and beliefs, which Mingus may or may not answer. Intercut with the loft scenes are shots from his last engagement, one week before, at a jazz spot near Boston. Also included are scenes on Harlem streets, at an anti-Vietnam War demonstration where Mingus was asked to march with a contingent of Sioux Indians, and a scene from his historic Town Hall concert in 1961. The film ends with the jazzman's eviction, and his arrest on a mistaken charge of heroin possession. *Musicians. Sioux Indians. Eviction. Jazz. Demonstrations. New York City—Harlem. Charles Mingus.*

Note: Filmed on location in New York City and at Lenny's in Peabody, Mass. The footage of Mingus before his eviction was shot in Nov 1966.

THE MINI-AFFAIR (Great Britain)   **F6.3197**
United Screen Arts. 22 May **1968** [Albany, New York, opening]. Sd (RCA); col (Technicolor). 35mm (Techniscope). 92 min.

Prod Richard A. Herland. *Exec Prod* Thomas M. Vickers. *Assoc Prod* Geoffrey Forster. *Dir-Writ* Robert G. Amram. *Orig Story Idea* Richard A. Herland. *Dir Photog* Derek Waterman. *Art Dir* Edwin Florence. *Titl Dsgn* Sydney King. *Film Ed* John Ireland, ed. *Mus* The Bee Gees. *Song:* "The Mini-Affair" Howard Blaikley. *Song:* "Words" Barry Gibb, Maurice Gibb, Robin Gibb. *Sung by* Georgie Fame. *Mus Dir* Bill Shepherd. *Sd Ed* Jim Atkinson. *Prod Mgr* Bernard Hanson. *Wardrobe* Gay Florence. *Makeup* Renee Claff.

Cast: Georgie Fame (*Georgie Hart*), Rosemary Nicols (*Charlotte*), John Clive (*Joe*), Bernard Archard (*Sir Basil Grinling*), Lucille Soong (*Lucille*), Rick Dane (*Mike Maroon*), Julian Curry (*Ronnie*), Gretchen Regan (*Marianne*), Madeline Smith (*Samantha*), Clement Freud (*Stephen Catchpole*), Totti Truman-Taylor (*Aunt Grace*), Clive Dunn (*Tyson*), Roy Kinnear (*fire extinguisher salesman*), Eric Pohlmann (*world banker*), William Rushton (*chancellor of the exchequer*), Irene Handl (*Chinese restaurant cook*).

Romantic comedy. In their fashionable London apartment, Charlotte, Marianne, and Samantha lament the lack of male companionship. While attending a demonstration of Kendo wrestling with her boyfriend Joe and reporter Ronnie, their roommate Lucille is inspired. Counseled in the ways of her Chinese ancestors, the women abduct their bachelor idols, including popular singer Georgie Hart; Minister of Popular Culture Sir Basil Grinling; and Radio Free Ruritania disc jockey Mike Maroon. Waking beside his captor at the island home of Joe's Aunt Grace, Sir Basil immediately falls in love with Charlotte. Samantha, however, is repelled by Georgie's lack of inhibition, while Georgie is attracted to Marianne. Preoccupied with his position and indifferent to Marianne's charms, Mike escapes at the first opportunity. Summoned by the disc jockey, police and army converge upon the island, terminating the idyll and apprehending the abductors. Nevertheless, Georgie and Sir Basil refuse to incriminate their captors, and Ronnie blackmails Mike into withdrawing the charges. The couples are then reunited, Samantha finding happiness with Ronnie. *Roommates. Lovelorn. Disc jockeys. Chinese. Bachelors. Singers. Bureaucrats. Nobility. Aunts. Reporters. Police. Abduction. Blackmail. Islands. Kendo. London. Great Britain—Army.*

Note: Location scenes filmed in London.

MINI-SKIRT LOVE   **F6.3198**
Cam-Scope Pictures. *Dist* Boxoffice International Film Distributors. 11 Oct **1967** [New York showing]. Sd; b&w (Pathé). 35mm. 74 min.

Prod-Dir-Writ Lou Campa. *Photog & Lighting* W. W. Lister. *Asst Lighting* Bob King. photog. *Film Ed* Bill Lister. *Mus* Musical Process. *Sd Rec* Ralph Berliner. *Post Rec* Murlyn Recording. *Asst Dir* Angie Giles. *Script Coörd* Cathy Campa. *Coöp* Albert J. Pogio. *Still Photog & Sp Tech Asst* George Cirello.

Cast: Marie Brent (*The Aunt?*), Donny Lee (*Billy [boy and man]*), Bella Donna (*mother*), Guy Sinclair (*father*), Mercedes je Morcerf (*saleswoman [see note]*), Marie Conti (*hooker*), Nick Harrison (*lover*), Lou Campa (*milkman*), Ancel Stiles (*policewoman*), Al Campa, Pete Brown, Louise Cirello, Jean Smith.

Melodrama. Billy, a 15-year-old camera buff, wanders through his home in search of subjects to photograph. He discovers his mother in bed with a lover, and he quietly snaps some revealing photos. There is a violent quarrel when Billy shows his father what he has found; Billy's mother accidentally kills his father and is committed to an institution for the criminally insane. Billy's aunt comes to care for him; she eventually seduces him, and they begin an affair. For 5 years, the incestuous relationship continues. Meanwhile, Billy's mother makes rapid strides toward recovery. At last she is deemed fit to return to society, and she arrives home to confront the overwhelming problems facing her family. *Aunts. Adolescence. Infidelity. Parenthood. Incest. Murder. Photographs. Insane asylums.*

Note: One source credits Mercedes je Morcerf as the aunt.

THE MINI-SKIRT MOB   **F6.3199**
American International Pictures. May **1968** [c22 May 1968; LP35943]. Sd; col (Perfect). 35mm. 82 min.

Prod-Dir Maury Dexter. *Screenplay* James Gordon White. *Photog* Arch R. Dalzell. *Film Ed* Sidney Levin. *Mus* Les Baxter. *Titl Song* Valjean Johns, Guy Hemric. *Sung by* The American Revolution, Patty McCormack. *Sd* Brad Trask. *Asst Dir* Jack Voglin. *Makeup* Ted Coodley. *Hairstyles* Wava Green.

Cast: Jeremy Slate (*Lon*), Diane McBain (*Shayne*), Sherry Jackson (*Connie Logan*), Patty McCormack (*Edie*), Ross Hagen (*Jeff Logan*), Harry Dean Stanton (*Spook*), Ronnie Rondell (*L. G.*).

Melodrama. Shayne, a mini-skirted cyclist, decides to break up the marriage of her ex-boyfriend, rodeo star Jeff Logan, by terrorizing the newlyweds. Accompanied by her younger sister, Edie, and a group of Jeff's former cronies, Shayne descends on the trailer where Jeff and Connie are honeymooning. Jeff

drives the mob away with a gun and moves to a new locale; and in the course of the chase that ensues, the wildly swinging trailer knocks one of the cyclists over a steep cliff. Shayne, goaded on by the sadistic Lon, now becomes more determined than ever to have her revenge. Edie, however, feels that the escapade has gone far enough, and she exchanges clothes with Connie and takes her place in the trailer while Jeff and Connie make their getaway on foot. The half-crazed mob hurl Molotov cocktails into the trailer, and Edie is burned to death. Blaming Jeff and Connie for Edie's death, Shayne and Lon attempt to run the couple down, but Lon crashes over an embankment and is killed while Shayne topples over a cliff and is left hanging by one hand. For a moment Connie feels compassion and goes to her rescue. But, remembering the past few hours, she releases her grip on Shayne and allows her to drop into the chasm below as Jeff arrives with the police. *Newlyweds. Sisters. Motorcycle gangs. Jealousy. Revenge. Honeymoons. Trailers. Molotov cocktails. Chases.*

Note: Location scenes filmed in Arizona and California.

MINI WEEKEND *see* **THE TOMCAT**

MINNESOTA CLAY (France/Italy/Spain)   **F6.3200**
Ultra Film–Jaguar Films–Franco London Film. *Dist* Harlequin International Pictures. Apr **1966** [Los Angeles showing]. Sd; col (Technicolor). 35mm (see note). 95 min.

Dir Sergio Corbucci. *Screenplay* Adriano Bolzoni, Sergio Corbucci. *Story* Adriano Bolzoni. *Photog* (see note) José Fernández Aguayo. *Art Dir* Carlo Simi. *Set Decor* Francisco Canet. *Film Ed* Franco Fraticelli. *Mus* Piero Piccioni. *Prod Mgr* Danilo Marciani, Faustino Ocaña.

Cast: Cameron Mitchell (*Minnesota Clay*), Georges Rivière (*Fox*), Ethel Rojo (*Estella*), Diana Martin (*Nancy*), Anthony Ross (*Scratchy*), Fernando Sancho (*Ortiz*), Alberto Cevenini (*Andy*), Antonio Casas (*Jonathan*), Julio Peña (*Lieutenant Evans*), Nando Poggi (*Tubbs*), Joe Kamel (*Millicet*), Gino Pernice, Madelaine Deheco, José Manuel Martín, Patricia del Frate.

Western drama. Former gunfighter Minnesota Clay, sentenced to 20 years of hard labor for a crime he did not commit, escapes from prison and makes his way to Mesa Encantada. The small Mexican town is ruled by two warring gangs; one is headed by Ortiz, and the other by Fox, the man who withheld information which could have proven Clay's innocence. Ortiz's mistress, Estella, offers to kill her lover and turn his gang over to Clay; when her proposal is rejected, she arranges for Clay to be captured by Fox. She then slays Ortiz and tries to win Clay's love by offering to help him kill Fox, but her treachery is discovered, and she is murdered by Fox, who sets out to kill Clay. Unknown to all, Clay is blind, and to further his chances, he hides out in a basement until it is dark. When the two men meet, Clay utilizes sound to trap and shoot down his opponent, although he himself is mortally wounded. *Gunfighters. Mistresses. Injustice. Prison escapes. Blindness. Frameup. Duplicity. Murder. Mexico.*

Note: Opened in Paris in Mar 1966 as *L'homme du Minnesota*; running time: 100 min. Released in Italy in 1965 and in Spain in Feb 1965 at 90 min as *Minnesota Clay*. Aguayo is also credited as Peppe Aguayo. Presented in an unidentified widescreen process.

THE MINOTAUR (Italy)   **F6.3201**
Agliani-Mordini–Illiria Film. *Dist* United Artists. May **1961** [c10 May 1961; LP22830]. Sd; col (Technicolor). 35mm (Totalscope). 95 min. [Also 92 min.]

Prod Giorgio Agliani, Gino Mordini, Rodolphe Solmsen. *Dir* Silvio Amadio. *2d Unit Dir* Giorgio Capitani. *Screenplay* Sandro Continenza, Gian Paolo Callegari. *English Adapt* Daniel Mainwaring. *Dir Photog* Aldo Giordani. *Art Dir* Piero Poletto. *Film Ed* Nella Nannuzzi. *Mus* Carlo Rustichelli. *Choreog* Adriano Vitale. *Sd* Mario Del Pezzo. *Asst Dir* Spartaco Conversi. *Prod Mgr* Pietro Merkel. *Cost* Peruzzi.

Cast: Bob Mathias (*Theseus, Prince of Athens*), Rosanna Schiaffino (*Ariadne/Phaedra*), Alberto Lupo (*Chryone*), Rick Battaglia (*Demetrius*), Nico Pepe (*Gerione*), Carlo Tamberlani (*King Minos*), Nerio Bernardi (*King Egeo [Aegeus]*), Tina Lattanzi, Elena Zareschi (*Queen Pasiphae [see note]*), Paul Muller (*doctor*), Tiziana Casetti (*Elea*), Alberto Plebani (*Xanto*), Susanne Loret (*Amphitrite*), Milo Malagoli (*The Minotaur*), Adriano Micantoni (*Sunis*), Amedeo Trilli (*Ctesiphorus*), Andrea Scotti (*Alcmene*), Vittorio Vaser (*Timon*), Vladimiro Picciafuochi (*jailer*).

Costume melodrama. In ancient Crete, Princess Phaedra learns that she has an identical twin sister, Ariadne, who was sent to Athens long ago because of a law requiring that one of each set of twins must be sacrificed to the Minotaur, a monster part-man and part-bull which lives in a labyrinth below the temple. To prevent her sister from threatening her ascendency to the throne of King Minos, Phaedra sends her lover, Chryone, to kill Ariadne, but the assassination attempt is thwarted by two young men, Theseus and Demetrius, who take Ariadne to the palace of Theseus' father, King Egeo [Aegeus] of Athens. Chryone threatens that unless Ariadne dies, Demetrius' father will be beheaded and his younger sister delivered to the Minotaur, who regularly devours sacrifice of a number of youths and virgins. Theseus and Demetrius return to Crete to save the people from the Minotaur but are captured by Phaedra. Demetrius and his family are killed, but Theseus pretends to love Phaedra to gain his freedom. Attempting to flee, he is fatally wounded and falls into the sea. The sea goddess Amphitrite restores him to health and falls in love with him, but, realizing that Theseus cannot return her love, she arms him with a charmed sword and sends him back to Crete. There he learns that Phaedra has imprisoned Ariadne. During a fight in the prison's torture chambers, Phaedra falls to her death in a pit of wild dogs. Theseus rescues Ariadne and then enters the labyrinth and slays the Minotaur. Ariadne follows him, trailing a gold thread from her dress which permits them to find their way out of the labyrinth. Theseus and Ariadne discover that in their absence the citizens of Crete have revolted and killed Chryone. With peace restored, King Minos outlaws human sacrifice forever. *Royalty. Twins. Sisters. Human sacrifice. Murder. Reviviscence. Prisons. Labyrinths. Swords. Crete. Athens. The Minotaur. Ariadne. Theseus. Phaedra. Amphitrite. Minos. Aegeus. Pasiphaë. Dogs.*

Note: Exteriors filmed in Italy and Yugoslavia. Rome opening: Jan 1961 as *Tesco contro il Minotauro.* Also known as *The Minotaur—The Wild Beast of Crete.* Sources conflict in crediting the actress portraying Queen Pasiphae.

A MINUTE TO PRAY, A SECOND TO DIE (United States/Italy)

F6.3202

Documento Film–Selmur Pictures. *Dist* Cinerama Releasing Corp. 22 May **1968** [New York opening]. Sd; col (Eastmancolor). 35mm. 103 min. [Also 97 min.]

Prod Albert Band. *Exec Prod* Selig J. Seligman. *Dir* Franco Giraldi. *Screenplay* Ugo Liberatore, Louis Garfinkle. *Story* Albert Band, Ugo Liberatore. *Photog* Aiace Parolin. *Art Dir* Massimiliano Capriccioli. *Set Dsgn* Guido Josia. *Film Ed* Alberto Gallitti. *Mus* Carlo Rustichelli. *Mus Dir* Bruno Nicolai. *Sd* Fernando Pescetelli. *Asst Dir* Franco Cirino. *Prod Mgr* Renato Iaboni. *Prod Supv* Fausto Saraceni. *Cost* Luciana Fortini. *Makeup* Michele Trimarchi. *Sp Eff* Erasmo Bacciucchi, Giovanni Corridoni.

Cast: Alex Cord (*Clay McCord*), Arthur Kennedy (*Roy Colby*), Robert Ryan (*Gov. Lem Carter*), Nicoletta Machiavelli (*Laurinda*), Mario Brega (*Kraut*), Renato Romano (*Cheap Charley*), Giampiero Albertini (*Fred Duskin*), Daniel Martin (*Father Santana*), Enzo Fiermonte (*Dr. Chase*), Pedro Canalejas (*Seminole*), Franco Lantieri (*Butler*), Osiride Pevarelli (*Fuzzy*), José Manuel Martín (*El Bailarín*), Antonio Molino Rojo (*Sein*), Rosita Palomar (*Ruby*), Paco Sanz (*barber*), Paolo Magalotti (*Sid*), Massimo Sarchielli (*Zack*), Ottaviano Dell'Acqua (*Clay, as a boy*), Alberto Dell'Acqua (*Ruby's son*), Antonio Vico (*Jonas*), Aldo Sambrell (*Jesus Maria*), Ivan Scratuglia, Silla Bettini.

Western melodrama. In the New Mexico Territory around 1870, gunman Clay McCord, who has a $10,000 dead-or-alive reward on his head, fears that he is doomed to die from periodic attacks of paralysis reminiscent of the epileptic fits that killed his father. Taking refuge in Escondido, a town filled with fugitive bandits converging there during the state of amnesty declared by Gov. Lem Carter, Clay is given shelter in the cabin of Laurinda, a half-starved young woman. Kraut, the town's outlaw boss, has his henchmen capture Clay and string him up by the hands. That night, however, Clay is rescued by a peddler, Cheap Charley Gamble, who informs him that Governor Carter wants to give him amnesty before the deadline is passed. Clay goes to a cabin outside the city of Tuscona [Tuscon?] for a prearranged meeting with the governor, but when Carter arrives, he finds Clay in the throes of one of his attacks. He summons U. S. Marshal Roy Colby, who is besieging Escondido, and Dr. Chase; and the physician, by extracting a bullet from the outlaw's arm, discovers that the paralytic seizures were brought about by the bullet's touching a nerve. Then, Kraut and his men attack the cabin and set it afire. In the ensuing battle, Dr. Chase and Marshal Colby are killed, but Clay and Carter escape through a cellar tunnel. Once on the outside, Clay kills off Kraut's gang and then rides to Tuscona to accept the governor's amnesty. As he rides out, he is shot by two bounty hunters who are unaware that there is no longer a price on his head. [In the shorter release version, McCord is not shot by the bounty hunters.] *Territorial governors. United States marshals. Outlaws. Bounty hunters. Peddlers. Paralysis. Amnesty. Epilepsy. New Mexico.*

Note: Produced in 1967 as *Escondido;* alternative Italian title: *Un minuto per pregare, un istante per morire.* Also known as *Dead or Alive.* Working titles: *McCord* and *Prodigal Gun.*

UN MINUTO PER PREGARE, UN ISTANTE PER MORIRE see A MINUTE TO PRAY, A SECOND TO DIE

THE MINX

F6.3203

Jara Productions. *Dist* Cambist Films. Sep **1969.** Sd; col (print by Movielab). 35mm. 84 min.

Pres by Lee Hessel. *Prod-Screenplay* Herbert Jaffey, Raymond Jacobs. *Dir* Raymond Jacobs. *Photog* Victor Petrashevic. *Film Ed* Larry Marinelli. *Mus Comp* Tom Dawes, Don Dannemann. *Mus Perf* The Cyrkle. *Sd* John Fodor.

Script Girl Elga Petrashevic. *Fashions* Teal Traina. *Sp Photog Eff* Raymond Jacobs. *Electrn* Janu Annus.

Cast: Jan Sterling (*Louise Baxter*), Robert Rodan (*Henry Baxter*), Shirley Parker (*Terry*), Adrienne Jalbert (*Nicole*), Robbie Heywood (*Susan*), Michael Beirne (*John Lawson*), Ned Cary (*Benjamin Thayer*), Allan Dellay (*Walter Harris*), Philip Faversham (*Charles Brennan*), William Gleason (*Sam Burke*), Russell Baker (*Oppenheimer*), Teal Traina (*himself*), The Cyrkle (*themselves*).

Melodrama. Ruthless, power-hungry Henry Baxter, president of Lawson Industries, makes plans for the corporate takeover of Benjamin Thayer's company, Eastern Devices, by covertly purchasing its stock through a Swiss bank. In order to remove Thayer as chairman of the board of Eastern Devices, Baxter must obtain the support of two board members to vote their proxies with his. Baxter arranges a weekend party at his hunting lodge for the two reluctant board members, and Baxter's brother-in-law, John Lawson, is told to provide women for the party. Unknown to Baxter, Lawson is secretly in league with Benjamin Thayer, and the women provided for the party—Terry, Nicole, and Susan—are experts in corporate spying and blackmail. Baxter needs the signature of his wife Louise, an older woman he married to gain control of Lawson Industries, on some essential documents; he persuades her to sign by making love to her. He then demands a divorce. She refuses and hires private detective Sam Burke to gather evidence that would make the separation impossible. Baxter discovers that the three party girls have been tape-recording and photographing the compromising sexual activities of the weekend, and he pursues Terry with a shotgun. Burke and Lawson give chase, and Burke kills Baxter in self-defense. Lawson takes the signed documents from Baxter's body, and on the following Monday morning, sitting at Baxter's desk, he tells Thayer that Lawson Industries will proceed with the takeover of Eastern Devices. *Executives. Detectives. Brothers-in-law. Spies. Marriage. Blackmail. Eavesdropping. Perfidy. Murder. Infidelity. Business competition. Documentation.*

Note: Location scenes were shot at Harlow's discotheque in New York City.

MIO FIGLIO NERONE see NERO'S MISTRESS

MIR VKHODYASHCHEMU see PEACE TO HIM WHO ENTERS

THE MIRACLE OF LOVE (West Germany)

F6.3204

Arca-Winston Films. *Dist* Times Film Corp. Jan **1969.** Sd; b&w with tinted sequences. 35mm. 83 min. *MPAA rating* X.

Prod-Screenplay Oswalt Kolle. *Exec Prod* Karin Wecker-Jacobsen. *Dir* Franz Josef Gottlieb. *Photog* Werner M. Lenz. *Mus* Johannes Rediske. *Titl Song (English Vers)* Curtis Lewis. *Sung by* Marge Dodson. *Scientific Cons* Dr. Hans Giese, Dr. Wolfgang Hochheimer.

Cast: Biggi Freyer, Katarina Haertel, Régis Vallée, Wilfred Gössler, Manfred Tümmler, Ortrud Gross, Matthias Grimm.

Sex instruction film. Source: Oswalt Kolle, *Das Wunder der Liebe* (Bielefeld, 1969). As Oswalt Kolle, a celebrated German columnist and marriage counselor, discusses the effects of sexual repression in marriage with two university professors, their exchange is illustrated by sequences depicting how the sexual development of the child is influenced by the repressions of a puritan society. Two dramatizations then demonstrate how unenlightened children often become unhappily married adults: After 6 months of marriage, Petra confesses to her husband, Thomas, that she has been unable to attain sexual satisfaction. Thomas' pride is hurt, and an argument ensues, but the couple are eventually able to examine their sexual inhibitions and hidden fears, enabling them to achieve mutual sexual satisfaction. Claudia and Martin, married 7 years, the parents of two children, face problems in their marriage stemming from Martin's preoccupation with his business and his neglect of Claudia's sexual needs. Claudia's frustration is expressed in a dream of self-gratification, and she blurts out her unhappiness to Martin in a moment of despair. Their sexual problems are resolved as Martin cancels his business plans and takes Claudia to the country hotel where they spent their first night together. *Businessmen. Professors. Columnists. Newlyweds. Marriage. Sex instruction. Sexuality. Autoeroticism. Marriage counsel. Sexual dysfunction. Puritanism. Dreams.*

Note: Released in West Germany in 1968 as *Oswalt Kolle: Das Wunder der Liebe—Sexualität in der Ehe;* running time: 81 min. A sequel, *Oswalt Kolle: Das Wunder der Liebe—Sexuelle Partnerschaft,* was also released in West Germany, but U. S. distribution is uncertain. Press material indicates that this is the first of a series, presenting the film as *Oswalt Kolle's "The Miracle of Love"* (Part 1—Sexuality in Marriage).

MIRACLE OF SAN SEBASTIAN see GUNS FOR SAN SEBASTIAN

THE MIRACLE OF SANTA'S WHITE REINDEER

F6.3205

Fantasy Films. 2 Nov **1963** [Phoenix, Arizona, opening]. Sd; b&w. 35mm. 60 min.

Cast: Charles Winninger, Fritz Feld, Ruthy Robinson, Dennis Holmes, Hal Smith.

Fantasy? No information about the precise nature of this film has been found. *Miracles. Santa Claus. Reindeer.*

Note: Also known as *The Miracle of the White Reindeer.*

MIRACLE OF THE WHITE STALLIONS   F6.3206

Walt Disney Productions. *Dist* Buena Vista Distribution Co. 29 Mar **1963** [Chicago opening; c11 Feb 1963; LP24526]. Sd (RCA); col (Technicolor). 35mm. 117 min.

Pres by Walt Disney. A Walt Disney Production. *Assoc Prod* Peter V. Herald. *Dir* Arthur Hiller. *Screenplay* A. J. Carothers. *Dir Photog* Günther Anders. *2d Unit Photog* Peter Pochlatko. *Art Dir* Werner Schlichting, Isabella Schlichting. *Film Ed* Alfred Srp, Cotton Warburton. *Mus* Paul Smith. *Orch* Franklyn Marks. *Song:* "Just Say, Auf Wiedersehen" Richard M. Sherman, Robert B. Sherman. *Sd* Kurt Schwarz, Robert O. Cook. *Asst Dir* Laci von Ronay. *Prod Mgr* Walter Tjaden, Robert Russ. *Script Supv* Auguste Bruenjes-Goldschwendt. *Cost* Leo Bei. *Makeup* Rudolf Ohlschmidt, Leopold Kuhnert. *Sp Eff* Paul Waldherr. *Tech Adv* Paul Waldherr. *Dial Coach* Kent McPherron. *Tech Supv in Vienna Filming* Alois Podhajsky, (Col.). *Adtl Lipizzan Horses* Lipica Stud Farms, Dakova Stud Farms.

Cast: Robert Taylor (*Colonel Podhajsky*), Lilli Palmer (*Verena Podhajsky*), Curt Jurgens (*General Tellheim*), Eddie Albert (*Rider Otto*), James Franciscus (*Major Hoffman*), John Larch (*General Patton*), Brigitte Horney (*Countess Arco-Valley*), Philip Abbott (*Colonel Reed*), Douglas Fowley (*U. S. general*), Charles Regnier (*General Stryker*), Fritz Wepper (*Rider Hans*), Günther Haenel (*Groom Sascha*), Hans Habietinek (*Innkeeper Hager*), Philo Hauser (*dispatcher*), Michael Janisch (*refugee leader*), Margarethe Dux (*woman railroad official*), Max Haufler (*engineer*), Robert Dietl (*German M. P. captain*), Josef Krastel (*Attendant Carl*), Peter Jost (*Kreisleiter*), Kurt Jager (*2d rider*), Olaf Tschierschke (*3d rider*), Herbert Prikopa (*Orderly Tellheim*), Erik Schuman (*German Captain Danhoff*), Helmut Janatsch (*intruder*), Michael Tellering (*Stryker's adjutant*), Hal Galili (*Brooklyn G. I.*), Harry Hornisch (*1st rider*), Hugo Lindinger, Larry Billman, Fritz Eckhardt.

Historical drama. Source: Alois Podhajsky, *Ein Leben für die Lipizzaner* (Munich, 1960). During the final critical months of World War II, Colonel Alois Podhajsky, the director of the Spanish Riding School in Vienna, is denied permission by General Stryker to evacuate the school's prized Lipizzan horses, endangered by the bombardment of the city. Desperate, he enlists the aid of General Tellheim, a sympathetic German who permits Podhajsky and his chief rider, Otto, to smuggle the white stallions to the safety of an old castle belonging to the Countess Arco-Valley. However, the mares had earlier been transferred to Czechoslovakia, and Podhajsky is now faced with the possibility of the rare breed becoming extinct. When an American advance guard arrives at the castle, Podhajsky stages a performance in order to persuade General Patton to include the Lipizzan mares as part of the Allied prisoner liberation program, and the Spanish Riding School becomes officially protected by the United States Army. Under the command of Colonel Reed, the Lipizzan mares are rounded up from Czechoslovakia before the arrival of the Russian force and returned to Podhajsky, thus insuring the continuation of the breed. Ten years later, on the 212th anniversary of the Riding Hall, the Lipizzans are once more performing at the Imperial Court in Vienna. *Equestrians. Bombardment. Riding schools. Horseshows. World War II. Vienna. Alois Podhajsky. George Smith Patton. United States Army. Germany—Army. Spanish Riding School. Horses.*

Note: Partially filmed in Vienna.

THE MIRACLE WORKER   F6.3207

Playfilms Productions. *Dist* United Artists. 23 May **1962** [New York opening; c23 May 1962; LP22317]. Sd; b&w. 35mm. 106 min.

Prod Fred Coe. *Dir* Arthur Penn. *Screenplay* William Gibson. *Dir Photog* Ernesto Caparros. *Camera Op* Jack Horton. *Art Dir* George Jenkins, Mel Bourne. *Film Ed* Aram Avakian. *Mus* Laurence Rosenthal. *Asst Dir* Larry Sturhahn, Ulu Grosbard. *Prod Mgr* Harrison Starr. *Script Supv* Maggie James. *Cost* Ruth Morley.

Cast: Anne Bancroft (*Annie Sullivan*), Patty Duke (*Helen Keller*), Victor Jory (*Captain Keller*), Inga Swenson (*Kate Keller*), Andrew Prine (*James Keller*), Kathleen Comegys (*Aunt Ev*), Beah Richards (*Viney*), Jack Hollander (*Mr. Anagnos*), Michael Darden (*Percy at 10*), Peggy Burke (*Helen at 7*), Dale Ellen Bethea (*Martha at 10*), Walter Wright, Jr. (*Percy at 8*), Donna Bryan (*Martha at 7*), Mindy Sherwood (*Helen at 5*), Diane Bryan (*Martha at 5*), Keith Moore (*Percy at 6*), Michele Farr (*Young Annie at 10*), Alan Howard (*Young Jimmie at 8*), Judith Lowry (*1st crone*), William F. Haddock (*2d crone*), Helen Ludlam (*3d crone*), Grant Code (*doctor*), Belle (*herself, a dog*).

Biographical drama. Source: William Gibson, *The Miracle Worker* (New York opening: 19 Oct 1959). In 1887 Annie Sullivan arrives in Tuscumbia, Alabama, to undertake the seemingly impossible task of teaching deaf, blind, 7-year-old Helen Keller "language" through the sense of touch. Blind herself as a child and hardened by both her early years in institutions and the death of her younger, crippled brother, Annie realizes that if Helen is to be helped she must be removed from the pampering influence of her mother and the shouting domination of her father. Though Annie succeeds in getting the family to allow her 2 weeks alone with Helen in a small garden house on the Keller property, the high-spirited and strong-willed child opposes her at every turn. At the end of the 2 weeks, however, Helen has learned to dress herself, eat with a fork, and understand the alphabet of touch. She is still unable, however, to comprehend that the words she spells are names for the objects she touches. Annie asks for another week alone with Helen, but the parents, seeing the progress that has been made, insist on bringing the child back into the household. There, she attempts to revert to her former willful savagery, but Annie again opposes her. Following an outburst at the dining room table, Annie drags the child to the pump on the front lawn and forces her to refill a pitcher from which she spilled the water. As the water pours over her hands, the sudden realization that what she feels is w-a-t-e-r dawns on the child, and she grasps Annie's hand and spells out the word. Wildly excited, Helen races about spelling the name of everything she touches—pump, tree, porch, bell, mother, father. Finally, Annie identifies herself by spelling out "teacher." *Tutors. Cripples. Blindness. Deafness. Brother-sister relationship. Family life. Tuscumbia (Alabama). Anne (Sullivan) Macy. Helen Keller.*

Note: Exteriors filmed in New Jersey.

MIRAGE   F6.3208

Universal Pictures. 26 May **1965** [New York opening; c5 Jun 1965; LP33026]. Sd (Westrex); b&w. 35mm. 107 min. [Copyright length: 109 min.]

Prod Harry Keller. *In Charge of Prod* Edward Muhl. *Dir* Edward Dmytryk. *Screenplay* Peter Stone. *Dir Photog* Joseph MacDonald. *Art Dir* Alexander Golitzen, Frank Arrigo. *Set Decor* John McCarthy, John Austin. *Film Ed* Ted J. Kent. *Mus* Quincy Jones. *Mus Supv* Joseph Gershenson. *Sd* Waldon O. Watson, Corson Jowett. *Asst Dir* Terence Nelson. *Unit Prod Mgr* Wallace Worsley. *Gowns Dsgn* Jean Louis. *Makeup* Bud Westmore. *Hairstyles* Larry Germain. *Matte Supv* Albert Whitlock.

Cast: Gregory Peck (*David Stillwell*), Diane Baker (*Shela*), Walter Matthau (*Ted Caselle*), Kevin McCarthy (*Josephson*), Jack Weston (*Lester*), Leif Erickson (*Major Crawford*), Walter Abel (*Charles Calvin*), George Kennedy (*Willard*), Robert H. Harris (*Dr. Broden*), Anne Seymour (*Frances Calvin*), House Jameson (*Bo*), Hari Rhodes (*Lieutenant Franken*), Syl Lamont (*Benny*), Eileen Baral (*Irene*), Neil Fitzgerald (*Joe Turtle*), Franklin Cover (*group leader*).

Melodrama. Source: Walter Ericson, *Fallen Angel* (Boston, 1952). As New York City's Unidyne Building is thrown into darkness, peace worker Charles Calvin falls from his 27th-floor window. David Stillwell descends the long stairway that leads to street level, but he soon realizes that he cannot remember people he meets, among them Shela, who apparently know him. When he returns to the building, he finds that there are no stairs and that offices he has remembered do not exist. Going to his own apartment, he meets Lester, a gunman who wants to take him to "the Major." David knocks Lester unconscious, then goes to the police, but his story is not believed because he cannot remember where or when he was born. He goes to psychiatrist Dr. Broden, who refuses to help him for fear of becoming involved with the police. Detective Ted Caselle takes on the challenge but is quickly murdered in his office. Threatened now by two gunmen, David returns to Dr. Broden, and together they deduce that he is a physiochemist and that he lost his memory when he saw his best friend, Calvin, fall to his death. Now it is recalled that David had discovered the secret of neutralizing radioactivity at its source, that he had taken his discovery to Calvin, and that then he had attempted to destroy the formula when it became apparent that Calvin, for mercenary gain, wanted to pass it on to his business associate, Major Crawford. Trying to prevent the burning of the formula, Calvin fell to his death. Now recalling everything, David returns to the Unidyne Building and comes face to face with Crawford. Intent on obtaining the formula, Crawford threatens David, but Shela comes to his rescue. *Pacifists. Psychiatrists. Detectives. Chemists. Police. Amnesia. Murder. Blackout. Radiation. Secret formulas. New York City.*

Note: Location scenes filmed in New York City.

MIRIAM *see* **TRILOGY**

THE MISADVENTURES OF MERLIN JONES   F6.3209

Walt Disney Productions. *Dist* Buena Vista Distribution Co. 5 Feb **1964** [Saint Louis opening; c20 Nov 1963; LP26808]. Sd (RCA); col (Technicolor). 35mm. 88 min. [Copyright length: 91 min.]

Pres by Walt Disney. A Walt Disney Production. *Assoc Prod* Ron Miller. *Dir* Robert Stevenson. *Screenplay* Tom August, Helen August. *Story* Bill Walsh. *Dir Photog* Edward Colman. *Art Dir* Carroll Clark, William H. Tuntke. *Set Decor* Emile Kuri, Hal Gausman. *Sp Titl* Bill Justice, Xavier Atencio. *Film Ed* Cotton Warburton. *Mus* Buddy Baker. *Orch* Bob Brunner. *Song* Richard M.

Sherman, Robert B. Sherman. *Sung by* Annette Funicello. *Sd* Robert O. Cook. *Mus Ed* Evelyn Kennedy. *Asst Dir* Joseph L. McEveety. *Cost* Chuck Keehne, Gertrude Casey. *Makeup* Pat McNalley. *Hairstyles* La Rue Matheron.

Cast: Tommy Kirk *(Merlin Jones)*, Annette Funicello *(Jennifer)*, Leon Ames *(Judge Holmby)*, Stuart Erwin *(Police Captain Loomis)*, Alan Hewitt *(Professor Shattuck)*, Connie Gilchrist *(Mrs. Gossett)*, Dal McKennon *(Detective Hutchins)*, Norman Grabowski *(Norman)*, Kelly Thordsen *(Muller)*, Stanley *(himself, a chimpanzee)*, June Ellis.

Comedy. College student Merlin Jones, constantly involved with mind experiments, devises an electronic helmet that when connected to an electroencephalographic tape records mental activity. Wearing the helmet while driving, he is stopped by traffic officer Muller and brought before Judge Holmby, who suspends his license. Returning to his laboratory, Merlin discovers accidentally that his equipment enables him to read minds. Judge Holmby visits the coffeeshop where Merlin has a part-time job, and through his powers Merlin discovers that the judge is planning a crime. He rushes to the police with the information but is brushed aside as a crackpot. Merlin and Jennifer, his girl friend, break into the judge's home looking for evidence but are arrested by the police. The judge confesses that he is the popular detective novelist Lex Fortis, and requests that this identity remain a secret. Merlin's next experimentation involves hypnotism. After successfully hypnotizing Stanley, the laboratory chimpanzee, into standing up for his rights against Norman, his bullying keeper, Merlin brawls with Norman, and as a result he is brought again before Judge Holmby. Fascinated by his experiments, the judge enlists Merlin's aid in devising a plot for his next mystery. Working on the assumption that no honest person can be made to commit a crime against his will, Merlin hypnotizes the judge and commands him to steal Stanley. Surprised when the judge actually commits the crime, Merlin and Jennifer return the chimp but are themselves charged with the theft. Unaware of his part in the crime, the judge sentences Merlin to jail. Jennifer, outraged at the injustice, convinces Judge Holmby of his own guilt, and he admits that perhaps there is a little dishonesty in everyone. *Students. Police. Judges. Novelists. College life. Electronics. Mental telepathy. Theft. Hypnotism. Honesty. Laboratories. Coffeeshops. Chimpanzees.*

MISCONDUCT   F6.3210
Continental Films—J. D. Palma—Herb Rossin. *Dist* CIP Ltd. 12 Aug **1966** [Knoxville, Tennessee, opening]. Sd; b&w with col sequences. 35mm. [Feature length assumed.]

Screenplay Earle Silver. *Cinematog* Jerry Denby, S. N. Johnsen. *Film Ed* C & W Associates. *Mus* Steve Karmen. *Titl Song* Bill Lucas.

Cast: Shad Higgins *(Harry Lovelace)*, Robin Zepp *(Felicia)*, Lisa Vohn *(nurse)*, Darlene Bennett *(secretary)*, Marianne *(Margo)*, Alvin Busch *(doctor)*, Penny Marleton *(Penny)*.

Comedy. Satyrist Harry Lovelace is advised by his doctor to abstain from sex. The doctor gives him a prescription as a substitute for sex and warns him that an overdose may cause undesirable side effects. The pills prove effective when several women try to seduce Harry, but he takes too many and imagines five naked women forcing themselves upon him. The doctor sends him to a secluded farmhouse with his faithful nurse, Arlene, who finds Harry irresistible. As a result, Harry takes an overdose, which brings back the vision of the five naked women. Harry escapes and returns, cured, to his doctor. Harry reveals that the solution to his problem was to give in to it and make love whenever the urge arose—with Felicia, his newfound, understanding girl friend. *Physicians. Nurses. Satyriasis. Seduction. Hallucinations.*

THE MISFITS   F6.3211
Seven Arts Productions. *Dist* United Artists. 1 Feb **1961** [New York opening; c1 Feb 1961; LP18965]. Sd; b&w. 35mm. 124 min.

Prod Frank E. Taylor. *Dir* John Huston. *2d Unit Dir* Tom Shaw. *Screenplay* Arthur Miller. *Dir Photog* Russell Metty. *Camera* Ledger Haddow. *1st Camera* Louis Schwartz. *2d Camera* Edwin Pyle. *Asst Camera* Michael Moramarco. *2d Unit Photog* Rex Wimpy. *2d Unit Camera Op* Harry Underwood, Richard Kelley. *Art Dir* Stephen Grimes, William Newberry. *Set Decor* Frank McKelvy. *Main Titl* George Nelson & Co. *Film Ed* George Tomasini. *Asst Film Ed* Stewart Linder. *Neg Cutter* Connie Roese. *Mus Comp & Cond* Alex North. *Sd Mix* Philip Mitchell. *Sd Rec* R. D. Cook. *Boom Op* Al Marsh. *Asst Dir* Carl Beringer, John Gaudioso, Tom Shaw. *Asst to the Prod* Edward Parone. *Prod Mgr* C. O. Erickson. *Script Supv* Angela Allen, Frank Remsden. *Cost* Jesse Munden. *Wardrobe* Shirlee Strahm. *Makeup Artist* Frank LaRue, Frank Prehoda, Allan Snyder. *Body Makeup* Bunny Gardel. *Hairstyles* Agnes Flanagan. *Sp Eff* Cline Jones. *Prop Master* Ross Burke. *Key Grip* Charles Cowie. *Dog Trainer* Cindy James. *Constr Coöd* Bud Pine. *Still Photog* Al St. Hilaire. *Dial Coach* J. Lewis Smith, Paula Strasberg. *Painter Gang Boss* Robert Stephen. *Stuntmen* John Day, Jim Palen, Richard Pasco, Chuck Roberson. *Gaffer* Lefty Budman. *Wranglers* Bobby Davenport, Bruce Galbraith, Bill Jones, Buford Randall, James (Buddy) Sherwood.

Cast: Clark Gable *(Gay Langland)*, Marilyn Monroe *(Roslyn Taber)*, Montgomery Clift *(Perce Howland)*, Thelma Ritter *(Isabelle Steers)*, Eli Wallach *(Guido)*, James Barton *(The Old Man in the Bar)*, Estelle Winwood *(The Church Lady)*, Kevin McCarthy *(Roslyn's husband)*, Dennis Shaw *(young boy in bar)*, Philip Mitchell *(Charles Steers)*, Walter Ramage *(old groom)*, Peggy Barton *(young bride)*, J. Lewis Smith *(fresh cowboy in bar)*, Marietta Tree *(Susan)*, Bobby LaSalle *(bartender)*, Ryall Bowker *(man in bar)*, Ralph Roberts *(ambulance attendant)*.

Drama. While staying at Isabelle Steers' roominghouse in Reno, newly-divorced showgirl Roslyn Taber meets Gay Langland, a ruggedly independent, aging cowboy. Immediately attracted to each other, they move into a partly completed ranchhouse belonging to Gay's friend Guido, a part-time mechanic who has turned into an aimless wanderer since the death of his wife in childbirth. The brief idyll ends when Guido devises a plan for rounding up some mustangs, wild horses often termed "misfits" because they are too small for riding. Gay and Guido need a third partner and take on Perce Howland, a battered and disillusioned rodeo performer. When Roslyn learns that the mustangs are to be sold to a dogfood manufacturer, she is revolted by this brutal destruction of life and begs Gay to call off the hunt. But he refuses, and the three men, accompanied by the reluctant Roslyn, ride up to the salt flats in the Nevada foothills. Six horses are driven out onto the flats by Guido's flivver plane and then chased and roped from a speeding truck. Sickened by the pathetic plight of the creatures, Roslyn appeals to the sensitive Perce, who sets the animals free. Enraged by this defiance of his authority, Gay recaptures the lead stallion and succeeds in subduing it. Then, having asserted his will, he sets the animal free. More understanding and respectful of each other, Gay and Roslyn return home, while Perce and Guido go their separate ways. *Showgirls. Cowboys. Mechanics. Wanderers. Roundups. Ranches. Airplanes. Salt flats. Reno. Nevada. Horses.*

Note: Location scenes filmed in and around Reno and Dayton, Nevada.

MISHPACHAT SIMCHON *see* **THE SIMCHON FAMILY**

MISS JESSICA IS PREGNANT   F6.3212
Triskele, Ltd. *Dist* Joseph Brenner Associates. 23 Sep **1970** [Greensboro, North Carolina, opening]. Sd; b&w. 35mm. 82 min. *MPAA rating* R.

Prod Franklin Miller, J. L. Anderson. *Dir* J. L. Anderson. *Screenplay* Doug Rapp, Franklin Miller, J. L. Anderson. *Photog* David Prince, Brian Blauser, Art Stifel. *Film Ed* J. L. Anderson, Franklin Miller. *Sd Rec* Bill Heim.

Cast: Larue Hall *(Jessie)*, Ted Heim *(Carl)*, Marj Johnson *(The Mother)*, John Crawford *(The Father)*, Tracy Smith *(Jessie's sister)*, David Ayres *(gas station owner)*.

Domestic drama. In southeastern Ohio, an old hillbilly, once a contented coal miner, must earn his living by subsistence farming. His eldest son, Carl, does most of the farm work, while his wife spends her time flirting in the local tavern. Jessie, the eldest daughter, has an affair with Carl, her half-brother. Although he flees to Columbus when their father learns that Jessie is pregnant, Carl returns to take Jessie away from the hostile environment. *Farmers. Coal miners. Rural life. Family life. Poverty. Brother-sister relationship. Incest. Infidelity. Pregnancy. Bars. Ohio. Columbus (Ohio).*

Note: Filmed in 1965 in and around Canaan, Ohio. Shown at the 1967 Pesaro Film Festival as *Spring Night, Summer Night.* Also known as *Jessica.* Ted Heim is also known as Ted Garrotte.

MISS JUDE *see* **THE TRUTH ABOUT SPRING**

MISS MUERTE *see* **THE DIABOLICAL DR. Z**

MISS NYMPHET'S ZAP-IN   F6.3213
Creative Film Enterprises. *Dist* Mayflower Pictures. **1970**. Sd; col (Eastmancolor). 35mm. 76 min.

Prod-Dir Sheldon Seymour. *Dir Cinematog* William R. Johnson. *Camera Op* Alex Ameripoor. *Ed Supv* Peter Guilfhoyle. *Mus Coörd* Larry Wellington. *Orig Mus* Robert Lewis. *Mus Backgrounds* The Zaps. *Sd Engr* Pat Dray. *Prod Mgr* Bethel Buckalew. *Unit Mgr* Dick Ozmun. *Prod Coörd* Pam Eddy. *Ch Electrn* Jim Andrian.

Cast: Dixie Donovan, Tony Mark, Christine Murray, Ed Pawlin, Sonora, Mij Shippen, Jessica Leland, Phyllis Stangel, Wendy Winders, Sonald South, Cathy Adams, Sonny Seymour, Elsie Wine, Ed Kelly, Michael Cheal, Astrid Stellar, Fern Tom, Robin Courtney, Tai Hamilton, Sylvia Sark, Tom Rogers, Alex Eliot, Donna Bradley, Bud Bogan, Mary Jane Shippen, Tony Halavah, Debbie Osborne, Paula Renault.

Comedy. The film presents a series of sex comedy skits: a French governess is seen with painted breasts; a couple have sexual intercourse on the *Candid Camera* television show; Little Lord Fauntleroy explores the female body; a "white hunter" is captured by African women; a female spy uncovers a secret password; and two topless dancers experiment with a new dance. *French. Governesses. Africans. Spies. Go-go dancers. Nudity. Lesbianism. Little Lord*

Fauntleroy. "Candid Camera".

Note: Also known as *Zap-In*. Sheldon Seymour is a pseudonym for Herschell Gordon Lewis.

MISSION BATANGAS   F6.3214
Batangas Productions–Diba Productions. *Dist* Manson Distributing Corp. Nov **1968**. Sd; col (Technicolor). 35mm. 100 min.

Prod-Dir Keith Larsen. *Screenplay* Lew Antonio. *Story* Keith Larsen. *Dir Photog* Herbert Theis. *Camera Asst* Francisco Magpayo. *Film Ed* Tony Di Marco, George Schrader. *Sd* Levy Principe. *Asst Dir* Francisco MacLang. *Prod Mgr* Vicente Nayve. *Prod Supv* James Cranston. *Prod Asst* Tony Dungan, Isidoro Rueda. *Script Supv* Maria Abelardo. *Makeup* Lily Joaquino. *Hairstyles* Cecilia Abelardo. *Sp Eff* Santos Hilario. *Gaffer* Silverstre Carianga, Jr.

Cast: Dennis Weaver *(Chip Corbett)*, Vera Miles *(Joan Barnes)*, Keith Larsen *(Colonel Turner)*, Leopoldo Salcedo, Helen Thompson, Vic Diaz, Bruno Punzalan, Fred Galang, Tony Dungan, Ernesto La Guardia.

War melodrama. As the Japanese invade the Philippines in 1942, U. S. pilot Chip Corbett agrees, for a price, to fly a Filipino war profiteer to safety. Forced to crashland on Corregidor, Corbett meets Colonel Turner, the commandant of the island, and missionary nurse Joan Barnes, who is aiding a small garrison in attempting to remove the Philippine government's stock of gold bullion to a waiting submarine. Before they can transfer the gold from a barge, however, the submarine is sunk by the Japanese. A decision is then made to sink the barge with a homemade bomb so that the gold will be safe at the bottom of the bay until the war is over. Corbett's interest in the gold increases, and he volunteers to drop the bomb if a plane can be found. When Joan says that they can obtain an aircraft at a missionary station some miles away, the small band of Americans and Filipinos set out through headhunter country. Although Colonel Turner is killed in a skirmish with the Japanese, Joan's friendship with the headhunters is rewarded when the natives use blowpipes against the pursuing enemy. Nevertheless, Joan is mortally wounded during the jungle fighting and dies when they reach the mission. Corbett, who had fallen in love with Joan, dedicates himself to the Filipinos' cause and flies off with the bomb, aware that his mission will probably be suicidal. *Air pilots. Nurses. Profiteers. Filipinos. Missionaries. Headhunters. Sabotage. Jungles. Gold. Submarines. Missions. World War II. Corregidor. Batangas. United States Army. Japan— Army.*

Note: Filmed on location in the Philippines in 1967. Prerelease titles: ... *Except People Get Killed* and *Batangas*.

MISSION BLOODY MARY (France/Italy/Spain)   F6.3215
Fida Cinematografica–Productions Jacques Roitfeld–Epoca Films–Estela Films. *Dist* Telefilm of Canada. 16 Aug **1967** [Seekonk, Massachusetts, opening]. Sd; col (Technicolor). 35mm (Techniscope). 102 min.

Dir Terence Hathaway. *Screenplay* Sandro Continenza, Marcello Coscia, Leonardo Martin. *Photog* Juan Julio Baena. *Art Dir* Franco Lolli, Nedo Azzini, Ramiro Gómez García. *Film Ed* Enzo Alfonsi, Petra Nieva. *Mus Comp & Cond* Angelo Francesco Lavagnino. *Prod Mgr* A. Campitelli, Manuel Pérez García.

Cast: Ken Clark *(Dick Malloy)*, Helga Liné *(Elsa Freeman)*, Mitsouko *(Kuan)*, Philippe Hersent *(Lester)*, Umberto Raho *(Professor Betz)*, Susan Terry *(Juanita)*, Antonio Gradoli, Andrea Scotti, Brand Lyonell, Peter Blades, Peter Bosch, Franca Polesello, Pulloa Coy, Mirko Ellis, Dario Michaelis, Erik Bianchi, Alfredo Mayo, Ignazio Leone, Tomás Blanco, John Fordan, Félix Fernández.

Adventure melodrama. Dick Malloy, CIA agent 077, is assigned to recover a powerful nuclear bomb called "Bloody Mary," stolen by the Black Lily, an international spy ring. In Paris, Dick contacts fellow agent Dr. Elsa Freeman of the Betz Clinic, who leads him to Kuan, a Chinese stripteaser and syndicate member. Although Kuan is killed before she can provide valuable information, Dick learns that the weapon is aboard the freighter *Trinidad*, in Barcelona, en route to Athens. His life threatened after boarding the ship, Dick escapes near Athens and contacts CIA agents Elsa and Lester. After several encounters with Russian and Chinese agents, Dick is abducted. Escaping, he recovers the bomb and reveals Elsa and Professor Betz to be the Black Lily's Chinese double agent and mastermind. Although Betz temporarily eludes capture, he is apprehended while boarding the *Trinidad* in Monte Carlo. *Secret agents. Physicians. Chinese. Stripteasers. Russians. Masterminds. Theft. Espionage. Murder. Abduction. Nuclear weapons. Syndicates. Freighters. Paris. Barcelona. Athens. Monte Carlo. United States—Central Intelligence Agency.*

Note: Location scenes filmed in Paris, Barcelona, Madrid, Rome, Athens, and Istanbul. Opened in Rome in Jul 1965 as *Agente 077—missione Bloody Mary*; in Paris in Jan 1966 as *Opération lotus bleu*; running time: 90 min; in Madrid in Sep 1966 as *La muerte espera en Atenas*; running time: 104 min. Alternative Spanish titles: *Agente 077, mision Bloody Mary* and *Operación loto azul*. Terence Hathaway is a pseudonym for Sergio Grieco.

MISSION MARS   F6.3216
Sagittarius Productions–Red Ram Productions. *Dist* Allied Artists. Jul **1968** [c1 Apr 1968; LP35650]. Sd; col (Berkey). 35mm. 87 min. [Copyright length: 95 min.]

Prod Everett Rosenthal. *Exec Prod* Mort Fallick. *Assoc Prod* Lawrence Applebaum. *Dir* Nicholas Webster. *Screenplay* Mike St. Clair. *Story* Aubrey Wisberg. *Photog* Clifford Poland. *Prod Dsgn* Hank Aldrich. *Film Ed* Paul Jordan. *Supv Ed* Michael Calamari. *Mus* Berge Kalajian, Gus Pardalis. *Songs Sung by* The Forum Quorum. *Sd* Sanford Rackow, John W. Barry. *Asst Dir* Sal Scoppa. *Cost* Grover Cole. *Sp Eff* Haberstroh Studios.

Cast: Darren McGavin *(Mike Blaiswick)*, Nick Adams *(Nick Grant)*, George De Vries *(Duncan)*, Heather Hewitt *(Edith Blaiswick)*, Michael De Beausset *(Cliff Lawson)*, Shirley Parker *(Alice Grant)*, Bill E. Kelly *(Russian astronaut)*, Chuck Zink *(Chuck)*, Ralph Miller *(Simpson)*, Art Barker *(doctor)*, Monroe Myers *(Lawson's aide)*.

Science fiction melodrama. U. S. astronauts Mike Blaiswick, Nick Grant, and Duncan blast off from Cape Kennedy on the first American space flight to Mars. As they approach their rendezvous with an orbiting supply ship, they are horrified to see the frozen, lifeless bodies of two Russian astronauts, the victims of an unsuccessful Soviet flight to Mars. Upon landing on the planet, the astronauts find the body of another Russian. While Grant takes the body back to the spaceship, Mike and Duncan are attacked by a strange mechanical object called a polarite, which is activated by the sun's rays. After immobilizing the polarite, they contact Earth and are ordered to terminate their mission immediately. Before they can do so, however, a huge glowing sphere neutralizes the ship's rocket power and engulfs Duncan. Mike and Grant notice that the Russian astronaut has returned to life, and he tells the Americans that the polarite can only be stopped by blocking its source of solar energy. Though it costs him his life, Grant uses his laser gun to temporarily reduce the magnetic hold of the planet, thereby enabling Mike and the Russian to return safely to Earth. *Astronauts. Russians. Space exploration. Reviviscence. Self-sacrifice. Spaceships. Laser. Solar energy. Cape Kennedy. Mars (planet).*

Note: Filmed on location in and around Miami.

MISSION STARDUST (Italy/Spain/West Germany)   F6.3217
P. E. A.–Aitor Films–Tefi. *Dist* Times Film Corp. Oct **1968** [Los Angeles opening]. Sd; col (Technicolor). 35mm (Techniscope). 95 min.

Dir Primo Zeglio. *Assoc Dir* Ricardo Sanz. *Screenplay* Karlheinz Vogelmann, Karlheinz Scheer, Sergio Donati, Primo Zeglio, Federico de Urrutia. *Story* Karlheinz Vogelmann. *Photog* Riccardo Pallottini, Manuel Merino. *Art Dir* Jaime Pérez Cubero. *Film Ed* Renato Cinquini. *Mus* Antón García Abril. *Song* Marcello Giombini. *Asst Dir* Renato Moretti. *Prod Supv* Jesús García Gárgoles.

Cast: Lang Jeffries *(Maj. Perry Rhodan)*, Essy Persson *(Thora)*, Gianni Rizzo *(criminal leader)*, John Karlsen *(Kress)*, Pinkas Braun *(Rotkin)*, Luis Dávila *(Captain Bull)*, Daniel Martín, Joachim Hansen, Ann Smyrner, Stefano Sibaldi, Janos Bartha, Giuseppe Addobbati, José Jaspe.

Science fiction melodrama. Based on the series of *Perry Rhodan* novels begun by: Clark Darlton. A group of American astronauts led by Maj. Perry Rhodan land on the moon and find Thora and Kress, two space beings from an advanced civilization stranded with their spaceship crippled. Kress is dying of a strange malady, discovered to be leukemia, and the entire group flies to East Africa in search of a famous blood specialist. A group of spies discover that Kress and Thora represent a form of life whose technology is greatly advanced beyond Earth's, and members of the spy ring disguised as the physician and his nurses attempt to capture the space people. Even though Major Rhodan's crew includes a traitor, the astronauts and their space friends defeat the spies, but some of them escape. Thora uses her advanced weapons to destroy their refuge, however, and Kress is cured when the real physician is found. It is then decided that the technology of the faraway planet should be withheld from Earth, since the human race appears ill-equipped to handle such power and responsibility. *Spacemen. Astronauts. Spies. Physicians. Nurses. Traitors. Technology. Impersonation. Conspiracy. Cancer. Spaceships. The Moon. East Africa.*

Note: Opened in Rome in Aug 1967 as *4... 3... 2... 1... morte*; running time: 95 min. Released in West Germany in Oct 1967 as *Perry Rhodan—SOS aus dem Weltall*; running time: 79 min; in Spain as *Órbita mortal*; running time 92 min.

MISSION TO HELL see SAVAGE!

MISSION TO HONG KONG see RED-DRAGON

MISSISSIPPI MERMAID (France/Italy)   F6.3218
Films du Carrosse–Les Productions Artistes Associés–Produzioni Associate Delphos. *Dist* Lopert Pictures, United Artists. 10 Apr **1970** [New York opening; c10 Apr 1970; LP38882]. Sd; col (DeLuxe). 35mm (Dyaliscope). 123 min. *MPAA rating* GP.

Prod Marcel Berbert. *Dir-Adapt-Dial* François Truffaut. *Dir Photog* Denys Clerval. *Camera* Jean Chiabaut. *Asst Camera* Jacques Assuerus. *Art Dir* Claude Pignot. *Film Ed* Agnès Guillemot. *Mus* Antoine Duhamel. *Sd* René Levert. *Sd Rec* Guy Chichignoud. *Asst Dir* Jean-José Richer, Jean-François Détré. *Prod Mgr* Claude Miler. *Script Girl* Suzanne Schiffman. *Gen Mgr* Roland Thénot. *Makeup* Michel Deruelle, J. P. Eychenne. *Hairdresser* Jacqueline Anatole. *Set Photog* Léonard de Reamy.

Cast: Jean-Paul Belmondo *(Louis Mahé [Durand, dubbed vers?])*, Catherine Deneuve *(Julie Roussel/Marion)*, Michel Bouquet *(Comolli)*, Nelly Borgeaud *(Berthe Roussel)*, Marcel Berbert *(Jardine)*, Martine Ferrière *(landlady)*, Roland Thénot *(Richard)*, Yves Drouhet.

Romantic melodrama. Source: William Irish, *Waltz Into Darkness* (New York, 1947). Louis Mahé, a millionaire tobacco plantation owner on the island of Réunion, has become engaged through the personals columns of a French newspaper to Julie Roussel and awaits her arrival on the steamer *Mississippi*. He is greeted by a young woman who surprises him by her beauty and explains that she sent her sister's photo to assure the sincerity of his intentions. They quickly marry, and Louis's adoration of his new bride makes him overlook incongruities with Julie's description of herself in her letters. One day, Louis's bride absconds after emptying his bank accounts. Louis meets Julie's sister, Berthe Roussel, who informs him that the woman he married was not Julie; together they hire a private detective, Comolli, to track down the impostor and find Berthe's sister. En route by plane to Nice, Louis is suddenly stricken ill. Recuperating in a sanitarium, he sees Julie on television, dancing at a nightclub in Antibes. He travels there and hides in her hotel room, intent on killing her. She offers no resistance, but, explaining that her name is Marion, she tells him of her past, including years spent in prison, and of her association with a heartless gangster, Richard. Richard was with her on the *Mississippi* when they met Julie Roussel and learned of her forthcoming marriage. He had fabricated a plot to kill Julie and send Marion in her place to rob Louis; and afterwards Richard had forced her to go through with the robbery. Louis quickly forgives Marion, and they decide to live together in France on profits from the plantation. In Aix-en-Provence their happiness is interrupted by Comolli, who has discovered Julie's murder. After trying in vain to bribe the detective to drop the case, Louis shoots him and buries him in the wine cellar of their house. He flees with Marion to Lyons, but she grows increasingly dissatisfied with their fugitive existence and longs to enjoy a life of luxury in Paris. To obtain funds, Louis returns briefly to Réunion and sells his share in the plantation, but upon his return he finds the police on their trail. They are again forced to flee, leaving behind the money; penniless, they hide out in a cabin in the French Alps, but Marion is restless and irritable. Louis becomes increasingly ill, and one day he becomes aware that Marion has been administering quantities of rat poison in his coffee. Near collapse, he makes an attempt to escape, but Marion brings him back to the cabin. He reveals his knowledge of her plan, and, urging her to fill his coffee glass, he affirms his acceptance of his fate, his lack of regrets, and his overwhelming love for her. Struck with shame, Marion knocks the glass from Louis's hand and vows to make amends. As he regains his strength, they flee the hut together into the snow. *Confidence women. Detectives. Plantations. Fugitives. Impersonation. Wealth. Marriage. Robbery. Murder. Poisoning. Ships. Sanitariums. Nightclubs. Hotels. Réunion. Nice. Antibes. Lyons. Alps. Aix-en-Provence. "Marseillaise" (Renoir).*

Note: Location scenes filmed in Réunion, Antibes, Aix-en-Provence, Lyons, and near Grenoble. Dedicated to Jean Renoir; a clip from Renoir's *La Marseillaise* appears in the film in an exposition of Réunion's history. Paris opening: Jun 1969 as *La sirène du Mississippi*; released in Italy in 1970(?) as *La mia droga si chiama Julie*.

MR. ARKADIN (Spain/Switzerland)   F6.3219

Filmorsa-Cervantes Films-Sevilla Studios. *Dist* Dan Talbot, Cari Releasing Corp. 11 Oct **1962** [New York opening]. Sd; b&w. 35mm. 99 min. [Also reviewed at 93 min.]

A Mercury Production. *Exec Prod* Louis Dolivet. *Dir-Screenplay-Story* Orson Welles. *Dir Photog* Jean Bourgoin. *Art Dir* Orson Welles. *Set Dsgn* Luis Pérez Espinosa, Gil Parrondo, Francisco Prósper. *Film Ed* Renzo Lucidi. *Mus* Paul Misraki. *Sd* Jacques Lebreton. *Sd Rec* Jacques Carrère. *Asst Dir* José María Ochoa, José Luis de la Serna, Isidoro Martínez Ferry. *Prod Mgr* Michel Boisrond, Juan Solórzano Piñares. *Cost* Orson Welles.

Cast: Orson Welles *(Gregory Arkadin)*, Robert Arden *(Guy Van Stratten)*, Paola Mori *(Raina)*, Michael Redgrave *(Burgomil Trebitsch)*, Patricia Medina *(Mily)*, Akim Tamiroff *(Jakob Zouk)*, Mischa Auer *(The Professor)*, Katina Paxinou *(Sophie)*, Jack Watling *(Marquis of Rutleigh)*, Grégoire Aslan *(Bracco)*, Peter Van Eyck *(Tadeus)*, Suzanne Flon *(Baroness Nagel)*, Frédéric O'Brady *(Oskar)*, Tamara Shane *(The Blonde)*, Gordon Heath *(pianist)*.

Additional Cast (Spanish Vers?): Irene López de Heredia *(Sophie)*, Amparo Rivelles *(Baroness Nagel)*, Mark Sharpe, Gustavo Re, Requena, Gary Land, Emilia Ruiz, Jacinto San Emeterio.

Melodrama. Bracco, the victim of a waterfront stabbing in Naples, confides the names Gregory Arkadin and Sophie to Mily, the girl friend of Guy Van Stratten, an unscrupulous American cigarette smuggler. These names, asserts Bracco, will prove the key to a fortune. Learning that Arkadin is a wealthy financier, Van Stratten obtains an introduction through the magnate's sheltered daughter, Raina. Arkadin engages Van Stratten to reconstruct his life before 1927, at which time he lost his memory. So empowered, the American sets out on a quest, during which he encounters a Copenhagen flea-trainer; an Amsterdam fence masquerading as an antiquary; a Polish baroness; a French secret service agent; Sophie, Arkadin's former partner in a white slave operation, now married to a retired general in Mexico; and Zouk, a Munich tailor. All are subsequently murdered, as is Mily. Van Stratten learns that they are the victims of Arkadin's henchmen and he himself is the financier's dupe. To forever bury his unsavory past from his daughter, Arkadin has used Van Stratten to locate all former associates. Realizing that he is in imminent danger, Van Stratten contacts Raina, who attempts to radio her father. Convinced that she has learned the truth, Arkadin jumps from his private plane. *Smugglers. Tycoons. Americans in foreign countries. Tailors. Fences (for stolen goods). Poles. Secret agents. French. Murder. Amnesia. White slave traffic. Narcotics. Suicide. Filial relations. Duplicity. Airplanes. Flea circus. Amsterdam. Copenhagen. Mexico. Munich. Naples.*

Note: Filmed in 1954 on locations in Spain, France, West Germany, Italy, Greece, and Mexico. Opened in Madrid in Mar 1955. Previously released abroad in English as *Confidential Report*.

MISTER BUDDWING   F6.3220

DDD Productions-Cherokee Productions. *Dist* Metro-Goldwyn-Mayer, Inc. 11 Oct **1966** [New York opening; c31 Dec 1965; LP33399]. Sd (Westrex); b&w. 35mm. 100 min.

A Delbert Mann-Douglas Laurence-Dale Wasserman Production. *Prod* Douglas Laurence, Delbert Mann. *Dir* Delbert Mann. *Screenplay* Dale Wasserman. *Dir Photog* Ellsworth Fredricks. *Art Dir* George W. Davis, Paul Groesse. *Set Decor* Henry Grace, Hugh Hunt. *Film Ed* Fredric Steinkamp. *Mus* Kenyon Hopkins. *Rec Supv* Franklin Milton. *Asst Dir* Eric Von Stroheim, Jr. *Miss Simmons' Gowns* Helen Rose. *Makeup* William Tuttle. *Hairstyles* Sydney Guilaroff. *Dial Supv* Norman Stuart.

Cast: James Garner *(Mister Buddwing)*, Jean Simmons *(The Blonde)*, Suzanne Pleshette *(Fiddle)*, Katharine Ross *(Janet)*, Angela Lansbury *(Gloria)*, George Voskovec *(shabby old man)*, Jack Gilford *(Mr. Schwartz)*, Joe Mantell *(1st cab driver)*, Raymond St. Jacques *(Hank)*, Ken Lynch *(Dan)*, Beeson Carroll *(policeman)*, Billy Halop *(2d cab driver)*, Michael Hadge *(counterman)*, Charles Seel *(printer)*, John Tracy *(Tony)*, Bart Conrad *(chauffeur)*, Romo Vincent, Wesley Addy, John Dennis, Kam Tong, Rafael Campos, Nichelle Nichols, James O'Rear, Pat Li, Rikki Stevens *(dice players)*, Paul Andor *(man on street)*.

Melodrama. Source: Evan Hunter, *Buddwing* (New York, 1964). A man awakens on a bench in Central Park and realizes that he is suffering from total amnesia; his life and his identity are a blank, and his only clue is a telephone number he finds in his pocket. He accidentally calls the wrong number and reaches a sleepy-voiced woman named Gloria who mistakenly assumes that he is her drunken husband. After he makes up the name of Buddwing from a passing beer truck and an overhead jet plane, he calls on Gloria in her shabby apartment. Touched by the man's dilemma, she gives him coffee, sympathy and $5. While he wanders the streets, Buddwing spots a young woman and shouts the name "Grace" as he sees a fleeting image from his past. When the woman tells him she is a college student named Janet, Buddwing relives his college romance with the young woman, Grace, who was his fiancée. While listening to records in the apartment of an actress named Fiddle, he remembers how poverty forced him to abandon his dream of becoming a composer. He then encounters a blonde socialite who needs a tall man in a grey suit to accompany her on a scavenger hunt. She persuades Buddwing to take her to Harlem where she must win a large sum of money in a dice game. During the frenzied gambling, a chance remark causes Buddwing to recall the shock that blotted out his memory. Finally aware of his identity, he goes to the hospital where his wife had been taken after attempting suicide because he had rejected her upon hearing of her pregnancy. *Students. Actors. Composers. Socialites. Amnesia. Mistaken identity. Gambling. Suicide. Pregnancy. Marriage. Hospitals. New York City—Central Park. New York City—Harlem. New York City— Greenwich Village.*

Note: Filmed in New York City. Locations include Washington Square, Central Park, Greenwich Village, New York University, Shubert Alley, Plaza Hotel, and the Queensboro Bridge. Also known as *Woman Without A Face.*

MISTER FREEDOM (France)   F6.3221

Les Films du Rond Point-O. P. E. R. A. *Dist* Grove Press. 30 Mar **1970** [New York opening]. Sd; col (Eastman Color). 35mm. 95 min.

Prod Guy Belfond, Michel Zemer, Christian Thivat. *Dir-Writ* William Klein. *Photog* Pierre Lhomme. *Art Dir* Jacques Dugied, André Piltant. *Film Ed* Anne-Marie Cotret. *Mus* Serge Gainsbourg. *Sd* Antoine Bonfanti. *Asst Dir* Alain Franchet, Didier Baudet. *Prod Mgr* Michel Zemer. *Cost* Janine Klein.

Cast: Donald Pleasence *(Dr. Freedom)*, Delphine Seyrig *(Marie-Madeleine)*, John Abbey *(Mister Freedom)*, Philippe Noiret *(Moujik Man)*, Catherine Rouvel *(Marie Rouge)*, Sami Frey *(Christ Man)*, Jean-Claude Drouot *(Dick)*, Serge Gainsbourg *(Mr. Drugstore)*, Yves Montand *(Capitain Formidable)*, Rufus *(Freddy Fric)*, Simone Signoret, Daniel Cohn-Bendit, Yves Lefebvre, Michel Creton, Rita Maiden, Sabine Sun, Colin Drake, Henry Pillsbury.

Satire. Mister Freedom, a United States sheriff dedicated to law and order, changes into his freedom-fighting costume and brutally apprehends a group of Negro looters before being ordered by his superior, Dr. Freedom, to save France from communism. He is taken by Marie-Madeleine to the headquarters of the French Freedom Movement, where he stirs masses of spectators with his fiery speech. Mister Freedom then contacts the United States Ambassador, whose office is located in a huge supermarket, and suggests that they grant freedom to France. He next visits Moujik Man, a Russian, and suggests a division of France. Their negotiations are interrupted by Red China Man and Christ Man, who knock Mister Freedom unconscious and place him in a jail cell. Mister Freedom escapes by killing Marie Rouge and then discovers that he has been betrayed by Marie-Madeleine, a Russian double agent. With all of his followers slaughtered, Mister Freedom decides that France is not ready for freedom, and he destroys the country, as well as himself, with an atom bomb. *Sheriffs. Negroes. Americans in foreign countries. Russians. Chinese. Secret agents. Race relations. Communism. Anti-communism. Cold war. Perfidy. Suicide. Christianity. Law and order. Atom bomb. United States—Diplomatic and consular service.*

Note: Opened in Paris in Jan 1969; running time: 102 min.

MR. HOBBS TAKES A VACATION   **F6.3222**

Jerry Wald Productions. *Dist* Twentieth Century–Fox Film Corp. 15 Jun **1962** [New York opening; c25 May 1962; LP22226]. Sd (Westrex); col (De Luxe). 35mm. (CinemaScope). 116 min.

Prod Jerry Wald. *Assoc Prod* Marvin A. Gluck. *Dir* Henry Koster. *2d Unit Dir* William Witney. *Screenplay* Nunnally Johnson. *Dir Photog* William C. Mellor. *Art Dir* Jack Martin Smith, Malcolm Brown. *Set Decor* Walter M. Scott, Stuart A. Reiss. *Film Ed* Marjorie Fowler. *Mus* Henry Mancini. *Song:* "Cream Puff" Johnny Mercer, Henry Mancini. *Sung by* Fabian. *Orch* Leo Shuken, Jack Hayes. *Sd* Alfred Bruzlin, Warren B. Delaplain. *Asst Dir* Joseph E. Rickards. *Cost Dsgn* Don Feld. *Makeup* Ben Nye. *Hairstyles* Helen Turpin. *Sp Photog Eff* L. B. Abbott.

Cast: James Stewart *(Mr. Hobbs)*, Maureen O'Hara *(Peggy Hobbs)*, Fabian *(Joe)*, Lauri Peters *(Katey)*, Lili Gentle *(Janie)*, John Saxon *(Byron)*, John McGiver *(Martin Turner)*, Marie Wilson *(Emily Turner)*, Reginald Gardiner *(Reggie McHugh)*, Valerie Varda *(Marika)*, Natalie Trundy *(Susan Carver)*, Josh Peine *(Stan Carver)*, Michael Burns *(Danny Hobbs)*, Minerva Urecal *(Brenda)*, Richard Collier *(Mr. Kagle)*, Peter Oliphant *(Peter Carver)*, Tom Lowell *(Freddie)*, Stephen Mines *(Carl)*, Dennis Whitcomb *(Dick)*, Michael Sean *(Phil)*.

Domestic comedy. Source: Edward Streeter, *Mr. Hobbs' Vacation* (New York, 1954). Roger Hobbs is a banker whose hopes for a quiet vacation are dashed when his wife, Peggy, decides that what they need is a little family "togetherness" at a cottage by the seashore. From the very beginning things go wrong. Their rented cottage turns out to be such a dilapidated Gothic eyesore that their cook, Brenda, leaves in a huff; son Danny prefers television to the beach; daughter Katey also refuses to go out because of the braces on her teeth; daughter Susan arrives with her unruly children and has a spat with her unemployed husband, Stan, who promptly leaves; daughter Janie's egghead husband, Byron, becomes the all-too-willing prey of Marika, a bikini-clad siren; and Peggy is openly wooed by Reggie McHugh, a yacht club romeo. But, by steady perseverance, Mr. Hobbs manages to restore family harmony. He conquers the house's rebellious pump, wins Danny's respect and admiration by guiding a small boat through a dense fog, overcomes Katey's shyness by introducing her to a good-looking youngster named Joe, helps Stan get a job by entertaining the privately alcoholic Mr. and Mrs. Turner, steers Byron away from Marika by implying that she is hopelessly schizophrenic, and outromances the pompous Reggie. When their vacation ends, Hobbs greets with something less than enthusiasm his wife's announcement that she has leased the cottage for the following summer. *Bankers. Playboys. Family life. Fatherhood. Adolescence. Filial relations. Alcoholism. Vacations. Beaches.*

MISTER INNOCENT *see* **THE HAPPENING**

MR. JIM—AMERICAN, SOLDIER, AND GENTLEMAN *see* **SERGEANT JIM**

MR. KENNEDY, MR. REAGAN AND THE BIG, BEAUTIFUL, BELEAGUERED AMERICAN DREAM (Canada)   **F6.3223**

Canadian Broadcasting Corp. *Dist* Film-Makers' Distribution Center. 22 Nov **1967** [New York showing]. Sd; b&w. 16mm. 60 min.

Prod-Dir Clifford Solway. *Screenplay* Clifford Solway, Philip Deane. *Photog* Robert Kaufman, photog.

Narrator: Philip Deane.

Documentary. The film is a compilation of newsreel clips of former actor Ronald Reagan and Sen. Robert F. Kennedy in California during the 1966 gubernatorial campaign. *Politicians. Political campaigns. California. Robert Francis Kennedy. Ronald Reagan.*

Note: Originally made for Canadian television; broadcast from Toronto on 30 Oct 1966.

MR. LIMPET *see* **THE INCREDIBLE MR. LIMPET**

MR. MAGOO'S HOLIDAY FESTIVAL   **F6.3224**

UPA Pictures. *Dist* Maron Films. 21 Nov **1970** [Las Vegas, Nevada, opening]. Sd; col. 35mm. 104 min. *MPAA rating* G.

Production Credits for *Mr. Magoo's Christmas Carol*: A Henry G. Saperstein Production. *Prod* Lee Orgel. *Exec Prod* Henry G. Saperstein. *Dir* Abe Levitow. *Seq Dir* Steve Clark, Gerard Baldwin, Duane Crowther. *Adapt* Barbara Chain. *Col Stylist* Phill Norman, Gloria Wood, Robert Inman, Jack Heiter, Dave Weidman. *Anim* John Walker, anim, Hank Smith, Xenia, Ed Solomon, Tom McDonald, Casey Onaitis. *Prod Dsgn* Lee Mishkin, Robert Singer, Richard Ung, Corny Cole, Shirley Silvey, Tony Rivera, Marty Murphy, Sam Weiss. *Film Ed* Sam Horta, Earl Bennett, George Probert, Wayne Hughes. *Songs:* "Alone in the World," "It's Great To Be Back on Broadway," "The Lord's Bright Blessing," "Ringle, Ringle," "We're Despicable," "Winter Is Warm" Jule Styne, Bob Merrill. *Mus Score & Cond* Walter Scharf. *Prod Mgr* Earl Jonas.

Production Credits for *Mr. Magoo's Snow White:* A Henry G. Saperstein Production. *Exec Prod* Henry G. Saperstein. *Supv Dir* Abe Levitow. *Adapt* Barbara Chain. *Mus* Carl Brandt.

Voices for *Mr. Magoo's Christmas Carol*: Jim Backus *(Mr. Magoo—Ebenezer Scrooge)*, Jack Cassidy *(Bob Cratchit)*, Joan Gardner *(Tiny Tim/Christmas Past)*, Jane Kean *(Belle Fezziwig)*, Royal Dano *(Marley's ghost)*, Morey Amsterdam *(Brandy/James)*, Les Tremayne *(Christmas Present)*, Marie Matthews *(Young Scrooge)*, Laura Olsher *(Mrs. Cratchit)*, Paul Frees *(Old Fezziwig/undertaker)*, John Hart.

Voices for *Mr. Magoo's Snow White*: Jim Backus *(Mr. Magoo/7 dwarfs)*, Julie Bennett *(Snow White)*, Howard Morris *(prince)*, Joan Gardner *(queen)*, Everett Sloane.

Animated fantasy. Source: Charles Dickens, *A Christmas Carol* (London, 1843). Jakob Grimm and Wilhelm Grimm, "Schneewittchen und die sieben Zwerge". Animated adaptations of *A Christmas Carol* and "Snow White and the Seven Dwarfs," in which Mr. Magoo enacts the roles of Scrooge and the seven dwarfs. *Misers. Ghosts. Cripples. Dwarfs. Hunters. Employer-employee relations. Poverty. Family life. Jealousy. Friendship. Poisoning. Churchyards. Christmas. London. Visions. Imaginary kingdoms. Snow White. Prince Charming.*

Note: *Mr. Magoo's Christmas Carol* was originally presented on NBC-TV on 18 Dec 1962; *Mr. Magoo's Snow White* was first shown on NBC-TV on 2 Jan and 9 Jan 1965 as a 2-part episode entitled *Mr. Magoo's Little Snow White*.

MR. MARI'S GIRLS   **F6.3225**

Dist American Film Distributing Corp. 1 Mar **1967** [New York showing]. Sd; b&w. 35mm. 63 min.

Dir William K. Hennigar.

Melodrama. Among the troubled women who seek help and advice from wealthy Mr. Mari are Alice, who finds sexual release through masturbation; Gloria, a housewife who uses her body to pay her gambling debts; Stella, a drug addict who is raped by a Negro drug dealer and performs an erotic dance under the influence of the LSD that Mr. Mari gives her; Diana, a high school student made pregnant by the teacher she seduced to improve her grades; Dirk and Barbara, a lesbian couple who ask Mr. Mari to perform a marriage ceremony for them; and Ann, who prostitutes herself for a teenage gang and is shot down when she tries to double-cross them. Mr. Mari invites his young friends to his home so that they might help one another, but the plan fails, and they end up fighting with each other, to Mr. Mari's ultimate amusement. *Housewives. Drug addicts. Students. Negroes. Drug dealers. Autoeroticism. Prostitution. Rape. Pregnancy. Lesbianism. Murder. Wealth. Seduction. Gambling. Debt. LSD. Street gangs.*

MISTER MOSES
F6.3226

Talbot Productions-Frank Ross Productions-Belmont Productions. *Dist* United Artists. 14 Apr **1965** [Houston opening; c8 Mar 1965; LP30560]. Sd; col (Technicolor). 35mm (Panavision). 113 min.

A Frank Ross Production. *Prod* Frank Ross. *Dir* Ronald Neame. *Screenplay* Charles Beaumont, Monja Danischewsky. *Dir Photog* Oswald Morris. *Art Dir* Syd Cain. *Asst Art Dir* Robert Laing. *Titl Backgrounds Painted by* Robin Anderson. *Film Ed* Peter Weatherley, Philip W. Anderson. *Mus Comp & Cond* John Barry. *Sd Mix* John W. Mitchell, Bob Jones. *Sd* Winston Ryder, James Shields. *Asst Dir* Colin Brewer. *Prod Supv* David Middlemas. *Makeup Supv* George Frost. *Hairdresser* Joan Smallwood.

Cast: Robert Mitchum (*Joe Moses*), Carroll Baker (*Julie Anderson*), Ian Bannen (*Robert*), Alexander Knox (*Reverend Anderson*), Raymond St. Jacques (*Ubi*), Orlando Martins (*Chief*), Reginald Beckwith (*Parkhurst*), "Susie" of Nairobi (*Emily, the elephant*).

Comedy-drama. Source: Max Catto, *Mister Moses* (London, 1961). Joe Moses, an American circus man, diamond smuggler, and self-styled medicine man, is dumped into a river by enraged African natives he has swindled. Left to float unconscious downstream, he is caught in the bullrushes near a village that is to be flooded upon the completion of an irrigation dam. Despite the pleadings of Anderson, a missionary, the natives refuse to leave by helicopter because they cannot take their animals with them. Joe appears and puts on a magic show by setting fire to a bush, and the natives hail him as a second Moses and demand that he lead them to "The Promised Land." Joe's reluctance to do so is quickly overcome by Anderson's daughter, Julie, who threatens to expose his diamond smuggling. Adding to Joe's problems during the long, arduous trek is Ubi, the U. S.-educated son of a witch doctor who resents Joe's influence with the natives. Attempting to expose Joe as a false prophet, Ubi accidentally perishes in flames. At the journey's end the district commissioner, Julie's former fiancé, fails to arrest Joe and allows him to walk into the African bush. Julie hurriedly tries to explain to her father why she loves Joe and then runs after him. *Americans in foreign countries. Swindlers. Smugglers. Medicine men. Missionaries. Witch doctors. Africans. Circus. Fraud. Magic. Irrigation. Filial relations. Helicopters. Africa. Fires. Elephants.*

Note: Filmed on location in Kenya, on the shores of Lake Naivasha, and in the Amboselli Game Preserve.

MR. MOTO AND THE PERSIAN OIL CASE see THE RETURN OF MR. MOTO

MR. PEEK-A-BOO'S PLAYMATES
F6.3227

Doe-Rae Pictures. *Dist* Pay Play Inc. 7 Aug **1962** [Los Angeles showing]. Sd; col. 35mm. 58 min.

Prod Ronnie Ashcroft, Lorraine Ashcroft. *Dir* Ronnie Ashcroft.

Cast: Denise Daniell, Stanton Prithert.

Comedy. Mr. Peek-a-Boo finds a pair of magic glasses that give him the power to see fully-clothed women nude. *Magic. Nudity. Voyeurism. Eyeglasses.*

Note: Also known as *Like Wow!*, *A Mad Escapade of a Playboy*, *Naked Like Wow!*, and *Wow!*

MR. PETERS' PETS
F6.3228

Dist Sonney Amusement Enterprises. 22 Mar **1962** [Los Angeles showing]. Sd; col. 35mm. 70 min.

Comedy. Irishman Willy Peters runs a pet shop, and he converses intimately with his animal friends. He receives an advertisement from the Maharajah of Poon Ja offering a secret formula which ensures the happiness of household pets. Willy tests the potion on himself and obtains the ability to transform himself into any member of the animal kingdom. Assuming a number of different animal guises, Willy goes spying in the homes of his prospective customers to determine their suitability as pet owners. He thus gains entrance to private situations and sees many female customers without their clothes, but finally he decides that he should rely on chance to select homes for his pets. *Irish. Metamorphosis. Nudity. Magic. Voyeurism. Pets. Pet shops. Potions.*

Note: May also be known as *Petey's Sweeties*.

MR. PULVER AND THE CAPTAIN see ENSIGN PULVER

MR. RADISH AND MR. CARROT see TWILIGHT PATH

MR. SARDONICUS
F6.3229

William Castle Productions. *Dist* Columbia Pictures. 18 Oct **1961** [New York opening; c1 Oct 1961; LP20642]. Sd (RCA); b&w. 35mm. 89 min.

Prod-Dir William Castle. *Assoc Prod* Dona Holloway. *Screenplay* Ray Russell. *Dir Photog* Burnett Guffey. *Art Dir* Cary Odell. *Set Decor* James M. Crowe. *Film Ed* Edwin Bryant. *Mus* Von Dexter. *Sd Supv* Charles J. Rice. *Sd* James Z. Flaster. *Asst Dir* R. Robert Rosenbaum, Les Gorall. *Script Supv* Eylla Jacobus. *Wardrobe* Pat Barto, Jack Angel. *Makeup Supv* Ben Lane. *Still Photog* Homer Van Pelt.

Cast: Ronald Lewis (*Sir Robert Cargrave*), Audrey Dalton (*Maude*), Guy Rolfe (*Sardonicus*), Oscar Homolka (*Krull*), Vladimir Sokoloff (*his father*), Erika Peters (*his first wife, Elenka*), Lorna Hanson (*Anna*), James Forrest (*Wainwright*), Tina Woodward (*The Girl*), Constance Cavendish (*Mrs. Higgins*), Mavis Neal (*head nurse*), Charles H. Radilac (*stationmaster*), David Janti (*Janku*), Franz Roehn (*gravedigger*), Annalena Lund (*1st girl*), Ilse Burkert (*2d girl*), Albert D'Arno (*gatekeeper*), William Castle (*narrator*).

Horror film. Source: Ray Russell, "Sardonicus," in *Playboy* (Jan 1961). English medical pioneer Sir Robert Cargrave, working on the use of toxic poisons as a cure for nervous disorders, is summoned to a central European castle by his former love, Maude, now the wife of Baron Sardonicus. Once there, Robert discovers that the baron wears a rubber mask to conceal his features, hideously contorted years before when he disinterred his father's corpse to recover a winning lottery ticket. For years Sardonicus has been trying to find a cure for his affliction by having Krull, a one-eyed, Neanderthal-looking man, experiment with leeches on the faces of young peasant girls. When the baron threatens to have Maude facially disfigured unless Robert attempts a cure with the toxic poisons, Robert uses distilled water in his hypodermic needle and, by means of "psychological shock," effects a complete recovery. Once Sardonicus sees his face restored to its normal appearance, he signs an annulment of his marriage to Maude and permits her to leave with Robert. They are overtaken by Krull, who reports that his master's jaws have locked tight: he cannot eat, drink, or speak. But Robert refuses to return, and he and Maude leave Sardonicus to his doom. *English. Physicians. Domestics. Peasants. Nobility. Disfiguration. Mutilation. Disinterment. Psychosomatic illness. Torture. Shock therapy. Marriage—Annulment. Castles. Masks. Leeches.*

Note: Working title: *Sardonicus*.

MISTER SEBASTIAN see SEBASTIAN

MR. TEASE AND HIS PLAYTHINGS see STEAM HEAT

MR. TOPAZE see I LIKE MONEY

I MISTERI DELLA GIUNGLA NERA see THE MYSTERY OF THUG ISLAND

MISTERIOS DE ULTRATUMBA see BLACK PIT OF DR. M

LOS MISTERIOS DEL ROSARIO see THE REDEEMER

MRS. BROWN, YOU'VE GOT A LOVELY DAUGHTER (Great Britain)
F6.3230

Metro-Goldwyn-Mayer Pictures-Ivorygate Films. *Dist* Metro-Goldwyn-Mayer, Inc. 12 Jun **1968** [Detroit opening; c16 Apr 1968; LP35708]. Sd; col (Metrocolor). 35mm (Panavision). 95 min.

An Allen V. Klein Production. *Prod* Allen V. Klein. *Assoc Prod* David Orton. *Dir* Saul Swimmer. *Screenplay* Thaddeus Vane. *Dir Photog* Jack Hildyard. *Camera Op* Dudley Lovell. *Art Dir* George Provis. *Film Ed* Tristam Cones. *Asst Ed* Denis Whitehouse. *Mus Supv* Mickie Most. *Songs:* "It's Nice To Be Out in the Morning," "Ooh, She's Done It Again," "Lemon and Lime," "The World Is for the Young," "Holiday Inn" Graham Gouldman. *Song:* "The Most Beautiful Thing in My Life" Kenny Young. *Song:* "Daisy Chain" Peter Noone, Keith Hopwood, Karl Green, Derek Leckenby. *Titl Song* Trevor Peacock. *Song:* "There's a Kind of Hush" Les Reed, Geoff Stephens. *Songs Arr* by John Paul Jones. *Adtl Mus Comp & Cond* Ron Goodwin. *Songs Sung by* Herman's Hermits. *Sd Ed* Jim Groom. *Sd* John Bramall, Bill Cook. *Dub Mix* Nolan Roberts, Bob Jones. *Prod Mgr* Dennis Hall. *Cont* Joan Davis. *Asst to the Prod* Ronald Schneider. *Cost* Beatrice Dawson. *Makeup* Eddie Knight. *Hairdresser* Pat McDermott.

Cast—Herman's Hermits: Peter Noone (*Herman Tulley*), Karl Green (*Karl*), Keith Hopwood (*Keith*), Derek Leckenby (*Derek*), Barry Whitwam (*Barry*).

Cast—Others: Stanley Holloway (*Mr. Brown*), Mona Washbourne (*Mrs. Brown*), Lance Percival (*Percy Sutton*), Marjorie Rhodes (*Gloria*), Sheila White (*Tulip*), Sarah Caldwall (*Judy Brown*), Hugh Futcher (*Swothard*), Drewe Henley (*Clive Wingate*), Avis Bunnage (*Tulip's mother*), John Sharp (*Oakshot*), Nat Jackley (*pub singer*), Rita Webb (*woman in pub*), Billy Milton (*landlord*), Dermot Kelly (*con man*), Tom Kempinski (*Vince Hobart*), Lynda Baron (*Miss Fisher*), Joan Hickson (*landlady*), Iris Salder (*Stewpot Iris*), Nan Munro (*mother at station*), Pamela Cundell (*woman on embankment*), Paul Farrell (*White City clerk*), Michelle Cook (*hippie girl*), James Myers (*page boy*), Margery Manners (*pub singer*).

Comedy with music. When 20-year-old Herman Tulley inherits his grandfather's most prized possession, a greyhound named Mrs. Brown, he and his friends (Barry, Keith, Karl, and Derek) decide to make their fortune racing the dog. After the animal has won the Manchester heat of the National Greyhound Derby, Herman meets wealthy Londoners Mr. and Mrs. Brown and their daughter Judy, a model. Hoping to see Judy again, Herman and his pop-singing friends decide to take the dog to London for the derby finals. Once there, however, they are swindled by a con man who takes all their money. Fortunately, the Honorable Percy Sutton, a good-natured tramp whom Herman once befriended in Manchester, appears and finds them beds for the night. The following day Mr. Brown gets them jobs as fruit-peddlers. Judy, who is attracted to Herman, invites them to a party, where they are offered a nightclub engagement. The next day, Herman's greyhound wins the preliminary heat of the London Derby. But Herman's enthusiasm turns to gloom when Judy goes to Rome for a 6-week modeling assignment, and the greyhound disappears at the station. After a futile search, Herman and his friends return to Manchester. Herman's spirits pick up when Percy arrives with the lost dog, and Herman discovers that his tomboy neighbor Tulip has become a very attractive woman. When Herman's dog gives birth to a mongrel pup, Herman and his friends give the pup to Judy's mother, the other Mrs. Brown. *Models. Singers. Confidence men. Tramps. Peddlers. Tomboys. Neighbors. Inheritance. Dogracing. Rock and roll. Nightclubs. Manchester (England). London.*

Note: Opened in London in Sep 1968.

A MISTRESS FOR THE SUMMER (France/Italy)   **F6.3231**
Boréal-Filmsonor-SPA Cinematografica. *Dist* American Film Distributing Corp. 27 Mar **1964** [New York opening]. Sd; col (Eastman Color). 35mm (Dyaliscope). 80 min.
Pres by Stan Borden. *Assoc Prod* Pierre Meyrat. *Dir* Edouard Molinaro. *Dial* Maurice Clavel. *Adapt* Maurice Clavel, Edouard Molinaro. *Dir Photog* Jean Bourgoin. *Camera* André Dumaître. *Asst Camera* René Guissard. *Art Dir* Georges Lévy. *Film Ed* Robert Isnardon. *Mus* Georges Delerue. *Sd* Jacques Lebreton. *Asst Dir* Serge Vallin, Pierre Cosson. *Prod Mgr* André Hoss. *Location Mgr* Guy Maugin. *Script Girl* Marie-José Darène. *Still Photog* Serge Beauvarlet.
Cast: Pascale Petit (*Manette*), Micheline Presle (*Paule*), Michel Auclair (*Philippe*), Georges Poujouly (*Michel*), Antoine Balpêtré (*poet*), Aimé Clariond (*Rosenkrantz*), Henri Vidon (*The King*), Claire Maurier (*Viviane*), Bernard Lajarrige (*bartender*), Eva Linkova, Geo Harry, Georges Meister, Sylvie Coste, Nicole Nantheuil, Ariana Galli, Giuseppe Porelli, Marina Malfatti.
Drama. Source: Maurice Clavel, *Une fille pour l'été* (Paris, 1957). A relatively unknown painter is invited to spend the summer with a wealthy friend. En route, he picks up an attractive young woman who agrees to join him at his friend's house. Their visit is disrupted by the arrival of the friend's teenaged son, who begins flirting with the young woman but suddenly leaves for Israel. As the summer comes to an end, the young woman, who by now has fallen in love with the painter, fears that he will leave her; and, while on a boat ride, she becomes reckless and falls overboard. The painter is unable to find her and only then realizes how much he loved her. *Painters. Friendship. Adolescence. Flirtation. Summer.*
Note: Filmed on location in Saint-Tropez and on Cap d'Antibes. Opened in Paris in Feb 1960 as *Une fille pour l'été*; in Rome in Feb 1960 as *Una ragazza per l'estate*. Alternative U. S. title: *A Lover for the Summer*.

MRS. STONE'S THING   **F6.3232**
Motion Picture Center. *Dist* Kalt-Robertson Productions. 30 Oct **1970** [Chicago opening]. Sd; col. 35mm. 82 min.
Prod Joseph F. Robertson, Harry Kay. *Dir-Writ* Joseph F. Robertson. *Cinematog* Hal Guthu, Bob Maxwell. *Film Ed* Executive Artists. *Mus* Synchrofilm.
Melodrama. George Stone's wife, Martha, is curious about the parties her husband attends at the home of his boss, McMahon. At dinner with friends one evening, she imagines George and their friends engaging in sex games and fantasies, and longs to be a part of them. She persuades George to let her go to a party at McMahon's the next day, but is stunned to find that an orgy is under way: body painting, sadomasochism, autoeroticism, bestiality, homosexuality, lesbianism, transvestism, and sex games of all descriptions, are involved. Martha makes love to a stranger by the pool, participates in the whipping of a woman guest, has sex with McMahon, makes love to another woman and to George's friend Ron, and becomes involved with a female transvestite until George, in a fit of jealousy, interrupts them. At home the following day, George finds Martha contrite and tearful. They conclude that orgies are ill-suited to their lifestyle and decide to raise a family. *Employers. Marriage. Fantasy. Body painting. Sadomasochism. Autoeroticism. Bestiality. Male homosexuality. Lesbianism. Transvestism. Bisexuality. Flagellation. Jealousy. Marriage. Orgies.*

MISTY   **F6.3233**
Twentieth Century-Fox Film Corp. 17 Jul **1961** [New York opening; c23 Feb 1961; LP19489]. Sd (Westrex); col (DeLuxe). 35mm (CinemaScope). 92 min.
Prod Robert B. Radnitz. *Dir* James B. Clark. *Screenplay* Ted Sherdeman. *Dir Photog* Leo Tover, Lee Garmes. *Art Dir* Duncan Cramer, Maurice Ransford.

Set Decor Walter M. Scott, Stuart A. Reiss. *Film Ed* Fredrick Y. Smith. *Mus* Paul Sawtell, Bert Shefter. *Orch* Max Reese. *Sd* Bernard Freericks, Frank W. Moran. *Asst Dir* Stanley Hough. *Makeup* Ben Nye. *Hairstyles* Helen Turpin. *Coöp* People of Chincoteague (Virginia), Chincoteague National Wildlife Refuge.
Cast: David Ladd (*Paul Beebe*), Arthur O'Connell (*Grandpa Beebe*), Pam Smith (*Maureen Beebe*), Anne Seymour (*Grandma Beebe*), Duke Farley (*Eba Jones*), People of Chincoteague (Virginia).
Drama. Source: Marguerite Henry, *Misty of Chincoteague* (Chicago, 1947). Recently orphaned 12-year-old Paul Beebe and his younger sister, Maureen, go to live on their grandparents' pony ranch on the island of Chincoteague, Virginia. Each year, on Pony-Penning Day, the natives cross over to the nearby island of Assateague and round up herds of wild ponies to be sold at a community auction. When the two youngsters participate in their first roundup, they bring in The Phantom, an elusive mare never before caught, and her newborn colt, which they name Misty. The children, who had earned $100 doing odd jobs, are heartbroken when a stranger buys the two animals before they can bid. Through the intervention of the local fire chief, however, the stranger "sells" Paul and Maureen the two ponies for their $100. Misty takes to the youngsters at once, but The Phantom proves to be more obstinate. Eventually, though, Paul succeeds in "gentling" her into submission, and he decides to enter her in the next Pony-Penning Day race. Although The Phantom wins in a practice race against the local champion, the children realize that she is pining for the open freedom of Assateague, and they drive Misty after her into the water that separates the ponies from their former home. Although The Phantom swims away, Misty returns and gallops back to the jubilant Paul and Maureen. *Children. Orphans. Grandparents. Firemen. Horsetrainers. Ranches. Chincoteague (Virginia). Assateague (Virginia). Horses.*
Note: Filmed on location on the islands of Chincoteague and Assateague, Virginia.

MIT EVA FING DIE SÜNDE AN see **THE PLAYGIRLS AND THE BELLBOY**

IL MITO see **THE MYTH**

MIVTZA KAHIR see **TRUNK TO CAIRO**

MIXED FRUIT   **F6.3234**
caMay **1970**. Sd; b&w. 35mm? [Feature length assumed.]
Sex film. Among the episodes depicted are the seduction of a minister's wife by a notoriously virile man; a lesbian encounter; and the adventure of two sisters, one innocent, one experienced. *Clergymen. Sisters. Infidelity. Seduction. Lesbianism.*

MIXED FRUIT see **A FAIRY TALE FOR ADULTS; OR THE HALF-FAST LOVER**

MNASIDIKA   **F6.3235**
Dist American Film Distributing Corp. **1969**. Sd; col. 35mm. 70 min.
Prod Julian Marsh, Anna Riva.
Cast: Robert West, Denise Lemain, Rosine Martinique, Lyse Boule, Artimidia Grillet, Maria Lorello.
Fantasy. A man falls asleep on the beach. *He awakens in an arbor in ancient Greece. Through the trees he sees a scantily-clad wood nymph; he follows her and helps her when she falls and her leg becomes caught in a tree. She undresses and gives herself to him. The incidents are repeated from his awakening in an arbor to the wood nymph's disrobing. The man, revealing the other side of his personality, raises a club, beats the girl to death, and caresses her lifeless body. A group of women are enjoying themselves in lesbian embraces in a graveyard beside a river. They seize the man, tie him to the ground, and after dancing around him raise long knives and castrate him. The man suddenly awakens at the seashore in the present time.* Nymphs. Nudity. Murder. Lesbianism. Castration. Necrophilia. Beaches. Cemeteries. Greece—Ancient. Dreams.*
Note: Julian Marsh and Robert West are pseudonyms for Michael Findlay, Anna Riva for Roberta Findlay. Also known as *Manasadeeka*.

THE MODEL HUNTERS   **F6.3236**
MJ Productions. *Dist* MarJon Film Distributors. ca **1970**. Sd; col. 16mm. ca60 min.
Sex film. Three young women striving for a career in the modeling field are hired by photographers in the pornography business to undress and act out titillating erotic situations. *Models. Photographers. Sexual practices. Pornography.*

THE MODEL MURDER CASE (Great Britain)   **F6.3237**
Viewfinder Films. *For* British Lion/Bryanston Films. *Dist* Cinema V Distributing, Inc. 24 Nov **1964** [New York opening]. Sd; b&w. 35mm. 90 min.

Prod John Davis. *Dir* Michael Truman. *Screenplay* Vivienne Knight, Patrick Campbell. *Photog* Stanley Pavey. *Camera Op* Frank Watts. *Focus* Trevor Wrenn. *Art Dir* Alan Withy. *Asst Art Dir* Ron Benton. *Set Dresser* Peter James. *Draughtsman* Raymonde Reilly. *Scenic Artist* W. Simpson Robinson. *Film Ed* Frederick Wilson. *1st Asst Ed* Thom Noble. *2d Asst Ed* Richard Bryan. *Mus Comp & Cond* John Addison. *Song:* "Casta diva" sung by Elizabeth Vaughan. *Sd Dir* Stephen Dalby. *Sd Mix* Leonard Bulkley. *Sd Camera Op* Dave Goghan. *Boom Op* Fred Tomlin. *1st, 2d & 3d Asst Dir* Bill Cartlidge, Ernie Lewis, Alan Anzarut. *Prod Mgr* Al Marcus. *Prod Sec* Angela Cockill. *Cont* Renee Glynne. *Wardrobe Master* Harry Haynes. *Makeup* Wally Schneiderman. *Hairdresser* Elsie Alder. *Prod Buyer* Terry Parr. *Still Photog* Doug Luke. *Chargehand Prop* Alfred Pegley. *Elec Chargehand* F. Buckle. *Grip* M. McLaughlin.

Cast: Ian Hendry *(Inspector Birkett)*, Ronald Fraser *(Sergeant Saunders)*, Margaret Johnston *(Mrs. Gray)*, Natasha Parry *(Perlita Barker)*, Jeremy Brett *(Jordan Barker)*, Kieron Moore *(Herter)*, Peter Arne *(Hammond Barker)*, Jane Asher *(Lindy Birkett)*, Rosalie Crutchley *(Maude Klein)*, Robert Harris *(William Lamotte)*, Duncan MacRae *(Barney)*, Zena Walker *(Mildred Birkett)*, James Villiers *(David Dane)*, Alan White *(Inspector Blackwell)*, Martin Boddey *(superintendent)*, Marie Burke *(Madame Lavalle)*, Patrick Holt *(Walbrook)*, Griffith Davies *(Teddy boy)*, Gabrielle Brune *(Lamotte's secretary)*, Peter Elliott, actor *(waiter)*, Terence Brook *(Detective Sergeant Carter)*, David Randall *(P. C. Jackson)*, Douglas Robinson *(Harrison)*, John Forbes-Robertson *(porter)*, Hugh Latimer *(man in club)*, Amanda Bowman *(receptionist)*, Neville Becker *(steward)*, Peter Forbes-Robertson *(police doctor)*.

Crime melodrama. Source: Laurence Payne, *The Nose on My Face* (London, 1961). A glamorous London model is found shot to death and her flat ransacked, and police Inspector Birkett and his assistant Sergeant Saunders are assigned the case. They find some clues, the hidden gun, a ballpoint pen, and a diary entry, which informs them that the woman was being blackmailed by her neighbor David Dane, a television star. They also discover that she was a drug addict, leading Birkett to speculate that the murderer might be a dope smuggler. Further investigation, however, proves him to be wrong, although his suspicions help to crack a narcotics ring. After the murder of David Dane, Birkett and Saunders pursue and capture the drug traffickers, but none of them is the killer. Finally, the dead girl's mother, Mrs. Gray, confesses under pressure that, jealous of the attention her second husband paid to the daughter she had always despised, she killed her with her own gun. *Models. Drug addicts. Detectives. Neighbors. Actors. Murder. Blackmail. Smuggling. Jealousy. Motherhood. Guns. Diaries. Narcotics. London.*

Note: Location scenes filmed in London. Released in Great Britain in Nov 1963 as *Girl in the Headlines*; running time: 93 min. Working title: *The Nose on My Face.*

THE MODEL SHOP   F6.3238

Columbia Pictures. 11 Feb **1969** [New York opening; c1 Apr 1969; LP36707]. Sd; col (Perfect). 35mm. 95 min. *MPAA rating* M.

A Jacques Demy Production. *Prod-Dir-Writ* Jacques Demy. *Asst Prod* Richard Roth. *Engl Dial* Adrien Joyce. *Dir Photog* Michel Hugo. *Set Decor* Anthony Mondell. *Prod Dsgn* Kenneth A. Reid. *Film Ed* Walter Thompson. *Mus Comp & Perf by* Spirit. *Song:* "Nothing To Do and Little To Say" sung by Spirit. *Mus Sd Track Prod* Lou Adler. *Cond* Marty Paich. *Mus Selections* Johann Sebastian Bach, Robert Schumann. *Selections from "Scheherazade"* Nikolai Andreevich Rimski-Korsakov. *Sd Supv* Charles J. Rice. *Sd* Les Fresholtz, Arthur Piantadosi. *Mus Ed* Ralph Hall. *Asst Dir* Herbert Willis. *Cost* Rita Riggs, Gene Ashman. *Makeup Supv* Ben Lane. *Miss Aimée's Hairstyles* Carrie White.

Cast: Anouk Aimée *(Lola)*, Gary Lockwood *(George Matthews)*, Alexandra Hay *(Gloria)*, Carol Cole *(Barbara)*, Severn Darden *(portly man)*, Tom Fielding *(Gerry)*, Neil Elliot *(Fred)*, Jacqueline Miller *(model number one)*, Anne Randall *(model number two)*, Duke Hobbie *(David)*, Craig Littler *(Rob)*, Hilarie Thompson *(girl hippie)*, Jeanne Sorel *(secretary)*, Jon Lawson *(Tony)*, David Mink *(bearded hippie)*, Jay Ferguson *(Jay)*, Jon Hill *(Allan)*, Fred Willard *(gas station attendant)*, Ken Prymus *(short-order cook)*.

Romantic drama. George Matthews is a 26-year-old Los Angeles architect waiting to be drafted. Refusing to commit himself to anyone or anything, he walks out on a dull job designing gas pipes and also refuses to marry his ambitious actress girl friend, Gloria. While attempting to borrow money to stop repossession of his sports car, he notices an elegant woman and follows her to her place of employment, a "model shop" for amateur "photographers" willing to pay high prices for the privilege of taking pictures of semi-nude models. George spends part of the car payment money to take pictures of the young woman, but all he learns about her is that her name is Lola and that she is French. After an argument with Gloria, George returns to the model shop and learns from Lola that her husband left her in the United States for another

woman and that she took a job in the model shop to earn enough money to return to France and her young son. Although Lola, like George, is reluctant to give of herself, she invites him home and allows him to spend the night. After talking about his fears of the Vietnam War (he has now received his induction notice) and his doubts about the future, George declares his love for Lola. Although moved, the love-scarred Lola cannot return his feelings. Before leaving, George gives her the rest of the car payment money to help her get back to France, though he hopes that she will remain behind. Returning home, George finds that Gloria is leaving him for a man who is trying to get her a job in a television commercial. As the finance company tows away his car, George telephones Lola but learns from her friend Barbara that she has already left for Europe. When asked if the call was important, George replies that he just wanted to wish Lola luck and leaves word for her that he hopes to make a new beginning. *Architects. French. Actors. Models. Photographers. Desertion. Military draft. Finance—Personal. Vietnam War 1964-73. Los Angeles.*

Note: Location scenes filmed in Los Angeles. The film contains references to three earlier films directed by Jacques Demy: *Lola* (1961), *Bay of the Angels* (1963), and *The Umbrellas of Cherbourg* (1964), q. v.

MODELS IN CHARCOAL see **NUDE IN CHARCOAL**

MODERATO CANTABILE (France/Italy)   F6.3239

Iéna Production-Productions Jacques Companeez-Documento Film. *Dist* Royal Films International. 6 Jan **1964** [New York opening]. Sd; b&w. 35mm (CinemaScope). 95 min.

Prod Raoul J. Lévy. *Dir* Peter Brook. *Screenplay-Adapt-Dial* Marguerite Duras, Gérard Jarlot, Peter Brook. *Photog* Armand Thirard. *Art Dir* Jean André. *Film Ed* Albert Jürgenson. *Mus: Sonata no. 4 in B-flat, opus 168* Antonio Diabelli. *Sd* William R. Sivel. *Asst Dir* Serge Vallin. *Prod Mgr* Roger Debelmas.

Cast: Jeanne Moreau *(Anne Desbaredes)*, Jean-Paul Belmondo *(Chauvin)*, Didier Haudepin *(Pierre)*, Valerie Dobuzinsky *(assassin)*, Pascale de Boysson *(patronne)*, Colette Régis *(Miss Giraud)*.

Drama. Source: Marguerite Duras, *Moderato cantabile* (Paris, 1958). Anne Desbaredes is the bored wife of a steel industrialist in the half-forgotten village of Blaye on the Gironde estuary in southwest France. Typical of her unchanging and placid existence is her weekly accompaniment of her precocious son, Pierre, to his music teacher's. One day, while listening to the uninterested child practicing scales, she hears a woman scream from the cafe below the teacher's studio. Anne looks down upon the scene and witnesses a frightened man being taken away from the side of a dead woman. Curious about the passions that must have motivated the crime, she visits the cafe and encounters an employee of her husband's, Chauvin, whose inquisitive and reflective mood mirrors her own. For the next few days they meet often, discussing not only the murder but also their own lives. When Chauvin eventually realizes that Anne's morbidness stems from her own death wish, he rejects her offer of love and leaves her. *Housewives. Industrialists. Children. Music teachers. Death. Murder. Music. Steel industry. Cafes. Blaye-et-Ste. Luce (France).*

Note: Opened in Paris in May 1960; running time: 92 min; in Rome in Sep 1960; running time: 95 min. Also 92 min.

A MODERN MARRIAGE see **FRIGID WIFE**

MODESTY BLAISE (Great Britain)   F6.3240

Modesty Blaise Ltd. *Dist* Twentieth Century-Fox Film Corp. 1 Jul **1966** [Chicago opening; c1 Jul 1966; LP32928]. Sd (Westrex); col (DeLuxe). 35mm. 119 min.

A Joseph Janni Production. *Prod* Joseph Janni. *Prod in Assoc With* Stanley Dubens. *Assoc Prod* Norman Priggen, Michael Birkett. *Dir* Joseph Losey. *Screenplay* Evan Jones. *Orig Story* Peter O'Donnell, Stanley Dubens. *Dir Photog* Jack Hildyard. *Camera Op* Gerry Fisher. *Amsterdam Location Photog* Davis Boulton. *Art Dir* Jack Shampan. *Prod Dsgn* Richard MacDonald. *Film Ed* Reginald Beck. *Mus Comp & Cond* John Dankworth. *Theme Song:* "Modesty" John Dankworth, Benny Green. *Sung by* David and Jonathan. *Song:* "We Should've" John Dankworth, Benny Green, Evan Jones. *Sd Rec* Buster Ambler, John Cox. *Sd Ed* Gordon Daniel, John Aldred. *Asst Dir* Gavrik Losey, Claude Watson. *Pers Asst to the Dir (Italy)* Carlo Lastricati. *Asst to the Prod* John Goldstone. *Prod Mgr* Ed Harper, Mara Blasetti. *Cont* Ann Skinner. *Cost Supv* Bumble Dawson. *Wardrobe Mistress* Evelyn Gibbs. *Terence Stamp's Cost* Douglas Hayward. *Adtl Cost & Tattoos for Monica Vitti* Marissa Martelli. *Makeup* Neville Smallwood. *Hairdresser* Pearl Tipaldi.

Cast: Monica Vitti *(Modesty Blaise)*, Terence Stamp *(Willie Garvin)*, Dirk Bogarde *(Gabriel)*, Harry Andrews *(Tarrant)*, Michael Craig *(Paul Hagan)*, Clive Revill *(McWhirter/Sheik Abu Tahir)*, Alexander Knox *(minister)*, Rossella Falk *(Mrs. Fothergill)*, Scilla Gabel *(Melina)*, Michael Chow *(Weng)*, Joe Melia *(Crevier)*, Saro Urzi *(Basilio)*, Tina Marquand *(Nicole)*, Oliver MacGreevy *(tattooed man)*, Jon Bluming *(Hans)*, Lex Schoorel *(Walter)*, Marcello Turilli *(Strauss)*, Giuseppe Paganelli *(friar)*, Wolfgang Hillinger

(Handsome), Roberto Bisacco *(Enrico)*, John Karlsen *(Oleg)*, Silvan *(The Great Pacco)*, John Stacy *(Tyboria captain)*, Robin Hunter *(pilot)*, Denys Graham *(co-pilot)*, Patrick Ludlow *(Under Secretary)*, Robin Fox *(man who pushes the doorbell)*, George Fisher.

Action comedy-drama. Based on the comic strip by: Peter O'Donnell and Jim Holdaway, "Modesty Blaise," in the *Evening Standard* (London). Voluptuous adventuress Modesty Blaise is recruited by Secret Service chief Sir Gerald Tarrant to protect a shipment of diamonds to Abu Tahir, a Middle Eastern oil magnate. The shipment is menaced, however, by Modesty's presumedly dead enemy, the archcriminial Gabriel. Gabriel is assisted by the dotard McWhirter and the sadistic Mrs. Fothergill, to whom for chastisement he delivers abducted spy Crevier. In Amsterdam Modesty is reunited with her former lover, Secret Service agent Paul Hagen, while her partner, Willie Garvin, is reunited with an old flame, Nicole. Through Paul and Nicole, Modesty and Willie ascertain that Gabriel is alive. Though Modesty and Paul are surprised in their lovenest by Gabriel's agents, Walter, Hans, and Gunther, they are rescued by Willie. Aware that she has betrayed him, Gabriel orders Nicole's death. En route to a rendezvous with Willie, Nicole is pursued by a tatooed man and stabbed to death. Sought by the same assassins, Modesty disguises herself as a prostitute. When she discovers that she does not enjoy the complete confidence of the Secret Service, Modesty and Willie determine to steal the diamonds for themselves. Gabriel abducts Modesty. Holding her hostage aboard his barque, he forces Willie to steal the diamonds. Disguised as a monk, Modesty escapes with Willie and the booty. After slaying Mrs. Fothergill, Modesty presents Abu Tahir with the shipment. In reward for her stewardship, the sheik gives her the diamonds. Although staked in the sands, Gabriel is rescued by McWhirter. *Adventuresses. Sheiks. Oil magnates. Masterminds. Prostitutes. Kidnaping. Robbery. Torture. Disguise. Jewels. Amsterdam. London. Great Britain—Intelligence service.*

Note: Location scenes filmed in Amsterdam, Naples, London, Farnborough, and Sicily. Released in London in Technicolor in May 1966.

MODIGLIANI OF MONTPARNASSE (France/Italy)　　F6.3241

Franco London Film–Astra Cinematografica–Pallavicini. *Dist* Continental Distributing, Inc. 28 Feb **1961** [New York opening]. Sd (Westrex); b&w. 35mm. 110 min.

Assoc Prod Ralph Baum. *Dir* Jacques Becker. *Screenplay* Henri Jeanson, Max Ophuls. *Foreword* Jean Cocteau. *Dir Photog* Christian Matras. *Camera* Gilbert Chain. *Asst Camera* Ernest Bourreaud. *Art Dir* Jean d' Eaubonne. *Asst Art Dir* Jacques Gut. *Set Decor* Maurice Bourbotte. *Film Ed* Marguerite Renoir. *Asst Film Ed* Maryse Barbut. *Mus (see note)* Georges Van Parys, Paul Misraki. *Selections From the Works of* Johann Sebastian Bach. *Sd* Pierre Calvet. *Sd Rec* Christian Courmes. *Boom* Maurice Dagonneau. *Asst Dir* Serge Witta, Jean Becker. *Prod Mgr* André Hoss. *Location Mgr* Robert Christides. *Script Girl* Sophie Becker. *Prod Sec* Jacqueline Fauvel. *Cost Dsgn* Georges Annenkov. *Cost* Madeleine Rabusson. *Makeup* Yvonne Fortuna. *Hairstyles* Denise Lemoigne. *Still Photog* Henri Thibault. *Props* Raymond Lemoigne, prop.

Cast: Gérard Philipe *(Amedeo Modigliani)*, Lilli Palmer *(Beatrice Hastings)*, Anouk Aimée *(Jeanne Hébuterne)*, Gérard Séty *(Sborowski)*, Lila Kedrova *(Madame Sborowski)*, Léa Padovani *(Rosalie)*, Jean Lanier *(Monsieur Hébuterne)*, Denise Vernac *(Madame Hébuterne)*, Lino Ventura *(Morel)*, Marianne Oswald *(Berthe Weil)*, Antoine Tudal *(Cendrars)*, François Jone *(commissaire de police)*, Pâquerette *(Madame Salomon)*, Daniel Mendaille *(professor)*, Harry Max *(doctor)*, Arlette Poirier *(Lulu)*, Robert Ripa *(Marcel)*, Frank Edwards *(Mr. Dickson)*, Carol Sands *(Mrs. Dickson)*, Judith Magre.

Biographical drama. Source: Georges-Michel Michel, *Les Montparnos* (Paris, 1924). In Montparnasse young Amedeo Modigliani becomes embittered and dissolute over public indifference to his paintings. Though his wealthy mistress, English writer Beatrice Hastings, appreciates his genius, she encourages his life of drunkenness and debauchery rather than his work. One day, he meets Jeanne Hébuterne, a young art student with whom he falls in love, but after one night together, her outraged father takes her away from Paris. Modigliani's intensified drinking soon affects his lungs, and he is told by a doctor that he must go to southern France if he is to recover from tuberculosis. In Nice he again sees Jeanne, who returns to Paris with him and becomes his model and mistress. An exhibition of his paintings is arranged by his good friend and patron, Léopold Sborowski, but when it is generally ignored by the public, Modigliani again turns to alcohol. Other disappointments follow, and he is reduced to peddling sketches at sidewalk cafes. Eventually his weakened condition causes him to collapse on the street, and a few hours later he dies in a nearby hospital. Realizing that Jeanne is unaware of her lover's death, Morel, an unscrupulous art dealer, visits her and buys all of Modigliani's masterpieces. *Painters. Mistresses. Students. Models. Patrons. Art dealers. Drunkenness. Authors. Tuberculosis. Paris—Montparnasse. Nice. Amedeo Modigliani. Beatrice Hastings. Jeanne Hébuterne. Léopold Zborowski.*

Note: Location scenes filmed in Paris and Nice. Opened in Paris in Apr 1958 as *Montparnasse 19*; running time: 120 min; in Rome in Sep 1958 as *Montparnasse*; running time: 100 min. Sources conflict on music credit. The film is dedicated to Max Ophuls, who was the scheduled director before his death.

UNA MOGLIE AMERICANA see **RUN FOR YOUR WIFE**

MOIRA see **WOMEN WOMEN WOMEN MOIRA**

MOJU see **THE BLIND BEAST**

THE MOLESTER see **NEVER TAKE CANDY FROM A STRANGER**

THE MOLESTERS (Switzerland)　　F6.3242

Praesens Film. *Dist* Aristocrat Films. 26 Mar **1964** [Atlanta opening]. Sd; b&w. 35mm. 89 min.

Prod Lazar Wechsler. *Exec Prod* Max Dora. *Prod U. S. Vers* Bob Moscow, Theodore Mann. *Dir* Franz Schnyder. *Screenplay* Richard Schweizer, Wolfgang Menge. *Photog* Emil Berna. *Orig Mus* Walter Baumgartner. *Mus U. S. Vers* Bernard Bennett. *Zither* Martin Gotelcheck. *Sd Supv U. S. Vers* Bob Moscow. *Dub* Titra Sound Corp.

Cast: Mathias Wieman, Eva Kotthaus, Kurt Heintel, Wolfgang Reichmann, Peter Arens, Franz Matter, Fred Tanner, Walter Kiesler, Margrit Winter, Edwin Maechler, Pierre Tagmann, Ellen Widmann, Peter Ehrlich, Megge Lehmann, Maximilian Wolters, Olivia Oettli, Eva Mueller, Andrea Teuwen, Gaby Kaufmann, Freddy Karsten.

Documentary. In exploring sex offenses, particularly against children, this film reveals the inner workings of the Zurich police and INTERPOL as they pursue persons accused of voyeurism, rape, fetishism, sadism, and masochism. After the criminals are arrested and given psychological tests, they may be sentenced to an institution or undergo brain surgery (with their consent) in order to be rehabilitated. *Sex deviates. Police. Psychiatrists. Criminals—Rehabilitation. Voyeurism. Rape. Fetishism. Sadism. Masochism. Brain surgery. Zurich. INTERPOL.*

Note: Location scenes filmed in Zurich. Released in Switzerland in 1963 as *Der Sittlichkeitsverbrecher*. Additional footage may have been added by Moscow and Mann for U. S. release.

THE MOLLY MAGUIRES　　F6.3243

Tamm Productions. *Dist* Paramount Pictures. 27 Jan **1970** [Scranton, Pennsylvania, opening; c5 Jan 1970; LP37376]. Sd; col (Technicolor). 35mm (Panavision). 124 min. *MPAA rating* M.

A Martin Ritt Production. *Prod* Martin Ritt, Walter Bernstein. *Dir* Martin Ritt. *2d Unit Dir* Oscar Rudolph. *Writ* Walter Bernstein. *Dir Photog* James Wong Howe. *2d Unit Photog* Morris Hartzband. *Camera Op* Ed Garvin. *Asst Camera* Charles Termini. *2d Unit Camera* Fred Porrett. *Art Dir* Tambi Larsen. *Set Decor* Darrell Silvera. *Film Ed* Frank Bracht. *Mus* Henry Mancini. *Sd* John Muchmore. *Sd Rec* Bill Ford, Elden Ruberg. *Asst Dir* James Rosenberger. *Prod Mgr* David Golden. *Unit Prod Mgr* Wally Samson. *Script Supv* Marvin Weldon. *Location Mgr* Robert Crawford, Sr. *Cost Dsgn* Dorothy Jeakins. *Women's Wardrobe* Ruth Stella. *Men's Wardrobe* Gildo Scarano. *Makeup* Wally Westmore. *Hairstyles* Scotty Rachin. *Sp Eff* Willis Cook. *Tech Adv Mine Operations* Joseph Lawrence. *Constr Supv* Elmer Rodgers. *Prop Master* Robert McCrillis. *Key Grip* John Hennessy. *Gaffer* Warren Hoag. *Casting* Hoyt Bowers, Diane Schatten. *Stunt Dir* Roger Creed.

Cast: Richard Harris *(James McParlan/McKenna)*, Sean Connery *(Jack Kehoe)*, Samantha Eggar *(Mary Raines)*, Frank Finlay *(Davies)*, Anthony Zerbe *(Dougherty)*, Bethel Leslie *(Mrs. Kehoe)*, Art Lund *(Frazier)*, Anthony Costello *(Frank McAndrew)*, Philip Bourneuf *(Father O'Connor)*, Brendan Dillon *(Mr. Raines)*, Frances Heflin *(Mrs. Frazier)*, John Alderson *(Jenkins)*, Malachy McCourt *(bartender)*, Susan Goodman *(Mrs. McAndrew)*, Peter Rogan *(Gomer James)*, William Clune *(Franklin Gowen)*, Phillip Richards *(Gen. Charles Albright)*, Karen Machon *(girl at football game)*, Tom Jones, actor *(football player)*.

Historical drama. Suggested by: Arthur H. Lewis, *Lament for the Molly Maguires* (New York, 1964). In 1876 the Molly Maguires, a secret society of immigrant Irish coal miners terrorizing the eastern Pennsylvania anthracite belt, are infiltrated by company detective James McParlan, who poses as fugitive murderer James McKenna. McParlan rents a room in the home of disabled miner Raines, and courts Raines' ambitious daughter, Mary. Having secured a job as a miner, the detective ingratiates himself with coworkers by leading the Gaelic football team to victory over its Welsh rival and by beating a brutal policeman. Furthermore, McParlan allays the suspicions of Molly leader Jack Kehoe by casting the decisive vote to murder a mine superintendent, and by rescuing another Molly during the assassination. Following the death of Mary's father, Kehoe and McParlan, claiming Raines' right to a burial suit, break into, loot, and set afire the company store. When Mollies Kehoe and McAndrew attempt to sabotage a mine, however, McParlan alerts Police Chief Davies, and they are arrested. At the trial the detective's testimony results in the Mollies' conviction and death sentence. Shocked by McParlan's duplicity, Mary rejects the agent. While the gallows are being constructed in the jail yard, McParlan confronts the imprisoned Kehoe, then departs for reassignment as head of the Denver Pinkerton Agency. *Immigrants. Police. Coal miners. Irish. Detectives. Informers. Imposture. Perfidy. Coal mining. Assassination. Sabotage. Capital punishment. Secret societies. Trials. Mining towns. Pennsylvania. James McParlan. Jack Kehoe. Frank McAndrew. Daniel Dougherty. Molly Maguires. Pinkerton Detective Agency.*

Note: Location scenes filmed in Pennsylvania, in Eckley, Bloomsburg, Llewelyn, Wilkes-Barre, Hazelton, in the boroughs of Mauch Chunk, Weatherly, and Ashland, and in the counties of Luzerne, Carbon, Schuylkill, and Columbia. The musical score includes the traditional Irish tunes: "Eileen Aroon," "Cockles and Mussels," and "Gary Owen."

LA MÔME PIGALLE *see* **THE MAIDEN**

MOMENT OF DANGER *see* **MALAGA**

MOMENT OF TERROR (Japan)   **F6.3244**
Toho Co. Feb **1969** [Los Angeles showing]. Sd; b&w. 35mm (Tohoscope). 100 min.
Prod Masumi Fujimoto. *Dir* Mikio Naruse. *Screenplay* Zenzo Matsuyama. *Photog* Rokuro Nishigaki. *Mus* Masaru Sato.
Cast: Hideko Takamine *(The Mother)*, Yoko Tsukasa, Eitaro Ozawa, Hisashi Nakayama, Toshio Kurosawa, Daisuke Kato, Natsuko Kahara, Yutaka Sada.
Melodrama. The only child of a working-class mother is run over and killed by the philandering wife of a company president. The president has news of the accident suppressed, but the mother learns the identity of the driver and takes a job in her household, intending to kill her young son who is the same age as her own dead child. *Children. Philanderers. Domestics. Executives. Revenge. Motherhood. Murder. Automobile accidents.*
Note: Released in Japan in Apr 1966 as *Hikinige.*

THE MOMENT OF TRUTH (Italy/Spain)   **F6.3245**
Federiz–As Films Producción. *Dist* Rizzoli Film Distributors. 9 Aug **1965** [New York opening]. Sd; col (Technicolor). 35mm (Techniscope). 105 min. [Also 110 min.]
Prod Antonio Cervi, Francesco Rosi. *Dir-Screenplay-Story* Francesco Rosi. *Screenplay Collab* Pedro Portabella, Ricardo Muñoz Suay, Pedro Beltrán. *Adapt(?)* Raffaele La Capria. *Photog* Gianni Di Venanzo, Aiace Parolin, Pasquale De Santis. *Set Decor* José Antonio de la Guerra. *Film Ed* Mario Serandrei. *Mus* Piero Piccioni. *Sd* Claudio Maielli, Mario Ronchetti. *Asst Dir* Ricardo Muñoz Suay, Marco Guarnaschelli. *Prod Mgr* Enzo Provenzale.
Cast: Miguel "Miguelín" Mateo *(Miguel)*, Pedro Basauri *(Maestro Pedrucho)*, José Gómez Sevillano *(impresario)*, Linda Christian *(American woman)*.
Drama. Following the path of many boys from poor farming regions of southern Spain, Miguel makes his way north to seek his fortune in Barcelona. Like the others he soon finds that the only work available is as an unskilled laborer. Hand-in-hand with the job, however, is pressure to make kickback payments from his wages to corrupt agents. Finally, he enrolls in a school for bullfighters which is run by Pedrucho. In time, Miguel faces his first bull as an apprentice bullfighter. One Sunday afternoon, he leaps into the ring during a fight, angering the toreros but attracting the attention of the press. A modest provincial contract results, and contracts subsequently begin to mount. Soon he is enveloped by a daily schedule of fights; although the pace is hectic, he reaps the profits of a torero: automobiles, parties, wealthy women, and a new home for his parents. But the strain of his success begins to weigh on him heavily; he begins to lose his nerve, and his luck starts to run short. His fate now appears to be out of his control, as was his climb to the top, and one day he dies facing a stalwart bull. *Bullfighters. Employment. Poverty. Wealth. Death. Barcelona. Bulls.*
Note: Location scenes filmed in Spain. Opened in Rome in Mar 1965 as *Il momento della verità*; running time: 110 min; in Madrid in May 1966 as *El momento de la verdad*; running time: 107 min. Alternative Spanish title: *Vivir desviviéndose.*

MOMENT OF TRUTH *see* **NEVER LET GO**

MOMENT TO MOMENT   **F6.3246**
Mervyn LeRoy Productions. *Dist* Universal Pictures. 27 Jan **1966** [Miami, Florida, opening; c5 Feb 1966; LP35374]. Sd (Westrex); col (Technicolor). 35mm. 108 min.
Prod-Dir Mervyn LeRoy. *In Charge of Prod* Edward Muhl. *Screenplay* John Lee Mahin, Alec Coppel. *Dir Photog* Harry Stradling. *Art Dir* Alexander Golitzen, Alfred Sweeney. *Set Decor* John McCarthy, John Austin. *Main Titl* Pacific Title. *Film Ed* Philip W. Anderson. *Mus* Henry Mancini. *Mus Supv*

Joseph Gershenson. *Titl Song* Johnny Mercer, Henry Mancini. *Sd* Waldon O. Watson, John Moriarity. *Asst Dir* Phil Bowles. *Unit Prod Mgr* Bob Larson. *Honor Blackman's Wardrobe* Rosemary Odell. *Miss Seberg's Wardrobe* Yves Saint Laurent. *Makeup* Bud Westmore. *Hairstyles* Larry Germain. *Coöp* Fondation M. et A. Maeght, Hippodrome de la Côte d'Azur, Aéroport de Nice-Côte.
Cast: Jean Seberg *(Kay Stanton)*, Honor Blackman *(Daphne Fields)*, Sean Garrison *(Mark Dominic)*, Arthur Hill *(Neil Stanton)*, Grégoire Aslan *(Inspector DeFargo)*, Peter Robbins *(Timmy)*, Donald Woods *(Mr. Singer)*, Walter Reed *(Hendricks)*, Albert Carrier *(travel agency clerk)*, Lomax Study *(Albie)*, Richard Angarola *(Givet)*, Georgette Anys *(Louise)*.
Romantic melodrama. Source: Alec Coppel, "Laughs With a Stranger" (a story; publication undetermined). Psychiatrist Neil Stanton, his wife, Kay, and their son, Timmy, are living on the French Riviera while Neil is on sabbatical. Neil's frequent lecture trips leave Kay lonely, and one day she and Timmy meet an American naval ensign, Mark. Kay and Mark soon become emotionally involved. When Kay decides to break off the relationship because she really does love Neil, they quarrel and Mark is shot accidentally. Panic-stricken, Kay enlists the aid of her worldly neighbor, Daphne, in dumping the apparently dead body into a ravine and she telephones the police anonymously to inform them of the location of the body, giving no other details. Some days later, curious that the incident has not been in the news, Kay returns to the ravine. Back at her home, Inspectors DeFargo and Albie visit her and ask about her involvement. Her response is unconvincing, and DeFargo persuades Neil to help an amnesia victim who is recovering from a gunshot wound; the man is, in fact, Mark. DeFargo hopes that Mark's exposure to Kay will restore his memory. Even after he finally regains his memory, however, Mark does not disclose the truth about what happened. He departs for the States; and Neil, though he surmises the truth, realizes that Kay truly loves him. *Psychiatrists. Housewives. Detectives. Americans in foreign countries. Neighbors. Loneliness. Manslaughter. Marriage. Infidelity. Amnesia. Filial relations. France. Riviera.*
Note: Location scenes filmed on the French Riviera.

EL MOMENTO DE LA VERDAD *see* **THE MOMENT OF TRUTH**

IL MOMENTO DELLA VERITÀ *see* **THE MOMENT OF TRUTH**

LA MOMIA AZTECA CONTRA EL ROBOT HUMANO *see* **THE ROBOT VS. THE AZTEC MUMMY**

MOMMAN, LITTLE JUNGLE BOY *see* **LITTLE JUNGLE BOY**

MONA   **F6.3247**
Graffitti Productions. *Dist* Sherpix, Inc. 6 Aug **1970** [San Francisco showing]. Sd; col. 35mm. 72 min. [Also reviewed at 75 min.]
Prod-Dir-Writ Bill Osco. *Photog* Howard Ziehm.
Cast: Fifi Watson *(Mona)*, Judy Angel *(her mother)*.
Drama. Mona, a young woman who lives with her widowed mother, was badly traumatized as a child when her father forced her to perform an act of fellatio. Although the incident has left her with nymphomaniacal tendencies, she refuses to have premarital intercourse with her fiancé because she is determined to maintain her virginity until her wedding day. She does, however, give vent to her passion by stopping strangers and offering them oral sex. Following a row with her fiancé, Mona goes off by herself to a movie. When the young man comes looking for her at her home, he finds her mother masturbating with a tarantula-shaped vibrator. She tells him she is a lonely widow and they make love. Later, discovering that she has seduced a man in the balcony, serviced a passerby in an alley, and had a lesbian encounter, the fiancé drags Mona from the theater and forces her into an orgy with all of her former conquests. Reduced to near-hysteria, Mona tearfully returns to her mother; as she starts to divulge her past, however, her mother confides that she, too, has something to confess. *Widows. Oral sex. Filial relations. Child molesting. Incest. Virginity. Lesbianism. Nymphomania. Autoeroticism. Sex aids. Motion picture theaters.*
Note: Filmed in Los Angeles. Also known as *Mona the Virgin Nymph.*

MONA LISA TAILS   **F6.3248**
ca **1969**. Sd; b&w with col seq. 35mm. [Feature length assumed.]
Sex film. Two lesbians, Mona and Lisa, live together. One day a door-to-door photographic equipment salesman stops by. In demonstrating a new projector to the young women, the salesman shows sex films of himself and his girl friends. Inspired, Mona and Lisa enjoy sex with the salesman. *Traveling salesmen. Lesbianism. Troilism. Sex exploitation films.*

MONA THE VIRGIN NYMPH *see* **MONA**

LA MONACA DI MONZA *see* **THE LADY OF MONZA**

LE MONACHINE see **THE LITTLE NUNS**

UN MONDE NOUVEAU see **A YOUNG WORLD**

LE MONDE SANS SOLEIL see **WORLD WITHOUT SUN**

MONDO BALORDO (Italy)   F6.3249
Cineproduzioni Associate. *Dist* Crown International Pictures. 8 Mar **1967** [Los Angeles opening]. Sd; col (Eastman Color). 35mm. 87 min.
Pres by Albert T. Viola. *English Vers Prod* Ivanhoe Productions. *Dir* Roberto Bianchi Montero. *Orig Narr* Francesco Torti, Guido Castaldo. *English Vers Narr* Ted Weiss. *Photog* Giuseppe La Torre. *Film Ed* Enzo Alfonsi. *English Vers Ed* Fred Von Bernewitz. *Mus* Lallo Gori. *Mus With Participation of* Nini Rosso. *Sd* Franco Bassi.
Cast: Franz Drago (himself, a midget), Boris Karloff (narrator).
Documentary. A record of unusual and bizarre customs practiced throughout the world. Included in the footage are scenes of moviemakers utilizing special effects to make their film heroes look like modern-day Samsons; tourists in desert countries paying large fees to "go native" for a night; a Las Vegas beauty pageant; young girls in primitive locales being given in marriage at an age when their contemporaries in other lands are playing with dolls; the lottery craze in Italy; a visit to an oriental opium den; a transvestite bar; a man attempting to break through the Berlin Wall; Mediterranean fishermen secretly working for smugglers; children in Ecuador who are addicted to cocaine; the religious rites of India's "untouchables"; young boatmen in Capri taking foreign women out on fishing boats for the night; Arabian beauty parlors; a man living his life according to the conviction that he is the reincarnation of Rudolph Valentino; and Englishmen playing adult "parlor games" in Sherwood Forest. *Actors. Tourists. Fishermen. Arabs. English. Children. Social customs. Marriage. Smuggling. Transvestism. Prostitution. Reincarnation. Rites and ceremonies. Motion pictures. Beauty contests. Lotteries. Opium. Religious sects. Cocaine. Beauty shops. Las Vegas. Mediterranean Sea. Ecuador. Capri. Sherwood Forest. India. Berlin Wall. Rudolph Valentino.*
Note: Released in Italy in 1964; running time: 93 min.

MONDO BIZARRO   F6.3250
Olympic International Films. 25 Aug **1966** [San Francisco showing]. Sd; b&w and col. 35mm. 78 min.
Prod Felix Lomax. *Exec Coörd* Stan Russell. *Dir, Camera Unit No. 2* Seasu Hakasomi. *Narr* David Kayne. *Orig Idea* R. W. Cresse, R. L. Frost. *Dir Col Cinematog* R. L. Frost. *Photog, Camera Unit No. 1* Saul Resnick. *Photog, Camera Unit No. 2* Toki Matsumuri. *Op, Camera Unit No. 1* Lloyd Williamson. *Op, Camera Unit No. 2* Sam Tokahashi. *Mus Comp & Cond* Lawrence Van Lattman. *Sd Rec* Spectra Sound. *Unit Mgr, Camera Unit No. 1* Arnie Cohen.
Cast: Claude Emmand (narrator).
Documentary. Hidden cameras investigate facets of human behavior normally obscured beneath the surface of respectable life: worshipers perform a secret voodoo rite in Nassau; young men and women are auctioned like livestock at an illegal Lebanese slave market; a Sydney, Australia, man casually pierces his cheek with a needle to demonstrate the principle of mind over matter; Vito, a California artist, uses photographs of nude models to create his controversial sculptures; a Kyoto, Japan, massage parlor specializes in a "double massage"; demonstrators in Chicago protest the war in Vietnam; manufacturers of erotic underwear do a $7 million-a-year business; and, in a private neo-Nazi theater in Hamburg, Nazi sexual practices are revived for the entertainment of a jaded audience. *Models. Sculptors. Masseurs. Stoics. Demonstrations. Slavery. Sadism. Eroticism. Neo-nazism. Voodoo. Rites and ceremonies. Lingerie. Stag shows. Theater. Vietnam War 1964–73. Nassau. Lebanon. Sydney (Australia). California. Kyoto. Hamburg. Chicago.*
Note: Also known as *Bizarro*. Felix Lomax is a pseudonym for Bob Cresse; David Kayne for Bob Cresse and R. L. Frost; all Oriental names are pseudonyms.

MONDO CANE (Italy)   F6.3251
Cineriz. *Dist* Times Film Corp., Cinemation Industries. 3 Apr **1963** [New York opening]. Sd; col (Technicolor). 35mm. 105 min.
Prod-Dir-Story-Narr Gualtiero Jacopetti. *Assoc Prod-Assoc Dir-Writ* (see note) Paolo Cavara, Franco Prosperi. *Collab Dir (Australia)* Vine Vlasoff. *Collab Dir (Borneo)* Ling Beng Siew. *Collab Dir (China)* K.-C. Liang. *Collab Dir (Europe)* Carlo Chiarini, José Montaner, Garry, Marcel Boille, Henry Spack, Gunnar, Sergio Marcellini, Michel Obry. *Collab Dir (Japan)* Katznio Weda. *Collab Dir (Malaysia)* Charles Lake. *Collab Dir (New Guinea)* Capo Cavallo. *Collab Dir (North Pacific)* Cap F. B. *Collab Dir (Palestine)* Moïse Talbert. *Collab Dir (Polynesia)* De Putini. *Collab Dir (Sandwich Islands)* Henry Hoover. *Collab Dir (Solomon Islands)* Juppiter. *Collab Dir (United States)* Carlo Pavone, Bill Brownell. *Photog* Antonio Climati, Benito Frattari. *Film Ed* Gualtiero Jacopetti. *Mus & Theme Song:* "More" Nino Oliviero, Riz Ortolani.

Italian Lyr Marcello Ciorciolini. *English Lyr* Norman Newell. *Organizer of Location Photog* Stanis Nievo.
Cast: Stefano Sibaldi (English language narrator).
Documentary. A view of mores and customs throughout the world illustrates the proposition that "it's a dog's life": The people of Rudolph Valentino's hometown, Castellaneta, Italy, still revere his memory, while actor Rossano Brazzi is besieged by women who tear the shirt off his back. In pursuit of the male, New Guinea maidens are compared to bikini-clad girls on the French Riviera. A bereaved woman in New Guinea nurses a suckling pig; elsewhere in the region pigs are slaughtered as inhabitants break a fast. In Pasadena, California, pet dogs are given lavish funerals, while in Formosa puppies are eaten by gourmets. Food is forced into the throats of Strasbourg geese to provide paté de foie gras, and Tokyo calves are made to consume 6 quarts of beer daily. Women on the island of Tabar are not considered suitable for marriage to the king if they weigh less than 300 pounds. By contrast, American women work out at Vic Tanny's gyms to lose weight. Hong Kong markets sell crocodiles, toads, lizards, and snakes; a swank New York restaurant serves butterflies, muskrat, stuffed beetles, and ants. In Calabria, villagers lacerate their legs with glass in memory of Christ's crucifixion. Sydney beaches are guarded by 16-year-old female lifeguards. Turtles on Bikini, poisoned by atomic radiation, cannot find their way back to sea after laying their eggs on shore. Malaysian fishermen take revenge on sharks by forcing poisonous sea urchins into their jaws. Roman children polish the skulls of unknown victims of the black plague. Hamburg beer drinkers carouse all night. In Singapore, relatives feast while awaiting the death of one of the family in a "house of death." American tourists in Hawaii pay to learn "authentic" Hawaiian customs. Gurkha warriors show their strength by decapitating steers; runaway bulls in Portugal kill four people. Finally, the natives of Port Moresby, New Guinea, have built a miniature airstrip because they believe that airplanes come from paradise and will eventually be sent to them. *Lifeguards. Fishermen. Tourists. Gurkhas. Rites and ceremonies. Social customs. Sexuality. Drunkenness. Death. Obesity. Christianity. Food. Funerals. Health clubs. Restaurants. Atom bomb. Airplanes. Castellaneta. New Guinea. Pasadena. Riviera. Taiwan. Strasbourg. Tokyo. Tabar Islands. Hong Kong. New York City. Calabria. Sydney (Australia). Bikini. Malaysia. Rome. Hamburg. Singapore. Hawaii. Portugal. Port Moresby. Rudolph Valentino. Rossano Brazzi. Dogs. Pigs. Geese. Cows. Bulls. Animals.*
Note: Opened in Rome in Apr 1962. Rereleased by Cinemation Industries as *Mondo Cane No. 1*; running time: 97 min; MPAA rating: R. Also known as *A Dog's Life*. Italian sources credit scenario to Jacopetti, Cavara, and Prosperi. The first of a series of documentaries by Jacopetti.

MONDO CANE NO. 1 see **MONDO CANE**

MONDO CANE NO. 2 see **MONDO PAZZO**

MONDO DAYTONA   F6.3252
Mondo Productions. *Dist* Craddock Films. May **1968** [Bradenton, Florida, opening]. Sd; col (Capitol Color). 35mm. 80 min.
Prod Bill Packham, Gordon Craddock. *Dir* Frank Willard. *Mus Dir* Bill Lowry. *Background Mus & Songs:* "Spooky," "Breakthrough" played by Mike Sharp. *Songs:* "These Are Not My People," "Down in the Boondocks," "Hush" Joe South. *Sung by* Billy Joe Royal. *Song:* "She Drives Me out of My Mind" Arthur K. Adams. *Perf by* The Swinging Medallions. *Song:* "Double Shot of My Baby's Love" perf by The Swinging Medallions. *Songs:* "What Kind of Fool," "Laugh It Off" sung by The Tams.
Cast: Billy Joe Royal (narrator).
Documentary. Hidden cameras record the activities of vacationing college students in Daytona Beach during Spring at rock and roll parties, in motel suites, and frolicking on the beach. Motorcycle clubs are also observed. *Students. Motorcycle gangs. Rock and roll. Vacations. Spring. Daytona Beach.*
Note: Filmed on location in Daytona Beach, Florida. Subtitled: *How To Swing on Your Spring Vacation.*

MONDO DEPRAVADOS see **MUNDO DEPRAVADOS**

IL MONDO DI NOTTE see **WORLD BY NIGHT**

MONDO DI NOTTE N. 3 see **ECCO**

MONDO EXOTICA see **NAUGHTY DALLAS**

MONDO FREUDO   F6.3253
Olympic International Films. 27 Apr **1966** [Champaign, Illinois, showing]. Sd; col. 35mm. 80 min.
Overall Production Credits: *Prod* R. W. Cresse. *Dir* R. L. Frost.
Camera Unit No. 1: *Dir* Kasem Salhmadine. *Photog* Eldor Ishmahd. *Op* Kaldar Kashmald.
Camera Unit No. 2: *Dir* Seasu Hakasomi. *Photog* Jerome Matsumurie. *Op* Sam Tokahashi.

Camera Unit No. 3: *Dir* David Kayne. *Photog* Samual Hayatt. *Op* Lloyd Williamson.

Cast: Judy Adler.

Documentary. Hidden cameras record strange and unusual sexual practices around the world: two teenagers make love at night on a beach where a mother was nursing her baby earlier that day; strippers in a Tijuana nightclub invite male members of the audience to join them for sex play on stage; in San Francisco, customers are treated to a topless Watusi dance at a night spot; a restaurant improves its lunchtime business with a nude fashion show; nude girls are auctioned in a Mexican slave market; Puerto Rican immigrants celebrate a black mass in a loft near Times Square, preparing a 17-year-old virgin for sacrifice to the Devil; at the Saseiby club in Japan, performers are beaten sadistically for the titillation of the audience; two artists make their living by painting directly on the nude female form; strippers remove all of their clothes in a private London club exempt from censorship; and, at the Old Heidelberg restaurant in Berlin, customers are entertained by two young, female mud wrestlers. *Stripteasers. Dancers. Puerto Ricans. Virginity. Painters. Models. Immigrants. Stag shows. Nudity. Sadism. Striptease. Eroticism. Human sacrifice. Adolescence. Rites and ceremonies. White slave traffic. Fetishism. Wrestling. Nightclubs. Fashion shows. Watusi (dance). Clubs. Restaurants. San Francisco. Tijuana (Mexico). Mexico. Japan. London. Berlin. New York City. The Devil.*

Note: Also known as *The World of Freud*. David Kayne is a pseudonym for R. W. Cresse and R. L. Frost. All other production credits are pseudonyms.

MONDO GIRLS see MONDO TOPLESS

MONDO HOLLYWOOD   F6.3254

Omega–Cyrano Corp. *Dist* Emerson Film Enterprises, Hollywood International Pictures. Aug **1967**. Sd; col (Pathe). 35mm. 91 min.

Prod-Dir-Writ Robert Carl Cohen. *Exec Prod* Howard I. Cogan, Arthur Gilbert. *Assoc Prod* Gerald Alcan, Helene K. Cohen. *Photog* Robert Carl Cohen. *Aerial Photog* Doyle E. Fields. *Titl Dsgn* Allen Porter. *Film Ed* Robert Carl Cohen. *Mus Dir* Mike Curb. *Mus Perf by* The Mugwumps, Davie Allan and the Arrows, Bobby Jameson.

Cast—Those Seen in the Film: Lewis Beach Marvin, III *(creater of "Moonfire")*, Dale Davis *(surfing film producer)*, Jim Arender *(sky diver and actor)*, Vito *(art and dance instructor)*, Theodore Charack *("The Night Stalker")*, Sheryl Carson *(psychedelic body painter)*, Bobby Jameson *(folksinger)*, Richard Alpert, Ph.D. *(clinical psychologist)*, Valerie Porter *(sculptress)*, Jennie Lee *("Bazoom Girl")*, Jack Gerard *(Hollywood agent)*, Jay Sebring *(men's hair stylist)*, Hope Chest *(exotic dancer)*, Carazini *("The Cigarette Comic")*, Mrs. Herbert White *(silent film star)*, Rudi Gernreich *(designer)*, Peanuts *(transvestite)*, Mary Ewaldt *(artist)*, Murry Schwimmer *("Pan")*, King Solomon *(metaphysician)*, Dee Dee Cartier *(model)*, Helene Frank *(model)*, Gypsy Boots.

Documentary. This film looks at untraditional Hollywood: the people swept up in the whirl of current fads and trends. Scenes of sundry actors, would-be actors, models, artists, transvestites, flower children, and politicians, among others, take place at film premieres, parties, on streets, and in cemeteries. Psychologist Richard Alpert talks about LSD; sculptor Valerie Porter talks about her art; a woman submits to body painting; and skydiver Jim Arender leaps out of an airplane in a free fall to earth. *Motion picture producers. Actors. Art teachers. Dance teachers. Sculptors. Couturiers. Artists. Models. Go-go dancers. Psychologists. Talent agents. Flower children. Transvestism. Skydiving. Body painting. LSD. Hollywood.*

Note: Also known as *Image* and *Hippie Hollywood: The Acid-Blasting Freaks.*

MONDO INFAME (Italy)   F6.3255

Cineproduzioni Associate. *Dist* Filmarco. 27 Dec **1963** [New York State license]. Sd; col (Eastmancolor). 35mm (Stereorama). 85 min.

Dir Roberto Montero. *Photog* Enzo Alfonsi.

Documentary. No information about the precise nature of this film has been found, although it is assumed that it deals with social customs. *Social customs.*

Note: Opened in Rome in May 1963; running time: 90 min.

MONDO INSANITY see MONDO PAZZO

MONDO KEYHOLE see THE WORST CRIME OF ALL!

MONDO MACABRO see MACABRO

MONDO MOD   F6.3256

Timely Motion Pictures. 21 Jun **1967** [Boston opening]. Sd; col (Eastman Color). 35mm. 89 min.

Prod-Dir Peter Perry. *Exec Prod* Gil Atamian, Harry Novak. *Asst Prod* John Cravin. *2d Unit Dir* Jack Starrett. *Writ* Sherman Greene. *Dir Photog* Leslie Kovacs, William Zsigmond. *2d Unit Photog* Ewing Brown, Ed DePriest. *Asst*

Camera Peter Sorel. *Lighting* Richard Aguilar. *Art Dir* Earl Marshall. *Film Ed* Peter Perry. *Mus* The Gretschmen. *Sd Rec* Bob Dietz. *Asst Dir* Jim Corvin. *Cost* Greta Meyers. *Makeup* Jim Martin.

Cast: Harve Humble *(narrator)*, Sam the Soul and The Inspirations, The Group.

Documentary. This documentary maintains that America's youth (aged 13 to 25) have more resources, more leisure, more knowledge, and more money than any other generation before them. Highlighted in the film are the small shops that specialize in original, handmade "mod" apparel; the craze for motorcycles and go-carts; the challenge of facing a 30-foot wall of water with only a 10-foot surfboard; the famed Sunset Strip "youth riot" that demonstrated against the injustices of modern society; the use of LSD and marijuana to increase self-awareness; and the coffee shops and discotheques that have become the "in" meeting places for the young. Above all, it is the music of love and protest (exemplified in the film by Sam the Soul and The Inspirations and The Group) that has the strongest appeal to this generation. The picture concludes at the Whiskey-A-Go-Go cafe on Sunset Strip. *Surfers. Motorcyclists. Youth. Wealth. Demonstrations. Music. Boutiques. Clothes. LSD. Marijuana. Discotheques. Go-carts. Coffeehouses. Los Angeles—Sunset Strip. Whiskey-A-Go-Go.*

IL MONDO NELLA MIA TASCA see THE WORLD IN MY POCKET

MONDO NUDO see NAKED WORLD

UN MONDO NUOVO see A YOUNG WORLD

MONDO OSCENITA   F6.3257

Dist American Film Distributing Corp. 30 Jun **1966** [San Francisco showing]. Sd; b&w. 35mm. 71 min.

Prod (see note) George Weiss, Gino Polizzo. *Dir (see note)* Joseph P. Mawra, Carlo Scappine.

Narrator: Joel Holt.

Compilation film. An investigation of changing attitudes toward sex in the motion picture industry from the early 1930's to the present day contrasts the outlooks of European and American producers, seeks out the women who act in sex films, traces the portrayal of lesbian relationships through the years, explores the connection between sex and violence in the movies, documents the increasingly uninhibited portrayal of sex on the screen with film clips from motion pictures banned in countries around the world, and examines the present trends in the sex film. Includes scenes from *Madame Olga's Massage Parlor* (q. v.), *My Baby Is Black* (q. v.), *Nudes of All Nations* (q. v.), *Olga's Girls* (q. v.), *Olga's House of Shame* (q. v.), *Paris Ooh-La-La* (q. v.), *The Sensualist* (q. v.), and *Sunswept* (q. v.). *Actors. Motion picture producers. Censorship. Lesbianism. Sex exploitation films. Motion pictures—History.*

Note: Maryland censorship records credit Gino Polizzo as producer and Carlo Scappine as director. These may be pseudonyms for George Weiss and Joseph P. Mawra. Also known as *World of Obscenity.*

MONDO PAZZO (Italy)   F6.3258

Federiz–Cineriz–Rizzoli Films. *Dist* Rizzoli Film Distributors, Cinemation Industries. 27 Jan **1965** [Los Angeles opening]. Sd; col (Technicolor). 35mm. 94 min. [Also 80 min.]

Prod Mario Maffei, Giorgio Cecchini. *Dir-Screenplay-Comm* Gualtiero Jacopetti. *Dir-Screenplay* Franco Prosperi. *Photog* Benito Frattari. *Film Ed* Mario Morra. *Mus & Theme Song:* "I'll Set My Love to Music" Nino Oliviero. *Orig Lyr* Guido Castaldo, Francesco Torti. *English Lyr* Marian Grudeff, Ray Jessel. *Mus Cond* Bruno Nicolai. *Mus Arr* Frank Metis. *Sung by* Steve Rossi.

Documentary. The film concentrates on the unusual, the bizarre, and the shocking aspects of life throughout the world: London surgeons remove dogs' vocal cords for experiments in vivisection; Italian peasant women cut and sell their hair to American wigmakers; Mexican peasants eat candy-filled skulls made of sugar in an ancient rite to insure the demise of Judas; they also get rid of parasitic insects by putting them in tortillas covered with hot sauce and eating them; Masai women use a mud and manure substance for fuel, building material, and an aphrodisiac; Americans sell kisses at a trade show. Other scenes include: automats and the rush hour in America; tourists taking mud baths in Hawaii; Masai women eating white pebbles to guarantee sterility for a month; hysteria over spiders in a deconsecrated church in Italy; a Buddhist monk publicly burning himself in Vietnam; American policemen disguised as women to trap robbers and sex offenders; Indian fakirs oblivious to pain as they walk over hot coals; Italian penitents climbing church steps on their bloody knees; factory pollution killing flamingoes in a lake; a tribe eating crocodile meat near Lake Victoria and becoming sterile as a result; a photography studio specializing in sadistic covers for lurid detective novels; a slave market on the Red Sea coast selling African girls into prostitution; other slave traders torturing children; Britons making speeches in Hyde Park; a Greek painter spitting colors onto his canvas; coffins being bought on an installment plan;

Hamburg female impersonators in a nightclub chorus line; and a 94-year-old woman embalmed in a sitting position for her funeral. *Peasants. Masai. Monks. Tourists. Police. Fakirs. Photographers. Children. Painters. Slavers. Greeks. Surgery. Vivisection. Rites and ceremonies. Suicide. Sterility (sexual). Female impersonation. Prostitution. Buddhism. Water pollution. Hysteria. Torture. Slavery. Self-immolation. Sadism. Embalming. Funerals. Churches. Factories. Coffins. Credit. Nightclubs. London. Italy. Vietnam. Africa. Greece. Mexico. Los Angeles. India. Lake Victoria. Red Sea. Hamburg. Pasadena. Dogs. Spiders. Flamingos. Birds.*

Note: Released in Italy in Nov 1963 as *Mondo cane ... n. 2*; running time: 97 min. Rereleased by Cinemation Industries as *Mondo Cane No. 2*; running time: 80 min; MPAA rating: R. Also known as *Crazy World, Insane World,* and *Mondo Insanity.* One of a series of documentaries by Jacopetti.

MONDO ROCCO   F6.3259

Bizarre Productions. *Dist* Signature Theatres, Continental Theatres. 25 Feb 1970 [Los Angeles opening]. Sd; col (Eastmancolor). 16mm. 163 min.

Prod-Dir-Writ Pat Rocco. *Photog* Pat Rocco. *Camera* Wayne Schotten, James Prestridge. *Film Ed* Pat Rocco. *Sd* Wayne Schotten, James Prestridge. *Sd Transfer* Sam Kopetsky. *Prod Mgr* Jack Pierce, dir. *Prod Coörd* Mike T. Oberholtzer. *Prod Asst* Dean Chambers.

Narrator: Pat Rocco.

Cast—"A Night at Joani's": Jim Bailey, Warren Fremming, Joani Waldor.

Anthology. The program consists of six short films and one feature length film, including: *Homosexuals on the March, Meat Market Arrest, Hair Revisited, Groovy Guy, Screen Test, Kiss,* and *A Night at Joani's* (feature). The feature focuses on a Halloween celebration at a North Hollywood nightclub, including entertainment by women and featuring Jim Bailey impersonating Barbra Streisand, Mae West, and Judy Garland. *Entertainers. Male homosexuality. Female impersonation. Nightclubs. Hallowe'en. Hollywood.*

IL MONDO SENZA SOLE *see* **WORLD WITHOUT SUN**

MONDO SEXO   F6.3260

Trans-Continental Artists. Apr 1967 [San Francisco showing]. Sd (RCA); b&w. 35mm. 69 min.

Prod-Writ Fanny Frankenstein. *Dir* Dale Berrystein. *Photog* Charles Martinistein. *Film Ed* Big Daddy Epstein, III. *Mus* Enrique Madariaga.

Cast: Frenchy Larue (*Frenchy*), Conrad Marcus (*Baby Face*), Claudine Manson (*Stella*), Jimmy Green (*Lieutenant Wolfgang*), Knockers O'Hare (*Knockers*), Sylvia Bardette (*Sylvia*), April Friday, Candy Stick, Bunny Bare (*themselves, the Tia-Juana Strippers*).

Comedy. Released after 10 years at hard labor for rape, Baby Face Riley immediately reverts to his former pursuit, lurking about nightclubs and raping intoxicated customers. Although his victims crave return engagements, Riley rapes but once. After a futile search for her assailant, a disappointed woman reports her attack to the police, who sound a city-wide alarm. Hearing of the alert, Riley's victims form a vigilante organization, determined to punish the criminal in their own way. One by one the vigilantes find and rape Riley, whom the police subsequently discover dead from sexual exhaustion. *Ex-convicts. Police. Vigilantes. Rape. Murder. Drunkenness. Lust. Nightclubs.*

Note: Compiled from outtakes of *The Hot Bed* (q. v.), *Passion in the Sun* (q. v.), and *Hot Blooded Woman* (q. v.). Dale Berrystein is a pseudonym for Dale Berry; Charles Martinistein for Carlos Martinez; and Big Daddy Epstein III for Harry Epstein.

MONDO TEENO (United States/Great Britain)   F6.3261

Unger Productions–James Garrett & Partners, Ltd.–Lanrus Pictures. *Dist* Trans American Films. Apr 1967 [c19 Apr 1967; LP35526]. Sd; b&w. 35mm. 81 min.

An Oliver A. Unger Production. *Prod-Dir-Writ* Norman Herman. *Dir U. S. Seq* George Lefferts. *Dir British Seq* Richard Lester. *Dir Swedish Seq* Jörn Donner. *Dir French Seq* Jean Herman. *Dir Japanese Seq* Walter J. Sheldon. *Dir Italian Seq* Eriprando Visconti. *Mus Comp* Mike Curb, Mike Summers. *Mus Score* Al Simms.

Narrator: Burt Topper.

Documentary. The film depicts teenagers throughout the world in revolt against society. In sequences filmed in the United States, Great Britain, Sweden, France, Italy, and Japan, the teenagers are shown to share a belief that no restrictions should be placed on their actions or their thoughts. The picture concentrates on sexual freedom, the drug problem, birth control, fashion, and rock music. The scenes include American youth using marijuana and LSD, teenagers engaging in sex, and a discussion of campus morals with a college student. Also included are investigations into teenaged prostitution in Japan and Italy and of homosexuality among Italian youth. The birth of a child to an unwed mother concludes the film. *Adolescence. Birth control. Fashion. Rock and roll. Pregnancy. Male homosexuality. College life. Childbirth. Marijuana. LSD. Sweden. France. Italy. Japan.*

Note: Also known as *Teenage Rebellion.*

MONDO TOPLESS   F6.3262

Eve Productions. 17 Nov 1966 [Maryland license; c1 Oct 1966; LP33019]. Sd; col (Eastmancolor). 35mm. 61 min.

Prod-Dir Russ Meyer.

Cast: Babette Bardot (*Bouncy*), Sin Lenee (*Lucious*), Diane Young (*Yummy*), Donna "X" (*'Xciting*), Pat Barringer (*Bumptious*), Darla Paris (*Delicious*), Darlene Grey (*Buxotic*), Lorna Maitland, Veronique Gabriel, Greta Thorwald, Denise Duval, Gigi La Touche, Abundavita, Heide Richter, Yvette Le Grand (*themselves*).

Documentary. In San Francisco some professional topless dancers are interviewed and shown at work, among them Pat Barringer, Darlene Grey, Sin Lenee, Darla Paris, Diane Young, Donna "X," and Babette Bardot. In Brussels' Moulin Rouge, topless dancer Veronique Gabriel performs her "dance of the leather belt." Greta Thorwald is interviewed in Copenhagen at the Atlantic Palace; and Denise Duval is seen at Le Cabaret Sexy in Nancy, France. Lorna Maitland, star of the sex exploitation film *Lorna,* is interviewed, and her screen test for *Lorna* is shown. In Paris, Gigi La Touche is seen at the Place Pigalle; and Abundavita is shown at work in Berlin's Fair Lady Film Bar. Heide Richter performs at Casino de Paris in Hamburg, and Yvette Le Grand is interviewed and seen onstage in the Crazy Horse Saloon in Paris. *Go-go dancers. Actors. Eroticism. Employment—Women. Nightclubs. Sex exploitation films. San Francisco. Brussels. Copenhagen. Nancy. Paris. Berlin—West. Hamburg. Moulin Rouge. Atlantic Palace. Place Pigalle (Paris). Cabaret Sexy (Nancy). Fair Lady Film Bar. Casino de Paris. Crazy Horse Saloon (Paris). "Lorna".*

Note: Also known as *Mondo Girls* and *Mondo Top.* Includes footage from *Europe in the Raw,* q.v.

MONDO TRASHO   F6.3263

Dreamland Productions. *Dist* Film-Makers' Distribution Center. 14 Mar 1970 [Baltimore opening]. Sd; b&w. 16mm. 90 min.

Prod-Dir-Writ John Waters. *Photog* John Waters. *Film Ed* John Waters. *Prod Asst* Vince Peranio.

Cast: Mary Vivian Pearce (*girl*), John Leisenring (*shrimper*), Sharon Sandrock, Berenica Cipcus (*stepsisters*), Divine (*hit-and-run driver*), Margie Skidmore (*madonna*), Lizzy Temple Black (*madonna's helper*), Jack Walsh, Chris Atkinson (*attendants*), Mink Stole (*tapdancer*), David Lochary (*Dr. Coathanger*), Berenica Cipcus (*nurse*), Bob Skidmore (*cop*), Mark P. Isherwood, Nancy P. Stoll.

Satire. In a spoof of contemporary films exploiting sex and violence, a young woman experiences a series of events during the course of a single day: a shrimper who is also a shoe fetishist attempts to convince her to perform acts involving unknown pleasures; recalling the Cinderella fable, her two evil stepsisters reappear; she is the victim of a hit-and-run accident involving a car driven by a 300-pound woman; she witnesses a "madonna" performing a miracle in a laundromat; she is committed to an insane asylum and eventually becomes the prey of a mad doctor conducting questionable experiments. Finally, she is struck down and killed during a knife fight in a pigsty. *Stepsisters. Physicians. Fishermen. Fetishism. Murder. Automobile accidents. Miracles. Insane asylums. Experiments. "Cinderella".*

Note: Filmed in Baltimore, Maryland. Press preview running time: 94 min.

MONDO WEIRDO *see* **THE THRILL KILLER**

MONEY   F6.3264

Dist Film-Makers' Distribution Center, Canyon Cinema Cooperative. 1968. Sd; b&w. 16mm. 45 min.

Prod-Dir Rudy Burckhardt. *Text* Joe Brainard.

Cast: Edwin Denby (*Hemlock Stinge*).

Comedy. A hard-drinking farmer inspires his son with the story of unlovable billionaire Hemlock Stinge. Included are documentary sequences contrasting the luxury and corruption of New York City with the serenity of rural Maine. *Farmers. Millionaires. Moral corruption. Ambition. Urban life. Rural life. New York City. Maine.*

MONEY IN MY POCKET   F6.3265

Erven Jourdan. *Dist* Metropolitan Motion Picture Theatres Association, Inc. 21 Dec 1962 [Los Angeles opening]. Sd; col? 35mm. [Feature film, length unknown.]

Prod-Dir-Writ Erven Jourdan. *Orig Mus* Geordie Hormel.

Cast: Robert Anson, Jan Brinker, Graham Archer, Anthony Rowse, Suzie William, Bill Anderson, actor, Nancy Allen, Frank Faro, Louis Zwere, Shirley Clark, Ernest Hurley, Roy Davenport.

Comedy. No information about the precise nature of this film has been found.

THE MONEY JUNGLE — F6.3266

United Pictures–Harold Goldman Associates. *Dist* Feature Film Corp. of America. Feb **1968** [Los Angeles showing]. Sd; col. 35mm. 95 min.

Pres by Commonwealth United Entertainment Inc. *Prod* Earle Lyon. *Dir* Francis D. Lyon. *Screenplay* Charles A. Wallace. *Photog* Alan Stensvold. *Art Dir* Paul Sylos. *Set Decor* Raymond G. Boltz. *Mus* Paul Dunlap. *Song:* "Two Lovers" Paul Dunlap. *Song:* "Help a Good Girl Go Bad" Bob Haymes, Alan Brandt. *Songs Sung by* Lola Albright. *Sd* Brad Trask. *Asst Dir* William Schwartz. *Prod Supv* Joe Wonder. *Cost* Frank Tauss. *Makeup* Gus Norin.

Cast: John Ericson *(Blake Heller)*, Lola Albright *(Peggy Lido)*, Leslie Parrish *(Treva Saint)*, Nehemiah Persoff *(Lieut. Dow Reeves)*, Charles Drake *(Harvey Sheppard)*, Kent Smith *(Paul Kimmel)*, Don Rickles *(Harry Darkwater)*, Michael Forest, Mark Roberts, Edy Williams, Marilyn Devin, Jim Adams, Leslie McRae, Dale Monroe, Dodie Warren, Dub Taylor, Tex Armstrong, John Cliff, George De Normand, Byrd Holland, Richard Norris, Ed Parker.

Crime melodrama. Five major U. S. oil companies have joined forces to bid on offshore fields offered for lease by the state of California. Five days before the date for submitting bids, four of the companies' head geologists meet "accidental" deaths. Harvey Sheppard, president of Far West Oil, calls in troubleshooter Blake Heller to investigate. Heller destroys a bomb planted at his beach house, and he meets and becomes romantically involved with his new neighbor, young widow Treva Saint. With the help of police lieutenant Dow Reeves and stock market expert Harry Darkwater, Heller learns that stocks from two of the oil companies have recently changed hands: one of the owners is Treva; the other is Peggy Lido, a nightclub singer. Despite attempts on his life and the murder of a geologist from the fifth oil company, Heller continues his assignment and eventually discovers that the person behind the killings is Peggy Lido, revealed to be the ex-wife of the oil company president who sold Treva her stock. Peggy, with the help of her fiancé, Paul Kimmel, is determined to prevent both her ex-husband and Treva, the woman Peggy thinks he loves, from enjoying their new-found wealth. Realizing what has occurred, Heller races to Treva's home in time to save her from being killed by Peggy. *Geologists. Investigators. Widows. Singers. Nightclub owners. Police. Oil business. Murder. Fraud. Oil lands. Bombs. Stock market. California.*

Note: Working title: *The Silken Trap*. Prerelease title: *The Billion Dollar Caper.*

MONEY-MAKER — F6.3267

Dist Stacey Distributors. ca **1970**. Sd; col. 16mm. 61-81 min.

Sex film. No information about the precise nature of this film has been found. *Sexuality.*

MONEY, MONEY, MONEY *see* THE COUNTERFEITERS OF PARIS

THE MONEY ORDER *see* MANDABI

THE MONEY TRAP — F6.3268

Metro-Goldwyn-Mayer, Inc. 2 Feb **1966** [Baltimore opening; c30 Nov 1965; LP31992]. Sd (Westrex); b&w. 35mm (Panavision). 92 min.

A Max E. Youngstein Production. *Prod* Max E. Youngstein, David Karr. *Dir* Burt Kennedy. *Screenplay* Walter Bernstein. *Dir Photog* Paul C. Vogel. *Art Dir* George W. Davis, Carl Anderson. *Set Decor* Henry Grace, Robert R. Benton. *Film Ed* John McSweeney. *Mus* Hal Schaefer. *Rec Supv* Franklin Milton. *Asst Dir* Hank Moonjean. *Makeup Supv* William Tuttle. *Miss Sommer's Hairstyles* Mary Keats. *Miss Hayworth's Hairstyles* George Masters.

Cast: Glenn Ford *(Joe Baron)*, Elke Sommer *(Lisa Baron)*, Rita Hayworth *(Rosalie Kenny)*, Joseph Cotten *(Dr. Horace Van Tilden)*, Ricardo Montalban *(Pete Delanos)*, Tom Reese *(Matthews)*, James Mitchum *(Detective Wolski)*, Argentina Brunetti *(aunt)*, Fred Essler *(Mr. Klein)*, Eugene Iglesias *(father)*, Teri Lynn Sandoval *(daughter)*.

Melodrama. Source: Lionel White, *The Money Trap* (New York, 1963). Homicide detective Joe Baron is financially desperate because of the extravagance of his wife, Lisa. Consequently, while investigating the shooting of a burglar by society physician Horace Van Tilden, Joe devises a plan to solve his money problems. Learning that Van Tilden is the head of a large dope syndicate, he plans to rob his safe of $1 million in cash. Joe's partner, Pete Delanos, a Mexican tired of being underprivileged, learns of the plot, and demands to be cut in on it. Meanwhile, Joe has resumed a romance with the dead burglar's wife, Rosalie, an alcoholic waitress. Aware that Rosalie knows of his narcotic dealings, Van Tilden has her pushed to her death and then interrupts Joe and Pete as they are robbing his safe. Following a gun fight, Joe and Pete return to Joe's house with two bags of heroin, but Joe agrees to return one bag if Van Tilden will treat the badly wounded Pete. The doctor agrees; but when Pete dies, the two men turn on each other, and Van Tilden is killed while Joe is severely injured. With no alternative open to him, Joe submits to Lisa's calling an ambulance, knowing that the police will soon follow. *Drug dealers. Physicians. Detectives. Thieves. Alcoholism. Waitresses. Mexicans. Infidelity. Murder. Marriage. Heroin.*

I MONGOLI *see* THE MONGOLS

THE MONGOLS (France/Italy) — F6.3269

Royal Film–France Cinéma Productions. *Dist* Colorama Features. 26 Sep **1966** [Los Angeles opening]. Sd; col (EastmanColor). 35mm (CinemaScope). 105 min.

Prod Guido Giambartolomei. *Dir (see note)* Andre De Toth, Leopoldo Savona. *Dir of Battle Scenes* Riccardo Freda. *Scen* Ugo Guerra, Luciano Martino, Ottavio Alessi. *Adapt & Dial* Ugo Guerra, Luciano Martino, Ottavio Alessi, Alessandro Ferraù. *Dir Photog* Aldo Giordani. *Art Dir* Ottavio Scotti. *Film Ed* Otello Colangeli. *Mus Comp* Mario Nascimbene. *Mus Cond* Franco Ferrara, Edrioni G. Campi. *Choreog* Dino Solari. *Sd* Leopoldo Rosi. *Prod Mgr* Carlo Bessi. *Cost* Enzo Bulgarelli.

Cast: Jack Palance *(Ogotai)*, Anita Ekberg *(Huluna)*, Antonella Lualdi *(Amina)*, Franco Silva *(Stephen)*, Gianni Garko *(Henry)*, Roldano Lupi *(Genghis Khan)*, Gabriella Pallotta *(Lutezia)*, Pierre Cressoy *(Igor)*, Gabriele Antonini *(Temugin)*, Tuen Wang *(Subodai)*.

Historical melodrama. In 1240, the Mongols are pushing at the boundaries of Europe. Stephen of Crakow and Henry de Valois are sent to Genghis Khan to negotiate a peace, but Genghis' son Ogotai and his mistress Huluna want the war to continue, and they stop the two men from reaching the Khan. Stephen escapes and is rescued by Igor, the leader of a band of rebels, and his girl friend Amina. Stephen and Igor vie for Amina's love, but they are captured by Ogotai and forced to fight a duel. Igor is only wounded by Stephen, but Ogotai then murders him. Stephen is able to reach Genghis and arrange a peace settlement, which Henry tries to convey to the Slavic armies. He is intercepted, however, by Ogotai, who tortures him into making a false confession to the Khan of a plot against the Mongols. Stephen is also captured, but Henry sacrifices his life to free his companion. Stephen persuades Genghis of the truth and goes to tell his armies of the peace. Meanwhile, Huluna kills Genghis, and Ogotai becomes the new Khan. He marches the Mongols into battle, but they are beaten by Stephen, who leads them into quicksand; after the defeat, Ogotai kills himself. Stephen and Amina are reunited, and the new Khan withdraws his armies to Asia. *Mongols. Royalty. Mistresses. Soldiers. Perfidy. Murder. Torture. Confession (law). Conspiracy. Self-sacrifice. Assassination. Suicide. Treaties. Quicksand. Genghis Khan. Ogadai. Duels.*

Note: Opened in Paris in Sep 1961 as *Les mongols* at 115 min; in Italy in 1961 as *I mongoli*. Sources conflict in crediting director.

LES MONGOLS *see* THE MONGOLS

MONICA'S THING — F6.3270

Fountain Films. *Dist* Astro–Jemco Film Distributors. 23 Apr **1969** [New York showing]. Sd; b&w. 35mm. 67 min.

Prod Bethel Buckalew. *Dir* Rex Brand.

Cast: Kathy Williams *(Monica)*, Bill Austin, Camille Grant, Vic Lazy, Vickie Carbe, Vic Lance, Marsha Jordan, Keith M. Connell.

Drama. Monica's parents, hopeful that she will remain a virgin until marriage, teach her from an early age the merits of chastity. The parents' friends, however—artists, hippies, lesbians—and even Monica's boyfriend all tempt Monica's willpower. She zealously defends her virginity, but she eventually succumbs to their wishes and proceeds to enjoy her new-found sexuality. *Artists. Hippies. Sexuality. Adolescence. Virginity. Sexual initiation. Lesbianism. Filial relations.*

MONIQUE (Great Britain) — F6.3271

Tigon British Film Productions. *Dist* Avco Embassy Pictures. 27 Mar **1970** [New York opening]. Sd; col (Eastmancolor). 35mm. 88 min. MPAA rating X.

Prod Michael Style. *Exec Prod* Tony Tenser. *Dir-Writ* John Bown. *Dir Photog* Moray Grant. *Camera Op* Peter Hendry. *Art Dir* Colin Southcott. *Film Ed* Richard Sidwell. *Mus* Jacques Loussier. *Sd Ed* Nestor Lovera. *Sd Rec* Alan Kane. *Sd Re-rec* Maurice Askew. *Asst Dir* Michael McKeag. *Prod Mgr* Christopher Neame. *Cont* Ann Edwards. *Wardrobe Mistress* Muriel Dickson. *Makeup* Betty Blattner. *Hairstyles* Olive Mills. *Constr Mgr* Alan Board.

Cast: Sibylla Kay *(Monique)*, Joan Alcorn *(Jean)*, David Sumner *(Bill)*, Jacob Fitz-Jones *(Edward)*, Nicola Bown *(Susan)*, Davilia O'Connor *(Harriet)*, Carol Anne Hawkins *(girl)*, Howard Rawlinson *(Richard)*.

Drama. Monique, a young Frenchwoman, is hired by a couple to care for their children and soon proves her competence with them. Bill, whose wife, Jean, is sexually unresponsive, is attracted by Monique's frank sexuality, and they begin an affair. Meanwhile, Jean and Monique become friends and eventually have a sexual relationship that teaches Jean how to respond to Bill. The situation resolves into a harmonious ménage à trois until it is time for Monique to return to Paris and her boyfriend, leaving Bill and Jean happier than before. *French. Governesses. Children. Marriage. Frigidity. Infidelity. Lesbianism.*

Note: Released in Great Britain in Jun 1970; running time: 87 min.

MONIQUE MY LOVE
F6.3272

Dekko Films. *Dist* Distribpix, Inc. 13 Aug **1969** [New York showing]. Sd; b&w. 35mm. 65 min.

Dir Peter Woodcock. *Photog* Max Busche.

Cast: Claudia Cheer, Jo Sweet, Maxine, Sue Akers, Carla Costa.

Sex film. Rita records her roommate Monique's adventures in a book she intends to call *Monique, My Love.* Monique hopes to become a film star, but the only opportunities for her to act are in sex exploitation films. As Monique relates the story of her experiences, they are relived in the imagination of the women. The sexual tension in the apartment builds, and Rita makes passionate love to Monique. *Roommates. Authors. Actors. Lesbianism. Sexual techniques. Sex exploitation films.*

Note: Generally advertised as *She's Monique My Love.*

THE MONITORS
F6.3273

Wilding, Inc.–Second City Productions. *Dist* Commonwealth United Entertainment, Inc. 8 Oct **1969** [New York opening]. Sd; col (Eastmancolor). 35mm. 92 min. *MPAA rating* M.

Pres by Bell & Howell Productions, Commonwealth United Corp. *Prod* Bernard Sahlins. *Dir* Jack Shea. *Screenplay* Myron J. Gold. *Camera* William Zsigmond. *Art Dir* Roy Henry. *Film Ed* Patrick Kennedy. *Mus* Fred Kaz. *Songs Sung by* Odetta, Sandy Holt. *Sd* Edit-Rite Inc. *Asst Dir* Rusty Meek.

Cast: Guy Stockwell (*Harry*), Susan Oliver (*Barbara*), Avery Schreiber (*Max*), Sherry Jackson (*Mona*), Shepperd Strudwick (*Tersh*), Keenan Wynn (*general*), Ed Begley (*The President*), Larry Storch (*Colonel Stutz*), Alan Arkin, Adam Arkin, Xavier Cugat, Barbara Dana, Everett Dirksen, Stubby Kaye, Fred Kaz, Lynn Lipton, Jackie Vernon (*themselves*), Mel Zellman, Thomas Erhart (*narrators*).

Science fiction comedy-drama. Source: Keith Laumer, *The Monitors* (New York, 1966). The United States is controlled by robot-like Monitors from another planet whose objective is to impose peace and good will by regimenting human emotions. Extending their worldwide control, the Monitors create a society in which the usual human preoccupations—war, violence, sex, politics—play no part. An underground faction consisting of right-wing militarists plots to overthrow the Monitors; and in the end the Monitors conclude that Earth isn't ready to be saved, and they return to their own world in space. *Space creatures. Militarism. Politics. Conspiracy. Utopia.*

Note: Filmed in Chicago.

A MONKEY IN WINTER (France)
F6.3274

Cipra–Cité Films. *Dist* Metro-Goldwyn-Mayer, Inc. 31 Jan **1963** [New York opening; c31 Dec 1962; LP24997]. Sd (Western Electric); b&w. 35mm (Totalscope). 104 min. [Copyright length: 101 min.]

Prod Jacques Bar. *Assoc Prod* Léon Sanz, Georges Valon. *Dir* Henri Verneuil. *Dial* Michel Audiard. *Screen Adapt* François Boyer. *Dir Photog* Louis Page. *Camera* André Dumaître. *Sets* Robert Clavel. *Film Ed* Monique Bonnot, Françoise Bonnot. *Mus* Michel Magne. *Tango:* "Caminito" Juan de Dios Filiberto. *Sd* Jean Rieul, Poste-Parisien. *Asst Dir* Constantin Gavras.

Cast: Jean Gabin (*Albert Quentin*), Jean-Paul Belmondo (*Gabriel Fouquet*), Suzanne Flon (*Suzanne Quentin*), Noël Roquevert (*Landru*), Paul Frankeur (*Esnault*), Gabrielle Dorziat (*Victoria*), Marcelle Arnold (*nurse*), Hella Petri (*Georgina*), Lucien Raimbourg (*Gardiner*), Geneviève Fontanel (*Marie-Jo*), Sylvianne Margolle (*Marie*), Charles Bouillaud (*chauffeur*), Camille Guérini (*mayor*), André Dalibert (*chief of police*), Anne-Marie Coffinet (*Simone*), Hélène Dieudonné (*Josephine*).

Comedy-drama. Source: Antoine Blondin, *Un singe en hiver* (Paris, 1959). Albert Quentin, a crusty, reformed alcoholic, runs an inn in a small Normandy town. One day a young stranger, Gabriel Fouquet, wanders into his tavern, and the old man senses at once that they are kindred spirits. Fouquet, after years of aimless drifting, has come to fetch the schoolgirl daughter he has never seen. Fearful he will be a disappointment to the child, he meets the crisis by building up his courage with alcohol. A sympathetic Quentin, despite his vow never to touch another drop, joins Fouquet in a drinking bout. In the course of their escapade, Quentin recaptures the spirit of his adventurous past in China as a French marine while his companion's imagination takes him to Spain where he fancies himself to be both a flamenco dancer and a toreador. With the coming of the sobering dawn, both men are forced to face reality and Fouquet goes to fetch his daughter. While Quentin is seeing them off, he recalls a Chinese legend according to which the bitter, cold winter would bring hundreds of small monkeys from the wilderness to the towns. They would wander aimlessly about until the kindly townspeople placed them on trains and sent them back to their familiar forests. When the child asks her father if Quentin really helped the lost monkeys, Fouquet replies, "Well, I know for a fact of one monkey he put on a train." *Innkeepers. Veterans. Drifters. Alcoholism. Drunkenness. Fatherhood. Fantasy. Inns. Myths. Normandy. China. Monkeys.*

Note: Released in France in 1962 as *Un singe en hiver.*

MONKEYS, GO HOME!
F6.3275

Walt Disney Productions. *Dist* Buena Vista Distribution Co. 8 Feb **1967** [San Francisco opening; c22 Dec 1966; LP33760]. Sd (RCA); col (Technicolor). 35mm. 101 min.

Pres by Walt Disney. *Co-prod* Ron Miller. *Dir* Andrew V. McLaglen. *Screenplay* Maurice Tombragel. *Dir Photog* William Snyder. *Art Dir* Carroll Clark, John B. Mansbridge. *Set Decor* Emile Kuri, Frank R. McKelvy. *Film Ed* Marsh Hendry. *Mus* Robert F. Brunner. *Orch* Cecil A. Crandall. *Song:* "Joie de Vivre" Robert B. Sherman, Richard M. Sherman. *Sd Supv* Robert O. Cook. *Sd Mix* Robert Post. *Mus Ed* Evelyn Kennedy. *Asst Dir* Tom Leetch. *Asst to the Prod* Louis Debney. *Cost Dsgn* Bill Thomas. *Cost* Chuck Keehne, Neva Rames. *Makeup* Pat McNalley. *Hairstyles* La Rue Matheron. *Matte Eff* Peter Ellenshaw, Jim Fetherolf. *Dial Supv* Stewart Raffill. *Animal Supv* Stewart Raffill.

Cast: Maurice Chevalier (*Father Sylvain*), Dean Jones (*Hank Dussard*), Yvette Mimieux (*Maria Riserau*), Bernard Woringer (*Marcel Cartucci*), Clément Harari (*Emile Paraulis*), Yvonne Constant (*Yolande Angelli*), Marcel Hillaire (*Mayor Gaston Lou*), Jules Munshin (*M. Piastillio*), Alan Carney (*grocer*), Maurice Marsac (*Fontanino*), Darleen Carr (*Sidoni Risera*), Peter Camlin (*cabinet maker*).

Comedy. Source: G. K. Wilkinson, *The Monkeys* (London, 1962). Hank Dussard, a young American, arrives in France to claim the olive farm left him by his late uncle. He is welcomed by the local priest, Father Sylvain, who explains that olive farmers usually have large families since olives must be removed from the ground immediately after the seasonal wind blows them off the trees. Ignoring the hint that he take a wife, Hank imports four female chimpanzees, castoffs from past space flights, and trains them to be olive pickers. The news throws the village into an uproar, and the irate citizens stage anti-monkey demonstrations. Furthermore, Hank finds himself confronted by a phony cousin, Yolande, who claims half of his property. But Hank's pretty housekeeper, Maria, uses the chimps to frighten off the imposter and expose the fraud. Then, the mistral starts to blow, and crowds of curious townspeople gather to watch Hank's chimps harvest the olive crop. All is going well until Maria appears with a huge male chimp. And Hank is left alone as his female chimps pursue their new playmate through the olive grove. But Father Sylvain persuades the villagers to help Hank in his hour of need and all the local citizenry begin picking olives as Hank embraces the delighted Maria. *Americans in foreign countries. Housekeepers. Farmers. French. Cousins. Priests. Inheritance. Fraud. Imposture. Demonstrations. Fruit. France. Chimpanzees. Weather.*

THE MONKEY'S UNCLE
F6.3276

Walt Disney Productions. *Dist* Buena Vista Distribution Co. 14 Jul **1965** [Los Angeles opening; c24 Mar 1965; LP31094]. Sd; col (Technicolor). 35mm. 87 min.

Prod Walt Disney. *Co-prod* Ron Miller. *Dir* Robert Stevenson. *2d Unit Dir* Arthur J. Vitarelli. *Screenplay* Tom August, Helen August. *Story* Bill Walsh. *Dir Photog* Edward Colman. *Art Dir* Carroll Clark, William H. Tuntke. *Set Decor* Emile Kuri, Hal Gausman. *Film Ed* Cotton Warburton. *Mus* Buddy Baker. *Orch* Walter Sheets. *Titl Song* Richard M. Sherman, Robert B. Sherman. *Sung by* Annette, The Beach Boys. *Sd* Robert O. Cook. *Mus Ed* Evelyn Kennedy. *Asst Dir* Joseph L. McEveety. *Cost* Chuck Keehne, Gertrude Casey. *Makeup* Pat McNalley. *Hairstyles* La Rue Matheron. *Sp Eff* Robert A. Mattey, Eustace Lycett.

Cast: Tommy Kirk (*Merlin Jones*), Annette (*Jennifer*), Leon Ames (*Judge Holmsby*), Arthur O'Connell (*Darius Green III*), Frank Faylen (*Mr. Dearborne*), Leon Tyler (*Leon*), Norman Grabowski (*Norman*), Cheryl Miller (*Lisa*), Connie Gilchrist (*Mrs. Gossett*), Alan Hewitt (*Professor Shattuck*), Gage Clarke (*college president*), Mark Goddard (*Haywood*), Harry Holcombe, Alexander Lockwood, Harry Antrim (*board of regents*), Stanley (*himself, a chimp*).

Comedy. Merlin Jones, an eccentric young inventor, receives permission from Judge Holmsby to legally adopt Stanley, a chimpanzee. He then embarks on his follow-up plan—to enroll Stanley as a student at Midvale College. Merlin attaches a phonograph to some electric curlers, puts the contraption on Stanley's head, and lulls the chimp to sleep with a recording that gives instructions on how to be a civilized human being. Meanwhile, the board of regents at Midvale is debating whether to allow football players with poor academic records to play on the team, but Judge Holmsby persuades Merlin to use his invention on two particularly stupid athletes, Norman and Leon. With the help of Jennifer, his girl friend, Merlin succeeds in getting them through their exams. Soon afterward, the president of Midvale is informed by wealthy Mr. Astorbilt that the college will receive $1 million from him if it will abandon football; however, Darius Green III, another millionaire, promises to donate 10 times that amount if someone at Midvale can prove the validity of a claim by one of Green's ancestors that man-powered flight is possible. Merlin is able to fulfill the conditions of the gift by inventing such a machine. As the school prepares to accept its $10 million, three men with a straitjacket appear to pick up Green, who is revealed to be Mr. Astorbilt, an escaped lunatic whose check is worthless. *Eccentrics. Inventors. Athletes. Students. Judges. Millionaires. Lunatics. Adoption. College life. Fraud. Inventions. Football. Chimpanzees.*

Note: A sequel to Walt Disney's *The Misadventures of Merlin Jones*, q. v.

MONSIEUR COGNAC *see* **WILD AND WONDERFUL**

UN MONSIEUR DE COMPAGNIE *see* **MALE COMPANION**

MONSIEUR ZIVACO (Japan)   F6.3277
Toho Co. Apr **1968** [Los Angeles showing]. Sd; col. 35mm. 110 min.
Dir Takashi Tsuboshima.
Cast: Mie Hama, The Crazy Cats.
Comedy. Although no information about the precise nature of this film has been found, sources indicate that the story centers around a notorious burglar. *Burglars.*
Note: Released in Japan in Oct 1968 as *Kaito Jibako.*

MONSTER A GO-GO!   F6.3278
Dist B. I. & L. Releasing Corp. **1965**. Sd; b&w. 35mm. 70 min.
Prod-Dir (see note) Sheldon Seymour, Bill Rebane. *Titl Song* Libby Quinn.
Cast: Phil Morton, June Travis, George Perry, Lois Brooks *(uncredited roles)*, Henry Hite *(Monster)*.
Horror film. An American astronaut returns from space transformed into a monster 10 feet tall. *Astronauts. Monsters. Space travel. Transmutation.*
Note: Produced by Bill Rebane in 1963-64 as *Terror at Halfday*; footage filmed by Herschell Gordon Lewis (under the pseudonym Sheldon Seymour) was added.

MONSTER FROM THE SURF *see* **THE BEACH GIRLS AND THE MONSTER**

THE MONSTER OF LONDON CITY (West Germany)   F6.3279
CCC-Filmkunst. *Dist* Producers Releasing Organization. Mar **1967**. Sd; b&w. 35mm (Ultrascope). 87 min.
Prod Artur Brauner. *Exec Prod* Heinz Willeg. *Dir* Edwin Zbonek. *Screenplay* Robert A. Stemmle. *Story* Bryan Edgar Wallace. *Photog* Siegfried Hold. *Art Dir* Hans Jürgen Kiebach, Ernst Schomer. *Film Ed* Walter Wischniewsky. *Mus* Martin Böttcher. *Sd* Erwin Schänzle. *Asst Dir* Lucie Berndsen. *Prod Supv* Erwin Dräger. *Prod Mgr* Heinz Götze. *Cost Cons* Trude Ulrich. *Makeup* Heinz Stamm, Ingrid Haas.
Cast: Hansjörg Felmy *(Richard Sand)*, Marianne Koch *(Ann Morlay)*, Dietmar Schönherr *(Dr. Morley Greely)*, Hans Nielsen *(Dorne)*, Chariklia Baxevanos *(Betty Ball)*, Fritz Tillmann *(Sir George)*, Walter Pfeil *(Horrlick)*, Peer Schmidt *(Teddy Flynn)*, Kurd Pieritz *(Maylor)*, Elsa Wagner *(housekeeper)*, Adelheid Hinz *(maid)*, Gerda Blisse *(assistant)*, Manfred Grothe *(detective)*, Kai Fischer *(Helen Capstick)*, Gudrun Schmidt *(Evelyn Nichols)*.
Mystery melodrama. Inspired by the works of: Edgar Wallace. Actor Richard Sand is appearing on the London stage in a new production based on the career of Jack the Ripper. When a series of actual murders are committed in a manner similar to those depicted in the play, police suspicion falls on all those connected with the production, Richard in particular. At the same time Richard is deeply troubled by his love for Ann Morlay, a Parliament member's daughter who is already engaged to one of Richard's best friends, Dr. Morley Greely. Despite intensive questioning by the police, Richard continues in his role, until, during a performance, he discovers that a real knife has been substituted for a stage prop. After rushing from the theater, he is led by a mysterious telephone message to the room of a prostitute who has just been slain. The police arrive and are about to arrest him when a little girl announces that she saw the real killer. Richard cooperates with Scotland Yard in setting a trap for the modern-day Jack the Ripper, who turns out to be Greely. Jealous of Richard's love for Ann, Greely had tried to frame his friend for the brutal murders. With Richard cleared of suspicion, Greely commits suicide before the police can close in on him. *Actors. Physicians. Police. Prostitutes. Murder. Frameup. Suicide. Theater. London. Scotland Yard. Great Britain— Parliament. Jack the Ripper.*
Note: Released in West Germany in Jul 1964 as *Das Ungeheuer von London City*; running time: 89 min.

MONSTER OF TERROR *see* **DIE, MONSTER, DIE!**

MONSTER OF THE WAX MUSEUM *see* **NIGHTMARE IN WAX**

MONSTER ZERO (Japan)   F6.3280
Toho Co. *Dist* Maron Films. 29 Jul **1970** [Houston opening]. Sd; col (Eastman Color). 35mm (Tohoscope). 92 min. *MPAA rating* G.
Pres by United Productions of America. *Exec Prod* Tomoyuki Tanaka. *Dir* Inoshiro Honda. *Screenplay* Shinichi Sekizawa. *Photog* Hajime Koizumi. *Art* *Dir* Takeo Kita. *Film Ed* Ryohei Fujii. *Mus* Akira Ifukube. *Sp Eff* Eiji Tsuburaya.
Cast: Nick Adams *(Glenn)*, Akira Takarada *(Fuji)*, Kumi Mizuno *(Namikawa)*, Keiko Sawai, Akira Kubo, Yoshio Tsuchiya, Jun Tazaki, Goro Naya.
Science fiction melodrama. Earth astronauts Glenn and Fuji are sent to Planet X to establish friendly ties with the ruler of that planet, The Controller. He promises Earth the formula for a universal panacea in return for the loan of two Earth monsters, Godzilla and Rodan, to combat the fearsome Ghidrah *(Monster Zero)* which is terrorizing the people. Returning home to Japan, Glenn becomes romantically involved with Namikawa, an enemy spy posing as a toy manufacturer's representative. Godzilla and Rodan, released from their lairs, are transported by huge space bubbles to Planet X. Glenn, Fuji, and a doctor follow in a spaceship. They soon discover that the tape which is supposed to contain the medical formula to end disease is actually an ultimatum for Earth's immediate surrender. Refusal would mean the Earth's destruction by the three monsters which are controlled by Planet X's computers. Namikawa is killed, and a toy created by Teri, the fiancé of Fuji's sister, is discovered to emit a sound that severs the light waves by which the creatures are controlled. The invaders are destroyed in a space battle with cannons and laser beams; Ghidrah defeats the Earth monsters and flies away. *Monsters. Astronauts. Spies. Duplicity. Space travel. Space warfare. Imaginary planets. Spaceships. Computers. Laser. Godzilla. Rodan. Ghidrah.*
Note: Released in Japan in 1966 as *Kaiju daisenso*; running time: 96 min. Also known as *Invasion of Astro-Monsters*, *Battle of the Astros*, and *Invasion of the Astros.*

THE MONSTERS ARE LOOSE *see* **THE THRILL KILLERS**

LES MONSTRES *see* **OPIATE '67**

MONSTROSITY   F6.3281
Cinema Ventures. *Dist* Emerson Film Enterprises. Sep **1963**. Sd; b&w. 35mm. 70 min. [Also reviewed at 65 and 67 min.]
Prod Jack Pollexfen. *Dir* Joseph V. Mascelli. *Screenplay (see note)* Jack Pollexfen, Dean Dillman, Jr., Sue Dwiggins, Vi Russell.
Cast: Frank Gerstle *(doctor)*, Erika Peters *(Nina)*, Judy Bamber *(Bee)*, Marjorie Eaton *(Hazel)*, Frank Fowler *(Victor)*, Margie Fisco *(zombie)*.
Horror film. Hazel, a wealthy, aging spinster, finances a mad doctor's brain transplant experiments in the hope that she can be rejuvenated. After they import servant girls from Europe for the surgery, the doctor uses Victor, a deformed victim of previous experiments, to assist him in the operations. They place a cat's brain in the head of one of the female prisoners and turn the other women into zombies; but the plot is foiled when one of the captives burns down the laboratory. *Surgeons. Spinsters. Zombies. Brain surgery. Rejuvenation. Disfiguration. Experiments. Laboratories. Fires. Cats.*
Note: Some sources list Pollexfen and Dillman as authors of the screenplay; others credit Dillman, Dwiggins, and Russell. Also known as *The Atomic Brain.*

MONTE CARLO OR BUST! *see* **THOSE DARING YOUNG MEN IN THEIR JAUNTY JALOPIES**

LE MONTE-CHARGE *see* **PARIS PICK-UP**

MONTE WALSH   F6.3282
Palladian Pictures. *For* Cinema Center Films. *Dist* National General Pictures. 7 Oct **1970** [New York opening; c28 Sep 1970; LP39810]. Sd; col (Technicolor). 35mm (Panavision). 99 min. [Also reviewed at 108 min.] *MPAA rating* GP.
A Hal Landers-Bobby Roberts Production. *Prod* Hal Landers, Bobby Roberts. *Dir* William A. Fraker. *Screenplay* Lukas Heller, David Z. Goodman. *Dir Photog* David M. Walsh. *Camera Op* John Hussey. *Camera Asst* Bob Byrne, Victor King. *Asst Art Dir* Ward Preston. *Set Decor* Philip Abramson. *Prod Dsgn* Albert Brenner. *Film Ed* Richard Brockway, Robert L. Wolfe, Raymond Daniels, Gene Fowler, Jr. *Mus* John Barry. *Song:* "The Good Times Are Comin'" John Barry, Hal David. *Sung by* Mama Cass. *Supv Sd Ed* Jack Finley. *Supv Mus Ed* Gene Feldman. *Sd* Jerry Kosloff. *Rec* Larry Hooberry. *Boom Op* Gino Contemessa. *Asst Dir* Jack Roe, Al Murphy. *Prod Mgr* William R. Finnegan, Chris Seiter. *Script Supv* John Franco. *Cost Dsgn* Albert Brenner. *Wardrobe* Alan Levine, Arnold Lipin, Patricia Norris. *Makeup* Emile La Vigne. *Hairstyles* Dionne Taylor. *Sp Eff* George Peckham, Roy Bolton. *Screenplay Supv* Associates & Aldrich Co. *Dial Dir* Deth Doughty. *Gaffer* Joseph Smith. *Key Grip* Tom May. *Prop* Richard M. Rubin, Jack Ianarelli. *Constr* Lowell Thomas, constr. *Casting* Lynn Stalmaster. *Animal Trainer* Les Hilton.
Cast: Lee Marvin *(Monte Walsh)*, Jeanne Moreau *(Martine Bernard)*, Jack Palance *(Chet Rollins)*, Mitch Ryan *(Shorty Austin)*, Jim Davis *(Cal Brennan)*, Bear Hudkins *(Sonny Jacobs)*, Raymond Guth *(Sunfish Perkins)*, John McKee *(Petey Williams)*, Michael Conrad *(Dally Johnson)*, Tom Heaton *(Sugar*

Wyman), G. D. Spradlin *(Hat Henderson)*, Ted Gehring *(Skimpy Eagans)*, Bo Hopkins *(Jumpin' Joe Joslin)*, Matt Clark *(Rufus Brady)*, Billy Bush *(Powder Kent)*, Allyn Ann McLerie *(Mary Eagle)*, John McLiam *(Fightin' Joe Hooker)*, Leroy Johnson *(marshal)*, Eric Christmas *(Colonel Wilson)*, Charles Tyner *(doctor)*, Dick Farnsworth, Fred Waugh *(cowboys)*, Jack Colvin *(card cheat)*, William Graeff, Jr. *(bartender)*, John Carter, actor *(farmer)*, Guy Wilkerson *(old man)*, Roy Bancroft *(proprietor)*, Blackie Escalante, Frank Green, Billy Fraker, Kurtis Roberts.

Western melodrama. Source: Jack Warner Schaefer, *Monte Walsh* (Boston, 1963). In the late 1880's Monte Walsh and Chet Rollins, two aging cowboys, ride into the town of Harmony, and manager Cal Brennan offers them a job at the Slash Y Ranch. There they meet an old friend, Shorty Austin, and the three men ride into town where Monte visits Martine Bernard, his mistress, at the local saloon, while Chet courts Mary Eagle, a widow who has inherited a hardware store. Soon after Shorty loses his job at the ranch, he becomes involved in a saloon brawl and kills a man who turns out to be a marshal. Chet, who marries Mary Eagle and settles down to work in the store, tells Monte that the day of the cowboy is gone and that he, too, should settle down. Martine, however, has moved to Charleyville to work in a more prosperous saloon. Monte follows her and proposes marriage. As he leaves Charleyville, the drunken Monte comes upon a wild horse that is part of a Wild West show and decides to tame the stallion. The owner of the show offers Monte a job, but Monte is too proud to become a carnival attraction and turns him down. He mounts the horse and destroys a large part of the town during the wild ride. Upon returning to Harmony, Monte is informed that Chet was killed by Shorty during a robbery of the hardware store. Monte sets out in pursuit of Shorty but learns that Martine is very ill. He rides to Charleyville to find Martine dead and Shorty waiting for him. The two men stalk each other throughout the town until Monte finally kills Shorty. *Cowboys. Ranchers. Mistresses. Widows. Outlaws. Broncobusters. Murder. Marriage. Drunkenness. Robbery. Saloons. Wild West shows. Horses.*

Note: Location scenes filmed near Tucson, Arizona.

MONTEREY POP   F6.3283

The Foundation. *Dist* Leacock Pennebaker, Inc. 29 Jan **1969** [New York opening]. Sd; col (Eastman Color). 35mm (see note). 79 min. [Also reviewed at 72 min.]

Dir & Conceived by D. A. Pennebaker. *Photog* James Desmond, Barry Feinstein, Richard Leacock, Albert Maysles, Roger Murphy, D. A. Pennebaker, Nicholas Proferes. *Adtl Photog* Bob Neuwirth, John Cooke, Tim Cunningham, Baird Hersey, Robert Leacock, Peter Pilafian, John Maddox, Nina Schulman, Robert Van Dyke, Brice Marden. *Main Titl* Tomi Ungerer. *Film Ed* Nina Schulman. *Song:* "Combination of the Two" Sam Andrew, Janis Joplin. *Perf By* Big Brother and the Holding Company. *With* Janis Joplin. *Song:* "San Francisco" John Phillips. *Sung by* Scott McKenzie. *Song:* "Creeque Alley" John Phillips, Michelle Gilliam. *Song:* "California Dreamin'" John Phillips. *Song:* "I've Got a Feelin'" John Phillips, Denny Doherty. *Sung by* Mamas and the Papas. *Song:* "Rollin' and Tumblin'" Morris Levy. *Perf by* Canned Heat. *Song:* "The 59th Street Bridge Song (Feelin' Groovy)" Paul Simon. *Sung by* Simon and Garfunkel. *Song:* "Bajabula Bonke" Miriam Makeba. *Perf by* Hugh Masekela, William Henderson, Chuck Carter, Henry Franklin, Al Abrau. *Song:* "High Flyin' Bird" Billy Edd Wheeler. *Song:* "Today" Marty Balin, Paul Kantner. *Perf by* Jefferson Airplane. *With* Grace Slick. *Song:* "Ball and Chain" Willie Mae "Big Mama" Thornton. *Perf by* Janis Joplin, Big Brother and the Holding Company. *Song:* "Paint It Black" Mick Jagger, Keith Richard. *Perf by* Eric Burdon and the Animals. *Song:* "My Generation" Peter Townshend. *Perf by* The Who. *Song:* "Section 43" Joe McDonald. *Perf by* Country Joe and the Fish. *Song:* "Shake" Sam Cooke. *Song:* "I've Been Loving You Too Long" Otis Redding, Jerry Butler. *Perf by* Otis Redding, Booker T. and the MG's. *Song:* "Wild Thing" Chip Taylor. *Perf by* Jimi Hendrix, Noel Redding, Mitch Mitchell. "Raga Bhimpalasi" *perf by* Ravi Shankar, Alla Rakha, Kamala. *Sd Rec* Wally Heider. *Prod Mgr* Peter Hansen. *Prod Asst* Pauline Marden, Peyton Fong, Larry Mong. *Monterey International Pop Festival Prod* John Phillips, Lou Adler. *Stage Lighting* Chip Monck. *Light Show* Headlights.

Documentary. A record of the 1967 Monterey International Pop Festival. Interviews are conducted with "flower children," festival producer John Phillips, policemen, and some of the sound and lighting crew. The Rolling Stones' Brian Jones is the festival's announcer, and the acts include Big Brother and the Holding Company (with Janis Joplin), The Mamas and the Papas, Canned Heat, Hugh Masekela, the Jefferson Airplane (with Grace Slick), Eric Burdon and The Animals, The Who, Country Joe and the Fish, Otis Redding (backed by Booker T and the MG's), Jimi Hendrix, and a final sequence with Ravi Shankar. *Flower children. Police. Rock and roll. Monterey International Pop Festival (1967). Monterey (California).*

Note: Filmed in 16mm.

MONTGOMERY TO MEMPHIS *see* KING: A FILMED RECORD ... MONTGOMERY TO MEMPHIS

MONTPARNASSE *see* MODIGLIANI OF MONTPARNASSE

MONTPARNASSE 19 *see* MODIGLIANI OF MONTPARNASSE

MOON PILOT   F6.3284

Walt Disney Productions. *Dist* Buena Vista Distribution Co. 5 Apr **1962** [New York opening; c27 Dec 1961; LP21310]. Sd (RCA); col (Technicolor). 35mm. 98 min.

Pres by Walt Disney. A Walt Disney Production. *Assoc Prod* Ron Miller. *Co-prod* Bill Anderson, prod. *Dir* James Neilson. *Screenplay* Maurice Tombragel. *Dir Photog* William Snyder. *Art Dir* Carroll Clark, Marvin Aubrey Davis. *Set Decor* Emile Kuri, William Stevens. *Film Ed* Cotton Warburton. *Mus* Paul Smith. *Orch* Joseph Oroop. *Songs:* "Seven Moons of Beta Lyrae," "True Love's an Apricot," "The Void" Richard M. Sherman, Robert B. Sherman. *Sd Supv* Robert O. Cook. *Sd Mix* Harry M. Lindgren. *Mus Ed* Evelyn Kennedy. *Asst Dir* Joseph L. McEveety. *Cost Dsgn* Bill Thomas. *Cost* Chuck Keehne, Gertrude Casey. *Makeup* Pat McNalley. *Hairstyles* Ruth Sandifer. *Sp Eff* Eustace Lycett. *Coöp* United States Air Force.

Cast: Tom Tryon *(Capt. Richmond Talbot)*, Brian Keith *(Maj. Gen. John Vanneman)*, Edmond O'Brien *(McClosky)*, Dany Saval *(Lyrae)*, Tommy Kirk *(Walter Talbot)*, Bob Sweeney *(Senator McGuire)*, Kent Smith *(Secretary of the Air Force)*, Simon Scott *(medical officer)*, Bert Remsen *(Agent Brown)*, Sarah Selby *(Mrs. Celia Talbot)*, Dick Whittinghill *(Colonel Briggs)*, Cheeta *(Charlie the Chimp)*, Nancy Kulp, William Hudson, Robert Brubaker.

Comedy. Source: Robert Buckner, "Moon Pilot," in *Saturday Evening Post* (19 Mar–2 Apr 1960). Following a successful trajectory around the moon by Charlie the Chimp, Maj. Gen. John Vanneman decides to orbit one of his top eight astronauts. There are, however, no volunteers until Charlie jabs Rich Talbot with his fork and the young captain leaps to his feet. While on a 3-day leave to visit his mother, Rich meets a mysterious girl with an equally mysterious name, Lyrae, who seems to appear wherever he goes. Believing her to be a spy, he notifies Vanneman, who, in turn, calls McClosky, head of Federal security. Lyrae finally confesses to the astounded Rich that she is from the friendly planet of Beta Lyrae and has been sent to warn him that he will die in outer space unless his rocket has a protective anti-proton ray coating. Certain no one will believe his story, Rich disappears and refuses to return unless his rocket is equipped with Lyrae's anti–proton ray formula. Vanneman agrees, and Rich finally sets out for the moon. He is hardly spaceborne before Lyrae appears in his cabin. And back on earth Vanneman and the space team are stupefied to hear on the space radio that Rich is delaying his moon orbit to spend a honeymoon visit on Beta Lyrae. *Astronauts. Space creatures. Space exploration. Defense—National. Space travel. Rockets. Imaginary planets. The Moon. United States Air Force. Chimpanzees.*

THE MOON-SPINNERS (United States/Great Britain)   F6.3285

Walt Disney Productions. *Dist* Buena Vista Distribution Co. 8 Jul **1964** [Chicago opening; c19 Jun 1964; LP28526]. Sd (RCA); col (Technicolor). 35mm. 119 min.

Pres by Walt Disney. A Walt Disney Production. *Co-Prod* Bill Anderson, prod. *Assoc Prod* Hugh Attwooll. *Dir* James Neilson. *2d Unit Dir* Arthur J. Vitarelli. *Screenplay* Michael Dyne. *Dir Photog* Paul Beeson. *Adtl Photog* Michael Reed, John Wilcox. *Camera Op* David Harcourt. *Art Dir* Tony Masters. *Film Ed* Gordon Stone. *Mus Comp & Cond* Ron Grainer. *Titl Song* Terry Gilkyson. *Sd Ed* Jonathan Bates. *Sd Rec* Dudley Messenger, Gordon McCallum. *Asst Dir* John Peverall. *Prod Mgr* Peter Manley. *Cont* Yvonne Axworthy. *Cost Dsgn* Anthony Mendleson. *Makeup* Harry Frampton. *Hairdressing* A. G. Scott. *Casting* Maude Spector. *Animals* Jimmy Chipperfield. *Constr Mgr* Gus Walker.

Cast: Hayley Mills *(Nikky Ferris)*, Eli Wallach *(Stratos)*, Pola Negri *(Madame Habib)*, Peter McEnery *(Mark Camford)*, Joan Greenwood *(Frances Ferris)*, Irene Papas *(Sophia)*, John Le Mesurier *(Anthony Gamble)*, Paul Stassino *(Lambis)*, Sheila Hancock *(Cynthia Gamble)*, Michael Davis *(Alexis)*, Andre Morell *(yacht captain)*, George Pastell *(police lieutenant)*, Tutte Lemkow *(Orestes)*, Steve Plytas *(hearse driver)*, Harry Tardios *(bus driver)*, Pamela Barrie *(Ariadne)*.

Adventure melodrama. Source: Mary Stewart, *The Moon-Spinners* (New York, 1963). Vacationing in Crete with her Aunt Frances, a musicologist, 17-year-old Nikky Ferris learns that their reservations at the Moon-Spinners Hotel have not been recognized, but hostile owners Stratos and his sister, Sophia, reluctantly give them a room. They meet Mark Camford, a young British expatriate, artist, and skindiver, apparently having a running feud with Stratos. Because of her attraction to Mark, Nikky becomes involved when she finds him wounded in a deserted church where he crawled after being ambushed and shot by Lambis, Stratos' cohort, the night before. Her complicity uncovered, Nikky is imprisoned by Stratos in a windmill. After being rescued by Mark and Sophia's son, Alexis, Nikky learns from Mark that he was sacked from his job as a messenger for a London bank because of a jewel robbery he believes Stratos to have committed. The couple then encounter Anthony Gamble, a self-styled British consul who as Stratos' partner is planning to sell the jewels to Madame Habib, a millionairess. These revelations send Mark on a chase after Stratos, while Nikky appeals to Madame. Following a struggle, the police board Madame's yacht, apprehend Stratos, and thereby exonerate Mark. *Tourists. Aunts. Thieves. Hotelkeepers. Millionaires. Expatriates. Brother-sister relationship. Robbery. Hotels. Jewels. Windmills. Yachts. Crete.*

Note: Locations filmed on Crete and in the town of Elounda, Greece. Opened in London in Jul 1964.

MOON WALK *see* A TICKLISH AFFAIR

MOON ZERO TWO (Great Britain)   F6.3286

Hammer Film Productions. *Dist* Warner Bros. Pictures. Mar **1970.** Sd; col (Technicolor). 35mm. 100 min. *MPAA rating* G.

Prod-Writ Michael Carreras. *Dir* Roy Ward Baker. *Story* Gavin Lyall, Frank Hardman, Martin Davison. *Photog* Paul Beeson. *Art Dir* Scott MacGregor. *Main Titl* Stokes Cartoons. *Film Ed* Spencer Reeve. *Mus* Don Ellis. *Mus Supv* Philip Martell. *Choreog* Jo Cook. *Sd Ed* Roy Hyde. *Sd Rec* Claude Hitchcock. *Sd Re-rec* Len Abbott. *Asst Dir* Jack Martin. *Prod Mgr* Hugh Harlow. *Cost* Carl Toms. *Sp Photog Eff* Kit West, Nick Allder. *Sp Eff* Les Bowie.

Cast: James Olson (*Bill Kemp*), Catherina von Schell (*Clementine Taplin*), Warren Mitchell (*Hubbard*), Adrienne Corri (*Liz Murphy*), Ori Levy (*Karminski*), Dudley Foster (*Whitsun*), Bernard Bresslaw (*Harry*), Neil McCallum (*space captain*), Joby Blanshard (*Smith*), Michael Ripper, Robert Tayman (*card players*), Sam Kydd (*barman*), The Gojos (*themselves*), Keith Bonnard (*junior customs officer*), Leo Britt (*senior customs officer*), Carol Cleveland (*hostess*), Roy Evans (*worker*), Tom Kempinski (*2d officer*), Lew Luton (*immigration officer*), Claire Shenstone (*female hotel clerk*), Chrissie Shrimpton (*boutique attendant*), Amber Dean Smith, Simone Silvera (*Hubbard's girl friends*).

Science fiction melodrama. Bill Kemp and his partner Karminski land their spaceship on the Moon City spaceport in the year 2021. Passing through customs, Kemp is approached by Clementine Taplin, a visitor from Earth looking for her brother Wally who disappeared from a mining expedition on the far side of the Moon. Police Chief Liz Murphy, however, tells Kemp that he will be grounded unless extensive repairs are made on his ship. Depressed about his poor prospects, Kemp encounters Hubbard, a millionaire space industrialist who offers to buy him a new ship if he will harness a certain sapphire asteroid and bring it back to the vicinity of the Moon. After completing his mission for Hubbard, Kemp agrees to help Clementine. Upon discovering Wally's dead body at the mining site, Kemp and Clementine are attacked by a group of Hubbard's men, but they escape back to Moon City and explain to Liz that Clementine's brother was killed by Hubbard's henchmen. Hubbard arrives, kills Liz, and orders Kemp to crash the asteroid into one of Wally's claims. Kemp and Karminski fly Hubbard and his men to the asteroid, where Kemp persuades them to examine the surface of the asteroid; Kemp and his partner then crash the asteroid into the Moon, killing Hubbard and his men. *Pilots. Miners. Missing persons. Policewomen. Millionaires. Industrialists. Brother-sister relationship. Space flights. Murder. Duplicity. Spaceships. Asteroids. The Moon. The Future.*

Note: Opened in London in Oct 1969.

MOONLIGHT IN THE RAIN (Japan)   F6.3287

Takarazuka Motion Picture Co. *Dist* Toho Co. Nov **1961** [Los Angeles showing]. Sd; col? 35mm. 95 min.

Dir Seiji Hisamatsu.

Cast: Yoshiko Kuga, Aiko Mimasu, Michiyo Aratama, Kazuyo Matsushita, Hikaru Mayuzumi, Tadao Takashima, Shoji Yasui, Jun Funato, Chieko Naniwa, Haruya Kato, Kenji Sahara, Michiyo Tamaki.

Drama. No information about the precise nature of this film has been found.

Note: Released in Japan in May 1961 as *Onna kazoku.*

MOONLIGHTING SECRETARIES   F6.3288

Dist Enrico Alexandros Releases. 1 Oct **1969** [Boston opening]. Sd; b&w. 35mm. 69 min.

Prod Jack Bravman, Al Marvin. *Dir* Wizard Glick.

Melodrama. Secretaries in an office work overtime to entertain businessmen. The women enjoy sex with their clients and with each other, and one secretary discovers emotions she has previously suppressed. Guilt-ridden by her complicity, one moonlighter rejects her husband's attentions; however, they resolve their problem. *Secretaries. Businessmen. Prostitution. Group sex. Lesbianism. Marriage. Guilt.*

MOONLIGHTING WIVES   F6.3289

Morgan Pictures. *Dist* Craddock Films, Cannon Releasing Corp. 21 Sep **1966** [Los Angeles showing]. Sd; col (De Luxe). 35mm. 86 min.

Assoc Prod Bob Moscow. *Dir-Writ* Joe Sarno. *Cinematog* Jerry Kalogerados. *Asst Camera* Anthony Lover. *Film Ed* Pat Follmer. *Mus* Stan Free. *Titl Song* Rosemary Heineman, Jim Heineman. *Sung by* Erin Malone. *Sd* Otis MacLay. *Mus Ed* Pat Follmer. *Prod Supv* Joseph A. Bellucci. *Prod Mgr* Gabriel Cicale. *Ch Electrn* George Quinn. *Still Photos* Helene Kalogerados.

Cast: Diane Vivienne (*Mrs. Joan Rand*), Jan Nash (*Nancy Preston*), John Aristedes (*Al Jordan*), Fatima (*belly dancer*), Chris Roberts, Jody Lynn, Tina Marie, Lisa Lillot, Shariaya Lee, Bill Sullivan, Joe Santos, Joe Jenckes, Jackie Farrel, Sue Gibson, George Windship.

Melodrama. Joan Rand, an attractive suburban housewife plagued with money troubles, decides to augment her stenographer's salary by accepting her employer's offer to pay for her physical favors. At the motel where she conducts her "moonlighting," she conceives the idea of organizing a group of housewives to perform similar services in exchange for money, all under the guise of doing temporary office work. After forming a partnership with a local golf pro named Al Jordan, Joan uses his contacts to find customers while she rounds up the necessary women. All goes well with the operation, despite Joan's quarrels with her husband, until another housewife, Nancy Preston, refuses to participate in the "parties" for businessmen. By informing Nancy's husband of her infidelity with Al, Joan manages to force the reluctant housewife into joining the stable of call girls. Eventually, when the ring's strong-arm beats up a local prostitute, the girl phones the police and identifies Joan as head of the operation. Although additional information is given to the authorities by Nancy, the police are unable to move in without a witness or a warrant. But, when a frightened newcomer flees from an orgy dressed only in her undergarments, the police arrest her, and she agrees to talk. The party is raided, and all members of the prostitution ring, Joan included, are apprehended. *Housewives. Stenographers. Prostitutes. Police. Suburbanites. Infidelity. Prostitution. Employment— Women. Revenge. Blackmail. Finance—Personal. Motels.*

Note: Filmed in Atlanta, Georgia.

MOONSHINE MOUNTAIN   F6.3290

Herschell Gordon Lewis Motion Picture Enterprises. *Dist* Creative Communications, Inc. 16 Sep **1964** [Charlotte, North Carolina, opening]. Sd; col (Eastman Color). 35mm. 90 min.

Pres by Herschell Gordon Lewis. *Prod-Dir* Herschell Gordon Lewis. *Screenplay* Charles Glore. *Film Ed* Robert Sinise, Ron Closky. *Asst Dir* J. G. Patterson, Jr. *Prod Mgr* Andy Romanoff. *Crew Ch* Bob Vercruse.

Cast: Chuck Scott (*Doug Martin*), Adam Sorg (*Asa Potter*), Jeffrey Allen (*Jeb Carpenter*), Bonnie Hinson (*Laura Carpenter*), Carmen Sotir (*Angeline*), Ben Moore (*Raf*), Pat Patterson (*Hutto*), Mark Douglas (*Ed Basham*), Karin March (*Ma Basham*), Gretchen Eisner (*Mary Lou*), Harry Hoffman (*Luther*), Bill Simpson (*Zero*), William Harris (*Harley*), Marilyn Walters (*Della Lawrence*), Harry Kerr (*Wilson*), Lee Collins (*Bentley*), Claude Casey (*TV announcer*), James Preddy (*TV singer*), James Stokes, Jr. (*electrician*), The Catalinas, Gay Land and the Thunderbirds, The Sweet Gum Sisters and Brother (*themselves*).

Rural melodrama. Doug Martin, a successful country-western singer, returns to the Carolina hills with the hope of restoring a country twang to his "citified" voice. Accompanied by his socialite fiancée, Della Lawrence, Doug takes part in folk-singing parties and meets the Carpenters, the Bashams, and Sheriff Asa Potter, who together run a still which supplies the surrounding area with moonshine. Doug flirts with Laura Carpenter, a college student who is home on vacation, and Della, jealous of Doug's new interest, decides to leave, but on the way to the airport, Sheriff Potter stops her and forces her to follow him to a secluded pond. When she laughs at his clumsy advances, he kills her. Aided by the ape-like Luther Basham, Potter then murders several federal agents and throws their bodies into the bubbling still. Doug discovers the sheriff's evil deeds and asks the Carpenters and the Bashams to help capture him. When Potter convinces Luther to dynamite the entire community, Luther bungles the job, and Potter shoots him to save his own life. Meanwhile, Mary Lou, Laura's retarded sister whom Potter once raped, arrives and kills the sheriff with an ax as the still explodes. After marrying Laura, Doug returns to the city with his bride, while the two families begin to rebuild the still. *Singers. Socialites. Moonshiners. Sheriffs. Students. Government agents. Halfwits. Country music. Mountain life. Family life. Jealousy. Murder. Rape. Stills. Axes. North Carolina. Explosions.*

Note: Filmed on location in the Blue Ridge Mountains in North Carolina. Also known as *White Trash on Moonshine Mountain.* Chuck Scott is a pseudonym for Charles Glore.

THE MOONSHINE WAR F6.3291

Filmways, Inc. *Dist* Metro-Goldwyn-Mayer, Inc. 8 Jul **1970** [Los Angeles opening; c25 Jun 1970; LP38100]. Sd; col (Metrocolor). 35mm (Panavision). 100 min. *MPAA rating* GP.

A Martin Ransohoff Production. *Prod* Martin Ransohoff. *Assoc Prod* James C. Pratt, Leonard Blair. *Dir* Richard Quine. *2d Unit Dir* Dick Crockett. *Screenplay* Elmore Leonard. *Dir Photog* Richard H. Kline. *Art Dir* George W. Davis, Edward Carfagno. *Set Decor* Robert R. Benton, Hugh Hunt. *Film Ed* Allan Jacobs. *Mus* Fred Karger. *Song:* "Ballad of the Moonshine" *comp & sung by* Hank Williams, Jr. *Song:* "It Takes All Kinds of People" *comp & sung by* Roy Orbison. *Song:* "Moonshine" *perf by* The Five Man Electrical Band. *Rec Supv* Franklin Milton. *Sd Rec* Bruce Wright. *Asst Dir* Mickey McCardle. *Prod Mgr* James T. Vaughn. *Script Supv* Esther Stephenson. *Cost* Edmund Kara. *Makeup* William Tuttle, Allan Snyder. *Hairstyles* Jean Austin. *Sp Eff* Earl McCoy. *Tech Adv* William "Big Siz" Henderson. *Casting* Leonard Murphy.

Cast: Patrick McGoohan *(Frank Long)*, Richard Widmark *(Dr. Taulbee)*, Alan Alda *(Son Martin)*, Lee Hazlewood *(Dual Meaders)*, Joe Williams *(Aaron)*, Will Geer *(Sheriff Baylor)*, Melodie Johnson *(Lizann Simpson)*, Suzanne Zenor *(Miley Mitchell)*, Max Showalter *(Mr. Worthman)*, Harry Carey, [Jr.] *(Stamper)*, Dick Peabody *(Boyd Caswell)*, Charles Tyner *(McClendon)*, Dick Crockett *(Carl)*, Claude Johnson *(tourist)*, Terry Garr *(tourist's wife)*, Patty Sauers *(waitress)*, John Schuck *(E. J. Royce)*, Tom Nolan *(Lowell)*, Bo Hopkins *(Bud Blackwell)*.

Melodrama. Source: Elmore Leonard, *The Moonshine War* (Garden City, New York, 1969). Revenue agent Frank Long schemes to make a profit from moonshine before the repeal of Prohibition by acquiring a large quantity of whiskey from his old army buddy, Son Martin, who operates a still in Kentucky. When Son and his black hired hand, Aaron, refuse to go along with the plan, however, Long hires ex-convicts Dr. Taulbee and Dual Meaders to frighten them into parting with the liquor. Later, the two paid killers and their gang murder Sheriff Baylor and his deputy, and Long decides to join Son in defending his still in return for a share of the whiskey. Taulbee's girl friend, Miley Mitchell, abandons the killers to join Long but is killed in the process. Taulbee then kidnaps four local residents and offers to exchange them for the moonshine. Son seemingly relents and informs Taulbee's gang that the supply is hidden in a nearby graveyard; however, when the killers begin digging, they detonate a charge of dynamite that Son has hidden. With the community now rid of the intruders, Son invites Long and the local people to join him in a celebration with some moonshine. *Revenue agents. Moonshiners. Negroes. Hired killers. Sheriffs. Prohibition. Murder. Kidnaping. Stills. Cemeteries. Kentucky. Explosions.*

Note: Location scenes filmed in Stockton, California.

MOONSHINER'S WOMAN F6.3292

Dist Worldwide Films, Starline Pictures, Tasbem. **1968.** Sd; b&w. 35mm. 79 min.

Prod-Dir D. E. Davison.

Cast: Alan Davis, Linda Lee, Roy Huston, "Georgeanne", Bill Crisp.

Melodrama. Claude, a Tennessee moonshiner, is killed by Jarvis, a big city gangster, who offers Claude's girl friend, Lorilee, a fancy wardrobe, money, and fame if she will work at his nightclub. Later, Lorilee vacations in Daytona and begins an affair with Mitch, one of Jarvis' henchmen. Returning home, Lorilee meets Rachel, who introduces her to marijuana and LSD. Jarvis discovers Lorilee and Mitch making love; he kills Mitch and beats Lorilee. At one of Jarvis' bookie parlors, Lorilee kills Jarvis' moll, Sharon, during a heated argument and then informs the police of the gangster's illegal activities. *Moonshiners. Gangsters. Bookies. Molls. Murder. Nightclubs. Vacations. Marijuana. LSD. Tennessee. Daytona Beach.*

Note: D. E. Davison and Alan Davis are the same person.

MOONSHOT see COUNTDOWN

MOONWOLF (Finland/West Germany) F6.3293

Alfa Film–Suomen Filmiteollisuus. *Dist* Allied Artists. Apr **1966.** Sd; b&w. 35mm. 74 min. [Also reviewed at 85 min.]

Prod Wolf Brauner, Martin Nosseck. *Dir* Martin Nosseck, George Freedland. *Screenplay* George Freedland. *Dial* Johannes Hendrich. *Photog* Herbert Körner, Anton Markic, Esko Töyri. *Art Dir* Aarre Koivisto, Max A. Bienek. *Film Ed* Ralph Cushman. *Mus* Henri Price, Albert Sendry, Peter Thomas. *Prod Mgr* Soitso, Hans-Bolko Marcard.

Cast: Carl Möhner *(Dr. Holm)*, Ann Savo *(Åra)*, Helmut Schmid *(woodsman)*, Paul Dahlke, Richard Häussler, Ingrid Lutz, Horst Janson, Åke Lindman.

Melodrama. In Switzerland, Dr. Holm, a veterinarian and zoologist, reluctantly allows his dog Wolf to be used in a space project to study survival techniques. Years before, the zoologist found the pup in Finland, and the dog led him to Åra, a young woman trapped on the side of a precipice. Although a romance developed between the two, it was complicated by her relationship with a jealous woodsman. The dog is launched, and his capsule lands in a dangerous Arctic terrain near Åra's home. Dr. Holm and the woodsman join in the recovery mission, but after starting a fight with Dr. Holm, the woodsman is killed by wolves. Dr. Holm retrieves his dog and is then reunited with Åra. *Veterinarians. Zoologists. Woodsmen. Space flights. Survival. Jealousy. Experiments. Arctic regions. Switzerland. Dogs. Wolves.*

Note: Location scenes filmed in the Arctic regions. Opened in Munich in May 1959 as *... Und immer ruft das Herz;* running times: 83 and 91 min.

THE MORALIST (Italy) F6.3294

Avers Film (Rome)–Napoleon Film. *Dist* United Motion Picture Organization. 22 Apr **1964** [New York opening]. Sd; b&w. 35mm. 120 min.

Dir Giorgio Bianchi. *Screenplay* Ettore M. Margadonna, Luciana Corda, Rodolfo Sonego, Vincenzo Talarico, Oreste Biancoli. *Story* Ettore M. Margadonna, Luciana Corda, Oreste Biancoli. *Photog* Alvaro Mancori. *Mus* Carlo Savina.

Cast: Alberto Sordi *(Agostino)*, Vittorio De Sica *(Il Presidente)*, Franca Valeri *(Virginia)*, Franco Fabrizi *(Giovanni)*, Maria Percy *(Monique)*, Sylvia Lopez, Mara Berni, Leopoldo Trieste, Christiane Nielsen.

Satire. Agostino, the recently appointed general secretary of a censorship board, is given wide authority by the group's elderly leader, Il Presidente, who is anxious to arrange a marriage for his daughter Virginia. Giovanni, whose nightclub is closed down by Agostino, solicits the help of Virginia in reopening his business. While attending a convention abroad, Agostino meets Monique, a stripteaser whom he persuades to return to Italy with him. When Il Presidente discovers that Agostino is using his position as a front for his own exploits, Agostino is arrested, Giovanni reopens his nightclub, and Virginia resumes her search for a husband. *Nightclub owners. Stripteasers. Censorship. Marriage—Arranged. Duplicity. Nightclubs.*

Note: Opened in Rome in Sep 1959 as *Il moralista*.

IL MORALISTA see THE MORALIST

MORD UND TOTSCHLAG see A DEGREE OF MURDER

MORDEI HA'OR see SANDS OF BEERSHEBA

DER MÖRDER see ENOUGH ROPE

MORE (Luxembourg) F6.3295

Jet Films–Doric Film. *Dist* Cinema V Distributing, Inc. 4 Aug **1969** [New York opening]. Sd; col (Eastman Color). 35mm. 110 min.

Prod Dave Lewis, Charles Lachman. *Exec Prod* Fred Junck. *Dir-Story* Barbet Schroeder. *Screenplay-Dial* Paul Gégauff, Barbet Schroeder. *Dir Photog* Nestor Almendros. *Art Dir* Fran Lewis, Nestor Almendros. *Film Ed* Denise de Casabianca. *Asst Ed* Monique Giraudy. *Mus Comp & Perf by* Pink Floyd. *Sd* Jack Julian. *Sd Eff* Robert Pouret. *Prod Asst* Carlos Duran, Michel Chanderli, Stéphane Tchalgadjieff, Alfred de Graaff. *Script Girl* Monique Giraudy. *Still Photog* Lester Waldman.

Cast: Mimsy Farmer *(Estelle)*, Klaus Grunberg *(Stefan)*, Heinz Engelmann *(Wolf)*, Michel Chanderli *(Charlie)*, Louise Wink *(Cathy)*, Henry Wolf, actor *(Henry)*, Georges Montant *(seller)*.

Drama. Upon completing his university studies, Stefan, a German student, hitchhikes from Lübeck to Paris in quest of experience and self-knowledge. In the Latin Quarter, he is befriended by Charlie, a petty crook and gambler. Despite Charlie's warnings, Stefan falls in love with Estelle, an American expatriate who introduces him to marijuana. When Estelle goes to the island of Ibiza in the Mediterranean, Stefan raises money to follow her by joining Charlie in a robbery. Upon his arrival, he discovers that Estelle is involved with Wolf, an ex-Nazi who runs a resort hotel and traffics in narcotics. Stefan persuades Estelle to leave Wolf's hotel and live with him in a villa he has borrowed. One day Stefan overhears Estelle discussing narcotics with her friend Cathy. Although shocked by Estelle's past history as a heroin user and her lesbian relationship with Cathy, Stefan succumbs to Estelle's wishes by first making love to Cathy and then sampling some heroin. Stefan and Estelle rapidly become addicts, and Stefan is forced to support their habit by tending bar and trafficking in drugs for Wolf. The couple make a desperate attempt to cure themselves through the use of LSD, but this tactic ultimately fails, and their emotional and physical relationship deteriorates. Eventually, Charlie arrives and tries to persuade Stefan to return with him to Paris, but by now Stefan is too dependent on Estelle and drugs to make the break. When Estelle walks out after a violent quarrel, Stefan takes an overdose of heroin and dies. *Germans. Students. Gamblers. Americans in foreign countries. Nazis. Drug dealers. Drug addicts. Bartenders. Robbery. Lesbianism. Drug overdose. Hotels. Marijuana. Heroin. LSD. Lübeck. Ibiza. Paris—Quartier Latin.*

Note: Filmed in Ibiza and Paris; original running time: 120 min.

MORE DEAD THAN ALIVE F6.3296

Aubrey Schenck Enterprises. *Dist* United Artists. 15 Jan **1969** [Los Angeles opening; c15 Jan 1969; LP37138]. Sd; col (De Luxe). 35mm. 101 min. [Also 87 & 99 min.] *MPAA rating* M.

An Aubrey Schenck Production. *Prod* Hal Klein. *Exec Prod* Aubrey Schenck. *Dir* Robert Sparr. *Writ* George Schenck. *Photog* Jack Marquette. *Art Dir* J. Arthur Loel. *Set Decor* William L. Kuehl. *Film Ed* John Schreyer. *Mus* Philip Springer. *Sd* Everett Hughes. *Asst Dir* Morris R. Abrams, Joe Nayfack. *Script Supv* Betty Crosby. *Wardrobe* Tye Oswald, Joyce Rogers. *Makeup* Gary Liddiard. *Hairstyles* Jean Burt Reilly. *Sp Eff* Ralph Webb. *Constr* Carl Lindstrom. *Still Photog* Don Christie. *Key Grip* Kenneth Taylor. *Prop Master* Louis Sluskin. *Casting* Jack Roberts.

Cast: Clint Walker *("Killer" Cain)*, Vincent Price *(Ruffalo)*, Anne Francis *(Monica)*, Paul Hampton *(Billy)*, Mike Henry *(Luke Santee)*, Craig Littler *(Karma)*, Beverly Powers *(Sheree)*, Clarke Gordon *(Carson)*, William Woodson *(warden)*.

Western melodrama. In the 1890's four desperadoes headed by Luke Santee attempt to free Luke's younger brother from the Arizona Territorial Prison. When the break is thwarted by Cain, a man serving 18 years for the killing of a marshal, Luke vows revenge on Cain. After his release from prison, Cain finds that there is no place in the new, less violent West for professional gunfighters. Refusing an offer to appear as a sharpshooter in a traveling sideshow owned by Ruffalo, Cain takes a job driving a supply wagon but is ambushed by the Santee gang, beaten up, and left for dead in a ghost town. After being nursed back to health by Monica Alton, an artist from the East, he reluctantly signs on with Ruffalo and is billed as "Killer" Cain, the outlaw with 12 notches in his gun. Now he finds that he has incurred the angry jealousy of young Billy Eager, the former star of the show. Bothered by Billy's attempts to provoke a gunfight and annoyed when his old enemy Linus Carson tries to make him draw his gun, Cain leaves the show, encounters Monica at a rundown ranch, and stays to help her fix up the place. Meanwhile, Billy Eager goes berserk and murders Ruffalo but is himself killed by Luke Santee. After aiding in the apprehension of Luke, Cain marries Monica and settles down to raise cattle on their ranch. A short time later, lawyer Rafe Karma appears, opens a briefcase, pulls out a gun and kills Cain, claiming that, years before, Cain had killed his father. *Desperadoes. Brothers. Artists. Convicts. Gunfighters. United States marshals. Sharpshooters. Revenge. Lawyers. Criminals—Rehabilitation. Prison escapes. Jealousy. Murder. Marriage. Sideshows. Ranches. Arizona.*

Note: Location scenes filmed at Vasquez Rocks, California.

MORE DEADLY THAN THE MALE (Great Britain) F6.3297

U. N. A. *Dist* Schoenfeld Film Distributing Corp. 11 Jan **1961** [Hartford, Connecticut, opening]. Sd; col (Eastman Color). 35mm. 60 min.

Dir Robert Bucknell. *Screenplay* Paul Chevalier. *Film Ed* Robert Bucknell. *Mus* Louis Nordish. P. Gibbon.

Cast: Jeremy White *(Saul Coe)*, John Mahoney *(Godfrey LeFol)*, Ann Davy *(Estelle LeFol)*, Edna Dore *(Ruth LeFol)*, Lorraine Peters *(Rita)*, Don Mason *(narrator)*.

Melodrama. Source: Paul Chevalier, *More Deadly Than the Male* (London, 1960). While vacationing in England, American Saul Coe has an affair with unhappily married Estelle LeFol. Goaded on by the woman, Saul kills her wealthy husband, Godfrey, and places his body in an abandoned blockhouse on the beach. With her husband out of the way, Estelle no longer needs Saul and rejects him. Rita, Saul's fiancée, arrives and becomes suspicious of the strained relationship between Saul and Estelle. Knowing that the young woman is a threat to her safety, Estelle murders her. Saul comes to realize the truth about Estelle's ruthlessness and decides to kill her; during a chase along a cliff path, Estelle loses her footing and falls to her death. He carries her body to the blockhouse, where Godfrey's suspicious and vengeful mother, Ruth, suddenly appears and locks him in with the murder victims. Hysterical, Saul shoots himself. *Americans in foreign countries. Murder. Infidelity. Revenge. Motherhood. Suicide. Vacations.*

Note: Released in Great Britain in 1959.

MORE HEAD F6.3298

Boss Productions. *Dist* Enrico Alexandros Releases. ca **1969**. Sd; b&w. 35mm. 69 min.

Prod-Dir Wizard Glick, Robert Ruttenberg. *Photog* Bob Sumner. *Main Titl* Helen Hersch. *Film Ed* Snip Johnson. *Prod Asst* Jean Paiva.

Sex film. Based on a novel by: Linda Vair. Dr. Von Clapp operates a sex clinic designed to help women with their sexual problems. His techniques include group oral sex play and group bathing. His assistant, Morgan the Organ, helps in solving the clients' problems. *Physicians. Sexual techniques. Oral sex. Group sex. Bathing customs. Sex clinics.*

MORE MILK EVETTE F6.3299

Dist Film-Makers' Cooperative. 8 Feb **1966** [New York opening]. Sd; b&w with col seq. 2 × 16mm. 70 min.

Prod-Dir Andy Warhol. *Writ* Ronald Tavel. *Photog* Andy Warhol. *Mus* The Velvet Underground. *Prod Asst* Paul Morrissey.

Cast: Mario Montez *(mother)*, Paul Caruso, Richard Schmidt, Larry Kent.

Satire. An "opera" in which a son murders his mother's lover. Two images appear side by side on the screen. On one side, a transvestite movie star who resembles Lana Turner eats a hamburger and a pear and drinks some milk in the company of a listless young man. On the other side, a smiling man is bound and lashed with ropes. In the second part of the film, a blonde is having her makeup applied by a makeup man on one side of the screen, while on the other she is eating an elegant meal. Finally, the woman is seen with her head in a toilet. *Murder. Transvestism. Sadism. Flagellation. Filial relations. Lana Turner.*

Note: Also known as *Lana Turner* and *More Milk Yvette.*

MORE THAN A MIRACLE (France/Italy) F6.3300

C. C. Champion–Les Films Concordia. *Dist* Metro-Goldwyn-Mayer, Inc. 1 Nov **1967** [New York opening; c28 Sep 1967; LP34785]. Sd; col (Metrocolor). 35mm (Franscope). 110 min. [Also reviewed at 102 min and 105 min.]

A Carlo Ponti Production. *Prod* Carlo Ponti. *Dir* Francesco Rosi. *Story & Screenplay* Tonino Guerra, Raffaele La Capria, Giuseppe Patroni Griffi, Francesco Rosi. *Orig Story* Tonino Guerra. *Dir Photog* Pasquale De Santis. *Camera* Mario Cimini. *2d Camera* Roberto Forges Davanzati. *Art Dir* Piero Poletto. *Asst Art Dir* Giantito Burchiellaro. *Film Ed* Iolanda Benvenuti. *Mus* Piero Piccioni. *Titl Song* Larry Kusik, Eddie Snyder, Piero Piccioni. *Perf by* Roger Williams Chorus & Orchestra. *Sd* Claudio Maielli, Mario Morigi. *Asst Dir* Marco Guarnaschelli, Roberto Pariante. *Gen Mgr* Ione Tuzi. *Prod Mgr* Gianni Cecchin, Claudio Mancini. *1st Asst* Camillo Teti, Dante Brini. *Prod Sec* Giovanna Pellegrino. *Script Girl* Franca Santi. *Cost Dsgn* Giulio Coltellacci. *Asst Cost Dsgn* Enrico Sabbatini. *Wardrobe* Anda Masseroni. *Miss Loren's Cost* Sartoria Safas. *Makeup for Miss Loren* Giuseppe Annunziata, Ada Palombi. *Makeup* Mario Van Riel. *Hairdresser* Paolo Borselli. *Master of Arms* Franco Fantasia. *Dial Supv* Olaf Pooley. *Prop Mgr* Aldo Colanzi. *1st Electrn* Orlando Pellegrini. *Sp Horses, Saddles, and Harnesses* Medyna y García Moreno S. L.

Cast: Sophia Loren *(Isabella)*, Omar Sharif *(Prince Ramon)*, Dolores Del Rio *(Princess Mother)*, Georges Wilson *(Monzu)*, Leslie French *(Brother Joseph)*, Carlo Pisacane *(1st witch)*, Marina Malfatti *(devout princess)*, Anna Nogara *(impatient princess)*, Rita Forzano *(greedy princess)*, Rosemary Martin *(vain princess)*, Carlotta Barilli *(superstitious princess)*, Fleur Mombelli *(haughty princess)*, Anna Liotti *(infant princess)*, Cris Huerta *(Spanish groom)*, Pietro Carloni *(village priest)*, Giovanni Tarallo *(elderly monk)*, Renato Pinciroli *(prince's chamberlain)*, Giacomo Furia *(prior)*, Gladys Dawson, Kathleen St. John, Beatrice Greack *(head witches)*, Pasquale Di Napoli, Francesco Coppola, Salvatore Ruvo, Vincenzo Danaro, Luciano Di Mauro, Luigi Criscuolo, Francesco Lo Como *(street urchins)*, Valentino Macchi.

Romantic comedy. In 17th-century Spain, the handsome, arrogant Prince Ramon refuses to choose a bride from the seven marriageable princesses whom his mother has selected as most deserving of becoming his wife. Ignoring his stately duties, he rides off on his white stallion, gets thrown in a meadow, and walks to a monastery. There he meets a simple and pure-hearted friar, Brother Joseph, who amuses the local children by leaping into the air and flying about the countryside. Brother Joseph presents the prince with a donkey and a bag of flour and instructs him to search for a woman who will make him seven dumplings. Leaving the monastery, the prince finds his stallion in the possession of a peasant girl, Isabella. Taken by her beauty he orders her to make the seven dumplings, but overcome by hunger Isabella eats the seventh dumpling. To taunt her for her disobedience, the prince feigns death and then disappears. In her distress, Isabella visits a group of witches, who give her a magic spell to bring the prince back to life; but she jumbles the incantation and renders the prince paralyzed. His soldiers find Isabella and bring her to the palace, and she breaks the spell with a magic kiss. Despite his growing affection for Isabella, the prince punishes her by nailing her in a barrel and rolling her toward the sea. Some street urchins rescue her, however, and she returns to the palace to work as a scullery maid. Meanwhile, the viceroy has ordered the prince to pick his bride from the seven princesses. By now in love with Isabella, he disguises her as a princess and enters her in a dishwashing contest to determine who will be his bride. Isabella fails to win when one of her rivals arranges for some of Isabella's dishes to break upon being touched. Filled with despair, she decides to drown herself, but Brother Joseph, now a heavenly saint, intervenes and sends her back to the castle. Once there, Isabella exposes those who plotted against her and is happily reunited with the prince. *Royalty. Peasants. Monks. Witches. Angels. Levitation. Magic. Marriage. Courtship. Suicide. Filial relations. Spells. Contests. Spain. Miracles. Horses. Donkeys.*

Note: Location scenes filmed in Italy. Released in Italy in 1967 as *C'era una volta.* Opened in Paris in May 1968 as *La belle et le cavalier.* Prerelease title: *Happily Ever After;* may also be known as *Once Upon a Time.*

MORGAN! (Great Britain)   **F6.3301**
Quintra Productions. *For* British Lion Films. *Dist* Cinema V Distributing, Inc. 4 Apr **1966** [New York opening]. Sd; b&w. 35mm. 97 min.
Prod Leon Clore. *Dir* Karel Reisz. *Screenplay* David Mercer. *Photog* Larry Pizer, Gerry Turpin. *Art Dir* Philip Harrison. *Film Ed* Victor Proctor, Tom Priestley. *Mus* John Dankworth. *Sd Rec* Peter Handford. *Asst Dir* Claude Watson. *Prod Mgr* Roy Baird.
Cast: Vanessa Redgrave *(Leonie Delt),* David Warner *(Morgan Delt),* Robert Stephens *(Charles Napier),* Irene Handl *(Mrs. Delt),* Newton Blick *(Mr. Henderson),* Nan Munro *(Mrs. Henderson),* Bernard Bresslaw *(policeman),* Arthur Mullard *(Wally),* Graham Crowden *(counsel),* Peter Cellier *(2d counsel),* John Rae *(judge),* Angus MacKay *(best man),* Peter Collingwood, John Garrie, Marvis Edwards, Robert Bridges.
Comedy-drama. Based on the BBC-produced teleplay by: David Mercer, *A Suitable Case for Treatment.* Morgan Delt is an eccentric and madcap London artist, who, though reared by his Marxist-minded mother to participate in the "great revolution," has disappointed her by marrying into a wealthy family and spending most of his life in a world of fantasy. He particularly identifies with the gorilla, and at times lapses into mimicking gorilla behavior. Morgan, supposedly in Greece while his wife, Leonie, obtains a divorce, suddenly reappears on the day of the hearing and demands that Leonie return to him. Leonie, despite her deep affection for Morgan and his world, feels compelled to shed the bizarre role of playing Jane to his Tarzan and intends to marry the "sensible" Charles Napier, an art dealer and friend of Morgan's. Undaunted by Leonie's decision, Morgan embarks on a diabolical campaign to win her back. He camps outside her house in her car, places a skeleton in her bed, wires the house so that the sound of a launching American rocket plays when Leonie and her fiancé embrace, draws and cuts hammer and sickle designs on her furnishings, seduces her during her moments of vulnerability, and plants a bomb under her bed to discourage her fiancé. The bomb explodes, shaking up Leonie's interfering mother. Between pranks, Morgan takes refuge with his mother, whose favorite diversion is to visit Karl Marx's tomb in Highgate Cemetery. Finally, aided by wrestler Wally Carver, Morgan abducts Leonie and takes her to a lake in Wales, but Leonie's parents rescue her, and Morgan is sent to prison. Released on the day Leonie and Charles are to marry, Morgan, who has been influenced by the movie *King Kong,* dons a gorilla suit; scales the walls of an apartment building; crashes bodily into the wedding reception; and succeeds only in setting his suit on fire. He escapes his pursuers by motorcycle and ends up in a rubbish heap, where he fantasizes that all the people with whom he has shared his life have come to execute him. Some time later Leonie, now pregnant, visits Morgan at a mental institution. She finds him busily engaged in planting a hammer-and-sickle-shaped flower garden. He asks her if she is carrying his child; and she smiles, nods, and walks away. *Eccentrics. Artists. Art dealers. Wrestlers. Mothers-in-law. Divorce. Marxism. Motherhood. Wealth. Insanity. Fantasy. Seduction. Abduction. Pregnancy. Disguise. Weddings. Social classes. Bombs. Prisons. London. Wales. Highgate Cemetery (England). Chases. Tarzan. "King Kong". Gorillas.*
Note: Filmed in London. Opened in London in Apr 1966 as *Morgan, a Suitable Case for Treatment* and also known there as *A Suitable Case for Treatment.* Included in the film are clips from RKO's *King Kong* (1933) and a Tarzan sequence.

MORGAN, A SUITABLE CASE FOR TREATMENT *see* **MORGAN!**

MORGAN IL PIRATA *see* **MORGAN THE PIRATE**

MORGAN THE PIRATE (France/Italy)   **F6.3302**
C. C. F. Lux–Lux Film–Adelphia Compagnia Cinematografica. *Dist* Metro-Goldwyn-Mayer, Inc. 21 Jun **1961** [Los Angeles opening; c2 May 1961; LP20383]. Sd (Fonolux); col (Eastman Color). 35mm (CinemaScope). 93 min. [Copyright length: 95 min.]
Pres by Joseph E. Levine. *Dir* Primo Zeglio. *Supv Dir* Andre De Toth. *Story & Screenplay* Filippo Sanjust, Andre De Toth, Primo Zeglio. *Dir Photog* Tonino Delli Colli. *Camera* Franco Delli Colli. *Set Dsgn* Gianni Polidori, Renato Cardone. *Film Ed* Maurizio Lucidi, Cesare Cavagna. *Mus Comp & Cond* Franco Mannino. *Asst Dir* Alberto Cardone. *Prod Mgr* Aldo Pomilia. *Prod Supv* Nicolo Pomilia. *Cost Dsgn* Filippo Sanjust. *Sp Eff* Eros Bacciucchi.
Cast: Steve Reeves *(Sir Henry Morgan),* Valérie Lagrange *(Doña Inez),* Chelo Alonso *(Concepción),* Lidia Alfonsi *(Doña María),* Armand Mestral *(L'Olannais),* Ivo Garrani *(The Governor),* Giulio Bosetti *(Sir Thomas Modyford),* Giorgio Ardisson *(Walter),* Angelo Zanolli *(David),* Dino Malacrida *(The Duke),* Anita Todesco, Mimmo Poli.
Adventure melodrama. In the late 17th century, a freeborn Englishman, Henry Morgan, is enslaved by the Spaniards in Panama and sold to Doña Inez,

daughter of the governor. Morgan falls in love with his mistress, and her father punishes him by sentencing him to a life of hard labor aboard a Spanish galleon. Morgan leads his fellow slaves in mutiny, takes over the ship, and becomes a pirate. Before long his daring exploits on the Spanish Main arouse the interest of King Charles II of England, and Morgan agrees to attack only Spanish vessels in return for English ships and men. In one raid he captures Doña Inez, but when she spurns him he permits her to return to Panama. Once there, she warns her father of Morgan's planned invasion of Panama, and the pirate ships are easily sunk or routed by the alerted Spanish. Undaunted, Morgan leads his men overland and attacks the city from the rear. The maneuver succeeds, Panama falls to the pirates, and Doña Inez finally admits her love for Morgan. *English. Spanish. Pirates. Slavery. Filial relations. Mutiny. Panama. Henry Morgan. Charles II (England).*
Note: Opened in Rome in Nov 1960 as *Morgan il pirata;* running time: ca105 min; in Paris in Jun 1961 as *Capitaine Morgan;* running time: ca95 min.

MORIANERNA *see* **MORIANNA (I, THE BODY)**

MORIANNA (I, THE BODY) (Sweden)   **F6.3303**
Bison Film–Inge Ivarson. *Dist* Mondial Films. 10 Feb **1967** [Los Angeles opening]. Sd; b&w. 35mm. 90 min.
Pres by Gaston Hakim. *Prod* Inge Ivarson, Ewert Granholm. *Dir* Arne Mattsson. *Screenplay* Per Wahlöö, Arne Mattsson. *Photog* Max Wilén. *Art Dir* Poa Sivertzen. *Film Ed* Lennart Wallen. *Mus* Georg Riedel. *Sd* Wilhelm Aring.
Cast: Lotte Tarp *(Rita),* Anders Henrikson *(Verner Vade),* Eva Dahlbeck *(Anna Vade),* Olle Andersson *(Durell),* Valter Norman *(Jonas),* Elsa Prawitz *(Agda),* Ella Henrikson *(Monika),* Ove Tjernberg *(Bengt),* Anne Thorstensson *(Lisa),* Erik Hell *(Ragnar),* Tor Isedal *(Valter Velin),* Elisabeth Oden *(Miss Nilsson),* Heinz Hopf *(Boris).*
Melodrama. Source: Jan Ekström, *Morianerna* (Stockholm, 1964). Millionaire Verner Vade, lustful despite the impotence of his nearly 80 years, plans to show his contempt for the family who fear and despise him by leaving his entire fortune to charity. He pays Rita, the wanton housemaid, to disrobe while he watches. Later, seeking to track down a mysterious phone call from "Death," he goes to an apartment in a condemned building, which, as he suspects, is a trysting place for his young wife, Anna, and her architect lover, Ragnar. While Vade watches Rita taking a shower at the apartment, he is knocked unconscious by an unseen assailant and dragged into a closet. Regaining consciousness, he overhears an encounter between Anna and Ragnar. He stumbles back to his own home, where his 8-year-old niece, Lisa, burns a rag doll and recites a rhyme about his death. Inspector Durell, who has been investigating Vade, arrests Rita's brutal fiancé, waiter Valter Velin, on suspicion of assault. Vade confronts Anna with her infidelity and tells her he intends to prosecute her brother-in-law, Bengt, for embezzlement. Meanwhile, Anna's evil and demented nephew, Boris, attemps to rape Rita but is stopped and ordered out of the house by Vade. Vade is stabbed to death as he returns to his room, and his body is discovered while the family celebrates his 80th birthday. Inspector Durell confronts the assembled hopeful heirs and unmasks the killer. *Millionaires. Housemaids. Architects. Detectives. Waiters. Family life. Infidelity. Voyeurism. Rape. Murder. Inheritance. Embezzlement.*
Note: Released in Sweden in 1965 as *Morianerna;* running time: 100 min. Also known as *I, The Body* and *Morianna.*

MORIRE GRATIS (Italy)   **F6.3304**
Fedel Film. *Dist* New Yorker Films. 30 Mar **1969** [New York opening]. Sd; b&w. 35mm. 88 min.
Prod Enzo Giulioli. *Dir-Writ* Sandro Franchina. *Photog* Guido Cosulich de Pecine. *Mus* Stefano Torossi.
Cast: Franco Angeli *(sculptor),* Karen Blanguernon *(Michèle),* Mario Pisu, Gerard Herter, Isabel D'Avila, Adrano Amedei Migliano, Madeleine Santoro, Sandro Brunori.
Drama. A bored young sculptor who describes himself as "impotent, alcoholic, and drugged," leaves Rome on a motor trip to Paris, smuggling a shipment of narcotics inside his statue of the she-wolf giving suck to Romulus and Remus. En route he encounters a hitchhiker—Michèle, the elegant Parisian mistress of a rich, middle-aged Italian—and she abandons her lover to accompany him. Along the way, he ruminates bitterly on the waste and coarseness of modern life, insulting and abusing both Michèle and himself, finding satisfaction only in his skill as a driver. In an episode on board a yacht on the Riviera, he gets drunk, uses narcotics, reveals his divorce, and exhibits suicidal tendencies. At an inn, the two switch bed partners in a sexual encounter with a brother and sister, but they resume their trip together. They rush to a hospital with a screaming woman who has been injured in an automobile accident, then arrive in Paris with their cargo intact, only to be murdered by members of the dope ring. *Sculptors. Mistresses. Hitchhikers. Smuggling. Narcotics. Drunkenness. Suicide. Mate swapping. Murder. Impotence. Yachts. Rome. Paris. Riviera. Automobile accidents.*
Note: Produced in Italy in 1968.

MORITURI   F6.3305

Arcola-Colony Productions. *Dist* Twentieth Century-Fox Film Corp. 14 Jul **1965** [Santa Catalina, California, opening; c4 Aug 1965; LP31752]. Sd (Westrex); b&w. 35mm. 123 min. [Also reviewed at 116 min.]

Prod Aaron Rosenberg. *Assoc Prod* Barney Rosenzweig. *Dir* Bernhard Wicki. *Screenplay* Daniel Taradash. *Dir Photog* Conrad Hall. *Art Dir* Jack Martin Smith, Herman A. Blumenthal. *Set Decor* Walter M. Scott, Jerry Wunderlich. *Film Ed* Joseph Silver. *Mus* Jerry Goldsmith. *Orch* Arthur Morton. *Sd* Garry Harris, David Dockendorf, Elmer Raguse. *Asst Dir* David Silver, Joseph Behm. *Unit Prod Mgr* William Eckhardt. *Cost Dsgn* Moss Mabry. *Wardrobe* Wesley Trist, Truman Eli. *Makeup Supv* Ben Nye. *Makeup* Phil Rhodes, Dan Striepeke, Jack Obringer. *Hairstyles* Margaret Donovan. *Sp Photog Eff* L. B. Abbott, Emil Kosa, Jr. *Dial Coach* Walon Green, Sam Gilman. *Prop* Don Greenwood, prop. *Grip* Jack Richter. *Still Photog* James Mitchell, Larry Prather.

Cast: Marlon Brando *(Robert Crain),* Yul Brynner *(Captain Mueller),* Janet Margolin *(Esther Levy),* Trevor Howard *(Colonel Statter),* Martin Benrath *(Kruse),* Hans Christian Blech *(Donkeyman),* Wally Cox *(Dr. Ambach),* Max Haufler *(Branner),* Rainer Penkert *(Milkereit),* William Redfield *(Baldwin),* Oscar Beregi *(admiral),* Martin Brandt *(Nissen),* Charles De Vries *(Kurz),* Carl Esmond *(Busch),* Martin Kosleck *(Wilke),* Norbert Schiller *(steward),* Robert Sorrells *(German crew member),* Rick Traeger *(crew member),* Ivan Triesault *(Lieutenant Brandt).*

War melodrama. Source: Werner Jörg Lüddecke, *Morituri* (Bayreuth, 1963). Wealthy Robert Crain, a deserter from the German Army posing as a Swiss national in India during World War II, is coerced by British Intelligence Colonel Statter into masquerading as a Gestapo officer. Installing himself as a passenger aboard a German blockade runner which is carrying a valuable cargo of rubber from the Orient, Crain, using the name Hans Keil, is to deactivate the scuttling charges by which the captain would destroy the ship if faced with capture. Captain Mueller, unsympathetic to the Nazi philosophy, regards the presence of the "Gestapo officer" on his ship with fear and suspicion. Mueller refuses to allow Crain the run of the ship, thus making it almost impossible for him to find and deactivate the explosives before the Allies intercept the vessel at a predetermined point. Two German submarine officers bring aboard the freighter a group of survivors of a sunken ship, among them some American refugees and Esther Levy, a German Jew who has been the victim of Nazi atrocities. Crain, aware that his identity is about to be exposed by the suspicious submarine officers, decides to lead the new arrivals and some of the crew members to mutiny. By the time the Germans learn that Crain is a fraud, mutiny has broken out and the ship is sinking. Crain and Mueller, left alone on the ship, discover that the vessel probably will not sink for a few hours. Crain convinces Mueller that he owes no allegiance to the Nazis, and Mueller radios a nearby Allied ship to save them and the cargo. *Secret agents. Nazis. Sea captains. Germans. Ship crews. Jews. Deserters—Military. Imposture. Sabotage. Mutiny. Sea rescue. War crimes. Rubber. Freighters. World War II. India. Gestapo. Great Britain—Intelligence service. Ship explosions.*

Note: Location scenes filmed off Santa Catalina, California. Also known as: *The Saboteur: Code Name—Morituri.*

THE MORNING AFTER   F6.3306

Dist Sam Lake Enterprises. **1970.** Sd; col. 35mm. 76 min.

Prod Jean Jacques Robeau. *Dir* Sidney Knight. *Writ* Harvey Green. *Camera* Robert Morgenstern. *Film Ed* Sidney Knight. *Sd* Ronald Nort. *Prod Asst* Luigi D'Arc.

Cast: Sammy Cole *(John),* Jean Parker, actress *(Gay),* David Marcus *(inspector),* Richard Zunt *(Larry),* Linda Shall *(Maureen),* Thomas Strangle *(father),* Nessa Trou *(bodyguard),* Steve Dario *(man),* Susan Cono *(woman).*

Melodrama. John returns from a vacation and finds his sister Gay, a stripper at a nightclub, dead from stab wounds. He calls an inspector to investigate the case and visits Larry, Gay's boss and lover. Maureen, Gay's best friend and lesbian lover, who also works at the club, tells John that she has a clue to the murder. When he arrives at Maureen's apartment, she insists that they have sex. She then reveals that an older man with a limp became upset by Gay's striptease act the night of the murder; knowing that his father has a limp, John returns to the old man's house. He forces his father to confess that he had been drunk at the club, and, enraged at seeing his daughter's act, he went to her apartment and stabbed her to death. *Stripteasers. Cripples. Murder. Brother-sister relationship. Lesbianism. Filial relations. Drunkenness. Nightclubs.*

MORNING STAR (U.S.S.R.)   F6.3307

Lenfilm-Frunze Film Studio. *Dist* Artkino Pictures. 18 Aug **1962** [New York opening]. Sd; col. 35mm. 75 min.

Dir Roman Tikhomirov. *Screenplay* I. Menaker, Nikolay Tugelov, Apollinariy Dudko, Roman Tikhomirov. *Story Ed* I. Glikman. *Photog* Apollinariy Dudko. *Camera* K. Sobol, V. Kovzel. *Art Dir* A. Blek. *Mus* Mikhail Rafailovich Raukhverger. *Perf by* Leningrad Philharmonic Orchestra. *Cond* G. Mironovich. *Ballet Master* Nikolay Tugelov. *Sd* Ye. Nesterov. *Asst Dir* N. Rusanova. *Prod Mgr* V. Yakovlev, prod mgr. *Makeup* V. Goryunov. *Sp Eff* A. Zavyalov, G. Senotov, M. Krotkin.

Cast: Reina Chokoyeva *(Cholpon),* Uran Sarbagishev *(Nurdin),* Nikolay Tugelov *(Temir Khan),* Bibisara Beyshenaliyeva *(Ayday),* S. Abduzhalilov *(genie),* Kirgiz State Opera Company Corps de Ballet.

Dance film. Source: Mikhail Rafailovich Raukhverger, L. Kramarevskiy and O. Sarbagishev, *Cholpon—Utrennyaya zvezda* (a ballet interpretation of the legend from the Tien Shan of Kirgiz; Frunze(?) production: 1944). Nurdin, the son of the omnipotent Temir Khan, is in love with Cholpon [Morning Star], though her poverty is a barrier to their love. Ayday, an evil, 100-year-old sorceress whose kiss turns men to stone, tries to separate them. Temir Khan arranges for Nurdin to choose a bride from among five well-born beauties, but none sways him from his love for Cholpon. Suddenly Ayday appears, transformed into a young woman of extraordinary beauty, and tempts Nurdin. He is on the point of drinking her love potion when Cholpon appears. He affirms his love for her and asks his father's blessing on his choice. Temir Khan, enraged that his son would choose a low-born bride, has the lovers thrown into the well of death. They remain true lovers in the underground kingdom, but one day Cholpon awakens to find Nurdin gone. The fear of losing her beloved gives Cholpon strength, and in a struggle with Ayday's servant she wrests away Ayday's magic scarf. In Ayday's lair, Cholpon tears the scarf, saving Nurdin from death. Ayday and her servant are turned to stone, and Nurdin and Cholpon celebrate their wedding. *Sorcerers. Royalty. Temptresses. Social classes. Magic. Kirgiz. Tien Shan. Imaginary kingdoms.*

Note: Released in the U.S.S.R. in Jan 1960 as *Cholpon—Utrennyaya zvezda.*

MORO WITCH DOCTOR (United States/Philippines)   F6.3308

Associated Producers, Inc.–Hemisphere Pictures. *Dist* Twentieth Century-Fox Film Corp. 28 Oct **1964** [New York opening; c28 Oct 1964; LP30821]. Sd; b&w. 35mm. 61 min.

Prod-Dir-Writ Eddie Romero. *Exec Prod* Kane W. Lynn. *Co-dir* Gerardo de Leon. *Dir Photog* Felipe Sacdalan. *Art Dir* Vincente Bonus. *Film Ed* Joven Calub. *Asst Film Ed* Ben Barcelón. *Mus* Ariston Avelino. *Sd Engr* Demetrio de Santos. *Sd Eff* Tony Gosalves. *Sd Mix* Pat Del Rosario. *Asst Dir* Jose Dagumboy. *Unit Mgr* Carpi Asturias. *Makeup* Remy Amazan. *Sp Eff* Santos Hilario.

Cast: Jock Mahoney *(Jefferson Stark),* Margia Dean *(Paula Cameron),* Pancho Magalona *(Martin Gonzaga),* Reed Hadley *(Robert Collins),* Paraluman *(Selisa Noble),* Michael Parsons *(Ackerman),* Dale Ishimoto *(Manuel Romblon),* Vic Diaz *(Salek),* Jay Ilagan *(Mahmud),* Bruno Punzalan *(Datu Sumlang),* Nemia Velasco *(Mulan),* Jerry Uslander *(Tom Cameron),* Paul Edwards, Jr. *(Arthur Kruger),* Jess Montalban, Paquito Salcedo, Bill Kane.

Adventure melodrama. CIA agent Jefferson Stark is sent to the Philippines to investigate the murder of two American plantation owners, Cameron and Kruger. Authorities believe that the deaths are linked to gun and opium smuggling. Stark is assisted by Paula, Cameron's sister, who is informed that her brother is alive and hiding from a smuggling syndicate. Arriving at the plantation with Martin, Cameron's financial partner, Stark and Paula discover that the caretaker is a drug addict and the plantation is actually a cover for smuggling activities. When Paula refuses to sell the plantation to Datu Sumlang, the reputed leader of a group of religious fanatics, a wave of terror and murder breaks out on the island. Many of those loyal to Cameron are killed; Stark, Paula, and Martin are attacked and barely escape death. Cameron telephones Paula, telling her to take a briefcase full of money from a bank deposit box and meet him in Manila. Stark and Martin follow her; she is attacked by the supposedly dead Kruger; and Stark and Martin kill him in a gun battle. Kruger's death leads to the breaking up of the smuggling ring and to Cameron's exoneration. *Caretakers. Drug addicts. Fanatics. Murder. Smuggling. Brother-sister relationship. Guns. Opium. Plantations. Partnerships. Manila. United States—Central Intelligence Agency.*

Note: Filmed in the Philippines; working title: *Amok.*

MOROZKO see **JACK FROST**

LA MORT A PONDU UN OEUF see **PLUCKED**

LA MORT DE BELLE see **THE PASSION OF SLOW FIRE**

LA MORT EN CE JARDIN see **GINA**

LA MORTE HA FATTO L'UOVO see **PLUCKED**

LA MORTE NON HA SESSO see **A BLACK VEIL FOR LISA**

LA MORTE-SAISON DES AMOURS see **THE SEASON FOR LOVE**

LA MORTE SALE IN ASCENSORE see **PARIS PICK-UP**

LA MORTE VESTITA DI DOLLARI see **DOG EAT DOG**

LA MORTE VIENE DALLO SPAZIO see **THE DAY THE SKY EXPLODED**

MOSQUITO SQUADRON (Great Britain)   F6.3309
Oakmont Productions. *Dist* United Artists. 6 May **1970** [Salt Lake City, Utah, opening; c29 Apr 1970; LP38125]. Sd; col (De Luxe). 35mm. 90 min. MPAA rating G.

Pres by Mirisch Films. *Prod* Lewis J. Rachmil. *Dir* Boris Sagal. *Screenplay* Donald S. Sanford, Joyce Perry. *Dir Photog* Paul Beeson. *Art Dir* Bill Andrews. *Film Ed* John S. Smith. *Mus* Frank Cordell. *Sd Rec* Norman Bolland. *Asst Dir* Anthony Waye. *Prod Supv* William S. Gilmore, Jr. *Prod Mgr* Victor Peck. *Wardrobe Supv* David Baker. *Ch Makeup* Benny Royston. *Sp Eff* Les Bowie. *Tech Adv* Allen Wheeler, (Commodore), John Roast.

Cast: David McCallum *(Quint Munroe)*, Suzanne Neve *(Beth Scott)*, David Buck *(Sqdn. Ldr. David Scott)*, David Dundas *(Flt. Lieut. Douglas Shelton)*, Dinsdale Landen *(Wing Commander Penrose)*, Charles Gray *(Air Commodore Hufford)*, Michael Anthony *(Father Bellague)*, Vladek Sheybal *(Lieutenant Schack)*, Gordon Sterne *(resistance leader)*, Robert Urquhart *(Major Kemble)*, Brian Grellis, George Layton *(pilot officers)*, John Landry, Derek Steen *(flight sergeants)*, Bryan Marshall *(Neale)*, Michael Latimer *(Clark)*, Nicky Henson *(Wiley Bunce)*, Peggy Thorpe-Bates, Peter Copley, Michael McGovern.

War melodrama. David Scott, a Royal Air Force bomber pilot in World War II, is shot down and presumably killed in a mission over France. His friend, Quint Munroe, assumes command of the squadron and tells David's wife, Beth, of her husband's death. When Quint's reconnaissance flight over France confirms that the Germans are developing a V3 rocket in the Château de Charlon, the British commanders order its destruction with a specially developed bomb. Meanwhile, Quint has fallen in love with Beth, who was his girl friend before she married Scott. Reconnaissance reports indicate that the Germans are holding several hundred British prisoners of war, including Scott, in the château. Consequently, Quint formulates a plan whereby the first wave of bombers will merely breach the château's walls, allowing the prisoners to escape; Father Bellague, a priest working with the French resistance, conveys this information to the prisoners so they will be prepared. The raid is carried out successfully, but although many British prisoners escape, Scott is killed. *Air pilots. Missing persons. Widows. Germans. Prisoners of war. Priests. Reconnaissance. Prison escapes. Bombers. World War II. France. Great Britain—Royal Air Force. Maquis.*

Note: Location scenes filmed at Bovingdon Airfield, England. Released in Great Britain in 1970.

THE MOST BEAUTIFUL AGE (Czechoslovakia)   F6.3310
Barrandov Film Studio. *For* Československý Film. *Dist* Grove Press. 22 Mar **1970** [New York opening]. Sd; b&w. 35mm. 80 min.

Prod Jaroslav Solnička. *Exec Prod* Jiří Šebor, Vladimír Bor. *Assoc Prod* Ludmila Tikovská, František Jaderník. *Asst Prod* Milan Stěch. *Dir-Writ* Jaroslav Papoušek. *Photog* Josef Ort-Šnep. *Art Dir* Karel Černý. *Film Ed* Jiřina Lukešová. *Mus* Karel Mareš. *Mus Perf by* Rudolf Rokl Quartet. *Sd* Adolf Bohm, František Fabián. *Asst Dir* Milan Kadlec.

Cast: Jan Stöckl *(Hanzlik)*, Anna Pisariková *(Kulharková)*, Hana Brejchová *(Vránová)*, Josef Šebánek *(Vosta)*, Ladislav Adam *(Ada)*, Jiří Hálek *(Franta)*, Vladimír Šmeral *(professor)*, Věra Kresadlová *(Susan)*, Milada Ježková *(Vosta's wife)*, Jiří Sýkora *(Vránová's husband)*, M. Kříž, O. Marcin, B. Zemánek, Antonín Soukup, Josef Bartůněk, J. Vošalik, S. Banzet, Josef Kolb, Helena Růžičková, V. Černý, M. Otava, J. Mrázek-Horický, Bohuslav Kupšovský, M. Veselý.

Comedy. An art school selects its models from a group of elderly pensioners who arrive each day seeking work either because they are bored or because they want to earn a little extra money. Hanzlik, a very old man, is chosen, and the young students contemplate his face as he sits and dozes. An elderly woman who is interested in Hanzlik tries to persuade a student to remove the moustache from his bust of Hanzlik because she has been trying to convince Hanzlik that he would look younger without it; but Hanzlik prefers to keep his moustache, even if it means losing his lady friend. The next day Vránová, a young woman who arrives with her baby, is asked to pose in the nude. Her jealous husband later arrives and destroys the students' work. Vránová returns the next day in defiance of her husband, only to find that her services are no longer required because Vosta, a middle-aged, temporarily unemployed coalman who is recovering from an injury, has been selected to pose as a wounded soldier. Vosta learns of the nude modeling that takes place at the school and returns there at night with two of his cronies in the hope of secretly watching the models. Irritated because they cannot see anything, they go off

to get drunk in a nearby bar and to complain about being middle-aged. *Models. Students. Artists. Old age. Middle age. Youth. Employment. Vanity. Nudity. Jealousy. Drunkenness.*

Note: Released in Czechoslovakia in 1969 as *Nejkrásnější věk.*

MOST DANGEROUS MAN ALIVE   F6.3311
Trans-Global Films. *Dist* Columbia Pictures. 28 Jun **1961** [Los Angeles opening; c1 Jun 1961; LP20446]. Sd; b&w. 35mm. 82 min.

Prod Benedict Bogeaus. *Dir* Allan Dwan. *Screenplay* James Leicester, Phillip Rock. *Dir Photog* Carl Carvahal. *Film Ed* Carlo Lodato. *Mus* Louis Forbes. *Sd Ed* Joe Kavigan. *Prod Supv* Clarence Eurist. *Wardrobe* Gwen Wakeling.

Cast: Ron Randell *(Eddie Candell)*, Debra Paget *(Linda Marlow)*, Elaine Stewart *(Carla Angelo)*, Anthony Caruso *(Andy Damon)*, Gregg Palmer *(Lieutenant Fisher)*, Morris Ankrum *(Captain Davis)*, Tudor Owen *(Dr. Meeker)*, Steve Mitchell *(Devola)*, Joel Donte *(Franscetti)*.

Science fiction drama. Source: Phillip Rock and Michael Pate, "The Steel Monster" (a story; publication undetermined). Racketeer Eddie Candell is framed on a murder charge. He escapes from the police and wanders into a blast area where scientists are conducting an experiment in cobalt mutation. He survives the explosion and discovers that his body is now capable of absorbing steel. He then pursues Andy Damon, the rival gangster who not only framed him but also took over both his mob and his moll, Linda Marlow. Damon attempts to kill his old enemy but flees when he learns that Eddie is impervious to bullets. Realizing that his body is slowly turning to steel, Eddie seeks comfort from Carla Angelo, a woman he once befriended. After Damon has fatally wounded Linda, Eddie kills him. He meets his own end when a National Guardsman turns a flamethrower on him and burns his body of steel into powdery dust. *Gangsters. Molls. Murder. Mutation. Revenge. Frameup. Cobalt. Flamethrowers. National Guard.*

THE MOST DANGEROUS MAN IN THE WORLD see **THE CHAIRMAN**

THE MOST PROHIBITED SEX see **SEXY PROIBITISSIMO**

THE MOST WANTED MAN (France/Italy)   F6.3312
Cité Films-Fidès-Cocinor-Peg Produzione. *Dist* Astor Pictures. 7 Feb **1962** [New York opening]. Sd (Western Electric); b&w. 35mm. 85 min.

Prod Jacques Bar. *Assoc Prod* Walter Rupp. *Dir* Henri Verneuil. *Screenplay* Michel Audiard, Jean Manse. *Dial* Michel Audiard. *Story* Max Favalelli. *Photog* Armand Thirard. *Camera* Louis Née, Jean Dicop, Robert Florent. *Art Dir* Robert Giordani. *Asst Set Dsgn* Jean Mandaroux, Jacques d' Ovidio, Gorellik. *Set Decor* André Molles. *Film Ed* Christian Gaudin. *Asst Film Ed* Jacqueline Brédillon, Jacqueline Brachet. *Mus* Nino Rota, Raymond Legrand. *Sd* William Sivel. *Sd Rec* Arthur Van Der Meeren. *Boom* Pierre Zahn. *Asst Dir* Marcel Camus, J. Stocane, Dattino. *Prod Mgr* Louis Manella. *Location Mgr* Charles Auvergne. *Prod Sec* Marguerite Chevalier. *Script Girl* Ginette Diamant-Berger. *Cost* Rosine Delamare. *Dresser* Tina Conte, Marguerite Brachet. *Makeup* Lina Gallet. *Hairstyles* Michèle Dumont. *Still Photog* Gaston Thonnart. *Props* Charpeau.

Cast: Fernandel *(Joe Calvet)*, Zsa-Zsa Gabor *(Lola)*, Alfred Adam *(sheriff)*, Jean Marchat *(attorney general)*, Louis Seigner *(prison director)*, Saturnin Fabre *(W. W. Stone)*, David Opatoshu *(Slim)*, Bob Ingarao *(policeman)*, Paolo Stoppa *(Tony Fallon)*, Nicole Maurey, Gianfanelli, Arturo Bragaglia, Tino Buazzelli, Carlo Ninchi, Guglielmo Barnabo.

Crime comedy. Timid Joe Calvet is fired from his job in a department store due to his nearsightedness and decides to go to a movie. He sits next to Slim, a gangster, and by mistake takes Slim's coat when he leaves the theater. In the subway, he reaches for his glasses but pulls out Slim's gun instead and is arrested by the police who believe him to be Public Enemy No. 1. Slim's gang, headed by Lola, rescues Joe and takes him to their farm hideout. Joe later leads the police to the hideout; there the gang is apprehended, and Joe becomes a national hero. *Gangsters. Police. Eyesight. Timidity. Mistaken identity. Motion picture theaters.*

Note: Location scenes filmed in New York City. Opened in Nice in Dec 1953 as *L'ennemi public no. 1*; running time: 105 min; in Italy in 1953 as *Il nemico pubblico n. 1*. Also known as *The Most Wanted Man in the World.*

I MOSTRI see **OPIATE '67**

IL MOSTRO DI VENEZIA see **THE EMBALMER**

MOSURA see **MOTHRA**

MOTEL CONFIDENTIAL   F6.3313
A. F. P. I. Productions–Monarex. *Dist* SCA Distributors, Sack Amusement Enterprises, Crest Film Distributors. **1967**. Sd; b&w. 35mm (Astravision). 85 min.

Prod-Dir A. C. Stephen. Orig Screenplay Mark Del Monde. Dir Photog Robert Ruben. Art Dir Bud Costello. Post Prod Marco Macaroni. Mus Score Igor Gigagusky. Sd Rec Sam Kopetzky. Wardrobe Hollywood Men's Store. Makeup Artist Sidney Moore.

Cast: Mark Shannon (Stanley Buddington III), Desire D'Andre (Ann Pepper), Vic Lance (Romeo Rampart), Sharron Patino (Daisy Ferguson), John Bealy (Casper Murk), Helena Clayton (Phyllis Doogoodie), John Patino (Harry Ferguson), Diana Denning (Helen Gibbons), Harvey Shane (Willy King), Pat Neice (Susan Harrison), Robert Dodson (Masher Jones), Timothy Paola (Chi-Chi), Hugh Johnson (Donald Harrison), Paula Allison (Sadie Jones).

Sex film. Catering to the "instant sex" market, the Quickie Motel is kept busy night and day: business tycoon Stanley Buddington III seduces his young secretary, Ann Pepper; Chi-Chi, the bellhop, finds Phyllis Doogoodie, a spinster, doing her exercises, and he rapes her, much to her enjoyment; Donald and Susan Harrison save their foundering marriage with a second honeymoon, and Susan displays the sexual prowess she lacked on the first; newlyweds Harry and Daisy Ferguson consummate their marriage; Romeo Rampart makes a pickup at a nearby bar, only to discover at the motel that his date is not a woman; Casper Murk is forced to flee the Quickie when his date's husband, Masher Jones, breaks in and takes over in order to satisfy his own sadistic urges; and nymphomaniac Helen Gibbons picks up a hitchhiking sailor, Willy King, and wears him to a frazzle. Tycoons. Secretaries. Bellboys. Spinsters. Sailors. Hitchhikers. Newlyweds. Pickups. Seduction. Rape. Marriage. Nymphomania. Infidelity. Sadism. Transvestism. Sexual techniques. Motels. Honeymoons.

MOTEL WIVES   F6.3314
Mitam Productions. 21 Feb **1968** [New York showing]. Sd; b&w. 35mm. 63 min.

Dir Adam Clay.

Cast: Capri, Wayne Howser, Carol Long, Virginia Luce, Ginny Smith.

Melodrama. Capri, the owner of a motel, arranges for husbands and wives to meet their lovers in privacy. When a woman fails to show up for a tryst, Capri herself substitutes for the woman. She joins in an orgy with two men and two women, and watches a young couple make love for the first time. Businesswomen. Infidelity. Group sex. Voyeurism. Motels.

Note: Also known as Motel Lives.

MOTHER AND DAUGHTER (U.S.S.R.)   F6.3315
Dovzhenko Film Studio. Dist Artkino Pictures. 30 Oct **1965** [New York opening]. Sd; b&w. 35mm. 80 min.

Dir Yevgeniy Bryunchugin, Anatoliy Bukovskiy. Screenplay Yuriy Zbanatskiy. Story Ed N. Orlova. Photog V. Tyshkovets. Camera A. Kravchenko, P. Pastukhov. Art Dir A. Mamontov, V. Migulko. Sets V. Tsirlina. Film Ed I. Karpenko. Mus German Zhukovskiy. Song Lyr A. Novitskiy. Cond V. Tolba. Sd N. Avramenko. 1st & 2d Asst Dir I. Levchenko, A. Khoryakov. Prod Mgr T. Kulchitskaya. Cost G. Nesterovskaya. Makeup Ye. Shayner. Sp Eff I. Tregubova, G. Lukashov.

Cast: Vera Maretskaya (Mikhaylina), Soraya Pavlova (Olga Dmitriyevna), Ira Mitsik (Natasha), Yura Leontyev (Roman), Lyuda Zabrodskaya (Magda), B. Borisenok (Martsinyuk), Yu. Kritenko (Tikhonyuk), N. Antonova (Yaroshka), Oksana Sluzhenko (Tanya), Nina Borisova, N. Gnepovskaya, L. Danchishin, S. Karamash, O. Nozhkina, A. Nikolayeva, N. Naum, A. Poddubinskiy, N. Rushkovskiy, N. Talyura.

Melodrama. In a Carpathian border village, at a monument erected to the heroic frontier guards of World War II, the school director Martsinyuk meets Olga Kosacheva, widow of the frontier guard commander. At the beginning of the war Martsinyuk had evacuated Olga and her little daughter, Tanya, from the village, but Olga had been captured and her daughter lost. After the war, Olga had left the village to live and work along the Volga. Martsinyuk learns that Mikhaylina Yasen, an older widow, adopted a lost child near the village at the beginning of the war. Over the years, Mikhaylina has been a devoted mother to the girl, whom she named Natasha. Martsinyuk visits Mikhaylina, and, unwilling to deceive the girl and her natural mother, she relates the story of Natasha's adoption. Natasha and her two mothers meet at last, and Mikhaylina finds the strength to give up the girl. Widows. School principals. War victims. Motherhood. Adoption. World War II. Carpathian Mountains. Volga River. Ukraine.

Note: Released in the U.S.S.R. in Nov 1962 as Sredi dobrykh lyudey. Shown in New York as part of a program entitled Ukrainian Festival.

MOTHER GOOSE À GO-GO   F6.3316
Tonylyn Productions. Dist Jack H. Harris Enterprises, VIP Distributors, U. S. Films. 12 Oct **1966** [Albuquerque, New Mexico, opening; c6 Jun 1966; LP33714]. Sd; col (Panacolor). 35mm. 82 min.

Pres by Jack H. Harris. Prod-Dir-Writ Jack H. Harris. Co-prod Muriel G. Harris. Dir Photog Vilis Lapenieks. Art Dir James E. Bechtold. Prod Dsgn Muriel G. Harris. Film Ed Hank Gotzenberg. Mus Douglas Lackey, Gene

Kauer. Songs Tony Harris. Titl Song Sung by Tom Kirk. Song: "Queen of Soul" sung by Barbara McNair. Sd Nigel Noble. Cost Maxwell Shieff.

Cast: Tom Kirk (Ted), Anne Helm (Margie), Jacques Bergerac (Jacques Phillipe), Danica D'Hondt (Dr. Marilyn Richards), Robert Ball (Ernest Sinclair), Joe Pyne, Henny Youngman (themselves), Melinda Fee, Margaret Teele.

Comedy. Newlyweds Ted and Margie Hastings immediately begin to have marital problems on their honeymoon at the hotel of Margie's uncle, Jacques Phillipe. Margie, to overcome her nervousness during lovemaking preliminaries, picks up a copy of Mother Goose and begins to read aloud from it, whereupon Ted faints. A secret visit to psychiatrist Dr. Marilyn Richards reveals that Ted has a "Mother Goose" complex. Hotel detective Ernest Sinclair complicates Dr. Richards' treatment (conducted for convenience's sake in the hotel) by his overzealousness—he believes that Ted, like his employer, Jacques Phillipe, is being unfaithful to his wife. Dr. Richards solves Ted's problem by treating him with an LSD spray while he sleeps, causing him to hallucinate and thus incorporate into reality the fairy tale characters from his fantasies. Newlyweds. Uncles. Psychiatrists. Detectives. Hotelkeepers. Sexual dysfunction. Infidelity. Hotels. Honeymoons. LSD. Hallucinations. "Mother Goose".

Note: Also known as Unkissed Bride.

MOTHER JOAN OF THE ANGELS? see JOAN OF THE ANGELS?

MOTHER KNOWS BEST   F6.3317
Kirt Films International. Dist Distribpix, Inc. ca **1970**. Sd; col. 35mm. 65 min.

Melodrama. Carma, an attractive 45-year-old prostitute who has been in the business since she was 16, rears her daughter in the same trade. Carma's daughter gets married, unaware that her husband is a weak, impotent, ineffectual man. The daughter secretly returns to the trade, and once more Carma's apartment rings with laughter. The husband, unable to effect a reconciliation with his wife, visits a whorehouse, and there he is unwittingly entertained by his mother-in-law. As a special treat, Carma offers him the opportunity to watch another couple having intercourse, and she leads him to a room where he sees his wife in a lesbian embrace. The sight is too much for him and he goes berserk. Prostitutes. Filial relations. Mothers-in-law. Marriage. Infidelity. Lesbianism. Voyeurism. Whorehouses.

MOTHER OUGHT TO MARRY see THE SECOND TIME AROUND

MOTHER RILEY MEETS THE VAMPIRE see MY SON THE VAMPIRE

MOTHER SUPERIOR see THE TROUBLE WITH ANGELS

THE MOTHERS see THE MUTHERS

MOTHRA (Japan)   F6.3318
Toho Co. Dist Columbia Pictures. May **1962** [c1 Mar 1962; LP21393]. Sd; col (Eastman Color, print by Pathé). 35mm (Tohoscope). 101 min. [Copyright length: 91 min.]

Prod Tomoyuki Tanaka. Prod English Vers David D. Horne. Dir Inoshiro Honda. Dir English Vers Lee Kresel. Screenplay Shinichi Sekizawa. Story Shinichiro Nakamura, Takehiko Fukunaga, Yoshie Hotta. Screenplay English Vers Robert Myerson. Dir Photog Hajime Koizumi. Lighting Toshio Takashima. Art Dir Takeo Kita, Kimei Abe. Film Ed Ichiji Taira. Mus Yuji Koseki. Sd Rec Shoichi Fujinawa, Masanobu Miyazaki. Asst Dir Masaji Nonagase. Sp Eff Eiji Tsuburaya, Hiroshi Mukouyama. English Dub Titra Sound Corp.

Cast: Franky Sakai (reporter), Hiroshi Koizumi (photographer), Kyoko Kagawa (showman), Emi Ito, Yumi Ito (twins), Jerry Ito, Ken Uehara, Takashi Shimura, Seizaburo Kawazu, Kenji Sahara, Akihiko Hirata, Yoshio Kosugi, Yoshifumi Tajima, Yasushi Yamamoto, Haruya Kato, Ko Mishima, Tetsu Nakamura.

Science fiction melodrama. An expedition of Japanese and Rosilican scientists visit an island in the Pacific which has been used as an atomic testing ground. They find the island inhabited by tiny tribesmen and discover foot-tall twin maidens guarding a huge egg which is held sacred by the islanders. Nelson, an unscrupulous Rosilican, later kidnaps the twins to exhibit them as freaks in Tokyo. The egg hatches, and a giant larva crawls toward the Japanese capital to rescue the women. Leaving a trail of destruction behind it, the creature finally spins an invulnerable cocoon. Atomic rays are used in an attempt to destroy the cocoon, but the tremendous heat generated speeds up the creature's metamorphosis, and a monstrous moth emerges. As it pursues Nelson to Rosilica, the monster creates powerful wind storms with its wings, destroying the Rosilican metropolis and killing thousands. Angry citizens kill Nelson; and to ensure world peace, the two governments surrender the twins to Mothra, who returns with them to their island. Twins. Showmen. Scientists. Radiation.

Mutation. Metamorphosis. Abduction. Eggs. Monsters. Atom bomb. Islands. Tokyo. Pacific Ocean. Mothra.

Note: Released in Japan in Jul 1961 as *Mosura.* According to one source, the film is based on the story "Shukan Asahi" by Shinichiro Nakamura.

LA MOTOCYCLETTE see THE GIRL ON A MOTORCYCLE

MOTOR PSYCHO   F6.3319

Eve Productions. Aug **1965** [c1 Aug 1965; LP31264]. Sd; b&w. 35mm. 73 min.

Prod-Dir Russ Meyer. *Assoc Prod* Eve Meyer. *Screenplay* William E. Sprague, Russ Meyer. *Based on a story by* Russ Meyer, James Griffith, Hal Hopper. *Dir Photog* Russ Meyer. *Ed* Charles Schelling. *Mus* Igo Kantor. *Theme Song* Paul Sawtell, Bert Shefter. *Sd* Carl G. Sheldon. *Asst Dir* George Costello. *Prod Mgr* Fred Owens. *Prod Asst* Richard Brummer. *Sp Photog Eff* Orville Hallberg.

Cast: Haji *(Ruby Bonner),* Alex Rocco *(Cory Maddox),* Stephen Oliver *(Brahmin),* Holle K. Winters *(Gail Maddox),* Joseph Cellini *(Dante),* Thomas Scott *(Slick),* Coleman Francis *(Harry Bonner),* Sharon Lee *(Jessica Fannin),* Steve Masters *(Frank),* Arshalouis Aivazian *(wife),* E. E. Meyer *(sheriff),* George Costello *(doctor),* F. Rufus Owens *(Rufus),* Richard Brummer *(ambulance driver).*

Action melodrama. Three motorcyclists—Brahmin, a medically discharged Vietnam veteran, Dante, and Slick—wreak havoc in a California desert town. Cory Maddox, the local veterinarian whose wife was assaulted and raped by the gang, chases the three hoodlums into a desert canyon when the town sheriff refuses to help. Taking with him Ruby, whose husband was murdered by the gang, Cory is bitten by a poisonous snake. Slick is killed by Brahmin during an argument, and Ruby kills Dante when he attacks her. Cory takes refuge in a deserted mine shaft and finds a stick of dynamite. He ignites it and it explodes, killing Brahmin. *Motorcyclists. Veterans. Veterinarians. Sheriffs. Rape. Murder. Deserts. Mines. Explosives. California. Snakebites.*

Note: Working title: *Rio Vengeance.*

MOTSART I SALYERI see REQUIEM FOR MOZART

LA MOUCHARDE see WOMAN OF SIN

MOUCHETTE (France)   F6.3320

Argos Films–Parc Film. *Dist* Cinema Ventures. Mar **1970.** Sd; b&w. 35mm. 80 min.

Prod Anatole Dauman. *Dir-Screenplay-Adapt-Dial* Robert Bresson. *Photog* Ghislain Cloquet. *Camera Op* Jean Chiabaut. *Asst Photog* Emmanuel Machuel, Paul Bonis. *Art Dir* Pierre Guffroy. *Asst Art Dir* Jean Catala. *Film Ed* Raymond Lamy. *Asst Film Ed* Arlette Lalande. *Excerpt from "Magnificat"* Claudio Monteverdi. *Sung by* Saint-Eustache Chorus. *Dir by* Emile Martin. *Adtl Mus* Jean Wiener. *Sd* Séverin Frankiel, Jacques Carrère. *Sd Eff* Daniel Couteau. *Asst Dir* Jacques Kébadian, Mylène Van Der Mersch. *Prod Mgr* Philippe Dussart, Michel Choquet. *Cost* Odette Le Barbenchon.

Cast: Nadine Nortier *(Mouchette),* Marie Cardinal *(mother),* Paul Hébert *(father),* Jean Vimenet *(Mathieu),* J. C. Guilbert *(Arsène),* Marie Susini *(Mathieu's wife),* Liliane Princet *(teacher),* Raymonde Chabrun *(grocer),* Suzanne Huguenin *(layer out of the dead),* Marie Trichet *(Louisa),* Robert Bresson.

Drama. Source: Georges Bernanos, *Nouvelle histoire de Mouchette* (Paris, 1937). Mouchette is the 14-year-old daughter of an alcoholic bootlegger and a mother who is bedridden and dying. Cruelly treated by her father, Mouchette is friendless and harassed by her classmates, and she takes her revenge with glaring looks and by hurling mudballs at her young persecutors. Caught in a sudden downpour while walking home from school one day, she takes shelter under a tree. From there she witnesses a fight between Arsène, a poacher, and Mathieu, the gamekeeper. Arsène later finds Mouchette and takes her to his shack to dry her clothes. Drunk, he believes he has killed the gamekeeper; and Mouchette tries to console him and offers to provide him with an alibi. Arsène has an epileptic seizure, and when Mouchette cradles his head and sings to him, he misunderstands her gestures of sympathy and rapes her. Mouchette returns home to confide in her mother, who dies before Mouchette can speak. The next day Mouchette learns that the gamekeeper is still alive and that he and Arsène were fighting over a local barmaid, Louisa. Mouchette's encounters with the local grocer, the gamekeeper's wife, and an old woman who is obsessed with death all contribute to her isolation and growing hostility to those around her; and she commits suicide by rolling herself down a hill into a pond. *Bootleggers. Poachers. Gamekeepers. Invalids. Adolescence. Alcoholism. Village life. Drunkenness. Rape. Death. Parenthood. Suicide. Epilepsy.*

Note: Opened in Paris in Mar 1967; running time: 90 min.

LE MOULIN DES SUPPLICES see MILL OF THE STONE WOMEN

MOURIR À MADRID see TO DIE IN MADRID

THE MOUSE ON THE MOON (Great Britain)   F6.3321

Walter Shenson Films. *Dist* Lopert Pictures. 17 Jun **1963** [New York opening; c3 May 1963; LP25389]. Sd (Westrex); col (Eastmancolor). 35mm. 85 min.

A Walter Shenson Production. *Prod* Walter Shenson. *Dir* Richard Lester. *Screenplay* Michael Pertwee. *Anim* Trevor Bond. *Dir Photog* Wilkie Cooper. *Camera Op* Kelvin Pike. *Asst Art Dir* Bill Alexander. *Prod Dsgn* John Howell. *Main Titl Dsgn* Maurice Binder. *Ed* Bill Lenny. *Dub Ed* Roy Hyde. *Sd Rec* Dudley Messenger, Bill Daniels. *Asst Dir* Ross MacKenzie. *Prod Mgr* Robert E. Dearing. *Cont* Eileen Head. *Cost Dsgn* Anthony Mendleson. *Wardrobe* Laurel Staffell. *Makeup* George Blackler. *Hairdresser* Stella Rivers.

Cast: Margaret Rutherford *(The Grand Duchess, Gloriana),* Ron Moody *(Mountjoy),* Bernard Cribbins *(Vincent),* David Kossoff *(Kokintz),* Terry-Thomas *(Spender),* June Ritchie *(Cynthia),* John Le Mesurier *(British delegate),* John Phillips, British *(American delegate),* Eric Barker *(M. I. 5 man),* Roddy McMillan *(Benter),* Tom Aldredge *(Wendover),* Michael Trubshawe *(British aide),* Peter Sallis *(Russian delegate),* Clive Dunn *(bandleader),* Hugh Lloyd *(plumber),* Graham Stark *(standard bearer),* Mario Fabrizi *(valet),* Jan Conrad *(Russian aide),* John Bluthal *(Von Neidel),* Archie Duncan *(American general),* Guy Deghy *(Russian scientist),* Richard Marner *(Russian general),* Allan Cuthbertson, Robin Bailey, Gerald Andersen *(members of Whitehall Conference),* Gordon Phillott *(civil servant),* John Wood *(countryman),* George Chisholm *(wine waiter),* Rosemary Scott *(launching lady),* Vincent Ball *(pilot),* Frank Duncan *(news announcer),* Edward Bishop, Billy Edwards *(American astronauts),* Laurence Herder, Harvey Hall *(Russian astronauts),* Frankie Howerd *(himself),* Coral Morphew *(peasant girl),* Stuart Saunders *(sergeant),* Frank Lieberman *(American civilian),* Bruce Lacey *(bandleader),* Lucy Griffiths, Carol Dowell *(ladies-in-waiting),* Stringer Davis *(first councillor),* Carolyn Pertwee *(June),* Sandra Hampton *(April),* Michael Caspi, Paul Cole, Murray Kash, Larry Cross, Robert Haynos, Beverly Bennett.

Comedy. Source: Leonard Wibberley, *The Mouse on the Moon* (New York, 1962). The Duchy of Fenwick, which is ruled by the addled dowager Grand Duchess Gloriana XIII, falls into dire financial straits when its only source of income, the sale of wine, falls off because each bottle explodes when opened. The local beatniks are protesting conditions, but Prime Minister Mountjoy is more concerned about his inability to raise funds for improving the indoor plumbing at the royal castle. Striking upon the idea of once more asking the United States for financial aid, he does so by pretending that Fenwick wants to participate in the race for putting a man on the moon. Washington promptly responds with a million-dollar grant, and the Russians, anxious to offset America's propaganda advantage, give the tiny nation one of their obsolete rockets. Britain becomes suspicious and sends their master spy, Spender, to investigate the international intrigue. At this point, Professor Kokintz, the Duchy's scientist, discovers that Fenwick's wine is perfect for rocket fuel, and he and Mountjoy's son, Vincent, who wants to impress his beatnik girl friend Cynthia, decide to attempt a launching. Although the launching is expected to be disastrous, the rocket actually takes off and sails to the moon, pursued by American and Russian spaceships. As the Fenwick flag is triumphantly placed on the moon, the American and Russian rockets get sucked into the moon's soft surface. Gracious to the end, the Fenwickians gallantly offer their rivals a free trip back to a rejoicing Fenwick. *Astronauts. Royalty. Beatniks. Spies. Scientists. Russians. Prime ministers. Imaginary kingdoms. Rockets. Wine. Castles. The Moon.*

Note: Released in Great Britain in Jun 1963, this film is a sequel to *The Mouse That Roared,* released in the United States in 1959 by Columbia Pictures.

MOVE   F6.3322

Pandro S. Berman Productions. *Dist* Twentieth Century–Fox Film Corp. 31 Jul **1970** [New York opening; c31 Jul 1970; LP38146]. Sd (Westrex); col (De Luxe). 35mm (Panavision). 90 min. *MPAA rating* R.

A Pandro S. Berman–Stuart Rosenberg Production. *Prod* Pandro S. Berman. *Assoc Prod* Kathryn Hereford. *Dir* Stuart Rosenberg. *Screenplay* Joel Lieber, Stanley Hart. *Dir Photog* William H. Daniels. *Art Dir* Jack Martin Smith, Philip Jefferies. *Set Decor* Walter M. Scott, William Kiernan. *Main Titl* Pacific Title. *Film Ed* Rita Roland. *Mus* Marvin Hamlisch. *Titl Song* Marvin Hamlisch, Alan Bergman, Marilyn Bergman. *Sung by* Larry Marks. *Orch* Leo Shuken, Jack Hayes, Ralph Burns. *Sd* Larry Jost, Vinton Vernon. *Asst Dir* Hank Moonjean. *Asst to the Prod & Unit Prod Mgr* Hank Moonjean. *Cost Dsgn* Anthea Sylbert. *Makeup Supv* Dan Striepeke, Lynn Reynolds. *Hairstyles* Edith Lindon. *Sp Photog Eff* L. B. Abbott, Art Cruickshank.

Cast: Elliott Gould *(Hiram Jaffe),* Paula Prentiss *(Dolly),* Genevieve Waite *(girl),* John Larch *(mounted patrolman),* Joe Silver *(Oscar),* Graham Jarvis *(Dr.*

Picker), Ron O'Neal (*Peter*), Garrie Beau (*Andrea*), David Burns (*doorman*), Richard Bull (*Keith*), Mae Questel (*Mrs. Katz*), Aly Wassil (*Gupta*), John Wheeler (*brown package*), Rudy Bond (*Detective Sawyer*), Yvonne D'Angers (*Jeanine*), Amy Thomson (*Miss Landry*), Roger Bowen (*rabbi*), Stanley Adams (*new tenant*).

Comedy. Source: Joel Lieber, *Move!* (New York, 1968). Hiram Jaffe, a part-time playwright, pornographer, and professional dog walker, and his wife, Dolly, attempt to move to a new apartment on New York's West Side. Hiram is troubled by a succession of maddening events—the disappearance of the moving men, troubles with the transfer of telephone service, a persecuting mounted policeman, and a recurring suspicion that his apartment is being burglarized. In Central Park, he meets a beautiful blonde woman who asks him to her apartment, where, despite his clumsy approach, they make love. Meanwhile, the moving men call to say that they are having a meeting to decide whether or not to deliver his furniture. Throughout these misadventures, Hiram is beset by fantasies of the neighbors staging a gunfight in the hallways and the moving men having sex with Dolly. He also fantasizes about his Jewish wedding during which he is unable to break the glass, the traditional symbol of virility. After learning that his furniture will not be delivered, he realizes that all he wants is Dolly. He races to the new apartment and jumps into the bathtub with Dolly, who tells him the good news that she is pregnant. *Playwrights. Pornographers. Movers. Police. Jews. Marriage. Paranoia. Infidelity. Pregnancy. Weddings. Bathtubs. New York City—West Side. New York City—Central Park. Fantasy. Dogs.*

Note: Filmed in New York City.

MOVE OVER, DARLING   **F6.3323**
Melcher-Arcola Productions. *Dist* Twentieth Century-Fox Film Corp. 25 Dec **1963** [New York opening; c19 Dec 1963; LP27018]. Sd (Westrex); col (DeLuxe). 35mm (CinemaScope). 103 min.

Prod Aaron Rosenberg, Martin Melcher. *Dir* Michael Gordon. *Screenplay* Hal Kanter, Jack Sher. *Orig Story* Bella Spewack, Samuel Spewack, Leo McCarey. *Dir Photog* Daniel L. Fapp. *Camera Op* James Knott. *Art Dir* Jack Martin Smith, Hilyard Brown. *Set Decor* Walter M. Scott, Paul S. Fox. *Film Ed* Robert Simpson. *Mus* Lionel Newman. *Orch* Arthur Morton, Warren Barker. *Titl Song* Joe Lubin, Hal Kanter, Terry Melcher. Song: "Twinkle Lullaby" Joe Lubin. *Songs Sung by* Doris Day. *Sd* Alfred Bruzlin, Elmer Raguse. *Asst Dir* Ad Schaumer. *Unit Prod Mgr* Gaston Glass. *Script Supv* Dolores Rubin. *Cost Dsgn* Moss Mabry. *Wardrobe* Marjorie Plecher, Mickey Sherrard. *Makeup* Ben Nye. *Miss Day's Hairstyles* George Masters. *Hairstyle Supv* Margaret Donovan, Barbara Lampson. *Sp Photog Eff* L. B. Abbott, Emil Kosa, Jr. *Dial Coach* Carl Shain. *Still Photog* James Mitchell. *Prop* Glenn "Skippy" Delfino. *Gaffer* Jack Brown. *Grip* Walter Fitchman.

Cast: Doris Day (*Ellen Wagstaff Arden*), James Garner (*Nick Arden*), Polly Bergen (*Bianca Steele Arden*), Chuck Connors ("*Adam*" [*Stephen Burkett*]), Thelma Ritter (*Grace Arden*), Fred Clark (*Codd*), Don Knotts (*shoe salesman*), Elliott Reid (*Dr. Herman Schlick*), Edgar Buchanan (*Judge Bryson*), John Astin (*Clyde Prokey*), Pat Harrington, Jr. (*district attorney*), Eddie Quillan (*bellboy*), Max Showalter (*desk clerk*), Alvy Moore (*waiter*), Pami Lee (*Jenny Arden*), Leslie Farrell (*Didi Arden*), Rosa Turich (*Maria*), Harold Goodwin (*bailiff*), Alan Sues (*court clerk*), Pat Moran (*drunk*), Bess Flowers (*woman*), Rachel Romen (*injured man's wife*), Jack Orrison (*bartender*), Kelton Garwood, Joel Collins (*ambulance attendants*), Sid Gould (*waiter at pool*), Ed McNally (*commander*), James Patridge (*skipper*), Christopher Connelly (*executive seaman*), Billy Halop, Med Flory (*seamen*), Emile Meyer, Brad Trumbull (*process servers*), Michael Romanoff (*floorwalker*), John Harmon (*cabdriver*).

Comedy. Ellen Arden is rescued from a South Seas island and brought back to the United States 5 years after she disappeared in an airplane crash. On the same day, her husband, Nick, is in court to hear Judge Bryson declare Ellen legally dead. Nick then marries beautiful but dumb Bianca Steele, and they go to a resort hotel for their honeymoon. Meanwhile, Ellen returns home and is distressed when her two children fail to recognize her. Learning from Nick's mother that he has just remarried, Ellen proceeds to the honeymoon hotel, where Nick immediately catches a glimpse of her. Still in love with Ellen, Nick feigns a back injury and returns home with Bianca. Ellen flies home and arrives ahead of the newlyweds, pretending to be Nick's masseuse. Nick learns that a man was also stranded with Ellen, but she describes him as small and unappealing. Unknown to Ellen, Nick goes to see this man, who is actually a handsome athlete, while Ellen hires a meek shoeclerk to impersonate him. Afterwards, Nick listens to the story told by Ellen and the shoeclerk but reveals that he knows the truth. Enraged, Ellen rushes home, with Nick in pursuit. Bianca is there, and Nick confesses that Ellen is his wife as detectives enter to arrest him for bigamy, a charge brought by his mother. Judge Bryson annuls Nick and Bianca's marriage, but when Ellen's real island companion arrives to identify her so that she can be declared legally alive, she becomes flustered and

Nick storms off in a jealous rage. Later, at home, Ellen is about to tell the children that she is their mother when she learns that Nick has already informed them. *In-laws. Missing persons. Shoeclerks. Athletes. Masseurs. Marriage. Marriage—Annulment. Motherhood. Jealousy. Impersonation. Bigamy. Hotels. Honeymoons.*

Note: Remake of *My Favorite Wife* (R.K.O., 1940).

MOVIE STAR, AMERICAN STYLE OR; LSD, I HATE YOU   **F6.3324**
Famous Players Corp. Jul **1966** [c24 Jun 1966; LP33482]. Sd; b&w with col seq (see note). 35mm. 99 min.

A Morris Corson Production. *Prod* Robert Caramico. *Assoc Prod* Art Names, Joanne Wholey, Karen Arney. *Exec Prod* Arnold Stoltz. *Dir-Story* Albert Zugsmith. *Screenplay* Albert Zugsmith, Graham Lee Mahin. *Dial* Lulu Talmadge. *Photog* Robert Caramico. *Film Ed* Herman Freedman. *Mus Comp & Cond* Joe Greene. *Titl Song Sung by* T. C. Jones.

Cast: Robert Strauss (*Joe Horner, producer*), Del Moore (*Dr. Horatio*), T.C.Jones(*Skippy Roper, designer*), Steve Drexel (*Dr. Oscar Roscoe*), Paula Lane (*Honey Bunny, great screen star*), Steve Rogers (*Barry James, super-star*), Richard Clair (*David Erickson, writer*), Jill Darling (*Miranda Song, nurse*), Cara Garnett (*movie queen*), Sandra Lynn (*countess*), Peter Van Boorn (*Harvey Homantash, director*), Ned York (*Crash Dramm, all-American*), Frank Delfino (*midget photographer*), Juliet Picaud (*Miss Bee*), Albert Zugsmith (*director [see note]*).

Comedy. Film star Honey Bunny makes the latest in a series of suicide attempts, and studio head Joe Horner sends her to a lavish rest home operated by Dr. Horatio, a mentally unbalanced psychiatrist. Also at the institution are Skippy Roper, an effeminate dress designer; Barry James, a Hollywood matinee idol; David Erickson, an avant-garde writer; and an overweight femme fatale movie queen. As part of his therapy, Dr. Horatio uses LSD to bring about each patient's personal hallucination. The experiments often result in the surfacing of their hidden frustrations and innermost thoughts. *Actors. Psychiatrists. Authors. Couturiers. Suicide. Mental illness. Effeminacy. Motion pictures. Sanitariums. LSD. Hallucinations.*

Note: The LSD sequence is filmed in black and white and tinted. Albert Zugsmith's role in the film is unconfirmed.

MOVIE STRUCK (Reissue)   **F6.3325**
Metro-Goldwyn-Mayer, Inc. *Dist* Astor Pictures. 18 Mar **1963** [Maryland license]. Sd; b&w. 35mm. 70 min.

Note: Originally released by M-G-M in 1937 as *Pick a Star*; c18 May 1937; LP7164.

THE MOVING TARGET see HARPER

MOVING VIOLATION   **F6.3326**
Kirt Films International. *Dist* Distribpix, Inc. ca **1970**. Sd; col. 35mm. 64 min.

Sex film. On an excursion to the beach in a Volkswagen bus, three young men and their two female companions decide to relieve the boredom of the trip. One couple makes love in the rear of the van, and later the others join them. Soon the group is paired off, and the odd man out is forced out, onto the road. The excluded man follows on foot, bent on revenge, and when he comes upon their nude revel on the beach, he is provoked to violence. *Sexuality. Revenge. Group sex. Beaches.*

MOZAMBIQUE (Great Britain)   **F6.3327**
Towers of London–London & Overseas Film. *Dist* Seven Arts Pictures. 9 Feb **1966** [New York opening]. Sd; col (Technicolor). 35mm (Techniscope). 98 min.

Prod (see note) Harry Alan Towers, Oliver A. Unger. *Dir* Robert Lynn. *2d Unit Dir* Egil S. Woxholt. *Screenplay* Peter Yeldham. *Story* Peter Welbeck. *Photog* Martin Curtis. *2d Unit Photog* Egil S. Woxholt. *Mus Comp & Cond* Johnny Douglas. Song: "Das geht beim ersten Mal vorbei" Charly Niessen. Song: "Hey You" Gus Backus. *Miss Neff's Wardrobe* Pierre Balmain.

Cast: Steve Cochran (*Brad Webster*), Hildegard Neff (*Ilona Valdez*), Vivi Bach (*Christina*), Paul Hubschmid (*Commarro*), Martin Benson (*Da Silva*), Dietmar Schönherr (*Henderson*), Gert Van den Bergh (*Arab*), George Leech (*Carl*), Vic Perry (*himself*).

Melodrama. Brad Webster, an unemployed American pilot looking for work in Lisbon, becomes involved in a brawl and is jailed. Commarro, a police inspector, forces Webster to take a job in Mozambique as pilot for a Colonel Valdez. En route, Webster becomes friendly with Christina, a girl hired to sing at Valdez' nightclub. Upon arrival in Mozambique, Webster learns that Valdez is dead and that his widow, Ilona, and two men, Da Silva and Henderson, are all rivals for control of the Valdez business. Ilona tells Webster that Valdez had a fortune in Swiss banks known only to her husband's lawyer, who was murdered. Webster learns that the Valdez operation involved the smuggling of narcotics. Christina is kidnaped by an Arab and taken to Zanzibar; Webster rescues her and, with Da Silva along, escapes in his plane, which develops engine trouble and is forced down. While Christina and Webster are away from the plane, Da Silva is stabbed by the dwarf who killed the lawyer and has stowed away on Webster's plane. Webster repairs the plane, and he and Christina return to Mozambique, where he is taken into police custody. Commarro reveals that he has been using Webster as a front to get information on the Valdez operations. Webster then learns that Ilona, with Henderson as an accomplice, is behind the entire intrigue. When she learns the whereabouts of her husband's bank accounts, she prepares to kill Henderson, but he persuades her to flee with him across the border at Victoria Falls. Commarro and Webster pursue them, and Henderson falls to his death. Ilona is arrested and charged with plotting the murders. Webster and Christina leave Mozambique together. *Air pilots. Police. Singers. Widows. Lawyers. Dwarfs. Arabs. Americans in foreign countries. Murder. Smuggling. Abduction. Nightclubs. Narcotics. Lisbon. Mozambique. Zanzibar. Victoria Falls.*

Note: Filmed in Mozambique and at Victoria Falls. Released in Great Britain in Aug 1965. Sources conflict in crediting production company and producer. Peter Welbeck is a pseudonym for Harry Alan Towers.

MUČEDNÍCI LÁSKY see MARTYRS OF LOVE

MUD HONEY see ROPE OF FLESH

MUD MAIDENS   F6.3328
Dist Able Film Co. ca **1970**. Sd; col. 16mm. [Feature length assumed.]

Sex film. No information about the precise nature of this film has been found, although press material indicates that it concerns greed, human passion, and includes scenes of group sex, lesbianism, oral sex, and an orgy in mud. *Greed. Lesbianism. Group sex. Oral sex. Orgies.*

LA MUERTE EN ESTE JARDÍN see GINA

LA MUERTE ESPERA EN ATENAS see MISSION BLOODY MARY

LA MUERTE TENIA UN PRECIO see FOR A FEW DOLLARS MORE

MUHAIR (Argentina)   F6.3329
Sifa. *Dist* Haven International Pictures. 26 Feb **1970** [New York opening]. Sd; col (Eastman Color). 35mm. 84 min. *MPAA rating* X.

Prod Carl Pasqualini. *Dir-Writ* Armando Bo. *Dir Photog* Aníbal González Paz. *Mus* Luis Alberto del Paraná. *Songs Sung by* Los Paraguayos.

Cast: Isabel Sarli (*Eva*), Armando Bo (*José*), Víctor Bo (*Mario*), Mario Lozano (*Simon*).

Romantic melodrama. In a mountain forest in northeastern Argentina, José tends his ranch. [In the original version he is a woodcutter.] He meets Eva, a beautiful, mysterious woman from the nearby village, makes love with her near Iguaçu Falls, and is visited by her each weekend. Neither speaks of the past. During the week in town Eva works as a bar entertainer and prostitute; she has been the mistress of Simon, a hoodlum. José's son, Mario, returns after a long absence. [In the original José had deserted Mario and his mother.] Like his father, he falls in love with Eva, and she is attracted to both. José learns of the life she has led and becomes bitterly jealous when he discovers her relationship with his son. A fight between father and son ends when José holds an ax poised over Mario's head, then stops and comes to his senses. Believing that Eva loves Mario, José packs and prepares to leave the ranch to the two lovers. At the last moment, Eva reveals her love for José, and it is Mario who ventures from the mountain paradise. *Ranchers. Woodsmen. Prostitutes. Mistresses. Hoodlums. Entertainers. Mountain life. Filial relations. Desertion. Jealousy. Bars. Forests. Iguaçu Falls.*

Note: Location scenes filmed at Iguaçu Falls. Produced in Argentina in 1967 as *La mujer de mi padre*; running time: 90 min.

LA MUJER DE MI PADRE see MUHAIR

LA MUJER DEL GATO see FEMALE ANIMAL

IL MULINO DELLE DONNE DI PIETRA see MILL OF THE STONE WOMEN

MULTIPLE MANIACS   F6.3330
Dreamland Productions. 10 Apr **1970** [Baltimore opening]. Sd; b&w. 16mm. 90 min.

Prod-Dir-Writ John Waters. *Photog* John Waters. *Ed* John Waters.

Cast: Divine (*Lady Divine*), David Lochary (*Mr. David*), Mary Vivian Pearce (*Bonnie*), Mink Stole (*Mink Stole*), Cookie Mueller (*Cookie*), Paul Swift (*Steve*), Rick Morrow (*Ricky*), Edith Massey (*Barmaid*), George Figgs (*Jesus Christ*), Michael Renner, Jr. (*The Infant of Prague*), Susan Lowe, Howard Gruber, Vince Peranio, Jim Thompson, Dee Vitolo, Ed Peranio, Tom Wells, Gilbert McGill (*The Freaks*), Bob Skidmore, Margie Skidmore, Jack Walsh, Susan Walsh, Pat Moran, actor, Harvey Freed, Mark Lazarus (*The Straight People*).

Melodrama. Lady Divine, a woman of obese proportions, and her boyfriend, Mr. David, operate "The Cavalcade," a traveling freak show. Young housewives and businessmen from the suburbs are lured into a small tent to observe a bevy of their favorite horrors, such as junkies, homosexuals, and pornographers, only to be bullied, robbed, and even murdered by Lady Divine and her gang. Mr. David, realizing that his long-standing romance with Lady Divine is on the decline, takes up with Bonnie, whom he met at the world premiere of *Inga*, a sex exploitation film. Lady Divine, upon hearing of the affair, recedes into depression, and decides to seek spiritual contact with a superior force. She goes to an empty church and there she unexpectedly meets a woman named Mink Stole, a religious fanatic who gives her the moral support she needs; indeed, with the aid of a rosary, Mink Stole seduces her on the spot while Lady Divine has hallucinatory visions of a blasphemous crucifixion and of Jesus transforming five loaves and two fish into tons of a well-known brand of bread and cans of tuna. With Mink's help, Lady Divine sets out to murder the lovers. The murders having supposedly been carried out, she loses complete control of her behavior, and in the process is attacked by Lobstora, a 15-foot broiled lobster. Dazed by the experience, she makes her way into the street, causing mass hysteria, and is subsequently gunned down by the National Guard as a mob of thrill-seeking citizenry looks on. *Confidence women. Housewives. Businessmen. Suburbanites. Drug addicts. Fanatics. Lesbianism. Male homosexuality. Jealousy. Infidelity. Murder. Robbery. Seduction. Religion. Freak shows. Sex exploitation films. Miracles. Jesus. National Guard. "Inga". Visions.*

Note: Filmed in Baltimore, Maryland.

THE MUMMY'S SHROUD (Great Britain)   F6.3331
Seven Arts Productions–Hammer Film Productions. *Dist* Twentieth Century-Fox Film Corp. Mar **1967** [c31 Dec 1966; LP34488]. Sd (RCA); col (Technicolor, print by DeLuxe). 35mm. 90 min.

Prod Anthony Nelson Keys. *Dir-Writ* John Gilling. *Orig Story* John Elder. *Dir Photog* Arthur Grant. *Camera Op* Moray Grant. *Art Dir* Don Mingaye. *Prod Dsgn* Bernard Robinson. *Supv Film Ed* James Needs. *Ed* Chris Barnes. *Mus Comp (see note)* Don Banks, Franz Reizenstein. *Mus Supv* Philip Martell. *Sd Rec* Ken Rawkins. *Sd Ed* Roy Hyde. *Asst Dir* Bluey Hill. *Prod Mgr* Ed Harper. *Cont* Eileen Head. *Wardrobe* Larry Stewart. *Wardrobe Mistress* Molly Arbuthnot. *Makeup* George Partleton. *Hairstyles* Frieda Steiger. *Sp Eff* Bowie Films. *Casting* Irene Lamb.

Cast: Andre Morell (*Sir Basil Walden*), John Phillips, British (*Stanley Preston*), David Buck (*Paul Preston*), Elizabeth Sellars (*Barbara Preston*), Maggie Kimberley (*Claire*), Michael Ripper (*Longbarrow*), Tim Barrett (*Harry Newton*), Richard Warner (*Inspector Barrani*), Roger Delgado (*Hasmid Ali*), Catherine Lacey (*Haiti*), Dickie Owen (*Prem*), Bruno Barnabe (*Pharaoh*), Toni Gilpin (*Pharaoh's wife*), Toolsie Persaud (*Kah-to-Bey*), Eddie Powell (*mummy*), Andreas Malandrinos (*curator*).

Horror film. In 1920, British industrialist Stanley Preston finances an expedition to find the lost tomb of an Egyptian pharaoh buried in 2,000 B. C. (The mummified figure of the pharaoh's faithful slave has already been unearthed and placed in a museum.) Although the four members of the expedition—archeologist Sir Basil Walden, linguist Claire de Sangre, photographer Harry Newton, and Preston's son Paul—become lost in the desert, they eventually locate the tomb shortly after being joined by the elder Preston. Despite warnings from the crazed Hasmid Ali, guardian of the crypt, the pharaoh's shrouded mummy is carried from its resting place and displayed in the museum alongside the mummy of the slave. Determined to receive sole credit for the discovery, the egotistical senior Preston has Sir Basil committed to an insane asylum. At the same time, Hasmid Ali visits the museum and brings the mummified slave back to life by intoning the hieroglyphic "Words of Life" emblazoned on the pharaoh's shroud. The first to die at the hands of the vengeful mummy is Sir Basil, who had managed to escape from the asylum. One by one Hasmid Ali orders the deaths of all the others involved in disinterring the pharaoh from his tomb. Soon, only Claire and Paul are left alive, trapped in the museum by Hasmid Ali and the mummy. As they are about to be killed, Claire cries out the "Words of Death" inscribed on the pharaoh's shroud, and the mummy disintegrates into dust. *Industrialists. Archeologists. Linguists. Photographers. Revenge. Disinterment. Reviviscence. Mummies. Tombs. Museums. Egypt.*

Note: Released in Great Britain in Jun 1967; running time: 84 min. Sources conflict in crediting music composer. John Elder is a pseudonym for Anthony Hinds.

MUMSY, NANNY, SONNY, AND GIRLY (Great Britain)   F6.3332
Fitzroy–Francis Films–Brigitte Films. *Dist* Cinerama Releasing Corp. 12 Feb **1970** [New York opening; c12 Feb 1970; LP38514]. Sd; col (Eastman Color). 35mm. 101 min. *MPAA rating* R.

Prod Ronald J. Kahn. *Assoc Prod* Peter J. Thompson. *Dir* Freddie Francis. *Screenplay* Brian Comport. *Dir Photog* David Muir. *Camera Op* Moray Grant.

Art Dir Maggie Pinhorn. *Set Dresser* Dimity Collins. *Titl Dsgn* Michael Bastow. *Film Ed* Tristam Cones. *Mus Comp, Arr & Cond* Bernard Ebbinghouse. *Sd Mix* John Brommage. *1st Asst Dir* John Stoneman. *Prod Mgr* Jilda Smith. *Cont* Pamela Davies. *Asst to the Prod* Katherine Haber. *Wardrobe* Dulcie Midwinter. *Makeup* Phil Leakey. *Hairdresser* Gladys Leakey. *Casting Dir* Rose Tobias Shaw.

Cast: Michael Bryant ("*New Friend*"), Ursula Howells (*Mumsy*), Pat Heywood (*Nanny*), Howard Trevor (*Sonny*), Vanessa Howard (*Girly*), Robert Swann (*soldier*), Imogen Hassall (*girl friend*), Michael Ripper (*zoo attendant*), Hugh Armstrong ("*Friend in #5*").

Horror film. Source: Maisie Mosco, *The Happy Family* (London opening: 13 Mar 1966). In a large Victorian house outside of London, Mumsy and Nanny encourage teenagers Sonny and his sister Girly to bring strange men home as playmates. The victims are held captive until the four decide to murder them. On one of their forays, Sonny and Girly see a young man and his date drunkenly leaving a party. Girly invites the couple to play with them at a playground, where Sonny murders the young man's date and convinces him that he was responsible. "New Friend," as he is now called, is brought to the house under the threat of blackmail and soon learns of the strictly enforced rules of the house which, if violated, could result in a fate similar to that of "Friend in #5" who was murdered by bow and arrow. "New Friend" joins in the deadly games in order to attempt an escape; in addition to the permissible lovemaking with Mumsy, he seduces Girly and Nanny to create discord in the family. Girly bludgeons her jealous brother to death for his threats against "New Friend" and then beheads Nanny. Girly and Mumsy finally arrive at an agreement to share "New Friend," but he plots to do away with both of them. *Adolescence. Brother-sister relationship. Abduction. Murder. Sadism. Blackmail. Seduction. Fratricide. Decapitation. Jealousy. Playgrounds. London.*

Note: Opened in London in Apr 1970. Also known as *Girly*.

MUMU (U.S.S.R.)   F6.3333

Mosfilm. *Dist* Artkino Pictures. 3 Jun **1961** [New York opening]. Sd; b&w. 35mm. 71 min. [Also reviewed at 65 min.]

Dir Anatoliy Bobrovskiy, Yevgeniy Teterin. *Screenplay* Khrisanf Khersonskiy. *Story Ed* Valeriy Karen. *Photog* Konstantin Petrichenko. *Art Dir* Aleksandr Borisov, art dir, Arnold Vaysfeld. *Film Ed* V. Chekan. *Mus* Aleksey Muravlev. *Cond* V. Smirnov. *Sd* Ye. Indlina. *Asst Dir* A. Golyshev. *Prod Mgr* M. Khavkin. *Cost* G. Ganevskaya. *Makeup* Yu. Yemelyanov. *Sp Eff* V. Alekseyeva, S. Khizhnyak, B. Noskov.

Cast: Afanasiy Kochetkov (*Gerasim*), Nina Grebeshkova (*Tatyana*), Yelena Polevitskaya (*The Mistress*), Igor Bezyayev (*Kapiton*), Ivan Ryzhov (*Gavrila*), Yevgeniy Teterin (*Khariton*), Leonid Kmit (*Stepan*), V. Myasnikova (*Lyubimovna*), A. Denisova (*housekeeper*), A. Fyodorova (*Ustinya*), G. Belov (*Potap*), A. Dobronravov (*Uncle Khvost*), L. Volskaya, A. Danilova, L. Korolyova, P. Lyubeshkin, A. Pavlova, A. Rumyanova, K. Rumyantseva, G. Sayfulin, V. Khmara.

Drama. Source: Ivan Sergeyevich Turgenev, "Mumu," in *Sovremennik* (no.3, 1854). In 19th-century Russia, Gerasim, a huge, deafmute peasant, lives a simple and peaceful life working in the fields around his native village. One day the mistress of the estate, impressed by Gerasim's great strength, brings him to her Moscow mansion and makes him a porter. Though he intensely dislikes the life of the city, he falls in love with Tatyana, a laundress as unhappy as himself, and becomes her adoring protector. But once again the capricious mistress intervenes, this time forcing Tatyana to marry Kapiton, a drunken shoemaker. Gerasim's life becomes more lonely than ever until one day he finds a starved, half-frozen puppy by the riverside. Choosing a sound he is able to articulate, he names her Mumu and tenderly nurses her back to health. As the days pass, Gerasim lavishes all of his love upon the little dog. But the peasant's happiness comes to an abrupt end when Mumu snarls at the mistress, and she orders the dog destroyed. Gerasim rows out to the middle of the river with Mumu and drowns her. Then, turning his back on the mansion, he begins the long walk back to the village of his childhood. *Deafmutes. Peasants. Landed gentry. Porters. Laundresses. Domestics. Marriage—Arranged. Friendship. Drunkenness. Moscow. Dogs.*

Note: Released in the U.S.S.R. in Nov 1959.

MUNDO DEPRAVADOS   F6.3334

Monique Productions. *Dist* Monique Productions, Boxoffice International Pictures. 26 Jul **1967** [Champaign, Illinois, showing]. Sd; b&w. 35mm. [Feature length assumed.]

Prod Leroy C. Griffith. *Dir-Screenplay* Herb Jeffries. *Story* Herb Jeffries. *Dir Photog* Manuel S. Conde. *Art Dir* Marco Beline. *Set Dsgn* Herbert Ball. *Supv Film Ed* Howard Warren. *Mus* Francesco Ballantine. *Sd Mix* Richard Pierce. *Prod Mgr* David F. Friedman. *Script Supv* Sali Heller. *Cost* Andre. *Makeup Artist* Wallace Westland. *Hairstyles* Juanita Griffith. *Ch Gaffer* Chester Phebus.

Cast: Tempest Storm, Ron Von Klausen, Bunny Ware, Gene Burk, Morrey Spiegel, Dolores Carlos, Sali Heller, Tracy Carroll, Marcy Blayne, Amy Aris, Johnnie Decker, Larry Reed, Bob Morris.

Mystery drama. No information about the precise nature of this film has been found, but publicity material and photographs suggest that it concerns women in the power of a madman. Rape and murder are depicted. *Psychopaths. Murder. Rape.*

Note: Also known as *World of the Depraved* and *Mondo Depravados*.

UN MUNDO PARA MÍ *see* SOFT SKIN ON BLACK SILK

MUÑECOS INFERNALES *see* THE CURSE OF THE DOLL PEOPLE

MUNSTER, GO HOME!   F6.3335

Universal Pictures. 15 Jun **1966** [New York opening; c16 Jul 1966; LP35383]. Sd (Westrex); col (Technicolor). 35mm. 90 min. [Also 96 min.]

Prod Joe Connelly, Bob Mosher. *Assoc Prod* Irving Paley. *Dir* Earl Bellamy. *Writ* George Tibbles, Joe Connelly, Bob Mosher. *Dir Photog* Benjamin H. Kline. *Camera Op* William Dodds. *Asst Camera* William Renaldi. *Art Dir* Alexander Golitzen, John J. Lloyd. *Set Decor* John McCarthy, Julia Heron. *Film Ed* Bud S. Isaacs. *Asst Ed* Dale Johnson. *Mus* Jack Marshall. *Sd* Waldon O. Watson, Corson Jowett. *Asst Dir* Dolph Zimmer, Wendell Franklin, Tom Connors. *Unit Prod Mgr* James Hogan. *Asst to the Prod* Keith Vincent. *Script Supv* Marshall Wolins. *Cost* Grady Hunt. *Wardrobe* Sally Wood, Jesse Munden. *Makeup* Bud Westmore, Perc Westmore, Carl Silvera, Abe Haberman. *Hairstyles* Larry Germain. *Matte Supv* Albert Whitlock. *Stunt Coörd* Carey Loftin. *Still Photog* Jack Harris, still photog.

Cast: Fred Gwynne (*Herman*), Yvonne De Carlo (*Lily*), Al Lewis (*Grandpa*), Butch Patrick (*Eddie*), Debbie Watson (*Marilyn*), Terry-Thomas (*Freddie*), Hermione Gingold (*Lady Effigie*), Robert Pine (*Roger*), John Carradine (*Cruikshank*), Bernard Fox (*Squire Moresby*), Richard Dawson (*Joey*), Jeanne Arnold (*Grace*), Maria Lennard (*Millie*), Cliff Norton (*Herbert*), Diana Chesney (*Mrs. Moresby*), Arthur Malet (*Alfie*), Ben Wright (*Hennesy*).

Comedy. Based on the television series "The Munsters." Ghoulish-looking Herman Munster inherits an estate from a British uncle and takes his family—wife Lily, son Eddie, niece Marilyn, and mischief-making Grandpa—to England by boat to claim both his title and his manor house. On board, Marilyn strikes up a romance with Roger Moresby, a race-driving champion. On arriving, they receive a less than effusive welcome from their foreign relatives (Lady Effigie, her children Freddy and Grace, and their sinister butler Cruikshank), who are using the manor house as the headquarters of a counterfeiting ring. All attempts to scare off the Munsters fail miserably, for they are delighted by screams in the night, white-sheeted apparitions, and other ghostly phenomena. Desperate to be rid of the Munsters, Lady Effigie persuades Herman to save the family honor by entering an automobile race against Roger, as their families have been longtime rivals. Roger is knocked unconscious, and the head of the counterfeiting ring substitutes another driver, planning harm to Herman as the race proceeds. Herman, however, driving his Dragula, a special coffin-shaped car, wins the race and unmasks his opponent, who turns out to be the barmaid at the local pub. The Munsters donate their property for a village park, and Roger promises to visit Marilyn in the States. *Uncles. Grandfathers. Butlers. Barmaids. Counterfeiters. Ghosts. Inheritance. Feuds. Automobile racing. Family life. Ocean liners. Haunted houses. England.*

MURDER A LA MOD   F6.3336

Aries Documentaries. 1 May **1968** [New York opening]. Sd; b&w. 35mm. 80 min.

Pres by Tambellini's Gate Theater. *Prod* Ken Burrows. *Dir-Writ* Brian De Palma. *Photog (see note)* Bruce Torbet, Jack Harrell. *Main Titl* Dyn Productions. *Film Ed* Brian De Palma. *Mus Comp & Cond* John Herbert McDowell. *Titl Song Comp & Sung by* William Finley. *Sd* Robert Fiore. *Prod Asst* Riva Freifeld, Beth Hertig.

Cast: Margo Norton (*Karen*), Andra Akers (*Tracy*), Jared Martin (*Christopher*), William Finley (*Otto*), Ken Burrows (*Wiley*), Lorenzo Catlett (*policeman*), Jennifer Salt, Melanie Mander, Laura Rubin, Laura Stevenson ("*birds*").

Mystery comedy-melodrama. During a day of shopping at Manhattan's mod boutiques, Karen, an impressionable young woman, tells her socialite friend Tracy about a filmmaker, Christopher, with whom she has fallen in love. While Tracy is at her bank, Karen catches sight of Christopher and follows him to his studio. There she finds him screening the rushes of a sex film which he admits is his own. Angry and humiliated at having been discovered, Christopher confesses that he is being forced to do the film in order to make enough money to divorce his wife. When Karen pleads with him to allow her to raise the money, he refuses and storms out. Returning to Tracy's car, Karen finds an envelope full of jewels and a fortune in bonds and cash. Thrilled at her good luck, she races back to Christopher's studio, where she is stabbed with a trick icepick and squirted with catsup by Otto, the prankster star of Christopher's film. After cleaning herself up, Karen decides to remain in the studio and wait for Christopher. Suddenly, the blinding lights go on, and she is brutally murdered, this time in earnest, with an icepick. The three principal suspects then relate their individual versions of the events surrounding the slaying: Tracy sees Otto carry a trunk, apparently containing Karen's body, to a cemetery; Otto tries to lure the murderer to a cemetery by means of an empty trunk from which a blood-stained dress is protruding; and Christopher, who seems to have been following the two women, is an eyewitness to the murder. Once the three conflicting stories have been told, it is revealed that Christopher is the real killer. *Socialites. Filmmakers. Actors. Finance—Personal. Divorce. Practical jokes. Murder. Sex exploitation films. Motion picture studios. Cemeteries. New York City.*

Note: Filmed on location in New York City, including Greenwich Village. Sources conflict in crediting photographer.

MURDER AHOY (Great Britain) **F6.3337**

Metro-Goldwyn-Mayer Pictures. *Dist* Metro-Goldwyn-Mayer, Inc. 30 Sep **1964** [Washington, D. C., opening; c8 Sep 1964; LP29237]. Sd (Westrex); b&w. 35mm. 93 min.

A Lawrence P. Bachmann Production. *Assoc Prod* Ben Arbeid. *Dir* George Pollock. *Orig Screenplay* David Pursall, Jack Seddon. *Dir Photog* Desmond Dickinson. *Camera Op* Alan McCabe. *Art Dir* Bill Andrews. *Film Ed* Ernest Walter. *Mus Comp & Cond* Ron Goodwin. *Rec Supv* A. W. Watkins. *Sd Rec* Fred Turtle. *Dub Mix* J. B. Smith. *Sd Ed* Allan Sones. *Asst Dir* David Tomblin. *Prod Mgr* Sydney Streeter.

Cast: Margaret Rutherford (*Miss Marple*), Lionel Jeffries (*Captain de Courcy Rhumstone*), Charles Tingwell (*Detective Inspector Craddock*), William Mervyn (*Commander Breeze-Connington*), Joan Benham (*Matron Alice Fanbraid*), Stringer Davis (*Mr. Stringer*), Nicholas Parsons (*Dr. Crump*), Miles Malleson (*Bishop Faulkner*), Henry Oscar (*Lord Rudkin*), Derek Nimmo (*Sub-Lieutenant Humbert*), Gerald Cross (*L. W. Brewer Dimchurch*), Norma Foster (*Asst. Matron Shirley Boston*), Terence Edmond (*Sergeant Bacon*), Francis Matthews (*Lieutenant Compton*), Lucy Griffiths (*Millie*), Bernard Adams (*Dusty Miller*), Tony Quinn (*Kelly, a tramp*), Edna Petrie (*Miss Pringle*), Roy Holder (*Petty Officer Lamb*), Henry Longhurst (*Cecil Ffolly-Hardwicke*).

Mystery comedy. Based on the character of Miss Marple created by: Agatha Christie. At a board meeting of the Cape of Good Hope Youth Reclamation Trust, trustee Cecil Ffolly-Hardwicke drops dead before he can reveal some vital information concerning H. M. S. *Battledore*, the naval cadet ship used by the trust to rehabilitate juvenile delinquents. Miss Marple, a fellow trustee and private detective, discovers that Hardwicke has been poisoned, though the police discount her theory. To the dismay of Captain de Courcy Rhumstone, she boards the ship to continue her investigation, leaving her trusted assistant, Mr. Stringer, on shore to aid her. While Miss Marple searches for clues to the murder, Lieutenant Compton, discovered by the detective instructing a group of cadets in the profitable sideline of housebreaking, and Shirley Boston, an assistant matron, are murdered. Miss Marple learns that Commander Breeze-Connington has been embezzling funds for a number of years and has committed the murders in order to protect himself. She confronts Breeze-Connington; a fencing match ensues; and Miss Marple holds the murderer off until the police arrive. *Detectives. Police. Cadets. Juvenile delinquents. Murder. Embezzlement. Poisoning. Ships. Charitable organizations. Fencing (sport). Miss Marple.*

Note: Released in Great Britain in Oct 1965; running time: 74 min.

MURDER AT 45 R. P. M. (France) **F6.3338**

Cité Films. 18 Aug **1965** [New York showing]. Sd; b&w. 35mm. 98 min.

Prod Jacques Bar. *Dir* Etienne Périer. *Screenplay* Dominique Fabre, Etienne Périer, Albert Valentin. *Dial* Dominique Fabre. *Photog* Marcel Weiss. *Art Dir* Jean Mandaroux. *Film Ed* Robert Isnardon. *Mus* Yves Claoué. *Sd* Jean Rieul. *Prod Mgr* Jacques Juranville.

Cast: Danielle Darrieux (*Eve Faugères*), Michel Auclair (*Jean Le Prat*), Jean Servais (*Maurice Faugères*), Henri Guisol (*Georges Méliot*), Jacqueline Danno (*Florence*), Bernard Lajarrige (*Moureu*), Raymond Gérome, Julien Verdier, Bernard Musson, Peggy Lonaty, Madeleine Barbulée, Hubert Deschamps, Mathilde Casadesus, Philippe Prince.

Mystery drama. Source: Pierre Boileau and Thomas Narcejac, *À coeur perdu* (Paris, 1959). Famed singer Eve Faugères, separated from her jealous husband, Maurice, a songwriter, falls in love with her accompanist, Jean Le Prat. Maurice is killed in a mysterious automobile accident, and (because they felt that Maurice stood in the way of their happiness) Eve and Jean begin to suspect each other of foul play. Their concern is intensified when Eve receives a recorded message from Maurice, and Maurice's friend and publisher, Georges Méliot, receives a new song from him. Eve and Jean's affair is nearly destroyed by their fear of Maurice's return. Finally Jean forces the publisher to admit to perpetrating a hoax. The publisher falls down an elevator shaft before he can

explain why he carried out the hoax, and Eve and Jean are reunited. *Singers. Composers. Musicians. Publishers. Murder. Hoaxes. Recorders. Automobile accidents.*

Note: Opened in Paris in May 1960 as *Meurtre en 45 tours;* running time: 105 min. Also reviewed in France at 93 and 110 min.

MURDER AT THE GALLOP (Great Britain) **F6.3339**

Metro-Goldwyn-Mayer Pictures. *Dist* Metro-Goldwyn-Mayer, Inc. 24 Jun **1963** [New York opening; c12 Jun 1963; LP25631]. Sd (Westrex); b&w. 35mm (Panavision). 81 min.

A Lawrence P. Bachmann Production. *Prod* George H. Brown. *Exec Prod* Lawrence P. Bachmann. *Dir* George Pollock. *Screenplay* James P. Cavanagh, David Pursall, Jack Seddon. *Dir Photog* Arthur Ibbetson. *Camera Op* Paul Wilson. *Art Dir* Frank White. *Asst Art Dir* Jonathan Barry. *Film Ed* Bert Rule. *Mus Comp & Cond* Ron Goodwin. *Rec Supv* A. W. Watkins. *Sd Ed* Dennis Rogers. *Dub Mix* J. B. Smith. *Sd Rec* David Bowen. *Boom Op* Geoffrey Kidd. *1st & 2d Asst Dir* Basil Rayburn, Edward Dorian. *Prod Mgr* Sydney Streeter. *Cont* Betty Harley. *Prod Sec* Cynthia Palmer. *Wardrobe Supv* Maude Churchill. *Women's Wardrobe* Masada Wilmot. *Men's Wardrobe* Charles Monet. *Makeup* Eddie Knight. *Hairdressing* Pearl Orton. *Sp Eff* Tom Howard. *Casting Dir* Irene Howard. *Still Photog* John Hardman. *Prod Buyer* John Bigg. *Electrn/Gaffer* Fred Pretty. *Grip* T. Kelly.

Cast: Margaret Rutherford (*Miss Marple*), Robert Morley (*Hector Enderby*), Flora Robson (*Miss Gilchrist*), Charles Tingwell (*Detective Inspector Craddock*), Stringer Davis (*Mr. Stringer*), Duncan Lamont (*Hillman*), James Villiers (*Michael Shane*), Robert Urquhart (*George Crossfield*), Katya Douglas (*Rosamund Shane*), Gordon Harris (*Sergeant Bacon*), Noel Howlett (*Mr. Trundell*), Finlay Currie (*Old Enderby*), Kevin Stoney (*Dr. Markwell*).

Mystery comedy. Source: Agatha Christie, *After the Funeral* (London, 1953). While collecting for one of her favorite charities, "The Reformed Criminals Assistance League," Miss Marple and her librarian friend, Mr. Stringer, see an elderly recluse named Mr. Enderby fall to his death after being frightened by a cat. Immediately suspecting foul play, Miss Marple listens in on the reading of the dead man's will and learns that his estate will be divided among four relatives. Miss Marple also overhears Enderby's sister declare that her brother was murdered; before any further sleuthing can be accomplished, the sister is also slain. The dead woman's companion, Miss Gilchrist, suspects Miss Marple of the crime, but she is cleared by the long-suffering Inspector Craddock. Determined to solve the mystery, Miss Marple moves into the riding academy inn, The Gallop, which is owned by Enderby's nephew, Hector. She discovers that the three surviving relatives are all anxious to obtain a supposedly worthless painting belonging to the murdered sister. The painting is actually an old French masterpiece worth a fortune. After the murder of another relative, George Crossfield, Miss Marple deduces the identity of the killer but still lacks the proof. Miss Marple fakes a heart attack while dancing the Twist after pretending to have evidence enough to convict the killer, and she permits herself to be placed in a room alone. The murderer, Miss Gilchrist, attacks, but Miss Marple is able to hold her off until Inspector Tingwell arrives. As she prepares to leave The Gallop, Hector proposes marriage, but Miss Marple gracefully declines. *Detectives. Librarians. Recluses. Inheritance. Murder. Paintings. Twist (dance). Inns. Riding schools. Miss Marple.*

Note: Released in Great Britain in 1963.

MURDER BY AGREEMENT see **JOURNEY INTO NOWHERE**

MURDER CAN BE DEADLY (Great Britain) **F6.3340**

Mancunian Film Corp.–Doverton Films. *Dist* Colorama Features, Schoenfeld Film Distributing Corp. 9 Apr **1963** [Maryland license]. Sd; b&w. 35mm. 60 min.

A Blakeley's Films Production. *Prod* Tom Blakeley. *Dir* Lance Comfort. *Screenplay* Pip Baker, Jane Baker. *From an Orig Idea by* Brock Williams. *Photog* Basil Emmott. *Art Dir* George Provis. *Film Ed* John Trumper. *Mus* Martin Slavin. *Titl Song* Martin Slavin, Abbe Gail. *Song:* "Another You" Norrie Paramor, Bunny Lewis, Michael Carr, mus. *Sd Rec* Norman Bolland.

Cast: Liz Fraser (*Jo Lake*), Kenneth Griffith (*Kleinie*), Peter Reynolds (*Mark Davies*), Anthony Wickert (*Tom*), Craig Douglas (*nightclub singer*), Nanette Newman (*Mary*), Ray Smith (*Glynn*), David Hemmings (*Roy*), Harold Berens (*Mikhala*), Grazina Frame (*Lucy*), Lionel Ngakane (*barman*), Richard McNeff (*police inspector*), Gerald Sim (*plainclothes policeman*), Rosemary Chalmers (*Gloria*), Mia Karam (*Dawn*), Terence Maidment, Bill Stevens (*henchmen*), Ann Wrigg (*manageress*).

Crime melodrama. Tom, a student, gets drunk in a Soho clip joint run by Kleinie, a gangster. Jo Lake, who has been working the "outraged husband" con game, arrives home with Tom and discovers Mark, her partner in crime, stabbed to death by Kleinie, under whose auspices the pair had operated. Inebriated, Tom touches the murder weapon and thus involves himself; whereupon Jo forces him to dispose of the corpse. Tom drives the automobile so erratically, however, that he attracts the police and becomes the prime suspect. To clear himself, Tom, helped by his fiancée, Mary, and by his friends Glynn and Roy, tracks down Jo. Subsequently, Jo and Tom are kidnaped by Kleinie, who fatally shoots the woman when the police corner him. *Students. Gangsters. Confidence women. Police. Drunkenness. Murder. Blackmail. Kidnaping. Reckless driving. Clip joints. Corpses. London—Soho.*

Note: Released in Great Britain in May 1962 as *The Painted Smile.*

THE MURDER CLINIC (France/Italy)   **F6.3341**

Leone Film–Orphée Productions–Société Française de Cinématographie. *Dist* Europix-Consolidated Corp. 25 Jun **1969** [San Francisco opening]. Sd; col (Technicolor). 35mm (Techniscope). 86 min.

Prod-Dir Michael Hamilton. *English Vers Dir* Lewis E. Ciannelli. *Screenplay* Julian Berry, Martin Hardy. *Photog* Marc Lane. *Camera* Antonio Schiavolena. *Art Dir (see note)* Alberto Salvatori. *Film Ed* Richard Hartley. *Mus Comp & Cond* Frank Mason. *Sd* Oliver Scott. *Asst Dir* Montague Jackson. *Prod Mgr* Piero Lazzari. *Makeup* Massimo Giustini.

Cast: William Berger *(Dr. Robert Vance)*, Françoise Prévost *(Claudine)*, Mary Young *(Lizabeth)*, Barbara Wilson *(Mary)*, Delphi Maurin *(Laura)*, Max Dean *(Fred)*, Harriet White *(Sheena)*, Philippe Hersent, Ann Sherman, William Gold, Grant Laramy, Patricia Carr, Anne Field.

Horror film. Source: Robert Williams, *The Knife in the Body* (a novel; publication undetermined). At the turn of the century, Dr. Robert Vance runs a psychiatric clinic in a remote part of England. Plagued by a series of violent killings at the clinic in which young female deafmutes have been slashed to death with a razor, the doctor has few patients and lives in isolation with his wife, Lizabeth. Unknown to the small community, Lizabeth's sister Laura is also living at the clinic. Once a beautiful girl, she is now horribly disfigured from falling into a pit of quicklime. Although Vance had been blamed for the accident, he was acquitted because of lack of evidence. Mary, a new nurse, and a young woman arrive at the clinic; when the woman is brutally murdered with a razor, Vance persuades Mary to help him secretly dispose of the body. A short time later, Mary is attacked in her bedroom but saved by the cloak-shrouded Laura, who unmasks Lizabeth as the killer. When Laura accuses her sister of causing the quicklime accident because she was jealous of Vance's attentions, Lizabeth kills Laura and then commits suicide. With the death of the two sisters, Vance is free to begin a new life with Mary. *Psychiatrists. Deafmutes. Sisters. Nurses. Murder. Disfiguration. Jealousy. Suicide. Clinics. England.*

Note: Opened in Rome in Jun 1966 as *La lama nel corpo*; in Paris in Oct 1967 as *Les nuits de l'épouvante*. May also be known as *The Murder Society*. Michael Hamilton is a pseudonym for Elio Scardamaglia, Julian Berry for Ernesto Gastaldi, Martin Hardy for Sergio Martino, Marc Lane for Marcello Masciocchi, Richard Hartley for Alberto Gallitti, Frank Mason for Francesco De Masi, Oliver Scott for Dino Fronzetti, Montague Jackson for Roberto Pariante. One British source credits Walter Parkington as art director.

MURDER CZECH STYLE (Czechoslovakia)   **F6.3342**

Barrandov Film Studio. *For* Československý Film. *Dist* Royal Films International. 19 Aug **1968** [New York opening]. Sd; b&w with col seq. 35mm. 90 min.

A Feix-Broz Production. *Dir* Jiří Weiss. *Story-Screenplay* Ján Otčenášek, Jiří Weiss. *Photog* Jan Němeček. *Art Dir* Karel Lier. *Film Ed* Miroslav Hájek. *Mus* Zdeněk Liška. *Mus Dir* Luděk Hulan.

Cast: Rudolf Hrušínský *(Frantisek Pokorny)*, Květa Fialová *(Alice Pokorny)*, Václav Voska *(assistant manager)*, Vladimír Menšík *(Emil)*, Věra Uzelacová *(Bindrova)*, Libuše Svormová *(Jindriska)*, Vjačeslav Irmanov *(dandy)*, František Šlégr, Jaroslav Solnička, Jindřich Narenta.

Comedy-drama. While on a holiday, Frantisek Pokorny, a fat, aging clerk, meets and falls in love with Alice, an attractive young woman from Prague. To his surprise, she reciprocates his interest, and, encouraged by the assistant manager at the office, Frantisek clumsily courts and marries her. Despite the fact that the marriage is not consummated because Alice claims to be still suffering from a childhood trauma, Frantisek is blissfully happy. Even his week-long separations from Alice at first do not bother him, since they have the weekends together after she completes her work in Prague. Hoping to spend every night with his wife, Frantisek later asks to be transferred to Prague but instead is given a promotion by the assistant manager. Frantisek becomes suspicious, follows Alice to Prague, and learns that his wife and the assistant manager, who is already married, are having an affair. Frantisek dreams of killing both of them but realizes that the result would be his own arrest; he also considers suicide but realizes that this solution would only lead to his own funeral—and freedom for the lovers. He finally decides to blackmail the assistant manager for a better job and ignore his wife's infidelities. Content with his solution to the problem, Frantisek now controls the fate of the adulterous lovers. *Clerks. Courtship. Marriage. Infidelity. Revenge. Blackmail. Vacations. Dreams. Prague.*

Note: Released in Czechoslovakia in 1967 as *Vražda po česku* and *Vražda po našem.*

THE MURDER GAME (Great Britain)   **F6.3343**

Lippert Films. *Dist* Twentieth Century–Fox Film Corp. 30 Mar **1966** [New York opening; c7 Mar 1966; LF68]. Sd; b&w. 35mm. 75 min.

Prod Robert L. Lippert, Jack Parsons. *Dir* Sidney Salkow. *Screenplay* Harry Spalding. *Story* Irving Yergin. *Photog* Geoffrey Faithfull. *Camera* Gerry Massy-Collier. *Art Dir* Harry White. *Film Ed* Robert Winter. *Mus* Carlo Martelli. *Sd* Clive Smith. *Sd Rec* Jock May. *Asst Dir* Gordon Gilbert. *Prod Mgr* Clifton Brandon. *Wardrobe* Jean Fairlie. *Makeup* Harold Fletcher. *Hairstyles* Joyce James.

Cast: Ken Scott *(Steve Baldwin)*, Marla Landi *(Marie Aldrich)*, Trader Faulkner *(Chris Aldrich)*, Conrad Phillips *(Peter Shanley)*, Gerald Sim *(Larry Lindstrom)*, Duncan Lamont *(Inspector Telford)*, Rosamund Greenwood *(Mrs. Potter)*, Victor Brooks *(Rev. Francis Hood)*, Ballard Berkeley *(Sir Colin Chalmers)*, Jimmy Gardner *(Arthur Gillett)*, Peter Bathurst *(Dr. Knight)*, Jenny White *(secretary)*, Frank Thornton *(radio announcer)*, Gretchen Franklin *(landlady)*, John Dunbar *(Parkhill)*, Clement Freud *(croupier)*, Derek Partridge *(police sergeant)*, John Richmond *(prosecutor)*.

Crime melodrama. Marie Baldwin leaves her husband, Steve, changes her name to that of a nurse killed in African riots, and marries engineer Chris Aldrich. Steve tracks her down, gets a job as a handyman on Chris's estate, and tries to blackmail Marie. Marie, while appearing to yield to the blackmail demands, plans to murder Steve. She tampers with the car, but the plan goes wrong, and Chris is injured instead. While recuperating, Chris overhears Steve and Marie discussing a murder and thinks they plan to kill him. He decides to retaliate. The local vicar, who had known the nurse whose name Marie assumed, comes to see her and is murdered by Steve and buried in the backyard. Chris disappears after fabricating evidence of his own murder. Steve and Marie are brought to trial for the murder of Chris, but they are acquitted. Chris then confronts Steve and Marie and is nearly killed in a fight with Steve. The police stop the fight, but Steve is sure he won't be charged with assaulting a supposedly dead man. His confidence wanes as he hears police shovels digging in the backyard where the vicar is buried. Steve and Marie know they won't be acquitted this time. *Nurses. Engineers. Handymen. Clergymen. Police. Personal identity. Desertion. Marriage. Bigamy. Blackmail. Murder. Frameup. Trials. Automobile accidents.*

Note: Released in Great Britain in May 1966; running time: 76 min.

MURDER IN EDEN (Great Britain)   **F6.3344**

Luckwell Productions. *Dist* Colorama Features, Schoenfeld Film Distributing Corp. 5 Dec **1962** [New York opening]. Sd; b&w. 35mm. 63 min.

A Bill Luckwell–Michael Luckwell Production. *Prod* Bill Luckwell, Jock MacGregor. *Dir* Max Varnel. *Screenplay* H. E. Burdon. *Story* John Haggarty. *Photog* Walter J. Harvey. *Art Dir* Tony Inglis. *Film Ed* Robert Hill. *Mus* Wilfred Burns. *Sd Rec* Bill O'Neil.

Cast: Ray McAnally *(Inspector Sharkey)*, Catherine Feller *(Genevieve Beaujean)*, Yvonne Buckingham *(Vicky Woolf)*, Norman Rodway *(Michael Lucas)*, Mark Singleton *(Arnold Woolf)*, Jack Aranson *(Bill Robson)*, Robert Lepler *(Max Aaronson)*, Angela Douglas *(beatnik)*, Francis O'Keefe *(Sergeant Johnson)*, Noel Sheridan *(Frenchman Jack)*, Ronald Walsh *(bodyguard)*, John Sterling *(art expert)*, Frank O'Donovan *(manservant)*, Eithne Lydon *(receptionist)*.

Mystery melodrama. Art critic Max Aaronson is killed by a hit-and-run driver after informing London art dealers Arnold and Vicky Woolf that their famous Van Meerbeke painting is a fake. Texas oil magnate Bill Robson offers to pay any price for the original painting, and he buys another by the same artist. Assigned to investigate the case, Scotland Yard Inspector Sharkey learns of Aaronson's death from Genevieve Beaujean, a French magazine reporter; later, Sharkey rescues her from an unknown assailant who is subsequently found murdered. The detective goes to the bungalow of Michael Lucas, an art restorer and Mrs. Woolf's lover, and proves that Lucas was the killer and forger. *Art appraisers. Hit-and-run drivers. Art dealers. Detectives. Art collectors. Oil magnates. Texans. Americans in foreign countries. French. Reporters. Murder. Forgery. Infidelity. London. Scotland Yard.*

Note: Released in Great Britain in 1961; running time: 64 min.

MURDER IN MISSISSIPPI   **F6.3345**

Tiger Productions. *Dist* Supreme Films, Waldman Films. Oct **1965**. Sd; b&w. 35mm. 84 min.

Prod-Writ Herbert S. Altman. *Assoc Prod* Art Raymond. *Dir* J. P. Mawra. *Camera* Warner Rose. *Asst Camera* Bob Bailin. *Ed* J. P. Mawra. *Asst Ed* Joanna Alexander. *Mus* Joe Lesko. *Sd Eff* Joe Lesko. *Sp Eff* Technical Film Studios.

Cast: Sheila Britton *(Carol Byrd)*, Sam Stewart *(Phil Loving)*, Derek Crane *(Sheriff Engstrom)*, Lou Stone *(Luther Barnes)*, Martin St. John *(Tyrone Carver)*, John Steel *(Deputy Sheriff Bob Engstrom)*, Wayne Foster *(Andy*

Loving), Dick Stone (*Dick Byrd*), Otis Young (*Paul Jackson*), Irv Seldin (*Bernie Samuelson*), Frank Philadelphia (*asst. U. S. attorney*), Millie Moran (*guitar player*).

Melodrama. Five young students volunteer to aid in registering Negro voters in Lovingboro, Mississippi. In an attempt to intimidate the civil rights workers, Sheriff Engstrom has one of the workers beaten up. When this fails to work, he tries to frighten three of the workers into returning to the North. One of the workers, Bernie Samuelson, is accidentally killed, and the sheriff decides that he must also kill Tyrone Carver and Carol Byrd, witnesses to the crime. Carver is killed, and the sheriff instructs the Loving brothers to bury the men and dispose of Carol. She persuades the Loving brothers to spare her in return for a ransom to be paid by her brother Dick, a Hollywood actor. Her brother arrives with the money, and he entertains himself with a black prostitute while he awaits his sister. Luther Barnes, a black civil rights worker, decides to try to find Carol on his own. In the meantime, Phil Loving sends his brother Andy to collect the ransom. Luther Barnes stumbles on the shack where Carol is held captive, and he battles Andy, who is trying to rape her. Carol and Luther flee and spend the night huddled in a thicket. The two are found by a posse, and Luther is castrated and killed while Carol watches, helpless. Carol is released, and she tells her story, causing the FBI to press charges against the sheriff. Although the prosecution fails, it stirs the Negro community into demonstrating for their rights. *Students. Negroes. Sheriffs. Prostitutes. Brothers. Civil rights. Brother-sister relationship. Murder. Rape. Ransom. Castration. Racial prejudice. Mississippi. United States—Federal Bureau of Investigation.*

Note: Made in and around Philadelphia. Also known as *Murder Mississippi.*

MURDER MOST FOUL (Great Britain)   F6.3346
Metro-Goldwyn-Mayer, Inc. 23 May **1965** [New York opening; c11 Jun 1964; LP28119]. Sd (Westrex); b&w. 35mm. 90 min.

A Lawrence P. Bachmann Production. *Prod* Ben Arbeid. *Dir* George Pollock. *Screenplay* David Pursall, Jack Seddon. *Dir Photog* Desmond Dickinson. *Camera Op* Alan McCabe. *Art Dir* Frank White. *Film Ed* Ernest Walter. *Mus Comp & Cond* Ron Goodwin. *Rec Supv* A. W. Watkins. *Sd Rec* Cyril Swern. *Dub Mix* J. B. Smith. *Sd Ed* Allan Sones. *Asst Dir* David Tomblin. *Prod Mgr* Sydney Streeter.

Cast: Margaret Rutherford (*Miss Marple*), Ron Moody (*Driffold Cosgood*), Charles Tingwell (*Inspector Craddock*), Andrew Cruickshank (*Justice Crosby*), Megs Jenkins (*Mrs. Thomas*), Dennis Price (*theatrical agent*), Ralph Michael (*Ralph Summers*), James Bolam (*Bill Hanson*), Stringer Davis (*Mr. Stringer*), Francesca Annis (*Sheila Upward*), Alison Seebohm (*Eva McGonigall*), Terry Scott (*Police Constable Wells*), Pauline Jameson (*Maureen Summers*), Maurice Good (*George Rowton*), Annette Kerr, Windsor Davies, Neil Stacey, Stella Tanner.

Mystery melodrama. Source: Agatha Christie, *Mrs. McGinty's Dead* (London, 1952). Amateur detective Miss Marple, the only member of a jury to vote "not guilty" in a murder trial, decides to find the real culprit on her own when a mistrial is declared. Along with her companion, Mr. Stringer, she searches the home of the victim, a former actress, and is led to a foundering repertory company headed by Driffold Cosgood. Posing as an actress, Miss Marple is accepted into the troupe by Cosgood, who believes she may be able to help the company out of financial straits. Miss Marple receives no help in her investigations from Inspector Craddock, who is convinced of the guilt of the accused, a lodger in the victim's home; but her suspicions gain credibility when one cast member is poisoned and another is gassed with cyanide. Later, almost at the cost of her life, she discovers that the murderer is actor Bill Hanson, whose mother, a former member of the theater company, was hanged for murdering her husband; the victim, it is revealed, had been blackmailing Hanson. *Detectives. Actors. Lodgers. Murder. Poisoning. Blackmail. Capital punishment. Theatrical troupes. Juries. Trials. Miss Marple.*

MURDER ON THE CAMPUS (Great Britain)   F6.3347
Border Film Productions. *Dist* Colorama Features, Capitol Films. 17 Apr **1963** [Los Angeles opening]. Sd; b&w. 35mm. 61 min.

Prod Negus Fancey. *Assoc Prod-Dir-Screenplay* Michael Winner. *Photog* Richard Bayley. *Art Dir* Derek Barrington. *Mus* Jackie Brown, Cy Payne.

Cast: Terence Longdon (*Mark Kingston*), Donald Gray (*Inspector Wills*), Diane Clare (*Mary Johnson*), Robertson Hare (*Ronald Fortescue*), Dermot Walsh (*Research Professor Taylor*), Felicity Young (*waitress*), Douglas Muir (*killer*).

Mystery melodrama. Returning to England from an overseas assignment, newsman Mark Kingston learns that his younger brother, Tony, a student at Cambridge University, has presumedly killed himself. Refusing to believe that the death was a suicide, Mark goes to Cambridge to investigate, but he receives little coöperation from scandal-wary students and others, with the exception of Mary Johnson, daughter of a professor who has disappeared. After three more deaths, the newsman proves that his brother was murdered by a member of a gang of jewel thieves. *Reporters. Brothers. Students. Professors. Missing persons. Thieves. Murder. Suicide. Jewels. Cambridge University.*

Note: Released in Great Britain in Jun 1961 as *Out of the Shadow.*

MURDER SHE SAID (Great Britain)   F6.3348
Metro-Goldwyn-Mayer Pictures. *Dist* Metro-Goldwyn-Mayer, Inc. 20 Dec **1961** [San Francisco opening; c31 Dec 1961; LP21547]. Sd (Westrex); b&w. 35mm. 87 min.

Prod George H. Brown. *Dir* George Pollock. *Screenplay* David Pursall, Jack Seddon. *Adapt* David Osborn. *Dir Photog* Geoffrey Faithfull. *Camera Op* Austin Dempster. *Art Dir* Harry White. *Film Ed* Ernest Walter. *Mus Comp & Cond* Ron Goodwin. *Rec Supv* A. W. Watkins. *Dub Ed* Robert Carrick. *Sd Rec* Cyril Swern, J. B. Smith. *Asst Dir* Douglas Hickox. *Prod Mgr* Jan Darnley-Smith. *Cont* Beryl Booth. *Wardrobe* Felix Evans. *Makeup* Eddie Knight. *Hairdressing* Pearl Orton. *Sp Eff* Tom Howard. *Stills Camera* Norman Hargood.

Cast: Margaret Rutherford (*Miss Jane Marple*), Arthur Kennedy (*Dr. Quimper*), Muriel Pavlow (*Emma Ackenthorpe*), James Robertson-Justice (*Ackenthorpe*), Thorley Walters (*Cedric Ackenthorpe*), Charles Tingwell (*Inspector Craddock*), Conrad Phillips (*Harold*), Ronald Howard (*Brian Eastley*), Joan Hickson (*Mrs. Kidder*), Stringer Davis (*Mr. Stringer*), Ronnie Raymond (*Alexander Eastley*), Gerald Cross (*Albert*), Michael Golden (*Hillman*), Barbara Leake (*Mrs. Stainton*), Gordon Harris (*Bacon*), Peter Butterworth (*ticket collector*), Richard Briers ("*Mrs. Binster*"), Lucy Griffiths (*Lucy*).

Mystery melodrama. Source: Agatha Christie, *4:50 From Paddington* (London, 1957). While reading a mystery novel on a train from London, the elderly Miss Marple sees a woman being strangled by a man on a passing train. The police, however, are unable to find any trace of the body and dismiss her story as the imaginings of a doddering old woman. Highly indignant, she decides to investigate for herself. Believing the body was thrown from the passing train near the Ackenthorpe estate, she takes a job there as a maid; and her suspicions prove correct when her snooping uncovers the woman's body in a deserted outbuilding. At first the victim is believed to be a French girl once married to an Ackenthorpe killed in World War II. Consequently, suspicion naturally falls on the elderly Ackenthorpe's four remaining children, each of whom might resort to murder to prevent sharing their inheritance with another heir. Two more sons of the aged patriarch are murdered, and Miss Marple deduces the identity of the murderer and sets a trap. Her plan exposes the family physician, Quimper, as the killer. (Quimper murdered his own wife on the train and made it appear that she was the French-born wife. He then planned to kill off the sons before marrying Emma Ackenthorpe, the only daughter, who would eventually inherit the entire fortune.) *Spinsters. Detectives. Housemaids. Physicians. Murder. Inheritance. Brother-sister relationship. Trains. London. Miss Marple.*

Note: Released in Great Britain in Sep 1961. Working title: *Meet Miss Marple.* Actors Barbara Leake and Peter Butterworth are listed in several sources as Barbara Hicks and A. N. Other, respectively.

THE MURDER SOCIETY *see* **THE MURDER CLINIC**

THE MURDERER *see* **ENOUGH ROPE**

MURDERERS' ROW   F6.3349
Meadway-Claude Productions #2. *Dist* Columbia Pictures. 20 Dec **1966** [Chicago opening; c1 Dec 1966; LP34011]. Sd; col (Technicolor). 35mm. 108 min.

An Irving Allen Production. *Prod* Irving Allen. *Assoc Prod* Euan Lloyd. *Dir* Henry Levin. *2d Unit Dir* James Havens. *Screenplay* Herbert Baker. *Dir Photog* Sam Leavitt. *2d Unit Photog* Mark Davis. *Camera Op* Al Myers. *Art Dir* Joe Wright. *Set Decor* George R. Nelson. *Set Dsgn* Stewart Campbell. *Film Ed* Walter Thompson. *Mus* Lalo Schifrin. *Song:* "If You're Thinking What I'm Thinking" Tommy Boyce, Bobby Hart. *Song:* "I'm Not the Marrying Kind" Lalo Schifrin, Howard Greenfield. *Sung by* Dean Martin. *Choreog* Miriam Nelson. *Sd Supv* Charles J. Rice. *Sd* Lambert Day, Jack Haynes. *Rec* Vic Carpenter. *Boom Op* Dick Keener. *Asst Dir* Ray Gosnell, Leonard Kunody. *Prod Supv* Ivan Volkman. *Script Supv* Frances McDowell. *Cost Dsgn* Moss Mabry. *Wardrobe* Seth Banks, Morris Brown, Dina Joseph. *Makeup Supv* Ben Lane. *Makeup* Joseph Di Bella, Loren Cosand. *Ann-Margret's Hairstyles* Cherie. *Sp Eff* Danny Lee, Howard Jensen. *Still Photog* Sterling Smith. *Prop* Max Frankel, Irving Lipschutz. *Gaffer* Les Everson. *Grip* Al Becker, Henry Wood.

Cast: Dean Martin (*Matt Helm*), Ann-Margret (*Suzie*), Karl Malden (*Julian Wall*), Camilla Sparv (*Coco Duquette*), James Gregory (*MacDonald*), Beverly Adams (*Lovey Kravezit*), Richard Eastham (*Dr. Norman Solaris*), Tom Reese (*Ironhead*), Duke Howard (*Billy Orcutt*), Ted Hartley (*guard*), Marcel Hillaire (*Captain Deveraux*), Corinne Cole (*Miss January*), Robert Terry (*Doctor Rogas*), Dino, Desi & Billy (*themselves*), Mary Jane Mangler, Amedee Chabot,

Luci Ann Cook, Marilyn Tindall, Dee Duffy, Jan Watson, Dale Brown, Mary Hughes, Lynn Hartoch, Rena Horten, Barbara Burgess (*The Slaygirls*).

Action melodrama. Source: Donald Hamilton, *Murderers' Row* (New York, 1962). As part of his plan for world conquest, archvillain Julian Wall has kidnaped Dr. Norman Solaris, the inventor of a helio-beam, a device capable of destroying the earth by harnessing the sun's rays. Wall has also eliminated most of America's ICE (Intelligence and Counter-Espionage) agents, including the famous Matt Helm. Unknown to him, however, the ever-resourceful Helm is alive and traveling incognito. Arriving on the Riviera, Matt finds his contact woman murdered, but he meets Solaris' daughter, Suzie, who is worried about her father's disappearance. Matt poses as an American gunman on the lam; and Wall hires him but becomes suspicious when Matt rescues Suzie from being killed by one of Wall's henchmen. Matt and Suzie escape and make their way to Wall's island stronghold. After numerous misadventures, they rescue Dr. Solaris and destroy Wall and his gang, thereby preventing the imminent destruction of Washington, D. C., by the helio-beam. *Secret agents. Inventors. Scientists. Gangsters. Megalomania. Abduction. Imposture. Espionage. Murder. Inventions. Islands. Riviera. Washington (District of Columbia). Matt Helm.*

Note: Location scenes filmed on the French Riviera and the Isle of Wight.

MURIEL (France/Italy)   **F6.3350**

Argos Films–Alpha Productions–Eclair–Films de la Pléiade–Dear Film. *Dist* Lopert Pictures. 30 Oct 1963 [New York opening; c2 Oct 1963; LP27333]. Sd; col (Eastmancolor). 35mm. 115 min.

Prod Anatole Dauman. *Dir* Alain Resnais. *Orig Story, Screenplay & Dial* Jean Cayrol. *Dir Photog* Sacha Vierny. *Camera Op* Philippe Choquet, Philippe Brun. *Art Dir* Jacques Saulnier. *Film Ed (see note)* Kenout Peltier, Claudine Merlin, Eric Pluet. *Mus* Hans Werner Henze. *Singer* Rita Streich. *Song:* "Déjà" Paul Colline, Paul Maye. *Sung by* Jean Champion. *Sd Engr* Antoine Bonfanti. *Asst Dir* Jean Léon. *Prod Supv* Philippe Dussart. *Prod Mgr* Michel Choquet. *Script Girl* Sylvette Baudrot. *Still Photog* Liliane de Kermadec. *English Subtitl* Jan Lenica.

Cast: Delphine Seyrig (*Hélène*), Jean-Pierre Kérien (*Alphonse*), Nita Klein (*Françoise*), Jean-Baptiste Thierrée (*Bernard*), Claude Sainval (*de Smoke*), Laurence Badie (*Claudie*), Jean Champion (*Ernest*), Jean Dasté (*The Goat Man*), Martine Vatel (*Marie-Dominique*), Philippe Laudenbach (*Robert*), Robert Bordenave (*The Croupier*), Gaston Joly (*Antoine, the tailor*), Catherine de Seynes (*Angèle*), Julien Verdier (*The Stableman*), Gérard Lorin, Françoise Bertin, Wanda Kérien, Jean-Jacques Lagarde, Yves Vincent.

Drama. Hélène Aughain is a widow in her late thirties who lives in the French port of Boulogne-sur-Mer and earns her living by selling antiques from her apartment. Also living at the apartment is her stepson Bernard, who is haunted by the part he took during the Algerian War in the torture and ultimate death of a young Algerian named Muriel. Despite the fact that she has a devoted lover, de Smoke, Hélène cannot forget Alphonse, who had been her first love when she was 16 and from whom she had become separated during World War II. Consequently, she invites him to visit her when she learns of his present whereabouts. Alphonse arrives with his mistress Françoise, whom he passes off as his niece. Françoise, a young actress, becomes attracted to the introspective Bernard. During the 2 weeks the four spend together, despite mutual experiences and memories, they remain strangers to each other. Bernard, in a fit of remorse, kills a war buddy, Robert, who was directly involved in the death of Muriel. Hélène, unable to recapture her lost youth, finds it impossible to establish a rapport with Alphonse; and the arrival of Ernest, Alphonse's brother-in-law who has come to take Alphonse home, makes Hélène realize the truth about Alphonse that he is a self-satisfied "dreamer" who never amounted to much. Françoise returns to Paris; she cannot find happiness with either Bernard or Alphonse. Bernard packs up and leaves; Alphonse evades Ernest by running away; Hélène goes to visit some old, tranquil friends; and a strange woman, Alphonse's wife, wanders through the now empty apartment. *Antique dealers. Stepmothers. Actors. Veterans. Houseguests. Mistresses. Memory. Guilt. War crimes. Murder. Death. Boulogne-sur-Mer.*

Note: Released in France in 1963 as *Muriel, ou le temps d'un retour* at 120 min. Italian title: *Muriel, il tempo di un ritorno*. Claudine Merlin is credited by only one source as film editor.

MURIEL, IL TEMPO DI UN RITORNO *see* **MURIEL**

MURIEL, OU LE TEMPS D'UN RETOUR *see* **MURIEL**

MURIETA (Spain)   **F6.3351**

Pro Artis Ibérica. *Dist* Warner Bros. Pictures. 1 Sep 1965 [Kansas City, Missouri, opening; c1 Sep 1965; LP32090]. Sd; col (Eastman Color). 35mm. 108 min.

Supv Prod Francisco Molero. *Exec Prod* José Sainz de Vicuna. *Dir* George Sherman. *Screenplay & Story* James O'Hanlon. *Cinematog* Miguel F. Mila. *Camera Op* Hans Burman. *Asst Camera* José de la G. Cruz, Guillermo Peña.

Asst Art Dir Rafael Salazar. *Set Dsgn* Enrique Alarcón. *Set Asst* Enrique Alarcón, Jr. *Film Ed* Alfonso Santacana. *Asst Ed* Alicia Castillo, Margarita Ibáñez. *Mus Comp & Dir* Antonio Pérez Olea. *Songs:* "Rosita," "Corrido of Joaquin Murieta" *writ & sung by* Paco Michel. *Sd Engr* Enrique Molinero. *Ref Sd* Jesús Ocana. *1st Asst Dir* Stan Torchia, Frederico Vaquero. *Unit Mgr* Augusto Boué. *Prod Asst* Juan José Molina. *Script* Maria Watchman, Daniel Mendoza. *Prod Sec* Jesús Sánchez. *Wardrobe* Catalina Moreno. *Makeup* José Maria Sanchez. *Hairstyles* Dolores Clavel. *Sp Eff* Manuel Baquero. *Asst Sp Eff* Luis Castro. *English Vers* Intersync S. A. *Still Photog* Julio Sánchez.

Cast: Jeffrey Hunter (*Joaquin Murieta*), Arthur Kennedy (*Captain Love*), Diana Lorys (*Kate*), Sara Lezana (*Rosita Murieta*), Roberto Camardiel (*Three Fingers*), Pedro Osinaga (*Claudio*), Mike Brendel, Gonzalo Esquiroz, Juan Cazalilla, Julio Pérez Tabernero, David Thomson, actor, Francisco Braña, Fernando Villena, Hector Quiroga, Maria Jesús Corella, Andy Anza, Pedro Barbero, Rufino Inglés.

Western melodrama. Joaquin Murieta and his wife, Rosita, emigrate from Mexico to seek their fortune in the California Gold Rush of 1849. They encounter fierce anti-Mexican bigotry on the part of local miners but gain a friend in Captain Love, the territorial marshal. Several toughs attack Murieta when he makes a strike and rape and murder his wife. Convinced that the killers will not be brought to justice, Murieta becomes a professional gambler until he finds the guilty men and murders them. Captain Love arrests Murieta, and he is sent to prison, where he meets Three Fingers, leader of a band of Mexican outlaws, and his sidekick Claudio. Kate, a restaurant owner who has befriended Murieta, smuggles a gun into his cell, and the three men escape to join the outlaw gang. Murieta takes over the leadership of the gang and trains the outlaws as a disciplined army to chastise the "gringos." Seriously wounded in a gunfight, Murieta visits Rosita's grave. He is followed by Captain Love, who allows him to remain free in return for a promise that he will end his raids. While Murieta lies unconscious from his wounds, Three Fingers assumes his identity and continues to plunder the countryside. Murieta recovers and leads his gang to surrender, but along the way they are ambushed by Captain Love, and Murieta is killed. *Mexicans. Outlaws. Gamblers. Desperadoes. Immigrants. United States marshals. Restaurateurs. Gangs. Racial prejudice. Rape. Murder. Revenge. Gold rushes. Jailbreaks. Impersonation. California. Joaquín Murieta.*

Note: Madrid opening: Feb 1965 as *Joaquín Murrieta*.

MUSCLE BEACH PARTY   **F6.3352**

Alta Vista Productions. *Dist* American International Pictures. 25 Mar 1964 [San Francisco opening; c25 Mar 1964; LP28148]. Sd; col (Pathé). 35mm (Panavision). 94 min.

Prod James H. Nicholson, Robert Dillon. *Exec Prod* Samuel Z. Arkoff. *Dir* William Asher. *2d Unit Dir* Anthony Carras. *Screenplay* Robert Dillon. *Story* Robert Dillon, William Asher. *Dir Photog* Harold Wellman. *Art Dir* Lucius Croxton. *Set Decor* Harry Reif. *Titl* Butler-Glouner Inc. *Film Ed* Eve Newman. *Mus* Les Baxter. *Mus Coörd* Al Simms. *Songs:* "Muscle Beach Party," "Runnin' Wild," "Muscle Bustle," "My First Love," "Surfin' Woodie," "Surfer's Holiday" Roger Christian, Gary Usher, Brian Wilson. *Songs:* "Happy Street," "A Girl Needs a Boy" Guy Hemric, Jerry Styner. *Songs Perf by* Frankie Avalon, Annette Funicello, Dick Dale and the Del Tones, Little Stevie Wonder, Donna Loren. *Sd* Don Rush. *Sd Ed* Kay Rose. *Rec* George Anderson. *Mus Ed* Lloyd Young. *Asst Dir* Clark Paylow, Lew Borzage. *Prod Supv* Joe Wonder. *Prod Asst* Jack Cash. *Script Supv* Stanley Scheuer. *Cost* Marjorie Corso. *Makeup* Ted Coodley. *Hairdresser* Betty Pedretti. *Photog Sp Eff* Butler-Glouner Inc., Pat Dinga. *Prop* Karl Brainard. *Constr Coörd* Ross Hahn. *Still Photog* Bill Creamer.

Cast: Frankie Avalon (*Frankie*), Annette Funicello (*Dee Dee*), Luciana Paluzzi (*Julie*), John Ashley (*Johnny*), Don Rickles (*Jack Fanny*), Peter Turgeon (*Theodore*), Jody McCrea (*Deadhead*), Dick Dale (*Dick*), Candy Johnson (*Candy*), Little Stevie Wonder (*himself*), Morey Amsterdam (*Cappy*), Buddy Hackett (*S. Z. Matts*), Rock Stevens (*Flex Martian*), Dolores Wells (*Sniffles*), Donna Loren (*Donna*), Valora Noland (*Animal*), Alberta Nelson (*Lisa*), Amedee Chabot (*Floe*), Larry Scott (*Biff*), Bob Seven (*Rock*), Steve Merjanian (*Tug*), Don Haggerty (*Riff*), Chester Yorton (*Sulk*), Gene Shuey (*Mash*), Gordon Cohn (*Clod*), Luree Holmes, Laura Nicholson, Lorie Summers, Darlene Lucht (*beach girls*), Duane Ament, Gary Usher, Roger Christian, Guy Hemric (*beach boys*), Mary Hughes, Kathy Kessler, Salli Sachse, Linda Opie, Linda Benson, Patricia Rane (*surfer girls*), Butch Van Artsdalen, Mike Diffenderfer, Bill Graham, actor, Charles Hasley, Larry Shaw, Duane King, Mike Nader, Ed Garner, John Fain, Mickey Dora (*surfer boys*), Peter Lorre (*Mr. Strangdour*), Peter Lupus, Jr., The Del Tones.

Comedy with music. Surfers Frankie and Dee Dee and their friends become uneasy when muscleman Flex Martian and his friends from Jack Fanny's gym invade their section of the beach. On a yacht offshore, a wealthy contessa named Julie is arranging for her business manager S. Z. Matts to obtain Flex as the latest in a long string of boyfriends. Julie is temporarily content with Flex until she meets Frankie. When he returns her affection, Dee Dee becomes jealous, and the rift between the surfers and the musclemen widens. S. Z. tells Frankie about Julie's past affairs, and he goes back to Dee Dee. The surfers and the musclemen finally battle in a night brawl, but the fight is broken up by a Mr. Strangdour, who convinces Flex to concentrate on his muscles and forget Julie, who then decides to settle down with S. Z. *Surfers. Body-builders. Nobility. Business managers. Jealousy. Gymnasiums. Beaches. Yachts.*

Note: Location scenes filmed at Topanga and Malibu, California. This is a sequel to *Beach Party*, q. v.

MUSCLES AND FLOWERS
F6.3353

Hawk Serpent Productions. *Dist* Film-Makers' Cooperative, Canyon Cinema Cooperative. 4 Apr **1969** [New York opening]. Sd; col. 16mm. 90 min.
Prod-Dir Walter Gutman.

Cast—Participants: Suzanne Perry, Hanne Weaver, David Bourdon, Michael Benedikt, Emmett Williams.

Documentary. Circus acrobats Suzanne Perry and Hanne Weaver appear in three sequences, a total of 45 minutes in length, which focus on muscularity as an erotic attribute of the ultimate woman. In two of the segments, Suzanne Perry performs on a trapeze in the studio of avant-garde dancers Patricia Brown Schlichter and Joseph Schlichter. In the third segment, Hanne Weaver is seen engaged in everyday activities such as washing dishes, trying on clothes, playing with flowers from an admirer, and lying on a bed dreaming. The soundtrack provides a male contrast, as three writers—art critic David Bourdon and poets Michael Benedikt and Emmett Williams—discuss the acrobats and the visual segments. Their discussions also comprise four purely audio passages which separate the visual sequences. *Acrobats. Trapezists. Critics. Poets. Eroticism.*

MUSIC CITY U. S. A.
F6.3354

Gemini Pictures. 24 Aug **1966** [Knoxville, Tennessee, opening]. Sd; col (Eastmancolor). 35mm. ca80 min.

Prod-Dir Preston Collins, James Dinet. *Exec Prod* Edward W. Alfriend, IV. *Assoc Prod* John Giddens, Hillous Butrum. *Prod Assoc* Richard O'Connell, Vincent Youmans. *Dir Photog* Del Ankers. *Set Decor* Bill Gernert. *Song:* "Memory No. 1" Wayne Walker, Max Powell. *Sung by* Webb Pierce. *Song:* "Who Do I Think I Am?" Max Powell, Webb Pierce, Jerry Lane. *Sung by* Webb Pierce. *Song:* "Trouble's Back in Town" Dick Flood. *Sung by* The Wilburn Brothers. *Song:* "It's Another World" Darrell Statler. *Sung by* The Wilburn Brothers. *Songs:* "Wine, Woman, and Song," "The Home You're Tearing Down" Betty Sue Perry. *Sung by* Loretta Lynn. *Song:* "Six Days on the Road" Earl Green, Carl Montgomery. *Sung by* Dave Dudley. *Song:* "What We're Fighting For" Tom T. Hall. *Sung by* Dave Dudley. *Song:* "Second Fiddle (to an Old Guitar)" Betty Amos. *Sung by* Jean Shepard. *Song:* "Sittin' on a Rock (Cryin' in a Creek)" Jimmy Louis, Mart Melshee. *Sung by* Warner Mack. *Song:* "I Think I'll Go Somewhere (and Cry Myself To Sleep)" Bill Anderson. *Sung by* Charlie Louvin. *Song:* "Bayou Talk" *writ & sung by* Jimmy Newman. *Song:* "Artificial Rose" Tom T. Hall. *Sung by* Jimmy Newman. *Song:* "One of Them" Lorene Mann, Marie Wilson, *mus. Sung by* Lorene Mann. *Song:* "Hurry, Mr. Peters" Steve Karliski, Larry Kolber. *Sung by* Lorene Mann, Justin Tubb. *Song:* "Orange Blossom Special" Erwin T. Rouse. *Sung by* Gordon Terry. *Song:* "Don't Monkey Round on Me" *writ & sung by* Gordon Terry. *Songs:* "If He Only Knew," "One Woman" Tommy Fail, Arthur Smith. *Sung by* Wayne Haas. *Song:* "Mr. Trouble Maker" *sung by* Autry Inman. *Song:* "I'll Be All Right Tomorrow" Bobby Osborne, Pete Goble. *Sung by* The Osborne Brothers. *Asst Dir* Janet Mokarzel. *Unit Mgr* Noel Barrett, Vincent Youmans, Jr.

Cast: Webb Pierce, The Wilburn Brothers, Loretta Lynn, Dave Dudley, Jean Shepard, Warner Mack, Charlie Louvin and His Band, The Osborne Brothers, Lorene Mann, Justin Tubb, T Tommy Coutrer, Bob Jennings, Wayne Haas, Shot Jackson, Autry Inman, Hillous Butrum, Jimmy Newman, Gordon Terry, The Calloway Sisters, Bashful Brother Oswald, The Music City All Stars, Russell Sims, Weno A-Go-Go, Vincent Youmans, Jr., Bob Austin.

Musical revue. Disc jockey T Tommy returns to Nashville in 1965 for the country music DJ convention. He meets many friends and invites them to tour the city with him. They visit Roy Acuff's Museum of Music, Ernie's (Ernest Tubb's) Record Shop, and the music store Sho'Bud to see Shot Jackson and some of the newest musical instruments he has made. The group then stops at a television studio to see a live show emceed by disc jockey Bob Jennings and featuring Lorene Mann. Jennings and Hillous Butrum later watch Wayne Haas cut his first record, while T Tommy's group goes to meet Webb Pierce at his home. After attending the Record World Awards, emceed by Bob Austin, the disc jockeys visit a nightclub to see many country music and comedy groups perform. *Disc jockeys. Musicians. Entertainers. Country music. Conventions. Television studios. Nightclubs. Nashville (Tennessee).*

Note: Filmed entirely in Nashville, Tennessee.

THE MUSIC MAN
F6.3355

Warner Bros. Pictures. 19 Jun **1962** [Mason City, Iowa, opening; c31 Dec 1961; LP27116]. Sd; col (Technicolor). 35mm (Technirama). 151 min.

Prod-Dir Morton DaCosta. *Screenplay* Marion Hargrove. *Photog* Robert Burks. *Art Dir* Paul Groesse. *Set Decor* George James Hopkins. *Film Ed* William Ziegler. *Mus Supv & Cond* Ray Heindorf. *Mus & Lyr* Meredith Willson. *Vocal Arr* Charles Henderson. *Orch* Ray Heindorf, Frank Comstock, Gus Levene. *Minuet in G* Wolfgang Amadeus Mozart. *Choreog & Asst Choreog* Onna White, Tom Panko. *Sd* M. A. Merrick, Dolph Thomas. *Asst Dir* Russell Llewellyn. *Prod Supv* Joel Freeman. *Makeup* Gordon Bau. *Supv Hair Stylist* Jean Burt Reilly. *Miss Jones's Hairstyles* Myrl Stoltz.

Cast: Robert Preston (*Harold Hill*), Shirley Jones (*Marian Paroo*), Buddy Hackett (*Marcellus Washburn*), Hermione Gingold (*Eulalie MacKecknie Shinn*), Paul Ford (*Mayor Shinn*), Al Shea (*Ewart Dunlop*), Wayne Ward (*Oliver Hix*), Vern Reed (*Jacey Squires*), Bill Spangenberg (*Olin Britt*), Pert Kelton (*Mrs. Paroo*), Timmy Everett (*Tommy Djilas*), Susan Luckey (*Zaneeta Shinn*), Ronny Howard (*Winthrop Paroo*), Harry Hickox (*Charlie Cowell*), Charles Lane (*Constable Locke*), Mary Wickes (*Mrs. Squires*), Monique Vermont (*Amaryllis*), Ronnie Dapo (*Norbert Smith*), Jesslyn Fax (*Avis Grubb*), Patty Lee Hilka (*Gracie Shinn*), Garry Potter (*Dewey*), J. Delos Jewkes (*Harley MacCauley*), Ray Kellogg (*Harry Joseph*), William Fawcett (*Lester Lonnergan*), Rance Howard (*Oscar Jackson*), Roy Dean (*Gilbert Hawthorne*), David Swain (*Chet Glanville*), Arthur Mills (*Herbert Malthouse*), Rand Barker (*Duncan Shyball*), Jeannine Burnier (*Jessie Shyball*), Shirley Claire (*Amy Dakin*), Natalie Core (*Truthful Smith*), Therese Lyon (*Dolly Higgins*), Penelope Martin (*Lila O'Brink*), Barbara Pepper (*Feril Hawkes*), Anne Loos (*Stella Jackson*), Peggy Wynne (*Ada Nutting*), Hank Worden (*undertaker*), Milton Parsons (*farmer*), Natalie Masters (*farmer's wife*), Peggy Mondo, Sarah Seegar, Adnia Rice (*townswomen*), Casey Adams, Charles Perchesky (*salesmen*).

Musical comedy-drama. Source: Meredith Willson and Franklin Lacey, *The Music Man* (New York opening: 19 Dec 1957). "Professor" Harold Hill, a fast-talking traveling salesman, schemes to take money from the citizens of River City, Iowa, in the summer of 1912, by convincing them that a boys' band will put an end to the moral corruption resulting from the presence of a pool hall in the community. He sells instruments and uniforms to River City parents with the understanding that he will organize a band and teach the children to play; however, he intends to abscond with the money before the arrival of the instruments. Assisted by Marcellus Washburn, the town stableboy who helped Harold defraud customers in the East, Harold convinces the stubborn Iowa townspeople that he is an accomplished musician with a degree from a conservatory in Gary, Indiana. Marian Paroo, the piano teacher and librarian, uncovers evidence of his trumped-up credentials; but before she can tell Mayor Shinn, the owner of the pool hall, Harold charms her into believing he has developed the "think system" of learning to play musical instruments by humming Mozart's Minuet in G. Harold's influence transforms the quarreling school board into a harmonizing barbershop quartet, petty gossips into a ladies' dance committee, shy and lisping Winthrop Paroo into a happy child with dreams of playing in a band, and the high-strung "old maid" Marian into a young woman in love. The instruments and uniforms arrive, but Marcellus cannot convince Harold to leave town. On the evening of the ice-cream social, Charlie Cowell, a traveling anvil salesman, arrives in River City to expose Harold's scheme. Marian tries to stop him at first, but he tells her that Harold has romanced piano teachers in many towns. The alerted citizens chase Harold, planning to tar and feather him, but his love for Marian prevents him from escaping the mob. They handcuff the music man and bring him to Town Hall where the uniformed boys have assembled with their instruments. Harold pleads with the boys to employ the "think system"; and to his surprise, a ragged form of the Minuet in G escapes from the instruments. The shabby band becomes a splendid parade of color and music marching down the main street of River City, led by Harold with Marian at his side. Musical numbers: "Rock Island," "Iowa Stubborn," "Trouble," "Piano Lesson," "Goodnight My Someone," "Seventy-Six Trombones," "Sincere," "The Sadder-but-Wiser Girl," "Pickilittle," "Goodnight My Ladies," "Marian the Librarian," "Being in Love," "Wells Fargo Wagon," "It's You," "Shipoopi," "Lida Rose," "Will I Ever Tell You," "Gary, Indiana," "Till There Was You." *Traveling salesmen. Children. Librarians. Band leaders. Music teachers. Swindlers. Mayors. Music. Fraud. Moral corruption. Courtship. Parades. Bands. Billiard parlors. Barbershop quartets. Iowa. Chases.*

Note: Al Shea, Wayne Ward, Vern Reed, and Bill Spangenberg appear in the film as a barbershop quartet called the Buffalo Bills.

THE MUSIC ROOM (India)
F6.3356

Satyajit Ray Productions. *Dist* Harrison Pictures. 15 Oct **1963** [New York opening]. Sd; b&w. 35mm. 95 min.

Prod-Dir-Writ Satyajit Ray. *Photog* Subrata Mitra. *Art Dir* Bansi Chandragupta. *Sets* R. R. Sinde. *Film Ed* Dulal Dutta. *Mus Dir* Ustad Vilayat Khan. *Sd* Durgadas Mitra. *Asst Dir* Sailen Dutta, Nityananda Dutta, Tapeswar Prasad.

Cast: Chhabi Biswas *(Bishambar Rai)*, Padma Devi *(his wife)*, Pinaki Sengupta *(his son)*, Tulsi Lahari *(manager of Rai's estate)*, Kali Sarkar *(Rai's servant)*, Gangapada Basu *(Ganguly)*, Akhtari Bai, Salamat Khan *(singers)*, Roshan Kumari, Begum Akhtar, Ustad Waheed Khan, Bismilla Khan *(musicians and dancers)*, Pratap Mukhopdhya, Tarapada Nandy.

Drama. Source: Tarashankar Banerjee, *Jalsaghar* (Calcutta, 1937). In India in 1920 wealthy landowner Bishambar Rai lives in a palace with his wife and son. Most of the family fortune has been spent on elaborate music festivals. Bishambar feels a strong disdain for his nouveau riche neighbor, Ganguli, who is introducing an unwelcome note of modernity to the area. When the time comes to hold a ceremony for his adolescent son, the landowner finds that his credit is exhausted; but the event is held anyway in the greatest splendor, financed by the sale of his wife's jewels. Later, when Ganguli invites him to his house-warming party, Bishambar curtly refuses and arranges another festivity of his own. Since his wife and son are away, he sends for them; but on their return trip, they both die when their boat capsizes during a thunderstorm. The tragedy shatters the old man, and he retreats from reality, living a hermit-like existence. After 4 years, he is roused from his apathy when he hears that Ganguli has built a music room and is planning an extravagant festival. Bishambar reopens his music room, scrapes together the rest of his money, and holds a lavish party. This final victory over his neighbor strains his mental balance; he orders his dead son's horse to be saddled and gallops away toward the river. From the palace steps, his two remaining servants watch as he is thrown from the horse; they arrive in time for him to die in their arms. *Neighbors. Nouveaux riches. Hermits. Domestics. Music. Family life. Envy. Death.*

Note: Produced in India in 1958 and released there as *Jalsaghar*; running time: 100 min.

MUSICAL MUTINY F6.3357

Cinetron Corp. *Dist* CineWorld Corp. 7 May **1970** [New Orleans opening]. Sd; col. 35mm. 74 min. *MPAA rating* G.

Prod Barry Mahon. *Song:* "Soul Experience" Doug Ingle, Ron Bushy, Erik Brann, Lee Dorman. *Song:* "In the Time of Our Lives" Doug Ingle, Ron Bushy. *Song:* "In-A-Gadda-Da-Vida" Doug Ingle.

Cast: Iron Butterfly, Fantasy, The New Society Band, Grit *(themselves)*.

Musical comedy-drama. The Caribbean pirate, Don Williams the Great, returns to life, and comes from the sea to survey the land where he once made his rollicking hideaway. An amusement park called "Pirate's World" now occupies the spot. Don wanders unnoticed around the park, since the attendants are all dressed as buccaneers. The famous rock group Iron Butterfly is scheduled to perform in concert. In the spirit of piracy, Don poses as the park's publicity manager and tells the gatekeeper to allow free admission as a publicity stunt. Rock fans from miles around flock to hear the free music. As Iron Butterfly finishes its first song, an irate manager cancels the free performance. Several local groups fill in, and the young audience loves the music. Spirits are so high that one wealthy hippie agrees to pay the price of the concert if Iron Butterfly will continue. The group agrees, and the show moves on to a wild musical climax. *Pirates. Hippies. Reincarnation. Amusement parks. Rock and roll. Bands.*

MUSIK I MÖRKER see NIGHT IS MY FUTURE

MUSUME TO WATASHI see MY DAUGHTER AND I

THE MUTHERS F6.3358

Hollywood Cinema Associates. *Dist* Crest Film Distributors, Dekko Films. Nov **1968**. Sd; col. 35mm. 74 min.

Cast: Marsha Jordan *(The Mother)*, Kathy Williams *(Susan)*.

Drama. A group of thrill-seeking, Southern California suburban women ignore the effects of their extramarital sexual activities on their children until Susie, teenage daughter of one of the women, mortally wounds her boyfriend when she finds him in bed with her mother. *Housewives. Motherhood. Suburban life. Jealousy. Filial relations. Infidelity. Murder. California.*

Note: Also known as *The Mothers*.

THE MUTINEERS see DAMN THE DEFIANT!

MUTINY IN OUTER SPACE F6.3359

Woolner Bros. Pictures-Hugo Grimaldi Productions. *Dist* Allied Artists. 12 May **1965** [Los Angeles opening; c5 Jun 1964; LP29247]. Sd; b&w. 35mm. 85 min. [Also reviewed at 80 min.]

A Hugo Grimaldi Production. *Prod* Hugo Grimaldi, Arthur C. Pierce. *Exec Prod* Bernard A. Woolner, Lawrence Woolner, David E. Woolner. *Dir* Hugo Grimaldi. *Screenplay* Arthur C. Pierce. *Orig Story* Arthur C. Pierce, Hugo Grimaldi. *Photog* Arch R. Dalzell. *Art Dir* Paul Sylos. *Film Ed* George White. *Mus Dir* Gordon Zahler. *Sd Eff Supv* Gordon Zahler. *Asst Dir* Philip N. Cook. *Prod Mgr* Jack Voglin. *Miniatures* Edwards Art Studios.

Cast: William Leslie *(Major Towers)*, Dolores Faith *(Faith Montaine)*, Pamela Curran *(Connie)*, Richard Garland *(Colonel Cromwell)*, James Dobson *(Dr. Hoffman)*, Carl Crow *(Captain Webber)*, Harold Lloyd, Jr. *(enlisted man)*, Ron Stokes, Robert Palmer, Gabriel Curtis, Glenn Langan.

Science fiction melodrama. Upon returning to their outer space orbiting station after an exploratory mission to the moon, Webber, one of two astronauts, dies of a fungus infection. Faith Montaine, the station biochemist, begins an analysis of the samples brought back by Webber and Towers, his colleague. The station doctor, Hoffman, also contracts the infection and joins Towers in recommending that Earth be notified. Colonel Cromwell, afraid of being recalled, overrules the suggestion, and Tower's and Hoffman's attempt to make contact is foiled by Connie, the communication officer who is in love with Cromwell. A collision with meteors tears a hole in the outer wall of the station, and fungus from the laboratory escapes and surrounds the station. Realizing that the fungus thrives on heat, Hoffman puts himself in a refrigerated tube while Towers leads a mutiny, refrigerates the station, and contacts Earth. Earth scientists then surround the station with sub-zero particles to kill the fungus. *Astronauts. Biochemists. Physicians. Space exploration. Fungi. Meteors. The Moon.*

Note: Working titles: *Space Station-X* and *Invasion From the Moon*. Also known as *Space Station X-14*.

MUTINY ON THE BOUNTY F6.3360

Arcola Pictures. *Dist* Metro-Goldwyn-Mayer, Inc. 8 Nov **1962** [New York opening; c19 Nov 1962; LP24820]. Sd (Westrex); col (Technicolor). 35mm & 70mm (Ultra Panavision 70). 179 min. [Previewed at 185 min.]

Prod Aaron Rosenberg. *Dir (see note)* Lewis Milestone, Carol Reed. *2d Unit Dir* James Havens. *Screenplay (see note)* Charles Lederer, Eric Ambler, William L. Driscoll, Borden Chase, John Gay, Ben Hecht. *Dir Photog* Robert Surtees. *Adtl Photog* Harold E. Wellman. *Col Cons* Charles K. Hagedon. *Art Dir* George W. Davis, J. McMillan Johnson. *Set Decor* Henry Grace, Hugh Hunt. *Film Ed* John McSweeney, Jr. *Assoc Ed* Thomas J. McCarthy. *Mus* Bronislau Kaper. *Orch Cond* Robert Armbruster. *Choreog* Hamil Petroff. *Rec Supv* Franklin Milton. *Asst Dir* Ridgeway Callow. *Cost* Moss Mabry. *Makeup* William Tuttle. *Hairstyles* Mary Keats. *Sp Vis Eff* A. Arnold Gillespie, Lee LeBlanc, Robert R. Hoag. *Tech Adv* Donald MacIntyre, Bengt Danielsson, Aurora Natua, Leo Langomazino.

Cast: Marlon Brando *(Fletcher Christian)*, Trevor Howard *(Capt. William Bligh)*, Richard Harris *(John Mills)*, Hugh Griffith *(Alexander Smith)*, Richard Haydn *(William Brown)*, Tarita *(Maimiti)*, Tim Seely *(Edward Young)*, Percy Herbert *(Matthew Quintal)*, Gordon Jackson *(Edward Birkett)*, Noel Purcell *(William McCoy)*, Duncan Lamont *(John Williams)*, Chips Rafferty *(Michael Byrne)*, Ashley Cowan *(Samuel Mack)*, Eddie Byrne *(John Fryer)*, Keith McConnell *(James Morrison)*, Frank Silvera *(Minarii)*, Ben Wright *(Graves)*, Henry Daniell *(court martial judge)*, Torin Thatcher *(Staines)*, Matahiarii Tama *(Chief Hitihiti)*.

Historical drama. Source: Charles Bernard Nordhoff and James Norman Hall, *Mutiny on the Bounty* (Boston, 1932). In December of 1787, H. M. S. *Bounty* sets sail from Portsmouth, England. Her destination is Tahiti, and her mission is to transplant thousands of breadfruit plants from that island to Jamaica in the hope that the plants will become a food staple for plantation slaves. The vessel is commanded by William Bligh, an experienced but tyrannical captain who quickly arouses the ire of the crew. His first officer is Fletcher Christian, a somewhat foppish country gentleman, though an excellent sailor, whose genteel family background irritates the lowborn Bligh. As a result of Bligh's disastrous attempt to reach Tahiti by rounding Cape Horn in midwinter, the ship loses a month of sailing time and arrives in Tahiti at a time when the breadfruit plants are dormant. Bligh is enraged, but the crew is delighted at the prospect of spending 4 months on the beautiful tropical isle. Once the *Bounty* is again at sea, trouble erupts anew. Goaded on by seaman John Mills and by his own mounting anger against Bligh's cruelty, Christian leads a mutiny and takes control of the ship. Bligh and 18 other men are set adrift in a boat and eventually reach Timor. Christian takes the *Bounty* back to Tahiti to pick up supplies and those natives, including his own beloved Maimiti, who wish to start a new life with the mutineers. Aware that the British Navy will soon send ships in search of them, Christian looks for a new home and eventually finds the remote and uncharted Pitcairn Island. He soon realizes that he and his men must return to England or forever be hunted as criminals, but he loses the possibility of a choice when some of the mutineers set fire to the *Bounty*. In a hopeless attempt to save the ship, Christian is fatally burned. Before dying, he urges his men to stifle their rebellious natures and live in peace with one other. *Sea captains. Sailors. Mutiny. Class conflict. Portsmouth (England). Tahiti. Cape Horn. Pitcairn Island. Timor. Fletcher Christian.*

William Bligh. John Mills. Great Britain—Royal Navy. H. M. S. "Bounty". Ship fires.

Note: Location scenes filmed in Tahiti. Remake of the 1935 M-G-M film of the same title. Carol Reed began directing the 1962 film but was replaced by Lewis Milestone. Charles Lederer is given sole screen credit for writing the screenplay, although Ambler, Driscoll, Chase, Gay, and Hecht assisted.

MY BABY IS BLACK! (France)   F6.3361

Lodice–Général France Film–G. E. F.–Athos Films. *Dist* American Film Distributing Corp., U. S. Films. 10 Feb **1965.** Sd; b&w. 35mm. 75 min. [Originally 90 min.]

Pres by Stan Borden. *Prod-Dir-Orig Screenplay* Claude Bernard-Aubert. *Adtl Dial* Jean Rousselot. *Dir Photog* Jean Collomb. *Film Ed* Claude Bernard-Aubert. *Mus* Michel Magne. *Sd* André Louis. *Prod Asst* Geneviève Cortier.

Cast: Gordon Heath *(Daniel),* Françoise Giret *(Françoise),* Aram Stephan *(The Professor),* Mag-Avril *(The Concierge),* Hervé Watine *(The Guitarist),* Fred Carault *(Françoise's father),* Viviane Méry *(Françoise's mother),* Claude Berri, Jacques Champreux, Arlette Didier, Philippe Prince.

Melodrama. Françoise, a young Parisian who enjoys the company of bohemian friends in the Latin Quarter, meets Daniel, a Negro fellow-student. Although they are immediately attracted to each other, Daniel stresses the obstacles to their love, reluctant to encourage a relationship that Françoise may later regret. She allays his fears, however, and they begin a tender love affair. Françoise becomes pregnant and tries to tell Daniel, but he is enraged by a vicious attack on a fellow black by a group of young toughs, and she does not tell him about the baby. When Françoise confesses her predicament to her parents, they accuse her of disgracing their name. She returns to Daniel, but he is gone, having been arrested for rescuing a small Negro boy who was being maltreated by a shopkeeper. Feeling unloved, Françoise plans to have the baby alone. When the baby is born, however, Daniel appears with a group of their friends to celebrate, and the lovers set out to build a future together. *Students. Negroes. Racial prejudice. Pregnancy. Childbirth. Filial relations. Bohemianism. Miscegenation. Paris.*

Note: Originally released in Paris in Mar 1961 as *Les laches vivent d'espoir.*

MY BARE LADY (Great Britain)   F6.3362

Meadway Productions, Ltd.–Morton M. Lewis. *Dist* Union Film Distributors. 19 Jun **1963** [New York showing]. Sd; col (Eastmancolor). 35mm. 64 min.

Pres by Advent Film Productions. *Prod* Phineas Lonestar, Jr. *Exec Prod* Dick Randall. *Dir* Arthur Knight. *Screenplay* Jervis MacArthur. *Photog* Alf Hicks, Tony Young, photog, Michael Reed, Sidney Davies, Alan Blowey. *Art Dir* Denys Pavitt. *Mus* De Wolfe. *Asst Dir* Cino Bassi.

Cast: Julie Martin *(Tina Murray),* Carl Conway *(Pat Kneely),* Nina Huntredos *(Mrs. Darwell),* Kenneth McLelland *(Mr. O'Hanrahan),* Chantal Delor, Gilly Gerard, Jack Taylor, Bob Bryant, Leslie Crawford.

Nudist film. Tina Murray, an American vacationing in England, meets and falls in love with Pat Kneely, an American Korean War veteran. Taken in by kindly housekeeper Mrs. Darwell, Tina is horrified when she learns that both Pat and Mrs. Darwell are nudists and that she is in a nudist camp. Although she is at first shy and inhibited, Tina eventually comes to enjoy the leisurely life of swimming and sunbathing there. Mrs. Darwell tells her a story about a young couple who met in Paris and were later married in an English nudist camp. *Americans in foreign countries. Housekeepers. Veterans. Tourists. Nudism. Inhibition. Nudist camps. Paris.*

Note: Filmed at Kent Sun Club, Orpington, England. Released in Great Britain in 1963; running time: 59 min. May also be known as *My Seven Little Bares, Bare Lady, Bare World,* and *It's a Bare World.*

MY BLOOD RUNS COLD   F6.3363

Warner Bros. Pictures. 24 Mar **1965** [New York opening; c20 Mar 1965; LP32092]. Sd; b&w. 35mm (Panavision). 104 min.

Prod-Dir William Conrad. *Screenplay* John Mantley. *Story* John Meredyth Lucas. *Dir Photog* Sam Leavitt. *Art Dir* LeRoy Deane. *Set Decor* Ralph S. Hurst. *Film Ed* William Ziegler. *Mus* George Duning. *Sd* Stanley Jones. *Asst Dir* Russell Llewellyn. *Asst to the Prod* James Lydon. *Makeup Supv* Gordon Bau. *Hairstyles* Jean Burt Reilly.

Cast: Troy Donahue *(Ben Gunther),* Joey Heatherton *(Julie Merriday),* Barry Sullivan *(Julian Merriday),* Nicolas Coster *(Harry Lindsay),* Jeanette Nolan *(Aunt Sarah),* Russell Thorson *(sheriff),* Ben Wright *(Lansbury),* Shirley Mitchell *(Mrs. Courtland),* Howard McNear *(Henry),* Howard Wendell *(mayor),* John Holland *(Mr. Courtland),* John McCook *(Owen).*

Melodrama. Wealthy, reckless Californian Julie Merriday, accompanied by her boyfriend Harry Lindsay, an attorney, narrowly avoids crashing into a motorcycle driven by young Ben Gunther. Ben temporarily abandons his damaged cycle and accepts a ride from Julie but insists upon calling her Barbara. Later, at the Merriday beachhouse, Julie's Aunt Sarah tells Julie that her great

great grandmother was named Barbara, and furthermore, that ancestress had an illegitimate child fathered by one Benjamin Gunther. Despite her father's protestations and Ben's irrational conviction that she and he are reincarnations of the past lovers, Julie breaks off with Harry and elopes with Ben. While aboard a small ketch Ben claims he owns, Julie finds the earlier Benjamin's diary, reads of his affair with her ancestress, and realizes that Ben lied. Meanwhile, Mr. Merriday has learned of Ben's escape from an asylum for the criminally insane and his murder of the owner of the ketch. Ben, spotting a police helicopter, beaches the ketch and drags Julie to a sandblasting plant. As rescuers close in, he climbs a tower and tries to strangle the pursuing Harry, but in a fit, he plunges to his death. Once home with Harry, Julie scatters the pages of the diary onto the sea. *Lawyers. Aunts. Police. Reincarnation. Elopement. Insanity. Murder. Sailboats. Diaries. Helicopters. Chases. California. Motorcycle accidents.*

Note: Location scenes filmed in California.

MY BODY HUNGERS   F6.3364

Amalfi Films No. 3. *Dist* Haven International Pictures, Boxoffice International Pictures. Sep **1967.** Sd; b&w. 35mm. 80 min.

Prod Gerard Conti. *Dir-Writ* Joe Sarno. *Cinematog* Anthony Lover. *Asst Camera* Robert Gage. *Final Ed* Kemper Peacock. *Orig Mus* Stan Free. *Sd* Vincent De Leo. *Prod Mgr* Bruce Sparks.

Cast: Gretchen Rudolph *(Marcia Teel),* John Aristedes *(Detective Rod Loring),* Tammy Latour *(Joan Reynolds),* Tony King *(George Harvey),* Liz Love *(Mavis Harvey),* Joe Santos *(truck driver),* Rose Marie Stadler, Rickey Bell, Carolyn Fawcett, Lola Adams *(Olga & Her Oomphettes),* Joy Durden *(pianist/Geri),* George Winship *(Detective Pete Forsythe),* Bob Franklin *(newscaster),* Laurene Claire *(Lynn Phillips),* Geraldine Baron *(Janet Teel),* Pat Powers *(m.c.),* Diane Moss *(waitress),* Brandy Case *(woman clerk).*

Melodrama. In a small New England town, roadhouse hostess Janet Teel is strangled by a sex maniac as her sister Marcia hitchhikes from across the country for a visit. Marcia vows to find the killer, and with the help of Detective Rod Loring, she gets a job at the roadhouse under an assumed name. She mixes with the strippers in an effort to learn all she can about Janet's contacts and discovers that a group of them have formed an after-hours prostitution ring without the knowledge of manager Joan Reynolds. Wealthy George Harvey, whose possessive mother, Mavis, operates the local newspaper, falls in love with Marcia because of her resemblance to Janet, and he reveals that they had planned to elope. One night, Marcia is raped by an unknown assailant as she steps out of the bath. After two attempts are made on her life, she is taken hostage by the killer, George Harvey, who begins to strangle her in his careening car as Detective Loring helplessly watches. Finally, Marcia leaps to safety as the car speeds out of control, and Harvey plunges to his death. *Nightclub hostesses. Nightclub owners. Detectives. Stripteasers. Murder. Rape. Personal identity. Prostitution. New England. Chases.*

MY BROTHER'S WIFE   F6.3365

Juri Productions. *Dist* J. E. R. Pictures. 9 Nov **1966** [Fresno, California, showing]. Sd; b&w. 35mm. 72 min.

Prod-Dir-Writ Doris Wishman. *Photog* Tony Spalla. *Film Ed* Film-Rite Inc. *Mus* Music Sound Recorders. *Sd* Titra Sound Corp. *Sd Eff Ed* Film-Rite Inc.

Cast: June Roberts, Sam Stewart, Bob Oran, S. Stewart, Darlene Bennett, Joni Roberts, D. Swanson.

Melodrama. After 2 years on the road, Frankie Gordon returns home and finds that his older brother Bob has married Mary, a beautiful young woman. Frankie seduces her, and she falls in love with him. Frankie falsely promises to run off to Mexico with her. She cleans out Bob's bank account when Bob discovers that Mary loves Frankie, and he is brokenhearted. Frankie's girl friend Zena leaves town and writes to him asking him to join her with the money he received from Mary. Mary reads the letter and commits suicide. Bob finds his wife's body and threatens to kill Frankie. *Brothers. Newlyweds. Infidelity. Finance—Personal. Suicide.*

MY DAUGHTER AND I (Japan)   F6.3366

Tokyo Eiga Co. *Dist* Toho Co. 1 Feb **1963** [Los Angeles opening]. Sd; b&w. 35mm. [Feature film, length unknown.]

Prod Ichiro Sato. *Dir* Hiromichi Horikawa. *Screenplay* Sakae Hirosawa.

Cast: Yuriko Hoshi *(Mari),* So Yamamura *(Mari's father),* Setsuko Hara *(Mari's mother),* Yoko Aonuma, Reiko Obashi *(Mari as a child),* Françoise Mollechand *(French wife),* Haruko Sugimura *(aunt).*

Domestic drama. Based on the serial by: Bunroku Shishi, "Musume to watashi," in *Shufu no tomo* (Jan 1953–May 1956). A distinguished writer is left to rear his 4-year-old daughter, Mari, when his French wife dies from tuberculosis. Placed in a convent, the child becomes seriously ill. Realizing his neglect, the father takes Mari home and arranges to remarry, thus providing his daughter with a mother and allowing himself more time to devote to his writing. The new wife cherishes Mari, although she and the writer never consummate their marriage. The family grows closer, despite the writer's inability to sell his work, the daughter's racial harassment at school, and the wife's unrequited yearning for affection. By the end of World War II, the author has gained success but is left again to tend Mari alone when his wife dies of a heart attack. Mari, now 20 years old, decides to leave home and marry. *Authors. French. Widowers. Halfcastes. Children. Family life. Fatherhood. Marriage. Miscegenation. Racial prejudice. Tuberculosis. Convents.*

Note: Released in Japan in 1962 as *Musume to watashi.*

MY DAYS WITH JEAN-MARC *see* ANATOMY OF A MARRIAGE; MY DAYS WITH JEAN-MARC

MY ENEMY, THE SEA (Japan) F6.3367

Ishihara International Productions. 15 Apr **1964** [San Francisco opening]. Sd; col (Eastmancolor). 35mm (CinemaScope, see note). 100 min. [Also 97 min.]

Prod Akira Nakai. *Assoc Prod* Isao Zeniya. *Dir* Kon Ichikawa. *Screenplay* Natto Wada. *Photog* Yoshihiro Yamazaki. *Art Dir* Takashi Matsuyama. *Film Ed* Masanori Tsujii. *Mus* Yasushi Akutagawa, Toru Takemitsu. *Sd* Fumio Hashimoto. *Prod Mgr* Isao Zeniya.

Cast: Yujiro Ishihara *(The Youth, Ken'ichi Horie)*, Masayuki Mori *(His Father)*, Kinuyo Tanaka *(His Mother)*, Ruriko Asaoka *(His Sister)*, Hajime Hana *(His Friend)*, Gannosuke Ashinoya *(ship's carpenter)*, Shiro Osaka *(shipyard master)*.

Adventure drama. Based on the log-book by: Ken'ichi Horie, *Taiheiyo hitoribotchi* (Tokyo, 1963). For years, 23-year-old Ken'ichi Horie has dreamed of sailing his 18-foot yacht, *Mermaid*, across the Pacific. Despite the opposition of his father and friends and his mother's apprehension, he persists in his determination and outfits his boat. One night, in 1962, he leaves without telling anyone. Ken'ichi sneaks out of Osaka Bay without papers and must elude the coast guard. Once on the open sea, he runs into bad weather and also gets sick. Worse, the winds are forcing him back to Japan. Ken'ichi manages to surmount this hazard as he does all others: the rough seas, a typhoon, loneliness, and all the inherent dangers of a solo sea voyage. Through flashbacks, mirroring his thoughts, his life and character are revealed: during the typhoon he longs for his mother; a drifting newspaper picture reminds him of his dog at home. When Ken'ichi reaches Hawaii, a large American ship passes him, but he refuses all help. Instead he sails on, finally reaching San Francisco, and sails under the Golden Gate Bridge in triumph. *Sailors. Typhoons. Filial relations. Yachts. Osaka. San Francisco. Hawaii. Pacific Ocean. Ken'ichi Horie. The Sea.*

Note: Location scenes filmed in San Francisco and Hawaii. Released in Japan in 1963 as *Taiheiyo hitoribotchi;* running time: 104 min. Japanese release in CinemaScope; wide-screen process for U. S. release uncertain. Shown at the 1963 San Francisco International Film Festival as *The Enemy, the Sea* and at the 1964 New York Film Festival as *Alone on the Pacific.*

MY FAIR LADY F6.3368

Warner Bros. Pictures-First National Pictures. *Dist* Warner Bros. Pictures. 21 Oct **1964** [New York opening; c23 Apr 1964; LP33509]. Sd; col (Technicolor). 35mm & 70mm (Super Panavision 70). 170 min.

Prod Jack L. Warner. *Dir* George Cukor. *Screenplay* Alan Jay Lerner. *Dir Photog* Harry Stradling. *Art Dir* Gene Allen. *Scenery Dsgn* Cecil Beaton. *Set Decor* George James Hopkins. *Prod Dsgn* Cecil Beaton. *Film Ed* William Ziegler. *Mus* Frederick Loewe. *Lyr* Alan Jay Lerner. *Vocal Arr* Robert Tucker. *Orch* Alexander Courage, Robert Franklyn, Al Woodbury. *Mus Supv & Cond* Andre Previn. *Singing Voice for Audrey Hepburn* Marni Nixon. *Singing Voice for Jeremy Brett* Bill Shirley. *Choreog* Hermes Pan. *Sd* Francis J. Scheid, Murray Spivack. *Asst Dir* David Hall. *Unit Mgr* Sergei Petschnikoff. *Cost Dsgn* Cecil Beaton. *Makeup* Gordon Bau. *Supv Hairstylist* Jean Burt Reilly.

Cast: Audrey Hepburn *(Eliza Doolittle)*, Rex Harrison *(Henry Higgins)*, Stanley Holloway *(Alfred Doolittle)*, Wilfrid Hyde-White *(Colonel Pickering)*, Gladys Cooper *(Mrs. Higgins)*, Jeremy Brett *(Freddie Eynsford-Hill)*, Theodore Bikel *(Zoltan Karpathy)*, Mona Washbourne *(Mrs. Pearce)*, Isobel Elsom *(Mrs. Eynsford-Hill)*, John Holland *(butler)*, John Alderson, John McLiam *(Doolittle's cronies)*, Veronica Rothschild *(Queen of Transylvania)*, Marjorie Bennett *(Cockney with pipe)*, Barbara Pepper *(Doolittle's dancing partner)*, Owen McGivney *(man at coffee stand)*, Betty Blythe *(ad lib at ball)*, Henry Daniell *(Prince of Transylvania)*, Alan Napier *(ambassador)*, Jack Greening *(George)*, Ron Whelan *(Algernon/bartender)*, Dinah Anne Rogers, Lois Battle *(maids)*, Jacqueline Squire *(parlor maid)*, Gwendolyn Watts *(cook)*, Charles Fredericks *(king)*, Lily Kemble-Cooper *(lady ambassador)*, Moyna MacGill *(Lady Boxington)*, Ben Wright *(footman at ball)*, Oscar Beregi *(Greek ambassador)*, Buddy Bryan *(prince)*, Nick Navarro *(dancer)*, Jennifer Crier *(Mrs. Higgins' maid)*, Olive Reeves-Smith *(Mrs. Hopkins)*, Miriam Schiller *(landlady)*, Ayllene Gibbons *(fat woman at pub)*, Grady Sutton *(Ascot extra/ guest at ball)*, Major Sam Harris *(guest at ball)*, Queenie Leonard.

Musical comedy. Source: George Bernard Shaw, *Pygmalion* (London opening: 11 Apr 1914). Alan Jay Lerner and Frederick Loewe, *My Fair Lady* (New York opening: 15 Mar 1956). Phonetics professor Henry Higgins gets involved in an altercation with Cockney flowergirl Eliza Doolittle as he is taking notes on her speaking accent outside of London's Covent Garden in 1912. Colonel Pickering, another language enthusiast, quiets the argument, and Higgins boasts to him that after training Eliza for 3 months he could pass her off as a duchess. The next day Eliza arrives at Higgins' house, prepared to pay for diction lessons so that she may realize her dream of obtaining a position in a shop. With Pickering's help, Higgins begins a complete transformation of Eliza. Her first public appearance at the Ascot horseraces is a dubious success. A few months later, Eliza is a greater success at the season's biggest social event. After the affair, Higgins and Pickering congratulate each other on Eliza's transformation, completely ignoring her and her part in the process. She leaves Higgins' house in anger. Finding her father preparing to marry, Eliza seeks refuge with Higgins' mother. She is paid court to by Freddie Eynsford-Hill, a young admirer. Higgins finds Eliza at his mother's, but they quarrel and he returns home. Sitting alone in his study, Higgins realizes that he cannot be happy without Eliza. As he sits listening to recordings of her voice made during her diction lessons, Eliza quietly enters the room through the door behind him. *Songs:* "Why Can't the English?" (Higgins), "Wouldn't It Be Loverly?" (Eliza and chorus), "I'm an Ordinary Man" (Higgins), "With a Little Bit of Luck" (Alfred Doolittle, Harry, Jamie), "Just You Wait" (Eliza), "The Servant's Chorus" (servants), "The Rain in Spain" (Eliza, Higgins, Pickering), "I Could Have Danced All Night" (Eliza and maids), "Ascot Gavotte" (chorus), "On the Street Where You Live" (Freddie), "The Embassy Waltz" (instrumental), "You Did It" (Pickering, Higgins, servants), "Show Me" (Eliza), "The Flower Market" (instrumental), "Get Me to the Church on Time" (Doolittle, chorus), "A Hymn to Him" (Higgins), "Without You" (Eliza), "I've Grown Accustomed to Her Face" (Higgins). *Cockneys. Professors. Flower vendors. Phonetics. Marriage. Horseracing. Social classes. Filial relations. Recorders. London. Ascot. Covent Garden.*

MY FATHER'S MISTRESS *see* BAMSE

MY FIRST TIME F6.3369

Dist Able Film Co. ca **1970**. Sd; col. 16mm. [Feature length assumed.]

Sex film. No information about the precise nature of this film has been found. *Sexual initiation.*

MY GEISHA F6.3370

Sachiko Productions. *Dist* Paramount Pictures. 13 Jun **1962** [New York showing; c31 Dec 1961; LP22371]. Sd; col (Technicolor). 35mm (Technirama). 120 min.

Prod Steve Parker. *Dir* Jack Cardiff. *Screenplay* Norman Krasna. *Cinematog* Shunichiro Nakao. *2d Unit Photog* Stanley Sayer. *Art Dir* Hal Pereira, Arthur Lonergan, Makoto Kikuchi. *Film Ed* Archie Marshek. *Mus* Franz Waxman. *Song:* "You Are Sympathy to Me" Hal David, Franz Waxman. *Selections from "Madame Butterfly"* Giacomo Puccini. *Sd* Harold Lewis, Charles Grenzbach. *Asst Dir* Harry Kratz. *Prod Mgr* Harry Caplan. *Cost* Edith Head. *Makeup* Frank Westmore. *Dial Dir* George Tyne.

Cast: Shirley MacLaine *(Lucy Dell/Yoko Mori)*, Yves Montand *(Paul Robaix)*, Edward G. Robinson *(Sam Lewis)*, Bob Cummings *(Bob Moore)*, Yoko Tani *(Kazumi Ito)*, Tatsuo Saito *(Kenichi Takata)*, Alex Gerry *(Leonard Lewis)*, Nobuo Chiba *(Shig)*, Ichiro Hayakawa *(Hisako Amatsu)*, George Furness *(George)*, Tamae Kiyokawa, Tsugundo Maki.

Comedy. Irritated because he is known merely as the director of his wife Lucy's pictures, Paul Robaix decides to go to Japan and make an art film starring an unknown geisha in the title role of Puccini's *Madama Butterfly*. The outraged Lucy, accompanied by producer Sam Lewis, follows Paul to Japan and disguises herself as a geisha. When Paul sees her in a tea house and fails to recognize her, she assumes the name of Yoko Mori, takes lessons from Kazumi, a real geisha, passes a screen test and becomes Paul's new discovery. Complications arise when her wolfish leading man, Bob Moore, falls in love with her and asks Paul to help him win Yoko's hand. Shortly before filming is completed, Paul accidentally discovers the deception. Deeply hurt, he feels Lucy has deprived him of his one chance to win recognition without her support. But when *Madama Butterfly* premieres in Tokyo, Lucy, now wise in the ways of a geisha, appears as herself and tells the applauding audience that Yoko Mori has entered a convent and retired from the screen. She then proudly introduces her husband and gives him the entire credit for the picture. *Actors. Motion picture directors. Motion picture producers. Geishas. Disguise. Jealousy. Marriage. Motion pictures. Opera. Tea houses. Japan. Tokyo. "Madama Butterfly".*

Note: Filmed on location in Japan.

MY GIRLFRIEND'S WEDDING
F6.3371

Paradigm Films. *Dist* Paradigm Films, New Yorker Films. 21 Dec **1969** [New York showing]. Sd; col (Kodachrome). 16mm. 60 min.

Dir-Writ Jim McBride. *Photog* Michael Wadley. *Film Ed* Jim McBride, Mike Levine. *Mus* Al Kooper.

Film diary. An Englishwoman lives with her lover, a filmmaker, in New York City. The subject of his film, she reveals herself to the camera, beginning by describing the objects in her purse; discussing her 7-year-old son, her abortions, her former lovers; and reading a letter from her father, whose longstanding sexual interest in her prompts her to disclose some deep resentments about him. Subsequently, in a face-to-face interview with the filmmaker, she explains that her visitor's permit is about to expire. In order to remain in the United States she plans to marry an acquaintance, the Red Menace, a casual anarchist who has political reasons for entering into this marriage of convenience. The wedding, with the filmmaker/lover present as a witness, takes place in the municipal building; and afterwards the three sit in a sidewalk cafe and argue the pros and cons of the new bride starting a new job in a restaurant before bidding the Red Menace goodby. The next day she describes a visit to a doctor to have a pregnancy test. Finally, in a sequence of rapid shots of the American landscape, the filmmaker and the Englishwoman drive to California. *English. Filmmakers. Anarchists. Marriage of convenience. Naturalization. Pregnancy. Abortion. Motherhood. Filial relations. Weddings. New York City.*

MY GUN IS JAMMED see THE BARE HUNT; OR MY GUN IS JAMMED

MY HOBO (Japan)
F6.3372

Tokyo Eiga Co. *Dist* Toho International, Inc. 23 Jul **1963** [New York opening]. Sd; col (Eastmancolor). 35mm. 98 min.

Exec Prod Sanezumi Fujimoto, Hideyuki Shiino. *Dir-Writ* Zenzo Matsuyama. *Photog* Hiroshi Murai. *Mus* Hikaru Hayashi.

Cast: Keiju Kobayashi *(Jumpei)*, Hideko Takamine *(Komako)*, Norihei Miki *(Takeo)*, Reiko Dan *(Mariko)*.

Comedy. Jumpei, a hobo, has managed to collect a small fortune through begging and petty thievery. He keeps this money taped to his side as he wanders through the Japanese countryside. After refusing to pay for a meal, Jumpei is arrested and meets Komako, a woman hobo. Komako makes a living by fraudulently collecting money for atomic bomb victims [or by claiming to be a bomb victim herself]. They travel together until one night Komako gets Jumpei drunk and steals his money. Jumpei wanders on alone, looking for her, and along the way picks up two abandoned children, Takeo and Mariko. The three of them return to Jumpei's home, and he finds a letter from Komako saying that she is in Tokyo and inviting him to marry her when he is prepared to find a job and settle down. He sets off for Tokyo with the children, and after many adventures trying to provide for himself and his charges, he finally finds her. She reveals that she has invested his money; and the future looks bright for the four of them. *Hoboes. Beggars. Children. Fraud. Theft. Adoption. Tokyo.*

Note: Released in Japan in 1960 as *Burari burabura monogatari.*

MY HUSTLER
F6.3373

Dist Film-Makers' Distribution Center, Andy Warhol Films. Oct **1965** [New York opening]. Sd; b&w. 16mm. 72 min.

Prod-Dir Andy Warhol. *Co-dir & Writ* Chuck Wein. *Photog* Andy Warhol. *Prod Asst* Paul Morrissey.

Cast: Paul America *(hustler)*, Ed Hood *("john")*, Ed Wiener *(balding man)*, John MacDermott *(houseboy)*, S. P. Farry *(2d hustler)*, Genevieve Charbon *(next door neighbor)*, Jeanne Vieve *(beach girl)*, Joseph Campbell *(Sugar Plum Fairy)*, Dorothy Dean *(hustler's prospective client)*, Arthur Hooks.

Drama. A wealthy, balding homosexual hires a young blond hustler to spend a weekend with him at his summer cottage on Fire Island, New York. As the young man suns himself on the beach, the older man boasts of his "possession" to a female neighbor who delights in trying to entice young hustlers away from their weekend lovers. When an older hustler joins them on the porch of the beachhouse, the balding man bets his two companions that they cannot lure away his blond houseguest. After the young woman has made an unsuccessful attempt to do so, the older hustler joins the younger man in the bathroom of the beachhouse. As they shower and shave, they discuss the life of a professional hustler, its rewards and its drawbacks. Their lengthy conversation is interrupted several times as other people, including the balding man, stop by to chat with the young hustler. Through it all, however, he remains noncommittal, seemingly indifferent to the swarm of admirers competing for his attention. *Prostitutes. Male homosexuality. Fire Island.*

Note: Filmed on Fire Island, New York.

MY LAST DUCHESS see ARRIVEDERCI, BABY!

MY LIFE TO LIVE (France)
F6.3374

Films de la Pléiade. *Dist* Union Film Distributors, Pathé Contemporary Films. 23 Sep **1963** [New York opening]. Sd; b&w. 35mm. 85 min. [Also reviewed at 80 min.]

Prod Pierre Braunberger. *Dir-Writ* Jean-Luc Godard. *Adtl Narr (see note)* Judge Marcel Sacotte. *Photog* Raoul Coutard. *Asst Photog* Claude Beausoleil. *Asst Camera* Charles Bitsch. *Film Ed* Agnès Guillemot. *Asst Ed* Lila Lakshmanan. *Mus* Michel Legrand. *Song:* "Ma môme, elle joue pas les starlettes" Jean Ferrat, Pierre Frachet. *Sd* Guy Villette, Jacques Maumont. *Sd Asst* Jean Philippe. *Asst Dir* Bernard Toublanc-Michel, Jean-Paul Savignac. *Prod Supv* Roger Fleytoux. *Prod Mgr* Jean-François Adam. *Prod Sec* Ida Fassio. *Script Girl* Suzanne Schiffman. *Cost* Christiane Fageol. *Makeup* Jackie Reynal. *Hairstyles* Simone Knapp. *Created by* Alexandre of Paris.

Cast: Anna Karina *(Nana)*, Saddy Rebbot *(Raoul)*, André S. Labarthe *(Paul)*, Giselle Schlumberger *(Yvette)*, Gérard Hoffman *(The Cook)*, Monique Messine *(Elizabeth)*, Paul Pavel *(a journalist)*, Dimitri Dineff *(a youth)*, Peter Kassowitz *(a young man)*, Eric Schlumberger *(Luigi)*, Brice Parain *(The Philosopher)*, Henri Attal *(Arthur)*, Gilles Quéant *(a man)*, Odile Geoffroy *(barmaid)*, Marcel Charton *(a policeman)*, Jack Florency *(a bystander)*, Gisèle Hauchecorne *(concierge)*, Jean-Luc Godard *(voice)*.

Melodrama. Twelve episodes trace the story of Nana, a Parisian streetwalker. Separated from her husband, Nana takes a position as a salesclerk in a record shop. She attends a showing of Carl Dreyer's *La Passion de Jeanne d'Arc*, and it makes her weep. She drifts from one affair to another until she meets an old friend, a prostitute, and, beset by financial difficulties, she also becomes a prostitute working for Raoul, a pimp. Later, she meets and begins an affair with a young student. Her love for the boy grows, and after a philosophic conversation with an acquaintance, Nana decides to break with Raoul. The procurer, however, wants to "sell" Nana to another procurer because the girl has refused a cash customer. Before she has a chance to end her association with Raoul, he gets into a quarrel with the procurer to whom he wished to sell Nana, and as gun shots are exchanged between the two, Nana is killed in the crossfire. *Salesclerks. Pimps. Students. Separation (marital). Prostitution. Finance—Personal. Paris. "Passion de Jeanne d'Arc". "The Oval Portrait".*

Note: Filmed on location in Paris. Opened in Paris in Sep 1962 as *Vivre sa vie.* Portions of Judge Marcel Sacotte's work *Où en est la prostitution?* are read in the narrative. The voice of Jean-Luc Godard is dubbed onto the soundtrack when Nana's lover reads Edgar Allan Poe's "The Oval Portrait."

MY LOVER, MY SON (United States/Great Britain)
F6.3375

Sagittarius Productions. *Dist* Metro-Goldwyn-Mayer, Inc. 13 May **1970** [New York opening; c31 Dec 1969; LP38147]. Sd; col (Metrocolor). 35mm. 96 min. *MPAA rating* R.

Prod Wilbur Stark. *Dir* John Newland. *Screenplay* William Marchant, Jenni Hall. *Dir Photog* David Muir. *Camera Op* Moray Grant. *Art Dir* Bill Andrews. *Titl Col Eff Created by* Carlotta Brown, Michael Hanaker. *Film Ed* Peter Musgrave. *Mus & Mus Dir* Mike Vickers, Norrie Paramor. *Songs:* "I Want the Good Things," "What's on Your Mind," "Summer's Here" Mike Vickers, Sue Vickers, Norrie Paramor. *Sd Ed* Bill Creed. *Sd Rec* Gerry Turner. *Dub Mix* J. B. Smith. *Asst Dir* David Alexander. *Prod Mgr* Al Marcus. *Location Mgr* Alec Gibb. *Cost Dsgn* Gail Ansell.

Cast: Romy Schneider *(Francesca Anderson)*, Donald Houston *(Robert)*, Dennis Waterman *(James)*, Patricia Brake *(Julie)*, Peter Sallis *(Sir Sidney Brent)*, William Dexter *(Parks)*, Alexandra Bastedo *(Cicely Clarkson)*, Mark Hawkins *(Macer)*, Maggie Wright *(prostitute)*, Janet Brown *(Mrs. Woods)*, Tom Chatto *(Mr. Woods)*, Michael Forest *(Detective Inspector Chidley)*, Peter Gilmore *(barman)*, Rosalie Horner *(receptionist)*, Arthur Howard *(judge)*, Chrissie Shrimpton *(Kenworthy's girl friend)*, David Warbeck *(Kenworthy)*, Robert Wilde *(Parks's assistant)*, Cleo Sylvestre *(dressmaker)*, Paul Dawkins *(foreman of the jury)*.

Melodrama. Source: Wilbur Stark, "Second Level" (a short story; publication undetermined). Edward Grierson, *Reputation for a Song* (London, 1966). Depressed by the drowning of her lover and her unhappy marriage to Robert, a wealthy but insensitive man, Francesca Anderson becomes increasingly dependent on her son James. Robert, who sees the potential problems of the relationship, enrolls James in a university in London so that he will have to leave home. Francesca tries to persuade James to remain with her, but he goes to London and meets Julie, with whom he has sex for the first time. Upon returning home from a trip, Robert finds James and Francesca locked in an embrace, and a violent quarrel ensues. Francesca and James leave together. Robert follows them and fights with James, who knocks him to the ground with a golf club and then falls back in a daze; while James is unconscious, Francesca murders her husband with the club. Subsequently James is tried for murder but acquitted on the grounds that he was defending his mother. Later, when he learns that Francesca was the murderer and that her dead lover was his real father, he abandons her and returns to Julie. *Students. Infidelity. Incest. Oedipus complex. Sexual initiation. Murder. Trials. Illegitimacy. London.*

Note: Filmed on location in England. Released in Great Britain in 1970. Prerelease title: *Don't You Cry.* Working title: *Hush-a-Bye Murder.*

MY MOUNTAIN, SONG 27   **F6.3376**
Dist Brakhage, Canyon Cinema Cooperative. 28 Feb **1969** [New York opening]. Si; col. 8mm. ca62 min. [See note.]

Dir Stan Brakhage. *Assoc* Jane Brakhage. *Photog* Stan Brakhage. *Film Ed* Stan Brakhage.

Experimental film. The first reel (ca30 min) is a study of Arapahoe Peak in Colorado, in which the mountain's unity with its surroundings is emphasized. The mountain is shown in all the seasons of the 2 years during which it was photographed, at all times of the day, in many colors and exposures. The second reel, "Rivers," consists of eight short films which expand on the unity of the mountain with its surroundings. Each "River" begins with shots of the mountain or clouds. The first four "Rivers" include images of fire and a street scene as well as the mountain and the sky. "Five" brings the previous four "Rivers" together, utilizing footage from each of them. "Six" is comprised primarily of shots of motionless horses and leads into "Seven," which shows familiar human activities. "Eight" returns to the mountain as the film's central image. *Nature. Arapahoe Peak.*

Note: Photographed in large part one frame at a time; comprised of shots lasting only a few seconds. Although it is assumed that both reels were shown at the film's opening, they were released separately, each in two versions. The first reel was released as *My Mountain, Song 27* in 26 and 50 min versions by Brakhage and Canyon, respectively; *Rivers* was released in 36 and 50 min versions. Also known as *Song 27.*

MY NAME IS IVAN (U.S.S.R.)   **F6.3377**
Mosfilm. *Dist* Sig Shore. 26 Jun **1963** [New York opening]. Sd; b&w. 35mm. 95 min. [Also reviewed at 84 min.]

Dir Andrey Tarkovskiy. *Screenplay* Vladimir Osipovich Bogomolov, Mikhail Papava. *Story Ed* E. Smirnov. *Photog* Vadim Yusov. *Art Dir* Ye. Chernyayev. *Film Ed* L. Feyginova. *Mus* Vyacheslav Ovchinnikov. *Cond* E. Khachaturyan. *Sd* E. Zelentsova. *Asst Dir* G. Natanson. *Prod Mgr* G. Kuznetsov. *Makeup* L. Baskakova. *Sp Eff* V. Sevostyanov, S. Mukhin. *Military Cons* G. Goncharov.

Cast: Kolya Burlyayev *(Ivan),* Valentin Zubkov *(Captain Kholin),* Ye. Zharikov *(Lieutenant Galtsev),* S. Krylov *(Corporal Katasonov),* N. Grinko *(Colonel Gryaznov),* D. Milyutenko *(old man),* V. Malyavina *(Masha),* I. Tarkovskaya *(Ivan's mother),* A. Konchalovskiy, Ivan Savkin, V. Marenkov, Vera Miturich.

War melodrama. Source: Vladimir Osipovich Bogomolov, *Ivan* (a short story; Moscow, 1959). Having lost his father, mother, and sister in the early days of World War II, 12-year-old Ivan thinks only of vengeance. All that remains of his childhood appears at night in his restless dreams. Joining a military intelligence unit, he moves behind enemy lines in the Pripet Marshes, reporting on troop movements and locations of equipment and supplies. The proud, resolute boy is well liked by his superior Captain Kholin and by Colonel Gryaznov, the head of the intelligence unit. They decide, however, that he should be placed in a school to the rear, away from the dangers of war. Rebelling against the plan, Ivan runs away but returns shortly and is permitted to rejoin the group. He is given a dangerous assignment: to cross the river and gather information on the enemy's strength. On a cold autumn night, the boy makes the crossing and disappears into the dark forest. After the victory of the Soviet army, Captain Kholin and Lieutenant Galtsev, another of Ivan's friends, are sorting captured Gestapo documents when they find a dossier containing the boy's picture. Across his face is stamped the word "executed." *Gestapo. War victims. Childhood. Revenge. Combat zone life. Resistance (political). World War II. Polesye. Union of Soviet Socialist Republics—Army—Intelligence.*

Note: Released in the U.S.S.R. in May 1962 as *Ivanovo detstvo.* Also known as *Ivan's Childhood.*

MY NAME IS WOMAN (France)   **F6.3378**
PRI. *Dist* Astro-Jemco Film Distributors. Sep **1970** [periodical notice]. Sd; b&w. 35mm. 82 min.

Cast: Ellen Bahl, Dany Domange.

Melodrama. Bored with her marriage, Adrian begins to experiment with unconventional sex when her husband, Warren, leaves on an extended business trip. With the help of her friend Rene, Adrian has several affairs and eventually ends up in bed with Rene and her lover, Tony. She meets Maurice, a hippie, who after having sex with her, sells her favors for cash. She burns the ill-gotten money and throws him out, but he later returns with a group of his friends, and they gang rape Adrian in the midst of a wild orgy. Adrian, after another

encounter with Rene and Tony, becomes aware of her degradation and unsuccessfully attempts suicide. Warren returns home during her recuperation, and inspires her to give her marriage another chance. *Housewives. Businessmen. Hippies. Pimps. Infidelity. Marriage. Troilism. Rape. Group sex. Suicide.*

Note: Original language title and French release not found.

MY NIGHT AT MAUD'S (France)   **F6.3379**
F. F. P.–Les Films du Losange–Films du Carrosse–Renn Productions–Films des Deux Mondes–Productions de la Guéville–Simar-Films-Films de la Pléiade. *Dist* Pathé Contemporary Films. 22 Mar **1970** [New York opening]. Sd; b&w. 35mm. 105 min. *MPAA rating* GP.

Prod Pierre Cottrell, Barbet Schroeder. *Dir-Writ* Eric Rohmer. *Photog* Nestor Almendros. *1st & 2d Asst Op* Emmanuel Machuel, Philippe Rousselot. *Art Dir* Nicole Rachline. *Film Ed* Cécile Decugis. *Asst Film Ed* Christine Lecouvette. *Sd* Jean-Pierre Ruh. *Sd Mix* Jacques Maumont. *Asst Sd* Alain Sempé. *Asst Dir* Pierre Grimberg. *Prod Supv* Pierre Cottrell. *Prod Mgr* Alfred de Graaff. *Ch Electrn* Jean-Claude Gasché.

Cast: Jean-Louis Trintignant *(Jean-Louis),* Françoise Fabian *(Maud),* Marie-Christine Barrault *(Françoise),* Antoine Vitez *(Vidal),* Léonide Kogan *(concert violinist),* Anne Dubot *(blonde friend),* Guy Léger *(preacher),* Marie Becker *(Marie, Maud's daughter).*

Drama. Jean-Louis, a 32-year-old Catholic engineer living a solitary life in Clermont-Ferrand, regularly sees a student, Françoise, at Mass but is too shy to approach her. One evening Jean-Louis meets Vidal, an old school friend, now a Marxist and philosophy professor. They have a Christmas drink together, and afterwards Vidal invites Jean-Louis to join him for dinner at the apartment of his friend Maud, a recent divorcée and intellectual with whom he has been conducting a rather dispirited affair. The dinner is a success, Pascal's philosophy and the relationship of principle to practice being the primary topics of conversation. Vidal finally excuses himself, suggesting that Jean-Louis avoid the inclement weather by staying in Maud's spare room; and Jean-Louis, who has drunk too much wine, gives in to the coaxing of Vidal and Maud. On a personal note, Maud tells Jean-Louis about the breakup of her marriage: her husband became involved with a student, a devout Catholic. She then reveals that she has no spare room; and, irresistibly witty and charming, she tries to seduce him. He insists on remaining chaste, having resolved to sleep in a chair. Although he later joins her on the bed, they do not make love. They part on friendly terms the next morning, and Jean-Louis finds the courage to introduce himself to Françoise. Jean-Louis and Françoise fall in love, though Jean-Louis continues for a time to see Maud. Françoise confesses that she once had an affair with a married man, but Jean-Louis forgives her, implying that he recently had an affair with a divorcée. Five years later Jean-Louis and Françoise, now married, meet Maud at the seashore: Françoise and Maud recognize each other, whereupon Jean-Louis realizes that Françoise was the student in Maud's former husband's life. He quickly forestalls his wife's embarrassment by telling her that Maud was the divorcée he slept with in the past. *Catholics. Engineers. Intellectuals. Students. Professors. Philosophy. Seduction. Divorce. Chastity. Marriage. Infidelity. Marxism. Confession. Christmas. Clermont-Ferrand. Blaise Pascal.*

Note: Opened in Paris in Jun 1969 as *Ma nuit chez Maud;* running time: 110 min.

MY NIGHTS WITH FRANÇOISE *see* **ANATOMY OF A MARRIAGE; MY NIGHTS WITH FRANÇOISE**

MY SEVEN LITTLE BARES *see* **MY BARE LADY**

MY SIDE OF THE MOUNTAIN (United States/Canada)   **F6.3380**
Robert B. Radnitz Productions. *Dist* Paramount Pictures. Mar **1969** [Los Angeles opening: 28 May; c31 Dec 1968; LP36736]. Sd; col (Technicolor). 35mm (Panavision). 100 min. *MPAA rating* G.

Prod Robert B. Radnitz. *Dir* James B. Clark. *Screenplay* Ted Sherdeman, Jane Klove, Joanna Crawford. *Photog* Denys Coop. *Art Dir* George Lack. *Set Decor* Johnny Allett. *Film Ed* Peter Thornton, Alastair McIntyre. *Mus* Wilfred Josephs. *Cond* Muir Mathieson. *Sd* Gordon Everett. *Asst Dir* Tom Glynn, Ray Freeborn. *Prod Mgr* Clifton Brandon.

Cast: Teddy Eccles *(Sam Gribley),* Theodore Bikel *(Bando),* Tudi Wiggins *(Miss Turner),* Frank Perry, actor *(Mr. Gribley),* Peggi Loder *(Mrs. Gribley),* Gina Dick *(daughter no. 1),* Karen Pearson *(daughter no. 2),* Danny McIlravey *(little boy),* Cosette Lee *(Mrs. Fielder),* Larry Reynolds *(hunter no. 1),* Tom Harvey *(hunter no. 2),* Paul Hébert *(hunter no. 3),* Ralph Endersby *(1st boy),* George Allan *(2d boy),* Patrick Pervion *(ranger),* Ed Persons, Max Rosenbloom.

Drama. Source: Jean Craighead George, *My Side of the Mountain* (New York, 1969). Disappointed when his father reneges on a promised camping trip, Sam Gribley, a 13-year-old Canadian boy, decides to emulate his hero, Thoreau, by living close to nature. Explaining in a note to his parents that he intends to live on his own for a year, Sam packs his camping equipment and sets out with his pet raccoon, Gus, for the Laurentian Mountains. After traveling by bus and foot, he finds a mountain meadow near a stream and makes a home for himself in a hollow tree trunk. While conducting algae experiments, learning to forage for food, and hiding from people who pass his campsite, Sam decides to capture and train a baby falcon, a project that succeeds largely because of a trip to town and a helpful discussion with Miss Turner, a friendly librarian. One day Bando, an itinerant folksinger, happens upon Sam's hideout, and a warm friendship develops between the two as Bando contributes to the boy's knowledge of survival tactics. When it is time for Bando to move on, Sam asks him to mail a letter he has written to his parents. With the coming of winter, Sam suffers his first sorrow when a passing hunter kills his pet falcon. This, accompanied by the increasing cold, begins to depress his spirits. On Christmas Day, he awakens to find himself frozen by ice and snow inside his tree house. He is rescued by the timely arrival of Bando and Miss Turner, who has brought him a Christmas dinner. While they are finishing their holiday feast, Bando shows Sam newspaper clippings on the extensive search his parents have been conducting for their son. Touched by their concern and satisfied that he has accomplished what he set out to do, Sam takes Gus and leaves for home. *Runaways. Librarians. Singers. Adolescence. Nature. Survival. Friendship. Animals—Domestication. Winter. Christmas. Laurentian Mountains. Henry David Thoreau. Raccoons. Falcons.*

Note: Filmed on location in Toronto and Knowlton, Quebec.

MY SISTER, MY LOVE (Sweden)   **F6.3381**
Sandrews. *Dist* Sigma III Corp. 19 Feb **1967** [New York opening]. Sd; b&w. 35mm. 97 min.

Prod Göran Lindgren. *Dir-Writ* Vilgot Sjöman. *Photog* Lars Björne. *Art Dir* P. A. Lundgren. *Film Ed* Lennart Wallen. *Prod Mgr* Bertil Ohlsson. *Cost* Björn Nelstedt.

Cast: Per Oscarsson (*Jacob [Jakob]*), Bibi Andersson (*Charlotte*), Jarl Kulle (*Alsmeden*), Gunnar Björnstrand (*Count Schwartz*), Tina Hedström (*Ebba Livin*), Berta Hall (*Mrs. Kuller*), Åke Lindström (*Mrs. Kuller's son*), Rune Lindström (*Pastor Storck*), Sonya Hedenbratt (*Mrs. Storck*), Gudrun Östbye (*dressmaker*), Lena Hansson, Leif Hedberg, Lasse Pöysti.

Drama. Suggested by: John Ford, *'Tis Pity She's a Whore* (a play; 1633). In 1782 Jacob, a young Swedish nobleman, returns home after 5 years abroad. Greeted with the news that his sister Charlotte is about to marry Count Alsmeden, a nobleman connected with the court of King Gustavas III, Jacob finds himself greatly disturbed by pangs of jealousy. Charlotte experiences the same feelings when she watches her brother in the company of the flirtatious Ebba Livin. As time passes, brother and sister admit their love for each other and spend a night together. Charlotte is willing to accept social disgrace and live with her brother as his wife. But Jacob is unwilling to sacrifice everything for this forbidden and illicit love. When Charlotte becomes pregnant, she confronts the count and informs him that she is carrying another man's child. But he refuses to believe that the baby is not his, and the wedding takes place after one postponement. Some time later the count, already incensed by his wife's coolness, has a violent quarrel with Jacob. Ebba witnesses the scene, grasps the truth of the situation and, in a fit of insane jealousy, shoots Charlotte. An old peasant woman whose ears were cut off years before because of an incestuous relationship with her father and who gave birth to an abnormal child, arrives to act as midwife. Charlotte dies during childbirth but her baby, delivered by Caesarean section, is a healthy and normal child. *Nobility. Peasants. Incest. Pregnancy. Jealousy. Marriage. Murder. Brother-sister relationship. Childbirth. Mutilation. Gustavus III.*

Note: Released in Sweden in Feb 1966 as *Syskonbädd 1782*. The score consists of music of the rococo period.

MY SISTER'S BUSINESS   **F6.3382**
Carl R. Carter Productions. *Dist* Hollywood Cinema Associates, Jack Vaughn Productions. ca **1970**. Sd; b&w. 35mm. 65 min.

A Carl R. Carter Production. *Prod-Dir-Story-Screenplay* Bobby Davis. *Camera* William Cole. *Sets* Ty Fowler. *Mus* Eddie Levine. *Sd* Fred Meeks. *Makeup* Colier. *Still Photog* Jim Beckham. *Gaffer* Robert Jay.

Cast: Constance Sirifem, LuAnn Cox, Karen Withers, Angel Albright, Eddie Levine, Sterling Eilert, III, George Mason, John Stober, Jack Miles, David Good.

Drama. "Big Sister," a prostitute who enjoys masturbation as a prelude to sexual intercourse, instructs "Little Sister," a naive virgin, in sex techniques. Later at a marijuana party, Little Sister practices what she has learned. *Sisters. Prostitutes. Autoeroticism. Virginity. Lesbianism. Group sex. Sexual techniques. Marijuana.*

MY SIX LOVES   **F6.3383**
Paramount Pictures. 3 Apr **1963** [New York opening; c31 Dec 1962; LP24448]. Sd; col (Technicolor). 35mm (VistaVision). 105 min. [Copyrighted at 101 min.]

Prod Gant Gaither. *Assoc Prod* Doane Harrison. *Dir* Gower Champion. *Screenplay* John Fante, Joseph Calvelli, William Wood. *Photog* Arthur E. Arling. *Col Cons* Richard Mueller. *Art Dir* Hal Pereira, Roland Anderson. *Set Decor* Sam Comer, Grace Gregory. *Film Ed* John Woodcock. *Mus* Walter Scharf. *Song:* "It's a Darn Good Thing" Sammy Cahn, James Van Heusen. *Sung by* Debbie Reynolds. *Piano Solo by* Peter Nero. *Choreog* Jack Regas. *Sd* Hugo Grenzbach, John Wilkinson. *Asst Dir* Michael Caffey. *Prod Mgr* Frank Caffey. *Unit Prod Mgr* Kenneth DeLand. *Script Supv* Charles Merton. *Cost* Edith Head. *Makeup* Wally Westmore. *Hairstyles for Miss Reynolds* Sydney Guilaroff. *Hairstyles* Nellie Manley. *Sp Photog Eff* John P. Fulton. *Proc Photog* Farciot Edouart.

Cast: Debbie Reynolds (*Janice Courtney*), Cliff Robertson (*Rev. Jim Larkin*), David Janssen (*Martin Bliss*), Eileen Heckart (*Ethel Swenson*), Jim Backus (*The Sheriff*), Pippa Scott (*Diane Soper*), John McGiver (*Judge Harris*), Hans Conried (*Kingsley Cross*), Mary McCarty (*Doreen Smith*), Alice Ghostley (*Selina*), Alice Pearce (*bus driver*), Max Showalter (*B. J. Smith*), Claude Stroud (*doctor*), Darlene Tompkins (*Ava*), Leon Belasco (*Mario*), Billy Hughes (*Leo*), Colleen Peters (*Amy*), Sally Smith (*Brenda*), Barry Livingston (*Sherman*), Debbie Price (*Dulcie*), Teddy Eccles (*Sonny*).

Romantic comedy. Source: Peter V. K. Funk, *My Six Loves* (New York, 1963). Broadway star Janice Courtney collapses from exhaustion during a frantic press conference, and she is ordered to take a long vacation at her Connecticut home. Janice and her secretary-companion, Ethel Swenson, get little rest, however, because of the boisterous housekeeper, Selina, and her beatnik daughter, Ava. The day after her arrival, Janice discovers that six children and a large dog are living in a shack at the back of her property. Aided by the local parson, Jim Larkin, Janice moves the children into her home and is granted temporary custody of them. When her producer, Martin Bliss, insists she begin rehearsing a new show, Janice leaves the children with Ethel and returns to New York. When Jim phones to say that one of the children has run away, Janice quits the play, forsaking her career. As she and Jim find the youngsters back in their shack, they decide to marry and adopt the entire brood. *Actors. Secretaries. Housekeepers. Beatniks. Children. Theatrical producers. Clergymen. Adoption. New York City—Broadway. Connecticut.*

MY SON, THE HERO (France/Italy)   **F6.3384**
Vides–Ariane–Filmsonor. *Dist* United Artists. 18 Sep **1963** [New York opening; c24 Jan 1963; LP27016]. Sd; col (Technicolor). 35mm. 111 min. [Copyright length: 119 min.]

Prod (see note) Alexandre Mnouchkine, Franco Cristaldi. *Assoc Prod* Giorgio Cristallini. *Dir-Writ* Duccio Tessari. *Screenplay* Ennio De Concini, Duccio Tessari. *English Dial* Tom Rowe. *Dir Photog* Alfio Contini. *Decor* Ottavio Scotti. *Film Ed* Renzo Lucidi. *Mus* Carlo Rustichelli. *Sd* Adriano Taloni. *Cost* Vittorio Rossi. *Sp Eff* Joseph Natanson.

Cast: Pedro Armendariz (*Cadmus*), Jacqueline Sassard (*Antiope*), Antonella Lualdi (*Hermione*), Giuliano Gemma (*Crios*), Gérard Séty (*Hippolytos*), Serge Nubret (*Rator*), Tanya Lopert (*Licina*), Ingrid Schoeller (*Emerate*), Franco Lantieri, Monika Berger, Isarco Ravaioli, Luisa Ruspoli.

Action melodrama. In ancient times, Cadmus, King of Thebes, destroys Jove's temple and proclaims himself head god. Crios, strongest and most clever of the Titans, is sent by Jove to Thebes to right matters. In return he will be given the freedom of his brothers imprisoned in the infernal regions. After Crios defeats a huge Negro, Rator, in the arena, both he and Rator are freed. Later, Crios meets and falls in love with Cadmus' daughter, Antiope, and steals Pluto's helmet, which renders its wearer invisible at night. He then rescues the exiled Antiope and slays the Gorgon put there to guard her; as he is about to be captured by Cadmus' men, his brother Titans, freed by Jove, appear and disperse the soldiers. Meanwhile, at a victory celebration in Thebes, Rator is dragged in to be executed in the arena, and the statues there come to life, turning out to be the Titans, who attack the guards. However, the king's men are made invulnerable by dragon's blood until Crios floods the passages, thereby washing the blood away and enabling the Titans to defeat the tyrant's soldiers. Crios rescues Antiope, hurls a thunderbolt which fells Cadmus, and frees the Titans and the Thebans. *Titans. Royalty. Negroes. Soldiers. Usurpers. Magic. Theft. Capital punishment. Thebes. Floods. Mythological characters. Jupiter.*

Note: Released in France as *Les Titans* in 1962; running time: 122 min. Released in Italy as *Arrivano i Titani* in 1962. One British source lists Franco Cristaldi as producer.

MY SON THE VAMPIRE (Reissue) (Great Britain)   **F6.3385**
Renown Pictures. *Dist* Blue Chip Productions. caSep **1963** [c1 Aug 1963; LP32192]. Sd; b&w. 35mm. 72 min.

Titl Song Allan Sherman.

Note: Released in Great Britain in 1952 as *Mother Riley Meets the Vampire* and *Old Mother Riley Meets the Vampire*; running time: 74 min. Original U.S. release in 1952 as *Vampire Over London.*

MY SOUL RUNS NAKED *see* **RAT FINK**

MY SWEDISH COUSINS F6.3386
Kirt Films International. *Dist* Distribpix, Inc. ca **1970**. Sd; col. 35mm. 63 min.

Sex film. Two young, Swedish women, arriving at the home of their American relatives, find that the youngest son is sexually naive. They seduce the boy and introduce him to their candid style of sex—anything goes, in any number or sex combination. The boy permits his two cousins to initiate him into their hedonistic life-style because he is infatuated with them, but the sight of them in a lesbian embrace convinces him that his cousins are not interested in romantic love. *Cousins. Swedes. Sexual initiation. Sexual practices. Lesbianism. Hedonism.*

MY SWEET CHARLIE F6.3387
Universal Studios Productions-Bob Banner Associates. *Dist* Universal Pictures. 11 Feb **1970** [New York opening; c20 Jan 1970; LP40568]. Sd; col (Technicolor). 35mm. 97 min. *MPAA rating* G.
Prod-Writ Richard Levinson, William Link. *Exec Prod* Bob Banner. *Dir* Lamont Johnson. *Photog* Gene Polito. *Art Dir* Robert Luthardt. *Set Decor* John McCarthy, George Milo. *Film Ed* Edward M. Abroms. *Mus (see note)* Gil Melle, Sid Sheinberg, Stanley Wilson. *Sd* Melvin M. Metcalfe, Sr. *Asst Dir* Ralph Ferrin. *Cost* Charles Waldo.
Cast: Patty Duke *(Marlene Chambers)*, Al Freeman, Jr. *(Charles Roberts)*, Ford Rainey *(Treadwell)*, William Hardy *(Mr. Larrabee)*, Chris Wilson *(Mrs. Larrabee)*, Noble Willingham *(Grady)*, Dave Ward *(sheriff)*.
Melodrama. Source: David Westheimer, *My Sweet Charlie* (New York, 1965). David Westheimer, *My Sweet Charlie* (New York opening: 6 Dec 1966). Charles Roberts, a black activist lawyer from the North who is working in Texas, kills a white man in self-defense. Fearing for his life, he flees to a dilapidated lighthouse cabin on the Gulf Coast, and there he finds Marlene Chambers, a pregnant, unwed white girl who has been cast out of her home by her father. Racial tension develops between them, but they eventually grow to respect each other when they realize that they are mutually dependent. One day, Marlene goes into labor, whereupon Charles hurries to the nearby town for supplies and help. He tries to act like a deferential southern Negro toward Treadwell, the prejudiced owner of a small country store, but Charles is quickly offended, and he allows his northern accent to come out. Treadwell begins a row, and Charles runs away; but Treadwell catches up with him, pulls a gun, and kills him. *Negroes. Lawyers. Southerners. Fugitives. Storekeepers. Race relations. Racial prejudice. Pregnancy. Illegitimacy. Imposture. Murder. Lighthouses. Gulf of Mexico. Texas.*
Note: Location scenes filmed in Galveston and Point Bolivar, Texas. First shown 20 Jan 1970 on NBC-TV's "World Premiere." Sources conflict in crediting music.

MY TALE IS HOT F6.3388
Dist Sonney Amusement Enterprises. 23 Oct **1964** [Los Angeles showing]. Sd; col. 35mm. [Feature length assumed.]
Prod-Dir Seymour Tokus.
Cast: Little Jack Little, Candy Barr, Hells Bells.
Comedy. Lucifer U. Devil is persuaded by his irascible wife to try to tempt into sin Ben Hur Ova, recently named "husband of the year" by a popular ladies' magazine. Lucifer visits Ben Hur and tempts him with a succession of lovely women. Ben Hur remains unmoved, however, and the defeated Lucifer returns to Hell after learning that Ben Hur is an Arabian sheik who has a harem of his own. *Sheiks. Arabs. Harems. Magazines (periodicals). Awards. The Devil. Hell.*
Note: Also known as *Always on Monday* and *My Tale Is Told.*

MY THIRD WIFE GEORGE F6.3389
K & W Pictures. *Dist* Monique Productions, J. E. R. Pictures. 1 Jan **1968** [New York opening]. Sd; b&w. 35mm. 66 min.
Prod-Dir Harry E. Kerwin. *Assoc Prod* Terry Merrill. *Screenplay* Wayne Rafferty. *Dir Photog* Tom Barnett. *Camera Op* Earl Wainwright. *Asst Camera* Kerry Whitenack. *Set Dsgn* Pierre Du Kane. *Film Ed* Harry E. Kerwin, Earl Wainwright. *Mus Sol* Tosco. *Sd & Mixer* John McGrath, sd. *Asst Sd* Harold Glaze. *Asst Dir* Joan Wainwright. *Script Supv* Betty Kerwin. *Prod Mgr* Bob Davidson. *Makeup* Edith Johns. *Hairstyles* Jeré. *Casting Dir* Jeff Partin. *Stills* James Bice. *Head Electrn* Claude Pounds. *Head Grip* Bob Barnett.
Cast: Thomas Wood *(Ralph Higbee)*, Ingrid Kerr *(Gigi)*, Duke Moberly *(Doc Holliday)*, Joseph Sexhauer *(Charlie)*, Douglas Blake *(Mother Higbee)*, Regina Koo *(maid)*, Erika Von Zaros *(Josephine Higbee)*, Bunny Ware *(Polly, 1st hippy)*, Barbara Walker *(Trixie, 2d hippy)*, Sheila Howard *(Chloe, 3d hippy)*, Dan Roper *(swimming instructor)*, Olivar Farquat *(fencing instructor)*, Chris Martell *(gorilla)*, Gene Burk *(private detective)*, Bonnie Laurant *(public*

stenographer), Claude Pounds *(photographer)*, Majesta *(stripper)*, Jeri Winters *(Georgie Higbee)*, Cal Slade, Belle Teleone *(The Couple)*.
Comedy. Inhibited and mother-dominated, Ralph Higbee is introduced to the facts of life at the age of 40 when his mother dies and three hippie girls give him LSD and include him in an all-night orgy. Ralph marries Josephine, but he is unable to satisfy her desires, and he leaves her when he discovers that her lovers include both other men and the family pet, a gorilla. Ralph marries for a second time and discovers that his new wife Amanda married him for his money. She wants a divorce, and Ralph will not grant it. She hires detectives who, unable to prove that Ralph is unfaithful, force him, at gunpoint, to rape a virgin. Ralph grants Amanda the divorce and marries for the third time. It is a good marriage, but Ralph is unfaithful to his new wife. Insanely jealous, she sets out to teach him a lesson he will never forget. *Hippies. Marriage. Infidelity. Bestiality. Jealousy. Momism. Rape. Nymphomania. LSD. Orgies. Gorillas.*
Note: Filmed in Miami. Also known as *My Third Wife by George.*

MY WIFE'S ENEMY (Italy) F6.3390
Dino De Laurentiis Cinematografica. *Dist* Magna Pictures Distribution Corp. Mar **1967**. Sd; b&w. 35mm. 90 min.
Dir Gianni Puccini. *Screenplay* Bruno Baratti, Renato Castellani, Pipolo, Gianni Puccini. *Photog* Gianni Di Venanzo.
Cast: Marcello Mastroianni *(Marco)*, Giovanna Ralli *(Luciana)*, Memmo Carotenuto *(Nando)*, Luciana Paluzzi *(Giulia)*, Andrea Checchi, Giacomo Furia, Vittorio De Sica, Teddy Reno, Riccardo Garrone, Gisella Sofio, Salvo Libassi, Raimondo Vianello.
Domestic comedy. Marco, a soccer referee, places more importance on sports than on his wife, Luciana, manager of a knitted goods store. Their relationship is further strained by Marco's father's rejection of Luciana and disdain for soccer. Both husband and wife indulge in disappointing extramarital affairs, but at a soccer match they realize that they love each other. *Storekeepers. Marriage. Infidelity. Filial relations. Soccer.*
Note: Opened in Rome in Mar 1959 as *Il nemico di mia moglie.* Pipolo is a pseudonym for Giuseppe Moccia; Teddy Reno for Ricordi Ferruccio.

MY WIFE'S HUSBAND (France/Italy) F6.3391
Les Films Corona-Dear Film. *Dist* Lopert Pictures. 26 Jan **1965** [New York opening]. Sd; b&w. 35mm (Franscope). 85 min. [Also 90 min.]
Prod (see note) Robert Dorfmann, Louis Manella. *Assoc Prod* Claude Heymann. *Dir* Gilles Grangier. *Screenwriter (see note)* Jean Lévitte, Pierre Lévy-Corti, Michel Galabru. *Dial* Raymond Castans, Jean Manse. *Photog* Roger Hubert. *Art Dir* Rino Mondellini. *Film Ed* Madeleine Gug. *Mus* Jean Marion. *Sd* Jean Bertrand. *Asst Dir* Serge Piollet.
Cast: Fernandel *(Fernand Jouvin)*, Bourvil *(André Colomber)*, Claire Maurier *(Christiane Colomber)*, Henri Vilbert *(Serrazin, the lawyer)*, Michel Galabru *(Maximin)*, Andrex *(Pellatan)*, Mag-Avril *(Madame Rose)*, Evelyne Selena *(Louise)*, Laurence Lignères *(Marinette)*, Henri Arius *(The Mayor)*, Gaston Rey *(Espinasse)*, Ardisson *(Carlotti)*, André Tomasi *(Gervasoni)*, Anne Marie Carrière *(Gerda)*, Roger Bernard *(Fernand's nephew)*.
Comedy. During World War II, Fernand Jouvin, a slothful Frenchman, becomes a prisoner of war; he escapes, however, and takes refuge in an inn run by Gerda. At the end of the war, he decides not to return to his wife, Christiane, and remains with Gerda for 10 years. Eventually, Gerda's husband returns, and Fernand is forced to rejoin his wife in Martigues. The changes are extraordinary; their little cafe has been turned into a lavish restaurant, and his wife, believing him dead, has married Fernand's former chef, André. Realizing that Fernand is still her husband, Christiane denies André his marriage rights until Fernand agrees to a divorce. The two men become great friends, until André begins to believe that Fernand is double-crossing him and returns to his home in Normandy. Fernand becomes so despondent that he visits André and agrees to divorce Christiane if André will marry her and assume the responsibility of running the restaurant. Gerda suddenly appears and announces that her husband is in Siberia, and she is now free to marry Fernand. The men soon find themselves back in the kitchen being dominated by their wives. *Prisoners of war. Innkeepers. Cooks. Infidelity. Divorce. Marriage. Friendship. Restaurants. World War II. Martigues. Normandy.*
Note: Opened in Paris in Dec 1963 as *La cuisine au beurre*; running time: 82 min (cut from 100 min); opened in Rome in Mar 1965 as *Cucina al burro*; running time: 105 min. Only one source credits Manella as producer and Galabru as screenwriter.

MYRA BRECKENRIDGE F6.3392
Twentieth Century-Fox Film Corp. 23 Jun **1970** [New York opening; c1 Jul 1970; LP38117]. Sd (Westrex); col (De Luxe). 35mm (Panavision). 94 min. *MPAA rating* X.
Prod Robert Fryer. *Assoc Prod* James Cresson. *Dir* Michael Sarne. *Screenplay* Michael Sarne, David Giler. *Dir Photog* Richard Moore. *Art Dir* Jack Martin Smith, Fred Harpman. *Set Decor* Walter M. Scott, Reg Allen.

Main Titl Pacific Title. *Film Ed* Danford B. Greene. *Co-Film Ed* Hugh K. Cummings. *Mus Supv & Cond* Lionel Newman. *Song:* "Secret Place" John Phillips. *Sung by* Rex Reed. *Song:* "Hard To Handle" Allen Jones, mus, Alvertis Isbell, Otis Redding. *Sung by* Mae West. *Song:* "You Gotta Taste All the Fruit" sung by Mae West. *Orch* Jack Elliott, Jeff Alexander, Allyn Ferguson, Lyn Murray. *Choreog* Ralph Beaumont. *Sd* Don Bassman, David Dockendorf. *Asst Dir* Richard Glassman. *Unit Prod Mgr* William Eckhardt. *Cost* Theadora Van Runkle. *Miss Mae West's Cost* Edith Head. *Makeup Supv* Dan Striepeke. *Makeup Artist* Del Acevedo. *Hairstyles* Edith Lindon. *Sp Photog Eff* L. B. Abbott, Art Cruickshank. *Casting Supv* Michael McLean.

Cast: Mae West (*Leticia*), John Huston (*Buck Loner*), Raquel Welch (*Myra*), Rex Reed (*young man [Myron]*), Farrah Fawcett (*Mary Ann*), Roger C. Carmel (*Dr. Montag*), Roger Herren (*Rusty*), George Furth (*Charlie Flager, Jr.*), Calvin Lockhart (*Irving Amadeus*), Jim Backus (*doctor*), John Carradine (*surgeon*), Andy Devine (*Coyote Bill*), Grady Sutton (*Kid Barlow*), Robert Lieb (*Charlie Flager, Sr.*), Skip Ward (*Chance*), Kathleen Freeman (*Bobby Dean Loner*), B. S. Pully (*Tex*), Buck Kartalian (*Jeff*), Monty Landis (*Vince*), Tom Selleck (*stud*), Peter Ireland (*student*), Nelson Sardelli (*Mario*), William Hopper (*parole officer*), Genevieve Waite (*dentist's patient*), Charlene Jones (*masseuse*).

Comedy. Source: Gore Vidal, *Myra Breckenridge* (Boston, 1968). When New York film critic Myron Breckenridge undergoes a sex-change operation in Copenhagen, he ceases to exist, except as a white-suited phantom alter ego that hovers around his new identity, Myra Breckenridge, the All-American Woman whom "no man will ever possess." Myra, posing as the "late" Myron's widow, arrives at her Uncle Buck Loner's acting academy in Westwood, California, to claim an inheritance of half the land on which the ex-cowboy star has created his lavish training ground for screenstruck Hollywood hopefuls. Outraged, Buck and his attorneys begin a series of desperate legal attempts to invalidate her claim; meanwhile, Myra is offered a position on the faculty as instructress for a posture and empathy class. The crusading Myra begins her true quest: the ruination of American manhood. After ingratiating herself with a young acting student, Rusty, she lures him to the infirmary after hours so they may be alone. On the pretext of measuring him for a special orthopedic brace, Myra straps the naked Rusty to an operating table and rapes him mercilessly from the rear, whipping him in the process. Later, the disillusioned youth ends up at the beach retreat of singer and talent agent Leticia Van Allen, who finds him the best in a long and illustrious list of studs. Mary Ann, Rusty's adoring girl friend, is distraught over his behavior and comes to Myra for consolation, but instead her teacher tries to seduce her. When the attorneys discover that no evidence exists of Myron's marriage or demise, Myra hoists her skirt and reveals to the shocked witnesses the scar from her operation. After leaving the estate, she is hit by a car but awakens in the hospital as Myron. He is disturbed to find himself without large breasts, but later he seems resigned to coexistence with his feminine counterpart as he and Myra dance down the street together. *Critics. Actors. Students. Schoolteachers. Uncles. Lawyers. Talent agents. Bisexuality. Male homosexuality. Lesbianism. Rape. Seduction. Inheritance. Dual personality. Sex change operations. Copenhagen. Hollywood. Automobile accidents. "Stowaway".*

Note: Clips from *Stowaway* (1936), featuring Shirley Temple singing "You Got To S-M-I-L-E" are shown over the beginning and end titles. Clips from other Twentieth Century-Fox films appear throughout the film. One source credits Gore Vidal with screenplay collaboration and Mae West with additional material.

MYRA'S BED   F6.3393

William Gaston. *Dist* Gunter Productions. 27 Sep **1967** [New York showing]. Sd; b&w. 35mm. 52 min.

Dir William Gaston.

Cast: Patricia Moore (*Myra Brown*), Ralph G. Edwards.

Melodrama. Myra Brown has married an older man who is unaware of her infidelities with the customers at their cafe across the street. One day, he informs her that he will be away all night, and she entices a number of customers, both men and women, to come to her house for sex. During the evening, two men sexually abuse her, a lesbian fights her for the favors of another woman, and another lesbian and a handsome stranger have sex with her. She is murdered by a vicious sadist, who is in turn killed by her vengeful husband. *Restaurateurs. Infidelity. Marriage. Lesbianism. Rape. Troilism. Murder. Sadism. Revenge. Cafes.*

Note: This film may also be known as *Violent Sex Affair*. Also advertised as *Myra's Den*.

LE MYSTÈRE KOUMIKO *see* THE KOUMIKO MYSTERY

MYSTERIOUS ISLAND (United States/Great Britain)   F6.3394

Ameran Films. *Dist* Columbia Pictures. 20 Dec **1961** [New York opening; c1 Nov 1961; LP20499]. Sd; col (Eastman Color by Pathé). 35mm

(SuperDynamation). 101 min.

A Charles H. Schneer Production. *Prod* Charles H. Schneer. *Dir* Cy Endfield. *Screenplay* John Prebble, Daniel Ullman, Crane Wilbur. *Photog* Wilkie Cooper. *Underwater Photog* Egil Woxholt. *Camera Op* Jack Mills, photog. *Art Dir* Bill Andrews. *Titl Dsgn* Bob Gill. *Film Ed* Frederick Wilson. *Mus Comp & Cond* Bernard Herrmann. *Played by* London Symphony Orchestra. *Sd Supv* John Cox. *Sd Rec* Peter Handford, Bob Jones. *Asst Dir* Rene Dupont. *Prod Supv* Raymond Anzarut. *Prod Mgr* Robert Sterne. *Cont* Marjorie Lavelly. *Sp Visual Eff* Ray Harryhausen.

Cast: Michael Craig (*Capt. Cyrus Harding*), Joan Greenwood (*Lady Mary Fairchild*), Michael Callan (*Herbert Brown*), Gary Merrill (*Gideon Spilett*), Herbert Lom (*Captain Nemo*), Beth Rogan (*Elena*), Percy Herbert (*Sergeant Pencroft*), Dan Jackson (*Neb*), Nigel Green (*Tom*).

Science fiction melodrama. Source: Jules Verne, *L'ile mystérieuse* (Paris, 1874). In 1865, following the siege of Richmond toward the close of the Civil War, three Union soldiers, a Northern newspaperman, and a Rebel sergeant escape from a Confederate prison in an observation balloon and are carried across the country and far out over the Pacific. A violent storm forces them down on a tiny tropical island; there they find giant creatures (land crabs, roosters, and bees) but no signs of human life. One day they are joined by two women, the sole survivors of a shipwreck. As the little community grows, a pirate ship enters the lagoon and is mysteriously exploded and sunk. At this point a stranger emerges from the sea and announces himself as Captain Nemo. For the past 8 years he has been living on the island and experimenting in the mutation of animals in the hope that the development of such mammoth creatures may solve the world's food problems. The island's volcano will erupt in a few days, he tells the group, and they must try to refloat the sunken pirate ship. By means of the observation balloon, the vessel is raised; and all scramble aboard just as the volcano erupts—all, that is, except Captain Nemo; for by remaining behind until everyone else is safe, he is trapped by tons of rock and lava. *Newspapermen. Soldiers. Prisoners of war. Pirates. Balloons (ascent). Prison escapes. Mutation. Volcanoes. United States—History—Civil War. Shipwrecks. Richmond (Virginia). Crabs. Roosters. Bees.*

Note: Filmed in England and released there in 1962.

THE MYSTERY OF THUG ISLAND (Italy/West Germany)   F6.3395

Liber Film–Eichberg Film. *Dist* Columbia Pictures. May **1966** [c1 May 1966; LP34502]. Sd; col (Eastmancolor, print by Pathé). 35mm. 96 min.

Exec Prod Nino Battiferri. *Dir* Luigi Capuano. *Screenplay* Arpad De Riso, Ottavio Poggi. *Dir Photog* Guglielmo Mancori. *Camera Op* Mario Sbrenna. *Art Dir* Ernesto Kromberg. *Sets* Camillo Del Signore. *Scenery Asst* Giuseppe Ranieri. *Film Ed* Antonietta Zita. *Orig Mus* Carlo Rustichelli. *Sd* Vittorio Massi. *Asst Dir* Francesco Massaro. *Prod Mgr* Gino Fanano. *Prod Sec* Arrigo Peri. *Wardrobe* Giancarlo Bartolini Salimbeni. *Wardrobe Asst* Elio Micheli. *Cost* Casa d'Arte Firenze. *Makeup* Anacleto Giustini. *Wigs* Ditta Rocchetti. *Hairdresser* Marcella Favella. *Still Photog* Rinascimento Vaselli. *Exterior Constr* Giovar Battista Siciliano. *Exterior Tech* Antonio Colaiacono. *Fencing Master* Nando Poggi.

Cast: Guy Madison (*Souyadhana [Boujdhans]*), Ingeborg Schöner (*Edy [Ada]*), Giacomo Rossi Stuart (*Tremal-Naik*), Ivan Desny (*Maciadi*), Giulia Rubini (*Gundali*), Nando Poggi (*Kammamuri*), Peter Van Eyck (*MacPherson*), Aldo Bufi-Landi, Aldo Cristiani, Romano Giomini.

Adventure melodrama. Source: Emilio Salgari, *I misteri della jungla nera* (Genoa, 1895). Edy, the 3-year-old daughter of British Army Captain MacPherson, is abducted by the Thugs of India. Fifteen years later, the British captain commands an expedition to exterminate the murderous tribe, unaware that his daughter has been ceremonially invested as a virgin handmaiden in the temple of the goddess Kali. Meanwhile, a young snake hunter meets and falls in love with the young woman before he is captured by the Thugs. As punishment, he is ordered to kill MacPherson; if he fails, Edy will be sacrificed to Kali. The snake hunter and the captain unite against the Thugs, kill Souyadhana, their leader, and rescue Edy. *Thugs (of India). Hunters. Filial relations. Abduction. Rites and ceremonies. Human sacrifice. Rescue. India. Great Britain—Army.*

Note: Released in Italy in 1964 as *I misteri della giungla nera*; in West Germany in Jul 1965 as *Das Geheimnis der Lederschlinge*; running time: 86 min. A remake of the 1953 film released in Italy under the same Italian title.

MYSTERY SUBMARINE (Great Britain)   F6.3396

Bertram Ostrer Productions. *For* Britannia Film Distributors. *Dist* Universal-International. 23 Jan **1963** [Boston opening; c2 Mar 1963; LP35481]. Sd; b&w. 35mm. 92 min.

Prod Bertram Ostrer. *Dir* C. M. Pennington-Richards. *Screenplay* Hugh Woodhouse, Bertram Ostrer, Jon Manchip White. *Dir Photog* Stanley Pavey. *Camera Op* Derek Browne. *Focus* Ronnie Fox-Rogers. *Art Dir* Charles Bishop. *Asst Art Dir* Roy Dorman. *Draughtsman* Wallis Smith. *Film Ed* Bill Lewthwaite. *1st Asst Ed* Michael Rabiger. *2d Asst Ed* Adrian McDonald. *Mus*

Comp Clifton Parker. *Mus Cond* John Hollingsworth. *Sd Rec* George Stephenson, Bob Jones. *Dub Ed* Jim Sibley. *Boom Op* Jack W. Davies. *Sd Camera Op* Ernie Webb. *1st, 2d & 3d Asst Dir* Colin Brewer, Scott Wodehouse, Barry Langley. *Prod Mgr* Albert Becket. *Cont* Pamela Davies. *Prod Sec* Angela Cockill. *Wardrobe Mistress* Bridget Sellers. *Makeup* Phil Leakey. *Hairdresser* Henry Montsash. *Sp Eff* Wally Veevers. *Prop Buyer* Ronald Baker. *Still Photog* Laurie Ridley. *Rigger* A. McNeil. *Dressing Prop* John Feehan.

Cast: Edward Judd (*Lieutenant Commander Tarlton*), James Robertson-Justice (*Rear-Admiral Rainbird*), Laurence Payne (*Lieutenant Seaton*), Joachim Fuchsberger (*Commander Scheffler*), Arthur O'Sullivan (*Mike Fitzgerald*), Albert Lieven (*Captain Neymarck*), Robert Flemyng (*Vice-Adm. Sir James Carver*), Richard Carpenter (*Lieutenant Hoskins*), Richard Thorp (*Lieutenant Chatterton*), Jeremy Hawk (*Admiral Saintsbury*), Robert Brown (*Coxswain Drage*), Frederick Jaeger (*Lieutenant Henze*), George Mikell (*Lieutenant Remer*), Peter Myers, actor (*Telegraphist Packshaw*), Leslie Randall (*Leading Seaman Donnithorne*), Ewen Solon (*Lieutenant Commander Kirklees*), Roberta D'Esti (*3d Officer Mather*), Brian Peck (*Able Seaman Winner*), Fulton Mackaw (*Leading Torpedoman McKerrow*), Gerard Heinz (*German admiral*), Hamilton Deck (*Commander Sivewright*), Peter Stanwick (*Lieutenant Lyncker*), Peter Zander (*Lieutenant Jahn*), Sean Kelly (*Lieutenant Heilborn*), Dennis Edwards (*Lieutenant Neumann*), Keith Anderson (*German radio operator*), Brandon Brady (*pilot of Catalina*), John Chappell (*bomb aimer*), Desmond Davies (*radar operator*), Nigel Green (*Chief ERA Lovejoy*), Ray Smith (*Signalman Lewis*), Anthony Wickert (*ERA Barnes*), David Glover (*P. O. Tel. Hubbard*), Hedger Wallace (*Stoker Thompson*), Michael Ritterman (*Lieutenant Commander Torgau*), Graeme Bruce (*Lieutenant Schliemann*), Dixon Adams (*Lieutenant Anstey*), Norman Johns (*German ASDIC operator*), Declan Mulholland (*duty chef*), Frank Wilson Taylor (*1st sailor*), William Semour (*Leading Seaman Grant*), Derek Smek (*Leading Seaman Boydell*), Dusty Hood (*Leading Seaman Fuller*), Henry Kaufman (*Stoker Mechanic Parham*).

War drama. From a play by: Jon Manchip White. The crew of a German submarine, U-153, abandon their ship after being depth-charged, despite their captain's orders to the contrary. The submarine is then captured with its codebook and log intact and is hastily renovated by the British Navy, which then mans it with a British crew and sends it out to rejoin the Nazi wolfpack. Captained by Lieutenant Commander Tarlton, U-153 finds the pack after several times risking discovery while surfacing for repairs. U-153's message to the British command giving the submarine's position is intercepted by the Germans; and in the battle that ensues, U-153 torpedoes one of the other boats. The head of the pack follows U-153 as it submerges, then attempts to ram U-153 but is destroyed on a shallow reef. A British frigate sights U-153 and also attacks—successfully. U-153's men are rescued by the frigate, whose crew is amazed to find that the prisoners are fellow Britishers. *Submarines. World War II. Great Britain—Royal Navy. Germany—Navy. Documentation.*

Note: Released in Great Britain in May 1963. Working title: *Decoy.*

THE MYSTIFIERS *see* **SYMPHONY FOR A MASSACRE**

THE MYTH (Italy)   F6.3397
Jamir Cinematografica. *Dist* Times Film Corp. Jun **1965.** Sd; b&w. 35mm. 80 min.
Prod Umberto Ghignone. *Dir* Adimaro Sala. *Story-Screenplay* Adimaro Sala, Ugo Guerra. *Ch Camera* Franco Villa. *Mus Comp & Cond* Armando Trovajoli. *Asst Dir* Roberto Tamburrino. *Prod Mgr* Silvano Marabotti.
Cast—"Violence": Lisa Gastoni (*Luisa*), Raoul Grassilli (*Marco*), Dino Mele (*Nando*), Nini Rosso (*Renzino*), Gino Barbacane, Aldo Berti, Bruno Cattaneo, Peter Martell (*The Toughs*), Rossella D'Aquino, Erika Di Centa, Mauro Del Vecchio, Jacques Stany, Renato Terra.
Cast—"Love": Norma Bengell (*Anna*), Umberto Orsini (*Roberto*), Lidia Alfonsi (*Lucia*), Vittorio Caprioli (*poet*), Mario Pisu, Annie Gorassini, Stelvio Rosi, Evi Farinelli, Carlo Lima, Filippo Sallustri, Ermanno Adriani, Isabel Hurt.
Drama. VIOLENCE: After spending a dull evening with boorish friends, Marco and Luisa leave the party. On their way home they are assaulted by a group of teenagers. Marco is attacked and restrained while Luisa is raped. They return home and pretend that nothing happened. LOVE: After a formal ball, a group of people dance sensually atop a bridge. One of the guests, Lucia, attempts suicide. In the hospital, she is comforted by the attractive Anna, who is aroused by Lucia's husband, Roberto. Lucia dies; and Roberto, who feels guilty because of his attentions to Anna, calls in vain to Lucia. *Gangs. Adolescence. Rape. Marriage. Suicide. Infidelity. Bridges. Hospitals.*
Note: Released in Italy in 1963 as *Il mito.* Alternative Italian title: *La violenza e l'amore.* Original episode titles: "La violenza" and "La solitudine." Also known as *The Pushover.*

NA SEMI VETRAKH *see* **THE HOUSE ON THE FRONT LINE**

DAS NACHTLOKAL ZUM SILBERMOND *see* **5 SINNERS**

NACHTS, WENN DER TEUFEL KAM *see* **NAZI TERROR AT NIGHT**

NACKT UNTER WÖLFEN *see* **NAKED AMONG THE WOLVES**

DIE NACKTE UND DER SATAN *see* **THE HEAD**

NAISENKUVIA *see* **PORTRAITS OF WOMEN**

NAKED AMONG THE WOLVES (East Germany)   F6.3398
DEFA. *Dist* Lopert Pictures. 18 Apr **1967** [New York opening]. Sd; b&w. 35mm (Totalscope). 100 min.
Prod Hans Mahlich. *Dir* Frank Beyer. *Screenplay* (*see note*) Bruno Apitz, Alfred Hirschmeier. *Adtl Dial* Willi Schafer. *Photog* Günther Marczinowski. *Art Dir* Alfred Hirschmeier. *Film Ed* Hildegard Conrad. *Sd* Bernd Gerwein. *Asst Dir* Bernd Braun. *Cost* Günther Schmidt. *Makeup* Kurt Tauchmann.
Cast: Erwin Geschonneck (*Kramer*), Fred Delmare (*Pippig*), Gerry Wolff (*Bockow*), Armin Mueller-Stahl (*Höfel*), Bolesław Płotnicki (*Janowski*), Krystyn Wójcik (*Kropinski*), Peter Sturm (*Rose*), Viktor Avdyushko (*Bogorski*), Wolfram Handel (*Zweiling*), Fred Ludwig (*Mandrill*), Gerd Ehlers (*Gay*), Erik S. Klein, Herbert Köfer, Heinz Scholz, Zygmunt Malanowicz, Jan Pohan, Leonid Swjetlow, Bruno Apitz, Werner Mohring, Joachim Tomaschewsky, Hermann Eckhardt, Peter-Paul Goest, Günter Ruger, Angela Brunner, Albert Zahn, Werner Dissel, Christoph Engel, Hans-Helmut Krüger, Joachim Jablouski, Jürgen Strauch, Hans Hardt-Hardtloff, Richard Hilgert, Steffen Klaus, Janusz Roszkowski, Boris Suchow, Klaus Urban.
War drama. Source: Bruno Apitz, *Nackt unter Wölfen* (Halle, East Germany, 1958). During the closing days of World War II the Germans transfer a group of prisoners from the concentration camp at Auschwitz to one at Buchenwald. Among the arrivals is an elderly Pole bearing a heavy suitcase. Hiding inside the valise is Pippig, a small Jewish boy who managed to escape the gas chambers at Auschwitz. Although the child's presence in the camp presents a terrible danger, the prisoners decide to hide him from the Nazi guards. A young German officer overhears the inmates discussing Pippig and, at first, chooses to remain silent in order to ingratiate himself with the prisoners. Later, however, he anonymously informs the German commandant that a Jewish child has been hidden in the camp. As an intensified search is organized, the child becomes a symbol of the future to the prisoners, and despite torture and executions, they refuse to reveal Pippig's hiding place. When American planes are seen over the camp, preparations are made to evacuate Buchenwald. Fearing extermination, the prisoners break into open revolt, defending themselves with a meagre store of stolen weapons, knives, sticks, and even their bare hands. Although some die, most of the prisoners, including little Pippig, are set free. *Prisoners of war. Poles. Nazis. Children. Jews. Informers. Survival. Torture. Prison revolts. Concentration camps. World War II. Auschwitz. Buchenwald.*
Note: Produced in East Germany in 1963 and released there as *Nackt unter Wölfen;* running time: 125 min. Hirschmeier is credited with screenplay only in two U. S. sources.

NAKED ANGELS   F6.3399
David R. Dawdy Productions. *Dist* Crown International Pictures, Goldstone Film Enterprises. 14 May **1969** [San Francisco opening]. Sd; col (Eastman Color, print by Pathé). 35mm. 83 min. *MPAA rating* R.
Pres by Distributors International. *Prod* David R. Dawdy. *Exec Prod* Roger Corman. *Dir-Writ* Bruce Clark. *Camera* Robert Eberlein, Bill Kaplan. *Film Ed* Johanna Bryant. *Asst Dir* Marc Siegler.
Cast: Michael Greene (*Mother*), Jennifer Gan (*Marlene*), Richard Rust (*Fingers*), Art Jenoff, Felicia Guy, Leonard Coates, Tedd King, Bruce Sunkees, Corey Fischer, Sahn Berti, Howard Lester, Joe Kasey, Glenn Lee, Penelope Sprerris, Carol Ries, Pat McChrystle.
Action melodrama. Mother, leader of the Angels, a Los Angeles motorcycle gang, is hospitalized after being beaten up by members of the Hotdoggers, a rival Las Vegas gang. Upon his release, he leads the Angels to Las Vegas on a mission of vengeance. After a spree on Fremont Street, they pursue their enemies to their mine hideout. The trip through the desert takes its toll as hunger, thirst, and empty gasoline tanks dampen the group's spirits. Mother's girl friend defies him when he decides to leave behind a disabled motorcycle, and Mother tries but fails to persuade his fellow Angels to rape her as punishment. Leaving him behind, the gang goes on to complete its mission. Mother finds his way back through the desert, rejoining his gang for the final battle. *Motorcycle gangs. Rape. Revenge. Gang wars. Deserts. Los Angeles. Las Vegas.*

NAKED ARE THE CHEATERS see **THE POLITICIANS**

NAKED AS NATURE INTENDED see **AS NATURE INTENDED**

NAKED AS THE WIND FROM THE SEA see **ONE SWEDISH SUMMER**

NAKED AUTUMN (France)   F6.3400
Editions Cinégraphiques. *Dist* United Motion Picture Organization. 14 Nov 1963 [New York opening]. Sd; b&w. 35mm (Dyaliscope). 98 min.
Prod Jean Thuillier. *Assoc Prod* Irénée Leriche. *Dir* François Leterrier. *Screenplay* Roger Vailland, François Leterrier. *Dial* Roger Vailland. *Photog* Jean Badal. *Art Dir* Pierre Charbonnier. *Film Ed* Léonide Azar. *Mus* Maurice Le Roux. *Sd* André Hervée.
Cast: Simone Signoret *(Roberte)*, Reginald Kernan *(Milan)*, Alexandra Stewart *(Hélène)*, Marcel Pagliero *(Luigi)*, Serge Rousseau *(Duval)*, Serge Sauvion, Marie-Claude Poirier, Dorian Leigh Parker, Nicole Chollet, Marcelle Ranson, Antoine Roblot, José Luis de Vilallonga.
Melodrama. Source: Roger Vailland, *Les mauvais coups* (Paris, 1959). Roberte and Milan have been bound with an all-consuming love. After 10 years of marriage, however, they must face the realities of life in their middle age. They retire to a country estate, where Milan, formerly a sportscar racer, unsuccessfully tries to write his memoirs. Roberte, seeking to stem the erosion of their love, finds solace in gambling and drinking. The couple meet Hélène, a schoolteacher in the nearby village; and despite the objections of Hélène's fiancé (Duval, a soldier), the married couple and the teacher become constant companions. Roberte's attachment to the girl is such that through Hélène she relives her early and happier years with Milan; for Milan's part, he falls in love with Hélène but is fearful of causing her the kind of unhappiness that has befallen Roberte. His dilemma is solved when he accepts an offer to resume his racing career; and though either of the two women would willingly accompany him, he decides to leave them both behind. [In the original version, Roberte commits suicide when her husband leaves.] *Schoolteachers. Soldiers. Authors. Marriage. Alcoholism. Automobile racing. Gambling. Middle age. Suicide.*
Note: Paris opening: May 1961 as *Les mauvais coups*; running time: 103 min.

THE NAKED BRIGADE (United States/Greece)   F6.3401
Box Office Attractions–Alfa Studios. *Dist* Universal Pictures. 16 Jun 1965 [New York opening]. Sd; b&w. 35mm. 99 min. [New York opening: 101 min.]
Prod Albert J. Cohen. *Assoc Prod* A. Sanford Wolf. *Dir* Maury Dexter. *Screenplay* Albert J. Cohen, A. Sanford Wolf. *Story* Irwin Winehouse, A. Sanford Wolf. *Cinematog* Aristedes Karides-Fuchs. *Art Dir* Em Zampelas. *Film Ed* El Siaskas. *Mus* Theo Fanidi. *Sd* Antony Bairaktaris. *Asst Dir* Eric Andreou, George Kosmatos. *Prod Mgr* Michalis Lambinos. *Sp Eff* John Samiotis.
Cast: Shirley Eaton *(Diana Forsythe)*, Ken Scott *(Christo)*, Mary Chronopoulou *(Katina)*, John Holland *(Major Hamilton)*, Sonia Zoidou *(Athena)*, Eleni Zaferiou *(Sofia)*, Aris Vlachopoulos *(Father Nicholas)*, Patrick Kavanaugh *(Lieutenant Bentley)*, Clive Russell *(Corporal Reade)*, Nicholas Papakonstantantinou *(Major Heilmann)*, Karl Nurk *(Professor Forsythe)*, Christ Himaras *(Spyros Karrayiannis)*, Socrates Corres *(Lefteris Karrayiannis)*, Zanino Papadopoulos *(Yannis Karrayiannis)*, Gikas Biniaris *(Stavros Karrayiannis)*, Kostas Balademas *(Manolakakis)*.
War drama. Diana Forsythe, on Crete in 1941 to persuade her archeologist father to return to England before the Nazis take over the island, is taken by her Greek friend, Athena, to the hideout of a group of women guerrillas led by Katina after her father is killed during an attack by the Germans. Diana offers to help the guerrillas, and they assign her to drive a supply truck. She meets Christo, a Greek lieutenant who works under Major Hamilton, coordinator of the resistance forces on Crete. Christo agrees to help Diana escape to England. After an unsuccessful escape attempt, Diana continues to assist the Greek guerrillas in harassing the Nazis who occupy the island. Meanwhile, Katina, in love with Christo, grows increasingly resentful as she observes his attraction to Diana. Christo discovers that a Nazi munitions ship is docked at the harbor, and Diana joins the guerrillas on a dangerous sabotage mission. Swimming underwater, they attach explosives to the ship and narrowly escape the blast. The mission complete, Christo arranges for Diana's safe passage to England. *British. Archeologists. Nazis. Guerrillas. Resistance (political). Sabotage. Jealousy. Military occupation. Demolition—Underwater. Ammunition. World War II. Crete. Athens. Ship explosions.*
Note: Filmed in Athens and on location on Crete. Greek title: *Hē gymnē taxiarchia.*

NAKED CHILDHOOD see **ME**

NAKED COMPLEX   F6.3402
U. S. American Films. *Dist* Inter–American Film Distributors. 10 Apr 1964 [Los Angeles showing]. Sd; col (Eastman Color). 35mm. 64 min.

Dir Roy Mart. *Camera Op* Minervino Rojas. *Film Ed* Cesar (ed), Sergi Castello. *Mus* Chirino. *Makeup* Sergi Castello. *Still Photog* Dick Falcon.
Cast: Dolores Carlos *(Helen)*, Roy Savage *(Johnny)*, Mary Margaret *(Stella)*, Selina North *(Sussie)*, Tammy Baran *(Dorothy)*, Dawn Meridith *(Anna)*, Debbi Winters *(Mary)*, Sussy James *(Julieta)*, Mario Mark *(capitan)*, Esmeralda Pijuan *(snake dancer)*, Abby Rios *(twist dancer)*.
Nudist film. Handsome, athletic Johnny Smith, who suffers from a fear of women, spends his spare time swimming alone in the ocean off Miami Beach. His nervous reactions to a woman in a bikini and a snake dancer lead him to seek isolation on a deserted island. By mistake, he parachutes onto a Caribbean island which has been given to a group of women nudists by a wealthy philanthropist. Johnny tries to escape by swimming away from the island, but sharks send him back to shore. Gradually, he becomes accustomed to the presence of the nude women and becomes romantically involved with one of their number, Helen. The women perform a Hawaiian dance to welcome the crew of an arriving supply ship. As the ship prepares to depart again, Johnny makes his decision to remain on the island with Helen and asks the captain to perform the marriage ceremony. The ship leaves, and Johnny, who is now cured of his fear of women, removes his bathing trunks to join the nudists for a swim. *Exotic dancers. Sea captains. Phobias. Swimming. Nudism. Parachuting. Islands. Weddings. Nudist camps. Miami Beach. Caribbean.*
Note: Filmed at the Sunshine Beach Club of Florida, in Tampa.

THE NAKED EDGE (United States/Great Britain)   F6.3403
Pennebaker, Inc.-Baroda Productions-Jason, Inc.-Monica Corp.-Monmouth, Inc.-Bentley Productions. *Dist* United Artists. 28 Jun 1961 [Helena, Montana, opening: c28 Jun 1961; LP20320]. Sd; b&w. 35mm. 99 min.
Prod George Glass, Walter Seltzer. *Exec Prod* Marlon Brando, Sr. *Dir* Michael Anderson. *Screenplay* Joseph Stefano. *Photog* Erwin Hillier. *Camera Op* Tony White. *Focus* Wally Byatt. *Camera Grip* Sid Payne. *Art Dir* Carmen Dillon. *Asst Art Dir* Ernest Archer. *Set Dresser* Vernon Dixon. *Scenic Artist* Bill Beavis. *Draughtsman* Ron Benton, Robert Cartwright. *Film Ed* Gordon Pilkington. *Assembly Ed* Deveril Goodman. *2d Asst Ed* Tony West. *Mus Comp* William Alwyn. *Played by* Sinfonia of London. *Cond* Muir Mathieson. *Sd Mix* Norman Coggs. *Boom Op* Bill Cook. *Sd Camera Op* G. Lee. *Dub Ed* Rusty Coppleman. *1st, 2d & 3d Asst Dir* Peter Bolton, Gordon Gilbert, Bill Cartlidge. *Prod Supv* William Kirby. *Asst to the Prod* Jock MacGregor. *Location Mgr* Bluey Hill. *Prod Sec* Inez Easton. *Cont* Angela Martelli. *Dress Dsgn* Julie Harris, cost. *Wardrobe Master* Ernie Farrer. *Wardrobe Mistress* Eileen Sullivan. *Ch Makeup* Tony Sforzini. *Hairdresser* Gordon Bond. *Constr Mgr* Gus Walker. *Prop Buyer* Dudley May. *Still Photog* Ted Reed. *Casting Dir* Robert Lennard. *Ch Electrn* Ted Hallowes. *Prop* Len Alexander.
Cast: Gary Cooper *(George Radcliffe)*, Deborah Kerr *(Martha Radcliffe)*, Eric Portman *(Jeremy Clay)*, Diane Cilento *(Mrs. Heath)*, Hermione Gingold *(Lilly Harris)*, Peter Cushing *(Mr. Wrack)*, Michael Wilding *(Morris Brooke)*, Ronald Howard *(Mr. Claridge)*, Ray McAnally *(Donald Heath)*, Sandor Eles *(Manfridi)*, Wilfrid Lawson *(Mr. Pom)*, Martin Boddey *(Jason Roote)*, Helen Cherry *(Miss Osborne)*, Joyce Carey *(Victoria Hicks)*, Diane Clare *(Betty)*, Frederick Leister *(judge)*, Peter Wayn *(chauffeur)*.
Mystery melodrama. Source: Max Ehrlich, *First Train to Babylon* (New York, 1955). The courtroom testimony of George Radcliffe, an American businessman working in London, is so persuasive that a coworker, Donald Heath, is convicted of robbing and murdering the owner of the trucking firm where they were both employed. Although no trace of the money is found, Heath is sentenced to life imprisonment. Immediately after the trial, George tells his wife, Martha, that he has made a "killing" in the stock market and is using his new wealth to join Morris Brooke in buying out a shipping concern. The venture proves to be enormously successful and within 5 years George has become extremely wealthy. Then a blackmail note arrives in which a disbarred attorney, Jeremy Clay, accuses George of having himself committed the murder. Recalling the vagueness of the circumstances under which George acquired his money, Martha begins to doubt her husband. Hoping for reassurance, she conducts a series of private investigations, but each effort only makes her more certain of George's guilt. Finally, she visits Clay, who tells her he actually saw George commit the murder. Fearing that George will now kill her, Martha returns home. As she enters the bathroom she is seized by Clay, who tapes her mouth and attempts to slash her wrists. But George bursts into the room and subdues Clay. Before the police arrive, Clay admits he committed the crime for which Heath was convicted. *Businessmen. Americans in foreign countries. Lawyers. Robbery. Murder. Injustice. Blackmail. Stock market. Trucking agencies. Shipping companies. London.*
Note: Filmed in London; opened there in Aug 1961.

THE NAKED FLAME (Canada)   F6.3404
Corona Productions. *Dist* Headliner Productions. 3 Apr 1970 [Chicago opening]. Sd; col (Eastman Color). 35mm. ca90 min.

Prod-Dir Larry Matanski. *Assoc Prod* A. W. Mokry. *Screenplay* Al Everett Dennis. *Dir Photog* Paul Ivano. *Camera Op* Jack McCoskey. *Art Dir* Meredith Evans. *Sd Ed* Jack Kirschner. *Prod Coörd* Frank Leonetti. *Script Supv* Dixie McCoy.

Cast: Dennis O'Keefe, Kasey Rogers, Al Ruscio, Linda Bennett, Tracey Roberts, Barton Heyman, Robert Howay.

Drama. An outsider becomes engaged to a member of a small community of Dukhobors, a Christian sect of 18th-century Russian origin, who completely reject priesthood, the sacraments, and other symbols of the Orthodox Church. There are several murders, a suicide, and two love affairs in the farming settlement. The Sons of Freedom, a Dukhobor sect, adhere to the cult's traditions, including nudism. *Dukhobors. Strangers. Farmers. Religion. Village life. Murder. Suicide. Nudism.*

Note: Filmed in 1963 in Calgary, Canmore, and Banff, Canada.

NAKED FOG   **F6.3405**
Amalfi Films. *Dist* Rossmore Film Distributors, Boxoffice International Film Distributors. 23 Mar **1966** [Champaign, Illinois, showing]. Sd; b&w. 35mm. 80 min.

Prod Gabriel Cicale. *Dir-Writ* Joe Sarno.

Cast: Tammy Latour *(Marge)*, Jan Nash *(Marina)*, Mike Higgins *(Jack)*, Phil Mason *(Evan)*, Judy Young *(Lucille)*, Susan Winters *(Helga)*, Rick Sheldon *(Jeff)*, Dusty Martin *(Kirk)*, Shep Wild *(Judd)*, Sylvia Grant *(Marta)*, Pat Williams, actress *(Lynn)*, Johnny Kuhl *(Rok)*, Karen Cooper *(Tina)*, Pat Revere *(Cora)*, Beth Adams *(Claire)*, Robin Marks *(Anna)*, Jo Ann London *(Dino)*, Marla Ellis *(Nancy)*, John Fontayne *(Matt)*, Otis Maclay *(Berkey)*.

Melodrama. Marge, a jet set playgirl, visits relatives in a small harbor town. She meets Jack, owner of a marina, and is attracted by his rugged charm. Marge's brief affair with Jack ends when she discovers that he is a pimp; one night his teenage cousin, Marina, interrupts their lovemaking to hand him her evening's earnings. Revolted, she turns in vain to an old boyfriend for consolation. Finally, she pairs off with Evan, an unsophisticated young man who is the son of the local madam. The film concludes with the happy couple planning their future together. *Playgirls. Jet set. Pimps. Madams. Cousins. Prostitution. Smalltown life. Waterfronts.*

Note: Also known as *Night Fog.*

NAKED FURY *see* **THE PLEASURE LOVERS**

THE NAKED GENERAL (Japan)   **F6.3406**
Toho Co. 15 Dec **1964** [New York opening]. Sd; col (AgfaColor). 35mm (Tohoscope). 92 min.

Dir Hiromichi Horikawa. *Screenplay* Yoko Mizuki. *Photog* Asaichi Nakai. *Art Dir* Yasuhide Kato.

Cast: Keiju Kobayashi *(Kiyoshi Yamashita)*, Aiko Mimasu *(his mother)*, Yasuko Nakada *(girl in a lunch shop)*, Daisuke Kato *(master of an eating house)*, Kyoko Aoyama *(girl in an eating house)*, Eijiro Tono *(commander)*, Reiko Dan *(bus conductor)*.

Biographical comedy. The film examines the life of Japanese artist Kiyoshi Yamashita. At the beginning of World War II, he spends most of his time dodging the draft and living a tramp-like existence. In order to escape the insanity of war, he strips naked in the street and succeeds in getting himself placed in an asylum. At the end of the film, Kiyoshi has achieved international fame as an artist and is seen fleeing from a mob of autograph-seeking fans. *Draft dodgers. Tramps. Artists. Insane asylums. World War II. Kiyoshi Yamashita.*

Note: Released in Japan in Oct 1958 as *Hadaka no taisho.*

THE NAKED GODDESS *see* **THE DEVIL'S HAND**

NAKED HEARTS (France)   **F6.3407**
Films Raoul Ploquin–Sodor Films. *Dist* Altura Films International. 18 May **1970** [New York opening]. Sd; b&w. 35mm. 90 min.

Prod Raoul Ploquin. *Dir-Writ* Edouard Luntz. *Photog* Jean Badal. *Film Ed* Suzanne Sandberg, Colette Kouchner. *Mus* Serge Gainsbourg, Henri Renaud. *Song:* "Be-Bop-a-Lula" Gene Vincent, Sheriff Tex Davis. *Sd* René Longuet, Antoine Bonfanti. *Asst Dir* Maurice Dugowson.

Cast: Gérard Zimmermann *(Zim)*, Marise Maire *(Jacqueline)*, Erick Penet *(Jean-Pierre)*, Françoise Bonneau *(Patricia)*, Ariette Thomas *(Jean-Pierre's mother)*, Elliott Stein, Nat Lilienstein.

Melodrama. Zim, an adolescent living in suburban Paris, is apprehended by the police as he is siphoning gas from a car and is sent to a reformatory. He and Jean-Pierre, a fellow inmate, become friends when they are released on the same day and discover that they come from the same suburb of Paris. Zim tries to find a job, but Jean-Pierre spends the days with his friends in a cafe. Jean-Pierre's friends goad him into meeting Jacqueline, a young factory worker. Later that night, the gang forces Jacqueline to have sex with Jean-Pierre; afterwards, the others go to her in turn. Zim, happy to have found a job in the construction industry, attends a local dance and meets an attractive girl,

Patricia; but before the evening is over she departs with a group of young men from the well-to-do suburb of Neuilly. Fighting breaks out when a rival gang appears. Police arrive; the youngsters scatter; and after the melee Zim finds Patricia waiting for him. Jean-Pierre joins Zim at the construction site, but the work proves too hard and he leaves. Returning to the cafe, Jean-Pierre is rejected by Jacqueline. Zim is offered a position in a trade school, and he goes to tell his friend the news, only to find Jean-Pierre being arrested for attempting to steal a car. *Juvenile delinquents. Police. Gangs. Construction workers. Factory workers. Theft. Adolescence. Criminals—Rehabilitation. Rape. Reformatories. Cafes. Paris.*

Note: Opened in Paris in Nov 1966 as *Les coeurs verts*; running time: 105 min.

NAKED IN THE NIGHT *see* **ONE NAKED NIGHT**

NAKED IN THE WIND (France)   **F6.3408**
Carmina Films. *Dist* William Mishkin. ca **1962**. Sd; b&w. 35mm. 74 min.

Prod Michel d' Olivier. *Dir-Adapt* Henri Lepage. *Screenplay-Dial* Jacques de Bénac. *Photog* Enzo Riccioni. *Underwater Photog* Michel Rocca. *Film Ed* Marity Cléris. *Mus* Guy Lafarge. *Sd* Roger Cosson. *Sd Rec* Louis Bertone. *Prod Mgr* André Labrousse.

Cast: Armand Bernard *(Darcepoil)*, Antonin Berval *(Farigoul)*, Félix Oudart *(Lespinasse)*, Jeanne Sourza *(Madame Lespinasse)*, Lili Bontemps *(Pantaflon)*, Jean Tissier, Alice Tissot, Jim Gérald, Henri Arius, Saint-Granier, Michel Flamme, Nicole Besnard, Irène Ladrina.

Nudist film. Smalltown confectioner Lespinasse, hopeful of being reelected as chief councillor, is opposed by Darcepoil, the local druggist. Darcepoil arranges for the incumbent's defeat by having Pantaflon, a nightclub singer, lure him to the nudist camp on the Isle of Levant, where Lespinasse is photographed surrounded by half-naked women. At home, he is berated by his wife and thrown out of office; but he returns to Levant with the penitent Pantaflon and is welcomed by the nudists and voted camp president. His forgiving wife follows him and herself becomes a nudist. *Politicians. Singers. Confectioners. Pharmacists. Nudism. Smalltown life. Reputation. Nudist camps. Elections. Photographs. Government—Local. Île du Levant.*

Note: Released in France in 1952 as *L'île aux femmes nues*; running time: 95 min. Jeanne Sourza is also known as Jane Sourza. Also advertised as *Naked in the Mind.*

NAKED ISLAND: "THE LAND OF 1001 NUDES" (France)   **F6.3409**
Carmina Films–Louis Noel. *Dist* Union Film Distributors, Kingsley International Pictures. Nov **1961**. Sd; b&w with col seq (Eastman Color). 35mm. 67 min.

Pres by William Mishkin, Constitution Films. *Dir* Michel d'Olivier, Gerald Tor. *Scen* Michel d'Olivier, Jean-Albert Fox, Robert Rocca, Helene Chat. *Adapt* Marquis Monde. *Photog* Joseph Le Clerq, H. Bernard. *Film Ed* Pierre Smilet. *Mus* Roger Roger, Jean Rotart.

Cast—Featuring: Robert Rocca, Helene Chat.

Cast—Narrator: Marquis Monde.

Nudist film. On the Isle of Levant, a nudist resort off the southern coast of France, an American woman, a Norwegian woman, French students, and others frolic on the beaches. *Americans in foreign countries. Students. Norwegians. Nudism. Resorts. Île du Levant.*

Note: Original title and release undetermined. This may be a U. S. reedition of a French film.

THE NAKED KISS   **F6.3410**
Leon Fromkess–Sam Firks. *Dist* Allied Artists. 4 May **1964** [Chicago opening]. Sd; b&w. 35mm. 93 min.

Prod-Dir-Writ Samuel Fuller. *Exec Prod* Leon Fromkess, Sam Firks. *Photog* Stanley Cortez. *Camera Op* Frank Dugas. *Asst Camera Op* Gene Liggett, Julian Wilson. *Art Dir* Eugene Lourié. Victor Gangelin. *Main Titl* Pacific Title. *Film Ed* Jerome Thoms. *Mus* Paul Dunlap. *Song:* "Santa Lucia" sung by John Guarniere. *Rec Supv* Al Overton, Jr. *Mus Ed* Peter Zinner. *Sd Eff Ed* Leonard Corso. *Asst Dir* Nate Levinson, John Gaudioso. *Prod Mgr* Herbert G. Luft. *Script Supv* John Dutton. *Cost* Einar Bourman. *Makeup* Harry Thomas. *Hairstyles* Marie Walter-Temme. *Still Photog* Ed Jones.

Cast: Constance Towers *(Kelly)*, Anthony Eisley *(Griff)*, Michael Dante *(Grant)*, Virginia Grey *(Candy)*, Patsy Kelly *(Mac)*, Betty Bronson *(Miss Josephine)*, Marie Devereux *(Buff)*, Karen Conrad *(Dusty)*, Linda Francis *(Rembrandt)*, Barbara Perry *(Edna)*, Walter Mathews *(Mike)*, Betty Robinson *(Bunny)*, Gerald Michenaud *(Kip)*, Christopher Barry *(Peanuts)*, George Spell *(Tim)*, Patty Robinson *(Angel Face)*, Neyle Morrow *(Officer Sam)*, Monte Mansfield *(Farlunde)*, Fletcher Fist *(Barney)*, Gerald Milton *(Zookie)*, Breena Howard *(Redhead)*, Sally Mills *(Marshmallow)*, Edy Williams *(Hatrack)*, Michael Barrere *(young delinquent)*, Patricia Gayle *(nurse)*, Sheila Mintz *(receptionist)*, Bill Sampson *(Jerry)*.

Melodrama. Kelly, a prostitute, leaves town after a fight with her procurer and takes the money he owes her. She comes to the small town of Grantville, where her first customer is Griff, the police chief, who advises her to avoid arrest by going to work for Candy's bordello across the state line. Instead, Kelly remains in town and takes a job as nurse's aid at a hospital, where she soon establishes a close rapport with the children in her ward. Griff discovers that she is still in town, and although he does not believe that she desires to reform, he reluctantly agrees to give her a chance. Later she falls in love with Grant, a wealthy grandson of the town's founder. Meanwhile, Kelly completes her reformation by helping two associates. Buff, an innocent girl, decides to become a prostitute at Candy's after the madam gives her some cash, but Kelly changes Buff's mind, returns the money, and assaults Candy. When an unmarried nurse's aid becomes pregnant, Kelly borrows money from Grant so that the woman can leave town to have her baby rather than undergo an abortion. Kelly is gratified by Grant's indifference to her past, until she makes a surprise visit to his home and discovers him molesting a little girl. Shocked at the scene and hurt by Grant's pleas for understanding because they are both "abnormal," she kills him and surrenders herself to Griff. The police chief does not believe her story, and Kelly's position is weakened by both Candy and her former procurer, who testify that she is a blackmailer. Although the nurse's aid describes Kelly's help during her pregnancy, Griff believes that the money she got from Grant was extorted. Kelly then reveals her real reason for visiting Candy, and Buff finally corroborates her testimony. Uncertain, Griff locates the girl Grant molested, and Kelly is cleared. Vindicated, Kelly leaves Grantville, despite the townspeople's pleas and Griff's marriage proposal. *Prostitutes. Pimps. Police. Madams. Children. Nursing aids. Prostitution. Smalltown life. Child molesting. Pregnancy. Murder. Infidelity. Hospitals. Whorehouses.*

Note: Working title: *The Iron Kiss.*

NAKED LIKE WOW! see **MR. PEEK-A-BOO'S PLAYMATES**

THE NAKED LOVERS see **THE NAKED ZOO**

THE NAKED PEOPLE see **WORLD WITHOUT SHAME**

THE NAKED PREY (United States/South Africa)   **F6.3411**
Theodora Productions–Sven Persson Films. *Dist* Paramount Pictures. 23 Mar 1966 [Boston opening; c31 Dec 1965; LP32305]. Sd (RCA); col (Eastmancolor, print by Technicolor). 35mm (Panavision). 96 min.
Prod-Dir Cornel Wilde. *Co-prod* Sven Persson. *Story & Screenplay* Clint Johnston, Donald A. Peters. *Dir Photog* H. A. R. Thomson. *Camera Op* Ray Sturgess. *Titl Backgrounds* Andrew T. Motjuoadi. *Film Ed* Roger Cherrill. *Mus Adv* Andrew Tracey. *Theme Song:* "The Naked Prey" *sung by* The Principal Warriors. *Sd Rec* James Chapman. *Asst Sd Rec* Luke Broadley. *Sd Ed* Les Wiggins. *Mus Ed* Archie Ludski. *Dub Mix* Len Shilton. *1st & 2d Asst Dir* Bert Batt, Howard Rennie. *Prod Supv* Basil Keys. *Prod Mgr* John Merriman. *Unit Mgr* Dawie Van Heerden. *Cont* Muirne Mathieson. *Wardrobe Supv* Freda Thompson. *Makeup* Trevor Crole-Rees. *Coöp* National Parks Board of Trustees of South Africa, Government of South Africa. *Ch Electrn* Corrie Van Wyk. *Constr Mgr* Edu Masuch.
Cast: Cornel Wilde (*man*), Gert Van den Bergh (*ivory hunter*), Ken Gampu (*warrior leader*), Patrick Mynhardt (*safari overseer*), Bella Randles (*little girl*), Morrison Gampu (*tribal chief*), Sandy Nkomo, Eric Mcanyana, John Marcus, Richard Mashiya, Franklyn Mdhluli, Joe Dlamini, Fuzi Zazayokwe, Jose Sithole, Horace Gilman (*warriors*).
Adventure drama. In the 19th century, a white hunter is preparing to lead a safari into the South African jungle. Through the rudeness of the hunter's employer, the natives are stirred to anger and revenge, and as a result, he and his party are attacked and brutally tortured to death by the tribesmen. The hunter's punishment is to be stripped of his clothing, weapons, and food and set free. Given a headstart, he is to compete in "The Chance of the Lion," an ancient game of survival in which he will be hunted by tribe members who have killed 10 lions. He wards off starvation by eating raw plants and snakes and stealing food; cornered, he uses his cunning to escape; when trapped, he saves his life by killing his foe. After days of fighting both the jungle and his pursuers, the man reaches sight of a mission fort. Although he is almost caught, his luck and courage carry him through, and he crawls to safety. As he does so, he looks back and sees the chief tribesman award him with a salute of respect. *Hunters. Africans. Survival. Torture. Murder. Tribal life. Courage. Safaris. Jungles.*
Note: Filmed in the Transvaal, including the Kruger National Park; Botswana; Mozambique; and Rhodesia.

NAKED PURSUIT (Japan)   **F6.3412**
Dist Boxoffice International Film Distributors. Nov 1969. Sd; b&w with col seq. 35mm. 73 min.
Cast: Masayoshi Nogami (*student*), Mari Oaki (*girl*), Ranko Mizukami (*mother*), Kyuozo Fuyuki.

Melodrama. During a demonstration, a student accidentally kills a policeman. En route to prison, the captive eludes his guard and escapes to the seacoast. There he sees a young woman wandering aimlessly. Overwhelmed by the discovery that her mother has taken a lover, she has come to commit suicide. The student, seized by uncontrollable lust, pursues and rapes her. Her passions awakened by the attack, the girl leaves the scene with a renewed interest in life. *Students. Police. Fugitives. Rape. Filial relations. Murder. Suicide. Adolescence. Demonstrations.*
Note: Original title and release undetermined.

THE NAKED ROAD (Reissue)   **F6.3413**
Simar Productions. 27 Apr 1962 [New York opening]. Sd; b&w. 35mm. 71 min.
Note: Original title: *Naked Set.*

THE NAKED RUNNER (Great Britain)   **F6.3414**
Artanis Productions. *Dist* Warner Bros.–Seven Arts, Inc. 19 Jul 1967 [New York opening; c31 Dec 1966; LP35741]. Sd; col (Technicolor). 35mm (Techniscope). 104 min.
A Sinatra Enterprises Production. *Prod* Brad Dexter. *Dir* Sidney J. Furie. *Screenplay* Stanley Mann. *Dir Photog* Otto Heller. *Camera Op* Godfrey Godar. *Art Dir* Peter Proud. *Asst Art Dir* Bill Alexander. *Main Titl* Don Record. *Film Ed* Barry Vince. *Asst Film Ed* Alan Brett. *Mus Comp* Harry Sukman. *Mus Cond* Morris Stoloff. *Sd Rec* Maurice Askew, Peter Davies. *Sd Ed* Alan Bell, Arthur Ridout. *Asst Dir* Michael Dryhurst. *Prod Mgr* Fred Slark. *Cont* Pat Moon. *Hairdresser* Barbara Ritchie.
Cast: Frank Sinatra (*Sam Laker*), Peter Vaughan (*Martin Slattery*), Derren Nesbitt (*Colonel Hartmann*), Nadia Gray (*Karen Gisevius*), Toby Robins (*Ruth*), Inger Stratton (*Anna*), Cyril Luckham (*cabinet minister*), Edward Fox (*Ritchie Jackson*), J. A. B. Dubin-Behrmann (*Joseph*), Michael Newport (*Patrick Laker*).
Drama. Source: Francis Clifford, *The Naked Runner* (London, 1966). Sam Laker, an American widower who designs furniture in England, is planning to take his 14-year-old son, Patrick, on a business trip to the Leipzig Fair behind the Iron Curtain. Before his departure, he is contacted by a wartime colleague, Martin Slattery, who asks him to deliver a message in Leipzig. Slattery, now a chief in British Intelligence, wins Sam's consent when he tells him that delivery of the message could mean life or death to Karen Gisevius, a European agent who had helped Sam during the war. Actually, Slattery has devised an elaborate plan to force Sam into killing an international spy who has defected to the Communists. Shortly after arriving in East Germany, young Patrick is kidnaped, and Sam is informed by a Colonel Hartmann, presumably an East German, that in exchange for his son's safety he must assassinate a man in Copenhagen. Unable to think of anything but his son, Sam agrees; but his victim fails to show up. He then is told that Patrick has been killed by Hartmann because the assignment was never carried out. Now driven to an almost maniacal determination to avenge his son's murder, Sam gathers information about Hartmann's scheduled movements and sights his rifle on the roadway Hartmann is expected to travel. When the car passes, Sam fires two bullets into the back seat of the car and kills the occupant. As Sam makes his getaway, he is met by Slattery and Hartmann and informed that the man he killed was the defector-spy. *Widowers. Americans in foreign countries. Furniture designers. Secret agents. Defectors. Communists. Fatherhood. Espionage. Assassination. Duplicity. Kidnaping. Revenge. Iron Curtain. Leipzig. German Democratic Republic. Great Britain—Intelligence service.*
Note: Location scenes filmed in London and Copenhagen. Released in Great Britain in Aug 1967; running time: 102 min.

THE NAKED SEARCH see **THE SHAMELESS**

NAKED SET see **THE NAKED ROAD**

THE NAKED SPUR see **HOT SPUR**

NAKED TEMPTATION see **WOMAN AND TEMPTATION**

THE NAKED TEMPTRESS see **THE NAKED WITCH**

NAKED TERROR   **F6.3415**
Dist Joseph Brenner Associates. Aug 1961. Sd; col (Eastmancolor). 35mm. 74 min.
Documentary. Highlighted in the film on the ancient traditions and superstitions of the African Zulu tribes are: Zulu virgins being initiated into the tribe; a witch doctor teaching young girls the dance of the deadly pythons; murder by witchcraft; and the water truth test in which the arms of suspected liars are thrust into caldrons of scalding water. *Zulus. Witch doctors. Rites and ceremonies. Tribal life. Superstition. Witchcraft. Virginity. Murder. Trials. Africa. Snakes.*
Note: Filmed in Africa. Country of origin undetermined.

NAKED UNDER LEATHER *see* **THE GIRL ON A MOTORCYCLE**

THE NAKED WEST—AND HOW IT WAS LOST *see* **THE IMMORAL WEST—AND HOW IT WAS LOST**

THE NAKED WINDS OF THE SEA *see* **ONE SWEDISH SUMMER**

THE NAKED WITCH   F6.3416

Alexander Enterprises. *Dist* Alexander Enterprises, William Mishkin. Jun 1964 [c28 Aug 1961; LP27580]. Sd; col (Eastmancolor). 35mm. 60 min. [See note.]

Prod Claude Alexander. *Dir* Andy Milligan. *Screenplay* Clay Guss. *Photog* Andy Milligan.

Cast: Beth Porter *(Beth)*, Robert Burgos *(Stephen)*, Bryarly Lee *(Bella)*, Lee Forbes *(deaf-and-dumb hunchback)*, Maggie Rogers *(Mary)*, Esther Travers *(Stephen's mother)*, Vernon Newman *(Robert)*, Haal Borske *(Willie)*, Josef Bush *(Bud)*, Phyllis Newman *(Robert's mother)*, Robert Likala *(Jay)*.

Horror film. Stephen, a college student who is researching witchcraft, goes to an Atlantic coast village where a woman was executed as a witch in the 1800's. He digs up her shallow grave one night and removes the stake from her heart. She rises from the dead to once again tempt the men of the town and terrorize the populace. Stephen falls in love with Bella, a village girl who has befriended a deaf-and-dumb hunchback, but he comes under the spell of Beth, the vampire. Bella becomes pregnant, and Stephen must decide whether to marry Bella and destroy Beth, or desert Bella for Beth, knowing that she will continue to terrorize the town. *Witches. Vampires. Hunchbacks. Students. Grave robbers. Temptresses. Witchcraft. Village life. Pregnancy. New England.*

Note: Location scenes filmed in Dallas. Rereleased in 1967 by Mishkin with 20 min additional footage. Alternative title: *The Naked Temptress.*

NAKED WORLD (Italy)   F6.3417

Mida Film–Film Columbus. *Dist* Times Film Corp. May 1968 [New York opening]. Sd; col (Eastmancolor). 35mm. 92 min.

A Film by Giuseppe Marotta. *Dir* Francesco De Feo. *Dir Adtl Scenes (see note)* Albert T. Viola. *Screenplay* Giuseppe Marotta, Giancarlo Fusco. *Photog* Adalberto Albertini. *Mus* Teo Usuelli.

Documentary. This documentary of bizarre human behavior begins with tourists arriving in Hiroshima and at Alamogordo Air Base, site of the first man-made atomic explosion. The travelog continues with prisoners on a Pacific island practicing free love; Danish teenagers sunbathing in the nude; and Mexican Indians treating the dead in a lighthearted fashion. Diverse scenes include sexual practices among students from the Free School of Devonshire; the manufacture of cheese in the Pô valley; a fashion show for male homosexuals in the Philippines; a "happening" in New York City; Latin American men bathing in waters reputed to restore diminished sexual powers; hypnotism as practiced in Ceylon; the story of Japan's last Kamikaze pilot; and a drum-beating rite to accompany the birth of a child in an African tribe. *Tourists. Kamikazes. Convicts. Indians of North America. Rites and ceremonies. Sexual practices. Nudism. Impotence. Childbirth. Male homosexuality. Hypnotism. Atom bomb. Cheese. Fashion shows. Hiroshima. Mexico. Africa. Philippines. Denmark. Pacific Ocean. New York City. England. Ceylon. Alamogordo Air Base.*

Note: Released in Italy in Dec 1963 as *Mondo nudo*; running time: 105 min. Purportedly based on the diary of Giuseppe Marotta. U. S. version includes 10 min of footage filmed by Al Viola.

THE NAKED WORLD OF HARRISON MARKS (Great Britain)
                                                       F6.3418

Token Films. *Dist* Manson Distributing Corp. 19 Oct 1967 [San Francisco showing]. Sd; col. 35mm. 84 min.

Prod-Dir George Harrison Marks. *Exec Prod* Harry Reuben. *Narrative* William Templeton. *Scen* George Harrison Marks, Terry Maher, Jim McDonald. *Camera* Len Harris. *Dsgn* Tony Roberts, art. *Film Ed* Jim Connock. *Mus Comp, Arr & Cond* John Hawksworth.

Cast: Harrison Marks *(himself/Al Capone/Toulouse-Lautrec/James Bond/Napoleon/Alfie/Count Dracula)*, Pamela Green, June Palmer, Chris Williams, Jutka Goz, Annette Johnson, Chris Bromfield, Ken Hayes, Derek Nichols, David Roberts.

Narrators: Valentine Dyall, Beryl Gilchrist.

Fantasy. Renowned fashion and nude-study photographer Harrison Marks runs a large organization which specializes in the packaging and distribution of feminine beauty—advertising, set design, the judging of beauty contests, and cheesecake photography. Harrison Marks sits in the center of his complex organization and daydreams. He "becomes" Al Capone, Toulouse-Lautrec, James Bond, Napoleon, Alfie, and Count Dracula, and he fantasizes that he is charged with the prostitution of art. He awakens surrounded by the nude women who form the nucleus of his organization. *Entrepreneurs. Photographers. Models. Sexuality. Nudity. Advertising. Art. Beauty contests.*

Fantasy. Al Capone. Henri de Toulouse-Lautrec. Napoleon I. James Bond. Alfie. Dracula.

Note: Also known as *The Dream World of Harrison Marks.*

NAKED YOUTH (Japan)   F6.3419

Shochiku Co. *Dist* Shochiku Films of America. Jul 1961 [Los Angeles showing]. Sd; col (Eastman Color by Shochiku). 35mm (Shochiku GrandScope). 96 min.

Dir-Writ Nagisa Oshima. *Photog* Ko Kawamata. *Mus* Riichiro Manabe.

Cast: Yusuke Kawazu, Miyuki Kuwano, Yoshiko Kuga, Fumio Watanabe, Shinji Tanaka, Shinjiro Matsuzaki, Toshiko Kobayashi.

Drama. A schoolgirl in search of excitement begins accepting rides from strange men. A college student rescues her from the advances of a middle-aged driver and seduces her himself. Although he is having an affair with an older woman, he becomes more involved with the girl, whose family offers her little guidance in such matters. The girl moves in with the student, but they are threatened by hoodlums who demand money in exchange for the girl's safety. To obtain cash, the couple devises a scheme in which the girl accepts a ride with a stranger and is "rescued" by the student, who demands money through intimidation. The girl becomes pregnant, however, and one of the drivers reports the couple to the police. They are arrested and after their release, the student decides to leave the girl, feeling he cannot protect her. He is murdered by the hoodlums and, sensing her lover is in danger, the girl rushes to him, only to be killed trying to avoid a speeding car. *Students. Hitchhikers. Hoodlums. Extortion. Pregnancy. Family life. Murder.*

Note: Released in Japan in 1960 as *Seishun zankoku monogatari.*

NAKED YOUTH *see* **WILD YOUTH**

NAKED ZODIAC   F6.3420

Dist Canyon Cinema Cooperative, Sherpix, Inc. 26 Nov 1969 [San Francisco showing]. Sd; col. 16mm. 85 min.

Prod-Dir Ben Van Meter. *Photog* Ben Van Meter.

Experimental film. Comprised of 12 segments, this underground film uses nudity and sexual activity to illustrate the various signs of the astrological table. For each of three different signs a pregnant woman, a "wood nymph," and a young woman who takes hallucinogens shed their clothes as they expound their personal philosophies on freedom, and in another sequence a couple disrobe and perform sexual intercourse. *Astrology. Nudity. Eroticism. Hallucinogens.*

Note: Subsequently released by Canyon Cinema as a series of short films.

THE NAKED ZOO   F6.3421

Film Artists International. *Dist* R & S Film Enterprises. 18 Sep 1970 [New York opening]. Sd; col (Eastman Color). 35mm. 91 min. *MPAA rating* R.

Prod-Dir William Grefé. *Assoc Prod* Stuart Merrill. *Screenplay* Ray Preston. *Songs Sung by* Steve Alaimo.

Cast: Rita Hayworth *(Mrs. Golden)*, Stephen Oliver *(Terry Shaw)*, Ford Rainey *(Mr. Golden)*, Fay Spain *(Goldens' daughter)*, Fleurette Carter *(black woman)*, Willie Pastrano, Joe E. Ross, Canned Heat.

Domestic melodrama. Mrs. Golden, married to a crippled millionaire, has an affair with Terry Shaw, a young writer and swinging member of the artists' community of Miami's Cocoanut Grove district. At one of his LSD parties, Terry goes off with a black woman. Disappointed by his gigolo antics, Mrs. Golden cuts off Terry's subsidy. While Terry attempts a reconciliation with Mrs. Golden, Mr. Golden discovers them and, although the police believe Mr. Golden's death to be accidental, Mrs. Golden threatens to blackmail her lover. Terry resolves the situation by administering to his mistress a fatal overdose of narcotics. Terry later becomes a successful novelist. When the Goldens' daughter returns home from school, the writer seduces her. Afterwards, she slays him. *Cripples. Millionaires. Authors. Gigolos. Widows. Infidelity. Finance—Personal. Murder. Blackmail. Drug overdose. Seduction. LSD. Miami.*

Note: Location scenes filmed in and around Miami, Florida. Working title: *The Grove.* Alternative title: *The Naked Lovers.* Also released as *The Hallucinators*; running time: 78 min.

NAM ANGELS *see* **THE LOSERS**

THE NAME OF THE GAME IS KILL!   F6.3422

Poore-Todd Productions. *Dist* Fanfare Films. 29 May 1968 [Detroit opening]. Sd; col (Eastman Color, print by Pathé). 35mm. 88 min. [Cut from 92 min.]

Prod Robert A. Poore. *Exec Assoc Prod* Richard J. Todd. *Assoc Prod* Robert L. Rosen. *Exec Prod* Joe Solomon. *Dir* Gunnar Hellström. *Screenplay* Gary Crutcher. *Dir Photog* William Zsigmond. *1st Asst Camera* Tom Ellsberg. *Art Dir* Ray Markham. *Film Ed* Louis Lombardo. *Mus Comp & Cond* Stu Phillips. *Song:* "Shadows" Stu Phillips, Mike Gordon, mus. *Sung by* The Electric Prunes. *Sd* Producers Sound Service, J. Young. *Asst Dir* Wilbur D'Arcy. *Wardrobe* Sara Anderson. *Makeup* Louis Lane.

Cast: Jack Lord (*Symcha Lipa*), Susan Strasberg (*Mickey Terry*), Collin Wilcox (*Diz Terry*), Tisha Sterling (*Nan Terry*), T. C. Jones (*Mr. & Mrs. Terry*), Mort Mills (*Sheriff Fred Kendall*), Marc Desmond (*doctor*).

Melodrama. While making his way across the Arizona desert, a transient Hungarian refugee, Symcha Lipa, accepts a lift from a young woman, Mickey Terry, who drives him to her family's gas station in a ghost town. He is met by Mrs. Terry, a nervous, fidgety woman, and by Mickey's two hostile sisters, the masculine-looking Diz and the child-like, spider-loving Nan, both of whom make sexual overtures to the visitor. After spending the night, Symcha tries to sneak away but is run down by someone driving the family's old black Packard. When he recovers in a small adjacent town, the local sheriff advises him to stay away from the family and tells him of the disappearance of Mickey's fiancé. Despite this warning, Symcha returns to the gas station and accepts a job from Mickey, with whom he falls in love. He hears conflicting stories concerning the family's past and the possible murder of Mr. Terry; he decides to marry Mickey and take her away to San Francisco. Diz becomes incensed at the impending breakup of the family, and at a Halloween party, Symcha is knocked unconscious with a Venus de Milo statue and dragged by Diz and Nan toward the filling station's incinerator. He is saved from cremation when the family bulldog begins howling, and Mickey and Mrs. Terry race to the rescue. As Diz goes insane in her attempt to destroy Symcha, it is revealed that Mrs. Terry is actually Mr. Terry, who has masqueraded as his wife since her murder years ago. Now concerned only with getting Mickey away from her family, Symcha drives off with her as Mr. Terry prepares to poison himself and his two murderous daughters. An enigma remains as to the murderer of Mickey's mother. *Hungarians. Refugees. Sheriffs. Sisters. Family life. Insanity. Murder. Female impersonation. Matricide. Deserts. Ghost towns. Filling stations. Automobiles. Hallowe'en. Arizona. Spiders.*

Note: Location scenes filmed in Jerome, Arizona. Working title: *Lovers in Limbo.*

THE NAME OF THE GAME IS SEX see **THE GAME IS SEX**

NAMELESS see **FRAULEIN DOKTOR**

NAMONAKU MAZUSHIKU UTSUKUSHIKU see **HAPPINESS OF US ALONE**

NAMU, THE KILLER WHALE   F6.3423

Ivan Tors Enterprises. *Dist* United Artists. 1 Aug **1966** [Seattle opening; c1 Aug 1966; LP33017]. Sd; col (DeLuxe). 35mm. 89 min.

Prod-Dir Laslo Benedek. *Exec Prod* Ivan Tors. *Assoc Prod* Lamar Boren. *Screenplay* Arthur Weiss. *Cinematog* Lamar Boren. *Art Dir* Eddie Imazu. *Film Ed* Warren Adams. *Mus* Samuel Matlovsky. *Song:* "The Ballad of Namu, the Killer Whale" ("*Live and Let Live*") comp & sung by Tom Glazer. *Sd Mix* Al Strasser. *Asst Dir* Jack R. Berne. *Asst to the Prod* Don Leonard, prod asst. *Script Supv* Joseph Gannon. *Unit Prod Mgr* Herman Webber. *Tech Adv* Ted Griffin.

Cast: Robert Lansing (*Hank Donner*), John Anderson (*Joe Clausen*), Robin Mattson (*Lisa Rand*), Richard Erdman (*Deke*), Lee Meriwether (*Kate Rand*), Joe Higgins (*Burt*), Michael Shea (*Nick*), Clara Tarte (*Carrie*), Edwin Rochelle (*Charlie*).

Adventure drama. Naturalist Hank Donner, studying whales with his assistant Deke, witnesses two salmon fishermen, Joe and Burt, pursuing killer whales, a species that feeds on salmon. The fishermen shoot a female whale, which, followed by her mate, swims into the cove that Hank has rented. When the wounded female dies, her mate stays in the cove. Hank decides to study the whale and with a 200-ft. net bought from general store owner Kate Rand, who sells it to him despite the protests of the villagers, blocks off the entrance from the sea to the cove. The whale, belying the reputation of its species, becomes friendly with Hank and allows him to ride on its back. The good-natured whale is instrumental in dispelling the fear of the sea held by Kate's young daughter, Lisa, whose father drowned while skin-diving. Hank and Lisa christen the whale Namu. One day Lisa and her friends are feeding Namu when a sadistic boy secretly tosses Namu a fishhead imbedded with barbed hooks, and the whale's pained thrashing destroys the dock on which the children are standing. Two of the children are only mildly scratched, but the villagers use the incident as an excuse to demand Namu's destruction. Hank produces the barbed fishhead but the villagers are not dissuaded from their judgment until both Hank and Kate get into the water and play with Namu. Joe and Burt, however, begin to shoot at Namu from outside the cove. Deke opens the net, and Namu swims out, hits the boat, and knocks Joe unconscious and into the water. Namu holds Joe above the surface until Hank rescues him, then swims seaward as the onlookers watch a female whale join him. The two vanish in the distance. *Naturalists. Fishermen. Children. Sadism. Animal life. Phobias. General stores. Whales. Salmon.*

NANAMI: INFERNO OF FIRST LOVE (Japan)   F6.3424

Japan Art Theater Guild–Hani Productions. *Dist* Golden Eagle Films, RAF Industries. 11 Jun **1969** [Birmingham, Alabama, opening]. Sd; b&w. 35mm. 87 min. *MPAA rating* X.

Prod Satoshi Fujii. *Dir* Susumu Hani. *Screenplay* Susumu Hani, Shuji Terayama. *Photog* Yuji Okumura. *Mus* Akio Yashiro, Toru Takemitsu. *Sd* Yukio Kubota. *Prod Mgr* Yoshimoto Tsutsumi.

Cast: Akio Takahashi (*Shun*), Kuniko Ishii (*Nanami*), Koji Mitsui (*foster father*), Kazuko Fukuda (*foster mother*), Minoru Yuasa (*bearded man*), Shinatora (*gang leader*), Ichiro Kimura (*psychiatrist*), Haruo Asano (*Algebra*).

Melodrama. In present-day Tokyo, a 17-year-old boy named Shun accidentally meets a young girl, Nanami, and is immediately attracted to her. Although they rent a hotel room for a few hours, Shun is too embarrassed and insecure to go through with his intentions, and instead of making love to Nanami he talks about his life. He tells the attentive girl that he lost his father when he was very young and that his mother abandoned him in order to remarry. He was taken in by foster parents, and his home life became uncomfortable because of his foster father's unfatherly attentions. He now finds escape from his dull job as a metal worker by going to the park to feed the pigeons and play games with a little girl. After listening to Shun's story, Nanami explains that when she came to the city she soon discovered that the most lucrative way to earn her living was to become a nude model. Several days later, while he is innocently playing with the little girl in the park, Shun's behavior is misconstrued, and, after being accused of being a child molester, he is beaten up and arrested. A psychiatrist examines him and concludes that Shun's past is preventing him from having a normal attitude toward girls and the world in general. Nanami, meanwhile, has progressed from mere nude modeling to posing for lesbian sado-masochistic photo sessions. Eventually, the two teenagers meet again and attend a university carnival where they watch a student film made by one of Nanami's friends. Although the picture, *A Record of First Love*, is amateurish and awkward, both Nanami and Shun are moved by its honesty, and they make a date to meet again at the same hotel. Shun, on his way to the hotel, runs into the men for whom Nanami performs in the nude. When they demand to know where she is, Shun refuses to tell them and breaks away. Running wildly through the streets, he is struck down by an automobile and dies in front of the hotel where Nanami is waiting to keep their rendezvous. *Orphans. Factory workers. Foster fathers. Models. Psychiatrists. Adolescence. Family life. Male homosexuality. Child molesting. Nudity. Sadomasochism. Lesbianism. Employment—Women. Photography. Hotels. Motion pictures. Automobile accidents.*

Note: Released in Japan in 1968 as *Hatsukoi jigokuhen* at 108 min.

THE NANNY (Great Britain)   F6.3425

Seven Arts Productions–Hammer Film Productions. *Dist* Twentieth Century-Fox Film Corp. 27 Oct **1965** [Detroit opening; c3 Nov 1965; LP32095]. Sd (RCA); b&w. 35mm. 93 min.

Prod-Writ Jimmy Sangster. *Exec Prod* Anthony Hinds. *Dir* Seth Holt. *Dir Photog* Harry Waxman. *Camera Op* Kelvin Pike. *Prod Dsgn* Edward Carrick. *Supv Ed* James Needs. *Ed* Tom Simpson. *Mus Comp* Richard Rodney Bennett. *Mus Supv* Philip Martell. *Rec Supv* A. W. Lumkin. *Sd Rec* Norman Coggs. *Sd Ed* Charles Crafford. *Asst Dir* Christopher Dryhurst. *Prod Mgr* George Fowler. *Cont* Renee Glynne. *Wardrobe* Rosemary Burrows. *Wardrobe Mistress* Mary Gibson. *Makeup* Tom Smith. *Hairstyles* A. G. Scott.

Cast: Bette Davis (*Nanny*), Wendy Craig (*Virgie Fane*), Jill Bennett (*Pen*), James Villiers (*Bill Fane*), William Dix (*Joey*), Pamela Franklin (*Bobby*), Jack Watling (*Dr. Medman*), Alfred Burke (*Dr. Wills*), Maurice Denham (*Dr. Beamaster*), Nora Gordon (*Mrs. Griggs*), Sandra Power (*Sarah*), Harry Fowler (*milkman*), Angharad Aubrey (*Susy*).

Mystery melodrama. Source: Evelyn Piper, *The Nanny* (New York, 1964). Nanny has always taken care of Virgie Fane and is now in charge of her two children. The elder, Joey, is being released after spending 2 years in a home for disturbed children; Joey was placed in the home because of his implication in the drowning of his sister, but he still maintains that Nanny was responsible. Both Virgie and her husband, Bill, are nervous about Joey returning home, especially Virgie, who depends on Nanny to run the house for her. Joey refuses to have anything to do with Nanny, but no one believes his story except Bobby, the girl upstairs. Bill, a diplomatic courier, is called away on business, and Virgie suffers an attack of food poisoning that forces her to enter a hospital. Aunt Pen, an invalid dependent on heart medicine, comes to take care of the children, and she becomes convinced that Joey is telling the truth when she sees Nanny about to smother him with a pillow. Later, Nanny tries unsuccessfully to drown Joey. When Aunt Pen has a heart attack, Nanny withholds her medicine and tells her story to the dying woman: Joey's sister's death had been a preventable accident for which Nanny was responsible; that, plus the death of her own illegitimate daughter, have caused Nanny to go mad. After Aunt Pen dies, Nanny again tries to kill Joey, but she cannot. Joey and his mother are reunited in the hospital, as Nanny is taken away by the authorities. *Nursemaids. Children. Invalids. Aunts. Diplomats. Insanity. Sororicide. Murder. Motherhood. Heart disease. Children's homes.*

Note: Opened in London in Nov 1965.

NARAYAMA-BUSHI-KO see **BALLAD OF NARAYAMA**

THE NARCO MEN (Italy/Spain)   **F6.3426**

Pan-Latina Films-P. E. A. *Dist* RAF Industries. 19 Oct **1969** [Tuscaloosa, Alabama, opening]. Sd; col (Eastman Color). 35mm (Techniscope). 95 min. *MPAA rating* M.

Prod Sam X. Abarbanel, Angel Ibarra, Santiago Moncada. *Dir* Julio Coll. *Screenplay* Howard Berk, Santiago Moncada, Sergio Donati, Julio Coll. *Photog* Oberdan Trojani. *Camera Op* Carlo Carlini. *Art Dir* Eduardo Torre de la Fuente. *Film Ed* Mercedes Alonso. *Mus* Marcello Giombini. *Prod Supv* Manuel Caño. *Prod Mgr* Pedro Villanueva.

Cast: Tom Tryon *(Harry Bell)*, Lorenza Guerrieri *(Jill)*, Ana Castor *(Sonia)*, José Bódalo *(Marcos)*, Richard Deacon, Mirko Ellis, Jesús Puente, Aurora de Alba, Franco Fantasia, Paul Muller, José María Prada, Wolfgang Hillinger, Robert Hundar, Carlos Ballesteros, Franco Ressel, Emilio Redondo, Raf Baldassarre, Carlos Mendy, Angel Jordán, Carlos Riera, Luis Gasper, Saturno Cerra, Diego Santiesteban, José Ignacio Pidal, Francisco Braña, Victor Israel, Hector Quiroga, Angel Menéndez.

Crime melodrama. When a smuggled shipment of heroin is hijacked, Marcos Aristoulas is threatened with murder by the Mediterranean Syndicate if he fails to retrieve it. He meets embittered ex-convict and former INTERPOL agent Harry Bell in Madrid and enlists his aid. In Barcelona, Harry meets Jill, a hippie who agrees to help him. Upon learning that the heroin is in Rome, Harry and Jill leave for Italy, followed by Max Mainzhoffer, an INTERPOL agent. Max is found murdered by the syndicate, but Harry apprehends the thief and killer—Sonia, Marcos' girl friend who was responsible for doublecrossing Harry and sending him to prison. He kills her, finds Jill dead, and returns to Athens. He informs Marcos that the heroin has been turned over to the authorities. His deadline passed, Marcos is murdered by a syndicate member. *Smugglers. Hijackers. Thieves. Ex-convicts. Hippies. Murder. Perfidy. Heroin. Syndicates. Madrid. Barcelona. Rome. Athens. INTERPOL.*

Note: Filmed in Madrid, Rome, Barcelona, Naples, Valencia, and Athens. Released in Spain in 1968 as *Persecución hasta Valencia*; running time: 102 min. Italian title: *Il sapore della vendetta.*

THE NARCOTIC STORY see **THE DREAD PERSUASION**

NASHVILLE REBEL   **F6.3427**

Fred A. Niles Productions. *For* Show Biz, Inc. *Dist* American International Pictures. 16 Nov **1966** [Nashville, Tennessee, opening; c22 Nov 1966; LP33713]. Sd; col (Technicolor). 35mm (Techniscope). 91 min. [Cut from 95 min.]

Prod Fred A. Niles. *Assoc Prod* Jane Dowden. *Dir* Jay Sheridan. *Screenplay* Ira Kerns, Jay Sheridan. *Orig Story* Click Weston. *Photog* John Elsenbach. *Film Ed* James Miller. *Mus* Robert Blanford. *Songs:* "Nashville Rebel," "Green River," "Long Way From Home," "Nashville Bum," "Silver Ribbons" sung by Waylon Jennings. *Song:* "Hillbilly Heaven" sung by Tex Ritter. *Song:* "Country Music's Gone to Town" sung by Porter Wagoner. *Song:* "Sweet Dream of You" sung by Faron Young. *Song:* "Do What You Do, Do Well" sung by Sonny James. *Song:* "Christmas at the Opry" sung by The Wilburn Brothers, Loretta Lynn. *Song:* "You Ain't Woman Enough" sung by Loretta Lynn. *Prod Mgr* Donald L. Lawrence. *Cost* Mary Ann Curtis.

Cast: Waylon Jennings *(Arlin Grove)*, Gordon Oas-Heim *(Wesley Lang)*, Mary Frann *(Molly Morgan)*, Cece Whitney *(Margo Powell)*, Tex Ritter, Henny Youngman, Sonny James, The Wilburn Brothers, Faron Young, Loretta Lynn, Porter Wagoner, Cousin Jody, Archie Campbell *(themselves).*

Melodrama with music. Arlin Grove, just out of the Army, hitches a ride with some drunken revelers who rob and beat him. He awakens in the bedroom of Molly Morgan, whose uncle owns a grocery store and filling station. Arlin stays on as a clerk and soon falls in love with Molly. When a hootenanny is held in the town, Arlin performs and becomes a local attraction. As he celebrates with Molly, her uncle bursts into her room and demands that they marry. Arlin's guitar playing attracts Wesley Lang, a conniving talent manager who signs him to a personal contract. Arlin soon realizes his mistake and attempts to break the contract. To get even, Lang tries to break up Arlin's marriage by introducing him to voluptuous Margo Powell and then books him into a plush Chicago nightclub, where he is laughed off the stage. He begins to drink heavily, and Molly enlists the aid of Tex Ritter to arrange for Arlin's comeback at the Grand Ole Opry House. Just before his performance, Arlin learns that Molly is pregnant and seriously ill. Instead of singing his number, he broadcasts his love for Molly and rushes to the hospital, where he finds Molly holding their newborn son. *Veterans. Guitarists. Singers. Uncles. Salesclerks. Talent agents. Country music. Marriage. Revenge. Alcoholism. Pregnancy. Infidelity.*

Hootenannies. Contracts. Nightclubs. Chicago. Grand Ole Opry.

Note: Filmed in and around Nashville; additional location scenes filmed in Chicago.

NASILJE NA TRGU see **SQUARE OF VIOLENCE**

THE NASTY RABBIT   **F6.3428**

Rushmore Productions. *Dist* Fairway-International Films. Jan **1965**. Sd; col (Technicolor). 35mm (Techniscope). 85 min.

Pres by Arch Hall, [Sr.]. *Prod* Nicholas Merriwether. *Dir* James Landis. *Screenplay* Arch Hall, [Sr.], Jim Critchfield. *Photog* William Zsigmond. *Asst Camera* Leslie Kovacs. *Art Dir* Don Schneider. *Film Ed* Anthony M. Lanza. *Songs:* "The Robot Walk," "Jackie," "The Spy Waltz," "The Jackrabbit Shuffle" writ by Pat Vegas, Lolly Vegas. *Perf & Sung by* Arch Hall, [Jr.], Pat Vegas, Lolly Vegas, The Archers. *Sd* Robert Dietz. *Asst Dir* David Reed, III. *Prod Mgr* Don Russell. *Makeup* Rafaelle Harrod. *Prop Master* Vic Goss.

Cast: Mischa Terr *(Mischa Lowzoff)*, Arch Hall, Jr. *(Britt Hunter)*, Melissa Morgan *(Cecelia)*, William Watters *(Marshall Malouf/Malcolm McKinley)*, Little Jack Little *(Maxwell Stoppic)*, Ray Vegas *(Gonzales)*, John Akana *(Colonel Kobayaski)*, Harold Bizzy *(Heinrich Krueger)*, Sharon Ryker *(Jackie)*, Hal Bokar *(Gavin)*, George J. Morgan *(Hubert Jackson)*, Leslie Kovacs *(The Idiot)*, Pat Vegas, Lolly Vegas, The Archers *(themselves).*

Farce. Soviet agent Mischa Lowzoff arrives in America with a rabbit bearing a vial of dangerous bacteria. His orders are to free the rabbit on the Continental Divide, from which the germs will spread, killing millions of Americans. Disguised as a cowboy, Lowzoff boards at a dude ranch, where his movements are observed by similarly disguised agents from Germany, Mexico, Japan, and Israel, and by the ranch's owner, an undercover agent for the FBI. The landlord joins forces with singer Britt Hunter, a Pentagon employee, to deactivate the deadly capsule. *Secret agents. Singers. Russians. Germans. Mexicans. Israelis. Japanese. Biological warfare. Espionage. Disguise. Dude ranches. Continental Divide. United States—Federal Bureau of Investigation. The Pentagon. Rabbits and hares.*

Note: Filmed on location in Wyoming. Also known as *Spies-A-Go-Go.* Nicholas Merriwether and William Watters are pseudonyms for Arch Hall, Sr.

IL NATALE CHE QUASI NON FU see **THE CHRISTMAS THAT ALMOST WASN'T**

NATHANIEL HAWTHORNE'S "TWICE TOLD TALES" see **TWICE TOLD TALES**

NATIONAL CHAMPIONSHIP DRAG RACING   **F6.3429**

Dist Boxoffice Attractions. 4 Dec **1966** [Maryland license]. Sd; b&w. 35mm. 114 min.

Documentary. No information about the precise nature of this film has been found. *Automobile racing.*

NATSUKASHIKI FUE YA TAIKO see **EYES, THE SEA AND A BALL**

NATTLEK see **NIGHT GAMES**

NATTVARDSGÄSTERNA see **WINTER LIGHT**

NATURE CAMP CONFIDENTIAL   **F6.3430**

Dawn Productions. *Dist* Atlantic Pictures, Jerand Film Distributors. 27 Dec **1961** [New York opening; c27 Dec 1961; LP22793]. col (Eastman Color, print by Movielab). 35mm. 70 min.

Prod-Dir Doris Wishman. *Screenplay* Melvin Stanley. *Dir Photog* Raymond Pheelan. *Supv Film Ed* Martin Samuels. *Mus* Harry Glass. *Song:* "Sun Lovers Blues" Judith J. Kushner. *Sung by* Rosemary June. *Sd Eff Ed* Morris Sands.

Cast: Davee Decker *(Stacey Taylor)*, Norman Casserly *(Arthur Sherwood)*, Zelda R. Suplee *(herself, director of Sunny Rest Lodge, Palmerton, Pa.; and Sunny Palms Lodge, Homestead, Fla.)*, Dolores Carlos, Allan Blacker, Joan Bamford, Maria Stinger, Harry W. Stinger, Brigitte Bernard, Bunny Downe, Ronald M. Ziegler, June Marko, Gustave A. Hoek, Nellie Hoek, Phyliss Hoek, Sandra Hoek, Charles Allen, Warrene Gray, Una Diehl, Gloria Flowers.

Nudist film. Arthur Sherman, a smalltown Florida newspaper editor, loses his way while hunting and comes upon a nudist camp. Shocked, he determines to expose nudism. He returns to his office and assigns reporter Stacey Taylor to visit the camp, instructing her to pose as a nudist so that she may send back daily articles. She agrees to carry out the assignment on Arthur's insistence because she is secretly in love with him. Once she overcomes her initial embarrassment, however, she is greatly impressed with the friendliness and sincerity of the nudists, and her articles reflect her new outlook. Arthur protests; she challenges him to write the articles himself; and she is aghast to see him at the camp a few days later. Finally Stacey sees a newspaper with the headline "Nudist Exposé, Page 5." Furious, she confesses to the camp director her initial purpose in visiting the camp. On reading the article, however, she finds that it tells of the virtues of nudism. *Reporters. Editors. Nudism.*

Duplicity. Newspapers. Florida.

Note: Registered for copyright as *Nature Camp Diary*; also known as *Diary of a Nudist*, *Nudist Confidential*, and *Nudist Camp*.

NATURE CAMP DIARY *see* **NATURE CAMP CONFIDENTIAL**

NATURE GIRLS UNLIMITED *see* **BEHIND THE NUDIST CURTAIN**

NATURE'S BEAUTIFUL PLAYMATES *see* **NATURE'S SWEETHEARTS**

NATURE'S CURE   F6.3431

Dist Stacey Distributors. ca **1970**. Sd; col. 16mm. 61-81 min.

Sex film. No information about the precise nature of this film has been found. *Sexuality.*

NATURE'S PLAYGIRLS, INTERNATIONAL *see* **PLAYGIRLS INTERNATIONAL**

NATURE'S PLAYMATES   F6.3432

D & R Pictures. *Dist* Dore Productions. 26 Dec **1962** [Chicago opening]. Sd; col (Eastman Color). 35mm. 62 min.

Prod Thomas J. Dowd, Davis Freeman. *Dir* Lewis H. Gordon. *Screenplay* Bentley Williams. *Camera* William R. Johnson. *Mus* Lawrence W. Brady. *Sd* Davis Mason. *Tech Dir* Fred Gordon.

Cast: Vickie Miles *(Diana)*, Scott Osborne *(Russ Harper)*, Peter Lathrop *(Ellsworth)*, Teri Stevens *(The Wife)*, Al Glick, Fred Gordon *(camp directors)*, Craig Maudslay, Jr., Warrene Gray, Ingrun Albert, Marsha Monnet, Elaine Roberts, Judy Parsons, Shirley Gresham, Doris Wisher, Amy O'Donnell.

Nudist film. Chicago private detective Russell Harper and his assistant, Diana, are hired by Mrs. Sandra Elliott to find her husband who has disappeared. Mrs. Elliott tells the detective team that her husband, formerly a nudist, may be found in a Florida nudist camp. Mrs. Elliott explains that the sole identifying mark on her husband is a tattoo on his arm. The detective team leaves for Miami, and after some reluctance on the part of Diana to remove her clothing, they begin to search the nudist camps in the Miami area. Diana soon begins to enjoy nudism; at one of the camps she enters a Twist contest with one of the nudists. They win the contest, and she introduces the man to Russell. Russell notices a mark on the man's arm that he suspects is covering a tattoo. When confronted, the man admits he is the missing Mr. Elliott. A confirmed nudist, Elliott states that he will not live with his wife who continually harangues him on the subject. Russell and Diana call Mrs. Elliott and ask her to come to the camp to persuade her husband to leave. Mrs. Elliott arrives the next day, and the two detectives persuade her to remove her clothing and enter the camp. She does so, and the Elliotts are happily reunited. The two detectives, who have fallen in love in the course of the case, leave the camp with the intention of marrying. *Detectives. Missing persons. Nudism. Nudist camps. Tattoos. Dance contests. Twist (dance). Chicago. Florida.*

NATURE'S SWEETHEARTS   F6.3433

Ikay Beautiful Films. 16 Aug **1963** [Los Angeles showing]. Sd; col (Eastman Color). 35mm. 63 min.

Prod Irving Klaw. *Dir* Larry Wolk. *Ed* Paul Falkenberg, Joseph P. Mawra. *Tech Coörd* Bunny Yeager.

Cast: Maria Stinger *(herself)*, Dick Powers *(himself)*, Suzy Crandle, Cindy Lee, Lori Shaw, Habala Hopkins, Cindy Connors, Jody Evans, Viv Boyd, Lacy Kelly, Ina Mays, Una Diehl, Jo Davis.

Nudist film. Maria Stinger narrates how she became a nudist. While in Florida on a modeling assignment, Maria meets rancher Dick Powers, who invites her to visit a nudist colony of which he is a member. She takes part in a fashion show, and later, after a swimsuit modeling session, Maria and some of her model friends relax in the nude on board a yacht. Powers spends much of his time showing Maria the sights of Miami and Miami Beach. In the Japanese gardens, he proposes to Maria, and she accepts. They are married in a nude ceremony with all the nudists as witnesses. *Models. Ranchers. Nudism. Nudist camps. Yachts. Weddings. Miami.*

Note: Also known as *Nature's Beautiful Playmates*.

NAUGHTY CUTIES *see* **NAUGHTY DALLAS**

NAUGHTY DALLAS   F6.3434

Double Bob Productions. *Dist* Paul Mart Productions, Diamond International Pictures. 19 Feb **1964** [San Antonio, Texas, opening]. Sd; col. 35mm. 78 min. [Also reviewed at 62 min.]

Dir Larry Buchanan.

Cast: Jada, Kim Athas, Peggy Steele, Breck Wall, Bill Fanning, Bill Demar, Buddy Raymon *(themselves)*.

Burlesque film. The film surveys night life in Dallas, focusing on Jack Ruby's Carousel Club and its exotic dancers performing striptease and burlesque.

Exotic dancers. Striptease. Nightclubs. Dallas. Jack Ruby.

Note: Also known as *Naughty Cuties* and *Mondo Exotica*.

NAUGHTY NUDES   F6.3435

F-T Productions. *Dist* Cinema Syndicate, Inc., Chancellor Films. 22 Oct **1965** [Maryland license]. Sd; col (Eastman Color). 35mm. ca65 min.

Prod Richard Sunderland, James Michael. *Dir-Writ* James Michael. *Cinematog* Richard Sunderland. *Film Ed* Sande Johnsen. *Mus Comp* Henri Woode. *Asst Dir* Ben Anthony.

Cast: Jackie LaMont, Sande Johnsen, Gigi Darlene, James Short, Nadja Swenson, Rita Ham, Priscilla Hadley, Oliver Silver, Jean Fairfield, Ben Anthony, Darlene Bennett.

Comedy. Art teacher Jackie takes a group of college girls on a short trip to complete their art studies. From the estate of one of the girl's parents, the group takes a boat to a deserted island. On the boat, they model for each other and become the focal point of several sailors' interest. On the island, Jackie agrees to allow the sailors to visit the girls that night at the estate. The gathering is rather tame until one of the sailors spikes the punch with rum. The group winds up in the swimming pool as the dean's secretary comes to call. Jackie is fired from her post at the college. *Art teachers. Students. Models. Sailors. Nudity. Drunkenness. College life. Islands.*

THE NAUGHTY SHUTTER   F6.3436

Dist Sack Amusement Enterprises. Dec **1963** [periodical notice; Los Angeles showing: 14 Feb 1964]. Sd; b&w. 35mm. 55 min.

Prod Charles Martinez. *Dir* Sammy Helm.

Comedy. At the Thunderbird Hotel, Danny, a reporter, sees camera buff Jerry take a picture of a passing maid. The photograph, developed in seconds, shows that the maid is nude; the camera apparently undresses the dressed. Danny and Jerry agree to cover a story with the camera; they drink to their partnership and pass out. The camera is stolen by a dishonest bystander, who sells it to another shady character, Bill. Bill leaves his room to run an errand, hiding the camera in a waste basket. During his absence, the maid enters and empties the waste basket into the garbage. Mrs. Silvers, the secretary of a sunbathers association, goes through the garbage looking for her lost address book and finds the camera. She and her nudist friends play with the camera, discovering that the photos show them dressed. They also find out that the camera is stolen. The police are called, and they eventually locate the camera after it passes through the hands of an undertaker and many others. *Reporters. Chambermaids. Photographers. Drunkenness. Nudity. Theft. Nudism. Hotels. Cameras.*

NAVAJO JOE (Italy/Spain)   F6.3437

Dino De Laurentiis Cinematografica–C. B. Films. *Dist* United Artists. 6 Dec **1967** [New York opening]. Sd; col (Technicolor). 35mm (Techniscope). 89 min.

Pres by Dino De Laurentiis. *Prod* Ermanno Donati, Luigi Carpentieri. *Dir* Sergio Corbucci. *Screenplay* Dean Craig, Fernando Di Leo, Ugo Pirro. *Story* Ugo Pirro. *Photog* Silvano Ippoliti. *Art Dir* Aurelio Crugnola. *Mus* Ennio Morricone. *Sd* Fernando Terol. *Asst Dir* Deodato Ruggero. *Gen Supv* Piero Donati. *Head of Prod* Eduardo Torre de la Fuente. *Prod Mgr* Giorgio Baldi. *Wardrobe* Marcella De Marchis. *Makeup* Franco Freda. *Hairstyles* Adalgisa Favella.

Cast: Burt Reynolds *(Navajo Joe)*, Aldo Sambrell *(Marvin "Vee" Duncan)*, Nicoletta Machiavelli *(Estella)*, Tanya Lopert *(Maria)*, Fernando Rey *(Parson Rattigan)*, Franca Polesello *(Barbara)*, Lucia Modugno *(Geraldine)*, Pierre Cressoy *(Lynne)*, Nino Imparato *(Chuck)*, Alvaro de Luna *(Sancho Ramirez)*, Valeria Sabel *(Honor)*, Mario Lanfranchi, actor *(Mayor Jefferson Clay)*, Lucio Rosato *(Jeffrey Duncan)*, Simón Arriaga *(Monkey)*, Cris Huerta *(El Gordo)*, Angel Ortiz *(El Cojo)*, Gianni Di Stolfo *(Sheriff Elmo Reagan)*, Angel Alvarez *(Oliver Blackwood)*, Rafael Albaicín, Lorenzo Robledo *(bandits)*.

Western melodrama. Marvin "Vee" Duncan and his band of outlaws destroy an entire Indian village; the sole survivor is Navajo Joe, who swears revenge. He slits the throats of two of Duncan's men sent to capture him, shoots two more, and knifes a third as the outlaws are about to capture three saloon hostesses. Finally, he thwarts a railroad holdup. The townspeople quickly forget their gratitude to Navajo Joe, however, in their fear of an assault from Duncan and his gang. Joe demands a dollar from every family for each bandit he kills, and after some argument, the obligation is met. While saving an Indian girl, Estella, from the outlaws, Joe is captured and hanged from the ankles. With the help of the saloon pianist, he cuts himself loose, knifes his guard, and stampedes the gang's horses. When he learns of Joe's escape, Duncan fills the church with hostages, and his men take over the town. The outlaws then rush off to rob the train, but they are again foiled by Joe, who dynamites the train. Duncan and his surviving followers pursue Joe as he rides back to the Indian village. In a final confrontation, Joe chokes his enemy to death, returns the bank money to the townspeople, hands over his bounty to Estella, and rides away. *Navajo Indians. Outlaws. Hostages. Massacres. Revenge. Murder. Train robberies.*

Extortion. Explosives.

Note: Released in Italy in 1966 as *Un dollaro a testa*; in Madrid in Nov 1967 as *Joe, el implacable*; running time: 93 min. Actor Aldo Sambrell is also known as Sam Brell.

NAVAJO RUN											F6.3438

LoraJon Productions. *Dist* American International Pictures. Nov **1964** [c9 Dec 1964; LP29783]. Sd; b&w. 35mm. 83 min. [Copyright length: 75 min.]

Prod-Dir Johnny Seven. *Assoc Prod* Edward J. Forsyth. *Exec Prod* Mark Lipsky, Maxwell Rubin. *Co-dir* Miles Dickson. *Screenplay* Jo Heims. *Photog* Gregory Sandor. *Camera* Frank Ruttencutter. *Film Ed* Lee Gilbert. *Asst Film Ed* Hal Brazeal. *Mus* William Loose, Emil Cadkin. *Sd Ed* Joseph Von Stroheim, Dick Maier, Jack Jackson, Sid Lubow, Jim Bullock. *Asst Dir* John Irwin. *Prod Mgr* Paul Lewis. *Script Supv* Hannah Scheel.

Cast: Johnny Seven *(Mathew Whitehawk)*, Warren Kemmerling *(Luke Grog)*, Virginia Vincent *(Sarah Grog)*, Ron Soble *(Jesse Grog)*.

Western melodrama. Mathew Whitehawk, a half-breed Navajo, is bitten by a rattlesnake and seeks aid at the ranch of Sarah and Luke Grog. Sarah tries to turn Mathew away, but Luke orders her to nurse him back to health. Mathew becomes attracted to Sarah and makes friends with Luke's mute brother, Jesse, but he discovers that Luke's earlier gesture of friendship was merely a trap. Luke invites Mathew to go hunting and then turns him loose in the forest without food or water and hunts him down the way he hunted and killed 16 other Indians. When Luke finally corners him, Mathew sees a rattlesnake, grabs it, and uses it as a whip to kill Luke. *Navajo Indians. Mutes. Halfcastes. Hunters. Brothers. Murder. Snakebites. Ranches. Snakes.*

Note: Working title: *The Last Grave.*

LA NAVE DELLE DONNE MALEDETTE *see* **THE SHIP OF CONDEMNED WOMEN**

THE NAVY VS. THE NIGHT MONSTERS							F6.3439

Standard Club of California Productions. *Dist* Realart Pictures. 8 Jun **1966** [Boston opening; c15 Apr 1966; LP32414]. Sd; col (De Luxe). 35mm. 87 min.

A George Edwards Production. *Prod* George Edwards. *Assoc Prod* Madelyn Broder. *Dir-Screenplay* Michael A. Hoey. *Photog* Stanley Cortez. *Art Dir* Paul Sylos. *Film Ed* George White. *Mus* Gordon Zahler. *Sd* Clarence Peterson. *Asst Dir* Dick Dixon. *Makeup* Harry Thomas. *Sp Eff* Edwin Tillman.

Cast: Mamie Van Doren *(Lieut. Nora Hall)*, Anthony Eisley *(Lieut. Charles Brown)*, Pamela Mason *(Maria, a scientist)*, Billy Gray *(Petty Officer Fred Twining)*, Bobby Van *(Ens. Rutherford Chandler)*, Walter Sande *(Dr. Arthur Beecham)*, Phillip Terry *(Spalding)*, Edward Faulkner, Russ Bender.

Horror film. Source: Murray Leinster, *Monster From the Earth's End* (Greenwich, Connecticut, 1959). In the absence of his commanding officer, Lieut. Charles Brown takes charge of a remote U. S. Naval base in the South Pacific. His first project is to refuel an incoming plane en route from Antarctica with a passenger load of VIPs and samples of ice-age vegetation. When the craft crash-lands, Brown and a rescue team, including Navy nurse Nora Hall and biologist Arthur Beecham, find only the pilot aboard, frozen to his controls in a state of extreme shock. In an attempt to preserve the vegetation, Beecham plants some 6-foot trees in warm soil near the island's hot springs. Shortly thereafter, several Navy personnel disappear. In time it is discovered that they have been devoured by the omnivorous trees which can propel themselves on their snakelike, furry roots. As the menacing threat of the trees intensifies, Brown hurls "Molotov Cocktails" at them, and they perish in the flames. *Sailors. Nurses. Biologists. Air pilots. Monsters. Airplanes. Molotov cocktails. Airplane accidents. Carnivorous plants. Pacific Ocean. Antarctic regions. United States Navy.*

Note: Working title: *The Night Crawlers.*

NAZARIN (Mexico)										F6.3440

Producciones Barbachano Ponce. *Dist* Azteca Films, Altura Films International. 5 Sep **1962**. Sd; b&w. 35mm. 92 min.

Prod Manuel Barbachano Ponce. *Exec Prod* Federico Amérigo. *Dir* Luis Buñuel. *Screenplay* Julio Alejandro, Luis Buñuel. *Dir Photog* Gabriel Figueroa. *Lighting* Daniel López. *Camera* Ignacio Romero. *Asst Camera* Pablo Rios. *Art Dir* Edward Fitzgerald. *Film Ed* Carlos Savage. *Mus (see note)* Rodolfo Halffter. *Song:* "Dios nunca muere" Macedonio Alcala. *Sd Supv* James L. Fields. *Sd Engr* José de Pérez. *Dub Mix* Galdino Samperio. *Sd Eff* Abraham Cruz. *Asst Dir* Ignacio Villarreal. *Prod Mgr* Enrique Morfin. *Cont* Aguila. *Admin* Antonio de Salazar. *Wardrobe* Georgette Somohano. *Makeup* Armando Meyer. *Hairstyles* Miguel Horasitas, Berta Chiu. *Prod Cons* Carlos Velo. *Dial Supv* Emilio Carballido. *Still Photog* Manuel Alvarez Bravo.

Cast: Francisco Rabal *(Nazario)*, Marga López *(Beatriz)*, Rita Macedo *(Andara)*, Jesús Fernández *(Ujo, the dwarf)*, Ignacio López Tarso *(The Sacrilegist)*, Luis Aceves Castañeda *(The Parricide)*, Ofelia Guilmain *(Chanfa)*, Noé Murayama *(El Pinto)*, Rosenda Monteros *(La Prieta)*, Ada Carrasco, Antonio Bravo, Aurora Molina, David Reynoso, Manuel Arvide, Edmundo Barbero, Raúl Dantés, Pilar Pellicer.

Drama. Source: Benito Peréz Galdós, *Nazarín* (Madrid, 1895). In turn-of-the-century Mexico, Father Nazario lives on alms and tries to follow the precepts of Christ, mutely enduring disparagement and mockery for his lack of worldly perspective. The prostitute Andara, having killed another woman in a brawl, takes shelter in his room, and he nurses her back to health. He is stripped of his pastoral duties when church authorities learn that she has shared his room, and he takes to the road to beg his way like Christ among the poor. Seeing a construction crew, he asks to work for food alone and precipitates bloodshed as the workers revolt. Arriving in a village, he is reunited with Andara and with Beatriz, a woman whom he consoled when he attempted suicide over the departure of her brutal and faithless lover, El Pinto. Nazario is dismayed to find himself regarded as a saint but consents to pray for a fevered child, whose condition thereupon improves. The two women now insist upon following him as his disciples. In a plague-stricken village, he is troubled to discover that a dying woman thinks of her lover rather than of God. He chastises his companions for their carnal interest in him. Andara gains the devotion of a lascivious dwarf, and he tags after her. Nazario is arrested with Andara as her accomplice, and Beatriz returns to El Pinto. Savagely beaten in prison, Nazario is saved by a church thief. Ecclesiastical authorities intervene, and Nazario is separated from the group of chained prisoners and given a private guard. Taking pity on the thirsty priest, an old peasant woman offers him a pineapple, and, after hesitating, he gratefully accepts her charity. *Priests. Prostitutes. Beggars. Dwarfs. Thieves. Murder. Christianity. Jails. Chain gangs. Catholic Church.*

Note: Released in Mexico in Jun 1959 as *Nazarín*; running time: 94 min. Released by Azteca Films in 1962, by Altura Films International in 1968. Music is credited by a Mexican source only. Soundtrack includes Holy Week songs from Càlanda (Spain).

NAZI TERROR AT NIGHT (Reissue) (West Germany)					F6.3441

Divina Film. *Dist* Zenith International Film Corp. 14 Jun **1961** [New York opening]. Sd; b&w. 35mm. 104 min.

Note: Originally released in 1959 as *The Devil Strikes at Night*; running time: 97 min. Released in West Germany in 1958 as *Nachts, wenn der Teufel kam.*

NEAPOLITAN CAROUSEL (Italy)							F6.3442

Lux Film. *Dist* Lux Film America, Inc. 11 Oct **1961** [New York opening]. Sd; col (PathéColor). 35mm. 116 min.

Dir Ettore Giannini. *Adapt & Dial* Giuseppe Marotta, Remigio Del Grosso, Ettore Giannini. *Story* Ettore Giannini. *Photog* Piero Portalupi. *Art Dir* Mario Chiari. *Film Ed* Nicolo Lazzari. *Orig Mus, Transcriptions & Elaborations* Raffaele Gervasio. *Choreog* Léonide Massine. *Cost* Maria De Matteis. *English Subtitl* Clare Catalano. *Fireworks* Serafina Coccia & Sons.

Cast: Paolo Stoppa *(Salvatore Esposito)*, Clelia Matania *(his wife)*, Vittoria Barracaracciolo *(Maria)*, Jean Quick *(Angela)*, Nadia Gray *("The Spirit of Naples")*, Maria Fiore *(Brigida)*, Maria Pia Casilio *(her rival, the hairdresser)*, Antonio *(their flame)*, Yvette Chauviré *(Donna Margherita)*, Folco Lulli *(Don Raffaele)*, Sophia Loren *(Sisina)*, Giacomo Rondinella *(Luigino)*, Alberto Bonucci, Vittorio Caprioli *(Luigino's pals)*, Léonide Massine *(Leonide Punchinello)*, Loris Gizzi *(Mr. Gustafson)*, Vera Nandi *(Lily Kangy/singing voice)*, Joan Baron *(French can-can dancer)*, Franco Coop, Enrico Viarisio, Guglielmo Barnabò, Galeazzo Benti *(conquerors)*, Beniamino Gigli, Carlo Tagliabue, Mario Cioffi, Marinelli Meli *(singing voices)*, Antonio Cifariello, Aldo Bufi Landi, Dolores Palumbo, Rosita Segovia, Rosella Hightower, Marjorie Tallchief, The African Ballet Keita Fodeba, The Grand Ballet of the Marquis de Cuevas, Rome Opera Theatre Corps de Ballet, Italian State Radio Orchestra of Rome.

Musical epic. Based on the stage musical *Carosello Napoletano*. Music, ballet, folk dances, and mime eliciting the spirit of Naples from the 16th century to the postwar era are loosely tied together by the comedic wanderings and exploits of the Esposito family, whose lives as itinerant street musicians scarcely change throughout the centuries. Salvatore Esposito, an organ grinder, and other members of his family introduce and comment on each episode before moving on to their next stop in time. In the "Sailor's Lament," the paintings of Salvator Rosa inspire sketches of the Moorish invasion; a Neapolitan girl is admired by men dressed in the costumes of many countries in "Naples Incarnate"; the legendary birth of the barter system is told; and the boyfriend of a model for risqué postcards is killed during World War I. There is also a ballet interpretation of the invasion of the Saracens and Naples' subsequent occupation by the French, the Spanish, and the Germans; performances of the *Michelemma*, the oldest known Neapolitan melody; the dance of the tarantella; and a festival of fireworks. Finally, the Esposito family prepare to resume their travels. *Neapolitans. Street musicians. Musicians. Organ grinders. Moors. Models. Saracens. French. Spanish. Germans. Family life. Music. Ballet. Folk dancing. Mime. Trade. Paintings. Fireworks. World War I. Naples. Salvator Rosa. "Michelemma".*

Note: Location scenes filmed in Naples. Opened in Rome in Oct 1954 as *Carosello Napoletano*; running time: 125 min.

NEARLY A NASTY ACCIDENT (Great Britain)   **F6.3443**
Marlow Productions. *For* Britannia Film Distributors. *Dist* Universal-International. 28 Mar **1962** [Boston opening; c28 Apr 1962; LP35479]. Sd (Westrex); b&w. 35mm. 86 min.
Pres by Bertram Ostrer. *Prod* Bertram Ostrer. *Dir* Don Chaffey. *Screenplay* Jack Davies, Hugh Woodhouse. *Dir Photog* Paul Beeson. *Camera Op* Herbert R. Smith. *Art Dir* Charles Bishop. *Film Ed* Bill Lenny. *Mus Comp & Cond* Ken Jones. *Sd Rec* Norman Bolland, Bob Jones. *Dub Ed* Ted Mason. *Asst Dir* Dennis Bertera. *Prod Mgr* Albert Becket. *Cont* Olga Brook. *Wardrobe* Maggie Lewin. *Makeup* Ernest Gasser. *Hairdressing* Barbara Barnard. *Sp Eff* Wally Veevers.
Cast: Jimmy Edwards (*Group Captain Kingsley*), Kenneth Connor (*A.C.2 Alexander Wood*), Shirley Eaton (*Cpl. Jean Briggs*), Richard Wattis (*Wagstaffe*), Ronnie Stevens (*Flight Lieutenant Pocock*), Jon Pertwee (*General Birkenshaw*), Eric Barker (*minister*), Peter Jones (*Flight Lieutenant Winters*), Jack Watling (*Grogan*), Cyril Chamberlain (*Warrant Officer Breech*), John Forrest (*Bunthorpe*), Charlotte Mitchell (*Miss Chamberlain*), Joyce Carey (*Lady Trowborough*), Terry Scott (*Sam Stokes*), Vincent Ball (*Crybwyth Sergeant*), Harold Goodwin (*aircraft mechanic*), Joe Baker (*Watkins*), Jack Douglas, actor (*Balmer*), Ian Whittaker, actor (*railway transport officer*), Emrys Leyshon (*ambulance driver*).
Comedy. Source: David Stringer and David Carr, *Touch Wood* (a play; production undetermined). Aircraftsman Alexander Wood, a mechanic in the R.A.F., is forever fixing things, an obsession leading to such disastrous accidents as the premature launching of rocket missiles and the wrecking of aircraft. As a result, his group captain, distraught by this threat to his own promotion, tries to get Wood dismissed from the service. But en route to his home for discharge, Wood fixes the train's heating system and then disappears. As an extensive search is organized, Wood, unaware of the panic he is causing, conscientiously tries to get back to camp. He meets and falls in love with Jean Briggs, a comely WRAF who has the same destination. After accidentally flooding all of South Wales and blacking out the area's electrical supply, he arrives back at his base. The group captain's delight at retrieving him is suddenly shattered by the arrival of the air minister. Wood attempts to fix something for the minister, and the group captain's frantic effort to stop him results in a final, disastrous calamity. *Mechanics. Handymen. Missing persons. Obsession. Missiles. Airplanes. Trains. Floods. Blackout. Wales. Great Britain—Royal Air Force. Great Britain—Women's Royal Air Force.*
Note: Opened in London in May 1961; running time: 92 min.

NEBO ZOVYOT *see* **BATTLE BEYOND THE SUN**

NECRONOMICON—GETRÄUMTE SÜNDEN *see* **SUCCUBUS**

NED KELLY (Great Britain)   **F6.3444**
Woodfall Films. *Dist* United Artists. 10 Jun **1970** [Denver, Colorado, opening; c10 Jun 1970; LP38089]. Sd; col (Technicolor). 35mm. 103 min. *MPAA rating* GP.
Prod Neil Hartley. *Dir* Tony Richardson. *Screenplay* Tony Richardson, Ian Jones. *Dir Photog* Gerry Fisher. *Art Dir* Andrew Sanders. *Prod Dsgn* Jocelyn Herbert. *Film Ed* Charles Rees. *Mus Cond* Ron Haffkine. Songs: "Ned Kelly," "The Wild Colonial Boy," "Son of a Scoundrel," "Shadow of the Gallows," "Lonigan's Widow," "Stony Cold Ground," "The Kellys Keep Comin'," "Marchin' in the Evenin'," "Blame It on the Kellys," "Pleasures of a Sunday Afternoon," "Hey Ned" Shel Silverstein. Sung by Waylon Jennings. Song: "She Moved Through the Fair" sung by Glen Tomasetti. *Sd* Ian Masters, Peter Keen. *Sd Mix* Tony Jackson. *Asst Dir* Andrew Grieve. *Prod Mgr* Gavrik Losey. *Cost Dsgn* Jocelyn Herbert.
Cast: Mick Jagger (*Ned Kelly*), Allen Bickford (*Dan Kelly*), Geoff Gilmour (*Steve Hart*), Mark McManus (*Joe Byrne*), Serge Lazareff (*Wild Wright*), Peter Sumner (*Tom Lloyd*), Ken Shorter (*Aaron Sherritt*), James Elliott (*Pat O'Donnell*), Clarissa Kaye (*Mrs. Kelly*), Diane Craig (*Maggie Kelly*), Susan Lloyd (*Kate Kelly*), Alexi Long (*Grace Kelly*), Bruce Barry (*George King*), Janne Wolmsley (*Caitlyn*), Ken Goodlet (*Nicholson*), Nigel Lovell (*Standish*), Martyn Sanderson (*Fitzpatrick*), Robert Bruning (*Sergeant Steele*), John Laws (*Kennedy*), Liam Reynolds (*Lonigan*), Lindsay Smith (*McIntyre*), John Gray (*Stratton*), Reg Gorman (*Bracken*), John Hopkins, actor (*O'Connor*), Peter Whittle (*Devine*), Anne Harvey (*Mrs. Devine*), Bill Charlton (*Richards*), Graham Keating (*1st trooper*), Ben Blakeney (*tracker*), Bill Hunter (*officer*), Frank Thring (*Judge Barry*), Alexander Cann (*McInnes*), Gerry Duggan (*Father O'Hea*), John Dease (*Whitty*), Andrew Sanders (*Farrell*), Patsy Dance (*Mrs. Whitty*), Erika Crowne (*Mrs. Farrell*), Tony Bazell (*Mr. Scott*), Jessica Noad (*Mrs. Scott*), Colin Tilley (*bank clerk*), Tim Van Rellim, Patrick McCarville (*sportsmen*), Kamahl (*Gloster*), Ronald Golding (*Casement*), Gordon McDougall (*Tarleton*), Clifford Neate (*Living*), Brian Niland

(*Mackie*), Doreen Warburton (*Mrs. Jones*), Gary Fisher (*Jack Jones*), Karin Altman (*Jane Jones*), David Copping (*Mr. Curnow*), Penny Stehli (*Mrs. Curnow*), Francis Yin (*sympathizer*), Shirley May Donald (*Mrs. Byrne*), Mary Marshall (*Mrs. Barry*), Claire Balmford (*Nell Sherritt*), Kurt Beimel (*Anton Wicks*), Moshe Kedem (*Baumgarten*), Keith Peterson (*referee*), Terry Erwin (*Chinese*), Harry Kelly (*aborigine*), Jack Allen (*Melbourne*), Michael Boddy.
Adventure melodrama. In the mid-19th century, Ned Kelly, the 16-year-old son of an Irishman deported to Australia for stealing two pigs, is unjustly sent to prison. He returns home 3 years later to find his widowed mother engaged to George King, an American horse thief, and his brother in jail for cattle theft. In an attempt to lead an honest life, Ned opens a sawmill, but the authorities continue to watch him. One night in a bar, Fitzpatrick, a resentful British policeman, drugs one of Ned's drinks and arrests him for drunkenness. After a short stay in jail, Ned is released and, with his brothers and King, steals a herd of horses and heads for the outback. Fitzpatrick and two other policemen pursue the Kelly gang but are killed in an ambush. Upon learning that his pregnant mother has been falsely arrested for murder, Ned offers himself in exchange, but the provincial governor refuses to accept the trade. The gang, protected with make-shift suits of armor, manages to elude the police for a while, until they are trapped in a saloon. Surrounded, and with no hope of escape, Ned's two brothers honor the gang's vow never to be taken alive, and both commit suicide. Ned, who temporarily escapes, is captured, quickly tried, and hanged. *Irish. Widows. Americans in foreign countries. Brothers. Gangs. Police. Deportation. Imprisonment. Injustice. Filial relations. Frameup. Colonial administration. Rustling. Pregnancy. Suicide. Capital punishment. Sawmills. Armor. Australia. Edward "Ned" Kelly. Horses.*
Note: Filmed on location in Australia. Opened in London in Jul 1970.

NEFERTITE, REGINA DEL NILO *see* **QUEEN OF THE NILE**

NEGATIVES (Great Britain)   **F6.3445**
Kettledrum Productions–Narizzano Productions. *For* Paramount Pictures. *Dist* Continental Distributing, Inc. 14 Oct **1968** [New York opening]. Sd; col (Eastman Color by Technicolor). 35mm. 90 min. [Also 98 min.]
A Judd Bernard-Silvio Narizzano Production. *Prod* Judd Bernard. *Dir* Peter Medak. *Screenplay* Peter Everett, Roger Lowry. *Dir Photog* Ken Hodges. *Camera* George Minassian. *Art Dir* Ted Tester. *Set Decor* Dimity Collins. *Titl* Ptolemy Productions. *Film Ed* Barry Vince. *Mus* Basil Kirchin. *Sd Rec* Buster Ambler. *Sd Re-rec* Maurice Askew. *Sd Ed* Christopher Lancaster. *Asst Dir* Gordon Gilbert. *Prod Mgr* David Korda. *Gowns* Clive Evans.
Cast: Peter McEnery (*Theo*), Diane Cilento (*Reingard*), Glenda Jackson (*Vivien*), Maurice Denham (*Father*), Stephen Lewis (*The Dealer*), Norman Rossington (*auctioneer*), Billy Russell (*old man*).
Drama. Source: Peter Everett, *Negatives* (London, 1964). Theo and Vivien, an unmarried couple, live above an antique store owned by Theo's father, who is slowly dying of cancer in a nearby hospital. The two can function sexually only by acting out a fantasy in which Theo becomes turn-of-the-century wife murderer Dr. Crippen, and Vivien alternately assumes the roles of Crippen's wife, Belle, and his mistress, Ethel. One day an attractive German photographer, Reingard, witnesses the couple, dressed in their Edwardian costumes and acting out their fantasy. Fascinated with the game, Reingard photographs the action, and she soon moves in as a lodger. While Vivien enjoys the Crippen drama, Theo finds his part humiliating. Reingard convinces him that he looks like World War I ace pilot Baron Manfred von Richthofen, and he assumes the role totally, burning the Crippen clothes when his father dies. Vivien becomes jealous of Theo's solitary fantasy and tries to destroy the plane that he has installed on the roof-garden; but Theo beats her unmercifully, and she is taken to the hospital. Reingard decides that the situation has gotten out of hand and leaves Theo in his plane, embroiled in an imaginary battle. He is last seen slumped in the plane with blood trickling from his mouth. *Antique dealers. Mistresses. Photographers. Fantasy. Murder. Filial relations. Death. Airplanes. Manfred von Richthofen. Hawley Harvey Crippen. Belle Crippen. Ethel Le Neve.*
Note: Released in Great Britain in 1970 in a 98 min. version. Location scenes filmed in London. Producer Judd Bernard re-purchased film from Paramount Pictures, which co-financed production.

NEHÉZÉLETŰEK *see* **THE ROUND UP**

NEJKRÁSNĚJŠÍ VĚK *see* **THE MOST BEAUTIFUL AGE**

NEL LABIRINTO DEL SESSO *see* **SESSO**

NELLA CITTÀ L'INFERNO *see* **...AND THE WILD, WILD WOMEN**

IL NEMICO DI MIA MOGLIE *see* **MY WIFE'S ENEMY**

IL NEMICO PUBBLICO N. 1 *see* THE MOST WANTED MAN

NEMURERU BIJO *see* THE HOUSE OF THE SLEEPING VIRGINS

NEOTPRAVLENNOYE PISMO *see* THE LETTER THAT WAS NEVER SENT

NERO SU BIANCO *see* BLACK ON WHITE

NERO'S BIG WEEKEND *see* NERO'S MISTRESS

NERO'S MISTRESS (France/Italy)   **F6.3446**

Les Films Marceau-Titanus-Vides. *Dist* Manhattan Films International. 6 Nov **1962** [Los Angeles opening]. Sd; col (Eastman Color). 35mm (CinemaScope). 86 min.

Prod Franco Cristaldi. *Dir* Steno. *Screenplay* Rodolfo Longo, Sandro Continenza, Diego Fabbri, Ugo Guerra, Steno. *Photog* Mario Bava. *Art Dir* Piero Filippone.

Cast: Alberto Sordi (*Nero*), Gloria Swanson (*Agrippina*), Brigitte Bardot (*Poppaea*), Vittorio De Sica (*Seneca*), Giorgia Moll (*Lidia*), Ciccio Barbi (*Anicetus*), Mario Carotenuto, Mino Doro, Furlanetto, Carlo Tamberlani, Arturo Bragaglia.

Farce. Much to the despair of his mother, Agrippina, Roman Emperor Nero prefers orgies, ballet, and singing at his estate in Baia to the military life imposed on him. He tries many times to murder his domineering mother, but every attempt fails. Despite her efforts, he continues to lead a carefree life with his mistress Poppaea and his advisor Seneca. When Agrippina returns from a sea trip, German troops are threatening the city. Nero finally agrees to his mother's wishes and dresses as a soldier, but he plays the lyre while Rome burns and the enemy takes control of the city. *Royalty. Mistresses. Filial relations. Matricide. Orgies. Ballet. Rome—History—Empire. Baia (Italy). Nero. Agrippina the Younger. Poppaea Sabina. Lucius Annaeus Seneca.*

Note: Opened in Paris in Oct 1957 as *Les week-ends de Néron*; running time: 90 min; in Rome in Sep 1956 as *Mio figlio Nerone*; running time: 100 min. Also known as *Nero's Big Weekend*.

THE NEST OF THE CUCKOO BIRDS   **F6.3447**

Bert Williams Motion Picture Producers & Distributors. Aug **1965** [Dania, Florida, showing]. Sd; b&w. 35mm. 88 min.

Prod-Dir-Writ Bert Williams. *Titl Song* Peggy Williams. *Sung by* The Four Bits.

Cast: Bert Williams, Ann Long.

Melodrama. No information about the precise nature of this film has been found, but press material indicates that there are scenes of sadism, horror, and moonshiners. *Moonshiners. Sadism.*

NEUNZIG MINUTEN NACH MITTERNACHT *see* TERROR AFTER MIDNIGHT

NEVADA SMITH   **F6.3448**

Solar Productions–Embassy Pictures. *Dist* Paramount Pictures. 10 Jun **1966** [Miami, Florida, opening; c31 Dec 1965; LP32761]. Sd; col (Eastman Color). 35mm (Panavision). 128 min. [Copyright length: 139 min.]

Pres by Joseph E. Levine. *Prod-Dir* Henry Hathaway. *Exec Prod* Joseph E. Levine. *Screen Story & Screenplay* John Michael Hayes. *Dir Photog* Lucien Ballard. *Art Dir* Hal Pereira, Tambi Larsen, Al Roelofs. *Set Decor* Robert R. Benton. *Film Ed* Frank Bracht. *Mus* Alfred Newman. *Orch* Leo Shuken, Jack Hayes. *Sd Rec* Harold Lewis, Charles Grenzbach. *Asst Dir* Daniel J. McCauley, Joseph Lenzi. *Prod Mgr* Frank Caffey. *Unit Prod Mgr* Howard Roessel, Herbert Coleman, Howard Joslin. *Cost* Frank Beetson, Jr. *Makeup Supv* Wally Westmore. *Makeup* Del Acevedo. *Hairstyle Supv* Nellie Manley. *Hairdresser* Gertrude Reade. *Sp Eff* George C. Thompson. *Sp Photog Eff* Paul K. Lerpae. *Coöp* United States Department of Agriculture—Forest Service, United States Department of Interior—Bureau of Land Management. *Prop* Frank A. Wade.

Cast: Steve McQueen (*Nevada Smith/Max Sand*), Karl Malden (*Tom Fitch*), Brian Keith (*Jonas Cord*), Arthur Kennedy (*Bill Bowdre*), Suzanne Pleshette (*Pilar*), Raf Vallone (*Father Zaccardi*), Janet Margolin (*Neesa*), Pat Hingle (*Big Foot*), Howard Da Silva (*Warden*), Martin Landau (*Jesse Coe*), Paul Fix (*Sheriff Bonnell*), Gene Evans (*Sam Sand*), Josephine Hutchinson (*Mrs. Elvira McCanles*), John Doucette (*Uncle Ben McCanles*), Val Avery (*Buck Mason*), Sheldon Allman (*sheriff*), Lyle Bettger (*Jack Rudabough*), Bert Freed (*Quince*), David McLean (*Romero*), Steve Mitchell (*Buckshot*), Merritt Bohn (*riverboat pilot*), Sandy Kenyon (*clerk in bank*), Ricardo Roman (*Cipriano*), John Lawrence (*Hogg*), Stanley Adams (*storekeeper*), George Mitchell (*paymaster*), John Litel (*doctor*), Ted De Corsia (*Hudson*).

Western melodrama. Based on a character in the novel by: Harold Robbins, *The Carpetbaggers* (New York, 1961). Max Sand is a young halfbreed living in the mountain and desert West of the 1890's. One day three gunslingers torture and kill his parents. Swearing an oath of vengeance, Max makes a funeral pyre out of the family shack and sets out to track down the killers. He is befriended by Jonas Cord, a traveling gunsmith and ammunition maker, who tries to dissuade him from his mission but, failing that, teaches him how to defend himself with a gun. Searching town after town, Max eventually finds one of his parents' murderers, Jesse Coe, and kills him in a brutal knife fight. After his own wounds have been cared for by Neesa, a Kiowa girl, Max heads for Louisiana, where a second killer is serving a prison sentence. Max stages a fake holdup, is thrown into jail, feigns friendship with the man, Bill Bowdre, and joins him in an escape. Aided by an amorous Cajun girl, the two men make their way through the swamps. As they reach freedom, Max reveals his true identity and guns down Bowdre; the girl also dies from a snakebite. Five years have passed since Max began his vendetta, and he has changed from a naive cowhand into a hardened criminal. Finally, Max finds the last man, Tom Fitch. In the showdown, Max shoots his opponent in both legs but is unable to kill him. He throws away his guns and rides off to ask Jonas Cord for a job; calling himself Nevada Smith, he hopes to make a new life for himself. *Halfcastes. Gunfighters. Gunsmiths. Kiowa Indians. Cajuns. Murder. Revenge. Obsession. Prison escapes. Personal identity. Swamps. Louisiana.*

Note: Location scenes filmed in the Inyo National Forest and in Owens Valley, California.

NEVER A DULL MOMENT   **F6.3449**

Walt Disney Productions. *Dist* Buena Vista Distribution Co. 26 Jun **1968** [Philadelphia opening; c18 Jan 1968; LP35367]. Sd (RCA); col (Technicolor). 35mm. 100 min.

Pres by Walt Disney. *Prod* Ron Miller. *Dir* Jerry Paris. *Screenplay* A. J. Carothers. *Dir Photog* William Snyder. *Art Dir* Carroll Clark, John B. Mansbridge. *Set Decor* Emile Kuri, Frank R. McKelvy. *Film Ed* Marsh Hendry. *Mus* Robert F. Brunner. *Orch* Cecil A. Crandall. *Sd Supv* Robert O. Cook. *Sd Mix* Dean Thomas. *Mus Ed* Evelyn Kennedy. *Asst Dir* John C. Chulay. *Asst to the Prod* Tom Leetch. *Cost Dsgn* Bill Thomas. *Cost* Chuck Keehne, Neva Rames. *Makeup* Gordon Hubbard. *Hairstyles* La Rue Matheron. *Sp Eff* Eustace Lycett, Robert A. Mattey. *Matte Artist* Alan Maley. *Artists* Peter Ellenshaw, Bill Fannon, John Popararo, Roland Crump.

Cast: Dick Van Dyke (*Jack Albany*), Edward G. Robinson (*Leo Joseph Smooth*), Dorothy Provine (*Sally Inwood*), Henry Silva (*Frank Boley*), Joanna Moore (*Melanie Smooth*), Tony Bill (*Florian*), Slim Pickens (*Cowboy Schaeffer*), Jack Elam (*Ace Williams*), Ned Glass (*Rinzy Tobreski*), Richard Bakalyan (*Bobby Macoon*), Mickey Shaughnessy (*Francis*), Philip Coolidge (*Fingers Felton*), James Millhollin (*museum director*), Johnny Silver (*prop man*), Anthony Caruso (*Tony Preston*), Paul Condylis (*Lenny*), Dick Winslow (*1st TV actor*), Robert Homel (*2d TV actor [Police Captain Jacoby]*), Jackie Russell (*sexy girl*), Rex Dominick (*Sam*), Ken Lynch (*police lieutenant*), Eleanor Audley (*matron*), John Cliff, John Dennis (*museum guards*), Tyler McVey (*Police Chief Grayson*), Jerry Paris (*police photographer*).

Crime farce. Source: John Godey, *A Thrill a Minute With Jack Albany* (New York, 1967). On his way home after doing a bit on television, struggling actor Jack Albany, thinking that he is being followed by a mugger, ducks into an open doorway and is confronted by a young hoodlum, Florian, who mistakes him for Ace Williams, a notorious hired killer he has been assigned to meet. Fearing for his life, Jack does not correct the error and is driven to the estate of Florian's employer, gangster Leo Joseph Smooth, who is a lover of art. Smooth is planning to steal a painting recently acquired by a New York museum. Desperate, Jack tries to convince Smooth's pretty art instructress, Sally Inwood, that he is not really Ace Williams, but she refuses to believe him. When the real Ace appears, Smooth locks the two men in a room to determine which of them is the killer. Aided by a now-convinced Sally, Jack emerges as the victor; and the next afternoon he joins Smooth's gang for the raid on the museum. Once there, however, he prevents the mobsters from taking the painting and leads them on a wild chase from one gallery to another, ending up in a pop art exhibition. While Jack is holding his adversaries, the police, alerted by a telephone call from Sally, arrive on the scene and round up the would-be thieves. Acclaimed as a hero, Jack wins both Sally and enough publicity to assure future acting offers. *Actors. Art teachers. Gangsters. Art collectors. Hired killers. Guards. Police. Robbery. Mistaken identity. Impersonation. Publicity. Television. Museums. New York City. Chases.*

NEVER BACK LOSERS (Great Britain)   **F6.3450**

Merton Park Studios. *Dist* Schoenfeld Film Distributing Corp. 27 Sep **1967** [Newark, New Jersey, opening]. Sd; b&w. 35mm. 61 min.

Prod Jack Greenwood. *Dir* Robert Tronson. *Screenplay* Lukas Heller. *Dir Photog* Bert Mason. *Art Dir* Peter Mullins. *Film Ed* Derek Holding. *Mus Dir* Bernard Ebbinghouse. *Sd* Brian Blamey.

Cast: Jack Hedley (*Jim Mathews*), Jacqueline Ellis (*Marion Parker*), Patrick Magee (*Ben Black*), Richard Warner (*Crabtree*), Derek Francis (*R. R. Harris*), Austin Trevor (*Colonel Warburton*), Harry Locke (*Burnside*), Larry Martyn (*Clive Parker*), Howard Pays (*Freddie*), Hilda Barry (*Mrs. Sanders*), George

Tovey (*Wally Sanders*), Larry Taylor (*Reilly*), Harold Goodwin (*Floyd*), Douglas Bradley-Smith (*Carter*), Tenniel Evans (*doctor*).

Crime melodrama. Source: Edgar Wallace, *The Green Ribbon* (London, 1929). Wally Sanders, a well-known jockey, fails to win a horserace in which he rides the favorite. Shortly afterward, Sanders' car crashes, and he claims £20,000 in damages from his insurance company. Jim Mathews, a shrewd and energetic insurance investigator, follows up the company's suspicion of foul play and interviews several men who control the district's betting. Mr. Burnside, who operates Trigger Turf Accountants, admits to no involvement in illegal gambling organizations, but he tells Mathews to contact "Lucky" Ben Black, a professional gambler. Black admits to gambling crimes but insists that horseracing must be run legitimately. Sanders dies, and Clive Parker, a young jockey, takes over Sanders' mounts. When several near accidents occur, Clive's sister Marion seeks aid from Mathews. Mathews traces the death of Wally Sanders to Burnside, and soon afterward Burnside falls and breaks his neck. The police round up others in the gambling ring with the help of Black. Jim and Marion leave together holding hands. *Gamblers. Bookies. Jockeys. Police. Investigators. Horseracing. Brother-sister relationship. Murder. Insurance. Automobile accidents.*

Note: Released in Great Britain in Jan 1962.

NEVER LET GO (Great Britain)   **F6.3451**
Independent Artists. *For* Rank Organisation. *Dist* Continental Distributing, Inc. 16 May **1962** [San Francisco opening]. Sd; b&w. 35mm. 90 min.

A Julian Wintle–Leslie Parkyn Production. *Prod* Peter De Sarigny. *Dir* John Guillermin. *Screenplay* Alun Falconer. *Story* John Guillermin, Peter De Sarigny. *Photog* Christopher Challis. *Camera Op* Paul Wilson. *Focus Puller* Mervyn Wilson. *Art Dir* George Provis. *Draughtsman* Tony Rimmington. *Film Ed* Ralph Sheldon. *1st Asst Ed* Pamela Tomling. *2d Asst Ed* Barry McCormick. *Mus Comp & Cond* John Barry. *Titl Song* John Barry, Lionel Bart. *Sung by* Adam Faith. *Sd* Lionel Selwyn. *Sd Rec* Len Page, Ken Cameron. *Sd Camera Op* George Rice. *1st, 2d & 3d Asst Dir* Kip Gowans, Ron Jackson, John Danischewsky. *Prod Supv* Arthur Alcott. *Prod Sec* Joy Mercer. *Cont* Sue Dyson. *Wardrobe Mistress* Vi Murray. *Makeup Artist* Trevor Crole-Rees, John Wilcox, makeup. *Hairdresser* Maud Onslow. *Still Photog* Harry Gillard. *Prop Buyer* George Durant. *Prop Master* Fred Eames. *Constr Mgr* Bert Roberts.

Cast: Richard Todd (*John Cummings*), Peter Sellers (*Lionel Meadows*), Elizabeth Sellars (*Anne Cummings*), Adam Faith (*Tommy Towers*), Carol White (*Jackie*), Mervyn Johns (*Alfie Barnes*), Noel Willman (*Inspector Thomas*), David Lodge (*Cliff*), Peter Jones (*Alec Berger*), John Bailey (*MacKinnon*), Nigel Stock (*Regan*), John Le Mesurier (*Pennington*), Charles Houston (*Cyril Spink*), John Dunbar (*station sergeant*), Cyril Shaps (*Cypriot*).

Crime melodrama. John Cummings, an unsuccessful cosmetics salesman, has his unpaid-for car stolen by one of the hoods in the employ of Lionel Meadows, the sadistic organizer of a London car conversion racket. The auto was not insured, and since the police appear indifferent to his plight, Cummings decides to find it himself. An old newsvendor, Alfie, leads Cummings to Tommy Towers, the youngster who stole the car. Although Tommy is of no help to Cummings, he relates the incident to Meadows. Furious that the boy might be under police surveillance, Meadows beats him. After Alfie's suicide, Meadows' young mistress, Jackie, runs away from him and goes to live with Tommy, telling him that he must inform on Meadows if they are ever to be free of him. Acting on the boy's information, the police raid Meadows' garage, but all the stolen cars have been removed. Cummings, however, returns that night and finds his car. Meadows attacks him, and in the brutal fight that ensues, Cummings fells his adversary with a length of chain and a piece of wood. Alerted by Tommy, the police arrive and take Meadows into custody, leaving Cummings free to drive his car home. *Salesmen. Hoodlums. Racketeers. Police. Informers. Mistresses. Theft. Suicide. Cosmetics. Automobiles. Insurance. Garages. London.*

Note: Opened in London in Jun 1960; running time: 91 min. Working title: *Moment of Truth.*

NEVER PUT IT IN WRITING (Great Britain)   **F6.3452**
Andrew L. Stone–Virginia Stone. *For* Seven Arts Productions. *Dist* Allied Artists. Apr **1964.** Sd; b&w. 35mm. 93 min.

Prod Andrew L. Stone, Virginia Stone. *Assoc Prod* Harry Woolveridge. *Dir-Screenplay* Andrew L. Stone. *Photog* Martin Curtis. *Camera* Alan McCabe. *Supv Ed* Virginia Stone. *Film Ed* Noreen Ackland. *Asst Ed* Michael Round. *Mus* Frank Cordell. *Titl Song Writ & Sung by* Pat Boone. *Sd Mix* Laurie Clarkson. *Sd Eff Ed* Thelma Orr. *Dub Mix* Hugh Strain. *Asst Dir* Ted Wallis. *Prod Controller* Jack Smith. *Miss Murphy's Wardrobe* Norman Hartnell. *Stunt Flying* Charlie O'Hara.

Cast: Pat Boone (*Stephen Cole*), Milo O'Shea (*Danny O'Toole*), Fidelma Murphy (*Katie O'Connell*), Reginald Beckwith (*Lombardi*), Harry Brogan (*Mr. Breeden*), Nuala Moiselle (*Miss Bull*), John Le Mesurier (*Adams*), Sarah Ballantine (*Adams' secretary*), John Gardiner (*security officer*), Colin Blakely

(*Oscar*), Derry Power (*taxi driver*), Bill Foley (*tower man*), Polly Adams (*receptionist*), Julia Nelson (*maid*), Ed Devereaux (*Pringle*), Seamus Healy (*sorting office foreman*), Karal Gardner (*young woman*), John Dunbar (*judge*), Susan Richards (*judge's wife*), Liz Lanchbury (*Basil's girl friend*), Peadar Lamb, Georgina Cookson, Paul Farrell, Sylva Davies, Michael O'Briain, Eddie Golden, Pat Layde, Geoffrey Golden, Philip O'Flynn.

Comedy. Stephen Cole, a London insurance executive in Ireland on business, learns that his boss's nephew, Oscar, has received the promotion he himself expected. Cole writes a letter of resignation accusing his boss of nepotism. After posting the protest, however, he is informed that he has been promoted to vice president and has been made a junior partner. Danny O'Toole, an executive with a rival firm which has attempted to recruit Cole for O'Toole's position, and Katie O'Connell, a postal clerk, accompany Cole on an unsuccessful chase after the letter. In the process, the trio become entangled in postal red tape and encounter the police; as a result, Katie loses her job. They hire a rickety plane owned by a pilot to take them to London, where Cole tries to retrieve the letter. To his horror, he discovers that it has already been intercepted and read by Oscar, who plans to give it to his uncle at a banquet in Cole's honor. Although Oscar places the letter before his uncle at the testimonial dinner, Katie creates a diversion, during which Cole replaces the letter with one written by O'Toole, which reveals that Cole has refused a job with the rival firm at twice his present salary. Oscar is praised for his selflessness, Cole for his loyalty, and O'Toole retains his position. Cole then dances off with Katie, his new secretary and romantic interest. *Executives. Mail clerks. Secretaries. Police. Uncles. Pilots. Nepotism. Employer-employee relations. Loyalty. Insurance. Airplanes. London. Ireland. Documentation. Chases.*

Note: Filmed in England and Ireland. Released in Great Britain in Jul 1964; running time: 90 min.

NEVER STEAL ANYTHING WET *see* **CATALINA CAPER**

NEVER TAKE CANDY FROM A STRANGER (Great Britain)   **F6.3453**
Hammer Film Productions. *Dist* Sutton Pictures, Pathé-America Distributing Co., Omat Films. 15 Aug **1961** [Maryland license]. Sd; b&w. 35mm (Megascope). 81 min.

Prod Anthony Hinds. *Exec Prod* Michael Carreras. *Assoc Prod* Anthony Nelson Keys. *Dir* Cyril Frankel. *Screenplay* John Hunter. *Photog* Freddie Francis. *Art Dir* Bernard Robinson, Don Mingaye. *Film Ed* James Needs, Alfred Cox. *Mus Comp* Elisabeth Lutyens. *Mus Dir* John Hollingsworth. *Sd* Jock May, Arthur Cox. *Asst Dir* John Peverall. *Prod Mgr* Clifford Parkes. *Wardrobe* Molly Arbuthnot. *Makeup* Roy Ashton. *Hairstyles* Henry Montsash.

Cast: Gwen Watford (*Sally Carter*), Patrick Allen (*Peter Carter*), Felix Aylmer (*Olderberry Senior*), Niall MacGinnis (*defense counsel*), Alison Leggatt (*Martha*), Bill Nagy (*Olderberry Junior*), Macdonald Parke (*judge*), Michael Gwynn (*prosecutor*), Janina Faye (*Jean Carter*), Frances Green (*Lucille*), Estelle Brody (*Eunice Kalliduke*), James Dyrenforth (*Dr. Stevens*), Robert Arden (*Tom Demarest*), Vera Cook (*Mrs. Demarest*), Bud Knapp (*Hammond*), Hazel Jennings (*Mrs. Olderberry*), Cal McCord (*Charles Kalliduke*), Gaylord Cavallaro (*Neal Phillips*), Sheila Robins (*Miss Jackson*), Larry O'Connor (*Sam Kingsley*), Helen Horton (*Sylvia Kingsley*), Shirley Butler (*Mrs. Nash*), Michael Hammond (*Sammy Nash*), Patricia Marks (*nurse*), Peter Carlisle (*usher*), Mark Baker (*clerk of the court*), Sonia Fox (*receptionist*), John Bloomfield (*foreman of jury*), Charles Maunsell (*janitor*), Andre Dakar (*Olderberry's chauffeur*), Bill Sawyer (*taxi driver*), Jack Lynn (*Dr. Montfort*), William Abney (*state trooper*), Tom Busby (*2d policeman*).

Melodrama. Source: Roger Garis, *The Pony Cart* (London opening: 22 Feb 1959). Clarence Olderberry, a senile psychopath living in a Canadian town, is sexually attracted to little girls. High school principal Peter Carter and his wife, Sally, new arrivals from England, discover that their 9-year-old daughter Jean and her playmate Lucille have undressed in front of Olderberry in exchange for candy. Peter takes the matter to court, but the wealthy Olderberry's son, a powerful influence in the community, is able to conceal the fact that his father is a former mental patient and at the same time arouse public sentiment against the Carters. The prosecution is dropped when the defense counsel, a clever "family" lawyer, bullies and confuses Jean, and the old man is acquitted. Peter resigns his post and prepares to leave town when he discovers that Jean and Lucille have vanished, as has Clarence Olderberry. A search party finds the old man beside the murdered body of Lucille. Jean is found wandering around, unaware of the fate that has befallen her friend. *School principals. Psychopaths. Sex deviates. Children. Police. Lawyers. Child molesting. Injustice. Smalltown life. Murder. Trials. Canada.*

Note: Opened in London in Mar 1960 as *Never Take Sweets From a Stranger.* Also known as *The Molester.*

NEVER TAKE SWEETS FROM A STRANGER *see* **NEVER TAKE CANDY FROM A STRANGER**

NEVER TOO LATE   F6.3454

Tandem Enterprises. *Dist* Warner Bros. Pictures. 4 Nov **1965** [New York opening; c25 Dec 1965; LP32665]. Sd; col (Technicolor). 35mm (Panavision). 105 min.

Prod Norman Lear. *Dir* Bud Yorkin. *Screenplay* Sumner Arthur Long. *Dir Photog* Philip Lathrop. *Art Dir* Edward Carrere. *Set Decor* Ralph S. Hurst. *Film Ed* William Ziegler. *Mus* David Rose. *Titl Song* Jay Livingston, Ray Evans, David Rose. *Sung by* Vic Damone. *Sd* Everett Hughes. *Asst Dir* Bud Grace, Michael Daves. *Unit Mgr* James T. Vaughn. *Cost Dsgn* Sheila O'Brian. *Makeup Supv* Gordon Bau. *Supv Hairstylist* Jean Burt Reilly. *Dial Supv* William Giorgio.

Cast: Paul Ford *(Harry Lambert)*, Connie Stevens *(Kate Clinton)*, Maureen O'Sullivan *(Edith Lambert)*, Jim Hutton *(Charlie Clinton)*, Jane Wyatt *(Grace Kimbrough)*, Henry Jones *(Dr. James Kimbrough)*, Lloyd Nolan *(Mayor Crane)*.

Domestic comedy-drama. Source: Sumner Arthur Long, *Never Too Late* (New York opening: 27 Nov 1962). Middle-aged Harry Lambert, the owner of a lumber company, lives in a small New England town with a free-loading son-in-law, Charlie, a lazy daughter, Kate, and an aging wife, Edith. Prodded by her friend Grace, Edith goes to see a doctor for her persistent fatigue and learns that she is pregnant. After the initial shock, she goes on a buying spree and comes home with a new dress and coiffure. Spendthrift Harry becomes upset over her impulsiveness until she announces the doctor's diagnosis. The entire family is stunned, and Harry, much older than the typical new father, feels that he cannot contend with the responsibility. Kate, forced to do all the housework because Harry refuses to hire a maid, counters her father's stubbornness by also trying to have a baby, but her unsuccessful attempts only keep Charlie away from his job at the lumber yard and make him too tired to do anything else. One night, Harry and Charlie go on a wild drinking spree and insult Mayor Crane, who defeated Harry in the last town election. The insults cause Crane to retract a previously arranged deal for Harry to supply the lumber for the town's new stadium. Upon arriving home, Harry finds that Edith has left him. He follows her to Boston and convinces her that he is ready to become a father again. Meanwhile, Charlie regains the contract from Crane, and he and Kate begin to plan their own home. Edith and Harry celebrate their reconciliation by starting a second honeymoon. *Businessmen. In-laws. Spendthrifts. Mayors. Middle age. Family life. Pregnancy. Drunkenness. New England. Boston.*

THE NEW ANGELS (Italy)   F6.3455

Arco Film–Titanus–Galatea. *Dist* Promenade Films. 3 May **1965** [New York opening]. Sd; b&w. 35mm. 94 min.

Prod Alfredo Bini. *Dir* Ugo Gregoretti. *Screenplay* Mino Guerrini, Ugo Gregoretti. *Stories (see note)* Mino Guerrini. *Photog* Tonino Delli Colli, Mario Bernardo. *Art Dir* Flavio Mogherini. *Film Ed* Nino Baragli. *Mus* Piero Umiliani.

With: Rochelle Young *(American girl)*.

Documentary. Various aspects of Italian youth are examined in eight episodes: A group of morally righteous Roman youths find a couple necking in a car, strip the girl, and paint her red. In Sicily, where the sexes are strictly segregated, all marriages are arranged by matchmakers, and the only opportunity for premarital sex is with unattractive prostitutes. Wealthy young Neapolitans go yachting with working class girls, whom they seduce but would never marry. In the Chianti region, children persuade their parents to abandon the family farm for employment in a factory in Florence. A young Sicilian tries to find more gainful employment at a new factory but is bewildered by the tests he must take for the job. In a rural area, youths pledge to maintain their religious beliefs and high standards of morality. At the Rimini beach resort, an American girl seduces Italian men recommended by her friends. In Rome at a New Year's Eve party the son of the hosts and his girl friend deride their extravagant elders, preferring to watch television in the luxurious family bomb shelter. *Prostitutes. Americans in foreign countries. Social customs. Youth. Marriage—Arranged. Seduction. Family life. Yachts. Factories. Beaches. Bomb shelters. Rome. Sicily. Naples. Florence. Chianti Mountains. Rimini.*

Note: Opened in Rome in Feb 1962 as *I nuovi angeli*; running time: 95 min (cut from 105 min). Some U. S. sources credit Guerrini's stories as "The 20-Year-Olds Are Not Madmen."

NEW BUSHWACKERS   F6.3456

8 Aug **1968** [New York opening]. Sd; col. 16mm. [Feature length assumed.]

Sex film. No information about the precise nature of this film has been found. *Sexuality.*

NEW FACE IN HELL *see* P. J.

THE NEW INTERNS   F6.3457

Robert Cohn Productions. *Dist* Columbia Pictures. 19 Aug **1964** [New York opening; c1 Jun 1964; LP28210]. Sd (RCA); b&w. 35mm. 123 min.

Prod Robert Cohn. *Dir* John Rich. *Writ* Wilton Schiller. *Dir Photog* Lucien Ballard. *Art Dir* Don Ament. *Set Decor* Richard Mansfield, William Stevens. *Film Ed* Gene Milford, Eda Warren. *Mus* Earle Hagen. *Orch* Arthur Morton. *Song:* "Come On, Let Yourself Go" Jan Berry, Artie Kornfeld. *Sung by* The Matadors. *Sd Supv* Charles J. Rice. *Sd* Jack Solomon. *Asst Dir* Mike Moder. *Unit Prod Mgr* Ray Gosnell. *Makeup Supv* Ben Lane. *Makeup* Dave Grayson. *Tech Adv* Richard Soskin.

Cast: Michael Callan *(Dr. Alec Considine)*, Dean Jones *(Dr. Lew Worship)*, Barbara Eden *(Laura Rogers)*, Stefanie Powers *(Gloria Worship)*, Inger Stevens *(Nancy Terman)*, George Segal *(Dr. Tony Parelli)*, Kay Stevens *(Didi Loomis)*, Telly Savalas *(Dr. Riccio)*, George Furth *(Dr. Phil Osterman)*, Ellie Wood *(Madeline Osterman)*, Greg Morris *(Clark)*, Gordon Kee *(Chaum)*, Jimmy Mathers *(Freddie)*, Mike Vandever *(Beep)*, Lee Patrick *(Mrs. Hitchcock)*, Adam Williams *(Wolanski)*, Sue Ane Langdon *(Stella)*, Dawn Wells *(Bobbie)*, Gregory Morton *(Dr. Granchard)*, Michael Fox *(Dr. Hellman)*, Eddie Ryder, Rusty Lane, Alan Reed, Jr., Adrianne Ellis, Peter Hobbs, Ken Mayer, Norman Cole, Charles Lane, Marianna Hill, David Winters, Ken Drake.

Melodrama. Based on characters from: Richard Frede, *The Interns* (New York, 1960). Playboy Alec Considine returns to New North Hospital for another year's internship after suffering a mental breakdown during his first attempt at internship. Among the new interns he guides around the hospital are the explosive Tony Parelli, a former slum boy who is soon at odds with Dr. Riccio, head of the hospital; and Phil Osterman, who smuggles his bride into the intern's quarters to live. Parelli falls in love with Nancy Terman, a social worker who goes to pieces when she is raped by delinquents whom Parelli knew from the slums. Newly married resident Dr. Lew Worship learns that he is sterile, and the news nearly wrecks his marriage, but he and his wife, Gloria, solve their problem by deciding to adopt children. Nancy's assailants are brought into the hospital following a gang fight, and they confront Parelli. After a fight in which Considine is wounded, Parelli conquers his hatred enough to make a sincere attempt to save his enemy's life. Meanwhile, Dr. Osterman's pregnant wife is discovered in the men's quarters by Mrs. Hitchcock, the house-mother, but she promises to remain silent so that the couple can live together until he completes his year of duty. Considine, who has unsuccessfully been chasing student nurse Laura Rogers, finally succumbs to her wishes and agrees to marry her. As the year ends and the interns leave the hospital, Parelli, whose rebelliousness has been tempered, decides to remain at New North as a resident. *Hospital interns. Physicians. Newlyweds. Nurses. Juvenile delinquents. Social workers. Mental illness. Rape. Sterility (sexual). Pregnancy. Marriage. Gang wars. Hospitals.*

Note: A sequel to *The Interns*, q. v.

THE NEW JAPANESE CINEMA (Japan)   F6.3458

Film-Makers' Distribution Center. 2 May **1968** [New York opening]. Sd; b&w and col. 16mm. [Feature film, length unknown.]

Anthology film. A program of award-winning Japanese films from the 1968 Sogetsu Experimental Film Festival: Tatsuo Shimamura's *White City*, Fumio Ohi's *Folk Mythology*, Masataka Nakano's *One, Two, Three, Four-shi-Death*, Michio Okabe's *Doctrine of Creation*, Shoji Hosokawa's *Won't You Have Some Milk?*, Sanpei Kasu's *Trap* and Teruo Okumura's *Man Possessed of His Own Shadow*.

A NEW KIND OF LOVE   F6.3459

Llenroc Productions. *Dist* Paramount Pictures. 30 Oct **1963** [New York opening; c20 Sep 1963; LP26413]. Sd; col (Technicolor). 35mm. 110 min.

Prod-Dir-Orig Screenplay Melville Shavelson. *Cinematog* Daniel Fapp. *Col Cons* Hoyningen-Huene. *Art Dir* Hal Pereira, Arthur Lonergan. *Set Decor* Sam Comer, James Payne. *Film Ed* Frank Bracht. *Mus* Leith Stevens. *Adtl Themes* Erroll Garner. *Titl Song Sung by* Frank Sinatra. *Sd* John Carter. *Asst Dir* Arthur Jacobson. *Unit Prod Mgr* Andrew J. Durkus. *Asst to the Prod* Hal C. Kern. *Cost* Edith Head. *Paris Originals* Christian Dior, Lanvin-Castillo, Pierre Cardin. *Makeup* Wally Westmore. *Props* Carl Coleman.

Cast: Paul Newman *(Steve Sherman)*, Joanne Woodward *(Samantha Blake)*, Thelma Ritter *(Lena O'Connor)*, Eva Gabor *(Félicienne Courbeau)*, George Tobias *(Joseph Bergner)*, Marvin Kaplan *(Harry Gorman)*, Robert Clary *(Albert Sardou)*, Jan Moriarty *(Suzanne)*, Valerie Varda *(Mrs. Chalmers)*, Robert F. Simon *(Bertram Chalmers)*, Joan Staley *(stewardess)*, Maurice Chevalier *(himself)*.

Romantic comedy. Newspaper columnist Steve Sherman, sent to Paris by his publisher to cover the fashion shows, meets Samantha Blake on the plane. Samantha, who pirates fashions for a large New York department store, is accompanied by her boss, Joseph Bergner, and a buyer, Lena O'Connor. Steve and Samantha feel an instant dislike for each other: he because of her boyish haircut and superior air, she because of his boorish behavior and constant drinking. In Paris, Samantha is invited to the traditional St. Catherine's Day celebration when all the young unmarried girls pray for a husband. Caught up in the gala occasion, Samantha gets slightly intoxicated; and when St.

Catherine, the patron saint of unmarried women, seems to give her advice, she goes to a leading beauty salon and emerges wearing a beautiful blonde wig. Lena, meanwhile, forlornly watches her beloved employer, Bergner, fall for Félicienne, the firm's French agent. Later Samantha is picked up by Steve, who does not recognize her, and she sustains his idea that she is a high-priced prostitute. Steve uses her fantasies as a basis for his new column, which is an instant success. By this time they are in love, and Steve eventually learns that his new "discovery" is really Samantha. Bergner and Lena finally are united when Félicienne characteristically leaves him and turns to her next conquest. *Reporters. Columnists. Publishers. Couturiers. Americans in foreign countries. Buyers. Alcoholism. Drunkenness. Mistaken identity. Imposture. Fashion shows. Saint Catherine's Day. Paris.*

Note: Christian Dior, Pierre Cardin and Lanvin-Castillo present their new fashions in the St. Catherine's Day sequence of the film, while Maurice Chevalier sings a medley of his classics, including "Mimi" and "Louise." Working title: Samantha.

THE NEW LIFE STYLE (West Germany)   **F6.3460**
CCC-Filmkunst. *Dist* Dot Distributing Co. 29 Jul **1970** [New York opening]. Sd; col (De Luxe). 35mm. 91 min.

Pres by Peter Savage. *Prod-Dir-Writ English Seq (see note)* Peter Savage. *Dir* Jerzy Macc. *Screenplay* Jerzy Macc, Jürgen Knop. *Photog* Bob Klebig. *Photog English Seq* Bob Baldwin. *Mus* Maris Musik. *English Mus Score* Danny DiMinno, Horace Diaz, Athena Hosey.

Cast: Horst Tappert (*Walter Bergman*), Renate von Holt (*Renate*), Alexy Burg (*Alexy*), Ursula Moot (*Uschi [see note]*), Jennifer Stone (*Ava*), Rocky Graziano, Jake La Motta (*guest stars, U. S. version*), Charlotte Kerr, Babsi Zimmermann, Rolf Eden, Reinhold Timm, André Esterhazy, Francis Heym, Jürgen Knop.

Drama. Walter Bergman, a successful, middle-aged businessman, travels to the resort isle of Sylt for a convention. Despite his status as a professional and family man, he falls in love with Renate, a promiscuous blonde. To his chagrin, Walter soon discovers that physically and mentally he cannot cope with the frolics of the uninhibited group of young people with which the young woman associates. Overcome by the implications of this new lifestyle after finding Renate in bed with another man, he returns home to his wife and daughter. *Businessmen. Infidelity. Promiscuity. Youth. Middle age. Conventions. Sylt.*

Note: Released in West Germany in Jan 1968 as *Heisser Sand auf Sylt*; running time: 94 min. Producer Peter Savage reedited the film before U. S. release; several scenes were deleted, others added by Savage, and Jennifer Stone added to the cast. Ursula Moot is also known as Uschi Mood. Also known as *Just To Be Loved*.

NEW YORK APPELLE SUPER DRAGON *see* **SECRET AGENT SUPER DRAGON**

NEW YORK CHIAMA SUPERDRAGO *see* **SECRET AGENT SUPER DRAGON**

NEW YORK CITY—THE MOST   **F6.3461**
Spectrum Associates. *Dist* New York Times. Jul **1968**. Sd; col. 35mm. 50 min.

Prod-Dir George Pitt. *Screenplay* Harry Muheim. *Photog* Victor Lukens, George Silano, Gayne Rescher. *Film Ed* Reva Schlesinger. *Mus Score* Sol Kaplan. *Songs* Robert Leeman, Frank Lauria. *Perf by* The Salvation Navy.

Cast: Eli Wallach (*a cabdriver*).

Documentary. A friendly taxi driver takes the viewer on an extensive tour of New York City. The grace of the city's cultural institutions, its art galleries and concert halls, is contrasted with the gaudiness of Times Square. Protest groups are given exposure, as are the bigoted remarks scrawled in graffiti throughout the metropolis. The New York subway system is shown in detail. Mayor John V. Lindsay appears in several scenes. *Taxi drivers. New York City. John Vliet Lindsay.*

NEW-YORK-SUR-MER *see* **ONLY ONE NEW YORK**

NEWPORT FESTIVAL *see* **FESTIVAL**

A NICE GIRL LIKE ME (Great Britain)   **F6.3462**
Partisan Film Productions-Anglo Embassy Productions. *Dist* Avco Embassy Pictures. 13 Aug **1969** [Buffalo, New York, opening]. Sd; col (Eastman Color). 35mm. 91 min. *MPAA rating* M.

Pres by Joseph E. Levine. *Prod* Roy Millichip. *Exec Prod* Leonard Lightstone. *Dir* Desmond Davis. *Screenplay* Anne Piper, Desmond Davis. *Photog* Gilbert Taylor, Manny Wynn. *Art Dir* Ken Bridgeman. *Film Ed* Ralph Sheldon. *Mus* Pat Williams. *Titl Song* Pat Williams, Hal Shaper. *Sung by* Vikki Carr. *Sd* Robin Gregory. *Asst Dir* Ronnie Appleton. *Prod Mgr* Bruce Sharman.

Cast: Barbara Ferris (*Candida*), Harry Andrews (*Savage*), Gladys Cooper (*Aunt Mary*), Bill Hinnant (*Ed*), James Villiers (*Freddie*), Joyce Carey (*Aunt*

Celia), Christopher Guinee (*Pierre*), Fabia Drake (*Miss Grimsby*), Irene Prador (*Madame Dupont*), Erik Chitty (*vicar*), Totti Truman-Taylor (*Miss Charter*), John Serret (*museum attendant*), John Clive (*supermarket shopper*), Ann Lancaster (*Miss Garland*), Shelagh Wilcox (*labor ward sister*), Susan Whitman (*labor ward nurse*), Douglas Wilmer (*postnatal clinic doctor*), Carol Gilles (*Marie*), Madge Brindley, Miriam Margoyles (*Pensione "Mama" [see note]*), John Gurnsey, Tom Gill (*customs officers*), Barbara Keogh (*maternity night nurse*), Robert Sidaway (*shipping line assistant*), Beryl Cook (*bridal gowns assistant*), Sidney Johnson (*Mr. Wright*), Bartlett Mullins (*male basket weaver*), Sylvia Tysick (*supermarket shopper's wife*), Sarah Golding (*1st schoolgirl*), Cunitia Knight (*2d schoolgirl*), Christine Dingle (*3d schoolgirl*), Sorrel Breuning (*4th schoolgirl*), Terry Duggan (*radio cab driver*), Alistair Hunter (*country hire car driver*), Carmen Carpoldi (*Mrs. Lamplugh*), Bill Clancy (*Mr. Lamplugh*), Elisabeth Gordon (*Mrs. Newton*), David Armour (*Mr. Newton*), Nichola Cowper (*Valentine, age 6 months*), Rebecca Bridge (*Valentine, age 12 months*), Angela Jones (*Angelina, age 6 months*), Kate Harman (*Angelina, age 12 months*).

Comedy-drama. Source: Anne Piper, *Marry at Leisure* (New York, 1959). Candida leaves school and is taken to live with her two maiden aunts, Celia and Mary, when her father dies. Bored with her aunts, she travels to Paris where she has an affair with a French student and returns to England pregnant. No longer able to live with her aunts, she moves into her father's house where she and her newly-born child are looked after by the family caretaker, Savage. Candida again gets the urge to travel and visits Italy with Miss Grimsby, an elderly schoolteacher. There, a desperate mother hands Candida a baby and disappears. Candida smuggles the baby back to England and discovers that she is again pregnant, this time after a brief encounter with an American. Celia and Mary then negotiate for Candida to marry her dimwitted cousin, Freddie. Forced by circumstances into accepting the proposal, Candida, at the last moment, tells Freddie that she cannot go through with the loveless marriage. Returning to her father's house, she realizes that she has always been in love with Savage. *Aunts. Students. Caretakers. Schoolteachers. Infants. Cousins. Pregnancy. Motherhood. Marriage—Arranged. London. Paris. Venice.*

Note: Location scenes filmed in London, Paris, and Venice. Opened in London in Nov 1969. Sources conflict in crediting the role of the pensione "Mama."

NICHT VERSÖHNT ODER "ES HILFT NUR GEWALT, WO GEWALT HERRSCHT" *see* **NOT RECONCILED, OR "ONLY VIOLENCE HELPS WHERE IT RULES"**

THE NIGHT *see* **LA NOTTE**

NIGHT AFFAIR (France)   **F6.3463**
Orex Films. *Dist* President Films. 12 Oct **1961** [New York opening]. Sd; b&w. 35mm. 92 min.

Prod Lucien Viard. *Assoc Prod* Paul Joly. *Dir* Gilles Grangier. *Screenplay* Michel Audiard, Gilles Grangier, Jacques Robert. *Dial* Michel Audiard. *Photog* Louis Page. *Camera* Henri Tiquet. *Asst Camera* Marc Champion. *Art Dir* Robert Bouladoux. *Asst Art Dir* James Allan, Georges Richard. *Set Decor* Robert Pilat. *Scenic Artist* Fernand Chauviret. *Film Ed* Jacqueline Douarinou. *Asst Film Ed* Eric Pluet. *Mus* Jean Yatove. *Lyr* Henri Contet. *Sd* Jean Rieul. *Rec* Christian Courmes. *Boom Op* Marcel Corvaisier. *Asst Dir* Jacques Deray. *Prod Mgr* Paulette Boréal. *Asst Prod Mgr* Lucien Denis. *Script Girl* Martine Guillou. *Prod Sec* Yvonne Eblagond. *Cost* Irène Pawloff, Nanda Belloni. *Makeup* Yvonne Gasperina. *Hairstyles* Jean Lalaurette. *Still Photog* Robert Joffré. *Prop* René Albouze, Pierre Barbet.

Cast: Jean Gabin (*Inspector Vallois*), Danielle Darrieux (*Thérèse Marken*), Nadja Tiller (*Lucky*), Paul Frankeur (*Inspector Chaville*), Hazel Scott (*Valentine Horse*), Robert Manuel (*Blasco*), Robert Berri (*Marquis*), Roger Hanin (*Simoni*), Harald Wolff (*Lucky's father*), François Chaumette (*Commissioner Janin*), Raoul Saint-Yves, Amy Colin, Edouard Fleming.

Crime melodrama. Source: Jacques Robert, *Le désordre et la nuit* (Paris, 1955). While investigating the murder of nightclub owner Albert Simoni, Inspector Vallois of the Paris police becomes emotionally involved with the victim's German mistress Lucky Friedel, a would-be singer who takes dope. Hoping to prove her innocence, Vallois tries to induce Lucky to tell him all she knows, but she refuses to cooperate. Eventually, however, she leads him to Thérèse Marken, a clever woman pharmacist who also knew Simoni. Vallois' slow but methodical handling of the case so irritates the police commissioner that he decides to take over and arrest Lucky for drug addiction as well as complicity in Simoni's murder. Before he can do so, however, Lucky disappears. Vallois finds her, heavily doped, in Thérèse's home. Confronted by Vallois, Thérèse admits to having killed Simoni when she tired of her affections. Lucky witnessed the crime and used her knowledge of it to blackmail Thérèse into supplying her with morphine. After telling headquarters where they can find the killer, Vallois takes Lucky to a sanitarium, promising to return for her once she has been cured. *Nightclub owners. Drug addicts. Police. Pharmacists. Mistresses. Germans. Murder. Blackmail. Morphine. Paris.*

Note: Location scenes filmed in Paris. Paris opening in May 1958 as *Le désordre et la nuit.*

A NIGHT AT JOANI'S *see* **MONDO ROCCO**

A NIGHT BEFORE CHRISTMAS (U.S.S.R.)   **F6.3464**

Gorky Film Studio. *Dist* Artkino Pictures. 14 Dec **1963** [New York opening]. Sd; col. 35mm. 60 min.

Dir-Writ Aleksandr Rou. *Story Ed* V. Biryukova. *Anim* G. Kozlov, I. Davydov. *Photog* Dmitriy Surenskiy. *Art Dir* Aleksandr Dikhtyar. *Set Decor* A. Ivashchenko. *Film Ed* K. Blinova. *Mus* A. Filippenko. *Cond* V. Tolba. *Sd* Anatoliy Dikan. *Asst Dir* V. Losev. *Prod Mgr* A. Demyanenko. *Cost* L. Dushina. *Makeup* S. Filenova. *Sp Eff* L. Akimov, V. Nikitchenko, Yu. Lupandin.

Cast: Aleksandr Khvylya (*Chub*), L. Myznikova (*Oksana*), Yu. Tavrov (*Vakula*), L. Khityayeva (*Solokha*), S. Martinson (*Osip, the sacristan*), Anatoliy Kubatskiy (*Panas*), Vera Altayskaya (*his wife*), D. Kapka (*Shanuvalenko*), N. Yakovchenko (*Patsyuk*), M. Sidorchuk (*Odarka*), A. Radunskiy (*The Head*), Georgiy Millyar (*The Devil*), A. Ablova, V. Bubnova, M. Vasilyev, Ye. Grigoryev, A. Demyanenko, L. Korolyova, I. Murzayeva, N. Skvortsova, A. Smirnov, Mark Troyanovskiy, Z. Chekulayeva, Yu. Chekulayev.

Comedy. Source: Nikolay Vasilyevich Gogol, "Noch pered rozhdestvom," in *Vechera na khutore bliz Dikanki; chast vtoraya* (1832). On Christmas Eve in the Ukrainian village of Dikanka, the pig-faced Devil steals the moon. His purpose is to discourage the Cossack Chub from attending a party given by a kinsman of the sacristan's and leaving his beautiful daughter, Oksana, alone and vulnerable to a visit by the blacksmith Vakula, whose fine religious paintings the Devil finds offensive. However, the plan backfires as Chub sets out from home in the darkness with his friend Panas. Inside the house, Oksana sits in front of her mirror, talking to herself of her own beauty. Vakula, who is head-over-heels in love with Oksana, arrives to woo her, but she mocks him. The Devil creates a snowstorm to send Chub home, but the Cossack, roughly turned away from his own door by Vakula, believes he has stopped at the wrong house. He proceeds to the home of Vakula's mother, the witch Solokha, who counts among her lovers the Devil, the sacristan, and the Head, as well as Chub. Each of them arrives at her house in turn, believing her to be alone, and at each knock on the door she hides her current visitor in a coal sack to prevent his discovery. Meanwhile, Oksana taunts Vakula in front of her friends, who have gathered to sing carols, promising that she will marry him if he can bring her the czarina's slippers. The lovelorn Vakula visits the sorcerer Patsyuk to enlist the Devil's help, carrying with him a small coal sack from his mother's house. He discovers that he has been carrying the Devil in the sack and catches him by the tail. Forced to do Vakula's bidding, the Devil takes him to Saint Petersburg, and there the blacksmith joins a troop of Zaporozhian Cossacks who are to be reviewed by the czarina. The czarina is touched by Vakula's simple-hearted request for a pair of her slippers and gladly complies. By the time Vakula is returned home by the Devil, gossip has it that he has taken his own life. Meanwhile, Oksana, fearing that she has lost him, has fallen madly in love with him. Oksana and Vakula wed, and Vakula paints the church as an act of penance. *Blacksmiths. Painters. Witches. Cossacks. Royalty. Vanity. Magic. Courtship. Infidelity. Gossip. Shoes. Christmas. The Moon. Dikanka. Saint Petersburg. Ukraine. Blizzards. The Devil.*

Note: Released in the U.S.S.R. in Dec 1961 as *Vechera na khutore bliz Dikanki.* Synopsis follows Gogol's story.

THE NIGHT CALLER *see* **BLOOD BEAST FROM OUTER SPACE**

THE NIGHT CRAWLERS *see* **THE NAVY VS. THE NIGHT MONSTERS**

NIGHT CREATURES (Great Britain)   **F6.3465**

Hammer Film Productions-Major Productions. *Dist* Universal-International. 13 Jun **1962** [Kansas City, Missouri, opening; c19 Apr 1962; LP24731]. Sd; col (Eastman Color, print by Pathé). 35mm. 81 min.

Prod John Temple-Smith. *Dir* Peter Graham Scott. *Screenplay* John Elder. *Adtl Dial* Barbara S. Harper. *Dir Photog* Arthur Grant. *Camera Op* Len Harris. *Art Dir* Don Mingaye. *Prod Dsgn* Bernard Robinson. *Supv Film Ed* James Needs. *Ed* Eric Boyd-Perkins. *Mus Comp* Don Banks. *Mus Dir* Philip Martell. *Sd* Jock May. *Sd Ed* Terry Poulton. *1st & 2d Asst Dir* John Peverall, Peter Medak. *Prod Mgr* Don Weeks. *Cont* Tilly Day. *Wardrobe Supv* Molly Arbuthnot. *Wardrobe Mistress* Rosemary Burrows. *Makeup* Roy Ashton. *Hairdresser* Frieda Steiger. *Sp Eff* Les Bowie. *Stills Camera* Tom Edwards. *Fight Seq Supv* Bob Simmons.

Cast: Peter Cushing (*Dr. Blyss*), Yvonne Romain (*Imogene*), Patrick Allen (*Captain Collier*), Oliver Reed (*Harry Crabtree*), Michael Ripper (*Mipps*), Martin Benson (*Rash*), David Lodge (*bosun*), Derek Francis (*squire*), Daphne

Anderson (*Mrs. Rash*), Milton Reid (*mulatto*), Jack MacGowran (*frightened man*), Peter Halliday (*Jack Pott*), Terry Scully (*Dick Tate*), Sydney Bromley (*Tom Ketch*), Rupert Osborne (*Gerry*), Gordon Rollings (*Wurzel*), Bob Head (*peg-leg*), Colin Douglas (*pirate bosun*).

Melodrama. In 18th-century England, naval officer Captain Collier and a company of king's men are sent to the village of Dymchurch to rid the area of smuggling, but they are warned by Dr. Blyss, a tight-lipped vicar, not to expect any help from the villagers, who profit from smugglers' trade. Upon learning that his sole informant has drowned the previous night in the marshes, Collier marches his men to the site, where they are terrified by ghostly "marsh phantoms," later revealed to be decoys assisting in the smuggling of contraband liquor out of the local coffinmaker's shop. A mute mulatto in Collier's party recognizes Blyss as the notorious Captain Clegg, a pirate supposedly buried years before in the village graveyard. When Collier confronts Blyss with the information, the vicar avoids acknowledging the charges until his daughter Imogene can elope with young Harry Crabtree, the squire's son. The villagers, grateful that smuggling profits have been used to help the poor, rally to his defense; however, the vengeful mulatto, who was once tortured by Blyss, murders him. *Clergymen. Pirates. Mutes. Personal identity. Mulattoes. Smuggling. Filial relations. Elopement. Murder. Revenge. Liquor. Swamps. Great Britain—Royal Navy.*

Note: Opened in London in Jun 1962 as *Captain Clegg.* John Elder is a pseudonym for Anthony Hinds.

NIGHT ENCOUNTER (France/Italy)   **F6.3466**

S. N. E. Gaumont-Film Costellazione. *Dist* Shawn International, Inc. 15 Oct **1963.** Sd; b&w. 35mm. 80 min.

Dir-Story Robert Hossein. *Screenplay* Robert Hossein, Louis Martin, Alain Poiré. *Set Dsgn* Rino Mondellini. *Film Ed* Gilbert Natot. *Mus* André Gosselain. *Sd* Pierre Bertrand. *Prod Dir* Robert Sussfeld. *Prod Asst* Alain Poiré.

Cast: Robert Hossein (*Peter*), Marina Vlady (*Helene*), Robert Le Béal, Roger Crouzet, Clément Harari, Georges Vitaly, Michel Etcheverry.

War drama. During an air raid in London in 1941, a female German secret agent receives instructions from her superior to deliver some secret documents to a German officer at a rendezvous in an isolated cabin on the Normandy coast. The officer, in turn, is to give the woman instructions regarding future German espionage in Britain. The British learn of the plot, and they plan to intercept the German agent and send a British agent in her place. Another British agent is to kill the German officer, seize his documents, and retrieve the British female agent in the cabin. Two days later, Helene, ostensibly a German agent, meets Peter, a man in a German SS uniform, at the cabin. It is possible that they are two German spies, or the two British spies sent to replace them, or, if the British mission has been only partially successful, one German and one British spy. As the two attempt to discover each other's true identity during the night, they fall in love. By morning, there is no definite evidence as to the real nationality of either spy. [In the original version, the British intercept the German female agent but fail in their attempt to replace the SS officer. At the conclusion of the encounter between the agents at the cabin, they discover that they are enemies, and the British agent is shot by the German officer.] *Germans. British. Secret agents. Espionage. Personal identity. Impersonation. World War II. SS. London. Normandy.*

Note: Opened in Paris in Sep 1959 as *La nuit des espions*; running time: 85 min. Italian title: *La notte delle spie.*

NIGHT FOG *see* **NAKED FOG**

NIGHT GAMES (Sweden)   **F6.3467**

Sandrews. *Dist* Mondial Films. 2 Nov **1966** [San Francisco opening]. Sd (AGA-Baltic); b&w. 35mm. 104 min.

Pres by Gaston Hakim. *Prod* Lena Malmsjö. *Dir* Mai Zetterling. *Screenplay* Mai Zetterling, David Hughes. *Dir Photog* Rune Ericson. *Camera Op* Björn Thermaenius. *Asst Camera Op* Curt Persson. *Studio Photog* David Hughes. *Art Dir* Jan Boleslaw. *Film Ed* Paul Davies. *Mus Comp* Jan Johansson, Georg Riedel. *Sd* P. O. Pettersson. *Boom Op* Lennart Engholm. *Sd Mix* Olle Jacobsson. *Asst Dir* Peter Hald. *Prod Mgr* Göran Lindgren. *Script Girl* Kerstin Berg. *Location Mgr* Christer Abrahamsen. *Cost* Birgitta Hahn. *Makeup* Tina Johansson. *Hairstyles* Bengt Ottekil. *Sp Eff* Paul Davies. *Prop Master* Sven Björling.

Cast: Ingrid Thulin (*Irene*), Keve Hjelm (*Jan, as a man*), Jörgen Lindström (*Jan, age 12*), Lena Brundin (*Mariana*), Naima Wifstrand (*Aunt Astrid*), Rune Lindström (*Albin*), Monica Zetterlund (*Lotten*), Lauritz Falk (*Bruno*), Christian Bratt (*Erland*), Lissi Alandh (*Melissa*), Georg Årlin (*Dicksson*), Willy Koblanck (*doctor*), Axel Fritz (*Alex*), Fylgia Zadig, Chris Wahlström, Bo Hederström, Harry Schein, Cécile Ossbahr, Ragnar Arvedson, Siv Ericks, Sten Lonnert, Kai Reiners, Kurt Falk, Britt-Mari Råberg, Stig de la Berg, Tom Brown, Jan Johansson, Georg Riedel, Jan Allan, Rune Falk, Arne Domnerus,

Egil Johansen, Claes Rosendahl, Andreas Skjold, Kurt Kimsjö (guests).

Drama. Source: Mai Zetterling, *Night Games* (New York and London, 1966). When emotional and sexual inhibitions threaten to destroy his pending marriage, 35-year-old Jan returns to the manor home of his youth to reflect on the causes of his dilemma. As he recalls his childhood, his most vivid memories are of his beautiful and extravagant mother, Irene. At the age of 12, Jan was present while Irene gave birth to a stillborn child at an orgiastic party attended by all of her bizarre and perverted friends. Always eager to attract his mother's attention, Jan would crawl under her skirts while she made love, or if she were alone, he would put on her jewelry and makeup and parade before her. His feelings soon became more incestuous, and he was delighted when she dried his naked body or allowed him to sleep in her bed. Following her death in an automobile accident, he remained for a while with his eccentric Aunt Astrid, who read to him from the Bible and taught him to believe in the Resurrection. But his aunt also died, and Jan grew into manhood alone. His fiancée, Mariana, who bears a striking resemblance to Irene, stays with Jan at the mansion and tries desperately to help him by offering her love and understanding. Realizing that he can never be truly free while the mansion and its memories of his grotesque childhood remain, Jan invites all of his mother's parasitic friends to a final party and tells them that he intends to blow up the mansion. As they race from the premises, they carry off any treasures they can lift. When they are gone, Jan and Mariana watch as the mansion is destroyed by fire. *Orphans. Eccentrics. Aunts. Marriage. Inhibition. Filial relations. Childhood. Stillbirth. Incest. Death. Memory. Manors. Fires.*

Note: Filmed at Penningby Castle, Sweden. Released in Sweden in Sep 1966 as *Nattlck*; running time: 105 min. Working title: *Längtan.*

NIGHT GAMES see EROS

NIGHT HUNT see IF HE HOLLERS, LET HIM GO!

THE NIGHT HUSTLERS   F6.3468
Barracuda Productions. *Dist* Inter-American Film Distributors. 10 Jul **1968** [Champaign, Illinois, showing]. Sd; col (Eastman Color). 35mm. 66 min.

Prod James A. Neal, Jr. *Dir-Writ* Bobby O'Donald.

Cast: Marcel Delage, James Neal, China Valle, Carol Baillie, Jose Varo, Manola Rodriguez, Cielito Lindo, Andrea Barr, Linda Lee, Ami Amar, Lisa Hall, Margo Billings.

Drama. A French writer seeking material for a new novel invites two vice squad officers to his apartment to relate some of their case histories. Between listening to stories of drug raids, prostitution, and stag shows, the writer talks on the telephone to his women friends. Each woman is shown engaged in a leisure-time activity while she talks on the telephone—one plays with her stuffed tiger; one is shown being bathed by her maid; one, a stripper, is shown relaxing in her dressing room between acts; and one is given a rubdown by a masseur. The writer refuses invitations from all these women when he perceives that his private secretary would like to spend the evening with him. *French. Novelists. Masseurs. Secretaries. Stripteasers. Prostitution. Narcotics. Telephone. Sex shows. Vice squads.*

NIGHT IN BANGKOK (Japan)   F6.3469
Toho Co.-Taiwan Film Studios-The Cathay Organization. *Dist* Toho Co. Jun **1966** [Los Angeles showing]. Sd; col (Eastmancolor). 35mm (Tohoscope). 105 min.

Prod Sanezumi Fujimoto. *Dir* Yasuki Chiba. *Screenplay* Ryozo Kasahara. *Photog* Taiichi Kankura. *Mus* Naozumi Yamamoto.

Cast: Chang Mei Yao (*Meilan*), Yuzo Kayama (*Shuichi*), Yuriko Hoshi (*Masayo*), Praprapon Pureem, Takashi Shimura.

Romantic melodrama. Shuichi, a young doctor, has been raised by foster parents whose own daughter, Masayo, has been in love with him for years. Shuichi, however, meets Meilan, the daughter of a Chinese trader living in Bangkok, and their romance causes Masayo to drift away from him. After Shuichi takes a position at a Bangkok hospital, he and Meilan discover that her parents have arranged a marriage for her with a Thai prince. Despite their disappointment, the couple pledge their eternal love for each other. *Physicians. Chinese. Foster parents. Merchants. Royalty. Thais. Orphans. Marriage—Arranged. Bangkok.*

Note: Location scenes filmed in Taipei, Kyoto, Nara, Tokyo, and Bangkok. Released in Japan in 1966 as *Bankokku no yoru.*

A NIGHT IN HONG KONG (Japan)   F6.3470
Toho Co.-The Cathay Organization. *Dist* Toho Co. Dec **1961** [Los Angeles showing]. Sd; col (Eastmancolor). 35mm (Tohoscope). 119 min.

Exec Prod Sanezumi Fujimoto, Robert Chung. *Dir* Yasuki Chiba. *Screenplay* Toshiro Ide. *Photog* Rokuro Nishigaki. *Mus* Hachiro Matsui.

Cast: Akira Takarada (*Hiroshi Tanaka*), Yu Ming (*Wu Li Hung*), Yoko Tsukasa (*Keiko Kimura*), Mitsuko Kusabue, Ken Uehara, Daisuke Kato, Yu Fujiki, Won Inn, Ma Ree, Kang Pak King, Tetsu Nakamura, Hiroshi Koizumi,

Michiyo Kogure, Mie Hama.

Romantic melodrama. Hiroshi Tanaka, a journalist, stops on his way back from Europe in Hong Kong, where he meets a Chinese girl, Wu Li Hung, who nurses him to health when he falls ill. Their friendship develops into romance, and Hiroshi leaves for Tokyo promising to return to Hong Kong. In Tokyo, he is met by Keiko Kimura, a childhood friend in love with him. Some months later, on assignment in Hong Kong, Hiroshi finds Wu Li Hung is engaged to marry her boss's son. Hiroshi traces Wu to Macao, where he proposes marriage. She refuses, saying she is against mixed marriages because her Japanese mother had deserted her and fled to Japan during the war. Keiko arrives in Hong Kong and discovers the romance between Hiroshi and Wu. At first jealous, she finally resigns herself to their love and departs for Paris. Meanwhile, Hiroshi tries unsuccessfully to effect a happy reunion between Wu and her mother, whom he has found living in Japan. On his way to cover a war in Laos, Hiroshi stops off in Hong Kong once more. Wu finally consents to marry him, and he continues on to his assignment. As Wu is being fitted for her wedding gown, she is told of her fiancé's death on the Laotian front. *Journalists. Chinese. Social customs. Jealousy. Marriage—Mixed. Tokyo. Hong Kong. Laos. Macao.*

Note: Released in Japan in 1961 as *Honkon no yoru.*

NIGHT IS MY FUTURE (Sweden)   F6.3471
Terrafilm. *Dist* Embassy Pictures. 8 Jan **1963** [New York opening]. Sd; b&w. 35mm. 87 min.

Pres by Joseph E. Levine. *Prod* Lorens Marmstedt. *Dir* Ingmar Bergman. *Screenplay* Dagmar Edqvist. *Photog* Göran Strindberg. *Art Dir* P. A. Lundgren. *Film Ed* Lennart Wallén. *Mus* Erland von Koch. *Sd* Olle Jakobsson. *Prod Mgr* Allan Ekelund.

Cast: Mai Zetterling (*Ingrid Olofsdotter*), Birger Malmsten (*Bengt*), Bengt Eklund (*Ebbe*), Olof Winnerstrand (*vicar*), Naima Wifstrand (*Mrs. Schröder*), Bibi Skoglund (*Agneta*), Hilda Borgström (*Lovis*), Douglas Håge (*Druge*), Gunnar Björnstrand (*Klasson*), Åke Claesson, John Elfström, Sven Lindberg, Bengt Logardt, Marianne Gyllenhammar, Barbro Flodquist, Ulla Andreasson, Rune Andreasson.

Drama. Source: Dagmar Edqvist, *Musik i mörker* (Stockholm, 1946). During his military service, Bengt is blinded while rescuing a puppy on a rifle range. He tries to adjust to his affliction, but tensions mount when he rejects help and pity from others. He hires Ingrid, a destitute young woman, to be his maid and introduces her to the wonders of books and music; their relationship soon develops into an unspoken feeling of tenderness. Failing to gain admission to the Music Academy, he takes a job playing the piano in a restaurant but leaves because the owner is crooked and a young man whom he trusted robs him. He enrolls in a school for the blind and regains his self-respect, but his old feeling of inferiority returns when Ingrid introduces him to one of her boyfriends. Beset with despair and loneliness, he runs along a railroad track and is almost killed by a train. Ingrid finds him on a bridge, but her boyfriend follows and knocks Bengt down, giving Bengt the satisfaction of feeling that he has been treated as an equal. Despite the objections of the local parson, he asks Ingrid to marry him, and she accepts. *Veterans. Housemaids. Pianists. Blindness. Jealousy. Marriage. Schools for the Blind.*

Note: Opened in Stockholm in Jan 1948 as *Musik i mörker*; running time: 90 min.

NIGHT IS THE PHANTOM see WHAT!

NIGHT MUST FALL (Great Britain)   F6.3472
Metro-Goldwyn-Mayer Pictures. *Dist* Metro-Goldwyn-Mayer, Inc. 18 Mar **1964** [New York opening; c13 Feb 1964; LP28120]. Sd (Westrex); b&w. 35mm. 105 min. [Copyright length: 101 min.]

Prod Albert Finney, Karel Reisz. *Exec Prod* Lawrence P. Bachmann. *Dir* Karel Reisz. *Screenplay* Clive Exton. *Dir Photog* Freddie Francis. *Camera Op* Gerry Fisher. *Art Dir* Lionel Couch. *Prod Dsgn* Timothy O'Brien. *Ed Supv* Fergus McDonell. *Ed* Philip Barnikel. *Mus Comp & Cond* Ron Grainer. *Sd Ed* Malcolm Cooke. *Dub Mix* J. B. Smith. *Sd Rec* Cyril Swern. *Rec Supv* A. W. Watkins. *Asst Dir* David Tomblin. *Prod Mgr* Timothy Burrill.

Cast: Albert Finney (*Danny*), Mona Washbourne (*Mrs. Bramson*), Susan Hampshire (*Olivia*), Sheila Hancock (*Dora*), Michael Medwin (*Derek*), Joe Gladwin (*Dodge*), Martin Wyldeck (*Inspector Willet*), John Gill (*Foster*).

Drama. Source: Emlyn Williams, *Night Must Fall* (London opening: 31 May 1935). Danny, a Welsh hotel bellboy, commits an axe murder in the woods near the home of Mrs. Bramson, a wealthy widow, and disposes of his female victim's body and the axe in a lake. The following morning he is summoned to Mrs. Bramson's house because Dora, her maid, is pregnant by him. He charms the women, however, and soon he is living in the house, supposedly to redecorate it. There he plays games with Mrs. Bramson in which he pretends to be her child. He also becomes the lover of Olivia, Mrs. Bramson's daughter. Alone in his room, he performs lunatic rituals with the severed heads of his victims which he keeps in a black hatbox. Meanwhile, the police uncover the headless body and the axe in the lake. Dora discovers Danny and Olivia's relationship and refuses his offer to accompany her home. Rejected, he turns to Mrs. Bramson, and when Olivia witnesses one of their strange games, she flees in panic from the house. Frustrated because the tired old lady wishes to discontinue a game of chase in her wheelchair, Danny hacks her to death. Olivia returns and summons the police while Danny, cowered by Olivia's unexpected determination, huddles in the bathroom, completely withdrawn in his private world of madness. *Welsh. Bellboys. Psychopaths. Housemaids. Invalids. Widows. Police. Insanity. Murder. Pregnancy. Decapitation. Rites and ceremonies. Games. Axes.*

Note: Released in Great Britain in 1964 at 101 min. This is a remake of the 1937 Metro-Goldwyn-Mayer film.

NIGHT OF ANUBIS *see* **NIGHT OF THE LIVING DEAD**

NIGHT OF BLOODY HORROR   F6.3473

Taste of Blood, Inc.–Cinema IV International Pictures. *Dist* Howco International. 9 Aug **1969** [New Orleans opening; c1 May 1969; LP37500]. Sd; col. 35mm. 89 min. *MPAA rating* R.

Prod-Dir Joy N. Houck, Jr. *Exec Prod* Albert J. Salzer. *Assoc Prod* 1968 Equities, Sidney H. Lazard, Max Durham, James Morton, Gordon Ogden, Joseph C. Elmer. *Story-Screenplay* Robert A. Weaver, Joy N. Houck, Jr. *Dir Photog* Robert A. Weaver. *Camera Op* Bob Allen. *Asst Camera* Doug Sherr. *Titl* Consolidated Film Industries. *Film Ed* Robert A. Weaver. *Neg Cutter* Jack LaMantain. *Mus* General Music Corp. *Perf by* The Bored. *Sd* Ryder Sound Service. *Sd Rec* Sol Alzer. *Prod Supv* Russ M. Herman. *Exec Supv* Joy N. Houck, Sr. *Script Supv* Annuncetta Crump. *Makeup* Philip St. Jon. *Hairstyles* Louis Truxillo, Joellen Dearie. *Opticals* Consolidated Film Industries. *Grip* Ken Harrison, Ricky Wolsch. *Casting* Albert J. Salzer.

Cast: Gerald McRaney (*Wesley Stuart*), Gaye Yellen (*Angelle Miliot*), Herbert Nelson (*Dr. Bennett Moss*), Evelyn Hendricks (*Agatha Stuart*), Lisa Dameron (*Susan Collins*), Charlotte White (*Kay Jensen*), Nicholous R. Krieger (*Lieut. James Cole*), Michael Anthony, U. S. actor (*Mario Spenelli*), Bert Roberts, actor (*Mark Lewis*), Gordon Ogden (*Tucker Fredricks*), Murray Solow (*bartender*), Nigel Strangeways, Burt Love, Louis Grapes (*hoods*), George Spelvin (*priest*), Anthony Herrero (*man in club*), Mark Fleming, Philip Fleming (*altar boys*), Farley Dennis (*Wesley as a boy*), Emile Weaver, III (*Johnathan*), John Barber, Sheri Sherwood, The Bored.

Horror film. Stricken with a violent headache, Wesley Stuart, son of a wealthy New Orleans family, leaves the home of his fiancée, Susan, soon after they make love. Overcome by guilt, Susan goes to church, where she is brutally murdered as she makes her confession. Wesley, after a year-long drinking binge, becomes engaged again, this time to Kay Jensen, a nurse. She is soon murdered with an ax, and Wesley is held by police as the prime suspect. Agatha, Wesley's mother, sends for Bennett Moss, her son's doctor during the 13 years he was confined in a mental institution after he accidentally killed his brother Johnathan. Meanwhile, Wesley is released on bond and meets Angelle, a reporter. He takes her to a nightclub where a drunk recognizes him from a photo and intimidates him. Wesley beats the man brutally and is returned to jail, but Dr. Moss arrives and takes custody of his former patient. That night at the Stuart home, Wesley dreams about Angelle and awakens in a cold sweat. As Dr. Moss tries to find his patient, his hand is sliced off and he is murdered with a meat cleaver. Wesley, extremely agitated, visits Angelle and tries to become intimate. He affirms his innocence of the murders; and Angelle leaves to find Dr. Moss, who might be able to provide an alibi. Wesley is arrested by police, who believe that he has murdered Angelle. He persuades them to return with him to the family home. Arriving in time to prevent Angelle from being killed by Agatha, they learn that Agatha has murdered Wesley's girl friends and the resulting suicide of her husband. *Physicians. Nurses. Police. Reporters. Guilt. Murder. Filial relations. Mental illness. Confession. Alcoholism. Mutilation. Suicide. New Orleans.*

NIGHT OF EVIL   F6.3474

Galbreath Pictures. *Dist* Astor Pictures, Sutton Pictures. 27 Jan **1962** [Fort Wayne, Indiana, opening; c27 Jan 1962; LP21210]. Sd; b&w. 35mm. 88 min.

Prod Richard Galbreath, Lou Perry. *Dir* Richard Galbreath. *Screenplay* Louis Perino. *Story* Lou Perry. *Mus* Arnold Holop.

Cast: Earl Wilson (*narrator*), Lisa Gaye, William Campbell, Lynn Bernay, Remo Pisani, George Dietsel, Joseph Garri, Don De Leo, Burtt Harris, actor, Gary Gage, Sammy Mannis, Patricia Dahling, David Dunstone, Barbara Bricker, Marjorie Suter, Eric Anthony Pregent, Ira Gaskill, Jack Morey, Barbara Meyers, Lary Beauchamp, Walt Rearick, Virginia Carter, Les Podwell, Margaret Silverman, James Foland, George Fruechtenicht, James Voors, Paul Dawson, Manny Silverman, Lois Broad, John Renforth, Morey Copeland, Karlton Kadell, Bob Durham, Merrill C. Johnson, Sara Gage, John Himes, Jack Nichols, actor.

Melodrama. Dixie Ann Dikes, a Colorado teenager living with her foster parents, is assaulted by her school's football hero, who is jealous because she is dating another student. Her parents refuse to believe her explanation, and the courts send her to a girls' home. Released two years later, she goes to live with a former schoolmate. Soon, Dixie meets a promoter who enters her in the Miss Colorado contest. After Dixie wins the competition, she becomes involved with ex-convict Chuck Logan, who marries her after a whirlwind courtship. Logan reverts to a life of crime; he tries to kidnap a policeman, but is arrested. Dixie's marriage thus is made public, and she must withdraw from the Miss America pageant. Despondent, she obtains work as a stripper. Later, she is injured in a scuffle with a drunk. She then buys a gun, but her suicide attempt is aborted. Finally, she is arrested for trying to hold up a drugstore. The gun, however, has no firing pin, and she is given a light prison sentence. *Foster parents. Publicists. Ex-convicts. Stripteasers. Adolescence. Jealousy. Marriage. Suicide. Robbery. Girls' homes. Beauty contests. Guns. Colorado.*

Note: Filmed on location in Fort Wayne, Indiana.

NIGHT OF LUST (France)   F6.3475

Les Films Univers–Aurora Films. *Dist* Olympic International Films. 19 Feb **1965** [Los Angeles showing]. Sd (Western Electric); b&w. 35mm. 58 min.

Prod-Dir-Dial José Bénazéraf. *English Vers Dial* R. L. Frost. *Adapt* Guy Fanelli. *Photog* Edmond Richard. *Film Ed* Georges Marschalk. *Orig Mus* Chet Baker.

Cast: Hans Verner · (*Eric Voltay*), Jean-Pierre Kalfon (*Sacha Markriff*), Marcel Champel (*Fred Voltay*), Yvonne Monlaur (*Nora*), Michel Lemoine, Régine Rumen, Willy Braque, André Rouyer, Jean Claude, Christiane Arnaud.

Crime melodrama. Source: Dominique Dorn, *Le parfum de la peur* (Paris, 1960). Eric Voltay, a Parisian gangster, controls one of the three major narcotics syndicates in the city. Voltay's former employee, Sacha Markriff, heads a rival gang which is attempting to gain control of the narcotics trade. Sacha kidnaps Eric's brother Fred to blackmail Eric into revealing the source of his narcotics. Eric retaliates by kidnaping Nora, Sacha's sister. The two gangs agree to exchange hostages, but Sacha plots to destroy Eric's organization during the exchange. A heated gun battle ensues, and both sides are decimated. [According to a French source, Nora is not related to Sacha but becomes involved in the gang rivalry when she accepts a date with Chevrel, a member of Eric's gang. She is taken prisoner by the gang after Chevrel is murdered and Fred is kidnapped by Sacha's men. Nora accidentally kills her brutal guard, Fred's fiancée, and attempts to flee but allows herself to be seduced by Eric, a blind trumpet player. While the two gangs exterminate each other, Sacha visits Eric, and the two chiefs kill each other.] *Gangsters. Brothers. Hostages. Trumpeters. Perfidy. Murder. Kidnaping. Brother-sister relationship. Seduction. Gang wars. Blindness. Syndicates. Lesbianism. Narcotics. Paris. Crazy Horse Saloon (Paris).*

Note: Paris opening: Nov 1963 as *La drogue du vice*: running time: 75 min. Alternative French title: *Le concerto de la peur*. Also known in the United States as *Notte Erotique*; advertised as *Night of Love*. U. S. release version includes footage of a lesbian nightclub act filmed at the Crazy Horse Saloon in Paris. This additional material also appears in *Sexus*, q. v.

NIGHT OF PASSION *see* **DURING ONE NIGHT**

NIGHT OF THE EAGLE *see* **BURN, WITCH, BURN**

NIGHT OF THE FLESH EATERS *see* **NIGHT OF THE LIVING DEAD**

THE NIGHT OF THE FOLLOWING DAY   F6.3476

Gina Productions. *Dist* Universal Pictures. 22 Jan **1969** [Los Angeles opening; c29 Mar 1968; LP38878]. Sd (RCA); col (Technicolor). 35mm. 93 min. *MPAA rating* R.

A Jerry Gershwin–Elliott Kastner Production. *Prod-Dir* Hubert Cornfield. *Exec Prod* Jerry Gershwin, Elliott Kastner. *Assoc Prod* Alfredo Lettieri. *Screenplay* Hubert Cornfield, Robert Phippeny. *Dir Photog* (see note) Willy Kurant, Jean Klissak. *Camera Op* Jean Orjollet. *Art Dir* Jean Boulet. *Main Titl* Bob Gill. *Film Ed* Anne Vogler, Gordon Pilkington. *Mus* Stanley Myers. *Song:* "One Early Morning" Stanley Myers, Jon Hendricks. *Sung by* Annie Ross. *Sd Mix* Guy Rophé, Ken Scrivener. *Sd Ed* Alban Streeter. *Asst Dir* Georges Pellegrin. *Prod Mgr* Louis Fleury. *Asst to the Prod* Marion Rosenberg. *Cont* Elisabeth Rappeneau. *Wardrobe Master* Pierre Marcadé. *Makeup* Jackie Reynal. *Hairstyles* Antoine Garabédian.

Cast: Marlon Brando (*Bud, the chauffeur*), Richard Boone (*The Leer*), Rita Moreno (*Vi*), Pamela Franklin (*girl*), Jess Hahn (*Wally*), Gérard Buhr (*fisherman/cop*), Hugues Wanner (*father*), Jacques Marin (*bartender*), Alfredo Lettieri (*pilot*).

Melodrama. Source: Lionel White, *The Snatchers* (New York, 1953). At Paris' Orly Airport a young woman is kidnaped by a burly chauffeur, Bud, and his sadistic companion, The Leer. Quartered in an isolated beachhouse, she is introduced to the other gang members, including Vi, whom the victim recognizes as the stewardess on her flight, and Vi's brother Wally. Discovering that Vi is addicted to drugs and suspecting that The Leer intends to assault and rape their hostage, Bud suggests ending the scheme. Wally, however, dissuades him. While Bud, Wally, and Vi, drive to the village café to pick up the ransom, The Leer guards the woman. At the café the gang murders its proprietor and a gendarme. As Vi and Wally alight from the car they are shot down by the perfidious Leer, who is in turn murdered by Bud. Upon entering the house Bud discovers the expiring victim hanging from the wall, stripped, lacerated, and shot in the back. As Bud frees her body, the victim awakens in the plane. Awaiting her is the chauffeur. . . . *Hostages. Chauffeurs. Airline stewardesses. Police. Kidnaping. Murder. Perfidy. Sadism. Airfields. Cafes. Ransom. Narcotics. Orly Airport. Paris. Dreams.*

Note: Location scenes filmed in France. Sources conflict in crediting director of photography. Copyright claimant: Universal Pictures, Ltd.

THE NIGHT OF THE GENERALS (France/Great Britain)   **F6.3477**
Horizon Pictures-Filmsonor. *Dist* Columbia Pictures. 2 Feb **1967** [New York opening; c1 Feb 1967; LP34167]. Sd (Westrex); col (Technicolor). 35mm (Panavision). 148 min.
    Prod Sam Spiegel. *Dir* Anatole Litvak. *Screen Adapt* Joseph Kessel, Paul Dehn. *Adtl Dial* Paul Dehn. *Dir Photog* Henri Decaë. *Camera Op* Charles-Henry Montel. *Art Dir* Auguste Capelier. *Set Dresser* Maurice Barnathan. *Prod Dsgn* Alexander Trauner. *Titl Seq Dsgn* Robert Brownjohn. *Film Ed* Alan Osbiston. *Asst Ed* Willy Kemplen, Ginou Billo. *Mus Comp & Cond* Maurice Jarre. *Mus Perf* New Philharmonia Orchestra. *Sd Rec* William Sivel, Jacques Carrère. *Dub Ed* Ted Mason. *Mus Cutter* Dominique Amy. *Asst Dir* Tom Pevsner, Jean-Pierre Perier. *Prod Mgr* Louis Wipf. *Unit Mgr* Lucien Lippens. *Cont* Alice Ziller. *Cost* Rosine Delamare, J. Claude Philippe. *Makeup* Jean Zay. *Hairstyles* Marc Blanchard, A. G. Scott. *Polish Location Asst* Zjednoczone Zespoly Realizatorow Filmowych Groupe Studios. *Casting* Maude Spector, Margot Capelier.
    Cast: Peter O'Toole (*General Tanz*), Omar Sharif (*Major Grau*), Tom Courtenay (*Corporal Hartmann*), Donald Pleasence (*General Kahlenberge*), Joanna Pettet (*Ulrike von Seidlitz-Gabler*), Philippe Noiret (*Inspector Morand*), Charles Gray (*General von Seidlitz-Gabler*), Coral Browne (*Eleanore von Seidlitz-Gabler*), John Gregson (*Colonel Sandauer*), Nigel Stock (*Otto*), Christopher Plummer (*Field Marshal Rommel*), Juliette Greco (*Juliette*), Yves Brainville (*Liecsowski*), Sacha Pitoëff (*doctor*), Charles Millot (*Wionczek*), Raymond Gérôme (*colonel in war room*), Véronique Vendell (*Monique*), Pierre Mondy (*Kopatski*), Eléonore Hirt (*Melanie*), Nicole Courcel (*Raymonde*), Jenny Orléans (*Otto's wife*), Gérard Buhr (*Von Staffenberg*), Michael Goodliffe (*Hauser*), Gordon Jackson (*Captain Engel*), Patrick Allen (*Colonel Mannheim*), Harry Andrews (*Stupnagel*).
    War drama. Source: Hans Hellmut Kirst, *Die Nacht der Generale* (Munich, 1962). James Hadley Chase, *The Wary Transgressor* (London, 1952). A prostitute, who is also a German agent, is brutally murdered in Warsaw in 1942, and Major Grau of German Intelligence investigates three top-ranking Nazi generals: Kahlenberge, Seidlitz-Gabler, and Tanz, a ruthless sadist. Major Grau's persistence in bringing to justice one murderer during wartime irritates the High Command, and he is transferred. Two years later, the three generals and Grau are all present in Paris when the pathological Tanz murders a second prostitute. Aware that Grau is still on his trail, Tanz blames the crime on Hartmann, his orderly, who is having an affair with Seidlitz-Gabler's daughter Ulrike. After fleeing from Paris, Tanz uses the failure of the 1944 plot to assassinate Hitler as an excuse for killing Grau and naming him as one of the traitors involved in the plot. Years later, after his imprisonment as a war criminal, Tanz arrives in Hamburg for a neo-Nazi rally. He is confronted by Inspector Morand of the French police who, during the war, helped Grau with his investigation. Morand produces Hartmann, who identifies Tanz as the murderer of the Parisian prostitute. Faced with inevitable disgrace and humiliation Tanz kills himself. *Prostitutes. Nazis. Orderlies (military). Investigators. War criminals. Germans. Murder. Sadism. Frameup. Suicide. Germany—History—Third Reich. World War II. Warsaw. Paris. Erwin Rommel. Germany—Army. Germany—Intelligence service.*
    Note: Location scenes filmed in Warsaw and Paris. Released in Great Britain in 1967; in France in Apr 1967 as *La nuit des généraux*; running time: 140 min.

THE NIGHT OF THE GRIZZLY   **F6.3478**
Paramount Pictures. 20 Apr **1966** [Denver, Colorado, opening; c20 Apr 1966; LP32466]. Sd; col (Technicolor). 35mm (Techniscope). 102 min.
    Prod Burt Dunne. *Dir* Joseph Pevney. *Screenplay* Warren Douglas. *Dir Photog* Harold Lipstein, Loyal Griggs. *Art Dir* Hal Pereira, William Campbell, art dir. *Set Decor* Robert R. Benton, Anthony Mondell. *Film Ed* Philip W. Anderson. *Mus* Leith Stevens. *Song:* "Angela" Jay Livingston, Ray Evans. *Song:* "Pine Tree Tall" Clint Walker, Charlie Aldrich. *Sd* Garry Harris, John Wilkinson. *Asst Dir* Howard Roessel. *Prod Mgr* Kenneth DeLand. *Makeup*

Supv Wally Westmore. *Hairstyle Supv* Nellie Manley. *Sp Photog Eff* Paul K. Lerpae. *Proc Photog* Farciot Edouart. *Casting Supv* Kerwin Coughlin.
    Cast: Clint Walker (*Jim Cole*), Martha Hyer (*Angela Cole*), Keenan Wynn (*Jed Curry*), Nancy Kulp (*Wilhelmina Peterson*), Kevin Brodie (*Charlie Cole*), Ellen Corby (*Hazel Squires*), Jack Elam (*Hank*), Ron Ely (*Tad Curry*), Med Flory (*Duke Squires*), Leo Gordon (*Cass Dowdy*), Don Haggerty (*Sam Potts*), Sammy Jackson (*Cal Curry*), Victoria Meyerink (*Gypsy Cole*), Candy Moore (*Meg*), Regis Toomey (*Cotton Benson*).
    Western drama. Former sheriff Jim Cole comes to Hope, Wyoming, in 1880 with his wife and family to claim the ranch left him by his grandfather. Jed Curry, the town's leading citizen, wants the ranch for his sons, but Cole refuses to sell despite its poor condition. When spring comes, a marauding grizzly bear comes down from the hills and wreaks havoc at the ranches. Cole's prize bull is decapitated by the beast, his fences are knocked down, Curry's sheep flock is destroyed, a man is clawed to death, and another is maimed. Cole pledges all he owns for a loan to rebuild; and when the ranchers post a reward for the death of the grizzly, Cole sees a way out of debt. The reward also attracts Cass Dowdy, a man Cole once sent to prison and who is now out to get the former lawman. Both set out after the grizzly; and after some vicious encounters between Dowdy and Cole, Dowdy is killed by the bear, which in turn is killed by Cole. *Sheriffs. Homesteaders. Ranchers. Revenge. Inheritance. Debt. Rewards. Wyoming. Bears. Bulls. Sheep.*
    Note: Location scenes filmed at Holcomb Valley, California.

THE NIGHT OF THE IGUANA   **F6.3479**
Seven Arts Productions. *Dist* Metro-Goldwyn-Mayer, Inc. 6 Aug **1964** [New York opening; c15 Jun 1964; LP28231]. Sd (Westrex); b&w. 35mm. 125 min. [Copyright length: 118 min.]
    A John Huston-Ray Stark Production. *Prod* Ray Stark. *Prod Exec* Abe Steinberg. *Assoc Prod* Alexander Whitelaw. *Dir* John Huston. *Assoc Dir* Emilio Fernandez. *Screenplay* Anthony Veiller, John Huston. *Dir Photog* Gabriel Figueroa. *Art Dir* Stephen Grimes. *Film Ed* Ralph Kemplen. *Mus Comp & Cond* Benjamin Frankel. *Sd* Basil Fenton-Smith. *Sd Ed* Leslie Hodgson. *Asst Dir* Tom Shaw. *Prod Mgr* Clarence Eurist. *Assoc to Mr. Huston* Gladys Hill. *Script Supv* Angela Allen. *Cost* Dorothy Jeakins. *Makeup* Jack Obringer, Eric Allwright. *Hairstyles Created* Sydney Guilaroff.
    Cast: Richard Burton (*Rev. T. Lawrence Shannon*), Ava Gardner (*Maxine Faulk*), Deborah Kerr (*Hannah Jelkes*), Sue Lyon (*Charlotte Goodall*), James Ward (*Hank Prosner*), Grayson Hall (*Judith Fellowes*), Cyril Delevanti (*Nonno*), Mary Boylan (*Miss Peebles*), Gladys Hill (*Miss Dexter*), Billie Matticks (*Miss Throxton*), Fidelmar Duran (*Pepe*), Roberto Leyva (*Pedro*), C. G. Kim (*Chang*), Eloise Hardt, Thelda Victor, Betty Proctor, Dorothy Vance, Liz Rubey, Bernice Starr (*teachers*), Barbara Joyce.
    Drama. Source: Tennessee Williams, *The Night of the Iguana* (New York opening: 27 Dec 1961). The Reverend T. Lawrence Shannon, a defrocked clergyman working in Mexico as a guide for Blake's Tours, is leading a group of lady schoolteachers headed by Judith Fellowes through the country. The youngest of the group, 18-year-old Charlotte, becomes attracted to Shannon and goes to his hotel room. They are discovered by Miss Fellowes, who has been making Shannon's life miserable because she is jealous of Charlotte's interest in him; and she threatens to have Shannon fired. Although they are scheduled to stay at an air-conditioned hotel, Shannon leads the group past it and into the jungle to the Coste Verde, a crumbling hotel owned by his old friend, Maxine, whose husband has recently died. To make sure the teachers remain at Maxine's, which is closed for the season, Shannon disables the tour bus. The fever-racked Shannon tells Maxine of Miss Fellowes' plan to have him dismissed, and Maxine blocks her attempts to telephone Shannon's boss. Meanwhile, artist Hannah Jelkes and her poet grandfather, Nonno, arrive at the hotel after wandering across Mexico meagerly subsisting on the sale of their sketches and poems. Hank, the bus driver, takes up with Charlotte, repairs the bus, proclaims himself tour leader, and drives away with the teachers leaving Hannah, Nonno, Shannon and Maxine at the hotel. The frustrations of his life lead Shannon to the brink of madness, but he is comforted and calmed by Hannah. Noticing that his ravings held a note of sympathy and love for Hannah, Maxine offers her hotel to Hannah and Shannon, despite her own love for Shannon. Nonno dies after completing his final poem, and Hannah leaves the hotel alone. Shannon and Maxine remain together at the Coste Verde. *Clergymen. Guides. Hotelkeepers. Widows. Schoolteachers. Americans in foreign countries. Tourists. Grandfathers. Poets. Artists. Bus drivers. Spinsters. Jealousy. Alcoholism. Hotels. Buses. Mexico. Lizards.*

NIGHT OF THE LIVING DEAD   **F6.3480**
Image Ten. *Dist* Continental Distributing, Inc. 1 Oct **1968** [Pittsburgh opening]. Sd; b&w. 35mm. 90 min.
    Prod Russell Streiner, Karl Hardman. *Dir & Orig Story* George A. Romero. *Screenplay* John A. Russo. *Photog* George A. Romero. *Lighting Supv* Joseph Unitas. *Titl Seq* The Animators. *Film Ed* George A. Romero. *Sd* Gary R.

Streiner, Marshall Booth. *Prod Dir* Vincent D. Survinski. *Prod Mgr* George Kosana. *Cont* Jacqueline Streiner, Betty Ellen Haughey. *Makeup* Karl Hardman, Marilyn Eastman. *Hairstyles* Bruce Capristo. *Sp Eff* Regis Survinski, Tony Pantanello.

Cast: Judith O'Dea *(Barbara)*, Russell Streiner *(Johnny)*, Duane Jones *(Ben)*, Karl Hardman *(Harry Cooper)*, Keith Wayne *(Tom)*, Judith Ridley *(Judy)*, Marilyn Eastman *(Helen Cooper)*, Kyra Schon *(Karen Cooper)*, Bill Heinzman, Charles Craig, Frank Doak, George Kosana.

Horror film. While visiting their father's grave, a sister and brother, Barbara and Johnny, are attacked by a strange, disheveled man. Leaving the unconscious Johnny behind, Barbara flees to a nearby farmhouse and discovers a horribly mutilated corpse. Meanwhile, the strange man has been joined by several other ghoulish figures who are trying to help him break into the farmhouse. Suddenly, Ben, a young black salesman also seeking refuge, appears and fights his way past them into the house. While barricading the windows and doors, he explains to Barbara that a mutation resulting from radiation has caused the dead to arise and devour the living. Ben learns from a television report that fire frightens the ghouls and that they can be killed by a bullet or blow to the brain. Barbara and Ben then find that they are not alone in the farmhouse: in the basement are teenaged couple Judy and Tom as well as married couple Helen and Harry and their young daughter, Karen. Unknown to Helen and Harry, Karen has been injured by the ghouls and is slowly acquiring their disease. Ben improvises a plan to help Tom and Judy escape; but they panic and die in a fire and are devoured by the zombies. The ghouls finally burst through the barricades, and Ben accidentally shoots Harry; Barbara is dragged away by her brother Johnny, who has become a ghoul; and Helen is murdered and eaten by her infected daughter. By morning, when the living have succeeded in suppressing the dead, only Ben has survived by barricading himself in the basement of the farmhouse. But he is mistaken for a ghoul and shot through the head when he bursts out to greet a posse sent to destroy the zombies. *Salesmen. Negroes. Zombies. Radiation. Mutation. Cannibalism. Murder. Death. Brother-sister relationship. Filial relations. Corpses. Cemeteries. Fires.*

Note: Filmed in Evans City, Pennsylvania. Working titles: *Night of the Flesh Eaters* and *Night of Anubis.*

THE NIGHT OF THE SEAGULL (Japan)　　　　　　F6.3481
Toho Co. 11 Feb **1970** [Los Angeles opening]. Sd; col (Eastman Color). 35mm. 90 min.

Exec Prod Yorihiko Yamada. *Dir* Katsumi Iwauchi. *Screenplay* Mitsura Majima, Katsumi Iwauchi. *Photog* Choichi Nakai. *Mus* Chemei Watanabe.

Cast: Mie Hama *(woman)*, Jin Nakayama *(young man)*, Megumi Matsumoto, Jitsuko Yoshimura, Natsuko Kahara.

Melodrama. Source: Matsutaro Kawaguchi, *Mermaid* (a novel; publication undetermined). While out on bail awaiting the verdict of her trial for the murder of her husband's mistress, a woman returns to her seaside home. On the beach she meets a young man with whom she has a brief, passionate affair. The woman is finally acquitted on the grounds of self-defense, but instead of leaving with the youth, she presumably returns to her husband. *Murder. Infidelity. Justifiable homicide. Trials.*

Note: Released in Japan in Oct 1968 as *Suna no kaori.*

NIGHT OF THE SILICATES see **ISLAND OF TERROR**

THE NIGHT OF THE THREE LOVERS (France)　　　　F6.3482
Les Films du Griffon. *Dist* Audubon Films. **1970.** Sd; b&w. 35mm. 98 min.

Exec Prod Max Pécas. *Dir* Max Pécas. *Screenplay* Pierre Unia, Max Pécas. *Photog* Robert Lefèvre. *Film Ed* Nicole Cayatte. *Mus* Louiguy. *Prod Mgr* Yves Prigent.

Cast: Philippe Lemaire *(Max)*, Donna Michelle, Chantal Deberg, Agnès Ball, Michel Vocoret, J.-P. Dorat, Roland Charbeaux.

Melodrama. Lesbian strippers Jenny and Vera are held in their apartment by Max, a fugitive wanted for the murder of his wife, Nathalie. After spending a sleepless night, Max explains to the women that Nathalie was killed by her lover. Having locked Jenny in the closet, Max makes love to Vera. When the fugitive runs out of medication for his heart condition, Vera accompanies him to the drugstore. There she slips a note to the pharmacist, who consequently contacts the police. Upon their return to her apartment, Vera slips a sleeping potion into Max's coffee. The police arrive and exonerate Max, explaining that the murderer has confessed. *Stripteasers. Pharmacists. Police. Fugitives. Murder. Lesbianism. Heart disease. Medicines.*

Note: Opened in Paris in Feb 1968 in color as *La nuit la plus chaude*; running time: 90 min.

THE NIGHT OF THE TIGER see **RIDE BEYOND VENGEANCE**

NIGHT OF THE VIBRATOR　　　　　　　　　　　F6.3483
Dist Canyon Distributing Co. 23 Jan **1969** [San Francisco showing]. Sd; col. 16mm. [Feature length assumed.]

Sex film. A handsome, young, blond man is looking for sexual contacts. He first finds a masseuse and they both use vibrators to obtain satisfaction. After this he picks up a woman and they go to her apartment, where they are joined by another couple in their lovemaking. In the midst of the group sex, the two women make love while the men watch. *Masseurs. Group sex. Lesbianism. Sex aids.*

NIGHT OF THE WITCHES　　　　　　　　　　　F6.3484
Matchpoint Productions. *Dist* Medford Film Corp. 26 Aug **1970** [Scranton, Pennsylvania, opening]. Sd; col (DeLuxe). 35mm. 78 min. *MPAA rating* GP.

Prod-Writ Keith Erik Burt, Vincent Fotre. *Dir* Keith Erik Burt. *Photog* Herbert Theis. *Songs:* "Me and God and You," "Man of Many Pleasures" Sean Bonniwell. *Sung by* The Baby.

Cast: Keith Erik Burt *(preacher)*, Kathryn Loder *(high priestess)*, Marta, Juana *(black witches)*, Ron Taft, Randy Stafford, Leru Charles, Ernest Lawrence Rossi, Beverly LaRue, Louise Blain.

Horror film. A preacher wanders through Mexico seducing the young women he is supposed to be saving. He meets a man (Ron Taft) who sells offshore islands, and they go to a mansion. There, a high priestess, her servant (Ernest Lawrence Rossi), and her cult of witches and disciples (Randy Stafford, Beverly LaRue, Louise Blain, Marta, and Juana) murder people they believe are evil. The preacher learns that a fortune is hidden in the mansion, and he insists on being cut in in exchange for remaining silent. The high priestess, however, serves him the same poison brew that killed the other victims. *Preachers. Witches. Salesmen. Seduction. Murder. Poisoning. Greed. Cults. Mexico.*

Note: May also be known as *Night of Witches.*

NIGHT SHIFT see **A HARD MAN'S GOOD TO FIND**

NIGHT THE CREATURES CAME see **ISLAND OF TERROR**

NIGHT THE SILICATES CAME see **ISLAND OF TERROR**

THE NIGHT THE SUN CAME OUT see **WATERMELON MAN**

THE NIGHT THEY KILLED RASPUTIN (France/Italy)　　F6.3485
Wanguard Film-Faro Film-Explorer Film-C. F. P. C.-Rialto Film. *Dist* Brigadier Film Associates. Jul **1962.** Sd; b&w. 35mm. 87 min.

Prod Vincent Fotre. *Dir* Pierre Chenal. *Screenplay* Pierre Chenal, André Tabet, Ugo Liberatore. *Story* Pierre Chenal, André Tabet. *Photog* Adalberto Albertini. *Art Dir* Arrigo Equini. *Film Ed* Antonietta Zita. *Mus* Angelo Francesco Lavagnino. *Prod Mgr* Gianpaolo Bigazzi.

Cast: Edmund Purdom *(Rasputin)*, Gianna Maria Canale *(Czarina Alexandra)*, John Drew Barrymore *(Yousoupoff)*, Jany Clair *(Irina Yousoupoff)*, Ugo Sasso *(czar)*, Giulia Rubini, Livio Lorenzon, Nerio Bernardi, Miranda Campa, Marco Guglielmi, Ivo Garrani, Maria Grazia Buccella, Michele Malaspina, Rita Rubirosa, Feodor Chaliapin, Enrico Glori, Yvette Lebon, Elida Day.

Historical drama. Rasputin, a lustful peasant monk, cures Alexei, heir apparent to the Russian throne, of hemophilia and wins the complete confidence of the czarina. Thus begins Rasputin's rise to power and influence in the imperial court. Enemies dispatch a woman to stab the monk, but their plot is foiled when Rasputin miraculously recovers from his wounds. After Russia enters the Great War, Rasputin's association with arms merchants and other speculators lends credence to the supposition that he is a German spy. He is attracted to Irina, Prince Yousoupoff's wife, and Yousoupoff, one of a group of conspirators determined to kill Rasputin, lures him to his home on the pretext of meeting Irina. There, they attempt to poison him, but he merely falls asleep from the cyanide. Panic-striken, Yousoupoff empties a revolver into Rasputin, who even then does not die but bellows in his rage. He eventually falls to the ground, and the assassins dump his body into the Neva. *Peasants. Monks. Royalty. Spies. Miracles. Conspiracy. Assassination. Poisoning. Hemophilia. World War I. Russia. Neva River. Grigori Efimovich Rasputin. Alexei Nikolaievitch. Alexandra Feodorovna. Nicholas II (Russia). Felix Felixovich Yousoupoff.*

Note: Opened in Paris in July 1960 as *Les nuits de Raspoutine*; running time: 93 min; in Italy in 1960 as *L'ultimo zar.* Also known as *Giant Monster.*

THE NIGHT THEY RAIDED MINSKY'S　　　　　　F6.3486
Tandem Productions. *Dist* United Artists. 22 Dec **1968** [New York opening; c18 Dec 1968; LP36627]. Sd; col (DeLuxe). 35mm. 100 min. *MPAA rating* M.

A Bud Yorkin-Norman Lear Production. *Prod* Norman Lear. *Assoc Prod* George Justin. *Dir* William Friedkin. *2d Unit Dir* Pablo Ferro. *Screenplay* Arnold Schulman, Sidney Michaels, Norman Lear. *Dir Photog* Andrew Laszlo. *Camera* Dick Kratina. *Vis Cons* Pablo Ferro. *Art Dir* John Robert Lloyd. *Set Decor* John Godfrey. *Prod Dsgn* William Eckart, Jean Eckart. *Film Ed* Ralph

Rosenblum. *Mus* Charles Strouse. *Orch & Cond* Philip J. Lang. *Songs* Lee Adams, Charles Strouse. *Dances, Mus Numbers & Sketches Staged by* Danny Daniels. *Sd Ed* Jack Fitzstephens. *Sd* Richard Vorisek. *Asst Dir* Burtt Harris. *Prod Mgr* Jim Di Gangi. *Asst to the Prod* William Giorgio. *Cost* Anna Hill Johnstone. *Makeup* Irving Buchman. *Hairstyles* Robert Grimaldi. *Tech Adv* Morton Minsky.

Cast: Jason Robards, [Jr.] *(Raymond Paine)*, Britt Ekland *(Rachel Schpitendavel)*, Norman Wisdom *(Chick Williams)*, Forrest Tucker *(Trim Houlihan)*, Harry Andrews *(Jacob Schpitendavel)*, Joseph Wiseman *(Louis Minsky)*, Denholm Elliott *(Vance Fowler)*, Elliott Gould *(Billy Minsky)*, Jack Burns *(candy butcher)*, Bert Lahr *(Professor Spats)*, Gloria LeRoy *(Mae Harris)*, Eddie Lawrence *(Scratch)*, Dexter Maitland *(Duffy)*, Ernestine Barrett, Kelsey Collins, Marilyn D'Honau, Kathryn Doby, Joann Lehmann, Dorothea MacFarland, Billie Mahoney, Carolyn Morris, June Eve Story, Helen Wood *(The Minsky Girls)*, Lillian Hayman *(singer in speakeasy)*, Will B. Able *(Clyde)*, Judith Lowry *(Mother Annie)*, Richard Libertini *(Pockets)*, Mike Elias, Frank Shaw *(immigration officers)*, Herbie Faye *(waiter)*, Joe E. Marks *(costume shop proprietor)*, Chanin Hale *(Valerie)*, Fats Thomas, Reno Pesaturi *(stagehands)*, Rudy Vallee *(narrator)*.

Comedy. Source: Rowland Barber, *The Night They Raided Minsky's* (New York, 1960). In 1925, young Billy Minsky is in danger of losing the National Winter Garden theater which houses his famous burlesque show. Despite the fact that Billy's father, Louis, owns the theater, he is threatening not to renew his son's lease because of the harassment of Vance Fowler's Society for the Suppression of Vice. The outlook becomes even gloomier when racketeer Trim Houlihan refuses to buy the theater from the elder Minsky. Then Rachel Schpitendavel arrives on the scene. A young Pennsylvania Amish woman who has run away from her strict father in order to dance Bible scenes on the stage, she attracts the attention of the show's top banana, Raymond Paine, and fall guy, Chick Williams. Chick's interest is purely romantic, but the conniving Paine has an ulterior motive; he circulates the rumor that Rachel will do a special midnight show featuring the indecent dance of Mademoiselle Fifi, the French heroine of popular pornographic pamphlets. The plan is to provoke Fowler's society and the police into raiding the theater, whereupon they will discover Rachel doing an innocent Bible dance and be forced to make an embarrassed retreat. On the day of the performance, however, several complications arise: Rachel's father, Jacob, arrives to take his daughter home; Trim decides to make "Mademoiselle Fifi" his moll; and Chick's rivalry with the philandering Paine over Rachel leads to a series of brawls. When Rachel defies everyone by going on stage, her father tries to stop her and accidentally tears her dress. Encouraged by the enthusiastic response of the audience, Rachel abandons her Bible story dance and begins to peel off her clothes. Noticing Paine's disapproval, she reaches out to him, and the top of her dress falls away. As the performers are herded out of the theater by the police, they are hailed as heroes by the cheering crowd. The striptease has been born. *Songs and performers:* "The Night They Raided Minsky's" (Rudy Vallee); "Take 10 Terrific Girls, but Only 9 Costumes" (Duffy & Rudy Vallee); "You Rat, You" (singer in speakeasy); "How I Love Her," "Perfect Gentleman" (Raymond Paine & Chick Williams); "Penny Arcade." *Racketeers. Entertainers. Dancers. Jews. Police. Amish. Philanderers. Vigilantes. Burlesque. Filial relations. Striptease. New York City—Lower East Side. Louis Minsky. Billy Minsky. Raymond Paine. National Winter Garden.*

Note: Location scenes filmed in New York City.

NIGHT TIDE   F6.3487
Virgo Productions. *Dist* American International Pictures. 13 Feb **1963** [Detroit opening]. Sd; b&w. 35mm. 84 min. [See note.]
Pres by Filmgroup Inc. *Prod* Aram Kantarian. *Exec Prod* Jules Schwartz. *Assoc Prod* H. Duane Weaver. *Dir-Writ* Curtis Harrington. *Cinematog* Vilis Lapenieks. *Adtl Photog* Floyd Crosby. *Prod Dsgn* Paul Mathison. *Film Ed* Jodie Copelan. *Mus Comp* David Raksin. *Bongo Drums* Chaino. *Choreog* Benjamin Zemach. *Asst Dir* Karl Romaine.

Cast: Dennis Hopper *(Johnny Drake)*, Linda Lawson *(Mora)*, Gavin Muir *(Captain Murdock)*, Luana Anders *(Ellen Sands)*, Marjorie Eaton *(Madame Romanovitch)*, Cameron *(woman in black)*, H. E. West *(Lieutenant Henderson)*, Tom Dillon *(merry-go-round owner)*, Ben Roseman.

Melodrama. While on leave in California, Johnny Drake, a lonely sailor, meets Mora, who works as a mermaid at the Goldfish Bowl, a boardwalk concession owned by Captain Murdock. Johnny is warned by Murdock to beware of Mora, and he learns from Ellen Sands, who works at a nearby merry-go-round, that at least two men have died mysteriously shortly after being seen with her. Undaunted, Johnny follows a mysterious woman dressed in black to Murdock's house. Murdock discloses that he reared Mora and that she is descended from the Sea People, who, under the spell of a full moon, feel impelled to kill. Johnny remains skeptical and accepts an invitation from Mora to go skindiving. While they are underwater, she removes his air hose, but he

escapes and surfaces, while she disappears. Later Johnny returns to the amusement pier and is startled to see Mora's body on display at the Goldfish Bowl. Apprehended by the police, Murdock confesses that to prevent Mora from leaving him he cast a spell over her, making her believe that she was descended from the Sea People. Out of love for Johnny, she had chosen to swim into the depths rather than continue to kill lonely young men. *Sailors. Mermaids and mermen. Entertainers. Police. Murder. Sideshows. Adoption. Ancestry. Diving. Spells. Merry-go-rounds. Waterfronts. California.*

Note: Filmed in Venice, Santa Monica, and Malibu, California. Shown at the 1961 Venice Film Festival at 95 min, and at the 1961 Spoleto Festival of Two Worlds at 90 min.

NIGHT TRAIN TO MUNDO FINE   F6.3488
Cardoza–Francis Productions. *Dist* Hollywood Star Pictures. Nov **1966**. Sd; b&w. 35mm. 89 min.
Prod Anthony Cardoza, Coleman Francis. *Dir-Writ* Coleman Francis. *Photog* Herb Roberts. *Film Ed* J. H. Russell. *Mus* John Bath. *Titl Song* Ray Gregory.

Cast: Coleman Francis *(Griffin)*, Anthony Cardoza *(Landis)*, Harold Saunders *(cook)*, John Carradine *(train engineer)*, John Morrison, actor *(Joe)*, George Prince *(Cherokee Jack)*, Lanell Cado *(Ruby Chastain)*, Tom Hanson *(Bayiev Chastain)*, Julian Baker *(sheriff)*, Charles Harter *(old man)*, Elaine Gibford *(old man's daughter)*, Bruce Love *(newspaper reporter)*, Nick Raymond, Clarence Walker *(policemen)*, Richard Lance *(Jaime Russell)*.

Melodrama. Griffin, an escaped convict, takes up with two drifters. In need of money, they join a band of soldiers of fortune preparing to invade Cuba; though Griffin and the drifters have no intention of actually going there, they are forced to participate in the invasion. Captured, they escape by stealing an airplane. After a variety of adventures in Cuba, Griffin finally returns to the United States, where he is recaptured by the police. *Prison escapees. Drifters. Soldiers of fortune. Americans in foreign countries. Police. Airplanes. Cuba.*

NIGHT TRAIN TO PARIS (Great Britain)   F6.3489
Lippert Films. *Dist* Twentieth Century-Fox Film Corp. 23 Sep **1964** [Los Angeles opening; c23 Sep 1964; I.P29244]. Sd; b&w. 35mm. 65 min.
Prod Robert L. Lippert, Jack Parsons. *Dir* Robert Douglas. *Screenplay-Screen Story* Henry Cross. *Dir Photog* Arthur Lavis. *Camera Op* Len Harris. *Art Dir* George Provis. *Supv Film Ed* Robert Winter. *Asst Ed* Clive Smith. *Mus* Kenny Graham. *Mus Cond* Philip Martell. *Songs:* "Night Train to Paris," "Chit Chat," "Look After My Baby," "Hey There Girl" Brian Potter, Graham Dee. *Rec by* Troy Dante and the Infernos. *Sd Ed* Spencer Reeve. *Sd Rec* George Stephenson. *Asst Dir* Gordon Gilbert. *Prod Mgr* Clifton Brandon. *Cont* Renee Glynne. *Prod Sec* Angela Cockill. *Wardrobe* Jean Fairlie. *Makeup* Harold Fletcher. *Hairdresser* Joyce James.

Cast—Principals: Leslie Nielsen *(Alan Holiday)*, Alizia Gur *(Catherine Carrel)*, Dorinda Stevens *(Olive Davies)*, Eric Pohlmann *(Krogh)*, Edina Ronay *(Julie)*, Andre Maranne *(Louis Vernay)*, Cyril Raymond *(Inspector Fleming)*, Stanley Morgan *(plainclothesman)*, Hugh Latimer *(Jules Lemoine)*, John Quayle *(Jackson)*, Simon Oates *(Saunders)*, John Busby *(Bearman)*, Jenny White *(Vernay's model)*, George Little *(train porter)*, Jacques Cey *(Coffier)*, Jack Melford *(P. C. inspector)*, Trevor Reid *(policeman on train)*, Neal Arden *(Inspector Escalier)*.

Cast—Model Girls: Alexandra Beauclerc *(Anna)*, Sylvia Lewis Jones *(Christine)*, Juliet Hunt *(June)*, Patricia Maynard *(Gail)*.

Drama. Alan Holiday, a former OSS officer now living in London, is visited on New Year's Eve by Catherine Carrel, who claims to be a close friend of Jules Lemoine, one of Alan's wartime colleagues. Lemoine wants Alan to deliver a tape recording containing secret defense information to the French government. After receiving the tape from Lemoine, Alan poses as a photographer's assistant and leaves on the boat train to Paris with Catherine, who is masquerading as a model. Before their departure, Lemoine is murdered by a counterintelligence agent who, unable to find the tape, also boards the train. Because of the confusion of a wild New Year's party, Alan is able to elude the assassin until the train reaches France, but once there, he is confronted by another counterespionage agent seeking the tape. Although Alan escapes, he is stopped by Catherine, who, it develops, is also in league with the foreign agents; but he disarms her and turns her over to the police, along with the vital tape recording. *Intelligence agents. Photographers. Foreign agents. Models. Murder. Espionage. Defense—National. Disguise. Trains. Recorders. New Year's Eve. London. Paris. United States—Office of Strategic Services.*

Note: Released in Great Britain in 1965; running time: 64 min. Henry Cross is a pseudonym for Harry Spalding.

THE NIGHT WALKER   F6.3490
Castle Co. *Dist* Universal Pictures. 30 Dec **1964** [Los Angeles opening; c13 Feb 1964; LP33024]. Sd (Westrex); b&w. 35mm. 86 min.

Prod-Dir William Castle. *In Charge of Prod* Edward Muhl. *Assoc Prod* Dona Holloway. *Screenplay* Robert Bloch. *Photog* Harold Stine. *Camera Op* Eddie Albert, photog. *Camera Asst* Stuart Higgs, William Brown. *Art Dir* Alexander Golitzen, Frank Arrigo. *Set Decor* John McCarthy, Julia Heron. *Main Titl* Pacific Title. *Film Ed* Edwin H. Bryant. *Mus* Vic Mizzy. *Mus Supv* Joseph Gershenson. *Sd* Waldon O. Watson, David H. Moriarty, Don Bolger, William Griffith, Victor Goode. *Asst Dir* Terence Nelson, Bill Gilmore. *Unit Prod Mgr* Herman Webber. *Script Supv* Luanna Poole. *Cost* Helen Colvig. *Wardrobe* Bucky Rous, Viola Thompson. *Makeup* Bud Westmore, Carl Silvera, Dick Blair. *Hairstyles* Larry Germain, Merle Reeves. *Sp Eff* Charles Spurgeon. *Still Photog* Jack Geraghty. *Gaffer* Edward Hobson. *Grip* Lloyd Stafford, Eugene Barragy. *Prop* Ace Holmes, Robert Rentch, Jr.

Cast: Robert Taylor *(Barry Morland)*, Barbara Stanwyck *(Irene Trent)*, Judi Meredith *(Joyce)*, Hayden Rorke *(Howard Trent)*, Rochelle Hudson *(Hilda)*, Marjorie Bennett *(manager)*, Jess Barker *(Malone)*, Tetsu Komai *(gardener)*, Lloyd Bochner *(The Dream)*, Ted Durant *(narrator)*.

Horror film. Based on the story & screenplay by: Elizabeth Kata, *Witches' Friday* (publication undetermined). Irene Trent's sleep-talking convinces her blind husband, Howard, that she is having an affair with another man. He suspects his attorney, Barry Morland, who denies the charge. Irene reveals to Barry that she repeatedly dreams of an unknown lover. After a quarrel with Howard, Irene leaves the house; shortly thereafter, Howard is killed in an explosion in his laboratory. Irene's dreams continue. She is visited repeatedly by her lover, who transports her to a chapel peopled by wax dummies, where a bizarre wedding ceremony is enacted. Irene enlists Barry's aid, and the lawyer reveals that Howard had hired George Fuller, a private detective, to spy on her. Fuller is later identified as the dream lover. Joyce, a new beautician in Irene's shop, is murdered by a man resembling Howard. Barry then informs Irene that Howard is alive and has attempted to slay him. In Howard's laboratory, however, Barry removes the mask with which he had impersonated the dead man. He further reveals that he had murdered Howard, having first named himself the blind man's beneficiary. As Barry attempts to stab Irene, he is shot and wounded by George, who informs Irene that he is the husband of the dead Joyce. Although George menaces Irene, Barry revives. During a final struggle, Barry and George fall through a gaping hole in the laboratory floor. Irene is now safe. *Somniloquists. Lawyers. Detectives. Cosmetologists. Marriage. Blindness. Murder. Impersonation. Explosions. Laboratories. Waxworks. Dreams.*

THE NIGHT WATCH (France/Italy)   F6.3491

Playart-Filmsonor-Titanus. *Dist* Consort/Orion Films. 26 May **1964** [New York opening]. Sd (Western Electric); b&w. 35mm. 118 min.

Exec Prod Serge Silberman. *Assoc Prod* Georges Charlot. *Dir* Jacques Becker. *Screenplay* Jacques Becker, José Giovanni, Jean Aurel. *Dial* Jacques Becker, José Giovanni. *Photog* Ghislain Cloquet. *Camera* Gilbert Chain. *Asst Camera* Jean Chiabaut, François Lauliac. *Sets* Rino Mondellini. *Asst Decor* Jean Thaillandier. *Film Ed* Marguerite Renoir, Geneviève Vaury. *Sd* Pierre Calvet. *Rec* Jean Bareille, Maurice Dagonneau. *Asst Dir* Jean Becker. *Prod Supv* Paul Laffargue. *Prod Admin* Jacqueline Dudilleux. *Prod Mgr* Georges Charlot, Jean Mottet. *Prod Sec* Odette Laeupplée. *Script Girl* Sophie Becker. *Sp Eff* Philippe Arthuys. *Still Photog* Henri Thibault. *Props* René Albouze.

Cast: Michel Constantin *(Geo Cassid)*, Jean Kéraudy *(Roland Darban)*, Philippe Leroy *(Manu Borelli)*, Raymond Meunier *("Monseigneur")*, Marc Michel *(Gaspard)*, André Bervil *(The Warden)*, Eddy Rasimi *(The Guard, Bouboule)*, Jean-Paul Coquelin *(The Guard, Grinval)*, Catherine Spaak *(Nicole)*.

Drama. Source: José Giovanni, *Le trou* (Paris, 1957). At La Santé prison in France, Claude Gaspard awaits trial for the attempted murder of his wife. By French law a man is guilty until proven otherwise. Gaspard is moved into a cell with Roland Darban, Geo Cassid, Manu Borelli, and "Monseigneur," who decide to include him in their escape plan, devised by Roland. Two dummies are constructed to deceive the guards in their nightly check; a hole is dug in the cell floor and covered during daylight hours by cardboard cartons which the prisoners have been assigned to assemble; a piece of mirror and a toothbrush are made into a periscope with which to watch the guards; medicine bottles and sand are fashioned into an hourglass to time the work; and an iron bunk leg is used as a digging implement. Working in shifts by pairs, the men dig into the subterranean areas of the prison, from there into the prison's sewer tunnels, and from there through a 9-foot tunnel into the city's sewer system. On the day the tunnel is completed and the men plan to escape, Gaspard is called to the warden's office. He returns to the cell and announces that his wife has withdrawn her charges. However, he explains that he plans to escape with the others because he still faces a 5-year prison term and succeeds in allaying his cellmates' suspicions. That night, as they are preparing to leave, Geo informs the group that he is not going because his mother's health is at stake. Just then the alarm rings and, as the guards rush into the cell, the men realize that they have been betrayed by Gaspard. *Perfidy. Murder. Prison escapes. Prisons.*

Tunnels.

Note: Opened in Paris in Mar 1960 as *Le trou*; in Rome in Apr 1960 as *Il buco*. Original running time: 145 min.

THE NIGHT WE DROPPED A CLANGER *see* MAKE MINE A   DOUBLE

A NIGHT WITH THE GREAT ONE   F6.3492

Dist Joseph Brenner Associates. 10 Sep **1969** [Detroit opening]. Sd; b&w. 35mm. 50 min.

Anthology film. Three W. C. Fields short comedies: *Pool Sharks* (1915), his first screen appearance; *The Golf Specialist* (1930), his first film with sound; and *The Dentist* (1932), one of four shorts he did for Mack Sennett. *Actors. Motion pictures—History. W. C. Fields.*

Note: May also be known as *The Great One* and *W. C. Fields*.

NIGHT WOMEN (France)   F6.3493

Dist Olympic International Films. 16 Feb **1967** [Atlanta showing]. Sd; b&w. 35mm. 67 min.

Prod-Dir Claude Lelouch.

Documentary. Female sexuality is investigated in major European capitals. "Miss Spaghetti" is chosen in Rome; cosmetic surgery, including rhinoplasty, is performed in Paris; transvestites in Brussels are interviewed; stripteasers dance in Frankfurt and at the Lido in Paris; prostitutes ply their trade in the Bois de Boulogne; a soldier on leave in Paris visits a masseuse; and a woman performs childbirth exercises and gives birth. [Press material suggests that the incidents take place in various European cities; some sources indicate that Paris is the setting of the entire film.] *Stripteasers. Prostitutes. Masseurs. Soldiers. Transvestism. Childbirth. Plastic surgery. Beauty contests. Sexual techniques. Paris. Rome. Brussels. Frankfurt am Main. Paris—Bois de Boulogne. Lido (Paris).*

Note: Produced in France as *La femme spectacle* in 1964; running time: 84 min. Apparently banned in France.

NIGHTMARE (Great Britain)   F6.3494

Hammer Film Productions. *Dist* Universal Pictures. 8 May **1964** [Chicago opening; c13 Jun 1963; LP33272]. Sd (RCA); b&w. 35mm (Hammerscope). 83 min.

Prod-Writ Jimmy Sangster. *Dir* Freddie Francis. *Dir Photog* John Wilcox. *Camera Op* Ronnie Maasz. *Focus Puller* Geoff Glover, Ronnie Fox-Rogers. *Art Dir* Don Mingaye, Ken Ryan. *Prod Dsgn* Bernard Robinson. *Supv Ed* James Needs. *Asst Ed* Chris Barnes. *2d Asst Ed* Alan Willis. *Mus Comp* Don Banks. *Mus Supv* John Hollingsworth. *Sd Rec* Ken Rawkins. *Sd Ed* James Groom. *Boom Op* Jim Perry. *Sd Transfer Op* Michael Sale. *Sd Camera Op* Al Thorne. *1st & 2d Asst Dir* Douglas Hermes, Hugh Harlow. *Prod Mgr* Don Weeks. *Cont* Pamela Wise. *Prod Sec* Maureen White. *Wardrobe Supv* Molly Arbuthnot. *Wardrobe Mistress* Rosemary Burrows. *Makeup Artist* Roy Ashton. *Hairstyles* Frieda Steiger. *Sp Eff* Les Bowie. *Still Photog* Tom Edwards. *Constr Mgr* Arthur Banks. *Ch Electrn* Jack Curtis, electrn. *Elec Supv* George Robinson. *Prop Master* Tommy Money. *Prop Buyer* Eric Hillier. *Grip* Albert Cowland.

Cast: David Knight *(Henry Baxter)*, Moira Redmond *(Grace)*, Jennie Linden *(Janet)*, Brenda Bruce *(Mary Lewis)*, George A. Cooper *(John)*, Clytie Jessop *(woman in white)*, Irene Richmond *(Mrs. Gibbs)*, John Welsh *(doctor)*, Timothy Bateson *(barman)*, Elizabeth Dear *(Janet as a child)*, Hedger Wallace *(Sir Dudley)*, Julie Samuel *(maid)*, Isla Cameron *(mother)*.

Mystery melodrama. Janet, a girl at finishing school who 6 years ago saw her mother stab her father to death, is plagued by nightmares. (Her mother, following the tragedy, was committed to an asylum.) Miss Lewis, a teacher, takes Janet home; and in the absence of Henry Baxter, Janet's guardian, they are met by John (the chauffeur), Mrs. Gibbs (the housekeeper), and Grace Maddox (an attractive nurse-companion hired by Henry). Miss Lewis leaves Janet in Grace's care. The nightmares continue: a white-shrouded woman roams the corridors, inviting Janet to burst into her parents' room where she finds the same woman on the bed with a knife in her chest. When Henry returns he finds Janet under sedation; her doctors recommend psychiatric care; but he refuses, and Janet tries to commit suicide. Henry's wife comes to tea, and because she seems to be the woman in Janet's nightmares, Janet stabs the woman to death and is promptly committed to an institution. The woman in white is revealed to be Grace, disguised with a wig and mask and in cahoots with Henry. They marry, but Grace begins believing that Henry is trying to drive her mad. Under the impression that Janet has escaped from the asylum, Grace stabs Henry to death, expecting Janet to be blamed. Janet, however, never left the asylum, and Grace is brought to justice. *Schoolteachers. Guardians. Chauffeurs. Housekeepers. Physicians. Murder. Insanity. Disguise. Filial relations. Suicide. Boarding schools. Insane asylums. Dreams.*

Note: Released in Great Britain in May 1964; running time: 82 min. Working title: *Here's the Knife, Dear: Now Use It.*

NIGHTMARE CASTLE (Italy)   F6.3495
Produzione Cinematografica Emmeci. *Dist* Allied Artists. 5 Jul **1966**. Sd; b&w. 35mm. 90 min.

Prod Carlo Caiano. *Dir* Allan Grunewald. *Screenplay* Mario Caiano, Fabio De Agostini. *Photog* Enzo Barboni. *Art Dir* Massimo Tavazzi. *Film Ed* Renato Cinquini. *Mus* Ennio Morricone. *Sd* Dino Fronzetti. *Asst Dir* Angelo Sangermano. *Cost* Mario Giorsi.

Cast: Barbara Steele *(Muriel/Jenny)*, Paul Miller *(Dr. Stephen Arrowsmith)*, Helga Line *(Solange)*, Lawrence Clift *(Dr. Derek Joyce)*, Rik Battaglia *(David)*, John McDouglas *(Jonathan)*.

Horror film. Dr. Stephen Arrowsmith, an insane scientist, experiments with the possibilities of regenerating blood with electricity. He electrocutes his wife, Muriel, and her lover, David, the gardener at the castle. With their blood, Stephen rejuvenates his aging and faithful servant, Solange, and hides the hearts of Muriel and David in an urn. When Stephen discovers that Muriel's fortune has been willed to her neurotic sister, Jenny, rather than himself, he persuades her to marry him. Together with Solange, who is now a beautiful young woman, Stephen conspires to drive Jenny insane. When Derek Joyce, Jenny's doctor, is summoned to the castle, he refuses to pronounce her insane, but he senses that supernatural forces are at work. As Stephen is planning another blood transfusion for Solange, Derek discovers the hearts hidden in the urn and liberates the ghosts of Muriel and David. Anxious for revenge, Muriel burns Stephen alive, and David sucks Solange's blood, thereby reducing her to a skeleton. Jenny and Derek flee the castle. *Physicians. Scientists. Gardeners. Sisters. Ghosts. Electricity. Insanity. Infidelity. Murder. Inheritance. Rejuvenation. Revenge. Blood transfusion. Castles. Experiments.*

Note: Produced in Italy in 1965 as *Amanti d'oltretomba*; running time: 105 min.

NIGHTMARE IN THE SUN   F6.3496
Afilmco Productions. *Dist* Zodiac Films. Dec **1964** [Los Angeles showing]. Sd; col (De Luxe). 35mm. 81 min.

Prod Marc Lawrence, John Derek. *Assoc Prod* Douglas Stewart. *Dir* Marc Lawrence. *Screenplay* Ted Thomas, Fanya Lawrence. *Story* Marc Lawrence, George Fass. *Dir Photog* Stanley Cortez. *Art Dir* Paul Sylos. *Set Decor* Ray Boltz. *Ed* Douglas Stewart, William Shenberg. *Mus Comp & Cond* Paul Glass. *Sd* Glen Glenn Sound. *Asst Dir* Frank Parmenter. *Prod Mgr* Jerry A. Baerwitz. *Unit Mgr* Jay O. Lawrence. *Script Supv* John Dutton. *Wardrobe Supv* Patrick Cummings. *Harry* Thomas. *Hairstyles* Carmen Dirigo. *Prop Master* George MacKinnon. *Key Grip* Fred Russell. *Head Electrn* Joe Edesa.

Cast: Ursula Andress *(Marsha)*, John Derek *(The Hitchhiker)*, Aldo Ray *(The Sheriff)*, Arthur O'Connell *(Sam Wilson)*, Sammy Davis, Jr. *(truckdriver)*, Allyn Joslyn *(junk dealer)*, Keenan Wynn *(song-and-dance misfit)*, Chick Chandler *(tavern owner)*, Richard Jaeckel, Robert Duvall *(motorcyclists)*, Lurene Tuttle, George Tobias *(bird lovers)*, Douglas Fowley, John Marley, William Challee, Michael Petit, James Waters, John Sebastian, actor.

Melodrama. Marsha, who lives on a ranch owned by her wealthy, jealous husband, Sam Wilson, picks up a hitchhiker on the road and brings him back to the ranch to make love. The hitchhiker refuses to take Marsha with him when he leaves, intending to restore his own broken marriage. Sam sees him departing and kills Marsha in a drunken rage. An unscrupulous sheriff decides to blackmail Sam and arrest the hitchhiker for Marsha's murder. The hitchhiker is arrested; he escapes and is recaptured, but in the meantime Sam Wilson kills the blackmailing sheriff and confesses to both murders. The hitchhiker is exonerated and allowed to go on his way. *Hitchhikers. Ranchers. Sheriffs. Marriage. Infidelity. Murder. Blackmail. Frameup. Drunkenness.*

Note: Filmed in and around Calabasas, California.

NIGHTMARE IN WAX   F6.3497
Paragon International Pictures–Productions Enterprises–A & E Film Corp. *Dist* Crown International Pictures. 14 May **1969** [Charlotte, North Carolina, opening]. Sd; col (Pathé). 35mm. 95 min. *MPAA rating* M.

Prod Herbert Sussan, Martin B. Cohen. *Exec Prod* Rex Carlton, Herbert Sussan. *Assoc Prod* William Martin. *Dir* Bud Townsend. *Writ* Rex Carlton. *Dir Photog* Glen Smith. *Lighting Supv* Richard Aguilar. *Set Dsgn* James Freiberg. *Film Ed* Leonard Kwit. *Mus Supv* Igo Kantor. *Sd Supv* Robert Dietz. *Sd Ed* Edward Sandlin. *Asst Dir* Herman Webber. *Prod Mgr* Bud Cardos. *Asst Prod Mgr* Rick Jackson. *Script Supv* Winifred Gibson. *Mr. Mitchell's Wardrobe* Sy Devore. *Makeup Supv* Martin Varnaud. *Hairstyles* Lee Davis.

Cast (see note): Cameron Mitchell *(Vince Rinaud [Renard])*, Anne Helm *(Marie Morrison [Morgan])*, Scott Brady *(Detective Haskell)*, Berry Kroeger *(Max Block [Black])*, Victoria Carroll *(Carissa)*, Phillip Baird *(Tony Deane)*, Hollis Morrison *(Nick)*, John Cardos *(Sergeant Carver)*, James Forrest *(Alfred)*, The T-Bones, The Gazzari Dancers, Reni Martin.

Horror film. At a Hollywood party, Max Block, the head of Paragon Pictures, learns that his star actress, Marie Morrison, has become engaged to makeup man Vince Rinaud. Enraged, Max throws a glass of brandy which

ignites and deeply scars Rinaud's face. Brooding over the disfigurement, Rinaud becomes a recluse and sets up a wax museum. Within a few months, four Paragon stars disappear, including Tony Deane, now affianced to Marie. A police detective notices that the missing stars quickly become immortalized in Rinaud's museum. Rinaud uses a go-go dancer, Carissa, to lure Max to the museum, and there he is given a drugged drink. He then learns that the missing actors have been turned into living statues by injections of a formula perfected by Rinaud. Rinaud kills Carissa and leaves evidence to frame Max for the murder, then impersonates Max and fakes suicide. Just as Max is about to be lowered into a cauldron of boiling wax, a thunderstorm negates the effects of the drug; and the statues come to life and force Rinaud into the vat. A phone call from Marie awakens Rinaud, and he realizes that he has had a bizarre nightmare. She reminds him of their plan to tell Max of their engagement at a party that night. *Actors. Cosmetologists. Go-go dancers. Motion picture producers. Police. Recluses. Murder. Disfiguration. Insanity. Abduction. Waxworks. Hollywood. Dreams.*

Note: Filmed in 1966 at the Movieland Wax Museum in Los Angeles; working title: *Monster of the Wax Museum*. Also known as *Crimes in the Wax Museum*. Sources conflict in crediting production companies and role names.

NIGHTS OF SHAME (France)   F6.3498
Vascos Films. *Dist* Union Film Distributors. 6 Nov **1961** [New York State license]. Sd; b&w. 35mm. 81 min.

A Raoul André Production. *Assoc Prod* Raymond Logeart. *Dir* Raoul André. *Screenplay* Raymond Caillava, René Blancard. *Dir Photog* Roger Fellous. *Camera* Noël-Claude Martin. *Asst Camera* Maurice Fellous, Jean-Paul Schwartz. *Art Dir* Louis Le Barbenchon. *Asst Art Dir* Pierre Duquesne. *Film Ed* Gabriel Rongier. *Asst Film Ed* Fernand Manella. *Mus* Daniel Lesur. *Sd Dir* Pierre-Henri Goumy. *Sd Rec* Jean Bareille. *Boom* Urbain Loiseau. *Asst Dir* Tony Saytor, Jean Léon, Marc Montagu Telli. *Prod Mgr* Michel Mombailly. *Location Mgr* Pierre Lefait. *Script Girl* Brigitte Dubois. *Prod Sec* Micheline Robert. *Cost* Almine. *Wardrobe Mistress (see note)* Renée Rouzot, Anita Poirier. *Makeup* Louis Dor. *Still Photog* Serge Jacques. *Prop* Alphonse Lebeuf.

Cast: Nicole Courcel *(Maria)*, Raymond Pellegrin *(René)*, Giselle Pascal *(Marie-Thérèse)*, Philippe Lemaire *(Pierre)*, Louise Carletti *(Marcelle)*, Michel Ardan *(Ferdinand)*, Gina Manès *(Mathilde)*, Abel Jacquin, Paul Demange, Lisette Lebon, Evelyne Corman, René Blancard, Jérôme Goulven, René Havard, Simone Logeart, Jacques Muller, Simone Berthier, Julia Maffre, Rita Stoya.

Melodrama. Marie-Thérèse, a social worker for an institution known as Le Nid, attempts to rehabilitate Parisian prostitutes. Ignorant of her profession, the artist Pierre falls in love with the streetwalker Marcelle, while his friend René is magnetized by her companion, Maria. When Marcelle's middle-aged friend, the paralyzed Mathilde, is murdered by her former employer, the gangster Ferdinand, the prostitute comes under suspicion. After Ferdinand is killed in an automobile accident, Marie-Thérèse, anxious to clear Marcelle, informs the police that the prostitute was with Pierre at the time of Mathilde's death. Despite police promises to keep all information confidential, Pierre and René learn the truth. Although René accepts Maria, Pierre, disgusted by Marcelle's sordid past, rejects her. The distraught Marcelle is comforted by Marie-Thérèse. *Prostitutes. Paralytics. Artists. Social workers. Gangsters. Police. Disillusionment. Murder. Paris. Automobile accidents.*

Note: Filmed in Paris. Opened in Paris in May 1954 as *Marchandes d'illusions*; running time: 88 min. Renée Rouzot is also known as Renée Rouzeau.

NIGHTS ON THE CAMPUS see HOT NIGHTS ON THE CAMPUS

NIHON NO ICHIBAN NAGAI HI see THE EMPEROR AND A GENERAL

NIHONKAI DAIKAISEN see BATTLE OF THE JAPAN SEA

NIKKI, WILD DOG OF THE NORTH (United States/Canada)   F6.3499
Walt Disney Productions–Cangary, Ltd.–Westminster Films, Ltd. *Dist* Buena Vista Distribution Co. 12 Jul **1961** [Los Angeles opening; c9 Feb 1961; LP19838]. Sd (RCA); col (Technicolor). 35mm. 74 min.

Overall Production Credits: *Pres by* Walt Disney. A Walt Disney Production. *Prod* Winston Hibler. *Writ for the Screen* Ralph Wright, Winston Hibler. *Adtl Narr* Dwight Hauser.

For Walt Disney Productions: *Assoc Prod* Erwin L. Verity. *Cont Sketches* Sam McKim, Dale Hennesy. *Film Ed* Grant K. Smith. *Mus* Oliver Wallace. *Orch* Clifford Vaughan. *Sd* Robert O. Cook. *Mus Ed* Evelyn Kennedy. *Coöp Canada*—Department of Northern Affairs and National Resources—Forestry Branch.

For Cangary, Ltd.: *Dir* Jack Couffer. *Photog* Lloyd Beebe, Jack Couffer, Ray Jewell, William W. Bacon, III.

For Westminster Films: *Dir* Donald Haldane. *Photog* Donald Wilder. *Set Decor* Jack McCullagh. *Sd Rec* George Mulholland, Andre de Tonnancour. *Asst Dir* Phil Hirsch, Jerry Stoll. *Unit Mgr* Leo Ewaschuk. *Cost* Jan Kemp. *Makeup* Ken Brooke, Barry Nye.

Cast: Jean Coutu (*André Dupas*), Emile Genest (*Jacques Lebeau*), Uriel Luft (*Makoki*), Robert Rivard (*Durante*), Nikki ("*The Malemute Wonder Dog*"), Neewa (*The Bear*), Taao (*old champion fighting dog*), Jacques Fauteux (*narrator*), The Nomads (*performers of French-Canadian folk songs*).

Adventure melodrama. Source: James Oliver Curwood, *Nomads of the North* (Garden City, New York, 1919). While on a canoe trip in the Canadian Rockies, trapper André Dupas, his Malemute pup, Nikki, and an adopted bear cub, Neewa, are capsized in rough water. André struggles ashore, but the two animals, tied together by a leash, are pulled downstream. When they reach land they are forced to overcome the instinct that makes them natural enemies and join together in a search for food and shelter. Despite many fights, they eventually become friends and remain together even after their leash breaks. With the coming of winter Neewa goes into hibernation and Nikki wanders off alone. He steals the bait from traps until he is captured by a vicious trapper, Jacques Lebeau, and Lebeau's reluctant Indian companion, Makoki. After watching the now full-grown dog kill a wolf in spite of the trap, Lebeau decides to train Nikki as a fighting dog although pit-fighting is illegal. When André, the new factor, challenges Lebeau for breaking the law, he is pushed into the pit with the brutalized killer dog. Nikki recognizes his old master, however, and joins André in fighting Lebeau, who is accidentally killed with his own knife. Later, while on a trip to André's trap line, Nikki spots his old friend, Neewa; but the dog realizes that the full-grown bear is happier roaming the wilds, and he chooses to remain by André's side. *French Canadians. Traders. Indians of North America. Friendship. Animal life. Survival. Pit-fighting. Canadian Rockies. Dogs. Bears. Wolves.*

Note: Filmed in French and English in the Kananaskis Valley of the Canadian Rockies.

NIKUTAI NO GAKKO *see* **SCHOOL OF LOVE**

NIKUTAI NO MON *see* **GATE OF FLESH**

9 AGES OF NAKEDNESS (Great Britain)   **F6.3500**
Token Films. *Dist* Manson Distributing Corp. 2 Dec **1970** [Champaign, Illinois, showing]. Sd; col (Eastman Color). 35mm. 85 and 90 min.

Prod-Dir-Writ George Harrison Marks. *Exec Prod* Harry Reuben. *Assoc Prod* Terry Maher. *Dir Photog* Terry Maher. *Prod Dsgn* Tony Roberts, art. *Film Ed* Peter Mayhew. *Mus & Mus Dir* Peter Jeffries. *Sd* John Latham. *Prod Mgr* Derek Horne, Hector Elwes.

Cast: Harrison Marks (*himself and his ancestors*), Charles Gray (*narrator*), Max Wall, Max Bacon, Julian Orchard, Cardew Robinson, Bruno Elrington, June Palmer, Oliver MacGreevy, Rita Webb.

Farce. Surrounded by women, professional photographer Harrison Marks is suffering from "feminophobia." On a psychiatrist's couch he recalls how his ancestors were similarly affected with this phobia. These ancestors include Harrison Stone Marks of the Stone Age, Harrison Hubergritz of Ancient Egypt, Chinese mandarin Ha-Ri-Son, retired Greek sculptor Professor Marks, "Frankenstein" Marks, cavalier portraitist Sir Harrison Chandelier, romantic poet Byron Marks, and music hall performer The Great Marco. His final vision is of a futuristic computer age in which he is the lone surviving male, being preserved merely for breeding purposes. No medical assistance is supplied by the psychiatrist, who, although she has a man's voice, is revealed to be a woman. *Photographers. Psychiatrists. Man—Prehistoric. Mandarins. Greeks. Sculptors. Painters. Poets. Entertainers. Ancestry. Phobias. Eugenics. Music halls. Computers. Stone Age. Egypt—Ancient. Frankenstein. The Future.*

Note: Released in Great Britain in 1969; running time: 95 min.

NINE DAYS OF ONE YEAR (U.S.S.R.)   **F6.3501**
Mosfilm. *Dist* Artkino Pictures. 28 Dec **1964** [New York opening]. Sd; b&w. 35mm. 107 min.

Dir Mikhail Romm. *Screenplay* Mikhail Romm, Daniil Khrabrovitskiy. *Story Ed* I. Tsizin. *Photog* German Lavrov. *Art Dir* G. Kolganov. *Film Ed* Ye. Ladyzhenskaya. *Mus* D. Ter-Tatevosyan. *Sd* B. Volskiy. *1st & 2d Asst Dir* L. Indenbom, Daniil Khrabrovitskiy, L. Averbakh, A. Mkrtchan. *Prod Mgr* I. Vakar. *Cost* V. Kiselyova. *Makeup* V. Fetisov.

Cast: Aleksey Batalov (*Dmitriy Gusev*), Innokentiy Smoktunovskiy (*Ilya Kulikov*), Tatyana Lavrova (*Lyolya*), Nikolay Plotnikov (*Professor Sintsov*), Yevgeniy Teterin (*surgeon*), Nikolay Sergeyev (*Gusev's father*), Zinoviy Gerdt (*narrator*), S. Blinnikov, Yevgeniy Yevstigneyev, Mikhail Kozakov, I. Grabbe, V. Nikulin, P. Shpringfeld, A. Pelevin, Ada Voytsik, V. Belyayeva, Lyudmila Ovchinnikova, Yu. Kireyev, B. Yashin, I. Dobrolyubov, A. Smirnov, A. Pavlova, R. Esadze, Georgiy Yepifantsev, L. Durov, N. Batyryova, Z. Chekulayeva, I. Yasulovich.

Drama. Dmitriy Gusev, a nuclear physicist, receives a dangerously high dose of radiation as a result of an accident in which his professor, Sintsov, is fatally exposed. Warned that another exposure would prove fatal, Dmitriy nevertheless refuses a safer job and continues the experimentation. Lyolya, Dmitriy's girl friend, feels that their relationship means little to him and decides to marry their best friend, theoretician Ilya Kulikov. Learning that Dmitriy's life is in danger, however, she realizes that he loves him, and they marry despite his misgivings. From the outset of the marriage, Dmitriy's singular devotion to his work keeps them apart. At a Siberian research center, Dmitriy works together with Ilya, and though Ilya's cynical manner is so different from his own, their disagreements do nothing to mar their friendship and mutual respect. As a new success is obtained, Dmitriy is again exposed to radiation. He persuades Ilya to keep the accident a secret until the experiments are completed. Lyolya, misunderstanding Dmitriy's remoteness, feels that she has failed as a wife. Dmitriy's health deteriorates, and, aware of his doom, he makes a visit to his family. At a Moscow clinic he asks doctors to perform an experimental bone marrow transplant with little chance of success. Ilya comes to visit him on the day before the operation and tells him that their experiments produced a new type of radiation which was not thermonuclear, as anticipated, but nonetheless would be an important contribution to science. As Ilya and Lyolya await the outcome of the operation at the hospital, they receive a note from Dmitriy promising a celebration. *Researchers. Physicists. Radiation. Nuclear energy. Marriage. Friendship. Surgery. Self-sacrifice. Experiments. Siberia. Moscow.*

Note: Released in the U.S.S.R. in Mar 1962 as *Devyat dney odnogo goda*; running time: 110 min.

NINE HOURS TO RAMA (United States/Great Britain)   **F6.3502**
Red Lion Productions. *Dist* Twentieth Century-Fox Film Corp. 3 Apr **1963** [New York opening; c31 Dec 1962; LP23684]. Sd (Westrex); col (DeLuxe). 35mm (CinemaScope). 125 min.

Overall Production Credits: A Mark Robson Production. *Prod-Dir* Mark Robson. *Assoc Prod* Bob McNaught. *Screenplay* Nelson Gidding. *Dir Photog* Arthur Ibbetson. *Camera Op* Paul Wilson. *Camera Focus* Freddie Cooper. *Art Dir* Elliot Scott. *Asst Art Dir* Ivor Beddoes. *Set Dresser* John Jarvis. *Draughtsman* Reg Bream, Tony Pratt, John Graysmark. *Location Art Dir* Ram Yedekar. *Titl Dsgn* Saul Bass. *Film Ed* Ernest Walter. *Assembly Ed* Peter Elliott. *Asst Ed* Margaret Miller. *Mus Comp & Cond* Malcolm Arnold. *Sd Ed* Harry Miller. *Sd Rec* Gerry Turner, J. B. Smith. *Sd Camera Op* Mickey Hickey. *Boom Op* John Streeter. *1st & 2d Asst Dir* Kip Gowans, Tom Sachs, David Giffard. *Location Assoc Prod* Chimankant Gandhi. *Location Asst Dir* Baba Shaikh. *Prod Mgr* David Middlemas. *Location Mgr* R. L. M. Davidson. *Cont* Elaine Schreyeck. *Prod Sec* Joyce Herlihy. *Wardrobe* David Ffolkes, Betty Adamson, Barbara Gillett. *Makeup* Harold Fletcher, Wally Schneiderman. *Hairdressing* Pearl Tipaldi. *Casting Dir* Harvey Woods, Irene Howard. *Prod Buyer* Bill Isaacs. *Still Photog* Norman Gryspeerdt. *Stagehand* Tom Ramsey, Michael Dempsey, P. L. Pace. *Chargehand Prop* Tommy Ibbetson. *Chargehand Electrn* Anthony Condon.

Production Credits for Second Unit: *Dir Photog* Ted Moore. *Camera Op* John Winbolt. *Focus* Tony Spratling. *Cont* Rita Davison. *Constr Mgr* Larry Cleary. *Grip* L. Kelly, Maurice Budge. *Rigger* Harry Hunt, rigger.

Cast: Horst Buchholz (*Naturam Godse*), Jose Ferrer (*Superintendent Gopal Das*), Valerie Gearon (*Rani Mehta*), Don Borisenko (*Naryan Apte*), Robert Morley (*P. K. Mussadi*), Diane Baker (*Sheila*), Harry Andrews (*General Singh*), Jairaj (*G. D. Birla*), David Abraham (*Detective Munda*), Achla Sachdev (*mother*), Marne Maitland (*Karnick*), Harold Goldblatt (*Selvrag Prahlad*), Wolfe Morris (*Detective Bose*), Francis Matthews (*Rampure*), Nagendra Nath (*Magin Mehta*), Jack Hedley (*Kilpatrick*), Bobby Naidoo (*retiring room manager*), Allan Cuthbertson (*Captain Goff*), Peter Illing (*Frank Ramamurti*), Jagdev (*detective*), Frank Olegario (*Barburao*), Joseph Cuby (*Chacko*), Shay Gorman (*duty officer*), Nigel Phoenix (*S.N.S. boy*), Harold Kasket (*Datta*), Christopher Carlos (*Shankar*), S. N. Selk (*father*), Julian Sherrier (*P. K.'s secretary*), M. Y. Shaikh, Manohargin (*policemen*), Jagdish Raj, Keshov Singh, Sheri Mohan (*detectives*), Kurt Christian (*young Natu*), Shashi Pameholi (*young Apte*), Thali Kouri (*The Madame*), Ishaq Bux (*gardener*), Kunlan Malik (*bus conductor*), Lal Bahadur (*beggar*), R. S. Bansal (*astrologer*), Rani Verma (*Sita*), Baseo Panday (*laundryman*), J. S. Casshyap (*Mahatma Gandhi*).

Historical drama. Source: Stanley Wolpert, *Nine Hours to Rama* (New York, 1962). Following his rejection from the British Army because of his Brahmin ancestry, a young Indian, Naturam Godse, learns that his child bride and his father have been killed during communal riots. After promising his mother to fight violence with violence, Natu joins a reactionary political group opposing Mahatma Gandhi and his policy of nonviolence. While employed as a newspaper editor, he falls in love with Rani Mehta, a beautiful married woman who is a firm believer in the teachings of the Mahatma, but their affair ends because of political differences. Natu is then ordered to assassinate Gandhi during a prayer meeting at the home of an Indian industrialist. As Natu and his confederate, Naryan Apte, await the appointed hour of the execution, Natu recalls the events of his early life. Suddenly beset by doubts, he spends a few drunken hours with a Punjabi prostitute named Sheila and then seeks out Rani. When she once more rejects him, he decides to go through with his assignment. Although Gopal Das, the local police chief, has learned of the assassination plot, he is unable to persuade Gandhi to postpone the prayer meeting. Rani also learns of the plan but arrives too late to prevent Natu from firing the fatal shots. Knowing he has killed a great man and that he must be executed for his crime, Natu allows himself to be dragged off by Das's officers. *Hindus. Editors. Prostitutes. Police. Politics. Assassination. Nonviolence. India. Mahatma Gandhi. Naturam Godse.*

Note: Location scenes filmed in India. Opened in London in Mar 1963. Also known as *Nine Hours To Live.*

9 MILES TO NOON   F6.3503
Daron Enterprises. *Dist* Falcon Pictures, Taurus Film Co. **1963** [Maryland license: 4 Mar 1964]. Sd; b&w. 35mm. 67 min.

A Herbert J. Leder-Norman Kantor Production. *Prod* Herbert J. Leder, Norman Kantor. *Dir & Orig Screenplay* Herbert J. Leder. *Mus Comp & Cond* Manos Hadjidakis.

Cast: Renato Baldini *(Dio Dimou)*, Dolores Sutton *(Julia Dimou)*, Peter Lazer *(Jamie Dimou)*, Morgan Sterne *(Jeff Faulkner)*, Shelly Leder *(Pazzo)*, Anna Marie Ralli *(Nella)*.

Melodrama. Jeff Faulkner, an American, arrives in Athens to look for Julia, his ex-wife, whom he deserted after the birth of their son, Jamie, 9 years earlier. Julia has recently married Dio Dimou, a wealthy Greek architect, and will probably inherit money from her family. Jeff intends to obtain her money at any cost. He befriends his son, Jamie, a youngster who does not get along well with others (most notably his new stepfather), by promising Jamie that he will help him find his real father. Julia learns about Jamie's encounter with Jeff, and she warns her ex-husband to stay away from the boy. Desperate because his funds are running low, Jeff persuades Jamie to poison his stepfather by pouring poison into the thermos bottle that Dio takes to work each day for his lunchtime beverage. Jamie regrets his action early the next morning; and he and his friend Pazzo, a deafmute teenager, race to the construction site 9 miles away to save Dio. En route they encounter Jeff, who attempts to delay them by telling Jamie that he is Jamie's father. The boys break away, whereupon Jeff chases after them to the construction site and up the 15 stories of scaffolding to the place where Dio always eats lunch. In the melee that follows, Jeff shoots and injures Dio, and Pazzo falls off the scaffolding to his death after courageously attempting to wrest the gun from Jeff. Jeff gives himself up, and Jamie is reconciled with his stepfather at his friend's funeral. *Americans in foreign countries. Greeks. Architects. Stepfathers. Deafmutes. Desertion. Divorce. Wealth. Poisoning. Murder. Filial relations. Adoption. Greed. Self-sacrifice. Athens.*

Note: Filmed on location in Athens in 1961.

1967 see PENIS

90 DEGREES IN THE SHADE (Czechoslovakia/Great Britain)   F6.3504
Raymond Stross Productions-Barrandov Film Studio–Československý Film. *Dist* Landau/Unger Co. 15 Nov **1966** [New York opening]. Sd; b&w. 35mm. 90 min.

Prod Raymond Stross. *Assoc Prod* Ladislav Hanuš. *Dir* Jiří Weiss. *Screenplay* David Mercer. *Story* Jiří Weiss, Jiří Mucha. *Photog* Bedřich Baťka. *Photog Asst* Jiří Knotek. *Art Dir* Bohuslav Kulič. *Asst Art Dir* Věra Líznerová. *Film Ed* Jan Chaloupek, Russell Lloyd. *Asst Film Ed* Jana Kulhánková. *Mus Comp* Luděk Hulan. *Sd* Miloslav Hůrka, Milan Novotný. *Sd Eff* Bohumír Brunclík. *Asst Dir* Miloš Kohout, Hynek Bočan, Stanislava Hutková. *Prod Mgr* Vlastimil Maršálek, Jaromír Lukáš. *Prod Asst* Dagmar Rašilovová, Eva Hrubá. *Film Unit* Feix-Brož.

Cast: Anne Heywood *(Alena)*, James Booth *(Vorell)*, Rudolf Hrušínský *(Kurka)*, Ann Todd *(Mrs. Kurka)*, Donald Wolfit *(Bažant)*, Jiřina Jirásková *(Vera)*, Jorga Kotrbová *(Hanka)*, Vladimír Menšík *(Emil)*, Jiří Sovák *(director)*, Valtr Taub *(doctor)*, Věra Tichánková *(Vavrova)*, Věra Uzelacová *(Prochazkova)*, Jan Skopeček *(head waiter)*, Stella Zázvorková *(salesgirl)*, Taťána Vavřincová *(secretary)*, Jan Cmíral *(judge)*, Vlasta Jelínková, Eva Svobodová *(women)*, Jiří Šašek *(man with briefcase)*, Jan Libíček *(man in the booth)*, Mirko Musil *(saloon keeper)*, Karel Pavlík *(salesman)*, Ladislav Potměšil *(Jirka Kurka)*, Oldřich Velen *(criminal investigator)*.

Drama. At a grocery store in Prague, Alena, an attractive young woman, is having an affair with Vorell, the store's married manager. Although she is fully aware that Vorell is a scoundrel who has been stealing liquor from the stock shelves, Alena's physical need for him is so great that she is unable to break off their relationship. Then, an inventory is held, and it is discovered that 80 brandy bottles contain tea. When the two company auditors, Kurka and Bažant,

question the employees, Alena panics and races from the store. Kurka, an intolerant man whose sense of duty has wrecked his marriage, immediately places the guilt on Alena. When the disturbed woman turns to Vorell for advice, he callously suggests that she assume the blame since she would only be placed on probation while he would be sent to prison. Believing her life to be ruined, she commits suicide. Her death profoundly moves Kurka, who finally sees himself as a man devoid of human understanding. Vorell is hardly affected, however; as life at the store returns to normal, he begins training a new assistant to replace Alena. *Storekeepers. Thieves. Shopgirls. Infidelity. Embezzlement. Suicide. Grocery stores. Liquor. Prague.*

Note: Opened in Prague in Oct 1965 as *Třicet jedna ve stínu.*

99 WOMEN (Italy/Spain/West Germany)   F6.3505
Cineproduzioni Associate–Hesperia Films–Corona Filmproduktion. *Dist* Commonwealth United Entertainment, Inc. 5 Mar **1969** [San Francisco opening]. Sd; col (Eastman Color). 35mm (SuperScope). 86 min. *MPAA rating* X.

A Towers of London Production. *Prod* Harry Alan Towers. *Exec Prod* Luis Laso Moreno. *Dir* Jesús Franco. *Screenplay* Peter Welbeck, Carlo Fadda, Milo G. Cuccia, Jesús Franco. *Camera* Manuel Merino, Javier Pérez. *Art Dir* Santiago Ontañón. *Film Ed (see note)* Bruno Mattei, María Luisa Soriano. *Mus* Bruno Nicolai. *Prod Mgr* Francisco Moreno.

Cast: Maria Schell *(Leonie)*, Luciana Paluzzi *(Natalie)*, Mercedes McCambridge *(Thelma)*, Herbert Lom *(The Governor)*, Maria Rohm *(Marie)*, Rosalba Neri *(Zoe)*, Valentina Godoy *(Rosalie)*, Elisa Montés *(Helga)*, Maria Perschy.

Drama. On an island off the coast of Panama are situated two penal colonies. Supervising the women's penitentiary is the sadistic Thelma. Overseeing the brother institution is a lecherous warden who disports himself with inmates of the women's prison. When a number of prisoners die under suspicious circumstances, the cruel Thelma is replaced by liberal penologist Leonie, who retains the former supervisor as her assistant. Leonie's indulgence is her undoing. She is accused of a lesbian relationship with Marie, an inmate whom she has naively befriended. Accompanied by prisoners Helga and Rosalie, Marie attempts an escape into the surrounding jungle. One of the fugitives dies of injuries sustained during her rape by a gang of male convicts; the remaining escapees are recaptured and flogged. After a prison riot occurs Leonie is dismissed and Thelma reinstated. Nevertheless, Leonie learns of impending penal investigation and reform. *Prison matrons. Prison wardens. Penology. Sadism. Lesbianism. Prison reform. Conspiracy. Prison escapes. Rape. Flogging. Prison revolts. Penal colonies. Islands. Panama.*

Note: Location scenes filmed in Alicante and Madrid. Released in West Germany in Mar 1969 as *Der heisse Tod*; running time: 94 min; released in Spain as *99 mujeres*; running time: 84 min. Italian title: *99 donne*. Also known in U. S. as *Prostitutes in Prison*. Sources conflict on crediting editor. Peter Welbeck is a pseudonym for Harry Alan Towers.

NINGEN NO JOKEN *see* **NO GREATER LOVE**

NINGEN NO JOKEN II *see* **ROAD TO ETERNITY**

NINGEN NO JOKEN III *see* **A SOLDIER'S PRAYER**

NINJUTSU *see* **SECRET SCROLLS (PART II)**

THE NINTH CIRCLE (Yugoslavia)   F6.3506
Jadran Film. *Dist* Interprogress Trading Co. 14 Sep **1961** [New York opening]. Sd; b&w. 35mm. 90 min.

Dir France Štiglic. *Screenplay* Zora Dirnbach. *Adapt* France Štiglic, Vladimir Koch. *Photog* Ivan Marinček. *Art Dir* Željko Zagota. *Film Ed* Lidija Branis. *Mus* Branimir Sakač. *Asst Marijan Meglič. *Asst Dir* Krešo Golik, Vanja Pinter. *Prod Mgr* Stipe Gurdulic. *Cost* Vanda Pavelić.

Cast: Dušica Žegarac *(Ruth)*, Boris Dvornik *(Ivo)*, Ervina Dragman *(Mrs. Vojnovic)*, Branko Tatić *(Vojnovic)*, Dragan Milivojević *(Zvonko)*, Beba Lončar *(Magda)*, Mihajlo Kostić, Vera Misitá, Božidar Drnić, Djurdjica Delić.

Drama. In Nazi-occupied Zagreb kindly Mr. Vojnovic arranges a marriage of convenience between his Catholic son Ivo and family friend Ruth, a 17-year-old Jewess. Although Ivo, ostracized by schoolmates and his former girl friend, initially rebels and reproaches Ruth, the couple fall deeply in love. While enjoying a rare outing, however, Ruth is captured by the Nazis and interned in a concentration camp brothel. Her husband traces her to the camp, run by a former comrade. During their escape attempt Ruth's strength fails her and she is unable to scale the barbed wire fence. As the current is turned on, Ivo takes her hand and both are killed. *Jews. Catholics. Students. Nazis. Anti-Semitism. Military occupation. Marriage of convenience. Concentration camps. World War II. Zagreb.*

Note: Released in Yugoslavia in 1960 as *Deveti krug*; running time: 107 min.

NIPPON ICHINO HORAFUKI OTOKO *see* **THE GAY BRAGGART**
NIPPON KONCHUKI *see* **THE INSECT WOMAN**
NIPPON NO ICHIBAN NAGAI HI *see* **THE EMPEROR AND A GENERAL**

NO BLADE OF GRASS (Great Britain)   **F6.3507**
  Symbol Productions. *Dist* Metro-Goldwyn-Mayer, Inc. 4 Nov **1970** [San Francisco opening; c14 Dec 1970; LP38521]. Sd; col (Metrocolor). 35mm (Panavision). 97 min. *MPAA rating* R.
  Prod-Dir Cornel Wilde. *Screenplay* Sean Forestal, Jefferson Pascal. *Dir Photog* H. A. R. Thomson. *Camera Op* Wally Byatt. *Art Dir* Elliot Scott. *Film Ed* Frank Clarke, Eric Boyd-Perkins. *Mus Arr & Cond* Burnell Whibley. *Titl Song:* "No Blade of Grass" Louis Nelius, Charles Carroll. *Sung by* Roger Whittaker. *Theme:* "Lead Us On" Charles Carroll. *Sd Rec* Cyril Swern. *Dub Mix* Ken Barker. *Sd Ed* Roy Baker. *Asst Dir* John Stoneman. *Prod Supv* Sydney Streeter. *Unit Mgr* Terry Clegg. *Cont* Kay Rawlings. *Wardrobe Supv* Dorothy Edwards. *Cost Dsgn* Tony Armstrong Boutique. *Makeup* George Blackler. *Hairstyles* Biddy Chrystal. *Sp Eff* Terry Witherington.
  Cast: Nigel Davenport (*John Custance*), Jean Wallace (*Ann Custance*), John Hamill (*Roger Burnham*), Lynne Frederick (*Mary Custance*), Patrick Holt (*David Custance*), Anthony May (*Andrew Pirrie*), Wendy Richard (*Clara*), Nigel Rathbone (*Davey*), George Coulouris (*Mr. Sturdevant*), Ruth Kettlewell (*fat woman*), M. J. Matthews (*George*), Michael Percival (*police constable*), Tex Fuller (*Mr. Beaseley*), Simon Merrick (*TV interviewer*), Anthony Sharp (*Sir Charles Brenner*), Max Hartnell (*lieutenant*), John Lewis (*corporal*), Norman Atkyns (*Dr. Cassop*), Christopher Lofthouse (*Spooks*), John Avison (*Yorkshire sergeant*), Jimmy Winston, Richard Penny, R. C. Driscoll (*huns*), Geoffrey Hooper (*Tweed Jacket*), Christopher Wilson (*farmer*), William Duffy (*murdered farmer*), Mervyn Patrick (*Joe Ashton*), Denise Mockler (*Emily Ashton*), Ross Allan (*Alf Parsons*), Karen Terry (*Parsons' daughter*), Joan Ward (*Mrs. Parsons*), Brian Crabtree (*Joe Harris*), Susan Sydney (*Liz Harris*), Michael Landy (*Jess Arkwright*), Louise Kay (*Susan Arkwright*), Bruce Myers (*Bill Riggs*), Margaret Chapman (*Prudence Riggs*), Christopher Neame (*Locke*), Bridget Brice (*Jill Locke*), Reg Staniford (*Mr. Blennit*), Maureen Rutter (*Mrs. Blennit*), Derek Keller (*Scott*), Suzanne Pinkstone (*Mrs. Scott*), Surgit Sood (*Surgit*), Dick Offord (*Joe*), Joanna Annin (*Joe's wife*), John Buckley (*captain*), Malcolm Toes (*sergeant major*).
  Drama. Source: John Christopher, *The Death of Grass* (London, 1956). Environmental pollution turns a normally harmless virus into an uncontrollable plague that is deadly to crops, and famine spreads throughout Britain. Biochemist Roger Burnham convinces his friend John Custance that Custance and his family must leave London immediately. On the way to the well-stocked farm owned by Custance's brother, they stop to steal firearms from a supermarket. The shopkeeper tries to stop them, but hoodlum Andrew Pirrie, who with his wife, Clara, has joined the party, shoots the man, and the group escape. Later, Custance's party is attacked by a band of motorcyclists who steal their cars and supplies and rape Custance's wife, Ann, and their daughter Mary. When they finally camp for the night, Clara attempts to seduce John, but the outraged Pirrie shoots her. Continuing on foot the next morning, they join another escaping group and finally reach the farm. John's brother David is unwilling to permit such a large number of people on his farm, however, and John, unwilling to abandon the rest of the people, leads an attack on the farm. David and many others are killed; the Custances and other survivors take over the land, determined to live in peace. *Farmers. Biochemists. Hoodlums. Motorcyclists. Escapees. Brothers. Pollution. Famine. Robbery. Rape. Survival. Riots. Murder. London.*
  Note: Filmed on location in Cumberland, Westmorland, and Yorkshire, England. Released in Great Britain in 1972; running time: 80 min.

NO DEADLY MACHINE *see* **THE YOUNG DOCTORS**

NO ESCAPE *see* **ANY MAN'S WOMAN**

NO EXIT (United States/Argentina)   **F6.3508**
  Aries Cinematográfica. *Dist* Zenith International Film Corp. 5 Dec **1962** [New York opening; c1 Jul 1962; LP22538]. Sd; b&w. 35mm. 85 min. [Also 91 min.]
  Prod Fernando Ayala, Hector Olivera. *Assoc Prod* Julio Kaufman, James G. Zea. *Dir* Tad Danielewski. *Screenplay* George Tabori. *Dir Photog* Ricardo Younis. *Camera Op* Domingo Bugallo. *Art Dir* Mario Vanarelli. *Titl Dsgn* Carlos Parera. *Supv Ed* Carl Lerner. *Ed* Atilio Rinaldi, Jacques Bart. *Mus* Vladimir Ussachevsky. *Sd* José Feijoo. *Asst Dir* Esteban Etcheverrito, Ricardo Becher. *Prod Mgr* Emilio A. Keller. *Unit Mgr* Guillermo Smith. *Script Supv* Michelle Sutherland. *Cost Dsgn* Horace Lannes. *Makeup* Aida Fernández. *Hairstyles* Haydee Aued.
  Cast: Viveca Lindfors (*Inez*), Rita Gam (*Estelle*), Morgan Sterne (*Garcin*), Ben Piazza (*Camarero*), Susana Mayo (*Florence*), Orlando Sacha (*Gómez*), Manuel Roson (*Capitan*), Mirtha Miller (*Carmencita*), Miguel A. Irarte

(*Robert*), Elsa Dorian (*Shirley*), Mario Horna (*Albert*), Carlos Brown (*Roger Delaney, III*).
  Drama. Source: Jean-Paul Sartre, *Huis clos* (Paris opening: 27 May 1944). Three strangers are ushered into a brightly-lit hotel room. They are: Garcin, a self-proclaimed heroic journalist who considers himself to be of high moral standards; Estelle, a narcissistic society wife; and Inez, a lesbian. As the trio become aware that they are doomed to spend eternity together in the single room, they begin pairing off in conspiracies against one another. All attempted liaisons fail, however, because each has contempt for the others' weaknesses. It is discovered that Garcin was actually shot for cowardice; Estelle is revealed to be a nymphomaniac who married for money, killed her unwanted child, and then destroyed her husband; and Inez is exposed as a frustrated woman who took her own life after seducing a married woman and driving her to suicide. After a violent quarrel, Estelle stabs Inez with a paper knife, but it is in vain. Following the final realization that they can never escape from each other, the three break into hysterical laughter and then become silent. *Journalists. Socialites. Appearances. Narcissism. Lesbianism. Cowardice. Nymphomania. Infanticide. Suicide. Hotels. Hell.*
  Note: Filmed in Argentina and released there as *Huis clos*. Also known as *Sinners Go to Hell.*

NO GREATER LOVE (Reissue) (Japan)   **F6.3509**
  Shochiku Co. *Dist* Shochiku Films of America, Beverly Pictures. 3 Jun **1970** [Los Angeles showing]. Sd; b&w. 35mm (Shochiku Grandscope). 200 min. *MPAA rating* R.
  Prod Shigeru Wakatsuki. *Dir* Masaki Kobayashi. *Screenplay* Zenzo Matsuyama, Masaki Kobayashi. *Photog* Yoshio Miyajima. *Art Dir* Kazue Hirataka. *Film Ed* Keiichi Uraoka. *Mus* Chuji Kinoshita. *Sd Rec* Hideo Nishizaki.
  Cast: Tatsuya Nakadai (*Kaji*), Michiyo Aratama (*Michiko*), So Yamamura (*Okishima*), Eitaro Ozawa (*Okazaki*), Akira Ishihama (*Chen*), Shinji Nambara (*Kao*), Ineko Arima (*Yang Chun Lan*), Chikage Awashima (*Jin Tung Fu*), Keiji Sada (*Kageyama*), Toru Abe (*Watai*), Masao Mishima (*Kuroki*), Koji Mitsui (*Furya*), Kyu Sazanka (*Cho Meisan*), Seiji Miyaguchi (*Wang Heng Li*), Nobuo Nakamura (*chief of head office*).
  War drama. Source: Jumpei Gomigawa, *Ningen no joken*, vol 1 & 2 (Kyoto, 1958). In 1943 Kaji, a pacifist, takes a draft-exempt job as a labor supervisor at a mine in Manchuria. His attempts to treat the miners fairly conflict with their menial status and the cruelty of their overseer, Okazaki. Kaji is aided only by mine foreman Okishima and his Chinese assistant Chen. Kaji's problems are complicated by the arrival of 600 sick and starving prisoners of war, who are housed in a nearby compound under his supervision. His well-meaning treatment of the prisoners creates enemies among both his supervisors and the laborers. When the mine's production eventually increases by 20%, Kaji plans a short vacation with his wife, but an attempted escape by the prisoners, engineered by Kaji's enemies, throws the camp into turmoil. Kao, a prisoner whose trust Kaji has hoped to gain, attacks Okazaki, and the secret police (Kempei-tai) are summoned. Kao and six other prisoners are sentenced to die, and Kaji is forced to attend the execution. After Kao is beheaded, Kaji attempts to prevent the other executions and almost incites the prisoners to revolt. He is arrested, charged with conspiracy, tortured, and released, only to be served with a conscription notice. *Pacifists. Miners. Chinese. Prisoners of war. Humanitarianism. Prison revolts. Capital punishment. Conspiracy. Torture. Military draft. Mines. World War II. Manchuria. Kempei-tai.*
  Note: Released in Japan in 1959 as *Ningen no joken*; running time: 208 min. Originally released in the United States in Dec 1959 as *The Human Condition*; this film, part one of a trilogy entitled *The Human Condition*, will appear in its appropriate volume but has been included in this volume to complete coverage for the trilogy which was shown in its entirety in Los Angeles in 1970. The other parts are *Road to Eternity* (1961) and *A Soldier's Prayer* (1970), q. v.

NO GREATER LOVE THAN THIS (Japan)   **F6.3510**
  Nikkatsu Corp. *Dist* Toho Co. Nov **1969** [Los Angeles showing]. Sd; col (Fuji Color). 35mm (Nikkatsu Scope). 106 min.
  Dir Kenji Yoshida. *Screenplay* Shigeki Chiba. *Story* Keiichi Ito. *Photog* Kenji Hagiwara. *Art Dir* Motozo Kawahara. *Mus* Riichiro Manabe.
  Cast: Fumie Kashiyama (*Hatsuko Araki*), Homare Suguro (*Dr. Takaoka*), Izumi Ashikawa, Jukichi Uno, Gin Maeda, Terumi Niki, Jun Hamamura.
  Drama. Nurse Hatsuko Araki travels to Okino-shima, off southwestern Japan, where there is no doctor. The islanders are wary of Hatsuko at first, but she eventually wins their confidence, especially when she brings in a team of doctors from Kochi to study the parasite filaria, which causes a disease common to the islanders. Hatsuko becomes engaged to Dr. Takaoka, but she decides to remain unmarried when she realizes that she cannot leave the people of the island. *Nurses. Physicians. Self-sacrifice. Islands. Parasites. Okino-shima (Japan). Kochi (city).*
  Note: Released in Japan in 1968 as *Koto no taiyo.*

NO HOLDS BARRED   F6.3511

Dist Stacey Distributors. ca **1970**. Sd; col. 16mm. 61-81 min.

Sex film. No information about the precise nature of this film has been found. *Sexuality.*

NO KIDDING *see* BEWARE OF CHILDREN

NO LOVE FOR JOHNNIE (Great Britain)   F6.3512

Five Star Films. *For* J. Arthur Rank. *Dist* Embassy Pictures. 12 Dec **1961** [New York opening: c10 Feb 1961; LP20760]. Sd; b&w. 35mm (CinemaScope). 110 min.

Prod Betty E. Box. *Exec Prod* Earl St. John. *Dir* Ralph Thomas. *Screenplay* Nicholas Phipps, Mordecai Richler. *Photog* Ernest Steward. *Camera Op* James Bawden. *Focus Op* John Morgan. *Camera Grip* Reg Hall. *Art Dir* Maurice Carter. *Set Decor* Arthur Taksen. *Ch Draughtsman* Bert Davey. *Film Ed* Alfred Roome. *1st Asst Ed* Bill Creed. *2d Asst Ed* Paul Bijou. *Mus Comp & Cond* Malcolm Arnold. *Sd Rec* Dudley Messenger, Gordon K. McCallum. *Sd* Don Sharpe. *Boom Op* J. W. N. Daniel. *Sd Camera Op* Ron Butcher. *1st, 2d & 3d Asst Dir* Stanley Hosgood, Donald Toms, Anthony Waye. *Prod Mgr* Charles Orme. *Cont* Gladys Goldsmith. *Prod Sec* Lorely Farley. *Cost Dsgn* Yvonne Caffin. *Women's Wardrobe* Pat Baden. *Men's Wardrobe* Ben Foster. *Makeup* William Partleton. *Hairdresser* Biddy Chrystal. *Prop Buyer* Jim Baker. *Still Photog* Ian Jeayes. *Constr Mgr* Bert Jempson. *Ch Floor Electrn* Harry Black.

Cast: Peter Finch *(Johnnie Byrne)*, Stanley Holloway *(Fred Andrews)*, Mary Peach *(Pauline West)*, Donald Pleasence *(Roger Renfrew)*, Billie Whitelaw *(Mary)*, Hugh Burden *(Tim Maxwell)*, Rosalie Crutchley *(Alice Byrne)*, Michael Goodliffe *(Dr. West)*, Mervyn Johns *(Charlie Young)*, Geoffrey Keen *(prime minister)*, Paul Rogers *(Sydney Johnson)*, Dennis Price *(Flagg)*, Peter Barkworth *(Henderson)*, Fenella Fielding *(Sheilah)*, Gladys Henson *(constituent)*.

Drama. Source: Wilfred Fienburgh, *No Love for Johnnie* (London, 1959). Reelected to the House of Commons, Labour Party member Johnnie Byrne suffers two simultaneous setbacks: he fails to receive a Cabinet post, and his wife, Alice, a militant Communist, leaves him. The professional failure especially disturbs Johnnie and he is easily persuaded to join a left-wing splinter group bent on harassing the prime minister. One evening Johnnie's upstairs neighbor, Mary, who is in love with him, takes him to a party where he meets model Pauline West. After a few dates with Pauline, Johnnie is so desperately in love with her that he fails to appear in Parliament on the day he is scheduled to ask a crucial question to discredit the government. Pauline, however, decides that marrying a man twice her age is too great a risk, and she leaves London. In addition, Johnnie is summoned to a meeting of his constituents who bitterly attack him for his neglect. Failing to win back Pauline, Johnnie receives a surprise visit from his wife, who suggests they try again to achieve a successful marriage. Johnnie is inclined to accept her offer, but when the prime minister offers him a Cabinet post with the stipulation that he remain apart from his Communist wife, Johnnie decides against the reconciliation. Alone and without love or friends, he occupies one of the front seats reserved for Cabinet members. *Communists. Neighbors. Prime ministers. Models. Politics. Marriage. Ambition. Bribery. Infidelity. Separation (marital). London. Great Britain—Parliament. Labour Party (United Kingdom).*

Note: Opened in London in Feb 1961.

NO MAN IS AN ISLAND   F6.3513

Gold Coast Productions. *Dist* Universal-International. 20 Sep **1962** [Detroit opening; c8 Sep 1962; LP24724]. Sd (Westrex); col (Eastman Color). 35mm. 114 min.

Prod-Dir-Writ John Monks, Jr., Richard Goldstone. *Co-prod* Rolf Bayer. *Assoc Prod* Robert E. Lewis, Albert R. Joseph. *Dir Photog* Carl Kayser. *Adtl Photog* Mars Rasca. *Lighting* Joe Edesa. *Camera Op* William Grimmond. *Art Dir* Benjamin Resella. *Film Ed* Basil Wrangell. *Asst Ed* Howard French, Robert Fawcett. *Mus* Restie Umali. *Mus Played by* Manila Symphony Orchestra. *Song:* "Maulik Trabajo" Restie Umali. *Sung by* Barbara Perez. *Sd* Joseph Keener, Harry M. Leonard, Blandino Aquin, Tommy Santos. *Prod Mgr* Ron Whelan. *Prod Asst* Jose Velasco, Mario Barri, Ding Velasco, Fred Harris, II. *Cont Supv* Joy Cavill. *Sp Eff* Robert R. Joseph. *Cons for the Philippines* Lamberto V. Avellana. *Coöp* Tamaraw Studios, Armed Forces of the Republic of the Philippines.

Cast: Jeffrey Hunter *(George R. Tweed)*, Marshall Thompson *("Sonn" Sonnenberg)*, Barbara Perez *("Joe" Cruz)*, Ronald Remy *(Chico Torres)*, Paul Edwards, Jr. *(Al Turney)*, Rolf Bayer *(Chief Schultz)*, Vicente Liwanag *(Vicente)*, Fred Harris, II *(Roy Lund)*, Lamberto V. Avellana *(Mr. Shimoda)*, Amparo (Chichay) Custodio *(Mrs. Nakamura)*, Antonio de la Mogueis *(Florecito)*, Vic Silayan *(Major Hondo)*, Bert La Fortesa *(Comdr. Oto Harada)*, Eddie Infante *(Sus Quintagua)*, Nardo Ramos *(Tumon)*, Rosa Mia *(Primera*

Quintagua)*, Mike Anzures *(Santos)*, Joseph de Cordova *(Father Pangolin)*, Mario Barri *(Limtiago)*, Stevie Joseph *(Tommy Tanaka)*, Ding Tello *(Japanese sergeant major)*, Burt Olivar *(Antonio Cruz)*, Veronica Palileo *(Josefa Cruz)*, Bruno Punzalan, Nena Ledesma, Segundo Veloria.

War melodrama. When Guam is attacked by the Japanese during World War II, U. S. Navy radioman George R. Tweed and five other Americans escape to the center of the island. Though the other men are all eventually killed, Tweed evades capture and takes refuge in a leper hospital run by a dedicated priest, Father Pangolin. By using the priest's radio, Tweed issues encouraging news bulletins to the natives until the Japanese learn of the reports and burn the hospital. Tweed is then befriended by the Cruz family, who hide him in a cave and supply him with food. The daughter, "Joe," brings him a small hand mirror with which he flashes information on enemy artillery installations to a U. S. warship. He then successfully eludes a Japanese patrol and swims out to a small boat sent from the warship. His information enables the Navy to pinpoint and completely destroy the Japanese defenses. After the war, Tweed returns to Guam for a reunion with his many island friends. *Radiomen. Sailors. Priests. Resistance (political). Radio. Leprosy. Hospitals. World War II. George R. Tweed. United States Navy. Japan—Army. Guam.*

Note: Filmed in the Philippines. Based on experiences of George R. Tweed, USN, in World War II.

NO MAN WALKS ALONE *see* BLACK LIKE ME

NO MAN'S LAND   F6.3514

Dist Cinema-Video International, Inc. Feb **1964** [San Antonio, Texas, showing]. Sd; b&w. 35mm. 72 min.

Prod-Dir-Writ Russ Harvey. *Exec Prod* Bill Pierce. *Assoc Prod* Pat Boyette. *Dir Photog* James Houston. *Camera* Kent Moore. *Art Dir* Don Russell. *Supv Ed* Charles Kimball. *Mus* Jaime Mendoza-Nava. *Sd* Eddie Morris. *Asst Dir* Don Russell. *Prod Mgr* Don Russell. *Script Supv* Kenneth Miller. *Wardrobe* Nan Ruckman. *Makeup* Nan Ruckman. *Military Adv & Coörd* T. E. Lytle, (Capt.).

Cast: Russ Harvey *(Corp. Jerry Little)*, Kim Lee *(Anna Wong)*, Lee Morgan *(Old Sarge)*, Val Martinez, Tom Lytle, Henry Garcia, Eddie Retacy, Tom Drossis, Lyman Harrison, Don Russell, Percy Barbat.

War drama. American Corporal Jerry Little is assigned to a district during the Korean War called "No Man's Land." He thinks he hears something in the darkness, throws a hand grenade, and triggers a major battle. Afterwards, the corporal decides he will meet the enemy with more finesse. One afternoon he meets Anna Wong, an Oriental girl, walking her dog, and they become friends. One last patrol is ordered before the squad can retreat to a rest zone. When they meet the enemy, an old sergeant is wounded by a sniper, and one of the troops [Tom Lytle] leads volunteers back for medical aid. The corporal manages to find both the sniper, whom he shoots, and Anna, whom he marries. *Orientals. Combat zone life. Korean War 1950–53. United States Army. Dogs.*

Note: Filmed in and around San Antonio, Texas.

NO MORE EXCUSES   F6.3515

Phantasma Films. *Dist* Rogosin Films, Impact Films. 21 May **1968** [New York opening]. Sd; b&w. 16mm. 52 min. [Also reviewed at 55 min; cut from 62 min.]

Dir-Writ Robert Downey. *Film Ed* Robert Soukis.

Cast: Robert Downey *(Pvt. Stewart Thompson)*, Alan Abel *(himself)*, Lawrence Wolf *(President Garfield)*, Prentice Wilhite *(Charles Guiteau)*, Linda Diesem *(Mrs. Garfield)*, Amy Eccles *(Chinese girl)*, Don Calfa *(priest)*, Paula Morris *(his woman/prostitute)*.

Satire. Having received a superficial wound in the left buttock, Pvt. Stewart Thompson, a Confederate soldier, lies low until the battle passes him by and then flees to modern-day New York. He is immediately served a bad hamburger, which he dumps in the nearest mailbox. Meanwhile, Alan Abel of S.I.N.A. (Society for Indecency to Naked Animals) is campaigning to have animals clothed. Simultaneously, in cinema vérité interviews, some of the habitués of Manhattan's East Side singles bars reveal the crudity and singlemindedness of their attitude toward the mating game. A slightly-built, mustachioed rapist forces his way into the apartment of a heavyset woman. Intermittently, there are returns to the past as Charles Guiteau attempts to assassinate President Garfield. After three failures (he is too nervous; the day is too hot; a bird defecates on his head), his fourth attempt succeeds when he catches the President taking a shortcut through the ladies room at the Washington, D. C., railroad station. Private Thompson next picks up a prostitute near Riverside Church and pays for her services with his rifle. Later, he visits Yankee Stadium in his Confederate garb but is thrown out as a lunatic. Fed up with contemporary civilization, he returns to his war and is killed. The rapist, having conquered his prey, lolls in bed with her, while at the foot of the bed an American Broadcasting Company newsman questions them about their views on the war in Vietnam. When the rapist (who proves to be a priest) leaves to chase another victim, the newsman (who proves to be a chimpanzee) happily takes his place with the woman while strains of the "Hallelujah Chorus" ring forth. *Soldiers. Prostitutes. Priests. Reporters. Deserters—Military. Assassination. Rape. Bestiality. Personal identity. Singles bars. United States—History—Civil War. Vietnam War 1964–73. New York City. James Abram Garfield. Charles J. Guiteau. American Broadcasting Company. Society for Indecency to Naked Animals. Riverside Church (New York City). Yankee Stadium. Chimpanzees.*

Note: The Civil War segments are excerpts from Robert Downey's ca1963 short, *Balls Bluff.* The soundtrack includes music from *Goldfinger* and *A Man and a Woman.*

NO, MY DARLING DAUGHTER! (Great Britain)   F6.3516

Five Star Films. *Dist* Zenith International Film Corp. Feb **1964** [New York opening: 27 Mar]. Sd; b&w. 35mm. 85 min. [Also reviewed at 96 min.]

A Betty E. Box-Ralph Thomas Production. *Prod* Betty E. Box. *Exec Prod* Earl St. John. *Dir* Ralph Thomas. *Screenplay* Frank Harvey. *Photog* Ernest Steward. *Camera Op* James Bawden. *Focus Op* John Morgan. *Art Dir* Maurice Carter. *Ch Draughtsman* Bert Davey. *Draughtsmen* Bill Alexander, Nigel Curzon. *Set Dresser* Arthur Taksen. *Film Ed* Alfred Roome. *Mus* Norrie Paramor. *Titl Song* Herbert Kretzmer, David Lee. *Sd* Don Sharpe. *Sd Rec* Dudley Messenger, Gordon K. McCallum. *Boom Op* J. W. N. Daniel. *Sd Camera Op* Simon Kaye. *1st, 2d, & 3d Asst Dir* Stanley Hosgood, Donald Toms, Anthony Waye. *Prod Mgr* Charles Orme. *Cont* Gladys Goldsmith. *Prod Sec* Rhonda Grogan. *Producer's Sec* Margaret Child. *Dress Dsgn* Yvonne Caffin. *Ladies' Wardrobe* Pat Baden. *Men's Wardrobe* John Hilling. *Makeup* William Partleton. *Hairdresser* Betty Sherriff. *Prop Buyer* Harry Hannay. *Still Photog* Ian Jeayes. *Constr Mgr* Bert Jempson. *Grip* Reg Hall. *Ch Floor Electrn* Harry Black. *Prop* Tommy Gleed, Ken Wilkes.

Cast: Michael Redgrave *(Sir Mathew Carr),* Michael Craig *(Thomas Barclay),* Roger Livesey *(Gen. Henry Barclay),* Rad Fulton *(Cornelius),* Juliet Mills *(Tansy),* Renee Houston *(Miss Yardly),* Joan Sims, Carole Shelley *(typists),* Peter Barkworth *(Charles),* David Lodge *(Flanigan),* Victor Brooks *(policeman),* Court Benson *(Allingham),* Ian Fleming *(vicar),* Terry Scott *(constable).*

Comedy. Based on the play by: Harold Brooke and Kay Bannerman, *Handful of Tansy* (published as *Don't Tell Father;* London, 1961). Business tycoon Sir Mathew Carr withdraws his daughter Tansy from her British high school so that she can complete her education at a Paris finishing school. Tansy, who is most happy at home playing hockey and cricket, resists her father's plan. She meets Cornelius, an American boy whose father is a business associate of Sir Mathew's, and they discover that they have much in common. Cornelius neglects to deliver a letter from his father to Sir Mathew, and Tansy's father is compelled to fly to New York. In his absence, Sir Mathew sends Tansy fishing in Scotland with his friend General Barclay. Cornelius follows them, and he and Tansy go off camping, prompting newspaper headlines about their supposed elopement. General Barclay's son, Thomas, finds Tansy and returns her to Sir Mathew, who, upon discovering the boy's identity, agrees to let her marry Cornelius. Thomas and Tansy fall in love, however, thus interrupting the wedding plans. Tansy elopes with Thomas to Scotland, to the delight of Sir Mathew and General Barclay. *Businessmen. Tomboys. Americans in foreign countries. Tycoons. Soldiers. Fishing. Camping. Elopement. Filial relations. Adolescence. Boarding schools. Scotland.*

Note: Released in Great Britain in 1961; running time: 97 min.

NO. NO. IT'S A SIN (Italy)   F6.3517

5 May **1961** [New York State license]. Sd; b&w. 35mm. 93 min.

Pres by National Catholic Film Productions.

Religious drama. No information about the precise nature of this film has been found, but sources indicate that it concerns the life of Maria Goretti, an illiterate Italian peasant who was brutally stabbed at the age of 12 by a youth attempting to rape her. Subsequently, many miracles were associated with her name, and her slayer himself repented of his sin while in prison, upon release working for her beatification. In 1950, she was canonized a saint in the Catholic Church. *Peasants. Murder. Rape. Adolescence. Miracles. Maria Goretti. Catholic Church.*

Note: Original title and release undetermined. Alternative U. S. title: *The Life of St. Maria Goretti.*

NO PLACE LIKE HOMICIDE see WHAT A CARVE UP!

NO RETURN ADDRESS   F6.3518

Westwind Productions. *Dist* Century Releasing Co., Goldstone Film Enterprises. ca **1961**. Sd; b&w. 35mm. 76 min.

Prod-Dir Alexander Grattan. *Exec Prod* Robert Springer, Clark Bell. *Writ* Alexander Grattan, Robert Springer, Clark Bell. *Dir Photog* Andrew Janczak.

Cast: Harry Lovejoy *(Raymond Carver),* Alicia Hammond *(Selma Carver),* Shauna Dietlien *(Mary Carver),* Jo Armstrong *(grandmother),* Paul Spencer

(Moegle), Paul Timcho *(Ritter),* Jack Hammond *(lover),* John Vitale *(Gomez),* Cliff Medaugh *(psychiatrist),* Chuck Hastings *(truck driver).*

Melodrama. Raymond Carver relates his tragic history to a psychiatrist. Spurred by Selma, his neurotic wife, Carver stole from Moegle, his unscrupulous employer. Carver was consequently apprehended and incarcerated. Following his release from prison, he returned home, only to discover his wife in the arms of a lover. Deserted by Selma, Carver tried in vain to find work to support Mary, his beloved 9-year-old daughter, and his senile mother. Inspired by a minor automobile accident in which Mary bruised her knee, Carver defrauded the insurance company by having the child pretend to be lame. To his horror, however, Mary continues to believe that she is a cripple. *Psychiatrists. Employers. Children. Ex-convicts. Cripples. Imprisonment. Theft. Infidelity. Desertion. Filial relations. Marriage. Fraud. Psychosomatic illness. Insurance. Automobile accidents.*

Note: Filmed in Great Britain.

NO TEARS FOR THE DAMNED   F6.3519

Bonanza Film Productions. *Dist* Gold Star Pictures. 13 Jun **1968** [Maryland license]. Sd; b&w. 35mm. 85 min.

Prod Oliver Drake. *Exec Assoc* Frank E. Stranges. *Dir* William Collins. *Screenplay* June Drake, Oliver Drake. *Dir Photog* William Troiano. *Film Ed* Ewing Brown.

Cast: Robert Dix, Gillian Simpson, Liz Marshal, Gay Conway, Richard Jeffries, John Cardos, Perry Dell.

Melodrama. Las Vegas playboy Jeff Murray, the son of an overbearing woman, is tricked into marrying Lori, a prostitute he has rescued from the advances of a drunken truckdriver. Lori is unfaithful, and Jeff goes on a rampage, killing two prostitutes and assaulting a homosexual who has made a pass at him. He returns home, intent upon killing his mother, whom he blames for his illness, and is stopped just in time. *Playboys. Psychopaths. Prostitutes. Motherhood. Marriage. Infidelity. Murder. Male homosexuality. Drunkenness. Las Vegas.*

Note: Filmed in Las Vegas.

NO TIME FOR ECSTASY (France)   F6.3520

Les Films Univers. *Dist* European Producers International. ca **1963**. Sd; b&w. 35mm. [U. S. running time unknown.]

Prod José Bénazéraf. *Dir* Jean-Jacques Vierne. *Dial* Henri-François Rey. *Adapt* Henri-François Rey, Jean-Jacques Vierne. *Photog* Raymond Lemoigne. *Art Dir* René Moulaert. *Film Ed* Claudine Bouché, Eric Pluet. *Mus* Ricardo Biasco. *Sd* Louis Hochet. *Prod Mgr* Tonio Suné.

Cast: Peter Van Eyck *(Michel Georgenko),* Daliah Lavi *(Nathalie Conrad),* Roland Lesaffre *(Marcel Nancini),* Helmo Kindermann *(Walter),* Anne-Marie Coffinet *(Gina),* Henri Le Monnier, Billy Kearns, Emilio Carrère.

War drama. Source: Henri-François Rey, *La fête espagnole* (Paris, 1958). In 1936 during the Spanish Civil War, Michel Georgenko, a Ukrainian idealist, enlists in the International Brigade in Perpignan. Soon afterwards, he meets American journalist Nathalie, and they fall in love. After their arrival in Barcelona, Michel leaves to join his unit on the front near the commune of Albacete. Nancini, a comrade, is mutilated by captors. Michel deserts and rejoins Nathalie when his comrades set out to execute a group of their own prisoners. They reach the French border but are captured by anarchists. Michel is shot and killed; Nathalie, detained nearby, hears the gunshots and screams out her love and despair. *Ukrainians. Americans in foreign countries. Journalists. Idealists. Prisoners of war. Deserters—Military. Anarchists. Combat zone life. Mutilation. Spain—History—Civil War 1936–39. Perpignan. Barcelona. Albacete.*

Note: Opened in Paris in Sep 1961 as *La fête espagnole;* running time: 100 min.

NO TIME TO KILL (Great Britain/Sweden/West Germany)   F6.3521

Frejafilm, AB. *Dist* A. D. P. Productions. Mar **1963**. Sd; b&w. 35mm. 70 min.

Pres by Jerry Warren. *Prod* Tom Younger, Sven Nicou. *Dir-Writ* Tom Younger. *Photog* Bengt Lindström. *Film Ed* Lennart Wallen. *Mus* Harry Arnold.

Cast: John Ireland *(Johnny Greco),* Ellen Schwiers *(Nina Christians),* Birgitta Andersson *(Helle),* Frank Sundström *(Hopkins),* Hans Stråät *(Inspector Bergman),* Ralph Brown *(Jens),* Erik Strandmark *(concierge),* Charles Fawcett *(marine),* Marcia Ford *(receptionist),* John Starck *(bartender).*

Melodrama. Johnny Greco, erroneously convicted of arson, is released from prison after serving 8 years. An American, he travels to Sweden to avenge himself against the man who he believes framed him—businessman Nils Christians. Johnny meets Christians' wife, Nina, and has as affair with her, but her husband is nowhere to be found. Johnny's search finally leads him to a cemetery where he learns that Christians, who has been dead for several years, was not the one who framed him. Johnny continues to gather clues until Nina tries to kill him. Johnny kills her in self-defense and realizes that it was she who framed him. *Ex-convicts. Americans in foreign countries. Arson. Frameup. Revenge. Justifiable homicide. Perfidy. Cemeteries.*

Note: Produced in Sweden in 1958. Released in Great Britain in Dec 1961; running time: 75 min; opened in Stockholm in Jan 1963 as *Med mord i bagaget.*

NO TOYS FOR CHRISTMAS see **ONCE BEFORE I DIE**

NO TREE IN THE STREET (Great Britain)   **F6.3522**
Allegro. *Dist* Seven Arts Associated Corp. Jan **1964.** Sd; b&w. 35mm. 96 min.

A J. Lee Thompson-Frank Godwin-Ted Willis Production. *Prod* Frank Godwin. *Dir* J. Lee Thompson. *Screenplay* Ted Willis. *Photog* Gilbert Taylor. *Art Dir* Robert Jones. *Film Ed* Richard Best. *Mus* Laurie Johnson. *Sd Rec* Norman Coggs, Len Shilton.

Cast: Sylvia Syms *(Hetty),* Herbert Lom *(Wilkie),* Ronald Howard *(Frank),* Stanley Holloway *(Kipper),* Joan Miller *(Jess),* Liam Redmond *(Bill),* Carole Lesley *(Lova),* Lana Morris *(Marje),* Melvyn Hayes *(Tommy),* Lilly Kann *(Mrs. Jacobson),* Marianne Stone *(Mrs. Jokel),* Edwin Richfield *(Jackie),* David Hemmings *(Kenny),* Richard Shaw *(Reg),* Rita Wess *(Mrs. Brown),* Fred Griffiths *(street orator),* Victor Brooks *(bookie's clerk),* Campbell Singer *(inspector),* Lloyd Lamble *(superintendent).*

Crime melodrama. Source: Ted Willis, *No Trees in the Street* (Liverpool opening: 31 May 1948). In 1938 Wilkie, a dishonest turf accountant, rules Kennedy Street in the London slums. Anxious for her children to escape poverty, Jess persuades her son Tommy to work for Wilkie and attempts to marry her daughter Hetty to the petty criminal. When Hetty decides to leave home, Jess plies the girl with drink and panders for Wilkie. Having seduced Hetty, Wilkie freely humiliates her before his former mistresses. Forced to murder in the course of his employment, Tommy flees to his home, where he is shot by Hetty. As the ambulance pulls away, Hetty confronts Wilkie. In the street Jess lies screaming. *Mistresses. Bookies. Lower classes. Poverty. Motherhood. Drunkenness. Seduction. Murder. Brother-sister relationship. Slums. London.*

Note: Released in Great Britain in Apr 1959 as *No Trees in the Street.*

NO VIETNAMESE EVER CALLED ME NIGGER   **F6.3523**
Paradigm Films. Nov **1968** [Los Angeles opening]. Sd; b&w. 16mm. 76 min.
Prod-Dir David Loeb Weiss. *Camera* Michael Wadley, Richard Adams, Adam Guffard. *Film Ed* David Loeb Weiss, John Binder. *Sd* John Binder, Tom Cohen, Marshall Dodge.

Documentary. Three black veterans of the Vietnam War are interviewed. They explain that they have undergone more oppression at home in the United States and among their American comrades abroad than at the hands of the Vietnamese. They contend that national priorities set up by white society do not meet black peoples' needs and that promises made to black veterans, that upon their return to the United States their newly-acquired skills would advance their status in society, have not been fulfilled. Contrasted with the interview are sequences of the preparation for the 1967 Spring Mobilization March in Harlem and of interviews with spectators at the demonstrations that followed. *Negroes. Veterans. Racial prejudice. Social classes. Demonstrations. Interviews. Vietnam War 1964–73. New York City—Harlem. United States Army.*

NO WAY TO TREAT A LADY   **F6.3524**
Sol C. Siegel Pictures. *Dist* Paramount Pictures. 20 Mar **1968** [New York opening; c31 Dec 1967; LP35657]. Sd; col (Technicolor). 35mm. 108 min.
Prod Sol C. Siegel. *Dir* Jack Smight. *Screenplay* John Gay. *Dir Photog* Jack Priestley. *Exec Art Dir* Hal Pereira. *Art Dir & Set Decor* George Jenkins. *Film Ed* Archie Marshek. *Mus* Stanley Myers. *Song:* "A Quiet Place" Stanley Myers, Andrew Belling. *Arr* Bill Traut. *Sung by* The American Breed. *Song:* "The Miller of Dee" *adapt* Stanley Myers. *Sd Rec* William Nallan, Charles Grenzbach. *Asst Dir* Terence Nelson. *Unit Prod Mgr* William W. Gray. *Wardrobe Supv* Theoni V. Aldredge, George Newman. *Miss Remick's & Miss Heckart's Clothes* Theoni V. Aldredge. *Makeup Supv* Robert O'Bradovich. *Hairstyle Supv* Ernest Adler. *Coöp* Lincoln Center for the Performing Arts.

Cast: Rod Steiger *(Christopher Gill),* Lee Remick *(Kate Palmer),* George Segal *(Morris Brummel),* Eileen Heckart *(Mrs. Brummel),* Murray Hamilton *(Inspector Haines),* Michael Dunn *(Mr. Kupperman),* Martine Bartlett *(Alma Mulloy),* Barbara Baxley *(Belle Poppie),* Irene Dailey *(Mrs. Fitts),* Doris Roberts *(Sylvia Poppie),* Ruth White *(Mrs. Himmel),* Val Bisoglio *(Detective Monaghan),* David Doyle *(Lieutenant Dawson),* Kim August *(Sadie),* Vincent Sardi *(himself),* Tom Ahearne *(priest),* Glenn Kezer *(policeman).*

Mystery drama. Source: William Goldman, *No Way To Treat a Lady* (New York, 1964). Christopher Gill, the wealthy and elegant owner of a Broadway theater, is a psychotic killer who uses his knowledge of disguise and impersonation to gain admittance into the homes of lonely middle-aged women. Once he has strangled them, the only clue left behind is a lipstick kiss painted on the victim's forehead. Police detective Morris Brummel remarks to the press that the murderer is extremely clever, and Gill responds with a telephone call acknowledging the compliment, thus beginning a series of bizarre conversations between the two men. The one bright aspect of the case is that Brummel has met and fallen in love with Kate Palmer, a young woman who spoke to Gill when he was disguised as an Irish priest. Brummel tells reporters that his opponent is obviously sexually disturbed, and Gill calls up to complain and inadvertently reveals an obsessive love for his mother, a famous actress who is now dead. In an attempt to trick the killer into revealing his identity, the police falsely report another "lipstick murder." His ego wounded, Gill telephones to protest and is kept talking long enough for the call to be traced. When he realizes that he has been tricked, Gill decides to get even with Brummel by murdering Kate. Posing as a caterer, he presents himself at Kate's apartment and announces that Brummel has sent over a surprise feast. Brummel arrives in time to save Kate, but Gill escapes to his theater, where he is finally trapped and shot down by Brummel. *Theater owners. Psychopaths. Detectives. Murder. Disguise. Imposture. Telephone. Oedipus complex. Publicity. Revenge. New York City—Broadway.*

Note: Location scenes filmed in New York City.

NOBI see **FIRES ON THE PLAIN**

NOBODY LOVES A DRUNKEN INDIAN see **FLAP**

NOBODY LOVES FLAPPING EAGLE see **FLAP**

NOBODY RUNS FOREVER see **THE HIGH COMMISSIONER**

NOBODY WAVED GOODBYE (Canada)   **F6.3525**
National Film Board of Canada. *Dist* Cinema V Distributing, Inc. 21 Apr **1965** [New York opening; c17 Aug 1964; LF01]. Sd; b&w. 35mm. 80 min.
Prod Roman Kroiter, Don Owen. *Exec Prod* Tom Daly, prod. *Dir-Writ* Don Owen. *Photog* John Spotton. *Film Ed* Donald Ginsberg, John Spotton. *Mus* Eldon Rathburn. *Sd* Roger Hart.

Cast: Peter Kastner *(Peter),* Julie Biggs *(Julie),* Claude Rae *(father),* Toby Tarnow *(sister),* Charmion King *(mother),* Ronald Taylor *(boyfriend),* Robert Hill, actor *(patrolman),* Jack Beer *(sergeant),* John Sullivan, Canadian *(probation officer),* Lynne Gorman *(Julie's mother),* Ivor Barry *(interviewer),* Sharon Bonin *(waitress),* Norman Ettlinger *(landlord),* John Vernon *(lot supervisor).*

Drama. Peter is an 18-year-old high school senior in a middle-class suburb of Toronto. Although his parents want him to attend college after graduation, Peter rebels against all authority; he skips school, gets arrested for reckless driving in a demonstrator car from his father's automobile agency, and is put on probation after spending a night in jail. His only confidante is his girl friend, Julie, who is more mature, even though she shares Peter's desire for more personal freedom. After a bitter argument with his mother, Peter moves into a roominghouse and begins working as an attendant in a parking lot, where his boss teaches him to shortchange the customers. Peter's parents insist that he return home, prepare himself for college, and stop seeing Julie—conditions which he cannot accept. Later, Julie leaves her parents, and when Peter asks his father to loan him the money to go away with her, he is refused. Angrily, Peter steals a car, and they drive off together. Realizing the implications of what he has done, Julie pleads to return and reveals that she is pregnant. Peter stops the car, lets her out, and drives on alone. *Students. Juvenile delinquents. Runaways. Adolescence. Filial relations. Theft. Employer-employee relations. Reckless driving. Pregnancy. Automobiles. Roominghouses. Automobile agencies. Toronto.*

Note: Released in Canada in 1964.

NOBODY'S PERFECT   **F6.3526**
Universal Pictures. Jan **1968** [Los Angeles showing: Feb; c3 Feb 1968; LP36897]. Sd (Westrex); col (Technicolor). 35mm (Techniscope). 103 min.
Prod Howard Christie. *Dir* Alan Rafkin. *Screenplay* John D. F. Black. *Dir Photog* Robert Wyckoff. *Art Dir* Alexander Golitzen, Alexander A. Mayer. *Set Decor* John McCarthy, Robert C. Bradfield. *Titl* Universal Title. *Film Ed* Gene Palmer. *Mus Supv* Joseph Gershenson. *Mus* Irving Gertz. *Sd* Waldon O. Watson, Ed Somers. *Asst Dir* George Bisk. *Unit Prod Mgr* Jim Paisley. *Ladies Cost* Rosemary Odell. *Makeup* Bud Westmore. *Hairstylist* Larry Germain. *Tech Adv* Bernard M. Hillman, Marcus G. Klein, United States Defense Department, United States Navy.

Cast: Doug McClure *(Doc Willoughby),* Nancy Kwan *(Tomiko Momoyama),* James Whitmore *(Mike Riley),* David Hartman *(Boats McCafferty),* Gary Vinson *(Walt Purdy),* James Shigeta *(Toshi O'Hara),* Steve Carlson *(Johnny Crane),* George Furth *(Hamner),* Keye Luke *(Gondai-San),* Jill Donahue *(Marci Adler),* Bea Bradley *(Lieutenant Large),* Jim Creech *(Mr. Bayless),* Jerry Fujikawa *(Watanabe),* Edward Faulkner *(John Abelard),* Marian Collier *(Terry Abelard),* Ella Edwards, Maida Severn.

Comedy. Source: Allan R. Bosworth, *The Crows of Edwina Hill* (New York, 1961). While on a drunken liberty in Japan, Doc Willoughby and a group of fellow sailors from the U. S. S. *Bustard*, a submarine rescue vessel, steal a statue of the Smiling Buddha and hide it in a cave. When the ship returns to Japan a few years later, Willoughby—now a chief petty officer—falls in love with Tommy, a pretty Japanese woman who is a U. S. Navy nurse. Restricted to his quarters for starting a barroom brawl, Willoughby convinces his captain, Mike Riley, that the ship is infested with cockroaches and that he should be permitted to go ashore for exterminating supplies. Once there, Willoughby learns from Tommy's uncle, Gondai-San, that his village has been plagued with bad luck ever since their Smiling Buddha disappeared years before. Recalling his drunken escapade, Willoughby retrieves the statue from the cave and arranges for a jeep to take it back to the village. En route, however, both the jeep and the statue roll over a cliff into the ocean. Another of Tommy's admirers, wealthy Japanese diver Toshi O'Hara, insists upon a rescue attempt, despite the stormy weather. When Toshi's life is endangered, Willoughby dons a diving suit to save him and radios the *Bustard* for help. Once the Smiling Buddha has been returned to its shrine, Willoughby is rewarded with a Navy medal—and Tommy's love. *Sailors. Nurses. Divers. Japanese. Drunkenness. Theft. Religious objects. Japan. United States Navy. Storms. Automobile accidents.*

Note: Prerelease title: *The Winning Position.*

NOBORIRYU TEKKAHADA *see* **THE FRIENDLY KILLER**

LA NOIA *see* **THE EMPTY CANVAS**

LA NOIRE DE ... *see* **BLACK GIRL**

NOITE VAZIA *see* **EROS**

NON TIRATE IL DIAVOLO PER LA CODA *see* **THE DEVIL BY THE TAIL**

NONE BUT THE BRAVE   F6.3527
Ken-San Productions. *Dist* Parallel Film Distributors. **1963**. Sd; b&w. 35mm. [Feature film, length unknown.]
Exec Prod Earl Podolnik, Wroe Owens. *Dir* Ken Richardson. *Screenplay* James E. McLarty. *Orig Story* Ken Richardson, Sandra Richardson. *Dir Photog* Ronald Perryman. *Film Ed* Ronald Perryman. *Sd* Ronald Perryman.
Cast: James E. McLarty *(patrol member).*
War melodrama. During World War II, two U. S. patrols are sent to destroy two German radar stations. The first unit accomplishes its goal and waits for the second unit before moving to the last German installation. When it becomes clear that the other U. S. patrol is not coming, it is left to the single unit to destroy the station. The lieutenant in charge of the unit refuses to order the attack because he believes it to be suicidal. After the lieutenant is killed, however, a sergeant leads the patrol on a successful assault on the radar station. *Combat zone life. World War II. United States Army. Germany—Army.*
Note: Filmed on location in and around Austin, Texas.

NONE BUT THE BRAVE (United States/Japan)   F6.3528
Tokyo Eiga Co.-Artanis Productions. *Dist* Warner Bros. Pictures. 11 Feb **1965** [Chicago opening; c27 Feb 1965; LP31748]. Sd; col (Technicolor). 35mm (Panavision). 105 min.
A Sinatra Enterprises Production. *Prod-Dir* Frank Sinatra. *Japanese Prod-Story* Kikumaru Okuda. *Assoc Prod* William H. Daniels. *Exec Prod* Howard W. Koch. *Screenplay* John Twist, Katsuya Suzaki. *Dir Photog* Harold Lipstein. *Art Dir* LeRoy Deane. *Art Adv* Haruyoshi Oshita. *Set Decor* George James Hopkins. *Film Ed* Sam O'Steen. *Mus Comp* Johnny Williams. *Mus Supv & Cond* Morris Stoloff. *Japanese Mus Adv* Kenjiro Hirose. *Sd* Stanley Jones. *Asst Dir* David Salven, Mitsushige Tsurushima. *Makeup Supv* Gordon Bau. *Makeup* Shu Uemura. *Sp Eff Dir* Eiji Tsuburaya. *Sp Eff* Toho Special Effects Group. *Tech Adv* Kazuo Inoue. *Coöp* United States Department of Defense, United States Marine Corps, United States Navy, Hawaiian National Guard. *Dial Coach* Thom Conroy, Satoshi Nakamura.
Cast—Japanese: Tatsuya Mihashi *(Lieutenant Kuroki),* Takeshi Kato *(Sergeant Tamura),* Homare Suguro *(Lance Corporal Hirano),* Kenji Sahara *(Corporal Fujimoto),* Masahiko Tanimura *(Lead. Private Ando),* Toru Ibuki *(Private Arikawa),* Ryucho Shunputei *(Private Okuda),* Hisao Dazai *(Private Tokumaru),* Susumu Kurobe *(Private Goro),* Takashi Inagaki *(Private Ishii),* Kenichi Hata *(Private Sato).*
Cast—Americans: Frank Sinatra *(Chief Pharmacist's Mate Maloney),* Clint Walker *(Capt. Dennis Bourke),* Tommy Sands *(2d Lieutenant Blair),* Brad Dexter *(Sergeant Bleeker),* Tony Bill *(Air Crewman Keller),* Sammy Jackson *(Corporal Craddock),* Richard Bakalyan *(Corporal Ruffino),* Rafer Johnson *(Private Johnson),* Jimmy Griffin *(Private Dexter),* Christopher Dark *(Private Searcy),* Don Dorrell *(Private Hoxie),* Phil Crosby *(Private Magee),* John Howard Young *(Private Waller),* Roger Ewing *(Private Swensholm),* Richard Sinatra *(Private Roth),* Laraine Stephens.

War drama. Isolated on a South Pacific island in World War II, a Japanese platoon with no radio equipment is joined by American marines whose plane crash-lands on the island. The marines' radio also is damaged. The two groups discover each other's presence on the island, and fighting breaks out between them. The Japanese control a freshwater spring the marines want to use; and when one of his men is seriously injured in the leg, Lieutenant Kuroki, in charge of the Japanese platoon, trades water, fish, and potatoes to the marines for the services of Chief Pharmacist's Mate Maloney, who successfully amputates the man's leg and thereby saves his life. A truce is arranged between the two factions with the condition that if either side again becomes part of the war, fighting will be resumed. All is peaceful until an incident sets the two groups in preparation to fight again, but a typhoon diverts attention to the need to save the water supply. The Americans' radio is repaired, and they learn that a U. S. ship is on the way. Captain Bourke, the marine leader, offers Lieutenant Kuroki surrender terms, but he refuses them because of the conditions of their original agreement. The warship arrives, and fighting resumes. All the Japanese are killed, and only five marines, including Bourke and Maloney, survive. Kuroki leaves his journal for Bourke to deliver to his widow. *Pharmacists. Amputation. Radio. World War II. South Sea Islands. United States Marines. Japan—Army. Typhoons. Airplane accidents.*
Note: Filmed on Kauai, Hawaii. Released in Japan in 1965 as *Yusha nomi.*

NORA INU *see* **STRAY DOG**

NORMA   F6.3529
Lima Productions. *Dist* Eve Productions, Emco Productions. Mar **1970**. Sd; col (Eastmancolor). 35mm. 77 min.
Prod William Christian. *Dir* Ted Roter. *Screenplay* Norma Stevens. *Dir Photog* Joe Bardo. *Asst Camera* K. Lemmon. *Mus* John Barber, mus. *Location Rec* George Eddy. *Post Prod Ed* Commercial Sound Recorders. *Prod Mgr* Burt Powers. *Tech Adv* Waco. *Paintings Courtesy of* Aaron Brothers. *Grip* Les Watson. *Sets & Props* L. Levin.
Cast: Mady Maguire *(Norma),* Chris Warfield *(Dr. Bradley),* Teresa Thaw *(car hop),* Valda Hansen *(roommate),* Art Metrano *(delivery man),* Robert Redding *(party queen),* Lilli Diamond *(hostess),* Beverly Carter *(nurse),* Harve Selsby *(cyclist),* Don Snyder *(Tommy),* Joe Sigmund *(Jimmy),* Buck Flower *(Mother),* Ted Roter *(theater manager).*
Drama. Based on a novel by: Norma Stevens. Norma Stevens, who at the age of 13 watched in horror as an assailant killed a boyfriend with whom she was about to make love, has become, at 23, a guilt-ridden nymphomaniac. She goes to Dr. Bradley, a psychiatrist, and tells him of her recent, disturbing sex experiences. *Her lovemaking with a delivery man is interrupted by the appearance of a strange man at the window. Later, she has sex with the manager of a sex exploitation movie theater, and the figure again appears.* Dr. Bradley dismisses Norma's fears as fantasy. Norma has a disappointing experience with a lesbian and is raped by a sadistic motorcyclist. She is taken on a date to a sex party, and the mysterious intruder again appears as she is making love with two men in an upstairs room. Dr. Bradley hypnotizes the distraught Norma, and she remembers the identity of the man who killed her boyfriend and realizes that he is the same man who has been stalking her. *Psychiatrists. Guilt. Nymphomania. Voyeurism. Murder. Lesbianism. Sadism. Rape. Group sex. Hypnotism. Troilism. Motion picture theaters. "Like It Is". "Shannon's Women".*
Note: Clips from *Like It Is* and *Shannon's Women* are used in the theater sequence.

NORSE ADVENTURE   F6.3530
25 Jan **1970** [Los Angeles showing]. Si; col. 35mm. ca120 min.
Pres by Exploramia. A *Film by* Hjordis Kittel Parker.
Travelog. A travel host describes the history of Norway, from the Ice Age to the present. Featured are the Bergen International Music Festival, the royal wedding of Crown Prince Harald and Sonja Haraldsen in 1968, the Spitsbergen archipelago, native Laplanders, Oslo, Telemark, and winter sports. *Royalty. Travel. Weddings. Sports. Norway. Bergen (Norway). Spitsbergen. Lapland. Oslo. Telemark.*
Note: Narration delivered live on stage.

NORWOOD   F6.3531
Paramount Pictures. 21 May **1970** [Dallas opening; c10 Apr 1970; LP37950]. Sd; col (Technicolor). 35mm. 95 min. *MPAA rating* G.
A Hal B. Wallis Production. *Prod* Hal B. Wallis. *Assoc Prod* Paul Nathan. *Dir* Jack Haley, Jr. *Screenplay* Marguerite Roberts. *Dir Photog (see note)* Robert Hauser, Vilis Lapenieks. *Art Dir* Walter Tyler. *Set Decor* Arthur Parker. *Ed Cons & Film Ed* Warren Low. *Film Ed* John W. Wheeler. *Mus Score & Cond* Al De Lory. *Orch* Gus Levene. *Songs:* "Ol' Norwood's Comin' Home," "Marie" Mitchell Torok, Ramona Redd. *Songs Sung by* Glen Campbell. *Songs:* "The Repo Man," "I'll Paint You a Song," "Norwood (Me and My Guitar)," "Down Home," "Everything a Man Could Ever Need" Mac Davis. *Songs Sung*

by Glen Campbell. *Instrumentals:* "Country Girl," "The Brass Ensemble of Ralph, Texas," "Hot Wheels," "The Fring Thing," "Chicken Out (Joann's Theme)," "A Different Kind of Rock" Al De Lory. *Song:* "Village Raga" Bill Plummer. *Song:* "Smoke on the Water" Earl Nunn, Zeke Clements. *Song:* "Rock of Ages" Thomas Hastings, A. M. Toplady. *Sd Rec* Barry Thomas, Elden Ruberg, Noell Bartlett. *Boom Op* Michael Mekjian. *1st & 2d Asst Dir* Gene Marum, Bill Poole. *Prod Mgr* William W. Gray. *Asst to the Prod* Dona Holloway. *Unit Prod Mgr* Frank Beetson, Jr. *Script Supv* Marvin Weldon. *Men's Cost* Luster Bayless. *Women's Cost* Agnes Henry. *Makeup* Jack Wilson, Ben Nye, Jr. *Body Makeup* Sue Bower. *Hairstyles* Sherry Wilson. *Sp Eff* Bob Dawson. *Constr Coörd* Buzz Newhouse. *Prop Master* Martin Pendleton. *Grip* John Hennessy. *Gaffer* Ross Maehl. *Casting Dir* Hoyt Bowers. *Still Photog* Frank Shugrue.

Cast: Glen Campbell (*Norwood Pratt*), Kim Darby (*Rita Lee Chipman*), Joe Namath (*Joe William Reese*), Carol Lynley (*Yvonne Phillips*), Pat Hingle (*Grady Fring*), Tisha Sterling (*Marie*), Dom De Luise (*Bill Bird*), Leigh French (*Vernell Bird*), Meredith MacRae (*Kay*), Sammy Jackson (*Wayne T. E. B. Walker*), Billy Curtis (*Edmund B. Ratner*), Merie Earle (*Grandma Whichcoat*), Jack Haley, Sr. (*Mr. Reese*), Jimmy Boyd (*Jeeter*), David Huddleston (*Uncle Lonnie*), Edith Atwater (*irate bus passenger*), Gil Lamb (*Mr. Remley*), Cass Daley (*Mrs. Remley*), Joe Oakie (*Tilmon Fring*), Virginia Capers (*Ernestine*), Jay Ripley (*Pete*).

Melodrama. Source: Charles Portis, *Norwood* (New York, 1966). Marine veteran Norwood Pratt returns to Ralph, Texas, to live with his sister Vernell and brother-in-law Bill Bird. Although his ambition is to be a country and western singer, Pratt resumes his life as a service station attendant. Offered a television audition in exchange for transporting two cars, Norwood accepts, hoping to collect in New York $70 owed him by Marine comrade Joe William Reese. En route companion Yvonne Phillips informs Pratt that the vehicles are stolen, and the pair is pursued by police. Abandoning the auto, the veteran hitchhikes to New York, only to find Reese departed to Old Carthage, Arkansas, and his apartment now occupied by hippie student Marie. Singing in a Greenwich Village coffeehouse, Norwood finds its patrons indifferent to his ballad about an auto repossessor. On a southbound bus he meets Rita Lee Chipman, whose destination is Jacksonville, North Carolina, where she hopes to marry Marine T. E. B. Walker. In Jacksonville, however, Walker rejects her proposal. Accompanied by midget Edmund B. Ratner and Joann the Wonder Hen, Rita Lee and Pratt travel to Old Carthage. While visiting Reese, Rita Lee informs Pratt that she is pregnant, but declines his offer of marriage. Upon returning to Ralph the friends are confronted by the indecisive Walker, who beats Pratt and departs with Rita Lee. As Pratt auditions, however, he espies Rita Lee returning, having realized her love for him. *Veterans. Filling station attendants. Singers. Brothers-in-law. Hippies. Students. Midgets. Pregnancy. Brother-sister relationship. Marriage. Coffeehouses. Buses. New York City—Greenwich Village. Texas. Arkansas. Jacksonville (North Carolina). United States Marines. Chickens.*

Note: Location scenes filmed in Corona and Lake Elsinore, California. Vilis Lapenicks was replaced as photographer during production. Copyright claimants: Hal B. Wallis and Joseph H. Hazen.

THE NOSE ON MY FACE see **THE MODEL MURDER CASE**

NOT FOR HONOR AND GLORY see **LOST COMMAND**

NOT MINE TO LOVE (Israel)   **F6.3532**
S. Y. V. Ltd. *Dist* Edward Meadow. 26 Mar **1969** [New York opening]. Sd; b&w. 35mm. 90 min.

Prod Amatsia Hiuni. *Dir* Uri Zohar. *Script* Uri Zohar, Amatsia Hiuni, David Gurfinkel, Dan Ben-Amotz. *Story* A. B. Yehoshua. *Photog* David Gurfinkel. *Film Ed* Jacques Erlich. *Mus* Dov Seltzer.

Cast: Oded Kotler (*Eli*), Shuy Osherov (*Shuy*), Judith Soleh (*Noa*), Misha Asherov (*Shuy's father*), Illy Gorlitzky (*Zvi*), Germaine Unikovsky (*Yael*), Stella Avni (*neighbor*), Baruch David (*neighbor's husband*), Shoshana Duer (*Yael's mother*), Nissan Yatir (*Yael's father*).

Melodrama. Eli, a young teacher in Jerusalem, receives a telephone call from Noa, a former girl friend, who asks him to look after her 3-year-old son, Shuy, for a few days. Recalling the night that he and Noa spent together in a kibbutz several years before, Eli consents to the request in the hope that it will rekindle their affair, even though his romantic life is already complicated by the fact that Yael, his current mistress, is also being pursued by his best friend, Zvi. When Shuy responds to his temporary guardian with warmth and affection, Eli finds himself speculating on the possibility that he is the child's father. His reaction to Shuy wavers between love and hate because the child is Noa's, but he cannot claim him as his own. When Noa avoids any contact during the 3 days that Eli cares for the boy, Eli gradually develops an acute hostility toward the child and places him in dangerous situations, even letting loose a poisonous snake in the room where Shuy is sleeping. After Zvi is nearly bitten by the snake, Eli regains

his balance and, realizing that the past cannot be recaptured, accepts the fact that Noa is lost to him. *Schoolteachers. Mistresses. Babysitters. Children. Jealousy. Parentage. Kibbutzim. Jerusalem. Snakes.*

Note: Produced in Israel in 1966 and released there as *Shlosha yamim ve yeled.* Also known as *Three Days and a Child.*

NOT ON YOUR LIFE (Italy/Spain)   **F6.3533**
Naga Films–Zebra Film. *Dist* Pathé Contemporary Films. 29 Mar **1965** [New York opening]. Sd; b&w. 35mm. 90 min.

Dir Luis García Berlanga. *Screenplay* Luis García Berlanga, Rafael Azcona, Ennio Flajano. *Story* Luis García Berlanga. *Photog* Tonino Delli Colli. *Art Dir* José Antonio de la Guerra. *Film Ed* Alfonso Santacana. *Mus* Miguel Asins-Arbó. *Asst Dir* Ricardo Muñoz Suay. *Prod Mgr* José Manuel M. Herrero.

Cast: Nino Manfredi (*José Luis*), Emma Penella (*Carmen*), José Luis López Vázquez (*Antonio*), Angel Alvarez (*Alvarez*), José Isbert (*Amedeo*), María Luisa Ponte (*Stefania*), Guido Alberti (*governor of prison*), Maruja Isbert (*Ignazia*), Félix Fernández (*1st sacristan*), Alfredo Landa (*2d sacristan*), José Luis Coll (*organist*), Julia Caba Alba, Xan Das Bolas, José Sazatornil, Lola Gaos, Chus Lampreabe.

Comedy. José Luis, an undertaker's assistant, is attracted to Carmen, the daughter of the local executioner, Amedeo. The couple decide to marry when Amedeo is awarded a new apartment; besides, Amedeo has already caught them in bed and Carmen is pregnant. Amedeo wishes to retire, but he must forfeit his new apartment if he retires from government service. Therefore José Luis reluctantly takes over his father-in-law's job, intending to resign at duty's first call. Several months later, José Luis is ordered to perform an execution on Majorca at Palma de Majorca. His first impulse is to resign, but he is dissuaded from resigning by Amedeo, who believes that the criminal will be reprieved because of the upcoming carnival, and by Carmen, who wants to enjoy a holiday at the vacation spot with her new baby. They all set off for a holiday, but the reprieve never comes through, and José Luis distastefully performs the grim task, later claiming to his family it will be his last, though Amedeo notes that that was his own reaction to his first execution. *Undertakers. Executioners. Fathers-in-law. Civil servants. Marriage. Employment. Capital punishment. Fraud. Retirement. Pregnancy. Housing. Majorca.*

Note: Opened in Madrid in Feb 1964 as *El verdugo;* Italian title: *La ballata del boia.* Original running time: 110 min.

NOT ON YOUR LIFE see **ISLAND OF LOVE**

NOT RECONCILED, OR "ONLY VIOLENCE HELPS WHERE IT RULES" (West Germany)   **F6.3534**
Straub-Huillet. *Dist* New Yorker Films. 23 Feb **1969** [New York opening]. Sd; b&w. 35mm. 51 min.

Prod-Writ Jean-Marie Straub, Danièle Huillet. *Dir* Jean-Marie Straub. *Dir Photog* Wendelin Sachtler. *Camera Op* Gerhard Ries, Christian Schwarzwald, Jean-Marie Straub. *Lighting* R. Iblherr, D. Kein. *Film Ed* Jean-Marie Straub, Danièle Huillet. *Mus: Sonata for Two Pianos and Percussion* Béla Bartók. *Suite no. 2 in B minor, BWV 1067* Johann Sebastian Bach. *Mus Cond* François Louis. *Sd* Lutz Grübnau, Willi Hanspach. *Sd Mix* Paul Schöler, Aventin München. *Prod Supv* Danièle Huillet. *Prod Asst* Max Dietrich Willutzki, Uschi Fritsche. *Tech* Herbert Martin. *Tech Asst* Charlie Putzgruber, Hartmut Koldeway, Wilhelm Eschweiler.

Cast: Heinrich Hargesheimer (*Heinrich Fähmel, aged 80*), Carlheinz Hargesheimer (*Heinrich Fähmel, aged 30-35*), Martha Ständner (*Johanna Fähmel, aged 70*), Danièle Straub (*Johanna Fähmel as a young woman*), Henning Harmssen (*Robert Fähmel, aged 40*), Ulrich Hopmann (*Robert Fähmel, aged 18*), Joachim Weiler (*Joseph Fähmel*), Eva-Maria Bold (*Ruth Fähmel*), Hiltraud Wegener (*Marianne*), Ulrich von Thüna (*Schrella, aged about 35*), Ernst Kutzinski (*Schrella, aged 15*), Heiner Braun (*Nettlinger, aged 35-40*), Georg Zander (*Hugo/Ferdinand Progulske*), Erika Brühl (*Edith*), Werner Brühl (*Trischler*), Heljo Brühl (*Frau Trischler*), Lutz Grübnau (*1st abbot*), Martin Trieb (*2d abbot*), Karl Bodenschatz (*hotel porter*), Wendelin Sachtler (*Mull*), Anita Bell (*old woman playing cards*), Margrit Borstel (*blonde knitting stockings*), Eduard von Wickenburg (*M*), Huguette Sellen (*Robert's secretary*), Jochem Grüner, Günter Göbel, Peter Berger, Klaus Weyer, Eberhard Ellrich, Norbert Pritz, Bernd Wagner, Michael Krüger, Joseph Vollmert, Dieter Hornberg, Egbert Meiers, Ralf Kurth, Jürgen Beier, Michael Holy, Engelbert Greis, Wolfgang Kück, Herbert Gammersbach, Rolf Buhl, Peter Kneip, Gerd Lenze, Erdmann Dortschy, Piero Poli, Diana Schlesinger, Karin Kraus, Claudia Wurm, Frouwke von Herwynen, Ise Maassen, Dagmar von Netzer, Hartmut Kirchner, Jürgen Kraeft, Achim Wurm, Max Dietrich Willutzki, Hannelore Langhoff, Johanna Odry, Günther Becker, Willy Bruno Wange, Stefan Odry, Paul Esser, Hans Zander, Walter Brenner, Rudolf Thome, Claudio Domberger, Hans Schönberger, Karsten Peters, Kai A. Niemeyer, Franz Menzel, Kim Sachtler, Walter Talman-Gros, Joe Hembus, Max Zihlmann, Maurie Fischbein, Christel Meuser, Kathrin Bold, Annie Lautner,

Johannes Buzalski, Gottfried Bold, Victor von Halem, Beate Speith.

Domestic drama. Source: Heinrich Böll, *Billard um halbzehn* (Cologne, 1959). Reunited in Cologne in 1956, three generations of the Fähmel family reminisce. Among their memories are the deaths of two children of the matriarch Johanna and her husband Heinrich during the Great War, Johanna's subsequent arrest for slandering the kaiser, and her intermittent incarceration in mental institutions. Also remembered are the death of the couple's Nazi son Otto during World War II, the flight of their student son Robert to Amsterdam after conspiring with classmates Schrella and Progulske to kill the fascist teacher Vacano, Robert's subsequent repatriation, and his demolition of Heinrich's architectural masterpiece, the Abbey of St. Anthony, as a protest against war. During the celebration of Heinrich's 80th birthday, Johanna states her intention of slaying Vacano at a military parade, but is dissuaded by her husband, who suggests instead the assassination of a prominent minister. Following her abortive attempt on the bureaucrat's life, Heinrich reassures his family that Johanna will escape punishment because of her psychiatric history. *Grandparents. Architects. Students. Expatriates. Veterans. Nazis. Family life. Insanity. Death. Assassination. Abbeys. World War I. World War II. Cologne. Amsterdam.*

Note: Filmed on location in Cologne and Munich. First shown in West Germany in Jul 1965 at the Berlin Film Festival as *Nicht versöhnt oder "Es hilft nur Gewalt, wo Gewalt herrscht"*; running time: 53 min. Shown at the 1965 New York Film Festival as *Unreconciled.* Forms one segment of *Three by Jean-Marie Straub,* q. v. Danièle Straub and Danièle Huillet are the same person.

NOT SO QUIET DAYS see QUIET DAYS IN CLICHY

NOT WANTED see STREETS OF SIN

NOT WITH MY WIFE, YOU DON'T!   F6.3535
Fernwood Productions–Reynard Productions. *Dist* Warner Bros. Pictures. 2 Nov **1966** [New York opening; c19 Nov 1966; LP36585]. Sd; col (Technicolor). 35mm. 118 min.

A Norman Panama Production. *Prod-Dir* Norman Panama. *Assoc Prod* Joel Freeman. *Screenplay* Norman Panama, Larry Gelbart, Peter Barnes. *Story* Norman Panama, Melvin Frank. *Dir Photog* Charles Lang. *European Photog* Paul Beeson. *Set Decor* George James Hopkins. *Prod Dsgn* Edward Carrere. *Titl & Vis Consult* Saul Bass & Associates. *Film Ed* Aaron Stell. *Mus Comp & Cond* Johnny Williams. *Mus:* "A Big, Beautiful Ball," "My Inamorata" Johnny Williams. *Lyr* Johnny Mercer. *Choreog* Shelah Hackett. *Sd* Stanley Jones. *Asst Dir* Jack Aldworth. *Miss Lisi's Wardrobe Dsgn* Edith Head. *Makeup Supv* Gordon Bau. *Supv Hairstylist* Jean Burt Reilly. *Aviation Liaison* Hamish Mahaddie, (Group Capt.).

Cast: Tony Curtis (*Tom Ferris*), Virna Lisi (*Julie Ferris*), George C. Scott ("*Tank*" *Martin*), Carroll O'Connor (*General Parker*), Richard Eastham (*General Walters*), Eddie Ryder (*Sergeant Gilroy*), George Tyne (*Sergeant Dogerty*), Ann Doran (*Doris Parker*), Donna Danton (*Nurse Sally Ann*), Natalie Core (*Lillian Walters*), Buck Young (*air police colonel*), Maurice Dallimore (*BBC commentator*), Robert Cleaves ("*Time*" *reporter*), Karla Most (*Italian maid*), Betty Bresler (*Miss Ephron*), Alfred Shelley (*bartender*).

Comedy. London-based Col. Tom Ferris is so absorbed in his duties of making life comfortable for Air Force and civilian dignitaries that he neglects his beautiful Italian wife, Julie. But things change abruptly with the arrival of Col. Tank Martin, Tom's Korean War buddy. Tom has good reason to be jealous of the girl-chasing Tank because years before both of them fell in love with Julie and Tom won out only by convincing Julie that Tank was killed in action. Delighted to be reunited with Julie and eager to repay an old debt, Tank uses his influence to have Tom shipped to Labrador for an Arctic survival course. But when Tom learns that Julie is planning to divorce him and is in Rome with Tank, he abandons his post, steals a jet plane, masquerades as an Arab potentate, and eventually makes his way to Rome. Tank, however, persuades Tom he has no intention of changing his single status, and Julie is only too anxious to kiss and reconcile. Two years later, Julie, who loves everything in pairs, gives birth to twin boys while Tom continues making life easy for military V.I.P.'s, Brig. Gen. Tank Martin included. *Americans in foreign countries. Italians. Bachelors. Arabs. Twins. Marriage. Friendship. Jealousy. Divorce. Infidelity. Theft. Disguise. Airplanes—Jet. London. Labrador. Rome. United States Air Force.*

NOTHING BARRED see TWO-WAY STRETCH

NOTHING BUT A MAN   F6.3536
DuArt Film Laboratories. *Dist* Cinema V Distributing, Inc. 27 Nov **1964** [New York opening]. Sd; b&w. 35mm. 92 min. [Cut from 95 min.]

Prod Robert Young, Michael Roemer, Robert Rubin. *Assoc Prod* Irwin Young. *Dir* Michael Roemer. *Screenplay* Michael Roemer, Robert Young. *Photog* Robert Young. *Film Ed* Luke Bennett. *Asst Ed* Robert Machover. *Mus Writ & Sung by* Mary Wells, The Gospel Stars, Martha and the Vandellas, The

Miracles, Eddie Holland, Brian Holland, Lamont Dozier, Little Stevie Wonder, The Marvelettes, Wilbur Kirk. *Sd* Robert Rubin, Albert Gramaglia. *Prod Mgr* William Rhodes. *Cost* Nancy Ruffing.

Cast: Ivan Dixon (*Duff Anderson*), Abbey Lincoln (*Josie Dawson*), Gloria Foster (*Lee*), Julius Harris (*Will Anderson*), Martin Priest (*driver*), Leonard Parker (*Frankie*), Yaphet Kotto (*Jocko*), Stanley Greene (*Reverend Dawson*), Helen Lounck (*Effie Simms*), Helene Arrindell (*Doris*), Walter Wilson (*car owner*), Milton Williams (*Pop*), Melvin Stewart (*Raddick*), Alfred Puryear (*Barney*), Charles McRae (*Joe*), Ed Rowan (*Willie*), Tom Ligon, William Jordan, actor (*teenagers*), Gertrude Jeanette (*Mrs. Dawson*), Richard Webber (*Bud Ellis*), Eugene Wood (*schoolteacher*), Jim Wright (*bartender*), Jary Banks (*Bessie*), Dorothy Hall, Gil Rogers, Arland Schubert, Bill Riola, Pater Carew, Jay Brooks, Richard Ward, Moses Gunn, Sylvia Ray, Esther Rolle, Esther Davis, Jim Wright.

Drama. Duff Anderson, a Negro railroad worker, meets Josie Dawson, a Baptist minister's daughter, at a church social in an Alabama town. They fall in love in spite of Anderson's unwillingness to accept responsibility and in spite of Josie's middle-class father's objections to Anderson. They go to nearby Birmingham, and there Anderson visits his father, a sick, bad-tempered alcoholic who owes his life to Lee, the woman who lives with him. Anderson also visits his illegitimate son, who has been deserted by his mother and left with a woman who is reluctantly taking care of him. Anderson and Josie marry, and although Josie wants the child to join them, Anderson refuses. He takes a job in a sawmill but is fired because he will not defer to his bigoted white employers; he advises the other millhands to organize a union. His father-in-law helps him get a job in a filling station, but vigilantes threaten to wreck the station unless he leaves. Frustrated, Anderson strikes out at his pregnant wife, claiming she does not know what it is like to be a Negro because she has never had to live like one. Once more he visits his father, watches him die, and observes Lee's terrible loneliness. Finally, he takes his son and returns home to Josie, determined to raise his family in dignity and peace. *Railroad workers. Clergymen. Mill workers. Southerners. Fathers-in-law. Vigilantes. Negro life. Filial relations. Alcoholism. Illegitimacy. Marriage. Racial prejudice. Employer-employee relations. Pregnancy. Pride. Sawmills. Filling stations. Alabama. Birmingham (Alabama).*

Note: Location scenes filmed in Georgia, Alabama, Mississippi, Maryland, and New Jersey.

NOTHING BUT THE BEST (Great Britain)   F6.3537
Domino Productions. *Dist* Royal Films International. 13 Jul **1964** [New York opening; c1 Apr 1964; LP30013]. Sd; col (Eastman Color). 35mm. 99 min.

Prod David Deutsch. *Assoc Prod* George Willoughby. *Dir* Clive Donner. *Screenplay* Frederic Raphael. *Photog* Nicolas Roeg. *Art Dir* Reece Pemberton. *Set Decor* Helen Thomas. *Main Titl* James Baker. *Film Ed* Fergus McDonell. *Mus Comp & Cond* Ron Grainer. *Titl Song* Frederic Raphael, Ron Grainer. *Sung by* Millicent Martin. *Sd Rec* Robert Allen, Len Abbott. *Asst Dir* Peter Price. *Asst to the Dir* Miriam Brickman.

Cast: Alan Bates (*Jimmy Brewster*), Denholm Elliott (*Charlie Prince*), Harry Andrews (*Mr. Horton*), Millicent Martin (*Ann Horton*), Pauline Delany (*Mrs. March*), Godfrey Quigley (*Coates*), Alison Leggatt (*Mrs. Brewster*), Lucinda Curtis (*Nadine*), Nigel Stock (*Ferris*), James Villiers (*Hugh*), Drewe Henley (*Denis*), Avice Landon (*Mrs. Horton*), Ernest Clark (*Roberts*), William Rushton (*Gerry*), Peter Madden (*ex-politician*), Robert Bruce (*Basil*), Howard Lang (*Jutson*), Paul Curran (*Mr. Brewster*), Joe Levine (*taxi driver*), Donald Pickering (*Adrian Slater*), Joanna Morris (*Jimmy's secretary*), June Watts (*waitress*), Angus MacKay (*clergyman*), Diane Appleby (*secretary*), Bernard Levin (*himself*).

Farce. Source: Stanley Ellin, "The Best of Everything," in *Ellery Queen's Mystery Magazine* (Nov 1952). Jimmy Brewster, a young and excessively ambitious English real estate clerk, is determined to climb to the top of the social ladder. To improve himself, he moves a seedy character, Charlie Prince, into his lodgings and receives from Charlie a quick course in proper manners, speech, and behavior. Then, with calculated charm and strategy, he makes rapid progress both in his job and with his boss's daughter, Ann Horton. Though Ann is perceptive enough to see Jimmy as a ruthless opportunist, she encourages his advances simply because he is more desirable than her other suitors. Charlie wins at the racetrack and, suddenly financially independent, threatens to expose Jimmy as a fraud. Jimmy strangles Charlie with Charlie's own school tie, stows the body in a trunk, and, assisted by his amorous landlady, Mrs. March, hides the trunk in the basement. Jimmy then becomes a partner in his firm and marries Ann; but returning from his honeymoon, he discovers that Mrs. March's house is being demolished (the landlady herself has departed for South Africa). Jimmy watches as the house crumbles and wonders whether Charlie's corpse will be discovered. *Real estate agents. Opportunists. Landladies. Social climbers. Courtship. Etiquette. Fraud. Murder.*

Honeymoons.

Note: Opened in London in Feb 1964.

NOTORIOUS BIG SIN CITY *see* BIG SIN CITY

THE NOTORIOUS CLEOPATRA   F6.3538

Global Pictures. *Dist* Boxoffice International Pictures. Mar 1970. Sd; col (Eastman Color). 35mm. 88 min.

Pres by Harry Novak. *Prod-Dir* A. P. Stootsberry. *Screenplay* Jim Macher. *Photog* Dwayne Rayven. *Asst Camera* Ken Stewart. *Light Dir* Phil Zippo. *Art Dir* Earl Marshall. *Asst Art Dir* Sandy Root. *Ed* Dwayne Rayven. *Mus Score* Vic Lance. *Sd Mixer* Paul Hunt. *Asst Dir* Tony Rand. *Prod Coörd* James Brand. *Prod Mgr* Bethel Buckalew. *Script Girl* Pam Eddy. *Cost* Logan Costumes. *Cost Coörd* Sandy Root. *Makeup* Ray Sebastian. *Grip-Electrn* Dick Osmun. *Boom Op* Mike Franklin. *Prop* Jim Andrian. *Still Photog* William Rotsler.

Cast: Sonora *(Cleopatra)*, Johnny Rocco *(Mark Antony)*, Jay Edwards *(Caesar)*, Dixie Donovan *(Charmian)*, Mason Bakman *(Enobarbus)*, Christopher Stone *(Demetrius)*, Michael Cheal *(Cicero)*, Ron Smith *(Lepius)*, Woody Lee *(Cassius)*, Tom Huorn *(Brutus)*, Tai Hamilton *(high priest)*, James Brand *(centurion)*, Bobby Love *(devil dancer)*, Joe Pepi *(auctioneer)*, Jess White *(dungeon guard)*, Frank James *(messenger)*, Tommy Davis *(nubian guard)*.

Melodrama. Caesar, bored with the women of his country, is informed by his eunuch Cicero of the beautiful, dark princess of the Nile, Cleopatra. Caesar dispatches his trusted general Mark Antony to bring her to Rome, warning him that she is not to be molested in transit. Antony, with his two lieutenants Enobarbus and Demetrius, departs for Egypt. Despite Caesar's warning, Antony and Cleopatra become lovers. The evening of Antony's arrival, Cleopatra and her lady-in-waiting, Charmian, initiate the three Romans into their cult of love during the sacrifice of a virgin. An orgy follows as the assembled crowd pays homage with their bodies to the god of love. In the morning, a messenger arrives from Caesar bringing news that there is war in the capital and that Mark Antony is to return at once. Cleopatra, abandoned by Antony, finds solace in Charmian's kisses. Cleopatra then decides that she will follow Antony to Rome and destroy Caesar. She arrives in Rome and proceeds to seduce Caesar, only to be seen by Enobarbus. Antony, upon hearing this news, orders that Cleopatra be thrown into the dungeon. Charmian, disguised as a love goddess, seduces the guards and frees Cleopatra. They flee to Egypt. The Roman senators in the meantime plot the overthrow of Caesar and stab him to death on the steps of the senate. The senators then make Antony the scapegoat for their crime, forcing him to flee to Egypt. Despite Cleopatra's navy, Antony is defeated at sea. Enobarbus and Demetrius, foreseeing Antony's imminent defeat, switch their allegiance and proceed to loot Cleopatra's palace. Enobarbus finds Cleopatra and rapes her. Antony discovers them and murders both of them in a jealous rage. As two Roman centurians appear to take him to trial for murder and treason, he commits suicide with his dagger out of grief for Cleopatra. *Human sacrifice. Bisexuality. Perfidy. Assassination. Treason. Rape. Suicide. Orgies. Rome. Gaius Julius Caesar. Mark Antony. Cleopatra.*

THE NOTORIOUS CONCUBINES *see* THE CONCUBINES

THE NOTORIOUS DAUGHTER OF FANNY HILL   F6.3539

F-S & P Productions-Permax Enterprises. *Dist* Sonney Amusement Enterprises, Fantasy Films, David F. Friedman. 4 Jan 1966 [c28 Jan 1966; LP32212]. Sd; col. 35mm. 74 min.

Prod Bradford Hallworth. *Dir* Peter Stootsberry. *Orig Screenplay* Jim Markham. *Photog (see note)* Leslie Kovacs, Dino Grennell, Lee Ganther, Art Radford. *Mus* Chet More, Sam Brown. *Still Photog* William Rotsler, David McDaniel.

Cast: Stacey Walker *(Miss Kissy Hill)*, James Brand *(The Orgymaster)*, Orlando Fenwick *(Count de Sade)*, Ora Kittle *(Duke of Roxbury)*, Ginger Hale *(Meg)*, Lydia Farrell *(Beth)*, John Andrews *(peasant)*, Tony Sarcone *(Sir Philip)*, Tom Duncan *(Miss Hill's lackey)*, Leigh Cochran *(Duchess of Roxbury)*, William Rotsler *(Sir Alec)*, Frank Coe, Bill Markey, Earl Marshall.

Sex film. Kissy Hill, Fanny's daughter, caters to an exclusive upper-class clientele, including knights, counts, and dukes, as she follows in her mother's footsteps as a prostitute. Born in a London bordello, she has grown up with a businesswoman's attitude toward her profession, scorning false modesty and sentimentality. Her one small slip is an act of charity toward a husky peasant. The Duke of Roxbury, a regular patron at Kissy's establishment, joins her in the erotic delights of a lusty feast before proceeding to other pleasures. The Count de Sade is another client who finds his needs expertly served at Kissy's. Kissy dons black boots and gloves and beats the Count until he climaxes. Kissy is bathing following an orgy when the jealous Duchess of Roxbury, a lesbian, brings the thriving enterprise to an untimely conclusion by murdering the young woman of pleasure. *Prostitutes. Nobility. Upper classes. Sadomasochism. Murder. Flagellation. Lesbianism. Jealousy. Whorehouses.*

Orgies. London. Fanny Hill. Donatien Alphonse François [Marquis de] Sade.

Note: Permax Enterprises is copyright claimant. Sources conflict in crediting photography.

THE NOTORIOUS LANDLADY   F6.3540

Kohlmar-Quine Production Co. *Dist* Columbia Pictures. 27 Jun 1962 [Chicago opening; c27 Jun 1962; LP22246]. Sd (RCA); b&w. 35mm. 123 min.

Prod Fred Kohlmar. *Dir* Richard Quine. *Screenplay* Larry Gelbart, Blake Edwards. *Dir Photog* Arthur Arling. *Art Dir* Cary Odell. *Set Decor* Louis Diage. *Film Ed* Charles Nelson. *Mus* George Duning. *Orch* Arthur Morton. *Background Mus:* "I Am the Very Model of a Modern Major-General" William S. Gilbert, Arthur Sullivan. *Sd Supv* Charles J. Rice. *Sd* Josh Westmoreland. *Asst Dir* Carter DeHaven, Jr., Burt Astor. *Location Mgr* Hal Fisher. *Script Supv* Esther Stephenson. *Miss Novak's Gowns* Kim Novak. *Gowns Executed by* Elizabeth Courtney. *Makeup* Ben Lane, Harry Ray. *Hairstyles* Maudlee McDougall. *Sp Eff* David Koehler. *Still Photog* Mel Traxel.

Cast: Kim Novak *(Carlye Hardwicke)*, Jack Lemmon *(William Gridley)*, Fred Astaire *(Franklyn Ambruster)*, Lionel Jeffries *(Inspector Oliphant)*, Estelle Winwood *(Mrs. Dunhill)*, Maxwell Reed *(Miles Hardwicke)*, Philippa Bevans *(Mrs. Brown)*, Henry Daniell *(stranger)*, Ronald Long *(coroner)*, Richard Peel *(Dillings)*, Doris Lloyd *(Lady Fallott)*, Florence Wyatt *(Ambruster's secretary)*, Frederic Worlock *(elderly colonel)*, Dick Crockett *(Carstairs)*, Scott Davey *(Henry)*, Jack Livesey *(counsel)*, Tom Dillon *(coroner's officer)*, Benno Schneider *(man)*, Carter DeHaven, Sr. *(old man)*, Cecil Weston *(woman)*.

Comedy melodrama. Source: Margery Sharp, "The Notorious Tenant," in *Collier's* (3 Feb 1956). Young Bill Gridley, an American State Department official, is transferred to London, and he rents a room in a stately old town house belonging to American Carlye Hardwicke. The next day he learns from his superior, Franklyn Ambruster, that Scotland Yard suspects Carlye of having murdered her husband, a Britisher who is reported to be missing. Bill refuses to believe the accusation, though he reluctantly agrees to spy on his beautiful landlady. Then one night, he hears sounds of a scuffle and races into Carlye's room to find her holding a revolver over the lifeless body of her husband. At the coroner's inquest, Carlye is vindicated by the testimony of Agatha Brown, a private nurse who cares for Carlye's crippled next door neighbor, Mrs. Dunhill. The nurse claims that she saw Carlye struggling with her husband and that the murder was committed in self-defense. What she does not tell the court is that the husband had become enraged when he discovered that Carlye had innocently pawned a candelabra in which he had hidden a number of stolen jewels. Following the trial, Mrs. Brown murders the pawnbroker, obtains the jewels, and goes to a seaside resort to kill old Mrs. Dunhill, who also knows about the jewels. Carlye and Bill learn of Mrs. Brown's intent and take frantic pursuit. Mrs. Brown pushes Mrs. Dunhill's wheelchair down a winding cliff edge, but Bill makes a wild dash and catches it just in time. A flying tackle by Carlye subdues Mrs. Brown as Ambruster and Scotland Yard's Inspector Oliphant arrive on the scene by helicopter. *Landladies. Americans in foreign countries. Spies. Nurses. Cripples. Neighbors. Pawnbrokers. Justifiable homicide. Murder. Theft. Eavesdropping. Jewels. Trials. London. Scotland Yard. United States—State Department. Chases.*

LA NOTTE (France/Italy)   F6.3541

Nepi Film-Sofitedip-Silver Films. *Dist* Lopert Pictures. 19 Feb 1962 [New York opening; c22 Feb 1962; LP21952]. Sd; b&w. 35mm. 120 min.

Prod Emanuele Cassuto. *Dir* Michelangelo Antonioni. *Story-Screenplay* Michelangelo Antonioni, Ennio Flajano, Tonino Guerra. *Dir Photog* Gianni Di Venanzo. *Art Dir* Piero Zuffi. *Film Ed* Eraldo Da Roma. *Mus* Giorgio Gaslini and His Quartette. *Sd* Claudio Maielli. *Asst Dir* Franco Indovina. *Prod Mgr* Paolo Frasca. *English Subtitl* Rose Sokol.

Cast: Jeanne Moreau *(Lidia)*, Marcello Mastroianni *(Giovanni)*, Monica Vitti *(Valentina Gerardini)*, Bernhard Wicki *(Tommaso)*, Rosi Mazzacurati *(Resy)*, Maria Pia Luzi *(nymphomaniac)*, Vincenzo Corbella *(Gerardini)*, Gitt Magrini *(Signora Gerardini)*, Giorno Negro *(Roberto)*, Guido Aimone Marsan *(Fanti)*, Roberta Speroni *(Beatrice)*, Vittorio Bertolini, Ugo Fortunati, Pompiani.

Drama. After 10 years, the marriage of Lidia and Giovanni has become empty and meaningless; their only bond is mutual lethargy. Late one afternoon they visit a dying friend, Tommaso, in a Milan hospital. Distressed by the thought of death, Lidia leaves his bedside and weeps in anguish. When Giovanni rejoins her, he confesses that he allowed himself to be seduced by a nymphomaniacal patient in the hospital. Lidia, however, remains unmoved by the confession. They then attend a cocktail party celebrating the publication of Giovanni's latest book. Bored with the pseudo-sophisticated guests, Lidia steals away and wanders through the city, observing with fascination and revulsion the life around her. At dusk she telephones Giovanni from a park and asks him to pick her up. Back home, she tries but fails to reawaken Giovanni's sexual desires, and then she suggests they go to a nightclub. After watching an erotic dance, they attend a party given by a millionaire who wants Giovanni to become his director of literary publicity. While at the party, Lidia calls the hospital and learns that Tommaso has died. As she watches Giovanni unashamedly pursuing Valentina Gerardini, the millionaire's daughter, Lidia's despair drives her to flirt with a young playboy; but she is soon bored and returns to her husband, whose pursuit of Valentina proved fruitless. At dawn they leave the party, and Lidia reads Giovanni a love letter he wrote years before. He fails to recognize it and is suddenly forced to face the shallowness of his life. He tries to rekindle their love by making advances to Lidia; at first she resists, but gradually she yields. *Authors. Dancers. Millionaires. Playboys. Socialites. Marriage. Seduction. Nymphomania. Infidelity. Death. Hospitals. Nightclubs. Milan.*

Note: Filmed on location in Milan. Released in Italy in Feb 1961; in France as *La nuit* in Feb 1961. Also known as *The Night.*

LA NOTTE BRAVA (France/Italy)   F6.3542

Ajace Cinematografica–Franco London Film. *Dist* Miller Producing Company, Medallion Pictures. 24 Jan **1962** [New York opening]. Sd; b&w. 35mm. 96 min. [Reduced to ca85 min.]

Prod Antonio Cervi, Alessandro Jacovoni. *Exec Prod* Sante Chimirri. *Dir* Mauro Bolognini. *Story-Screenplay* Pier Paolo Pasolini. *Dial-Adapt* Jacques-Laurent Bost. *Dir Photog* Armando Nannuzzi. *Camera Op* Marcello Gatti. *Art Dir* Carlo Egidi. *Film Ed* Nino Baragli. *Mus* Piero Piccioni. *Asst Dir* Rinaldo Ricci. *Prod Mgr* Vittorio Glori Musy. *Set Mgr* Renato De Pasqualis. *English Lang Vers* (see note) Miller-King Productions.

Cast: Elsa Martinelli *(Anna)*, Antonella Lualdi *(Supplizia)*, Jean-Claude Brialy *(Scintillone)*, Laurent Terzieff *(Ruggeretto)*, Franco Interlenghi *(Bella-Bella)*, Anna Maria Ferrero *(Nicoletta)*, Mylène Demongeot *(Laura)*, Rosanna Schiaffino *(Rossana)*, Tomas Milian *(Achille)*, Marcella Valeri *(Rossana's mother)*.

Drama. Ruggeretto, Scintillone, and Bella-Bella, three indolent young cynics, steal some rifles and pick up two prostitutes on their way to a "fence" on the outskirts of Rome. During the transaction, they pick up a third prostitute who wants a ride back to the city. En route, the youths stop the car, take the women into the woods for the afternoon, and then leave without paying them. They soon discover, however, that one of the women has stolen all their money. Back in Rome, the companions attempt to steal a movie camera from an automobile and get into a brawl with its occupants, three wealthy homosexuals who then treat them to an evening of drinking. At the apartment of one of their newfound friends, Achille, the inquisitive Ruggeretto wanders into a bedroom and finds Laura. He seduces her, although he is unsure whether she is Achille's sister or the maid. Bella-Bella then steals his host's wallet, and the three hoodlums race from the apartment. As Bella-Bella and Ruggeretto argue over the money, Scintillone picks up the wallet and skulks off. He meets an old flame, Rossana, and promises her a night on the town, but he creates a disturbance at a posh restaurant and is led away to jail. Ruggeretto arrives on the scene, grabs the wallet, and takes Rossana to the most expensive club in Rome. When morning comes, he crumples his last bill and tosses it over the side of a bridge. *Hoodlums. Prostitutes. Fences (for stolen goods). Youth. Male homosexuality. Urban life. Perfidy. Seduction. Theft. Wealth. Nightclubs. Rome.*

Note: Released in Italy in 1959; running time: 105 min. Released in Paris in Jan 1961 as *Les garçons.* Also known as *On Any Street.* Re-released in 1965 by Medallion Pictures as *Bad Girls Don't Cry.* English language version credited as a Miller-King production.

LA NOTTE DELLE SPIE *see* **NIGHT ENCOUNTER**

NOTTE EROTICA *see* **NIGHT OF LUST**

LE NOTTI BIANCHE *see* **WHITE NIGHTS**

NOTTI CALDE D'ORIENTE *see* **ORIENT BY NIGHT**

99 DONNE *see* **99 WOMEN**

99 MUJERES *see* **99 WOMEN**

LA NOVICE *see* **RITA**

NOW *see* **THE EMBRACERS**

NOW CINEMA!   F6.3543

Grove Press. 9 Apr **1968** [New York showing]. Sd; b&w with col seq. 35mm. 114 min.

Anthology. This film includes "Rite of Love and Death," "Malcolm X: Struggle for Freedom," "Super Artist, Andy Warhol," "Film," "The Game," and "Psychomontage."

NOW I LAY ME DOWN *see* **RACHEL, RACHEL**

NOW IT CAN BE TOLD *see* **THE SECRET DOOR**

NÓŻ W WODZIE *see* **KNIFE IN THE WATER**

THE NUDE AND THE PRUDE   F6.3544

Dist Emerson Film Enterprises. 22 Aug **1969** [Champaign, Illinois, showing]. Sd; col. 35mm. 65 min.

Comedy. Warned by his mother of the evils of sex, Harry Truehart goes off to college. He shuns the attentions of campus co-eds and even chides his teacher, Miss Gardner, a nudist, for her behavior. The dean, concerned about Harry's "arrested" development, writes to the boy's mother. Harry's playboy father comes to the school and spies through a telescope on Miss Gardner and the college president's daughter as they sunbathe in the nude. Later, he arranges to join them on a double date with his son and accepts their invitation to a nudist camp. Once the barrier of inhibition is overcome, all savor the joys of nudism. Harry's mother arrives to storm the gates of the camp, but she at last sheds her clothes and joins the fun. In the end, Harry and the president's daughter fall in love. *Students. Deans. Playboys. College teachers. Filial relations. College life. Voyeurism. Nudism. Momism. Sunbathing. Nudist camps.*

NUDE CAMERA *see* **BUNNY YEAGER'S NUDE CAMERA**

NUDE HEAT WAVE *see* **THE TOUCHABLES**

NUDE IN CHARCOAL   F6.3545

Tempest Productions. *Dist* Premier Pictures, Sam Lake Enterprises. Mar **1963**. Sd; b&w. 35mm. 75 min.

Dir Joe Sarno.

Cast: Richard Kronold, Sally Ardrey, Peter Craig, Burtt Harris, actor, Dina Paisner.

Melodrama. Art student June Barton, in love with classmate Jimmy Fuller, unknowingly becomes the object of instructor Najlas Sarto's sexual obsession. Financial difficulties force June to seek work, and she accepts her teacher's offer to pose in the nude at his country home. She tells Jimmy that she must return to her family. As the work progresses, Sarto's self-control grows weaker. His mentally unbalanced housekeeper, Elia, who is also his mistress, smoulders with resentment at June's intrusion, and attempts to strangle the girl. Back in New York, Jimmy discovers that June is not at home in North Carolina, but at Sarto's estate. On the eve of June's departure, Sarto tries to force himself upon his student. Elia goes berserk, strangles Sarto, and accuses June of the murder. Jimmy arrives just in time to save June from the deranged housekeeper. *Art teachers. Models. Students. Housekeepers. Mistresses. Rape. Murder. Insanity. Finance—Personal. Employer-employee relations. New York City. North Carolina.*

Note: Also known as *Sinners à la Carte,* an alternative title shared by the 1960 release *For Lovers and Others.* Also known as *Models in Charcoal* and *Secrets of Venus.*

NUDE IN HIS POCKET (France)   F6.3546

Madeleine Films–S. N. E. Gaumont–Contact Organisation. *Dist* Cosmic Films. Mar **1962**. Sd; b&w. 35mm. 82 min.

Exec Prod Gilbert de Goldschmidt. *Dir* Pierre Kast. *Adapt & Dial* France Roche. *Dir Photog* Ghislain Cloquet. *Camera* Guy Suzuki. *Asst Op* René Guissard. *Art Dir* Sidney Bettex. *Asst Art Dir* Daniel Villerois. *Scenic Artist* Jean Alexandre. *Film Ed* Robert Isnardon. *Mus* Cogo Goragher, Georges Delerue, Marc Lanjean. *Ch Sd* Jean Bertrand. *Sd Rec* Claude Orhon. *Boom Op* Bernard Souverbie. *Asst Dir* Bernard Toublanc-Michel. *Prod Supv* René Thévenet. *Tech Prod Supv* Jacques Garcia. *Prod Mgr* Pierre Cottance. *Asst Prod Mgr* Maurice Fouhati. *Prod Sec* Edwige Jaeger. *Script Girl* Claude Levillain. *Jean Marais' Makeup* Alexandre Marcus. *Makeup* Blanche Picot. *Still Photog* Jean Schmidt.

Cast: Jean Marais *(Professor Jérôme)*, Geneviève Page *(Edith)*, Agnès Laurent *(Monette)*, Régine Lovi, Amédée, Pasquali, Joëlle Janin, Jean-Claude Brialy, Flip.

Comedy. Source: Waldemar Kaempfert, "The Diminishing Draft," in *Astounding Science Fiction* (9 Feb 1918). Professor Jérôme has been performing some experiments on suspended animation. Edith, his fiancée, attempts to persuade him to give up this work and go into the soft drink business. On his final day in the laboratory, Monette, Professor Jérôme's assistant, accidentally spills a jar containing an experimental solution. A pet dog drinks the liquid and is reduced in size to a statue 3 inches high. Jérôme restores its size by immersing it in salt water. During the course of their work, Jérôme and Monette fall in love. When Edith demands entry into the laboratory, Monette, not wanting to be found with Jérôme, swallows some of the solution and is reduced to a 3-inch nude statue which Jérôme hides in his pocket. The next day Jérôme takes Monette to the ocean, immerses her in salt water, and returns her to normal size. Using their discovery they have many intimate liaisons, and Jérôme decides to abandon his fiancée and remain with Monette.

[According to French sources, Edith becomes aware of their discovery and places the statue of Monette on an ocean liner bound for the United States, but Jérôme follows in a motorboat and rescues her.] *Professors. Scientists. Laboratory technicians. Experiments. Suspended animation. Miniaturization. Dogs.*

Note: Location scenes filmed in and around Marseilles. Opened in Paris in Nov 1957 as *Amour de poche* at 85 min. May also be known as *Girl in His Pocket.*

NUDE LAS VEGAS see **BUNNY YEAGER'S NUDE LAS VEGAS**

NUDE ODYSSEY (France/Italy) **F6.3547**
P. C. M.–Cineriz–Francinex. *Dist* Royal Films International. 26 Oct **1962** [New York opening]. Sd; col (Eastman Color). 35mm (Totalscope). 97 min.
Prod Golfiero Colonna, Luciano Ercoli, Alberto Pugliese. *Dir* Franco Rossi. *Screenplay* Ennio De Concini, Franco Rossi, Ottavio Alessi, Golfiero Colonna. *Story* Franco Rossi, Ennio De Concini, Golfiero Colonna. *Photog* Alessandro D'Eva. *Camera Op* Giovanni Scarpellini. *Set Decor* Giuseppe Ranieri. *Film Ed* Otello Colangeli. *Mus Comp & Cond* Angelo Francesco Lavagnino. *Songs:* "Roi Mata" & "The Legend of Hinano" Yves Roche. *Song:* "Bon Voyage" Danny Small.
Cast: Enrico Maria Salerno *(Enrico),* Venantino Venantini *(film maker),* Patricia Dolores Donlon *(Margaret),* Elizabeth Logue *(Matae),* Nathalie Gasse *(Tepare),* Pauline Rey *(Hinano),* Vaea Bennett *(Turere),* Jack Russel, Karl Schönbourg, Charles Mau, Giulia Meserve, Arona.
Adventure drama. Disillusioned with his jaded life in Rome, Enrico, a middle-aged Italian film director and novelist, travels to Polynesia to film a travelogue. He meets an American fellow-passenger, Margaret, and takes part in an unsuccessful search for her missing husband. He becomes romantically involved with a young Tahitian woman, Matae, and rapidly becomes immersed in the hedonistic lifestyle of Papeete with its endless round of drinking and lovemaking. Later he leaves his group to live with two other women, Tepare and Turere, in a deserted mansion. The news of his mother's death comes as a painful shock, and he finds that his aimless existence no longer satisfies him. He finds no solace in Margaret's materialistic outlook and he retires to a small uncharted island whose native inhabitants lead a simple existence. He becomes friendly with a young boy and meets a devoted priest who teaches Christianity to the natives. From this encounter comes the realization that all of his efforts to escape from his responsibilities have been futile. Enriched by his new perspective on life, Enrico returns to Rome. *Authors. Motion picture directors. Americans in foreign countries. Priests. Missionaries. Hedonism. Materialism. Islands. Rome. Tahiti. South Seas. Papeete.*
Note: Released in Italy in 1961 as *Odissea nuda*; running time: 120 min; opened in Paris in Aug 1961 as *L'odyssée nue*; running time: 105 min. Also known as *Love—Tahiti Style* and *Diary of a Voyage in the South Pacific.*

NUDE ON THE RUN see **RUN SWINGER RUN!**

NUDE RESTAURANT **F6.3548**
Dist Factory Films, Film-Makers' Cooperative. 13 Nov **1967** [New York opening]. Sd; col (Eastman Color). 16mm. 100 min.
Pres by Andy Warhol. *Prod-Dir-Writ* Andy Warhol. *Photog* Andy Warhol. *Film Ed* Andy Warhol. *Prod Asst* Paul Morrissey.
Cast: Viva *(the waitress),* Taylor Mead *(harmonica player),* Louis Waldon *(painted man),* James Davis *(man in tub),* Brigid Polk *(girl in tub),* Julian Burroughs *(draft dodger),* Allen Midgette *(silent man).*
Comedy-drama. Before going to work, a Greenwich Village waitress takes a bath. As she sits in her tub, she is joined by a young man, apparently "high" on marijuana. The waitress chats about friends, coiffures, and sex while thwarting the man's advances. Eventually they become a threesome with the arrival of a second girl. At the restaurant, where everyone is nude except for bikini briefs, the waitress serves her customers in a desultory manner, talking mostly about the men in her life and about her old-fashioned father. She also finds time to weave flowers in the hair of a husky young man whose body has been painted with psychedelic designs and engage in an involved bout of kissing with a man who doesn't speak. Occasionally, a patron plays a guitar or talks. A young draft dodger speaks out against the war in Vietnam, and another man intersperses snatches of autobiographical discourse with harmonica music. Dominating everything, however, is the sound of the waitress' voice as she talks on and on. *Waitresses. Harmonica players. Draft dodgers. Nudity. Sexuality. Marijuana. Restaurants. Body painting. Bathtubs. Vietnam War 1964–73. New York City—Greenwich Village.*
Note: Restaurant sequences filmed on location in New York City. Also known as *Andy Warhol's Restaurant.*

NUDE SCRAPBOOK **F6.3549**
Barry Mahon Productions. *Dist* Cinema Syndicate, Inc. 24 Jun **1965** [Maryland license]. Sd; col (Eastman Color). 35mm. 64 min.

A Barry Mahon Production. *Prod-Dir* Barry Mahon. *Script* Clelle Mahon. *Photog* Barry Mahon. *Film Ed* Al Ruban. *Sd* Magno Sound. *Asst Dir* Byron Mabe.
Cast: Bernie Allen *(The Photographer).*
Comedy. One of New York's most successful pinup photographers enjoys thumbing through his scrapbook of the world's most beautiful women whenever he has a few free minutes. As he reminisces, his vivid imagination brings the models to life again. At the same time, he maintains a busy schedule. Before he can steal some time with his scrapbook, he must photograph the beautiful pinup models who wait in his studio. *Photographers. Models. Nudity.*

NUDE ... SI MUORE see **THE YOUNG, THE EVIL AND THE SAVAGE**

NUDES, INC. **F6.3550**
Barry Mahon. 9 Jul **1964** [San Francisco showing]. Sd; col. 35mm. 62 min.
Prod-Dir Barry Mahon. *Script* Clelle Mahon. *Photog* Barry Mahon. *Film Ed* Al Ruban. *Sd* Magno Sound. *Asst Dir* Byron Mabe.
Sex film. Barbara Jo travels from her small southern hometown to New York and finds it difficult to find employment. Eventually she becomes desperate enough to call Nudes, Inc., the largest studio in the world producing pinup photographs. Barbara Jo is at first reluctant to pose in the nude, but Mr. Lewis, the managing director, gives her a tour of the studio to convince her of the studio's legitimacy. Mr. Lewis points out that the models are also employed elsewhere as school teachers, airline stewardesses, housewives, and professional models. Barbara is reassured, and after lunch she begins work. *Models. Southerners. Photography. Nudity. Employment—Women. New York City.*
Note: May also be known as *The Pin-up Factory; Broadway Pin-up Honeys;* and *Pin-Up Camera.*

NUDES OF ALL NATIONS (Great Britain) **F6.3551**
Searchlight Productions–Miracle Film Productions. *Dist* Advent Film Productions, American Film Distributing Corp. 3 Jul **1962** [New York State license]. Sd; col (Eastman Color). 35mm. 65-70 min.
Prod Harry Green. *Dir* Arnold Louis Miller. *Dir Photog* Stanley A. Long. *Film Ed* Stanley Marks. *Mus Dir* Keith Papworth. *Song:* "Oo-la-la" Nat Mills. *Coöp* The British Sunbathing Association.
Cast: Vivienne Raimon *(Miss England),* Margherita Lopez *(Miss Mexico),* Monique Ammon *(Miss France),* Susan Clift *(Miss Germany),* Julia Nicholaides *(Miss Greece),* Janet Ash *(Miss New Zealand),* Elizabeth Standing *(Miss Holland),* Minush Thuillier *(Miss Brazil),* Chantal Favre *(Miss Belgium),* Diana Dorlay *(Miss Denmark),* Sue Chang *(Miss Hong Kong),* Elaine Desmond *(Miss U. S. A.),* Jutka Goz *(Miss Hungary),* Antony Dell *(Ron Wilson),* Colin Goddard *(Peter Graham),* Douglas Cameron *(Sergeant Roberts),* Geoffrey Denton *(Lord Greystone),* Joyce Gregg *(Mrs. Haines),* Stephanie Rovert *(Helen, Mrs. Haines' daughter),* Valerie Singleton *(narrator).*
Comedy. Carol Wilson, winner of an international beauty contest, convinces the other contestants to join her for a summer of nudist camping. Unaware of their plans, Lord Greystone gives them permission to camp on his English estate while he is away, on the condition that they raise money for a deserving charity. The local villagers strongly disapprove of the manor activities; Mrs. Haines, the dour shopkeeper, refuses even to sell the women provisions, and they realize that their neighbors will never support a fund-raising event. They decide, however, to organize a carnival and fireworks display and invite other nudists. The operation is an enormous success, but the villagers intervene and stage an anti-nudism demonstration. Summoned by sympathetic local police officer Sergeant Roberts, Lord Greystone arrives unexpectedly to help restore peace to the village. The women present the proceeds of the carnival to the unfriendly shopkeeper so that her crippled daughter can be sent to America for an operation, and Lord Greystone reveals that he has been an ardent nudist all his life. *Nobility. Storekeepers. Nudism. Charity. Nudist camps. Beauty contests. Carnivals. Fireworks. Manors.*
Note: Filmed on location in England and originally released there in 1961 as *Nudes of the World.* Also known as *The Sun, the Place & the Girls.*

NUDES OF THE WORLD see **NUDES OF ALL NATIONS**

NUDES ON CREDIT see **LOVE NOW ... PAY LATER**

NUDES ON THE ROCKS see **50,000 B. C. (BEFORE CLOTHING)**

NUDES ON TIGER REEF **F6.3552**
Barry Mahon Productions. 6 Aug **1965** [Los Angeles showing]. Sd; col (Eastman Color). 35mm. 64 min.
A Barry Mahon Production. *Prod-Dir* Barry Mahon. *Script* Clelle Mahon. *Photog* Barry Mahon. *Film Ed* Al Ruban. *Sd* Magno Sound.
Cast: Nadja Swenson, Sande Johnsen.
Comedy-drama. After the closing of a very successful Broadway play, the producer-director and leading lady tell each other of their plans for the summer.

She plans to work in summer stock in the Catskills, and he will make a film spectacular in the Midwest. They part, and the director heads instead for the exclusive Tiger Reef Nudist Colony, on an island off the Florida coast. Tiger Reef has been chosen by the Sunbathing Association as the setting for a documentary on nudism, and the camp manager is anxious to have the Broadway director, a nudist himself, make the film. The director is unenthusiastic because he would have no professional help on the island. The manager announces happily that a famous Broadway actress has recently become a member of Tiger Reef. The new recruit turns out to be the leading lady, who has not gone to the Catskills after all. There is some initial embarrassment, after which the two set out to make the movie. They film attractive camp members and the beautiful surroundings. With the film completed and the summer over, the team returns to Broadway together. *Theatrical directors. Actors. Nudism. Duplicity. Nudist camps. Motion pictures. Florida. New York City—Broadway.*

Note: Filmed in Florida. Also known as *Girls on Tiger Reef.*

NUDIST CAMP *see* **NATURE CAMP CONFIDENTIAL**

NUDIST CONFIDENTIAL *see* **NATURE CAMP CONFIDENTIAL**

NUDIST CURTAIN *see* **BEHIND THE NUDIST CURTAIN**

LA NUIT *see* **LA NOTTE**

LA NUIT DES ESPIONS *see* **NIGHT ENCOUNTER**

LA NUIT DES GÉNÉRAUX *see* **THE NIGHT OF THE GENERALS**

LA NUIT LA PLUS CHAUDE *see* **THE NIGHT OF THE THREE LOVERS**

LA NUIT LA PLUS LONGUE *see* **SEXUS**

NUITS BLANCHES *see* **WHITE NIGHTS**

LES NUITS D'AMÉRIQUE *see* **AMERICA BY NIGHT**

LES NUITS DE L'ÉPOUVANTE *see* **THE MURDER CLINIC**

LES NUITS DE RASPOUTINE *see* **THE NIGHT THEY KILLED RASPUTIN**

NUITS D'EUROPE *see* **EUROPEAN NIGHTS**

NUMBER ONE   F6.3553
Walter Seltzer Productions. *Dist* United Artists. 21 Aug **1969** [New Orleans opening; c21 Aug 1969; LP37334]. Sd; col (DeLuxe). 35mm. 105 min. *MPAA rating* M.
A Walter Seltzer Production. *Prod* Walter Seltzer. *Assoc Prod* Frank Baur. *Dir* Tom Gries. *Screenplay* David Moessinger. *Photog* Michel Hugo. *Photog Football Seq* Kirk Wooster. *Art Dir* Art Loel. *Film Ed* Richard Brockway. *Mus* Dominic Frontiere. *Sd* Robert Martin. *Asst Dir* Phil Parslow. *Prod Mgr* Frank Baur. *Cost Dsgn* Rita Riggs.
Cast: Charlton Heston (*Ron "Cat" Catlan*), Jessica Walter (*Julie Catlan*), Bruce Dern (*Richie Fowler*), John Randolph (*Coach Jim Southerd*), Diana Muldaur (*Ann Marley*), G. D. Spradlin (*Dr. Tristler*), Richard Elkins (*Kelly Williams*), Mike Henry (*Walt Chaffee*), Ernie Barnes (*Deke Coleman*), Steve Franken (*Robin*), Bart Burns (*Ed Davis*), Forrest Wood (*attendant*), George Sperdakos (*Dr. Overstreet*), Roy Jenson (*Roy Nelson*), Bob Bennett (*Penny Forber*), Billy Holiday (*trainer*), Bobby Troup (*Harvey Hess*), Al Hirt (*himself*), The New Orleans Saints (*themselves*).
Drama. Ron "Cat" Catlan, 40-year-old star quarterback of the New Orleans Saints, experiences a professional crisis after suffering a knee injury in a final preseason game. In spite of Coach Jim Southerd's assurance that he has three good seasons left, Catlan realizes his days are numbered, particularly since rookie Kelly Williams is improving with every practice session. Catlan receives attractive business offers from both Richie Fowler and Harvey Hess, but he sees the business world as dull compared to pro football. He also fears starting a new career at his age. Further complicating Catlan's crisis is the collapse of his marriage. His wife, Julie, neglected by her husband, has immersed herself in fashion designing and has become something of a celebrity. Though she understands her husband's predicament, she can neither console nor counsel him since they are barely able to communicate. Depressed, Catlan enters into an affair with Ann Marley, a socialite in the sporting goods business, but she is also unable to help resolve his conflict. After being shaken further by stormy scenes with Julie and Richie, and an encounter with an impoverished former football pro, Catlan prepares for the season opener by using novocain and a steel brace to fortify his injured knee. At first the fans boo the veteran quarterback, but they cheer him when he engineers a spectacular touchdown drive. Following a fumble, Catlan takes over again; but as he prepares to pass, he is crushed by several defensive linemen. He lies motionless in the center of the playing field, while the crowd sits in stunned silence. *Athletes. Athletic*

coaches. Businessmen. Couturiers. Socialites. Football. Middle age. Marriage. Infidelity. New Orleans. New Orleans Saints.

Note: Location scenes filmed in New Orleans. Working title: *Pro.*

NO. 13 DEMON STREET *see* **THE DEVIL'S MESSENGER**

NO. 12   F6.3554
Dist Film-Makers' Cooperative. 15 Mar **1965** [New York opening]. Sd; b&w. 16mm. 66 min.
Dir Harry Smith. *Anim* Harry Smith. *Photog* Harry Smith. *Film Ed* Harry Smith.
Experimental animated film. A woman's dental dilemma, her visit to paradise, and return to earth are depicted, with allusions to historical personages (including Edward VII and Max Müller), and remembrances of Israel and Montreal. *Israel. Montreal. Edward VII (England). Max Müller. Heaven.*

Note: In production ca1950-62. Also known as *Heaven & Earth Magic Feature* and *The Magic Feature.* Comprised mainly of cutouts from 19th-century catalogs and books and of scratch-board drawings. First shown as a segment of the filmmaker's whole work; initial program title undetermined; subsequently known as *The Films of Harry Smith.* The soundtrack consists of rock music.

THE NUN AND THE SERGEANT   F6.3555
Springfield Productions–Eastern Film Enterprises. *Dist* United Artists. 27 Jun **1962** [Los Angeles opening]. Sd; b&w. 35mm. 73 min.
Prod Eugene Frenke. *Assoc Prod* Harold N. Even. *Dir* Franklin Adreon. *Screenplay* Don Cerveris. *Photog* Paul Ivano. *Art Dir* Bob Kinoshita. *Film Ed* John Hoffman, Carl Mahakian. *Mus* Jerry Fielding. *Sd* Woodruff H. Clark. *Asst Dir* Robert Agnew. *Prod Mgr* Bartlett A. Carre. *Cost* Marjorie Corso. *Makeup* Carlie Taylor. *Sp Eff* Norman Breedlove.
Cast: Robert Webber (*Sergeant McGrath*), Anna Sten (*nun*), Leo Gordon (*Dockman*), Hari Rhodes (*Hall*), Robert Easton (*Nupert*), Dale Ishimoto (*Pak*), Linda Wong (*Bok Soon*), Linda Ho (*Soon Cha*), Tod Windsor (*Nevins*), Valentin De Vargas (*Rivas*), Kenny Miller (*Quill*), Norman Du Pont (*Mossback*), Roger Torrey (*Turnbridge*), Gregori F. Kris (*Johnson*), Caroline Kido (*Myung Hee*), King Moody (*Pollard*), Yashi (*Kil Cha*), Anna Shin (*Ok-Cha*).
War melodrama. During the Korean War, U. S. Marine Sergeant McGrath and his Korean guide Pak are assigned to a critical mission which offers little chance for survival. Rather than sacrifice good fighting men, McGrath falsifies orders and takes along a motley assortment of men from the brig. Dropped behind enemy lines, the men encounter a nun and a group of Korean schoolgirls whose bus has been destroyed by a bomb. Fearful that the nun, whose leg has been injured, may reveal their position to the enemy, McGrath orders the women to accompany him. As they approach their destination, McGrath gradually wins the admiration of the nun and the girls as well as most of the men. One exception is Dockman, a burly coward who tries to rape one of the schoolgirls while McGrath is away from camp; he is stopped by the other soldiers who turn against him and refuse to participate in an escape attempt. When it becomes apparent that the nun will die from her leg wound unless she receives immediate medical care, McGrath permits the girls to carry her to a nearby village. Confident that his men will follow him, he leads them into action. *Guides. Convicts. Nuns. Koreans. Students. Combat zone life. Cowardice. Rape. Courage. Korean War 1950–53. United States Marines.*

A NUN AT THE CROSSROADS (Italy/Spain)   F6.3556
Izaro Films–Filmes Cinematografica. *Dist* Universal Pictures. Mar **1970**. Sd; col (Eastman Color). 35mm. 99 min. *MPAA rating* GP.
Exec Prod José Maria Reyzabal. *Dir* Julio Buchs. *Screenplay* Federico de Urrutia, Manuel Sebares, Victor Auz, José Luis Hernández Marcos, Julio Buchs. *Orig Story* José Frade. *Photog* Gabor Pogany. *2d Unit Camera* Manuel Hernández Sanjuan. *Art Dir* Ottavio Scotti, Jaime Perez Cubero. *Film Ed* Gaby Penalba. *Mus* Giovanni Fusco. *Sd* Eduardo Fernandez. *Asst Dir* José Puyol.
Cast: Rosanna Schiaffino (*Sister Maria*), John Richardson (*Dr. Pierre Lemon*), Mara Cruz (*Lisa*), Angel Picazo (*Father Raymond*), Paloma Valdes (*Sister Blanche*), Lili Murati (*Mother Claire*), Lex Monson (*Nangu*), Margot Cottens (*Madeleine*), Andres Mejuto (*Michel*), Willie P. Elie (*Isaku*), Claudia Gravy (*Yvonne*), Lorenzo Terzon (*Jean*), María Fernanda Ladrón de Guevara (*mother superior*), Antonio Pica (*officer*), Alicia Altabella (*Sister Genevieve*), Porfiria Sanchis (*Sister Marcella*), Matilde Muñoz Sampedro (*Sister Herminia*), Petra Lacey (*Sister Lucille*).
Drama. A violent struggle for power follows the Congo's independence from Belgium in 1960. A group of black Simba rebels, led by Isaku, warn the nuns at a Belgian Roman Catholic mission that all whites and colonialists are in danger, but the nuns cannot leave until they receive the orders from the bishop. Sister Maria leaves the mission to help a native woman and is raped in the woods by Simba marauders led by Nangu. Nangu and his men then plunder the

mission, killing Isaku and the mother superior. They prepare to murder the rest of the sisters, but a group of white mercenaries saves the day. Sister Maria returns to Brussels and discovers that she is pregnant from the attack in the Congo. Scorned by her family and rejected by her sister Lisa, Sister Maria receives an ultimatum from Rome: she must either give the child to the Church or renounce her vows. Dr. Pierre Lemon, a childhood sweetheart, proposes to Sister Maria and offers to accept her child. Though Sister Maria decides to keep the child and leave the religious order, she refuses to marry Pierre because she is already married to Christ. *Nuns. Africans. Simbas. Belgians. Mercenaries. Religion. Rape. Pregnancy. Murder. Race relations. Missions. Catholic Church. Congo—History—Independence. Belgium.*

Note: Produced in 1967 under the title *Encrucijada para una monja*. Filmed in Guinea, elsewhere in Africa, and in Belgium. Italian title: *Violenza per una monaca.*

THE NUN OF MONZA see **THE LADY OF MONZA**

I NUOVI ANGELI see **THE NEW ANGELS**

NUR TOTE ZEUGEN SCHWEIGEN see **HYPNOSIS**

NUREMBERG   F6.3557
CR Enterprises. *Dist* Unitel of California. Dec **1961** [Los Angeles showing; c24 Oct 1961; LP20624]. Sd; b&w. 35mm. 75 min. [Copyright length: 72 min.]
   Assoc Prod Alan Kane.
   Cast: Lee Bonnell, Roy Bennett, Marta Mithovitch.
   War melodrama. United States Supreme Court Associate Justice Robert Jackson delivers the opening indictment of war criminals at Nuremberg. In another part of Germany, two U. S. Army officers question a young woman who, despite her pleas that she is not a Nazi, reveals her true Nazi beliefs while she explains her life under fascism. Documentary footage of Nazi Germany is interpolated with her remarks. Sequences include marching Nazi soldiers, aerial warfare by the Germans against the Allied air forces, V bombs, youth camps, Hitler's speeches, Nazi propaganda, concentration camps, and methods of torture. The woman finishes her monolog, is judged to be innocent, and is given her freedom. *Nazis. Nazism. War crimes. World War II. Germany. Robert Houghwout Jackson. Adolf Hitler. International Military Tribunal. Germany— History—Third Reich.*

DER NÜRNBERGER PROZESS see **HITLER'S EXECUTIONERS**

NURSE-MADE   F6.3558
Dist Distribpix, Inc. ca **1970**. Sd; col. 35mm. 60 min.
   Comedy-drama. An attractive young woman applies for a job as a nurse and determines to become an heiress when she visits the rich old man for whom she would work and overhears him tell his lawyer that if he should die in the arms of a woman while making love, all of his money would go to that woman. She gets the job and makes love with the old man day and night. When it appears that she (not the old man) will succumb, she recruits a buxom friend to help kill him. The elderly satyr foils the plot, however, and he turns the tables on his nurse. *Nurses. Old age. Inheritance. Murder. Satyriasis. Employer-employee relations. Greed.*

NURSE ON WHEELS (Great Britain)   F6.3559
G. H. W. Productions. *For* Anglo Amalgamated Productions. *Dist* Janus Films. Nov **1963**. Sd; b&w. 35mm. 86 min.
   Prod Peter Rogers. *Assoc Prod* Frank Bevis. *Dir* Gerald Thomas. *Screenplay* Norman Hudis. *Photog* Alan Hume. *Art Dir* Lionel Couch. *Film Ed* Archie Ludski. *Mus Comp & Cond* Eric Rogers. *Sd* Leslie Wiggins. *Sd Rec* Robert MacPhee, Colin Le Mesurier. *Asst Dir* Anthony Waye.
   Cast: Juliet Mills *(Joanna Jones)*, Ronald Lewis *(Henry Edwards)*, Joan Sims *(Deborah)*, Noel Purcell *(Abel Worthy)*, Esma Cannon *(Mrs. Jones)*, Raymond Huntley *(vicar)*, Athene Seyler *(Mrs. Farthingale)*, Norman Rossington *(George Judd)*, Barbara Everest *(Nurse Merrick)*, Ronald Howard *(Dr. Harold)*, Joan Hickson *(Mrs. Wood)*, George Woodbridge *(Mr. Beacon)*, Renee Houston *(Mrs. Beacon)*, Jim Dale *(Tim Taylor)*, David Horne *(Dr. Golfrey)*, Deryck Guyler *(examiner)*.
   Comedy. Source: Joanna Jones, *Nurse Is a Neighbour* (London, 1958). Joanna Jones, an attractive young woman, is the new district nurse in the rural community of Blandley. Many of the villagers subject her to unkind gossip and compare her with her predecessor, Nurse Merrick. She becomes friends with Dr. Golfrey and his son, Dr. Harold, and is also accepted by the local storekeeper, Abel Worthy. When her car collides with one driven by farmer Henry Edwards, they meet and fall in love. They soon quarrel, however, when Henry wants to evict a destitute young couple whose caravan is parked on his land. Joanna objects because the woman is pregnant. Joanna delivers the couple's baby out in the fields and wins the respect of the rest of the community. *Nurses. Farmers. Physicians. Storekeepers. Gossip. Rural life. Eviction. Childbirth. Automobile accidents.*
   Note: Released in Great Britain in Jun 1963.

NUTTY, NAUGHTY CHATEAU (France/Italy)   F6.3560
   Les Films Corona–Spectacles Lubroso–Euro International Films. *Dist* Lopert Pictures. 13 Oct **1964** [New York opening]. Sd; col (Technicolor). 35mm (Franscope). 102 min.
   Exec Prod Robert Dorfmann. *Dir* Roger Vadim. *Adapt* Roger Vadim, Claude Choublier. *Dir Photog* Armand Thirard. *Art Dir* Jean André. *Film Ed* Victoria Mercanton. *Mus* Raymond Le Sénéchal. *Prod Mgr* Georges Valon.
   Cast: Monica Vitti *(Eleanore)*, Curt Jurgens *(Hugo)*, Jean-Claude Brialy *(Sebastian)*, Suzanne Flon *(Agathe)*, Jean-Louis Trintignant *(Eric)*, Françoise Hardy *(Ophelie)*, Sylvie *(Grandmother)*, Daniel Emilfork *(Gunther)*, Michel Le Royer *(Gosta)*.
   Farce. Source: Françoise Sagan, *Château en Suède* (Paris opening: 11 Mar 1960). In an isolated castle on a lake island in Sweden, aging Hugo Falsen jealously guards his second wife Eleanore, a seductive young woman passionately devoted to her idle, parasitic brother, Sebastian. The family dresses in 18th century costumes under orders from Hugo's elder sister Agathe, an authoritarian eccentric who lives in the past. A senile grandmother cackles from her wheelchair, while a solemn butler glides about the premises. The arrival of Hugo's cousin Eric, who has left a scandal behind him in Stockholm, throws the household into turmoil. He soon falls in love with Eleanore and discovers the scope of Hugo's jealousy; what at first appears to be a ghost is actually Hugo's first wife, Ophelie, believed to have drowned in the lake but actually very much alive, albeit half crazy. Since divorce would be impossible, Hugo hides her in a secret bedroom, where she carries on an affair with Sebastian. Eric also learns from Eleanore that Christian, a friend who disappeared the year before, was murdered by Hugo in a fit of jealousy, and he begins to fear for his own safety. Despite several attempts by Hugo and Agathe to murder him, Eric escapes across the newly-frozen lake to inform his uncle, the Minister of Justice in Stockholm, of the strange goings-on at the chateau. Soon afterwards, a handsome reporter arrives at the castle to profile the family for a magazine article. *Swedes. Cousins. Eccentrics. Grandmothers. Butlers. Family life. Jealousy. Incest. Infidelity. Bigamy. Insanity. Murder. Scandal. Seduction. Marriage. Castles. Sweden. Stockholm.*
   Note: Exteriors filmed in Lapland. Opened in Paris in Nov 1963 as *Château en Suède* running time: 110 min; in Italy in 1963 as *Il castello in Svezia.*

THE NUTTY PROFESSOR   F6.3561
   Jerry Lewis Enterprises. *Dist* Paramount Pictures. 4 Jun **1963** [Houston opening; c4 Jun 1963; LP25315]. Sd; col (Technicolor). 35mm. 107 min.
   A Jerry Lewis Production. *Prod* Ernest D. Glucksman. *Assoc Prod* Arthur P. Schmidt. *Dir* Jerry Lewis. *Screenplay* Jerry Lewis, Bill Richmond. *Photog* W. Wallace Kelley. *Camera Op* Kyme Meade. *Asst Camera* James Grant. *Col Cons* Richard Mueller. *Art Dir* Hal Pereira, Walter Tyler. *Set Decor* Sam Comer, Robert R. Benton. *Film Ed* John Woodcock. *Mus* Walter Scharf. *Played by* Les Brown & His Band. *Song:* "We've Got a World That Swings" Louis Y. Brown, Lil Mattis. *Sd* Hugo Grenzbach, Charles Grenzbach. *Asst Dir* Ralph Axness, Bill Poole, Jack Barry. *Prod Mgr* William C. Davidson. *Asst Prod Mgr* Hal Bell. *Script Supv* Dorothy Yutzi, Martin Pendleton. *Asst to the Prod* Marshall Katz. *Cost Dsgn* Edith Head. *Men's Wardrobe* Sy Devore, Nat Wise. *Wardrobe* Ruth Stella, Jim George. *Makeup Supv* Wally Westmore. *Makeup* Jack Stone. *Hairstyles* Nellie Manley, Agnes Flanagan. *Sp Photog Eff* Paul K. Lerpae. *Dial Dir* Marvin Weldon. *Still Photog* Sterling Smith. *Casting Dir* Ed Morse.
   Cast: Jerry Lewis *(Prof. Julius F. Kelp/Buddy Love)*, Stella Stevens *(Stella Purdy)*, Del Moore *(Dr. Hamius Warfield)*, Kathleen Freeman *(Millie Lemmon)*, Med Flory, Norman Alden, Skip Ward *(football players)*, Howard Morris *(Father Kelp)*, Elvia Allman *(Mother Kelp)*, Milton Frome *(Dr. Leevee)*, Buddy Lester *(bartender)*, Marvin Kaplan *(English boy)*, David Landfield, Julie Parrish, Henry Gibson *(college students)*, Les Brown & His Band, Dave Willock *(bartender)*, Doodles Weaver *(Rube)*, Mushy Callahan *(cab driver)*, Gavin Gordon *(salesman clothier)*, Celeste Yarnall, Francine York *(students)*, Joe Forte *(faculty member)*, Terry Higgins *(cigarette girl)*, Murray Alper *(judo instructor)*, Gary Lewis.
   Comedy. Eccentric maladroit Prof. Julius Kelp often gets into trouble with the dean of the large university where he teaches chemistry because his experiments frequently result in the demolition of his laboratory. Wishing to impress Stella Purdy, a beautiful student sympathetic to his difficulties, Kelp tries gym exercises and chemical formulas to improve his appearance. He stumbles on to a mixture that transforms him into singer Buddy Love, a swaggering, handsome bully; and in that personality, he tries to make love to Stella, who is alternately repelled and fascinated. Whenever the effect of the potion wears off, however, he must dash to his laboratory lest he change back to Professor Kelp. At the senior prom, where Kelp is ordered to act as chaperon and is also slated to appear as Buddy Love, the formula wears off during Buddy's number, and his personality reverts to that of the professor. Stella

realizes that Buddy is really Professor Kelp and confesses that she has always preferred the quiet. sensitive professor to brash Buddy Love. The two make plans to be married. *Eccentrics. Professors. Deans. Singers. College life. Dual personality. Experiments. Self-confidence.*

Note: Location scenes filmed at Arizona State University. Tempe, Arizona, using members of the student body as extras.

LES NYMPHETTES *see* **FIRST TASTE OF LOVE**

NYMPHO   F6.3562
Dist I. R. M. I. Films. ca **1965**. Sd: col (Eastman Color). 35mm. 63 min.
Prod-Dir Alfredo Nicola. *Assoc Prod* S. S. Millard. *Asst Prod* Jack Nelson. *Story* Michael Brown. *Photog* David Fields. *Camera Op* George Serran. *Film Ed* Nick Mattox. *Asst Dir* Bob Loh. *Prod Mgr* Syd Gold. *Gaffer* Dick Simms.

Cast: Laurie Davis. Leigh Sands. Alfredo Nicola. Herman Rose. Virginia Shay. Linda Richards. Tom Alexander. Mike Stimms. Suzy Sanders.

Drama. Buck. a 19th-century man. is mysteriously transported 100 years through time into the present. He is curious about the modern world's attitudes toward sex. and he witnesses seduction. lesbianism. mate swapping. nymphomania. fetishism. and wild parties. Although he is at first amused by what he sees. his amusement soon turns to disgust. *Seduction. Time travel. Lesbianism. Fetishism. Nymphomania. Mate swapping.*

NYMPHO *see* **A WOMAN'S URGE**

THE NYMPHS (Great Britain)   F6.3563
Dist Trans-Oceanic Films. 6 Mar **1967** [Maryland license]. Sd: col. 35mm. 53 min.
Prod-Dir Michael Keatering.
Narrator: Ingrid Sullivan.
Nudist film. No information about the precise nature of this film has been found. but one source indicates that it deals with nudists who take a boating trip to several summer resorts. May be the same as *Sunswept*, q. v. *Nudism. Resorts.*

NYMPHS ANONYMOUS   F6.3564
Great Empire Films. *Dist* Hollywood Cinemart. 24 May **1968** [Los Angeles showing]. Sd: b&w. 35mm. 90 min.
Prod-Writ J. Van Hearn. *Exec Prod* Elsa Singman. *Dir* Manuel S. Conde. *Dir Photog* Gregory Sandor. *Ed* M. & M. Samaniego.

Cast: Lois Lane. Natasha. Karen Lee, pseud. Elena. Betty Boop. Banana Peel. Jymi. Mia. Michelle Angelo. Barbara Dooley. Nancy O'Malley *(The Nymphs)*. Gordon Cohn. Wallace De Keth. Ralph Esor. Jack James. Phillip Brady. Tony Rittner. Bob Strong. Steve Goodwyn. Bethel Buckalew. Jerry Patterson. Don Jones. Mike Weldon. Arthur Williams. Ken Konopka *(The Employees)*.

Comedy. Suspicious of his wife's activities. a man engages in a search which leads him to a group of wealthy women who call themselves "Nymphs Anonymous." Among the women are lesbians. masochists. exhibitionists. fetishists. and voyeurs. and their activities involve luring unsuspecting men to their Hollywood Hills headquarters and forcing them to satisfy their sexual whims. *Nymphomania. Jealousy. Fetishism. Voyeurism. Lesbianism. Abduction. Suburban life. Hollywood.*

Note: Also known as *Nymphs*.

NYUJIRANDO NO WAKADAISHO *see* **YOUNG GUY ON MT. COOK**

O-GIN SAMA *see* **LOVE UNDER THE CRUCIFIX**

"O" GIRLS 1969 *see* **ORGY GIRLS '69**

O. K. CONNERY *see* **OPERATION KID BROTHER**

O SLAVNOSTI A HOSTECH *see* **A REPORT ON THE PARTY AND THE GUESTS**

OBCHOD NA KORZE *see* **THE SHOP ON MAIN STREET**

DIE "OBEN-OHNE" STORY *see* **THE TOPLESS STORY**

THE OBLONG BOX (United States/Great Britain)   F6.3565
American International Productions. *Dist* American International Pictures. 11 Jun **1969** [Los Angeles opening; c11 Jun 1969; LP37238]. Sd: col (Berkey Pathé). 35mm. 91 min. [Cut from 101 min.] *MPAA rating* M.
Prod-Dir Gordon Hessler. *Exec Prod* Louis M. Heyward. *Screenplay* Lawrence Huntington. *Adtl Dial* Christopher Wicking. *Dir Photog* John Coquillon. *Art Dir* George Provis. *Film Ed* Max Benedict. *Mus* Harry Robinson. *Sd* Bob Jones. *Asst Dir* Derek Whitehurst.

Cast: Vincent Price *(Julian Markham)*. Christopher Lee *(Dr. Neuhartt)*. Alister Williamson *(Sir Edward Markham)*. Hilary Dwyer *(Elizabeth Markham)*. Peter Arne *(Samuel Trench)*. Harry Baird *(N Galo)*. Carl Rigg *(Mark Norton)*. Maxwell Shaw *(Tom Hackett)*. Michael Balfour *(Ruddock)*. Godfrey James *(Weller)*. Rupert Davies *(Joshua Kemp)*. Sally Geeson *(Sally*

Baxter). Ivor Dean *(Hawthorne)*. Uta Levka. James Mellor. Danny Daniels. John Barrie. Hira Talfrey. John Wentworth. Betty Woolfe. Martin Terry. Anne Clune. Jackie Noble. Ann Barrass. Janet Rossini. Zeph Gladstone. Tara Fernando. Tony Thawnton. Anthony Bailey. Richard Cornish. Colin Jeavons. Andreas Malandrinos. Hedger Wallace. Martin Wyldeck. Oh! Ogunde Dancers.

Horror film. Source: Edgar Allan Poe. "The Oblong Box." in *Godey's Lady's Book* (1844). Julian Markham returns from Africa to his ancestral estate in 19th-century England with his deranged brother Edward. who has been so horribly mutilated by the natives that he is kept chained in an upstairs room. The dishonest family lawyer. Samuel Trench. agrees to help Edward by obtaining a special capsule from N'Galo. an African witch doctor. to make Edward appear dead so that he may be removed from Julian's care. The device works. but Julian decides that his brother's body must be displayed to the villagers and blackmails Trench into providing a substitute corpse. Trench and his colleague. Mark Norton. murder the owner of a London lodging house: and Julian secretly buries Edward. That night grave robbers take Edward's coffin fo Dr. Neuhartt. a local surgeon who is amazed to find Edward very much alive. Edward dons a crimson mask and remains at the doctor's lodgings while he undertakes an elaborate revenge against all those who have failed him. He begins a search for Sally Baxter. a servant employed by Dr. Neuhartt. and accidentally kills a London prostitute whom he mistakes for Sally. The madman then asks N'Galo to heal his face and attacks the witch doctor when he fails. Following the murder of Trench. Sally. now employed by Julian. reveals that a man in a crimson mask has been living with Dr. Neuhartt. Julian rushes to the doctor's house and finds him dying from wounds inflicted by Edward. who by now has gone to the manor house to abduct Sally. Returning home: Julian seeks out his brother in the woods and shoots him. He then confesses that he committed the crime for which Edward was tortured in Africa. Before he dies. Edward viciously bites Julian's hand. A few days later. Julian's wife. Elizabeth. enters Edward's room to call her husband for dinner and watches. horrified. as Julian's face takes on the mutilated appearance of his dead brother. *Brothers. Africans. Lawyers. Witch doctors. Surgeons. Prostitutes. Grave robbers. Domestics. Mutilation. Insanity. Catalepsy. Murder. Revenge. Frameup. Transmutation. Masks. London.*

Note: Opened in London in Jun 1970. Also known as *Edgar Allan Poe's "The Oblong Box"*.

THE OBLONG COUCH *see* **THE SAUCY AUSSIE**

OBON'S DIPPING CONTEST (Japan)   F6.3566
Tokyo Eiga Co. *Dist* Toho Co. Nov **1961** [Los Angeles showing]. Sd: col? 35mm. 73 min.
Dir Kozo Saeki.
Cast: Yoshie Mizutani. Sonomi Nakajima. Masumi Harukawa. Michiyo Yokoyama. Kiyoshi Atsumi. Ichiro Nakatani. Ichiro Arishima. Shizuko Kasagi.
Comedy. No information about the nature of this film has been found. *Contests.*

Note: Released in Japan in May 1961 as *Atomic no Obon. onna oyabun taiketsu no maki.*

OBRAS MAESTRAS DEL TERROR *see* **MASTER OF HORROR**

THE OBSCENE COUCH *see* **THE SAUCY AUSSIE**

OBSESSION (Sweden)   F6.3567
Nordisk Tonefilm. *Dist* O. R. P. Co. 28 Aug **1968** [New York opening]. Sd: col (Eastman Color). 35mm. 104 min.
Pres by Vernon P. Becker. Mel May. *Prod* Georg Eriksson. Lars Werner. *Dir* Gunnar Höglund. *Screenplay* Gunnar Höglund. Bosse Gustafson. *Photog* Bertil Wiktorsson. *Film Ed* Jan Persson. *Mus* Karl-Erik Welin. *Sd* Kurt Holmberg. *Asst Dir* Seivi Everstein. *Prod Mgr* Olle Lenander.

Cast: Matthias Henrikson ("You"). Maude Adelson *(Leni Wodak)*. Lars Lind *(The Other Man)*. Guy De la Berg *(German tourist)*. Johannes Blind *(Andreas)*.

Melodrama. Source: Bosse Gustafson. *Kungsleden* (Stockholm. 1963). As a man identified only as "You" walks along the Kungsleden. an extended mountain trail in Lapland. he recalls a time. 10 years earlier. when he spent 3 days in the same region with Leni. a young Jewish refugee from a concentration camp. *On their first night together. Leni virtually seduces You: the next evening. they quarrel when Leni accuses You of anti-Semitism: and. on the third night. You rapes Leni when she first encourages. then rejects. his advances.* After reminiscing about their brief. unhappy affair. You finds evidence that Leni also has returned to the trail and is somewhere in the vicinity. Arriving at the spot where they parted 10 years ago. You finds Leni's dead body in a mountain stream. You buries her. then goes to a nearby cottage where he and Leni once spent some time. Discovering that another man has been sleeping there. he concludes that this stranger must have murdered Leni.

Though he becomes lost in the mountains, You—obsessed with a feeling of guilt and a need for vengeance—tracks down the stranger, who offers to help him get back on the trail. You causes his death and then walks off uncertainly into the mountain mist. *Refugees. Strangers. Jews. Anti-Semitism. Rape. Murder. Seduction. Revenge. Guilt. Concentration camps. Lapland. Kungsleden.*

Note: Released in Sweden in Dec 1964 as *Kungsleden*; running time: 107 min. Shown at the 1965 San Francisco Film Festival as *The Royal Track.*

OBYKNOVENNYY FASHIZM *see* **TRIUMPH OVER VIOLENCE**

OCCHI SENZA VOLTO *see* **THE HORROR CHAMBER OF DR. FAUSTUS**

L'OCCHIO SELVAGGIO *see* **THE WILD EYE**

OCHAZUKE NO AJI *see* **TEA AND RICE**

THE ODD COUPLE F6.3568
Paramount Pictures. 2 May **1968** [New York opening; c2 May 1968; LP36430]. Sd: col (Technicolor). 35mm (Panavision). 105 min.
Prod Howard W. Koch. *Dir* Gene Saks. *Screenplay* Neil Simon. *Photog* Robert Hauser. *Art Dir* Hal Pereira, Walter Tyler. *Set Decor* Robert R. Benton, Ray Moyer. *Film Ed* Frank Bracht. *Mus* Neal Hefti. *Sd Rec* John Carter, Charles Grenzbach. *Asst Dir* Hank Moonjean. *Unit Prod Mgr* William C. Davidson. *Script Cont* Luanna Poole. *Cost Dsgn* Jack Bear. *Men's Wardrobe* John A. Anderson. *Makeup Supv* Wally Westmore. *Makeup Artist* Harry Ray, Jack Petty. *Hairstyle Supv* Nellie Manley. *Sp Photog Eff* Paul K. Lerpae.
Cast: Jack Lemmon *(Felix Ungar)*, Walter Matthau *(Oscar Madison)*, John Fiedler *(Vinnie)*, Herbert Edelman *(Murray)*, David Sheiner *(Roy)*, Larry Haines *(Speed)*, Monica Evans *(Cecily)*, Carole Shelley *(Gwendolyn)*, Iris Adrian *(waitress)*, Heywood Hale Broun *(sportswriter)*, John C. Becher *(hotel clerk)*, Roberto Clemente, Matty Alou, Maury Wills, Vernon Law, Ken Boyer, Bud Harrelson, Jerry Buchek, Ed Kranepool *(themselves, baseball players)*.
Comedy. Source: Neil Simon, *The Odd Couple* (New York opening: 10 Mar 1965). Following the collapse of his marriage, TV newsreporter Felix Ungar decides to commit suicide in a cheap hotel room near Times Square. He fails at even this, however, and dejectedly makes his way to the weekly poker game being held at the Riverside Drive apartment of his best friend, Oscar Madison, a divorced sportswriter. Felix accepts an invitation to share the 8-room apartment, but his hypochondria and his compulsion for order and cleanliness drive the slovenly Oscar to distraction, and the two men soon quarreling. Eventually, Oscar suggests they double-date Cecily and Gwendolyn Pigeon, two giddy English sisters who also live in the building, and Felix agrees on the condition that he be permitted to cook dinner. The evening ends disastrously when Felix's meatloaf burns, and he breaks down into a sobbing account of his broken marriage that elicits sympathetic tears from the Pigeon sisters. Finally, Felix's refusal to accompany the women upstairs so enrages Oscar that he restores his apartment to its original disorder and throws Felix out. After Felix departs, the card-playing cronies turn on Oscar and criticize his harsh treatment of their friend. They conduct a futile search for Felix, but he suddenly reappears and announces that he is moving in with Cecily and Gwendolyn until he can straighten out his life. Once Felix has left, the "boys" sit down for their weekly poker game, and they are surprised when Oscar rebukes them for spilling ashes on the table. *Roommates. Sportswriters. Reporters. English. Sisters. Divorce. Marriage. Friendship. Suicide. Poker. Hypochondriacs. New York City—West Side.*

Note: Exteriors filmed in Manhattan and at Shea Stadium.

ODD OBSESSION (Japan) F6.3569
Daiei Motion Picture Co. *Dist* Harrison Pictures. 12 May **1961** [Los Angeles opening]. Sd: col (Daiei-Agfa Color). 35mm (Daiei Scope). 96 min.
Pres by Edward Harrison. *Prod* Hiroaki Fujii. *Exec Prod* Masaichi Nagata. *Dir* Kon Ichikawa. *Screenplay* Natto Wada, Keiji Hasebe, Kon Ichikawa. *Photog* Kazuo Miyagawa. *Lighting* Yukio Ito. *Col Cons* Shozo Tanaka. *Art Dir* Tomoo Shimogawara. *Film Ed* Hiroaki Fujii, Kon Ichikawa. *Mus* Yasushi Akutagawa. *Sd* Kenichi Nishii. *Prod Mgr* Asao Kumada. *English Subtitl* Frederick Laing.
Cast: Machiko Kyo *(Ikuko Kenmochi)*, Ganjiro Nakamura *(Mr. Kenmochi)*, Junko Kano *(Toshiko Kenmochi)*, Tatsuya Nakadai *(Kimura)*, Tanie Kitabayashi *(Hana)*, Ichiro Sugai *(masseur)*, Jun Hamamura *(Dr. Soma)*, Mantaro Ushio *(Dr. Kodama)*, Kyu Sazanka *(curio dealer)*.
Melodrama. Source: Jun'ichiro Tanizaki, *Kagi* (Tokyo, 1957). Perturbed by his failing virility, Mr. Kenmochi, an elderly Japanese art critic and antiquarian with a young and beautiful wife, secretly takes injections to rejuvenate himself. When this treatment becomes no longer feasible, he chooses another method, jealousy. By encouraging a handsome young intern, Kimura, to show interest in his wife, Kenmochi discovers that his own aroused jealousy succeeds where the injections had failed. One night, his wife, Ikuko, faints in her bath after drinking too much brandy, and Kenmochi insists that the young doctor

examine her naked body. Furthermore, the old man begins taking nude photographs of Ikuko, forcing Kimura to develop them in his hospital laboratory. Such incidents finally lead Ikuko and Kimura into a passionate affair, much to the disgust of Kenmochi's homely daughter, Toshiko, who has hoped to win Kimura for herself. The old man now suffers a stroke while in bed with Ikuko, and this situation allows her to nurse Kenmochi by day and make love to Kimura at night. When Toshiko sees Kimura letting himself into the house, Ikuko removes her clothing in Kenmochi's presence and thereby causes him to have a second—and fatal—attack. Ikuko suggests that Kimura marry Toshiko and that the three of them live together. But Kimura, upon learning that Kenmochi died penniless, has lost interest in both mother and daughter. In any event, at an evening meal all three are poisoned by the old servant, Hana, who has despised them for their selfishness. The police find Ikuko's diary and refuse to believe Hana's confession, certain that out of grief over Kenmochi's death, the three had committed suicide. *Hospital interns. Antique dealers. Critics. Domestics. Murder. Nudity. Marriage. Jealousy. Infidelity. Impotence. Filial relations. Poisoning. Old age. Strokes. Photographs. Diaries.*

Note: Released in Japan in Jun 1959 as *Kagi*; running time: 107 min.

ODD TASTES F6.3570
Hollywood Cinema Associates. *Dist* Crest Film Distributors. May **1968**. Sd: col. 35mm. 74 min.
Prod-Dir Don Davis.
Cast: Joe Bonaparte *(Charles Odman)*.
Drama. The "sexual biography" of hedonist Charles Odman carries its subject through increasing degeneracy. A love affair in Malaya is succeeded by a homosexual affair in a Swiss school, culminating in the accidental death of his masochistic French teacher. Later, discovering his childhood sweetheart in a Hong Kong brothel, Odman is driven by guilt into an opium and sex orgy with the madam. His lust for bizarre pleasures takes him to Africa's jungles and Timbuktu's slave markets. Becoming increasingly perverted, he ultimately falls victim to his own devices: he is destroyed in a sadistic "experiment" with a personal vibrator saleswoman. *Adventurers. Schoolteachers. French. Madams. Prostitutes. Saleswomen. Hedonism. Male homosexuality. Sadomasochism. Opium. Orgies. Slavery. Sex aids. Hong Kong. Malaya. Africa. Timbuktu.*

Note: Filmed on location in Hong Kong, Singapore, the Pigmy forests of the Congo, the Sahara, and Timbuktu. Also known as *The Tasters* and *Great Taste.*

ODD TRIANGLE F6.3571
Rasnel Films. *Dist* A. L. Shackleton Films. 21 May **1969** [Dallas opening]. Sd; b&w. 35mm. 76 min.
Dir-Writ Joseph W. Sarno.
Cast: Barbara Lance *(Allison Harvey)*, Sidney Laird *(Dick Harvey)*, Blanche Robins *(Janet Kerr)*, Seymour Bradley *(Roger Kerr)*, Beth Manning *(Greta Barzak)*, Howard Dale *(Harry Zahn)*, René Howard *(Winnie Anderson)*.
Drama. Suburban housewife Allison Harvey is dissatisfied because her husband takes her for granted. She relieves her boredom at the swimming pool of neighbor Janet Kerr, and one afternoon she inadvertently observes Janet and a muscular gardener in a passionate embrace; she returns home only to find Greta, her maid, having sex with a boyfriend. Allison's attempts at self-arousal fail, and she goes to Janet for advice in expanding her own sexual horizons. The women rent a houseboat, and before long they are involved in a triangular affair with Winnie Anderson, a younger woman who makes a living guiding fishing parties through Florida's bays. Overwhelmed by the intensity of her erotic feelings, the guilt-ridden Allison tells her husband that she is leaving him, and she goes to Janet's house. When Allison sees Winnie and Janet embracing, she realizes that her need for love will never be fulfilled there, and she wanders off into the night. *Housewives. Guides. Gardeners. Housemaids. Suburban life. Marriage. Autoeroticism. Lesbianism. Troilism. Guilt. Houseboats.*

Note: Also reviewed as *The Odd Triangle.* Conflicting source information credits the following cast: Ulla Jensen, Dale Rene, Susan Whiteman, Susan Thomas.

ODDO F6.3572
Montgomery-C. I. T. Productions. *Dist* I. R. M. I. Films. **1967**. Sd; b&w. 35mm. 61 min.
Dir Joe Davis. *Camera Asst* V. Rodney. *Sd* Dave Vost. *Post Rec* C. I. T. Films. *Prod Mgr* Robert Shortusey. *Script Clerk* Jean Barth. *Cost* Anna Saro.
Cast: Martin Donley *(Alan Jaffeo [Dick])*, Nicki Holt, Brigitta Reim.
Melodrama. Vietnam war hero Alan Jaffeo returns home to San Francisco and finds his father passed out on the floor and the telegram announcing his arrival unopened. He takes a nap and awakens to find his young stepmother making love with another woman. Alan kills them both and goes for a walk. He visits a prostitute and kills her. Intent on rape, he breaks into the apartment of a young woman, and when she becomes seductive he kills her. Alan returns home and blows his brains out. *War heroes. Psychopaths. Prostitutes. Stepmothers. Filial relations. Lesbianism. Rape. Murder. Suicide. San Francisco.*

ODISSEA NUDA *see* **NUDE ODYSSEY**

L'ODYSSÉE NUE *see* **NUDE ODYSSEY**

OEDIPUS THE KING (Great Britain)   **F6.3573**
Crossroads Films–World Film Service Productions–Universal Pictures, Ltd. *Dist* Universal Pictures. 18 Sep 1968 [New York opening; c7 Dec 1967; LP37900]. Sd; col (Technicolor). 35mm. 97 min.
A Michael Luke–Philip Saville Production. *Prod* Michael Luke. *Assoc Prod* Timothy Burrill. *Dir* Philip Saville. *Screen Adapt* Michael Luke, Philip Saville. *Dir Photog* Walter Lassally. *Camera* Aristedes Karides-Fuchs, George Antonakis. *Art Dir* Yannis Migadis. *Scenic Artist* Nikos Stefanou. *Film Ed* Paul Davies. *Mus* Jani Christou. *Sd* Nikos Despotides. *Sd Ed* Rusty Coppleman. *Asst Dir* George Stamboulopoulos, Christos Kefalas, Simon Willson. *Prod Mgr* George Sarris. *Cont* May Kapsaskis. *Asst to the Prod* Paulle Clark. *Cost* Denny Vachlioti. *Wardrobe Mistress* Anna Stavropoulou. *Makeup* Ron Berkeley. *Fight Adv* Alf Joint. *Constr Mgr* Mikes Karapiperis.
Cast: Christopher Plummer *(Oedipus)*, Lilli Palmer *(Jocasta)*, Richard Johnson *(Creon)*, Orson Welles *(Tiresias)*, Cyril Cusack *(messenger)*, Roger Livesey *(shepherd)*, Donald Sutherland *(chorus leader)*, Alexis Mantheakis *(palace official)*, Dimos Starenios *(priest)*, Friedrich Ledebur *(King Laius)*, Oenone Luke *(Antigone)*, Cressida Luke *(Ismene)*, Minos Argyrakis, Manos Destounis, George Dialegmenos, Takis Emmanouel, Alexandros Maniatakis, George Oekonomou, Pan Panagiotopoulos, Nikos Paschalides, Paul Roche, Achilleas Skordilis, Grigoris Stefanides, Kostas Themos, George Zaifides *(The Chorus)*, Mary Xenoudaki, Jenny Damianopoulou, Diana J. Reed *(Jocasta's handmaidens)*.
Drama. Source: Sophocles, *Oedipus Rex*. The film is a screen version of the famous Greek tragedy by Sophocles. *Greeks. Royalty. Brothers-in-law. Widows. Prophets. Shepherds. Murder. Patricide. Parentage. Incest. Suicide. Mutilation. Plague. Thebes. Oedipus. Blindness. Exile.*
Note: Location scenes filmed in Dodona, Greece. Opened in London in Jun 1968.

L'OEIL DU MALIN *see* **THE THIRD LOVER**

OF BEDS AND BROADS *see* **TALES OF PARIS**

OF FLESH AND BLOOD (France/Italy)   **F6.3574**
Copernic Films–Films du Saphrène–Dear Film. *Dist* Times Film Corp. **1964**. Sd; col (Eastmancolor). 35mm (Franscope). ca83 min.
Prod Raymond Danon. *Supv Prod* (see note) Roger Vadim. *Dir* Christian Marquand. *Dial* Paul Gégauff. *Adapt* Christian Marquand, Pierre La Salle. *Photog* Andréas Winding. *Art Dir* Jean André. *Film Ed* Nadine Trintignant. *Mus* Michel Magne. *Sd* René Sarrazin. *Prod Mgr* Guy Lacourt.
Cast: Robert Hossein *(Samuel)*, Renato Salvatori *(Francis)*, Anouk Aimée *(Anna)*, Bervil *(garage owner)*, Jean Lefebvre *(card player)*, Andrée Turcy *(old woman)*, Serge Marquand *(mechanic)*, Fernand Sardou *(gendarme)*, Robert Dalban *(man in fairground)*.
Melodrama. Source: Jean Giono, *Les grands chemins* (Paris, 1951). Francis is delivering a jeep to Grenoble when he picks up Samuel. They become friends, but Francis soon discovers that Samuel has stolen part of the jeep's engine. At a carnival Francis meets, seduces, and falls in love with Anna, a young widow. The jeep breaks down, and they stay in a nearby hotel while it is being repaired. Meanwhile, Samuel has been playing poker with the local farmers. The cardplayers catch him cheating and in a fury, beat him up and break his hands. Francis and Anna nurse him for a while, but Samuel goes off, despairing over the mutilation. In a wooded area, he meets an old woman and tries to show her a card trick. When she laughs at him, he goes mad and strangles her. Francis joins a group of men who include the cardplaying farmers, to hunt Samuel down. When they confront him, Samuel shoots and kills the men who maimed him. Francis then shoots his friend so that he will not be captured. *Hitchhikers. Vagabonds. Widows. Cardsharps. Friendship. Theft. Pickups. Seduction. Cheating. Poker. Mutilation. Murder. Insanity. Manhunts. Hotels. Jeeps. Grenoble.*
Note: Screen credit: "A Film by Roger Vadim." Opened in Paris in Jul 1963 as *Les grands chemins;* running time: 93 min; in Italy as *Il baro.*

OF HUMAN BONDAGE (Great Britain)   **F6.3575**
Seven Arts Productions. *Dist* Metro-Goldwyn-Mayer, Inc. 2 Sep **1964** [Detroit opening; c24 Jul 1964; LP28887]. Sd (Westrex); b&w. 35mm. 98 min.
Prod James Woolf. *Assoc Prod* Ernest Holding. *Dir* Ken Hughes. *Dir Adtl Scenes* (see note) Henry Hathaway, Bryan Forbes. *Screenplay* Bryan Forbes. *Dir Photog* Oswald Morris. *Adtl Photog* Denys Coop. *Camera Op* Brian West. *Focus* Jimmy Turrell. *Col Cons* Eric Regan. *Asst Art Dir* Terence Marsh, Roy Rossotti. *Ch Draughtsman* Wallis Smith. *Draughtsman* Arden Gantley. *Scenic Artist* A. Van Montagu. *Prod Dsgn* John Box. *Graphic Dsgn* Maurice Binder.

Film Ed Russell Lloyd. *1st Asst Ed* William Butler. *Mus Comp & Cond* Ron Goodwin. *Sd Ed* Tom Simpson. *Sd Rec* Norman Bolland, Bob Jones. *Boom Op* John Salter. *1st, 2d & 3d Asst Dir* John Quested, Christopher Stamp, Michael Purcell. *Prod Mgr* Geoffrey Helman. *Cont* Angela Martelli. *Prod Sec* Myfanwy F. Jones. *Cost Dsgn* Beatrice Dawson. *Wardrobe Mistress* Laurel Staffell, Eileen Long. *Wardrobe Master* Brian Owen-Smith. *Makeup* George Frost. *Hairdressing* Olga Angelinetta. *Casting* Jenia Reissar. *Studio Constr Mgr* Peter McGoldrick. *Still Photog* Bert Cann. *Chargehand Electrn* Tom Chapman, W. B. Holmes.
Cast: Kim Novak *(Mildred Rogers)*, Laurence Harvey *(Philip Carey)*, Robert Morley *(Dr. Jacobs)*, Siobhan McKenna *(Norah Nesbitt)*, Roger Livesey *(Thorpe Athelny)*, Jack Hedley *(Griffiths)*, Nanette Newman *(Sally Athelny)*, Ronald Lacey *(Mathews)*, David Morris *(young Philip Carey)*, Anthony Booth *(Martin)*, Anna Manahan *(waitress)*, Jacqueline Taylor *(cook/woman patient)*, Derry O'Donovan *(2d waitress)*, Helen Robinson *(manageress-cashier)*, Michael Doolan *(man with club foot)*, John Sutton *(Kingsford)*, Leo McCabe *(elderly man in railway carriage)*, Olive White *(Griffiths' girl friend)*, Blanaid Irvine *(distinguished girl)*, Eamonn Morrisey *(bespectacled student)*, Ann Manceer *(girl patient)*, Robert Lepler *(jeweler)*, Evelyn McNeice *(Mrs. Harding)*, Norman Smythe *(attendant in dissecting theater)*, Caroline Swift *(nurse)*, Cecil Nash *(father of boy with club foot)*, Peter Nash *(young boy)*, May Cluskey *(Sister I)*, Terry Clinton *(barmaid)*, Danny O'Shea *(head waiter)*, Martin Crosbie, Alex Dignam *(porters)*, Brendan Mathews *(technician)*, Bryan Forbes, Peter Moray *(students)*.
Melodrama. Source: Somerset Maugham, *Of Human Bondage* (London, 1915). Philip Carey, a young man sensitive about his clubfoot, arrives in Edwardian London to study medicine after 2 years of failure as an artist in Paris. He becomes friendly with fellow students Griffiths and Mathews and falls in love with Mildred, a Cockney waitress who is impressed by his social superiority. Philip proposes to Mildred, but she announces her intention to marry a man named Miller. Soon thereafter, Philip accompanies Griffiths to a party and meets Norah, a widow, who returns his attentions. Under Norah's influence, Philip becomes successful in his studies, but soon Mildred, pregnant, unmarried, and deserted by Miller, returns. Philip forgets about Norah and takes Mildred in until her baby arrives. After the birth, Philip, Mildred, and Griffiths celebrate, but Mildred begins a flirtation with Griffiths. She and Philip quarrel when she shows him Griffiths' love letters; and, after telling Philip that his crippled foot has always revolted her and that her only interest in him was financial, Mildred leaves. Philip passes his final examinations and, during his internship, becomes friendly with Thorpe Athelny, a patient, and his daughter Sally. Philip learns that Mildred has become a prostitute, and he takes her, now a travesty of her former self, and her baby out of the brothel where they live and installs them in his flat. Finding she can no longer interest Philip, Mildred destroys everything valuable in the apartment and leaves again. She returns to prostitution; her baby dies; and she is admitted to the hospital where Philip works. It is discovered that she is incurably ill with syphilis. She dies in Philip's arms after asking for a proper funeral. Philip buries her in the style she wished and, despondent, decides to return to his artist's studio in Paris. But as his boat-train leaves the station, he looks up to find Sally standing over him. *Artists. Cripples. Barmaids. Widows. Medical students. Social classes. Childbirth. Prostitution. Infidelity. Illegitimacy. Hospitals. Venereal disease. London. Paris.*
Note: Opened in London in Nov 1964. Director Henry Hathaway resigned after shooting some footage; he was replaced temporarily by Bryan Forbes and finally by Kenneth Hughes. Previously filmed in 1934 (R.K.O.) and 1946 (Warner Bros.).

OF LOVE AND DESIRE   **F6.3576**
New World Film Corp. *Dist* Twentieth Century–Fox Film Corp. 11 Sep **1963** [New York opening; c21 Aug 1963; LP26270]. Sd (RCA); col (De Luxe). 35mm. 97 min.
Prod Victor Stoloff. *Dir* Richard Rush. *Screenplay* Laslo Gorog, Richard Rush. *Story* Victor Stoloff, Jacquine Delessert. *Photog* Alex Phillips. *Art Dir* Roberto Silva. *Film Ed* Harry Gerstad. *Assoc Film Ed* George Crone. *Song:* "Katherine's Theme" Ronald Stein. *Sung by* Sammy Davis, Jr. *Sd Rec* Manuel Topete. *Asst Dir* Henry Spitz, Mario Cisneros. *Prod Supv* Henry Spitz. *Prod Mgr* Felipe Subervielle. *Unit Prod Mgr* Antonio Tello. *Prod Asst* Nelly Levy. *Coiffure* Carita.
Cast: Merle Oberon *(Katherine Beckman)*, Steve Cochran *(Steve Corey)*, Curt Jurgens *(Paul Beckman)*, John Agar *(Gus Cole)*, Steve Brodie *(Bill Maxton)*, Eduardo Noriega *(Mr. Dominguez)*, Rebeca Iturbide *(Mrs. Renard)*, Elsa Cardenas *(Mrs. Dominguez)*, Tony Carbajal *(Dr. Renard)*, Aurora Muñoz *(Maria, the housemaid)*, Felix Gonzalez *(engineer)*, Felipe Flores *(Julio)*.
Society melodrama. Among the wealthy socialites living in Mexico City are Katherine Beckman and her half brother, Paul. When Paul hires Steve Corey, an American engineer, to supervise the construction of some mining operations,

the promiscuous Katherine lures him to her house for the night. As their affair blossoms into love, Paul becomes so jealous that he arranges for Katherine to see her former lover, Gus Cole. Although Katherine resists Gus's advances, she eventually has too much to drink and Gus forces himself upon her. When she awakens, she attempts to kill herself by slashing her wrists, but Steve arrives in time to save her. During her convalescence she explains to Steve that her behavior is an attempt to compensate for having refused to give herself to her first love, a young soldier killed during World War II. The understanding Steve persuades her to marry him and leave Mexico City. As she returns home to pack, she is confronted by Paul, who confesses his incestuous desires. Shocked by the revelation, she runs out into the night. But Steve finds her and promises her a new life. *Socialites. Americans in foreign countries. Engineers—Civil. Brother-sister relationship. Promiscuity. Jealousy. Suicide. Drunkenness. Rape. Incest. Mexico City.*

Note: Filmed in Mexico. Working titles: *The Forsaken Garden* and *In a Secret Garden.*

OF STARS AND MEN F6.3577

Storyboard Productions. *Dist* Brandon Films. 28 Apr **1964** [New York opening; c17 Jul 1961; LU3186]. Sd; col (Eastman Color). 35mm. 53 min. [Also 63 min.]

Prod-Writ John Hubley, Faith Hubley. *Dir* John Hubley. *Anim Dir* Bill Littlejohn, Gary Mooney. *Photog* John Buehre. *Film Ed* Faith Hubley. *Mus Dir* Walter Trampler. *Mus* Johann Christoph Pezel, Andrea Gabrieli, Johann Sebastian Bach, George Frederick Handel, Antonio Vivaldi, Wolfgang Amadeus Mozart, Ludwig van Beethoven. *Screenplay Cons* Harlow Shapley.

Cast: Mark Hubley, Hampy Hubley (*children's voices*), Harlow Shapley (*narrator*).

Animated instructional film. Source: Harlow Shapley, *Of Stars and Men* (Boston, 1958). Man, in the person of a small boy, assumes leadership of the animal kingdom. A comet streaks across the sky, and he begins to question the nature of his existence in the limitless universe. The time-space and matter-energy theories are interpreted in symbols of balls and cubes; building blocks, as atoms and electrons, are arranged in different configurations to explain these concepts in simple, yet cosmic, terms. Man's conclusion is that there may be other human species in the universe. *Astronomy. Human race. The Universe. Animal life.*

OF THE SAME GENDER F6.3578

Dove Productions. *Dist* Distribpix, Inc. 4 Oct **1968** [Champaign, Illinois, showing]. Sd; b&w. 35mm. [Feature length assumed.]

Dir Phyllis Stein. *Screenplay* Shirley White. *Photog* Jo Taunt. *Art Dir* Alice Spike. *Film Ed* Gertrude Scott. *Mus* Paula Starr. *Makeup* Emily Dick.

Cast: Bebe Dill (*Katherine Stone*), Michaelangelo Jones (*Robbie Stone*), Pussy Willow (*Joan Rheinheart*), Shirley White (*Bonnie Black*), Sudden Storm (*Helen, dancer*), Janet Mary Prance (*Mary, dancer*), Robert Marcus (*John, dancer*).

Melodrama(?). No precise information about the nature of this film has been found. Press material suggests that it contains scenes of lesbianism, prostitution, nymphomania, and sadism. *Lesbianism. Prostitution. Nymphomania. Sadism.*

Note: Also known as *Same Gender.*

OF WAYWARD LOVE (Italy/West Germany) F6.3579

Spa Cinematografica–Eichberg Film. *Dist* Pathé-Contemporary Films. 23 Mar **1964** [New York opening]. Sd; b&w. 35mm. 91 min. [Also 87 min.]

Overall Production Credits: *Prod* Achille Piazzi. *Film Ed* Eraldo Da Roma. *Mus* Piero Umiliani.

Production Credits for "The Women": *Dir* Sergio Sollima. *Screenplay* Alessandro Continenza, Ettore Scola. *Story* Ercole Patti. *Photog* Carlo Carlini. *Camera Op* Luigi Filippo Carta.

Production Credits for "The Serpent": *Dir* Alberto Bonucci. *Screenplay* Fabio Carpi, Guglielmo Santangelo, Renato Mainardi. *Story* Mario Soldati. *Photog* Erico Menczer. *Camera Op* Gastone Di Giovanni.

Production Credits for "The Soldier": *Dir* Nino Manfredi. *Screenplay* Fabio Carpi, Giuseppe Orlandini, Ettore Scola, Nino Manfredi. *Story* Italo Calvino. *Photog* Carlo Carlini.

Cast—"The Women": Enrico Maria Salerno (*Antonio*), Catherine Spaak (*Valeria*), Claudia Mori (*Bruna*).

Cast—"The Serpent": Lilli Palmer (*Hilde Brenner*), Bernhard Wicki (*Professor Brenner*), Gastone Moschin (*police marshal*).

Cast—"The Soldier": Nino Manfredi (*Tomagra, the soldier*), Fulvia Franco (*The Widow*).

Romantic comedy. THE WOMEN: Antonio, a middle-aged bachelor, finds that his regular mistresses are busy and calls Bruna, a woman with whom he has been having a casual affair. She arrives and shocks him by announcing that she has just been married, but she goes to bed with him anyway, claiming that her marriage will not alter their relationship. That afternoon, Antonio goes to

the beach with Valeria, another girl friend, who lures him into bed and afterwards reveals that she was a virgin. Antonio is left perplexed and realizes that, despite his worldliness, his life is vacant and absurd. THE SERPENT: Professor Brenner and his wife, Hilde, a couple whose marriage is unstable, are vacationing in Sicily. While visiting Aphrodite's temple, Hilde tries to arouse her husband's attention by pretending that she mistakes a snakeskin belt for a real snake, but he only scoffs at her. Later, their car breaks down on a lonely road, and two truckdrivers give Hilde a ride to town to get help. She half hopes that they will attack her, but they are uninterested so she vindictively accuses them of rape. Her husband arrives at the police station to explain Hilde's fantasies and clear the drivers. He realizes that he has neglected Hilde and decides to pay more attention to her. THE SOLDIER: In a stuffy train compartment, a soldier, Tomagra, attempts to seduce a voluptuous widow, despite the presence of three other people. The widow remains impassive, but after the others leave the train, Tomagra and the widow wordlessly make love. When the widow disembarks, Tomagra eagerly follows, but she is whisked off by relatives, leaving him alone and confused. *Bachelors. Mistresses. Professors. Truckdrivers. Police. Soldiers. Widows. Infidelity. Seduction. Virginity. Marriage. Vacations. Trains. Sicily.*

Note: Opened in Rome in Dec 1962 as *L'amore difficile*; running time: 125 min; in West Germany in Aug 1963 as *Erotica*; running time: 121 min. Italian titles for segments: "Le donne," "Il serpente," and "L'avventura di un soldato." The German and Italian release versions include a fourth segment, "L'avaro," directed by Luciano Lucignani.

OFFBEAT (Great Britain) F6.3580

Northiam. *Dist* Schoenfeld Film Distributing Corp. 18 Feb **1966** [Boston opening]. Sd; b&w. 35mm. 72 min.

Prod E. M. Smedley-Aston. *Dir* Cliff Owen. *Orig Story & Screenplay* Peter Barnes. *Photog* Geoffrey Faithfull. *Art Dir* George Provis. *Film Ed* Antony Gibbs. *Mus Dir* Ken Jones. *Sd Rec* Bill Salter, Red Law. *Prod Mgr* Clifton Brandon.

Cast: William Sylvester (*Steve Layton/Steve Ross*), Mai Zetterling (*Ruth Lombard*), Anthony Dawson, British (*James Dawson*), John Meillon (*Johnny Remick*), John Phillips, British (*Chief Superintendent Gault*), Victor Brooks (*Inspector Adams*), Joseph Furst (*Paul Varna*), Neil McCarthy (*Leo Farrell*), Harry Baird (*Gill Hall*), Diana King (*Maggie Dawson*), Gerard Heinz (*Jake*), Nan Munro (*Sarah Bennett*), Ronald Adam (*J. B. Wykeham*), Anthony Baird (*constable*), Neil Wilson (*Pat Ryan*).

Crime melodrama. In London, Steve Layton, an MI5 agent, is assigned to work with Scotland Yard as an undercover agent. Posing as a Tangiers bank robber, Layton infiltrates the gang led by James Dawson, who poses as an exporter. Layton becomes a trusted member of the gang and is attracted to Ruth Lombard, a widow. Soon his ideas about criminals begin to change with his growing respect for their sense of honor. Ruth sees him talking to Inspector Adams, his contact, but Layton convinces her that he is now a loyal member of the gang and would not reveal the planned jewel robbery. After the robbery, a fence identifies Layton as an agent, but he is able to talk his way out of it until Adams arrives to arrest the gang. Layton is unable to convince them of his sincere loyalty, and he is deeply troubled to receive congratulations and the reward money. *Secret agents. Gangsters. Widows. Informers. Police. Imposture. Robbery. Loyalty. Conscience. London. Scotland Yard.*

Note: Opened in London in Feb 1961. Working title: *The Devil Inside.*

OFFICE LOVE-IN, WHITE COLLAR STYLE F6.3581

A. F. P. I. Productions. *Dist* SCA Distributors, Sack Amusement Enterprises. ca **1968**. Sd; b&w. 35mm. 82 min.

Prod-Dir A. C. Stephen. *Orig Story* J. T. Casey. *Photog* Robert Ruben. *Sets* Bud Costello. *Ed* Sir Gay. *Mus* Igor Gigagusky. *Still Photog* CinemaGraphics.

Cast: Kathy Williams (*Stephanie Morris*), Forman Shane, Carol Saunders, Ray Cyr, Colleen Murphy, Nemo Nomus, Felicia Phark, Hugh Thelman, Lynn Harris, Michael Di Rosa, Vincent Barbi, Clete Bennett.

Drama. Winthrop A. Albertson, Sr., president of the Date-A-Mate Corp., finds that his new secretary, Stephanie Morris, compensates with her skills in the bedroom for those she lacks in the office. Winthrop, Jr., invites Stephanie for a drive and tries to follow in his father's footsteps, but he fails to measure up at the crucial moment and throws Stephanie out of his car when she makes an unkind comparison. She accepts a ride from Anne, an attractive lesbian. Meanwhile, Mae Flowers of the computer department succeeds in luring her boss, Lionel Smythe, to her apartment, and both of them end up in the bathtub. In spite of himself, gay Personnel Officer Vincent Sowash falls in love with clerk-typist applicant Jane Leary, who agrees to help him find his manhood. Only by dressing as a woman can he perform as a man; she gives him her clothes, and they become lovers. Stephanie and her friend from the payroll office, Marie Corbin, meet bank official Tom Brandon while they are cashing their checks. Tom and Stephanie go out to dinner and invite Marie and Tom's friend Cosmo to join them for a party. After movies at Tom's, all four end up in the same bed. The next day, Stephanie is promoted to executive secretary and meets Mr. Albertson's family. When she discovers that her lesbian lover, Anne, is her boss's wife, Tom's sister, and young Winthrop's mother, she nearly faints away. *Executives. Secretaries. Business managers. Office clerks. Bankers. Seduction. Lesbianism. Male homosexuality. Impotence. Group sex. Transvestism. Computer dating services. Employer-employee relations.*

Note: Also known as *Swinging Secretary.*

THE OFFICE PARTY — F6.3582

B. & P. Enterprises. *Dist* Crescent International Pictures. 12 Sep **1968** [San Francisco showing]. Sd; col. 35mm. 80 min.

Prod Whit Boyd, Ludwig Moner. *Dir* Ron Scott. *Screenplay* William E. Hamelman. *Photog* Ludwig Moner. *Asst Camera* Jeff Hipp. *Art Dir* X. O. Vangam. *Sd Rec* Danny Brown. *Script Girl* Peggie O'Neal. *Makeup* Byron Lord. *Hairstyles* Judy Farr.

Cast: Byron Lord (*Mr. Marks, the boss*), Judy Farr (*Maxine, his secretary*), Larry Tanner (*Carl, office manager*), Michelle Michelle (*Joyce, his secretary*), Ron Scott (*Bob, cashier*), Dianne Davis (*Janet, head steno*), Jimmie Raye (*Chunky, office boy*), Jeannie Hart (*steno 1*), Linda Lang (*steno 2*), Marlo Martin (*steno 3*), Dennis Adams (*janitor*), Danny Brown (*switchboard operator*), Barbara Bolyn (*elevator operator*), Chastity Fox (*Susan*), Artie Brooks (*Mr. Jacobs*).

Comedy. Sexual adventures occupy the staff of the Harris Company to the exclusion of business. A frenzy of sexual activity at every level from the top echelons of management through the stenographers' pool to the supply room culminates in an orgy for all. *Stenographers. Business managers. Office clerks. Group sex. Sexuality. Employer-employee relations. Orgies.*

OGGI, DOMANI E DOPODOMANI see **KISS THE OTHER SHEIK**

OGGI, DOMANI E DOPODOMANI see **THE MAN WITH THE BALLOONS**

OGNUNO PER SÈ see **THE RUTHLESS FOUR**

LES OGRESSES see **THE QUEENS**

OH DAD, POOR DAD, MAMA'S HUNG YOU IN THE CLOSET AND I'M FEELIN' SO SAD — F6.3583

Seven Arts Productions–Ray Stark. *Dist* Paramount Pictures. 15 Feb **1967** [New York opening; c15 Feb 1967; LP34059]. Sd; col (Technicolor). 35mm. 86 min.

Prod Ray Stark, Stanley Rubin. *Assoc Prod* Carter De Haven, Jr. *Dir* Richard Quine. *Adtl Dir* (see note) Alexander Mackendrick. *Screenplay* Ian Bernard. *Narr* Pat McCormick, Herbert Baker. *Cinematog* Geoffrey Unsworth. *2d Unit Photog* Skeets Kelly. *Co-photog* Charles Lawton. *Art Dir* Phil Jeffries. *Set Decor* William Kiernan. *Film Ed* Warren Low, David Wages. *Mus* Neal Hefti. *Sd* Josh Westmoreland, John Wilkinson. *Asst Dir* Mickey McCardle. *Prod Mgr* John Coonan. *Miss Russell's Cost* Galanos. *Cost* Howard Shoup. *Makeup* Robert Schiffer. *Hairstyles* Jane Shugrue. *Sp Eff* Charles Spurgeon. *Proc Photog* Farciot Edouart.

Cast: Rosalind Russell (*Madame Rosepettle*), Robert Morse (*Jonathan*), Barbara Harris (*Rosalie*), Hugh Griffith (*Commodore Roseabove*), Jonathan Winters (*Dad/narrator*), Lionel Jeffries (*airport commander*), Cyril Delevanti (*Hawkins*), Hiram Sherman (*Brechenduff*), George Kirby (*Moses*), Janis Hansen (*The Other Woman*).

Farce. Source: Arthur L. Kopit, *Oh Dad, Poor Dad, Mama's Hung You in the Closet and I'm Feelin' So Sad* (New York opening: 26 Feb 1962). As Madame Rosepettle arrives at a tropical island with her doting 25-year-old son, Jonathan, her collection of Venus flytrap plants, and a coffin containing the stuffed body of her late husband, her actions are carefully watched from a heavenly cloud by Dad himself. Determined to make a man of his simpering son, Dad arranges for Rosalie, a seductive babysitter, to meet Jonathan. Madame Rosepettle is so arrogantly confident of her son that she interrupts her own pursuit of Commodore Roseabove, a wealthy lecher, to allow Rosalie to attempt a seduction. Although Jonathan obeys his mother's teachings, he later secretly watches some home movies she shows to the commodore and is so appalled by her past that he destroys all of her possessions. Hearing the commotion, Rosalie barges in on him, seizes the opportunity to fling him on his mother's bed, and refuses to interrupt her seduction even when Dad's corpse falls out of a closet on top of them. Jonathan, however, is so upset by the experience that he strangles Rosalie and then flees from the scene. When Madame Rosepettle returns from her wedding to the commodore and discovers what has happened, she sets out to find Jonathan. During the chase that follows, the commodore suffers a heart attack while attempting to rescue Jonathan from a runaway motorboat. Once her son has been returned to her, Madame Rosepettle, dressed in mourning, leaves the island with her entourage, which now includes two coffins. As she beams proudly at her untainted son, Dad, defeated, climbs back on to his cloud. *Temptresses. Fatherhood. Momism. Lechery. Virginity. Seduction. Murder. Islands. Corpses. Home movies.*

Heaven.

Note: Location scenes filmed in Jamaica. Following previews in 1965, release was delayed to add a prolog and inserts, directed by Alexander Mackendrick.

OH! THOSE MOST SECRET AGENTS! see **00-2 MOST SECRET AGENTS**

OH! WHAT A LOVELY WAR (Great Britain) — F6.3584

Accord Productions. *Dist* Paramount Pictures. 3 Oct **1969** [New York opening; c9 Apr 1969; LF52]. Sd; col (Technicolor). 35mm (Panavision). 132 min. [Also reviewed at 136 and 139 min.] *MPAA rating* G.

Prod Brian Duffy, Richard Attenborough. *Assoc Prod* Mack Davidson. *Dir* Richard Attenborough. *Screenplay* (see note) Len Deighton. *Dir Photog* Gerry Turpin. *Camera* Ron Taylor. *Camera Asst* Michael Sarafian. *Art Dir* Harry White. *Set Dresser* Peter James. *Scenic Artist* Peter Wood. *Prod Dsgn* Don Ashton. *Main Titl* Raymond Hawkey. *Film Ed* Kevin Connor. *Songs Orch & Incidental Mus Comp & Cond by* Alfred Ralston. *Choreog* Eleanor Fazan. *Sd Mix* Simon Kaye. *Mus Ed* Michael Clifford. *Sd Ed* Don Challis, Brian Holland, ed. *Dub Mix* Gerry Humphreys. *Sp Sd Eff* Peter Handford. *Mus Rec* Eric Tomlinson. *Boom Op* Tom Buchanan. *Asst Dir* Claude Watson. *Prod Mgr* John Comfort. *Location Mgr* Bryan Coates. *Prod Sec* Ann Paterson. *Cont* Ann Skinner. *Cost Dsgn* Anthony Mendleson. *Wardrobe Master* Brian Owen-Smith. *Wardrobe Mistress* Eileen Sullivan. *Makeup Supv* Stuart Freeborn. *Ch Hairdresser* Biddy Chrystal. *Sp Eff* Ron Ballanger. *Military Adv* Douglas Campbell, (Maj.-Gen.). *Casting* Miriam Brickman. *Constr Mgr* Albert Blackshaw. *Camera Grip* Pat Newman. *Prop Buyer* Ronald Baker. *Elec Supv* Fred Anderson. *Prod Res* May Routh.

Cast: Ralph Richardson (*Sir Edward Grey*), Meriel Forbes (*Lady Grey*), Wensley Pithey (*Archduke Franz Ferdinand*), Ruth Kettlewell (*Duchess Sophie*), Ian Holm (*President Poincaré*), John Gielgud (*Count Berchtold*), Kenneth More (*Kaiser Wilhelm II*), John Clements (*General von Moltke*), Paul Daneman (*Tsar Nicholas II*), Pamela Abbott (*Tsarina*), Stella Courtney (*Poincaré's lady*), Kathleen Helme (*Berchtold's lady*), Ruth Gower (*Von Moltke's lady*), Elizabeth Craven (*Kaiserin*), Joe Melia (*The Photographer*), Anthony Morton (*Italian military attache*), Steve Plytas (*Turkish military attache*), Jack Hawkins (*Emperor Franz Josef*), John Hussey, actor (*soldier on balcony*), Kim Smith (*Dickie Smith*), Mary Wimbush (*Mary Smith*), Paul Shelley (*Jack Smith*), Wendy Allnutt (*Flo Smith*), John Rae (*Grandpa Smith*), Kathleen Wileman (*Emma Smith, age 4*), Corin Redgrave (*Bertie Smith*), Malcolm McFee (*Freddie Smith*), Colin Farrell (*Harry Smith*), Maurice Roeves (*George Smith*), Angela Thorne (*Betty Smith*), John Mills (*Field Marshal Sir Douglas Haig*), Julia Wright (*his secretary*), Jean-Pierre Cassel (*French colonel*), David Scheuer (*French soldier*), Michael Wolf (*German officer*), Jeremy Child (*wealthy young man*), Ambrose Coghill (*his father*), Penny Allen (*solo chorus girl*), Sheila Cox, Sue Robinson, Hermione Farthingale, Joyce Franklin, Carole Gray, Dinny Jones, Delia Linden (*chorus girls*), Maggie Smith (*music hall star*), David Lodge (*recruiting sergeant*), Michael Redgrave (*Gen. Sir Henry Wilson*), Laurence Olivier (*Field Marshal Sir John French*), Peter Gilmore (*Private Burgess*), Derek Newark (*shooting gallery proprietor*), Richard Howard (*young soldier at Mons*), John Trigger (*officer at station*), Ron Pember (*corporal at station*), Juliet Mills, Nanette Newman (*nurses at station*), Susannah York (*Eleanor*), Dirk Bogarde (*Stephen*), Norman Jones, actor (*1st Scottish soldier*), Andrew Robertson (*2d Scottish soldier*), Ben Howard (*Private Garbett*), Angus Lennie (*3d Scottish soldier*), Brian Tipping (*4th Scottish soldier*), Christian Doermer (*Fritz*), Tony Vogel (*German soldier*), Paul Hansard (*German officer*), John Woodnutt (*British officer*), Tony Thawnton (*officer on telephone*), Frank Coda, Kim Grant, Richard Loring, Tom Mashall (*soldiers in "Goodbyee"*), Annie Bee, Valerie Smith, Isabelle Metcalfe, Jenny Morgan (*girl friends in "Goodbyee"*), Cecil Parker (*Sir John*), Zeph Gladstone (*his chauffeuse*), Stanley McGeagh, Stanley Lebor (*soldiers in gassed trench*), Robert Flemyng (*staff officer in gassed trench*), Thorley Walters, Norman Shelley (*staff officers in ballroom*), Isabel Dean (*Sir John French's lady*), Guy Middleton (*Gen. Sir William Robertson*), Natasha Parry (*his lady*), Cecilia Darby (*Sir Henry Wilson's lady*), Phyllis Calvert (*Lady Haig*), Raymond S. Edwards (*3d staff officer in ballroom*), Freddie Ascott ("*Whizzbang*" *soldier*), Edward Fox, Geoffrey Davies (*aides*), Pippa Steel, Elisabeth Murray (*scoreboard girls*), Christian Thorogood, Paddy Joyce, John Dunhill, John Owens, P. G. Stephens (*Irish soldiers*), Vanessa Redgrave (*Sylvia Pankhurst*), Clifford Mollison, Dorothy Reynolds, Harry Locke, George Ghent, Bette Vivian (*hecklers*), Michael Bates (*drunken lance corporal*), Charles Farrell, British (*policeman*), Pia Colombo (*estaminet singer*), Vincent Ball (*Australian soldier*), Anthony Ainley (*3d aide*), Gerald Sim (*chaplain*), Maurice Arthur (*soldier singer in church parade*), Richard Davies (*sergeant in* burial party), Arthur White (sergeant in dugout), Christopher Cabot (soldier in shell hole), Lind Joyce, Mary Yeomans (other scoreboard girls), Fanny Carby, Christine Noonan, Marianne Stone (mill girls), Charlotte Attenborough (Emma Smith, age 8), Joanne Browne (singer), Frank Forsyth (Woodrow Wilson), John Gabriel (Nikolai Lenin).

War farce with music. Source: Charles Chilton, Oh! What a Lovely War (Stratford-upon-Avon opening: 19 Mar 1963). In the summer of 1914, leaders of European royalty gather together for a group photograph. As the camera's flashpan explodes, Archduke Franz Ferdinand and his wife fall dead. Accusations are exchanged, impossible ultimatums are delivered, and the heads of state choose sides for the inevitable war. A flashing electric sign at the seaside resort of Brighton announces World War I, and the Smith family falls in line to purchase tickets for patriotic sideshows from England's Gen. Sir Douglas Haig. Young Harry Smith responds to an enthusiastic music hall singer and enlists; a short time later, his brother Jack wins at a shooting gallery and is rewarded with a uniform and a one-way ticket to the war. Meanwhile, as Haig haggles with Sir John French and Sir Henry Wilson over strategy, a giant cricket scoreboard tallies deaths in battle. The social set, represented by Stephen and Eleanor, contributes to the effort by vowing not to drink German wine for the war's duration and by requiring their servants to knit mittens for the troops. On Christmas Eve, as the scoreboard tallies 1 1/2 million dead, Allied and German soldiers meet in the no-man's-land between their trenches to exchange liquor, cigarettes, and addresses. While Bertram and George Smith live knee-deep in mud, the military brass drink champagne at lavish balls, and Haig mounts his tower at Brighton Pier to order 300,000 men into the Battle of Somme. Meanwhile, suffragette Sylvia Pankhurst is heckled by a street-corner crowd as she reads anti-war letters written by George Bernard Shaw. At the front lines, a chaplain announces that the Dalai Lama in Tibet is offering his prayers, and the troops answer by singing their own bitter lyrics to traditional church hymns. At a field hospital, Harry Smith dies in the arms of his sister Betty, a nurse, while Haig cheerfully announces that, although no ground was taken at Somme, there were only 60,000 casualties. In 1917, the Americans enter the war, and victory is imminent. As a final tally shows 9 million dead, military representatives meet on Brighton Pier to sign the peace treaty. On that day, Jack Smith is killed in action; following a maze of red tape, he walks through patches of swirling smoke to a path strewn with red poppies. Simultaneously, the Smith women picnic on the green hillside where the five Smith boys lie buried along with all the other millions of war dead. Songs: "Oh! What a Lovely War," "Oh I Do Like To Be Beside the Seaside," "Belgium Put the Kibosh on the Kaiser" (French colonel), "Are We Downhearted?" "Your King and Country Need You" (chorus girl), "I'll Make a Man of You" (music hall star), "Send for the Boys of the Girls' Brigade" (young soldier at Mons), "We're 'Ere Because We're 'Ere," "Pack Up Your Troubles," "Heilige Nacht," "Christmas Day in the Cookhouse" (Private Garbett), "Goodbyee" (photographer and Bertie Smith), "Gassed," "Roses of Picardy," "Row, Row, Row," "Comrades" (photographer), "La Paloma," "She Was One of the Early Birds," "Hush Here Comes a Whizzbang," "There's a Long, Long Trail," "Rule Britannia," "I Don't Want To Be a Soldier," "Mademoiselle From Armentières," "The Moon Shines Bright on Charlie Chaplin," "Adieu la vie" (estaminet singer), "They Were Only Playing Leapfrog," "Forward Joe Soap's Army," "When This Lousy War Is Over" (soldier in church parade), "Whiter Than the Whitewash on the Wall," "I Want To Go Home," "The Bells of Hell," "Never Mind," "Far, Far From Wipers" (young soldier at Mons), "If You Want the Old Battalion," "Keep the Home Fires Burning," "Over There," "They'll Never Believe Me." Royalty. Brothers. Singers. Idle rich. Pacifists. Suffragettes. Chaplains. Nurses. War heroes. War victims. Patriotism. Death. Combat zone life. Social classes. Assassination. Sideshows. Music halls. Contests. Hospitals. Picnics. Christmas. World War I. Somme River. Brighton (England). Edward Grey. Franz Ferdinand. Nicholas II (Russia). Franz Josef. Douglas Haig. Henry Hughes Wilson. John Denton Pinkstone French. Estelle Sylvia Pankhurst. Thomas Woodrow Wilson. Nikolai Lenin. Great Britain— Army. France—Army. Germany—Army. United States Army.

Note: Location scenes filmed in Brighton and Sheepscote, England. Opened in London in Apr 1969; running time: 144 min. Deighton, originally a co-producer, requested that he not be given screen credit.

OHAYO (Japan)   F6.3585
Shochiku Co. Dist Shochiku Films of America. Feb **1962** [Los Angeles showing]. Sd; b&w (see note). 35mm. 93 min.
Prod Shizuo Yamanouchi. Dir Yasujiro Ozu. Screenplay Kogo Noda, Yasujiro Ozu. Photog Yushun Atsuta. Art Dir Tatsuo Hamada. Mus Toshiro Mayuzumi.
Cast: Koji Shidara (Minoru [The Elder Brother]), Masahiko Shimazu (Isamu [The Younger Brother]), Chishu Ryu (their father), Kuniko Miyake (their mother), Yoshiko Kuga (their aunt), Keiji Sada (their teacher), Haruo Tanaka (Tatsuko), Haruko Sugimura (Kikue, his wife), Teruko Nagaoka, Toyoko

Takahashi (neighbors), Eijiro Tono.
Domestic comedy-drama. The families in a middle-class housing development just outside Tokyo share in one another's lives. Only one house in the community has television, and a favorite pastime of the young boys in the neighborhood is to gather there to watch wrestling matches. Minoru and Isamu, the two Hayashi brothers, are frustrated in their attempts to persuade their parents to buy a television set. Told to shut up, the boys go on a silence strike, which offends their courtesy-conscious neighbors, who blame the boys' parents for their behavior. The brothers run away, are found, and are returned to their parents by their teachers, but their "strike" has been effective. They arrive home to find their own television set awaiting them. Brothers. Schoolteachers. Neighbors. Family life. Urban life. Middle classes. Parenthood. Television. Wrestling. Tokyo.
Note: Released in Japan in May 1959 in color; running time: 96 min. Also known as Good Morning.

OIL TOWN (Reissue)   F6.3586
Paramount Pictures. Dist Paramount Pictures, Citation Films. 20 Nov **1961** [Maryland license]. Sd; col. 35mm (VistaVision). 104 min.
Note: Originally released in 1955 as Lucy Gallant; c18 Oct 1955; LP5483.

L'OISEAU DE PARADIS see **DRAGON SKY**

LES OISEAUX VONT MOURIR AU PÉROU see **BIRDS IN PERU**

EL OJO DE LA CERRADURA see **THE EAVESDROPPER**

THE OLD DARK HOUSE (United States/Great Britain)   F6.3587
William Castle Productions–Hammer Film Productions. Dist Columbia Pictures. 31 Oct **1963** [New York opening; c1 Jun 1963; LP25415]. Sd (RCA); col (Eastman color by Pathé). 35mm. 86 min.
Prod (see note) William Castle, Anthony Hinds. Assoc Prod (see note) Dona Holloway, Basil Keys. Dir William Castle. Screenplay Robert Dillon. Dir Photog Arthur Grant. Camera Op Moray Grant. Focus Wally Byatt. Camera Grip Albert Cowland. Art Dir Bernard Robinson. Asst Art Dir Ken Ryan, Burt Evans. Titl Backgrounds Charles Addams. Supv Film Ed James Needs. Asst Ed Chris Barnes. 2d Asst Ed Pat Foster. Mus Comp & Cond Benjamin Frankel. Sd Mix Jock May. Sd Ed James Groom. Sd Camera Op H. C. Allan. 1st, 2d & 3d Asst Dir Douglas Hermes, Dominic Fulford, Hugh Harlow. Prod Mgr John Draper. Prod Sec Maureen White. Cont Pauline Wise. Wardrobe Supv Molly Arbuthnot. Wardrobe Mistress Rosemary Burrows. Makeup Roy Ashton. Hairdresser Frieda Steiger. Sp Eff Les Bowie. Still Photog Tom Edwards. Studio Mgr A. F. Kelly. Constr Mgr Arthur Banks. Ch Electrn Jack Curtis, electrn. Prop Master Tommy Money. Prop Buyer Eric Hillier.
Cast: Tom Poston (Tom Penderel), Robert Morley (Roderick Femm), Janette Scott (Cecily), Joyce Grenfell (Agatha Femm), Peter Bull (Casper Femm/Jasper Femm), Mervyn Johns (Potiphar), Fenella Fielding (Morgana), Danny Green (Morgan Femm).
Mystery farce. Source: J. B. Priestley, Benighted (London, 1928). Tom Penderel, an American car salesman in London, delivers a car to an old mansion in Wales and discovers that his eccentric client, Casper Femm, is dead. The car crashes in a raging storm, and Tom is invited to stay at the house by members of Casper's family, including his nieces, the demure young Cecily and the seductive Morgana, and his Uncle Potiphar, who has been building an ark in anticipation of another great flood. Each of the relatives is required to return to the dilapidated mansion before midnight each evening or forfeit his share of the family fortune. During the night, one of the Femm family dies every hour. First Agatha Femm, Casper's mother, is discovered with her knitting needles stuck in her throat. Casper's twin brother, Jasper, is the next victim, followed by Roderick, the head of the family. Tom stumbles upon the fact that the killer is a woman, and he accuses Morgana, but Cecily confesses, explaining that she wanted the entire family estate. Cecily runs from the house, and Tom discovers that she has placed time bombs in all of the clocks in the house. Racing against time, he frantically defuses each of the bombs. With moments to spare, he hurls the last bomb out of the window, and it explodes at Cecily's feet. Salesmen. Americans in foreign countries. Eccentrics. Brothers. Twins. Murder. Family life. Inheritance. Bombs. Manors. Wales. Automobile accidents. Storms.
Note: Filmed in Great Britain in 1962 and released there in Jul 1966; running time: 77 min. Sources conflict in crediting producer and associate producer.

THE OLD GROUCHY see **THE GROUCH**

THE OLD MAN'S BRIDE   F6.3588
Gunter Productions. 7 Sep **1967** [San Francisco showing]. Sd; b&w. 35mm. [Feature film, length unknown.]
Prod-Dir George Gunter. Screenplay Milton F. Beggs.
Cast: Patricia Moore (Julie), Doc Barrington, Mercy O'Tool, Ralph G. Edwards, Erick Von Ryan, Wayne Gaston.

Melodrama. Party girl Julie marries an elderly man, but he is unable to satisfy her sexual desires. Julie is constantly looking for new sexual partners, and she finds satisfaction with another woman. In addition, she participates in group sexual encounters until a jealous husband arrives and mayhem results. *Old age. Infidelity. Group sex. Lesbianism. Jealousy. Murder.*

Note: Based on a story that appeared in *Adam's Bedside Reader* in 1965. May also be known as *The Bride.*

OLD MOTHER RILEY MEETS THE VAMPIRE *see* **MY SON THE VAMPIRE**

OLD ŠETERHEND *see* **SHATTERHAND**

OLD SHATTERHAND *see* **SHATTERHAND**

OLD SUREHAND, 1. TEIL *see* **FLAMING FRONTIER**

THE OLDEST CONFESSION *see* **THE HAPPY THIEVES**

THE OLDEST PROFESSION (France/Italy/West Germany)   **F6.3589**
Gibé–Francoriz–Franco London Film–Rialto Film–Rizzoli Films. *Dist* Goldstone Film Enterprises, VIP Distributors. Jun **1968** [Los Angeles showing; c26 Jun 1968; LP36226]. Sd; col (Eastmancolor). 35mm. 97 min.

Overall Production Credits: *Pres by* Jack H. Harris. *Prod* Joseph Bergholz. *Camera* Pierre Lhomme. *Art Dir* Max Douy, Bernard Evein, Maurice Petri. *Mus* Michel Legrand. *Prod Mgr* André Cultet.

Production Credits—"Prehistoric Era": *Dir* Franco Indovina. *Scen* Ennio Flajano.

Production Credits—"Roman Nights": *Dir* Mauro Bolognini. *Scen* Ennio Flajano.

Production Credits—"Mademoiselle Mimi": *Dir* Philippe de Broca. *Scen* Daniel Boulanger.

Production Credits—"The Gay Nineties": *Dir* Michael Pfleghar. *Scen* Georges Tabet, Andre Tabet. *Photog* Heinz Hölscher. *Art Dir* Herta Hareiter. *Film Ed* Susanne Paschen. *Prod Mgr* Wolfgang Kühnlenz.

Production Credits—"Paris Today": *Dir* Claude Autant-Lara. *Scen* Jean Aurenche.

Production Credits—"Anticipation": *Dir-Scen* Jean-Luc Godard. *Film Ed* Agnès Guillemot. *Asst Dir* Charles Bitsch.

Cast—"Prehistoric Era": Michèle Mercier *(Brit)*, Enrico Maria Salerno *(Braque)*, Gabriele Tinti *(seaman)*.

Cast—"Roman Nights": Elsa Martinelli *(empress)*, Gastone Moschin *(Caesar)*.

Cast—"Mademoiselle Mimi": Jeanne Moreau *(Mimi)*, Jean-Claude Brialy *(Philibert)*, Jean Richard *(constable)*.

Cast—"The Gay Nineties": Raquel Welch *(Nini)*, Martin Held *(banker)*, Siegfried Schurenberg *(Edouard)*, Tilly Lauenstein.

Cast—"Paris Today": Nadia Gray *(Nadia)*, France Anglade *(Catherine)*, Jacques Duby *(doctor)*, Francis Blanche *(visitor)*, Marcel Dalio *(older man)*.

Cast—"Anticipation": Anna Karina *(Miss Conversation)*, Marilu Tolo *(Miss Physical)*, Jacques Charrier *(space traveler)*, Jean-Pierre Léaud *(bellboy)*, Daniel Bart, Jean-Patrick Lebel.

Comedy-drama. The history of prostitution is traced in six episodes, from prehistoric times. PREHISTORIC ERA depicts a tribe of cave dwellers who are happily engaging in sex. One girl, Brit, however, discovers the art of makeup, as well as the fact that she can get things in exchange for sleeping with men. In ROMAN NIGHTS a bored emperor leaves his wife, only to find her disguised as a slave girl in a bawdy house. MADEMOISELLE MIMI lives during the French Revolution, and she is delighted when a young man bursts into her room explaining that he wants to watch his uncle's execution from her window. He convinces Mimi that he will inherit his uncle's fortune, and she permits him to join her in bed. After they make love he leaves, revealing that he is actually a penniless student. During THE GAY NINETIES Nini, a stripteaser, picks up an elderly banker. She pretends to believe that he is very poor and that she really loves him. Nini is successful in getting him to marry her. The next episode, PARIS TODAY, involves a prostitute, Catherine, who works from a car driven by her friend, Nadia. When the car is impounded, they use an ambulance instead. They are chased by police but are saved in the end by the fact that their client is a doctor. Looking towards the future in the final segment, ANTICIPATION, a man from outer space visits Earth where prostitution has been automated and divided into its physical and sentimental aspects. He is equally unmoved by "Miss Conversation," who recites romances, and "Miss Physical," a silent bedmate, until he realizes that the mouth is one part of the body that can play a part in both aspects. Together, the spaceman and the chattering girl rediscover the kiss! *Prostitutes. Cave dwellers. Stripteasers. Uncles. Royalty. Bankers. Physicians. Police. Spacemen. Prostitution. Prehistory. Slavery. Perfidy. Marriage. Whorehouses. Rome—History—Empire. France—History—Revolution 1789-93. Gay Nineties. The Future.*

Note: Opened in Paris in Apr 1967 as *Le plus vieux métier du monde;* running time: 115 min; released in West Germany in Apr 1967 as *Das älteste Gewerbe der Welt;* running time: 119 min; in Italy in 1967 as *L'amore attraverso i secoli.* The episode entitled "The Gay Nineties" may also be known as "The Good Old Days," and "Paris Today" as "Today." Original titles of the six episodes are as follows: "Ère préhistorique," "Nuits romaines," "Mademoiselle Mimi," "La belle époque," "Aujourd'hui," and "Anticipation."

OLGA'S GIRLS   **F6.3590**
American Film Distributing Corp. *Dist* American Film Distributing Corp., Olympic International Films. 30 Sep **1964** [San Francisco opening]. Sd; b&w. 35mm. 70 min.

Pres by Stan Borden. *Prod* George Weiss. *Dir* Joseph P. Mawra. *Photog* Werner Rose. *Set Dsgn* Sande Johnsen. *Orig Theme Mus* Clyde Otis. *Sd* Magno Sound.

Cast: Audrey Campbell *(Olga)*, Rickey Bell *(Collette)*, Ava Denning *(Susie)*, Darlene Bennett *(Connie)*, Jean Laloni *(Bunny)*, Ann Pepper *(Kitty)*, Cynthia Grey *(Lela)*, Giselle Swan *(Dolores)*, Dolly Simmons *(Judy)*, Jane Hill *(Lorraine)*, Rita Barrie *(1st party girl)*, June Vega *(2d party girl)*, Gil Adams *(white slaver)*, Perry Peters, Audrey Campbell *(narrators)*.

Melodrama. Headquartered in New York's Chinatown, where Communists provide a steady stream of dangerous drugs from the Orient, sadist Olga Saglo deals in narcotics and white slavery. Her drug-addicted slaves, brutally tortured for the slightest offense, some of them locked into chastity belts, have only one another for comfort. Olga punishes an informer discovered in their midst by cutting out her tongue. Collette, Olga's assistant, leaves to establish a rival call girl business, taking many of the best girls with her. Pressured by the syndicate to eliminate the competition, Olga kidnaps Lorraine, one of Collette's favorites, to force her rival to a confrontation. After a knockdown fight, Olga emerges victorious, and business continues as usual under the old management. *Madams. Communists. Drug addicts. Prostitution. Sadism. Torture. Organized crime. Abduction. Lesbianism. White slave traffic. Mutilation. Narcotics. Chastity belts. New York City—Chinatown.*

Note: Said to be a sequel to *White Slaves of Chinatown*, q. v.

OLGA'S HOUSE OF SHAME   **F6.3591**
American Film Distributing Corp. 6 Feb **1964** [Los Angeles showing]. Sd; b&w. 35mm. 70 min.

Prod George Weiss. *Dir* Joseph P. Mawra.

Cast: Audrey Campbell *(Olga)*.

Melodrama. In a deserted mining shack in upstate New York, Olga operates her School of Torture, forcibly training young girls in prostitution and narcotics peddling. She metes out fiendish punishments for the slightest offense and terrorizes her slaves into complete obedience. *Madams. Drug dealers. Prostitutes. White slave traffic. Sadism. Torture. New York State.*

Note: May also be known as *36 Hours of Terror* and *House of Shame.*

OLGA'S MASSAGE PARLOR *see* **MME. OLGA'S MASSAGE PARLOR**

OLIMPIADA EN MEXICO *see* **THE OLYMPICS IN MEXICO**

THE OLIVE TREES OF JUSTICE (France)   **F6.3592**
Société Algérienne de Production des Studios Africa. *Dist* Pathé Contemporary Films. 4 May **1967** [New York opening]. Sd; b&w. 35mm. 81 min.

Prod Georges Derocles. *Dir* James Blue. *Screenplay* Jean Pelegri, Sylvain Dhomme, James Blue. *Dial* Jean Pelegri. *Photog* Julius Rascheff. *Asst Photog* Ouakil Boubekeur. *Film Ed* Suzanne Gaveau, Marie-Claude Bariset. *Asst Film Ed* Huguette Cheltiel, Brigitte Guérin. *Mus* Maurice Jarre. *Perf* Parrenin Quartet. *Sd* Henri Blondeau, Jacques Lebreton. *Sd Rec* Ali Moulahcène. *Asst Dir* Jean Pelegri. *Prod Supv* Frantz Schmidt. *Prod Mgr* G. Sarthouret, Kader Boudjemia.

Cast: Pierre Prothon *(Jean/narrator)*, Jean Pelegri *(his father)*, Marie Decaitre *(his mother)*, Huguette Poggi *(Cousin Louise)*, Saïd Achaibou, Mohamed Bennour, Boralfa, Mathilde Gau, Kaoudoune, Amar Metchiek, Fatima Moktari, Ali Moulahcène, Djama Precigout, Gesomina Ros, Alexandre Sagols, Mohamed Saour, Bounedine Sekkal, Mustapha Smaili, Josiane Solal, Lucienne Terrades, Janine Vila.

Drama. Source: Jean Pelegri, *Les oliviers de la justice* (Paris, 1959). Jean, a young Frenchman born and reared in Algiers, returns to his native land from Paris to be with his dying father. It is during the Algerian war of independence, and as Jean sits at his father's bedside, he recalls his happy childhood in the family vineyards, where he played with French and Arab friends. Later he walks through the strife-torn Algerian streets and feels the terrible presence of war. One day his father dies peacefully in his sleep, and relatives and friends, both French and Arab, come to pay their respects. Jean has a long discussion with an Arab friend and attempts to explain why he must return to the peaceful life he has made for himself in Paris. After his father's funeral Jean sees his normally chauvinistic aunt hasten to help an Arab boy who has been struck by a passing truck. Moved by this genuine expression of human concern regardless of nationality, Jean decides to remain in Algeria. *Arabs. Aunts. Filial relations. Death. Memory. Childhood. Chauvinism. Funerals. Algeria—History—War of Independence. Algiers. Automobile accidents.*

Note: Filmed in Algeria. Opened in Paris in Jun 1962 as *Les oliviers de la justice.*

OLIVER! (Great Britain)　　　　　　　　　　　　　　F6.3593

Warwick Film Productions–Romulus Films. *Dist* Columbia Pictures. 11 Dec **1968** [New York opening; c1 Dec 1968; LP36464]. Sd (Westrex); col (Technicolor). 35mm (Panavision, see note). 153 min. [Running time includes musical overture.] *MPAA rating* G.

Prod John Woolf. *Prod by & Arr in Assoc With* Donald Albery. *Dir* Carol Reed. *Screenplay* Vernon Harris. *Dir Photog* Oswald Morris. *2d Unit Photog* Brian West. *Camera Op* Freddie Cooper. *Art Dir* Terence Marsh. *Asst Art Dir* Roy Walker, Bob Cartwright. *Set Dresser* Vernon Dixon, Ken Muggleston. *Prod Dsgn* John Box. *Titl Backgrounds* Graham Barkley. *Film Ed* Ralph Kemplen. *Asst Film Ed* Marcel Durham. *Mus, Lyr & Book* Lionel Bart. *Mus Supv, Arr, Orch, Choral Arr & Cond* John Green. *Assoc Mus Supv & Adtl Orch* Eric Rogers. *Mus Coörd* Dusty Buck. *Choreog, see note* Onna White, Tom Panko, Larry Oaks, George Baron, Ray Holder. *Sd Supv* John Cox. *Sd Ed* Jim Groom. *Sd Rec* Buster Ambler, Bob Jones. *Mus Ed* Kenneth Runyon. *Assoc Mus Ed* Robert Hathaway. *1st & 2d Asst Dir* Colin Brewer, Ray Corbett. *Prod Supv* Denis Johnson. *Unit Prod Mgr* Denis Johnson, Jr. *Cont* Pamela Davies. *Prod Sec* Loretta Ordewer. *Cost Dsgn* Phyllis Dalton. *Wardrobe Supv* John Wilson-Apperson. *Makeup Supv* George Frost. *Ch Hairdresser* Bobbie Smith. *Sp Eff* Allan Bryce. *Constr Mgr* Peter Dukelow. *Casting* Jenia Reissar. *Prod Buyer* Percy Godbold.

Cast: Ron Moody *(Fagin)*, Shani Wallis *(Nancy)*, Oliver Reed *(Bill Sikes)*, Harry Secombe *(Mr. Bumble)*, Mark Lester *(Oliver)*, Jack Wild *(The Artful Dodger)*, Hugh Griffith *(The Magistrate)*, Joseph O'Connor *(Mr. Brownlow)*, Peggy Mount *(Widow Corney [Mrs. Bumble?])*, Leonard Rossiter *(Mr. Sowerberry)*, Hylda Baker *(Mrs. Sowerberry)*, Kenneth Cranham *(Noah Claypole)*, Megs Jenkins *(Mrs. Bedwin)*, Sheila White *(Bet)*, Wensley Pithey *(Dr. Grimwig)*, James Hayter *(Mr. Jessop)*, Elizabeth Knight *(Charlotte)*, Fred Emney *(chairman of workhouse governors)*, Edwin Finn, Foy Evans *(workhouse paupers)*, Norman Mitchell *(arresting policeman)*, Robert Barlett, Graham Buttrose, Jeffrey Chandler, Kirk Clugeston, Dempsey Cook, Christopher Duff, Nigel Grice, Ronnie Johnson, Nigel Kingsley, Robert Langley, Brian Lloyd, Peter Lock, Ian Ramsey, Peter Renn, Bill Smith, British, Kim Smith, Freddie Stead, Raymond Ward, John Watters *(Fagin's boys)*, Clive Moss *(Charlie Bates)*, Veronice Page *(Oliver's mother)*, Henry Kay *(doctor)*, Jane Peach *(Rose, the maid)*, Keith Roberts *(policeman in magistrate's court)*, Peter Hoar *(court clerk)*. John Baskcomb, Norman Pitt, Arnold Locke, Frank Crawshaw *(workhouse governors)*.

Musical melodrama. Source: Lionel Bart, *Oliver* (London opening: 30 Jun 1960). Charles Dickens, *Oliver Twist* (London, 1838). During mealtime at a 19th-century English orphanage, 9-year-old Oliver Twist loses at a draw of straws and asks for a second helping of gruel. Shocked by the child's audacity, the workhouse proprietor, Mr. Bumble, sells him as an apprentice to Sowerberry, a miserly undertaker. Derisive remarks about his mother are made by Sowerberry's assistant, Noah Claypole, and Oliver runs away to London to make his fortune. There he meets the Artful Dodger, a slightly older boy who offers him friendship and lodging. Arriving at a dilapidated, abandoned building, Oliver is introduced to Fagin, a crafty old thief who trains homeless boys to be pickpockets. After demonstrating his many techniques, Fagin sends Oliver, accompanied by the Artful Dodger, out on the streets to test his newly-learned skills. Oliver is caught and arrested when the Dodger and another boy attempt to filch the wallet of wealthy and wellborn Mr. Brownlow, and the real culprits escape. At Oliver's trial, however, Mr. Brownlow is so touched by the boy's pleas of innocence that he brings him home to live at his house in Bloomsbury. Certain that Oliver will give information to the police, Bill Sikes, a villainous associate of Fagin's, orders his common-law wife, Nancy, to lure Oliver into a trap. Once the boy is retaken, however, and Nancy realizes that Sikes means to kill him, she contacts Mr. Brownlow and arranges to bring Oliver to London Bridge at midnight. But Sikes follows, seizes Oliver, and clubs Nancy to death. As Sikes desperately drags Oliver across the rooftops, his old dog leads the police and a rapidly gathering mob to Fagin's hideout. Forced to relinquish his hold on Oliver, Sikes tries to leap to safety on a rope but is shot dead. With Oliver safe and sound, Mr. Brownlow—who has since learned that the little foundling is the long-lost son of his dead niece—joyously brings him back home to Bloomsbury. And Fagin, who dropped his life savings in a muddy stream while evading the police, joins with the Artful Dodger in setting off on their never-ending search for new and unpicked pockets. *Musical numbers* include: "Food, Glorious Food" (Oliver & Boys); "Oliver!" (Mr. Bumble,

Widow Corney & Boys); "Boy for Sale" (Mr. Bumble); "Where Is Love?" (Oliver); "Consider Yourself" (Artful Dodger, Oliver & Ensemble); "Pick a Pocket or Two" (Fagin & Boys); "I'd Do Anything" (Artful Dodger, Nancy, Bet, Oliver, Fagin & Boys); "Be Back Soon" (Fagin & Boys); "As Long as He Needs Me" (Nancy); "Who Will Buy?" (Oliver & Ensemble); "It's a Fine Life" (Nancy, Bet & "The Three Cripples" Crowd); "Reviewing the Situation" (Fagin); "Oom-Pah-Pah" (Nancy & "The Three Cripples" Crowd); Finale— "Where Is Love?" "Consider Yourself" (Ensemble). *Orphans. Undertakers. Pickpockets. Police. Evildoers. Guardians. Childhood. Child labor. Theft. Injustice. Upper classes. Kidnaping. Murder. Wealth. Personal identity. Orphanages. London. Dogs.*

Note: Opened in London in Sep 1968; running time: 146 min with an additional overture. Filmed in 35mm Panavision and blown up to 70mm Panavision for some roadshow presentations. Choreography and staged musical numbers by Onna White; associate choreographer, Tom Panko; assistant choreographers, Larry Oaks and George Baron; choreographic music layouts, Ray Holder.

LES OLIVIERS DE LA JUSTICE *see* **THE OLIVE TREES OF JUSTICE**

DER ÖLPRINZ *see* **RAMPAGE AT APACHE WELLS**

OLTRAGGIO AL PUDORE *see* **ALL THE OTHER GIRLS DO**

THE OLYMPICS IN MEXICO (Mexico)　　　　　　　　F6.3594

Film Unit of the Organizing Committee for the Games of the XIX Olympiad. *Dist* Columbia Pictures. 29 Jul **1970** [Washington, D. C., opening]. Sd; col (Technicolor). 35mm (Techniscope). 120 min. *MPAA rating* G.

Prod Federico Amérigo. *Dir-Script* Alberto Isaac. *Text* Fernando Macotela. *English Adapt* Lawrence H. Lipskin. *Tech Dir Photog* Antonio Reynoso, Benjamin Montano. *Photog* Everardo de Anda, Jimmy Allen, John Barnard, Guillermo Bravo, Mike Boultbee, Ricky Briggs, Ricardo Carretero, Claude Caillet, Alfredo Coss, Gordon Clark, Rafael Corkidi, Tony Coggans, Ron Collins, Agustín Coma, Mike Davis, Roger Eastell, Jean Elissalde, Jean-Jacques Flori, Andrew Fraser, Manuel González, Ruben García, Ken Goddard, Terry Gould, Alexis Grivas, Martin Gray, photog, Raúl González, Harry Hart, Harvey Harrison, Bob Hunter, photog, Genaro Hurtado, Alan Hewison, Anthony Imi, Nic Knowland, Toni Kuhn, Marcelo López, Walter Lassally, Dick Lorimore, Agustín Luna, Nick Lera, Jean-Pierre Lemoine, Max Liszt, Jack Lesage, Ramón Muñoz, Bill Miller, Luis Medina, Jesús Moreno, Ian McFarlane, Ernesto Martínez, Jorge Mejia, Mario Noviello, Ron Osborn, Juan Manuel Palomino, Terry Permane, Maurice Picot, Benito Pliego, Brian Probyn, Eduardo Ramos, Walter Reuter, Guillermo Romero, Antonio Reynoso, Roberto Salas, David Samuelson, Michael Samuelson, Alfonso Sánchez, León Sánchez, Robert Sánchez Uribe, Paddy Seale, Alex Sheridan, Andres Torres, Alfredo Uribe, Eduardo Valdéz, Eric Van Haren Noman, Bertrand Van Munster, Encarnacion Vega, Ronnie Whitehouse, Douglas Williams, Louis Wolfers, Arthur Wooster. *Film Ed* Carlos Savage, Alberto Valenzuela, Rafael Ceballos, Reynoldo P. Portillo, Eufemio Rivera. *Mus* Joaquín Gutiérrez Heras. *Sd* Galdino Samperio, Jesús González Gancy. *Asst to the Dir* Julio Pliego, Rafael Castañedo, Rafael Corkidi, Paul Leduc, Giovanni Korporaal, Felipe Cazals, José Ma, Sánchez Ariza. *Prod Mgr* Antonio de Salazar. *Photog Cons* Michael Samuelson.

Narrator: Allan Jeffreys.

Documentary. A record of the 19th summer Olympic Games held in Mexico City in 1968. Coverage includes track and field, swimming and diving, water polo, boxing, soccer, and equestrian events. *Athletes. Olympic Games.*

Note: Mexican title: *Olimpiada en Mexico.*

OMBRE BIANCHE *see* **THE SAVAGE INNOCENTS**

L'OMBRELLONE *see* **WEEKEND, ITALIAN STYLE**

L'OMICIDA *see* **ENOUGH ROPE**

ON A CLEAR DAY YOU CAN SEE FOREVER　　　　　F6.3595

Paramount Pictures. 17 Jun **1970** [New York opening; c8 Jun 1970; LP38128]. Sd; col (Technicolor). 35mm (Panavision). 130 min. *MPAA rating* G.

A Howard W. Koch–Alan Jay Lerner Production. *Prod* Howard W. Koch. *Dir* Vincente Minnelli. *Screenplay* Alan Jay Lerner. *Dir Photog* Harry Stradling. *Aerial Photog* Tyler Camera Systems. *Set Decor* George James Hopkins, Raphael Bretton. *Prod Dsgn* John De Cuir. *Main Titl* Wayne Fitzgerald, Universal Title. *Film Ed* David Bretherton. *Asst Ed* Flo Williamson. *Mus Supv, Arr & Cond* Nelson Riddle. *Songs* Burton Lane, Alan Jay Lerner. *Choral Arr* Joseph J. Lilley. *Choreog* Howard Jeffrey. *Sd Rec* Ben Winkler, Elden Ruberg. *Asst Dir* William McGarry, William R. Poole, Gene Anderson, Jr. *Prod Mgr* Sergei Petschnikoff, Howard Roessel. *Script Cont* Molly Kent-Wade. *Miss Streisand's Contemporary Clothes Dsgn* Arnold Scassi. *Period*

Cost Dsgn & Created by Cecil Beaton. *Wardrobe Man* John A. Anderson. *Wardrobe Woman* Shirlee Strahm. *Makeup Supv* Harry Ray. *Miss Streisand's Hairstyles Dsgn & Created by* Frederick Glaser. *Time Lapse Photog* John Ott. *Vocal-Dance Arr* Betty Walberg. *Dial Coach* Walter Kelley.

Cast: Barbra Streisand *(Daisy Gamble)*, Yves Montand *(Dr. Marc Chabot)*, Bob Newhart *(Dr. Mason Hume)*, Larry Blyden *(Warren Pratt)*, Simon Oakland *(Dr. Conrad Fuller)*, Jack Nicholson *(Tad Pringle)*, John Richardson *(Robert Tentrees)*, Pamela Brown *(Mrs. Fitzherbert)*, Irene Handl *(Winnie Wainwhisle)*, Roy Kinnear *(Prince Regent)*, Peter Crowcroft *(divorce attorney)*, Byron Webster *(prosecuting attorney)*, Mabel Albertson *(Mrs. Hatch)*, Laurie Main *(Lord Percy)*, Kermit Murdock *(Hoyt III)*, Elaine Giftos *(Muriel)*, John Le Mesurier *(Pelham)*, Angela Pringle *(Diana Smallwood)*, Leon Ames *(Clews)*, Paul Camen *(Millard)*, George Neise *(Wytelipt)*, Tony Colti *(Preston)*.

Musical comedy-drama. Source: Burton Lane and Alan Jay Lerner, *On a Clear Day You Can See Forever* (New York opening: 17 Oct 1965). In order to break a smoking habit repugnant to her fiancé, Warren, New Yorker Daisy Gamble attends a class taught by psychiatrist Marc Chabot. Under hypnosis Daisy reads the professor's mind, demonstrates psychic power by making flowers grow rapidly, and reenacts earlier incarnations, including her life in England as Lady Melinda Winifred Waine Tentrees. As Daisy continues her sessions with Marc, her relationship with the rigid Warren deteriorates. For consolation she turns to stepbrother Tad. During a key interview Daisy discloses that in her life as Lady Tentrees she was born the illegitimate daughter of a kitchen maid. In the orphanage where her mother worked she acquired the paternity records of the orphans and subsequently blackmailed their wealthy sires, eventually marrying nobility. Publicity given Marc's research jeopardizes his position, but the psychiatrist is exonerated when the university's patron indicates an interest in extrasensory perception. Arriving early for her appointment, Daisy turns on Marc's tape recorder and hears the doctor lament that, while he is infatuated by Lady Tentrees, he finds Daisy quite limited. Enraged, she storms out of the office, but returns when summoned psychically by the physician. During their final encounter, she describes 14 lives, including her incarnation as Laura and marriage to the psychiatrist in 2038. Following the session, Chabot and Daisy separate. *Songs:* "Hurry! It's Lovely Up Here!" (Daisy), "On a Clear Day You Can See Forever" (Chorus), "Love With All the Trimmings" (Daisy), "Melinda" (Marc), "Go To Sleep" (Daisy), "He Wasn't You" (Daisy), "What Did I Have That I Don't Have?" (Daisy), "Come Back to Me" (Marc), "On a Clear Day..." (Marc), "On a Clear Day..." (Daisy). *Stepsisters. Students. Psychiatrists. Nobility. Stepbrothers. Extrasensory perception. Hypnotism. Reincarnation. Blackmail. Smoking. Orphanages. New York City. England.*

Note: Location scenes filmed in New York City and at the Royal Pavilion in Brighton, England.

ON ANY STREET see **LA NOTTE BRAVA**

ON HER BED OF ROSES   **F6.3596**

Famous Players Corp. 22 Jun **1966** [Chicago opening; c3 Mar 1966; LP32352]. Sd; b&w. 35mm. 104 min.

A Film by Albert Zugsmith. *Prod* Robert Caramico. *Exec Prod* Morris Corson. *Assoc Prod* Foster Denker, Art Names, Jill Murphy, Arnold Stoltz. *Asst Prod* Joanne Wholey, Mary Lou Whipple, Karen Arney. *Dir-Writ* Albert Zugsmith. *Photog* Robert Caramico. *Prod Dsgn* Ruth Zugsmith. *Film Ed* Herman Freedman. *Mus* Joe Greene. *Tech Adv* Lee Gladden.

Cast: Ronald Warren *(Stephen Long)*, Sandra Lynn *(Melissa Borden)*, Barbara Hines *(Joanna Borden)*, Lee Gladden *(Dr. Krafft-Ebing)*, Ric Marlow *(Arthur Borden)*, Regina Gleason *(Rachel Long)*, Lovey Song *(Sally Marsh)*, Richard Clair *(detective)*, Ned York *(Jimmy Blake)*, Pat Barringer *(belly dancer)*, Pamela Woolman *(Tahitian dancer)*, Elaine Poulos *(Middle Eastern dancer)*, Karen Arney *(flowershop girl)*, Sarah Nade *(Francine)*, Richard Tretter *(Drake)*.

Melodrama. Source: Richard von Krafft-Ebing, *Psychopathia Sexualis: Eine klinischforensische Studie* (Stuttgart, 1886). Stephen Long murders his mother, drives to the top of a hill, kills several passing motorists with a rifle, and then commits suicide. Melissa Borden, his teenaged fiancée, seeks psychiatric help from Dr. Krafft-Ebing and relates the events leading up to Stephen's death: Melissa and her mother Joanna were in constant competition for masculine attention. When their rivalry drove away Arthur, the man of the house, the women began to give lavish parties to see who could attract more men. Eventually Melissa turned her attention to Stephen, a mother-dominated neighbor who was raised to believe that sex is sinful. Learning of his fetish for roses, Melissa unsuccessfully attempted to seduce him in his flower garden. The doctor explains that Stephen was driven to despair by his impotence and became filled with a desire to commit evil acts. *Psychopaths. Psychiatrists. Neighbors. Matricide. Murder. Suicide. Adolescence. Filial relations. Momism. Fetishism. Seduction. Impotence. Flowers.*

ON HER MAJESTY'S SECRET SERVICE (Great Britain)   **F6.3597**

Eon Productions–Danjaq, S. A. *Dist* United Artists. 17 Dec **1969** [Los Angeles opening; c18 Dec 1969; LP37433]. Sd; col (Technicolor). 35mm (Panavision). 140 min. *MPAA rating* M.

Pres by Albert R. Broccoli, Harry Saltzman, Albert R. Broccoli. *Prod* Harry Saltzman, Albert R. Broccoli. *Assoc Prod* Stanley Sopel. *Dir* Peter Hunt. *2d Unit Dir* John Glen. *Stock Car Seq Dir* Anthony Squire. *Screenplay* Richard Maibaum. *Adtl Dial* Simon Raven. *Dir Photog* Michael Reed. *Camera Op* Alec Mills. *Camera Focus* Ron Drinkwater. *2d Unit Camera* Egil Woxholt, Roy Ford. *Aerial Camera* John Jordan. *Skiing Camera* Willy Bogner, Jr., Alex Barbey. *Art Dir* Bob Laing. *Set Decor* Peter Lamont. *Prod Dsgn* Syd Cain. *Main Titl Dsgn* Maurice Binder. *Film Ed* John Glen. *Assembly Ed* Robert Richardson. *Mus Comp, Arr & Cond* John Barry. *Song:* "We Have All the Time in the World" John Barry, Hal David. *Sung by* Louis Armstrong. *Song:* "Do You Know How Christmas Trees Are Grown?" John Barry, Hal David. *Sung by* Nina. *James Bond Theme* Monty Norman. *Sd Mix* John Mitchell. *Sd Rec* Gordon K. McCallum. *Dub Ed* Nicholas Stevenson, Harry Miller. *Asst Dir* Frank Ernst. *Prod Supv* David Middlemas. *Prod Sec* Golda Offenheim. *Cont* Joan Davis. *Cost Dsgn* Marjory Cornelius. *Wardrobe Supv* Jackie Cummins. *Wardrobe Master* John Brady. *Makeup* Basil Newall, Paul Rabiger. *Hairdresser* Eileen Warwick. *Sp Eff* John Stears. *Sp Eff Ed* John Glen. *Coöp* Her Majesty's College of Arms and Heralds, Schil Thornbahn A. G. of Mürren (Switzerland). *Constr Mgr* Ron Udell. *Dial Coach* Job Stewart. *Stunt Arr* George Leech.

Cast: George Lazenby *(James Bond)*, Diana Rigg *(Tracy)*, Telly Savalas *(Ernst Stavros Blofeld)*, Gabriele Ferzetti *(Marc Ange Draco)*, Ilse Steppat *(Irma Bunt)*, Lois Maxwell *(Miss Moneypenny)*, George Baker *(Sir Hilary Bray)*, Bernard Lee *("M")*, Bernard Horsfall *(Campbell)*, Desmond Llewelyn *("Q")*, Yuri Borienko *(Grunther)*, Angela Scoular *(Ruby)*, Catherina von Schell *(Nancy)*, John Gay, actor *(Hammond)*, Norman McGlen *(janitor)*, Dudley Jones *(hall porter)*, Josef Vasa *(Piz Gloria receptionist)*.

Cast—Piz Gloria Girls: Dani Sheridan *(American girl)*, Julie Ege *(Scandinavian girl)*, Joanna Lumley *(English girl)*, Mona Chong *(Chinese girl)*, Anoushka Hempel *(Australian girl)*, Ingrit Back *(German girl)*, Jenny Hanley *(Italian girl)*, Zara *(Indian girl)*, Sylvana Henriques *(Jamaican girl)*, Helena Ronee *(Israeli girl)*.

Cast—Draco's Men: Geoffrey Cheshire *(Toussaint)*, Irvin Allen *(Che Che)*, Terry Mountain *(Raphael)*, Bill Morgan *(Klett)*, Richard Graydon *(driver)*, John Crewdson *(helicopter pilot)*.

Cast—Blofeld's Men: Leslie Crawford *(Felsen)*, George A. Cooper *(Braun)*, Reg Harding *(driver)*, James Bree *(Gumpold)*, Virginia North *(Olympe)*, Brian Worth *(Manuel)*.

Cast—At the Casino: Bessie Love *(American guest)*, Steve Plytas *(Greek tycoon)*, Robert Rietty *(chef de jeu)*, Elliott Sullivan *(American guest)*, Martin Leyder *(chef de jeu huissier)*.

Melodrama. Source: Ian Fleming, *On Her Majesty's Secret Service* (London, 1963). James Bond's perennial battle against international crime organization SPECTRE leads him to the shores of Portugal, where he prevents the suicide-by-drowning of Tracy, a beautiful "jet setter" with a penchant for heavy gambling. His search there for Ernst Stavros Blofeld, chief of SPECTRE, is aborted when Bond is recalled to London by "M," his superior, who insists the secret agent abandon his manhunt. Upon returning to Portugal on his own, Bond rescues Tracy once again by paying a gambling debt she cannot cover, an act of gallantry that earns him the key to her room. The following morning, however, Bond is brought by two hoodlums to see Tracy's father, Marc Ange Draco, head of the Union Corse crime syndicate, who thereupon offers the sleuth $1 million to marry Tracy. Bond refuses the money but makes use of Draco's underworld connections to trace Blofeld to Switzerland, where he is attempting to establish his right to the title of Count de Bleuchamp with London's College of Arms. After disguising himself as the College's director, Bond is taken in a helicopter by Irma Bunt, Blofeld's aide, to a heavily guarded Swiss mountaintop, where he is to research Blofeld's claim. At the Piz Gloria, as the retreat is called, Bond finds the Institute of Physiological Research, a front for another of Blofeld's attempts to rule the world. A dozen international beauties who have come there seeking cures for allergies have been brainwashed into introducing sterility spores into their respective nations' agricultural products. Bond samples some international love-making but has to escape Piz Gloria by skis when Irma penetrates his disguise and substitutes herself for one of his bedtime companions. Tracy rescues him with her car in Mürren, a skiing village, but Blofeld is so close behind that the couple must escape by skis immediately after Bond proposes marriage. Blofeld's attempt to bury them in an avalanche by exploding a grenade is a failure, but it enables him to kidnap Tracy as bait for a deal with the United Nations: in exchange for abandoning the destruction of the world, Blofeld will receive the title of Count de Bleuchamp in addition to total amnesty for his crimes. When Bond's objections to the plan are ignored by "M," he enlists Draco's help to bomb Blofeld's fortress by helicopter. The attack results in Tracy's rescue, and the final struggle between Bond and Blofeld on a speeding bobsled ends when an over-hanging branch sends the villain to an almost certain death. Bond and Tracy are finally married, but, as they begin their honeymoon, Blofeld and Irma arrive to machine-gun the bride to death. *Secret agents. Jet set. Racketeers. Masterminds. Murder. Kidnaping. Espionage. Allergy. Filial relations. Brainwashing. Suicide. Gambling. Impersonation. Genealogy. Organized crime. Automobile racing. Skiing. Sledding. Honeymoons. Helicopters. Portugal. London. Switzerland. United Nations. Chases. Avalanches. James Bond.*

Note: Location scenes filmed in Switzerland, London, and Portugal. Released in London in Dec 1969.

ON MY WAY TO THE CRUSADES, I MET A GIRL WHO ...
(United States/Italy)   F6.3598

Julia Film–Seven Arts Productions. *Dist* Warner Bros.–Seven Arts, Inc. 10 Sep **1969** [San Francisco opening; c1 Sep 1969; LP38135]. Sd; col (Technicolor). 35mm. 93 min. *MPAA rating* R.

Prod Francesco Mazzei. *Dir* Pasquale Festa Campanile. *Screenplay* Luigi Magni, Larry Gelbart. *Story* Ugo Liberatore. *Anim* Studio Favali. *Dir Photog* Carlo Di Palma. *Camera Op* Alberto Spagnoli. *Art Dir* Piero Poletto. *Titl* Studio Favali. *Film Ed* Gabrio Astori, Charles Nelson. *Mus* Riz Ortolani. *Sd Op* Aurelio Verona. *Asst Dir* Elvira D'Amico, Carlo Cotti. *Prod Mgr* Luciano Piperno. *Cost* Danilo Donati. *Makeup* Gianni Amedei. *Hairstyles* Luciano Vito. *Hairdresser for Miss Vitti* Elda Magnanti. *Tech Dir* Lamberto Pippia, Mario Cotone, Gilberto Scarpellini.

Cast: Tony Curtis (*Guerrando da Montone*), Monica Vitti (*Boccadoro*), Hugh Griffith (*Sultan of Bari*), John Richardson (*Drogone*), Ivo Garrani (*Duke of Pandolfo*), Nino Castelnuovo (*Marculfo*), Franco Sportelli (*Bertuccio*), Lauro Gazzolo (*hermit*), Francesco Mulè, Umberto Raho, Leopoldo Trieste, Gabriella Giorgelli, Mimmo Poli.

Costume farce. In medieval Italy, a greenhorn knight, Guerrando da Montone, receives a grant of all the land he can cover by horse in one day. Included in this territory is the house of Boccadoro, a peasant girl long infatuated with Guerrando, who now asks to be claimed as his property. Guerrando wants to share her with his servant, however, and she refuses his advances until marriage. Guerrando agrees to the marriage with the intention of burning Boccadoro as a witch when he grows tired of her, but she takes revenge and waits 3 days before she will allow the marriage to be consummated. At the moment of union, Guerrando is called away to the Crusades, and he locks Boccadoro in a chastity belt. Infuriated, she disguises herself as a knight and sets out to find him. In battle, she defeats another knight, Drogone, who then pledges to aid her in finding Guerrando. They finally catch up with Guerrando, but the key to unlock the belt is misplaced. Boccadoro and Guerrando are taken prisoner by Saracens. The Sultan of Bari wants to keep Boccadoro for his harem, but she escapes with Guerrando. They finally find the key but discover that it doesn't fit the lock. Drogone returns the right key, however, and reveals that he is actually King Ludwig of the Holy Roman Empire. He then leaves Boccadoro and Guerrando to fulfill their marriage vows. *Peasants. Royalty. Knighthood. Marriage. Disguise. Chastity belts. Harems. The Crusades. Saracens.*

Note: Opened in Rome in Jan 1968 as *La cintura di castità*; running time: 110 min. U. S. prerelease title: *The Chastity Belt.*

ON THE BRINK see THESE ARE THE DAMNED

ON THE DOUBLE
       F6.3599

Dena Pictures–Capri Productions. *Dist* Paramount Pictures. 19 May **1961** [New York opening; c19 May 1961; LP19799]. Sd; col (Technicolor). 35mm (Panavision). 92 min.

Prod Jack Rose. *Dir* Melville Shavelson. *Screenplay* Jack Rose, Melville Shavelson. *Dir Photog* Harry Stradling. *2d Unit Photog* Geoffrey Unsworth. *Col Cons* Richard Mueller. *Art Dir* Hal Pereira, Arthur Lonergan. *Set Decor* Sam Comer, Frank R. McKelvy. *Film Ed* Frank Bracht. *Mus Scored & Cond* Leith Stevens. *Songs:* "Darlin' Meggie," "The Mackenzie Hielanders," "On the Double" Sylvia Fine. *Mus Numbers Staged by* Bill Foster. *Sd* Lyle Figland, John Wilkinson. *Asst Dir* Harry Caplan, Arthur Jacobson. *Unit Prod Mgr* Bill Gray. *Prod Asst* Hal C. Kern. *Cost* Edith Head. *Makeup Supv* Wally Westmore. *Hairstyle Supv* Nellie Manley. *Sp Photog Eff* John P. Fulton. *Proc Photog* Farciot Edouart. *Tech Adv* Blake Owensmith.

Cast: Danny Kaye (*Pfc. Ernest Williams/Gen. Sir Lawrence Mackenzie-Smith*), Dana Wynter (*Lady Margaret Mackenzie-Smith*), Wilfrid Hyde-White (*Colonel Somerset*), Margaret Rutherford (*Lady Vivian*), Diana Dors (*Sgt. Bridget Stanhope*), Allan Cuthbertson (*Captain Patterson*), Jesse White (*Cpl. Joseph Praeger*), Gregory Walcott (*Col. Rock Houston*), Terence De Marney (*Sgt. Colin Twickenham*), Rex Evans (*Gen. Carleton "Puffy" Browne-Wiffingham*), Ben Astar (*General Zlinkov*), Rudolph Anders (*Oberkommandant*), Edgar Barrier (*Blankmeister*), Bobby Watson (*Hitler*), Pamela Light.

War comedy. Ernie Williams, a timid G. I. stationed in England shortly before the World War II Allied invasion of Normandy, is caught impersonating Gen. Sir Lawrence Mackenzie-Smith, England's foremost battle campaigner. American and British intelligence persuade Ernie to continue the impersonation in order to confuse Nazi spies. He first encounters the general's amorous chauffeur, Sgt. Bridget Stanhope. Though Ernie manages to fool her, he is less successful with the general's estranged wife, Lady Margaret, who, when she is informed of the situation, agrees to cooperate. A short time later the real general is killed in a plane disaster, and Ernie is free to end the deception; but the masquerade is now more important than ever, and he agrees to continue. He comes very close to being exposed by the general's eccentric aunt, Lady Vivian, but Lady Margaret saves the day by starting a family brawl that turns into a free-for-all. Later that night he is kidnaped by Bridget, who is actually a Nazi spy, and whisked off to Berlin for interrogation. After giving the Gestapo false information, Ernie eludes his captors, assumes numerous disguises, including one representing Marlene Dietrich, and makes his escape through an opera house and a beer hall. Once back in England he exposes an old chum of Mackenzie-Smith's, General Browne-Wiffingham, as the chief German agent in Britain. With the successful launching of the Allied invasion, Ernie returns to the waiting arms of Lady Margaret. *Soldiers. Spies. Chauffeurs. Aunts. Nazis. Gestapo. Timidity. Impersonation. Disguise. Kidnaping. World War II. Normandy. England. Berlin. Marlene Dietrich. Adolf Hitler.*

Note: Location scenes filmed in England.

ON THE FIDDLE see OPERATION SNAFU

ON THE RUN (Great Britain)
       F6.3600

Merton Park Studios. *Dist* Schoenfeld Film Distributing Corp. 1 Nov **1967** [Newark, New Jersey, opening]. Sd; b&w. 35mm. 59 min.

Prod Jack Greenwood. *Dir* Robert Tronson. *Screenplay* Richard Harris, writ. *Dir Photog* James Wilson. *Art Dir* Peter Mullins. *Film Ed* Derek Holding. *Mus Dir* Bernard Ebbinghouse. *Sd* Brian Blamey, Sidney Rider.

Cast: Emrys Jones (*Frank Stewart*), Sarah Lawson (*Helen Carr*), Patrick Barr (*Sergeant Brent*), Delphi Lawrence (*Yvonne*), Kevin Stoney (*Wally Lucas*), William Abney (*Jock Mackay*), Katy Wild (*Jean Stewart*), Philip Locke (*Dave Hughes*), Richard Warner (*prison governor*), Brian Haines (*Vance*), Garfield Morgan (*Meredith*), Brian Wilde (*Chief Warder*), Ken Wayne (*Bryce*), Bee Duffell (*Mrs Thomas*).

Mystery drama. Based on a story by: Edgar Wallace. Model prisoner Frank Stewart, convicted for burglarizing the Johannesburg Gold Trust, escapes with the assistance of Jock Mackay, the henchman of Wally Lucas. Lucas, the mastermind of the Johannesburg robbery, plans to have the fugitive arrested following his disclosure of the whereabouts of some missing bonds. When Stewart learns that Lucas is living with his wife, Yvonne, while laying his perfidious plans, the convict goes into hiding. In so doing he is assisted by Helen Carr, proprietress of a modeling agency and employer of Stewart's daughter Jean. Abducted by Lucas' gang and fearing for Helen's safety, Stewart discloses that the bonds are hidden in the sewer. During a confrontation in the sewer Lucas and Stewart are arrested by the police, who have been summoned by Helen. *Convicts. Fugitives. Gangsters. Police. Businesswomen. Jailbreaks. Robbery. Perfidy. Frameup. Infidelity. Abduction. Model agencies. Sewers. Johannesburg.*

Note: Released in Great Britain in Apr 1963.

ONCE A RAINY DAY (Japan)
       F6.3601

Toho Co. Feb **1968** [Los Angeles showing]. Sd; col (Eastmancolor). 35mm (Tohoscope). 85 min.

Dir Hideo Onchi. *Screenplay* Taichi Yamada. *Story* Keisuke Kinoshita. *Photog* Aizawa Yuzuru. *Mus* Toru Takemitsu.

Cast: Michiyo Aratama, Yoko Naito, Ryo Tamura, Daisuke Kato, Nobuko Otowa, Fukuko Sayo, Shoichi Ozawa.

Drama. A young man, deserted as a child by his mother, and a young woman, deserted in childhood by her father, meet and recall their days as playmates. When a romance develops between them, the man's foster parents express their disapproval and the woman's teacher claims they are too young for marriage; and the two lovers part. *Foster parents. Schoolteachers. Desertion. Filial relations.*

Note: Released in Japan in 1966 as *Akogare.*

ONCE A THIEF (United States/France)
       F6.3602

CIPRA–Ralph Nelson–Fred Engel. *Dist* Metro-Goldwyn-Mayer, Inc. 25 Aug **1965** [Detroit opening; c31 Dec 1964; LP30025]. Sd (Westrex); col. 35mm (Panavision). 106 min.

Prod Jacques Bar. *Dir* Ralph Nelson. *Screenplay* Zekial Marko. *Dir Photog* Robert Burks. *Art Dir* George W. Davis, Paul Groesse. *Set Decor* Henry Grace, Jack Mills. *Film Ed* Fredric Steinkamp. *Mus Comp & Cond* Lalo Schifrin. *Sd* Franklin Milton. *Asst Dir* Eric Von Stroheim, Jr. *Prod Mgr* J. Paul Popkin. *Makeup Supv* William Tuttle. *Hairstyles* Sydney Guilaroff. *Dial Coach* Walter

Kelley.

Cast: Alain Delon *(Eddie Pedak)*, Ann-Margret *(Kristine Pedak)*, Van Heflin *(Mike Vido)*, Jack Palance *(Walter Pedak)*, John Davis Chandler *(James Sargatanas)*, Jeff Corey *(Lieutenant Kebner)*, Tony Musante *(Cleve Shoenstein)*, Steve Mitchell *(Frank Kane)*, Zekial Marko *(Luke)*, Tammy Locke *(Kathy Pedak)*, Russell Lee *(drummer)*, Yuki Shimoda *(John Ling)*.

Crime melodrama. Source: Zekial Marko, *Scratch a Thief* (New York, 1961). Ex-convict Eddie Pedak and his wife, Kristine, attempt to build a new life for themselves and their daughter Kathy in San Francisco, but police officer Mike Vido is determined to send Eddie back to prison. Believing that Eddie was responsible for shooting him some years ago, Vido arrests Pedak for suspected robbery and murder but is forced to release him when the charges prove false. Eddie loses his job as a result of the suspicion, and Kristine is forced to go to work in a cheap nightclub. Frustrated and angry, Eddie is finally persuaded by his brother Walter and his accomplices, Sargatanas and Shoenstein, to assist in a $1 million robbery. The robbery is successful; but Walter is killed in an attempted doublecross, and Sargatanas kidnaps Kathy to force Eddie to turn over the truck with the stolen goods. Meanwhile, Vido has discovered that Eddie was framed for the previous robbery charges; and even though Eddie admits to wounding Vido, the policeman agrees to help him rescue Kathy. She is saved, but Eddie is shot and killed while protecting Vido. *Ex-convicts. Police. Brothers. Filial relations. Robbery. Murder. Perfidy. Kidnaping. Frameup. Nightclubs. San Francisco.*

Note: Filmed on location in San Francisco. Opened in Paris in Sep 1965 as *Les tueurs de San Francisco*; running time: 110 min.

ONCE A THIEF *see* THE HAPPY THIEVES

ONCE BEFORE I DIE (United States/Philippines)   F6.3603

F.8 Productions. *Dist* Goldstone Film Enterprises. Dec **1966**. Sd; col (Eastman Color). 35mm. 97 min.

Pres by Seven Arts Pictures. *Prod-Dir* John Derek. *Exec Prod* Wray Davis. *Screenplay* Vance Skarstedt. *Photog* Arthur Arling. *Film Ed* John Davisson. *Mus Comp & Cond* Emanuel Vardi. *Titl Song* Norman Gimbel, Ralph London. *Sd* Joseph Keener.

Cast: Ursula Andress *(Alex)*, John Derek *(Major Bailey)*, Rod Lauren *(captain)*, Richard Jaeckel *(Lieutenant Custer)*, Ron Ely, Vance Skarstedt, Allen Pinson, Gregg Martin, Renato Robles, Fred Galang, Nello Nayo, Mario Taquibulos, Rob Francisco, Eva Vivar, Lola Boy, Armando Lucero.

War drama. Source: Anthony March, *Quit for the Next* (New York, 1945). At a U. S. Cavalry station in the Philippines in 1941, Major Bailey and his Swiss fiancée, Alex, are caught in a surprise Japanese attack. After sending Alex ahead by car, Bailey and his men begin the long march through the jungles to Manila. After moving only a short distance, they overtake Alex, stalled in her car, and she joins the men on foot. During the journey that follows, Bailey is accidentally killed by an exploding hand grenade, Alex has sex with a virginal soldier before he dies, and the blood-thirsty Lieutenant Custer leads a senseless raid on an enemy stronghold. The horrified Alex watches the bloody massacre in which all of the Americans are killed. Left alone, she kills a young Japanese soldier and wanders down to a beach to await her fate. *Swiss. Combat zone life. Sexual initiation. Massacres. Jungles. World War II. Philippines. United States Army—Cavalry. Japan—Army. Explosions.*

Note: Filmed in 1964 on location in the Philippines. Working titles: *No Toys for Christmas* and *The 26th Cavalry*.

ONCE UPON A BODY   F6.3604

Chellee Films. 25 Jun **1970** [San Francisco showing]. Sd; b&w. 35mm. [Feature length assumed.]

Melodrama. Grace leaves her steady boyfriend Steve and joins Joyce and Ann in a scheme to support themselves and Joyce's boyfriend, Cochran, at the expense of Henry, an unsuspecting homosexual who associates with women in order to keep up appearances. Henry invites Ann to spend the night with him, and she robs him. Grace has a party, and there is an orgy in which Ann refuses to join. Later, Grace and Joyce seduce each other, and then they initiate Ann into lesbianism. Cochran beats Joyce when she does not steal enough money from Henry. Joyce dies; Ann is desolate; and Grace returns to Steve a changed woman. *Robbery. Fraud. Male homosexuality. Seduction. Lesbianism. Murder. Greed. Sadism. Orgies.*

ONCE UPON A COFFEE HOUSE   F6.3605

Fred Berney Productions. 29 Apr **1965** [Miami, Florida, opening]. Sd; col (Eastman Color). 35mm. ca91 min.

Prod Fred Berney. *Dir* Shepherd Traube. *Screenplay* Carl Yale. *Songs* Carl Yale. *Mus Arr* Jacques Donnet. *Choreog* Johnny Conrad.

Cast: Vince Martin *(rival)*, Karen Thorsell *(coffee house barmaid)*, Curtis Taylor *(playboy)*, Jerry Newby *(coffee house owner)*, Pedro Roman, Eve Tellegen, Oscar Brand, John Rivers, Deanna Lund, Jim, Jake, and Joan, Sherry Lou Shepherd, The Goldebriars, The Freewheelers.

Comedy. While visiting Miami, a rich playboy falls in love with a folksinging coffeehouse barmaid. The coffeehouse owner persuades the young man to buy his establishment to be near the woman. The playboy's jealous rival believes the barmaid has posed for him in the nude. *Playboys. Singers. Barmaids. Wealth. Folk music. Jealousy. Coffeehouses. Miami.*

Note: Filmed in Miami.

ONCE UPON A HORSE *see* HOT HORSE

ONCE UPON A KNIGHT   F6.3606

Cresse-Nyquist Productions. *Dist* Olympic International Films. **1961**. Sd; col (see note). 35mm. 72 min.

Prod-Writ Bob Cresse, Fred Nyquist. *Story* Bob Cresse.

Cast: Frank James *(Sir Seemore)*, Eric Nord *(King Bruiser)*, Virginia Gordon *(Lady Lauri)*.

Comedy. Sir Seemore, a bright young investigator for the Infidelity Insurance Company, receives an assignment to recover a stolen painting of a nude. Sir Seemore's allergy to nude women complicates the investigation because he bursts into uncontrollable sneezing at the first sight of exposed flesh. His search leads him to Venice, California, known as the stomping ground of the beatniks. He there encounters the Nudeniks, nude beauties who lead Sir Seemore on a wild chase after the stolen painting. *Investigators. Beatniks. Nudity. Theft. Paintings. Insurance. Allergy. Venice (California). Chases.*

Note: Re-released in b&w.

ONCE UPON A SUMMER *see* GIRL WITH GREEN EYES

ONCE UPON A TIME *see* MORE THAN A MIRACLE

ONCE UPON A TIME IN THE WEST (United States/Italy)   F6.3607

Rafran Cinematografica–Euro International Films. *Dist* Paramount Pictures. 28 May **1969** [New York opening; c20 Dec 1968; LF34]. Sd; col (Technicolor). 35mm (Techniscope). 165 min. [See note.] *MPAA rating* M.

A San Marco Production. *Assoc Prod* Bino Cicogna. *Exec Prod* Fulvio Morsella. *Dir* Sergio Leone. *Screenplay* Sergio Leone, Sergio Donati. *Story* Dario Argento, Bernardo Bertolucci, Sergio Leone. *Dir Photog* Tonino Delli Colli. *1st Asst Camera* Franco Di Giacomo. *2d Asst Camera* Giuseppe Lanci. *Art Dir* Carlo Simi. *Asst Art Dir* Tonino Palombi. *Set Decor* Carlo Leva. *Film Ed* Nino Baragli. *Mus Comp & Dir* Ennio Morricone. *Sd Rec* Claudio Maielli. *Asst Dir* Giancarlo Santi. *Unit Mgr* Ugo Tucci. *Prod Mgr* Claudio Mancini. *Asst Prod Mgr* Camillo Teti. *Prod Sec* George Risi. *Cont* Serena Canevari. *Cost* Carlo Simi. *Wardrobe* Marilù Carteny. *Makeup* Alberto De Rossi. *Hairdresser* Grazia De Rossi. *Still Photog* Angelo Novi.

Cast: Henry Fonda *(Frank)*, Claudia Cardinale *(Jill McBain)*, Jason Robards, [Jr.] *(Cheyenne)*, Charles Bronson *(The Man [Harmonica])*, Frank Wolff *(Brett McBain)*, Gabriele Ferzetti *(Morton)*, Keenan Wynn *(sheriff)*, Paolo Stoppa *(Sam)*, Marco Zuanelli *(Wobbles)*, Lionel Stander *(barman)*, Jack Elam *(Knuckles)*, John Frederick *(member of Frank's gang)*, Woody Strode *(Stony)*, Enzio Santianello *(Timmy)*, Dino Mele *(Harmonica as a boy)*, Robert Hossein, Benito Stefanelli, Livio Andronico, Salvo Basile, Aldo Berti, Marilù Carteny, Luigi Ciavarro, Spartaco Conversi.

Western melodrama. In the West during the 1870's, Frank, a ruthless killer, sends three of his henchmen to a remote railway depot to wait for The Man, an impassive gunman whose trademark is playing sad songs on a harmonica. The Man guesses their murderous intent when they refuse to answer a question about Frank, and he kills them before they can reach for their guns. Meanwhile, rancher Brett McBain and his three motherless children await the arrival of Jill, a New Orleans prostitute whom Brett has recently married. Suddenly, Frank and his gang appear and gun down Brett and the children. They plant evidence implicating Cheyenne, a notorious half-breed. Arriving at the ranch, Jill finds a burial service being conducted and learns that McBain's promise of wealth was for the future when his property, through which a new railroad must pass, would become the center of a thriving community. Too frightened to remain in the area, Jill is forced to auction off her property. Frank, who is employed by Morton, a crippled railroad executive, tries to fix the sale, but The Man appears with Cheyenne in tow and buys the land for $5,000—the exact amount of the reward money for capturing Cheyenne. The Man then returns the land rights to Jill but refuses to explain his actions. A short time later, he rescues Frank from an ambush by his own men who had sold their loyalty to the double-crossing Morton. The Man still refuses to explain his motives or reveal his true identity to Frank, but he returns to the ranch to help Jill with the work and to protect her from Frank. Cheyenne, who is now on friendly terms with The Man, also arrives after being cleared of the McBains' murders. He has been wounded in a gunfight with Morton's men. Frank eventually shows up to face The Man in a gun duel, and he is shot before he has time to draw his gun. Before Frank dies, The Man explains to him the reason for the vendetta: when The Man was 15 years old, Frank forced him to play the harmonica while his older brother was tortured and hanged. With his mission accomplished, The Man says goodby to Jill and rides off with the mortally wounded Cheyenne. Alone at the ranch, Jill distributes water to the men who are helping to build the new railroad town. *Harmonica players. Gunfighters. Strangers. Cripples. Prostitutes. Halfcastes. Ranchers. Brothers. Murder. Revenge. Frameup. Perfidy. Torture. Inheritance. Railroads. Ranches. Land rights. Auctions. Duels.*

Note: Filmed in the United States (Arizona and Utah) and Spain. Released in Italy in 1968 as *C'era una volta il West.* Subsequent release versions were cut to between 132 and 144 min.

ONCE YOU KISS A STRANGER F6.3608

Warner Bros.–Seven Arts, Inc. 12 Nov **1969** [Charlotte, North Carolina, opening; c1 Dec 1969; LP40875]. Sd; col (Berkey Pathé). 35mm. 106 min. *MPAA rating* M.

A Robert Goldstein Production. *Prod* Harold A. Goldstein. *Exec Prod* Robert Goldstein. *Assoc Prod* Mann Rubin. *Dir* Robert Sparr. *Screenplay* Frank Tarloff, Norman Katkov. *Dir Photog* Jacques Marquette. *Art Dir* Art Loel. *Set Decor* Jerry Miggins. *Film Ed* Marjorie Fowler. *Mus Comp & Cond* Jimmie Fagas. *Mus Supv* Sonny Burke. *Titl Song* Jimmie Fagas, Ken Darby. *Sung by* Dick Addrisi. *Sd* Robert B. Lee. *Asst Dir* Howard Kazanjian. *Prod Supv* Byron Roberts. *Script Supv* Della Ross. *Makeup* Perc Westmore. *Hairstyles* Billie Short. *Stunt Supv* Fred Carson.

Cast: Paul Burke *(Jerry)*, Carol Lynley *(Diana)*, Martha Hyer *(Lee)*, Peter Lind Hayes *(Peter)*, Philip Carey *(Mike)*, Stephen McNally *(Lieutenant Gavin)*, Whit Bissell *(Dr. Haggis)*, Elaine Devry *(Sharon)*, Kathryn Givney *(Aunt Margaret)*, Jim Raymond *(Johnny Parker)*, George Fenneman *(announcer)*, Orville Sherman *(Raymond)*, Maura McGiveney *(Harriet Parker)*, Ann Doran *(Lee's mother)*.

Melodrama. Suggested by: Patricia Highsmith, *Strangers on a Train* (New York, 1950). Knowing that psychiatrist Haggis has suggested her commitment, psychotic Diana is inspired by professional golfer Jerry's "sudden death" playoff against rival Mike. Seducing Jerry at the country club, Diana suggests a murder pact, according to which she will kill his opponent and he will slay her psychiatrist. Assuming that she is joking, the drunken Jerry agrees. As they make love Diana's concealed camera and tape recorder document the act. After stealing Jerry's club and lighter Diana locates Mike on the course, runs the golfer over with a cart, and clubs him to death. Diana now demands that Jerry fulfill his part of the bargain, threatening to incriminate him in Mike's murder if he refuses. As Jerry consults his estranged wife, Lee, Diana phones the couple and plays the tape. Following Jerry's departure, Diana attempts to run over Lee with a beach buggy. Fearing that Jerry has complied with Diana's demand, Lee rushes to Haggis' office, where she finds her husband conferring with the physician. Her plot discovered, Diana is arrested. *Athletes. Psychiatrists. Police. Insanity. Murder. Blackmail. Infidelity. Drunkenness. Country clubs. Golf. Recorders. Motion pictures.*

Note: Previously filmed by Alfred Hitchcock as *Strangers on a Train* (1951). Working titles: *You Can't Win 'Em All, Sudden Death,* and *The Perfect Set-Up.*

THE ONE AND ONLY, GENUINE, ORIGINAL FAMILY BAND
F6.3609

Walt Disney Productions. *Dist* Buena Vista Distribution Co. 21 Mar **1968** [New York opening; c8 Mar 1968; LP35652]. Sd (RCA); col (Technicolor). 35mm. 110 min. [Cut from 117 min.]

Pres by Walt Disney. *Prod* Bill Anderson, prod. *Dir* Michael O'Herlihy. *Story & Screenplay* Lowell S. Hawley. *Dir Photog* Frank Phillips. *Art Dir* Carroll Clark, Herman A. Blumenthal. *Set Decor* Emile Kuri, Hal Gausman. *Film Ed* Cotton Warburton. *Mus & Lyr* Richard M. Sherman, Robert B. Sherman. *Mus Supv, Arr & Cond* Jack Elliott. *Asst to the Cond* James MacDonald. *Choreog* Hugh Lambert. *Sd Supv* Robert O. Cook. *Sd Mix* Harold Lewis. *Mus Ed* Evelyn Kennedy. *Asst Dir* Paul Cameron. *Unit Prod Mgr* Joseph L. McEveety. *Cost Dsgn* Bill Thomas. *Costumers* Chuck Keehne, Emily Sundby. *Makeup* Gordon Hubbard. *Hairstylist* La Rue Matheron. *Matte Artist* Alan Maley.

Cast: Walter Brennan *(Grandpa Bower)*, Buddy Ebsen *(Calvin Bower)*, Lesley Ann Warren *(Alice Bower)*, John Davidson *(Joe Carder)*, Janet Blair *(Katie)*, Kurt Russell *(Sidney)*, Bobby Riha *(Mayo)*, Jon Walmsley *(Quinn)*, Smitty Wordes *(Nettie)*, Heidi Rook *(Rose)*, Debbie Smith *(Lulu)*, Pamelyn Ferdin *(Laura)*, Wally Cox *(Mr. Wampler)*, Richard Deacon *(Charlie Wrenn)*, Steve Harmon *(Ernie Stubbins)*, Goldie Jeanne Hawn *(giggly girl)*, John Craig *(Frank)*, Jonathan Kidd *(telegrapher)*, William Woodson *(Mr. Henry White)*.

Musical comedy-drama. Source: Laura Bower Van Nuys, *The Family Band* (Lincoln, Nebraska, 1961). During the 1888 presidential campaigns of Grover Cleveland and Benjamin Harrison, old Grandpa Bower organizes his son, daughter-in-law, and eight grandchildren into a family band that he hopes will be asked to perform his song, "Let's Put It Over With Grover," at the Democratic convention. Complications arise, however, when Alice, his eldest grandchild, falls in love with Joe Carder, a Republican newspaperman, who

persuades Papa Bower to move the family to the newly-formed Dakota Territory. Though Grandpa grudgingly accepts his son's decision and accompanies the family to Rapid City, his strongly partisan political views soon create disharmony. On election night, all the townspeople gather at Frontier Hall for the returns. Just as it appears that Cleveland has been reelected by popular vote, the telegrapher announces that the Electoral College has elected Harrison to the White House. The outraged Democrats start a brawl that continues until Papa Bower restores peace by ordering the family band to play the national anthem. As the disgruntled Grandpa pays off an election bet by giving Joe a wheelbarrow ride down Main Street, word arrives that Cleveland will divide the Dakota Territory into two states, both Republican, before leaving office. Furthermore, Washington and Montana, both Democratic territories, will be admitted to the Union, thus restoring the political balance in Congress. *Musical numbers:* "Dakota," " 'Bout Time" (Joe & Alice); "The One and Only, Genuine, Original Family Band," "Let's Put It Over With Grover," "Ten Feet Off the Ground" (The Family Band); "Drummin', Drummin', Drummin' " (Grandpa & youngsters); "The Happiest Girl Alive" (Alice); "Oh, Benjamin Harrison" (Papa & men's chorus); "West of the Wide Missouri" (entire cast). *Grandfathers. Newspapermen. Telegraph operators. Political campaigns. Family life. Political conventions. Elections. Wagers. Bands. Dakota Territory. Rapid City. Grover Cleveland. Benjamin Harrison. Democratic Party. Republican Party. Electoral College. United States Congress.*

ONE DAY WITH THE RUSSIANS *see* A DAY WITH THE RUSSIANS

ONE-EYED JACKS F6.3610

Pennebaker, Inc. *Dist* Paramount Pictures. 30 Mar **1961** [New York opening; c31 Dec 1960; LP19590]. Sd; col (Technicolor). 35mm (VistaVision). 141 min.

Prod Frank P. Rosenberg. *Exec Prod* George Glass, Walter Seltzer. *Dir* Marlon Brando. *Screenplay* Guy Trosper, Calder Willingham. *Dir Photog* Charles Lang, Jr. *2d Unit Photog* W. Wallace Kelley. *Technicolor Col Cons* Richard Mueller. *Art Dir* Hal Pereira, J. McMillan Johnson. *Set Decor* Sam Comer, Robert R. Benton. *Film Ed* Archie Marshek. *Mus* Hugo Friedhofer. *Dances Staged by* Josephine Earl. *Sd Rec* Hugo Grenzbach, Charles Grenzbach. *Asst Dir* Francisco Day, Harry Caplan. *Asst to the Prod* Carlo Fiore, prod asst. *Cost* Yvonne Wood. *Makeup Supv* Wally Westmore. *Marlon Brando's Makeup* Phil Rhodes. *Hairstyles* Nellie Manley. *Sp Photog Eff* John P. Fulton. *Proc Photog* Farciot Edouart. *Tech Adv* Rodd Redwing, Rosita Moreno. *Dial Coach* Henry Scott.

Cast: Marlon Brando *(Rio)*, Karl Malden *(Dad Longworth)*, Pina Pellicer *(Louisa)*, Katy Jurado *(Maria)*, Ben Johnson *(Bob Amory)*, Slim Pickens *(Lon)*, Larry Duran *(Modesto)*, Sam Gilman *(Harvey)*, Timothy Carey *(Howard Tetley)*, Miriam Colon *(redhead)*, Elisha Cook *(bank teller)*, Rudolph Acosta *(leader of the rurales)*, Ray Teal *(bartender)*, John Dierkes *(bearded townsman)*, Margarita Cordova *(flamenco dancer)*, Hank Worden *(Doc)*, Nina Martinez *(Margarita)*, Philip Ahn *(uncle)*, Clem Harvey *(Tim)*, William Forrest *(banker)*, Shichizo Takeda *(owner of cantina)*, Henry Wills *(posseman)*, Mickey Finn *(blacksmith)*, Fenton Jones *(squaredance caller)*, Joe Dominguez *(corral keeper)*, Margarita Martin *(Mexican vendor)*, John Michael Quijada *(rurales sergeant)*, Francy Scott *(cantina girl)*, Felipe Turich *(card sharp)*, Nesdon Booth *(townsman)*, Nacho Galindo *(Mexican townsman)*, Jorge Moreno *(bouncer in shack)*, Joan Petrone, Tom Webb.

Western melodrama. Source: Charles Neider, *The Authentic Death of Hendry Jones* (New York, 1956). In 1880, while fleeing from the Mexican police, two bank robbers, Rio and Longworth, have one of their horses shot out from under them. Rio agrees to remain behind while his friend rides off to get a new mount from a nearby ranch, but, motivated by self-preservation and greed, Longworth abandons Rio and rides off alone with the gold. After spending 5 years in the Sonora prison, Rio escapes with a cellmate, Modesto, and makes his way to the California border. There he learns that Longworth has become the sheriff of Monterey and has married a Mexican woman who has a grown daughter. Consumed by his passion for revenge, Rio joins forces with two outlaws, Amory and Harvey, who are planning to rob the Monterey bank. By feigning friendship and denying that he was ever caught, Rio wins the trust of the guilt-ridden Longworth. As part of his plan Rio seduces his arch-enemy's virginal stepdaughter, Louisa, and then brutally tells her the truth about himself. A short time later, Rio kills a drunken bully in self-defense, and Longworth uses the incident as an excuse for publicly whipping Rio, smashing his shooting hand, and driving him out of town. For several weeks Rio practices firing with his hand in a sling and once more returns to Monterey, but his growing love for Louisa, who is pregnant, has become stronger than his hatred of Longworth, and he decides to call off his vendetta. However, Amory and Harvey rob the Monterey bank; Longworth blames Rio, has him imprisoned, and arranges for a hanging. With the aid of a gun smuggled to him by Louisa, he overpowers the sadistic deputy sheriff, Lon, and escapes from jail. Just as he reaches the street, Longworth arrives. In the final meeting between the two enemies, it is Longworth who is killed. Rio says goodbye to Louisa, promises to return, and rides away. *Outlaws. Mexicans. Sheriffs. Stepfathers. Criminals—Rehabilitation. Bank robberies. Perfidy. Filial relations. Revenge. Guilt. Seduction. Murder. Flogging. Pregnancy. Sadism. Capital punishment. Marriage. Gold. Sonora (Mexico). Monterey (California).*

Note: Location scenes filmed in Monterey and Death Valley, California. Stanley Kubrick began directing the film but was replaced by Brando shortly after shooting began.

ONE-EYED SOLDIERS (United States/Great Britain/Yugoslavia)
F6.3611

Avala Film–BACO British–United Screen Arts. *Dist* United Screen Arts. Oct **1967** [Los Angeles showing]. Sd; col (Eastman Color by Technicolor). 35mm (Techniscope). 80 min.

Prod Clive Sharp. *Dir-Writ* Jean Christophe. *Story* Richard Fraink. *Photog* Branko Ivatović. *Mus* Avala Studios. *Asst Dir* Stevo Petrović.

Cast: Dale Robertson *(Richard Owen),* Luciana Paluzzi *(Gava Berens),* Guy Deghy *(Harold Schmidt),* Andrew Faulds *(Colonel Ferrer),* Mila Avramović *(Antonio Caporelli),* Dragan Nikolić *(The Mute),* Božidar Drnić *(Dr. Charles Berens).*

Adventure melodrama. A murdered United Nations official mutters the words "one-eyed soldiers" as he dies, thereby providing his daughter Gava with a clue to the whereabouts of the key to a Swiss bank vault containing $15 million in stolen money. On a train en route to the Eastern European town of Nassaum, Gava is followed by a mysterious fat man, later revealed to be Harold Schmidt, an international criminal. Gava knocks Schmidt unconscious and forces Richard Owen, an American journalist aboard the train, to drive her into town. The two are pursued by gunmen headed by former SS agent Antonio Caporelli, a sadistic dwarf. Caporelli captures and tortures Gava while Schmidt, disguised as an undertaker, rescues Owen in a hearse. Owen rescues Gava with Schmidt's help, and Gava directs Owen to the Nassaum cathedral where a statue with one eye contains the hidden vault key. Caporelli fires a machine gun into a crowd from his perch on top of the cathedral, but Schmidt's assistant, mute as a result of Caporelli's wartime tortures, throws himself on the dwarf, and the two fall to the ground. On the point of arresting Gava and Owens, Colonel Ferrer, the local police chief, allows himself to be corrupted by Schmidt. Locking his charges in adjoining hotel rooms, Ferrer departs with Schmidt and the key to the $15 million. *Journalists. Thieves. Dwarfs. Police. Mutes. Americans in foreign countries. Nazis. Murder. Theft. Sadism. Disguise. Trains. Cathedrals. Sculptures. Chases.*

Note: Filmed in Yugoslavia in 1966; running time: 83 min.

ONE-FOURTH OF HUMANITY: THE CHINA STORY see **THE CHINA STORY: ONE-FOURTH OF HUMANITY**

ONE HOUR WITH W. C. FIELDS see **THE BEST OF W. C. FIELDS**

101 ACTS OF LOVE   **F6.3612**

Xerxes Productions. *Dist* Films International Distribution Organization. Jul **1970** [Los Angeles showing]. Sd; col. 35mm. 90 min.

Prod Donn Greer. *Assoc Prod* Jerald Cormier. *Dir* Eric Jeffrey Haims. *Script* Ann Foster. *Cinematog* Jim Hastings. *Lighting-2d Unit Camera* David Worth. *Art Dir* Jim West. *Orig Mus & Song:* "Good Times" Randy Scott, Ernie Carter. *Sd* Frank Meadows. *Wardrobe* Jerry McCarter. *Sp Eff* David Worth.

Cast: Lindis Guiness *(Dr. Ann Foster),* Peter Forster *(narrator),* Marie Johnson, Bob Johnson, Rev Hansen, Frank and Janet Wilson, Lydia Freeman, Tom Freeman, Susan Westcott, John Keats, John Dunn, Diane Clark, Tony Hansen, Christine Murray, John Mandeville.

Sex instruction film. Marie Johnson, a young wife who has found sex with her husband unsatisfying, visits Dr. Ann Foster, a sexologist, for help. Dr. Foster tells Marie of the sexual frustrations of three other young couples she has treated and describes how she helped them to abandon the inhibitions which interfered with their full enjoyment of sex. Dr. Foster then describes 101 different positions for sexual gratification, including oral intercourse. Four couples demonstrate the sexual variations on a plexiglass platform suspended from the ceiling. *Housewives. Physicians. Sex instruction. Sexual techniques.*

Note: Portions of the narration are taken from Elizabeth Barrett Browning's sonnet "How Do I Love Thee? Let Me Count the Ways."

ONE HUNDRED AND ONE DALMATIANS   **F6.3613**

Walt Disney Productions. *Dist* Buena Vista Distribution Co. 10 Feb **1961** [New York opening; c18 Nov 1960; LP18715]. Sd (RCA); col (Technicolor). 35mm. 80 min.

Pres by Walt Disney. A Walt Disney Production. *Dir* Wolfgang Reitherman, Hamilton S. Luske, Clyde Geronimi. *Story* Bill Peet. *Dir Anim* Milt Kahl, Marc Davis, Ollie Johnston, Frank Thomas, John Lounsbery, Eric Larson. *Charact* *Anim* Hal King, Cliff Nordberg, Eric Cleworth, Art Stevens, Hal Ambro, Bill Keil, Dick Lucas, Les Clark, Blaine Gibson, John Sibley, Julius Svendsen, Ted Berman, Don Lusk, Amby Paliwoda. *Eff Anim* Jack Boyd, Ed Parks, Dan MacManus, Jack Buckley. *Layout* Basil Davidovich, McLaren Stewart, Vance Gerry, Richard Ung, Homer Jonas, Al Zinnen, Joe Hale, Dale Barnhart, Ray Aragon, Sammy June Lanham, Victor Haboush. *Col Stylist* Walt Peregoy. *Background* Al Dempster, Ralph Hulett, Anthony Rizzo, Bill Layne. *Layout Stylist* Don Griffith, Ernest Nordli, Colin Campbell. *Charact Stylist* Bill Peet, Tom Oreb. *Art Dir* Ken Anderson. *Prod Dsgn* Ken Anderson. *Film Ed* Donald Halliday, Roy M. Brewer, Jr. *Mus* George Bruns. *Orch & Song:* "Remember When" Franklyn Marks. *Songs:* "Cruella de Ville," "Dalmatian Plantation" Mel Leven. *Sung by* Jeanne Bruns, Bill Lee. *Song:* "Kanine Krunchies Kommercial" Mel Leven. *Sung by* Lucille Bliss. *Sd Supv* Robert O. Cook. *Mus Ed* Evelyn Kennedy. *Prod Supv* Ken Peterson. *Sp Proc* Ub Iwerks, Eustace Lycett.

With the Talents of: Rod Taylor, J. Pat O'Malley, Betty Lou Gerson, Martha Wentworth, Lisa Davis, Tom Conway, Tudor Owen, George Pelling, Micky Maga, Barbara Beaird, Mimi Gibson, Sandra Abbott, Paul Wexler, Mary Wickes, Barbara Luddy, Lisa Daniels, Ben Wright, Cate Bauer, David Frankham, Frederic Worlock, Ramsay Hill, Sylvia Marriott, Queenie Leonard, Marjorie Bennett, Thurl Ravenscroft, Bill Lee, Max Smith, Bob Stevens, Helene Stanley, Donald Barclay, Dal McKennon, Jeanne Bruns.

Animated comedy. Source: Dodie Smith, *One Hundred and One Dalmatians* (New York, 1957). Pongo is a male dalmatian living in London with his master, Roger, a bachelor songwriter who has yet to sell his first tune. Bored with their single existence, Pongo arranges for Roger to meet Anita, a pretty young woman who just happens to have a female dalmatian named Perdita. It is not long before love blossoms all around and a double wedding takes place. A few months later, Perdita gives birth to 15 puppies, much to the delight of Cruella De Vil, a wealthy, wicked former schoolmate of Anita's whose burning passion is to own a coat made of dalmatian pelts. When she is unable to purchase the puppies, she has them "dognapped" and brought to her castle, where 84 other dalmatians are also being held captive. All attempts by the police to find the missing pups fail, and the desperate Pongo and Perdita appeal to the dogs of London, via the "twilight bark." Led by The Colonel, an indomitable shaggy dog, all dogdom comes to the rescue and, aided by geese, cats, and horses, tracks down the missing puppies. A daring rescue is accomplished, and Cruella meets her death when her pursuing automobile sails off a cliff. All ends happily as Roger sells his first song, buys the De Vil estate, and moves in with Anita and the 101 dalmatians. *Bachelors. Composers. Evildoers. Fashion. Kidnaping. Wealth. Weddings. London. Chases. Dogs.*

$100 A NIGHT (West Germany)   **F6.3614**

Rex Film. *Dist* William Mishkin. 30 May **1968** [San Francisco showing]. Sd; b&w. 35mm. 85 min.

Dir Wolfgang Glück. *Screenplay* Hellmut Andics, August Rieger. *Photog* Walter Tuch. *Art Dir* Felix Smetana. *Film Ed* Ursula Norkus. *Mus* Willi Hoffmann, Gilbert Bécaud, Klaus Ogermann, Perez Prado, Sten Clift. *Choreog* Willy Dirtl. *Prod Mgr* Otto Stenzel, Karl Schmied. *Dir Prod* Ernst Müller, August Rieger.

Cast: Kai Fischer *(Olga),* Gerlinde Locker *(Eva),* Tommy Rupp *(Tommy Kersten),* Jimmy Makulis *(Jimmy),* Rolf Kutschera *(Martini),* Rolf Olsen *(Rutka),* Wolf Albach-Retty *(Krüger),* Horst Beck, Edith Elmay, Guido Wieland, Alfred Böhm, Raoul Retzer, Inge Rassaert, Renate Rohm, Aina Capell, Gaby King, Josef Hendrichs, Hansi Prinz, Mona Baptiste, Dalida, Macky Kasper, Habiba, Latin Bob Stars, Fatty George & His Orchestra.

Crime melodrama. Eva, a young woman intent on becoming a successful singer, goes to Martini, a man whom she has never seen, looking for employment. Martini, owner of the Mambo-Bar nightclub, finds her a job in the same building handling bookings for a theatrical agency. Tommy, the trumpeter in the jazz band at the club, encourages Eva to sing with his combo, thus angering Olga, the drug-addicted dancer at the cabaret. Olga tries to murder Eva but instead falls to her own death. Tommy, an undercover agent, intervenes in the bar's illicit operations in topless massage parlors, narcotics dealing, and espionage. Attempting to escape, Martini is fatally shot, but before dying he reveals to Tommy that he is Eva's father. Tommy keeps this information to himself, and he and Eva leave together. *Singers. Nightclub owners. Racketeers. Trumpeters. Secret agents. Dancers. Drug addicts. Drug dealers. Personal identity. Jealousy. Filial relations. Murder. Nightclubs.*

Note: Released in West Germany in Jul 1959 as *Mädchen für die Mambo-Bar* at 88 min.

$100 IS MY PRICE see **CANDY'S LUSTFUL NATURE**

100 RIFLES   **F6.3615**

Marvin Schwartz Productions. *Dist* Twentieth Century-Fox Film Corp. 26 Mar **1969** [New York opening; c30 Dec 1968; LP36630]. Sd (Westrex); col

(DeLuxe). 35mm. 110 min. *MPAA rating* R.

A Marvin Schwartz Production. *Prod* Marvin Schwartz. *Dir* Tom Gries. *2d Unit Dir* Chuck Roberson. *Screenplay* Tom Gries, Clair Huffaker. *Dir Photog* Cecilio Paniagua. *Art Dir* Carl Anderson. *Film Ed* Robert Simpson. *Mus* Jerry Goldsmith. *Orch* David Tamkin. *Sd* Roy Charman, David Dockendorf. *Asst Dir* Tony Tarruella. *Unit Prod Mgr* Joseph C. Behm. *Prod Mgr (Spain)* Tadeo Villalba. *Wardrobe* Oscar Rodriguez. *Makeup* Ramon de Diego. *Hairstyling* Mary Bredon. *Sp Photog Eff* L. B. Abbott, Art Cruickshank. *Mechanical Eff* Alex Weldon.

Cast: Jim Brown *(Lyedecker)*, Raquel Welch *(Sarita)*, Burt Reynolds *(Yaqui Joe)*, Fernando Lamas *(Verdugo)*, Dan O'Herlihy *(Grimes)*, Hans Gudegast *(Von Klemme)*, Michael Forest *(Humara)*, Aldo Sambrell *(Sergeant Paletes)*, Soledad Miranda *(girl in hotel)*, Alberto Dalbes *(Padre Francisco)*, Carlos Bravo *(Lopez)*, Jose Manuel Martin *(Sarita's father)*.

Western melodrama. Source: Robert MacLeod, *The Californio* (Greenwich, Connecticut, 1967). In the early 1900's, Yaqui Joe, a half-breed Indian, robs an Arizona bank and flees across the border into the Mexican town of Nogales where the governor, General Verdugo, aided by a German military advisor, Von Klemme, is waging a war of annihilation against the Yaqui Indians. Verdugo captures Joe and orders him shot, whereupon Lyedecker, a black American deputy assigned to bring the half-breed back to the States, intervenes and is himself arrested. The two men escape to the hills where they are joined by Sarita, a beautiful Indian revolutionary. After Joe has revealed that he used the bank loot to purchase 100 rifles for the Indians, General Verdugo once more captures the two men and orders them shot. Determined to see that the rifles reach her people, Sarita leads an attack on the General's hacienda and frees the two men as well as the rifles. Enraged, Verdugo retaliates by storming a Yaqui village and taking children as hostages. Lyedecker, finally won over to both Sarita and the Indian cause, rescues the children and vows to destroy Verdugo. Taking over the leadership of the Yaquis, Lyedecker ambushes Verdugo's train while Sarita distracts the attention of the soldiers on board by taking a public shower. The railroad manager, Grimes, captured by the Indians, escapes and warns Verdugo that the Indians plan to attack the town with the train, but Lyedecker outwits the General by filling the train with dead bodies. As Verdugo's men open fire on the corpses, the Yaquis attack from behind. During the bloody battle, Verdugo is killed and his men are defeated, but Sarita also pays with her life. Returning to the United States without his prisoner, Lyedecker leaves Yaqui Joe to take over the leadership of the Indians. *Yaqui Indians. Fugitives. Halfcastes. Mexicans. Negroes. Germans. Revolutionaries. Territorial governors. Railroad superintendents. Hostages. Genocide. Military government. Bank robberies. Firearms. Trains. Nogales. Mexico.*

Note: Location scenes filmed in Spain. Screenplay writer Clair Huffaker requested that his name be removed from the credits.

ONE LIFE *see* END OF DESIRE

ONE MAN'S WAY   F6.3616

Frank Ross Productions. *Dist* United Artists. 26 Feb **1964** [Kansas City, Missouri, opening; c26 Feb 1964; LP27679]. Sd; b&w. 35mm. 105 min.

Pres by Frank Ross. *Prod* Frank Ross. *Assoc Prod* Dick Ross. *Dir* Denis Sanders. *Screenplay* Eleanore Griffin, John W. Bloch. *Dir Photog* Ernest Laszlo. *Art Dir* Edward Jewell. *Set Decor* Morris Hoffman. *Film Ed* Philip W. Anderson. *Mus* Richard Markowitz. *Orch* Willard Jones. *Sd* Lambert Day. *Asst Dir* Herbert S. Greene. *Prod Supv* Ben Hersh. *Cost* Jack Angel, Grace Kuhn. *Makeup* Ben Lane, Joe Di Bella. *Hairstyles* Lillian Hokom.

Cast: Don Murray *(Norman Peale)*, Diana Hyland *(Ruth Peale)*, William Windom *(Rev. Clifford Peale)*, Virginia Christine *(Anna Peale)*, Carol Ohmart *(Evelyn)*, Veronica Cartwright *(Mary)*, Liam Sullivan *(Dr. Gordon)*, June Dayton *(Mrs. Gordon)*, Ian Wolfe *(Bishop Hardwick)*, Charles Lampkin *(Lafe)*, Arthur Peterson, Jr. *(instructor)*, Hope Summers *(Mrs. Thompson)*, Virginia Sale *(Miss Collingswood)*, Rory O'Brien *(Leonard Peale, as a child)*, David Bailey *(Robert Peale, as a child)*, Mickey Sholdar *(Norman Peale, as a child)*, Paul Marin *(Feldman)*, Hank Stanton *(Jack Wilson)*, Bryan O'Byrne *(organist)*, Eddie Ryder *(gas station attendant)*, Ed Peck *(Harry, the reporter)*, John Harmon *(Elder Marcus)*, Joseph Hamilton *(Elder Thompson)*, Tom Palmer *(Professor Aiken)*, Sandra Gale Bettin *(Alma)*, Wendy Ferdin *(Margaret Peale)*, Sharyl Locke *(Elizabeth Peale)*, Butch Patrick *(John Peale)*, Gerald Gordon *(Robert Peale, grown)*, Tom Skerritt *(Leonard Peale, grown)*, Vernon Rich *(Mr. Melton)*, Bing Russell *(Tom Rayburn)*, Ann Morgan Guilbert *(receptionist)*, Ed Prentiss *(Mr. Boardman)*, Arthur Marshall *(Rod Allenberry)*, Geraldine Wall *(Mae Michaels)*, Jon Lormer *(John Hellman)*, Jean Carson *(woman who shoots husband)*.

Biographical drama. Source: Arthur Gordon, *Norman Vincent Peale; Minister to Millions* (Englewood Cliffs, N. J., 1958). Twelve-year-old Norman Vincent Peale determines never to become a clergyman because of the insults he has suffered as the son of a smalltown Ohio minister. He changes his mind when, years later, as a Detroit crime reporter, he becomes frustrated by his inability to relieve much of the suffering and misfortune he reports. He enters a seminary and is there regarded as a rebel because he believes in a God of love rather than of vengeance, but his zeal increases church attendance wherever he preaches. In Syracuse he convinces pretty co-ed Ruth Stafford that the life of a minister's wife can be exciting; and after their honeymoon he accepts a position at New York City's Marble Collegiate Church. His methods and preachings are criticized as his fame grows; but through radio, articles in magazines, and a syndicated newspaper column he develops his thesis that God helps those who help themselves. With the publication of his book *The Power of Positive Thinking*, the condemnation of his theological attitudes reaches new heights; and he is about to resign from his pulpit when an experience with a critically ill child, who is given no chance for survival by medical science but nevertheless rallies after Peale keeps a night-long prayer vigil, renews his faith in all he has written and preached. He decides to remain with his church. *Clergymen. Reporters. Columnists. Filial relations. Seminaries. New York City. Ohio. Detroit. Syracuse (New York). Norman Vincent Peale. Methodist Episcopal Church. Marble Collegiate Reformed Church.*

Note: "Ohio" exteriors filmed in Pasadena, California. Marble Collegiate Reformed Church sequences filmed in New York City.

ONE MILLION AC/DC   F6.3617

Dist Canyon Distributing Co. **1969**. Sd; col. 35mm. 80 min.

Prod-Dir Ed DePriest. *Co-prod* Michael Welton. *Screenplay (see note)* Frederick Emerson, Akdov Telmig. *Story* Hayden Patterson, Everet Paine. *Photog* Michael Welton, Eric Torgesson, Ed DePriest. *Film Ed* Donald Larson. *Sd Rec* Sid Maitles. *Asst Dir* Bill Granding. *Sp Eff* Gary Mullet, Frank Hastings. *Historical Cons* R. L. Frost, Bob Cresse. *Grip* Tom Richman. *Op Dinosaur* Phil Otis.

Cast—Pressbook: Harvey Edmundt, Lawrence Richey, Douglass Martin, Robyn Glanz, Jacqueline Fox, Armondo Crain, Irwin Milton, Jesse Frandele, Barbara McNerney, Helen Mathew, Grace Hyfield, Ernest Caven, Evelyn Blaustein, Archie Leigh, Phil Otis, Francine Anton, Kevin Shirar, Sherrie Quinn, Noel Tavish, Gail Gralow, Morgana Hieb.

Cast—Review: Susan Berkely, Natasha, Sharon Wells, Pam English, Shari Stevens, Bonnie Walker, Chris Mathis.

Melodrama. During the age when primitive man fought giant reptiles, a band of people becomes trapped in a cave. Taking advantage of their confinement, they seek sexual fulfillment in an orgy, knowing that at the entrance to the cave a flesh-eating dinosaur waits for them. Eventually one of the group who can no longer bear his imprisonment kills the monster, thereby freeing his fellow prisoners from fear and oppression. *Man—Prehistoric. Orgies. Caves. Dinosaurs.*

Note: Sources conflict in crediting the screenplay writer.

ONE MILLION YEARS B. C. (Great Britain)   F6.3618

Seven Arts Productions–Hammer Film Productions. *Dist* Twentieth Century–Fox Film Corp. 21 Feb **1967** [New York showing; c31 Dec 1966; LP34065]. Sd (RCA); col (DeLuxe). 35mm. 91 min.

Prod-Writ Michael Carreras. *Assoc Prod* Hal E. Roach, Sr., Aida Young. *Dir* Don Chaffey. *Dir Photog* Wilkie Cooper. *Camera Op* David Harcourt. *2d Unit Camera* Jack Mills, photog. *Art Dir* Robert Jones. *Asst Art Dir* Kenneth McCallum Tait. *Prolog Dsgn* Les Bowie. *Supv Ed* James Needs. *Ed* Tom Simpson. *Mus & Sp Mus Eff* Mario Nascimbene. *Mus Supv* Philip Martell. *Sd Mix* Len Shilton, Bill Rowe. *Rec Dir* A. W. Lumkin. *Sd Ed* Roy Baker, Alfred Cox. *Asst Dir* Dennis Bertera. *Prod Mgr* John D. Wilcox. *Cont* Gladys Goldsmith, Marjorie Lavelly. *Cost Dsgn* Carl Toms. *Wardrobe Mistress* Ivy Baker. *Makeup Supv* Wally Schneiderman. *Hairdressing Supv* Olga Angelinetta. *Sp Vis Eff* Ray Harryhausen. *Sp Eff* George Blackwell.

Cast: Raquel Welch *(Loana)*, John Richardson *(Tumak)*, Percy Herbert *(Sakana)*, Robert Brown *(Akhoba)*, Martine Beswick *(Nupondi)*, Jean Wladon *(Ahot)*, Lisa Thomas *(Sura)*, Malya Nappi *(Tohana)*, Richard James *(young rock man)*, William Lyon Brown *(Payto)*, Frank Hayden *(1st rock man)*, Terence Maidment *(1st shell man)*, Micky De Rauch *(1st shell girl)*, Yvonne Horner *(Ullah)*.

Melodrama. Based on the film *One Million B. C.* (1940), screenplay by: Mickell Novak, George Baker and Joseph Frickert. In prehistoric times, Tumak of the Rock People violently quarrels with his father and is banished from his tribe. After escaping from an attack by a giant lizard and a brontosaurus, he reaches an ocean and collapses on the beach. He is found by the Shell People, a tribe considerably more advanced than his own. They nurse him back to health, and when he kills an allosaurus, they treat him as a member of their tribe. But he fights with the leader and is once more banished. Loana, a young woman who has fallen in love with him, decides to accompany him into the desert. After witnessing a fight between a triceratops and a ceratosaurus, they make their way to the caves of the Rock People. While Loana is teaching Tumak to swim, she is carried off in the claws of a pterodactyl and then dropped into the sea when the huge bird encounters another of its kind. She makes her way back to the Shell People and persuades some of them to return with her to Tumak's tribe. But they are attacked by the Rock People, and the fighting ends only when a giant volcano suddenly erupts. As the earth cracks and molten lava pours over the rocks, many members of both tribes are killed. Loana and Tumak join the other survivors in beginning a new life as the shadow of a huge mushroom cloud darkens the horizon. *Cave dwellers. Survival. Banishment. Volcanoes. Earthquakes. Atom bomb. Prehistory. Dinosaurs. Animals— Prehistoric.*

Note: Location scenes filmed on the Canary Islands. Released in Great Britain in Technicolor in Dec 1966 (100 min). A remake of the 1940 United Artists release *One Million B. C.*

ONE MORE TIME (United States/Great Britain)   **F6.3619**
Chrislaw Productions-Trace-Mark Productions. *Dist* United Artists. May **1970** [c27 May 1970; LP37959]. Sd; col (De Luxe). 35mm. 93 min. *MPAA rating* GP.

Prod Milton Ebbins. *Exec Prod* Peter Lawford, Sammy Davis, Jr. *Dir* Jerry Lewis. *Screenplay* Michael Pertwee. *Photog* Ernest Steward. *Set Dresser* Dimity Collins. *Prod Dsgn* Jack Stevens. *Film Ed* William Butler. *Mus & Mus Dir* Les Reed. *Titl Song* Les Reed, Jackie Rae. *Song:* "Where Do I Go From Here?" Les Reed, Geoff Stephens. *Song:* "When the Feeling Hits You" Bobby Doyle. *Sung by* Sammy Davis, Jr. *Sd Rec* Gerry Humphreys. *Sd Mix* Gerry Turner. *Prod Mgr* Frank Ernst, Ronnie Bear. *Wardrobe* Ken Lawton. *Makeup* George Frost. *Hairdresser* Alice Holmes. *Sp Eff* Terry Witherington.

Cast: Sammy Davis, Jr. (*Charlie Salt*), Peter Lawford (*Chris Pepper/Lord Sydney Pepper*), Maggie Wright (*Miss Tomkins*), Leslie Sands (*inspector*), John Wood (*Figg*), Sydney Arnold (*Tombs*), Edward Evans (*Gordon*), Percy Herbert (*Mander*), Bill Maynard (*Jenson*), Dudley Sutton (*Wilson*), Glyn Owen (*Dennis*), Lucille Soong (*Kim Lee*), Esther Anderson (*Billie*), Anthony Nicholls (*Candler*), Allan Cuthbertson (*Belton*), Cyril Luckham (*magistrate*), Moultrie Kelsall (*priest*), Julian D'Albie (*General Turpington-Mellish*), Gladys Spencer (*Lady Turpington-Mellish*), Joanna Wake (*Claire Turpington-Mellish*), Juliette Bora, Florence George, Amber Dean Smith, Lorraine Hall, Carmel Stratton, Thelma Neal (*Salt & Pepper Club girls*), Davie Trevena, Norman Mitchell, Richard Goolden, Geoffrey Morris, Norman Pitt, George McGrath, Mischa De La Motte, Walter Hopsburgh, John Nettles, Peter Reeves.

Comedy. Charlie Salt and Chris Pepper, owners of the Salt and Pepper Club, turn to Chris's influential twin brother, Lord Sydney Pepper, when their nightclub is closed by the police. Lord Sydney refuses to help pay the fine, but Chris manages to enjoy some good times in London's fashionable night spots by posing as his wealthy brother. Chris returns to Lord Sydney in a second attempt to borrow money, but finds his brother has been murdered. Seizing the opportunity, Chris changes clothing with the corpse and declares that it is Chris who has died. The Salt and Pepper Club holds an elaborate funeral for its owner, and the new Lord Sydney invites Charlie to his mansion for a reconciliation and offers his unsuspecting former partner a job as controller of the estate. Eventually, Charlie learns "Lord Sydney" 's true identity, and the two of them discover that Chris's brother was a diamond smuggler murdered by accomplices w¹ now believe Lord Sydney to still be alive. Following a hectic chase after th. murderers, the police take over, leaving Salt and Pepper free to resume their pleasure-seeking life. *Nightclub owners. Brothers. Twins. Smugglers. Police. Impersonation. Murder. Partnerships. Nightclubs. Funerals. London. Chases.*

Note: Released in Great Britain in Dec 1970. Film is a sequel to *Salt and Pepper*, q. v.

ONE NAKED NIGHT   **F6.3620**
Four Seasons Productions. *Dist* Sack Amusement Enterprises, Grads Corp. **1963**. Sd; b&w. 35mm. 65 min.

Cast: Barbara Morris (*Candy*), Joe Marshall (*Joe*), Audrey Campbell (*Barbara*), Ina Miller (*Charles*), Sally Lane (*Laura*), Allen Merson (*Bill*).

Drama. Smalltown girl Candy attends boarding school and sees her mother only occasionally. She is shocked at the news that her mother is a prostitute, and that she has taken her own life. Candy goes to New York City, moves in with several fast women, and meets nude study photographer Charles Stern. Barbara, a lesbian and one of Candy's roommates, interferes with her affair with Stern by seducing the still naive Candy. Candy is disappointed at losing Charles and attends a wild party; she awakes the next morning amidst a mass of nude, drunken revellers. *Innocents. Roommates. Photographers. Prostitutes. Motherhood. Suicide. Lesbianism. Seduction. Group sex. Drunkenness. Boarding schools. New York City.*

Note: Also known as *Naked in the Night* and *One N—— Night.*

1 + 1 *see* **SYMPATHY FOR THE DEVIL (1 + 1)**

1 + 1 (EXPLORING THE KINSEY REPORTS)
(United States/Canada)   **F6.3621**
Fluorite, Ltd. *Dist* Selected Films. 23 Aug **1961** [Los Angeles opening; c23 Aug 1961; LP21175]. Sd; b&w. 35mm. 114 min.

Exec Prod-Dir-Writ Arch Oboler. *Assoc Prod* Susanne Warner. *Anim* Pistafilm. *Dir Photog* George Jacobson. *Camera* Sol Reigman. *Lighting* Norman Leigh, Robert Milligan. *Film Ed* Chester W. Schaeffer. *Asst Ed* David Nicholson. *Mus Comp & Cond* John Bath. *Sd* Frank Orban, Abe Dicesare. *Asst Dir* Richard Dixon, Gordon Milligan. *Prod Asst* Jerry Kay. *Makeup* Irene Kent. *Key Grip* Robert Gilham. *Casting* Eva Langborn.

Cast—Lecture Hall: Leo G. Carroll (*Professor Logan*), Arch McDonnell, Herman Ettlinger, Margot Christie, Norman Welsh, Daryl Masters, Eleanor Beecroft.

Cast—"Honeymoon": Hilda Brawner (*Clare Hollister*), William Traylor (*Hollister*), Madeleine Christie.

Cast—"Homecoming": Kate Reid (*Julia Bradley*), Ernest Graves (*John Bradley*), Richard Janaver (*Carlton*), Garrick Hagon, Toby Tarnow, Michael Stewart, Sharon Acker, Robert Christie, Alfred Scopp.

Cast—"The Divorcée": June Duprez (*Margaret Gaylord*), Austin Willis (*Sam Tooray*), Peggi Loder, Douglas Rain.

Cast—"Average Man": Jane Rose (*Mrs. Kingsley*), Truman Smith (*Mr. Kingsley*), Winifred Dennis (*Gertrude*), Virginia MacLeod (*Miss Pom*), Leslie Yeo.

Cast—"Baby": Rita Gardner (*Peggy Cannon*), Jack Betts (*Bill Cannon*), Alice Hill (*The Nurse*), Barbara Hamilton, Sydney Brown, Susan Fletcher, Frances Tobias, Ruth Springford, Judith Orban, Bena Schuster, William Ferguson, Cal Whitehead, Sammy Sales.

Drama. Source: Arch Oboler, *Mrs. Kingsley's Report* (a play; production undetermined). Professor Logan, a retired university professor, conducts a symposium on marriage and the sexual mores described in the Kinsey Reports. As he lectures, various members of the audience recall individual experiences. HONEYMOON: Hollister is worried about the premarital sexual relations he had with his wife but discovers on his honeymoon that they will have no effect on his marriage. HOMECOMING: Advertising executive Julia Bradley dreads her husband's homecoming because of a liaison she had with a fellow account executive on New Year's Eve. By telling her husband the truth, however, she saves her marriage. THE DIVORCÉE: Attractive divorcée Margaret Gaylord is shunned by her women friends who fear that she might steal their husbands. She hopes that Sam Tooray will end her loneliness by marrying her, but he turns out to be just another man looking for a good time. AVERAGE MAN: Mr. Kingsley makes a date with a former school friend when he learns that all average men have extramarital affairs, but the romance is short-lived upon his discovery that she is a plump grandmother interested only in getting home to babysit for her daughter. BABY: Young Peggy Cannon's pregnancy causes her to worry so much about her husband's lack of interest in children that she goes to an abortionist, even though she is unable to go through with the operation. Instead of being upset by his approaching fatherhood, however, her husband is delighted with the news. After the symposium, Professor Logan realizes that no one in the discussion has mentioned love, the most important ingredient in a successful marriage. *Professors. Lecturers. Advertising executives. Grandmothers. Sex research. Marriage. Infidelity. Divorce. Loneliness. Pregnancy. Abortion. Honeymoons. New Year's Eve. Kinsey Reports.*

Note: Location scenes filmed in Toronto. Released in Canada in 1961.

ONE POTATO, TWO POTATO   **F6.3622**
Bawalco Picture Co. *Dist* Cinema V Distributing, Inc. 29 Jul **1964** [New York opening]. Sd; b&w. 35mm. 92 min.

Prod Sam Weston. *Dir* Larry Peerce. *Screenplay* Raphael Hayes, Orville H. Hampton. *Story* Orville H. Hampton. *Photog* Andrew Laszlo. *Film Ed* Robert Fritch. *Mus & Mus Dir* Gerald Fried. *Sd* Jack F. Lilly, Don Jones. *Asst Dir* Bruce Bilson.

Cast: Barbara Barrie (*Julie Cullen Richards*), Bernie Hamilton (*Frank Richards*), Richard Mulligan (*Joe Cullen*), Harry Bellaver (*Judge Powell*), Marti Mericka (*Ellen Mary*), Robert Earl Jones (*William Richards*), Vinette Carroll (*Martha Richards*), Sam Weston (*Johnny Hruska*), Faith Burwell (*Ann Hruska*), Jack Stamberger (*minister*), Michael Shane (*Jordan Hollis*).

Drama. Having been deserted by her irresponsible husband, Joe, shortly before the birth of their daughter, Ellen, Julie Cullen struggles to raise her child in a midwestern town. She obtains a divorce from her husband, who has gone to South America to seek his fortune, moves to another town, goes to work at a local plant, and meets Frank Richards, a black office worker at the plant. They fall in love and marry, despite opposition from Frank's parents. They move to Frank's parents' farm, where Julie is immediately made welcome by Mrs. Richards, but it is only after she bears Frank a son that Frank's father accepts her. Some time later, Joe Cullen, learning of Julie's marriage to a black, returns and institutes legal action for custody of Ellen. Advised to leave the state with his family because chances of retaining custody of the child are slight, Frank decides to remain and fight. Although the judge is aware that Ellen is healthy and happy with Julie and Frank, he takes society's prejudices into account and awards custody to Joe. Bewildered and hurt, Ellen is taken away in a taxi by Joe as Julie helplessly chases the departing vehicle. *Office clerks. Negroes. Judges. Farmers. In-laws. Desertion. Divorce. Racial prejudice. Marriage— Mixed. Child custody. Smalltown life. Factories. United States—Midwest.*

Note: Location scenes filmed in Painesville, Ohio. Shown at the 1964 Cannes Film Festival at 102 min.

ONE SHOCKING MOMENT F6.3623

Mark Brown Productions. 23 Jul **1965** [Los Angeles showing]. Sd; b&w. 35mm. 71 min.

Exec Prod Jay Fineberg, Ron B. Fineberg. *Dir-Writ* Ted V. Mikels. *Dir Photog* Gregory Sandor. *2d Unit Camera* Ted V. Mikels. *Art Dir* Wally Moon. *Supv Film Ed* Theodore Mikacevich. *Mus* Icaras de Docaras. *Sd* Austin McKinney. *Asst Dir* Art Names. *Script Supv* Igo Monaco. *Wardrobe* Marc Khoury. *Makeup* Tony Tierney. *Still Photog* Stan Feldstein. *Prop Master* Waldo K. Berns.

Cast: Phillip Brady (*Cliff*), Lee Anna (*Mindy*), Verne Martine (*Tanya*), Jerry Fitzpatrick (*Rick*), Maureen Gaffney (*Joanie*), Victor Sandor, Shirl Simmons, Marie Moore, Dominic Levi, Robin Willas, Dick Bing, Zenobia.

Melodrama. Cliff and Mindy Newhall move to Los Angeles when Cliff gets a promotion. Two women in a neighboring apartment, Joanie and Tanya, welcome the Newhalls, and soon Cliff and Mindy are regular patrons at Tanya's small, intimate nightclub. Tanya specializes in bizarre sexual practices, one night earning a handsome fee for whipping a wealthy masochist in his palatial home. A bisexual, Tanya attempts to seduce both of the Newhalls, whose marriage has been severely shaken by the recent move. In the midst of a wild party Mindy does a striptease while Cliff in the next room tries to rape Joanie. Tanya bursts in, orders Joanie out, and commands Cliff to make love to her. Shocked into awareness, Cliff leaves the women and the party, planning to start afresh with Mindy. *Businessmen. Nightclub owners. Neighbors. Roommates. Marriage. Bisexuality. Seduction. Masochism. Infidelity. Flagellation. Rape. Striptease. Nightclubs. Los Angeles.*

ONE SPY TOO MANY *see* WHERE THE SPIES ARE

ONE STEP TO HELL (United States/Italy/Spain) F6.3624

Copercines-Metheus Film-Harris Associates. *Dist* World Entertainment Corp. 28 Jun **1969** [Los Angeles opening]. Sd; col (Eastman Color). 35mm. 94 min. *MPAA rating G.*

Pres by Harris Associates. *Prod-Dir* Sandy Howard. *Exec Prod* Jack O. Lamont. *Assoc Prod* Sven Persson, Eduardo Manzanos. *Screenplay* Jack DeWitt, Sandy Howard, Robert L. Joseph. *Co-writ* Eduardo M. Brochero. *Dir Photog* Julio Ortas, Sven Persson. *Art Dir* Jaime Pérez Cubero, José Luis Galicia. *Film Ed* Juan Serra. *Mus Comp & Cond* Gianni Marchetti. *Theme Mus* Bob Harris, mus. *Asst Dir* Nino Scolaro. *Prod Mgr* Ignacio Gutiérrez.

Cast: Ty Hardin (*King Edwards*), Pier Angeli (*Ann Peterson*), Rossano Brazzi (*Dr. Hamilton*), George Sanders (*Captain Phillips*), Helga Liné (*Deborah Vinton*), Dale Cummings (*bartender*), George Rigaud, Julio Peña, Charles Fawcett, Alan Collins, Pamela Tudor, Michael Castillo, John Anthony Mayans, Fred Coplan, Martha Valardi, Fernando Villena, Salvadore Lago, Simon Sibela, Aldo Bufi-Landi, Valentino Macchi.

Adventure melodrama. In 1905 King Edwards, a police officer in South Africa, pursues three sadistic killers who have escaped en route to jail. Col. Albert Vinton, a prospector, is tortured to death by the fugitives in an attempt to locate his gold mine. Through Dr. Hamilton, a missionary, King learns the direction in which the killers are headed. He finds one of the men and learns that Vinton's wife, Deborah, is unwittingly leading the other escapees to the mine. Upon arriving in the coastal region, King visits a bar and learns the whereabouts of Baker, the man who is arranging the transportation of the gold out of the country. A gang of men paid by the fugitives ambush King, but he is rescued by Ann Peterson, a saloon girl who is later tortured to death for her interference. Meanwhile, King trails the killers to the mine, rescues Deborah, and eliminates the remaining prisoners in an explosion during the gunfight. *Police. Fugitives. Prospectors. Missionaries. Smugglers. Bar girls. Murder. Torture. Gold mines. South Africa. Chases. Explosions.*

Note: Location scenes filmed in South Africa and Spain. Working title: *King of Africa.* Opened in Madrid in Apr 1968 as *Rey de Africa;* running time: 98 min; released in Italy as *Caccia ai violenti.* Anglicized names include: Alan Collins (Luciano Pigozzi), George Rigaud (Jorge Rigaud), Michael Castillo (Miguel del Castillo), and John Anthony Mayans (Antonio Mayans).

ONE SWEDISH SUMMER (Sweden) F6.3625

Swedish Filmproduction. *Dist* U-M Film Distributors. **1968.** Sd; col (print by Movielab). 35mm. 104 min.

Prod-Dir Gunnar Höglund. *Screenplay* Gustav Sandgren, Gunnar Höglund. *Photog* Lars Björne, Lars Jahnson. *Mus* Bengt-Arne Wallin. *Sd* Kjell Westman.

Cast: Hans Gustafsson (*Leander*), Lillemor Ohlson (*Mae [Mejt]*), Barbro Hiort af Ornäs (*Ada [Aida]*), Gudrun Brost (*Torinna*), Gio Petré (*Aunt*), Birger Malmsten (*Uncle*), Anne Nord (*Gerda [Gärda]*), Ingrid Swedin (*Susanne*), Barbro Hedström (*Lola*), Siw Mattson (*Aine [Aino]*), Stephan Karlsen (*Ture*), Charlie Elvegård (*Adolf*), Annie Andersson (*Agnes*), Chris Wahlström (*The Mother*), Ulf Tistam (*The Priest*).

Drama. Source: Gustav Sandgren, ... *Som havets nakna vind* (Stockholm, 1965). Leander, a young music student, discovers that his awakening sexual desires are disturbing his ability to concentrate. After an embarrassing failure with a prostitute, Leander leaves Switzerland to spend the summer with his widowed mother in Sweden and, returning home, discovers that his relationship with his sister Mae is jeopardized by their mutual desire for each other. Aino, the Finnish maid, provides Leander with sexual fulfillment, but she soon rejects him for a young fisherman. Becoming increasingly uncertain of himself, Leander meets three young women vacationing nearby. The candid aggressiveness and gaiety of Gerda, Susanne, and Lola change Leander's outlook on life, and during the following days he makes love with each of them. Mae becomes jealous of the girls, and when Leander discovers that she is only his half-sister, he makes love to her also. At the summer's end, Leander asks Susanne to stay with him; her answer is mysterious to everyone but Leander, to whom she gives a private token of her affection. *Students. Widows. Prostitutes. Housemaids. Adolescence. Sexual initiation. Incest. Brother-sister relationship. Summer. Switzerland.*

Note: Opened in Stockholm in Oct 1968 as *Som havets nakna vind;* running time: 111 min. Alternative titles: *The Naked Winds of the Sea* and *Naked as the Wind From the Sea.*

1,000 FEMALE SHAPES *see* 1,000 SHAPES OF A FEMALE

THE 1,000 PLANE RAID F6.3626

Oakmont Productions. *Dist* United Artists. 18 Jun **1969** [Portland, Oregon, opening; c1 Mar 1969; LP37630]. Sd; col (DeLuxe). 35mm. 94 min. *MPAA rating G.*

Pres by Mirisch Films. *Prod* Lewis J. Rachmil. *Dir* Boris Sagal. *Screenplay* Donald S. Sanford. *Story* Robert Vincent Wright. *Dir Cinematog* William W. Spencer. *Art Dir* Harold Michelson. *Film Ed* Henry Batista, Jodie Copelan. *Mus Comp & Cond* Jimmie Haskell. *Sd* Robert Martin. *Mus Ed* Richard Carruth. *Asst Dir* Eric Von Stroheim, Jr. *Asst to the Prod* Marshall M. Borden. *Prod Supv* Allen K. Wood. *Sp Eff* Justus Gibbs, Henry Millar, Jr. *Tech Adv* Robert Gossman, (Maj.).

Cast: Christopher George (*Col. Greg Brandon*), Laraine Stephens (*W.A.C. Lieut. Gabrielle Ames*), J. D. Cannon (*Gen. Cotten Palmer*), Gary Marshall (*R.A.F. Wing Cmdr. Trafton Howard*), Michael Evans (*British Group Cmdr. Leslie Hardwicke*), Ben Murphy (*Lieutenant Archer*), James Gammon (*Major Varga*), Gavin MacLeod (*Sergeant Kruger*), Scott Thomas (*Richman*), Tim McIntire (*Quimby*), Bo Hopkins (*Douglas*), Henry Jaglom (*Worchek*), Noam Pitlik (*Jacobi*), Barry Atwater (*General Conway*), John Carter, actor (*Middleton*), Charles Dierkop (*Railla*), Mac McLaughlin (*waist gunner*), Wayne Sutherlin (*waist gunner*), Philip Proctor (*turret gunner*), Larry Perkins (*navigator*), Carl Reindel (*bombardier*).

War drama. Source: Ralph Barker, *The Thousand Plan* (London, 1965). Col. Greg Brandon, stationed at an American Air Force base in England, repeatedly attempts to persuade superiors that massive daylight bombing will hasten the end of World War II. In spite of the mission's extreme difficulty, his plan is finally put into effect against a German aircraft factory. During preparation for the raid, Brandon alienates his men by insisting that normal bombing operations continue. His disdain for cautious Lieutenant Archer and brash R.A.F. Wing Cmdr. Trafton Howard further antagonizes his associates, including his girl friend, WAC Lieut. Gabrielle Ames. When his plane crashes the morning of the mission, Brandon boards a bomber manned by Archer and Howard. During the effective air raid, he is impressed by Archer's courage and Howard's judgment. *Military life. Aerial bombardment. Airplane accidents. World War II. England. Germany. United States Air Force. United States Army—Women's Army Corps. Great Britain—Royal Air Force.*

Note: Location scenes filmed in Santa Maria, California.

1,000 SHAPES OF A FEMALE F6.3627

Artlife Pictures. *Dist* Cinema Syndicate, Inc., Chancellor Films. 18 Oct **1963** [Los Angeles showing]. Sd; col (Eastman Color). 35mm. 79 min.

A Barry Mahon Production. *Prod-Dir* Barry Mahon. *Screenplay* Sande N. Johnsen. *Photog* Barry Mahon. *Art Dir* Sande N. Johnsen. *Film Ed* Maurice McEndree. *Mus Comp* Arlene Corwin. *Sd* Al Ruban. *Asst Dir* Sande N. Johnsen. *Script Clerk* Clelle Mahon. *Optical Eff* Eastern Effects.

Cast: Dan Craig, Marty Devine, Byron Mabe, Sande Johnsen, Al Ruban, Faith Gilbert, Kimberly Harris, Doris Dane, Linda Bennet, Christine Kingsley, Jimmy Gavin, Monica Davis, Bob Bensen, Alicia Douglas, Vernon Marsh, Patricia Darling, Joey Naudic, Terri Powers, Rosebud O'Toole, Irene Charles,

Nell Murray, Gigi Darlene, Jane Day, Priscilla Hadley, Andrea Sinclair.

Comedy. Art gallery owner David Green takes a friend on a tour of his latest exhibition, a collection of contemporary nudes painted on commission by New York artists. He compares each painting with the work of the masters who influenced the artist. At the same time, the camera travels back to Green's first contact with each artist at a Greenwich Village coffeehouse, tracing the creation of the painting. Green makes contact with the artist, who hires a model, and poses her in his studio. The coffeehouse artists employ some unexpected techniques. One artist uses his hair as a brush. Another spatters his colors on canvas spread on the floor and tramps the paint with his feet. A painter who wants to cover his model with paint and smear her body against his canvas has trouble finding a woman who will work for him. One model is frightened away by an artist who throws darts at paint-filled balloons stuck to a canvas-covered wall. *Art dealers. Artists. Models. Nudity. Paintings. Coffeehouses. New York City—Greenwich Village.*

Note: Also known as *1,000 Female Shapes.*

ONE TOUCHING ONE   **F6.3628**
Taurus Films. May **1970** [Los Angeles showing]. Sd; col 35mm? 120 min. *Dir* Mark Eden, dir.

Sex film. No information about the precise nature of this film has been found, but press material suggests that it portrays male homosexuality as one of the life forces of the 20th century. *Male homosexuality.*

ONE, TWO, THREE   **F6.3629**
Mirisch Co.-Pyramid Productions, A. G. *Dist* United Artists. 15 Dec **1961** [Los Angeles showing; c18 Dec 1961; LP21926]. Sd; b&w. 35mm (Panavision). 108 min. [Also reviewed at 115 min.]
Prod-Dir Billy Wilder. *Assoc Prod* I. A. L. Diamond, Doane Harrison. *2d Unit Dir* André Smagghe. *Screenplay* Billy Wilder, I. A. L. Diamond. *Cinematog* Daniel Fapp. *Art Dir* Alexander Trauner. *Film Ed* Daniel Mandell. *Mus Adapt & Cond* Andre Previn. *Sd* Basil Fenton-Smith. *Asst Dir* Tom Pevsner. *Prod Mgr* William Calihan, Werner Fischer. *Makeup* Josef Coesfeld. *Sp Eff* Milt Rice.
Cast: James Cagney (*C. R. MacNamara*), Horst Buchholz (*Otto Ludwig Piffl*), Pamela Tiffin (*Scarlett Hazeltine*), Arlene Francis (*Phyllis MacNamara*), Lilo Pulver (*Ingeborg*), Howard St. John (*Hazeltine*), Hanns Lothar (*Schlemmer*), Lois Bolton (*Mrs. Hazeltine*), Leon Askin (*Peripetchikoff*), Peter Capell (*Mishkin*), Ralf Wolter (*Borodenko*), Karl Lieffen (*Fritz*), Henning Schlüter (*Dr. Bauer*), Hubert von Meyerinck (*Count von Droste-Schattenburg*), Til Kiwe (*newspaperman*), Karl Ludwig Lindt (*Zeidlitz*), John Allen (*Tommy MacNamara*), Christine Allen (*Cindy MacNamara*), Rose Renee Roth (*Bertha*), Ivan Arnold (*MP corporal*), Helmut Schmid (*East German corporal*), Otto Friebel (*East German interrogator*), Werner Buttler (*East German sergeant*), Klaus Becker, Siegfried Dornbusch (*policemen*), Paul Bos (*Krause*), Max Buchsbaum (*tailor*), Jaspar von Oertzen (*haberdasher*), Inga De Toro (*stewardess*), Jacques Chevalier (*Pierre*), Werner Hessenland (*shoeman*), Abi von Hasse (*jeweler*), Red Buttons (*MP sergeant*).
Comedy. Source: Ferenc Molnár, *One, Two, Three* (New York opening: 20 Sep 1930; trans. of *Egy, kettő, három*; Budapest, 1929). C. R. MacNamara, a fast-talking Coca-Cola sales representative in West Berlin, is attempting to introduce the beverage behind the Iron Curtain, hopeful that such a coup will result in his promotion to head of European operations. His hopes are dashed, however, when he learns that his company is not interested in dealing with the Russians; instead, he is ordered to chaperone his boss's daughter, 17-year-old Scarlett Hazeltine, during her 2-week stay in Berlin. The girl's visit lasts 2 months, in which time she secretly marries Otto Ludwig Piffl, a beatnik Communist from East Berlin. MacNamara learns the horrifying news at the same time he receives word that Hazeltine is arriving in West Berlin the next day. Frantic, MacNamara plants on Otto a copy of the *Wall Street Journal*, which gets him arrested by the East German police. After arranging to have the marriage certificate removed from official files, MacNamara learns that Scarlett is pregnant; aware that he must present Hazeltine with an ideal son-in-law, MacNamara gets Otto out of the East Berlin jail, buys him a royal title, and converts him into a well-groomed capitalist. He is so successful that Hazeltine decides that Otto is the man to head Coca-Cola's European operations; MacNamara must settle for a vice-presidency in the Atlanta office. *Americans in foreign countries. Sales managers. Executives. Chaperons. Beatniks. Communists. In-laws. Employer-employee relations. Adolescence. Marriage. Pregnancy. Coca-Cola. Berlin—West. Berlin—East. Iron Curtain. "Wall Street Journal".*
Note: Filmed on location in West Germany.

ONE WAY PENDULUM (Great Britain)   **F6.3630**
Woodfall Film Productions. *Dist* Lopert Pictures. 2 Mar **1965** [New York opening]. Sd; b&w. 35mm. 90 min.

Prod Michael Deeley. *Exec Prod* Oscar Lewenstein. *Assoc Prod* Michael Holden, Leigh Aman. *Dir* Peter Yates. *Screenplay* N. F. Simpson. *Photog* Denys Coop. *Prod Dsgn* Reece Pemberton. *Film Ed* Peter Taylor. *Mus Comp* Richard Rodney Bennett. *Mus Cond* Marcus Dods. *Mus Played by* Tommy Scott Quintet. "Halleluja Chorus" From "The Messiah" George Frederick Handel. *Sd Rec* Robin Gregory. *Asst Dir* Claude Watson. *Wardrobe* Barbara Gillett. *Makeup* Tom Smith. *Hairstyles* Betty Sherriff.
Cast: Eric Sykes (*Mr. Groomkirby*), George Cole (*defense counsel/friend*), Julia Foster (*Sylvia*), Jonathan Miller (*Kirby*), Peggy Mount (*Mrs. Gantry*), Alison Leggatt (*Mrs. Groomkirby*), Mona Washbourne (*Aunt Mildred*), Douglas Wilmer (*judge/maintenance man*), Kenneth Farrington (*Stan*), Glyn Houston (*Detective Inspector Barnes*), Graham Crowden (*prosecuting counsel/caretaker*), Walter Horsbrugh (*clerk of the court/drycleaner's assistant*), Frederick Piper (*usher/office clerk*), Vincent Harding (*policeman/bus conductor*), Tommy Bruce (*voice of Gormless*).
Comedy. Source: N. F. Simpson, *One Way Pendulum* (London opening: 22 Dec 1959). The Groomkirbys are an eccentric English family: Mr. Groomkirby is constructing a replica of Old Bailey in the living room of his home; his wife solves the leftover food problem by hiring a housemaid, Mrs. Gantry, to eat it; his son, Kirby, is trying to get his collection of scales to play the "Hallelujah Chorus"; his daughter, Sylvia, devotes her time to admiring the apes at the zoo; and Aunt Mildred sits in her wheelchair taking fanciful journeys. One Saturday, Mr. Groomkirby arrives home and begins a make-believe murder trial in his living-room Old Bailey, with his son as the defendant and his wife as a chief witness. As the imaginary trial ends, Mr. Groomkirby is remanded to custody, and his son is acquitted. Finally in bed, Mr. Groomkirby uses ear plugs to block out the sound of Kirby's triumphal "Hallelujah Chorus." *Eccentrics. Housemaids. Aunts. Invalids. Family life. Fantasy. Trials. Old Bailey. "Messiah". Apes.*
Note: Opened in London in Jan 1965; running time: 85 min.

ONE WAY WAHINE   **F6.3631**
Continental Pictures-Cal-Hawaiian Productions. *Dist* United Screen Arts. Oct **1965** [c17 Feb 1965; LU3352]. Sd; col (Technicolor). 35mm (Techniscope). 80 min.
Prod-Dir William O. Brown. *Exec Prod* Leon E. Whiteman. *In Charge of Prod* Larry E. Jackson. *2d Unit Dir* Don Laiffer. *Screenplay* Rod Larson. *Camera Op* John Arthur Morrill. *Film Ed* George White. *Mus Score* Jo Hansen. *Titl Song Sung by* Jody Miller. *Songs:* "When the One Way Wahine Does the Bird," "When I Look at You," "Hawaiian Rock" sung by Ray Peterson. *Sd* Rod Sutton. *Sd Ed* Bill Keith. *Mus Ed* Joseph Von Stroheim. *Script Supv* Bri Murphy. *Wardrobe* Maudine Adair. *Makeup Artist* Lillian Lawson. *Key Grip* Tom Ramsey. *Prop Master* Mike Ezzes.
Cast: Joy Harmon (*Kit Williams*), Anthony Eisley (*Chick Lindell*), Adele Claire (*Brandy Saveties*), David Whorf (*Lou Talbot*), Edgar Bergen (*Sweeney*), Lee Krieger (*Charley Rossi*), Ken Mayer (*Hugo Sokol*), Harold Fong (*Quong*), Alvy Moore (*Maxwell*), Aime Luce (*Tahitian dancer*), Ralph Nanalei (*Paulo*).
Comedy. Two runaway teenage girls, Kit Williams and Brandy Saveties, buy one-way tickets to Hawaii, and 2 weeks after they arrive they meet Lou Talbot. Talbot has found the hideout of two men whom he believes are clerks who have absconded with large sums of money from a Chicago bank, and he convinces Kit and Brandy to come to the beach house where they are hiding. Talbot has promised the thieves that he will bring two girls to them—he hopes to steal the money while the men are distracted. Talbot also promises Chick Lindell some of the money in order to enlist him in the scheme. The four plan to drug the thieves, and they try some knockout pills on Sweeney, a beach bum, before proceeding with their scheme. Once inside the beach house, Kit is nearly raped by one of the men, but she manages to knock him out, put the money in a plastic bag, and drop it out the window to Chick. The bag breaks, and Chick is forced to stuff the money into a trash can. The next day, Talbot and his friends discover that their victims are actually gangsters. They return to try to retrieve the money only to see Sweeney, who has found the loot in the trash, proudly showing it to the police. *Runaways. Gangsters. Bank clerks. Beachcombers. Theft. Robbery. Tranquilizers. Hawaii. Chicago.*
Note: Filmed on location at Lanakai Beach, Oahu, Hawaii.

ONE WILD NIGHT   **F6.3632**
Cherry Productions. ca **1969**. Sd; col (Eastmancolor). 16mm. [Feature length assumed.]
Orig Screenplay Woodrow Olivetti.
Sex film. No information about the precise nature of this film has been found, but pressbook photographs suggest it contains scenes of fellatio, cunnilingus, and lesbianism. *Oral sex. Lesbianism.*

ONE WISH TOO MANY (Great Britain)   **F6.3633**
Realist Film Unit. *For* Children's Film Foundation. *Dist* Sterling Educational Films. 29 Mar **1962** [Maryland license]. Sd; b&w. 16mm & 35mm.

56 min.

Prod Basil Wright. *Dir* John Durst. *Screenplay* John Eldridge. *Adapt* Mary Cathcart Borer. *Story* Norah Pulling. *Photog* Adrian Jeakins. *Art Dir* Bernard Sarron. *Film Ed* James Clark. *Mus* Douglas Gamley. *Sd* Terry Cotter, Ken Cameron. *Sp Eff* Bowie and Margutti.

Cast: Anthony Richmond *(Peter)*, Rosalind Gourgey *(Nancy)*, John Pike *(Ian)*, Terry Cooke *(Bert)*, Arthur Howard *(headmaster)*, Gladys Young *(Miss Mint)*, Sam Costa *(Mr. Pomfrett)*, Bay White *(Mrs. Brown)*, Frank Hayden *(Mr. Brown)*, Paddy Joyce *(barrow boy)*.

Comedy-drama. Peter, a London schoolboy, finds a magic marble which grants his every wish. As Peter withdraws into a world of fantasy, his strange behavior puzzles his parents and outrages the landlady, Miss Mint. The student uses the marble to play tricks on his teacher and to get even with the school bully. When he transforms his toy steamroller into a real machine, however, it runs amok on the London docks. Rescued by his father, the boy is delighted to discover the marble missing. *Children. Schoolteachers. Bullies. Landladies. Magic. Toys. Docks. London.*

Note: Location scenes filmed in London's East End. Released in Great Britain in 1956.

THE ONE WITH THE FUZZ *see* **SOME KIND OF A NUT**

ONEICHAN MAKARI TORU *see* **THREE DOLLS FROM HONG KONG**

ONI NO SUMU YAKATA *see* **DEVIL'S TEMPLE**

ONI SHLI NA VOSTOK *see* **ITALIANO BRAVA GENTE**

ONIBABA (Japan)   **F6.3634**
Kindai Eiga Kyokai–Tokyo Eiga Co. *Dist* Toho International, Inc. 9 Feb **1965** [New York opening]. Sd; b&w. 35mm (Tohoscope). 100–104 min.

Prod Toshio Konya. *Exec Prod* Hisao Itoya, Setsuo Noto, Tamotsu Minato. *Dir-Writ* Kaneto Shindo. *Photog* Kiyomi Kuroda. *Art Dir* Kaneto Shindo. *Film Ed* Toshio Enoki. *Mus* Hikaru Hayashi.

Cast: Nobuko Otowa *(The Mother)*, Jitsuko Yoshimura *(The Daughter-in-law)*, Kei Sato *(Hachi)*, Jukichi Uno *(The Warrior)*, Taiji Tonomura *(Ushi, the merchant)*.

Horror film. In a small hut in the marshland of medieval Japan, a country ravaged by civil war, pestilence, and starvation, live a mother and her daughter-in-law. They support themselves by selling the weapons and armor removed from bodies of exhausted samurai and soldiers they have ambushed and murdered. News of the death of the mother's son is brought from the battlefield by Hachi, a local farmer who has escaped from the army. He attempts to win the young woman's affections, and a passionate affair develops, looked upon with jealousy by the mother, also desirous of Hachi and fearful of losing her livelihood if she should be left alone. The older woman finds a horribly-masked warrior wounded and lost among the tall reeds of the swamp. Though he professes to conceal his face because of its renowned beauty, she kills him, then removes his mask, which actually covers a horribly-disfigured face. The mother plans to frighten the superstitious daughter-in-law away from Hachi by disguising herself as a hellish demon, but the mask shrinks in the rain and cannot be removed, causing her great pain. The young woman breaks the mask when the mother confesses the truth. Her face revealed to be a mass of decomposing flesh, the older woman dies. The young woman then returns to the hut to find her lover murdered. *Soldiers. Deserters—Military. Farmers. Mothers-in-law. Samurai. Murder. Jealousy. Disfiguration. Superstition. Supernatural. Swamps. Masks. Japan—History—Period of civil wars 1480–1568.*

Note: Produced in Japan in 1964; running time: 105 min. Hikaru Hayashi is also known as Mitsu Hayashi. Also known as *The Demon*. May also be known as *Devil Woman*.

ONKEL TOMS HÜTTE *see* **UNCLE TOM'S CABIN**

ONLY A WOMAN (West Germany)   **F6.3635**
Rialto Film. *Dist* Comet Film Distributors. Jan **1966**. Sd; col (Eastman Color). 35mm. 86 min.

Prod Horst Wendlandt. *Dir* Alfred Weidenmann. *Screenplay* Johanna Sibelius, Eberhard Keindorff. *Photog* Heinz Hölscher. *Art Dir* Helmut Nentwig. *Film Ed* Walter Wischniewsky. *Mus* Peter Thomas. *Sd* Clemens Tütsch. *Asst Dir* Wieland Liebske. *Prod Mgr* Fritz Klotzsch. *Cost* Hannelore Wessel.

Cast: Maria Schell *(Dr. Lilli König)*, Paul Hubschmid *(Martin Bohlen)*, Hans Nielsen *(Dr. Katz)*, Anita Höfer *(Pauline)*, Ingrid van Bergen *(Annabella)*, Hannelore Auer *(Gerda)*, Tilly Lauenstein *(Mrs. Starke)*, Agnes Windeck *(housekeeper)*.

Romantic comedy. Psychiatrist Lilli König advises an overweight female patient. During their consultations she suggests that the woman's boyfriend is

an inadequate lover. Enraged, the patient's lover, Martin Bohlen, a philandering fashion photographer, poses as a patient. In the course of treatment, the patient and physician fall in love and marry. *Psychiatrists. Philanderers. Photographers. Duplicity.*

Note: Location scenes filmed in West Berlin. Opened in West Berlin in Nov 1962 as *Ich bin auch nur eine Frau*; running time: 89 min.

THE ONLY GAME IN TOWN   **F6.3636**
Twentieth Century–Fox Film Corp.–George Stevens Films. *Dist* Twentieth Century–Fox Film Corp. 21 Jan **1970** [Los Angeles opening; c30 Dec 1969; LP37645]. Sd (Westrex); col (DeLuxe). 35mm. 113 min. *MPAA rating* M.

A George Stevens–Fred Kohlmar Production. *Prod* Fred Kohlmar. *Dir* George Stevens. *2d Unit Dir* Robert Swink. *Screenplay* Frank D. Gilroy. *Dir Photog* Henri Decaë. *Art Dir* Herman Blumenthal, Auguste Capelier. *Set Decor* Walter M. Scott, Jerry Wunderlich. *Film Ed* John W. Holmes, William Sands, Pat Shade. *Mus Comp & Cond* Maurice Jarre. *Orch* Michel Mention. *Alto Saxophone Solo* Ernie Watts. *Flugel Horn Solo* Bobby Bryant. *Sd* Jo de Bretagne, David Dockendorf. *Asst Dir* Robert Doudell, Jean-Michel Lacor. *Unit Prod Mgr* Christian Ferry. *Elizabeth Taylor's Cost* Mia Fonssagrives, Vicki Tiel. *Miss Taylor's Makeup* Frank Larue. *Mr. Beatty's Makeup* John Jiras. *Miss Taylor's Hairstyles* Alexandre of Paris. *Hairstyles* Claudie Ettori. *Sp Photog Eff* L. B. Abbott, Art Cruickshank.

Cast: Elizabeth Taylor *(Fran Walker)*, Warren Beatty *(Joe Grady)*, Charles Braswell *(Thomas Lockwood)*, Hank Henry *(Tony)*, Olga Valery *(woman with purple wig)*.

Comedy-drama. Source: Frank D. Gilroy, *The Only Game in Town* (New York opening: 23 May 1968). While awaiting her married lover's divorce, Las Vegas chorus girl Fran Walker has sex with compulsive gambler and barroom pianist Joe Grady. Their affair is punctuated by Grady's wins and losses, and complicated by the appearance of Fran's lover, Thomas Lockwood, now free to marry his former mistress. Fran, however, has fallen in love with the gambler. Having finally accumulated the money necessary to reestablish himself in New York, Grady decides instead to gamble on marriage to Fran. *Mistresses. Chorus girls. Pianists. Gamblers. Marriage. Divorce. Bars. Las Vegas.*

Note: Location scenes filmed in Las Vegas, Nevada.

THE ONLY HOUSE IN TOWN   **F6.3637**
The Professionals. *Dist* Stacey Distributors. ca **1970**. Sd; col. 16mm. 60 min.

Sex film. A group of hippies—four sex-crazed women and their three male partners—perform "unspeakable" sexual acts in an old house on the outskirts of town. Press material indicates the film concerns prostitutes, bootleggers, ghosts, rape, lesbianism, and orgies. *Hippies. Prostitutes. Bootleggers. Ghosts. Orgies. Lesbianism. Rape.*

ONLY IN MY DREAMS   **F6.3638**
CineCentrum, Inc. *For* MFD Productions. *Dist* MFD Productions. 12 Nov **1970** [Maryland license]. Sd; col. 35mm. 80 min.

Dir-Writ Victor Peters. *Photog* Victor Peters. *2d Unit Camera* Joao Fernandes. *Film Ed* Alfred Behary. *Sd Man* Charles Pitts. *Prod Mgr* Norman Berns. *Script Girl* Alexandra Berns. *Gaffer* Joe Rivers, Lucky Kargo.

Cast: Linda Boyce *(Linda)*, Toni Talley, Bal Johnson, Burt Bertez, Sharon Spitz, Nasser Salem.

Drama. Troubled by sex dreams, Linda relates to her psychiatrist her latest nightmare in which she is compelled to make love with a deformed dwarf. She admits to the psychiatrist that, to her surprise, she actually liked the experience. In another dream, Linda has sex with a fish, and she recalls that the sensation was pleasurable. The psychiatrist diagnoses Linda's problem as fear of being unable to achieve orgasm, and he asks to see her boyfriend Johnny before he recommends a course of treatment. That night, Johnny and Linda have an argument in a nightclub when Linda, inspired by the decor, vividly imagines a Roman orgy. As a result, Linda visits a photographer, a lesbian who seduces her, thus jolting her back to reality. Johnny returns to Linda's apartment, makes love to her, and apologetically offers to go to the psychiatrist to help with her therapy, but she coyly denies having a problem. *Psychiatrists. Dwarfs. Photographers. Lesbianism. Nightclubs. Orgies. Dreams. Hallucinations. Fish.*

ONLY ONE NEW YORK (United States/France)   **F6.3639**
S. I. C. A.–Embassy Pictures. *Dist* Embassy Pictures. 30 Sep **1964** [New York opening]. Sd; b&w. 35mm. 72 min.

Pres by Joseph E. Levine. *Prod* Serge de Dietrich. *Dir, Writ & Conceived by* Pierre-Dominique Gaisseau. *Assoc Dir* Jan Yoors, Jean Hamon. *French Narr* Philippe Labro. *Photog* Pierre-Dominique Gaisseau. *Film Ed* Georges Arnstam. *Mus* Milton DeLugg.

Narrators: Norman Rose *(English vers)*, Philippe Labro *(French vers)*.

Documentary. French explorer and documentarian Pierre-Dominique Gaisseau spent 7 months in New York City filming this pictorial essay. He primarily concentrates on the mores and customs of the various ethnic groups comprising part of the city's population. The opening sequence moves from a construction site where a demolition ball is knocking down an old building to modern glass skyscrapers. Other scenes include: a New Year's celebration in Chinatown, Hasidic Jews taking part in a ritual bath of purification, a gypsy wedding party, Japanese Buddhists celebrating their "Festival of Flowers," a Ukrainian wedding, and a German colony in a traditional dance. More familiar sights are the St. Patrick's Day parade, a fashion show, a revival meeting in Harlem, the Fulton Fish Market, and Broadway at night. *Hasidim. Gypsies. Japanese. Germans. Ukrainians. Social customs. Urban life. Demolition. Rites and ceremonies. Buddhism. Weddings. Parades. Fashion shows. Revivals. Saint Patrick's Day. New York City. New York City—Chinatown. New York City—Harlem. Fulton Fish Market (New York City). New York City—Broadway.*

Note: Filmed on location in New York City. French title: *New-York-Sur-Mer.*

ONLY TWO CAN PLAY (Great Britain)   **F6.3640**
Vale Film Productions. *For* British Lion Films. *Dist* Kingsley International Pictures, Columbia Pictures. 20 Mar **1962** [New York opening; c1 May 1962; LP22242]. Sd; b&w. 35mm. 106 min. [Copyright length: 80 min.]

Prod Leslie Gilliat. *Exec Prod* Frank Launder, Sidney Gilliat. *Dir* Sidney Gilliat. *Screenplay* Bryan Forbes. *Camera* John Wilcox. *Camera Op* Peter Allwork. *Focus* Geoffrey Glover. *Camera Grip* Frank Batt. *Art Dir* Albert Witherick. *Set Decor* Robert Cartwright. *Scenic Artist* Alan Evans. *Draughtsman* Tony Woollard. *Film Ed* Thelma Connell. *Asst Ed* Michael Hart. *Mus Comp* Richard Rodney Bennett. *Mus Cond* Muir Mathieson. *Sd* Baron Mason, Red Law. *Boom Op* Derek Kavanagh. *Sd Camera* Jack Smart. *1st, 2d & 3d Asst Dir* Douglas Hermes, Ernie Lewis, Don Webb. *Prod Mgr* Jim Pellatt. *Prod Sec* Sheila Hawkins. *Cont* Lee Turner. *Wardrobe Supv* Muriel Dickson. *Makeup* Phil Leakey. *Hairstyles* Eileen Bates. *Stills* Norman Hargood. *Casting Dir* Paul Sheridan. *Prop Buyer* Terry Parr.

Cast: Peter Sellers *(John Lewis)*, Mai Zetterling *(Elizabeth Gruffydd-Williams)*, Virginia Maskell *(Jean Lewis)*, Richard Attenborough *(Gareth Probert)*, Kenneth Griffith *(Ieuan Jenkins)*, Marjie Edwards *(Mrs. Davies)*, Frederick Piper *(Davies)*, Graham Stark *(Hyman)*, John Arnatt *(Bill)*, Sheila Manahan *(Mrs. Jenkins)*, John Le Mesurier *(Salter)*, Raymond Huntley *(Vernon)*, David Davies *(Beynon)*, Meredith Edwards *(clergyman)*, Eynon Evans *(town hall clerk)*, Marjie Lawrence *(girl in bus)*.

Comedy. Source: Kingsley Amis, *That Uncertain Feeling* (London, 1955). John Lewis works in a library in a provincial Welsh town. Bored with his lowly position, irritated by his family life in a cluttered, three-room, apartment, and frustrated by his humdrum social life, he escapes by imagining himself involved in numerous clandestine affairs with beautiful women. Then one day the glamorous Elizabeth Gruffydd-Williams, the wife of the town's wealthiest businessman, enters the library, offers to satisfy his secret passions, and, in the bargain, help him attain a more important library post. One evening she persuades him not to attend an amateur theatrical performance he is supposed to review for the local newspaper but, instead, take her for a drive. Their tryst is interrupted by a cow peering through the car window and, later at her home, by the unexpected appearance of her husband. Furthermore, John writes a review of the play and submits it to the newspaper, unaware that the theater burned to the ground before the performance. Though he loses his standing on the paper, his benefactress succeeds in getting him the head librarian's job. He realizes that the acceptance of the post would cost him his independence, and he walks out on both Mrs. Gruffydd-Williams and the job. He returns to his wife, Jean (who has been encouraging the attentions of a would-be poet), apologizes for his behavior, and decides to take over a mobile library, a position that will enable him to travel and still remain with his wife and two children. *Librarians. Poets. Socialites. Critics. Infidelity. Family life. Libraries. Wales. Cows.*

Note: Location scenes filmed in Swansea, Wales. Opened in London in Jan 1962. Working title: *That Uncertain Feeling.*

ONLY WHEN I LARF (Great Britain)   **F6.3641**
Beecord Productions. *Dist* Paramount Pictures. 23 Oct **1968** [New York opening; c20 Jun 1968; LF37]. Sd; col (Eastman Color). 35mm. 104 min.

Pres by Deighton/Duffy Productions. *Prod* Len Deighton, Brian Duffy. *Assoc Prod* Hugh Attwooll. *Dir* Basil Dearden. *Screenplay* John Salmon. *Dir Photog* Tony Richmond. *Camera Op* Roy Ford. *Focus Puller* Frank Gell. *Art Dir* John Blezard. *Asst Art Dir* Anthony Reading. *Film Ed* Fergus McDonell. *Mus* Ron Grainer. *Titl Theme Perf by* Whistling Jack Smith. *Sd Mix* Sydney Squires. *Sd* Dino Di Campo. *1st & 2d Asst Dir* John Peverall, Terry Marcel. *Prod Mgr* Mack Davidson. *Location Mgr* Timothy Pitt Miller. *Cont* Sue Dyson. *Wardrobe Dsgn* Beatrice Dawson. *Wardrobe Mistress* Brenda Dabbs. *Makeup* Freddie Williamson. *Hairdresser* Barbara Ritchie.

Cast: Richard Attenborough *(Silas)*, David Hemmings *(Bob)*, Alexandra Stewart *(Liz)*, Nicholas Pennell *(Spencer)*, Melissa Stribling *(Diana)*, Terence Alexander *(Gee Gee Gray)*, Edric Connor *(Awana)*, Clifton Jones *(General Sakut)*, Calvin Lockhart *(Ali Lin)*, Brian Grellis *(Spider)*, David Healy *(Jones)*,

Alan Gifford *(Poster)*.

Crime comedy. Source: Len Deighton, *Only When I Larf* (London, 1968). After successfully fleecing two New York businessmen out of $250,000, three confidence tricksters, Silas, Bob, and Liz, return to London and set up a scheme to sell to a militant African diplomat-revolutionary crates of weapons that will, in fact, contain only scrap metal. The plan backfires, and the revolutionary ends up being shipped back to Africa in one of the sealed crates. Bob blames Silas for bungling the deal and asserts himself as the new brains behind the trio's operations. Relegating Silas to the role of secretary and replacing him as Liz's lover, Bob devises his own plan for swindling Spencer, a wealthy young tycoon, by inducing him to provide the $500,000 investment for a forged bond deal which is to be carried out in Lebanon on behalf of the British government. But while Bob and Liz are planning to doublecross Silas, their senior partner is scheming with Spencer's assistant, Diana, to seize the money. Once in Lebanon, Silas collects the money from the unsuspecting Spencer, then switches bags with Diana before rejoining Bob and Liz in their getaway car. Liz discovers the ruse in time, however, and, when they all meet at a desert ruin, she alerts Bob as to the whereabouts of the money. Drawing Silas and Diana away from the car, Bob grabs the money bag and throws it to Liz, who runs to the car with it. As Bob prepares to jump into the car with her, Liz steps on the gas and drives off alone with all the money. Completely outwitted and stranded in the desert, Bob, Silas, and Diana collapse into helpless laughter. *Confidence men. Confidence women. Revolutionaries. Diplomats. Africans. Secretaries. Businessmen. Fraud. Perfidy. Forgery. Guns. Deserts. New York City. London. Lebanon.*

Note: Location scenes filmed in New York City, London, and Beirut. Opened in London in Jun 1968.

ONNA GA KAIDAN O AGARUTOKI *see* **WHEN A WOMAN ASCENDS THE STAIRS**

ONNA GOROSHI ABURA JIGOKU *see* **THE PRODIGAL SON**

ONNA KAZOKU *see* **MOONLIGHT IN THE RAIN**

ONNA NO MIZUUMI *see* **THE LAKE**

ONNA NO NAKANI IRU TANIN *see* **THE THIN LINE**

ONNA NO REKISHI *see* **A WOMAN'S LIFE**

ONNA NO UZU TO FUCHI TO NAGARE *see* **WHIRLPOOL OF WOMAN**

ONNA NO ZA *see* **THE WISER AGE**

ONNA ONNA ONNA MONOGATARI *see* **WOMEN ... OH, WOMEN!**

ONNA TOBAKUSHI *see* **THE WOMAN GAMBLER**

ONNA UKIYOBURO *see* **THE HOUSE OF STRANGE LOVES**

ONSEN GERIRA DAI SHOGEKI *see* **HOTSPRINGS HOLIDAY**

OPEN AIR BEDROOM   **F6.3642**
Kirt Films International. *Dist* Distribpix, Inc. ca **1970**. Sd; col. 35mm. 64 min.

Melodrama. Laura and Edie, two young lesbians, find the bedroom confining for their lovemaking and occasionally leave their apartment in favor of the secluded woods. A young man comes into their lives and it isn't long before Edie has lured him into the woods. Laura follows them and witnesses their wild lovemaking. Edie returns home alone, and Laura throws her out of the apartment. Laura then becomes a prostitute in order to prove that she is attractive to men as well as to women. *Roommates. Lesbianism. Jealousy. Prostitution.*

OPEN THE DOOR AND SEE ALL THE PEOPLE   **F6.3643**
Jerome Hill. *Dist* Noel Productions, Barney Pitkin Associates, Film-Makers' Cooperative, Film-Makers' Distribution Center. 1 Apr **1964** [New York opening]. Sd; b&w. 35mm & 16mm. 82 min. [Cut from 91 min.]

Prod-Dir-Writ Jerome Hill. *Dir Photog* Gayne Rescher. *Op* Peter Garbarini. *Asst Camera* Peter Norman. *Film Ed* Henry A. Sundquist. *Mus* Alec Wilder. *Orch Cond* Samuel Baron. *Sd* Robert C. Fine. *Sd Mix* Stanley Kasper. *Asst Dir* Tony La Marca. *Prod Coörd* Otto Lang. *Asst Prod Coörd* David C. Stone. *Prod Asst* William Stevenson. *Asst to Prod* Julia Knowlton. *Script Supv* Sascha Laurence. *Prod Sec* Belle Lacobellis. *Wardrobe Mistress* Francesca Kennedy. *Sp Photog* William Kennedy. *Gaffer* Frank Leonetti. *Still Photog* Muky.

Cast: Maybelle Nash *(Alma Blake/Thelma Fahnstock)*, Alec Wilder *(Dan)*, Jeremiah Sullivan *(Jerry)*, Charles Rydell *(Andrew)*, Chris Schroll *(Chris)*, Johanna Hill *(Jo)*, Paul Chu *(Luke)*, Melvina Boykin *(Melvina)*, Ellen Martin *(Mimosa)*, Lester Judson *(Raoul)*, Louise Rush *(Veronica)*, Harry Rigby *(Steadman)*, Tony Ballen *(Paul)*, Day Tuttle *(Wei #1)*, Douglas Ho *(Wei #2)*, Chao Li Chi *(Wei #3)*, John Holland *(Antoine)*, Susana De Mello *(Amaryllis)*,

Gwen Davies (Gypsy mother), Gene Fallon (mayor), Astride Lance (solitary girl), Sheilah Chang (cashier), Taylor Mead (tramp), Billy Leavitt (Archibald Davies, Jr.).

Comedy. Thelma Fahnstock and Alma Blake are identical 70-year-old twins, but there is no similarity between them. Thelma is wealthy, morose, hypochondriacal, and domineering, while Alma is an easygoing and industrious supermarket cashier who takes care of her invalid husband, Dan, and opens her home to all those in need. Their respective households come into constant conflict. Thelma, who lives in a dreary mansion, is trying to force her granddaughter, Mimosa, into the image of the girl's late mother, a famous actress. To this end, Thelma keeps Mimosa a virtual prisoner in a tower room. Meanwhile, Mimosa's obese brother, Raoul, proudly erects a bomb shelter in the front yard. Alma is finally successful in causing Mimosa to run off with Jerry, a footloose young man who dances for the girl on a scaffold near her window. Mimosa's liberation is accomplished by a swami. In addition, Alma arranges a romance between her tenant Andrew, a dog fancier, and Amaryllis, a refugee who works in a Gypsy palm-reading parlor. Alma also settles a feud between the owners of rival Chinese restaurants before settling back to await the arrival of new houseguests and adventures. Twins. Sisters. Grandmothers. Restaurateurs. Chinese. Swamis. Houseguests. Gypsies. Hypochondriacs. Cashiers. Invalids. Actors. Family life. Imprisonment. Feuds. Wealth. Bomb shelters. Castles. Dogs.

Note: Filmed in 1962 on location in Greenwich, Connecticut; working title: Peacock Feathers. Original commercial release in 35mm by Noel Productions and Barney Pitkin Associates; released in 16mm by Film-Makers' Cooperative; subsequently released in 35mm by Film-Makers' Distribution Center.

OPERACIÓN DALILA see OPERATION DELILAH

OPERACIÓN GOLDMAN see LIGHTNING BOLT

OPERACIÓN LOTO AZUL see MISSION BLOODY MARY

OPERATION ABOLITION   F6.3644
Fulton Lewis, III-House Un-American Activities Committee-Washington Video Producers. Dist Missionary Film Service. 29 Jan 1962 [New York showing]. Sd; b&w. 16mm. 45 min.

Narration: Fulton Lewis, III.

Documentary. On 12 May 1960, the House Un-American Activities Committee under Chairman Designate Edwin E. Willis convenes its San Francisco hearings on Communist infiltration of American institutions. Among witnesses refusing to testify is Archie Brown, who is ejected from the hearings. The next day a crowd of protestors seeks admission. In the ensuing melee a police officer is assaulted, and water hoses are turned on the crowd. Speakers include committee members Gordon Scherer and August E. Johansen and Chairman Francis E. Walter. Police. Investigators. Communism. Interrogation. Demonstrations. San Francisco. Edwin E. Willis. Francis E. Walter. Gordon Scherer. Archie Brown. August E. Johansen. United States Congress—House Un-American Activities Committee.

Note: Assembled under the auspices of the House Un-American Activities Committee by Washington Video and Fulton Lewis III. See also Operation Correction.

OPERATION BIKINI   F6.3645
Alta Vista Productions. Dist American International Pictures. 26 Mar 1963 [Groton, Connecticut, opening; c3 Apr 1963; LP25626]. Sd; b&w. 35mm. 84 min. [Also reviewed at 80 min.]

Pres by James H. Nicholson, Samuel Z. Arkoff. Prod James H. Nicholson, Lou Rusoff. Exec Prod Samuel Z. Arkoff. Dir Anthony Carras. Screenplay John Tomerlin. Photog Gilbert Warrenton. Art Dir Daniel Haller. Film Ed Anthony Carras, Homer Powell. Mus Les Baxter. Mus Coörd Al Simms. Song: "The Girl Back Home" Bob Marcucci, Russ Faith. Sung by Frankie Avalon. Sd Al Bird, Gene Corso, Don Rush. Asst Dir Robert Agnew. Prod Mgr Bartlett A. Carre. Wardrobe Marjorie Corso. Makeup Ted Coodley. Sp Eff Charles Moody. Photog Eff Butler-Glouner Inc. Adv Charles L. Freeman, (Capt. USN Ret.).

Cast: Tab Hunter (Lieut. Morgan Hayes), Frankie Avalon (Seaman Joseph Malzone), Scott Brady (Capt. Emmett Carey), Jim Backus (Bosun's Mate Ed Fennelly), Gary Crosby (Seaman Floyd Givens), Michael Dante (Lieut. William Fourtney), Jody McCrea (Seaman William Sherman), Eva Six (Reiko), Aki Aleong (Seaman Ronald Davayo), David Landfield (Lieutenant Cale), Richard Bakalyan (Seaman Hiller), Joe Finnegan (Seaman Morris), Vernon Scott (Seaman Fowler), Raymond Guth (Seaman Rich), Tony Scott (C. P. O. Perez), Steve Mitchell (Seaman Nolan), Mickey McDermott (Seaman Fairly), Wayne Winton (Seaman Patterson), Duane Ament (Seaman Kingsley), Jody Daniels (Seaman Jones), Marc Cavell (Paul), Raynum K. Tsukamoto (Kawai), Lan Nam Tuttle (Mika), Alicia Li (3d native girl), Nancy Dusina (dream girl back home), Judy Lewis (dream siren).

War melodrama. In the Pacific in 1943, an underwater demolition team (UDT) headed by Lieut. Morgan Hayes is picked up by an American submarine commanded by Capt. Emmett Carey. The team's mission is to destroy a sunken submarine to prevent its top-secret equipment from being salvaged by the Japanese; and Carey is ordered to avoid contact with the enemy until this mission is accomplished. Carey's crew resents both the alteration of the submarine's course and the overcrowding. They proceed to Bikini Island, where, aided by guerrillas, they determine the exact location of the sunken ship. In the course of these developments a romantic attachment is formed between Hayes and Reiko, one of the guerrilla band, but she is killed in a skirmish with the Japanese. The UDT successfully plants the explosives, however, and the men escape to the waiting American submarine. Guerrillas. Japanese. Demolition—Underwater. Submarines. World War II. Bikini. United States Navy.

Note: Prerelease titles: The Seafighters, Bikini, and Bikini Beach.

OPERATION BLUE BOOK see THE BAMBOO SAUCER

OPERATION BULLSHINE (Great Britain)   F6.3646
Associated British Picture Corp. Dist Seven Arts Associated Corp., Manhattan Films International. 17 Jan 1963 [Los Angeles opening]. Sd; col (Technicolor). 35mm. 84 min.

Prod Frank Godwin. Dir Gilbert Gunn. Screenplay Anne Burnaby, Rupert Lang, Gilbert Gunn. Orig Story: "Mixed Company" Anne Burnaby. Photog Gilbert Taylor. Camera Op Val Stewart. Art Dir Robert Jones. Film Ed E. B. Jarvis. Mus Laurie Johnson. Song Laurie Johnson, Frank Godwin. Sung by The Polka Dots. Sd A. Southgate, A. W. Lumkin. Sd Rec H. L. Bird, Len Shilton. Sd Mix Richard Best. Asst Dir Frederic Goode. Makeup Eric Aylott. Hairstyles Polly Young. Still Photog Ronnie Pilgrim.

Cast: Donald Sinden (Lieut. Gordon Brown), Barbara Murray (Pvt. Betty Brown), Carole Lesley (Pvt. Marge White), Ronald Shiner (Gunner Slocum), Naunton Wayne (Major Pym), Dora Bryan (Private Cox), John Cairney (Gunner Willie Ross), Fabia Drake (Junior Commander Maddox), Joan Rice (Private Finch), Daniel Massey (Bombardier Palmer), Peter Jones (Gunner Perkins), Barbara Hicks (Sergeant Merrified), John Welsh (brigadier), Judy Grinham (p. t. instructress), Cyril Chamberlain (orderly sergeant), Ambrosine Phillpotts (reporter), Naomi Chance (Subaltern Godfrey), Marianne Stone (Sergeant Cock), Harry Landis (Gunner Wilkinson), Brian Weske (Gunner Pooley), George Mikell (German airman), Blockbuster Bridget (a bulldog), Dorinda Stevens, Amanda Barrie, Marigold Russell, Julie Hopkins, Beverly Prowse, Margaret Simons, Pamela Searle, Eve Eden, Julie Alexander, Pat Gibson.

War farce. In 1942 A. T. S. (Auxiliary Territorial Service) Pvt. Betty Brown is among the many women assigned to a remote Ack-Ack gunsight on the British coast. The post's commanding officer, Major Pym, does not know that camp casanova Lieut. Gordon "Killer" Brown is Betty's husband. Pym suspects Lieutenant Brown of having an affair with man-chasing Pvt. Marge White, whereupon he suggests that Gordon go on leave to visit his wife. Gordon is unable to reveal that his wife is stationed at the post, and he goes home to London, followed by Marge and an extremely suspicious Betty. In London Major Pym discovers the three in the Brown flat, and the trio return ignominiously to camp. There they learn that the brigadier is making a spot inspection. A series of misadventures ensues, but all ends well when the A. T. S. shoot down an enemy airplane and capture the pilot. Playboys. Personal identity. Military life. Infidelity. World War II. London. Great Britain—Auxiliary Territorial Service.

Note: Opened in London in Jul 1959. Working title: Girls in Arms.

OPERATION CAMEL (Denmark)   F6.3647
Merry Filmproduktion–Dansk-Svensk Film. Dist American International Pictures. 14 Jun 1961 [Omaha, Nebraska, opening]. Sd; b&w (see note). 35mm. 74 min. [Also reviewed at 70 min.]

Prod Henrik Sandberg. Dir Sven Methling, Jr. Screenplay Bob Ramsing, Preben Kaas. Photog Aage Wiltrup, Ole Lytken, Ib Lønvang, Per Staehr. Mus Comp Ib Glindemann, Simon Rosenbaum, Gustav Winckler, George Swensson. Sd Georg Jensen, Poul Nyrup, Morten Reesen. Military Adv Allan Adolph, (Lieut. Col.).

Cast: Nora Hayden (The Dancer), Paul Hagen, Ebbe Langberg, Preben Kaas, Carl Ottosen, Louis Miehe-Renard, Klaus Pagh, Svend Johansen, Ole Dixon, Tor Stokke, Lisbet Kurt, Mogens Brandt, Vera Stricker, Annie Birgit Garde, Raggah Jussef, Maria Velasco, Major Poulsen, Addison Mayers.

Comedy. A group of Danish soldiers are reunited with their sergeant-major after undergoing training in Denmark. As part of the United Nations patrol in Gaza, they run into a series of misadventures and finally rescue a French nightclub dancer from a cabaret where she is being held to perform against her will. Soldiers. Dancers. French. Military life. Gaza. United Nations.

Note: Opened in Copenhagen in Oct 1960 as *Soldaterkammerater på vagt*. Released in Denmark in Eastmancolor as part of the *Soldaterkammerater* series.

OPERATION CIA   F6.3648

Hei-Ra-Matt. *Dist* Allied Artists. 8 Sep **1965** [New York opening]. Sd; b&w. 35mm. 90 min.

A Peer J. Oppenheimer Production. *Prod* Peer J. Oppenheimer. *Assoc Prod* Leonard Blair. *Dir* Christian Nyby. *Story-Screenplay* Peer J. Oppenheimer, Bill S. Ballinger. *Photog* Richard Moore. *Film Ed* Joseph Gluck, George Watters. *Mus* Paul Dunlap. *Sd* Cyril Collick. *Asst Dir* Santa Pestonji. *Gowns* Thelma Nyby.

Cast: Burt Reynolds (*Mark Andrews*), Kieu Chinh (*Kim-chinh*), Danielle Aubry (*Denise*), John Hoyt (*Wells*), Cyril Collick (*Withers*), Vic Diaz (*Professor Yen*), Bill Catching (*Frank Decker*), Marsh Thomson (*Stacey*), John Laughinghouse, Frank Estes (*American officers*), Chaiporn (*terrorist*), Santi (*Porter*), Juanita (*Ming-tah*), Michael Schwiner (*embassy marine*), Robert Gulbranson (*man in bed*), Janet Russell (*girl in bed*).

Action melodrama. CIA agent Stacey is murdered in Saigon while attempting to deliver a message to the U. S. Embassy. Another agent, Mark Andrews, is sent to investigate. He poses as an agriculture professor, and after being briefed in Hong Kong by Denise, a French agent, he heads for Saigon. There he is greeted by Professor Yen of the university. He also meets his contact, Kim-chinh, who informs Mark that Yen is one of a group of terrorists who plan to assassinate the American ambassador by injecting cyanide gas into the embassy's air-conditioning system. Mark is kidnaped by Yen, but a daring escape, concluding with Yen's death, leads Mark back to his hotel. There he learns that Denise is a double agent and that her information has led him into a trap set by terrorist leader Decker. He arrives at the embassy in time to save the ambassador and overcomes Decker in a fight to the death. *Secret agents. Americans in foreign countries. French. Professors. Terrorists. Murder. Hong Kong. Saigon. United States—Central Intelligence Agency. United States—Diplomatic and consular service.*

Note: Filmed in Bangkok, Saigon, and Hong Kong. Working title: *Last Message From Saigon.*

OPERATION CORRECTION   F6.3649

American Civil Liberties Union (Northern California). 29 Jan **1962** [New York showing]. Sd; b&w. 16mm. 47 min.

Narration: Ernest Besig.

Documentary. Using the same footage as did the House Un-American Activities Committee, the American Civil Liberties Union of Northern California attempts to prove that *Operation Abolition* is a distortion of the events surrounding the May 12-14, 1960, hearings in San Francisco. Committee investigator William A. Wheeler's distribution of passes to selected individuals is questioned, as is the committee's assertion that those protesting the hearings were Communists. *Investigators. Communism. Interrogation. Demonstrations. San Francisco. William A. Wheeler. American Civil Liberties Union. United States Congress—House Un-American Activities Committee.*

Note: See also *Operation Abolition.*

OPERATION CROSS EAGLES (United States/Yugoslavia)   F6.3650

Noble Productions-Walter Reade Organization-Triglav Film. *Dist* Continental Distributing, Inc. **1969** [c15 Jan 1969; LP37219]. Sd; col (Eastmancolor). 35mm. 90 min. [Copyright length: 84 min.]

Prod Ika Panajotović. *Dir* Richard Conte. *Screenplay* Vincent Fotre. *Photog* Nenad Jović. *Art Dir* Bob Radley. *Sd* Mike Neglich. *Asst Dir* (see note) Casey Diamond. *Prod Mgr* Gor Končar, Chris Whittaker.

Cast: Richard Conte (*Lieutenant Bradford*), Rory Calhoun (*Sgt. Sean MacAfee*), Aili King (*Anna*), Phil Brown (*Sergeant Tunley*), Rada Djuričin, Relja Bašić, Abdul Rahman, Rick West.

War melodrama. Sgt. Sean MacAfee and two survivors of his commando unit, Sergeant Tunley and Corporal Bell, are waiting to be picked up in Yugoslavia after completing their mission during World War II. They are intercepted by a group of Germans who take them to a secluded farmhouse where they meet American Lieutenant Bradford, who had enlisted the aid of some local partisans to impersonate the Germans in order to bring back MacAfee and his men. Bradford is recovering from wounds he received when his mission to rescue a captured American officer was betrayed by an informer. Bradford's plan to capture a German commandant and pretend to exchange him for the American officer, who supposedly knows the Allied invasion plans, is almost foiled by a traitor among them. However, Bradford's plan is finally successful: the officer is rescued, and the Americans, by a trick, retain the German commandant as their prisoner. The traitor, Corporal Bell, is discovered and killed when he attempts to free the commandant. Bradford explains that the Allied invasion plan was a fabrication to divert the Germans, and that the purpose of the mission was to capture the commandant. *Commandos. Traitors.*

Impersonation. Resistance (political). World War II. United States Army. Germany—Army.

Note: Location scenes filmed in Piran, Yugoslavia, and Trieste. Yugoslav title: *Unakrsna vatra*. A Yugoslav source credits Casey Diamond as director.

OPERATION CROSSBOW (Great Britain/Italy)   F6.3651

Metro-Goldwyn-Mayer Pictures-Carlo Ponti. *Dist* Metro-Goldwyn-Mayer, Inc. 1 Apr **1965** [New York opening; c13 Apr 1965; LP30349]. Sd (Westrex); col (Metrocolor). 35mm (Panavision). 116 min.

A Carlo Ponti Production. *Prod* Carlo Ponti. *Dir* Michael Anderson. *Screenplay* Richard Imrie, Derry Quinn, Ray Rigby. *Story* Duilio Coletti, Vittoriano Petrilli. *Dir Photog* Erwin Hillier. *Camera Op* Robert Kindred. *Art Dir* Elliot Scott. *Film Ed* Ernest Walter. *Mus Comp & Cond* Ron Goodwin. *Sd* A. W. Watkins. *Sd Rec* Gerry Turner. *Dub Mix* J. B. Smith. *Sd Ed* Allan Sones. *Asst Dir* Basil Rayburn. *Prod Mgr* Sydney Streeter. *Sp Eff* Tom Howard. *English Subtitl* Bernard Doret.

Cast: Sophia Loren (*Nora*), George Peppard (*Lieut. John Curtis*), Trevor Howard (*Professor Lindemann*), John Mills (*Boyd of M.I. 6*), Richard Johnson (*Duncan Sandys*), Tom Courtenay (*Robert Henshaw*), Jeremy Kemp (*Phil Bradley*), Anthony Quayle (*Bamford*), Lilli Palmer (*Frieda*), Paul Henreid (*General Ziemann*), Helmut Dantine (*General Linz*), Barbara Rütting (*Hanna Reitsch*), Richard Todd (*Wing Commander Kendall*), Sylvia Syms (*Constance Babington Smith*), John Fraser (*Flight Lieutenant Kenny*), Maurice Denham (*R.A.F. officer*), Patrick Wymark (*Winston Churchill*), Karel Stepanek (*Professor Hoffer*), Moray Watson (*Col. Kenneth Post*), Richard Wattis (*Sir Charles Sims*), Allan Cuthbertson (*German technical examiner*), Robert Brown (*air commodore*), Wolf Frees, William Mervyn, Milo Sperber, George Mikell, Ferdy Mayne.

War drama. Allied Intelligence in London in December of 1942 receives reports that the Germans are developing long-range rockets. Though key advisers such as Professor Lindemann are skeptical of the reports, Prime Minister Churchill appoints Duncan Sandys, deputy supply minister, to head an investigation studying photographs for clues and pinpointing possible enemy launching sites. Then, when V-1 robot bombs begin to fall on London, three agents—Lieut. John Curtis, Phil Bradley, and Robert Henshaw—parachute into Holland and cross into Germany to infiltrate the underground plant at Peenemünde. They are posing as German agents known by the Allies to be deceased, but Henshaw is recognized by Gestapo agent Bamford and dies without giving any information. Curtis is confronted by the wife of the man he is impersonating. He locks her in his room and exacts her promise of secrecy; but she is ruthlessly killed by Frieda, an underground leader, to avoid any possible security leak. Bradley and Curtis get jobs at Peenemünde and transmit their findings to London. When London decides to bomb the site before long-range rockets can be launched, the agents are instructed to light the way for a squadron of Allied bombers. At the cost of their lives the two men make possible the total destruction of the Nazi installation. *Secret agents. Saboteurs. Espionage. Impersonation. Resistance (political). Self-sacrifice. Rockets. Aerial bombardment. World War II. London. Peenemünde. Gestapo. Winston Leonard Spencer Churchill.*

Note: Opened in London in Aug 1965; in Rome in Oct 1965 as *Operazione Crossbow*; running time: 110 min. Also shown as *The Great Spy Mission* and *Code Name: Operation Crossbow.*

OPERATION DELILAH (United States/Spain)   F6.3652

S. W. P. Productions-Esamer Films. *Dist* Comet Film Distributors. Jan **1966**. Sd; col (Eastman Color). 35mm. 86 min.

Prod Sidney W. Pink, Harry Eller. *Dir* Luis de los Arcos. *Assoc Dir* Sidney W. Pink, David Elias. *Screenplay* Luis de los Arcos, Sidney W. Pink. *Photog* Mario Pacheco. *Art Dir* Antonio Simont. *Film Ed* Margarita Lauvergeon, Kurt Herrnfeld. *Mus* Adolfo Waitzmann. *Prod Mgr* Antonio Sau.

Cast: Rory Calhoun (*Rory*), Gia Scala (*Delilah*), Marvin Kaplan, Enrique Guitart, Manolo Morán, Angel Alvarez, José Manuel Martín, José Isbert, Jackie Mason, Angel Del Pozo, José Luis López Vázquez, Jorge Rigaud.

Satire. On a Caribbean island, a coup d'état replaces President González with President Ramón, whose beard symbolizes a Marxist influence. "Operation Delilah" is organized by an alarmed Western power to remove the new leader. Rory, owner of a razor company, goes to the capital with Delilah, who charms Ramón but falls in love with Rory. At a party, she drugs Ramón and, as she begins to shave him, discovers that his beard is false and that he is actually former President González. *Presidents. Businessmen. Coups d'état. Marxism. Espionage. Disguise. Islands. Drugs. Caribbean. Delilah.*

Note: Filmed on location in Madrid and Barcelona. Opened in Madrid in Aug 1967 as *Operación Dalila*; running time: 93 min. Margarita Lauvergeon is also known as Margarita Ochoa.

OPERATION EICHMANN   **F6.3653**

Bischoff–Diamond Corp. *Dist* Allied Artists. 15 Mar **1961** [Detroit opening; c7 Mar 1961; LP18565]. Sd; b&w. 35mm. 92 min.

Prod Samuel Bischoff, David Diamond. *Dir* R. G. Springsteen. *Screenplay* Lewis Copley. *Photog* Joseph Biroc. *Art Dir* Rudi Feld. *Set Dresser* George Sawley. *Film Ed* Roy Livingston. *Mus Supv* Mischa Terr. *Mus Dir* Alex Alexander. *Mus Comp* June Starr. *Orch* Herbert Doerfel. *Song:* "Es muss nur der Richtige kommen" ("The Right One Must Come Along") Franz Steininger, Gustav Heimo. *"The Prayer"* Sung by Cantor Sholom Katz. *Sd Mixer* Charles Althouse. *Sd Rec* Art Smith. *Sd* Charles Schelling, Marty Greco. *Asst Dir* Maurie M. Suess. *Prod Mgr* Maurie M. Suess. *Script Supv* Bobbie Sierks. *Wardrobe* Wally Harton, Rose Rockne. *Makeup* Anthony Lloyd. *Hairstyles* Irene Beshon. *Sp Eff* Charles Duncan. *Props* Max Frankel, Allen Gordon. *Gaffer* Don Carstensen. *Constr Supv* Howard Reed.

Cast: Werner Klemperer (*Adolf Eichmann*), Ruta Lee (*Anna Kemp*), Donald Buka (*David*), Barbara Turner (*Sara*), John Banner (*Rudolf Hoess*), Hanna Landy (*Frau Hoess*), Lester Fletcher (*Kurt Kessner*), Steve Gravers (*Jacob*), Jim Baird (*David, as boy*), Debbie Cannon (*Sara, as girl*), Jackie Russo (*Jacob, as boy*), Paul Thierry (*Lopez*), Rodolfo Hoyos (*Sanchez*), Norbert Schiller (*Uri Goldmann*), Luis Van Rooten (*Heinrich Himmler*), Oscar Beregi (*Kuwait Chief of Police*), Theodore Marcuse (*Felsner*), Otto Reichow (*Rostich*), Walter Linden (*Eichmann's driver*), Hans Hermann (*Hans*), Hans Gudegast (*Klaus*), Robert Christopher (*Ben, pilot*), Carla Lucerne (*cafe singer*), Austin Green, Robert H. Harris.

Historical drama. Under orders from Hitler to find a final solution of the Jewish problem, Gestapo chief Adolf Eichmann personally organizes a series of mass exterminations, mostly in concentration camps like Auschwitz, which take the lives of 6 million Jews. When Germany is defeated, he flees to Barcelona with his mistress, Anna Kemp. Two Jewish agents, David and Jacob, both of whom as young boys miraculously escaped from one of Eichmann's mass murders, track him down. But when they disagree on whether the archcriminal should be killed or captured, Eichmann escapes to a port in Kuwait. Israeli agents force Eichmann to move on, and he takes refuge in Argentina, where Anna joins him. Meanwhile, the Nazi underground, led by Kurt Kessner, has decided that Eichmann is to be eliminated for disobeying orders. Before they can succeed, however, David and Jacob capture Eichmann and fly him to Israel to await trial. *Jews. Nazis. Israelis. War crimes. Genocide. Concentration camps. World War II. Germany. Kuwait. Auschwitz. Barcelona. Argentina. Adolf Eichmann. Rudolf Hess. Anna Kemp. Heinrich Himmler.*

Note: Includes newsreels of World War II concentration camp atrocities.

OPERATION ENEMY FORT (Japan)   **F6.3654**

Toho Co. Aug **1964** [Los Angeles showing]. Sd; col (Eastmancolor). 35mm (Tohoscope). 95 min.

Exec Prod Tomoyuki Tanaka. *Dir* Senkichi Taniguchi. *Screenplay* Shinichi Sekizawa. *Photog* Fukuzo Koizumi. *Mus* Masaru Sato.

Cast: Makoto Sato, Yuriko Hoshi, Yosuke Natsuki, Toru Ibuki, Kumi Mizuno, Jun Tazaki.

War drama. During the China Incident, two Japanese army lieutenants, Wakana and Taira, are assigned to Major Otawara's battalion in the northern China mountains. Although the Chinese army is 70 miles away, the battalion has been plagued by General Lung's guerrillas, who have just blown up a bean warehouse owned by Lee, a Japanese sympathizer. Fearing a second explosion, Lee decides to move his stock, and as Wakana escorts the convoy, it is attacked by the guerrillas. Wakana unsuccessfully pursues them, only to find on his return that the entire shipment is missing. After Taira is ordered to an observation post, he is taken prisoner and Otawara, suspecting he has deserted, assigns Lieutenant Isshiki, Otawara's rival, and Wakana to locate Taira. In disguise, the two lieutenants penetrate the enemy fort and discover that Lee is actually General Lung and the shipment of beans was a cache of arms for the guerrillas. Thrown into the same cell as Taira, the men watch in horror as Somemaru, a geisha Taira loves, is tortured. Taira then agrees to write a letter to the battalion which will lead them into a trap. However, Isshiki breaks out of the cell and blows up a powder magazine. The soldiers secure a machine gun and a fight ensues. *Chinese. Guerrillas. Geishas. Combat zone life. Disguise. Perfidy. Torture. Forts. Sino-Japanese Conflict 1937–45. China. Japan—Army.*

Note: Released in Japan in 1962 as *Yamaneko sakusen*.

OPERATION KID BROTHER (Italy)   **F6.3655**

Produzione D. S. *Dist* United Artists. 25 Oct **1967** [Denver, Colorado, opening]. Sd; col (Technicolor). 35mm (Techniscope). 104 min.

Prod Dario Sabatello. *Dir* Alberto De Martino. *Screenplay* Paolo Levi, Frank Walker, Stanley Wright, Stefano Canzio, Vincenzo Mannino, Carlo Tritto. *Photog* Alejandro Ulloa, Gianni Bergamini. *Art Dir* Franco Fontana. *Set Decor* Massimo Tavazzi. *Film Ed* Otello Colangeli. *Mus* Bruno Nicolai, Ennio Morricone. *Song:* "The Man for Me" Bruno Nicolai, Ennio Morricone, Audrey Nohra. *Sd* Deliberti. *Asst Dir* Carlo Moscovini. *Prod Mgr* Nino Masini. *Cost*

Gaia Romanini. *Sp Eff* Gagliano.

Cast: Neil Connery (*Neil Connery*), Daniela Bianchi (*Maya*), Adolfo Celi (*Thair Beta*), Agata Flori (*Mildred*), Bernard Lee (*Commander Cunningham*), Anthony Dawson (*Alpha*), Lois Maxwell (*Max*), Yachuco Yama (*Yachuco*), Guido Lollobrigida (*Kurt*), Franco Giacobini (*Juan*), Nando Angelini (*Ward Jones*), Mario Soria (*Gamma*), Anne-Marie Noé (*Lotte*), Leo Scavini, Francesco Tensi, Enzo Consoli, Mirella Pamphili, Antonio Gradoli, Franco Ceccarelli.

Action melodrama. After Dr. Ward Jones is assassinated while investigating underworld organization THANATOS, Neil Connery, a plastic surgeon, hypnotist, archer, and lip reader, is recruited by the secret service. By hypnotizing Mildred, mistress to THANATOS kingpin Thair, the doctor discovers the whereabouts of Yachuco, Jones' missing girl friend, whom he rescues. The grateful victim reveals that Thair plans a universal power failure, through which THANATOS will blackmail the world. Alarmed, Connery begins a desperate search for the syndicate's headquarters. In Tetuán, he discovers a carpet factory staffed by blind workers, in which are woven radioactive rugs. Accompanied by former THANATOS agent Maya, Connery penetrates the organization's palatial Bavarian headquarters. In retaliation Thair activates the power shortage and in so doing neutralizes his own weapons, thereby enabling Maya and a team of Scottish archers to decimate THANATOS. When secret service commander Cunningham presses Connery to remain in his employ, the surgeon hypnotizes the chief, thereby declining the invitation. *Surgeons. Secret agents. Mistresses. Organized crime. Megalomania. Kidnaping. Hypnotism. Archery. Blackmail. Blackout. Bavaria. Tetuán.*

Note: Locations filmed in Monaco; Tetuán, Morocco; and Spain. Anthony Dawson is a pseudonym for Antonio Margheriti. Released in Italy in 1967 as *O. K. Connery*.

OPÉRATION LOTUS BLEU *see* **MISSION BLOODY MARY**

OPERATION LOVEBIRDS (Denmark)   **F6.3656**

Nordisk Films. *Dist* Emerson Film Enterprises. Jun **1968**. Sd; col (Eastmancolor). 35mm. 102 min. [Also reviewed at 90 min.]

Pres by Marshall Schacker. *Prod* Bo Christensen. *Dir* Erik Balling. *Screenplay* Bengt Janus, Henning Bahs, Erik Balling. *Photog* Jørgen Skov, Arne Abrahamsen. *Art Dir* Henning Bahs. *Mus Comp* Bent Fabricius-Bjerre. *Sd* Hans Sørensen.

Cast: Essy Persson (*Sonja*), Morten Grunwald (*Freddy*), Ove Sprogøe (*Smith*), Poul Bundgaard (*Kolick*), Martin Hansen (*Dr. Pax*), John Wittig, Frankie Steele, Jørgen Blaksted, Edward Fleming, Valsø Holm, Lisbeth Frandsen, Søren Rode, Philippe Decaux, Freddy Koch, Karl Stegger, André Sallyman, Knud Rex, Arthur Jensen, Ebba With, Else Marie, Anne Marie Lie, Jan Priiskorn Schmidt, Michael Sprehn, Olaf Lindfors, Bjørn Spiro, Hans Ejner Jensen, Gunnar Strømvad, Anne Werner Thomsen.

Farce. As novelties salesman Freddy returns from a business trip, his sample case becomes confused with the valise of secret agent Smith. While Freddy's bag is full of trick gadgets, Smith's briefcase contains incriminating evidence against the sinister Dr. Pax. Because Freddy has unwittingly become privy to its intelligence he is recruited by the secret service, which he enters under the tutelage of Smith. En route to an encounter with Pax's paramour, Sonja, the pair is unsuccessfully attacked by one-handed henchman Kolick. At the Stockholm cabaret in which Sonja is a performer the agents are again menaced by Kolick. Although Freddy escapes with the help of his sample case, Kolick abducts Sonja and Smith. The salesman follows them to Pax's island headquarters, from which the megalomaniac plans to mount a missile attack spearheaded by a flight of trained pigeons. The scheme is foiled by Freddy, who deflects the missiles from their Russian target by substituting homing pigeons for Pax's flock. Freddy rescues Sonja and Smith, and the trio departs in a helicopter as the avian army approaches its target. *Salesmen. Secret agents. Entertainers. Amputees. Espionage. Practical jokes. Aerial bombardment. Megalomania. Islands. Missiles. Stockholm. Pigeons.*

Note: Filmed on location in and around Copenhagen. Released in Denmark in Dec 1965 as *Slå først, Frede!*

OPERATION M *see* **HELL'S BLOODY DEVILS**

OPERATION MASQUERADE *see* **MASQUERADE**

OPERATION MERMAID *see* **PATTERN FOR PLUNDER**

OPÉRATION SAN GENNARO *see* **TREASURE OF SAN GENNARO**

OPERATION SNAFU (Great Britain)   **F6.3657**

S. Benjamin Fisz. *Dist* American International Pictures. 27 Jan **1965** [Cleveland opening; c20 Jan 1965; LP30615]. Sd; b&w. 35mm. 97 min. [Also 89 min.]

An S. Benjamin Fisz Production. *Prod* S. Benjamin Fisz. *Assoc Prod* Ben Arbeid. *Dir* Cyril Frankel. *Screenplay* Harold Buchman. *Photog* Edward Scaife. *Art Dir* John Blezard. *Film Ed* Peter Hunt. *Mus Comp & Dir* Malcolm Arnold. *Sd* Bill Salter, Bob Jones.

Cast: Alfred Lynch (*Horace Pope*), Sean Connery (*Pedlar Pascoe*), Cecil Parker (*Group Captain Bascombe*), Stanley Holloway (*Mr. Cooksley*), Alan King (*Technical Sergeant Buzzer*), Eric Barker (*doctor*), Wilfrid Hyde-White (*Trowbridge*), Kathleen Harrison (*Mrs. Cooksley*), Eleanor Summerfield (*Flora McNaughton*), Terence Longdon (*air gunner*), Victor Maddern (*1st airman*), Harry Locke (*Huxtable*), John Le Mesurier (*Hixon*), Viola Keats (*sister*), Peter Sinclair (*Mr. Pope*), Edna Morris (*Lil*), Thomas Heathcote (*sergeant*), Brian Weske (*corporal*), Jack Lambert (*police constable*), Cyril Smith (*ticket collector*), Simon Lack (*Flight Lieutenant Baldwin*), Graham Stark (*Sergeant Ellis*), Jean Aubrey (*WAAF corporal*), Ann Beach (*Iris*), Miriam Karlin (*WAAF sergeant*), Bill Owen (*Corporal Gittens*), Barbara Windsor (*Mavis*), Ian Whittaker, actor (*Lancing*), Harold Goodwin (*Corporal Reeves*), Kenneth J. Warren (*Dusty*), Beatrix Lehmann (*Lady Edith*), Gary Cockrell (*U. S. Snowdrop*), Lance Percival (*MacTaggart*), Monty Landis (*conductor*), Jack Smethurst, Patsy Rowlands, Priscilla Morgan, Richard Hart, Stuart Saunders, Toni Palmer, Norman Coburn, Michael Sarne.

War comedy. Source: Ronald Frederick Delderfield, *Stop at a Winner* (London, 1961). In World War II Horace Pope is drafted into the Royal Air Force in lieu of serving a jail sentence. He decides to make the best of the situation, and with the assistance of a Gypsy, Pedlar Pascoe, he turns his wartime service into a life of easy profit. With Pope serving as the brains for the team of opportunists and Pascoe supplying the muscle, the two begin their first assignment by selling transfers and leave passes to fellow airmen. At their next station, Pope and Pascoe become butchers and arrange to sell fresh beef to Cooksley, a local butcher. Pope is attracted to Iris, the butcher's daughter, until Cooksley begins to hint of marriage. A quick transfer saves Pope; and after a brief stay in a hospital following an air raid, the two men find themselves at an American air base near Cornwall, where they turn a rundown pub owned by Trowbridge into a financial success. Sergeant Buzzer, a greedy American, wants the pub business for himself, however, and manages to have Pascoe and Pope sent overseas to France. For the first time, the two men find themselves in a combat zone. Pascoe takes over this time, and both men leave the service as decorated heroes. They return to civilian life at Cornwall and once again take over the profitable pub, but no sooner do they arrive than Iris also arrives with a baby that is obviously Pope's. *Profiteers. Gypsies. Butchers. Military life. Aerial bombardment. Combat zone life. Illegitimacy. Greed. Pubs. World War II. Cornwall (England). France. Great Britain—Royal Air Force. United States Army—Air Force.*

Note: Opened in London in Oct 1961 as *On the Fiddle*; running time: 97 min. U. S. prerelease titles: *War Head* and *Operation War Head*.

OPERATION SNATCH (Great Britain)   F6.3658

Keep Films. *Dist* Continental Distributing, Inc. 24 Sep **1962** [New York opening]. Sd; b&w. 35mm. 83 min.

Prod Jules Buck. *Assoc Prod* Roy Simpson. *Dir* Robert Day. *Screenplay* Alan Hackney. *Adtl Material* John Warren, Len Heath. *Story* Paul Mills. *Photog* Geoffrey Faithfull. *Art Dir* Ivan King. *Film Ed* Bert Rule. *Mus Comp & Cond* Ken Jones. *Sd Rec* Norman Coggs, Len Shilton. *Asst Dir* Ross MacKenzie.

Cast: Terry-Thomas (*Lieut. "Piggy" Wigg*), George Sanders (*Major Hobson*), Lionel Jeffries (*Evans*), Jackie Lane (*Bianca Tabori*), Lee Montague (*Miklos Tabori*), Michael Trubshawe (*Colonel Marston*), James Villiers (*Lieutenant Keen*), Dinsdale Landen (*Captain Whittington*), Jeremy Lloyd (*Captain James*), John Gabriel (*Major Frink*), Warren Mitchell (*contact man*), Mario Fabrizi (*tall man*), Bernard Hunter (*Captain Baker*), Mark Singleton (*prime minister's secretary*), John Meillon (*medical officer*), Gerard Heinz (*Colonel Waldock*), Howard Lang (*p.t. sergeant*), Graham Stark (*1st soldier*), John Scott (*Lieutenant-General Hepworth*), Ian Whittaker, actor (*Dyson*).

War comedy. Stationed at Gibraltar in World War II, Lieut. "Piggy" Wigg has the difficult task of looking after the Rock's famous Barbary apes. Legend has it that as long as the apes are on the Rock, Gibraltar will remain British; consequently, when a mysterious disease threatens the ape colony, Major Hobson, the intelligence officer, realizes that if the apes all die the Germans will take advantage of the legend for propaganda purposes. Hobson is also faced with another crisis: the death of the sole male ape has made the females so listless and morose that it is imperative that another male be found immediately. He therefore orders Wigg and his batman, Evans, to steal one from a German circus in Zurich. After smuggling the animal out of the circus by putting it into a prop horse, they successfully return to Gibraltar and thereby save the ape colony. Despite Wigg's promotion, he and Evans are transferred to the Tower of London to guard its ravens. It is believed that if the birds were to leave, the British Kingdom would fall. *Guards. Orderlies (military). Animal care.*

Propaganda. Smuggling. Theft. Myths. Circus. World War II. Gibraltar. Zurich. Great Britain—Army. Great Britain—Intelligence service. Tower of London. Apes. Ravens.

Note: Opened in London in Mar 1962: running time: 87 min.

OPERATION WAR HEAD *see* **OPERATION SNAFU**

OPERATION X (Japan)   F6.3659

Toho Co. 11 Jan **1963** [Los Angeles opening]. Sd; b&w. 35mm (Tohoscope). 102 min.

Exec Prod Tomoyuki Tanaka, Ken-ichiro Tsunoda. *Dir-Writ* Kihachi Okamoto. *Photog* Yuzuru Aizawa. *Mus* Masaru Sato.

Cast: Yuzo Kayama, Yosuke Natsuki, Makoto Sato, Kumi Mizuno, Ichiro Nakatani, Tadao Nakamaru, Kunie Tanaka, Mickey Curtis, Nami Tamura.

War drama. In the waning days of World War II, Captain Seki, an idealistic young officer, is assigned to a beleaguered garrison on the north China frontier. Eager to make good on his first command and ignoring the advice of experienced officers, Seki leads a platoon against the Chinese only to have his unit slaughtered and himself taken prisoner. Because he is the son of the division commander and may have gained knowledge of Chinese activities, a search for Seki is organized and a reward is offered. Byakko, the leader of a Chinese guerrilla band who prefer Japanese occupation to the Chinese Communists, offers to head the expedition, and he selects four soldiers about to undergo punishment for various crimes to accompany him. At the scene of the massacre, Byakko meets Muso, the head of Chinese intelligence, and while Byakko learns where Seki is being held, Muso is told of the reward. The two men race to recapture Seki, with Byakko's group winning. Returning to the garrison, Byakko finds Seki has already been reported dead, and Seki joins the guerrilla band as the war continues. *Chinese. Guerrillas. Idealists. Prisoners of war. Combat zone life. Rewards. Massacres. Sino-Japanese Conflict 1937–45. China. Japan—Army.*

Note: Released in Japan in 1962 as *Dobunezumi sakusen.*

OPERAZIONE CROSSBOW *see* **OPERATION CROSSBOW**

OPERAZIONE GOLDMAN *see* **LIGHTNING BOLT**

OPERAZIONE PARADISO *see* **KISS THE GIRLS AND MAKE THEM DIE**

OPERAZIONE PAURA *see* **KILL BABY KILL**

OPERAZIONE SAN GENNARO *see* **TREASURE OF SAN GENNARO**

OPHÉLIA (France)   F6.3660

Boréal. *Dist* Trans-Lux Distributing Corp. **1964**. Sd; b&w. 35mm. 100 min. [Unconfirmed.]

Dir Claude Chabrol. *Screenplay* Claude Chabrol. *Literary Collab* Martial Matthieu. *Photog* Jean Rabier. *Camera* Alain Levent. *Film Ed* Jacques Gaillard. *Mus Comp* Pierre Jansen. *Mus Cond* André Girard. *Sd* Jean-Claude Marchetti. *Asst Dir* Paul Seban, Francis Cognani. *Prod Mgr* Jean Lavie.

Cast: Alida Valli (*Claudia Lesurf*), Claude Cerval (*Adrien Lesurf*), André Jocelyn (*Yvan Lesurf*), Juliette Mayniel (*Lucie*), Robert Burnier (*André Lagrange*), Jean-Louis Maury (*Sparkos*), Sacha Briquet (*gravedigger*), Liliane David (*Ginette*), Pierre Vernier (*Paul*), Serge Bento (*François*), Roger Carel (*worker*), Laszlo Szabo (*foolish guard*), Henri Attal, Dominique Zardi, Jean-Marie Arnoux (*guards*).

Drama. Yvan, the outlandish son of the Lesurf family, is obsessed with his father's death and his mother's sudden marriage to his uncle, Adrien. He takes pleasure in subjecting the latter to scorn and sarcasm in the family mansion, which Adrien has placed under guard to prevent attacks by strikers from the Lesurf factory. Lucie, whose father, André, presides over the family estate, is Yvan's only consolation, in spite of her father's disapproval of him. While watching Laurence Olivier's film of *Hamlet* at a nearby theater, it occurs to Yvan that his situation is similar to that of Hamlet. Pretending insanity, Yvan intensifies his taunting of Adrien and his mother, Claudia. He sets out to make a film about a couple who poison the unwitting husband; Ginette the barmaid, his friend François, and a happy-go-lucky gravedigger play the roles. At the gala family showing of the film, Adrien and his mother become upset, as Yvan had intended. In desperation, Adrien tries unsuccessfully to murder Yvan but poisons himself instead. As he dies, Adrien explains that he has taken the poison because he was forced to believe that he was guilty, although he insists that neither he nor Claudia have done anything wrong. Feeling guilty himself, Yvan turns for consolation to Lucie, who assures him that he is not the Prince of Denmark, but Yvan Lesurf. *Stepfathers. Uncles. Barmaids. Gravediggers. Death. Marriage. Obsession. Duplicity. Murder. Insanity. Poisoning. Suicide. Guilt. Motion pictures. "Hamlet" (1948 film).*

Note: Location scenes filmed at Villepreux (Yvelines). Opened in Paris in Feb 1963; running times: 105 min. and 102 min. Martial Matthieu is a pseudonym for Paul Gégauff in this film; Chabrol uses the name in *The Third Lover*, q. v.

OPIATE '67 (France/Italy)   **F6.3661**

Fair Film–Incei Film–Mountfluor Films–Dicifrance. *Dist* McAbee Pictures, Janus Films. 30 Jun 1967 [Portland, Oregon, opening]. Sd; b&w. 35mm. 87 min.

Pres by Ian McGlashan. *Prod* Mario Cecchi Gori. *Dir* Dino Risi. *Story & Screenplay* Age & Scarpelli, Elio Petri, Ettore Scola, Ruggero Maccari, Dino Risi. *Photog* Alfio Contini. *Art Dir* Ugo Pericoli. *Film Ed* Maurizio Lucidi. *Mus* Armando Trovajoli.

Cast: Vittorio Gassman, Ugo Tognazzi, Marisa Merlini, Michèle Mercier, Lando Buzzanca, Luisa Ruspoli, Marino Masè, Rick Tognazzi, Franco Castellani, Nino Nini, Angela Portaluri, Rika Dialina, Daniele Vargas, Riccardo Paladini, Carlo Ragno, Ugo Attanasio, Mario Laurentino, Maria Mannelli, Luciana Vincenzi, Salvatore Borgese, Francesco Caracciolo, Yacinto Yaria, Carlo Kechler, Mario Brega, Lucia Modugno.

Comedy-drama. Fifteen "monsters" of present-day Rome are presented from every class and profession: a terrified old woman, abducted by filmmakers for use in their production, is repeatedly thrown into a pool; a husband [Ugo Tognazzi] watches television soap operas about infidelity, while his wife [Michèle Mercier] conducts her own extra-marital activities in the adjoining room; his family being too large for him to provide proper care, a poverty-stricken father continues to impregnate his wife in order to receive bigger welfare payments to bet on soccer games; after preening and fussing about his appearance, a priest [Vittorio Gassman] goes on television to denounce vanity; unsuccessful in approaching a young woman on the beach, two Don Juans [Gassman and Tognazzi] comfort each other; when a father [Tognazzi] teaches his young son nonconformist moral principles, the boy responds by killing him for money; while calling his employer to ask his aid in determining if his wife is unfaithful, a cuckold discovers her sleeping with the employer; on furlough because of the murder of his sister, a "grief-stricken" soldier [Tognazzi] rises above his misery to offer his exclusive story to the best-paying newspaper; the beggar partner [Gassman] of a young blind musician prefers to wait until they save up enough money to go to Lourdes rather than allow a doctor to restore his friend's sight for free; after persuading his mistress that he must end their 6-year affair because he feels guilty in deceiving his newly pregnant wife, a married man [Gassman] goes off to meet his new girl friend; almost killed by several ferocious drivers, a pedestrian gets into his car and becomes a public menace; testifying at a criminal trial, an honest witness [Tognazzi] is badgered by a cunning lawyer; during the showing of a horrifying war film in which peasants are lined up against a wall for execution, a wealthy man [Tognazzi] whispers to his bored wife, "That's the kind of wall I want for our villa, only with tiles along the top"; a retired boxing champion [Gassman], persuaded by a former manager [Tognazzi] to return to the ring, barely survives one round. *Filmmakers. Cuckolds. Clergymen. Soldiers. Beggars. Physicians. Mistresses. Lawyers. Peasants. Prizefighters. Fight managers. Abduction. Infidelity. Poverty. Fatherhood. Family life. Pregnancy. Public welfare. Vanity. Gambling. Murder. Greed. Blindness. Reckless driving. Motion pictures. Wealth. Television. Soccer. Beaches. Newspapers. Trials. Rome. Lourdes.*

Note: Opened in Rome in Oct 1963 as *I mostri*; running time: 120 min (20 vignettes); in Paris in May 1964 as *Les monstres*; running time: 112 min (18 vignettes). U. S. title changed to *15 From Rome*. Cast credits derived from foreign sources; some actors may have been cut for U. S. release.

L'OPTIMISME AU XXᴱ SIÈCLE *see* **CANDIDE**

THE OPTIMISTIC TRAGEDY (U.S.S.R.)   **F6.3662**

Mosfilm. *Dist* Artkino Pictures. 22 Feb 1964 [New York opening]. Sd; b&w. 35mm. 120 min.

Dir Samson Samsonov. *Screenplay* Sofiya Vishnevetskaya, Samson Samsonov. *Story Ed* N. Glagoleva. *Photog* Vladimir Monakhov. *Camera* I. Bogdanov, V. Zakharchuk. *Asst Camera* E. Borkman, Ye. Shvedov. *Art Dir* I. Novoderezhkin, Sergey Voronkov. *Film Ed* A. Kamagorova. *Mus* Vasiliy Dekhteryov. *Song Lyr* M. Matusovskiy. *Cond* V. Dudarova. *Asst Dir* Grigoriy Korenblyum. *1st & 2d Asst Dir* Lyutsiya Okhrimenko, M. Koldobskaya, N. Solovyov. *Prod Mgr* A. Yablochkin. *Cost* V. Perepyolov. *Makeup* S. Kalinin. *Sp Eff* I. Felitsyn, A. Klimenko. *Military Cons* N. Molotkov, N. Smirnov, N. Oslikovskiy, S. Kornilov. *Sculptor* L. Berlin.

Cast: Margarita Volodina *(The Commissar)*, Boris Andreyev *("The Boss" ["Vozhak"])*, Vyacheslav Tikhonov *(Aleksey)*, Vsevolod Sanayev *("Husky" ["Siplyy"])*, Orko Byerninen *(Vaynonen)*, Vsevolod Safonov *(Bering)*, I. Zhevago *(boatswain)*, D. Netrebin *("Pock-marked" ["Ryaboy"])*, Grigoriy Mikhaylov *(old sailor)*, P. Sobolevskiy *(ship's doctor)*, Erast Garin *(Vozhachok)*, Oleg Strizhenov *(1st officer)*, Gleb Strizhenov *(2d officer)*, A. Glazyrin, V. Belokhvostik *(leaders)*, I. Vankov *(tattooed sailor)*, V. Nedobrovo-Buzhinskaya *(woman in black)*, V. Shulgin *(tall sailor)*, I. Bychkov, I. Bondar, V. Grave, V. Demidovskiy, V. Zabavin, Ye. Zosimov, Yu. Kireyev, L. Knyazev, N. Kondratyev, P. Kononykhin, A. Milyukhin, V. Novikov, D. Orlovskiy, V.

Prikhodko, A. Sakhnovskiy, S. Svashenko, V. Skuridin, A. Stroyev, N. Khryashchikov.

Historical melodrama. Source: Vsevolod Vitaliyevich Vishnevskiy, *Optimisticheskaya tragediya* (Moscow opening: 1934). In 1917, shortly after the October Revolution, the Communist Party sends a former tsarist officer as commander and a pretty young woman commissar aboard the cruiser *Emperor Paul* to consolidate political power and convert the sailors, who have embraced anarchism, into an effective fighting force. Despite the opposition of the anarchist "Boss," the crew, who at first abuse the commissar, are gradually won over. The ship sails to the Black Sea. The woman's courage and the corrupt actions of the Boss and his mute henchman, "Husky," cause the crew to rethink their anarchism. The Boss's former ally Aleksey, who has grown to love the woman, shoots the anarchist leader, and the crew fight by the side of the commissar. Aided by Husky's treachery, the Whites carry out a raid and take prisoners, including the commissar and Aleksey. A counteroffensive is made to rescue them, but it is too late to save the woman, who is tortured and dies, a martyr to the revolution. *Anarchists. Communists. Mutes. Revolutionaries. War heroes. Women in public office. Perfidy. Russia—History—1917–21 Revolution. Black Sea. Union of Soviet Socialist Republics—Navy.*

Note: Released in the U.S.S.R. in Jun 1963 as *Optimisticheskaya tragediya.* Shown at the 1963 Cannes Film Festival in 70mm Kinopanorama. Soldiers from the Kiev military district and sailors from the Black Sea fleet participated in the production.

OPTIMISTICHESKAYA TRAGEDIYA *see* **THE OPTIMISTIC TRAGEDY**

L'OR DES CÉSARS *see* **GOLD FOR THE CAESARS**

OR POUR LES CÉSARS *see* **GOLD FOR THE CAESARS**

ORAZI E CURIAZI *see* **DUEL OF CHAMPIONS**

ÓRBITA MORTAL *see* **MISSION STARDUST**

ORDERED TO LOVE (West Germany)   **F6.3663**

Alfa–Film. *For* FTR. *Dist* M. C. Pictures. Aug 1963. Sd; b&w. 35mm. 82 min.

Prod Wolf Brauner. *Dir* Werner Klingler. *Screenplay* Will Berthold. *English Dial* Jack Dunn Trop. *Photog* Igor Oberberg. *Art Dir* Paul Markwitz, Max Vorberg. *Mus* Gerhard Becker. *Prod Mgr* Heinz Götze.

Cast: Maria Perschy *(Doris Korff)*, Joachim Hansen *(Klaus Steinbach)*, Harry Meyen *(Dr. Hagen)*, Emmerich Schrenk *(Meyer Westroff)*, Joachim Mock *(Kempe)*, Marisa Mell *(Erica Meuring)*, Gert Günter Hoffmann *(Mertens)*, Waldemar Tepel *(Hellmich)*, Lothar Mann *(Koss)*, Michael Welchberger *(Gühne)*, Helmut Lange *(Nietermann)*, Eva Bubat *(Irmgard)*, Rosemarie Kirstein, Renate Küster, Hannelore Jüterbock, Birgitt Bergen, Elke Eichwede, Dinah Berger.

Drama. Based on unidentified articles in *Revue* by: Will Berthold. During World War II, a group of German women are selected to participate in the breeding of a master race by mating with a chosen group of young men from the armed forces and the SS. Dr. Hagen, head of the Lebensborn camp, becomes attracted to Doris Korff, although emotions are not supposed to affect the selection of mates. Before her scheduled mating, Doris falls in love with Klaus Steinbach, a lieutenant who escaped execution for his anti-Nazi sentiments by assuming the identity of an SS man killed in an air raid. Appalled by the cold-blooded mating practices and the prospect of forced breeding with Dr. Hagen, Doris attempts to escape to Switzerland with Klaus, but he is shot and killed. Temporarily spared because she is pregnant, Doris is sentenced to die after the birth of her baby. Later, Doris discovers that her new-born baby has been killed. During an air raid, she manages to escape from the camp. *Nazis. Scientists. Eugenics. Imposture. Pregnancy. World War II. Germany—History—Third Reich. SS.*

Note: Released in West Germany in Jan 1961 as *Lebensborn*; running time: 88 min.

LE ORE DELL'AMORE *see* **THE HOURS OF LOVE**

LOS ORGANILLOS *see* **THE UNINHIBITED**

THE ORGANIZER (France/Italy/Yugoslavia)   **F6.3664**

Lux Film–Vides–Méditerranée Cinéma–Avala Film. *Dist* Continental Distributing, Inc. 6 May 1964 [New York opening]. Sd; b&w. 35mm. 126 min.

Prod Franco Cristaldi. *Dir* Mario Monicelli. *Story & Screenplay* Age & Scarpelli, Mario Monicelli. *Photog* Giuseppe Rotunno. *Camera* Giuseppe Maccari. *Art Dir* Mario Garbuglia. *Film Ed* Ruggero Mastroianni. *Mus* Carlo Rustichelli. *Mus Cond* Pierluigi Urbini. *Sd* Adriano Taloni. *Asst Dir* Renzo Marignano, Fernando Morandi, Bata Stojanović. *Prod Supv* Giorgio Adriani, Fausto Lupi. *Cost* Piero Tosi. *English Subtitl* Herman G. Weinberg.

Cast: Marcello Mastroianni *(Professor Sinigaglia)*, Renato Salvatori *(Raoul)*, Annie Girardot *(Niobe)*, Gabriella Giorgelli *(Adele)*, Bernard Blier *(Martinetti)*, Folco Lulli *(Pautasso)*, François Périer *(Maestro Di Meo)*, Vittorio Sanipoli *(Baudet)*, Giuseppe Cadeo *(Cenerone)*, Elvira Tonelli *(Cesarina)*, Giampiero Albertini *(Porro)*, Pippo Starnazza *(Bergamasco)*, Pippo Mosca *(Cerioni)*, Franco Ciolli *(Omero)*, Raffaella Carrà *(Bianca)*, Antonio Casa Monica *(Arró)*, Enzo Casini *(Antonio)*, Kenneth Kove *(Luigi)*, Mario Pisu *(manager)*, Gino Manganello *(Uncle Spartaco)*, Edda Ferronao *(Maria)*, Anna Di Silvio *(Gesummina)*, Antonio Di Silvio *(Pietrino)*, Sara Simoni *(Cenerone's wife)*, Piero Traiannoni *(bookkeeper)*, Anna Glori *(Signora Cravetto)*, Bruno Scipioni, Anselmo Silvio, Giuseppe Marchetti, Fred Borgognoni, Giulio Bosetti.

Drama. At the end of the 19th century, employees of a textile mill in Turin are working a 14-hour day. When a worker is injured due to carelessness fostered by overlong hours, Pautasso, Martinetti, and Cesarina petition the management for improved conditions, but they are brushed off by Baudet, a foreman. It is later decided that all workers will leave an hour early in protest, but when Pautasso gives the signal, Baudet forces the workers to remain. Pautasso is suspended for 2 weeks without pay, and others are fined. Professor Sinigaglia, a political refugee, arrives in Turin to stay with schoolteacher Maestro Di Meo. He outlines a strike, and the workers agree to the conditions. The only concession management will make, however, is the lifting of Pautasso's suspension and cancellation of the fines. The strike continues and strikebreakers are called in; when the workers meet them at the train, violence erupts and Pautasso is killed. The incident is reported by the press, and the police commissioner orders the strikebreakers out of Turin. The mill owner, realizing that he may have to concede, pressures the police into ordering the arrest of Sinigaglia, but the professor is hidden by Niobe, a prostitute. When Baudet convinces Martinetti that a return to work would be a sign of strength, Sinigaglia comes out of hiding and rallies the workers. They march to the mill where the militia fires on them and kills a 15-year-old striker. The professor is arrested, and the workers return to their jobs. Although nothing is won, the united strength of the workers has been felt for the first time. *Mill workers. Factory management. Labor agitators. Political refugees. Police. Prostitutes. Strikes. Mills. Turin.*

Note: Opened in Rome in Oct 1963 as *I compagni*; running time: 130 min. French title: *Les camarades.*

ORGASMO see PARANOIA

THE ORGY AT LIL'S PLACE   F6.3665

Extraordinary Films. *Dist* William Mishkin. 25 Dec **1963** [Boston opening]. Sd; b&w with col sequences (Eastman Color). 35mm. 77 min.

Pres by William Mishkin. *Prod-Dir* J. Nehemiah. *Exec Prod* William Mishkin. *Scen* Allan Naidob. *Story* Neil Lewis. *Dir Photog* Ben Zvi.

Cast: Carrie Knudsen *(Ann)*, Bob Curtis *(Charles)*, June Ashlyn *(Sally)*, John Lyon *(Bob)*, Myles Stuart *(Mark)*, Terri Powers *(Lil)*, Karen Lynn, Anita Ventura, Don Paradise, Chase Decker, Joyce Bonner, Princess Zobeide.

Melodrama. Ann, an aspiring actress, joins her sister Sally in New York City. To earn money for dance lessons, Sally poses in the nude for art classes; she meets Bob, a young artist, and they become engaged. Bob introduces Ann to his friend Charles, a writer, and the two are immediately attracted. Ann eventually decides, however, that Charles is a confirmed bachelor, and she concentrates on establishing her career. She makes the rounds of theatrical agencies without success; in desperation, she answers an advertisement for a photographer's model and meets Mark, a smooth-talking agent who devotes his energies to finding her jobs. Her poses become increasingly revealing, but she continues to be treated with respect. Mark eventually presents Ann with an invitation to a party given by the influential Lil Duncan, who is actually a procuress. Lil's affair degenerates into an orgy, and Mark attempts to rape Ann, but she escapes just in time. Sally and Bob are married; Charles' novel is published at last, and he proposes to Ann, whose happiness is now complete. *Actors. Sisters. Dancers. Models. Artists. Authors. Talent agents. Pimps. Courtship. Employment—Women. Nudity. Orgies. Pornography. New York City.*

Note: Also known as *At Lil's Place.*

ORGY GIRLS '69   F6.3666

Kirt Films International. *Dist* Alexander Beck Productions. 20 Nov **1968** [New York showing]. Sd; b&w. 35mm. 80 min.

Prod Leonard Kirtman. *Dir-Writ* Robert Canton. *Narr* Philip Burrell. *Dir Photog* Moe Odegaard. *2d Camera* David Howe. *Film Ed* Robert Canton. *Mus & Songs* Harmon Thornbury, The Ends and Outs. *Sd Rec* Fred Turner. *Prod Asst* Burt Fox. *Script Cont* Francis Baker. *Cost* Frank Lewis. *Makeup* Bill Pinkney. *Grip* Carl Vinas, Grant Willis. *Gaffer* Sam Rider.

Cast—"The Housewife": Sandra Harris *(Abigail)*, Sam Hart *(salesman)*.

Cast—"Roommates": Jane Austin *(Jane)*, Mary Stacy *(Ann)*, Frank Rogers *(Harry)*.

Cast—"The Sensualists": Marilyn Stevens *(Tia)*, Rochelle Francis *(Marilyn)*.

Cast—"The Fashion Model": Steve Louis *(Memming, the photographer)*, Lois Wingate *(model)*.

Cast—"The Hippie": Gale Farrell *(Mary Ellen)*, Frank Simpson, [2] *(father)*.

Comedy-drama. This is a five-part film. THE HOUSEWIFE: A door-to-door salesman makes love to a lonely housewife. ROOMMATES: A woman and her date make love and awaken the woman's roommate; she joins in their lovemaking. THE SENSUALISTS: Two women make love. THE FASHION MODEL: A fashion model discovers that there is more to posing in the nude than taking one's clothes off. THE HIPPIE: A hippie smokes marijuana with a man who wants to take her away from the bohemian life. *Salesmen. Housewives. Roommates. Hippies. Models. Troilism. Lesbianism. Seduction. Marijuana.*

Note: Working title: *Girls of the City*. Alternative title: *"O" Girls 1969;* may also be known as *Orgy Girls.*

ORGY IN THE OZARKS   F6.3667

MJ Productions. *Dist* MarJon Film Distributors. ca **1970**. Sd; col. 16mm. ca60 min.

Comedy-drama. Two families in the Ozarks, the Humpers and the Comes, decide to end the 100-year-long feud which has reduced their surviving numbers to one brother and two sisters on each side. During their celebration supper party, they attempt to make up for all the time lost in fighting each other. The sisters become sexually intimate and are interrupted by the brothers, who first attempt to separate their kin but then decide to join them for an orgy. *Feuds. Incest. Lesbianism. Group sex. Mountain life. Ozarks.*

ORGY OF BLOOD see BRIDES OF BLOOD

ORGY OF THE DEAD   F6.3668

Astra Productions. *Dist* F. O. G. Distributors, Crest Film Distributors. 1 Jun **1965** [Atlanta opening]. Sd; col. 35mm (Astravision). 82 min.

Prod-Dir A. C. Stephen. *Screenplay* Edward Davis Wood, Jr. *Dir Photog* Robert Caramico. *Art Dir* Robert Lathrop. *Post Prod* Don Davis. *Choreog* Mark Desmond. *Cost* Robert Darieux.

Cast: Criswell *(The Emperor)*, Pat Barringer *(Shirley)*, Fawn Silver *(Black Ghoul)*, William Bates *(Bob)*, Louis Ojena *(The Mummy)*, John Andrews *(The Wolfman)*, Rod Lindeman *(giant)*, John Bealy *(detective)*, Arlene Spooner *(nurse)*.

Cast—Dancers: Pat Barringer *(Gold)*, Colleen O'Brien *(The Street Walker)*, Barbra Norton *(The Skeleton)*, Mickey Jines *(Hawaiian)*, Nadejda Dobrev *(The Slave)*, Dene Starnes *(The Zombie)*, Texas Starr *(The Cat)*, Bunny Glaser *(Indian)*, René De Beau *(Seven Veils)*, Stephanie Jones *(The Skull)*.

Melodrama. Source: Edward Davis Wood, Jr., *Orgy of the Dead* (a novel, publication undetermined). On a stormy night, a young writer and his fiancée travel through the mountains in search of an ancient cemetery where they hope to find material for a new novel. Knocked unconscious when their car hits a lightning-felled tree, they awaken to find the cemetery illuminated by the light of a full moon. They stumble upon a strange rite: The Master of the Dead and The Princess of Darkness have arisen from their graves to judge the newly dead, who dance naked before their throne. The Master orders the young couple bound to ceremonial posts, so that they may watch as he judges the female sinners: The Main Street Prowler, who lured men to her apartment to rob and murder them, is now condemned to eternal punishment; The Slave Girl, once a princess, is beaten by those who had been her slaves; The Bride who murdered her husband must now reside eternally with his skeleton; The Indian Girl who tossed her lovers into the flames must leap into flames throughout eternity; The Island Girl, who used her beloved snakes to dispose of her lovers, is restricted to the companionship of snakes; a woman who loved cats is condemned to remain a cat forever; and one who worshiped gold is turned into a gold statue. As The Princess of Darkness prepares to take the writer's fiancée for her slave, the morning sun returns the dead creatures to dust, and the young couple are rescued from the wreckage of their car. *Authors. Prostitutes. Brides. Royalty. Murder. Rites and ceremonies. Slavery. Death. Demonology. Cemeteries. Gold. Automobile accidents. Snakes. Cats.*

ORGY OF THE GOLDEN NUDES see HONEYMOON OF HORROR

ORIENT BY NIGHT (Italy)   F6.3669

Cineproduzioni Associate. *Dist* Filmarco. 27 Dec **1963** [New York State license]. Sd; col (Eastmancolor). 35mm (Supertotalscope). 98 min.

Dir Roberto Montero.

Documentary. The world of the cabaret is explored, with particular attention given to oriental acts. *Entertainers. Orientals. Cabarets.*

Note: Opened in Rome in Nov 1962 as *Notti calde d'Oriente*; running time: 103 min. Filmarco, an Italian distributor, may be associated with U. S. distribution only as an importer.

ORO PER I CESARI *see* **GOLD FOR THE CAESARS**

L'ORRIBILE SEGRETO DEL DR. HICHCOCK *see* **THE HORRIBLE DR. HICHCOCK**

OSAKA-JO MONOGATARI *see* **DAREDEVIL IN THE CASTLE**

THE OSCAR   F6.3670

Greene-Rouse Productions. *For* Embassy Pictures. *Dist* Embassy Pictures. 15 Feb **1966** [Los Angeles opening]. Sd; col (PathéColor). 35mm. 119 min.

Pres by Joseph E. Levine. *Prod* Clarence Greene. *Exec Prod* Joseph E. Levine. *Dir* Russell Rouse. *Screenplay* Harlan Ellison, Russell Rouse, Clarence Greene. *Photog* Joseph Ruttenberg. *Art Dir* Hal Pereira, Arthur Lonergan. *Set Decor* Robert R. Benton, James Payne. *Film Ed* Chester W. Schaeffer. *Mus* Percy Faith. *Song:* "Thanks for the Memory" Leo Robin, Ralph Rainger. *Song:* "All the Way" Sammy Cahn, James Van Heusen. *Mus Supv* Irving Friedman. *Orch* Leo Shuken, Jack Hayes. *Choreog* Stephen Peck. *Sd* Harry Lindgren, John Wilkinson. *Asst Dir* Dick Moder. *Prod Mgr* Frank Caffey. *Unit Prod Mgr* Maurie M. Suess. *Gowns* Edith Head. *Mr. Boyd's Wardrobe* Robert Magahay. *Women's Wardrobe* Glenita Dineen. *Makeup* Wally Westmore. *Hairstyles* Nellie Manley. *Sp Photog Eff* Paul K. Lerpae. *Proc Photog* Farciot Edouart. *Dial Coach* Leon Charles.

Cast: Stephen Boyd (*Frank Fane*), Elke Sommer (*Kay Bergdahl*), Milton Berle (*Kappy Kapstetter*), Eleanor Parker (*Sophie Cantaro*), Joseph Cotten (*Kenneth H. Regan*), Jill St. John (*Laurel Scott*), Tony Bennett (*Hymie Kelly*), Edie Adams (*Trina Yale*), Ernest Borgnine (*Barney Yale*), Ed Begley (*Grobard*), Walter Brennan (*Orrin C. Quentin*), Broderick Crawford (*sheriff*), James Dunn (*network executive*), Peter Lawford (*Steve Marks*), Jack Soo (*Sam*), Jean Hale (*Cheryl Barker*), Edith Head, Bob Hope, Hedda Hopper, Merle Oberon, Frank Sinatra, Nancy Sinatra (*themselves*), Eddie Ryder, Chris Alcaide, John Dennis, Peter Leeds, John Holland, Jean Bartel, John Crowther.

Drama. Source: Richard Sale, *The Oscar* (New York, 1963). On Oscar night, nominee Frank Fane anticipates he will be the winner of the award for best actor. His longtime friend, Hymie Kelly, reflects on Fane's rise to fame. In flashback, Fane's career unrolls from its tawdry beginnings: Small-time cabaret performers Frank Fane, Hymie Kelly, and Laurel Scott run afoul of the law and are falsely arrested. They drift to New York, where the ruthlessly ambitious Frank rejects Laurel for a beautiful dress designer, Kay Bergdahl, unaware that Laurel is pregnant by him. Frank's good looks and fast temper arouse the interest of drama coach Sophie Cantaro, who gets him a small acting part and offers to help launch his career. Persuading her agent, Kappy Kapstetter, to take Frank as a client, she manages to get Frank a Hollywood contract with producer Kenneth H. Regan. Frank plunges into a life of extravagance and publicity seeking. He sends for his old friend Hymie to serve as companion and public relations man and asks him about Laurel. Hymie tells him that he married her and she died. During his drive for fame, Frank pauses long enough to arrange for Kay's promotion to studio designer and then to marry her in Tijuana. Before long, Frank's behavior has made him countless enemies and has caused him to become a boxoffice failure despite the critical acclaim given his most recent picture. Dropped by Regan, Frank is promoted by Kapstetter for a TV pilot but walks out on the project when he learns that he has been nominated for an Oscar. Determined to win the award, Frank hires a private detective, Barney Yale, to leak the story of his past arrest to the press, in hopes of turning Academy voter sympathy to himself; but his scheme backfires as Yale tries to blackmail him. Abandoned by everyone, Frank attends the ceremonies alone. Emcee Bob Hope calls Merle Oberon to present the best actor award. Shattered, Frank rises from his seat when the actress reads the name of Frank Sinatra as the winner. *Actors. Drama coaches. Couturiers. Talent agents. Motion picture producers. Publicists. Detectives. Ambition. Blackmail. Motion pictures. New York City. Tijuana (Mexico). Hollywood. Academy of Motion Picture Arts and Sciences—Awards.*

Note: Additional song: "Carmen Carmelo" (traditional). Footage of actual Academy Awards presentations is included in the film.

OŠETŘOVNA *see* **SIGN OF THE VIRGIN**

OSS 117 FURIA A BAHÍA *see* **OSS 117—MISSION FOR A KILLER**

OSS 117 MINACCIA BANGKOK *see* **SHADOW OF EVIL**

OSS 117—MISSION FOR A KILLER (France/Italy)   F6.3671

P. A. C.–P. C. M.–DA. MA. Film. *Dist* Embassy Pictures. 12 Oct **1966** [New York opening]. Sd; col (Eastmancolor, print by Pathé). 35mm (Franscope). 84 min.

Prod Paul Cadéac. *Dir* André Hunebelle. *2d Unit Dir* Jacques Besnard. *Screenplay* André Hunebelle, Jean Halain, Pierre Foucaud. *Photog* Marcel

Grignon. *Art Dir* Paul-Louis Boutié. *Film Ed* Jean Feyte. *Mus* Michel Magne. *Sd* René Forget. *Prod Mgr* Cyril Grize. *Cost* Jo Ranzato.

Cast: Frederick Stafford (*OSS 117*), Mylène Demongeot (*Anna Maria Sulza*), Raymond Pellegrin (*Leandro*), Perrette Pradier (*Consuela 1*), Annie Andersson (*Consuela 2*), François Maistre (*Carlos*), Jacques Riberolles (*Miguel*), Yves Furet (*Clark*), Guy Delorme (*Karl*), Jean-Pierre Janic (*Ludwig*), Claude Carliez (*Thomas Ellis*).

Adventure melodrama. Source: Jean Bruce, *Le dernier quart d'heure* (Paris, 1955). Secret agent OSS 117 is sent to Rio de Janeiro to investigate a series of explosions that killed several government leaders. The puzzling aspect of the case is that the crimes were committed by trusted assistants who also died in the blasts. OSS 117 arrives for a meeting with Thomas Ellis, chief of special agents, and is greeted by a woman claiming to be Consuela, Ellis' secretary. After escaping from a trap set by the imposter Consuela, 117 learns that Ellis has been hospitalized from a car explosion injury. At the hospital 117 meets Anna Maria, a friend of the wounded man, but before the two can speak to Ellis, he is murdered on the operating table by a man disguised as a surgeon. The secret agent and Anna Maria then find evidence of a plant which induces a hypnotic trance. Realizing that this was the method used to make the assistants kill the government leaders, 117 and Anna Maria go to Bahía to contact a tribe of Indians who extract the drug from the plant. Leandro, a friend of the tribe, offers to take them to the native village, but instead he takes them to the secret headquarters of an international organization planning world domination through use of the drug. When 117 and Anna Maria are taken prisoner because they refuse to join the conspiracy, Leandro, who is a member of the organization, has qualms of conscience and sends Brazilian Paratroopers to rescue 117 and Anna Maria and break up the organization's headquarters. *Secret agents. Surgeons. Indians of South America. Imposture. Assassination. Conspiracy. Drugs. Rio de Janeiro. Bahía. Explosions.*

Note: Location scenes filmed in Brazil. Opened in Paris in Jul 1965 as *Furia à Bahia pour OSS 117*; running time: 110 min; in Rome in Oct 1965 as *OSS 117 furia a Bahía*; running time: 100 min.

OSTŘE SLEDOVANÉ VLAKY *see* **CLOSELY WATCHED TRAINS**

OSTRVA *see* **SEDUCTION BY THE SEA**

OSWALT KOLLE: DAS WUNDER DER LIEBE—SEXUALITÄT IN DER EHE *see* **THE MIRACLE OF LOVE**

OTCHIY DOM *see* **A HOME FOR TANYA**

OTETS SOLDATA *see* **FATHER OF A SOLDIER**

OTHELLO (Great Britain)   F6.3672

B. H. E. Productions. *Dist* Warner Bros. Pictures. 15 Dec **1965** [Los Angeles opening; c31 Dec 1965; LP35739]. Sd; col (Technicolor). 35mm (Panavision). 166 min.

Prod Anthony Havelock-Allan, John Brabourne. *Assoc Prod* Richard Goodwin. *Dir* Stuart Burge. *Stage Dir for National Theatre of Great Britain* John Dexter. *Dir Photog* Geoffrey Unsworth. *Camera* John Harris, Cecil Cooney, Peter Allwork. *Film Art Dir* William Kellner. *Asst Art Dir* Peter Howitt. *Stage Dsgn for National Theatre of Great Britain* Jocelyn Herbert. *Film Ed* Richard Marden. *Mus* Richard Hampton. *Sd Mix* John Cox, Dickie Bird. *Asst Dir* Christopher Dryhurst. *Prod Mgr* Julian Mackintosh, Margaret Unsworth. *Cost for National Theatre of Great Britain* Jocelyn Herbert. *Wardrobe* William Walsh. *Makeup* George Partleton, R. L. Alexander. *Hairdresser* A. G. Scott. *Fight Arr* William Hobbs.

Cast: Laurence Olivier (*Othello*), Frank Finlay (*Iago*), Maggie Smith (*Desdemona*), Robert Lang (*Roderigo*), Anthony Nicholls (*Brabantio*), Roy Holder (*clown*), Derek Jacobi (*Cassio*), Joyce Redman (*Emilia*), Sheila Reid (*Bianca*), Harry Lomax (*Duke of Venice*), Michael Turner (*Gratiano*), Kenneth Mackintosh (*Lodovico*), Terence Knapp (*Duke's officer*), Keith Marsh (*senator*), Tom Kempinski (*sailor*), David Hargreaves, Malcolm Terris (*senate officers*), Nicholas Edmett (*messenger*), Edward Hardwicke (*Montano*), William Hobbs, Trevor Martin, Christopher Timothy (*Cypriot officers*), Petronella Barker, Janie Booth, Andrew Bradford, Peter Cellier, Nicholas Edmett, Mike Gambon, Reginald Green, Peter John, Lewis Jones, John McEnery, Bruce Purchase, Dan Meaden, Malcolm Reynolds, Robert Russell, Clive Rust (*senators, soldiers, Cypriots*).

Tragedy. Source: William Shakespeare, *Othello*. A film version of the National Theatre of Great Britain stage production, which opened in London on 21 Apr 1964. *Moors. Nobility. Soldiers. Perfidy. Jealousy. Ambition. Murder. Suicide. Miscegenation. Fatherhood. Venice. Cyprus.*

Note: London opening: May 1966.

OTHELLO *see* **BALLET OF OTHELLO**

THE OTHER SIDE OF BONNIE AND CLYDE F6.3673
Dist Dal-Art Films. 22 Aug **1968** [San Antonio, Texas, opening]. Sd; b&w. 35mm. 75 min.

Prod-Dir Larry Buchanan.

Cast: Jo Enterentree *(Bonnie Parker)*, Lucky Mosley *(Clyde Barrow)*, Floyd Hamilton, Mrs. Frank Hamer, Frank Hamer, Jr. *(themselves)*, Burl Ives *(narrator)*.

Biographical drama. The story of Bonnie Parker and Clyde Barrow, told in documentary style, includes actual footage taken by the police after the couple was killed, scenes of Barrow gang member Floyd Hamilton being questioned, and scenes of Texas Ranger Frank Hamer and his family. *Gangs. Bonnie Parker. Clyde Barrow. Floyd Hamilton. Texas Rangers.*

Note: Filmed on location in Texas and Louisiana. Jo Enterentree and Lucky Mosley are pseudonyms for Bonnie Shefield and Sonny Wayne, respectively.

OTHER VOICES F6.3674
Dist Dorowite Corp. 26 Jan **1970** [New York opening]. Sd; b&w. 35mm. 100 min.

Prod-Dir David H. Sawyer. *Exec Prod* Mary W. Ellis. *Co-dir* Robert Elfstrom. *Photog* Robert Elfstrom. *Film Ed* J. Michaels.

Participants: Albert M. Honig, Emil Ondra, Dan Lieberman, Sylvia Honig.

Documentary. This study of the Delaware Valley Mental Health Foundation at Doylestown, Pennsylvania, deals specifically with a handful of patients. There is a close examination of Foundation Director Dr. Albert M. Honig's method of treatment, known as "reality confrontation," by which a doctor will use any manner of physical or verbal prodding, from wrestling and hugging to screaming and bullying, to arouse the patient from his or her psychotic withdrawal. The patients live with their respective doctors in the therapists' homes as part of therapy. Therapy sessions are employed at the institution, and these sessions become, at times, highly demonstrative and violent. Dr. Honig claims no status as a miracle worker: one young boy appears headed toward a healthier state, but he suddenly reverts to former tendencies and commits suicide; Peter and Pat, two other patients, come very close to being cured of their mental disturbances. *Mental illness. Psychiatry. Hospitals. Delaware Valley Mental Health Foundation.*

Note: Filmed in 16mm; original running time: 103 min.

OTKLONENIE *see* DETOUR

OTLEY (Great Britain) F6.3675
Open Road Films-Bruce Cohn Curtis Films-Highroad Productions. *Dist* Columbia Pictures. 11 Mar **1969** [New York opening; c1 Mar 1969; LP36586]. Sd; col (Pathé). 35mm. 90 min.

Pres by Carl Foreman. *Prod* Bruce Cohn Curtis. *Dir* Dick Clement. *Screenplay* Ian La Frenais, Dick Clement. *Photog* Austin Dempster. *Adtl Photog* Brian West. *Camera Op* Freddie Cooper. *Art Dir* Carmen Dillon. *Asst Art Dir* Paul Huson, Russell Hagg. *Titl Dsgn* Paul Huson. *Film Ed* Richard Best. *Asst Ed* Denis Whitehouse. *Mus Comp & Cond* Stanley Myers. *Mus:* "Homeless Bones" Stanley Myers. *Lyr & Sung by* Don Partridge. *Sd Rec* Peter Davies, John Cox. *Sd Ed* William Trent. *Asst Dir* Dominic Fulford. *Prod Mgr* Basil Rayburn. *Loc Mgr* Richard Gill. *Cont* Eileen Head. *Wardrobe Supv* Jean Fairlie. *Mr. Courtenay's "CIA" Suit* Cecil Gee of London. *Makeup* Michael Morris. *Hairdresser* Joyce James. *Casting Dir* Irene Lamb.

Cast: Tom Courtenay *(Gerald Arthur Otley)*, Romy Schneider *(Imogen)*, Alan Badel *(Hadrian)*, James Villiers *(Hendrickson)*, Leonard Rossiter *(Johnston)*, James Bolam *(Albert)*, Fiona Lewis *(Lin)*, Freddie Jones *(Proudfoot)*, James Cossins *(Jeffcock)*, James Maxwell *(Rollo)*, Edward Hardwicke *(Lambert)*, Ronald Lacey *(Curtis)*, Phillyda Law *(Jean)*, Geoffrey Bayldon *(Hewitt)*, Frank Middlemas *(Bruce)*, Damian Harris *(Miles)*, Robert Brownjohn *(Paul)*, Maureen Toal *(landlady)*, Barry Fantoni *(Larry)*, Bernard Sharpe *(Tony)*, Paul Angelis *(constable)*, David Kernan *(ground steward)*, Sheila Steafel *(ground stewardess)*, Katherine Parr *(newsagent)*, Katherine Helm *(dietician)*, Ron Owen *(hotel waiter)*, Stella Tanner *(traffic warden)*, Jonathan Cecil *(young man at party)*, Georgina Simpson *(young girl at party)*, Norman Shelley *(1st businessman)*, John Savident *(2d businessman)*, Ken Parry *(3d businessman)*, Robin Askwith *(1st kid)*, Kevin Bennett *(2d kid)*, Kenneth Cranham *(3d kid)*, Robert Gillespie *(policeman)*, Donald McKillop *(police driver)*, The Herd, Jimmy Young, Pete Murray.

Comedy. Source: Martin Waddell, *Otley* (London, 1966). Lacking a place to sleep, Gerald Arthur Otley, an easygoing drifter who dabbles in petty thievery and womanizing, beds down at the flat of a friend who, unknown to him, is involved in smuggling state secrets. During the night, the friend is murdered, and Otley, suffering from a dreadful hangover, wakes up 2 days later in the middle of an airfield. After returning to London and learning that he is wanted by the police, he is kidnaped, interrogated, and beaten up by Hendrickson, an arrogant bully, and Imogen, a beautiful woman. They release Otley, and he falls into the hands of an effeminate spy, Philip Proudfoot, who turns him over to

still another agent, Johnston, for extermination. Otley, it seems, lifted a tobacco holder from his murdered friend, unaware that it contained a tape-recorded message which is wanted by all of his captors. Baffled, Otley turns himself over to the police in the hope of finding a little peace and safety. But Imogen has him released and explains to him that she is a member of Sir Alec Hadrian's Parliament-sanctioned counter-spy organization. Following several more murders and aborted blackmail schemes, Otley is sent to a health farm to trap a treacherous double agent. Although Hendrickson is suspected, Sir Alec is eventually exposed as the true villain. No longer of use to either spy faction, the battered and confused Otley looks with disgust at his brief fling at espionage and returns happily to his Soho life of petty thievery—and the comfort of a Thames houseboat belonging to his girl friend, Lin. *Philanderers. Thieves. Secret agents. Police. Espionage. Murder. Kidnaping. Blackmail. Effeminacy. Health resorts. London. Great Britain—Intelligence service. Chases. Documentation.*

Note: Released in Great Britain in 1968; location scenes filmed in and around London.

OTOKO TAI OTOKO *see* MAN AGAINST MAN

OTTO E MEZZO *see* 8 1/2

OUR MAN FLINT F6.3676
Twentieth Century-Fox Film Corp. 19 Jan **1966** [Philadelphia opening; c31 Dec 1965; LP32292]. Sd (Westrex); col (DeLuxe). 35mm (CinemaScope). 107 min.

Prod Saul David. *Dir* Daniel Mann. *Sp Action Seq Dir* Buzz Henry. *Screenplay* Hal Fimberg, Ben Starr. *Story* Hal Fimberg. *Dir Photog* Daniel L. Fapp. *Camera Op* Paul Lockwood. *Asst Camera* Hugh Crawford. *Art Dir* Jack Martin Smith, Ed Graves. *Set Decor* Walter M. Scott, Raphael Bretton. *Prod Illus* Fred Harpman. *Film Ed* William Reynolds. *Asst Ed* William Navarro. *Mus* Jerry Goldsmith. *Orch* Arthur Morton. *Sd* Carlton W. Faulkner, Elmer Raguse, Harry Proodian. *Boom Op* Frank McWhorter. *Asst Dir* David Silver, Al Murphy. *Unit Prod Mgr* Saul Wurtzel. *Script Supv* June Santantonio. *Cost Dsgn* Ray Aghayan. *Wardrobe* Ed Wynigear, Willie Mae Neal. *Makeup* Ben Nye. *Hairstyles* Margaret Donovan. *Sp Photog Eff* L. B. Abbott, Howard Lydecker, Emil Kosa, Jr. *Still Photog* James Mitchell. *Prop* Allen Levine, Dennis Parrish. *Gaffer* Jack Brown. *Grip* Walter Fitchman.

Cast: James Coburn *(Derek Flint)*, Lee J. Cobb *(Cramden)*, Gila Golan *(Gila)*, Edward Mulhare *(Malcolm Rodney)*, Benson Fong *(Dr. Schneider)*, Gianna Serra *(Gina)*, Sigrid Valdis *(Anna)*, Shelby Grant *(Leslie)*, Helen Funai *(Sakito)*, Michael St. Clair *(Gruber)*, Rhys Williams *(Dr. Krupov)*, Russ Conway *(American general)*, Ena Hartman *(WAC)*, Bill Walker *(American diplomat)*, Peter Brocco *(Dr. Wu)*.

Action comedy. At a subterranean secret meeting, the international delegates of ZOWIE (Zonal Organization World Intelligence Espionage) learn that a mysterious organization called GALAXY is planning to rule the world by controlling the weather. Computers indicate that the man best qualified to prevent such a catastrophe is Derek Flint, an irresponsible but expert secret agent who lives in luxurious bliss with four exotic international beauties. At first Flint is reluctant to accept the assignment, but he changes his mind when several murder attempts are made not only upon him but also on Cramden, the head of ZOWIE. Using as his only weapon a cigarette lighter with 83 functions, Flint learns that the three mad scientists heading GALAXY are operating out of Marseilles. Once there, he is almost killed by Gila, a GALAXY agent. He trails her to Rome but is captured and taken to GALAXY headquarters on a remote volcanic island. Playing dead, he learns that his four exotic roommates are also captives and that GALAXY has demanded that the entire world surrender or be destroyed within one hour. After killing a guard and switching clothing, Flint makes a quick tour of the electric weather controlling plant and formulates a plan of action. Although he is once more captured by the three scientists, he again escapes and makes a desperate attempt to rescue his four roommates and Gila, by now among the women in love with him. He disrupts the electrical equipment, saves the women and rides them to safety down a waterfall as the entire island and its personnel are blown up. *Secret agents. Playboys. Scientists. Hostages. Roommates. Megalomania. Weather. Computers. Waterfalls. Islands. Marseilles. Rome. Explosions.*

OUR MAN IN MARRAKESH *see* BANG! BANG! YOU'RE DEAD!

OUR MAN IN MARRAKESH *see* THAT MAN GEORGE

OUR MOTHER'S HOUSE (United States/Great Britain) F6.3677
Heron Film Productions-Filmways, Inc. *Dist* Metro-Goldwyn-Mayer, Inc. 9 Oct **1967** [New York opening; c29 Sep 1967; LP34779]. Sd; col (Metrocolor). 35mm. 105 min.

Exec Prod Martin Ransohoff. *Prod-Dir* Jack Clayton. *Assoc Prod* Roy Baird. *Screenplay* Jeremy Brooks, Haya Harareet. *Dir Photog* Larry Pizer. *Camera Op* Denis Lewiston. *Camera Asst* Ken Goodman, David MacDonald, photog.

Camera Grip Dick Savery. *Art Dir* Reece Pemberton. *Set Decor* Ian Whittaker. *Film Ed* Tom Priestley. *Asst Ed* Rex Pyke. *Mus Comp & Cond* Georges Delerue. *Solo Piano* Peter Katin. *Sd Rec* Ken Ritchie. *Sd Ed* Terry Rawlings. *Dub Mix* Hugh Strain. *Asst Sd Ed* Hazel Harste. *Boom Op* John Salter. *1st & 2nd Asst Dir* Claude Watson, Grania O'Shannon. *Script Ed* Jeanie Sims. *Cont* Pamela Davies. *Asst to the Prod* Roger Peek. *Wardrobe* Sue Yelland. *Makeup* Bill Lodge. *Hairstyles* Olga Angelinetta. *Constr Mgr* Terry Apsey. *Ch Electrn* Bernie Prentice. *Floor Props* John Graham, prop, Terry Barrett.

Cast: Dirk Bogarde (*Charlie Hook*), Margaret Brooks (*Elsa Hook*), Pamela Franklin (*Diana Hook*), Louis Sheldon Williams (*Hubert Hook*), John Gugolka (*Dunstan Hook*), Mark Lester (*Jiminee Hook*), Sarah Nicholls (*Gerty Hook*), Gustav Henry (*Willy Hook*), Parnham Wallace (*Louis*), Yootha Joyce (*Mrs. Quayle*), Claire Davidson (*Miss Bailey*), Anthony Nicholls (*Mr. Halbert*), Annette Carell (*mother*), Gerald Sim (*bank clerk*), Edina Ronay (*Doreen*), Diana Ashley (*girl friend*), Garfield Morgan (*Mr. Moley*), Faith Kent (*woman client*), John Arnatt (*man client*), Jack Silk (*motorcyclist*).

Melodrama. Source: Julian Gloag, *Our Mother's House* (New York, 1963). Because their mother has long been bedridden, the seven Hook children have learned to take care of themselves in their old Victorian house. Never having known a father, their whole existence centers around "mothertime"—an evening visit to their mother's room for Bible reading and family guidance. Then one night their mother dies. Mingled with grief is their fear of the outside world and of being sent to an orphanage. Unable to bear a separation from their mother, they secretly bury her in the garden and set up a shrine in the backyard shed. After dismissing the cleaning woman, they resume their everyday habits, continuing to attend school and running the household on their own, meeting expenses by forging their mother's signature on her annuity checks. Each night they gather in the shed for "mothertime," which now has become a rite in which one of the girls, Diana, communes with the spirit of the mother "who is always with us." Eventually they adopt a schoolmate, Louis, who has run away from home, but the youngster's absence precipitates a visit from a schoolteacher, who almost discovers their secret. The danger is averted by the arrival of their father, Charlie, who has been summoned by the oldest boy, Hubert. A charming opportunist, Charlie quickly captivates the children; before long he has squandered most of their savings, accustomed himself to bringing home women at late hours, and even made plans to sell the house. One day he commits the ultimate sin by attempting to destroy their mother's shrine, and the children finally turn on him. To their horror, he confronts them with the knowledge that they are all illegitimate, the result of their mother's promiscuity. Upon hearing the truth about their beloved, pious mother, Diana seizes a fireplace poker and strikes Charlie a fatal blow. Now that their world of innocence is destroyed, the seven youngsters leave the home of their childhood. *Children. Orphans. Invalids. Housemaids. Opportunists. Family life. Illegitimacy. Forgery. Death. Promiscuity. Patricide. Spiritualism.*

Note: Location scenes filmed in Croydon, England.

OUR SILENT LOVE (Japan)   F6.3678

Tokyo Eiga Co. *Dist* Toho Co. Jun **1969** [Los Angeles showing]. Sd; b&w. 35mm (Tohoscope). 114 min.

Exec Prod Sanezumi Fujimoto, Hideyuki Shiino. *Dir-Writ* Zenzo Matsuyama. *Photog* Kozo Okazaki. *Mus* Yuro Funamura.

Cast: Kinya Kitaoji, Keiju Kobayashi, Yoko Naito, Mayumi Ozora, Hideko Takamine, Izumi Hara, Daisuke Kato, Nobuko Otowa, Ryo Tamura.

Domestic drama. Young Ichiro Katayama finds that he cannot get a good job because he is the son of deafmute parents, even though he is healthy and well-educated. At a bar, Ichiro nearly begins a fight when the hostess taunts his father, but Sakai, a factory owner, intervenes and offers Ichiro a job. Sakai sees the young man as a prospect for his daughter Miyo, also a deafmute, although she has her own deaf lover, Norio. Sakai tries to break up this relationship, fearing his grandchildren would inherit their parents' affliction, and although Michio, Ichiro's father, is delighted, his son is critical of Sakai's meddling. Michio, trying to help his son's chances, takes Norio to visit two deafmutes whose children are similarly afflicted. The two lovers despair of a happy future together and agree to a suicide pact. Both are saved, however, and with Ichiro's encouragement, Miyo and Norio decide to pledge their eternal love. *Deafmutes. Prejudice. Fatherhood. Heredity. Family life. Suicide. Factories.*

Note: Released in Japan in May 1967 as *Chichi to ko.*

L'OURS see THE BEAR

OUT OF IT   F6.3679

Pressman–Williams Enterprises. *Dist* United Artists. Dec **1969** [c26 Nov 1969; LP38053]. Sd; b&w. 35mm. 97 min. *MPAA rating* M.

Prod Edward Pressman. *Assoc Prod* John G. Avildsen, Thomas Sand. *Dir-Writ* Paul Williams. *Assoc Dir* David Feldshuh, Elizabeth Rosenwald. *Dir Photog* John G. Avildsen. *Lighting* Moe Odegaard. *Adtl Photog* Martin Smith. *Titl* Dick Hess. *Film Ed* Ed Orshan. *Asst Ed* Glenn Ross, Martin Smith. *Mus*

Comp & Dir Michael Small. *Lyr* Michael Benedikt. *Perf by* The New York Rock and Roll Ensemble. *Sd* Fred Daniel. *Sd Ed* Dan Sable. *Sd Mix* Al Gramaglia. *Asst Dir* Nyles Gradus. *Prod Mgr* Alvin Shapiro. *Prod Asst* Leeds Levy, Curtis Dowds, Joyce Sunila. *Creative Cons* Carl Lerner.

Cast: Barry Gordon (*Paul*), Jon Voight (*Russ*), Lada Edmund, Jr. (*Christine*), Gretchen Corbett (*Barbara*), Peter Grad (*Steve*), Martin Gray, Oliver Bery, Leonard Gelber, Richard Coyler.

Comedy-drama. As summer comes to an end on Long Island, Paul and his friends Steve and Barbara are discussing their forthcoming year of high school. Russ, a football hero and the school bully, arrives with his beautiful girl friend, Christine. When Christine shows an interest in Paul, an introverted intellectual, he secretly makes a date with her, and they go to New York City to see a performance of *Romeo and Juliet*. Feigning sickness, however, Christine is brought home early, and Paul later discovers that she also had a date with Russ that night. His pride hurt, Paul turns to Barbara, who is eager to go out with him. When Paul is injured by Russ during football practice, Christine, tired of Russ's rough ways, decides to see Paul again, but he is confronted by the jealous Russ, who burns Paul's varsity jacket. The next day, Paul humiliates Russ in the locker room when he frightens him with a cigarette lighter shaped like a gun. Although pleased with his revenge, and certain that Barbara still loves him, Paul is still unsure of himself as he watches Russ and Christine frolic on the beach. *Bullies. Athletes. Students. Adolescence. High school life. Jealousy. Revenge. Beaches. Football. Summer. Long Island. New York City. "Romeo and Juliet".*

OUT OF SIGHT   F6.3680

Universal Pictures. 12 May **1966** [New Orleans opening; c2 Jul 1966; LP35391]. Sd (Westrex); col (Technicolor). 35mm. 87 min.

A Bart Patton–Lennie Weinrib Production. *Prod* Bart Patton. *Dir* Lennie Weinrib. *Screenplay* Larry Hovis. *Story* Dave Asher, Larry Hovis. *Dir Photog* Jack Russell, photog. *Art Dir* Lloyd S. Papez. *Set Decor* Audrey Blasdel. *Main Titl* Pacific Title. *Film Ed* Jack Woods. *Mus* Al De Lory, Fred Darian, Nick Venet. *Mus Supv* Nick Venet. *Song:* "Malibu Run" Jim Karstein, Leon Russell, Gary Lewis, T. Leslie. *Sung by* Gary Lewis and The Playboys. *Song:* "Out on the Floor" Fred Darian, Al De Lory. *Sung by* Dobie Gray. *Song:* "She'll Come Back" Nita Garfield, Howard Kaylan. *Sung by* The Turtles. *Song:* "Baby Please Don't Go" Joe Williams. *Sung by* The Astronauts. *Song:* "It's Not Unusual" Gordon Mills, Les Reed. *Sung by* The Knickerbockers. *Song:* "Funny Over You" Freddie Garrity. *Sung by* Freddie and the Dreamers. *Song:* "A Love Like You" Quinn & Jones. *Sung by* Freddie and the Dreamers. *Songs:* "What's Her Name," "Hip City" Fred Darian, Al De Lory. *Sd* Corson Jowett. *Asst Dir* Thomas J. Schmidt. *Unit Prod Mgr* Abby Singer. *Cost Dsgn* Helen Colvig. *Makeup* Bud Westmore. *Hairstyles* Larry Germain. *Custom Car* George Barris.

Cast: Jonathan Daly (*Homer*), Karen Jensen (*Sandra*), Carole Shelyne (*Marvin*), Robert Pine (*Greg*), Forrest Lewis (*Mr. Carter*), Wende Wagner (*Scuba*), Maggie Thrett (*Wipeout*), Deanna Lund (*Tuff Bod*), Rena Horten (*Girl from FLUSH*), John Lawrence (*Big D*), Jimmy Murphy (*Mousie*), Norman Grabowski (*Huh*), Billy Curtis (*FLUSH assistant*), Deon Douglas (*Mike*), Bob Eubanks (*M. C.*), Pamela Rodgers (*Madge*), Vicki Fee (*Janet*), Coby Denton (*Tom*), John Lodge (*John Stamp*), Gary Lewis and The Playboys, Freddie and The Dreamers, Dobie Gray, The Turtles, The Astronauts, The Knickerbockers (*guest stars*).

Comedy with music. When Sandra, a teenaged beach beauty, overhears Big D, a man driven mad by rock and roll, discussing with his henchmen, Mousie and Huh, plans to sabotage an upcoming fair, she telephones secret agent John Stamp for help. Homer, Stamp's butler, answers the telephone, however, and, wishing to be a secret agent himself, agrees to take on the case. Big D learns of Homer's involvement in the affair and tries to divert him with three beautiful assistants (Scuba, Wipeout, and Tuff Bod); but the bumbling Homer manages to elude them. Homer is also hampered in his investigations by the mysterious Girl from FLUSH, who constantly pursues Homer in a motorcycle with an assistant in the sidecar. Homer manages to prevent Big D from ruining the fair. And the Girl from FLUSH turns out to be Homer's boss in disguise, indignant because Homer has been using his custom-built automobile without permission. *Gangsters. Secret agents. Butlers. Musicians. Rock and roll. Mental illness. Sabotage. Fairs. Automobiles.*

OUT OF THE SHADOW see MURDER ON THE CAMPUS

OUT OF THE TIGER'S MOUTH   F6.3681

Ruggles-Whelan Enterprises. *Dist* Pathé-America Distributing Co., Astor Pictures. Dec **1962** [Los Angeles showing]. Sd; b&w. 35mm. 78 min.

Prod Wesley Ruggles, Jr. *Asst Prod* John Russey. *Dir* Tim Whelan, Jr. *Story-Screenplay* Wesley Ruggles, Jr., Tim Whelan, Jr. *Photog* Emmanuel Rojas. *Film Ed* Jack Ruggiero. *Mus* Howard Wells. *Sd* Leroy Robbins.

Cast: Loretta Han-Yi Hwong (*Little Moon*), David Fang (*Peaceful*), Lillian Wai (*Grandma Yang*), T'ang Juo Ch'ing (*Madame Pang*), Mario Barri (*Mario*), Lolita Shek (*Su Mei*), Feng I (*Boatman Feng*), Victoria Chan (*beggar girl*).

Drama. Little Moon and Peaceful, two Chinese children, are smuggled from the mainland to Hong Kong in the bottom of a boat. The unscrupulous boatman, instead of delivering the sister and brother to their uncle, goes to Macao and sells them to a whorehouse, where a prostitute takes pity on the children and helps them to gain passage to Hong Kong. Unfamiliar with the urban way of life, the children are soon robbed of what little money they have and are forced into begging and stealing. They finally learn that their uncle has died and realize that they must face the bleak future alone. *Children. Refugees. Prostitutes. Boatmen. Brother-sister relationship. Urban life. Smuggling. Whorehouses. Hong Kong. Macao.*

Note: Location scenes filmed in Hong Kong and Macao.

THE OUT-OF-TOWNERS   F6.3682

Jalem Productions. *Dist* Paramount Pictures. 28 May **1970** [New York opening; c31 Dec 1969; LP37717]. Sd; col (print by Movielab). 35mm. 98 min. *MPAA rating* G.

Prod Paul Nathan. *Dir* Arthur Hiller. *Screenplay* Neil Simon. *Dir Photog* Andrew Laszlo. *Camera Op* Kyme Meade. *Camera Asst* Walter Rankin. *Art Dir* Charles Bailey, Walter Tyler. *Set Decor* Arthur Parker. *Main Titl* Don Record. *Film Ed* Fred Chulack. *Mus* Quincy Jones. *Sd Rec* Dennis Maitland, Elden Ruberg. *Asst Dir* Peter Scoppa, Larry Albucher, Peter Bogart. *Prod Mgr* William W. Gray. *Unit Mgr* Dale Hutchinson. *Script Supv* Barbara Robinson. *Wardrobe* Forrest T. Butler, Grace Harris. *Makeup* Clay Lambert, Armand Delmar. *Hairstyles* William Farley. *Casting Dir* Hoyt Bowers. *Dial Coach* Alan DeWitt. *Prop* Earl Olin, John Ferry. *Key Grip* Norbert Haring.

Cast: Jack Lemmon (*George Kellerman*), Sandy Dennis (*Gwen Kellerman*), Milt Kamen (*counterman*), Sandy Baron (*TV man*), Anne Meara (*woman in police station*), Robert Nichols (*man in airplane*), Ann Prentiss (*airline stewardess*), Ron Carey (*cab driver, Boston*), Phil Bruns (*Officer Meyers*), Graham Jarvis (*Murray*), Carlos Montalban (*Cuban diplomat*), Robert King (*agent in Boston*), Johnny Brown (*waiter on train*), Dolph Sweet (*police sergeant*), Jack Crowder (*police officer*), Jon Korkes (*looter*), Robert Walden (*looter*), Richard Libertini (*baggage man, Boston*), Paul Dooley (*hotel clerk, day*), Anthony Holland (*hotel clerk, night*), Billy Dee Williams (*lost and found, Boston*), Bob Bennett (*man in phone booth, Boston*), Mary Norman (*stewardess*), Paul Jubara (*1st hippie*), Hash Howard (*2d hippie*), Maxwell Glanville (*redcap*), Meredith Vincent (*washroom lady*), B. Paipert (*sweeper*), J. French (*cleaning woman*), A. P. Westcott (*porter*), Ray Ballard (*attendant*).

Comedy. George Kellerman, a successful Dayton businessman, is invited by his company to visit their New York City offices and discuss his possible promotion to an executive position there. George and his wife, Gwen, fly to New York with the intention of having dinner there, spending the night in a luxury hotel, and after George's interview the next morning returning to Dayton. In the course of 24 hours, the Kellermans are beset with difficulties. Their plane is rerouted to Boston when air traffic and fog make landing in New York impossible; and in Boston the Kellermans learn that their luggage has been lost, and moreover, they must take a crowded train to New York. Tired and hungry, George and Gwen reach New York during a downpour and find that the city is in the midst of strikes by garbage collectors and transit workers. They walk the 10 blocks to their hotel, the Waldorf-Astoria, only to find that, owing to the Kellermans' lateness, the hotel has canceled their reservation. A friendly stranger offers them accomodations, but he soon reveals himself to be a mugger and takes all their money. Destitute, they go to the police and are told they will be put up at the armory, but the police car which takes them to the armory is hijacked by robbers, who deposit the Kellermans in Central Park. They spend the night there and are again mugged and George's watch is stolen. The next morning two athletes mistake George for a rapist and beat him up. Later a mounted policeman chases George, who he thinks is a child molester. George hitches a ride with a passing motorist, whereupon the car, belonging to a Cuban diplomat, is assailed by demonstrators. George finally arrives at his interview, looking dirty and disheveled, and though he is offered the position he declines. The couple are soon aboard a plane to Dayton, only to find when they are aloft that the plane is being hijacked to Cuba. *Businessmen. Muggers. Diplomats. Cubans. Police. Robbers. Employer-employee relations. Urban life. Theft. Mistaken identity. Rape. Child molesting. Hijackers. Airplanes. Taxicabs. Trains. Strikes. Demonstrations. Dayton. New York City. New York City—Central Park. Boston. Waldorf-Astoria Hotel. Fog. Storms.*

Note: Location scenes filmed in New York City and Boston.

THE OUT-OF-TOWNERS see DEAR HEART

THE OUTCRY see IL GRIDO

THE OUTDOORSMAN   F6.3683

W. A. B. Motion Picture Productions. *Dist* Theatre Management, Inc. 10 Jan **1968** [Minneapolis opening; c10 Jan 1968; MP18331]. Sd; col. 35mm (see note). 90 min. [Copyright length: 112 min.]

Prod William A. Bryant, Ned Payne. *Photog* William A. Bryant, Ned Payne, Don Redinger, Charles Beery. *Mus & Score* The Silhouettes. *Sd* Olaf Kuuskler. *Acknowledgements to* The Management of Chober River Lodge (South Africa), The Management of Osric Bristow (Southern Rhodesia), The Wardens of Kalahari Gemsbuck Park (South-West Africa), C. H. Visser (Etosha Game Reserve—South-West Africa), P. S. Daniel (Umfolozi Game Reserve—South-Africa). *Post Prod Supv* Don Redinger.

Narrator: Bill Steinbach.

Documentary. A group of outdoorsmen demonstrate duck hunting as a preliminary to traveling the various hunting and fishing centers of the world. They begin their journey with a trip to the Rocky Mountains to hunt elk and mountain lions and to fish in the freshwater lakes. They travel to Lac la Ronge in Saskatchewan and to Anchorage and the Katmai Peninsula in Alaska to fish for trout, salmon, and grayling and hunt moose and bear. In the Arctic, the hunters go with a group of Eskimos for their biggest catch, the polar bear. The hunters travel south by plane, to the Fishing Club of Panama to fish for marlin, tuna, shark, and dolphin in the Gulf of Panama. In South Africa and the Zambesi River basin, they often hunt with only a camera. Accompanied by native beaters, they hunt elephants, antelope, buffalo, crocodiles, and hippopotami. As conservationists they capture some almost extinct white rhinoceros and take them to a game preserve for protection. *Americans in foreign countries. Sportsmen. Eskimos. Africans. Hunting. Fishing. Photography. Big game. Airplanes. Safaris. Game preserves. Rocky Mountains. Lac la Ronge. Saskatchewan. Alaska. Arctic regions. Gulf of Panama. South Africa. Zambesi River. Fishing Club of Panama. Ducks. Elk. Mountain lions. Bears. Trout. Salmon. Moose. Sharks. Dolphin (fish). Marlin. Tuna. Elephants. Antelope. Buffalo. Crocodiles. Rhinoceros.*

Note: Filmed on location in the Rocky Mountains, Saskatchewan, Alaska, Panama, Zambia, Southern Rhodesia, South-West Africa, and South Africa. Production started in 1964. Filmed in 16mm.

OUTER AND INNER SPACE   F6.3684

Dist Film-Makers' Cooperative. 8 Feb **1966** [New York opening]. Sd; b&w. 2 x 16mm. 70 min.

Prod-Dir Andy Warhol.

Cast: Edie Sedgwick.

Experimental film. A young woman has a conversation with her videotape image on a television set. The dialog centers on space, mysticism, and aspects of herself. *Mysticism. Television.*

Note: At the New York opening, reels one and two were projected simultaneously, side by side. The frame remains fixed throughout.

OUTLAW MOTORCYCLES   F6.3685

Hollywood Star Pictures. *Dist* Gillman Film Corp. 28 Dec **1967** [San Francisco showing]. Sd; col. 35mm. [Feature film, length unknown.]

A Film by Titus Moody.

Action melodrama. Motorcyclists who belong to various "outlaw" clubs organize a state-wide "run" and participate in other activities: a wedding, meetings, confrontations with law enforcement officers, and a gang member's funeral. *Motorcycle gangs. Police. Outlaws. Weddings. Funerals.*

THE OUTLAWS IS COMING   ~F6.3686

Normandy Productions. *Dist* Columbia Pictures. 14 Jan **1965** [San Antonio, Texas, opening; c1 Jan 1965; LP30327]. Sd; b&w. 35mm. 89 min.

Prod-Dir-Story Norman Maurer. *Screenplay* Elwood Ullman. *Dir Photog* Irving Lippman. *Camera Op* Arnold Rich. *Camera Asst* H. L. Bettcher, Moe Bauchman. *Art Dir* Robert Peterson. *Set Decor* James M. Crowe. *Film Ed* Aaron Nibley. *Mus* Paul Dunlap. *Sd Supv* Charles J. Rice. *Sd* James Z. Flaster, Win Hancock, William Bernds. *Asst Dir* Don Gold, Norman August. *Script Supv* Marie Kenney. *Makeup* Joe Dibella. *Sp Eff* Richard Albain. *Coöp* Bud Basolo, B-Bar-B Buffalo Ranch. *Still Photog* Homer Van Pelt. *Gaffer* Hal Franklin. *Prop Master* Clarence Peet. *Best Boy* Henry Stevens. *Grip* Al Becker.

Cast: Larry Fine, Moe Howard, Joe De Rita (*The Three Stooges*), Adam West (*Kenneth Cabot*), Nancy Kovack (*Annie Oakley*), Mort Mills (*Trigger Mortis*), Don Lamond (*Rance Roden*), Rex Holman (*Sunstroke Kid*), Emil Sitka (*Mr. Abernathy/witch doctor/cavalry colonel*), Henry Gibson (*Charlie Horse*), Murray Alper (*Chief Crazy Horse*), Tiny Brauer (*bartender*), Joe Bolton (*Rob Dalton*), Bill Camfield (*Wyatt Earp*), Hal Fryar (*Johnny Ringo*), Johnny Ginger (*Billy the Kid*), Wayne Mack (*Jesse James*), Ed T. McDonnell (*Bat Masterson*), Bruce Sedley (*Cole Younger*), Paul Shannon (*Wild Bill Hickok*), Sally Starr (*Belle Starr*), Marilyn Fox, Sidney Marion, Audrey Betz, Jerry Allan, Lloyd King.

Western farce. The publisher of Boston's wildlife magazine assigns his editor Kenneth Cabot, along with the Three Stooges, who have been bungling their work in the magazine's pressroom, to go out West and halt the slaughter of buffalo. There they encounter every gunslinger, from Wild Bill Hickok to Jesse James and Billy The Kid, as they inadvertently hamper the gang leaders' plans.

Annie Oakley saves them with her many trick gunshots. The gang leaders are exposed; the Three Stooges persuade them to mend their ways; and Annie asks Kenneth to marry her. *Editors. Gunfighters. Clerks. Wildlife—Conservation. Magazines (periodicals). Boston. Phoebe Ann Oakley. Crazy Horse. Wyatt Earp. William Barclay Masterson. Belle Starr. James Butler Hickok. William H. Bonney. Cole Younger. Robert Dalton. John Ringo. Jesse Woodson James. Buffalo.*

Note: Location scenes filmed near Ventura, California. Working title: *The Three Stooges Meet the Gunslingers.*

OUTPOST OF HELL (Japan)   F6.3687

Toho Co. Apr **1966** [Los Angeles showing]. Sd; b&w. 35mm (Tohoscope). 98 min.

Exec Prod Tomoyuki Tanaka, Kenjiro Tsunoda. *Dir* Senkichi Taniguchi. *Screenplay* Masato Ide. *Photog* Kazuo Yamada.

Cast: Tatsuya Mihashi, Makoto Sato, Yosuke Natsuki, Makoto Terada, Hiroshi Tachikawa.

War drama. In the closing days of World War II Japanese defenses are strung thinly along the Manchurian border, always susceptible to attack by the advancing Soviet army. Five Japanese soldiers occupy a pillbox in the face of enemy fire, despite the fact that all other pillboxes in the area have been captured. One by one, the Japanese soldiers are killed, and the pillbox is captured. *Combat zone life. World War II. Manchuria. Japan—Army. Union of Soviet Socialist Republics—Army.*

Note: Released in Japan in 1963 as *Dokuritsu kikanjutai imada shagekichu.*

THE OUTRAGE   F6.3688

KHF Productions. *Dist* Metro-Goldwyn-Mayer, Inc. 7 Oct **1964** [New York opening; c17 Sep 1964; LP28886]. Sd (Westrex); b&w. 35mm (Panavision). 97 min.

A Martin Ritt Production. *Prod* A. Ronald Lubin. *Assoc Prod* Michael Kanin. *Dir* Martin Ritt. *2d Unit Dir* Lesley Selander. *Screenplay* Michael Kanin. *Dir Photog* James Wong Howe. *Camera Op* Robert Johannes. *Camera Asst* Dewey Wrigley. *Art Dir* George W. Davis, Tambi Larsen. *Set Decor* Henry Grace, Robert R. Benton. *Film Ed* Frank Santillo. *Mus Comp & Cond* Alex North. *Rec Supv* Franklin Milton. *Sd Mix* Larry Jost. *Asst Dir* Daniel J. McCauley, Al Murphy, Roger Duchowny. *Unit Mgr* Stanley Goldsmith. *Script Supv* Mae Wale-Wright. *Cost Dsgn* Don Feld. *Wardrobe* Lambert Marks, Sylvia Posner. *Makeup Supv* William Tuttle. *Makeup* Ron Berkeley. *Hairstyles* Sydney Guilaroff, Alma Johnson. *Sp Vis Eff* J. McMillan Johnson, Robert R. Hoag. *Dialect Adv* Julie Gibson, Walon Green. *Still Photog* Sterling Smith.

Cast: Paul Newman *(Juan Carrasco)*, Laurence Harvey *(husband)*, Claire Bloom *(wife)*, Edward G. Robinson *(con man)*, William Shatner *(preacher)*, Howard Da Silva *(prospector)*, Albert Salmi *(sheriff)*, Thomas Chalmers *(judge)*, Paul Fix *(Indian)*.

Western melodrama. Source: Fay Kanin and Michael Kanin, *Rashomon* (a play; New York opening: 27 Jan 1959). Akira Kurosawa, screenplay for the film *Rashomon* (Daiei Co., 1950). Late in the 19th century a disillusioned preacher, a grizzled prospector, and a cynical con man meet by chance at a southwestern railway station. The first two relate events in the recent trial of Juan Carrasco, the territory's most notorious outlaw, who has been sentenced to death for murdering a southern gentleman and raping his wife. The trial was confusing because three witnesses each told conflicting versions of what had occurred: Carrasco claimed that he bound the husband, forced him to watch the rape, and then killed the husband in a duel; the wife claimed that after Carrasco raped her and fled, she killed her husband in a fit of rage when he accused her of having encouraged the bandit; and an old Indian testified that the husband killed himself because of the humiliation he had suffered. After this last account a cry is heard, and the three men discover an abandoned baby. The con man attempts to steal some gold that has been left for the child, and an ensuing argument reveals that the prospector was also involved in the incident: he had witnessed the crime but did not testify because he had stolen the jeweled dagger from the dying man's chest. The prospector claims that the bandit showed remorse after the rape and begged his victim to come away with him, but fancying herself as a prize to be won, she shamed the two unwilling men into a fight over her, and her husband accidentally fell on the dagger. When the prospector offers to raise the child, even though he has five others at home, the preacher's faith in humanity is somewhat restored, and he is able to return to his congregation and the Lord's work. *Bandits. Mexicans. Southerners. Preachers. Prospectors. Confidence men. Indians of North America. Foundlings. Rape. Murder. Perjury. Infidelity. Disillusionment. Suicide. Trials. Duels. Gold.*

Note: Working title: *Judgment in the Sun.*

THE OUTSIDER   F6.3689

Universal Pictures. 27 Dec **1961** [Los Angeles opening; c21 Dec 1961; LP24331]. Sd; b&w. 35mm. 108 min.

Prod Sy Bartlett. *Dir* Delbert Mann. *Screenplay* Stewart Stern. *Photog* Joseph La Shelle. *Art Dir* Alexander Golitzen, Edward S. Haworth. *Set Decor* Oliver Emert. *Film Ed* Marjorie Fowler. *Mus Comp & Cond* Leonard Rosenman. *Mus Supv* Joseph Gershenson. *Sd* Waldon O. Watson, Joe Lapis. *Asst Dir* Ray Gosnell, Jr., Charles Scott, Jr., Douglas Green. *Prod Mgr* Marshall Green. *Makeup* Bud Westmore. *Hairstyles* Larry Germain. *Tech Adv* Clement J. Stadler, (Lieut. Col.).

Cast: Tony Curtis *(Ira Hamilton Hayes)*, James Franciscus *(Jim Sorenson)*, Gregory Walcott *(Sergeant Kiley)*, Bruce Bennett *(Major-General Bridges)*, Vivian Nathan *(Nancy Hayes)*, Edmund Hashim *(Jay Morago)*, Paul Comi *(Sergeant Boyle)*, Stanley Adams *(Noomie)*, Wayne Heffley *(Corporal Johnson)*, Ralph Moody *(uncle)*, Jeff Silver *(McGruder)*, James Beck *(Tyler)*, Forrest Compton *(Bradley)*, Peter Homer, Sr. *(Mr. Alvarez)*, Mary Patton *(chairlady)*, Charley Stevens *(Joseph Hayes)*, Ray Daley *(Gagnon)*, Miriam Colon *(Anita Goode)*, Vincent Edwards *(George)*.

Biographical drama. Source: William Bradford Huie, "Torture Execution of a Hero Marine" ("The Hero of Iwo Jima"), in *Cavalier* (Dec 1958). In World War II, 17-year-old Ira Hamilton Hayes, a shy Pima Indian who has never set foot outside his tribal reservation in Arizona, enlists in the Marine Corps. Though most of his white companions either deride or ignore him, he strikes up a deep and lasting friendship with another marine, Jim Sorenson. In February of 1945 the two buddies are among the five marines who raise the U. S. flag on Mt. Suribachi during the bloody fighting at Iwo Jima. Shortly thereafter Sorenson is killed by enemy fire, and a stunned and heartbroken Ira is returned to the United States to take part in a war bond drive. Disturbed at being singled out as a national hero, and feeling unworthy of the role, the simple Indian turns to whisky for courage. His drinking becomes a scandal, and he is returned to his unit in disgrace. Following the war, anonymity eludes him as his tribal chief persuades him to go to Washington to seek funds for an irrigation project. There he begins drinking again and lands in jail. The dedication of the Iwo Jima Memorial in Arlington, Virginia, inspires him to pull himself together, and he returns home to work on the reservation; but he is shattered when his people do not elect him to the tribal council. Sneaking away with a supply of liquor, he seeks refuge on a lonely mountainside. There he dies of exposure at the age of 32. *Pima Indians. War heroes. Alcoholism. Friendship. War bonds. Irrigation. World War II. Iwo Jima. Mount Suribachi. Pima-Maricpa Indian Reservation. Washington (District of Columbia). Ira Hamilton Hayes. James Sorenson. United States Marines. Iwo Jima Memorial.*

Note: Location scenes filmed in San Diego; on the Pima-Maricpa Indian Reservation; at Camp Matthews; Soldier Field (Chicago); Camp Pendleton; in the San Fernando Valley; and at the Iwo Jima Memorial in Arlington, Virginia. Prerelease title: *The Sixth Man.*

OVER 18, ... AND READY!   F6.3690

Dist Paul Mart Productions. Aug **1969**. Sd; b&w. 35mm. 70 min.

Prod Ted Lake. *Dir* Lloyd Allen. *Screenplay* Don Lambert. *Photog* Stan Landers. *Camera Op* Len Randall. *Mus* John Barnett. *Sd Rec* David McDaniel. *Asst Dir* Ed Lawrence. *Script Girl* Peggy Stevens. *Prod Mgr* Lee Grant, prod. *Makeup* Laurel Kenyon. *Stills Photog* Bob Rhoades.

Cast: Mary McRea *(Lyn)*, Larry Martinelli *(Barney Merritt)*, Margot Stevens *(Billie Merritt)*, Michelle LeGrande *(maid)*, Gary Fox *(Gerry Blair)*, Sylvia Thorne *(Jane)*, Herb Henry *(Howie)*.

Drama. Sex exploitation filmmaker Barney Merritt conducts extensive interviews for the female lead in his next picture, but he is bothered by his secretary, Lyn, who wants the job. He refuses. Lyn includes in a batch of pictures of applicants nude photographs of herself, and her physical endowments attract the attention of Barney's wife, who is both a lesbian and the financial support for Barney's film company. She forces Barney to give Lyn the part, and he seduces his young secretary in the bargain. Lyn moves in with the Merritts during the filming, and becomes involved in their sexual rituals. Gerry, the photographer who shot Lyn's nude portfolio, arrives at the Merritt house to declare his love for her, but he leaves in disgust when he finds her in bed with her employer. Lyn quickly realizes what has happened and, grasping at the chance to regain her decency, drives frantically after Gerry. On a hairpin curve the distraught woman loses control of her car and dies in the crash. *Motion picture producers. Secretaries. Actors. Houseguests. Photographers. Ambition. Lesbianism. Seduction. Nudity. Employer-employee relations. Sex exploitation films. Photographs. Automobile accidents.*

Note: The following are credited under pseudonyms: Ted Leversuch (Ted Lake), John Bath (Lloyd Allen and John Barnett), and Stanley Lipinski (Stan Landers).

OVER-EXPOSED   F6.3691

Lima Productions. 22 Jan **1969** [Baltimore opening]. Sd; col. 35mm. 73 min. *Dir* W. A. Chrisfield. *Photog* Shannon Carse. *Mus* Greg Poree.

Sex film. A film consisting of several vignettes. One concerns a black woman who practices voodoo; another is about a doll's fantasies; a third concerns two women fighting. Press material suggests that the film depicts nudity, sadism, lesbianism, hedonism, group sex, seduction, and autoeroticism. *Negroes. Nudity. Sadism. Hedonism. Lesbianism. Voodoo. Fantasy. Group sex. Seduction. Autoeroticism. Dolls.*

Note: A sequel to *Exposure*, q. v.

OVER THERE, 1914–1918 (France)   F6.3692

Zodiaque Productions. *Dist* Pathé-Contemporary Films. 10 Mar **1965** [New York opening]. Sd; b&w. 35mm. 90 min.

Dir Jean Aurel. *Comm* Cécil Saint-Laurent. *Film Ed (see note)* Jean Aurel, Cécil Saint-Laurent, Anne-Marie Cotret. *Mus* Serge Kaufmann. *English Adapt* Titra Sound Corp.

Documentary. Newsreel footage is used to present the history of World War I, the leaders, the causes, and the battles which led to the signing of the treaty at Versailles. Highlights include the assassination of Archduke Ferdinand; the German invasion of Belgium, Luxembourg, and France; the battles of the Marne and Verdun; the decisive entrance of the United States into the war; the Russian Revolution; and the final offensives which forced Germany to accept the treaty and quell its own revolution. Also included are scenes of the persons named in the following subject list. *World War I. Russia—History—1917–21 Revolution. Versailles Treaty (1919). Germany. Belgium. Luxembourg. Russia. Verdun. Marne. Franz Ferdinand. Henri Philippe Pétain. William II (Germany). Nicholas II (Russia). Nikolai Lenin. Joseph Jacques Césaire Joffre. Ferdinand Foch. Paul von Hindenburg. Erich Friedrich Wilhelm Ludendorff. Georges Clemenceau. John Joseph Pershing. Margaretha Geertruida Zelle. United States Army.*

Note: Opened in Paris in Feb 1963 as *14–18*; running time: 95 min. Sources conflict in crediting film editor.

THE OVERCOAT (U.S.S.R.)   F6.3693

Lenfilm. *Dist* Cinemasters International, Ltd. 1 Mar **1965** [New York opening]. Sd; b&w. 35mm. 78 min.

Pres by J. Jay Frankel. *Dir* Aleksey Batalov. *Screenplay* L. Solovyov. *Story Ed* I. Tarsanova. *Photog* G. Marandzhyan. *Art Dir* B. Manevich, I. Kaplan. *Mus* N. Sidelnikov. *Sd* A. Shargorodskiy. *Asst Dir* Ye. Serdechkova. *Prod Mgr* A. Arshanskiy. *Cons* B. Eykhenbaum, V. Glinka.

Cast: Rolan Bykov *(Akakiy Akakiyevich)*, Yuriy Tolubeyev *(Petrovich)*, A. Yezhkina *(Petrovich's wife)*, Ye. Ponsova *(landlady)*, T. Teykh *(Important Person)*, N. Urgant, Aleksandr Sokolov, V. Maksimov, R. Lebedev, P. Lobanov, G. Kolosov, M. Ladygin, G. Voropayev, N. Kuzmin.

Drama. Source: Nikolay Vasilyevich Gogol, "Shinel," in *Sochineniya Nikolaya Gogolya; Tom tretiy* (Saint Petersburg, 1842). Akakiy Akakiyevich Bashmachkin, a lowly copy clerk in a Saint Petersburg court office, is obsessed with his work. Mocked by his fellow clerks for the determination with which he pursues the colorless routine of his life, he pays no heed, having tailored his life to fit within the bounds dictated by his meager means. As winter draws on, Akakiy Akakiyevich begs the drunken tailor Petrovich to repair his threadbare coat, but the tailor declares the garment unsalvageable and recommends the fashioning of a new overcoat. The clerk undertakes new economies to make the eventual purchase possible; and a Christmas bonus added to the accumulated savings of years brings the hope to fruition. With excitement Akakiy Akakiyevich sets out with Petrovich to choose fabric, and the tailor devotes himself to the task of producing a new overcoat. A new spark of life enters Akakiy Akakiyevich as he dons the finished coat. His fellow clerks, who had jeered at his old garment, now congratulate him, and one of the wealthier of their number invites them all for champagne in his honor. Akakiy Akakiyevich, who for years has not ventured outside his house at night, makes his way from the poor, drab district where he lives to the more prosperous section of the city. He feels disoriented in the party atmosphere he finds upon his arrival; supped and made to drink two glasses of champagne, he is unable to leave until long after the hour he is usually in bed. As he regains the poorer district of the city, he is set upon by thieves, who make off with his precious overcoat. Frantic, he is advised at work that the police will not help him but that he should visit a certain Important Person. However, the Important Person preemptorily dismisses him so as to create an impression. The clerk walks out into the snow a broken man and catches a chill which leads to delirium and death. Subsequently his ghost snatches overcoats from the shoulders of sundry Saint Petersburg citizens until at last it steals the overcoat of the Important Person and is heard from no more. [The inclusion of the ghost sequences is uncertain.] *Clerks. Civil servants. Tailors. Poverty. Employer-employee relations. Theft. Insanity. Bureaucracy. Death. Winter. Saint Petersburg.*

Note: Released in the U.S.S.R. in Feb 1960 as *Shinel*; running time: 74 min(?).

OVERDOSE OF DEGRADATION   F6.3694

Hollywood Cinema Associates. *Dist* Distribpix, Inc., Hollywood Cinema Associates. Sep **1970**. Sd; col. 35mm. 62 min.

Sex film. No information about the precise nature of this film has been found, but press photographs suggest that it includes scenes of group sex, lesbianism, and sadomasochism. *Lesbianism. Group sex. Sadomasochism.*

ÖVERGREPPET see LE VIOL

THE OWL AND THE PUSSYCAT   F6.3695

Rastar Productions. *Dist* Columbia Pictures. 3 Nov **1970** [New York opening; c1 Nov 1970; LP38197]. Sd; col (Eastman Color). 35mm (Panavision). 96 min. *MPAA rating* R.

A Ray Stark–Herbert Ross Production. *Prod* Ray Stark. *Assoc Prod* George Justin. *Dir* Herbert Ross. *Screenplay* Buck Henry. *Dir Photog (see note)* Harry Stradling, Andrew Laszlo. *Camera Crew* Edward Brown, Harvey Jenkins, Thomas Priestley, Jr., James S. Brown, Jr., Josh Weiner. *Art Dir* Robert Wightman, Philip Rosenberg. *Dsgn Supv* Ken Adam. *Set Decor* Leif Pedersen. *Prod Dsgn* John Robert Lloyd. *Titl Dsgn* Wayne Fitzgerald. *Supv Film Ed* Margaret Booth. *Ed* John F. Burnett. *Mus Comp and Arr* Richard Halligan. *Lyr Writ & Mus Perf by* Blood, Sweat and Tears. *Sd* Arthur Piantadosi, Dennis Maitland. *Mus Ed* William Saracino. *Asst Dir* William C. Gerrity. *Unit Prod Mgr* Robert Greenhut. *Script Supv* Marguerite James. *Prod Asst* Leo Garen. *Cost* Ann Roth. *Wardrobe* Shirlee Strahm, George Newman. *Makeup* Lee Harman, Joe Cranzano. *Hairstyles* Robert Grimaldi. *Gaffer* Rich Quinlan. *Grip* Edward Knott. *Casting* Marion Dougherty.

Cast: Barbra Streisand *(Doris)*, George Segal *(Felix)*, Robert Klein *(Barney)*, Allen Garfield *(dress shop proprietor)*, Roz Kelly *(Eleanor)*, Jacques Sandulescu *(Rapzinsky)*, Jack Manning *(Mr. Weyderhaus)*, Grace Carney *(Mrs. Weyderhaus)*, Barbara Anson *(Ann Weyderhaus)*, Kim Chan *(theater cashier)*, Stan Gottlieb *(coatcheck man)*, Joe Madden, Fay Sappington *(old neighbors)*, Evelyn Lang *(Barney's girl)*, Dominic T. Barto *(man in bar)*, Marshall Ward, Tom Atkins, Stan Bryant *(gang in car)*, Buck Henry *(man looking through Doubleday bookstore)*.

Romantic comedy. Source: Bill Manhoff, *The Owl and the Pussycat* (New York opening: 18 Nov 1964). After Felix Sherman, an aspiring author and bookshop clerk in New York City, reports to landlord Rapzinsky that neighbor Doris is a prostitute, the woman is evicted, immediately moves into his apartment in the middle of the night, and denounces Felix as a homosexual informant. Astonished, Felix allows her to stay. When his guest develops hiccups he attempts to cure her by appearing in a skeleton costume. Her screams, however, attract so much attention that Felix himself is instantly evicted. The two go to the apartment of Felix's friend Barney, where, after a tumultuous argument between Felix and Doris which forces Barney and his girl friend out on the street, Doris seduces Felix. The next morning they argue violently and part angrily. Doris becomes a go-go dancer, but her audience prefers to watch a televised football game. In a sleazy theater Felix uneasily watches *Cycle Sluts*, a film featuring Doris. When Doris' friend Eleanor informs him of the prostitute's whereabouts, Felix takes Doris to the home of his fiancée, prim concert pianist Ann Weyderhaus. After smoking marijuana, Felix and Doris are bathing when the Weyderhaus family returns home unexpectedly, and Doris recognizes Mr. Weyderhaus as one of her most peculiar customers. As Felix and Doris walk in Central Park, they argue and then confess their love for each other. *Prostitutes. Authors. Clerks. Landlords. Go-go dancers. Courtship. Eviction. Seduction. Bookshops. Sex exploitation films. Marijuana. New York City. New York City—Central Park.*

Note: Filmed on location in New York City. After his death, Stradling was replaced by Laszlo. Evelyn Lang is a pseudonym for Marilyn Chambers.

OYOME NI OIDE see COME MARRY ME

P. J.   F6.3696

Universal Pictures. 9 Feb **1968** [Chicago opening; c23 Mar 1967; LP38593]. Sd (Westrex); col (Technicolor). 35mm (Techniscope). 109 min.

Prod Edward J. Montagne. *Dir* John Guillermin. *Screenplay* Philip Reisman, Jr. *Story* Philip Reisman, Jr., Edward J. Montagne. *Dir Photog* Loyal Griggs. *Art Dir* Alexander Golitzen, Walter M. Simonds. *Set Decor* John McCarthy, Robert Priestley. *Main Titl* Cinefx. *Film Ed* Sam E. Waxman. *Mus* Neal Hefti. *Mus Supv* Joseph Gershenson. *Song:* "Welcome to St. Crispin" Percy Faith, Philip Reisman, Jr. *Sung by* King Charles MacNiles. *Sd* Waldon O. Watson, Lyle Cain. *Asst Dir* Phil Bowles, Skip Cosper. *Unit Prod Mgr* Wes Thompson. *Asst to the Prod* Billy Sands. *Gowns* Jean Louis. *Makeup* Bud Westmore. *Hairstyles* Larry Germain. *Matte Supv* Albert Whitlock.

Cast: George Peppard *(P. J. Detweiler)*, Raymond Burr *(William Orbison)*, Gayle Hunnicutt *(Maureen Preble)*, Brock Peters *(Police Chief Waterpark)*, Wilfrid Hyde-White *(Billings-Browne)*, Jason Evers *(Jason Grenoble)*, Coleen Gray *(Betty Orbison)*, Susan Saint James *(Linette Orbison)*, Severn Darden *(Shelton Quell)*, H. Jane Van Duser *(Elinor Silene)*, George Furth *(Sonny*

Silene), Barbara Dana (*Lita*), Herbert Edelman (*Charlie*), John Qualen (*Poppa*), Bert Freed (*police lieutenant*), Ken Lynch (*Thorson*), Jim Boles (*landlord's agent*), Arte Johnson (*Jackie*), King Charles MacNiles (*calypso singer*), Don Haggerty (*Ape*), Kay Farrington (*Mrs. Thorson*), Lennie Bremen (*Greavy*).

Crime melodrama. Desperate for employment, New York private investigator P. J. Detweiler takes a position as bodyguard to Maureen Preble, mistress of wealthy William Orbison. After several attempts are made on Maureen's life, Orbison moves wife, mistress, relatives, and business associates to his small island in the Bahamas. There P. J., suspecting another attempt on Preble, slays Jason Grenoble, Orbison's business partner. Although jailed for the murder, P. J. is reprimanded and freed. Upon release the detective discovers his entourage departed and rightly suspects that Maureen and Orbison have engineered Grenoble's death. Back in Manhattan, P. J. documents Orbison's motivations and confronts the magnate with proof of his crime. During the encounter Maureen and Orbison shoot and kill one another, freeing P. J. for another assignment. *Detectives. Bodyguards. Mistresses. Businessmen. Police. Duplicity. Murder. Bahamas. New York City.*

Note: Location scenes filmed at Santa Catalina, California, and New York City. Working title: *Criss Cross*; prerelease title: *New Face in Hell*.

P. P. S. (PROSTITUTES' PROTECTIVE SOCIETY)   F6.3697

Barry Mahon Productions. 15 Jun **1966** [Fresno, California, showing]. Sd; b&w. 35mm. 63 min.

Pres by Barry Mahon. *Prod-Dir* Barry Mahon. *Photog* Barry Mahon. *Ed* Dan Quinn. *Sd* Magno Sound.

Cast: Madame Sue, Barry Mahon (*see note*), The Times Square Girls.

Melodrama. The New York World's Fair draws a huge tourist business for Madame Sue and her Times Square prostitutes. Petty racketeer Carney Bill decides to muscle in on the profits. To announce his intentions, he machine-guns one of the prostitutes and her lover. Unless the others agree to turn over 10 per cent of the profits, he promises that there will be more violence. Madame Sue discusses the proposition with the frightened girls, who decide that a 10 per cent share would be only the beginning if they were to give in. Carney Bill carries out his threats of murder, knifing and strangling several women. When the nude body of a popular member of the group is found hanging from a light fixture, the others decide that they must fight back. They steal guns and set traps to make their protective society work. Finally they capture Carney Bill and castrate him, thus bringing peace to Times Square. *Madams. Racketeers. Extortion. Prostitution. Murder. Castration. Revenge. Protective associations. New York World's Fair (1964–65). New York City—Times Square.*

Note: May also be known as *The Secret Society*. Mahon's participation as an actor is unconfirmed.

PACIFIC VIBRATIONS   F6.3698

John Severson Productions. *Dist* Surfer Magazine, American International Pictures. 22 Oct **1970** [Santa Monica, California, opening]. Sd; col (Eastmancolor, print by Movielab). 16mm & 35mm. 92 min. *MPAA rating* G.

Prod-Dir-Writ John Severson. *Photog* John Severson. *Adtl Photog* Spyder Wills, Robert Grant, Curt Mastalka, Brad Barrett. *Film Ed* John Severson. *Assoc Film Ed* Fred Talmage. *Mus* Cream, Steve Miller Band, Wolfgang, Ry Cooder, Crosby, Stills & Nash, Sky Oats, Colorado Purple Gang, Paul Beaver, Bernie Krause, Ashish Khan, Pranesh Khan, Zakir Hussain. *Prod Asst* Bryan Heath.

Featuring: Jock Southerland, Billy Hamilton, Rolf Aurness, David Nuuhiwa, Merv Larson, Jeff Hakman, Mike Tabeling, Corky Carroll, Rick Griffin, Angie Reno, Brad McCaul, Spyder Wills, Mickey Dora, Chuck Dent, Steve Bigler, Mike Purpus.

Documentary. The film examines surfing communities in California and Hawaii and the growing ecological problems facing them. Surfers are seen riding huge waves from California's Hermosa and Huntington beaches to Oahu's north shore, Waikiki Beach, and Maui's Honolua Bay. Also depicted are overcrowded beaches, decaying sea life, and the erosion of surfland by the onslaught of industrial expansion and private communities. *Surfers. Ecology. Beaches. Hawaii. California. Hermosa Beach. Huntington Beach. Oahu. Maui. Waikiki Beach. Pacific Ocean.*

Note: Filmed and originally shown in 16mm.

THE PAD (AND HOW TO USE IT)   F6.3699

Ross Hunter Productions–Universal Pictures. *Dist* Universal Pictures. 17 Aug **1966** [New York opening; c1 Oct 1966; LP35393]. Sd (Westrex); col (Technicolor). 35mm. 86 min.

Prod Ross Hunter. *Dir* Brian G. Hutton. *Screenplay* Thomas C. Ryan, Ben Starr. *Dir Photog* Ellsworth Fredricks. *Art Dir* Alexander Golitzen, George Webb. *Set Decor* John McCarthy, George H. Henshaw. *Main Titl* Pacific Title. *Film Ed* Milton Carruth. *Mus* Russ Garcia. *Mus Supv* Joseph Gershenson. *Titl Song* Robert Allen, mus. *Sung by* The Knickerbockers. *Sd* Waldon O. Watson, Corson Jowett. *Asst Dir* Phil Bowles. *Unit Prod Mgr* John Morrison. *Cost*

Rosemary Odell. *Makeup* Bud Westmore. *Hairstyles* Larry Germain.

Cast: Brian Bedford (*Bob*), Julie Sommars (*Doreen*), James Farentino (*Ted*), Edy Williams (*Lavinia*), Nick Navarro (*beatnik*), Pearl Shear (*fat woman on bus*), Barbara London (*waitress*), Barbara Reid (*girl on phone*), Roger Bacon (*Larry*), Don Conreaux (*Ralph*).

Comedy-drama. Source: Peter Shaffer, *The Private Ear* (London opening: 10 May 1962). Bob Handman, a shy, introverted lover of classical music, attends a Mozart concert and meets Doreen Marshall by accidentally spilling a soft drink on her. Doreen accepts his invitation to dinner at his Los Angeles apartment for the following evening; but preparing to entertain her, he panics and seeks the help of his best friend, Ted, a successful ladies' man. Ted coaches Bob, then prepares and serves the dinner; and Doreen is fascinated by Bob's suave friend. Bob gets drunk and fights with Ted, who leaves without bidding Doreen goodby. After playing recorded music from *Madama Butterfly*, which intrigues Doreen, Bob spoils his chances by making an awkward pass at her. As she leaves, Bob gives her Ted's telephone number and resigns himself to his lonely existence. *Playboys. Timidity. Friendship. Loneliness. Los Angeles. "Madama Butterfly".*

Note: Location scenes filmed in Los Angeles at the Whiskey-A-Go-Go and the Greek Theatre.

PADDY (Ireland)   F6.3700

Dun Laoghaire Productions. *Dist* Allied Artists. 29 Apr **1970** [Los Angeles opening]. Sd; col (Eastman Color by Pathé). 35mm. 97 min. *MPAA rating* GP.

Prod Tamara Asseyev. *Dir* Daniel Haller. *Screenplay & Adapt* Lee Dunne. *Photog* Daniel Lacambre. *Set Decor* Tim Booth. *Film Ed* Christopher Holmes. *Mus Supv* John Caper, Jr. *Mus* John Rubenstein. *Song:* "Paddy" John Rubenstein, David Colloff. *Sung by* Emmy Lou Harris. *Song:* "Maureen" John Rubenstein, Stephen Michaels. *Sung by* The Happenings. *Song:* "Oop Oomp Ee Doo" John Rubenstein, David Colloff. *Sd* Producers Sound Service. *Sd Eff Ed* Fred Brown, Jack Cheap. *Asst Dir* Seamus Byrne.

Cast: Milo O'Shea (*Harry Redmond*), Des Cave (*Paddy Maguire*), Dearbhla Molloy (*Maureen*), Maureen Toal (*Mrs. Kearney*), Peggy Cass (*Irenee*), Judy Cornwell (*Breeda*), Donal LeBlanc (*Larry Maguire*), Lillian Rapple (*Mrs. Doyle*), Desmond Perry (*Cahill*), Maire O'Donnell (*Mrs. Maguire*), Vincent Smith (*Billy Maguire*), Ita Darcy (*Josie Maguire*), Desmond Walter Ellis (*butcher's apprentice*), Dominic Roche (*Duncan Stuart*), Clive Geraghty (*Tony Deugan*), Alec Doran (*graveyard priest*), Mary Larkin (*Liz O'Boyle*), Pat Layde (*Mr. Hayes*), John Kavanagh (*Willie Egan*), John Molloy (*Watchbox*), Bill Foley (*priest*), Brendan Dunne (*Barney*), Mary Jo Kennedy (*Mary*), Mark Mulholland (*Jack Sloan*), Danny Cummins (*taxi driver*).

Drama. Source: Lee Dunne, *Goodbye to the Hill* (London, 1965). Paddy, a butcher boy in Dublin, Ireland, helps to support his family which has been deserted by his father. He seldom stays home, however, since he is constantly nagged by his mother, his sister, Josie, and his older brother, Billy. Paddy's pub companion, middle-aged Harry Redmond, has never held a job, but he nevertheless encourages Paddy to improve himself. After being seduced by one of his butcher store customers, a lusty widow named Claire Kearney, Paddy becomes her paid nightly companion until he takes a job as a mail clerk with an insurance company. In his new position, he falls in love with Maureen, a pretty secretary, and also becomes involved with Breeda, a woman of masochistic sexual inclinations who prefers making love with two men at once. Depressed by the death of his invalid younger brother, Larry, and upset by Maureen's suggestions of marriage, Paddy quits his job. Maureen reveals that she is pregnant and announces that she will marry another man since Paddy is unwilling to assume the responsibility. The two part, and Paddy resumes his carefree pursuits, while Harry latches onto a wealthy American tourist, Irenee. *Butchers. Ne'er-do-wells. Widows. Mail clerks. Secretaries. Tourists. Gigolos. Invalids. Family life. Desertion. Employment. Marriage. Sadomasochism. Seduction. Pregnancy. Troilism. Pubs. Dublin.*

Note: Released in Ireland in 1970. British running time: 87 min. Also known as *Goodbye to the Hill*.

IL PADRE DI FAMIGLIA see THE HEAD OF THE FAMILY

IL PAESE DI PAPERINO see THE SECRET OF MAGIC ISLAND

O PAGADOR DE PROMESSAS see THE GIVEN WORD

PAGAN HELLCAT see MAEVA

PAGAN ISLAND   F6.3701

Barry Mahon Productions. *Dist* Cinema Syndicate, Inc., Century Releasing Co. Jul **1961**. Sd; b&w (print by Movielab). 35mm. 67 min. [Also reviewed at 60 min.]

Prod-Dir Barry Mahon. *Script* Clelle Mahon. *Dir Photog* Mark Dennis, photog. *Sd* Peter Genung. *Re-rec* Magno Sound. *Asst Dir* Maurice McEndree. *Makeup* Richard Kereszi. *Opticals* B. & O. Film Specialists. *Casting* Bunny Yeager. *Master Electrn* Harry Duncan.

Cast: Edward Dew (*Stanton*), Nani Maka (*"Princess" Nani Maka*).

Adventure drama. Shipwrecked in the South Seas, Stanton is cast up on a mysterious island inhabited only by beautiful native women. At a feast given in his honor, he consumes too much liquor. Taken prisoner, he learns of the island's first contact with white men: long ago, pirates invaded, ravaging the women and destroying the underwater temple of the sea god. He learns that the beautiful women he sees have been sent from surrounding islands to care for Princess Nani Maka, who has been chosen to join in a sacrificial marriage to the sea god. The princess saves Stanton's life when he is left to die in the sun, and he in turn saves the islanders from enemy tribesmen. He is given his freedom but is forbidden to woo Nani Maka. Nevertheless, Stanton and the princess are irresistibly drawn to each other. On the day appointed for the sacrificial ceremony, Stanton joins Nani Maka on her journey beneath the water, and leads her to a dry cave. There they discover the ruins of the temple of the sea god and three chests of pirate treasure. They perform a marriage ceremony and stay the night. As they emerge from the cave entrance the next morning to return to Stanton's homeland, Nani Maka is caught in the jaws of a giant clam. Unable to save her, Stanton carries her body to his raft and sets out in anguish from the island. He drifts upon the seas until he is fished up by a schooner to tell his unhappy tale. *Royalty. Pirates. Human sacrifice. Marriage. Rites and ceremonies. South Seas. Shipwrecks. Clams.*

Note: Underwater sequence filmed at Seaquarium, Miami, Florida.

THE PAGANS see THE BARBARIANS

I PAGLIACCI (Austria/Switzerland/West Germany)   F6.3702
Cosmotel–Zweiten Deutschen Fernsehen–Österreichischen Rundfunk-Fernsehen. *Dist* Beta Film. 25 Jul **1970** [New York opening]. Sd; col (Eastman Color). 35mm. 79 min.

Prod Fritz Buttenstedt. *Dir* Herbert von Karajan. *Orig Staging* Paul Hager. *Photog* Ernst Wild. *Art Dir* Georges Wakhévitch. *Film Ed* Gela-Marina Runne. *Mus:* "I Pagliacci" Ruggero Leoncavallo. *Mus Cond* Herbert von Karajan. *Mus Played by* La Scala Orchestra. *Mus Sung by* La Scala Chorus. *Sd* Hans Weber, Günter Hermanns. *Asst Dir* Peter Busse. *Prod Asst* Dieter Meyer, Horant H. Hohlfeld. *Cost* Georges Wakhévitch.

Cast: Jon Vickers (*Canio*), Raina Corsi-Kabaiwanska (*Nedda*), Peter Glossop (*Tonio*), Sergio Lorenzi (*Beppe*), Rolando Panerai (*Silvio*), Carlo Ricciardi (*young farmer*), Carlo Moresi (*farmer*).

Opera film. Source: Ruggero Leoncavallo, *I Pagliacci* (first performance: Milan, 21 May 1892). A film adaptation of Leoncavallo's *I Pagliacci*. *Actors. Italians. Clowns. Cuckolds. Theater. Infidelity. Murder. Revenge. Theatrical troupes. Parades. Calabria.*

PAI-SHE CHUAN see MADAME WHITE SNAKE

PAIN AND PLEASURE   F6.3703
Americana Entertainment Association. *Dist* Boxoffice International Film Distributors. 30 Mar **1967** [San Francisco showing]. Sd; col. 35mm. 68 min.

Cast: Sammy Arena, Angelique.

Melodrama. Sammy, a deranged alcoholic, tries to escape from his past life and the pain of his present existence by drinking, going to erotic movies, and dreaming of nude dancers. He attempts to pick up a young blonde woman who reminds him of his former wife. The girl turns him down, and he rapes another young woman in a deserted warehouse. He is later seduced by a nymphomaniac. Sammy goes to another sex exploitation film and returns to the nymphomaniac's home. She is gone, but he discovers that the blonde girl who resembles his former wife is a houseguest. He attacks the girl and discovers in horror that she is his own daughter. She kills him with a liquor bottle. *Alcoholism. Rape. Nymphomania. Seduction. Filial relations. Incest. Murder. Mistaken identity. Insanity. Sex exploitation films.*

PAINT YOUR WAGON   F6.3704
Alan Jay Lerner Productions. *Dist* Paramount Pictures. 15 Oct **1969** [New York opening; c9 Oct 1969; LP38115]. Sd; col (Technicolor). 35mm (Panavision, see note). 166 min. [Also reviewed at 137 min.] *MPAA rating* M.

Prod-Screenplay Alan Jay Lerner. *Assoc Prod* Tom Shaw. *Dir* Joshua Logan. *2d Unit Dir* Tom Shaw, Fred Lemoine. *Adapt* Paddy Chayefsky. *Dir Photog* William A. Fraker. *2d Unit Photog* Loyal Griggs. *Aerial Photog* Nelson Tyler. *Camera Op* David M. Walsh. *Camera Asst* Bob Byrne. *Art Dir* Carl Braunger. *Set Decor* James Berkey. *Prod Dsgn* John Truscott. *Titl Dsgn* David Stone Martin. *Film Ed* Robert C. Jones. *Mus* Frederick Loewe. *Songs* Frederick Loewe, Alan Jay Lerner. *Adtl Songs* "The First Thing You Know," "A Million Miles Away Behind the Door," "The Gospel of No Name City," "Best Things," "Gold Fever" Andre Previn, Alan Jay Lerner. *Choral Mus Cond* Roger Wagner. *Orch Mus Scored & Cond* Nelson Riddle. *Choral Arr & Mus Asst to the Prod* Joseph J. Lilley. *Choreog for* "Gold Fever" *and* "Best Things" Jack Baker. *Sd Mix* William Randall, Jr. *Stereophonic Re-rec Supv* Fred Hynes. *Asst Dir & 2d Unit Asst Dir* Jack Roe, Al Murphy. *Prod Mgr* Carl

Beringer, Fred Lemoine. *Asst to the Prod* Jonas Halperin. *Prod Coörd* Gene Levy. *Script Supv* Marshall Wolins. *Cost* John Truscott. *Cost Supv* Bill Jobe. *Cost Coörd* Anne Laune. *Makeup* Frank McCoy. *Hairdresser* Vivienne Zavitz. *Sp Eff* Maurice Ayers, Larry Hampton. *Coöp* United States Forest Service. *Dial Coach* Joseph Curtis. *Gaffer* Joseph Smith. *Key Grip* Tom May. *Prop* Robert Eaton.

Cast: Lee Marvin (*Ben Rumson*), Clint Eastwood (*Pardner*), Jean Seberg (*Elizabeth*), Harve Presnell (*Rotten Lucky Willie*), Ray Walston (*Mad Jack Duncan*), Tom Ligon (*Horton Fenty*), Alan Dexter (*parson*), William O'Connell (*Horace Tabor*), Ben Baker (*Haywood Holbrook*), Alan Baxter (*Mr. Fenty*), Paula Trueman (*Mrs. Fenty*), Robert Easton (*Atwell*), Geoffrey Norman (*Foster*), H. B. Haggerty (*Steve Bull*), Terry Jenkins (*Joe Mooney*), Karl Bruck (*Schermerhorn*), John Mitchum (*Jacob Woodling*), Sue Casey (*Sarah Woodling*), Eddie Little Sky (*Indian*), Harvey Parry (*Higgins*), H. W. Gim (*Wong*), Roy Jenson (*Hennes*), Pat Hawley (*Clendennon*), William Mims (*frock-coated man*), The Nitty Gritty Dirt Band.

Musical comedy. Source: Alan Jay Lerner and Frederick Loewe, *Paint Your Wagon* (New York opening: 12 Nov 1951). During the California Gold Rush, while digging a grave for the victim of a covered wagon accident, prospector Ben Rumson discovers gold. Vowing to share the sizable stake with the dead man's surviving brother, Pardner, Rumson founds No Name City. At an auction Rumson purchases a Mormon's spare wife, Elizabeth, whom he also shares with Pardner. To alleviate the jealousy her presence causes in the mining camp, Rumson diverts a coach of French prostitutes to No Name City, where they quickly establish a brothel. In order to conserve loose gold dust, Rumson and Pardner honeycomb the town's streets and buildings with shallow mines. The depletion of the area's gold resources coincides with the arrival of the Fentys, a respectable New England couple. Taking pity on the couple's inhibited son, Rumson introduces the youth to the pleasures of Mother's Darling Hotel, the French whorehouse. Horrified, Elizabeth ejects Rumson from their home. As a traveling evangelist prophesies the town's destruction, a raging bull butts the supports of Rumson's tunnels, causing the collapse of No Name City. Following the camp's demise Rumson leaves for new adventures, while Elizabeth and Pardner farm the land. *Songs:* "I'm on My Way" (Ben, Pardner, Willie, Wong, Duncan, Clendennon, Foster, Schermerhorn, Tabor, Mooney, Holbrook, Woodling, and Miners), "I Still See Elisa" (Pardner), "The First Thing You Know" (Ben), "Hand Me Down That Can o' Beans" (Ben, Miners, and the Nitty Gritty Dirt Band), "They Call the Wind Maria" (Willie and Miners), "A Million Miles Away Behind the Door" (Elizabeth), "I Talk to the Trees" (Pardner), "There's a Coach Comin' In" (Miners), "Whoop-Ti-Ay!" (Miners), "The Gospel of No Name City" (The Parson), "Best Things" (Ben, Pardner, Duncan, Clendennon, and Foster), "Wand'rin Star" (Ben and Miners), "Gold Fever" (Pardner, Miners, and Dance Hall Girls), "I'm on My Way" (Miners). *Prospectors. Prostitutes. French. Evangelists. Frontier and pioneer life. Gold mining. Polygamy. Friendship. Gold rushes. Mining camps. Auctions. Whorehouses. California. Church of Jesus Christ of Latter-day Saints. Bulls.*

Note: Location scenes filmed in Oregon. Blown up to 70mm for some roadshow presentations.

THE PAINTED SMILE see MURDER CAN BE DEADLY

A PAIR OF BRIEFS (Great Britain)   F6.3705
Rank Organisation. *Dist* Davis Film Distributors. 16 Oct **1963** [Philadelphia opening]. Sd; b&w. 35mm. 90 min.

A Betty E. Box–Ralph Thomas Production. *Prod* Betty E. Box. *Exec Prod* Earl St. John. *Dir* Ralph Thomas. *Screenplay* Nicholas Phipps. *Photog* Ernest Steward. *Art Dir* Maurice Carter. *Film Ed* Alfred Roome. *Mus* Norrie Paramor. *Sd* Don Sharpe, Robert T. MacPhee. *Asst Dir* Anthony Waye. *Prod Mgr* Charles Orme.

Cast: Michael Craig (*Tony Stevens*), Mary Peach (*Frances Pilbright*), Brenda De Banzie (*Gladys Pudney*), James Robertson Justice (*Justice Hadden*), Roland Culver (*Sir John Pilbright*), Liz Fraser (*Pearly Girl*), Ron Moody (*Sid Pudney*), Jameson Clark (*George Lockwood*), Charles Heslop (*Peebles*), Bill Kerr (*Victor*), Nicholas Phipps (*Peter Sutcliffe*), Joan Sims (*Beryl*), John Standing (*Hubert Shannon*), Amanda Barrie (*Golly*), Judy Carne (*Maude*), Barbara Ferris (*Gloria Lockwood*), Myrtle Reed (*barmaid*), Terry Scott (*court attendant*), Graham Stark (*police officer*), Ronnie Stevens (*house detective*).

Farce. Source: Harold Brooke and Kay Bannerman, *How Say You?* (London opening: 22 Apr 1959). Fledgling barristers Frances Pilbright and Tony Stevens begin their careers at the same time in the London law offices of Sir John Pilbright, Frances' eminent uncle. Frances' first assignment is to defend Gladys Pudney in a suit for restitution of conjugal rights. Tony's solicitor friend Hubert Shannon takes pity on him and offers him the assignment of defending Cockney Sid Pudney against Gladys' claim. Gladys, dressed in a sable coat, leaves her Rolls Royce and enters a hotel, to emerge soon afterwards with the accent and attire of a poor North Country woman. She claims that she was married during the war, although the witnesses have since disappeared and the records of the marriage were destroyed. She explains that she suffered amnesia and that her husband, Sid, left her shortly thereafter. Upon regaining her memory she contacted Sid, but he denied ever having married her. Frances and Tony incur the wrath of Justice Hadden through their courtroom inexperience, and the irascible judge threatens to have them disbarred. The judge finally rules that there is no legal proof that Gladys was ever married to Sid Pudney. Frances immediately sets an appeal in motion, but Tony accidentally discovers that Gladys initiated the case with the intention of losing it. Now happily married to a millionaire, she feared that Sid would find out that she was wealthy and try to blackmail her. Tony and Frances declare their love and plan to marry. *Barristers. Judges. Cockneys. Uncles. Millionaires. Trials. Marriage. Marriage—Common law. Amnesia. Hoaxes. Desertion. London.*

Note: Released in Great Britain in Apr 1962.

PAJAMA PARTY F6.3706

American International Pictures. 11 Nov **1964** [Chicago opening; c11 Nov 1964; LP29677]. Sd; col (Pathécolor). 35mm (Panavision). 85 min. [Copyright length: 75 min.]

Prod James H. Nicholson, Samuel Z. Arkoff. *Co-prod* Anthony Carras. *Dir* Don Weis. *Screenplay* Louis M. Heyward. *Photog* Floyd Crosby. *Camera Asst* Travis Hill, Fred Pearce. *Art Dir* Daniel Haller. *Set Decor* Harry Reif. *Main Titl* Butler-Glouner Inc. *Film Ed* Fred Feitshans, Eve Newman. *Mus Score* Les Baxter. *Mus Supv* Al Simms. *Songs:* "It's That Kind of Day," "There Has To Be a Reason," "Where Did I Go Wrong?" "Pajama Party," "Beach Ball," "Among the Young," "Stuffed Animal" Guy Hemric, Jerry Styner. *Choreog* David Winters. *Sd Ed* James Nelson. *Mus Ed* Milton Lustig. *Sd* Phil Mitchell. *Rec* Howard Wallman. *Boom Op* Ronald Sterling. *Asst Dir* Clark Paylow, Robert J. Rubin. *Prod Supv* Joe Wonder. *Prod Asst* Jack Cash. *Script Supv* Betty Crosby. *Cost & Dsgn* Marjorie Corso. *Makeup* Bob Dawn. *Hairdresser* Eve Newing. *Photog Sp Eff* Butler-Glouner Inc. *Sp Eff* Roger George, Joe Zomar. *Constr Coörd* Ross Hahn. *Prop* Karl Brainard. *Motorcycle Coörd* George Dockstader. *Still Photog* John Monte. *Grip* Charles Hannawalt. *Gaffer* Charles Beckett.

Cast: Tommy Kirk (*Go-Go*), Annette Funicello (*Connie*), Elsa Lanchester (*Aunt Wendy*), Harvey Lembeck (*Eric Von Zipper*), Jesse White (*J. Sinister Hulk*), Jody McCrea (*Big Lunk*), Ben Lessy (*Fleegle*), Donna Loren (*Vikki*), Susan Hart (*Jilda*), Bobbi Shaw (*Helga*), Cheryl Sweeten (*Francine*), Luree Holmes (*perfume girl*), Candy Johnson (*Candy*), Buster Keaton (*Chief Rotten Eagle*), Dorothy Lamour (*head saleslady*), Andy Romano, Linda Rogers, Alan Fife, Alberta Nelson, Jerry Brutsche, Bob Harvey (*The Rat Pack*), Renie Riano (*maid*), Joi Holmes (*topless bathing suit model*), Kerry Kollmar (*little boy*), Joan Neel, Patricia O'Reilly, Marion Kildany, Linda Opie, Mary Hughes, Patti Chandler, Laura Nicholson, Linda Benson, Carey Foster, Stacey Maxwell, Teri Hope, Margo Mehling, Diane Bond, Keva Page, Toni Basil, Kay Sutton, Connie Ducharme, Joyce Nizzari, Leslie Wenner (*The Pajama Girls*), Ray Atkinson, Frank Alesia, Ned Wynn, Ronnie Rondell, Howard Curtis, John Fain, Mike Nader, Rick Newton, Guy Hemric, Ed Garner, Frank Mortiforte, Ronnie David, Gus Trikonis, Bob Pane, Roger Bacon, Ronnie Dayton (*The Pajama Boys*), Nooney Rickett Four (*themselves*).

Comedy with music. A Martian invasion of Earth is planned, and Go-Go is the envoy sent to prepare the way. He lands in Aunt Wendy's garden and meets Big Lunk, her muscular nephew, and his friend Connie. Aunt Wendy, an eccentric who owns a dress shop, is reputedly hiding a small fortune in her house, and therefore she is the object of a robbery plan by con men J. Sinister Hulk and Fleegle. There is also trouble brewing from motorcycle gang leader Eric Von Zipper, who is jealous of Big Lunk's affection for Connie. Meanwhile, Go-Go tries in vain to convince Aunt Wendy and Connie that he is really a Martian and that an invasion is imminent. Aided by Chief Rotten Eagle and Helga, a sexy Swede sent to pry information from Big Lunk about the hidden money, the con men crash a pajama party given by Aunt Wendy for the teenagers; but Go-Go saves the day by "teleporting" the would-be robbers to Mars. The motorcycle gang and Eric Von Zipper are also dealt with, and Go-Go persuades the Martians to call off the invasion. Go-Go, who has fallen in love with Connie, decides to stay on Earth, and Big Lunk wins the affection of Helga, who does not understand English. *Spacemen. Aunts. Eccentrics. Confidence men. Swedes. Indians of North America. Motorcycle gangs. Adolescence. Robbery. Jealousy. Teleportation. Mars (planet).*

Note: Working title: *The Maid and the Martian.*

PAJAMA PARTY IN THE HAUNTED HOUSE *see* **THE GHOST IN THE INVISIBLE BIKINI**

A PÁL UTCAI FIÚK *see* **THE BOYS OF PAUL STREET**

PALACE OF NUDES (France/Italy) F6.3707

Lutétia–U. E. C. *Dist* William Mishkin. Feb **1961** [New York showing]. Sd; b&w. 35mm. 96 min.

Assoc Prod Robert Florat. *Dir* Pierre Méré. *Screenplay* Jacques Chabannes, Lucien Rimmels. *Dial & Adapt* Jacques Chabannes. *Photog* Pierre Dolley. *Camera* Roger Duculot. *Mus* Marcel Landowski. *Sd* Maurice Carrouet. *Asst Dir* Danny Fox. *Prod Mgr* Marc Hellain. *Script Girl* Andrey de Ryan. *Makeup* Lala Janvier.

Cast: Claude Godard (*Mado*), Daniel Clérice (*Max*), Jean-Pierre Kérien (*Inspector Million*), Robert Berri (*Fred*), Jean Tissier (*Grumeau*), Magda, Paul Demange, Paul Ensia, Jean Daurand, Célia Cortez, Ariane Lancel, Monique Vivin, Gina Manès, Ballets d'Evelyne Gray.

Crime melodrama. At the Concert Mayol, which features lavish striptease shows, Mado, the star, drinks poison in a glass of champagne used in a production number and is rushed to a hospital, where her life is saved. Some time later, however, Mado's understudy, Lydia, is found shot while wearing one of Mado's costumes. Inspector Million is brought in, and after numerous embarrassing experiences he realizes that the murderer was after Lydia all the time. The director of the show, who recently quarrelled with Lydia, comes under suspicion, as does Fred, a narcotics dealer and pimp with whom she has been having an affair. Soon the evidence against Max, Mado's lead singer and current lover, builds up in spite of his efforts to incriminate Bob, Lydia's protector. Although Max eludes the police, Bob eventually captures him. *Stripteasers. Police. Theatrical directors. Drug dealers. Pimps. Singers. Poisoning. Mistaken identity. Murder. Concert Mayol (Paris).*

Note: Filmed on location at the Concert Mayol in Paris. Opened in Paris in Sep 1954 as *Crime au Concert Mayol*; running time: 97 min. Also known as *Palace of Shame.*

PALACES OF A QUEEN (Great Britain) F6.3708

Rank Organisation. *Dist* Universal Pictures. 26 Jun **1967** [New York opening]. Sd; col (Eastmancolor). 35mm. 80 min. [Also reviewed at 75 min.]

Prod George Grafton Green. *Asst Prod* Antony Barrier. *Dir* Michael Ingrams. *Comm* Christopher Hibbert. *Treatment Devised by* Alec Clifton-Taylor. *Photog* Peter Cannon. *Aerial Photog* Albert Werry. *Main Titl* Albert Urry. *Film Ed* Roy Drew. *Mus Arr & Cond* Malcolm Sargent. *Mus Played by* Royal Philharmonic Orchestra. *Musical Selections* George Frederick Handel, Edward Elgar, Walford Davies, Arthur Bliss. *Sd* Alfred Witcomb, Edward Drake, Arthur Irwin. *Asst Dir* Roger Pennington. *Prod Mgr* E. A. Candy.

Narrator: Michael Redgrave.

Documentary. This filmed tour of Windsor Castle, Buckingham Palace, St. James's Palace, Hampton Court, Kensington Palace, and the Palace of Holyrood House at Edinburgh explores both the grounds and interiors of the individual structures. Aerial views establish the Thames as a river of palaces, and the accompanying narration relates both the historical background and present use of these official residences. In addition, sidelights focus on Henry VIII's suit of armor that made allowances for the size of his stomach, Queen Victoria's extensive collection of dolls and family photographs, the room in Holyrood House where Mary of Scotland's secretary, David Rizzio, was murdered, and the study used by Queen Elizabeth II. *Royalty. Armor. Dolls. Photographs. Thames River. London. Edinburgh. Henry VIII (England). Queen Victoria. David Rizzio. Elizabeth II (England). Windsor Castle. Buckingham Palace. Saint James's Palace. Hampton Court. Kensington Palace. Palace of Holyrood House.*

Note: Released in Great Britain in 1967.

PALM SPRINGS WEEKEND F6.3709

Warner Bros. Pictures. 5 Nov **1963** [New York opening; c23 Nov 1963; LP29432]. Sd; col (Technicolor). 35mm. 100 min.

Prod Michael A. Hoey. *Dir* Norman Taurog. *Screenplay* Earl Hamner, Jr. *Dir Photog* Harold Lipstein. *Camera Op* George Nogle. *Asst Camera* Alan MacKenzie, J. B. Allen. *Art Dir* LeRoy Deane. *Asst Art Dir* Charles Clarke. *Set Decor* George James Hopkins. *Film Ed* Folmar Blangsted. *Asst Ed* Tom Martin. *Mus* Frank Perkins. *Song:* "Live Young" Larry Kusik, Paul Evans. *Sung by* Troy Donahue. *Sd Mix* Stanley Jones. *Rec* Robert J. Miller. *Boom Op* John Jensen. *Asst Dir* Charles L. Hansen, Stanley Goldsmith, Phil Ball, Mecca Graham, Bob Templeton. *Prod Asst* Charles L. Hansen. *Script Supv* Dorothy Aldrin. *Location Mgr* Joseph Barry. *Men's Cost* B. Richards, M. Butler. *Women's Cost* Joyce Rogers, May Booth, Norma Brown. *Makeup Supv* Gordon Bau. *Makeup* Norman Pringle, Fred Williams. *Body Makeup* Faye Chaney. *Supv Hairstyles* Jean Burt Reilly. *Hairstyles* Ray Foreman, Fae Smith. *Prop Master* Robert Cooper. *Dial Dir* Jack Mintz. *Still Photog* Bert Six. *Gaffer* Charles O'Bannon. *Grip* Harold Noyes.

Cast: Troy Donahue (*Jim Munroe*), Connie Stevens (*Gail Lewis*), Ty Hardin (*Stretch Fortune*), Stefanie Powers (*Bunny Dixon*), Robert Conrad (*Eric Dean*), Andrew Duggan (*Chief Dixon*), Jack Weston (*Coach Campbell*), Carole Cook (*Mrs. Yates*), Jerry Van Dyke (*Biff Roberts*), Zeme North (*Amanda*

North), Billy Mumy *(Boom-Boom),* Dorothy Green *(Cora Dixon),* Robert Gothie *(Gabby),* Greg Benedict *(Hap),* Gary Kincaid *(Fred),* Mark Dempsey *(Mike),* Jim Shane *(Dave),* Tina Cole *(Ruth Stewart),* Sandy Kevin, Roger Bacon, Margo Spinker, The Modern Folk Quartet.

Comedy. Every Easter, Palm Springs, California, is invaded by youngsters seeking fun and adventure, to the distress of Police Chief Dixon and his wife, Cora. On one of the buses headed for the vacation spot is a college basketball team with its captain, medical student Jim Munroe, and Coach Campbell. On the same bus is Hollywood High School senior Gail Lewis, who pretends to be a wealthy college girl. The bus breaks down, and Gail gets a ride to the resort with playboy Eric Dean, the spoiled son of a millionaire. On the way they meet Stretch Fortune, a Hollywood stuntman from Texas, to whom Gail becomes attracted. In Palm Springs, Jim meets Chief Dixon's daughter Bunny, who works in a record shop; and he takes her to a party, which is invaded by local hoodlums. After a brawl that ends up at the police station, everyone is released with a warning, but Chief Dixon forbids Jim to see his daughter again. Meanwhile, Eric tries to force himself on Gail, but she is rescued by Stretch, who gives Eric a beating. Stretch is pursued by the maddened Eric, who sideswipes Stretch's car, causing it to overturn. Jim, who has been trailing the two, pulls Stretch from the burning wreck. Gail visits Stretch at the hospital, confesses that she is only a high school student, and obtains his forgiveness. Meanwhile, Coach Campbell has won the affections of Mrs. Yates, a widow who owns the hotel where the team is staying, and Gail's homely roommate, Amanda North, has paired off with Biff Roberts, a bumbling member of the basketball team. As the students leave Palm Springs, Bunny promises to wait for Jim until he finishes medical school, and even Chief Dixon softens enough to invite the young people back next Easter. *Police. Athletes. Students. Playboys. Texans. Widows. Roommates. Athletic coaches. Stuntmen. Filial relations. Basketball. Vacations. Duplicity. Buses. Easter. Palm Springs. Hollywood. Chases. Automobile accidents.*

Note: Location scenes filmed in Palm Springs, California.

PAMELA, PAMELA YOU ARE ...   F6.3710

Dist Distribpix, Inc., Schooner Bay Productions. 20 Dec **1968** [New York opening]. Sd; b&w with col seq. 35mm. 90 min. *MPAA rating* X.

Pres by Howard Farber, Arthur Morowitz. A William L. Rose Production. *Prod-Dir* William L. Rose. *Assoc Prod* Milton Meshel, Edward Jacobs. *Story-Screenplay* William L. Rose, Richard B. Shull. *Camera* Victor Petroshevic, Sherman Price, Victor Hurwitz. *Film Ed* William D. Gordy, Sherman Price. *Mus Score* Graham Forbes, Sherman Price. *Titl Song Mus* Graham Forbes. *Titl Song Lyr* William L. Rose. *Sung by* Molly Lion. *Prod Mgr* William D. Gordy. *Cont* Harold Cherry, Anne Hancock. *Prod Asst* Judith Ettinger.

Cast: Elaine Edwards *(Pamela),* Paul Hardy *(Calvin),* Mary Lindsay *(Susan),* Sherman Lloyd *(Felix),* Henry Andrews *(Charles),* Margaret Ann Cathell *(Evelyn),* Paul Zayas *(Nazi),* Barbara Ellen *(secretary).*

Drama. Wealthy Pamela Browning meets profligate Calvin Miller at a party and, as a protest against middle age, makes love to him in her Long Island home. Her stepdaughter, Susan, finds them together, and Calvin later seduces her as well. Calvin uses Pamela's home for a party and invites many of his debauched friends. There is an orgy, and Pamela takes drugs offered her by Calvin. She finds Calvin in a parked car with Susan and begins to hallucinate. *The party guests, dressed as monks and nuns, throw garbage at her and watch as Calvin rapes her in a muddy alley. She walks naked on the beach, and hands reach up out of the sand to pull her down.* Pamela's husband returns home, and he gives Pamela strength to put Calvin out of her life. *Rakes. Housewives. Socialites. Marriage. Infidelity. Filial relations. LSD. Hallucinations. Middle age.*

PAMPA SALVAJE *see* SAVAGE PAMPAS

PANDA AND THE MAGIC SERPENT (Japan)   F6.3711

Toei Animation Studio Co. *For* Toei Co. *Dist* Globe Pictures. 8 Jul **1961** [New Orleans opening]. Sd; col (Eastman Color). 35mm. 76 min.

Exec Prod Hiroshi Okawa. *Assoc Prod* Hideyuki Takahashi, Koichi Akagawa, Sanae Yamamoto. *Dir* Kazuhiko Okabe, Teiji Yabushita. *Screenplay* Teiji Yabushita, Shin Uehara. *Orig Dial* Seiichi Yashiro. *Anim* Yasuo Otsuka, Yusaku Sakamoto. *Orig Drawing* Akira Daikubara, Yasuji Mori. *Background* Kazuo Kusano. *Dir Photog* Takamitsu Tsukahara. *Art Dir* Kazuhiko Okabe, Kiyoshi Hashimoto. *Film Ed* Shintaro Miyamoto. *Mus* Chuji Kinoshita. *Sd Rec* Takeshi Mori.

Narrator: Marvin Miller.

Animated melodrama. Inspired by the Chinese fairy tale "Pai she chuan." Hsü Hsien falls in love with Pai Niang, a lovely immortal who is the incarnation of a white snake. Accompanied by Panda and a raccoon named Mimi, they travel across the countryside of ancient China. Fa Hai, a wizard who knows of Pai Niang's transformation, tries to break up the lovers by drowning them in the Yangtze River; after that attempt fails, he arranges for Hsü Hsien's arrest on a robbery charge. The boy is exiled, but Panda and Mimi help him escape.

Later Hsü Hsien falls from a precipice while chasing Pai Niang's shadow and is killed. To bring Hsü Hsien back to life, Pai Niang sacrifices her immortality to the dragon god, and after being rescued during a storm at sea, the lovers are reunited. *Sorcerers. Reincarnation. Immortality. Frameup. Exile. Sea rescue. Self-sacrifice. China. Yangtze River. Storms. Snakes. Pandas. Raccoons.*

Note: Released in Japan in 1958 as *Hakuja den;* running time: 90 min.

PANIC (Great Britain)   F6.3712

Ingram Films. *Dist* Schoenfeld Film Distributing Corp. 5 Jan **1966** [Newark, New Jersey, opening]. Sd; b&w. 35mm. 69 min.

Prod Guido Coen. *Dir-Writ* John Gilling. *Story* Guido Coen, John Gilling. *Photog* Geoffrey Faithfull. *Art Dir* Duncan Sutherland. *Film Ed* Bill Lewthwaite. *Sd* Stephen Dalby. *Sd Rec* Syd Wiles. *Asst Dir* Ernie Lewis. *Prod Mgr* Al Marcus.

Cast: Janine Gray *(Janine Heining),* Glyn Houston *(Mike),* Dyson Lovell *(Johnnie Cobb),* Duncan Lamont *(Inspector Saunders),* Stanley Meadows *(Tom),* Brian Weske *(Ben),* Charles Houston *(Louis Cobb),* Philip Ray *(Jessop),* Marne Maitland *(Lantern),* John Horsley *(Inspector Malcolm),* Dermot Kelly *(Murphy),* Paul Carpenter *(flight commentator),* Sean Lynch *(layabout in cafe),* Colin Rix *(Detective Sergeant Rose),* Roland Curram *(Frinton),* Milton Reid *(Dan),* Julie Mendez *(Lucette),* Duncan Lewis *(Joe),* Jeremy Hawk *(Spike),* Leonard Sachs *(Len Collier),* Vic Wise *(Benny),* Garry Davis *(Bobby Shark),* Manning Wilson *(policeman).*

Crime drama. Janine Heining, Swiss secretary to a diamond merchant, lives with her musician boyfriend, Johnnie Cobb, who secretly plots a get-rich-quick scheme. Johnnie intercepts a letter from Janine's boss to a German jewelry firm and has his friends Ben and Tom pose as diamond merchants sent by the firm to pick up a valuable stone. The ruse is discovered and the two crooks kill Janine's boss and knock her out. As a result of the blow, Janine suffers from amnesia and wanders through London as Johnnie worries about her going to the police. Visiting his brother Louis, he finds Janine has been there and in the argument that ensues, Louis is accidentally killed. Meanwhile, Janine is befriended by an ex-boxer, Mike Connor, who is aware of her true identity through newspapers and broadcasts. To raise money for Janine's safe passage out of the country, Mike enters the ring for one more bout. Finally tracking Janine down, Johnnie appears outside the arena just as Mike emerges, and when he begins to beat the weary fighter, Janine shoots him. *Musicians. Secretaries. Prizefighters. Diamond merchants. Theft. Imposture. Amnesia. Murder. Gems. London. Motion picture producers. Actors. Accountants. Detectives. Police. Murder. Fraud. Infidelity.*

Note: Released in Great Britain in Apr 1965.

PANIC BUTTON   F6.3713

Yankee Productions. *Dist* Gorton Associates. Apr **1964.** Sd; b&w. 35mm (Totalscope). 90 min.

Prod-Orig Story Ron Gorton. *Dir* George Sherman. *Screenplay* Hal Biller. *Adapt* Mort Friedman. *Story* Ron Gorton. *Cinematog* Enzo Serafin. *Songs & Mus* Georges Garvarentz.

Cast: Maurice Chevalier *(Philippe Fontaine),* Eleanor Parker *(Louise Harris),* Jayne Mansfield *(Angela),* Michael Connors *(Frank Pagano),* Akim Tamiroff *(Pandowski),* Carlo Croccolo *(Guido),* Vincent Barbi *(Mario).*

Comedy. Faced with the ruinous prospect of having to pay income tax on $500,000, business executive Frank Pagano decides to invest the money in a project that he believes is doomed to financial ruin: a television pilot film based on the story of Romeo and Juliet. Pagano hires Pandowski, an eccentric disciple of Stanislavski, to direct the film and casts Philippe Fontaine, a faded French actor long forgotten in Hollywood, as Romeo. For the role of Juliet, Pagano hires Angela, a starlet with a voluptuous body but no talent. When the film is finished, Philippe and his ex-wife Louise steal a print and, disguised as nuns, take it to the Venice Film Festival. The film is mistaken for a satire by the festival jury and is awarded the Golden Lion for the best comedy. Fontaine swallows his wounded pride and accepts his new reputation as a comedian. Pagano arrives on the scene and, making the best of the situation, decides to become a film producer. *Businessmen. Eccentrics. Motion picture directors. Actors. French. Motion picture producers. Finance—Personal. Motion pictures. Theft. Disguise. Income tax. Awards. Venice. Venice Film Festival. "Romeo and Juliet".*

Note: Filmed in Rome and Venice.

PANIC IN THE CITY   F6.3714

United Pictures-Harold Goldman Associates. *Dist* Commonwealth United Entertainment, Inc. Feb **1968** [Los Angeles showing]. Sd; col (Eastman Color). 35mm. 97 min.

Prod Earle Lyon. *Dir* Eddie Davis. *Screenplay* Eddie Davis, Charles E. Savage. *Photog* Alan Stensvold. *Art Dir* Paul Sylos, Jr. *Film Ed* Terry O. Morse. *Mus* Paul Dunlap. *Sd* Brad Trask. *Asst Dir* William Schwartz.

Cast: Nehemiah Persoff (*August Best*), Anne Jeffreys (*Myra Pryor*), Howard Duff (*Dave Pomeroy*), Linda Cristal (*Dr. Paula Stevens*), Stephen McNally (*James Kincade*), Oscar Beregi (*Dr. Paul Cerbo*), Gregory Morton (*Steadman*), Dennis Hopper (*Goff*), George Barrows, John Hoyt, Steve Franken, Wesley Lau, Jim Adams, Hank Brandt, Eddie Firestone, John Pickard, Cal Currens, Jan Watson, Elaine Beckett, Stanley Clements, Walter Reed, Leon Lontoc, Deanna Lund, Edith Loder, Wendy Stuart, Robert Terry, Bee Tompkins, Mike Farrell, Eilene Janssen, Jim Kline, William Tannen, Dodie Warren, Rush Williams, Douglas Evans, Maurice Wells, James Seay, Al Shafran, Renee Redman, Tex Armstrong, Walter Scott, George Sawaya.

Action melodrama. Dave Pomeroy, an agent for the National Bureau of Investigation (NBI), is called to investigate the death of a distinguished European nuclear scientist who was admitted to a hospital suffering from severe radiation burns and was murdered there before he could be questioned. Pomeroy discovers that the only person in the United States to have worked with the dead man is Czech scientist Dr. Paul Cerbo. Aided by radiologist Dr. Paula Stevens, Pomeroy learns that Cerbo is in league with two Communist conspirators, August Best and his assistant Myra Pryor, who plan to start World War III by detonating an atom bomb in the heart of Los Angeles. By the time Pomeroy locates the Communist headquarters, the deranged Best has triggered the bomb's reactor so that no one can prevent it from exploding. In an unsuccessful attempt to deactivate the device, Pomeroy is exposed to a fatal overdose of radiation. Warning everyone to stay clear of him, he calls a helicopter, replaces the pilot, flies out over the Pacific with the bomb, and sacrifices himself to save Los Angeles and the world from catastrophe. *Secret agents. Scientists. Communists. Physicians. Czechoslovakians. Espionage. Murder. Nuclear warfare. Conspiracy. Self-sacrifice. Atom bomb. Helicopters. Hospitals. Radiation. Los Angeles.*

Note: Location scenes filmed in Los Angeles.

PANIC IN YEAR ZERO!　　　　　　　　　　F6.3715
Alta Vista Productions. *Dist* American International Pictures. 4 Jul **1962** [Miami, Florida, opening; c18 Jun 1962; LP23129]. Sd; b&w. 35mm. 92 min.

A James H. Nicholson–Samuel Z. Arkoff Production. *Prod* Arnold Houghland, Lou Rusoff. *Exec Prod* James H. Nicholson, Samuel Z. Arkoff. *Dir* Ray Milland. *Screenplay* Jay Simms, John Morton. *Story* Jay Simms. *Dir Photog* Gilbert Warrenton. *Art Dir* Daniel Haller. *Set Dsgn* Daniel Haller. *Set Decor* Harry Reif. *Opticals & Titl* Ray Mercer. *Film Ed* William Austin, Anthony Carras. *Asst Film Ed* Jerry Irvin. *Mus* Les Baxter. *Mus Coörd* Al Simms. *Sd* Steve Bass. *Sd Ed* Al Bird. *Mus Ed* Eve Newman. *Asst Dir* Jim Engle, Les Gorall. *Prod Supv* Bartlett A. Carre. *Unit Mgr* Robert Agnew. *Script Supv* Billy Vernon. *Prod Asst* Jack Cash. *Wardrobe* Marjorie Corso. *Makeup* Ted Coodley. *Hairstyles* Betty Pedretti. *Sp Eff* Pat Dinga, Larry Butler. *Prop Master* Dick Rubin. *Constr* Ross Hahn. *Still Photog* Ed Jones.

Cast: Ray Milland (*Harry Baldwin*), Jean Hagen (*Ann Baldwin*), Frankie Avalon (*Rick Baldwin*), Mary Mitchell (*Karen Baldwin*), Joan Freeman (*Marilyn Hayes*), Richard Garland (*Mr. Johnson*), Richard Bakalyan (*Carl*), Rex Holman (*Mickey*), Neil Nephew (*Andy*), Willis Bouchey (*Dr. Strong*), O. Z. Whitehead (*Hogan*), Byron Morrow (*Haenel*), Shary Marshall (*Mrs. Johnson*), Russ Bender (*Harkness*), Hugh Sanders (*Becker*), Andrea Lane, Scott Peters, Bud Slater, Kelton Crawford.

Melodrama. Harry Baldwin, his wife, Ann, and their two children, 17-year-old Karen and 19-year-old Rick, leave their home in Los Angeles for a fishing trip. Two hours after their departure, they hear a tremendous explosion and learn that the city has been demolished by a nuclear attack. It soon becomes apparent that the greatest danger facing them is from the hordes of frightened looters running rampant. After deciding their safest course is to proceed to their vacation spot, they stop to pick up provisions and ammunition. When they reach their fishing spot, they set up home in a cave, where they will be protected from radiation. Nearby, three young hoodlums have taken over a farmhouse and are ravaging the countryside. They murder a couple who have followed the Baldwins to the area. Two of the thugs come upon Karen when she is alone and brutally rape her. They are shot by Harry and Rick, who also find that the youths have been holding a girl, Marilyn Hayes, as their prisoner. Taken to the cave, she is menaced by the third thug, but she takes Rick's rifle and kills him. When the radio reports that Los Angeles is safe, the family and Marilyn prepare to return to civilization and face the enormous task of rebuilding. *Hoodlums. Nuclear warfare. Looting. Murder. Survival. Rape. Caves. Los Angeles.*

Note: Working titles: *Survival* and *The End of the World*. Rereleased in Mar 1965 under the latter title.

PANORAMA OF RUSSIA (U.S.S.R.)　　　　　F6.3716
Leningrad Newsreel Studio. *Dist* Artkino Pictures. 4 Jul **1964** [New York opening]. Sd; col. 35mm. 65 min.

Dir Yefim Uchitel. *Screenplay* I. Kotenko, Yefim Uchitel. *Photog* N. Blazhkov, N. Vinogradskiy, F. Ovsyannikov. *Mus* V. Chistyakov, S. Tombak. *Sd* Ye. Belskiy, N. Zinina.

Cast: Irina Arkhipova, Boris Shtokolov.

Documentary. A musical tour of Russia, featuring Soviet opera singers Irina Arkhipova and Boris Shtokolov. Selections include "Moscow Evenings" ("Podmoskovnyye vechera"), "Song of the Volga Boatmen" ("Ey, ukhnem!"), and solos from Musorgski's opera *Boris Godunov*. *Singers. Opera. Folk music.*

Note: Released in the U.S.S.R. in 1963 as *Pesni Rossii*.

PAPARAZZI　　　　　　　　　　　　　　F6.3717
C. I. T. Films. *Dist* I. R. M. I. Films. 19 Feb **1969** [New York showing]. Sd; col (Eastman color). 35mm. 55 min.

Dir Bruno Geller.

Sex film. No information about the precise nature of this film has been found. *Photographers. Sexuality.*

Note: Press material indicates filming in Paris, Cannes, and London.

PAPA'S DELICATE CONDITION　　　　　　F6.3718
Amro Productions. *Dist* Paramount Pictures. 6 Mar **1963** [New York opening; c28 Feb 1963; LP24121]. Sd; col (Technicolor). 35mm. 98 min.

Prod-Screenplay Jack Rose. *Dir* George Marshall. *Camera* Loyal Griggs. *Art Dir* Hal Pereira, Arthur Lonergan. *Set Decor* Sam Comer, James Payne. *Film Ed* Frank P. Keller. *Mus Scored & Cond* Joseph J. Lilley. *Song:* "Call Me Irresponsible" Sammy Cahn, James Van Heusen. *Sd* Gene Merritt, Charles Grenzbach. *Asst Dir* Arthur Jacobson. *Cost* Edith Head. *Sp Photog Eff* Paul K. Lerpae.

Cast: Jackie Gleason (*Jack "Papa" Griffith*), Glynis Johns (*Ambolyn Griffith*), Laurel Goodwin (*Augusta Griffith*), Linda Bruhl (*Corinne Griffith*), Charlie Ruggles (*Grandpa Anthony Ghio*), Ned Glass ("*Sparrow*" *Wildman*), Murray Hamilton (*Mr. Harvey*), Elisha Cook (*Mr. Keith*), Charles Lane (*Hiram Cosgrove*), Benny Baker (*Douglas*), Claude Johnson (*Norman*), Ken Renard (*Walter*), Don Beddoe (*Mr. Looby*), Trevor Bardette (*Stanley Henderson II*), Juanita Moore (*Ellie*).

Biographical comedy-drama. Source: Corinne Griffith, *Papa's Delicate Condition* (Boston, 1952). Jack Griffith, a boisterous and hard-drinking railroad supervisor who lives in turn-of-the-century Texas, is worshiped by his 6-year-old daughter, Corinne, although his behavior is a constant source of embarrassment to his wife, Ambolyn, and his elder daughter, Augusta. One of his more extravagant gestures is the purchase of a drugstore so that he and his cronies can drink on Sunday. He also buys a bankrupt circus in order to get a pony and its gaily decorated cart for Corinne. When he is forced to use all the family savings to pay the circus' debts, the disgusted Ambolyn takes their two daughters and moves to Texarkana, where her father, Anthony Ghio, is the mayor. In order to get back in his family's good graces, Jack takes his circus to Texarkana and uses it to insure his father-in-law's reelection. He tries to take Corinne back with him, but Ambolyn goes after them and in the struggle Corinne falls and injures her hand. Jack becomes so despondent over the incident that he disappears. Months later, Papa Ghio realizes that the family sorely misses the flamboyant Jack. After tracking him down in Louisiana, he persuades him to return to Texas. At first Jack is reluctant to enter the family house; but when he hears Ambolyn playing "Won't You Come Home Bill Bailey" on the piano, he makes his entrance and is reunited with his family. *Railroad superintendents. Eccentrics. Fathers-in-law. Mayors. Grandfathers. Fatherhood. Family life. Debt. Elections. Drugstores. Circus. Texarkana. Texas. Louisiana. John Lewis Griffith. Corinne Griffith.*

PAPER LION　　　　　　　　　　　　　F6.3719
Stuart Millar Productions. *Dist* United Artists. 2 Oct **1968** [Detroit opening; c30 Oct 1968; LP36690]. Sd; col (Technicolor). 35mm (Techniscope). 105 min.

Pres by Stuart Millar. *Prod* Stuart Millar. *Assoc Prod* Nicholas Masci. *Dir* Alex March. *Screenplay* Lawrence Roman. *Dir Photog* Morris Hartzband, Peter Garbarini. *Sp Game Photog* Steve Sabol, Fred Hoffman, Al Taffet, Jack Schatz, Joseph Wheeler, Eugene Friedman, David Marx, Richard Pollister, Fred Porrett, Morris Kellman. *Set Dsgn* Hank Aldrich. *Titl Dsgn* Joe Caroff. *Film Ed* Sidney Katz, John Carter, ed, Louis San Andres. *Mus* Roger Kellaway. *Sd Ed* Dan Sable, Al Nahmias, Vincent Connelly. *Mus Ed* John Strauss. *Asst Dir* Peter Scoppa, Ted Zachary. *Prod Supv* Roger Michael Rothstein. *Prod Mgr* Willard W. Goodman, Fred Gallo. *Vis Cons* Elliott Erwitt.

Cast: Alan Alda (*George Plimpton*), Lauren Hutton (*Kate*), David Doyle (*Oscar*), Ann Turkel (*Susan*), Sugar Ray Robinson (*himself*), Frank Gifford (*himself*), Vincent Lombardi (*himself*), Joe Schmidt (*himself*), Alex Karras, John Gordy, Mike Lucci, Pat Studstill, Roger Brown (*themselves, members of the Detroit Lions*), Detroit Lions' Coaching Staff & Players (*themselves*).

Comedy. Source: George Plimpton, *Paper Lion* (New York, 1966). In order to gain first-hand experience for articles published by *Sports Illustrated* magazine, writer George Plimpton has pitched in baseball's all-star game and gone a few rounds in the fight ring with Sugar Ray Robinson. One day, while George is playing touch football in Central Park, his editor, Oscar Barnes, stops by and gets the inspired idea that George write about a rookie quarterback's indoctrination and training during tryouts for a pro football team. After several teams have rejected the idea, George is finally accepted by the Detroit Lions, provided he agrees to sign a waiver in case of injury. Although George's assignment is kept a secret from the other players, his unfamiliarity with the basic facts of the game ultimately betrays him, and he becomes the butt of team jokes in the classroom, on the playing field, in the locker rooms, and in the Lions' living quarters. Initially, several members of the team resent his status as a magazine writer; but, due mainly to the protective custody of defensive tackle Alex Karras, George eventually convinces the players of his sincerity. Following a visit from his secretary, Kate, George starts showing some proficiency in learning the intricacies of the game. Uncomplaining despite his not inconsiderable bruises, he is finally assigned a jersey bearing the numeral "0" and—once Detroit is safely ahead—permitted to play the final minutes in a pre-season game against the St. Louis Cardinals. His debut, however, is a disaster: within three plays he loses 32 yards, fumbles a pass, runs into his own goal post, and knocks himself unconscious. Despite his mortification, George's spirits pick up when his teammates give him credit for having spunk, and they award him the game ball. Deeply touched, he says goodby and leaves with Kate to write his article for *Sports Illustrated*. Athletes. Secretaries. Authors. Football. New York City—Central Park. George Plimpton. Saint Louis Cardinals. Detroit Lions. "Sports Illustrated".

Note: Location scenes were filmed in Central Park in New York City, at Busch Stadium in St. Louis, and at Boca Raton, Florida.

PAR LE FER ET PAR LE FEU see **INVASION 1700**

PARADISE ALLEY   F6.3720

Sutton Pictures. *Dist* Pathé-America Distributing Co. 15 Feb **1962** [Maryland license]. Sd; b&w. 35mm. 81 min.

Prod-Dir-Writ Hugo Haas. *Assoc Prod* Robert Erlik. *Mus* Franz Steininger. *Asst Dir* Marty Moss.

Cast: Hugo Haas (*himself*), Carol Morris, Marie Windsor, Corinne Griffith, Billy Gilbert, Don Sullivan, Chester Conklin, Margaret Hamilton, William Forrest, Tom Fadden, Jesslyn Fax, Almira Sessions, Jan Englund, Tom Duggan, William Schallert, Clegg Hoyt, Tim Johnson, Bob Dennis, James Canino, Skipper McNally.

Comedy-drama. A once-great European film director moves into a seedy boarding house in Paradise Alley, a rundown section of Los Angeles. The boarders, who include the teenaged children of quarreling parents, an unwed mother, a stripper, a landlady, and the local busybody, all have their personal problems, and the ex-director sets out to prove that, in spite of the day-to-day bickerings, each of them is basically kind. With the aid of a former motion picture cameraman, the director announces he is shooting a film and asks for volunteers from the boarders; unknown to them, the movie does not exist— there is no film in the camera. Central Casting then calls on the director to accept a bit part in a movie, and when the director reveals his plan to the head of Central Casting, the latter supplies him with means to make an actual movie featuring the people of Paradise Alley. Motion picture directors. Motion picture cameramen. Landladies. Stripteasers. Actors. Urban life. Family life. Illegitimacy. Motion pictures. Los Angeles.

Note: Working title: *Stars in Your Backyard*.

PARADISE—HAWAIIAN STYLE   F6.3721

Hal Wallis Productions. *Dist* Paramount Pictures. 15 Jun **1966** [New York opening; c31 Dec 1965; LP32470]. Sd; col (Technicolor). 35mm. 91 min.

Prod Hal B. Wallis. *Assoc Prod* Paul Nathan. *Dir* Michael Moore. *Screenplay* Allan Weiss, Anthony Lawrence. *Orig Story* Allan Weiss. *Dir Photog* W. Wallace Kelley. *Helicopter Photog* Nelson Tyler. *Art Dir* Hal Pereira, Walter Tyler. *Set Decor* Sam Comer, Ray Moyer. *Film Ed* Warren Low. *Background Mus Comp & Cond* Joseph J. Lilley. *Songs:* "Paradise, Hawaiian Style," "Scratch My Back (Then I'll Scratch Yours)," "Stop Where You Are," "This Is My Heaven" Bill Giant, Bernie Baum, Florence Kaye. *Songs:* "House of Sand," "Queenie Wahine's Papaya" Bill Giant, Bernie Baum, Florence Kaye, Donna Butterworth. *Song:* "Datin'" Fred Wise, Randy Starr, Donna Butterworth. *Song:* "Drums of the Islands" Sid Tepper, Roy C. Bennett. *Song:* "A Dog's Life" Sid Wayne, Ben Weisman. *Song:* "Sand Castles" Herb Goldberg, David Hess, Donna Butterworth. *Song:* "Bill Bailey, Won't You Please Come Home?" Hughie Cannon. *Songs Sung by* Elvis Presley. *Choreog* Jack Regas. *Sd* John Carter, Charles Grenzbach. *Asst Dir* James Rosenberger. *Prod Mgr* Robert Goodstein. *Asst to the Prod* Jack Saper. *Cost* Edith Head. *Makeup* Wally Westmore. *Hairdresser* Nellie Manley. *Sp Eff* Romaine Birkmeyer. *Proc Photog* Farciot Edouart.

Cast: Elvis Presley (*Rick Richards*), Suzanna Leigh (*Judy Hudson*), James Shigeta (*Danny Kohana*), Donna Butterworth (*Jan Kohana*), Marianna Hill (*Lani*), Irene Tsu (*Pua*), Linda Wong (*Lehua*), Julie Parrish (*Joanna*), Jan Shepard (*Betty Kohana*), John Doucette (*Donald Belden*), Philip Ahn (*Moki*), Grady Sutton (*Mr. Cubberson*), Don Collier (*Andy Lowell*), Doris Packer

(*Mrs. Barrington*), Mary Treen (*Mrs. Belden*), Gigi Verone (*Peggy Holdren*), Shanon Hale (*blonde applicant*).

Melodrama with music. Airline pilot Rick Richards, unemployed because of his playboy ways, returns to Hawaii. There, with his old friend Danny Kohana, he establishes a charter helicopter service to fly tourists around the islands. Judy Hudson, hired as a secretary, intrigues Rick with her aloofness, although he continues to see other girl friends who work in the hotels. When dogs in his helicopter cause Rick accidentally to buzz the car of a Federal aviation agent and force him into a ditch, Rick is grounded until a hearing can determine if his license should be revoked. He violates the order, however, to rescue Danny, whose leg is broken when his helicopter crashes in a remote section of the islands. At a big party, Rick's girl friends learn of his deals with other girls and gang up on him. He escapes, successfully pleads his case with the aviation agent, and wins Judy's affection. Air pilots. Playboys. Tourists. Secretaries. Helicopters. Hotels. Hawaii. United States—Federal Aviation Agency.

Note: Filmed in Hawaii.

PARADISE ISLAND   F6.3722

Dist Stacey Distributors. ca **1970**. Sd; col. 16mm. 61-81 min.

Sex film. No information about the precise nature of this film has been found. Sexuality.

PARADISE NOW   F6.3723

Paradise Productions–Victor Herbert. *Dist* Paradise Productions, Victor Herbert, New Line Cinema. 14 Aug **1970** [New York opening]. Sd; col. 16mm. 110 min. [Also 95 min.]

Dir Sheldon Rochlin. *Photog* Sheldon Rochlin. *Adtl Photog* Diane Rochlin, Jack Moore. *Film Ed* Sheldon Rochlin. *Electronic Ed* Mike Corby. *Collab Ed* Julian Beck, Judith Malina. *English Subtitl* Julian Beck, Judith Malina, Pierre Biner.

Cast: Members of The Living Theatre.

Documentary. The film is a videotaped recording of the final staging of The Living Theatre's production at the Sportpalast in Berlin on 10 January 1970. It is meant to emphasize the participation and reaction of the audience, which is considered by the production company to be a decisive factor in the direction of each performance depicting steps toward a permanent, nonviolent revolution. Theatrical troupes. Theater. Revolutions. Berlin. The Living Theatre.

Note: Partially filmed in Brussels. Dialog originally recorded in French, German, and English.

PARADISE ROAD see **BIG DADDY**

PARADISIO (Great Britain)   F6.3724

Tonylyn Productions. *Dist* Fanfare Films, Evelyn Place Productions. 23 Feb **1962** [Los Angeles showing; c15 Apr 1962; LP23346]. Sd; b&w. 35mm (seq in 3-D). 82 min.

Pres by Dramatis Personal, Jack H. Harris. *Prod* Jacques Henrici. *Story-Screenplay* Lawrence Zeitlin, Henri Haile, Jacques Henrici. *Mus Score* John Bath. *Played by* Kurt Graunke Orchestra. *Casting Dir* Steve Waen.

Cast: Arthur Howard (*Professor Sims*), Eva Waegner (*Lisa Hinkle*).

Comedy. Professor Sims of Oxbridge University arrives at the Austrian physics laboratory of Dr. Krapotkin just as the building is demolished by an explosion under the watchful eye of Russian spy Lisa Hinkle. Sims receives a package left by Krapotkin, with a note enclosed urging him to deliver a pair of sunglasses to Honschmeier, a Munich physicist; later, he is shocked to discover that everyone appears naked when seen through the glasses. Unaware that he is being followed by Lisa, Sims arrives in Munich to find Honschmeier dead, then proceeds to Paris, where another contact is murdered, and then to Venice, where he reluctantly turns the glasses over to Signore Capone. The spies kill Capone and steal the glasses, but Sims retrieves them and discovers that they can decode a secret message, which leads him to Florence and another murder. Posing as a friend of Krapotkin, Lisa lures Sims to West Berlin, where she arranges to abduct and take him to the Eastern sector. The Englishman escapes by motor scooter with the Russians in pursuit and manages to drive into a cargo plane just as it takes off. Leaving Lisa and her companions to their failures, he puts the glasses to use on the beaches of the Riviera. Professors. Spies. Russians. Physicists. French. Italians. Espionage. Nudity. Murder. Abduction. Eyeglasses. Austria. Munich. Paris. Venice. Berlin—West. Berlin—East. Riviera. Florence. Explosions. Chases.

Note: Location scenes filmed in Paris, Vienna, Berlin, Florence, London, Venice, Munich, and the Riviera. Parts of the film are in a 3-D process called "Tri-Optique." One source lists the year of production as 1956, but this information is unconfirmed.

PARANOIA (France/Italy)   F6.3725

Tritone Filmindustría–S. N. C. *Dist* Commonwealth United Entertainment, Inc. Aug **1969**. Sd; col (Eastman Color). 35mm (Cromoscope). 91 min. *MPAA* *rating* X.

Pres by Commonwealth United Entertainment, Inc., Titanus. *Prod* Salvatore Alabiso. *Dir* Umberto Lenzi. *Screenplay* Ugo Moretti, Marie Claire Solleville, Umberto Lenzi. *Story* Umberto Lenzi. *Photog* Guglielmo Mancori. *Art Dir* Giorgio Bertolini. *Film Ed* Enzo Alabiso. *Song Sung* by Lydia MacDonald. *Sd* Del Harris. *Asst Dir* Marcello Pandolfi. *Gen Dir* Adriano Merkel. *Prod Dir* Averoe Stefani. *Cost* Gianni Pancani.

Cast: Carroll Baker (*Kathryn West*), Lou Castel (*Peter Donovan*), Colette Descombes (*Eva*), Tino Carraro (*Brian Sanders*), Lilla Brignone (*Teresa*), Franco Pesce (*Martino*), Jacques Stany (*police inspector*), Tina Lattanzi, Sara Simoni (*Kathryn's aunts*), Gaetano Imbro, Calisto Calisti, Mario Rosiello, Alberto Cocchi.

Melodrama. Following the death of her wealthy husband, socialite Kathryn West seeks seclusion at an Italian villa rented by her lawyer, Brian Sanders. She soon becomes bored, however, and welcomes the sudden appearance of Peter Donovan, a young American student whose car has broken down near the villa. After Peter seduces the willing Kathryn in the shower, he brings his "sister" Eva into the household and initiates a series of nightly orgies in which Kathryn's sexual desires are stimulated by alcohol and drugs. As the debauchery progresses, Peter dismisses the servants and makes Kathryn his prisoner by blackmailing her with erotic photographs showing her participation in various sexual combinations with himself and Eva. Reduced to near-hysteria, Kathryn tries to contact Brian, but she is duped into thinking that he has been killed in a plane crash. While in a drugged stupor, Kathryn makes a clumsy attempt to escape and falls from the roof of the villa. Brian arrives in time to see the fall; he finds Kathryn still alive and finishes the job his cohorts began by hurling her body over a balustrade. Their plot a success, the three murderers arrive in London to collect the inheritance which Brian had tricked Kathryn into signing over to him. But Brian is arrested by Scotland Yard police, and Peter and Eva are killed when their flashy sports car crashes into a huge delivery van. *Widows. Socialites. Lawyers. Students. Americans in foreign countries. Conspiracy. Seduction. Blackmail. Murder. Perfidy. Drunkenness. Tranquilizers. Photographs. Inheritance. Troilism. London. Automobile accidents.*

Note: Released in Italy in 1968 as *Orgasmo.*

PARANOIA see **KISS THE OTHER SHEIK**

PARANOIA see **THE MAN WITH THE BALLOONS**

PARANOIAC (Great Britain)   F6.3726
Hammer Film Productions. *Dist* Universal Pictures. 15 May **1963** [Boston opening; c1 Jun 1962; LP33411]. Sd (RCA); b&w. 35mm. 80 min.
Prod Anthony Hinds. *Assoc Prod* Basil Keys. *Dir* Freddie Francis. *Screenplay* Jimmy Sangster. *Dir Photog* Arthur Grant. *Camera Op* Moray Grant. *Focus Puller* David Osborne, Robin Higginson. *Art Dir* Don Mingaye. *Asst Art Dir* Ken Ryan. *Prod Dsgn* Bernard Robinson. *Supv Ed* James Needs. *Mus Comp* Elisabeth Lutyens. *Mus Supv* John Hollingsworth. *Sd Rec* Ken Rawkins. *Sd Ed* James Groom. *Boom Op* Ken Nightingall. *Sd Transfer Op* H. C. Allan. *Sd Camera Op* Al Thorne. *1st, 2d & 3d Asst Dir* Ross Mackenzie, Hugh Harlow, Ray Corbett. *Prod Mgr* John Draper. *Cont* Pauline Wise. *Prod Sec* Maureen White. *Wardrobe Supv* Molly Arbuthnot. *Wardrobe Mistress* Rosemary Burrows. *Makeup Artist* Roy Ashton. *Hairstyles* Frieda Steiger. *Sp Eff* Les Bowie, Kit West. *Still Photog* Curtis Reeks. *Studio Mgr* A. F. Kelly. *Constr Mgr* Arthur Banks. *Ch Electrn* Jack Curtis, electrn. *Master Carpenter* Charles Davis. *Prop Master* Tommy Money. *Prop Buyer* Eric Hillier. *Camera Grip* Albert Cowland.

Cast: Janette Scott (*Eleanor Ashby*), Oliver Reed (*Simon Ashby*), Liliane Brousse (*Françoise*), Alexander Davion (*Tony Ashby*), Sheila Burrell (*Aunt Harriet*), Maurice Denham (*John Kossett*), John Bonney (*Keith Kossett*), John Stuart (*Williams*), Colin Tapley (*vicar*), Harold Lang (*RAF type*), Laurie Leigh, Marianne Stone (*women*), Sydney Bromley (*tramp*), Jack Taylor (*sailor*).

Horror film. Attending a memorial service for her deceased parents, Eleanor Ashby glimpses a shadowy figure which she believes to be her brother Tony, who supposedly committed suicide 7 years earlier. The incident provides Eleanor's other brother, Simon, and her Aunt Harriet with further proof that the highstrung girl is mentally unbalanced and therefore not entitled to her share of the family fortune. Now doubting her own sanity, Eleanor attempts to throw herself off a cliff but is rescued by Tony, who claims that he merely disappeared and that there was no suicide. After convincing the family solicitor of his identity, Tony moves into the Ashby mansion, where he experiences several violent attacks upon his life. While conducting his own investigation, Tony falls in love with Eleanor and, to justify her incestuous feelings, is forced to admit that he is only posing as her brother. Simon is unmasked as a paranoid who murdered the real brother and hid his body in the house's chapel. When Tony's corpse is discovered, Simon, by now hopelessly insane, knocks the imposter unconscious and ties him up in the chapel. Aunt Harriet sets fire to

it in an effort to destroy all evidence of Simon's crime; but Eleanor rescues her friend and leads him to safety. Simon, overcome with guilt, races into the burning chapel to save his brother and perishes in the flames. *Heirs. Lawyers. Psychopaths. Aunts. Brother-sister relationship. Suicide. Insanity. Disguise. Paranoia. Murder. Impersonation. Fires.*

Note: Released in Great Britain in Sep 1963.

LES PARAPLUIES DE CHERBOURG see **THE UMBRELLAS OF CHERBOURG**

EL PARASOL see **WEEKEND, ITALIAN STYLE**

PÁRBESZÉD see **DIALOGUE**

PARDON MY BRUSH   F6.3727
Active-Stardust Productions. *Dist* Gillman Film Corp., S. I. E. International. 26 Nov **1964** [San Francisco showing]. Sd; col. 35mm. 60 min.
Prod-Dir-Writ John K. McCarthy.
Cast: Maureen Gaffney.
Comedy. Alvie and his partner are the owners of a painting firm called the Peekaboo Paint Co. They are contracted to paint an apartment building that is inhabited by beautiful young women. They unintentionally mix some vanishing cream into the paint, and when the paint is applied, the wall begins to vanish, enabling them to see the tenants going through their daily routines. They are especially interested in the view of nudie model Maureen Gaffney, who is preparing for her day's work. Alvie falls into a swimming pool to get a closer look at a nude woman swimming there, but what he sees coming toward him is an atomic submarine that shoots a missile at him. The painters are finally cornered and shot at when they invade the privacy of the property owner's bathroom. *Painters. Models. Landlords. Nudity. Voyeurism. Submarines. Swimming pools.*

THE PARENT TRAP   F6.3728
Walt Disney Productions. *Dist* Buena Vista Distribution Co. 21 Jun **1961** [New York opening; c14 Apr 1961; LP19429]. Sd (RCA); col (Technicolor). 35mm. 124 min. [Copyright length: 129 min.]
Pres by Walt Disney. A Walt Disney Production. *Assoc Prod* George Golitzen. *Dir-Writ* David Swift. *Dir Photog* Lucien Ballard. *Art Dir* Carroll Clark, Robert Clatworthy. *Set Decor* Emile Kuri, Hal Gausman. *Sp Titl* T. Hee, Bill Justice, Xavier Atencio. *Film Ed* Philip W. Anderson. *Mus* Paul Smith. *Orch* Franklyn Marks. *Songs:* "The Parent Trap," "For Now for Always," "Let's Get Together" Richard M. Sherman, Robert B. Sherman. *Sung by* Tommy Sands, Annette Funicello. *Sd Supv* Robert O. Cook. *Sd Rec* Dean Thomas. *Mus Ed* Evelyn Kennedy. *Asst Dir* Ivan Volkman. *Seq Cons* Don DaGradi. *Cost Dsgn* Bill Thomas. *Cost* Chuck Keehne, Gertrude Casey. *Makeup* Pat McNalley. *Hairstyles* Ruth Sandifer. *Sp Photog Eff* Ub Iwerks. *Dial Coach* Leon Charles.

Cast: Hayley Mills (*Sharon McKendrick/Susan Evers*), Maureen O'Hara (*Maggie McKendrick*), Brian Keith (*Mitch Evers*), Charlie Ruggles (*Charles McKendrick*), Una Merkel (*Verbena*), Leo G. Carroll (*Reverend Mosby*), Joanna Barnes (*Vicky Robinson*), Cathleen Nesbitt (*Louise McKendrick*), Ruth McDevitt (*Miss Inch*), Crahan Denton (*Hecky*), Linda Watkins (*Edna Robinson*), Nancy Kulp (*Miss Grunecker*), Frank De Vol, actor (*Mr. Eaglewood*).

Comedy. Source: Erich Kästner, *Das doppelte Lottchen* (Vienna, 1949). Sharon McKendrick and Susan Evers are identical twins whose parents were divorced when the girls were infants. Sharon has lived with her mother, Maggie, while Susan has lived with her father, Mitch; neither knows of the other's existence. Now, after 14 years, the twins are accidentally reunited when they are sent to the same summer camp. They take an initial dislike to each other (Sharon is a proper Bostonian while Susan is a rowdy Californian), but before long they discover their relationship, and as the summer progresses they become close friends. They decide to get their parents together again, and when camp is over, they switch places in order that each may meet the parent she has never known. Neither parent is aware of the deception until Sharon learns their father is planning to marry a conniving gold digger, Victoria Robinson. The two children then reveal their true identities and force Maggie to bring Susan back to her California home. In their efforts to get rid of their father's fiancée, the girls enlist Maggie's aid and then proceed to make life so miserable for Victoria that she abandons all thoughts of marrying Mitch. Goaded on by the scheming youngsters, Mitch and Maggie resolve their marital differences and decide to make a second trip to the altar. *Twins. Sisters. Gold diggers. Adolescence. Divorce. Impersonation. Personal identity. Filial relations. Summer camps.*

Note: Location scenes filmed in Monterey and Boston. Working title: *Petticoats and Bluejeans.*

LE PARIGINE *see* **TALES OF PARIS**

PARIS AU MOIS D'AOÛT *see* **PARIS IN THE MONTH OF AUGUST**

PARIS BELONGS TO US (France)   F6.3729

Ajym Films–Films du Carrosse. *Dist* Merlyn Films. 5 Nov **1962** [New York opening]. Sd; b&w. 35mm. 120 min.

Assoc Prod Roland Nonin. *Dir* Jacques Rivette. *Screenplay* Jacques Rivette, Jean Gruault. *Photog* Charles Bitsch. *Film Ed* Denise de Casabianca. *Mus* Philippe Arthuys. *Sd* Christian Hackspill.

Cast: Betty Schneider *(Anne Goupil)*, Giani Esposito *(Gérard Lenz)*, Françoise Prévost *(Terry Yok)*, Daniel Crohem *(Philip Kaufman)*, François Maistre *(Pierre Goupil)*, Jean-Claude Brialy *(Jean-Marc)*, Jean Marie Robain *(de Georges)*, Brigitte Juslin, Noëlle Leiris, Monique Le Poirier, Malka Ribovska, Louise Roblin, Henri Poirier, Jean Martin, Anne Zamire, Paul Bisciglia, Claude Chabrol, Jacques Demy, Jean-Luc Godard, Jean-Pierre Delage, André Thorent.

Mystery melodrama. While attending a party on the Left Bank in Paris, student Anne Goupil overhears a discussion of the mysterious suicide of Juan, a young Spaniard. Later she meets Gérard Lenz, a theatrical director, and Philip Kaufman, an American victim of McCarthyism. Philip tells her that Juan died because he had learned the secret of a worldwide conspiracy; Gérard also knows the secret and will be the next victim. Hoping to save Gérard's life by remaining near him, Anne takes a part in a play he is directing. Her further efforts to unravel the mystery lead her to Terry, the former mistress of all three men. Terry admits that she learned the secret from Philip and confided it to both Juan and Gérard. Anne fails to save Gérard, and after Gérard's suicide, Philip is revealed as a paranoiac who, suffering from an old war wound, invented the story of the worldwide organization. Anne realizes that the deaths of Juan and Gérard are attributable not to any conspiracy, but rather to the motivations of their own lives. *Students. Spanish. Americans in foreign countries. Theatrical directors. Mistresses. Suicide. Conspiracy. Paranoia. McCarthyism. Paris—Quartier Latin.*

Note: Opened in Paris in Jun 1960 as *Paris nous appartient*; running time: 140 min. Also known as *Paris Is Ours.*

PARIS BLUES   F6.3730

Pennebaker, Inc.—Diane Productions—Jason, Inc.—Monica Corp.—Monmouth, Inc. *Dist* United Artists. 27 Sep **1961** [Chicago opening; c27 Sep 1961; LP21032]. Sd; b&w. 35mm. 98 min.

Prod Sam Shaw. *Exec Prod* George Glass, Walter Seltzer. *Dir* Martin Ritt. *2d Unit Dir* Andre Smagghe. *Screenplay* Jack Sher, Irene Kamp, Walter Bernstein. *Adapt* Lulla Adler. *Camera* Christian Matras. *Art Dir* Alexander Trauner. *Film Ed* Roger Dwyre. *Mus* Duke Ellington. *Mus Adv* Billy Byers. *Sd* Jo de Bretagne. *Asst Dir* Bernard Farrel, Andre Smagghe. *Prod Mgr* Michel Rittener.

Cast: Paul Newman *(Ram Bowen)*, Joanne Woodward *(Lillian Corning)*, Sidney Poitier *(Eddie Cook)*, Louis Armstrong *(Wild Man Moore)*, Diahann Carroll *(Connie Lampson)*, Serge Reggiani *(Michel Duvigne)*, Barbara Laage *(Marie Seoul)*, André Luguet *(Rene Bernard)*, Marie Versini *(Nicole)*, Moustache, Aaron Bridgers, Guy Pederson *(Members of Ram's Band)*, Maria Velasco *(pianist)*, Roger Blin *(Gypsy guitarist)*, Hélène Dieudonné *(pusher)*, Niko *(Ricardo)*.

Drama. Source: Harold Flender, *Paris Blues* (New York, 1957). Ram Bowen and Eddie Cook are two expatriate American jazzmen working in a Left Bank nightclub in Paris. Ram is there hoping to attain stature as a musician, and Eddie has come to escape the racism a Negro encounters in the United States. Among their friends are Wild Man Moore, a trumpeter helping Ram with his concerto; Marie Seoul, who owns the club and is having a casual affair with Ram; and Michel Duvigne, a Gypsy guitarist addicted to drugs. One day Ram and Eddie meet two American tourists, Lillian Corning and Connie Lampson, who are on a 2-week vacation in Paris. Eventually the two couples pair off, and Eddie decides to marry Connie and return to the United States, despite the discrimination he will face. Though Ram falls in love with Lillian, he is reluctant to give up his independence and become a second-rate trombone player in the States. When an impresario rejects his concerto, Ram at first decides to leave Paris and marry Lillian; but ultimately he realizes that he must stay until he can determine whether he has a real talent for composing. Sadly he says goodby to Lillian and returns to his music. *Americans in foreign countries. Negroes. Expatriates. Composers. Guitarists. Drug addicts. Musicians. Tourists. Gypsies. Nightclub owners. Jazz. Nightclubs. Vacations. Paris—Quartier Latin.*

Note: Location scenes filmed in Paris.

PARIS BRÛLE-T-IL? *see* **IS PARIS BURNING?**

PARIS EROTIKA *see* **PARIS OOH-LA-LA!**

PARIS IN THE MONTH OF AUGUST (France)   F6.3731

Sirius. *Dist* Trans–Lux Distributing Corp. 10 Jul **1968** [Atlanta opening]. Sd; b&w. 35mm (Totalvision). 94 min.

Prod Louis Emile Galey. *Dir* Pierre Granier-Deferre. *Screenplay* Rodolphe M. Arlaud, Pierre Granier-Deferre. *Dial* Henri Jeanson. *Photog* Claude Renoir. *Art Dir* Bernard Evein. *Main Titl* Jean Fouchet. *Film Ed* Jean Ravel. *Mus* Georges Garvarentz. *Song:* "August Days in Paree" Georges Garvarentz, Charles Aznavour. *Sung by* Charles Aznavour. *Sd* Julien Coutellier. *Asst Dir* Jean-Michel Lacor. *Prod Mgr* Jean Darvey.

Cast: Charles Aznavour *(Henri Plantin)*, Susan Hampshire *(Patricia Seagrave)*, Michel de Ré *(Gogaille)*, Daniel Ivernel *(Civadusse)*, Alan Scott *(Peter)*, Etchika Choureau *(Simone Plantin)*, Jacques Marin *(Bouvreuil)*, Héléna Manson *(concierge)*, Dominique Davray *(model)*, Léonce Corne, André Certes, Marcel Charvey, Bernard Musson, Ann Lewis, Dominique Zardi, Henri Attal, Joëlle Cazal, Amarande, Max Amyl, Jean Sylvère, Patricia Aznavour.

Comedy-drama. Source: René Fallet, *Paris au mois d'août* (Paris, 1964). With his wife and children at the seashore during the month of August, department store clerk Henri Plantin is left alone in Paris. At a cafe he meets Patricia Seagrave, a young Englishwoman who claims to be a fashion model; she asks him directions to the Panthéon, and soon he becomes her guide, pretending to be a famous artist. After a night spent wandering through the streets of Paris, Patricia disappears, but Henri eventually finds her. Their reunion is marred by the presence of Patricia's boss, Peter, who maliciously reminds her of the broken love affair that she has just experienced in England. Despite Peter's intrusion and her initial reluctance to repeat a past mistake, Patricia falls in love with Henri, and they spend all of their time in his apartment, which has been converted to resemble an artist's studio. Even Henri's confession that he is not a painter and Patricia's that she is not a fashion model do not spoil their bliss. When the time comes for Patricia to leave for London, Henri at first decides to accompany her, but his family returns from their vacation, and he decides to rejoin them. *Salesclerks. English. Models. Guides. Duplicity. Infidelity. Summer. Paris.*

Note: Filmed on location in Paris. Opened in Paris in Jan 1966 as *Paris au mois d'août*; running time: 98 min (may have been cut to 90 min).

PARIS IS OURS *see* **PARIS BELONGS TO US**

PARIS NOUS APPARTIENT *see* **PARIS BELONGS TO US**

PARIS OOH-LA-LA! (United States/France)   F6.3732

Les Films Univers–American Film Distributing Corp. *Dist* American Film Distributing Corp. Dec **1963** [Baltimore showing]. Sd; col (Eastman Color). 35mm (CinemaScope). 80 min.

Pres by Stan Borden. *Prod-Dir-Writ* José Bénazéraf. *Photog* Alain Derobe. *Mus* Louiguy.

Cast: Dick Randall *(Sam Smith)*, Jessica Rubicon, Poupée La Rose, Dodo From Hamburg, The Heros, Roberto Talamo, Pamela Holhouse, Claudine Hogleenel, Stephanie Underdorn, Cosette Blanche, Ballet of the Folies Pigalle, Chantal Delor, Monique Sivers, Jane Jonason, Béatrice de L'Etang, Nancy Holloway.

Comedy. Sam Smith, a cigar-smoking American businessman, arrives in Paris for a 24-hour visit and immediately runs into difficulties as he seeks fun and romance. He is approached by an attractive sidewalk beatnik, but discovers that she is a hawker for the *Herald Tribune*. Unable to find a date in his hotel lobby, he attends a bikini beauty contest; mistaken for a judge, he is thrown into the pool for ungentlemanly behavior. He goes to see the striptease at the Crazy Horse Saloon and in the dark places his arm around the woman sitting next to him; she remains impassive through the show and then gets up to leave with her husband. The businessman's imagination runs wild: as he dictates a letter, his stenographer's clothes seem to disappear. Attempting to strike up a conversation with three young women at a restaurant, he discovers that they are lesbians. He rescues a woman from drowning in the Seine, but she rushes to rejoin the man who inspired her suicide attempt. Thoroughly discouraged, Mr. Smith gets drunk, makes a nuisance of himself at a nightclub, and returns to his hotel, where a beautiful young woman from Peoria, Illinois, mistakes him for a Frenchman and follows him into his room to make love. *Businessmen. Tourists. Americans in foreign countries. Mistaken identity. Striptease. Lesbianism. Suicide. Drunkenness. Nightclubs. Beauty contests. Paris. Seine River. Crazy Horse Saloon (Paris). Fantasy.*

Note: Filmed in Paris; locations include The Crazy Horse Saloon, Le Sexy Club, and the Folies Pigalle. Opened in Paris in Oct 1964 as *24 heures d'un Américain à Paris*; French title changed to *Paris Erotika*; running time: 74 min; may have been cut from 90 min. French sources do not indicate U. S. involvement in production; one French source lists production company as Films du Chesne.

PARIS PICK-UP (France/Italy)   F6.3733
S. N. E. Gaumont-Marianne Productions-Galatea. *Dist* Paramount
Pictures. 28 Aug 1963 [New York opening; c28 Aug 1963; LP26342]. Sd; b&w.
35mm. 90 min. [Copyright length: 85 min.]
  Prod Alain Poiré, Michel Bernheim. *Dir* Marcel Bluwal. *Screenplay* Frédéric
Dard, Marcel Bluwal. *Photog* André Bac. *Art Dir* Jean Mandaroux. *Film Ed*
Germaine Vaury. *Mus* Georges Delerue. *Sd* René Forget. *Asst Dir* André Fay.
Prod Mgr Robert Sussfeld, André Deroual.
  Cast: Robert Hossein (*Robert Herbin*), Léa Massari (*Martha Dravet*),
Maurice Biraud (*Adolphe Ferry*), Robert Dalban (*The Inspector*), Pascale
Brouillard.
  Mystery melodrama. Source: Frédéric Dard, *Le monte-charge* (Paris, 1961).
One Christmas Eve in Paris, Robert Herbin picks up an attractive young
woman, Martha Dravet. After leaving her daughter at their apartment on the
upper floor of her husband's book warehouse, Martha goes with Robert to his
lodgings. On returning to her home later, they find her husband dead, an
obvious suicide. Robert, an ex-convict who is breaking parole by being in Paris,
persuades her not to call the police. He leaves, but his curiosity makes him
linger long enough to see Martha and her child leave and head toward a church.
She faints at mass, and a tipsy automobile salesman named Adolphe Ferry takes
her back to her apartment. Robert is amazed that the body has disappeared, and
he watches the two leave. He waits until they return, hours later, but this time
the body is again in the apartment. Adolphe telephones the police and leaves
after they come and take the body away. Robert confronts Martha, and she
shows him two identical rooms on separate floors and admits that she had
fatally drugged her husband and faked his suicide; she needed a stranger,
Robert, in order to establish an alibi. They burn all the furnishings of the
upstairs apartment, but Martha accidentally places the wallet left by Adolphe
in Robert's coat. Later, when the police arrive at the ex-convict's apartment to
question his presence in Paris, he unwittingly hands them the wrong wallet.
Upon seeing Adolphe's papers, they urge Robert to reveal his part in the death,
but Martha arrives and confesses everything. *Pickups. Ex-convicts. Police.
Murder. Parole. Suicide. Drunkenness. Corpses. Elevators. Christmas. Paris.*
  Note: Opened in Paris in May 1962 as *Le monte-charge*; running time: 85
min. Italian release title: *La morte sale in ascensore*.

PARIS SECRET (France)   F6.3734
Ulysse Productions-Primex Films-Carlton Continental. *Dist* Cinema V
Distributing, Inc. 23 Jul 1965 [Maryland license; New York opening: 3 Sep].
Sd; col (Eastman Color). 35mm. 84 min.
  Prod Arthur Cohn, Pierre Roustang. *Dir* Edouard Logereau. *Screenplay*
Tom Rowe, Pierre Roustang, Claude Brulé, Edouard Logereau. *English Narr*
Tom Rowe. *Photog* Roland Pontoiseau. *Art Dir* Claude Brulé. *Film Ed* Pierre
Gillette. *Mus Comp* Alain Goraguer.
  Cast: Tom Rowe (*narrator*).
  Documentary. This documentary depicts aspects of Paris which normally
remain hidden from view. There are scenes of transvestites in bars attempting
to pick up unsuspecting men, and of prostitutes using an ambulance as a mobile
brothel. A circus orphan gives a party for the freaks who reared her; a young
woman sells a piece of her skin tattooed with a picture of the Eiffel Tower; at
night, upper-class women dressed as birds and deer are hunted through the
woods; ice-packed corpses are imported from India for medical study; a group
of interns at a party cover a nude young woman with jelly; a widow orders a
lifelike statue of her dead husband; vagabonds seek shelter in the famous Paris
sewers, which they share with the rats; a "sculptor" allows his beloved bees to
swarm over him; old horses are brought to a factory for slaughter. Cult practices
such as moon and egg worship, navel contemplation, and voodoo are also
examined. A man navigates the Seine in his private submarine; another attends
a school for seduction; and a secret gypsy restaurant serves roast bat to a group
of gourmets. *Prostitutes. Orphans. Freaks. Vagabonds. Gourmets. Cults.
Gypsies. Sculptors. Hospital interns. Widows. Transvestism. Nudity. Voodoo.
Rites and ceremonies. Masquerades. Seduction. Female impersonation.
Ambulances. Whorehouses. Circus. Tattoos. Restaurants. Submarines.
Corpses. Paris. Rats. Bats. Horses. Bees.*
  Note: Filmed in Paris; opened in Paris in Jun 1965. May also be known as
Paris Secrets.

PARIS TOPLESS (Reissue)   F6.3735
Dist American Film Distributing Corp. ca 1966. Sd; b&w. 35mm. 62 min.
  Note: Originally released in the 1950's as *Paris After Midnight*.

PARIS VU PAR ... *see* **SIX IN PARIS**

PARIS WHEN IT SIZZLES   F6.3736
Richard Quine Productions-Charleston Enterprises. *Dist* Paramount
Pictures. 8 Apr 1964 [New York opening; c31 Dec 1963; LP27553]. Sd; col
(Technicolor). 35mm. 110 min.

A Richard Quine-George Axelrod Production. *Prod* Richard Quine, George
Axelrod. *Assoc Prod* Carter De Haven, Jr., John Coonan. *Dir* Richard Quine.
Screenplay George Axelrod. *Dir Photog (see note)* Charles Lang, Jr., Claude
Renoir. *Art Dir* Jean d' Eaubonne. *Set Decor* Gabriel Bechir. *Film Ed* Archie
Marshek. *Mus* Nelson Riddle. *Orch* Arthur Morton. *Asst Dir* Paul Feyder. *Miss Hepburn's
Wardrobe* Hubert de Givenchy. *Makeup* Frank McCoy. *Sp Photog Eff* Paul K. Lerpae.
  Cast: William Holden (*Richard Benson*), Audrey Hepburn (*Gabrielle
Simpson*), Grégoire Aslan (*police inspector*), Raymond Bussières (*gangster*),
Christian Duvalleix (*maître d'hôtel*), Noel Coward (*Alexander Meyerheimer*),
Tony Curtis (*second policeman*), Marlene Dietrich, Mel Ferrer (*themselves*),
Fred Astaire, Frank Sinatra (*themselves [voices]*), Thomas Michel, Dominique
Boschero, Evi Marandi.
  Romantic comedy. Based on the film *La fête à Henriette* (1951), screenplay
written by: Julien Duvivier and Henri Jeanson. Film producer Alexander
Meyerheimer is in Cannes and upset because scriptwriter Richard Benson is
late delivering the script for *The Girl Who Stole the Eiffel Tower*,
Meyerheimer's latest production. He wires Benson in Paris that he has only 2
days to complete the script; and Benson, who has written nothing, hires a
secretary, Gabrielle Simpson, to move in and assist him. As they grind out a
script that combines all the elements of a spy thriller, a comedy, a love story,
a western, a musical, and every other basic motion picture genre, Richard and
Gabrielle project themselves into the story and actually become the hero,
heroine, and villain of each scene they create. They return to reality only for
story changes, champagne suppers, and romantic interludes. When the deadline
is reached the script is still unfinished, but Richard and Gabrielle have fallen
in love. *Motion picture producers. Motion picture scriptwriters. Secretaries.
Motion pictures. Fantasy. Paris. Cannes.*
  Note: Working title: *Together in Paris*. Lang replaced Renoir during
production.

LES PARISIENNES *see* **TALES OF PARIS**

PARLIAMO DI DONNE *see* **LET'S TALK ABOUT WOMEN**

PARMI LES VAUTOURS *see* **FRONTIER HELLCAT**

PAROXISMUS *see* **VENUS IN FURS**

PARRISH   F6.3737
Warner Bros. Pictures. 4 May 1961 [New York opening; c1 Jul 1960;
LP25363]. Sd; col (Technicolor). 35mm. 137 min.
  Prod-Dir-Writ Delmer Daves. *Photog* Harry Stradling, Sr. *Art Dir* Leo K.
Kuter. *Set Decor* William L. Kuehl. *Film Ed* Owen Marks. *Mus* Max Steiner.
Orch Murray Cutter. *Sd* Stanley Jones. *Asst Dir* Charles L. Hansen, Russell
Llewellyn. *Cost* Howard Shoup. *Makeup* Gordon Bau.
  Cast: Troy Donahue (*Parrish McLean*), Claudette Colbert (*Ellen McLean*),
Karl Malden (*Judd Raike*), Dean Jagger (*Sala Post*), Connie Stevens (*Lucy*),
Diane McBain (*Alison Post*), Sharon Hugueny (*Paige Raike*), Dub Taylor (*Teet
Howie*), Hampton Fancher (*Edgar Raike*), David Knapp (*Wiley Raike*),
Saundra Edwards (*Evaline Raike*), Sylvia Miles (*Eileen*), Bibi Osterwald
(*Rosie*), Madeleine Sherwood (*Addie*), Hayden Rorke (*Tom Weldon*), Hope
Summers (*Mary Howie*), Frank Campanella (*foreman*), Carroll O'Connor (*fire
chief*), Vincent Gardenia (*gas station attendant*), Alfonso Marshall
(*Gladstone*), John Barracudo (*Willis*), Terry Carter (*Cartwright*), Ford Rainey
(*John Donati*), Edgar Stehli, Sara Taft, Gertrude Flynn, House Jameson.
  Melodrama. Source: Mildred Savage, *Parrish* (New York, 1958). Widow
Ellen McLean and her son, Parrish, arrive at widower Sala Post's Connecticut
tobacco farm, where Ellen has taken a position as chaperon to Sala's willful
daughter, Alison. Sala, however, resents the handsome young man's presence
about the house, and Parrish strikes out on his own as a laborer in the tobacco
fields. Almost immediately he has an affair with a farm girl, Lucy, and a short
time later he becomes romantically involved with young Alison. When his
mother marries unscrupulous tobacco tycoon Judd Raike, Parrish goes to work
for his stepfather. The ruthless competitive tactics used by Judd and his two
sons, Edgar and Wiley, repulse Parrish, and he quits his job and joins the navy.
Offended, Alison promptly marries Wiley. Meanwhile, Lucy has become
pregnant by Edgar. Two years later, Parrish returns and leases land from Sala,
who has given up trying to fight Judd. Parrish is unable to hire fieldhands, who
are terrified lest there be reprisals by the Raikes, but he gets unexpected support
from young Paige Raike, Judd's daughter, who enlists her schoolmates to work
weekends in the fields. The final showdown occurs when Edgar tries to set fire
to Parrish's fields. As Parrish beats his opponent into abject submission before
the watching fieldhands, Judd stands by without raising a hand to protect his
son, silently acknowledging that Parrish has won his fight—and Paige. *Farmers.
Widows. Widowers. Manhood. Incendiarism. Filial relations. Tycoons.
Chaperons. Tobacco. Business competition. Connecticut.*
  Note: Location scenes filmed in Connecticut.

LE PARTAGE DE CATHERINE *see* **SIX DAYS A WEEK**

PARTINGS (Poland)   F6.3738

Syrena Film Unit. *For* Film Polski. *Dist* Telepix Corp. 28 Nov **1962** [New York opening]. Sd; b&w. 35mm. 101 min.

Dir Wojciech J. Has. *Screenplay* Stanisław Dygat, Wojciech J. Has. *Photog* Mieczysław Jahoda. *Film Ed* Zofia Dwornik. *Mus* Lucjan Kaszycki.

Cast: Maria Wachowiak (*Lidka*), Tadeusz Janczar (*Paul [Paweł]*), Gustaw Holoubek (*Mirek*), Saturnin Żurawski (*Felix*), Irena Netto (*owner of the villa "Quo Vadis"*), Zdzisław Mrożewski (*Paul's father*), Stanisław Milski (*professor*), Hanna Skarżanka (*Maryna*), Helena Sokołowska (*Paul's aunt*), Irena Starkówna (*countess*).

Drama. *Source:* Stanisław Dygat, *Pożegnania* (Warsaw, 1948). Shortly before the outbreak of World War II, Paul, a young, disillusioned Polish aristocrat, indulges in a flirtation with Lidka, a dancehall hostess. He refuses to consummate their affair since the act would affirm a life force he wishes to renounce. He is called into the army and does not return to his village for 5 years. Now even more disillusioned because of his war and prison-camp experiences, he discovers that the ante bellum aristocracy in which he grew up is rapidly disintegrating; his family has fled the country; and his once complacent friends are struggling for survival. Although Lidka has bettered herself by marrying a count, she has only contempt for her husband because of his collaboration with the Nazis; and when she reencounters Paul, she seduces him and breaks irrevocably with her husband. Following their first night together, she leads Paul to a roadside to watch Soviet tanks rolling into the village. Confident that the upheaval and change are for the better, she tells Paul that they will begin a new life together. *Dancehall hostesses. Prisoners of war. Aristocrats. Nazis. Traitors. Seduction. Military occupation. World War II. Union of Soviet Socialist Republics—Army.*

Note: Released in Poland in 1958 as *Pożegnania*. Also known as *Lydia Ate the Apple.*

THE PARTNER (Great Britain)   F6.3739

Merton Park Studios. *Dist* Schoenfeld Film Distributing Corp. 27 Apr **1966** [Patchogue, New York, opening]. Sd; b&w. 35mm. 58 min.

Prod Jack Greenwood. *Dir* Gerard Glaister. *Screenplay* John Roddick. *Photog* James Wilson. *Art Dir* Scott MacGregor. *Film Ed* Derek Holding. *Mus & Mus Dir* Bernard Ebbinghouse. *Sd* Brian Blamey.

Cast: Yoko Tani (*Lin Siyan*), Guy Doleman (*Wayne Douglas*), Ewan Roberts (*Detective Inspector Simons*), Mark Eden (*Richard Webb*), Anthony Booth (*Buddy Forrester*), Helen Lindsay (*Helen Douglas*), Noel Johnson (*Charles Briers*), Denis Holmes (*Sergeant Rigby*), John Forgeham (*Adrian Marlowe*), Virginia Wetherell (*Karen*), Yvette Wyatt (*Pam*), Norman Scace (*Dr. Ambrose*), John Forbes-Robertson (*Alwood*), Brian Haines (*surgeon*), Earle Green (*Peter*), Neil Wilson (*security officer*), Guy Standeven (*counterhand*), Norma Parnell (*day nurse*).

Mystery drama. *Source:* Edgar Wallace, *The Million Dollar Story* (London, 1926). Charles Briers, an accountant working on a delicate financial deal with film producer Wayne Douglas, is found murdered and a large sum of money missing. Under suspicion by Detective Inspector Simons are Lin Siyan, star of Douglas' new film, who is involved in the deal with Douglas; Helen, Douglas' wife; her brother, Buddy; and Douglas himself. Helen has already hired a private detective, Richard Webb, to keep an eye on her husband, whom she suspects of infidelity, and when Douglas becomes aware of Webb's efficiency, he hires him to find the lost money. An attempt on Douglas' life is made, and as he recuperates in the hospital, he begins to piece together clues and reaches the same conclusions as Inspector Simons: that Briers had been planning to swindle Wayne but the mastermind behind the crime is none other than detective Webb. *Motion picture producers. Actors. Accountants. Detectives. Police. Murder. Fraud. Infidelity.*

Note: Released in Great Britain in Nov 1963.

THE PARTY   F6.3740

Mirisch-Geoffrey Productions. *Dist* United Artists. 4 Apr **1968** [New York opening; c3 Apr 1968; LP35521]. Sd; col (DeLuxe). 35mm (Panavision). 99 min.

A Blake Edwards Production. *Prod-Dir-Story* Blake Edwards. *Assoc Prod* Ken Wales. *Screenplay* Blake Edwards, Tom Waldman, Frank Waldman. *Dir Photog* Lucien Ballard. *Set Decor* Reg Allen, Jack Stevens. *Prod Dsgn* Fernando Carrere. *Film Ed* Ralph Winters. *Mus* Henry Mancini. *Song:* "Nothing To Lose" Henry Mancini, Don Black. *Sung by* Claudine Longet. *Sd* Robert Martin, Ben Smith. *Mus Ed* Richard Carruth. *Asst Dir* Mickey McCardle. *Prod Mgr* Patrick J. Palmer. *Prod Supv* Allen K. Wood. *Cost* Jack Bear. *Makeup* Allan Snyder, Lynn Reynolds. *Hairstyles* Alice Monte, Pat Whiffing. *Sp Eff* Norman Breedlove.

Cast: Peter Sellers (*Hrundi V. Bakshi*), Claudine Longet (*Michele Monet*), Marge Champion (*Rosalind Dunphy*), Sharron Kimberly (*Princess Helena*), Denny Miller (*Wyoming Bill Kelso*), Gavin MacLeod (*C. S. Divot*), Buddy Lester (*Davey Kane*), Corinne Cole (*Janice Kane*), J. Edward McKinley (*Fred Clutterbuck*), Fay McKenzie (*Alice Clutterbuck*), Kathe Green (*Molly Clutterbuck*), Carol Wayne (*June Warren*), Tom Quine (*Congressman Dunphy*), Timothy Scott (*Gore Pontoon*), Elianne Nadeau (*Wiggy*), Al Checco (*Bernard Stein*), Steve Franken (*Levinson*), James Lanphier (*Harry*), Jerry Martin (*Bradford*), Danielle De Metz (*Stella D'Angelo*), Dick Crockett (*Wells*), Frances Davis (*maid*), Allen Jung (*cook*), Herb Ellis (*film director*), Natalie Borisova, Jean Carson, Paul Ferrara, Ken Wales.

Comedy. Hrundi V. Bakshi, an actor on the New Delhi stage, is brought to Hollywood to play the title role in *Son of Gunga Din*. Bakshi is a bungler, however, and before long he has accidentally blown up the picture's most expensive location set. The enraged studio head, Fred Clutterbuck, vows that the Indian will never work in Hollywood again and writes his name on a slip of paper. Clutterbuck's secretary, however, misinterprets the memo and adds Bakshi's name to the guest list for a lavish party her boss is giving at his home. Once at the party, Bakshi stumbles into the producer's flower bed, loses his muddy shoe in the hors d'oeuvres, knocks a servant through a plate glass window, inadvertently turns on the lawn sprinklers, and slides off the roof into the pool. Then Clutterbuck's daughter Molly arrives with some of her college friends and a baby elephant painted in psychedelic colors. Shocked that one of India's revered beasts should be treated with such disrespect, Bakshi talks Molly and her fellow students into washing the elephant in one of the indoor pools. As some of the other guests join in, the house and lawn become engulfed in mountains of soapsuds, and before the party finally ends, the driveway is jammed with fire engines, police cars, an ambulance, and an SPCA truck. Clutterbuck eventually recognizes Bakshi and tries to strangle him, but the Indian manages to escape with a pretty starlet, Michele Monet. *Actors. East Indians. Secretaries. Motion picture producers. Swimming pools. Hollywood. Elephants.*

THE PARTY AT KITTY AND STUD'S PLACE   F6.3741

Dist Able Film Co., Cinex International Film Distributors, Clamil Productions. ca **1970**. Sd; col. 16mm. 60 min.

Sex film. No information about the precise nature of this film has been found. *Sexuality.*

PARTY GIRL   F6.3742

Dist Stacey Distributors. 17 Sep **1969** [New York showing]. Sd; col. 16mm. 61-81 min.

Sex film. No information about the precise nature of this film has been found. *Sexuality.*

Note: Also known as *Partygirls.*

PARTY GIRLS   F6.3743

Bo-Har Productions. *Dist* Crescent International Pictures. 19 Nov **1969** [Champaign, Illinois, showing]. Sd; col. 35mm. 80 min.

Pres by Whit Boyd. *Prod* Whit Boyd. *Dir* Ron Scott. *Screenplay* William E. Hamelman. *Photog* Ludwig Moner. *Art* X. O. Vangam. *Sd* Danny Brown.

Cast: Adrainne (*Helen*), Judy Farr (*Bobbie*), Gail Caraway (*Doris*), Sandi Gram (*Jean*), Artie Brooks (*Frank*), Byron Lord (*Dr. Peters*), Jimmie Raye (*Paul*), Rod Laws, Mike Johnson, Jack Chitte (*college boys*), Helen Ware (*sun bather*), Ron Scott (*policeman*), Ron Mann (*boyfriend #1*), Si Gamma (*boyfriend #2*), Milton Halligan (*train station attendant*), Bob Jett (*bartender*).

Drama. In the course of a weekly bridge party, four young suburban housewives relax with a few drinks and relate their first extra-marital sexual adventures. Afterwards, they join in an orgy with their current lovers. *Housewives. Group sex. Infidelity. Suburban life. Bridge.*

PARTY GIRLS FOR THE CANDIDATE *see* **THE CANDIDATE**

THE PARTY'S OVER (Great Britain)   F6.3744

Tricastle Films. *Dist* Allied Artists. Mar **1966**. Sd; b&w. 35mm. 94 min.

Prod Anthony Perry. *Exec Prod* Jack Hawkins, Jules Buck. *Dir* Guy Hamilton. *Screenplay* Marc Behm. *Photog* Larry Pizer. *Art Dir* Peggy Gick. *Film Ed* John Bloom. *Mus Comp & Cond* John Barry. *Titl Song Sung by* Annie Ross. *Sd* Robert Allen, Matt McCarthy. *Asst Dir* David Bracknell. *Prod Assoc* Roy Simpson. *Prod Mgr* Donald Toms. *Makeup* Bunty Phillips. *Hairstyles* Bobbie Smith.

Cast: Oliver Reed (*Moise*), Clifford David (*Carson*), Catherine Woodville (*Nina*), Ann Lynn (*Libby*), Louise Sorel (*Melina*), Eddie Albert (*Ben*), Mike Pratt (*Geronimo*), Maurice Browning (*Tutzi*), Jonathan Burn (*Phil*), Roddy Maude-Roxby (*Hector*), Annette Robertson (*Fran*), Mildred Mayne (*countess*), Alison Seebohm (*Ada*), Barbara Lott (*Almoner*).

Melodrama. Ben, an American industrialist, urges Carson, his daughter Melina's fiancé, to go to Chelsea and locate the girl. To her father's dismay,

Melina has joined "The Pack," a band of depraved beatniks led by Moise. In England Carson discovers that Melina is missing and that Phil, a medical student and fellow member of The Pack, has committed suicide. Carson is joined by Ben, who finds his daughter, supposedly the victim of an auto accident, in a morgue. Aided by Nina, a benevolent beatnik artist, Carson learns from Moise that Nina died after a drunken fall, and that Phil, believing her to be alive, had sex with her corpse. Although Moise threatens to tell Ben the details of his daughter's demise, he relents. Nina's body is shipped to America, and Carson and Nina acknowledge their love for one another. *Americans in foreign countries. Beatniks. Industrialists. Artists. Medical students. Necrophilia. Suicide. Filial relations. London.*

Note: Filmed on location in London in 1962. Released in Great Britain in 1965. British release delayed because of censorship problems.

PAS DE MENTALITÉ see **THE WORLD IN MY POCKET**

PAS QUESTION LE SAMEDI see **IMPOSSIBLE ON SATURDAY**

PASAŻERKA see **THE PASSENGER**

LE PASSAGE DU RHIN see **TOMORROW IS MY TURN**

PASSAGE OF LOVE see **TIME LOST AND TIME REMEMBERED**

LE PASSAGER DE LA PLUIE see **RIDER ON THE RAIN**

PASSAGES FROM "FINNEGANS WAKE"   **F6.3745**
Expanding Cinema. *Dist* Grove Press. 9 Oct **1967** [New York opening]. Sd; b&w. 35mm. 97 min.
Prod-Dir Mary Ellen Bute. *Assoc Prod* Ted Nemeth, Jr. *Shooting Script* Mary Ellen Bute, Ted Nemeth, Jr., Romana Javitz. *Screen Treatment* Mary Ellen Bute, Mary Manning. *Dir Photog* Ted Nemeth, Jr. *Film Ed* Mary Ellen Bute, Yoshio Kishi, Paul Ronder, Thelma Schoonmaker, Catherine Pichonnier. *Mus Comp & Cond* Elliot Kaplan. *Accordion Player* Luke J. O'Malley. *Sd* Richard Vorisek. *Asst Dir* Ted Nemeth, Jr. *Location Mgr in Dublin* John Manning. *Art Cons* Ronnie Solbert, Eleanor Fast, John Duanne Kelly. *Sp Acknowledgments* The Avon Foundation, Eric Barnouw, Clinton House, Padraic Colum, Damon Runyon Fund, Gotham Book Mart, James Joyce Estate, James Joyce Society, University of Minnesota, Niall Montgomery, New York Public Library Picture Collection, Charles E. Feinberg, William York Tindall, Trans World Airlines, Isabelle Wilder, Thornton Wilder, Gene Moore. *Textual Mus Cons* Mabel P. Worthington, Zack Bowen, Leslie Wendell. *Still Photog* James Nemeth.
Cast: Martin J. Kelly *(Finnegan)*, Jane Reilly *(Anna Livia Plurabelle)*, Peter Haskell *(Shem)*, Page Johnson *(Shaun)*, John V. Kelleher *(commentator)*, Ray Flanagan *(Young Shem)*, Maura Pryor *(Young Iseult)*, Jo Jo Slavin *(Young Shaun)*, Joseph Alderham, Ray Allen, Virginia Blue, Sean Brancato, Joan Campbell, Paddy Croft, Leonard Frey, Eileen Koch, Joe Maher, Janis Markhouse, Kevin O'Leary, Herbert Prah, Jan Thompson, Virginia J. Wallace, Carmen P. Zavick *(celebrants)*.
Drama. Source: Mary Manning, *Finnegans Wake, a Dramatization in Six Scenes of the Book of James Joyce* (Cambridge, Massachusetts, opening: 25 Apr 1955). James Joyce, *Finnegans Wake* (New York, 1939). Finnegan, an Irish tavernkeeper, dreams of being present at his own riotous wake. He envisions himself as part of the cosmic universe, embracing all of humanity and traversing the whole of history in a neverending process of reawakening. His wife, Anna Livia, and his two sons, Shem and Shaun, also participate in the nightmarish chronicle of the reincarnation of man through the ages. As Finnegan envisions himself a monarch, a business tycoon, and a political candidate, he periodically "wakes" from his death, only to once more lapse into deep slumber. With the coming of the dawn, he is released from the myriad but purging dreams of the night and rises to greet another day. *Saloon keepers. Irish. Death. Sleep. Reincarnation. Dreams.*
Note: Location scenes filmed in Dublin, Ireland. Also known as *Finnegans Wake* and *Passages From James Joyce's "Finnegans Wake."* The film is dedicated to Frances Steloff of the Joyce Society. Production completed in 1963.

IL PASSAGGIO DEL RENO see **TOMORROW IS MY TURN**

THE PASSENGER (Poland)   **F6.3746**
Kamera Film Unit. *For* Film Polski. *Dist* Altura Films International. 18 May **1970** [New York opening]. Sd; b&w. 35mm (Dyaliscope). 60 min.
Dir Andrzej Munk. *Screenplay* Zofia Posmysz-Piasecka. *Dial-Adapt* Zofia Posmysz-Piasecka, Andrzej Munk. *Comm* Wiktor Woroszylski, *Photog* Krzysztof Winiewicz. *Camera* Wiesław Rutowicz. *Asst Op* Tadeusz Jakuczyn. *Lighting* Stanisław Matuszewski. *Art Dir* Jerzy Possak. *Sets* Tadeusz Wybult. *Interiors* Leonard Mokicz. *Set Execution* Romuald Korczak. *Film Ed* Zofia Dwornik. *Compilation (see note)* Witold Lesiewicz. *Mus* Tadeusz Baird. *Orch* Filharmonii Narodowej. *Cond* Stanisław Wislocki. *Sd Engr* Jerzy Szawlowski.

Asst Dir Andrzej Brzozowski, Anna Dyrka. *Asst Prod Mgr* Barbara Pec Slesicka, Wiesław Grzelczak. *Prod Mgr* Wilhelm Hollender. *Script Girl* Tamara Gawrys. *Cost* Wiesława Chojkowska. *Makeup* Teresa Tomaszewska, Mieczysław Posmiechowicz. *Dial Dir* Jerzy Stefan Stawiński. *Stills & Post-prod Collab* Włodzimierz Kamiński, Andrzej Piotrowski, Maria Piątkowska, Henryk Wasilewski, Władysław Tomaszewski. *English Vers Prepared by* John Minchinton.
Cast: Aleksandra Śląska *(Liza)*, Anna Ciepielewska *(Marta)*, Jan Kreczmar *(Walter)*, Marek Walczewski *(Tadeusz)*, Maria Kościałkowska *(Inga)*, Irena Malkiewicz *("Ober")*, Leon Pietraszkiewicz *(commandant)*, Janusz Bylczyński *(Kapo)*, A. Golebiowska *(female commandant)*, John Rees *(English narrator)*, Vanda Jones *(voice of Liza)*, Barbara Horawianka, Anna Jaraczówna, Andrzej Krasicki, S. Musial, L. Olszewska, W. Swaryczewska, Zbigniew Szymborski, Barbara Walkówna, Kazimierz Rudzki, Bogusław Sochnacki, Elżbieta Czyżewska, Maria Ciesielska.
Drama. Source: Zofia Posmysz-Piasecka, *Pasażerka* (publication undetermined). When Liza and her husband, Walter, arrive at Southampton on an ocean liner from the United States, she is shocked to see a woman whom she believes to be Marta, a former prisoner at the concentration camp at Auschwitz. Liza tells her husband that as an overseer at the camp, she had helped Marta arrange a rendezvous with her fiancé, Tadeusz, who was also a prisoner. The last Liza knew of Marta was that she had been taken to one of the death cells where the prisoners were kept before execution. Liza then recalls the details of the situation in which she was intensely jealous of Marta's love for Tadeusz. Marta and Tadeusz had been brought together by the Resistance and had been sent to prison together. Liza had tried to dominate Marta with her knowledge of the lovers' secret meetings. Eventually Marta was taken to the death cell, and Liza was promoted to a position with the SS in Berlin. *Prisoners of war. Memory. Jealousy. War crimes. Resistance (political). Ocean liners. Concentration camps. World War II. Southampton (England). Auschwitz. Berlin. SS.*
Note: Opened in Warsaw in Sep 1963 as *Pasażerka*. After the death of director Munk, Lesiewicz compiled the final version from completed footage and still photographs. Original Polish narrator is Tadeusz Łomnicki.

PASSION (Japan)   **F6.3747**
Daiei Motion Picture Co. ca **1968**. Sd; col (Eastman Color). 35mm (Daiei Scope). 90 min.
Prod Yonejiro Saito. *Dir* Yasuzo Masumura. *Screenplay* Kaneto Shindo. *Photog* Setsuo Kobayashi. *Mus* Tadashi Yamauchi.
Cast: Ayako Wakao *(Mitsuko Tokumitsu)*, Kyoko Kishida *(Sonoko Kakiuchi)*, Yusuke Kawazu *(Eijiro Watanuki)*, Eiji Funakoshi *(Kotaro Kakiuchi)*.
Melodrama. Source: Jun-ichiro Tanizaki, "Manji," in *Kaizo* (Mar 1928-Apr 1930). Sonoko, the childless wife of successful lawyer Kotaro Kakiuchi, falls in love with Mitsuko, a beautiful model whom she meets at art school. The two women are very happy with their relationship until Sonoko discovers that Mitsuko has a male lover as well. Eijiro Watanuki, the lover, offers to share Mitsuko with Sonoko, but the jealous Sonoko decides that she will instead lavish attention and affection on her husband. This resolution, however, is short-lived. To rid themselves of Watanuki, the women pretend to commit suicide. Awakening from a drug-induced sleep, Sonoko discovers Mitsuko in bed with her husband. This new triangle becomes even more confusing. When Watanuki reports their story to the newspapers, Mitsuko suggests a suicide pact with Sonoko and her husband. The next morning Sonoko awakens to find that she is the only survivor; she suspects that Mitsuko planned the results. *Lawyers. Models. Lesbianism. Infidelity. Jealousy. Suicide. Scandal. Troilism. Marriage.*
Note: Opened in Tokyo in Aug 1964 as *Manji*.

EN PASSION see **THE PASSION OF ANNA**

PASSION FEVER   **F6.3748**
Mostest Productions. *Dist* Jerand Film Distributors. 29 Oct **1969** [Champaign, Illinois, showing]. Sd; b&w. 35mm. 75 min.
Drama. Playboy Yarkos Fillip, disowned by his wealthy family because he is lazy and dissolute, has one ambition: to seduce as many women as possible. Yarkos goes to the city to pursue his sex fantasy, and he has casual affairs with many women until he becomes infatuated with his 16-year-old neighbor, Doba. He charms Doba into a relationship, meaning little to him, but signifying true love to her. Soon thereafter Yarkos is reacquainted with Mickel, a childhood friend who has matured into a beautiful woman. They become lovers; Yarkos declares that he will abandon his old ways, and Mickel silently plans to separate from her lover, an older man whom she describes to Yarkos as her Uncle Nuru. Yarkos becomes enraged when he sees Mickel in a parting embrace with Nuru. Mickel follows Yarkos home to explain her real relationship with Nuru, and the lovers are reconciled. Doba, who has become pregnant, goes to Yarkos' room, sees him with another woman, and becomes hysterical. Returning home, she

leaps off the roof of her apartment building. A crowd gathers and Yarkos and Mickel go out to investigate. As Yarkos is bent over Doba's shattered body, she reveals the reason for her suicide and dies. Mickel claims that Yarkos is responsible for the girl's death, and she leaves him. *Playboys. Innocents. Neighbors. Mistresses. Promiscuity. Seduction. Desertion. Pregnancy. Suicide.*

Note: Country of origin undetermined; possibly Yugoslavia.

PASSION HOLIDAY   F6.3749

Flamingo Productions. *Dist* Davis Film Distributors, Paul Mart Productions. 2 Oct **1963** [Providence, Rhode Island, opening]. Sd; col (Eastman Color). 35mm. 75 min.

Prod (see note) Hal Marsh, Irwin Meyer, Herb Meyer. *Dir* Wynn Miles. *Photog* Hal Carrington. *Film Ed* Larry Bennet. *Sd* Warren Rose, sd. *Asst Dir* Sam Segal. *Prod Coörd* Gloria Izzo. *Makeup* Rudolph Liszt. *Hairdresser* Irene Aparicio. *Sp Eff* Jack Johnson.

Cast: Christy Foushee *(Cathy)*, Linda Hall *(Anne)*, Yanka Mann *(Dixie)*, Stella Palma *(Betty)*, Bruce Brown, actor *(Frank)*, Harry Hocker *(Harry)*, Fred Kost *(Eddie)*, Bob Lee *(George)*, Ed Ross *(Emil)*, Larry Roberts *(Sam)*, Dick Kennedy *(Joe)*, Sam Segal, Jack Gundersen *(truck drivers)*, Monroe Myers, Harold Richter *(crooks)*, Leon Label *(boss)*, Wynona, Habibi, Kismet *(exotic dancers)*, Victor Charles, Peg Rayborn, Sharon Lee, Virginia Horn, Bobbi Shaw, Lanita Kent, Connie Crump, Ludovic Huot, Owen Negrin, Pearl Rubin, Gertrude Dean, Lou Horn, Ed Bell, Sid Katz, Marion Webber, Eva Bartfield, Charles Bartfield, John Wentz, Frances Glick, Bob Krantz, Jr.

Comedy-drama. Four women meet in Miami Beach: Ann, escaping a tenant farm and her drunken, lecherous stepfather; Betty, tired of her job as secretary to a sex-crazed executive; nightclub singer Kathy, fleeing a suitor; and Dixie, a truckstop waitress who has obtained a package of money as a result of the murder of a truck driver. Soon they become friends and decide to spend their holiday together. They meet four men beside a pool and spend an evening together. The next day the couples rent a yacht. The motor breaks down near an island, and the men fix the boat while the women picnic on the island. Two crooks come to the island, bury a parcel, and chase the women. The four men subdue the crooks, retrieve the parcel, a fortune in jewels, and call in the Coast Guard. The eight return to Miami Beach to continue their holiday. *Runaways. Stepfathers. Secretaries. Singers. Waitresses. Thieves. Murder. Theft. Drunkenness. Yachts. Islands. Jewels. Miami Beach. United States Coast Guard.*

Note: Filmed in Crandon Park, Florida, with interiors at the Barcelona Hotel in Miami Beach. Also released in an expurgated version under the working title: *Miami Rendezvous.* Producers Irwin and Herb Meyer are mentioned only in pre-release production information.

PASSION IN HOT HOLLOWS   F6.3750

Cinetex Industries. *Dist* Craddock Films. 10 Oct **1969** [Champaign, Illinois, showing]. Sd; b&w. 35mm. 83 min.

Prod Peggy Steffans. *Dir-Writ* Joe Sarno. *Dir Photog* Steve Silverman. *Mus* Pir Marini.

Cast: Britt Hansen *(Jean)*, Lola Valentine *(Norma Lou)*, Charlie Dobson *(Billy Joe)*, Aaron Green *(Luke)*, June Daley *(Linda)*, Monique Drevon *(Anna)*, Luther Braun *(Parker)*.

Drama. The people of the mountain town of Hot Hollows suffer inactivity, unemployment, and poverty when the local mill closes. Young widow Jean Bullock, owner and proprietress of a small hotel, receives a visit from her younger sister, Norma Lou, who arrives with traveling companion Parker Greer. The visit renews difficulties the sisters have experienced since their childhood. The frustrations and tensions of the financial depression provoke erratic behavior among the townspeople: Billy Joe Fenton's wife, Linda Sue, is testy because her husband is indulging his motorcycle racing passion, and she commits adultery with one of his best friends, Luke Herman. Billy Joe responds by making love to Anna Kovaks, whose husband has recently been committed to a mental institution. Linda Sue then falls in with Norma Lou and Parker; together, they lie in wait for Jean one night, and when she returns from the tavern to her room, Parker rapes her. Then Norma Lou embraces her. Finally, Jean realizes that much of the tension between them as children arose from repressed sexual yearnings. Norma Lou and Parker Greer abruptly depart Hot Hollows, leaving Jean and her newly-awakened passions. *Sisters. Hotelkeepers. Motorcyclists. Rape. Incest. Lesbianism. Smalltown life. Unemployment. Poverty. Infidelity. Mills.*

Note: Originally titled *Hot Hollows.*

PASSION IN THE SUN   F6.3751

Trans American Pictures. 27 Oct **1964** [Houston opening]. Sd; b&w. 35mm. 73 min.

Prod-Dir Dale Berry. *Exec Prod* Carlos Martinez. *Orig Story* Enrique Madariaga.

Cast: Dale Berry, Josette Valague, Sans Souci Girls.

Melodrama. Two Antiguan police officers assigned to investigate the escape of a carnival freak are suddenly called away from their duties and instructed to go to the airport and intercept the delivery of some stolen government documents. Foreign agents Raul and Ernesto are to pick up the documents; and when the police move in, the two agents abduct exotic dancer Josette and take her hostage. Raul kills Ernesto in the melee, and Josette, after escaping from Raul, finds herself on the outskirts of the city, clad only in her underwear. She is bathing in a stream when the escaped freak rushes out of the woods and captures her. Raul intervenes and frees Josette but is himself drowned in the stream. Josette flees in an old pickup truck with the freak, who has jumped onto the truck bed, an unwelcome passenger. Turning off the highway, Josette parks at the carnival grounds. The freak finds her hiding in one of the carnival rides and starts up the ride. When the ride is running at full speed, he climbs onto the track and is struck by the speeding car. Police arrive and escort Josette to her nightclub, and there they witness her exotic dancing, backed up by a nude chorus. *Exotic dancers. Foreign agents. Police. Freaks. Abduction. Murder. Nightclubs. Carnivals. Antigua. Documentation.*

Note: One source indicates filming in and around Houston and Galveston, Texas; press material denotes location filming in Antigua. Also known as *Passion of the Sun.*

THE PASSION OF ANNA (Sweden)   F6.3752

Svensk Filmindustri–Cinematograph. *Dist* United Artists. 28 May **1970** [New York opening; c28 May 1970; LP38433]. Sd; col (Eastmancolor, print by DeLuxe). 35mm. 100 min. *MPAA rating* R.

Exec Prod Lars-Owe Carlberg. *Dir-Writ* Ingmar Bergman. *Dir Photog* Sven Nykvist. *Asst Camera* Roland Lundin. *Prod Dsgn* P. A. Lundgren. *Film Ed* Siv Kanälv. *Sd* Lennart Engholm. *Sd Mix* Olle Jacobsson. *Asst Dir* Jan Söderkvist. *Prod Mgr* Brian Wikström. *Unit Mgr* Lennart Blomkvist. *Asst Prod Mgr* Arne Carlsson. *Script Girl* Katherina Farago. *Cost* Mago. *Cost Asst* Ethel Sjöholm. *Makeup* Cecilia Drott. *Hairstyles* Börje Lundh. *Sp Eff* Ulf Nordholm. *Prop Master* Karl-Arne Bergman. *Ch Electrn* Gerhard Carlsson. *Grips* Einar Carlsson, Stig Limer, Börje Krogstad. *Still Photog* Christer Strömholm, Lennart Nilsson.

Cast: Liv Ullmann *(Anna Fromm)*, Bibi Andersson *(Eva Vergerus)*, Max von Sydow *(Andreas Winkelman)*, Erland Josephson *(Elis Vergerus)*, Erik Hell *(Johan Andersson)*, Sigge Fürst *(Verner)*, Svea Holst *(Verner's wife)*, Annika Kronberg *(Katarina)*, Hjördis Petterson *(Johan's sister)*, Lars-Owe Carlberg, Brian Wikström *(policemen)*, Barbro Hiort af Ornäs, Malin Ek, Britta Brunius, Brita Öberg, Marianne Karlbeck, Lennart Blomkvist.

Drama. Andreas Winkelman, who has spent time in prison for forgery, lives alone in a farmhouse on a sparsely populated island. One day Anna Fromm, a young woman crippled by an automobile accident, asks to use his telephone and afterwards leaves behind her handbag. Andreas examines the contents of the purse to learn her address and discovers a letter addressed to Anna from her husband, also named Andreas, which describes their unhappy marriage and explains his reasons for leaving her. When Andreas returns the handbag, he meets Elis Vergerus, a cynical architect and amateur photographer, and Eva, his wife. The four dine together, and in the course of the conversation Anna refers to the happy marriage in her past. Later, Andreas learns that her husband and young son were killed in the accident that left Anna crippled. When Elis goes to Milan on a business trip, Eva, who is haunted by a feeling of purposelessness, visits Andreas, and they have a brief affair. Before long, Andreas and Anna begin living together on the farm. Elis employs Andreas as an assistant, while Anna works as a translator. Anna finds, however, that her relationship lacks the warmth that existed in her marriage. Meanwhile, a maniac has been torturing and killing animals on the island, and Johan Andersson, a solitary islander who has been one of Andreas' few human contacts, falls under suspicion. Assaulted and humiliated by the outraged townspeople, the pathetic loner kills himself, leaving behind a suicide note for Andreas. Anna and Andreas have their most serious quarrel to date, during which he tries to strike her with an ax. Soon the island madman strikes again, setting fire to a barn. Anna picks up Andreas in her car at the scene of the blaze; they resume their argument, and Andreas confronts her with the contents of her husband's letter. Anna drives wildly, and Andreas suggests that she is trying to kill him in an auto accident, as she may have done with her husband and child. Andreas gets out of the car and walks away alone as Anna drives off. [The film contains four brief interludes in which actors Ullmann, Andersson, von Sydow, and Josephson relate their impressions of their characters.] *Widows. Mistresses. Cripples. Recluses. Ex-convicts. Suicide. Insanity. Marriage. Infidelity. Sadism. Memory. Islands. Automobile accidents. Fires. Animals.*

Note: Filmed entirely on the island of Fårö. Opened in Stockholm in Nov 1969 as *En passion.*

THE PASSION OF SLOW FIRE (France)   **F6.3753**

Cinéphonic–François Chavane–Les Films Odéon. *Dist* Trans-Lux Distributing Corp. 11 Oct **1962** [New York opening; c4 Oct 1962; LP27579]. Sd; b&w. 35mm. 91 min.

A François Chavane Production. *Prod* François Chavane. *Dir* Edouard Molinaro. *English Vers Dir-Writ* Terry Curtis. *Screenplay* Jean Anouilh. *Photog* Jean-Louis Picavet. *Art Dir* Robert Clavel. *Film Ed* Robert Isnardon, Monique Isnardon. *Mus* Georges Delerue. *Sd* Antoine Petitjean. *Dir Prod* Jean Darvey.

Cast: Jean Desailly (*Stephane Blanchon*), Alexandra Stewart (*Belle*), Monique Mélinand (*Madame Blanchon*), Yvette Etiévant (*judge's secretary*), Jacques Monod (*Judge Bechman*), Marc Cassot (*police officer*), Jacques Pierre (*Belle's admirer*), Yves Robert (*bartender*), Louisa Colpeyn (*Belle's mother*), Van Doude (*doctor*), Maurice Teynac (*Stephane's friend*).

Mystery drama. Source: Georges Simenon, *La mort de Belle* (Paris, 1952). While attending a university near Geneva, a young American, Belle, stays at the home of Professor Stephane Blanchon and his frigid wife. Stephane becomes the principal suspect when Belle is found murdered in the Blanchon home. At the inquest it is revealed that although Belle dated often and was quite promiscuous, she had secretly been in love with Stephane. The news shocks Stephane into the realization that because of the brittle relationship with his wife, he has permitted his life to become aimless and listless, and as circumstantial evidence against him mounts, he shakes off his former passiveness and has a brief affair. Obsessed by the death of Belle and all he has missed in life, he kills the woman—ironically, he commits this murder at the very moment the police get a confession from Belle's killer. *Americans in foreign countries. Students. Professors. Murder. Promiscuity. Marriage. Circumstantial evidence. Infidelity. Confession (law). Geneva.*

Note: Opened in Paris in Mar 1961 as *La mort de Belle* at 100 min. Also known as *The End of Belle.*

PASSION OF THE SUN *see* **PASSION IN THE SUN**

THE PASSION PIT *see* **THE ICE HOUSE**

THE PASSION PIT *see* **SCREAM OF THE BUTTERFLY**

PASSION STREET, U. S. A.   **F6.3754**

Nu Wave Productions. *Dist* Gillman Film Corp. 21 Sep **1964** [Maryland license; San Francisco showing: 9 Nov 1967]. Sd; b&w. 35mm. 90 min.

Prod (see note) James C. Dunne, Oscar Daley. *Dir* Oscar Daley. *Jazz Score* Bob Emenegger.

Cast: Tanya Conway (*Lorrie Owens*), Steve Ihnat (*Dick Dudman*), Gary Clarke (*Joseph Redding*).

Melodrama. Beautiful Lorrie Owens moves from Memphis to the French Quarter of New Orleans and enters into a relationship with detective Dick Dudman. She becomes despondent over the affair, and in a church she meets minister Joe Redding, a childhood sweetheart. They renew their love and marry. Dick spots Lorrie, follows her to her apartment, and seduces her. Lorrie confesses her action and Joe sends her to a psychiatrist, but an incident in which her mother, a physician, examined her after a teenage date has given her a fear of all doctors. She attempts suicide, fails, and is taken to a police station. Dick continues to plot to wreck her marriage. Trying to claim her, Dick makes advances to Lorrie at her home and prods Joe into a fight in which Joe is badly beaten. Lorrie rushes to Joe's aid and angrily drives Dick away. *Detectives. Clergymen. Physicians. Psychiatrists. Marriage. Suicide. Seduction. Jealousy. Memphis. New Orleans—French Quarter.*

Note: Filmed in New Orleans in 1962. Also known as *Passion Street, Passion Streets,* and *Bourbon Street.* Sources conflict in crediting producer; pressbook lists Dunne, while Maryland license records give Daley as producer-director.

THE PASSIONATE DEMONS (Norway)   **F6.3755**

Concord Film Productions–Norsk Film. *Dist* Manson Distributing Corp., Albex Films. 12 Sep **1962** [Los Angeles opening]. Sd; b&w. 35mm. 86 min.

Prod Sverre Gran. *Dir* Nils Reinhardt Christensen. *Screenplay* Pål Løkkeberg. *Dir Photog* Ragnar Sørensen. *Art Dir* H. C. Hansen. *Film Ed* Olav Engebregtsen. *Mus* Egil Monn-Iversen. *Sd* Dagfin Akselsen.

Cast: Margaret Robsahm (*Line*), Toralv Maurstad (*Jacob*), Henki Kolstad (*Gabriel Sand*), Sissel Tuul (*Hanne*), Elisabeth Bang (*Jacob's sister*), Rønnaug Alten (*Jacob's mother*), Truuk Doyer (*a passionate demon*), Rolf Christensen (*Jacob's father*), Atle Merton (*Laffen*), Per Lillo Stenberg (*Jeno*), Ragnhild Hjorthøy (*Ellen*), Per Christensen (*Putte*), Odd Borg (*Kalle*), Ulf Wengaard.

Melodrama. Source: Axel Jensen, *Line* (Oslo, 1959). Jacob, a young Norwegian seaman who has written a novel, comes home to Oslo after years at sea but refuses to see his ailing father because he blames him for his mother's insanity. He falls in love with Line, an uninhibited girl who runs around with a wild crowd, and they begin living together and enjoying a carefree way of life. At a party, Jacob is humiliated by Laffen, a writer friend of Jacob's and Line's former lover, and challenges him to a fight. Laffen adds to Jacob's humiliation by beating him soundly. Line later informs Jacob that she thinks she is pregnant, and they argue about an abortion. Jacob becomes increasingly jealous of Line's attention to others and, on a yachting holiday, his jealousy reaches such an exaggerated state that he almost kills her. Realizing that he is no better than his father, Jacob finally visits him before going back to sea. He indicates to Line that he may return to her. *Seamen. Novelists. Filial relations. Jealousy. Pregnancy. Abortion. Yachts. Oslo.*

Note: Released in Norway in 1961 as *Line* at 90 min. Sources conflict in crediting production company. Pressbook claims film was set in Stockholm; British source gives Oslo.

THE PASSIONATE STRANGERS (Philippines)   **F6.3756**

MJP Productions. *Dist* RAF Industries. 26 Sep **1968** [Maryland license]. Sd; b&w. 35mm. 78 min. [Original length: 101 min.]

Prod M. J. Parsons. *Dir-Screenplay* Eddie Romero. *Story* Cesar Amigo, Reuben Canoy. *Camera* Justo Paulino. *Mus* Nestor Robles.

Cast: Michael Parsons (*Adam Courtney*), Valora Noland (*Margaret Courtney*), Mario Montenegro (*Roberto Valdez*), Celia Rodriguez (*Lydia Trasmonte*), Vic Diaz (*Attorney Angel Mascardo*), Butch Aquino (*District Attorney Julio Lazatin*), Claude Wilson (*J. V. Harrison*), Jose Dagumboy (*Yoyong*), Bong Calumpang (*Yoyong's companion*), Cesar Aguilar (*Manuel Hidalgo*).

Melodrama. Adam Courtney, an American who owns a Philippine sugar mill, doubts his wife's fidelity and accidentally kills the uncle of his wife's lover. The body is found by the roadside. The uncle, Manuel Hidalgo, was an employee of the mill and a major figure in the workers' union. Two of the townspeople, Lydia Trasmonte and Angel Mascardo, take advantage of the old labor organizer's death to incite the town against the Americans. An innocent boy is charged with Hidalgo's murder, and Yoyong, the town drunk and companion to the boy, pleads in vain with Courtney to exonerate him. Courtney is finally arrested, but the case against him becomes clouded: Margaret Courtney breaks off with her lover and comes to her husband's defense. Courtney, however, refuses to make public his wife's infidelity. Yoyong ends the intrigue by stabbing Courtney to death. *Businessmen. Factory workers. Uncles. Americans in foreign countries. Waifs. Labor agitators. Murder. Infidelity. Injustice. Drunkenness. Jealousy. Revenge. Sugar mills. Labor unions.*

PASSIONATE SUNDAY *see* **DARK ODYSSEY**

THE PASSIONATE THIEF (Italy)   **F6.3757**

Titanus. *Dist* Embassy Pictures. 11 Sep **1963** [San Francisco opening]. Sd; b&w. 35mm. 95 min.

Prod Silvio Clementelli. *Dir* Mario Monicelli. *Screenplay* Suso Cecchi D'Amico, Agenore Incrocci, Furio Scarpelli, Mario Monicelli. *Adapt* Suso Cecchi D'Amico. *Photog* Leonida Barboni. *Art Dir* Piero Gherardi, Giuseppe Ranieri. *Film Ed* Adriana Novelli. *Mus* Lelio Luttazzi.

Cast: Anna Magnani (*Tortorella*), Totò (*Umberto*), Ben Gazzara (*Lello*), Fred Clark (*The American*), Edy Vessel (*Mimi*), Gina Rovere, Mac Ronay, Toni Ucci, Rik von Nütter, Marcella Rovena, Kurt Polter, Alberto De Amicis, Gianni Bonagura, Peppino De Martino, Mara Ombra, Dori Dorika, Carlo Pisacane.

Crime comedy. Source: Alberto Moravia, "Ladri in chiesa," in *Racconti Romani* (Milan, 1954). Alberto Moravia, "Risate di gioia" (publication undetermined). Tortorella, a movie extra, is left alone by her friends on New Year's Eve. She meets Umberto, another extra who is working as part of a pickpocket team with Lello. Unaware of what the two men are doing, Tortorella tags along with them. Despite the thieves' efforts to get rid of her, she shows up just as they are preparing to rob a rich American; he immediately becomes attracted to her, and they drive off together. Followed by Umberto and Lello, the couple go to the Trevi Fountain, where the drunken American tries to jump into the water. Tortorella calls the police, and the man is taken away. The trio next find themselves invited to a party at a German prince's home, only to be thrown into the street when Lello is discovered plying his trade on the guests. Tortorella and Umberto seek shelter in a church where Lello steals a necklace from a statue of the Madonna. The police arrive to find Tortorella holding the necklace, and after several months in jail, she is released and finds Umberto waiting for her. *Actors. Pickpockets. Americans in foreign countries. Germans. Royalty. Theft. Drunkenness. Frameup. New Year's Eve. Rome. Trevi Fountain.*

Note: Opened in Rome in Oct 1960 as *Risate di gioia;* running time: 105 min.

PASSPORT TO CHINA (Great Britain)   **F6.3758**

Hammer Film Productions–Swallow Productions. *Dist* Columbia Pictures. 18 Jan **1961** [Detroit opening; c1 Feb 1961; LP20410]. Sd; b&w (see note). 35mm. 75 min.

Prod-Dir Michael Carreras. *Assoc Prod* Anthony Nelson Keys. *Screenplay-Screen Story* Gordon Wellesley. *Photog* Arthur Grant. *Art Dir* Bernard Robinson, Thomas Goswell. *Supv Film Ed* James Needs. *Ed* Alfred Cox. *Mus*

Comp & Cond Edwin Astley. *Sd* Jock May. *Asst Dir* Arthur Mann. *Prod Mgr* Clifford Parkes. *Wardrobe* Molly Arbuthnot. *Makeup* Roy Ashton. *Hairstyles* Frieda Steiger.

Cast: Richard Basehart *(Don Benton)*, Lisa Gastoni *(Lola Sanchez)*, Athene Seyler *(Mao Tai Tai)*, Eric Pohlmann *(Ivano Kang)*, Alan Gifford *(Charles Orme)*, Bernard Cribbins *(Pereira)*, Burt Kwouk *(Jimmy)*, Hedger Wallace *(Inspector Taylor)*, Marne Maitland *(Han Po)*, Milton Reid *(bodyguard)*, Yvonne Shima *(Liang Ti)*, Robert Lee *(Chinese Officer)*, Zoreen Ismail *(Swee Kim)*, Paula Lee Shiu *(girl croupier)*, Soraya Ra Fat *(hostess)*, Gerry Lee Yen *(room boy)*, Ronald Ing *(sentry)*, Kevin Scott.

Action melodrama. Don Benton, a former World War II pilot now running a travel agency in Hong Kong, refuses to take political sides and flatly rejects an offer to do espionage work for the United States. Mao Tai Tai, an aged Chinese woman who more or less adopted Benton during the war years, asks him to try to find her missing grandson. Knowing that the grandson was piloting a Formosan plane that disappeared over mainland China, Benton obtains a passport through a Russian friend, Ivano Kang, goes to the mainland, and rescues the pilot. Then, to clear the young man's name, he goes to Canton to bring back one of the plane's passengers—an American agent, Lola Sanchez, who has memorized a vital scientific formula and is willing to sell it to the highest bidder. Kang tries to get the formula from her, and she kills him. Benton hopes to get Lola out of the city, but as they work their way through holiday street crowds she is fatally wounded by Kang's bodyguard and dies with her secret. Back in Hong Kong, Benton once more turns down an offer to do undercover work for the U. S. government. *Americans in foreign countries. Air pilots. Travel agents. Communists. Russians. Secret agents. Murder. Missing persons. Passports. Secret formulas. People's Republic of China. Republic of China. Hong Kong. Canton.*

Note: Location scenes filmed in Hong Kong. Released in Great Britain in Technicolor in Dec 1960 as *Visa to Canton*.

PASSPORT TO OBLIVION see **WHERE THE SPIES ARE**

THE PASSWORD IS COURAGE (Great Britain)   F6.3759
   Andrew L. Stone–Virginia Stone. *Dist* Metro-Goldwyn-Mayer, Inc. 21 Dec **1962** [New York opening; c19 Dec 1962; LP23598]. *Sd* (Westrex); b&w. 35mm (Metroscope). 116 min.
   Prod Andrew L. Stone, Virginia Stone. *Assoc Prod* Sydney Streeter. *Dir-Writ* Andrew L. Stone. *Dir Photog* Davis Boulton. *Art Dir* Wilfred Arnold. *Supv Ed* Virginia Stone. *Ed* Noreen Ackland. *Asst Ed* Alma Godfrey. *Songs Arr by* Jack Chaindlin, Tommy Riley, Virginia Stone, Christopher Stone, mus, Derek New. *Harmonica Played by* Tommy Riley. *Rec Supv* A. W. Watkins. *Sd Rec* Cyril Swern. *Dub Mix* J. B. Smith. *Asst Dir* George Pollard. *Cont* Joan Kirk. *Wardrobe* Larry Stewart. *Sp Eff* Bill Warrington. *Tech Adv* Charles Coward. *Coöp* Great Britain—War Office, British Railways. *Casting Dir* Irene Howard. *Drawings* Henri Pieck.
   Cast: Dirk Bogarde *(Charles Coward)*, Maria Perschy *(Irena)*, Alfred Lynch *(Corporal Pope)*, Nigel Stock *(Cole)*, Reginald Beckwith *(unterofficer)*, Richard Marner *(Schmidt)*, Ed Devereaux *(Aussie)*, Lewis Flander *(Pringle)*, George Mikell *(Necke)*, Richard Carpenter *(Robinson)*, Margaret Whiting *(French farmwoman)*, Olaf Pooley *(German doctor)*, Ferdy Mayne *(German officer)*, Colin Blakely *(German goon)*, Michael Mellinger *(Feldwebal)*, Bernard Archard, George Pravda, Mark Eden, Douglas Livingstone, John Gardiner, Howard Pays, Tommy Elliott, Bernard Proctor, Philo Hauser.
   Biographical drama. Source: John Castle, *The Password Is Courage* (New York, 1955). While being marched to a German prisoner-of-war camp in World War II, British Sgt. Maj. Charles Coward escapes by lying down with wounded German soldiers. He is taken to a German hospital and decorated with the Iron Cross before his true identity is discovered. Transferred to prison camp, Coward immediately begins making plans for a tunnel escape. Through a ruse, he is able to get an afternoon pass into the neighboring town, where he contacts a member of the Polish underground, Irena, who gives him the necessary maps and escape information. Back in camp, he completes the tunnel and escapes with his friend Billy Pope, only to be recaptured in Vienna. Near the end of the war, Coward and Pope steal a fire engine and make a successful lunge to freedom through enemy villages. *Poles. Prisoners of war. Resistance (political). Prison escapes. Sabotage. Hospitals. Tunnels. Iron Cross. World War II. Germany. Vienna. Charles Coward. Great Britain—Army. Germany—Army.*
   Note: Opened in London in Oct 1962.

PATATE see **FRIEND OF THE FAMILY**

PATCH see **DEATH OF A GUNFIGHTER**

A PATCH OF BLUE   F6.3760
   Pandro S. Berman Productions. *Dist* Metro-Goldwyn-Mayer, Inc. 10 Dec **1965** [Los Angeles opening; c24 Nov 1965; LP32176]. *Sd* (Westrex); b&w. 35mm (Panavision). 105 min.

A Pandro S. Berman–Guy Green Production. *Prod* Pandro S. Berman. *Assoc Prod* Kathryn Hereford. *Dir-Writ* Guy Green. *Dir Photog* Robert Burks. *Camera Op* Leonard South. *Asst Camera* George Hollister. *Art Dir* George W. Davis, Urie McCleary. *Henry* Grace, Charles S. Thompson. *Film Ed* Rita Roland. *Asst Ed* Hal Davis. *Mus* Jerry Goldsmith. *Rec Supv* Franklin Milton. *Mix* Larry Jost. *Rec* Bruce Wright. *Boom Op* Larry Hadsell. *Asst Dir* Hank Moonjean, Herb Hirst, William R. Finnegan. *Script Supv* Dorothy Aldrin. *Makeup* William Tuttle. *Sp Vis Eff* Robert R. Hoag. *Still Photog* Ken Bell. *Gaffer* Wesley Shanks. *Grip* Lloyd Isbell. *Prop* Bob Murdock, Bill Graham, prop.
   Cast: Sidney Poitier *(Gordon Ralfe)*, Shelley Winters *(Rose-Ann D'Arcey)*, Elizabeth Hartman *(Selina D'Arcey)*, Wallace Ford *(Ole Pa)*, Ivan Dixon *(Mark Ralfe)*, Elisabeth Fraser *(Sadie)*, John Qualen *(Mr. Faber)*, Kelly Flynn *(Yanek Faber)*, Debi Storm *(Selina, age 5)*, Renata Vanni *(Mrs. Favaloro)*, Saverio LoMedico *(Mr. Favaloro)*.
   Melodrama. Source: Elizabeth Kata, *Be Ready With Bells and Drums* (New York, 1961). Selina D'Arcey, an 18-year-old girl accidentally blinded by her mother, Rose-Ann, in a family quarrel 13 years ago, lives in a shabby tenement with her prostitute mother and alcoholic grandfather, Ole Pa. She never leaves the apartment, has never attended school, knows nothing about braille, and spends her days cleaning, cooking, and stringing beads. When Ole Pa offers to take her to the park one morning and pick her up on his way home from work, Selina eagerly agrees. In the park she screams when a caterpillar lands on her shoulder, and Gordon Ralfe, a friendly young black man comes to her aid. They become friends, and Selina persuades Ole Pa to take her to the park every day. When Gordon introduces Selina to his brother Mark, Mark tries to discourage the couple's friendship. Then Sadie, an aging prostitute neighbor, sees the two together and tells Rose-Ann. Rose-Ann starts to beat Selina and tries to explain Gordon's racial difference, but Selina is unmoved. Gordon arranges to have Selina admitted to a school for the blind, a plan that interferes with Rose-Ann and Sadie's plan to start a whorehouse with Selina as a special attraction. Selina recalls to Gordon the last image she remembers seeing, a patch of blue sky, and tells him that one of her mother's customers raped her when she was 5 years old. Gordon insists upon removing her from the tenement into the school but will not marry her until she experiences other people and knows her mind more fully. Though Selina wants to marry Gordon, she heeds his advice and enters the school. *Negroes. Prostitutes. Grandfathers. Neighbors. Brothers. Blindness. Racial prejudice. Adolescence. Alcoholism. Rape. Filial relations. Whorehouses. Tenements. Schools for the Blind.*

LES PÂTRES DU DÉSORDRE see **THANOS AND DESPINA**

LA PATROUILLE ANDERSON see **THE ANDERSON PLATOON**

THE PATSY   F6.3761
   Patti Enterprises. *Dist* Paramount Pictures. 8 Jul **1964** [Los Angeles opening; c11 Jun 1964; LP28699]. *Sd*; col (Technicolor). 35mm. 101 min.
   A Jerry Lewis Production. *Prod* Ernest D. Glucksman. *Assoc Prod* Arthur P. Schmidt. *Dir* Jerry Lewis. *Screenplay* Jerry Lewis, Bill Richmond. *Dir Photog* W. Wallace Kelley. *Camera Op* James Knott. *Art Dir* Hal Pereira, Cary Odell. *Set Decor* Sam Comer, Ray Moyer. *Film Ed* John Woodcock. *Mus Score* David Raksin. *Song:* "I Lost My Heart in a Drive-In Movie" David Raksin, Jack Brooks. *Sd* Ray Cossar. *Mix* Hugo Grenzbach. *Boom Op* Bud Parman. *Asst Dir* Ralph Axness, Howard Roessel, Dale Coleman. *Unit Prod Mgr* William C. Davidson. *Script Supv* Dorothy Yutzi. *Cost Dsgn* Edith Head. *Cost* Karlice Burkhart, Buddy Clark. *Haberdashery* Sy Devore. *Makeup Supv* Wally Westmore. *Makeup* Harry Ray, Jack Stone. *Casting* Ed Morse. *Dial Coach* Marvin Weldon. *Still Photog* Larry Barbier. *Prop* Earl Olin, Jim Cottrell. *Grip* Robert Dabke. *Gaffer* Lorne Netten.
   Cast: Jerry Lewis *(Stanley Belt)*, Everett Sloane *(Caryl Fergusson)*, Ina Balin *(Ellen Betz)*, Keenan Wynn *(Harry Silver)*, Peter Lorre *(Morgan Heywood)*, John Carradine *(Bruce Alden)*, Phil Harris *(Chic Wymore)*, Hans Conried *(Dr. Mule-rrr)*, Phil Foster *(Mayo Sloan)*, Richard Deacon *(Sy Devore)*, Del Moore *(policeman)*, Nancy Kulp *(theatre-goer)*, Neil Hamilton *(barber)*, Jerry Dunphy *(television newscaster)*, Jerry Dexter *(radio newscaster)*, Scatman Crothers *(shoe-shine boy)*, Fritz Feld *(maitre d')*, Benny Rubin *(waiter)*, Jerome Cowan *(executive)*, Ned Wynn *(page)*, Henry Slate *(Paul)*, Ed Wynn, Ed Sullivan, Mel Torme, Hedda Hopper, Rhonda Fleming, George Raft, The Step Brothers *(themselves)*, Gavin Gordon, Buddy Lester, Jack Albertson, Norman Alden, Lloyd Thaxton.
   Comedy. A famous singer dies in a plane accident, and his management team—producer Caryl Fergusson, writer Chic Wymore, press agent Harry Silver, director Morgan Heywood, valet Bruce Alden, and secretary Ellen Betz—decides to make an unknown into a star. They pick Stanley Belt, a shy bellboy, whose nervous bumbling is mistaken for comic ability. Despite singing and acting lessons, Stanley is extremely nervous, and a recording session and nightclub tryout are disastrous. However, a publicity campaign gains him an

appearance on the Ed Sullivan Show, but his management team—with the exception of Ellen, who loves him—abandons him before he goes on. Contrary to the team's expectations, Stanley is a hit on the show. He later forgives the others because they made him a star; he gives each back his old job and proposes to Ellen. *Bellboys. Secretaries. Entertainers. Press agents. Television producers. Television directors. Television scriptwriters. Valets. Publicity. Timidity. Nightclubs. Television. Ed Sullivan Show.*

PATTERN FOR PLUNDER (Great Britain)   **F6.3762**
Trionyx Film Productions. *Dist* Herts-Lion International Corp. Dec **1964**. Sd; b&w. 35mm. 90 min.

Prod-Dir John Ainsworth. *Assoc Prod* John Brason. *Screenplay* Christopher Davis. *Photog* Stephen Dade. *Art Dir* Duncan Sutherland. *Film Ed* Tristam Cones. *Mus & Mus Dir* Johnny Douglas. *Sd* Robert Macphee, Ken Cameron. *Asst Dir* Peter Weingreen.

Cast: Keenan Wynn (*Nick Rawlings*), Mai Zetterling (*Helene Bretton*), Ronald Howard (*Bill Webb*), Rona Anderson (*Pru Lawson*), Trader Faulkner (*Dave Newton*), Edward Underdown (*Colonel Harvey*), Michael Peake (*Captain Starkey*), Victor Beaumont (*man in the "Boîte d'or"*), Rudolph Offenbach (*Father Laurent*), Paul Bogdan (*General von Kreisling*), Rita Webb (*landlady*), Murray Kash (*boorish man*), Mike Jenkinson (*drunken sailor*), Harvey Hall (*SS officer*), Sidney Gross (*barman*), Patrick Darren (*Stuart*), Sally Aylward (*barmaid*), Michael Landeau (*French officer*).

Adventure drama. Three former naval commandos—bank executive Bill Webb, nightclub pianist Pru Lawson, and Dave Newton—are summoned by their ex-commander, Nick Rawlings, to participate in a secret mission dubbed "Operation Mermaid." Once at sea, they learn that they are to recover $10 million in stolen war booty. The treasure was hidden by German General von Kreisling with the collaboration of two Allied officers, an American and a Frenchman, to whom he gave pieces of a map pinpointing its hiding place. Nick Rawlings holds the American's segment, which he explains was obtained through intelligence sources. In Cherbourg, contact is made with Helene Bretton, purported agent for the recently released von Kreisling, and she supplies his third of the puzzle. The final portion, originally held by the French collaborator, who is now dead, is discovered behind a painting of a mermaid. The group quickly put to sea toward Mont-Saint-Michel in Normandy, where the loot is said to be hidden in a family tomb. The bullion and works of art are found, and with them a painting of Helene's mother. She reveals herself to be a French secret agent and identifies Rawlings as the American traitor with whom the German general had made his deal. Rawlings escapes but is killed in the quicksands on the beach of Mont-Saint-Michel. *Great Britain—Royal Navy. Veterans. Bankers. Pianists. Americans in foreign countries. Nazis. French. Secret agents. Traitors. Theft. Imposture. Tombs. Treasure. Quicksand. Beaches. Cherbourg. Mont-Saint-Michel. Documentation.*

Note: Released in Great Britain in 1963 as *The Bay of Saint-Michel* at 73 min. Also known as *Operation Mermaid*.

PATTERN OF EVIL *see* **FORNICON—PATTERN OF EVIL**

PATTERN OF EVIL *see* **SATAN IN HIGH HEELS**

PATTON   **F6.3763**
Twentieth Century-Fox Film Corp. 4 Feb **1970** [New York opening; c30 Dec 1969; LP38179]. Sd (Westrex); col (De Luxe). 35mm & 70mm (Dimension 150, see note). 170 min. MPAA rating M.

A Frank McCarthy-Franklin J. Schaffner Production. *Prod* Frank McCarthy. *Assoc Prod* Frank Caffey. *Dir* Franklin J. Schaffner. *2d Unit Dir* Michael Moore. *Screenplay-Screen Story* Francis Ford Coppola, Edmund H. North. *Dir Photog* Fred Koenekamp. *2d Unit Photog* Clifford Stine, Cecilio Paniagua. *Art Dir* Urie McCleary, Gil Parrondo. *Set Decor* Antonio Mateos, Pierre-Louis Thévenet. *Main Titl* Pacific Title. *Film Ed* Hugh S. Fowler. *Mus* Jerry Goldsmith. *Orch* Arthur Morton. *Sd Supv* James Corcoran. *Sd Re-rec* Douglas O. Williams, Ted Soderberg, Murray Spivack. *Sd Prod* Don Bassman. *Asst Dir* Eli Dunn, José López Rodero. *Unit Prod Mgr* Francisco Day, Eduardo G. Maroto, Tadeo Villalba. *Makeup Supv* Dan Striepeke. *Makeup Artist* Del Acevedo. *Sp Photog Eff* L. B. Abbott, Art Cruickshank. *Proc Cons* Richard Vetter, Carl Williams. *Tech Adv* Paul D. Harkins, (Gen.), Glover S. Johns, Jr. (Col.). *Sr Military Adv* Omar N. Bradley, (Gen.). *Spanish Military Adv* Luis Martin Pozuelo, (Lieut. Col.). *Action Coörd* Joe Canutt. *Mechanical Eff* Alex Weldon. *Casting* Michael McLean.

Cast: George C. Scott (*Gen. George S. Patton, Jr.*), Karl Malden (*Gen. Omar N. Bradley*), Michael Bates (*Field Marshall Sir Bernard Law Montgomery*), Edward Binns (*Maj. Gen. Walter Bedell Smith*), Lawrence Dobkin (*Col. Gaston Bell*), John Doucette (*Maj. Gen. Lucian K. Truscott*), James Edwards (*Sgt. William George Meeks*), Frank Latimore (*Lieut. Col. Henry Davenport*), Richard Münch (*Col. Gen Alfred Jodl*), Morgan Paull (*Capt. Richard N. Jenson*), Siegfried Rauch (*Capt. Oskar Steiger*), Paul Stevens (*Lieut. Col. Charles R. Codman*), Michael Strong (*Brig. Gen. Hobart Carver*), Karl Michael

Vogler (*Field Marshall Erwin Rommel*), Stephen Young (*Capt. Chester B. Hansen*), Peter Barkworth (*Col. John Welkin*), John Barrie (*Air Vice-Marshal Sir Arthur Coningham*), David Bauer (*Lieut. Gen. Harry Buford*), Tim Considine (*soldier who gets slapped*), Albert Dumortier (*Moroccan minister*), Gerald Flood (*Air Chief Marshal Sir Arthur Tedder*), Jack Gwillim (*Gen. Sir Harold Alexander*), David Healy (*clergyman*), Bill Hickman (*General Patton's driver*), Sandy Kevin (*correspondent*), Carey Loftin (*General Bradley's driver*), Alan MacNaughtan (*British briefing officer*), Lionel Murton (*Third Army chaplain*), Clint Ritchie (*tank captain*), Douglas Wilmer (*Maj. Gen. Francis de Guingand*), Patrick J. Zurica (*1st Lieut. Alexander Stiller*), Lowell Thomas (*narrator [see note]*), Abraxas Aaran (*Willy, a dog*).

Biographical drama. Source: Ladislas Farago, *Patton: Ordeal and Triumph* (New York, 1964). Omar N. Bradley, *A Soldier's Story* (New York, 1951). In 1943, after German Field Marshal Erwin Rommel's Afrika Korps has severely defeated American tank units in the Kasserine Pass, Tunisia, Gen. George S. Patton is sent to spearhead the U. S. sector of the North African campaign. His dramatic flair for leadership revitalizes the tank corps; an avid student of military history, he indulges his mystical belief in reincarnation and envisions the succession of great warriors and battles that have preceded him. Aided by his deputy commander, Gen. Omar N. Bradley, Patton scores a decisive victory over Rommel at El Guettar, which eventually leads to the German expulsion from North Africa. His next assignment is to lead the 7th Army into Sicily by taking Palermo, but instead he is ordered to protect the flank of his chief rival, British Field Marshal Montgomery, while Montgomery leads the attack. On his own initiative, Patton pushes forward and takes Messina, the island's main port and primary objective of the campaign, thereby intensifying his feud with Montgomery. Shortly thereafter, Patton visits a field hospital where, in a fit of rage, he slaps a weeping, battle-fatigued soldier; his action causes Allied Commander Dwight D. Eisenhower to demand the general's public apology and to eventually relieve Patton of his command. In spite of his probation, Patton's worth as a decoy during a tour of the Mediterranean is acknowledged, and he eventually assumes leadership of the 3rd Army under the command of Bradley. He forces his men through an impasse at Normandy and comes to a dramatic rescue of the beleaguered 101st Airborne under siege at Bastogne during the Battle of the Bulge. Patton pushes his troops all the way to Czechoslovakia where, with total victory imminent, he is ordered to allow Montgomery and the Russian troops to rout the already disorganized German army. At the war's end, Patton cannot refrain from insulting America's current ally, Russia; unable to make the transition to peacetime, he is removed from command and bids a sad farewell to his staff. *Military life. Combat zone life. Ambition. Reincarnation. Battle fatigue. Hospitals. Tanks (armored cars). World War II. Battle of the Bulge. Kasserine Pass (Tunisia). North Africa. El Guettar (Tunisia). Sicily. Palermo. Messina. Normandy. Bastogne. Czechoslovakia. George Smith Patton. Omar Nelson Bradley. Bernard Law Montgomery. Dwight David Eisenhower. Erwin Rommel. Alfred Jodl. United States Army. United States Army—General Staff. United States Army—Armored Forces. Great Britain—Army. Union of Soviet Socialist Republics—Army.*

Note: Location scenes filmed in Spain, England, Morocco, and Greece. Also known as *Patton: A Salute to a Rebel*. Dimension 150 process used only in 70mm roadshow prints. Fox Movietone News clips were accompanied by a revised narration delivered by Lowell Thomas, who also narrated the original clips.

PAULETTE *see* **THE SEX PERILS OF PAULETTE**

PAW *see* **BOY OF TWO WORLDS**

THE PAWN   **F6.3764**
Carmen Productions-Frank Sollento. *Dist* Carmen Productions. 20 Nov **1968** [Port Chester, New York, opening]. Sd; b&w. 35mm. [Feature length assumed.]

Pres by Seven Arts Pictures. *Prod-Dir-Writ* Jean Carmen Dillow. *Cons Prod* Ben Berk. *Financial Backers* Serge Semenenko, Eliot Hyman. *Dir Photog* François Farkas. *Film Ed* Aram Avakian. *Mus* Mario Nascimbene. *Prod Mgr* Kathryn Hastings.

Cast: Guy "Buz" Dillow, Lisa Jonson, Roger Landry, Lou Steele, Jean Carmen Dillow.

Drama. No information about the precise nature of this film has been found, but press material indicates that it concerns a small boy involved in the Hungarian revolution in 1956. *Children. Hungary—History—Revolt 1956.*

Note: Production begun in Dec 1961; location scenes filmed in Ipswich and Boston, Massachusetts; Newport, Rhode Island; upstate New York; and Amalfi, Italy. Working title: *Tears Are for Tomorrow.*

THE PAWNBROKER
F6.3765

Landau/Unger Co.-Pawnbroker Co. *Dist* Landau Releasing Organization, Allied Artists, American International Pictures. 20 Apr **1965** [New York opening; c20 Apr 1965; LP34701]. Sd; b&w. 35mm. 114 min. [Copyright length: 119 min.]

Pres by Ely Landau, Herbert R. Steinmann. An Ely Landau Production. *Prod* Roger Lewis, Philip Langner. *Exec Prod* Worthington Miner. *Assoc Prod* Joseph Manduke. *Dir* Sidney Lumet. *Screenplay* David Friedkin, Morton Fine. *Dir Photog* Boris Kaufman. *Art Dir* Richard Sylbert. *Set Decor* Jack Flaherty. *Film Ed* Ralph Rosenblum. *Mus* Quincy Jones. *Sd* Dennis Maitland. *Asst Dir* Dan Eriksen. *Prod Coörd* Alfred Markim. *Prod Mgr* Ulu Grosbard. *Cost* Anna Hill Johnstone. *Makeup* Bill Herman. *Hairdresser* Ed Callaghan.

Cast: Rod Steiger *(Sol Nazerman)*, Geraldine Fitzgerald *(Marilyn Birchfield)*, Brock Peters *(Rodriguez)*, Jaime Sanchez *(Jesus Ortiz)*, Thelma Oliver *(Ortiz' girl)*, Marketa Kimbrell *(Tessie)*, Baruch Lumet *(Mendel)*, Juano Hernandez *(Mr. Smith)*, Linda Geiser *(Ruth)*, Nancy R. Pollock *(Bertha)*, Raymond St. Jacques *(Tangee)*, John McCurry *(Buck)*, Charles Dierkop *(Robinson)*, Eusebia Cosme *(Mrs. Ortiz)*, Warren Finnerty *(Savarese)*, Jack Ader *(Morton)*, E. M. Margolese *(Papa)*, Marianne Kanter *(Joan)*, Ed Morehouse *(Robinson)*, Marc Alexander *(Rubin)*.

Drama. Source: Edward Lewis Wallant, *The Pawnbroker* (New York, 1961). With the rise of Hitler, Prof. Sol Nazerman, a Jew, and his family were dragged to a concentration camp, where he saw his two children die and his wife raped by Nazi officers. Now he operates a pawnshop in Spanish Harlem. Numbed by the horrors of his past, he considers himself conditioned against any emotion. His assistant at the shop is a brash but sensitive young Puerto Rican, Jesus Ortiz, who senses that there is another being under the cold exterior Nazerman presents. But the boy's attempts to break through this exterior are rebuffed, as are those of Marilyn Birchfield, a neighborhood social worker. When Nazerman learns that Rodriguez, the pawnshop's flamboyant black backer, makes his money through prostitution, the old man recalls his wife's death and swears that he wants no part of the business; but Rodriguez forces him to admit that he knew all along where the money came from. One day Ortiz tries to get assurance from Nazerman that there is more to life than the ugliness he sees around him. When Nazerman responds by being thoughtlessly cruel, the boy spitefully arranges for the pawnshop to be robbed. Facing armed thugs, Nazerman refuses to hand over his money and readily—almost eagerly—awaits death. But Ortiz takes the bullet intended for Nazerman and dies in the old man's arms. In frustration, Nazerman impales his hand on the receipt spindle and wanders into the street. *Jews. Negroes. Germans. Professors. Pawnbrokers. Puerto Ricans. Social workers. Nazis. Anti-Semitism. Mutilation. Rape. Prostitution. Robbery. Urban life. Concentration camps. Pawnshops. Slums. Germany—History—Third Reich. New York City—Spanish Harlem.*

Note: Filmed on location in New York City.

PAY THE BABY-SITTER
F6.3766

Dist Distribpix, Inc. ca **1969**. Sd; col. 35mm. 61 min.

Drama. A young woman works as a babysitter to earn money for college. She is often surprised by the early return of the father, and he has no trouble seducing her. On lonely nights, the babysitter invites her boyfriend to visit. On one such night, she is caught with her beau in the parents' bedroom, and they are forced to participate in group sex to "atone" for their indiscretion. *Babysitters. Seduction. Employer-employee relations. Group sex.*

PAYMENT IN BLOOD (Italy)
F6.3767

Circus Film–Fono Roma. *Dist* Columbia Pictures. 4 Dec **1968** [New York opening; c1 Dec 1968; LP36360]. Sd; col (Technicolor). 35mm (Techniscope). 90 min. *MPAA rating* R.

Exec Prod Francesco Orefici. *Dir* E. G. Rowland. *Story-Screenplay* Tito Carpi, E. G. Rowland. *Dir Photog* Aldo Pennelli. *Camera* Renato Fait. *1st Asst Camera* Renato Lomiry. *2d Asst Camera* Dario Garbarino. *3d Asst Camera* Marcello Gallinelli. *Art Dir* Saverio D'Eugenio. *Set Decor* Antonio Fratalocchi. *Main Titl* Diamante & Grisanti. *Film Ed* Antonietta Zita. *Mus Comp & Cond* Francesco De Masi. *Gen Mus* Fono Roma. *Song:* "Seven Men" Francesco De Masi, Audrey Nohra, Alessandroni. *Sung by* Raul. *Sd Engr* Manlio Magara. *Sd Op* Ugo Pace. *Asst Dir* Maurizio Mancini. *Prod Mgr* Adriano Merkel. *Gen Organization* Marino Girolami, Francesco Orefici. *Cont* Amelia Zurlini. *Prod Sec* Pietro Nardi. *Cost* Giorgio Desideri. *Makeup* Massimo De Rossi. *Hairdresser* Fausto De Lisio. *Sp Eff* F. Bacciucchi. *Ch Electrn* Attivo Bevilacqua. *Stagehand* Spartaco Pizzi.

Cast: Edd Byrnes *(Stuart)*, Guy Madison *(Colonel Blake)*, Louise Barrett *(Manuela)*, Enio Girolami *(Chamaco)*, Rick Boyd, Rossella Bergamonti, Mario Donen, Alfred Aysanoa, Marco Mariani, Attilio Severini, Adriana Facchetti, Giulio Maculani, Piero Vida, Mirella Pamphili.

Western melodrama. Along the Texas-Mexican border in the years following the Civil War, a band of former Confederate soldiers under the leadership of an ex-officer, Colonel Blake, terrorize the countryside. As one of their number faces a military firing squad, he is rescued by Stuart, a stranger who claims to know the hiding place of a fabulous treasure in gold hidden by General Beauregard. After proving himself in several tests of courage, Stuart joins the marauders in their raids. They encounter Manuela, a fiery young woman, and Blake appropriates her as his girl friend. Stuart claims that the treasure is hidden in an Indian burial ground near the town of Durango. Blake comes to realize that Stuart is actually a bounty hunter who has planned to lure him into a trap. Blake kills the town sheriff and leaves Stuart tied in a barn which he sets afire; but Manuela, who is actually Stuart's partner, slips him a knife which enables him to escape. Gunning down a posse, the outlaws make their way to the burial ground and unearth the "treasure"—worthless Confederate money. Stuart arrives and shoots the ex-soldiers in turn, leaving the wounded Blake to the vengeance of his victims' widows. Stuart then collects the bounty money and rides off with Manuela. *Confederate veterans. Outlaws. Strangers. Bounty hunters. Gangs. Sheriffs. Murder. Duplicity. Gold. Treasure. Cemeteries. Texas. Mexican border. Pierre Gustave Toutant de Beauregard.*

Note: Opened in Rome in Jul 1967 as *7 Winchester per un massacro*; running time: ca100 min. Registered for copyright by St. Regis Films International. E. G. Rowland is a pseudonym for Enzo Girolami; Louise Barrett for Luisa Baratto.

PAYROLL (Great Britain)
F6.3768

Lynx Films. *Dist* Allied Artists. Jun **1962** [c25 May 1962; LP21898]. Sd; b&w. 35mm. 94 min. [Also 80 min.]

Pres by Nat Cohen, Stuart Levy. A Julian Wintle–Leslie Parkyn Production. *Prod* Norman Priggen. *Dir* Sidney Hayers. *Screenplay* George Baxt. *Dir Photog* Ernest Steward. *Camera Op* Godfrey Godar. *Art Dir* Jack Shampan. *Main Titl* Gil Kirk. *Film Ed* Tristam Cones. *Mus Comp & Dir* Reg Owen. *Song:* "It Happens Every Day" Tony Osborne. *Sung by* Eddie Ellis. *Sd Ed* Lionel Selwyn. *Sd Rec* John W. Mitchell. *Re-rec* Ken Cameron. *Asst Dir* Clive Reed. *Prod Supv* Arthur Alcott. *Unit Mgr* Geoffrey Haine. *Cont* Marjorie Owens. *Cost* Morris Angel. *Wardrobe* Vi Murray. *Makeup* Trevor Crole-Rees. *Hairstyles* Maud Onslow.

Cast: Michael Craig *(Johnny Mellors)*, Françoise Prévost *(Katie Pearson)*, Billie Whitelaw *(Jackie Parker)*, William Lucas *(Dennis Pearson)*, Kenneth Griffith *(Monty)*, Tom Bell *(Blackie)*, Barry Keegan *(Bert Landridge)*, Edward Cast *(Det. Sgt. Mark Bradden)*, Andrew Faulds *(Detective Inspector Carberry)*, William Peacock *(Harry Parker)*, Glyn Houston *(Frank Moore)*, Joan Rice *(Madge Moore)*, Vanda Godsell *(Doll)*, Stanley Meadows *(Bowen)*, Brian McDermott *(Brent)*, Hugh Morton *(Mr. John)*, Keith Faulkner *(Alf)*, Bruce Beeby *(Worth)*, Murray Evans *(Billy)*, Kevin Bennett *(Archie)*, Michael Barrington.

Crime melodrama. Source: Derek Bickerton, *Payroll* (London, 1959). During the gang robbery of an armored truck carrying a factory payroll, the driver of the getaway car is killed. His wife, Jackie Parker, vows to avenge her husband's death and, upon learning that Dennis Pearson, a wages clerk at the factory, was the thieves' inside man, begins showering him with anonymous letters and telephone calls. Pearson's greedy wife, Katie, has meanwhile fallen in love with the gang's leader, Johnny Mellors. With pressure coming at them from all sides, the crooks start quarreling among themselves, and Johnny is forced to kill two of his cohorts. After Katie has tried to doublecross him, he decides to flee the country, but he is confronted by Jackie Parker as he boards a cruiser. When the suitcase containing the payroll money slips overboard, Johnny dives in after it and is killed by a speeding motorboat as the money floats out to sea. *Clerks. Robbery. Revenge. Infidelity. Murder. Perfidy. Armored car services. Cruisers. Motorboats.*

Note: Location scenes filmed in Newcastle. Opened in London in Apr 1961; running time: 105 min. Working title: *I Promise To Pay*.

PEACE FOR A GUNFIGHTER
F6.3769

Cable Springs, Ltd. *Dist* Cable Springs, Ltd., Crown International Pictures. Jan **1967** [c26 Oct 1965; LP32463]. Sd; col (Technicolor). 35mm (Techniscope). 82 min.

Prod Robert J. Allen, Harold W. Johnson. *Dir* Raymond Boley. *Screenplay* Michael W. Fuller. *Dir Photog* Robert J. Allen. *Set Dsgn* Red Johnson. *Film Ed* James L. Royer. *Mus Score & Songs:* "Peace for a Gunfighter," "Sometime" Dolan Ellis. *Sd Ed* Motteram.

Cast: Burt Berger *("The Preacher")*, JoAnne Meredith *(Melody)*, Everett King *(Smiley)*, Stirling Welker *(Sloan)*, Danny Zapien *(Igmagio)*, John Scovern *(Rafe)*, Mark Farrington *(The Minister)*, Bob Pollard *(old man)*, Ray Odom *(gambler)*, Mark Sanchez *(boy)*, Allen Wood *(Wells Fargo agent)*.

Western melodrama. "The Preacher," weary of the life of blood and violence which has earned him the reputation as the fastest gunfighter alive, arrives in Reata Pass, a small town where he hopes to begin a new life. Several townspeople seek his assistance: Melody, a Reata Saloon dancehall girl whose former romance with her unscrupulous employer, Rafe, is proving to be a threat to her newfound love for Preacher; the minister, who wants his church saved;

and Sloan, who wishes to hire Preacher to protect his ore shipments. Preacher's attempt to lay down his guns is scorned by many of the townspeople, and they eventually taunt him into battle once again. Following a showdown in the churchyard, Preacher finally lays down his guns and turns to Melody to begin a new life. *Gunfighters. Dancehall girls. Saloon keepers. Clergymen. Smalltown life. Reputation. Employer-employee relations.*

PEACE TO HIM WHO ENTERS (U.S.S.R.)   F6.3770

Mosfilm. *Dist* Artkino Pictures. 23 Nov **1963** [New York opening]. Sd; b&w. 35mm. 90 min.

Dir Aleksandr Alov, Vladimir Naumov. *Screenplay* Leonid Zorin, Aleksandr Alov, Vladimir Naumov. *Story Ed* L. Belova. *Photog* Anatoliy Kuznetsov. *Art Dir* Ye. Chernyayev. *Film Ed* N. Anikeyeva. *Mus* Nikolay Karetnikov. *Cond* G. Gamburg. *Sd* V. Sharun. *Asst Dir* V. Ivanov, dir. *Prod Mgr* I. Gurman. *Cost* T. Kasparova. *Makeup* Ye. Yevseyeva.

Cast: Viktor Avdyushko *(Yamshchikov)*, Aleksandr Demyanenko *(Ivlev)*, Stanislav Khitrov *(Rukavitsyn)*, Lidiya Shaporenko *(Barbara)*, V. Bokadoro *(Frenchwoman)*, N. Grinko *(American)*, Nikolay Timofeyev *(battalion commander)*, I. Izvitskaya *(traffic controller)*, A. Fayt *(Serb)*, Viktor Koltsov, G. Nikitin, V. Zhilkin, S. Krylov, M. Logvinov, E. Knausmyuller, V. Marenkov, V. Makarov, G. Samokhina, A. Seryozhkin.

War melodrama. In the final days of World War II, Ivlev, a lieutenant newly graduated from officers' school, receives as his first assignment the task of escorting Barbara, a pregnant German woman, to a field hospital in the rear lines at Kvikau [Zwickau?]. He is accompanied by Yamshchikov, a mute, shell-shocked sergeant who has lost everything dear to him, and by Rukavitsyn, the group's good-hearted, undisciplined truckdriver. The four are forced to overcome mutual hostilities and join together to surmount obstacles of nature and war. Ivlev initially insists upon following military regulations to the letter, but he gains flexibility with experience. At one point they lose their way, and Barbara, frightened and hysterical, directs them toward remnants of German forces. Rukavitsyn is killed, and his truck is destroyed. Ivlev, in the heat of the moment, is tempted to shoot Barbara, but Yamshchikov prevents him from firing and teaches him a lesson in humanitarianism. Liberated concentration camp prisoners aid them, and finally they are picked up by an American soldier. With his help they reach the hospital; and, as news of peace arrives, Barbara's baby is born. *Truckdrivers. Mutes. Germans. Refugees. Combat zone life. Shell shock. Childbirth. Humanitarianism. V-E Day (7 May 1945). World War II. Zwickau. Union of Soviet Socialist Republics—Army. Germany—Army. United States Army.*

Note: Released in the U.S.S.R. in Sep 1961 as *Mir vkhodyashchemu*. Also known as *Peace to Him.*

THE PEACH THIEF (Bulgaria)   F6.3771

Sofiya Film Studios. *For* Bulgarian State Films. *Dist* Brandon Films. 15 Sep **1969** [New York opening]. Sd; b&w. 35mm. 84 min. *MPAA rating* M.

Dir-Writ Vulo Radev. *Photog* Todor Stoyanov. *Art Dir* Nedelcho Nanev. *Mus* Simeon Pironkov.

Cast: Nevena Kokanova *(Lisa)*, Rade Marković *(Ivo Obrenovich)*, Mikhail Mikhailov *(The Colonel)*, Vasil Vachev *(The Colonel's Orderly)*.

War drama. Source: Emiliian Stanev, *Kradetsüt na praskovi* (Sofia, 1948). During the final months of World War I when Bulgaria is aligned with Germany, Ivo Obrenovich, a Serbian officer, is among the inmates at a prisoner of war camp in Trnovo commanded by a Bulgarian colonel. One day, Ivo sneaks into the Colonel's garden to steal some peaches and meets the Colonel's wife, Lisa. Bored with her life and lonely for companionship, Lisa not only ignores the theft but agrees to meet with Ivo again. Lisa finds Ivo's optimism about the future a refreshing change from her husband's preoccupation with military matters. As the friendship between Ivo and Lisa blossoms into love, the Colonel's fears multiply, and he orders the prisoners evacuated. As they are being marched out of town, Ivo breaks away and races to Lisa in the hope of persuading her to run away with him. He is shot and killed by an orderly who had been instructed by the Colonel to protect the peaches in the garden from thieves. *Prisoners of war. Serbians. Theft. Infidelity. Gardens. World War I. Trnovo.*

Note: Released in Bulgaria in 1964 as *Kradetsüt na praskovi.*

PEACOCK FEATHERS see **OPEN THE DOOR AND SEE ALL THE PEOPLE**

THE PEARL OF TLAYUCAN (Mexico)   F6.3772

Producciones Matouk. Sep **1964** [Los Angeles showing]. Sd; b&w. 35mm. 105 min.

Dir-Writ Luis Alcoriza. *Photog* Rosalío Solano. *Art Dir* Jesús Bracho. *Film Ed* Carlos Savage. *Mus* Sergio Guerrero. *Sd* Javier Mateos.

Cast: Andrés Soler *(Don Carlos)*, Julio Aldama *(husband [Euphemio])*, Jorge Martínez de Hoyos *(priest)*, Norma Angélica *(wife)*, Anita Blanch *(spinster)*, Noé Murayama *(blind man)*, Francisco Córdova, José Gálvez,

Antonio Bravo, José Chávez, Dolores Camarillo, José Carlos Ortiz.

Comedy. Based on a novel by: Jesús Murciélago Velázquez. In a small Mexican village, the local priest berates the peasants for not contributing to church fêtes and pilgrimages. When a small boy sickens, his grieving father steals a pearl from the crown of the statue of Santa Lucia to pay for medicine. The father is caught, but the pearl is lost. His neighbors, however, rally to the father's support, and he is allowed to go free. His wife finds the missing pearl, passed by a swine that had swallowed it. She returns it to the statue, and the village thinks that a miracle has occurred. *Priests. Peasants. Catholics. Village life. Theft. Family life. Pearls. Miracles. Pigs.*

Note: Produced in Mexico in 1961 as *Tlayucan.*

PEAU DE BANANE see **BANANA PEEL**

PEAU D'ESPION see **TO COMMIT A MURDER**

LA PEAU DOUCE see **THE SOFT SKIN**

IL PECCATO DI ANNA see **ANNA'S SIN**

I PECCATORI DELLA FORESTA NERA see **THE BURNING COURT**

PECCATORI IN BLUE-JEANS see **THE CHEATERS**

PEDDLERS OF SIN   F6.3773

Mitam Productions. ca **1966** [Champaign, Illinois, showing: 6 Sep 1967]. Sd; b&w. 35mm. 64 min.

Cast: Jerry Harris, Capri, Carole Lang, Virginia Luce, Wayne Howser.

Melodrama. Talent agent John receives a telephone call from Hollywood producer Max, who wants a number of women to come to his party. John and his partner, Chris, procure a young actress and other women who want to break into show business. The actress is invited into Max's bedroom where he asks her to read a part for his new film. He ignores her acting talent, but he fails in his efforts to seduce, and then rape her. Meanwhile, two disillusioned actresses find solace with each other while drug addict Joan tries to get a fix from Chris, who is really a dope pusher for a syndicate. Chris degrades Joan before he gives her the narcotics, but when he tries to seduce her, she accidentally kills him with an ice pick. The police arrive to break up the party. *Talent agents. Motion picture producers. Actors. Drug dealers. Drug addicts. Seduction. Lesbianism. Manslaughter. Rape. Sadism. Narcotics.*

Note: Also known as *Peddlers of Evil.*

PEE WEE KING'S "COUNTRY WESTERN HOEDOWN" see **COUNTRY WESTERN HOEDOWN**

PEEK-A-BOO (France)   F6.3774

Optimax Films—C. C. F. Lux. *Dist* Fanfare Films, U. S. Films. 20 Apr **1961** [Los Angeles showing]. Sd; col (Agfacolor). 35mm. 65 min.

Prod Edgar Bacquet. *Exec Prod* Emile Flavin. *Prod Administrator* Paul Deschamps. *Dir* Jean Loubignac. *Screenplay* Robert Dhéry. *Dial* Francis Blanche. *Photog* René Colas. *Camera* Gricha Willy. *Asst Camera* Paul Gobet, Pierre Darasse. *Art Dir* Roger Briaucourt. *Asst Art Dir* Yves Olivier. *Film Ed* Jacques Mavel. *Asst Film Ed* Janine Verneau. *Mus* Gérard Calvi. *Lyr* Francis Blanche. *Choreog* Colette Brosset. *Sd* André Louis. *Sd Rec* André Soler. *Boom* Gabriel Motus. *Asst Dir* Roger de Fontaine, Guy Labourrasse, François Trives. *Prod Mgr* André Bertoux. *Prod Asst* Pierre Vouillon. *Location Mgr* Robert Testard. *Script Girl* Alice Ziller. *Prod Sec* Jacqueline Robin. *Cost Dsgn* Catherine (cost), Raymonde. *Wardrobe Mistress* Georgette Dubois. *Wardrobe Master* Marcelle Malherbe. *Makeup* Claudie Milhau. *Hairstyles* Rosy Rouff. *Still Photog* Henry Carnel.

Cast: Robert Dhéry *(himself)*, Colette Brosset *(herself)*, Louis de Funès *(Inspector Leboeuf)*, Raymond Bussières *(plumber)*, Rosine Luguet *(plumber's wife)*, Jacqueline Maillan *(theatre manageress)*, Sophie Mallet, Simone Claris, Liliane Autran, Caccia, Jacques Legras, Robert Saget, Gérard Calvi, Francis Blanche, Michel Serrault, Guy Pierrault, Jacques Jouanneau, The Bluebell Girls, Ballets Colette Brosset, Ballets de La Loïe Fuller.

Farce. In a small French provincial town, the local theater announces a new variety show entitled "Ah! les belles bacchantes". Police Inspector Leboeuf attends several rehearsals to determine if any rules of decency have been violated. Several numbers are executed: "The Creation of the World," "American Strip Tease," "In the Rain," and "The Bathing Huts." The show succeeds in arousing both the inspector and a plumber working at the theater. The plumber's wife, enraged by her husband's interest in the nude women on stage, performs a striptease. Leboeuf mounts the stage and begins to sing and dance. The producer becomes annoyed at the interruptions, but Leboeuf finally takes part in the show, along with the plumber and his wife. *Police. Theatrical troupes. Plumbers. Singers. Dancers. Theatrical producers. Nudity. Striptease. Smalltown life. Rehearsals.*

Note: Premiered in Paris in Oct 1954 under the title *Ah! les belles bacchantes*; running time (apparently cut): 71 min. Interiors filmed at the Théâtre de Suresnes.

THE PEEK SNATCHERS   F6.3775
Dist Broadway Roadshow Distributors. 25 Feb **1965** [San Francisco showing]. Sd; b&w. 35mm. 72 min.

Sex film. No information about the precise nature of this film has been found, but pressbook materials indicate that it deals with voyeurism. *Voyeurism.*

PEEP SHOWS OF PARIS (Reissue)   F6.3776
Pad Productions. *Dist* Pad Productions, William Mishkin. 18 Oct **1962** [Los Angeles showing]. Sd; col (Eastman Color). 35mm. 70 min. [Also 60 min.]

Note: Originally released in 1952 as *French Peep Show*; running time: 72 min. Also known as *French Post Cards*.

THE PEEPING PHANTOM   F6.3777
All American Film Producers, Inc. *Dist* Inter-American Film Distributors. 30 Jul **1964** [San Francisco showing]. Sd; col (Eastman Color). 35mm. [Feature film, length unknown.]

Horror comedy. In the court of Judge Goodbody, several chorus girls in a musical revue relate their experiences with the Peeping Phantom, whose method of operation was to lurk in the dressing rooms to watch the girls as they changed clothes. The trial concludes with the Peeping Phantom's own surprise testimony. *Judges. Chorus girls. Voyeurism. Trials. Nightclubs. Musical revues.*

Note: Also known as *How To Succeed With Girls*.

PEEPING TOM (Great Britain)   F6.3778
Michael Powell Productions. *Dist* Astor Pictures. 16 May **1962** [Hartford, Connecticut, opening]. Sd; col (Eastman Color). 35mm. 86 min. [Also reviewed at 90 min.]

Prod-Dir Michael Powell. *Assoc Prod* Albert Fennell. *Screenplay-Orig Story* Leo Marks. *Photog* Otto Heller. *Art Dir* Arthur Lawson. *Set Decor* Ivor Beddoes. *Film Ed* Noreen Ackland. *Mus Comp & Cond* Brian Easdale. *Rhythm Dance* Wally Stott. *Sd* C. C. Stevens, Gordon McCallum. *Sd Ch* Simon Kaye. *Prod Mgr* Al Marcus.

Cast: Karl Boehm *(Mark Lewis)*, Moira Shearer *(Vivian)*, Anna Massey *(Helen Stephens)*, Maxine Audley *(Mrs. Stephens)*, Esmond Knight *(Arthur Baden)*, Bartlett Mullins *(Mr. Peters)*, Shirley Ann Field *(Diane Ashley)*, Michael Goodliffe *(Don Jarvis)*, Brenda Bruce *(Dora)*, Martin Miller *(Dr. Rosan)*, Pamela Green *(Milly)*, Jack Watson *(Inspector Gregg)*, Nigel Davenport *(Sergeant Miller)*, Brian Wallace *(Tony)*, Susan Travers *(Lorraine)*, Maurice Durant *(publicity chief)*, Brian Worth *(assistant director)*, Veronica Hurst *(Miss Simpson)*, Miles Malleson *(elderly gentleman)*, Alan Rolfe *(store detective)*, Michael Powell *(Mr. Lewis)*, John Dunbar.

Crime melodrama. Mark Lewis is a cameraman in a British film studio who is addicted to pornography. He has been so perverted by his sadistic father, who used him as a guinea pig in his psychology-of-fear experiments, that he becomes a psychotic killer obsessed with photographing the fear on the faces of those he kills. His first victim is a prostitute, his second a film actress, and his third a model. In the course of these murders, Mark meets Helen Stephens and her blind mother, and the two women rent a flat in his house. One day he shows Helen some film depicting his father's experiments on himself; the film both fascinates and repels Helen. Learning that Mark is the son of the notorious Dr. Lewis, the police put Mark under surveillance. The truth is revealed when Helen accidentally switches on Mark's projector and views the murder of the actress. Now completely insane, Mark struggles with his impulse to kill Helen; but hearing the police arrive downstairs, he switches on the recorded screams of his own childhood and films his own suicide. *Motion picture cameramen. Psychologists. Psychopaths. Prostitutes. Actors. Models. Police. Photography. Pornography. Sadism. Blindness. Filial relations. Murder. Suicide. Experiments.*

Note: Opened in London in Apr 1960; running time: 109 min.

PEER GYNT   F6.3779
Willow Corp. *Dist* Brandon Films. Nov **1965** [c27 Jul, 15 Sep 1965; LU3373, LP31910]. Sd; b&w. 16mm & 35mm. 85 min.

Prod-Dir David Bradley. *Assoc Dir* Thomas A. Blair, Roy Eggert, Jr. *Photog* David Bradley, Richard Roth, Robert Cooper, *photog. Mus Selections* Edvard Grieg. *Cost* Sally Hyde, Elizabeth Cole, *makeup,* Katherine Elfstrom. *Makeup Artist* Roy Eggert, Jr. *Prop* Roy Eggert, Jr. *Tech Staff* Rod Maynard, John Jerrard, Philip McConnell, George B. Moll.

Cast: Charlton Heston *(Peer Gynt)*, Betty Hanisee *(Aase)*, Mrs. Herbert Hyde *(old woman)*, Lucielle Powell *(Kari)*, Sue Straub *(old woman)*, Charles Pactow *(Aslak)*, Katherine Elfstrom *(Solveig)*, Morris Wilson *(Haegstad)*, George B. Moll *(drunk/Bedouin chief)*, Betty Barton *(Ingrid)*, Alan Eckhart *(Mads Moen)*, Katharine Bradley, Anty Ball, Alice Badgerow *(three cowherd girls)*, Audrey Wedlock *(Woman in Green)*, Roy Eggert, Jr. *(Dovre-King/ Monsieur Ballon/priest)*, Francis X. Bushman *(Boyg, a voice in the darkness)*, Sarah Merrill *(Woman in Green, now a hag)*, Alan Heston *(ugly urchin)*, David Bradley *(Herr Trumpetterstraale/bailiff)*, Warren McKenzie *(MacPherson)*, Rose Andrews *(Anitra)*, Robert Cooper, *photog (man in mourning)*, Rod Maynard *(lad)*, Jane Wilimovsky *(old woman)*, Thomas A. Blair *(button moulder/thin person)*.

Fantasy. Source: Henrik Ibsen, *Peer Gynt* (1867). Aase tells her son, Peer Gynt, that his betrothed will marry the village dullard. Peer travels to the nearby Norwegian village to attend the wedding and meets Solveig, a pretty young maiden who rejects his advances. Angered, Peer abducts the bride and carries her into the mountains, where he seduces and abandons her. The Woman in Green finds him asleep in the forest and takes him to her father, the Troll-King. He becomes a captive of the trolls and goblins in a nightmare fantasy but eventually escapes from the Hall of the Mountain King and leaves the court of the trolls. He returns to Solveig, and they live happily in a mountain hut until the Woman in Green, transformed into a hag, claims that Peer fathered an ugly troll urchin. Peer leaves Solveig and returns to his mother, who becomes ill and dies. Traveling around the world, Peer acquires wealth and plans to become emperor of the world; but he is robbed and left stranded off the coast of Morocco. After stealing the sacred robes and favorite horse of the Bedouin chief, Peer tries to win the favor of a Mohammedan dancing girl, whose tribe chases Peer across the desert. Years later, Peer returns to the village of his youth, where the people are attending a funeral; and Peer discovers that the corpse bears his own image. Soon he encounters a button-moulder, a spirit who threatens to melt his body into a base for buttons, and Peer tries to prove to the button-moulder that he has not failed in life. The love of Solveig saves him from the button-moulder's pot, and Peer claims that he will become good. Now an old man, he rejoins Solveig, who has spent her life awaiting his return. *Wanderers. Royalty. Trolls. Goblins. Bedouins. Dancers. Village life. Abduction. Seduction. Parentage. Filial relations. Robbery. Weddings. Forests. Deserts. Funerals. Buttons. Norway. Morocco. Dreams.*

Note: Filmed in 1941 on location in northern Illinois and Wisconsin, including the shores of Lake Michigan. Originally produced as a silent film with synchronized music score; revised and reedited in 1965 with new material and the voice of Francis X. Bushman.

PEKING BLONDE (France/Italy/West Germany)   F6.3780
Hans Eckelkamp Film Produktion-Copernic Films-Clesi Cinematografica. *Dist* Ben Barry & Associates. **1969.** Sd; col (Eastmancolor). 35mm (Franscope). 95 min.

Prod Raymond Danon. *Dir* Nicolas Gessner. *Screenplay* Nicolas Gessner, Marc Behm. *Adapt* Jacques Vilfrid. *Photog* Claude Lecomte. *Camera Op* Gilbert Chain. *Art Dir* Georges Petitot. *Film Ed* Jean-Michel Gautier. *Mus* François de Roubaix.

Cast: Mireille Darc *(Christine)*, Claudio Brook *(Mark Girland [Gandler?])*, Edward G. Robinson *(Douglas)*, Pascale Roberts *(secretary)*, Françoise Brion *(Erika Olsen)*, Jo Warfield *(doctor)*, Giorgia Moll *(Ginny)*, Carl Studer *(Hardy)*, Jean-Jacques Delbo *(Olsen)*, Yves Elliot *(Jackson)*, Valery Inkijinoff, Tiny Young, Aimé de March, Anne Marie Blanc, Guido Celano.

Adventure melodrama. Source: James Hadley Chase, *You Have Yourself a Deal* (London, 1966). In Paris a blonde amnesiac is tentatively identified as Erika Olsen, the mistress of Chinese ballistics expert Feng Hoh Kung. American and Soviet agents, anxious to elicit rocket secrets, pursue the blonde, while their Chinese counterparts seek to kill her. Hired by CIA chief Douglas to pose as Erika's husband, American actor Mark Girland [Gandler?] hides the woman in a Swiss villa. There she reveals that she is neither a spy nor Erika Olsen, but Erika's sister Christine, and that this elaborate imposture will allow Erika to escape from Peking with Feng Hoh Kung's priceless Black Grape pearl. Together Mark and Christine travel to Hong Kong, where they witness Erika's murder by Chinese agents. Falling from Erika's neck, the pearl drops into the sea. *Mistresses. Chinese. Scientists. Americans in foreign countries. Russians. Secret agents. Actors. Sisters. Amnesia. Impersonation. Murder. Theft. Pearls. Paris. Switzerland. Peking. Hong Kong. United States—Central Intelligence Agency.*

Note: Location scenes filmed in Hong Kong. Opened in Paris in Jan 1968 as *La blonde de Pékin*; running time: 90 min; cut to 80 min? Released in West Germany in Oct 1967 as *Die Blonde von Peking*; running time: 87 min. Italian title: *La bionda di Pechino*. Alternative U. S. title: *Professional Blonde.*

THE PEKING MEDALLION *see* THE CORRUPT ONES

IL PELO NEL MONDO *see* GO, GO, GO WORLD!

PENDULUM   F6.3781
Pendulum Productions. *Dist* Columbia Pictures. Jan **1969** [New York opening: 21 Mar; c1 Jan 1969; LP36398]. Sd; col (Technicolor). 35mm. 106 min. MPAA rating M.

Prod-Writ Stanley Niss. *Dir* George Schaefer. *Dir Photog* Lionel Lindon. *Set Decor* Morris Hoffman. *Prod Dsgn* Walter M. Simonds. *Film Ed* Hugh S.

Fowler. *Mus* Walter Scharf. *Song:* "The Pendulum Swings Both Ways" Mack David, Walter Scharf. *Sung by* The Lettermen. *Sd Supv* Charles J. Rice. *Sd* William Randall, Jr., Arthur Piantadosi. *Asst Dir* David Salven. *Makeup Supv* Ben Lane. *Hairstyles* Virginia Jones.

Cast: George Peppard *(Capt. Frank Matthews)*, Jean Seberg *(Adele Matthews)*, Richard Kiley *(Woodrow Wilson King)*, Charles McGraw *(Deputy Chief Hildebrand)*, Madeleine Sherwood *(Eileen Sanderson)*, Robert F. Lyons *(Paul Martin Sanderson)*, Frank Marth *(Lieutenant Smithson)*, Marj Dusay *(Lieutenant Tennant)*, Paul McGrath *(Sen. Augustus Cole)*, Stewart Moss *(Richard D'Angelo)*, Isabell Sanford *(Effie)*, Dana Elcar *(Detective Thornton)*, Harry Lewis *(Brooks Elliot)*, Mildred Trares *(Mary Schumacher)*, Robin Raymond *(Myra)*, Phyllis Hill *(Mrs. Wilma Elliot)*, Jock MacKelvie *(U. S. Attorney Grady Butler)*, S. John Launer *(Judge Kinsella)*, Richard Guizon *(Deputy Marshal Barnes)*, Jack Grimes *(Artie)*, Gene Boland *(Garland)*, Logan Ramsey *(Detective Jelinek)*, Douglas Henderson *(Detective Hanauer)*.

Crime melodrama. After securing the conviction of rapist-murderer Paul Sanderson, Washington, D. C., Police Capt. Frank Matthews is awarded a medal of honor and granted a leave of absence to serve on a Senate subcommittee studying law and order. However, the Supreme Court reverses the death penalty against Sanderson when his attorney, Woodrow Wilson King, establishes the fact that Sanderson was not advised of his constitutional rights before making a voluntary confession. Adding to Matthew's bitterness over the fact that an admitted killer has been freed on a technicality is the growing suspicion that his wife, Adele, is carrying on an affair with a married man. Upon being told that he is to speak on law and order in Baltimore, Matthews tells Adele that he is going to New York and will not return until the next day. That night while Adele and her lover, Brooks Elliot, are in bed, they are shot to death. When it is discovered that Matthews returned to Washington on the night of the murder, he becomes the prime suspect and is assumed guilty even by his colleagues. Retracting his initial hostility towards King's "civil rights" legal tactics, Matthews hires the liberal lawyer as his defense attorney. Despite King's efforts, however, circumstantial evidence against Matthews mounts, and eventually he is arrested for manslaughter. Convinced that he knows who the real killer is, Matthews escapes and makes his way to McKeesport, Pennsylvania, the home of Paul Sanderson. After admitting that he shot Adele and her lover, Sanderson tries to kill Matthews but is prevented from committing still another murder by his mother. Although cleared of all charges, Matthews returns to Washington to face an uncertain future with the police force. *Police. Lawyers. Judges. Murder. Rape. Confession (law). Infidelity. Circumstantial evidence. Civil rights. Law and order. Capital punishment. Filial relations. McKeesport. Washington (District of Columbia). United States Congress. United States Supreme Court.*

PENELOPE
F6.3782

Euterpe, Inc. *Dist* Metro-Goldwyn-Mayer, Inc. 10 Nov **1966** [New York opening; c20 Oct 1966; LP33601]. Sd (Westrex); col (Metrocolor). 35mm (Panavision). 97 min.

Prod Arthur Loew, Jr. *Exec Prod* Joe Pasternak. *Dir* Arthur Hiller. *Screenplay* George Wells. *Dir Photog* Harry Stradling. *Art Dir* George W. Davis, Preston Ames. *Set Decor* Henry Grace, Keogh Gleason. *Film Ed* Rita Roland. *Mus* Johnny Williams. *Lyr:* "Penelope" Leslie Bricusse. *Mus* Johnny Williams. *Song:* "The Sun Is Gray" Gale Garnett. *Sung by* Natalie Wood. *Rec Supv* Franklin Milton. *Asst Dir* Terence Nelson. *Unit Prod Mgr* Robert Vreeland. *Cost Dsgn* Edith Head. *Miss Wood's Cost* Ann Landers. *Makeup* William Tuttle. *Miss Wood's Hairstyles* Maryce Bates. *Hairstyles* Sydney Guilaroff.

Cast: Natalie Wood *(Penelope)*, Ian Bannen *(James B. Elcott)*, Dick Shawn *(Dr. Gregory Mannix)*, Peter Falk *(Lieutenant Bixbee)*, Jonathan Winters *(Professor Klobb)*, Lila Kedrova *(Sadaba)*, Lou Jacobi *(Ducky)*, Norma Crane *(Mildred)*, Arthur Malet *(Major Higgins)*, Jerome Cowan *(bank manager)*, Arlene Golonka *(Honeysuckle Rose)*, Amzie Strickland *(Miss Serena)*, Bill Gunn *(Sergeant Rothschild)*, Carl Ballantine *(Boom Boom)*, Iggie Wolfington *(store owner)*.

Comedy. Source: E. V. Cunningham, *Penelope* (New York, 1965). Although Penelope Elcott's banker husband James is in love with her, he is constantly preoccupied with business. On a whim, Penelope disguises herself as a sweet old lady and holds up her husband's bank for $60,000. She then goes to the ladies' room, removes her disguise, emerges wearing a yellow suit, informs the guards that a little old lady with a gun is in the washroom, and leaves the bank. Afterwards, she goes to her mentally unbalanced psychiatrist, Gregory Mannix, and confesses her history of kleptomania. A concealed camera has photographed the crime and has caught a rear view of the yellow-suited woman leaving the bank. Police Lieutenant Bixbee begins to suspect Penelope when he notices that the little old lady and the yellow-suited woman in the film have the same walk as she does. Penelope disposes of the yellow suit in a thrift shop, and it is purchased by Sadaba, who runs a fashion boutique. Sadaba learns of

the suit's significance, and she and her partner, Ducky, try to blackmail Penelope. Penelope confesses to Dr. Mannix, who attempts to return the $60,000 through the bank's night deposit box and, in his haste, leaves the cash exposed. Penelope confesses to her husband when a streetwalker who finds the money is accused of committing the crime. She is forced to take drastic measures to convince him of the truth of her story, but he refuses to press charges. Penelope reforms, having gained the renewed interest of her husband. *Bankers. Police. Psychiatrists. Marriage. Bank robberies. Disguise. Kleptomania. Blackmail. Wealth. Boutiques. Clothes. Documentation.*

PENIS
F6.3783

Dist Film-Makers' Cooperative. 28 Jun **1965** [New York opening]. Si; b&w. 16mm. 45 min. [See note.]

Dir A. J. Rose, Jr. No information about the precise nature of this film has been found. *Sexuality.*

Note: Filmed in Chicago. Released in a revised version in 1967 as *1967;* running time: 29 min.

PENNY WISE
F6.3784

Dist Pictograph Corp., Distribpix, Inc. ca **1970**. Sd; col (Eastmancolor). 35mm. 65 min.

Prod-Dir-Writ Emilio Portici. *Dir Photog* Thomas Casey. *Camera* Tom Kolowrath. *Asst Camera* Randy Gritner. *Sd Eff & Mus* Warren Sound Studios. *Sd Rec* Larry Fisher, Marty Jones. *Asst to Prod* Gina Fellucci. *Makeup* Barbara Kerwin. *Gaffer* William Kerwin. *Ch Grip* Harold Glaze.

Cast: Iris Rogers, Don Terri.

Drama. Three escaped convicts force their way into the Jones home. They interrupt Mr. and Mrs. Jones taking a bath and come upon two women houseguests making love. The men lash Mr. Jones to a chair and force the women to wine and dine them. A radio bulletin announces $10 thousand reward for their capture, and the women, formerly helpless in their dangerous situation, now greedily plot to get the reward. A fourth woman, selling cosmetics door-to-door, joins forces with the others to seduce the sexually naive criminals. The convicts are eventually captured and the reward goes to the women. *Prison escapees. Houseguests. Hostages. Traveling saleswomen. Lesbianism. Seduction. Rewards.*

THE PENTHOUSE (Great Britain)
F6.3785

Tahiti Films. *Dist* Paramount Pictures. 3 Oct **1967** [New York opening; c3 Oct 1967; LP34994]. Sd; col (Eastmancolor). 35mm. 100 min. [See note.]

Prod Harry Fine. *Exec Prod* Michael Klinger, Guido Coen. *Dir-Writ* Peter Collinson. *Dir Photog* Arthur Lavis. *Art Dir* Peter Mullins. *Film Ed* John Trumper. *Mus* John Hawksworth. *Song:* "World Full of Lonely Men" Harold Shaper, John Hawksworth. *Sung by* Lisa Shayne. *Sd* Laurie Clarkson. *Asst Dir* Barry Langley. *Makeup* George Partleton. *Hairstyles* Barbara Barnard.

Cast: Suzy Kendall *(Barbara Willason)*, Terence Morgan *(Bruce Victor)*, Tony Beckley *(Tom)*, Norman Rodway *(Dick)*, Martine Beswick *(Harry)*.

Drama. Source: C. Scott Forbes, *The Meter Man* (London opening: 10 Sep 1964). Adulterers Barbara and Bruce use a furnished penthouse in an unfinished apartment building for their trysts. A real estate agent with a wife and two children, Bruce has prolonged his affair with Barbara by assuring her that he is only waiting for the right moment to divorce his wife. Early one morning Barbara answers the door to the apartment and is confronted by a man who claims he has come to read the gas meter. After introducing himself as Tom, the stranger brings in his assistant, Dick. Within a few moments, Tom has produced a switchblade, Bruce has been bound with satin ribbons in a chair, and Barbara has been pushed onto a couch and forced to drink tumblers of scotch. The two intruders, in a "party" mood, persuade Barbara to smoke marijuana, dance a striptease to seductive music, and join them one at a time in the bedroom. Through it all, the helpless Bruce is taunted and ridiculed at knife point. Eventually the two men leave abruptly and Barbara unties Bruce. A few minutes later the doorbell rings again, and a bizarre-looking woman who calls herself Harry explains that she is the parole officer for the two intruders and that they wish to apologize for their bad manners. To Barbara's disgust, Bruce not only agrees but also promises not to notify the police. Immediately upon re-entering the apartment, Tom and Dick, goaded on by the sadistic Harry, tie up the couple and perform a weird dance around them. Then they leave. Bruce and Barbara free themselves, leave the building, and go off in separate directions. *Real estate agents. Hoodlums. Parole officers. Meter readers. Infidelity. Rape. Imposture. Striptease. Drunkenness. Marijuana.*

Note: Released in Great Britain in 1967 at 96 min. Press material lists running time as 97 min; also reviewed at 90 min.

PEOPLE MEET AND SWEET MUSIC FILLS THE HEART
(Denmark/Sweden)
F6.3786

Henning Carlsen-Nordisk Films-Sandrews. *Dist* Trans-Lux Distributing Corp. 14 May **1969** [New York opening]. Sd; b&w with tinted seq. 35mm. 94 min.

Prod Göran Lindgren, Henning Carlsen. *Exec Prod* Bertil Ohlsson. *Dir-Scen* Henning Carlsen. *Script* Poul Borum. *Photog* Henning Kristiansen. *Asst Camera* Leif Jappe. *Art Dir* P. A. Lundgren. *Film Ed* Henning Carlsen. *Mus* Krzysztof Komeda. *Choreog* Eske Holm. *Sd* Erik Jensen, Birger Swan. *Asst Dir* Anja Breien, Leif Jappe, Tom Hedegaard, Christian Hartkopp, Niels Heie. *Prod Mgr* Bjarne Westergaard, J. O. Bohlin, Robert McCarty. *Cost* Ulla-Britt Söderlund, Lotte Ravnholt. *Still Photog* Elliot Landy.

Cast: Harriet Andersson *(Sofia Petersen)*, Preben Neergaard *(Sjalof Petersen)*, Erik Wedersøe *(Hans Madsen)*, Eva Dahlbeck *(Devah Sörensen)*, Lone Rode *(Evangeline Hansen)*, Georg Rydeberg *(Robert Clair de Lune)*, Lotte Horne *(Mithra)*, Bent Christensen *(Falconetti)*, Mona Chong, Cassandra Mahon *(girls of the house)*, Elin Reimer *(Madam Calcura)*, Knud Rex *(Ramon Salvador)*, Lotte Tarp *(Kose)*, Eske Holm, Zito Kerras, Ove Rud, Benny Juhlin, Arne Weel, Claus Nissen, Armand Miehe, Jimmy Moore, Per Gundemann.

Romantic comedy-drama. Source: Jens August Schade, *Mennesker mødes og sød musik opstår i hjertet* (Copenhagen, 1945). Sofia Petersen, a promiscuous dancer, meets student Hans Madsen while traveling on a train to South America, and the two make love. Hans has just left his girl friend, Evangeline, and is on his way to meet his fiancée, Mithra, a woman who is admittedly seeing other men and eventually reveals herself to be a lesbian. Sofia meets Evangeline's husband, an actor named Sjalof, on the train when Hans has departed; and after making love, they decide to travel to South America together. Ramon, Sofia's stepfather, tries to seduce her; but Sjalof kills him, gets Sofia a job at a brothel in Rio de Janeiro, and then returns to Evangeline in Denmark. Evangeline has since become a streetwalker, and Sjalof encourages her to continue supporting them in this fashion. Sofia cheerfully enjoys the wanton life of the brothel. She travels to New York City and, with the help of theater impresario Robert Clair de Lune, becomes a dancing star. Meanwhile Hans, who has since married Mithra, travels to Rio de Janeiro and then to New York in search of Sofia. They meet again, and Hans fantasizes about living with Sofia and two of the prostitutes from the brothel. Again on a train in Denmark, Sofia is accosted by a masked man who forces her to disrobe; the next morning she awakens to find herself alone. *Dancers. Students. Actors. Prostitutes. Impresari. Infidelity. Promiscuity. Seduction. Murder. Marriage. Lesbianism. Trains. Whorehouses. Copenhagen. Rio de Janeiro. New York City. Fantasy.*

Note: Filmed in Rio de Janeiro, New York City, and Copenhagen. Released in 1967 in Denmark as *Mennesker mødes og sød musik opstår i hjertet* and in Sweden as *Människor möts och ljuv musik uppstår i hjärtat*; running time: 105 min.

THE PEOPLE NEXT DOOR   F6.3787
Avco Embassy Pictures–The People Next Door Co. *Dist* Avco Embassy Pictures. 26 Aug **1970** [New York opening]. Sd; col (DeLuxe, print by Movielab). 35mm. 93 min. *MPAA rating* R.
Prod Herbert Brodkin. *Exec Prod* Joseph E. Levine. *Assoc Prod* Kenneth Utt. *Dir* David Greene. *Screenplay* J. P. Miller. *Dir Photog* Gordon Willis. *Set Decor* Richard Adee. *Prod Dsgn* Charles Bailey. *Supv Ed* Brian Smedley-Aston. *Ed* Arline Garson. *Mus* Don Sebesky. *Song:* "Mama, Don't You Wait Up for Me" sung by The Glass Bottle. *Songs:* "Sweet Medusa" and "My Life in Review" sung by The Bead Game. *Sd* Chris Newman, Jack Fitzstephens, Richard Vorisek. *Asst Dir* Terence A. Donnelly, Ronald Walsh. *Prod Exec* Alan R. Morris. *Prod Mgr* Paul Ganapoler. *Cost* Ann Roth.
Cast: Eli Wallach *(Arthur Mason)*, Julie Harris *(Gerrie Mason)*, Deborah Winters *(Maxie Mason)*, Stephen McHattie *(Artie Mason)*, Hal Holbrook *(David Hoffman)*, Don Scardino *(Sandy Hoffman)*, Cloris Leachman *(Tina Hoffman)*, Rue McClanahan *(Della)*, Nehemiah Persoff *(Dr. Salazar)*, Mike Kellin *(Dr. Margolin)*, Sandy Alexander *(Elliott)*, Anthony Call *(Dr. Lauran)*, Matthew Cowles *(Wally)*, Joseph Leon *(Price Whitehead)*, Bruce Scott *(Jack)*, Anita Dangler *(blonde mother)*, Bobby Sandler, Jay Savino, Steve Kanyon, Ron Panvini *(party musicians)*, The Bead Game *(Artie's group)*, Jan Sarno *(night nurse)*, Paul Ganapoler *(club owner)*, Marilyn Chris *(discotheque waitress)*, Ben Yaffee *(discotheque owner)*, John Batiste *(therapist)*.
Drama. Source: J. P. Miller, *The People Next Door* (a teleplay; first presented on CBS's "Television Playhouse" 8 Oct 1968). Suburban residents Arthur and Gerrie Mason are shocked to discover their daughter Maxie hallucinating under the influence of LSD. Accusing his musician son Artie of supplying her with drugs, Mason demands that he leave home. Mason then seeks advice from his next door neighbor, high school principal David Hoffman. Hoffman, the father of model son Sandy, advises Mason to get to know his daughter better. The Masons try family therapy, which fails abysmally. During a party Maxie takes STP and is disabled. When Hoffman discovers that Sandy has been Maxie Mason's supplier, he calls the police. Although charges are brought against Sandy, they are dropped because of a technicality. At the hospital where Maxie is being treated, Gerrie becomes infuriated by her daughter's recalcitrance and slaps the adolescent repeatedly, eliciting a positive reaction. *Suburbanites. Musicians. Neighbors. Drug dealers. Adolescence.*

Family life. Group therapy. LSD. Drugs. Hospitals. Hallucinations.
Note: Location scenes filmed in New York City.

PER IL BENE E PER IL MALE *see* ANATOMY OF A MARRIAGE; MY DAYS WITH JEAN-MARC

PER IL BENE E PER IL MALE *see* ANATOMY OF A MARRIAGE; MY NIGHTS WITH FRANÇOISE

PER QUALCHE DOLLARO IN PIÙ *see* FOR A FEW DOLLARS MORE

PER UN PUGNO DI DOLLARI *see* A FISTFUL OF DOLLARS

LE PÈRE NOËL A LES YEUX BLEUS *see* BAD COMPANY

PERFECT FRIDAY (Great Britain)   F6.3788
Sunnymede Film Productions. *Dist* Chevron Pictures. 10 Nov **1970** [New York opening]. Sd; col (print by Movielab). 35mm. 94 min. *MPAA rating* R.
A Dimitri De Grunwald Production. *Prod* Jack Smith, British. *Assoc Prod* William Kirby. *Dir* Peter Hall. *Screenplay* Anthony Greville-Bell, C. Scott Forbes. *Story* C. Scott Forbes. *Dir Photog* Alan Hume. *Camera Op* Derek Browne. *Art Dir* Robert Laing. *Set Decor* Hugh Scaife. *Prod Dsgn* Terence Marsh. *Film Ed* Rex Pyke. *Mus Comp, Arr & Dir* John Dankworth. *Sd Ed* Nicholas Stevenson, Peter Horrocks. *Sd Rec* Robert Allen. *Sd Re-rec* Hugh Strain. *Asst Dir* Christopher Dryhurst. *Prod Mgr* John Bremer. *Cont* Angela Allen. *Cost Dsgn* Kiki Byrne. *Miss Andress' Cost* Rahvis. *Wardrobe Master* Ron Beck. *Wardrobe Mistress* Jean Fairlie. *Makeup* W. T. Partleton. *Miss Andress' Makeup* John O'Gorman. *Hairdresser* Ann Fordyce. *Constr Mgr* Jock Lyall.
Cast: Ursula Andress *(Britt)*, David Warner *(Nick Dorsett)*, Stanley Baker *(Graham)*, Patience Collier *(Nanny)*, T. P. McKenna *(Smith)*, David Waller *(Williams)*, Joan Benham *(Miss Welsh)*, Julian Orchard *(Thompson)*, Trisha Mortimer *(Janet)*, Ann Tirard *(Miss Marsh)*, Johnny Briggs, Fred Griffiths, Sidney Jennings *(taxi drivers)*, Hugh Halliday *(cyclist)*, Max Faulkner *(strongroom guard)*, Carleton Hobbs *(elderly Peer)*, Eric Longworth *(House of Lords messenger)*, Brian Peck *(chauffeur)*, Howard Lang *(bank commissioner)*, Patrick Jordan *(bank guard)*, Malcolm Johns *(Swiss boyfriend)*, Garfield Morgan, Derek Cox *(airport officials)*, Barbara Ogilvie *(woman airport official)*, Georgina Simpson *(stewardess)*.
Crime comedy-drama. Mr. Graham, an assistant bank manager who works in the West End of London, is dissatisfied with his boring life. He becomes acquainted with Britt (Lady Dorset), one of the bank's wealthiest patrons, and they devise a plan, along with the indolent Lord Nicholas Dorset, to rob the bank. Their plan—to be enacted on the day that the manager plays golf—is for Britt to seduce the main security guard and for Lord Dorset, posing as a bank inspector, to substitute counterfeit money. The scheme almost fails when a real inspector arrives, but a second opportunity arises, and Lady Dorset absconds with the funds. She fails to show up for the scheduled division of the loot, however, and Graham and Lord Dorset realize that they have been doublecrossed. Undaunted, they begin to plan another robbery for the following year. *Bankers. Idle rich. Aristocrats. Guards. Bank robberies. Seduction. Imposture. Perfidy. London—West End.*
Note: Locations scenes filmed in London. Opened in London in Dec 1970.

THE PERFECT SET-UP *see* ONCE YOU KISS A STRANGER

PERFORMANCE (Great Britain)   F6.3789
Goodtimes Enterprises. *Dist* Warner Bros. Pictures. 3 Aug **1970** [New York opening; c3 Aug 1970; LP40892]. Sd; col (Technicolor). 35mm. 106 min. *MPAA rating* X.
Prod Sanford Lieberson. *Assoc Prod-Screenplay* Donald Cammell. *Dir* Donald Cammell, Nicolas Roeg. *Dir Photog* Nicolas Roeg. *Art Dir* John Clark. *Set Decor* Peter Young. *Dsgn Cons for Turner's House* Christopher Gibbs. *Film Ed* Antony Gibbs, Brian Smedley-Aston. *Mus* Jack Nitzche. *Mus Dir* Randy Newman. *Song:* "Memo From Turner" Mick Jagger, Keith Richard. *Sung by* Mick Jagger. *Song:* "Gone Dead Train" Jack Nitzsche, Russ Titelman. *Sung by* Randy Newman. *Songs:* "Rolls Royce and Acid," "Harry Flowers," "Natural Magic," "Performance," "Poor White Hound Dog," "Turner's Murder," "Get Away," "Powis Square," "The Hashishin," "Dyed, Dead, Red" Jack Nitzsche. *Vocals in:* "Performance" and "Poor White Hound Dog" Merry Clayton. *Vocals in:* "Turner's Murder" Merry Clayton Singers. *Bottleneck Guitar Solo in:* "Get Away" and "Powis Square" Ry Cooder. *Dulcimer Solo in:* "The Hashishin" Ry Cooder. *Mouth Bow Solo in:* "The Hashishin" Buffy Sainte-Marie. *Mouth Bow Solo and Vocal in:* "Dyed, Dead, Red" Buffy Sainte-Marie. *Sd Ed* Alan Pattillo. *Sd Rec* Ron Barron. *Asst Dir* Richard Burge. *Prod Mgr* Robert Lynn. *Tech Adv* David Litvinoff.
Cast: James Fox *(Chas Devlin)*, Mick Jagger *(Turner)*, Anita Pallenberg *(Pherber)*, Michèle Breton *(Lucy)*, Ann Sidney *(Dana)*, John Bindon *(Moody)*, Stanley Meadows *(Rosebloom)*, Allan Cuthbertson *(lawyer)*, Anthony Morton *(Dennis)*, Johnny Shannon *(Harry Flowers)*, Anthony Valentine *(Joey*

Maddocks), Kenneth Colley *(Tony Farrell)*, John Sterland *(chauffeur)*, Laraine Wickens *(Lorraine)*.

Drama with music. Chas Devlin, sadistic henchman of decadent business magnate Harry Flowers, flees the syndicate after brutally murdering his boss's client. Disguised as a juggler, he seeks shelter at the London townhouse of reclusive rock star Turner. There he is plied with hallucinogens by the androgynous entertainer and his sapphic concubines, Pherber and Lucy. When Devlin, his face heavily made-up, is properly receptive, Turner enacts for him his final performance. In search of Devlin, Flowers' minions penetrate Turner's sanctuary. As they escort the unfortunate Devlin from the townhouse, the infuriated thug shoots Turner to death. *Entertainers. Doubles. Businessmen. Recluses. Gangsters. Sadism. Murder. Rock and roll. Bisexuality. Lesbianism. Disguise. Male homosexuality. Hallucinogens. London.*

Note: Released in London in Jan 1971; running time: 102 min. Working title: *The Performers.*

THE PERFORMERS (Japan)   **F6.3790**
 Shochiku Co. *Dist* Shochiku Films of America. Aug **1970** [Los Angeles showing]. Sd; col (Eastmancolor). 35mm (Shochiku GrandScope). 94 min.
 Dir-Writ Umeji Inoue. *Photog* Keiji Maruyama. *Art Dir* Gohei Morita. *Mus* Seitaro Omori.
 Cast: Hibari Misora *(Kasumi Fujihana)*, Shinichi Mori *(Ryusuke)*, Shogo Shimada *(Seijuro Fujihana)*, Yoichi Hayashi *(Hiroshi)*, Yataro Kitagami *(Kisaburo)*, Nana Ozaki *(Hamako)*, Takamaru Sasaki, Osami Nabe, Shin-ichi Yanagizawa, Fujio Murakami, Ryusuke Kita, Kentaro Imai, Kyoko Mizuki, Natsuko Shiga, Michiko Yashima, Yoshisaburo Owa, Nobuko Suzuki, Fusako Maki.
 Drama. Seijuro Fujihana, the headmaster of the struggling Fujihana dance school, hopes that his daughter Kasumi will some day take over the school. Kasumi, however, is more interested in her affair with Hiroshi, a jazz musician whom her father dislikes. Meanwhile, Kisaburo, Seijuro's closest follower, wants to marry Kasumi and take charge of the school himself. Hiroshi informs Kasumi that their affair is over, and to console herself she takes up with Ryusuke, a strolling singer. Soon the couple are performing in the same nightclub show, and Seijuro, already opposed to the romance, orders Kasumi not to see Ryusuke again. Kisaburo now realizes that he will never marry Kasumi, and he forms his own school from the Fujihana staff and students. Seijuro is so shocked by this action that he becomes ill and decides to apologize to Kasumi for interfering in her romantic affairs. Feeling that Ryusuke should be more independent, Kasumi stops supporting him and concentrates all of her efforts on a forthcoming recital. Kasumi is unable to raise the necessary money, however, until Hiroshi gives her 5 million yen that Ryusuke received for signing with an agent. *Headmasters. Dancers. Musicians. Singers. Filial relations. Courtship. Finance—Personal. Dance schools. Nightclubs.*
 Note: Released in Japan in Jan 1970 as *Hana to namida to honoo.*

THE PERFORMERS see **PERFORMANCE**

THE PERILOUS PEARLS OF PAULINE see **THE HOT PEARL SNATCH**

PERILS OF BANGAKU (Japan)   **F6.3791**
 Takarazuka Motion Picture Co. *Dist* Toho Co. 7 Apr **1961** [Los Angeles opening]. Sd; col? 35mm. [Feature film, length unknown.]
 Cast: Keiju Kobayashi, Reiko Dan, Takashi Shimura, Manami Fuji, Hiroshi Koizumi, Yukiko Shimazaki, Kyu Sazanka, Toru Abe, Chishu Ryu, Toru Yuri, Mutoshi Happa, Michiyo Tamaki, Ikio Sawamura. Although no information about the precise nature of this film has been found, sources indicate that it involves the adventures of a master fencer.
 Note: Original title and release undetermined.

THE PERILS OF PAULINE   **F6.3792**
 Universal Pictures–Herbert B. Leonard Enterprises. *Dist* Universal Pictures. 9 May **1967** [Fort Lee, New Jersey, opening; c1 Jul 1967; LP35385]. Sd (Westrex); col (Technicolor). 35mm. 107 min.
 Prod Herbert B. Leonard. *Assoc Prod* Willetta Leonard. *Dir* Herbert B. Leonard, Joshua Shelley. *2d Unit Dir* Joseph E. Kenny. *Writ* Albert Beich. *Dir Photog* Jack Marta. *Art Dir* Alexander Golitzen, John T. McCormack. *Set Decor* John McCarthy, Julia Heron. *Film Ed* Sam E. Waxman. *Mus & Song:* "My Pretty Pauline" Vic Mizzy. *Sung by* Pat Boone. *Sd* Waldon O. Watson, Melvin M. Metcalfe, Sr. *Asst Dir* Joseph E. Kenny. *Unit Prod Mgr* Ernest B. Wehmeyer. *Cost* Grady Hunt. *Makeup* Bud Westmore. *Hairstyles* Larry Germain. *Stunt Coörd* Max Kleven.
 Cast: Pat Boone *(George)*, Terry-Thomas *(Sten Martin)*, Pamela Austin *(Pauline)*, Edward Everett Horton *(Casper Coleman)*, Hamilton Camp *(Thorpe)*, Doris Packer *(Mrs. Carruthers)*, Kurt Kasznar *(consul general)*, Vito Scotti *(Frandisi)*, Leon Askin *(commissar)*, Aram Katcher *(vizier)*, Ric Natoli *(Prince Benji)*, Jeanne Gerson *(Pauline's foster mother)*, Joe Higgins *(Pauline's*

foster father), Keith Taylor *(Henry)*, Max Kleven *(gorilla)*.
 Comedy. Suggested by: Charles W. Goddard, *The Perils of Pauline, a Drama in One Act* (New York?, 1914). Two orphans, Pauline and George, fall in love at the Baskerville Foundling Home. Before leaving the orphanage George vows to return as a millionaire and marry Pauline. Seven years later he fulfills his promise, only to find that Pauline has gone to Arabia as the governess of 12-year-old Prince Benji. Arriving in Arabia, George learns that Pauline, having frustrated the precocious prince's plan to make her the first member of his harem, has been sold to white pygmies in the Congo. Abducted by a gorilla, Pauline is rescued by the renowned hunter Sten Martin. While George is recovering in New York City from an African disease, Pauline falls into a sewer. Her elderly savior, millionaire Casper Coleman, freezes Pauline in anticipation of his grandson's maturity. Disconsolate, George has himself frozen. Both are thawed prematurely, but are separated again when Pauline is persuaded by Soviet agents to join the Wolf of Siberia in a spacewalk. Returning to Earth, Pauline finds George impecunious and consents to star in a film directed by Frandisi. During the filming she is abducted by her co-star, her former gorilla captor, but rescued by George. As Pauline and George honeymoon in Venice, their gondola sinks. *Adventuresses. Governesses. Orphans. Millionaires. Pygmies. Hunters. Motion picture directors. Secret agents. Russians. Italians. Grandfathers. Royalty. Actors. Spaceship crews. Rescue. Abduction. Marriage. Harems. Honeymoons. Sewers. Cryogenics. Arabia. Congo. New York City. Venice. Apes.*
 Note: Previously filmed as a 20-chapter serial (Pathé, 1914) and as a feature (Paramount, 1947).

PERIOD OF ADJUSTMENT   **F6.3793**
 Marten Productions. *Dist* Metro-Goldwyn-Mayer, Inc. 31 Oct **1962** [New York opening; c11 Oct 1962; LP23324]. Sd (Westrex); b&w. 35mm. 112 min.
 A Lawrence Weingarten Production. *Prod* Lawrence Weingarten. *Dir* George Roy Hill. *Screenplay* Isobel Lennart. *Dir Photog* Paul C. Vogel. *Art Dir* George W. Davis, Edward Carfagno. *Set Decor* Henry Grace, Dick Pefferle. *Film Ed* Fredric Steinkamp. *Mus* Lyn Murray. *Rec Supv* Franklin Milton. *Asst Dir* Al Jennings. *Makeup* William Tuttle. *Hairstyles* Sydney Guilaroff.
 Cast: Tony Franciosa *(Ralph Baitz)*, Jane Fonda *(Isabel Haverstick)*, Jim Hutton *(George Haverstick)*, Lois Nettleton *(Dorothea Baitz)*, John McGiver *(Stewart P. McGill)*, Mabel Albertson *(Mrs. Alice McGill)*, Jack Albertson *(desk sergeant)*.
 Comedy-drama. Source: Tennessee Williams, *A Period of Adjustment* (New York opening: 31 Oct 1961). Shortly after his discharge from the hospital where he has been treated for the shakes, Korean War veteran George Haverstick marries Isabel, his nurse, a good-natured, romantic Southern belle. Their honeymoon gets off to a bad start when Isabel discovers that George has quit his job, that his "station wagon" is actually a hearse, and that their wedding night is to be spent in a cheap motel. Despite his conspicuous display of masculinity, George feels inadequate, and to avoid failure on his wedding night he gets drunk and passes out in a chair. The next morning, he takes his disenchanted bride to Tennessee to visit a wartime buddy, Ralph Baitz, who married for money but now genuinely loves his wife, Dorothea. Because of trouble with his domineering in-laws, the McGills, Ralph has decided to quit the family business, and Dorothea has left him, convinced by her parents that she, too, will be abandoned. When Ralph's in-laws arrive to claim their daughter's possessions, a fight ensues, and everyone ends up at the police station. George and Isabel, forgetting their own problems, commiserate with Ralph and Dorothea. With their help and Ralph's gift of a fur coat to convince Dorothea that he isn't after her money, the Baitzes become reconciled. George confesses his nervous anxiety, and Isabel lovingly reminds him that the best thing about marriage is that there is so much time to work out problems. *Newlyweds. Southerners. Nurses. Veterans. Neurosis. In-laws. Fortune hunters. Marriage. Impotence. Drunkenness. Filial relations. Honeymoons. Motels. Shell shock. Korean War 1950–53. Tennessee.*

LA PERMISSION see **THE STORY OF A THREE DAY PASS**

PERRY RHODAN—SOS AUS DEM WELTALL see **MISSION STARDUST**

PERSECUCIÓN HASTA VALENCIA see **THE NARCO MEN**

THE PERSECUTION AND ASSASSINATION OF JEAN-PAUL MARAT AS PERFORMED BY THE INMATES OF THE ASYLUM OF CHARENTON UNDER THE DIRECTION OF THE MARQUIS DE SADE (Great Britain)   **F6.3794**
 Marat Sade Productions. *Dist* United Artists. 22 Feb **1967** [New York opening]. Sd; col (DeLuxe). 35mm. 115 min. [Also reviewed at 120 min.]
 Pres by Royal Shakespeare Co. *Prod* Michael Birkett. *Dir* Peter Brook. *Screen Adapt* Adrian Mitchell. *Photog* David Watkin. *Art Dir* Ted Marshall. *Prod Dsgn* Sally Jacobs. *Film Ed* Tom Priestley. *Mus* Richard Peaslee. *Choreog*

Malcolm Goddard. *Sd* Hugh Strain. *Sd Rec* Robert Allen. *Asst Dir* Anthony Waye. *Prod Mgr* Jack Swinburne. *Cost* Gunilla Palmstierna-Weiss. *Makeup* Bunty Phillips.

Cast: Clifford Rose (*Monsieur Coulmier*), Brenda Kempner (*Madame Coulmier*), Ruth Baker (*Mademoiselle Coulmier*), Michael Williams (*herald*), Freddie Jones (*Cucurucu*), Hugh Sullivan (*Kokol*), Jonathan Burn (*Polpoch*), Jeanette Landis (*Rossignol*), Robert Lloyd (*Jacques Roux*), Glenda Jackson (*Charlotte Corday*), Ian Richardson (*Jean-Paul Marat*), Susan Williamson (*Simonne Evrard*), Patrick Magee (*Marquis de Sade*), John Steiner (*Duperret*), Mark Jones (*abbot*), Morgan Sheppard (*a mad animal*), James Mellor (*schoolmaster*), Ian Hogg (*military representative*), Mark Jones (*mother*), Henry Woolf (*father*), John Hussey, actor (*newly-rich lady*), John Harwood (*Voltaire*), Leon Lissek (*Lavoisier*), Heather Canning, Jennifer Tudor (*nuns*), Timothy Hardy, Stanford Trowell (*guards*), Patrick Gowers, Richard Callinan, Michael Gould, Nicholas Moes, Rainer Schuelein, Paul Hiley (*musicians*), Mary Allen, Michael Farnsworth, Maroussia Frank, Tamara Fuerst, Guy Gordon, Sheila Grant, Michael Percival, Lyn Pinkney, Carol Raymont (*patients*).

Drama. Source: Peter Weiss, *The Persecution and Assassination of Jean-Paul Marat as Performed by the Inmates of the Asylum of Charenton Under the Direction of the Marquis de Sade* (trans. by Geoffrey Skelton and Adrian Mitchell of *Die Verfolgung und Ermordung Jean Paul Marats, dargestellt durch die Schauspielgruppe des Hospizes zu Charenton unter Anleitung des Herrn de Sade*; Berlin opening: 29 Apr 1964; London opening: 20 Aug 1964). In the early 19th century it becomes fashionable for Parisians to attend the theatrical performances given as a form of therapy by inmates of mental institutions. In the bathhouse at the asylum of Charenton, where the Marquis de Sade is destined to spend the last years of his life, an audience arrives to witness a play with music directed by de Sade, in which he has an imaginary conversation with the embittered writer Jean-Paul Marat, one of the motivating forces behind the French Revolution. Soaking in his tub, Marat calls for violent upheaval as the only means to effect social reform. De Sade, conversely, remains the pessimistic individualist: firm in his conviction that revolutions solve nothing, he expounds the theory that violence is beneficial only if used for personal gratification. During the course of the play, Charlotte Corday travels alone from Caen to Paris. Upon her arrival at the home of Marat, she calls three times before being admitted. Once in Marat's presence, she draws a dagger from between her breasts and pierces his chest as he sits in his tub. As the play ends, de Sade tries to advise the spectators that there are no ready answers to the questions raised; the polemical debate has been offered only to stimulate thought and guide the observer to his own personal conclusion. But the 30-odd patients who have performed the various roles have too strongly identified with their parts and their oft-repeated revolutionary cry for freedom. Consumed by an insane fury that has nearly surfaced several times in the course of the play, they turn upon their guards, their keepers, their audience, and even themselves. *Playwrights. Theatrical directors. Lunatics. Invalids. Guards. Group therapy. Sadism. Social reform. Assassination. Riots. Theater. Baths. France—History—Revolution 1789–93. Donatien Alphonse François [Marquis de] Sade. Charlotte Corday. Jean Paul Marat. La Maison de Santé de Charenton.*

Note: The Royal Shakespeare Co. repeats its original stage performance for the film. Also known as *Marat/Sade* or *Marat-Sade*.

PERSONA (Sweden)   F6.3795

Svensk Filmindustri. *Dist* Lopert Pictures. 6 Mar **1967** [New York opening]. Sd; b&w. 35mm. 81 min. [Also 85 and 90 min.]

An Ingmar Bergman Production. *Dir-Writ* Ingmar Bergman. *Photog* Sven Nykvist. *Art Dir* Bibi Lindström. *Film Ed* Ulla Ryghe. *Mus* Lars-Johan Werle. *Sd* P. O. Pettersson, Lennart Engholm. *Asst Dir* Lenn Hjörtzberg. *Prod Mgr* Lars-Owe Carlberg. *Cost* Mago. *Makeup* Borje Lundh, Tina Johansson. *Sp Eff* Evald Andersson.

Cast: Bibi Andersson (*nurse Alma*), Liv Ullmann (*actress Elisabeth Vogler*), Gunnar Björnstrand (*Mr. Vogler*), Jörgen Lindström (*boy*), Margaretha Krook (*doctor*).

Drama. During a performance of *Electra*, noted stage actress Elisabeth Vogler stops speaking for a moment before continuing with the play. The next day she withdraws completely into a mental and physical inertia. When hospital tests and examinations fail to identify the source of her problem, her psychiatrist sends her to an isolated beach house on the Baltic Sea for a rest. She is attended by Alma, a trained nurse who attempts to penetrate the silence by freely talking about herself. As the days pass, a warm friendship develops between the two women; the nurse gradually bares all of her innermost secrets, and the actress silently absorbs all that she hears. For Alma, the relationship becomes an almost complete merging of personalities, until she reads a letter Elisabeth has written to her doctor describing how she has drawn strength from listening to the somewhat naive confessions of her nurse. Feeling betrayed by Elisabeth's apparent indifference, Alma angrily rebukes her patient for her

selfish withdrawal from life. During the recrimination, Alma seems to become Elisabeth and experiences all the pain that had forced Elisabeth into her retreat. Alma finally breaks down, and the two women silently pack their bags and leave the house. *Actors. Nurses. Psychiatrists. Personality. Mental illness. Hospitals. Beaches. Baltic Sea. "Electra".*

Note: Released in Sweden in Oct 1966.

PERVERSION CITY U. S. A.   F6.3796

Dist Able Film Co. ca **1970.** Sd; col. 16mm. [Feature length assumed.]

Sex film. No information about the precise nature of this film has been found. *Sexuality.*

PERVYY DEN MIRA *see* **THE DAY THE WAR ENDED**

PESNI RODNOY STORONY *see* **FROM THE KREMLIN TO THE COSMOS**

PESNI ROSSII *see* **PANORAMA OF RUSSIA**

PETEY'S SWEETIES *see* **MR. PETERS' PETS**

LE PETIT SOLDAT (France)   F6.3797

Productions Georges de Beauregard–S. N. C. *Dist* West End Films, Inc. 20 Apr **1967** [New York opening]. Sd; b&w. 35mm. 88 min.

Prod Georges de Beauregard. *Dir-Writ* Jean-Luc Godard. *Dir Photog* Raoul Coutard. *Camera Op* Michel Latouche. *Film Ed* Agnès Guillemot. *Asst Film Ed* Nadine Marquand, Lila Herman. *Mus* Maurice Le Roux. *Sd* Jacques Maumont. *Asst Dir* Francis Cognani. *Script Girl* Suzanne Schiffman.

Cast: Michel Subor (*Bruno Forestier*), Anna Karina (*Véronica Dreyer*), Henri-Jacques Huet (*Jacques*), Paul Beauvais (*Paul*), Laszlo Szabo (*Laszlo*), Georges de Beauregard (*Beauregard*), Jean-Luc Godard (*bystander at railway station*), Gilbert Edard.

Drama. During the Algerian crisis of 1958, Bruno Forestier, a deserter from the French Army, works as a photographer with a news agency in Geneva. Although two of his friends, Jacques and Paul, are right-wing terrorists plotting against the Algerian rebels, Bruno himself is without political ideals; he is concerned only with personal freedom. The terrorists suspect him of being a double agent and attempt to use his position as a deserter to blackmail him into assassinating a Swiss radio commentator who has been broadcasting on behalf of the Algerian rebels. Determined to follow his personal convictions, Bruno makes plans to escape to Brazil with Véronica Dreyer, a young woman with whom he has fallen in love. But he is captured by Algerians who use torture in an attempt to make him talk about his friends' activities. Bruno, however, stubbornly refuses to submit and eventually escapes by hurling himself out a window without knowing how far above street level he is being held. Desperate to get out of the country, he now consents to kill the news commentator in exchange for passports for himself and Véronica. Once the murder has finally been committed after several attempts, he discovers that he has been betrayed: his friends became suspicious of Véronica's Algerian sympathies and tortured her to death in a futile attempt to gain information about the Algerians. Bruno, left alone, reflects, "Only one thing remained, to learn not to be bitter. But I was happy, for I had a lot of time in front of me." *Algerians. Terrorists. Photographers. Deserters—Military. Radio announcers. Perfidy. Assassination. Blackmail. Torture. Algeria—History—War of Independence. Geneva.*

Note: Filmed in Geneva Apr–May 1960. Banned by French censors until Jan 1963, when film was first shown in Paris with minor cuts; running time: 87 min.

LES PETITS CHATS *see* **WILD ROOTS OF LOVE**

PETTICOATS AND BLUEJEANS *see* **THE PARENT TRAP**

PETULIA (United States/Great Britain)   F6.3798

Petersham Films. *Dist* Warner Bros.–Seven Arts, Inc. 10 Jun **1968** [New York opening; c29 Feb 1968; LP35719]. Sd (RCA); col (Technicolor). 35mm. 105 min.

A Richard Lester–Raymond Wagner Production. *Prod* Raymond Wagner. *Exec Prod* Denis O'Dell. *Exec Assoc Prod* Don Devlin. *Dir* Richard Lester. *Screenplay* Lawrence B. Marcus. *Adapt* Barbara Turner. *Dir Photog* Nicolas Roeg. *Camera Op* Paul Wilson, Freddie Cooper. *Assoc Art Dir* Dean Tavoularis. *Dsgn Cons* David Hicks. *Set Decor* Audrey Blasdel. *Prod Dsgn* Tony Walton. *Film Ed* Antony Gibbs. *Mus Comp & Cond* John Barry. *Sd* Francis E. Stahl. *Dub Ed* Don Challis. *Dub Mix* Gerry Humphreys. *Asst Dir* John Bloss. *Prod Mgr* Emmett Emerson. *Location Mgr* Harry Zubrinsky. *Cont* Rita Davison. *Cost Dsgn* Tony Walton. *Wardrobe* Rita Riggs, Ray Summers. *Miss Christie's Cost* Arlette Nastat "Real". *Makeup* Gus Norin. *Hairdresser* Vivienne Zavitz. *Prop Master* Stephen Ferry. *Casting* Fred Roos. *Ch Electrn* Gibby Germaine. *Light Show* Paul Hawkins.

Cast: Julie Christie (*Petulia Danner*), George C. Scott (*Archie Bollen*), Richard Chamberlain (*David Danner*), Arthur Hill (*Barney*), Shirley Knight

(Polo), Pippa Scott (May), Kathleen Widdoes (Wilma), Roger Bowen (Warren), Richard Dysart (motel receptionist), Ruth Kobart, Ellen Geer (nuns), Lou Gilbert (Mr. Howard), Nate Esformes (Mr. Mendoza), Maria Val (Mrs. Mendoza), Vincent Arias (Oliver), Eric Weiss (Michael), Kevin Cooper (Stevie), Joseph Cotten (Mr. Danner), Austin Pendleton (intern), Barbara Colby (patient), Rene Auberjonois (salesman), Josephine Nichols (neighbor), De Ann Mears (nurse), The Grateful Dead, Big Brother and the Holding Company, The Ace Trucking Co., The Committee, Members of the American Conservatory Theatre.

Comedy-drama. Source: John Haase, *Me and the Arch Kook Petulia* (New York, 1966). Disillusioned with her 6-month-old marriage, Petulia Danner attends a San Francisco charity ball and flagrantly attempts to entice Archie Bollen, a divorced surgeon. Archie had first attracted Petulia's attention because of Oliver, a Mexican boy who hitched a ride from Tijuana with Petulia and her moody husband, David. When David suddenly insisted that Oliver return to Mexico, Petulia took the boy to a bus station, where, in trying to run away, he was hit by a car. Oliver was taken to a hospital, where Archie performed surgery. Archie and Petulia now go to an automated motel, but Petulia balks at following through on her plan and Archie sends her off in a taxi. Petulia then impulsively steals a tuba and the next morning brings it to Archie's apartment. In time, Archie's casual attitude toward her gives way to love, and he rejects any thought of reconciliation with Polo, his ex-wife; he is also unresponsive to the devotion of his mistress, May. After spending a night with Petulia in his apartment, Archie leaves her for a Sunday outing with his children. Upon returning, he finds her brutally beaten. Though Archie has her hospitalized, David's millionaire father uses his influence to have her released in her husband's custody. Archie then visits her at the Danner estate, charging David with responsibility for the beating, but David maintains that he was out of town. His father corroborates his story, and Archie is dismayed when Petulia says nothing to deny the coverup. A year later, after David and Petulia have returned from a cruise, Archie encounters her in a hospital maternity ward. Recalling their affair, he asks Petulia to go away with him; though she consents, Archie cannot bring himself to make the necessary arrangements. After he has kissed her goodby, Petulia is wheeled into the delivery room, calling his name. *Surgeons. Mistresses. Mexicans. Hitchhikers. Marriage. Divorce. Infidelity. Filial relations. Childbirth. Balls (formal gatherings). Motels. Hospitals. Tubas. San Francisco. Tijuana (Mexico). Automobile accidents.*

Note: Location scenes filmed in San Francisco and Tijuana. Opened in London in Jun 1968.

LA PEUR ET L'AMOUR *see* **TORMENT**

LA PEUR ET LE DÉSIR *see* **TORMENT**

PHAEDRA (United States/France/Greece)   **F6.3799**
Melinafilm–Jorilie Productions. *Dist* Lopert Pictures. 18 Oct **1962** [New York opening; c15 Oct 1962; LP23096]. Sd; b&w. 35mm. 115 min.
Prod-Dir Jules Dassin. *Asst Prod* Noel Howard. *Screenplay* Jules Dassin, Margarita Liberaki. *Orig Scen* Margarita Liberaki. *Cinematog* Jacques Natteau. *Art Dir* Max Douy. *Set Decor* Maurice Barnathan. *Film Ed* Roger Dwyre. *Mus Score* Mikis Theodorakis. *Toccata and Fugue in F-major* Johann Sebastian Bach. *Sd Engr* Jacques Carrère. *Sd Rec* M. Karakeusian. *Sd* Jacques Lebreton, Athanassis Giorgiadiss. *Asst Dir* Ginette Diamant-Berger. *Prod Mgr* Michel Rittener, Marios Stavropoulos, George Mills. *Cost Dsgn* Denny Vachlioti. *Makeup* Jill Carpenter, Janine Casse. *Hairstyles* Marc Blanchard.
Cast: Melina Mercouri (Phaedra), Anthony Perkins (Alexis), Raf Vallone (Thanos), Elizabeth Ercy (Ercy), Olympia Papadouka (Anna), George Sarris (Ariadne), Andreas Philippides (Andreas), Giorgos Karoussos (old man), Alexis Pezas (Dimitri), Kostas Baldemas (Dimo), Nikos Tzoyias (Felere), Depy Martini (Heleni), Stelios Vokovits (Stavros), Jules Dassin (Christo), Marc Bohan (himself), Lillia Ralli (herself).
Drama. Inspired by: Euripides, *Hippolytus*. Phaedra, the second wife of Thanos Kyrilis, a powerful Greek shipowner, is persuaded by her husband to go to London and urge Alexis, his 24-year-old son by a previous marriage, to return to Greece for the summer. Immediately attracted to each other, the young man and the older woman become involved in a passionate love affair in Paris. When they return to Thanos' home on the Aegean island of Hydra, Alexis is racked with guilt. Thanos, delighted to have his son back, makes plans for him to enter the family business and marry the daughter of another shipbuilding tycoon with whom he is planning to merge. The jealous Phaedra, determined not to give up Alexis, confronts Thanos and tells him that she has been unfaithful with his son. In a rage, Thanos denounces his wife and mercilessly beats his son. As Alexis is about to leave, Phaedra asks him to take her with him, but he refuses and drives his car off a seacliff road. Phaedra goes to her room and swallows a lethal dose of sleeping pills, leaving Thanos to face the death of his son and his wife. *Stepmothers. Shipowners. Filial relations. Infidelity. Guilt. Marriage—Arranged. Jealousy. Suicide. London. Paris.*

Hydra. Phaedra.

Note: Filmed in Greece, France, and Great Britain. Jorilie Productions is credited only by U. S. copyright source; French coproduction status is unconfirmed.

PHANTOM FIEND *see* **THE RETURN OF DR. MABUSE**

THE PHANTOM OF SOHO (West Germany)   **F6.3800**
CCC–Filmkunst. *Dist* Producers Releasing Organization. Mar **1967**. Sd; b&w. 35mm (Ultrascope). 92 min.
Prod Artur Brauner. *Exec Prod* Heinz Willeg. *Dir* Franz Josef Gottlieb. *Screenplay* Ladislaus Fodor. *Photog* Richard Angst. *Art Dir* Hans Jürgen Kiebach, Ernst Schomer. *Film Ed* Walter Wischniewsky. *Mus* Martin Böttcher. *Sd* Erwin Schänzle. *Dir Prod* Heinz Götze. *Prod Mgr* Felix Siebenrogg, Horant H. Hohlfeld. *English Dub Supv* Jacques Willmetz.
Cast: Dieter Borsche (Hugh Patton), Barbara Rütting (Clarinda Smith), Hans Söhnker (Sir Philip), Elisabeth Flickenschildt (Joanna Filiati), Peter Vogel (Hallam), Helga Sommerfeld (Corinna Smith), Werner Peters (Dr. Dalmar), Hans Nielsen (Lord Malhouse), Stanislav Ledinek (Gilard), Otto Waldis ("Liver-Spot"), Hans W. Hamacher (Captain), Emil Feldmar (Daddy), Harald Sawade (Charlie).
Mystery melodrama. Source: Bryan Edgar Wallace, *Murder by Proxy* (publication undetermined). In the Soho section of London, several people are murdered by a phantom killer dressed in black and wearing gloves. When Inspector Hugh Patton of Scotland Yard reports on the case to his superior, Sir Philip, he meets the latter's fiancée, Clarinda Smith, a writer of mystery novels who announces that the identity of the phantom will be disclosed on the last page of her next book. Patton discovers that all of the murder victims were shipmates on a pleasure voyage, but his suspicions center on Joanna Filiati, the crippled proprietress of a Soho nightclub, and on Sir Philip, who appears to know more about the crimes than Patton has told him. After several more murders, Joanna and her physical therapist, Dr. Dalmar, attempt to leave the country, but Dr. Dalmar is killed at the airport. Joanna is saved by Patton, and the phantom is revealed to be Clarinda; all of her victims had been members of a vice racket and had raped her on the pleasure voyage. As Patton turns to the last page of the unfinished novel, Clarinda swallows a poison pill. *Detectives. Novelists. Cripples. Nightclub owners. Physical therapists. Murder. Disguise. Rape. Revenge. Suicide. Airfields. London—Soho. Scotland Yard.*
Note: Released in West Germany in Feb 1964 as *Das Phantom von Soho*; running time: 97 min.

THE PHANTOM OF THE OPERA (Great Britain)   **F6.3801**
Hammer Film Productions. *Dist* Universal–International. 15 Aug **1962** [Los Angeles opening; c25 Jul 1962; LP24527]. Sd; col (Eastman Color, print by Pathé). 35mm. 84 min.
Prod Anthony Hinds. *Dir* Terence Fisher. *Assoc Prod* Basil Keys. *Screenplay* John Elder. *Dir Photog* Arthur Grant. *Camera Op* Len Harris. *Art Dir* Don Mingaye. *Prod Dsgn* Bernard Robinson. *Supv Film Ed* James Needs. *Ed* Alfred Cox. *Mus Comp & Cond* Edwin Astley. *Sd* Jock May. *1st & 2d Asst Dir* John Peverall, Peter Medak. *Prod Mgr* Clifford Parkes. *Cont* Tilly Day. *Wardrobe Supv* Molly Arbuthnot. *Wardrobe Mistress* Rosemary Burrows. *Makeup* Roy Ashton. *Hairdresser* Frieda Steiger. *Stills Camera* Tom Edwards.
Cast: Herbert Lom (phantom), Heather Sears (Christine Charles), Thorley Walters (Lattimer), Edward De Souza (Harry Hunter), Michael Gough (Lord Ambrose D'Arcy), Martin Miller (Rossi), Miles Malleson (philosophical cabby), Miriam Karlin (charwoman), John Harvey (Vickers), Harold Goodwin (Bill), Ian Wilson (dwarf), Marne Maitland (Xavier), Michael Ripper (long-faced cabby), Sonya Cordeau (Yvonne), Patrick Troughton (rat catcher), Liane Aukin (Maria), Leila Forde (Teresa), Geoffrey L'Oise (Frenchman), Renee Houston (Mrs. Tucker).
Horror film. Source: Gaston Leroux, *Le fantôme de l'Opéra* (Paris, 1910). During the London opening of *Saint Joan*, a new opera by Lord Ambrose D'Arcy, the body of a murdered stagehand swings out of the wings on a rope into full view of the terrified audience. The prima donna quits the production after the ghastly occurrence, forcing D'Arcy and producer Harry Hunter to audition for a replacement. They discover Christine Charles, a talented but unknown singer, but D'Arcy refuses to use her after she rejects his romantic advances. Shortly thereafter, Christine is abducted by a dwarf and carried to a grotto under the opera house, where she is confronted by a masked figure who offers to give her vocal training. Meanwhile, Harry has discovered that *Saint Joan* was actually written by an unknown composer who supposedly drowned in the Thames after suffering severe burns. Following the victim's trail, Harry finds himself in an underground sewer tunnel, which leads to Christine and her captor. Touched by the phantom's tale of D'Arcy's thievery, Harry agrees not to interfere with Christine's lessons, and a few weeks later she performs at the opera's reopening. As she takes her bow, however, the dwarf is spotted watching the performance, and in his attempt to flee, he accidentally breaks

loose a heavy chandelier directly above Christine. Aware of her danger, the phantom rips off his mask, leaps to the stage, and throws Christine to safety before the chandelier kills him. *Singers. Composers. Theatrical producers. Theatrical directors. Dwarfs. Stagehands. Opera. Murder. Abduction. Plagiarism. Disfiguration. Self-sacrifice. Sewers. London. Thames River.*

Note: Opened in London in Jun 1962. Previously filmed in the United States in 1925 and 1943. John Elder is a pseudonym for Anthony Hinds.

THE PHANTOM PLANET   F6.3802

Four Crown Productions. *Dist* American International Pictures. 13 Dec **1961** [San Diego, California, opening]. Sd; b&w. 35mm. 82 min.

Prod-Screenplay Fred Gebhardt. *Exec Prod* Leo Handel. *Assoc Prod* Bob Kinoshita, Hugo Grimaldi. *Dir* William Marshall, dir. *Photog* Elwood J. Nicholson. *Camera Op* Ned Davenport. *Art Dir* Bob Kinoshita. *Set Dresser* Joe Kish. *Film Ed* Hugo Grimaldi, Donald Wolfe. *Mus* Hayes Pagel. *Sd* Al Overton. *Asst Dir* Maurice Vaccarino, Lindsley Parsons, Jr. *Script Supv* Hazel Hall. *Cost* Marla Craig. *Men's Wardrobe* Oscar Rodriguez. *Makeup* David Newell. *Hairstyles* Mary Moreland. *Sp Eff* Studio Film Service. *Still Photog* Bruce Bailey. *Gaffer* Frank Leonetti. *Grip* Lou Kusley.

Cast: Dean Fredericks *(Capt. Frank Chapman)*, Coleen Gray *(Liara)*, Anthony Dexter *(Herron)*, Dolores Faith *(Zetha)*, Francis X. Bushman *(Sesom)*, Richard Weber *(Lieutenant Makonnen)*, Al Jarvis *(Judge Eden)*, Dick Haynes *(Colonel Lansfield)*, Earl McDaniel *(Pilot Leonard)*, Michael Marshall *(Lieutenant White)*, John Herrin *(Captain Beecher)*, Mel Curtis *(Lieutenant Cutler)*, Jimmy Weldon *(Navigator Webb)*, Akemi Tani *(communications officer)*, Lori Lyons *(radar officer)*, Richard Kiel *(Solarite)*, Susan Cembrowska, Marissa Mathes, Gloria Moreland, Judy Erickson, Marya Carter, Allyson Ames, Marion Thompson, Warrene Ott.

Science fiction melodrama. Investigating the disappearance of a second Pegasus rocket, American astronaut Capt. Frank Chapman is forced to land his spaceship on Rehton, a mysterious asteroid. Upon opening his spacesuit he is reduced in size by the atmospheric conditions and captured by a race of tiny people, ruled by Sesom. Liara, Sesom's daughter, is attracted to Chapman, but he becomes attached to Zetha, a mute. After befriending the jealous Herron, Liara's admirer, Chapman wins the respect of the Rehtons. The astronaut helps the tiny kingdom defend itself when unexpectedly attacked by the Solarites, an ancient enemy. Zetha, rescued by Chapman when she is abducted by a Solarite, regains her speech in the excitement. Donning his space suit, Chapman regains his normal size and returns to earth, realizing that his experiences on Rehton will not be believed. *Astronauts. Space creatures. Mutes. Space exploration. Miniaturization. Abduction. Friendship. Jealousy. Military invasion. Spaceships. Asteroids. Imaginary kingdoms. Imaginary planets.*

THE PHANTOM TOLLBOOTH   F6.3803

Metro-Goldwyn-Mayer, Inc. 7 Nov **1970** [San Francisco opening; c31 Dec 1969; LP38522]. Sd; col (Metrocolor). 35mm. 90 min. *MPAA rating* G.

Overall Production Credits: A Chuck Jones Production. *Co-prod* Abe Levitow, Les Goldman. *Dir* Chuck Jones, Abe Levitow. *Screenplay* Chuck Jones, Sam Rosen, writ. *Anim Supv* Ben Washam, Hal Ambro, George Nicholas. *Anim* Irv Spence, Bill Littlejohn, Richard Thompson, Tom Ray, Philip Roman, Alan Zaslove, Edwin Aardal, Ed DeMattia, Xenia, Lloyd Vaughan, Carl Bell. *Layout* Tony Rivera, Don Morgan, Oscar Dufau, Rosemary O'Connor, Corny Cole, Phyllis Graham. *Typographics* Don Foster. *Backgrounds* Philip DeGuard, Irving Weiner, Robert McIntosh. *Checker* Buf Nerbovig, Carol Barnes, Ted Bemiller. *Ink & Paint Supv* Auril Thompson. *Anim Camera* Jack Stevens, photog. *Prod Dsgn* Maurice Noble. *Film Ed* Jim Faris. *Mus Score* Dean Elliott. *Songs:* "Milo's Song," "Time Is a Gift," "Word Market," "Numbers Are the Only Thing That Count," "Rhyme and Reason Reign" Lee Pockriss, Norman Gimbel. *Songs:* "Don't Say There's Nothing To Do in the Doldrums," "Noise, Noise, Beautiful Noise" Lee Pockriss, Paul Vance. *Rec Supv* Franklin Milton. *Prod Mgr* Earl Jonas.

Production Credits for Live Action Seq: *Dir* David Monahan. *Photog* Lester Shorr. *Art Dir* George W. Davis, Charles K. Hagedon. *Set Decor* Henry Grace, Chuck Pierce. *Asst Dir* Charles Bonniwell, Jr. *Unit Prod Mgr* Robert Vreeland. *Makeup* William Tuttle.

Cast—Voices in Animation Seq: Mel Blanc, Daws Butler, Candy Candido, Hans Conried, June Foray, Patti Gilbert, Shep Menken, Cliff Norton, Larry Thor, Les Tremayne.

Cast—Live Action Seq: Butch Patrick *(Milo)*.

Fantasy. Source: Norman Juster, *The Phantom Tollbooth* (New York, 1961). Upon returning from school one day, a bored San Francisco youth, Milo, finds a huge candy-striped package in his bedroom. Tearing off the wrappings, he uncovers a magic tollbooth, a red car, and a roadmap of the Kingdom of Wisdom. He drives through the tollbooth and discovers himself in a mystical cartoon world. There Milo encounters Officer Short Shrift, who gives him a traffic ticket with "I am" written on it, and the Whether Man, who is unable to make up his mind. He eventually winds up in the swampy Doldrums, where

the yellow-eyed Lethargians try to convert him to their slothful way of life. Rescued from the Lethargians by a ticking "watch"-dog called Tock, Milo and the dog travel to the towns of Dictionopolis and Digitopolis. Tock explains that the two towns were at one time united under King Wisdom and his twin daughters, Sweet Rhyme and Pure Reason; but when Wisdom died, warfare broke out between King Azaz of Dictionopolis (who believes words are more important than numbers) and his brother, the Mathemagician of Digitopolis (who values numbers above words). Furthermore, the kings have banished Rhyme and Reason to the Castle-in-the-Air, which is guarded by the demons who inhabit the Mountains of Ignorance. Determined to restore peace to the land, Milo—with the help of Tock, the Spelling Bee, and the foxlike Humbug—subdues the forces of ignorance, returns Rhyme and Reason to the Kingdom of Wisdom, and joins in the celebration as the two kings finally realize that numbers and words are of equal importance. Although reluctant to leave his new friends, Milo drives back through the tollbooth into his bedroom. Transformed by his adventures into an alert and active boy, Milo runs outdoors to immerse himself in the real world. *Children. Police. Royalty. Twins. Youth. Fantasy. Imaginary kingdoms. San Francisco.*

DAS PHANTOM VON SOHO *see* **THE PHANTOM OF SOHO**

THE PHARAOHS' WOMAN (Italy)   F6.3804

Vic Films–Faro Film. *Dist* Universal-International Films. May **1961** [New York opening: 18 Apr 1962; c15 Mar 1961; LP24528]. Sd; col (Eastmancolor). 35mm (Techniscope). 88 min.

A Victor Tourjansky Production. *Prod* Giorgio Venturini. *Dir* Giorgio Rivalta, Wenceslav Tourjansky. *Screenplay* Ugo Liberatore, Remigio Del Grosso, Virgilio Tosi, Massimo Vitalo. *Story* Virgilio Tosi, Massimo Vitalo. *Photog* Pier Ludovico Pavoni. *Art Dir* Arrigo Equini. *Film Ed* Antonietta Zita. *Mus* Giovanni Fusco. *Choreog* Adriano Vitale. *Prod Mgr* Gianpaolo Bigazzi. *Cost* Giancarlo Bartolini Salimbeni. *Tech Adv for Battle Scenes* Giorgio Rivalta. *Tech Adv in Egypt* Charles Lifshitz.

Cast: John Drew Barrymore *(Sabaku)*, Linda Cristal *(Akis)*, Armando Francioli *(Ramsisu)*, Pierre Brice *(Amosi)*, Lilly Lembo *(Mareth)*, Guido Celano, Ugo Sasso, Andreina Rossi, Nerio Bernardi, Nando Angelini, Nadia Brivio, Enzo Fiermonte, Fedele Gentile, Nino Marchetti, Anna Placido, Wilma Sempetery, Anita Todesco.

Costume melodrama. In ancient Egypt, two cousins, Prince Sabaku and Prince Ramsisu, become rivals for the hand of a beautiful village girl named Akis. Unknown to them, however, she has fallen in love with the young Amosi, the court physician and one of Ramsisu's close friends. Amosi is forced to accompany his friend back to Thebes when Ramsisu's father, the ruling pharaoh, dies. Akis, mistakenly thinking herself abandoned by Amosi, agrees to become Sabaku's bride. Ramsisu is crowned pharaoh, and the jealous Sabaku declares himself pharaoh of lower Egypt, therby precipitating a war. The two armies meet and clash at dawn in the desert. Sabaku is killed, his army defeated, and Akis is taken as a slave by Ramsisu. During the long homeward trek to Thebes, Amosi manages to free Akis and the two escape into the desert. But Ramsisu captures them, chains them together, and leaves them to die. Fortunately, a merchant caravan passes by and saves them. *Royalty. Physicians. Cousins. Slavery. Courtship. Jealousy. Deserts. Egypt—Ancient.*

Note: Location scenes filmed in Egypt. Opened in Rome in Dec 1960 as *La donna dei Faraoini*; running time: 100 min.

PHENOMENA 7.7   F6.3805

Empire Studios. May **1965** [Socorro, New Mexico, showing]. Sd; col. 35mm. 70 min.

Documentary. An examination of verified sightings of unidentified flying objects, this film is based on an actual incident in 1964 involving Lonnie Zamora, a Socorro, New Mexico, policeman, who claimed to see a UFO alight and take off. Approximately 7.7 percent of the reported sightings cannot be explained by the Federal Government. *Police. Unidentified flying objects. Socorro (New Mexico).*

Note: Location scenes filmed in Socorro, New Mexico.

PHILIP *see* **RUN WILD, RUN FREE**

THE PHONY AMERICAN (West Germany)   F6.3806

Astra–Filmkunst. *Dist* Signal International Films. 2 Oct **1964** [New Haven, Connecticut, opening]. Sd; b&w. 35mm. 72 min.

Prod Alfred Strauss, Harold N. Even. *Prod Supv* Rudolf Kalmowicz. *Dir* Akos von Rathony. *Screenplay* Michael Krims, Alexander Badal. *Photog* Ernst W. Kalinke. *Art Dir* Hans Sohnle, Friedrich Thaler. *Film Ed* Annaliese Schoennenbeck, Margot Mohrbutter. *Mus* Herbert Jarczyk. *Sd* Günther Bloch. *Asst Dir* Felix von Podmanitzky. *Prod Mgr* Adolf Rosen.

Cast: Christine Kaufmann *(Inge)*, Michael Hinz *(Helmut)*, William Bendix *(Sergeant Harrigan)*, Ron Randell *(Captain Smith)*, Walter Gross *(Max)*, Alfred Pongratz *(Rudolf)*, Karl Lieffen *(Moritz)*, Gary Marshall *(McNulty)*, Oskar

Paulig *(Hermann)*, Wera Frydtberg *(Mary)*, Götz Burger, Bob Cunningham, Charles Hickman, Mal Sondock, Holger Hagen, Stefan Schnabel, Fred Dürr, William H. Taylor, Inge Benz, Leonardo Putzgruber, Al Hoosman, Burt Bertez, Paula Braend, Cheril Bernard, James Saeger, Frithjof Vierock, Karl Otto Alberty, Axel Scholz.

Comedy-drama. Source: Heinz Gross and Egon G. Schleinitz, *Toller Hecht auf krummer Tour, die amüsanteste Köpenickiade unserer Zeit* (Bad Wörishofen, 1959). Helmut, a German war orphan, is unofficially adopted by Captain Smith, an American pilot based in Berlin during the 1948 airlift. The boy is treated as Smith's own son until the pilot is reassigned to Korea and killed in action. Teenaged Helmut then goes to live with a German family and wins the love of the daughter, Inge, and the hatred of the son. Later, Helmut is unjustly accused of theft and imprisoned. When he is freed, he sets out to fulfill his ambition of joining the United States Air Force. With a stolen uniform, ID card, and other papers, he enters an American military camp. There he is befriended by Sergeant Harrigan; but just as he is about to be flown to the United States, Helmut's identity is discovered. Although Sergeant Harrigan offers to adopt him, Helmut decides to remain in Germany with Inge. *Air pilots. Orphans. War victims. Adoption. Adolescence. Family life. Imposture. Berlin Blockade 1948–49. United States Air Force. Documentation.*

Note: Released in West Germany in Feb 1962 as *Toller Hecht auf krummer Tour*; running time: 91 min. German prerelease title: *Toller Hecht auf krummen Touren*; original length: 97 min.

PHOTO FINNISH-STYLE   F6.3807
Dist Distribpix, Inc. ca 1970. Sd; col. 35mm. 65 min.
Drama. A young photographer starts a new job doing child and baby portraits in the home. On one house call he is confronted by a 19-year-old woman who poses *au naturel*, and the boy discovers another dimension to his work. The number of these "special" jobs increases until one day he is hired by a couple to record their lovemaking on film. The young man develops the film and determines to blackmail the couple, but he meets violence when they refuse to acquiesce to his demands. *Photographers. Exhibitionism. Sexuality. Blackmail.*

THE PHYNX   F6.3808
Cinema Organization. *Dist* Warner Bros. Pictures. 6 May 1970 [Indianapolis, Indiana, opening]. Sd; col (Technicolor). 35mm. 91 min. *MPAA rating* GP.
Prod Bob Booker, George Foster. *Dir* Lee H. Katzin. *Screenplay* Stan Cornyn. *Story* Bob Booker, George Foster. *Photog* Michel Hugo. *Set Decor* Ralph S. Hurst. *Prod Dsgn* Stan Jolley. *Film Ed* Dann Cahn. *Mus* Mike Stoller. *Lyr* Jerry Leiber. *Mus Supv* Sonny Burke. *Sd* Jean Kean, Dan Wallin. *Asst Dir* Les Sheldon, Bruce Chevillat. *Prod Supv* Leon Chooluck. *Cost* Donfeld. *Sp Eff* Westheimer Co.
Cast: A. Michael Miller, Ray Chippeway, Dennis Larden, Lonny Stevens *(The Phynx)*, Lou Antonio *(Corrigan)*, Mike Kellin *(Bogey)*, Michael Ansara *(Colonel Rostinov)*, George Tobias *(Markevitch)*, Joan Blondell *(Ruby)*, Larry Hankin *(Philbaby)*, Teddy Eccles *(Wee Johnny Wilson)*, Ultra Violet *(herself)*, Pat McCormick *(Father O'Hoolihan)*, Joseph Gazal *(Yakov)*, Bob Williams *(Number One)*, Barbara Noonan *(Bogey's secretary)*, Rich Little *(voice in box)*, Sue Bernard, Ann Morell, Sherry Miles *(belly girls)*.
Guest Stars: Patty Andrews, Rona Barrett, Edgar Bergen, Busby Berkeley, James Brown, singer, Dick Clark, Xavier Cugat, Cass Daley, Andy Devine, Fritz Feld, Leo Gorcey, Huntz Hall, John Hart, Louis Hayward, George Jessel, Ruby Keeler, Patsy Kelly, Dorothy Lamour, Joe Louis, Guy Lombardo, Trini Lopez, Marilyn Maxwell, Butterfly McQueen, Pat O'Brien, Maureen O'Sullivan, Richard Pryor, Martha Raye, Harold Sakata, Col. Harlan Sanders, Jay Silverheels, Ed Sullivan, Rudy Vallee, Clint Walker, Johnny Weissmuller.
Farce. The U. S. Super Secret Agency (SSA) is disturbed by the kidnaping of a number of American show business people by Communist Albania. SSA Agent Corrigan tries to penetrate Albania but is blocked by Albanian Army Chief Rostinov. Number One holds a secret meeting to decide how SSA can solve the problem, and Wee Johnny Wilson of the Underage Underground suggests that they consult MOTHA (Mechanical Oracle That Helps Americans). The computer responds with a scheme to form a rock group, "The Phynx", to tour Albania. An athlete, a campus militant, a Negro model, and an American Indian form the group; and with the help of record producer Philbaby, The Phynx record an album that is pushed to fame by SSA force tactics. After a farewell orgy provided by the government, The Phynx are sent to London where a double agent (played by Martha Raye) reveals that maps giving directions to the secret castle in Albania where the prisoners are confined are tattooed on the bellies of her three daughters, living respectively in London, Copenhagen, and Rome. Finally arriving at the castle, the group is greeted by Marshal Markevitch and his American wife (played by Joan Blondell), for whose sake Markevitch has kidnaped her former colleagues. A loud rock guitar

session welcomes The Phynx, the walls of the castle crumble in the resulting vibrations, and the American prisoners escape. *Communists. Secret Agents. Americans in foreign countries. Entertainers. Kidnaping. Show business. Rock and roll. Espionage. Recording. Computers. Tattoos. Castles. Orgies. London. Copenhagen. Rome. Albania.*

IL PIACERE E L'AMORE *see* CIRCLE OF LOVE

IL PIANETA DEGLI UOMINI SPENTI *see* BATTLE OF THE WORLDS

LOS PIANOS MECÁNICOS *see* THE UNINHIBITED

LES PIANOS MÉCANIQUES *see* THE UNINHIBITED

PICK A STAR *see* MOVIE STRUCK

THE PICK-UP   F6.3809
Dementia Productions. *Dist* Republic Amusements Corp., Olympic International Films. 21 Nov 1968 [San Francisco showing]. Sd; b&w. 35mm. 92 min. [Also released at 80 min.] *MPAA rating* X.
Prod Wesdon Bishop. *Assoc Prod* Stefan Zema. *Dir* R. L. Frost. *Screenplay* Wesdon Bishop, R. L. Frost. *Orig Story* R. L. Frost. *Photog* R. L. Frost. *Film Ed* R. L. F. Enterprises. *Mus* Synchrofilm, Mischa Terr. *Sd* Mike Beardsley. *Asst Dir* James E. McClarty.
Cast: Wesdon Bishop, Stefan Zema, Tracy Saunders, Lynn Harris, David F. Friedman, R. W. Cresse, Maria Lease, Antoinette Maynard, Warren James, John Alderman, John Riazzi, James E. McClarty, Jim Sullivan.
Crime melodrama. Frankie and Tony, two couriers whose job is delivering bags of money skimmed by a crime syndicate from Las Vegas gambling tables, lose $1 million when they disobey instructions to make no stops by picking up two women who are apparently stranded on the highway. The two thugs lose the money when the women, Dana and Marcia, suggest that they stop at a roadside motel, and there the women seduce Frankie and Tony, pull a gun, and speed off with the million dollars. Frankie and Tony hire an airplane, follow the women to an apartment, and torture the women into telling where the money is hidden. *Couriers. Gangsters. Gambling. Seduction. Robbery. Torture. Syndicates. Airplanes. Las Vegas. Chases.*
Note: Also known as *The Pickup.*

PICKPOCKET (France)   F6.3810
Agnès Delahaie Production. *Dist* New Yorker Films. 21 May 1963 [New York opening]. Sd; b&w. 35mm. 75 min.
Prod Agnès Delahaie. *Assoc Prod* Annie Dorfmann. *Dir-Writ* Robert Bresson. *Photog* Léonce-Henri Burel. *Camera* Henri Raichi. *Asst Camera* Jean Charvein. *Art Dir* Pierre Charbonnier. *Film Ed* Raymond Lamy. *Mus From the Works of* Jean Baptiste Lully. *Sd* Antoine Archimbaud. *Asst Dir* Michel Clément, Claude Clément. *Prod Mgr* Michel Choquet. *Asst Prod Mgr* Jean-Jacques Lecot. *Location Mgr* Jacques Ballanche. *Script Girl* Odette Lemarchand.
Cast: Martin Lasalle *(Michel)*, Marika Green *(Jeanne)*, Jean Pelegri *(inspector)*, Dolly Scal *(Michel's mother)*, Pierre Leymarie *(Jacques)*, Kassagi, Pierre Etaix *(accomplices)*, César Gattegno *(detective)*.
Crime drama. Michel, an educated young man, has been a kleptomaniac since he first stole money from his mother. When caught in an unsuccessful theft, he attempts to justify his chosen way of life: a failure by society's standards, he can feel superior to society only by disobeying its rules. Shortly after Michel is released from custody, his mother dies, and he tries to heed the advice of his friends Jacques and Jeanne; but when he meets a master pickpocket who offers to train him, Michel resumes his life of crime and quickly becomes an accomplished thief. Eventually he senses that he is being closely observed by both Jeanne, who is in love with him, and an inspector, who wants to catch him, and he abruptly leaves France. After spending his spoils in England, he returns 2 years later and finds Jeanne alone and abandoned after having had a child by Jacques. Once more taking to picking pockets in order to provide for Jeanne, he is caught and sent to prison. When Jeanne visits him, he realizes how much he cares for her and suddenly finds himself at peace. *Pickpockets. Detectives. Kleptomania. Criminals—Rehabilitation. Prisons. England.*
Note: Filmed on location in Paris. Opened in Paris in Dec 1959.

PICKUP IN ROME *see* FROM A ROMAN BALCONY

PICTURE MOMMY DEAD   F6.3811
Berkeley Productions. *Dist* Embassy Pictures. Sep 1966. Sd; col (PathéColor). 35mm. 88 min.
A Bert I. Gordon Production. *Prod-Dir* Bert I. Gordon. *Screenplay* Robert Sherman. *Photog* Ellsworth Fredricks. *Set Decor* Ray Moyer, Robert R. Benton. *Film Ed* John Bushelman. *Mus* Robert Drasnin. *Sd* Harry Lindgren, James E. Murphy. *Sd Rec* John Wilkinson. *Asst Dir* Dennis Connelly. *Prod Mgr* Dale Coleman. *Cost* Leah Rhodes. *Makeup* Dan Striepeke, Hal Lierley.

Hairstyles Sherry Wilson. *Sp Eff* Charles Spurgeon.

Cast: Don Ameche *(Edward Shelly)*, Martha Hyer *(Francene Shelly)*, Zsa Zsa Gabor *(Jessica)*, Susan Gordon *(Susan Shelly)*, Maxwell Reed *(Anthony)*, Wendell Corey *(Clayborn)*, Signe Hasso *(Sister Rene)*, Anna Lee *(Elsie Kornwald)*, Paulle Clark *(1st woman)*, Marlene Tracy *(2d woman)*, Steffi Henderson *(3d woman)*, Robert Sherman *(father)*, Kelly Corcoran *(boy)*.

Horror film. Young Susan Shelly, suffering from shock and amnesia, is confined to a sanitarium-convent following the death of her mother, Jessica, in a fire. After 3 years Susan returns home to her father, Edward, and his new wife, Francene, Susan's former governess. Francene, who married Edward because she thought he would inherit his wife's total estate, applies pressure on Edward to have Susan recommitted, knowing that her inheritance would revert to Edward should she be declared insane or die before her 25th birthday. Failing this, Francene persuades her lover, Anthony, the caretaker, to help her recover from Susan a valuable necklace once belonging to Jessica and now missing. During a thunderstorm Susan reconstructs the events leading up to the fire in which her mother perished. She realizes that she did steal the necklace and finds it but refuses to give it to Francene, believing in her hysteria that the woman is Jessica. A chase ensues; Francene discovers Anthony calling the police and stabs him to death. Edward joins in the fray and strangles Francene, just as he killed Jessica, and for the same reason, because of her adultery with Anthony. The scene is witnessed by Susan, who, as she did 3 years before, sets fire to the house and departs with her father, happy in the thought that she is the only woman in his life. *Stepmothers. Governesses. Filial relations. Amnesia. Inheritance. Greed. Infidelity. Jealousy. Murder. Arson. Insanity. Theft. Sanitariums. Storms. Fires.*

Note: Location scenes filmed at Greystone Mansion, Beverly Hills.

PIE IN THE SKY *see* TERROR IN THE CITY

A PIECE OF HER ACTION   F6.3812
Jode Productions. *Dist* CIP Ltd. 5 Jun **1968** [Champaign, Illinois, showing]. Sd; b&w. 35mm. 64 min.

Prod-Dir Jerry Denby.

Drama. Beach boys Rick and Bermuda team up in Miami, looking for "easy money." Bermuda, a confidence man, is fleeing the law, and Rick, a drifter, has been hitchhiking his way south. Bermuda begins a romance with Margo, vacationing away from her rich husband, while Rick seduces April, who arrives with her father in a Cadillac convertible. Margo and Bermuda engage in exotic sexplay, and they watch while Rick and April make love. Rick, Bermuda, and April plan to rob Margo and share the booty, but April double-crosses the men, takes the money, and drives off with the older man who, it turns out, is not her father but an accomplice. *Drifters. Confidence men. Fugitives. Seduction. Wealth. Theft. Perfidy. Voyeurism. Miami.*

Note: Also known as *A Piece of the Action.*

PIECES   F6.3813
Chellee Films. ca **1969**. Sd; b&w. 35mm. 66 min.

Pres by Chellee Wilson.

Sex film. The film "documents" the private lives of the makers of sex exploitation films. Press material suggests that the film contains scenes depicting lesbianism, nymphomania, sexual intercourse, and nudity. *Actors. Lesbianism. Nudity. Nymphomania. Sex exploitation films.*

PIECES OF DREAMS   F6.3814
RFB Enterprises. *Dist* United Artists. 23 Sep **1970** [Los Angeles opening; c26 Aug 1970; LP38967]. Sd; col (DeLuxe). 35mm. 100 min. *MPAA rating* GP.

Pres by Robert F. Blumofe. *Prod* Robert F. Blumofe. *Assoc Prod* J. Paul Popkin. *Dir* Daniel Haller. *Screenplay* Roger Hirson. *Dir Photog* Charles F. Wheeler. *Camera Op* Jack Whitman. *Art Dir* Herman A. Blumenthal. *Set Decor* James Payne. *Film Ed* William Chulack. *Mus Comp & Cond* Michel Legrand. *Titl Song* Michel Legrand, Alan Bergman, Marilyn Bergman. *Sung by* Peggy Lee. *Sd* Don Rush. *Asst Dir* Victor Vallejo, Fred Giles. *Sec to the Prod* Robert M. Blumofe. *Prod Sec* Sandy Delaney. *Prod Asst* Michael Rachmil. *Location Mgr* LeRoy Hollis. *Wardrobe* Halston, Ray Phelps, Phyllis Garr. *Makeup* Gustaf M. Norin. *Still Photog* Lee Green. *Prop* Arthur Friedrich, Fred Westcott. *Grip* Dick Borland. *Gaffer* Harry Sundby.

Cast: Robert Forster *(Gregory Lind)*, Lauren Hutton *(Pamela Gibson)*, Will Geer *(The Bishop)*, Ivor Francis *(Father Paul Schaeffer)*, Richard O'Brien *(Monsignor Francis Hurley)*, Edith Atwater *(Mrs. Lind)*, Mitzi Hoag *(Anne Lind)*, Rudy Diaz *(Police Sgt. Bill Walkingstick)*, Sam Javis *(Leo Rose)*, Gail Bonney *(Mrs. Tietgens)*, Helen Westcott *(Mrs. Straub)*, Joanne Moore Jordan *(girl in bar)*, Miriam Martinez *(Mrs. Rios)*, Kathy Baca *(Estella)*, Eloy Phil Casados *(Charlie)*, Robert McCoy *(employment agency interviewer)*, Raimundo Baca *(gunshot victim)*.

Melodrama. Source: William E. Barrett, *The Wine and the Music* (Garden City, New York, 1968). Father Gregory Lind, a young Catholic priest, meets divorced social worker Pamela Gibson in an Albuquerque hospital where a man, whom they have been trying to help, dies of gunshot wounds after an attempted robbery. Father Lind, who is strongly opposed to abortion, argues with Pamela about the fate of the young man's pregnant 15-year-old girl friend. The girl miscarries, however, and Father Lind goes to comfort Pamela, but his attempt at consolation leads him to make love to her, and they begin an affair despite his vow of celibacy. Finding it difficult to work within the confines of the church and the conservative Father Schaeffer, Father Lind visits his domineering mother and spinster sister, who rebuke him for his doubts about the church. Later that night, he is propositioned by a prostitute and beaten up by a group of hoodlums who call him a homosexual. After taking a leave of absence from the church, Father Lind goes to see Pamela, realizes his love for her, and decides to leave the priesthood immediately, even though he faces excommunication. *Priests. Social workers. Prostitutes. Abortion. Miscarriage. Celibacy. Conscience. Hospitals. Albuquerque. Catholic Church.*

Note: Location scenes filmed in Albuquerque, New Mexico, and Kansas City, Missouri. Working title: *The Wine and the Music.*

THE PIED PIPER *see* THE CLOWN AND THE KIDS

THE PIED PIPER OF HAMELIN   F6.3815
Hal Stanley Productions. *Dist* International Film Distributors. **1961**. Sd; col (EastmanColor). 35mm. 90 min.

Prod Hal Stanley. *Dir* Bretaigne Windust. *Screenplay* Irving Taylor, Hal Stanley. *Photog* William Snyder. *Art Dir* Arthur Lonergan. *Film Ed* Floyd Knudtson. *Mus Selections* Edvard Grieg. *Lyr* Irving Taylor, Hal Stanley. *Mus Dir* Pete King. *Choreog* Ward Ellis. *Sp Eff* Jack Rabin, Louis DeWitt, Irving Block.

Cast: Van Johnson *(The Pied Piper)*, Claude Rains *(mayor)*, Lori Nelson *(Myra)*, Jim Backus *(king's emissary)*, Kay Starr, Doodles Weaver.

Fantasy. Freely based on the legend. In 12th-century Bavaria, the town of Hamelin is overrun with rats. The Pied Piper offers to rid the town of the rats for 50,000 guilders. The schoolteacher Trusson, who is a near-double for the Piper, supports the Piper's offer. The avaricious mayor and council come to terms with the Pied Piper, but they refuse to pay him after he has led the rats into the river, preferring instead to buy gold chimes for the church. The Piper retaliates by leading all the children of Hamelin into an impregnable mountain retreat. The mothers of Hamelin force the mayor to resign; Trusson takes over the office and pays for the release of the children; and the money is given to the poor. *Musicians. Magicians. Doubles. Schoolteachers. Mayors. Children. Greed. Charity. Hameln. Pied Piper. Rats.*

Note: First shown as an NBC-TV special on 26 Nov 1957.

LE PIÈGE *see* ANY MAN'S WOMAN

PIEL DE VERANO *see* SUMMERSKIN

PIERROT LE FOU (France/Italy)   F6.3816
Rome Paris Films–Productions Georges de Beauregard–Dino De Laurentiis Cinematografica–S. N. C. *Dist* Pathé Contemporary Films. Nov **1968** [Los Angeles showing]. Sd; col (Eastman Color). 35mm (Techniscope). 110 min.

Prod Georges de Beauregard. *Dir-Writ* Jean-Luc Godard. *Dir Photog* Raoul Coutard. *Camera* Georges Liron, Jean Garcenot. *Studio Photog* Marilou Parolini, Georges Pierre. *Art Dir* Pierre Guffroy. *Film Ed* Françoise Colin. *Mus* Antoine Duhamel. *Songs:* "Ma ligne de chance," "Jamais je ne t'ai dit que je t'aimerai toujours" Antoine Duhamel, Bassiak. *Flute Concerto* Antonio Vivaldi. *Sd* René Levert. *Sd Mix* Antoine Bonfanti. *Asst Dir* Philippe Fourastié, Jean-Pierre Léaud. *Gen Prod Mgr* René Demoulin. *Prod Mgr* Roger Scipion. *Prod Admin* Roger Ferret.

Cast: Jean-Paul Belmondo *(Ferdinand Griffon [Pierrot])*, Anna Karina *(Marianne Renoir)*, Dirk Sanders *(Marianne's brother)*, Raymond Devos *(man on the pier)*, Graziella Galvani *(Ferdinand's wife)*, Roger Dutoit, Hans Meyer *(gangsters)*, Jimmy Karoubi *(dwarf)*, Christa Nell *(Madame Staquet)*, Pascal Aubier *(2d brother)*, Pierre Hanin *(3d brother)*, Aicha Abidir *(herself, a princess)*, Samuel Fuller *(himself)*, Alexis Poliakoff *(sailor)*, Laszlo Szabo *(political exile)*, Jean-Pierre Léaud *(young man in cinema)*, Pascal Aubier, Pierre Hanin.

Drama. Source: Lionel White, *Obsession* (New York, 1962). French television director Ferdinand Griffon becomes bored by the pretentious chatter of people at a party given by his wife's wealthy parents and returns home alone. Upon finding that the babysitter for his two children is a former girl friend, Marianne Renoir, he leaves with her. The next morning, after a man is murdered in her flat, Ferdinand, whom Marianne insists on calling Pierrot, agrees to flee to the Riviera and search for her brother, a gunrunner. On an idyllic island, Ferdinand decides to take advantage of the serenity by writing; Marianne, however, soon becomes bored and once more involves him in violence. He receives a phone call from Marianne asking for help and arrives to find the body of a dwarfish gangster, stabbed with a pair of scissors, and two gangsters waiting to torture him to learn Marianne's whereabouts. After escaping, Ferdinand discovers that Marianne's brother is actually her lover. Following a double-cross in which he is involved in another murder, the disillusioned Ferdinand returns to the island and kills both lovers in a gun battle. Unable to reach his wife in Paris by telephone, he paints his face blue, ties dynamite around his head, and lights the fuse. Although he changes his mind, it is too late to snuff out the burning fuse. *Television directors. Babysitters. Gunrunners. Gangsters. Infidelity. Duplicity. Murder. Suicide. Islands. Explosives. Riviera. Paris.*

Note: Filmed on location in Paris and in southern France. Opened in Paris in Nov 1965 as *Pierrot le fou*; working title: *Le démon de 11 heures*; running time: 90 min; opened in Rome in Feb 1966 as *Il bandito della 11*; running time: 95 min.

THE PIGEON THAT TOOK ROME   F6.3817

Llenroc Productions. *Dist* Paramount Pictures. 22 Aug **1962** [New York opening; c22 Aug 1962; LP23299]. Sd; b&w. 35mm (Panavision). 101 min.

A Melville Shavelson Production. *Prod-Dir-Writ* Melville Shavelson. *Dir Photog* Daniel L. Fapp. *Art Dir* Hal Pereira, Roland Anderson. *Set Decor* Sam Comer, Frank R. McKelvy. *Film Ed* Frank Bracht. *Mus Score* Alessandro Cicognini. *Orch* Leo Shuken, Jack Hayes. *Cond* Irvin Talbot. *Sd Rec* Hugo Grenzbach, John Wilkinson. *Asst Dir* Daniel J. McCauley. *Prod Mgr* Andrew J. Durkus, Mario Del Papa. *Asst to the Prod* Hal C. Kern. *Script Supv* Mae Wale-Wright. *Makeup Supv* Wally Westmore. *Hairstyle Supv* Nellie Manley. *Sp Photog Eff* John P. Fulton. *Proc Photog* Farciot Edouart. *Dial Coach* Harriet White, Argentina Brunetti.

Cast: Charlton Heston *(Capt. Paul MacDougall)*, Elsa Martinelli *(Antonella Massimo)*, Harry Guardino *(Sgt. Joseph Contini)*, Baccaloni *(Ciccio Massimo)*, Marietto *(Livio Massimo)*, Gabriella Pallotta *(Rosalba Massimo)*, Debbie Price *(Luigina Massimo)*, Brian Donlevy *(Col. Sherman Harrington)*, Bob Gandett *(The General)*, Arthur Shields *(Monsignor O'Toole)*, Rudolph Anders *(Oberst Wilhelm Krafft)*, Gary Collins *(Major Wolff)*, Vadim Wolkonsky *(Conte Danesi)*, Richard Nelson *(The Chief [Franklin Delano Roosevelt])*.

War comedy. Source: Donald C. Downes, *The Easter Dinner* (New York, 1960). After the fall of Mussolini in 1944 Capt. Paul MacDougall and his radioman, Sgt. Joseph Contini, are smuggled into Nazi-occupied Rome to investigate enemy activities, though neither has had any training in espionage. They are met on the beach by Livio Massimo, an 11-year-old resistance fighter, who leads them to his father, Ciccio, leader of the Italian resistance. Massimo's daughter, Antonella, who is friendly with German officers, resents the intrusion of the American spies because the family is hungry, but she changes her mind when she learns that her sister, Rosalba, is pregnant and in need of a husband. Contini and Rosalba fall in love, and Massimo plans to announce their engagement at a feast, providing he can find enough food. Antonella innocently serves all but one of the carrier pigeons used by MacDougall to carry messages. Livio, trying to be helpful, replaces them with stolen German pigeons, which fly MacDougall's messages directly to the Nazis. Frantic, MacDougall sends insane, contradictory reports, but the surviving American pigeon carries one of these to the Americans at Anzio. The Americans decide to attack; Rome is liberated; Rosalba is married just as her baby arrives; MacDougall marries Antonella on the spur of the moment; and the lone American pigeon receives the Medal of Honor. *Spies. Radiomen. Italians. Germans. Nazis. Children. Espionage. Resistance (political). Marriage. Pregnancy. Family life. World War II. Italy—History—German occupation. Rome. Anzio. Franklin Delano Roosevelt. United States Army. Pigeons.*

Note: Location scenes filmed in Rome. Working title: *The Easter Dinner.*

PIGEONS *see* **THE SIDELONG GLANCES OF A PIGEON KICKER**

PIKOVAYA DAMA *see* **QUEEN OF SPADES**

A PILGRIMAGE FOR PEACE: POPE PAUL VI VISITS AMERICA
                                                F6.3818

Roberts Productions. 20 Jul **1966** [New York opening]. Sd; col. 35mm. 56 min.

Pres by Davis International. *Prod* Joseph L. Roberts. *Dir-Narr* Carl Allensworth.

Narrator: Phil Tonkin.

Documentary. On October 4, 1965, Pope Paul VI arrives at John Fitzgerald Kennedy International Airport, beginning an historic peace mission, the first American visit of a Catholic pontiff. At Saint Patrick's Cathedral he is welcomed by members of the New York archdiocese. After meeting with President Lyndon Baines Johnson in the Waldorf-Astoria Hotel, Paul VI proceeds to the United Nations. In the General Assembly his impassioned plea for peace in Vietnam is heard by an audience of 3,000. At Holy Family Church the pope addresses representatives of divers faiths. Before 90,000 spectators Paul VI celebrates Mass in Yankee Stadium. Following a visit to the Vatican Pavilion of the World's Fair, the pontiff departs for Rome, concluding his 14-

hour visit. *Clergymen. Travel. New York World's Fair (1964–65). Vietnam War 1964–73. New York City. Lyndon Baines Johnson. Paul VI (pope). United Nations. Catholic Church. Saint Patrick's Cathedral. Waldorf-Astoria Hotel. John Fitzgerald Kennedy International Airport. New York City—Yankee Stadium.*

THE PILL   F6.3819

Screen Classics. *Dist* American Film Distributing Corp. 26 Sep **1967** [Maryland license]. Sd; col. 35mm. 70 min.

Prod George Weiss. *Dir* W. Merle Connell.

Cast: Monica Davis, John Maitland.

Sex instruction film. Little information has been found on this film, but the press release claims that a number of topics pertaining to sex education and marriage are covered, particularly from a medical point of view, including artificial insemination and birth control. *Sex instruction. Marriage. Birth control. Artificial insemination.*

Note: Rerelease of *Test Tube Babies*, a 1950's feature; additional footage, filmed in Los Angeles, is included.

THE PILL *see* **THE GIRL, THE BODY, AND THE PILL**

THE PILLAR OF FIRE (Israel)   F6.3820

Larry Frisch Productions–Geva Films. *Dist* Noel Meadow Associates, Hoffberg Productions, Frank Kassler. 6 Apr **1963** [New York opening]. Sd; b&w. 35mm. 75 min.

A Larry Frisch Production. *Prod* Izhak Agadati, Mordechai Navon, Larry Frisch. *Dir* Larry Frisch. *Screenplay* Hugh Nissenson, Larry Frisch. *Photog* Haim Shreiber. *Film Ed* Nelly Bogor. *Mus Comp & Cond* Moshe Willensky. *Played by* Israel Symphony Orchestra.

Cast: Michael Shillo *(Uri)*, Lawrence Montaigne *(David)*, Nehama Hendel *(Rachel)*, Moshe Yaari *(Moshe)*, Amos Mocadi *(Kantrowitz)*, Uri Zohar *(Yossi)*.

War drama. During the 1948 Israeli War of Independence, six Jewish reconnaissance fighters defend a tiny settlement in the Negev desert from Arab invasion. Uri, David, Rachel, Moshe, Kantrowitz, and Yossi learn that the Arabs are planning to attack a major Israeli city; but in an attempt to return to the outpost with the information, all but David and Rachel are killed. David, an American idealist living in Israel, and Rachel, a product of Nazi concentration camps, fall in love on the trip back to the post, where they give the warning. The Israelis are once again attacked by the Arabs; they sustain heavy losses but organize another patrol for the following day. *Jews. Soldiers. Americans in foreign countries. Arabs. Reconnaissance. Israeli-Arab War 1948–49. Negev.*

Note: Sources conflict in crediting distributor.

PIN-UP CAMERA *see* **NUDES, INC.**

THE PIN-UP FACTORY *see* **NUDES, INC.**

THE PINK JUNGLE   F6.3821

Cherokee Productions. *Dist* Universal Pictures. Aug **1968** [c7 Sep 1968; LP37967]. Sd (Westrex); col (Technicolor). 35mm (Techniscope). 104 min.

Prod Stan Margulies. *Dir* Delbert Mann. *Screenplay* Charles Williams. *Dir Photog* Russell Metty. *Art Dir* Alexander Golitzen, Alfred Ybarra. *Set Decor* John McCarthy, James S. Redd. *Main Titl* Universal Title. *Film Ed* William B. Murphy. *Mus* Ernie Freeman. *Mus Supv* Joseph Gershenson. *Sd* Waldon O. Watson, William Russell. *Asst Dir* Phil Bowles, Ted Swanson. *Prod Mgr* Ernest B. Wehmeyer. *Cost Dsgn* Edith Head. *Makeup* Bud Westmore. *Hairstyles* Larry Germain. *Stunt Coörd* John Daheim.

Cast: James Garner *(Ben Morris)*, Eva Renzi *(Alison Duquesne)*, George Kennedy *(Sammy Ryderbeit)*, Nigel Green *(Crowley)*, Michael Ansara *(Raul Ortega)*, George Rose *(Stopes)*, Fabrizio Mioni *(Colonel Celaya)*, Vincent Beck *(Sanchez)*, Val Avery *(Rodriguez)*, Robert Carricart *(Benavides)*, Victor Millan *(helicopter pilot)*, Natividad Vacio *(Figueroa)*, Nacho Galindo *(hotel proprietor)*, Pepito Galindo *(bellboy)*, Than Wyenn *(customs agent)*, Pepe Callahan *(hoodlum)*.

Adventure comedy. Source: Alan Williams, *Snake Water* (London, 1965). While working on a lipstick ad campaign in a South American village, photographer Ben Morris and fashion model Alison Duquesne are stranded when their helicopter is stolen by adventurer Sammy Ryderbeit. After convincing the local authorities that they are not secret agents or smugglers, Ben and Alison run into Sammy, who has crashed the helicopter. Upon hearing Sammy's story about a lost diamond mine, the couple are skeptical until they discover the dead body of Captain Stopes, the only man aware of the mine's location. Equipped with Stopes's map to the mine, Ben, Alison, and Sammy set off on a diamond safari, joined by Crowley, a scheming Australian who claims to be Stopes's ex-partner. Intending to take the diamonds for himself, he steals the trio's supplies and leaves them stranded in the middle of the desert without mules. Sammy catches up with Crowley and kills him in a shoot-out. When the trio finally reaches the mine, they discover that a rival gang headed by Raul Ortega has beaten them to the treasure. In the ensuing skirmish, Ortega is taken prisoner, his henchmen killed, and the diamonds retrieved by Sammy, who then steals another helicopter and takes off with the loot. Colonel Celaya, a village police official, is unperturbed by Sammy's disappearance, since Ortega, the head of a revolutionary movement, has been captured. Ben, revealed to be a CIA agent, is confident that he can overtake Sammy and the diamonds. *Adventurers. Models. South Americans. Australians. Photographers. Police. Revolutionaries. Robbery. Imposture. Helicopters. Diamond mines. Deserts. South America. United States—Central Intelligence Agency. Documentation.*

THE PINK PANTHER
F6.3822

Mirisch-G & E Productions. *Dist* United Artists. 18 Mar **1964** [Chicago opening; c18 Mar 1964; LP27578]. Sd; col (Technicolor). 35mm (Technirama, see note). 113 min.

Pres by Mirisch Co. A Blake Edwards Production. *Prod* Martin Jurow. *Assoc Prod* Dick Crockett. *Dir* Blake Edwards. *Screenplay* Maurice Richlin, Blake Edwards. *Cinematog* Philip Lathrop. *Camera Op* Cliff King. *Asst Camera* Richard Kline. *Art Dir* Fernando Carrere. *Set Decor* Reg Allen, Jack Stevens, Arrigo Breschi. *Main Titl* DePatie-Freleng. *Film Ed* Ralph E. Winters. *Asst Ed* Marshall M. Borden, David B. Zinnemann. *Mus* Henry Mancini. *Song:* "It Had Better Be Tonight" Henry Mancini. *English Lyr* Johnny Mercer. *Italian Lyr* Franco Migliacci. *Sung by* Fran Jeffries. *Tenor Sax Solos* Plas Johnson. *Choreog* Hermes Pan. *Sd* Alexander Fisher. *Boom Op* William Hamilton. *Asst Dir* Ottavio Oppo. *Prod Mgr* Jack McEdward. *Prod Supv* Guy Luongo. *Script Supv* Betty Abbott. *Wardrobe for Miss Cardinale and Capucine* Yves Saint-Laurent. *Sp Eff* Lee Zavitz. *Dial Coach* James Lanphier. *Still Photog* Sherman Clark.

Cast: David Niven (*Sir Charles Lytton*), Peter Sellers (*Inspector Jacques Clouseau*), Capucine (*Simone Clouseau*), Robert Wagner (*George Lytton*), Claudia Cardinale (*Princess Dala*), Fran Jeffries (*The Greek "Cousin"*), Brenda De Banzie (*Angela Dunning*), James Lanphier (*Saloud*), Colin Gordon (*Tucker*), John Le Mesurier (*defense attorney*), Guy Thomajan (*Artoff*), Michael Trubshawe (*The Novelist*), Riccardo Billi (*Greek shipowner*), Meri Welles (*Hollywood starlet*), Martin Miller (*photographer*).

Comedy. Sir Charles Lytton, who is really the famous jewel thief, the Phantom, wants the Pink Panther, a priceless jewel owned by beautiful Princess Dala. Inspector Jacques Clouseau wants the Phantom, whom he has been chasing unsuccessfully for 15 years. Clouseau also wants the Phantom's female accomplice, unaware that she is really his own wife, Simone, the Phantom's mistress. Princess Dala visits the ski resort of Cortina; and there Sir Charles, Clouseau, and Simone also appear. George, Sir Charles's nephew, who supposedly has been attending school in America at his uncle's expense but is actually an amateur in the same "profession" as his uncle, also arrives unexpectedly at Cortina. After many complications, Clouseau learns that Sir Charles is the Phantom, but he cannot capture him. Later, when Princess Dala plans a costume party at her villa in Rome, Clouseau warns her that the Phantom will undoubtedly attempt to steal the Panther from the library safe during the party. Sir Charles and George come to the party, both dressed as gorillas, and begin to work on the safe from opposite ends. They crack it simultaneously only to find it empty except for a white glove, the Phantom's trademark. The lights go out and when they come on again it is announced that the Panther is missing. After a wild car chase, Clouseau apprehends Sir Charles and George. Simone goes to Princess Dala to ask help to free them. At their trial, Clouseau testifies that he was present at each of the Phantom's thefts. Suspicion is thrown on Clouseau as the actual Phantom, and Clouseau is arrested when he pulls a handkerchief from his pocket with the Panther attached to it—the work of Simone and Dala. Sir Charles and George are freed and whisked off by Simone to South America. Clouseau, enveloped in the admiration of the crowd attending the trial and basking in the first adulation of his life, protests his innocence less vigorously as he is taken to prison. Sir Charles promises Simone that, as soon as they are safely in South America, he will send a letter to the Italian government clearing the innocent Clouseau. *Thieves. Detectives. Royalty. Infidelity. Duplicity. Robbery. Disguise. Imprisonment. Jewels. Ski resorts. Masquerades. Safes. Trials. Evidence. Cortina d'Ampezzo. Rome. South America. Chases. Inspector Clouseau.*

Note: Filmed in Italy; location scenes filmed in the Swiss Alps. Press material indicates that the film was photographed in 70mm Super Technirama.

THE PINK PUSSY (WHERE SIN LIVES) (Argentina)
F6.3823

Dist Cambist Films. 1 Jun **1966** [Champaign, Illinois, showing]. Sd; b&w. 35mm. 80 min.

Prod Emilio Spitz. *Dir-Writ* Albert Dubois. *Dial* Jack Curtis. *Story* Albert Diego. *Dir Photog* Ignacio Souto. *Camera* Lorenzo Capra. *Asst Camera* Albert Curreri. *Mus* Amadeo Monges. *Sd* Louis Capriles. *Dial Rec* Titra Sound Corp. *Asst Dir* Carlos Lopez. *Prod Asst* Petro Pereira. *Makeup* Miguel Casal. *Electrn* Jaime Alvarado.

Cast: Libertad Leblanc (*Mara Doran*), Nestor Zavarce (*Alex*), Teresa Marti (*Elvira*), Francis Ferrari, Joe Jorda, Albert Alvarez, Adolf Alcala, Gilbert Pinto, Herbert Scalona, Carl Flores, Brigitte Blum, Georgette White, Vikky Roger, Eva Moreno.

Melodrama. Exotic dancer Mara Doran signs a contract in New York to entertain at The Pink Pussy in Caracas, Venezuela, unaware that the contract is phony and that no hotel reservation has been made for her. In Caracas, her passport and money are stolen, and she is abducted and raped. Alex, in reality a Caracas vice lord who has engineered the fraud, comes to her "rescue," takes her to his hotel, and gets her the job at The Pink Pussy. At the club, Mara meets and falls in love with Ernest, another entertainer. Elvira, Alex's drug-addicted girl friend, is jealous of Mara and calls her to tell her who he really is—a vice lord who lures women to Caracas, drugs them, and forces them into white slavery. Mara is kidnaped by Alex's henchmen, but Ernest, realizing the danger she is in, rescues her. During a fight in a cable car high above the city, Alex and his henchmen nearly triumph over Ernest and Mara, but Elvira arrives and kills Alex. *Exotic dancers. Racketeers. Drug addicts. Mistresses. Abduction. Fraud. Rape. Jealousy. White slave traffic. Contracts. Nightclubs. Cable cars. Caracas.*

Note: Filmed in Caracas in 1963 as *Acosada*. Also known as *The Pink Pussy, The Pink Pussy Cat, The Pink Pussy Club, The Exploiteers,* and *Where Sin Lives.*

PINOCCHIO (East Germany)
F6.3824

DEFA. *Dist* Childhood Productions. 1 Feb **1969** [Brooklyn, New York, opening]. Sd; col. 35mm. 74 min.

Pres by Omega Productions. *English Vers Prod-Dir* Ron Merk. *German Vers Dir* Walter Beck. *German Vers Screenplay* Margot Beichler, Gudrun Rammler, Walter Beck. *Adapt* Wilhelm Päch. *English Vers Screenplay* Ellen Prince, Ron Merk. *Photog* Günter Haubold. *Camera* Wolfgang Braumann. *Sets* Harald Horn. *Film Ed* Margrit Brusendorf. *Mus German Vers* Gerhard Wohlgemuth. *Mus English Vers* Joseph Scott. *Song:* "A Boy Named Pinocchio" Ron Merk, Joseph Scott. *Sung by* Jason Cane. *Sd* Klaus Wolter. *Prod Dir* Heinz Kuschke, Siegfried Kabitzke. *Prod Mgr* Waldemar Döring. *Cost* Dorit Gründel. *Makeup* Bernhard Kalisch, Irmgard Lippmann, Liane Wilk. *Puppets Supv by* Prague Marionette Theatre "Spejl and Hurvínek", Klara Hakenová, Miloš Haken, Radko Haken.

Cast: Martin Flörchinger (*Papa Geppetto*), Alfred Müller (*Stromboli*), Martin Hellberg (*Arturo*), Vera Oelschlegel (*Mirzilla, the fox*), Peter Pollatschek (*Eusebius, the cat*), Marianne Wünscher (*Euphrosina, the Good Fairy*), Detlef Wolf (*Pippifax*), Herwart Grosse (*Mr. Lehrer, schoolmaster*), Helmut Schreiber (*ringmaster*), Carola Zschockelt (*Pudel*), Harald Popig (*Malte*), Hans Hardt-Hardtloff (*Karsten*), Jürgen Marten (*a father*), Detlef Salzsieder (*Thomas*), Andreas Nehring (*Alfons*), Lutz Krüger (*Eduard*), Heinz Müller (*Konrad*), Uwe Thielisch (*Pinocchio as a boy*), Klaus-Dieter Thiedemann (*young boy*), Kerstin Berger (*young girl*), Gerhard Rosenlöcher (*trumpeter*), Ellen Prince (*voice of Pinocchio*).

Puppet film. Source: Carlo Collodi, *Le avventure di Pinocchio* (Rome, 1882). The film combines performances of actors and puppets in presenting the tale of Pinocchio, the little puppet carved by Papa Geppetto who magically comes to life. *Toymakers. Puppets. Mendacity. Children. Fairies. Metamorphosis. Circus. Sea rescue. Cats. Fox. Donkeys. Whales. Pinocchio.*

Note: Released in East Germany in 1967 as *Turlis Abenteuer.*

PINOCCHIO IN OUTER SPACE (United States/Belgium)
F6.3825

Swallow Ltd.–Belvision Productions. *Dist* Universal Pictures. 22 Dec **1965** [New York opening; c1 Jan 1964; LP35001]. Sd; col (Pathé Color). 35mm. 71 min.

Prod Norm Prescott, Fred Ladd. *Dir* Ray Goossens. *Screenplay* Fred Laderman. *Based on an idea by* Norm Prescott. *Songs* Robert Sharp, Arthur Korb. *Mus* F. Leonard, H. Dobbelaere, E. Schurmann. *Prologue* Douglas Aircraft Co.

Cast—Voices: Arnold Stang (*Nurtle the Turtle*), Peter Lazer (*Pinocchio*), Conrad Jameson, Cliff Owens, Mavis Mims, Kevin Kennedy, Minerva Pious, Jess Cain, Norman Rose.

Animated science fiction fantasy. Based on the character created by: Carlo Collodi, *Le aventure di Pinocchio* (Rome, 1882). Geppetto punishes Pinocchio for bad behavior by changing him back into a puppet. While he is watching television, Pinocchio learns of a contest to capture Astro, a spaceborne flying whale who swallows rockets. Nurtle the Turtle, from the planet of Twurtle Dum Twurtle Dee, accidentally lands his spaceship on Earth, and he invites Pinocchio to accompany him on a flight into outer space. On the trip the two discover a lost city and are attacked by giant crabs before they run into Astro, the menacing whale. Astro swallows Pinocchio and Nurtle, but they extricate themselves and lead the whale back to Earth. There Pinocchio, now a hero, is turned back into a boy by the Blue Fairy. The film features the following songs:

"The Little Toy Shop," "Doin' the Impossible," and "Goody Good Morning." *Contests. Space travel. Heroism. Puppets. Spaceships. Imaginary planets. Fairies. Space creatures. Pinocchio. Turtles. Whales. Crabs.*

Note: Released in Belgium as *Pinocchio dans le space.* Prerelease title: *Pinocchio's Adventure in Outer Space.*

PIONEER, GO HOME! see **FOLLOW THAT DREAM**

THE PIPER see **THE CLOWN AND THE KIDS**

IL PIRATA DELLO SPARVIERO NERO see **THE PIRATE OF THE BLACK HAWK**

THE PIRATE AND THE SLAVE GIRL (France/Italy) F6.3826
Romana Film–Fortunato Misiano–S. N. C. *Dist* Crest Film Distributors. 13 Dec **1961** [Los Angeles opening]. Sd; col (Eastmancolor). 35mm (Colorscope). 87 min.

Dir Piero Pierotti. *Story-Screenplay* Luciano Martino, Bruno Rasia, Piero Pierotti. *Photog* Augusto Tiezzi. *Art Dir* Bruno Rasia. *Film Ed* Iolanda Benvenuti. *Mus* Michele Cozzoli.

Cast: Lex Barker (*Dragut*), Chelo Alonso (*Miriam*), Massimo Serato (*Captain Diego*), Graziella Granata (*Bianca*), Daniele Vargas (*Gamal*), Luigi Tosi (*Francisco*), Bruno Corelli (*Selim*), Enzo Maggio (*Candela*), Michele Malaspina, Anna Arena, Franco Fantasia, Ubaldo Lay, Evelina Laudani, Nadia Brivio, Valeria Gramignani, Geneviève Audry, Rina Mascetti, Gianni Rizzo.

Adventure melodrama. During a raid, the 15th century pirate Dragut obtains some Venetian military documents and abducts Bianca, the daughter of the governor of Rhodes. Dragut adds the young woman to his collection of captive females destined for delivery to Princess Miriam, a slave dealer with whom he is in love. Desperate, the governor pardons Diego, an imprisoned adventurer, on the condition that he retrieve both Bianca and the documents. Diego joins Dragut's crew but is flogged for eyeing Bianca and then left to die in the desert. He nevertheless makes his way to Miriam's oasis to have his wounds treated. By the time Dragut arrives with Bianca and the documents (which he plans to sell to the highest enemy bidder), Miriam has fallen in love with Diego. Diego steals the documents and makes his escape, but he is captured and sentenced to death by Dragut and the vengeful Miriam. Catalan fishermen drive off Dragut, Miriam, and the pirates, however, and return Diego, Bianca, and the documents to the Venetian Republic. *Pirates. Adventurers. Slavers. Royalty. Theft. Abduction. Jealousy. Revenge. Rhodes. Venice. Documentation.*

Note: Produced in Italy in 1959 as *La scimitarra del Saraceno*; opened in Paris in Jul 1960 as *La vengeance du Sarrasin*; running time: 99 min.

LE PIRATE DE L'ÉPERVIER NOIR see **THE PIRATE OF THE BLACK HAWK**

THE PIRATE OF THE BLACK HAWK (France/Italy) F6.3827
Emmepi Cinematografica–C. F. P. C. *Dist* Filmgroup, Inc. 29 Nov **1961** [Boston opening]. Sd; col (Ferraniacolor, print by Technicolor). 35mm (SuperCinescope). 75 min.

Prod Giorgio Pescino, Carlo Pescino. *Dir* Sergio Grieco. *Screenplay* Sergio Grieco, Enzo Alfonsi, Mario Caiano, Guido Zurli. *Photog* Vincenzo Seratrice. *Art Dir* Saverio D'Eugenio. *Set Decor* Luigi D'Andria. *Film Ed* Enzo Alfonsi. *Mus* Roberto Nicolosi. *Sd* Franco Groppioni. *Asst Dir* Mario Caiano. *Cost* Giulia Mafai.

Cast: Mijanou Bardot (*Eleanor*), Gérard Landry (*Richard*), Andrea Aureli (*Manfred*), Ettore Manni (*Johnny*), Pina Bottin (*Eva*), Eloisa Cianni (*Stella*), Germano Longo (*Mark*), Andrea Miano.

Adventure melodrama. In the 16th century, the usurper Manfred seizes the Duchy of Monteforte and uses Saracen pirates to control the state. His tyrannical rule is opposed by Richard, the pirate of the Black Hawk, and a group of the murdered Duke of Monteforte's loyal subjects. Manfred captures the Duke's daughter Eleanor and her younger brother and then threatens to kill the boy unless Eleanor agrees to become his wife. Richard and his men pose as the ambassador of France and his delegation and infiltrate the wedding. During the battle that ensues, the women flee to the castle's dungeons. Knowing Eleanor is there, Manfred orders the rooms sealed and flooded. Richard and his men capture the fortress, however, and rescue the women, as Manfred is killed by an execution device planned for Richard. *Despots. Usurpers. Pirates. Nobility. Saracens. Kidnaping. Imposture. Marriage—Arranged. Weddings. Castles.*

Note: Released in Italy in 1958 as *Il pirata dello Sparviero Nero*; opened in Paris in Aug 1959 as *Le pirate de l'Epervier Noir*. Original running time: 95 min.

THE PIRATES OF BLOOD RIVER (Great Britain) F6.3828
Hammer Film Productions. *Dist* Columbia Pictures. Aug **1962** [c1 Aug 1962; LP22997]. Sd; col (Eastman Color). 35mm (Megascope). 87 min.

Prod Anthony Nelson Keys. *Exec Prod* Michael Carreras. *Dir-Writ* John Gilling. *Screenplay* John Hunter, John Gilling. *Story* Jimmy Sangster. *Dir*

Photog Arthur Grant. *Camera Op* Len Harris. *Art Dir* Don Mingaye. *Prod Dsgn* Bernard Robinson. *Supv Ed* James Needs. *Ed* Eric Boyd-Perkins. *Mus Comp* Gary Hughes. *Mus Dir* John Hollingsworth. *Sd Rec* Jock May. *Sd Ed* Alfred Cox. *Asst Dir* John Peverall. *Prod Mgr* Clifford Parkes. *Cont* Tilly Day. *Wardrobe Supv* Molly Arbuthnot. *Wardrobe Mistress* Rosemary Burrows. *Makeup* Roy Ashton. *Hairstyles* Frieda Steiger. *Sp Eff* Les Bowie. *Casting* Stuart Lyons. *Horsemaster & Master at Arms* Bob Simmons.

Cast: Kerwin Mathews (*Jonathon*), Glenn Corbett (*Henry*), Christopher Lee (*LaRoche*), Marla Landi (*Bess*), Oliver Reed (*Brocaire*), Andrew Keir (*Jason Standing*), Peter Arne (*Hench*), Michael Ripper (*Mac*), Jack Stewart, British (*Mason*), David Lodge (*Smith*), Marie Devereux (*Maggie*), Diane Aubrey (*Margaret Blackthorne*), Jerold Wells (*commandant*), Dennis Waterman (*Timothy*), Lorraine Clewes (*Martha Blackthorne*), John Roden (*2d settler*), Desmond Llewelyn (*Blackthorne*), Keith Pyott (*Silas*), Richard Bennett (*Seymour*), Michael Mulcaster (*Martin*), Denis Shaw (*Silver*), Michael Peake (*Kemp*), John Collin (*Lance*), Don Levy, actor (*Carlos*), John Bennett (*penal colony guard*), Ronald Blackman (*Pugh*).

Action drama. In the 18th century, Jonathon Standing, the heir of the leader of a Huguenot settlement on a Caribbean island, is unjustly accused of immoral conduct with a married woman who drowned herself. Imprisoned in a penal colony, he escapes and falls into the hands of a band of pirates. Their leader, LaRoche, believes the Huguenots have a treasure concealed on their island and forces Jonathon to lead him to the settlement. A battle ensues, and LaRoche methodically executes the captured Huguenots in the hope that they will reveal the whereabouts of the treasure; but some of the settlers, including Jonathon's half sister, Bess, and her fiancé, Henry, manage to escape into the jungle. When LaRoche discovers that a large statue of Jonathon's grandfather is made of solid gold, he and his crew drag it to the beach. While they are floating it on a raft, Jonathon, Henry, Bess, and other settlers ambush them, and the statue sinks. Jonathon kills LaRoche and the pirates and returns with Bess and Henry to the settlement. *Huguenots. Pirates. Heirs. Injustice. Prison escapes. Treasure. Gold. Sculptures. Penal colonies. Caribbean.*

Note: Released in Great Britain in Aug 1962; running time: 84 min.

PIRATES OF TORTUGA F6.3829
Clover Productions. *Dist* Twentieth Century–Fox Film Corp. 25 Oct **1961** [Los Angeles opening; c20 Sep 1961; LP20643]. Sd (Westrex); col (De Luxe). 35mm (CinemaScope). 97 min.

Prod Sam Katzman. *Dir* Robert D. Webb. *Screenplay* Melvin Levy, Jesse Lasky, Jr., Pat Silver. *Story* Melvin Levy. *Dir Photog* Ellis W. Carter. *Art Dir* Jack Martin Smith, George Van Marter. *Set Decor* Walter M. Scott, Lou Hafley. *Film Ed* Hugh S. Fowler. *Mus* Paul Sawtell, Bert Shefter. *Orch* Max Reese. *Choreog* Hal Belfer. *Sd* E. Clayton Ward, Frank W. Moran. *Asst Dir* Jack R. Berne. *Makeup* Ben Nye. *Hairstyles* Helen Turpin.

Cast: Ken Scott (*Bart Paxton*), Leticia Roman (*Meg Graham*), David King (*Pee Wee*), John Richardson (*Percy*), Rafer Johnson (*John Gammel*), Robert Stephens (*Henry Morgan*), Rachel Stephens (*Phoebe*), Stanley Adams (*Captain Montbars*), Edgar Barrier (*Sir Thomas Modyford*), James Forrest (*Reggie*), Patrick Sexton (*Randolph*), Arthur Gould-Porter (*Bonnett*), Hortense Petra (*Lola*), Malcolm Cassell (*Kipper*), Maxwell Reed (*Fielding*), Alan Caillou (*Ringose*), Kendrick Huxham (*Sir Francis Day*).

Adventure melodrama. In the 17th century privateer Bart Paxton is commissioned by Charles II of England to capture the villainous pirate Henry Morgan, who has been spiriting English cargoes to his hideout on the island of Tortuga, near Jamaica. Once at sea, Paxton is enraged to discover that Meg Graham, a Gypsy guttersnipe he once rescued from a lecherous butcher, has stowed away on his ship. The young woman charms three of Paxton's officers into teaching her how to act like a lady, and, when the vessel docks in Jamaica, she manages to pass herself off as a noblewoman, fooling even the governor himself. Paxton makes contact with Morgan, offers him a chest of gold in partnership, and lures him into revealing information about his pirate headquarters at Tortuga. When Paxton attacks, however, Morgan is waiting for him and the two men engage in single combat. But they are both knocked into unconsciousness and taken prisoners by the governor when Morgan's pirate arsenal explodes. At their trial, Morgan accuses Paxton of being a fellow pirate, but Meg wins an acquittal for Paxton by revealing her true identity and convincing the governor that Paxton is in the employ of King Charles II. *Pirates. Gypsies. Nobility. Stowaways. Impersonation. Tortuga. Jamaica. Charles II (England). Henry Morgan.*

LA PISCINA see **THE SWIMMING POOL**

LA PISCINE see **THE SWIMMING POOL**

A PISTOL FOR RINGO (Italy/Spain) F6.3830
P. C. M.–Balcázar P. C. *Dist* Embassy Pictures. 2 Nov **1966** [New York opening]. Sd; col (Technicolor). 35mm (Techniscope). 97 min.

Prod Luciano Ercoli, Alberto Pugliese. *Dir-Writ* Duccio Tessari. *Script* Duccio Tessari, Alfonso Balcázar. *Photog* Francisco Marín. *Art Dir* Juan Alberto Soler, Carlo Gentili. *Film Ed* Licia Quaglia. *Mus & Song:* "Angel Face" Ennio Morricone. *Sung by* Graf Maurizio. *Mus Cond* Bruno Nicolai. *Sd* Alberto Bartolomei. *Asst Dir* Manahen Velasco. *Prod Mgr* Antonio Negri. *Cost* Carlo Gentili.

Cast: Montgomery Wood (*Ringo*), Fernando Sancho (*Sancho*), Hally Hammond (*Ruby*), Nieves Navarro (*Dolores*), Antonio Casas (*Major Clyde*), George Martin, actor (*sheriff*), Paco Sanz, José Holupi, Nazzareno Zamperla, José Manuel Martín, Juan Cazalilla, Pajarito, Frank Oliveras.

Western melodrama. A group of Mexican bandits cross the Rio Grande and rob the bank at Quemado, brutally shooting down all opposition. During the getaway, the gang leader, Sancho, is wounded, and the outlaws take refuge at a small ranch operated by Major Clyde and his daughter Ruby. Sancho warns the local sheriff, who is Ruby's fiancé, that unless he and his gang are allowed to go free, a hostage will be killed each day at dawn and sunset. In desperation, the sheriff calls upon a famous professional killer named Ringo for help, and he accepts the offer in return for 30% of the stolen money. Ringo poses as a fellow bandit, contacts Sancho's gang, and offers to escort them to safety for 40% of the loot. After saving Ruby from being raped by one of the bandits, Ringo eliminates several members of the gang. Eventually his deception is discovered, but he manages to kill all but Sancho. After taking his share of the money, Ringo goes after Sancho, shoots him down, and then rides off alone. *Mexicans. Bandits. Ranchers. Hostages. Sheriffs. Hired killers. Bank robberies. Imposture. Rape. Ranches. Rio Grande.*

Note: Opened in Madrid in Dec 1965 as *Una pistola para Ringo;* in Rome in May 1965 as *Una pistola per Ringo.* Montgomery Wood is a pseudonym for Giuliano Gemma, Hally Hammond for Lorella De Luca, and George Martin for Jorge Martin.

UNA PISTOLA PARA RINGO *see* **A PISTOL FOR RINGO**

UNA PISTOLA PER RINGO *see* **A PISTOL FOR RINGO**

PISTOLERO *see* **THE LAST CHALLENGE**

LOS PISTOLEROS DE CASA GRANDE *see* **GUNFIGHTERS OF CASA GRANDE**

LE PISTONNÉ *see* **THE MAN WITH CONNECTIONS**

THE PIT *see* **FIVE MILLION YEARS TO EARTH**

THE PIT AND THE PENDULUM F6.3831

Alta Vista Productions. *Dist* American International Pictures. 23 Aug **1961** [New York opening; c5 Aug 1961; LP21143]. Sd; col (Pathé Color). 35mm (Panavision). 85 min. [Copyright length: 80 min.]

Pres by James H. Nicholson, Samuel Z. Arkoff. *Prod-Dir* Roger Corman. *Exec Prod* James H. Nicholson, Samuel Z. Arkoff. *Screenplay* Richard Matheson. *Dir Photog* Floyd Crosby. *Art Dir* Daniel Haller. *Set Decor* Harry Reif. *Prod Dsgn* Daniel Haller. *Film Ed* Anthony Carras. *Mus* Les Baxter. *Mus Coörd* Al Simms. *Sd Rec* Roy Meadows. *Sd Ed* Kay Rose. *Mus Ed* Eve Newman. *Asst Dir* Jack Bohrer, Lou Place. *Prod Mgr* Bartlett A. Carré. *Unit Mgr* Robert Agnew. *Prod Asst* Jack Cash. *Script Supv* Betty Crosby. *Wardrobe* Marjorie Corso. *Makeup* Ted Coodley. *Sp Eff* Pat Dinga. *Scenic Eff* Tom Matsumoto. *Photog Eff* Butler-Glouner Inc., Ray Mercer. *Prop* Richard M. Rubin. *Constr Coörd* Ross Hahn.

Cast: Vincent Price (*Nicholas Medina*), John Kerr (*Francis Barnard*), Barbara Steele (*Elizabeth Barnard Medina*), Luana Anders (*Catherine Medina*), Antony Carbone (*Dr. Charles Leon*), Patrick Westwood (*Maximillian*), Lynn Bernay (*Maria*), Larry Turner (*Nicholas as a child*), Mary Menzies (*Isabella*), Charles Victor (*Bartolome*).

Horror film. Source: Edgar Allan Poe, "The Pit and the Pendulum," in *The Gift* (Philadelphia, 1843). In 16th-century Spain Francis Bernard journeys to the foreboding castle of Nicholas Medina, the husband of Francis' recently deceased sister, Elizabeth. Francis is told that his sister, although very much in love with Nicholas, had become increasingly depressed by the gloomy atmosphere of the castle and had spent most of her time in the dungeons built by Nicholas' father during the Inquisition. One night, after locking herself inside an iron box in the torture chamber, she died of fright. The explanation fails to satisfy Francis, and he decides to remain for a few days. Gradually it becomes apparent that Nicholas has become obsessed with the thought that he may have buried his wife alive, a fate that befell his adulterous mother. One night Nicholas hears a woman's voice calling his name, and he follows it to the burial room where Elizabeth, very much alive, rises from her coffin. She is joined by Dr. Leon, Nicholas' closest friend, and, as Nicholas' mind snaps, the two lovers gloat over their plot to drive him mad and inherit his wealth. The crazed Nicholas suddenly assumes his father's identity, battles with Dr. Leon, who falls to his death in the pendulum pit, and locks his unfaithful wife in the

iron box. Francis enters the chamber and is seized by the insane Nicholas and lashed to a table under a swinging, razor-sharp pendulum. But before the blade reaches him he is rescued by Nicholas' sister, Catherine, and the butler, Maximillian. In the struggle Nicholas meets the same fate as Dr. Leon, when he falls into the pit. Catherine decides to seal up the torture chamber forever—unaware that imprisoned in the iron box is the terror-stricken Elizabeth. *Widowers. Brother-sister relationship. Death. Obsession. Torture. Infidelity. Insanity. Personal identity. Castles. Spain.*

PIT STOP F6.3832

Jack Hill Productions. *Dist* Goldstone Film Enterprises, Crown International Pictures. 14 May **1969** [San Francisco opening]. Sd; b&w. 35mm. 92 min. *MPAA rating* R.

Pres by Distributors International. *Prod* Lee Strosnider. *Exec Prod* Roger Corman. *Dir-Writ* Jack Hill. *Photog* Austin McKinney. *Film Ed* Jack Hill. *Sd* Lee Strosnider. *Prod Mgr* Frank Zuniga.

Cast: Brian Donlevy (*Grant Willard*), Richard Davalos (*Rick Bowman*), Ellen McRae (*Ellen McLeod*), Sid Haig (*Hawk Sidney*), Beverly Washburn (*Jolene*), George Washburn (*Ed McLeod*).

Action melodrama. Grant Willard, head of a stock-car racing organization, sponsors ambitious driver Rick Bowman in competition against local track hero Hawk Sidney. Rick causes Hawk to crash, wins the race, then leaves with Hawk's ex-girl friend Jolene. Hawk follows them, forces them off the road, terrorizes Jolene, and destroys Rick's car. Entering the Phoenix Internationals, Rick works closely with Willard's star Ed McLeod, while having an affair with Ed's wife, Ellen. Rick's desire for personal glory emerges when the race begins; he wins after forcing McLeod out of the race in a spectacular crash. At the hospital, Ellen informs Rick of her husband's death. Willard offers Rick another opportunity to become a racing star. *Stock car drivers. Automobile racing. Ambition. Infidelity. Phoenix (Arizona).*

Note: Location scenes filmed in and around Los Angeles. Filmed in 1967; working title: *The Winner.*

IL PIÙ GRANDE COLPO DEL SECOLO *see* **ACTION MAN**

THE PIZZA TRIANGLE (Italy/Spain) F6.3833

Dean Film–Juppiter Generale Cinematografica–Midega Film. *Dist* Warner Bros. Pictures. 1 Nov **1970** [New York opening]. Sd; col (Technicolor). 35mm (Panavision). 99 min. *MPAA rating* R.

Prod Pio Angeletti, Adriano De Micheli. *Dir* Ettore Scola. *Screenplay* Ettore Scola, Age & Scarpelli. *Story* Age & Scarpelli. *Dir Photog* Carlo Di Palma. *Art Dir* Luciano Ricceri. *Film Ed* Alberto Gallitti. *Mus* Armando Trovajoli. *Mus Dir* Gianfranco Plenizio. *Sd* Vittorio Massi. *Asst Dir* Giorgio Scotton, Adriano Incrocci. *Prod Mgr* Mario D'Alessio. *Cost* Ezio Altieri.

Cast: Marcello Mastroianni (*Oreste*), Monica Vitti (*Adelaide*), Giancarlo Giannini (*Nello*), Manuel Zarzo (*Uto*), Marisa Merlini (*Silvana*), Hercules Cortes (*Ambleto Di Meo*), Fernando Sanchez Polack (*district head of Communist Party*), Gioia Desideri (*Adelaide's friend*), Juan Diego (*Antonia's son*), Bruno Scipioni (*pizza maker*), Josefina Serratosa (*Antonia*), Corrado Gaipa (*president of tribunal*), Giuseppe Maffioli (*lawyer*), Paola Natale, Brizio Montinaro.

Romantic comedy. Oreste, a middle-aged bricklayer, meets young Adelaide, a flower vendor, after a Communist rally. Adelaide convinces Oreste that she is deeply in love with him, and Oreste makes her his wife for her. They live happily together until Oreste introduces to Adelaide his friend Nello, a baker in a restaurant. Adelaide takes up with the gallant pizza-maker, eventually leaving Oreste when he finds out. Oreste starts a street brawl over the matter and accidentally causes Adelaide to be hospitalized. Uncertain of whom she loves, Adelaide visits a psychiatrist, but, having found no solution to her problem, she attempts suicide. Upon her sister's advice, Adelaide moves in with Ambleto, a good-natured butcher, but she leaves him when she is told of Nello's attempted suicide, and, rushing to Nello's bedside, she promises to marry him. Meanwhile Oreste has lost his job and become a bum. Adelaide sees him as she and Nello are on their way to church. She wavers; another fight breaks out, and by accident Adelaide is fatally wounded by Oreste with a pair of flower shears. *Flower vendors. Construction workers. Bakers. Psychiatrists. Sisters. Butchers. Middle age. Desertion. Communism. Infidelity. Jealousy. Suicide. Manslaughter. Hospitals. Weddings.*

Note: Produced in 1970. Italian title: *Dramma della gelosia—tutti i particolari in cronaca.* Also known as *A Drama of Jealousy (and Other Things).*

A PLACE CALLED GLORY (Spain/West Germany) F6.3834

CCC–Filmkunst–Midega Film. *Dist* Embassy Pictures. 10 Aug **1966** [New York opening]. Sd; col (Pathé Color). 35mm (Techniscope). 92 min.

Prod Bruce Balaban, Danilo Sabatini. *Exec Prod* Fred S. Wallach, Michael Echarry. *Dir* Sheldon Reynolds. *2d Unit Dir* Enrique Bergier. *Screenplay* Edward Di Lorenzo, Jerold Hayden Boyd, Fernando Lamas. *Orig Story* Jerold Hayden Boyd. *Photog* Federico G. Larraya. *Art Dir* Enrique Alarcón, Heinrich

Weidemann. *Film Ed* Roberto Cinquini, Teresa Alcocer. *Mus* Angel Arteaga. *Mus Arr & Cond* Bruno Nicolai. *Sd* Renato Cadueri. *Asst Dir* Enrique Bergier. *Prod Supv* Peter Hahne. *Prod Mgr* Andrés Velasco. *Cost* Itala Scandariato.

Cast: Lex Barker *(Brenner)*, Pierre Brice *(Reece)*, Marianne Koch *(Jade Grande)*, Jorge Rigaud *(Seth Grande)*, Gérard Tichy *(Jack Vallone)*, Angel Del Pozo *(Josh)*, Santiago Ontañón *(mayor of Glory)*, Hans Nielsen *(judge of Glory)*, Wolfgang Lukschy *(barman)*, Victor Israel *(clerk)*, Antonio Molino Rojo, Aldo Sambrell, Carlos Casaravilla, Roberto Martín.

Western melodrama. Every year the town of Glory celebrates its founding with a gunfight between the two fastest gunmen in the West. The participants are to be Deakes and Brenner, but plans change when a drifter named Reece announces that he has killed Deakes. He agrees to take Deakes' place in the fight, but the men behind the celebration decide to keep the substitution a secret. With the fight some time away, Reece goes to Powder City where, without knowing each other's identity, he and Brenner become friends and decide to unite to rid Glory of crime. They return to Glory together and remain unaware that they are opponents until they meet in the street for the duel. At first they are unwilling to fight, but the townspeople force them. They stage the gunfight without killing each other, however, and also manage to eliminate the men behind the bloody custom. *Gunfighters. Drifters. Smalltown life. Personal identity. Contests. Duels.*

Note: Opened in Munich in Aug 1965 as *Die Hölle von Manitoba*; in Madrid in May 1966 as *Un lugar llamado "Glory"*. Sheldon Reynolds is also known as Ralph Gideon.

A PLACE FOR LOVERS (France/Italy)   F6.3835
C. C. Champion–Les Films Concordia. *Dist* Metro-Goldwyn-Mayer, Inc. 22 Aug 1969 [New York opening; c31 Dec 1968; LP36698]. Sd; col (Technicolor). 35mm. 88 min. *MPAA rating* R.

A Carlo Ponti Production. *Prod* Carlo Ponti, Arthur Cohn. *Dir* Vittorio De Sica. *Screenplay (see note)* Julian Halevy, Peter Baldwin, Ennio De Concini, Tonino Guerra, Cesare Zavattini, Vittorio De Sica. *Dir Photog* Pasquale De Santis. *Art Dir* Piero Poletto. *Film Ed* Adriana Novelli. *Mus Comp* Manuel De Sica. *Mus Dir* Zeno Vukelich. *Song:* "A Place for Lovers" Norman Gimbel, Manuel De Sica. *Sung by* Ella Fitzgerald. *Sd* Carlo Palmieri, Renato Cadueri. *Rec* International Recording. *1st & 2d Asst Dir* Peter Baldwin, Luisa Alessandro. *Prod Supv* Ione Tuzi. *Script Girl* Elvira D'Amico. *Cost Dsgn* Enrico Sabbatini. *Cost Dsgn for Miss Dunaway* Theadora Van Runkle. *Cost Executed by* Forquet's House. *Makeup for Miss Dunaway* Mario Van Riel. *Makeup for Mr. Mastroianni* Giuseppe Banchelli. *Hairstyles for Miss Dunaway Created by* Sydney Guilaroff. *Hairdresser* Lina Cassini. *Dial Coach* Margaret Anderson.

Cast: Faye Dunaway *(Julia)*, Marcello Mastroianni *(Valerio)*, Caroline Mortimer *(Maggie)*, Karin Engh *(Griselda)*, Esmeralda Ruspoli, Enrico Simonetti, Mirella Pamphili.

Romantic drama. Source: Brunello Rondi and Renaldo Cabieri, *Amanti* (a play; production undetermined). Julia, an American divorcée and fashion designer, moves into a sumptuously furnished villa near Venice lent her by a friend. She turns on the television set and watches an interview with an Italian engineer. Recognizing the man as Valerio, a stranger who once stopped her at an airport, gently declared his infatuation, and then gave her his calling card, Julia impulsively telephones him and asks him to visit her at the villa. Elated by the invitation, Valerio drives all night, and before the morning is over he and Julia have become lovers. Other guests arrive at the villa that night and join in such hedonistic pleasures as a slide show of erotic art and an orgy. Valerio becomes disgusted at Julia's compliance and drives off. The next day Julia goes to an autodrome where Valerio is testing a new racing car accident-prevention device and persuades him to take her to the Italian Alps. Resuming their affair in the intimacy of an Alpine chalet, the couple are idyllically happy, although Julia reveals little about herself and shows little interest in Valerio's future plans. Eventually, Julia is traced to the chalet by Maggie, her friend and business associate, who informs Valerio that Julia is terminally ill and should be hospitalized so that morphine can ease the pain that will come with the final throes of her illness. Julia runs away, intent on suicide, but Valerio follows her to the heights of a nearby mountain and commits an act of faith by asking her to drive their jeep back to the chalet. Though she speeds off at a furious pace that could kill them both, she steers to avoid an impending crash and then asks Valerio to take the wheel. The split-second decision brings Julia the strength to finally accept her illness as well as the love offered to her by Valerio. *Americans in foreign countries. Couturiers. Engineers. Incurable illness. Suicide. Hedonism. Orgies. Inventions. Alps. Venice.*

Note: Released in Italy in 1968 as *Amanti*; opened in Paris in Sep 1969 as *Le temps des amants*. Italian sources credit Vittorio De Sica as an additional screenplay writer.

PLACER SANGRIENTO *see* **THE DEADLY ORGAN**

THE PLAGUE OF THE ZOMBIES (Great Britain)   F6.3836
Seven Arts Productions–Hammer Film Productions. *Dist* Twentieth Century-Fox Film Corp. 12 Jan **1966** [Detroit opening; c12 Jan 1966; LP32698]. Sd (RCA); col (DeLuxe). 35mm. 90 min.

Prod Anthony Nelson Keys. *Exec Prod* Anthony Hinds. *Dir* John Gilling. *Screenplay* Peter Bryan, John Elder. *Dir Photog* Arthur Grant. *Camera Op* Moray Grant. *Art Dir* Don Mingaye. *Prod Dsgn* Bernard Robinson. *Supv Ed* James Needs. *Ed* Chris Barnes. *Mus Comp* James Bernard. *Mus Supv* Philip Martell. *Sd Rec* Ken Rawkins. *Sd Ed* Roy Baker. *Asst Dir* Bert Batt, Martyn Green. *Prod Mgr* George Fowler. *Cont* Lorna Selwyn. *Wardrobe* Rosemary Burrows. *Makeup* Roy Ashton. *Hairstylist* Frieda Steiger. *Sp Eff* Bowie Films.

Cast: Andre Morell *(Sir James Forbes)*, Diane Clare *(Sylvia)*, Brook Williams *(Dr. Peter Tompson)*, Jacqueline Pearce *(Alice)*, John Carson *(Clive Hamilton)*, Alexander Davion *(Denver)*, Michael Ripper *(Sergeant Swift)*, Marcus Hammond *(Martinus)*, Dennis Chinnery *(Constable Christian)*, Louis Mahoney *(servant)*, Roy Royston *(vicar)*, Ben Aris *(John Martinus)*, Tim Condron, Bernard Egan, Norman Mann, Francis Willey *(The Young Bloods)*, Jerry Verno *(landlord)*, Jolyan Booth *(coachman)*.

Horror film. A strange plague strikes a Cornish village, and local doctor Peter Tompson enlists the aid of Sir James Forbes, his former professor, who comes to the town with his daughter, Sylvia. When the two doctors open the graves of the victims to perform autopsies, they find the coffins empty. The walking corpses are seen near an abandoned mine on the estate of Clive Hamilton, the local squire who learned voodoo in Haiti and created the zombies to work the mine. Peter's wife is killed; and Sylvia, under Hamilton's evil spell, goes to the mine where she is captured by Hamilton and his zombies. Peter and Sir James arrive in time to save Sylvia from being sacrificed and to start a fire in which Hamilton and all his zombies are destroyed. *Physicians. Professors. Zombies. Plague. Filial relations. Disinterment. Voodoo. Human sacrifice. Cemeteries. Mines. Cornwall (England). Fires.*

Note: Opened in London in Jan 1966. John Elder is a pseudonym for Anthony Hinds.

THE PLAINSMAN   F6.3837
Universal Pictures. Sep **1966** [c1 Oct 1966; LP35476]. Sd (Westrex); col (Eastman Color by Pathé). 35mm. 92 min.

Prod Richard E. Lyons. *Assoc Prod* Jack Leewood. *Dir* David Lowell Rich. *Writ* Michael Blankfort. *Dir Photog* Bud Thackery. *Col Coörd* Robert Brower. *Art Dir* Alexander Golitzen, William D. DeCinces. *Set Decor* John McCarthy, Ralph Sylos. *Film Ed* Danny B. Landres, Bud Small. *Mus Score* Johnny Williams. *Mus Supv* Stanley Wilson. *Sd* Waldon O. Watson, David H. Moriarty. *Asst Dir* Edward K. Dodds. *Cost Dsgn* Helen Colvig. *Cost Supv* Peter Saldutti. *Makeup* Bud Westmore. *Hairstylist* Larry Germain.

Cast: Don Murray *(Wild Bill Hickok)*, Guy Stockwell *(Buffalo Bill Cody)*, Abby Dalton *(Calamity Jane)*, Bradford Dillman *(Lieutenant Stiles)*, Henry Silva *(Crazy Knife)*, Simon Oakland *(Black Kettle)*, Leslie Nielsen *(Col. George A. Custer)*, Edward Binns *(Lattimer)*, Michael Evans *(Estrick)*, Percy Rodriguez *(Brother John)*, Terry Wilson *(Sergeant Womack)*, Walter Burke *(Abe Ireland)*, Emily Banks *(Louisa Cody)*.

Western melodrama. Source: Waldemar Young, Harold Lamb and Lynn Riggs, screenplay for the film *The Plainsman*, 1937. Wild Bill Hickok is ambushed by a band of Cheyenne Indians headed by Crazy Knife. Chief Black Kettle intercedes, and Wild Bill is allowed to leave, but without his horse and boots. After hitching a ride on a stage driven by Calamity Jane, he reports to Army Lieutenant Stiles that the Indians now have repeater rifles. The inexperienced officer, however, treats the intelligence with indifference. Later, at the local saloon, Wild Bill meets his old friend Buffalo Bill Cody and Cody's new bride, Louisa. After they have parted, Wild Bill catches Lattimer, a stranger, cheating at poker and forces him to leave. Soon after, Wild Bill and Cody are captured by Indians armed with repeater rifles, and Calamity is taken prisoner by Crazy Knife. During his captivity Wild Bill learns that the repeater rifles are being supplied by Lattimer. Consequently, when Calamity and Wild Bill are rescued, Lattimer is arrested and delivered to the sheriff. As Col. George Custer takes over the Army post, Calamity declares her undying love for Wild Bill. *Cheyenne Indians. Soldiers. Newlyweds. Friendship. Cheating. Firearms. Poker. James Butler Hickok. Black Kettle. Martha Jane Burke. William Frederick Cody. George Armstrong Custer.*

Note: Previously filmed by Cecil B. De Mille and released through Paramount Pictures in 1937.

THE PLAINSMAN *see* **THE RAIDERS**

PLANET OF BLOOD *see* **PLANET OF THE VAMPIRES**

PLANET OF BLOOD *see* **QUEEN OF BLOOD**

PLANET OF THE APES   F6.3838

APJAC Productions. *Dist* Twentieth Century-Fox Film Corp. 8 Feb **1968** [New York opening; c30 Dec 1967; LP35407]. Sd (Westrex); col (De Luxe). 35mm (Panavision). 112 min.

An Arthur P. Jacobs Production. *Prod* Arthur P. Jacobs. *Assoc Prod* Mort Abrahams. *Dir* Franklin J. Schaffner. *Screenplay* Michael Wilson, Rod Serling. *Dir Photog* Leon Shamroy. *Art Dir* Jack Martin Smith, William Creber. *Set Decor* Walter M. Scott, Norman Rockett. *Film Ed* Hugh S. Fowler. *Mus* Jerry Goldsmith. *Orch* Arthur Morton. *Sd* Herman Lewis, David Dockendorf. *Asst Dir* William Kissel. *Unit Prod Mgr* William Eckhardt. *Cost Dsgn* Morton Haack. *Sp Makeup Dsgn* John Chambers. *Makeup* Ben Nye, Dan Striepeke. *Hairstyling* Edith Lindon. *Sp Photog Eff* L. B. Abbott, Art Cruickshank, Emil Kosa, Jr.

Cast: Charlton Heston (*George Taylor*), Roddy McDowall (*Cornelius*), Kim Hunter (*Dr. Zira*), Maurice Evans (*Dr. Zaius*), James Whitmore (*president of the assembly*), James Daly (*Honorious*), Linda Harrison (*Nova*), Robert Gunner (*Landon*), Lou Wagner (*Lucius*), Woodrow Parfrey (*Maximus*), Jeff Burton (*Dodge*), Buck Kartalian (*Julius*), Norman Burton (*hunt leader*), Wright King (*Dr. Galen*), Paul Lambert (*minister*), Dianne Stanley (*female astronaut*).

Science fiction melodrama. Source: Pierre Boulle, *La planète des singes* (Paris, 1963). While traveling some 2,000 years through time and space, four astronauts crashland on an unknown planet. After finding the female of their quartet dead, the three male survivors cross the barren wasteland of the planet until they encounter a tribe of mute sub-humans living amidst lush vegetation. They are set upon and captured by uniformed gorillas on horseback. One of the astronauts, Dodge, is killed and his body is placed in the simian museum of natural history; another, Landon, is subjected to a frontal lobotomy; the third, George Taylor, who has been rendered speechless by a throat wound, is placed in a hospital cage. Taylor, although aware that he is a prisoner in a society where humans are treated as beasts, persuades the sympathetic chimpanzees, Dr. Zira and her archeologist fiancé Cornelius, that he can speak, read, and write. Intrigued by the possibility that man may be the missing link in the evolution of the ape, Dr. Zira and Cornelius spare Taylor from experimental vivisection, intending to mate him with a female captive, Nova. Taylor eventually regains his power of speech and is able to communicate with the apes. Chief of state Dr. Zaius, an orangutan, demands that he be silenced by a lobotomy. Deeply resentful of this infringement upon their freedom of thought, Dr. Zira, Cornelius, and their young assistant Lucius help Taylor and Nova escape to the Forbidden Zone, a vast territory where earlier Cornelius had found human artifacts. When they are pursued by the ape militia, Taylor seizes Dr. Zaius and threatens to kill him unless he orders the gorillas to retreat. Zaius, after confessing that he has long been aware of man's reputation as "the harbinger of death," permits Taylor and Nova to continue into the Forbidden Zone, provided they never return with evidence of their superior human culture. Some distance down the coastline, Taylor discovers the half-buried remnants of the Statue of Liberty and realizes the destiny of man's civilization. *Astronauts. Scientists. Archeologists. Mutes. Space exploration. Time travel. Evolution. Lobotomy. Vivisection. Statue of Liberty. The Future. Apes. Chimpanzees.*

Note: Location scenes filmed in Utah and Arizona. The first in a series of films based on Boulle's novel.

PLANET OF THE VAMPIRES (United States/Italy/Spain)   F6.3839

Castilla Cinematográfica Cooperativa–Italian International Film–American International Productions. *Dist* American International Pictures. Oct **1965** [c27 Oct 1965; LP32040]. Sd; col (Pathé). 35mm (Colorscope). 86 min.

Prod Fulvio Lucisano. *Assoc Prod* Salvatore Billitteri. *Dir* Mario Bava. *Screenplay* Alberto Bevilacqua, Callisto Cosulich, Mario Bava, Antonio Román, Rafael J. Salvia. *Story English Vers* Ib Melchior. *English Screenplay* Ib Melchior, Louis M. Heyward. *Dir Photog* Antonio Rinaldi. *Art Dir* Giorgio Giovannini. *Film Ed* Antonio Gimeno. *Mus* Gino Marinuzzi, Jr., Antonio Pérez Olea. *Sd* Mario Ronchetti. *Prod Mgr* Mario Silvestri. *Cost* Gabriele Mayer.

Cast: Barry Sullivan (*Capt. Mark Markary*), Norma Bengell (*Sanya*), Angel Aranda (*Wess*), Evi Marandi (*Tiona*), Fernando Villena (*Karan*), Stelio Candelli (*Mud*), Massimo Righi (*Nordeg*), Mario Morales (*Eldon*), Franco Andrei (*Garr*), Ivan Rassimov (*Kell/Derry*), Rico Boido (*Keir/Key*), Alberto Cevenini (*Wan/Toby*).

Science fiction melodrama. Source: Renato Pestriniero, "One Night of 21 Hours," in *Interplanet No. 3* (trans. of "Una notte di 21 ore"; publication undetermined). Spaceships *Argos* and *Galliot* carry crews of explorer-scientists to Aura, a distant planet which transmits radio signals and has an oxygen atmosphere. As Capt. Mark Markary of the *Argos* lands his ship, the crew members go berserk and attack one another. Later, they find the wreckage of the *Galliot* with the mutilated bodies of its crew, who were apparently killed fighting among themselves. The crew of the *Argos* find no signs of life on Aura,

but Professor Karan speculates that the planet is inhabited by invisible minds seeking to control the wills of the visitors. That night, the bodies of the *Galliot*'s crew are seen to move through the planet's eerie mists; and one by one Mark's crew are killed or disappear. Mark captures one of the missing crew members and discovers that his body is inhabited by a being from Aura, whose survivors hope to leave their dying planet in the visitors' spaceships. The survivors of the *Argos* foil the Aurans' attempt to disable their craft, and Mark escapes with his assistant, Sanya, and second-in-command, Wess. However, he perceives that his companions have been vampirized by the Aurans, who now prepare to land on an unknown planet—Earth. [Sources disagree on the precise ending of the film; according to some sources, Mark and Sanya escape unharmed.] *Spaceship crews. Scientists. Vampires. Space exploration. Disembodiment. Thought control. Spaceships. Imaginary planets.*

Note: Opened in Rome in Oct 1965 as *Terrore nello spazio*; running time: ca100 min.; in Madrid in Apr 1966 as *Terror en el espacio*; running time: 88 min. Also known as *Planet of Blood*. United States co-production status unconfirmed.

PLANTS FROM THE DUNES (Japan)   F6.3840

Toho Co. 25 Mar **1966** [Los Angeles opening]. Sd; col? 35mm. [Feature film, length unknown.]

Cast: Noboru Nakaya, Kazuko Ineno, Mieko Nishio, Yukiko Shimazaki. No information about the nature of this film has been found.

Note: Original title and release undetermined.

THE PLASTIC DOME OF NORMA JEAN   F6.3841

Juleen Compton. 10 Mar **1970** [New York showing]. Sd; b&w. 35mm. 82 min.

Prod-Dir-Writ Juleen Compton. *Co-prod* Stuart Murphy. *Dir Photog* Roger Barlow. *Asst Camera* Stuart Day. *Set Decor* Sterling Merritt. *Film Ed* Stuart Murphy. *Asst Ed* Bud Hamilton. *Mus Comp & Cond* Michel Legrand. *Songs Sung by* The Dupres, The Vocals. *Orig Sd* Leroy Robbins. *Asst Sd* Sam Kopetsky. *Sd Ed* Claud Plugano. *Sd Mix* Paul Boistelle. *Location Coörd* Mark Trimble. *Head Electrn* Chris Meadows. *Key Grip* Hal Meadows. *Casting Dir* Terry Fay.

Cast: Robert Gentry (*Vance*), Sharon Henesy (*Norma Jean*), Marco St. John (*BoBo*), Samuel Waterston (*Andy*), Skip Hinnant (*Francis*), Arthur Hughes (*Chris*), Henry Oliver (*mayor*), Jack Murray, actor (*announcer*), Jerry Serempa (*spelunker*), Emma Coody (*Mrs. Meekas*), Gilbert Elmore (*Chance Lawson*), Stanley Tiffany (*Johnny*), Carl Wallace (*sheriff*), George Jackson (*Elmer*), Robert Kreiger (*Finch*).

Drama. Norma Jean, an innocent 15-year-old living in the Ozarks, possesses natural powers of clairvoyance. She and her brother Vance [her boyfriend according to another source] meet a rock and roll band leader, BoBo, who is attempting to establish an entertainment center in the Plastic Dome, a large circus-tent structure. Faced with disappointing crowds, BoBo persuades Norma Jean to allow him to exploit her visionary abilities. Box office receipts begin to soar, but Norma Jean is nearly driven insane in the process. After her prediction of a suicide materializes, she suffers a breakdown and is hidden by Vance, who resists the temptation to cash in on the enterprise. In another incident, a spelunker becomes trapped in a nearby cave, attracting a reporter and would-be rescuers. Meanwhile, the public clamors for Norma Jean's return. The local mayor, anxious to retain the business revenue generated by Norma Jean's presence, and BoBo, who has acquired wealth and fame as a result of the promotion, set out to bring her back but accidentally shoot her dead. *Clairvoyants. Entrepreneurs. Band leaders. Musicians. Mayors. Spelunkers. Brother-sister relationship. Rock and roll. Murder. Insanity. Bands. Ozarks.*

Note: Filmed in the Ozarks ca1966.

PLAY DIRTY (Great Britain)   F6.3842

Lowndes Productions. *Dist* United Artists. 15 Jan **1969** [Washington, D. C., opening; c2 Jan 1969; LF32]. Sd; col (Technicolor). 35mm (Panavision). 117 min. *MPAA rating* M.

Prod Harry Saltzman. *Exec Prod–Dir* Andre De Toth. *Screenplay* Lotte Colin, Melvyn Bragg. *Orig Story* George Marton. *Photog* Edward Scaife. *Art Dir* Tom Morahan. *Film Ed* Alan Osbiston, Jack Slade. *Mus* Michel Legrand. *Sd* Paddy Cunningham. *Asst Dir* Roger Good. *Prod Mgr* Eva Monley. *Sp Eff* Kit West.

Cast: Michael Caine (*Captain Douglas*), Nigel Davenport (*Cyril Leech*), Nigel Green (*Colonel Masters*), Harry Andrews (*Brigadier Blore*), Aly Ben Ayed (*Sadok*), Vivian Pickles (*German nurse*), Bernard Archard (*Colonel Homerton*), Daniel Pilon (*Captain Attwood*), Takis Emmanouel (*Kostas Manou*), Enrique Avila (*Kafkarides*), Scott Miller (*Boudesh*), Mohamed Kouka (*Assine*), Mohsen Ben Abdullah (*Hassan*), Tony Stamboulieh (*barman in Arab bar*), Patrick Jordan (*Major Watkins*), Mike Stevens (*Captain Johnson*), Martin Burland ("*dead*" *officer*), Bridget Espeet (*Ann, A.T.S. officer*), George McKeenan (*corporal at Quayside*), Rafael Albaicin (*chief Arab at oasis*), Jose

Halufi *(Arab at oasis)*, Jeremy Child, Dennis Brennan.

War drama. During the North African campaign of World War II, Douglas, an inexperienced British Army captain, is assigned to lead a band of mercenaries into the desert to dispose of a vital German oil depot 650 miles behind Rommel's front lines. From the moment Douglas assumes command, he is treated with open hostility by the men, all of whom are ex-convicts, and especially by their unofficial leader, Cyril Leech. What Douglas and the mercenaries do not know is that the Commander of Special Forces, Brigadier Blore, has sent a regular army unit on the same mission in case the mercenaries should be annihilated. Ironically, the second unit is ambushed and slaughtered as Douglas and his men press forward. After capturing and attempting to rape a German nurse, the mercenaries reach their destination but discover that it is only a decoy. While Douglas and Leech argue over whether or not to continue their search for the real depot, word arrives at command headquarters that Montgomery has broken through the German lines. Brigadier Blore, realizing that the British now need the depot fuel for themselves and unable to stop the mercenaries, secretly gives their location to the Germans through a double agent. Despite this betrayal, the mercenaries, wearing German uniforms, succeed in blowing up their objective. But the waiting Germans shoot them down one by one, and only Douglas and Leech survive. Carrying a white rag on a stick and still wearing enemy uniforms, the two men approach the British forces and are shot down. *Mercenaries. Ex-convicts. Germans. Nurses. Commandos. Rape. Disguise. Sabotage. Perfidy. World War II. North Africa. Great Britain—Army. Germany—Army.*

Note: Location scenes filmed in Almería, Spain. Opened in London in Dec 1968. Working title: *Written on the Sand.*

PLAY IT COOL (Great Britain)   **F6.3843**

Independent Artists–Coronado Productions–Lynx Films. *Dist* Allied Artists. May **1963** [New York opening: 17 Jul; c22 Mar 1963; LP24142]. Sd; b&w. 35mm. 74 min. [Copyright length: 82 min.]

A Julian Wintle–Leslie Parkyn Production. *Prod* David Deutsch. *Assoc Prod* Denis Holt. *Exec Prod* Julian Wintle. *Dir* Michael Winner. *Orig Screenplay* Jack Henry. *Dir Photog* Reginald Wyer. *Camera Op* Gerry Turpin. *Focus Op* Gerry Anstiss. *Art Dir* Lionel Couch. *Set Dresser* Peter Russell. *Draughtsman* Ted Ambrose. *Film Ed* Tristam Cones. *1st Asst Ed* John Beaton. *2d Asst Ed* Michael Clifford. *Mus Comp & Cond* Norrie Paramor. *Mus Assoc* Harold Shampan. *Songs:* "Who Can Say," "It's Gonna Take Magic," "Take It Easy," "Twist," "Cry My Heart Out," "But I Don't Care," "Play It Cool" Norrie Paramor, Richard B. Rowe, Bernard Jewry, Norman Newell, Bob Barratt, Ronald Fraser, Larry Parnes. *Song:* "Who Can Say" *sung by* Danny Williams. *Song:* "It's Gonna Take Magic" *sung by* Shane Fenton and the Fentones. *Song:* "Take It Easy" *sung by* Jimmy Crawford. *Song:* "Twist" *perf by* Lionel Blair and His Dancers. *Songs:* "Cry My Heart Out," "But I Don't Care" *sung by* Helen Shapiro. *Song:* "Play It Cool" *sung by* Billy Fury. *Sd Ed* Allan Morrison. *Sd Rec* Dudley Messenger, Gordon K. McCallum. *Sd Camera Op* Ted Karnon. *Boom Op* J. W. N. Daniel. *Asst Boom Op* Charles McFadden. *1st, 2d & 3d Asst Dir* Eric Rattray, Christopher Dryhurst, Ken Softley. *Unit Mgr* Donald Toms. *Cont* Splinters Deason. *Prod Sec* Maureen Hensby. *Producer's Sec* Josephine Baker. *Wardrobe Master* Jim Dunlevy. *Wardrobe Mistress* Laurel Staffell. *Makeup* W. T. Partleton. *Hairdresser* Stella Rivers. "*Twist*" *Paintings* Leroy Nieman. *Prop Buyer* Michael McCarthy. *Constr Mgr* Bert Jempson. *Still Photog* Harry Gillard. *Grip* M. Beauchamp. *Prop* Tommy Davies. *Elec Supv* Harold Cooke.

Cast: Billy Fury *(Billy Universe)*, Michael Anderson, Jr. *(Alvin)*, Dennis Price *(Sir Charles Bryant)*, Richard Wattis *(nervous man)*, Anna Palk *(Ann)*, Keith Hamshere *(Ring-a-Ding)*, Ray Brooks *(Freddy)*, Jeremy Bulloch *(Joey)*, Maurice Kaufmann *(Larry Granger)*, Peter Barkworth *(Skinner)*, Max Bacon *(Lotus proprietor)*, Felicity Young *(Yvonne)*, Helen Shapiro, Bobby Vee, Danny Williams, Shane Fenton and the Fentones, Jimmy Crawford, Lionel Blair and His Dancers.

Comedy with music. Sir Charles Bryant sends his daughter Ann to Europe in order to break up her romance with Larry Granger, a singer of ill repute. At the London airport Ann becomes acquainted with Billy Universe and the Satellites, a rock and roll group who are en route to Brussels. Fog grounds the plane, and Billy and the boys take Ann on a nightclub tour of London in hopes of finding her lover. They find Larry romancing one of the club's dancers. Ann realizes that Larry is not for her; she is reconciled with her father; and the boys depart for Brussels. *Singers. Musicians. Ne'er-do-wells. Upper classes. Rock and roll. Filial relations.*

Note: Coronado Productions, cited in copyright source as production company, has not been confirmed. Released in Great Britain in 1962; running time: 82 min.

PLAY IT COOL (Japan)   **F6.3844**

Daiei Motion Picture Co. Nov **1970** [Los Angeles showing]. Sd; col (Fuji Color). 35mm (Daiei Scope). 93 min.

Dir-Writ Yasuzo Masumura. *Orig Story* Masayuki Toyama. *Photog* Setsuo Kobayashi. *Art Dir* Takesaburo Watanabe. *Mus* Hikaru Hayashi.

Cast: Mari Atsumi *(Yumi)*, Yusuke Kawazu *(Nozawa)*, Akemi Negishi *(Tomi)*, Akira Nishimura *(Kada)*, Ryoichi Tamagawa *(Yoshimura)*, Sanae Nakahara *(madam)*.

Melodrama. Tomi works at a whorehouse and has a 19-year-old illegitimate daughter, Yumi, who goes to dressmaking school and is Tomi's one consolation in a life of broken affairs. Tomi's latest man, Yoshimura, forces himself on Yumi, and the enraged mother kills him and is sentenced to prison. Yumi becomes a hostess in a Ginza nightclub where she plays poker with men who may sleep with her only if they win, an event which rarely happens. Kada, the club owner, asks Yumi to become his mistress, but her devotion to another man, Nozawa, causes her to refuse until Nozawa makes it clear he will defer to Kada's wishes. Kada dies suddenly, and Nozawa impregnates Yumi so that she can claim the child as Kada's and thereby obtain Kada's fortune. *Prostitutes. Nightclub hostesses. Nightclub managers. Mistresses. Motherhood. Murder. Pregnancy. Illegitimacy. Inheritance. Tokyo—Ginza District.*

Note: Released in Japan in May 1970 as *Denki kurage.*

THE PLAY PEN GIRLS   **F6.3845**

Leo–Todd Productions. *Dist* Chellee Films, Leo–Todd Motion Picture Producing and Distributing Ltd. **1967**. Sd; b&w. 35mm. 63 min.

Prod Paul Leonardi, Phil Todaro. *Created & Dir by* Victor Burton. *Dir Photog* Victor Peters.

Melodrama. The Girl comes to the city and visits a nightclub that features topless waitresses and Go-go girls. She attends an orgy at which the participants smoke marijuana and becomes involved in the sadistic practices of a motorcycle gang. *Go-go dancers. Waitresses. Orgies. Sadism. Marijuana. Nightclubs. Motorcycle gangs.*

THE PLAYBOY OF THE WESTERN WORLD (Ireland)   **F6.3846**

Four Provinces Films. *Dist* Janus Films, Lion International Films. 18 Mar **1963** [New York opening]. Sd; col (Eastman Color). 35mm. 100 min.

Prod Brendan Smith, Denis O'Dell. *Exec Prod* Michael Killanin. *Dir-Screenplay* Brian Desmond Hurst. *Photog* Geoffrey Unsworth.

Cast: Siobhan McKenna *(Pegeen Mike)*, Gary Raymond *(Christy Mahon)*, Elspeth March *(Widow Quin)*, Michael O'Briain *(Shawn Keogh)*, Liam Redmond *(Michael James)*, Brendan Cauldwell *(Jimmy Farrell)*, John Welsh *(Philly Cullen)*, Niall MacGinnis *(Old Mahon)*, Eithne Lydon *(Susan)*, Finnuala O'Shannon *(Sara)*, Anne Brogan *(Nelly)*, Katie Fitzroy *(Honor)*.

Comedy-drama. Source: John Millington Synge, *Playboy of the Western World* (Dublin, 1907). Christy Mahon stumbles into a remote tavern on the Irish coast of County Mayo and announces that he has murdered his tyrannical father by splitting his head with a single blow from a spade. The villagers are impressed, and Christy becomes a hero to the town's young women, including Pegeen Mike, the innkeeper's daughter, who has listened to his tale in awe. Pegeen competes for his love with the amorous Widow Quin. As Christy reaches the height of his popularity, his father, Old Mahon, unexpectedly arrives, alive but with a bandaged head. When the villagers discover that Christy is not really a murderer, he is ridiculed, and Pegeen breaks with him. To regain his former status, he once again strikes his father and this time is apparently successful in killing him. The villagers, now faced with the actuality of the murder, are incensed, and they make plans to hang young Christy; but once more the old man recovers, and he rescues his son. Bowing to Christy's superior strength, the old man asks him to return home, and the two men depart together, leaving Pegeen to grieve over her loss. *Widows. Braggarts. Filial relations. Patricide. Village life. Hero worship. Pubs.*

Note: Produced in 1962. Location scenes filmed in Kerry, Ireland. Cast includes members of the Abbey Players.

PLAYBOY PRESIDENT (Japan)   **F6.3847**

Toho Co. Mar **1962** [Los Angeles showing]. Sd; col? 35mm. 91 min.

Dir Shue Matsubayashi.

Cast: Hisaya Morishige, Keiju Kobayashi.

Comedy. No information about the precise nature of this film has been found. *Playboys.*

Note: Released in Japan in Apr 1960 as *Shacho dochuki.*

PLAYGIRL see **THAT WOMAN**

PLAYGIRL AFTER DARK see **TOO HOT TO HANDLE**

THE PLAYGIRL AND THE WAR MINISTER (Great Britain)   **F6.3848**

Covent Garden Films. *Dist* Miller-King Productions, Medallion Pictures, Union Film Distributors. 3 Oct **1963** [Maryland license]. Sd; b&w. 35mm. 90 min.

Prod Leslie Gilliat. *Dir* Anthony Kimmins. *Screenplay* Anthony Kimmins, Nicholas Phipps. *Dir Photog* Wilkie Cooper. *Camera Op* Peter Allwork. *Focus Puller* Gerry Anstiss. *Camera Grip* J. Vincent. *Art Dir* Albert Witherick. *Asst Art Dir* Bill Bennison. *Set Dresser* Pamela Cornell. *Scenic Artist* Alan Evans. *Film Ed* Thelma Connell. *1st Asst Ed* Michael Hart. *2d Asst Ed* Gillian Scott. *Mus Comp & Cond* John Barry. *Sd Rec* H. L. Bird, Red Law. *Dub Ed* Michael Hart. *Boom Op* Ken Ritchie. *Sd Camera Op* Sandy Fairlie. *1st, 2d & 3d Asst Dir* Douglas Hermes, Gordon Gilbert, Henry Emery. *Prod Mgr* John Pellatt. *Cont* Eileen Head. *Prod Sec* Doreen Jones. *Miss Greenwood's Cost* Hardy Amies. *Wardrobe Mistress* Bridget Sellers. *Makeup* George Partleton. *Hairdressing* Eileen Bates. *Drill Adv* Ronald Brittain. *Prop Buyer* Percy Godbold. *Still Photog* Norman Hargood. *Casting Dir* Paul Sheridan. *Chargehand Prop* Bobby Murrell. *Prop* Chuck Ferango.

Cast: Joan Greenwood (*Lady Fitzadam*), Cecil Parker (*General Fitzadam*), Ian Carmichael (*Cpl. Sidney Green*), Robert Beatty (*Larry Hoffman*), Dennis Price (*Prawn*), Liz Fraser (*Suzie Tidmarsh*), Bridget Armstrong (*Biddy O'Hara*), Derek Nimmo (*Willie Maltravers*), Harry Locke (*Albert Huggins*), Robert Nichols (*Sam Goulansky*), Roddy McMillan (*Mac*), Ronald Brittain (*parade sergeant major*), Patrick Jordan (*sergeant of guard*), Godfrey James (*sergeant at exchange*), Gerald Sim (*1st operator*), Geoffrey Bayldon (*2d operator*), Eric Woodburn (*landlord*), John Dunbar (*1st man in bar*), Jack Stewart, British (*2d man in bar*), Sandra Dorne (*Dusty Babs*), Finlay Currie (*Lochaye*), Eric Francis (*postman*), Reg Lye (*Uncle Joe*), Michael Ripper (*Angus*), Drew Russell (*airman*), Michael Hunt (*Royal Air Force sergeant*).

Comedy. Source: Anthony Kimmins, *The Amorous Prawn* (London opening: 9 Dec 1959). Gen. Hamish Fitzadam, due to retire from the military, needs money to buy the country cottage of his dreams. When the general leaves on an overseas mission, Lady Fitzadam devises a scheme to raise money by turning Glenmally, the general's Scottish Highland headquarters, into a luxurious salmon fishing resort for rich American tourists. The army staff agree to cooperate for a share of the profits, and Cpl. Sidney Green becomes hotel manager. The first guests, Americans Larry Hoffman and Sam Goulansky, settle down to enjoy the pleasures of the resort. While Hoffman fishes for salmon, Goulansky pursues Corporal Green's girl friend, the chambermaid. Hoffman soon becomes enamored of Lady Fitzadam, who poses as a widow. The general returns unexpectedly, but he is so outraged by the war minister's refusal to allow army trucks to move his furniture that he joins forces with his wife in the new business venture. They welcome a new guest, known as "the amorous Prawn" because of his notorious romances in the United States. Prawn arouses suspicion when he telephones the War Office, and it soon becomes apparent that he is the war minister. The hotelkeepers learn that the woman posing as Prawn's wife is a local barmaid, and in order to avoid a public scandal, Prawn agrees to allow the army trucks to move the General's furniture to his new cottage. *Americans in foreign countries. Tourists. Hotelkeepers. Barmaids. Chambermaids. Philanderers. Retirement. Finance—Personal. Imposture. Resorts. Scotland. Great Britain—Army. Great Britain—War Office.*

Note: Released in Great Britain in 1962 as *The Amorous Prawn.* Also known as *The Amorous Mr. Prawn.*

THE PLAYGIRLS AND THE BELLBOY (West Germany)   **F6.3849**
Rapid-Film. *Dist* Joseph Brenner Associates, United Producers Releasing Organization. 12 Feb **1962** [Los Angeles showing]. Sd; b&w with col seq. 35mm. 94 min.

Prod Wolfgang Hartwig. *Prod U. S. Vers* Harry Ross, prod. *Dir* Fritz Umgelter. *Dir-Writ Addl U. S. Seq* Francis Ford Coppola. *Screenplay* Dieter Hildebrandt, Margh Malina. *Photog* Paul Grupp. *Art Dir* Walter Dörfler. *Mus* Klaus Ogermann. *Prod Mgr* Ludwig Spitaler.

Cast: June Wilkinson, Gigi Held, Louise Lawson, Lori Shea, Ann Myers, Laura Cummins, Jan Davidson, Don Kenney, Karin Dor, Willy Fritsch, Michael Cramer, Gigi Martine, Merwin Goldsmith, Mady Rahl, Thomas Fabian, Maria Malden-Madsen, Otto Storr, Hanne Weider, Klaus Havenstein, Hans J. Dietrich, Angeles Durand, Max Greger.

Comedy. George, a bellboy, takes a correspondence course in detective work in hopes of becoming the hotel's house detective. Disguising himself as a stagehand, he studies the techniques of psychology that a director in a nearby theater uses on his female actors. A bevy of lingerie models checks into the hotel, and George, believing that the models are up to immoral purposes, dons various disguises in order to gain entrance into the models' suite. George finds nothing immoral in their activities, and he returns to the theater to learn more about women. *Bellboys. Detectives. Stagehands. Theatrical directors. Actors. Models. Disguise. Voyeurism. Correspondence courses. Hotels. Theater. Lingerie.*

Note: Released in West Germany in Aug 1958 in black and white as *Mit Eva fing die Sünde an;* running time: 85 min. Re-edited with color sequences added for U. S. release. Also known as *The Bellboy and the Playgirls.*

THE PLAYGIRLS AND THE VAMPIRE (Italy)   **F6.3850**
Nord Film Italiana. *Dist* Fanfare Films. 4 Jul **1963** [Atlanta opening]. Sd; b&w. 35mm. 76 min.

Pres by Richard Gordon. *Prod* Tiziano Longo. *Dir-Screenplay* Piero Regnoli. *Photog* Ugo Brunelli. *Camera* Aldo Greci. *Art Dir* Giuseppe Ranieri. *Film Ed* Mario Arditi. *Mus* Aldo Piga. *Mus Dir* Pierluigi Urbini.

Cast: Lyla Rocco (*Vera*), Walter Brandi (*Count Gabor Kernassy/vampire*), Maria Giovannini (*Katia*), Alfredo Rizzo (*Lucas*), Tilde Damiani, Antoine Nicos, Corinne Fontaine, Erika Di Centa, Marisa Quattrini, Leonardo Botta, Ivy Holzer.

Horror film. Vera, Katia, Ilona, Magda, and Erica, five showgirls stranded with their boss, Lucas, and their accompanist, Frank, in an area isolated by floods, take refuge in a mysterious-looking castle. Their host, Count Gabor Kernassy, is startled at the sight of Vera, who has the strange feeling of having been in the castle before. The Count tells her that she is the exact double of an ancestor of his. Although the seven guests are warned against leaving their rooms at night, Katia does and is later found dead. Soon after, the dead Katia, transformed into a vampire, attacks Lucas, but his cries attract help, and she vanishes. When Vera sees the Count lurking in the bushes, she notices that he looks strange, and it is discovered that he is not the Count, but his ancestor, a vampire. While exploring, Vera is attacked in an underground crypt by the vampire who, mistaking her for his long-lost love, places her in a tomb. When Katia jealously intervenes, she is disposed of. The Count rescues Vera by attacking the vampire and kills him by pulling aside the window curtains to allow the sunlight to strike him. *Vampires. Showgirls. Ancestry. Murder. Jealousy. Doubles. Floods. Castles. Tombs.*

Note: Originally released in Italy in 1960 as *L'ultima preda del vampiro;* running time: 85 min. Also known as *Curse of the Vampire.*

PLAYGIRLS INTERNATIONAL   **F6.3851**
Westfield Productions. 30 Oct **1963** [Philadelphia opening]. Sd; col (Eastman Color, print by Movielab). 35mm. 71 min.

Prod-Dir Doris Wishman. *Screenplay* Cy Eichman. *Narr* Andrew J. Kuehn. *Dir Photog* Larry Wolk. *Film Ed* Cy Eichman. *Sd* Titra Sound Corp. *Script girl* Gloria Fariello. *Cons* Jack Alexander.

Cast: Leslie Daniel (*narrator*), Betty Andrews, Eileen Traynor, Kenneth Andrews, Betsi Warton, Lee Sinclair, Christy Fanshee, Maria Stinger, Martha J. Pryor, Harry W. Stinger, Janice Coughlin, Sylvia Bayner, Louis Prima Twist Show, Sam Butera and the Witnesses, French Can-Can, Roller Stars, La Marionette de Valdes.

Travelog. The film is a travelog exploring "The Good Life" in various parts of the world where hedonism is practiced. The first sequence shows cancan dancers performing in Paris. Similar scenes are shown taking place in Hawaii, Thailand, Japan, Germany, Austria, and Mexico. In the American segment of the film, the Louis Prima Twist Show and Sam Butera and the Witnesses perform in Las Vegas, Nevada. The film concludes with footage of two Florida nudist camps showing patrons dancing the Twist, the Hula, and an Apache war dance. *Chorus girls. Hedonism. Nudist camps. Paris. Homestead (Florida). Miami. New York City. Hawaii. Las Vegas. Mexico. Haiti. Berlin—West. Austria. Japan. Thailand. Hong Kong. Twist (dance). Hula. Cancan.*

Note: Location scenes filmed at Sunny Palms Lodge, Homestead (Florida) and at Spartans nudist camp in Miami. Other footage filmed in New York, Hawaii, Mexico, Haiti, Paris, West Berlin, Austria, Japan, Thailand, and Hong Kong. Also known as *Nature's Playgirls, International.* Florida nudist camp sequences added by Westfield Productions, and certain nightclub sequences appeared later in *Behind the Nudist Curtain,* q. v.

PLAYGIRLS OF FRANKFURT *see* **CALL GIRLS OF FRANKFURT**

THE PLAYGROUND   **F6.3852**
General Films. *Dist* Jerand Film Distributors. 3 Oct **1965** [New York opening]. Sd; b&w. 35mm. 95 min.

Prod-Dir Richard Hilliard. *Screenplay* George Garrett. *Photog* Urs Furrer. *Mus* Elliot Kaplan.

Cast: Rees Vaughn (*Thomas Smith*), Inger Stratton (*Eva*), Edmon Ryan (*Jason Porter*), Andrea Blayne (*Mrs. Porter*), Loretta Leversee (*Mary*), Richard Kilbride (*Father Williams*), Marian Blake (*Mrs. Williams*), Carol White, U. S. (*Virginia Williams*), Peter MacLean (*Dr. Ronald*), Conrad Jameson (*Dr. Jacques*), Roger Talbot (*John*), Stanley Greene (*Clayton*), Philip Brown (*Fishback*), Sol Schwade (*Dr. Zimmerman*), Ethel Shutta (*Mrs. Cartwright*). Paul Schmidt (*Duncan Cartwright*).

Farce. Inspired by: Cyrus Leo Sulzberger, *My Brother Death* (New York, 1961). Boston theatrical director Thomas Smith is having an affair with Danish nurse Eva when he becomes involved with Irene, the lustful wife of Jason Porter, an actor playing the lead role in Smith's new play about the death of Socrates. Meanwhile, Jason, an atheist, meets Mary, a prostitute with religious obsessions. Walking in a cemetery with Mary, Jason taunts her by lying in a grave and blaspheming—then he suddenly dies of a heart attack. Terrified, Mary runs from the cemetery, encounters actor Duncan Cartwright, whom she believes to be Jesus Christ, and falls into religious ecstasy. Dr. Zimmerman, Mary's psychiatrist, also runs into Cartwright and has a similar religious experience, believing the actor to be Sigmund Freud. A motorcycle accident that leaves Irene dead and Smith unconscious and paralyzed prompts Eva to disconnect his heart-and-lung machine to end his misery. Unable to cope with her guilt, Eva wanders into a playground where a group of children push her in a swing until she is happy again, not knowing that Dr. Zimmerman has scheduled a lobotomy for her. *Theatrical directors. Danes. Nurses. Actors. Atheists. Prostitutes. Psychiatrists. Children. Infidelity. Obsession. Blasphemy. Religion. Paralysis. Mercy killing. Guilt. Theater. Cemeteries. Motorcycles. Playgrounds. Lobotomy. Motorcycle accidents.*

Note: Filmed in Boston.

PLAYMATES (France/Italy)   **F6.3853**
Paris Inter Productions-Capitole Films-Super International Pictures. *Dist* Goldstone Film Enterprises, VIP Distributors, Blue Chip Productions. Dec **1969** [c1 Jul 1969; LP37003]. Sd; col (De Luxe). 35mm (Techniscope). 86 min. *MPAA rating* R.
Pres by Jack H. Harris. *Prod* Joël Lifschutz. *Dir-Writ* Jean-Claude Dague. *Co-Dir-Screenplay* Louis Soulanes. *Dir Photog* Jacques Robin. *Film Ed* Monique Isnardon. *Mus* Norbert Glanzberg. *Asst Dir* Lionel Bernier.

Cast: Jean-Claude Bercq (*Henri Verdier*), Marc Briand (*Robert*), Donna Michelle (*Karine*), Michel LeRoyer (*Philippe Leroy*), Linda Veras (*Sophie Verdier*), Roland Lesaffre (*Inspector Fougas*), Jean Distinghin (*himself, a photographer*), Luigi Bellini (*Luigi*), Georges Bellec (*Paulo*), Kim Camba (*Jack*), Katia Chenko (*Ginette*), Renate Wolfle, Edith Catry, Cathy Reghin (*playgirls*).

Crime melodrama. Bank manager Henri Verdier meets fashion model Karine when her car breaks down. He falls in love with her and is persuaded by her brother, Robert, to embezzle some money from his bank to finance a uranium venture. Henri subsequently discovers that Robert and Karine are not related, and he starts a fight with Robert, but Robert forces Henri at gunpoint to help rob the bank. Their plot to incriminate Philippe, Henri's wife's lover, is successful, and Philippe is falsely arrested for the robbery. Fashion photographer Jean Distinghin, however, while working in the area, photographs Henri during the robbery. Inspector Fougas shoots Robert while attempting to apprehend the two robbers, but Henri escapes on a motorboat with Karine as a hostage. Distinghin pursues them, and Fougas arrives to rescue him from Henri, who is killed in the ensuing struggle. *Bankers. Models. Photographers. Police. Imposture. Embezzlement. Frameup. Infidelity. Bank robberies. Motorboats. Chases.*

Note: Opened in Paris in Jul 1968 as *Le bal des voyous*. Also known as *Les femmes.*

THE PLAYPEN   **F6.3854**
American Art Films. *Dist* Warren St. Thomas. 16 Nov **1967** [San Francisco showing; c12 Apr 1967; LP35675]. Sd; col. 35mm. 86 min.
Prod-Dir-Writ Warren St. Thomas.
Cast: Tiger Lilly, Jerry Jordan, Corby Drake, John Shimick, Rich Schmidt, Bonnie Blue.
Drama. Farm girl Tiger Lilly dreams of becoming a ballet dancer. She is forced by Len, her stepfather, to perform endless menial tasks and to sleep in a goatshed. Two hill boys attack her, and Len only watches; later he offers her to his cronies for money. Tiger runs away to the city, becomes a dancer in a nightclub, and is desired by both a bisexual stripper and the club operator. The stripper forces her to have relations with men in hopes that Tiger will become a lesbian. Tiger learns that her mother has died; she leaves the city and goes to her mother's grave. There she encounters her stepfather, and she accuses him of killing her mother. Enraged, he kills her. After death, she recalls the things she would have liked to have done while alive. *Farmers. Stepfathers. Dancers. Farm life. Rape. Prostitution. Bisexuality. Seduction. Lesbianism. Murder. Filial relations. Death. Nightclubs. Supernatural.*

PLAYTIME (France)   **F6.3855**
Général Productions-Elite Films. *Dist* Audubon Films. 15 Jan **1963** [New York opening]. Sd; b&w. 35mm. 87 min.
Pres by Radley H. Metzger. *Prod* Hervé Messir. *Dir* François Moreuil. *Co-dir* Fabien Collin. *Screenplay* François Moreuil, Daniel Boulanger. *Dial* Daniel Boulanger. *Story* Françoise Sagan. *Photog* Jean Penzer. *Film Ed* René Le Hénaff. *Mus* Georges Delerue. *Sd* Jean-Claude Marchetti, Pierre Goumy, Jacques Bonpunt. *Prod Mgr* Paul de Saint-André.
Cast: Jean Seberg (*Kate Hoover*), Christian Marquand (*Philippe*), Françoise Prévost (*Anne de Limeuil*), Evelyn Ker (*Kate's friend*), Paulette Dubost (*Anne's maid*).

Drama. Kate Hoover, an American student at an exclusive school in Versailles, spies from her dormitory window on Philippe, a sculptor living next to the school at the home of his wealthy patron and mistress, widow Anne de Limeuil. Unable to sleep one night because of a party at Anne's, Kate dresses and clambers down a wall into the garden. Fearful of joining in the activities, she wanders down a street and witnesses a fatal hit-and-run automobile accident which she mentions to no one. In the days that follow, Kate frequently waves to Philippe, and after he surprises her in the garden, he becomes intrigued with the fact that she is obviously infatuated with him. The worldly Anne, fearful of the threat to her own relationship with Philippe, suggests he get the young girl out of his system by having an affair with her, and to make things easier, she leaves town for a few days. Kate spends several happy days with Philippe, but when he takes her for a drive, she recognizes his car as the one belonging to the hit-and-run driver. Afterwards she makes love with Philippe, but her infatuation quickly pales at his lack of candor about the accident; and she leaves while he is sleeping and returns to school. *Students. Mistresses. Patrons. Americans in foreign countries. Sculptors. Widows. Voyeurism. Adolescence. Wealth. Versailles. Automobile accidents.*

Note: Opened in Paris in Feb 1961 as *La récréation*; running time: 89 min. Some U. S. sources list Elite Films as production company, while foreign sources credit Général Productions. Also known as *Love Play.*

PLEASE, NOT NOW! (France/Italy)   **F6.3856**
Productions Jacques Roitfeld-Francos Films-Vides. *Dist* International Classics, Twentieth Century-Fox Film Corp. 3 Jul **1963** [Minneapolis opening; c14 Mar 1963; LP25768]. Sd; b&w. 35mm (CinemaScope). 74 min.
A Jacques Roitfeld-Francis Cosne Production. *Prod* Jacques Roitfeld. *Assoc Prod* Francis Cosne. *Dir* Roger Vadim. *English Vers Writ-Dir* Jack Dunn Trop. *Screenplay* Claude Brulé, Roger Vadim. *Dial* Claude Brulé. *Conceived by* Jean Aurel. *Photog* Robert Le Febvre. *Art Dir* Robert Clavel. *Film Ed* Albert Jurgenson. *Mus* James Campbell. *Choreog* Michel Renault. *Sd* William R. Sivel. *Asst Dir* Claude Clément. *Prod Mgr* Louis Wipf.
Cast: Brigitte Bardot (*Sophie*), Joséphine James (*Barbara*), Mireille Darc (*Marie-Jeanne*), Edith Zetline (*Josette*), Michel Subor (*Alain*), Jacques Riberolles (*Philippe*), Claude Brasseur (*Claude*), Serge Marquand (*prince*), Jean Tissier (*concierge*), Bernard Fresson (*Serge*), Claude Berri (*Bernard*), Max Montavon (*waiter*).

Romantic comedy. Sophie, a Parisian cover girl, discovers that Philippe, the photographer with whom she is in love, has been two-timing her with Barbara, an American heiress. Alain, a medical student, suggests that Sophie sleep with him to make Philippe jealous, but she decides to shoot Barbara the same way that her Corsican grandmother got rid of a rival. Meanwhile, Alain warns Philippe, who leaves with Barbara for the Swiss Alps. Sophie and Alain follow them, the latter still trying unsuccessfully to win Sophie's affections. After several fruitless attempts to win back Philippe, Sophie convinces Barbara that he is only after her money; Philippe, in turn, convinces Sophie that Alain's intentions are dishonorable. The women then team up against the men. Sophie realizes she loves Alain when he threatens her with her own shotgun and forces her to disrobe. *Models. Photographers. Americans in foreign countries. Heiresses. Medical students. Jealousy. Revenge. Paris. Alps.*

Note: Produced in France; opened in Paris in Apr 1961 as *La bride sur le cou*; running time: 91 min. Italian release title: *A briglia sciolta.*

PLEASURE CRUISE   **F6.3857**
Kirt Films International. *Dist* Distribpix, Inc. 9 Oct **1969** [San Francisco showing]. Sd; col. 35mm. 60 min.
Melodrama. An owner of a pleasure cruiser and his wife make a living by renting out their yacht on a daily basis. Two young women hire the yacht and, once out of port, turn the cruise into an orgy by seducing the whole crew. The captain ignores the illicit activities until the party anchors off a deserted island to have a picnic, and his wife leaves him behind to go ashore with the group. The captain becomes suspicious, swims ashore, and discovers that his wife has joined in the orgy. Distraught, he murders the whole group to teach them a lesson in morality. *Sea captains. Infidelity. Murder. Yachts. Orgies. Picnics.*

THE PLEASURE GAME   **F6.3858**
Wodwo Productions. *Dist* Eve Productions. Mar **1970**. Sd; col (Eastman Color). 35mm. 78 min.
Prod Joseph Feury. *Dir* John Vittoli. *Screenplay* Chase Frank. *Photog* Frank Murphy. *Sd* Art Names.
Cast: Leah James (*Jenny*), William Borsella (*David*), Daniel Ades (*Robert*), Victor Sandor (*Harry*), Ann Staunton (*Susan*), Angela Martell (*Zelda*), Erica Von Kessler (*Shirley*).
Drama. David brings his girl friend Jenny home from college for a weekend at his wealthy parents' home, and there they plan to make love for the first time. David's mother, Susan, accustomed to the appearance of uninvited female guests, sends Robert, the family chauffeur, to carry Jenny's bags to her room.

Robert surreptitiously watches Jenny as she stands naked in front of her bathroom mirror until she becomes aware of his presence and angrily throws him out. Harry, David's father, arrives home with two women, Zelda and her deafmute companion, Shirley. Unbeknownst to David and Jenny, Harry is impotent, and he finds sexual satisfaction by arranging weekend gatherings in which the participants have sex while he watches through secret peepholes. The next morning, David and Jenny make love, and it develops that David, like his father, is impotent. Meanwhile, Zelda and Shirley make love under the influence of marijuana. After they shower together, Shirley offers herself to Robert, while Zelda makes overtures to Susan. Jenny helps David overcome his impotency while Harry watches. *Students. Chauffeurs. Deafmutes. Voyeurism. Impotence. Wealth. Lesbianism. Family life. Marijuana.*

PLEASURE GIRL see **GIRL WITH A SUITCASE**

THE PLEASURE GIRLS (Great Britain)   F6.3859
Compton-Tekli Film Productions. *Dist* Times Film Corp. 20 Apr **1966** [New York opening]. Sd; b&w. 35mm. 88 min.
Pres by Michael Klinger, Tony Tenser. *Prod* Harry Fine. *Assoc Prod* Robert Sterne. *Dir-Writ* Gerry O'Hara. *Dir Photog* Michael Reed. *Camera Op* Dennis Lewiston. *Art Dir* Peter James. *Film Ed* Tony Palk, ed. *Mus Comp & Cond* Malcolm Lockyer. *Song:* "The Pleasure Girls" Bob Barratt. *Sung by* The Three Quarters. *Sd* John Mitchell. *1st Asst Dir* Christopher Dryhurst. *Makeup* Ken MacKay. *Hairdresser* Henry Montsash. *Still Photog* Laurie Turner.
Cast: Ian McShane *(Keith)*, Francesca Annis *(Sally)*, Klaus Kinski *(Nikko)*, Mark Eden *(Prinny)*, Tony Tanner *(Paddy)*, Rosemary Nicols *(Marion)*, Suzanna Leigh *(Dee)*, Annika Wills *(Angela)*, Coleen Fitzpatrick *(Cobber)*.
Melodrama. Young Sally Feathers arrives in London to become a model and moves into an apartment with Angela, an old school friend. Also living in the house are three other girls, Dee, Marion, and Cobber, an Australian, as well as Dee's brother, Paddy. On her first night Sally goes to a party where she meets and is strongly attracted to Keith Dexter, a photographer. Marion, who has become pregnant by her callous lover Prinny, breaks off with him when he suggests an abortion and then sells her grandmother's brooch for gambling money. Dee discovers that her wealthy boyfriend is already married and is a disreputable character involved in a slum rental racket. Sally's weekend affair comes to an abrupt end when the overly-anxious Keith tries to seduce her. Bitterly disappointed, Sally rushes home to seek comfort from the understanding Paddy. Instead she is shocked to find him embracing his boyfriend. Leaving for her first modeling class on Monday morning, Sally's spirits are lifted considerably when she finds the repentant Keith waiting to drive her to school. *Roommates. Students. Australians. Models. Photographers. Seduction. Brother-sister relationship. Male homosexuality. Pregnancy. Gambling. Infidelity. Theft. Abortion. Jewels. London.*
Note: Released in Great Britain in May 1965 at 88 min.

THE PLEASURE LOVERS (Great Britain)   F6.3860
Butcher's Film Distributors. *Dist* Joseph Brenner Associates. 7 Oct **1964** [New York State license; Champaign, Illinois, showing: 25 Dec 1964]. Sd; b&w. 35mm. 73 min.
Prod-Orig Story Guido Coen. *Dir* Charles Saunders. *Screenplay* Brock Williams. *Dir Photog* James Harvey. *Camera* Val Stewart. *Art Dir* Duncan Sutherland. *Film Ed* Peter Pitt. *Mus Dir* Edwin Astley. *Sd* Norman Coggs. *Asst Dir* Patrick Marsden. *Prod Mgr* Fred A. Swann. *Wardrobe* Gladys James. *Makeup* Tom Smith.
Cast: Leigh Madison *(Carol)*, Reed De Rouen *(Eddie)*, Kenneth Cope *(Johnny)*, Arthur Lovegrove *(Syd)*, Thomas Eytle *(Steve)*, Alexander Field *(Vic)*, Arthur Gross *(Tom Parker)*, Ann Lynn *(Judy)*, Marianne Brauns *(Joy)*, Redmond Phillips *(Inspector Stevens)*, Michael Collins, actor *(detective)*, Eric Woodburn *(Frank)*, Anne Sharpe *(nurse)*, Petite *(The Exotic Dancer)*.
Crime melodrama. Eddie, an American in England, leads a trio of professional criminals—Johnny, a strong-arm; Syd, a safecracker; and Steve, the Nigerian driver—in a daring robbery. Their getaway is hindered by the sudden appearance of the night watchman's daughter, Carol, whom they kidnap after beating up the old man. Johnny votes to kill Carol, while Syd and Steve agree to leave the decision to Eddie. During the 2-day wait for the delayed getaway boat, Carol's hostility toward Eddie, who is guarding her, excites him and he rapes her. To his surprise, Carol becomes aroused and eagerly turns to him for satisfaction. Meanwhile, Steve and Syd plan to force Eddie to divide the money, and Johnny picks up an ex-convict who also wants a share. When Carol's father dies from the beating, the men rendezvous at their warehouse hideout to plan their strategy. Johnny and the ex-con try to take the money, and Eddie kills the ex-con. As Eddie struggles with Johnny, the staircase gives way and the dilapidated building begins to collapse. The men scramble greedily for the money, but Eddie, realizing his love for Carol, pushes her to safety and is crushed with the others when the building crumbles. *Robbers. Safecrackers. Watchmen. Americans in foreign countries. Nigerians. Ex-convicts. Kidnaping.*

Rape. Robbery. Murder. Greed. Self-sacrifice. Warehouses.
Note: Originally released in Great Britain in Feb 1960 under the title *Naked Fury;* running time: 60 min. Also known as *Pleasure Lover.*

THE PLEASURE MACHINES   F6.3861
Pacific International Films. *Dist* Republic Amusements Corp. 26 Mar **1969** [Champaign, Illinois, showing]. Sd; b&w. 35mm. 70 min.
Exec Prod Paul Hunt, Ron Garcia. *Dir* Ron Garcia. *Screenplay* R. G. Vicry. *Cinematog* Paul Hunt. *Lighting* Stan Century. *Sd Rec* Mike Beardsley. *Sd Mix* Hollywood Picture Recorders. *Set Constr* Paul Wilmoth, Jim Feazell. *Boom* Darwin Joston. *Key Grip* Ken Haeger. *Still Photog* Joel Sussman.
Cast: Barbara Lynn, Beverly Walker, Patricia Miller.
Comedy. Harry Short, an inventor, builds a love machine. His wife, Martha, catches him in the garage with the lifelike, female robot and demands that Harry build a male robot for her own use. Soon, all the neighbors want love machines, and Harry cannot keep up with their requests and his wife's orders for a variety of additional male robots for herself. He constructs two robots for Martha—omitting the on-off switch—and Martha dies of overexertion. *Inventors. Marriage. Lust. Sex aids. Robots.*
Note: Also known as *Pleasure Machine, Love Machine,* and *The Love Machines.*

THE PLEASURE OF HIS COMPANY   F6.3862
Perlsea Co.–Paramount Pictures. *Dist* Paramount Pictures. 1 Jun **1961** [New York opening; c26 May 1961; LP20109]. Sd; col (Technicolor). 35mm. 115 min.
A Perlberg-Seaton Production. *Prod* William Perlberg. *Dir* George Seaton. *Screenplay* Samuel Taylor. *Dir Photog* Robert Burks. *Technicolor Col Cons* Richard Mueller. *Art Dir* Hal Pereira, Tambi Larsen. *Set Decor* Sam Comer, Frank R. McKelvy. *Titl Background Photog* Bud Fraker. *Film Ed* Alma Macrorie. *Mus Scored & Cond* Alfred Newman. *Orch* Herbert Spencer, Edward B. Powell. *Titl Song* Alfred Newman, Sammy Cahn. *Choreog* Fred Astaire, Hermes Pan. *Sd* Hugo Grenzbach, Charles Grenzbach. *Asst Dir* Harry Caplan, Donald Roberts. *Asst to the Prod* Theodore Taylor. *Cost* Edith Head. *Makeup Supv* Wally Westmore. *Hairstyle Supv* Nellie Manley. *Sp Photog Eff* John P. Fulton. *Proc Photog* Farciot Edouart.
Cast: Fred Astaire *(Biddeford "Pogo" Poole)*, Debbie Reynolds *(Jessica Poole)*, Lilli Palmer *(Katharine Dougherty)*, Tab Hunter *(Roger Henderson)*, Gary Merrill *(James Dougherty)*, Charlie Ruggles *(Mackenzie Savage)*, Harold Fong *(Toy)*, Elvia Allman *(wedding counsellor)*, Edith Head *(dress designer)*.
Romantic comedy. Source: Samuel Taylor and Cornelia Otis Skinner, *The Pleasure of His Company* (New York opening: 22 Oct 1958). After an absence of 15 years, international playboy Biddeford "Pogo" Poole returns unexpectedly to San Francisco for the wedding of his daughter Jessica. Though the young girl is immediately captivated by her father's savoir faire, her mother, Pogo's ex-wife, Kate, remains skeptically aloof. In the few remaining days before the wedding, Pogo takes over the household, rearranges the nuptial plans, and escorts Jessica on a whirlwind tour of the city. Overwhelmed by her father's charm, Jessica begins quarreling with her comparatively dull and unsophisticated rancher fiancé, Roger Henderson. Delighted by the turn of events, Pogo concentrates on wrecking both Jessica's pending marriage and Kate's current one to her second husband, wealthy industrialist Jim Dougherty. When Pogo sprains his arm at Roger's ranch, Jessica has a stormy argument with Roger, cancels the wedding, and announces that she is going around the world with her father in order to comfort him "in his old age." Hurt and dismayed by the implications of this declaration, Pogo insists that the wedding proceed, and when it is over he leaves town, taking with him Kate's treasured childhood portrait of Jessica and Jim's prized Chinese houseboy, Toy. All agree, however, that these deprivations are a small price to pay for having had the pleasure of Pogo Poole's company. *Playboys. Ranchers. Houseboys. Chinese. Industrialists. Marriage. Divorce. Filial relations. Weddings. San Francisco.*
Note: Location scenes filmed in San Francisco.

PLEASURE PLANTATION   F6.3863
Dist Republic Amusements Corp. 18 Mar **1970** [Champaign, Illinois, showing]. Sd; col (Eastmancolor). 35mm. 80 min.
Prod Anthony Scaretti. *Dir* Jerry Denby. *Screenplay* Jon Statkis. *Camera* Harry August, Joe Mangine. *Sets* Dick May. *Film Ed* Jet Motion Pictures. *Mus* DAS Associates. *Prod Mgr* Ian Merrick.
Cast: William Scope *(Jonah Hunt)*, Gerald Nomes *(Jason Hunt)*, Karil Holmes *(Rachel Hunt)*, Kim Bishop *(Lee Hunt)*, Mike Naylor *(Terrence Black)*, Bob Charles *(Cogswell)*, Linda Boyers *(Ruby)*, Jackie Glenn *(Lorna)*, Sheba Brittan *(Prissy)*, Matt Fortune *(Billy Joe)*, Susan Winters, Jean Parks, Phyllis Randall *(sporting house girls)*.
Drama. The Hunt family, consisting of two brothers and two sisters, lives on a declining Virginia plantation during the 1860's. Jonah, the eldest and owner of the plantation, spends most of his time in the local sporting house; brother

Jason is a drunkard; Lee is the mentally retarded, promiscuous "little sister"; and Rachel, ambitious, dreams of becoming the plantation's sole owner. To effect her plan, Rachel hires New Orleans prostitute Lorna to seduce Jonah and lure him away from the plantation. Rachel's scheme runs afoul when Lee is "raped" by Cogswell, the field boss, and Jason is killed in a duel to defend Lee's honor. Jonah locks himself in his room and drinks himself to death, and Rachel murders Cogswell and Lorna when she finds them in bed together in the whorehouse. The family honor restored, Rachel returns home only to find that the plantation has been seized by the Confederate Army: she goes insane and kills herself. *Landed gentry. Prostitutes. Farm foremen. Halfwits. Family life. Greed. Brother-sister relationship. Revenge. Murder. Alcoholism. Rape. Promiscuity. Suicide. Plantations. Duels. Whorehouses. United States—History—Civil War. Virginia.*

THE PLEASURE SEEKERS F6.3864

Twentieth Century-Fox Film Corp. 25 Dec **1964** [New York opening; c1 Jan 1965; LP29824]. Sd; col (DeLuxe). 35mm (CinemaScope). 107 min.

Prod David Weisbart. *Dir* Jean Negulesco. *Screenplay* Edith Sommer. *Dir Photog* Daniel L. Fapp. *Art Dir* Jack Martin Smith, Edward Carrere. *Set Decor* Walter M. Scott, Stuart A. Reiss. *Film Ed* Louis R. Loeffler. *Mus Score & Cond* Lionel Newman. *Assoc* Alexander Courage. *Songs:* "The Pleasure Seekers," "Something To Think About," "Everything Makes Music When You're in Love," "Next Time" Sammy Cahn, James Van Heusen. *Sung by* Ann-Margret. *Orch* Herbert Spencer, Warren Barker, Billy May. *Choreog* Robert Sidney. *Sd* Robert O'Brien, Elmer Raguse. *Asst Dir* Joseph Lenzi. *Cost Dsgn* Renie. *Makeup* Ben Nye. *Hairstyles* Margaret Donovan. *Adv* Prado Museum (Madrid). *Flamenco Dances* Antonio Gades.

Cast: Ann-Margret (*Fran Hobson*), Tony Franciosa (*Emilio Lacaye*), Carol Lynley (*Maggie Williams*), Gardner McKay (*Pete Stenello*), Pamela Tiffin (*Susie Higgins*), Andre Lawrence (*Dr. Andrés Briones*), Gene Tierney (*Jane Barton*), Vito Scotti (*neighborhood man*), Isobel Elsom (*Doña Teresa Lacaye*), Maurice Marsac (*José*), Shelby Grant (*American girl*), Raoul de Leon (*Martínez*), Brian Keith (*Paul Barton*), Antonio Gades (*flamenco dancer*), Emilio Diego (*guitarist*), Ida Romero, Peter Brocco.

Comedy-drama with music. Source: John H. Secondari, *Coins in a Fountain* (Philadelphia, 1952). Three young American women come to Madrid in search of romance and adventure. Maggie Williams finds a job as a secretary with an American news agency and falls in love with bureau chief Paul Barton, who is married. When Barton eventually realizes that he loves his wife and family more than Maggie, Maggie turns to Pete Stenello, a handsome young reporter who has admired her since her arrival in Spain. Fran, an ambitious, passionate singer and dancer, has a weekend affair with Andrés Briones, a shy provincial doctor who tries not to become involved with Fran but falls in love in spite of himself. Meanwhile, Susie Higgins has an affair with wealthy playboy Emilio Lacaye, who proposes marriage merely to fulfill his romantic desires but later realizes that he loves Susie and makes good his promise. The affairs culminate at a party given by Paul Barton before he and his family return to the United States. *Americans in foreign countries. Spanish. Secretaries. Reporters. Singers. Dancers. Physicians. Playboys. Newspapermen. Infidelity. Marriage. Madrid.*

Note: Filmed in Madrid and Toledo, Spain, with scenes shot inside the Prado museum in Madrid. Previously filmed in 1954 as *Three Coins in the Fountain*.

PLEASURES AND VICES (France) F6.3865

Lutétia. *Dist* William Mishkin. 21 Nov **1962** [New York opening]. Sd; col. 35mm. 86 min.

Assoc Prod Georges Sénamaud, Albert Mazaleyrat. *Dir-Adapt-Dial* Marcel Blistène. *Dir Photog* Jean Isnard. *Camera* Jacques Klein. *Asst Camera* Roland Paillas, Robert Alliel. *Art Dir* Fred Marpeaux. *Asst Art Dir* Robert Guisgand. *Film Ed* Jacques Mavel. *Asst Film Ed* Janine Verneau. *Sd Rec* Norbert Gernolle. *Sd Rec* André Soler. *Boom* Urbain Loiseau. *Asst Dir* Jacques Poitrenaud, Maurice Cartier. *Prod Mgr* Pierre Caudrelier. *Prod Asst* Pierre Cottance. *Location Mgr* Maurice Jumeau. *Script Girl* Denise Morlot. *Prod Sec* Blanche Mazaleyrat. *Wardrobe* Lily Caudrelier. *Makeup* Louis Bonnemaison. *Still Photog* Roger Forster. *Prop* Roger Bollangier, Padovani.

Cast: Maurice Ronet (*Angel Face*), Viviane Romance (*Loina*), Geneviève Kervine (*Marie*), Simone Paris (*Madame de Fourcroy*), René Havard (*"Caniche"*), Dora Doll, France Roche, Elisa Lamothe, Louis Viret, Rosy Varte, Danik Patisson, Roger Normand, Jean-Jacques Lecot, San Juan, Catherine Michard, Robert Seller, Jacques Herrien, Gérard Rolland, Colette Mareuil, Paul Demange.

Melodrama. Based on a play by: Roger Normand. Angel Face, a handsome young gigolo, supports himself by selling the gifts given to him by his lovers. One of his women, Marie, tells him that she is pregnant, hoping that this will have a stabilizing effect on him, but he is merely annoyed at her naiveté and leaves her. Despondent over the loss of her lover, Marie has an accident that causes a miscarriage. Later, Angel Face meets a man in a bar who tells him of Loina, a beautiful woman who preys upon the men who love her. Angel Face

decides to take the challenge and meets Loina, who invites him to join her in selling forged art work. He attempts to make love to her, and she agrees, with the stipulation that he not become jealous of her other sexual encounters. The arrangement succeeds for a while, but finally the love-sick Angel Face pleads with Loina for them both to stop their promiscuous behavior. She refuses to be possessed solely by Angel Face and leaves him. Angel Face is heartbroken but soon realizes that he has done the same thing to women many times before. *Gigolos. Confidence women. Promiscuity. Double standard. Forgery. Jealousy. Pregnancy. Miscarriage.*

Note: Filmed in Paris and Switzerland. Opened in Paris in Sep 1955 as *Gueule d'Ange* at 100 min.

THE PLEASURES OF THE FLESH (Japan) F6.3866

Sozo-sha. *Dist* Shochiku Films of America. Dec **1965** [Los Angeles showing]. Sd; col (Eastmancolor). 35mm (Shochiku GrandScope). 104 min.

Prod Masayuki Nakajima. *Dir-Writ* Nagisa Oshima. *Photog* Akira Takada. *Art Dir* Yasutaro Kon. *Mus Comp* Joji Yuasa.

Cast: Katsuo Nakamura (*Wakizaka*), Mariko Kaga (*Shoko*), Yumiko Nogawa (*Hitomi*), Masako Yagi (*Shizuko*), Toshiko Higuchi (*Keiko*), Hiroko Shimizu (*Mari*), Shoji Kobayashi, Mitsuhiro Toura, Akira Hamada, Fumio Watanabe, Naramasa Komatsu, Mamoru Hirata, Daigo Kusano, Kei Sato.

Melodrama. Source: Futaro Yamada, "Kan no naka no etsuraku," in *Josei no kiroku* (2 Sep 1961–19 Jan 1962). Wakizaka, a young college graduate working for a small company, is deeply hurt when he receives a marriage announcement from Shoko, a girl whom he has loved for years. As her tutor, he learned she was being blackmailed by a hoodlum who had raped her in her childhood. Wakizaka followed the man and killed him by pushing him off a moving train. The police were unable to solve the murder, and Wakizaka's crime went undetected. In time Hayami, a witness to the murder and a government official, confronts Wakizaka and promises his silence if Wakizaka will hold 30 million yen Hayami has embezzled. Hayami is soon arrested and sentenced to 5 years in prison. Four years pass, and Wakizaka remains disconsolate over losing Shoko. Moreover, he is still a virgin. Desperately lonely and living in a shabby apartment, he decides to spend the stolen money in the last year of Hayami's sentence. He falls in love with a bar hostess, Hitomi, and begins to support her in luxury; but a former lover of Hitomi's eventually drives him away. Another bar hostess, Shizuko, becomes his lover and willingly accepts his money to support her child and sick husband, but Wakizaka awakens one night to find them embracing. In a rage, he tells them of the murder and blackmail and beats Shizuko's husband. Wakizaka takes the injured man to a hospital and there meets a woman doctor, Keiko, who has just quit her job rather than submit to the advances of another doctor. Wakizaka decides to seduce her; they fall in love and are eventually married. Soon Wakizaka becomes disillusioned with his bride's obsession for cleanliness. One night he awakens from a recurring nightmare about Hayami returning to claim his money; he goes out and picks up Mari, a mute street girl. Mari's boyfriend unwittingly informs Wakizaka that Hayami died in prison. The next day Wakizaka meets his old love, Shoko, who promises her body in exchange for a loan to help her bankrupt husband. Wakizaka tells Shoko that he is penniless, having spent Hayami's money, and relates the story of the murder and subsequent blackmail. Soon afterwards the police arrest Wakizaka and inform him that Shoko turned him in. *Students. Bar girls. Executives. Physicians. Mutes. Mistresses. Prostitutes. Murder. Blackmail. Embezzlement. Theft. Marriage. Perfidy. Finance—Personal. Guilt. Dreams.*

Note: Released in Japan in 1965 as *Etsuraku*.

PLEIN SOLEIL see PURPLE NOON

PLISETSKAYA DANCES (U.S.S.R.) F6.3867

Central Documentary Film Studio. *Dist* Artkino Pictures. 17 Apr **1965** [New York opening]. Sd; b&w. 35mm. 70 min.

Dir Vasiliy Katanyan. *Scen* V. Komissarzhevskiy. *Photog* A. Khavchin. *Art Dir* V. Sedov. *Selections From:* "The Swan Lake" ("Lebedinoye ozero"), "The Sleeping Beauty" ("Spyashchaya krasavitsa") Pëtr Ilich Tchaikovsky. "Laurencia" ("Laurensiya") Aleksandr Abramovich Kreyn. "Spartacus" ("Spartak") Aram Ilich Khachaturyan. "The Little Humpbacked Horse" ("Konyok-Gorbunok") Rodion Konstantinovich Shchedrin. "Khovanshchina" Modest Petrovich Musorgski. "Raymonda" Aleksandr Konstantinovich Glazunov. "The Stone Flower" ("Skaz o kamennom tsvetke"), "Romeo and Juliet" ("Romeo i Dzhulyetta") Sergei Sergeevich Prokofiev. "Walpurgis Night" ("La Nuit de Walpurgis") Charles François Gounod. "Don Quixote" ("Don Kikhot") Ludwig Minkus. *Sd* Z. Uzdin.

Cast: Bolshoi Theater Ballet.

Featuring: Maya Plisetskaya, D. Begak, Vladimir Vasilyev, Yuriy Zhdanov, M. Liyepa, V. Tikhonov, Nikolay Fadeichev.

Documentary dance film. A portrait of Maya Plisetskaya, the prima ballerina of the Bolshoi Ballet, who is seen as a 14-year-old student at the Bolshoi Theater school, in current interviews, at home in Moscow, and on stage. *Dancers. Ballet. Maya Plisetskaya. Bolshoi Theater (Moscow).*

Note: Produced in the U.S.S.R. in 1964 as *Mayya Plisetskaya.*

PLUCKED (France/Italy)   **F6.3868**
   Summa Cinematografica-Ciné Azimut-Les Films Corona. *Dist* U-M Film Distributors. Apr **1969**. Sd; col (Eastman Color, print by Movielab). 35mm. 90 min.

   Prod Franco Marras. *Dir* Giulio Questi. *Screenplay* Giulio Questi, Franco Arcalli. *Photog* Dario Di Palma. *Art Dir* Sergio Canevasi. *Film Ed* Franco Arcalli. *Mus* Bruno Maderna.

   Cast: Gina Lollobrigida *(Anna)*, Jean-Louis Trintignant *(Marco)*, Ewa Aulin *(Gabri)*, Jean Sobieski *(Mondaini)*, Renato Romano *(Luigi)*, Giulio Donnini *(motel manager)*, Vittorio André, Ugo Adinolfi, Cleofe Del Cile, Biagio Pelligra, Conrad Anderson, Livio Ferraro.

   Melodrama. Marco operates a modern chicken breeding factory financed by his beautiful but domineering wife, Anna. He visits a local brothel to reduce his sadistic tensions, until Anna's orphan niece Gabri comes to live with them. He has an affair with her and tells her of his plan to kill Anna. Gabri, however, is secretly in love with art designer Mondaini, and the two lovers plan to kill both Anna and Marco so that Gabri will inherit the chicken farm. An anonymous letter tips off Anna to her husband's antics with the town's prostitutes. Assisted by Gabri, she disguises herself as a prostitute and goes to find Marco. At the motel, Gabri and Mondaini murder Anna, phone the police, and wait for the authorities to arrest Marco. Their plan backfires, however, when Marco takes the body to his factory. While attempting to dump it into a chicken food machine, he falls in and is killed. The police arrive and find Gabri and Mondaini standing guiltily near Anna's corpse. *Prostitutes. Aunts. Orphans. Commercial artists. Infidelity. Sadism. Disguise. Murder. Frameup. Factories. Whorehouses. Inheritance. Documentation. Chickens.*

   Note: Released in Italy in 1968 as *La morte ha fatto l'uovo* at 105 min; in Paris in Nov 1969 as *La mort a pondu un oeuf* at 87 min.

LES PLUS BELLES ESCROQUERIES DU MONDE see **THE BEAUTIFUL SWINDLERS**

LE PLUS VIEUX MÉTIER DU MONDE see **THE OLDEST PROFESSION**

PLUSHETTE'S SWEET REVENGE   **F6.3869**
   Century Cinema Corp. *Dist* Chancellor Films. ca **1970**. Sd; col. 35mm. 61 min.

   Melodrama. Syndicate executioner Tony has just strangled a victim, Bill, and as always after a kill, he begins to lust after sexual kicks. He hungrily watches two lesbians making love and joins them for a *ménage à trois*. Then he has them purge his guilt by using a steel claw hammer on him. Bill's girl friend, Jo Ann, gives Tony her body willingly, but he still has an occasional though compelling need for perverse sexual activity. Knowing this, Plushette, Bill's sister, lures him into her boudoir under the pretense of an ecstatic revel and exacts deadly revenge. *Hired killers. Psychopaths. Brother-sister relationship. Murder. Revenge. Lesbianism. Troilism. Voyeurism.*

POCIĄG see **BALTIC EXPRESS**

POCKETFUL OF MIRACLES   **F6.3870**
   Franton Productions. *Dist* United Artists. 18 Dec **1961** [New York opening; c18 Dec 1961; LP21109]. Sd; col (Technicolor). 35mm (Panavision). 136 min.

   Prod-Dir Frank Capra. *Assoc Prod* Glenn Ford, Joseph Sistrom. *Screenplay* Hal Kanter, Harry Tugend. *Dir Photog* Robert Bronner. *Art Dir* Hal Pereira, Roland Anderson. *Set Decor* Sam Comer, Ray Moyer. *Film Ed* Frank P. Keller. *Mus Scored & Cond* Walter Scharf. *Orch* Gil Grau. *Titl Song* Sammy Cahn, James Van Heusen. *Selections from the Works of* Pëtr Ilich Tchaikovsky. *Choreog* Nick Castle. *Sd Rec* Hugo Grenzbach, Charles Grenzbach. *Asst Dir* Arthur S. Black, Jr., Frank Capra, Jr., Ralph Axness. *Unit Prod Mgr* Kenneth DeLand. *Women's Cost* Edith Head. *Men's Cost* Walter Plunkett. *Makeup Supv* Wally Westmore. *Hairstyles* Nellie Manley. *Process Photog* Farciot Edouart.

   Cast: Glenn Ford *(Dave the Dude)*, Bette Davis *(Apple Annie)*, Hope Lange *(Queenie Martin)*, Arthur O'Connell *(Count Romero)*, Peter Falk *(Joy Boy)*, Thomas Mitchell *(Judge Henry G. Blake)*, Edward Everett Horton *(butler)*, Mickey Shaughnessy *(Junior)*, David Brian *(governor)*, Sheldon Leonard *(Steve Darcey)*, Peter Mann *(Carlos Romero)*, Ann-Margret *(Louise)*, Barton MacLane *(police commissioner)*, John Litel *(police inspector)*, Jerome Cowan *(mayor)*, Fritz Feld *(Pierre)*, Benny Rubin *(Flyaway)*, Jay Novello *(Spanish consul)*, Frank Ferguson, Willis Bouchey *(newspaper editors)*, Ellen Corby *(Soho Sal)*, Gavin Gordon *(hotel manager)*, Jack Elam *(Cheesecake)*, Mike Mazurki *(Big Mike)*, Hayden Rorke *(Captain Moore)*, Doodles Weaver *(pool player)*, Paul E. Burns *(Mallethead)*, Angelo Rossitto *(Angie)*, Edgar Stehli *(Gloomy)*, George E. Stone *(Shimkey)*, William F. Sauls *(Smiley)*, Tom Fadden

(Herbie), Snub Pollard *(Knuckles)*.

   Comedy. Source: Robert Riskin, *Lady for a Day* (a screenplay written for the film *Lady for a Day*, 1933). Damon Runyon, "Madame La Gimp," in *Cosmopolitan* (Oct 1929). One of the panhandlers working the Broadway beat in the early 1930's is Apple Annie, a gin-guzzling, bedraggled old woman whose apples are a good luck charm for Dave the Dude, king of New York's bootleggers. Unknown to her cronies, Annie has a daughter, Louise, who has been reared since infancy in an exclusive Spanish convent. The girl believes her mother to be a wealthy socialite, Mrs. E. Worthington Manville, whose weak heart has prevented her from making a trip to Spain. One day Annie's world collapses; she receives word that Louise is engaged to a Spanish nobleman and is coming to New York with her fiancé and future father-in-law. As the despairing Annie slips into a drunken stupor, Dude's girl friend, Queenie, hits upon a wild Cinderella scheme—using Dude's influence and connections, they will transform Annie into a society dowager and set her up in a lavish penthouse. The ruse works, and Annie is accepted by her daughter and guests as Mrs. E. Worthington Manville. But another crisis develops when Louise's prospective father-in-law, Count Romero, asks Annie to give an engagement party and introduce him to New York's "Four Hundred." All appears to be doomed until Dude crashes a reception and cons the governor, the mayor, and a host of socialites into coming to Annie's rescue. The party is a huge success; and Louise, her fiancé, and Count Romero return to Spain still unaware of the truth. Dude, converted to a belief in miracles, decides to give up the rackets and settle down in a little cottage with Queenie, and Annie happily returns to selling her apples. *Beggars. Bootleggers. Socialites. Nobility. Spanish. Filial relations. Imposture. New York City—Broadway.*

   Note: Remake of *Lady for a Day* (Columbia, 1933), also produced and directed by Frank Capra.

THE POEM OF THE BLUE STAR (Japan)   **F6.3871**
   Takarazuka Motion Picture Co. *Dist* Toho Co. Oct **1961** [Los Angeles showing]. Sd; col? 35mm. [Feature film, length unknown.]

   Cast: Akira Takarada, Tadao Takashima, Izumi Yukimura, Yukiji Asaoka, Ichiro Kanbe, Hiroshi Mizuhara, Shinichi Yanagisawa, Ebara Tatsuji, Michiyo Tamaki, Mitsuko Mito, Toru Abe, Kingoro Yanagiya, Shin Morikawa, Kyu Sazanka.

   Drama. Although no information about the precise nature of this film has been found, press material suggests that the story concerns the leader of a jazzband. *Band leaders. Jazzbands.*

   Note: Original title and release undetermined.

POE'S TALES OF TERROR see **TALES OF TERROR**

POI TI SPOSERÒ see **MALE COMPANION**

POIGNANT STORY (Japan)   **F6.3872**
   Toho Co. Mar **1962** [Los Angeles showing]. Sd; col? 35mm. [Feature film, length unknown.]

   Cast: Masayuki Mori, Hideko Takamine, Chikage Awashima, Yuriko Hoshi, Tatsuya Nakadai, Keiko Awaji, Kumi Mizuno, Choko Iida, Chieko Nakakita.

   Drama. No information about the precise nature of this film has been found.

   Note: Original title and release undetermined.

POINT BLANK   **F6.3873**
   Metro-Goldwyn-Mayer, Inc. 30 Aug **1967** [San Francisco opening; c19 Sep 1967; LP34744]. Sd; col (Metrocolor). 35mm (Panavision). 92 min.

   A Judd Bernard-Irwin Winkler Production. *Prod* Judd Bernard, Robert Chartoff. *Dir* John Boorman. *Screenplay* Alexander Jacobs, David Newhouse, Rafe Newhouse. *Dir Photog* Philip H. Lathrop. *Camera Op* Cliff King. *Asst Camera* William Clark. *Col Cons* William Stair. *Art Dir* George W. Davis, Albert Brenner. *Set Decor* Henry Grace, Keogh Gleason. *Film Ed* Henry Berman. *Mus* Johnny Mandel. *Song:* "Mighty Good Times" Stu Gardner. *Sung by* Stu Gardner Trio. *Rec Supv* Franklin Milton. *Mix* Larry Jost. *Rec* Frank Antunez. *Boom Op* Clint Althouse. *Asst Dir* Al Jennings, Mickey Lewis, Chris Seitz. *Unit Prod Mgr* Edward Woehler. *Location Mgr* Bob Sunderland. *Prod Assoc* Patricia Casey. *Asst to the Prod* Rafe Newhouse. *Script Supv* Doris Grau. *Wardrobe* Lambert Marks, Margo Weintz. *Makeup* William Tuttle, Jim Truwe. *Hairstyles* Sydney Guilaroff. *Sp Visual Eff* J. McMillan Johnson. *Sp Photog for Prod* David Steen. *Dial Coach* Norman Stuart. *Still Photog* Virgil Apger.

   Cast: Lee Marvin *(Walker)*, Angie Dickinson *(Chris)*, Keenan Wynn *(Yost/ Fairfax)*, Carroll O'Connor *(Brewster)*, Lloyd Bochner *(Frederick Carter)*, Michael Strong *(Stegman)*, John Vernon *(Mal Reese)*, Sharon Acker *(Lynne)*, James Sikking *(hired gun)*, Sandra Warner *(waitress)*, Roberta Haynes *(Mrs. Carter)*, Kathleen Freeman *(first citizen)*, Victor Creatore *(Carter's man)*, Lawrence Hauben *(car salesman)*, Susan Holloway *(girl customer)*, Sid Haig, Michael Bell *(penthouse guards)*, Priscilla Boyd *(receptionist)*, John McMurtry *(messenger)*, Ron Walters, George Strattan *(two young men in apartment)*,

Nicole Rogell (Carter's secretary), Rico Cattani, Roland LaStarza (Reese's guards).

Crime melodrama. Source: Richard Stark, *The Hunter* (New York, 1963). After taking part in the robbery of a large shipment of cash being transferred by helicopter on deserted Alcatraz, a man known as Walker is shot and left for dead by his partner Mal Reese, who then runs off with Walker's faithless wife, Lynne. Two years later, while on a guided tour around the island, Walker is stopped by a stranger, Yost, who offers to help him recover his share of the money by leading him to both Lynne and the criminal organization to which Reese now belongs. After Lynne has killed herself in despair, Walker takes up with her sister, Chris, who helps get him into Reese's heavily-guarded penthouse. As Walker threatens him, Reese plunges from a terrace to his death. Still determined to get his money, Walker continues to hunt down other members of the organization in Los Angeles. After two of them, Carter and car dealer Stegman, die in a trap intended for him, Walker makes his way to the combine's second-in-command, Brewster. Greedy to take over the number one spot in the organization, Brewster proposes that Walker outwit the top man, Fairfax, by pulling a hijack job similar to the previous one at Alcatraz. Walker accompanies Brewster to Fort Point, San Francisco, where the cash transfer is to take place. As Brewster picks up the packet of money, a shot rings out and he falls dead. Then Yost—who is actually Fairfax—appears to acknowledge Walker's unwitting assistance in eliminating those organization men who were a threat to his power. After offering Walker a job, Fairfax points to the packet of money and tells him to come and take it. Standing in the darkness, Walker considers the proposition for a moment and then disappears into the shadows. *Gangsters. Sisters. Infidelity. Perfidy. Murder. Suicide. Revenge. Organized crime. Robbery. Automobiles. Los Angeles. San Francisco—Fort Point. Alcatraz.*

Note: Location scenes filmed at Alcatraz Prison and in Los Angeles and San Francisco.

POINT BLANK *see* **PRESSURE POINT**

POINT OF ORDER!   F6.3874

Point Films. *Dist* Continental Distributing, Inc. 14 Jan **1964** [New York opening]. Sd; b&w. 35mm. 97 min.

Prod Emile De Antonio, Dan Talbot. *Assoc Prod* Eliot D. Pratt. *Ed Dir* Emile De Antonio. *Based on an Idea by* Dan Talbot. *Film Ed* Robert Duncan, ed. *Ed Cons* David T. Bazelon, Richard Rovere.

Documentary. This editorial condensation of 188 hours of television kinescopes chronicles the United States Senate's Army–McCarthy Hearings, which occupied 36 days between 22 April and 16 June 1954 in the Senate Caucus Room. As the film begins, Sen. Joseph R. McCarthy of Wisconsin, chairman of the Senate Permanent Subcommittee on Investigations (known as the "McCarthy Committee"), has accused the United States Army of permitting Communist infiltration of its ranks. The Army has countercharged that McCarthy and his chief counsel, Roy M. Cohn, have used threats to obtain special privileges for Cohn's friend and committee staff investigator G. David Schine, who had been drafted and sent to Fort Dix. McCarthy, in turn, has accused the Army of holding Schine for ransom to blackmail the committee into stopping its investigation. The principals in the hearing are introduced, and although several people on McCarthy's staff are pictured, including Robert F. Kennedy, it is primarily Cohn and McCarthy who are pitted against Secretary of the Army Robert T. Stevens, Army counselor John G. Adams, and special counsel Joseph N. Welch. The subcommittee also includes special counsel Ray Jenkins and his assistant Robert Collier; Senators John L. McClellan, Stuart M. Symington, and Henry M. Jackson; and Sen. Karl E. Mundt, who has temporarily taken over as chairman for McCarthy, who is now, in effect, on trial. Stevens testifies about Army efforts to resist pressures from the McCarthy staff to give special consideration to Private Schine. In retaliation the McCarthy Committee produces a photograph of Stevens and Schine together at an Air Force base, which gives the impression that the Secretary has been particularly friendly toward the private. The next day Welch produces a photograph identical to the other in every way, except that the second picture contains a third party, an Air Force colonel. From cross-examination of McCarthy staff member James Juliana it is established that the original group photo was cropped to make it seem as if only Stevens and Schine were in the picture. Later McCarthy submits to the committee a document identified as a 1951 report by FBI Director J. Edgar Hoover summarizing espionage activities at Fort Monmouth, New Jersey, but Hoover, through an intermediary, disclaims any knowledge of the paper. Welch, who establishes that McCarthy has possessed the document for months, asks Cohn why the incriminating information was never relayed to Stevens. McCarthy, riled at the lawyer's intensive questioning of his colleague, divulges that a member of Welch's law firm, Fred Fisher, once belonged to the National Lawyer's Guild, an organization labeled as subversive by the House Un-American Activities Committee. Dismayed that McCarthy has used national television both to slander his associate and to exploit a minor

occurrence that was already reported in the press, Welch castigates the senator in a long speech that receives loud applause from the spectators. Later McCarthy accuses Senator Symington of having advised Stevens of ways to frustrate the McCarthy staff's investigations of the Army, demanding that Symington rebut the accusations under oath. Symington criticizes the McCarthy staff's research and describes their files as the sloppiest and most carelessly handled he has seen in his government career. As Mundt calls a recess and the caucus room begins to clear, McCarthy likens Symington's statement to a Communist smear. Angrily, Symington answers that anyone critical in any way of the McCarthy staff is always certain to be branded a Communist, and he leaves the room with the others as McCarthy is left alone shouting into his microphone. *Investigators. Politicians. Lawyers. Anticommunism. Slander. Espionage. Television. Documentation. Photographs. United States—History—Army-McCarthy Hearings. Washington (District of Columbia). Fort Dix (New Jersey). Fort Monmouth (New Jersey). Joseph Raymond McCarthy. Roy M. Cohn. Joseph Nye Welch. Gerard David Schine. Stuart M. Symington. Robert T. Stevens. John G. Adams. John L. McClellan. Karl E. Mundt. Henry M. Jackson. Ray Jenkins. Robert A. Collier. James Juliana. Robert Francis Kennedy. Frederick G. Fisher, Jr. United States—Federal Bureau of Investigation. United States Congress—Senate Permanent Subcommittee on Investigations. United States Army. United States Congress—House Un-American Activities Committee. National Lawyer's Guild.*

POLICE NURSE   F6.3875

Associated Producers, Inc. *Dist* Twentieth Century–Fox Film Corp. May **1963** [c7 May 1963; LP26795]. Sd; b&w. 35mm (CinemaScope). 64 min.

Prod-Dir Maury Dexter. *Writ* Harry Spalding. *Dir Photog* John Nickolaus, Jr. *Set Decor* Harry Reif. *Supv Film Ed* Jodie Copelan. *Film Ed* Richard Einfeld. *Mus Comp & Cond* Richard La Salle. *Sd* William Bernds, Harry M. Leonard. *Asst Dir* Clarence Eurist. *Script Supv* Mary Chaffee. *Wardrobe* Bob Mark. *Prop Master* John Orlando.

Cast: Ken Scott (*Art Devlin*), Merry Anders (*Joan Olson*), Oscar Beregi (*Dr. Leon Claudel*), Barbara Mansell (*Irene Kersey*), John Holland (*Edward Mayhall*), Byron Morrow (*Capt. Pete Ingersoll*), Ivan Bonar (*Dr. C. F. Sears*), Jerry Murray (*Terry*), Justin Smith (*pharmacist*), Carol Brewster (*Mrs. Mayhall*), Lorna Thayer, Lee Henry, Glen Marshall.

Mystery melodrama. Arriving in southern California, nurse Joan Olson finds her recently divorced sister, Grace, dead from an overdose of sleeping tablets. She and her sister's ex-husband, police detective Art Devlin, learn that Grace recently gave birth to a child fathered by Devlin. Although nurse Irene Kersey and Dr. Leon Claudel, who delivered Grace's baby, deny knowledge of the drug prescription, Joan takes a job on the doctor's staff and discovers records proving that her sister had been a patient in his nursing home. Irene, beaten by Terry, one of Claudel's orderlies, escapes and reveals that Claudel is a heroin addict dealing in black-market babies. Devlin forces Claudel to confess that he has sold Grace's infant to the Mayhalls, a wealthy childless couple. Upon finding the baby in a happy home, Devlin returns to Joan. *Nurses. Physicians. Infants. Sisters. Detectives. Drug addicts. Suicide. Childbirth. Black market. Adoption. Drug overdose. Heroin. Tranquilizers. California. Documentation.*

THE POLICEMAN OF THE 16TH PRECINCT (Greece)   F6.3876

Dist Greek Motion Pictures. 21 Apr **1963** [New York showing]. Sd; b&w. 35mm. 84 min.

Dir Alekos Sakellarios. *Screenplay* Christos Yannakopoulos, Alekos Sakellarios.

Cast: Kostas Hadjichristos (*Elias*), Marika Krevata (*Lucy*), Kyveli Theochari (*Alice*), Thanassis Vengos (*Thomas*), Stavros Xenidis (*Angelo*), D. Papagianopoulos (*Lambros*), George Gavrilidis (*Orestis*), Alice Georguli (*maid*), Thanos Generalis (*chief of police*).

Comedy. A variety of small-time crooks congregate at a restaurant and discuss their financial problems and ways of solving them. *Thieves. Police. Finance—Personal. Restaurants.*

Note: No information on original title or release date has been found.

POLISH PASSION *see* **IT BEGAN ON THE VISTULA**

THE POLITICIANS   F6.3877

Fountain Films. *Dist* Ellman Enterprises. Oct **1970**. Sd; col (Eastman Color). 35mm. 82 min.

Prod N. E. Shane. *Dir-Writ* Derek Ashburne. *Photog* Michael Neyman, Paul Hipp. *Film Ed* N. E. Shane. *Mus* John Bath. *Sd* William Oliver.

Cast: Angela Carnon (*Sandra Dixon*), Bob Warner (*Larry Channing*), Vickie Carbe (*Karen Green*), Douglas Frey (*Dr. Ernie Maddox*), Neola Graef (*Laurie Saunders*), Vincent Mongol (*Bud Chandler*), Dixie Donovan (*Susan*), Richard Gonzales (*Senator Portman*), Heidi Sohler (*Lisa, the masseuse*), Robert Copple (*Dwight Dixon*), Nanci Sheldon, Gil Francassa, Rick Rivera, John B. Lewis,

Tony Marasca, Bruce Martin, actor, Alex Roseff.

Drama. Larry Channing is a Washington, D. C., procurer whose social secretary, Sandra Dixon, an ex-manicurist, keeps him and a number of prominent politicians sexually satisfied. Larry matches two of his girls, Laurie and Susan, to an Arab sheik, and Karen to Bud Chandler, a prominent politician who is being groomed for a cabinet post. They are shown having sexual intercourse with their clients. Bud falls in love with Karen; and Susan becomes pregnant. When Susan goes to have an abortion, however, she is raped by the abortionists. In addition, Sandra is involved in a lesbian encounter. Sandra leaves town to visit her mentally retarded brother, Dwight, in North Carolina and assists him in masturbating, to make his birthday that much happier. *Pimps. Politicians. Arabs. Sheiks. Prostitution. Lesbianism. Autoeroticism. Brothersister relationship. Mental retardation. Rape. Abortion. Washington (District of Columbia). North Carolina.*

Note: Also known as *Naked Are the Cheaters.*

POLIZEIREVIER DAVIDSWACHE (ST. PAULI) *see* **SEVEN CONSENTING ADULTS**

LE PONT VERS LE SOLEIL *see* **BRIDGE TO THE SUN**

POOR COW (Great Britain)   **F6.3878**
Vic Films–Fenchurch Films. *Dist* National General Pictures. 31 Jan **1968** [New York opening]. Sd; col (Technicolor). 35mm. 104 min.

Prod Joseph Janni. *Assoc Prod* Edward Joseph. *Dir* Kenneth Loach. *Screenplay* Nell Dunn, Kenneth Loach. *Photog* Brian Probyn. *Art Dir* Bernard Sarron. *Film Ed* Roy Watts. *Mus* Donovan. *Mus Cond* John Cameron. *Song:* "*Be Not Too Hard*" Donovan, Christopher Logue. *Songs:* "*Colours,*" "*Poor Love*" Donovan. *Songs Sung by* Donovan. *Pop Programs for Background Mus* David Symonds. *Sd Rec* Kevin Sutton, Gerry Humphreys. *Asst Dir* Andrew Grieve. *Asst to the Prod* John Goldstone. *Prod Mgr* David Anderson.

Cast: Carol White *(Joy)*, Terence Stamp *(Dave)*, John Bindon *(Tom)*, Kate Williams *(Beryl)*, Queenie Watts *(Aunt Emm)*, Geraldine Sherman *(Trixie)*, James Beckett, Billy Murray *(Tom's mates)*, Simon King *(Jonny, age 1 1/2)*, Stevie King *(Jonny, age 3)*, Winnie Holman *(woman in park)*, Rose Hillier *(customer in hairdresser's)*, Ellis Dale *(solicitor)*, Gerald Young *(judge)*, Paddy Joyce *(governor in photo studio)*, Gladys Dawson *(Bet)*, Ron Pember *(Petal)*, Malcolm McDowell *(Billy)*, George Tovey, Will Stampe, Bernard Stone, John Halstead *(photographers)*, Peter Claughton *(driving examiner)*, Julie May *(woman in Sheppey)*, Philip Rose, actor *(Shelley)*, Martin King *(prison warden)*, Muriel Hunte *(woman at prison)*, James Thornhill *(prisoner)*, Mo Dwyer *(prisoner's wife)*, Terry Duggan *(2d prisoner)*, Ian Christain, Liza Carrol, Tony Selby, Ray Barron, Sian Davis, Mike Negal, George Sewell, Chris Gannon, Philip Newman, Alan Selwyn, Wally Patch, Hilda Barry, Joe Palmer *(customers in pub)*.

Drama. *Source:* Nell Dunn, *Poor Cow* (London, 1967). After giving birth to a son, 18-year-old Joy returns to her dingy London flat and her husband, Tom, an abusive and insensitive petty thief. Money from a successful robbery enables the couple to move to a better apartment, but Joy's happiness is ended when Tom is arrested and sent to jail. Joy stays with her aging Aunt Emm before moving in with Dave, one of Tom's friends. Dave's tender nature and affection for Joy's son, Jonny, arouses a loving response in Joy, but even this happiness ends abruptly when Dave is also convicted of robbery. After promising to wait for Dave, Joy begins divorce proceedings against Tom and sets out to earn a living for herself and Jonny. Following jobs as a barmaid and a nude model, Joy drifts into a life of promiscuity; then Tom returns from prison, and Joy tries to revive their marriage. Eventually, however, Tom beats her up during an argument, and she runs from their flat. When she returns, she discovers that Jonny is missing. Frantic, she races through the neighborhood until she finds him playing in a demolition site. Realizing how much her child means to her, Joy compromises her life by remaining with Tom but hopes for future happiness with Dave. *Thieves. Aunts. Infants. Barmaids. Models. Childbirth. Motherhood. Marriage. Infidelity. Promiscuity. Survival. Employment—Women. Prisons. London.*

Note: Filmed on location in London, Wales, and the Isle of Sheppey. Opened in London in Dec 1967.

POOR LITTLE RICH GIRL   **F6.3879**
Dist Film-Makers' Cooperative. 26 Apr **1965** [New York opening]. Sd; b&w. 16mm. 70 min.

Prod-Dir Andy Warhol. *Directorial Asst* Chuck Wein. *Prod Asst* Gerard Malanga.

Cast: Edie Sedgwick.

Satire. A young woman has just spent her inherited fortune in a few months. The film depicts a day in her life at this juncture. She talks about her inheritance, moves between the bed and telephone in her room, and shows off a beautiful new coat. The first reel is out of focus. *Heiresses. Spendthrifts. Inheritance.*

Note: The frame remains fixed throughout.

POOR WHITE TRASH (Reissue)   **F6.3880**
American National Films. *Dist* Cinema Distributors of America, International Film Organization. 26 Jul **1961** [Mobile, Alabama, opening]. Sd; b&w. 35mm. 88 min.

Note: Originally released by United Artists in 1957 as *Bayou.*

POP GEAR *see* **GO GO MANIA**

POPCORN; AN AUDIO/VISUAL ROCK THING (United States/ Australia)   **F6.3881**
United Screen Arts. *Dist* Sherpix, Inc. 16 Nov **1969** [New York opening]. Sd; col (Eastman Color). 35mm. 85 min. *MPAA rating* G.

Prod Peter Ryan. *Exec Prod* Louis K. Sher. *Dir* Peter Clifton. *Photog* Graham Lind. *Film Ed* Alan Lake, ed, David Lewis, ed. *Prod Mgr* Paul Quincy.

Starring: Mick Jagger, The Rolling Stones, Jimi Hendrix, Otis Redding, Vanilla Fudge, The Bee Gees, Joe Cocker, The Small Faces, The Beach Boys, The Fifth Dimension, Stevie Winwood, Eric Burdon, Emperor Rosko, Traffic, Twiggy, Spencer Davis, Russell Morris, Johnny Farnham, Sebastian Jorgensen.

Also with: Tim Walker, The Groove.

Documentary. This documentary includes a series of on-stage performances by a number of singers and groups, purportedly filmed in Paris, London, New York, Los Angeles, Hawaii, and Australia. These sequences are intercut with ones representing current myths, images, and ideas of the youth culture. Besides a fashion show featuring Twiggy and an interview with Mick Jagger, lead singer of the Rolling Stones, there are: an interview with and character study of Emperor Rosko, a European disc jockey, sequences of surfers in the Pacific, protesters on the streets of the United States, and vagabond youths traveling in Katmandu. The following numbers are included, either live onstage, or on the sound track over the various montage sequences: "Relax Me" (The Groove), "Jumping Jack Flash" and "2,000 Light Years From Home" (The Rolling Stones), "Hey, Joe" and "Wild Thing" (Jimi Hendrix), "To Love Somebody" (The Bee Gees), "Respect" and "Satisfaction" (Otis Redding), "Itchykoo Park" and "Lazy Sunday" (Small Faces), "Heroes and Villains" (The Beach Boys), "Everybody Ought To Sing a Song" (Johnny Farnham), "With a Little Help From My Friends (Joe Cocker), "Albatross" (Stevie Winwood and Traffic), "The Beat Goes On" (Vanilla Fudge), "Sonata in F Major" (Sebastian Jorgensen and Tim Walker), "Gimme Some Lovin' " (Stevie Winwood and Spencer Davis), "The Real Thing" (Russell Morris), and "Have You Tried Love?" (The Fifth Dimension). *Singers. Youth. Rock and roll. Bands. Paris. London. New York City. Los Angeles. Hawaii. Australia.*

THE POPE ONDINE STORY *see* **THE CHELSEA GIRLS**

POPI   **F6.3882**
Leonard Films. *Dist* United Artists. 27 May **1969** [New York opening; c27 May 1969; LP37110]. Sd; col (DeLuxe). 35mm. 115 min. *MPAA rating* G.

Pres by Herbert B. Leonard. *Prod* Herbert B. Leonard. *Exec in Charge of Prod* Stanley Neufeld. *Dir* Arthur Hiller. *Writ* Tina Pine, Les Pine. *Dir Photog* Andrew Laszlo. *2d Unit Photog* Russ Lowell. *Art Dir* Robert Gundlach. *Film Ed* Anthony Ciccolini. *Mus* Dominic Frontiere. *Song* Dominic Frontiere, Norman Gimbel. *Sd Rec* Stanley Mitteldorf. *Asst Dir* Peter Scoppa, Don Moody. *Cost* Albert Wolsky. *Makeup* Mike Maggi. *Hairstyles* William Farley.

Cast: Alan Arkin *(Abraham Rodriguez)*, Rita Moreno *(Lupe)*, Miguel Alejandro *(Junior Rodriguez)*, Ruben Figueroa *(Luis Rodriguez)*, John Harkins *(Harmon)*, Joan Tompkins *(Miss Musto)*, Anthony Holland *(Pickett)*, Arny Freeman *(Diaz)*, Barbara Dana *(receptionist)*, Antonia Rey *(Mrs. Cruz)*, Arnold Soboloff *(Dr. Perle)*, Victor Junquera *(Novitas man)*, Gladys Velez *(Silvia)*, Anita Dangler *(nurse)*, Judith Lowry *(old lady)*.

Comedy-drama. Popi (Abraham Rodriguez), a Puerto Rican widower struggling to raise his two young sons amid the squalor of New York's Spanish Harlem, has two aims in life. One is to marry Lupe, his warmhearted, voluptuous girl friend, and move to Brooklyn. But before he can do this, Popi feels obligated to realize his other aim—assuring his sons a decent future. For years he has managed to provide for them by simultaneously working several jobs, but in his mind has always lurked the fear that he would one day lose them to the ghetto. And it isn't long before this fear is realized: he learns that his sons are telling school friends that their father is the gangster brother of a notorious underworld figure. The problem preoccupies him, but the solution presents itself one evening while he is catering a banquet for Cuban refugees. Popi is a shrewd man, and his experience has taught him that America is more altruistic toward political refugees than toward the common poor. His scheme is to set his sons adrift in a rowboat somewhere off the coast of Miami in the hope that they will be spotted, taken for Cuban refugees, and rescued. Following rowing sessions in Central Park and some lessons in motorboat handling on the East River, Popi reveals his plan to the boys. Despite their reluctance to leave New York (they even try running away), Popi has his way, and the family soon arrives in Florida. After stealing a boat Popi instructs his sons to take the boat out until fuel runs out, jettison the motor, and start rowing back. The boys have qualms but nevertheless obey. With the scheme underway Popi attempts to alert the Coast Guard but fails. Believing that all is lost, he is near suicide when a report comes over the radio concerning the rescue of "two brave Cuban boys." The two are rushed to a hospital in critical condition, suffering from dehydration and sunburn. Thousands of well-wishers send flowers and toys; adoption offers pour in, and the boys receive an invitation to visit the White House. When Popi, variously disguised, finally reaches his sons, they try to make him see how they value his love far more than the security that adoption by wealthy parents would provide. He tries to reason with them, but his noisy protests alert the hospital staff. When he tries to flee, the boys follow, and the entire hoax is exposed. The young boys are overjoyed as a somewhat bewildered Popi returns with them to the old neighborhood. *Widowers. Puerto Ricans. Cubans. Hoaxes. Political refugees. Fatherhood. Poverty. Urban life. Adoption. Slums. Hospitals. Motorboats. New York City—Spanish Harlem. Miami. United States Coast Guard.*

Note: Location scenes filmed in New York City and Miami, Florida.

POPIÓŁ I DIAMENT *see* ASHES AND DIAMONDS

THE POPPY IS ALSO A FLOWER   F6.3883
Telsun Foundation. *For* United Nations. *Dist* Comet Film Distributors, Morin M. Scott. 26 Oct **1966** [Austin, Texas, opening]. Sd; col (Eastmancolor). 35mm. 100 min.

Prod Euan Lloyd. *Exec Prod* Edgar Rosenberg. *U. N. Delegate Prod* Simon Schiffrin. *Dir* Terence Young. *2d Unit Dir* Georges Lampin. *Screenplay* Jo Eisinger. *Story Idea* Ian Fleming. *Photog* Henri Alekan. *2d Unit Photog* Tony Braun. *Art Dir* Maurice Colasson, Tony Roman. *Set Decor* Freda Pearson. *Film Ed* Monique Bonnot, Peter Thornton, Henry Richardson. *Mus* Georges Auric. *Sd Rec* Jean Monchablon. *Prod Supv* Mickey Delamar. *Prod Mgr* Dennis Hall, Clo D'Alban, Hushang Shafti. *Sp Eff* Paul Pollard.

Cast: E. G. Marshall *(Jones)*, Trevor Howard *(Lincoln)*, Gilbert Roland *(Marco)*, Rita Hayworth *(Monique)*, Anthony Quayle *(captain)*, Angie Dickinson *(Linda)*, Yul Brynner *(Colonel Salem)*, Eli Wallach *(Locarno)*, Harold Sakata *(Martin)*, Senta Berger *(nightclub entertainer)*, Hugh Griffith *(tribal chief)*, Marcello Mastroianni *(Inspector Mosca)*, Georges Géret *(Superintendent Roche)*, Howard Vernon *(police analyst)*, Stephen Boyd *(Benson)*, Jocelyn Lane *(society photographer)*, Amedeo Nazzari *(Captain Dinonno)*, Jean-Claude Pascal *(leader of tribesmen)*, Omar Sharif *(Dr. Rad)*, Nadja Tiller *(Dr. Bronovska)*, Barry Sullivan *(Chasen)*, Jack Hawkins *(General Bahar)*, Trini Lopez *(himself)*, Gilda Dahlberg *(guest at Marco's table)*, Luisa Rivelli, Laya Raki, Sylvia Sorente, Marilù Tolo, Violette Marceau, Morteza Kazerouni, Bob Cunningham, Ali Oveisi.

Crime drama. When Benson, a U. S. narcotics investigator, is killed in the Iranian desert after offering to buy opium from a nomadic tribal chief, the United Nations sends agents Lincoln and Jones to smash the dope ring. Their trail leads first to Tehran, where they meet Linda, who, after claiming to be Benson's widow, disappears. The agents plot with U. N. scientists to intercept a cargo of opium, mark it with radioactive tracers, and use Geiger counters to follow it through underworld channels to the drug traffic center. For a while the agents maintain contact with the cargo but then lose it. Eventually the Naples police report having seized the cargo, which is traced to Marco, a wealthy playboy in Monte Carlo. Lincoln finds Marco aboard his yacht, hosting a party attended by Linda, and he questions Marco's wife, Monique, who is a drug addict. The following morning Lincoln's dead body is found, and Jones continues the pursuit alone. He tracks Marco to a Paris-bound train, where he again meets Linda, and she reveals herself to be a U. N. agent. After escaping an attack by Marco's henchmen, they return to Marco's yacht and succeed in implicating him in both the murder and the narcotics ring. *Americans in foreign countries. Narcotics agents. Drug dealers. Drug addicts. Scientists. Police. Playboys. Imposture. Murder. Smuggling. Opium. Yachts. Tehran. Iran. Naples. Monte Carlo. United Nations.*

Note: Location scenes filmed in Iran, Nice, Naples, Rome, Monte Carlo, and Switzerland. First shown on ABC-TV on 22 Apr 1966.

POR UN PUÑADO DE DOLARES *see* A FISTFUL OF DOLLARS

PORNOGRAFI *see* THE EVIL PLEASURE

PORNOGRAPHY: COPENHAGEN 1970   F6.3884
Signature Films, Inc. 17 Apr **1970** [Los Angeles opening]. Sd; col (Eastmancolor). 35mm. 77 min. [Cut from 102 min.]

Dir Jorgen Lyhne. *Photog (see note)* Jefferson Burke, Jeff Stein. *Film Ed* Nils Madsen. *Mus* Frederik Magius. *Sd* Karl Jacobson.

Participants: Mariann Lund, Rodney Aarup, Jorgen Lyhne, Harold R. Shuman *(interviewers)*, Elizabeth Bundgaard.

Narrator: Roy Whaley.

Documentary. Sexual freedom in Copenhagen is explored by several means: interviews on pornography and sexuality are conducted with, among others, a man chosen at random on the street, the clerk of a pornographic bookstore, and a sex exploitation filmmaker; clips from sex films and scenes from the making of an 8mm sex film are shown; and a live sex show club offers both lesbian and heterosexual acts. An actor and participant in three daily group shows reveals in an interview that she is married with two children and commutes every day to her job. "Sex for the Millions," the second annual sex trade fair held in 1970 at Odense, Denmark, is shown with its large displays of pornographic literature offered for sale. The film concludes with a long interview on the topics covered in the film between California psychiatrist Harold R. Shuman and Elizabeth Bundgaard, a Danish sexologist and Copenhagen newspaper columnist. *Danes. Filmmakers. Actors. Psychiatrists. Booksellers. Sex researchers. Columnists. Sexuality. Pornography. Lesbianism. Interviews. Sex clubs. Sex shows. Magazines (periodicals). Fairs. Sex exploitation films. Copenhagen. Odense (Denmark).*

Note: Title changed to *Wide-Open Copenhagen 70* during New York release. Sources conflict on photography credit.

PORNOGRAPHY IN DENMARK: A NEW APPROACH   F6.3885
Dist Sherpix, Inc. 24 Feb **1970** [San Francisco opening]. Sd; col (Eastman Color). 35mm (see note). 90 min. [Cut to 75 min.]

Prod-Dir Alex DeRenzy. *Camera* Jack Kerpan, Paul Gerber, Michael Martin. *Film Ed* Jack Kerpan, Michael Martin, Paul Gerber.

Documentary. This film explores the results of the abolition of all restrictions in Denmark on pornography. Persons attending the first annual sex fair in Copenhagen in 1969 are interviewed, and women wearing see-through clothing are shown selling books and magazines in pornography shops. Scenes of a couple having intercourse before an 8mm movie camera crew are shown, as well as the activities inside Copenhagen's "porno clubs" where members view striptease acts and live sex shows. *Danes. Censorship. Pornography. Striptease. Sex clubs. Bookshops. Sex shows. Sex exploitation films. Fairs. Copenhagen. Denmark.*

Note: Filmed in Denmark in 16mm and blown up to 35mm for theatrical release. Title changed to *Censorship in Denmark: A New Approach.*

PORT OF CALL (Sweden)   F6.3886
Svensk Filmindustri. *Dist* Janus Films. 1 Aug **1963** [New York showing]. Sd; b&w. 35mm. 100 min.

Prod Allan Ekelund. *Dir-Writ* Ingmar Bergman. *Story* Olle Länsberg. *Photog* Gunnar Fischer. *Art Dir* Nils Svenwall. *Film Ed* Oscar Rosander. *Mus* Erland von Koch. *Sd* Sven Hansen.

Cast: Nine-Christine Jönsson *(Berit)*, Bengt Eklund *(Gösta)*, Berta Hall *(Berit's mother)*, Erik Hell *(Berit's father)*, Mimi Nelson *(Gertrud)*, Birgitta Valberg *(welfare worker)*, Stig Olin *(Thomas)*, Sif Ruud *(Mrs. Krona)*, Hans Strååt *(engineer Vilander)*, Nils Dahlgren *(Gertrud's father)*, Nils Hallberg *(Gustav)*, Harry Ahlin *(Skåningen)*, Sven-Eric Gamble.

Drama. Gösta, a disenchanted seaman, is hired as a dockworker in Göteborg. At a dancehall he meets Berit, a young factory worker whom he rescued on the waterfront when she tried to commit suicide; they soon become lovers. Intent on being honest with Gösta, Berit tells him of her poor relationship with her mother, her life in reform school, and her unsuccessful relationships with men. Gösta is disturbed by Berit's past and decides to leave her. Meanwhile, Gertrud, a friend of Berit, asks her for a loan to get an abortion. Berit lends her the money and accompanies her to the abortionist, but Gertrud dies during the operation. Under pressure from her probation officer, Berit gives the police the name of the doctor. Gösta, aware of his loneliness, decides to return to Berit, and the couple prepare to flee to Stockholm, but at the last moment, they decide to remain in Göteborg and face their difficulties together. *Seamen. Factory workers. Suicide. Probation. Abortion. Docks. Göteborg.*

Note: Opened in Stockholm in Oct 1948 as *Hamnstad*; running time: 100 min.

PORT OF SHAME (Reissue) (France)   F6.3887
Entreprise Générale Cinématographie–Hoche Productions–Fidès. 10 Jan **1961** [Los Angeles opening]. Sd; b&w. 35mm. [Feature film, length unknown.]

Note: Released in the United States in 1957 by Times Film Corp. as *Lovers' Net*; distributor of reissue unknown. Opened in Paris in Jan 1955 as *Les amants du Tage*; running time: 123 min.

PORT SINISTER *see* BEAST OF PARADISE ISLE

PORTRAIT *see* DAVID, CAROL, DON, WILL: A PORTRAIT

PORTRAIT OF A MOBSTER   F6.3888
Warner Bros. Pictures. 19 Apr **1961** [New York opening; c22 Apr 1961; LP25362]. Sd; b&w. 35mm. 108 min.

Dir Joseph Pevney. *Screenplay* Howard Browne. *Dir Photog* Gene Polito. *Art Dir* Jack Poplin. *Set Decor* George James Hopkins. *Film Ed* Leo H. Shreve. *Mus* Max Steiner. *Sd* M. A. Merrick. *Asst Dir* Charles Hansen. *Cost Dsgn* Howard Shoup. *Makeup Supv* Gordon Bau. *Supv Hairstylist* Jean Burt Reilly.

Cast: Vic Morrow (*"Dutch" Schultz*), Leslie Parrish (*Iris Murphy*), Peter Breck (*Frank Brennan*), Ray Danton (*"Legs" Diamond*), Norman Alden (*Bo Wetzel*), Robert McQueeney (*Michael Ferris*), Ken Lynch (*Lieut. D. Corbin*), Frank De Kova (*Anthony Parazzo*), Stephen Roberts (*James Guthrie*), Evan McCord (*Vincent "Mad Dog" Coll*), Arthur Tenen (*Steve Matryck*), Frances Morris (*Louise Murphy*), Larry Blake (*John Murphy*), Joseph Turkel (*Joe Noc*), Eddie Hanley (*Matty Krause*), Jon Kowal (*Lou Rhodes*), Harry Holcombe (*Captain Bayridge*), Anthony Eisley (*legal advisor*), Poncie Ponce (*master of ceremonies*).

Crime melodrama. Source: Harry Grey, *Portrait of a Mobster* (New York, 1958). In New York City during Prohibition, two smalltime hoodlums, Dutch Schultz and Bo Wetzel, join Legs Diamond's gang. While on a project for Diamond, Schultz oversteps his authority and kills a bootlegger, John Murphy, who has an attractive daughter named Iris. Though Schultz leaves Diamond to form his own mob, he is unable to forget Iris, and he persuades her to date him, despite her engagement to Frank Brennan, a young police detective. Upon learning that Schultz is a hoodlum, however, she rejects him and marries Frank. The newlyweds have a rough time of it financially, and before long the weak Frank is on Schultz's payroll of corrupt officials. When Iris learns of her husband's duplicity, she leaves him, becomes Schultz's mistress, and turns to alcohol for solace. After eliminating Legs Diamond and Mad Dog Coll, Schultz beats a criminal conspiracy rap and becomes New York's number one underworld czar. When Iris finally learns that it was Schultz who murdered her father, she moves into a rundown boarding house and becomes a hopeless alcoholic. Frank eventually finds her there, and the two decide to make a new life together. Schultz, meanwhile, is having trouble with the Mafia and he attempts to placate them by agreeing to allow his top lieutenants, including Bo, to be killed. The attack takes place, but, unknown to Schultz, the assassins have orders to kill him, too. Though he escapes, he is shot and killed by Bo, who, mortally wounded himself, mistakes Schultz for one of the assassins. *Hoodlums. Gangsters. Gangs. Bootleggers. Duplicity. Alcoholism. Mafia. Prohibition. Police. Murder. Marriage. Legs Diamond. Mad Dog Coll. Dutch Schultz. New York City.*

PORTRAIT OF A SINNER (Great Britain)
F6.3889

Renown Pictures. *Dist* American International Pictures. 22 Feb **1961** [Cincinnati, Ohio, opening; c23 Jan 1961; LP21142]. Sd (Westrex); b&w. 35mm. 96 min.

Pres by George Minter. A Minter-Siodmak Production. *Prod* George Minter. *Dir* Robert Siodmak. *Screenplay* Audrey Erskine Lindop, Dudley Leslie. *Photog* Otto Heller. *Camera Op* Harold Haysom. *Focus* Manny Wynn. *Camera Grip* Pat Newman. *Art Dir* Ken Adam. *Asst Art Dir* Herbert Smith. *Draughtsman* Thomas Goswell, Bill Bennison. *Film Ed* Gordon Pilkington. *Asst Ed* Don Challis. *Mus Comp* Douglas Gamley. *Cond* Muir Mathieson. *Played by* Sinfonia of London. *Dance Mus* Ken Jones. *Rec Supv* A. W. Watkins. *Sd Rec* Cyril Swern, J. B. Smith. *Dub Ed* Rusty Coppleman. *Boom Op* Bill Baldwin. *Sd Camera Op* Bill Robson. *1st, 2d & 3d Asst Dir* Tom Pevsner, Gerry Arbeid, Peter Honri. *Prod Mgr* Al Marcus. *Cont* Doreen Francis. *Prod Sec* Trix Wilkin. *Dress Dsgn* Julie Harris, cost. *Wardrobe Supv* Harry Haynes. *Wardrobe Mistress* Tina Swanson. *Makeup* Harold Fletcher. *Hairstyles* Joan White. *Dial Adv* Elizabeth Montagu. *Casting Dir* Maude Spector. *Prop Buyer* Bill Isaacs. *Still Photog* Joe Pearce.

Cast: Nadja Tiller (*Ila Hansen*), Tony Britton (*Mike Thompson*), William Bendix (*Reg Barker*), Natasha Parry (*Margaret Goreham*), Norman Wooland (*David Fraser*), Donald Wolfit (*Lord Drewell*), Tony Wright (*Jack*), Adrienne Corri (*Jane Buller*), Joyce Carey (*Mrs. Thompson*), John Welsh (*Dr. Thompson*), Martin Miller (*Piggy*), Michael Ward (*head waiter*), Edward Chapman (*Willy Catch*), Norman Pierce (*barman*), Beatrice Varley (*hotel manageress*), Myles Eason (*Bobby Montagu-Jones*), Cyril Smith (*taxi driver*), Geoffrey Bayldon (*Ransom*).

Drama. Source: Robin Maugham, *The Rough and the Smooth* (London, 1951). Angered with his overbearing fiancée, young archeologist Mike Thompson becomes involved with the mysterious Ila Hansen, a German woman who, at 16 years of age, was raped by Jack, a friend of her sailor brother. As their affair progresses, Mike learns that Ila is sharing a flat with her boss, Reg Barker. Mike's anger is moderated when the older man explains that he is impotent and that the arrangement is strictly for business purposes. Soon thereafter, Jack appears and demands that Ila give him £1,500 he needs to avoid imminent trouble. When Ila is unable to get the money from either Mike or Reg, she turns on them and brazenly admits that Jack is the only man capable of satisfying her sexual appetite. Unable to face the future without Ila, Reg commits suicide. Ila then goes to Mike's fiancée, Margaret Goreham, and tries

to barter Mike for cash. When she is scorned, Ila, realizing she has lost all three men, walks out and picks up the first man who comes along. *Archeologists. Germans. Sailors. Rape. Brother-sister relationship. Employer-employee relations. Impotence. Suicide.*

Note: Opened in London in Oct 1959 as *The Rough and the Smooth*; running time: 99 min.

PORTRAIT OF CHIEKO (Japan)
F6.3890

Shochiku Co. 13 Mar **1968** [Los Angeles opening]. Sd; col (Eastmancolor). 35mm. 125 min.

Dir Noboru Nakamura. *Screenplay* Minoru Hirose, Noboru Nakamura. *Photog* Hiroshi Takemura. *Art Dir* Tatsuo Hamada. *Mus* Masaru Sato.

Cast: Tetsuro Tamba (*Kotaro Takamura*), Shima Iwashita (*Chieko*), Eiji Okada (*Tsubaki*), Takamaru Sasaki (*Koun Takamura*), Jin Nakayama (*Hoshu*), Yoko Minamida (*Kazuko*).

Drama. Source: Haruo Sato, *Shosetsu Chieko Sho* (Japan, 1963). Chieko, wife of the renowned Japanese poet and sculptor Kotaro Takamura, desperately seeks to express her own artistry as a painter. She passionately devotes herself to the creation of beauty, but critical response is discouraging, and the dawning realization that she lacks the creative capacity to achieve her goal begins to drive her mad. Kotaro grows to the task of understanding his wife's problem and tenderly ministers to her wants, writing moving poems to and about her. Chieko finally admits defeat and abortively attempts suicide. Her mental condition deteriorates rapidly, and she finally dies of pneumonia. *Painters. Poets. Sculptors. Marriage. Insanity. Suicide. Pneumonia. Art. Kotaro Takamura. Chieko Takamura.*

Note: Released in Japan in 1967 as *Chieko-sho*.

PORTRAIT OF HELL (Japan)
F6.3891

Toho Co. ca18 Nov **1969** [Los Angeles showing]. Sd; col (Eastmancolor). 35mm (Panavision). 91 min.

Prod Tomoyuki Tanaka. *Dir* Shiro Toyoda. *Screenplay* Toshio Yasumi. *Photog* Kazuo Yamada. *Art Dir* Shinobu Muraki. *Mus* Yasushi Akutagawa.

Cast: Kinnosuke Nakamura (*Lord Hosokawa*), Tatsuya Nakadai (*Yoshihide*), Yoko Naito (*Yoshika*), Shun Oide.

Melodrama. Source: Ryunosuke Akutagawa, "Jigokuhen," serialized in *Tokyo Nichi Nichi* (1918). In 10th-century Japan, Yoshihide, a headstrong Korean painter, lives with his daughter, Yoshika, who is courted by her father's Japanese apprentice. Both the suitor's youth and his Japanese heritage are repugnant to Yoshihide, and the young man is banished from the house and forbidden to see Yoshika. The girl flees to the court of the despotic, arrogant Lord Hosokawa. Yoshihide is ordered to paint a mural for the lord's temple in exchange for his daughter's return, but the painter agrees only to create a depiction of hell. The bargain is struck, whereupon the two men begin a contest of wills. In the interest of artistic truth, Yoshihide ties up the youth assigned to assist him and releases a crock of snakes. He then demands a burning carriage to be occupied by the lord. Lord Hosokawa responds by providing a carriage with Yoshika chained inside, and he threatens that she will burn to death if Yoshihide does not apologize for his impudent behavior. The artist, disbelieving the threat, refuses, and his daughter dies in the flames. Yoshihide completes the portrait, depicting Lord Hosokawa in the burning carriage, and then hangs himself. The painting casts a spell over the despot, and he goes mad. *Koreans. Painters. Despots. Hostages. Filial relations. Nationalism. Supernatural. Pride. Insanity. Suicide. Spells. Fires. Snakes.*

Note: Released in Japan in Sep 1969 as *Jigokuhen*; running time: 95 min.

PORTRAIT OF JASON
F6.3892

Film-Makers' Distribution Center-Shirley Clarke. *Dist* Film-Makers' Distribution Center. 2 Oct **1967** [New York opening]. Sd; b&w. 16mm & 35mm. 105 min.

Prod-Dir Shirley Clarke. *Photog* Jeri Sapanen. *Film Ed* Shirley Clarke. *Sd* Francis Daniel. *Prod Asst* Robert Fiore. *Asst* Jim Hubbard.

Cast: Jason Holliday (*himself*).

Documentary. This cinema vérité portrait of Jason Holliday, a 33-year-old black male prostitute who dreams of a career as a nightclub entertainer, is drawn from 12 consecutive hours of filming in a New York City apartment. As Jason reminisces about his past and speculates about his future, all the while smoking marijuana and drinking, the filmmaker and some friends prod him with questions and taunts from off camera. Jason, born Aaron Paine in Newark, New Jersey, describes in frequently humorous fashion his traumatic confrontations with his family, the orgies he has attended, and the hustling that has formed the pattern of his life as a black, homosexual outcast. His "performance" includes brief impersonations of Mae West, Butterfly McQueen, and Pearl Bailey. He recalls that he was a college dropout, worked as a bar hustler and as a servile houseboy in San Francisco, has been a heroin addict, and has spent time in jail, on the Bowery, and in a hospital mental ward. *Negroes. Drug addicts. Houseboys. Ex-convicts. Male homosexuality. Prostitution. Female* *impersonation. Mental illness. Marijuana. New York City. New York City—Bowery. San Francisco.*

Note: Filmed in 16mm.

PORTRAIT OF LENIN (Poland/U.S.S.R.) **F6.3893**
Mosfilm–Studio Film Unit–Film Polski. *Dist* Artkino Pictures, Brandon Films. 10 Nov **1967** [New York opening]. Sd; b&w. 35mm (Sovscope). 98 min.

Dir Sergey Yutkevich. *Screenplay* Yevgeniy Gabrilovich, Sergey Yutkevich. *Photog* Jan Laskowski. *Camera* Kazimierz Madejski, Vladimir Pishchalnikov. *Art Dir* Jan Grandys. *Asst Art Dir* Feliks Zbarskiy. *Mus* Adam Walaciński. *Sd* Józef Bartczak. *Asst Dir* Jan Rutkiewicz, Lyutsiya Okhrimenko. *Sp Eff* Boris Travkin, A. Rudachenko.

Cast: Maksim Shtraukh *(V. I. Lenin)*, Anna Lisyanskaya *(Krupskaya)*, Antonina Pavlycheva *(Krupskaya's mother)*, Ilona Kuśmierska *(Ulka)*, Edmund Fetting *(Hanecki)*, Krzysztof Kalczyński *(Andrzej)*, Tadeusz Fijewski *(secretary of the prison)*, Henryk Hunko, Ludwik Benoit *(guards)*, Gustaw Lutkiewicz *(investigator)*, Kazimierz Rudzki *(priest)*, Zbigniew Skowroński *(Matyszczuk)*, Jarema Stępowski *(photographer)*, Vladimir Akimov, Nikolay Kashirskiy, Vladimir Monakhov, Andrey Petrov, actor, Gennadiy Yukhtin, J. Gruca, E. Jeżewska, W. Jakubińska, A. Jurczak, A. Łodziński, J. Marchand, B. Michalski, Jerzy Moes, Józef Nowak, A. Nowak, A. Potapov, W. Rajewski, A. Skupień, R. Zaorski, A. Żuliński.

Biographical drama. In Poland shortly after the outbreak of the First World War, Austrian police arrest Vladimir Ilich Lenin as a suspected Russian spy and confine him in the prison of the town of Nowy Targ. He passes the time in thinking of the events preceding his arrest: Lenin, his wife Krupskaya, and her mother live in the town of Poronin in the Tatra foothills. From this point in exile, Lenin writes articles for the revolutionary journal *Pravda*. Ulka, a Polish peasant girl beloved by the family, helps with household tasks. She joins Lenin on a mountain hike and is profoundly impressed by his rapport with the peasants. Lenin meets her boyfriend, Andrzej, a shepherd devoted to the Polish nationalist cause. Andrzej sets his dogs against the town gendarme, Matyszczuk, when the gendarme accuses him of trespassing. Lenin shelters Andrzej from the police and tries unsuccessfully to sway him from national to class loyalty. Meanwhile, the young couple celebrate their betrothal. Lenin helps to smuggle Andrzej to Krakow and along the way learns of the assassination of Archduke Ferdinand. Shortly afterwards, Ulka disappears; Lenin later learns that she was jailed and beaten when she refused to inform on him. Lenin is arrested by Matyszczuk, and Andrzej dies in the cause of Polish freedom. Released from prison at last, Lenin travels into neutral Switzerland with Krupskaya and her mother to continue his work for the revolution. *Revolutionaries. Domestics. Peasants. Shepherds. Police. Nationalism. Communism. Marxism. Exile. Class conflict. Prisons. World War I. Krakow (Poland). Tatra Mountains. Poronin (Poland). Nowy Targ (Poland). Nikolai Lenin. Nadezhda Konstantinovna Krupskaya.*

Note: Released in the U.S.S.R. in 1966 as *Lenin v Polshe*; in Poland as *Lenin w Polsce*.

PORTRAITS OF WOMEN (Finland) **F6.3894**
FJ-Filmi–Jörn Donner Productions. *Dist* Allied Artists. 30 Dec **1970** [San Francisco opening]. Sd; col (Eastmancolor). 35mm. 90 min. *MPAA rating* X.

Prod Arno Carlstedt. *Dir-Writ* Jörn Donner. *Photog* Heikki Katajisto. *Film Ed* Jörn Donner, Erkii Seiro. *Mus* Claes af Geijerstam. *Sd* Paul Jyrala. *Asst Dir* Jaakko Talaskivi.

Cast: Ritva Vepsä *(Saara)*, Kirsti Wallasvaara *(Liisa)*, Marianne Holmström *(Ulla)*, Jörn Donner *(Pertti)*, Aarre Elo *(Jussi)*, Henrik Granö *(Sven)*, Jaakko Talaskivi *(Peter Von Spaak)*, Lennart Laurama *(producer)*, Helena Makela *(journalist)*, Jukka Sipilä *(agent)*, Heli Sakki *(actress)*, Hannu Oravisto *(pupil)*, Juhani Kumpulainen.

Comedy. Pornographic film director Pertti returns from the United States to his native Finland. At a dinner party in his honor given by married friends Liisa and Jussi, the drunken director makes an unsuccessful pass at Saara, a neurotic schoolteacher. Although he is the houseguest of Jussi, he seduces his host's wife. Inspired to make a pornographic film in Finland, Pertti hires a compliant couple, Ulla and Sven, and transports the pair to a remote island. During a break in the filming, Pertti resumes his pursuit of Saara, whom he finds not only acquiescent, but possessive. Relationships are further complicated by Liisa's threat to tell Jussi of their affair, and by Saara's insistence on moving in with him at Liisa and Jussi's home. Furthermore, when Sven quits the film because of its lack of political commitment, Pertti succeeds him as Ulla's lover. Learning that a warrant has been issued for his arrest on a charge of obscenity, Pertti flees Finland on an ocean liner. Following in a speedboat, Saara boards the ship, hurls the cans of film overboard, and forces Pertti into his stateroom. Satisfying himself that the negative is securely hidden, Pertti complies with Saara's sexual demands. *Pornographers. Houseguests. Motion picture directors. Schoolteachers. Actors. Mistresses. Seduction. Infidelity. Jealousy. Drunkenness. Sex exploitation films. Islands. Ocean liners. Speedboats.*

Note: Released in Finland in 1970 as *Naisenkuvia*.

POSITIONS *see* **PUT UP OR SHUT UP**

POSITIONS OF LOVE *see* **PUT UP OR SHUT UP**

POSSE FROM HELL **F6.3895**
Universal Pictures. May **1961** [c23 Mar 1961; LP24332]. Sd; col (Eastman Color). 35mm. 89 min.

Prod Gordon Kay. *Asst Prod* Willard Willingham. *Dir* Herbert Coleman. *Screenplay* Clair Huffaker. *Photog* Clifford Stine. *Camera Op* William Dodds. *Art Dir* Alexander Golitzen, Alfred Sweeney. *Set Decor* Oliver Emert. *Film Ed* Frederic Knudtson. *Mus Supv* Joseph Gershenson. *Sd* Waldon O. Watson, Joe Lapis. *Asst Dir* Ray Gosnell, Jr., Douglas Green. *Prod Mgr* Norman Deming. *Script Supv* Marshall Schlom. *Makeup* Bud Westmore. *Hairstyles* Larry Germain.

Cast: Audie Murphy *(Banner Cole)*, John Saxon *(Seymour Kern)*, Zohra Lampert *(Helen Caldwell)*, Vic Morrow *(Crip)*, Robert Keith *(Captain Brown)*, Ward Ramsey *(Marshal Webb)*, Rudolph Acosta *(Johnny Caddo)*, Royal Dano *(Uncle Billy Caldwell)*, Frank Overton *(Burt Hogan)*, James Bell *(Benson)*, Paul Carr *(Jack Wiley)*, Lee Van Cleef *(Leo)*, Ray Teal *(Larson)*, Forrest Lewis *(Dr. Welles)*, Charles Horvath *(Hash)*, Harry Lauter *(Russell)*, Henry Wills *(Chunk)*, Stuart Randall *(Luke Gorman)*, Allan Lane *(Burl Hogan)*.

Western melodrama. Source: Clair Huffaker, *Posse From Hell* (New York, 1958). Four killers escape from prison and invade the small Western town of Paradise, where they murder four men and rob the local bank. They abduct young Helen Caldwell as they depart, rape her on the trail, and then leave her to die. Former gunslinger Banner Cole sets out after the gang with a posse of seven, including city-born bank clerk Seymour Kern, who has volunteered to join the hunters. After finding and rescuing Helen, they track down and kill one of the outlaws. The posse dwindles as the hunt continues until only Banner, Helen, and Seymour remain. They manage to round up the remaining outlaws, however, and with peace once more restored, Banner agrees to become the marshal of Paradise, and Helen agrees to remain by his side. *Prison escapees. Gunfighters. Bank clerks. Murder. Bank robberies. Abduction. Rape.*

Note: Location scenes filmed in the Lone Pine area of California.

THE POSTGRADUATE **F6.3896**
Kariofilms–Haljay Film. *Dist* Kariofilms. 26 Aug **1970** [New York opening]. Sd; col. 16mm. 75 min.

Prod John Flanders. *Dir* Harold Kovner. *Screenplay* Harold Kovner, Jay Campbell. *Photog* Wes Belson. *Film Ed* Harold Kovner, Jay Campbell. *Mus* Cheyenne. *Sd* Jay Campbell.

Cast: John Dugan *(Professor Collins)*, Bert Lewison, Babs Lewison *(1st couple)*, Darwin Burke, Randi Sablon *(2d couple)*, Danny Sillman, Fran Carston *(3d couple)*, Robert Weaver, Don Jones *(boys)*, Michael Barber, Jan Barber *(hippies)*, Candy Bacardi, Linda Bloom, Barry Cornwall, Allan Figaro, Michael Garson, Pamela Garson, Danny Ireland, Eric Van West, Louis Velez, Marcie Webster *(students)*, Alan Saunders *(venereal disease doctor)*, Leo Slezak *(boy)*, Bonnie Podrid *(girl)*.

Sex film. A teacher lectures to a class of students. Five of the students have erotic daydreams during the lecture. At the conclusion of the film, the teacher warns the students of the dangers of venereal disease. *Schoolteachers. Students. Venereal disease. Sexuality. Fantasy.*

THE POSTMAN GOES TO WAR (France) **F6.3897**
Les Films J.-J. Vital–Alcinter-Régina. *Dist* Trans-Lux Distributing Corp. Nov **1967**. Sd; col (Eastman Color). 35mm (Techniscope). 95 min.

Pres by Official Films. *Prod* Jean-Jacques Vital, André Cotton. *Dir* Claude Bernard-Aubert. *Screenplay* René Hardy, Claude Bernard-Aubert, Claude Accursi, Pascal Jardin. *Photog* Marcel Grignon. *Film Ed* Gabriel Rongier. *Mus* Georges Garvarentz.

Cast: Charles Aznavour *(Thibon)*, Daniel Ceccaldi *(Cassagne)*, Jacques Richard *(Klein)*, Maria Minh *(Vang)*, Helmut Schneider *(Maury)*, Jess Hahn *(Jess)*, Franco Fabrizi *(Ritoni)*, Doudou Babet *(Clementine)*, Lucien Barjon.

War comedy-drama. Source: Gaston-Jean Gautier, *Le facteur s'en va-t-en guerre* (Paris, 1966). Thibon, a resourceful Parisian postman, enlists for the French-Indochina War and is sent to Cambodia. He soon becomes disenchanted with the war, however, and is injured in a mine explosion. Thibon is released from the infirmary, and his regiment receives orders to defend Dien Bien Phu, but the group is captured by the Communists. They manage to escape, narrowly missing news of the armistice. Thibon returns to France with a Cambodian woman with whom he has fallen in love. *Mail carriers. Prisoners of war. Combat zone life. Mines (war explosives). French-Indochina War 1945–54. Indochina. Cambodia. Dien Bien Phu. France—Army.*

Note: Released in France in 1966 as *Le facteur s'en va-t-en guerre*; running time: 90 min. Filmed in Cambodia.

IL POSTO see THE SOUND OF TRUMPETS

POSTORONNIM VKHOD VOSPRESHCHEN see WELCOME KOSTYA!

DER POSTZUG-ÜBERFALL see THE GREAT BRITISH TRAIN ROBBERY

POTPOURRI F6.3898

MDO Enterprises. *Dist* Distribpix, Inc. Jul **1969**. Sd; col 35mm. 62 min. *Dir* Max Bush, II. *Writ* Joe Russo. *Mus* P. J. Vols.

Cast: Avery Akers, Betty Bruce.

Documentary. This film is a documentary view of the New York sex scene; it contains sequences of live sex shows filmed in several underground nightclubs by hidden cameras and scenes from a highly erotic striptease recorded for "peep show" viewing. Among the acts shown are: two models making love with a photographer, a black prostitute servicing a shoe fetishist, a voyeur watching two lesbians play, and a couple fornicating and then performing mutual oral intercourse. *Models. Photographers. Prostitutes. Sexuality. Striptease. Fetishism. Lesbianism. Oral sex. Voyeurism. Stag shows. New York City.*

POUND F6.3899

Pound Films. *Dist* United Artists. 17 Aug **1970** [New York opening; c17 Aug 1970; LP40363]. Sd; col (De Luxe). 35mm. 92 min. *MPAA rating* X.

Prod Floyd L. Peterson. *Assoc Prod* Ronald Nealy. *Dir-Writ* Robert Downey. *Dir Photog* Gerald Cotts. *Lighting* Jack Reidel. *Art Dir* Salvatore Romano. *Film Ed* Bud Smith. *Mus* Charley Cuva. *Lyr* Robert Downey. *Sd* Francis Daniel. *Sp Asst to the Dir* Sharon Sachs. *Cost* Wendy Appel.

Cast: Joe Madden *(Colonel)*, James Greene *(Honky Killer)*, Mari-Claire Charba *(his wife)*, Errol Jaye *(Lieutenant Weintraub)*, Carolyn Cardwell *(keeper)*, Charles Dierkop *(airedale)*, Lawrence Wolf *(Mexican hairless)*, Ching Yeh *(Siamese cat)*, Marshall Efron *(dachshund)*, Eric Krupnik *(Montana sheepdog)*, Elsie Downey *(mutt bitch)*, Chuck Green *(mutt)*, Don Calfa *(Italian terrier)*, Stan Gottlieb *(boxer)*, Carolyn Groves *(pedigreed bitch)*, George Morgan *(Irish setter)*, Harry Rigby *(penguin)*, Eric Crawley *(Baltimore pointer)*, Lucille Rogers *(old Pekingese bitch)*, Buddy Butler *(singing water spaniel)*, Robert Downey *(puppy)*, Carl Lee *(thief)*, Antonio Fargas *(greyhound)*, Robert Kocourek *(uniformed lackey)*, Allison Downey *(angel)*, Barry "Spider" Rubin *(visitor to pound)*.

Allegory. Source: Robert Downey, *The Comeuppance* (a play; production undetermined). As a group of canines awaits execution at the city pound, a mass murderer, the Honky Killer, stalks the streets of New York. Over the objections of a pedigreed bitch, an Italian terrier plans their keeper's death. A gentle airedale, however, assures his fellows that the governor's pardon is imminent. After unsuccessfully propositioning the pound's female populace, an Irish setter masturbates before the enthusiastic male inmates. While a mutt bemoans her impending destruction, a Mexican hairless proclaims his sky-diving prowess and loudly laments his baldness, and a Baltimore pointer fantasizes literary fame. As a Siamese cat philosophizes, an expiring penguin is eulogized by a water spaniel. The afternoon ends and gas seeps into the cell, killing the prisoners one by one. *Murder. Autoeroticism. Death. Funerals. Pounds. New York City. Dogs. Cats. Penguins.*

Note: Location scenes filmed in New York City.

LA POUPÉE (France) F6.3900

Films Franco Africains. *Dist* Lionex Films, Gaston Hakim Productions International. 28 Aug **1963** [New York opening]. Sd; col (Eastmancolor). 35mm (Franscope, see note). 90 min.

Pres by Lionex Films. *Prod-Dir* Jacques Baratier. *Screenplay* Jacques Audiberti. *Photog* Raoul Coutard. *Art Dir* Georges Koskas. *Film Ed* Léonide Azar. *Mus* Joseph Kosma, Jorge Milschberg, Bernard Parmeggiani. *Songs* Jorge Milschberg. *Sung by* Catherine Sauvage. *Sd* Raymond Gauguier. *Prod Mgr* Antoine Maestratti.

Cast: Zbigniew Cybulski *(Colonel Prado Roth/Coral)*, Sonne Teal *(Marion/La Poupée)*, Claudio Gora *(Moren)*, Catherine Milinaire *(Mirt)*, Jean Aron *(Professor Palmas)*, Sacha Pitoëff *(Sayas)*, Daniel Emilfork *(Gant de Crin [Horsehair])*, Jacques Dufilho *(The Indian)*, Gabriel Jabbour *(Joachim)*, Michel de Ré *(Gervasio)*, Laszlo Szabo *(Pascuel)*, Roger Karl *(Terremoche)*, Jean Galland *(Gonziano)*, Max Montavon *(scientist)*.

Comedy-drama. Source: Jacques Audiberti, *La poupée* (Paris, 1958). Colonel Prado Roth, a brutal South American dictator, is having an affair with Marion, wife of the great industrialist Moren. A revolutionary group, including Coral, Gant de Crin, and Pascuel, plan to assassinate the dictator. Moren sees the revolution as a useful business proposition, and his daughter, Mirt, becomes involved by falling in love with Coral. Professor Palmas, another revolutionary, has discovered the means of duplicating matter and creates a doll in the image of Marion, which can only live for 36 hours. He enters the body of the doll in order to control it, and as a nightclub dancer and stirring speaker, the doll

becomes a symbol of revolt. Gant de Crin, unable to control his urge to kill, assassinates the dictator at a banquet before the appointed hour. Afterwards, practically everybody is revealed to be associated with the revolutionary party. Fearing that the revolution may collapse without the impetus of a well-staged assassination, Coral, the dictator's double, is forced to impersonate him and be assassinated in public at the proper time. Unwittingly Coral agrees, but once in the dictator's uniform, he begins to act as the dictator. The people who have risen in response to the doll are led into a trap and shot. [Other sources indicate that Moren orders Coral not to shoot the people.] The doll vanishes, and the dictatorship continues. *Dictators. Doubles. Revolutionaries. Inventors. Industrialists. Dancers. Revolts. Assassination. Infidelity. Impersonation. Dolls. Nightclubs. South America.*

Note: Opened in Paris in Nov 1962 at 95 min; Cannes Film Festival running time: 100 min. U. S. press material lists wide-screen process as CinemaScope. Also known as *He, She or It!*

LES POUPÉES see BAMBOLE

THE POWER F6.3901

Galaxy Productions. *Dist* Metro-Goldwyn-Mayer, Inc. 21 Feb **1968** [Boston opening; c20 Dec 1967; LP35000]. Sd; col (Metrocolor). 35mm (Panavision). 109 min. [Also reviewed at 104 min.]

A George Pal Production. *Prod* George Pal. *Dir* Byron Haskin. *Screenplay* John Gay. *Dir Photog* Ellsworth Fredricks. *Art Dir* George W. Davis, Merrill Pye. *Set Decor* Henry Grace, Don Greenwood, Jr. *Film Ed* Thomas J. McCarthy. *Mus Comp & Cond* Miklos Rozsa. *Rec Supv* Franklin Milton. *Sp Electronic Sd Eff* Lovell Norman. *Asst Dir* E. Darrell Hallenbeck. *Unit Prod Mgr* Ralph W. Nelson. *Asst to the Prod* Gae Griffith. *Makeup* William Tuttle. *Hairstyles* Sydney Guilaroff. *Sp Vis Eff* J. McMillan Johnson, Gene Warren, Wah Chang.

Cast: George Hamilton *(Jim Tanner)*, Suzanne Pleshette *(Margery Lansing)*, Richard Carlson *(N. E. Van Zandt)*, Yvonne De Carlo *(Sally Hallson)*, Earl Holliman *(Talbot Scott)*, Gary Merrill *(Mark Corlane)*, Ken Murray *(Grover)*, Barbara Nichols *(Flora)*, Arthur O'Connell *(Henry Hallson)*, Nehemiah Persoff *(Carl Melniker)*, Aldo Ray *(Bruce)*, Michael Rennie *(Arthur Nordlund)*, Miiko Taka *(Mrs. Van Zandt)*, Celia Lovsky *(Mrs. Hallson)*, Vaughn Taylor *(Mr. Hallson)*, Lawrence Montaigne *(Briggs)*.

Science fiction melodrama. Source: Frank M. Robinson, *The Power* (Philadelphia, 1956). At a space laboratory meeting presided over by naval liaison officer Arthur Nordlund, scientists involved in a research project on human endurance are warned by fellow member Henry Hallson that one of them possesses a super-intelligence capable of controlling other minds and effecting destruction through sheer willpower. None of Hallson's co-workers—including biochemist Jim Tanner, geneticist Margery Lansing, physicist Carl Melniker, chairman N. E. Van Zandt, and biologist Talbot Scott—is convinced until Hallson is found murdered with the name Adam Hart scrawled near his dead body. Tanner, Insp. Mark Corlane's chief suspect, begins an investigation of his own and learns from Hallson's widow, Sally, that her husband had a childhood friend named Adam Hart. Although Tanner loses his job at the laboratory, he persists in his search as one by one the other members of the research group are killed off, Tanner himself barely escaping death at the hands of the mysterious force. Eventually Tanner learns that Nordlund (alias Adam Hart) is the villain, and that he hopes to conquer the world for the sake of "good." Tanner, who also possesses a superhuman brain, finally summons sufficient strength to destroy Nordlund. *Scientists. Biochemists. Physicists. Biologists. Megalomania. Researchers. Murder. Telekinesis. Laboratories.*

Note: Locations filmed in Lancaster, California.

POŻEGNANIA see PARTINGS

IL POZZO DELLE TRE VERITÀ see THREE FACES OF SIN

PRAVDA (France) F6.3902

Dziga-Vertov Group–Centre Européen pour le Cinéma, la Radio et la Télévision. *Dist* Grove Press. 21 May **1970** [New York opening]. Sd; col (Agfa-Gevaert). 16mm. 76 min.

Prod-Dir-Writ Jean-Luc Godard, Jean-Pierre Gorin, Jean-Henri Rober, Paul Burron. *Exec Prod* Claude Nedjar.

Film essay. The setting of the film is Czechoslovakia after the Soviet invasion of 1968. In an imaginary conversation in which they attack Soviet revisionism, narrators Vladimir and Rosa (Vladimir Ilyich Lenin and Rosa Luxemburg) discuss, among other topics, the evolution of Communism, the state of the proletariat, and the problems of bureaucracy. The images in the film are dominated by the color red; and the recurring visual metaphor is a red rose, which is finally destroyed. The film ends with a view of a truck moving toward the left and flying a red flag while a revolutionary song is played. However, since the camera is tracking left, the red flag disappears to the right in the final scene. *Communism. Marxism. Czechoslovakia. Czechoslovakia—History—*

Soviet Invasion 1968. Union of Soviet Socialist Republics. Nikolai Lenin. Rosa Luxemburg.

Note: Filmed in Czechoslovakia in 1969.

EL PRECIO DE UN HOMBRE *see* **THE UGLY ONES**

PRECIOUS JEWELS   F6.3903

Art in Motion (A. I. M.) Productions–Times Ten. *Dist* Grads Corp., Clamil Productions. 2 Sep **1969** [Maryland license]. Sd; col (Eastman Color). 35mm. 58-77 min.

Dir-Writ William Stagg. *Film Ed* Moe Macky.

Cast: Don Auld, Peter Deb, Dee Lockwood, Chet Washington, Bob Ball, Rose M. Howard, Antoinette Maynard, Mary Jane Wallace, Mickey Jines, Marlon Harper, Stuart Lancaster.

Drama. Retired jewel thief Jeff Fielding, owner of a gambling casino, agrees to help his longtime friend and client Ralph Taylor, who needs $30,000 to pay back his losses at Jeff's club. Jeff's mission is to steal a valuable necklace from Ralph's daughter Kathy, so that Ralph can collect the insurance. Kathy, however, hits on the same idea, and hires Jeff's archenemies Max and Ray to steal the necklace. Complications arise when Kathy falls for Jeff, who makes love to a number of women in his efforts to find the jewels. *Thieves. Gamblers. Theft. Debt. Jewels. Casinos. Insurance.*

PREHISTORIC PLANET WOMEN *see* **WOMEN OF THE PREHISTORIC PLANET**

PREHISTORIC WOMEN (Great Britain)   F6.3904

Seven Arts Productions–Hammer Film Productions. *Dist* Twentieth Century-Fox Film Corp. 25 Jan **1967** [Detroit opening; c31 Dec 1966; LP34063]. Sd (RCA); col (De Luxe). 35mm (CinemaScope). 91 min. [Also reviewed at 95 min.]

Prod-Dir Michael Carreras. *Exec Prod* Anthony Hinds. *Assoc Prod* Aida Young. *Screenplay* Henry Younger. *Dir Photog* Michael Reed. *Camera Op* Robert Thomson. *Art Dir* Robert Jones. *Supv Ed* James Needs. *Ed* Roy Hyde. *Mus Comp* Carlo Martelli. *Mus Supv* Philip Martell. *Choreog* Denys Palmer. *Sd Mix* Sash Fisher, Len Shilton. *Rec Dir* A. W. Lumkin. *Dub Ed* Charles Crafford. *Asst Dir* David Tringham. *Prod Mgr* Ross Mackenzie. *Cont* Eileen Head. *Cost Dsgn* Carl Toms. *Wardrobe Mistress* Jackie Breed. *Makeup Supv* Wally Schneiderman. *Hairdressing Supv* Olga Angelinetta. *Sp Eff* George Blackwell.

Cast: Martine Beswick *(Kari)*, Edina Ronay *(Saria)*, Michael Latimer *(David Marchant)*, Stephanie Randall *(Amyak)*, Carol White *(Gido)*, Alexandra Stevenson *(Luri)*, Yvonne Horner *(1st Amazon)*, Sydney Bromley *(Ullo)*, Frank Hayden *(Arja)*, Robert Raglan *(Colonel Hammond)*, Mary Hignett *(Mrs. Hammond)*, Louis Mahoney *(head boy)*, Bari Johnson *(high priest)*, Danny Daniels *(Jakara)*, Steven Berkoff *(John)*, Sally Caclough *(Amazon)*.

Adventure drama. David Marchant, hunting on an African safari, goes into some brush after a wounded leopard and comes to a tree trunk bearing a carved white rhinoceros. When his native guides refuse to go any farther, he ventures on alone and is captured by warriors who take him to a strange prehistoric land ruled by brunette Amazon women. Kari, their cruel queen, commands the intruder to dine with her and later summons him to make love; David rejects her advances, however, and is thrown into a dungeon with other male captives. Saria, a beautiful blonde slave, is about to be offered as a tribal sacrifice, but David breaks his manacles to free her and the other prisoners. During the ensuing fight, a white rhinoceros suddenly charges out of the bush and kills Kari. Free once again, David reluctantly leaves Saria, with whom he has fallen in love, to return to his own world. Back on the trail, he wakes up seemingly from a dream, but in his hand is a rhinoceros talisman she gave him. Upon arriving at camp, he is introduced to a new member of the safari, who is the exact image of Saria. *Hunters. Man—Prehistoric. Amazons. Human sacrifice. Slavery. Imprisonment. Rescue. Safaris. Talismans. Africa. Rhinoceros.*

Note: Produced in Great Britain in 1966 and opened in London in Jul 1968 as *Slave Girls*; running time: 74 min.

PRELUDE TO ECSTASY (Finland)   F6.3905

Suomen Filmiteollisuus. *Dist* Manson Distributing Corp. 5 Apr **1963** [Los Angeles showing]. Sd; b&w. 35mm. 84 min.

Prod-Dir-Writ Toivo Särkkä. *Photog* Olavi Tuomi. *Art Dir* Aarre Koivisto. *Film Ed* Elmer Lahti. *Mus Score* Einar Englund. *Sd* Kuru Vilija.

Cast: Liana Kaarina *(Elsie)*, Toivo Makela *(Sten Lehtoja)*, Esko Salminen *(Reino)*, Eero Roine *(his father)*, Rose-Marie Precht *(Maja)*, Åke Lindman *(sheriff)*, Kaarlo Wilska *(policeman)*.

Melodrama. Source: Hans Severinsen, *Besaettelse* (Copenhagen, 1942). Sten Lehtoja, a married, middle-aged businessman, picks up a young hitchhiker, Elsie, while driving to his summer home. Elsie spends the night and becomes his mistress. Later during the summer, Elsie also begins an affair with Reino, the teenage son of a local storekeeper. Sten offers to divorce his wife, and Elsie,

attracted by the prospect of a secure social position, agrees to marry him when the divorce becomes final. One night when the couple are in bed, Reino climbs a ladder and attempts to force his way into their room; he falls and breaks his neck, and to avoid scandal Sten hides the body. But the strain of guilt ruins the romance, and Elsie contacts the police, who arrest her lover. *Businessmen. Hitchhikers. Mistresses. Infidelity. Divorce. Guilt. Middle age.*

Note: Produced in Finland in 1961 under the title *Kuu on vaarallinen*; running time: 105 min. Pressbook credits film as a "Swedish International Motion Pictures" production, although it is a Finnish film.

PREMATURE BURIAL   F6.3906

Santa Clara Productions. *Dist* American International Pictures. 7 Mar **1962** [Chicago opening; c11 Mar 1962; LP22342]. Sd; col (Eastman Color by Pathé). 35mm (Panavision). 81 min.

Pres by Filmgroup Inc. A Roger Corman Production. *Prod-Dir* Roger Corman. *Exec Prod* Gene Corman. *Screenplay* Charles Beaumont, Ray Russell. *Dir Photog* Floyd Crosby. *Lighting* Lloyd Garnell. *Art Dir* Daniel Haller. *Set Decor* Harry Reif. *Film Ed* Ronald Sinclair. *Mus* Ronald Stein. *Sd* John Bury. *Asst Dir* Jack Bohrer. *Prod Mgr* Jack Bohrer. *Asst to the Prod* Jonathan Haze. *Film Asst* David Blangsted. *Script Supv* Betty Crosby. *Cost* Marjorie Corso. *Makeup* Louis LaCava. *Sp Eff* Pat Dinga. *Paintings* Burt Shonberg. *Key Grip* Charles Hannawalt. *Prop* Richard Rubin.

Cast: Ray Milland *(Guy Carrell)*, Hazel Court *(Emily Gault)*, Richard Ney *(Miles Archer)*, Heather Angel *(Kate Carrell)*, Alan Napier *(Dr. Gideon Gault)*, John Dierkes *(Sweeney)*, Richard Miller *(Mole)*, Brendan Dillon *(minister)*, Clive L. Halliday.

Horror film. Source: Edgar Allan Poe, "The Premature Burial," in *Dollar Newspaper* (31 July 1844). Guy Carrell, a medical researcher in 19th-century London, fears that his father's catalepsy is hereditary, and that he, too, will be buried alive during a seizure. He postpones marriage to Emily Gault, daughter of his physician and professor, Dr. Gideon Gault, and withdraws with his sister Kate to their country home on the moors, where he paints portraits of death. Emily visits him and persuades him to go through with the marriage, but following the ceremony, Guy builds a tomb containing every possible escape device to counteract his visions of grave robbers and nightmares of live burial. Guy's friend Miles Archer explains to Emily that catalepsy is not hereditary, but that given Guy's susceptible condition, any morbid reminder might precipitate a seizure; she then insists the tomb be destroyed, and Guy complies. Miles suggests that Guy open the family crypt and see for himself that his father was not buried alive. When the coffin is opened and a contorted skeleton is found, Guy collapses and falls lifeless to the ground, whereupon Miles and Dr. Gault pronounce him dead. Two grave robbers try to steal the body directly after the interment, but when they lift the lid from the casket, Guy leaps out and kills them. After murdering the doctor, Guy goes to Emily's room, drags her from her bed, carries her to the cemetery, and buries her alive. He is then confronted by Miles, who has discovered Gault's body and learned of Emily's disappearance. As the two men struggle, a shot rings out and Guy falls to the ground, killed by Kate, who was aware all along that Emily was using her knowledge of Guy's fears in a scheme to inherit his fortune. *Researchers. Physicians. Professors. Grave robbers. Obsession. Catalepsy. Death. Perfidy. Murder. Insanity. Heredity. Inheritance. Brother-sister relationship. Tombs. Coffins. Paintings. Dreams. Moorlands. London.*

Note: Also known as *The Premature Burial.*

PRESCRIPTION SEX   F6.3907

Dist Stacey Distributors. ca **1970**. Sd; col. 16mm. 61-81 min.

Sex film. No information about the precise nature of this film has been found. *Sexuality.*

THE PRESIDENT'S ANALYST   F6.3908

Panpiper Productions. *Dist* Paramount Pictures. 21 Dec **1967** [New York opening; c20 Dec 1967; LP35321]. Sd; col (Technicolor). 35mm (Panavision). 104 min. [Copyright length: 106 min.]

Prod Stanley Rubin. *Exec Prod* Howard W. Koch. *Dir-Writ* Theodore J. Flicker. *Anim* DePatie-Freleng. *Dir Photog* William A. Fraker. *Camera Op* David M. Walsh. *Art Dir* Hal Pereira, Al Roelofs. *Set Decor* Robert R. Benton, Arthur Krams. *Prod Dsgn* Pato Guzman. *Film Ed* Stuart H. Pappé. *Mus* Lalo Schifrin. *Song:* "Inner Manipulations" Barry McGuire, Paul Potash. *Sung by* Barry McGuire. *Song:* "She's Ready To Be Free" comp & sung by The Clear Light. *Song:* "Hey, Me" Lalo Schifrin, Theodore J. Flicker. *Sd Rec* Robert Post, John Wilkinson. *Asst Dir* Kurt Neumann. *Unit Prod Mgr* William C. Davidson. *Cost Dsgn* Jack Bear. *Makeup Supv* Wally Westmore. *Makeup Artist* Emile LaVigne. *Hairstyle Supv* Nellie Manley. *Hairstyles* Maryce Bates. *Sp Photog Eff* Westheimer Co.

Cast: James Coburn *(Dr. Sidney Schaefer)*, Godfrey Cambridge *(Don Masters)*, Severn Darden *(Kropotkin)*, Joan Delaney *(Nan Butler)*, Pat Harrington *(Arlington Hewes)*, Barry McGuire *(Old Wrangler)*, Jill Banner

(*Snow White*), Eduard Franz (*Ethan Allen Cocket*), Walter Burke (*Henry Lux*), Will Geer (*Dr. Lee-Evans*), William Daniels (*Wynn Quantrill*), Joan Darling (*Jeff Quantrill*), Sheldon Collins (*Bing Quantrill*), Arte Johnson (*Sullivan*), Martin Horsey (*1st Puddlian*), William Beckley (*2d Puddlian*), Kathleen Hughes (*White House tourist*).

Satire. Unknown to successful New York psychiatrist Dr. Sidney Schaefer, one of his patients, CEA (Central Enquiries Agency) agent Don Masters, has been evaluating him for the important task of becoming the President's analyst. After being sworn to secrecy, Schaefer and his newfound girl friend, Nan, move to Washington. Here he meets CEA head Ethan Allen Cocket and FBR (Federal Board of Regulations) chief Henry Lux, who are suspicious of each other. Though a great help to the President, Schaefer, unable to speak with anyone, soon acquires the President's tensions, constantly feels that he is being followed, and even becomes wary of Nan. Seeking relief, Schaefer mingles with a White House tour group and leaves Washington for New Jersey with the Quantrills, a typical gun-carrying, karate-practicing, eavesdropping American family, who boast of being liberals and are cautious of their rightwing neighbors. Schaefer, now being pursued by secret agents of other nationalities as well, escapes with a group of nomadic hippies. Kidnaped by Canadian Secret Service agents disguised as a Liverpool rock group, they are additionally abducted by Russian spy Kropotkin. Schaefer convinces Kropotkin that he needs an analyst, and they set out together for Washington. En route, Schaefer is kidnaped by the Telephone Company, which, angered over constant complaints about its inefficiency, plans to take over the country and use Schaefer to brainwash the President. Masters and Kropotkin, old friends from previous clandestine assignments, join forces, rescue Schaefer, and destroy the Telephone Company's headquarters. Returning to Washington, Schaefer resumes his job and marries Nan, who has been cleared on a security level equal to his own. The couple, accompanied by Masters and Kropotkin, enjoy Christmas evening together, unaware they are being watched by Telephone Company automatons. *Psychiatrists. Secret agents. Presidents of the United States. Hippies. Canadians. Russians. Musicians. British. Tourists. Government agents. Robots. Paranoia. Electronic surveillance. Kidnaping. Disguise. Brainwashing. Coups d'état. Family life. Guns. Karate. Rock and roll. Telephone. Christmas. New York City. Washington (District of Columbia). New Jersey. The White House.*

Note: Locations scenes filmed in New York City and Washington, D. C. Working title: *T. P. A. (The President's Analyst).*

PRESSURE OF GUILT (Japan)   F6.3909

Toho Co. 31 Jan **1964** [Los Angeles opening]. Sd; b&w. 35mm. 113 min.

Prod Ichiro Sato, Hideyuki Shiino. *Dir* Hiromichi Horikawa. *Screenplay* Shinobu Hashimoto. *Photog* Hiroshi Murai. *Art Dir* Hiroshi Mizutani. *Mus* Toru Takemitsu. *Sd* Toshio Harashima.

Cast: Keiju Kobayashi (*Ochiai*), Tatsuya Nakadai (*Hamano*), Hisashi Igawa (*Wakida*), Koreya Senda (*Munakata*), Akira Nishimura (*Hirao*), Mayumi Ozora (*Muramatsu*), Chikage Awashima (*Munakata's wife*), Nobuko Otoba (*Ochiai's wife*).

Crime melodrama. Hamano, lawyer to Munakata, an elderly attorney, is also the young Mrs. Munakata's lover. During an argument with her one evening, Hamano loses his temper and strangles her. Under intensive questioning by the police, the young lawyer is about to confess to the crime when the police announce they have arrested Wakida, a burglar suspected of entering the Munakata house on the night of the murder. Prosecutor Ochiai now focuses his investigation on Wakida and after five days of interrogation, Ochiai obtains a confession. Hamano, wracked with guilt when he realizes that Wakida could be executed for a crime he did not commit, arranges for Munakata, a noted opponent of capital punishment, to defend the burglar. Meanwhile, Ochiai becomes suspicious when Hamano taunts him for not having complete proof of Wakida's guilt. Investigating further, the prosecutor learns of the affair between Hamano and Mrs. Munakata and that, when she had found her lover was planning to marry the daughter of a millionaire, she accused him of opportunism and he strangled her. Confronted with the evidence, Hamano confesses to the crime. Ochiai's efforts are made public, but it is then revealed that Mrs. Munakata made a phone call shortly after the time Hamano claims to have strangled her. Further investigation discloses that Mrs. Munakata had recovered from Hamano's attack only to be killed by the burglar, who entered the house after Hamano left. Ochiai, exhausted by his efforts, is hospitalized, while Hamano, publicly disgraced by the investigation, commits suicide. *Lawyers. District attorneys. Burglars. Opportunists. Police. Murder. Guilt. Confession (law). Capital punishment. Infidelity. Suicide.*

Note: Released in Japan in 1963 as *Shiro to kuro.*

PRESSURE POINT   F6.3910

Larcas Productions. *Dist* United Artists. 19 Sep **1962** [Los Angeles opening; c21 Sep 1962; LP23094]. Sd; b&w. 35mm. 91 min. [Also reviewed at 87 min.]

A Stanley Kramer Production. *Prod* Stanley Kramer. *Dir* Hubert Cornfield. *Screenplay* Hubert Cornfield, S. Lee Pogostin. *Cinematog* Ernest Haller.

Camera Op Conrad Hall. *Art Dir* George C. Webb. *Set Decor* George Milo. *Prod Dsgn* Rudolph Sternad. *Film Ed* Frederic Knudtson. *Mus* Ernest Gold. *Sd* James Speak. *Asst Dir* Phil Bowles, Douglas Green. *Prod Mgr* Clem Beauchamp. *Makeup* George Lane. *Hairstyles* Larry Germain. *Optical Eff* Pacific Title. *Spider Web Spinner* Malcolm Wheel.

Cast: Sidney Poitier (*doctor*), Bobby Darin (*patient*), Peter Falk (*young psychiatrist*), Carl Benton Reid (*chief medical officer*), Mary Munday (*bar hostess*), Barry Gordon (*patient as a boy*), Howard Caine (*tavern owner*), Anne Barton (*mother*), James Anderson (*father*), Yvette Vickers (*drunken woman*), Clegg Hoyt (*Pete*), Richard Bakalyan (*Jimmy*), Butch Patrick (*playmate*), Leonard Geiger, Gilbert Green, Lynn Loring.

Melodrama. Source: Robert Mitchell Lindner, "Destiny's Tot," in *The Fifty-Minute Hour: A Collection of True Psychoanalytic Tales* (New York, 1955). A young psychiatrist is unable to make progress with a black patient who hates whites, and he asks his superior, a black, to remove him from the case. The superior, however, tells the younger man of a similar assignment he dealt with years before. *While serving on the staff of a Federal prison during World War II, the psychiatrist is asked to treat a young Nazi imprisoned for subversion. The prisoner suffers from sleeplessness, nightmares, and blackouts. Despite his hatred of Negroes, the patient submits to therapy in hopes that it will end his terror. Events from the man's past help explain some of his disturbances: his father was a drunken sadist who resented the boy for being the cause of his marriage to a whining semi-invalid; the patient created an imaginary playmate whom he bullied; he left home at an early age and exhibited sadistic tendencies in a drunken barroom orgy; and he joined the Nazi party after he was barred from the home of a Jewish girl whose father felt him unworthy of his daughter. The patient finds relief after the psychiatrist explains the causes of his nightmares, but, once able to sleep, he refuses to continue his therapy. Because the patient is still a Nazi, the psychiatrist refuses to recommend his release, but prison authorities prevail and the patient is paroled. The psychiatrist regards himself as a failure because the patient's racism has swayed him from a disinterested role as an analyst. Shortly after his release, the patient brutally murders an old man and is executed.* After hearing of his superior's experience, the younger doctor decides to continue with his case. *Psychiatrists. Negroes. Psychopaths. Nazis. Jews. Drunkenness. Invalids. Psychiatry. Mental illness. Racism. Sleep. Filial relations. Murder. Fantasy. Sadism. Prisons. Bars. Orgies. World War II. Dreams.*

Note: Included in the film are newsreel clips of a wartime Nazi Bund rally in Madison Square Garden and march music from *Judgment at Nuremberg.* Working title: *Point Blank.*

PRETTY BUT WICKED (Brazil)   F6.3911

Dist Victoria Films, Times Film Corp. 7 May **1965** [Los Angeles showing]. Sd; b&w. 35mm. 90 min.

Prod Joffre Rodrigues, Jece Valadão. *Dir* J. P. de Carvalho. *Script* Jece Valadão. *Photog* Amleto Daissè. *Camera* José Rosa. *Film Ed* Rafael Velledde. *Mus* Carlos Lyra. *Sd* Antônio Gomes.

Cast: Jece Valadão (*Edgar*), Odete Lara (*Rita*), Lia Rossi (*Maria Cecilia*), Fregolente (*Hector Wernek*), André Villion (*Perrault*).

Melodrama. Source: Nélson Rodrigues, *Bonitinha, mas ordinária* (publication undetermined). In Rio de Janeiro, Perrault, assistant to wealthy industrialist Hector Wernek, suggests to Edgar, a clerk, that he marry Wernek's daughter Maria Cecilia. Edgar dates Maria, and she tells him that three motorcycle hoodlums once raped her in Perrault's disabled car while Perrault went to find a mechanic. Wernek tries to bribe Edgar into marrying his daughter, but the resentful clerk informs him that he loves Rita, his next door neighbor. One night in a cemetery, Edgar tells Rita of Wernek's offer. After they make love in an open grave, Rita confesses that as an adolescent she allowed a policeman to seduce her so that her invalid mother would not be sent to jail. To support her mother and sisters, she became a prostitute. At home, Rita discovers that her virgin sisters have gone to an orgy at Wernek's house, but she arrives there too late to prevent their humiliating seduction in front of the guests. Edgar, who left the party before the orgy began, visits Maria and learns that she cannot enjoy lovemaking without violence and that the rape by the motorcyclists had been staged for her pleasure by Perrault. Edgar leaves, disgusted by Maria's perversion, and goes to find Rita. Meanwhile, Perrault arrives at Maria's house, and after an argument he kills her and then commits suicide. *Industrialists. Clerks. Hoodlums. Neighbors. Police. Sisters. Motorcyclists. Rape. Filial relations. Bribery. Seduction. Prostitution. Virginity. Masochism. Murder. Suicide. Cemeteries. Orgies. Rio de Janeiro.*

Note: Produced in Brazil in 1963 as *Bonitinha, mas ordinária.*

PRETTY POISON   F6.3912

Lawrence Turman Films–Molino Productions. *Dist* Twentieth Century-Fox Film Corp. 18 Sep **1968** [Los Angeles opening; c18 Sep 1968; LP36050]. Sd (Westrex); col (Deluxe). 35mm. 89 min.

A Lawrence Turman Production. *Prod* Marshal Backlar, Noel Black. *Exec Prod* Lawrence Turman. *Assoc Prod* Jack Grossberg. *Dir* Noel Black. *Screenplay* Lorenzo Semple, Jr. *Dir Photog* David Quaid. *Art Dir* Jack Martin Smith, Harold Michelson. *Set Decor* John Mortensen. *Film Ed* William Ziegler. *Mus* Johnny Mandel. *Sd* Dennis Maitland, David Dockendorf. *Asst Dir* Roger Rothstein. *Unit Prod Mgr* Jack Grossberg. *Cost Dsgn* Ann Roth. *Makeup* Robert Jiras. *Sp Eff* Ralph Winigar, Billy King, sp eff.

Cast: Anthony Perkins *(Dennis Pitt)*, Tuesday Weld *(Sue Ann Stepanek)*, Beverly Garland *(Mrs. Stepanek)*, John Randolph *(Azenauer)*, Dick O'Neill *(Bud Munsch)*, Clarice Blackburn *(Mrs. Bronson)*, Joseph Bova *(Pete)*, Ken Kercheval *(Harry Jackson)*, Don Fellows *(detective)*, Parker Fennelly *(night watchman)*, Tim Callahan *(plainclothesman)*, George Fisher *(burly man)*, William Sorrells *(cop at beanery)*, Dan Morgan, Mark Dawson, Gil Rogers *(men in police station)*, John Randolph Jones, Maurice Ottinger *(highway policemen)*, Tom Gorman *(1st detective)*, Bill Fort, Ed Wagner *(cops)*, George Ryan's Winslow High-Steppers.

Drama. Source: Stephen Geller, *She Let Him Continue* (New York, 1966). As a teenager, Dennis Pitt was institutionalized for burning down his home and accidentally killing his aunt. Now years later, he is on parole working in a chemical factory in a small New England town. Living in a paranoic's world, he becomes convinced that the factory is polluting the river and poisoning the entire Eastern seaboard. One day he meets Sue Ann Stepanek, a pretty high school drum majorette, who complains of the restrictions placed on her by her widowed mother. Dennis then poses as a CIA agent on orders to destroy the factory, and Sue Ann delightedly agrees to help him. On the night they attempt to sabotage the factory and unexpectedly encounter the night watchman, Sue Ann knocks the watchman unconscious and drowns him. When Dennis becomes the prime suspect because of his record, Sue Ann consents to run away with him to Mexico, but they return home for her clothes and are interrupted by the arrival of Mrs. Stepanek. Realizing that Dennis is incapable of murder, Sue Ann shoots her mother and orders Dennis to dispose of the body. Instead, he calls the police. At the hearing, Sue Ann denounces Dennis and watches casually as he is accused of the murders. Dennis, hopelessly in love with Sue Ann and aware that no one would believe him if he told the truth, makes no effort to defend himself, although Azenauer, his probation officer, believes him innocent. Some time later, Sue Ann meets another young man and begins to complain about the trouble she is having with her new foster parents. *Students. Drum majorettes. Widows. Watchmen. Police. Parole officers. Arson. Parole. Paranoia. Water pollution. Filial relations. Murder. Imposture. Factories. Chemicals. New England.*

Note: Location scenes filmed in Great Barrington, Massachusetts. Working title: *She Let Him Continue.*

PRETTY POLLY see A MATTER OF INNOCENCE

THE PRICE OF FLESH (France)   F6.3913

Horizons Cinématographiques. *Dist* Triad Films, Audubon Films. 31 Mar 1962 [New York opening]. Sd; b&w. 35mm. 89 min.

Prod Edgar Roulleau. *Dir* Walter Kapps. *Screenplay* Pierre Chichério. *Dial-Adapt* Bernard Dimey, Gérard Gohier, Georges Tabet. *Photog* Jacques Klein. *Art Dir* Claude Bouxin. *Film Ed* Françoise Diot. *Mus* Michel Magne. *Sd* Louis Olivier, André Louis. *Prod Mgr* Stany Cordier.

Cast: Hélène Chanel *(Christine)*, Frank Villard *(Daniel)*, Louis Seigner *(Max)*, Michel Roux *(Jean)*, Josette Demay *(Gisèle)*, Maria Vincent *(Conchita)*, Nathalie Nattier *(Michka)*, Madeleine Barbulée *(Christine's mother)*, Robert Burnier *(Christine's father)*, Jean Payen *(Philippe)*, Yvette Sautereau, Gib Grossac.

Melodrama. Christine Lambert decides to become a dancer in spite of her parents' disapproval. She is introduced to Max, a photographer who is reputed to be a specialist in the theatrical field. Max sends Christine to Madame Michka for dancing lessons but since she has no money to pay for the lessons Christine is forced to return to Max to pose for him in the nude. At Max's home Christine meets "producer" Daniel Gerard, who asks her to become the star of his revue which will soon tour North Africa. As a publicity stunt, Daniel arranges for Christine's false abduction, and he secretly flies her to Tangiers. Meanwhile, Jean, a newspaper reporter and the fiancé of Christine's sister, Gisèle, suspects that all is not well and begins to search for Christine. In Tangiers, Daniel secures lodgings for Christine in a local cabaret run by Conchita, a madam who immediately undertakes to make Christine a prostitute. Jean arrives in Tangiers just in time to save Christine from being abused by Daniel. Jean is rescued from an unequal fight by the police, and Christine is returned to her family. *Dancers. Photographers. Theatrical producers. Madams. Reporters. White slave traffic. Imposture. Publicity. Abduction. Hoaxes. Rape. Finance—Personal. Cabarets. Tangiers.*

Note: Opened in Paris in Dec 1959 as *Détournement de mineures.*

PRIDE OF THE CAMPUS (Japan)   F6.3914

Toho Co. Dec 1962 [Los Angeles showing]. Sd; col. 35mm. [Feature film, length unknown.]

Cast: Yuzo Kayama, Yuriko Hoshi, Reiko Dan, Yoko Fujiyama, Tatsuyoshi Ehara, Machiko Naka, Akemi Kita, Ken Uehara, Ichiro Arishima, Kunie Tanaka, Asami Kuji, Choko Iida, Bokuzen Hidari.

Comedy-drama. No information about the precise nature of this film has been found. *College life.*

Note: Original title and release undetermined.

LA PRIGIONIERA see LA PRISONNIÈRE

PRIMA DELLA RIVOLUZIONE see BEFORE THE REVOLUTION

THE PRIME OF MISS JEAN BRODIE (Great Britain)   F6.3915

Twentieth Century-Fox Productions. *Dist* Twentieth Century-Fox Film Corp. 2 Mar 1969 [New York opening; c31 Dec 1968; LP36762]. Sd; col (DeLuxe). 35mm. 116 min. MPAA rating M.

Prod Robert Fryer. *Co-prod* James Cresson. *Dir* Ronald Neame. *Screenplay* Jay Presson Allen. *Dir Photog* Ted Moore. *Camera Op* Robert Kindred. *Art Dir* Brian Herbert. *Set Dresser* Pamela Cornell. *Prod Dsgn* John Howell. *Film Ed* Norman Savage. *Orig Mus Comp* Rod McKuen. *Arr & Cond* Arthur Greenslade. *Sd Mix* Jock May. *Sd Rec* Gordon McCallum. *Sd Ed* Winston Ryder. *Asst Dir* Ted Sturgis. *Prod Supv* David Anderson. *Cont* Annabel Davis-Goff. *Location Adv* Lorna Rhind. *Col Cost Dsgn* Elizabeth Haffenden, Joan Bridge. *Wardrobe Supv* Jackie Cummins. *Chief Makeup* Ernest Gasser. *Hairstyles* Pat McDermott. *Casting* Anne Donne. *Dial Coach* Margaret Gordon.

Cast: Maggie Smith *(Jean Brodie)*, Robert Stephens *(Teddy Lloyd)*, Pamela Franklin *(Sandy)*, Gordon Jackson *(Gordon Lowther)*, Celia Johnson *(Miss MacKay)*, Diane Grayson *(Jenny)*, Jane Carr *(Mary McGregor)*, Shirley Steedman *(Monica)*, Lavinia Lang *(Emily Carstairs)*, Antoinette Biggerstaff *(Helen McPhee)*, Margo Cunningham *(Miss Campbell)*, Isla Cameron *(Miss McKenzie)*, Rona Anderson *(Miss Lockhart)*, Ann Way *(Miss Gaunt)*, Molly Weir *(Miss Alison Kerr)*, Helena Gloag *(Miss Kerr)*, John Dunbar *(Mr. Burrage)*, Heather Seymour *(Clara)*, Lesley Paterson *(prefect)*, Kristen Hatfield, Hilary Berlin, Jennifer Irvine, Gillian Evans, Janette Sattler, Diane Robillard, Helen Wigglesworth, Antonia Moss *(schoolgirls)*.

Drama. Source: Jay Presson Allen, *The Prime of Miss Jean Brodie* (Torquay, England, opening: 5 Apr 1966). Muriel Spark, *The Prime of Miss Jean Brodie* (London, 1961). In 1932 Miss Jean Brodie, a middle-aged spinster, teaches at Edinburgh's exclusive Marcia Blaine School. A romantic devoted to art and music, as well as a fascist sympathizer, Miss Brodie belittles those who do not share her enthusiasms. From her students she recruits a coterie, including the attractive Jenny; the impressionable Mary McGregor, a wealthy orphan; and the subtle Sandy, who proves to be her nemesis. Courted by Lowther, a retiring music instructor at whose ancestral home she spends the weekends, Miss Brodie carries on an affair with Lloyd, an earthy art teacher and the father of a large Catholic family. Miss Brodie's antagonist is the humorless headmistress, Miss MacKay, who repeatedly attempts to dismiss her. Jealous of Miss Brodie's eulogies to Jenny's beauty and stung by the teacher's indifferent prediction that she will make a superior secret service agent, Sandy takes Lloyd as her lover. When she discovers that his portrait of her resembles Miss Brodie, she breaks with the artist, assuring him that he is an aging mediocrity. Learning that Mary's brother has run off to Spain, Miss Brodie assumes that he has joined Franco's forces and encourages her to join him. En route to Spain, her train is bombed and Mary is killed. At a school convocation Lloyd informs Miss Brodie of Lowther's impending marriage to the chemistry teacher, Miss Lockhart. Shortly thereafter, Miss Brodie is dismissed for propagandizing in the classroom. Stunned, she asks Sandy who has betrayed her. Sandy spitefully proclaims her liaison with Lloyd and reveals her treachery, citing as justification the absurdity of Mary's death. *Schoolteachers. Spinsters. Students. Art teachers. Music teachers. Adolescence. Fascism. Boarding schools. Spain—History—Civil War 1936–39. Francisco Franco. Edinburgh.*

Note: Location scenes filmed in London and Edinburgh. London opening: Feb 1969.

PRIMITIVE LONDON (Great Britain)   F6.3916

Searchlight Productions–Troubadour Films. *Dist* Steve Prentoulis Films. 22 Nov 1967 [New York showing]. Sd; col (Eastman Color). 35mm. 76 min.

Prod Arnold Louis Miller, Stanley A. Long. *Exec Prod* Michael Klinger, Tony Tenser. *Dir-Screenplay* Arnold Louis Miller. *Photog* Stanley A. Long. *Film Ed* Stephen Cross. *Mus* Basil Kirchin. *Sd* Dudley Plummer.

Cast: David Gell *(narrator)*, Ray Martine, McDonald Hobley, Vicki Grey, Billy J. Kramer, Diana Noble.

Documentary. A tour of modern London begins with the birth of a baby and goes beneath the city's façade of respectability to reveal its primitive, violent undercurrents: the Rockers, riding fast motorcycles, express contempt for the fashion-conscious Mods; beatniks advocate free love; the aggressive arts of judo and kendo gain new popularity; brutal wrestling matches attract large audiences; teenage girls sit in hot water baths in order to shrink their dungarees skin-tight; striptease establishments flourish at every economic level in the West End; young women attend the "London School of Strip" to learn the techniques of the art, and one young graduate rushes from club to club to perform; lavish drinking clubs present a variety of "girlie" shows; and married Londoners attend parties where housekeys are swapped and couples exchange partners for the night. *Rockers. Mods. Beatniks. Stripteasers. Childbirth. Wrestling. Adolescence. Mate swapping. Judo. Kendo. Stag shows. Free love. Nightclubs. London. London—West End.*

Note: Released in Great Britain in 1965. Also known as *Primitive London Exposed, Swinging London, Swinging London Exposed, Swinging London Exposé,* and *London Exposed.*

PRIMITIVE LOVE (Italy)   F6.3917

Italian International Film-G. L. M. *Dist* American Film Distributing Corp. 3 Nov **1966** [San Francisco showing]. Sd; col (Eastman Color). 35mm. 83 min.

Pres by Stan Borden. *Prod* Dick Randall, Joel Holt, Fulvio Lucisano, Pietro Paolo Giordani. *Dir* Luigi Scattini. *Screenplay* Luigi Scattini, Amedeo Sollazzo. *Story* Luigi Scattini, D. M. Pupillo. *Photog* Claudio Racca. *Art Dir* Gastone Carsetti. *Film Ed* Otello Colangeli. *Mus* Lallo Gori.

Cast: Jayne Mansfield *(Jayne)*, Franco Franchi, Ciccio Ingrassia *(hotel porters)*, Luigi Scattini *(commentator)*, Mickey Hargitay, Lucia Modugno, Carlo Kechler, Alfonso Sarlo, Eugenio Galadini.

Farce. Jayne, an anthropologist, arrives in Rome to show to a prominent anthropology professor a documentary film she has made illustrating the sexual practices and marriage customs of "primitive" peoples around the world. The film, seen also by two hotel porters who secretly have followed Jayne to her room, fails to convince the professor of her thesis—that love is universally primitive, affecting "civilized" man in much the same way it does "primitive." To prove her point, Jayne performs a striptease, which powerfully affects the professor as well as the porters. *Anthropologists. Bellboys. Professors. Sexual practices. Marriage. Social customs. Striptease. Primitive life. Motion pictures. Rome. Paris. Kenya. Morocco. Senegal. Guinea. Tanganyika. Singapore. Tokyo. Hong Kong. South Sea Islands.*

Note: Location scenes filmed in Rome, Paris, Kenya, Morocco, Senegal, Guinea, Tanganyika, Singapore, Tokyo, Hong Kong, and the South Sea Islands. Released in Italy in 1964 as *L'amore primitivo.*

PRIMITIVE PARADISE   F6.3918

Dist Excelsior Pictures. 24 May **1961** [New York opening]. Sd; col. 35mm. 66 min.

Prod-Dir Lewis Cotlow. *Cinematog* Bede Whitman. *Mus Supv* Herman Fuchs. *Prod Supv* Francis Wood, Jr. *Prod Asst* Alan Frazer.

Narrator: Lewis Cotlow.

Documentary. Lewis Cotlow leads an expedition into the Sepik River country of New Guinea to photograph the tribes living in the jungle. Accompanied by Australian- and Dutch-trained patrol officers and native policemen, the crew films daily habits and special ceremonies of native life, including music, customs, and beliefs of the primitive tribesmen. There are scenes of a pig feast, canoe races, and a type of soccer game, as well as a huge song-and-dance fest with the natives dressed in costumes for the finale. *Explorers. Police. Tribal life. Music. Rites and ceremonies. Jungles. Sepik River. New Guinea.*

Note: Filmed in New Guinea.

THE PRINCE AND THE NATURE GIRL   F6.3919

Juri Productions. 28 Sep **1965** [New York showing]. Sd; col (Eastman Color). 35mm. 70 min.

Prod-Dir Doris Wishman. *Screenplay & Narr* Andrew J. Kuehn. *Dir Photog* Nouri Haviv. *Film Ed* Stuart Allen. *Mus* Picture Scores. *Sd* Titra Sound Corp. *Optical Eff* B & O Film Specialists.

Cast: Mari Hara *(narrator)*, Joni Roberts, Jeffery Niles, Sandy, William Meyer, Lee Abell, Warrene Gray, Barbara Taylor, Stephen Bloom, Dolores K. Norris, Ingrid Martinsen, Shirley Perratto.

Nudist film. The wealthy, handsome prince of a mythical kingdom works at an office job just in case he is deposed by a revolution. Twins Sue and Eve Pringle, from the faraway kingdom of Ohio, come to work in the same office. The prince becomes attracted to blonde Eve, who joins the nudist camp where the prince is also a member, but it is brunette Sue who loves him. Eve returns to Ohio for a visit; and Sue dons a blonde wig, pretends to be her sister, and wins the love of the prince. Although she is hurt and angry when she returns from Ohio, Eve bows out and seeks the cheery atmosphere of the nudist camp. There she meets Alfred King, and as they walk off, Eve remarks, "Why settle for a prince when you can get a king?" *Royalty. Twins. Sisters. Mistaken identity. Disguise. Nudist camps. Imaginary kingdoms. Ohio.*

Note: Filmed on location at Sunny Palms Lodge in Homestead, Florida, and Sunny Heights Lodge in Trenton, New Jersey.

THE PRINCE AND THE PAUPER   F6.3920

Storyland Films. *Dist* Childhood Productions. 4 Oct **1969** [Chicago opening]. Sd; col (Eastman Color, print by Movielab). 35mm. 68 min.

Prod Elliot Geisinger, Ronald Saland. *Assoc Prod* Marcel Broekman. *Dir* Elliot Geisinger. *Screenplay* Elliot Geisinger, Alex Tartaglia. *Photog* Al Mozell. *2d Unit Photog* Vincent Corcoran. *Art Dir* Charles Stockton. *Film Ed* Howard Kuperman. *Sd* Chris Newman. *Asst Dir* John Quill. *Prod Mgr* John Quill.

Cast: Gene Bua *(Miles Hendon)*, Ken Shaffel.

Adventure drama. Source: Mark Twain, *The Prince and the Pauper* (New York, 1881). Tony, a beggar boy, trades places with his look-alike, Prince Edward, the day before young Edward's coronation. *Royalty. Beggars. Doubles. Impersonation. Coronations.*

Note: Filmed in Ireland. Also known as *The Adventures of the Prince and the Pauper.*

THE PRINCESS *see* A TIME IN THE SUN

THE PRINCESS AND THE MAGIC FROG   F6.3921

Fantasy Films. 25 Oct **1965** [Maryland license]. Sd; col (Eastman Color). 35mm. 80 min.

Prod-Dir Austin Green. *Screenplay* Harold Vaughn Taylor. *Photog* Donald Gundrey. *Film Ed* Gary Lindsay. *Mus* Billy Allen, Dave Roberts. *Makeup* Rod Wilson.

Cast: David Bailey, Ernest Vaio, Frank Delfino, Clive L. Halliday, Dick Reeves, Nancy DeCarl, Lindsay Workman.

Fantasy. Schoolboys Matthew O'Brien and Timothy Ryan play hooky on Saint Patrick's Day to go fishing. At the end of the day, Tim goes home but Matt stays on, hopeful of catching a fish. He has no luck, however, and is about to leave when he sees a big frog at the water's edge. He captures it, puts it in his pocket, and, running to catch up with Tim, becomes lost in a dark forest. He meets a leprechaun whose beard is caught in a log and frees the little man in exchange for his bag of seven gold coins. The leprechaun warns Matt that the coins will do good only for others, and he disappears. Matt learns that each coin is capable of granting a wish, and, paying no attention to the leprechaun's admonition, he uses one of them to ask a signpost the way to his home. The signpost tells Matt to consult the wizard who dwells in a cave. On the way to the cave, Matt learns from a grove of talking trees that the frog is actually an enchanted knight, and he therefore uses a coin to return the knight to his human state. The two travel on and suddenly meet the wizard, who banishes them to the Impossible Desert, but there a genie returns them to the forest. Matt meets an old puppeteer who has lost his ability to move his puppets' strings, and with a coin Matt brings the puppets to life to take care of the puppeteer in his old age. Matt meets a gypsy girl who as a princess was kidnaped by the wizard. Restoring her to her former self, Matt learns that the knight has been seeking the princess for many years. Matt is told that his home will be found at the end of a rainbow. He looks for the rainbow, but the wizard appears and blocks Matt's way, whereupon Matt turns the wizard into a kindly old man. He finds a rainbow and after bidding his newfound friends goodby follows it into his own backyard. *Children. Fairies. Sorcerers. Gypsies. Royalty. Puppeteers. Truancy. Fishing. Metamorphosis. Magic. Wish fulfillment. Knighthood. Banishment. Rainbows. Gold. Forests. Puppets. Saint Patrick's Day. Frogs.*

Note: Working title: *At the End of the Rainbow.* Included in the film is the song "At the End of the Rainbow."

PRINSESSAN *see* A TIME IN THE SUN

LA PRISE DE POUVOIR PAR [DE] LOUIS XIV *see* THE RISE OF LOUIS XIV

PRISONER OF THE IRON MASK (France/Italy)   F6.3922

Cineproduzioni Associate–Mida Film–Comptoir Français du Film. *Dist* American International Pictures. 7 Feb **1962** [Detroit opening; c23 Jan 1962; LP22539]. Sd; col (Eastmancolor). 35mm (Techniscope). 80 min.

Pres by James H. Nicholson, Samuel Z. Arkoff. *Prod* Francesco Thellung. *Supv English Vers* Salvatore Billitteri. *Dir* Francesco De Feo. *Dir English Vers* Lee Kresel. *Screenplay* Silvio Amadio, Ruggero Jacobbi, Francesco De Feo. *Dir Photog* Raffaele Masciocchi. *Camera Op* Antonio Schiavolena, Remo Grisanti, Bruno Letizia. *Art Dir* Piero Poletto. *Set Dsgn* Ennio Michettoni. *Film Ed* Luciano Cavalieri. *Mus* Carlo Innocenzi. *Sd* Pietro Ortolani. *Cost* Adriana Berselli. *Makeup* Oscar Pacheli.

Cast: Michel Lemoine *(Marco)*, Wandisa Guida *(Christina)*, Andrea Bosic, Jany Clair, Giovanni Materassi, Pietro Albano, Tiziana Casetti, Alan Evans, Mimmo Poli, Francesco De Leone, Nando Tamberlani, Marco Tulli, Joe Camel, Silvio Bagolini, Erminio Spalla, Emma Baron, Andrea Fantasia, Piero Pastore.

Adventure drama. Source: Alexandre Dumas, père, *Le Vicomte de Bragelonne, ou dix ans plus tard* (Paris, 1848–50). In 18th-century Italy, a duke is being slowly poisoned by his treacherous advisor, Count Astolfo. The duke's son, Marco, and his friend, Andrea, are returning home with documentary proof of the count's treachery but are captured; Marco is put into an iron mask but not before he has hidden the document. Andrea, who has escaped, thinking that Marco has been killed, rescues him as he is being exiled from the country. Marco's sister, to save her brother's life, has consented to marry the count. After being defeated in a duel by Marco, the count is put into the iron mask and sent to the battle field where the French are awaiting him. *Royalty. Poisoning. Filial relations. Treason. Exile. Brother-sister relationship. Masks. Documentation. Duels.*

Note: Opened in Paris in Jul 1962 as *La vengeance du masque de fer;* running time: 89 min; in Italy as *Vendetta della maschera di ferro.* Copyright claimant: Alta Vista Productions.

LA PRISONNIÈRE (France/Italy)   F6.3923

Les Films Corona–Vera Film–Fono Roma. *Dist* Avco Embassy Pictures. 26 Mar **1969** [New York opening]. Sd; col (Eastman Color). 35mm. 104 min. *MPAA rating* M.

Pres by Joseph E. Levine. *Prod* Robert Dorfmann. *Dir* Henri-Georges Clouzot. *2d Unit Dir* Robert Menegoz. *Screenplay* Henri-Georges Clouzot, Monique Lange, Marcel Moussy. *Photog* Andréas Winding. *2d Unit Photog* Raymond Picon Borel. *Art Dir* Jacques Saulnier. *Film Ed* Noëlle Balenci. *Dream Montage* Dominique Amy. *Mus Dir* Gilbert Amy. *Sd* Jean-Louis Ducarme, William Sivel. *Asst Dir* Serge Witta. *Gen Prod Mgr* Pierre Darcay. *Prod Mgr* Claude Hauser. *Makeup* Michel Deruelle. *Artistic Collab* Stein-Yvaral. *English Subtitl* Sonya Mays Friedman.

Cast: Laurent Terzieff *(Stanislas Hassler),* Bernard Fresson *(Gilbert Moreau),* Elisabeth Wiener *(Jose),* Dany Carrel *(Maguy),* Dario Moreno *(Sala),* Daniel Rivière *(Maurice),* Michel Etcheverry, Claude Pieplu, Noëlle Adam, Gilberte Géniat, Michel Piccoli, Charles Vanel, André Luguet, Annie Fargue, Germaine Delbat.

Drama. Stanislas Hassler is the owner of a fashionable art gallery in Paris. While exhibiting the work of sculptor Gilbert Moreau, Hassler invites Gilbert's mistress Jose to his apartment and shows her some of his photographs, including one of a naked woman bound in chains. Although unnerved to discover that Hassler's avocation is sadomasochistic photography, Jose cannot erase the image from her mind, and eventually she persuades Hassler to let her observe him work. As Hassler demands that his nude model strike numerous poses simulating erotic bondage, Jose becomes so distraught that she leaves. Bored with her life with Gilbert, however, and fascinated by Hassler's obsession, she later offers to pose for him. Reduced to total submission, Jose lies to Gilbert about her frequent absences and accepts without question Hassler's humiliating arrogance. Hoping to disprove Gilbert's charge that Hassler is impotent, Jose accompanies him to a seaside resort and succeeds in seducing him. Their idyll ends abruptly when Hassler discovers a photograph of himself and Jose taken by a street photographer. Upon learning the details of Jose's affair, Gilbert goes to Hassler's and finds him standing on the roof of his apartment building. Realizing that Hassler wants to be pushed to his death, Gilbert denies him an escape from reality and pulls him back from the ledge. Meanwhile, Jose, who is convinced that she has lost both men, drives off in her car, stalls on a railroad crossing, and is gravely injured in a crash. When Gilbert visits her at the hospital, she is delirious and only murmurs Hassler's name. *Art dealers. Sculptors. Mistresses. Models. Photography. Sadomasochism. Seduction. Art galleries. Resorts. Paris. Automobile accidents.*

Note: Opened in Paris in Nov 1968; running time: 110 min. Italian title: *La prigioniera.* Also known as *The Female Prisoner.*

PRIVATE ARRANGEMENT   F6.3924

Mitam Productions. 4 Feb **1970** [Champaign, Illinois, showing]. Sd; col (Eastman Color). 35mm. 72 min.

Dir Wes Ransom.

Cast: Lynne Lori, Jeanne Lund.

Melodrama. Office workers Gloria, Emily, Linda, and Beverly join sailors Terry, Bob, and the skipper for a weekend cruise on the *Playpen.* Bob and Linda and Terry and Beverly pair off while Gloria divides her time between Emily and the skipper. The boat anchors at a cove where the voyagers enjoy a lazy day. That evening, everyone takes off their clothes and engages in group sex. Freddy, the skipper's deafmute helper, tries to make love to Emily. The next morning Freddy is found beside Emily's dead body. The police are informed and Freddy is taken into custody. *Office clerks. Sailors. Deafmutes. Group sex. Lesbianism. Murder.*

THE PRIVATE LIFE OF SHERLOCK HOLMES (United States/
(Great Britain)   F6.3925

Phalanx Productions–Mirisch Productions–Sir Nigel Films. *Dist* United

Artists. 29 Oct **1970** [New York opening; c29 Oct 1970; LP38886]. Sd; col (DeLuxe). 35mm (Panavision). 125 min. *MPAA rating* GP.

Prod-Dir Billy Wilder. *Assoc Prod* I. A. L. Diamond. *Screenplay* Billy Wilder, I. A. L. Diamond. *Dir Photog* Christopher Challis. *Art Dir* Tony Inglis. *Set Decor* Harry Cordwell. *Prod Dsgn* Alexander Trauner. *Main Titl* Maurice Binder. *Film Ed* Ernest Walter. *Mus:* Score and Concerto for Violin and Orchestra, opus 24 Miklos Rozsa. *Dances Arr & Ballet Adv* David Blair. *Sd Ed* Roy Baker. *Sd Rec* J. W. N. Daniel, Dudley Messenger, Gordon K. McCallum. *Asst Dir* Tom Pevsner. *Prod Supv* Larry De Waay. *Prod Mgr* Eric Rattray. *Cost Dsgn* Julie Harris, cost. *Makeup* Ernest Gasser. *Sp Eff* Wally Veevers, Cliff Richardson.

Cast: Robert Stephens *(Sherlock Holmes),* Colin Blakely *(Dr. John H. Watson),* Irene Handl *(Mrs. Hudson),* Stanley Holloway *(1st gravedigger),* Christopher Lee *(Mycroft Holmes),* Geneviève Page *(Gabrielle Valladon),* Clive Revill *(Rogozhin),* Tamara Toumanova *(Petrova),* George Benson *(Inspector Lestrade),* Catherine Lacey *(old lady),* Mollie Maureen *(Queen Victoria),* Peter Madden *(Von Tirpitz),* Robert Cawdron *(hotel manager),* Michael Elwyn *(Cassidy),* Michael Balfour *(cabby),* Frank Thornton *(porter),* James Copeland *(guide),* Alex McCrindle *(baggage man),* Kenneth Benda *(minister),* Graham Armitage *(Wiggins),* Eric Francis *(2d gravedigger),* John Garrie, Godfrey James *(carters),* Ina De La Haye *(Petrova's maid),* Ismet Hassan, Charlie Young Atom, Teddy Kiss Atom, Willie Shearer *(submarine crew),* Daphne Riggs *(lady-in-waiting),* John Gatrell *(equerry),* Martin Carroll, John Scott *(scientists),* Philip Anthony *(lieutenant commander),* Phillip Ross *(McKellar),* Annette Kerr *(secretary),* Kynaston Reeves *(old man),* Anne Blake *(madame),* Marilyn Head, Anna Matisse, Wendy Lingham, Penny Brahms, Sheena Hunter *(girls),* Tina Spooner, Judy Spooner *(twins),* David Kossoff, Paul Stassino, Paul Hansard.

Mystery comedy-drama. Based on the characters created by: Arthur Conan Doyle. Bored by a lack of interesting cases, detective Sherlock Holmes begins using cocaine, despite the disapproval of his biographer and friend, Dr. Watson. One evening the two associates receive complimentary tickets to a Russian ballet, after which the famous ballerina Petrova proposes that she and Holmes produce a child that will combine her beauty and his intellect. Holmes declines, implying that he and Watson are lovers, much to Watson's dismay. Later, as Holmes prepares to investigate the disappearance of a family of midgets, he finds a half-drowned, amnesiac woman at the door of his home. He takes her in and learns that she is Gabrielle Valladon and has come from Belgium in search of her husband. The detective takes the case and travels to Inverness, Scotland, where Holmes's mysterious brother Mycroft warns him not to pursue the case. Holmes nevertheless continues the investigation. When he and Watson take a small boat onto Loch Ness to observe some strange activity in a Scottish castle, their boat is overturned by what appears to be the Loch Ness monster, but Holmes and Watson manage to paddle ashore. Holmes is then summoned to the castle by Mycroft, who shows him a submarine to be manned by the missing midgets. Queen Victoria learns of the bizarre project and orders a halt to it. Mycroft informs his brother that Gabrielle is actually a German spy who duped him into locating the submarine. Dejected, Holmes returns home, and upon learning that Gabrielle has been executed by the Japanese for her espionage activities, he again turns to the use of cocaine. *Detectives. Russians. Dancers. Missing persons. Brothers. Germans. Spies. Midgets. Ballet. Amnesia. Perfidy. Imposture. Capital punishment. Male homosexuality. Cocaine. Castles. Submarines. Inverness (Scotland). Loch Ness. Queen Victoria. Sherlock Holmes. Dr. Watson.*

Note: Location scenes filmed at Inverness, Scotland. Opened in London in Dec 1970.

THE PRIVATE NAVY OF SGT. O'FARRELL   F6.3926

John Beck–Naho Productions. *Dist* United Artists. 8 May **1968** [New York opening; c8 May 1968; LP35838]. Sd; col (Technicolor). 35mm. 92 min.

Prod John Beck. *Dir-Writ* Frank Tashlin. *Story* John L. Greene, Robert M. Fresco. *Photog* Alan Stensvold. *Art Dir* Bob Kinoshita. *Set Decor* Fred Price. *Film Ed* Eda Warren. *Mus* Harry Sukman. *Sd Engr* Harold Lewis. *Asst Dir* Kurt Neumann. *Prod Supv* Austen Jewell. *Location Mgr* Wally Samson. *Wardrobe* Oscar Rodriguez. *Makeup* Mike Moschella. *Hairstyles* Jane Chabra. *Sp Eff* Charles Spurgeon.

Cast: Bob Hope *(M. Sgt. Dan O'Farrell),* Phyllis Diller *(Nellie Krause),* Jeffrey Hunter *(Lieut. j. g. Lyman P. Jones),* Gina Lollobrigida *(Maria),* Mylene Demongeot *(Gaby),* John Myhers *(Lieut. Comdr. Roger Snavely),* Henry Wilcoxon *(Rear Adm. Arthur L. Stokes),* Dick Sargent *(Capt. Elwood Prohaska),* Mako *(Calvin Coolidge Ishimura),* Christopher Dark *(Pvt. George Strongbow),* Michael Burns *(Pvt. Johnny Bannon),* William Wellman, Jr. *(Corporal Kennedy),* Robert Donner *(Marine Private Ogg),* Jack Grinnage *(Private Roberts),* William Christopher *(Pvt. Jack Schultz),* John Spina *(Corporal Miller).*

Comedy. Fearing for his men's morale after a beer boat is sunk off Funapee Atoll during World War II, M. Sgt. Dan O'Farrell persuades Army Capt. Elwood Prohaska to import a battalion of beautiful nurses from the United States. Lieut. Cmdr. Roger Snavely sends nurse Nellie Krause, hardly a soldier's vision of feminine charm. While searching for the missing beer, O'Farrell stumbles upon Calvin Coolidge Ishimura, an American Japanese drafted into the Japanese army and now AWOL. In their continued search for the beer supply, the two men launch an enemy torpedo boat, but instead they discover Maria, O'Farrell's pre-war fiancée, and Gaby, a mysterious beauty, unconscious on a wrecked sailboat. O'Farrell then organizes his crew, consisting of Navy Lieut. Lyman P. Jones, Ishimura, Nellie, Maria and Gaby, and continues his hunt, despite Snavely's order that they return. A Japanese fighter plane attacks, and Jones scores a direct hit. When the plane explodes underwater, thousands of beer cans spew up from the wreck and are quickly loaded aboard O'Farrell's boat. O'Farrell then captures an enemy submarine that has surfaced nearby, fooled by the PT boat's Imperial Navy markings. Days later, as O'Farrell paddles a raft toward Funapee beach, towing the submarine behind him, he hears his own memorial service being conducted. After loudly asserting that he is alive, he claims Maria for his bride. *Nurses. Halfcastes. War heroes. Military life. Submarines. PT boats. Airplanes. Funerals. World War II. South Sea Islands. Japan—Navy. Japan—Army. United States Army. United States Navy.*

PRIVATE RELATIONS   F6.3927

Lark Film Productions. *Dist* Cinex Film Industries. 9 Jul **1968** [Maryland license]. Sd; b&w. 35mm. 75 min.

Prod Lou Campa. *Dir* Larry Crane. *Screenplay* Walter M. Berger. *Dir Cinematog* Eric Breitbart. *Sets* Thomas D. Trovato, Donald Purdy, Frank Wakula. *Ed* Lou Campa. *Songs:* "Never Is a Long Long Time," "I'm Cute," "How Could You Be Such a Liar" Larry Crane. *Songs Arr & Cond* Lorenzo Fuller. *Sung by* Biff Williams. *Song:* "I Want a Doll for Christmas" Larry Crane. *Song Arr & Cond* Lorenzo Fuller. *Sung by* Mario Manzini. *Sd Rec* Michael Rauch. *Locations* John Wagerer.

Cast: Don Canfield *(Earl Dudley)*, Carla Erikson *(Willi Trublood)*, Anne Brent *(Katie Mallory)*, Joe Kugel *(Romney Elrod)*, Elizabeth Easter *(Cynthia)*, Biff Williams *("Corny" Wilson)*, Stanley McEvoy *(Irv Stone)*, Edith Rodewald *(Mrs. Barracuda)*, Linda Boyce *(stripper)*, Laura Kreyn *(Elly Mae)*, Lou Campa.

Comedy. When wealthy Texas entrepreneur Romney Elrod brings hillbilly singer "Corny" Wilson to Earl Dudley's New York office, the public relations man sees an opportunity to rid his company of its indebtedness. With the help of his dedicated secretary, Cynthia, his society girl friend, Willi Trublood, her young actress friend, Katie Mallory, and a pornographer, he sets up hidden cameras in an old Long Island house to set the scene for blackmail. Katie is given the job of seducing Corny before the cameras. Instead, she falls in love with the strait-laced singer, who remains completely within the bounds of propriety while she takes off her clothes. Earl forces Katie to continue with their plan, and she seduces the wealthy Texan, Elrod. When Elrod is presented with the incriminating evidence, he counters with a stag film of his own. For years he has made sex films to excite his frigid wife. Earl is the only one shocked by what he has caught on film, since Willi is revealed in the midst of the orgy. A call comes for Katie from New York. The owner of the Club Mogador has seen her with Corny on film and wants to hire them as a team, stripping and singing. Meanwhile, Willi uses another of Elrod's stag films to break down Earl's resistance to marriage. The Texan tells Earl that he would prefer to do business with a married man. Earl gives in, while Corny and Katie leave for their New York nightclub engagement. *Publicists. Singers. Secretaries. Actors. Socialites. Pornographers. Blackmail. Seduction. Voyeurism. Marriage. Sex exploitation films. New York City. Long Island.*

Note: Pressbook photographs suggest that portions of the footage of *Private Relations* and *Sugar Daddy* are identical.

PRIVILEGE (Great Britain)   F6.3928

World Film Service Productions–Memorial Enterprises. *Dist* Universal Pictures. 24 Jul **1967** [New York opening; c7 Oct 1967; LP43777]. Sd; col (Technicolor). 35mm. 103 min.

Prod John Heyman. *Assoc Prod* Timothy Burrill. *Dir-Adtl Dial* Peter Watkins. *Dir Action Seq* Derek Ware. *Screenplay* Norman Bogner. *Story* Johnny Speight. *Photog* Peter Suschitzky. *Camera Op* Jimmy Turrell. *Focus* Colin Corby. *Art Dir* William Brodie. *Film Ed* John Trumper. *Mus* Mike Leander. *Songs:* "Bad, Bad Boy," "Free Me" Mike Leander, Mark London. *Sung by* Paul Jones, singer. *Sd* Iain Bruce. *Boom Op* Kevin Gurry. *Dub Ed* Roy Taylor. *Dub Mix* Ken Scrivener. *Asst Dir* Scott Wodehouse. *Location Mgr* David Griffith. *Cont* Valerie Booth. *Cost* Vanessa Clarke. *Wardrobe Supv* Barbara Gillett. *Makeup* Jill Carpenter. *Hairstyles* Daphne Vollmer. *Casting Dir* Miriam Brickman. *Still Photog* Patrick Ward & Duffy.

Cast: Paul Jones, singer *(Steve Shorter)*, Jean Shrimpton *(Vanessa Ritchie)*, Mark London *(Alvin Kirsch)*, Max Bacon *(Julie Jordan)*, Jeremy Child *(Martin Crossley)*, William Job *(Andrew Butler)*, James Cossins *(Professor Tatham)*, Frederick Danner *(Marcus Hooper)*, Victor Henry *(Freddie K.)*, Arthur Pentelow *(Leo Stanley)*, Steve Kirby *(Squit)*, Michael Barrington *(Bishop of Essex)*, Edwin Fink *(Bishop of Cornwall)*, John Gill *(Bishop of Surrey)*, Norman Pitt *(Bishop of Hersham)*, Alba *(Bishop of Rutland)*, Malcolm Rogers *(Rev. Jeremy Tate)*, Doreen Mantle *(Miss Crawford)*, Michael Graham *(TV director)*, George Bean Group *(The Runner Beans)*.

Drama. The most celebrated figure in England in 1970 is young pop singer Steve Shorter. Attending his performances are thousands of adoring teenagers who give vent to their feelings of rebellion by wildly cheering his stage presentations in which he is manacled, beaten up, and locked in a cage by sadistic police officers. Quick to sense the potential of controlling and channeling the emotions of the impressionable young, the coalition government of Church and State, with the help of Shorter's managers, forces Shorter to change his image from that of a symbol of modern youth in revolt to that of an inspirational leader of a world-wide evangelical crusade. Although he personally loathes his new identity, he is too deeply entrenched to make a break with the Establishment. His only hope of salvation is provided by Vanessa Ritchie, an individualistic young artist who has been commissioned to paint his portrait. As she follows his daily routine and witnesses the cold and calculating manipulation of his life, she gradually realizes that beneath his celebrated image is a confused young man. When the relationship between Vanessa and Shorter deepens, she urges him to publicly destroy his manufactured facade. Eventually, after a mock demonstration in which he supposedly effects a miraculous healing of the sick, Shorter is ordered to attend a banquet where he is to receive an award. Once there, he suddenly screams out in angry defiance against both the system and the public that has created him. The outburst is met with stunned horror, and he is denounced by the State, the Church, and the conformist audience. *Singers. Theatrical managers. Artists. Evangelists. Rock and roll. Youth. Sadism. Propaganda. Personal identity. Hoaxes. Church and state. Faith cure. Church of England. The Future.*

Note: Filmed in London and Birmingham. Released in Great Britain in 1967.

THE PRIZE   F6.3929

Roxbury Productions. *Dist* Metro-Goldwyn-Mayer, Inc. 25 Dec **1963** [Los Angeles opening; c24 Oct 1963; LP26499]. Sd (Westrex); col (Metrocolor). 35mm (Panavision). 135 min.

A Pandro S. Berman Production. *Assoc Prod* Kathryn Hereford. *Dir* Mark Robson. *Screenplay* Ernest Lehman. *Dir Photog* William H. Daniels. *Art Dir* George W. Davis, Urie McCleary. *Set Decor* Henry Grace, Dick Pefferle. *Film Ed* Adrienne Fazan. *Mus* Jerry Goldsmith. *Rec Supv* Franklin Milton. *Asst Dir* Hank Moonjean. *Wardrobe* Bill Thomas. *Makeup Creat* William Tuttle. *Hairstyles* Sydney Guilaroff. *Sp Vis Eff* J. McMillan Johnson, A. Arnold Gillespie, Robert R. Hoag.

Cast: Paul Newman *(Andrew Craig)*, Edward G. Robinson *(Dr. Max Stratman)*, Elke Sommer *(Inger Lisa Andersen)*, Diane Baker *(Emily Stratman)*, Micheline Presle *(Dr. Denise Marceau)*, Gérard Oury *(Dr. Claude Marceau)*, Sergio Fantoni *(Dr. Carlo Farelli)*, Kevin McCarthy *(Dr. John Garrett)*, Leo G. Carroll *(Count Bertil Jacobsson)*, Sacha Pitoeff *(Daranyi)*, Jacqueline Beer *(Monique Souvir)*, John Wengraf *(Hans Eckart)*, Don Dubbins *(Ivar Cramer)*, Virginia Christine *(Mrs. Bergh)*, Rudolph Anders *(Mr. Bergh)*, Martine Bartlett *(Saralee Garrett)*, Karl Swenson *(Hilding)*, John Qualen *(Oscar)*, Ned Wever *(Clark Wilson)*.

Melodrama. Source: Irving Wallace, *The Prize* (New York, 1962). Newly arrived in Stockholm to receive their Nobel prizes are American novelist Andrew Craig (literature), refugee Max Stratman (physics), John Garrett and Carlo Farelli (medicine), and a French couple, Claude and Denise Marceau (chemistry). Communist agents kidnap Stratman, enlisting the aid of his niece, Emily, on the pretense that the man whom they will put in Stratman's place is her father, the scientist's identical twin, whom she believed dead. The Communists plan to take the real Stratman behind the Iron Curtain, leaving the impostor behind to denounce the United States in his acceptance speech. The frustrated, alcoholic Craig, whose professed interest in the prize is purely financial, proclaims at a press conference that he no longer writes serious literature but produces only detective stories; and he promptly improvises a story about the kidnaping of a Nobel Prize winner. Having known Stratman, Craig soon becomes suspicious of the impostor; starts his own investigation; and finds himself at the center of an intrigue. Though several attempts are made upon Craig's life, the police and Inger Lisa Andersen, a pretty Swedish official assigned to keep him out of trouble, refuse to believe his story; but eventually he convinces Inger that Stratman is being smuggled out of the country. Almost singlehanded he rescues Stratman from a freighter and brings him back to his hotel. Exhausted by his experience, the old man suffers a heart attack but is revived by Garrett and Farelli, who had previously been enemies. When

Stratman makes his appearance at the Nobel ceremonies, his brother flees from the scene and is mistakenly killed by a Communist. It is then revealed that the impersonator was a professional actor, the twin having died years before in Russia. With a changed attitude, Craig then accepts the award and begins a romance with Inger. *Americans in foreign countries. Novelists. Physicists. Physicians. Chemists. Uncles. Brothers. Twins. Communists. Actors. Police. French. Italians. Swedes. Impersonation. Kidnaping. Espionage. Murder. Iron Curtain. Alcoholism. Heart disease. Stockholm. Nobel Prize.*

Note: Exteriors filmed in Stockholm.

PRIZED AS A MATE! see **SPOILED ROTTEN**

PRO see **NUMBER ONE**

THE PRO SHOP   F6.3930
Dist Distribpix, Inc. ca 1970. Sd; col. 35mm. 65 min.

Sex film. Newlyweds take an apartment in a brownstone and are immediately confronted with a problem: the woman has strong sexual desires which her husband is unable to appease. He determines to alleviate her mounting frustration by selling her favors to other men who will be able to satisfy her, and accordingly plies her with liquor until she passes out. The wife soon awakens to find herself coupled with a stranger; quickly realizing this may be her only means of satisfaction, she submits. Her husband thereafter produces an assorted collection of men and women who come to her with a variety of requests, most of which she submits to willingly as her husband looks on. *Newlyweds. Prostitutes. Pimps. Impotence. Drunkenness. Lesbianism. Sexual practices. Voyeurism.*

LE PROCÈS see **THE TRIAL**

PROCÈS DE JEANNE D'ARC see **TRIAL OF JOAN OF ARC**

IL PROCESSO see **THE TRIAL**

THE PROCURER   F6.3931
Dist Distribpix, Inc. 25 Sep 1968 [Boston opening]. Sd; b&w. 35mm. 72 min.
Prod E. V. Loew. *Dir* Graham Place. *Film Ed* Graham Place.

Cast: Stephen Treadwell (*Wilson, The Procurer*), Elizabeth Hartley, Cherie Winters, Louise Violet, Donald Warren.

Sex film. No precise information about the nature of this film has been found, but the title and press materials suggest that it is concerned with prostitution. *Prostitutes. Pimps.*

PRODIGAL GUN see **A MINUTE TO PRAY, A SECOND TO DIE**

THE PRODIGAL SON (Japan)   F6.3932
Toho Co. 29 Jan 1964 [New York opening]. Sd; col (Eastmancolor). 35mm. 99 min.

Assoc Prod Shiro Horie, Koji Toita. *Dir* Hiromichi Horikawa. *Screenplay* Shinobu Hashimoto. *Photog* Asaichi Nakai. *Art Dir* Yasuhide Kato. *Mus* Koji Taku.

Cast: Senjaku Nakamura (*Yohei*), Ganjiro Nakamura (*his father*), Eiko Miyoshi (*his mother*), Kyoko Kagawa (*his sister*), Michiyo Aratama (*Okichi*), Takako Fujino (*Kogiku*).

Melodrama. Source: Monzaemon Chikamatsu, *Onna-goroshi abura no jigoku* (a play; 1721). In 18th-century Japan Yohei, the son of a merchant, takes money from his father's shop in order to court Kogiku, a geisha whose wealthy patron proves to be too much competition for the young man. Desperate for revenge, Yohei is disgraced when his attack on the patron accidentally soils a passing samurai. Now Yohei's creditors demand that he pay his debts, and after his parents refuse to help him, he turns to Okichi, the wife of a fellow trader. As he is pleading to her for aid, his parents arrive at her shop with some money, but the sum is still insufficient. When Okichi refuses to give him more money, the desperate Yohei stabs her to death. *Merchants. Geishas. Samurai. Theft. Finance—Personal. Jealousy. Murder. Family life.*

Note: Released in Japan in 1958 as *Onna goroshi abura jigoku*.

THE PRODUCERS   F6.3933
Sidney Glazier-Springtime Productions-Crossbow Productions. *Dist* Embassy Pictures. 22 Nov 1967 [Pittsburgh opening]. Sd; col (PathéColor). 35mm. 88 min. [Also reviewed at 100 min.]

Pres by Joseph E. Levine. A Sidney Glazier Production. *Prod* Sidney Glazier. *Assoc Prod* Jack Grossberg. *Dir-Writ* Mel Brooks. *Photog* Joseph Coffey. *Art Dir* Charles Rosen. *Set Decor* James Dalton. *Film Ed* Ralph Rosenblum. *Mus Comp & Cond* John Morris. *Mus Supv* Felix Giglio. *Titl Song* John Morris, Mort Goode. *Song:* "Love Power" Norman Blagman, Herb Hartig. *Sung by* Dick Shawn. *Song:* "Springtime for Hitler" Mel Brooks. *Sung by* Michael Davis. *Song:* "Prisoners of Love" Mel Brooks. *Sung by* Zero Mostel. *Choreog* Alan Johnson. *Sd* Alan Heim. *Asst Dir* Michael Hertzberg, Martin Danzig. *Prod Supv* Robert Porter. *Unit Mgr* Louis A. Stroller. *Cost* Gene Coffin. *Makeup* Irving Buchman.

Cast: Zero Mostel (*Max Bialystock*), Gene Wilder (*Leo Bloom*), Dick Shawn (*Lorenzo St. Du Bois*), Kenneth Mars (*Franz Liebkind*), Estelle Winwood ("*Hold me, touch me*" *old lady*), Christopher Hewett (*Roger De Bris*), Andreas Voutsinas (*Carmen Giya*), Lee Meredith (*Ulla*), Renee Taylor (*Eva Braun*), Michael Davis (*production tenor*), John Zoller ("*New York Times*" *critic*), Madlyn Cates (*woman at window*), Frank Campanella (*bartender*), Arthur Rubin, Zale Kessler, Bernie Allen, Rusty Blitz, Anthony Gardell (*auditioning Hitlers*), Mary Love, Amelie Barleon, Nell Harrison, Elsie Kirk (*old ladies*), Barney Martin (*German officer in play*), Diana Eden (*showgirl*), Tucker Smith, David Evans (*lead dancers*), Josip Elic (*violinist*), William Hickey (*drunk in theater bar*).

Farce with music. Max Bialystock is a seedy, disreputable, has-been Broadway producer who ekes out a living by charming love-starved little old ladies into investing in his disastrous productions. One day a timorous and neurotic accountant, Leo Bloom, arrives at Max's office to check the books on his latest theatrical fiasco. He finds a $2,000 difference in the books and naively mentions that a producer could make a killing by finding a sure-fire flop, over-financing it, and then pocketing the remainder of the investors' money after the show closes. Max becomes wildly excited and cons the reluctant Bloom into becoming his partner in producing the worst play in theatrical history. After rejecting hundreds of manuscripts, they finally find the ideal script in *Springtime for Hitler*, a musical comedy about Adolf Hitler and Eva Braun romping in Berchtesgaden, written by Franz Liebkind, an unregenerate Nazi who keeps pigeons and staunchly maintains that Hitler was "a swell guy with a song in his heart." After oversubscribing by 25,000%, Max and Bloom insure disaster by hiring Roger De Bris, a flagrant transvestite generally regarded as the world's worst director, to stage their play, and Lorenzo St. Du Bois, a mind-blown hippie known as LSD, to play the young Führer who danced his way to glory. On opening night, they add a final touch to their scheme by wrapping a $100 bribe around the ticket of the drama critic from the *New York Times*. But the play and production are so unremittingly awful that the audience interprets it as a gigantic put-on and roars with approval. Stunned to discover they are stuck with a smash hit, Max, Bloom, and Liebkind frantically try to close their show, even to the point of blowing up the theater. Apprehended and sent to jail after a trial in which they are found "incredibly guilty," they soon revert to their former tactics by producing a prison show called *Prisoners of Love* and selling shares—well over 100%—to their fellow inmates and the warden. *Theatrical producers. Accountants. Playwrights. Theatrical directors. Theatrical backers. Critics. Nazis. Actors. Hippies. Convicts. Embezzlement. Fraud. Transvestism. Theater. Prisons. New York City—Broadway. Adolf Hitler. Eva Braun.*

Note: Location scenes filmed in New York City.

PROFESSIONAL BLONDE see **PEKING BLONDE**

THE PROFESSIONALS   F6.3934
Pax Enterprises. *Dist* Columbia Pictures. 2 Nov 1966 [New York opening; c1 Nov 1966; LP33771]. Sd; col (Technicolor). 35mm (Panavision). 117 min.

Prod-Dir-Writ Richard Brooks. *Dir Photog* Conrad Hall. *Art Dir* Edward S. Haworth. *Set Decor* Frank Tuttle. *Film Ed* Peter Zinner. *Mus Comp & Cond* Maurice Jarre. *Sd Supv* Charles J. Rice. *Sd* William Randall, Jr., Jack Haynes. *Sd Eff* Del Harris, Kay Rose, Maury Winetrobe. *Asst Dir* Tom Shaw. *Unit Prod Mgr* Lee Lukather. *Script Supv* John Franco. *Wardrobe* Jack Martell. *Makeup* Robert Schiffer. *Hairdresser* Jackie Bone. *Sp Eff* Willis Cook. *Ch Electrn* Harry Sundby.

Cast: Burt Lancaster (*Bill Dolworth*), Lee Marvin (*Henry Rico Fardan*), Robert Ryan (*Hans Ehrengard*), Woody Strode (*Jacob Sharp*), Jack Palance (*Capt. Jesús Raza*), Claudia Cardinale (*Maria Grant*), Ralph Bellamy (*J. W. Grant*), Joe DeSantis (*Ortega*), Rafael Bertrand (*Fierro*), Jorge Martinez de Hoyos (*Padilla*), Marie Gomez (*Chiquita*), José Chavez, Carlos Romero (*revolutionaries*), Vaughn Taylor (*banker*).

Western melodrama. Source: Frank O'Rourke, *A Mule for the Marquesa* (New York, 1964). After the 1917 Mexican revolution, American millionaire J. W. Grant offers to pay four professional soldiers-of-fortune $1,000 apiece to rescue his Mexican wife, Maria, who was kidnaped by guerrilla-bandit Raza. The men employed are dynamite expert Bill Dolworth; professional soldier Henry Rico Fardan; wrangler-packmaster Hans Ehrengard; and black tracker-scout Jacob Sharp, an expert archer. They ride deep into Mexican desert territory until they reach Raza's encampment. A careful plan of strategy is worked out to split-second timing as they secretly break into Maria's room, fight off her guards, and carry her back into the desert. Then they learn that Maria was purchased by Grant, but she is Raza's lover and has no intention of returning to her husband. The adventurers, however, are determined to collect the reward, and they make for the border with Maria. Raza and his men eventually catch up with the four men and Maria at a narrow rock canyon. Dolworth sends the others on ahead and stays behind to await a showdown. Raza is badly wounded in the gunplay, and Dolworth rides on to the border.

Once they all rendezvous, Maria exposes her husband's ruthlessness and begs to be allowed to return to Mexico. Raza arrives to claim Maria, and the four professionals hold Grant and his men at bay until the lovers have safely started back to their desert stronghold. *Scouts—Frontier. Soldiers of fortune. Mexicans. Millionaires. Negroes. Bandits. Guerrillas. Kidnaping. Deserts. Mexico—History—1910-17. Mexican border.*

Note: Filmed on the Mexican border.

PROFESSOR LUST   F6.3935
Biolane Corp. *Dist* American Film Distributing Corp. 30 Nov **1967** [San Francisco showing]. Sd; b&w. 35mm. 95 min.

Prod Herbert Lannard. *Dir* Warner Rose. *Screenplay* Herbert Lannard, W. Pox. *Photog* W. Pox. *Mus* Martin Ammon.

Cast: Larry Swenson, Madison Arnold, Herbert Lannard, Jacqueline Michelin.

Sex film. Dr. Lust (pronounced "Loost"), a chemistry professor experimenting with mind-altering drugs, discovers a chemical which, when sniffed, drastically changes the personality. Lust inhales the vapor and becomes a sneering tyrant. He organizes a world-wide prostitution ring that caters to bizarre tastes. Gathering prostitutes from internationally-known brothels, Lust permits his clients to brutally assault the women. He administers hallucinogenic gases to both the prostitutes and the customers in order to create in their minds appropriate fantasies. One man, a wealthy degenerate, imagines that he is at Versailles with Madame de Pompadour. Another client, a shy introvert, imagines that he is a dashing cavalier with numerous mistresses. Lust's colleague, Miss Zimmerman, investigates the professor's illegal activities and puts an end to the prostitution ring. *Professors. Pimps. Cavaliers. Sex deviates. Dual personality. Prostitution. Hallucinogens. Hallucinations. Versailles Palace. Jeanne Antoinette Poisson.*

PROHIBITED SEX see **SEXY PROIBITISSIMO**

PROIBITISSIMO see **SEXY PROIBITISSIMO**

PROJECT X   F6.3936
Paramount Pictures–Hanna–Barbera Productions. *Dist* Paramount Pictures. May **1968** [c31 Dec 1967; LP35846]. Sd; col (Technicolor). 35mm. 97 min.

Overall Production Credits: A William Castle Production. *Prod-Dir* William Castle. *Assoc Prod* Dona Holloway. *Screenplay* Edmund Morris. *Dir Photog* Harold Stine. *Camera Op* Frank Dugas. *Asst Camera* Paul Weddell. *Art Dir* Hal Pereira, Walter Tyler. *Set Decor* Robert R. Benton, Joseph J. Stone. *Film Ed* Edwin H. Bryant. *Mus* Nathan Van Cleave. *Sd Rec* Garry Harris, John Wilkinson, Rocky Nelson, Robert J. Callen. *Asst Dir* Michael Caffey, Charles Bohart. *Unit Prod Mgr* William W. Gray. *Prod Mgr* Frank Caffey. *Asst Prod Mgr* Curtis Mick. *Script Supv* Luanna Poole. *Wardrobe* Shirlee Strahm, Robert Magahay. *Makeup Supv* Wally Westmore. *Makeup* Marvin Westmore. *Hairstyle Supv* Nellie Manley. *Sp Photog Eff* Paul K. Lerpae. *Sp Eff* Chet Johns. *Opticals* The Optical House. *Dial Coach* Howard W. Koch, Jr. *Still Photog* Bob Full.

Production Credits—Special Sequence: *Prod* William Hanna, Joseph Barbera. *Live Action Dir* Wally Burr. *Dir Photog* Kenneth Peach. *Prod Dsgn* Carl Urbano, Alex Toth. *Asst Dir* Willard Kirkham.

Cast: Christopher George (*Hagen Arnold*), Greta Baldwin (*Karen Summers*), Henry Jones (*Dr. Crowther*), Monte Markham (*Gregory Gallea*), Harold Gould (*Colonel Holt*), Phillip Pine (*Lee Craig*), Lee Delano (*Dr. Tony Verity*), Ivan Bonar (*Colonel Cowen*), Robert Cleaves (*Dr. George Tarvin*), Charles Irving (*Major Tolley*), Sheila Bartold (*Sybil Dennis*), Patrick Wright (*Stover*), Maryesther Denver (*overseer*), Keye Luke (*Sen Chiu*), Ed Prentiss (*Hicks*).

Science fiction melodrama. Source: L. P. Davies, *The Artificial Man* (London, 1965). L. P. Davies, *Psychogeist* (London, 1966). Returning to America from Sino-Asia in the year 2118, government agent Hagen Arnold radios a warning that the West will be destroyed in 14 days. He is found unconscious and with his memory gone as a result of a serum having been injected into his brain. A team of scientists under Dr. Crowther, intent upon learning the nature of the Sinoese secret weapon, freeze Hagen's body, give him the identity of a 1968 bank robber, and place him in a deserted location where a farmhouse environment of that year has been re-created. By scientifically exploring his brain each night, in the hope he will recall the meaning of the message, the scientists learn that a man named Gregory Gallea vanished 2 years earlier on a similar mission. One day Hagen wanders off and meets Karen Summers, an absentee from a nearby factory who is as puzzled by his archaic garb as he is by her futuristic clothing. The nightly experiments continue until an amorphous mass nearly kills Hagen; the mass, explains Dr. Crowther, is Hagen's subconscious, released by the experimentation and capable of killing Hagen in the future. Crowther insists the experiments be continued, but he is overruled by security officer Colonel Holt. Meanwhile Gallea, later revealed as a turncoat working for the enemy, persuades Karen to help him abduct Hagen;

Gallea is killed, however, by the amorphous mass. A final experiment on Hagen's brain explains the cryptic message: Gallea has injected a Sinoese bacterial culture of medieval diseases into Hagen, and in 14 days he will be a living death bomb capable of spreading disease, panic, and death. When the doctors grimly point out that more than 14 days have elapsed since Hagen was injected, Crowther recalls that for much of that period Hagen was frozen and there is still time to immunize him and save the West. Once the threat to mankind is averted, Arnold is given a third identity and, upon regaining consciousness, he finds himself already married to Karen. *Government agents. Scientists. Robbers. Factory workers. Traitors. Cryogenics. Amnesia. Biological warfare. Thought control. Personal identity. Experiments. The Future.*

Note: Location scenes filmed in Placerita Canyon, California.

THE PROJECTED MAN (Great Britain)   F6.3937
M. L. C. Productions. *Dist* Universal Pictures. Feb **1967**. Sd; col (Eastman Color, U. S. print by Technicolor). 35mm (Techniscope). 77 min.

Pres by Protelco Films. *Prod* John Croydon, Maurice Foster. *Exec Prod* Richard Gordon, Gerald A. Fernback. *Assoc Prod* Pat Green. *Dir* Ian Curteis. *Screenplay* John C. Cooper, Peter Bryan. *Story* Frank Quattrocchi. *Photog* Stanley Pavey. *2d Unit Photog* Brian Rhodes. *Art Dir* Peter Mullins. *Film Ed* Derek Holding. *Mus Comp & Cond* Kenneth V. Jones. *Played by* Sinfonia of London. *Sd* Sidney Rider, Red Law. *Asst Dir* Derek Whitehurst, Tom Sachs. *Sp Eff* Flo Nordhoff, Robert Hedges, Mike Hope.

Cast: Bryant Halliday (*Professor Steiner*), Mary Peach (*Dr. Pat Hill*), Norman Wooland (*Dr. Blanchard*), Ronald Allen (*Christopher Mitchell*), Derek Farr (*Inspector Davis*), Tracey Crisp (*Sheila Anderson*), Derrick De Marney (*Latham*), Gerard Heinz (*Professor Lembach*), Sam Kydd (*Harry*), Terry Scully (*Steve*), Norma West (*Gloria*), Frank Gatliff (*Dr. Wilson*).

Science fiction melodrama. At the Farber Research Foundation Professor Steiner and his aide, Christopher Mitchell, succeed in disintegrating objects into energy and reassembling them elsewhere through laser power; a similar experiment on a live guinea pig, however, makes the reassembled animal electrically charged. Dr. Pat Hill, a female associate, helps correct the miscalculation, and Steiner decides to demonstrate his discovery for Professor Lembach, an important visiting scientist. Meanwhile, the head of the foundation, Dr. Blanchard, is being blackmailed into sabotaging Steiner's equipment by Latham, an outsider who wants to take credit for the study. The experiment fails again, and Steiner decides to perform the test on himself in an attempt to vindicate his theories. Jealous of Mitchell, who has fallen in love with Hill, Steiner forces his secretary, Sheila Anderson, to assist him. He is initially successful in projecting himself from one room to another but emerges from the experiment as an electrically charged and facially disfigured monster. After Steiner kills several people, including Blanchard, Hill tries to persuade him to reverse the experiment in the hope that he can change back into a human being. Instead, the crazed scientist chooses to destroy both himself and his equipment. *Scientists. Secretaries. Monsters. Transmutation. Experiments. Sabotage. Blackmail. Disfiguration. Murder. Suicide. Laser. Electricity.*

Note: Released in Great Britain in 1966; running time: 90 min.

PROLOGUE (Canada)   F6.3938
National Film Board of Canada. *Dist* Vaudeo Inc. 29 Jan **1970** [New York opening]. Sd; b&w. 35mm. 87 min.

Prod Tom Daly, prod, Robin Spry. *Dir* Robin Spry. *Screenplay* Sherwood Forest. *Story* Sherwood Forest, Robin Spry. *Photog* Douglas Kiefer. *Film Ed* Christopher Cordeaux. *Mus (see note)* Saz Williams. *Go-Go Mus Perf by* The Ventures. *Sd Ed* Bernard Bordelau, Christopher Cordeaux. *Sd Rec* Roger Lamoureux, Ron Alexander. *Location Sd Rec* Russel Heise. *Asst Dir* Jerry Krepakevich, Myna Lee Johnstone.

Cast: John Robb (*Jesse*), Elaine Malus (*Karen*), Gary Rader (*David*), Christopher Cordeaux (*Neil*), Peter Cullen (*Allen*), Henry Gamer (*Karen's father*), Victor Knight (*judge*), Robert Girolami (*newscaster*), Frank Edwards (*janitor*), Abbie Hoffman, Allen Ginsberg, Dick Gregory, Jean Genêt, Kenneth Galbraith, William S. Burroughs (*themselves*), Magnus Flynn, Caroline Cordeaux, Howard Perry, Daniel Cordeaux, Tanya Mackay, Bruce Mackay, Renée Hébert, John Wildman, Fred Smith, Terrence Ross.

Drama. Jesse, a law school dropout selling underground newspapers, lives in Montreal with his girl friend, Karen, a nightclub waitress. Both are political activists, but when Jesse is beaten up on the street for selling his papers, Karen begins to long for a peaceful country life. David, an American draft dodger, comes to live with them, and Karen becomes intrigued by his mystic beliefs and unpolitical attitudes. Unable to bring legal action against his attackers, Jesse plans to join the protesters in Chicago for the 1968 Democratic Convention; but Karen leaves with David to join a pacifist commune in the Canadian woods. In Chicago, Jesse records the actions of the protesters, including interviews with Abbie Hoffman, and witnesses the violence and bloody clashes with the police. Shaken and disillusioned, Jesse returns to Montreal and is reunited with

Karen, who also has been disillusioned with the escapist life of the commune. *Law students. Lawyers. Hippies. Waitresses. Police. Draft dodgers. Americans in foreign countries. Pacifists. Riots. Communal living. Newspapers— Underground. Democratic National Convention 1968. Montreal. Chicago.*

Note: Filmed in 16mm in Montreal and in Chicago during the riots at the 1968 Democratic National Convention. Opened in Toronto in Feb 1970. First shown at the Venice Film Festival in 1969 with a music score by William Brooks.

LA PROMESSE *see* **SECRET WORLD**

LA PROMESSE DE L'AUBE *see* **PROMISE AT DAWN**

THE PROMISCUOUS SEX   **F6.3939**
All American Film. *Dist* William Mishkin. 22 Jun **1967** [New York opening]. Sd; b&w. 35mm. 94 min.

Dir Andy Milligan. *Screenplay* Clay Guss. *Photog* Andy Milligan.

Cast: Judith Rentzer *(Liz)*, Richard Mangoode *(Michael)*, Judy Eckhardt *(Maxine)*, Lee Forbes *(Mr. Contronia)*, Candy Hammond *(Hazel)*, Stanley Brock *(Sam)*, Kay Carney *(Michael's mother)*, Flora Morrell *(Liz's mother)*, Henry Ansel *(Walter)*, Sylvia Lesser *(Bobbie)*.

Melodrama. At 25, Michael attempts to break away from his over-protective mother and spends an evening making the rounds of Greenwich Village bars. He picks up Liz, a model, and makes love with her in the apartment of her lesbian friend, Maxine. Liz leads Michael to believe that their affair is her first, although she regularly entertains buyers, good-naturedly accommodating their demands in order to help Sam, her middle-aged employer. In spite of Liz's efforts, business declines, and Sam asks her to approach Mr. Contronia for financial help. Liz discovers that Contronia is a gangster, and she barely escapes being raped when she rejects his advances. Maxine is beaten to death by Contronia's gang when she refuses to help them find Liz. Feeling responsible for her friend's death, Liz confesses to Michael that she is a prostitute. He asks her to forget the past, but she dashes into the street and is killed beneath the wheels of a speeding car. *Innocents. Couturiers. Models. Gangsters. Buyers. Filial relations. Promiscuity. Rape. Lesbianism. Murder. Employer-employee relations. Prostitution. New York City—Greenwich Village. Automobile accidents.*

PROMISE AT DAWN (United States/France)   **F6.3940**
Avco Embassy Pictures–Nathalie Films. *Dist* Avco Embassy Pictures. 16 Dec **1970** [Los Angeles opening]. Sd; col (De Luxe). 35mm. 101 min. *MPAA rating* GP.

Pres by Joseph E. Levine. A Jules Dassin Production. *Prod-Dir-Writ* Jules Dassin. *Exec Prod* Joseph E. Levine. *Photog* Jean Badal. *Set Decor* Charles Mérangel. *Prod Dsgn* Alexandre Trauner. *Film Ed* Robert Lawrence. *Mus Comp & Cond* Georges Delerue. *English Song Lyr* Richelle Dassin. *Sd* Jacques Lebreton. *Asst Dir* Jean-Michel Lacor. *Prod Mgr* André Cultet. *Cost* Theoni V. Aldredge. *Makeup* Otello Fava. *Hairstyles* Renata Magnanti. *Location Filming in U.S.S.R. Coöp* Lenfilm.

Cast: Melina Mercouri *(Nina Kacew)*, Assaf Dayan *(Romain, age 25)*, Didier Haudepin *(Romain, age 15)*, François Raffoul *(Romain, age 9)*, Despo *(Aniela)*, Jean Martin *(Igor Igorevitch)*, Fernand Gravey *(Jean-Michel Serusier)*, Jacqueline Porel *(Madame Mailler)*, Elspeth March *(Polish matron)*, Maria Machado *(Nathalia Lissenko)*, Julie Dassin *(Royal Navy Wren)*, René Clermont *(Mr. Piekielny)*, Carol Cole *(Louison)*, Marina Nestora *(Mariette)*, Audrey Berindey *(Valentine)*, Jacqueline Duc *(Madame de Rare)*, Muni *(Angélique)*, Thérèse Thoreaux *(silent film heroine)*, Perlo Vita *(Ivan Mosjoukine)*, Denis Berry.

Biographical melodrama. Source: Samuel Taylor, *First Love* (New York opening: 25 Dec 1961). Romain Gary, *La promesse de l'aube* (Paris, 1960). Nina Kacew, a flamboyant Russian actress who appears in silent films made in Leningrad during the 1920's, has grandiose ambitions for her 9-year-old son, Romain, and devotes her life to making them come true. Attempting to end her affair with movie idol Ivan Mosjoukine (who Romain later learns is his father), Nina joins an acting troupe that ends its tour in Krakow, Poland, where Nina pretends to represent a Paris designer and opens a dress shop. When her fraud is exposed, Nina takes Romain to Nice and befriends Jean-Michel Serusier, a jeweler. In order to pay for Romain's education, Nina plunges into a variety of jobs. Encouraged by his mother to pursue a literary career, Romain attempts to fulfill her ambitions, especially when he learns that she is suffering from diabetes. When World War II breaks out, Romain joins the French Air Force and later the R.A.F. in England. Wounded in action, he recuperates in a North African hospital, where Nina's letters still manage to reach him, each one expressing her love and belief in him. After France's liberation, Romain returns to Nice a hero and plans to present to Nina the Cross of the Liberation he was awarded by General de Gaulle. He learns, however, that Nina died more than 2 years ago but had written 250 letters in advance to sustain him through the war. *Russians. Actors. Couturiers. Jewelers. War heroes. Ambition. Filial*

relations. Motherhood. Fraud. Diabetes. Hospitals. Documentation. World War II. Leningrad. Krakow (Poland). Nice. North Africa. Paris. Nina Kacew. Romain Gary. Ivan Mosjoukine. France—Air Force. Great Britain—Royal Air Force.

Note: Location scenes filmed in Nice, Paris, and the U.S.S.R. Opened in Paris in Nov 1970 as *La promesse de l'aube.* Perlo Vita is a pseudonym for Jules Dassin.

PROMISE HER ANYTHING (Great Britain)   **F6.3941**
Seven Arts Productions. *Dist* Paramount Pictures. 22 Feb **1966** [New York opening; c31 Dec 1965; LP32241]. Sd (Westrex); col (Technicolor). 35mm. 98 min.

Pres by Ray Stark, Seven Arts Productions. *Prod* Stanley Rubin. *Prod Exec* Jack Smith, British. *Dir* Arthur Hiller. *2d Unit Dir* Ernie Robinson. *Screen Story & Screenplay* William Peter Blatty. *Story* Arne Sultan, Marvin Worth. *Dir Photog* Douglas Slocombe. *Camera Op* Chic Waterson. *2d Unit Camera* Bert Mason. *Set Decor* David Ffolkes. *Prod Dsgn* Wilfrid Shingleton. *Main Titl Dsgn* Maurice Binder. *Film Ed* John Shirley. *Mus* Lyn Murray. *Titl Song* Hal David, Burt Bacharach. *Sung by* Tom Jones. *Orch* Johnny Keating. *Choreog* Lionel Blair. *Sd* George Stephenson, John Cox. *Dub Ed* Christopher Lancaster. *Asst Dir* Ted Sturgis. *Prod Mgr* Ronnie Bear. *Unit Mgr* John Wakefield. *Script Supv* Angela Allen. *Cost Dsgn* Beatrice Dawson. *Wardrobe* Jean Fairlie, John Briggs. *Makeup Supv* Bob Lawrence. *Miss Caron's Makeup* Charles Parker. *Hairdresser* Pat McDermott. *Casting Dir* Maude Spector.

Cast: Warren Beatty *(Harley Rummel)*, Leslie Caron *(Michele O'Brien)*, Bob Cummings *(Dr. Peter Brock)*, Keenan Wynn *(Angelo Carelli)*, Hermione Gingold *(Mrs. Luce)*, Lionel Stander *(Sam)*, Asa Maynor *(Rusty)*, Cathleen Nesbitt *(Mrs. Brock)*, Michael Bradley *(John Thomas)*, Bessie Love *(pet shop customer)*, Riggs O'Hara *(glue sniffer)*, Mavis Villiers *(Rusty's mother)*, Hal Galili *(1st moving man)*, Warren Mitchell *(Frank Focus/panel moderator)*, Ferdy Mayne *(Vittorio Fettucini)*, Sydney Tafler *(panel participant)*, Margaret Nolan, Viviane Ventura *(mail-order film girls)*, Anita Sharp Bolster *(babysitter)*, George Moon, Charlotte Holland *(neighbors)*, Chuck Julian *(grocery clerk)*, Michael Chaplin *(beatnik)*, Michael Kane *(staff doctor)*, Libby Morris *(clinic mother)*, Jill Adams *(Mrs. B. M. von Crispin)*, Donald Sutherland *(baby's father)*.

Romantic comedy. Widowed Michele O'Brien moves into a Greenwich Village apartment with her infant son, John Thomas. Her neighbor Harley Rummel, who wants to make art films but supports himself by making burlesque movies, becomes interested in her; but she is interested in her boss, Peter Brock. Brock, a psychologist, is an authority on children (though he hates them) and is considered the country's sixth most eligible bachelor. With Harley's help, Michele keeps John Thomas' existence a secret from Brock. Harley, unknown to Michele, is using the baby in his burlesque movies. Harley convinces Michele that Brock would love the baby, and the child is installed in Brock's clinic. Harley has to make another of his burlesque films in John Thomas' hospital room, but his activities are discovered by a camera hidden in the room to record the child's behavior. Michele is furious but forgives Harley because he saves John Thomas when the baby crawls onto a crane and sets it in motion. Harley, not Brock, is to be John Thomas' new father. *Widows. Infants. Neighbors. Filmmakers. Psychologists. Bachelors. Motherhood. Employer-employee relations. Clinics. New York City—Greenwich Village.*

Note: Released in Great Britain in 1966.

PROMISE HER ANYTHING *see* **PROMISES! PROMISES!**

A PROMISE OF BED *see* **THIS, THAT AND THE OTHER**

PROMISES! PROMISES!   **F6.3942**
Noonan-Taylor Productions. *Dist* NTD, Inc. 2 Aug **1963** [Los Angeles opening; c2 Aug 1963; LP28696]. Sd; b&w. 35mm. 75 min.

Prod Tommy Noonan, Donald F. Taylor. *Dir* King Donovan. *Screenplay* William Welch, Tommy Noonan. *Dir Photog* Joseph Biroc. *Art Dir* Serge Krizman. *Set Decor* Victor Gangelin. *Supv Film Ed* Edward Dutko. *Mus* Hal Borne. *Songs:* "Lu-Lu-Lu, I'm in Love," "Promise Her Anything" Hal Borne. *Sung by* Jayne Mansfield. *Song:* "Fairy Tales" Roberta Day. *Sung by* Marie McDonald. *Sd Mix* Frank McWhorter. *Asst Dir* Cy Roth. *Prod Mgr* William J. Magginetti. *Script Supv* Dixie McCoy. *Cost* Patrick Cummings, Vou Lee Giokaris. *Miss Mansfield's Wardrobe Dsgn* "Mr. Blackwell". *Marie McDonald's Wardrobe Dsgn* Ceil Chapman. *Makeup Artist* Sidney Perell. *Miss Mansfield's Coiffure* Marc Britton. *Marie McDonald's Coiffure* "Fredric". *Hairstyles* Fritzy Merrick. *Prop Master* Irving Sindler. *Ch Electrn* Vaughan Asher.

Cast: Jayne Mansfield *(Sandy Brooks)*, Marie McDonald *(Claire Banner)*, Tommy Noonan *(Jeff Brooks)*, Mickey Hargitay *(King Banner)*, Fritz Feld *(ship's doctor)*, T. C. Jones *(Babbette)*, Claude Stroud *(steward)*, Marjorie Bennett *(Mrs. Snavely)*, Eddie Quillan *(bartender)*, Vic Lundin *(gigolo)*, Eileen Barton *(herself, a girl in doctor's office)*, Pat O'Moore *(ship's captain)*, Imogene

Coca (herself).

Comedy. Source: Edna Sheklow, *The Plant* (a play; production undetermined). Television writer Jeff Brooks, vacationing on a world cruise with his wife, Sandy, finds himself in a cabin next door to muscleman actor King Banner and his wife, Claire. Sandy has been unable to become pregnant because Jeff is too nervous and tense. Hoping that a restful trip will solve the problem, Jeff consults the ship's doctor, who gives him aspirin in the guise of a fertility pill. The couples' frequent drinking parties and trips to each others' cabins create confusion when Sandy and Claire both become pregnant. Jeff remains in a state of drunkenness because he recalls seeing Sandy, clad only in a revealing negligee, entertaining King; in addition, he remembers awakening one morning to the sight of Claire passed out in the same room. Some questions about the babies' parentage obviously remain to be answered. *Television scriptwriters. Body-builders. Actors. Physicians. Impotence. Marriage. Mate swapping. Drunkenness. Parentage. Pregnancy. Vacations. Ocean liners.*

Note: Location scenes filmed on the *S. S. Independence.* Working title: *Promise Her Anything.*

PROSHCHAYTE, GOLUBI! *see* **FAREWELL, DOVES**

PROSTITUTES IN PRISON *see* **99 WOMEN**

PROSTITUTES' PROTECTIVE SOCIETY *see* **P. P. S. (PROSTITUTES' PROTECTIVE SOCIETY)**

PROSTITUTION (France)   F6.3943
Cocifrance. *Dist* Stratford Pictures. 30 Mar **1967** [San Francisco showing]. Sd; b&w. 35mm (CinemaScope). 115 min.

Prod-Dir Maurice Boutel. *Screenplay-Dial* Maurice Boutel. *Screenplay Supv* Marcel Sicot. *Photog* Quinto Albicocco, Paul Fabian, Enzo Riccioni, Jacques Mercanton. *Ed* Etiennette Muse. *Mus* Roger-Roger. *Sd* Jacques Gallois. *Coöp* Interpol.

Cast: Etchika Choureau *(Olga)*, Evelyne Dassas *(Irene)*, Alain Lionnel *(Mario)*, Jean Verner *(Hans)*, Alicia Gutirrez *(Concepcion)*, Anne Darden *(Martha)*, Rita Cadillac *(Rita)*, Gabrielle Robinne *(Honorine)*, Victor Guyau *(Pauwels)*, Robert Dalban *(Robert)*, Carl Eich *(Franck)*, Raoul Dantes *(Joaquin)*, Hinsing Chow *(Bangchow)*, Jacques Devos.

Melodrama. Newly arrived in Paris from the country, Irene is befriended by Mario who invites her to dinner and afterwards brings her to a roominghouse. They meet for lunch the next day, and Mario buys Irene a wardrobe. Irene falls in love with Mario and, believing he wants to marry her, becomes his mistress. Olga, a friend of Mario's who lives at the roominghouse, persuades Irene to take up prostitution in order to prevent Mario from committing a robbery to get enough money to open a small business for himself and Irene. Irene soon becomes trapped in the vice ring and is sent to Hamburg, Holland, and Mexico, always with the promise that Mario will join her. Finally, in Hong Kong Irene is drugged until she becomes an addict. A well-meaning sea captain persuades Irene to tell her story to Interpol when she learns that Mario has betrayed her. Then, resigned to her predicament, Irene is confident that the drugs will help her die quickly. *Pimps. Drug addicts. Innocents. Perfidy. Prostitution. Roominghouses. Paris. Hamburg. Netherlands. Mexico. Hong Kong. INTERPOL.*

Note: Location scenes filmed in Paris, Hamburg, Vera Cruz, Hong Kong, and The Netherlands. Opened in Paris in Mar 1963 as *La prostitution.* Scenes from this film are also included in *To Be a Woman,* q. v.

LA PROSTITUTION *see* **PROSTITUTION**

LA PROSTITUTION *see* **TO BE A WOMAN**

THE PROTECTORS *see* **COMPANY OF KILLERS**

PROTEST AND COMMUNICATION *see* **CIVILISATION: PROTEST AND COMMUNICATION**

PROWL GIRLS   F6.3944
Barry Mahon Productions. *Dist* Chancellor Films. Jun **1968.** Sd; b&w. 35mm. 70 min.

A Barry Mahon Production.

Cast: Leo Schell *(narrator)*.

Melodrama. When Sally Mae's boyfriend Tarzan is expelled from high school for peddling marijuana, she rebels against her middle-class background, thinking that he has been treated unfairly. She joins Tarzan in his East Village hippie "crash pad." He organizes a profitable racket, luring suckers from uptown to watch the wild parties that take place in the "pad." He appeals to their sympathy to extract large sums of money for the supposed rehabilitation of the young female participants. The racket is so successful that other operators, including Big Daddy and Butterfly, join in the enterprise. After several months, Sally Mae learns about the racket and goes to live with a businessman she met at one of the parties. Big Daddy, Tarzan, and Butterfly

seek her out to make sure that she doesn't talk to the police. They abduct her, give her an overdose of heroin, and leave her dead in the basement of a Village flop house. *Hippies. Racketeers. Runaways. Juvenile delinquents. Drug dealers. Voyeurism. Abduction. Murder. Adolescence. Fraud. Drug overdose. Marijuana. Orgies. New York City—East Village.*

Note: Also known as *Runaway Daughters.*

DER PROZESS *see* **THE TRIAL**

PRUDENCE AND THE PILL (Great Britain)   F6.3945
Prudence Films. *Dist* Twentieth Century-Fox Film Corp. 23 May **1968** [New York opening; c23 May 1968; LP35849]. Sd (Westrex); col (DeLuxe). 35mm. 92 min. [Cut from 100 min.]

A Kahn–Harper Production. *Prod* Kenneth Harper, Ronald J. Kahn. *Dir* Fielder Cook. *Uncredited Adtl Dir (see note)* Ronald Neame. *Screenplay* Hugh Mills. *Anim* Errol Le Cain. *Dir Photog* Ted Moore. *Camera Op* Robert Kindred. *Art Dir* Fred Carter. *Set Decor* John Jarvis. *Prod Dsgn* Wilfred Shingleton. *Titl* Richard Williams. *Film Ed* Norman Savage. *Mus & Songs:* "The Pill," "Too Soon To Tell You" Bernard Ebbinghouse. *Sd Rec* Bert Ross. *Dub Ed* Don Sharpe. *Asst Dir* Ted Sturgis. *Prod Mgr* Michael F. Johnson. *Cont* Pamela Carlton. *Cost Dsgn* Julie Harris, cost. *Wardrobe Supv* Eileen Sullivan. *Makeup Ch* Tony Sforzini. *Hairdresser* Gordon Bond.

Cast: Deborah Kerr *(Prudence Hardcastle)*, David Niven *(Gerald Hardcastle)*, Robert Coote *(Henry Hardcastle)*, Irina Demick *(Elizabeth)*, Joyce Redman *(Grace Hardcastle)*, Judy Geeson *(Geraldine Hardcastle)*, Keith Michell *(Dr. Alan Hewitt)*, Edith Evans *(Lady Roberta Bates)*, David Dundas *(Tony Bates)*, Vickery Turner *(Rose)*, Hugh Armstrong *(Ted)*, Peter Butterworth *(chemist)*, Moyra Fraser *(woman in teashop)*, Annette Kerr *(Gerald's secretary)*, Harry Towb *(racetrack official)*, Jonathan Lynn *(chemist's assistant)*.

Comedy. Source: Hugh Mills, *Prudence and the Pill* (London, 1965). Gerald and Prudence Hardcastle hardly talk to each other and have separate bedrooms. Gerald consoles himself with his mistress, Elizabeth, while Prudence is having an affair with her doctor, Alan Hewitt. Henry and Grace Hardcastle, Gerald's brother and sister-in-law, are most happily married, but their snug world is upset when Grace becomes pregnant as a result of daughter Geraldine's having substituted aspirin for her mother's birth control pills. Heeding Elizabeth's advice, Gerald decides to do the same with Prudence's pills, hoping she will become pregnant by Alan and get a divorce. His plan is foiled, however, by the family maid, Rose. Thinking Prudence's pills are real, Rose steals them and substitutes what she thinks are vitamins but actually are birth control pills given her by her boyfriend, Ted, the family chauffeur. When Rose rather than Prudence becomes pregnant, Gerald realizes the error and again substitutes aspirin for his wife's pills. Meanwhile, young Geraldine, having run out of pills, becomes pregnant by her boyfriend, Tony Bates, to the consternation of her parents and the delight of Tony's guardian, Lady Roberta Bates. Eventually Prudence does get pregnant by Alan, but her request for a divorce is rejected by Gerald, who has been deserted by Elizabeth. Later, learning that Elizabeth has already given birth to his child, Gerald happily agrees not to contest Prudence's suit, and all the couples celebrate with their babies. *Mistresses. Physicians. Brothers. Sisters-in-law. Housemaids. Chauffeurs. Guardians. Marriage. Infidelity. Birth control. Divorce. Pregnancy.*

Note: Location scenes filmed in Oxfordshire and Berkshire, England. Released in London in Aug 1968; running time: 92 min. Neame completed direction of the film following Fielder Cook's resignation.

PSYCH-OUT   F6.3946
Dick Clark Enterprises. *Dist* American International Pictures. 6 Mar **1968** [San Francisco opening; c13 Mar 1968; LP35618]. Sd; col (Pathé Color). 35mm. ca88 & 101 min. [Copyright length: 55 min.]

Pres by James H. Nicholson, Samuel Z. Arkoff. *Prod* Dick Clark. *Dir* Richard Rush. *Screenplay (see note)* E. Hunter Willett, Betty Ulius, Betty Tusher. *Story* E. Hunter Willett. *Dir Photog* Leslie Kovacs. *Camera Op* Frank Ruttencutter, Peter Heiser. *Art Dir* Leon Ericksen. *Set Decor* James Cotton. *Titl & Eff Cinefx.* *Film Ed* Ken Reynolds. *Asst Film Ed* Herb Steinore. *Orig Score & Adapt* Ronald Stein. *Song:* "The Pretty Song" The Strawberry Alarm Clock. *Sung by* The Storybook. *Song:* "Rainy Day Mushroom Pillow" Steven Bartek, George Bunnell, Jr. *Sung by* The Strawberry Alarm Clock. *Song:* "Two Fingers Pointing on You" Sky Saxon. *Sung by* The Seeds. *Song:* "Ashbury Wednesday" Rusty Young, Mitchell Mitchell, Joe E. Neddo, George Grantham, S. Bush. *Sung by* Cryque Boenzee. *Song:* "The World's on Fire" *writ & sung by* The Strawberry Alarm Clock. *Songs:* "Psych-Out Sanctorum," "The Love Children," "Psych-Out" Ronald Stein. *Sung by* The Storybook. *Song:* "Beads of Innocence" Harlene Stein, Ronald Stein. *Sung by* The Storybook. *Song:* "Incense and Peppermints" John S. Carter, Jr., Tim Gilbert. *Sung by* The Strawberry Alarm Clock. *Sd Mix* Leroy Robbins. *Sd Boom* James Contrares. *Sd Eff* Edit-Rite Inc. *Asst Dir* Elliot Schick. *Prod Mgr* Paul Lewis. *Script Supv*

Joyce King. *Prod Sec* Sheila Scott. *Wardrobe Mistress* Sara Anderson. *Makeup Artist* Rafaelle Patterson. *Hairstyles* Evelyn Talavera. *Sp Eff* Gary Kent. *Sp Lighting Eff* Jim Morrissett. *Ch Electrn* Aggie Aguilar. *Still Photog* Peter Sorel. *Key Grip* Bill Pecchi, Jack Oliver. *Prop Master* Robert V. O'Neil.

Cast: Susan Strasberg *(Jennie Davis)*, Dean Stockwell *(Dave)*, Jack Nicholson *(Stoney)*, Bruce Dern *(Steve Davis)*, Adam Roarke *(Ben)*, Max Julien *(Elwood)*, Henry Jaglom *(Warren)*, Linda Gaye Scott *(Lynn)*, I. J. Jefferson *(Pandora)*, Tommy Flanders *(Wesley)*, Ken Scott *(preacher)*, Garry Marshall *(plainclothesman)*, Geoffrey Stevens *(Greg)*, Susan Bushman *(little girl)*, John Cardos *(thug)*, Madgal Dean *(mother)*, William Gerrity *(little boy)*, Robert Kelljan *(Arthur)*, Gary Kent *(thugs' leader)*, Beatriz Monteil *(landlady)*, David Morick *(stuntman)*, Barbara London *(Sadie)*, The Strawberry Alarm Clock, The Seeds.

Melodrama. Jennie Davis, a 17-year-old deaf runaway, arrives in San Francisco's Haight-Ashbury district to search for her missing brother Steve, an artist. Wandering into a hippie coffee shop, she meets Stoney, Ben, and Elwood—three members of an unsuccessful rock group. They help her elude two policemen who are looking for her and persuade her to exchange her "square" clothing for something more suitable. With the help of Stoney's friend Dave, they continue to search for Steve but find no trace of him. After learning that some young thugs are also looking for Steve, Stoney runs into Steve and talks him into visiting Jennie at the hangout where Stoney's combo is performing. Though Steve appears there the next day, he is forced to flee when he is spotted by the thugs. Dave takes the near-hysterical Jennie to Stoney's apartment, where he attempts to quiet her down and then seduce her by giving her a psychedelic drug. Unaware of what she has swallowed, Jennie runs out in the night to continue her search for her brother, who, unable to escape from his pursuers, has barricaded himself in his house and set fire to it. Jennie arrives in the area and wanders into the traffic on the Golden Gate Bridge. Stoney and Dave come to her rescue; but Dave, also in a daze, is killed by a car while carrying Jennie to safety. United by their mutual contempt for the outside world, Jennie and Stoney leave together. *Runaways. Artists. Hippies. Musicians. Missing persons. Hoodlums. Adolescence. Deafness. Brother-sister relationship. Suicide. Coffeehouses. Hallucinogens. San Francisco—Haight-Ashbury. Golden Gate Bridge. Fires. Psychedelic states.*

Note: Location scenes filmed in the Haight-Ashbury district of San Francisco. Working title: *The Love Children.* Leslie Kovacs is also known as Laszlo Kovacs. Some sources credit Tusher, rather than Willett, with screenplay and story.

PSYCHE 59 (Great Britain)   **F6.3947**
Troy-Schenck Productions. *Dist* Columbia Pictures, Royal Films International. 29 Apr **1964** [New York opening; c1 Apr 1964; LP28066]. Sd (Westrex); b&w. 35mm. 94 min.
Prod Phillip Hazelton. *Dir* Alexander Singer. *Screenplay* Julian Halevy. *Dir Photog* Walter Lassally. *Camera* Len Harris. *Art Dir* John Stoll. *Asst Art Dir* Frank Willson. *Set Decor* Josie MacAvin. *Main Titl* Romek Marber, Robert Ellis. *Film Ed* Max Benedict. *Mus Comp & Cond* Kenneth V. Jones. *Sd Rec* George Stephenson, Red Law. *Sd Ed* Peter Thornton. *Asst Dir* David Bracknell. *Prod Mgr* R. L. M. Davison. *Cont* Pamela Carlton. *Cost Dsgn* Julie Harris, cost. *Wardrobe Supv* Laura Nightingale. *Makeup* Harold Fletcher. *Hairdresser* Pearl Tipaldi. *Casting* James Liggat.

Cast: Patricia Neal *(Allison)*, Curt Jurgens *(Eric Crawford)*, Samantha Eggar *(Robin)*, Ian Bannen *(Paul)*, Beatrix Lehmann *(grandmother)*, Elspeth March *(Madame Valadier)*, Sandra Lee *(Susan)*, Shelley Crowhurst *(Jean)*, Peter Porteous, Gladys Spencer, Michael McStay.

Drama. Source: Françoise Des Ligneris, *Psyché 58* (Paris, 1958). Allison has been blind since a fall 5 years earlier during a pregnancy. Doctors have decided that her blindness is psychosomatic, induced by the desire to forget a traumatic event in her past. Allison's younger sister, Robin, arrives in London for a visit, much to the annoyance of Eric, Allison's industrialist husband. Robin begins seeing Paul, a family friend who is in love with her, but Allison senses a curious tension between Eric and Robin. Later, Eric tells Paul that he seduced Robin when she was a schoolgirl, and Robin admits that she is still attracted to Eric. Allison's sight begins to return following a fall in the garden, but she hides the fact. After Robin announces her intention to marry Paul, Allison discovers Robin and Eric embracing. She remembers that her earlier fall and blindness resulted from seeing her husband and sister in a similar situation. Paul leaves Robin, and Allison abandons Eric. *Sisters. Industrialists. Houseguests. Blindness. Pregnancy. Psychosomatic illness. Infidelity. Marriage. London.*

Note: Released in Great Britain in 1964; running time: 94 min.

PSYCHEDELIC SEX KICKS   **F6.3948**
Pad Productions. *Dist* Distribpix, Inc. 14 Sep **1967** [San Francisco showing]. Sd; col. 35mm. 48 min.
Pres by Pot Heads Experimental Films.

Cast: Janie Boyde, Dixie Darling, Glen McKay.

Drama. A hippie lures two women who are enjoying the sun in San Francisco's Golden Gate Park to his apartment. There they smoke marijuana, take LSD, and dream of making love among a thousand balloons. They paint each other's nude bodies, and one of the women plays with a pet snake. *Hippies. Body painting. Marijuana. LSD. Balloons (toy). San Francisco. San Francisco—Golden Gate Park. Hallucinations. Snakes.*

Note: Also known as *Psychedelics ... Kicks* and *Psychedelic Love.*

THE PSYCHIC LOVER (Italy/West Germany)   **F6.3949**
La Regina Produzione–Thor Film. *Dist* Cinema Arts Distributing Co., William Rowland. ca **1969**. Sd; b&w. 35mm. [Feature film, length unknown.]
Original Production Credits: *Prod* Joseph Justman. *Dir* Edward Dein. *Screenplay* Edward Dein, Karlheinz Deikert. *Photog* Franco Delli Colli. *Film Ed* Giancarlo Cappelli. *Mus* Ugo Calise. *Sd* Domenico Luria.
Original Cast: Marisa Solinas, Dan Harrison, Henrik Reinkwell, Georg Hauke, Gianluigi Crescenzi.

Cast—Additional U. S. footage: Marsha Jordan.

Melodrama. Phil, on the run with a fortune in jewels for which he has doublecrossed his accomplice, arrives in a remote Mediterranean village where he meets and is attracted to Carmencita, the lovely and innocent owner of a local cantina. Phil, an obsessive womanizer, attempts to seduce Carmencita, but she continually rejects his advances. Finally, Phil's accomplice locates him, but he murders the man and makes the death appear accidental. His pretended grief arouses Carmencita's sympathy, and she agrees to marry him. After a night of passionate lovemaking, Phil abandons her, but her humiliation is eased by the comforts brought to her by Paco, her mute and adoring helper. [Press photographs suggest that the film also includes scenes of lesbianism.] *Thieves. Peasants. Mutes. Saloon keepers. Philanderers. Desertion. Village life. Seduction. Murder. Marriage. Lesbianism. Perfidy. Jewels. Mediterranean Sea.*

Note: The U. S. version contains sex scenes filmed in the United States. The original version was shown in the U. S. as *Sweet Smell of Love,* q. v.

PSYCHO A GO-GO!   **F6.3950**
Tal Productions. *Dist* Hemisphere Pictures, American General Pictures. Nov **1965**. Sd; col (Technicolor). 35mm (Techniscope). 85 min. [See note.]
Prod-Dir-Story Al Adamson. *Assoc Prod* Don Guiss. *Screenplay* Chris Martino, Mark Eden, writ. *Dir Photog* William Zsigmond. *Rock Mus Score* Don McGinnis, Billy Storm. *Perf by* The Vendells.

Cast: Roy Morton *(Joe Corey)*, Tacey Robbins *(Linda Clarke)*, Kirk Duncan *(David Clarke)*, John Talbert *(Curtis)*, K. K. Riddle *(Nancy Clarke)*, Tanya Maree *(Vicky, a moll)*, John Armond *(Nicky, a thug)*, Lyle Felice *(Vito)*, Joey Benson *(Lieutenant Ward)*, Shary Richards *(his wife)*, The Vendells *(themselves)*, John Carradine *(Dr. Vanard [see note])*.

Melodrama. A group of jewel thieves, led by Vito, hide their loot in a pickup truck. Nancy, the young daughter of trucker David Clarke, finds the jewelry and conceals it in a new doll. Confronted by the gang, David is unable to give them any information. Vito sends Joe Corey, a Vietnam veteran whose mind has been deranged by a device implanted in his brain by Dr. Vanard, to abduct David's wife, Linda, and daughter. Corey picks up and murders a go-go dancer. Accompanied by Curtis, another henchman, Corey abducts the pair and drives them to a deserted farmhouse. During an attempted rape of Linda, the two men fight, enabling mother and daughter to flee. The thugs pursue them into the mountains, where Nancy hurls her doll at Corey. As the fortune falls into a deep gorge, David comes to his family's rescue. Corey is killed, and the Clarkes are reunited. *Thieves. Truckdrivers. Veterans. Scientists. Psychopaths. Go-go dancers. Brain surgery. Murder. Abduction. Rape. Rescue. Jewels. Dolls. Chases.*

Note: Filmed in and around Los Angeles; working title: *Echo of Terror.* Revised, with additional footage featuring Carradine, and released in Sep 1966 as *The Fiend With the Electronic Brain;* running time: 90 min.

PSYCHO-CIRCUS (Great Britain)   **F6.3951**
Circus Film. *Dist* American International Pictures. May **1967**. Sd; b&w (see note). 35mm. 65 min.
Prod Harry Alan Towers. *Exec Prod* David Henley. *Dir* John Moxey. *Screenplay* Peter Welbeck. *Photog* Ernest Steward. *2d Unit Photog* John Kotze. *Camera Op* Dudley Lovell. *Art Dir* Frank White. *Asst Art Dir* George Lack. *Film Ed* John Trumper. *1st Asst Ed* John Colville. *Mus* Johnny Douglas. *Sd Rec* John Brommage, Ken Cameron. *Asst Dir* Barrie Melrose. *Prod Mgr* Peter Manley. *Cont* Eve Willson. *Wardrobe* Charles Guerin. *Makeup* Frank Turner. *Hairstyles* Ann Box.

Cast: Christopher Lee *(Gregor)*, Leo Genn *(Inspector Elliott)*, Anthony Newlands *(Barberini)*, Heinz Drache *(Carl)*, Eddi Arent *(Eddie)*, Klaus Kinski *(Manfred)*, Margaret Lee *(Gina)*, Suzy Kendall *(Natasha)*, Cecil Parker *(Sir John)*, Victor Maddern *(Mason)*, Maurice Kaufmann *(Mario)*, Lawrence James *(Manley)*, Tom Bowman *(Jackson)*, Skip Martin *(Mr. Big)*, Fred Powell *(Red)*, Gordon Petrie *(Negro)*, Henry Longhurst *(hotel porter)*, Dennis Blakely *(armored van guard)*, George Fisher *(4th man)*, Peter Brace, Roy Scammel *(speedboat men)*, Geoff Silk, Keith Peacock *(security men)*.

Mystery drama. Following the hold-up of an armored truck, some stolen bank notes show up at the winter quarters of Barberini's Circus, and Scotland Yard's Inspector Elliott is sent to investigate. The murdered body of one of the robbers is found, and a short time later Gina, a circus starlet, also is slain. The chief suspects are: Gregor, the lion tamer, who wears a black mask to conceal his disfigured face; Carl, the ringmaster, who believes his father was killed by Gregor's twin brother; Mario, the knife thrower, who was insanely jealous of the dead Gina's suitors; Mr. Big, a dwarf who is blackmailing Gregor; Eddie, the bookkeeper, who never realized his ambition of becoming a circus performer; and Natasha, Gregor's niece, the daughter of the man Carl is seeking. Eventually it is established that Gregor found the missing robbery money and hid it in a suitcase. He tries to escape with his loot but is murdered by a masked figure. Furthermore, it is revealed that Gregor is actually Natasha's father and that Carl's father died accidentally from a fall. Although this aspect of the mystery is solved, Inspector Elliott adheres to his belief that Gregor was not responsible for the two murders. Acting on a hunch, he arranges for Eddie to be given a chance to assist Mario in his knife-throwing act. When Mario switches weapons and uses knives identical to the ones used in the murders, Eddie breaks down and admits that his envy of the performers led him to commit the murders. *Detectives. Lion tamers. Ringmasters. Dwarfs. Accountants. Robbery. Murder. Jealousy. Envy. Confession (law). Circus. Masks. Scotland Yard.*

Note: Location scenes filmed at Billy Smart's Circus Grounds in Winkfield, England. Released in Great Britain in Eastmancolor in Nov 1967 as *Circus of Fear*; running time: 83 min. Peter Welbeck is a pseudonym for Harry Alan Towers.

PSYCHO KILLER *see* **THE PSYCHO LOVER**

PSYCHO KILLERS *see* **MANIA**

THE PSYCHO LOVER　　　　　　　　　　　　　　　　　　　　　　F6.3952

Taos-Libra Productions. *Dist* Medford Film Corp. Sep **1970**. Sd; col (Eastman Color). 35mm. 75 min. *MPAA rating* X.

Prod-Dir-Writ Robert Vincent O'Neil. *Exec Prod* Lou Horowitz. *Assoc Prod* Gerry Huffaker. *Photog* Robert Maxwell. *Art Dir* Ray Markham. *Film Ed* Steve Faber, Stanley E. Rabjohn. *Mus* Gary LeMel, Norma Green, Jim Helms. *Songs Sung by* Gary LeMel, Ginger Blake. *Sd* Don Jones. *Prod Mgr* Gary Kent.

Cast: Lawrence Montaigne *(Kenneth)*, Joanne Meredith *(Valerie)*, Elizabeth Plumb *(Stacy)*, Frank Cuva *(Marco)*, John Vincent *(district attorney)*, Sharon Cook, Dianne Jones, Luanne Roberts, David Astor, Judy Lang, Charles Victor, Lynn Lyon.

Melodrama. Psychotic sex murderer Marco is put under the care of Kenneth, a psychiatrist. Kenneth is unable to obtain a divorce from his alcoholic wife, Valerie. Kenneth's mistress, Stacy, tells Kenneth of the use of brainwashing in the film version of *The Manchurian Candidate* and inadvertently gives Kenneth an idea of how to kill his wife: Kenneth hypnotizes Marco and instructs him to kill Valerie. Valerie learns of the plot and arranges for Stacy to be in her place. Marco attacks Stacy, and both are killed when they fall on the live wires of a television set. *Psychopaths. Psychiatrists. Mistresses. Infidelity. Murder. Brainwashing. Hypnotism. Divorce. Electrocution—Accidental. Alcoholism. "The Manchurian Candidate".*

Note: Also known as *Psycho Killer*, *The Loving Touch*, and *The Lovely Touch*.

PSYCHODRAMA　　　　　　　　　　　　　　　　　　　　　　　　F6.3953

MJ Productions. *Dist* Able Film Co. ca **1970**. Sd; col. 16mm. [Feature length assumed.]

Sex film. No information about the precise nature of this film has been found. *Sexuality. Psychiatry.*

PSYCHOMANIA *see* **VIOLENT MIDNIGHT**

THE PSYCHOPATH (Great Britain)　　　　　　　　　　　　　　　F6.3954

Amicus Productions. *Dist* Paramount Pictures. 25 May **1966** [Minneapolis opening; c31 Dec 1965; LP32624]. Sd; col (Technicolor). 35mm (Techniscope). 83 min.

Prod Max J. Rosenberg, Milton Subotsky. *Dir* Freddie Francis. *Screenplay* Robert Bloch. *Dir Photog* John Wilcox. *Art Dir* Bill Constable. *Main Titl* Sam Suliman. *Film Ed* Oswald Hafenrichter. *Mus* Elisabeth Lutyens. *Mus Comp & Cond* Philip Martell. *Sd* Baron Mason. *Asst Dir* Peter Price. *Prod Mgr* Ted Wallis. *Makeup* Jill Carpenter. *Hairdresser* Henry Montsash. *Sp Eff* Ted Samuels.

Cast: Patrick Wymark *(Inspector Holloway)*, Margaret Johnston *(Mrs. Von Sturm)*, John Standing *(Mark Von Sturm)*, Alexander Knox *(Frank Saville)*, Judy Huxtable *(Louise Saville)*, Don Borisenko *(Donald Loftis)*, Colin Gordon *(Dr. Glyn)*, Thorley Walters *(Martin Roth)*, Robert Crewdson *(Victor Ledoux)*,

Tim Barrett *(Morgan)*, Frank Forsyth *(Tucker)*, Olive Gregg *(Mary)*, Harold Lang *(Briggs)*, John Harvey *(Reinhardt Klermer)*, Greta Farrer *(cigarette girl)*, Gina Gianelli, Peter Diamond.

Horror film. Four men are brutally murdered with each victim found lying next to a doll fashioned in his own image, and Inspector Holloway of Scotland Yard is assigned to the case. Holloway learns that all four men were members of an Allied commission which convicted German industrialist Von Sturm of using slave labor during World War II. Von Sturm had committed suicide, and when Holloway learns that the dolls had been purchased by his widow, he visits the crippled woman at her London home. Mrs. Von Sturm's house is filled with dolls with which she converses when her neurotic son, Mark, is not at home. Holloway visits Mark at the boathouse where he works, and during questioning, the young man becomes violent and knocks the inspector unconscious. Following Mark's disappearance, Louise Saville, the daughter of one of the murdered men, visits Mrs. Von Sturm and finds Mark's dead body propped up in a chair like a doll. The truth exposed, Mrs. Von Sturm rises from her wheelchair and walks menacingly toward the terrified Louise, but the crazed woman loses her balance and plummets down a flight of stairs to her death. *Detectives. Germans. Industrialists. Widows. Cripples. Psychopaths. Murder. Revenge. Filial relations. Dolls. World War II. London. Scotland Yard.*

Note: Released in Great Britain caOct 1966.

PSYCHOUT FOR MURDER (Argentina / Italy)　　　　　　　　　F6.3955

Chiara Films Internazionali–Banco Film–Glori Art. *For* International Co-Productions. *Dist* Times Film Corp. Dec **1970**. Sd; col (Eastman Color, print by Movielab). 35mm. 88 min. *MPAA rating* R.

Prod-Story Oscar Brazzi. *Dir* Edward Ross, Ted Kneeland. *Screenplay* Oscar Brazzi, Mario Proietti, Diana Crispo. *Photog* Luciano Trasatti. *Art Dir* Francesco Della Noce, Giovanni Fratalocchi. *Film Ed* Amedeo Giomini. *Mus* Benedetto Ghiglia. *Song:* "Daddy Said the World Was Lovely" Benedetto Ghiglia, Jo Anna Kneeland.

Cast: Adrienne La Russa *(Licia)*, Rossano Brazzi *(Brigoli)*, Nino Castelnuovo *(Mario)*, Paola Pitagora *(Giovanna)*, Alberto de Mendoza *(Francesco)*, Idelma Carlo *(Laura)*, Renzo Petretto *(Paterlini)*, Nestor Garay *(politician)*.

Melodrama. Licia, the hedonistic daughter of Brigoli, a wealthy industrialist, falls in love with Mario, a conniving young man. Mario lures her to a brothel, where their lovemaking is disrupted by a police raid and press photographers. In order to suppress the scandal, Licia's family commits her to a mental institution, and her father is forced to pay off Mario, who had arranged the event for purposes of blackmail. Some time later, Licia is released from the asylum and returns home. Although Licia convinces her family that she is happy to be home, she systematically plots to destroy everyone who conspired in sending her away. First, she persuades Mario to secretly film her father making love to his mistress; when Brigoli shows his business associates movies of himself on a holy pilgrimage, the sex footage appears on the screen. Next, Licia seduces her brother-in-law, thereby driving her sister Giovanna to suicide. Finally, learning that her father is planning to call on Mario, Licia drugs Mario's champagne, props him up in bed, points a revolver at his face, and ties the trigger to the doorknob; when Brigoli arrives, the gun goes off, killing Mario. Back home, Licia tells her father that she knows he killed Mario but has decided not to inform the police. To make her revenge complete, Licia tells him that she will devote herself to making the rest of his life a living nightmare. *Industrialists. Police. Photographers. Mistresses. Frameup. Blackmail. Revenge. Family life. Seduction. Suicide. Murder. Scandal. Whorehouses. Insane asylums.*

Note: Filmed in Italy and released there in 1969 as *Salvare la faccia*; running time: 92 min. U. S. prerelease title: *Daddy Said the World Was Lovely*. Edward Ross is a pseudonym for Rossano Brazzi.

PSYCOSISSIMO (Italy)　　　　　　　　　　　　　　　　　　　　F6.3956

Variety Film–Flora Film. *Dist* Ellis Films, Trans-Lux Distributing Corp. 7 Sep **1962** [New York opening]. Sd; b&w. 35mm. 88 min.

Prod Leo Cevenini, Vittorio Martino. *Dir* Steno. *Adapt for the Screen by* Vittorio Metz, Roberto Gianviti, Steno. *Photog* Tino Santoni. *Art Dir* Ivo Battelli. *Film Ed* Giuliana Attenni. *Mus Comp* Carlo Rustichelli.

Cast: Ugo Tognazzi *(Ugo)*, Raimondo Vianello *(Raimondo)*, Edy Vessel *(Annalisa)*, Monique Just *(Marcella)*, Spiros Focas *(Arturo)*, Francesco Mulè *(The Butler)*, Franca Marzi *(The Widow Scarfoni)*.

Crime comedy. While rehearsing a crime skit in the bedroom of a boardinghouse, three unemployed actors—Marcella, Ugo and Raimondo—are observed by a neighbor, Arturo, a butcher, who assumes that Ugo and Raimondo are professional killers and Marcella their victim. Since Arturo would like his unfaithful wife, Annalisa, eliminated, he offers to hire the two men to do the job. Hoping to obtain a fee without actually killing anyone, the actors agree. Unbeknownst to them, Annalisa and her lover plan to get rid of Arturo by causing him to have a heart attack. Following several mishaps in which the individuals become involved in each other's plots, Arturo actually dies of a heart attack. When the police become suspicious, Annalisa and her lover decide they must murder Ugo and Raimondo to protect themselves. They lure the actors to a sausage factory and attempt to hurl them into a meat-mincing machine. But Annalisa and her companion are apprehended and accused of murdering Arturo, a crime they did not actually commit. Ugo and Raimondo return to their profitless acting careers. *Actors. Neighbors. Butchers. Swindlers. Hired killers. Police. Murder. Mistaken identity. Fraud. Injustice. Boardinghouses. Factories. Rehearsals.*

Note: Released in Italy in 1961; running time: 95 min. An Italian source lists Focas' role as Michele and Mulè's as Arturo.

PT 109   F6.3957
Warner Bros. Pictures. 19 Jun **1963** [Boston opening; c27 Jan 1963; LP29447]. Sd; col (Technicolor). 35m (Panavision). 140 min.

Prod Bryan Foy. *Pers Supv* Jack L. Warner. *Dir* Leslie H. Martinson. *2d Unit Dir* Russell Saunders. *Screenplay* Richard Breen. *Adapt* Howard Sheehan, Vincent X. Flaherty. *Photog* Robert Surtees. *2d Unit Photog* Mark Davis. *Camera Op* John Schmitz. *Art Dir* Leo K. Kuter. *Set Decor* John P. Austin. *Film Ed* Folmar Blangsted. *Mus* William Lava, David Buttolph. *Orch* David Strech, Carl Brandt, Gus Levene. *Sd* Francis M. Stahl. *Asst Dir* William Kissel, Russell Saunders, Jack Cunningham, C. M. Florance. *Script Supv* Edward Hohler. *Wardrobe* Alexis Davidoff. *Makeup* Gordon Bau, Norman Pringle. *Sp Eff* Ralph Webb. *Tech Adv* J. E. Gibbon, (Capt.). *Dial Dir* Lew Gallo. *Still Photog* Ed Cronenweth. *Gaffer* Lee Wilson. *Grip* Harold Noyes. *Prop* Red Turner.

Cast: Cliff Robertson *(Lieut. (j.g.) John F. Kennedy)*, Ty Hardin *(Ens. Leonard J. Thom)*, James Gregory *(Comdr. C. R. Ritchie)*, Robert Culp *(Ens. "Barney" Ross)*, Grant Williams *(Lieut. Alvin Cluster)*, Lew Gallo *(Yeoman Rogers)*, Errol John *(Benjamin Kevu)*, Michael Pate *(Lieut. Reginald Evans)*, Robert Blake *("Bucky" Harris)*, William Douglas *(Gerard E. Zinser)*, Biff Elliott *(Edgar E. Mauer)*, Norman Fell *(Edmund Drewitch)*, Sam Gilman *(Raymond Starkey)*, Clyde Howdy *(Leon Drawdy)*, Buzz Martin *(Maurice Kowal)*, James McCallion *(Patrick McMahon)*, Evan McCord *(Harold Marney)*, Sammy Reese *(Andrew Kirksey)*, Glenn Sipes *(William Johnston)*, John Ward, actor *(John Maguire)*, David Whorf *(Raymond Albert)*.

Biographical war drama. Source: Robert J. Donovan, *PT 109, John F. Kennedy in World War II* (New York, 1961). In the early days of World War II, Lieut. (j.g.) John F. Kennedy arrives in the Solomon Islands to assume command of the battle-scarred PT 109. After making hasty repairs, he and his crew are sent to rescue a Marine patrol trapped on Choiseul. Though the mission is successful, the boat runs out of fuel and has to be towed back to base. Then, on the morning of August 2, 1943, while attempting to prevent the Japanese from landing troops at Vila, PT 109, having no radar equipment, is rammed and split in two by an enemy destroyer. Two of the men are killed, and Kennedy decides the only chance he and the other survivors have is to swim to a nearby island. One of the men is too badly burned to swim, and Kennedy tows him through the water. All efforts to make their location known fail until Kennedy writes a message on a coconut, which friendly natives take to nearby Rendova. They return with a canoe, hide Kennedy under palm fronds, and deliver him to an Australian coastwatcher. After directing the rescue of his men, Kennedy learns he is eligible for transfer home; instead, he elects to assume command of another PT boat. *Heroism. Sea rescue. PT boats. Coast patrol. World War II. Solomon Islands. John Fitzgerald Kennedy. United States Marines. Japan—Navy. United States Navy.*

Note: Location scenes filmed in Florida.

A PUBLIC AFFAIR   F6.3958
Girard-Lewis Productions. *Dist* Parade Releasing Organization. 21 Mar **1962** [Los Angeles opening]. Sd; b&w. 35mm. 75 min.

Prod Bernard Girard, Robert E. Lewis. Lawrence Hanson, Jr. *Dir-Writ* Bernard Girard. *Photog* Howard Schwartz. *Set Decor* Harry Reif. *Film Ed* Robert Seiter. *Mus* Joe Greene. *Mus Ed* Graham Makin. *Asst Dir* Nathan R. Barragar, Edward Haldeman. *Prod Mgr* Nathan R. Barragar.

Cast: Myron McCormick *(Sam Clavell)*, Edward Binns *(Sen. Fred Baines)*, Judson Pratt *(Hal Green)*, Jacqueline Loughery *(Phyllis Baines)*, Paul Birch *(Malcomb Hardy)*, Harry Carey, Jr. *(Bill Martin)*, Grace Lee Whitney *(Tracey Phillips)*, Peter Brocco *(Leonard Lohman)*, Mack Williams *(Senator Armstrong)*, Noel Drayton *(George Babcock)*, Tyler McVey *(Senator Hopkins)*, Lou Kane *(Marshall Thor)*, Armand Alzamora *(gardener)*, Paul Frees *(narrator)*.

Drama. Aroused by public indignation over the unscrupulous and illegal methods of many bill collectors, California State Sen. Fred Baines introduces a resolution to establish a committee to investigate collection agency abuses, and it is passed by the legislature. Committee coordinator Sam Clavell, assisted by Bill Martin and Tracey Phillips, is determined to document collectors' illegal activities before the legislature adjourns. Hal Green, a conniving lobbyist, and

Malcomb Hardy, boss of the collection agency league, attempt to stall the investigation by launching an attack on Baines's integrity. On the brink of adjournment, the senate rejects an emasculating amendment to Baines's bill and passes his measure to curb the unprincipled tactics of collection agencies. *Bill collectors. Investigators. Politicians. Politics. Political corruption. Slander. Social consciousness. State legislatures. California.*

Note: Location scenes filmed in Sacramento and Los Angeles.

LA PUCE À L'OREILLE see **A FLEA IN HER EAR**

PUFNSTUF   F6.3959
Sid & Marty Krofft Productions. *Dist* Universal Pictures. 4 Jun **1970** [San Antonio, Texas, opening; c4 Jun 1970; LP38935]. Sd; col (Technicolor). 35mm. 98 min. [Copyright length: 95 min.] MPAA rating G.

Prod Si Rose. *Exec Prod* Sid Krofft, Marty Krofft. *Assoc Prod* Malcolm Alper. *Dir* Hollingsworth Morse. *Screenplay* John Fenton Murray, Si Rose. *Photog* Kenneth Peach. *Camera Op* Kenneth Peach, Jr. *Asst Camera* John Greer, William McGovern. *Art Dir* Alexander Golitzen, Walter Scott Herndon, Joe Alves. *Set Decor* Arthur Parker. *Film Ed* David Rawlins. *Asst Ed* Skip Greene. *Mus* Charles Fox. *Songs:* "Pufnstuf," "Angel Raid," "Charge," "Fire in the Castle," "Happy Hour," "Leaving Living Island," "Rescue Racer to the Rescue," "Witchiepoo's Lament," "Different" Charles Fox, Norman Gimbel. *Choreog* Paul Godkin. *Mix* David H. Moriarty. *Sd Asst* Don Bolger, Ed Somers, Jr. *Asst Dir* Chuck Colean, Warren Smith. *Prod Mgr* Joseph Kenny. *Asst to the Prod* Trudy Bennett. *Prod Coörd* Don Ramsey. *Script Supv* Dee Cooper. *Men's Wardrobe* Ken Harvey, cost. *Women's Wardrobe* Barbara Harootunia. *Makeup* Ziggy Geike. *Sp Eff* Luke Tillman, Roland Chiniquy. *Puppet Creation* Rolf Roediger, Evenda Leeper, Troy Barrett. *Gaffer* Lloyd Peter. *Prop* Sol Martino, John Faltis. *Casting* Harold Rossmor. *Dial Coach* Dale Ross.

Voices: Jack Wild *(Jimmy)*, Billie Hayes *(Witchiepoo)*, Martha Raye *(Boss Witch)*, Mama Cass *(Witch Hazel)*, Roberto Gamonet *(H. R. Pufnstuf)*, Sharon Baird *(Shirley Pufnstuf)*, Johnny Silver *(Dr. Blinkey)*, Andrew Ratoucheff *(alarm clock)*, Billy Barty *(Googy Gopher)*, Felix Silla *(polkadotted horse)*, Jane Dulo, Jan Davis, Princess Livingston, Joy Campbell, Angelo Rossitto, Van Snowden, Lou Wagner, Hommy Stewart, Pat Lytell, Buddy Douglas, Jon Linton, Bob Howland, Scutter McKay, Roberta Keith, Penny Krompier, Brooks Hunnicutt, Barrie Duffus, Evelyn Dutton, Tony Barro, Ken Creel, Fred Curt, Dennis Edenfield, Allison McKay.

Fantasy. Jimmy, a happy young boy, decides one day to miss band practice and go with his talking flute, Freddie, to Living Island, a magical kingdom where animals, plants, and inanimate objects are able to speak. Witchiepoo, flying on her jet broom, sees Jimmy and decides to steal his flute in order to be named "Witch of the Year" at the upcoming witches' convention. Jimmy discovers the cave in which the inhabitants of Living Island reside and meets H. R. Pufnstuf, a friendly dragon who is the island's mayor. Disguised as a hippy, Witchiepoo manages to steal Freddie Flute. To recover the flute, Jimmy and Pufnstuf get Googy Gopher to burrow into Witchiepoo's castle and release bags of smoke in the basement so that Pufnstuf can enter as a fireman. The attempt fails, however, and Pufnstuf is captured and locked in a dungeon. Meanwhile, Witchiepoo prepares for the witches' convention by thinking of a way to serve Pufnstuf to her guests for dinner. Jimmy then disguises the inhabitants of Living Island as angels and frightens away the witches to save Pufnstuf and Freddie. *Children. Witches. Dragons. Mayors. Gophers. Angels. Magic. Theft. Disguise. Rescue. Flutes. Caves. Castles. Imaginary kingdoms.*

Note: Based on the characters in the NBC television series *Pufnstuf.*

I PUGNI IN TASCA see **FIST IN HIS POCKET**
LE PUITS AUX TROIS VÉRITÉS see **THREE FACES OF SIN**
PULGARCITO see **TOM THUMB**
PUMP PRIMER   F6.3960
Dist Stacey Distributors. ca **1970.** Sd; col. 16mm. 61-81 min.

Sex film. No information about the precise nature of this film has been found. *Sexuality.*

THE PUMPKIN EATER (Great Britain)   F6.3961
Romulus Films–Jack Clayton. *Dist* Royal Films International. 9 Nov **1964** [New York opening; c1 Nov 1964; LP30019]. Sd (Westrex); b&w. 35mm. 110 min.

Pres by Columbia Pictures. *Prod* James Woolf. *Assoc Prod* James Ware. *Dir* Jack Clayton. *Screenplay* Harold Pinter. *Script Ed* Jeanie Sims. *Dir Photog* Oswald Morris. *Camera Op* Brian West. *Camera Grip* Ray Jones. *Art Dir* Edward Marshall. *Set Dresser* Peter James. *Film Ed* James Clark. *Mus* Georges Delerue. *Sd Rec* Peter Handford, John Aldred. *Dub Ed* Peter Musgrave. *Boom Op* Ken Ritchie. *Asst Dir* Claude Watson. *Prod Mgr* Charles Blair. *Cont* Pamela Davies. *Cost* Motley. *Makeup Supv* George Frost. *Hairdresser* Gordon Bond. *Casting Dir* Jenia Reissar. *Supv Floor Electrn* Maurice Gillett. *Trained Animals* John Holmes.

Cast: Anne Bancroft *(Jo Armitage)*, Peter Finch *(Jake Armitage)*, James Mason *(Bob Conway)*, Janine Gray *(Beth Conway)*, Cedric Hardwicke *(Jo's father)*, Rosalind Atkinson *(Jo's mother)*, Alan Webb *(Jake's father)*, Richard Johnson *(Giles)*, Maggie Smith *(Philpot)*, Eric Porter *(psychiatrist)*, Cyril Luckham *(doctor)*, Anthony Nicholls *(surgeon)*, John Franklin Robbins *(parson)*, John Junkin *(undertaker)*, Yootha Joyce *(woman in hairdresser's)*, Leslie Nunnerley *(waitress at zoo)*, Gerald Sim *(man at party)*, Frank Singuineau *(The King of Israel)*, Faith Kent *(nanny)*, Gregory Phillips, Rupert Osborne *(Pete)*, Michael Ridgeway, Martin Norton *(Jack)*, Frances White, Kate Nicholls *(Dinah)*, Fergus McClelland, Christopher Ellis *(Fergus)*, Elizabeth Dear, Sarah Nicholls *(Elizabeth)*, Sharon Maxwell, Mimosa Annis *(Sharon)*, Kash Dewar *(Mark)*, Mark Crader *(youngest child)*.

Drama. Source: Penelope Mortimer, *The Pumpkin Eater* (London, 1962). Jo, the mother of seven children, divorces her second husband, Giles, in order to marry Jake, a successful but promiscuous screenwriter. Though they are physically and emotionally compatible, they are torn apart by Jo's strict marital morality. Following the birth of another child and a terrifying experience with a mentally unbalanced woman, Jo seeks psychiatric advice. Still perturbed, she refuses to accompany Jake to Morocco for location shooting but does agree to undergo sterilization. Following her recovery, she is informed by a sardonic friend, Conway, that Jake has been having an affair with Beth, Conway's wife. Horrified, Jo has a savage fight with Jake and then returns to her second husband. Jake's father dies, and at his funeral, Jo is ignored. Shattered, she retreats alone to an old house in a converted windmill. One day Jake arrives with the children, offering hope that perhaps there will be a new beginning. *Motion picture scriptwriters. Children. Psychiatrists. Recluses. Motherhood. Family life. Divorce. Insanity. Infidelity. Funerals. Sterility (sexual). Windmills. Morocco.*

Note: Opened in London in Aug 1964; running time: 110 min. Original length: 118 min (1964 Cannes Film Festival).

PUÒ UNA MORTA RIVIVERE PER AMORE? *see* VENUS IN FURS

THE PURE HELL OF ST. TRINIAN'S (Great Britain) F6.3962

Vale Film Productions-British Lion Films-Hallmark Productions-Tudor Productions. *Dist* Continental Distributing, Inc. 25 Sep **1961** [New York opening]. Sd; b&w. 35mm. 94 min.

Prod Sidney Gilliat, Frank Launder. *Assoc Prod* Leslie Gilliat. *Dir* Frank Launder. *Screenplay* Frank Launder, Val Valentine, Sidney Gilliat. *Photog* Gerald Gibbs. *2d Unit Photog* Freddie Ford. *Art Dir* Wilfred Shingleton, Tony Woollard. *Film Ed* Thelma Connell. *Mus Comp & Cond* Malcolm Arnold. *Sd* Frederick Cook. *Sd Rec* H. C. Pearson, Red Law. *Prod Mgr* John Pellatt. *Sp Eff* Wally Veevers, George Samuels.

Cast: Cecil Parker *(Professor Canford)*, Joyce Grenfell *(Sgt. Ruby Gates)*, George Cole *(Flash Harry)*, Thorley Walters *(Butters)*, Eric Barker *(Culpepper-Brown)*, Irene Handl *(Miss Harker-Packer)*, Sidney James *(Alphonse O'Reilly)*, Dennis Price *(Gore-Blackwood)*, Raymond Huntley *(judge)*, Lloyd Lamble *(Superintendent Kemp-Bird)*, Liz Fraser *(Miss Partridge)*, Elwyn Brook-Jones *(emir)*, Nicholas Phipps *(major)*, Cyril Chamberlain *(army captain)*, Harold Berens *(British consul)*, Julie Alexander *(Rosalie)*, Ann Wain *(Lolita Chatterly)*, Gilda Emmanuelli *(Minnie Hen)*, Sally Bulloch *(Maud Birdhanger)*, Mark Dignam *(prosecuting counsel)*, George Benson *(defense counsel)*, Michael Ripper *(liftman)*, John Le Mesurier *(minister)*, Lisa Lee *(Miss Brenner)*, Wensley Pithey *(chief constable)*, Monty Landis *(Octavius)*, Clive Morton *(v.i.p.)*, Maria Lennard *(Millicent)*, Dawn Beret *(Jane)*.

Comedy. Inspired by the original "St. Trinian's" drawings by: Ronald Searle. The fiendish girls of St. Trinian's, brought to trial at Old Bailey for burning down their school, are freed when the mysterious Professor Canford, recently arrived from the University of Baghdad, claims that he can rehabilitate them. Unaware that his benefactor, Alphonse O'Reilly, is a white slaver who plans to abduct and sell the students to an Eastern potentate seeking wives for his many sons, Canford arranges for the older students to take a cultural tour of the Greek islands. Hidden aboard the students' luxury yacht is longsuffering police Sgt. Ruby Gates, who has been ordered to relay information about the girls' activities to Superintendent Kemp-Bird, her fiancé of many years. Ruby learns that the ship is off course and wires headquarters. Before any action can be taken, however, O'Reilly sets adrift in a lifeboat Professor Canford, Ruby, and Flash Harry, the unofficial matrimonial agent of St. Trinian's. Butters and Culpepper-Brown, a team sent from the ministry of education to rescue the girls, are also put out to sea by St. Trinian's younger students, who believe that they are helping their older classmates. Although the older students are delivered to the emir's palace, they hold off his ardent sons during a free-for-all. Rescued by police and the younger students, the girls celebrate their homecoming by burning down St. Trinian's. *Students. Professors. Juvenile delinquents. Police. Stowaways. Potentates. Castaways. Arson. White slave traffic. Abduction. Rescue. Yachts. Middle East. Greece. Old Bailey.*

Note: Opened in London in Dec 1960.

PURLIE VICTORIOUS *see* GONE ARE THE DAYS!

THE PURPLE HILLS F6.3963

Associated Producers, Inc. *Dist* Twentieth Century-Fox Film Corp. Oct **1961** [c20 Sep 1961; LP20641]. Sd; col (De Luxe). 35mm (CinemaScope). 60 min.

Prod-Dir Maury Dexter. *Writ* Edith Cash Pearl, Russ Bender. *Dir Photog* Floyd Crosby. *Art Dir* John Mansbridge. *Supv Film Ed* Jodie Copelan. *Mus Comp & Cond* Richard La Salle. *Sd* Frank McWhorter. *Supv Sd Ed* Jack Cornall. *Asst Dir* Frank Parmenter. *Prod Mgr* Harold E. Knox. *Script Supv* Dixie McCoy. *Wardrobe* Ray Summers, Paula Giokaris. *Makeup* Bob Mark. *Prop Master* Ted Ross. *Head Grip* Chuck Hanawalt.

Cast: Gene Nelson *(Gil Shepard)*, Joanna Barnes *(Amy Carter)*, Kent Taylor *(Johnny Barnes)*, Russ Bender *(deputy sheriff)*, Jerry Summers *(Martin Beaumont)*, Danny Zapien *(Chito)*, Jack Carr *(A. J. Beaumont)*, Medford Salway *(young brave)*, Jack Riggs.

Western melodrama. In the Arizona of the 1870's, cowboy Gil Shepard kills a notorious outlaw, Beaumont, and then rides into town to collect the $8,000 reward. The dead man's partner, Johnny Barnes, however, also shows up to claim the reward. A further complication is the sudden appearance of 18-year-old Martin Beaumont, who has sworn to slay his brother's killer. The sheriff decides to settle the matter by taking all concerned out to Beaumont's grave. On the trail, young Martin's pretty guardian, Amy Carter, becomes attracted to Shepard but is unable to understand his lust for money. When the outlaw's grave is opened, it is discovered that the Apaches, who worshiped Beaumont, have removed his body. Barnes turns on the sheriff and kills him but is himself mortally wounded during an Indian raid. Before dying, however, he provides cover for the others to escape. Once safe, Shepard decides that Amy's love is more important than the reward, and a more mature Martin realizes that his brother deserved to die. *Brothers. Outlaws. Sheriffs. Guardians. Apache Indians. Grave robbers. Rewards. Revenge. Arizona.*

Note: Filmed at Apacheland, Arizona.

PURPLE NOON (France/Italy) F6.3964

Paris-Films Production-Panitalia-Titanus. *Dist* Times Film Corp. 25 Aug **1961** [New York opening]. Sd; col (Eastman Color). 35mm. 115 min.

Prod Raymond Hakim, Robert Hakim. *Dir* René Clément. *Screenplay* René Clément, Paul Gégauff. *Dial* Paul Gégauff. *Photog* Henri Decae. *Art Dir* Paul Bertrand. *Film Ed* Françoise Javet. *Mus* Nino Rota. *Choreog* Jean Guélis. *Sd* Jean-Claude Marchetti.

Cast: Alain Delon *(Tom Ripley)*, Marie Laforêt *(Marge)*, Maurice Ronet *(Philippe Greenleaf)*, Elvire Popesco *(Madame Popova)*, Erno Crisa *(Inspector Riccordi)*, Frank Latimore *(O'Brien)*, Billy Kearns *(Freddy)*, Ave Ninchi *(Signora Gianna)*, Viviane Chantel *(La Belge)*.

Crime drama. Source: Patricia Highsmith, *The Talented Mr. Ripley* (New York, 1955). Tom Ripley and Philippe Greenleaf are two young, pleasure-seeking Americans vacationing in Italy. Tom has been promised $5,000 by Philippe's father if he can persuade Philippe to return to America, but Tom soon realizes that he will never collect his fee. Envious of Philippe's boat, his expensive clothes, and his desirable mistress, Marge, Tom plots to take Philippe's place. While alone with Philippe on the boat, Tom stabs his friend with a fishknife, wraps his body in a tarpaulin, and drops it over the side. Back in port, he assumes Philippe's identity, forging checks and passports, and living Philippe's kind of life. Tom explains to Marge that Philippe no longer loves her and does not wish to see her again. Then, suddenly, the impersonation is discovered by an old friend of Philippe's and Tom is once more forced to kill. Realizing that "Philippe" will be the chief suspect, Tom fakes Philippe's suicide and signs Philippe's name to a note bequeathing his fortune to Marge. He then resumes his own identity as Tom Ripley and begins wooing Marge. All goes as planned: the now-wealthy Marge falls in love with him, Philippe's death is accepted by both his father and the police, and Tom has within his grasp all the things he envied. His doom is sealed, however, when Marge decides to sell Philippe's boat. As it is hauled out of the water into dry-dock, the corpse is found hanging from the propeller. *Americans in foreign countries. Mistresses. Police. Heiresses. Vacations. Friendship. Murder. Wealth. Impersonation. Inheritance. Envy. Yachts. Wills.*

Note: Opened in Paris in Mar 1960 as *Plein soleil*; running time: 119 min; in Rome in Sep 1960 as *In pieno sole*; running time: 110 min.

PURSE SNATCH F6.3965

Impressive Art Productions. *Dist* MarJon Film Distributors. ca **1970**. Sd; col. 16mm. ca60 min.

Pres by MJ Productions.

Drama. A nymphomaniac photographer takes advantage of the naive male models who pose nude for her. After a lovemaking session with one model, she notices that her purse is missing. The photographer's neighbor becomes sexually intimate with a virile young man, and she discovers that he is involved in a plot to burglarize the photographer's well-furnished home. *Photographers. Thieves. Models. Nymphomania. Burglary. Nudity.*

THE PURSUIT OF HAPPINESS see **CIVILISATION: THE PURSUIT OF HAPPINESS**

THE PUSHER   F6.3966
Coastal Cheese Co.–Caldwell Productions. *Dist* Film-Makers' Distribution Center. 5 Jun **1965** [New York opening]. Sd; b&w. 16mm. 60 min.
Dir Gregory Burke. *Camera* Francisco Bautista, Steve Ashton. *Mus* The Sparrow. *Sd* Richard Smith. *Prod Dir* Derek Roome. *Cont* John Chase.
Cast: Gene Horton, Katrina Boratynski, Glen McKay, Sarah Paul, Yaya.
Drama. The film portrays the lifestyle of Gene, a drug pusher living in the Haight-Ashbury district of San Francisco. *Drug dealers. San Francisco—Haight-Ashbury.*

THE PUSHERS see **THE HOOKED GENERATION**

THE PUSHOVER see **THE MYTH**

PUSS 'N BOOTS (Mexico)   F6.3967
Películas Rodríguez. *Dist* K. Gordon Murray Productions. 7 Mar **1964** [New York showing]. Sd; col (Eastman Color). 35mm. 90 min.
Pres by K. Gordon Murray. *Prod-Dir-Adapt* Roberto Rodríguez. *Prod English Vers* K. Gordon Murray. *Dir English Vers* Manuel San Fernando. *Story* Sergio Magaña. *Photog* Rosalío Solano. *Set Dsgn* Roberto Silva. *Film Ed* José Bustos. *Mus* Sergio Guerrero. *Sd* Ernesto Caballero.
Cast: Rafael Muñoz, Humberto Dupeyrón, Antonio Raxell, Luis Manuel Pelayo, Armando Gutiérrez, Rocío Rosales, Santanón.
Fantasy. Source: Charles Perrault, "Le maître chat ou le chat botté," in *Contes de ma mère l'oye* (Paris, 1695). The film follows Charles Perrault's tale of the heroic cat in red boots. *Evildoers. Monsters. Royalty. Duplicity. Magic. Courage. Castles. Cats.*
Note: Released in Mexico in 1961 as *El gato con botas.*

PUSS 'N BOOTS (West Germany)   F6.3968
Förster Film. *Dist* Childhood Productions. Oct **1967**. Sd; col (Agfacolor). 35mm. 68 min.
Prod Alfred Förster. *Dir* Herbert B. Fredersdorf. *Screenplay* Christof Schulz-Gellen. *Photog* Ted Kornowicz. *Art Dir* Alfred Bütow. *Film Ed* Anneliese Krigar. *Mus* Richard Stauch. *Sd* Hermann Birkhofer. *Prod Mgr* Werner Lehndorff.
Cast: Margitta Sonke (*Puss*), Christa Oenicke (*princess*), Harry Wüstenhagen, Günter Hertel, Martin Volkmann, Helmut Ziegner, Wilhelm Grothe, F. W. Schröder-Schrom, Brigitte Fredersdorf, Waltraud Förster.
Fantasy. Source: Jakob Grimm and Wilhelm Grimm, "Der gestiefelte Kater". A film version of the Grimm brothers' adaptation of Charles Perrault's tale. *Evildoers. Monsters. Royalty. Magic. Courage. Castles. Cats.*
Note: Location scenes filmed near Bergisch Gladbach. Released in West Germany in Sep 1955 as *Der gestiefelte Kater.*

PUSS OCH KRAM see **HUGS AND KISSES**

PUSSY GALORE   F6.3969
Dist American Film Distributing Corp. 30 Dec **1965** [San Francisco showing]. Sd; col (Eastman Color). 35mm. 68 min.
Cast: Henry Crawford (*playboy-drunk*), Joseph S. Franklin (*teacher*), Larry W. Kiss (*artist*), Leon Lesley (*waiter*), Joann Maguire (*teacher's pet*), Barbara Mansfield (*flower girl*), Margaret Manley, Pam McDonald (*artist's models*), Doris A. Meyer (*teacher's pet*), Donna L. Parish (*hostess*), Barbara Bowen (*lead chorus dancer*), Ruth Ann (*beauty contest winner*), Blanch Toy (*2d beauty contest winner*).
Comedy. An arithmetic teacher with an overwhelming interest in the female form visits a nudist camp, where he watches the vacationers participate in athletics and a beauty contest. One evening he falls asleep and dreams that his pillow and blankets turn into beautiful nude women. *Schoolteachers. Nudism. Beauty contests. Nudist camps. Dreams.*

PUSSYCAT see **FASTER, PUSSYCAT! KILL! KILL!**

PUSSYCAT ALLEY (Great Britain)   F6.3970
Cyclops Film Productions. *Dist* Goldstone Film Enterprises. 15 Dec **1965** [New York showing]. Sd (RCA); b&w. 35mm. 93 min.
Prod Michael Luke. *Assoc Prod* Roy Simpson. *Dir-Writ* Wolf Rilla. *Scen Ed* Frederick Gotfurt. *Dir Photog* Larry Pizer. *Camera Op* Frank Drake. *Art Dir* Peggy Gick. *Ed* Jack Slade. *Assembly Ed* Lois Gray. *Mus Comp & Dir* Edwin Astley. *Dub Ed* Roy Baker. *Sd Rec* Edgar Vetter, Len Abbott. *Rec Dir* A. W. Lumkin. *Asst Dir* David Bracknell. *Prod Mgr* John Merriman. *Cont* Phyllis Crocker. *Wardrobe Mistress* Ivy Baker. *Makeup* Jim Hydes. *Hairdresser* Polly Young. *Miss Syms' and Miss Ritchie's Hairstyles* René. *Casting Dir* Robert

Lennard. *Asst Casting* Judith Jouard.
Cast: Sylvia Syms (*Billa*), Edward Judd (*Bob*), June Ritchie (*Ginnie*), William Hartnell (*Dad*), Sarah Lawson (*Elizabeth*), Francis De Wolff (*Shelbourne*), Davy Kaye (*Compere*), Linda Marlowe (*Penny*), Jack Gwillim (*Bolton*), Kevin Brennan (*Brian*), Alan White (*Freddy*).
Melodrama. Billa and Ginnie, two nightclub hostesses who find refuge from their public lives in the London flat they share, grow to depend on each other for emotional stability. (Ginnie is a capricious extrovert, freely attracted to men, while Billa is older and vulnerable beneath her cynical facade.) Embittered by her own failure to achieve satisfying relationships with men, Billa grows disturbed at Ginnie's involvement with Bob Shelbourne, a father-dominated young business tycoon estranged from his socialite wife, Elizabeth. Ginnie insists that, to prove his sincerity, Bob find a position for her in the family business, and Bob is openly defiant for the first time when his father sarcastically offers the position of "hostess" to his firm's clients. Meanwhile, Billa's weak but well-meaning father, a country schoolmaster, arrives for a visit. All affection having faded, Billa's attempt to confide goes awry, and she deliberately tries to shock him with details of her life. When he leaves, she tearfully confesses to Ginnie that she is pregnant. Refusing to abandon her friend, Ginnie puts aside plans of a trip to the Bahamas with Bob. Having broken with his wife at last, Bob tries to convince Ginnie to leave with him, but she drunkenly dismisses his protestations of love and vulgarly taunts him. Alone at the flat, Ginnie bungles an attempt at suicide, and both women conclude that their only chance for future happiness is with each other. *Nightclub hostesses. Roommates. Businessmen. Filial relations. Infidelity. Friendship. Wealth. Divorce. Pregnancy. Suicide. Employment—Women. Social classes. London.*
Note: Released in Great Britain in 1963 under the title *The World Ten Times Over.*

PUSSYCAT, PUSSYCAT, I LOVE YOU   F6.3971
Three Pictures Corp.–CKF Productions. *Dist* United Artists. 18 Mar **1970** [Chicago opening; c18 Mar 1970; LP37961]. Sd; col (De Luxe). 35mm. 99 min. MPAA rating GP.
Prod Jerry Bresler. *Dir-Writ* Rod Amateau. *Dir Photog* Tonino Delli Colli. *Camera Op* Franco Di Giacomo. *Art Dir* Toni Sarzi-Braga. *Set Decor* Arrigo Breschi. *Main Titl* Pacific Title. *Film Ed* Larry Heath. *Mus & Mus Dir* Lalo Schifrin. *Song:* "Groove Into It" Lalo Schifrin, Gene Lees. *Sung by* Henry Shed. *Song:* "What's New, Pussycat?" Burt Bacharach, Hal David. *Sd* Cyril Collick. *Asst Dir* Francesco Cinieri. *Prod Mgr* Alessandro Von Norman. *Script Girl* Bona Magrini. *Cost for Mr. McShane* Nikki of Just Men. *Cost* Adriana Berselli. *Sp Eff* Danny Lee.
Cast: Ian McShane (*Fred Dobbs*), Anna Calder-Marshall (*Millie Dobbs*), Severn Darden (*Dr. Fahrquardt*), Joyce Van Patten (*Anna Fahrquardt*), John Gavin (*Grant Granite*), Beba Loncar (*Ornella*), Samy Pavel (*Ottavio*), Katia Christina (*Angelica*), Veronica Carlson (*Liz*), Gaby André (*Flavia*), Marino Masè (*Franco*), Dari Lallou (*Hester*), Ian Trigger (*Dr. Ponti*), Leopoldo Trieste (*desk clerk*), Paul Muller (*Amo Amas Amat*), Madeline Smith (*Gwendolyn*), Maurizio Lucidi (*director*), Linda Morand (*Moira*), Solvi Stubing (*girl with door*), John Frederick (*heavy*), Richard Harrison (*hero*), Janos Prohaska (*gorilla*), Jean Sobieski, Josiane Tanzilli, Janeth Aigren.
Farce. Living in Rome, plagued by incipient baldness and recurrent dreams of a sex-starved gorilla, American playwright Fred Dobbs consults Dr. Fahrquardt, a bewigged and henpecked psychiatrist. During therapy Dobbs describes numerous marital misadventures, including liaisons with a mistress, Ornella; his sister-in-law, Gwendolyn; his masseuse, Liz; and a nymph, Angelica. Dobbs also relates the escapades of his wife, Millie, recounting her dalliance with two Italian gigolos, Ottavio and Franco, and subsequent affair with movie idol Grant Granite, who, desirous of rights to Dobbs' play, "When in Rome Do As the Romanians," introduces himself to Millie while she is bathing. Dobbs further describes the denouement of these adventures, in which Granite, Millie, and an assortment of lovers converge upon vacationing Dobbs and Angelica, stimulating a slapstick chase through the Cinecitta studios where they unwittingly participate in the filming of a Western. Dobbs' session is abruptly concluded when the sex-starved gorilla enters through the window of Dr. Fahrquardt's office. *Mistresses. Playwrights. Sisters-in-law. Actors. Psychiatrists. Gigolos. Italians. Marriage. Infidelity. Motion pictures. Motion picture studios. Rome. Cinecittà (Rome). Dreams. Chases. Apes.*
Note: Location scenes filmed in Rome.

PUT UP OR SHUT UP (Argentina)   F6.3972
Armando Bo. *Dist* Cambist Films. 14 Aug **1968** [Baltimore showing]. Sd; b&w. 35mm. 84 min.
Prod-Dir-Screenplay Armando Bo. *Story* Augusto Roa Bastos. *Photog* Alfredo Traverso. *Mus* Alberto Gnecco. *Asst Dir* Joseph Martinez.
Cast: Isabel Sarli (*Angela*), Armando Bo, Alba Mujica, Ernesto Báez, Joaquín Petrosino, Alberto Barcel, Adolfo Lenvell, M. Velich, Celso Vidal,

Oscal L. Par, Joe Delk.

Crime melodrama. The people of a primitive fishing village are divided into two factions. Angela, the daughter of the man who leads one faction and serves a corrupt political boss, falls in love with Bruno, the son of the principled leader. Angela's father kills Bruno's father, and Bruno assumes his father's place. Angela's father attempts to kill Bruno, and Bruno is forced to kill him in self-defense; thus the lovers are separated. The mistress of Angela's father takes control of the corrupt faction and plans to murder two witnesses against the abuses of the corrupt regime. Angela warns Bruno. One witness is killed, but Bruno helps the other to safety across the border. The testimony of the surviving witness will serve to destroy the corrupt regime. *Mistresses. Fishermen. Fatherhood. Courtship. Murder. Political corruption. Feuds. Fishing villages.*

Note: Opened in Buenos Aires in Feb 1959 as *Sabaleros;* running time: 100 min. Spanish language version released in the U. S. in Aug 1962; pre-1968 general release unconfirmed. Also known as *Put Out or Shut Up;* title changed to *Positions;* probably the same as *Positions of Love.*

PUTNEY SWOPE   F6.3973

Herald Productions. *Dist* Cinema V Distributing, Inc. 10 Jul **1969** [New York opening]. Sd; b&w with col seq (Eastman Color). 35mm. 84 min.

Assoc Prod Ron Sullivan. *Dir-Writ* Robert Downey. *Photog* Gerald Cotts. *Art Dir* Gary Weist. *Main Titl* Chermayeff and Geismar Associates. *Film Ed* Bud Smith. *Asst Ed* Pat Dobie. *Orig Mus* Charley Cuva. *Sd* Mike Scott, Bruce Perlman, Tom Dillinger. *Prod Supv* Ron Sullivan. *Prod Coörd* Barbara Wise. *Prod Asst* Wendy Appel, Eric Krupnik. *Sp Eff* Bill Daley, Tom Daniel, Dan List, Josh Zander. *Coöp* John Simon Guggenheim Foundation.

Cast—In Order of Appearance: Arnold Johnson *(Putney Swope),* Stan Gottlieb *(Nathan),* Allen Garfield *(Elias, Jr.),* Archie Russell *(Joker),* Ramon Gordon *(Bissinger),* Bert Lawrence *(Hawker),* Joe Engler *(Mr. Syllables),* David Kirk *(Elias, Sr.),* Don George *(Mr. Cards),* Buddy Butler *(Putney's bodyguard),* Vincent Hamill *(man in white suit),* Tom Odachi *(Wing Soney),* Ching Yeh *(Wing Soney, Jr.),* Spunky-Funk Johnson *(Mr. Major),* Joe Fields *(Pittsburgh Willie),* Norman Schreiber *(messenger),* Bob Staats *(Mr. War Toys),* Alan Abel *(Mr. Lucky),* Sol Brawerman *(Mr. Dinkleberry),* Ben Israel *(Mr. Pit Stop),* Mel Brooks *(Mr. Forget It),* Louise Heath, Barbara Clarke *(secretaries),* Catherine Lojacono *(Lady Beaver),* Johnjohn Robinson *(Wayne),* Charles Buffum *(director),* Ron Palombo *(assistant director),* Wendy Appel *(script girl),* Antonio Fargas *(The Arab),* Geegee Brown *(secretary),* Vance Amaker *(Wall Man),* Al Green *(1st cowboy),* Chuck Ender *(2d cowboy),* Anthony Chisholm *(3d cowboy),* Walter Jones *(Jim Keranga),* Khaula Bakr *(Mrs. Keranga),* Melvia Marshall, Annette Marshall, Andrea Marshall *(little Kerangas),* Laura Greene *(Mrs. Swope),* Ed Gordon *(Mr. Victrola Cola),* Eric Krupnik *(Mark Focus),* George Morgan *(Mr. Token),* Abdul Hakeim *(bouncer),* Allan Arbus *(Mr. Bad News),* Jesse McDonald *(young militant),* C. Robert Scott *(militant #1),* Leopoldo Mandeville *(militant #2),* Vince Morgan, Jr. *(West Indian),* Al Browne *(moderate),* Marie Claire *(Eugenie Ferlinger/nun),* Eileen Peterson *(narrator),* William H. Boesen *(Bert/Mr. Lunger),* Carol Farber *(secretary),* Cerves McNeil *(Youngblood),* Carolyn Cardwell *(Borman Six girl),* Chuck Green *(Myron X [Rufus]),* Pepi Hermine *(President of the United States),* Ruth Hermine *(First Lady),* Paul Storob *(secret service man),* Lawrence Wolf *(Mr. Borman Six),* Jeff Lord *(Mr. Bald),* Tom Boya *(Mr. O'Dinga),* Major Cole *(Idea Man #1),* David Butts *(Idea Man #2),* Franklin Scott *(Idea Man #3),* Paul Alladice *(Idea Man #4),* Exit *(Idea Man #5),* Ronald Dyson *(Face Off boy),* Shelley Plimpton *(Face Off girl),* Elżbieta Czyżewska *(Putney's maid),* Paulette Marron *(air conditioner girl),* Delilah *(1st stewardess),* Carol Hobbs *(2d stewardess),* Birgitta *(3d stewardess),* Marco Heiblim *(lucky passenger),* Grania *(interviewer),* Peter Maloney *(Putney's chauffeur),* Larry Greenfield *(lead reporter),* Lloyd Kagin *(Billy Reilly),* Perry Gewirtz *(Sonny Williams),* Herbert Kerr *(bodyguard #2),* Hal Schochet *(President Mimeo's chauffeur),* George Marshall, actor *(Mr. Executive),* Donald Lev *(poet),* Fred Hirshhorn *(Mr. Bourbon),* Donahl Breitman *(Mr. Ethereal Cereal),* Peter Benson *(Mr. Jingle).*

Satire. Putney Swope is the token black man on the executive board of a large Madison Avenue advertising agency. During a promotional meeting, the elderly company chairman, while addressing the board, drops dead of a heart attack. The other board members vote to elect a successor and, through a company rule which prohibits voting for oneself, Swope wins by a landslide. Putney promptly replaces all the white board members with blacks (leaving one token white man), renames the agency Truth and Soul, Inc., and refuses accounts for commercials on liquor, cigarettes, and war toys. Truth and Soul revolutionizes television advertising by creating shock-effect commercials for such products as Face-Off Acne Cream and Ethereal Cereal. The agency's unorthodox policies are regarded by the President of the United States, Mimeo, a marijuana-smoking midget, as a serious threat to his vested interests. As cash deposits accumulate in the Truth and Soul basement, dissidents in the agency threaten Putney's authority. Putney meets with Mimeo, who tells him that

unless Truth and Soul begins advertising liquor, cigarettes, and war toys, as well as promoting the unsafe "Borman Six" German roadster, the government will picket Truth and Soul. Following an assassination attempt by a white messenger boy who has been continuously abused by Putney and his staff, Putney abandons the agency, dressed in Castro garb and carrying a sack of money. As he does so, a dissident Arab tosses a Molotov cocktail into the plexiglass vault containing the company loot—and all of Truth and Soul's cash assets go up in smoke. *Negroes. Advertising executives. Militants. Midgets. Arabs. Presidents of the United States. Racism. Business ethics. Employer-employee relations. Television commercials. Elections. Heart disease. Marijuana. Molotov cocktails. Food. Cosmetics. Automobiles. New York City—Madison Avenue. Fidel Castro Ruz.*

Note: Location scenes filmed in New York City.

PUZZLE OF A DOWNFALL CHILD   F6.3974

Newman-Foreman Productions–Schatzberg Productions. *Dist* Universal Pictures. 16 Dec **1970** [Los Angeles opening; c18 Dec 1970; LP39253]. Sd; col (Technicolor). 35mm. 104 min. *MPAA rating* R.

Pres by Jennings Lang. *Prod* John Foreman. *Assoc Prod* Frank Caffey. *Prod Assoc* Neil Machlis. *Dir* Jerry Schatzberg. *Screenplay* Adrien Joyce. *Story* Jerry Schatzberg, Adrien Joyce. *Photog* Adam Holender. *Art Dir* Richard Bianchi. *Set Decor* Hubert J. Oates. *Film Ed* Evan Lottman. *Mus Comp & Cond* Michael Small. *Electronic Mus Programmed by* Sear Electronic Music Production. *Sd Rec* William Gramaglia. *Sd Re-rec* Richard Vorisek. *Asst Dir* Robert P. Schneider, Martin E. Miller. *Prod Supv* Roger Michael Rothstein. *Prod Mgr* James Inch. *Cost Supv* Jo Ynocencio. *Cost Dsgn* Terry Leong. *Men's Wardrobe* Roland Meledandri. *Makeup* Richard Philippe. *Hairstyles* Colleen Callaghan.

Cast: Faye Dunaway *(Lou Andreas Sand),* Barry Primus *(Aaron Reinhardt),* Viveca Lindfors *(Pauline Galba),* Barry Morse *(Dr. Galba),* Roy Scheider *(Mark),* Ruth Jackson *(Barbara Casey),* John Heffernan *(Dr. Sherman),* Sydney Walker *(psychiatrist),* Clark Burckhalter *(Davy Bright),* Shirley Rich *(Peggy McCavage),* Emerick Bronson *(Falco),* Joe George *(1st man in bar),* John Eames *(1st doctor),* Harry Lee, actor *(Mr. Wong),* Jane Halleran *(Joan),* Susan Willis *(neighbor),* Barbara Carrera *(T. J. Brady),* Sam Schacht *(George).*

Drama. At an isolated beach cottage, Lou Andreas Sand, a once-famous fashion model, relates her past (often contradicting herself) to Aaron Reinhardt, her close friend and photographer. Aaron records her conversation for a film he is making about her. Reminiscing about her first affair, Lou describes her love for a respected older man; in reality, he brutally raped her. Describing herself as an unresponsive lover, Lou omits mentioning her desire to have sex with strangers in cheap hotels. Recalling her rise in the fashion world under the sponsorship of fashion photographer Pauline Galba, Lou minimizes the woman's lesbian dominance and her mentor's rage when Lou became engaged to marry Mark, an advertising executive. Lou is vague in relating the details of this affair—how she fled from the courthouse on the day she was to be married, and how she later accused Mark of forbidding her to go to Paris for a magazine layout when the magazine had actually decided to use another model. When her career began to ebb because of her neurotic behavior, she blamed others. After an attempted suicide, Lou resorted to using alcohol and tranquilizers to calm herself; finally, she had a nervous breakdown and was hospitalized. Now alone in the cottage, she still lives on medication, trying to pull herself together. As she walks on the beach with Aaron, Lou expresses surprise that they never made love together; when he informs her that they did have an affair and that she was a good lover, Lou smiles. *Models. Photographers. Advertising executives. Memory. Mental illness. Rape. Lesbianism. Suicide. Alcoholism. Beaches. Recorders. Tranquilizers.*

Note: Filmed in New York City. Adrien Joyce is a pseudonym for Carol Eastman.

PYRO (United States/Spain)   F6.3975

S. W. P. Productions–Esamer Films. *Dist* American International Pictures. Feb **1964** [c27 Nov 1963; LP27091]. Sd; col (Panacolor). 35mm. 99 min.

A Sidney W. Pink–Harry Eller Production. *Prod* Sidney W. Pink, Richard C. Meyer. *Dir* Julio Coll. *Screenplay* Luis de los Arcos, Sidney W. Pink. *Orig Story* Sidney W. Pink. *Dir Photog* Manuel Berenguer. *Set Dsgn* Antonio Simont. *Film Ed* Margarita Ochoa. *Orig Mus Comp & Cond by* José Solá. *Prod Mgr* José Puyol. *Orig Cost & Dresses for Miss Hyer Dsgnd by* Mitzou of Madrid. *Makeup* Carmen Martin. *Hairdresser* Marita Sánchez. *Sp Eff* Tony Molina.

Cast: Barry Sullivan *(Vance Pierson),* Martha Hyer *(Laura Blanco),* Sherry Moreland *(Verna Pierson),* Soledad Miranda *(Liz Frade),* Luis Prendes *(police inspector),* Fernando Hilbeck *(Julio),* Carlos Casaravilla *(Frade),* Marisenka *(Isabella Blanco),* Hugo Pimentel, Francisco Morán.

Horror film. British engineer Vance Pierson invents a new generator in the shape of a Ferris wheel and moves his family to Spain to supervise its construction. Looking for a house, he meets Laura Blanco and stops her from setting fire to her house in an effort to collect the insurance. He moves into

Laura's house with his family but is drawn into a passionate affair with Laura that so jeopardizes his family life and his career that he ends the affair. Maddened by the rejection, Laura sets fire to the house, and Vance's wife and daughter burn to death. He is horribly disfigured trying to save them and vows revenge. He escapes from the hospital, perfects a presentable disguise, and sets out to find and kill Laura and her daughter. He sets fires that kill Laura's mother, brother, and sister-in-law, and Laura flees to a small coastal town and goes into seclusion. Vance travels with a carnival, and the owner's daughter, Liz, falls in love with him. Finding Laura, Vance starts a fire that burns her to death. He then takes her child back to the carnival, intending to throw her from the Ferris wheel, but the police and Liz convince him the child should be spared. After placing the child safely in the gondola seat, Vance leaps to his death, losing his mask as he falls. *British. Inventors. Engineers. Mistresses. Pyromaniacs. Fraud. Infidelity. Murder. Disfiguration. Disguise. Suicide. Arson. Revenge. Insurance. Ferris wheels. Carnivals.*

Note: Opened in Madrid in May 1964 as *Fuego.* Also known as *Pyro—The Thing Without a Face* and *Pyro—Man Without a Face.* Working title: *A Cold Wind From Hell.*

QUACKSER FORTUNE HAS A COUSIN IN THE BRONX   F6.3976
UMC Pictures. 13 Jul **1970** [New York opening]. Sd; col (Eastman Color). 35mm. 90 min. *MPAA rating* R.

Prod Mel Howard, John H. Cushingham. *Exec Prod* Sidney Glazier. *Dir* Waris Hussein. *Screenplay* Gabriel Walsh. *Dir Photog* Gilbert Taylor. *Art Dir* Herbert Smith. *Film Ed* Bill Blunden. *Mus* Michael Dress. *Harmonica Solo* Tommy Reilly. *Sd Ed* David Campling. *Sd* John Ireland, ed. *Sd Rec* Hugh Strain. *Asst Dir* Ferdinand Fairfax. *Prod Supv* Barrie Melrose.

Cast: Gene Wilder (*Quackser Fortune*), Margot Kidder (*Zazel Pierce*), Eileen Colgan (*Betsy Bourke*), Seamus Ford (*Mr. Fortune*), May Ollis (*Mrs. Fortune*), Liz Davis (*Kathleen Fortune*), Caroline Tully (*Vera Fortune*), Paul Murphy (*Damien*), Dave Kelly (*Tom Maguire*), Tony Doyle (*Mike*), John Kelly (*Tim*), Liam Sweeney, Robert Somerset, Danny Cummins (*men in pub*), Julie Hamilton (*charlady*), Cecil Sheehan (*coal merchant*), Charles Byrne (*blacksmith*), Brendan Mathews (*attendant*), Robert Garrickford (*Walter*), Lillian Rapple (*woman*), Jeremy Jones (*student*), John Hoey (*hall porter*), Martin Crosbie (*policeman*), Marjorie McHenry (*Elaine Boland*), Patrick Smyth (*man at foundry*), David Hogarty.

Comedy-drama. Instead of working in the local foundry like his father, Quackser Fortune earns a living in Dublin by collecting horse manure and selling it to housewives for their gardens. He carries on an affair with Betsy Bourke, one of his customers, until he meets and immediately falls in love with Zazel Pierce, a wealthy American student at Trinity College. She begins to instruct him on Dublin's history and then invites Quackser to a dress ball; once there, however, she ignores him in favor of her more affluent and sophisticated classmates. The students' taunting of Quackser results in a scuffle, but he manages to escape with Zazel to an elegant hotel. She completes her seduction of him and leaves during the night. In the morning, Quackser goes to her room at Trinity only to find that she has moved out. Quackser's more immediate concern, however, is a new city ordinance which bans horses from the streets of Dublin, thereby ruining his livelihood. Dejected, he releases the horses into the city's streets to prevent them from being taken to the glue factory and then goes on a drinking spree. His luck changes when he learns that a distant cousin in the Bronx in New York has died and left him over £200; Quackser purchases a bus and uses it to give historical tours of Dublin. *Housewives. Students. Americans in foreign countries. Cousins. Guides. Seduction. Drunkenness. Manure. Balls (formal gatherings). Hotels. Inheritance. Buses. Dublin. Trinity College (Dublin). Horses.*

Note: Filmed on location in Dublin.

THE QUARE FELLOW (Great Britain/Ireland)   F6.3977
Anthony Havelock-Allan Productions. *Dist* Astor Pictures, Ajay Film Co. Nov **1962.** Sd; b&w. 35mm. 85 min.

Prod Anthony Havelock-Allan. *Dir-Writ* Arthur Dreifuss. *Adapt* Jacqueline Sundstrom, Arthur Dreifuss. *Dir Photog* Peter Hennessy. *2d Unit Photog* Vincent Corcoran. *Art Dir* Ted Marshall. *Film Ed* Gitta Zadek. *Mus Comp & Cond* Alexander Faris. *Vocal Arr* Kathleen O'Connor. *Sd* Stephen Dalby. *Asst Dir* Roy Baird. *Coöp* Kilmainham Gaol Restoration Society.

Cast: Patrick McGoohan (*Thomas Crimmin*), Sylvia Syms (*Kathleen*), Walter Macken (*Regan*), Dermot Kelly (*Donelly*), Jack Cunningham, actor (*chief warder*), Hilton Edwards (*Holy Healy*), Philip O'Flynn (*prison governor*), Leo McCabe (*Dr. Flyn*), Norman Rodway (*Lavery*), Marie Kean (*Mrs. O'Hara*), Pauline Delany (*Mickser's wife*), Geoffrey Golden, Tom Irwin (*customs officers*), Joe O'Donnell (*poet*), Agnes Bernelle (*Meg*), Iris Lawler (*Minna*), Dominic Roche (*prison chaplain*), Brian Hewitt-Jones (*Jenkinson*), Arthur O'Sullivan (*himself*), Aubrey Morris (*Silvertop*), Eamonn Brennan (*Flaherty*), Robert Bernal (*Mickser*), John Welsh (*Carroll*), Harry Brogan (*Dunlavin*), Frank O'Donovan (*Clancy*).

Drama. Source: Brendan Behan, *The Quare Fellow* (London opening: 24 May 1956). Thomas Crimmin, a staunch advocate of capital punishment, is beginning his duties as a Dublin prison warder. Regan, a senior warder, is opposed to hanging on the grounds that it solves nothing. Among the inmates are two "quare" (condemned) fellows awaiting execution for murder. After one of them commits suicide in his cell in spite of a reprieve, Crimmin visits the other man's wife, Kathleen. Mutually attracted, they drift into an affair; and Kathleen confesses that her husband killed his brother because he had found him in bed with her. Learning that the quare fellow withheld this evidence at his trial, Crimmin persuades Kathleen to tell her story to the prison governor. The appeal is denied, however, and Crimmin is forced to assist at the hanging. When Regan is retired, Crimmin knows that he will continue the old man's efforts to abolish capital punishment. *Prison guards. Prison wardens. Capital punishment. Murder. Suicide. Infidelity. Prisons. Dublin.*

Note: Filmed on location in Ireland. Released in Great Britain in Nov 1962; running time: 90 min.

QUATERMASS AND THE PIT *see* **FIVE MILLION YEARS TO EARTH**

14–18 *see* **OVER THERE, 1914–1918**

LES QUATRES VÉRITÉS *see* **THREE FABLES OF LOVE**

LE QUATRIÈME SEXE *see* **THE FOURTH SEX**

I QUATTRO DELL'AVE MARIA *see* **ACE HIGH**

LE QUATTRO GIORNATE DI NAPOLI *see* **THE FOUR DAYS OF NAPLES**

4... 3... 2... 1... MORTE *see* **MISSION STARDUST**

LE QUATTRO VERITÀ *see* **THREE FABLES OF LOVE**

QUE LA BÊTE MEURE *see* **THIS MAN MUST DIE**

THE QUEEN   F6.3978
Si Litvinoff–Vineyard Films–MDH Enterprises–The Queen Co. *Dist* Grove Press. 17 Jun **1968** [New York opening]. Sd; col (Technicolor). 35mm. 68 min.

Prod Si Litvinoff, Don Herbert. *Exec Prod* Lewis Allen, John Maxtone-Graham. *Dir* Frank Simon. *Assoc Dir* Sven Lukin. *Photog* Frank Simon, Ken Van Sickle, Robert Elfstrom, Alfonse Schilling, Joseph Zysman. *Film Ed* Fred Shore, Geraldine Fabrikant. *Sd* Sven Lukin, Gwen Brown, Nigel Noble. *Sp Cons* Sidney Meyers.

Cast: Jack Doroshow (*Flawless Sabrina/narrator*), Bernard Giquel (*interviewer*), Mario Montez.

Cast—The Finalists: Harlow [Richard Finochio] (*Miss Philadelphia*), Crystal (*Miss Manhattan*), Sonya (*Miss Boston*), Emory (*Miss New Jersey*), Alfonse (*Miss Chicago*).

Cast—The Judges: Andy Warhol, Edie Sedgwick, Terry Southern, Larry Rivers.

Documentary. This documentary centers around the 1967 Miss All-America Camp Beauty Contest for female impersonators held at New York City's Town Hall. As the film opens, the pageant's organizer and "mistress" of ceremonies, Jack Doroshow (Flawless Sabrina when in "drag"), calls his mother to invite her to the event. Doroshow sets forth the ground rules and the point breakdown for judging: 5 points each for walking, talking, bathing suit, gown, and makeup and hairdo; 10 points for beauty. The contestants get settled in their hotel rooms, gossip, share beauty secrets, and discuss their backgrounds. Topics of discussion include "gay" life, sex change operations, problems with the draft, and "husbands" in the service. Following rehearsal scenes, including a patriotic production number to the tune of "You're a Grand Old Flag," the participants begin transforming themselves into women. A problem arises when Harlow, Doroshow's 18-year-old protégé from Philadelphia, discovers that his hair fall has not been sent; a few frantic phone calls avert the crisis. The show gets under way: Flawless Sabrina introduces the contestants to the audience; Andy Warhol's superstar Mario Montez makes a guest appearance and sings "Diamonds Are a Girl's Best Friend"; the bathing suit parade is held while the orchestra plays "Am I Blue?"; and ultimately, five finalists are announced. Harlow is crowned the winner, and an after-contest squabble ensues as Crystal (Miss Manhattan) casts aspersions on Harlow's charms and accuses Doroshow of rigging the contest. The Town Hall owner and workers, by now unable to conceal their distaste, rush everyone out of the theater. The evening over, Harlow, in regular street garb, sits in a phone booth holding his rhinestone tiara while waiting for the bus back to Philadelphia. *Female impersonation. Male homosexuality. Sex change operations. Beauty contests. New York City.*

Note: The Queen Co. is given as copyright claimant in notice on film. Filmed in Kodachrome 16mm and blown up to 35mm. Billed as an Evergreen Film by distributor Grove Press. Harlow is a pseudonym for Richard Finochio.

QUEEN BEE *see* **THE CONJUGAL BED**

QUEEN OF BLOOD   F6.3979

Cinema West Productions. *Dist* American International Pictures. 2 Mar **1966** [Cincinnati, Ohio, opening; c2 Mar 1966; LP32464]. Sd; col (PathéColor). 35mm. 81 min. [Copyright length: 78 min.]

A George Edwards Production. *Prod* George Edwards. *Assoc Prod* Stephanie Rothman. *Dir-Writ* Curtis Harrington. *Photog* Vilis Lapenieks. *Art Dir* Albert Locatelli. *Set Decor* Leon Smith. *Titl From the Paintings of* John Cline. *Film Ed* Leo Shreve. *Mus* Leonard Morand. *Sd* Harold Garver. *Prod Mgr* Gary Kurtz. *Script Supv* Barbara Bohrer. *Cost Supv* Sharon Compton. *Makeup* William Condos. *Hairstyles* George Spicer. *Prop* Karl Schanzer.

Cast: John Saxon *(Allan)*, Basil Rathbone *(Dr. Farraday)*, Judi Meredith *(Laura)*, Dennis Hopper *(Paul)*, Florence Marly *("Queen of Blood")*, Robert Boon, Don Eitner, Virgil Frye, J. Robert Porter, Teri Lee, Forrest J. Ackerman.

Science fiction melodrama. Based on an unidentified story, "The Veiled Woman." In the year 1990 a spaceship from another solar system crashlands on Mars and appeals to Earth for help. When a rescue crew headed by Dr. Farraday is sent to Mars, they find that the only survivor of the crash is an unconscious, green-complexioned female. On the trip back to Earth the woman reveals herself to be a vampire, and the crew members are eliminated one by one as the woman overcomes their resistance with her hypnotic stare and then drains their blood. On the final day of the return voyage, Allan and Laura, the only two crew members remaining, discover that the creature is a hemophiliac, and when she is scratched during a struggle she quickly bleeds to death. *Vampires. Space creatures. Spaceship crews. Space travel. Murder. Hemophilia. Mars (planet).*

Note: Also known as *Planet of Blood.*

QUEEN OF CLUBS *see* **LOVE CYCLES**

THE QUEEN OF SHEBA MEETS THE ATOM MAN   F6.3980

Dist Film-Makers' Cooperative. 28 Jan **1963** [New York opening]. Si; b&w. 16mm. ca70 min.

Dir Ron Rice. *Photog* Ron Rice. *Asst (see note)* Howard Everngam.

Cast: Winifred Bryan *(woman)*, Taylor Mead *(beatnik)*, Jack Smith.

Comedy-drama. A slighty-built beatnik cavorts and clowns his way through everything he does. In contrast, a stout black woman moves around her apartment naked, expressing vitality in all of her actions, whether shaving with an electric razor, making a telephone call, or playing with her cat. She fights affectionately with the beatnik; and later, after a grotesque ball, the two embrace and collapse amidst the disorder of her apartment. *Beatniks. Negroes. Balls (formal gatherings).*

Note: The film was first shown in rough cut and was unfinished at the time of the filmmaker's death in 1964. A posthumous release version, prepared by Howard Everngam, opened in New York 14 Mar 1968; running time: 71 min.

QUEEN OF SPADES (U.S.S.R.)   F6.3981

Lenfilm. *Dist* Artkino Pictures. 2 Sep **1961** [New York opening]. Sd; col (Magicolor). 35mm. 105 min. [Also 100 min.]

Dir Roman Tikhomirov. *Screenplay* Georgiy Vasilyev, Sergey Vasilyev, Pavel Veysbrem, Roman Tikhomirov, Boris Yarustovskiy. *Story Ed* I. Glikman. *Dir Photog* Yevgeniy Shapiro. *Camera* N. Shifrin. *Art Dir* I. Vuskovich. *Film Ed* R. Izakson. *Mus Perf* Bolshoi Theater Orchestra, Bolshoi Theater Chorus. *Mus Cond* Yevgeniy Svetlanov. *Choirmaster* A. Rybnov. *Sd* G. Elbert. *Asst Dir* N. Rusanova. *Prod Mgr* M. Shostak. *Cost* Ye. Slovtsova. *Makeup* V. Goryunov. *Sp Eff* M. Krotkin. *Mus Cons* A. Dmitriyev.

Cast: Oleg Strizhenov *(Germann)*, Olga Krasina *(Liza)*, Yelena Polevitskaya *(countess)*, V. Kulik *(Yeletskiy)*, Vadim Medvedev *(Tomskiy)*, I. Gurzo-Gubanova *(Polina)*, A. Gustavson, I. Daryalov, V. Kosarev, A. Olevanov, D. Radlov, Yuriy Solovyov, V. Tsitta.

Voices: Zurab Andzhaparidze *(Germann)*, Tamara Milashkina *(Liza)*, Sofya Preobrazhenskaya *(countess)*, Yevgeniy Kibkalo *(Yeletskiy)*, V. Nechipaylo *(Tomskiy)*, Larisa Avdeyeva *(Polina)*, V. Volodin, V. Kirpalov, M. Reshetin, V. Vlasov, G. Shulgin, L. Maslov, N. Yaroslavtsev.

Opera film. Source: Pëtr Ilich Tchaikovsky and Modest Ilich Tchaikovsky, *Pikovaya dama* (St. Petersburg staging: 19 Dec 1890). Aleksandr Sergeevich Pushkin, *Pikovaya dama* (1834). Obsessed with the desire to gain fortune, Germann, a poor young officer in St. Petersburg, learns of an aged countess who as a young woman learned the secret of three winning cards from a lover and gained the epithet "The Queen of Spades." Were she to reveal the secret to another lover she would die. By approaching her granddaughter, Liza, with whom he falls in love, Germann one night gains entrance to the countess' bedchamber. He confronts her with a pistol and demands that she reveal her secret, but the shock proves too great for the old woman and she dies of fright. Later, Germann arranges to meet Liza on the canal bank near the Winter Palace. A funeral procession passes, and the countess' ghost appears to Germann, advising him to wager on three cards: the three, the seven, and the

ace. Liza, fearful of the consequences, tries to dissuade Germann from going to the gambling rooms, and, when he persists, she drowns herself in the canal. At the gaming tables, Germann is challenged by Prince Yeletskiy, formerly Liza's suitor. Following the instructions of the ghost, Germann wins on the first two cards but loses everything on the third card when the Queen of Spades appears in place of the ace. Germann shoots himself, crawls to the banks of the canal where Liza's scarf blows in the night air, and dies. *Soldiers. Nobility. Grandmothers. Ghosts. Obsession. Gambling. Murder. Suicide. Poverty. Saint Petersburg.*

Note: Released in the U.S.S.R. in Oct 1960 as *Pikovaya dama*; running time: 106 min.

QUEEN OF THE NILE (Italy)   F6.3982

Max Production. 15 Jan **1964** [New York showing]. Sd; col (Eastman Color). 35mm (Supercinescope). 97 min.

Prod Ottavio Poggi. *Dir* Fernando Cerchio. *Screenplay* John Byrne, Ottavio Poggi, Fernando Cerchio. *Story* Emerico Papp, Ottavio Poggi. *Photog* Massimo Dallamano. *Art Dir* Ernesto Kromberg, Amedeo Mellone. *Film Ed* Renato Cinquini. *Mus* Carlo Rustichelli. *Choreog* Wilbert Bradley. *Sd* Mario Del Mezzo, Mario Amari. *Cost* Giancarlo Bartolini Salimbeni.

Cast: Jeanne Crain *(Tanit/Nefertiti)*, Vincent Price *(Benakon)*, Edmund Purdom *(Tumos)*, Amedeo Nazzari *(Amenophis IV)*, Liana Orfei *(Merith)*, Carlo D'Angelo, Clelia Matania, Alberto Farnese, Piero Palermini, Giulio Marchetti, Umberto Raho, Luigi Marturano, Raffaele Baldassarre, Romano Giomini, Adriano Vitale, Gino Talamo.

Melodrama. Tanit, a sheltered young woman living in ancient Thebes, is prevented by Benakon, the High Priest, from eloping with Tumos, a sculptor. Benakon then divulges that he is Tanit's father and that he intends that she fulfill her destiny by marrying Amenophis IV, the mentally disturbed son of the pharaoh and heir to the throne. Tumos is sentenced to death by the High Priest, but he escapes, intending to seek the aid of Amenophis, who is his friend. In time Amenophis ascends to the throne, and Tanit has her name changed to "Nefertiti" during a purification ceremony; meanwhile, Tumos finds some solace with Merith, a gypsy girl who loves him. Tumos is imprisoned once again by Benakon, and the High Priest threatens to kill him unless Nefertiti consents to marry Amenophis. He escapes a second time but later returns to Thebes, commissioned to do a bust of the new queen. During the sculpture session Nefertiti admits to Tumos that she still loves him, but she is unwilling to abandon her husband, who is becoming increasingly deranged. Benakon exploits Amenophis' condition by killing his close friend, the Priest of Ato, and besieging the palace. After Amenophis commits suicide, Nefertiti takes command, while Tumos and the army combine to save the kingdom; the queen is saved, and Benakon is killed by Merith. *Royalty. Sculptors. Priests. Gypsies. Perfidy. Marriage—Arranged. Filial relations. Murder. Suicide. Sculptures. Thebes. Egypt—Ancient. Nefertiti. Ikhnaton.*

Note: Opened in Rome in Jun 1962 as *Nefertite, regina del Nilo*; running time: 106 min.

QUEEN OF THE PIRATES (Italy/West Germany)   F6.3983

Max Production-Rapid-Film. *Dist* Columbia Pictures. 26 Jul **1961** [New York opening; c1 Aug 1961; LP20443]. Sd; b&w (see note). 35mm (SuperCinescope). 80 min.

Prod Ottavio Poggi. *Dir* Mario Costa. *Dir English Vers* Richard McNamara. *Screenplay* Nino Stresa, Ottavio Poggi. *Screenplay English Vers* John Byrne. *Story* Kurt Nachmann, Rolf Olsen. *Photog* Raffaele Masciocchi. *Art Dir* Ernesto Kromberg. *Set Dsgn* Amedeo Mellone. *Film Ed* Renato Cinquini. *Mus* Carlo Rustichelli. *Sd* Alessandro Sarandrea. *Asst Dir* Mario Tota. *Prod Mgr* Rino Merolle. *Cost* Giancarlo Bartolini Salimbeni. *Makeup* Maurizio Giustini. *Hairstyles* Adriana Cassini. *Fencing Master* Franco Fantasia.

Cast: Gianna Maria Canale *(Sandra)*, Massimo Serato *(Cesare)*, Scilla Gabel *(Isabella)*, Paul Müller *(The Duke)*, José Jaspé *(Mirko)*, Livio Lorenzon *(pirate chief)*, Giustino Durano *(Battista)*, Moira Orfei *(Jana)*, Andrea Aureli, Franco Fantasia, Nando Tamberlani, Raffaele Baldassarre, Giulio Battiferri, Luigi Marturano, Gianni Solaro, Anna Maria Mustari.

Adventure melodrama. In the 16th century, the Duchy of Doruzzo is under the tyrannical rule of Duke Zulian and his daughter, Isabella. When an unjustly accused sea captain, Mirko, and young and fiery Sandra, who believes Mirko to be her father, are brought before the duke, he decides to hang Mirko and sell Sandra into a Turkish harem. They are freed, however, by Cesare, Count of Santa Croce, a nobleman who the duke hopes will wed Isabella. Sandra and Mirko embark on a career of piracy, and Cesare sets out to capture them. Instead he falls in love with Sandra and joins her in planning an assault on the duke's palace. As the pirates battle their way ashore, they are joined by the oppressed peasants, and the attack is successful. The duke is fatally wounded by Cesare but before dying confesses that Sandra is the rightful heiress to the duchy. Many years ago, he reveals, he ordered Mirko to kill her, but the sea captain spared the young girl's life and reared her as his daughter. Isabella retires to a convent, and Sandra, now the Duchess of Doruzzo, prepares to marry Cesare and right the wrongs committed by Zulian. *Nobility. Sea captains. Despots. Peasants. Piracy. Filial relations. Personal identity. Harems.*

Note: Opened in Rome in Eastmancolor in Aug 1960 as *La venere dei pirati*; running time: ca85 min; released in West Germany in Apr 1961 as *Venus der Piraten*; running time: 78 min. West German coproduction status uncertain.

THE QUEENS (France/Italy)   **F6.3984**

Documento Film–Orsay Films. *Dist* Royal Films International. 10 Mar **1968** [New York opening]. Sd; col (Eastmancolor). 35mm. 110 min. [Cut from 122 min.]

Overall Production Credits: *Prod* Gianni Hecht Lucari. *Anim* M. C. S. Lodolo. *Mus* Armando Trovajoli. *Song:* "Walk Into My Life" sung by Rick Mantovani. *Prod Mgr* Fausto Saraceni. *English Subtitl* Mai Harris.

Production Credits—"Queen Sabina": *Dir* Luciano Salce. *Screenplay* Ruggero Maccari, Luigi Magni, Luciano Salce. *Story* Franco Indovina. *Photog* Ennio Guarnieri, Carlo Di Palma. *Art Dir* Luigi Sabatelli. *Film Ed* Sergio Montanari. *Sd* Augusto Troiani.

Production Credits—"Queen Armenia": *Dir* Mario Monicelli. *Screenplay* Suso Cecchi D'Amico, Tonino Guerra, Giorgio Salvioni. *Photog* Dario Di Palma. *Art Dir* Piero Gherardi. *Film Ed* Ruggero Mastroianni. *Sd* Fernando Pescetelli. *Asst Dir* Renzo Marignano.

Production Credits—"Queen Elena": *Dir* Mauro Bolognini. *Screenplay* Rodolfo Sonego. *Photog* Leonida Barboni. *Art Dir* Pier Luigi Pizzi. *Film Ed* Nino Baragli. *Sd* Fernando Pescetelli. *Asst Dir* Mariano Laurenti.

Production Credits—"Queen Marta": *Dir* Antonio Pietrangeli. *Screenplay* Rodolfo Sonego. *Photog* Armando Nannuzzi. *Art Dir* Mario Chiari. *Film Ed* Franco Fraticelli. *Sd* Massimo Jaboni. *Asst Dir* Marcello Ugolini.

Cast—"Queen Sabina": Monica Vitti *(Sabina)*, Enrico Maria Salerno *(Gianni)*, Franco Balducci *(1st motorist)*, Renzo Giovampietro *(2d motorist)*.

Cast—"Queen Armenia": Claudia Cardinale *(Armenia)*, Gastone Moschin *(Dr. Aldini)*.

Cast—"Queen Elena": Raquel Welch *(Elena)*, Jean Sorel *(Luigi)*, Pia Lindstrom *(Claudia)*, Massimo Fornari *(Alberto)*, Clothilde Sakharoff, Stelvio Rosi.

Cast—"Queen Marta": Capucine *(Marta)*, Alberto Sordi *(Giovanni)*, Anthony Steel *(The Professor)*, Gigi Ballista *(The Priest)*, Olga Villi *(Countess Rattazzi)*, Nino Marchetti *(The Guest)*.

Comedy. QUEEN SABINA: While hitchhiking home from the beach, Sabina arouses two motorists, who attempt to rape her. Rescued from the second assault by Gianni, a third driver, she finds herself becoming increasingly stimulated. Finally overcome by passion, Sabina chases Gianni through the woods. QUEEN ARMENIA: Armenia, a young gypsy woman who lives in a room with a juke box, uses friends' babies in various ways to make money. At first her advances to pediatrician Dr. Aldini are rebuffed, but when he succumbs and eventually becomes enamored of her, Armenia runs away with a truck driver. QUEEN ELENA: While her husband, Alberto, naps in the garden, Elena seduces Luigi, a handsome neighbor. Amazed at the ease with which the dalliance has been conducted, Luigi returns home to his wife, Claudia, who is calmly making love with one of their male friends. QUEEN MARTA: At a house party, Marta, a society woman, gets drunk and seduces Giovanni, a butler hired for the occasion. When Giovanni is hired by Marta's husband as a chauffeur the following morning, she appears to have no recollection of the previous evening. The servant still anticipates many evenings alone with his mistress, but after another passionate evening together, Marta again claims no knowledge of the affair and reacts angrily to Giovanni's further advances. Finally aware of the convenient games her memory plays, Giovanni decides to follow her lead and be aloof, confident that another drunken evening will soon occur. *Hitchhikers. Gypsies. Physicians. Neighbors. Socialites. Butlers. Chauffeurs. Seduction. Infidelity. Drunkenness.*

Note: Opened in Rome in Nov 1966 as *Le fate*; in Paris in Jul 1967 as *Les ogresses*; running time: 100 min. The four episodes may have also been titled "The Hitchhiker," "The Room With a Juke Box," "The Digestive Tablet," and "Giovanni."

THE QUEEN'S SWORDSMEN (Mexico)   **F6.3985**

Aurelio García Yévenes. *Dist* K. Gordon Murray Productions, Trans-International Films. **1963.** Sd; col. 35mm. 86 min.

Pres by K. Gordon Murray. *Prod* Aurelio García Yévenes. *Prod English Vers* K. Gordon Murray. *Dir* Roberto Rodríguez. *Story & Screenplay* Roberto Rodríguez, Manuel R. Ojeda. *Photog* Alex Phillips. *Art Dir* Roberto Silva. *Film Ed* José Bustos. *Mus* Sergio Guerrero. *Sd* Ernesto Caballero.

Cast: Elmo Michel, Rafael Muñoz, Marina Torres, Antonio Raxell, Ariadne Welter, Miguel Manzano, Javier Loyá, Ofelia Guilmain, Quintín Bulnes.

Fantasy. The beautiful princess of an enchanted kingdom is abducted by a wicked king who wants her to marry his son. A wolf and Stinky the Skunk become musketeers and rescue the princess from the king's soldiers. *Royalty.*

Musketeers. Abduction. Rescue. Imaginary kingdoms. Wolves. Skunks.

Note: Produced in Mexico in 1960 as *Los espadachines de la reina*.

QUEENS WILD   **F6.3986**

Dist Rossmore Film Distributors. 30 Aug **1963** [Los Angeles showing]. Sd; col (Eastman Color). 35mm. 67 min.

Pres by Harry H. Novak.

Special guest appearance: Virginia Bell.

Sex film. No information about the precise nature of this film has been found, but press material suggests that it includes scenes of nudity and poker-playing in a Wild West milieu. *Nudity. Poker. Frontier and pioneer life.*

QUEI DISPERATI CHE PUZZANO DI SUDORE E DI MORTE *see* **A BULLET FOR SANDOVAL**

QUEI TEMERARI SULLE LORO PAZZE, SCATENATE, SCALCINATE CARRIOLE *see* **THOSE DARING YOUNG MEN IN THEIR JAUNTY JALOPIES**

QUEIMADA! *see* **BURN!**

QUELLI CHE NON MUOIONO *see* **GUILT IS NOT MINE**

QUEMADA! *see* **BURN!**

QUESTI FANTASMI *see* **GHOSTS—ITALIAN STYLE**

QUESTION 7 (United States/West Germany)   **F6.3987**

Louis de Rochemont Associates–Lutheran Film Associates–Luther-Film. *Dist* Louis de Rochemont Associates. 1 Mar **1961** [Washington, D. C., opening; c2 Mar 1961; MP13057]. Sd; b&w. 35mm. 107 min.

Prod Lothar Wolff. *Prod Assoc* Robert E. A. Lee. *Dir* Stuart Rosenberg. *Screenplay* Allan Sloane. *Photog* Günter Senftleben. *Art Dir* Dieter Bartels. *Film Ed* Georges Klotz. *Mus* Hans-Martin Majewski. *Sd* Werner Schlagge. *Prod Supv* Harry Endress, Oswald C. J. Hoffmann, Johannes Stuhlmacher. *Adv* Paul C. Empie, Richard Solberg.

Cast: Michael Gwynn *(Friedrich Gottfried)*, Margaret Jahnen *(Maria Gottfried)*, Christian de Bresson *(Peter Gottfried)*, Almut Eggert *(Anneliese Zingler)*, Erik Schuman *(Rolf Starke)*, Max Buchsbaum *(Police Inspector Herrmann)*, John Ruddock *(Martin Kraus)*, Leo Bieber *(Herr Rettmann)*, Fritz Wepper *(Heinz Dehmert)*, Eduard Linkers *(Otto Zingler)*, Marianne Schubarth *(Marta Zingler)*, Philo Hauser *(barber)*, Rolf von Nauckhoff *(Karl Marschall)*, Helmo Kindermann *(Luedtke)*, Manfred Furst *(Professor Stefl)*, Lutz Altschul *(Herr Durfel)*, Sigurd Lohde *(Herr Kesselmaier)*, Erik Jelde *(A. A. Tritschler)*, Ernst Constantin *(bishop)*, Galina Probandt-Frank *(Gerda Laube)*, Günter Meisner *(Schmidt)*, Gerd Vespermann, Nora Minor, Richard Handwerk, Stefan Schnabel, Gabriele Mascher, Hans Schumm, Hans Piper, Willy Trenk-Trebitsch, Annemarie Braun, Reginald Pasch.

Drama. The East German Communist Party is involved in a campaign to turn students away from their Christian heritage by denying higher education to youths who do not hold politically "correct" views. Peter Gottfried is a 15-year-old pastor's son who hopes to enter a music conservatory, but before he can be accepted, he must answer seven questions, the last of which asks him to name the major influence on his social development. Aware that he must deny his religious beliefs, the boy turns to those around him for advice. His teacher encourages him to make the "right" decision, but his girl friend, Anneliese, and his father urge him to stand by his principles. When the Party gives him an opportunity to participate in the annual Berlin Youth Festival, Peter accepts despite the protests of his father. Once in Berlin, Peter realizes that he is merely a pawn being used by the Party to refute charges that religious youth are denied opportunity under communism. He flees from the festival and takes refuge in the West. *Clergymen. Defectors. Communism. Adolescence. Filial relations. Religious persecution. German Democratic Republic. Berlin.*

Note: Location scenes filmed in Berlin. Released in West Germany in 1961 as *Frage 7*; running time: 106 min.

QUESTIONE DI PELLE *see* **CHECKERBOARD**

THE QUICK AND THE DEAD   **F6.3988**

Manson Distributing Corp. *Dist* Beckman Film Corp. Jan **1963**. Sd; b&w. 35mm. 92 min.

Prod Sam Altonian. *Exec Prod* Edmund Goldman. *Assoc Prod* Paul Mart. *Dir* Robert Totten. *Screenplay* Robert Totten, Sheila Lynch. *Photog* John Arthur Morrill. *Art Dir* O. R. C. Totten. *Film Ed* Weber Ford. *Mus* Jaime Mendoza. *Sd* Van Ditmars, Richard Carpenter, sd.

Cast: Larry D. Mann *(Parker)*, Victor French *(Riley)*, Jon Cedar *(Lieutenant Rogers)*, James Almanzar *(Giorgio)*, Louis Massad *(Donatelli)*, Majel Barrett *(Teresa)*, Sandy Donigan *(Maria)*, Joseph Locastro, William Kirschner, Frank D'Agostino, Stuart Nisbet, Ted French.

War drama. In the last days of the German occupation of Italy during World War II, an American patrol led by Lieutenant Rogers receives orders to destroy a hidden Nazi ammunition dump in northern Italy. After suffering many casualties, the men are captured by the Germans. Maria and Teresa, two Italian partisans, join the Americans, and during an air raid the group escapes. Two of the Americans locate the Nazi ammunition supply and destroy it before they are killed, while the women lead the rest of the group to a partisan hideout. Only two Americans and one of the women survive the trip back to American lines. *Nazis. Italians. Prisoners of war. Survival. Military occupation. Resistance (political). Bombardment. Ammunition. World War II. United States Army. Italy. Explosions.*

QUICK, BEFORE IT MELTS   F6.3989

Biography Productions. *Dist* Metro-Goldwyn-Mayer, Inc. 20 Jan **1965** [Chicago opening; c5 Oct 1964; LP29208]. Sd (Westrex); col (Metrocolor). 35mm (Panavision). 98 min.

A Douglas Laurence–Delbert Mann Production. *Prod* Douglas Laurence, Delbert Mann. *Dir* Delbert Mann. *Screenplay* Dale Wasserman. *Dir Photog* Russell Harlan. *Art Dir* George W. Davis, Preston Ames. *Set Decor* Henry Grace, Hugh Hunt. *Film Ed* Fredric Steinkamp. *Mus Comp & Cond* David Rose. *Rec Supv* Franklin Milton. *Asst Dir* Eric Von Stroheim, Jr. *Makeup Supv* William Tuttle. *Hairstyles* Sydney Guilaroff. *Dial Supv* Norman Stuart.

Cast: George Maharis (*Peter Santelli*), Robert Morse (*Oliver Cromwell Cannon*), Anjanette Comer (*Tiare Marshall*), James Gregory (*vice admiral*), Michael Constantine (*Mikhail Drozhensky*), Howard St. John (*Harvey T. Sweigert*), Norman Fell (*George Snell*), Janine Gray (*Diana Grenville-Wells*), Bernard Fox (*Leslie Folliott*), Richard LePore (*Ben Livingston*), Conlan Carter (*Orville Bayleaf*), Yvonne Craig (*Sharon Sweigert*), Hal Baylor (*prison guard*), Doodles Weaver (*ham operator*), Frank London (*shaggy type*), Nelson Olmsted (*scientist*), Tom Vize, John Dennis, Hugh "Slim" Langtry, Fletcher Allen, Davis Roberts, Dale Malone (*military men*), Marjorie Bennett, Karen Scott (*barmaids*), Philip Benjamin (*guest at admiral's party*), Milton Fox (*a penguin*).

Comedy. Source: Philip Benjamin, *Quick, Before It Melts* (New York, 1964). Oliver Cannon, a shy reporter for *Sage Magazine*, is assigned to cover a naval expedition in Little America by Harvey Sweigert, his managing editor, who is also the father of Oliver's fiancée, Sharon. Pete Santelli, a photographer, is assigned to accompany Oliver, and the two become fast friends. Their first stop is Christchurch, New Zealand, and there Pete meets and falls in love with Diana. Oliver is strongly attracted to Tiare, a half-Maori, and a brawl ensues when George Snell, a rival journalist, makes some unkind remarks about her. While in Antarctica, Oliver tries to create a scoop for himself by trying to influence Mickey, a pleasant Russian scientist with the expedition, to defect, but the admiral in charge of the expedition, having been informed of the plan by Snell, objects to Oliver's plan. Pete and Oliver persuade the admiral to have some women flown in to demonstrate the habitability of the Antarctic region, and they are not surprised when Diana and Tiare are among the group who arrive. Mickey falls in love with Tiare, marries her, and announces his intention to defect to New Zealand, thus providing Oliver and Pete with their much-wanted defection scoop. The admiral, however, refuses to allow the information to be released and orders the radio shack to be placed out of bounds to the reporters. The celebration that takes place when Pete and Diana are married, however, provides Oliver the opportunity to sneak into the shack and radio his story to the magazine. Oliver goes home, having established the reputation of being an ace reporter, and marries Sharon. *Reporters. Editors. Photographers. Scientists. Russians. Maori. Halfcastes. Defectors. Timidity. Employer-employee relations. Marriage. Exploration. Magazines (periodicals). Radio. Little America. Christchurch (New Zealand). Penguins.*

Note: Location scenes filmed on the Bering Sea near Nome, Alaska.

THE QUICK GUN   F6.3990

Admiral Pictures. *Dist* Columbia Pictures. Apr **1964** [c1 May 1964; LP28067]. Sd (Westrex); col (Technicolor). 35mm (Techniscope). 88 min.

Prod Grant Whytock. *Dir* Sidney Salkow. *Screenplay* Robert E. Kent. *Dir Photog* Lester Shorr. *Art Dir* Robert Purcell. *Set Decor* Frank Tuttle. *Film Ed* Grant Whytock. *Mus* Richard LaSalle. *Sd Supv* Charles J. Rice. *Sd* Josh Westmoreland. *Asst Dir* Herbert S. Greene. *Makeup Supv* Ben Lane.

Cast: Audie Murphy (*Clint Cooper*), Merry Anders (*Helen Reed*), James Best (*Scotty Grant*), Ted De Corsia (*Spangler*), Walter Sande (*Tom Morrison*), Rex Holman (*Rick Morrison*), Charles Meredith (*Reverend Staley*), Frank Ferguson (*Dan Evans*), Mort Mills (*Cagle*), Gregg Palmer (*Donovan*), Frank Gerstle (*George Keely*), Stephen Roberts (*Dr. Stevens*), Paul Bryar (*Mitchell*), Raymond Hatton (*elderly man*), William Fawcett (*Mike*).

Western melodrama. Source: Steve Fisher, "The Fastest Gun" (a story; publication undetermined). Clint Cooper, who left his home town after being forced into a duel in which the sons of a powerful rancher were killed, decides to return and claim his right to his father's ranch. He also plans to resume his relationship with his girl friend, Helen Reed. On the way home, he learns that a large gang plans to rob the town bank. He arrives in town and finds that most

of the townsmen have left on a cattle drive, but he agrees to help his long-time friend Scotty, the sheriff, defend the town against the gang. In the ensuing battle, many of the raiders are killed, as well as Scotty and most of the town's defenders. Only Clint, the minister, and an elderly man remain. These three manage to defeat the surviving raiders, and Clint stays on to become the new sheriff. *Cattlemen. Ranchers. Heirs. Sheriffs. Gangs. Clergymen. Murder. Bank robberies.*

Note: Locations scenes filmed in the San Fernando Valley, California. Working title: *The Fastest Gun.*

QUIEN SABE? see A BULLET FOR THE GENERAL

QUIET DAYS IN CLICHY (Denmark)   F6.3991

S. B. A. Film–Dansk-Svensk Film–Merry Filmproduktion. *Dist* Grove Press, Sherpix, Inc. 21 Sep **1970** [New York opening]. Sd; b&w. 35mm. 90 min. MPAA rating X.

Prod Klaus Pagh. *Dir-Writ* Jens Jørgen Thorsen. *Photog* Jesper Høm, Teit Jørgensen. *Art Dir* Elith Nykjaer Jørgensen. *Film Ed* Anker Sørensen. *Mus & Songs* Country Joe McDonald, Ben Webster, The Young Flowers, Andy Sundstrøm, Papa Blue's Viking Jazz Band. *Sd* Peter Stamer. *Asst Dir* Ivar Søe. *Prod Mgr* Bent Nykjaer Jørgensen, Roger de Monenstral. *Dub Voice for Paul Valjean* Bruce Johansen.

Cast: Paul Valjean (*Joey*), Louise White (*surrealist*), Wayne John Rodda (*Carl*), Ulla Lemvigh-Müller (*Nys*), Elsebeth Reingaard (*Colette*), Susanne Krage (*Christine*), Petronella (*Adrienne*), Avi Sagild (*Mara*), Lisbeth Lundquist (*Jeanne*), Olaf Ussing (*father*), Noemi Roos (*mother*), Anne Kehlet (*Corinne*), Ben Webster (*himself*), Herman Woldsgaard-Iversen, Britten Jensen, Elsa Jackson, Mette Aarre Thorsen, Marianne Bergh, Mai Weckselman, Maria Stentz, "Bamse" Kragh-Jacobsen, Marie-France Hamou, Roger de Monenstral, Marcel Doumerg, Jacques Spezia, Françoise Hesselman, Jens Jørgen Thorsen.

Autobiographical comedy. Source: Henry Miller, *Quiet Days in Clichy* (Paris, 1956). Joey, an American choreographer living in Denmark, and his friend Carl are poor but happy in Paris where they spend most of their time in Montmartre picking up and seducing young women. In a series of scenes, Joey, the Henry Miller counterpart in the author's autobiographical novel, is seen in bed with a succession of women, displaying his lecherous character. An excursion to Luxembourg by Carl and Joey is presented in the film as a series of still photographs. Back in Paris, a teenaged nymphomaniac, Colette, moves in with them and is shared by both men until her parents discover the sordid affair. After an angry confrontation with Colette's parents and the girl's departure from the apartment, Joey and Carl continue their pursuit of pickups. *Americans in foreign countries. Choreographers. Pickups. Nymphomania. Lechery. Poverty. Seduction. Adolescence. Paris—Montmartre. Clichy. Luxembourg.*

Note: Filmed in Paris. Released in Denmark in Jun 1970 as *Stille dage i Clichy*; running time: 95 min. Rereleased by Sherpix, Inc., as *Not So Quiet Days.*

A QUIET PLACE IN THE COUNTRY (France/Italy)   F6.3992

P. E. A.–Les Productions Artistes Associés. *Dist* Lopert Pictures. 28 Aug **1970** [New York opening]. Sd; col (Technicolor). 35mm (Techniscope). 106 min. MPAA rating R.

Prod Alberto Grimaldi. *Dir* Elio Petri. *Screenplay* Elio Petri, Luciano Vincenzoni. *Story* Tonino Guerra, Elio Petri. *Photog* Luigi Kuveiller. *Art Dir* Sergio Canevari. *Supv Film Ed* Enzo Ocone. *Film Ed* Ruggero Mastroianni. *Mus* Ennio Morricone. *Mus Perf by* Gruppo di Improvvisazioni Nuova Consonanza. *Sd Ed* Mario Bramonti. *Sd Rec* Emilio Rosa. *Asst Dir* Mario Chiari. *Prod Mgr* Gino Millozza. *Cost* Giulio Coltellacci. *Paintings* Jim Dine.

Cast: Franco Nero (*Leonardo Ferri*), Vanessa Redgrave (*Flavia*), Georges Géret (*Attilio*), Gabriella Grimaldi (*Wanda*), Madeleine Damien (*Wanda's mother*), Rita Calderoni (*Egle*), Renato Menegotto (*Egle's friend*), John Francis Lane (*asylum attendant*), David Maunsell (*medium*), Mirta Simionato, Graziella Simionato, Arnaldo Momo, Sara Momo, Otello Cazzola, Marino Bagiola, Piero De Franceschi, Camillo Besenzon, Costantino De Luca, Giulia Menin (*villagers*), Valerio Ruggeri, Umberto Di Grazia, Bruno Simionato, Elena Vicini, Renato Lupi, Giuseppe Bella, Onofrio Fulli.

Mystery melodrama. Leonardo Ferri, a popular artist, is disturbed by nightmares in which he and Flavia, his mistress and sales agent, engage in sadistic sexual practices. Thinking that the urban life of Milan is oppressing him, Leonardo rents a villa in the country. On the first night there, several of his canvases are damaged, and a few nights later, Flavia is seriously injured in a bizarre accident. Leonardo discovers that a bouquet of flowers is being left in the garden every night, and he is informed by Attilio, the caretaker, that Wanda, the promiscuous daughter of the former owner of the villa, died in the garden during a World War II air raid. Excited by the possibility of living in a haunted house, Leonardo hires a medium to conduct a seance to contact Wanda. During the seance, Leonardo goes berserk and kills Flavia. When the police arrive to arrest Attilio, who has confessed to Wanda's murder, they find Leonardo guarding a refrigerator which supposedly contains the mutilated body of Flavia. Leonardo is committed to an asylum where he continues his work, and Flavia, who was murdered only in Leonardo's mind, continues to sell his paintings. *Artists. Mistresses. Art dealers. Caretakers. Mediums. Police. Seances. Insanity. Confession (law). Murder. Mutilation. Paintings. Gardens. Haunted houses. Insane asylums. Milan. Dreams. Hallucinations.*

Note: Location scenes filmed in Milan and Venice. Released in Italy in 1968 as *Un tranquillo posto di campagna;* opened in Paris in Aug 1969 as *Un coin tranquille à la campagne;* running time: 105 min (cut from 109 min).

THE QUILLER MEMORANDUM (United States/Great Britain) F6.3993

Rank Organisation-Ivan Foxwell Productions-Carthay Films. *For* National General Productions. *Dist* Twentieth Century-Fox Film Corp. 15 Dec **1966** [New York opening; c15 Dec 1966; LP34061]. Sd; col (De Luxe). 35mm (Panavision). 105 min.

An Ivan Foxwell Production. *Prod* Ivan Foxwell. *Dir* Michael Anderson. *Screenplay* Harold Pinter. *Dir Photog* Erwin Hillier. *Camera Op* John Winbolt. *2d Unit Camera* H. A. R. Thomson. *Art Dir* Maurice Carter. *Assoc Art Dir* Jack Maxsted. *Set Dresser* Arthur Taksen. *Film Ed* Frederick Wilson. *Mus Comp & Cond* John Barry. *Song:* "Wednesday's Child" John Barry, David Mack. *Sung by* Matt Monro. *Sd Ed* Archie Ludski. *Sd Rec* C. C. Stevens, John Aldred. *Asst Dir* Clive Reed. *Prod Supv* Sydney Streeter. *Unit Mgr* Bernard Williams. *Cont* Joan Kirk. *Wardrobe* Carl Tom. *Makeup* W. T. Partleton. *Hairstyles* Stella Rivers. *Sp Eff* Les Bowie, Arthur Beavis.

Cast: George Segal *(Quiller),* Alec Guinness *(Pol),* Max von Sydow *(Oktober),* Senta Berger *(Inge),* George Sanders *(Gibbs),* Robert Helpmann *(Weng),* Robert Flemyng *(Gibbs's associate),* Peter Carsten *(Hengel),* Edith Schneider *(headmistress),* Gunter Meisner *(Hassler),* Robert Stass *(Jones),* Ernst Walder *(Grauber),* Philip Madoc, John Rees *(Oktober's men).*

Drama. Source: Adam Hall, *The Berlin Memorandum* (London, 1965). When two British Intelligence agents are murdered in Berlin, Quiller, an American agent, is given the task of finding the leader of a neo-Nazi movement attempting to infect German thinking. Under the watchful eye of Pol, head of Berlin Control, Quiller follows a newspaper lead and visits a school where a teacher convicted of Nazi war crimes recently hanged himself. There Quiller is attracted to the teacher's replacement, Inge, and visits her at her apartment. Upon leaving, he is picked up by the Nazis, drugged, and brought for questioning to their headquarters. When he refuses, despite torture, to reveal the location of Berlin Control, the Nazi leader, Oktober, orders him dumped into the icy waters of a canal. Realizing Oktober expects him to report to Berlin Control, Quiller goes instead to Inge and asks for her help. Her "contact"—her headmistress—leads them both back to Oktober. The Nazi informs Quiller that he is to be set free, but unless he reveals the location of Berlin Control by daylight, both he and Inge will be murdered. By deliberately setting off a bomb which has been placed in his rented car, Quiller slips from the scene as the blazing explosion convinces the Nazis that he has been killed. Once he has reported the address of Oktober's headquarters to Pol, and the Nazis have been quickly rounded up, Quiller learns that Inge is not among the prisoners. He finds her back at her school; she tells him only that Oktober let her go. As Quiller leaves, Inge returns to "teaching" the younger generation of Berlin children. *Secret agents. Nazis. Schoolteachers. Americans in foreign countries. Neo-nazism. Espionage. Murder. Suicide. Torture. Kidnaping. Perfidy. Berlin—West. Great Britain—Intelligence service. Explosions.*

Note: Location scenes filmed in West Berlin. Opened in London in Nov 1966 at 103 min.

QUIXOTE F6.3994

Dist Canyon Cinema Cooperative, Film-Makers' Cooperative. 22 Dec **1965** [New York opening]. Sd; b&w with color seq. 16mm. 45 min.

Prod-Dir-Writ Bruce Baillie. *Photog* Bruce Baillie. *Film Ed* Bruce Baillie.

Experimental film. This nonfiction film is in part compiled from television and motion picture footage. A boxer roams through New York City at dawn; two aging Indians, their faces wrinkled and proud, converse in a cafe; blacks march past rigid policemen in battle gear; and migrant workers amble across fields. Constantly recurring in the film are shots of newspaper clippings, billboards, and television commercials intruding upon landscape and quixotic sequences: desert sunsets, Midwest snowscapes, human faces, an Indian chief in full regalia, and a herd of sheep on a hillside. The film ends with shots of the Vietcong juxtaposed with shots of blacks in groups—both types of "Quixotes" protesting their corrupt societies. *Negroes. Boxers. Police. Migratory workers. Indians of North America. Materialism. Idealists. Airplanes—Jet. Computers. Billboards. Television commercials. Vietnam War 1964–73. New York City.*

Note: Revised in 1967 with some scenes deleted, and the final section reshot.

QUOI DE NEUF, PUSSYCAT? see WHAT'S NEW PUSSYCAT?

R. P. M. F6.3995

Columbia Pictures. 16 Sep **1970** [New York opening; c1 Sep 1970; LP38167]. Sd; col (Eastman Color). 35mm. 92 min. *MPAA rating* R.

A Stanley Kramer Production. *Prod-Dir* Stanley Kramer. *Assoc Prod* George Glass. *Screenplay* Erich Segal. *Dir Photog* Michel Hugo. *Camera Op* Roger Sherman, Jr. *Set Decor* George James Hopkins. *Prod Dsgn* Robert Clatworthy. *Titl Dsgn* Wayne Fitzgerald. *Film Ed* William A. Lyon. *Mus Writ & Comp* Barry DeVorzon, Perry Botkin, Jr. *Adtl Lyr & Songs Sung by* Melanie. *Sd* Les Fresholtz. *Sd Eff* Edit-Rite Inc. *Mus Ed* Robert Tracy. *Asst Dir* Jack Roe. *Prod Supv* Ivan Volkman. *Script Supv* Marshall Schlom. *Cost Dsgn* Moss Mabry. *Wardrobe Supv* Joe King. *Makeup* Fred Phillips. *Hairstyles* Virginia Jones. *Sp Eff* Geza Gaspar. *Prop Master* Joe La Bella. *Grip* John Livesley. *Ch Electrn* Ralph McCarthy.

Cast: Anthony Quinn *(Paco Perez),* Ann-Margret *(Rhoda),* Gary Lockwood *(Rossiter),* Paul Winfield *(Dempsey),* Graham Jarvis *(Thatcher),* Alan Hewitt *(Hewlett),* Ramon Bieri *(Brown),* John McLiam *(Reverend Blauvelt),* Don Keefer *(Dean Cooper),* Donald Moffat *(Perry Howard),* Norman Burton *(Coach McCurdy),* John Zaremba *(Tyler),* Inez Pedroza *(Estella),* Teda Bracci, Linda Meiklejohn, Bruce Fleischer, David Ladd, John David Wilder, Bradjose, Raymond Cavaleri, Henry Brown, Jr., Frank Alesia, Robert Carricart, Jr. *(students).*

Melodrama. After a coalition of black and white students occupies the administration building of Hudson University and forces the college president to resign, the revolutionaries submit to the board of trustees a list of people whom they respect, among them Paco Perez. Consequently, Perez, a Puerto Rican sociology professor, is appointed acting president of the university to facilitate negotiations, thereby pitting the aging radical against many of his former student friends. Dempsey and Rossiter, respective leaders of the black and white factions, disagree on some matters, but when Perez informs them that three of their demands cannot be met, all the radicals stand fast in their refusal to leave the building. In addition to his lack of success with the negotiations, Perez' graduate student mistress, Rhoda, accuses him of sexual inadequacy. When the harassed Perez learns of a threat by Rossiter to destroy the university's $2,000,000 computer if their demands are not met, he calls in the police who provoke a riot by exploding tear gas and beating students, including Rhoda, who has joined the radicals. At the courthouse, Perez is congratulated by the board of directors for ending the crisis, but he is aware that the goals of the students were right, even if their methods were not; as he leaves the courthouse, he is booed by the student body. *Students. Professors. Puerto Ricans. Negroes. Mistresses. Police. College life. Sit-ins. Radicalism. Race relations. Extortion. Riots.*

Note: Location scenes filmed at the University of the Pacific in Stockton, California, and in San Francisco. Also reviewed as *R.*P. M.* Revolutions Per Minute.*

RABBIT, RUN F6.3996

Solitaire/Worldcross Productions. *Dist* Warner Bros. Pictures. 28 Oct **1970** [Reading, Pennsylvania, opening]. Sd; col (Technicolor). 35mm (Panavision). 94 min. *MPAA rating* R.

A Howard B. Kreitsek Production. *Prod-Writ* Howard B. Kreitsek. *Assoc Prod* Joanne Deane. *Dir* Jack Smight. *Photog* Philip Lathrop. *Art Dir* Alfred Sweeney. *Set Decor* Marvin March. *Film Ed* Archie Marshek. *Mus Supv* Sonny Burke. *Mus Coörd* Frank Kay. *Song:* "Anything Happening?" Ray Burton, Brian King, M. K. Gregory. *Song:* "Gonna Love Me" Ray Burton, G. K. Michael. *Songs Sung by* Inner Sense. *Sd* Tom Overton. *Asst Dir* James H. Brown. *Prod Mgr* Maurie M. Suess. *Asst to the Prod* Bert Remsen. *Makeup* Gordon Bau. *Hairstyles* Jean Burt Reilly.

Cast: James Caan *(Rabbit Angstrom),* Anjanette Comer *(Ruth),* Jack Albertson *(Marty Tothero),* Melodie Johnson *(Lucy Eccles),* Henry Jones *(Mr. Angstrom),* Carmen Mathews *(Mrs. Springer),* Virginia Vincent *(Margaret),* Nydia Westman *(Mrs. Smith),* Marc Antony Van Der Nagel *(Nelson),* Josephine Hutchinson *(Mrs. Angstrom),* Don Keefer *(Mr. Springer),* Margot Stevenson *(Mrs. Tothero),* Sondra Scott *(Miriam Angstrom),* Ken Kercheval *(Barney),* Carrie Snodgress *(Janice Angstrom),* Arthur Hill *(Rev. Jack Eccles).* Joanne Deane.

Domestic drama. Source: John Updike, *Rabbit, Run* (New York, 1960). In Reading, Pennsylvania, former high school basketball star Rabbit Angstrom is dissatisfied with both his failure to find a career and with his loveless marriage to Janice, an alcoholic who is pregnant with a child neither of them wants. Following an argument with Janice, Rabbit looks up his old basketball coach Marty Tothero, who is now living in squalor. Marty decides that Rabbit needs a woman, and he introduces him to Ruth, a part-time prostitute. When Rabbit moves in with Ruth, Jack Eccles, the family minister, tries to persuade him to return to his wife, but Rabbit refuses. Eventually, Rabbit also becomes disenchanted with Ruth, and when Janice has her baby, Rabbit goes to the hospital and effects a reconciliation. For a time, they live in relative harmony, but Janice's insistence on a less active sex life leads to bitterness, and Rabbit again takes off. Janice resumes her solitary drinking, this time with tragic results; while in a drunken stupor, she accidentally drowns the baby. Learning of his child's death, Rabbit returns home and finds that everyone holds him responsible. At the funeral, Rabbit responds to his parents' and in-laws' accusing glances by screaming his innocence. Fleeing from the cemetery, he goes to Ruth's apartment; but Ruth, who is now pregnant with his child, refuses to let him in unless he agrees to divorce Janice and marry her. Although he promises to do so, Rabbit is still unable to make a commitment to anyone and runs away again. *Athletic coaches. Prostitutes. Clergymen. Infants. Marriage. Family life. Disillusionment. Alcoholism. Pregnancy. Infidelity. Desertion. Infanticide. Funerals. Reading (Pennsylvania).*

Note: Location scenes filmed in Reading, Pennsylvania.

THE RABBLE (Japan)   **F6.3997**
Toho Co. *Dist* Toho Co., Frank Lee International. 25 Mar **1965** [Los Angeles showing]. Sd; col (Eastman Color). 35mm (Tohoscope). 116 min.

Prod Tomoyuki Tanaka, Hiroshi Inagaki. *Dir* Hiroshi Inagaki. *Screenplay* Shintaro Mimura, Masato Ide, Hiroshi Inagaki. *Photog* Kazuo Yamada. *Mus* Ikuma Dan.

Cast: Somegoro Ichikawa (*Kanzaburo*), Yuriko Hoshi (*Midori*), Mayumi Ozora (*Makie*), Tadao Nakamaru, Ichiro Arishima.

Costume melodrama. In feudal Japan the harbor city of Sakai is a haven for farmers left homeless by pillaging warlords. Kanzaburo, a sturdy young farmer's son newly arrived in the city, sells himself to a wealthy merchant and is assigned to guard a parrot belonging to Midori, one of the merchant's two granddaughters. The second granddaughter, Makie, is being wooed both by a samurai and a nobleman of high rank, the ambitious merchant's choice. A cruise on his new ship is arranged for the rival suitors, with Makie and Midori also on board as well as Kanzaburo and many other attendants. Fulfilling the captain's premonitions, a violent storm suddenly comes up and all aboard are stranded on a deserted island when the ship sinks. Under the primitive conditions of this new environment, the nobleman and the samurai become cringing cowards while Kanzaburo emerges as a calm, effective leader. Makie, who has heretofore treated Kanzaburo haughtily, now clamors for his attentions, but he realizes that the change is temporary; besides, his romantic hopes lie with Midori. Finally, rescue arrives, but Kanzaburo is left behind as a result of the samurai's treachery and must find his way back to Sakai alone against tremendous odds. But the love of Midori and a future full of hope are his ultimate rewards. [A Japanese source suggests that Midori joins Kanzaburo as he sets out on his own.] *Merchants. Samurai. Nobility. Social classes. Jealousy. Survival. Feudalism. Perfidy. Courtship. Islands. Sakai. Shipwrecks.*

Note: Released in Japan in 1964 as *Garakuta*; running time: 120 min.

LA RABIA (THE RAGE) (United States/Mexico)   **F6.3998**
Cronos Productions. 25 Jul **1963** [Miami, Florida, opening]. Sd; b&w. 35mm. ca90 min.

Prod Massey Creamer. *Dir* Myron J. Gold.

Cast: June Wilkinson (*stripper*), Armando Silvestre (*gigolo*).

Crime melodrama. In Mexico City an American stripper and her gigolo boyfriend conspire to steal $80,000 by making the loot appear to have been lost in an airplane explosion. *Americans in foreign countries. Stripteasers. Gigolos. Theft. Mexico City. Airplane accidents.*

Note: Location scenes filmed in Mexico City. Also reviewed as *The Rage Within.*

RACCONTI D'ESTATE *see* **LOVE ON THE RIVIERA**

RACHEL CADE *see* **THE SINS OF RACHEL CADE**

RACHEL, RACHEL   **F6.3999**
Kayos Productions. *Dist* Warner Bros.–Seven Arts, Inc. 26 Aug **1968** [New York opening; c1 Sep 1968; LP37144]. Sd; col (Technicolor). 35mm. 101 min.

A Paul Newman Production. *Prod-Dir* Paul Newman. *Assoc Prod* Arthur S. Newman, Jr., Harrison Starr. *Screenplay* Stewart Stern. *Photog* Gayne Rescher. *Camera* Dick Mingalone. *Asst Camera* Thomas Priestley, Jr. *Art Dir* Robert Gundlach. *Set Decor* Richard Merrell. *Scenic Art* Sante Fiore. *Film Ed* Dede Allen. *Assoc Ed* Robert Q. Lovett. *Asst Ed* Lynn Lewis. *Mus Comp & Cond* Jerome Moross. *Song* Jerome Moross, Stewart Stern. *Perf by* The Phaetons. *Selections From the Mus of* Erik Satie, Robert Schumann. *Sd* Jack Jacobsen. *Re-rec* Dick Vorisek. *Sd Ed* Alan Heim. *Asst Dir* Alan Hopkins, Robert Koster. *Prod Mgr* Florence Nerlinger. *Script Cont* Roberta Hodes. *Cost* Domingo Rodriguez. *Wardrobe* Bev Langer. *Makeup* Bob Philippe. *Prod & Location Cons* Larry Sturhahn, Emil Morey Associates. *Still Photog* Muky. *Constr Mgr* Merle Eckhart. *Key Grip* Larry Barr. *Casting* Shirley Rich. *Prop Master* Thomas Wright. *Ch Gaffer* Willie Meyerhoff.

Cast: Joanne Woodward (*Rachel Cameron*), James Olson (*Nick Kazlik*), Kate Harrington (*Mrs. Cameron*), Estelle Parsons (*Calla Mackie*), Geraldine Fitzgerald (*Reverend Wood*), Donald Moffat (*Niall Cameron*), Terry Kiser (*preacher*), Frank Corsaro (*Hector Jonas*), Bernard Barrow (*Leighton Siddley*), Nell Potts (*Rachel, as a child*), Shawn Campbell (*James*), Violet Dunn (*Verla*), Izzy Singer (*Lee Shabab*), Tod Engle (*Nick, as a child*), Bruno Engl (*bartender*), Beatrice Pons, Dorothea Duckworth, Simm Landres, Connie Robinson, Sylvia Shipman, Larry Fredericks, Wendell MacNeal.

Drama. Source: Margaret Laurence, *A Jest of God* (New York, 1966). Rachel Cameron, a 35-year-old spinster schoolteacher, feels that her life has been meaningless. She lives in a small New England town with her simpering widowed mother in an apartment over the funeral parlor that once belonged to her father. Haunted by memories of her childhood and her mortician father, Rachel spends each frustrating day taking care of her mother and working with the schoolchildren. Her closest friend is Calla Mackie, another unmarried teacher who persuades Rachel to attend a revival meeting led by Reverend Wood. There, to Rachel's astonishment, all of her pent-up frustrations are released when a visiting preacher urges her to give expression to her repressed emotions. Despite a near-hysterical breakdown and her revulsion at Calla's tentative overtures of lesbian love, Rachel realizes that only by exposing herself to life can she experience it. She therefore gives herself to a former high school friend, Nick Kazlik, who is in town for a visit with his parents. Mistaking her first sexual encounter for love, she fantasizes about a future with Nick. Her hopes are shattered, however, when Nick, put off by her seriousness, abruptly ends their affair. A short time later, Rachel discovers that she may be pregnant. Determined to accept the consequences of her actions, she decides to go away and have the child. After Calla has helped her find a teaching post in Oregon, Rachel learns that her pregnancy is merely a cyst requiring minor surgery. Though she is disappointed at her loss, Rachel's new respect for herself remains, and she decides to move to Oregon. As she leaves with her somewhat reluctant mother and looks for the last time at the familiar sights of her home town, she speculates on what the future may bring. *Spinsters. Schoolteachers. Widows. Undertakers. Evangelists. Loneliness. Memory. Filial relations. Lesbianism. Sexual initiation. Pregnancy. Revivals. New England.*

Note: Filmed in Connecticut in Bethel, Georgetown, and Danbury. Working title: *A Jest of God*; prerelease title: *Now I Lay Me Down.*

RACING FEVER   **F6.4000**
Racing Fever Productions. *Dist* Allied Artists. 1 Oct **1964** [Miami, Florida, opening]. Sd; col (Eastmancolor). 35mm. 90 min.

Prod-Dir-Writ William Grefé. *Assoc Prod* Joe A. Rodero. *Dir Photog* Julio C. Chavez. *Camera Op* J. R. Remy. *Lighting* M. Lavilla. *Camera Asst* F. Navila. *Film Ed* Oscar Barber. *Songs & Mus* Al Jacobs. *Title Song Sung by* Gerry Granahan. *Sd* Raul Corvizon. *Boom Op* R. Arias. *Unit Mgr* Theodore Gannon. *Script Supv* Perry Mavrelis. *Makeup* Carlos Perez, Francisca Perez. *Tech Adv* Ray Derome, Bob Moore, Bob Allard. *Prop* Doris Bernhardt. *Still Photog* Tony Gulliver. *Stunt Supv* Ron Von Klausen.

Cast: Joe Morrison (*Lee Gunner*), Charles G. Martin (*Gregg Stevenson*), Barbara G. Biggart (*Connie Stevenson*), Maxine Carroll (*Linda Gunner*), Dave Blanchard (*Pop Gunner*), Ruth Nadel (*Martha Stevenson*), John Vella (*Johnny*), Martha Coastworth (*dancer*), Ross Stone (*TV announcer*), Ben Hawkins (*mechanic*), Perry Mavrelis (*Richard Thompson*), Tony Gulliver (*man in bar*), Patty Morrison (*waitress*), Gerry Granahan.

Action melodrama. At the International Gran Prix boat race in Miami, hydroplane racer Lee Gunner sees his father killed by a boat piloted by millionaire playboy Gregg Stevenson. Linda, Lee's sister and Gregg's mistress, claims the killing was an accident. Suspicious, Lee visits Gregg's home and is told by his wife, Martha, that although she knows Gregg has other mistresses, she will not divorce him. Lee and Connie, Gregg's daughter, fall in love, and over the objections of her father, decide to marry. Linda discovers Gregg in a hotel room with a dancer, reveals that she is pregnant, and insists that he marry her. He refuses, and after the next race, during which Lee saves Gregg's life, Linda shoots Gregg as he returns to his yacht. Connie and Lee are reunited over Gregg's dead body. *Playboys. Mistresses. Boat racing. Infidelity. Pregnancy. Divorce. Revenge. Brother-sister relationship. Hydroplanes. Miami. Boating accidents.*

Note: Racing events filmed at the Miami Marine Stadium in Pelican Harbor, Florida.

RADIOGRAFIA D'UN COLPO D'ORO *see* **THEY CAME TO ROB LAS VEGAS**

RADISHES AND CARROTS *see* **TWILIGHT PATH**

RAFFICA DI COLTELLI *see* **KNIVES OF THE AVENGER**

RAG DOLL see **YOUNG, WILLING AND EAGER**

UNA RAGAZZA A SAINT TROPEZ see **THE GENDARME OF ST. TROPEZ**

LA RAGAZZA CHE SAPEVA TROPPO see **EVIL EYE**

LA RAGAZZA CON LA VALIGIA see **GIRL WITH A SUITCASE**

LA RAGAZZA DI BUBE see **BEBO'S GIRL**

LA RAGAZZA E IL GENERALE see **THE GIRL AND THE GENERAL**

LA RAGAZZA IN PRESTITO see **ENGAGEMENT ITALIANO**

UNA RAGAZZA PER L'ESTATE see **A MISTRESS FOR THE SUMMER**

RAGE (United States/Mexico)   **F6.4001**
Cinematográfica Jalisco–Joseph M. Schenck Enterprises. *Dist* Columbia Pictures. 30 Nov **1966** [Boston opening; c31 Dec 1966; LP34009]. Sd (RCA); col (Eastman Color by Pathé). 35mm. 103 min.
Prod-Dir Gilberto Gazcón. *Exec Prod* Richard Goldstone. *Exec in Charge of Prod for Cinematográfica Jalisco* Edgardo Gazcón. *Screenplay* Teddi Sherman, Gilberto Gazcón, Fernando Méndez. *Story* Jesús Velázquez, writ, Guillermo Hernández, Gilberto Gazcón. *Dir Photog* Rosalío Solano. *Art Dir* Ramón Rodríguez Granada. *Film Ed* Carlos Savage, Walter Thompson. *Mus Comp & Cond* Gustavo César Carrión. *Mus Perf by* Filarmónicos del S.T.P.C. de la R.M. *Sd Eff Ed* José Li' Ho. *Sd Engr* Luis Fernández. *Re-rec* Galdino Samperio. *Sd Supv* James L. Fields. *Asst Dir* Sigfrido García, Jesús Marin. *Prod Mgr* Jorge Cardena. *Script Supv* José Luis Ortega. *Miss Stevens' Dresses* Mario Huarte. *Hairstyles* Dorothy White, Guadalupe Gorraez. *Dial Coach* Harold Clifton, Stim Segar.
Cast: Glenn Ford *(Reuben)*, Stella Stevens *(Perla)*, David Reynoso *(Pancho)*, Armando Silvestre *(Antonio)*, Ariadne Welter *(Blanca)*, José Elías Moreno *(Fortunato)*, Dacia González *(Maria)*, Pancho Cordova *(old man)*, Susana Cabrera *(his wife)*, David Silva *(bus driver)*, Quintín Bulnes *(Pedro)*, Valentín Trujillo *(José)*, Maura Monti, Isala Vega, Jorge Russek, Raúl Martínez, José Angel Espinosa, Gilda Miros, Stim Segar, Alicia Gutirrez, Anita Morgan.
Melodrama. At an isolated construction camp in the barren Mexican desert, Reuben, an American doctor, ministers to the sick while simultaneously trying to drown in alcohol the memory of his wife and unborn child who died when he was forced to perform an emergency delivery. One day a troupe of girl "entertainers" led by the worldly-wise Perla pays a visit to the camp. Perla is attracted to the brooding Reuben, but he repulses her advances, preferring to be alone with his bottle of whiskey. Shortly after Perla is left behind accidentally by the troupe, one of the construction workers dies from rabies; and, after Perla has moved on, Reuben discovers that he too has contracted the disease from his pet dog. With only 48 hours to reach a medical center where treatment is available, Reuben's departure is delayed when one of the workers, Pancho, forces him at gunpoint to perform a cesarean delivery on his wife. Once the baby has safely arrived, the grateful Pancho insists upon joining Reuben in his race against time. En route, they pick up Perla and—despite a shortage of fuel, the agonizing breakdown of their jeep, a blinding sandstorm, and a torturous trek under the blistering sun—they eventually reach their destination. Mainly through Perla's persistent encouragement, Reuben has found a new will to live. Perla, however, is less certain of her own future. *Physicians. Prostitutes. Americans in foreign countries. Alcoholism. Guilt. Death. Childbirth. Construction camps. Rabies. Deserts. Dogs.*
Note: Location scenes filmed in Mexico. Produced in Mexico in 1965 as *El mal.*

RAGE OF THE BUCCANEERS (Italy)   **F6.4002**
Max Production. *Dist* Colorama Features. 25 Apr **1963** [Maryland license]. Sd; col (Eastmancolor). 35mm (Totalscope). 90 min.
An Ottavio Poggi Production. *Prod* Ottavio Poggi. *Dir* Mario Costa. *Screenplay* Ottavio Poggi, John Byrne. *Photog* Mario Bellero. *Art Dir* Ernesto Kromberg, Amedeo Mellone. *Film Ed* Renato Cinquini. *Mus* Carlo Rustichelli. *Sd* Raffaele Del Monte, Fiorenzo Magli. *Fencing Master* Andrea Fantasia, Franco Fantasia.
Cast: Ricardo Montalban *(Gordon, the Black Buccaneer)*, Vincent Price *(Romero)*, Giulia Rubini *(Manuela)*, Liana Orfei *(Luana)*, Mario Feliciani *(Tortuga)*, Gisella Sofio, Giustino Durano, José Jaspe, Edoardo Toniolo, Andrea Fantasia, Gino Marturano.
Action melodrama. In his campaign against the slave trade, Gordon, the Black Buccaneer, who once was a slave, disguises himself and goes to the slavers' base in San Salvador. Unmasked by his old enemy Tortuga, whose life he had spared in return for a promise to renounce the slave trade, Gordon is condemned to death through the treachery of the governor's secretary,

Romero, who is the secret head of the slave traffic. The buccaneer escapes from prison, however, with the help of his devoted Creole companion, Luana, and the governor's daughter, Manuela. After Romero seizes power and imprisons Manuela, the buccaneer mounts an attack. Though Luana is killed in the fighting, the buccaneer captures the villain, frees Manuela, and then, with the governor's consent, marries her. *Pirates. Slavers. Creoles. Disguise. Slavery. Prison escapes. Colonial administration. San Salvador.*
Note: Opened in Rome in Jul 1962 as *Gordon il Pirata Nero*; running time: 91 min.

A RAGE TO LIVE   **F6.4003**
Mirisch Corp.–Rage Productions. *Dist* United Artists. 15 Sep **1965** [Chicago opening; c26 Jul 1965; LP32178]. Sd (Westrex); b&w. 35mm (Panavision). 101 min.
Pres by Mirisch Corp. *Prod* Lewis J. Rachmil. *Dir* Walter Grauman. *Screenplay* John T. Kelley. *Dir Photog* Charles Lawton. *Art Dir* James Sullivan. *Set Decor* Ray Boltz. *Film Ed* Stuart Gilmore. *Mus* Nelson Riddle. *Orch* Gil Grau. *Theme:* "Rage To Live" *comp & played by* Arthur Ferrante, Louis Teicher. *Lyr by* Noel Sherman. *Sd* Al Overton, Jr. *Mus Ed* Richard Carruth. *Sd Eff Ed* Gil Marchant. *Asst Dir* Emmett Emerson. *Prod Mgr* Allen K. Wood. *Script Supv* Doris Grau. *Cost Dsgn* Howard Shoup. *Wardrobe* Russ Hamlin, Paula Giokaris. *Makeup* Stanley Campbell. *Hairdresser* Doris Durkus. *Sp Eff* Norman Breedlove. *Prop* Arthur Friedrich. *Dial Supv* Leon Charles. *Casting* Lynn Stalmaster.
Cast: Suzanne Pleshette *(Grace Caldwell)*, Bradford Dillman *(Sidney Tate)*, Ben Gazzara *(Roger Bannon)*, Peter Graves *(Jack Hollister)*, Bethel Leslie *(Amy Hollister)*, Carmen Mathews *(Emily Caldwell)*, Linden Chiles *(Brock Caldwell)*, James Gregory *(Dr. O'Brien)*, Ruth White *(Mrs. Bannon)*, Mark Goddard *(Charlie Jay)*, Sarah Marshall *(Connie Schoffstall)*, George Furth *(Paul Reichelderfer)*, Virginia Christine *(Emma)*, Brett Somers *(Jessie Jay)*, Frank Maxwell *(George Jay)*.
Melodrama. Source: John O'Hara, *A Rage To Live* (New York, 1949). Grace Caldwell, a wealthy college student who craves male attention, has an affair with Charlie Jay, whose parents find out and tell Grace's widowed mother. Mrs. Caldwell, who suffers from a heart condition, suspects the extent of her daughter's promiscuity and travels with her to Nassau for a vacation. While Grace becomes involved with a hotel waiter, her mother has a heart attack and dies from lack of care. Her brother Brock introduces Grace to a college friend, Sidney Tate, who consoles her after her mother's death, and they decide to marry. Grace explains her past to Sidney, but he insists that their love will overcome her desire for other men. For 2 1/2 years they live happily on a farm and have a baby boy; then Roger Bannon, a self-made building construction manager and the son of one of her mother's former servants, rebuilds their barn. He makes advances to Grace, and she succumbs. Jack Hollister, a successful editor and self-righteous hypocrite, tries to make love to Grace, but she refuses his attentions. Fearing the impairment of relations with her husband, she decides to end her affair with Roger; and when she notifies Roger he gets drunk, mistreats a waitress, and dies in a subsequent car crash. When police investigate the death, Grace's affair becomes public knowledge, whereupon Sidney threatens to leave her if her promiscuity continues. At a charity bazaar, the jealous wife of Jack Hollister publicly denounces Grace as the cause of her own failing marriage. Though Grace insists upon her innocence, Jack, bitter from rejection, does not deny the accusation, and Sidney abandons Grace. *Students. Widows. Construction foremen. Editors. Waiters. Police. Promiscuity. Filial relations. Marriage. Farm life. Infidelity. Hypocrisy. Drunkenness. Scandal. Jealousy. Heart disease. Nassau. Pennsylvania. Automobile accidents.*
Note: Copyright claimants: Mirisch Corp. and Araho Corp.

THE RAGE WITHIN see **LA RABIA (THE RAGE)**

RAGINA'S SECRETS   **F6.4004**
Fine-Flick-Film Productions. *Dist* Fine Products. 17 Sep **1969** [New York showing]. Sd; col. 35mm. 67 min.
Prod Jerry Jackson. *Dir-Script* Fletcher Hand. *Film Ed* Slash Cutts, Rip N. Tear. *Mus* The Chastity Belts.
Cast: Elizabeth Traylor, Konnie Kooze, Sandy Paws, Gloria Gold, The Degenerate.
Sex film. Ragina, seeking to understand her own sexuality, visits Dr. Will C. Byrd. Ragina tells her life story: an odyssey of sex, sadism, orgies, and drugs. Telling the tale so arouses her that Dr. Byrd's office soon becomes the scene of an all-out orgy involving the nurse, the doctor, another patient, and Ragina. *Psychiatrists. Nurses. Promiscuity. Sadism. Lesbianism. Lust. Group sex. Orgies. Narcotics.*
Note: This film is also known as *Dr. Byrd, Dr. Byrd Unlocks Ragina's Secrets,* and *Regina's Secret.*

THE RAIDERS
F6.4005

Revue Productions. *Dist* Universal Pictures. 12 Feb **1964** [Los Angeles opening; c23 May 1964; LP35485]. Sd (RCA); col (Eastman Color by Pathé). 35mm. 75 min.

Prod Howard Christie. *Dir* Herschel Daugherty. *Screenplay* Gene L. Coon. *Ed Dept Head* David J. O'Connell. *Dir Photog* Bud Thackery. *Art Dir* Alexander A. Mayer. *Set Decor* John McCarthy, Robert C. Bradfield. *Main Titl* Pacific Title. *Film Ed* Gene Palmer. *Mus* Morton Stevens. *Sd* David H. Moriarty. *Asst Dir* Edward K. Dodds. *Cost Supv* Vincent Dee. *Makeup* Jack Barron. *Hairstyles* Florence Bush.

Cast: Robert Culp (*James Butler "Wild Bill" Hickok*), Brian Keith (*John G. McElroy*), Judi Meredith (*Martha "Calamity Jane" Canary*), James McMullan (*William F. "Buffalo Bill" Cody*), Alfred Ryder (*Captain Benton*), Simon Oakland (*Sgt. Austin Tremaine*), Ben Cooper (*Tom King*), Trevor Bardette (*"Uncle Otto" Strassner*), Harry Carey, Jr. (*Jellicoe*), Richard Cutting (*Jack Goodnight*), Addison Richards (*Huntington Lawford*), Cliff Osmond (*Duchamps*), Paul Birch (*Paul King*), Richard Deacon (*Commissioner Mailer*), Michael Burns (*Jimmy McElroy*).

Western drama. After the Civil War, former Confederate Col. John G. McElroy leaves west Texas with six neighboring ranchers to drive their cattle to the nearest railway stockyard at Hays City, Kansas, but they lose their entire stock to a gang of rustling carpetbaggers as they enter the Six Nations Indian lands in Oklahoma territory. This convinces them that they must have an extension of the railroad to their area. They continue on to Hays City to make their demands and are told by the manager of the Kansas and Pacific Railroad, who is behind schedule in building tracks to Pueblo, that the planned routes west will not detour south into Texas. Impatient, they band together into a group known as the Raiders, attacking only the railroad. Wild Bill Hickok and Buffalo Bill Cody are working for the Army under the command of Captain Benton, who is determined to avenge the railroad's losses and those of Calamity Jane, who is shipping equipment west for the railroad construction. Benton plans an ambush and orders the Raiders machine-gunned, but Hickok and Buffalo Bill intervene and take McElroy and his friends into custody. They persuade the Raiders to return to their ranches and then convince the Kansas and Pacific officials to push a line through to Abilene, Kansas. *Confederate veterans. Cattlemen. Rustlers. Carpetbaggers. Railroad superintendents. Revenge. Texas. Hays City (Kansas). Oklahoma. Indian Territory. Martha Jane Burke. William Frederick Cody. James Butler Hickok. United States Army—Cavalry. Kansas and Pacific Railroad.*

Note: Working title: *The Plainsman.*

RAIDERS FROM BENEATH THE SEA
F6.4006

Lippert, Inc. *Dist* Twentieth Century-Fox Film Corp. 16 Dec **1964** [Los Angeles opening; c25 Nov 1964; LP29685]. Sd; b&w. 35mm. 73 min.

Prod-Dir Maury Dexter. *Assoc Prod-Story* F. Paul Hall. *Screenplay* Harry Spalding. *Dir Photog* Floyd Crosby. *Set Decor* Harry Reif. *Supv Film Ed* Carl Pierson. *Mus Supv* "By" Dunham. *Song:* "The Raiders Theme" Hank Levine. *Song:* "Two Lovers Theme" Hank Levine, Jim Economides. *Sd* Burdick S. Trask. *Asst Dir* Willard Kirkham. *Prod Mgr* Willard Kirkham. *Asst to the Prod* Hank Tani. *Script Supv* Betty Crosby. *Wardrobe* Joseph Dimmitt. *Makeup* Harry Thomas. *Prop Master* Jockey Liebgold.

Cast: Ken Scott (*Bill Harper*), Merry Anders (*Dottie Harper*), Russ Bender (*Tucker*), Booth Colman (*Purdy*), Garth Benton (*Buddy*), Bruce Anson, Walter Maslow (*policemen*), Stacey Winters (*bank teller*), Ray Dannis (*Bowman*), Larry Barton (*bank manager*), Roger Creed (*bank guard*).

Crime melodrama. Ex-diver Bill Harper is an apartment house manager who lives with his wife, Dottie, and his brother Buddy. Bill, a failure in life, plans to rob a bank, and he recruits the aid of an old friend, Tucker. They are visited by Purdy, who originally gave Bill the idea for the robbery, and Bill and Tucker reluctantly include him in the robbery. While Bill and Tucker are taking their diving equipment to Catalina Island, Buddy attempts to rape Dottie. Bill returns in time to witness the violent scene. Dottie throws Buddy out and announces that she is planning to leave Bill. On the day of the robbery, Bill and Tucker swim underwater to Catalina Island while Buddy and Purdy cruise around the bay in a rented boat. Emerging from the water carrying spear guns, Bill and Tucker enter a bank and are forced to kill a man. They place the money in a waterproof bag and race to a pier. Tucker suffers a heart attack, and a police bullet pierces Bill's air tank as he dives into the water. He reaches the steamer where Buddy and Purdy are waiting, but the steamer's propellers suck him to his death. While Dottie watches from the pier, Buddy and Purdy are arrested by the police, and the money sack floats to the surface. *Brothers. Divers. Apartment house managers. Police. Bank robberies. Rape. Murder. Motorboats. Spear guns. Ships. Heart disease. Santa Catalina (California).*

THE RAIDERS OF LEYTE GULF (United States/Philippines)
F6.4007

Lynro Pictures. *Dist* Hemisphere Pictures, Manhattan Films International. 19 Aug **1963** [New York showing]. Sd; b&w. 35mm. 80 min.

Prod-Dir Eddie Romero. *Exec Prod* Kane W. Lynn. *Screenplay* E. F. Romero, Carl Kuntze. *Photog* Felipe Sacdalan. *Film Ed* E. F. Romero. *Mus* Tito Arevalo.

Cast: Jennings Sturgeon (*Emmett Wilson*), Michael Parsons (*Lieut. Robert Grimm*), Efren Reyes (*Capt. Shirai Akira*), Eddie Mesa (*Angel Zabala*), Leopoldo Salcedo (*Col. Lino Sebastian*), Liza Moreno (*Aida Rivas*), Oscar Keesee (*Leon Magpayo*).

War melodrama. U. S. intelligence officer Emmett Wilson is captured by the Japanese while making a coastal survey of Leyte during World War II. Torture fails to extract the American invasion plans from him, and the Japanese begin to execute one Filipino a day, threatening to continue until Wilson talks. Another American soldier, Lieut. Robert Grimm, parachutes into the hills held by Filipino guerrillas and persuades the guerrillas to attack the Japanese and rescue Wilson. The attack fails, the executions continue, and the horrified Wilson goes to Captain Akira, the Japanese commander, to reveal the plans. A Filipino, one of an angry crowd protesting the executions, sees Wilson and Akira together and, suspecting treachery, shoots Wilson. The Japanese turn their guns on the crowd, but the guerrillas attack again before Akira can organize his men. The dying Wilson bayonets Akira, the guerrillas defeat the Japanese garrison, and, a short time later, Gen. Douglas MacArthur leads the American invasion of the islands. *Guerrillas. Military invasion. Torture. Capital punishment. Perfidy. World War II. Leyte. Douglas MacArthur. United States Army. Japan—Army.*

Note: Filmed at Leyte in the Philippines. Closing sequences include newsreel footage of Gen. Douglas MacArthur returning to the Philippines.

THE RAILROAD MAN (Italy)
F6.4008

Carlo Ponti-Dino De Laurentiis Cinematografica-ENIC. *Dist* Continental Distributing, Inc. 24 Oct **1965** [New York opening]. Sd; b&w. 35mm. 105 min.

Prod Carlo Ponti. *Dir* Pietro Germi. *Screenplay (see note)* Pietro Germi, Alfredo Giannetti, Luciano Vincenzoni, Ennio De Concini. *Story* Alfredo Giannetti. *Photog* Leonida Barboni. *Cinematog (see note)* Aiace Parolin. *Art Dir* Carlo Egidi. *Film Ed* Dolores Tamburini. *Mus* Carlo Rustichelli. *Mus Dir* Franco Ferrara. *Sd* Roy Mangano. *Prod Mgr* Luigi Giacosi. *Cost* Mirella Morelli.

Cast: Pietro Germi (*Andrea Marcocci*), Luisa Della Noce (*Sara Marcocci*), Sylva Koscina (*Giulia*), Saro Urzi (*Liverani*), Renato Speziali (*Renato*), Carlo Giuffre (*Marcello*), Edoardo Nevola (*Sandrino*), Amedeo Trilli.

Drama. Andrea Marcocci, an aging but proud railroad engineer, is the idol of his young son Sandrino. The rest of the family, however, finds Andrea difficult to get along with. Although the family frequently engages in bitter arguments, Andrea would rather drink and play the guitar than discuss matters of importance. Andrea forces his daughter Giulia to marry the man whose child she is expecting, though Giulia knows that the man does not love her. She loses the baby and takes up with another man. Shaken when his train kills a suicide, Andrea drives through a red light. As a result, he is removed from his job on the passenger train and demoted to driving a freight train. Andrea loses all his friends by taking a train out on the regular schedule during an official strike, and he quits work. Meanwhile, the family situation deteriorates: Marcello, the elder son, and Giulia are thrown out of the house, and even Sandrino is taken to the police station for throwing a rock through the window of Giulia's boyfriend's car. Andrea, now out of work and friendless, finds solace in Sandrino's good performance in school. The two visit the pub where in former days Andrea enjoyed drinking. Unprepared for the welcome he receives from his old friends, Andrea suffers a serious stroke. The family gathers to celebrate Christmas, and reconciliations seem to be near, but Andrea, already broken in spirit, dies while playing his guitar. *Railroad engineers. Pregnancy. Pride. Family life. Infidelity. Marriage. Strokes. Bars.*

Note: Released in Italy in 1965 under the title *Il ferroviere*; running time: 116 min. Also known as *Man of Iron*. Aiace Parolin is credited as cinematographer by one source, while other sources credit Leonida Barboni. Ennio De Concini is not given screenplay credit in most sources.

THE RAIN PEOPLE
F6.4009

American Zoetrope. *Dist* Warner Bros.-Seven Arts, Inc. 27 Aug **1969** [New York opening; c1 Oct 1969; LP37990]. Sd; col (Technicolor). 35mm. 102 min. *MPAA rating* R.

Pres by Francis Ford Coppola. *Prod* Bart Patton, Ronald Colby. *Prod Assoc* George Lucas, Mona Skager. *Dir-Writ* Francis Ford Coppola. *Photog* Wilmer Butler. *Camera Op* Ralph Gerling. *Art Dir* Leon Ericksen. *Film Ed* Blackie Malkin. *Mus* Ronald Stein. *Mus Assoc* Carmen Coppola. *Sd* Nat Boxer. *Sd Montage* Walter Murch. *Asst Dir* Richard C. Bennett, Jack Cunningham. *Participating in Prod* John Blair, prod, Tony Dingman, Marcia Griffin, William Neil, Sully Sullivan, Sharon Compton, Ken Gagnon, Charles Hannawalt, Tom

Ryan, Fred Talmage, Joel Cox, Tom Gavin, Richard Marks, James Sabat, Steve Wilson.

Cast: James Caan (*Jimmie "Killer" Kilgannon*), Shirley Knight (*Natalie Ravenna*), Robert Duvall (*Gordon*), Marya Zimmet (*Rosalie*), Tom Aldredge (*Mr. Alfred*), Laurie Crewes (*Ellen*), Andrew Duncan (*Artie*), Margaret Fairchild (*Marion*), Sally Gracie (*Beth*), Alan Manson (*Lou*), Robert Modica (*Vinny Ravenna*).

Drama. Pregnant Long Island housewife Natalie Ravenna deserts her husband. While driving on the Pennsylvania Turnpike she picks up former college athlete Jimmie Kilgannon. Touched by the revelation that the young man has suffered brain damage during a football game, the housewife drives the athlete to West Virginia, where he has been promised employment by the father of his former girl friend. The family, however, is repelled by Kilgannon, and Natalie persuades him to accompany her to Chattanooga, where she tries unsuccessfully to drop him off. In Nebraska she places the youth as a handyman at a reptile zoo. Speeding from the town she is apprehended by widowed motorcycle policeman Gordon and subsequently fined by Justice of the Peace Alfred, Kilgannon's treacherous employer. When the athlete releases abused animals from their cages, Alfred fires Kilgannon, exacting $800 from the young man's $1,000 savings. As Gordon entertains Natalie in his mobile home, the couple is observed by the athlete and the policeman's adolescent daughter Rosalie. When the officer attempts to make love to the housewife he is assaulted by Kilgannon. Alarmed, Rosalie shoots and kills the youth. *Housewives. Hitchhikers. Handymen. Athletes. Police. Widowers. Justices of the peace. Desertion. Brain damage. Marriage. Pregnancy. Murder. Trailers. Football. Zoos. Long Island. West Virginia. Pennsylvania. Chattanooga. Nebraska. Snakes.*

Note: Location scenes filmed in New York, West Virginia, Tennessee, Nebraska, and Colorado.

A RAISIN IN THE SUN   F6.4010

Paman-Doris Productions. *Dist* Columbia Pictures. 29 Mar **1961** [New York opening; c1 Apr 1961; LP20541]. Sd; b&w. 35mm. 128 min.

Prod David Susskind, Philip Rose. *Dir* Daniel Petrie. *Screenplay* Lorraine Hansberry. *Photog* Charles Lawton, Jr. *Art Dir* Carl Anderson. *Film Ed* William A. Lyon, Paul Weatherwax. *Mus* Laurence Rosenthal. *Orch* Arthur Morton. *Sd* Charles J. Rice, George Cooper. *Asst Dir* Sam Nelson. *Makeup* Ben Lane. *Hairstyles* Helen Hunt.

Cast: Sidney Poitier (*Walter Lee Younger*), Claudia McNeil (*Lena Younger*), Ruby Dee (*Ruth Younger*), Diana Sands (*Beneatha Younger*), Ivan Dixon (*Asagai*), John Fiedler (*Mark Lindner*), Louis Gossett (*George Murchison*), Stephen Perry (*Travis Younger*), Joel Fluellen (*Bobo*), Roy Glenn (*Willie Harris*), Ray Stubbs (*bartender*), Rudolph Monroe (*taxi driver*), George DeNormand (*employer*), Louis Terkel (*Herman*), Thomas D. Jones (*chauffeur*).

Drama. Source: Lorraine Hansberry, *A Raisin in the Sun* (New York opening: 11 Mar 1959). The Youngers are a Negro family living in three crowded, sunless rooms on Chicago's South Side. The squalid routine of their lives is suddenly disrupted when Lena Younger receives a $10,000 check from the company that insured her late husband. Lena wants to use the money to buy a house and to help her daughter, Beneatha, finish medical school. Lena's son, Walter Lee, however, wants to invest the money in a liquor store so he can rise above his status of chauffeur for a wealthy white man. Lena disapproves of the idea and makes a down payment of $3,500 on a small house in a white neighborhood. Frustrated and enraged, Walter Lee quarrels with his mother and his wife, Ruth, and storms out of the flat. He stays away from work for 3 days, and Lena finds him in a bar. She offers him the remaining $6,500 ($3,500 of which is to be set aside for Beneatha's education). Once more united and optimistic, the family prepares to move into their new home. Not even a visit from a hypocritical representative of an "improvement association," who offers to buy back the house at a higher price to preserve the community's all-white character, can alter their decision to move. Then their world collapses. Unknown to the rest of the family, Walter Lee invests the entire $6,500 in a liquor store and is swindled. Realizing he has betrayed his mother's trust, threatened his sister's future, and thrown away his father's life savings, Walter Lee desperately decides to accept the "improvement association" 's offer. But under the eyes of his entire family, he sees that such a move is only a step backwards, and he once more rejects the offer. Though it means hard work and years of sacrifice for all, the Youngers make their move. *Widows. Chauffeurs. Swindlers. Negro life. Family life. Racial integration. Racial prejudice. Insurance. Inheritance. Liquor stores. Chicago—South Side.*

Note: Location scenes filmed in Chicago.

RAISING THE WIND *see* ROOMMATES

LA RAISON AVANT LA PASSION (Canada)   F6.4011

Dist Film-Makers' Cooperative. Dec **1969** [New York showing]. Sd; col. 16mm. 80 min. [Cut from 90 min.]

Prod-Dir Joyce Wieland. *Photog* Joyce Wieland. *Film Ed* Joyce Wieland.

Documentary. In a prelude, the singing of Canada's national anthem, "O Canada," is filmed without sound, and images of Canada's maple leaf flag, adopted in 1965, appear. The body of the film is structured in three sections. The first and third parts are comprised of recorded impressions of a journey across Canada, beginning on Cape Breton and ending in Vancouver. The landscape is seen in all seasons and hours, in varying exposures, photographed in many cases from moving trains or cars. Prime Minister Pierre Elliott Trudeau's assertion "La raison avant la passion; c'est le thème de tous mes écrits" ("reason over passion; that is the theme of all my writing") introduces the first section. While images of Canada succeed each other, the phrase "reason over passion" appears as a yellow superimposition on the lower half of the frame in 537 permutations. In the middle section, a French lesson (a reference to Trudeau's affirmation of the principle of bilingualism) is heard on the soundtrack. A study of Trudeau follows, in which the prime minister, filmed at the 1968 Liberal Party convention, is viewed in intimate slow motion and freeze-frame passages. *Bilingualism. Political conventions. Pierre Elliott Trudeau. Liberal Party (Canada).*

Note: Shown in Canada caJun 1969. Also known as *Reason Over Passion* and *La raison avant la passion, Reason Over Passion, a Corrective Film.*

RAMPAGE   F6.4012

Talbot Productions–Seven Arts Productions. *Dist* Warner Bros. Pictures. 9 Oct **1963** [Los Angeles opening; c12 Oct 1963; LP29449]. Sd; col (Technicolor). 35mm. 98 min.

Prod William Fadiman. *Assoc Prod* Thomas D. Tannenbaum. *Dir* Phil Karlson. *2d Unit Dir* Richard Talmadge. *Screenplay* Robert I. Holt, Marguerite Roberts. *Photog* Harold Lipstein. *Art Dir* Herman Blumenthal. *Set Decor* George James Hopkins. *Film Ed* Gene Milford. *Mus* Elmer Bernstein. *Titl Song* Elmer Bernstein, Mack David. *Sd* Stanley Jones. *Asst Dir* Clark Paylow. *Miss Martinelli's Clothes* Oleg Cassini. *Makeup* Gordon Bau. *Hairstyles* Jean Burt Reilly.

Cast: Robert Mitchum (*Harry Stanton*), Elsa Martinelli (*Anna*), Jack Hawkins (*Otto Abbot*), Sabu (*Talib*), Cely Carrilo (*Chep*), Emile Genest (*Schelling*), Stefan Schnabel (*Sakai chief*), David Cadiente (*Baka*), John Keaka (*Malay warrior*).

Adventure drama. Source: Alan Caillou, *Rampage* (New York, 1961). Big game trapper Harry Stanton is commissioned by a West German zoo to go to the Malay jungle and capture a rare breed of cat called "The Enchantress," a combination of tiger and leopard. Accompanying him is Otto Abbot, a professional hunter, and Otto's mistress Anna. After netting two tigers, they set out after their prize quarry. Friction develops between the two men when Harry makes it apparent that he intends to take Anna away from Otto, although Anna rejects the trapper's advances. They trap the sought-after animal in a cave, and Otto tries to prove himself by entering the cave armed only with a blazing torch. He is badly mauled; but Harry comes to the rescue and captures the huge cat. Once back in Germany, Anna admits to Otto that she has fallen in love with Harry. While they are taking the Enchantress to its destination by freight train, the jealous Otto releases the animal when Harry is alone with it in the baggage car; but his life is saved when the van doors are opened, and the cat leaps from the train. After killing a janitor, the cat stalks the roof of an apartment house. Harry and Anna, both armed, follow it, only to discover that Otto is already on the trail. He attempts to shoot Harry but instead is killed by the snarling cat, which is then shot by Anna. *Trappers. Hunters. Mistresses. Jealousy. Revenge. Zoos. Jungles. Caves. Trains. Malaya. Federal Republic of Germany. Tigers. Leopards.*

Note: Location scenes filmed in Hawaii and the San Diego Zoo. Also known as *Jungle Rampage.*

RAMPAGE AT APACHE WELLS (West Germany/Yugoslavia)   F6.4013

Rialto Film-Jadran Film. *Dist* Columbia Pictures. Jan **1966**. Sd; col (Eastmancolor). 35mm (UltraScope). 91 min.

Prod Horst Wendlandt. *Dir* Harald Philipp. *Screenplay* Fred Denger, Harald Philipp. *Photog* Heinz Hölscher. *Art Dir* Duško Jeričević. *Film Ed* Hermann Haller. *Mus* Martin Böttcher. *Sd* Matija Barbalić. *Prod Supv* Wolfgang Kühnlenz. *Prod Mgr* Alfred Arbeiter, Herbert Kerz, Wolfgang Hantke. *Cost* Irms Pauli. *Wardrobe* Helmut Preuss. *Makeup* Erich-Lothar Schmekel, Claire Fussbach. *Sp Eff* Erwin Lange. *Prop* Otto Fechtner.

Cast: Stewart Granger (*Old Surehand*), Pierre Brice (*Winnetou*), Macha Méril (*Lizzy*), Harald Leipnitz (*The Oil Prince*), Mario Girotti (*Richard Forsythe*), Antje Weisgerber (*Frau Ebersbach*), Walter Barnes (*Campbell*), Gerd Frickhöffer (*Kovacz*), Paddy Fox (*Old Wabble*), Heinz Erhardt (*Kantor Hampel*), Vladimir Leib (*Duncan*), Dušan Janićijević (*Butler*), Slobodan Dimitrijević (*Knife*), Davor Antolić (*Paddy*), Veljko Maričić (*Bergmann*). Ilija

Ivezić (*Webster*), Zvonimir Črnko (*Billy Forner*), Petar Petrović (*Jimmy*), Slobodan Vedernjak (*John*), Branko Supek (*Jack*), Marinko Ćosić (*Tobby*).

Western drama. Source: Karl Friedrich May, *Der Ölprinz* (Stuttgart, 1893). When Old Surehand and his Apache blood brother Winnetou learn that their friend, Billy Forner, a wagon master, was killed by the Fingers Gang, Surehand volunteers to lead the wagon train. Winnetou negotiates with the Navajos to ensure the settlers' safe passage to Lake Shelly, but the Oil Prince, intent on keeping settlers' land for an oil well swindle, frames the Navajo chief's son as a robber and then kills him. The Navajos, who believe that the settlers are responsible for the murder, attack the wagon train, but Surehand arrives and exposes the Oil Prince's guilt. Surehand and Winnetou apprehend the Oil Prince and the Fingers Gang, and the wagon train moves on to Lake Shelly. *Wagon masters. Apache Indians. Blood brothers. Settlers. Navajo Indians. Swindlers. Oilmen. Frameup. Murder. Revenge. Wagon trains. Winnetou.*

Note: Released in West Germany in Aug 1965 as *Der Ölprinz*; in Yugoslavia in 1965 as *Kralj petroleja*.

THE RAMRODDER   **F6.4014**
  E. S. I. Productions. *Dist* Entertainment Ventures, Inc. 23 Jan **1969** [San Francisco showing]. Sd; col (Eastmancolor). 35mm. 92 min.
  Dir-Writ Van Guylder. *Dir Photog* Bob Maxwell. *Art Dir* Bud Costello. *Mus Supv* Giovanni. *Sd Rec* Jim Economides. *Asst Dir* Roger Gentry. *Asst to the Prod* Jim Economides. *Script Supv* Nancy Barney.
  Cast: Jim Gentry (*The Ramrodder*), Julia Blackburn (*Lucy*), Brave Eagle (*Chief*), Kathy Williams (*Tuwana*), David Rosenkranz, Bob Beausoleil, Kathy Share, Kedric Wolfe, Marsha Jordan.
  Western melodrama. In the late 19th century American West, Rick, a ramrodder, builds a personal empire using his friendship with the Indians. He is the only white man to have an affair with Princess Tuwana. A trail bum rapes and kills an Indian maiden, and Rick is unjustly accused. In retaliation, the Indians rape a settler's daughter. When Tuwana confesses that she has slept with Rick, her Indian fiancé whips her. Rick captures the white rapist, who is given to the Indians and castrated. Rick's heroics prevent an Indian war, and he marries Tuwana. *Ranchers. Indians of North America. Royalty. Rape. Injustice. Revenge. Castration. Murder. Miscegenation.*
  Note: Also known as *Ramrodders*.

RANCH HAND   **F6.4015**
  Dist Stacey Distributors. ca **1970**. Sd; col. 16mm. 61-81 min.
  Sex film. No information about the precise nature of this film has been found. *Sexuality. Ranch life.*

LA RANCUNE *see* **THE VISIT**

RANI RADOVI *see* **EARLY WORKS**

THE RANSOM   **F6.4016**
  Dist Stacey Distributors. ca **1970**. Sd; col. 16mm. 61-81 min.
  Sex film. No information about the precise nature of this film has been found. *Sexuality. Ransom.*

THE RAPE (Greece)   **F6.4017**
  Finos Films. *Dist* Zenith International Film Corp. 8 Sep **1965** [New York opening]. Sd; b&w. 35mm. 86 min.
  Dir Dinos Dimopoulos. *Screenplay* Dinos Dimopoulos, Lazaros Montanaris. *Photog* Nikos Kavoudikis. *Mus Comp & Cond* Stavros Xarhakos.
  Cast: Lefteris Vournas (*Peter*), Zoras Tsapelis (*Johann*), Zetta Apostolou (*Fanny*), Floretta Zana (*Sarah*), Anna Veneti (*Anna*).
  Melodrama. Ten women escape from a reformatory in Greece and hide on an island they believe to be deserted; but seven men, led by ex-Nazi Johann and his son Peter, are searching for a treasure buried on the island. The men find the fugitive women and force them to do the digging for the treasure. The women, believing that they will be murdered when the treasure is found, attempt to kill the men with dynamite they have stolen from Johann's boat. Sarah, a Jew, cannot tolerate further violence, and she throws the dynamite into the sea, where it explodes harmlessly. The Germans then beat and rape the women at Johann's orders. The women force Sarah to lure Peter into a trap so that he may be used as a hostage. Peter is captured, but his companions release him; he then demands that he personally be granted the privilege of disposing of Sarah. He takes her to the other side of the island, but, instead of killing her, he sets her free to swim to the mainland. One of the women, Fanny, subsequently dies of a beating administered by Johann's men, and her best friend digs a grave for her. In the process of digging the grave, she finds the treasure but buries Fanny with it. Sarah then returns with the police, and Johann is shot while trying to resist arrest. *Germans. Fugitives. Hostages. Nazis. Jews. Police. Rape. Treasure. Explosives. Islands.*
  Note: Produced in Greece in 1964 as *Amok*.

RAPE (Austria)   **F6.4018**
  Dist Yoko Ono, John Lennon. Dec **1969** [Berkeley, California, showing]. Sd; 16mm. 80 min.
  Dir Yoko Ono. *Assoc* (see note) John Lennon.
  Allegory. The camera follows a young German woman in London as she takes a walk in a cemetery, moves through the streets, and eventually reaches her apartment. The woman is annoyed by the presence of the camera; she becomes increasingly upset and tries to escape its persistent shadow. Locked in her apartment, she frantically seeks an exit. *Rape. Voyeurism. Motion pictures. London.*
  Note: Filmed in London. Country of origin unconfirmed. One source indicates that the film was produced by Austrian television. The apartment sequence was later shown as *Rape—Part II*; running time: 40 min. John Lennon's precise function in the production is undetermined.

THE RAPE *see* **LE VIOL**

THE RAPE OF THE SABINES *see* **THE SHAME OF THE SABINE WOMEN**

RAPE! THE WORST CRIME OF ALL *see* **THE WORST CRIME OF ALL!**

EL RAPTO DE LAS SABINAS *see* **THE SHAME OF THE SABINE WOMEN**

RAPTURE (United States/France)   **F6.4019**
  Panoramic Productions. *Dist* International Classics. 23 Aug **1965** [New York opening; c23 Aug 1965; LP32238]. Sd (Westrex); b&w. 35mm (CinemaScope). 104 min.
  Prod Christian Ferry. *Dir* John Guillermin. *Screenplay* Stanley Mann. *Screen Treatment* Ennio Flajano. *Dir Photog* Marcel Grignon. *Camera* Charles-Henry Montel, Gilles Bonneau. *Art Dir* Jean André. *Film Ed* Max Benedict, Françoise Diot. *Mus Comp & Cond* Georges Delerue. *Sd Ed* Peter Thornton. *Sd Rec* Joseph de Bretagne, Gordon McCallum. *Asst Dir* Louis Pitzele, Rik Wise. *Prod Mgr* Paul Joly. *Cont* Lucie Lichtig. *Cost* Jacques Fonteray. *Makeup* Janine Jarreau, Jeanine Lankshear. *Hairdresser* Renée Guidet. *Sp Eff* René Albouze. *Prop* Paulette Boréal, Jacques Pradel.
  Cast: Patricia Gozzi (*Agnes*), Melvyn Douglas (*Larbaud*), Dean Stockwell (*Joseph*), Gunnel Lindblom (*Karen*), Leslie Sands (*1st gendarme*), Murray Evans (*young gendarme*), Sylvia Kay (*Genevieve*), Peter Sallis (*Armand*), Christopher Sandford (*young man*), Ellen Pollock (*landlady*).
  Drama. Source: Phyllis Hastings, *Rapture in My Rags* (London, 1964). Sixteen-year-old Agnes considers herself to be retarded. In reality, the lonely girl is normal, her situation a product of her father's retreat from reality after the death of her mother. He resigned from his post as a judge and lives on the coast of Brittany with Agnes, who was taken out of school at age 12. Agnes has made a scarecrow to be her companion and has dressed it in her father's old suit. When she finds Joseph, an escaped prisoner, wearing the suit, she believes that her creation has come alive. Agnes and her father, with Karen, their servant, take Joseph in and nurse his wounds. Joseph becomes part of the household, but when Agnes discovers Joseph and Karen making love, she tries to kill Karen. Karen leaves, and soon Agnes and Joseph are lovers. Her father discovers them and beats her. The gendarme whom Joseph injured in his escape dies, and so Joseph is sought for murder. Joseph and Agnes run away to the city, which so bewilders Agnes that she returns home. Joseph is killed by the police when he follows Agnes; and Agnes and her father resume their life in a new adult relationship. *Domestics. Judges. Prison escapees. Police. Adolescence. Loneliness. Mental retardation. Fatherhood. Murder. Scarecrows. Brittany.*
  Note: Filmed in Brittany.

RAQ LO B'SHABBAT *see* **IMPOSSIBLE ON SATURDAY**

RAQUEL'S MOTEL   **F6.4020**
  Dist Distribpix, Inc. ca **1970**. Sd; col. 35mm. 64 min.
  Sex film. A young man and his girl friend stop one afternoon at Raquel's Motel. As Raquel shows them to their room and begins to prepare the bed, she notices that they have already begun to make love; she goes outside but continues to watch through the window. The experience arouses her sexually, and later in her room she stimulates herself by massaging with baby oil. The next morning Raquel runs into the woman, and soon they are back in Raquel's room making love. The man occupies himself with a maid who arrives to clean the room. When Raquel and the young woman return, the foursome join in an orgy, indulging in a variety of sexual activities. *Innkeepers. Chambermaids. Lesbianism. Voyeurism. Infidelity. Autoeroticism. Group sex. Motels.*

THE RARE BREED
F6.4021

Universal Pictures. 2 Feb **1966** [Fort Worth, Texas, opening; c5 Mar 1966; LP35371]. Sd (Westrex); col (Technicolor). 35mm (Panavision). 97 min.

Prod William Alland. *In Charge of Prod* Edward Muhl. *Dir* Andrew V. McLaglen. *Writ* Ric Hardman. *Dir Photog* William H. Clothier. *Art Dir* Alexander Golitzen, Alfred Ybarra. *Set Decor* John McCarthy, Oliver Emert. *Main Titl* Pacific Title. *Film Ed* Russell F. Schoengarth. *Mus* Johnny Williams. *Mus Supv* Joseph Gershenson. *Sd* Waldon O. Watson, Corson Jowett. *Asst Dir* Terry Morse, Jr. *Unit Prod Mgr* Norman Deming. *Action Coörd* Hal Needham. *Cost* Rosemary Odell. *Makeup* Bud Westmore. *Hairstyles* Larry Germain. *Matte Supv* Albert Whitlock. *Tech Adv* D. R. O. Hatswell, Al Sherman. *Dial Coach* Michael Audley.

Cast: James Stewart (*Sam Burnett*), Maureen O'Hara (*Martha Price*), Brian Keith (*Alexander Bowen*), Juliet Mills (*Hilary Price*), Don Galloway (*Jamie Bowen*), David Brian (*Charles Ellsworth*), Jack Elam (*Deke Simons*), Ben Johnson (*Jeff Harter*), Harry Carey, Jr. (*Ed Mabry*), Perry Lopez (*Juan*), Larry Domasin (*Alberto*), Alan Caillou (*Taylor*), Silvia Marino (*Conchita*), Gregg Palmer (*Rodenbush*), Barbara Werle (*Gert*), Joe Ferrante (*Estaban*), Jim O'Hara (*Sagamon*).

Western drama. Martha Price, an English widow, arrives in Saint Louis in 1884 with her daughter Hilary, 4 milking cows, and Vindicator, a hornless Hereford bull. She hopes to sell the bull for breeding purposes, believing that the crossbreeding process will improve upon the lean longhorn cattle prevalent in the West. Vindicator is sold to cattle baron Alexander Bowen, a widower originally from Scotland, and saddle tramp Sam Burnett is hired to deliver the bull to Bowen's Texas ranch. Burnett is skeptical of Martha's theories and is at first party to a scheme to swindle her, but he soon changes sides. En route to Texas, James, Bowen's son, is injured in an unsuccessful attempt by roughnecks to steal Vindicator. Martha and Hilary also go to Bowen's ranch, and Bowen falls in love with Martha. Hilary and James fall in love while she is nursing him back to health, and they plan to marry. That winter, Vindicator and some of the other cattle are lost on the range. When the bull is found dead and it is not known whether he mated successfully, Martha resigns herself to marrying Bowen. But Sam, converted to Martha's theories and a new man because he has something to believe in, goes on a long search of the range and returns with a Hereford calf. Martha then decides to stay in Texas, marry Sam, and raise Herefords. *English. Widows. Widowers. Swindlers. Cowboys. Cattlemen. Scotch. Filial relations. Rustling. Ranches. Texas. Saint Louis (Missouri). Cattle.*

THE RARE ONES *see* THE RAW ONES

RASCAL
F6.4022

Walt Disney Productions. *Dist* Buena Vista Distribution Co. 11 Jun **1969** [c25 Apr 1969; LP36995]. Sd (RCA); col (Technicolor). 35mm. 85 min. *MPAA rating* G.

Prod James Algar. *Dir* Norman Tokar. *2d Unit Dir* Arthur J. Vitarelli. *Screenplay* Harold Swanton. *Dir Photog* William Snyder. *Art Dir* John B. Mansbridge. *Set Decor* Emile Kuri, Frank R. McKelvy. *Film Ed* Norman R. Palmer. *Mus* Buddy Baker. *Orch* Walter Sheets. *Song:* "Summer Sweet" Bob Russell. *Sd Supv* Robert O. Cook. *Sd Mix* Dean Thomas. *Mus Ed* Evelyn Kennedy. *Asst Dir* Christopher Hibler. *Unit Prod Mgr* John Bloss. *Cost Dsgn* Rosemary O'Dell. *Cost* Chuck Keehne, Emily Sundby. *Makeup* Otis Malcolm. *Hairstyles* La Rue Matheron. *Sp Eff* Eustace Lycett. *Matte Artist* Alan Maley. *Animal Supv* Henry L. Cowl, Gerry Lynn Warshauer.

Cast: Steve Forrest (*Willard North*), Bill Mumy (*Sterling North*), Pamela Toll (*Theo*), Elsa Lanchester (*Mrs. Satterfield*), Henry Jones (*Garth Shadwick*), Bettye Ackerman (*Miss Whalen*), Jonathan Daly (*Reverend Thurman*), John Fiedler (*Cy Jenkins*), Richard Erdman (*Walt Dabbitt*), Herbert Anderson (*Mr. Pringle*), Robert Emhardt (*constable*), Steve Carlson (*Norman Bradshaw*), Maudie Prickett (*Miss Pince-nez*), Walter Pidgeon (*voice of Sterling North*).

Comedy-drama. Source: Sterling North, *Rascal, a Memoir of a Better Era* (New York, 1963). In the summer of 1918 in the little town of Brailsford Junction in central Wisconsin, 11-year-old Sterling North saves a raccoon from a lynx, and the two become boon companions. Sterling's father, a widower and traveling salesman, spends much of his time on the road; and Rascal, the raccoon, is often Sterling's only companion. Three friendly neighbors keep an eye on the pair, however: Miss Whalen, his teacher; Mr. Thurman, the new minister; and Mr. Pringle, a kindly merchant. Rascal gets into trouble often, and when he digs up a neighbor's corn patch, Sterling frees him rather than putting him in a cage. Rascal is again almost killed by the lynx, and Sterling must once more save him. On his way home, Sterling takes Rascal to a race between a Stanley Steamer and a sulky, and the presence of the animal inspires Donnybrook, the horse pulling the sulky, to win the race. Sterling's sister, Theo, returns home from Chicago with her fiancé and finds the North home in a terrible mess. She takes her father to task for neglecting Sterling, and, as a result, Mr. North takes an office in Brailsford Junction. Sterling sets Rascal free

in the company of a female raccoon, knowing that together the two animals will be able to protect themselves from the lynx. *Children. Traveling salesmen. Widowers. Housekeepers. Cashiers. Schoolteachers. Clergymen. Family life. Rural life. Brother-sister relationship. Animal care. Stanley Steamer automobiles. General stores. Wisconsin. Lynx. Dogs. Raccoons. Horses.*

RASPUTIN—THE MAD MONK (Great Britain)
F6.4023

Seven Arts Productions–Hammer Film Productions. *Dist* Twentieth Century-Fox Film Corp. 6 Apr **1966** [Detroit opening; c6 Apr 1966; LP32662]. Sd (RCA); col (DeLuxe). 35mm (CinemaScope). 92 min.

Prod Anthony Nelson Keys. *Exec Prod* Anthony Hinds. *Dir* Don Sharp. *Screenplay* John Elder. *Dir Photog* Michael Reed. *Camera Op* Cece Cooney. *Art Dir* Don Mingaye. *Prod Dsgn* Bernard Robinson. *Supv Ed* James Needs. *Ed* Roy Hyde. *Mus Comp* Don Banks. *Mus Supv* Philip Martell. *Sd Rec* Ken Rawkins. *Sd Ed* Roy Baker. *Asst Dir* Bert Batt. *Prod Mgr* Ross Mackenzie. *Cont* Lorna Selwyn. *Wardrobe* Rosemary Burrows. *Makeup* Roy Ashton. *Hairstylist* Frieda Steiger.

Cast: Christopher Lee (*Rasputin*), Barbara Shelley (*Sonia*), Richard Pasco (*Dr. Zargo*), Francis Matthews (*Ivan*), Suzan Farmer (*Vanessa*), Nicholas Pennell (*Peter*), Renee Asherson (*Tsarina*), Derek Francis (*innkeeper*), Alan Tilvern (*patron*), Joss Ackland (*The Bishop*), John Welsh (*The Abbott*), Robert Duncan (*Tsarevitch*), John Bailey (*court physician*).

Historical melodrama. In Russia during the rule of Nicholas II, Rasputin, a debauched monk with strange powers of healing, renounces his holy vows and goes to St. Petersburg to further his own ambitions. There he uses his mystical powers to influence two court aristocrats, the alcoholic Dr. Zargo and Sonia, lady-in-waiting to Tsarina Alexandra. After making love to Sonia, Rasputin hypnotizes her into causing Alexandra's young son to have a serious accident. He then miraculously cures the boy and wins the tsarina's gratitude and a place in the palace, where he slowly gains both social and political power. Zargo, who has become court physician, becomes disturbed by the monk's evil designs; and after Sonia has been driven to suicide, he joins a plot to do away with Rasputin. Poisoned food and a deadly hypodermic injection fail to have the intended effect; but in a climactic struggle, the mortally wounded Zargo forces Rasputin off a balcony into the frozen river below. *Monks. Aristocrats. Physicians. Royalty. Mysticism. Ambition. Alcoholism. Hypnotism. Suicide. Conspiracy. Assassination. Russia. Saint Petersburg. Grigori Efimovich Rasputin. Nicholas II (Russia). Alexandra Feodorovna.*

Note: Opened in London in Mar 1966. John Elder is a pseudonym for Anthony Hinds.

RAT FINK
F6.4024

Genesis Productions. *Dist* Cinema Distributors of America, International Film Organization. 22 Dec **1965** [Los Angeles opening]. Sd; b&w. 35mm. 80 min.

Pres by M. A. Ripps. *Prod* Lewis Andrews. *Dir-Writ* James Landis. *Story* Matthew Cheney, Jack Miller. *Camera* William Zsigmond. *Art Dir* Daniel Toledo. *Film Ed* Tom Boutross. *Mus* Ronald Stein. *Songs:* "My Soul Runs Naked" & "One on Every Corner" sung by Don Snyder. *Asst Dir* Hank Sheldon, Don Russell. *Stuntman* Steve Karkus.

Cast: Schuyler Hayden (*singer*), Hal Bokar (*singer's manager*), Warrene Ott (*wife*), Judy Hughes (*teenager*), Don Snyder, Eve Brenner, Alice Reinheart, Jack Lester, Sirkka Ottonen, Anna Stephen, Peter Wilkins, The Futuras, David Reed, Ernie Crites, Chuck Harrod, Richard Jeffries, Sharon Sutton, Jill Quinn.

Melodrama. A handsome rock and roll singer ruthlessly works his way to the top. After sleeping with a woman older than himself, he steals from her purse and leaves for Hollywood where he buys the services of a top agent. The young singer and his agent become close friends, but the singer has an affair with the agent's wife and then becomes involved with a teenaged fan. The teenager becomes pregnant, and the singer takes her to a veterinarian for an abortion, then leaves her to continue his push toward stardom, complete with Hollywood-style beach parties and underhanded business methods. In the end, the manager's wife provokes a violent argument with the singer, and in the scuffle he falls to his death from a balcony. *Singers. Opportunists. Theatrical agents. Veterinarians. Rock and roll. Robbery. Ambition. Infidelity. Pregnancy. Abortion. Adolescence. Hollywood.*

Note: Location scenes filmed in Los Angeles and in southern California. Working title: *My Soul Runs Naked*; also known as *Wild and Willing* and *The Swinging Fink.*

RAT PFINK AND BOO BOO
F6.4025

Morgan–Steckler Productions. *Dist* Craddock Films. caSep **1966**. Sd; b&w. 35mm. 72 min.

Prod-Dir-Story Ray Dennis Steckler. *Screenplay* Ronald Haydock. *Camera* Ray Dennis Steckler. *Film Ed* Keith Wester. *Mus* Henry Price.

Cast: Vin Saxon (*Lonnie Lord/Rat Pfink*), Titus Moede (*Titus Twimbly/Boo Boo*), Carolyn Brandt (*Cee Bee Beaumont*), George Caldwell (*Linc*), Mike

Kannon *(Hammer)*, James Bowie *(Benjie)*, Keith Wester *(cowboy)*, Mary Jo Curtis *(Irma La Streetwalker)*, Romeo Barrymore *(ape trainer)*, Dean Danger *(narrator)*, Kogar *(himself, the "Swinging Ape")*.

Comedy. Rock and roll singer Lonnie Lord and his bumbling gardener friend Titus Twimbly are the hero characters in this spoof on the *Batman* television series. When three villains abduct Lonnie's girl friend, Cee Bee Beaumont, Lonnie and Titus transform themselves into Rat Pfink and Boo Boo and rush to her assistance. The chase results in several mixups and crises, including a confrontation with Kogar, the Swinging Ape, but Cee Bee is eventually rescued. *Singers. Gardeners. Rock and roll. Abduction. Rescue. Chases. Batman. Apes.*

RATAI see **THE BODY**

RATTLE OF A SIMPLE MAN (Great Britain)   F6.4026

Sydney Box Associates. *For* Associated British Productions. *Dist* Continental Distributing, Inc. 20 Dec **1964** [New York opening]. Sd; b&w. 35mm. 96 min.

A Sydney Box Production. *Prod* William Gell. *Dir* Muriel Box. *Assoc Dir* Gerry O'Hara. *Screenplay* Charles Dyer. *Photog* Reg Wyer. *Art Dir* Robert Jones. *Film Ed* Frederick Wilson. *Mus* Stanley Black. *Sd Rec* Les Hammond, Len Shilton. *Prod Mgr* Al Marcus.

Cast: Harry H. Corbett *(Percy)*, Diane Cilento *(Cyrenne)*, Thora Hird *(Mrs. Winthram)*, Michael Medwin *(Ginger)*, Charles Dyer *(Chalky)*, Hugh Futcher *(Ozzie)*, Brian Wilde *(Fred)*, Alexander Davion *(Ricardo)*, David Saire *(Mario)*, Barbara Archer *(Iris)*, Michael Robbins *(George)*, George Roderick *(Papa)*, Marie Burke *(Mama)*, Carole Gray *(district nurse)*, John Ronane *(Willie)*, Ingrid Anthofer *(1st stripper)*, Karen Kaufman *(2d stripper)*.

Comedy-drama. Source: Charles Dyer, *Rattle of a Simple Man* (London opening: 19 Sep 1962). Percy Winthram, a 39-year-old virginal bachelor who is an avid football fan, comes to London to see the Cup Final. Before his scheduled bus trip back to Manchester, he joins his friends Ginger, Chalky, Ozzie, and Fred, a rowdy group of Manchester millworkers, for a night on the town. In a Soho striptease club, Ginger insults Cyrenne, an attractive, blonde, Italian bar hostess/prostitute, and soon Percy's companions trick him into wagering his motorcycle against £50 that he will take her home and sleep with her. Cyrenne overhears this and playfully lets Percy escort her home. Percy's inhibitions overcome him when Cyrenne begins to undress and invites him to bed, and the two end up talking through the night. During the conversation, Percy begins to shed his timidity while Cyrenne's earlier claims of an aristocratic background are revealed as a fantasy she employed to conceal her sordid family life. They finally agree to go away on a holiday together, and, if all goes well, to get married. Before dawn, Percy races away to catch his bus, but a view of Cyrenne's face on an advertisement compels him to stop the bus, leave his friends, and hurry back to her. *Bachelors. Prostitutes. Barroom hostesses. Italians. Mill workers. Soccer. Wagers. Timidity. Virginity. London.*

Note: Released in Great Britain in 1964; running time: 96 min.

RAUTHA SKIKKJAN see **HAGBARD AND SIGNE**

RAVAGED see **AFTER MEIN KAMPF**

THE RAVAGER   F6.4027

Green Dolphin Productions. *Dist* Manson Distributing Corp. 14 Jan **1970** [Champaign, Illinois, showing]. Sd; col (Eastman Color). 35mm. 76 min.

Prod Dave Ackerman. *Dir* Charles Nizet. *Photog* Carl Johnston. *Set Decor* Herman Thyson. *Asst Dir* Ebby Rhodes. *Script Girl* Mary Martin, cont. *Prod Mgr* Lyle Cabot.

Cast: Pierre Gostin, Pierre Gaston *(Joe Salkow, see note)*, Jo Long *(landlady)*, Lynn Hayes, Luana Wilcox, Ann Hollis, Diane Thurman, Darlene Dawes *(The Ravager's victims)*.

Melodrama. Joe Salkow, a naturalized citizen, enters the United States Army and is sent to Vietnam as a demolition expert. There Joe becomes separated from his unit and witnesses the brutal rape and murder of a young Vietnamese woman by two Vietcong. Joe is found in a dazed condition and sent back to the States for rehabilitation. Six months later he is presumed to be cured and released from the Army hospital, but the memory of the outrage he witnessed has produced a compulsion to destroy anyone he finds engaging in sex. Joe comes upon a young couple making love in a car, and he quietly sets a charge of dynamite nearby. He watches the completion of their lovemaking and explodes the charge, killing them both. Joe satisfies his voyeuristic cravings as he carries out a series of rapes and dynamite murders. On one occasion he becomes upset by the discovery of two lesbians making love, but he does not harm them. Soon, running low on money and dynamite, Joe is forced to become simply a voyeur. He saves his last charge of dynamite for his landlady, whom he kills on the day of his eviction. Joe now perceives that a private detective is following him. Joe bides his time until he feels that he is safe, and then he rapes and murders the detective's wife. The detective arrives home to find Joe leaving his house. He apprehends Joe and kills him when he attempts to escape.

Immigrants. Veterans. Psychopaths. Detectives. Landladies. Rape. Voyeurism. Obsession. Murder. Lesbianism. Eviction. Explosives. Vietnam War 1964-73. United States Army. Vietcong.

Note: Sources conflict in rendering the name of the leading actor. Production company has not been confirmed.

THE RAVAGERS   F6.4028

Hemisphere Pictures. 24 Nov **1965** [Boston opening]. Sd; b&w. 35mm. 88 min. [Also 79 min.]

Exec Prod Kane W. Lynn. *Dir* Eddie Romero. *Screenplay* Cesar Amigo, E. F. Romero. *Film Ed* Joven Calub. *Mus Score* Tito Arevalo. *Sd* Demetrio de Santos. *Wardrobe* Paquito Salcedo. *Makeup* Remy Amazan.

Cast: John Saxon *(Capt. Kermit Dowling)*, Fernando Poe, Jr. *(Gaudiel)*, Bronwyn Fitzsimmons *(Sheila)*, Michael Parsons *(Reardon)*, Kristina Scott *(mother superior)*, Robert Arevalo *(Captain Araullo)*, Vic Diaz *(Cruz)*, Vic Silayan *(Captain Mori)*, José Dagumboy *(Joe)*.

War drama. The Philippines, 1945. One of the last Japanese forces in the South Pacific receives orders to obtain for transport back to Japan a shipment of gold bullion stored at an island convent. The Japanese take over the convent, making virtual prisoners of the nuns and convent girls. Kermit Dowling, an American officer, and ex-convict Gaudiel lead a group of native guerrillas against the Japanese. Gaudiel, accompanied by demolition experts, infiltrates the convent and is attracted to Sheila, an American the nuns have been hiding and whom the Japanese are anxious to find. Soon, fighting breaks out between the two forces; initially repulsed, the guerrillas defeat the Japanese and save the gold. *Japanese. Americans in foreign countries. Filipinos. Guerrillas. Ex-convicts. Nuns. Convents. Gold. World War II. Philippines. Japan—Army.*

Note: Filmed on location in the Philippines.

THE RAVEN   F6.4029

Alta Vista Productions. *Dist* American International Pictures. 25 Jan **1963** [New York opening; c27 Jan 1963; LP24570]. Sd; col (Pathé). 35mm (Panavision). 86 min.

Prod-Dir Roger Corman. *Exec Prod* James H. Nicholson, Samuel Z. Arkoff. *Screenplay* Richard Matheson. *Photog* Floyd Crosby. *Camera Op* Harry Underwood. *Art Dir* Daniel Haller. *Set Decor* Harry Reif. *Film Ed* Ronald Sinclair. *Mus* Les Baxter. *Mus Coörd* Al Simms. *Sd* John Bury, Gene Corso. *Asst Dir* Jack Bohrer, Paul Rapp. *Prod Supv* Bartlett A. Carre. *Unit Mgr* Robert Agnew. *Cost* Marjorie Corso. *Wardrobe* Tom Welsh. *Makeup* Ted Coodley. *Hairstyles* Betty Pedretti. *Sp Eff* Pat Dinga. *Raven Trainer* Moe Disesso. *Still Photog* Bill Creamer. *Constr Coörd* Ross Hahn.

Cast: Vincent Price *(Dr. Erasmus Craven)*, Peter Lorre *(Dr. Adolphus Bedlo)*, Boris Karloff *(Dr. Scarabus)*, Hazel Court *(Lenore Craven)*, Olive Sturgess *(Estelle Craven)*, Jack Nicholson *(Rexford Bedlo)*, Connie Wallace *(maidservant)*, William Baskin *(Grimes)*, Aaron Saxon *(Gort)*, Jim Jr. *(The Raven)*.

Comedy-drama. Source: Edgar Allan Poe, "The Raven," in *American Review* (Feb 1845). Dr. Erasmus Craven, a 15th-century English magician, goes into retirement following the apparent death of his wife, Lenore. He is startled one night by the appearance of a talking raven, who turns out to be Dr. Adolphus Bedlo, a former magician turned into a bird for daring to challenge the power of the master sorcerer, Dr. Scarabus. After Craven returns him to human form, Bedlo divulges that a woman resembling Lenore is living at the Scarabus castle. Accompanied by Craven's daughter, Estelle, and Bedlo's son, Rexford, the two magicians visit the castle and learn that Lenore feigned death to become Scarabus' mistress. The master sorcerer imprisons his guests and threatens to torture Estelle unless Craven reveals the secrets of his magical powers. Bedlo, who is actually a party to a plot with Scarabus to get Craven to divulge his magic secrets, tries to back out of the agreement, and Scarabus changes him into a raven once more. The bird, however, cuts Craven's bonds, enabling him to challenge Scarabus to a duel of magic, which results in the death of Scarabus and Lenore in a castle fire. Later, Craven takes the raven home with him, but he is in no hurry to change Bedlo back into a man. *Magicians. Sorcerers. English. Mistresses. Death. Duplicity. Transmutation. Imprisonment. Infidelity. Magic. Castles. Ravens. Duels. Fires.*

RAVEN'S END (Sweden)   F6.4030

Europa Film. *Dist* New Yorker Films. 21 May **1970** [New York opening]. Sd; b&w. 35mm. 100 min.

Dir-Writ Bo Widerberg. *Photog* Jan Lindeström. *Art Dir* Einar Nettelbladt. *Film Ed* Wic Kjellin. *Mus:* "Trumpet Concerto in D Major" Giuseppe Torelli. *Sd* Sven Fahlen. *Prod Mgr* Waldemar Bergendahl.

Cast: Thommy Berggren *(Anders)*, Keve Hjelm *(father)*, Emy Storm *(mother)*, Ingvar Hirdwall *(Sixten)*, Christina Frambäck *(Elsie)*, Agneta Prytz *(neighbor)*.

Domestic drama. In 1936, Anders works in a factory in Malmö and dreams of becoming a writer. He lives with his parents in a small apartment in Raven's

End, a poor section of the city. Anders' father is an alcoholic ne'er-do-well whose desire for an upper-class life prevents him from accepting working-class employment; his mother, a washerwoman, works incessantly to earn money to support their meager existence. Anders' first book is rejected for publication, though he is offered encouragement by a publisher, and he despondently turns to the girl next door for consolation. When she becomes pregnant and expects Anders to marry her, he realizes that he is about to become trapped in Raven's End, and he and a friend set out in search of a better life in Stockholm. *Lower classes. Factory workers. Novelists. Laundresses. Family life. Youth. Alcoholism. Ambition. Pregnancy. Slums. Malmö. Stockholm.*

Note: Released in Sweden in Dec 1963 as *Kvarteret Korpen.*

A RAVISHING IDIOT (France/Italy)   **F6.4031**
Belles Rives–Flora Film. *Dist* Seven Arts Pictures. Jan **1966** [Baltimore showing]. Sd; b&w. 35mm. 105 min.
Pres by Seven Arts Productions. *Prod* Michel Ardan. *Dir* Edouard Molinaro. *Screenplay* Edouard Molinaro, André Tabet, Georges Tabet. *Dir Photog* Andréas Winding. *Camera* Daniel Diot. *1st Asst Camera* André Dubreuil. *Art Dir* Jean André, Robert Clavel. *Film Ed* Robert Isnardon. *Mus* Michel Legrand. *Sd* Robert Biart. *Prod Supv* Robert Florat. *Cost* Tanine Autre. *Ch Makeup* Odette Berroyer.
Cast: Anthony Perkins *(Harry Compton),* Brigitte Bardot *(Penelope Lightfeather),* Grégoire Aslan *(Bagda),* André Luguet *(Reginald Dumfrey),* Charles Millot *(Balaniev),* Hélène Dieudonné *(Mamie),* Jacques Monod *(surgeon),* Jean-Marc Tennberg *(Cartwright),* Hans Verner *(Farrington),* Paul Demange *(bank director),* Denise Provence *(Lady Barbara),* Robert Murzeau.
Comedy. Source: Charles Exbrayat, *Une ravissante idiote* (Paris, 1962). Harry Compton, the orphan son of a Russian, loses his job at the Bank of England as a result of courting Penelope Lightfeather during his lunch hour. Despising the capitalist system, he reveals to East End restaurateur Bagda, a friend of his late father, that he intends to go to the Soviet Union. Bagda, a secret Soviet agent, instead recruits him to steal the secret Admiralty file "Avalanche," dealing with the mobilization of NATO forces in time of war, from the safe of security chief Sir Reginald Dumfrey. Unbeknownst to the conspirators, false plans have been fabricated for the purpose of tracing the chief Soviet agents. To facilitate the theft, Sir Reginald gives the file to his gossip-loving wife, Lady Barbara, and arranges a reception to attract the spies. Harry discovers that Penelope works as a couturière at the home of Lady Barbara, and he enlists her aid in gaining entrance to the reception. The file is alternately lost and found as a series of misadventures threaten to compromise the entire Admiralty project. In the end, however, the spy chiefs, Bagda included, are destroyed in a shootout, and Harry is united with Penelope, who, as it turns out, is a British agent. *Bank clerks. Orphans. Spies. Restaurateurs. English. Couturiers. Courtship. Theft. Espionage. London. Great Britain—Intelligence service. North Atlantic Treaty Organization.*
Note: Released in France in 1964 as *Une ravissante idiote;* running time: 110 min. Italian title: *Adorabile idiota.* Also known as *The Ravishing Idiots* and *Agent 38-24-36 (The Warm-Blooded Spy).*

UNE RAVISSANTE IDIOTE *see* **A RAVISHING IDIOT**

RAW LOVE   **F6.4032**
Stardust Productions. *Dist* Gold Star Pictures, Grads Corp. **1965**. Sd; b&w. 35mm. 62 min.
Prod John Petrells, Mary Grace Gordon. *Dir* Kent Osborne.
Cast: Suzanne Anderson, Mike Perry.
Rural melodrama. Skeeter, a moonshiner in a backwoods section of the United States, lives and loves in an uninhibited fashion. To protect his unlawful manufacture of corn liquor, Skeeter offers his voluptuous daughter, Bessie Lou, to Sheriff Bird. Both the sheriff and Bessie Lou enjoy their unrestrained lovemaking. Candy, one of Skeeter's relatives, is sought after by three men: Skeeter, Jed the handyman, and Sweet Billie. Skeeter rapes Candy; and Mae, his wife, seduces Sweet Billie in retaliation for her husband's infidelity. This provokes a fight between Mae and Candy. Sweet Billie subsequently makes love to Candy, but Candy seduces Jed in a barn in revenge for Sweet Billie's affair with Mae. Skeeter, who has been spying on Sweet Billie and Candy, becomes enraged and savagely whips both of them. No longer willing to put up with this abuse, Sweet Billie decides to take Candy away. Skeeter tries to rape Candy as she is preparing to leave the house. Skeeter chases Candy out of the house but the rape is prevented by Sweet Billie, who fights Skeeter for Candy. Skeeter is about to crush Sweet Billie's skull with a rock when Sweet Billie knocks his legs from under him, causing Skeeter to fall off a cliff to his death. *Moonshiners. Sheriffs. Handymen. Rape. Infidelity. Seduction. Rural life. Stills. Flagellation.*

THE RAW ONES   **F6.4033**
Pacifica Films. *Dist* Art Films International. 31 Dec **1965** [Los Angeles showing]. Sd; b&w. 35mm. 75 min.

Prod-Dir John Lamb. *Photog* Jack Hill, Robert Wilson.
Documentary. A narrator quotes statements by Albert Ellis, Thomas Jefferson, Bertrand Russell, Hugh Hefner, and Justice Hugo Black regarding nudity and censorship, as extensive footage shows nudists swimming, boating, playing, and exercising in a nudist colony. *Censorship. Nudist camps. Thomas Jefferson. Bertrand Arthur William Russell. Hugh Marston Hefner. Hugo Lafayette Black. Albert Ellis.*
Note: Also advertised as *The Rare Ones.*

RAW WEEKEND   **F6.4034**
Dist Boxoffice International Film Distributors. 3 Sep **1964** [San Francisco opening]. Sd; b&w. 35mm. 62 min.
Exec Prod J. Willard Evans. *Dir* Sidney Niehoff. *Screenplay* Michal Locke. *1st Camera* Armond Selz. *2d Camera* Franklin Holmes. *Asst Camera* Bill Jordan. *Sd* Avery McCaulif. *Grip* Tommy Fields.
Cast: Toni Warren, Shannon Harris, Tim Robinson, Randi Morrow, Ondine (actress), Ralph Conners, Annette Varsi.
Drama. A small movie crew shooting a love scene in a wooded valley with Tammy and Pete, is surprised by the appearance of Dolores, a semi-nude woman who wanders through the background. The crew follows her, in hopes of photographing her for the motion picture. They find Dolores and her friend, Lee, sunbathing amidst the rocks and waterfalls, and the women invite the crew to picnic beside their cabin. After lunch Dolores and Lee row and swim in the lake while Tammy stays inside the cabin studying her script. Tammy grows restless, takes off her nightgown, and joins Dolores and Lee outside. *Actors. Motion picture crews. Nudity. Motion pictures.*

THE RAWHIDE HALO *see* **SHOOT OUT AT BIG SAG**

IL RE DEI FALSARI *see* **THE COUNTERFEITERS OF PARIS**

REACH FOR GLORY (Great Britain)   **F6.4035**
Blazer Films. *Dist* Royal Films International, Columbia Pictures. 9 Sep **1963** [New York opening]. Sd; b&w. 35mm. 89 min.
Prod Jud Kinberg, John Kohn. *Dir* Philip Leacock. *Screenplay* Jud Kinberg, John Kohn, John Rae. *Photog* Bob Huke. *Art Dir* John Blezard. *Titl Dsgn* Maurice Binder. *Film Ed* Frederick Wilson. *Mus & Sp Lyr* Bob Russell. *Mus Cond* Raymond Premru. *Sd* Cyril Collick, Maurice Askew, Don Sharpe. *Asst Dir* David Tomblin. *Prod Mgr* Frederick Gunn.
Cast: Harry Andrews *(Captain Curlew),* Kay Walsh *(Mrs. Curlew),* Oliver Grimm *(Mark Stein),* Michael Anderson, Jr. *(Lewis Craig),* Martin Tomlinson *(John Curlew),* Alexis Kanner *(Steven),* Michael Trubshawe *(Major Burton),* George Pravda *(Mr. Stein),* Peter Furnell *(Arthur Chettle),* James Luck *(Michael),* John Pike *(Felix),* Freddie Eldrett *(Willie),* John Coker *(Peter),* Cameron Hall *(headmaster),* John Rae *(Lance Freeman),* Melvin Baker *(Chettle's lieutenant),* Arthur Hewlett *(vicar),* Alan Jeayes *(Crabtree),* Richard Vernon *(Dr. Aldrich),* Russell Waters *(Mr. Freeman),* Pay Hayess *(Mrs. Freeman).*
Drama. Source: John Rae, *The Custard Boys* (London, 1960). During World War II, several hundred London school children are evacuated to the small coastal town of Hollysea. Several of the boys attending a local school form a gang under the leadership of Lewis Craig and play war games. Attacks on stray animals and raids against local teenagers form the military activities. John Curlew, whose father has an unimpressive military record from the previous war and whose mother is upset by his court-martialed stance as a conscientious objector, dreams of becoming a war hero but does not get along with the tough gang members. Mr. Stein, a Jewish refugee from Austria, comes to teach at the school, and John is ordered by the headmaster to take care of the teacher's young son, Mark. The rest of the boys torment Mark because of his Austrian-Jewish background and refuse to admit him into their gang. John finally convinces them to allow Mark to join, but during a battle with some local teenagers, Mark panics and betrays the others. Lewis decides he should be court-martialed and shot, and a mock execution is planned. One of the rifles used by the children accidentally contains live ammunition, however, and Mark is killed. *Children. Austrians. Jews. Schoolteachers. Refugees. Militarism. Gangs. War games. Capital punishment. Anti-Semitism. Filial relations. Firearms. World War II.*
Note: Released in Great Britain in 1962.

READY FOR ANYTHING!   **F6.4036**
Timely Productions. *Dist* Signature Releasing Organization. 3 Dec **1968** [Maryland license]. Sd; b&w. 35mm. 77 min.
Prod-Dir-Writ Darcia. *Photog* R. L. Buchanan. *Asst Camera* Ludwig Moner. *Film Ed* R. L. Dancer. *Mus* New Music Co. *Sd* Danny Brown. *Prod Asst* Nick Nicholas, Rosemarie McKay, Jeff Kimball, T. Weems.
Cast: Gerrie Grant *(Penny),* Larry Tanner, Carol Ann Lee, J. P. Cranshaw, Jim Clark, Terry Smith, Dianne Davis, Kenneth Wayne, Byron Lord, Cherrie LaMour, R. Eubank, Barnett Shaw.

Drama. Penny, a materialistic young woman, seeks employment with an agency that provides companionship for males, especially visiting businessmen. During the interview Lola, the agency's owner, asks Penny to take off her clothes, and she realizes that she is entering the life of prostitution. Lola advances Penny the money to buy new clothes and rent an apartment, and Penny quickly learns her new trade. She falls in love with a man, but the affair ends badly. Penny returns to prostitution, is seduced by Lola, and becomes a partner in the business. *Businesswomen. Escorts. Prostitution. Seduction. Lesbianism. Employment—Women.*

READY FOR THE PEOPLE F6.4037
Warner Bros. Pictures. Oct **1964** [c17 Oct 1964; LP32385]. Sd; b&w. 35mm. 54 min. [Copyright length: 57 min]
An Anthony Spinner Production. *Prod* Anthony Spinner. *Exec Prod* William T. Orr. *Dir* Buzz Kulik. *Screenplay* E. M. Parsons, Sy Salkowitz. *Photog* Carl Guthrie. *Art Dir* Perry Ferguson. *Set Decor* Hoyle Barrett. *Film Ed* Robert B. Warwick. *Mus* Frank Perkins. *Sd* B. F. Ryan. *Asst Dir* Russell Llewellyn. *Makeup* Gordon Bau. *Hairstyles* Jean Burt Reilly.
Cast: Simon Oakland (*Murray Brock*), Everett Sloane (*Paul Boyer*), Anne Helm (*Connie Zelenko*), Richard Jordan (*Eddie Dickinson*), Karl Held (*Dave Ryan*), Bartlett Robinson (*John T. McGrane*), Simon Scott (*district attorney*), Louis Guss (*Joe Damico*), Harold Gould (*Arnie Tomkins*), Don Keefer (*Dr. Michaels*), Jo Helton (*Karen Brock*), William Bramley (*Nick Williams*), Robert Lieb (*judge*), King Calder (*chaplain*).
Drama. Based on an unidentified magazine story by: Eleazar Lipsky. In a barroom fight over Connie Zelenko, Eddie Dickinson is badly wounded and Connie's boyfriend is killed. Witnesses claim Dickinson is the killer, but he maintains his innocence despite public prosecutor Murray Brock's advice that he plead guilty and take a life-imprisonment sentence rather than risk capital punishment. When Connie comes out of hiding, she confirms the other witnesses' stories, but Brock believes Dickinson is innocent. Dickinson sticks to his story at his trial but receives the death sentence. In the death house, Dickinson continues to maintain his innocence, but after the execution of the sentence, Brock receives a letter from Dickinson confessing to the murder. *Public prosecutors. Murder. Capital punishment. Confession (law). Bars. Trials.*
Note: Location scenes filmed in Brooklyn.

THE REAL GONE GIRLS *see* **THE MAN FROM O. R. G. Y.**

THE REAL THING F6.4038
Dist Film-Makers' Cooperative. 7 Jan **1966** [New York opening]. Si with Sd-on-tape; b&w. 16mm. 50 min.
Dir Raymond Saroff. *Mus* Ornette Coleman.
Cast: Lucas Samaras, Peter Holbrook.
Satire. Elements of live action, Dada, collage, and "happenings" are combined. In the film's opening, television commercials that use sex to glamorize such products as beer and vacations are juxtaposed with sequences from a sex film featuring a couple having intercourse. *Television commercials. Sex exploitation films. Sexuality.*
Note: Filmed in 1964.

THE REALLY BIG FAMILY F6.4039
Wolper Pictures. 17 Feb **1967** [Los Angeles opening]. Sd; b&w. 35mm. 51 min.
A David L. Wolper Production. *Prod-Dir* Alex Grasshoff. *Assoc Prod* Sam Farnsworth. *Narr* Arthur Bramble. *Camera* Vilis Lapenieks. *2d Camera* Guy Adenis. *Asst Camera* Mindaugis Bagdon. *Film Ed* John Soh. *Neg Supv* Elva Fraser. *Asst Neg Cutter* Christina Friedgen. *Sd* Rod Sutton. *Sd Eff Supv* James OwYoung. *Rec Engr* Don Lusby. *Business Admin* Harvey Bernhard. *Film Coörd* Bert Gold. *Optical Eff* Modern Film Effects. *Coöp* Doces Sixth Avenue. *Gaffer* John Morrill.
Narrator: Henry Fonda.
Participants: Bill Dukes, Louise Dukes.
Documentary. This film records the daily lives of Bill and Louise Dukes and their 18 children. The camera shows the chaos of living conditions for this Catholic family in their small Seattle home and the resulting strain on family relations and budgetary considerations. Bill Dukes is a Boeing assembly inspector whose understanding of his parental role is influenced by the compassion of his wife. The film focuses on preparations for the marriage of the eldest daughter, Bobbi. Narrator Henry Fonda appears at the beginning and at the end of the film, while the greater part of the dialog reflects the conversations of the family. *Catholics. Parenthood. Family life. Marriage. Finance—Personal. Seattle.*

REASON OVER PASSION *see* **LA RAISON AVANT LA PASSION**

THE REBEL *see* **CALL ME GENIUS**

REBEL ANGEL F6.4040
Greyhawk Studios. *Dist* Hoffman Distributors. Jun **1962** [c13 Mar 1961; LU3175]. Sd; col (DeLuxe). 35mm. 96 min.
A James J. Gannon Production. *Prod* James J. Gannon. *Dir* Lamont Douglas. *Screenplay* Denny Ross, Elliott Tyne. *Photog* E. H. Witt. *Mus* The Stardusters.
Cast: Patricia Manning, Richard Flynn, Tom Falk, Denny Ross.
Melodrama. Lori Nelson, a 17-year-old high school student, is torn between Paul, her boyfriend who mistreats her, and Todd, a more mature college senior. When Paul is revealed to be the murderer of a child for whom Lori was babysitting, Todd leaves her. *Students. Babysitters. Murder. Adolescence.*

THE REBEL GLADIATORS (Italy) F6.4041
Splendor Film. *Dist* Medallion Pictures. **1963**. Sd; col (Eastman Color). 35mm (Techniscope). 98 min.
Pres by Palisades International Corp. *Prod* Ignazio Luceri. *Dir* Domenico Paolella. *Story-Screenplay* Domenico Paolella, Sergio Sollima, Alessandro Ferraù. *Photog* Carlo Bellero. *Art Dir* Alfredo Montori. *Mus* Carlo Savina.
Cast: Dan Vadis (*Ursus*), José Greci (*Commodus*), Gloria Milland (*Arminia*), Alan Steel, Andrea Aureli, Gianni Santuccio, Carlo Delmi, Tullio Altamura, Pietro Ceccarelli, Consalvo Dell'Arti, Marco Mariani, Claudio Marzulli, Bruno Scipioni.
Action melodrama. In 180 Roman Emperor Marcus Aurelius dies, and his cruel and powerful son Commodus ascends to the throne. His conduct incenses Laetus, a wise senator, and his son Septimus, who openly supports the oppressed barbarians. Ursus, a mighty gladiator, is anxious to win freedom for his fiancée, Arminia, one of Laetus' slaves. Commodus kidnaps Arminia to force Ursus into fighting him in the arena. Marcia, Commodus' concubine, protects Arminia while Commodus, humiliated in battle by Ursus, accuses him of conspiring with Laetus against him. Commodus' reaction causes Ursus to join the rebel army, led by Septimus, to defeat the Roman legions and kill Commodus. *Royalty. Despots. Gladiators. Slavery. Kidnaping. Conspiracy. Assassination. Rome—History—Empire. Lucius Aelius Aurelius Commodus. Ursus.*
Note: Opened in Rome in Jul 1963 as *Ursus gladiatore ribelle.* Alternative Italian title: *Ursus, il gladiatore ribelle.* Alan Steel is a pseudonym for Sergio Ciani.

REBEL ROUSERS F6.4042
Paragon International Pictures. *Dist* Four Star Excelsior Releasing Co. 20 May **1970** [San Francisco opening]. Sd; col (Eastman Color). 35mm. 78 min. *MPAA rating* R.
Prod-Dir Martin B. Cohen. *Screenplay* Abe Polsky, Michael Kars, Martin B. Cohen. *Dir Photog* Leslie Kovacs, Glen Smith. *Film Ed* Thor Brooks. *Sd* Robert Dietz. *Asst Dir* Bud Cardos. *Prod Mgr* John Gardes.
Cast: Cameron Mitchell (*Mr. Collier*), Jack Nicholson ("*Bunny*"), Bruce Dern ("*J. J.*"), Diane Ladd (*Karen*), Dean Stanton, Neil Burstyn, Lou Procopio, Earl Finn, Philip Carey (*The Rebels*), Robert Dix, Jim Logan, Sid Lawrence, Johnny Cardas.
Melodrama. A motorcycle gang known as the Rebel Rousers arrive in the town of Chloride, Arizona, and proceed to a local bar where they hold a wild party until the local sheriff drives them away. Meanwhile, Mr. Collier, an architect who knows J. J., the leader of the gang, from high school, is meeting with his girl friend Karen at a motel. She informs him that she is pregnant by him, but she refuses his proposal of marriage. On their way to the beach to further talk over the problem, they are attacked by the gang. J. J., feeling some loyalty to Mr. Collier, proposes a drag race to stall for time. Collier is beaten up but manages to slip away and contact a Mexican family related to the sheriff. Back at the beach, Bunny, one of the gang members, wins the race and the right to spend the night with Karen. Later that night, the Mexican family confront the Rebel Rousers with pitchforks and rescue Karen, and the gang moves on. *Motorcycle gangs. Architects. Mexicans. Abduction. Pregnancy. Motorcycle racing. Rescue. Chloride (Arizona).*
Note: Filmed in 1967; working title: *Limbo.* Location scenes filmed in Los Angeles, Arizona, and southern California.

REBEL WITH A CAUSE *see* **THE LONELINESS OF THE LONG DISTANCE RUNNER**

LA REBELIÓN DE LOS ESCLAVOS *see* **THE REVOLT OF THE SLAVES**

REBELLION (Japan) F6.4043
Toho Co.-Mifune Productions. *Dist* Toho Co. Dec **1967** [Los Angeles showing]. Sd; b&w. 35mm (Tohoscope). 120 min.
Prod Tomoyuki Tanaka. *Dir* Masaki Kobayashi. *Screenplay* Shinobu Hashimoto. *Photog* Kazuo Yamada. *Art Dir* Yoshiro Muraki. *Mus* Toru

Takemitsu.

Cast: Toshiro Mifune *(Isaburo Sasahara)*, Takeshi Kato *(Yogoro)*, Yoko Tsukasa *(Ichi)*, Tatsuya Nakadai *(Tatewaki Asano)*, Tatsuyoshi Ebara *(Bunzo)*, Michiko Otsuka *(Suga)*, Tatsuo Matsumura *(Lord Matsudaira)*, Shigeru Koyama *(Steward Takahashi)*, Masao Mishima *(Chamberlain Yanase)*, Isao Yamagata *(Kotani)*, Etsuko Ichihara.

Historical drama. Source: Yasuhiko Takiguchi, *Haiyo zuma shimatsu yori* (publication undetermined). In the 18th century Ichi, mistress to Lord Matsudaira and mother of his younger son, is banished from the castle after striking her master for taking a new mistress. Court official and swordsman Isaburo Sasahara is commanded to marry his son Yogoro to Ichi, and though reluctant in view of his own unhappy marriage with the shrewish Suga, the loyal vassal at last agrees to the marriage. Initial mistrust gives way to admiration as Ichi proves to be a perfect wife and daughter-in-law. Sasahara, moved by the love between the young couple, loves their infant daughter as his own child. Two years later, however, Matsudaira recalls Ichi to his castle since his elder son has died and Ichi, as mother of his heir, cannot remain the wife of a vassal. Sasahara urges the young couple to open rebellion against Matsudaira's tyranny. Father and son refuse a command to commit harakiri, and Ichi commits suicide rather than return to Matsudaira. In the ensuing battle with the lord's men Yogoro is killed. After burying the young couple together, Sasahara takes his grandchild and sets out for Edo, determined to appeal to the Tokugawa Shogunate. En route he is stopped by Tatewaki Asano, Lord Matsudaira's loyal gatekeeper. Despite their long friendship Sasahara is forced to battle Asano. Sasahara slays the gatekeeper but is mortally wounded by frontier guardsmen armed with muskets and dies in despair. *Nobility. Mistresses. Samurai. Marriage—Arranged. Suicide. Loyalty. Family life. Japan—History—Tokugawa period 1600–1867.*

Note: Released in Japan in 1967 as *Joi-uchi*; running time: 128 min.

REBELLION IN CUBA see **CHIVATO**

THE REBELLIOUS ONE see **WILD SEED**

REBELS AGAINST THE LIGHT see **SANDS OF BEERSHEBA**

REBELS DIE YOUNG see **TOO YOUNG, TOO IMMORAL!**

REBIRTH OF A NATION see **ACID MANTRA, OR REBIRTH OF A NATION**

RECORD OF A LIVING BEING see **I LIVE IN FEAR**

LA RÉCRÉATION see **PLAYTIME**

THE RED AND THE WHITE (Hungary/U.S.S.R.)   **F6.4044**
Mafilm Studios–Mosfilm. *Dist* Brandon Films. 26 Mar **1969** [New York opening]. Sd; b&w. 35mm (Agascope). 92 min.

Dir Miklós Jancsó. *Screenplay* Georgiy Mdivani, Gyula Hernádi, Miklós Jancsó. *Photog* Tamás Somló. *Asst Photog* János Kende, Tibor Banok. *Art Dir* Boris Chebotaryov. *Film Ed* Zoltán Farkas. *Sd* Zoltán Toldy. *Asst Dir (see note)* Zsolt Kézdi Kovács, Ferenc Grunwalski, Vladimir Glazkov, Liliya Kelshteyn. *Prod Mgr* Jenő Götz, Yu. Rogozovskiy, András Németh, M. Shadur, Kirill Siryayev, István Daubner. *Script Ed* Luca Karall, Valeriy Karen. *Cost* Mayya Abar-Baranovskaya, Gyula Várdai.

Cast: József Madaras *(Hungarian commander)*, Tibor Molnár *(András)*, András Kozák *(László)*, Jácint Juhász *(István)*, Anatoliy Yabbarov *(Captain Chelpanov)*, Sergey Nikonenko *(Cossack officer)*, Mikhail Kozakov *(Nestor)*, Bolot Beyshenaliyev *(Chingiz)*, Tatyana Konyukhova *(Yelizaveta, the matron)*, Krystyna Mikolajewska *(Olga)*, Viktor Avdyushko *(sailor)*, Gleb Strizhenov *(colonel)*, Nikita Mikhalkov *(White officer)*, Vladimir Prokofyev, Valentin Bryleyev, Vera Bykova, Ye. Yermolayeva, Vitaliy Konyayev, Valeriy Glebov, K. Karyolskikh, Pyotr Savin, Nikolay Sergeyev, Sándor Szili, Roman Khomyatov, Károly Eizler, Mika Ardova, Vera Berezutskaya, Gabi Dániel, Yelena Kazelkova, Nikolay Parfyonov, Nina Sorina, Natalya Zheromskaya, Julia Coglin.

Historical drama. In Russia in the summer of 1918, a band of Hungarian internationalists and their Red Army comrades take refuge from the White Guards in a deserted hillside monastery. In keeping with the practice of both sides, the Reds force their prisoners to remove their shirts and boots before execution. A short time later, the tide of battle turns as the Whites surround the monastery and take captive the Reds and their Hungarian allies. The Hungarian commander jumps to his death from the bell tower, and a White officer rebukes the Hungarians for interfering in a Russian conflict. The Red prisoners are given 15 minutes to attempt an escape made virtually impossible by White troops surrounding the building. Following the slaughter, a Hungarian sheltered by a Russian peasant woman is shot down by a Cossack, who in turn is executed by a Tsarist officer for attempting to rape a peasant girl. Some of the revolutionaries find shelter in a military field hospital where a dedicated staff of nurses refuses to make distinctions between wounded soldiers. The

Whites soon arrive, bent on ferreting out the insurgents, but none will aid them until Olga, a Polish nurse, loses the reason for her silence when the Hungarian she loves is killed. László, a young Hungarian, escapes and brings back Red reinforcements as their comrades are being executed. Nevertheless, the Red commander realizes that his decimated ranks stand little chance against the vast White forces encamped in the vicinity. After lining up the White prisoners and firing into the air, he divides his group, orders one half to remove their shirts, and leads them against the White forces, who have regrouped by a river. As the men march toward certain death singing the "Marseillaise," some in Russian, some in Hungarian, the Whites are duped into believing that this is all that remains of the Red Army. Later, when the second group of revolutionaries, including László, reach the front lines, they pause to salute their fallen comrades. *Revolutionaries. Prisoners of war. Cossacks. Soldiers. Nurses. Poles. Traitors. Suicide. Monasteries. Hospitals. Russia—History—1917–21 Revolution. Russia—History—1917–21 Revolution (Foreign participation). "Marseillaise".*

Note: Filmed in the Kostroma Region of central Soviet Russia. Hungarian opening: Nov 1967 as *Csillagosok, katonák*. Released in the U.S.S.R. in 1968 as *Zvyozdy i soldaty*; running time: ca70 min. Sources conflict in crediting assistant directors and production managers.

RED BEARD (Japan)   **F6.4045**
Kurosawa Films–Toho Co. *Dist* Toho International, Inc., Frank Lee International. Jan **1966** [Los Angeles showing]. Sd; b&w. 35mm (Tohoscope). 185 min.

Prod Tomoyuki Tanaka, Ryuzo Kikushima. *Dir* Akira Kurosawa. *Screenplay* Masato Ide, Hideo Oguni, Ryuzo Kikushima, Akira Kurosawa. *Photog* Asaichi Nakai, Takao Saito. *Lighting* Hiromitsu Mori. *Art Dir* Yoshiro Muraki. *Mus* Masaru Sato. *Sd* Shin Watarai.

Cast: Toshiro Mifune *(Dr. Niide, Red Beard)*, Yuzo Kayama *(Dr. Noboru Yasumoto)*, Yoshio Tsuchiya *(Dr. Mori)*, Terumi Niki *(Otoyo)*, Tsutomu Yamazaki *(Sahachi)*, Yoko Naito *(Masae)*, Reiko Dan *(Osuki)*, Akemi Negishi *(Okumi)*, Kyoko Kagawa *(mental patient)*, Kamatari Fujiwara *(Rokusuke)*, Miyuki Kuwano *(Onaka)*, Takashi Shimura *(Tokubei Izumiya)*, Eijiro Tono *(Goheiji)*, Tatsuyoshi Ehara *(Genzo Tsugawa)*, Haruko Sugimura *(Kin)*, Ken Mitsuda *(Masae's father)*, Kinuyo Tanaka *(Yasumoto's mother)*, Chishu Ryu *(Yasumoto's father)*, Yoshitaka Zushi *(Choji [Chobo?])*, Reiko Nanao, Koji Mitsui.

Drama. Source: Shugoro Yamamoto, *Akahige shinryo tan* (Tokyo, 1962). In the early 19th century, hoping to become a court physician, young Dr. Noboru Yasumoto completes his medical training in Nagasaki and returns to the city of Edo. He is dismayed to find himself assigned as an intern at the impoverished public health clinic run by the dedicated Dr. Niide, known as Red Beard. Attempting to get himself discharged, Yasumoto rebels against the clinic rules by drinking heavily, refusing to wear medical attire, and venturing into a cell-like room forbidden to everyone but Red Beard himself. While locked in the room, Yasumoto encounters a deranged young woman, who almost kills him before Red Beard intervenes. Yasumoto is unprepared for his experiences with a dying man and as an assistant at an operation, but gradually he is won over by the older doctor's understanding of the charity patients in the clinic. Red Beard rescues a mistreated 12-year-old girl from a brothel and places her in Yasumoto's care. Working patiently with the youngster, Yasumoto is finally able to overcome her bitterness, and she rewards his efforts by nursing him back to health when he falls ill. As he learns from Red Beard, Yasumoto finds the understanding to forgive his ex-fiancée for marrying another man. Later Yasumoto marries his ex-fiancée's sister, and he finally comprehends Red Beard's conviction that a doctor must fight poverty as well as disease. Resolved to follow in his mentor's footsteps, he rejects an offer to become a shogunate physician in order to remain at the clinic. *Physicians. Children. Poverty. Insanity. Death. Clinics. Whorehouses. Edo.*

Note: Released in Japan in 1965 as *Akahige*.

THE RED CLOAK (France/Italy)   **F6.4046**
Franca Film–Trio Films–Centra Cinéma. *Dist* Sefo Films International, Allied Artists. 4 Oct **1961** [Buffalo, New York, opening]. Sd; col (Eastmancolor). 35mm. 95 min.

Prod Elios Vercelloni. *Exec Prod* Albino Principe. *Dir* Giuseppe Maria Scotese. *Screenplay* Riccardo Pazzaglia, Albino Principe, Jacopo Corsi, Giuseppe Maria Scotese. *Dial* France Roche, Pierre Kast. *Story* Albino Principe. *Photog* Adalberto Albertini. *Art Dir* Umberto Giovagnoli. *Mus* Gino Marinuzzi. *Songs* Domenico Modugno.

Cast: Patricia Medina *(Laura Lanfranchi)*, Bruce Cabot *(Raniero d'Anversa)*, Fausto Tozzi *(Luca de Bardi)*, Guy Mairesse *(Guercio)*, Domenico Modugno *(Saro)*, Lyla Rocco *(Stella)*, Jean Murat *(Cosimo)*, Nyta Dover, Jean François Calvé, Jeanne Fusier-Gil.

Adventure melodrama. In 1500, the citizens of Pisa are subjected to unjust taxes, which are collected by Capt. Raniero d'Anversa. His men murder a prominent banker, and the banker's son, Luca de Bardi, vows revenge. Posing as an artist during the day, he sketches the beautiful Laura Lanfranchi, d'Anversa's fiancée; at night, Luca dons a mask and red cloak and attacks d'Anversa's men one by one. Eventually he is captured and sentenced to death. Laura gets help from the Grand Duke, however, and Luca is set free on the way to his execution. He then challenges d'Anversa to a duel to the death on the Tower of Pisa. Luca wins both the duel and Laura's affection. *Revenue agents. Bankers. Artists. Murder. Revenge. Imposture. Disguise. Capital punishment. Taxes. Pisa. Tower of Pisa. Duels.*

Note: Released in Italy in 1955 as *Il mantello rosso*; in Paris in Jul 1956 as *Les révoltés* or *Le manteau rouge*; running time: 102 min.

RED DESERT (France/Italy)   **F6.4047**

Film Duemila-Federiz-Francoriz. *Dist* Rizzoli Film Distributors. 8 Feb **1965** [New York opening]. Sd (Westrex); col (Eastmancolor, print by Technicolor). 35mm. 116 min.

Prod Antonio Cervi. *Exec Prod* Angelo Rizzoli. *Dir* Michelangelo Antonioni. *Story & Screenplay* Michelangelo Antonioni, Tonino Guerra. *Photog* Carlo Di Palma. *Camera Op* Dario Di Palma. *Asst Op* Alberto Spagnoli, Gianni Antinori. *Art Dir* Piero Poletto. *Asst Art Dir* Sergio Dona. *Film Ed* Eraldo Da Roma. *Asst Film Ed* Mariza Mengoli. *Mus* Giovanni Fusco. *Sung by* Cecilia Fusco. *Electronic Mus* Vittorio Gelmetti. *Mus Dir* Carlo Savina. *Sd* Claudio Maielli, Renato Cadueri. *Boom Op* Mario Bramonti. *Asst Dir* Gianni Arduini, Flavio Nicolini. *Prod Mgr* Ugo Tucci. *Unit Mgr* Rodolfo Martello, Dino Di Salva. *Script Girl* Serena Canevari. *Prod Sec* Eros Lanfranconi. *Cost* Gitt Magrini. *Created by* Battistoni, De Luca of Rome, Zenobi. *Wardrobe Mistress* Paola Carloni. *Hairstyles* Giancarlo De Leonardis. *Trick Shots* Franco Freda, sp eff. *Prop Master* Sergio Dona. *Still Photog* Glauco Cortini, Sergio Strizzi. *Ch Mechanic* Romolo Romagnoli. *Ch Electrn* Emiro Rubeo.

Cast: Monica Vitti (*Giuliana*), Richard Harris (*Corrado Zeller*), Carlo Chionetti (*Ugo*), Xenia Valderi (*Linda*), Rita Renoir (*Emilia*), Aldo Grotti (*Max*), Valerio Bartoleschi (*Valerio*), Giuliano Missirini (*workman*), Lili Rheims (*workman's wife*), Emanuela Pala Carboni (*girl in the fable*), Bruno Borghi, Beppe Conti, Giulio Cotignoli, Giovanni Lolli, Hiram Mino Madonia, Arturo Parmiani, Carla Ravasi, Ivo Scherpiani, Bruno Scipioni.

Drama. Ugo, an electronics engineer, his neglected young wife, Giuliana, and their 5-year-old son, Valerio, live in industrialized Ravenna. Corrado, a mining engineer, arrives from London to recruit skilled workers. He meets Giuliana, and the two are immediately attracted to each other. Corrado learns from Ugo that Giuliana is suffering from nightmares and depression as a result of shock from an automobile accident, but he soon realizes that her mental condition is much worse and that she had tried to commit suicide. When Ugo goes away on a business trip, Valerio pretends to be paralyzed, a trick which badly frightens his mother. Upon learning of the deception, Giuliana angrily leaves him and goes to Corrado's hotel room. She compels the reluctant man to make love to her, but she realizes that the affair will not "cure" her. Wandering aboard a ship, she and a Turkish sailor have an uncommunicative sexual encounter. The next morning, she and her son walk calmly by Ugo's factory where yellow smoke pours from the chimney; Giuliana explains to Valerio that the poisonous smoke does not kill the birds, because they have learned to fly around it. *Industrialists. Engineers. Turks. Sailors. Family life. Shock. Mental illness. Suicide. Infidelity. Factories. Automobile accidents. Ravenna (Italy).*

Note: Filmed in Ravenna and Sardinia. First shown at Venice Film Festival in Sep 1964 as *Il deserto rosso*; running time: 120 min; in Paris in Oct 1964 as *Le désert rouge*; running time: 115 min.

RED-DRAGON (Italy/West Germany)   **F6.4048**

Arca-Film-P. E. A. *Dist* Woolner Bros. Pictures. 16 Mar **1967** [Maryland license]. Sd; col (Eastman Color, print by Technicolor). 35mm (Ultrascope). 89 min.

Prod Gero Wecker. *Dir* Ernst Hofbauer. *Screenplay* Hans-Karl Kubiak, W. P. Zibaso. *Adtl Dial* George Higgins, III. *Dir Photog* Werner M. Lenz. *Camera Op* Wolfgang Hannemann. *Asst Camera Op* Klaus Jahnel. *Art Dir* Max Mellin. *Film Ed* Werner M. Lenz, Hella Faust, Eugenio Alabiso. *Mus Comp & Cond* Riz Ortolani. *Sd* Gunther Kortwich. *Asst Dir* Eberhard Schröder. *Prod Mgr* Bruno Michalk, Dieter Hirsch. *Prod Asst* Wolfgang Hartwig. *Wardrobe* Margarete Simon. *Makeup* Werner Schröder, Ruth Lorenz. *Sp Eff* Richard Richtsfeld. *Prop Master* Otto Arndt.

Cast: Stewart Granger (*Michael Scott*), Rosanna Schiaffino (*Carol*), Harald Juhnke (*Smoky*), Paul Klinger (*Norman*), Margit Saad (*Blanche*), Sieghardt Rupp (*Pierre Milot*), Paul Dahlke (*Harris*), Hilda Somers, Frank Fontana, Horst Frank, Chitra Ratana, Suzanne Roquette.

Crime melodrama. Source: Georges Godefroy, *La rivière des trois jonques* (Paris, 1956). An FBI agent and a woman involved in a smuggling racket are both murdered in Hong Kong, and another FBI agent, Michael Scott, is called in to investigate. Carol, assigned to assist Scott, is placed as a telegraphist in

an organization suspected of conducting the smuggling operation. She is supervised by Pierre Milot and his mistress, Blanche, but the identity of the mastermind behind the combine remains a mystery. Scott contacts the regular Hong Kong FBI agent, Norman, who keeps in touch with both Scott and Carol by means of transmitters concealed in their wristwatches. Later Blanche discovers Carol trying to steal Milot's code book and subjects her to torture. Scott, meanwhile, has learned that river junks are being used to smuggle gems and electrical equipment to mainland China. After several attempts have been made upon his life, he suddenly finds himself face to face with the mysterious gang leader, who is revealed to be Norman. In a climactic fight aboard one of the junks, Scott succeeds in overpowering Norman and blowing up the boat. Satisfied with a job well done, Scott is reunited with Carol. *Americans in foreign countries. Secret agents. Mistresses. Telegraph operators. Smuggling. Murder. Torture. Cryptography. Jewels. Junks. Hong Kong. People's Republic of China. United States—Federal Bureau of Investigation. Ship explosions.*

Note: Location scenes filmed in Hong Kong. Released in West Germany in Jul 1965 as *Das Geheimnis der drei Dschunken*; in Rome in Aug 1965 as *A-009 missione Hong Kong*. U. S. pre-release title: *Mission to Hong Kong*. The following are credited in the United States under anglicized names: Hilda Somers (Helga Sommerfield), Frank Fontana (Franco Fantasia).

THE RED HANGMAN see **BLOODY PIT OF HORROR**

RED LANTERNS (Greece)   **F6.4049**

Th. A. Damaskinos-V. G. Michaelides, A. E. *Dist* Times Film Corp. 31 Mar **1965** [New York opening]. Sd; b&w. 35mm. 85 min.

Prod Theophanis A. Damaskinos, Viktor G. Michaelides. *Dir* Vassilis Georgiades. *Screenplay* Alekos Galanos. *Camera* Nikos Gardelis. *Art Dir* Petros Kapoularis. *Mus* Stavros Xarhakos. *Songs* Grigori Bithikotsis, Georges Zambetas.

Cast: Jenny Karezi (*Helen ["Princess"]*), George Foundas (*Mike*), Mary Chronopoulou (*Mary*), Katerina Helmi (*Marina*), Despo Diamantidou (*The Madam*), Dimitris Papamichael (*Peter*), Kostas Kourtis (*Doris*), Phaedon Georgitsis (*Angelo*), Ero Kyriakaki (*Katerina*), Alexandra Ladikou (*Anna*), Manos Katrakis (*Captain Nicholas*), Eleni Anousaki (*Myrsini*), Notis Peryalis.

Melodrama. Source: Alekos Galanos, *Ta kokkina phanaria* (a play; production undetermined). The film explores the lives of five prostitutes working for a madam and her partner Mike in the red light district of the Greek port of Piraeus. Helen, a young woman from the banks of the Danube, comes to work at the brothel after her career as a sculptress is destroyed by the Nazi invasion. Mike becomes attracted to Helen, but Helen, attempting to escape from her sordid life, becomes romantically involved with Peter, a man who is unaware of her current occupation. After the jealous Mike tells him the truth about Helen, Peter leaves; but he returns when the house is closed and asks her to marry him. Mary, another member of the household, falls in love with Angelo, a teenaged student who asks her to marry him; but their relationship becomes strained and finally ends at the insistence of his relatives. The mentally retarded Marina, a nymphomaniac, lives a tragic life, exploited by a sadistic pimp. Anna, proud despite poverty, carefully hides her life from her young son whom she secretly supports with her earnings. She finally marries Captain Nicholas, one of her steady customers, who convinces her that he will be a good father to her son. Myrsini, the newest member of the house, loves the lustful life of prostitution and its financial rewards. When the Greek government closes down the red light district, Myrsini decides to continue clandestinely the business with some of the other women. *Madams. Sculptors. Pimps. Sea captains. Prostitution. Jealousy. Mental retardation. Nymphomania. Sadism. Adolescence. Motherhood. Poverty. Waterfronts. Whorehouses. World War II. Piraeus.*

Note: Produced in Greece in 1962 as *Kokkina phanaria*; running time: 120 min.

RED LINE 7000   **F6.4050**

Laurel Productions. *Dist* Paramount Pictures. 9 Nov **1965** [Charlotte, North Carolina, opening; c10 Nov 1965; LP31985]. Sd; col (Technicolor). 35mm. 110 min.

Pres by Howard Hawks. *Prod-Dir-Story* Howard Hawks. *Assoc Prod* Paul Helmick. *2d Unit Dir* Bruce Kessler. *Screenplay* George Kirgo. *Dir Photog* Milton Krasner. *Adtl Photog (see note)* Haskell Boggs. *Photog Racing Seq* Larry Frank. *Art Dir* Hal Pereira, Arthur Lonergan. *Set Decor* Sam Comer, Claude Carpenter. *Film Ed* Stuart Gilmore, Bill Brame. *Mus Score & Cond* Nelson Riddle. *Song:* "Wildcat Jones" Carol Connors, Buzz Cason. *Song:* "Let Me Find Someone New" Carol Connors, Nelson Riddle. *Sd Ed* Keith Stafford. *Sd Rec* John Carter, John Wilkinson. *1st & 2d Asst Dir* Dick Moder, Dale Coleman. *Unit Prod Mgr* Andrew J. Durkus. *Prod Mgr* Frank Caffey. *Script Supv* Della Ross. *Cost* Edith Head. *Wardrobe* Buddy Clark. *Hairstyle Supv* Nellie Manley. *Sp Photog Eff* Paul K. Lerpae. *Proc Photog* Farciot Edouart. *Coöp* NASCAR. *Prop Master* Earl Olin, Carl Coleman.

Cast: James Caan *(Mike Marsh)*, Laura Devon *(Julie Kazarian)*, Gail Hire *(Holly MacGregor)*, Charlene Holt *(Lindy Bonaparte)*, John Robert Crawford *(Ned Arp)*, Marianna Hill *(Gabrielle Queneau)*, James Ward *(Dan McCall)*, Norman Alden *(Pat Kazarian)*, George Takei *(Kato)*, Carol Connors *(singer)*, Idell James *(server)*, Diane Strom, Anthony Rogers, Cissy Wellman, Dee Hartford, John Gabriel, Ann Morell, Beryl Hammond, Leslie Summers, Forrest Lewis.

Action melodrama. Jim Loomis, a stock car driver on Pat Kazarian's racing team, is killed in a Daytona race the day before his fiancée, Holly MacGregor, arrives. Holly, who is befriended by members of the racing team, feels that she is responsible for Jim's death, but she regains her self-control and joins another racing widow, Lindy Bonaparte, in operating a cafe. A new driver, Ned Arp, arrives to take Loomis' place on the team, and Pat Kazarian's sister Julie falls in love with him. Ned leaves the team after winning a race, however, feeling that he can do better on his own. Dan McCall comes to join the team, bringing with him from Paris his girl friend, Gabrielle Queneau. He falls in love with Holly; and Mike Marsh, another driver on the team, becomes interested in Gabrielle. Mike is jealous of Gabrielle's earlier affection for Dan, and, thinking them still lovers, tries to kill Dan on the racetrack. Dan survives the crash and forgives Mike, who is reconciled with Gabrielle. Holly agrees to marry Dan, and Ned, who has lost a hand in an accident, is comforted by Julie. *Stock car drivers. Widows. French. Amputees. Automobile racing. Brother-sister relationship. Jealousy. Cafes. Daytona Beach. Automobile accidents.*

Note: Racetrack location scenes filmed in Daytona Beach (Florida), Darlington (South Carolina), Charlotte (North Carolina), Riverside (California), and Ascot (England). Boggs replaced Krasner as photographer during production.

RED LION (Japan)   F6.4051
Mifune Productions. *Dist* Toho International, Inc. 17 Dec **1969** [Los Angeles opening]. Sd; col (Eastmancolor). 35mm. 116 min.
Prod Toshiro Mifune, Yoshio Nishikawa. *Dir* Kihachi Okamoto. *Screenplay* Kihachi Okamoto, Sakae Hirosawa. *Photog* Takao Saito. *Art Dir* Hiroshi Ueda. *Mus* Masaru Sato.
Cast: Toshiro Mifune *(Gonzo)*, Etsushi Takahashi *(Hanzo)*, Shigeru Koyama *(Staff Chief Aragaki)*, No Terada *(Sanji)*, Shima Iwashita *(Tomi)*, Yunosuke Ito *(magistrate)*, Tokue Hanazawa *(Komatora)*, Takahiro Tamura *(Sozo Sagara)*, Kaai Okada, Nobuko Otowa, Jitsuko Yoshimura, Yuko Mochizuki.
Historical drama. In 1868 the Emperor is restored to the throne, and the Imperial Army's Sekiho Troop, led by Sozo Sagara, marches toward Edo. Tozan Army Staff Chief Aragaki gives the Troop the right to halve land taxes in each town they pass to bring the people under control. Gonzo, a soldier in the Troop, volunteers to make the announcement to Sawando, which is his hometown, and he rides into town wearing the scarlet headdress resembling a lion's mane as his symbol of authority. However, Sawando is under the control of a ruthless magistrate and Komatora, a gambler, who tax the people so heavily that many parents are forced to sell their daughters into prostitution. Gonzo begins to notify the villagers of the reduction in taxes, while men still loyal to the old Tokugawa Shogunate calling themselves Mobile Unit One persuade the magistrate and Komatora to hire a swordsman, Hanzo, to kill Gonzo. Meanwhile, Tozan Army Headquarters, desperate for revenue and envious of the Sekiho Troop's growing popularity, rescinds the tax cut and executes Sozo Sagara, declaring his men impostors. The army's main unit arrives in Sawando and defeats Mobile Unit One, also killing Hanzo and his wife. Disillusioned, confused, and embittered, Gonzo attacks the entire army by himself. *Hired killers. Gamblers. Magistrates. Military occupation. Prostitution. Suicide. Taxes. Japan—Army. 1853-70 Japan—History—Restoration.*
Note: Released in Japan in Oct 1969 as *Akage.*

RED LIPS (France/Italy)   F6.4052
Rotor Film-Gray Films-Orsay Films. *Dist* Royal Films International. 18 Mar **1964** [New York opening]. Sd; b&w. 35mm. 90 min.
Prod Carmine Bologna. *Dir* Giuseppe Bennati. *Screenplay* Paolo Levi, Federico Zardi, Giuseppe Bennati. *Story* Giuseppe Bennati, Paolo Levi. *Photog* Tino Santoni. *Art Dir* Amedeo Mellone. *Film Ed* Franco Fraticelli. *Mus* Piero Umiliani.
Cast: Gabriele Ferzetti *(Paolo Martini)*, Giorgio Albertazzi *(Carrei)*, Jeanne Valérie *(Irene)*, Christine Kaufmann *(Baby)*, Marina Bonfigli *(Signora Martini)*, Laura Betti *(The Painter)*, Elvy Lissiak *(Baby's sister)*, Gabriella Serafini, Tullio Altamura, Carla Bizzari, Fabrizio Capucci, Giuseppe Colizzi, Elena Forte, Jacqueline Julien.
Drama. Paolo Martini, a lawyer investigating the disappearance of his teenaged daughter, Baby, learns from Baby's school friend Irene that Baby has been having an affair with an older married man and has apparently gone away with him. Martini goes on their trail, and Irene, interested in him, insists on accompanying him and attempts to seduce him into an affair with her. When they finally meet Carrei, the man with whom Baby was involved, they learn that

she has left him for a boy her own age. Martini finds Baby in a hotel bed with her new lover, and, although he realizes it is too late to help her, he takes her from the hotel. He returns home and breaks his relationship with Irene only to realize that his younger daughter shows signs of following in Baby's footsteps. *Lawyers. Sisters. Filial relations. Adolescence. Missing persons. Seduction. Hotels. Promiscuity.*

Note: Produced in Italy and released there in 1960 as *Labbra rosse*; running time: 100 min. Opened in Paris in Mar 1961 as *Fausses ingénues.* Most sources credit Gray Films as French production company, while others credit Orsay Films.

RED MAN COMETH   F6.4053
Dist Able Film Co. ca **1970**. Sd; col. 16mm. [Feature length assumed.]
Sex film. No information about the precise nature of this film has been found. *Sexuality.*

THE RED MANTLE see **HAGBARD AND SIGNE**

RED OVER RED see **COME SPY WITH ME**

RED ROSES OF PASSION   F6.4054
Amalfi Films. *Dist* Haven International Pictures, Boxoffice International Pictures. Apr **1967**. Sd; b&w. 35mm. 85 min.
Exec Prod Gabriel Cicale. *Dir-Writ* Joe Sarno. *Cinematog* Anthony Lover. *Asst Camera* Robert Gage. *Film Ed* David Durston. *Mus* Ross-Gaffney Inc. *Sd* Vincent De Leo. *Script Girl* Vivian Parciasepe. *Gaffer* Bruce Sparks.
Cast: Judson Todd *(Jay)*, Jean James *(Jean)*, Carol Halleck *(Enid)*, Helena Clayton *(Martha)*, Steve Barton *(Dick)*, Johnny Kuhl *(Peter)*, Liz Love *(Julie)*, Laura London *(Tracey)*, Laurene Claire *(Carla)*, Robin Marks *(Pam)*, Laurie Andrews *(Ruth)*, Pat Daverese *(delivery boy)*, Joanna Mills.
Melodrama. Carla lives with her moralizing Aunt Julie and her prudish cousin Tracey. Carla's friend Enid advises her to see Martha Kag, a mystic who will help Carla with her family problems. Carla does not realize that Enid is employed by Martha to lure young women to her seances, where they are given aphrodisiacs and forced to pay homage to Pan, the god of love. On the first night that Carla visits Martha, she witnesses a woman being sacrificed to Pan, and she flees in terror. She returns later, however, after Enid reassures her that no harm is done to the women. Martha instructs Carla to put a vial of aphrodisiac in Aunt Julie's tea. That night after Aunt Julie has drunk the tea, Pan, disguised as a delivery man, brings her a poisoned rose. She touches the enchanted rose, loses control of herself, and has sex with the delivery man. Tracey is shocked to witness this, but later she is also given the aphrodisiac and reacts in the same manner as her mother. Carla, temporarily satisfied with the revenge on her relatives, asks Martha to release Aunt Julie and Tracey from the spell. Martha agrees, on the condition that Carla become the bride of Pan. Carla gives herself to Pan, who is actually Martha's sexually deranged brother, and though she is able to free her aunt and cousin, she falls victim in their place. *Aunts. Cousins. Mystics. Delivery men. Psychopaths. Human sacrifice. Eroticism. Brother-sister relationship. Disguise. Aphrodisiacs. Seances. Spells. Flowers. Pan (god).*

RED RUNS THE RIVER   F6.4055
Bob Jones University. *Dist* Unusual Films. 26 Apr **1963** [Glenside, Pennsylvania, opening; c1 Apr 1963; LP26575]. Sd; col. 16mm. 90 min.
Dir Katherine Stenholm. *Screenplay* Charles Applegate. *Story* Eva Carrier. *Cinematog* Wade K. Ramsey. *Art Dir* Tim Morris. *Film Ed* George Jensen. *Mus Comp & Cond* Dwight L. Gustafson. *Mus Perf* Bob Jones University Symphony Orchestra. *Sd Engr* William Phillips. *Sd Tech* Grant Erikson. *Wardrobe* Alice Cromley, Jane Morris. *Makeup* Charles Applegate. *Adv* Willard Webb, (Gen.), Mrs. Dewey Wood, Lucy Kurtz, Virgil Carrington Jones, E. H. Hoffman, (Col.), Laura Virginia Hale, Roy Christie, R. M. Verner. *Prop* Gere Stratton.
Cast: Bob Jones, Jr. *(Gen. Richard Stoddert Ewell)*, Bob Jones, III *(Gen. "Jeb" Stuart)*, Jack Buttram *(Gen. Thomas "Stonewall" Jackson)*, Lonnie Iglesias *(Apache)*, Stephen Green *(Charlie)*, Jon Jones *(Maj. G. Campbell Brown)*, Truman Conley *(Sam Sweeney)*, Mike Greene *(Captain Crossman)*, Laura Pratt *(Lizinka Brown Ewell)*, Gwen Rees *(Mrs. Thomas J. Jackson)*, Charles Applegate *(photographer)*, Nancy Astinger *(Martha Fairfield)*, Eddie Beck *(Private Williams)*, Miriam Bonner *(Winchester lady)*, Brad Boynton *(Winchester rebel)*, David Bryan *(Private Maxwell)*, Tom Butts *(Dr. (Major) Hunter McGuire)*, Eva Carrier *(Winchester hostess)*, Jim Carter *(Yankee corporal)*, Philip Courter *(Yankee sentry)*, Ray Hansel *(Lieut.-Gen. A. P. Hill)*, Doris Harris *(Mrs. Cy Fairfield)*, Joseph Henson *(artillery captain)*, Ronald Hill, U. S. actor *(Corporal Woods)*, Donald Hudgins *(Private Hall)*, Eva P. Kelley *(Mrs. Jackson's maid)*, Leland Klinetop *(farm boy)*, Billy Lanier *(Private Downs)*, Charles Luttrell *(Private Jacobs)*, Phillip Luttrell *(Private Russell)*, William Moose *(Maj. "Sandie" Pendleton)*, Paul Morris *(Federal private)*, Marshall Neal, Jr. *(drummer boy)*, Robert Pratt *(Brig.-Gen. Richard B.*

Garnett), Tim Rogers (Binghamton Yankee), Philip Russell (Federal flag bearer), Robert Sizelove (Private Jordan), Peter Skelly (Sergeant McDaniel), Beryl Smith (Captain Robinson), Donnella Smith (Winchester lady), Mel Stratton (Private Roberts), Arend J. Ten Pas (Col. John S. Mosby), William G. Williams (sentry), Zeb Wolfe (Cy Fairfield), Robert Woodward (General Ewell's aide), David Yearick (Gen. Robert E. Lee).

Historical melodrama. Confederate Gen. Richard Stoddert Ewell scorns the Christian values of fellow officers Gen. "Stonewall" Jackson and Gen. "Jeb" Stuart. Ewell lusts for the excitement of war and becomes irked when delayed orders force him to miss the first battle of Manassas. Shortly before the second battle of Manassas, Ewell enters the tent of General Jackson to confirm battle orders and finds Jackson praying. He is struck by the sincerity and humility of the officer and leaves in silence. During the fight that follows, Ewell is wounded and his aide is killed. That night, through the guidance of Jackson, Ewell finds solace in the Christian philosophy; once a battle-hardened cynic, Ewell develops an attitude of piety, and after Jackson's death, he takes over the general's command. *Christianity. United States—History—Civil War. Manassas. James Ewell Brown Stuart. Thomas Jonathon Jackson. Richard Stoddert Ewell. Robert Edward Lee.*

THE RED SHEIK (Italy)   F6.4056
Explorer Film. *Dist* Medallion Pictures. 11 Dec **1963** [New York showing]. Sd; col (Eastman Color). 35mm (Euroscope). 90 min.

Dir Fernando Cerchio. *Screenplay* Gino De Santis, Luigi Capuano, Vittoriano Petrilli, Remigio Del Grosso, Montanari. *Photog* Gianni Narzisi, Angelo Lotti. *Mus* Giovanni Fusco.

Cast: Channing Pollock (Ruiz/The Red Sheik), Luciana Gilli (Amina), Mel Welles (Hassan), Mary Welles, Ettore Manni, Pietro De Vico, Rosalba Neri, Glauco Onorato, Giulio Battiferri, Alberto Archetti, Ahmed Amer.

Adventure melodrama. In 19th-century Morocco, amid festivities celebrating the end of combat between the sultan and those who have revolted against him, several rebels are slaughtered by the sultan's men. Among those who refuse to forget the massacre are rebel leader Ajabar; his next-in-command, Mohamed; and the mysterious "Red Sheik," who rides through the streets at night calling on the people to avenge the massacre. Fifteen years later a Spanish architect, Ruiz, takes refuge in Ajabar's camp when he is caught in a sandstorm en route to visit Hassan, who has usurped the sultan's throne. There Ajabar's daughter, Amina, prevents the suspicious Mohamed from killing their visitor, and Ruiz continues his journey to the city. Several rebels are later attacked by Hassan's forces, and their lives are saved only when the Red Sheik appears; and Amina, having been abandoned in the desert on orders from Hassan's ex-wife, Rammel, is rescued by Ruiz. Meanwhile, the Sultan's men have lost a series of battles with Ajabar's men, forcing Hassan to take shelter in a fort, which is eventually blown up by the Red Sheik. The mysterious figure is revealed to be Ruiz, seeking vengeance for the death of his father, and after killing Hassan in hand-to-hand combat, Ruiz and Amina are married. *Spanish. Royalty. Sheiks. Architects. Revolts. Massacres. Revenge. Disguise. Deserts. Forts. Morocco. Sandstorms. Explosions.*

Note: Opened in Rome in 1962 as *Lo sceicco rosso.*

THE RED TERROR (West Germany)   F6.4057
Dist Hoffberg Productions. 19 May **1961** [New York State license]. Sd; b&w. 35mm. 90 min. No information about the nature of this film has been found.

Note: Filmed in the Baltic States, Sweden, the Netherlands, and France. Country of origin unconfirmed.

RED TOMAHAWK   F6.4058
A. C. Lyles Productions. *Dist* Paramount Pictures. Jan **1967** [c22 Dec 1966; LP33643]. Sd; col (Pathé). 35mm (see note). 82 min.

Prod A. C. Lyles. *Dir* R. G. Springsteen. *Screenplay* Steve Fisher. *Story* Steve Fisher, Andrew Craddock. *Dir Photog* W. Wallace Kelley. *Art Dir* Hal Pereira, Al Roelofs. *Set Decor* Robert R. Benton, Ray Moyer. *Film Ed* John F. Schreyer. *Mus Comp* Jimmie Haskell. *Sd* Harold Lewis, John Wilkinson. *Asst Dir* James Rosenberger.

Cast: Howard Keel (Capt. Tom York), Joan Caulfield (Dakota Lil), Broderick Crawford (Columbus Smith), Scott Brady (Ep Wyatt), Wendell Corey (Elkins), Richard Arlen (telegrapher), Tom Drake (Bill Kane), Tracy Olsen (Sal), Ben Cooper (Lieutenant Drake), Donald Barry (Bly), Reg Parton (3d prospector), Gerald Jann (Wu Sing), Roy Jenson (2d prospector), Dan White (1st prospector, Ned Crone), Henry Wills (Samuels), Saul Gorss (townsman).

Western melodrama. Following the massacre of General Custer and the 7th Cavalry at Little Big Horn, Army Captain Tom York rides into nearby Deadwood to warn the townspeople that the rampaging Sioux may attack. York is suspected of being a deserter until gunfighter Ep Wyatt identifies him as a special agent of the Army. Two huge Gatling guns are buried somewhere in the town, but only Dakota Lil of the local dance hall knows where, and she refuses

to disclose the hiding place, claiming that they have already caused enough tragedy, including the deaths of her husband and little boy. York persuades her that the guns are vital to warding off an Indian attack, and she eventually leads him to where they are buried. Before they can be assembled, however, they are stolen by Elkins, a gambler who intends to sell them to the Sioux. Banded together by York, the townspeople kill Elkins, build barricades, mount the Gatlings, and prepare for the attack. York, Wyatt and old Columbus Smith ride off with the Gatlings to help a cavalry troop pinned down by the Sioux. Although Smith is killed, cavalry troops are found, and the Sioux quickly scatter. With peace restored, York decides to settle down in Deadwood with Dakota Lil. *Gunfighters. Gamblers. Sioux Indians. Dancehall girls. Ordnance. Little Big Horn. United States Army—Cavalry. Deadwood (South Dakota).*

Note: Some sources give Panavision as film's anamorphic process.

THE RED, WHITE AND BLACK   F6.4059
Hirschman-Northern Productions. 16 Dec **1970** [Los Angeles opening]. Sd; col (Eastman Color). 35mm. 103 min. [Also 97 min.] MPAA rating GP.

Prod Stuart Z. Hirschman, James M. Northern. *Dir* John Cardos. *Screenplay* Marlene Weed. *Photog* Lewis J. Guinn. *Camera Op* Jack Steeley, Leo Rousseau. *Art Dir & Set Decor* Phedon Papamichael. *Film Ed* Lewis J. Guinn, Mort Tubor. *Mus Score* Stu Phillips. *Song:* "Ordinary Huckleberry" Stu Phillips, Bob Stone. *Sung by* Don Reed. *Sd* Robert Dietz. *Asst Dir* Russ Nannarello, Dick Dixon. *Prod Mgr* Stan Thorne. *Wardrobe* Frances Dennis. *Makeup* Barry Noble. *Sp Eff* Harry Woolman. *Prop* James O'Donnell, Gene Jesso. *Gaffer* John Murray. *Orig Paintings* Kelly Pruitt.

Cast: Robert DoQui (Trooper Eli Brown), Janee Michelle (Julie), Lincoln Kilpatrick (Sergeant Hatch), Isaac Fields (1st Sergeant Robertson), Rafer Johnson (Private Armstrong), Cesar Romero (Colonel Grierson), Barbara Hale (Mrs. Grierson), Isabell Sanford (Isabel), Steve Drexel (Captain Carpenter), Russ Nannarello, Jr. (Lieutenant Bigelow), Robert Dix (Walking Horse), Otis Taylor (Private Adams), Bill Collins (Private Washington), John Fox (The Signifier), Byrd Holland (The Sutler), Bobby Clark (Kayitah), Bernard Brown, Clarence Comas, Donald Diggs, Jeff Everett, Cal Fields, Perry Fluker, Noah Hobson, Earl Humphrey, DeVaughn LaBon, Rod Law, Jim Pace, John Nettles, Eric Richmond (troopers of the 10th Cavalry), Jon-Jon, Rava Malmuth, John Ramsey, Charles Wells, George Wells, actor, Paul Wheaton, David White, Barbara Brown, U. S. actress, Edith Hazley, Lee James, Hank Lowery, Barry Noble, Maurishka, Steve Paullada, Wanda Roberts, Marchita Stanton, Mollie Stevenson, Leah Weed, Stuart Z. Hirschman.

Western melodrama. In 1871 a regiment of U. S. Colored Troops (the 10th Cavalry) is stationed at Fort Davis, Texas. Despite the fact that all recruits and noncommissioned officers are Negroes, the garrison commander, Colonel Grierson, is a white man. Among the new recruits is Eli Brown, a fun-loving man with an eye for women, who immediately begins wooing the post's young seamstress, Julie. Arrogant Sergeant Hatch has long coveted Julie for himself, but Julie consents to become Brown's wife. Shortly after their wedding, Chief Walking Horse arrives to protest the stealing of horses from the Indians. Colonel Grierson responds by sending Private Armstrong, a close friend of Walking Horse, and a contingent of soldiers, including Trooper Brown, against the white marauders. Aware that Julie was always intrigued and flattered by his sexual advances, Sergeant Hatch waits for Brown to leave the fort and then seduces her. Brown returns to learn of the perfidy and attempts to kill Hatch, an action for which he is punished. After Julie and Brown are reconciled, the Indians, outraged by the slaying of one of their braves, go on a rampage; and the entire regiment is sent into action. The Indians are defeated in a bloody battle, but Trooper Brown and many other soldiers die. As the survivors return to Fort Davis with their Indian prisoners, they reflect on the irony of black men waging war against red men. *Indians of North America. Negroes. Seamstresses. Horsethieves. Marriage. Seduction. Infidelity. Race relations. United States—History—Indian campaigns. Fort Davis (Texas). United States Army—Cavalry. United States Army—Negro troops.*

Note: Filmed in Los Angeles and Fort Davis, Texas. Working title: *Men of the Tenth.*

THE REDEEMER (United States/Spain)   F6.4060
Cruzada del Rosario en Familia. *Dist* Empire Pictures. 4 Nov **1965** [San Antonio, Texas, opening]. Sd; col (Eastman Color, print by DeLuxe). 35mm. 93 min.

Prod Patrick Peyton. *Assoc Prod* Jerome Lawyer. *Dir* Joseph Breen. *Script* Tom Blackburn, Robert Hugh O'Sullivan, John T. Kelley, James O'Hanlon. *Photog* Edwin Du Par. *Art Dir* Enrique Alarcón. *Spanish Vers Mus* José Muñoz-Molleda. *U. S. Vers Mus* David Raksin. *Script Girl* Mary Jane Buchenau.

Cast: Luis Alvarez (Jesus Christ), Maruchi Fresno (Virgin Mary), Manuel Monroy (Judas Iscariot), Félix Acaso (Joseph Caiaphas), Antonio Vilar (Pontius Pilate/Saint Peter), Virgilio Teixeira, José Marco Davó, Carlos Casaravilla, Hebe Donay, Jacinto San Emeterio, Félix de Pomés, Antonio

Casas, Carlota Bilbao, Francisco Arenzana.

Voices U. S. Vers: MacDonald Carey *(Jesus Christ)*, Sebastian Cabot *(prolog-epilog narrator)*.

Religious drama. The last 3 days in the life of Jesus Christ are enacted, beginning with Judas' betrayal. Christ is arrested in the garden of Gethsemane and taken to the court of Caiaphas. The next morning he is brought before Pontius Pilate, Roman governor of Judea, who orders him crucified. After his interment, a group of faithful disciples visit his tomb, which they find empty; later, the resurrected Christ appears before them. *Romans. Religion. Christianity. Perfidy. Crucifixion. Tombs. The Resurrection. Gethsemane. Judea. Jesus. Mary Magdalene. Judas Iscariot. Joseph Caiaphas. Pontius Pilate.*

Note: Filmed in Spain in 1957. Opened in Madrid in Mar 1959 as *Los misterios del rosario.*

REFLECTIONS IN A GOLDEN EYE   F6.4061

Warner Bros.-Seven Arts International, Ltd. 11 Oct **1967** [New York opening; c28 Oct 1967; LP35799]. Sd (Westrex); col (Technicolor, see note). 35mm (Panavision). 109 min.

A John Huston-Ray Stark Production. *Prod* Ray Stark. *Assoc Prod* C. O. Erickson. *Dir* John Huston. *Screenplay* Chapman Mortimer, Gladys Hill. *Dir Photog* Aldo Tonti. *Camera Op* Michele Cristiani. *Art Dir* Bruno Avesani. *Set Dir* William Kiernan, Joe Chevalier. *Prod Dsgn* Stephen Grimes. *Film Ed* Russell Lloyd. *Mus Comp* Toshiro Mayuzumi. *Mus Cond* Marcus Dods. *Sd* Basil Fenton-Smith, John Cox. *Sd Ed* Leslie Hodgson. *Asst Dir* Vana Caruso. *Prod Mgr* Mario Del Papa, Milton Feldman. *Script Supv* Angela Allen. *Cost* Dorothy Jeakins. *Wardrobe* Anna Maria Fea. *Makeup* Frank Larue, Phil Rhodes, Amato Garbini. *Hairstyles for Elizabeth Taylor* Alexandre of Paris. *Hairdresser* Agnes Flanagan, Paola Borzelli. *Sp Eff* Augie Lohman. *Horsemaster* Friedrich von Ledebur.

Cast: Elizabeth Taylor *(Leonora Penderton)*, Marlon Brando *(Maj. Weldon Penderton)*, Brian Keith *(Lieut. Col. Morris Langdon)*, Julie Harris *(Alison Langdon)*, Zorro David *(Anacleto)*, Gordon Mitchell *(stables sergeant)*, Irvin Dugan *(Captain Weincheck)*, Fay Sparks *(Susie)*, Robert Forster *(Private Williams)*, Douglas Stark *(Dr. Burgess)*, Al Mulock *(old soldier)*, Ted Beniades *(sergeant)*, John Callaghan *(soldier)*.

Drama. Source: Carson McCullers, *Reflections in a Golden Eye* (Boston, 1941). In 1948 Major Weldon Penderton and his wife, Leonora, are living at an Army post in Georgia. A latent homosexual, the major tries to hide his sexual impotence by maintaining a brusque and authoritative attitude toward his men. Leonora, on the other hand, treats her husband with obvious contempt, making little effort to conceal her adulterous affair with a neighbor, Lieut. Col. Morris Langdon. Langdon's wife, Alison, is a brooding psychotic who, following the birth of a deformed child, mutilated her breasts and now finds solace only in the company of her effeminate houseboy, Anacleto. Also living on the post is withdrawn young Private Williams, who works in the stables and takes care of Leonora's favorite stallion. Unknown to all, Williams is in the habit of sneaking into the Penderton house late at night to gaze intently at Leonora's sleeping body and lovingly fondle her lingerie. After observing Williams, stark naked, riding a horse in the nearby forest, the major secretly begins to lust after the young man, following him on the post and into the woods where he sunbathes in the nude. Late one night, Alison spies Williams entering the Penderton house and follows him to Leonora's room. Upon witnessing his voyeuristic ritual, she suffers an emotional breakdown and makes plans to divorce her husband and go away with Anacleto. Langdon, believing her to be mad, has her committed to a sanitarium, and there she dies of heart failure. Then, during a driving rainstorm, Private Williams makes another trip to the Penderton house. The major sees him and mistakenly assumes that he is the reason for the soldier's visit. When Williams enters Leonora's room instead, Penderton takes a revolver and kills him. *Neighbors. Houseboys. Stableboys. Male homosexuality. Impotence. Marriage. Military life. Infidelity. Mental illness. Effeminacy. Voyeurism. Divorce. Murder. Sanitariums. Georgia. United States Army.*

Note: Filmed in Rome. In initial engagements, prints were specially treated so that color appeared washed out and sepia-toned. Later engagements featured full Technicolor prints.

DIE REGENSCHIRME VON CHERBOURG *see* THE UMBRELLAS OF CHERBOURG

LA REGINA DEI TARTARI *see* THE HUNS

REGINA'S SECRET *see* RAGINA'S SECRETS

LA RÈGLE DU JEU *see* RULES OF THE GAME

EL REGRESO DE LOS SIETE MAGNÍFICOS *see* RETURN OF THE SEVEN

REHEARSAL FOR SIN *see* THE SHOCKING SEX

LA REINE DES BARBARES *see* THE HUNS

THE REIVERS   F6.4062

Duo Productions-Solar Productions. *Dist* National General Pictures. 25 Dec **1969** [New York opening; c17 Nov 1969; LP39331]. Sd; col (Technicolor). 35mm (Panavision). 107 min. *MPAA rating* M.

Pres by Cinema Center Films. An Irving Ravetch-Arthur Kramer Production. *Prod* Irving Ravetch. *Exec Prod* Robert E. Relyea. *Assoc Prod* Rick Rosenberg. *Dir* Mark Rydell. *Screenplay* Irving Ravetch, Harriet Frank, Jr. *Cinematog* Richard Moore. *Art Dir* Charles Bailey, Joel Schiller. *Set Decor* Philip Abramson. *Film Ed* Thomas Stanford. *Mus Comp* Johnny Williams. *Sd Mix* Jack Solomon. *Asst Dir* Tim Zinnemann. *Prod Mgr* Jack N. Reddish. *Script Supv* Meta Rebner, Marshall Wolins. *Cost Dsgn* Theadora Van Runkle. *Men's Cost* Alan Levine. *Women's Cost* Joanne Haas. *Makeup* Emile Lavigne. *Hairstyles* Pat Davey. *Sp Eff* A. Paul Pollard. *Prop Master* Frank Agnone, Tommy Fairbanks. *Dial Dir* Stanley Beck.

Cast: Steve McQueen *(Boon Hogganbeck)*, Sharon Farrell *(Corrie)*, Will Geer *(Boss McCaslin)*, Michael Constantine *(Mr. Binford)*, Rupert Crosse *(Ned McCaslin)*, Mitch Vogel *(Lucius McCaslin)*, Lonny Chapman *(Maury McCaslin)*, Juano Hernandez *(Uncle Possum)*, Clifton James *(Butch Lovemaiden)*, Ruth White *(Miss Reba)*, Dub Taylor *(Dr. Peabody)*, Allyn Ann McLerie *(Alison McCaslin)*, Diane Shalet *(Hannah)*, Diane Ladd *(Phoebe)*, Ellen Geer *(Sally)*, Pat Randall *(May Ellen)*, Charles Tyner *(Edmonds)*, Vinette Carroll *(Aunt Callie)*, Gloria Calomee *(Minnie)*, Sara Taft *(Sarah)*, Lindy Davis *(Otis)*, Raymond Guth *(Uncle Ike)*, Shug Fisher *(Cousin Zack)*, Logan Ramsey *(Walter Clapp)*, Jon Shank *(Joe Poleymus)*, Ella Mae Brown *(Mrs. Possum)*, Florence St. Peter *(Mary Possum)*, John McLiam *(Van Tosch)*, Lou Frizzell *(Doyle)*, Roy Barcroft *(Ed)*, Burgess Meredith *(narrator)*.

Comedy-drama. Source: William Faulkner, *The Reivers, a Reminiscence* (New York, 1962). As the McCaslins' first automobile, a new 1905 yellow Winton Flyer, arrives in Jefferson, Mississippi, 11-year-old Lucius McCaslin is the most excited of all the family. Boon Hogganbeck, a loyal but irrepressible hired hand, is given the position of "official driver." The elder McCaslins—Maury, the father, and Boss, the grandfather—are called away to a funeral in St. Louis. They leave Lucius in the care of old Aunt Callie, but Boon's influence takes over. He persuades Lucius to lie so that both of them can take the car for a pleasure trip to Memphis. As they reach the countryside, Ned, a Negro who as a baby was found in the McCaslin backyard, pops up from his hiding place in the back seat. The three travel to Memphis, 80 miles and nearly 24 hours away. At their destination, Ned goes his own way while Boon takes Lucius to Miss Reba's "boardinghouse for women." Boon finds his favorite of Miss Reba's women, Corrie, and discovers that she wants to change her ways and get married. Corrie's nephew, Otis, sleeps with Lucius that night, and when Otis calls his aunt a whore, Lucius defends her honor and receives a knife wound for his effort. Ned arrives the next morning and boasts of a trade he has made—the car for a racehorse named Lightning. To soothe Boon's temper, Ned explains that the car is the prize in a race between Lightning and another horse, Coppermine. At a makeshift track, Lightning proves to be anything but swift until Ned unwittingly opens a sardine sandwich in the horse's presence. Lightning demolishes his stall and later breaks the track's speed record. Sheriff Butch Lovemaiden's racial slurs against Ned lead Boon to defend his friend violently. The group is jailed, but Corrie comes to the rescue, returning to her old profession for the sheriff. Boon, incensed, blackens her eye and cuts her mouth. Disappointed by Boon, Lucius threatens to go home instead of riding Lightning, but after he sees the prized car arrive at the track, he changes his mind. The race is close, but at the last moment, Coppermine jumps the rail and crosses the finish line ahead of Lightning. Because of the infraction, the race is rerun and Lightning easily wins. After the race, Boss arrives to escort the trio, the horse, and the car back to Jefferson. At home, Maury is stern with Lucius. As he prepares the razor strap for punishment, Boss intervenes, prevents the whipping, and tells Lucius that he must accept the consequences of his wrongdoing. Somewhat heartened by his grandfather's advice, Lucius is made even happier when he hears that Boon and Corrie will marry—and will name their first child after him. *Farmhands. Grandfathers. Negroes. Foundlings. Prostitutes. Aunts. Sheriffs. Adolescence. Horseracing. Family life. Smalltown life. Wagers. Whorehouses. Mississippi. Memphis. Winton Flyer automobiles. Horses.*

Note: Filmed in Carrollton, Mississippi.

RĘKOPIS ZNALEZIONY W SARAGOSSIE *see* THE SARAGOSSA MANUSCRIPT

RELATIONS (Denmark)   F6.4063

Athena Film. *Dist* Cambist Films. Sep **1970**. Sd; col (Eastman Color). 35mm. 91 min. *MPAA rating* X.

Pres by Lee Hessel, Ron Richards. *Prod* Sam Lomberg. *Dir-Writ* Hans Abramson. *2d Unit Dir* Ron Richards. *Photog* Mikael Salomon. *Film Ed* Niels Ulrich Meyer-Pederson. *Mus* Made in Sweden.

Cast: Gertie Jung *(Sonja),* Bjørn Puggaard-Müller *(J.P.),* Paul Glargaard *(Egon),* Jeanne Darville *(J.P.'s wife),* Isa Sørensen *(Dora),* Dorothea Ross *(Rigmor),* Rita Angela.

Drama. Source: Johannes Allen, *Nu* (Copenhagen, 1967). J.P., an affluent, middle-aged businessman, is frustrated by the frigidity of his wife, whom he nevertheless still loves. One night he is harassed by a gang of unruly teenagers, and he meets 16-year-old Sonja, a callous, promiscuous working-class girl. Sonja propositions J.P., and they begin an affair. J.P. gradually perceives that Sonja is merely using him to get money for Egon, her pimp. Sonja must eventually choose between J.P. and Egon; she shows some compassion for sad, victimized J.P., but eventually she goes off with Egon. *Businessmen. Pimps. Prostitutes. Marriage. Middle age. Frigidity. Promiscuity. Perfidy. Adolescence.*

Note: Opened in Copenhagen in Sep 1969 as *Tumult.*

RELAZIONI PERICOLOSE *see* **LES LIAISONS DANGEREUSES**

IL RELITTO *see* **THE WASTREL**

THE RELUCTANT ASTRONAUT　　　　　　　　　　**F6.4064**
　　Universal Pictures. 25 Jan **1967** [Houston opening; c4 Mar 1967; LP35395]. Sd (Westrex); col (Technicolor). 35mm. 102 min.
　　Prod-Dir Edward J. Montagne. *Assoc Prod* Billy Sands. *Writ* Jim Fritzell, Everett Greenbaum. *Based on the Idea by* Don Knotts. *Dir Photog* Rex Wimpy. *Art Dir* Alexander Golitzen, William D. DeCinces. *Set Decor* John McCarthy, John Austin. *Set Coörd* Walter Woodworth. *Main Titl* Pacific Title. *Film Ed* Sam E. Waxman. *Mus* Vic Mizzy. *Mus Supv* Joseph Gershenson. *Sd* Waldon O. Watson, Earl N. Crain, Sr., Bill Schwartz, James Alexander. *Asst Dir* Phil Bowles, James Welch. *Unit Prod Mgr* Wes Thompson. *Script Supv* Robert Forrest. *Cost* Rosemary Odell. *Wardrobe* Peter Saldutti, Ron Roberts, Sally Wood. *Makeup* Bud Westmore, Hank Edds. *Hairstylist* Larry Germain. *Matte Supv* Albert Whitlock. *Sp Eff* Dave Lee, George Brown, sp eff. *Still Photog* Jack Harris, still photog. *Prop* Bill Nunley. *Gaffer* Earl Kennedy. *Grip* Dean Paup, Joe Riggio.
　　Cast: Don Knotts *(Roy Fleming),* Leslie Nielsen *(Maj. Fred Gifford),* Joan Freeman *(Ellie Jackson),* Jesse White *(Donelli),* Jeanette Nolan *(Mrs. Fleming),* Frank McGrath *(Plank),* Arthur O'Connell *(Buck Fleming),* Joan Shawlee *(blonde in bar),* Guy Raymond *(Bert),* Nydia Westman *(Aunt Zana),* Paul Hartman *(Rush),* Robert F. Simon *(Cervantes),* Robert Pickering *(Moran),* Burt Mustin *(Ned),* Ceil Cabot *(waitress),* Fay De Witt *(secretary),* Fabian Dean *(bus driver).*
　　Comedy. Timid Roy Fleming is so terrified of heights that he becomes dizzy operating the space ride at an amusement park. One day he learns that he has been accepted by the astronaut training program after his father entered him as an applicant. Arriving at the space center, he is given the assignment of apprentice janitor. His father and two friends come to pay him a visit, and Roy dons a space suit and attempts to demonstrate some equipment. The results prove disastrous, and Roy is dismissed from his janitor's post. Roy is called back to duty, however, as the Russians prepare to launch a fully automated capsule. The United States decides to prove the efficacy of their own capsule by manning it with the least-qualified individual. In orbit, Roy loses contact with the ground and is left on his own, but, recalling his amusement park experience, he maneuvers the rocket and guides his craft back to earth. Now a national hero, he marries his childhood sweetheart, Ellie Jackson. As their honeymoon plane takes off, Roy is hiding in a patch of tall grass watching Ellie's solo departure. *Astronauts. Janitors. Timidity. Acrophobia. Filial relations. Heroism. Space capsules. Amusement parks.*

THE RELUCTANT NATURE GIRL *see* **SANDY, THE RELUCTANT NATURE GIRL**

THE RELUCTANT NUDIST *see* **SANDY, THE RELUCTANT NATURE GIRL**

THE RELUCTANT SADIST *see* **I, A NOBLEMAN**

THE RELUCTANT SAINT (United States/Italy)　　　　**F6.4065**
　　Dmytryk-Weiler Productions. *Dist* Davis-Royal Films International. 3 Dec **1962** [New York opening]. Sd; b&w. 35mm. 105 min.
　　A Dmytryk-Weiler Production. *Prod-Dir* Edward Dmytryk. *Screenplay* John Fante, Joseph Petracca. *Photog* C. M. Pennington-Richards. *Camera Op* Sergio Bergamini. *Art Dir* Mario Chiari, Pasquale Romano. *Film Ed* Manuel Del Campo. *Mus* Nino Rota. *Sd* Claude Hitchcock. *Prod Mgr* Giorgio Morra. *Unit Mgr* Mara Blasetti. *Cost* Maria De Matteis. *Makeup* Otello Fava. *Hairstyles* Renata Magnanti.

Cast: Maximilian Schell *(Giuseppe Desa),* Ricardo Montalban *(Father Raspi),* Lea Padovani *(Francesca Desa),* Akim Tamiroff *(Bishop Durso),* Harold Goldblatt *(Father Giovanni),* Arnoldo Foa *(Felixa Desa),* Mark Damon *(Aldo),* Luciana Paluzzi *(Carlotta),* Carlo Croccolo *(Gobbo),* Giulio Bosetti *(Brother Orlando),* Elisa Cegani *(Sister Nunziata).*

Biographical drama. Giuseppe Desa, a simple and good-natured peasant boy who lives in Cupertino, Italy, during the 17th century, loses his job as a laborer because of his ineptness. In desperation, Francesca, his mother, arranges for him to enter a Franciscan monastery run by her brother Giovanni and Father Raspi. Given the task of cleaning the abbey, the clumsy Giuseppe breaks a statue of the Madonna. Later he is placed in charge of the stable and shows a natural affinity with the animals, although the stable remains a mess. Giuseppe wins the friendship of Bishop Durso, who orders that he be trained for the priesthood. By sheer luck, he passes the first examination; and while praying before the broken Madonna, he is seen rising off the floor. Father Raspi believes that Giuseppe has become possessed by the Devil and forces him to undergo an exorcism, but the young monk rises again in spite of the chains placed on him during the ceremony. The monastery and Father Raspi then accept him as saintly, and he is later canonized by the church. *Peasants. Stableboys. Catholic Church. Exorcism. Levitation. Monasteries. Religious objects. Copertino. Franciscans. Saint Joseph of Cupertino. Animals.*

Note: Filmed in Italy. Italian title: *Cronache di un convento.* Working title: *Joseph Desa.*

RENEGADE POSSE *see* **BULLET FOR A BADMAN**

RENFRO VALLEY BARN DANCE *see* **JOHN LAIR'S RENFRO VALLEY BARN DANCE**

"RENT-A-GIRL"　　　　　　　　　　　　　　　　**F6.4066**
　　Corsair Films. *Dist* Cambist Films, Lambs Films. 15 Oct **1965** [Omaha, Nebraska, opening]. Sd; b&w. 35mm. 77 min.
　　Prod-Dir-Orig Screenplay William L. Rose. *Exec Prod* Charles Rosenthal. *Assoc Prod* Anton Holden. *Camera* Maximillian Strasser. *2d Camera* Bernie Smith. *Set Decor* Eda Buschatzky. *Supv Ed* Anton Holden. *Sd* Riccardo Widmaier. *Asst Dir* Anton Holden. *Prod Assoc* Ted Estabrook.
　　Cast: Barbara Wood, Frank Spencer, Inge Christopher, David Ransom, Teresa Morgano, Elizabeth Walker, Gary Takata, Darlene Bennett, Paul Dare, June Roberts, Margareta Lindblom, Gigi Darlene.
　　Melodrama. Careerwoman Karen Anderson takes a job at a New York City model agency run by Evelyn Marshall and her brother, Adam. The agency actually procures women as sexual playthings for wealthy, depraved clients. Karen's boyfriend suspects that the Marshalls do not confine their activities to arranging photography sessions, and he insists that she quit. The Marshalls persuade Karen to attend a party given by one of the agency's clients, a sadist. During the party (in reality an orgy in which Karen is the feature attraction) Karen becomes hysterical and tries to escape when her host whips and brands her. In the confusion that follows, the other women turn on the clients. A police raid and investigation put an end to the model agency and its activities. *Models. Careerwomen. Pimps. Police. Model agencies. Brother-sister relationship. Fraud. Prostitution. Sadism. Flagellation. Photography. New York City.*
　　Note: Also advertised as *Rented.*

A REPORT ON THE PARTY AND THE GUESTS (Czechoslovakia)　　**F6.4067**
　　Barrandov Film Studio. *For* Československý Film. *Dist* Sigma III Corp. 27 Sep **1968** [New York opening]. Sd; b&w. 35mm. 70 min.
　　Pres by Carlo Ponti. *Dir* Jan Němec. *Screenplay* Ester Krumbachová, Jan Němec. *Story* Ester Krumbachová. *Photog* Jaromír Šofr. *Art Dir* Oldřich Bosák. *Film Ed* Miroslav Hájek. *Mus* Karel Mareš. *Sd* Jiří Pavlik. *Asst Dir* Pavel Horák. *Cost* Ester Krumbachová.
　　Cast: Ivan Vyskočil *(host),* Jan Klusák *(Rudolf),* Jiří Němec *(Josef),* Zdena Škvorecká *(Eva),* Pavel Bosek *(František),* Helena Pejšková *(Marta),* Karel Mareš *(Karel),* Jana Pracharová *(wife),* Evald Schorm *(husband).*
　　Allegory. Seven people decide to make the most of a beautiful day by having a picnic in the woods. After enjoying their food and washing themselves in a stream, they are startled by the sudden appearance of a group of strangers, led by Rudolf, who take them to a clearing in the woods where an interrogation game is held. When Carl, one of the guests, challenges Rudolf's authority, he is treated abusively until another man arrives, apologizes for the behavior of Rudolf, and explains that the game was merely a practical joke. The man invites them to his birthday banquet, and the guests proceed to the lake where the others are waiting. Once the meal has begun, it is discovered that they are not sitting in their proper seats, and they are told to reseat themselves. One of the female guests bursts into tears because her husband, unable to forgive Rudolf's rudeness, has left the table. Irked by this nonconformist behavior, Rudolf declares that the husband's lack of cooperation is ruining the banquet. He then organizes a search party with police dogs and guns to find the missing husband.

Strangers. Picnics. Games. Practical jokes. Etiquette.

Note: Released in Czechoslovakia in 1966 as *O slavnosti a hostech.*

LE REPOS DU GUERRIER *see* **LOVE ON A PILLOW**

REPRIEVE *see* **CONVICTS 4**

THE REPTILE (Great Britain)   **F6.4068**

Seven Arts Productions–Hammer Film Productions. *Dist* Twentieth Century–Fox Film Corp. 6 Apr **1966** [Detroit opening; c6 Apr 1966; LP32663]. Sd (RCA); col (DeLuxe). 35mm. 90 min.

Prod Anthony Nelson Keys. *Exec Prod* Anthony Hinds. *Dir* John Gilling. *Screenplay* John Elder. *Dir Photog* Arthur Grant. *Camera Op* Moray Grant. *Art Dir* Don Mingaye. *Prod Dsgn* Bernard Robinson. *Supv Ed* James Needs. *Ed* Roy Hyde. *Mus Comp* Don Banks. *Mus Dir* Philip Martell. *Sd Rec* Bill Bulkley. *Sd Ed* Roy Baker. *Asst Dir* Bill Cartlidge. *Prod Mgr* George Fowler. *Cont* Lorna Selwyn. *Wardrobe* Rosemary Burrows. *Makeup* Roy Ashton. *Hairstylist* Frieda Steiger. *Sp Eff* Bowie Films.

Cast: Noel Willman *(Dr. Franklyn)*, Jennifer Daniel *(Valerie)*, Ray Barrett *(Harry)*, Jacqueline Pearce *(Anna)*, Michael Ripper *(Tom Bailey)*, John Laurie *(Mad Peter)*, Marne Maitland *(Malay)*, David Baron *(Charles Spalding)*, Charles Lloyd Pack *(vicar)*, Harold Goldblatt *(solicitor)*, George Woodbridge *(Old Garnsey)*.

Horror film. Harry, a British Grenadier Guard, decides to investigate when he learns that his brother has mysteriously died in a Cornish village. Although the townspeople are secretive and hostile to Harry and his wife, Valerie, the two learn that the brother died from a snakebite on his neck. Subsequent investigation reveals that Anna, the daughter of Dr. Franklyn, the local physician, had been cursed by Malayan natives when she and her father lived in Borneo. As a result, Anna turns into a snake when exposed to intense heat. After Harry is lured to the house and bitten by the snake creature, Valerie also visits the house and a struggle ensues during which an overturned lamp sets fire to Dr. Franklyn's home. The blaze transforms Anna into a huge reptile, and she buries her fangs in her father before perishing in the flames. Harry manages to save Valerie, and the two escape from the burning house. *Investigators. Physicians. Murder. Filial relations. Metamorphosis. Curses. Snakebites. Cornwall (England). Fires. Snakes.*

Note: Opened in London in Mar 1966. John Elder is a pseudonym for Anthony Hinds.

REPTILICUS (United States/Denmark)   **F6.4069**

Saga Film–Cinemagic, Inc.–Alta Vista Productions. *Dist* American International Pictures. Nov **1962** [c21 Nov 1962; LP23589]. Sd; col (Pathécolor). 35mm. 81 min. [Cut from 90 min.]

A Sidney Pink Production. *Prod* Sidney Pink. *Exec Prod* J. H. Zalabery. *Dir* (see note) Sidney Pink, Poul Bang. *Screenplay* Sidney Pink, Ib Melchior. *Danish Adapt* Poul Bang, Bob Ramsing. *Story* Sidney Pink. *Photog* Aage Wiltrup. *Set Decor* Otto Lund, Helge Hansen, Kai Koed. *Film Ed* (see note) Svend Mehling, Edith Nisted Nielsen. *Mus Comp & Cond* Sven Gyldmark. *Sd* Georg Jensen, Poul Nyrup. *Prod Supv* Erik Larsen.

Cast: Carl Ottosen *(Mark Grayson)*, Ann Smyrner *(Lise Martens)*, Mimi Heinrich *(Karen Martens)*, Asbjørn Andersen *(Professor Martens)*, Marla Behrens *(Connie Miller)*, Bent Mejding *(Svend Viltofft)*, Poul Wildaker *(Dr. Dalby* [see note]*)*, Dirk Passer *(Dirk Mikkelsen)*, Ole Wisborg *(Captain Brandt)*, Bodil Miller, Mogens Brandt, Kjeld Petersen, Alex Suhr, Alfred Wilken, Bent Vejlby, Knud Hallest, Benny Juhlin, Martin Stander, Børge Møller Grimstrup, Hardy Jensen, Poul Thomsen, Svend Johansen, Jørgen Blaksted, Birthe Wilke, Claus Toksvig.

Science fiction melodrama. Danish engineers drilling for minerals in Lapland find the tail of a prehistoric beast and send it to the distinguished Professor Martens in Copenhagen. The door of the refrigerated room in which the remains are stored is accidentally left ajar, and the rise in temperature enables the tail to grow new tissue. American Gen. Mark Grayson of the United Nations arrives in Copenhagen to maintain an alert on the creature, which continues to regenerate itself and grows to an enormous size. Though the general undertakes the mission reluctantly, he becomes attracted to the professor's daughters, Lise and Karen. One night, the monster escapes into the forest and begins to terrorize the countryside. The armed forces fail in their efforts to combat the monster with conventional weapons. A flamethrower forces the creature into the ocean, and a depth charge severs one of its feet, but the creature returns to wreak destruction on Copenhagen. As a last resort, a deadly narcotic is fired into its mouth with a rocket. Though the monster appears to have been destroyed, its severed foot begins the process of regeneration. *Americans in foreign countries. Scientists. Monsters. Regeneration. Copenhagen. Lapland. United Nations. Animals—Prehistoric.*

Note: Filmed in Copenhagen; Copenhagen opening: Feb 1961. U. S. sources credit Pink as producer-director and Mehling as editor, while a Danish source credits Bang as director and Nielsen as editor. Actor Poul Wøldike is credited by U. S. sources as Poul Wildaker.

REPULSION (Great Britain)   **F6.4070**

Compton-Tekli Film Productions. *Dist* Royal Films International. 2 Oct **1965** [New York opening]. Sd; b&w. 35mm. 105 min.

A Michael Klinger–Tony Tenser Production. *Prod* Gene Gutowski. *Assoc Prod* Robert Sterne, Sam Waynberg. *Dir* Roman Polanski. *Screenplay* Roman Polanski, Gérard Brach, David Stone. *Photog* Gilbert Taylor. *Camera* Alan Hall. *Art Dir* Seamus Flannery. *Film Ed* Alastair McIntyre. *Mus Comp & Cond* Chico Hamilton. *Mus Arr* Gabor Szabo. *Sd* Stephen Dalby, Leslie Hammond. *Asst Dir* Ted Sturgis.

Cast: Catherine Deneuve *(Carol Ledoux)*, Ian Hendry *(Michael)*, John Fraser *(Colin)*, Patrick Wymark *(landlord)*, Yvonne Furneaux *(Helen Ledoux)*, Renee Houston *(Miss Balch)*, Helen Fraser *(Bridget)*, Valerie Taylor *(Madame Denise)*, James Villiers *(John)*, Hugh Futcher *(Reggie)*, Mike Pratt *(workman)*, Monica Merlin *(Mrs. Rendlesham)*, Imogen Graham *(manicurist)*, Roman Polanski *(a spoon player)*.

Drama. Carol Ledoux, a beautiful, reserved Belgian woman, works in London as a manicurist and lives in an apartment with her sister Helen. Although she has an admiring boyfriend, Colin, Carol is repulsed by sexuality, and particularly by Michael, her sister's married lover. Carol is repelled by his razor and toothbrush in their bathroom and especially by the sounds of their lovemaking at night. Helen and Michael leave for a vacation in Italy, and left alone, Carol falls into a tortured state of mind. She leaves her job at the beauty salon and barricades herself in the apartment. Her mind becomes further unhinged when she receives an abusive telephone call, intended for her sister, from Michael's wife. She tears out the telephone, shutting herself in totally. She imagines a rapist coming through the door and sees arms reaching out of the walls to ravish her. The slight cracks in the apartment walls appear to enlarge and the walls to crumble. An uncooked rabbit in a dish decays and appears grotesque and hideous. Colin, concerned about Carol's condition, breaks down the door; when he turns his back, she bludgeons him with a candlestick and places his lifeless body in the bathtub. The landlord comes to collect the rent, and when he interprets Carol's scanty dress as a sexual invitation, she slashes him to death with Michael's razor. Returning from their vacation, Helen and Michael find Carol in a trance on the floor and telephone the police. *Belgians. Manicurists. Sisters. Landlords. Fear. Murder. Rape. Insanity. Sexuality. Food. Beauty shops. London. Hallucinations.*

Note: Filmed on location in London. Opened in London in Jun 1965.

REQUIEM FOR A GUNFIGHTER   **F6.4071**

Premiere Productions. *Dist* Embassy Pictures. Jun **1965**. Sd; col (Technicolor). 35mm (Techniscope). 91 min.

An Alex Gordon Production. *Prod* Alex Gordon. *Exec Prod* Pat. B. Rooney. *Dir* Spencer Gordon Bennet. *Screenplay* R. Alexander. *Story* Evans W. Cornell, Guy J. Tedesco. *Photog* Frederick E. West. *Art Dir* Don Ament. *Film Ed* Charles H. Powell. *Mus* Ronald Stein. *Sd* Harry Lindgren. *Asst Dir* Clark Paylow. *Prod Mgr* Clark Paylow.

Cast: Rod Cameron *(Dave McCloud)*, Stephen McNally *(Red Zimmer)*, Chet Douglas *(Larry Young)*, Mike Mazurki *(Ivy Bliss)*, Tim McCoy *(Judge Irving Short)*, Johnny Mack Brown *(Enkoff)*, Chris Hughes *(Billy Parker)*, Olive Sturgess *(Bonnie Young)*, Lane Chandler *(Bryan Comer)*, Bob Steele *(Max)*, Raymond Hatton *(Hoops)*, Dick Jones *(Fletcher)*, Rand Brooks *(Gentry)*, Dale Van Sickel *(Kelly)*, Doris Spiegel, Zon Murray, Frank Lackteen, Ronn Delanor, Edmund Cobb, Margo Williams, Dick Alexander, Fred Carson, Red Morgan.

Western melodrama. Dave McCloud, a professional gunfighter, has a gun duel with a killer and then sees Judge Irving Short (on his way to investigate a murder in the town of Stopover Flats) ambushed and killed. After burying Short, McCloud rides into town and breaks up a fight between rancher Larry Young and another man. McCloud is mistaken for the judge by the townspeople and soon learns that Red Zimmer and his henchmen are terrorizing the town. Larry and his wife, Bonnie—the only two who know McCloud's true identity—persuade him to continue to pose as Judge Short and to hold court to try Zimmer's man, Comer, for murder. In the midst of the trial, Fletcher, a gunslinger who witnessed McCloud's gunfight, calls him an imposter and challenges him to a duel. McCloud accepts the challenge, shoots the gun out of his opponent's hand, throws away his own gun, and rides out of town, abandoning his career as a gunfighter. Zimmer and his men are arrested, and the townspeople persuade McCloud to return. *Gunfighters. Judges. Ranchers. Murder. Mistaken identity. Imposture. Smalltown life. Trials. Duels.*

REQUIEM FOR A HEAVYWEIGHT   **F6.4072**

Paman Productions. *Dist* Columbia Pictures. 17 Oct **1962** [New York opening; c1 Sep 1962; LP22965]. Sd; b&w. 35mm. 85 min.

Prod David Susskind. *Assoc Prod* Jack Grossberg. *Dir* Ralph Nelson. *Screenplay-Adapt* Rod Serling. *Dir Photog* Arthur J. Ornitz. *Art Dir* Burr

Smidt. *Set Decor* Francis J. Brady. *Film Ed* Carl Lerner. *Mus Comp & Cond* Laurence Rosenthal. *Sd* Edward Johnstone, Richard Vorisek, Jack Fitzstephens. *Asst Dir* Tony La Marca, Michael Hertzberg. *Wardrobe* John Boxer. *Makeup* Dick Smith.

Cast: Anthony Quinn (*Mountain Rivera*), Jackie Gleason (*Maish Rennick*), Mickey Rooney (*Army*), Julie Harris (*Grace Miller*), Stanley Adams (*Perelli*), Madame Spivy (*Ma Greeny*), Herbie Faye (*bartender*), Jack Dempsey (*himself*), Cassius Clay (*ring opponent*), Steve Belloise (*hotel desk clerk*), Lou Gilbert (*ring doctor*), Arthur Mercante (*referee*), Val Avery, Rory Calhoun ([*participation unconfirmed*]), Barney Ross, Alex Miteff, Willie Pep, J. J. Ballargeon, Michael Conrad, Gus Lesnevich, Paoli Rossi, Abe Simon, Stan Ross.

Drama. Source: Rod Serling, *Requiem for a Heavyweight* (a teleplay; first presented on CBS's "Playhouse 90," 11 Oct 1956). Heavyweight prizefighter Mountain Rivera is knocked out in the 7th round after suffering a brutal beating from a young contender. Upon learning from his doctor that he may become blind, Mountain quits the ring. Army, his trainer, and Maish Rennick, his manager, are equally distressed that Mountain's 17-year career has ended, especially since Maish assured gambler Ma Greeny that Mountain would not last beyond the early rounds; the manager is now faced with repaying her losses. Desperate for work, Mountain visits a state unemployment agency and wins the sympathy of Grace Miller, a young social worker. When Grace arranges an interview between Mountain and an elderly couple seeking an athletic director for their summer camp, Maish ruins the deal by deliberately getting Mountain drunk before the meeting. The manager, who needs $3000 to pay Ma Greeny, then proposes that Mountain commercialize on his American Indian ancestry by becoming a wrestler. Mountain, appalled to learn that Maish bet against him in the final bout, initially refuses the deal but finally relents when he realizes that Maish's life will be endangered if he fails to raise the money. As Mountain walks into the arena in his Indian suit, the crowd starts laughing at him; stripped of all dignity, he performs a war dance and waves his tomahawk at the jeering audience. *Prizefighters. Wrestlers. Fight managers. Athletic coaches. Social workers. Indians of North America. Halfcastes. Gamblers. Hoodlums. Prizefighting. Unemployment. Duplicity. Drunkenness. Employment agencies.*

Note: Location scenes filmed in New York City.

REQUIEM FOR MOZART (U.S.S.R.) F6.4073
Riga Film Studio. *Dist* Artkino Pictures, Brandon Films. 12 Nov **1967** [New York opening]. Sd; b&w. 35mm. 47 min.
Dir Vladimir Gorikker. *Photog* Vadim Mass. *Art Dir* U. Pauzers. *Film Ed* M. Chardynina. *Mus* Nikolai Andreevich Rimski-Korsakov. *Cond* S. Samosud. *Sd* T. Koroteyev. *Asst Dir* Yu. Tselms. *Prod Mgr* Kh. Kinstler. *Makeup* V. Kuznetsova. *Mus Cons* N. Avenarius.

Cast: Innokentiy Smoktunovskiy (*Mozart*), Pyotr Glebov (*Salieri*), A. Milbret (*blind musician*).

Singing voices: Sergey Lemeshev (*Mozart*), Aleksandr Pirogov (*Salieri*).

Opera film. Source: Nikolai Andreevich Rimski-Korsakov, *Motsart i Salyeri* (Moscow opening: 7 Dec 1898). Aleksandr Sergeevich Pushkin, *Motsart i Salyeri* (1830). The proud composer Salieri, for whom success has been difficult to attain, envies Mozart, whose unrivaled talents have come to him naturally and who does not have to labor as others do to create his music. Mozart walks into the room in a jovial mood and forces Salieri to listen as a blind tavern fiddler plays Mozart's music. Salieri is disgusted by what he regards as the debasement of Mozart's art. After Mozart plays a new composition, Salieri invites him to dinner. Alone again, Salieri bemoans the height of his rival's artistry. He fears that the need to write music will end with Mozart, and, becoming enraged, he vows to poison the genius that night. At the inn that evening, Mozart is dejected and explains that he is working on a requiem. He reveals that he was approached 3 weeks ago by an unknown man dressed in black, who commissioned him to write the funeral work; since then Mozart has been haunted by his patron's presence. As the two composers drink to their health and friendship, Salieri poisons Mozart. Mozart begins to play his requiem and weeps; then, feeling ill, he goes home to sleep. Alone, Salieri attempts to rationalize his act of murder by comparing himself to Michelangelo, who, according to legend, killed for the sake of art. *Composers. Violinists. Pride. Music. Poisoning. Murder. Jealousy. Blindness. Inns. Antonio Salieri. Wolfgang Amadeus Mozart. Michelangelo. "Requiem" (Mozart).*

Note: Released in the U.S.S.R. in Nov 1962 as *Motsart i Salyeri.*

LA RESA DEI CONTI see **THE BIG GUNDOWN**

RESTLESS see **MAN-TRAP**

THE RESTLESS NIGHT (West Germany) F6.4074
Carlton Film–Filmaufbau–Real Film. *Dist* Casino Films. Apr **1964**. Sd; b&w. 35mm. 102 min.
Prod Günther Stapenhorst. *Dir* Falk Harnack. *Screenplay* Horst Budjuhn. *Photog* Friedl Behn-Grund. *Set Decor* Franz Bi, Bruno Monden. *Film Ed* (see

note) Eva Kroll, Georg Jaun. *Mus* Hans-Martin Majewski. *Sd* Hans Ebel. *Prod Dir* Eberhard Krause.

Cast: Bernhard Wicki (*pastor*), Ulla Jacobsson (*Melanie*), Hansjörg Felmy (*Fedor*), Ann Savo (*Ljuba*), Erik Schuman (*Ernst*), Werner Hinz (*Arnim*), Richard Münch, Werner Peters, Paul Esser, Joseph Offenbach, Emmerich Schrenk, Albert Bessler, Werner Fölger, Karlheinz Kreienbaum, Erik von Loewis, Hans Krull, Peter A. Lehmbrock.

Melodrama. Source: Albrecht Goes, *Unruhige Nacht* (Hamburg, 1950). During the German retreat from Stalingrad in World War II, military discipline is rigorously enforced. Accordingly, the deserter Fedor is sentenced to death. Assigned to prepare the prisoner for his execution, the chaplain familiarizes himself with Fedor's history. In so doing he discovers that the deserter's motivation was to protect a Russian widow from outrage by either army. Despite the prisoner's purity of purpose, he is executed in the morning. *Chaplains. Widows. Russians. Deserters—Military. Capital punishment. Self-sacrifice. World War II. Stalingrad. Germany—Army.*

Note: Opened in West Berlin in Oct 1958 as *Unruhige Nacht.* Sources conflict in crediting editor.

THE RESTLESS ONES F6.4075
World Wide Pictures–Billy Graham Associates. *Dist* World Wide Pictures. 2 Dec **1965** [San Antonio, Texas, opening]. Sd; b&w. 35mm. 103 min.
Prod-Dir Dick Ross. *Screenplay* James F. Collier. *Photog* Ernest Haller. *Art Dir* Stan Jolley. *Set Decor* William Calvert. *Film Ed* Eugene Pendleton. *Mus & Songs:* "The Restless Ones," "Sing, Sing, Sing a Song of Strength," "He's Ev'rything to Me" Ralph Carmichael. *Sd* Frank Goodwin. *Asst Dir* James Rosenberger. *Prod Mgr* Robert Vreeland.

Cast: Georgia Lee (*Mrs. Winton*), Robert Sampson (*Mr. Winton*), Johnny Crawford (*David*), Kim Darby (*April*), Jean Engstrom (*April's mother*), Billy Graham (*himself*), Jerome Courtland, Lurene Tuttle, Don O'Rourke, Rick Murray, Bob Random, Patrick Moore, Joy Eilers, Timothy Sims, I. Stanford Jolley, Burt Douglas, Kay Cousins, Robert Clarke, Pam McMyler, Marlene Ludwig, Rick Kelman, Paula Baird, David Wright.

Melodrama. Mr. and Mrs. Winton, a television scriptwriting team, are shocked when their teenaged son David is arrested for drunken driving. In hopes of discovering the causes of David's problems, they decide to write a television program about teenagers. As part of their research, they attend one of Billy Graham's Los Angeles Crusade meetings and are so impressed that they convert to Christianity. David scorns them and runs away to Palm Springs with a seductive friend, April. En route, he discovers that April has merely come for the ride and intends to elope with Ray, a truckdriver by whom she is pregnant. Ray does not turn up, and April attempts to commit suicide by slashing her wrists. While Mrs. Winton comforts April's anguished mother at the hospital, David and his father have a long talk. At the next Crusade meeting, when Billy Graham asks for those who believe in Christ to stand up, David does so. *Television scriptwriters. Runaways. Family life. Adolescence. Pregnancy. Drunkenness. Religious conversion. Suicide. Palm Springs. Los Angeles. Billy Graham.*

RESURRECTION (U.S.S.R.) F6.4076
Mosfilm. *Dist* Artkino Pictures. 5 Oct **1963** [New York opening]. Sd; b&w. 35mm. 152 min. [Also 146 and 148 min.]
Dir-Screenplay Collab Mikhail Shveytser. *Screenplay* Yevgeniy Gabrilovich. *Story Ed* L. Nekhoroshev. *Photog* Era Savelyeva, Sergey Poluyanov. *2d Camera* O. Zguridi. *Art Dir* David Vinitskiy, A. Freydin. *Set Decor* O. Alikin. *Film Ed* K. Aleyeva. *Mus* Georgiy Sviridov. *Cond* A. Roytman. *Sd* Valeriy Popov, K. Gordon. *1st & 2d Asst Dir* S. Milkina, O. Shulgina, L. Sadikova, Ye. Yegorov. *Prod Mgr* Viktor Tsirgiladze, A. Ashkinazi. *Cost* G. Ganevskaya. *Makeup* A. Patenovskaya. *Sp Eff* A. Vinokurov, G. Ayzenberg.

Cast: Tamara Syomina (*Katyusha Maslova*), Yevgeniy Matveyev (*Prince Nekhlyudov*), Pavel Massalskiy (*presiding judge*), V. Kulakov, V. Bokaryov (*members of the court*), Leonid Zolotukhin (*prosecutor*), V. Sez (*court secretary*), V. Sushkevich (*prison warden* [*bailiff*]), N. Svobodin (*retired colonel*), Aleksandr Khvylya (*merchant*), A. Smirnov (*Nikiforov*), V. Vanyshev (*teacher*), Sergey Kalinin (*member of workers' collective*), A. Kasapov (*shopkeeper*), Nina Samsonova (*Bochkova*), V. Boriskin (*Kartinkin*), Nikolay Sergeyev (*supervisor of prisons*), A. Zuyeva (*Matryona Kharina*), V. Gusev (*Simonson*), K. Rumyanova (*Bogodukhovskaya*), V. Lanovaya (*Shchetinina*), Vasiliy Livanov (*Kryltsov*), V. Belokurov (*Maslennikov*), N. Pazhitnov (*Maslova's lawyer*), Valentina Telegina (*Korablyova*), L. Ivanova (*red-headed woman*), M. Vinogradova (*Khoroshavka*), L. Arkhipova (*Fenichka*), M. Sidorkin (*lawyer Fonarin*), G. Konskiy (*Korchagin*), L. Zhukovskaya (*Missi Korchagina*), Ye. Yelina (*Sofya Ivanovna*), S. Garel (*Marya Ivanovna*), A. Panova (*Agrafena Petrovna*), N. Bogoyavlenskaya (*Matryona Pavlovna*), A. Konsovskiy (*commentator*), A. Georgiyevskaya, Boris Smirnov, V. Makhov, N. Ofitserov, S. Tikhonravov, P. Voloshin, P. Mikhaylov, Ye. Volskaya, Ye.

Sokolova, V. Vladimirova, Larisa Kadochnikova, A. Zarzhitskaya, V. Burlakova, V. Marenkov, G. Nechayev, N. Agapova, P. Vinnik, N. Grabbe, V. Dukhina, I. Zhevago, V. Kostina, S. Krylov, B. Lyaush, M. Novikova, A. Plavan, M. Semenikhin, Lena Sugrobova, V. Chayeva, G. Shapovalov, Gennadiy Yukhtin.

Drama. Source: Leo Nikolaevich Tolstoy, *Voskreseniye* (Moscow, 1900). Prince Nekhlyudov sits on a jury for the trial of a young woman accused of robbing and poisoning a merchant. He recognizes the woman as Katyusha, recalling their meeting 10 years earlier: As a young army officer, Nekhlyudov spent the summer at the countryside home of his maiden aunts. Here he met their ward, Katyusha, a peasant girl, and they fell in love. He seduced her and returned to his career, giving her a sum of money and leaving her in the care of his aunts, who sent her away upon discovering that she was pregnant. The baby died shortly after birth, and Katyusha slipped into a life of prostitution. At the conclusion of the trial, Katyusha is sentenced to 4 years at hard labor, and Nekhlyudov feels that he is to blame for her situation. He uses his influence to appeal the verdict and visits Katyusha in prison, seeking to make amends for his past conduct and proposing marriage. Hardened by her life of the past 10 years, she rebuffs his efforts, but gradually, in the light of his continued solicitude, her attitude toward him softens. He follows her into Siberia and eventually succeeds in having her sentence reduced. Again she refuses his marriage proposal; having found a new life among the political prisoners, she decides to remain in exile at the side of a fellow convict, Simonson. *Royalty. Peasants. Convicts. Political prisoners. Seduction. Illegitimacy. Trials. Conscience. Injustice. Prostitution. Desertion. Poisoning. Murder. Robbery. Siberia.*

Note: Released in the U.S.S.R. in two parts, the first in Nov 1960 and the second in Mar 1962; running times: 100 and 107 min. Soviet title: *Voskreseniye.*

LE RETOUR DE SURCOUF see **THE SEA PIRATE**

LE RETOUR DU DOCTEUR MABUSE see **THE RETURN OF DR. MABUSE**

THE RETURN　　　　　　　　　　　　　　　　　　　　　**F6.4077**
　Dist Stacey Distributors. ca **1970**. Sd; col. 16mm. 61-81 min.
　Sex film. No information about the precise nature of this film has been found. *Sexuality.*

RETURN FROM THE ASHES (United States/Great Britain)　**F6.4078**
　Mirisch Corp.-Orchard Productions. *Dist* United Artists. 13 Oct **1965** [Pittsburgh opening; c13 Oct 1965; LP32308]. Sd (Westrex); b&w. 35mm (Panavision). 107 min.
　Pres by Mirisch Corp. A J. Lee Thompson Production. *Prod-Dir* J. Lee Thompson. *Assoc Prod* Cecil F. Ford. *Exec Prod* Lewis J. Rachmil. *Screenplay* Julius J. Epstein. *Dir Photog* Christopher Challis. *Camera Op* Austin Dempster. *Set Dresser* Terence Morgan, II. *Prod Dsgn* Michael Stringer. *Film Ed* Russell Lloyd. *Mus Comp & Cond* John Dankworth. *Sd Ed* William Butler. *Sd Rec* John Bramall, Fred Turtle. *Asst Dir* Kip Gowans. *Prod Mgr* Charles Blair. *Cont* Connie Willis. *Cost Dsgn* Margaret Furse. *Makeup* John O'Gorman, Tom Smith. *Hairdresser* Pearl Tipaldi.
　Cast: Maximilian Schell (*Stanislaus Pilgrin*), Samantha Eggar (*Fabienne*), Ingrid Thulin (*Dr. Michele Wolf*), Herbert Lom (*Dr. Charles Bovard*), Talitha Pol (*Claudine*), Vladek Sheybal (*manager of chess club*), Jacques Cey (*hotel desk clerk*), Jacques Brunius (*1st detective*), André Maranne (*2d detective [see note]*), André Charise (*restaurant captain*), Daniele Noel (*nurse*), Arnold Diamond (*neighbor*), Franco DeRosa (*boy in nightclub*), Doreen Moore, Harriet Harper (*girls in nightclub*), Yvonne André (*woman in train*), John Serret, Henri Vidon (*man in train*), Pamela Stirling (*mother in train*), Eugene Keeley (*boy in train*), Jean Driant (*train conductor*), Mischa De La Motte (*Mr. Friedheim*), Rica Fox (*Mrs. Friedheim*), Viviane Ventura (*receptionist*).
　Melodrama. Source: Hubert Monteilhet, *Le retour des cendres* (Paris, 1961). Scarred and prematurely aged Michele Wolf returns to Paris in 1945 after having been liberated from the German concentration camp at Dachau. She persuades an old friend and fellow doctor, Bovard, to reconstruct her face to look as it did before the war. As Bovard goes to work on her, she dreams of her past. *Because she is Jewish, Michele flees from Germany to Paris and there meets the brilliant chess player and handsome gigolo, Stanislaus Pilgrin. She falls in love with him, and they are married. Shortly afterward, the Germans, who have occupied Paris, arrest her, leaving no traces of her; and Stanislaus and her friends assume that she is dead.* Meanwhile, Stanislaus and Michele's stepdaughter, Fabienne, have been living together in her house and now plan to obtain a large inheritance bequeathed to Michele. Since they cannot prove that Michele is dead, however, they must wait 30 years before they can control the estate. Michele's operation is a success, and Fabienne, who does not recognize her stepmother, proposes to use the resemblance to gain the money.

When Michele reveals her true identity, Stanislaus still plans to get the money and run away with Fabienne. Michele catches them conspiring and orders Fabienne from her house. Fabienne plots Michele's murder, but Stanislaus murders Fabienne while also planning the death of Michele. Dr. Bovard intervenes and thwarts Stanislaus' plans. Stanislaus is arrested, and Michele and Bovard remain together. *Physicians. Jews. Gigolos. Stepmothers. Plastic surgery. Marriage. Murder. Personal identity. Perfidy. Inheritance. Germany. Paris. Dachau.*

　Note: Opened in London in Feb 1966; running time: 104 min. Sources conflict in crediting the actors portraying the roles of the 2d detective and the man in the train.

RETURN FROM THE PAST see **DR. TERROR'S GALLERY OF HORRORS**

THE RETURN OF DR. MABUSE (France/Italy/West Germany) **F6.4079**
　CCC Filmkunst–Critérion Film–SPA Cinematografica. *Dist* Ajay Film Co. 6 Apr **1966** [Boston opening]. Sd; b&w. 35mm. 88 min.
　Dir Harald Reinl. *Screenplay* Ladislaus Fodor, Marc Behm. *Photog* Karl Löb. *Asst Camera* Karl-Heinz Linke, Ernst Zahrt. *Art Dir* Otto Erdmann, Hans-Jürgen Kiebach. *Film Ed* Hermann Haller. *Mus* Peter Sandloff. *Sd* Eduard Kessel. *Asst Art Dir* Carl von Barany. *Prod Mgr* Heinz Götze, Manfred Koritowsky. *Prod Dir* Wolf Brauner. *Prod Supv* Artur Brauner. *Cost* Gisela Nixdorf. *Makeup* Willi Nixdorf, Charlotte Schmidt-Kersten.
　Cast: Gert Fröbe (*Inspector Lohmann*), Lex Barker (*Joe Como*), Daliah Lavi (*Maria Sabrehm*), Wolfgang Preiss (*Dr. Mabuse*), Fausto Tozzi (*prison governor*), Joachim Mock (*Voss*), Rudolf Forster (*Professor Sabrehm*), Rudolf Fernau (*Parson Brietenstein*), Werner Peters (*Böhmler*), Laura Solari (*Madame Pizarro*), Lou Seitz (*Mrs. Lohmann*), Albert Bessler (*Trödler*), Adi Berber (*Sandro*), Henri Coubet (*blind man*), Jean-Roger Caussimon, Alexander Engel, Zeev Berlinski.
　Crime melodrama. A series of particularly brutal murders leads Inspector Lohmann to suspect that the master criminal Dr. Mabuse, believed dead, is actually alive and operating in collusion with the Chicago Mafia. Aiding Lohmann in his investigations are reporter Maria Sabrehm and FBI agent Joe Como, who poses as a Mafia chief and learns of the doctor's plan to take over the city. Lohmann finds that Mabuse in some way controls the local prison, whose inmates and staff have been turned into mindless slaves, committing murder on command. Mabuse controls the wills of his slaves by means of a drug invented by Maria's father, Professor Sabrehm, a prison inmate manipulated by the archcriminal. Como poses as one of Mabuse's human robots to prevent an attack against the city's nuclear reactor, but Mabuse discovers the ruse at the last moment and imprisons Como and Maria. Though they escape and join Lohmann's men in foiling the attack, Mabuse escapes. Lohmann follows and discovers that the mad doctor has been masquerading as the prison warden. After a struggle Mabuse disappears into a fire, but no trace of his body is found. *Masterminds. Reporters. Prison wardens. Scientists. Murder. Hypnotism. Disguise. Prisons. Drugs. Nuclear energy. United States—Federal Bureau of Investigation. Mafia. Doktor Mabuse.*
　Note: Released in West Germany in Jan 1961 as *Im Stahlnetz des Dr. Mabuse*; running time: 91 or 89 min; Rome opening: May 1962 as *FBI contro Dr. Mabuse*; running time: 88 min; Paris opening: Jan 1965 as *Le retour du Docteur Mabuse*; running time: 91 or 100 min. Also known as *Phantom Fiend.*

THE RETURN OF MR. H see **THE MADMEN OF MANDORAS**

THE RETURN OF MR. MOTO (Great Britain)　　　　**F6.4080**
　Lippert Films. *Dist* Twentieth Century-Fox Film Corp. 3 Nov **1965** [Los Angeles opening; c29 Dec 1965; LP32094]. Sd (Westrex); b&w. 35mm. 71 min.
　Prod Robert L. Lippert, Jack Parsons. *Dir* Ernest Morris. *Screenplay* Fred Eggers. *Story Cons* Randall Hood. *Dir Photog* Basil Emmott. *Camera Op* Frank Drake. *Art Dir* Harry White. *Supv Film Ed* Robert Winter. *Asst Ed* Dave Bennett. *Mus Comp* Douglas Gamley. *Sd Ed* Clive Smith. *Sd Rec* Jock May. *Asst Dir* Gordon Gilbert. *Prod Mgr* Clifton Brandon. *Wardrobe Supv* Jean Fairlie. *Makeup* Harold Fletcher. *Hairdresser* Joyce James.
　Cast: Henry Silva (*Mr. Moto*), Terence Longdon (*Jonathan Westering*). Suzanne Lloyd (*Maxine Powell*), Marne Maitland (*Wasir Hussein*), Martin Wyldeck (*Dargo*), Brian Coburn (*Magda*), Stanley Morgan (*Inspector Halliday*), Peter Zander (*Ginelli*), Harold Kasket (*Shahrdar*), Anthony Booth (*Hovath*), Gordon Tanner (*McAllister*), Henry Gilbert (*David Lennox*), Richard Evans (*Chief Inspector Marlow*), Dennis Holmes (*Chapel*), Ian Fleming (*Rogers*), Tracy Connell (*Arab*), Alister Williamson (*maître d'hôtel*), Sonya Benjamin (*belly dancer*).
　Mystery melodrama. Based on the "Mr. Moto" character in the novels by: John Phillip Marquand. Mr. Moto, an INTERPOL agent, investigates a sabotage plot at the Beta Oil Company in London after Dargo, a ruthless ex-Nazi, and his gunman Hovath kill McAllister, an executive of Beta Oil, at the onset of an important oil conference held at British intelligence agent Jonathan

Westering's estate. Dargo discovers the INTERPOL agent's interference, throws him into the river, and acclaims Mr. Moto's death. At the meeting, David Lennox, head of Beta Oil, persuades the Shahrdar of Wadi Shamar to renew Middle East oil concessions to the British firm, and Mr. Moto, disguised as a Japanese oil magnate, learns that McAllister may have tried to turn over the Beta concessions to an underground syndicate forming an oil trust along the Persian Gulf as a step toward world control. Dargo and Hovath kidnap Maxine Powell, Lennox' secretary, and hold her hostage at a nightclub to extract company secrets from her. Mr. Moto follows them to the nightclub; a gun battle ensues; and Moto kills Dargo, arrests syndicate members Westering and Wasir Hussein, adviser to the Shahrdar, and rescues Maxine. *Detectives. Nazis. Secretaries. Oil magnates. Royalty. Kidnaping. Sabotage. Disguise. Nightclubs. Conferences—International. Syndicates. Middle East. London. Persian Gulf. Great Britain—Intelligence service. INTERPOL.*

Note: Released in Great Britain in Oct 1965. Working title: *Mr. Moto and the Persian Oil Case.*

RETURN OF THE SECRET SOCIETY see **BABETTE IN RETURN OF THE SECRET SOCIETY**

RETURN OF THE SEVEN (United States/Spain)   **F6.4081**
Mirisch Productions-C. B. Films. *Dist* United Artists. 19 Oct **1966** [New York opening; c12 Oct 1966; LP33186]. Sd; col (DeLuxe). 35mm (Panavision). 95 min.

Prod Ted Richmond. *Dir* Burt Kennedy. *Screenplay* Larry Cohen. *Dir Photog* Paul C. Vogel. *Art Dir* José Algueró. *Set Decor* Antonio Mateos. *Film Ed* Bert Bates. *Mus* Elmer Bernstein. *Sd* Wally Milner, J. B. Smith. *Asst Dir* José López Rodero. *Prod Supv* Allen K. Wood. *Prod Mgr* Robert Goodstein. *Unit Mgr* Eduardo G. Maroto. *Wardrobe* Eric Seelig. *Makeup* José Maria Sanchez. *Sp Eff* Dick Parker.

Cast: Yul Brynner *(Chris)*, Robert Fuller *(Vin)*, Julián Mateos *(Chico)*, Warren Oates *(Colbee)*, Jordan Christopher *(Manuel)*, Claude Akins *(Frank)*, Virgilio Teixeira *(Luis)*, Emilio Fernández *(Lorca)*, Rodolfo Acosta *(Lopez)*, Elisa Montés *(Petra)*, Fernando Rey *(priest)*, Gracita Sacromonte, Carlos Casaravilla, Ricardo Palacios, Felisa Jiménez, Pedro Bermúdez, Francisco Antón, Moises Menedez, Hector Quiroga, José Telavera.

Western melodrama. Fifty gunmen force all of the men in a small Mexican village to ride off with them into the desert. Among the captured farmers is Chico, who years before was one of seven men responsible for ridding the village of a tyrannical bandit. Chico's wife, Petra, seeks out the other members of the band of whom only two, Chris and Vin, survive; and she begs them to save the village once more. To replace the deceased members of the group, Chris buys the release of Frank and Luis, held in the local jail, and also recruits Colbee, a ladies' man, and Manuel, a young bullfighter. The six men discover that the missing villagers are being used as slave labor to rebuild a desert village and church as a memorial to the dead sons of wealthy rancher Lorca. In a surprise attack, the six force Lorca's men to leave, and, with Chico, prepare for a counterattack. The cowed farmers offer no assistance, but the seven defenders successfully repulse Lorca's initial attack. The rancher then gathers all of the gunmen on his land to rout the seven. The situation seems bleak until Manuel discovers a supply of dynamite which the seven use in a counteroffensive. They are eventually overrun, but Chris emerges victorious from a shootout with Lorca. The rancher's gang flee, leaving Frank, Luis, and Manuel dead in the fighting. Chico plans to resettle the village on Lorca's fertile land, and Colbee remains to help teach the villagers how to defend themselves against future attacks. Chris and Vin once more ride off as the church bell rings seven times. *Farmers. Ranchers. Bandits. Gunfighters. Abduction. Slavery. Village life. Explosives. Churches. Mexico.*

Note: Filmed in Alicante and Colmenar de Oreja. Opened in Madrid in Feb 1967 as *El regreso de los siete magníficos.* The second in a series preceded by *The Magnificent Seven* (1960) and followed by *Guns of the Magnificent Seven,* q. v.

RETURN TO PEYTON PLACE   **F6.4082**
Jerry Wald Productions-Associated Producers, Inc. *Dist* Twentieth Century-Fox Film Corp. 5 May **1961** [New York opening; c4 May 1961; LP19491]. Sd (Westrex); col (De Luxe). 35mm (CinemaScope). 122 min.

A Jerry Wald Production. *Prod* Jerry Wald. *Assoc Prod* Curtis Harrington. *Dir* Jose Ferrer. *Screenplay* Ronald Alexander. *Photog* Charles G. Clarke. *Art Dir* Jack Martin Smith, Hans Peters. *Set Decor* Walter M. Scott, Fred Maclean. *Film Ed* David Bretherton. *Mus* Franz Waxman. *Orch* Leonid Raab. *Song:* "The Wonderful Season of Love" Paul Francis Webster, Franz Waxman. *Sung by* Rosemary Clooney. *Sd* Bernard Freericks, Warren B. Delaplain. *Asst Dir* David Hall. *Cost Dsgn* Don Feld. *Makeup* Ben Nye. *Hairstyles* Helen Turpin.

Cast: Carol Lynley *(Allison MacKenzie)*, Jeff Chandler *(Lewis Jackman)*, Eleanor Parker *(Connie)*, Mary Astor *(Roberta Carter)*, Robert Sterling *(Mike Rossi)*, Luciana Paluzzi *(Raffaella)*, Tuesday Weld *(Selena Cross)*, Brett Halsey

(Ted Carter), Gunnar Hellström *(Lars)*, Kenneth MacDonald *(Dexter)*, Joan Banks *(Mrs. Humphries)*, Emerson Treacy *(Bud Humphries)*, Bob Crane *(Peter White)*, Bill Bradley *(Mark Steele)*, Tim Durant *(John Smith)*, Casey Adams *(Nick Parker)*, Pitt Herbert *(Mr. Wadley)*, Warren Parker *(Lupus Wolf)*, Arthur Peterson *(selectman)*, Jennifer Howard *(Mrs. Jackman)*, Wilton Graff *(Dr. Fowlkes)*, Laura McCann *(Miss Wentworth)*, Hari Rhodes *(Arthur)*, Leonard Stone *(Steve Swanson)*, Alex Dunand *(Pierre Galante)*, Jack Carr *(postman)*, Reedy Talton *(Frank O'Roark)*, Tony Miller *(photographer)*, Max Mellinger *(Nevins)*, Collette Lyons *(Mrs. Bingham)*, Charles Seel *(counterman)*, Carol Veazie, Helen Bennett *(interviewers)*.

Drama. Source: Grace Metalious, *Return to Peyton Place* (New York, 1959). Young Allison MacKenzie, who is called to New York for the final editing of her first novel (a thinly disguised case history of the residents of her hometown of Peyton Place), falls in love with her publisher, Lewis Jackman, an older married man. When the novel is published, many townspeople are outraged, particularly Roberta Carter, a domineering and snobbish woman determined to wreck her son Ted's marriage to his Italian-born wife, Raffaella. Hounded by her lurid past, Selena Cross is unable to face her lover, ski instructor Lars Hedlom. Allison's mother, Connie, shocked by her daughter's exposé of the town's citizens, becomes enraged when her husband, school principal Mike Rossi, is fired because he refuses to remove the novel from the school library. Meanwhile, Roberta has finally succeeded in driving her daughter-in-law out of the house. Emotionally upset, Raffaella races to the ski slopes and nearly causes herself to have a miscarriage. Events come to a head when a town meeting is called to discuss Rossi's defense of the controversial novel. Allison and Lewis are present when Connie publicly stands by her daughter and denounces Roberta Carter as a hypocritical bigot. The crisis over, Mike is reinstated at the school, Selena is reunited with Lars, and Ted is reconciled with Raffaella when he finally stands up to his mother. A more mature and wiser Allison realizes that she could never find true happiness by destroying Lewis' marriage. *Novelists. Publishers. Ski instructors. School principals. Mothers-in-law. Italians. Freedom of the press. Smalltown life. Marriage. Infidelity. Libraries. Miscarriage. Filial relations. Bigotry. Hypocrisy. New York City.*

Note: A sequel to *Peyton Place* (Twentieth Century-Fox, 1957).

RETURN TO THE HORRORS OF BLOOD ISLAND see **BEAST OF BLOOD**

RÉVEILLE-TOI ET MEURS see **WAKE UP AND DIE**

REVENGE OF A SWORDSWOMAN (Hong Kong)   **F6.4083**
Shaw Brothers (H. K.) Ltd. 30 Mar **1966** [New York showing]. Sd; col? 35mm. [Feature film, length unknown.]

Action melodrama. No information about the nature of this film has been found. *Revenge.*

Note: Original title and release undetermined.

REVENGE OF DRACULA see **DRACULA—PRINCE OF DARKNESS**

THE REVENGE OF THE BLOOD BEAST see **THE SHE BEAST**

REVENGE OF THE GLADIATORS (Italy)   **F6.4084**
Leone Film. *Dist* Paramount Pictures. 29 Sep **1965** [Detroit opening]. Sd; col (Technicolor). 35mm (Techniscope). 100 min.

Prod Elio Scardamaglia. *Dir* Michele Lupo. *Screenplay* Lionello De Felice, Ernesto Guida. *Story* Lionello De Felice. *Photog* Guglielmo Mancori. *Art Dir* Pier Vittorio Marchi. *Film Ed* Alberto Gallitti. *Mus* Francesco De Masi.

Cast: Roger Browne *(Valerius)*, Scilla Gabel *(Cynthia)*, Gordon Mitchell *(Arminius)*, Giacomo Rossi Stuart *(Fulvius Trasone)*, Daniele Vargas *(Lucius Trasone)*, Germano Longo *(Marcellus)*, Gianni Solaro.

Action melodrama. In 73 B. C., a slave revolt led by Spartacus is quelled by Roman sentries. After all of his cohorts have been crucified, a rumor spreads that Spartacus has been freed by Marcellus. The ambitious senator Lucius Trasone is then sent from Rome to crush the rebels. Marcellus' younger brother Valerius, an ex-soldier and legionary from Spain, returns home to find that his family has been brutally murdered by Roman troops. To avenge their death, Valerius, with the assistance of his sweetheart Cynthia, joins a band of escaped gladiators led by Arminius. It becomes evident that a traitor is in their ranks, however, when Trasone's belligerent son Fulvius is captured by the slaves and mysteriously escapes. In pursuit, Valerius stumbles upon the fatally wounded Marcellus, who explains that Spartacus is dead, that Trasone planted the rumor to become more powerful, and that he has been betrayed by Arminius. His ruse discovered, Arminius plots the freedom fighters' slaughter, but Valerius orders the survivors to hide among the dead. After Trasone, Fulvius, and Arminius arrive to oversee the massacre, the slaves arise and kill the villains. *Politicians. Brothers. Gladiators. Traitors. Revolts. Slavery. Crucifixion. Ambition. Conspiracy. Murder. Revenge. Massacres. Rome—History—Empire. Spartacus.*

Note: Produced in Italy in 1964 as *La vendetta di Spartacus.*

REVOLT OF THE MERCENARIES (Italy/Spain)　　　**F6.4085**
Prodas Film–Chapalo Film. *Dist* Warner Bros. Pictures. 15 Jan **1964** [New York showing]. Sd; col (Eastman Color). 35mm (Totalscope). 102 min.
Prod Antonio Canelli. *Dir* Piero Costa. *Screenplay* Luciano Vincenzoni, Carlo Musso, E. Falletti, Antonio Boccacci, Piero Costa. *Photog* Godofredo Pacheco. *Prod Mgr* Julián Esteban.
Cast: Virginia Mayo *(Lady Patrizia)*, Conrado Sanmartin *(Lucio di Rialto)*, Susana Canales *(Katia)*, Livio Lorenzón *(Keller)*, Carla Calò *(Miriam)*, Tomas Blanco, Franco Fantasia, Alfredo Mayo, John Kitzmiller, Luciano Benetti, Marco Tulli, Alberto Tedecco.
Action melodrama. While traveling to Venice for her wedding to Prince Stefano, widowed duchess Lady Patrizia meets Lucio di Rialto, leader of a band of mercenaries. Later, Lucio returns a jewel that one of his men stole from her, and Patrizia invites him to a feast. Keller, one of Patrizia's neighbors, wants her money, and Lucio offers to protect the duchess from his advances. When Lucio is offered more money to side with Keller, he accepts, and the startled Patrizia accelerates her wedding plans, even though she is attracted to her former protector. Lucio is imprisoned after a second clash with his new master but escapes to rescue Patrizia's wedding party from an attack by Keller's forces. After he slays Keller in a duel, Lucio is reunited briefly with the duchess and admits to her that he could never adapt to her way of life. As he rejoins his men, Lucio finds solace with Katia, a woman who has always loved him. *Mercenaries. Royalty. Nobility. Widows. Neighbors. Employer-employee relations. Greed. Prison escapes. Weddings. Venice. Duels.*
Note: Opened in Rome in Aug 1962 as *La rivolta dei mercenari*; running time: 100 min; in Madrid in Apr 1962 as *Los mercenarios*.

THE REVOLT OF THE SLAVES (Italy/Spain/West Germany)　　**F6.4086**
Ambrosiana Cinematografica–C. B. Films–Ultra Film. *Dist* United Artists. 10 May **1961** [Chicago opening]. Sd; col (Eastman Color, print by Technicolor). 35mm (Totalscope). 102 min. [Also 99 min.]
Prod Paolo Moffa. *Dir* Nunzio Malasomma. *2d Unit Dir* Duccio Tessari. *Story-Screenplay* Duccio Tessari, Stefano Strucchi. *English Dial* Daniel Mainwaring. *Photog* Cecilio Paniagua. *2d Unit Photog* Carlo Bellero. *Art Dir* Ramíro Gómez García, Francisco R. Asensio. *Film Ed* Eraldo Da Roma. *Mus* Angelo Francesco Lavagnino. *Prod Mgr* Manuel Pérez, Mario Bisi, Jesús García Gargóles. *Cost* Vittorio Rossi. *Makeup* Carmen Martin, Mario Bonotti. *Hairstyles* Carmen Sánchez.
Cast: Rhonda Fleming *(Fabiola)*, Lang Jeffries *(Vibio)*, Gino Cervi *(Fabio)*, Ettore Manni *(Sebastian)*, Wandisa Guida *(Agnese)*, Rafael Rivelles *(Rutilio)*, Dario Moreno *(Emperor Massimiano)*, Fernando Rey *(Valerio)*, Serge Gainsbourg *(Corvino)*, José Nieto *(Sesto)*, Julio Peña *(Torquato)*, Dolores Francine *(Ljubala)*, Van Aikens *(Iface)*, Burt Nelson *(Catulo)*, Benno Hoffmann *(Pretoriano)*, Rainer Penkert *(Massimo)*, Antonio Casas *(Tertulio)*.
Action melodrama. Source: Nicholas Patrick Stephen Wiseman, *Fabiola; or, The Church of the Catacombs* (London, 1854). Three hundred years after the death of Christ, when Roman Christians are forced to practice their religion in underground caves, a slave named Vibio is purchased by Fabio, a Roman patrician. For his refusal to fight against a professional wrestler, Vibio is whipped by the patrician's daughter Fabiola. Vibio is defended by Fabiola's gentle cousin, Agnese, and the emperor's favorite tribune, Sebastian, both of whom are secretly Christians. When the hiding place of the Christians is discovered, Fabiola agrees to help them, although she does not share their faith. She falls in love with Vibio and remains with him until word arrives that Sebastian's religion has been discovered and he has been sentenced to death. Fabiola tries to intervene in his behalf, but she is imprisoned and Sebastian is executed. Vibio then rallies the Christians, and they break into the sewers beneath the jail where hundreds of Christians, including Agnese, are waiting to be dragged into the arena. Before many of them can be saved, however, they are burned on crosses or slaughtered by condemned criminals. As Vibio and his men forcibly enter the arena and witness the gory spectacle, they drop their swords in horror. The massacre affects even the blood-thirsty crowd, and they prevail upon the emperor to spare Vibio, Fabiola, and the remaining Christians. *Romans. Aristocrats. Cousins. Magistrates. Royalty. Religious persecution. Christianity. Slavery. Flogging. Capital punishment. Uprisings. Massacres. Caves. Arenas. Rome—History—Empire. Rome.*
Note: Filmed in Spain. Opened in Rome in Jan 1961 as *La rivolta degli schiavi*; in West Berlin in Mar 1961 as *Die Sklaven Roms*; and in Madrid in Sep 1961 as *La rebelión de los esclavos*. Previously filmed in Italy in 1920 and 1951 as *Fabiola*.

LA RÉVOLTE DES INDIENS APACHES *see* **APACHE GOLD**

LES RÉVOLTÉES DE L'ALBATROS *see* **WHITE SLAVE SHIP**

LES RÉVOLTÉS *see* **THE RED CLOAK**

REVOLUTION　　　**F6.4087**
Robert J. Leder Co.–Omicron Films. *Dist* Lopert Pictures. 7 Aug **1968** [New York opening; c17 May 1968; LP37360]. Sd; col (DeLuxe). 35mm. 87 min.
Prod-Dir-Writ Jack O'Connell. *Exec Prod* Robert J. Leder. *Cons Writ* W. H. Manville. *Photog* Bill Godsey. *Film Ed* Carl Lerner. *Mus Coörd* Ben Shapiro. *Titl Song* Norman Martin, Jack O'Connell. *Sung by* Mother Earth. *Closing Song* Sung by Kenny Karen and the Family Album. *Song:* "Cod'ne" Buffy Sainte-Marie. *Sung by* Quicksilver Messenger Service. *Song:* "Super Byrd" Steve Miller. *Sung by* Steve Miller Band. *Song:* "Your Old Lady" O'Kelly Isley, E. Glick, K. Curtis. *Sung by* Steve Miller Band. *Song:* "Babe, I'm Gonna Leave You" E. Darling, P. Bennett, A. Bredon. *Sung by* Quicksilver Messenger Service. *Song:* "Without Love" D. Small. *Sung by* Mother Earth. *Song:* "Mercury Blues" Steve Miller, K. C. Douglas. *Sung by* Steve Miller Band. *Song:* "Stranger in My Own House" P. Mayfield. *Sung by* Mother Earth. *Adtl Mus* Country Joe and the Fish. *Dance Dir* Ann Halprin. *Sd* Vincent De Leo, John Brumbaugh.
Cast—Principals: Today Malone, Herb Caen, Ronnie Davis, Louis Gottlieb, Jurt Hirschhorn.
Cast—From the City of San Francisco: Ellis Sox *(Director of Public Health)*, J. Barry Decker *(Director of Clinical Psychiatry)*, Thomas Cahill *(Chief of Police)*, Dancers Workshop Company of San Francisco.
Documentary. The film examines the hippie culture in San Francisco's Haight-Ashbury district and features Today Malone, a middle-class girl who left home for the new lifestyle. There are scenes of LSD trips, "acid rock" music performed against a background of psychedelic lights, nude swimming and dancing, Indian religious services, a discussion on guerrilla theater by San Francisco Mime Troupe director Ronnie Davis, and a marijuana-smoking session in Golden Gate Park. Throughout the film the positive attitudes of the hippies are contrasted with comments by doctors, psychiatrists, and policemen about the physical and mental dangers involved with the hippie lifestyle. *Hippies. Psychiatrists. Physicians. Police. Rites and ceremonies. Rock and roll. Psychedelic states. Nudity. Theater. Communal living. LSD. Marijuana. San Francisco—Haight-Ashbury.*
Note: Working title: *Revolution ... The Flowering of the Hippies.*

THE REVOLUTION IS IN YOUR HEAD　　　**F6.4088**
Eugene Rosenthal. *Dist* Adelphi Films. 10 Mar **1970** [Washington, D. C., opening; c17 Aug 1969; MP20138]. Sd; col. 16mm. 75 min. [Copyright length: 70 min.]
Prod-Dir Eugene Rosenthal. *Photog* William Hatfield, Joel Jacobson. *Film Ed* Joel Jacobson, William Hatfield, Gayle Moore. *Sd* Kurt Wittig, Van Wood.
Featuring: Phil Ochs, Paul Krassner, Urch Perch, The Fugs, The Fallen Angels, Hog Farm, Pigasus the Pig, Pat Pig.
Documentary. The film concerns the counter-inaugural activities of January 17-20, 1969 (coinciding with the inauguration of President Nixon), organized by the Mobilization Committee to End the War in Vietnam (Mobe). The events of the weekend are depicted in chronological order, beginning with scenes in the offices of Mobe, showing preparation for the march. Next are the activities in the workshops at the Hawthorne School and the tent raising on Friday and Saturday. The middle section shows the rallies, speeches, the march, and the mock inauguration of Pigasus and Pat Pig, two pigs representing the new President and his wife. The Young Americans for Freedom Ball at the Washington Hilton Hotel is also shown. The final section of the film is devoted to the Mobe-Yippie Ball held under the circus tent. *Yippies. Demonstrations. Hotels. Balls (formal gatherings). Washington (District of Columbia). Mobilization Committee To End the War in Vietnam. Young Americans for Freedom. Pigs.*

REVOLUTION ... THE FLOWERING OF THE HIPPIES *see*
　　REVOLUTION

THE REVOLUTIONARY　　　**F6.4089**
Pressman–Williams Enterprises. *Dist* United Artists. 15 Jul **1970** [New York opening; c15 Jul 1970; LP38141]. Sd; col (DeLuxe). 35mm. 100 min. *MPAA rating* GP.
Prod Edward Pressman. *Assoc Prod* John Pellatt, Hans Koningsberger. *Dir* Paul Williams. *Screenplay* Hans Koningsberger. *Dir Photog* Brian Probyn. *Prod Dsgn* Disley Jones. *Film Ed* Henry Richardson. *Mus & Mus Dir* Michael Small. *Sd Ed* Michael Hart. *Sd Rec* David Bowen, Gerry Humphreys. *Asst Dir* Patrick Marsden, Richard Dalton. *Prod Mgr* David Griffith.
Cast: Jon Voight *(A)*, Jennifer Salt *(Helen Peret)*, Seymour Cassel *(Leonard)*, Robert Duvall *(Despard)*, Collin Wilcox-Horne *(Anne)*, Lionel Murton *(professor)*, Reed De Rouen *(mayor)*, Warren Stanhope *(A's father)*, Mary Barclay *(A's mother)*, Richard Pendry *(N.C.O.)*, Alexandra Berlin

(nurse), Julie Garfield *(girl)*, Libby Glenn *(Mrs. Peret)*, Tucker McGuire *(lady guest)*, Tom Duggan *(man guest)*, Alan Tilvern *(Sid)*, Kenneth J. Warren *(sergeant)*, Reginald Cornish *(judge)*, Bill Nagy *(Gansard)*, Earl Cameron *(speaker)*, James Dyrenforth, Bruce Boa *(guests at party)*, Julian Close, Henry Gilbert.

Drama. Source: Hans Koningsberger, *The Revolutionary* (New York, 1967). In an unspecified country, a radical student called "A" is disenchanted with the university leftist group to which he belongs because of its policy of cooperation with the system it wishes to change. He abandons it and his girl friend Anne to join a more militant group led by Despard, a radical factory worker. Working hard to foment a general strike, he is forced to go into hiding when the government enforces a crackdown on radical activities. He is drafted by the army, but when he finds that he will be sent to put down a workers' strike, he deserts and finds shelter with Helen, a pretty bourgeois woman whom he had met earlier. Soon A becomes dissatisfied with Despard's group, which has become very careful due to increased government pressure, and he agrees to join Leonard, a fanatic far-left activist planning to assassinate a judge. A's part in this conspiracy is to detonate a second bomb in case Leonard's bomb does not explode. After the judge has sentenced several convicted strikers, Leonard's bomb malfunctions, and A is left holding the bomb and facing the judge. *Student activism. Militants. Factory workers. Deserters—Military. Fanatics. Judges. Radicalism. Strikes. Military draft. Conspiracy. Assassination. Bombs.*

Note: Filmed on location in London.

THE REVOLUTIONARY *see* **LE RÉVOLUTIONNAIRE**

LE RÉVOLUTIONNAIRE (Canada)   **F6.4090**
Les Films J. P. Lefebvre. *Dist* Film-Makers' Distribution Center. 3 Apr **1967** [New York opening]. Sd; b&w. 16mm. 74 min.

Prod-Dir-Writ Jean-Pierre Lefebvre. *Anim* Pierre Hébert. *Photog* Michel Régnier. *Main Titl* Ciné-Clair. *Film Ed* Marguerite Duparc. *Song* Jean-Pierre Lefebvre. *Folk Songs Perf by* Lionel Renaud. *Sd* Roger Leclerc. *Sd Mix* Barry Lucking. *Asst Dir* Christian Rasselet.

Cast: Louis St. Pierre *(Le révolutionnaire)*, Louise Rasselet *(woman)*.
With the Participation of: Alain Chartrand, Robert Daudelin, Michel Gauthier, René Goulet, Pierre Hébert, Camil Houle, Richard Lacroix, Jacques Monette, Michel Patenaude, Jean-Pierre Payette, Yves Robillard, Jean-Guy Simard, Jacques Soublières, André Théberge, André Leduc, Réal Leduc, Jean-Pierre Roy, Christian Rasselet.

Comedy-drama. A group of youths go out into the snowy Quebec countryside to train in revolutionary tactics under a fanatical, authoritarian leader. He dictates their aims—discipline, silence, and action; forbids them to dream; and rigidly regulates their daily routine. A sequence follows in which Canada's history unfolds. The group capture a young woman who has fled from her husband and hold her for execution. The leader's attention is totally occupied by her presence as the possibility of love enters his horizon. He reviews his troops and forces Yves, who has confessed his fear of death, to place an apple on his head as a shooting target for another youth, Jean. Jean misses his shot, killing Yves, and afterwards kills himself. One of the group, walking in the forest, catches his leg in a bear trap, and his cries for help go unanswered. The woman's husband arrives, and he commits suicide. The members of the group finish by killing each other. The leader, decorated by the government, is shot by the last surviving group member. Only the woman is left alive. *Revolutionaries. French Canadians. Death. Suicide. Winter. Canada—History. Quebec.*

Note: Released in Canada in 1965. Also known as *The Revolutionary.* "Winter" is credited at the head of the cast. Shown at the New York opening in French language version.

REVOLUTIONS PER MINUTE *see* **R. P. M.**

THE REWARD   **F6.4091**
Arcola Pictures. *Dist* Twentieth Century-Fox Film Corp. 15 Sep **1965** [New York opening; c22 Sep 1965; LP31751]. Sd; col (De Luxe). 35mm (CinemaScope). 92 min.

Prod Aaron Rosenberg. *Dir* Serge Bourguignon. *Screenplay* Serge Bourguignon, Oscar Millard. *Dir Photog* Joseph MacDonald. *Art Dir* Jack Martin Smith, Robert Boyle. *Set Decor* Walter M. Scott, Lucien Hafley. *Film Ed* Robert Simpson. *Mus* Elmer Bernstein. *Orch* Leo Shuken, Jack Hayes. *Sd* Jack F. Lilly, Elmer Raguse. *Asst Dir* Joseph E. Rickards. *Cost Dsgn* Moss Mabry. *Makeup* Ben Nye. *Hairstyles* Margaret Donovan. *Sp Photog Eff* L. B. Abbott, Emil Kosa, Jr.

Cast: Max von Sydow *(Scott Swenson)*, Yvette Mimieux *(Sylvia)*, Efrem Zimbalist, Jr. *(Frank Bryant)*, Gilbert Roland *(Captain Carbajal)*, Emilio Fernandez *(Sargento Lopez)*, Henry Silva *(Joaquin)*, Nino Castelnuovo *(Luis)*, Rodolfo Acosta *(patron)*, Julian Rivero *(El Viejo)*, Rafael Lopez *(Indian boy)*, Carmen Rivero, Roque Ybarra.

Drama. Source: Michael Barrett, *The Reward* (London, 1955). In an accident caused by a buried pipeline, Scott Swenson, who operates a crop dusting service based in El Paso, crashes his plane into the water tower of a Mexican village. In town he sees a friend, Frank Bryant, accompanied by a woman, Sylvia, driving in a sports car. At the police station, Scott discovers that $50,000 has been offered for Bryant's capture, dead or alive, on the charge of kidnaping and murdering a boy in the United States. To avoid paying for repairs to the water tower, Swenson offers to help the police chief, Captain Carbajal, find Bryant and Sylvia in return for half the bounty. Accompanying them are Police Sergeant Lopez, a young Indian, Joaquin, and Luis, who dreams of becoming a bullfighter. In the desert 2 days later, the posse captures Bryant and Sylvia, but he insists that he is innocent. Then Lopez finds out about the $50,000 reward and demands that the bounty be shared. Joaquin tries to escape with the prisoners, but Lopez kills both him and Bryant. The horses are lost in the gunplay, and Luis dies attempting to recover one of them. Scott confronts Lopez as he tries to carry Bryant's body away, and the sergeant's horse bolts. Lopez runs into the desert after his mount, leaving behind Carbajal, delirious from an attack of malaria. Scott and Sylvia set off together for help. *Air pilots. Police. Fugitives. Bounty hunters. Mexicans. Indians of North America. Greed. Murder. Posses. Rewards. Deserts. Malaria. Mexico. Airplane accidents.*

Note: Location scenes filmed in Death Valley.

REY DE AFRICA *see* **ONE STEP TO HELL**

RHAPSODIE IN BLEI *see* **HOT MONEY GIRL**

RHINO!   **F6.4092**
Ivan Tors Films. *Dist* Metro-Goldwyn-Mayer, Inc. 20 May **1964** [San Francisco opening; c31 Dec 1963; LP27332]. Sd (Westrex); col (Metrocolor). 35mm. 91 min.

Prod Ben Chapman. *Assoc Prod* Sven Persson, Art Arthur. *Dir* Ivan Tors. *Screenplay* Art Arthur, Arthur Weiss. *Story* Art Arthur. *Dir Photog* Sven Persson, Lamar Boren. *Film Ed* Warren Adams. *Mus Comp & Cond* Lalo Schifrin. *Sd Rec* Fred Turtle. *Prod Supv* Mel Bledsoe. *Asst to the Prod* Joseph Gannon. *Coöp* Natal Parks Game & Fish Preservation Board. *Animal Immobilization Adv* Ian Player. *Psychopharmacology Adv* Keith S. Ditman, (M.D.).

Cast: Harry Guardino *(Alec Burnett)*, Shirley Eaton *(Edith Arleigh)*, Robert Culp *(Dr. Jim Hanlon)*, Harry Mekela *(Jopo)*, George Lane, actor *(Haragay)*.

Adventure melodrama. Dr. Jim Hanlon, devoted to saving African animals from extinction, unknowingly hires poacher Alec Burnett as his guide in seeking to capture two white rhinos to help propagate the rare species. Burnett, who has also been hired by a black marketeer to capture the animals, is certain that his task will be simplified by Hanlon's tranquilizer guns, and he steals the zoologist's car and equipment. Burnett's girl friend, nurse Edith Arleigh, is anxious to reform him and divulges his hiding place. The two men clash, but Burnett changes his attitude when he is bitten by a cobra and Hanlon saves his life. Later, the two rhinos are captured, and the former enemies decide to join forces in animal research. *Zoologists. Guides. Poachers. Nurses. Theft. Snakebites. Safaris. Tranquilizers. Black market. Africa. Rhinoceros.*

Note: Filmed at the Umfolozi Game Reserve in Zululand, South Africa.

THE RIBALD TALES OF ROBIN HOOD   **F6.4093**
P. B. S. Co.–Mondo Films. *Dist* Entertainment Ventures, Inc., Adam Academy of Adult Cinema. 29 Oct **1969** [Fresno, California showing]. Sd; col (Eastmancolor). 35mm. 83 min.

Prod Edward E. Paramore, John Harvey, prod. *Assoc Prod* Murray Perlstein. *Dir-Screenplay* Richard Kanter. *Orig Story* Lawrence Morse. *Dir Photog* Paul Hipp. *Titl* Earl Marshall. *Mus* Amphion Music. *Sd Mix* Sam Kopetzky. *Prod Mgr* Jax T. Carroll. *Script Girl* Mindy Kanter. *Wardrobe* Lee Fischer. *Makeup Artist* Mark Teller. *Head Grip* Paul Wilmoth.

Cast: Ralph Jenkins *(Robin Hood)*, Dee Lockwood *(Maid Marion)*, Lawrence Adams *(Prince John)*, Danielle Carver *(Lady Sallyforth)*, Scott Sizemore *(Young Robin)*, C. S. Poole *(The Sheriff)*, Frank Nathan *(Little John)*, James Brand *(Sir Guy)*, Eddie Nova *(Friar Tuck)*, Ray Benard *(Robin's father)*, Barbara Sanderson *(Robin's mother)*, L. Crandon *(Allan-A-Dale)*, Bambi Allen *(Polly)*, Paul Smith, actor 2 *(Will Scarlet)*, Terry Sands *(Tina)*, Capri, Karen Nichols, Ingred Young, Norma Vanden, Dee Howard, Wendel Swink.

Costume comedy-drama. While King Richard is imprisoned by the Normans, his evil brother John usurps the throne and wreaks pillage, rape, and oppressive taxation on the populace. John and his men forcibly enter the castle of young Robin's father and kill the Earl when he refuses to pledge allegiance. Young Robin watches the brutes rape and kill his mother, and he vows revenge against John and his band. Five years later young Robin is known as Robin Hood, champion of the common people, and he has cleverly resisted John's attempts to capture him. Lady Sallyforth, the sister of John and Richard who has allied herself with John, sends Maid Marion, Robin Hood's childhood sweetheart, into Sherwood Forest to lure Robin Hood out of the forest. Robin

Hood's men take Maid Marion to their leader, and the lovers are reunited. Marion relates to Robin Hood the evil king's efforts to capture him; and Robin allows himself to be captured. He confronts John and leads his men in a spirited battle in which John is killed and his allies subdued, thus restoring Richard to the throne. [Film may include scenes of nudity, sexual intercourse, fellatio, and torture.] *Royalty. Usurpers. Bandits. Orphans. Despots. Rape. Murder. Torture. Sexuality. Revenge. Perfidy. Great Britain—History—Plantagenets. John (England) 1167–1216. Richard the Lion-Hearted. Robin Hood.*

Note: Also known as *Robin Hood.*

RICE GIRL (France/Italy)   F6.4094

Excelsa Film–Carlo Ponti. *Dist* Ultra Pictures. 9 Jan **1963** [Newark, New Jersey, opening]. Sd; col (EastmanColor). 35mm (CinemaScope). 90 min.

Prod Carlo Ponti. *Dir* Raffaello Matarazzo. *Screenplay* Aldo De Benedetti, Ennio De Concini, Carlo Musso. *Photog* Luciano Trasatti. *Art Dir* Enrico Cerrelli. *Film Ed* Mario Serandrei. *Mus* Angelo Francesco Lavagnino. *Sd* Mario Morici.

Cast: Elsa Martinelli *(Elena),* Folco Lulli *(Pietro),* Michel Auclair *(Mario),* Rik Battaglia *(Gianni),* Vivi Gioi *(Elena's mother),* Lilla Brignone *(Pietro's wife),* Gianni Santuccio *(lawyer),* Susanne Levesy *(Carmen),* Liliana Gerace *(little boy's mother),* Edith Jost *(field crew captain),* Emilia Ristori, Bianca Maria Fabbri.

Melodrama. Pietro Guerrini, a middle-aged Italian rice farmer, suffers from an unhappy marriage. At the start of the planting season hundreds of migratory women come to work for him. When Pietro thinks that he recognizes Elena, one of the workers, he journeys to Milan and learns that she is his illegitimate daughter. Although he cannot admit their relationship to anyone, Pietro gives Elena special treatment, and his motives are misunderstood by the other workers, as well as by his wife and their nephew Mario. Mario tries to seduce Elena in his car, but she escapes and meets Gianni, an automobile mechanic, on the way back to camp. The two soon fall in love, but Gianni becomes jealous of Pietro. After Elena is saved from a fire by Pietro, the lovers quarrel and temporarily separate. At the harvest festival, Mario attempts to rape Elena, but Gianni, who has just learned the truth from Pietro, hears her screams and rescues her. In the ensuing struggle, Mario dies after being knocked unconscious. Pietro then tells Elena that she is his daughter and instructs Elena and Gianni to go away and marry, explaining that he will take the blame for Mario's death and claim self defense. *Farmers. Migratory workers. Mechanics. Uncles. Illegitimacy. Marriage. Fatherhood. Seduction. Jealousy. Rape. Self-sacrifice. Justifiable homicide. Rice. Milan. Fires.*

Note: Opened in Nice in Sep 1959 as *La fille de la rizière* at 96 min; in Italy in 1956 as *La risaia.*

THE RICHARD TAUBER STORY see YOU ARE THE WORLD FOR ME

RICOCHET (Great Britain)   F6.4095

Merton Park Studios. *Dist* Schoenfeld Film Distributing Corp. 19 Jan **1966** [Patchogue, New York, opening]. Sd; b&w. 35mm. 64 min.

Prod Jack Greenwood. *Dir* John Moxey. *Screenplay* Roger Marshall. *Photog* James Wilson. *Camera Op* Peter Allwork. *1st Camera Asst* John Stanier. *Art Dir* Peter Mullins. *Film Ed* Derek Holding. *Mus* Bernard Ebbinghouse. *Sd Rec* Sid Rider. *Boom Op* Tom Otter. *Sd Camera Op* Robin Clare. *Dub Ed* Brian Blamey. *1st, 2d & 3d Asst Dir* Derek Cracknell, Peter Dolman, Nigel Watts. *Prod Mgr* Ron Fry. *Prod Sec* Joan Woodgate. *Cont* Marjorie Owens. *Wardrobe Mistress* Eileen Welch. *Makeup* Michael Morris. *Hairdresser* Hilda Fox. *Still Photog* Eddie Orton. *Casting Dir* Ronald Curtis. *Ch Electrn* Jim Axtell. *Prop Master* Dennis Griffin. *Constr Mgr* Eddie Turner. *Grip* Freddie Williams.

Cast: Maxine Audley *(Yvonne Phipps),* Richard Leech *(Alan Phipps),* Alex Scott *(John Brodie),* Dudley Foster *(Peter Dexter),* Patrick Magee *(Inspector Cummins),* Frederick Piper *(Siddall),* June Murphy *(Judy),* Virginia Wetherell *(Brenda),* Alec Bregonzi *(Max),* Keith Smith *(Porter),* Peter Torquill *(Sergeant Walters),* Nancy Nevinson *(Elsie Siddall),* William Dysart *(1st skater),* Barbara Roscoe *(pretty girl skater),* Anne Godley *(wardress).*

Crime melodrama. Source: Edgar Wallace, *The Angel of Terror* (London, 1922). Solicitor Alan Phipps formulates a plan to blackmail his wealthy wife, Yvonne, and at the same time gain revenge against her former lover, John Brodie. Phipps instructs Brodie to demand payment from Yvonne in return for his silence about the affair, and he and Brodie will split the money. Phipps then supplies his wife with a gun, which he assures Brodie contains blanks but which actually is loaded with live ammunition. Brodie, acting his part, is shot dead, and Yvonne is arrested for the crime. Unknown to Phipps, however, Brodie had an accomplice, Peter Dexter, who now begins to blackmail both Phipps and his wife. Driven to desperation, Phipps is about to kill Dexter when the police arrive and arrest them both. *Lawyers. Infidelity. Blackmail. Revenge. Murder. Duplicity.*

Note: Released in Great Britain in Jul 1963.

RIDE A WILD STUD   F6.4096

Vega International Pictures. *Dist* Gold Star Pictures. 5 Jun **1969** [San Francisco showing]. Sd; col (Eastman Color). 35mm. 76 min.

Prod William Edwards. *Assoc Prod* Cliff Alexander. *Dir* Revilo Ekard. *Screenplay* William Edwards, Rachel Edwards. *Camera* William Troiano. *Asst Camera* Edwin Gadden. *Lighting* James Parks. *Ed* Ewing Brown. *Sd* James Fullerton. *Asst Sd* Jim Evans. *Unit Mgr* Chuck Alford, Burke Reynolds. *Makeup* William Fosterwick. *Stunt Coörd* Frenchy LeBoyd, William Fosterwick.

Cast: Hale Williams *(Mike),* Josie Kirk *(Marsha),* Frenchy LeBoyd *(Bill Doolen),* Cliff Alexander *(Sam Bass),* William Fosterwick *(Frank James),* C. C. Chase *(Irene),* Barbara Parks *(Carol),* Bill Ferrill *(Quantrill),* Burke Reynolds *(Pancho),* Helga Honshue *(older sister),* Richard Smedly *(sheriff),* Bill Johnson *(Lefty),* Chuck Alford *(Burt Wilson),* Tex Gates *(Butch Cassidy),* S. T. Alexander, Sr. *(Jennings),* Bob Goldfarb *(Shorty).*

Western melodrama. Quantrill, the leader of a gang of outlaws based in Kansas and Missouri, murders Burt Wilson, a traitor to the gang, and rapes his oldest daughter. The gang then abducts Wilson's younger daughter Marsha and takes her to Quantrill's "pleasure house," where the nightly entertainment includes exotic dancers, wild parties, and orgies. Marsha, a virgin, is disgusted by the easy morals of the women who are kept by the gang. Irene, Quantrill's personal mistress, is murdered when she attempts to save Marsha from Bill Doolen's sexual advances. Marsha then steals a horse and attempts to escape on her own, but Doolen, warned by Frank James, pursues her on horseback and rapes her in a mountain stream. Quantrill's Raiders are brought to justice, and Marsha is released from her captors. *Outlaws. Exotic dancers. Mistresses. Rape. Virginity. Murder. Orgies. Abduction. Whorehouses. Kansas. Missouri. William Clarke Quantrill. Frank James. George "Butch" Cassidy. Sam Bass. Quantrill's Raiders.*

Note: Alternative title: *Ride the Wild Stud.*

RIDE BEYOND VENGEANCE   F6.4097

Tiger Co.–Sentinal Films–Fenady Associates. *Dist* Columbia Pictures. 21 Apr **1966** [Houston opening; c1 Apr 1966; LP32618]. Sd (Westrex); col. 35mm. 100 min. [Also 110 min.]

A Mark Goodson–Bill Todman Production. *Prod-Writ* Andrew J. Fenady. *Dir* Bernard McEveety. *Dir Photog* Lester Shorr. *Camera Op* Leonard South. *Asst Camera* Dennis Dalzell, Jordan Cronenweth. *Art Dir* Stan Jolley. *Set Decor* William Calvert. *Film Ed* Otho Lovering. *Mus* Richard Markowitz. *Orch* Willard Jones. *Song:* "You Can't Ever Go Home Again" Richard Markowitz, Andrew J. Fenady. *Sung by* Glenn Yarbrough. *Sd Rec* Terry Kellum, Joel Moss. *Mus Ed* John Caper, Jr. *Rec* R. D. Cook. *Boom Op* Frank Ami. *Asst Dir* Lee H. Katzin, Harry F. Hogan, III. *Prod Mgr* Harry F. Hogan. *Script Supv* George Rutter. *Exec Assoc* Ann St. Lawrence. *Men's Cost* Gordon Dawson. *Women's Cost* Frances Hamilton. *Makeup Artist* Fred Phillips. *Makeup* William Morley, William Reynolds, makeup. *Hairstyles* Virginia Darcy. *Sp Eff* Lee Vasque. *Casting Cons* Marvin Paige. *Prop* Richard M. Rubin. *Constr Mgr* Harold Nyby. *Still Photog* Homer Van Pelt. *Gaffer* George Marqueenie. *Grip* Herb Bomey, Glenn Maschmeyer.

Cast—Prolog: James MacArthur *(Delahay, the census taker),* Arthur O'Connell *(narrator),* Ruth Warrick *(Aunt Gussie),* Buddy Baer *(Mr. Kratz),* Frank Gorshin *(Tod Wisdom),* Robert Q. Lewis *(hotel clerk).*

Cast—Main Story: Chuck Connors *(Jonas Trapp),* Michael Rennie *(Brooks Durham),* Kathryn Hays *(Jessie),* Joan Blondell *(Mrs. Lavender),* Gloria Grahame *(Bonnie Shelley),* Gary Merrill *(Dub Stokes),* Bill Bixby *(Johnsy Boy Hood),* Claude Akins *(Elwood Coates),* Paul Fix *(Hanley),* Marissa Mathes *(Maria),* Harry Harvey, Sr. *(Vogan),* William Bryant *(bartender),* Jamie Farr *(Pete),* Larry Domasin *(Mexican boy),* Bill Catching *(a drunk).*

Western melodrama. Source: Al Dewlen, *The Night of the Tiger* (New York, 1956). The bartender in a modern-day Texas town tells Delahay, a census taker, the following story: Jonas Trapp marries Jessie in the 1880's, and it soon becomes apparent that everyone believes he married Jessie for her ailing Aunt Gussie's money. Determined to make good on his own, he sets out alone and returns 11 years later with $17,000 earned from hunting buffalo. Outside of town, he is stopped by three men—banker Brooks Durham and two sadistic cowboys, Johnsy Boy and Elwood Coates—who accuse him of being a rustler and brand a "T" on his chest. He awakens from his delirium to find himself in the care of old Hanley who, along with Durham, is the real rustler. Jonas swears revenge after discovering that his money is gone and that Jessie, believing him dead, is engaged to marry Durham. He hunts down Johnsy Boy, who is ignorant of the $17,000 but becomes so terrified of Jonas that he commits suicide. Upon hearing of the money, Coates kills Hanley before realizing that Durham must have taken it. Durham then openly admits his guilt and offers to return the money, but before he can do so, Jonas clubs him down and then kills Coates. When Jessie asks Jonas to remain, he hands her the money and rides away.

Census takers. Bartenders. Aunts. Cowboys. Bankers. Rustlers. Marriage. Hunting. Branding. Robbery. Revenge. Suicide. Pride. Texas. Buffalo.

Note: Working title: *The Night of the Tiger.*

RIDE HARD, RIDE WILD (Denmark)   F6.4098

BT København. *Dist* Phoenix International Films. 28 Oct **1970** [Dallas opening]. Sd; col. 35mm. 70 min.

Dir Elov Peterssons. *Screenplay* Lennart Neilsen. *Photog* Toruald Nyheter. *Ed Supv* Stig Saltström. *Mus* Daniel Sydow. *Sd Rec* Gert Hägberg. *Asst Dir* Lars Nyberg. *Prod Mgr* Eric Malmsjö. *English Dub Dir* R. L. Frost.

Cast: Brigit Krøyer *(Annelise)*, Halger Strøbye *(Leif Vederin)*, Dahl Kullenberg *(Karl Borsch)*, Nicke Bjurström, Vera Ryssen, Åke Nardenskiöld.

Action melodrama. Source: Lennart Neilsen, *Krosor 500* (publication undetermined). Motorcyclist Leif Vederin and his girl friend, Annelise, travel by camper to a cross-country motorcycle race. With the winnings Leif hopes to finance their marriage. Karl Borsch, a competitor who blames Leif for an accident at Le Mans which disfigured his face, threatens revenge. The evening of the contest, Karl, hippies Ruhl and Orla, and two female adolescents participate in a sadistic orgy at which drugs abound. Attempting to murder Leif during the competition, Karl eliminates himself from the race. Angered by Leif's victory, Karl and his pack abduct the lovers. Annelise is raped aboard a motorcycle and compelled to perform lesbian acts and fellatio. When Karl attempts to mutilate Leif's face, however, Annelise seizes a rifle and shoots Karl in the face. Horrified by the homicide, Ruhl and Orla flee as the lovers depart in their camper. *Motorcyclists. Hippies. Motorcycle racing. Disfiguration. Revenge. Sadism. Murder. Abduction. Rape. Lesbianism. Oral sex. Drugs. Orgies. Camper buses. Le Mans.*

Note: Country of origin unconfirmed. Original title and release undetermined.

RIDE MISTER?   F6.4099

Unit Ten Productions. *Dist* Bernhard Films. 18 Feb **1970** [Champaign, Illinois, showing]. Sd; col. 35mm. 82 min.

Prod-Dir-Writ Don Hallstrom. *Exec Prod* Charles H. Leonard. *Dir Photog* Al Denney. *Film Ed* Go! Film Enterprises. *Sd Rec* J. B. Sharpe. *Asst Dir* Bob Dix. *Asst to Prod* J. Bovard. *Makeup* Ray Sebastian.

Cast: Michelle Marke, Lori Brown, Jeanette Mills, Joe O'Conner, Woody Lee, J. E. Meyers, Christopher Stone, Lillian "Chick" Cochran.

Melodrama. Teenaged cousins Wanda and Chris skip school one day to sunbathe in the desert where they are attacked and raped by three drunken men. Thereafter, the two girls seek revenge for their mistreatment. Each weekend they drive to the outskirts of the city and abandon their car. They then pretend to be hitchhikers and lure their victims off the road with the promise of sex. Afterwards, the girls brashly rob their victims' car and money, confident that the men will not report the incident to the police. One day the girls lure homosexual Claude off the road, but his sexual requests are so strange that the girls leave him stranded without his clothes. With nothing to lose, he reports the incident to the police. *Cousins. Students. Statutory rape. Male homosexuality. Revenge. Drunkenness.*

RIDE THE HIGH COUNTRY   F6.4100

Metro-Goldwyn-Mayer, Inc. 9 May **1962** [Washington, D. C., opening; c9 Mar 1962; LP21459]. Sd; col (Metrocolor). 35mm (CinemaScope). 94 min.

Prod Richard E. Lyons. *Dir* Sam Peckinpah. *Screenplay* N. B. Stone, Jr. *Dir Photog* Lucien Ballard. *Col Cons* Charles K. Hagedon. *Art Dir* George W. Davis, LeRoy Coleman. *Set Decor* Henry Grace, Otto Siegel. *Film Ed* Frank Santillo. *Mus* George Bassman. *Rec Supv* Franklin Milton. *Asst Dir* Hal Polaire. *Makeup* William Tuttle. *Hairstyles* Mary Keats. *Coöp* United States Forest Service.

Cast: Randolph Scott *(Gil Westrum)*, Joel McCrea *(Steve Judd)*, Mariette Hartley *(Elsa Knudsen)*, Ron Starr *(Heck Longtree)*, Edgar Buchanan *(Judge Tolliver)*, R. G. Armstrong *(Joshua Knudsen)*, Jenie Jackson *(Kate)*, James Drury *(Billy Hammond)*, L. Q. Jones *(Sylvus Hammond)*, John Anderson *(Elder Hammond)*, John Davis Chandler *(Jimmy Hammond)*, Warren Oates *(Henry Hammond)*, Carmen Phillips *(saloon girl)*, Percy Helton.

Western melodrama. His days of glory as a legendary lawman have passed, and aging Steve Judd accepts the job of transporting gold from a remote mining camp in the Sierras to a smalltown bank. Assisting him are Gil Westrum, another forgotten lawman reduced to earning his living as a carnival sharpshooter, and Heck Longtree, an adventurous young drifter. Secretly, Gil and Heck plan to steal the gold deposits, with or without Steve's help. En route to the mining camp the three men are joined by Elsa Knudsen, the rebellious daughter of a religious zealot. Elsa is running away to join her boyfriend, Billy Hammond, at the mining camp. When they arrive, she marries Billy; but a brawl starts immediately after the ceremony, and Elsa refuses to stay with her husband and his drunken brothers. Instead, she leaves the camp with Steve, Gil, and Heck, who have collected the gold for transport. On the way back to the

lowlands, Gil and Heck attempt to steal the gold, but Steve outwits them. Later, Gil slips away but returns when his comrades are attacked by the Hammond brothers. In a blazing shootout, the Hammonds are slain, but Steve also is mortally wounded. Before Steve dies, Gil promises him that he will deliver the gold and do what he can for Elsa and Heck, who have become attracted to each other. *Sharpshooters. Carnival workers. Guards. Runaways. Brothers. Filial relations. Drunkenness. Robbery. Weddings. Gold. Mining camps. Banks. Sierras.*

Note: Location scenes filmed in the Inyo National Forest, California. Prerelease title: *Guns in the Afternoon.*

RIDE THE HIGH WIND (South Africa)   F6.4101

Killarney Film Studio. *Dist* Feature Film Corp. of America. 1 May **1967** [Maryland license]. Sd; col. 35mm. 77 min.

Pres by Harold Goldman Associates. *Prod* Hyman Kerstein. *Assoc Prod* David Millin, Roscoe C. Behrmann. *Dir* David Millin. *Mus* Joe Kentridge, Bob Adams. *Titl Song Sung by* Michael McGovern.

Cast: Darren McGavin *(Mike Gregory)*, Maria Perschy *(Helena Hansen)*, Albert Lieven *(Karl Du Val)*, Alison Seebohm *(Maria Du Val)*, Michael McGovern *(Jack Dillon)*, John Hayter *(Major Dillon)*, Brian O'Shaughnessy, Michael Todd, Eric Egan, Fiona Fraser, Valerie Miller, Jan Fenn, Geoffrey Morris.

Melodrama. Source: George Harding, *North of Bushman's Rock* (London, 1965). Mike Gregory, an airline pilot, crash lands in the desert of South-West Africa near the remains of an old wagon. Maria and Karl Du Val, the managers of a copper mine, nurse him back to health, and they express interest in the wagon. Maria attempts unsuccessfully to seduce Mike, but he returns to Johannesburg and learns that a wagon loaded with gold bullion was lost in the desert during the Boer War. Major Dillon suggests that he and Mike form an expedition; and with Dillon's son Jack, and Jack's girl friend, Helena, they set out for the desert to find the gold. During the trip they are attacked by an unknown assailant; their plane is burned, Major Dillon is wounded, and Jack and a desert policeman are killed. Maria and Karl Du Val, who are responsible for the sabotage, take Mike and Helena prisoner. Although Maria's advances are once again rejected by Mike, she repents of her role in the kidnaping and helps the hostages to escape. Du Val, now totally deranged, shoots Maria. Mike and Helena trace the gold bullion to a cave. Standing at the entrance is the skeleton of the original escort, still holding a machine gun. Du Val appears; Mike reveals that the bullion is actually lead, and Du Val lunges toward them. The machine gun discharges, and Du Val is killed. *Air pilots. Greed. Murder. Seduction. Sabotage. Kidnaping. Insanity. Deserts. Mines. Gold. Caves. South-West Africa. Johannesburg.*

Note: Filmed in the Namib Desert of South-West Africa. Opened in Johannesburg in Sep 1965.

RIDE THE WILD STUD see RIDE A WILD STUD

RIDE THE WILD SURF   F6.4102

Jana Film Enterprises. *Dist* Columbia Pictures. 5 Aug **1964** [Detroit opening; c1 Jul 1964; LP29187]. Sd (RCA); col (Eastman Color by Pathé). 35mm. 101 min.

Prod-Writ Jo Napoleon, Art Napoleon. *Dir (see note)* Don Taylor. *Dir Photog* Joseph Biroc. *Art Dir* Edward S. Haworth. *Film Ed* Eda Warren, Howard Smith. *Mus* Stu Phillips. *Titl Song* Jan Berry, Brian Wilson, Roger Christian. *Sung by* Jan and Dean. *Sd Supv* Charles J. Rice. *Sd* Don Rush. *Asst Dir* R. Robert Rosenbaum. *Hawaiian Fashions* Sun Fashions of Hawaii Ltd. *Sportswear and Swimwear* Catalina. *Makeup Supv* Ben Lane. *Hairstyles* Virginia Jones. *Coöp* James Campbell. *Surfboards* Phil.

Cast: Fabian *(Jody Wallis)*, Shelley Fabares *(Brie Matthews)*, Tab Hunter *(Steamer Lane)*, Barbara Eden *(Augie Poole)*, Peter Brown *(Chase Colton)*, Susan Hart *(Lily Kilua)*, James Mitchum *(Eskimo)*, Anthony Hayes *(Frank Decker)*, Roger Davis *(Charlie)*, Catherine McLeod *(Mrs. Kilua)*, Murray Rose *(Swag)*, Robert Kenneally *(Russ)*, David Cadiente *(Ally)*, Alan LeBuse *(Phil)*, Paul Tremaine *(Vic)*, John Kennell *(TV commentator)*, Yankee Chang *(Mr. Chin)*.

Comedy-drama. Surfers Steamer Lane, Jody Wallis, and Chase Colton come to Oahu Island to ride the world's biggest waves and compete against surfers from all over the world. Steamer falls in love with Lily Kilua, whose mother objects to the romance because she considers surfers to be "beach bums." Jody falls in love with Brie Matthews, who convinces him that he can be more than a surf bum if he wishes. The stuffy Chase falls in love with fun-loving Augie Poole, who teaches him to enjoy life. Jody continues the sport despite his mounting fear after he is nearly killed while surfing. To make a Hawaiian legend connected with bringing in the big waves come true, Chase makes a dangerous 80-foot dive into a rocky pool. The big waves come and the competition begins. Chase almost drowns and Jody risks his life to save him. Steamer is dropped from competition when his surfoard breaks, but his disappointment is compensated for by Mrs. Kilua's decision to give her approval to his romance with Lily. Only Jody and Eskimo, the previous year's champion, remain in competition. Eskimo quits and Jody, exhausted but triumphant, rides a 40-foot wave alone to the waiting Brie. *Surfers. Hawaiians. Youth. Courtship. Filial relations. Contests. Myths. Oahu.*

Note: Filmed in Hawaii. Don Taylor replaced Art Napoleon as director early in production.

THE RIDE TO HANGMAN'S TREE   F6.4103

Universal Pictures. 19 Apr **1967** [New York opening; c5 Aug 1967; LP36900]. Sd (Westrex); col (Technicolor). 35mm. 90 min.

Prod Howard Christie. *Dir* Alan Rafkin. *Screenplay* Luci Ward, Jack Natteford, William Bowers. *Story* Luci Ward, Jack Natteford. *Dir Photog* Gene Polito. *Art Dir* Alexander Golitzen, John T. McCormack. *Set Decor* John McCarthy, Ralph Sylos. *Film Ed* Gene Palmer. *Mus* Frank Skinner. *Mus Supv* Joseph Gershenson. *Choreog* Hal Belfer. *Sd* Waldon O. Watson, Ed Somers. *Asst Dir* Joseph Kenny. *Unit Prod Mgr* William S. Gilmore, Jr. *Cost* Rosemary Odell. *Makeup* Bud Westmore. *Hairstyles* Larry Germain.

Cast: Jack Lord *(Guy)*, Melodie Johnson *(Lillie)*, James Farentino *(Matt)*, Don Galloway *(Nevada)*, Richard Anderson *(Carlson)*, Ed Peck *(Sheriff Stewart)*, Robert Yuro *(Scott)*, Robert Cornthwaite *(Harper)*, Paul Reed *(Corbett)*, Fabian Dean *(Indian)*, John Pickard *(Pete)*, Claudia Bryar *(Mrs. Harmon)*, Robert Sorrells *(Blake)*, Richard Cutting *(Ed Mason)*, Bing Russell *(Keller)*, Virginia Capers *(Teresa Moreno)*.

Western melodrama. Bandits Guy Russell and Matt Stone are about to be hanged when they are rescued by their buddy, Nevada Jones. The three then hold up a stagecoach for needed funds, and Matt heads for California, ostensibly to retire from crime. But in Sacramento he meets an old friend, lawyer Jeff Scott, and they become partners. Jeff supplies information about Wells Fargo shipments, and Matt, costumed and masked as The Black Bandit, holds up stagecoaches. In one holdup, singer-danseuse Lillie Malone attracts Matt's amorous eye; and Guy and Nevada, who also are on the stagecoach, become heroes by trying to prevent the robbery. After being hired as Wells Fargo drivers, they meet Matt in Sacramento and immediately suspect that he is the famed Black Bandit. Guy is no more successful in proving this suspicion, however, than he is in winning Lillie away from Matt. A $30,000 gold shipment sparks Guy and Matt to make rival robbery attempts. Unaware that T. L. Harper, the top Wells Fargo detective, is riding on the stagecoach, a decoy, Matt and Guy fail in their plans, but once again Nevada helps them escape. The three finally realize that there is no place left to hide and so they surrender. Before giving himself up, however, Matt spends his last night of freedom with Lillie, who has known for some time that he was the Black Bandit. *Bandits. Stagecoach drivers. Entertainers. Detectives. Lawyers. Capital punishment. Stagecoach robberies. Disguise. Criminals—Rehabilitation. California. Sacramento. Wells Fargo & Co.*

Note: Remake of *Black Bart* (Universal, 1948).

THE RIDER IN THE NIGHT (South Africa)   F6.4104

Suidafrikaanse Rolprentproduksies-Killarney Film Studio. *Dist* Barney Pitkin Associates. Jan **1968**. Sd; col (Eastman Color). 35mm (CinemaScope). 78 min.

Dir Jan Perold. *Camera* John Brown, photog. *Art Dir* George Canes, Sydney Mendoza. *Film Ed* Peter Grosset. *Sd* Edward Howes, Willie Du Toit.

Cast: Annette De Villiers, Johan Van Heerden, Brian O'Shaughnessy, Emsie Botha, Gert Van den Bergh, Willie Van Rensburg.

Drama. Source: Mikro, *Die Ruiter in die Nag* (Bloemfontein, 1936). During the Boer War, a mysterious courier plays a central part in efforts to prevent a key Boer regiment from being encircled by British forces. *British. Couriers. South Africa—History—Boer War 1899–1902.*

Note: Produced in Afrikaans as *Die Ruiter in die Nag*; running time: 103 min.

RIDER ON A DEAD HORSE   F6.4105

Phoenix Film Studios. *Dist* Allied Artists. May **1962** [c25 May 1962; LP21899]. Sd; b&w. 35mm. 72 min.

Prod Kenneth Altose. *Exec Prod* Jules Schwartz. *Assoc Prod* Alfred E. F. Stern. *Dir* Herbert L. Strock. *Screenplay* Stephen Longstreet. *Story* James Edmiston. *Photog* Frank Phillips. *Camera Op* Harry Stradling, Jr. *Lighting* Wilbur Kinnett. *Interiors* A. J. Bayless. *Supv Film Ed* Jack Ruggiero. *Film Ed* Melvin Shapiro. *Asst Film Ed* Harry Kaye. *Mus* Fairlane. *Song:* "Rider on a Dead Horse" Joseph Hooven, Edward Alperson, Jr., Jerry Winn. *Sung by* Millard Woods. *Sd* Robert Roderick. *Sd Ed* Kurt Herrnfeld. *Mus Ed* Peter Zinner. *Asst Dir* Lou Place. *Prod Supv* H. Duane Weaver. *Prod Secretary* Patti Drake. *Prod Asst* David McDonald. *Script Supv* Helen Gailey. *Wardrobe* Joseph Dimmitt. *Makeup* Ernie Park. *Prop Master* Meyer Gordon.

Cast: John Vivyan *(Hayden)*, Bruce Gordon *(Barney Senn)*, Kevin Hagen *(Jake Fry)*, Lisa Lu *(Ming)*, Charles Lampkin *(Taylor)*.

Western melodrama. Three prospectors—Senn, Taylor, and Hayden—divide and bury their gold to safeguard it from warring Apache Indians. Senn guns down Taylor as he rides away but permits Hayden to live, since he is the only one who knows the way back. The Indians attack and force the two men to abandon their horses, but Taylor's riderless horse appears and Senn shoots Hayden and rides off to the nearest settlement. Hayden is revived by Ming, a young Chinese girl who hopes that he will take her to San Francisco. Meanwhile, Senn tells bounty hunter Jake Fry that he saw Hayden murder Taylor, and the two men agree to share the $1,000 reward for Hayden's capture. Fry tracks down Hayden and Ming, while Senn goes off in search of the gold. After locking Hayden in jail, Fry forces Ming to take him to the buried gold. Hayden manages to escape and rescues Ming from Fry, who sets off a dynamite charge and unwittingly reduces the gold to dust. Senn goes berserk upon discovering the destruction and attacks Ming, but Hayden shoots him and leaves with Ming. [One source states that Senn attacks Hayden.] *Prospectors. Bounty hunters. Apache Indians. Chinese. Murder. Perfidy. Frameup. Gold.*

Note: Filmed in and around Phoenix, Arizona.

RIDER ON THE RAIN (France/Italy)   F6.4106

Greenwich Film Production-Medusa Film. *Dist* Avco Embassy Pictures. 24 May **1970** [New York opening]. Sd; col (Eastman Color, print by Movielab). 35mm. 119 min. [Also 115 min.] MPAA rating GP.

Pres by Joseph E. Levine. *Prod* Serge Silberman. *Dir* René Clément. *Screenplay* Sébastien Japrisot. *Adapt-Dial* Sébastien Japrisot, Lorenzo Ventavoli. *Photog* Andréas Winding. *Art Dir* Pierre Guffroy. *Film Ed* Françoise Javet. *Mus & Mus Cond* Francis Lai. *Sd* Jacques Gallois. *Asst Dir* Georges Grodzenczyk, Jacques Bourdon. *Prod Mgr* Ulrich Pickard. *Cost* Rosine Delamare.

Cast: Marlène Jobert *(Mellie)*, Charles Bronson *(Dobbs)*, Annie Cordy *(Juliette)*, Jill Ireland *(Nicole)*, Gabriele Tinti *(Tony)*, Jean Gaven *(Toussaint)*, Marc Mazza *(passenger)*, Corinne Marchand *(Tania)*, Jean Piat *(Mr. Armand)*, Marika Green *(hostess)*, Ellen Bahl *(Madeline Legauff)*, Marcel Pérès *(station master)*.

Mystery melodrama. Mellie, a young woman living in a seaside resort in France, sees a stranger disembark from a bus. The next day she sees him watching her as she tries on a dress at her friend Nicole's boutique. That night, while her jealous airline pilot husband, Tony, is away, the stranger breaks into the house and assaults and rapes her. When she regains consciousness, she hears the intruder in the basement and kills him with two blasts from a shotgun when he tries to attack her again. In fear of reporting the incident to the police, she decides to throw the body off a cliff into the sea. Several days later, she sees a newspaper headline announcing the discovery of a body washed ashore in the bay. Harry Dobbs, an American stranger, approaches her at a wedding reception and accuses her of the murder of a sex maniac who escaped from a military prison asylum and stole $60,000 in U. S. Army funds. Despite Mellie's steadfast denial of guilt, Dobbs continues to pressure her for a confession and demands that she turn over a red airline bag which the dead man was carrying. His relentless hounding evokes childhood memories of discovering her mother with a lover, her father's badgering the revelation from her, and his furious reaction and desertion of the family. Mellie finds the bag with the money and goes to Dobbs's hotel room, where in his absence she searches his suitcase and discovers that he is a colonel in the U. S. Army. Dobbs catches her in his room and tells her that another woman has been arrested for the murder. Mellie travels to Paris to warn the accused woman's sister, a madam, and is attacked by three gangsters who think she knows too much. Dobbs comes to her rescue, and the two return to the coast, where they are informed by a local detective that the body washed ashore was not that of the man sought by Dobbs. Dobbs later finds the missing body and in the dead man's hand a button from Mellie's dress. Content to recover the stolen money, he decides not to implicate her. *Strangers. Psychopaths. Air pilots. Americans in foreign countries. Investigators. Madams. Gangsters. Rape. Justifiable homicide. Murder. Confession (law). Theft. Infidelity. Jealousy. Personal identity. Resorts. Whorehouses. Paris. United States Army.*

Note: Location scenes filmed on Cap des Pins and in Paris. Opened in Paris in Jan 1970 as *Le passager de la pluie.*

RIFF RAFF GIRLS (France/Italy)   F6.4107

Les Productions de l'Etoile-Dismage-Transalpina-Techno Stampa Films. *Dist* Continental Distributing, Inc. 19 Oct **1962** [New York opening]. Sd; b&w. 35mm. 97 min.

Prod Jacques Mage. *Dir* Alex Joffé. *Dial* Auguste Le Breton. *Adapt* Auguste Le Breton, Alex Joffé, José Giovanni, Gabriel Arout, Jacques Mage. *Photog* Pierre Montazel. *Art Dir* Rino Mondellini. *Film Ed* Léonide Azar. *Mus & Song* Louiguy. *Lyr* Charles Aznavour. *Sd* Joseph de Bretagne. *Asst Dir* Dossia Mage, Marc Aurian. *Prod Mgr* Jacques Planté.

Cast: Nadja Tiller *(Vicky)*, Robert Hossein *(Marcel)*, Silvia Monfort *(Yoko)*, Roger Hanin *(The Bug)*, Pierre Blanchar *(The Pirate)*, Françoise Rosay

(Berthe), Eddie Constantine *(Williams)*, Jean Gaven *(James)*, Georges Rigaud *(The Marquis)*, André Cellier *(bank guard)*, Carlo Campanini, Tiberio Murgia.

Crime melodrama. Source: Auguste Le Breton, *Du rififi chez les femmes* (Paris, 1957). While major repairs are being made on the roof of the Bank of Belgium, a group of thieves are planning to rob the receipts from the Brussels Exposition. The plan, masterminded from Paris by an underworld figure known as The Marquis, involves Vicky, the money-hungry proprietress of a river barge nightclub, whose outlook has been marked by childhood memories of wartime; James, her assistant; and Marcel, who will execute the robbery while working as a laborer on the construction job. Their plans hit a snag, however, when Vicky refuses to sell her night spot to a deported gangster called The Bug. As a result, The Bug has his mistress, Yoko, and her band of women gangsters raid and demolish the club. Realizing that the robbery is in danger of discovery, Marcel arranges a meeting between The Bug and The Marquis; and another racketeer, The Pirate, arranges a truce whereby Vicky must sell the club within a week. But The Bug is threatened with another deportation unless he pinpoints a waterfront dope smuggling racket, and he mistakenly assumes that Vicky's barge is the ring's headquarters. After abducting James, he learns of the proposed robbery and tries to muscle in. During the violent gun battle that follows, the two gangs annihilate each other. *Nightclub owners. Gangsters. Mistresses. Bank robberies. Smuggling. Extortion. Abduction. Deportation. Gang wars. Waterfronts. Barges. Narcotics. Brussels.*

Note: Opened in Paris in May 1959 as *Du rififi chez les femmes*; running time: 110 min; in Rome in Oct 1959 as *Rififi fra le donne*; running time: 105 min. Prerelease title: *Rififi for Girls*.

RIFIFI À TOKYO *see* **RIFIFI IN TOKYO**

RIFIFI FOR GIRLS *see* **RIFF RAFF GIRLS**

RIFIFÌ FRA LE DONNE *see* **RIFF RAFF GIRLS**

RIFIFI IN PARIS *see* **THE UPPER HAND**

RIFIFI IN TOKYO (France/Italy)   **F6.4108**
CIPRA-C. C. M. *Dist* Metro-Goldwyn-Mayer, Inc. 13 Mar **1963** [Los Angeles opening; c31 Dec 1962; LP24888]. Sd; b&w. 35mm. 89 min.

A Jacques Bar Production. *Prod* Jacques Bar. *Dir* Jacques Deray. *Orig Screenplay* Auguste Le Breton. *Dial* José Giovanni. *Screen Adapt* José Giovanni, Jacques Deray, Rodolphe M. Arlaud. *Dir Photog* Tadashi Arakami. *Camera* Jean Charvein. *Decors* Hirataka. *Film Ed* Albert Jurgenson. *Asst Film Ed* Janine Oudoul, Eva Zora. *Mus* Georges Delerue. *Asst Dir* Claude Clément. *Prod Mgr* Jacques Juranville. *Script Girl* Annie Rozier.

Cast: Karl Boehm *(Carl Mersen)*, Michel Vitold *(Merigne)*, Charles Vanel *(Van Hekken)*, Eric Okada *(Danny Riquet)*, Keiko Kishi *(Asami)*, Barbara Lass *(Françoise Merigne)*, Eijiro Yanagi *(Ishimoto)*, Hideaki Suzuki, Dante Maggio, Masao Oda.

Crime drama. Van Hekken, an international jewel thief, arrives in Japan with a plan for stealing a priceless diamond which is kept in the electronically protected vault of the Bank of Tokyo. Also interested in the gem is an underworld ruler who, with his gangsters, arranges for the murder of Van Hekken's accomplice, Danny Riquet. Following Riquet's death, Riquet's old Army buddy Carl Mersen joins Van Hekken to avenge his friend's slaying. Further trouble arises when Mersen becomes involved with Françoise Merigne, the wife of Van Hekken's electrical expert. The trio eventually makes its way into the bank vault, and Van Hekken acquires the cherished jewel. As he is about to leave, however, an iron-barred door descends from the ceiling and imprisons him inside the vault. He offers the diamond to Mersen who refuses it. As Mersen escapes from the bank, he hears Van Hekken shoot himself to avoid capture. *Thieves. Gangsters. Theft. Revenge. Murder. Suicide. Jewels. Banks. Tokyo.*

Note: Filmed in Tokyo. Opened in Paris in Mar 1963 as *Rififi à Tokyo* at 98 min. Italian title: *Rififi a Tokyo*.

RIFIFÌ INTERNAZIONALE *see* **THE UPPER HAND**

THE RIGHT APPROACH   **F6.4109**
Twentieth Century-Fox Film Corp. 17 May **1961** [New York opening; c19 Apr 1961; LP19492]. Sd (Westrex); b&w. 35mm (CinemaScope). 92 min. [Copyright length: 98 min.]

Prod Oscar Brodney. *Dir* David Butler. *Screenplay* Fay Kanin, Michael Kanin. *Dir Photog* Sam Leavitt. *Art Dir* Duncan Cramer, Herman A. Blumenthal. *Set Decor* Walter M. Scott, Fred MacLean. *Film Ed* Tom McAdoo. *Mus* Dominic Frontiere. *Titl Song* Marilyn Keith, Alan Bergman, Lew Spence. *Song:* "When You Least Expect It" Sammy Stept. *Song:* "Lady, Love Me" Kirby Stone. *Sung by* The Kirby Stone Four, Frankie Vaughan. *Choreog* Josephine Earl. *Sd* Arthur Kirbach, Frank W. Moran. *Asst Dir* Ad Schaumer. *Makeup* Ben Nye. *Hairstyles* Helen Turpin.

Cast: Frankie Vaughan *(Leo Mack)*, Martha Hyer *(Anne Perry)*, Juliet Prowse *(Ursula Poe)*, Gary Crosby *(Rip Hulett)*, David McLean *(Bill Sikulovic)*, Jesse White *(Brian Freer)*, Jane Withers *(Liz)*, Rachel Stephens *(Helen)*, Steve Harris, actor *(Mitch Mack)*, Paul Von Schreiber *(Granny)*, Robert Casper *(Horace)*.

Drama. Source: Garson Kanin, *The Live Wire* (New York opening: 17 Aug 1950). Five young ex-army friends have turned an abandoned Pasadena restaurant, the Hut, into a sort of barracks apartment. The happy routine of their lives is suddenly disrupted when they take in a new member—Leo Mack, an unscrupulous would-be actor whose brother, Mitch, is one of the residents. Before long Leo not only has conned the young men out of money and clothing but has also made a secret deal with young Ursula Poe, a money-hungry carhop who hopes to marry one of the bachelors, Horace Tobey, whose mother is a millionaire. Though Leo expects to get a share of the profits if he helps Ursula catch her man, he is not above having an affair with the girl himself. He then takes up with *Life* magazine staffer Anne Perry and induces her to do a story on the Hut. Leo naturally receives most of the coverage (including a cover picture) and attracts an important agent and bids from the movie studios. Then, at a press party, his world collapses when Anne denounces him as a cad and Ursula, pregnant, threatens to expose him unless he marries her. Furthermore, the bachelors throw him out of the Hut and refuse to have anything more to do with him. Though Leo is on the threshold of fame, he has paid a high price. *Bachelors. Roommates. Opportunists. Actors. Gold diggers. Waitresses. Heirs. Ambition. Publicity. Seduction. Pregnancy. Motion pictures. "Life" (magazine). Pasadena.*

THE RIGHT HAND OF THE DEVIL   **F6.4110**
Aram Katcher. *Dist* Cinema-Video International, Inc. 31 Jul **1963** [Denver, Colorado, showing]. Sd; b&w. 35mm. 72 min. [Cut from 75 min.]

Prod-Dir-Orig Story Aram Katcher. *Screenplay* Ralph Brooke. *Photog* Fouad Said. *Titl Dsgn* Aram Katcher. *Supv Film Ed* Aram Katcher. *Mus* John Bath. *Asst to the Prod* Tom Boutross. *Makeup* Aram Katcher.

Cast: Aram Katcher *(Pepe Lusara)*, Lisa McDonald *(Miss Sutherland)*, Brad Trumbull *(Williams)*, James V. Christy *(Sammy)*, Chris Randall *(Spooky)*, Monte Lee *(Carter)*, Luigi Gardneri *(Dino's bartender)*, Georgia Holden *(The Dancer)*, Jack Elton *(Dino's pianist, uncredited)*.

Crime melodrama. Gangster Pepe Lusara arrives in Los Angeles and leases as his center of operations a deserted mansion in Laurel Canyon. He hires some local hoodlums, planning to rob the Hollywood Sports Arena, and romances Miss Sutherland, the arena's lonely, middle-aged cashier, into assisting him. Following the successful robbery and a wild chase, Lusara kills his accomplices, steals acids from a chemical warehouse, fills a bathtub with a solution of acid, dumps the bodies into the tub, and flees to Rio assuming he has killed off everyone who might incriminate him. He returns to Hollywood, broke and with a new plan in mind, but Miss Sutherland traps and kills him there. *Gangsters. Cashiers. Robbery. Murder. Seduction. Duplicity. Revenge. Laurel Canyon. Hollywood. Rio de Janeiro. Hollywood Sports Arena.*

Note: Location scenes filmed in Laurel Canyon, the Hollywood Sports Arena, and various Hollywood night spots.

RINDERCELLA   **F6.4111**
Janus II Productions–Academy Productions. *Dist* Stacey Distributors. Nov **1970** [periodical notice]. Sd; col. 16mm. 61-81 min.

Prod Richard Z. Evans. *Dir* Hardi Burton. *Camera* Jack White.

Sex film. A variation on the Cinderella theme, the film contains scenes of nudity, lesbianism, male homosexuality, and troilism. The role of the fairy godmother is played by a male actor. *Nudity. Lesbianism. Male homosexuality. Troilism. Female impersonation. "Cinderella".*

Note: Also known as *Rindercella and Her Fella*, and *Cindereller and Her Feller*.

RING-A-DING RHYTHM (Great Britain)   **F6.4112**
Amicus Productions. *Dist* Columbia Pictures. Sep **1962** [c1 Sep 1962; LP22826]. Sd; b&w. 35mm. 78 min. [Copyright length: 73 min.]

Prod-Dir Richard Lester. *Exec Prod-Writ* Milton Subotsky. *Dir Photog* Gilbert Taylor. *Camera Op* Gerry Turpin. *Focus* Neil Binney. *Art Dir* Maurice Carter. *Asst Art Dir* Don Picton. *Draughtsman* Geoffrey Tozer. *Film Ed* Bill Lenny. *Assembly Ed* Deveril Goodman. *Mus Supv* Norrie Paramor. *Incidental Mus* Ken Thorne. *Song:* "Tavern in the Town" perf by Terry Lightfoot. *Song:* "Nineteen-Nineteen March" perf by Kenny Ball. *Song:* "Space Ship to Mars" Norrie Paramor, Milton Subotsky. *Perf by* Gene Vincent. *Song:* "Double Trouble" Geoff Brook, Ricky Brook. *Perf by* The Brook Brothers. *Song:* "Everybody Loves My Baby" Jack Palmer, Spencer Williams. *Perf by* The Temperance Seven. *Song:* "Dream Away Romance" Paul McDowell, Clifford Bevan. *Perf by* The Temperance Seven. *Song:* "Bellissima" Milton Subotsky. *Perf by* Bob Wallis and His Storyville Jazzmen. *Song:* "In a Persian Market" Albert Ketelbey, Mack David. *Perf by* Mr. Acker Bilk and His Paramount Jazz

Band. *Song:* "*Lonely City*" Geoffrey Goddard. *Perf by* John Leyton. *Song:* "*High Society*" Clarence Williams, A. J. Piron. *Perf by* Mr. Acker Bilk and His Paramount Jazz Band. *Song Lyr:* "*Frankie & Johnny*" Milton Subotsky. *Perf by* Mr. Acker Bilk and His Paramount Jazz Band. *Song:* "*Aunt Flo*" Bob Wallis. *Perf by* Bob Wallis and His Storyville Jazzmen. *Song:* "*Rainbows*" Norrie Paramor, Bunny Lewis. *Perf by* Craig Douglas. *Song:* "*Let's Talk About Love*" Norrie Paramor, Bunny Lewis. *Perf by* Helen Shapiro. *Song:* "*Sometime Yesterday*" Clive Westlake. *Perf by* Helen Shapiro. *Song:* "*My Maryland*" arr & *perf by* Terry Lightfoot. *Song:* "*Beale Street Blues*" W. C. Handy. *Perf by* Kenny Ball. *Song:* "*Yellow Dog Blues*" W. C. Handy. *Perf by* Chris Barber's Jazz Band. *Song:* "*Down by the Riverside*" arr by Chris Barber. *Perf by* Ottilie Patterson. *Song:* "*When the Saints Go Marching In*" arr by Chris Barber. *Perf by* Chris Barber's Jazz Band. *Song:* "*Ring-a-Ding*" Norrie Paramor, Bunny Lewis. *Perf by* Helen Shapiro, Craig Douglas. *Song:* "*Seven Day Weekend*" Doc Pomus, Mort Shuman. *Perf by* Gary "U. S." Bonds. *Song:* "*What Am I To Do*" Doc Pomus, Mort Shuman. *Perf by* The Paris Sisters. *Song:* "*Another Tear Falls*" Hal David, Burt Bacharach. *Perf by* Gene McDaniels. *Song:* "*Lose Your Inhibition Twist*" Kal Mann, Dave Appell. *Perf by* Chubby Checker. *Song:* "*By and By*" *perf by* The Dukes of Dixieland. *Song:* "*You Never Talk About Me*" Doc Pomus, Mort Shuman. *Perf by* Del Shannon. *Sd Rec* H. L. Bird, Ken Cameron. *Dub Ed* James Shields. *Boom Op* Ken Ritchie. *Sd Camera Op* Sandy Fairlie. *1st, 2d & 3d Asst Dir* John D. Merriman, Stuart Freeman, Michael Meighan. *Prod Mgr* Al Marcus. *Cont* Jane Buck. *Prod Sec* Vivienne Eden. *Wardrobe for Craig Douglas* Gamp Ferris. *Wardrobe Mistress* Maude Churchill. *Makeup* Freddie Williamson. *Hairdresser* Joyce James. *American Supv U. S. A. Numbers* Paul Case. *Still Photog* Bert Cann. *Prod Buyer* Terry Parr. *Grip* R. Jones. *Elec Chargehand* Jack Sullivan.

Cast: Helen Shapiro (*Helen*), Craig Douglas (*Craig*), Felton Felton (*mayor*), Arthur Mullard (*police chief*), Timothy Bateson (*coffeeshop owner*), Hugh Lloyd (*usher*), Ronnie Stevens, Frank Thornton (*TV directors*), Derek Nimmo (*head waiter*), Mario Fabrizi (*spaghetti eater*), Arnold Diamond (*TV panelist*), Bruce Lacey (*gardener*), Deryck Guyler (*narrator*), John Leyton, The Brook Brothers, Chubby Checker, Del Shannon, Gary "U. S." Bonds, Gene Vincent, Gene McDaniels, The Paris Sisters, The Dukes of Dixieland, Chris Barber's Jazz Band, Ottilie Patterson, Mr. Acker Bilk and His Paramount Jazz Band, Kenny Ball and His Jazzmen, Bob Wallis and His Storyville Jazzmen, Terry Lightfoot and His New Orleans Jazz Band, The Temperance Seven, Sounds Incorporated, David Jacobs, Pete Murray, Alan Freeman.

Comedy with music. The mayor of an English town objects to the jukebox and television entertainment at a local coffeeshop and has its license revoked. Two of its patrons, Helen and Craig, decide to line up a number of acts appearing in London for a show to prove to the mayor the value of jazz and rock and roll. They visit a television studio in an attempt to enlist the help of disc jockeys and hear many acts, though they are rebuffed at first in their efforts. They finally succeed, but the performers have to get through a roadblock set up by the mayor. Local entertainers fill in until they arrive, and the show is a tremendous success. The mayor capitulates when he is praised for arranging the show, and he joins in dancing the twist. *Singers. Musicians. Disc jockeys. Mayors. Rock and roll. Jazz. Television. Coffeeshops. Jazzbands. London. Twist (dance).*

Note: Opened in London in Mar 1962 as *It's Trad, Dad!*; running time: 73 min.

RING OF BRIGHT WATER (Great Britain)   F6.4113

Brightwater Film–Palomar Pictures International. *Dist* Cinerama Releasing Corp. 18 Jun 1969 [New York opening]. Sd; col (Technicolor). 35mm. 107 min. *MPAA rating* G.

Prod Joseph Strick. *Exec Prod* Edgar J. Scherick. *Asst Prod* Betty Botley. *Screenplay* Jack Couffer, Bill Travers. *Photog* Wolfgang Suschitzky. *Art Dir* Ken Ryan. *Film Ed* Reginald Mills. *Mus Comp & Cond* Frank Cordell. *Titl Song* Frank Cordell, Betty Botley. *Sung by* Val Doonican. *Sd* Ivan Sharrock. *Asst Dir* Ernie Lewis, Brian Lawrence. *Prod Mgr* Terry Lens. *Wardrobe* Ernie Farrer. *Makeup* Catherine Shirley. *Hairstyles* Hilda Fox. *Wildlife Cons* Hubert Wells, Tom Beecham, Mabel Beecham.

Cast: Bill Travers (*Graham Merrill*), Virginia McKenna (*Mary MacKenzie*), Peter Jeffrey (*Colin Wilcox [Colin Clifford]*), Jameson Clark (*storekeeper*), Helena Gloag (*Mrs. Flora Elrich*), W. H. D. Joss (*lighthouse keeper*), Roddy McMillan (*bus driver*), Jean Taylor-Smith (*Mrs. Sarah Chambers*), Archie Duncan (*road mender*), Kevin Collins (*fisherman*), John Young (*guard*), James Gibson (*sleeping car attendant*), Michael O'Halloran (*Herman*), Philip McCall (*Frank*), Christopher Benjamin (*fishmonger*), Philippa Gail (*pet stall girl*), June Ellis (*barmaid*), Tommy Godfrey (*ticket seller*), Walter Hall, Bill Horsley, Philip Morant.

Comedy-drama. Source: Gavin Maxwell, *Ring of Bright Water* (London, 1960). Graham Merrill, a London clerk for the civil service, has become increasingly dissatisfied with both his computerized job and automated society

---

in general. While passing a pet shop one day, he catches the attention of a caged otter on display in the window; as he continues his daily walks by the store, Merrill gradually comes to believe the animal has singled him out from all the other pedestrians. He overhears two show promoters discussing the otter and decides to purchase it himself, but soon realizes his urban apartment is too small to house the rambunctious pet. When the otter's playfulness causes his landlady to evict him, Merrill buys a small cottage in the Argyllshire area of the Scottish highlands, where he plans to write a book on Arabian culture. Most of his working hours, however, are spent with the animal, which he nicknames "Mij"; in addition, the two of them enjoy the company of an attractive doctor, Mary MacKenzie, and her pet spaniel. One day, Mij runs away with a female otter, and is later found in a fishing net on a nearby island, badly injured and nearly drowned. After nursing the animal back to health, Merrill is called back to London. Mary agrees to care for Mij, but a road worker accidentally kills the pet during the writer's absence. Merrill returns and, upon hearing the news, becomes too distraught to work, until a female otter and three cubs suddenly appear at Mij's favorite watering spot. Inspired by the realization that they must be Mij's family, Merrill begins writing about otters. *Authors. Clerks. Highlanders. Physicians. Eviction. Pet shops. London. Argyllshire (Scotland). Otter. Pets. Dogs.*

Note: Filmed on location in London and Argyllshire, Scotland. Opened in London in Apr 1969.

RING OF FIRE   F6.4114

Andrew L. Stone. *Dist* Metro-Goldwyn-Mayer, Inc. 14 Jun **1961** [Vernonia, Oregon, opening; c15 Mar 1961; LP19147]. Sd (Westrex); col (Metrocolor). 35mm (CinemaScope). 91 min.

An Andrew L. Stone–Virginia Stone Production. *Dir-Writ* Andrew L. Stone. *Dir Photog* William H. Clothier. *Film Ed* Virginia Stone. *Titl Song* Duane Eddy. *Played by* Duane Eddy. *Sd Supv* Franklin Milton. *Asst Dir* Henry Spitz. *Prod Mgr* Henry Spitz. *Sp Eff* Herman Townsley. *Coöp* Simpson Timber Co., Georgia Pacific Corp., United States Army, State of Washington, People of Vernonia (Oregon).

Cast: David Janssen (*Sgt. Steve Walsh*), Joyce Taylor (*Bobbie Adams*), Frank Gorshin (*Frank Henderson*), Joel Marston (*Deputy Pringle*), James Johnson (*Roy Anderson*), Ron Myron (*Sheriff Niles*), Marshall Kent (*deputy*), Doodles Weaver (*Mr. Hobart*).

Melodrama. In the vast forest region of Oregon, Deputy Sheriff Steve Walsh arrests three teenagers—Bobbie Adams, Frank Henderson, and Roy Anderson—for the holdup of a filling station. En route to jail Bobbie produces a gun from beneath her shirt, and Walsh becomes the trio's prisoner. They abandon the sheriff's car and, by using Walsh as both hostage and guide, set out by foot through the mountainous forestland. When they stop for the night, Bobbie, aware of Walsh's growing interest in her, tries unsuccessfully to seduce him. The next day the drunken Roy tries to push Walsh off the edge of a ravine, but in the struggle Roy himself plunges to his death. Meanwhile, a search party has been organized; and when Walsh, Bobbie, and Frank reach a clearing the police are waiting. Once apprehended, the desperate and vengeful Frank falsely accuses Walsh of being intimate with Bobbie, who is still a minor. Before the argument can be settled, a forest fire breaks out, the result of a lit cigarette carelessly tossed aside by Frank. When the blaze gets out of control and sweeps through the town, Walsh herds the trapped citizens into two railway cars and, aided by Bobbie, drives the locomotive over a 200-foot-high trestle. Midway across, the train stalls, but the townspeople make their way across the ties to safety. In the panic and confusion, Frank escapes from his captors and begins climbing down the trestle. But as Walsh, Bobbie, and the last of the townspeople reach safety, the burning trestle collapses, and Frank is killed as the train crashes into the riverbed below. *Sheriffs. Adolescence. Hostages. Robbery. Seduction. Railroads. Vernonia (Oregon). Oregon. Forest fires.*

Note: Filmed in Vernonia, Oregon, and in Washington.

RING OF SPIES see RING OF TREASON

RING OF TERROR   F6.4115

Playstar Productions. *Dist* Ronnie Ashcroft Inc., Playstar Productions. 22 May **1962** [Maryland license]. Sd; b&w. 35mm. 71 min.

Prod Alfeo Bocchicchio. *Dir* Clark Paylow. *Screenplay* Lewis Simeon, G. J. Zinneman. *Photog* Brydon Baker. *Mus* James Cairncross. *Makeup* Roland Ray.

Cast: George Mather (*college student*), Esther Furst (*his girl friend*), Austin Green, Joseph Conway, Jerry Zinneman, June Smavey.

Horror film. A pre-medical student seems to fear nothing. He calmly watches his first dissection in anatomy class and later kills a rattlesnake threatening his girl friend at their lovers' lane rendezvous. However, at a mortuary where a friend recently killed in an automobile accident lies in his coffin, the student panics briefly when a gust of wind blows out a candle. The student admits that when his grandfather died some years before, he spent the night in terror waiting for the corpse to climb the stairs to his bedroom. During a fraternity initiation, the student's fearlessness earns him the most difficult stunt; he has to go to a tomb in a nearby cemetery and remove a finger ring from a corpse. In the crypt, the student forces himself to open the coffin and remove the ring, but later he dies of shock. *Medical students. Fear. College life. Tombs. Corpses. Fraternities. Snakes.*

RING OF TREASON (Great Britain)   F6.4116

British Lion Films. *Dist* Paramount Pictures. 28 May **1964** [New York opening; c31 Dec 1963; LP28700]. Sd; b&w. 35mm. 90 min.

Prod Leslie Gilliat. *Dir* Robert Tronson. *Screenplay* Frank Launder, Peter Barnes. *Dir Photog* Arthur Lavis. *Art Dir* Norman Arnold. *Film Ed* Thelma Connell. *Sd* Cecil Mason, Red Law. *Asst Dir* Derek Cracknell.

Cast: Bernard Lee *(Henry Houghton)*, William Sylvester *(Gordon Lonsdale)*, Margaret Tyzack *(Elizabeth Gee)*, David Kossoff *(Peter Kroger)*, Nancy Nevinson *(Helen Kroger)*, Thorley Walters *(Commander Winters)*, Gillian Lewis *(Marjorie Shaw)*, Brian Nissen *(Lieutenant Downes)*, Newton Blick *(Petty Officer Meadows)*, Philip Latham *(Captain Ray)*, Howard Pays *(Petty Officer Garton)*, Cyril Chamberlain *(Anderson)*, Justine Lord *(Christine)*, Richard Marner *(Colonel Monat)*, Norma Foster *(Ella)*, Anita West *(Tilly)*, Patrick Barr *(Captain Warner)*, Edwin Apps *(Blake)*, Derek Francis *(Chief Superintendant Croft)*, Garry Marsh *(1st member at Lord's)*, Basil Dignam *(2d member at Lord's)*, Hector Ross *(Superintendant Woods)*, Margaret Ward *(Superintendant Muriel)*, George Pravda.

Adventure melodrama. Warrant officer Henry Houghton, discharged from the staff of the British Embassy in Warsaw because of his disgraceful drinking, returns to England and is assigned to the Navy's Underwater Weapons Establishment at Portland. Soon afterwards he is contacted by a friend of his former Polish girl friend and blackmailed into the Soviet spy ring led by Gordon Lonsdale. Houghton becomes friendly with spinster Elizabeth Gee, who has access to keys to the department's safe. He gains her assistance in stealing documents and convinces her to give them to Lonsdale, in spite of the fact that Elizabeth believes Lonsdale to be a NATO officer. Lonsdale photographs the documents and passes them on to London book dealer Peter Kroger and his wife, Helen, who then transmit them by radio to Moscow. Houghton's free spending of money from his illegal income soon arouses the suspicion of the British intelligence service, and it is not long before they track down and arrest the members of the spy ring. *Spies. Communists. Spinsters. Booksellers. Espionage. Alcoholism. Blackmail. Radio. Portland (England) Spy Case. Union of Soviet Socialist Republics. London. Henry Houghton. Gordon Lonsdale. Elizabeth Gee. Peter Kroger. Helen Kroger. Great Britain—Royal Navy. Great Britain—Intelligence service. Documentation.*

Note: Released in Great Britain in 1964 as *Ring of Spies.* The film is based on the Portland (England) Spy Case, 1961. A narrator introduces the film with documentary footage of the actual spies.

RINGS AROUND THE WORLD   F6.4117

Caam Co. *Dist* Columbia Pictures. 27 Sep **1966** [Tallahassee, Florida, opening; c1 Oct 1966; LP33039]. Sd; col (Eastman Color, print by Technicolor). 35mm. 98 min. [Also 79 min.]

Prod-Dir Gilbert Cates. *Assoc Prod* Arthur Rosenblum. *Story & Screenplay* Victor Wolfson. *Dir Photog* Urs Furrer. *Camera Op* Alan McCabe. *2d Unit Op* Ronald Lautore. *Titl Dsgn* Urs Furrer. *Film Ed* John Oettinger. *Assoc Ed* Joan Chaffee. *Asst Ed* Don Sturges. *Mus Comp & Cond* Jacques Belasco. *Song:* "The Canvas Sky" sung by Neil Sedaka. *Sd* Recording Studios Inc. *Mus Engr* Elvin Campbell. *Courtesy Dir* Roland Johnson. *Prod Mgr* Peter G. Benzoni. *Asst to the Prod* Everett Rosenthal. *Prod Sec* Lillian Tobinson. *Optical Eff* Creative Opticals. *Res* Bruce MacDonell. *Talent Coörd* Aksel Glaesner.

Starring: Don Ameche *(John Shawcross)*.

Artists: Rudy Cardenas, The Flying Armors, The Four Titos, The Francesco Clowns, The Gaonas, Grey Arrow and Zuni, The Fredy Knie Horses, Carl Sembach Krone, Frieda Sembach Krone, The Larible Trapeze Act, La Mara, Marco, Mendez and Seitz, Pablo Noel, Pauline Schumann, Tarzan, Sahib; and Boy, The Tongas, The Two Mascotts, Gunther Gebel Williams, Lilly Yokoi.

Documentary. While writing a book on the circus, author John Shawcross reflects upon the great acts he has seen over the years and the mystique of circus people. He recalls: the solo trapeze act of La Mara; Tarzan, Sahib, and their elephant; Marco's sword-balancing act; an archery act in which Grey Arrow shoots an apple off the head of Zuni, his wife; the Mascott Sisters' head-to-head balancing act on a high ladder; the juggling of Rudy Cardenas; high bar specialists, the Tongas; Gunther Gebel Williams with his tiger; the flying bar act of the Laribles; Carl Sembach Krone's trained horses; lion tamer Pablo Noel; the Gaonas and the Four Titos on the trampoline; the Flying Armors on the flying trapeze; Frieda Krone and her elephants; Fredy Knie, Sr., and his Lippizaner; the Francesco Clowns; Lilly Yokoi on her bicycle; Mendez and Seitz on the tightrope; and Pauline Schumann on the trick horse. *Authors. Trapezists. Jugglers. Lion tamers. Clowns. Bicyclists. Tightrope walkers. Acrobats. Circus. Archery. Trampolines. Elephants. Tigers. Horses. Lions.*

Note: Filmed at the Smethport County Fair (Smethport, Pa.), the Circus Schumann (Copenhagen), the Circus Krone (Kiel), the Spanish National Circus (Munich), the Circus Scott (Stockholm), and the Circus Knie (Lausanne).

RIO CONCHOS   F6.4118

Twentieth Century–Fox Film Corp. 23 Oct **1964** [Cleveland opening; c23 Oct 1964; LP29353]. Sd (Westrex); col (De Luxe). 35mm (CinemaScope). 107 min.

Prod David Weisbart. *Dir* Gordon Douglas. *Screenplay* Joseph Landon, Clair Huffaker. *Dir Photog* Joseph MacDonald. *Camera Op* Duke Callaghan. *Asst Camera* Walt Kershner, William Cronjager. *Art Dir* Jack Martin Smith, William Creber. *Set Decor* Walter M. Scott, Lucien Hafley. *Film Ed* Joseph Silver. *Mus* Jerry Goldsmith. *Orch* Arthur Morton. *Sd* Alfred Bruzlin, Elmer Raguse. *Rec* Harry Proodian. *Boom Op* Gino Contemessa. *Asst Dir* Joseph E. Rickards. *Script Supv* Rose Steinberg. *Makeup* Ben Nye. *Hairstyles* Margaret Donovan. *Dial Dir* Eugene Busch. *Constr Coörd* Walt Wiley. *Still Photog* Robert Coburn. *Prop* Robert McLaughlin, Anthony Mazzola. *Gaffer* Earl Spicer.

Cast: Richard Boone *(Lassiter)*, Stuart Whitman *(Captain Haven)*, Tony Franciosa *(Rodriguez)*, Wende Wagner *(Sally)*, Warner Anderson *(Colonel Wagner)*, Jim Brown *(Sgt. Ben Franklyn)*, Rodolfo Acosta *(Bloodshirt)*, Barry Kelley *(croupier)*, Vito Scotti *(Mexican bandit)*, House Peters, Jr. *(Pardee officer)*, Kevin Hagen *(Blondebeard)*, Edmond O'Brien *(Col. Theron Pardee)*, Timothy Carey *(barman)*.

Western drama. Source: Clair Huffaker, *Guns of Rio Conchos* (Greenwich, Connecticut, 1964). A patrol headed by Captain Haven and Sergeant Franklyn is sent to investigate the theft of 2,000 rifles from a U. S. Cavalry command. The trail leads to James Lassiter, who owns one of the stolen rifles, but he refuses to reveal the name of his contact and is jailed with Rodriguez, a Mexican murderer. Haven plans to take a wagonload of gunpowder to Mexico, hoping to use it as bait for those who stole the rifles. In exchange for both his and the Mexican's freedom, Lassiter finally agrees to lead Haven to Pardee, the man from whom he obtained the rifle. Pardee, who was Lassiter's commander during the Civil War, is still fighting the war from Mexico. Captain Haven and his patrol have skirmishes with Indians and bandits along the way, and they pick up Sally, a young Indian woman. Lassiter, who hates Indians because they killed his family, wants to kill her, but they learn from her that Pardee is about to sell the rifles to Apaches. The traitorous Rodriguez escapes, but Lassiter finds and kills him. Lassiter begins talks with Pardee, but when Bloodshirt, the Indian who killed his family, appears, Lassiter goes berserk and attacks him. Pardee imprisons Lassiter, Haven, and Franklyn; but Sally frees them while Pardee negotiates with Bloodshirt. Lassiter and Franklyn sacrifice their lives to ignite the gunpowder wagon, destroying the camp and killing everyone except Haven and Sally, who return to Texas. *Mexicans. Apache Indians. Bandits. Theft. Murder. Self-sacrifice. Firearms. Mexico. Texas. United States Army—Cavalry. Explosions.*

Note: Location scenes filmed in Moab, Utah, Monument Valley, and elsewhere in Arizona.

RIO LOBO   F6.4119

Malabar Productions. *For* Cinema Center Films. *Dist* National General Pictures. 16 Dec **1970** [Chicago opening; c6 Nov 1970; LP39047]. Sd; col (Technicolor). 35mm. 114 min. *MPAA rating* G.

A Howard Hawks Production. *Prod-Dir* Howard Hawks. *Assoc Prod* Paul Helmick. *2d Unit Dir* Yakima Canutt. *Screenplay* Leigh Brackett, Burton Wohl. *Story* Burton Wohl. *Dir Photog* William H. Clothier. *Camera Op* William Dodds. *Asst Camera* Richard Barth, Frank Redmond. *Set Decor* William Kiernan. *Prod Dsgn* Robert E. Smith. *Main Titl* Don Record. *Film Ed* John Woodcock. *Mus* Jerry Goldsmith. *Sd* John Carter. *Mus Ed* Gene Feldman. *Asst Dir* Mike Moder, Mack Harding. *Prod Mgr* Robert Beche. *Script Supv* Marshall Wolins. *Exteriors Coörd* Denis Judd. *Cost* Luster Bayless. *Men's Cost* Ted Parvin. *Makeup* Monte Westmore, David Grayson, Dick Cobos. *Hairstyles* Jean Austin. *Sp Eff* A. D. Flowers, Clifford Wenger. *Tech Adv for Train Seq* William Byrne. *Prop Master* Ray F. Mercer, Jr. *Still Photog* David Sutton. *Gaffer* James Vaiana. *Key Grip* Carl Gibson. *Constr Coörd* Ed Shaley.

Cast: John Wayne *(Col. Cord McNally)*, Jorge Rivero *(Capt. Pierre Cordona)*, Jennifer O'Neill *(Shasta Delaney)*, Jack Elam *(Phillips)*, Victor French *(Ketcham)*, Susana Dosamantes *(Maria Carmen)*, Chris Mitchum *(Tuscarora)*, Mike Henry *(Sheriff Tom Hendricks)*, David Huddleston *(Dr. Jones)*, Bill Williams *(Sheriff Pat Cronin)*, Edward Faulkner *(Lieutenant Harris)*, Sherry Lansing *(Amelita)*, Dean Smith *(Bitey)*, Robert Donner *(Whitey Carter)*, Jim Davis *(Riley)*, Peter Jason *(Lieutenant Forsythe)*, Robert Rothwell, Chuck Courtney, George Plimpton *(Whitey's henchmen)*, Bob Steele *(deputy sheriff)*, Hank Worden *(Hank)*, Chuck Roberson *(corporal)*, William Byrne *(machinist)*, Don "Red" Barry, José Angel Espinosa, Anthony Sparrow Hawk, Charlie Longfoot, Frank Kennedy, John McKee, Stanley Corson, Chuck Hayward, Sandra Currie, Jim Prejean, Danny Sands, Harold Cops, Red

Morgan.

Western melodrama. As the Civil War nears its end, a band of Confederate guerrillas led by Capt. Pierre Cordona and his scout, Tuscarora, steal a shipment of gold from a Union train. Although they also capture Union Col. Cord McNally, he eventually outwits them and retrieves the gold. When the war ends and the men meet again, McNally asks Cordona for the names of the traitors who informed the Confederates of the gold shipments, but Cordona replies that he never knew their names. Shortly thereafter, McNally rides into a Texas town and aids Shasta, a young woman whose medicine show partner has been murdered by a sheriff's deputy from nearby Rio Lobo. Cordona is also in town, and he tells McNally that the Union traitors have taken over Rio Lobo. Accompanied by Shasta, the two former enemies ride into Rio Lobo and learn that Deputy Ketcham and Sheriff Hendricks have confiscated land from the people, with the exception of old man Phillips, Tuscarora's grandfather. To force the issue, Hendricks arrests Tuscarora on trumped-up charges and throws him in jail, but McNally, Cordona, and Phillips take Ketcham hostage, force him to sign back the stolen land, and make him order Hendricks to release Tuscarora. They then barricade themselves inside the jail while Cordona goes to the nearest Army post for help. He is captured, however, by Hendricks' men and brought back to Rio Lobo; Hendricks then demands that Ketcham be exchanged for Cordona. Forced to comply, McNally releases his hostage but informs Hendricks that his partner signed back all the stolen land. Enraged, Hendricks shoots Ketcham and starts a massive gunfight. Hendricks is killed by his former mistress, and McNally's forces emerge victorious as the timid townspeople rally to defeat their common enemy. *Guerrillas. Scouts—Frontier. Soldiers. Traitors. Hostages. Sheriffs. Train robberies. Murder. Theft. Frameup. Revenge. Gold. Land rights. Jails. United States—History—Civil War. Texas.*

Note: Location scenes filmed in Arizona and Cuernavaca, Mexico.

RIO NUDO   F6.4120

Chellee Films. 28 Sep **1969** [San Francisco opening]. Sd; col. 35mm. 70 min.

Prod S. Rachael, S. Sas. *Dir* Sinte S. Albert. *Photog* Yaron Danino. *Ed* Sam S. Catah. *Prod Mgr* Sam Jones. *Research* R. Sero.

Sex film. Hidden cameras sample the pleasures and perversions of Rio de Janeiro, the "sin capital of South America." Scenes show a nude woman, beautiful despite the ape-like hair that covers her body; a visit to Rio's "red light district" and the infamous clip joints of the waterfront; erotic dancing and a voodoo "dance of death"; Rio's uninhibited youth in an orgy; and finally, a 3-day carnival during which the entire city erupts in a frenzy of drinking, dancing, and sensual abandon. *Freaks. Exotic dancers. Prostitution. Orgies. Carnivals. Voodoo. Nightclubs. Rio de Janeiro. Dance of death.*

RIO VENGEANCE *see* **MOTOR PSYCHO**

RIOT   F6.4121

William Castle Enterprises. *Dist* Paramount Pictures. 15 Jan **1969** [New York opening; c9 Dec 1968; LP36890]. Sd; col (Technicolor). 35mm. 97 min. *MPAA rating* R.

Prod William Castle. *Assoc Prod* Dona Holloway. *Dir* Buzz Kulik. *Screenplay* James Poe. *Dir Photog* Robert Hauser. *Art Dir-Prod Dsgn* Paul Sylbert. *Film Ed* Edwin H. Bryant. *Mus* Christopher Komeda. *Song:* "100 Years" Christopher Komeda, Robert Wells. *Sung by* Bill Medley. *Song:* "Rag Mop" Johnnie Lee Willis, Deacon Anderson. *Sd* John Wilkinson, Clem Portman. *Sd Rec* Vic Carpenter, Walter Goss. *Asst Dir* Danny McCauley. *Prod Mgr* Bill Gray. *Unit Prod Mgr* William C. Davidson. *Script Supv* Duane Toler. *Makeup* Charles Blackman.

Cast: Jim Brown (*Cully Briston*), Gene Hackman (*Red Fletcher*), Ben Carruthers (*Joe Surefoot*), Mike Kellin (*Bugsy*), Gerald S. O'Loughlin (*Grossman*), Clifford David ("*Big Mary*" *Sheldon*), Bill Walker (*Jake*), Ricky Summers ("*Gertie*"), Michael Byron (*Murray*), Jerry Thompson (*Deputy Warden Fisk*), M. Gerri, John Neiderhauser (*homosexuals*), Frank A. Eyman (*The Warden*).

Melodrama. Source: Frank Elli, *The Riot* (New York, 1967). In the absence of the warden of a state penitentiary, black convict Cully Briston irritates a prison guard and is taken to the isolation block; and there he reluctantly becomes involved in a riot led by Red Fletcher. After several guards have been taken hostage and the rioters have taken over part of the prison, Red stalls for time by pretending that the revolt is the result of grievances; actually he is planning to escape by extending the shaft of a long-forgotten tunnel beneath the prison walls. The press plays up the inmates' grievances, and the prison authorities negotiate with Red. Meanwhile, the rioters get drunk on homemade whiskey; the homosexual prisoners throw a party; convicts who have informed on their fellow prisoners are judged by a kangaroo court; and Cully restrains a psychopathic Indian, Joe Surefoot, from murdering the hostages. When the warden returns, he ignores the peace negotiations and announces immediate steps to restore order. Red and 11 other men make their way into the tunnel shaft and conceal their escape route by sealing the entrance. Emerging on the outside, they are met by machine gun fire and gas grenades. But Cully, Red, and Surefoot are equipped with gas masks, and they escape through a steam pipe to the base of a guard tower. Surefoot kills the guard and tries to knife Cully in the back, but he is stopped by Red. The two men engage in fatal combat, and Cully escapes alone. *Prison wardens. Convicts. Negroes. Prison guards. Hostages. Psychopaths. Indians of North America. Informers. Prison revolts. Prison escapes. Drunkenness. Kangaroo courts. Male homosexuality. Murder. Tunnels.*

Note: Filmed on location at the Arizona State Penitentiary. Prison warden Frank A. Eyman and some 600 personnel and inmates of the prison appear in the film.

RIOT AT LAUDERDALE *see* **HELL'S PLAYGROUND**

RIOT ON SUNSET STRIP   F6.4122

Four Leaf Productions. *Dist* American International Pictures. Mar **1967** [c1 Mar 1967; LP34188]. Sd; col (Pathécolor). 35mm. 85 min.

Prod Sam Katzman. *Assoc Prod* Jerome F. Katzman. *Dir* Arthur Dreifuss. *Screenplay* Orville H. Hampton. *Photog* Paul C. Vogel. *Art Dir* George W. Davis, Merrill Pye. *Set Decor* Don Greenwood. *Film Ed* Ben Lewis. *Mus Scored & Cond by* Fred Karger. *Choreog* Hal Belfer. *Rec Supv* Franklin Milton. *Asst Dir* Donald C. Klune. *Prod Supv* Robert Stone. *Makeup* William Tuttle. *Hairstyles* Mary Keats.

Cast: Aldo Ray (*Lieut. Walt Lorimer*), Mimsy Farmer (*Andy*), Michael Evans (*Sergeant Tweedy*), Laurie Mock (*Siz-Ann*), Tim Rooney (*Grady*), Gene Kirkwood (*Flip*), Hortense Petra (*Marge*), Anna Mizrahi (*Helen Tweedy*), Schuyler Hayden (*Herby*), Dick Winslow, Bill Baldwin, Sr., Tony Benson, Jim LeFebvre, Al Ferrara, Pat Renella, The Standells, Forrest Lewis, George E. Carey, The Enemies, Deborah Travis, John Hart, The Longhairs, The Chocolate Watch Band.

Melodrama. As Hollywood's Sunset Strip becomes the favorite hangout for the restless younger generation, many of whom wear hippie garb and carry protest placards, police detective Walt Lorimer is torn between two duties: his obligation to property owners and the right of the young people to lawful assembly. For the past 4 years Lorimer has been separated from his alcoholic wife and his teenage daughter, Andy. When they move back to the city, Andy becomes involved in a brawl on the Strip and is brought to police headquarters for routine identification. Following the incident, Lorimer is told by the wife of a fellow officer that his daughter is headed for trouble and needs guidance. Although Andy at first resolves to stay away from the Strip, her life at home with her drunken mother soon drives her back. Joining her friends at a club, she meets Herby, the son of a movie star. Bored with the "nowhere" action at the club, Herby persuades the group to break into an unoccupied house for a party. And, as the search for kicks continues, drinking leads to marijuana and eventually to LSD. Because Andy refuses to join in, Herby serves her a doctored drink and then coerces her into accompanying him and several others into the bedroom. Ultimately the noise of the brawl arouses the neighbors who call in the police, including Lorimer. When Andy requires hospitalization, the enraged Lorimer violates his own code of nonviolence by seeking out Herby and his friends and all but killing them with his bare fists. With cries of "police brutality" echoing in his ears, Lorimer is forced to somehow cope with what may well be the worst riot on Sunset Strip. *Detectives. Hippies. Parenthood. Separation (marital). Adolescence. Police brutality. Nonviolence. Riots. LSD. Marijuana. Los Angeles—Sunset Strip.*

THE RIOTOUS BRUIN *see* **THE RUINED BRUIN**

IL RIPOSO DEL GUERRIERO *see* **LOVE ON A PILLOW**

LA RISAIA *see* **RICE GIRL**

RISATE DI GIOIA *see* **THE PASSIONATE THIEF**

RISE AGAINST THE SWORD (Japan)   F6.4123

Toho Co. Nov **1966** [Los Angeles showing]. Sd; b&w. 35mm (Tohoscope). 101 min.

Exec Prod Tomoyuki Tanaka. *Dir* Hiroshi Inagaki. *Screenplay* Masato Ide, Hiroshi Inagaki. *Photog* Kazuo Yamada.

Cast: Toshiro Mifune (*Abare Goemon*), Makoto Sato, Ryo Tamura, Yuriko Hoshi, Mayumi Ozora, Nobuko Otowa.

Action drama. During the Muromachi Era, the seven groups of Kaga, led by Abare Goemon, protect the peasants from the cruelties of the wealthy samurai class. Lord Asakura, a samurai, solicits the help of the Kaga for a clan war in which he is embroiled, and all groups except Goemon's agree to lend their support. To win over Goemon, Asakura has his daughter seduce Goemon's younger brother. When Goemon still withholds aid, Asakura orders the brother killed. As a result, all the Kaga join with Goemon in successful retaliation against Asakura. *Samurai. Brothers. Class conflict. Seduction. Revenge. Japan—History—Muromachi Era.*

Note: Released in Japan in 1966 as *Abare Goemon*.

THE RISE OF LOUIS XIV (France) F6.4124

O. R. T. F. *Dist* Brandon Films. 18 Aug **1970** [New York opening]. Sd; col (Eastman Color). 35mm. 100 min. *MPAA rating G.*

Dir Roberto Rossellini. *Screenplay* Philippe Erlanger, Jean Gruault. *Dial* Jean Gruault. *Photog* Georges Leclerc. *Camera* Claude Butteau. *Art Dir* Maurice Valay. *Film Ed* Armand Ridel. *Asst Ed* Yves Kovacs. *Sd* Jacques Gayet. *Sd Eff* Betty Willemetz. *Asst Dir* Yves Kovacs. *Prod Ch* Pierre Gout. *Cost* Christiane Coste. *Art Cons* Jean-Dominique de La Rochefoucauld.

Cast: Jean-Marie Patte *(Louis XIV)*, Raymond Jourdan *(Colbert)*, Silvagni *(Mazarin)*, Katharina Renn *(Anne of Austria)*, Dominique Vincent *(Mme du Plessis)*, Pierre Barrat *(Fouquet)*, Fernand Fabre *(Le Tellier)*, Françoise Ponty *(Louise de la Vallière)*, Joëlle Laugeois *(Marie-Thérèse)*, Maurice Barrier *(D'Artagnan)*, André Dumas *(Father Joly)*, François Mirante *(M. de Brienne)*, Pierre Spadoni *(Moni)*, Roger Guillo *(pharmacist)*, Louis Raymond *(1st physician)*, Maurice Bourbon *(2d physician)*, Michel Ferré *(M. de Gesvres)*, Guy Pintat *(master chef)*, Michèle Marquais *(Mme de Motteville)*, Jean-Jacques Daubin *(M. de Vardes)*, Georges Goubert *(M. de Soyecourt)*, Pierre Pernet *(Monsieur)*, Ginette Barbier *(Pierrette Dufour)*, Jean Obe *(Le Vau)*, Jacques Charby *(Le Vau's assistant)*, Micheline Muc *(Mlle de Pons)*, Michel Debrane *(tailor)*, René Rabault *(M. de Gramont)*, François Bennard *(archbishop)*, Georges Spanelly *(Séguier)*, Jean Soustre *(M. de Guiche)*, Axel Ganz *(ambassador)*, Jean-Jacques Lecomte *(1st chamberlain)*, Violette Marceau *(Mlle de Chemerault)*, Paula Dehelly *(Mlle d'Elboeuf)*, Jacques Préboist, Robert Cransac *(musketeers)*, André Daguenet *(master bargeman)*, Marc Fraiseau, Pierre Frag, Jean Coste *(bargemen)*, Rita Maiden *(peasant)*, Françoise Deville *(woman)*, M. le Marquis de Brissac, M. le Vicomte de Chabot *(leaders of the hunt)*, Le Rallye Boissière.

Historical drama. Upon the death of Mazarin in 1661 Louis XIV ascends the throne of France. Contrary to expectations the king immediately consolidates his power, denies his mother a place on the privy council, arrests Minister of Finance Nicolas Fouquet, appoints in his stead the incorruptible Colbert, and moves his court from Paris to Versailles, thereby separating the nobility from its power base. At court he further distracts the aristocracy by devising sumptuous fashions, lavish banquets, extravagant entertainments and elaborate rituals celebrating his exalted position, and by encouraging rivalry and intrigue. In middle age the king contemplates his royal isolation. *Royalty. Mistresses. Priests. Politics. Marriage of convenience. Catholic Church. Food preparation. Versailles. Versailles Palace. Paris. Louis XIV (France). Anne of Austria. Marie-Thérèse. Jean-Baptiste Colbert. Nicolas Fouquet. Jules Mazarin.*

Note: Produced for French television in 1966. Paris opening: Nov 1966 as *La prise de pouvoir par [de] Louis XIV.*

THE RISK (Great Britain) F6.4125

Charter Film Productions. *Dist* Kingsley International Pictures. 23 Sep **1961** [New York opening]. Sd; b&w. 35mm. 81 min.

A Boulting Brothers Production. *Prod-Dir* Roy Boulting, John Boulting. *Screenplay* Nigel Balchin. *Adtl Scenes & Dial* Jeffrey Dell, Roy Boulting. *Dir Photog* Max Greene. *Camera Op* Gerry Anstiss. *Focus Puller* Gerry Anstiss. *Art Dir* Albert Witherick. *Set Dresser* Peter James. *Draughtsman* Terry Addison. *Scenic Artist* Alan Evans. *Film Ed* John Jympson. *1st Asst Ed* Jeremy Saunders. *2d Asst Ed* Ron Pope. *Mus* Frédéric François Chopin, Aleksandr Nikolaevich Scriabin. *Mus Arr & Played by* John Wilkes. *Sd Mix* George Stephenson. *Boom Op* Jack W. Davies. *Sd Camera Op* Ernie Webb. *1st, 2d & 3d Asst Dir* Basil Rabin, Julian Mackintosh, Henry Emery. *Prod Mgr* Philip Shipway. *Prod Sec* Joan Parcell. *Cont* Beryl Booth. *Wardrobe Mistress* Maude Churchill. *Makeup Ch* Freddie Williamson. *Hairdresser* Ann Box. *Still Photog* Laurie Ridley. *Prod Buyer* Percy Godbold. *Ch Electrn* Jackie Sullivan. *Grip* Jack Roche.

Cast: Tony Britton *(Bob Marriott)*, Virginia Maskell *(Lucy Byrne)*, Peter Cushing *(Professor Sewall)*, Ian Bannen *(Alan Andrews)*, Raymond Huntley *(Sir George Gatling)*, Thorley Walters *(Mr. Prince)*, Donald Pleasence *(Brown)*, Spike Milligan *(Arthur)*, Kenneth Griffith *(Dr. Shole)*, Robert Bruce *(Levers)*, Anthony Booth *(Parkin)*, Basil Dignam *(Dr. Childs)*, Brian Oulton *(director)*, Sam Kydd *(Slater)*, John Payne, British *(Iverson)*, Murray Melvin *(Teddy boy)*, Andre Charise *(Heller)*, Geoffrey Bayldon *(Rosson)*.

Drama. Source: Nigel Balchin, *A Sort of Traitors* (London, 1949). In London, under the supervision of Professor Sewell, a group of dedicated British scientists have developed a serum which they believe could be used to stamp out typhus and bubonic epidemics. Since the serum involves using a particularly virulent germ which could be used for germ warfare, the minister of defense denies Sewell permission to publish his findings under the Official Secrets Act. Sewell accepts the decision, albeit angrily, but one of his assistants, Bob Marriott, is less resigned. Marriott is further troubled by his frustrated love for Lucy Byrne, a co-scientist tied to her former fiancé, Alan Andrews, an armless and embittered Korean war veteran. Alan learns Marriott is indignant over the Ministry's decision, and he puts him in touch with Mr. Brown, a shady individual who claims he can get the research papers published by an "international scientific exchange." Satisfied that he has had his revenge on humanity, Alan kills himself. Though Sewell catches Marriott stealing the secret file, he protects him from security officers who have been investigating Brown's connections. Realizing his error, Marriott aids the security men in trapping Brown and his confederates; and free of guilt, he prepares for a peaceful future with Lucy. *Professors. Scientists. Researchers. Cripples. Veterans. Government agents. Investigators. Defense—National. Chemical warfare. Revenge. Suicide. Theft. Espionage. Treason. Serums. Typhus. Bubonic fever. Epidemics. London. Documentation.*

Note: Opened in London in Nov 1960 as *Suspect;* working title: *The Risk.*

RITA (France/Italy) F6.4126

Les Films Modernes–Agiman–Euro International Films. *Dist* Parallel—49— Inc., Colorama Features. **1963.** Sd; b&w. 35mm. 93 min.

Pres by Telac. *Prod* Carlo Ponti. *Dir* Alberto Lattuada. *Screenplay-Adapt* Roger Vailland, Alberto Lattuada. *Photog* Roberto Gerardi. *Film Ed* Leo Catozzo. *Mus* Robert Nicolosi. *English Subtitl* Herman G. Weinberg.

Cast: Pascale Petit *(Margherita [Rita] Passi)*, Jean-Paul Belmondo *(Giuliano Verdi)*, Massimo Girotti *(Don Paolo Conti)*, Lilla Brignone *(Sister Giulietta)*, Hella Petri, Elsa Vazzoler, Emilio Cigoli.

Drama. Source: Guido Piovene, *Lettere di una novizia* (Verona, 1941). Margherita (Rita) Passi, a young novice at a convent near Venice, is about to take her vows when the bishop receives an anonymous letter which denounces the novice's past and casts doubt on her sincerity. Don Paolo, the bishop's secretary, hears Margherita's confession and discovers her true story. Upon leaving school, she had sex with Giuliano, a neighbor, and had fallen in love with him. She was aware that Giuliano was having an affair with an older woman, but when she discovered that the woman was Countess Passi, her own mother, and that Giuliano preferred her mother, Margherita killed him. The countess gave Margherita the choice of going to prison or entering a convent, and Margherita chose the convent. Don Paolo learns that the young woman's own guilt had led her to write the letter denouncing herself. She is subsequently expelled from the convent and arrested for her crime. At the trial, however, Margherita refuses to plead guilty, claiming extenuating circumstances. *Novices. Priests. Nobility. Filial relations. Murder. Confession. Guilt. Convents. Documentation. Trials.*

Note: Opened in Rome in Dec 1960 as *Lettere di una novizia;* running time: 105 min; in Paris in Mar 1961 as *La novice;* running time: 82 min. Also known as *Letter From a Novice.*

RITEN *see* **THE RITUAL**

THE RITUAL (Sweden) F6.4127

Svensk Filmindustri–Sveriges TV–Cinematograph. *Dist* Janus Films. 4 Dec **1970** [New York opening]. Sd; b&w. 35mm. 75 min.

Dir-Writ Ingmar Bergman. *Photog* Sven Nykvist. *Art Dir* Lennart Blomkvist. *Film Ed* Siv Kanalv. *Sd Rec* Olle Jacobsson. *Asst Dir* Christer Dahl. *Prod Mgr* Lars-Owe Carlberg. *Cost* Mago.

Cast: Ingrid Thulin *(Thea Winkelmann)*, Anders Ek *(Albert Emanuel Sebastian Fischer)*, Gunnar Björnstrand *(Hans Winkelmann)*, Erik Hell *(Judge Abramsson)*, Ingmar Bergman *(clergyman)*.

Drama. A performance by the theatrical company Les Riens is halted when one of their pieces is judged obscene. Magistrate Abramsson summons the troupe, consisting of Sebastian Fischer, Hans Winkelmann, and Hans' neurotic wife, Thea. To show the gravity of the case the judge investigates the artists' personal histories, finding that Sebastian has been convicted of manslaughter, that Thea and Sebastian are lovers, and that Thea was once married to her present husband's former partner. Confronting the offenders, Abramsson goads Sebastian into a violent outburst, tricks Hans into offering him a bribe, and attempts to rape Thea during her epileptic seizure. In retaliation the trio performs the censored piece, "The Ritual." Hans and Sebastian don beaked masks and enormous wooden phalli, and Thea appears bare-breasted. At the conclusion of the play, the judge is found dead of a heart attack. *Actors. Judges. Mistresses. Theatrical troupes. Censorship. Infidelity. Rape. Obscenity. Epilepsy. Heart disease. Bribery. Masks.*

Note: First shown as *Riten* on Swedish television in Mar 1969.

RIVALEN DER MANEGE *see* **BIMBO THE GREAT**

RIVER OF FOREVER (Japan) F6.4128

Tokyo Eiga Co. *Dist* Toho Co. Oct **1967** [Los Angeles showing]. Sd; b&w. 35mm (Tohoscope). 102 min.

Exec Prod Ichiro Sato, Hideyuki Shiino. *Dir* Shiro Toyoda. *Screenplay* Zenzo Matsuyama. *Photog* Kozo Okazaki. *Mus* Masaru Sato.

Cast: Kinya Kitaoji, Yuriko Hoshi, Mikijiro Hira, Ayumi Ishida, Kunie Tanaka.

Romantic melodrama. Hajime Goshokawa, a young truckdriver, is persuaded to take a physical examination while visiting a friend in the hospital. Although he is ordered back for further testing, Hajime, who is suspicious of doctors and hospitals, does not return to the doctor until persuaded to do so by Nami, a nurse to whom he is attracted. Unaware that he has leukemia, Hajime continues courting Nami until an automobile accident serves to disclose the nature of his illness. Desperate for a cure, Hajime goes from hospital to hospital until he finally realizes that there is no hope for his recovery. Nami takes him to her home in a river valley, where the two lovers spend the last few months of Hajime's life. *Truckdrivers. Nurses. Cancer. Death. Incurable illness. Hospitals. Automobile accidents.*

Note: Released in Japan in Feb 1967 as *Chikumagawa zessho.*

RIVERRUN   **F6.4129**
Korty Films. *Dist* Columbia Pictures. 22 Apr **1970** [Lawrence, Kansas, opening; c27 Apr 1970; LP37948]. Sd; col (Eastman Color). 35mm. 87 min. *MPAA rating* R.
Prod Stephen Schmidt. *Dir-Writ* John Korty. *Adtl Dial* Bill Brammer. *Dir Photog* John Korty. *Photog Asst* Hiro Narita. *Film Ed* Paddy Monk. *Asst Film Ed* Tom Berry, Robert Moore, ed. *Mus Score* Richard Greene, mus, Peter Berg, mus. *Quintet in B-minor for Clarinet and Strings, opus 115* Johannes Brahms. *Mus Perf by* David Oppenheim, The Budapest String Quartet. *Sd* J. Paul Oppenheim. *Sd Asst* Bruce Hatch. *Asst Dir* Rick Wise. *Prod Asst* Otis Johnson, Dorothy Browning, Mary Alice Rogers. *Script Girl* Cindy Harwood. *Wardrobe* Arleen Sterling. *Prop* Arleen Sterling.
Cast: Louise Ober (*Sarah*), John McLiam (*Jeffries*), Mark Jenkins (*Dan*), Josephine Nichols (*Sarah's mother*), Joseph Miksak (*bartender*), Stefanie Priest (*waitress*), George Hellyer, Jr. (*doctor*), Esther Sutherland (*madam*), Laura Kwong, Orion De Winter (*prostitutes*), Paula Preston, Wilhelm Joerres (*hippie couple*), Sheila Emmett (*Sarah as a child*), Roy Parks (*farmer*), Robert Bertrand (*sheriff's deputy*).
Drama. Conscientious objector Dan and student Sarah leave Berkeley for life on a San Marino County sheep farm. There they are visited by her father, veteran sailor Jeffries. Excluded from Sarah and Jeffries' reminiscences, Dan becomes jealous. His resentment is intensified by Jeffries' jibes at his pacifism. Jeffries, on the other hand, is shocked to learn that his pregnant daughter is unmarried and that her lover, a former medical student, intends to deliver the baby. When her drunken father and Dan argue violently Sarah runs from the farmhouse. Finding her in a field, Dan helps her home. While Sarah gives birth to a son, her drunken father lunges at the locked door and suffers a fatal heart attack. *Students. Medical students. Drunkenness. Sailors. Conscientious objectors. Filial relations. Jealousy. Pregnancy. Childbirth. Farm life. Heart disease. Berkeley (California).*
Note: Location scenes filmed in San Francisco and northern California. Original running time: 95 min.

RIVERS see **MY MOUNTAIN, SONG 27**

THE RIVERS OF FIRE AND ICE see **AFRICAN SAFARI**

LA RIVOLTA DEGLI SCHIAVI see **THE REVOLT OF THE SLAVES**

LA RIVOLTA DEI MERCENARI see **REVOLT OF THE MERCENARIES**

THE ROAD HUSTLERS   **F6.4130**
Saturn Productions. *Dist* Saturn Productions, American International Pictures. 28 Mar **1968** [San Antonio, Texas, opening; c1 Feb 1968; LP35676]. Sd; col (Eastman Color). 35mm. 95 min.
Prod Robert M. Newsom. *Dir-Exec Prod* Larry E. Jackson. *Assoc Prod* Tom Jenkins. *Screenplay* Robert Barron. *Photog* Gerhard Maser. *Mus Comp & Dir* Michael Colicchio. *Script Girl* Joyce King. *Tech Crew* Forest Carpenter. *Stuntman* Jeff Hunt.
Cast: Jim Davis (*Noah Reedy*), Scott Brady (*Earl Veasey*), Bruce Yarnell (*Matt Reedy*), Robert Dix (*Mark Reedy*), Victoria Carroll (*Nadine*), Andy Devine (*Sheriff Estep*), Sue Raney (*Helen*), Christian Anderson (*Luke Reedy*), Ted Lehmann (*Hagar*), John Cardos (*Chandler*), Bill McKinney (*Hays*), Bill MacDowell (*Basset*), Jack Lester (*Eskie*), Sid Lawrence (*Deke*), Monica Davis (*Martha Lu*), Derek Hughes (*Ted*), Marshall Lockhart (*Nelly*), Jim Quick (*Imhoff*), Jack Morey (*Harrison*).
Action drama. Patriarch Noah Reedy and his sons Matt, Mark, and Luke are engaged in a battle on three fronts to maintain their illegal liquor business located in the mountains of Carolina. Pursued by local sheriff Estep and federal revenue agents Chandler and Hays, the Reedy family faces the ruthless competition of syndicate boss Earl Veasey and his henchmen. After Veasey hijacks one of Reedy's sugar supply trucks, Reedy and his sons pay a visit to the luxurious houseboat headquarters of the syndicate boss, but threats from both sides only increase the tension. Upon learning that the Reedy sons are entertaining his two playgirls, Martha Lu and Nadine, Veasey sends Deke to kill Mark Reedy. Deke succeeds in running Mark's car off a cliff, but Mark survives, and Noah Reedy launches an all-out war against the syndicate. Reedy fights Veasey's sabotage attempts with booby-trapped fireworks and electronic devices designed to protect the family stills, then lures Veasey's gang into a speed boat chase that ends with a dynamite ambush. Noah and his sons locate Veasey's stills using hogs to follow the scent of sour mash. After a raid on Veasey's houseboat headquarters, Reedy tricks the federal agents into arresting the syndicate gangsters, while at the same time protecting his own secret stills and the million-dollar moonshine business. *Moonshiners. Sheriffs. Revenue agents. Gangsters. Business competition. Murder. Sabotage. Stills. Houseboats. United States—South. Automobile accidents. Chases.*
Note: Filmed in North and South Carolina.

ROAD REBELS   **F6.4131**
Starlite-Henrietta Corp. **1963.** Sd; b&w. 35mm. 64 min.
Prod Don R. Stevenson. *Dir* Reno D. Calarco.
Cast: Julie Francis, Bernie Rose.
Action melodrama. No information about the precise nature of this film has been found, but press material suggests that it concerns teenaged hot rod enthusiasts. *Adolescence. Automobile racing.*

ROAD TO ETERNITY (Japan)   **F6.4132**
Shochiku Co. *Dist* Shochiku Films of America, Beverly Pictures. Feb **1961** [Los Angeles showing]. Sd; b&w. 35mm (Shochiku GrandScope). 181 min. *MPAA rating* GP.
Prod Tatsuo Hasoya. *Dir* Masaki Kobayashi. *Screenplay* Masaki Kobayashi, Zenzo Matsuyama. *Photog* Yoshio Miyajima. *Art Dir* Kazue Hirataka. *Film Ed* Keiichi Uraoka. *Mus* Chuji Kinoshita. *Sd Rec* Hideo Nishizaki.
Cast: Tatsuya Nakadai (*Kaji*), Michiyo Aratama (*Michiko*), Keiji Sada (*Kageyama*), Michio Minami (*Yoshida*), Hideo Kisho (*Kudo*), Kei Sato (*Shinjo*), Taketoshi Naito (*Tange*), Kunie Tanaka (*Obara*), Kokinjo Katsura (*Sasa*), Kaneko Iwasaki (*nurse*), Yusuke Kawazu, Hideo Kidokoro, Jun Tatara.
War drama. Source: Jumpei Gomigawa, *Ningen no joken*, vol 3 & 4 (Kyoto, 1958). Toward the end of World War II Kaji, a new recruit in the Kwantung Army, is sent to Manchuria for basic training. When he protests the cruel treatment of the soldiers at the hands of their drill instructors, he is suspected of being a communist. Kaji becomes friendly with Shinjo, a communist sympathizer who plans to desert and escape to Russia. Kaji receives a surprise visit from his wife, Michiko, and the couple are allowed to spend the night together. The harsh discipline quickly resumes, however, as the soldiers are sent into the field on a forced march that proves too much for many of the men; one of the soldiers, Obara, commits suicide to escape being humiliated by his troop. Shinjo attempts to escape, and Kaji comes to his aid when Shinjo is trapped in a swamp. Kaji himself is injured and taken to a hospital where he recuperates, until the head nurse discovers that he is becoming too friendly with the other nurses and discharges him. He is then reassigned to another unit as an assistant to an old friend, Lieutenant Kageyama. Now in a position to help the enlisted soldiers, Kaji succeeds only in arousing the contempt of the career officers and nearly kills one of them while defending himself from a beating. After the surrender of Germany, the Russians launch a powerful tank attack that throws the poorly-equipped Kwantung Army into a rout. During the attack, Kaji strangles one of his fellow soldiers who tries to break ranks, but eventually the Japanese forces are decimated, and Kaji is left alone on the battlefield. *Communists. Nurses. Russians. Basic military training. Combat zone life. Deserters—Military. Suicide. Hospitals. Tanks (armored cars). World War II. Manchuria. Japan—Army. Union of Soviet Socialist Republics—Army.*
Note: Released in Japan in 1959 as *Zoku ningen no joken*; alternative Japanese title: *Ningen no joken II.* Film is the second part of the trilogy entitled *The Human Condition*, released in its entirety in Los Angeles in 1970. The other parts are *The Human Condition* (1959) and *A Soldier's Prayer* (1970), q. v.

THE ROAD TO FORT ALAMO (France/Italy)   **F6.4133**
Protor Film–Piazzi Produzione Cinematografica–Comptoir Français du Film. *Dist* World Entertainment Corp. Jul **1966** [New York showing]. Sd; col (Eastman Color). 35mm (Totalscope). 82 min.
Dir John M. Old. *Screenplay* Vincent Thomas, Charles Price, Jane Brisbane. *Story* Vincent Thomas. *Photog* Bud Third.
Cast: Ken Clark, Jany Clair, Michel Lemoine, Andreina Paul, Kirk Bert, Antonio Gradoli, Dean Ardow.
Western melodrama. In Wagon City, Utah, eight bandits disguised as federal soldiers rob a bank. Bud, critical of his leader Carson's brutal killing of an elderly woman, is abandoned in the desert along with the faithful Little Slim. They are rescued by Captain Hull and his wagon train, bound for Fort Alamo. Bud is attracted to Janet, a prisoner accused of theft. Although Sergeant

Warwick realizes that Bud is impersonating a federal officer, he allows him to order a retreat when the wagon train is surrounded by the hostile Sioux. Bud courageously ventures to Fort Alamo and returns with reinforcements to repulse the Indians. Attempting to flee with the bank loot, Carson, rescued by the wagon train after his men have been slain by the Indians, is chased and killed by Bud. Having returned the money to the authorities, Bud, Janet, and Little Slim leave the wagon train to begin a happy life together. *Bandits. Sioux Indians. Wagon masters. Disguise. Bank robberies. Murder. Rescue. Deserts. Wagon trains. Forts. Utah. United States Army. Chases.*

Note: Opened in Rome caJan 1965 as *La strada per Fort Alamo*; in Paris in Mar 1965 as *Arizona Bill*; running time: 100 min. John M. Old is a pseudonym for Mario Bava.

THE ROAD TO HONG KONG (United States/Great Britain)   **F6.4134**

Melnor Films. *Dist* United Artists. 23 May **1962** [Chicago opening; c23 May 1962; LP22380]. Sd; b&w. 35mm. 91 min.

A Norman Panama–Melvin Frank Production. *Prod* Melvin Frank. *Dir* Norman Panama. *Screenplay* Norman Panama, Melvin Frank. *Anim* Biographic Cartoon Films. *Dir Photog* Jack Hildyard. *Camera Op* Gerry Fisher. *Focus Puller* Jimmy Devis. *Camera Grip* Frank Howard. *Art Dir* Syd Cain, Bill Hutchinson. *Asst Art Dir* Bob Cartwright. *Set Decor* Maurice Fowler. *Sketch Artist* Sidney Braham. *Scenic Artist* Basil Mannin. *Draughtsmen* Jim Sawyer, Brian Ackland-Snow, Ted Clements, Joel Schiller. *Prod Dsgn* Roger Furse. *Main Titl* Maurice Binder. *Supv Film Ed* Alan Osbiston. *Film Ed* John Victor Smith. *1st Asst Ed* Joan Morduch. *2d Asst Ed* Ray Thorne. *Mus Comp & Cond* Robert Farnon. *Mus Assoc* Douglas Gamley, Bill McGuffie. *Songs Comp* Sammy Cahn, James Van Heusen. *Mus Numbers Staged by* Jack Baker, Sheila Meyers. *Sd* A. G. Ambler, Red Law, Chris Greenham. *Boom Op* Peter Dukelow. *Sd Camera Op* Jimmy Dooley. *Mus Ed* Lee Doig. *1st & 2d Asst Dir* Bluey Hill, Gordon Gilbert, Edward Dorian, Ken Softley. *Prod Supv* William Kirby. *Prod Sec* Inez Easton. *Cont* Angela Martelli. *Cost Dsgn* Anthony Mendleson. *Wardrobe Mistress* May Walding. *Wardrobe Master* Ernie Farrer. *Makeup* Dave Aylott, Eric Allwright. *Hairstyles* Joan White, Joyce James. *Sp Eff* Wally Veevers, Ted Samuels. *Chinese Adv* Mrs. Fei. *Still Photog* Ted Reed. *Casting* Sally Nicholl. *Prod Buyer* Terry Parr. *Constr Mgr* Harry Phipps. *Prop Chargehand* Bobby Murrell. *Chargehand Electrn* Maurice Gillett.

Cast: Bing Crosby (*Harry Turner*), Bob Hope (*Chester Babcock*), Joan Collins (*Diane*), Dorothy Lamour (*herself*), Robert Morley (*The Leader*), Walter Gotell (*Dr. Zorbb*), Roger Delgado (*Jhinnah*), Felix Aylmer (*Grand Lama*), Peter Madden (*lama*). Alan Gifford, Robert Ayres, Robin Hughes (*U. S. officials*), Julian Sherrier (*doctor*), Bill Nagy (*agent*), Guy Standeven (*photographer*), John McCarthy, actor (*messenger*), Simon Levy (*servant*), Jacqueline Jones (*lady at airport*), Victor Brooks, Roy Patrick, John Dearth, David Randall, Michael Wynne (*leader's men*), Mei Ling (*Chinese girl*), Katya Douglas (*receptionist*), Harry Baird, Irvin Allen (*Nubians*), Yvonne Shima, Camilla Brockman, Lena Margot, Sheree Winton, Edwina Carroll, Diane Valentine, April Ashley, Jacqueline Leigh, Sein Short, Lier Hwang, Michele Mok, Zoe Zephyr (*girls*), Frank Sinatra, Dean Martin, Peter Sellers, David Niven, Jerry Colonna (*guest stars*).

Farce with music. Harry Turner and Chester Babcock are two vaudeville song-and-dance men touring the Far East. While hawking a phony do-it-yourself space kit in India, Chester is knocked unconscious and loses his memory. Harry takes him to a Tibetan Lamasery, where he is given a special herb that cures his amnesia and provides him with a photographic memory. At the airport, Chester meets Diane, a beautiful spy for the Third Echelon, an organization of mad scientists planning to conquer the universe. She mistakes him for a photographer assigned to copy a secret Russian formula for rocket fuel, and Chester is able to memorize the information merely by glancing at the equations. Later, the two men are captured by the organization and inadvertently become substitutes for a pair of apes on a moon reconnaissance flight when they try to escape. Upon their return the Third Echelon decides to sacrifice them to science but quarters the two men in a harem to make their final hours more pleasant. They evade their captors and flee through Hong Kong with Diane, who has come to realize that the organization's leader is a madman. An old friend, Dorothy Lamour, who is appearing at a local nightclub, helps the trio outwit their pursuers and alert the Hong Kong police. As the Third Echelon headquarters are raided, however, Harry, Chester, and Diane are trapped in a rocket that takes them to Plutonium, a remote planet, where they are met by Frank Sinatra and Dean Martin, who have arrived in another spacecraft. *Musical numbers:* "Let's Not Be Sensible" (Harry), "Teamwork" and "It's the Only Way To Travel" (Harry and Chester), "We're on the Road to Hong Kong" (Harry, Chester, and Diane), "Warmer Than a Whisper" (Dorothy Lamour). *Entertainers. Confidence men. Spies. Scientists. Entertainers. Police. Priests. Megalomania. Espionage. Amnesia. Memory. Mistaken identity. Space flights. Buddhism. Secret formulas. Harems.*

Nightclubs. Rockets. India. Tibet. Hong Kong. Chases.

Note: Filmed in England. Opened in London in Mar 1962. Seventh in the series of *Road* films starring Crosby, Hope, and Lamour.

ROAD TO NASHVILLE   **F6.4135**

Robert Patrick Productions. *Dist* Crown International Pictures. 21 Sep **1966** [Charlotte, North Carolina, opening]. Sd; col (Technicolor). 35mm (Techniscope). 109 min.

Prod Robert Patrick. *Assoc Prod* Marty Robbins. *Dir-Writ* Will Zens. *Photog* Leif Rise. *Adtl Photog* William Zsigmond. *Songs:* "Devil Woman," "Beggin' to You," "El Paso" *Writ & Sung by* Marty Robbins. *Song* "Working My Way Through a Heartache" Buddy Mize. *Song:* "Count Me Out" Jerry Reed. *Sung by* Marty Robbins. *Song:* "Love's Somethin' I Can't Understand" *Writ & Sung by* Webb Pierce. *Song:* "You Ain't No Better Than Me" Wayne Walker. *Sung by* Webb Pierce. *Song:* "Anita, You're Dreaming" *Writ & Sung by* Waylon Jennings. *Song:* "Annie Lou" H. Whittaker. *Sung by* Don Winters. *Song:* "Put It Off Until Tomorrow" Dolly Parton. *Sung by* Bill Phillips, singer. *Song:* "I Miss You Already" *Writ & Sung by* Faron Young. *Song:* "I Love You Drops" *Writ & Sung by* Bill Anderson. *Song:* "Po' Folks" Monda Dick. *Sung by* Bill Anderson. *Songs:* "Would You Hold It Against Me," "Here Comes My Baby" *Writ & Sung by* Dottie West. *Song:* "Just a Faded Petal From a Beautiful Bouquet" *Writ & Sung by* Hank Snow. *Song:* "I've Been Everywhere" Geoffrey Mack. *Sung by* Hank Snow. *Song:* "Up This Hill and Down" R. Staedtler. *Sung by* The Osborne Brothers. *Song:* "Howdy, Neighbor, Howdy" J. Morris. *Sung by* Porter Wagoner. *Song:* "I Wouldn't Buy a Used Car From Him" Harlan Howard. *Sung by* Norma Jean. *Song:* "I Walk the Line" Johnny Cash. *Sung by* The Carter Family. *Song:* "Were You There (When They Crucified My Lord)" *Arr & Sung by* Johnny Cash. *Song:* "The One on the Right Is on the Left" Jack Clement. *Sung by* Johnny Cash. *Song:* "Nobody but a Fool Would Love You" Bill Anderson. *Sung by* Connie Smith. *Song:* "I Hope You'll Learn" *Sung by* Bobby Sykes. *Song:* "A Woman Half My Age" *Sung by* Kitty Wells. *Song:* "No Dreams Like My Dreams" *Sung by* Faron Young. *Song:* "A Thousand Ways" *Sung by* Lefty Frizzell. *Song:* "I'll Never Get Over Lovin' You" *Sung by* Connie Smith. *Song:* "It Seemed That You'd Never Been Gone" *Sung by* Margie Singleton. *Songs:* "Write Me a Letter," "Goin', Goin', Gone" *Sung by* The Stonemans. *Song:* "My Baby's Coming Home" *Sung by* The Osborne Brothers. *Song:* "Skid Row Joe" *Sung by* Porter Wagoner.

Cast: Doodles Weaver (*Colonel Fiedelbaum*), Richard Arlen (*himself*), Connie Smith, Marty Robbins, The Stonemans, Webb Pierce, The Carter Family, Waylon Jennings, Margie Singleton, The Osborne Brothers, Porter Wagoner, Norma Jean, Johnny Cash, Hank Snow, Dottie West, Faron Young, Kitty Wells Show, Bill Anderson, Lefty Frizzell, Bill Phillips, singer.

Musical comedy. Colonel Fiedelbaum, theatrical agent for Hollywood producer Richard Arlen, is sent to Nashville to line up the top professionals in country music for an upcoming film. With the help of Connie Smith and Marty Robbins, the blundering colonel meets some of the best talent in the field, but in his enthusiasm he forgets to secure any of the stars for Arlen's picture. Consequently, the production crew arrive and discover an empty stage, but Fiedelbaum's new friends save the day by putting on an exciting performance. *Theatrical agents. Motion picture producers. Singers. Country music. Nashville (Tennessee).*

THE ROAD TO SHAME (France)   **F6.4136**

Sirius–Productions Jacques Roitfeld. *Dist* Atlantic Pictures. Jul **1962** [New York showing: 29 Aug]. Sd; b&w. 35mm. 85 min.

Assoc Prod Jean Mottet. *Dir* Edouard Molinaro. *Story-Scen* Gilles-Maurice Morris-Dumoulin. *Adapt-Dial* Albert Simonin. *Dir Photog* Robert Juillard. *Art Dir* Georges Levy. *Film Ed* Laurence Mery. *Mus Art* Blakey, The Jazz Messengers. *Sd* Jean Rieul.

Cast: Robert Hossein (*Pierre Rossi*), Magali Noël (*Coraline*), Estella Blain (*Beatrice*), Philippe Clay (*Tom*), Pierre Collet (*Nasol*), Jacques Dacqmine (*Quaglio*), Monique Vita (*Nina*), Liliane David (*Madeleine*), Anita Treyens (*Brigitte*), Claudie Laurence (*Jacqueline*), Jane Marken (*Madame Cassini*), Robert Lombard (*Merlin*), François Darbon, Jean Juillard, Jean Degrave, Dominique Boschero, Yvon Sarray, Olivier Mathot, William Sabatier.

Crime melodrama. Source: Gilles-Maurice Morris-Dumoulin, *Des femmes disparaissent* (Paris, 1958). Beatrice leaves her family's apartment in Marseilles to meet Coraline, the wife of Quaglio, a society figure who heads a white slave ring. The gangsters, posing as members of the upper classes to entrap young women, rape their victims and then put them to work as streetwalkers. Pierre, Beatrice's fiancé, follows her to the dancehall where she is to meet Coraline. Nasol and Tom, two gangsters employed by Quaglio, knock Pierre unconscious and steal his wallet to throw police off the track. Beatrice, Coraline, and several other young women leave the dancehall to spend the evening at Quaglio's lavish villa. Pierre regains consciousness, eludes police, and rushes to the villa, where he is overpowered by Tom, who has since murdered Nasol for insubordination. The young women now realize for the first time that they have been trapped by a prostitution ring, and Coraline attempts unsuccessfully to help them escape. Police surround the villa, and the criminals meet their deaths in a gun battle just before dawn. The young women are rescued, and Pierre is reunited with Beatrice. [According to foreign sources Coraline is the wife of one of the gang members.] *Socialites. Police. Gangsters. White slave traffic. Murder. Theft. Rape. Dancehalls. Marseilles.*

Note: Opened in Paris in May 1959 as *Des femmes disparaissent* at 90 min. Originally intended for American release as *Girls Disappear.*

ROBBERY (Great Britain) F6.4137

Oakhurst Productions. *Dist* Embassy Pictures. 27 Sep **1967** [New York opening]. Sd; col (Eastman Color, print by Pathé). 35mm. 114 min.

Prod Stanley Baker, Michael Deeley. *Exec Prod* Joseph E. Levine. *Assoc Prod* Jonathan Clowes, Alec Natas. *Dir* Peter Yates. *Screenplay* Edward Boyd, Peter Yates, George Markstein. *Screen Treatment* Gerald Wilson. *Photog* Douglas Slocombe. *Art Dir* Michael Seymour. *Film Ed* Reginald Beck. *Mus* Johnny Keating. *Sd* Dudley Plummer. *Asst Dir* Derek Cracknell. *Prod Mgr* Gavrik Losey. *Wardrobe* Brian Owen-Smith. *Makeup* Wally Schneiderman.

Cast: Stanley Baker (*Paul Clifton*), Joanna Pettet (*Kate Clifton*), James Booth (*Inspector Langdon*), Frank Finlay (*Robinson*), Barry Foster (*Frank*), William Marlowe (*Dave*), Clinton Greyn (*Jack*), George Sewell (*Ben*), Michael McStay (*Don*), Patrick Jordan (*Freddy*), Kenneth Farrington (*7th robber*), Glynn Edwards (*squad chief*), Anthony Sweeney (*detective inspector*), David Pinner (*constable in information room*), Frank Williams (*prison contact*), Barry Stanton (*car lot owner*), Rachel Herbert (*teacher*), Michael David (*C.I.D. chief on track*), Martin Wyldeck (*chief constable on track*), Malcolm Taylor (*Delta One observer*), Linda Marlowe (*debutante at nightclub*), Roger Booth (*detective*).

Crime drama. Criminal mastermind Paul Clifton executes a jewel theft in order to finance a more ambitious heist, the looting of a government mail train transporting millions from Glasgow to London. For the train robbery he recruits various specialists, and he engineers the escape from jail of convicted currency expert Robinson. After the theft the gang, anxious to divide the loot, retreats to an abandoned airfield. When Robinson phones his wife, however, the police trace his call and discover the band's whereabouts. All are apprehended but Clifton, who escapes to New York with his booty. *Robbers. Police. Prison escapees. Train robberies. Jewels.*

Note: Location scenes filmed in London at Trafalgar Square, Paddington Station, and the New Scotland Yard. Released in Great Britain in Nov 1967.

ROBBO see ROBIN AND THE 7 HOODS

ROBBY F6.4138

Bluewood Films. 14 Aug **1968** [New York opening]. Sd; col (Eastman Color, print by Movielab). 35mm. 91 min.

Prod Stacy Enyeart, Ralph C. Bluemke. *Assoc Prod* John Woodbridge. *Dir-Writ* Ralph C. Bluemke. *Photog* Al Mozell. *Film Ed* Bill Buckley. *Mus Comp & Cond* John Randolph Eaton. *Vocals* Norvin Baskerville. *Asst Dir* Jeff Mullin. *Prod Mgr* John Woodbridge. *Exec Asst* James Adonis.

Cast: Warren Raum (*Robby*), Ryp Siani (*Friday*), John Garces (*Horton Crandall/Lloyd Woodruff*), Rita Elliot (*Janet Woodruff*), John Woodbridge (*Simmons*), Ralph C. Bluemke (*chauffeur*).

Melodrama. A *National Geographic* writer and his wife place their 8-year-old son, Robby, in a tiny lifeboat before perishing in stormy seas. After being washed up on the shore of a lush tropical island, Robby attempts to apply the knowledge of self-survival taught him by his nature-loving parents. He appears doomed despite his valiant efforts, until he spies a black boy his age, who was banished with his now-deceased mother to the island years before by a wrathful tribal chief. Terrified by the stranger, Robby remains guarded even after the boy saves him from drowning. Eventually, however, they become friends, and Robby names him "Friday" to commemorate the day they met. Robby soon discovers that the civilized ways he tries to teach Friday are not as practical as Friday's ways. Together they enjoy many idyllic days and adventures until Horton Crandall, a drunken beachcomber, lands on their island in a battered little boat. The next day Crandall, a writer, recognizes Robby from newspaper photographs. He tells Robby that his wealthy aunt and uncle, Janet and Lloyd Woodruff, have offered a reward for information about the boy and takes Robby, and also Friday, back to the States in his leaky boat. Arriving at the aunt's estate, Crandall speaks glowingly of the boys to the aunt, who assures him that the boys will be allowed to remain together. But when Robby's uncle, a fortune hunter, arrives home and sees the situation, he persuades his wife to place Friday in an adoption agency. There, Lloyd Woodruff reasons, a black family can adopt him. Thus disposed of, Friday will no longer threaten the Woodruffs' social standing. When a man from the orphanage comes for Friday, Robby desperately, but futilely, tries to prevent him from taking his friend. Perplexed as to why he and Friday cannot remain together, Robby tearfully watches as Friday is taken away. *Authors. Castaways. Children. Orphans.*

Negroes. Beachcombers. Missing persons. Aunts. Uncles. Fortune hunters. Survival. Friendship. Rescue. Adoption. Alcoholism. Wealth. Racial prejudice. Tropics. Islands. National Geographic Society. Shipwrecks. Robinson Crusoe.

Note: Filmed on location in Puerto Rico and Connecticut.

ROBIN AND THE 7 HOODS F6.4139

P-C Productions. *Dist* Warner Bros. Pictures. 24 Jun **1964** [Chicago opening; c27 Jun 1964; LP29469]. Sd; col (Technicolor). 35mm (Panavision). 123 min. [Copyright length: 120 min.]

Prod Frank Sinatra. *Exec Prod* Howard W. Koch. *Assoc Prod* William H. Daniels. *Dir* Gordon Douglas. *Story-Screenplay* David R. Schwartz. *Photog* William H. Daniels. *Art Dir* LeRoy Deane. *Set Decor* Raphael Bretton. *Film Ed* Sam O'Steen. *Mus Score & Cond* Nelson Riddle. *Songs* Sammy Cahn, James Van Heusen. *Orch* Gil Grau. *Sd* Everett Hughes, Vinton Vernon. *Asst Dir* David Salven, Lee White. *Cost* Don Feld. *Makeup* Gordon Bau. *Hairstyles* Jean Burt Reilly. *Dial Supv* Thom Conroy.

Cast: Frank Sinatra (*Robbo*), Dean Martin (*Little John*), Sammy Davis, Jr. (*Will*), Bing Crosby (*Allen A. Dale*), Peter Falk (*Guy Gisborne*), Barbara Rush (*Marian*), Edward G. Robinson (*Big Jim*), Victor Buono (*Crocker*), Barry Kelley (*police chief*), Hank Henry (*Six Second*), Robert Carricart (*Blue Jaw*), Allen Jenkins (*Vermin*), Jack LaRue (*Tomatoes*), Hans Conried (*Mr. Ricks*), Sig Ruman (*Hammacher*), Robert Foulk (*Sheriff Glick*), Sonny King, Phil Crosby, Richard Bakalyan (*Robbo's hoods*), Phil Arnold (*Hatrack*), Harry Swoger (*Soup Meat*), Joseph Ruskin (*Tick*), Bernard Fein (*Liver Jackson*), Carol Hill (*cocktail waitress*), Diane Sayer ("*Booze*" *witness*), William Zuckert, Richard Simmons (*prosecutor [see note]*), Milton Rudin (*judge*), Maurice Manson (*dignitary*), Chris Hughes (*Jud*), Harry Wilson, Joe Brooks, Richard Sinatra, Roger Creed (*Gisborne's hoods*), Carolyn Morin (*house guard*), Aldo Silvani (*guard*), Joe Gray, John Delgado, Boyd "Red" Morgan, John Pedrini, Al Wyatt, Tony Randall (*hoods*), Eddie Ness, Frank Scannell (*lawyers*), Thom Conroy, Joey Jackson (*butler*), Linda Brent (*woman derelict*), Jerry Davis, Manuel Padilla, Mark Sherwood (*boys*).

Comedy with music. During the Depression, gangster chieftain Big Jim is assassinated by Guy Gisborne and his cronies while celebrating his birthday. A war of attrition between rival gangsters Robbo and Gisborne is interrupted when Big Jim's daughter, Marian, posts a reward of $50,000 to avenge her father's death. Believing Glick, a crooked sheriff whom Gisborne has killed, to be her father's murderer and Robbo to be her avenger, Marian gives Robbo the reward. Aware that he is undeserving, Robbo donates the money to an orphanage administered by Allen A. Dale. When Robbo consequently acquires a reputation as a philanthropist, he hires Dale as his minister of finance. Marian, however, charms the rivals, instigating a gang war during which Robbo is imprisoned for the sheriff's murder and Gisborne is slain. Although the freed Robbo vows vengeance, Marian persuades the women of Chicago to rid the city of racketeers. Under reformist guise, she attains gangland supremacy. She then installs herself in the offices of the Women's League for Better Government, from which, aided by Allen A. Dale, she conducts her illegal operations. *Songs:* "My Kind of Town" (*Robbo*); "Don't Be a Do-Badder" (*Allen & kids*); "Mr. Booze" (*Robbo, John, Will, Allen*); "Any Man Who Loves His Mother" (*John*); "Bang Bang" (*Will*); "Style" (*Robbo, John, Allen*); "All for One and One for All" (*Guy*); "Charlotte Couldn't Charleston" (*chorus*). *Gangsters. Police. Murder. Gang wars. Revenge. Charity. Frameup. Duplicity. Political corruption. Rewards. Orphanages. The Great Depression (1929–34). Chicago. Indiana. Robin Hood.*

Note: Prerelease title: *Robbo.* Sources conflict in crediting the role of the prosecutor.

ROBIN CRUSOE F6.4140

Fearless Productions. Dec **1968** [San Francisco showing]. Sd; col. 16mm? [Feature film, length unknown.]

Sex film. Four lesbians stranded on a deserted island engage in group sex. *Lesbianism. Group sex. Islands. Robinson Crusoe.*

ROBIN HOOD see THE RIBALD TALES OF ROBIN HOOD

ROBINSON CRUSOE ON MARS F6.4141

Devonshire Pictures-Paramount Pictures. *Dist* Paramount Pictures. 17 Jun **1964** [Providence, Rhode Island, opening; c4 Jun 1964; LP28209]. Sd; col (Technicolor). 35mm (Techniscope). 110 min.

An Aubrey Schenck-Edwin F. Zabel Production. *Prod* Aubrey Schenck. *Exec Prod* Edwin F. Zabel. *Dir* Byron Haskin. *Screenplay* Ib Melchior, John C. Higgins. *Dir Photog* Winton C. Hoch. *Col Cons* Richard Mueller. *Art Dir* Hal Pereira, Arthur Lonergan. *Film Ed* Terry O. Morse. *Mus* Nathan Van Cleave. *Sd* Harold Lewis, John Wilkinson. *Asst Dir* Arthur Jacobson, Robert Goodstein. *Makeup* Wally Westmore, Bud Bashaw. *Sp Photog Eff* Lawrence W. Butler. *Tech Adv* Edward V. Ashburn.

Cast: Paul Mantee (*Comdr. Christopher "Kit" Draper*), Vic Lundin (*Friday*), Adam West (*Col. Dan McReady*), Mona the Woolly Monkey (*herself*).

Science fiction drama. Source: Daniel Defoe, *The Life and Strange Surprising Adventures of Robinson Crusoe* (1719). The U. S. spaceship *Elinor M*, while circling Mars to test its gravity, is drawn into the planet's gravitational field when it tries to avoid colliding with a meteor. Astronauts Christopher Draper and Dan McReady, accompanied by Mona, a pet monkey taken along for scientific observation, are forced to abandon their ship in ejector capsules. McReady is killed, but Draper and Mona safely reach Mars' surface. Conditions are rugged, but Draper soon learns to make fire by igniting certain stones that burn like coal, and when his oxygen gives out, he discovers that the stones give off the essential element. The monkey leads Draper to underground caves where he finds drinkable water and edible tubers. A slave escapes from an aircraft belonging to a strange planet and joins Draper on Mars. Draper christens him "Friday" and teaches him English, and the two become fast friends. When Friday's former captors begin to bombard Mars in an attempt to kill the escaped slave, Draper, Friday, and Mona escape through the underground canals of Mars and emerge at the planet's icecap. Just as a volcano erupts, melting the ice and causing a flood, the three are rescued by a U. S. spaceship. *Astronauts. Slaves—Runaway. Space exploration. Survival. Space rescue. Spaceships. Mars (planet). Volcanoes. Floods. Robinson Crusoe. Monkeys.*

Note: Location scenes filmed in Death Valley.

ROBINSON SOLL NICHT STERBEN *see* **THE GIRL AND THE LEGEND**

ROBINSON'S PLACE *see* **BAD COMPANY**

ROBO DE DIAMANTES *see* **RUN LIKE A THIEF**

ROBO NO ISHI *see* **THE WAYSIDE PEBBLE**

EL ROBOT HUMANO *see* **THE ROBOT VS. THE AZTEC MUMMY**

THE ROBOT VS. THE AZTEC MUMMY (Mexico) **F6.4142**
Cinematográfica Calderón. *Dist* K. Gordon Murray Productions. 17 Nov 1965 [Cincinnati, Ohio, opening]. Sd; b&w. 35mm. 65 min.
Prod William C. Stell. *Prod U. S. Vers* K. Gordon Murray. *Dir* Rafael Portillo. *Screenplay* William C. Stell, Alfredo Salazar. *Adapt* Alfredo Salazar. *Photog* Enrique Wallace. *Art Dir* Javier Torres Torija. *Film Ed* Jorge Bustos, José Li-Ho. *Mus* Antonio Díaz Conde. *Sd* Luis Fernández.
Cast: Ramón Gay, Rosita Arenas, Crox Alvarado, Luis Aceves Castañeda, Angel d' Esteffani, Arturo Martínez, Jaime González Quiñones, Julián de Meriche, Alberto Yáñez, Enrique Yáñez, Guillermo Hernández, Jesús Velázquez, Alejandro Cruz, Francisco Segura.
Horror film. Dr. Krupp, a mad scientist, creates a robot with a human brain, but both are destroyed by the curse of the Aztec mummy. *Scientists. Brain surgery. Robots. Mummies. Curses.*
Note: Produced in Mexico in 1959 and released there as *El robot humano*; alternative Mexican title: *La momia azteca contra el robot humano*. William C. Stell is a pseudonym for Guillermo Calderón.

ROCCO AND HIS BROTHERS (France/Italy) **F6.4143**
Titanus–Les Films Marceau. *Dist* Astor Pictures. 27 Jun **1961** [New York opening]. Sd; b&w. 35mm. 175 min. [Also 144 and 149 min.]
Prod Goffredo Lombardo. *Dir* Luchino Visconti. *Screenplay* Luchino Visconti, Suso Cecchi D'Amico, Pasquale Festa Campanile, Massimo Franciosa, Enrico Medioli. *Dial* Luchino Visconti, Claude Brulé. *Story* Luchino Visconti, Vasco Pratolini, Suso Cecchi D'Amico. *Photog* Giuseppe Rotunno. *Camera Op* Nino Cristiani, Silvano Ippoliti, Franco Delli Colli. *Art Dir* Mario Garbuglia. *Film Ed* Mario Serandrei. *Mus* Nino Rota. *Sd* Giovanni Rossi. *Asst Dir* Rinaldo Ricci. *Prod Mgr* Giuseppe Bordogni. *Cost* Piero Tosi. *Makeup* Giuseppe Banchelli. *Hairstyles* Vasco Reggiani.
Cast: Alain Delon (*Rocco Parondi*), Renato Salvatori (*Simone Parondi*), Annie Girardot (*Nadia*), Katina Paxinou (*Rosaria Parondi*), Roger Hanin (*Morini*), Paolo Stoppa (*boxing impresario*), Suzy Delair (*Luisa*), Claudia Cardinale (*Ginetta*), Spiros Focas (*Vincenzo Parondi*), Max Cartier (*Ciro Parondi*), Rocco Vidolazzi (*Luca Parondi*), Corrado Pani (*Ivo*), Alessandra Panaro (*Ciro's fiancée*), Claudia Mori, Adriana Asti (*laundry workers*), Franca Valeri (*Vedova*), Enzo Fiermonte.
Drama. Source: Giovanni Testori, *I segretti di Milano: il ponte della Ghisolfa* (Milan, 1958). Searching for a better life, Rosaria Parondi and her sons Rocco, Simone, Ciro, and Luca, arrive in Milan from their impoverished farm in southern Italy. Recently widowed, Rosaria has come uninvited to join her oldest son, Vincenzo. Although not steadily employed, Vincenzo is engaged to Ginetta, the daughter of a middle-class family, but the engagement causes a rift with Rosaria, and Vincenzo leaves Milan with his fiancée. The Parondis move into a working-class section of the city and begin to experience the difficulties of city life and the pressure of unemployment. Simone, the most ambitious of the brothers, makes a name for himself as a prizefighter and takes Nadia, a

disillusioned prostitute, as his mistress; but when he becomes possessive, Nadia tires of him and leaves. Eventually, Rocco is called into military service, and one day he sees Nadia, recently released from prison; the gentleness of Rocco awakens a new hope in her, and she promises to begin a new life. Upon returning to Milan, they find that Ciro has started to work at the Alfa Romeo auto factory and is supporting the family, while Vincenzo and Ginetta have returned to the city. Simone, who has turned to petty crime, learns that Rocco and Nadia are lovers and decides to take revenge. He brutally rapes Nadia while a group of fellow hoodlums forces Rocco to watch. Blaming himself for his brother's despair, Rocco persuades Nadia to return to Simone. Rocco, unable to find employment, enters professional boxing and goes to live with Vincenzo and Ginetta. Simone, evicted from his hotel, goes back to his mother, taking Nadia with him, but Nadia has returned to her former ways, and Rosaria soon throws her out. At the depths of despair, Simone cajoles money from his brothers and cavorts with his homosexual boxing patron, whom he robs. Rocco then signs a 10-year boxing contract in order to repay Simone's patron. The same day that Rocco wins his first fight, Simone finds Nadia, and when she rejects him again, he stabs her to death. At the family celebration of Rocco's victory, Simone confesses to Nadia's murder. The family, though shocked and grief-stricken, tries to protect Simone, but Ciro turns him over to the police. Luca, the youngest brother, cannot understand this act of betrayal; Ciro, now ostracized by the family, explains that Simone was doomed and that all of them were responsible. As he leaves his little brother, Ciro hopes that Luca, the only one still uncorrupted by city life, will return to the country where the Parondis' roots still lie. *Widows. Brothers. Prizefighters. Prostitutes. Mistresses. Family life. Urban life. Unemployment. Moral corruption. Revenge. Rape. Male homosexuality. Theft. Murder. Milan.*
Note: Filmed on location in Milan and Rome. Opened in Rome in Oct 1960 as *Rocco e i suoi fratelli*; running time: 180 min; in Paris in Mar 1961 as *Rocco et ses frères*; running time: 165 min. One French source lists a 120 min version. Cocinor, a French production company affiliated with Marceau, is credited as co-producer in French sources.

ROCCO E I SUOI FRATELLI *see* **ROCCO AND HIS BROTHERS**

ROCCO ET SES FRÈRES *see* **ROCCO AND HIS BROTHERS**

ROCK '70 *see* **GROUPIES**

DEN RÖDA KAPPAN *see* **HAGBARD AND SIGNE**

DEN RØDA KAPPE *see* **HAGBARD AND SIGNE**

LE ROI DE COEUR *see* **KING OF HEARTS**

ROKUJO YUKIYAMA TSUMUGI *see* **DARK THE MOUNTAIN· SNOW**

ROLLER SKATE *see* **DANCE MOVIE**

ROMA CONTRO ROMA *see* **THE WAR OF THE ZOMBIES**

ROMAN LOVE TEMPLE **F6.4144**
Topar Productions. *Dist* Probe Films. 6 Feb **1970** [Los Angeles opening]. Sd; col. 16mm. [Feature film, length unknown.]
Sex film. No information about the precise nature of this film has been found. *Sexuality. Temples. Rome.*

THE ROMAN SPRING OF MRS. STONE (United States/Great Britain) **F6.4145**
A. A. Productions. *For* Seven Arts Productions. *Dist* Warner Bros. Pictures. 25 Dec **1961** [Boston opening; c30 Dec 1961; LP23793]. Sd; col (Technicolor). 35mm. 104 min.
Prod Louis De Rochemont. *Assoc Prod* Lothar Wolff. *Dir* José Quintero. *Screenplay* Gavin Lambert. *Adtl Dial* Jan Read. *Dir Photog* Harry Waxman. *Camera Op* Ernest Day. *Focus* Alec Mills. *Art Dir* Herbert Smith. *Set Decor* John Jarvis. *Sr Draughtsman* Ron Benton. *Prod Dsgn* Roger Furse. *Supv Ed* Ralph Kemplen. *Assembly Ed* Graham Shipham. *2d Asst Ed* Eunice Mountjoy. *Mus Comp* Richard Addinsell. *Mus Cond* Douglas Gamley. *Song*: "Che noia l'amour" Paddy Roberts, Richard Addinsell. *Sung by* Cleo Laine. *Sd Mix* Cecil Mason. *Boom Op* Denis Whitlock. *Sd Camera Op* Stanley Samworth. *1st, 2d & 3d Asst Dir* Peter Yates, Jake Wright, Tony Wallis. *Prod Mgr* Basil Somner. *Location Mgr* Bob Porter. *Unit Mgr* Ted Wallis. *Prod Sec* Midge Warnes. *Cont* June Faithfull. *Miss Leigh's Gowns* Pierre Balmain. *Cost Dsgn* Bumble Dawson. *Wardrobe Mistress* Betty Adamson. *Wardrobe Master* John Briggs. *Ch Makeup* Bob Lawrence. *Ch Hairdresser* Daphne Vollmer. *Sketch Artist* Ivor Beddoes. *Prop Buyer* Joan Croft. *Scenic Artist* Peter Wood. *Stills Camera* Bert Cann. *Casting Dir* Robert Lennard. *Chargehand Electrn* Stephen Birtles.
Cast: Vivien Leigh (*Karen Stone*), Warren Beatty (*Paolo di Leo*), Lotte Lenya (*Countess Magda Terribili-Gonzales*), Coral Browne (*Meg*), Jill St. John (*Barbara Bingham*), Jeremy Spenser (*young man*), Stella Bonheur (*Mrs.*

Jamison-Walker), Josephine Brown (Lucia), Peter Dyneley (L. Greener), Carl Jaffé (baron), Harold Kasket (tailor), Viola Keats (Julia), Cleo Laine (singer), Bessie Love (Bunny), Elspeth March (Mrs. Barrow), Henry McCarthy (C. Kennedy), Warren Mitchell (Giorgio), John Phillips, British (Tom Stone), Paul Stassino (barber), Ernest Thesiger (Stefano), Mavis Villiers (Mrs. Coogan), Thelma D'Aguiar (Mita).

Drama. Source: Tennessee Williams, *The Roman Spring of Mrs. Stone* (New York, 1950). A disastrous performance in an ingenue role convinces actress Karen Stone that it is time to give up her fading career and vacation in Italy. En route, her wealthy, ailing, husband suffers a fatal stroke. In Rome, after admitting to her journalist friend, Meg, that she is restless, Karen is introduced to handsome gigolo Paolo di Leo by Countess Magda Terribili-Gonzales, a cynical procuress. Karen is unable to resist his charm, and in time they become lovers. The countess, however, is dissatisfied with Karen's insistence upon giving Paolo expensive gifts rather than money, and she introduces him to Barbara Bingham, a rich young Hollywood star. The younger woman so arouses Karen's jealousy that she loses all restraint and creates an ugly scene; Paolo, however, defiantly rejects her with the taunting accusation that her pursuit of him has made her the laughing stock of Rome. When she learns later that Paolo and Barbara are having an affair, Karen returns to her apartment and stares down at a young man who has silently followed her ever since her arrival in Rome; she walks to the balcony, wraps the keys to her apartment in a handkerchief, and throws them to the waiting stranger. *Actors. Widows. Idle rich. Journalists. Gigolos. Pimps. Nobility. Jealousy. Vacations. Rome.*

Note: Location scenes filmed in London and Rome. Opened in London in Feb 1962. Also known as *The Widow and the Gigolo.*

ROMANCE AND REALITY see **CIVILISATION: ROMANCE AND REALITY**

ROMANCE EXPRESS (Japan)   F6.4146
Toho Co. 18 Aug **1961** [Los Angeles opening]. Sd; col? 35mm. 86 min.
Dir Yuzo Kawashima.

Cast: Frankie Sakai, Reiko Dan, Yumi Shirakawa, Eitaro Ozawa, Sonomi Nakajima, Sadako Sawamura, Yusuke Takida, Kan Tachikawa, Shin Morikawa, Keiko Yanagawa, Michiyo Yokoyama, Keiko Sata, Sachio Sakai, Akihiko Tanimura, Bontaro Hei.

Comedy. No information about the precise nature of this film has been found. *Trains.*

Note: Released in Japan in Apr 1961 as *Tokkyu Nippon.*

ROMANCE ON THE BEACH see **SIN ON THE BEACH**

ROMANOFF AND JULIET   F6.4147
Pavor, S. A. *Dist* Universal-International. 8 Jun **1961** [New York opening; c23 Dec 1960; LP25018]. Sd; col (Technicolor). 35mm. 103 min.

Prod-Dir-Writ Peter Ustinov. *Assoc Prod* Walter Thompson. *Dir Photog* Robert Krasker. *Art Dir* Alexander Trauner. *Set Decor* Maurice Barnathan. *Film Ed* Renzo Lucidi. *Mus Comp & Cond* Mario Nascimbene. *Sd* Sash Fisher. *Asst Dir* Gus Agosti, Franco Cirino. *Prod Supv* Edward Woehler. *Prod Mgr* Orazio Tassara. *Cost* Orietta Nasalli-Rocca, Annalisa Nasalli-Rocca. *Miss Dee's Cost* Bill Thomas. *Makeup* Jack Freeman, Giuseppe Annunziata. *Hairstyles* Larry Germain.

Cast: Peter Ustinov (The General), Sandra Dee (Juliet Moulsworth), John Gavin (Igor Romanoff), Akim Tamiroff (Vadim Romanoff), Alix Talton (Beulah Moulsworth), Rik von Nutter (Freddie van der Stuyt), John Phillips, British (Hooper Moulsworth), Peter Jones (Otto), Tamara Shayne (Evdokia Romanoff), Suzanne Cloutier (Marfa Zlotochienko), Edward Atienza (patriarch), John Alderson (Randle Wix), Thomas Chalmers (chief executive), Carl Don (spy), Tonio Selwart (president at United Nations), Renato Chiantoni (Joseph the pilot), Booth Colman (customs officer), Moura Budberg (cook), Gianpaolo Maffei, Strelsa Brown.

Comedy. Source: Peter Ustinov, *Romanoff and Juliet* (New York opening: 10 Oct 1957). Concordia, a tiny country not even on the map, becomes important when a United Nations debate ends in a deadlock and Concordia's president, known as "The General," holds the deciding vote. Because The General does not understand the issue in debate, he abstains from voting and hurries home, with the Soviet and U. S. ambassadors in pursuit and wooing him with economic aid. Determined to remain neutral, he fosters a romance between Juliet Moulsworth, the American ambassador's daughter, and Igor Romanoff, son of the Russian ambassador. As the two world powers plunge desperately into such diplomatic activities as spying, bribery, and wiretapping, The General arranges an Independence Day ceremony and has the young couple secretly married in historical disguises. Their horrified parents initially are outraged, but The General eventually makes them see the humor of the situation. *Diplomats. Americans in foreign countries. Russians. Spies. Politics. Marriage. Filial relations. Disguise. Electronic surveillance. Bribery. United Nations. Imaginary republics.*

Note: Location scenes filmed in Italy. Also known as *Dig That Juliet.*

ROME ADVENTURE   F6.4148
Warner Bros. Pictures. 15 Mar **1962** [New York opening; c21 Apr 1962; LP27101]. Sd; col (Technicolor). 35mm. 119 min.

A Delmer Daves Production. *Prod-Dir-Writ* Delmer Daves. *Photog* Charles Lawton. *Art Dir* Leo K. Kuter. *Set Decor* John P. Austin. *Film Ed* William Ziegler. *Mus Score* Max Steiner. *Orch* Murray Cutter. *Song:* "Al-di-La" C. Donida, Mogol. *Sung by* Emilio Pericoli. *Titl Song* Max Steiner, Hugo Peretti, Luigi Creatore, George David Weiss. *Sd* M. A. Merrick. *Asst Dir* Russell Llewellyn, Ottavio Oppo. *Prod Mgr* Orazio Tassara. *Cost* Howard Shoup. *Makeup* Gordon Bau. *Hairstyles* Jean Burt Reilly.

Cast: Troy Donahue (Don Porter), Angie Dickinson (Lyda), Rossano Brazzi (Roberto Orlandi), Suzanne Pleshette (Prudence Bell), Constance Ford (Daisy), Al Hirt (himself), Hampton Fancher (Albert Stillwell), Iphigenie Castiglioni (contessa), Chad Everett (young man), Gertrude Flynn (Mrs. Riggs), Pamela Austin (Agnes), Lili Valenty (Angelina), Mary Patton (Mrs. Bell), Maurice Wells (Mr. Bell).

Romantic melodrama. Source: Irving Fineman, *Lovers Must Learn* (New York, 1932). Librarian Prudence Bell, reprimanded for allowing a student to read a classified book on love, quits her job to go to Italy in order to learn about love and romance herself. En route by ship, she meets Roberto Orlandi, a sophisticated Italian whose offers to teach her all she wants to know are rejected. Arriving in Rome, Prudence finds a job in a bookstore and moves into a boardinghouse where American architecture student Don Porter is also staying. Lyda, Don's wealthy and spoiled girl friend, returns to the States, and he consoles himself by dating Prudence. They spend the August holidays together on a tour of Italy, and Prudence falls in love with Don. When they return to Rome, however, the glamorous Lyda is waiting to reclaim her man. Heartsick because she is still too inexperienced to compete, Prudence puts on her most alluring dress and visits Roberto, who declines her advances and advises her not to imitate Lyda. Prudence decides to return to the United States, and when her ship docks in New York, Don is there waiting for her. *Librarians. Americans in foreign countries. Italians. Students. Vacations. Lovelorn. Bookshops. Summer. Italy. Rome. New York City.*

Note: Location scenes filmed in Italy. Working title: *Lovers Must Learn.*

ROMEO AND JULIET (Great Britain)   F6.4149
Poetic Films. *Dist* Embassy Pictures. 5 Oct **1966** [New York opening]. Sd; col (Eastman Color, print by Pathé). 35mm. 126 min.

Pres by Joseph E. Levine. A Paul Czinner Production. *Prod-Dir* Paul Czinner. *Photog* S. D. Onions. *Camera Op* Neil Binney, Cecil Cooney, Leslie Dear, David Harcourt, Dudley Lovell, George Minassian. *Scenery* Nicholas Georgiadis. *Film Ed* Philip Barnikel. *Asst Ed* Jim Atkinson. *Mus* Sergei Sergeevich Prokofiev. *Played by* Orchestra of the Royal Opera House (Covent Garden). *Cond* John Lanchbery. *Choreog* Kenneth MacMillan, choreog. *Sd Supv* Edgar Vetter. *1st & 2d Asst Dir* A. Pearl, Peter Baynham-Honri. *Prod Mgr* Pamela Paulet. *Cont Sec* K. Climie. *Asst to Prod* Ben Harrison. *Cost* Nicholas Georgiadis. *Makeup Dir* George Claff. *Ch Hairdressing* Olga Angelinetta. *Tech Supv* Hans Nieter. *Lighting Engr* T. E. Knight.

Cast: Margot Fonteyn (Juliet), Rudolf Nureyev (Romeo), David Blair (Mercutio), Desmond Doyle (Tybalt), Anthony Dowell (Benvolio), Derek Rencher (Paris), Michael Somes (Lord Capulet), Julia Farron (Lady Capulet), Leslie Edwards (Escalus, Prince of Verona), Georgina Parkinson (Rosaline), Gerd Larsen (nurse), Ronald Hynd (Friar Laurence), Christopher Newton (Lord Montague), Betty Kavanagh (Lady Montague), Ann Jenner, Ann Howard, Carol Hill, Margaret Lyons, Jennifer Penney, Diane Horsham (Juliet's friends), Deanne Bergsma, Monica Mason, Carole Needham (harlots), Keith Rosson, Robert Mead, Lambert Cox, Ian Hamilton, Kenneth Mason, Laurence Ruffell (mandolin dancers), Royal Ballet (ballroom guests and townspeople).

Ballet film. Source: William Shakespeare, *Romeo and Juliet*. Sergei Sergeevich Prokofiev, *Romeo and Juliet* (first performance: Moscow, 24 Nov 1936). Prokofiev's ballet, *Romeo and Juliet*, as choreographed by Kenneth MacMillan premiered at the London Royal Opera House on Feb 9, 1965. The film was made in a studio during a stage performance with the entire stage cast present and using original costumes and settings. *Nobility. Nursemaids. Clergymen. Cousins. Feuds. Adolescence. Friendship. Family life. Banishment. Murder. Revenge. Marriage—Arranged. Suicide. Balls (formal gatherings). Potions. Poisoning. Verona.*

Note: Opened in London in Nov 1966.

ROMEO AND JULIET (Italy/Spain)   F6.4150
Imprecine–Hispamer Films. *Dist* World Entertainment Corp. Sep **1968**. Sd; col (Eastman Color). 35mm (Cromoscope). 90 min.

Dir-Writ Riccardo Freda. *Photog* Gabor Pogany. *Art Dir* Teddy Villalba. *Set Dsgn* Piero Filippone. *Film Ed* Anna Amidei, Antonio Gimeno. *Mus* Pětr Ilich Tchaikovsky, Sergei Rachmaninoff. *Arr* Bruno Nicolai. *Spanish Vers Mus* José

Pagán, Antonio Ramírez Angel. *Sd* Giovanni Rossi. *Prod Mgr* Angel Rossón. *English Dub Dir* George Higgins, III.

Cast: Gerald Meynier *(Romeo)*, Rosemarie Dexter *(Juliet)*, Carlos Estrada *(Mercutio)*, Umberto Raho *(Friar Laurence)*, Toni Soler *(nurse)*, Andrea Bosic *(Capulet)*, Antonella Della Porta *(Lady Capulet)*, José Marco Davó *(Paris)*, German Grech *(Tybalt)*, Mario De Simone *(Peter)*, Bruno Scipioni *(Balthasar)*, Franco Balducci *(Benvolio)*, Elsa Vazzoler *(Lady Montague)*, Antonio Gradoli *(Montague)*.

Tragedy. Source: William Shakespeare, *Romeo and Juliet*. A film adaptation of Shakespeare's play. *Nobility. Nursemaids. Clergymen. Cousins. Feuds. Adolescence. Family life. Banishment. Murder. Revenge. Marriage— Arranged. Friendship. Suicide. Potions. Poisoning. Balls (formal gatherings). Verona.*

Note: Location scenes filmed in Rome, Verona, Ávila, and Madrid. Released in Italy in 1964 as *Giulietta e Romeo*; in Spain as *Los amantes de Verona*; running time: 95 min. Spanish working title: *Julieta y Romeo*. Gerónimo Meynier and Tadeo Villalba are credited in the United States under their anglicized names.

ROMEO AND JULIET (Great Britain / Italy)   F6.4150a
  B. H. E. Productions–Verona Produzione–Dino De Laurentiis Cinematografica. *Dist* Paramount Pictures. 8 Oct **1968** [New York opening; c4 Mar 1968; LF27]. Sd; col (Technicolor). 35mm. 139 min.
  A Franco Zeffirelli Production. *Prod* Anthony Havelock-Allan, John Brabourne. *Assoc Prod* Richard Goodwin. *Dir* Franco Zeffirelli. *Screenplay* Franco Brusati, Franco Zeffirelli, Masolino D'Amico. *Dir Photog* Pasquale De Santis. *Camera Op* Mario Tomassoni. *Art Dir* Luciano Puccini, Emilio Carcano. *Set Decor* Christine Edzard. *Prod Dsgn* Renzo Mongiardino. *Film Ed* Reginald Mills. *Asst Ed* John Rushton. *Mus* Nino Rota. *Song:* "What Is Youth" Nino Rota, Eugene Walter. *Sung by* Bruno Filippini. *Sd Rec* Alexander Fisher. *Asst Dir & Dial Asst* Isa Bartalini, Dyson Lovell, Rinaldo Ricci, Anna Davini, Carlos Barbieri, Lamberto Pippia. *Prod Mgr* Giuseppe Bordogni. *Cost Dsgn* Danilo Donati. *Makeup Artist* Mauro Gavazzi. *Artistic Adv* Antoni Fedeli. *Dial Dir* Margaret Anderson. *Fencing Master* Niccolo Perna. *Dance Instr* Albert Testa.
  Cast: Murray Head *(Chorus)*, Keith Skinner *(Balthazar)*, Richard Warwick *(Gregory)*, Dyson Lovell *(Sampson)*, Ugo Barbone *(Abraham)*, Michael York *(Tybalt)*, Bruce Robinson *(Benvolio)*, Paul Hardwick *(Lord Capulet)*, Natasha Parry *(Lady Capulet)*, Antonio Pierfederici *(Lord Montague)*, Esmeralda Ruspoli *(Lady Montague)*, Robert Stephens *(The Prince of Verona)*, Leonard Whiting *(Romeo)*, Paola Tedesco *(Rosaline)*, Roberto Bisacco *(Count Paris)*, Roy Holder *(Peter)*, Olivia Hussey *(Juliet)*, Pat Heywood *(nurse)*, John McEnery *(Mercutio)*, Milo O'Shea *(Friar Laurence)*, Aldo Miranda *(Friar John)*, Dario Tanzini *(page to Tybalt)*, Maria Fracci, Roberto Antonelli, Carlo Palmucci.
  Narrator: Laurence Olivier.
  Tragedy. Source: William Shakespeare, *Romeo and Juliet*. Teenagers are cast in the roles of Romeo and Juliet in this version of Shakespeare's play. *Nobility. Nursemaids. Clergymen. Cousins. Feuds. Adolescence. Family life. Banishment. Murder. Revenge. Marriage—Arranged. Friendship. Suicide. Poisoning. Balls (formal gatherings). Potions. Verona. Mantua.*
  Note: Location scenes filmed in Tuscany, including Pienza, in Tuscania, Artena, Gubbio, and at the Borghese Palace. Opened in London in Mar 1968; released in Italy in 1968 as *Romeo e Giulietta*. Original running time: 152 min.

ROMEO E GIULIETTA see **ROMEO AND JULIET**

ROMEO, JULIE A TMA see **SWEET LIGHT IN A DARK ROOM**

ROMMEL'S TREASURE (Italy)   F6.4151
  Imperial Film. *Dist* Medallion Pictures. Jun **1962** [Los Angeles showing]. Sd; col (Technicolor). 35mm (CinemaScope). 85 min.
  Prod Luigi Rovere. *Dir* Romolo Marcellini. *Screenplay* Romolo Marcellini, Gino De Santis, Ugo Guerra. *Scen* Frank Gervasi, Duncan Elliott. *Photog* Renato Del Frate. *Underwater Photog* Hans Haas, Raimondo Bucher. *Mus* Carlo Rustichelli. *Prod Mgr* Antonio Musu.
  Cast: Dawn Addams *(Sofia)*, Paul Christian *(von Brunner)*, Bruce Cabot *(Wells)*, Isa Miranda *(Mrs. Fischer)*, Vittorio Massimo *(Krikorian)*, Luigi Visconti, Andrea Checchi, Wolfgang Lukschy, John Stacy.
  Adventure melodrama. Various people are seeking a huge fortune and accompanying documents which were allegedly hidden in Egypt by Field Marshal Rommel during World War II. The searchers include: von Brunner, a former Rommel aide who wants to use the treasure to assist families of men killed during the war; Wells, an American photographer looking for a big story; and Mrs. Fischer, who hopes to sell the documents to a foreign power, with the help of her henchman Krikorian. Aided by Sofia, an entertainer in Mrs. Fischer's nightclub, von Brunner learns that the treasure is hidden beneath the sea. The other people seeking the treasure also learn this secret, and as von

Brunner and Sofia are diving for it, Fischer and Krikorian try to steal it. Sofia saves von Brunner's life, but the treasure is destroyed when a mine explodes, killing Fischer and Krikorian. [One source indicates that Fischer and Krikorian are shot to death during the fight for the treasure.] *Germans. Americans in foreign countries. Photographers. Nightclub owners. Entertainers. Diving. Treasure. Documentation. Mines (war explosives). Egypt. Explosions.*
  Note: Location scenes filmed in Cairo and North Africa. Released in Italy in 1965 as *Il tesoro di Rommel*; running time: 94 min.

ROMOLO E REMO see **DUEL OF THE TITANS**

ROMP OF FANNY HILL see **FANNY HILL: MEMOIRS OF A WOMAN OF PLEASURE**

LA RONDE see **CIRCLE OF LOVE**

THE ROOK see **SOMETHING FOR EVERYONE**

ROOM AND BROAD   F6.4152
  Baldwin Films. *Dist* Distribpix, Inc. 13 Nov **1968** [Champaign, Illinois, showing]. Sd; b&w. 35mm. 62 min.
  Prod Vera Mandelova. *Dir* Graham Place. *Dir Photog* Arthur Marks. *Sd* Hugh Little.
  Cast: Janice Petrie, Gina May, Rex Johnson, Gregory Hope, Harlow Winthrop, III.
  Sex film. No information about the precise nature of this film has been found, but press material suggests that it includes scenes of troilism, adultery, and prostitution. *Troilism. Infidelity. Prostitution.*
  Note: Also known as *Room and Board*.

ROOM 11   F6.4153
  Bud-Bun Productions. *Dist* A. L. Shackleton Films. ca **1970**. Sd; col. 35mm. 70 min.
  Dir-Writ Bud Irwin. *Song:* "Room 11" *Comp by* Bunny Yeager.
  Cast: Terri Juston *(The Prostitute)*, Arthur Davis *(hotel desk clerk)*, Don Plourde *(The Cop)*, Joani Cruthirds *(The Maid)*, Gene Helton *(man in the car pool)*, Rhonda Campus *(girl in the car pool)*, Betty Andrews *(The Lesbian)*, Rubi Allyn *(The Virgin)*, Tito Carr *(The Thief)*, Dan Roper *(The Businessman)*, Mary Howard *(The Secretary)*, Marc Brock *(man with the whipped cream)*, Cherry Sundie *(his girl friend)*, Lynn Lyckles *(wealthy widow)*, Dan Archer *(muscular young lover)*, Hal Ross *(The Drunk)*, Harry Freeman *(Bub)*, Nicole Vadim *(Cheryl)*, Clay Waldron *(Ed)*, Lee Stevens *(Allison)*.
  Drama. Max, a hotel desk clerk who has free access to one of the rooms, decides that he can best profit by renting the room on an hourly basis. During one day, the room is successively used by Doll, a prostitute who has sex with a policeman so that he will not report her and Max; a businessman and his secretary who spend their lunch hour there; a lesbian and a virgin; a couple from a local car pool; a thief; a couple who use whipped cream in their lovemaking; two mate-swapping couples; and a wealthy widow and her muscular lover. *Hotel clerks. Businessmen. Prostitutes. Secretaries. Police. Thieves. Widows. Lesbianism. Mate swapping. Hotels.*

ROOM FOR A STRANGER see **ADULTEROUS AFFAIR**

ROOMMATES (Great Britain)   F6.4154
  G. H. W. Productions. *Dist* Herts-Lion International Corp. 26 Oct **1962** [Los Angeles opening]. Sd; col (Eastmancolor). 35mm. 91 min.
  A Peter Rogers Production. *Prod* Peter Rogers. *Dir* Gerald Thomas. *Story-Screenplay* Bruce Montgomery. *Dir Photog* Alan Hume. *Art Dir* Carmen Dillon. *Film Ed* John Shirley. *Mus Comp & Cond* Bruce Montgomery. *Mus Perf* Lincoln Sinfonia Orchestra. *Prod Mgr* Bill Hill.
  Cast: James Robertson Justice *(Sir Benjamin)*, Leslie Phillips *(Mervyn)*, Sidney James *(Sid)*, Paul Massie *(Malcolm)*, Kenneth Williams *(Harold)*, Eric Barker *(Morgan Rutherford)*, Liz Fraser *(Miranda)*, Jennifer Jayne *(Jill)*, Esma Cannon *(Mrs. Deevens)*, Geoffrey Keen *(Sir John)*, Jill Ireland *(Janet)*, Jimmy Thompson *(Alex)*, David Lodge *(taxi driver)*, Lance Percival *(Harry)*, Ambrosine Phillpotts *(Mrs. Featherstone)*, Joan Hickson *(Mrs. Bostwick)*, Michael Nightingale *(invigilator)*, Oliver Johnston *(Professor Parkin)*, Cyril Chamberlain *(L.A.M.A. porter)*, Dorinda Stevens *(Doris)*, Brian Oulton *(concert agent)*, George Woodbridge *(Yorkshire orchestra leader)*, Peter Howell *(Professor Lumb)*, Frank Forsyth *(Professor Abrahams)*, Michael Miller *(barman)*, Henry Davies *(carpenter)*, Horace Seguira *(old professor)*, Victor Maddern, Charles Stanley *(removal men)*, Erik Chitty *(elderly man)*, Douglas Ives, Ian Wilson, Tom Clegg, John Antrobus, Kenneth Cove *(street musicians)*, Bernard Hunter *(1st flute)*, Peter Burton *(1st viola)*, Terence Holland *(1st trombone)*, Jim Dale *(bass trombone)*, Nigel Arkwright *(4th cellist)*, Peter Byrne *(1st horn)*.
  Comedy. Aspiring musicians Jill, Malcolm, Alex, Mervyn, and Miranda meet for the first time at the London Academy of Music and Arts and decide to share a house. At school, they are fearful of the fiery-tempered conductor,

Sir Benjamin, and angered by Harold, a smug student. All are competing for the Strauss Scholarship, given to the student of the year. On a dare, Mervyn composes a song, which he sells to Sid, a music agent. Realizing that his act may cost him the scholarship, Mervyn attempts to buy back the song, but Sir Benjamin reveals that the tune was actually stolen from a classical piece. Miranda eventually wins the scholarship, after Harold fails his conducting test. She and Mervyn fall in love, as do Malcolm and Jill. *Students. Music teachers. Plagiarism. Conservatories (schools). Contests. Scholarships.*

Note: Opened in London in Sep 1961 as *Raising the Wind.*

ROOMMATES see MARCH OF THE SPRING HARE

ROOMMATES SOCIABLE   F6.4155
Enrico Alexandros. *Dist* Boss Distributors. Sep **1969**. Sd; b&w. 35mm. 69 min.

Prod-Dir Wizard Glick. *Camera* John Meroa.

Cast: Sheba Swengire, Sandra Sture, Roza Madre, Tulip Moyst, Linda Lust.

Sex film. No information about the precise nature of this film has been found, but press material suggests that it concerns sexual playmates who are also roommates. *Roommates. Sexuality.*

ROPE OF FLESH   F6.4156
Delta Films, Inc. *Dist* Eve Productions. Aug **1965** [c1 Jan 1965; LP29822]. Sd; b&w. 35mm. ca92 min.

Prod Russ Meyer, George Costello. *Assoc Prod* Eve Meyer. *Dir* Russ Meyer. *Screenplay* Raymond Friday Locke, William E. Sprague. *Photog* Walter Schenk. *Ed* Charles Schelling. *Mus Dir* Henri Price. *Rec* Charles Schelling. *Prod Asst* Gil Haimson. *Prod Mgr* Fred Owens. *Dial Dir* George Costello. *Gaffer* William Maley.

Cast: Hal Hopper (*Sidney Brenshaw*), Antoinette Cristiani (*Hannah Brenshaw*), John Furlong (*Calif McKinney*), Stuart Lancaster (*Lute Wade*), Rena Horten (*Eula*), Princess Livingston (*Maggie Marie*), Lorna Maitland (*Clara Belle*), Sam Hanna (*Injoys*), Nick Wolcuff (*Sheriff Abel*), Frank Bolger (*Brother Hanson*), Lee Ballard (*Sister Hanson*), Mickey Foxx (*Thurmond Pate*), F. Rufus Owens (*Milton*).

Melodrama. At the end of the Great Depression, Calif McKinney, having completed a 5-year prison term for manslaughter, settles down in a small Missouri farming community. Calif soon becomes intimately involved with Hannah, the niece of his employer, Lute Wade. Hannah's husband, sadistic Sidney Brenshaw, continually attempts to goad Calif into violence, but Calif refuses to become involved and turns for comfort to local prostitutes Clara Belle and Eula. Using Brother Hanson, the town preacher, as his spokesman, Sidney attempts to provoke the townspeople into lynching Hannah, Calif, and Lute Wade. Sidney's plan goes awry, however, and, enraged, he burns his farm, attempts to frame Calif, and rapes and murders the preacher's wife. Sidney falls victim to the lynch mob, and Calif, while trying to rescue him, accidentally kills the preacher. *Ex-convicts. Farmers. Preachers. Prostitutes. Sadism. Jealousy. Rape. Lynching. Arson. Murder. The Great Depression (1929-34). Missouri.*

Note: Also known as *Mud Honey* and *Mudhoney!*; may also be known as *Rope.*

LA ROSA DI BAGDAD see THE SINGING PRINCESS

UNA ROSA PER TUTTI see A ROSE FOR EVERYONE

LA ROSE ÉCORCHÉE see THE BLOOD ROSE

A ROSE FOR EVERYONE (Italy)   F6.4157
Vides. *Dist* Royal Films International. 29 Jun **1967** [New York opening]. Sd; col (Technicolor). 35mm. 107 min.

Prod Franco Cristaldi. *Dir* Franco Rossi. *Screenplay* Eduardo Borras, Ennio De Concini, Franco Rossi, Nino Manfredi. *Photog* Alfio Contini. *Art Dir* Gianni Polidori. *Film Ed* Giorgio Serralonga. *Mus* Luis Enriquez Bacalov. *Song:* "Rosamor" Luis Enriquez Bacalov, Juca Chaves. *Sung by* Juca Chaves. *Sd* Franco Bassi, Alberto Tinebra. *Sd Rec* Angelo Curi. *Asst Dir* Mario Forges Davanzati, Maurizio Rotundi, Nello Vanin. *Prod Mgr* Roberto Machado. *Cost* Gaia Romanini. *Makeup* Giannetto De Rossi. *Hairstyles* Vito Luciani.

Cast: Claudia Cardinale (*Rosa*), Nino Manfredi (*The Doctor*), Mario Adorf (*Paolo*), Akim Tamiroff (*Basilio*), Lando Buzzanca (*Lino*), Luis Pellegrini (*Silvano*), Milton Rodríguez (*Sergio*), Oswaldo Loureiro (*Nino*), José Lewgoy (*Floreal*), Grande Otelo (*Zé Amoro*), Celia Bilar (*Nilse*), Laura Soares (*Donna Natalia*).

Comedy. Source: Gláucio Gill, *Procura-se uma Rosa* (a play; production undetermined). In Rio de Janeiro, beautiful Rosa dedicates herself to bringing happiness to as many men as possible. Though she lives with one man, hotheaded Lino who owns a coffeeshop, she continuously resists his offers of marriage, claiming that her capacity for love is too great to expend on just one individual. Aside from sharing her charms—with Sergio, a bus driver; Nino, a musician; Basilio, a sculptor; Paolo, a fisherman; a student; and a bookshop

owner—she takes an active interest in her lovers' family problems and helps them in domestic and business affairs. Rosa also spends time giving people drug samples for all sorts of ailments, obtaining her medications, some of which are outdated, from a local hospital. One day the jealous Lino flies into a rage because of Rosa's frequent absences and beats her so severely that she requires medical attention at the hospital. The attending doctor attempts to explain to her that love should not be dispensed freely, like inoculations, but should be shared with only one other person. For a brief time Rosa experiments with this new theory but quickly discovers that she has succeeded only in causing quarrels, hurt feelings, and discontent among her friends. Incensed by the poor advice given to her by the doctor, Rosa smashes most of his research equipment and then goes to look up her former male companions and resume her happy and carefree life. *Physicians. Bus drivers. Musicians. Sculptors. Students. Fishermen. Booksellers. Free love. Marriage. Infidelity. Jealousy. Hospitals. Medicines. Coffeeshops. Rio de Janeiro.*

Note: Filmed in Rio de Janeiro. Opened in Rome in Jan 1967 as *Una rosa per tutti*; running time: 109 min. Also known as *Every Man's Woman* and *Everyman's Woman.*

ROSEMARY IS PREGNANT AGAIN   F6.4158
Dist Gunter Productions. ca **1969**. Sd; col. 35mm. 63 min.

Comedy. Rosemary is the beautiful daughter of "Filthy Phil." Phil has organized a club for people with no sexual inhibitions. One of the members is Rosemary's husband, Tony Danton, who seldom has sex with his wife. He is, however, regularly making love to Fanny Hill and Brenda Wyndham, Rosemary's cousin. "Filthy Phil" throws an initiation party that results in the accidental death of one of the male club members. The man is buried during a humorous ceremony in the forest. Rosemary continues to search for her husband; her cousin Brenda is seduced by a lesbian; and "Filthy Phil" is raped by his estranged wife with the assistance of Phil's brother, "Nasty Ned." The supposedly dead member returns cold, hungry, and naked, the victim of a premature burial. *Philanderers. Brothers. Cousins. Infidelity. Rape. Filial relations. Seduction. Lesbianism. Sex clubs.*

ROSEMARY'S BABY   F6.4159
William Castle Enterprises. *Dist* Paramount Pictures. 12 Jun **1968** [New York opening; c12 Jun 1968; LP36431]. Sd; col (Technicolor). 35mm. 137 min.

A William Castle Production. *Prod* William Castle. *Assoc Prod* Dona Holloway. *Dir-Writ for the Screen by* Roman Polanski. *Dir Photog* William A. Fraker. *Art Dir* Joel Schiller. *Set Decor* Robert Nelson. *Prod Dsgn* Richard Sylbert. *Film Ed* Sam O'Steen, Robert Wyman. *Mus* Krzysztof Komeda. *Sd Rec* Harold Lewis, John Wilkinson. *Asst Dir* Daniel J. McCauley. *Unit Prod Mgr* William C. Davidson. *Script Cont* Luanna Poole. *Cost Dsgn* Anthea Sylbert. *Makeup* Allan Snyder. *Miss Farrow's Hairstyles Created by* Sydney Guilaroff, Vidal Sassoon. *Hairstylist* Sherry Wilson. *Process Photog* Farciot Edouart. *Dial Coach* Howard W. Koch, Jr.

Cast: Mia Farrow (*Rosemary Woodhouse*), John Cassavetes (*Guy Woodhouse*), Ruth Gordon (*Minnie Castevet*), Sidney Blackmer (*Roman Castevet*), Maurice Evans (*Hutch*), Ralph Bellamy (*Dr. Sapirstein*), Angela Dorian (*Terry*), Patsy Kelly (*Laura-Louise*), Elisha Cook (*Mr. Nicklas*), Emmaline Henry (*Elsie Dunstan*), Marianne Gordon (*Joan Jellico*), Philip Leeds (*Doctor Shand*), Charles Grodin (*Dr. Hill*), Hanna Landy (*Grace Cardiff*), Hope Summers (*Mrs. Gilmore*), Wende Wagner (*Tiger*), Gordon Connell (*Guy's agent*), Janet Garland (*nurse*), Joan Reilly (*pregnant woman*), Tony Curtis (*voice of Donald Baumgart*), William Castle (*man at telephone booth*), Walter Baldwin, Charlotte Boerner, Sebastian Brook, Ernest Harada, Natalie Masters, Elmer Modlin, Patricia O'Neal, Robert Osterloh, Almira Sessions, Bruno Sidar (*members of the coven*).

Horror film. Source: Ira Levin, *Rosemary's Baby* (New York, 1967). Newlyweds Rosemary and Guy Woodhouse move into The Bramford, an old New York apartment building, which, they are told by their friend Hutch, has an infamous history. Shortly thereafter Terry, the ward of their intrusive next door neighbors, the Castevets, leaps to her death. Although Rosemary avoids Roman and Minnie, Guy, an ambitious television actor, enjoys Roman's flattery and spends his evenings with the old couple. When a rival actor is mysteriously blinded, Guy is awarded a choice part in a Broadway show. In celebration of his good fortune, Guy and Rosemary plan to conceive a child. Minnie presents Rosemary with an unappetizing dessert, which she eats out of politeness. Rosemary becomes dizzy, and Guy carries her to bed. Upon awakening, Rosemary remembers having intercourse with a rough beast before an elderly coven, but Guy assures her that the scratches on her body are the result of his drunken lovemaking. Finding herself pregnant, Rosemary consults Dr. Sapirstein, a noted obstetrician recommended by the Castevets. Instead of vitamins, Sapirstein prescribes a tonic concocted by Minnie. Alarmed by Rosemary's subsequent loss of weight and cramps, Hutch investigates Minnie's potion. Alarmed by his findings, Hutch arranges to meet Rosemary, but he falls into a coma and dies. At his funeral Rosemary receives his legacy, a book entitled *All of Them Witches*, from which she deduces that the name Roman Castevet is an anagram of the celebrated warlock, Steven Marcato. Certain that the Castevets, Guy, and Sapirstein have conspired to murder her unborn child, Rosemary seeks refuge with Dr. Hill, her former gynecologist, who betrays her to the conspirators. In her apartment, Rosemary is delivered of a son. When she asks to see the baby, Guy informs her that the boy was born dead. Having heard an infant crying in the next apartment, Rosemary arms herself with a butcher knife. In the Castevets' living room she discovers the coven and her son Adrian, the antichrist, nestled in a black basinet. Although Rosemary recoils at the sight, she hums him a lullaby. *Actors. Witches. Sorcerers. Physicians. Witchcraft. Marriage. Rape. Pregnancy. Suicide. Ambition. Talismans. Herbs. New York City. Dreams. The Devil.*

Note: Location scenes filmed in New York City and at Playa del Rey, California.

ROSEN FÜR DEN STAATSANWALT see **ROSES FOR THE PROSECUTOR**

DER ROSENKAVALIER (Great Britain)   F6.4160
Poetic Films. *Dist* Rank Overseas Film Distribution Ltd. 3 Oct **1962** [Boston opening; c9 Jul 1962; LF171]. Sd; col (Eastmancolor). 35mm. 195 min. [Also 192 min.]

A Paul Czinner Production. *Prod-Dir* Paul Czinner. *Stage Prod* Rudolf Hartmann. *Libretto* Hugo von Hofmannsthal. *Photog* S. D. Onions. *Decor* Theo Otto. *Film Ed* Philip Barnikel. *Mus Comp* Richard Strauss. *Mus Perf* Vienna Philharmonic Orchestra, Vienna State Opera Chorus, The Mozarteum Orchestra. *Mus Cond* Herbert von Karajan. *Sd* Edgar Vetter. *Tech Supv* Hans Nieter. *Cost* Erni Kniepert.

Cast: Elisabeth Schwarzkopf (*Princess von Werdenberg*), Otto Edelmann (*Baron Ochs von Lerchenau*), Sena Jurinac (*Octavian*), Erich Kunz (*Herr von Faninal*), Anneliese Rothenberger (*Sophie*), Judith Hellwig (*The Duenna*), Renato Ercolani (*Valzacchi*), Hilde Rossel-Majdan (*Annina*), Alois Pernerstorfer (*a commissary of police*), Josef Knapp (*a notary*), Fritz Sperlbauer (*landlord*), Giuseppe Sampieri (*a singer*), Hermann Tichavsky (*Leopold*), Hans Kres (*hairdresser*), Mary Richards (*milliner*), Kurt Equiluz (*animal vendor*), Erich Majkut (*major-domo*), Liselotte Maikl, Ute Frey, Evelyn Labruce (*3 orphans*), Vienna State Opera Ballet.

Opera film. Source: Richard Strauss and Hugo von Hofmannsthal, *Der Rosenkavalier* (first performance: Dresden, 26 Jan 1911). The 1960 Salzburg Festival performance of the opera by Strauss is presented. *Royalty. Aristocrats. Duplicity. Jealousy. Vienna. Salzburg.*

Note: Released in Great Britain in 1962. Previously filmed in Great Britain and opened in London in 1926.

ROSES FOR THE PROSECUTOR (West Germany)   F6.4161
Kurt Ulrich Film. *Dist* American Metropolitan Enterprises, Altura Films International. 9 Oct **1961** [New York opening]. Sd; b&w. 35mm. 92 min.

Prod Kurt Ulrich. *Dir-Story* Wolfgang Staudte. *Screenplay* Georg Hurdalek. *Photog* Erich Claunigk. *Art Dir* Walter Haag, Hans Kutzner. *Mus* Raimund Rosenberger. *Sd* Heinz Martin.

Cast: Walter Giller (*Rudi Kleinschmidt*), Martin Held (*Dr. Wilhelm Schramm*), Ingrid van Bergen (*Lissy*), Camilla Spira (*Hildegard Schramm*), Roland Kaiser (*Werner Schramm*), Werner Peters (*Otto Kügler*), Wolfgang Wahl (*defense counsel*), Werner Finck (*Haase*), Ralf Wolter (*Hessel*), Paul Hartmann (*Diefenbach*), Burkhard Orthgies, Inge Meysel, Wolfgang Neuss, Wolfgang Müller, actor, Wolfgang Preiss, Ingrid Andree.

Drama. For buying two bars of chocolate on the black market during the last days of World War II, Pvt. Rudi Kleinschmidt is given the death penalty by Wilhelm Schramm, a fanatical Nazi prosecutor, but an Allied air raid enables Rudi to escape before the sentence can be carried out. Years later, Rudi, now a street vendor, arrives in the small German town where a former girl friend, Lissy, owns the local inn. Though Lissy is still fond of Rudi, she cannot understand his easy-going nature and encourages him to be more aggressive. Also living in the town is Schramm, who has managed to obscure his past and has become a public prosecutor. Despite the fact that Rudi does not hold a grudge against Schramm, the prosecutor fears that his background will be discovered, and he uses his influence to have Rudi put out of town. When Rudi is unable to win the support of the local citizens, he smashes a store window and steals some chocolate in order to be brought to trial. Schramm again prosecutes, but his mounting fear leads him into hysterically demanding the death penalty and exposing his past. He flees in panic from the court, and Rudi is set free. *Nazis. Fanatics. Peddlers. Innkeepers. Public prosecutors. Injustice. Capital punishment. Smalltown life. Paranoia. Theft. Black market. Trials. World War II.*

Note: Opened in Hamburg in Sep 1959 as *Rosen für den Staatsanwalt*; running time: 98 min.

ROSIE   F6.4162
Ross Hunter Productions. *Dist* Universal Pictures. 3 Nov **1967** [Atlanta opening; c2 Dec 1967; LP37877]. Sd (Westrex); col (Technicolor). 35mm (Techniscope). 98 min.

Prod Jacque Mapes. *Exec Prod* Ross Hunter. *Dir* David Lowell Rich. *Screenplay* Samuel Taylor. *Dir Photog* Clifford Stine. *Camera Asst* William Dodds, John Hussey, Max Wolk. *Art Dir* Alexander Golitzen, George C. Webb. *Set Decor* Howard Bristol. *Main Titl* Universal Title. *Film Ed* Stuart Gilmore. *Asst Ed* Robert Daniels. *Mus* Lyn Murray. *Mus Supv* Joseph Gershenson. *Titl Song* Johnny Mercer, Harry Warren. *Sung by* The Boyfriends. *Sd* Waldon O. Watson, Melvin M. Metcalfe, Sr. *Asst Dir* Joseph Kenny, Phil Parslow, John Anderson, Jr. *Unit Prod Mgr* Ernest B. Wehmeyer. *Gowns* Jean Louis. *Makeup* Bud Westmore. *Hairstyles* Larry Germain. *Dial Coach* Betty Abbott.

Cast: Rosalind Russell (*Rosie Lord*), Sandra Dee (*Daphne Shaw*), Brian Aherne (*Oliver Stevenson*), Audrey Meadows (*Mildred Deever*), James Farentino (*David Wheelwright*), Vanessa Brown (*Edith Shaw*), Leslie Nielsen (*Cabot Shaw*), Margaret Hamilton (*Mae*), Reginald Owen (*Patrick*), Juanita Moore (*nurse*), Virginia Grey (*Mrs. Peters*), Dean Harens (*Willetts*), Richard Derr (*lawyer*), Harry Hickox (*1st detective*), Eddie Ness (*2d detective*), Hal Lynch (*telephone man*), Ann Doran (*old lady*), Than Wyenn (*psychiatrist*), Walter Woolf King (*judge*), Ronald Chisolm (*pianist*), Doris Lloyd (*Sedalia*), Ron Stokes (*taxi driver*), Gene Roth (*Joseph*), Kathleen O'Malley (*secretary*), Doodles Weaver (*florist*).

Comedy-drama. Source: Ruth Gordon, *A Very Rich Woman* (New York opening: 30 Sep 1965). Philippe Hériat, *Les joies de famille* (Paris opening: 6 Oct 1960). Mercenary daughters Mildred Deever and Edith Shaw contrive to cheat their widowed mother Rosie out of her millions. Alarmed by her purchase of the Los Angeles theater in which their father proposed, they incarcerate Rosie in an old age home and attempt to have her declared incompetent. To the widow's rescue, however, come granddaughter Daphne Shaw, old friend and lawyer Oliver Stevenson, and Stevenson's young assistant, David Wheelwright. At the trial the discouraged Rosie refuses to testify in her own defense. When Stevenson declares his love, however, she takes the stand, tricks her daughters into admitting their sanity, and wins the court's confidence. *Widows. Lawyers. Heiresses. Millionaires. Greed. Filial relations. Old age. Inheritance. Abduction. Mental incompetency. Wills. Trials. Old age homes. Los Angeles.*

ROSMUNDA E ALBOINO see **SWORD OF THE CONQUEROR**

IL ROSSETTO see **LIPSTICK**

THE ROTTEN APPLE   F6.4163
Dist Studio 10,001 Inc., Headliner Productions. caApr **1963** [c20 Apr 1963; LP25413]. Sd; b&w. 35mm. 85 min.

Dir John Hayes. *Screenplay* William Norton. *Writ* Paul Leder, William Norton.

Cast: Paul Leder (*Harry*), King Moody (*Blowhard*), Will Gregory (*Ben*), Rue McClanahan (*Sally [Poochie]*), Gail Gordon (*Edna*), Geraldine Leder (*Ben and Edna's daughter*).

Melodrama. Ben and Edna, an impoverished couple with an infant, are on their way to San Diego to find work for Ben when their car breaks down. Ben goes to a nearby automobile junkyard, hopeful of buying with his last $5 the part he needs. There Harry, the unscrupulous proprietor who deals in stolen automobiles and parts, teases Ben before promising that his mechanic, Blowhard, will try to find the necessary part. Sally, Harry's whorish girl friend, attempts to seduce Ben while Blowhard looks for the part. Meanwhile Harry, who knows that he is about to be arrested, plans to get himself out of trouble by turning in Ben as an automobile thief. Ben is taken aside and questioned by a police sergeant who has accepted bribes from Harry. Hoping to obtain a written confession from Ben, the sergeant permits his sadistic partner to beat Ben, but to no avail. Edna becomes worried about her husband and goes to the junkyard to find him. There Blowhard harasses her, telling her that Ben has been unfaithful, and attempts to seduce her. Police release Ben and attempt to arrest Blowhard, whom Harry has chosen to be his scapegoat. The police shoot Blowhard, and in a struggle Ben kills Harry. *Junk dealers. Fences (for stolen goods). Automobile mechanics. Police. Theft. Frameup. Bribery. Seduction. San Diego.*

Note: Working title: *The Wrecking Yard*. Also known as *5 Minutes To Love* and *It Only Takes 5 Minutes*. Copyright claimants: Paul Leder and William Norton.

ROTTEN TO THE CORE (Great Britain)   F6.4164
Tudor Productions. *For* British Lion Films. *Dist* Cinema V Distributing, Inc. 19 Jul **1965** [New York opening]. Sd; b&w. 35mm (Panavision). 90 min.

A Boulting Brothers Production. *Prod* Roy Boulting. *Assoc Prod* Philip Shipway. *Dir* John Boulting. *Screenplay* Jeffrey Dell, Roy Boulting, John

Warren, Len Heath. *From an Idea by* John Warren, Len Heath. *Photog* Freddie Young. *2d Unit Photog* Skeets Kelly. *Art Dir* Alex Vetchinsky. *Film Ed* Teddy Darvas. *Mus* Michael Dress. *Mus Played by* The New Jazz Voices. *Titl Song Sung by* Pamela Michaels. *Sd* John Aldred. *Asst Dir* Roy Baird. *Sp Eff* Wally Veevers. *Tech Adv* Ronald Brittain.

Cast: Eric Sykes *(Hunt)*, Ian Bannen *(Vine)*, Charlotte Rampling *(Sara)*, Dudley Sutton *(Jelly)*, Kenneth Griffith *(Lenny)*, James Beckett *(Scapa)*, Avis Bunnage *("Countess")*, Anton Rodgers *(The Duke)*, Victor Maddern *(Anxious O'Toole)*, Thorley Walters *(Preston)*, Peter Vaughan *(Sir Henry)*, Raymond Huntley *(prison governor)*, Ian Wilson *(Chopper Parsons)*, Kenneth Dight *(Dirty Bertie)*, John Baker *(Drainpipe Fred)*, Frank Jarvis *(Moby)*, Arthur Skinner *(Nick the Bible)*, Margaret Lacey *(Miss Rossiter)*, Richard Coleman *(Inspector Hewlett)*, Barbara Everest *(Mrs. Dick)*, Cameron Hall *(The Admiral)*, Basil Dignam *(The General)*, Robert Bruce *(War Office major)*, Neil Hallett *(guard commander)*.

Crime comedy. Upon their release from prison, dull-witted robbers Lenny, Jelly, and Scapa seek out their ringleader, The Duke, who has safeguarded the proceeds of their crime. They are met by Sara, The Duke's wealthy girl friend, who informs them that he is dead and that the money from the robbery has been spent on hospital bills. Without The Duke, who served as the brains of the group, the three crooks must resort to picking pockets. They learn by chance, however, that The Duke is actually alive and running a health clinic while planning to rob an enormous army payroll. The Duke agrees to let his old partners in on the plan, which already involves a number of London's petty criminals, but complications soon arise, including the scheduled arrival of a N.A.T.O. general on the train carrying the payroll. Meanwhile, Sara, who is assigned to extract information from the payroll guard, Lieutenant Vine, is being followed by a detective engaged by her father, who is worried about the company she keeps. The detective, Hunt, tips off the police, who board the train carrying the payroll and arrest most of the gangsters. The three ex-convicts escape with Sara and The Duke and follow the payroll to the bank. Tricked into believing that he is protecting the money, Lieutenant Vine borrows a tank for the robbers to smash through the wall of the bank, but the tank crashes through the floor. Narrowly escaping capture, Sara is taken home by her father, and The Duke is reduced to picking pockets. *Ex-convicts. Molls. Detectives. Police. Pickpockets. Thieves. Perfidy. Train robberies. Bank robberies. Impersonation. Jails. Clinics. Tanks (armored cars). London. Great Britain—Army.*

Note: Opened in London in Jul 1965; running time: 88 min.

LE ROUBLE À DEUX FACES see **THE DAY THE HOT LINE GOT HOT**

THE ROUGH AND THE SMOOTH see **PORTRAIT OF A SINNER**

ROUGH NIGHT IN JERICHO   F6.4165

Martin Rackin Productions. *Dist* Universal Pictures. 11 Aug 1967 [Dallas opening; c30 Sep 1967; LP37876]. Sd (Westrex); col (Technicolor). 35mm (Techniscope). 104 min.

Prod Martin Rackin. *Assoc Prod* Alvin G. Manuel. *Dir* Arnold Laven. *2d Unit Dir* James Havens. *Screenplay* Sydney Boehm, Marvin H. Albert. *Dir Photog* Russell Metty. *Art Dir* Alexander Golitzen, Frank Arrigo. *Set Decor* John McCarthy, James S. Redd. *Film Ed* Ted J. Kent. *Mus Comp* Don Costa. *Mus Supv* Joseph Gershenson. *Songs:* "The Devil Rides in Jericho," "Hold Me Now and Forever" Don Costa, Phil Zeller. *Sung by* The Kids Next Door. *Sd* Waldon O. Watson, Frank H. Wilkinson. *Asst Dir* Joseph Kenny. *Prod Mgr* Hal Polaire. *Cost* Rosemary Odell, Helen Colvig. *Makeup* Bud Westmore. *Hairstyles* Larry Germain. *Matte Supv* Albert Whitlock. *Dial Coach* Irvin Berwick.

Cast: Dean Martin *(Alex Flood)*, George Peppard *(Dolan)*, Jean Simmons *(Molly Lang)*, John McIntire *(Ben Hickman)*, Slim Pickens *(Yarbrough)*, Don Galloway *(Jace)*, Brad Weston *(Torrey)*, Richard O'Brien *(Ryan)*, Carol Andreson *(Claire)*, Steve Sandor *(Simms)*, Warren Vanders *(Harvey)*, John Napier *(McGivern)*.

Western melodrama. Source: Marvin H. Albert, *The Man in Black* (publication undetermined). On the outskirts of the western town of Jericho, Alex Flood, an ex-lawman turned gang boss, ambushes a stagecoach carrying a single passenger—Dolan, once a U. S. marshal and now a professional gambler. After arriving in Jericho with the wounded stage driver, Ben Hickman, Dolan learns that the ruthless Flood is determined to wrest control of the stagecoach line from Ben and his attractive partner, Molly Lang. Molly refuses to yield to Flood's demands, however, and tries to rouse the townspeople into taking a stand against his lawlessness. Although Dolan is attracted to Molly, he considers her cause a hopeless one, and he leaves town, but he has a change of heart and returns to challenge Flood. Hastily formulating a plan of attack, Dolan and a handful of volunteers steal Flood's cattle, dynamite his ranch house and granary, and blow up his mine. As Flood makes plans to invade the town, Dolan and Molly rally enough supporters to wage a bloody gunfight.

Flood shoots Ben in the back and then flees to a mountain wilderness, pursued by Dolan. When the two men confront each other in a clearing, Dolan kills Flood. *Sheriffs. Gunfighters. Gamblers. Cowboys. Stagecoach robberies. Partnerships. Rustling. Dynamite. Ranches. Chases. Explosions. Cattle.*

Note: Location scenes filmed in Kanub, Utah.

ROUND TRIP   F6.4166

Chablis Productions. *Dist* Continental Distributing, Inc. 19 Jul 1967 [New York opening]. Sd; col (Movielab). 35mm. 86 min.

Prod Mitchell R. Leiser. *Dir* Pierre Dominique Gaisseau. *Screenplay* William Duffy. *Photog* Victor Petroshevic. *Film Ed* Sidney Katz.

Cast: Venantino Venantini *(Marc Daumel)*, Ellen Faison *(Ellen Tracy)*, Larry Rivers *(Larry)*, Joan Thornton *(Diana Evremont)*, Clarice Rivers *(Clarice)*, Jacques Kaplan *(Jacques)*, Sheila Clarke *(Sheila)*, Melinda Lasson *(drama coach)*, Henri Abehsera *(Travis, playwright)*, Silverstein the Loft King *(Silverstein)*, Boscoe Holder *(Boscoe)*.

Romantic drama. Marc Daumel, a French artist, leaves behind his divorced wife and 6-year-old daughter in Paris and comes to New York City in the hope of finding a new approach to life. Following an art gallery showing of his work, he attends a pop art party on a boat off Manhattan and meets Ellen Tracy, a beautiful black model. After several dates, they fall in love and move into a loft rented by Marc. However, their different attitudes toward life result in a conflict: Marc is interested in absorbing black culture via firsthand trips to Harlem, while Ellen prefers the things from which Marc is trying to escape—cocktail parties attended by wealthy, jaded bohemians, and the status symbols that go with gracious living. Before they can resolve their dilemma, Marc receives a message that his daughter has been injured in an accident. Forced to return to Paris, he says goodby to Ellen. Although he leaves their future in doubt, Ellen feels certain that she will never see him again. *Artists. Models. Negroes. French. Social classes. Negro life. Miscegenation. New York City. New York City—Harlem.*

Note: Filmed in New York City. May also be known as *Roundtrip.*

THE ROUND UP (Hungary)   F6.4167

Mafilm Studios. *Dist* Altura Films International. 4 May 1969 [New York opening]. Sd; b&w. 35mm (Agascope). 94 min. [Also reviewed at 89 min.]

Pres by Fleetwood Films, Clem Perry. *Dir* Miklós Jancsó. *Screenplay* Gyula Hernádi. *Photog* Tamás Somló. *Asst Photog* József Halom. *Art Dir* Tamás Banovich. *Film Ed* Zoltán Farkas. *Sd* Zoltán Toldy. *Asst Dir* Zsolt Kézdi Kovács. *Prod Mgr* András Németh. *Script* Luca Karall. *Cost* Zsuzsa Vicze.

Cast: János Görbe *(János Gajdor)*, Tibor Molnár *(Kabai)*, András Kozák *(Kabai's son)*, Gábor Agárdy *(Torma)*, Zoltán Latinovits *(Veszelka)*, István Avar *(1st interrogator)*, Lajos Öze *(2d interrogator)*, Béla Barsi, János Koltai, Attila Nagy, József Madaras, Rudolf Somogyvári, Zoltán Basilides, György Bárdi, Zsigmond Fülöp, László Csurka, Ida Siménfalvy, Sándor Siménfalvy, László György, József Horváth, Lörinc G. Szabó, László Horváth, Gyula Szersén, Jácint Juhász, Tibor Szilágyi, József Kautzky, Endre Tallós, József Konrád, Géza Tordy, István Velenczei.

Historical drama. Some years after the abortive revolution of 1848, Hapsburg monarch Franz Josef of Austria ruthlessly eliminates Hungarian nationalists. Attempting to capture the famous revolutionary Sándor Rósza and his band, the Austrian army sequesters hundreds of peasants in an impregnable stockade, isolating key prisoners. So segregated, prisoner János Gajdor turns informer. The acknowledged murderer of two herdsmen, Gajdor is falsely offered his freedom on the condition that he identify an inmate with a larger number of victims. A self-confessed assassin of six is executed after an escape attempt before he can be named by Gajdor. The informer's next target is the outlaw Veszelka. After the Austrians publicly strip and beat the suspect's wife, he and two comrades leap to their deaths rather than betray the Hungarian cause. Now that his usefulness is exhausted, the captors open Gajdor's cell door, and the prisoners strangle the traitor. The Austrian interrogators exploit filial relationships, causing father and son Kubai to betray terrorist Torma in order to save each other. Torma's punishment is forestalled by an announcement of general conscription. The Austrians arrange a test of horsemanship between Torma and the older Kubai which Torma easily wins. As a prize, he is directed to choose from the stockade's inmates a core cavalry squadron. Following the selection Torma boasts that he has chosen the revolutionary band of Sándor Rósza. The Austrians announce that Rósza, who has eluded capture, has been pardoned, but they seize his contingent, which Torma has unwittingly exposed. *Political prisoners. Revolutionaries. Peasants. Informers. Soldiers. Terrorists. Nationalism. Loyalty. Filial relations. Interrogation. Torture. Suicide. Prison escapes. Murder. Military draft. Prisons. Hungary—History—Uprising 1848–49. Austria-Hungary. Franz Josef.*

Note: Released in Hungary in Jan 1966 as *Szegénylegények (Nehézéletűek).* Alternative U. S. title: *The Hopeless Ones.*

THE ROUNDERS
F6.4168

Metro-Goldwyn-Mayer, Inc. 3 Mar **1965** [Denver, Colorado, opening; c31 Dec 1964; LP29467]. Sd; col (Metrocolor). 35mm (Panavision). 85 min.

Prod Richard E. Lyons. *Dir-Writ* Burt Kennedy. *Photog* Paul C. Vogel. *Art Dir* George W. Davis, Urie McCleary. *Set Decor* Henry Grace, Jack Mills. *Film Ed* John McSweeney. *Mus* Jeff Alexander. *Sd* Franklin Milton. *Asst Dir* Al Jennings. *Makeup* William Tuttle. *Hairstyles* Sydney Guilaroff. *Tech Adv* Buzz Henry.

Cast: Glenn Ford (*Ben Jones*), Henry Fonda (*Howdy Lewis*), Sue Ane Langdon (*Mary*), Hope Holiday (*Sister*), Chill Wills (*Jim Ed Love*), Edgar Buchanan (*Vince Moore*), Kathleen Freeman (*Agatha Moore*), Joan Freeman (*Meg Moore*), Denver Pyle (*Bull*), Barton MacLane (*Tanner*), Doodles Weaver (*Arlee*), Allegra Varron (*Mrs. Norson*), Casey Tibbs (*Rafe*).

Western comedy. Source: Max Evans, *The Rounders* (New York, 1960). Ben Jones and Howdy Lewis, two itinerant horse wranglers tired of spending their winters rounding up stray horses in the New Mexico hills, make a pledge to give up the carousing that keeps them forever in debt to their stingy employer, rancher Jim Ed Love. They also attempt to solve another of their problems by getting rid of Ol' Fooler, a wild roan that stubbornly refuses to be broken. They let moonshiner Vince Moore have him in exchange for some corn liquor, but the horse also likes whisky, and he is returned. With time, however, the two men develop a grudging admiration for the animal and accept him as partial payment for their winter's work, planning to enter him as a bucking bronco in a rodeo. Before the event Ben and Howdy join two Las Vegas strippers for a midnight swim in the state fish hatchery but are forced to flee from a pursuing game warden. At the rodeo, Ol' Fooler lives up to expectations but sustains what the vet calls a fatal injury. Ben agrees to have the horse shot; but as soon as Ol' Fooler sees the gun, he bolts up and wildly lashes out at the two cowboys. Ben and Howdy pay the vet for his demolished barn and set out with Ol' Fooler to seek another job from Jim Ed Love. *Broncobusters. Wranglers. Ranchers. Moonshiners. Stripteasers. Veterinarians. Employer-employee relations. Swimming. Ranches. Rodeos. Fish hatcheries. New Mexico. Las Vegas. Horses.*

Note: Location scenes filmed in Arizona's Coconino National Forest.

ROUNDTRIP *see* **ROUND TRIP**

ROUSTABOUT
F6.4169

Hal Wallis Productions. *Dist* Paramount Pictures. 10 Nov **1964** [New York opening; c10 Nov 1964; LP29277]. Sd; col (Technicolor). 35mm (Techniscope). 101 min.

Prod Hal B. Wallis. *Assoc Prod* Paul Nathan. *Dir* John Rich. *Screenplay* Anthony Lawrence, Allan Weiss. *Story* Allan Weiss. *Cinematog* Lucien Ballard. *Art Dir* Hal Pereira, Walter Tyler. *Set Decor* Sam Comer, Robert R. Benton. *Film Ed* Warren Low. *Mus* Joseph J. Lilley. *Songs:* "Roustabout," "Poison Ivy League," "One Track Heart" Bill Giant, Bernie Baum, Florence Kaye. *Songs:* "Wheels on My Heels," "It's a Wonderful World" Sid Tepper, Roy C. Bennett. *Song:* "It's Carnival Time" Ben Weisman, Sid Wayne. *Song:* "Carny Town" Fred Wise, Randy Starr. *Songs:* "Hard Knocks," "There's a Brand New Day on the Horizon" Joy Byers. *Song:* "Big Love, Big Heartache" Dolores Fuller, Lee Morris, Sonny Hendrix. *Song:* "Little Egypt" Jerry Leiber, Mike Stoller. *Songs Sung by* Elvis Presley. *Vocal Accompaniment* The Jordanaires. *Choreog* Earl Barton. *Sd* Charles Grenzbach, John Carter. *Asst Dir* D. Michael Moore. *Prod Mgr* Frank Caffey. *Cost* Edith Head. *Sp Photog Eff* Paul K. Lerpae. *Process Photog* Farciot Edouart. *Tech Adv* Col. Tom Parker.

Cast: Elvis Presley (*Charlie Rogers*), Barbara Stanwyck (*Maggie Morgan*), Joan Freeman (*Cathy Lean*), Leif Erickson (*Joe Lean*), Sue Ane Langdon (*Madame Mijanou*), Pat Buttram (*Harry Carver*), Joan Staley (*Marge*), Dabbs Greer (*Arthur Nielsen*), Steve Brodie (*Fred*), Norman Grabowski (*Sam*), Jack Albertson (*Lou*), Jane Dulo (*Hazel*), Joel Fluellen (*Cody Marsh*), Wilda Taylor (*Little Egypt*), Raquel Welch.

Melodrama with music. Charlie Rogers, an embittered orphan who makes his living as a singer-guitarist, is involved in a motorcycle accident with a jeep driven by Joe Lean. Annoyed at Charlie's shouted advances to his daughter Cathy, Joe runs Charlie off the highway, wrecking his motorcycle and guitar. Maggie, who owns a carnival where Cathy is an assistant, promises to have the motorcycle repaired and the guitar replaced; in the meantime, she hires Charlie as a roustabout at her carnival. Although Charlie is unhappy with the work, his increasing fondness for Cathy keeps him on the job after the motorcycle and guitar are returned. Charlie soon becomes a featured attraction as a singer, and the carnival, which was on the verge of bankruptcy, begins to make money. Harry Carver, an unscrupulous businessman, makes Charlie an offer to perform in a nightclub for more money, and, after an argument with Joe and squabbles with Cathy and Maggie, he accepts. Charlie is an immense success, but Maggie's carnival is again on the verge of closing. Cathy comes to one of Charlie's performances, and they realize that they are in love. Charlie leaves Carver and returns to Maggie's carnival in time to save it. *Orphans. Singers. Guitarists. Roustabouts. Filial relations. Bankruptcy. Carnivals. Nightclubs. Motorcycle accidents.*

Note: Copyright claimants: Hal B. Wallis and Joseph H. Hazen.

LA ROUTE DE CORINTHE *see* **WHO'S GOT THE BLACK BOX?**

ROYAL FLESH
F6.4170

Vox Pop Productions. *Dist* All-State International Film Distributors. 27 May **1970** [Champaign, Illinois, showing]. Sd; col. 35mm. 84 min.

Prod (see note) Lawrence Morse, Michael Kraike, Harry Essex. *Dir* Carlton De Serge. *Screenplay* Lawrence Morse. *Dir Photog* Manuel Whitaker. *Mus* Jaime Mendoza-Nava. *Sd Rec* John Koester. *Re-rec* Hollywood Picture Recorders. *Post Prod* Go! Film Enterprises.

Cast: Lawrence Adams (*King Henry VIII*), Elizabeth Ada (*Queen Anne Boleyn*), Dee Lockwood (*Maria*), Whit Dickington (*Lord Lansing*), Forman Shain (*William*), William Keys (*Douglas*), Lori Brown (*Maureen*), Najila (*The Snake Dancer*).

Historical melodrama. Anne Boleyn, Queen of England, provides for the extra-marital sexual needs of her husband, King Henry VIII, from among a group of young women kept at court expressly for that purpose. After the beheading of Henry's most recent concubine, Amanda, Anne supplies the King with the beautiful Maria. Maria lies nude on the banquet table and spends her first night with Henry in an orgy of sex and food. In the meantime Douglas, a member of the palace guard and Anne Boleyn's secret lover, joins William, the brother of the recently executed Amanda, in fomenting a rebellion. One night while Henry is preoccupied with a snake dancer, Anne slips out of the palace to make love with Douglas in the forest. Henry's adviser, Lord Lansing, informs the King of Anne's infidelity, and a trap is set for the lovers. Henry has Douglas thrown into the dungeon and tortured. He then brings Anne to the dungeon to prove her loyalty by whipping the final breath from Douglas. Instead, she turns the whip on Henry, who masochistically enjoys the punishment. Douglas is put to death, and Anne is beheaded. Maria, fearing that the same fate awaits her, flatters Henry into undertaking to have sex with eight women at one time. Her intention is to overtax Henry to the point of death. *Mistresses. Exotic dancers. Marriage. Group sex. Masochism. Infidelity. Orgies. Torture. Flagellation. Capital punishment. England. Anne Boleyn. Henry VIII (England). Snakes.*

Note: Also known as *The Undercover Scandals of Henry VIII.* Lawrence Morse is credited as producer by one source, and the team of Michael Kraike and Harry Essex by another. Morse may be a pseudonym for Kraike or Essex. Pre-release version reviewed under the title *Henry VIII* in Sep 1968.

THE ROYAL GAME *see* **BRAINWASHED**

THE ROYAL HUNT OF THE SUN (United States/Great Britain)
F6.4171

Royal Films–Benmar Productions–Security Pictures. *For* Cinema Center Films. *Dist* National General Pictures. 6 Oct **1969** [New York opening; c2 Oct 1969; LP38736]. Sd; col (Technicolor). 35mm. 121 min. [Also 110 and 113 min.] MPAA rating G.

Prod Eugene Frenke, Philip Yordan. *Dir* Irving Lerner. *Screenplay* Philip Yordan. *Lighting Camera* Roger Barlow. *2d Unit Photog* Francisco Sempere. *Art Dir* Eugene Lourié. *Film Ed* Peter Parasheles. *Mus* Marc Wilkinson. *Sd* Ed Roy Baker. *Sd Rec* Wally Milner. *Sd Re-rec* Ken Barker. *Asst Dir* José Maria Ochoa. *Prod Supv* Gregorio Sacristan. *Cont* Eva del Castillo. *Cost Dsgn* Anthony Powell. *Wardrobe* Charles Simminger. *Makeup* Julian Ruiz. *Hairdresser* Antonia López. *Sp Eff* Manuel Baquero. *Stills Camera* Antonio Luengo, Fernando Montejano. *Dial Coach* John Kirby.

Cast: Robert Shaw (*Pizarro*), Christopher Plummer (*Atahualpa*), Nigel Davenport (*De Soto*), Michael Craig (*Estete*), Leonard Whiting (*young Martin*), Andrew Keir (*Valverde*), James Donald (*King Carlos V*), William Marlowe (*Candia*), Percy Herbert (*Diego*), Alexander Davion (*De Nizza*), Sam Krauss (*Felipillo*), David Bauer, Danny Yordan, Alfredo Porras, Joaquín Parra, José Panzio, Oscar Alvarez, Lisarao de la Inglesia.

Historical drama. Source: Peter Shaffer, *The Royal Hunt of the Sun* (London opening: 8 Dec 1964). Spanish explorer Francisco Pizarro persuades King Carlos V to finance another Peruvian expedition in search of the Incas' gold. Provided only with two priests and Estete, the king's personal representative, Pizarro recruits 167 volunteers and appoints Hernando De Soto second in command. Upon arriving in Peru, Pizarro arranges a meeting with Atahualpa, the divine king of the Incas who has been warned by his followers that the Spanish invasion will lead to disaster. After Pizarro announces to the Inca priests that he, too, is a god, the Peruvian ruler arrives at Spanish headquarters, where Dominican priest Valverde tries to convert him to Christianity. The conversion proves unsuccessful, however, and the Spanish priests demand that Atahualpa be taken prisoner, whereupon the Inca ruler is seized and his escort murdered. Pizarro asks for a ransom in gold large enough to fill Atahualpa's cell, and as the Incas work to fulfill the demand, Pizarro becomes acquainted with the noble leader and is partially convinced of his divinity. As the ransom is delivered, officers in Pizarro's command, fearing Inca reprisals, threaten to mutiny unless Atahualpa is executed, and the priests, unsuccessful in their attempts to convert the Incas, concur. Although Atahualpa guarantees Pizarro's personal safety, the Spanish soldiers sentence Atahualpa, despite Pizarro's protests. The Inca leader dons a golden mask, assuring everyone that the Sun God will not allow him to die. After the execution, Pizarro, with faith in the ruler's prediction, removes the mask to find Atahualpa dead. He then begins to realize the enormity of the crimes he has perpetrated against the Incas. *Spanish. Explorers. Soldiers. Royalty. Incas. Priests. Hostages. Greed. Religious conversion. Kidnaping. Capital punishment. Gold. Ransom. Spain. Peru. Francisco Pizarro. Atahualpa. Hernando De Soto. Catholic Church.*

Note: Location scenes filmed in Spain and Peru. Opened in London in Oct 1969.

THE ROYAL TRACK *see* OBSESSION

ROZMARNÉ LÉTO *see* CAPRICIOUS SUMMER

RUB IT IN   F6.4172
Dist Distribpix, Inc. ca **1970**. Sd; col. 35mm. 63 min.
Sex film. When he enters an illicit massage parlor, the client has nearly limitless resources at his disposal if he has the price, for the establishment caters to the most frenetic and extreme forms of sexual demand. The girls prove to be adept at group sex, lesbianism, and bestiality. The activity in the back room finally becomes so notorious that the police arrive and close down the massage parlor. *Prostitutes. Sexual techniques. Lesbianism. Bestiality. Group sex. Massage parlors.*

RUBA AL PROSSIMO TUO *see* A FINE PAIR

EL RUBLO DE LAS DOS CARAS *see* THE DAY THE HOT LINE GOT HOT

LA RUE DES AMOURS FACILES *see* RUN WITH THE DEVIL

LA RUÉE DES VIKINGS *see* ERIK THE CONQUEROR

RUINED   F6.4173
Mitam Productions. 14 Feb **1968** [periodical notice; Champaign, Illinois, showing: 29 May]. Sd; b&w. 35mm. 63 min.
Cast: Capri *(Honey)*, Jerry Harris.
Melodrama. Jerry and his cellmate escape from prison. While fleeing, they see Honey taking a dip in the stream. The men force her to take them to her home, and there they terrorize her father, her virgin sister, and her adopted Japanese sister. The men threaten the girls, and Honey offers herself to the men if they will not molest her sisters. The men have sex with her and then rape the others. The men leave the house with Honey as a hostage, and they rape two girls whose car is stalled on the highway. Honey escapes; the men fight with each other; and Jerry kills his cellmate. Honey goes to the sheriff for help, and Jerry is arrested. *Prison escapees. Hostages. Japanese. Rape. Virginity. Murder.*

THE RUINED BRUIN   F6.4174
T. I. C., Inc. *Dist* Rossmore Film Distributors. 9 Nov **1961** [Los Angeles showing]. Sd; col (DeLuxe). 35mm. 65 min.
Pres by Harry H. Novak. *Prod* Bob Felderman, Walter Hoffman. *Dir-Writ* John K. McCarthy. *Photog* William Troiano.
Cast: Myron Griffin *(Buddy)*, Maureen Jansen *(The Nurse)*, Marilyn Frazier, Mary Garcia, Luanda Banks, Kathy Martinez, Patty Wade, Arline Hunter, Bob Felderman.
Comedy. Buddy, an enormous, black grizzly bear, escapes from the zoo and falls in love with a voluptuous nurse he finds sitting on a park bench. Discouraged by her cool reception, he swallows a bottle of male hormone pills to make himself into a human, so that women will no longer flee his embraces. Instead, the pills merely inflame his desire and provoke a series of misadventures. He crashes a poolside party while the men are indoors playing poker, and creates a panic among the nude sunbathers. At the Los Angeles Artists and Models Ball, attended by a variety of scantily-clothed guests, he is mistaken for a man dressed in a bear costume. He tries unsuccessfully to woo one woman away from her drunken boyfriend and dances with another, who nearly falls for him until she realizes that he is not in costume. *Nudity. Drunkenness. Swimming pools. Masquerades. Los Angeles. Bears.*
Note: Also known as *The Bare and the Shapely* and *The Riotous Bruin.* Production company unconfirmed; Maryland license records give T. I. C. as copyright claimant.

DIE RUITER IN DIE NAG *see* THE RIDER IN THE NIGHT

RULES OF THE GAME (Reissue) (France)   F6.4175
La Nouvelle Edition Française. *Dist* Janus Films. 18 Jan **1961** [New York opening]. Sd; b&w. 35mm. 110 min.
Reissue Vers Assembled by Jean Gaborit, Jacques Durand, Jean Renoir.
Note: Originally released in France in 1939 as *La règle du jeu*; running time: 113 min. First released in the United States in 1950 by Cine-Classics, Inc.; running time: 85 min. For the reissue, Jean Gaborit and Jacques Durand collected 25 min of footage not included in the 1950 version and reassembled it with the advice of director Jean Renoir in 1958. The reassembled footage is comprised almost entirely of scenes from the hunt. The reconstituted version opened in Paris in Apr 1965.

RUMPELSTILTSKIN (West Germany)   F6.4176
Förster Film. *Dist* K. Gordon Murray Productions, Trans-International Films. 13 Nov **1965** [New York opening]. Sd; col (Agfacolor). 35mm. 79 min.
Pres by K. Gordon Murray. *Prod English Vers* K. Gordon Murray. *Dir* Herbert B. Fredersdorf. *Screenplay* Christof Schulz-Gellen. *Photog* Ted Kornowicz. *Art Dir* Alfred Bütow. *Film Ed* Lisa Thiemann. *Mus* Richard Stauch. *Sd* Hermann Birkhofer.
Cast: Werner Krüger *(Rumpelstiltskin)*, Liane Croon *(miller's daughter)*, Wilhelm Grothe, Günter Hertel, F. W. Schröder-Schrom, Harry Wüstenhagen, Helmut Ziegner.
Fantasy. Source: Jakob Grimm and Wilhelm Grimm, "Rumpelstilzchen." A film adaptation of the German folktale. *Dwarfs. Royalty. Millers. Children. Abduction. Gold. Rumpelstiltskin.*
Note: Released in West Germany in 1955 as *Rumpelstilzchen.*

RUMPELSTILZCHEN *see* RUMPELSTILTSKIN

RUN ACROSS THE RIVER   F6.4177
Cameo Productions. *Dist* Citation Films, Sutton Pictures, Pathé America Distributing Co. 12 Nov **1961** [Detroit opening]. Sd; b&w. 35mm. 74 min.
Prod Everett Chambers, Charles Weiss, David J. Cogen. *Dir* Everett Chambers. *Screenplay* Lee Gillen.
Cast: William Lazarus *(artist)*, Joan Calistri *(artist's sister)*, Curt Conway *(engineer)*, Gordon Peters *(gang leader)*, George Cathery *(gang leader's partner)*, Shirley Grayson, Robert Carricart.
Crime melodrama. After returning from overseas to his Greenwich Village apartment, a young engineer is abducted by three gangsters who believe he possesses documentation showing the location of South African uranium deposits. A young artist, in love with the engineer's sister, follows them to their hideout in a deserted warehouse; later, after the engineer is murdered, the artist assists police in discovering that the leader of the killers is a successful businessman. The murderers are arrested, the missing information is returned to the proper authorities, and the artist returns to his girl friend. *Engineers. Police. Artists. Gangsters. Businessmen. Abduction. Murder. Brother-sister relationship. Uranium. New York City—Greenwich Village. Documentation.*
Note: Filmed on location in Greenwich Village, New York City.

RUN, ANGEL, RUN!   F6.4178
Fanfare Film Productions. 18 Apr **1969** [New York opening]. Sd; col (Eastman Color). 35mm. 95 min. *MPAA rating* R.
Pres by Joe Solomon. *Prod* Joe Solomon. *Assoc Prod* Paul Rapp. *Dir* Jack Starrett. *Screenplay (see note)* Jerome Wish, V. A. Furlong. *Story* Richard Compton. *Photog* John M. Stephens. *Camera Op* Don Birnkrant. *Art Dir* Paul Sylos. *Set Decor* Ray Boltz. *Film Ed* Renn Reynolds. *Mus Comp & Cond* Stu Phillips. *Song:* "Run, Angel, Run" *writ by* Billy Sherrill, Stu Phillips. *Sung by* Tammy Wynette. *Other Songs* Byron Cole, James East, Stu Phillips. *Perf by* The Windows. *Sd Rec* Bud Alper. *Asst Dir* Dave Marks. *Prod Supv* Peter Fain, Madeleine Oolie. *Asst to the Prod* Pearl Kempton. *Script Supv* Marie Messinger. *Post Prod* Synchrofilm. *Wardrobe* Frank Tauss. *Makeup* Harry Thomas. *Stunt Coörd* Bill Catching. *Prop Master* Walter Starkey. *Gaffer* Bobby Petzoldt. *Key Grip* John Murray.
Cast: William Smith *(Angel)*, Valerie Starrett *(Lauri)*, Gene Shane *(Ron)*, Lee De Broux *(Pappy)*, Eugene Cornelius *(Space)*, Paul Harper *(Chic)*, Earl Finn *(Turk)*, William Bonner *(Duke)*, Dan Kemp *(Dan Felton)*, Ann Fry *(Flo Felton)*, Margaret Markov *(Meg Felton)*, Brian Rapp, Jennifer Starrett, Jeb Adams *(The Felton Children)*, Lou Robb *(Roger)*, Homer Thurman *(Elmo)*, Austin Roberts *(Harry)*, Stafford Morgan *(Stan)*, Rachel Romen *(Maggy)*, Joy Wilkerson *(Estelle)*, Wally Berns *(doctor)*.
Melodrama. Angel, a renegade member of the Devil's Advocates motorcycle gang, exposes the lurid story of the gang in a national magazine and sets out on his bike with his girl friend Lauri to collect his $10,000 fee, which has been deposited in a San Francisco bank. With his former buddies in murderous pursuit, Angel outwits the gang by driving through a railroad freight yard and finding refuge at a northern California sheep ranch. Dan Felton, the

owner of the ranch and a former cyclist himself, gives Angel a job and rents him a shack, which Lauri converts into a comfortable home. As four of the Advocates continue to search for him, Angel gradually comes to accept his new, peaceful life with Lauri. Eventually, Dan's teenaged daughter, Meg, meets the four Advocates at a roadhouse and tells them about the young man with a beautiful motorcycle living on her father's ranch. Now certain of Angel's whereabouts, the gang brutally gang-rapes Meg and then rides to the shack and attacks Lauri. When Angel appears, a fierce battle ensues between the four gang members on bikes and Angel on foot. Dan, who has mistakenly assumed that Angel was responsible for the assault on Meg, arrives on the scene, quickly sizes up the situation, and uses his shotgun to chase the hoodlums away, leaving Angel and Lauri free to start a new life. *Motorcycle gangs. Sheepmen. Ranchers. Authors. Revenge. Rape. Filial relations. Magazines (periodicals). California. San Francisco.*

Note: Screenplay writer V. A. Furlong is actress Valerie Starrett.

RUN, APPALOOSA, RUN   F6.4179

Walt Disney Productions. *Dist* Buena Vista Distribution Co. 29 Jun **1966** [Los Angeles opening: c13 May 1965; LP32536]. Sd (RCA); col (Technicolor). 35mm. 48 min.

Pres by Walt Disney. *Prod-Dir-Story* Larry Lansburgh. *Screenplay* Janet Lansburgh. *Photog* Larry Lansburgh. *Film Ed* Fred W. Berger. *Mus* Richard Shores. *Song:* "Ballad of the Appaloosa" Bobby Wayne. *Sung by* Rex Allen. *Sd* Robert O. Cook. *In Charge of Prod* Robert Baron. *Tech Asst* George Hatley, Richard Stranger, Gordon Eastman, Rodeo Cowboys Association. "Holy Smoke" *Trained by* Jimmy Williams. "Silver" *Trained by* Jay Sisler.

Cast: Adele Palacios (*Mary Blackfeather*), Wilbur Plaugher (*The Clown*), Jerry Gatlin (*Gilly Trask*), Walter Cloud (*tribal chief*), Jack Keran (*The Dude*), Ray Patnaude (*Mary's brother*), Pete Logan (*rodeo announcer*), Stan Bergstein (*race caller*), Rex Allen (*narrator*).

Adventure drama. Joe Blackfeather and his daughter, Mary, who own a band of Appaloosas—spotted horses bred by the Nez Percé Indians in northern Idaho—find one of the horses, Sky Princess, dead. Her colt is being followed by a mountain lion, and, panic-struck, jumps into a river; but Mary's dog, Silver, leads him to safety. Mary, though only a "squaw," is the tribe's finest equestrian, and she receives permission from the chief, who disapproves of her rodeo activities, to take care of the colt, named Holy Smoke by the tribe. She trains him for the difficult terrain that a cattle horse must endure; but when the tribe needs money, Mary is forced to sell him. The man who buys Holy Smoke cannot control him, and he is sold cheap to a rodeo rider, Gilly, who treats him roughly. After Holy Smoke again proves too wild to tame, Gilly's mate, Wilbur, the rodeo clown, gently tries his luck. Meanwhile, the date of the treacherous Hell's Mountain Stampede and Suicide Relay Race approaches. At the rodeo, Mary is shocked to see Holy Smoke performing in Wilbur's clown act. When a bull becomes uncontrollable in the ring, Silver leaps to help Holy Smoke. Sympathetic, Wilbur sells the horse back to Mary, and she trains him for the big race. In that race, Holy Smoke's endurance proves itself when Mary's partner, her brother Dale, is thrown by his mount. Holy Smoke makes up the lost time and, with help from Silver and skillful riding by Mary, wins. *Nez Percé Indians. Clowns. Equestrians. Tribal chiefs. Adolescence. Brother-sister relationship. Rodeos. Horseracing. Idaho. Dogs. Horses. Bulls.*

RUN FOR COVER see COLORADO

RUN FOR YOUR WIFE (France/Italy)   F6.4180

Sancro Film-Films Borderie. *Dist* Allied Artists. Oct **1966**. Sd; col (Technicolor). 35mm (Techniscope). 97 min.

Prod Enrico Chroscicki, Alfonso Sansone. *Assoc Prod* Gray Frederickson. *Dir* Gian Luigi Polidoro. *Screenplay* Rafael Azcona, Ennio Flajano, Gian Luigi Polidoro. *Story* Rodolfo Sonego. *Photog* Benito Frattari, Marcello Gatti, Enzo Serafin. *Art Dir* Maurizio Chiari. *Film Ed* Eraldo Da Roma. *Mus* Nino Oliviero. *Prod Mgr* John G. Avildsen.

Cast: Ugo Tognazzi (*Riccardo Vanzi*), Marina Vlady (*Nicole*), Rhonda Fleming (*Nita*), Juliet Prowse (*Jenny*), Graziella Granata (*Louise*), Carlo Mazzone (*Carlo*), Ruth Laney (*teenager*), Sharon Obeck (*Mary*), Cherie Latimer, Louisette Rousseau (*call girls*), Robert Hulsh, Gigette Reiner, George Clow, Deanna Lund, Alex Johnson, Soni Compagna, Raniero Di Giovanbattista, Jamie Wyatt, Nancy McCarter, Michele Weigand, Carol Landric, Marisa Malachini, Egidio Casolari, Michael Briggs.

Comedy. While on a business trip to the United States, Riccardo Vanzi, a 40-year-old bachelor, becomes so enchanted with an old friend's story of marrying a rich widow and then divorcing her to marry a younger woman that he decides to become a citizen by finding an American wife. He selects his first prospect, Jenny, at Miami Beach. After a pleasant evening together, he discovers that she has a husband at Cape Kennedy. Riccardo is flown by the wealthy Nita in her private plane to a huge party at her Texas ranch. After he discovers her succession of husbands, Riccardo returns to New York on a commercial airliner. En route he meets the stewardess Louise. Although the two make love, Louise laughs at his proposal of marriage. Hitchhiking to New Orleans, Riccardo has a brief encounter with a teenager but is afraid of her. His next lover is Nicole, a divorcée with children and a house in the suburbs. Riccardo's praise of Nicole, however, persuades her former husband to seek a reconciliation. Riccardo returns to New York for the final humiliation: he proposes to a call girl who rejects him. The fruits of his American adventure are a very angry boss and a return flight back to his Italian fiancée of 13 years. *Idle rich. Bachelors. Ranchers. Hitchhikers. Suburbanites. Prostitutes. Airline stewardesses. Marriage. Infidelity. Cape Kennedy. Miami. New Orleans. Texas. New York City.*

Note: Filmed on location in Miami, New Orleans, Texas, and Cape Kennedy. Opened in Paris in Apr 1966 as *Mes femmes américaines*; running time: 90 min; in Rome in Sep 1965 as *Una moglie americana*; running time: 115 min.

RUN HERO RUN see THE HELL WITH HEROES

RUN HOME SLOW   F6.4181

Joshua Productions. *Dist* Emerson Film Enterprises. 15 Dec **1965** [Los Angeles opening]. Sd; b&w. 35mm. 75 min.

Prod Tim Sullivan.

Cast: Mercedes McCambridge, Linda Gaye Scott, Allen Richards, Gary Kent.

Western melodrama. Outraged by a patriarch's death, his daughter, daughter-in-law, and two sons become bank robbers. Despite their defiance, they are undone by human frailty. *In-laws. Robbers. Revenge. Filial relations. Bank robberies.*

RUN LIKE A THIEF (United States/Spain)   F6.4182

Twincraft Productions-Coral, P. C. For Harold Goldman Associates. *Dist* Feature Film Corp. of America. Jan **1967**. Sd; col (Eastmancolor, print by Technicolor). 35mm (Techniscope). 92 min.

A Bernard Glasser Production. *Prod-Dir* Bernard Glasser. *Exec Prod* Harry Spalding. *Assoc Prod* Tibor Reves. *Prod Exec* Harold Goldman, Rafael Gil. *Screenplay* Myron J. Gold. *Photog* Jack Willoughby, Federico Gutiérrez Larraya. *Art Dir* Juan Estelrich, Santiago Ontañón. *Supv Ed* Peter Parasheles, Nicholas Wentworth. *Mus* Johnny Douglas. *Sd* John Hopkins, sd. *Stunt Ch* Joe Zboran.

Cast: Kieron Moore (*Johnny Dent*), Ina Balin (*Mona Shannon*), Keenan Wynn (*Willy Gore*), Fernando Rey (*Colonel Romero*), Charles Regnier (*Piet De Jonge*), Victor Maddern (*Abel Baker*), Sancho Gracia, Bobby Hall, Luis Rivera, Vicente Roca, Scott Miller, Mike Brendel, Román Ariznavaretta, Xan Das Bolas.

Crime melodrama. Concealed in the Mexican jungle, American soldier of fortune Johnny Dent watches as gangsters hijack a sack of blue diamonds from an armored car. Gangster Whitey Keller, the sole survivor of the gun battle, makes off into the brush, where Johnny kills him. He takes the gems and later hides them in the ice cube tray of his hotel room refrigerator. Shortly thereafter, his belongings are searched in vain by American mobster Willy Gore, his henchmen, and his moll Mona Shannon. Johnny is kidnaped and savagely beaten by the henchmen, but Mona helps him escape. Despite their distrust of each other, they band together and head for the American border with the gems. They are followed, however, by Piet De Jonge, a ruthless diamond broker. Johnny kills De Jonge in self-defense, and he and Mona take flight on a riverboat, only to fall once more into the hands of Gore and his gang. They are rescued by Colonel Romero of the Diamond Syndicate Police, but it soon becomes apparent that the colonel is actually the brains behind the original hijacking scheme. The colonel shoots down Gore and his men and chases Johnny and Mona into a glass factory, and he is attempting to take the diamonds from Johnny when he crashes to his death in a fiery furnace. Realizing they are two of a kind, Johnny and Mona decide to stay together. *Soldiers of fortune. Americans in foreign countries. Gangsters. Molls. Hired killers. Diamond merchants. Police. Masterminds. Theft. Murder. Kidnaping. Torture. Jungles. Diamonds. Armored cars. Riverboats. Factories. Mexico. Mexican border. Chases.*

Note: Location scenes filmed in Madrid. Working titles: *Diamond Country* and *Diamond Hunters*. Opened in Madrid in Apr 1967 as *Robo de diamantes*; running time: 91 min.

RUN LIKE A THIEF see MAKE LIKE A THIEF

RUN SHADOW RUN see COVER ME BABE

RUN SWINGER RUN!   F6.4183

Barry Mahon Productions. *Dist* Chancellor Films. Apr **1967**. Sd; b&w. 35mm. 72 min.

A Barry Mahon Production. *Prod-Dir* Barry Mahon. *Story* William K. Hennigar.

Melodrama. Laura throws herself into a life of sexual abandon in an attempt to erase the shame of a rape she secretly enjoyed. She becomes a call girl and seduces dope pushers, petty thieves, and big-time gunmen. Her involvement in the intimate operations of a smuggling ring becomes so deep that when she discovers that munitions are being shipped to communists, she tries to make a break with the gangsters. They send their most ruthless hired killer to prevent her from talking to the police. She flees in terror and is picked up, apparently unaware of her danger, by the trigger man in his car. The FBI arrives just in time to save Laura from serious harm. *Prostitutes. Gangsters. Smugglers. Hired killers. Communists. Gunrunners. Promiscuity. Seduction. Rape. Murder. United States—Federal Bureau of Investigation. Chases.*

Note: May also be known as *Nude on the Run.*

RUN WILD, RUN FREE (Great Britain)　　　　　　　　F6.4184
Irving Allen, Ltd. *Dist* Columbia Pictures. 28 May **1969** [Los Angeles opening; c1 Jun 1969; LP37135]. Sd (Westrex); col (Technicolor). 35mm. 100 min. MPAA rating G.

An Irving Allen Production. *Prod* John Danischewsky. *Exec Prod* Andrew Donally. *Dir* Richard C. Sarafian. *Screenplay* David Rook. *Dir Photog* Wilkie Cooper. *Camera Op* Frank Drake. *Art Dir* Ted Tester. *Film Ed* Geoffrey Foot. *Mus Comp & Cond* David Whitaker. *Titl Song* David Whitaker, Don Black. *Sung by* Nina and Frederik, New Christy Minstrels. *Sd Rec* David Price, Ken Scrivener. *Sd Ed* Charles Crafford. *Asst Dir* William M. Graf. *Prod Supv* Ed Harper. *Cont* Leonora Hale. *Sp Eff Supv* Bill Warrington.

Cast: John Mills *(The Moorman)*, Gordon Jackson *(Mr. Ransome)*, Sylvia Syms *(Mrs. Randsome)*, Mark Lester *(Philip Ransome)*, Bernard Miles *(Reg)*, Fiona Fullerton *(Diana)*.

Drama. Source: David Rook, *The White Colt* (New York, 1967). As the result of an early traumatic experience, 10-year-old Philip Ransome is mute, a psychological affliction that is worsened by the overbearing love of his mother and the exasperated impatience of his father. Following the failure of an attempt to cure the boy at a local clinic, Philip's mother gives up in despair and allows him to wander freely about the moors that surround his home in Devonshire. During these days Philip makes two friends: a retired army colonel known as The Moorman and a white pony that runs wildly about the moors. Naming the colt after himself, Philip devotes all of his time to his new companion—until the pony suddenly disappears. Realizing that Philip responds more to animals than people, The Moorman persuades a neighbor's little girl, Diana, to lend the boy her pet kestrel. While training the falcon under the tutelage of The Moorman and Diana, Philip catches a glimpse of his pony and chases after it, completely ignoring the bird attached to his arm. As a result, Diana's pet is badly wounded. The kestrel recovers, but it is accidentally killed a short time later. As Philip lapses into listlessness, The Moorman recaptures the colt and patiently teaches Philip to ride. During this learning process The Moorman discovers that Philip is capable of speech. Then, while riding on the moors, Philip, Diana, and the colt get lost in a heavy mist and the colt becomes mired in a bog. A search party, including The Moorman and Philip's parents, find them but cannot rescue the colt. Looking at his apparently doomed pony, Philip speaks a few loving words of encouragement, and the colt struggles to safety. *Children. Mutes. Neighbors. Veterans. Parenthood. Friendship. Psychosomatic illness. Moorlands. Devonshire (England). Horses. Falcons.*

Note: Filmed on location in Dartmoor, England. Opened in London in Jun 1969; running time: 98 min. Working title: *The White Colt.* Prerelease title: *Philip.*

RUN WITH THE DEVIL (France/Italy)　　　　　　　　F6.4185
Documento Film–Le Louvre Films. *Dist* Jillo Film Productions. 15 Jul **1963** [New York opening]. Sd; b&w. 35mm. 93 min.

Pres by Richard L. Rosenfeld. *Prod* Gianni Hecht Lucari. *Dir* Mario Camerini. *Story-Screenplay* Franco Brusati, Mario Camerini, Ennio De Concini, Ugo Guerra. *Photog* Leonida Barboni. *Art Dir* Dario Cecchi, Massimiliano Capriccioli. *Film Ed* Giuliana Attenni. *Mus* Piero Piccioni. *Prod Mgr* Paolo Giovanardi.

Cast: Antonella Lualdi *(Donata)*, Gérard Blain *(Stefano)*, Franco Fabrizi *(Giosué)*, Yvonne Furneaux *(Marta)*, Cristina Gajoni *(Marisa Maccesi)*, Spiros Focas *(Marco Belli)*, Claudio Gora *(Pippo Cantigliani)*, Corrado Pani *(youth)*, Alex Nicol *(Bill Rogers)*, Marion Marshall *(Grace)*, Wera Dekormos *(Greta)*, Walter Brofferio.

Comedy-drama. Source: Ugo Moretti, *Gente al Babuino* (Florence, 1957). The artists' quarter in Rome is the Via Margutta where many aspiring artists seek to gain recognition. Stefano, a dedicated but unsuccessful painter, shares his misery and bitterness with actress Donata, until Pippo, a homosexual antique dealer, organizes an exhibition for him and secretly buys several of his paintings. When Stefano learns that Pippo has been sponsoring him, he commits suicide. Giosué, another artist, decides to end the struggle for success and marries Greta, a wealthy German tourist 20 years his senior. Marta, a beautiful singer, spends her time flitting from one love affair to another. Marco Belli sells his own paintings fraudulently signed by Marisa, a peasant housemaid whose suicide attempt had made news headlines. Expatriate American actor Bill Rogers indulges his laziness, occasionally molding a sculpture. One artist and his girl friend decide to leave, but his place is soon taken by a newcomer, filled with optimism about his future on the Via Margutta. *Artists. Painters. Actors. Patrons. Antique dealers. Germans. Tourists. Gigolos. Singers. Housemaids. Americans in foreign countries. Sculptors. Ambition. Male homosexuality. Suicide. Fraud. Art exhibits. Rome—Via Margutta.*

Note: Location scenes filmed in Rome. Opened in Rome in Sep 1960 as *Via Margutta;* running time: 108 min; in Paris in Jun 1962 as *La rue des amours faciles;* running time: 105 min.

RUNAROUND　　　　　　　　　　　　　　　　　　　F6.4186
Cosmos Films. *Dist* Able Film Co. ca **1970**. Sd; col. 16mm. [Feature length assumed.]

Sex film. Jack, a middle-class suburban husband, leaves his domestic sex life for many adventures with beautiful women, only to return to his wife. *Suburbanites. Infidelity. Sexuality.*

RUNAWAY DAUGHTERS *see* PROWL GIRLS

RUNAWAY GIRL　　　　　　　　　　　　　　　　　F6.4187
Caren Productions. *For* Laurel Films. *Dist* United Screen Arts. Feb **1966.** Sd; b&w. 35mm. 62 min.

Prod-Dir Hamil Petroff. *Assoc Prod* Vernon Keays. *Orig Story & Screenplay* Stewart Cohn. *Dir Photog* Ed Fitzgerald. *Mus Comp & Cond* Richard LaSalle. *Guitarist* Laurindo Almeida. *Prod Supv* Vernon Keays.

Cast: Lili St. Cyr *(Edella)*, Jock Mahoney *(Randy Marelli)*, Ron Hagerthy *(Mario Marelli)*, Laurie Mitchell *(Winnie Bernay)*, Booth Colman *(Angelo Guglietta)*, Robert Shayne *(Walter Quillen)*, June Jocelyn *(Louise)*, Lisa Pons *(Tina)*, Shary Layne *(Betsy)*, Suzi Carnell *(Ruth)*, Dusty Enders *(Jeanette)*, Sandra Phelps *(Cleo)*, Anne Graves *(Ginger)*.

Drama. Exhausted from an endless string of nightclub performances, an exotic dancer and stripteaser takes a job as a grape picker in a California vineyard. Her mysterious presence causes resentment among the other girls as well as a bitter rivalry between the vineyard manager and his younger brother. The dancer's true identity is eventually revealed, and she gives her perfumes and jewelry to the other girls in her bunkhouse and prepares to leave with her agent. At the last minute she changes her mind, however, and decides to remain at the vineyard and become the manager's wife. *Stripteasers. Farm workers. Talent agents. Jealousy. Vineyards. California.*

THE RUNNING MAN (Great Britain)　　　　　　　　F6.4188
Peet Productions. *Dist* Columbia Pictures. 2 Oct **1963** [New York opening; c1 Oct 1963; LP26601]. Sd (Westrex); col (Eastman Color by Pathé). 35mm (Panavision). 103 min. [Copyright length: 109 min.]

A Carol Reed Production. *Prod-Dir* Carol Reed. *Assoc Prod* John R. Sloan. *2d Unit Dir* Harold Haysom. *Screenplay* John Mortimer. *Dir Photog* Robert Krasker. *Camera Op* John Harris. *Art Dir* John Stoll. *Asst Art Dir* Herbert Smith. *Film Ed* Bert Bates. *Mus Comp* William Alwyn. *Cond* Muir Mathieson. *Played by* Sinfonia of London. *Sd Rec* Claude Hitchcock, Bob Jones. *Sd Ed* Peter Thornton. *Asst Dir* Peter Bolton, Pedro Vidal. *Prod Supv* John Dark. *Spanish Prod Mgr* Roberto Roberts. *Unit Mgr* John Quested. *Cont* Angela Allen. *Makeup* George Frost. *Hairstyles* George Scott.

Cast: Laurence Harvey *(Rex Black)*, Lee Remick *(Stella Black)*, Alan Bates *(Stephen Maddox)*, Felix Aylmer *(parson)*, Eleanor Summerfield *(Hilda Tanner)*, Allan Cuthbertson *(Jenkins)*, Harold Goldblatt *(Tom Webster)*, Noel Purcell *(Miles Bleeker)*, Ramsay Ames *(Madge Penderby)*, Fernando Rey *(police official)*, Juan Jose Menendez *(Roberto)*, Eddie Byrne *(Sam Crewdson)*, Colin Gordon *(Solicitor)*, John Meillon *(Jim Jerome)*, Roger Delgado *(Spanish doctor)*, Fortunio Bonanova *(bank manager)*, Shirley Gale *(Florence)*, Jose Calvo, Joe Lynch, Freddy Roberts, Adriano Dominguez, James Neylin, Pamela Mant, Herbert Curiel, Antonio Padilla Ruiz, Lockwood West, Bob Cunningham.

Crime drama. Source: Shelley Smith, *The Ballad of the Running Man* (London, 1961). Rex Black, a pilot running a private airline, learns he cannot collect insurance when his glider plane crashes because he failed to renew his policy the day before the accident. Infuriated, he formulates a plan for defrauding the insurance company of £50,000. After faking a supposedly fatal crash, he changes his name and appearance and goes to Malaga, Spain, while his wife, Stella, remains in England to collect his life insurance money. Company agent Stephen Maddox investigates, finds everything in order, and puts through Stella's claim. In accordance with Rex's instructions, Stella also goes to Spain. She is distressed to discover that he is posing as Australian millionaire Jim Jerome, whose passport he found and whom he plans to kill off on another policy. Stephen Maddox suddenly appears, ostensibly on a holiday. The three become friendly as Rex tries to discover whether or not Maddox is suspicious. Then, convinced that their scheme will soon be exposed, Rex forces

Stella to flee with him to Gibraltar, unaware that Maddox is no longer an insurance man and really is on vacation. Maddox, in love with Stella, follows them, and Rex becomes panic-stricken and tries unsuccessfully to force Maddox's car over a cliff. Stella jumps out of Rex's car as he races to an airport to steal a small plane. Unaware that the fuel tank is almost empty, he takes off and crashes into the sea. *Air pilots. Insurance agents. Swindlers. Insurance. Vacations. Imposture. Airplanes. Passports. Málaga (Spain). Gibraltar. Chases. Airplane accidents.*

Note: Location scenes filmed in Spain. Released in Great Britain in 1963; running time: 103 min.

RUNNING SCARED see **THE GHOST AND MR. CHICKEN**

RUSH TO JUDGMENT   F6.4189
Judgment Films. *Dist* Impact Films. 30 Mar **1967** [New Orleans opening; c16 Jan 1967; MP25659]. Sd; b&w. 35mm. 122 min. [Also 116 min.]
Prod Mark Lane, Emile De Antonio. *Dir* Emile De Antonio. *Screenplay* Mark Lane. *Photog* Robert Primes. *Film Ed* Daniel Drasin.
Narrator: Mark Lane.
Film essay. Source: Mark Lane, *Rush to Judgment: A Critique of the Warren Commission Inquiry Into the Murders of President John F. Kennedy, Officer J. D. Tippit and Lee Harvey Oswald* (New York, 1966). Contending that the Warren Commission did not establish conclusively that Lee Harvey Oswald was the sole assassin of President Kennedy, lawyer Mark Lane interviews numerous eyewitnesses. Lane concludes that Oswald's killer, Jack Ruby, was well-known by the Dallas police, that the circumstances surrounding the death of officer J. D. Tippit have been insufficiently investigated, and that much evidence was mishandled. Lane's discussion of a possible conspiracy is illustrated by television newsreel footage of the assassination. *Lawyers. Assassination. John Fitzgerald Kennedy. Lee Harvey Oswald. Jack Ruby. J. D. Tippit. The President's Commission on the Assassination of President John F. Kennedy.*

RUSS MEYER'S VIXEN see **VIXEN**

RUSSIA IN THE 70'S   F6.4190
Clay Francisco. 20 Oct **1970** [San Diego, California, showing]. Sd eff & mus score; col. 35mm. ca120 min.
Prod-Dir Clay Francisco.
Travelog. Among the featured cities and attractions are: Moscow, Kiev, Novgorod, Leningrad, Kazakhstan, the Bolshoi Theater, the Moscow Circus, the Gregorian State Dance Company, and the Kremlin. *Moscow. Kiev. Novgorod. Leningrad. Kazakhstan. Bolshoi Theater (Moscow). Moscow Circus. Gregorian State Dance Company. The Kremlin (Moscow).*
Note: Narration is delivered on stage.

RUSSIAN ROULETTE see **TWO BEFORE ZERO**

THE RUSSIANS ARE COMING THE RUSSIANS ARE COMING
                                                                                                       F6.4191
Mirisch Corp. *Dist* United Artists. 25 May **1966** [New York opening; c25 May 1966; LP32950]. Sd; col (DeLuxe). 35mm (Panavision). 126 min.
A Norman Jewison Production. *Prod-Dir* Norman Jewison. *Screenplay* William Rose. *Photog* Joseph Biroc. *Art Dir* Robert Boyle. *Set Decor* Darrell Silvera. *Set Dsgn* James F. McGuire, Lewis E. Hurst. *Sketch Artist* Thomas J. Wright, Jr. *Titl* Pablo Ferro, Inc. *Film Ed* Hal Ashby, J. Terry Williams. *Mus* Johnny Mandel. *Sd* Al Overton, Jr., John Romness. *Sd Ed* Sidney E. Sutherland. *Mus Ed* Richard Carruth. *1st & 2d Asst Dir* Kurt Neumann, Les Gorall. *Prod Supv* Allen K. Wood. *Prod Mgr* James E. Henderling. *Unit Mgr* Fred Lemoine. *Asst to the Prod* Peter Nelson. *Script Supv* Betty Levin. *Wardrobe* Wes Jeffries. *Makeup* Del Armstrong. *Hairstyles* Sydney Guilaroff. *Hairdresser* Naomi Cavin. *Sp Eff* Daniel W. Hays. *Dial Dir* Leon Belasco. *Casting* Lynn Stalmaster.
Cast: Carl Reiner (*Walt Whittaker*), Eva Marie Saint (*Elspeth Whittaker*), Alan Arkin (*Rozanov*), Brian Keith (*Link Mattocks*), Jonathan Winters (*Norman Jonas*), Theodore Bikel (*Russian captain*), Paul Ford (*Fendall Hawkins*), Tessie O'Shea (*Alice Foss*), John Phillip Law (*Kolchin*), Andrea Dromm (*Alison*), Ben Blue (*Luther Grilk*), Sheldon Golomb (*Pete Whittaker*), Cindy Putnam (*Annie Whittaker*), Guy Raymond (*Lester Tilly*), Cliff Norton (*Charlie Hinkson*), Richard Schaal (*Oscar Maxwell*), Philip Coolidge (*Mr. Porter*), Don Keefer (*Irving Christiansen*), Parker Fennelly (*Mr. Everett*), Doro Merande (*Muriel Everett*), Vaughn Taylor (*Mr. Bell*), Johnnie Whitaker (*Jerry Maxwell*), Danny Klega (*Polsky*), Ray Baxter (*Brodsky*), Paul Verdier (*Maliavin*), Nikita Knatz (*Gromolsky*), Constantine Baksheef (*Vasilov*), Alex Hassilev (*Hrushevsky*), Milos Milos (*Lysenko*), Gino Gottarelli (*Kregitkin*), Michael J. Pollard (*airport worker*), Peter Brocco (*Reverend Hawthorne*).
Comedy. Source: Nathaniel Benchley, *The Off-Islanders* (New York, 1961). Early one September morning a Russian submarine draws too close to the New England coast when its captain wants to take a good look at America and runs

aground on a sandbar near an island off Cape Cod. A 9-man landing party headed by timorous Lieutenant Rozanov is sent in search of a motor launch to help free the submarine. The men arrive at the house of Walt Whittaker, a New York City playwright anxious to get his wife and two children off the forever-damp island now that summer is over. Failing to convince the Whittakers that his group are Norwegians, Rozanov draws a gun and promises no harm to Walt if he will simply tell them how to get a boat so that they can quietly go away. Walt agrees and the Russians depart, leaving a young sailor, Kolchin, to guard the Whittakers and their attractive 18-year-old neighbor, Alison Palmer. The Russians steal an old sedan from Muriel Everett, the postmistress; she calls Alice Foss, the gossip telephone switchboard operator, and before long, wild rumors throw the entire island into confusion. As levelheaded Sheriff Mattocks and his bumbling assistant Norman Jonas try to squelch the civil resistance movement of blustering Fendall Hawkins, the Russians run into Walt, who has escaped from Kolchin, and together they obtain a boat. As the remaining Russians race back to their submarine, Rozanov goes to find Kolchin, who by now is falling in love with Alison. The captain takes his submarine into the small harbor and threatens to blow up the town unless Rozanov and Kolchin are returned to him. As tension mounts, a small boy falls from his perch on the church steeple and hangs perilously from a gutter. Forgetting their differences, islanders and Russians unite to form a human pyramid and rescue the child. With peace and harmony enveloping everyone, the Russians leave the island—with a convoy of villagers in small boats protecting the submarine from overhead Navy planes until it reaches safe waters. *New Englanders. Russians. Playwrights. Postmistresses. Telephone operators. Sheriffs. Civil defense. Village life. Imposture. Rescue. Islands. Submarines. Cape Cod. Union of Soviet Socialist Republics—Navy. United States Navy.*
Note: Filmed in Mendocino County, California.

THE RUTHLESS FOUR (Italy/West Germany)   F6.4192
P. C. M.–Eichberg Film. *Dist* Goldstone Film Enterprises. Nov **1969**. Sd; col (Technicolor). 35mm (Techniscope). 96 min. *MPAA rating* M.
Pres by Walter Manley Enterprises. *Prod* Alberto Pugliese, Luciano Ercoli. *Dir* Giorgio Capitani. *Story & Screenplay* Fernando Di Leo, Augusto Caminito. *Dir Photog* Sergio D'Offizi. *Cameraman* Giuseppe Oall. *Prod Dsgn* Franco Bottari. *Film Ed* Renato Cinquini. *Mus Comp* Carlo Rustichelli. *Mus Dir* Bruno Nicolai. *Asst Dir* Marcello Crescenzi. *Prod Mgr* Antonio Negri. *Prod Mgr for Germany* Hans Gerber. *Unit Mgr* Paolo Zaccario. *Unit Prod* Kadin Hellman, Fausto Benelli. *Script Girl* Paola Colonna. *Makeup* Giulio Natalucci.
Cast: Van Heflin (*Sam Cooper*), Gilbert Roland (*Mason*), Klaus Kinski (*Blond*), George Hilton (*Manolo*), Sarah Ross, Rick Boyd, Sergio Doria, Ivan Scratuglia, Giorgio Gruden, Hardy Reichelt, Doro Carrà.
Western melodrama. Sam Cooper, an old prospector who has at last discovered a rich vein of gold, invites young Manolo, whom he describes to dancehall hostess Annie as the only man he trusts, to help him dig out his gold in Nevada. Manolo brings with him Blond, a ruthless killer. Sam counters by asking Mason, his old army buddy, to join the group. (Mason deserted with Sam and, though he blames Sam for the 3 years he spent in prison, joins the party for the money.) On the way, the four men wipe out a gang, and Blond kills a man lost in the hills who turns out to be a marshal. Sam collects all the guns, and Mason beats Blond to death when he attempts to grab one. Manolo is killed by Sam in order to save Mason; then Mason dies after saving Sam from two killers hired for protection. The gold is now entirely Sam's. *Prospectors. Dancehall hostesses. United States marshals. Hired killers. Deserters—Military. Murder. Greed. Gold. Nevada.*
Note: Released in West Germany in Aug 1968 as *Das Gold von Sam Cooper*; running time: 106 min; in Italy in 1968 as *Ognuno per sè.* Prerelease U. S. titles: *Sam Cooper's Gold* and *Each Man for Himself.*

RUUSUJEN AIKA see **TIME OF ROSES**

RYAN'S DAUGHTER (Great Britain)   F6.4193
Faraway Productions. *Dist* Metro-Goldwyn-Mayer, Inc. 9 Nov **1970** [New York opening; c29 Dec 1970; LP38482]. Sd; col (Metrocolor). 35mm & 70mm (Super Panavision). 192 min. *MPAA rating* R.
Prod Anthony Havelock-Allan. *Assoc Prod* Roy Stevens. *Dir* David Lean. *2d Unit Dir* Charles Frend. *2d Unit Dir for Storm Seq* Roy Stevens. *Screenplay* Robert Bolt. *Dir Photog* Freddie Young. *2d Unit Photog* Denys Coop, Bob Huke. *Camera Op* Ernest Day. *Art Dir* Roy Walker. *Asst Art Dir* Derek Irvine. *Set Decor* Josie MacAvin. *Prod Dsgn* Stephen Grimes. *Film Ed* Norman Savage. *Mus Comp & Cond* Maurice Jarre. *Sd Ed* Ernie Grimsdale, Winston Ryder. *Sd Rec* John Bramall. *Sd Re-rec* Gordon K. McCallum. *Mus Rec* Eric Tomlinson. *Asst Dir* Pedro Vidal, Michael Stevenson. *Prod Mgr* Douglas Twiddy. *Cont* Phyllis Crocker. *Location Mgr* Eddie Fowlie. *Cost Dsgn* Jocelyn Rickards. *Makeup* Charles Parker. *Hairstyles* A. G. Scott. *Sp Eff* Robert MacDonald. *Ch Electrn* Bernie Prentice, Roy Rodhouse. *Constr* Peter Dukelow. *Prod Liaison* William O'Kelly. *Prop* Eddie Fowlie.

Cast: Robert Mitchum (*Charles Shaughnessy*), Trevor Howard (*Father Collins*), Sarah Miles (*Rosy Ryan*), Christopher Jones (*Randolph Doryan*), John Mills (*Michael*), Leo McKern (*Tom Ryan*), Barry Foster (*Tim O'Leary*), Archie O'Sullivan (*McCardle*), Marie Kean (*Mrs. McCardle*), Evin Crowley (*Moureen*), Barry Jackson (*corporal*), Douglas Sheldon (*driver*), Philip O'Flynn (*Paddy*), Ed O'Callaghan (*Bernard*), Gerald Sim (*captain*), Des Keogh (*lanky private*), Niall Toibin (*O'Keefe*), Donal Meligan (*Moureen's boyfriend*), Brian O'Higgins (*Constable O'Connor*), Niall O'Brien (*Joseph*), Owen O'Sullivan (*Peter*), Emmet Bergin (*Sean*), May Cluskey (*storekeeper*), Anne Dalton (*old woman*), Pat Layde (*policeman*).

Romantic drama. In an Irish seaside town in 1916, Rosy Ryan, daughter of tavern owner Tom Ryan, accepts the marriage proposal of her former schoolteacher, widower Charles Shaughnessy. After the marriage, Rosy quickly realizes that Charles lacks interest in sex, and she goes to talk with Father Collins, who reprimands her and tries to convince her that she is a lucky woman to have such a good man for a husband. Maj. Randolph Doryan, a shell-shocked British soldier, arrives in town to help control contact between the Irish Republican Army and the Germans, and soon Rosy and the young soldier fall in love. They make love in the meadow outside of town, and Michael, the town idiot, finds a button torn from Randolph's clothing and walks through the town displaying the evidence. The townspeople begin to gossip, but the talk does not affect Charles, who is confident that the romance will weaken by itself. When IRA leader Tim O'Leary arrives seeking aid to retrieve munitions from the offshore ruins of a German ship, Tom Ryan, fearful of reprisals, informs on O'Leary, and the British soldiers quickly arrest him. The townspeople, however, believe Rosy to be the traitor because of her relationship with Randolph and descend on Charles's house, strip her, and cut off her hair, while Charles and Tom helplessly watch. Randolph, realizing that he has lost Rosy, shoots himself. Rosy, meanwhile, decides to leave town with Charles, who is willing to try and start a new life in Dublin. *Bartenders. Widowers. Schoolteachers. Priests. Idiots. Informers. Traitors. Marriage. Infidelity. Scandal. Injustice. Village life. Suicide. Ireland. Irish Republican Army. Great Britain—Army.*

Note: Filmed on location on the western coast of Ireland. Opened in London in Dec 1970.

RYMDINVASION I LAPPLAND see **INVASION OF THE ANIMAL PEOPLE**

RYOJIN NIKKI see **THE HUNTER'S DIARY**

RYSOPIS see **IDENTIFICATION MARKS: NONE**

S. O. S. CLUB   **F6.4194**
Mitam Productions. 26 Nov **1969** [Champaign, Illinois, showing]. Sd; col (Eastmancolor). 35mm. 72 min.

Drama. Norma arrives destitute in Hollywood to find fame and stardom. She meets Ray, who invites her to live with him. When he is arrested, Norma takes in Irma. Their funds soon run out, and they find two men to support them. Joan and Cheryl move in next, and together the four women form the "S. O. S. Club." They recruit a lesbian and stage sensual performances, eventually allowing the audience to participate for an extra fee. One night four men reserve the club, but one of them reveals himself to be a police officer, and everybody is arrested. *Actors. Police. Exhibitionism. Prostitution. Lesbianism. Group sex. Finance—Personal. Sex clubs. Stag shows. Hollywood.*

SABALEROS see **PUT UP OR SHUT UP**

SABATA (Italy)   **F6.4195**
P. E. A.-Produzioni Associate Delphos. *Dist* United Artists. 2 Sep **1970** [New York opening; c16 Sep 1969; LF71]. Sd; col (Technicolor). 35mm (Techniscope). 106 min. *MPAA rating* GP.

Prod Alberto Grimaldi. *Dir* (see note) Frank Kramer. *Screenplay* Renato Izzo, Gianfranco Parolini. *Photog* Sandro Mancori. *Camera Op* Mario Sbrenna. *Art Dir* Carlo Simi. *Film Ed* Edmondo Lozzi. *Mus* Marcello Giombini. *Sd Engr* Tonino Palombi. *Sd* Pietro Spadoni. *Asst Dir* Ignazio Dolce. *Prod Supv* Arrigo Peri, Ubaldo Izzo. *Prod Mgr* Alberto De Stefanis. *Cost* Carlo Simi. *Makeup* Gianfranco Mecacci. *Sp Eff* Stacchini.

Cast: Lee Van Cleef (*Sabata*), William Berger (*Banjo*), Franco Ressel (*Stengel*), Linda Veras (*Jane*), Pedro Sanchez (*Carrincha*), Gianni Rizzo (*Judge O'Hara*), Anthony Gradwell (*Fergusson*), Nick Jordan (*Alley Cat [Indio]*), Robert Hundar (*Oswald*), Spanny Convery (*Slim*), Marco Zuanelli (*Sharky*), Gino Marturano (*McCallum*), Joseph Mathews (*Frankie*), Franco Ukmar (*Cutty*), Bruno Ukmar ("*Jumping Kid*"), Rodolfo Lodi (*Father Brown*), Alan Collins (*false Father Brown*), Vittorio Andre (*Logan*), Romano Puppo (*Rocky Bendato*), Andrew Ray, pseud (*Daniel*), Franco Marletta (*captain*), John Bartha (*sheriff*), Charles Tamblyn (*Nickols*), Mimmo Poli (*hotel workman*).

Western melodrama. Stengel, a wealthy landowner in Dougherty, Texas, masterminds a bank robbery of U. S. Army gold, and then, together with his co-conspirators Judge O'Hara and saloon owner Fergusson, he arranges for a $5,000 reward for the capture of the robbers. A mysterious stranger named Sabata rides into town, apprehends and kills the bank robbers, and collects the reward. Sabata also suspects the acrobatic Virginian Brothers of taking part in the robbery, but Stengel has them murdered before they can confess. After locating evidence that implicates Stengel, Sabata attempts to blackmail him for $10,000. A succession of assassins is hired by Stengel to kill Sabata, but they all fail. Finally Banjo, an old friend of Sabata's, is hired, but he, too, fails although Sabata spares his life. Sabata attacks Stengel's ranch and kills Judge O'Hara and Fergusson with bullets and dynamite; later, Sabata kills Stengel in one of the latter's favorite shooting games. Sabata and Banjo then fight for the blackmail money, and Banjo shoots Sabata. Banjo takes the money and throws Sabata's body over his saddle. Outside of town, Sabata regains consciousness, overpowers Banjo, tosses the bag to Banjo, and rides off as the money scatters in the wind. *Judges. Saloon keepers. Bounty hunters. Brothers. Acrobats. Hired killers. Bank robberies. Conspiracy. Murder. Blackmail. Gold. Explosives. Texas.*

Note: Location scenes filmed in Almería, Spain. Released in Italy in 1969 as *Ehi, amico ... C'è Sabata, hai chiuso*. Frank Kramer is a pseudonym for director Gianfranco Parolini. The following actors appear under anglicized names: Ignazio Spalla (Pedro Sanchez), Antonio Gradoli (Anthony Gradwell), Claudio Undari (Robert Hundar), Spartaco Conversi (Spanny Convery), Pino Mattei (Joseph Mathews), Janos Bartha (John Bartha), Carlo Tamberlani (Charles Tamblyn), Luciano Pigozzi (Alan Collins), and Andrea Aurell (Andrew Ray).

THE SABOTEUR: CODE NAME—MORITURI see **MORITURI**

IL SACCO DI ROMA see **THE BARBARIANS**

SADISMO   **F6.4196**
Trans American Films. Sep **1967** [c6 Sep 1967; LP35279]. Sd; col (Colorscope). 81 min.

Prod Salvatore Billitteri. *Writ* Philip Marx. *Film Ed* Fred Feitshans, Salvatore Billitteri. *Mus* Les Baxter. *Mus Supv* Al Simms.

Narrators: Burt Topper, Terry Telli.

Documentary. Bizarre customs, rites, and ceremonies practiced throughout the world include the torture of both animals and humans, love cult rituals, Japanese women succumbing to men who are wearing devil masks, a Caesarian operation, men and women immersing themselves in vats of multicolored paints, the pagan worship of reptiles, ancient fertility rites, and scenes of Oriental girls being prepared for marriage by being shown sexually stimulating symbols. A brief sequence contains footage of Nazi concentration camps showing thousands of victims of Nazi atrocities. *Japanese. Orientals. Social customs. Rites and ceremonies. Nazis. Paganism. Torture. Body painting. Masks. Cults. Concentration camps. War crimes. Reptiles.*

Note: Withdrawn from distribution in Nov 1967 and altered to eliminate some footage; distribution began again on 15 Dec 1967.

THE SADIST   **F6.4197**
Fairway Productions. *Dist* Fairway-International Films. Apr **1963** [c1 Oct 1963; LU3318]. Sd; b&w. 35mm. 94 min.

Prod L. Steven Snyder. *Exec Prod* Nicholas Merriwether. *Dir-Writ* James Landis. *Photog* William Zsigmond. *Art Dir* Mark Von Berblinger. *Film Ed* Anthony M. Lanza. *Mus Dir* Rod Moss. *Sd Mix* Alan O'Day. *Prod Mgr* Don Russell. *Script Supv* Joan Howard. *Wardrobe* Addalyn Fay. *Makeup* Lynn Noonkester. *Prop Master* Doug Kersting.

Cast: Arch Hall, Jr. (*Charley Tibbs*), Helen Hovey (*Doris Page*), Richard Alden (*Ed Stiles*), Marilyn Manning (*Judy Bradshaw*), Don Russell (*Carl Oliver*).

Melodrama. En route to a baseball game at Dodger Stadium, three smalltown high school teachers—Ed Stiles, Carl Oliver, and Doris Page—develop engine trouble and seek parts at a garage, which proves to be deserted. However, they are soon confronted by sadistic killer Charley Tibbs and his companion Judy Bradshaw, both wanted by the law in connection with a series of gruesome highway murders. The three victims are held at gunpoint as Stiles tries to fix the auto. When Tibbs learns Oliver's occupation he kills him, because Judy has always hated teachers. After two unsuspecting motorcycle policemen are shot by Tibbs, Stiles tries to kill the psychopath but succeeds only in temporarily blinding him with gasoline. In the confusion, Tibbs accidentally shoots and kills Judy. Chasing Stiles, he murders him, then pursues Doris, who is now on the verge of insanity, into the desert. She escapes to safety when Tibbs falls into a pit of rattlesnakes and meets his death. *Schoolteachers. Police. Psychopaths. Sadism. Murder. Insanity. Automobiles. Deserts. Gasoline. Filling stations. California. Chases. Snakes.*

Note: Location scenes filmed in California. Nicholas Merriwether is a pseudonym for Arch Hall, Sr.

THE SADISTIC HYPNOTIST see **WANDA (THE SADISTIC HYPNOTIST)**

THE SADISTIC LOVER   **F6.4198**

Gunter Productions. 1 Apr **1966** [Fresno, California, showing]. Sd; b&w. 35mm. [Feature length assumed.]

Prod-Dir George Gunter. *Exec Prod* F. T. Gardner. *Orig Screenplay* Dale Berry.

Cast: Ralph G. Edwards, Diane Durette, Ann Lane, Durline Dunham.

Melodrama. Haunted by the memory of his victims, voyeur Dane Harris confesses to Professor Foray, a psychic adviser, to having committed a series of sex crimes: *Dane watches an exotic dancer perform, follows her to her apartment, and beats her to death. In a lovers' lane, he locks a couple in the trunk of their car, shoots them, and sets fire to the gas tank. On several occasions, he hides in women's bedrooms, watches them undress, and fondles them as they sleep.* After listening to Dane's confession, the professor telephones the police, in hopes of getting a reward for turning Dane in; but, Dane, who has overheard the call, murders him. Dane then rapes the professor's secretary and holds her hostage as the police close in. The secretary is shot as she breaks away, and Dane is killed in the ensuing gun battle. *Psychopaths. Fortune-tellers. Exotic dancers. Secretaries. Hostages. Police. Murder. Rape. Voyeurism. Sadism. Confession.*

SADKO see **THE MAGIC VOYAGE OF SINBAD**

SAFARI IN ALASKA   **F6.4199**

Alaskan Shows. Jan **1965** [Eugene, Oregon, showing]. Sd; col. 35mm. ca90 min.

A Ron Hayes Production. *Prod-Dir* Ron Hayes, Bev Hayes. *Photog* Ron Hayes.

Documentary. The film is comprised of footage of hunting and fishing expeditions in the 49th state. *Hunting. Fishing. Alaska.*

Note: Filmed in 16mm. Combined with *Arctic Safari*, q. v., this film was reedited into a feature entitled *Alaskan Safari*, q. v.

SAFARI MOJA (ALASKA TO AFRICA)   **F6.4200**

4 Nov **1970** [Dallas opening]. Sd; col. 35mm. [Feature film, length unknown.]

A Willy Taber Production.

Documentary. No information about the precise nature of this film has been found, but press material suggests that it includes scenes of wild game. *Animal life. Safaris. Alaska. Africa. Big game.*

SAFE AT HOME!   **F6.4201**

Naud-Hamilburg Productions. *Dist* Columbia Pictures. 13 Apr **1962** [New York opening; c1 Apr 1962; LP22252]. Sd (Westrex); b&w. 35mm. 83 min.

Prod Tom Naud. *Dir* Walter Doniger. *Screenplay* Robert Dillon. *Story* Tom Naud, Steve Ritch. *Dir Photog* Irving Lippman. *Set Decor* James M. Crowe. *Film Ed* Frank P. Keller. *Mus* Van Alexander. *Sd Supv* Charles J. Rice. *Sd* James Z. Flaster. *Asst Dir* Leonard Katzman.

Cast: Mickey Mantle *(himself)*, Roger Maris *(himself)*, William Frawley *(Bill Turner)*, Patricia Barry *(Johanna Price)*, Don Collier *(Ken Lawton)*, Bryan Russell *(Hutch Lawton)*, Eugene Iglesias *(Mr. Torres)*, Flip Mark *(Henry)*, Scott Lane *(Mike Torres)*, Charles G. Martin *(Henry's father)*, Ralph Houk *(himself)*, Whitey Ford *(himself)*, Desiree Sumarra *(Mrs. Torres)*, Joe Hickman *(Joe)*, Chris Hughes *(Phil)*, James R. Argyras *(Jackie)*, Fred A. Schwarb *(Coach Benton)*, Joe Morrison *(Hank)*.

Sports film. Hutch Lawton has recently moved from New York to Florida with his widower father, who runs a charter fishing boat. When Hutch boasts to his Little League teammates that Mickey Mantle and Roger Maris are his father's friends, his lie snowballs and he is forced into promising that he will deliver the two Yankee stars to a Little League banquet. While his father is away on a three-day fishing trip, Hutch hitchhikes a ride to the Yankee spring training camp at Fort Lauderdale. Although he meets Mantle and Maris, the two men refuse to be a party to his deceit. Heartbroken, Hutch returns home to tell the truth to the Little Leaguers and their fathers. Just as he finishes his confession, however, word arrives that Mantle and Maris have invited the Little Leaguers to join them for spring training. *Braggarts. Widowers. Hitchhikers. Fishermen. Honesty. Baseball. Filial relations. Florida. Fort Lauderdale. New York Yankees. Little League.*

Note: Location scenes filmed in Fort Lauderdale, Florida.

SAFFO, VENERE DI LESBO see **THE WARRIOR EMPRESS**

THE SAGA OF THE FLYING HOSTESSES see **GIRL GAME**

SAGA OF THE VAGABONDS (Japan)   **F6.4202**

Toho Co. 6 Oct **1964** [New York opening]. Sd; col (Agfacolor). 35mm (Tohoscope). 115 min.

Exec Prod Sanezumi Fujimoto, Kazuo Nishino. *Dir* Toshio Sugie. *Screenplay* Sadao Yamanaka, Akira Kurosawa. *Story* Juro Miyoshi. *Photog* Akira Suzuki. *Mus* Ikuma Dan.

Cast: Koji Tsuruta *(Taro Tarao)*, Toshiro Mifune *(Rokuro Kai)*, Misa Uehara *(Princess Koyuki)*, Takashi Shimura *(Toki Saemon-no-jo)*, Akihiko Hirata *(Jiro Hidekuni)*, Seizaburo Kawazu *(Hyoe Yamano)*, Yoko Tsukasa *(Tazu)*.

Melodrama. In feudal Japan, a group of bandits led by Rokuro Kai take advantage of the chaotic conditions of civil war and oppressive taxation to overrun many provinces and steal from the wealthy lords. Taro Tarao is ordered by his father to deliver war funds to Lord Hojo, but he is attacked by the bandits and the money is stolen. His younger brother, Jiro, is persuaded by Hyoe Yamano, the treacherous family retainer, to spread a rumor that Taro actually absconded with the money himself. Unaware of the plot against him Taro searches for the thieves, until he is stopped by local officials. Rescued by Rokuro and his men, Taro joins the bandits and calls himself the Red Demon of Amagi. He learns that because of Hyoe and Jiro's actions, his father has been murdered and his fiancée, Princess Koyuki, has committed suicide. Taro gains entry to the family castle with his fellow bandits, kills Kyoe, and then watches as his demented brother jumps to his death from the castle wall. *Bandits. Brothers. Feudalism. Revenge. Robbery. Frameup. Suicide. Murder. Castles.*

Note: Released in Japan in Aug 1959 as *Sengoku gunto-den*.

LA SAGE-FEMME, LE CURÉ ET LE BON DIEU see **JESSICA**

SAIKAKU ICHIDAI ONNA see **LIFE OF OHARU**

SAIL A CROOKED SHIP   **F6.4203**

Philip Barry Productions. *Dist* Columbia Pictures. 3 Jan **1962** [Boston opening; c1 Jan 1962; LP21332]. Sd (RCA); b&w. 35mm. 88 min.

Prod Philip Barry, Jr. *Dir* Irving Brecher. *Screenplay* Ruth Brooks Flippen, Bruce Geller. *Dir Photog* Joseph Biroc. *Art Dir* Robert Peterson. *Set Decor* James M. Crowe. *Film Ed* William A. Lyon. *Mus* George Duning. *Orch* Arthur Morton. *Song:* "Opposites Attract" Bob Marcucci, Russ Faith. *Sung by* Frankie Avalon. *Sd Supv* Charles J. Rice. *Sd Rec* Lambert Day. *Asst Dir* Sam Nelson, Michael Vidor. *Script Supv* Frances McDowell. *Wardrobe* Jack Angel. *Makeup Supv* Ben Lane. *Hairstyles* Alice Monte.

Cast: Robert Wagner *(Gilbert Barrows)*, Dolores Hart *(Elinor Harrison)*, Carolyn Jones *(Virginia)*, Ernie Kovacs *(Bugsy F. Foglemeyer)*, Frankie Avalon *(Rodney)*, Frank Gorshin *(George Wilson)*, Jesse White *(McDonald)*, Harvey Lembeck *(Nickels)*, Sid Tomack *(Sammy)*, Guy Raymond *(Helmut)*, Buck Kartalian *(Finster)*, Wilton Graff *(Simon J. Harrison)*, Marjorie Bennett *(Mrs. Chowder)*, Terry Huntingdon *(young lady pilgrim)*, Graeme Ferguson *(1st man)*, Tom Symonds *(2d man)*, Howard Wendell *(Mr. Caldingham)*, Mary Young *(woman)*, Bru Mysak *(newsboy)*, Hope Sansberry *(Biddy)*, Mark Myer *(cop)*.

Comedy. Source: Nathaniel Benchley, *Sail a Crooked Ship* (New York, 1960). Gilbert Barrows, an inept ex-Navy officer, tries to impress his boss's daughter, Elinor, by ignoring her father's order to scrap a fleet of Liberty ships. Attempting to prove the vessels seaworthy by having one of them refit for cargo transport, he mistakes petty thief Bugsy F. Foglemeyer for a ship builder and turns the project over to him. The ambitious Bugsy, nicknamed "The Captain," decides to use the ship for his getaway after robbing a Boston bank. Gilbert and Elinor arrive and are taken prisoner as Bugsy prepares to sail from New York City with his girl friend Virginia, his nephew Rodney, and his crew of crooks. Gilbert helps skipper the ship to Boston, triumphing over such potential disasters as seasickness, fire, hurricane, and collision, but he is unable to halt the bank robbery itself. Meanwhile, gang member George Wilson tries to gain leadership of the crew by killing Gilbert, Bugsy, and the two women; Gilbert, however, uses Elinor's brassiere as a slingshot and attracts the attention of the Coast Guard, who arrest the crooks. Later, Gilbert and Elinor are married, Virginia becomes the godmother of their child, and Bugsy receives a light prison sentence. *Veterans. Shipowners. Robbers. Uncles. Mistaken identity. Abduction. Bank robberies. Salvage. Employer-employee relations. Ambition. Sea rescue. Ships. Boston. New York City. United States Coast Guard. Fires. Hurricanes.*

THE SAILOR FROM GIBRALTAR (Great Britain)   **F6.4204**

Woodfall Films. *Dist* Lopert Pictures. 24 Apr **1967** [New York opening; c3 Apr 1967; LF9]. Sd; b&w. 35mm. 89 min.

Prod Oscar Lewenstein, Neil Hartley. *Dir* Tony Richardson. *Screenplay* Christopher Isherwood, Don Magner, Tony Richardson. *Camera* Raoul Coutard. *Camera Unit* Georges Liron, Jean Garcenot. *Set Dsgn* Marilena Aravantinou. *Set Dresser* Josie Macavin. *Supv Film Ed* Anthony Gibbs. *Ed* Bill Blunden, Brian Smedley-Aston. *Mus* Antoine Duhamel. *Song:* "Jo le rouge" Antoine Duhamel, Bassiak. *Sung by* Jeanne Moreau. *Sd Unit (see note)* André Hervée, Gérard Manneveau, Kevin Connor. *Asst Dir* Christian de Chalonges, Marc Grunebaum, Marcello Ugolini, Spyros Spyromilios. *Prod Mgr* Marc Maurette, Orazio Tassara, Mohamed Ragai. *Cont* Suzanne Schiffman. *Prod*

Asst Gérard Crosnier, Don Magner, Valerio De Paolis, Cyrus Edes. *Cost Dsgn* Jocelyn Rickards. *Wardrobe Mistress* Ruth Myers. *Wardrobe Asst* Anna Pradella. *Makeup* Simone Knapp. *Prop* Angelo Rizzi. *Electrn* Fernand Coquet, Henri Schickel. *Grip* Jean Gimello.

Cast: Jeanne Moreau *(Anna)*, Ian Bannen *(Alan)*, Vanessa Redgrave *(Sheila)*, Zia Mohyeddin *(Noori)*, Hugh Griffith *(Legrand)*, Orson Welles *(Louis of Mozambique)*, Umberto Orsini *(postcard vendor)*, Erminio Spalla *(Eolo)*, Eleanor Bron *(Carla)*, Gabriella Pallotta *(girl at dance)*, Arnoldo Foa *(man on train)*, Claudio De Renzi *(Jeannot)*.

Cast—Sailors: Fausto Tozzi *(captain)*, John Hurt *(John)*, Theo Roubanis *(Theo)*, Brad Moore *(Brad)*, Massimo Sarchielli *(Massimo)*, Guglielmo Spoletini *(Guglielmo)*, Wolfgang Hillinger *(Wolf)*.

Drama. Source: Marguerite Duras, *Le marin de Gibraltar* (Paris, 1952). While on a holiday in Italy, Alan, a young Englishman, encounters the mysterious Anna, a wealthy French widow who has spent the years following her husband's suicide in an endless search for a sailor from Gibraltar with whom she once passed a moment of true happiness. Sailing from port to port on her luxurious yacht, Anna forms brief liaisons as she looks for the sailor, a suspected murderer, in every waterfront dive and hangout. Fascinated by the woman, Alan abandons his longtime mistress, Sheila, as well as his London office job, and joins Anna in her quest for the elusive sailor. En route to the next port of call, Athens, Alan finds himself falling in love; and now he too must find the sailor to determine if Anna's passion is real. When the sailor is not found in Athens, Anna sails to Alexandria for a visit with Louis of Mozambique, a florid peddler of information who assures her that the true whereabouts of the sailor can be learned from a white hunter in Ethiopia. The hunter, Legrand, also fails to produce the sailor, but Anna and Alan have fallen in love in the course of the search, and they set sail once more together. *French. Widows. Sailors. Hunters. Informers. Wealth. Yachts. Italy. Athens. Alexandria (Egypt). Ethiopia.*

Note: Released in Great Britain in 1967; running time: 91 min. U. S. sources credit André Hervée and Gérard Manneveau as sound unit, while Kevin Connor is credited with sound by a British source.

ST. GEORGE AND THE 7 CURSES *see* THE MAGIC SWORD

THE ST. VALENTINE'S DAY MASSACRE   F6.4205
Corman Co.-Los Altos, Inc. *Dist* Twentieth Century-Fox Film Corp. 30 Jun **1967** [Chicago opening; c30 Jun 1967; LP34594]. Sd (Westrex); col (De Luxe). 35mm (Panavision). 100 min.

Prod-Dir Roger Corman. *Assoc Prod* Paul Rapp. *Screenplay* Howard Browne. *Dir Photog* Milton Krasner. *Camera Op* Alfred Lebowitz. *Art Dir* Jack Martin Smith, Phil Jeffries. *Set Decor* Walter M. Scott, Steven Potter. *Film Ed* William B. Murphy. *Mus—Main & End Titl* Fred Steiner. *Mus Cond* Lionel Newman. *Sd* Herman Lewis, David Dockendorf. *Asst Dir* Wesley E. Barry. *Unit Prod Mgr* David Silver. *Makeup* Ben Nye. *Hairstyles* Margaret Donovan. *Sp Photog Eff* L. B. Abbott, Art Cruickshank, Emil Kosa, Jr. *Adv* Chicago Historical Society.

Cast: Jason Robards, [Jr.] *(Al Capone)*, George Segal *(Peter Gusenberg)*, Ralph Meeker *(Bugs Moran)*, Jean Hale *(Myrtle)*, Clint Ritchie *(Jack McGurn)*, Frank Silvera *(Sorello)*, Joseph Campanella *(Wienshank)*, Richard Bakalyan *(Scalise)*, David Canary *(Frank Gusenberg)*, Bruce Dern *(May)*, Harold J. Stone *(Frank Nitti)*, Michele Guayini *(Patsy Lolardo)*, Kurt Kreuger *(James Clark)*, Paul Richards *(Charles Fischetti)*, Joseph Turkel *(Guzik)*, Milton Frome *(Adam Heyer)*, Mickey Deems *(Schwimmer)*, John Agar *(Dion O'Banion)*, Celia Lovsky *(Josephine Schwimmer)*, Tom Reese *(Newberry)*, Jan Merlin *(Willie Marks)*, Alex D'Arcy *(Aiello)*, Reed Hadley *(Hymie Weiss)*, Gus Trikonis *(Rio)*, Charles Dierkop *(Salvanti)*, Tom Signorelli *(Bobo Borotto)*, Rico Cattani *(Albert Anselmi)*, Alex Rocco *(Diamond)*, Leo Gordon *(Heitler)*, Barboura Morris *(woman)*, Mary Grace Canfield *(landlady)*, Daniel Ades *(Little Jerry Molina)*, Richard Krisher *(desk clerk)*, Paul Frees *(narrator)*, Jack Nicholson *(Gino)*.

Crime melodrama. In the late 1920's Chicago is the crime capital of the world. In 9 years 618 known murders have been committed, none of them officially solved, and gang lords have grossed over $350 million from prohibition and illegal operations. Undisputed king of the underworld is the notorious Al Capone, who sends hoodlums like Peter and Frank Gusenberg to force bar owners into buying his beer instead of that of Bugs Moran, leader of the rival North Side gang. Determined to wrest control from Capone, Moran is planning to slay Patsy Lolardo, head of the dreaded Mafia and a close friend of Capone's. Similarly, Capone has ordered his right-hand man, Jack McGurn, to arrange for the mass murder of Moran and his mob. First to act is Moran, who has the Mafia boss shot down, hoping that his successor will withdraw support from Capone. But Capone quickly evens the score by trapping the potential successor on a train and slashing his throat with a razor. He then puts into motion his plan to get Moran. On the morning of February 14, 1929, some of Capone's gang pose as hijackers and sell a shipment of booze to Moran's

hoodlums. The rest of the gang, dressed as policemen, raid the garage where the exchange is being transacted and mow down seven of Moran's men with tommyguns. Capone, who is establishing his alibi in Florida, learns that Moran was not present at the massacre. Though no one is ever brought to trial for the slaughter, the killers all die violent deaths within 22 months; and public indignation eventually effects Capone's downfall. *Gangsters. Police. Hired killers. Saloon keepers. Prohibition. Feuds. Murder. Organized crime. Roaring Twenties. Saint Valentine's Day Massacre. Chicago. Florida. Al Capone. George "Bugs" Moran. Pasqualino "Patsy" Lolardo. Jack McGurn. Peter Gusenberg. Frank Gusenberg. Mafia.*

SAINTLY SINNERS   F6.4206
Harvard Film Corp. *Dist* United Artists. 28 Feb **1962** [Los Angeles opening; c6 Dec 1961; LP21107]. Sd; b&w. 35mm. 78 min.

Prod Robert E. Kent. *Dir* Jean Yarbrough. *Screenplay* Kevin Barry. *Photog* Gilbert Warrenton. *Set Decor* Harry Reif. *Film Ed* Robert Carlisle. *Mus* Richard LaSalle. *Sd* Stan Cooley, Paul Wolfe. *Asst Dir* Frank Mayer. *Prod Mgr* Joseph Small. *Wardrobe* Einar Bourman, Sabine Manela. *Sp Eff* Barney Wolff.

Cast: Don Beddoe *(Father Dan)*, Paul Bryar *(Duke)*, Stanley Clements *(Slim)*, Ellen Corby *(Mrs. McKenzie)*, Ron Hagerthy *(Joe)*, Erin O'Donnell *(Sue)*, Clancy Cooper *(Idaho)*, William Fawcett *(Horsefly)*, Addison Richards *(monsignor)*, Willis Bouchey *(Harrihan)*, Earl Hodgins *(Uncle Clete)*, Norman Leavitt *(Phineas)*, Marjorie Bennett *(Mrs. Madigan)*, Tommy Farrell *(Mike)*, Max Mellinger *(Sam)*, Robert B. Williams *(Hank)*, David Tyrell *(Tubber)*, Bobs Watson *(attendant)*, Bob Hopkins *(Honest Jim)*, Marla Craig *(Maybelle)*.

Comedy-drama. Duke and Slim, two smalltime sharpies, steal a car belonging to Joe Braden, an ex-convict who is having a difficult time making a living as a salesman. They then rob a bank and hide the loot in the car's spare tire. Before they can retrieve the money, however, the automobile is repossessed by a finance company. The local parish priest, Father Dan, buys the used car to take a long-postponed fishing trip. En route, he is stopped by a police officer and, because he is unrecognizable as a priest in his fishing attire, arrested for the bank robbery. Though he is freed the next day, young Joe Braden is arrested for the crime. When the police complain that Father Dan is coddling criminals in his parish, the monsignor decides to transfer him to another church. The parishioners become so upset by this decision that Duke and Slim, thoroughly ashamed of the trouble they have caused Father Dan and Joe, confess to the robbery. The resultant publicity has a beneficial effect upon Joe's career. *Ex-convicts. Salesmen. Priests. Police. Bank robberies. Theft. Finance—Personal. Mistaken identity. Publicity. Fishing.*

SAIYU-KI *see* ALAKAZAM THE GREAT

SALAMMBO *see* THE LOVES OF SALAMMBO
SALARIO PARA MATAR *see* THE MERCENARY
SALESMAN   F6.4207
Maysles Films. 17 Apr **1969** [New York opening]. Sd; b&w. 35mm. 90 min. MPAA rating G.

Prod-Dir David Maysles, Albert Maysles, Charlotte Zwerin. *Photog* Albert Maysles. *Film Ed* David Maysles, Charlotte Zwerin. *Contrib Ed* Ellen Giffard. *Asst Ed* Barbara Jarvis. *Sd* Dick Vorisek.

With: Paul Brennan *("The Badger")*, Charles McDevitt *("The Gipper")*, James Baker, U. S. *("The Rabbit")*, Raymond Martos *("The Bull")*, Kennie Turner *(sales manager)*, Melbourne I. Feltman *(theological consultant)*, Margaret McCarron *(motel maid)*.

Documentary. A record of the experiences of four door-to-door salesmen for the Mid-American Bible Company. While working the snowbound area around Boston, one of the men, 55-year-old Paul Brennan ("The Badger"), has a bad day and returns to his motel headquarters with only one sale. Despite a pep talk from his sales manager, his subsequent days are no better; and he discusses the difficulties of his job with his fellow salesmen. The men then travel to Chicago for a sales meeting of the Mid-American Bible Company, where the firm's theological consultant reminds them of the "self-satisfaction" they should receive from "going about their Father's business." Following a poker game, the men leave for Florida, and there Paul is assigned to the town of Opa-Locka, northwest of Miami. Despite the confusion and irritation caused by the maze of unfamiliar and exotically-named streets (Sinbad Avenue, Sesame Street, Sharazad Boulevard), he has a fairly successful day and feels slightly encouraged. But his optimism is short-lived as the following days of no-sale rejections reduce him to despondency and the "ultimate sin" of negative thinking. Paul accompanies a more successful colleague, Charlie ("The Gipper"), on his rounds; but this act serves only to exhaust Paul rather than build up his confidence, and as he packs his bags to leave Florida, Paul faces his future with uncertainty and fear. *Traveling salesmen. Sales managers. Salesmanship. Employer-employee relations. Middle age. Motels. Poker. Boston. Chicago. Opa-Locka (Florida). The Bible.*

Note: Filmed in 16mm.

SALLAH (Israel)   F6.4208

Sallah Ltd. *Dist* Palisades International Corp. 10 Mar **1965** [Los Angeles opening]. Sd; b&w. 35mm. 105 min.

Prod Menahem Golan. *Dir-Orig Story-Screenplay* Ephraim Kishon. *Dir Photog* Floyd Crosby. *Art Dir* Joseph Carl. *Film Ed* Dani Schick, Jacques Erlich, Roberto Cinquini. *Mus* Yohanan Zarai. *Sd* Wally Milner. *Sd Rec* Yair Podolsky. *Asst Dir* Joseph Gross. *Prod Coörd* Roni Yaacov. *Cost* Gina Rosenbach. *Makeup* Rachel Golan.

Cast: Haym Topol (*Sallah Shabati*), Geula Noni (*Habbubah Shabati*), Gila Almagor (*Bathsheva Sosialit*), Arik Einstein (*Ziggi*), Shraga Friedman (*Neuman*), Zaharira Harifai (*Frieda*), Shaika Levi (*Shimon Shabati*), Nathan Meisler (*Mr. Goldstein*), Esther Greenberg (*Sallah's wife*), Mordecai Arnon (*Mordecai*).

Comedy. Sallah Shabati, an Oriental Jew, arrives with his family in the young nation of Israel in 1949 and finds housing in a ramshackle transit camp until he can afford a modern flat. Sallah, habitually lazy, devises various schemes to get money, such as selling his vote to each of the several political parties. Habbubah, Sallah's beautiful daughter, falls in love with Ziggi, a handsome member of a kibbutz, and Sallah tricks an admiring taxi driver into buying his daughter for Ziggi. Meanwhile, Sallah's son Shimon has fallen in love with kibbutznik Bathsheva, thus prompting the kibbutz director to demand reimbursement. Through his antics, Sallah not only exposes the maladies of Israeli society but also succeeds in forcing the housing authorities to move his family out of the transit camp and into a new apartment. *Orientals. Taxi drivers. Immigration. Filial relations. Elections. Housing. Kibbutzim.*

Note: Released in Tel Aviv in Jun 1964 as *Sallah Shabati.*

SALLAH SHABATI see SALLAH

SALON DE MASSAGE   F6.4209

Dist Jo-Jo Distributors. ca **1970**. Sd; col. 16mm. 61-81 min.

Sex film. No information about the precise nature of this film has been found. *Sexuality. Massage parlors.*

SALT & PEPPER (United States/Great Britain)   F6.4210

Chrislaw Productions-Trace-Mark Productions. *Dist* United Artists. 31 Jul **1968** [Baltimore opening; c21 Jun 1968; LP36083]. Sd; col (DeLuxe). 35mm. 101 min. [Copyright length: 110 min.]

Prod Milton Ebbins. *Exec Prod* Peter Lawford, Sammy Davis, Jr. *Prod Exec* James Waters. *Assoc Prod* Ted Wallis. *Dir* Richard D. Donner. *Screenplay* Michael Pertwee. *Photog* Ken Higgins. *Art Dir* Don Mingaye. *Set Decor* Scott Slimon, Andrew Low. *Prod Dsgn* Bill Constable. *Film Ed* Jack Slade. *Mus Comp & Cond* John Dankworth. *Song:* "I Like the Way You Dance" George Rhodes, Sammy Davis, Jr. *Titl Song* Leslie Bricusse. *Sung by* Sammy Davis, Jr. *Staged by* Lionel Blair. *Sd* John Poyner. *Sd Rec* Dickie Bird. *Sd Mix* Nolan Roberts. *Asst Dir* Derek Parr. *Prod Mgr* John Comfort. *Cost* Cynthia Tingey. *Mr. Davis' Wardrobe* Charles Glenn. *Mr. Lawford's Wardrobe* Douglas Hayward. *Makeup* Jimmy Evans. *Hairstyles* Bill Griffiths. *Sp Eff* Kit West.

Cast: Sammy Davis, Jr. (*Charles Salt*), Peter Lawford (*Christopher Pepper*), Michael Bates (*Inspector Crabbe*), Ilona Rodgers (*Marianne Renaud*), John Le Mesurier (*Colonel Woodstock*), Graham Stark (*Sergeant Walters*), Ernest Clark (*Colonel Balsom*), Jeanne Roland (*Mai Ling*), Robert Dorning (*club secretary*), Robertson Hare (*Dove*), Geoffrey Lumsden (*foreign secretary*), William Mervyn (*prime minister*), Llewellyn Rees ("*fake*" *prime minister*), Mark Singleton ("*fake*" *home secretary*), Michael Trubshawe ("*fake*" *1st lord*), Francisca Tu (*Tsai Chan*), Oliver MacGreevy (*Rack*), Peter Hutchins (*Straw*), Jeremy Lloyd (*Lord Ponsonby*), Sean Lynch (*black jack player*), Ivor Dean (*police commissioner*), Brian Harrison (*1st policeman*), Harry Hutchinson (*manservant*), Max Faulkner (*lieutenant*), Beth Rogan (*Greta*), Rifat Shenel (*Mario*), Calvin Lockhart (*Jones*), Nicholas Smith (*constable*), Susan Blair (*Janice*), Christine Pocket (*Jill*), Cassandra Mowan (*Jean*), Joe Wadham (*Colonel Woodstock's aide*).

Comedy-drama. Charles Salt and Christopher Pepper, owners of a Soho gambling club, find themselves in trouble when a man and a Chinese woman are murdered on their premises. Implicated in the killings by an anonymous tipster, Salt and Pepper are questioned by Scotland Yard Inspector Crabbe, who has often harassed them for minor violations at their club. Finally released, they are kidnaped by Colonel Balsom of the British Secret Service. After informing them that the murdered woman was a British agent, the colonel also questions the two men, but to no avail. When Salt and Pepper find the woman's diary which contains the names of four men marked for murder, they decide to solve the case themselves. Despite their efforts, three of the men are murdered, and an attempt is made on their own lives by Colonel Woodstock, a madman who is masterminding a plot to overthrow the British government by threatening nuclear warfare. Salt and Pepper discover this plot when they are abducted and taken aboard a landlocked submarine. They escape and go to Colonel Balsom;

but the three men return only to find the submarine gone, and Balsom begins to doubt their sanity. Later, at their club, Marianne, who is a party to the conspiracy, is about to kill Pepper when Salt bursts in and shoots her. Uncovering the conspirators' secret headquarters at the War Museum, Salt and Pepper commandeer an ancient army tank and manage to dispose of the enemy. The two heroes are then brought to Buckingham Palace where they are knighted by the queen. *Nightclub owners. Secret agents. Masterminds. Informers. Royalty. Murder. Gambling. Abduction. Conspiracy. Nuclear warfare. Diaries. Nightclubs. Submarines. Museums. Tanks (armored cars). London—Soho. Scotland Yard. Buckingham Palace.*

Note: Location scenes filmed in London. Released in Great Britain in 1968. Sequel: *One More Time,* q. v.

SALTO (Poland)   F6.4211

KADR Film Unit. *For* Film Polski. *Dist* Kanawha Films. 3 Oct **1966** [New York opening]. Sd; b&w. 35mm. 104 min.

Dir-Writ Tadeusz Konwicki. *Photog* Kurt Weber. *Mus* Wojciech Kilar.

Cast: Zbigniew Cybulski (*Kowalski/Malinowski*), Gustaw Holoubek (*The Host*), Marta Lipińska (*Helena*), Irena Laskowska (*Cecylia, a fortune-teller*), Wojciech Siemion (*The Poet*), Włodzimierz Boruński (*Blumenfeld*), Zdzisław Maklakiewicz (*The Captain*), Andrzej Łapicki (*The Drunkard*), Jerzy Blok (*The Mayor*), Iga Cembrzyńska (*Kowalski's wife*).

Comedy-drama. A man leaps from a moving train and goes to a small Polish village where he claims to have lived before. Although no one remembers him, the stranger does find refuge with a family there, but his past remains a secret. All that he will divulge is that he has changed his name from Kowalski to Malinowski because he is being hunted by unidentified people who wish to see him dead. Mysteriously and insidiously, the stranger creates an atmosphere of anxiety and death, and the almost apathetic villagers respond to it by exposing their innermost feelings. After apparently curing two dying children, the man seduces his host's daughter, and during an annual town celebration he teaches the villagers the steps of the salto, a dreamlike dance which brings them completely under his hypnotic influence. The illusion—or reality—of the man's power is broken by the sudden appearance of a woman accompanied by two children. She claims the man is her husband, a woman-chasing charlatan, and the townspeople hurl stones and force the stranger to board another passing train. *Strangers. Fugitives. Charlatans. Village life. Fear. Seduction. Hypnotism. Desertion. Trains.*

Note: Released in Poland in 1965.

O SALTO see VOYAGE OF SILENCE

A SALUTE TO A REBEL see PATTON

SALVARE LA FACCIA see PSYCHOUT FOR MURDER

SALVATORE GIULIANO (Italy)   F6.4212

Lux Film-Vides-Galatea. *Dist* Royal Films International. Apr **1966** [Los Angeles showing]. Sd; b&w. 35mm. 125 min.

Prod Franco Cristaldi. *Dir* Francesco Rosi. *Screenplay* Francesco Rosi, Suso Cecchi D'Amico, Enzo Provenzale, Franco Solinas. *Photog* Gianni Di Venanzo. *Camera* Pasquale De Santis. *Art Dir* Sergio Canevari, Carlo Egidi. *Film Ed* Mario Serandrei. *Mus* Piero Piccioni. *Sd* Claudio Maielli. *Asst Dir* Roberto Pariante, Franco Indovina, Fernando Cicero. *Prod Mgr* Enzo Provenzale. *Prod Asst* Luciano Cattania, Aldo Pace, Bruno Sassaroli, Lamberto Pippia. *Cost* Marilù Carteny.

Cast: Frank Wolff (*Gaspare Pisciotta*), Salvo Randone (*President of Viterbo Assize Court*), Federico Zardi (*Pisciotta's defense counsel*), Pietro Cammarata (*Salvatore Giuliano*), Fernando Cicero (*bandit*), Sennuccio Benelli (*reporter*), Bruno Ekmar (*spy*), Max Cartier (*Francesco*), Giuseppe Calandra (*minor official*), Cosimo Torino (*Frank Mannino*), Giuseppe Teti (*priest of Montelepre*), Ugo Torrente.

Historical drama. The bullet-ridden corpse of Salvatore Giuliano, a Sicilian Mafia leader, is found in a sunny courtyard on July 5, 1950. As his wake and funeral unfold, his career is traced in a series of flashbacks. Postwar Sicily had been the scene of numerous separatist guerrilla activities, one of which had been led by Giuliano. Although his group had been disbanded, Giuliano managed to retain many of his followers and carried on a constant war against the police. After the massacre by Giuliano's followers of peasants at a Communist rally at Portella della Ginestra, the authorities launched a fierce war against Giuliano and other outlaws like him. Eventually he was abandoned by most of his associates, including Gaspare Pisciotta, his second-in-command. The outlaws were ushered through a confusing trial at Viterbo, and subsequently Pisciotta was poisoned in jail by members of a Mafia organization he had recently joined. In a continuation of the vendetta, another Mafia member is murdered much later by anonymous gunmen. *Guerrillas. Police. Communists. Nationalism. Murder. Trials. Poisoning. Funerals. Jails. Italy—History—Sicilian separatist movement. Sicily. Viterbo. Salvatore Giuliano.*

Gaspare Pisciotta. Mafia.

Note: Filmed on location in Sicily. Opened in Rome in Mar 1962.

SAM COOPER'S GOLD see **THE RUTHLESS FOUR**

SAM WHISKEY   **F6.4213**

Brighton Pictures. *Dist* United Artists. 19 Feb **1969** [Denver, Colorado, opening; c1 Mar 1969; LP37339]. Sd; col (DeLuxe). 35mm. 96 min. *MPAA rating* M.

Prod Jules Levy, Arthur Gardner, Arnold Laven. *Dir* Arnold Laven. *Story & Screenplay* William Norton. *Dir Photog* Robert Moreno. *Art Dir* Lloyd S. Papez. *Set Decor* Charles Thompson. *Main Titl* Phill Norman. *Film Ed* John Woodcock. *Mus* Herschel Burke Gilbert. *Sd* Robert R. Bertrand. *Asst Dir* Burt Astor, Russell Vreeland. *Prod Mgr* Ben Bishop. *Cost* William T. Zacha, Helen Colvig. *Makeup* Dan Greenway.

Cast: Burt Reynolds (*Sam Whiskey*), Clint Walker (*O. W. Bandy*), Ossie Davis (*Jedidiah Hooker*), Angie Dickinson (*Laura Breckinridge*), Rick Davis (*Fat Henry Hobson*), Del Reeves (*fisherman*), William Schallert (*Mint Superintendent Perkins*), Woodrow Parfrey (*mint inspector*), Virgil Warner (*narrator*), Anthony James, John Damler, Bud Adler, Chubby Johnson, Ayllene Gibbons, Sidney Clute, Amanda Harley, William Boyett, Tracey Roberts.

Western comedy. Shortly after the Civil War, Sam Whiskey, a gambler and adventurer, is seduced into helping Laura Breckenridge retrieve a quarter of a million dollars in gold bars from a sunken riverboat in Colorado's Platte River. The gold had been stolen from the Denver mint by Laura's late husband, and she is willing to pay $20,000 to have it returned before the theft is discovered and her family name is ruined. After teaming up with Jedidiah Hooker, a local blacksmith, and O. W. Bandy, an Army friend turned inventor, Sam heads for the sunken riverboat, unaware that he is being watched by Fat Henry Hobson. A diving helmet made by O. W. enables Sam to find the gold, but he loses it to Fat Henry and his henchmen. With the help of one of O. W.'s homemade machine guns, Sam and his cronies recover the loot, meet Laura, and head for Denver. Assuming the identity of a government inspector, Sam enters the mint and deliberately damages a bronze bust of George Washington. He then insists on having it repaired and takes it to a blacksmith's shop, where Jedidiah recasts the gold into the shape of the bust. Fat Henry later breaks into the shop and steals the bronze original. Sam and his men, posing as plumbers, return to the mint and recast the bust into gold bars. On a train leaving Denver the next morning, Sam splits the $20,000 with Jedidiah and O. W. but keeps Laura for himself. *Adventurers. Blacksmiths. Gamblers. Widows. Inventors. Theft. Imposture. Gold. Riverboats. Inventions. Sculpture. Guns. Platte River. Denver. United States Mint.*

Note: Location scenes filmed in Denver, Colorado. Prerelease title: *Whiskey's Renegades.*

SAMANTHA see **A NEW KIND OF LOVE**

SAMAR   **F6.4214**

Winchester & MAM. *Dist* Warner Bros. Pictures. 11 Apr **1962** [New York opening; c10 Dec 1961; LP27112]. Sd; col (Technicolor). 35mm. 89 min. [Also reviewed at 85 min.]

Prod-Dir George Montgomery. *Assoc Prod* Al Wyatt, Ferde Grofé, Jr. *Story-Screenplay* Ferde Grofé, Jr., George Montgomery. *Photog* Emmanuel Rojas. *Film Ed* Walter Thompson. *Mus Comp & Cond* Harry Zimmerman. *Sd Eff Ed* Mort Tubor. *Asst Dir* Mario Barri, Vicente Nayve, Jairo Mullin.

Cast: George Montgomery (*Dr. John Saunders*), Gilbert Roland (*Colonel Salazar*), Ziva Rodann (*Ana*), Joan O'Brien (*Cecile Salazar*), Nico Minardos (*De Guzman*), Mario Barri (*Sergeant Nanding*), Tony Fortich, Danny Jurado, Henry Feist, Esperanza Garcia, Luciano Lasam, Carmen Austin, Pedro Faustino, Johnny Cortez, Pam Saunders, Rita Moreno.

Adventure melodrama. In the 1870's Spanish political prisoners are exiled to the penal colony of Samar in the Philippines. Newly arrived are Ana Rodriguez, halfcaste daughter of a Spanish official, and Dr. John Saunders, a soldier of fortune sentenced to five years imprisonment for killing a jealous husband in a duel. Saunders is startled to discover that the colony is being operated by the humane Colonel Salazar more as a model community than as a prison. When Spanish inspector Captain De Guzman demands that Salazar explain his actions to the officials in Manila, the colonel decides to destroy the camp and lead his prisoners to a remote, interior valley. Taking De Guzman prisoner, Salazar burns every structure in the area and leads his charges into the dense jungle. During the trek they are attacked by headhunters and De Guzman is mortally wounded. They are also confronted by towering mountains and drenching typhoons but manage to push forward steadily. Salazar is felled by a poisoned dart and Saunders is forced to amputate his arm in order to save his life. Eventually the little group reaches a lush valley, where they decide to establish a new community free from Spanish oppression. *Spanish. Political prisoners. Physicians. Soldiers of fortune. Halfcastes. Headhunters. Exile. Humanitarianism. Amputation. Penal colonies. Jungles. Typhoons. Samar.*

Note: Filmed in the Philippines.

SAME GENDER see **OF THE SAME GENDER**

SAMMA NO AJI see **AN AUTUMN AFTERNOON**

SAMMY GOING SOUTH see **A BOY TEN FEET TALL**

SAMPO see **THE DAY THE EARTH FROZE**

SAMSON AND THE SEVEN MIRACLES OF THE WORLD
(France/Italy)   **F6.4215**

Panda Film–Gallus Films–Agiman. *Dist* American International Pictures. Dec **1962**. Sd; col (Technicolor, print by Pathé). 35mm (Colorscope). 80 min.

Prod Ermanno Donati, Luigi Carpentieri. *Dir* Riccardo Freda. *Screenplay* Oreste Biancoli, Duccio Tessari. *Story* Oreste Biancoli. *Photog* Riccardo Pallottini. *Art Dir* Piero Filippone. *Film Ed* Ornella Micheli. *Orig Mus* Carlo Innocenzi. *Mus U. S. Vers* Les Baxter. *Choreog* Wilbert Bradley. *Asst Dir* Giuliano Betti. *Cost* Massimo Bolongaro.

Cast: Gordon Scott (*Samson*), Yoko Tani (*Princess Lei-ling*), Gabriele Antonini (*Cho*), Leonardo Severini (*Garak*), Valery Inkijinoff (*high priest*), Hélène Chanel (*Liutai*), Dante Di Paolo (*Bayan*), Chu-Lai-Chit, Luong-Ham-Chau, Franco Ressel, Antonio Cianci, Ely Yeh, Giacomo Tchang.

Adventure melodrama. After a Tartar tyrant murders the emperor of China during the 13th century, Samson rescues the young prince while the princess is taken to safety by the leader of the rebels. The tyrant again seizes the princess and plans to marry her, thus legitimizing his succession to the throne. Samson rescues her and takes her to the monastery that serves as the rebels' hideout. The monastery is attacked again, and the prince is killed. The enslaved Chinese finally revolt when Samson rings the great "Gong of Freedom," but he is knocked down by the swinging bell and buried in an underground vault by Tartars. In freeing himself from his tomb, Samson creates an earthquake, and the tyrant and his men are defeated, leaving the princess free to ascend the throne and marry the leader of the Chinese rebels. *Despots. Royalty. Tartars. Usurpers. Assassination. Rescue. Abduction. Revolts. Feats of strength. Monasteries. China. Earthquakes. Samson. Maciste.*

Note: Produced in Italy in 1961 as *Maciste alla corte del Gran Khan;* running time: 95 min; opened in Paris in Mar 1963 as *Le géant à la cour de Kublai Khan;* running time: 92 min.

SAMSON AND THE SLAVE QUEEN (Italy)   **F6.4216**

Romana Film. *Dist* American International Pictures. Dec **1963** [New York opening: 4 Mar 1964; c18 Dec 1963; LP27090]. Sd; col (Eastmancolor). 35mm (Colorscope, see note). 86 min.

Prod Fortunato Misiano. *Dir* Umberto Lenzi. *Screenplay* Guido Malatesta, Umberto Lenzi. *Dir Photog* Augusto Tiezzi. *Set Dsgn* Peppino Piccolo. *Film Ed* Iolanda Benvenuti. *Mus Comp & Cond* Angelo Francesco Lavagnino. *Prod Mgr* Nino Misiano. *Cost* Walter Patriarca.

Cast: Pierre Brice (*Zorro/Ramón*), Alan Steel (*Samson*), Moira Orfei (*Malva*), Maria Grazia Spina (*Isabella*), Andrea Aureli (*Rabek*), Massimo Serato (*Garcia*), Aldo Bufi Landi, Andrea Scotti, Loris Gizzi, Rosy De Leo, Nazzareno Zamperla, Gaetano Scala, Attilio Dottesio.

Adventure melodrama. During the 15th century, Philip II, King of Navarra, dies, and his two nieces, the evil Princess Malva and the virtuous Princess Isabella, struggle to determine which one will ascend the throne. The successor's name is hidden in the royal treasure chest which contains the king's will. The ambitious Malva thinks Isabella is the king's choice and engages Samson to bring the chest to her so that Garcia, her lover and the captain of the guards, can replace the document with one naming Malva queen. Isabella engages Zorro, a superb swordsman, for the same purpose after being so advised by Ramón, a poet with whom she is in love. After many contests of strength and will with Zorro, Samson finally gets the chest and takes it to the palace. He prevents Malva from receiving it, however, when he realizes that the gentle Isabella should be queen. Samson and Zorro, no longer enemies, then join forces and fight together to overthrow Garcia's guards. Isabella becomes queen and finds that the unmasked Zorro is really Ramón. *Royalty. Strongmen. Sisters. Poets. Ambition. Inheritance. Contests. Disguise. Personal identity. Swords. Wills. Navarre. Feats of strength. Duels. Maciste. Samson.*

Note: Released in Italy in 1964 as *Zorro contra Maciste;* running time: 92 min. Copyright claimant: Alta Vista Productions. Some sources list Totalscope or Techniscope as the widescreen process.

SAMSON VS. THE GIANT KING (Italy)   **F6.4217**

Cineluxor. *Dist* John Alexander Film Associates. Aug **1965**. Sd; b&w. 35mm. 91 min.

Prod Luigi Rovere. *Dir* Amerigo Anton. *Screenplay* Mario Moroni, Alberto De Rossi, Amerigo Anton. *Photog* Aldo Giordani. *Art Dir* Amedeo Mellone. *Mus* Carlo Rustichelli. *Cost* Walter Patriarca.

Cast: Kirk Morris (*Samson [Maciste]*), Massimo Serato (*czar*), Gloria Milland (*Nadia [Sonia]*), Ombretta Colli, Tom Felleghi, Giulio Donnini, Dada Gallotti, Ugo Sasso, Armando Arnaldi, Renato Rossini, Attilio Dottesio, Luigi Scavran, Giorgio Bixio.

Adventure melodrama. Preserved for centuries in a state of frozen animation beneath the Russian tundra, Samson is unearthed and revived by an anthropological expedition sent by the tyrannical czar to find buried treasure. The anthropologists, ambushed by the czar's men while returning to Saint Petersburg, are rescued by the legendary warrior. The czar plans to use Samson for his own cruel deeds, but Nadia, a maiden at court, informs Samson of the czar's intentions. With the promise of freedom for slaves and political prisoners, Samson undergoes a trial of strength; the czar reneges on his word, however, and poisons Samson. After recovering with an antidote found by Nadia, Samson leads the people in a successful revolt against the czar. *Anthropologists. Despots. Reviviscence. Cryogenics. Slavery. Feats of strength. Perfidy. Poisoning. Revolts. Russia. Saint Petersburg. Maciste. Samson.*

Note: Opened in Rome in Aug 1964 in Technicolor as *Maciste alla corte dello zar.* Amerigo Anton is a pseudonym for Tanio Boccia.

SAMURAI *see* **SAMURAI ASSASSIN**

SAMURAI ASSASSIN (Japan)   **F6.4218**
Toho Co.-Toshiro Mifune. *Dist* Toho International, Inc. 5 Mar **1965** [Honolulu, Hawaii, opening]. Sd; b&w. 35mm (Tohoscope). 123 min.
Prod Tomoyuki Tanaka, Reiji Miwa. *Dir* Kihachi Okamoto. *Screenplay* Shinobu Hashimoto. *Photog* Hiroshi Murai. *Mus* Masaru Sato.
Cast: Toshiro Mifune (*Niino*), Keiju Kobayashi (*Kurihara*), Michiyo Aratama (*Okiko Kukuhime*), Yunosuke Ito (*Hoshino*), Koshiro Matsumoto (*Lord Naosuke Ii*), Nami Tamura, Kaoru Yachigusa, Haruko Sugimura, Takashi Shimura, Chusha Ichikawa, Susumu Fujita.
Action melodrama. Source: Jiromasa Gunji, *Samurai Nippon* (Tokyo, 1969). Niino, a swordsman of exceptional ability, is denied admittance to a house of nobility because the identity of his father is unknown. Frustrated in his desire to become a great warrior, Niino joins a band of outlaws planning to assassinate the Chief Minister, who has been advocating more open relations with Western nations. Niino escapes his own murder by the assassins and finally gains admittance to the minister's palace after a vicious fight with the palace guards. He succeeds in assassinating the minister, only to discover that the dead man was his father. *Samurai. Nobility. Outlaws. Prime ministers. Assassination. Illegitimacy. Patricide. Duels.*
Note: Released in Japan in 1965 as *Samurai.*

SAMURAI BANNERS *see* **UNDER THE BANNER OF SAMURAI**

SAMURAI FROM NOWHERE (Japan)   **F6.4219**
Shochiku Co. *Dist* Shochiku Films of America. 20 May **1964** [Los Angeles opening]. Sd; b&w. 35mm (Shochiku GrandScope). 93 min.
Prod Gin-ichi Kishimoto. *Dir* Seiichiro Uchikawa. *Screenplay* Hideo Oguni. *Story* Shoguro Yamamoto. *Photog* Yoshiharu Ota. *Art Dir* Jun-ichi Osumi. *Mus* Masaru Sato.
Cast: Isamu Nagato (*Ihei Misawa*), Tetsuro Tamba (*Gunjuro Ohba*), Shima Iwashita (*Tae*), Chieko Baisho (*Chigusa*), Seiji Miyaguchi (*Tatewaki Komuro*).
Action drama. During the 17th century, Ihei, a ronin, or unemployed samurai, rescues Tae from Lord Kotani, who wishes to make her his concubine. Pursued by the lord's henchmen, the couple take on menial jobs, desperate for money with which to pay their debts and bribe border guards to ensure safe passage. Ihei's income is so meager, however, that he challenges a local fencing master to a match and then blackmails the man after defeating him, despite the tradition that a samurai not use his skills for monetary gain. The local governor, made aware of Ihei's extraordinary skills during an authorized fencing tournament, offers him the post of master of martial arts, but he withdraws the offer when he learns that Ihei had participated for money in a common fencing contest. As Ihei and Tae continue on their journey, they are attacked by the lord's henchmen. Aided by Gunjuro Ohba, another ronin and formerly Ihei's tournament rival, Ihei subdues his opponents and proceeds in safety with Tae. *Samurai. Nobility. Personal identity. Social customs. Fencing (sport). Wagers.*
Note: Released in Japan in 1964 as *Dojo yaburi.* Also reviewed as *Kempo samurai.*

SAMURAI (PART II) (Japan)   **F6.4220**
Toho Co. *Dist* Toho International, Inc. 20 Oct **1967** [New York opening]. Sd; col (Eastmancolor). 35mm. 102 min.
Prod Kazuo Takimura. *Dir* Hiroshi Inagaki. *Screenplay* Tokuhei Wakao, Hiroshi Inagaki. *Photog* Asushi Atumoto, Jun Yasumoto. *Mus* Ikuma Dan.
Cast: Toshiro Mifune (*Musashi Miyamoto*), Koji Tsuruta (*Kojiro Sasaki*), Sachio Sakai (*Matahachi Honiden*), Akihiko Hirata (*Seijuro Yoshioka*), Yu Fujiki (*Denshichiro Yoshioka*), Daisuke Kato (*Toji Gion*), Eijiro Tono (*Baiken Shishido*), Kuninori Kodo (*Old Priest Nikkan*), Kenjim Iida (*Jotaro*), Kaoru

Yachigusa (*Otsu*), Mariko Okada (*Akemi*), Mitsuko Mito (*Oko*), Michiyo Kogure (*Yoshino*), Kuroemon Ono.
Adventure drama. Source: Eiji Yoshikawa, *Miyamoto Musashi* (Tokyo, 1936-39). Musashi Miyamoto, a samurai wandering through feudal Japan, learns during his adventures that along with strength and swordsmanship a warrior must display mercy and kindness. He is pursued by several women, but his devotion to martial life precludes any romantic involvements. *Samurai. Feudalism.*
Note: Released in Japan in 1955 as *Ichijoji no ketto,* the second film in the Musashi Miyamoto trilogy. The first part was released in the United States in 1955 as *Samurai;* the third part in 1967 as *Samurai (Part III),* q. v. Japanese alternative title: *Zoku Miyamoto Musashi.*

SAMURAI (PART III) (Japan)   **F6.4221**
Toho Co. *Dist* Toho International, Inc. 10 Nov **1967** [New York showing]. Sd; col (Eastmancolor). 35mm. 102 min.
Prod Kazuo Takimura. *Dir* Hiroshi Inagaki. *Screenplay* Tokuhei Wakao, Hiroshi Inagaki. *Story* Eiji Yoshikawa. *Photog* Kazuo Yamada. *Art Dir* Kisaku Ito. *Mus* Ikuma Dan.
Cast: Toshiro Mifune (*Musashi Miyamoto*), Koji Tsuruta (*Kojiro Sasaki*), Kaoru Yachigusa (*Otsu*), Michiko Saga (*Omitsu*), Mariko Okada (*Akemi*), Takashi Shimura (*court official*), Kyo Shimura.
Action melodrama. Musashi Miyamoto, a wandering samurai, is challenged to a duel by his rival, Kojiro Sasaki, but Miyamoto requests a meeting at a later time. Followed by two women who love him, Miyamoto settles in an area where local farmers have been plagued by bandits. He teaches his neighbors self-defense, but the bandits use one of his women and through trickery attack the village. The woman dies, and Miyamoto is about to settle down with Otsu, his other follower, when he receives a new challenge from Sasaki. The two samurai meet on Ganryu Island; Miyamoto wins the duel and afterwards returns to his home, hoping for an end to his troubles. *Samurai. Farmers. Bandits. Duels. Islands.*
Note: Released in Japan in 1956 as *Ketto Ganryu Jima,* this is the third part of the Musashi Miyamoto trilogy. Alternative U. S. title: *Duel at Ganryu Island.* Part I of the trilogy was released in Japan in 1954 as *Miyamoto Musashi* and in the United States in 1955 as *Samurai.* Part II was released in Japan in 1955 as *Ichijoji no ketto* and in the United States as *Samurai (Part II),* q. v.

SAMURAI PIRATE (Japan)   **F6.4222**
Toho Co. *Dist* American International Pictures. Mar **1965** [c3 Mar 1965; LP30616]. Sd; col (Eastman Color by Pathé). 35mm (Tohoscope). 95 min. [Also reviewed at 90 min.]
Exec Prod Tomoyuki Tanaka. *Dir* Senkichi Taniguchi. *Screenplay* (see note) Takeshi Kimura, Shinichi Sekizawa. *Photog* Takao Saito. *Mus* Masaru Sato. *Sp Eff* Eiji Tsuburaya.
Cast: Toshiro Mifune (*Sukezaemon/"Luzon"*), Makoto Sato, Jun Funato, Ichiro Arishima, Mie Hama, Kumi Mizuno, Akiko Wakabayashi, Mitsuko Kusabue, Tadao Nakamaru, Jun Tazaki, Takashi Shimura.
Fantasy. Sukezaemon, alias "Luzon," the wealthiest citizen in a 16th-century seaport, is suspected of piracy by the townspeople, and after a hasty trial he is found guilty and sentenced to death. Luzon escapes by bribing the guards, and he sets out to sea, determined to make his fortune in piracy. His ship is attacked by pirates during a typhoon, and Luzon is forced to swim to an island for safety. An old wizard, Sennin, gives him shelter and tells him of the cruel lord chamberlain who rules the island. The lord chamberlain, who is the leader of the pirates who attacked Luzon's ship, keeps the ailing king a prisoner with the aid of a witch, and he plots to marry the king's daughter, Princess Yaya, and usurp the throne. While attending a state procession, Luzon sees Princess Yaya wearing a necklace that was among the treasures stolen from him by the pirates, and he vows revenge. In order to marry the princess, the lord chamberlain orders the execution of her fiancé, the Prince of Ming. Luzon rescues the prince and, with the aid of Sennin and his magic powers, attacks the castle. He flies over the castle walls on a huge kite and interrupts the wedding ceremony. Luzon kills the lord chamberlain in a sword fight, restores the king to the throne, and goes off in search of more excitement. *Pirates. Sorcerers. Royalty. Witches. Usurpers. Magic. Revenge. Treasure. Castles. Swords. Kites. Islands. Typhoons.*
Note: Released in Japan in 1964 under the title *Daitozoku;* running time: 97 min. Title changed to *The Lost World of Sinbad.* U. S. sources credit only Kimura with screenplay while Japanese sources list both Kimura and Sekizawa as writers.

SAN FRANCISCO COWBOY   **F6.4223**
AAF Productions. *Dist* Grads Corp. **1969.** Sd; col. 35mm. 70 min.
Sex film. Romeo Bruno, a notorious philanderer living in San Francisco, seduces five women in the course of a single day. *Philanderers. Seduction. San Francisco.*

SAN SIMEON DEL DESIERTO *see* **SIMON OF THE DESERT**

SANCTUARY
F6.4224

Darryl F. Zanuck Productions. *Dist* Twentieth Century–Fox Film Corp. 21 Feb **1961** [New York opening; c21 Feb 1961; LP18689]. Sd (Westrex); b&w. 35mm (CinemaScope). 90 min.

Prod Richard D. Zanuck. *Dir* Tony Richardson. *Screenplay* James Poe. *Dir Photog* Ellsworth Fredricks. *Art Dir* Duncan Cramer, Jack Martin Smith. *Set Decor* Walter M. Scott, Fred Maclean. *Film Ed* Robert Simpson. *Mus* Alex North. *Orch* Edward B. Powell. *Song Sung by* Julie London. *Sd* Charles Peck, Harold A. Root. *Asst Dir* David Hall. *Cost Dsgn* Don Feld. *Makeup* Ben Nye. *Hairstyles* Helen Turpin.

Cast: Lee Remick *(Temple Drake)*, Yves Montand *(Candy Man)*, Bradford Dillman *(Gowan Stevens)*, Harry Townes *(Ira Bobbitt)*, Odetta *(Nancy Mannigoe)*, Howard St. John *(Governor Drake)*, Jean Carson *(Norma)*, Reta Shaw *(Miss Reba)*, Strother Martin *(Dog Boy)*, William Mims *(Lee)*, Marge Redmond *(Flossie)*, Jean Bartel *(Swede)*, Hope Du Bois *(Mamie)*, Enid James *(Jackie)*, Dana Lorenson *(Connie)*, Pamela Raymond *(Cora)*, Linden Chiles *(Randy)*, Robert Gothie *(Gus)*, Wyatt Cooper *(Tommy)*, Kim Hector *(Bucky Stevens)*, Voltaire Perkins *(The Judge)*.

Melodrama. Source: William Faulkner, *Sanctuary* (New York, 1931). William Faulkner, *Requiem for a Nun* (New York, 1951). Ruth Ford, *Requiem for a Nun* (a stage adaptation of Faulkner's novel; London opening: 26 Nov 1957). In 1928, in the county of Yoknapatawpha, Mississippi, Nancy Mannigoe, a 30-year-old Negro woman, is condemned to death for the willful murder of the infant son of Mrs. Gowan Stevens, the former Temple Drake. On the eve of the scheduled execution, Temple tries to save Nancy by telling her father, the governor, of the events leading up to the murder. *Six years earlier, Temple was a pleasure-loving college girl carrying on a flirtatious romance with young Gowan Stevens. One night Gowan got drunk and took her to a backwoods still where she was raped by Candy Man, a Cajun bootlegger. The next morning, although in a state of semi-shock, she willingly submitted to more of his lovemaking and then agreed to live with him in a New Orleans brothel. Nancy became her personal maid, and Temple reveled in her new life, until Candy Man was reported killed in an auto accident and Temple was forced to go home. Marriage to Gowan followed; but for Temple it was a dull life, and she hired Nancy as a servant to remind her of the brothel life she had loved so much. Suddenly, Candy Man returned, and Temple decided to abandon her home and marriage and once more run off with him. To bring Temple to her senses and prevent her from ruining her life, Nancy sacrificed the infant child by smothering it to death.* Though shocked by the candor of his daughter's confession, the governor is unable to grant a pardon for Nancy. The next morning Temple visits Nancy in her cell. As the two women beg each other's forgiveness, Temple realizes that it is only through Nancy's sacrifice that she has been able to find salvation. *Negroes. Housemaids. State governors. Bootleggers. Cajuns. Infanticide. Capital punishment. Drunkenness. Rape. Prostitution. Marriage. Self-sacrifice. Stills. Whorehouses. Mississippi. New Orleans. Automobile accidents.*

Note: Faulkner's *Sanctuary* was filmed by Paramount in 1933 and released as *The Story of Temple Drake.*

THE SAND CASTLE
F6.4225

Noel Productions. *Dist* Louis de Rochemont Associates, Barney Pitkin Associates, Contemporary Films. 15 Aug **1961** [New York opening]. Sd; b&w with col seq (Eastman Color). 16mm & 35mm. 70 min. [Also 64 min.]

Prod-Dir-Writ Jerome Hill. *Photog* Lloyd Ahern. *Film Ed* Julia Knowlton, Henry A. Sundquist. *Mus* Alec Wilder. *Sd* Robert C. Fine. *Sp Eff Cons* Francis Thompson. *Dream Seq Art Work Dsgn and Painted by* Jerome Hill.

Cast: Barry Cardwell *(boy)*, Laurie Cardwell *(girl)*, George Dunham *(artist)*, Alec Wilder *(fisherman)*, Maybelle Nash *(shade lady)*, Erica Speyer *(sun lady)*, Charles Rydell *(young man)*, Allegra Ahern *(young girl)*, Lester Judson *(fat man)*, Martin Russ *(frogman)*, Ghislain Dussart *(priest)*, Mabel Mercer *(voice of the shell)*.

Drama. Early on a summer day in California, a mother leaves her young son and daughter at a nearby beach while she goes shopping. Unwelcome in the war games of a group of older boys, the youngsters wander off alone along the water's edge. The boy finds a lovely seashell and imagines that he hears a voice inside it telling him to build a sand castle. As he works on his fortress, the beach attracts other visitors: a fat woman burdened down with paraphernalia, including a canopy, a radio, a bird in a cage, and binoculars; a bikini-clad sun worshiper; an eccentric painter; two lovers; a fisherman; a fat man who drinks from a bottle of gin; muscle-builders; a skin diver; and a group of nuns who play softball. The visitors mill about, admiring the boy's beautiful castle until a sudden rainstorm drives them away. Sheltered by a beach umbrella, the boy and his little sister fall asleep near the castle. His head filled with the events of the day, the boy has a dream in which his sand castle becomes real and the people he has seen on the beach become its inhabitants. An alarm sounds; the castle

begins to tremble; and the boy awakens to the voice of his mother calling in the distance. As he leaves the beach, the tide rushes in, and the sand castle is washed into the sea. *Children. Painters. Fishermen. Body-builders. Nuns. Divers. Brother-sister relationship. Sunbathing. Sand castles. Beaches. Dreams.*

Note: Filmed in 16mm. Live-action, black-and-white sequences filmed on location in Laguna Beach, California. The style of the animated, color dream sequences, involving stop-motion photography of paper figurines against paper sets, was inspired by the "juvenile drama" paper cutout theaters of the 19th century. Originally released in 16mm by Louis de Rochemont Associates; subsequently released in 35mm by Barney Pitkin Associates and in 16mm by Contemporary Films.

THE SAND PEBBLES
F6.4226

Argyle Enterprises–Solar Productions. *Dist* Twentieth Century–Fox Film Corp. 20 Dec **1966** [New York opening; c28 Dec 1966; LP34734]. Sd (Westrex); col (DeLuxe). 35mm (Panavision). 155-195 min. [See note.]

A Robert Wise Production. *Prod-Dir* Robert Wise. *Assoc Prod* Charles Maguire. *Prod Assoc* Maurice Zuberano. *2d Unit Dir* Charles Maguire. *Screenplay* Robert W. Anderson. *Dir Photog* Joseph MacDonald. *2d Unit Photog* Richard Johnson, photog. *Set Decor* Walter M. Scott, John Sturtevant, William Kiernan. *Prod Dsgn* Boris Leven. *Film Ed* William Reynolds. *Mus* Jerry Goldsmith. *Cond* Lionel Newman. *Orch* David Tamkin, Arthur Morton. *Sd* Murray Spivack, Douglas O. Williams, Bernard Freericks, James Corcoran. *Asst Dir* Ridgeway Callow. *Unit Prod Mgr* Saul Wurtzel. *Cost Dsgn* Renie. *Wardrobe* Ed Wynigear. *Makeup* Ben Nye, Bill Turner, Del Acevedo. *Hairstyles* Margaret Donovan. *Sp Eff* Jerry Endler. *Sp Photog Eff* L. B. Abbott, Emil Kosa, Jr. *Tech Adv* Harley Misiner, (USN Ret.). *Location Constr Mgr* Herbert Cheek.

Cast: Steve McQueen *(Jake Holman)*, Richard Attenborough *(Frenchy Burgoyne)*, Richard Crenna *(Captain Collins)*, Candice Bergen *(Shirley Eckert)*, Marayat Andriane *(Maily)*, Mako *(Po-han)*, Larry Gates *(Jameson)*, Charles Robinson *(Ensign Bordelles)*, Simon Oakland *(Stawski)*, Ford Rainey *(Harris)*, Joseph Turkel *(Bronson)*, Gavin MacLeod *(Crosley)*, Joseph Di Reda *(Shanahan)*, Richard Loo *(Major Chin)*, Barney Phillips *(Chief Franks)*, Gus Trikonis *(Restorff)*, Shepherd Sanders *(Perna)*, James Jeter *(Farren)*, Tom Middleton *(Jennings)*, Paul Chinpae *(Cho-jen)*, Tommy Lee *(Chien)*, Beulah Quo *(Mama Chunk)*, James Hong *(Victor Shu)*, Stephen Jahn *(Haythorn)*, Alan Hopkins *(Wilsey)*, Steve Ferry *(Lamb)*, Ted Fish *(CPO Wellbeck)*, Loren Janes *(Coleman)*, Glenn Wilder *(Waldron)*, Henry Wang *(Lop-eye Shing)*, Ben Wright *(Englishman)*, Walter Reed *(bidder)*, Gil Perkins *(customer)*.

War drama. Source: Richard McKenna, *The Sand Pebbles* (New York, 1962). In 1926, as strong feelings of nationalism are sweeping through China and the followers of Chiang Kai-shek, as well as the war lords and communists, are demanding that all foreigners leave Chinese soil, the U. S. gunboat *San Pablo* is patroling the Yangtze River. The newest member of the crew, who call themselves "sand pebbles," is Jake Holman, a machinist with 8 years previous Navy duty. Although Jake's independent nature is regarded with suspicion by most of the men, he wins the friendship of Frenchy, a sailor in love with an English-educated Chinese girl, Maily, who has been sold into enforced prostitution. When Chiang Kai-shek moves against the feudal war lords, the United States decides to treat the upheaval as a civil war, and the *San Pablo* is ordered to confine its function to protection of American civilians in the area. Included among them are Mr. Jameson, a missionary, and Shirley Eckert, a schoolteacher whom Jake met earlier. In an attempt to draw the *San Pablo*'s fire, the Chinese capture Jake's coolie assistant, Po-han, and torture him by slashing his chest with a knife. Unable to bear his friend's agonized screams, Jake grabs a gun and puts a bullet into Po-han's head. Later, Frenchy buys Maily's freedom and takes her as his common-law wife because they cannot legally marry. While the *San Pablo* is forced to remain in a state of siege, Frenchy swims ashore each night to visit his pregnant wife. But the icy waters precipitate pneumonia and he dies in Maily's room. When Jake visits the bereaved woman, the Chinese beat him and put Maily to death. They then brand Jake as the murderer and demand that the *San Pablo* hand him over for trial. The crew agrees that Jake should be tried, and when Captain Collins refuses the demand and orders the crew to fire on the Chinese the men nearly mutiny. The captain takes advantage of the rising tide and moves his ship into deep water. When word arrives that full-scale fighting has led to the landing of U. S. Marines in Shanghai, Captain Collins decides to give his humiliated ship and disgraced crew a chance for glory by heading for Jameson's mission and a rescue attempt. After a bloody fight, the *San Pablo* breaks through a Chinese blockade and reaches the mission. But Jameson and Shirley declare themselves stateless and rebuke the captain for interfering in China's affairs. Jake wants to desert, but neutrality is no longer possible. Nationalist troops, incensed by the *San Pablo*'s defiance of the blockade, storm the mission and kill both Jameson and Collins. Pushed into making a last stand, Jake orders the other crew members to take Shirley to safety while he covers their getaway. But he is killed by a Chinese bullet. As he dies, he cries "I was home. ... What the hell happened?" *Warlords. Communists. Sailors. Americans in foreign countries. Machinists. Chinese. Missionaries. Schoolteachers. Nationalism. Race relations. Prostitution. Torture. Mercy killing. Marriage—Common law. Miscegenation. Pneumonia. Murder. Frameup. Mutiny. Self-sacrifice. Gunboats. China—History—Republic 1912-49. Yangtze River. Shanghai. Chiang Kai-shek. United States Navy. United States Marines.*

Note: Location scenes filmed in Taiwan and Hong Kong. The running time has been listed at 155, 162, 182, 191, 193 and 195 min. Marayat Andriane is also known as Emmanuelle Arsan.

SANDA TAI GAILAH *see* **THE WAR OF THE GARGANTUAS**

SANDAI KAIJU CHIKYU SAIDAI NO KESSEN *see* **GHIDRAH, THE THREE-HEADED MONSTER**

THE SANDAL KEEPER (Japan)   **F6.4227**
Toho Co. Oct **1965** [Los Angeles showing]. Sd; col. 35mm (Tohoscope). 96 min.

Dir Kengo Furusawa.

Cast: Hitoshi Ueki, Hajime Hana, Kei Tani, Mie Hama, Mitsuko Kusabue, Ichiro Arishima, Yu Fujiki.

Comedy. No information about the precise nature of this film has been found.

Note: Released in Japan in 1964 as *Horafuki taikoki.*

SANDOKAN THE GREAT (France/Italy/Spain)   **F6.4228**
Comptoir Français du Film–Filmes Cinematografica–Ocean Film. *Dist* Metro-Goldwyn-Mayer, Inc. May **1965** [c31 Dec 1964; LP29466]. Sd; col (Technicolor). 35mm (Techniscope). 110 min. [Also reviewed at 105 min.]

Prod (see note) Solly V. Bianco, Joseph Fryd. *Dir* Umberto Lenzi. *Asst to the Dir* Victor Tourjansky, Jean Maumy, Giancarlo Romitelli. *Story & Screenplay* Fulvio Gicca, Umberto Lenzi. *Screenplay Collab* Victor A. Catena. *Photog* Angelo Lotti, Giovanni Scarpellini, Aurelio Gutiérrez Larraya. *Set Dsgn* Arrigo Equini, Juan Alberto Soler. *Film Ed* Iolanda Benvenuti, Antonietta Zita. *Mus* Giovanni Fusco. *Prod Mgr* Tommaso Sagone, Teodoro Herrero. *In Charge of Location Scenes* Sandha Ratnavira. *Cost* Giancarlo Bartolini Salimbeni. *Makeup* Raoul Ranieri.

Cast: Steve Reeves *(Sandokan)*, Geneviève Grad *(Mary Ann)*, Andrea Bosic *(Yanez)*, Maurice Poli *(Giro Batol)*, Rik Battaglia *(Sambigliong)*, Leo Anchóriz *(Lord Hillock)*, Joaquín Oliveras *(Lieutenant Appleton)*, Ananda Kumar *(Tuang Olong)*, Antonio Molino Rojo *(Lieutenant Tollbee)*, Mario Valdemarin *(Lieutenant Ross)*, Enzo Fiermonte *(Sergeant Mitchell)*, Gino Marturano *(Tananduriam)*, Wilbert Bradley, Pietro Capanna, Nazzareno Zamperla, Giovanni Cianfriglia.

Adventure melodrama. Source: Emilio Salgari, *Le tigri di Mompracem* (Genoa, 1900). During the reign of Queen Victoria, British forces led by Lord Hillock occupy Tapuah, subduing its population through mass murder. Among their victims are the mother and brothers of Sandokan, and he in reprisal organizes a revolutionary band. When Hillock attempts to entrap the rebel by threatening to hang his father, the Sultan of Mulaker, Sandokan penetrates Hillock's home, taking as hostage the Englishman's niece, Mary Ann. Although initially indignant, Mary Ann comes to love her captor. Following an encounter with headhunters, Sandokan and his men are surrounded by Hillock's forces, and an armistice is negotiated according to which Sandokan and his gang will be exiled in return for Mary Ann's release. Hillock immediately violates the agreement, however, imprisoning the rebels and planning for their immediate execution. Escaping, the insurgents, joined by Mary Ann, combine with the army of the native chieftain Tuang Olong to free their homeland from British domination. *British. Royalty. Uncles. Headhunters. Hostages. Colonialism. Revolts. Perfidy. Abduction.*

Note: Exteriors filmed in Spain. Opened in Madrid in Mar 1964 as *Sandokan;* in Paris in Dec 1964 as *Sandokan, le tigre de Bornéo* at 115 and 94 min; released in Italy in 1964 as *Sandokan, la tigre di Mompracem.* Fryd is credited as producer only by U. S. sources.

THE SANDPIPER   **F6.4229**
Venice Productions–Filmways, Inc. *Dist* Metro-Goldwyn-Mayer, Inc. 23 Jun **1965** [Washington, D. C., opening; c15 Jun 1965; LP30828]. Sd (Westrex); col (Metrocolor). 35mm (Panavision). 116 min.

A Martin Ransohoff Production. *Assoc Prod* John Calley. *Dir* Vincente Minnelli. *Coörd of the Big Sur Scene* Eduardo Tirella. *Screenplay* Dalton Trumbo, Michael Wilson. *Adapt* Irene Kamp, Louis Kamp. *Story* Martin Ransohoff. *Dir Photog* Milton Krasner. *Wildlife Photog* Richard Borden. *Art Dir* George W. Davis, Urie McCleary. *Set Decor* Henry Grace, Keogh Gleason. *Titl Art* Herb Rosenthal. *Film Ed* David Bretherton. *Mus & Song:* "The Shadow of Your Smile" Johnny Mandel. *Lyr* Paul Francis Webster. *Orch* Robert Armbruster. *Rec Supv* Franklin Milton. *Asst Dir* William McGarry.

Supv Prod Exec Ben Kadish. *Cost Dsgn* Irene Sharaff. *Makeup Supv* William Tuttle. *Hairstyles* Sydney Guilaroff. *Coöp* Don Bloom, Dorothy Bowman, The Bradford Children, Cyril M. Brown, Jr. *Laura's Paintings* Elizabeth Duquette. *Redwood Sculpture* Edmund Kara.

Cast: Elizabeth Taylor *(Laura Reynolds)*, Richard Burton *(Dr. Edward Hewitt)*, Eva Marie Saint *(Claire Hewitt)*, Charles Bronson *(Cos Erickson)*, Robert Webber *(Ward Hendricks)*, James Edwards *(Larry Brant)*, Torin Thatcher *(Judge Thompson)*, Tom Drake *(Walter Robinson)*, Douglas Henderson *(Phil Sutcliff)*, Morgan Mason *(Danny Reynolds)*, Rex Holman, Kelton Garwood, Mel Gallagher, Ron Whelan *(celebrants)*, Peter O'Toole *(voice)*.

Drama. Laura Reynolds, a freethinking artist, lives with her 9-year-old illegitimate son, Danny, in a beach house near Monterey. The boy's uninhibited upbringing has brought him into conflict with the law, and Laura is ordered by the court to enroll him in the private school headed by Episcopal clergyman Edward Hewitt or risk losing him. Convinced that she can better educate the boy herself, she complies reluctantly, resentful of the judge's interference. She is surprised, however, at the ease with which Danny settles down to the school routine. Despite the initial hostility between Laura and Hewitt, who is married and the father of two boys, they are drawn into a passionate love affair. Antagonized by her nonconformist friends, Hewitt nevertheless yields to his passion, though he is tormented by guilt and humiliation. He reveals his affair to his wife, Claire, who withdraws, brokenhearted; and he subsequently makes a public admission. Laura condemns him for making their private relationship into public gossip, and they sever their liaison. Hewitt now confronts the self-seeking politicians who have been using him and his school for their own ends, and he resigns his headmastership. Leaving both Claire and Laura behind, he sets off to regain his former ideals as a minister. *Artists. Nonconformists. Atheists. Clergymen. Headmasters. Judges. Politicians. Illegitimacy. Infidelity. Guilt. Motherhood. Beaches. Boarding schools. Monterey (California). Protestant Episcopal Church.*

Note: Working title: *The Flight of the Sandpiper.*

SANDRA (Italy)   **F6.4230**
Vides. *Dist* Royal Films International. 16 Jan **1966** [New York opening]. Sd; b&w. 35mm. 100 min.

Prod Franco Cristaldi. *Exec Prod* Oscar Brazzi. *Dir* Luchino Visconti. *Screenplay* Suso Cecchi D'Amico, Luchino Visconti, Enrico Medioli. *Photog* Armando Nannuzzi. *Camera* Nino Cristiani, Claudio Cirillo. *Art Dir* Mario Garbuglia. *Film Ed* Mario Serandrei. *Mus:* Prelude, Chorale & Fugue César Franck. *Sd* Claudio Maielli. *Asst Dir* Rinaldo Ricci, Albino Cocco. *Prod Mgr* Sergio Merolle. *Cost* Bice Brichetto. *Makeup* Michele Trimarchi. *Hairstyles* Jole Cecchini.

Cast: Claudia Cardinale *(Sandra)*, Jean Sorel *(Gianni)*, Michael Craig *(Andrew)*, Marie Bell *(mother)*, Renzo Ricci *(Gilardini)*, Fred Williams, actor *(Pietro Fornari)*, Amalia Troiani *(Fosca)*, Vittorio Manfrino, Renato Moretti, Giovanni Rovini, Paolo Pescini, Isacco Politi.

Drama. After a long absence, 25-year-old Sandra returns to Volterra, an ancient, crumbling Italian town which dates back to Etruscan times. Accompanying her is her American husband, Andrew, a practical man who is puzzled by the volatile emotions of his wife's family. Foremost among them is Sandra's younger brother, Gianni, an unstable, would-be author who has attempted suicide several times, but only when Sandra was there to save him. His reunion with Sandra rekindles the passionate feelings he had for her during their adolescence, but Sandra feels only remorse and guilt. Also living at the palazzo is their mother, once a beautiful woman who is now ravaged by physical and mental illness. Although Sandra has ostensibly returned because the family grounds are being given to the city in memory of her father, a prominent Jewish scientist who died in a Nazi concentration camp, her real reason is to confirm her suspicion that her mother arranged her husband's deportation and subsequent death in order to marry Gilardini, the former administrator of the estate. Unable to comprehend the mounting tensions, Andrew makes an attempt to reconcile Sandra and Gianni with their stepfather, but having failed miserably, he leaves for the United States. Gianni destroys his autobiographical novel and then kills himself. After staying for the dedication ceremony, Sandra leaves to rejoin her husband. *Jews. Americans in foreign countries. Novelists. Stepfathers. In-laws. Marriage. Family life. Brother-sister relationship. Incest. Guilt. Mental illness. Suicide. Volterra.*

Note: Filmed on location in Volterra, Geneva, the Alps, and other locations near Florence and in northern Italy. Opened in Rome in Sep 1965 as *Vaghe stelle dell'orsa.*

SANDRA, THE MAKING OF A WOMAN   **F6.4231**
Minifi Corp. *Dist* Grads Corp. May **1970**. Sd; col (Eastmancolor). 35mm. 90 min.

Prod Jay Fineberg, Ron Nicholas. *Dir* Gary Graver. *Screenplay* Robert Aiken, Gary Graver. *Photog* Gary Graver. *Set Dsgn* John Parker. *Film Ed*

Gary Graver. *Sd* Donald Dietz. *Prod Mgr* Gary Kent. *Makeup* Sherri Tilley. *Still Photog* Joel Sussman.

Cast: Monica Gayle *(Sandra)*, Daryll Largo, Raymond Zona, Jean Clark, James Ritter, Bobby Seasons, Bobbie Martin, Desiree Polove, Mark Trayle, Crack Laird, Keel Smythe, Ronald Mowry.

Drama. Sandra makes passionate love to a young sailor in her San Francisco apartment, and she recalls the path to her "sexual liberation:" Sandra's parents separate, and she remains on the family farm with her domineering, alcoholic father. He constantly accuses her of sexual wrongdoing when, in fact, she is chaste. Seduced by her childhood sweetheart, she awakens to the joys of sexuality. Her drunken father drives off a cliff to his death, and Sandra departs for the Coast, anxious to acquire more sexual experience. Hitchhiking, she is picked up by a traveling lingerie salesman, a fetishist who makes love to her while wearing one of his sample brassieres. In San Francisco Sandra broadens her sexual experience in encounters with a lesbian cosmetic saleswoman, a brutal motorcyclist, and a married businessman. She meets a psychiatrist who pronounces her uninhibited attitude entirely healthy. Her hometown lover arrives in San Francisco and is quickly rebuked for his possessive attitude—Sandra gives her body freely, and she refuses to confine her impulses. *Hitchhikers. Sailors. Traveling salesmen. Saleswomen. Motorcyclists. Businessmen. Psychiatrists. Adolescence. Filial relations. Sexual initiation. Sensualism. Rural life. Promiscuity. Alcoholism. Fetishism. Lesbianism. San Francisco.*

Note: Also known as *I Am Sandra.*

SANDS OF BEERSHEBA (United States/Israel)   **F6.4232**
David Productions. *Dist* American International Pictures. 5 May 1966 [New York opening]. Sd; b&w. 35mm. 90 min. [Original length: 93 min.]
Pres by Landau/Unger Co. *Prod-Dir-Writ* Alexander Ramati. *Exec Prod* Jack Grynberg. *Dir Photog* Wolfgang Suschitzky. *Film Ed* Helga Cranston. *Mus* Mel Keller. *Song* Naomi Shemer. *Sung by* Shoshana Damari. *Sd* Robert Allen. *Asst Dir* John Quested, Nellie Lenson. *Prod Mgr* Geoffrey Helman.

Cast: Diane Baker *(Susan)*, David Opatoshu *(Daoud)*, Tom Bell *(Dan)*, Paul Stassino *(Salim)*, Didi Ramati *(Naima)*, Theodore Marcuse *(Nuri)*, Wolfe Barzell *(Ayub)*, Oded Kotler, Avraham Ben-Yosef.

War drama. Source: Alexander Ramati, *Rebel Against the Light* (New York, 1960). Visiting the site of her fiancé's death in the 1948 Palestinian War, American gentile Susan meets and falls in love with her betrothed's best friend, Dan. Although he works in a potash factory, Dan is also an Israeli gunrunner. When ambushed by Arab terrorist Salim, Dan is given refuge by Daoud, Salim's father. Salim promptly lays siege to his father's house. In the ensuing battle the terrorist is killed. Wounded by Salim, Dan is comforted by Susan. *Factory workers. Arabs. Terrorists. Americans in foreign countries. Gunrunners. Filial relations. Israeli-Arab War 1948–49. Palestine.*

Note: Filmed on location in Israel in 1964; working title: *Rebels Against the Light.* Opened in Tel Aviv in May 1965 as *Mordei ha'or.*

SANDS OF ECSTASY   **F6.4233**
Kaws Productions. *Dist* Crescent International Pictures. **1968.** Sd; b&w. 35mm. 65 min.
Prod-Dir-Writ Larry Stouffer. *Camera* Jim Kerdorski. *Art* Tiz Sorri. *Ed* Jerry Caraway. *Sd* Victor Vibrator. *Script Girl* Juanita Harris.

Cast: Ken Haynie *(Johnny)*, Sandra Jenson *(Sandra)*, Adrainne *(Margo)*, Byron Lord *(Eddie)*, Denis Aaron *(Oriental)*, Jerry Caraway *(Jerry)*, Chastity Fox *(Janet)*, Lea Mission *(Barbara)*.

Melodrama. Johnny and Sandra meet and spend a day together on the beach. Though they feel a strong mutual attraction, memories of unhappy sexual experiences make them fearful of falling in love. Johnny is the victim of impotence, while Sandra has been sexually assaulted by one man and given LSD by another. Together, Johnny and Sandra overcome their inhibitions, and they at last unite in complete love. *Impotence. Seduction. Guilt. Rape. LSD. Beaches.*

Note: Also known as *Sands of Extasy.*

SANDS OF THE KALAHARI (Great Britain)   **F6.4234**
Pendennis Pictures. *Dist* Paramount Pictures. 10 Nov **1965** [Los Angeles opening; c3 Nov 1965; LP32195]. Sd; col (Technicolor). 35mm (Panavision). 119 min.
Pres by Joseph E. Levine. A Cy Endfield–Stanley Baker Production. *Prod* Cy Endfield, Stanley Baker. *Exec Prod* Joseph E. Levine. *Assoc Prod* Bob Porter. *Dir-Writ* Cy Endfield. *Dir Photog* Erwin Hillier. *Art Dir* Seamus Flannery. *Film Ed* John Jympson. *Mus* John Dankworth. *Sd* Les Hammond, John Aldred. *Asst Dir* Jack Causey, Jim Brennan. *Prod Mgr* Geoffrey Helman. *Cost* James Smith, cost. *Makeup* Wally Schneiderman. *Sp Eff* Cliff Richardson.

Cast: Stuart Whitman *(O'Brien)*, Stanley Baker *(Bain)*, Susannah York *(Grace Monckton)*, Harry Andrews *(Grimmelman)*, Theodore Bikel *(Bondarahkai)*, Nigel Davenport *(Sturdevant)*, Barry Lowe *(Detjens)*.

Adventure drama. Source: William Mulvihill, *Sands of the Kalahari* (New York, 1960). When the takeoff of a plane destined for Johannesburg is delayed, one of the stranded passengers, Dr. Bondarahkai, persuades some of the other passengers to join him in chartering a smaller aircraft. The party includes Grace Monckton, a recent divorcee looking for a new life; Bain, an unsuccessful mining engineer; Grimmelman, an elderly German; and Sturdevant, a suspicious character who pilots the chartered plane. Joining them just before takeoff is a man carrying two gun cases, O'Brien, who soon bribes Sturdevant to fly toward Capetown instead. The changed course puts them in the path of thousands of locusts, which splatter the windshield and clog the engines, causing the plane to crash in the desert. With the copilot killed and the plane on fire, their only hope is to set out on foot through the desert, but they disagree on their methods for survival. Sturdevant, after unsuccessfully trying to rape Grace, decides to go seek help alone. O'Brien takes command of the group, forcing Dr. Bondarahkai to set out by himself, and then murders Grimmelman when he refuses to do the same. This last act is witnessed by Bain, who relates it to Grace and induces her to steal O'Brien's rifle, even though she is attracted to him. Bain knocks O'Brien unconscious and throws him down a deep pit, but that night a tremendous rain storm fills the hole with water, permitting him to escape. Now alone and hidden in some rocks, O'Brien decides to remain in the desert instead of accompanying Grace and Bain in a rescue helicopter. As the survivors fly away, O'Brien is surrounded by several baboons who have been tormented by him ever since the crash. In almost ritualistic fashion they fall upon him and begin chewing. *Physicians. Engineers—Mining. Germans. Air pilots. Bribery. Rape. Murder. Survival. Airplanes. Firearms. Helicopters. Johannesburg. Cape Town. Kalahari Desert. Airplane accidents. Storms. Locusts. Apes.*

Note: Location scenes filmed in Africa. Opened in London in Dec 1965.

SANDU FOLLOWS THE SUN (U.S.S.R.)   **F6.4235**
Moldova-Film. *Dist* Artkino Pictures. 17 Apr **1965** [New York opening]. Sd; col (Sovcolor). 35mm. 66 min. [Also 60 min.]
Dir Mikhail Kalik. *Screenplay* Valeriu Gazhiu, Mikhail Kalik. *Story Ed* A. Konunov. *Photog* Vadim Derbenyov. *Camera* D. Motornyy. *Art Dir* S. Bulgakov, A. Roman. *Film Ed* K. Blinova. *Mus Comp* Mikhail Tariverdiyev. *Song Lyr* S. Kirsanov. *Mus Cond* E. Khachaturyan. *Sd* A. Chayka. *Asst Dir* A. Matveyev. *Prod Mgr* M. Usoltsev. *Makeup* P. Klimov.

Cast: Nika Krimnus *(Sandu)*, Tatyana Bestayeva, N. Volkov, G. Georgiu, M. Grekov, L. Dolgorukova, Yevgeniy Yevstigneyev, Valentin Zubkov, L. Kruglyy, N. Kavunovskiy, I. Levyanu, Larisa Luzhina, V. Markin, Anatoliy Papanov, G. Svetlani, G. Sovchis, Valentina Telegina, S. Troitskiy, I. Unguryanu, D. Fusu, S. Andreyev, G. Belov, V. Bogatyy, V. Grigoryeva, I. Gurzo-Gubanova, N. Doni, B. Yermolayev, L. Zimina, P. Zavtoni, V. Kulik, K. Kramarchuk, V. Minin, N. Nikitich, L. Naumov, A. Nagits, L. Panova, V. Filina, Yu. Khaso, Viktor Chetverikov, I. Shkurya, I. Shatokhin, A. Yurchak.

Comedy-drama. Five-year-old Sandu sets out to follow the sun around the earth. He rolls his hoop around his city and looks at the world through pieces of tinted glass. He finds himself at the maternity hospital and discovers how people are born. He becomes friendly with a shoeshine man whose chief passion in life is soccer; then notices that the man has no legs, having lost them in the war. In a park Sandu meets a young woman newly arrived in the city who works as a gardener. She tends roses and peonies, and in a corner of the flower bed grows a sunflower, which reminds her of her home and childhood. She tells Sandu how the sunflower turns its head to follow the sun. The parkkeeper cuts the flower down, and Sandu struggles with evil for the first time in his life. The boy dines with some good-natured young builders, encounters a passing funeral, meets the driver of a huge truck, and watches gymnasts at a stadium. When night falls, Sandu falls asleep against a stone lion. In his dream, the parkkeeper solemnly buries the sunflower and becomes a lifeless dummy; and the shoeshine man, having found his legs, takes Sandu into a beautiful street to meet the sun. In the morning, a military musician finds Sandu and takes him home. *Children. Bootblacks. Amputees. Veterans. Gardeners. Construction crews. Truckdrivers. Gymnasts. Childbirth. Bureaucracy. Flowers. Funerals. Parks. The Sun. Dreams.*

Note: Released in the U.S.S.R. in Jun 1962 as *Chelovek idyot za solntsem;* running time: 71 min.

SANDY, THE RELUCTANT NATURE GIRL (Great Britain)   **F6.4236**
Avon Films. *Dist* Production Releasing Corp., Jerand Film Distributors. 4 Dec **1964** [Champaign, Illinois, showing]. Sd; col! (Eastman Color). 35mm. 74 min.
Prod Michael Deeley. *Exec Prod* Bruce Yorke. *Dir* Stanley Pelc. *Story-Script* S. M. C. Mitchell. *Dir Photog* Terry Maher. *Camera Op* Jimmy Day. *Ed* Jim Connock. *Mus Dir* Dick Laurie. *Mus Arr & Cond* Keith Amos. *Mus Comp* Edwin Astley. *Sd Rec* Joe Charman. *Asst Dir* John Stoneman. *Prod Mgr* Robert Sterne. *Cont* Anne Deeley. *Wardrobe* Dulcie Midwinter. *Makeup* Dore Hamilton.

Cast: Annette Briand (Sandy), Jeremy Howes (David), Vivienne Taylor (Bridget), Peter Benison (Allan), John Atkinson (detective), Mary Chapman (Mrs. Schofield), Constance Feeher (Mrs. Henderson), Bertha Russell (Mrs. Dearlove).

Nudist film. David, a confirmed nudist, offers his young girl friend Sandy, who heartily disapproves of nudism and is unaware of David's activities, several feeble excuses for his inability to see her on weekends. Suspecting that David has another woman, Sandy hires a detective to follow him. The detective discovers David's secret, but since he is also a nudist, he declines to reveal the deception to Sandy. The detective telephones David and warns him of Sandy's suspicions. Sandy hides herself in the back of David's car one weekend, and David unwittingly drives her to the nudist camp. Sandy, expecting to be confronted with David's other woman, is shocked to find herself in the camp. She catches a glimpse of David without his clothes and, startled, falls into the pool. Allan and Bridget, two of David's friends, take Sandy on a tour of the camp in order to convince her of the benefits of nudism. She steals away that night, but the next day she daydreams of the camp's free and joyful atmosphere, and she returns to join David and his friends. *Detectives. Nudism. Duplicity. Jealousy. Nudist camps. Dreams.*

Note: Produced in Great Britain in 1963 as *The Reluctant Nudist.* Alternative title: *Sandy, the Reluctant Nudist.* Location scenes filmed in Spielplatz, Hertfordshire.

SANG ET LUMIÈRES see BEAUTY AND THE BULLFIGHTER

IL SANGUE E LA ROSA see BLOOD AND ROSES

SANJURO (Japan)   **F6.4237**
Toho Co. *Dist* Toho International, Inc. 14 Jun **1962** [Los Angeles opening]. Sd; b&w. 35mm (Tohoscope). 96 min.
Prod Ryuzo Kikushima, Tomoyuki Tanaka. *Dir* Akira Kurosawa. *Screenplay* Ryuzo Kikushima, Hideo Oguni, Akira Kurosawa. *Photog* Fukuzo Koizumi, Kozo Saito. *Lighting* Ichiro Inohara. *Art Dir* Yoshiro Muraki. *Film Ed* Akira Kurosawa. *Mus* Masaru Sato. *Sd* Wataru Konuma, Hisashi Shimonaga. *Swordplay Adv* Ryu Kuze.
Cast: Toshiro Mifune (Sanjuro), Tatsuya Nakadai (Muroto), Takashi Shimura (Kurofuji), Yuzo Kayama (Iori Izaka), Reiko Dan (chamberlain's daughter), Masao Shimizu (Kikui), Yunosuke Ito (Mutsuta, the chamberlain), Takako Irie (chamberlain's wife), Kamatari Fujiwara (Takebayashi), Keiju Kobayashi (spy), Akihiko Hirata, Kunie Tanaka, Hiroshi Tachikawa, Tatsuhiko Hari, Tatsuyoshi Ehara, Kenzo Matsui, Yoshio Tsuchiya, Akira Kubo (young samurai).

Action melodrama. Based on a "Tsubaki Sanjuro" story by: Shugoro Yamamoto. In mid-19th-century Japan, the chamberlain, who heads a powerful clan, is suspected by his nephew, Iori Izaka, of fomenting political unrest. Iori and eight samurai wait to meet with the superintendent, Kikui, in a deserted shrine when Sanjuro, a wild, unkempt samurai, bursts in to warn them that it is Kikui, not the chamberlain, who is to be feared. Sanjuro is proven correct when a party of Kikui's warriors attacks the shrine, but Sanjuro's devastating swordsmanship forces the attackers into retreat. Sanjuro consents to help the samurai in their mission, and returning to the chamberlain's house they discover that the chamberlain and his family have been kidnaped. Through Kurofuji, one of Kikui's allies, Sanjuro and the samurai find the chamberlain's wife and daughter and take them to a villa next door to Kurofuji's villa. Pretending to join with Kikui, Sanjuro meets Muroto, Kikui's troubleshooter, and learns that the chamberlain is being held at Kurofuji's villa. Sanjuro persuades Muroto to lead his warriors away from Kurofuji's villa but is captured by Kikui just as he is about to give the signal (by floating white camellias down the stream) for his own samurai to attack. Sanjuro nevertheless tricks Kikui into floating the camellias, and the samurai attack as planned and rescue the chamberlain. A victory celebration is held, but Sanjuro does not attend. Instead, he faces Muroto in a duel, and after winning he waves aside congratulations and walks away in solitude. *Samurai. Uncles. Hired killers. Government—Local. Politics. Kidnaping. Duplicity. Shrines. Duels. Flowers.*

Note: Released in Japan in Jan 1962 as *Tsubaki Sanjuro.*

SANS TAMBOUR NI TROMPETTE see DIE GANS VON SEDAN

SANSHO DAYU see THE BAILIFF

SANSHO THE BAILIFF see THE BAILIFF

SANTA AND THE THREE BEARS   **F6.4238**
R & S Film Enterprises. *Dist* Ellman Enterprises. 7 Nov **1970** [Miami, Florida, opening]. Sd; col (Eastman Color). 35mm (Colorscope). 63 min. MPAA rating G.
Prod-Dir-Writ Tony Benedict. *Anim* Bill Hutten, Tony Love, Volus Jones. *Art Dir* Walt Peregoy. *Mus Dir* Joe Leahy. *Songs* Doug Goodwin, Tony Benedict, Joe Leahy. *Sung by* Joyce Taylor.

Voices: Hal Smith, Jean Vanderpyl, Annette Ferra, Bobby Riha.
Animated fantasy. A Christmas fairy tale about two bear cubs living in Yellowstone National Park who are told about Christmas by a friendly forest ranger. The little cubs become so excited about Santa's forthcoming arrival that they postpone their hibernation until the ranger is persuaded by Mama Bear to impersonate Santa Claus. *Forest rangers. Christmas. Yellowstone National Park. Santa Claus. Bears.*

Note: Filmed partially in Dania, Florida. The film combines live action and animation.

SANTA CLAUS CONQUERS THE MARTIANS   **F6.4239**
Jalor Productions. *Dist* Embassy Pictures. 14 Nov **1964** [Chicago opening]. Sd; col (Eastman Color). 35mm. 81 min.
Pres by Joseph E. Levine. *Prod* Paul L. Jacobson. *Assoc Prod* Arnold Leeds. *Dir* Nicholas Webster. *Screenplay* Glenville Mareth. *Orig Story Idea* Paul L. Jacobson. *Dir Photog* David Quaid. *Art Dir* Maurice Gordon. *Song:* "Hurray for Santa Claus" Milton De Lugg, Roy Alfred. *Sd* Dennis Maitland. *Cost Dir* Ramse Mostoller. *Makeup Dir* George Fiala.
Cast: John Call (Santa Claus), Leonard Hicks (Kimar), Vincent Beck (Voldar), Victor Stiles (Billy), Donna Conforti (Betty), Bill McCutcheon (Dropo), Christopher Month (Bomar), Pia Zadora (Girmar), Leila Martin (Momar), James Cahill (Rigna), Charles G. Renn (Hargo), Carl Don (Von Green/Chochem), Al Nesor (Stobo), Josip Elic (Shim/Torg), Jim Bishop (Lomas), Doris Rich (Mrs. Claus), Ned Wertimer (Andy Henderson), Lin Thurmond (children's announcer), Don Blair (news announcer), Ivor Bodin (Winky), Gene Lindsey (polar bear), Glenn Schaffer, Ronald Rotholz, Tony Ross, Scott Aronesty (Santa's helpers).

Science fiction comedy-drama. The intellectual, fully-automated life on Mars has produced a generation of listless and dispirited children, who look enviously at a press conference with Santa Claus televised from the North Pole. When Martian leader Kimar detects these symptoms in his own children, Bomar and Girmar, he calls a council meeting at which Chochem, Mars' 800-year-old sage, suggests a kidnaping expedition to the Earth's North Pole. Kimar commands the Earthbound saucer but, upon arrival in December, is confused by the profusion of Santas on every street corner and lands out in the country where two children, Billy and Betty, direct the Martians to the North Pole. The skeptical Voldar, an evil Martian, convinces his shipmates that the two children must be abducted along with Santa to prevent their informing on the extra-terrestrial invaders. En route through space, Voldar attempts to oust Santa and the children and is banished upon landing on Mars. He takes up residence in a cave while plotting his revenge. Together with henchmen Shim and Stobo, Voldar raids Santa's Martian workshop, destroying the machinery and kidnaping Dropo, a happy Martian who happened to be dressed in a Santa Claus costume. Voldar is jailed when he returns to the workshop to negotiate for Santa's return, but he escapes and locks Kimar in a storeroom. Finally confronting the real Santa, Voldar must first contend with Billy, Betty, Bomar, and Girmar, who fend him off with a succession of toy weapons while Santa watches, gleefully blowing bubbles. Kimar is touched by the Christmas spirit, and he returns the Earthlings to their planet. Santa, who is happily rid of the automation that had manufactured his gifts on Mars, arrives just in time for Christmas. *Children. Abduction. Space travel. Sabotage. Banishment. Flying saucers. Toys. Christmas. Mars (planet). North Pole. Santa Claus.*

SANTA CLAUS HAS BLUE EYES see BAD COMPANY

SANTA IS COMING   **F6.4240**
Fleetan Films. 24 Dec **1969.** Sd; col. 16mm. [Feature film, length unknown.]
Sex film. Two couples are having a sex party on Christmas Eve when Santa Claus arrives. He and a woman join the group. A midget fairy watches the group's sex play, which includes oral intercourse. Santa Claus' ugly wife soon arrives to interrupt the party. *Midgets. Fairies. Group sex. Oral sex. Christmas. Santa Claus.*

Note: May also be known as *Santa Is Arriving.*

SANTA VISITS THE MAGIC LAND OF MOTHER GOOSE   **F6.4241**
J. Edwin Baker. 23 Dec **1967** [Baltimore opening; c20 Mar 1974; LU3667]. Sd; col. 35mm. 60 min.
Prod J. Edwin Baker.
Fantasy. No information about the precise nature of this film has been found. *Santa Claus. Mother Goose.*

Note: Copyrighted as *The Magic Land of Mother Goose.*

SANTA'S CHRISTMAS CIRCUS   **F6.4242**
Gold Star Pictures. *Dist* Mercury Film. 24 Sep **1966** [Kansas City, Missouri, showing]. Sd; col. 35mm. 60 min.
Prod Byers Jordan. *Dir* Frank Wiziarde. *Based on an Idea by* Byers Jordan. *Organ Mus* Harry Jenks.

Cast: Frank Wiziarde (*Whizzo the Clown*), John Bilyeu (*Santa Claus*), Dancing Children (*themselves*).

Fantasy. The film is a Christmas special for children based on the television show of Whizzo the Clown. Youngsters from the Johnny Miller Dance Studio in Kansas City, Missouri, perform as circus animals in Whizzoland. To cheer up one sad little girl, Whizzo takes the children to see the Christmas displays in town and then flies them on a magic carpet to the North Pole for a visit with Santa Claus, who introduces them to the elves and explains the true meaning of Christmas. Whizzo then returns the children to Whizzoland on the magic carpet. *Elves. Clowns. Children. Dancers. Circus. Christmas. North Pole. Kansas City (Missouri). Santa Claus. Flying carpets.*

SAPHO *see* **THE WARRIOR EMPRESS**

IL SAPORE DELLA VENDETTA *see* **THE NARCO MEN**

SAPPHO DARLING (Sweden)   **F6.4243**
   Svenska Film. *Dist* Cambist Films. 25 Dec **1968** [Boston opening]. Sd; col. 35mm. 100 min. [Also released in 78 min version.]
   Prod Hal Senter. *Exec Prod* Donald E. Leon. *Asst Prod* Knut Anderson. *Dir* Gunnar Steele. *Screenplay* Albert Zugsmith. *Art Dir* Wolf Bjorn. *Set Dir* Ingamar Swenson. *Mus* Henri Price. *Ed Cons* Ray Laurent.
   Cast: Carol Young (*Sappho*), Yvonne D'Angers (*Brigitte*), Alyn Darnay (*Sven*), Sally Sanford (*Luana*), Julia Blackburn (*Britt*).
   Drama. Because of her strict upbringing, Sappho refuses to become sexually intimate with her boyfriend, Sven. Brigitte, who suffered an unhappy sexual initiation in a gang rape, becomes Sappho's roommate. His desire frustrated, Sven attempts unsuccessfully to take Sappho by force; when he leaves, Luana and her girl friend try, also unsuccessfully, to seduce the two girls. Arriving to apologize for his behavior, Sven discovers the women together and leaves, appalled at the thought that his lover is a lesbian. Brigitte visits his apartment to convince him that he is mistaken, that Sappho truly loves him but is unable to overcome her fear of sex. Returning home, she surprises her new boyfriend attempting to rape Sappho. The two lonely girls are drawn together, and their intimacy culminates in a single homosexual experience. Sappho wants only to live with Brigitte, but Brigitte is attracted to men, and refuses. When Sven calls and asks Sappho to meet him at the beach, the two girls make the trip together, torn by doubts. Sappho at last runs off alone, unable to choose between her two loves. *Virginity. Roommates. Inhibition. Lesbianism. Rape. Sexual initiation. Bisexuality. Seduction. Friendship.*
   Note: Filmed in Stockholm in English.

SAPPHO '68   **F6.4244**
   C. I. T. Films. *Dist* I. R. M. I. Films. 10 Jan **1968** [New York opening]. Sd; b&w. 35mm. 65 min.
   Prod Sven Erikson. *Dir* Jan Anders. *Screenplay* Gunnel Kjellin.
   Cast: Myrna Lorni, Petra Andrews, Gary Boyd.
   Sex film. No information about the precise nature of this film has been found, but printed sources suggest that it includes scenes of lesbianism and fetishism. *Lesbianism. Fetishism.*

LOS SAQUEADORES DEL DOMINGO *see* **THAT MAN GEORGE**

SARABA MOSUKUWA GURENTAI *see* **GOODBYE, MOSCOW**

THE SARAGOSSA MANUSCRIPT (Poland)   **F6.4245**
   Kamera Film Unit. *For* Film Polski. *Dist* Amerpol Enterprise Films. Jan **1966** [Los Angeles showing]. Sd; b&w. 35mm (Dyaliscope). 155 min.
   Dir Wojciech J. Has. *Screenplay* Tadeusz Kwiatkowski. *Photog* Mieczysław Jahoda. *Art Dir* Jerzy Skarżyński, Tadeusz Myszorek. *Mus* Krzysztof Penderecki. *Prod Mgr* Ryszard Straszewski. *Cost* Lidia Skarżyński, Jerzy Skarżyński.
   Cast: Zbigniew Cybulski (*Capt. Alfons van Worden*), Kazimierz Opaliński (*hermit*), Iga Cembrzyńska (*Princess Emina*), Joanna Jędryka (*Princess Zibelda*), Sławomir Linder (*van Worden's father*), Mirosława Lombardo (*van Worden's mother*), Aleksander Fogiel (*Spanish nobleman*), Franciszek Pieczka (*Pascheco*), Ludwik Benoit (*Pascheco's father*), Barbara Krafftówna (*Camilla*), Pola Raksa (*Inezilla*), August Kowalczyk (*envoy of the Holy Inquisition*), Adam Pawlikowski (*cabalist*), Beata Tyszkiewicz (*Doña Rebeca Uzeda*), Gustaw Holoubek (*Don Pedro Velasquez*), Leon Niemczyk (*Don Avadoro*), Krzysztof Litwin (*Don Lopez Soarez*), Stanisław Igar (*Don Gaspar Soarez*), Bogumił Kobiela (*Toledo*), Juliusz Jabłczyński (*Aquillar*), Elżbieta Czyżewska (*Frasquetta*), Janusz Kłosiński (*Frasquetta's husband*), Jan Machulski (*Count Peña Flor*), Zdzisław Maklakiewicz (*Don Roque Busqueros*), Henryk Hunko (*thug from the Holy Inquisition*), Feliks Chmurkowski (*father of Don Lopez*), Jerzy Przybylski (*Don Moro*), Jadwiga Krawczyk (*Donna Inez Moro*), Edmund Fetting (*[see note]*).
   Drama. Source: Jan Potocki, *Manuscrit trouvé à Saragosse* (publication begun in St. Petersburg in 1804). While spending the night in a haunted hostel

in the Sierra Morena mountains, Capt. Alfons van Worden of the Walloon Guards dines with two Moorish princesses, Zibelda and Emina. Awakening at the foot of a gallows, van Worden is accosted by a hermit who regales him with tales of demonic possession and by a cabalist who invites him to a castle in Madrid. While a palace guest, van Worden is entertained by the raconteur gypsy king Avadoro. Taking leave of his host, the captain again finds himself at the inn, in the company of the Sheik of Gomelez, who asserts his identity with the hermit. Shortly thereafter, van Worden is invited to dine with two foreign princesses. *Royalty. Moors. Hermits. Gypsies. Sheiks. Impersonation. Supernatural. Inns. Castles. Haunted houses. Sierra Morena. Madrid.*
   Note: Released in Poland in 1965 as *Rękopis znaleziony w Saragossie;* running time: 180 min. Also known as *Adventures of a Nobleman* and *Manuscript Found in Saragossa.* One source credits Edmund Fetting with the role of Aquillar.

SARDONICUS *see* **MR. SARDONICUS**

SASAKI KOJIRO *see* **KOJIRO**

SASAYASHI NO JOE *see* **WHISPERING JOE**

SÅSOM I EN SPEGEL *see* **THROUGH A GLASS DARKLY**

THE SATAN BUG   **F6.4246**
   Mirisch Corp.–Kappa Corp. *Dist* United Artists. 24 Mar **1965** [Cleveland opening; c25 Feb 1965; LP29870]. Sd (Westrex); col (DeLuxe). 35mm (Panavision). 114 min. [Copyright length: 104 min.]
   Prod-Dir John Sturges. *Screenplay* James Clavell, Edward Anhalt. *Dir Photog* Robert Surtees. *Art Dir* Herman Blumenthal. *Set Decor* Charles Vassar. *Main Titl* De Patie-Freleng. *Film Ed* Ferris Webster. *Asst Film Ed* Marshall M. Borden. *Mus Comp & Cond* Jerry Goldsmith. *Sd* Harold Lewis. *Mus Ed* Richard Carruth. *Sd Eff Ed* Gilbert D. Marchant. *Asst Dir* Jack N. Reddish. *Prod Supv* Allen K. Wood. *Unit Mgr* J. Paul Popkin. *Script Supv* John Franco. *Wardrobe* Wes Jeffries. *Makeup* Emile Lavigne. *Sp Eff* Paul Pollard. *Prop* Frank Agnone. *Casting* Lynn Stalmaster.
   Cast: George Maharis (*Lee Barrett*), Richard Basehart (*Dr. Hoffman/Ainsley*), Anne Francis (*Ann*), Dana Andrews (*The General*), Edward Asner (*Veretti*), Frank Sutton (*Donald*), John Larkin (*Michaelson*), Richard Bull (*Cavanaugh*), Martin Blaine (*Martin*), John Anderson (*Reagan*), Russ Bender (*Mason*), Hari Rhodes (*Johnson*), John Clarke (*Raskin*), Simon Oakland (*Tasserly*), Henry Beckman (*Dr. Baxter*), Harold Gould (*Dr. Ostrer*), James Hong (*Dr. Yang*), Harry Lauter (*fake SDI agent*).
   Science fiction melodrama. Source: Ian Stuart, *The Satan Bug* (New York, 1963). Special government investigator Lee Barrett is sent to Station Three, a top-secret biological research installation in the desert, to investigate the disappearance of a flask which contains a newly-discovered virus known as the "satan bug" and of several flasks of botulinus organism. He learns from the general in charge of the investigation and from Dr. Hoffman, joint originator of the virus formula, that the satan bug is so virulent that if it were released in the atmosphere it could set off a chain reaction that would ultimately destroy all life on earth. Barrett eventually locates the stolen virus, but he and the general's daughter, Ann, are taken prisoner by Veretti and Donald, accomplices of Ainsley, a depraved millionaire who plans to use the virus to acquire power. Before the two accomplices are captured, they use some of the botulinus to wipe out a small community in Florida. Ainsley then threatens to destroy the entire city of Los Angeles with another flask of botulinus. Through frantic search efforts, the police find and disconnect the timing device which is set to spread the organism; but Ainsley remains at large with the flask of the satan bug. Barrett discovers that Ainsley and Dr. Hoffman are one and the same, and his pursuit of the madman climaxes in a struggle aboard a helicopter flying over Los Angeles. Hoffman falls to his death, and Barrett reaches safety with the flask of the satan bug still sealed. *Investigators. Researchers. Intelligence agents. Psychopaths. Millionaires. Biological warfare. Personal identity. Theft. Kidnaping. Deserts. Helicopters. Microorganisms. Florida. Chases.*
   Note: Filmed in Los Angeles and Palm Springs, California.

SATAN IN HIGH HEELS   **F6.4247**
   Vega Productions. *Dist* Cosmic Films. 23 Mar **1962** [New York opening]. Sd; b&w. 35mm. 89 min.
   Prod Leonard M. Burton. *Assoc Prod* Benedict Himmel. *Dir* Jerald Intrator. *Screenplay* John T. Chapman. *Story* Harold Bonnett, John T. Chapman. *Photog* Bernard Herschensen. *Film Ed* Armond Lebowitz. *Mus Comp & Cond* Mundell Lowe. *Songs* Jack Lawrence, Walter Marks, Mundell Lowe, Bobby Weil. *Asst to the Prod* Paul Porter.
   Cast: Meg Myles (*Stacey Kane*), Grayson Hall (*Pepe*), Mike Keene (*Arnold Kenyon*), Robert Yuro (*Laurence Kenyon*), Sabrina (*herself*), Nolia Chapman (*Felice*), Earl Hammond (*Rudy*), Del Tenney (*Paul*), Ben Stone (*Louie*), Paul Scott (*Vincent*), John Nicholas, actor (*Peter*), Pat Hamer (*stripper*), Sandra Dale (*cigarette girl*).

Melodrama. Stacey Kane, a cunning and ambitious striptease dancer in a cheap carnival, tricks her drug-addict husband out of his money and boards a plane for New York. A fellow passenger, Louie, sets her up in a hotel and introduces her to Pepe, the manager of a club on Manhattan's swank East Side. Arnold Kenyon, the club's owner, falls in love with Stacey and makes her his mistress, unaware that while he is lavishing her with expensive gifts and grooming her for a singing debut at his club, she is also having an affair with his playboy son, Laurence. On her opening night, Stacey's estranged husband, Rudy, arrives at the club. Using both emotional and sexual appeal, Stacey persuades him to kill Arnold; but Rudy bungles the murder attempt and confesses his intention to Arnold. Her double-dealing nature out in the open, Stacey is abandoned by all the men in her life, put out of her apartment, and left alone on the streets. *Stripteasers. Drug addicts. Mistresses. Singers. Playboys. Nightclub owners. Ambition. Infidelity. Murder. Nightclubs. New York City—East Side.*

Note: Filmed in New York City at La Martinique nightclub. Working title: *Pattern of Evil.*

SATAN NEVER SLEEPS (United States/Great Britain)   **F6.4248**

Twentieth Century-Fox Film Corp. 21 Feb **1962** [New York opening; c1 Mar 1962; LP21692]. Sd (Westrex); col (De Luxe). 35mm (CinemaScope). 126 min. [Also reviewed at 133 min.]

A Leo McCarey Production. *Prod-Dir* Leo McCarey. *Assoc Prod* Cecil F. Ford. *Dir Adtl Seq* Jack Cardiff. *Screenplay* Claude Binyon, Leo McCarey. *Dir Photog* Oswald Morris. *Camera Op* Brian West. *Camera Focus* Jimmy Turrell, Gerry Elliott. *Camera Grip* John Scott, grip. *Assoc Art Dir* Jim Morahan. *Asst Art Dir* John Hoesli, Ivor Beddoes. *Set Dresser* Jack Stephens. *Asst in Charge of Draughting* Jack Shampan. *Prod Dsgn* Tom Morahan. *Film Ed* Gordon Pilkington. *1st Asst Ed* Tony West. *2d Asst Ed* David Martindale. *Mus Comp* Richard Rodney Bennett. *Cond* Muir Mathieson. *Titl Song* Harry Warren, Harold Adamson, Leo McCarey. *Sung by* Timi Yuro. *Sd Rec* John Bramall. *Boom Op* Geoffrey Kidd, Bill Cook. *Sd Camera* Brian Knott. *1st, 2d & 3d Asst Dir* David Orton, Dennis Hall, Carl Mannin. *Prod Mgr* Jack Swinburne. *Cont* Connie Willis. *Prod Sec* Jean Hall. *Wardrobe Supv* Arthur Newman. *Wardrobe Master* Bob Rayner. *Wardrobe Mistress* Doris Turner. *Makeup Supv* George Frost. *Ch Hairdresser* Bill Griffiths. *Tech Adv* Edward MacElroy, (Rev.). *Casting Dir* Nora Roberts. *Still Photog* Robert Penn. *Chinese Extras Liaison* Eddie Powell. *Chinese Dial Coach* Juliet Yuen. *Ch Floor Electrn* Fred Pretty. *Prop Chargehand* Tommy Welsh. *Prod Buyer* Sid Palmer.

Cast: William Holden (*Father O'Banion*), Clifton Webb (*Father Bovard*), France Nuyen (*Siu Lan*), Athene Seyler (*Sister Agnes*), Martin Benson (*Kuznietsky*), Edith Sharpe (*Sister Theresa*), Robert Lee (*Chung Ren*), Weaver Lee (*Colonel Ho San*), Marie Yang (*Ho San's mother*), Andy Ho (*Ho San's father*), Burt Kwouk (*Ah Wang*), Lin Chen (*Sister Mary*), Anthony Chinn (*Ho San's driver*).

Comedy-drama. Source: Pearl S. Buck, *Satan Never Sleeps* (New York, 1962). In 1949 Catholic priests O'Banion and Bovard are constantly harassed by the Communist People's Party at their remote mission outpost in China. Adding to Father O'Banion's troubles is the mission's cook, Siu Lan, an attractive Chinese girl who makes no secret of her love for him. Under the leadership of Colonel Ho San the Communists wreck the mission dispensary and desecrate the chapel. Ho San straps O'Banion to a chair and rapes Siu Lan; later, when she gives birth to a son, Ho San displays paternal pride but refuses to stop persecuting the priests. Only after the villagers revolt and his superiors order the killing of all Christians, including his parents, does Ho San become convinced that Communism will never solve China's problems. He decides to smuggle Siu Lan, his son, and the two priests out of the compound, but their journey is halted within a few miles of freedom by a helicopter sent to prevent Ho San's defection. Before he can be restrained, the aged Father Bovard dons Ho San's military cap and coat and drives away in the colonel's car. He dies in a spray of bullets from the helicopter, but his sacrifice enables the others to escape. Later, at mission headquarters in Hong Kong, O'Banion marries Siu Lan and Ho San and baptizes their child. *Priests. Missionaries. Chinese. Communists. Defectors. Cooks. Soldiers. Christianity. Religious persecution. Rape. Illegitimacy. Fatherhood. Revolts. Self-sacrifice. Marriage. Helicopters. China—History—Republic 1912-49. Hong Kong.*

Note: Location scenes filmed in England and Wales. Opened in London in Feb 1962 as *The Devil Never Sleeps*; running time: 127 min; cut to 120 min. May also be known as *Flight From Terror*. Working title: *The China Story.*

SATANIS, THE DEVIL'S MASS   **F6.4249**

Dist Sherpix, Inc. 4 Mar **1970** [San Francisco opening]. Sd; col. 35mm. 80 min.

A Ray Laurent Production. *Prod-Dir* Ray Laurent.

Cast: Anton Szandor LaVey (*himself*).

Documentary. The film is a study of Anton Szandor LaVey, leader of a cult of devil worshipers in San Francisco. He and his Church of Satan are shown performing a black mass, in which a nude woman serves as an altar and a boa constrictor wraps itself around a naked witch. Newsreel footage is included in which LaVey's neighbors are interviewed about the lion which he kept in his house until complaints resulted in the animal's removal to a zoo. The ideology of the Church of Satan is discussed—guilt rejection, sexual freedom, and self-indulgence. *Witches. Neighbors. Demonology. Hedonism. Cults. San Francisco. Anton Szandor LaVey. The Devil. Snakes. Lions.*

THE SATANIST   **F6.4250**

Dist Olympic International Films. 2 Aug **1968** [Champaign, Illinois, showing]. Sd; b&w. 35mm. 64 min.

Dir Zoltan G. Spencer.

Melodrama. Joe, a writer recovering from a nervous breakdown, rents a cottage with his wife, Mary, in a small, peaceful village. The couple becomes acquainted with Shandra, a student of the occult, when Joe's car accidentally collides with the woman's bicycle. Soon, Shandra has introduced Joe to the occult, loaning him an ancient book on the subject. Mary, perceiving the insidious influence that the volume has on Joe, returns it to Shandra. She witnesses a strange rite that sends her, hysterical, back to Joe. At a party given by Shandra to celebrate the "Black Sabbath," Joe and Mary are drugged, and Mary becomes the "Devil's bride." Joe, helplessly watching, suffers another nervous collapse; in the hospital he becomes convinced that the entire incident was the invention of a troubled mind. Mary and Shandra (who Joe believes is his psychiatrist) arrive to take him to a homecoming party on the Sabbath. ... *Authors. Witches. Mental illness. Occult. Demonology. Rites and ceremonies. Tranquilizers. The Devil.*

Note: May also be known as *Succubus*. Zoltan G. Spencer is a pseudonym for Spence Crilly.

SATAN'S BED   **F6.4251**

Dist Prometheus Ventures, Inc., Sam Lake Enterprises. **1965.** Sd; b&w. 35mm. 72 min.

Prod Jerry Burke, Roger Wilson. *Dir* Marshall Smith. *Dir Adtl Material* Tamijian. *Photog* Julian Marsh. *Lighting* Anna Riva. *Ed* Michael Fenway. *Mus* Thomas J. Valentino. *Mus Ed* Douglas Fenway. *Makeup* Lem Amero.

Cast: Yoko Ono (*Ito*), Val Avery, Glen Nielson, Gene Wesson, Robert Williams, Steve Shaw, Lydia Martin, Cathy Stevens, Judy Young, Sarah Gold, William Stein, Marvin Holtz, Philip Dunn, Franklyn Clark, Ruth Rawson, Juanita Rodriguez, Thomas O'Reilly, Michael Ryan, Anna Riva, Madison Arnold, Neil Merk, Judy Adler.

Melodrama. Three sadistic young punks, Snake, Dip, and Angel, use heroin and unleash a wave of twisted violence upon the city. Their world is threatened when their source, Paul, decides to give up dealing drugs because of his approaching marriage with Ito, a beautiful Japanese girl. Lou, the local pusher, plans to keep Paul in the business by kidnaping Ito and disposing of her, but the three toughs decide to take care of Ito themselves. Lou learns Ito's whereabouts and tricks her into coming to his house. He rapes her, and then decides to keep her as a plaything until he is ready to kill her. Meanwhile, the hoodlums are told by the hotel desk clerk that Ito has gone to the Long Island estate of a friend, Cathey, and gives them the address. They steal a car, rape its owner, and drive to Long Island. They mistake Cathey for Ito, torment her, and force her to submit to Angel's lesbian embraces. As the point of a knife cuts away her clothing, Cathey breaks away, and Angel follows her with a gun. Cathey promises to satisfy any desire if Angel will protect her from the two men. As the two girls embrace, Cathey grabs the gun and shoots her three tormentors. Back at Lou's house, Ito finds the keys and slips out the door, but Lou awakens and chases her. Dashing across the street in a desperate attempt to escape, Ito is struck dead by a car. Lou hurries away, safe in the knowledge that Paul will now have no reason to stop dealing heroin. *Drug addicts. Drug dealers. Hoodlums. Japanese. Sadism. Rape. Lesbianism. Mistaken identity. Murder. Kidnaping. Heroin. Automobile accidents. Long Island.*

Note: Includes footage from a never-released film called *Judas City*, directed by Tamijian. The following are credited under their pseudonyms: Norman Berliner (Jerry Burke), Robert Renfield (Roger Wilson), Wally Martin (Marshall Smith), Michael Findlay (Julian Marsh and Michael Fenway), and Roberta Findlay (Anna Riva).

SATAN'S MISTRESS *see* **THE DEVIL'S MATE**

SATAN'S SADISTS   **F6.4252**

Kennis-Frazer Films. *Dist* Independent-International Pictures. Jun **1969.** Sd; col (Deluxe). 35mm. 86 min. *MPAA rating* R.

An Al Adamson Production. *Prod-Dir* Al Adamson. *Exec Prod* Dan Q. Kennis. *Assoc Prod* Sid Frazer. *Prod Cons* Samuel M. Sherman. *Screenplay* Dennis Wayne. *Dir Photog* Gary Graver. *Main Titl* Bob Lebar. *Film Ed* Gary Graver. *Neg Cutter* Howard Moore. *Mus & Songs:* "Satan," "Gotta Stop That Feeling," "I Like the Way You Work," "I'm on My Way Out," "Is It Better To Have Loved and Lost?" "Baby How I Feel for You" Harley Hatcher. *Perf by* The Nightriders. *Sd* Robert Dietz. *Unit Mgr* Bud Cardos. *Script Clerk* Sandy Portelli. *Asst to the Prod* Denver Dixon. *Makeup* Susan Arnold. *Tech Adv* John Gregoire. *Still Photog* Hedy Dietz. *Key Grip* Forest Carpenter.

Cast: Russ Tamblyn (*Anchor*), Scott Brady (*Charles Baldwin*), Kent Taylor (*Lew*), John Cardos (*Firewater*), Robert Dix (*Willie*), Gary Kent (*Johnny Martin*), Greydon Clark (*Acid*), Regina Carrol (*Gina*), Jackie Taylor (*Tracy Stewart*), William Bonner (*Muscle*), Bobby Clark (*Romeo*), Evelyn Frank (*Nora Baldwin*), Yvonne Stewart (*Carol*), Cheryl Anne (*Jan*), Randee Lynne (*Rita*), Bambi Allen (*Lois*), Breck Warwick (*Ben*).

Crime melodrama. On the edge of the California desert, an outlaw gang of motorcyclists led by the psychopathic Anchor brutally assaults and murders two young lovers. Later, the gang barges into a remote cafe where Charles and Nora Baldwin, a vacationing policeman and his wife, are dining with Johnny Martin, a hitchhiking Vietnam veteran. When cafe owner Lew insults Anchor's girl friend, Gina, the cyclists knock out Johnny and kill Lew and the Baldwins. Johnny regains consciousness and utilizes his combat training by smashing a mirror in the face of one of the thugs and drowning another in a toilet bowl. Johnny and the cafe waitress, Tracy Stewart, then flee into the desert in the young girl's dune buggy. Forced to abandon the buggy because of a broken gas tank, they proceed on foot until they reach a small natural cave. Meanwhile, the cyclists encounter a group of college girls on a field trip and rape and then murder them after dropping LSD in their coffee. Gina destroys herself by driving her motorcycle over a cliff after Anchor informs her that he is looking for a new girl friend. Johnny manages to kill two other members of the gang and then mistakenly kills Firewater, Anchor's Indian friend who had become disgusted with the leader's lunacy and attempted to help the runaways. Anchor finally overtakes Johnny and Tracy as they are heading toward town, but as the deranged biker hurdles toward them on his cycle, Johnny stops Anchor by hurling a knife into his neck. *Motorcycle gangs. Psychopaths. Police. Veterans. Waitresses. Students. Indians of North America. Murder. Rape. Suicide. Cafes. Deserts. Caves. LSD. California.*

Note: Location scenes filmed in Indio, California.

SATAN'S WOMAN *see* THE DEVIL'S MATE

THE SATIN MUSHROOM   F6.4253

Dist Grads Corp., Producers Releasing Organization. 18 Sep **1969** [San Francisco showing]. Sd; col. 35mm. 78 min.

Dir Don Brown. *Writ* Van Zurich. *Camera* Ray Nadeau. *Ed* Don Hallstrom. *Neg Cutter* Ray Nadeau. *Prod Mgr* Bethel Buckalew. *Unit Mgr* Sandy Root. *Prod Asst* Dick Osmun.

Cast: Matla Bridgestone (*Gail*), Jan Kent (*Pam*), John DeWar (*Gitano*), Vic Lance (*Manolo*), Vince Render (*Pepe*), Don Auld (*Jim*), Lynda Prish (*hooker*), Dick Osmun, Bethel Buckalew (*bartenders*), The Matadors (*band*), Briggette Weihnstraume (*stripper*), Stuart Lancaster (*Mexican lawyer*), Rachel Jablonski (*Manolo's girl friend*), Natasha Steele (*secretary*), Terry Hart (*drummer*), Vivian David, Don Hallstrom, Mark Lowhead.

Drama. Pam, heir to her uncle's Mexican estate, arrives from the United States with her friend Gail to take possession of her inheritance, but she is told by her uncle's attorney that she will have to await court clearance. In the meantime, the attorney provides a guide to help them get acquainted with the countryside. A local guitar player, Gitano, begins to romance Gail, and one day he takes the two women to watch the bullfights. Gitano's best friend, Manolo Rodriguez, is the featured matador; after a victorious afternoon he invites his friends to his home for a celebration. Pam's enticing sensuality captivates Manolo, and he sets out to make his second conquest of the day. *Heiresses. Uncles. Guitarists. Bullfighters. Bullfighting. Inheritance. Seduction. Mexico.*

Note: Filmed on location in the United States and Mexico. May also be known as *A Soft Warm Experience.*

SATURDAY NIGHT AND SUNDAY MORNING (Great Britain)
F6.4254

Woodfall Film Productions. *Dist* Continental Distributing, Inc. 3 Apr **1961** [New York opening]. Sd; b&w. 35mm. 90 min.

Prod Tony Richardson. *Exec Prod* Harry Saltzman. *Dir* Karel Reisz. *Screenplay* Alan Sillitoe. *Dir Photog* Freddie Francis. *Camera Op* Ron Taylor. *Art Dir* Ted Marshall. *Film Ed* Seth Holt. *Mus Comp & Cond* John Dankworth. *Played by* Johnny Dankworth Orchestra. *Sd* Peter Handford, Bob Jones. *Sd Ed* Chris Greenham. *Asst Dir* Tom Pevsner. *Prod Mgr* Jack Rix. *Cont* Pamela Mann.

Cast: Albert Finney (*Arthur Seaton*), Shirley Ann Field (*Doreen Gretton*), Rachel Roberts (*Brenda*), Hylda Baker (*Aunt Ada*), Norman Rossington (*Bert*), Bryan Pringle (*Jack*), Robert Cawdron (*Robboe*), Edna Morris (*Mrs. Bull*), Elsie Wagstaff (*Mrs. Seaton*), Frank Pettitt (*Mr. Seaton*), Avis Bunnage (*blowzy woman*), Colin Blakely (*loudmouth*), Irene Richmond (*Doreen's mother*), Louise Dunn (*Betty*), Peter Madden (*drunken man*), Cameron Hall (*Mr. Bull*), Alister Williamson (*policeman*), Anne Blake (*civil defense officer*).

Drama. Source: Alan Sillitoe, *Saturday Night and Sunday Morning* (London, 1958). Arthur Seaton is a 22-year-old factory worker in Nottingham, a sprawling industrial city in the British Midlands. All week long he works hard at his lathe, asking and expecting nothing more than his weekly pay; but on Saturday evenings he asserts his independence by drinking, brawling, and playing practical jokes at the local pub. Saturday nights he spends with Brenda, the wife of a fellow worker. He is also involved with Doreen, a girl with rigid ideas on sex and marriage. Brenda becomes pregnant, and Arthur takes her to his Aunt Ada in hopes of procuring an abortion, but without success. Arthur dutifully offers to marry Brenda, but she senses that their affair is over and decides to have the baby and accept the consequences. Eventually, her husband, Jack, learns of the affair; and his soldier brother and a friend waylay Arthur at a fair and beat him into senselessness. But this punishment Arthur accepts as part of life, and a week later he returns to his job. His attitude toward marriage has changed, however, and he agrees to marry Doreen and move into a new housing development. He warns her, nevertheless, that he has not yet lost his independence. *Factory workers. Philanderers. Aunts. Brothers. Soldiers. Infidelity. Drunkenness. Pregnancy. Abortion. Marriage. Practical jokes. Pubs. Nottingham.*

Note: Opened in London in Oct 1960; running time: 89 min.

SATURDAY NIGHT BATH IN APPLE VALLEY   F6.4255

Empire Productions. *Dist* Emerson Film Enterprises. 9 Nov **1965** [Chicago opening]. Sd; b&w. 35mm. 80 min.

Prod-Dir-Writ John Myhers. *Photog* Alan Stensvold. *Film Ed* John Myhers. *Mus* Foster Wakefield.

Cast: Phil Ford (*Big Man*), Mimi Hines (*Mimi Madison*), Cliff Arquette (*Charley Weaver/Mama Coot*), Shanton Granger (*Beau Coot*), Joan Benedict (*Poopsie Patata*), Marvin Miller, Anthony Dexter.

Satire. The film is a satire on the motion picture industry, its techniques and styles. The romance between Big Man and Mimi is a spoof on the old Hollywood combination of innocent virgin and tough guy. There are also scenes satirizing the extravagant use of symbolism. In the conclusion, a slot machine is shown lying on its side as Big Man and Mimi depart for a new life. *Actors. Virginity. Motion pictures. Hollywood.*

Note: Also known as *Saturday Night in Apple Valley.* Charley Weaver is a pseudonym for Cliff Arquette.

SATURDAY NIGHT OUT (Great Britain)   F6.4256

Tekli British Productions. *Dist* Topaz Film Corp. Jun **1964** [Los Angeles showing]. Sd; b&w. 35mm. 84 min.

A Michael Klinger–Tony Tenser Production. *Prod-Dir* Robert Hartford-Davis. *Assoc Prod* Robert Sterne. *Screenplay* Donald Ford, Derek Ford. *Dir Photog* Peter Newbrook. *Camera Op* Dennis Lewiston. *Focus* Ronnie Fox-Rogers. *Art Dir* Peter Proud. *Asst Art Dir* Ted Clements. *Ed* Alastair McIntyre, John Poyner. *Assoc Ed* David DeWilde, Ray Frift. *Mus Comp & Cond* Bobby Richards. *Sd Mix* Dickie Bird. *Sd Supv* John Cox. *Sd Rec* Red Law. *Dub Ed* Michael Hopkins, John Jeremy. *Boom Op* Don Wortham. *Asst Dir* Gordon Gilbert, Barry Langley, Laurie Turner. *Cont* June Faithfull. *Wardrobe Master* Harry Haynes. *Wardrobe Mistress* Tina Swanson. *Makeup* Jimmy Evans. *Hairdresser* Joyce James. *Stills* Laurie Turner. *Prop Master* Sidney Leggett. *Grip* Tommy Miller.

Cast: Heather Sears (*Penny*), Bernard Lee (*George Hudson*), Erika Remberg (*Wanda*), John Bonney (*Lee*), Francesca Annis (*Jean*), Colin Campbell (*Jamie*), Toni Gilpin (*Margaret*), Inigo Jackson (*Harry*), Nigel Green (*Paddy*), Caroline Mortimer (*Marlene*), Vera Day (*Arlene*), David Burke (*manager*), Freddie Mills (*Joe*), David Lodge (*Arthur*), Wendy Newton (*Cathy*), Barry Langford (*barman*), Margaret Nolan (*Julie*), Derek Bond (*Paul*), Shirley Cameron (*Edie*), Patsy Fagan (*barmaid*), Barbara Roscoe (*Miss Bingo*), Gerry Gibson (*doorman*), Patricia Hayes, The Searchers.

Drama. Five seamen and a passenger spend 14 hours in London as their cargo passenger boat unloads. At a West End bar, passenger George Hudson, a lonely, widowed businessman, meets Wanda, a seductive blackmailer working with a photographer partner, Paul. Before returning to ship, Hudson successfully foils their blackmail plot. Lee, an Australian with a love for music and travel, meets the zany beatnik Penny, and they fall in love. Arthur, a loner, goes off to visit his "mother," as he does in every port, but the others realize that he will spend the time with his standby prostitute. Paddy spends his leave in a drinking bout. Harry, a tough know-it-all, shakes off Margaret, a brash tart, and visits a Soho clip joint where he is robbed by Marlene and Arlene and thrown out, penniless. Jamie, shy and innocent, meets Jean, who is homeless, and falls in love while helping to find her a place to live. The next morning he jumps ship, marries her, and settles down as an electrician. *Seamen. Businessmen. Widowers. Photographers. Australians. Beatniks. Innocents. Waifs. Blackmail. Drunkenness. Pubs. Clip joints. London—Soho. London—West End.*

Note: Released in Great Britain in 1964; running time: 96 min.

SATYRICON see **FELLINI SATYRICON**

THE SAUCY AUSSIE   **F6.4257**

Pad Productions. *Dist* Sack Amusement Enterprises. 5 Jul **1963** [San Francisco opening]. Sd; col (Eastman Color). 35mm. 65 min.

Prod (see note) Walter Bowley, Richard W. Bomont. *Dir* Walter Bowley.

Cast: Sheree Steiner, Karen ([see note]).

Comedy. An Australian tourist, suffering from a severe headache, arrives at the Padre Hotel in San Francisco. The woman desk clerk gives him some pills, which he assumes are aspirin. The pills fail to relieve his headache, but they do enable him to see through women's clothing. In the elevator, he sees a woman who appears to be naked and gets slapped for staring. Before reaching his room, he accidentally opens a wrong door and finds a woman undressing; her screams cause him to flee. In his suite, he opens the door to the adjoining room and discovers a woman in bed, but he is chased away by her husband. The following day, after swallowing another dose of pills, the tourist amuses himself with his hallucinations, and in the evening he visits a burlesque house. The effect of the pills wears off, however, and he is unable to see through the strippers' remaining garments at the end of the act. *Australians. Tourists. Stripteasers. Eyesight. Nudity. Voyeurism. Burlesque. Hallucinations. San Francisco.*

Note: Location scenes filmed in and around San Francisco. Also known as *The Obscene Couch* and *The Oblong Couch*. Sources conflict in crediting producer. Press material for *The Saucy Aussie* gives star billing to Sheree Steiner, while press material for *The Obscene Couch* features Karen.

SAUL AND DAVID (Italy/Spain)   **F6.4258**

San Paolo Film-San Pablo Films. *Dist* Rizzoli Film Distributors, World Entertainment Corp. Jun **1968** [Wilmington, North Carolina, showing]. Sd; col (Eastmancolor). 35mm. 105 min.

Prod Emilio Cordero, Toni De Carlo. *Dir* Marcello Baldi. *Screenplay* Ottavio Jemma, Flavio Nicolini, Tonino Guerra, Marcello Baldi. *Story* Emilio Cordero. *Photog* Marcello Masciocchi, Juan Ruiz Romero. *Art Dir* Ottavio Scotti, Sigfrido Burman. *Film Ed* Giuliana Attenni. *Mus* Teo Usuelli.

Cast: Norman Wooland *(King Saul)*, Gianni Garko *(David)*, Elisa Cegani *(Akhinoam)*, Luz Márquez *(Abigail)*, Pilar Clemens *(Michal [Mikol])*, Virgilio Teixeira *(Abner)*, Antonio Mayans *(Jonathan)*, Carlos Casaravilla *(Samuel)*, Marco Paoletti *(David as a boy)*, Stefy Lang *(Goliath)*, Paolo Gozlino *(Joab)*, Dante Maggio *(Abdon)*, José Jaspe, Nino Parsello.

Biblical drama. During the wars between the Philistines and the Israelites, King Saul offers his daughter Michal in marriage to the person who can kill the Philistine giant Goliath. Among those who respond is David, a young shepherd. When the boy slays the giant with a slingshot, he is acclaimed a hero among all the Israelites and moved into Saul's palace where he is treated as though he were the king's own son. Following David's marriage to Michal, Akhinoam, Saul's wife, fears that the boy may ascend to the throne in place of her eldest son, Jonathan, and she hints to Saul that David plans to kill him. Despite his love for David, Saul heeds her warning and tries to kill the youth, but David escapes. As the years pass, Saul becomes so obsessed with the belief that David has been chosen by God to succeed him that he orders the execution of 50 priests suspected of being followers of David. Some time later, on the eve of a battle, David has an opportunity to kill Saul while he sleeps; instead, David professes his loyalty and berates him for his persecution. At the battle of Mount Gilboa, Saul, now an old man, rallies his men and charges courageously into the overwhelming might of the Philistines. The Israelites are defeated, Jonathan is killed, and Saul is badly wounded. When his servant refuses to kill him to prevent him from being captured by the Philistines, Saul deliberately falls upon his sword and, before dying, names David as his successor. As the battle ends, David walks among the dead calling out for his beloved king. *Royalty. Shepherds. Heirs. Israelites. Philistines. Marriage. Heroism. Conspiracy. Perfidy. Capital punishment. Loyalty. Suicide. Mount Gilboa. Saul. David. Goliath. Jonathan. Michal.*

Note: Opened in Rome in Jun 1965 as *Saul e David*; in Madrid in Jul 1965 as *Saúl y David*. Original running time: 118 min.

SAUL E DAVID see **SAUL AND DAVID**

SAÚL Y DAVID see **SAUL AND DAVID**

LE SAUT see **VOYAGE OF SILENCE**

SAUTERELLE see **FEMMINA**

SAVAGE!   **F6.4259**

Jones-Carpenter Corp. 8 Jun **1962** [Monroe, Louisiana, opening; c8 Jun 1962; LP23361]. Sd (Todd-AO); col (Eastman Color). 35mm (Ultrascope 50). 84 min.

An Arthur A. Jones-Bill Carpenter Production. *Prod-Dir-Writ* Arthur A. Jones. *Film Ed* Herbert Prechtel. *Sd Ed* Carl Mahakian. *Mus Ed* Richard Carruth.

Participants: Bill Carpenter, Roy Hurst, Peter Hankins, Francis Lindsey.

Adventure drama. The construction of the Kariba Dam on the Zambesi River drives a large number of inhabitants from their homeland. Relocated in an unfamiliar area where their fishing livelihood is threatened by crocodiles and hippos, one tribe begins illegally to trap protected wild animals. The Rhodesian government appeals for help to Bill Carpenter, an American hunter, who arrives with his young assistant, Mississippian Roy Hurst, to capture the crocodiles and move them away from the natives' fishing waters; frighten the hippos away from the crops; and stop the poaching of wild animals. The Americans are joined by Peter Hankins, a Rhodesian guide and white hunter, and Francis Lindsey, a South African who acts as overseer. Lindsey's harsh treatment of the natives nearly excites a rebellion and almost causes Lindsey and Hurst to come to blows. Despite these difficulties, Carpenter and his crew succeed in their mission, but in carrying out their assignment, the group survive a number of terrifying crises, including encounters with man-eating crocodiles and wounded, charging elephants. *Hunters. Americans in foreign countries. South Africans. Guides. Tribal life. Fishing. Poaching. Racism. Rhodesia. Zambesi River. Kariba Dam. Crocodiles. Hippopotami. Elephants.*

Note: Location scenes filmed in the Victoria Falls region. Rereleased in 1965 as *Mission to Hell*. Copyright claimant: J. C. Corp.

THE SAVAGE AMERICAN see **THE TALISMAN**

THE SAVAGE GUNS (United States/Spain)   **F6.4260**

Capricorn Productions-TECISA. *Dist* Metro-Goldwyn-Mayer, Inc. caAug **1962** [c31 Dec 1962; LP24328]. Sd (Westrex); col (Metrocolor). 35mm (MetroScope). 84 min.

Prod Jimmy Sangster, José G. Maesso. *Assoc Prod for Capricorn* Niels Larsen. *Dir* Michael Carreras. *Screenplay* Edmund Morris. *Dir Photog* Alfredo Fraile. *Camera Op* Ricardo Gonzales. *Art Dir* Francisco Canet. *Film Ed* David Hawkins, Pedro del Rey. *Mus Comp & Dir* Antón García Abril. *Sd Rec* Ramón Arnal. *Asst Dir* Paco Pérez Dolz. *Prod Mgr* Gustavo Quintana. *Cont* Margarita Delgras. *Wardrobe* Manuel Revuelta. *Makeup* Paco Puyol. *Hairdresser* Esther Martin.

Cast: Richard Basehart *(Steve Fallon)*, Don Taylor, actor *(Mike Summers)*, Alex Nicol *(Danny Post)*, Paquita Rico *(Franchea)*, María Granada *(Juana)*, José Nieto *(Ortega)*, Fernando Rey *(Don Hernán)*, Félix Fernández *(Paco)*, Francisco Camoiras *(Manola)*, Antonio Fuentes *(Captain Baez)*, Sergio Mendizábal *(Mayor)*, Rafael Albaicín *(Gonzales)*, José Manuel Martín *(Segura)*, Victor Bayo *(Sánchez)*, Pilar Caballero *(Sánchez' wife)*.

Western melodrama. In 1870 Mexico, wounded gunman Steve Fallon takes refuge at the ranch of ex-Confederate officer Mike Summers and his wife, Franchea. A romance develops between Fallon and Franchea's sister, Juana. Ortega, a ruthless landowner, is trying to take over all the ranches in the valley, by force if necessary. Any resistance is eliminated by his henchman, Danny Post, and his gang of mercenaries. Upon learning that Summers refuses to carry a gun because of all the bloodshed he saw in the Civil War, Fallon decides to stay and help put an end to Ortega's reign of terror. When Danny tries to collect "protection" money from Summers, Fallon disarms and thrashes him. After a second meeting with Fallon, in which three of the mercenaries are killed, the cowardly Danny leaves town. Ortega and the remnants of his gang then raid the Summers ranch and leave Fallon with his hands crippled. Believing Fallon dead, Danny returns, kills Ortega, takes over his holdings, and then proceeds to the Summers ranch. When he sees the helpless Fallon, he draws his gun, but Summers appears and shoots Danny to save his friend's life. Fallon decides to settle down with Juana. *Gunfighters. Confederate veterans. Pacifists. Ranchers. Hired killers. Sisters. Land rights. Extortion. Mutilation. Mexico.*

Note: Filmed in Spain. Released in Spain in Oct 1962 as *Tierra brutal*.

THE SAVAGE INNOCENTS (France/Great Britain/Italy)   **F6.4261**

Magic Film-Playart-Gray Films-Pathé Cinéma-Joseph Janni Productions-Appia Films. *Dist* Paramount Pictures. 15 Feb **1961** [Los Angeles opening; c31 Dec 1960; LP18680]. Sd; col (Technicolor). 35mm (Technirama, see note). 89 min. [Copyright length: 110 min.]

Prod Maleno Malenotti. *Co-prod* Joseph Janni. *Dir-Writ* Nicholas Ray. *2d Unit Dir* Baccio Bandini. *Adapt* Hans Ruesch, Franco Solinas. *Photog* Aldo Tonti, Peter Hennessy. *Photog 2d Unit(?)* Riccardo Pallottini, Patrick Carey. *Camera Op 2d Unit(?)* Allan Bryce. *Art Dir* Don Ashton, Dario Cecchi. *Film Ed* Ralph Kemplen, Eraldo Da Roma. *Mus* Angelo Francesco Lavagnino. *Cond* Muir Mathieson. *Song:* "Iceberg" comp & interpreted by The Four Saints. *Song:* "Sexy Rock" Angelo Francesco Lavagnino, Panzeri. *Interpreted by* Colin Hicks. *Sd* Geoff Daniels. *Sd Rec* Winston Ryder. *Asst Dir* Tom Pevsner, Jacques Giraldeau. *Prod Mgr* Douglas Peirce, Bianca Lattuada. *Cost* Vittorio Nino Novarese. *Makeup* Geoffrey Rodway. *Arctic Cons* Douglas Wilkinson.

Cast: Anthony Quinn *(Inuk)*, Yoko Tani *(Asiak)*, Carlo Giustini, Peter O'Toole *(troopers)*, Marie Yang *(Powtee)*, Marco Guglielmi *(missionary)*,

Kaida Horiuchi *(Imina)*, Lee Montague *(Itti)*, Andy Ho *(Anarvik)*, Anna May Wong *(Hiko)*, Yvonne Shima *(Iulik)*, Anthony Chin *(Kidok)*, Francis De Wolff *(trading post proprietor)*, Michael Chow *(Undik)*, Ed Devereaux *(pilot)*.

Adventure drama. Source: Hans Ruesch, *Top of the World* (New York, 1950). After years of borrowing other men's wives—a normal custom in a land where women are scarce—Inuk, an Eskimo hunter, decides to marry. At first he favors Imina, daughter of the aged Powtee, but later he marries her younger sister, Asiak. Inuk learns of a trading post miles away that will give him a rifle in exchange for fox skins; he takes his wife and mother-in-law on the long trek to the post. Once there, however, they decide to leave because Asiak does not care for the "civilized" ways of the white men. Inuk builds an igloo some distance from the post, and when a missionary visits them, Inuk extends his hospitality by offering the stranger his wife. The outraged missionary attempts to leave, and Inuk, incensed at this insult to his wife, accidentally kills him. They flee, and Powtee, realizing that she will be a burden on the trip, goes off alone to die in the snow. Shortly after the birth of his son, Inuk is arrested by two Canadian troopers for the murder of the missionary. As they take him south for trial, one of the troopers freezes to death, but Inuk saves the second one by taking him back to his igloo. Upon recovering, the trooper offers to allow Inuk to escape; when Inuk refuses to flee, the trooper insults him, spits at Asiak, and runs away. Baffled by the behavior of the white men, Inuk and Asiak return to the safety of their home in the wilderness. *Eskimos. Hunters. Sisters. Mothers-in-law. Missionaries. Canadians. Police. Social customs. Marriage. Race relations. Manslaughter. Childbirth. Trading posts. Igloos. Arctic regions.*

Note: Location scenes filmed around Hudson Bay and in Greenland. Opened in Paris in Sep 1960 as *Les dents du diable* at 90 min; in Rome in Mar 1960 as *Ombre bianche* at 110 min; in London in Jul 1960 at 107 min. Some sources list gauge as Technirama 70. Paramount Pictures was involved in financing the film but did not receive official coproduction credit.

SAVAGE PAMPAS (United States/Argentina/Spain)   **F6.4262**
Samuel Bronston Productions–Dasa Films–Jaime Prades, P. C. *Dist* Comet Film Distributors. Jul **1967**. Sd; col (Eastmancolor). 35mm (see note). 97 min.

Prod Jaime Prades. *Dir* Hugo Fregonese. *Screenplay* Hugo Fregonese, John Melson. *Photog* Manuel Berenguer. *Art Dir* Gil Parrondo, Angel Canizares. *Set Decor* Roberto Carpio. *Film Ed* Juan Serra. *Mus* Waldo de los Ríos. *Choreog* Alberto Masulli. *Sd* Alfonso Carvajal. *Asst Dir* Julio Sempere, Tony Tarruella. *Prod Mgr* Ramón Plana. *Cost* Marian Ribas. *Makeup* Juan Farsac. *Hairstyles* Antonia López. *Sp Eff* Pablo Pérez.

Cast: Robert Taylor *(Captain Martin)*, Marc Lawrence *(Sergeant Barril)*, Ron Randell *(Padron)*, Ty Hardin *(Carreras)*, Rosenda Monteros *(Rucu)*, Felicia Roc *(Camila)*, Angel Del Pozo *(Lieutenant del Rio)*, Mario Lozano *(Santiago)*, Enrique Avila *(Petizo)*, Laura Granados *(Carmen)*, Milo Quesada *(Alfonso)*, Hector Quiroga *(Pepe)*, Juan Carlos Galván *(Isidro)*, Charles Fawcett *(El Gato)*, Julio Peña *(Chicha)*, José Nieto *(General Chavez)*, José Jaspe *(Luis)*, José María Caffarel *(Vigo)*, Lucia Prado *(Chiquito)*, Barta Barri *(priest)*, Pastora Ruiz *(Magnolia)*, Sancho Gracia *(Carlos)*, Georges Rigaud *(old man)*, Isabel Pisano *(Lucy)*, Laya Raki *(Mimi)*.

Drama. Source: Homero Manzi and Ulises Petit de Murat, *Pampa bárbara* (publication undetermined). In the uncolonized pampas of Argentina in 1870, Captain Martin, the commanding officer of a lonely outpost, confronts the problem of an ever-increasing number of deserters. Behind the plot to decimate the army ranks is a renegade soldier, Padron, who is in league with hostile Indians. By offering each deserter a captive woman, Padron has succeeded in amassing a band of outlaws bent on attacking and plundering villages. Determined to defeat Padron at his own game, Captain Martin eventually persuades his superiors that the soldiers at the fort must be provided with female companionship. As a consequence, prostitutes are removed from prisons, granted a military escort, and forced to make the dangerous journey across the pampas to the fort. The soldiers, with a few exceptions, obey their instructions not to touch the women until they reach their destination. Once the women arrive at the fort, their presence not only bolsters morale but also brings about the return of some of the deserters. When his ranks have swelled to their original size, Captain Martin leads an attack on the Indians and the remaining rebels and restores peace to the pampas. *Soldiers. Prostitutes. Convicts. Deserters—Military. Outlaws. Indians of South America. Slavery. Looting. Military life. Forts. Pampas.*

Note: Location scenes filmed in Spain. Filmed in 70mm Super-Panorama. Opened in Madrid in Apr 1966 as *Pampa salvaje;* running time: 112 min. Remake of a 1945 Argentine film, *Pampa bárbara*, which was never released in the United States.

SAVAGE SAM   **F6.4263**
Walt Disney Productions. *Dist* Buena Vista Distribution Co. 17 Jul **1963** [Los Angeles opening; c16 May 1963; LP25088]. Sd (RCA); col (Technicolor). 35mm. 103 min.

Pres by Walt Disney. *Prod* Walt Disney. *Co-prod* Bill Anderson, prod. *Dir* Norman Tokar. *Screenplay* Fred Gipson, William Tunberg. *Dir Photog* Edward Colman. *Art Dir* Carroll Clark, Marvin Aubrey Davis. *Set Decor* Emile Kuri, Hal Gausman. *Film Ed* Grant K. Smith. *Mus* Oliver Wallace. *Orch* Walter Sheets. *Song:* "Savage Sam and Me" Terry Gilkyson. *Sd* Robert O. Cook. *Mus Ed* Evelyn Kennedy. *Asst Dir* Joseph L. McEveety. *Asst to the Prod* Louis Debney. *Cost* Chuck Keehne, Gertrude Casey. *Makeup* Pat McNalley. *Hairstyles* Ruth Sandifer. *Sp Eff* Eustace Lycett, Jim Fetherolf.

Cast: Brian Keith *(Uncle Beck Coates)*, Tommy Kirk *(Travis Coates)*, Kevin Corcoran *(Arliss Coates)*, Dewey Martin *(Lester White)*, Jeff York *(Bud Searcy)*, Royal Dano *(Pack Underwood)*, Marta Kristen *(Lisbeth Searcy)*, Rafael Campos *(Young Warrior)*, Slim Pickens *(Wily Crup)*, Rodolfo Acosta *(Bandy Legs)*, Pat Hogan *(Broken Nose)*, Dean Fredericks *(Comanche chief)*, Brad Weston *(Ben Todd)*.

Adventure melodrama. Source: Fred Gipson, *Savage Sam* (New York, 1962). In 1870 18-year-old Travis Coates is left in charge of his precocious 12-year-old brother, Arliss, on the family farm in Southwest Texas, while their parents visit an ailing grandmother. While Arliss and his dog, Savage Sam, are tracking a wildcat, Travis is warned by Bud Searcy that renegade Apache Indians are in the area. When Travis joins Bud's 17-year-old daughter, Lisbeth, in a search for Arliss, all three are captured by a band of Apaches led by a Comanche. The boys' Uncle Beck Coates witnesses the scene and manages to wound the Indian leader, but Beck's horse is shot by one of the braves, allowing the Comanche and his followers to escape with the captives. Beck alerts the U. S. Cavalry, but the Indians split into three groups and ride for the hills; in the confusion, Travis escapes but is knocked unconscious and left to die. Beck and his posse of five find Travis and his dog, set out in pursuit of the other captives, and eventually find the Indians in a valley fighting over Lisbeth. Although posse member Pack Underwood, bent on revenge for the massacre of his family, fires a shot that alerts the Indians to their planned ambush, the youngsters are saved and the renegades captured. *Brothers. Apache Indians. Comanche Indians. Uncles. Frontier and pioneer life. Farm life. Abduction. Revenge. Texas. United States Army—Cavalry. Dogs. Wildcats.*

Note: Location scenes filmed in the San Fernando Valley, California. Sequel to *Old Yeller* (1957).

THE SAVAGE SEVEN   **F6.4264**
Dick Clark Enterprises. *Dist* American International Pictures. 22 May **1968** [Portland, Oregon, opening; c24 Apr 1968; LP35619]. Sd; col (Perfect). 35mm. 97 min. [Also 94 min.]

Prod Dick Clark. *Dir* Richard Rush. *Screenplay* Michael Fisher. *Story* Rosalind Ross. *Photog* Laszlo Kovacs. *Art Dir* Leon Ericksen. *Film Ed* Renn Reynolds. *Mus Comp* Mike Curb, Jerry Styner. *Titl Theme:* "Anyone for Tennis" Cream. *Song:* "The Ballad of the Savage Seven" Valjean Johns, Guy Hemric. *Played by* The American Revolution. *Sd* Leroy Robbins. *Asst Dir* Gene H. De Ruelle. *Prod Mgr* Jack Bohrer. *Makeup* Louis Lane.

Cast: Robert Walker, Jr. *(Johnnie Little Hawk)*, Larry Bishop *(Joint)*, Adam Roarke *(Kisum)*, Joanna Frank *(Marie Little Hawk)*, John Garwood *(Stud)*, Max Julien *(Grey Wolf)*, Richard Anders *(Bull)*, Duane Eddy *(Eddie)*, Chuck Bail *(Taggert)*, Mel Berger *(Fillmore)*, Billy Rush *(Seely)*, John Cardos *(Running Buck)*, Susannah Darrow *(Nancy)*, Beach Dickerson *(Fat Jack)*, Alan Gibbs *(stunt man)*, Fabian Gregory *(Tommy)*, Gary Kent *(Lansford)*, Gary Littlejohn *(Dogface)*, Penny Marshall *(Tina)*, Walter Robles *(Walt)*, Eddy Donno.

Action melodrama. American Indians living in a squalid California desert shantytown are being victimized by greedy businessmen and terrorized by a gang of motorcyclists, led by Kisum, which arrives at Fat Jack's tavern and causes a disturbance. Kisum is impressed by the aloofness of Maria, the waitress; and her brother, Johnnie Little Hawk, steps in to protect her. Johnnie then has a run-in with Fillmore, the storekeeper, and Kisum forces him to pay the wages due Johnnie. This intercession softens Maria's attitude toward Kisum, and both groups join forces and loot Fillmore's store, whereupon Fillmore calls in the highway patrol, resulting in the arrest of several motorcyclists and Indians. After the Indians raid the cyclists' camp, prompted by Kisum's rough treatment of Marie, Kisum agrees to Fillmore's proposal to drop his charges if Kisum and his gang will do away with the Indians. Maria then makes love with Kisum, and he calls off the attack; but he decides to go ahead when one of his gang is murdered (apparently by the Indians for raping an Indian woman). While the destruction is underway, Kisum discovers it was Fillmore who raped the woman and murdered his friend. He and Maria gaze helplessly at each other as Indians (including Johnnie) and gang members alike are slaughtered. *Indians of North America. Businessmen. Waitresses. Motorcycle gangs. Police. Storekeepers. Greed. Brother-sister relationship. Rape. Murder. Bars. Shantytowns. California.*

THE SAVAGE WILD　　　　　　　　　　**F6.4265**

Gordon Eastman. *Dist* American International Pictures. Jan **1970**. Sd; col (Technicolor). 35mm (Techniscope). 103 min. *MPAA rating* G.

Prod-Dir-Writ Gordon Eastman. *Assoc Prod* Felix Buckingroth. *Camera* Gordon Eastman, Wes Marks, Brad Eastman, Rod Eastman, Art Bothum. *Ed Supv* Tom Boutross. *Mus Comp* Jaime Mendoza-Nava. *Titl Song* Earl E. Smith, Gordon Eastman. *Sung by* Cris Quesada. *Sd Eff* Sonic Editorial Service. *Mus Ed* John Caper, Jr. *Prod Mgr* Bruce Jacobson.

Cast: Gordon Eastman *(Gordon)*, Carl Spore *(Red)*, Maria Eastman *(Maria)*, Arlo Curtis *(Arlo)*, Jim Timiaough *(Jim)*, Robert Wellington Kirk *(Bob)*, John Payne *(John)*, Charles Abou *(Cha-Lay)*, Alex Dennis *(Cha-Lay's brother)*, Charley Davis *(Charley)*, Wilber O'Brian *(helicopter pilot)*, Yukon, Teton, Missy *(timber wolves)*.

Documentary drama. Nature photographer Gordon Eastman takes his family and a crew of filmmakers to northern Canada near the Arctic Circle to study the habits of timber wolves. The wolves, widely sought by bounty hunters, are among the vanishing species of animals in North America. Eastman and the crew capture three wolf cubs and raise them, eventually gaining the confidence and trust of the cubs. Red, a bounty hunter who shoots wolves from his airplane, loses control of his plane while trying to shoot one of Eastman's pet wolves and is killed. After the wolves are fully grown, Eastman sets them free. For a while, they hunt small game near the camp, but soon their instincts sharpen, and they kill a caribou. When they return to the camp area for the last time, they are completely wild and independent. *Photographers. Filmmakers. Bounty hunters. Wildlife—Conservation. Canada. Arctic regions. Airplane accidents. Wolves. Caribou.*

Note: Filmed on location in the Yukon Territory in Canada. Prerelease title: *Wild Arctic.*

SAVAGES FROM HELL *see* **BIG ENOUGH N' OLD ENOUGH**

LO SBARCO DI ANZIO *see* **ANZIO**

LO SCACCHIERE DI DIO *see* **MARCO THE MAGNIFICENT**

THE SCALPHUNTERS　　　　　　　　　　**F6.4266**

Norlan Productions–Bristol Pictures. *Dist* United Artists. 2 Apr **1968** [New York opening; c2 Apr 1968; LP38906]. Sd; col (Deluxe). 35mm (Panavision). 103 min.

Pres by Roland Kibbee. *Prod* Jules Levy, Arthur Gardner, Arnold Laven. *Dir* Sydney Pollack. *Screenplay* William Norton. *Story* William Norton. *Photog* Duke Callaghan, Richard Moore. *Art Dir* Frank Arrigo. *Main Titl* Phill Norman. *Film Ed* John Woodcock. *Mus* Elmer Bernstein. *Choreog* Alex Ruiz. *Sd* Jesús González Gancy. *Asst Dir* Charles Scott, Jr., Kevin Donnelly. *Prod Mgr* Henry Spitz, Jack Corrick. *Cost* Joe Drury. *Makeup* Gary Liddiard. *Sp Eff* Herman Townsley. *Stunt Coörd* Tony Epper. *Horse Supv* Kenneth Lee.

Cast: Burt Lancaster *(Joe Bass)*, Shelley Winters *(Kate)*, Telly Savalas *(Jim Howie)*, Ossie Davis *(Joseph Winfield Lee)*, Armando Silvestre *(Two Crows)*, Dan Vadis *(Yuma)*, Dabney Coleman *(Jed)*, Paul Picerni *(Frank)*, Nick Cravat *(Ramon)*, John Epper, Jack Williams, Chuck Roberson, Tony Epper, Agapito Roldan, Gregorio Acosta, Marco Antonio Arzate *(scalphunters)*, Angela Rodriguez, Amelia Rivera, Alicia del Lago *(scalphunters' women)*, Nestor Dominguez, Francisco Oliva, Benjamin Ramos, Enrique Tello, Raúl Martínez, José Martínez, actor, Rodolfo Toledo, José Salas, Cuco Velazquez, Alejandro López, Raúl Hernández, Pedro Aguilar *(Kiowas)*.

Western drama. Trapper Joe Bass confronts a party of Kiowa Indians. Led by Two Crows, the band compels Bass to exchange mule and furs for fugitive slave Joseph Winfield Lee. Hoping for an opportunity to retrieve his possessions, Bass follows them. While imbibing Bass' whiskey the Kiowas are ambushed by scalphunters. Only Two Crows escapes. As Bass stalks the whites, Lee is captured. The black quickly becomes the favorite of Kate, mistress to leader Jim Howie, and is given freedom of the camp. Aware that the gang's destination is Mexico, where slavery is illegal, Lee has little motivation to escape. Bereft of slave, mule, and furs, Bass launches a campaign of attrition, causing rockfalls, feeding the band's mounts loco weed, and slaying the marauders one by one. Under the pretense of returning the trapper's property Howie plans an ambush, but is himself slain by the black. Although Lee has saved Bass, the two immediately quarrel. As the pair grapple, vengeful Kiowa braves descend upon the remaining scalphunters, appropriating their women and sparing only slave and trapper. Together Lee and Bass scheme to recover the pelts. *Slaves—Runaway. Fur traders. Bounty hunters. Mistresses. Kiowa Indians. Frontier and pioneer life. Race relations. Revenge. Murder. Mexico. Horses.*

Note: Location scenes filmed in Mexico.

SCANDAL (Japan)　　　　　　　　　　**F6.4267**

Shochiku Co. *Dist* Shochiku Films of America. Jun **1964** [Los Angeles showing]. Sd; b&w. 35mm. 104 min.

Prod Takashi Koide. *Dir* Akira Kurosawa. *Screenplay* Ryuzo Kikushima, Akira Kurosawa. *Photog* Toshio Ubukata. *Art Dir* Tatsuo Hamada. *Mus* Fumio Hayasaka.

Cast: Toshiro Mifune *(Ichiro Aoye)*, Yoshiko Yamaguchi *(Miyako Saigo)*, Takashi Shimura *(Hiruta)*, Yoko Katsuragi *(Masako)*, Noriko Sengoku *(Sumic)*, Sakae Ozawa *(Hori)*, Bokuzen Hidari *(drunk)*, Kuninori Kodo *(farmer)*.

Melodrama. Ichiro Aoye, a young painter, goes off into the mountains to work and meets Miyako Saigo, a well-known singer, who is being annoyed by photographers from a fan magazine. The magazine prints a picture of the couple riding on Ichiro's motorcycle and a contrived story about a romance between them. Ichiro decides to sue the magazine for slander, but Hiruta, his lawyer, eager to provide for his invalid daughter, accepts a bribe from the magazine to lose the case. In court, however, Hiruta confesses his crime, realizing he will be disbarred for his actions. The magazine is restrained by a court order, but Hiruta's daughter dies. *Painters. Singers. Lawyers. Invalids. Yellow journalism. Bribery. Perfidy. Confession (law). Lawsuits.*

Note: Released in Japan in Apr 1950 as *Shubun.*

SCANDAL IN DENMARK (Denmark)　　　　　　**F6.4268**

Novaris Film. *Dist* Cinetex Industries. 17 Jun **1970** [Atlanta opening]. Sd; col (Eastman Color). 35mm. ca90 min. *MPAA rating* R.

A Peer Guldbrandsen Production. *Prod-Dir-Writ* Peer Guldbrandsen. *Photog* Erik Wittrup Willumsen. *Film Ed* Edith Nisted. *Mus* Sven Gyldmark. *Sd* Jon Branner, Torben Øksnebjerg.

Cast: Willy Rathnov *(The Soldier)*, Hanne Borchsenius *(The Witch)*, Poul Bundgaard *(Dobbermann)*, Olaf Ussing *(Pinchier)*, Karl Stegger *(Schaefer)*, Ove Sprogøe *(Baron Royal King von König)*, Astrid Villaume *(Baroness Regina King von König)*, Ullabella Johansson *(Countess Elise)*, Inger Bagger *(governess)*, Paul Hagen *(hotel porter)*.

Fantasy. Source: Hans Christian Andersen, "Fyrtøjet," in *Eventyr fortalte for Børn* (Copenhagen, 1835). An updated version of Hans Christian Andersen's fairy tale "The Tinder-Box" in which the tinderbox becomes a cigarette lighter, the underground cave a gambling casino, the three giant walleyed dogs corrupt gold brokers with enormous spectacles, and the princess voluptuous and seductive. *Soldiers. Witches. Royalty. Brokers. Magic. Wealth. Weddings. Casinos. Gold.*

Note: Released in Denmark in 1969 as *Der kom en soldat;* running time: 98 min.

SCANDAL '64 *see* **THE CHRISTINE KEELER AFFAIR**

LE SCANDALE *see* **THE CHAMPAGNE MURDERS**

THE SCANDALOUS ADVENTURES OF BURAIKAN (Japan)　**F6.4269**

Ninjin Club–Toho Co. *Dist* Toho International, Inc. Nov **1970** [Los Angeles showing]. Sd; col (Eastmancolor). 35mm (Panavision). 104 min.

Prod Ninjin Kurabu. *Dir* Masahiro Shinoda. *Screenplay* Shuji Terayama. *Photog* Kozo Okazaki. *Art Dir* Shigemasa Toda. *Mus* Masaru Sato.

Cast: Tatsuya Nakadai *(Naojiro)*, Suisen Ichikawa *(his mother)*, Shima Iwashita *(Michitose)*, Tetsuro Tamba *(Soshun)*, Shoichi Ozawa *(Ushimatsu)*, Masakane Yonekura *(Ichinojo Kaneko)*, Kiwako Taichi *(Namiji)*, Fumio Watanabe *(Seizo Moritaya)*, Hiroshi Akutagawa.

Melodrama. Based on a play by: Mokuami Kawatake. During the Tempo Reformation of 1842, which restricted the arts and pleasure-taking, Naojiro, an aspiring actor, falls in love with Michitose, a prostitute. At the same time Ushimatsu finds that his wife committed suicide after she sold their son to her lover, Goto, to pay her debts. Naojiro learns that he has a rival for Michitose in Seizo Moritaya, who hires killer Ichinojo Kaneko to eliminate Naojiro. Kaneko attacks a palanquin which he believes is carrying Naojiro, but the passenger is revealed to be Soshun Kochiyama, a samaritan who has befriended an actor fleeing from the police. Naojiro's mother refuses to allow him to marry a prostitute, and he throws her into a river, but Michitose rescues her. Moritaya attempts to win Michitose by insulting Naojiro and his mother, but the latter eavesdrops on the conversation. Naojiro joins a group paid to rescue a merchant's daughter, Namiji, from the court of Lord Izumonokami. Naojiro, disguised as a samurai, and Kochiyama, dressed as a priest, rescue Namiji, but Kochiyama is discovered and captured. Kaneko sets fire to police stations in protest of the Reformation, and Ushimatsu commits suicide. *Actors. Prostitutes. Nobility. Hired killers. Filial relations. Suicide. Disguise. Arson. Abduction. Japan—History—Tempo Reformation 1842.*

Note: Released in Japan in Apr 1970 as *Buraikan.*

SCANTY PANTIES　　　　　　　　　　**F6.4270**

Jacjay Productions. *Dist* William Mishkin. 7 Jul **1961** [Los Angeles showing]. Sd; b&w with col seq (Eastman Color). 35mm. 72 min.

Prod Eli Jackson. *Dir* Jay Hornick. *Photog* Donald Malkames. *Mus Dir* Merrick Valinote. *Orig Songs* Johnny Crawford, mus. *Sd* Jim Shields.

Cast: Billy "Cheese 'n' Crackers" Hagan (*Dr. Plumber*), Debra Dante (*patient*), Murray Briscoe (*doctor*), Maxie Furman (*husband*), Alma Maiben (*wife*), Irving Benson (*gambler*), Virginia Bell, Laurel Sands, Barbara Lane, Electrique, Debra Dante, Debbie Starr (*exotics*), Johnny Crawford, mus (*singer*), Prince Donnell, Arleena (*dancers in "Dance of the Fire God"*).

Burlesque film. The film consists of ribald comedy routines with burlesque house comics, striptease acts, and exotic dance numbers. *Stripteasers. Actors. Exotic dancers. Burlesque.*

SCAPPAMENTO APERTO *see* **BACKFIRE**

SCARAMOUCHE *see* **THE ADVENTURES OF SCARAMOUCHE**

SCARE THEIR PANTS OFF   F6.4271

Dist Distribpix, Inc. 29 May **1968** [New York showing]. Sd; b&w. 35mm. 75 min.

Prod Ron Sullivan. *Dir-Writ* John Maddox. *Photog* Arthur Marks. *Asst Camera* Peter McCreavy. *Art Dir* Joan Wendell. *Sd* Hugh Little. *Prod Mgr* Don Walters. *Cont* Vicky Pollack. *Cost* Alexandria Mitchell.

Cast: Mary St. Feint, Sean Laney, Jon Woods, Alou Mitsou, Claire Adams.

Drama. Two young men, bored with the normal process of seduction, devise a scheme to heighten the pleasure of sexual conquest. They determine to dress in costumes and enact fantastic tableaux in which three women are separately abducted, drugged, terrorized, and seduced. In the first adventure, one of the men forces one of the abducted women to submit to his friend, whose body and face appear to be monstrously deformed. The man agrees to cover his face, but in the course of their sexual frenzy, his headcover becomes dislodged. The terrified woman faints from fright, and the man removes the grotesque face which was only a mask. The second victim is forced to lie down covered by a shroud while one of the men, in the guise of a Tibetan guru, performs bizarre sexual rites on her. The third victim is interrogated, fascist-style, by the two men until she submits to their "good-natured" lovemaking. *Abduction. Seduction. Sadism. Disguise. Interrogation. Troilism. Voyeurism. Practical jokes. Rites and ceremonies.*

Note: Also known as *Scare the Girls Off, He Scared the Girls Off,* and *Scare Them Off.*

SCARF OF MIST, THIGH OF SATIN   F6.4272

Chellee Films. 29 Nov **1967** [Rochester, New York, opening]. Sd; b&w. 35mm. 82 min.

Prod Chellee Wilson. *Dir-Writ* Joe Sarno. *Cinematog* Bruce Sparks. *Film Ed* Kemper Peacock.

Cast: Cleo Nova (*Betta Clay*), Sheila Britt (*Drucilla Harmon*), Justin Moreau (*Neil Furman*).

Melodrama. Betta Clay and Drucilla Harmon own a financially unstable fashion house in New York's garment center. There is much tension between the two partners because Drucilla's designs are not selling well. One of their models, Jenya Radik, plans to steal some designs made by Hani, a young immigrant, as a means to further her own career and to help the failing business. Her plans are foiled, however, when she is fired from the company for having an indiscreet affair with another employee. She determines to follow through when her shiftless boyfriend, Neil Furman, beats her up for losing the job. Jenya appropriates Hani's designs and presents them to Betta as her own in order to reinstate herself with her former employer. Impressed with the sketches, Betta believes she has a new designer. She makes plans to oust Drucilla and hastily forms a new partnership with buyers Paul Dan and Norma Palmer. Betta and her new partners invite Drucilla to an office party where there are sure to be adult games played. As the susceptible Drucilla abandons her inhibitions and begins to participate in an orgy, Betta arrives, pretends anger, and dissolves the partnership with Drucilla. Jenya is toasted as the star designer of the new enterprise, but when Betta reveals that Jenya's salary is to be far less than Jenya had told Neil, he becomes enraged and pulls a gun. Neil is killed in the ensuing melee, and Betta seriously regrets her actions. *Businesswomen. Couturiers. Models. Immigrants. Gigolos. Fashion. Infidelity. Business ethics. Employer-employee relations. Reputation. Perfidy. Partnerships. Orgies. Drawings. New York City—Garment District.*

Note: Also advertised as *Scarf of Mist, Women of Satin.*

THE SCARFACE MOB   F6.4273

Desilu Productions. *Dist* Cari Releasing Corp., Desilu Film Distributing Co. Aug **1962**. Sd; b&w. 35mm. 105 min. [Also 98 min.]

Prod Quinn Martin. *Exec Prod* Bert Granet. *Assoc Prod* Jack Aldworth. *Dir* Phil Karlson. *Screenplay* Paul Monash. *Photog* Charles Straumer. *Art Dir* Ralph Berger, Frank T. Smith. *Set Decor* Sandy Grace. *Film Ed* Robert L. Swanson. *Mus* Wilbur Hatch. *Choreog* Jack Baker. *Sd Cam* McCulloch. *Asst Dir* Vincent McEveety. *In Charge of Prod* Desi Arnaz. *Wardrobe* Jerry Bos, Maria Donovan. *Makeup* Ed Butterworth. *Hairstyles* Lorraine Roberson.

Cast: Robert Stack (*Eliot Ness*), Keenan Wynn (*Joe Fuselli*), Barbara Nichols (*Brandy La France*), Patricia Crowley (*Betty Anderson*), Neville Brand (*Al Capone*), Bill Williams (*Martin Flaherty*), Joe Mantell (*George Ritchie*), Bruce Gordon (*Frank Nitti*), Peter Leeds (*Lamarr Kane*), Eddie Firestone (*Eric Hansen*), Robert Osterloh (*Tom Kopka*), Paul Dubov (*Jack Rossman*), Abel Fernandez (*William Youngfellow*), Paul Picerni (*Tony Liguri*), John Beradino (*Johnny Giannini*), Wolfe Barzell (*Picco*), Frank Wilcox (*Beecher Asbury*), Peter Mamakos (*Bomber Belcastro*), Wally Cassell (*Phil D'Andrea*), Herman Rudin (*Mops Volpe*), Richard Benedict (*Furs Sammons*), Bern Hoffman (*Jack Guzik*), Frank De Kova (*Jimmy Napoli*), James Westerfield (*Ed Marriatt*), Walter Winchell (*narrator*).

Crime drama. Source: Eliot Ness and Oscar Fraley, *The Untouchables* (New York, 1957). Eliot Ness is convinced that syndicate graft is buying local police protection when a raid on the headquarters of Al Capone's gang proves unsuccessful. After receiving the support of the district attorney, Ness picks several reliable men from the Treasury Department and sets up a special office in Chicago. The Treasury agents establish the whereabouts of one of Capone's stills, and Capone henchman Frank Nitti offers Ness a bribe to leave it alone; but Ness steps up the raids, and as a result the mob votes to have Ness killed. Ness places an informer in the gang's headquarters and closes six more breweries. Capone, released from jail, returns to declare an all-out war on Ness and his men. He breaks the wire tap, kills the informer, and hires Jimmy Napoli to murder Ness. Soon afterward, the government puts together a tax-evasion case against Capone, and he is sentenced to 11 years in prison. *District attorneys. Gangsters. Informers. Syndicates. Graft. Prohibition. Bribery. Murder. Income tax. Electronic surveillance. Prohibition. Chicago. Al Capone. Eliot Ness. United States—Treasury Department.*

Note: A theatrical release of Westinghouse-Desilu Playhouse's "The Untouchables," a 2-part television drama registered for copyright 27 Mar, 10 Apr 1959; LP14941, LP14942 and shown 20 Apr and 27 Apr 1959.

THE SCARLET BLADE *see* **THE CRIMSON BLADE**

THE SCARLET CAMELLIA (Japan)   F6.4274

Shochiku Co. *Dist* Shochiku Films of America. 26 Feb **1965** [Los Angeles showing]. Sd; col (Eastmancolor). 35mm (Shochiku GrandScope). 117 min.

Prod Shiro Kido. *Dir* Yoshitaro Nomura. *Screenplay* Masato Ide. *Photog* Ko Kawamata. *Art Dir* Takashi Matsuyama, Chiyoo Umeda. *Mus Comp* Yasushi Akutagawa.

Cast: Shima Iwashita (*Oshino*), Yoshi Kato (*Kihei Musashiya*), Sachiko Hidari (*Osono*), Takahiro Tamura (*Chodayu*), Yunosuke Ita (*Unno*), Shoichi Ozawa (*Seiichi*), Ko Nishimura (*Sakichi*), Eiji Okada (*Gen Maruu*), Go Kato (*Aoki*).

Crime melodrama. Source: Shugoro Yamamoto, *Goben no tsubaki* (Tokyo, 1959). A fire at the Edo villa of merchant Kihei Musashiya yields three bodies thought to be Musashiya, who had been ill with tuberculosis; his wife, Osono; and their only daughter, Oshino. Six months later, a musician, notorious as a ladies' man, is found stabbed to death with a silver hairpin; beside his body is a scarlet camellia. Soon another murder takes place under identical circumstances. The victim this time is a doctor who had become wealthy treating women who dared not go to legitimate physicians. On a tip from a police informer, Officer Aoki trails a female suspect, but as he is convinced that she is innocent he does not arrest her. Meanwhile, another murder occurs, and Aoki's suspicions about the girl are again aroused. He learns that the girl is Oshino, Musashiya's daughter, and that the corpse assumed to be hers was that of Kikutaro, one of her mother's lovers. After setting fire to the villa, Oshino, to avenge her father, killed the men with whom her promiscuous mother had affairs. Oshino eludes capture and next murders a teahouse handyman who had supplied many of her mother's lovers. Oshino intends to kill one more man before she surrenders to the police, but she cannot bring herself to stab him when she remembers that her mother had once said that he was Oshino's real father. Oshino gives herself up, satisfied that she has gained revenge. She feels remorse, however, when she learns that her real father's wife has hung herself. *Merchants. Musicians. Physicians. Police. Revenge. Murder. Infidelity. Promiscuity. Suicide. Parentage. Tuberculosis. Flowers. Edo. Fires.*

Note: Released in Japan in 1965 as *Goben no tsubaki.*

SCARLET NEGLIGEE   F6.4275

Dist Crescent International Pictures. 24 Jul **1968** [Charlotte, North Carolina, opening]. Sd; col. 35mm. 66 min.

Prod Whit Boyd. *Dir* Ron Scott. *Screenplay* Rosemarie McKay. *Photog* Ludwig Moner. *Art Dir* X. O. Von Gam. *Sd Rec* Forest Duval. *Wardrobe* Rosemarie McKay. *Makeup* Rosemarie McKay.

Cast: Byron Lord (*Craig*), Shirley Boyd (*Rita*), Nancy Reeves (*Catherine*), Ron Scott (*Joe*), Gene Wilson (*Billy Boy*), Rosemarie McKay (*Dee Dee*), Dianne Davis (*Jeannie*), Ann, Cher Lamait, Pat, Dee (*Rita's girls*), Scott Martin (*police lieutenant*), Helaine Bradshaw (*housewife*), Jeff Hipp (*policeman*), Whit

Field (drunk).

Melodrama. Three gunmen hold up a supermarket and take the cashier hostage. They hide out in an exclusive brothel, sheltered by Rita, the voluptuous madam, and entertained by her prostitutes. The cashier eventually persuades one of the robbers to reform, and they flee together, pursued by the other gunmen. A wild chase ends in a shootout with police, and all three robbers meet their deaths. *Cashiers. Madams. Police. Hostages. Robbery. Prostitution. Abduction. Criminals—Rehabilitation. Markets. Whorehouses. Chases.*

THE SCARS OF DRACULA (Great Britain)   F6.4276

Hammer Film Productions-EMI Film Productions. For Anglo-EMI Film Distributors. *Dist* American Continental Films. 23 Dec **1970** [Chicago opening]. Sd; col (Technicolor). 35mm. 96 min. [Also reviewed at 94 min.] *MPAA rating* R.

Pres by Levitt-Pickman Film Corp. *Prod* Aida Young. *Dir* Roy Ward Baker. *Screenplay* John Elder. *Dir Photog* Moray Grant. *Art Dir* Scott MacGregor. *Film Ed* James Needs. *Mus Comp* James Bernard. *Mus Supv* Philip Martell. *Sd Ed* Roy Hyde. *Sd Rec* Ron Barron. *Sd Re-rec* Denis Whitlock. *Asst Dir* Derek Whitehurst. *Prod Mgr* Tom Sachs. *Makeup* Wally Schneiderman. *Sp Eff* Roger Dicken.

Cast: Christopher Lee *(Count Dracula)*, Dennis Waterman *(Simon)*, Jenny Hanley *(Sarah Framsen)*, Christopher Matthews *(Paul)*, Patrick Troughton *(Klove)*, Michael Gwynn *(priest)*, Wendy Hamilton *(Julie)*, Anoushka Hempel *(Tania)*, Delia Lindsay *(Alice)*, Bob Todd, British *(burgomaster)*, Toke Townley *(elderly wagon master)*, Michael Ripper *(landlord)*, David Leland, Richard Durden *(officers)*, Morris Bush *(farmer)*, Margot Boht *(landlord's wife)*, Clive Barrie *(fat young man)*.

Horror film. Based on characters created by: Bram Stoker. Upon discovering a murdered girl with fang marks on her neck, the farmers of Kleinenberg set Count Dracula's castle ablaze in the hope of destroying the dreaded vampire. When they return to the village, however, they discover that giant vampire bats have killed all the women and children who were left behind in the church. Some time later, Paul, a rakish youth, flees from the bed of Alice, the burgomaster's daughter, when her father returns unexpectedly. Escaping into the night, Paul stops at his girl friend Sarah's birthday party, but is once again obliged to run off when the burgomaster's officers catch up with him. Wandering along a country road, Paul climbs into an abandoned black coach, falls asleep, and awakens to find himself in the presence of Tania, a seductive vampire who lures him to the ruined castle. When Count Dracula offers him a bed, Paul is too exhausted to refuse. During the night Tania joins him. When Paul awakens the next morning, he finds Dracula stabbing her to death. Eventually, Sarah and Paul's brother, Simon, trace him to the castle and are persuaded to stay the night, though the Count denies having seen Paul. Although Simon discovers that his brother is somewhere in the castle, Dracula's crippled servant, Klove, advises him to take Sarah away. Having sequestered Sarah in a church, Simon returns to the castle and finds his brother's mutilated corpse in Dracula's crypt. When the pastor is slashed to death by a horde of bats which invades the church, Sarah rushes back to the castle and joins Simon in a final confrontation with the Count. After killing Klove for his intrusion, Dracula is about to impale the young lovers when a bolt of lightning strikes. Consumed by fire, the Count falls from a castle turret. *Vampires. Farmers. Mayors. Brothers. Cripples. Domestics. Priests. Murder. Village life. Arson. Impalement. Churches. Castles. Corpses. Chases. Lightning. Dracula. Bats.*

Note: Opened in London in Oct 1970; running time: 96 min. John Elder is a pseudonym for Anthony Hinds.

LO SCATENATO *see* **CATCH AS CATCH CAN**

THE SCAVENGERS   F6.4277

Cresse-Frost Productions. *Dist* Republic Amusements Corp., Grads Corp. 13 May **1969** [Champaign, Illinois, showing]. Sd; col (Eastman Color). 35mm. 111 min. *MPAA rating* R.

Prod-Writ R. W. Cresse. *Dir* R. L. Frost. *Unit Dir* Fred Scarborough. *Dir Photog* Bob Maxwell. *Camera* James K. Shea, Joe Bardo. *Lighting Dir* Russ Nannarello. *Set Dsgn* Joe Anthony. *Set Decor* John Fry. *Film Ed* B. Richard Conners. *Title Song:* "The Scavengers Are Coming" Lee Frost, Paul Hunt. *Lyr* Tom Bowden, Jr., R. W. Cresse. *Perf by* Jody Berry. *Sd* Hollywood Picture Recorders. *Sd Engr* Sam Kopetzky. *Asst Dir* Don Baker. *Prod Supv* Wesdon Bishop. *Wardrobe* Steve Mooni. *Makeup* Dennis Marsh. *Sp Eff* Joe Zomar. *Prop Master* Alfred Garcia. *Set Constr* Dick Maddox. *Stunt Coörd* Chuck Bail. *Still Photog* Joel Sussman.

Cast: John Bliss *(The Captain)*, Maria Lease *(Faith)*, Michael Dikova *(Sergeant West)*, Roda Spain *(Nancy)*, John Riazzi, Wes Bishop, Bruce Kemp, Sanford Mitchell, Tom Siegel, Jody Berry, Paul Wilmoth, Uschi Digart, James E. McLarty, Claudia Siefried, Karen Swanson, Warren James, Paul Hunt, James K. Shea, Freddy Mizrahi, Ben Adams, Tom Bowden, Jr., Fig Blackman, Ben Cadlett, Robert Jones, actor, James Gorden.

Melodrama. Confederate Capt. Steven Harris and 10 survivors from the Army of Tennessee who are assigned to rob a Union gold shipment being delivered to the Army of the Potomac and scheduled to pass through the town of Tazewell, proceed with their plans, unaware that the Civil War has ended. The men invade Tazewell, take over a saloon, shoot the bartender, and lock up the prostitutes. Harris tortures Union Lieutenant Nelson and learns that no gold will be shipped, the truce having been signed. Harris tries unsuccessfully to rape Faith, Nelson's fiancée, and he gives Faith's Negro maid, Nancy, to his men for their own sport. Nancy kills one of the men with a knitting needle and flees to nearby Everett, a Negro tent city founded by freed slaves. The liberated slaves attack the rebels with a vengeance, losing their leader in the battle, but the rebels desert Harris when he tries to kill Faith, and they leave him pinned under his wounded horse—surrounded by vultures. *Soldiers. Negroes. Prostitutes. Robbery. Murder. Torture. Rape. Slavery. Revenge. Gold. Saloons. United States—History—Civil War. Tazewell (Tennessee).*

Note: Released by Grads Corp. as *The Grabbers*, an X-rated version including additional sex footage.

THE SCAVENGERS *see* **CITY OF SIN**

LO SCEICCO ROSSO *see* **THE RED SHEIK**

SCENES FROM UNDER CHILDHOOD: SECTION NO. 4   F6.4278

Dist Film-Makers' Cooperative, Canyon Cinema Cooperative, Brakhage. 18 Dec **1970** [New York opening]. Si; col. 16mm. 46 min.

Dir Stan Brakhage. *Assoc* Jane Brakhage. *Photog* Stan Brakhage. *Film Ed* Stan Brakhage.

Experimental film. A visual rendering of the world as experienced in the womb, in infancy, and in childhood. Objects, colors, and abstract images are combined in rapidly cut sequences. *Infants. Children. Childhood. Pregnancy.*

Note: A further elaboration of a theme developed in Sections 1, 2 & 3 of *Scenes From Under Childhood*, filmed 1967-69. Inspired by the music of Olivier Messiaen.

SCENT OF LOVE   F6.4279

Dist Stacey Distributors. ca **1970**. Sd; col. 16mm. 61-81 min.

Sex film. No information about the precise nature of this film has been found. *Sexuality.*

SCENT OF MYSTERY *see* **HOLIDAY IN SPAIN**

DIE SCHACHNOVELLE *see* **BRAINWASHED**

SCHATTEN ÜBER TIRAN—KOMMANDO SINAI *see* **SINAI COMMANDOS**

DIE SCHATTEN WERDEN LÄNGER *see* **THE SHADOWS GROW LONGER**

DER SCHATZ IM SILBERSEE *see* **TREASURE OF SILVER LAKE**

SCHEHERAZADE (France/Italy/Spain)   F6.4280

Spéva Films-Ciné-Alliance-Filmsonor-Dear Film-Tecisa. *Dist* Shawn International, Inc. 12 May **1965** [Chicago opening]. Sd; col (Eastman Color). 35mm (see note). 115 min.

Prod Michel Safra, Serge Silberman. *Dir* Pierre Gaspard-Huit. *2d Unit Dir* Jacques Bourdon. *Screenplay* Marc-Gilbert Sauvajon, Pierre Gaspard-Huit, José G. Maesso. *Orig French Dial* Marc-Gilbert Sauvajon. *Camera* Christian Matras, André Domage. *Art Dir* Georges Wakhévitch, Francisco Canet. *Film Ed* Louisette Hautecoeur. *Mus* André Hossein. *Sd* Antoine Petitjean. *Prod Mgr* Henri Baum. *Cost* Georges Wakhévitch.

Cast: Anna Karina *(Scheherazade)*, Gérard Barray *(Renaud de Villecroix)*, Antonio Vilar *(Haroun-al-Raschid)*, Marilù Tolo *(Shirin)*, Jorge Mistral *(Grand Vizier Zaccar)*, Fausto Tozzi *(Barmak)*, Giuliano Gemma *(Didier)*, Gil Vidal *(Thierry)*, Joëlle Latour *(Anira)*, Fernando Rey, José Manuel Martín.

Adventure melodrama. Renaud de Villecroix, nephew of Emperor Charlemagne, journeys to Bagdad to assure Caliph Haroun-al-Raschid that pilgrims to the Holy Land will not disrupt the lives of those who dwell in the Mesopotamian Desert. En route, Renaud rescues Princess Scheherazade from Bedouin bandits and escorts her to Bagdad. By the time they reach the city, they are lovers; Scheherazade must abandon Renaud, however, to join the caliph's harem. She competes with two rivals in tests of wisdom, beauty, and courage, and is chosen to wed the caliph. Jealous of Scheherazade's triumph, Shirin, who is the choice of Grand Vizier Zaccar, arranges for guards to find the princess and Renaud together in the harem of the caliph; the faithless bride is subsequently condemned to death. When Renaud offers to sacrifice himself in her place, the caliph agrees but further humiliates Scheherazade by throwing her to the beggars. Again rescued by Renaud's men, the princess and Renaud flee into the desert, but after suffering thirst and fever, they are forced to return to Bagdad. Touched by the lovers' devotion, the caliph frees Renaud on the condition that Scheherazade be the caliph's bride. When Renaud helps to quell a rebellion fomented by the traitorous grand vizier, the mortally wounded caliph releases Scheherazade from her vows and blesses the lovers. *Royalty. Bedouins. Bandits. Grand viziers. Traitors. Jealousy. Frameup. Capital punishment. Self-sacrifice. Revolts. Harems. Deserts. Bagdad. Mesopotamia. The Holy Land. Harun al-Rashid.*

Note: Opened in Paris in May 1963 as *Shéhérazade*; running time: 124 min; in Madrid in Jun 1963 as *Scheherazade*; in Rome in Sep 1963 as *La schiava di Bagdad*; running time: 105 min. Originally released in 70mm (Super Technirama-70 or Superpanorama-70).

LA SCHIAVA DI BAGDAD see **SCHEHERAZADE**

LE SCHIAVE ESISTONO ANCORA see **SLAVE TRADE IN THE WORLD TODAY**

GLI SCHIAVI PIÙ FORTI DEL MONDO see **SEVEN SLAVES AGAINST THE WORLD**

SCHIZO see **ALL WOMAN**

DIE SCHLANGENGRUBE UND DAS PENDEL see **THE BLOOD DEMON**

DAS SCHLOSS see **THE CASTLE**

SCHNEEWEISSCHEN UND ROSENROT see **SNOW WHITE AND ROSE RED**

SCHNEEWITTCHEN UND DIE SIEBEN ZWERGE see **SNOW WHITE**

THE SCHNOOK see **SWINGIN' ALONG**

SCHOOL FOR LOVE see **SCHOOL FOR SEX**

SCHOOL FOR SEX (Great Britain)   **F6.4281**
Pete Walker Film Productions. *Dist* Paul Mart Productions. 16 Jul 1969 [Champaign, Illinois, showing]. Sd; col (Eastman Color). 35mm. 68 min.

Prod-Dir-Writ Pete Walker. *Assoc Prod* Norman Lambert. *Dir Photog* Reg Phillips. *Camera Op* Derek Barclay. *Lighting* Key Lighting. *Supv Ed* Matt McCarthy. *Ed* John Black. *Mus Comp & Cond* Harry South. *Sd Rec* Bill Howell. *Mus Ed* Matt McCarthy. *Prod Mgr* John Regan. *Ch Electrn* Pat O'Keefe. *Ch Grip* Rex Stewart. *Post Prod* Cine Lingual Ltd.

Cast: Derek Aylward *(Giles Wingate)*, Rose Alba *(Duchess of Burwash)*, Hugh Latimer *(Hubert Berridge)*, Vic Wise *(Horace Clapp)*, Bob Andrews *(Sergeant Braithewaite)*, Nosher Powell *(Hector Shaughnessy)*, Cathy Howard *(Sue Randall)*, Sylvia Barlow *(Judy Arkwright)*, Amber Dean-Smith *(Beth Villiers)*, Françoise Pascal *(Jackie [Sally Reagan])*, Edgar K. Bruce *(Fred)*, Simon Cain *(Harry)*, Alec Bregonzi *(defense counsel [Harry])*, Robert Dorning *(minister)*, Wilfred Babbage *(judge)*, Maria Frost *(Polly)*, Cindy Neal *(stripper [Marianne])*, Dennis Castle *(Colonel Roberts)*, Sandra Gleeson *(Jenny)*, Gilly Grant *(striptease artist)*, Nicole Austen *(Tania)*, Jackie Berdet *(Ingeborg)*, The Annie Walker Lovelies, The Rosaleigh-Anne Girls *(unidentified roles)*.Giles Wingate inherits $1 million but loses his money to a succession of four wives in the space of as many years. Educated by this experience, Giles opens a private girls' school in his country mansion to train young women in the arts of love and sex. He hires the Duchess of Burwash to guide his pupils in attracting and ensnaring men. Giles also engages a male instructor to test and refine the students' lovemaking abilities. The school's first 20 graduates meet with great success in their endeavors, and respectable families unsuspectingly enroll their daughters. The authorities close in on Giles, but the judge who hears his case is so impressed with the venture that he frees Giles and decides to become a partner in the school upon his retirement from the bench. [In the British release version, Giles escapes an embezzlement conviction when his lawyer, Hugh Berridge, relates to the judge a moving account of the nine wives who tricked Giles into paying alimony. Giles then opens a school with Berridge to train women in the art of fleecing men in return for 10 percent of their profits. Berridge provides the students through a probation officer friend. Giles employs the drunken Duchess of Burwash; Hector, a punch-drunk boxer, whom he places in charge of physical instruction; and Fred, the 80-year-old butler, on whom the students practice their skills. A local vigilante group brings Giles before the same judge who had earlier freed him. The judge sentences Giles and Berridge to prison, and then assumes the management of the school.] *Students. Judges. Boxers. Butlers. Vigilantes. Nobility. Sex instruction. Drunkenness. Alimony. Partnerships. Moral corruption. Trials. Probation. Boarding schools. Inheritance.*

Note: Released in Great Britain in 1969; running time: 80 min. Also known as *School for Love*.

SCHOOL FOR SEX see **SCHOOL OF LOVE**

SCHOOL OF HARD KNOCKS   **F6.4282**
Kirt Films International. *Dist* Distribpix, Inc. ca 1970. Sd; col. 35mm. 64 min.

Melodrama. Two young women respond to a newspaper advertisement promoting a school for models, and are led to believe that great fame and riches will be theirs. The men who run the school are actually involved in the procurement of women to perform in stag shows, and they feed the women knockout drops to make them cooperate. Drugged and threatened with whipping, the women engage in erotic acts with their "schoolmasters." The women escape when one of their boyfriends discovers the school's true nature and determines to close its doors. *Models. Pimps. Fraud. Sadism. Stag shows. Tranquilizers. Flagellation. Advertisements.*

SCHOOL OF LOVE (Japan)   **F6.4283**
Toho Co. *Dist* Toho International, Inc. May 1966 [Los Angeles showing]. Sd; b&w. 35mm (Tohoscope). 95 min.

Prod Masakatsu Kaneko. *Dir* Ryo Kinoshita. *Screenplay* Toshiro Ide. *Photog* Jo Aizawa. *Mus* Shigeru Ikeno.

Cast: Kyoko Kishida *(Taeko)*, Tsutomu Yamazaki *(Senkichi)*, Yuki Nakagawa, So Yamamura.

Melodrama. Source: Yukio Mishima, *Nikutai no gakko* (Tokyo, 1964). Taeko, a lonely middle-aged divorcée, operates a successful dress shop in modern-day Japan. While lunching with two other divorcées, she hears gossip about Senkichi, a bartender in a homosexual club who earns additional money by satisfying the sexual needs of both men and women. Curious, Taeko visits the bar, becomes enamored of the handsome hustler, and brings him home with her. Before long he has moved into her apartment, passing as her nephew. Following an idyllic vacation together, Taeko invites Senkichi to accompany her to an afternoon party, and there he meets the daughter of one of Taeko's wealthy friends. Quick to seize an opportunity for advancing his social status, Senkichi begins courting the girl and eventually becomes engaged to her. Filled with jealous vindictiveness at being spurned, Taeko returns to the bar where she met Senkichi and obtains some incriminating photographs from one of his former homosexual friends. She then confronts Senkichi with the damaging evidence—evidence that could easily destroy his ambitious plans for the future. Senkichi's bravura attitude gradually crumbles as the vengeful Taeko forces him to agree to break off the engagement. As she watches his pathetic breakdown, however, she suddenly realizes the sordidness of her situation. Her infatuation over, she burns the photographs and returns to her former existence. *Storekeepers. Bartenders. Prostitutes. Gigolos. Social climbers. Divorce. Middle age. Male homosexuality. Imposture. Jealousy. Blackmail. Photographs.*

Note: Alternative title: *School for Sex*. Released in Japan in 1965 as *Nikutai no gakko*.

SCHOOL OF LOVE   **F6.4284**
Cherry Productions. ca 1969. Sd; col (Eastmancolor). 16mm. [Feature length assumed.]

Orig Screenplay Woodrow Olivetti.

Sex film. People go to a "school" featuring sex instruction. Includes scenes of whipping and oral intercourse. *Sex instruction. Flagellation. Oral sex.*

SCHWARZE NYLONS—HEISSE NÄCHTE see **INDECENT**

DER SCHWEIGENDE STERN see **FIRST SPACESHIP ON VENUS**

LA SCIMITARRA DEL SARACENO see **THE PIRATE AND THE SLAVE GIRL**

SCINTILLATING SIN see **VIOLATED PARADISE**

SCORPIO '70   **F6.4285**
Dist Sam Lake Enterprises. Jun 1970. Sd; col (Eastman Color). 35mm. 83 min.

Pres by Sam Lake. *Prod* Sam Lake. *Dir* Ron Sullivan. *Screenplay* Dario Finelli. *From an Idea by* Sam Lake. *Dir Photog* Arthur Marks. *Main Titl* Cineffects. *Film Ed* C. Davis Smith and Associates. *Mus* James Taylor, Robert Patterson. *Sd V & W* Sounds Inc. *Eff* Cineffects.

Cast: Jennifer Welles *(Layne)*, Stacey Michaels *(Glenn Lawrence)*, Iris Brooks *(Janet Hypes)*, Michael Haynes *(Bill Hypes)*, Hollis Solomon *(Dorothy Lindsay)*, Blaine Quincy *(Pete Lindsay)*, Jessica Stuart *(Christina)*, Tomba, Robin Elliot *(crewmen)*, Larry Hunter *(captain)*, Whitney Wayne *(Coast Guard lieutenant)*, Jud Phillips *(sailor)*.

Melodrama. Three couples set out on a weekend yachting party that ends tragically with the drowning of newlywed Bill Hypes. As his body is returned to the yacht, the others think back over the events of the weekend. Bill's widow, Janet, recalls their argument over the charms of Layne, a shapely member of the boating party. ... Bill and Janet exchange accusations of infidelity. Layne, a nymphomaniac and the secretary of Glenn Lawrence, is posing as Glenn's wife in order to complete a business scheme. Layne tempts the two crewmen, next turns her attentions to Bill, and finally joins the black crewman in the engine room. Pete Lindsay, an alcoholic, taunts his wife, Dorothy, for being a lesbian. Janet, after discovering Bill with Layne, joins Dorothy in lesbian lovemaking. Bill learns that Glenn is smuggling heroin, and in a scuffle with Glenn he is thrown overboard. Christina, the captain's daughter and a witness to the murder, forces Glenn to include her in the heroin deal. Pete learns of the murder and radios the Coast Guard. Glenn tries to escape but is killed by the black crewman, whose sister was a victim of Glenn's drug dealing. *Newlyweds. Drug dealers. Secretaries. Ship crews. Negroes. Murder. Jealousy. Infidelity. Imposture. Seduction. Nymphomania. Lesbianism. Smuggling. Alcoholism. Blackmail. Revenge. Yachts. Heroin. United States Coast Guard.*

Note: Also known as *Black Revenge.*

SCRATCH HARRY   F6.4286

Cannon Productions. ca15 Apr **1970** [Milwaukee, Wisconsin, opening]. Sd; col (Eastman Color). 35mm. 94 min. [Also 88 min.] *MPAA rating* R.

Prod Christopher C. Dewey. *Exec Prod* Dennis Friedland. *Assoc Prod* Donald Havens, Jr. *Dir* (see note) Alex Matter. *Screenplay* Stephen R. Winsten, Alex Matter. *Anim* Perpetual Motion Pictures. *Photog* Stephen R. Winsten, Alex Matter. *Film Ed* Matt Alexander. *Mus Score* Ken Lauber. *Sd* F. James Datri, Jr.

Cast: Harry Walker Staff *(Harry)*, Victoria Wilde *(Erica)*, Christine Kelly *(Christine)*, Mio Domani *("The Shadow")*.

Comedy-drama. Harry, a work-shy and selfish idler, is married to Erica, a wealthy woman who refuses to share her fortune with him. Harry takes advantage of Erica's frequent European vacations by picking up women and bringing them home. Erica, who is bisexual, returns and discovers Harry in bed with Christine, a playmate whom he found in New York City, and promptly makes Christine her own lover. The triangular affair ends abruptly when Harry, fearful of losing his income to his wife's new mate, shoots Christine and buries her along with the gun he used to kill her. He blackmails Erica into silence by vowing to produce the weapon (on which her fingerprints appear), thus forcing Erica to sell her estate and to make plans to leave the country. Erica refuses to depart without the revolver, so Harry reluctantly disinters Christine. Confronted in the garden by Erica with another gun, the couple shoot and kill each other, falling into the open grave. (The Shadow, a mysterious, devilish figure [invisible to the characters] dressed as a 1950's jazz musician, has seemingly been an off-stage force that led to Harry's demise. In a grim epilog, The Shadow guides Harry off through some trees—Harry apparently being the creation of his drug-inspired hallucination.) *Idlers. Pickups. Musicians. Wealth. Marriage. Infidelity. Lesbianism. Bisexuality. Murder. Disinterment. Narcotics. New York City. The Devil.*

Note: Shot in 16mm. Matt Alexander appears to be a pseudonym for Alex Matter. Also known as *The Erotic Three.*

SCREAM AND SCREAM AGAIN (Great Britain)   F6.4287

Amicus Productions–American International Productions. *Dist* American International Pictures. 11 Feb **1970** [Chicago opening; c11 Feb 1970; LP38183]. Sd; col (Eastman Color). 35mm. 94 min. *MPAA rating* M.

Prod Max J. Rosenberg, Milton Subotsky. *Exec Prod* Louis M. Heyward. *Dir* Gordon Hessler. *Screenplay* Christopher Wicking. *Dir Photog* John Coquillon. *Art Dir* Don Mingaye. *Prod Dsgn* Bill Constable. *Film Ed* Peter Elliott. *Mus* David Whitaker. *Mus Dir* Shel Talmy. *Titl Song* Dominic King, Tim Hayes. *Song:* "When We Make Love" Dominic King. *Sd Rec* Bert Ross. *Asst Dir* Ariel Levy. *Prod Mgr* Teresa Bolland. *Cont* Eileen Head. *Wardrobe Supv* Evelyn Gibbs. *Makeup* Jimmy Evans. *Hairstyles* Betty Sherriff.

Cast: Vincent Price *(Dr. Browning)*, Christopher Lee *(Fremont)*, Peter Cushing *(Benedek)*, Judy Huxtable *(Sylvia)*, Alfred Marks *(Superintendent Bellaver)*, Anthony Newlands *(Ludwig)*, Peter Sallis *(Schweitz)*, David Lodge *(Detective Inspector Strickland)*, Uta Levka *(Jane)*, Christopher Matthews *(David Sorel)*, Judi Bloom *(Helen Bradford)*, Clifford Earl *(Det. Sgt. Jimmy Joyce)*, Kenneth Benda *(Professor Kingsmill)*, Michael Gothard *(Keith)*, Marshall James *(Konratz)*, Julian Holloway *(Griffin)*, Edgar D. Davies *(Rogers)*, Yutte Stensgaard *(Erika)*, Lincoln Webb *(wrestler)*, Nigel Lambert *(Ken Sparten)*, Steve Preston *(Fryer)*, Lee Hudson *(matron)*, Leslie Ewin *(tramp)*, Kay Adrian *(nurse)*, Rosalind Elliot *(Valerie)*, The Amen Corner.

Horror film. Source: Peter Saxon, *The Disoriented Man* (London, 1966). Police Superintendent Bellaver, investigating the murder and mutilation of two young women and the disappearance of a young athlete, learns from American pathologist David Sorel that the women's bodies had been drained of blood. Helen Bradford, a police decoy, lures the suspected killer into the open, and police handcuff him. He proves to possess superhuman strength, however, and escapes by tearing off his hand and racing to the clinic of Dr. Browning, where he leaps into a vat of acid. Meanwhile, Konratz, a mysterious foreign agent who is systematically eliminating his political enemies, blackmails British agent

Fremont into persuading Scotland Yard to halt the investigation of the "vampire killings." Although unauthorized to continue work on the case, Sorel and Helen go to Dr. Browning's mansion and discover a modern operating room. They are caught by Dr. Browning, who reveals that he is creating human bodies by transplanting limbs and organs to form a perfect composite; the missing athlete was used for his strong arms and legs. Konratz, the mastermind behind the scheme, arrives and fights with Browning for allowing the murders to interrupt his political maneuvers. In the ensuing struggle, Konratz throws Browning into the vat, and Fremont arrives in time to save Helen and Sorel by pushing Konratz into the acid along with his victim. *Investigators. Athletes. Americans in foreign countries. Pathologists. Foreign agents. Physicians. Murder. Suicide. Amputation. Transplants. Organ transplants. Experiments. Scotland Yard.*

Note: Opened in London in Feb 1970.

SCREAM, BABY, SCREAM   F6.4288

Westbury Films. 22 May **1969** [San Antonio, Texas, opening]. Sd; col. 35mm. 83 min. *MPAA rating* R.

Prod-Dir Joseph Adler. *Assoc Prod* Boris Pritcher. *Story-Screenplay* Laurence Robert Cohen. *Photog* Julio C. Chavez. *Lighting Cons* Thomas Casey. *Camera Asst* David Lang. *Set Decor* David Trimble. *Main Titl* Paul Moore. *Film Ed* Joseph Adler. *Asst Ed* Ken Paulen. *Mus Comp & Perf by* Charles Austin Group. *Nightclub Songs* Chris Martell. *Perf by* The Odyssey. *Sd* Manuel Sole, Rafael Deairas. *Sd Eff* Larry Fisher. *Asst Dir* Michael Gallander. *Prod Supv* Joan Murphy. *Unit Mgr* Harry Kerwin. *Sp Makeup* Doug Hobart. *Key Grip* Duke McGrath.

Cast: Ross Harris *(Jason Grant)*, Eugenie Wingate *(Janet Wells)*, Chris Martell *(Scotty)*, Suzanne Stuart *(Marika Gold)*, Larry Swanson *(Charles Butler)*, Jim Vance *(Garrison)*, Naomi Fink *(Laura)*, Phil Philbin *(doctor)*, Gordon Walsh *(detective)*, Brad F. Grinter *(instructor)*, Jerry DeGennaro *(nightclub comic)*, Leona Resnick *(nurse)*, Candy Ernst, Bunny Ware *(models)*.

Horror film. Charles Butler, a demented artist, abducts live models and surgically remolds their faces, which inspire his macabre paintings. Jason Grant, jealous of irresponsible rock musician Scotty's attentions toward fellow student Janet Wells, provokes a fight which sends Janet and Scotty off together. On a deserted beach Butler strangles Scotty and abducts Janet. Marika Gold, a student in love with Jason, helps him determine Janet's whereabouts. Jason locates the artist's mansion, is captured by Butler's creatures, and escapes with the help of Janet, who has been hideously disfigured. Jason smashes Butler's face, flees the house, and is hospitalized following an automobile accident. He escapes police custody and returns to the mansion, where Marika screams at the sight of Jason's horribly disfigured face. *Painters. Psychopaths. Models. Musicians. Students. Abduction. Surgery. Disfiguration. Jealousy. Murder. Beaches. Automobile accidents.*

Note: Filmed in Miami. Working title: *Mayhem.*

SCREAM FREE *see* FREE GRASS

SCREAM OF FEAR (Great Britain)   F6.4289

Hammer Film Productions. *Dist* Columbia Pictures. 22 Aug **1961** [New York opening; c1 Sep 1961; LP20540]. Sd (RCA); b&w. 35mm. 81 min.

Prod-Writ Jimmy Sangster. *Exec Prod* Michael Carreras. *Dir* Seth Holt. *Dir Photog* Douglas Slocombe. *Camera Op* Desmond Davis. *Art Dir* Thomas Goswell. *Prod Dsgn* Bernard Robinson. *Supv Ed* James Needs. *Film Ed* Eric Boyd-Perkins. *Mus Comp* Clifton Parker. *Mus Supv* John Hollingsworth. *Sd Rec* Leslie Hammond, Ted Mason, Len Shilton. *Sd Ed* James Groom. *Asst Dir* David Tomblin. *Prod Mgr* Bill Hill. *Cont* Pamela Mann. *Wardrobe Mistress* Dora Lloyd. *Makeup Artist* Basil Newall. *Hairdresser* Eileen Bates. *Casting* Stuart Lyons. *Still Photog* George Higgins.

Cast: Susan Strasberg *(Penny Appleby)*, Ronald Lewis *(Bob)*, Ann Todd *(Jane Appleby)*, Christopher Lee *(Dr. Gerrard)*, John Serret *(Inspector Legrand)*, Leonard Sachs *(Spratt)*, Anne Blake *(Marie)*, Fred Johnson *(father)*, Bernard Brown, British *(gendarme)*, Richard Klee *(plainclothes sergeant)*, Madame Lobegue *(Swiss air hostess)*.

Mystery drama. After an absence of 10 years, crippled heiress Penny Appleby returns to her father's lavish villa on the French Riviera. Her stepmother, Jane, whom Penny meets for the first time, tells her that her father has been called away on business. That night, awakened by a flapping shutter, Penny rolls her wheelchair into the summerhouse and sees her father's corpse propped up in a chair. Jane and her father's close friend, Dr. Gerrard, try to persuade the hysterical girl that she was hallucinating; but the next night Penny again sees her father's corpse and becomes convinced that Jane and Dr. Gerrard have murdered him and are trying to drive her mad to deprive her of her inheritance. Aided by the family chauffeur Bob, Penny starts a search for her father's body, which eventually is found in the swimming pool. As Bob drives Penny to the police, he encounters Jane on a twisting mountain road. He gets out of the car, releases the brakes, embraces Jane, and smiles as Penny, the corpse, and the car plunge into the sea below. The next day, however, the lovers are startled by the appearance of Penny, who is revealed to be Penny's close friend. (The real Penny, after expressing concern for her father's safety, had died in a swimming accident; her friend assumed her identity and worked with Dr. Gerrard in exposing Jane's murderous plan.) Jane collapses in the wheelchair at the edge of the cliff, and Bob, believing her to be Penny, pushes it over the embankment as the police arrive to arrest him. *Cripples. Heiresses. Stepmothers. Physicians. Chauffeurs. Police. Filial relations. Murder. Inheritance. Impersonation. Corpses. Swimming pools. Riviera. Hallucinations. Automobile accidents.*

Note: Opened in London in Apr 1961 as *Taste of Fear.* Copyright claimant: Falcon Films.

SCREAM OF THE BUTTERFLY   F6.4290
Dist Emerson Film Enterprises. 15 Dec **1965** [Los Angeles opening]. Sd; b&w. 35mm. 76 min.

Dir Ebar Lobato. *Photog* Ray Dennis Steckler. *Film Ed* Don Snyder. *Prod Mgr* Joe Bardo.

Cast: Nelida Lobato *(Marla Williams),* Nick Novarro *(David),* William Turner, actor *(Paul Williams),* Leona Gage, Britt Nilsson.

Melodrama. David is arrested for the savage murder of his lover, Marla Williams, but to the consternation of the assistant district attorney in charge of the case, the district attorney seems strangely reluctant to prosecute, preferring to commit the murderer to a state hospital. Slowly, with the help of the public defender and the court psychiatrist, the sordid facts of the case are revealed: Marla marries millionaire Paul Williams after a whirlwind courtship, but he is unable to satisfy her boundless sexual desires, and she becomes involved in a clandestine affair with David. She plots to dispose of her husband, but she fails and discovers that she loves him after all. She visits David to break off the relationship and discovers that he has been trifling with her love. Unable to bear her taunts, he goes berserk and murders her. *District attorneys. Psychiatrists. Lawyers. Psychopaths. Millionaires. Marriage. Murder. Infidelity. Trials. Nymphomania. Sanitariums.*

Note: Filmed in Las Vegas. Working titles: *Four Cornered Triangle* and *The Passion Pit.*

THE SCREAMING HEAD *see* THE HEAD

SCREEN TEST   F6.4291
Dist Film-Makers' Cooperative. 12 Jun **1965** [New York opening]. Sd; b&w. 16mm. 70 min.

Prod-Dir Andy Warhol. *Writ* Ronald Tavel. *Prod Asst* Gerard Malanga.

Cast: Mario Montez *(transvestite),* Ronald Tavel *(off-camera voice).*

Satire. A transvestite is conducted through a screen test by a man off-camera. She is asked questions, ordered to perform certain actions, and compelled at the end to admit to being a man. *Transvestism. Female impersonation.*

Note: Also known as *Screen Test #2.* The frame remains fixed throughout.

SCREEN TEST #2 *see* SCREEN TEST

THE SCREENTEST GIRLS   F6.4292
Satyr IX Productions. *Dist* Sack Amusement Enterprises, Grads Corp. 10 Dec **1969** [New York showing; c29 Sep 1969; LU3585]. Sd; col. 35mm. 63 min. [Also available in 57 min. version.]

Prod-Dir Zoltan S.

Drama. Two naive young women, Sue and Linda, arrive in Hollywood seeking acting jobs and meet Mr. Zoltan, a producer of adult movies. They are required to strip for their interview, and afterwards Linda participates in a test lovemaking sequence with a young actor while Sue is made up by Barbara, Mr. Zoltan's secretary. Sue and Linda then watch the filming of a gorilla rape sequence involving Honey, a starlet who is chained, naked, to the wall. Sue and Linda are next asked to play a lesbian love scene, and because they are so inexperienced, Mr. Zoltan sends Barbara to teach them erotic techniques. At the end of the day, they learn that there is no immediate work available but that their screen tests will be shown in neighborhood theaters. *Actors. Secretaries. Motion picture producers. Lesbianism. Rape. Bestiality. Sexual techniques. Sex exploitation films. Hollywood. Gorillas.*

Note: Registered for copyright in 16mm.

SCROOGE (Great Britain)   F6.4293
Waterbury Films. *For* Cinema Center Films. *Dist* National General Pictures. 5 Nov **1970** [Los Angeles opening; c24 Oct 1970; LP39148]. Sd; col (Technicolor). 35mm (Panavision). 115 min. *MPAA rating* G.

Prod Robert H. Solo. *Exec Prod* Leslie Bricusse. *Assoc Prod* David Orton. *Dir* Ronald Neame. *Screenplay* Leslie Bricusse. *Dir Photog* Oswald Morris. *Camera Op* Jimmy Turrell. *Art Dir* Bob Cartwright. *Set Dresser* Pamela Cornell. *Prod Dsgn* Terence Marsh. *Main Titl* Ronald Searle. *Film Ed* Peter Weatherley. *Songs:* "A Christmas Carol," "Christmas Children," "I Hate

People," "Farver Chris'mas," "See the Phantoms," "December the Twenty-Fifth," "Happiness," "You ... You," "I Like Life," "The Beautiful Day," "Thank You Very Much," "I'll Begin Again" Leslie Bricusse. *Mus Cond & Supv* Ian Fraser. *Assoc Mus Supv* Herbert Spencer. *Mus Seq Stgd by* Paddy Stone. *Sd Mix* Jock May. *Dub Ed* James Shields. *Mus Ed* Kenneth Runyon. *Assoc Mus Ed* Robert Hathaway. *Asst Dir* Ted Sturgis. *Prod Mgr* Ed Harper. *Cont* Elaine Schreyeck. *Cost Dsgn* Margaret Furse. *Wardrobe Supv* Ivy Baker. *Ch Makeup Artist* George Frost. *Hairstyles* Bobbie Smith. *Sp Eff* Wally Veevers. *Sp Eff Photog* Jack Mills, photog.

Cast: Albert Finney *(Scrooge),* Alec Guinness *(Marley's ghost),* Edith Evans *(Ghost of Christmas Past),* Kenneth More *(Ghost of Christmas Present),* Laurence Naismith *(Fezziwig),* Michael Medwin *(nephew),* David Collings *(Bob Cratchit),* Anton Rodgers *(Tom Jenkins),* Suzanne Neve *(Isabel),* Frances Cuka *(Mrs. Cratchit),* Derek Francis, Roy Kinnear *(portly gentlemen),* Mary Peach *(nephew's wife),* Paddy Stone *(Ghost of Christmas Yet To Come),* Kay Walsh *(Mrs. Fezziwig),* Gordon Jackson *(nephew's friend),* Richard Beaumont *(Tiny Tim),* Geoffrey Bayldon *(toyshop owner),* Molly Weir, Helena Gloag *(women debtors),* Reg Lever *(Punch and Judy man),* Keith Marsh *(well wisher),* Marianne Stone *(party guest),* Philip Da Costa, Raymond Hoskins, Gaynor Hodgson, Nicholas Locise, Peter Lock, Joy Leigh, Sara Gibson, Clive Moss, John O'Brien, David Peacock, Michael Reardon, Karen Scargill, Terry Winter, Stephen Garlick.

Musical drama. Source: Charles Dickens, *A Christmas Carol* (London, 1843). Ebenezer Scrooge, a miserly London misanthrope who hates Christmas, is visited on Christmas Eve by the ghost of Marley, his former business partner, who informs him that three apparitions will come to him that night. Shortly after Marley vanishes, the Ghost of Christmas Past appears and takes Scrooge back in time to his youth and his courtship of Isabel; the ghost criticizes him for abandoning Isabel for the pursuit of money. It then disappears and the Ghost of Christmas Present materializes and takes Scrooge to the house of Bob Cratchit, one of Scrooge's underpaid employees. Scrooge watches as the Cratchits happily prepare for their Christmas dinner, despite the fact that Bob Cratchit is miserably poor. Of the Cratchit's five children, Scrooge is particularly drawn to Cratchit's crippled son, Tiny Tim. The ghost returns Scrooge to his house, and he is then taken to Tiny Tim's grave by the Ghost of Christmas Yet To Come. The old man is even more shocked when the ghost shows Scrooge his future, to be spent chained in Hell. Upon awakening on Christmas morning, Scrooge rushes from the house determined to celebrate Christmas. He buys a fine turkey and many toys and goes to the Cratchits' home. Although they are surprised by the old man's change of heart, they welcome him into their home. *Misers. Ghosts. Cripples. Children. Employer-employee relations. Poverty. Family life. Churchyards. Christmas. London. Visions. Hell.*

Note: Opened in London in Dec 1970; running time: 118 min.

SCUM OF THE EARTH!   F6.4294
Dist Box Office Spectaculars. 8 Oct **1963** [Maryland license]. Sd; b&w. 35mm. 71 min.

Prod Davis Freeman. *Dir* Lewis H. Gordon. *Camera* Marvin Lester. *Film Ed* Patrick Murphy. *Mus* Manuel Ortiz. *Sd* Davis Mason.

Cast: Vickie Miles *(Kim),* Thomas Sweetwood *(Harmon),* Sandra Sinclair *(Sandy),* Lawrence Wood *(Lang),* Mal Arnold *(Larry),* Craig Maudslay, Jr. *(Ajax),* Edward Mann, actor *(Mr. Sherwood),* Toni Calvert *(Marie).*

Melodrama. Sandra, who models for a teenaged gang that traffics in photographs of young women being abused and degraded, persuades her innocent teenage roommate, Kim, to replace her at one of the photography sessions. Kim is unwittingly photographed in a seemingly compromising pose, and she is blackmailed into continued posing. Members of the gang overhear another model discussing plans to go to the police, and they take brutal revenge. At another photography session, one of the leaders of the gang attacks Kim and is killed by the other gang leader. In the subsequent investigation, the gang leader is exposed along with the older mastermind of the operation. The two men meet their deaths, and the chief photographer destroys all evidence of Kim's past association with the gang. *Models. Roommates. Photographers. Innocents. Gangs. Pornography. Adolescence. Sadism. Blackmail. Murder.*

Note: Also known as *Devil's Camera.* Davis Freeman and Lewis H. Gordon are pseudonyms for David Friedman and Herschell Gordon Lewis.

SCUSI, FACCIAMO L'AMORE? *see* LISTEN, LET'S MAKE LOVE

SE PERMETTETE, PARLIAMO DI DONNE *see* LET'S TALK ABOUT WOMEN

SE TUTTE LE DONNE DEL MONDO *see* KISS THE GIRLS AND MAKE THEM DIE

THE SEA GULL (United States/Great Britain) F6.4295

Sidney Lumet Productions. *Dist* Warner Bros.–Seven Arts, Inc. 22 Dec **1968** [New York opening; c1 Dec 1968; LP37140]. Sd; col (Technicolor). 35mm. 141 min. *MPAA rating G.*

Prod-Dir Sidney Lumet. *Assoc Prod* Frank Sherwin Green. *Trans & Adapt* Moura Budberg. *Photog* Gerry Fisher. *Camera Op* Anders Bodin. *Scenic Artist* Erik Björk. *Dsgn Asst* Lennart Clemens, Philip Rosenberg. *Set Dresser* Rune Hjelm, Rolf Larsson. *Prod Dsgn* Tony Walton. *Titl Dsgn* F. Hillsberg Inc. *Film Ed* Alan Heim. *Ed Asst* Joanne Burke. *Sd Rec* Leslie Hammond. *Boom Op* Fred Tomlin. *Asst Dir* Waldemar Bergendahl. *Prod Mgr* Ronald Sundberg. *Cont* Inga-Lisa Britz. *Cost* Tony Walton. *Wardrobe* Eve Faloon, Maj Erikson. *Makeup & Hairstyles* Tina Johansson, Kjell Gustavsson.

Cast: James Mason *(Trigorin)*, Vanessa Redgrave *(Nina)*, Simone Signoret *(Arkadina)*, David Warner *(Konstantin)*, Harry Andrews *(Sorin)*, Denholm Elliott *(Dorn)*, Eileen Herlie *(Polina)*, Alfred Lynch *(Medvedenko)*, Ronald Radd *(Shamraev)*, Kathleen Widdoes *(Masha)*, Frej Lindqvist *(Yakov)*, Karen Miller *(housemaid)*.

Drama. Source: Anton Pavlovich Chekhov, *Chayka* (Saint Petersburg opening: 17 Oct 1896). In late 19th-century Russia Arkadina, a famous actress, visits the country estate where her brother Sorin, a retired official, is spending his remaining years. Self-centered and penurious, Arkadina pays only random attention to the needs of her son, Konstantin, and dismisses his playwriting attempts as absurdly experimental and "decadent." Already distressed by the realization that his vain mother does not care to be reminded that she has a son in his twenties, Konstantin is troubled further by the presence of her current lover, Trigorin, a successful novelist whose polished charm has completely captivated the naive and impressionable Nina, a young woman from a neighboring estate whom Konstantin has long loved. One afternoon Konstantin lays a sea gull he has killed at Nina's feet and warns her that someday he too will be dead. Also present during the long weekend is Masha, the bailiff Shamraev's daughter, who, hopelessly in love with Konstantin, wears only black, drinks too much, and openly sniffs snuff. Nina decides to go to Moscow and arranges to meet Trigorin there. Two years pass, and Arkadina and Trigorin return to the estate when Sorin falls ill. During the interim Masha has married the schoolteacher Medvedenko, whom she does not love, and Konstantin has had some of his writings published. Nina became Trigorin's mistress, but he deserted her after she bore him a child, who died. Now an actress in a provincial theater, Nina has refused to see Konstantin. The same group, except for Nina, assembles at the estate, and the self-indulgent Arkadina casually remarks that she has not read any of her son's works. Then, while the others are involved in a card game, Konstantin encounters Nina outside the house. He declares his undying love for her, but she replies that she still loves Trigorin. Despondent, Konstantin goes off and shoots himself. *Actors. Novelists. Playwrights. Schoolteachers. Neighbors. Mistresses. Brother-sister relationship. Filial relations. Vanity. Lovelorn. Suicide. Marriage. Russia. Sea gulls.*

Note: Location scenes filmed in Sweden. Opened in London in Dec 1969.

SEA NYMPHS *see* **VIOLATED PARADISE**

SEA OF SAND *see* **DESERT PATROL**

THE SEA PIRATE (France/Italy/Spain) F6.4296

Edic Films–Arco Film–Balcázar P. C. *Dist* Paramount Pictures. 28 Jun **1967** [New York opening; c28 Jun 1967; LP34741]. Sd; col (Eastman Color). 35mm (Techniscope). 83 min.

Exec Prod Georges de La Grandière, Francisco Balcázar. *Assoc Prod* Richard Hellman. *Dir* (see note) Sergio Bergonzelli. *English Vers Supv* Roy Rowland. *Screenplay* Georges de La Grandière, José Antonio de la Loma, Giovanni Simonelli. *Dial* Georges Farrel. *Adapt* Jacques Séverac. *Photog* Juan Gelpi. *Art Dir* Juan Alberto Soler. *Film Ed* Jean-Michel Gautier. *Mus* Georges Garvarentz. *Song:* "Surcouf" Georges Garvarentz, Joe Juliano. *Sung by* Les Compagnons de la Chanson. *Prod Mgr* Valentín Sallent. *Sp Photog Eff* John P. Fulton.

Cast: Gérard Barray *(Capt. Robert Surcouf)*, Antonella Lualdi *(Margaret Carruthers)*, Terence Morgan *(Lord Blackwood)*, Geneviève Casile *(Marie Catherine)*, Frank Oliveras *(Nicolas)*, Armand Mestral *(Captain Fell)*, Gérard Tichy *(Kernan)*, Alberto Cevenini *(Garneray)*, Giani Esposito *(Napoleon)*, Fernando Sancho *(jailer)*, Vidal Molina *(André Chamblés)*, Gonzalo Esquiroz *(Captain Toward)*, Jorge Rigaud *(admiral)*, Monica Randal *(Josephine)*, Aldo Sambrell, Tomas Blanco, Rossella Bergamonti.

Adventure melodrama. In 1795, on the island of Saint-Malo, Robert Surcouf, a young Frenchman, is denied the hand of his beloved Marie Catherine because her father wants a wealthy son-in-law. Vowing to make a fortune, Surcouf goes to the Île de France and joins the French pirates fighting the British in the Indian Ocean. Although he breaks through the English blockade with a ship bringing food to the starving natives on the island, he receives no recognition since he was not officially authorized for the voyage. Furious, Surcouf sets out for Paris to demand a reward, intending to take Marie Catherine along, but he is attacked on the road and manages to save himself by leaping into the carriage of Margaret Carruthers, a beautiful American woman. He remains with her for a time, but after a duel with her fiancé, Lord Blackwood, Surcouf returns to the Île de France. Later, he learns that Marie Catherine's father is forcing her into a loveless marriage, and he immediately sets sail for Saint-Malo. Arriving in time to stop the wedding, he defeats Marie Catherine's suitor and marries her himself. *Fortune hunters. Pirates. British. Americans in foreign countries. Courtship. Ambition. Filial relations. Marriage—Arranged. Ships. Rewards. Weddings. Saint-Malo. Île de France. Indian Ocean. Paris. Duels.*

Note: Opened in Paris in Aug 1966 as *Surcouf, le tigre des sept mers*; in Italy as *Surcouf l'eroe dei sette mari*; in Madrid in Dec 1967 as *El tigre de los siete mares*; running time: 98 min. One U. S. source indicates that the film is composed of footage from *Surcouf, le dernier corsaire* and *Le retour de Surcouf*, both produced in France in 1965. Also included is footage from *Son of Captain Blood*, q. v. French working title: *Tonnerre sur l'Océan Indien*. Roy Rowland is credited as director in some U. S. sources.

THE SEAFIGHTERS *see* **OPERATION BIKINI**

SEANCE ON A WET AFTERNOON (Great Britain) F6.4297

Beaver Films–Allied Film Makers. *Dist* Artixo Productions. 5 Nov **1964** [New York opening; c5 Jul 1964; LF165]. Sd; b&w. 35mm. 115 min.

Pres by Artie Shaw, Don Getz. A Richard Attenborough–Bryan Forbes Production. *Prod* Richard Attenborough, Bryan Forbes. *Assoc Prod* Jack Rix. *Dir-Screenplay* Bryan Forbes. *Photog* Gerry Turpin. *Art Dir* Ray Simm. *Set Decor* Peter James. *Film Ed* Derek York. *Mus Comp & Cond* John Barry. *Sd Rec* Bill Daniels. *Asst Dir* Christopher Dryhurst.

Cast: Kim Stanley *(Myra Savage)*, Richard Attenborough *(Billy Savage)*, Mark Eden *(Charles Clayton)*, Nanette Newman *(Mrs. Clayton)*, Judith Donner *(Amanda Clayton)*, Patrick Magee *(Superintendent Walsh)*, Gerald Sim *(Sergeant Beedle)*, Margaret Lacey *(woman at 1st seance)*, Maria Kazan *(other woman at seance)*, Lionel Gamlin *(man at seances)*, Marian Spencer *(Mrs. Wintry)*, Ronald Hines *(policeman at Clayton's)*, Hajni Biro *(maid at Clayton's)*, Diana Lambert *(Clayton's secretary)*, Godfrey James *(Clayton's chauffeur)*, Arnold Bell *(Mr. Weaver)*, Stanley Morgan *(man in Trilby)*, Michael Lees *(plainclothes policeman)*, Margaret McGrath *(woman at 2d seance)*, Frank Singuineau *(bus conductor)*.

Drama. Source: Mark McShane, *Seance on a Wet Afternoon* (London, 1961). Myra Savage, a professional medium, has contact with the "other world" through her dead son, Arthur, who was actually stillborn, a fact Myra refuses to accept. With her doting husband, Billy, she conceives a plan to gain recognition for herself; Billy will kidnap a child, and, after the ransom is paid, Myra will go to the parents and offer her help in locating the child through her supernatural powers. Billy reluctantly abducts Amanda Clayton, the young daughter of a wealthy industrialist. Myra contacts the parents and Billy collects the ransom, but the child's return is delayed when she contracts a fever. Billy wants to return her immediately but the mentally deranged Myra announces that she has contacted Arthur and he has said that he wants a playmate. Myra tells Billy to send the little girl to Arthur. Instead of killing the child, who has seen Billy's face, he leaves her in the woods where she is sure to be found by nearby scouts. Police Superintendent Walsh, knowing of Myra's call on the parents, comes to her and asks her to hold a seance for possible help in finding the missing girl. Myra goes into her trance, but instead of delivering the story prepared beforehand, she reveals the entire truth, while Billy watches helplessly. *Mediums. Children. Industrialists. Police. Ambition. Kidnaping. Death. Mental illness. Stillbirth. Seances.*

Note: Location scenes filmed in London. Opened in London in Jun 1964; running time: 116 min.

SEARCH FOR PEACE (United States/Netherlands) F6.4298

Mason Shaw. *Dist* Shaw Film Distributors. Oct **1968** [Los Angeles showing]. Sd; b&w and col (Technicolor). 35mm. 86 min.

Prod–Compilation Mason Shaw.

Anthology. Four short films are assembled to demonstrate how man expresses his desire for peace through music. HEARTBEAT OF A CITY features the city of Amsterdam, long a haven for refugees from political and religious persecution. The film focuses on the Jewish tradition of the cantor, who sings the prayers from the sacred texts, and the unique style developed by the Amsterdam school of liturgical singing. In PAN, a boy spies upon a nesting area for birds, and through the music he plays on his panpipe, he is accepted by the birds as part of nature. Attacked by a swan which guards the area, the boy defends himself and merges once again into nature through the power of his music. In BIG CITY BLUES, a small boy is playing with a rabbit near a partially completed concrete building. A girl snatches the rabbit from him; it escapes from her; and she follows it into the building, past two men lying drunk against a wall. One of the men chases her through the building and catches her. As she is struggling with him, she falls through a hole in the floor and is killed. The police arrive and take the two men away. The boy gets his rabbit back, only to have it taken away by another girl. SYMPHONY OF THE TROPICS depicts life in Surinam, where people of different races, religions, and cultural backgrounds live together in peace, developing their own music as a reflection of their harmonious daily lives. *Political refugees. Cantors. Jews. Children. Police. Music. Religious persecution. Nature. Urban life. Theft. Drunkenness. Race relations. Amsterdam. Surinam. Birds. Rabbits and hares.*

Note: *Big City Blues* was produced in the Netherlands in 1961 at 24 min (b&w); *Heartbeat of a City* at 24 min (col); *Pan* at 22 min (b&w); and *Symphony of the Tropics* at 17 min (col).

THE SEARCH OF THE CASTAWAYS *see* **IN SEARCH OF THE CASTAWAYS**

SEARCHING FOR VENUS *see* **AROUND THE WORLD WITH NOTHING ON**

SEASIDE SWINGERS (Great Britain) **F6.4299**
Fitzroy–Maycroft. *Dist* Embassy Pictures. Jun **1965**. Sd; col (Technicolor). 35mm (Techniscope). 94 min.

Prod Ronald J. Kahn. *Exec Prod* Maurice J. Wilson. *Dir* James Hill. *Screenplay* Anthony Marriott, Jeri Matos, James Hill. *Story* Anthony Marriott. *Photog* Nicolas Roeg. *Art Dir* Edward Carrick. *Film Ed* Tristam Cones. *Mus* Tony Osborne. *Song:* "Second Time Around" Clive Westlake. *Songs:* "All I Want Is You," "A Girl Needs a Boy" Clive Westlake, Kenny Lynch. *Song:* "Indubitably Me" Kenny Lynch. *Song:* "Love Me, Please" Clive Westlake, Kenny Lynch, Michael Sarne. *Songs:* "Now Ain't That Somethin'—Caw (Blimey)," "Romeo Jones" Mort Shuman, J. Leslie McFarland. *Song:* "What's Cookin'?" Jackie Rae, Tony Osborne. *Choreog* Gillian Lynne. *Sd* John Cox, Dickie Bird. *Asst Dir* Patrick Marsden. *Prod Mgr* John Pellatt.

Cast: John Leyton *(Gerry Pullman)*, Michael Sarne *(Timothy Gilbin)*, Freddie and the Dreamers *(The Chefs)*, Ron Moody *(Professor Bastinado)*, Liz Fraser *(Miss Slightly)*, Grazina Frame *(Christina Barrington de Witt)*, Jennifer Baker *(Jennifer)*, Susan Baker *(Susan)*, The Mojos *(themselves)*, Nicholas Parsons *(Julian Goddard)*, Hazel Hughes *(Mrs. Barrington de Witt)*, Michael Ripper *(Mr. Pullman)*, Richard O'Sullivan *(Jimmy)*, Tony Daines *(Mike)*, Peter Gilmore *(Kenneth)*, Patrick Newell *(Mr. Hoskins)*, Charles Lloyd Pack *(Mr. Close)*, Gaby Vargas *(Anne)*, Nicola Riley *(little girl)*, Marion Grimaldi *(vision mixer)*, Coral Morphew *(Serena)*, The Leroys *(themselves)*, The Gillian Lynne Dancers.

Comedy with music. At a popular English seaside resort, a group of teenagers recently employed for the summer are briefed by camp secretary Miss Slightly. The group includes Gerry Pullman, a would-be singer; Timothy Gilbin, a wealthy, egotistical playboy; Christina Barrington de Witt, a reluctant opera student who has run away from her snobbish aunt in order to sing pop music; identical twins Jennifer and Susan; and Jimmy and Mike, two former store clerks. Everyone, including the resort's zany chefs, becomes interested in winning a talent contest to be televised, and the young people join together to stage a musical act. Christina's aunt arrives to supervise her niece's singing lessons and social life. With the help of the chefs and Christina's sympathetic singing coach, Professor Bastinado, Mrs. Barrington de Witt's attention is diverted as Christina goes on stage with the "Lucky Seven." The group wins first place, and romance blooms between Christina and Gerry. *Singers. Aunts. Cooks. Playboys. Music teachers. Twins. Adolescence. Resorts. Talent contests. Opera. Snobbery. Summer.*

Note: Location scenes filmed at Clacton-on-Sea, Essex. Released in Great Britain in Jan 1965 as *Every Day's a Holiday.*

THE SEASON FOR LOVE (France) **F6.4300**
Jad Films. *Dist* Gaston Hakim Productions International. 8 May **1963** [New York opening]. Sd; b&w. 35mm. 100 min.

Prod Clara d' Ovar, Peter Oser. *Dir* Pierre Kast. *Screenplay* Pierre Kast, Alain Aptekman. *Dial* Pierre Kast. *Photog* Sacha Vierny. *Art Dir* Jacques Saulnier. *Film Ed* Yannick Bellon. *Mus* Georges Delerue. *Sd* Guy Chichignoud. *Prod Mgr* Georges Charlot.

Cast: Daniel Gélin *(Jacques Saint-Fond)*, Françoise Arnoul *(Geneviève)*, Pierre Vaneck *(Sylvain)*, Françoise Prévost *(Françoise)*, Alexandra Stewart *(Sandra)*, Anne-Marie Bauman *(Anne-Marie)*, Hubert Noël *(Hubert)*, Edouard Molinaro *(new male secretary)*, Michèle Vérez *(Michèle)*, Ursula Vian *(Ursula)*, Anne Colette, Claudie Bourlon, Frédéric Lambre, André Certes, Christiane Bréaud.

Drama. Sylvain and Geneviève are modern young sophisticates living an easy life among the ruins of one of Louis XV's unfinished cities. Sylvain was once regarded as a promising writer on the strength of his first book, but he has written nothing since. Geneviève has had a succession of love affairs; now that she is apparently settled with Sylvain, she wonders if their marriage can last. When the local squire, Jacques Saint-Fond, falls in love with Geneviève, she finds herself returning his affection; furthermore, Sylvain is momentarily drawn to Françoise, the squire's wife. Eventually, Geneviève reproaches Sylvain for his immaturity and lack of ambition. Following their argument, she decides to leave him and return to Paris with the squire, even though his political career will be ended. Saint-Fond is actually happy to rid himself of public office and a frigid wife. As they prepare to depart, Geneviève realizes that Sylvain is totally helpless without her, yet she needs the lonely and mature Saint-Fond. The only solution is an unorthodox one: the three of them agree to live together in Paris. *Authors. Landed gentry. Politicians. Marriage. Infidelity.*

Note: Released in France in Aug 1961 as *La morte-saison des amours.*

SEASON OF PASSION (Australia/Great Britain) **F6.4301**
Hecht-Hill-Lancaster Pty. *Dist* United Artists. 4 Oct **1961** [Cleveland opening; c29 Jan 1960; LP23379]. Sd; b&w. 35mm. 93 min.

Prod-Dir Leslie Norman. *Assoc Prod* Cecil F. Ford. *Screenplay* John Dighton. *Dir Photog* Paul Beeson. *Camera Op* Jeffrey Seaholme. *Art Dir* Jim Morahan. *Film Ed* Gordon Hales. *Mus* Benjamin Frankel. *Sd Mix* Alan Allen, sd. *Asst Dir* Alex Ezard. *Prod Mgr* Ron Whelan.

Cast: Ernest Borgnine *(Roo)*, Anne Baxter *(Olive)*, John Mills *(Barney)*, Angela Lansbury *(Pearl)*, Vincent Ball *(Dowd)*, Ethel Gabriel *(Emma)*, Janette Craig *(Bubba)*, Deryck Barnes *(Spruiker)*, Tom Lurich *("The Atomic Bomber")*, Al Thomas *(cane-cutter)*, Dana Wilson *(little girl)*, Al Garcia *(cane-cutter)*, Frank Wilson, actor *(cane-cutter)*, Jessica Noad *(Nancy)*.

Comedy-drama. Source: Ray Lawler, *Summer of the Seventeenth Doll* (first performance: Melbourne, Nov 1954). For 16 years, lusty cane-cutters Roo and Barney have been spending their 5-month layoffs in Sydney with their mistresses, Olive and Nancy. Annually, Roo presents Olive, a barmaid, with a doll as a souvenir of their idyll, but this year Roo has quit work after a fight with a young coworker, Dowd, and has no money. Furthermore, Nancy has married. Although Olive recruits in her stead the widow Pearl, the substitute lacks enthusiasm for the arrangement. The carefree gaiety of summers past is difficult to recapture, and there are numerous conflicts. During one such altercation, Roo questions Barney's virility, and Barney derides Roo's waning strength and leadership. Pearl and Barney part, and Olive and Roo, while lamenting loss of youth, decide to marry. *Migratory workers. Barmaids. Mistresses. Widows. Middle age. Unemployment. Marriage. Dolls. Sydney (Australia).*

Note: Opened in Sydney in Dec 1959 as *Summer of the Seventeenth Doll*; in Great Britain in 1960 as *Season of Passion*; running time: 95 min.

SEAT OF PASSION, PARK OF PLEASURE **F6.4302**
Athena Productions. 18 Sep **1969** [San Francisco showing]. Sd?; col? 35mm? [Feature length assumed.]

Sex film. A nude couple have intercourse while riding on a bus through a staid San Francisco neighborhood to Golden Gate Park. There they continue to make love. *Nudity. Sexuality. Buses. San Francisco. San Francisco—Golden Gate Park.*

Note: Filmed on location in San Francisco.

SEAWEED SANDWICH **F6.4303**
Merrill-Hammond Productions. 11 Sep **1970** [San Diego, California, showing]. Sd; col. 16mm. [Feature film, length unknown.]

Prod H. Glenn Merrill. *Co-prod* Steve Hammond. *Photog* Bert Kersey. *Film Ed* Bert Kersey. *Mus* Ann Shimeall, Tom Gunn, The Rugg. *Song:* "Every Day Is a Good Day" Ann Shimeall.

Documentary. Among the activities taking place at the San Diego beach area are two-man volleyball, board and body surfing, and the 1970 Over-the-Line World Championships. *Surfers. Beaches. Volleyball. San Diego.*

SEBASTIAN (Great Britain) **F6.4304**
Maccius Productions. *Dist* Paramount Pictures. 24 Jan **1968** [New York opening; c15 Dec 1967; LP36948]. Sd; col (Eastman Color, print by Technicolor). 35mm. 100 min.

A Herbert Brodkin-Michael Powell Production. *Prod* Herbert Brodkin, Michael Powell. *Prod Exec* Robert Berger. *Assoc Prod* John Pellatt. *Dir* David Greene. *Screenplay* Gerald Vaughan-Hughes. *Story* Leo Marks. *Photog* Gerry Fisher. *Camera Op* Jimmy Turrell. *Focus* Wally Byatt. *Art Dir* Fred Carter. *Set Dresser* Terence Morgan, II. *Prod Dsgn* Wilfrid Shingleton. *Main Titl* Richard Williams Films. *Film Ed* Brian Smedley-Aston. *Mus Comp & Cond* Jerry Goldsmith. *Song:* "Here Comes the Night" Jerry Goldsmith, Hal Shaper. *Sung by* Anita Harris. *Sd* H. L. Bird, Gerry Humphreys. *Asst Dir* Gordon Gilbert. *Prod Mgr* Clifton Brandon. *Cont* Ann Skinner. *Wardrobe Supv* Bridget Sellers. *Makeup* Bob Lawrence.

Cast: Dirk Bogarde *(Sebastian)*, Susannah York *(Becky)*, Lilli Palmer *(Elsa Shahn)*, John Gielgud *(Head of Intelligence)*, Margaret Johnston *(Miss Elliott)*, Nigel Davenport *(General Phillips)*, John Ronane *(Jameson)*, Susan Whitman *(Tilly)*, Ann Beach *(Pamela)*, Ann Sidney *(Naomi)*, Veronica Clifford *(Ginny)*, Jeanne Roland *(Randy)*, Lyn Pinkney *(Joan)*, Louise Pernell *(Thelma)*, Janet

Munro (Carol), Ronald Fraser (Toby), Donald Sutherland (American), Alan Freeman (TV disc jockey), Charles Lloyd Pack (chess player), Portland Mason (The "UG" Girl), Hayward Morse, James Belchamber, Charles Farrell, British, Jennifer Lautrec, Sally Douglas, David Toguri, Stuart Hoyle, Ann Norman, Edwina Carroll, Robin Tolhurst.

Comedy-drama. Sebastian, a former Oxford professor, heads the all-female decoding staff of British Intelligence. One day he has a chance meeting with young Becky Howard and is so impressed by her mental agility that he offers her a job deciphering codes used by foreign agents. A crisis develops when Elsa Shahn, a former Communist and one of Sebastian's most trusted associates, is accused of being a poor security risk by the brutish Inspector Phillips. But Sebastian persuades the Head of Intelligence that Elsa is vital to his operation. During all of this the headstrong Becky seduces Sebastian, thereby irritating his longtime mistress, Carol Fancy, a former pop singer. Elsa then betrays the trust placed in her by giving decoded information to a left-wing political organization. Obligated to resign, Sebastian leaves London and returns to his professorship at Oxford. Sometime later he is summoned back to his post by Head of Intelligence to help decode the signals emanating from a newly-launched Russian satellite. While looking for Becky (who has left the department), he runs into Carol and is lured to a party at her flat and drugged with LSD. He is saved from killing himself while hallucinating by the timely intervention of Inspector Phillips, who has been trailing him. Eventually, Sebastian locates Becky and learns that he is the father of her baby. A noise from the child's rattle provides Sebastian with the clue to the Russian signals; and, aided by his still-faithful team of girls, he breaks the sputnik code. *Professors. Communists. Mistresses. Cryptography. Seduction. Perfidy. Illegitimacy. Suicide. Satellites. LSD. London. Oxford University. Great Britain—Intelligence service.*

Note: Location scenes filmed at Manchester University. Opened in London in Mar 1968. Prerelease title: *Mister Sebastian.*

DER 6-TAGE-KRIEG see **SINAI COMMANDOS**

THE 2ND BEST SECRET AGENT IN THE WHOLE WIDE WORLD
(Great Britain)　　　　　　　　　　　　　　　　　　　F6.4305
Alistair Film Productions. *Dist* Embassy Pictures. 17 Nov **1965** [Houston opening]. Sd; col (Eastman Color, print by Pathé). 35mm. 96 min.

Pres by Joseph E. Levine. *Exec Prod* S. J. H. Ward. *Dir* Lindsay Shonteff. *Screenplay* Howard Griffiths, Lindsay Shonteff. *Photog* Terry Maher. *Film Ed* Ron Pope. *Mus Comp & Cond* Bertram Chappell. *Song:* "The Second Best Secret Agent in the Whole Wide World" (see note) Sammy Cahn, James Van Heusen. *Sung by* Sammy Davis, Jr. *Sd* Terry Rawlings, Joe Charman. *Asst Dir* Ernie Lewis. *Prod & Location Mgr* Estelle E. Richmond.

Cast: Tom Adams (*Charles Vine*), Karel Stepanek (*Henrik Jacobsen*), Veronica Hurst (*Julia Lindberg*), Peter Bull (*Masterman*), John Arnatt (*Rockwell*), Francis De Wolff (*Walter Pickering*), Felix Felton (*Tetchnikov*), George Pastell (*Russian commissar*), Judy Huxtable (*computer center girl*), Gary Hope (*army officer*), Denis Holmes (*Maltby*), Billy Milton (*Wilson*), Carole Blake (*crossword puzzle girl*), Tony Wall (*Sadistikov*), Oliver MacGreevy (*1st Russian commissar*), Stuart Saunders (*police inspector*), Paul Tann (*Vladimir Sheehee*), Shelagh Booth (*governess*), John Evitts ("*Killer*"), Robert Marsden (*August Jacobsen*), Mona Chong (*Chinese girl*), Michael Godfrey (*Roger*), Julian Strange (*hotel clerk*), Claire Gordon (*hospital doctor*), J. A. B. Dubin-Behrmann (*Slavonic official*), Sarah Maddern (*hotel maid*).

Action comedy-drama. Secret agent Charles Vine is assigned by the British Foreign Office the extremely dangerous job of protecting the life of Swedish scientist Henrik Jacobsen, the inventor of an anti-gravity machine. Jacobsen and his assistant, Julia Lindberg, arrive in England to negotiate the sale of the valuable invention to the British government. Agent Vine must protect him from Russian agents who would rather see him dead than imparting his knowledge to the British. From the time of their arrival in England, Jacobsen and Julia are continually ambushed by the Russian agents, but Vine always manages to save them. As the scientist and his assistant are departing for their homeland after selling the formula to Britain for a considerable sum, they are ambushed again, and Vine is injured. Shortly afterwards, it is revealed that Jacobsen tried to sell his secret to both the Russians and the British. *Secret agents. Swedes. Scientists. Russians. Perfidy. Inventions. Great Britain—Foreign Office.*

Note: Released in Great Britain in 1965 as *Licensed To Kill.* The title song was added by Embassy Pictures for U. S. release.

SECOND FIDDLE TO A STEEL GUITAR　　　　　　F6.4306
Marathon Pictures. 14 Sep **1965** [Cincinnati, Ohio, opening; c28 Jul 1965; LP34810]. Sd; col (Eastman Color). 35mm (SuperScope). 107 min.

Exec Prod Victor Lewis. *Assoc Prod* Edward R. Neely. *Dir* Victor Duncan. *Screenplay* Seymour D. Rothman. *Photog Dir* Gary Galbraith. *Camera Op* Pat Burke. *Asst Camera* Sid O'Berry. *Scenic Art* Bill Gernert. *Film Ed* John Mullin,

Zavala-Riss Productions. *Score & Mus Arr* Audrey Williams. *Rec Dir* Tommy Strong. *Rec Supv* Jack Sanders. *Sd Engr* Vilmars Zile. *Asst Dir* Robert Smawley. *Script Clerk* Pat Burton. *Makeup Artist* Allie Clayton. *Hairstyles* Marsha Kaye Gray.

Cast: Arnold Stang (*Jubal A. Bristol*), Pamela Hayes (*Mrs. Bristol*), Leo Gorcey, Huntz Hall (*stagehands*).

Cast—Guest Stars: Homer and Jethro, Kitty Wells, Webb Pierce, Faron Young, Minnie Pearl, Lefty Frizzell, Sonny James, Bill Monroe, George Hamilton, IV, Del Reeves, Carl Butler, Pearl Butler, Merle Kilgore, Little Jimmy Dickens, Johnnie Wright, Dottie West, Billy Walker, Connie Smith, The Cheatin' Hearts, Old Joe Clark, Delores Smiley, Marilyn Gallo, Pete Drake, Bill Phillips, singer, Buddy Spiker, Murv Shiner, Curly Fox, Clyde Smith, Lamar Morris, Dave Lewis, singer, Bob Perry.

Comedy with music. Jubal A. Bristol, like most of his Nashville neighbors, loves country and western music, even though his socialite wife fails to share his fervent interest. In fact, Mrs. Bristol is chairwoman for the city's biggest current social event, a benefit performance by an Italian opera company. At the last minute, the Italians are unable to appear, and Jubal is called upon to save the day by getting 30 top country entertainers to perform. The acts enthrall the audience, but backstage two inept stagehands create chaos when one of them dons a musketeer's outfit. Jubal, under the impression that the disguised bumbler is a member of the opera company, cracks him over the head with a mallet and hides the body. Nevertheless, the show is a tremendous hit and succeeds in converting Mrs. Bristol into a country and western music fan. *Songs include:* "Don't Let Me Cross Over," "Hello Walls," "John Henry," "Born To Lose," "Young Love," "Columbus Stockade Blues," "Honky Tonk Angels," "Ain't That a Shame," "Careless Love," and "Abilene." *Socialites. Stagehands. Entertainers. Country music. Charity. Opera. Nashville (Tennessee).*

Note: Filmed on location in Nashville, Tennessee.

THE SECOND TIME AROUND　　　　　　　　　　F6.4307
Cummings-Harman Productions. *Dist* Twentieth Century-Fox Film Corp. 26 Oct **1961** [Los Angeles showing; c1 Nov 1961; LP20618]. Sd (Westrex); col (De Luxe). 35mm (CinemaScope). 99 min.

A Jack Cummings Production. *Dir* Vincent Sherman. *Screenplay* Oscar Saul, Cecil Dan Hansen. *Art Dir* Jack Martin Smith, Walter M. Simonds. *Set Decor* Walter M. Scott, Stuart A. Reiss. *Main Titl* Pacific Title. *Film Ed* Betty Steinberg. *Mus* Gerald Fried. *Titl Song* Henry Mancini. *Sd* Alfred Bruzlin, Frank W. Moran. *Asst Dir* Jack R. Berne. *Cost Dsgn* Don Feld. *Makeup* Ben Nye. *Hairstyles* Helen Turpin.

Cast: Debbie Reynolds (*Lucretia Rogers*), Steve Forrest (*Dan Jones*), Andy Griffith (*Pat Collins*), Juliet Prowse (*Rena, a dancehall girl*), Thelma Ritter (*Aggie*), Ken Scott (*Sheriff John Yoss*), Isobel Elsom (*Mrs. Rogers*), Rudolph Acosta (*Rodriguez*), Timothy Carey (*Bonner*), Tom Greenway (*Shack*), Eleanor Audley (*Mrs. Trask*), Blossom Rock (*Mrs. Collins*), Tracy Stratford (*Cissie*), Jimmy Garrett (*Tobey*), Lisa Pons (*Mrs. Rodriguez*), Nicky Blair (*Mr. Stone*), Jack Orrison (*editor*).

Comedy. Source: Richard Emery Roberts, *Star in the West* (New York, 1951). In 1911, recently widowed Lucretia Rogers leaves her two small children and her frosty mother-in-law and travels to Charleyville, Arizona Territory, where she has been offered a storekeeper job by a friend of her late husband. Upon arrival, however, she learns that her benefactor has been killed in a holdup, and she takes a farmhand job on a ranch owned by Aggie Gates. Lu's outspoken nature and good looks win her the admiration of both Dan Jones, the handsome owner of the local saloon, and Pat Collins, a mother-dominated rancher. Aggie tries to marry off Lu to Pat, but Pat's mother discourages the match. When Lu proves that the dishonest sheriff, John Yoss, is in league with gunmen, the women and the law-abiding citizens of Charleyville elect her as the new sheriff. Yoss retaliates by attacking and looting the town and kidnaping Lu; but Dan, Pat, and the townspeople form a posse, raid the gunmen's hideout, and rescue Lu. The reward money enables Lu to bring her two children to the new state of Arizona. As she throws her arms around Dan, Lu tosses her sheriff's badge to Pat. *Widows. Employment—Women. Farmhands. Ranchers. Sheriffs. Saloon keepers. Law and order. Statehood. Kidnaping. Posses. Arizona. New York City.*

Note: Prerelease titles: *Star in the West, The Calico Sheriff,* and *Mother Ought To Marry.*

SECONDS　　　　　　　　　　　　　　　　　　　F6.4308
Douglas & Lewis Productions-Joel Productions-Gibraltar Productions. *Dist* Paramount Pictures. 5 Oct **1966** [New York opening; c14 Sep 1966; LP33179]. Sd; b&w. 35mm. 106 min.

Prod Edward Lewis. *Dir* John Frankenheimer. *Screenplay* Lewis John Carlino. *Dir Photog* James Wong Howe. *Art Dir* Ted Haworth. *Set Decor* John Austin. *Main Titl* Saul Bass. *Film Ed* Ferris Webster, David Webster. *Mus* Jerry Goldsmith. *Song:* "That Old Black Magic" Johnny Mercer, Harold Arlen. *Song:* "Love Is Just Around the Corner" Leo Robin, Lewis E. Gensler. *Sd Rec*

Joe Edmondson, John Wilkinson. *Sd Eff Ed* Howard Beals. *Asst Dir* Francisco Day, Michael Glick. *Prod Mgr* Lloyd Anderson. *Script Supv* John Franco. *Makeup* Jack Petty, Mark Reedall. *Miss Jens's Hairstyles* Sydney Guilaroff. *Paintings* John Hunter.

Cast: Rock Hudson *(Antiochus Wilson)*, Salome Jens *(Nora Marcus)*, John Randolph *(Arthur Hamilton)*, Will Geer *(The Old Man)*, Jeff Corey *(Mr. Ruby)*, Richard Anderson *(Dr. Innes)*, Murray Hamilton *(Charlie Evans)*, Karl Swenson *(Dr. Morris)*, Khigh Dhiegh *(Davalo)*, Frances Reid *(Emily Hamilton)*, Wesley Addy *(John)*, John Lawrence *(Texan)*, Elisabeth Fraser *(plump blonde)*, Dody Heath *(Sue Bushman)*, Robert Brubaker *(Mayberry)*, Dorothy Morris *(Mrs. Filter)*, Barbara Werle *(secretary)*, Frank Campanella *(man in station)*, Edgar Stehli *(tailor shop presser)*, Aaron Magidow *(meat man)*, De De Young *(nurse)*, Françoise Ruggieri *(girl in boudoir)*, Thom Conroy *(dayroom attendant)*, Ned Young *(Henry Bushman)*, Kirk Duncan *(Mr. Filter)*, William Richard Wintersole *(doctor in operating room)*, Tina Scala *(young girl)*.

Drama. Source: David Ely, *Seconds* (New York, 1963). Discontented middle-aged Scarsdale banker Arthur Hamilton is contacted by Charlie, a friend believed dead, and persuaded to submit to radical plastic surgery performed by a mysterious company. Transformed into a much younger man, he is relocated in California and given the identity of Antiochus Wilson, an established painter. Although he falls in love with the uninhibited Nora Marcus, Arthur quickly discovers that she is a company employee and his new friends mutants like himself. Disgusted, he returns to his Scarsdale home. He is, however, so altered that his wife does not recognize him. Unable to adjust to his new life, Arthur asks the company to restore him to his former self. When Arthur cannot refer another client to the organization, he is bound to a stretcher, gagged, given last rites by a nondenominational clergyman, and wheeled into an operating room to be murdered. *Bankers. Painters. Suburbanites. Widows. Clergymen. Plastic surgery. Personal identity. Middle age. Rejuvenation. California. Scarsdale (New York).*

Note: Location scenes filmed in Grand Central Station (New York City), Scarsdale (New York), and Malibu (California).

SECRET AGENT FIREBALL (France/Italy)   **F6.4309**
Nike Cinematografica-Devon Film-Radius Production. *Dist* American International Pictures. 12 Jan **1966** [Boston opening; c29 Dec 1965; LP32219]. Sd; col (Eastman Color). 35mm. 89 min.
Prod Mino Loy, Luciano Martino. *Dir* Martin Donan. *Screenplay* Julian Barry. *Photog* Richard Thierry. *Art Dir* Rick Sommers. *Film Ed* Robert Quintley. *Mus* Carlo Savina. *Sd* Mario Angeletti, Bruno Moreal. *Asst Dir* Charles Chelosi. *Prod Mgr* Floriano Trenker.
Cast: Richard Harrison *(Robert Fleming)*, Dominique Boschero *(Liz)*, Wandisa Guida *(Elena)*, Alcide Borik *(taxi driver)*, Jim Clay, Alan Collins *(Russian agents)*, Audry Fisher, Franklyn Fred, Clément Harari, Caroll Brown, Jean Ozenne, Freddy Unger.
Action drama. Two scientists escape from Russia with microfilm of military secrets. When one of them is murdered in Paris and the second killed in a Hamburg nightclub, CIA agent Robert Fleming learns that the missing microfilm has been handed over to a wealthy Lebanese financier. Russian agents arrive in Beirut ahead of Fleming, and the financier is tortured to death for refusing to hand over the microfilm. The financier's niece Liz flees to an ancient fort. Fleming finds her and wins her confidence, but they are both captured by Russian agents. To save Fleming's life, Liz confesses that the microfilm was hidden in the heel of a shoe her uncle was wearing. The financier's body is exhumed, and one of the Russians takes the microfilm and reveals that he is a double agent working for a third power. In the confusion Fleming escapes and sets out by helicopter in pursuit of the double agent, who has departed in a speedboat with Liz as hostage. Fleming sets fire to the boat, rescues Liz, and obtains the microfilm. Only then is it learned that the film contains the formula for the H-bomb. *Russians. Scientists. Foreign agents. Financiers. Hostages. Espionage. Murder. Torture. Disinterment. Microfilm. Helicopters. Speedboats. Hydrogen bomb. Paris. Hamburg. Beirut. United States—Central Intelligence Agency.*
Note: Location scenes filmed in Paris, Hamburg, Rome, and Beirut. Opened in Rome in Apr 1965 as *Le spie uccidono a Beirut*; running time: 95 min; in Paris in Dec 1965 as *Les espions meurent à Beyrouth*; running time: 70 min. The following are pseudonyms: Martin Donan (Mario Donen), Julian Barry (Sergio Martino), Rick Sommers (Riccardo Domenici), Robert Quintley (Roberto Cinquini), Jim Clay (Aldo Cecconi), Caroll Brown (Bruno Carotenuto), Richard Thierry (Riccardo Pallottini), and Alan Collins (Luciano Pigozzi).

SECRET AGENT SUPER DRAGON (France/Italy/West Germany)
F6.4310
Ramo Film-Fono Film-C. I. C. C.-Films Borderie-Gloria Film-Constantin Film. *Dist* United Screen Arts. May **1966**. Sd; col (Technicolor). 35mm. 95 min.
Prod Roberto Amoroso. *Dir-Story* Calvin Jackson Padget. *Screenplay* Bill Coleman, Mike Mitchell, Remigio Del Grosso, Calvin Jackson Padget, Roberto Amoroso. *Photog* Antonio Secchi. *Scene Dsgn* Arrigo Equini. *Mus* Benedetto Ghiglia.
Cast: Ray Danton *(Bryan Cooper)*, Marisa Mell *(Charity Farrell)*, Margaret Lee *(Cynthia Fulton)*, Jess Hahn *(Baby Face)*, Carlo D'Angelo *(Fernand Lamás)*, Adriana Ambesi *(Verna)*, Marco Guglielmi *(Professor Kurge)*, Solvi Stübing *(Elizabeth)*, Gerard Herter *(Coleman)*, Jacques Herlin *(Dumont)*, Carlo Hintermann, Pinkas Braun, Christia Hester.
Melodrama. CIA agent Bryan Cooper, known as Super Dragon, investigating the strange behavior of college students in a small town in Michigan, discovers that they are being drugged through chewing gum and candy. Investigations lead Cooper and agents Cynthia Fulton and Baby Face to Amsterdam, where they establish communication with another agent, Charity Farrell. Fernand Lamás, a Venezuelan, is discovered to be the wealthy ringleader behind an international organization plotting to sabotage the United States through the drug, which renders its victims helpless. Charity is revealed as a double agent in the power of Lamás, who is holding back the antidote needed for her release from the drug's effects. Cooper tricks Lamás into giving him the formula for the antidote, but he is too late to save Charity. *Secret agents. Students. Venezuelans. Sabotage. Conspiracy. Tranquilizers. Candy. Michigan. Amsterdam. United States—Central Intelligence Agency.*
Note: Filmed on location in Amsterdam. Opened in Paris in May 1966 as *New York appelle Super Dragon*; running time: 100 min. Released in West Germany in Jun 1966 as *Höllenjagd auf heisse Ware*; running time: 100 min; in Italy as *New York chiama Superdrago*. Also known as *Super Dragon*.

SECRET CEREMONY (Great Britain)   **F6.4311**
Universal Pictures, Ltd.-World Film Service Productions-Paul M. Heller Productions. *Dist* Universal Pictures. 23 Oct **1968** [New York opening; c21 Dec 1968; LP36934]. Sd (Westrex); col (Technicolor). 35mm. 109 min.
A John Heyman Production. *Prod* John Heyman, Norman Priggen. *Dir* Joseph Losey. *Screenplay* George Tabori. *Photog* Gerry Fisher. *Camera Op* Jimmy Turrell. *Art Dir* John Clark. *Set Decor* Jill Oxley. *Prod Dsgn* Richard MacDonald. *Film Ed* Reginald Beck. *Mus Comp* Richard Rodney Bennett. *Mus Cond* Marcus Dods. *Sd Rec* Leslie Hammond, Hugh Strain. *Dub Ed* Alan Pattillo. *Asst Dir* Richard Dalton. *Prod Supv* Geoffrey Haine. *Prod Orig & Developed* Paul M. Heller. *Cont* Pamela Davies. *Cost* Sue Yelland. *Wardrobe Supv* Klara Kerpen. *Miss Taylor's Wardrobe Created by* Marc Bohan, Christian Dior. *Makeup* Alex Garfath. *Miss Taylor's Hairstyles Dsgn & Created by* Alexandre of Paris. *Hairdressing* Bill Griffiths.
Cast: Elizabeth Taylor *(Leonora)*, Mia Farrow *(Cenci)*, Robert Mitchum *(Albert)*, Peggy Ashcroft *(Hannah)*, Pamela Brown *(Hilda)*.
Drama. Source: Marco Denevi, "Ceremonia secreta," in *Life en español* (12 and 26 Dec 1960). While riding on a bus in London, Leonora, a fading prostitute, discovers that she is being stared at by Cenci, a sad-faced girl who bears a remarkable resemblance to Leonora's deceased daughter. Cenci follows Leonora to her daughter's grave and invites her to the shuttered old mansion where she lives. There, Leonora learns that she closely resembles Cenci's dead mother. Touched by Cenci's need for love and intrigued by the luxury surrounding her, Leonora succumbs to the young girl's wish that she stay on and live with her as her mother. Explaining to Cenci's two greedy aunts, Hilda and Hannah, that she is the dead mother's sister, Leonora assumes her role with ease, settles down to a life of comfort, and becomes devoted to the child-like Cenci. Eventually, however, Leonora learns that Cenci is really 22 years old, that her stepfather, Albert, was banished from the house for attempting to seduce her, and that her mother was hopelessly insane. Returning to the mansion one day, Leonora finds Cenci cowering under a table after a visit from Albert. Cenci convinces Leonora that she has been raped by her stepfather, and the two leave for the seashore. Albert follows and confronts Leonora with the fact that Cenci is a sexual psychotic who has repeatedly tried to seduce him. Realizing the truth of his statement, which is supported by Cenci's infantile attempt to appear pregnant by stuffing her dress with a doll, Leonora desperately tries to force Cenci to face reality. Instead, Cenci seeks out Albert on the beach, consummates her love for him, and sends Leonora away. A short time later, Leonora visits Cenci, asks to be forgiven, and pleads for the chance to resume their former relationship. But Cenci sends her away once more and then commits suicide. When Leonora and Albert meet in silence at Cenci's funeral, Leonora pulls out a knife and plunges it into Albert. *Prostitutes. Aunts. Stepfathers. Motherhood. Imposture. Mental illness. Wealth. Rape. Seduction. Suicide. Murder. Funerals. London.*
Note: Opened in London in Jun 1969.

LE SECRET DE D'ARTAGNAN see **THE SECRET MARK OF D'ARTAGNAN**

THE SECRET DOOR
F6.4312

Dorton Productions-Fifeshire Productions. *Dist* Allied Artists. Feb **1964**. Sd; b&w. 35mm. 72 min.

Prod Charles Baldour. *Assoc Prod* Robert Hutton. *Dir* Gilbert L. Kay. *Screenplay* Charles Martin. *Photog* Robert Moss, Aurelio Rodriguez. *Film Ed* David Capey. *Mus Comp & Cond* Tony Osborne. Song: "Lisboa" Charles Baldour. *Asst Dir* Ed Parker.

Cast: Robert Hutton *(Joe Adams)*, Sandra Dorne *(Sonia)*, Peter Illing *(Buergher)*, Peter Allenby *(Edward Brentano)*, George Pastell *(Antonio)*, Shirley Lawrence *(Gretchen)*, Bob Gallico *(Lieut. Ted Avery)*, Peter Elliott, actor *(Japanese ambassador)*, Tony Arpino *(freighter captain)*, James Dyrenforth *(prison warden)*, Chris Lawrence *(Captain Hastings)*, Martin Benson *(Edmundo Vara)*, Joel Aldred *(narrator)*, Ed Parker, Moises Batista, Carlos Rodriguez, Antonio Faria, Yoshio Hikida.

War melodrama. Source: Stephen Longstreet, "Paper Door" (a story; publication undetermined). Following the Japanese attack on Pearl Harbor, two imprisoned safecrackers, Joe Adams and Edward Brentano, are released to U. S. Naval Intelligence for the purpose of photographing enemy documents located in the Japanese Embassy in Lisbon. Once there, they contact Buergher, a dealer in stolen government secrets, and Sonia, a Russian woman who tells Brentano that the documents are worth $1 million. Joe and Brentano enter the embassy through the sewers and photograph the documents, but Brentano double-crosses Joe in the hope that he can make off with both the profits and Sonia. He is killed by Buergher, who is revealed to be Sonia's husband; Sonia and Buergher are then killed in a car crash. Although the documents are retrieved by the U. S. Navy, Joe is captured and taken aboard a Japanese freighter. When the ship is sunk, Joe is rescued and granted a presidential pardon. *Safecrackers. Convicts. Spies. Russians. Espionage. Perfidy. Murder. Lisbon. United States Navy—Intelligence. Japan—Diplomatic and consular service. Documentation. Automobile accidents. Shipwrecks.*

Note: Filmed in Europe; working title: *Now It Can Be Told.*

SECRET FILE: HOLLYWOOD
F6.4313

Dist Crown International Pictures. 6 Jun **1962** [Detroit opening]. Sd; b&w. 35mm. 85 min.

Prod Rudolph Cusumano, James Dyer. *Dir* Ralph Cushman. *Story-Screenplay* Jack Lewis. *Photog* Gregory Sandor.

Cast: Robert Clarke *(Maxwell Carter)*, Francine York *(Nan Torr)*, Syd Mason *(Hap Grogan)*, Maralou Gray *(Gay Shelton)*, John Warburton *(James Cameron)*.

Crime melodrama. Maxwell Carter, an unemployed private detective, accepts an offer from Nan Torr to work as a candid photographer for the scandal magazine, *Secret File: Hollywood.* His first assignment is to take compromising pictures of director James Cameron with starlet Gay Shelton. Nan and her co-worker, Hap Grogan, blackmail Cameron and then publish the pictures anyway. The scandal causes Cameron's wife to commit suicide. Gay is cleared of complicity in the blackmail scheme, and she joins Carter, who is now working with the police, in trying to uncover the identity of the "Mr. Big" of the exposé racket. As a result of Carter's sleuthing, Hap is killed and Nan is found murdered. Investigating further, Carter finds some tapes on which Nan had received instructions from the mysterious boss of the magazine. Carter recognizes the voice as the one Hollywood news commentator Rutherford Pemberly used years before when he was a radio actor, and with this evidence Carter is able to expose "Mr. Big" and end *Secret File: Hollywood. Detectives. Photographers. Actors. Motion picture directors. Police. Radio announcers. Blackmail. Scandal. Suicide. Murder. Magazines (periodicals). Recording. Hollywood. Documentation.*

Note: Also known as *Secret Files of Hollywood.*

THE SECRET FILES OF DETECTIVE "X"
F6.4314

Dist EMCO Productions. 19 Jun **1968** [Boston opening]. Sd; b&w. 35mm. 74 min.

Prod-Dir Richard Hilliard. *Film Ed* Richard Hilliard.

Drama. Detective "X," a private investigator, makes available to the public secret films of his investigations in the hope of dissuading mankind from its follies and vices. They show an encounter between a young prostitute and a customer, filmed during a white slavery investigation; a woman who denies her husband sex and retreats into the woods to satisfy herself; a lab technician who secretly develops an aphrodisiac while working for a pharmaceutical firm; male prostitution; a wealthy citizen's nymphomaniac daughter filmed during a rendezvous; a madman who, posing as a doctor, subjects his female patients to sexual indignities; and the same prostitute revealed to be a lesbian. *Detectives. Prostitutes. Psychopaths. Laboratory technicians. Physicians. White slave traffic. Male homosexuality. Autoeroticism. Imposture. Nymphomania.*

Insanity. Lesbianism. Aphrodisiacs. Documentation.

Note: Also known as *Files of Detective X.*

SECRET FILES OF HOLLYWOOD see **SECRET FILE: HOLLYWOOD**

THE SECRET FORMULA (Mexico)
F6.4315

Salvador López. *Dist* Trans-National Film Corp. Jan **1967**. Sd; col. 35mm. 60 min.

Dir Rubén Gámez. *Screenplay* Juan Rulfo. *Photog* Rubén Gámez. *Film Ed* Rubén Gámez. *Mus Selections* Antonio Vivaldi, Igor Stravinsky, Leonardo Velázquez.

Narrator: Jaime Sabines.

Documentary. In a number of sequences, the Mexican character is examined in a historical perspective that encompasses Aztec blood rituals, the colonial experience, Catholic heritage, and the present day domination of Mexico by the United States. Poverty and oppression are shown in such scenes as a Mexican receiving Coca-Cola in place of blood in a transfusion and the mass hanging of priests and seminarians. *Peasants. Aztec Indians. Clergymen. Colonialism. Poverty. Blood transfusion. Coca-Cola. Catholic Church.*

Note: Released in Mexico in 1965 as *La fórmula secreta.*

THE SECRET INVASION
F6.4316

Corman Co.-San Carlos Productions. *Dist* United Artists. 16 Sep **1964** [New York opening; c16 Sep 1964; LP29155]. Sd; col (Eastmancolor, print by DeLuxe). 35mm (Panavision). 95 min. [Also reviewed at 107 min.]

Prod Gene Corman. *Dir* Roger Corman. *Story-Screenplay* R. Wright Campbell. *Dir Photog* Arthur E. Arling. *Art Dir* John Murray. *Set Decor* Ian Love. *Film Ed* Ronald Sinclair. *Mus* Hugo Friedhofer. *Sd Ed* Gene Corso. *Asst Dir* Charles Griffith. *Prod Mgr* Lou Place. *Location Mgr* Charles Hannawalt. *Wardrobe* Sharon Compton. *Makeup* Sandra James. *Sp Eff* George Blackwell. *Coöp* Citizens of Dubrovnik. *Electrn* William Huffman.

Cast: Stewart Granger *(Maj. Richard Mace)*, Raf Vallone *(Roberto Rocca)*, Mickey Rooney *(Terrence Scanlon)*, Edd Byrnes *(Simon Fell)*, Henry Silva *(John Durrell)*, Mia Massini *(Mila)*, William Campbell *(Jean Saval)*, Helmo Kindermann *(German fortress commandant)*, Enzo Fiermonte *(General Quadri)*, Peter Coe *(Marko)*, Nan Morris *(Stephana)*, Helmut Schneider *(German captain)*, Giulio Marchetti *(Italian officer)*, Nicholas Rend *(captain of fishing boat)*, Craig March *(Petar)*, Todd Williams *(partisan leader)*, Charles Brent *(1st monk)*, Richard Johns *(wireless operator)*, Kurt Bricker *(German naval lieutenant)*, Katrina Rozan *(peasant woman)*.

War melodrama. In Cairo during World War II British Intelligence selects five convicts—Durrell, a murderer; Rocca, the former head of a crime syndicate; Scanlon, a demolition expert; Fell, a forger; and Saval, an art thief and impersonator—to perform an essential mission in exchange for their freedom. Their mission, led by Maj. Richard Mace, is to rescue Italian General Quadri from a prison in Dubrovnik so that he can turn his troops against their German allies and facilitate the end of the war. They arrive in Dubrovnik and with the assistance of partisans Marko and Mila are making plans to tunnel into the prison when they are captured by the Nazis and imprisoned with the general. They escape, taking the Italian general with them, but lose Fell during the escape. Scanlon and Saval also are killed en route to the location of the Italian troops. They discover the general is an impostor substituted by the Nazis when the real general was killed, but they force him to address the Italian troops. Durrell, disguised as a Nazi and shouting Nazi slogans, kills the phony general before the eyes of his troops when he tries to convince the troops to remain loyal to the Nazis; and this turns the Italians against the Nazis. The mission is a success, but at its conclusion Roberto Rocca is the only surviving convict. *Convicts. Gangsters. Thieves. Italians. Germans. Nazis. Prison escapes. Demolition. Resistance (political). Imposture. World War II. Great Britain—Intelligence service. Italy—Army. Cairo. Dubrovnik.*

Note: Filmed on location in Dubrovnik and other parts of Yugoslavia. Working title: *Dubious Patriots.*

THE SECRET LIFE OF AN AMERICAN WIFE
F6.4317

Charleston Enterprises. *Dist* Twentieth Century-Fox Film Corp. 25 Jun **1968** [New York opening; c25 Jun 1968; LP35903]. Sd (Westrex); col (De Luxe). 35mm. 92 min.

Prod-Dir-Writ George Axelrod. *Assoc Prod* Hank Moonjean. *Dir Photog* Leon Shamroy. *Art Dir* Jack Martin Smith, Ed Graves. *Set Decor* Walter M. Scott, Raphael Bretton. *Film Ed* Harry Gerstad. *Mus* Billy May. *Sd* Bernard Freericks, David Dockendorf. *Asst Dir* Hank Moonjean. *Unit Prod Mgr* William Eckhardt. *Script Supv* Cleo Anton. *Gowns Dsgn by* Travilla. *Makeup* Dan Striepeke. *Hairstyles for Miss Jackson* Sydney Guilaroff. *Hairstyling* Edith Lindon. *Sp Photog Eff* L. B. Abbott, Art Cruickshank.

Cast: Walter Matthau *(Movie Star "Charlie")*, Anne Jackson *(Victoria Layton)*, Patrick O'Neal *(Tom Layton)*, Edy Williams *(Suzie Steinberg)*, Richard Bull *(Howard)*, Paul Napier *(Herb Steinberg)*, Gary Brown *(Jimmy)*,

Albert Carrier (Jean-Claude), Todd Baron (Peter Layton), Christy Hall (Susan Layton).

Comedy. Victoria Layton, a suburban housewife devoted to her husband Tom, a harried public relations man, resents his statement that she could never have been a successful call girl. Exaggerated recollections of past sexual adventures serve further to convince her that life is passing her by. After bolstering her courage with several brandies Victoria calls her husband's biggest client, movie star "Charlie," and sets up a date with him as a $100 call girl. Instead of a mad sexual fling in Charlie's New York hotel suite, however, Victoria finds herself nursing his sinus attack. At first upset that the screen's famed lover finds her no more desirable than does her husband, Victoria is somewhat assuaged when Charlie confesses that his prowess as a lover is based on press releases. After exchanging confidences and discovering that they are compatible, Victoria and Charlie eventually make love; but their idyll is shattered when Tom telephones from the lobby and announces that he is on his way up. While Victoria hides in the bedroom, Tom storms in, tells off Charlie, threatens to quit as his press agent, and punches Charlie in the nose. After ministering to Charlie's wounds, Victoria returns home. As she leaves, Charlie slips her a $100 bill for cab fare. *Housewives. Prostitutes. Actors. Marriage. Public relations. Infidelity. Hotels. New York City.*

Note: Location scenes filmed in Manhattan and New Canaan, Connecticut.

THE SECRET LIFE OF HERNANDO CORTEZ   F6.4318
Q Productions. *Dist* Hardrock Movies. 6 Feb **1969** [New York showing]. Sd; col. 16mm. 65 min.

Prod Alan Power. *Dir-Writ* John Chamberlain. *Photog* John Chamberlain, R. Davis, C. Williams. *Film Ed* John Chamberlain. *Cost* Tiger Morse.

Cast: Taylor Mead (Hernando Cortez), Ultra Violet (his mistress), Octavio, Mary Easy, Blackie Norton, Curly Atlas, Rami Pushkin, Tarzan, Fats.

Satire. Hernando Cortez struggles through the jungles of Mexico with his mistress. The two reach a small village where they are welcomed by the natives and treated as royalty. When the easy life of lust and pleasure begins to take root, Cortez discards earlier dreams of freedom for the conquered people and sees himself as a great dictator. His mistress, however, diverts his attention from this goal to sex and his own vanity. Finally, she leads him from a romp on the beach into the ocean, where they disappear into the waves. *Spanish. Indians of South America. Mistresses. Dictators. Village life. Jungles. Beaches. Mexico. Hernando Cortez.*

Note: Location scenes filmed on Long Island and in Mexico.

THE SECRET LOVE LIVES OF ROMEO AND JULIET see THE SECRET SEX LIVES OF ROMEO AND JULIET

THE SECRET MARK OF D'ARTAGNAN (France/Italy)   F6.4319
Liber Film-Agiman. *Dist* Medallion Pictures. **1963.** Sd; col (Eastman Color). 35mm (Totalscope). 95 min.

Exec Prod-Screenplay Ottavio Poggi. *Dir* Siro Marcellini. *Dial* Ottavio Poggi, Milton Krims, Siro Marcellini. *Photog* Alvaro Mancori. *Art Dir* Amedeo Mellone. *Set Decor* Ernesto Kromberg. *Film Ed* Renato Cinquini. *Mus* Carlo Rustichelli. *Sd* Franco Groppioni. *Asst Dir* Filiberto Fiaschi. *Prod Mgr* Nino Battiferri. *Fencing Master* Franco Fantasia.

Cast: George Nader (d'Artagnan), Magali Noël (Carlotta), Georges Marchal (Duke de Montserant), Mario Petri (Porthos), Alessandra Panaro (Diana), Massimo Serato (Cardinal Richelieu), Franco Fantasia, Raf Baldassarre, Giulio Marchetti.

Costume melodrama. Based on the characters created by: Alexandre Dumas, père. Cardinal Richelieu, advisor to Louis XIII of France, instructs musketeers d'Artagnan and Porthos to infiltrate a secret society which is plotting the assassination of the king. Learning that the Duke de Montserant is the leader of the insurgents, d'Artagnan enlists the help of Diana, the duke's innocent niece, and the two fall in love; Diana's maidservant Carlotta and Porthos also begin a romance. The musketeers brand Count Savignac and Montfort, an expert swordsman, as conspirators, marking an "x" on their foreheads. Montfort dons a mask to deceive the king, but Richelieu reveals his perfidy. Following a duel between the two musketeers and Montserant, the king's enemies are defeated. *Musketeers. Royalty. Uncles. Assassination. Conspiracy. Perfidy. Secret societies. Masks. Cardinal Richelieu. Louis XIII (France). Duels.*

Note: Opened in Paris in Dec 1962 as *Le secret de d'Artagnan*; in Rome in Mar 1963 as *Il colpo segreto di d'Artagnan*; running time: 105 min.

THE SECRET OF BLOOD ISLAND (Great Britain)   F6.4320
Hammer Film Productions. *Dist* Universal Pictures. Jun **1965** [c3 Jul 1964; LP33412]. Sd (RCA). b&w. 35mm. 84 min.

Prod Anthony Nelson Keys. *Dir* Quentin Lawrence. *Screenplay* John Gilling. *Dir Photog* Jack Asher. *Camera Op* Harry Gillam. *Prod Dsgn* Bernard Robinson. *Supv Ed* James Needs. *Ed* Tom Simpson. *Mus Comp* James Bernard. *Mus Supv* Marcus Dods. *Sd Rec* Ken Rawkins, James Groom. *Asst Dir* Peter

Price. *Prod Mgr* Don Weeks. *Cont* Pauline Harlow. *Wardrobe Mistress* Jean Fairlie. *Makeup Artist* Roy Ashton. *Hairstyles* Frieda Steiger. *Sp Eff* Syd Pearson.

Cast: Barbara Shelley (Elaine), Jack Hedley (Sergeant Crewe), Patrick Wymark (Major Jocomo), Charles Tingwell (Major Dryden), Bill Owen (Bludgin), Michael Ripper (Lieutenant Tojoko), Peter Welch (Richardson), Lee Montague (Levy), Edwin Richfield (O'Reilly), Glyn Houston (Berry), David Saire (KEMPI Chief), Philip Latham (Captain Drake), Ian Whittaker, actor (Mills), John Southworth (Leonard), Peter Craze (Red), Henry Davies (Taffy).

Action drama. During World War II, British secret agent Elaine parachutes from her disabled plane over Malaya. She is found in the jungle by Sergeant Crewe, who is held as a POW by the Japanese in a camp the inmates call "Blood Island" because of the sadistic officers in charge. She hides in Crewe's barracks with his fellow prisoners—Bludgin, Levy, O'Reilly, and Major Dryden. The Japanese are aware that a female enemy agent is in the area, and to obtain information about her, they torture Bludgin to death and begin to work on the other men. Elaine confides to her comrades that she must reach Kuala Lumpur, and they all work on her escape plans. But the Japanese beat Major Dryden and Levy until they produce Elaine. The Japanese begin to torture her; but because of her importance, they decide to take her to Singapore for interrogation. At the cost of their own lives, however, Crewe and Dryden assist Elaine to escape. *Secret agents. Prisoners of war. Torture. Self-sacrifice. Parachuting. Prison escapes. Airplanes. Jungles. World War II. Malaya. Great Britain—Army. Japan—Army.*

Note: Opened in London in Jun 1965 in Eastman Color.

SECRET OF DEEP HARBOR   F6.4321
Harvard Film Corp. *Dist* United Artists. 25 Oct **1961** [New York opening; c9 Sep 1961; LP21202]. Sd; b&w. 35mm. 70 min.

Prod Robert E. Kent. *Dir* Edward L. Cahn. *Screenplay* Owen Harris, Wells Root. *Dir Photog* Gilbert Warrenton. *Set Decor* Morris Hoffman. *Film Ed* Kenneth Crane. *Mus* Richard La Salle. *Sd* Stan Cooley. *Asst Dir* Herbert S. Greene. *Prod Mgr* Joseph Small. *Cost* Einar Bourman, Sabine Manela. *Sp Eff* Barney Wolff.

Cast: Ron Foster (Skip Hanlon), Barry Kelley (Milo Fowler), Merry Anders (Janey Fowler), Norman Alden (Barney Hanes), James Seay (Travis), Grant Richards (Rick Correll), Ralph Manza (Frank Miner), Billie Bird (Mama Miller), Elaine Walker (Rita), Max Mellinger (doctor).

Crime melodrama. Source: Max Miller, *I Cover the Waterfront* (New York, 1932). When his charter fishing business declines, Milo Fowler agrees to rent his boat to syndicate member Rick Correll for the purpose of smuggling an underworld big shot out of the country. Once out of port, however, Correll murders the big shot and dumps his anchor-weighted body overboard. Later that night, while drunk in a waterfront dive, Milo flashes a wad of bills and is closely observed by reporter Skip Hanlon. Milo's daughter, Janey, befriends Skip, and, when the gangster's body is found, she innocently identifies the anchor as belonging to her father. Skip notifies the police; and they lie in wait for Milo, who is doing another job for Correll. When the boat returns to port, the police board it; a battle ensues during which Correll is killed and Milo is wounded before escaping. Thinking that Skip ingratiated himself with her only to get a story, Janey breaks with him and decides to smuggle her father into Mexico. But, after a showdown with Skip, Milo dies from his wounds; and Janey realizes that Skip was only doing his duty. *Reporters. Police. Gangsters. Smuggling. Murder. Waterfronts. Fishing boats. Syndicates.*

Note: Remake of *I Cover the Waterfront* (United Artists, 1933).

THE SECRET OF DORIAN GRAY see DORIAN GRAY

THE SECRET OF MAGIC ISLAND (France/Italy)   F6.4322
Del Duca Films–Cino del Duca–Tourane Films. *Dist* Embassy Pictures. 19 Dec **1964** [Milwaukee, Wisconsin, opening]. Sd; col (Eastman Color). 35mm. 63 min.

Production Credits for Original Vers: *Pres by* Joseph E. Levine. *Prod* Pierre Bochart. *Dir-Story* Jean Tourane. *Screenplay* Louise de Vilmorin. *Photog* Maurice Fellous. *Art Dir* René Thévenet. *Film Ed* Albert Jurgenson. *Mus* Richard Cornu. *Sd* Jean Neny. *Tech Cons* Léonide Azar.

Production Credits for U. S. Preview Vers (see note): A William S. Miller—George Gudis Production. *Prod-Adapt* Jack Dunn Trop. *Screenplay* Jean Tourane, Frank Scully, Jack Dunn Trop. *Mus* Richard Cornu, Warren Baker.

Narrator: Robert Lamoureux (French version), Phil Tonkin (U. S. version).

Fantasy. During the annual fair in the animal village of Champfleury, a good fairy's magic wand is stolen from its caretaker, Chassidou (a white Persian cat), by the wicked Black Genie (a monkey). The Black Genie becomes master of the elements, takes the fairy prisoner, and petrifies Barbara (a duck), the animal tamer. Saturnin (a duck), who is Barbara's lover, and Chassidou embark in a balloon, parachute to safety when shot down by the Black Genie, and, after overcoming many perils, arrive in the Land of the Doves, where they are immunized against the petrifying power of the wand. Enraged when his magic fails against the two, the Black Genie is accidentally petrified when he touches himself with the wand. The wand is recaptured, and happiness is restored in Champfleury. *Fairies. Genii. Animal trainers. Abduction. Magic. Fairs. Balloons (ascent). Animals. Cats. Monkeys. Ducks.*

Note: Opened in Paris in Oct 1956 as *Une fée pas comme les autres;* running time: 65 min; in Rome in Dec 1956 as *Il paese di Paperino;* running time: 60 min. A U. S. revision was previewed in New York in Dec 1962 as *Secret of Outer Space Island.*

THE SECRET OF MONTE CRISTO (Great Britain)　　　F6.4323

Mid-Century Film Productions. *Dist* Metro-Goldwyn-Mayer, Inc. 5 Jul **1961** [San Francisco opening]. Sd; col (Eastmancolor). 35mm (DyaliScope). 80 min. [Also reviewed at 83 min.]

Prod-Dir Robert S. Baker, Monty Berman. *Exec Prod* Michael Green, Joe Vegoda. *Screenplay* Leon Griffiths. *Photog* Robert S. Baker, Monty Berman. *Art Dir* Allan Harris. *Film Ed* John Jympson. *Mus* Clifton Parker. *Mus Cond* Muir Mathieson. *Sd* Jeanne Henderson, Bill Daniels. *Asst Dir* Bert Batt.

Cast: Rory Calhoun *(Capt. Adam Corbett),* John Gregson *(Renato),* Patricia Bredin *(Pauline Jackson),* Peter Arne *(Count Boldini),* Gianna Maria Canale *(Lucetta Di Marca),* Ian Hunter *(Colonel Jackson),* Sam Kydd *(Albert),* David Davies *(Van Ryman),* Francis Matthews *(Louis Auclair),* Endre Muller *(Carlo),* Tutte Lemkow *(Gino),* Tony Thawnton *(militia officer),* C. Denier Warren *(French café proprietor),* Michael Balfour *(Beppo),* George Street *(English innkeeper),* Walter Randall *(sailor),* John Sullivan *(Jenkins),* Bill Cummings *(Ben),* Derek Prentice *(groom).*

Adventure melodrama. When his employer is murdered by unknown assailants, Capt. Adam Corbett, an 18th-century soldier of fortune, joins the dead man's daughter, Pauline Jackson, in a search party seeking a treasure hidden on the island of Monte Cristo. The group, each member of which holds a portion of the treasure map, includes Van Ryman, a Dutch sea captain, Auclair, a Frenchman, and Count Boldini, an Italian who is accompanied by his fiancée, Lucetta. When the adventurers land on the island, they are captured by Renato, the island's ruler, and his bandits. At first Renato orders his prisoners put to death, but he spares their lives when Corbett beats him in hand-to-hand combat. In uncovering the treasure in a cave, one of the men is wounded; and Corbett and Renato take the victim to a doctor on the mainland. They return in time to see Boldini escaping with the treasure. In the melee that follows, Lucetta attempts to shoot Corbett but accidentally kills Boldini. As Boldini falls, he overturns the treasure chest, revealing its contents—nothing but bits of rope and chain. (The real treasure was hidden in another ship by Pauline's manservant, and the ship has sunk to the bottom of the bay.) Corbett consoles himself with Pauline's love while Lucetta mourns her dead lover. *Soldiers of fortune. Adventurers. Bandits. Nobility. Italians. French. Dutch. Sea captains. Murder. Greed. Treasure. Montecristo. Duels. Documentation.*

Note: Location scenes filmed in southern Italy. Opened in London in Aug 1961 as *The Treasure of Monte Cristo;* running time: 95 min.

THE SECRET OF MY SUCCESS (Great Britain)　　　F6.4324

Andrew L. Stone-Virginia Stone. *Dist* Metro-Goldwyn-Mayer, Inc. 29 Sep **1965** [Detroit opening; c20 Jul 1965; LP31390]. Sd; col (Metrocolor). 35mm (Panavision). 112 min. [Copyright length: 103 min.]

Prod Andrew L. Stone, Virginia Stone. *Dir-Writ* Andrew L. Stone. *Dir Photog* Davis Boulton. *Camera Op* Alan McCabe. *Supv Ed* Virginia Stone. *Film Ed* Noreen Ackland. *Asst Film Ed* Ken Ross. *Mus Cond & Supv* Roland Shaw. *Sp Mus Comp* Lucien Cailliet. *Songs:* "Guandurian Anthem," "No Secrets" Derek New. *Song:* "Mangerico Verdi" João Baptista Laurenço. *Mus Box Waltz, Bicycle and Guitar Themes* Christopher Stone, mus. *Rec Supv* A. W. Watkins. *Sd Rec* John Bramall. *Dub Mix* Fred Turtle. *Asst Dir* Peter Price. *Prod Mgr* Tom Sachs. *Prod Asst* Americo Leite Rosa, Maria Eugenia Caldas. *Wardrobe Supv* Felix Evans. *Women's Cost Dsgn by* John Cavanagh. *Makeup* Tom Smith. *Hairdresser* Joan Smallwood.

Cast: Shirley Jones *(Marigold Marado),* Stella Stevens *(Violet Lawson),* Honor Blackman *(Baroness von Lukenburg),* James Booth *(Arthur Tate),* Lionel Jeffries *(Inspector Hobart/Baron von Lukenburg/President Esteda/Earl of Aldershot),* Amy Dalby *(Mrs. Tate),* Joan Hickson *(Mrs. Pringle),* Robert Barnete *(Colonel Armandez).* Nicolau Breyner *(Pallazio),* Richard Vernon, David Davenport, Peadar Lamb, Ann Lancaster, Martin Benson, Reginald Beckwith, Ernest Clark, Robert Harris.

Farce. Arthur Tate dutifully follows his mother's advice to have faith in mankind. Now the major beneficiary of a will, he relates to the group assembled how his mother's words helped him advance from constable in a small British town to ruler of Guanduria and heir to a fortune. *When redheaded dressmaker Violet Lawson reports her husband missing, Inspector Hobart suspects foul play and orders his men to dig up Lawson's cellar. Mrs. Lawson, the murderer, takes advantage of the digging to bury the corpse. Arthur's mother detects a* connection between the voluptuous dressmaker and the local magistrate and uses the information to gain a promotion for her ineffectual son. In his new capacity as police inspector, Arthur arrests Baron von Lukenburg for developing a variety of giant spiders which have crushed a man. While Arthur becomes involved with the Baroness von Lukenburg, who is the real mad scientist, Mrs. Tate's intervention with Scotland Yard wins her son the post of liaison officer with President Esteda of Guanduria. Marigold Murada, a revolutionary pretending to film a movie about the takeover of a South American government, tricks Arthur and President Esteda into appearing in the movie. Arthur's film role makes him a hero and the new ruler of Guanduria when the film turns out to be a real coup d'état. In England, the wealthy Earl of Aldershot hears about Arthur's heroism, wills him £15 million, and dies. Arthur leaves the group and returns to his South American mansion to enjoy his riches. Mrs. Tate, however, wants more than her son's praise; after Arthur wills his estate to her, she blows up the mansion with Arthur in it. *Heirs. Dressmakers. Constables. Magistrates. Scientists. Presidents. Revolutionaries. Nobility. Filial relations. Ambition. Murder. Blackmail. Duplicity. Coups d'état. Heroism. Murder. Greed. Wills. Motion pictures. South America. Scotland Yard. Explosions. Spiders.*

Note: Opened in London in Dec 1965 at 96 min.

SECRET OF OUTER SPACE ISLAND *see* **THE SECRET OF MAGIC ISLAND**

THE SECRET OF SANTA VITTORIA　　　F6.4325

Stanley Kramer Corp. *Dist* United Artists. 15 Oct **1969** [Los Angeles opening; c17 Oct 1969; LP37275]. Sd; col (Technicolor). 35mm (Panavision). 138 min. *MPAA rating* M.

Prod-Dir Stanley Kramer. *Assoc Prod* George Glass. *Screenplay* William Rose, Ben Maddow. *Dir Photog* Giuseppe Rotunno. *Set Decor* Ferdinando Ruffo. *Prod Dsgn* Robert Clatworthy. *Main Titl* Wayne Fitzgerald. *Film Ed* William A. Lyon, Earle Herdan. *Mus* Ernest Gold. *Sd* David Hildyard. *Asst Dir* Ray Gosnell, Franco Cirino. *Prod Supv* Ivan Volkman. *Prod Mgr* Giorgio Zambon, Luciano Piperno. *Cost* Joe King. *Sp Eff* Danny Lee.

Cast: Anthony Quinn *(Italo Bombolini),* Anna Magnani *(Rosa Bombolini),* Virna Lisi *(Caterina Malatesta),* Hardy Kruger *(Sepp von Prum),* Sergio Franchi *(Tufa),* Renato Rascel *(Babbaluche),* Giancarlo Giannini *(Fabio),* Patrizia Valturri *(Angela),* Valentina Cortese *(Gabriella),* Eduardo Ciannelli *(Luigi Lunghetti),* Leopoldo Trieste *(Vittorini),* Gigi Ballista *(Padre Polenta),* Quinto Parmeggiani *(Copa),* Carlo Caprioli *(Giovanni Pietrosanto),* Francesco Mulè *(Francocci),* Wolfgang Jansen *(Sergeant Zopf),* Aldo De Carellis *("Old Vines"),* Marco Tulli *(Mazzola),* Chris Anders *(Corporal Heinsick),* Peter Kuiper *(Sergeant Traub),* Dieter Wilken *(Hans),* Karl Otto Alberty *(Otto),* Gigi Bonos *(Benedetti),* Clelia Matania *(Julietta),* Pippo Lauricella *(Pulci),* Carlo Capannelle *(Capoferro),* Renato Chiantoni *(Bracolini),* Pino Ferrara *(Dr. Bara),* Curt Löwens *(Colonel Scheer),* Tim Donnelly *(Private Holtzmann).*

Comedy-drama. Source: Robert Crichton, *The Secret of Santa Vittoria* (New York, 1966). Italo Bombolini, a wine merchant in Santa Vittoria, celebrates news of Mussolini's death in 1945 by painting over an old fascist slogan. This act wins him the post of mayor. He imprisons the fascists as a gesture to the populace and, optimistic that a good government will work, reads Machiavelli's *The Prince* and forms a grand council. Soon Italo's son-in-law rushes into town with news that the retreating Germans are headed toward Santa Vittoria, intending to occupy the town and commandeer the wine supply, Santa Vittoria's chief source of wealth. Italo takes it upon himself to save the wine and commands the townspeople to form a "bucket brigade" to transport 1 million bottles to an old Roman cave just outside of town. The villagers complete their task just before the Germans, led by Captain Sepp von Prum, arrive and begin to look for the wine they know exists. Italo allows them to find a small cache of a few thousand bottles and the Germans decide to confiscate half. The SS arrives and informs von Prum that there is a great deal more than a few thousand bottles. Von Prum tries various means of obtaining the wine, but none work. Finally, von Prum and his men are ordered to leave. Von Prum, in a last attempt, puts a gun to Italo's head and asks the townspeople for information about the wine; no one comes forward. Von Prum admits defeat and departs, respectful of the man he had thought of as a buffoon. *Wine merchants. Fascists. Political prisoners. Mayors. Village life. Military occupation. Commandeering. Wine. World War II. Italy. Benito Mussolini. Germany—Army. "The Prince".*

Note: Filmed in Italy.

THE SECRET OF THE SACRED FOREST　　　F6.4326

William Copeland Productions-Sari-Manok Productions. *Dist* Shermart Distributing Co. 23 Jun **1970** [Biloxi, Mississippi, opening]. Sd; col (Eastmancolor, print by DeLuxe). 35mm. 87 min. *MPAA rating* G.

Pres by Art Jacobs. A William Copeland Production. *Prod-Writ* William Copeland. *Dir* Michael Du Pont. *Photog* Vincente Sempio. *Film Ed* Tony Di

Marco. *Mus Comp & Cond* Herschel Burke Gilbert. *Orch & Arr* Ernest Hughes. *Song:* "Has Any One Seen Chris?" William Copeland, Herschel Burke Gilbert, Ernest Hughes. *Song:* "Filipina Filipina" William Copeland, Angel Pena. *Sung by* Maurice Santa Lucia. *Sd* Demetrio Carrianga.

Cast: Gary Merrill (*Mike Parks*), Jon Provost (*Jimmy*), Henry Duval (*García*), Leo Martinez (*Bayani*), Michael Parsons (*Chris Carpenter*), Dave Harvey (*Brownie*), Laurie Agudo (*Annie*), Christina Ponce-Enrile (*Fely*), Vic Silayan, Rolf Bayer, Mona Morena, Lola Boy, Louis Florentino, Joseph de Cordova, Carol Varga, Bruno Punzalan, Poch Apostol, Fred Viray, Don Smith, Zenaida Amador, Gami Virray, Vincente Sempio.

Adventure drama. Chris Carpenter, an adventurous newspaperman set on exposing a drug-smuggling ring, is reported dead in an airplane crash in the Sacred Forest, a mountainous terrain in the Philippines that is still the habitat of headhunters. Jimmy, his teenaged brother, does not believe that he was killed and stows away on a Manila-bound merchant airship. Eluding the Philippine authorities, Jimmy befriends Bayani, a native boy who offers to help find Chris. Mike Parks, an American Embassy attaché eager to take Jimmy into custody for illegal entry into the country, finds him with Fely, Chris's secretary. The boy escapes with Bayani to the mountains, followed by García, a double agent for the government, and Brownie, a traitorous American black marketeer. Annie, a mountain girl, leads the boys into the Sacred Forest, but Jimmy is caught by Brownie, who is killed when they are attacked by headhunters. Jimmy escapes with the assistance of Parks, and the smugglers are apprehended, with Chris among them. He had planted the story of his own death to enable him to infiltrate the gang and bring the drug traffickers to justice. *Adventurers. Newspapermen. Headhunters. Stowaways. Americans in foreign countries. Government agents. Traitors. Smuggling. Black market. Drugs. Forests. Manila. Philippines. United States—Diplomatic and consular service. Airplane accidents.*

Note: Filmed in the Philippines.

SECRET OF THE TELEGIAN (Japan)   F6.4327
Toho Co. *Dist* Toho Co., Herts-Lion International Corp. Jul **1961** [Los Angeles showing]. Sd; col (Eastmancolor). 35mm (Tohoscope). 85 min.
Dir Jun Fukuda. *Screenplay* Shinichi Sekizawa. *Photog* Kazuo Yamada. *Dir Sp Eff* Eiji Tsuburaya.
Cast: Koji Tsuruta, Yumi Shirakawa, Akihiko Hirata, Tadao Nakamaru, Seizaburo Kawazu, Yoshio Tsuchiya, Sachio Sakai.

Science fiction melodrama. A murder in an amusement park provokes the interest of science reporter Kirioka, who finds a coil resembling a transistor near the victim's body. Another murder, also committed with a bayonet, soon follows. Both murders had been foretokened when identification tags of the old Imperial Japanese Army were sent to the victims. Taki, a veteran of the war, appeals to the police for protection when he too receives a tag. During questioning, he reveals that during the war he and three other soldiers had been ordered to hide Dr. Niki, a scientist working for the military, and his cases of research material. When Corporal Sudo discovered the cases actually contained gold bars, the four soldiers conspired to murder both Sudo and Dr. Niki by blowing up a cave where the two were trapped. Years later, the four returned to dig up the gold but found no trace of it or the bodies of the two men. Despite police protection, Taki is killed by Sudo, who, along with Dr. Niki, is still alive. It is revealed that Sudo, unknown to Dr. Niki, has been using the scientist's invention to teleport himself to different locations to commit the murders for revenge. Soon, the fourth veteran is also killed. [Sources are unclear as to whether Sudo is apprehended.] *Veterans. Scientists. Reporters. Police. Teleportation. Revenge. Murder. Gold. Inventions. World War II.*

Note: Released in Japan in 1960 as *Denso ningen.* Alternative title: *The Telegian.* Also reviewed at 75 min.

THE SECRET PARTNER (Great Britain)   F6.4328
Metro-Goldwyn-Mayer, Inc. 15 Mar **1961** [Seattle opening; c15 Feb 1961; LP18564]. Sd (Westrex); b&w. 35mm. 92 min.
Prod Michael Relph. *Dir* Basil Dearden. *Screenplay* David Pursall, Jack Seddon. *Photog* Harry Waxman. *Camera Op* Ernest Day. *Focus* Chic Anstiss. *Art Dir* Alan Withy. *Set Dresser* John Jarvis. *Draughtsman* Reg Bream. *Prod Dsgn* Elliot Scott. *Film Ed* Raymond Poulton. *Assembly Ed* Ernie Grimsdale. *Mus Comp & Cond* Philip Green. *Rec Supv* A. W. Watkins. *Sd Rec* Gerry Turner. *Dub Ed* Norman Savage. *Dub Mix* J. B. Smith. *Boom Op* Godfrey Bowen. *Sd Camera Op* Mickey Hickey. *1st, 2d & 3d Asst Dir* George Pollock, Ted Wallis, Ernie Lewis. *Prod Mgr* Basil Somner. *Cont* June Faithfull. *Prod Sec* Midge Warnes. *Wardrobe Supv* Felix Evans. *Wardrobe Mistress* Dolly Smith. *Makeup* Bob Lawrence. *Hairdresser* Alice Holmes. *Photog Eff* Tom Howard. *Grip* Wally Wheatley. *Prop Buyer* Bill Isaacs. *Still Photog* Davis Boulton. *Casting Dir* Irene Howard. *Supv Electrn* Arthur Pochetti.
Cast: Stewart Granger (*John Brent*), Haya Harareet (*Nicole Brent*), Bernard Lee (*Detective Superintendent Hanbury*), Hugh Burden (*Charles Standish*), Lee Montague (*Detective Inspector Henderson*), Melissa Stribling (*Helen*

Standish), Conrad Phillips (*Alan Richford*), John Lee (*Clive Lang*), Norman Bird (*Ralph Beldon*), Peter Illing (*Strakarios*), Basil Dignam (*Lyle*), William Fox (*Brinton*), George Tovey (*Vickers*), Sidney Vivian (*dock foreman*), Paul Stassino (*man in Soho street*), Colette Wilde (*girl in car*), Willoughby Goddard (*hotelkeeper*), Peter Welch (*P. C. Maclaren*), Joy Wood (*Brent's secretary*), Dorothy Gordon (*dentist's receptionist*).

Mystery melodrama. Because of his criminal past, London shipping magnate John Brent is being blackmailed by a disreputable dentist, Ralph Beldon, who is aware of Brent's prison sentence for embezzlement. When Brent refuses to explain what he does with his money, his spoiled wife, Nicole, voices the opinion that there is another woman in his life and walks out on him. One night Beldon is visited in his office by a hooded stranger who threatens to expose him unless he drugs Brent during a dental appointment and extracts from him the combination to his company's safe. Beldon agrees, and the safe is subsequently robbed of £13,000. Scotland Yard's Hanbury suspects Brent of the theft and has him picked up for questioning. But Brent escapes and at gunpoint forces Beldon to confess to Hanbury that he helped set up the robbery. Brent is cleared, and suspicion falls on Alan Richford, Nicole's lover. Nevertheless, Hanbury remains dissatisfied with the case, and when Nicole admits her love for Richford, Brent confesses that he was the hooded stranger and the robber, and that Nicole was his accomplice. Deserted and disillusioned, Brent returns the stolen money. *Ex-convicts. Shipping magnates. Dentists. Blackmail. Embezzlement. Disguise. Robbery. London. Scotland Yard.*

Note: Opened in London in May 1961. Working title: *The Sleeping Partner.*

THE SECRET PASSION *see* FREUD

SECRET SCROLLS (PART I) (Japan)   F6.4329
Toho Co. *Dist* Toho International, Inc. 11 Oct **1967** [Los Angeles opening]. Sd; col (Agfacolor). 35mm. 106 min.
Exec Prod Tomoyuki Tanaka. *Dir* Hiroshi Inagaki. *Screenplay* Hiroshi Inagaki, Takeshi Kimura. *Photog* Tadashi Iimura. *Art Dir* Takeo Kita, Hiroshi Ueda. *Mus* Akira Ifukube. *Sd* Yoshio Nishikawa.
Cast: Toshiro Mifune (*Tasaburo*), Koji Tsuruta (*Senshiro*), Yoshiko Kuga (*Yuhime*), Kyoko Kagawa (*Oki*), Mariko Okada (*Rika*), Denjiro Okochi (*Lord Yagyu*), Jotaro Togami (*Jubei*), Akihiko Hirata (*Tomonori*), Senjaku Nakamura (*Matajuro*), Hanshiro Iwai (*Iyemitsu*), Eijiro Tono (*Fugetsusai*).

Adventure melodrama. Source: Kosuke Gomi, *Yagyu Bugeicho* (Tokyo, 1956–59). In 17th-century Japan, three scrolls called *Yagyu Bugeicho* are secretly kept by three separate households. If put together, the scrolls could ruin the Yagyu family, overthrow the ruling government, and disrupt the country's peace. Although the three families zealously guard their scrolls, one of the households is robbed of its scroll by the Ryuzoji clan, led by Princess Yuhime. Jubei, eldest son of the Yagyu family and a master swordsman, pursues the princess and her clan in order to retrieve the scroll. Meanwhile, another clan, also desperately wanting the scrolls, assigns a magician-samurai, Tasaburo, and his brother Senshiro to steal them. *Royalty. Samurai. Magicians. Brothers. Family life. Theft. Scrolls.*

Note: Released in Japan in 1957 as *Yagyu Bugeicho.* Also known as *Yagyu Secret Scrolls.*

SECRET SCROLLS (PART II) (Japan)   F6.4330
Toho Co. *Dist* Toho International, Inc. 22 May **1968** [New York opening]. Sd; col (Agfacolor). 35mm (Tohoscope). 106 min.
Exec Prod Tomoyuki Tanaka. *Dir* Hiroshi Inagaki. *Screenplay* Hiroshi Inagaki, Takeshi Kimura, Tokuhei Wakao. *Photog* Tadashi Iimura, Asaichi Nakai. *Art Dir* Takeo Kita, Hiroshi Ueda. *Mus* Akira Ifukube. *Sd* Yoshio Nishikawa.
Cast: Toshiro Mifune (*Tasaburo*), Koji Tsuruta (*Senshiro*), Yoshiko Kuga (*Yuhime*), Kyoko Kagawa (*Oki*), Mariko Okada (*Rika*), Denjiro Okochi (*Lord Yagyu*), Jotaro Togami (*Jubei*), Akihiko Hirata (*Tomonori*), Senjaku Nakamura (*Matajuro*), Hanshiro Iwai (*Iyemitsu*), Eijiro Tono (*Fugetsusai*), Nobuko Otowa (*The Princess*).

Adventure melodrama. Source: Kosuke Gomi, *Yagyu Bugeicho* (Tokyo, 1956–59). The *Yagyu Bugeicho* scrolls, kept in three separate households, could bring war to 17th-century Japan and ruin to the Yagyu family if they are put together. The Ryuzoji clan, led by Princess Yuhime, steals one of the scrolls, and the Yagyus send Jubei, their eldest son, to retrieve it. A competing clan assigns magician-samurai Tasaburo and his brother Senshiro to find two of the three scrolls, but during a struggle for its possession, the stolen scroll is torn in half by the brothers. The two part, and Senshiro continues his mission, while Tasaburo stays behind with Princess Yuhime. Jubei encounters the princess with Tasaburo's half of the scroll and kills her, but not before she is able to drop the scroll into a river. Tasaburo pursues Jubei, who finds Senshiro with the other half of the stolen scroll. After a hard battle, the Yagyu clan recover the other portion of the scroll. *Royalty. Samurai. Magicians. Brothers. Family life. Theft. Scrolls.*

Note: Released in Japan in 1958 as *Ninjutsu* and *Soryu hiken.*

THE SECRET SEVEN (Italy/Spain)   **F6.4331**
Film Columbus-Atenea Films. *Dist* Metro-Goldwyn-Mayer, Inc. May **1966**
[c31 Dec 1964; LP32307]. Sd (Westrex); col (Eastman Color). 35mm
(Techniscope). 92 min.
  Prod Cleto Fontini, Italo Zingarelli. *Dir* Alberto De Martino. *Screenplay*
Alberto De Martino, Sandro Continenza, Tonino Guerra, Natividad Zaro. *Dir
Photog* Eloy Mella. *Camera* John Bergame. *Art Dir* Piero Poletto, Anthony
Guere. *Film Ed* Otello Colangeli. *Mus* Carlo Franci. *Sd Rec* Mario Morigi.
Post-Sync Gene Luotto. *Asst Dir* Jaime Bayarri. *Cont* Mary Rock. *Wardrobe*
Antonelli-Baston. *Cost* Mario Giorsi. *Makeup* Romolo Demartino. *Sp Eff*
S. P. E. S. *Sp Eff Mgr* Ettore Catallucci.
  Cast: Tony Russel (*Leslio*), Helga Liné (*Lydia*), Massimo Serato (*Axel*),
Gérard Tichy (*Rabirio*), Renato Baldini (*Kadem*), Livio Lorenzón (*Rubio*),
Barta Barri (*Baxo*), Joseph Marc (*Luzar*), Cris Huerta (*Gular*), Gianni Solaro
(*Nakasser*), Frank Sorman (*aristocrat*), Emma Baron (*mother*), Pedro Mari
(*Ario*), Tomás Blanco (*Panuzio*), Renato Montalbano (*aristocrat*), Nando
Gazzolo, Piero Lulli, Pietro Capanna, Paola Pitti, Walter Maestosi, Caetano
Quarraro, Fernando María Sánchez.
  Adventure drama. Toward the end of the 4th century B. C., after the fall of
Athens, Sparta continues its reign of terror throughout the Middle East. Led
by the tyrant Rabirio, the army enslaves the village of Tur. Axel, a rebel, is
condemned to death by starvation but is rescued by his brother Leslio and five
former galley slaves. Rabirio, in reprisal, destroys the entire village and kills its
citizens, including Leslio's mother and younger brother. Leslio, posing as the
architect who is to build Rabirio's new villa, gains entrance to his palace. When
he encounters Lydia, now Rabirio's mistress but once in love with Leslio, she
does not betray him; but Rabirio eventually learns Leslio's true identity. A
battle between Rabirio's army and the seven—Axel, Leslio, and the five former
slaves—leads to the tyrant's death and the rescue of Lydia from a burning stake.
*Despots. Soldiers. Brothers. Mistresses. Galley slaves. Starvation. Revenge.
Imposture. Greece—History—Peloponnesian War. Athens. Sparta. Middle
East.*
  Note: Released in Italy in Feb 1964 as *Gli invincibili sette*; in Spain in Jul
1964 as *Los invencibles*; running time: 91 min. Original language credit and cast
names: José Antonio de la Guerra (Anthony Guere), José Marco (Joseph
Marc), Francesco Sormano (Frank Sorman).

THE SECRET SEX LIVES OF ROMEO AND JULIET   **F6.4332**
Global Pictures. *Dist* Boxoffice International Film Distributors. Mar **1969**.
Sd; col (Eastman Color). 35mm. 96 min.
  Prod-Dir A. P. Stootsberry. *Screenplay* Jim Schumacher. *Photog* Duane
Rayven. *Photog Asst* Peter Sorel. *Lighting* Richard Aguilar. *Lighting Asst* John
Kirkland. *Art Dir* Earl Marshall. *Set Dsgn* Earl Marshall. *Ed* Mark Perri. *Sd
Mixer* Paul Taylor. *Sd* Ryder Sound Service. *Boom Boy* Mike Bennett. *Asst Dir*
John Taylor, asst dir. *Prod Mgr* Bethel Buckalew. *Script Girl* Pam Eddy. *Cost*
Logan Costumes. *Wardrobe Girl* Sandy Root. *Makeup* Tony Tierney. *Still
Photog* CinemaGraphics.
  Cast: Forman Shane (*Romeo*), Dicora Carse (*Juliet*), Mickey Jines (*Lady
Capulet*), Stuart Lancaster (*Capulet*), Adam Lawrence (*Montague*), Jay
Edwards (*Balthasar*), Wendel Swink (*Friar*), Vincene Wallace (*nurse*), Shannon
Carse (*The Prince*), Don Jones (*Gregory*), Marvin Sweetbody (*Paris*), Sydney
Carlysle (*Derek*), Karen Thomas (*maid no 1*), Pat Davis (*maid no 2*), Tiffany
Lane (*maid no 3*), Elenor Rigby (*maid no 4*), Antoinette Maynard (*maid no 5*),
Dorthea Cristie (*maid no 6*), Kelly (*stage hand*), James Brand (*narrator*).
  Farce. Source: William Shakespeare, *Romeo and Juliet*. The film claims to
present the play as it might have been performed in Shakespeare's time, in a
replica of the Globe Theatre, to an excited and drunken male audience.
Interspersed with sex scenes, such as the encounter between the mayor and
Juliet and a lesbian encounter between Juliet and her maid, the love affair
between young Romeo and Juliet unfolds. Lord Capulet, Juliet's father, and
Lord Montague, Romeo's father, exchange harsh words and involve their
guards in a swordfight. The Prince of Verona steps in to defend Juliet's honor,
although it is well known that she has led a promiscuous life. Seeking
consolation, Romeo fulfills his sexual desires with many women, including
Juliet's nurse and Lady Capulet. Meanwhile, Lord Capulet, in an attempt to
amuse himself, witnesses a beautiful housemaid being whipped and watches a
hunchback make love to her. In order to increase his own wealth, Lord Capulet
arranges for Juliet to marry Paris, a wealthy homosexual; this news horrifies
Juliet, but her nurse's tender love eases the pain. While an orgy among the
servants takes place in the Capulet house, the balcony scene between the two
lovers transpires, ending in a wild lovemaking scene. Friar Lawrence provides
Juliet with a sleeping potion so that she can feign death and thereby escape the
fate her father has planned. Romeo finds her, concludes that she has died, and
decides to join her by drinking the potion. The patriarchs Capulet and
Montague find their children asleep in the sepulchre. Supposing that Romeo

and Juliet have taken their own lives, the two men go off to drink together,
leaving the lovers to continue their romance. *Nobility. Patriarchs. Youth.
Hunchbacks. Nurses. Housemaids. Monks. Courtship. Wealth. Marriage.
Promiscuity. Lesbianism. Filial relations. Seduction. Male homosexuality.
Voyeurism. Drunkenness. Suicide. Orgies. Potions.*
  Note: Also known as *The Secret Love Lives of Romeo and Juliet* and *The
Sex Life of Romeo and Juliet*.

THE SECRET SOCIETY   **F6.4333**
Jode Productions–C & W Associates. *Dist* Olympic International Films. 15
Oct **1965** [Champaign, Illinois, showing]. Sd; b&w. 35mm. 67 min.
  Prod S. N. Johnsen, R. W. Cresse. *Assoc Prod* Jerry Denby. *Dir* S. N.
Johnsen.
  Cast: Judy Adler.
  Documentary. Hidden cameras document the activities of the "Secret
Society," a nationwide sex club whose members participate in mate swapping,
sadomasochism, lesbianism, fetishism, and group sex. The society's other
services include producing and distributing stag films and arranging abortions.
*Group sex. Mate swapping. Fetishism. Sadomasochism. Sex clubs. Abortion.
Sex exploitation films.*

THE SECRET SOCIETY *see* P. P. S. (PROSTITUTES' PROTECTIVE
    SOCIETY)

THE SECRET WAR OF HARRY FRIGG   **F6.4334**
Albion Film Corp. *Dist* Universal Pictures. 29 Feb **1968** [New York opening;
c27 Apr 1967; LP39024]. Sd (Westrex); col (Technicolor). 35mm
(Techniscope). 110 min.
  Prod Hal E. Chester. *Assoc Prod* Peter Stone. *Dir* Jack Smight. *Screenplay*
Peter Stone, Frank Tarloff. *Story* Frank Tarloff. *Dir Photog* Russell Metty. *Art
Dir* Alexander Golitzen, Henry Bumstead. *Set Decor* John McCarthy, John
Austin. *Film Ed* J. Terry Williams. *Mus Comp* Carlo Rustichelli. *Mus Supv*
Joseph Gershenson. *Sd* Waldon O. Watson, William Russell, Ronald Pierce.
Asst Dir Terence Nelson. *Unit Prod Mgr* Arthur S. Newman, Jr. *Cost Dsgn*
Edith Head. *Makeup* Bud Westmore. *Hairstyles* Larry Germain. *Tech Adv* D.
R. O. Hatswell. *Dial Coach* Leon Charles.
  Cast: Paul Newman (*Harry Frigg*), Sylva Koscina (*Countess di Montefiore*),
Andrew Duggan (*General Armstrong*), Tom Bosley (*General Pennypacker*),
John Williams (*General Mayhew*), Charles Gray (*General Cox-Roberts*), Vito
Scotti (*Colonel Ferrucci*), Jacques Roux (*General Rochambeau*), Werner Peters
(*Major von Steignitz*), James Gregory (*Gen. Homer Prentiss*), Fabrizio Mioni
(*Lieutenant Rossano*), Johnny Haymer (*Sergeant Pozzalo*), Norman Fell
(*Captain Stanley*), Buck Henry (*stockade commandant*), Horst Ebersberg
(*Lieutenant Gruber*), Richard X. Slattery (*M. P. sergeant*), George Ives (*major*).
  War comedy. In World War II, five general officers—three American, one
British, and one French—are captured in a Tunisian turkish bath by Italians and
detained in a luxurious villa in Italy under the command of Colonel Ferrucci.
Soon it becomes clear to the Allied powers that the five officers cannot agree
on a plan for escaping from their comfortable prison; consequently, public
relations head Homer Prentiss recruits Pvt. Harry Frigg, known for his
consistent, grandiose escapes from Army guardhouses, to spring the generals.
Promoted instantly to major general in order to facilitate his command of the
other officers, Frigg is then parachuted into Italy. After his capture by the
enemy and imprisonment in the villa, he immediately begins haranguing the
five men about their inability to organize an escape plan; when Frigg meets
Contessa Francesca di Montefiore, the neutral owner of the villa, however, he
becomes less intent on escape and delays the generals with a series of training
programs. The escape night finally arrives, but it is postponed as a favor to
Ferrucci, who is to be made a general at midnight. German officers arrive and
promptly at midnight announce that Italy has surrendered and all prisoners will
be transported to a German prison camp. Away from the comforts of both villa
and countess, Frigg reverts to his former self and swiftly engineers a successful
escape; as a reward, he is recommended for a commission by the five generals
and allowed to run an Army radio station located back at the villa. *Prisoners
of war. Nobility. Escape artists. Prison escapees. Parachuting. Radio. Turkish
baths. World War II. Italy. Tunisia. United States Army. France—Army.
Germany—Army. Great Britain—Army. Italy—Army.*
  Note: Location scenes filmed in the Sierra Madre section of southern
California. Working titles: *The Best Kept Secret of the War*; *Harry Frigg*; and
Meanwhile, Far from the Front.

THE SECRET WAYS   **F6.4335**
Heath Productions. *Dist* Universal-International. Apr **1961** [New York
opening: 24 May; c10 Apr 1961; LP25072]. Sd (Westrex); b&w. 35mm. 112
min.
  Prod Richard Widmark. *Assoc Prod* Euan Lloyd. *Dir* Phil Karlson.
Screenplay Jean Hazlewood. *Dir Photog* Max Greene. *Camera Op* Peter
Allwork. *Art Dir* Werner Schlichting, Isabella Schlichting. *Film Ed* Aaron Stell.

Mus Supv Joseph Gershenson. *Mus* Johnny Williams. *Sd* Kurt Schwarz. *Asst Dir* André Farsch, Eric Von Stroheim, Jr. *Prod Mgr* Herbert E. Mendelson, Georg von Block. *Cont* Hertha Friedl. *Wardrobe* Leo Bei. *Makeup* Rudolf Ohlschmidt. *Hair Stylist* Margarete Pitter. *Tech Adv* Tibor Simanyi. *Stunt Supv* Bob Simmons.

Cast: Richard Widmark *(Michael Reynolds)*, Sonja Ziemann *(Julia Jansci)*, Charles Regnier *(The Count)*, Walter Rilla *(Professor Jansci)*, Senta Berger *(Elsa)*, Howard Vernon *(Colonel Hidas)*, Heinz Moog *(Minister Sakenov)*, Hubert von Meyerinck *(Hermann Sheffler)*, Oskar Wegrostek *(The Fat Man)*, Stefan Schnabel *(border official)*, Elisabeth Neumann-Viertel *(Olga)*, Helmut Janatsch *(Janos)*, John Horsley *(Jon Bainbridge)*, Walter Wilz *(Peter)*, Raoul Retzer *(special agent)*, Georg Kovary *(language professor)*, Adi Berber *(Sandor)*, Jochen Brockmann *(The Commandant)*, Brigitte Brunmuller *(waitress)*, Reinhard Kolldehoff, Rudolf Rosner *(The Count's men)*.

Adventure melodrama. Source: Alistair MacLean, *The Secret Ways* (Garden City, N. Y., 1959). American adventurer Michael Reynolds is hired by an international espionage ring to smuggle a noted scholar and resistance leader, Professor Jansci, out of Communist-ruled Hungary. Reynolds goes to Vienna to see the professor's daughter, Julia, and he persuades her to accompany him to Budapest. Once there, Reynolds is kidnaped by freedom fighters who take him to the professor's secret headquarters. Meanwhile, one of Jansci's trusted aides is captured by the Hungarian Secret Police and forced to reveal the professor's hiding place. Reynolds, Julia, and Jansci are quickly rounded up and taken to Szarhaza Prison, where they are tortured by the sadistic Colonel Hidas. They are rescued by a resistance fighter known as The Count, who tricks the Communists into placing the prisoners in his custody. At the last moment the ruse is discovered, and The Count is killed as the other three race to the airport where a chartered plane is waiting. Hidas pursues them but is killed in an accident on the runway. Safe at last, Reynolds, Julia, and the professor leave Hungary. *Adventurers. Professors. Political refugees. Communists. Resistance (political). Espionage. Abduction. Torture. Hungary. Budapest. Vienna. Automobile accidents.*

Note: Filmed in Europe, principally Vienna and Zurich.

SECRET WORLD (France)　　　　　　　　　　F6.4336

Fox Europa–Les Films du Siècle. *Dist* Twentieth Century–Fox Film Corp. 9 Jul **1969** [New York opening; c9 Jul 1969; LP38326]. Sd; col (DeLuxe). 35mm. 94 min. [Copyright length: 111 min.] *MPAA rating* M.

Prod Jacques Strauss. *Dir* Robert Freeman, Paul Feyder. *Screenplay* Gérard Brach, Jackie Glass. *Photog* Peter Biziou. *Art Dir* Jacques Dugied. *Film Ed* Richard Bryan. *Mus* Antoine Duhamel. *Sd* Jean Labussière. *Asst Dir* Alain Franchet. *Prod Mgr* Louis Wipf. *Wardrobe* Colette Baudot. *Makeup* Michel Deruelle, Fernande Hugi.

Cast: Jacqueline Bisset *(Wendy)*, Giselle Pascal *(Florence)*, Pierre Zimmer *(Philippe)*, Marc Porel *(Olivier)*, Jean-François Maurin *(François)*, Paul Bonifas *(Gustave)*, Guy D'Avout *(Malevar)*, Jacques Riberolles *(Norbert)*, Judith Magre *(Eliane)*, Chantal Goya *(Monique)*, Yves Lefebvre *(Alain)*.

Melodrama. François, withdrawn and fearful of riding in cars as a result of an automobile crash that left him an orphan, lives with his middle-aged aunt and uncle, Florence and Philippe, in a chateau in Provence. The couple's arrogant 20-year-old son, Olivier, makes a stopover at the chateau in the course of his travels. Philippe announces that Wendy, the daughter of an old wartime friend, is arriving from England for a stay; actually she is Philippe's mistress. François, fascinated by the new houseguest, steals a bottle of perfume from her room and cuts off a lock of her hair while she is sleeping. Tensions in the household increase as the jealous Florence is suddenly forced to face her fading beauty, and Olivier tries unsuccessfully to seduce Wendy. Put off by Olivier's egomania and bored by Philippe's attentions, Wendy devotes more and more of her time to sharing François' secret world. Although her friendship gives the boy the courage to ride in an automobile again, he misunderstands her intentions and believes that she will take him with her when she returns to London. On the day of her departure, he readies himself to leave but finds that he is to be left behind. Desolate, François retreats to his private treehouse after Wendy has left and pours the bottle of her perfume over his face. *Children. Orphans. Mistresses. British. Houseguests. Infidelity. Loneliness. Middle age. Duplicity. Filial relations. Jealousy. Provence. Automobile accidents.*

Note: Paris opening: Jul 1969 as *La promesse*; running time: ca90 min; alternative French title: *L'échelle blanche*. Location scenes filmed in or near Arles.

SECRETARIES SPREAD　　　　　　　　　　　F6.4337

Kirt Films International. *Dist* Distribpix, Inc. ca **1970**. Sd; col. 35mm. 63 min.

Melodrama. Two roommates who work as secretaries in the same office have varying attitudes toward sex. One woman loves her employer, but she believes that marriage vows should precede physical love; the other is promiscuous. The first woman finally receives a marriage proposal from her employer and

consents to have sex with him. Her roommate meanwhile discovers that nymphomania has dangerous consequences, and she begins to feel victimized, unloved, and desperate after a night of marked horror. *Roommates. Secretaries. Promiscuity. Employer-employee relations.*

SECRETS OF A SOUL see CONFESSIONS OF AN OPIUM EATER

SECRETS OF A WOMEN'S TEMPLE (Japan)　　　　F6.4338

Daiei Motion Picture Co. Jul **1969** [Los Angeles showing]. Sd; b&w. 35mm (Daiei Scope). 79 min.

Dir Tokuzo Tanaka. *Screenplay* Shozaburo Asai. *Photog* Chishi Makiura. *Art Dir* Yoshinobu Nishioka. *Mus* Hajime Kaburagi.

Cast: Michiyo Yasuda *(Oharu)*, Shigako Shimegi *(Shigetsuin)*, Sanae Nakahara, Machiko Hasegawa, Naomi Kobayashi, Yasuyo Matsumura.

Melodrama. In late 18th-century Edo, Shigetsuin, cousin to the Shogun, is made mother superior of the convent at Hosho Temple as punishment for her misdeeds. Oharu pretends to join the convent in order to investigate her brother's mysterious disappearance in the convent area. Her suspicions are confirmed when she discovers that Shigetsuin has continued her evil ways inside the convent walls, luring young men to her and murdering them after sexually satisfying herself. Oharu decides to kill the mother superior, but Shigetsuin herself sets fire to the temple and perishes in the blaze. *Nuns. Brother-sister relationship. Sadism. Murder. Suicide. Convents. Edo. Fires.*

Note: Released in Japan in Jan 1969 as *Hiroku Onnadera*.

SECRETS OF AN UNCOVER MODEL　　　　　　　F6.4339

Lon Productions. 16 Sep **1965** [San Antonio, Texas, opening]. Sd; col (Eastmancolor, print by Movielab). 35mm. 68 min.

Dir Maurice Seymour. *Screenplay* Josephine O'Neill. *Photog* Arpad Makay, Manuel S. Conde, Lou Campa. *Lighting* Seymour Studio. *Ed* Gloria Pinoria. *Sd* Havilland Studio. *Cost* Vinnie. *Makeup* Irving Carlton.

Documentary(?). Lynne O'Neill, a nude model and burlesque star, guides the viewer on a behind-the-scenes tour leading from her backstage dressing rooms to the studios of artists and photographers for whom she poses, to a variety of Broadway show spots where she performs, and finally to a Florida nudist club where she relaxes during her vacation. *Models. Burlesque. Nudity. Nudist camps. New York City—Broadway. Florida.*

Note: Also known as *Secrets of an Undercover Model*. Nudist camp sequence filmed in Florida.

SECRETS OF THE CITY see CITY OF SECRETS

SECRETS OF THE NAZI CRIMINALS (Sweden)　　　F6.4340

Minerva International Films. *Dist* Trans-Lux Distributing Corp. 3 Oct **1962** [New York opening; c3 Oct 1962; LP26085]. Sd; b&w. 35mm. 84 min.

Prod-Dir Tore Sjöberg. *Screenplay* Erik Holm. *English Transl* Crawford Moller. *From an Idea by* Tore Sjöberg. *Film Ed* Tore Sjöberg, Ingemar Ejve, Erik Holm.

Cast: Claude Stephenson *(narrator)*, William Hurley *(narrator of American Prosecutor Jackson's speeches)*.

Documentary. Using authentic Russian, German, and British newsreel footage, the film traces the origins and rise of the Nazi party under the leadership of Adolf Hitler and his principal lieutenants, Hermann Göring, Joseph Goebbels, and Heinrich Himmler. In 1945, Göring heads the prisoners in the dock at the Nuremberg trials. Among the other defendants whose activities are detailed are Julius Streicher, Rudolf Hess, Wilhelm Keitel, and Karl Dönitz. American chief prosecutor Robert Houghwout Jackson reads the three main charges—crimes against peace, war crimes, and crimes against humanity—and they are documented in succession. German-made films depicting scenes of mass murder and concentration camp brutalities are intercut with reaction shots of the prisoners in the dock. Other footage shows Nazis massacring American soldiers at Malmédy and killing hostages as frightened citizens look on. Detailed documentation of mass exterminations, torture of Jewish prisoners, and corpses piled at concentration camps at Belsen, Buchenwald, and Dachau substantiate the charge of crimes against humanity, for which the prisoners were convicted. The history of the Nuremberg trials ends with the hanging of several of the war criminals. *Nazis. Jews. Judges. Prisoners of war. Genocide. Massacres. Torture. War crimes. Anti-Semitism. Capital punishment. Concentration camps. International Military Tribunal. World War II. Germany—History—Third Reich. Belsen. Dachau. Buchenwald. Malmédy. Joseph Paul Goebbels. Hermann Göring. Adolf Hitler. Julius Streicher. Robert Houghwout Jackson. Heinrich Himmler. Rudolf Hess. Karl Dönitz. Wilhelm Keitel. United States Army.*

Note: Sequel to *Mein Kampf*, q. v. Released in Sweden in 1962 as *Krigsförbrytare*; running time: 75 min. Also known as *Mein Kampf II*.

SECRETS OF VENUS *see* **NUDE IN CHARCOAL**

SECRETS OF WOMEN (Sweden)　　　　　　　　　　　**F6.4341**
Svensk Filmindustri. *Dist* Janus Films. 7 Apr **1961** [Los Angeles opening]. Sd; b&w. 35mm. 114 min. [Also reviewed at 108 min.]

An Ingmar Bergman Production. *Prod* Allan Ekelund. *Dir-Writ* Ingmar Bergman. *Photog* Gunnar Fischer. *Art Dir* Nils Svenwall. *Film Ed* Oscar Rosander. *Mus* Erik Nordgren. *Mus Dir* E. Eckert-Lundin. *Sd* Sven Hansen.

Cast: Anita Björk *(Rakel)*, Karl-Arne Holmsten *(Eugen)*, Jarl Kulle *(Kaj)*, Maj-Britt Nilsson *(Märta)*, Eva Dahlbeck *(Karin)*, Gunnar Björnstrand *(Fredrik)*, Birger Malmsten *(Martin)*, Gerd Andersson *(Maj)*, Björn Bjelvenstam *(Henrik)*, Aino Taube *(Annette)*, Håkan Westergren *(Paul)*, Naima Wifstrand *(family matriarch)*, Ingmar Bergman *(street character)*, Kjell Nordensköld, Carl Ström, Märta Arbin.

Romantic comedy-drama. While waiting for their husbands to join them at their lakeside summer home, three sisters-in-law pass the time by recounting an incident out of their pasts. The first, Rakel, recalls the time she had submitted to the advances of a neighbor, Kaj, and discovered that she was as frigid an adulteress as she was a wife. Upon hearing his wife's confession, Eugen grabbed his hunting rifle and threatened to kill himself but changed his mind. Rakel's marriage became bearable when she realized that her husband was completely dependent on her. The second wife, Märta, tells of meeting her husband, Martin, when he was an artist in Paris. She became pregnant and refused to marry him because of his wish to be free. After her baby was born, however, she agreed to become his wife. The third sister-in-law, Karin, announces that her story is nothing more than a comic anecdote. One night she and her business-minded and somewhat pompous husband, Fredrik, were trapped between floors in their apartment's elevator. After discussing extramarital activities, Fredrik made ardent love to Karin and promised to be a more devoted and loving husband. But with his release from the elevator in the morning, Fredrik automatically returned to his former ways. As Karin finishes her story, the husbands arrive at the summer house. While their wives rush to greet them, Märta's younger sister, Maj, who has listened to the tales of adultery and compromise, elopes with the boy she loves. Young and naive, she is certain that her marriage will be one of perfect bliss. *In-laws. Neighbors. Artists. Sisters. Marriage. Frigidity. Infidelity. Suicide. Pregnancy. Elopement. Elevators. Summer. Paris.*

Note: Released in Sweden in Nov 1952 as *Kvinnors väntan*.

SEDDOK, L'EREDE DI SATANA *see* **ATOM AGE VAMPIRE**

SEDMI KONTINENT *see* **THE SEVENTH CONTINENT**

SEDMIKRÁSKY *see* **DAISIES**

SEDMÝ KONTINENT *see* **THE SEVENTH CONTINENT**

SEDOTTA E ABBANDONATA *see* **SEDUCED AND ABANDONED**

SEDUCED AND ABANDONED (France/Italy)　　　**F6.4342**
Lux Film–Ultra Film–Vides–C. C. F. Lux. *Dist* Continental Distributing, Inc. 15 Jul **1964** [New York opening]. Sd; b&w. 35mm. 118 min.

Prod Franco Cristaldi. *Exec Prod* Antonio Musu. *Dir* Pietro Germi. *Screenplay* Pietro Germi, Luciano Vincenzoni, Age & Scarpelli. *Story* Pietro Germi, Luciano Vincenzoni. *Photog* Aiace Parolin. *Camera Op* Elio Polacchi. *Art Dir* Carlo Egidi. *Asst Art Dir* Gino Lazzari. *Set Decor* Andrea Fantacci. *Film Ed* Roberto Cinquini. *Asst Film Ed* Sergio Montanari, Giampiero Giunti. *Mus* Carlo Rustichelli. *Mus Cond* Pierluigi Urbini. *Sd* Guido Nardone, Mario Amari. *Asst Dir* Renzo Marignano, Francesco Massaro. *Prod Mgr* Luigi Giacosi. *Unit Mgr* Marcello Papaleo, Andrea Petricca. *Script Girl* Myrta Corbucci. *Admin* Renato Pieri. *Prod Sec* Silvana Benedetti. *Cost* (see note) Angela Sammaciccia. *Asst Cost* Lilli Menichelli. *Makeup* Raffaele Cristini. *Hairstyles* Vitaliana Patacca, Ditta Rocchetti. *Ch Electrn* Armando Luzi. *Key Grip* Guglielmo Maga. *Still Photog* Divo Cavicchioli. *English Subtitl* Herman G. Weinberg.

Cast: Stefania Sandrelli *(Agnese Ascalone)*, Aldo Puglisi *(Peppino Califano)*, Saro Urzì *(Vincenzo Ascalone)*, Lando Buzzanca *(Antonio Ascalone)*, Leopoldo Trieste *(Baron Rizieri)*, Rocco D'Assunta *(Orlando Califano)*, Lola Braccini *(Amalia Califano)*, Paola Biggio *(Matilde Ascalone)*, Umberto Spadaro *(Cousin Ascalone)*, Oreste Palella *(Police Chief Potenza)*, Lina La Galla *(Francesca Ascalone)*, Roberta Narbonne *(Rosaura Ascalone)*, Rosetta Urzì *(Consolata, the maid)*, Adelino Campardo *(Bisigato, policeman)*, Vincenzo Licata *(Profumo, the undertaker)*, Italia Spadaro *(Aunt Carmela)*, Gustavo D'Arpe *(Ciarpetta, lawyer)*, Salvatore Fazio *(Father Mariano)*, Bruno Scipioni, Attilio Martella.

Comedy. During the siesta in a Sicilian village, Peppino Califano seduces Agnese Ascalone, the 15-year-old sister of his fiancée, Matilde. Agnese becomes pregnant, whereupon her father, Vincenzo, ends Matilde's engagement to Peppino. Vincenzo finds a new fiancé for Matilde—the penniless Baron Rizieri—and tries to force Peppino to wed Agnese. Peppino perversely refuses to marry an unchaste girl and goes into seclusion. Vincenzo plans to have Peppino murdered, but Agnese warns the police. Peppino is ordered to marry the girl or go to prison for seducing a minor. He makes Agnese's family grovel for his assent and thereby turns Agnese against him so that she rejects him. The dishonored Agnese and her relatives are ridiculed in the streets by the villagers; the baron breaks his engagement to Matilde; Vincenzo has a heart attack; Matilde becomes a nun; and the baron attempts suicide. Vincenzo dies, but Agnese restores the family honor by finally agreeing to wed Peppino. *Nobility. Police. Seduction. Pregnancy. Family life. Marriage. Scandal. Murder. Suicide. Double standard. Village life. Heart disease. Sicily.*

Note: Opened in Rome caFeb 1964 as *Sedotta e abbandonata*. Opened in Paris in Jul 1964 as *Séduite et abandonnée*. Original running time: 123 min. An Italian source credits Carlo Egidi as costumer and Sammaciccia and Menichelli as assistants.

THE SEDUCERS　　　　　　　　　　　　　　　　　**F6.4343**
Boar's Head Films–Quest Productions. *Dist* Joseph Brenner Associates. 3 Aug **1962** [New York State license; released 21 Dec 1962]. Sd; b&w. 35mm. 88 min. [Original running time: 96 min.]

A Wilson Ashley Production. *Prod-Screenplay* Wilson Ashley. *Assoc Prod* William E. Maloney. *Dir* Graeme Ferguson. *Photog* Baird Bryant. *Asst Camera* Stephen R. Winsten. *Film Ed* Bernard Leslie. *Mus* Mort Lindsey. *Sd* David Jones. *Script Supv* Rita Call. *Grip* Donald Buchsbaum.

Cast: Nuella Dierking *(Jean Wells)*, Mark Saegers *(Joe)*, Robert Milli *(Robert Wells)*, Sheila Britt *(Wilma)*, John Coe *(Hank)*.

Melodrama. While driving her faithless husband, Robert, home from a party, heiress Jean Wells runs into a pedestrian and knocks his body into a nearby lake. Her fear that she has killed someone is substantiated the next day when an embittered stranger, Joe, arrives and threatens blackmail. But when the frantic Jean attempts suicide Joe confesses he saw the pedestrian walk away from the scene of the accident. Determined to find out for herself, Jean returns to the lake—and uncovers a muddy corpse. She is deranged by the incident and pleads with Joe to make love to her, but he refuses to take advantage of her. Joe then starts an investigation and discovers that the body is that of Jean's lawyer, who had learned of Robert's affair with a young girl named Wilma. The lovers had murdered the lawyer and then arranged the accident, using Wilma's father as the pedestrian, in order to put the blame on Jean and gain control over her inheritance money. Although Robert succeeds in drugging Joe, he is prevented from murdering him by the appearance of Jean. The failure of his plan causes Robert's mind to snap, and he kills Wilma's father and flees up the face of a huge dam. Wilma is waiting and she pushes him to his death. As the police arrive, Jean is comforted by the reformed Joe. *Heiresses. Lawyers. Marriage. Infidelity. Murder. Blackmail. Frameup. Suicide. Greed. Dams. Automobile accidents.*

Note: Filmed in Westchester County, New York, and at the Kensico Reservoir Dam. Working title: *Downfall*.

THE SEDUCERS (Italy)　　　　　　　　　　　　　**F6.4344**
A. I. C. A. Cinematografica. *Dist* Cinemation Industries. 30 Nov **1970** [New York opening]. Sd; col (De Luxe). 35mm (SuperScope). 86 min.

Pres by Jerry Gross. *Prod* Franco Cancellieri. *Dir* Ottavio Alessi. *Screenplay* Ottavio Alessi, Nelda Minucci, Lorenzo Ricciardi. *Story* Lorenzo Ricciardi. *Photog* Alessandro D'Eva. *Mus* Sante M. Romitelli.

Cast: Maud de Belleroche *(Mudy)*, Ruggero Miti *(Tony)*, Maurizio Bonuglia *(Aldo)*, Rosalba Neri *(Paula)*, Edwige Fenech *(Ulla)*, Ewa Thulin *(peasant girl)*, Salvatore Puntillo *(fisherman)*.

Melodrama. Wealthy and corrupt Mudy and her emotionally immature 20-year-old son Tony sail on their yacht with young married couple Paula and Aldo, two social climbers willing to do anything to gain the rights to one of Mudy's oil concessions. Ulla, a prostitute hired by Aldo to arouse Tony out of his sexual adolescence, is also on board. During the night Mudy has a lesbian encounter with Paula while Aldo, distracted by Ulla, leaves the ship's helm and permits the yacht to run aground on a small island. Tony runs ashore, and the other four set out in search of him. Aldo and Ulla find him talking with a peasant girl, whom they take aboard the yacht. Her fisherman husband, brought on board by Mudy and Paula, learns that his wife is also on the vessel, but, plied with liquor and seduced by Paula, he soon forgets about his wife, who has been coerced into helping Tony find his manhood. Mudy and Aldo are distracted by the drunken fisherman from watching on a closed-circuit television set directed at Tony's room what they hope will take place. But they return to the screen to find that Tony has strangled the young woman. The confused Mudy agrees to give Paula and her husband an oil concession if she will quiet the fisherman. Paula shoots him, places both corpses in their boat with a box of dynamite, and explodes it to make it appear an accident. Ulla, attempting to blackmail Mudy, is dissuaded by Paula. The saddened mother takes the helm and is soon joined by her son, whose strong, incestuous embraces eventually strangle her. Tony races the yacht toward a fate which the others, dreaming of their newfound riches, do not even suspect. *Fishermen. Prostitutes. Social climbers. Oil magnates. Peasants. Jet set. Seduction. Murder. Sexual initiation. Abduction. Adolescence. Blackmail. Incest. Drunkenness. Filial relations. Lesbianism. Infidelity. Matricide. Greed. Yachts. Islands. Explosions.*

Note: Filmed in Italy in 1968 as *Sensation.* Also known in Italy as *Top Sensation.*

SEDUCTION BY THE SEA (West Germany/Yugoslavia)   **F6.4345**
Alfa Film–Avala Film. *Dist* Europix–Consolidated Corp. Nov **1967**. Sd; col. 35mm. 80 min.
Dir Jovan Živanović. *Screenplay* Yug Grizely, Rolf Schulz. *Photog* Mišković.
Cast: Peter Van Eyck (*Peter*), Elke Sommer (*girl*).
Drama. Disillusioned with his marriage and life in general, Peter escapes to an island in the Adriatic Sea. His mother hires a beautiful young girl to lure him back to civilization. The girl falls in love with Peter, and over the objections of Peter's mother, they are married. *Disillusionment. Filial relations. Marriage. Islands. Adriatic Sea.*
Note: Released in West Germany in Aug 1963 as *Verführung am Meer.* Yugoslavian title: *Ostrva.*

SÉDUITE ET ABANDONNÉE see **SEDUCED AND ABANDONED**

SEE HOW THEY COME   **F6.4346**
Nadecelle, Ltd. *Dist* Goldstone Film Enterprises. 12 Dec **1968** [New York showing]. Sd; b&w. 35mm. 71 min.
Prod Harvey Green. *Dir* William K. Hennigar.
Cast: Jason Ellis (*Joe Link*), Maria Powers (*Honey Deer*), Alan Stanley (*Mr. Mallory*), Carla Erikson (*Mrs. Mallory*), Kenneth Lye (*Mr. Teal*), Jean Pell (*Teal's secretary*), Stephen Treadwell (*Stringer*), Larry Hunter (*1st henchman*), Byron Feldt (*photographer*).
Comedy-drama. Honey Deer, a girl friday working for private detective Joe Link, becomes innocently involved in blackmail, loan sharking, conspiracy, and suburban mate swapping. She pretends to be a secretary and is almost seduced by the Mallorys, a libertine suburban couple. Honey Deer delivers an envelope and finds herself in the middle of a penthouse orgy; she manages to escape, however, with her virtue intact. *Detectives. Secretaries. Suburbanites. Loan sharks. Blackmail. Conspiracy. Mate swapping. Seduction. Orgies.*
Note: Also advertised as *See How They Go* and *See How They Come and Go.*

SEE YOU AT MAO (Great Britain)   **F6.4347**
Kestrel Films. *For* London Weekend Television. *Dist* Grove Press. 21 May **1970** [New York opening]. Sd; col (Eastman Color). 16mm. 52 min.
Prod Irving Teitelbaum, Kenneth Trodd. *Prod-Dir-Writ* Jean-Luc Godard. *Photog* Charles Stewart. *Film Ed* Elizabeth Kozmian. *Sd* Fred Sharp. *Res Mo* Teitelbaum.
Film essay. The film attacks the bourgeois capitalist society from a radical left-wing point of view, examining the alienation of workers in an automobile assembly line, and the exploitation of women as sex objects and as consumers in the capitalistic society. The second part of the film deals with the need for political organization and class consciousness; militant workers discuss their plight, and students at Essex are shown making posters. *Students. Factory workers. Class conflict. Capitalism. Women's rights. Essex.*
Note: Filmed on location at the University of Essex and at the British Motor Corporation plant at Abingdon. Released in Great Britain in 1971 as *British Sounds.*

THE SEED OF MAN (Italy)   **F6.4348**
Polifilm. *Dist* S. R. L. Films. Apr **1970**. Sd; col (Eastman Color). 35mm. 101 min.
Dir Marco Ferreri. *Screenplay* Marco Ferreri, Sergio Bazzini. *Photog* Mario Vulpiani. *Mus* Teo Usuelli.
Cast: Marco Margine (*Ciro*), Anne Wiazemsky (*Dora*), Annie Girardot (*Anna*), Milva Frosini (*[see note]*), Rada Rassimov, Maria Teresa Piaggio, Angela Pagano.
Allegory. Ciro and Dora move into a primitive house by the sea after a global plague and warfare have destroyed most of the population of the world. Ciro wants to father a child, but Dora refuses to comply, arguing that it is absurd to repopulate a world bent on self-destruction. A group of horsemen from a government agency appear and tell Dora that it is her duty to produce children; they depart, and she still refuses to bear a child. When a whale washes up on the beach, Dora fears that it is an evil omen, and soon Anna, a woman who has been alone for many months, arrives. She is more receptive to Ciro's desire to procreate, and they have sex in the same bed with Dora, who pretends to sleep. The next day, Anna attacks Dora, but Dora clubs her to death, cuts off her leg, and serves it to Ciro for dinner. Eventually, the rotting whale forces the couple

to move into a cave, but they return to the beach when the carcass has been picked clean by birds. Ciro again expresses his wish to have a child; when Dora refuses, he drugs and impregnates her. She awakens complaining of an upset stomach, and some days later, Ciro tells her that she is pregnant. Suddenly, a great explosion destroys everything but the skeleton of the whale. *Equestrians. Reproduction. Murder. Mutilation. Cannibalism. Rape. Pregnancy. Holocausts. Explosions. Doomsday. Whales.*
Note: Location scenes filmed on the coast of the Adriatic Sea. Released in Italy in 1969 as *Il seme dell'uomo.* Milva Frosini is credited as Deanna Frosini in Italian sources.

SEEDS   **F6.4349**
Aquarian Productions. *Dist* Harrington Film Distributing Corp., Hoffberg Pictures. Dec **1968**. Sd; b&w. 35mm. 84 min.
An Allen Bazzini–Rosily Bazzini Production. *Dir* Andy Milligan. *Screenplay* John Borske, Andy Milligan. *Photog* Andy Milligan.
Cast: Maggie Rogers (*Claris*), Candy Hammond (*Carol*), Robert Service (*Michael*), Helena Velos (*Margaret*), Neil Flanagan (*Matthew*), Gene Connelly (*Buster*), David Hazard (*Drew*), Jonathan East (*Peter*), Paulene Ramsey (*Jessica*), Paul Eden (*Dr. Kram*), Jesse Bigelow (*Mortimer*), Liza Hart (*Barbara*), Eileen Haves (*Susan*), Jerry Cortez (*Jonathan*), Rita Benning (*Miss Bundy*), Maggie Dominic (*Bonita*), Lee Rand (*Slippery*).
Melodrama. Matriarch Claris Manning, an alcoholic invalid, tyrannizes her children, including: Carol, who enjoys muscle magazines; Matthew, a crackpot clergyman; Michael, in love with his sister Carol; Margaret, the eldest daughter; Buster, the youngest son; and Drew. Drew's fiancée undergoes a gruesome abortion performed by the family doctor, Kram, a blackmailer. At dinner a heated argument arises, and Claris reveals that Mortimer, her attendant, is Margaret's father. Later, Michael's pregnant, possessive wife Susan visits Claris, who informs her that Michael's father is confined in an asylum for the criminally insane. [Press material suggests that the film includes scenes of drug-taking, seduction, and murder.] *Invalids. Clergymen. Physicians. Domestics. Family life. Alcoholism. Incest. Blackmail. Murder. Seduction. Abortion. Insane asylums. Narcotics.*

SEGRETI CHE SCOTTANO see **DEAD RUN**

SEI DONNE PER L'ASSASSINO see **BLOOD AND BLACK LACE**

SEISHUN ZANKOKU MONOGATARI see **NAKED YOUTH**

SEKRET USPEKHA see **BOLSHOI BALLET 67**

SELLERS OF GIRLS (France)   **F6.4350**
C. F. P. C. *Dist* American Film Distributing Corp. 11 May **1967** [San Francisco showing]. Sd; b&w. 35mm. 100 min.
Assoc Prod Jean Maumy. *Dir-Screenplay-Dial* Maurice Cloche. *Dir Photog* Jacques Mercanton. *Cameraman* Charles-Henry Montel. *Art Dir* Raymond Nègre. *Asst Art Dir* Jean Forestier. *Set Dresser* Belin. *Film Ed* Franchette Mazin. *Mus* Guy Magenta. *Sd Dir* Jacques Gallois. *Sd Rec* Daniel Heron. *Boom* Jean Jak. *Asst Dir* Jean-Pierre Decourt, Odette Glenat. *Prod Mgr* Raymond Dupont. *Location Mgr* Roger Bar. *Script Girl* Colette Crochot, Régine Hernou. *Prod Sec* Janine Seri. *Cost* Monique Naussac, Luce Scatena. *Makeup* Gisèle Jacquin. *Still Photog* Henri Thibault. *Prop* François Robineau, Marcel Balland.
Cast: Georges Marchal (*Mister John*), Agnès Laurent (*Josette*), Daniela Rocca (*Bettina*), Saro Urzi (*Mottia*), Roger Duchesne (*Gofferi*), Richard Winckler (*Henri*), Pascale Roberts (*Gaby*), Jacques Dynam (*Mister Jean*), Evelyne Dandry (*Véra*), Renée Cosima, Florence Arnaud, Robert Porte, Luce Aubertin, Anne-Marie Mersen, Catherine Romane, Claude Cerval, Georges Lycan, Henri-Jacques Huet, Roger Coggio, Jorge Matthews, Clément Harari, Pierre Massimi.
Melodrama. Unable to find work in Paris, Josette, having been promised a job at a bar owned by Gofferi, a member of a vicious narcotics and white slavery ring, travels to South America. She becomes engaged to ship's crewman Henri in the course of the crossing. Gofferi soon sells Josette to Mottia, who uses drugs as well as violence to force women into compliance. Josette rebels and is brutally punished. Mister John, a mysterious character who has shown a strong interest in Josette, places her in a clinic, but Mottia fears that she will betray him and has her kidnaped. Gofferi's mistress, Bettina, falls in love with Mister John and aids him in feeding the rivalry between the two racketeers. The rival factions exterminate each other, and Gofferi, mortally wounded, reveals that Bettina is at the head of the whole operation. Mister John, actually a secret agent for Interpol, brings the case to a close, and Josette returns to Henri. *Prostitutes. Racketeers. Mistresses. Secret agents. White slave traffic. Murder. Kidnaping. Employment—Women. Sadism. Narcotics. Bars. Paris. South America. INTERPOL.*
Note: Opened in Nice in Sep 1957 as *Marchands de filles.* Role names, drawn from a French source, may not correspond to U. S. release version. Also known as *Girl Merchants.*

SEMBAZURU *see* THOUSAND CRANES

IL SEME DELL'UOMO *see* THE SEED OF MAN

SEN NOCI SVATOJANSKÉ *see* A MIDSUMMER NIGHT'S DREAM

SEND ME NO FLOWERS   **F6.4351**

Martin Melcher Productions. *Dist* Universal Pictures. 14 Oct **1964** [Los Angeles opening; c14 Sep 1964; LP33022]. Sd (Westrex); col (Technicolor). 35mm. 100 min.

Prod Harry Keller. *In Charge of Prod* Edward Muhl. *Exec Prod* Martin Melcher. *Dir* Norman Jewison. *Screenplay* Julius J. Epstein. *Dir Photog* Daniel Fapp. *Art Dir* Alexander Golitzen, Robert Clatworthy. *Set Decor* John McCarthy, Oliver Emert, John Austin. *Main Titl* Pacific Title. *Film Ed* J. Terry Williams. *Mus* De Vol. *Mus Supv* Joseph Gershenson. *Titl Song* Hal David, Burt Bacharach. *Sung by* Doris Day. *Choreog* David Winters. *Sd* Waldon O. Watson, Joe Lapis. *Asst Dir* Douglas Green. *Unit Prod Mgr* Norman Deming. *Gowns* Jean Louis. *Makeup* Bud Westmore. *Hairstyles* Larry Germain, Barbara Lampson. *Dial Coach* Norman Stuart.

Cast: Rock Hudson (*George Kimball*), Doris Day (*Judy Kimball*), Tony Randall (*Arnold Nash*), Clint Walker (*Bert Power*), Edward Andrews (*Dr. Ralph Morrisey*), Patricia Barry (*Linda Bullard*), Hal March (*Winston Burr*), Paul Lynde (*Mr. Akins*), Clive Clerk (*Vito*), Dave Willock (*milkman*), Aline Towne (*Cora*), Helene Winston (*woman commuter*), Christine Nelson (*nurse*).

Comedy. Source: Norman Barasch and Carroll Moore, *Send Me No Flowers* (New York opening: 5 Dec 1960). Judy and George Kimball have been happily married for 8 years despite George's hopeless hypochondria. One day George visits his doctor about an imaginary chest pain and overhears him discussing another patient. Assuming that the conversation is about him, George concludes that he has but a few weeks to live. After revealing the tragic news to Arnold Nash, his neighbor and best friend, George puts $1,000 down on three cemetery plots for himself, his wife, and her next husband and then sets out to find someone to take his place. He decides upon Bert Power, a college friend of Judy's who is now an oil magnate. But George's attempts to throw his wife and Bert together only serve to convince Judy that George is trying to cover up an affair of his own. Her suspicions double when she finds George in a compromising position with Linda Bullard, a recently-separated friend whom George is trying to protect from Winston Burr, a suburban wolf. To clear himself, George is forced to tell Judy his terrible news. Her initial horror quickly turns to rage when she learns from George's doctor that he is in perfect physical health. Arnold's advice, given while he is drunk, only worsens the situation, and Judy, now certain there is another woman, begins packing. But when she learns of George's purchase of the cemetery plots, she can no longer doubt his sincerity. George promises to forget his hypochondria forever, and as Judy throws away all his medicine bottles, he celebrates their reconciliation by opening a bottle of champagne and planting a punch on the jaw of the meddlesome Winston Burr. *Hypochondriacs. Physicians. Oil magnates. Neighbors. Death. Suburban life. Marriage. Jealousy. Infidelity. Drunkenness. Cemeteries.*

SENGOKU GUNTO-DEN *see* SAGA OF THE VAGABONDS

SENGOKU YARO *see* WARRING CLANS

SENJO NI NAGARERU UTA *see* WE WILL REMEMBER

SENSATION *see* THE SEDUCERS

SENSATION GENERATION   **F6.4352**

Gulf-United Productions. *Dist* Distribpix, Inc. **1969**. Sd; col (Eastman Color). 35mm. ca74 min.

1st Camera Rex Sampson. *2d Camera* Harry Orstein. *Lighting* George Kingston. *Sd* Herman Werner, Fritz Farenkoff. *Mus Ed* Lola Kersnoft. *Grip* Fred Saunders, Bob Mercy.

Cast: Sherry King (*June*), Mickie Thomas (*Penny*), Bill Emory (*The Hitchhiker*), Rud Arthur (*Jim Pritchard*), Cosmo Gumpkin (*Fred Eldridge*), Omar Hagerty (*Phil*), Ernest Swartz (*The Detective*), Harry Grove, Tom Johnson, Tony Douglas, June Sundae, Marie Marcus, Betty Wonder, Sandra Smilie.

Sex film. A group of young people, including students, drive around in automobiles, pick up a hitchhiker, and engage in various sex practices. Press photographs suggest that the film contains scenes of sexual intercourse, lesbianism, and flagellation. *Hitchhikers. Students. Youth. Flagellation. Lesbianism. Sexual practices.*

Note: May also be known as *Sensational Generation.*

A SENSATION ODYSSEY *see* 2069 A.D.: A SENSATION ODYSSEY

SENSATIONAL GENERATION *see* SENSATION GENERATION

SENSO (Italy)   **F6.4353**

Lux Film. *Dist* Fleetwood Films. Jun **1968** [New York showing]. Sd; col (Technicolor). 35mm. 125 min.

Prod Domenico Forges Davanzati. *Dir* Luchino Visconti. *Screenplay* Luchino Visconti, Suso Cecchi D'Amico, Giorgio Prosperi, Carlo Alianello, Giorgio Bassani. *Photog (see note)* Aldo Graziata, Robert Krasker, Giuseppe Rotunno. *Camera Op* Francesco Izzaretti. *Art Dir* Ottavio Scotti. *Set Decor* Gino Brosio. *Film Ed* Mario Serandrei. *Mus From Symphony no. 7* Anton Bruckner. *Played by* Orchestra della RAI-TV. *Cond* Franco Ferrara. *Mus from "Il trovatore"* Giuseppe Verdi. *Sd* Vittorio Trentino. *Asst Dir* Francesco Rosi, Franco Zeffirelli. *Cost* Marcel Escoffier, Piero Tosi.

Cast: Alida Valli (*Contessa Livia Serpieri*), Farley Granger (*Lieut. Franz Mahler*), Massimo Girotti (*Marquis Roberto Ussoni*), Heinz Moog (*Count Serpieri*), Rina Morelli (*Laura*), Marcella Mariani (*prostitute*), Christian Marquand (*Bohemian officer*), Tonio Selwart (*Colonel Kleist*), Sergio Fantoni (*patriot*), Cristoforo De Hartungen (*commander at Venetian square*), Tino Bianchi (*Meucci*), Marianna Leibl (*wife of Austrian general*), Ernst Nadherny, Goliarda Sapienza.

Drama. Source: Camillo Boito, *Senso: nuove storielle vane* (Milan, 1883). In Venice in 1866 as war threatens to erupt between Austria and Italy, the Countess Livia Serpieri is present when her patriot cousin, Marquis Roberto Ussoni, has a bitter exchange of words with a young Austrian lieutenant, Franz Mahler, because of the latter's disparaging remarks about the Italians. When Ussoni is subsequently arrested and sent into exile, Franz vows to Livia that he had nothing whatsoever to do with the charges. Although skeptical at first, Livia is so taken by the young officer's charm that she accepts his explanation. Despite her awareness that war is imminent, she suppresses her loyalty to both husband and country and becomes Franz's mistress. Ussoni secretly returns to the city and consigns to Livia a large sum of money for the Venetian patriot rebels. Despite her determination to end her affair with Franz, Livia once more succumbs to his charm and gives him the money intended for the rebels so that he can bribe his way out of military service. After he has left, war is declared, and Livia decides to join Franz in Verona; but bitter reality awaits her. Franz has taken another mistress, and when Livia finds him he is drunk and disillusioned, conscious of his baseness as a man and cowardice as a soldier. With brutal frankness, Franz admits to Livia that he only wanted her money and that he was responsible for Ussoni's arrest. For revenge, Livia impulsively delivers a letter to the Austrian command in which she exposes Franz as a deserter. Victimized by her own vengeance, Livia lapses into insanity, and after Franz has been executed by a firing squad, she runs through the streets calling his name. *Nobility. Cousins. Austrians. Mistresses. Deserters—Military. Exile. Resistance (political). Bribery. Perfidy. Revenge. Capital punishment. Insanity. Austro-Prussian War 1866. Venice. Verona. Austria—Army.*

Note: Location scenes filmed in Venice and the Villa di Valmarana. Rome opening in Jan 1955; running time: 120 min. An English version was filmed in 1954 with dialog by Tennessee Williams and Paul Bowles, but the 1968 U. S. release is the original version. A substantially cut dubbed version entitled *The Wanton Contessa* was shown on U. S. television before 1968. Photographers Krasker and Rotunno replaced Graziata, who died during production. Graziata is also known as G. R. Aldo.

THE SENSUAL WOMAN *see* **THE SENSUALLY LIBERATED FEMALE**

THE SENSUALIST   **F6.4354**

Dist American Film Distributing Corp. 16 Jun **1966** [San Francisco showing]. Sd; b&w. 35mm. 73 min.

Prod-Dir Aram Emanuel. *Camera* Peter Emanuel Goldman, Simon Nuchtern. *Asst Camera* Ansley W. Berlin. *Ed* Peter Rostov. *Orig Mus* The Connections. *Mix* Val Peters. *Sd* Sid Washer. *Script Girl* Riva Freifeld.

Cast: Ilona Lys (*Karina*), Ann Kirton (*Sharon*), Carolyn Carlton (*Louise*), Daniel Tomaso (*Robert*), Michelle Roberts (*Yvonne*), Astrid Paul, Kim Strong, Rachel Delarue, Michael Sims, Barbara Brent, Phillipe Lemari, John Stanton, Ondine Le Bourget, Peter W. Schneider, Janet Lund.

Melodrama. Karina leaves her home in Denmark after an unhappy love affair and comes to New York where she meets Sharon, a Greenwich Village coffee house waitress, who offers the shelter of her apartment. On the first night Sharon gives a wild party; Karina goes to the roof of the building to be alone, and there she meets a rapist. Meditating revenge on men, she agrees to meet Sharon's boyfriend, Robert, but her willpower fails, and they make love. Sharon tries to lead her friend into a lesbian affair; uninterested, Karina spends her days wandering alone. Convinced by Sharon that she is taking men too seriously, Karina has a series of superficial sexual encounters and finds no satisfaction. Reminded of happier days in Denmark by the visit of a couple in love, she performs a drunken striptease. The next morning, a boyfriend of Sharon's makes love to both women, and Karina at last submits to Sharon's lesbian embrace. Suddenly disgusted by the life she has been leading, she packs her bags to wander again through the streets of New York. *Danes. Waitresses. Roommates. Rape. Lesbianism. Troilism. Striptease. New York City— Greenwich Village.*

Note: Aram Emanuel is a pseudonym of Peter Emanuel Goldman. Also known as *The Sensualists.*

THE SENSUALLY LIBERATED FEMALE   F6.4355
New World Studios. *Dist* Institute for Adult Education. 16 Nov **1970** [New York opening]. Sd; col. 35mm. 67 min.

Narrator: Lindis Guiness.

Sex film. Several women masturbate with an assortment of aids in a clinical demonstration of woman's natural sexuality and ability to achieve orgasm. *Sexuality. Autoeroticism. Sex aids.*

Note: Also known as *The Sensual Woman; The Sexually Liberated Female; The Sexuous Female;* and *Woman and Lover.*

SEPARATION (Great Britain)   F6.4356
Bond Films. *For* Alliance International Pictures. *Dist* Continental Distributing, Inc. 25 Mar **1968** [New York opening]. Sd; b&w with col seq (Eastmancolor). 35mm. 90 min. [Also reviewed at 97 min.]

Prod-Dir Jack Bond. *Assoc Prod* Michael Pearson, Richard De La Mare, Frank Walsh, Jacob Seguev. *Story & Screenplay* Jane Arden. *Photog* David Muir, Aubrey Dewar. *Film Ed* Michael Johns. *Mus* Stanley Myers, Procol Harum. *Songs* Matthew Fisher. *Sd Rec* Barrie Copland, Charles Poulton. *Asst Dir* Adam Clapham.

Cast: Jane Arden *(Jane)*, David De Keyser *(husband)*, Ann Lynn *(woman)*, Iain Quarrier *(lover)*, Terence De Marney *(old man)*, Fay Brook, Leslie Linder, Joy Bang, Neil Holmes, Ann Norman, Malou Pantera, Theo Aygar, Kathleen Saintsbury, Peter Thomas, actor, Donald Sayer, Tom Corbett.

Drama. Following the break-up of her marriage, Jane, an Englishwoman in her mid-30's, is on the brink of a nervous breakdown. Unable to distinguish between reality and fantasy, she experiences a series of real and imaginary confrontations with her husband, her lover, and her analyst. The meetings reveal different aspects of the woman's complex personality as she futilely attempts to adjust to the demands of each man. Her husband appears as self-contained and detached, her younger lover as a man who will soon tire of her devotion, and her analyst as a relentless inquisitor. During the course of her mental wanderings, Jane sees herself as an old woman shoplifting in a department store, as a middle-aged wife lunching with her husband in a fashionable restaurant, and as a young married woman on the verge of her first illicit love affair. Ultimately, she and her lover appear in a park where they draw revolvers and shoot each other—but the incident may have occurred only in her mind. *Psychologists. Divorce. Mental illness. Marriage. Infidelity. Murder.*

Note: Opened in London in Jun 1968; running time: 93 min.

IL SEPOLCRO DEI RE *see* **CLEOPATRA'S DAUGHTER**

SEPPUKU *see* **HARAKIRI**

SEPT FOIS FEMME *see* **WOMAN TIMES SEVEN**

SEPT HOMMES EN OR *see* **SEVEN GOLDEN MEN**

LES SEPT PÉCHÉS CAPITAUX *see* **SEVEN CAPITAL SINS**

LE SEPTIÈME JURÉ *see* **THE SEVENTH JUROR**

I SEQUESTRATI DI ALTONA *see* **THE CONDEMNED OF ALTONA**

LES SÉQUESTRÉS D'ALTONA *see* **THE CONDEMNED OF ALTONA**

SERAFINO (France/Italy)   F6.4357
R. P. A.-Rizzoli Films-Francoriz. *Dist* Royal Films International. 3 May **1970** [New York opening; c4 May 1970; LP39044]. Sd (Westrex); col (Technicolor). 35mm. 94 min. *MPAA rating* GP.

Pres by Angelo Rizzoli. *Prod-Dir* Pietro Germi. *English Vers Dir* Lee Kresel. *Screenplay* Leo Benvenuti, Piero De Bernardi, Tullio Pinelli, Pietro Germi. *Orig Story* Alfredo Giannetti, Tullio Pinelli, Pietro Germi. *Dir Photog* Aiace Parolin. *Art Dir* Carlo Egidi. *Set Decor* Andrea Fantacci. *Film Ed* Sergio Montanari. *Mus* Carlo Rustichelli. *Mus Cond* Bruno Nicolai. *Sd* Guido Ortensi. *Sd Rec* Venanzio Biraschi. *Prod Mgr* Ottavio Oppo. *Cost* Angela Sammaciccia. *English Subtitl* Harold J. Salemson.

Cast: Adriano Celentano *(Serafino Fiorin)*, Ottavia Piccolo *(Lidia)*, Saro Urzì *(Uncle Agenore)*, Francesca Romana Coluzzi *(Asmara)*, Benjamin Lev *(Armido)*, Nazareno Natale *(Silio)*, Giosuè Ippolito *(Rocco)*, Ermelinda De Felice *(Aunt Armida)*, Nerina Montagnani *(Aunt Gesuina)*, Luciana Turina *(Aunt Lucia)*, Oreste Palella *(lawyer)*, Piero Gerlini *(1st policeman)*, Goffredo Canzano *(Uncle Olmo)*, Gino Santercole *(sergeant)*, Nestor Garay *(priest)*,

Amedeo Trilli *(Pasquale)*, Orlando D'Ubaldo *(Uncle Felicetto)*, Gustavo D'Arpe *(medical officer)*, Vittorio Fanfoni *(2d policeman)*, Mara Oscuro *(4th aunt)*, Gianni Pulone *(corporal of the guard)*, Clara Colosimo *(1st washerwoman)*, Nazzareno D'Aquilio *(town policeman)*, Lidia Mancani *(2d washerwoman)*.

Comedy-drama. Serafino Fiorin, a shepherd in the Abruzzi Mountains in Italy, is mainly concerned with the pursuit of pleasure. He is drafted into the army, but after spending most of his time in the brig, he is discharged. Returning to his home town, he falls in love with his naive 17-year-old cousin, Lidia, who allows him to have sex with her. Lidia tries to persuade him to marry her, but Serafino has no intention of marrying her and turns to Asmara, a local prostitute. Later, his eccentric Aunt Gesuina dies and wills him a small fortune, which he immediately begins to squander. Serafino's Uncle Agenore, to gain control of the inheritance, goes to court and has Serafino declared mentally incompetent; to further insure his trusteeship, Agenore tries to force Serafino to marry Lidia, his daughter. At the wedding Serafino's friends disrupt the ceremony, and Serafino escapes to marry Asmara. Asmara and her brood of illegitimate children move into a new house, and Serafino returns to the mountains and his simple life as a shepherd. *Shepherds. Cousins. Prostitutes. Eccentrics. Aunts. Uncles. Spendthrifts. Hedonism. Military draft. Mental incompetency. Marriage of convenience. Mountain life. Inheritance. Weddings. Italy—Army.*

Note: Released in Italy in 1968 as *Serafino*; in France in Sep 1969 as *Serafino ou l'amour aux champs.*

SERAFINO OU L'AMOUR AUX CHAMPS *see* **SERAFINO**

SERDTSE MATERI *see* **SONS AND MOTHERS**

SERENADE FOR TWO SPIES (Italy/West Germany)   F6.4358
Modern Art Film–Metheus Film. *Dist* United Film Enterprises. 4 Nov **1966** [Chicago opening]. Sd; col (Eastman Color). 35mm (Franscope). 90 min.

Prod Hansjürgen Pohland. *Dir* Michael Pfleghar. *Screenplay* Michael Pfleghar, Klaus Munro. *Photog* Ernst Wild. *Art Dir* Peter Scharff. *Film Ed* Margot von Schlieffen. *Mus* Francesco De Masi. *Prod Mgr* Peter Genée.

Cast: Helmut Lange *(John Krim)*, Tony Kendall *(Pepino)*, Barbara Lass *(Tamara)*, Heidelinde Weis *(Goldfeather)*, Wolfgang Neuss *(secret service chief)*, Dick Palmer *(Cormoran)*, Annie Giess.

Satire. Based on a novel by: K. H. Günther. An international band of arms smugglers steals a laser gun from a German laboratory. FBI agent Cormoran, assigned to the case, appears to have defected to the organization responsible for the theft. John Krim, German secret agent 006 1/2, arrives in San Francisco, escapes from the clutches of several hoodlums, and contacts female agents Tamara and Goldfeather. Krim's weakness for women nearly costs him his life when Goldfeather, posing as a hotel waitress, serves him a bomb disguised as a breakfast roll. Pursued to Las Vegas, New York, and the Nevada desert, Krim is abducted, buried in the sand, and left to die. Rescued by Tamara, Krim retrieves the stolen weapon. Piloting a plane, Tamara snatches Krim by lasso from the ground and informs him that they are leaving for Venice to be married. *Smugglers. Secret agents. Defectors. Hoodlums. Waitresses. Theft. Abduction. Rescue. Imposture. Laser. Bombs. Deserts. Airplanes. San Francisco. Las Vegas. New York City. Nevada. Venice. United States—Federal Bureau of Investigation. Chases.*

Note: Opened in West Germany in Aug 1965 as *Serenade für zwei Spione;* running time: 87 min. Opened in Rome in Mar 1966 as *Sinfonia per due spie;* running time: ca90 min. Tony Kendall and Dick Palmer are pseudonyms for Luciano Stella and Mimmo Palmara respectively.

SERENADE FÜR ZWEI SPIONE *see* **SERENADE FOR TWO SPIES**

SERENITY   F6.4359
Serenity Productions. Jul **1962** [New York opening]. Sd; col (Eastman Color). 35mm. 70 & 90 min.

Prod-Dir-Writ Gregory J. Markopoulos. *Mus* Peter Hartman. *Co-worker* Dimitri Trimbalis, Nikos Erressiou, Madame Goumas.

Cast: Norma Valdi *(Eirene Veni)*, Constantine Baldimas *(Dimitri Veni)*, Vivian Verrilli *(Anna)*, George Foundas *(Photis Glaros)*, Nina Bobbie *(Eleni Glaros)*, Koula Agagiotou *(Aunt Maria)*, Athena Mihalidou *(Aunt Sophia)*, Dimitri Maras *(Andreas, her son)*, Pandopoulos *(a water-diviner)*, Lili Yannikaki *(Zambeta)*, Margarita Goumas *(widow)*, Thanas Veloudios *(Barba-Stathys)*, Byron Pallis *(mechanic)*, Takis Cabouras *(Haritos)*, Dimitri Stamos *(a boy)*, Mike Papalexis *(Greek narrator)*, Brian Clark *(English narrator)*, Peter Schreicher *(German narrator)*, Mr. Kozowski *(Russian narrator)*.

Experimental film. Inspired by: Elias Venezis, *Galene* (Athens, 1939). In the early 1920's, after Greece and Turkey have signed a peace establishing new boundaries, the two countries exchange groups of displaced nationals. Among those forced to leave their traditional homes are the Greeks of Ionia in Asia Minor. Eirene Veni, whose husband, idealistic physician Dimitri Veni, is much older than she, recalls how she and her family first came to the village of Anávissos in Greece. Rather than cultivate wheat and grapes as the Greek government prescribed, Dimitri decided to grow a rose garden, as his family had always done in their homeland. Recurring throughout the film is an image of Dimitri at rest in a quiet orchard meditating over the collapse of his marriage with Eirene since the migration and over his relationship with the band of refugees who consider him their leader. Meanwhile, Photis Glaros and his wife, Eleni, who are also refugees, discover an ancient statue in their field, but a grave robber steals the statue and strangles Eleni. One day Anna, the daughter of Dimitri and Eirene, informs the villagers that the prisoners of war are returning from Asia Minor. The villagers go out to greet the returning soldiers but are dismayed to see a solitary, ragged man on the footpath. As they turn to head for home, Dimitri recognizes that the soldier is Andreas, the son of one of the Ionians. In Anávissos, Andreas experiences recurring reveries in which he makes love with Anna and in which Anna is raped and killed. [Some sources suggest that these are actual occurrences.] Eirene uproots her husband's rose garden, and a 30-second sequence ensues in which the scenes of the film follow one another in rapid succession. *Physicians. Prisoners of war. Refugees. Greeks. Immigration. Memory. Marriage. Murder. Theft. Rape. Flowers. Gardens. Greco-Turkish War (1921–22). Anávissos. Ionia. Fantasy.*

Note: Filmed on location in Greece, including Anávissos and Mitilíni, in 1958. Date of completion: 1961. Dedicated to Madame Tiggie Ghika.

THE SERGEANT   F6.4360

Warner Bros.-Seven Arts, Inc. 25 Dec **1968** [New York opening; c1 Nov 1968; LP37139]. Sd; col with b&w seq (Technicolor). 35mm. 108 min. *MPAA rating R.*

A Robert Wise Production. *Prod* Richard Goldstone. *Exec Prod* Robert Wise. *Dir* John Flynn. *Screenplay* Dennis Murphy. *Dir Photog* Henri Persin. *Camera Op* Gilles Bonneau. *Art Dir* Marc Frederix. *Prod Dsgn* Willy Holt. *Supv Film Ed* Charles Nelson. *Film Ed* Françoise Diot. *Mus* Michel Magne. *Sd* Julien Coutellier. *Asst Dir* Louis Pitzele. *Prod Mgr* Serge Lebeau. *Cont* Alice Ziller. *Makeup* Michel Deruelle. *Tech Adv* Donald Roth. *Dial Coach* Elliott Sullivan.

Cast: Rod Steiger (*M. Sgt. Albert Callan*), John Phillip Law (*Pfc. Tom Swanson*), Ludmila Mikael (*Solange*), Frank Latimore (*Captain Loring*), Elliott Sullivan (*Pop Henneken*), Ronald Rubin (*Corporal Cowley*), Philip Roye (*Aldous Brown*), Jerry Brouer (*Sergeant Komski*), Memphis Slim (*nightclub singer*), Gabriel Gascond (*Solange's brother-in-law*).

Drama. Source: Dennis Murphy, *The Sergeant* (New York, 1958). In 1952 M. Sgt. Albert Callan, who distinguished himself in World War II by strangling a German soldier with his bare hands, is assigned to a petroleum supply depot in France. Upon discovering that the camp lacks discipline under the leadership of insecure and alcoholic Captain Loring, Callan seizes command and imposes his own strict military standards on the resentful men. At the same time he is attracted, almost subconsciously, to handsome young Pfc. Tom Swanson. After forcing the hardworking Swanson to become his orderly room clerk, Callan tries to monopolize the private's time and even refuses to issue him passes to date his French girl friend, Solange. Mistaking the sergeant's attentions for loneliness, Swanson begins to spend more time with Callan, but after the sergeant succeeds in driving away Solange, Swanson realizes the truth and openly defies his superior. Driven to excessive drinking, Callan desperately attempts to make love to Swanson and is violently rejected. The next morning, when the sergeant comes to company formation in a state of drunken dishevelment, Loring relieves him of his duties. After spending that night in the orderly room, Callan takes a rifle from the company armory, goes into a nearby woods, and kills himself. *War heroes. French. Male homosexuality. Alcoholism. Drunkenness. Suicide. France. United States Army.*

Note: Location scenes filmed in France.

SERGEANT DEADHEAD   F6.4361

American International Productions. *Dist* American International Pictures. 18 Aug **1965** [Kansas City, Missouri, opening; c11 Aug 1965; LP31861]. Sd; col (Pathé Color). 35mm (Panavision). 90 min.

Prod James H. Nicholson, Samuel Z. Arkoff. *Co-prod* Anthony Carras. *Dir* Norman Taurog. *Screenplay* Louis M. Heyward. *Dir Photog* Floyd Crosby. *Art Dir* Howard Campbell. *Set Decor* Robert Nelson. *Film Ed* Ronald Sinclair, Fred Feitshans, Eve Newman. *Mus Dir* Al Simms. Songs: "Sergeant Deadhead," "The Difference in Me Is You," "Let's Play Love," "Two-Timin' Angel," "How Can You Tell," "You Should Have Seen the One That Got Away," "Hurry Up and Wait" Guy Hemric, Jerry Styner. *Songs Sung by* Frankie Avalon, Deborah Walley, Eve Arden. *Choreog* Jack Baker. *Sd* Don Rush. *Sd Rec* Wallace R. Bearden. *Asst Dir* Claude Binyon, Jr. *Prod Mgr* Jack Bohrer. *Sp Eff* Roger George.

Cast: Frankie Avalon (*Sgt. O. K. Deadhead/Sergeant Donovan*), Deborah Walley (*Col. Lucy Turner*), Cesar Romero (*Admiral Stoneham*), Fred Clark (*Gen. Rufus Fogg*), Gale Gordon (*Captain Weiskopf*), Harvey Lembeck

(*Private McEvoy*), John Ashley (*Private Filroy*), Buster Keaton (*Private Blinken*), Reginald Gardiner (*Lieutenant Commander Talbott*), Eve Arden (*Lieutenant Kinsey*), Pat Buttram (*The President*), Donna Loren (*Susan*), Romo Vincent (*tuba player*), Tod Windsor (*Sergeant Keeler*), Norman Grabowski, Mike Nader (*air police*), Edward Faulkner (*radioman*), Bobbi Shaw (*Gilda*), Patti Chandler (*Patti*), Salli Sachse (*Sue Ellen*), Luree Holmes (*Luree*), Sue Hamilton (*Ivy*), Jo Collins (*Gail*), Bob Harvey (*bellhop*), Jerry Brutsche (*newsman*), Andy Romano, John Macchia (*Marine MPs*), Sallie Dornan (*secretary*), Mary Hughes, Astrid De Brea, Jean Ingram, Peggy Ward, Stephanie Nader, Lyzanne Ladue, Janice Levinson, Alberta Nelson (*WAFs*).

Comedy with music. U. S. Air Force Sgt. O. K. Deadhead, stationed at Smedley Missile Base, accidentally explodes a rocket at a military parade, and Gen. Rufus Fogg sends him to the guardhouse. Under the guidance of a hardened criminal who shares his cell, the mild-mannered Deadhead escapes the stockade and takes refuge in a rocket; and he is accidentally launched into space along with a chimpanzee. Air Force officers retrieve the rocket and tell Deadhead that they will make him a public hero if he will keep the blunder secret. The ride in space has altered the sergeant's personality, however, and he becomes a power-mad girl-chaser who insists upon exposing the mistake to the press. To protect his reputation, General Fogg imprisons Deadhead, despite the sergeant's plans to marry Col. Lucy Turner the same day. Under Fogg's orders, Lieutenant Kinsey and other officers arrange for Sergeant Donovan, Deadhead's double, to pose as Deadhead for the wedding ceremony and the honeymoon. Deadhead escapes from the guardhouse and takes his rightful place at the honeymoon hotel. He reverts to his original personality and claims his bride. *Doubles. Personality. Military life. Imprisonment. Impersonation. Rocket-launching sites. Rockets. Weddings. Parades. Honeymoons. United States Air Force. United States Air Force—Women in the Air Force. Chimpanzees.*

Note: Also known as *Sergeant Deadhead the Astronut!*

SERGEANT JIM (Yugoslavia)   F6.4362

Triglav Film. *Dist* Cain Productions. 4 Jun **1962** [New York State license]. Sd; b&w. 35mm. 82 min.

Dir France Štiglic. *Screenplay* Ivan Ribič. *Photog* Rudi Vavpotič. *Mus* Marijan Kozina.

Cast: John Kitzmiller (*Sergeant Jim*), Evelyne Wohlfeiler (*Lotti*), Tugo Štiglic (*Marko*), Boris Kralj, Maks Furijan, Janez Čuk.

War drama. Marko, a Yugoslavian youth, and Lotti, a little German girl, are orphaned during an air raid in World War II. Determined to find a "valley of peace," they flee from the Germans. Sergeant Jim, an American Negro airman whose plane has been shot down, helps them find their way to Marko's uncle's valley, which the children believe to be their destination. When they arrive, however, fighting breaks out between the Germans and the partisans, and Jim is fatally wounded. The children escape and resume their search for the peaceful valley. *Orphans. Germans. Children. Negroes. Soldiers. Resistance (political). World War II.*

Note: Produced in Yugoslavia in 1956 as *Dolina mira*; running time: 89 min. U. S. prerelease title: *Mr. Jim—American, Soldier, and Gentleman.*

SERGEANT RYKER   F6.4363

Roncom Films. *Dist* Universal Pictures. 18 Feb **1968** [Charlotte, North Carolina, opening; c2 Mar 1968; LP38592]. Sd (Westrex); col (PathéColor). 35mm. 86 min.

Prod Frank Telford. *Assoc Prod* Joel Rogosin, Jo Swerling, Jr. *Dir* Buzz Kulik. *Screenplay* Seeleg Lester, William D. Gordon. *Story* Seeleg Lester. *Dir Photog* Walter Strenge. *Art Dir* John J. Lloyd. *Set Decor* John McCarthy, Robert C. Bradfield. *Main Titl* Universal Title. *Film Ed* Robert B. Warwick. *Mus* Johnny Williams. *Mus Supv* Stanley Wilson. *Sd* Waldon O. Watson, William Lynch. *Asst Dir* John Clarke Bowman. *Makeup* Bud Westmore. *Hairstyles* Larry Germain.

Cast: Lee Marvin (*Sgt. Paul Ryker*), Bradford Dillman (*Capt. David Young*), Vera Miles (*Ann Ryker*), Peter Graves (*Major Whitaker*), Lloyd Nolan (*Gen. Amos Bailey*), Murray Hamilton (*Captain Appleton*), Norman Fell (*Sgt. Max Winkler*), Walter Brooke (*Col. Arthur Merriam*), Francis DeSales (*president of court martial*), Don Marshall (*Corporal Jenks*), Charles Aidman (*Major Kitchener*).

Melodrama. During the Korean War, Sgt. Paul Ryker is arrested as a traitor, convicted, and sentenced to hang. His wife, Ann, charges that the trial was unfair and persuades the prosecuting attorney, Capt. David Young, to conduct a personal investigation. Convinced that, at least technically, Ryker's defense was improperly handled, Young attempts to investigate Ryker's claim that he was sent behind North Korean lines on a secret mission by Colonel Chalmers (who is now dead) to plug a security leak. Young talks Gen. Amos Bailey into granting a stay of execution and a new trial, and appointing Young as Ryker's defense attorney. Young's efforts to help Ryker are complicated, however, when Ryker flies into a rage upon learning that Young has fallen in love with

Ann. The new prosecuting attorney, Major Whitaker, produces two witnesses who add seemingly more proof of Ryker's defection, and the defendant only makes matters worse by losing his temper during cross-examination, bluntly stating that he has received only abuse from his own countrymen whereas the enemy made him an officer and treated him with honor. Even Young now feels that Ryker's case is lost, but last-minute testimony from Sgt. Max Winkler convinces the court that the dead colonel frequently gave secret orders without keeping an official record. Ryker is finally acquitted, and Ann decides to remain with her husband. *Traitors. Defectors. Lawyers. Secret agents. Combat zone life. Treason. Capital punishment. Marriage. Courts-martial. Korean War 1950–53. United States Army.*

Note: Originally presented on NBC's "Kraft Suspense Theatre" as a two-part episode *The Case Against Paul Ryker;* c10 Oct 1963, 17 Oct 1963; LP29836, LP29837; telecast on the same days as registered for copyright.

THE SERGEANT WAS A LADY   **F6.4364**
Twincraft Productions. *Dist* Universal-International. 4 Oct **1961** [Los Angeles opening; c29 Aug 1961; LP24450]. Sd; b&w. 35mm. 72 min.

Prod-Dir-Writ Bernard Glasser. *Dir Photog* Hal McAlpin. *Camera Op* Jack Willoughby. *Art Dir* Frank Sylos. *Set Decor* William Stevens. *Film Ed* John F. Link. *Choreog* Noel Parenti. *Sd* William Bernds. *Asst Dir* Robert Farfan, Buddy Messinger. *Prod Asst* Joan Glasser. *Script Supv* Billy Vernon. *Wardrobe* Thelma Hilborn. *Makeup* Larry Butterworth. *Hair Stylist* Doris Durkus. *Prop Master* George Bahr. *Ch Electrn* Robert Petzoldt.

Cast: Martin West *(Cpl. Gale Willard)*, Venetia Stevenson *(Sgt. Judy Fraser)*, Bill Williams *(Colonel House)*, Catherine McLeod *(Major Hay)*, Roy Engel *(Sergeant Bricker)*, Gregg Martell *(Red Henning)*, Chickie Lind *(Lenore Bliss)*, Jomarie Pettitt *(Marge McKay)*, Mari Lynn *(Rose Miller)*, Joan Barry *(Rita Waters)*, Francine York *(Tina Baird)*, Rhoda Williams *(Lieutenant Witt)*, Doris Fesette *(Lieutenant Read)*, Lonnie Blackman *(Captain Beal)*, Ric Turner *(Cy Turner)*, Richard Emory *(Major Zilker)*, Jim Dale *(Sergeant Thomas)*, Dan White *(General Payson)*, Hal Torey *(Colonel Burns)*, John Mitchum *(1st M. P.)*, Mike Masters *(2d M. P.)*.

Comedy. Owing to an error in the Army's data-processing classification system, Cpl. Gale Willard, a young missile technician, is assigned to a Pacific island military base staffed by 125 WAC's. Until Washington issues new orders, Gale is given temporary duties by Judy Fraser, an attractive top sergeant. The WAC's are trying to prove that they are as effective as men in missile tactics, and they are in heated competition with an all-male base on another island some miles away. After causing a romantic upheaval in the women's camp, Gale is sent to the rival base to learn the "enemy's" secret tactics. He accomplishes his mission and helps the women win the missile-firing exercise. When his replacement arrives, the grateful WAC's give him a farewell party, and Sergeant Fraser promises to meet him again. *Employment—Women. Mistaken identity. Computers. Missiles. Pacific Ocean. United States Army—Women's Army Corps.*

SERGEANTS 3   **F6.4365**
Essex-Claude Productions. *Dist* United Artists. 10 Feb **1962** [New York opening; c9 Feb 1962; LP21362]. Sd; col (Technicolor). 35mm (Panavision). 112 min.

Prod Frank Sinatra. *Exec Prod* Howard W. Koch. *Dir* John Sturges. *2d Unit Dir* Al Wyatt. *Writ* W. R. Burnett. *Dir Photog* Winton Hoch. *2d Unit Photog* Carl Guthrie. *Art Dir* Frank Hotaling. *Set Decor* Victor Gangelin. *Film Ed* Ferris Webster. *Mus* Billy May. *Song:* "And the Night Wind Sang" Johnny Rotella, Franz Steininger. *Sd* Harold Lewis, Harry Alphin. *Asst Dir* Jack Reddish. *Wardrobe* Wesley V. Jefferies, Angela Alexander. *Makeup* Beans Ponedel. *Hairstyles* Mary Westmoreland. *Sp Eff* Paul Pollard.

Cast: Frank Sinatra *(1st Sgt. Mike Merry)*, Dean Martin *(Sgt. Chip Deal)*, Sammy Davis, Jr. *(Jonah Williams)*, Peter Lawford *(Sgt. Larry Barrett)*, Joey Bishop *(Sgt. Maj. Roger Boswell)*, Henry Silva *(Mountain Hawk)*, Ruta Lee *(Amelia Parent)*, Buddy Lester *(Willie Sharpknife)*, Phil Crosby *(Corporal Ellis)*, Dennis Crosby *(Private Page)*, Lindsay Crosby *(Private Wills)*, Hank Henry *(blacksmith)*, Richard Simmons *(Col. William Collingwood)*, Michael Pate *(Watanka)*, Armand Alzamora *(Caleb)*, Richard Hale *(White Eagle)*, Mickey Finn *(Morton)*, Sonny King *(corporal)*, Eddie Little Sky *(ghost dancer)*, Rodd Redwing *(an irregular)*, James Waters *(colonel's aide)*, Madge Blake *(Mrs. Parent)*, Dorothy Abbott *(Mrs. Collingwood)*, Walter Merrill *(telegrapher)*, Ceffie *(herself)*.

Western comedy. Mike, Chip, and Larry are three lusty, brawling U. S. Cavalry sergeants stationed in Indian Territory in 1870. Mike and Chip are determined to prevent Larry from carrying out his decision to leave the Army at the end of his current hitch and marry beautiful Amelia Parent. One night the three cronies befriend a trumpet-playing former slave, Jonah Williams, who dreams of someday becoming a trooper. A tribe of fanatical Indians begins terrorizing the area, and the headstrong Chip decides to attempt the capture of their leader. Accompanied by Jonah, he sneaks into the Indians' secret meeting

place while they are conducting one of their mysterious rites, but he is discovered and taken prisoner. Jonah, however, escapes and races back to tell Mike and Larry. When Larry insists upon going to Chip's rescue, Mike makes him sign a reenlistment paper "just to make his help official" and promises to destroy the paper after the mission. Mike, Larry, and Jonah make their way to the Indian stronghold, but they too end up as prisoners. As the Cavalry rides into a trap where a thousand warriors are waiting to ambush them, Jonah blows the regiment's favorite tune on his trumpet as a warning. The ensuing battle ends in victory for the Cavalry; the three sergeants are decorated, and Jonah is made a trooper. Thinking himself discharged, Larry drives off in a buggy with Amelia, but the crafty Mike shows the post's commanding officer the reenlistment paper he had promised to destroy. Larry, it appears, will be forced to serve another hitch with Mike and Chip. *Musicians. Indians of North America. Negroes. Slavery. Perfidy. Rites and ceremonies. Friendship. Trumpeters. Indian Territory. United States Army—Cavalry.*

Note: Exteriors filmed on location near Kanab, Utah, and at Bryce Canyon National Park, Utah. The film is a comic reworking of *Gunga Din*, RKO, 1939. Working titles! *Badlands* and *Soldiers 3.*

SERIOUS CHARGE see **IMMORAL CHARGE**

THE SERVANT (Great Britain)   **F6.4366**
Springbok Films. *Dist* Landau Releasing Organization. 16 Mar **1964** [New York opening]. Sd; b&w. 35mm. 115 min.

Prod Joseph Losey, Norman Priggen. *Dir* Joseph Losey. *Screenplay* Harold Pinter. *Dir Photog* Douglas Slocombe. *Camera Op* Chic Waterson. *Art Dir* Ted Clements. *Asst Art Dir* Bill Alexander. *Prod Dsgn* Richard MacDonald. *Film Ed* Reginald Mills. *Mus Comp & Cond* John Dankworth. *Song:* "All Gone" sung by Cleo Laine. *Sd Supv* John Cox. *Sd Rec* Buster Ambler. *Sd Ed* Gerry Hambling. *Asst Dir* Roy Stevens. *Prod Mgr* Teresa Bolland. *Cont* Pamela Davies. *Cost Dsgn* Beatrice Dawson. *Makeup* Bob Lawrence. *Hairdresser* Joyce James. *Camera Grip* Frank Howard.

Cast: Dirk Bogarde *(Hugo Barrett)*, Sarah Miles *(Vera)*, Wendy Craig *(Susan)*, James Fox *(Tony)*, Catherine Lacey *(Lady Mounset)*, Richard Vernon *(Lord Mounset)*, Ann Firbank *(society woman)*, Doris Knox *(older woman)*, Patrick Magee *(bishop)*, Jill Melford *(younger woman)*, Alun Owen *(curate)*, Harold Pinter *(society man)*, Derek Tansley *(head waiter)*, Brian Phelan *(man in pub)*, Hazel Terry *(woman in bedroom)*, Philippa Hare *(girl in bedroom)*, Dorothy Bromiley *(girl in phone box)*, Colette Martin, Joanna Wake, Harriet Devine *(her friends)*, Alison Seebohm *(girl in pub)*, Chris Williams *(cashier in coffee bar)*, Gerry Duggan *(waiter)*, John Dankworth *(jazz band leader)*, Davy Graham *(guitarist)*, Bruce Wells *(sidewalk painter)*.

Drama. Source: Robin Maugham, *The Servant* (London, 1948). Tony—wealthy, spoiled, and class-conscious—returns to London from a trip abroad, buys a home, and hires Hugo Barrett, a manservant, to take care of the house. Barrett quickly and efficiently decorates and organizes the home, and Tony's dependence on him grows, though Susan, Tony's fiancée, is antagonistic toward Barrett, whom she feels is an evil influence. Barrett brings Vera to the house to serve as maid, introducing her as his sister. She soon seduces Tony, and he begins to ignore Susan. One evening Tony arrives to find Barrett and Vera making love, and when they admit that they are not brother and sister, Tony fires them. Tony's house becomes a shambles, and Susan rejects him; so when he sees Barrett in a pub, Tony quickly rehires him. Barrett increases his dominance, while Tony has fits of drunkenness and becomes so weak-willed that he loses all control of the house; Barrett becomes the master. Susan makes one last visit, and she finds Tony in a decrepit state, unaware of reality, and unable to grapple with her final statement of love. *Valets. Housemaids. Seduction. Drunkenness. Moral corruption. Social classes. London.*

Note: Opened in London in Nov 1963.

SERYOZHA see **A SUMMER TO REMEMBER**

A SESSION WITH THE COMMITTEE   **F6.4367**
Spectra Media. *Dist* Commonwealth United Entertainment, Inc. 29 Jan **1969** [Denver, Colorado, opening]. Sd; col (Technicolor). 35mm (see note). 88 min. MPAA rating G.

Prod-Dir Del Jack. *Exec Prod, Staged & Created by* Alan Myerson. *Screenplay* The Committee. *Camera* Joe Talosi, Ernest Hall. *Film Ed* Donn Cambern. *Mus* P. William Mathieu, Ellsworth Milburn. *Sd* Roger Standbridge. *Asst Dir* Bud Morrison.

Cast—The Committee: Peter Bonerz, Garry Goodrow, Jessica Myerson, Melvin Stewart, Barbara Bosson, Carl Gottlieb, Christopher Ross, Don Sturdy.

Comedy. This filmed presentation of a performance by The Committee is comprised of 19 satiric skits and blackouts. Following an introduction by Peter Bonerz, the highlights include a young man's frantic effort to avoid the draft by behaving like a frog; a "talking" elevator that argues with its occupants; a generation gap dispute between a hostile cyclist and a defensive old man; two housewives enjoying a break in their daily routine by smoking marijuana instead of drinking coffee; a takeoff on television commercials; the effect of Dale Carnegie on dating behavior; a TV audience applause warm-up session; a symphony concert in which the musicians vocally imitate orchestral instruments; an illustration of hypocrisy in the police force; a TV giveaway show called "Greed," in which the participants assault each other in the hope of winning prizes; a would-be Casanova's disastrous attempt to be suave while lighting a girl's cigarette; a white man posing as a black in order to understand the Negro's problems in contemporary society; a spoof of a well-known California car dealer who does his own television commercials; a girl on a blind date pretending that she actually is blind in order to test her date's sexual curiosity; and the entire company performing "The Star Spangled Banner." *Draft dodgers. Motorcyclists. Housewives. Police. Used-car dealers. Musicians. Hypocrisy. Greed. Race relations. Blindness. Imposture. Elevators. Marijuana. Television. Television commercials. Orchestras. "The Star Spangled Banner".*

Note: Videotaped before a live audience in Los Angeles, 22 Jul 1968. May also be known as *The Committee.*

SESSO (Italy)   **F6.4368**

Roas Produzioni. *Dist* Sherpix, Inc. Aug **1970** [San Francisco showing]. Sd; col (Eastman Color). 35mm (Colorscope). ca84 min. *MPAA rating* X.

Prod Ovisio G. Assonitis, Giorgio Carlo Rossi. *Dir* Alfonso Brescia. *Screenplay* Giacinto Ciaccio, Massimo D'Avack. *Story* Giorgio Carlo Rossi. *Photog* Fausto Rossi. *Art Dir* Claudio Giambanco. *Film Ed* Emilio Lopez. *Mus* Italo Fischetti. *Sd* Pietro Spadoni. *Asst Dir* Edgardo Siroli, Franco Fogagnolo. *Prod Mgr* Carlo Vassalle. *Cost* Gloria Cardi. *Scientific Cons* Professor Emilio Servadio.

Cast: Orchidea De Santis *(Anna),* Franco Ressel *(fetishist),* Susy Andersen *(nymphomaniac),* Edgardo Siroli *(sadist),* Maria Pia Conte, Elisabetta Fanti, Gioia Desideri, Sergio Doria, Willy Van Der Valle, Evaristo Maran, Massimo Foschi, Ilona Drasch, Marcello Tamborra.

Drama. In this documentary-style examination of sexuality, machines scientifically record the bodily responses of a couple having intercourse in a laboratory. Psychiatrists discuss various aspects of sexuality from infancy to adulthood and, in a series of dramatized episodes, illustrate and pose theories on the causes of such sexual deviations as nymphomania, lesbianism, homosexuality, necrophilia, voyeurism, exhibitionism, fetishism, and sadomasochism. *Sex researchers. Psychiatrists. Sexuality. Lesbianism. Male homosexuality. Necrophilia. Voyeurism. Exhibitionism. Fetishism. Sadomasochism.*

Note: Released in Italy in 1969 as *Nel labirinto del sesso* at 95 min. Also known as *The Labyrinth of Sex* and *Sexual Inadequacies.*

IL SESSO DEGLI ANGELI see **THE SEX OF ANGELS**

SETENTA VECES SIETE see **THE FEMALE; SEVENTY TIMES SEVEN**

SETTE CONTRO LA MORTE see **THE CAVERN**

SETTE DONNE PER I MACGREGOR see **UP THE MACGREGORS**

LE 7 FATICHE DI ALÌ BABÀ see **THE SEVEN TASKS OF ALI BABA**

I SETTE GLADIATORI see **GLADIATORS SEVEN**

I SETTE NANI ALLA RISCOSSA see **THE SEVEN DWARFS TO THE RESCUE**

I SETTE PECCATI CAPITALI see **SEVEN CAPITAL SINS**

7 PISTOLE PER I MACGREGOR see **SEVEN GUNS FOR THE MACGREGORS**

LE SETTE SFIDE see **THE SEVEN REVENGES**

SETTE UOMINI D'ORO see **SEVEN GOLDEN MEN**

SETTE VOLTE DONNA see **WOMAN TIMES SEVEN**

7 WINCHESTER PER UN MASSACRO see **PAYMENT IN BLOOD**

SEVEN AGAINST THE SUN (South Africa)   **F6.4369**

South African Screen Productions–David Millin–Roscoe C. Behrmann. *Dist* Emerson Film Enterprises. Mar **1968** [Los Angeles showing]. Sd; col (Eastmancolor). 35mm (CinemaScope). 115 min.

Prod David Millin, Roscoe C. Behrmann. *Dir* David Millin. *Sp Eff* Ike Honeyball. *Adv* George Duxbury.

Cast: Gert Van den Bergh *(Corporal Smit),* John Hayter *(Lieutenant Mitchell),* Brian O'Shaughnessy *(Sergeant MacCarthy),* Patrick Mynhardt *(Private Peters),* James White *(Private Irving),* Chris Robinson *(Private Louw),* Morne Coetzer, Jr. *(Private Harley),* Elizabeth Meyer *(Nursing Sister Bowley).*

War drama. In February 1941, South African troops on the northern frontier of Kenya attempt to repulse an Italian invasion. The South African command deceives the enemy by purporting to have large numbers of troops in the area. To this end, a seven-man patrol is assigned to set up an Abyssinian communications center to broadcast false reports of troop movements. Young and inexperienced Lieutenant Mitchell, the only member apprised of the mission, leads the patrol. Under his command are the radio operator, Sergeant MacCarthy; veteran trooper Corporal Smit; drunken Private Irving; a playboy, Private Louw; a music lover, Private Harley; and a loner, Private Peters. En route to their destination, the men are joined by Nurse Bowley, the sole surviver of a native uprising. As Mitchell attempts to carry out his orders, complications arise. Smit threatens his command; Sergeant MacCarthy and Nurse Bowley fall in love; Louw is obsessed with women; Irving mixes medicinal alcohol with his drinking water; and Harley plays his phonograph continuously. All seven soldiers, however, finally distinguish themselves in battle. *Nurses. Playboys. Combat zone life. Drunkenness. Military invasion. Music. Radio. World War II. Kenya. Abyssinia. Italy—Army. South Africa—Army.*

Note: Location scenes filmed in Senekal, South Africa. Released in South Africa in 1964.

SEVEN CAPITAL SINS (France/Italy)   **F6.4370**

Gibé–Franco London Film–Titanus. *Dist* Embassy Pictures. 16 Jan **1963** [New York opening]. Sd; b&w. 35mm (Dyaliscope). 113 min.

Overall Production Credits: *Pres by* Joseph E. Levine. *Film Ed* Jacques Gaillard, Jean Feyte.

Production Credits for "Anger": *Dir* Sylvain Dhomme, Eugène Ionesco, Max Douy. *Screenplay* Eugène Ionesco. *Photog* Jean Penzer. *Mus* Michel Legrand. *Prod Mgr* Jean Lavie, Tonio Suné.

Production Credits for "Envy": *Dir* Edouard Molinaro. *Screenplay* Claude Mauriac. *Photog* Louis Miaille. *Mus* Michel Legrand.

Production Credits for "Gluttony": *Dir* Philippe de Broca. *Screenplay* Daniel Boulanger. *Photog* Jean Penzer. *Mus* Michel Legrand.

Production Credits for "Lust": *Dir* Jacques Demy. *Screenplay* Jacques Demy, Roger Peyrefitte. *Photog* Henri Decaë. *Art Dir* Bernard Evein. *Mus* Michel Legrand.

Production Credits for "Laziness": *Dir-Writ* Jean-Luc Godard. *Photog* Henri Decaë. *Mus* Michel Legrand.

Production Credits for "Pride": *Dir* Roger Vadim. *Screenplay* Roger Vadim, Félicien Marceau. *Photog* Henri Decaë. *Mus* Sacha Distel.

Production Credits for "Greed": *Dir* Claude Chabrol. *Screenplay* Félicien Marceau. *Photog* Jean Rabier. *Mus* Pierre Jansen. *Prod Mgr* Jean Lavie, Tonio Suné.

Cast for "Anger": Marie-José Nat *(young wife),* Dominique Paturel *(young husband),* Jean-Marc Tennberg *(gendarme),* Perrette Pradier *(TV announcer).*

Cast for "Envy": Dany Saval *(Rosette),* Geneviève Casile *(Rita Gerly),* Claude Brasseur *(Riri),* Jean Murat *(Monsieur Duchemin),* Jacques Monod *(Monsieur Jasmin),* Paulette Dubost *(Madame Jasmin),* Paul Demange.

Cast for "Gluttony": Georges Wilson *(Valentin),* Marcelle Arnold *(his wife),* Magdelaine Berubet *(his mother-in-law),* Paul Préboist *(postman),* Henri Virlojeux.

Cast for "Lust": Laurent Terzieff *(Bernard),* Jean-Louis Trintignant *(Paul),* Paul Desailly *(father),* Micheline Presle *(mother),* Corinne Marchand *(girl on the street).*

Cast for "Laziness": Eddie Constantine *(himself),* Nicole Mirel *(herself).*

Cast for "Pride": Marina Vlady *(Catherine),* Jean-Pierre Aumont *(her husband),* Sami Frey *(her lover),* Michèle Girardon *(her husband's mistress).*

Cast for "Greed": Jacques Charrier *(Antoine),* Danièle Barraud *(girl),* Jean-Claude Brialy, Jean-Pierre Cassel, Claude Rich, Sacha Briquet, Jean-Claude Massoulier, André Jocelyn, Claude Berri, Michel Benoist, André Chanal, Serge Bento *(other students).*

Comedy. ANGER: One peaceful Sunday, several husbands find flies in their soups. As each one accuses his wife of deliberately creating the incident, domestic squabbles erupt. The mounting anger spreads throughout the town, and eventually the whole world destroys itself in an atomic holocaust. ENVY: Rosette, a discontented chambermaid at a country inn, seduces a wealthy industrialist who is the benefactor of a movie star. When she becomes the industrialist's mistress and returns to the inn as a guest, Rosette discovers that she envies the carefree pleasures of the new chambermaid. GLUTTONY: After his father dies from indigestion, Valentin, a farmer, takes his family to the funeral. Because of numerous stops for food, they arrive too late for the services but manage to make the banquet that follows. As they gorge themselves, they contemplate future funeral banquets. LUST: Two young artists, Bernard and Paul, sit at a sidewalk cafe and visualize the passersby without clothes. They attempt to pick up a pretty girl, but their efforts are unsuccessful. LAZINESS: Actor Eddie Constantine is so lazy that when a young starlet, Nicole, tries to seduce him, he resists the offer because it would be too much of an effort to remove his clothing and dress again. PRIDE: As a young wife plans to run off with her lover, she discovers that her husband has a mistress. Outraged, she abandons her lover to defend her home against the other woman. GREED: Twenty-five cadets pool their funds and draw lots for the money to buy the services of Paris' highest paid prostitute. The winner is Antoine, a shy virgin who impresses the girl; and she returns his share of the money. *Chambermaids. Industrialists. Actors. Farmers. Artists. Cadets. Prostitutes. Mistresses. Marriage. Holocausts. Seduction. Envy. Gluttony. Lust. Infidelity. Pride. Virginity. Sexual initiation. Greed. Inns. Funerals. Cafes. Paris.*

Note: Opened in Paris in Mar 1962 as *Les sept péchés capitaux;* running time: 110 min; in Rome in Apr 1962 as *I sette peccati capitali.* Episode titles: "La colère," "Ira" ("Anger"), "L'envie," "Invidia" ("Envy"), "La gourmandise," "Gola" ("Gluttony"), "La luxure," "Lussuria" ("Lust"), "La paresse," "Pigrizia" ("Laziness"), "L'orgueil," "Orgoglio" ("Pride"), "L'avarice," "Avarizia" ("Greed").

SEVEN CONSENTING ADULTS (West Germany)   F6.4371
Hans Eckelkamp & Sohn. *Dist* William Mishkin. Mar **1970**. Sd; b&w. 35mm. 88 min.

Prod Ernst Liesenhoff. *Dir* Jürgen Roland. *Screenplay* Wolfgang Menge. *Photog* Günter Haase. *Asst Camera* Dieter Form. *Art Dir* Dieter Bartels, Dietrich Reinecke. *Film Ed* Susanne Paschen. *Mus* Günter Marschner. *Sd* Horst Grosse. *Asst Dir* Alexander Ebermayer von Richthofen. *Prod Mgr* Dieter Pauker. *Prod Dir* Ernst Steinlechner. *Prod Staff* Felix Hock. *Cost* Hildegard Bürger. *Makeup* Ingeborg Ritter.

Cast: Wolfgang Kieling *(Police Sergeant Glantz),* Hannelore Schroth *(Margot),* Günter Neutze *(Schriever),* Günter Ungeheuer *(Bruno),* Horst Neutze *(Laepke),* Helmut Oeser *(Kohlhammer),* Johanna König *(Miss Schmelz),* Jürgen Draeger *(Manfred),* Fred Berthold *(Bruenjes),* Silvana Sansoni *(Cherie),* Kristen Steen, Hans Irle, Harald Heitmann, Günter Lüdke, Ingrid Andree, Hanns Lothar, Heinz Reincke, Herbert Malsbender, Horst Hesslin, Linda Fulda, Kurt Klopsch, Gerti Molzen, Marietta Storen, Joachim Richert, Helmut Kolar, Raymond Vargas, Christa Graf, Edeltraut Schmidt, Karin Büchel, Irmgard Wendt, Frank Nossack, Erna Nitter, Horst Beck, Günther Jerschke, Joachim Hammer, Marion Hartmann, Siegfried Graw, Frank Strass, Wolfgang Borchert, Christa Siems, Doris Masjos, Gerda-Maria Jürgens, Frieda Michalek, Hanns Gosslar, Eddie Arps.

Crime melodrama. During 48 hours in Hamburg's infamous Reeperbahn section, Sergeant Glantz sees a revealing cross-section of offenders culled from the city's tenderloin: a madam and her prostitutes, strippers, female impersonators, confidence men, lesbians, gangsters, racketeers, juvenile offenders, curio-seeking tourists, drunkards, and a contingent of American sailors out on the town. Bruno, a habitual criminal just out from a 4-year prison term, vows revenge against Glantz, the officer who caught him. Bruno attempts a theft, is surprised by Glantz, and lets himself be apprehended. His naive young bride appears at the police station carrying a concealed weapon, discovers the truth about Bruno, and turns the gun on him. Bruno pushes Glantz into the line of fire and thus accomplishes his revenge. *Police. Hoodlums. Confidence men. Theft. Revenge. Murder. Female impersonation. Lesbianism. Prostitution. Striptease. Hamburg.*

Note: Released in West Germany in 1964 as *Polizeirevier Davidswache (St. Pauli);* running time: 101 min. Also known as *7 Consenting Adults* and *Hamburg Off-Limits.* Sex footage apparently inserted for American release version.

SEVEN DARING GIRLS (West Germany)   F6.4372
Rapid-Film. *Dist* Manson Distributing Corp. 31 Aug **1962** [Los Angeles showing]. Sd; b&w. 35mm. 76 min.

Prod Wolfgang Hartwig. *Dir* Otto Meyer. *Screenplay* Johannes Kai. *Camera* Georg Krause. *Camera Op* Ernst Wild, Horst Philipp. *Mus* Karl Bette. *Asst Dir* Max Brandt. *Prod Mgr* Ludwig Spitaler. *Unit Mgr* Nusa Kozian. *Cost* Anna Hanoszek. *Makeup* Ladislaus Valíček.

Cast: Adrian Hoven *(Manuel),* Ann Smyrner *(Liz),* Jan Hendriks *(Murdok),* Dorothee Glöcklen *(Colette),* Beatrix Norden *(Trixi),* Demeter Bitenc *(Leblanc),* Kurt Ludwig *(Muhazzin),* Slavo Schwaiger *(Felipe),* Dora Carras *(Sonja),* Karin Heske *(Katrin),* Hertha Riedle *(Pat),* Nina Semona *(Merci).*

Crime melodrama. Seven young women who have graduated from Madame Degrelle's exclusive international boarding school in Switzerland set out on a cargo boat to vacation in the southern latitudes. Along the way, the girls enjoy the company of the ship's crew. Arriving at a southern port, they go dancing at the Blue Lagoon, and Liz, a graduate from South America, meets Manuel Cahilez. Anxious to see Liz again, Manuel invites the students to visit the meteorological station he operates on isolated Amazon Island where he lives with his father. Returning to the station Manuel learns that his father has found a crashed airplane with a cargo of gold ingots. Manuel goes to the mainland to report his father's discovery. He is overheard by Murdok, a gangster, who, with his accomplices Leblanc, Costa, and Chen-Fu, rushes to the island to steal the ingots. Murdok shoots Manuel's father, but Manuel escapes. At this moment, the girls arrive at the island. Seeing the meteorological station on fire, Liz, her sister Trixi, and the courageous Merci leave the other girls behind on the boat and proceed to the station, where they find Manuel's stricken father. Meanwhile, Murdok and his gang capture the remaining girls and hold them captive on the boat. Manuel finds Liz, and together they set out to rescue the girls. Murdok shoots Leblanc, who has attempted to cheat him. In the meantime, the captives attempt to ward off the advances of the drunken Costa and Chen-Fu, and Pat performs an exciting dance to distract their attention. Manuel and Liz then arrive on the scene and subdue Costa and Chen-Fu, but Murdok flees in a dinghy and is shot by police. *Students. Gangsters. South Americans. Ship crews. Chinese. Theft. Murder. Abduction. Islands. Boarding schools. Vacations. Gold. Freighters. Switzerland. Airplane accidents.*

Note: Released in 1960 in West Germany as *Insel der Amazonen;* running time: 88 min.

SEVEN DAYS IN MAY   F6.4373
Seven Arts Productions–Joel Productions. *Dist* Paramount Pictures. 12 Feb **1964** [Washington, D. C., opening; c12 Feb 1964; LP26986]. Sd; b&w. 35mm. 120 min.

A John Frankenheimer Production. *Prod* Edward Lewis. *Dir* John Frankenheimer. *Screenplay* Rod Serling. *Cinematog* Ellsworth Fredricks. *Camera Op* John Mehl. *Camera Asst* Kyme Meade, Paul Weddell. *Art Dir* Cary Odell. *Asst Art Dir* Phil Jeffries. *Set Decor* Edward G. Boyle. *Film Ed* Ferris Webster. *Asst Film Ed* Bill Brame. *Mus* Jerry Goldsmith. *Sd* Joe Edmondson. *Rec* R. D. Cook. *Boom Op* W. C. Smith. *Asst Dir* Hal Polaire, Dale Hutchinson, Robert J. Anderson. *Prod Mgr* Hal Polaire. *Prod Sec* Maggie Smith, sec. *Script Supv* John Franco. *Wardrobe* Wes Jeffries, Sid Mintz, Angela Alexander. *Makeup* Art Jones. *Opticals* Darryl Anderson. *Still Photog* Sterling Smith. *Gaffer* Vaughan Asher. *Grip* Dick Borland. *Prop* Ross Burke, Charles Gay. *Dial Coach* Thom Conroy. *Constr Coörd* William Maldonado.

Cast: Burt Lancaster *(Gen. James M. Scott),* Kirk Douglas *(Col. Martin "Jiggs" Casey),* Fredric March *(President Jordan Lyman),* Ava Gardner *(Eleanor Holbrook),* Edmond O'Brien *(Sen. Raymond Clark),* Martin Balsam *(Paul Girard),* George Macready *(Christopher Todd),* Whit Bissell *(Senator Prentice),* Hugh Marlowe *(Harold McPherson),* Bart Burns *(Arthur Corwin),* Richard Anderson *(Colonel Murdock),* Jack Mullaney *(Lieutenant Hough),* Andrew Duggan *(Colonel "Mutt" Henderson),* John Larkin *(Colonel Broderick),* Malcolm Atterbury *(White House physician),* Helen Kleeb *(Esther Townsend),* John Houseman *(Admiral Barnswell),* Colette Jackson *(bar girl),* Fredd Wayne, Rodolfo Hoyos, Clegg Hoyt.

Drama. Source: Fletcher Knebel and Charles Waldo Bailey, II, *Seven Days in May* (New York, 1962). U. S. President Jordan Lyman signs a nuclear treaty with the Soviet Union, arousing public displeasure and the disapproval of the military, particularly Gen. James M. Scott, Chairman of the Joint Chiefs of Staff, who considers the action almost treasonable. After Martin "Jiggs" Casey, Scott's aide, comes across some cryptic messages and learns of a top secret base in Texas, the existence of which is denied by others in the Pentagon, he suspects that Scott is leading the other Chiefs of Staff in a coup to occur seven days later when the President will be isolated from his civilian aides during a military alert. Casey reports his suspicions to the President, who sends Sen. Raymond Clark to investigate the secret base. Clark locates the base but is held there incommunicado until he breaks out with the help of an officer friend of Casey's. Presidential aide Paul Girard flies to Gibraltar, where he obtains a statement from Admiral Barnswell, a Joint Chief who isn't enthusiastic about the coup, but Girard is killed in a plane crash on the return trip, and Barnswell denies signing the statement. Later, Casey obtains some highly incriminating letters from Eleanor Holbrook, Scott's former mistress, but the President cannot bring himself to use them when he confronts Scott and demands his resignation. Scott, confident that public opinion is on his side and that his aides are behind him, refuses. The President goes on television to demand the guilty officers' resignations, and Scott's colleagues desert him. During the telecast it is learned that Barnswell's statement has been found in the plane wreckage, and Scott also resigns, squelching the coup before it occurs. *Presidents of the United States. Traitors. Politicians. Hostages. Mistresses. Treason. Conspiracy. Militarism. Nuclear control. Blackmail. Coups d'état. Treaties. Airplane accidents. Washington (District of Columbia). Union of Soviet Socialist Republics. Texas. Gibraltar. United States—Defense Department—Joint Chiefs of Staff. The White House. The Pentagon. Documentation.*

Note: Location scenes filmed in Washington, D. C., and in Arizona.

SEVEN DAYS TOO LONG   F6.4374
Cannon Productions. *Dist* Cannon Releasing Corp. **1970**. Sd; col. 35mm. 87 min.

Dir William K. Hennigar.

Cast: Maria Lease *(Linda),* Barry Titus *(The Husband),* Deanna Robinson, Robin Nolan, Christopher Pennock, Helen Stewart, Verne Williams, John Kress.

Drama. Linda, a rock and roll singer, seeks sexual satisfaction from her friends when her husband, a writer who is preoccupied with his work, goes to a mountain retreat to be alone. While he is there, he allows himself to be seduced by an attractive woman. When husband and wife are reunited, they keep secret their infidelities. Their separate experiences, however, serve to renew their love for each other. *Singers. Authors. Infidelity. Seduction. Marriage. Rock and roll.*

THE SEVEN DWARFS TO THE RESCUE (Italy)　　　　　　F6.4375

P. W. T. Produzione. *Dist* Childhood Productions. 30 Jan **1965** [Brooklyn, New York, opening]. Sd; b&w. 35mm. 84 min.

Prod-Dir-Writ Paolo William Tamburella. *Cinematog* Aldo Giordani. *Film Ed* Giuseppe Vari.

Cast: Rossana Podestà *(Snow White)*, Roberto Risso *(Prince Charming)*, Georges Marchal *(Prince of Darkness)*, Ave Ninchi, Salvatore Furnari, Francesco Gatto, Ulisse Lorenzelli, Mario Mastrantonio, Giovanni Solinas, Arturo Tosi, Domenico Tosi, Rossana Martini, Guido Celano, Pietro Tordi, Amedeo Trilli.

Fantasy. Source: Jakob Grimm and Wilhelm Grimm, "Schneewittchen und die sieben Zwerge". Snow White and Prince Charming are the married rulers of a peaceful kingdom where the Seven Dwarfs live. The evil Prince of Darkness invades the country, terrorizing the inhabitants. Prince Charming and his army ride off to confront the enemy, but he is captured and held for ransom. Learning of her husband's plight, Snow White goes to the Prince of Darkness with her crown in payment but is herself captured. The Seven Dwarfs, through a series of tricky charades, manage to free Prince Charming, who then rescues Snow White. *Royalty. Dwarfs. Kidnaping. Ransom. Imaginary kingdoms. Snow White. Prince Charming.*

Note: Released in Italy in 1952 as *I sette nani alla riscossa*; running time: 103 min.

7 FACES OF DR. LAO　　　　　　　　　　　　　　　　　F6.4376

Galaxy Productions–Scarus, Inc. *Dist* Metro-Goldwyn-Mayer, Inc. 18 Mar **1964** [Denver, Colorado, opening; c31 Dec 1963; LP28083]. Sd (Westrex); col (Metrocolor). 35mm. 100 min.

A George Pal Production. *Prod-Dir* George Pal. *Screenplay* Charles Beaumont. *Dir Photog* Robert Bronner. *Art Dir* George W. Davis, Gabriel Scognamillo. *Set Decor* Henry Grace, Hugh Hunt. *Film Ed* George Tomasini. *Mus* Leigh Harline. *Rec Supv* Franklin Milton. *Asst Dir* Al Shenberg. *Asst to the Prod* Gae Griffith. *Sp Makeup Created by* William Tuttle. *Hairstyles* Sydney Guilaroff. *Sp Vis Eff* Paul Byrd, Wah Chang, Jim Danforth, Ralph Rodine, Robert R. Hoag. *Adv of Magic* George L. Boston.

Cast: Tony Randall *(Dr. Lao/Merlin the Magician/Pan/The Abominable Snowman/Medusa/The Giant Serpent/Apollonius of Tyana)*, Barbara Eden *(Angela Benedict)*, Arthur O'Connell *(Clint Stark)*, John Ericson *(Ed Cunningham)*, Noah Beery *(Tim Mitchell)*, Lee Patrick *(Mrs. Howard T. Cassan)*, Minerva Urecal *(Kate Lindquist)*, John Qualen *(Luther Lindquist)*, Frank Kreig *(Peter Ramsey)*, Peggy Rea *(Mrs. Peter Ramsey)*, Eddie Little Sky *(George G. George)*, Royal Dano *(Carey)*, Argentina Brunetti *(Sarah Benedict)*, John Doucette *(Lucas)*, Dal McKennon *(lean cowboy)*, Frank Cady *(Mayor James Sargent)*, Chubby Johnson *(fat cowboy)*, Douglas Fowley *(toothless cowboy)*, Kevin Tate *(Mike Benedict)*.

Fantasy. Source: Charles G. Finney, *The Circus of Dr. Lao* (New York, 1961). The elderly Dr. Lao, a Chinese showman, rides into the desert town of Abalone, places an advertisement in the local newspaper announcing the impending arrival of his circus, and in the time preceding its arrival learns a great deal about Abalone's citizens. He becomes fond of Ed Cunningham, the newspaper editor, and takes an interest in Ed's romance—which is not progressing smoothly—with Angela Benedict, the local schoolteacher, librarian, and widowed mother of 8-year-old Mike. Ed, through his editorials, is conducting a war against Clint Stark, a local bully who is trying to buy up the town because he knows that a railroad will soon come through Abalone. The whole town attends Dr. Lao's circus, and as part of the evening's entertainment Dr. Lao assumes various disguises to show the townspeople how weak and small-minded they are. As the blind seer Apollonius he puts the mirror of truth before the town gossip; as Medusa he turns a shrewish housewife temporarily into stone; as Pan he cements Ed's romance with Angela; and as a serpent he shows Clint the error of his ways. Clint's unreformed henchmen wreck the newspaper office, but Dr. Lao magically restores it to its former condition. Seeking revenge on Dr. Lao, the frustrated wreckers shoot at a bowl containing, they assume, Dr. Lao's pet fish. The creature in the bowl, a huge sea serpent sworn to devour Dr. Lao, begins to grow, sprouts seven heads, and pursues Clint's henchmen. The appearance of Dr. Lao saves Clint's men but jeopardizes Dr. Lao, who magically reduces the monster to fish bowl size. The next morning Dr. Lao departs Abalone, leaving a better town than he found. *Showmen. Chinese. Editors. Schoolteachers. Librarians. Widows. Seers. Smalltown life. Courtship. Magic. Disguise. Revenge. Circus. Newspapers. Railroads. Deserts.*

Pan (god). Merlin. Medusa. Apollonius of Tyana. Abominable Snowman. Sea monsters. Fish.

SEVEN GOLDEN MEN (France/Italy/Spain)　　　　　　F6.4377

Atlantica Cinematografica–Paris Union Films–As Films Producción. *Dist* Warner Bros.–Seven Arts, Inc. 23 Apr **1969** [New York opening]. Sd; col (Eastman Color). 35mm. 87 min. [Also 84 min.] MPAA rating G.

Prod-Dir Marco Vicario. *Screenplay* Marco Vicario, Mariano Ozores. *English Adapt* Noelle Gillmor. *Photog* Ennio Guarnieri. *Art Dir* Piero Poletto, Arrigo Equini. *Set Decor* Dario Micheli. *Decor* Jaime Pérez Cubero. *Film Ed* Roberto Cinquini, Pedro del Rey. *Mus Comp & Cond* Armando Trovajoli. *Sd* Alberto Tinebra, Mario Amari. *Asst Dir* Francesco Massaro, F. Ariza. *Prod Supv* Ugo Tucci. *Cost* Gaia Romanini. *Makeup* Michele Trimarchi. *Hairstyles* Giancarlo De Leonardis.

Cast: Rossana Podestà *(Giorgia)*, Philippe Leroy *(Albert)*, Gastone Moschin *(Adolf)*, Gabriele Tinti *(Aldo)*, José Suárez *(bank manager)*, Giampiero Albertini *(August)*, Dario De Grassi *(Anthony)*, Manuel Zarzo *(Alfonso)*, Maurice Poli *(Alfred)*, Ennio Balbo *(police chief)*, Alberto Bonucci *(radio ham)*, Renzo Palmer, Renato Terra, Juan Luis Gagliardo, Juan Cortez, Gianni Di Benedetto.

Crime melodrama. After bungling a job in London, Albert, an international thief, masterminds a plan to rob a Geneva bank of 7 tons of gold. Assisted by the seductive Giorgia, who works from within the bank, and six other accomplices, Albert sets himself up in an expensive hotel with a battery of electronic devices to supervise the operation. Posing as a street-repair crew, the six accomplices tunnel their way into the city's water mains and, guided by a radar signalling device left by Giorgia in a safe-deposit box, swim to a spot beneath the bank vault. Albert, aided by a closed-circuit television camera hidden in the bank, steers his men by walkie-talkies to the vault. After the gold has been disguised as brass and shipped to Rome, Albert tries to doublecross his accomplices by notifying the police that the men are carrying fake passports; Giorgia, in turn, attempts to doublecross Albert while they are travelling to Rome by train. Both schemes backfire, however, and the eight thieves arrive in Rome to split the loot. Before they can do so, the truck carrying the gold crashes and scatters its contents on the street pavement. Frustrated but undaunted, the group begin making plans to rob the largest bank in Rome. *Robbers. Bank robberies. Electronic surveillance. Imposture. Perfidy. Gold. Radar. London. Geneva. Rome. Automobile accidents.*

Note: Location scenes filmed in Geneva and Rome. Opened in Rome in Oct 1965 as *Sette uomini d'oro*; running time: 91 min; in Madrid in Nov 1965 as *Siete hombres de oro*; in Paris in Mar 1966 as *Sept hommes en or*.

SEVEN GUNS FOR THE MACGREGORS (Italy/Spain)　　F6.4378

Produzione D. S.–Jolly Film–Estela Films. *Dist* Columbia Pictures. Nov **1968**. Sd; col (Technicolor). 35mm (Techniscope). 94 min.

Prod Dario Sabatello. *Dir* Frank Grafield. *Screenplay* Enzo Dell'Aquila, Fernando Di Leo, David Moreno, Duccio Tessari. *Story* David Moreno. *Photog* Alejandro Ulloa. *Art Dir* Jaime Pérez Cubero. *Film Ed* Nino Baragli, Mario Morra, Antonio Ramírez. *Mus Comp* Ennio Morricone. *Mus Cond* Bruno Nicolai. *Prod Mgr* Julián Esteban, George Bold. *Cost* Karl Kinds.

Cast: Robert Woods *(Gregor MacGregor)*, Manuel Zarzo *(David MacGregor)*, Nick Anderson *(Peter MacGregor)*, Paul Carter *(Kenneth MacGregor)*, Julio Pérez Tabernero *(Mark MacGregor)*, Saturnino Cerra *(Johnny MacGregor)*, Albert Waterman *(Dick MacGregor)*, Agatha Flory *(Rosita Carson)*, Leo Anchoriz *(Santillana)*, Perla Cristal *(Perla)*, Georges Rigaud *(Alastair MacGregor)*, Harry Cotton *(Harold MacGregor)*, Fernando Sancho *(Miguel)*, Anne-Marie Noé *(Mamie MacGregor)*, Margaret Horowitz *(Annie MacGregor)*, Raphael Bardem *(Justice Garland)*, Antonio Molino Rojo *(sheriff)*, Cris Huerta *(Crawford)*.

Western comedy. The MacGregors are ranchers of Scottish descent living near the Mexican border in 19th-century Texas. One day seven of the sons go into town to sell a herd of horses and clash with a crooked horsedealer, Crawford, who offers them a paltry sum for the animals. When the seven men start a brawl, the sheriff takes them to jail. Upon breaking out, the MacGregors discover that their horses have been stolen and that Crawford and the sheriff are in league with bandit chief Santillana. To break the power of the bandits, the oldest MacGregor son, Gregor, teams up with Santillana, wins his confidence, and passes on information about the gang's plans to the MacGregors; but after Santillana's men have been thwarted in several robbery attempts, the bandit chief suspects the deception and attacks the MacGregors, capturing all but Gregor. Gregor then steals into the enemy camp to free his brothers. In the gunfight that ensues, the brothers' ammunition is nearly exhausted when they hear the sound of approaching bagpipes. With the arrival of the older MacGregors, the bandits are routed or killed, and Santillana himself is slain by his discarded mistress, Perla. Once peace is restored, Gregor is betrothed to his sweetheart, Rosita, and the family celebrates the occasion. *Scotch. Ranchers. Horsetraders. Sheriffs. Horsethieves. Duplicity. Robbery.*

Jailbreaks. Bagpipes. Texas. Mexican border.

Note: Opened in Rome in Mar 1966 as *7 pistole per i MacGregor*; running time: 95 min; in Spain as *Siete pistolas para los MacGregor*; running time: 97 min. Pseudonyms include: Frank Grafield (Franco Giraldi), Alexander Ulloa (Alejandro Ulloa), Nick Anderson (Nazareno Zamperla), Paul Carter (Paolo Magalotti), Albert Waterman (Alberto Dell'Acqua), Agatha Flory (Agata Flori), Anne-Marie Noé (Ana María Noé), and Margaret Horowitz (Margherita Orowitz).

THE SEVEN REVENGES (Italy)   F6.4379
Adelphia Compagnia Cinematografica. *Dist* Avco Embassy Pictures. 9 Jul **1967** [New York showing]. Sd; col (Eastman Color). 35mm (Totalscope). 92 min.

Dir Primo Zeglio. *Screenplay* Sabatino Ciuffini, Sergio Leone, Primo Zeglio, Emimmo Salvi, G. Taffarel, Roberto Natale. *Story* Emimmo Salvi. *Photog* Adalberto Albertini. *Mus* Carlo Innocenzi.

Cast: Ed Fury, Elaine Stewart, Bella Cortez, Roldano Lupi, Paola Barbara, Furio Meniconi, Gabriele Antonini.

Adventure drama. Two rival chiefs, a Circassian and a Kirghiz, serving Genghis Khan must respond to seven challenges. *Tribal chiefs. Kirghiz. Circassians. Mongols. Contests. Genghis Khan.*

Note: Opened in Rome in Apr 1961 as *Le sette sfide*; running time: 95 min.

SEVEN SEAS TO CALAIS (Italy)   F6.4380
Adelphia Compagnia Cinematografica. *Dist* Metro-Goldwyn-Mayer, Inc. 6 Mar **1963** [Los Angeles opening; c29 Aug 1962; LP23374]. Sd (Westrex); col (Eastmancolor). 35mm (CinemaScope). 102 min. [Copyright length: 99 min.]

Exec Prod Paolo Moffa. *Dir* Rudolph Maté, Primo Zeglio. *Story & Screenplay* Filippo Sanjust, George St. George, Lindsay Galloway. *Dir Photog* Giulio Gianini. *2d Unit Photog* Gianni Narzisi. *Camera* Vittorio Bernini. *Art Dir* Nicola Cantatore. *Set Decor* Antonio Martini, Brunello Serena, Adele Tosi. *Film Ed* Franco Fraticelli. *Mus Comp & Cond* Franco Mannino. *Sd Dir* Mario Messina. *Asst Dir* Rinaldo Ricci. *Prod Mgr* Luciano Cattania. *Script Girl* Anna Gruber. *Cost Dsgn* Filippo Sanjust. *Makeup* Maurizio Giustini. *Hairdresser* Giancarlo Marin. *Sp Eff* Eros Bacciucchi. *Stills* Angelo Pennoni. *Fencing Master* Bruno Ukmar.

Cast: Rod Taylor (*Sir Francis Drake*), Keith Michell (*Malcolm Marsh*), Irene Worth (*Queen Elizabeth*), Hedy Vessel (*Arabella*), Basil Dignam (*Walsingham*), Anthony Dawson (*Burleigh*), Gianni Cajafi (*Tom Moone*), Mario Girotti (*Babington*), Esmeralda Ruspoli (*Mary of Scotland*), Marco Guglielmi (*Fletcher*), Arturo Dominici (*Mendoza*), Gianni Solaro (*Medina Sidonie*), Adriano Vitale (*Recalde*), Bruno Ukmar (*Emmanuel*), Franco Ukmar (*Francisco*), Aldo Bufi-Landi (*Vigeois*), Umberto Raho (*Philip of Spain*), Luciano Melani (*Winter*), Jacopo Tecchi (*Garcia*), Giuseppe Abbrescia (*Chester*), Rossella D'Aquino (*Potato*), Anna Santarsiero, Luciana Gilli (*other Indian wives*).

Melodrama. In 1577, England's supremacy on the high seas keeps her from falling under Spanish domination. Though Queen Elizabeth outwardly disapproves of Francis Drake and his band of pirates, she secretly finances his raids against the treasure ships of Spain. After pillaging the gold mines of the Incas and looting Spanish vessels off Panama, Drake lands in California and names the country New Albion. When he makes a triumphant return to England, Elizabeth knights him. Aided by his faithful friend, Malcolm, and Sir Francis Walsingham, Drake thwarts a Spanish plot to murder the queen and replace her with Mary of Scotland. Enraged, King Philip of Spain gives the order for his mighty armada to attack England. But during a storm, Drake turns the tables, and the tattered remnants of the Spanish fleet are forced to retreat. With England safe from invasion, Drake sails off to new adventures. *Pirates. Incas. Exploration. Gold. Spanish Armada. Panama. Peru. California. Francis Drake. Elizabeth I (England). Mary Stuart. Francis Walsingham. Philip II (Spain).*

Note: Opened in Rome in Aug 1962 as *Il dominatore dei sette mari.* Anthony Dawson is a pseudonym for Antonio Margheriti.

THE SEVEN SECOND LOVE AFFAIR   F6.4381
Robert Abel. c10 Oct **1966** [LP34003]. Sd; col. 16mm. 52 min.

Cast: Rick Stewart, Gene Adams, Jack Wayre.

Documentary. Drag racer Rick Stewart, a 24-year-old X-ray technician from Bakersfield, California, who is perfecting his fuel dragster to beat the quarter-mile record of 214.16 mph in 7.42 seconds, along with his partners, mechanic Gene Adams and financier Jack Wayre, enters a weekend race and wins. But the race destroys his engine, and the three men and their families, all racing enthusiasts, spend the greater part of their free time during the next week repairing it. The following weekend Rick nears the record-breaking speed in a qualifying run. In a subsequent record attempt, however, the engine explodes at the finish line, and the car careens end-over-end into an open field. In the final scene the three families are seen huddling around their new dragster. The camera drifts to photographs on the garage wall indicating that the car did indeed set a new record—219.65 mph in 7.30 seconds. The record lasted 8 weeks. *Mechanics. Automobile racing. California. Automobile accidents.*

SEVEN SLAVES AGAINST THE WORLD (Italy)   F6.4382
Leone Film. *Dist* Paramount Pictures. 18 Aug **1965** [New York opening]. Sd; col (Technicolor). 35mm (Techniscope). 96 min.

Prod Elio Scardamaglia. *Dir* Michele Lupo. *Screenplay* Roberto Gianviti, Michele Lupo. *Photog* Guglielmo Mancori. *Art Dir* Pier Vittorio Marchi. *Film Ed* Alberto Gallitti. *Mus* Francesco De Masi. *Sd* Fausto Ancillai, Vittorio Massi. *Cost* Walter Patriarca. *Fencing Master* Alfio Caltabiano.

Cast: Roger Browne (*Marcus*), Gordon Mitchell (*Balisten*), Scilla Gabel (*Claudia*), Giacomo Rossi Stuart (*Gaius*), Germano Longo (*Lucius Emilius*), Alfredo Rizzo (*Efrem*), Carlo Tamberlani (*Lucius Terentius*), Arnaldo Fabrizio (*Goliath*), Pietro Ceccarelli, Aldo Pini, Alfio Caltabiano, Adriano Vita, Luciana Vincenzi.

Action melodrama. Marcus, a Roman tribune, is sent to Asia to oversee the building of an aqueduct. Gaius, the former overseer, had been unpopular with the slaves because of his cruel treatment of them, and Marcus does not employ the same methods. Angered after Marcus beats him in a duel, Gaius incites a slave revolt in which all Romans are killed except Marcus, who is saved by Balisten, a slave whom he had befriended. The slaves are recaptured and crucified, but Marcus, who appeared to have been responsible for the revolt, escapes with Balisten and five other slaves. In the city, they meet Efrem, a gladiator organizer, and form a band of gladiators who fight with masks to avoid being captured by the Romans. Upon hearing of a conspiracy to overthrow the government, they help uncover the plotters, led by Gaius. The slaves thus regain their freedom, and Marcus preserves his reputation. *Gladiators. Slavery. Revenge. Revolts. Conspiracy. Masks. Rome—History—Empire. Asia. Duels.*

Note: Released in Italy in 1964 as *Gli schiavi più forti del mondo.*

7 SURPRISES (Canada)   F6.4383
National Film Board of Canada. *Dist* Quartet International, Inc. 26 Sep **1964** [New York opening]. Sd; b&w and col. 35mm. 77 min.

Prod Harvey Chertok. *Co-prod* Eric Albertson.

Anthology. The seven short features are: *Nahanni* (1962), *Le merle* (1958), *A Chairy Tale* (1957), *The Cars in Your Life* (1960), *Corral* (1954), *Wrestling* (1961), and *Neighbors* (1952).

Note: *Wrestling* was released in Canada as *La lutte.*

THE SEVEN TASKS OF ALI BABA (Italy)   F6.4384
Avis Film. *Dist* Medallion Pictures. **1963**. Sd; col (Eastman Color). 35mm (Totalscope). 95 min.

Dir Emimmo Salvi. *Screenplay* Emimmo Salvi, Ambrogio Molteni, Benito Ilforte. *Photog* Mario Paradetti. *Art Dir* Giovanni Amadei.

Cast: Rod Flash (*Ali Baba*), Bella Cortez (*Lota*), Furio Meniconi (*Mustapha*), Amedeo Trilli (*Hassam Bey*), Mario Polletin, Omero Gargano, Liliana Zagra, Salvatore Furnari, Aristide Massari.

Adventure melodrama. Ali Baba is given a sacred crown to help Hassam Bey, who has been deposed from power by the treacherous Mustapha. After hiding the crown, Ali Baba is arrested and put to several torturous tasks, which he overcomes with his Herculean strength. Princess Lota, Hassam Bey's daughter whom Mustapha wants to marry, helps Ali Baba escape, but she is captured by Mustapha's soldiers. Ali Baba and his 40 thieves arouse the populace against the evil ruler, and in the ensuing revolt Mustapha is killed, and Lota and her father are saved. Ali Baba and Lota return the crown to the genie of Sesame, and Hassam Bey brings peace to his kingdom. *Despots. Royalty. Thieves. Genii. Usurpers. Abduction. Treason. Torture. Feats of strength. Jewels. Revolts. Ali Baba.*

Note: Released in Italy in 1963 as *Le 7 fatiche di Alì Babà.* Rod Flash is also known as Rod Flash Ilush.

SEVEN WOMEN   F6.4385
John Ford Productions-Bernard Smith Productions. *Dist* Metro-Goldwyn-Mayer, Inc. 5 Jan **1966** [Los Angeles opening; c3 Nov 1965; LP31868]. Sd (Westrex); col (Metrocolor). 35mm (Panavision). 93 min. [Copyright length: 87 min.]

Prod Bernard Smith. *Dir* John Ford. *Screenplay* Janet Green, John McCormick. *Dir Photog* Joseph LaShelle. *Art Dir* George W. Davis, Eddie Imazu. *Set Decor* Henry Grace, Jack Mills. *Film Ed* Otho Lovering. *Mus* Elmer Bernstein. *Rec Supv* Franklin Milton. *Sd* Phil Mitchell. *Asst Dir* Wingate Smith. *Prod Mgr* G. Rex Bailey. *Cost Dsgn* Walter Plunkett. *Makeup* William Tuttle. *Hairstyles* Sydney Guilaroff. *Sp Vis Eff* J. McMillan Johnson.

Cast: Anne Bancroft (*Dr. D. R. Cartwright*), Sue Lyon (*Emma Clark*), Margaret Leighton (*Agatha Andrews*), Flora Robson (*Miss Binns*), Mildred Dunnock (*Jane Argent*), Betty Field (*Florrie Pether*), Anna Lee (*Mrs. Russell*), Eddie Albert (*Charles Pether*), Mike Mazurki (*Tunga Khan*), Woody Strode (*lean warrior*), Jane Chang (*Miss Ling*), Hans William Lee (*Kim*), H. W. Gim *(coolie),* Irene Tsu *(Chinese girl).*

Drama. Source: Norah Lofts, "Chinese Finale," in *I Met a Gypsy* (London, 1935). In the 1930's Mongol Tunga Khan is terrorizing the people of the Chinese border. In the area is an American mission headed by prim, iron-willed Agatha Andrews. Assisting her are admiring Jane Argent, young Emma Clark, ineffectual teacher Charles Pether, and his frightened, pregnant wife, Florrie. At first glad to hear that a Dr. Cartwright will soon be joining them, Agatha is displeased when the doctor turns out to be a cynical, worldly woman. The conflict between the two women is sharpened with the arrival of cholera-bearing refugees from the nearby ravaged British mission headed by Miss Binns, and matters are not helped by Agatha's refusal to provide the funds necessary to send Florrie to a hospital. When the Chinese soldiers protecting the area depart, Pether, with new courage, sets out to seek news but is killed. Tunga Khan and his forces storm into the mission as Florrie's labor pains begin. To pacify the invaders, Dr. Cartwright agrees to give herself to the warlord once she has delivered the baby; then, after the child is born, she uses her new power over Tunga Khan to provide for the pressing needs of the women and child. Miss Andrews, hysterically losing control, condemns Dr. Cartwright as a wanton and lustful woman, but the others understand her sacrifice. Dr. Cartwright then gets Tunga Khan's permission for the women to leave the mission. After their departure, she secretly poisons some wine and shares a toast with the warlord. *Warlords. Mongols. Missionaries. Americans in foreign countries. Schoolteachers. Physicians. English. Refugees. Spinsters. Pregnancy. Childbirth. Self-sacrifice. Suicide. Poisoning. Cholera. China—History— Republic 1912-49.*

SEVEN WOMEN FROM HELL   F6.4386

Associated Producers, Inc. *Dist* Twentieth Century-Fox Film Corp. Oct 1961 [New York opening: 31 Jan 1962; c27 Sep 1961; LP20619]. Sd; b&w. 35mm (CinemaScope). 88 min.

Prod Harry Spalding. *Dir* Robert D. Webb. *Writ by* Jesse Lasky, Jr., Pat Silver. *Dir Photog* Floyd Crosby. *Art Dir* Duncan Cramer. *Set Decor* Morris Hoffman. *Supv Film Ed* Jodie Copelan. *Mus Comp & Cond* Paul Dunlap. *Sd* Jack Cornall. *Sd Rec* Jack Solomon. *Asst Dir* Leon Chooluck, Willard Kirkham. *Prod Supv* Frank Parmenter. *Script Supv* Betty Crosby. *Men's Wardrobe* Patrick Cummings. *Women's Wardrobe* Della Fox. *Makeup* George Lane. *Sp Eff* Lee Zavitz. *Prop Master* Ygnacio Sepulveda.

Cast: Patricia Owens *(Grace Ingram),* John Kerr *(Bill Jackson),* Denise Darcel *(Claire Oudry),* Cesar Romero *(Luis Hullman),* Margia Dean *(Mara Shepherd),* Yvonne Craig *(Janet Cook),* Pilar Seurat *(Mai-Lu Ferguson),* Sylvia Daneel *(Ann Van Laer),* Richard Loo *(Sergeant Takahashi),* Bob Okazaki *(Captain Oda),* Lloyd Kino *(rapist guard),* Evadne Baker *(Regan),* Yuki Shimoda *(Doctor Matsumo),* Kam Fong Chun *(house guard),* Yankee Chang *(guard).*

War melodrama. When the Japanese invade New Guinea in 1942, Grace Ingram, an Australian member of a scientific expedition, is put in a women's detention camp. She shares her cell with six other women: Janet Cook, a pregnant American teenager; Ann Van Laer, a tightlipped but sympathetic German widow; Claire Oudry, a French waitress; Mai-Lu, a Eurasian nurse; and two other Americans, Mara and Regan. During a bombing raid, Janet's baby is born dead and the humane Captain Oda is killed. Sergeant Takahashi, his sadistic assistant, assumes command of the camp, and a friendly Japanese, Doctor Matsumo, helps the women escape. Mara is recaptured and tortured to death, and Claire and Regan are killed by rifle fire. The surviving four encounter a wounded American flyer, Bill Jackson, who helps them make their way to the beach but dies before they can reach safety. A wealthy planter, Luis Hullman, finds the girls, feigns friendship, and then attempts to hand them over to the Japanese. But the women learn of his plan, kill him, and escape by boat to the Allied lines. *Internees (wartime). Scientists. Waitresses. Nurses. Physicians. Pilots. Planters. Australians. Japanese. Germans. Widows. French. Eurasians. Torture. Pregnancy. Stillbirth. Murder. World War II. New Guinea.*

Note: Location scenes filmed in Hawaii.

SEVENTEEN see ERIC SOYA'S "17"

17TH PARALLEL: VIETNAM IN WAR (France)   F6.4387

Capi Films–Argos Films. *Dist* Rogosin Films, Impact Films. 26 Sep 1968 [New York showing]. Sd; b&w. 35mm. 110 min.

Conceived & Dir Joris Ivens. *Photog* Joris Ivens. *Collab* Marceline Loridan, Hanoi Documentary Studio.

Documentary. In 1965, Joris Ivens, a 70-year-old Dutch documentary filmmaker, spent 2 months in North Vietnam above the 17th parallel of the demilitarized zone to examine the extraordinary resistance of the Vietnamese people to the devastation of war. Although the film contains some scenes of the North Vietnamese bombing U. S. sites and shooting down planes, the major portion of the footage is devoted to the people themselves. Their village life, as depicted in the film, centers around building underground shelters, schools,

and hospitals, filling in bomb craters, and continuously constructing booby traps and fortifications against the enemy. *Village life. Aerial bombardment. Combat zone life. Civil defense. Vietnam War 1964–73. Democratic Republic of Vietnam.*

Note: Opened in Paris in Mar 1968 as *Le 17e parallèle: le Vietnam en guerre;* running time: 90 or 110 min.

THE 7TH COMMANDMENT   F6.4388

Irvmar Producing Corp. *Dist* Crown International Pictures. Dec 1961. Sd; b&w. 35mm. 82 min.

Prod-Dir Irvin Berwick. *Screenplay* Jack Kevan, Irvin Berwick. *Photog* Robert C. Jessup. *Asst Dir* Joseph Cavalier.

Cast: Jonathan Kidd *(Ted Mathews [Tad Morgan]),* Lyn Statten *(Terry James),* Frank Arvidson *(Noah Turnbull),* John Harmon *(Pete),* John Carpenter.

Crime melodrama. Ted Mathews and his girl friend, Terry James, have a highway accident in which Ted believes he has killed the driver of the other car. Shocked into amnesia by the crash, he wanders about until he is picked up by Noah Turnbull, a traveling evangelist. Under Noah's tutelage, and using the name of Tad Morgan, Ted becomes a world-renowned preacher. Terry learns of her former boyfriend's new identity and decides to blackmail Ted with the help of her lover, Pete. Confronted by a face from the past, Ted's memory returns and Terry realizes he is unaware that the driver of the other car was not killed but merely knocked into unconsciousness. Not satisfied with blackmail, she gets him drunk and marries him in a phony wedding ceremony. As Terry's demands increase, the nearly insane Ted pushes her off a bridge and returns to his congregation thinking he is at last free of her. She survives the fall, returns to her apartment, mistakes the sleeping Pete for Ted and kills him. Discovering her tragic error, she rushes to Ted's home obsessed with the idea of killing him. He wrests the pistol from her hand and strangles her to death. Filled with despair, Ted goes to his tabernacle and suffers a fatal heart attack as he prays for forgiveness. *Evangelists. Amnesia. Murder. Blackmail. Shock. Drunkenness. Marriage—Fake. Personal identity. Automobile accidents.*

THE SEVENTH CONTINENT (Czechoslovakia/Yugoslavia)   F6.4389

Jadran Film–Koliba Film Studio. *For* Československý Film. *Dist* U–M Film Distributors. 29 Jul 1968 [New York opening]. Sd; col (Eastman Color). 35mm (CinemaScope). 84 min.

Pres by Sidney Glazier. *Dir* Dušan Vukotić. *Screenplay* Dušan Vukotić, Andro Lušičić. *Story* Růžena Fišerová. *Photog* Karol Krška. *Art Dir* Rudolf Kováč, Branko Hundić. *Film Ed* Lidija Branis. *Mus Comp* Tomislav Simović. *Perf by* Praha Film Symphonic Orchestra. *Cond* František Belfín. *Sd* Milan Petovsky, Josef Fluge. *Asst Dir* Jozef Medveď. *Prod Mgr* Vladimir Džamonja. *Cost* Ivan Stefan. *English Subtitl* Herman G. Weinberg.

Cast: Iris Vrus *(Yellow Girl),* Tomislav Pasarić *(White Boy),* Abdoulaye Seck *(Black Boy),* Hermina Pipinić *(White Boy's mother),* Demeter Bitenc *(White Boy's father),* Oudy Rachmat Endang *(Yellow Girl's mother),* Mikuláš Huba *(general),* Karla Chadimová *(general's wife),* Viktor Starčić *(expert at conference),* Vanja Drach *(diplomat),* Dano Živojinović, Jindřich Láznička.

Fantasy. While on a ferryboat ride, the Yellow Girl sets down a basket containing sea gulls cut from cloth. When the basket is accidentally kicked into the water, the Yellow Girl and the White Boy go after it in a rubber raft. They land on a magical island, find the basket, and open it to see the cloth sea gulls fly out. After being joined by the Black Boy, who arrives on a raft made of a door, the children discover that they can make an entire forest materialize by drawing trees, and that by means of a map, they can summon children from other nations of the world; soon all the children are setting out for the "seventh continent," and panic seizes the grownups when there are no children left. An international conference is convened to study the situation, but it becomes entangled in bureaucratic red tape. As the adults become more bogged down by their inability to reach an agreement that would enable them to bring happiness (children) back into their lives, the youngsters continue to lead carefree lives, disturbed only by a beautiful conch shell which projects a loud and discordant sound. The Yellow Girl, the White Boy, and the Black Boy decide to return to the real world to see if something can be done to fix the shell. The grownups, incapable of achieving harmony in their own lives, are stymied by the challenge of achieving harmony in a simple shell. Disillusioned by the adults, the children embark once more for the "seventh continent." *Children. Magic. Parenthood. Race relations. Bureaucracy. Islands. Ferryboats. Forests. Conferences—International. Shells. Sea gulls.*

Note: Produced in 1966. Released in Yugoslavia as *Sedmi kontinent;* in Czechoslovakia as *Sedmý kontinent* and *Siedma pevnina.*

THE 7TH DAWN (United States/Great Britain)   F6.4390

Holdean Productions. *Dist* United Artists. 24 Jun 1964 [Boston opening; c24 Jun 1964; LP28504]. Sd; col (Technicolor). 35mm. 123 min.

Overall Production Credits: *Prod* Charles K. Feldman. *Co-prod* Karl Tunberg. *Assoc Prod* John Dark. *Dir* Lewis Gilbert. *Screenplay* Karl Tunberg. *Photog* F. A. Young. *Camera Op* Harry Gillam. *Focus Puller* David Osborne. *Camera Grip* Dick Savery. *Art Dir* Herbert Smith. *Set Decor* Josie MacAvin. *Draughtsman* Tony Rimmington. *Prod Dsgn* John Stoll. *Main Titl* Maurice Binder. *Film Ed* John Shirley. *Asst Ed* Jeremy Saunders. *Mus Comp & Cond* Riz Ortolani. *Sd* Basil Fenton-Smith, Red Law. *Sd Ed* Chris Greenham. *Boom Op* John Brommage. *Sd Camera Op* Terry Sharrett. *1st & 2d Asst Dir* Jack Causey, Jim Brennan. *Prod Mgr* Morris Aza. *Cont* Joan Davis. *Cost* Hylda Gilbert. *Wardrobe Supv* Betty Adamson. *Wardrobe* Charles Guerin. *Makeup* John O'Gorman. *Hairdresser* Betty Glasow. *Sp Eff* Cliff Richardson. *Constr Mgr* Harry Arbour. *Still Photog* Douglas Webb. *Chargehand Prop* Peter Guerin. *Ch Electrn* Peter Carey.

Production Credits for 2d Unit: *Dir* Harold Haysom. *Camera Op* Derek Browne. *Focus Puller* Roy Ford. *Camera Grip* Gwyn Godwin. *Asst Dir* John Gilbert. *Prop* Wilfred Allenby. *Stuntman* Keith Peacock, Tony Bushell.

Cast: William Holden *(Ferris)*, Susannah York *(Candace)*, Capucine *(Dhana)*, Tetsuro Tamba *(Ng)*, Michael Goodliffe *(Trumpey)*, Allan Cuthbertson *(Cavendish)*, Maurice Denham *(Tarlton)*, Sydney Tafler *(C.P.O.)*, Beulah Quo *(Ah Ming)*, Hugh Robinson *(judge)*, Tony Price *(Morley)*, Griffiths Alun *(Sedgwick)*, Christopher Allen *(C.I.D.)*, Yap Mook Fui *(Lim)*, David Keith *(aide)*, James Massang *(Malay engineer)*, R. William Koh *(General Osaki)*, Allan Wong *(Colonel Hsia)*, Ibrahim Bin *(Captain Chey)*, Noel Chow *(Captain Kiat)*, Hew Thian Choy *(Lieutenant Nelson)*, David Weinman *(Tamil cyclist)*, George Zakhariah *(Indian unionist)*, Seow *(Chinese unionist)*, Tomy Cheng *(Walter)*, Kip Bahadun *(Japanese prisoner)*.

Drama. Source: Michael Keon, *The Durian Tree* (New York, 1960). At the end of World War II in Malaya Ferris, Ng, and Dhana, three leaders of the guerrillas who fought the Japanese, part company. Ng, a Malayan-Chinese, goes to Moscow to complete his education, and Dhana and Ferris remain in Malaya. Eight years later Ferris is a successful plantation owner very much in love with Dhana, his mistress, who is now a prominent schoolteacher. Communist terrorists have launched a campaign of murder and destruction to drive the British from Malaya, but Ferris' interests are not touched. It is discovered that Ng is back in Malaya leading the terrorists, and Ferris reluctantly promises the British Resident to talk to Ng. Ng, though pleased to see Ferris, will not agree to a compromise. Returning from the meeting, Ferris meets Candace, the Resident's daughter, and agrees to attend a ball at the Residency that evening. A grenade is tossed among the dancers at the ball, and Ferris saves Candace's life by throwing her to the floor. In retaliation the British burn the village where Dhana teaches (which is thought to house many terrorists), despite Ferris and Dhana's protests. Dhana, whose sympathies are divided between the terrorists and the colonists, is arrested when police, acting on a tip, find grenades in her bicycle basket. She is sentenced to die but is offered her life if she or Ferris will reveal Ng's hideout. They refuse. Candace pleads with Dhana, who only asks Candace to look after Ferris after her death. Candace then goes to Ng and offers herself as a hostage, hoping her father will release Dhana. Ng holds her captive and distributes posters announcing that Candace will be killed unless Dhana is released by a certain time. Realizing old loyalties are dead, Ferris promises to flush Ng from his hideout. He needs 10 days to do this and Dhana has only 7 days to live. The Communists are routed and Ferris captures Ng and rescues Candace, who shoots Ng as he is about to kill Ferris. The dying Ng confesses he planted the grenades on Dhana's bicycle, hoping to start a revolt. Dhana is executed and several days later Ferris leaves Malaya, probably never to return, though Candace declares her love. *Guerrillas. Americans in foreign countries. Eurasians. Malayans. Chinese. Planters. Diplomats. Mistresses. Schoolteachers. Communists. Hostages. Friendship. Terrorism. Capital punishment. Self-sacrifice. Frameup. Murder. Jungles. Plantations. Rubber. Malaya.*

Note: Filmed on location in Malaysia, in and around Kuala Lumpur. Opened in London in Aug 1964. Working titles: *Wherever Love Takes Me*, and *The Third Road*.

THE SEVENTH JUROR (France)   **F6.4391**
Orex Films. *Dist* Trans-Lux Distributing Corp. 27 Jan **1964** [New York opening]. Sd; b&w. 35mm. 90 min.

Prod Paul Joly. *Dir* Georges Lautner. *Screenplay* Jacques Robert. *Dial* Pierre Laroche. *Cinematog* Maurice Fellous. *Art Dir* Robert Bouladoux. *Film Ed* Michèle David. *Mus* Jean Yatove. *Sd* Antoine Archimbaud.

Cast: Bernard Blier *(Grégoire Duval)*, Danièle Delorme *(Geneviève Duval)*, Maurice Biraud *(veterinarian)*, Francis Blanche *(attorney-general)*, Jacques Riberolles *(Sylvain Sautral)*, Robert Dalban *(fisherman)*, Françoise Giret *(Catherine)*, Charles Lavialle *(preceptor)*, Catherine Le Couey *(Madame Souchon)*, Raymond Meunier *(Monsieur Souchon)*, Jean-Pierre Moutier *(Testut)*, René Renal *(Laurent Duval)*, Anne Doat *(Alice Moreux)*, Madeleine Geoffroy *(Madame Sylvestre)*, Yves Barsacq *(Maître Adreux)*, Albert Rémy

(police superintendent), Jean Sylvère *(druggist)*, Barbara Brand *(dancer)*, Henri Crémieux *(coroner)*, Camille Guerini *(judge)*, Jacques Monod *(magistrate)*.

Crime drama. Source: Francis Didelot, *Le septième juré* (Paris, 1958). Grégoire Duval is a respected middle-aged druggist who lives with his family in a provincial French town. One Sunday afternoon while walking near a lake, he comes upon a girl sunbathing half-nude. Overcome by sudden sexual desire, he tries to make love to her and strangles her when she resists. Undetected, he returns to the company of others who have not noticed his absence. The girl's lover, Sylvain Sautral, an unsavory character shunned by the townspeople, is accused of the crime because of circumstantial evidence. Ironically, Duval is asked to serve as a juror at Sautral's trial. He has no desire to confess, but at the same time he does not want an innocent man convicted. Through some sharp questioning, Duval secures a reenactment of the crime and manages to win an acquittal for Sautral. His questioning causes his wife to suspect him of committing the murder, but she is willing to keep quiet for appearances' sake. The tormented Duval decides to confess, but the authorities refuse to believe him. He meets Sautral and begs him to leave town, but Sautral, who has been unable to stand the taunts of the townspeople, has decided to kill himself. In a scuffle for the gun, Sautral is killed. Again, Duval tries to confess, but the police label the death suicide. His wife arranges for Duval to be committed to an asylum until he can be cured, and Duval, whose life has been shattered by the past events, leaves in the custody of attendants and vows never to return. *Pharmacists. Police. Rape. Murder. Conscience. Confession (law). Suicide. Insanity. Trials. Juries. Circumstantial evidence.*

Note: Opened in Paris in Apr 1962 as *Le septième juré* at 105 min.

SEVENTY TIMES SEVEN see **THE FEMALE; SEVENTY TIMES SEVEN**

SEX AGENT see **THERE IS STILL ROOM IN HELL**

SEX AND ASTROLOGY   **F6.4392**
New World Studios. *Dist* Institute for Adult Education. Dec **1970**. Sd; col (Eastman Color). 35mm. 82 min.

Sex film. Couples perform sexual intercourse in accord with the zodiac as blue and pink dwarfs, obese women and hermaphrodites look on. *Dwarfs. Sexuality. Voyeurism. Astrology. Hermaphroditism.*

SEX AND THE ANIMALS see **LOVE AND THE ANIMALS**

SEX AND THE COLLEGE GIRL   **F6.4393**
Aura Productions. *Dist* Entertainment Enterprises. 27 Feb **1970** [Chicago opening]. Sd; col (Pathé Color). 35mm. 90 min.

Pres by Stanford S. Kohlberg. *Prod* Robert N. Langworthy, Ben Parker. *Dir* Joseph Adler. *Screenplay* Joseph Adler, William A. Bairn, Warren Spector. *Photog* Floyd Crosby. *Camera Op* Richard Moore. *Film Ed* George White. *Mus & Songs:* "Blue Latin," "Con-Cha-Cha-Cha" Robert N. Langworthy. *Songs:* "Love Cool," "Fun Lovers" Robert N. Langworthy, John Gabriel. *Titl Song Sung by* John Gabriel. *Sd* Al Overton, Jr. *Prod Mgr* Charles Hannawalt.

Cast: John Gabriel *(Larry Devon)*, Luana Anders *(Susan)*, Charles Grodin *(Bob)*, Julie Sommars *(Gwen)*, Richard Arlen *(Charles Devon)*, Valora Noland.

Drama. During semester break college students Susan and Gwen visit Puerto Rico, where Susan hopes to persuade Larry Devon, a dropout, to marry her, and Gwen intends to shed all inhibition and lose her virginity. Larry, now an aspiring composer and band leader, is supported by his father, Charles, a San Juan construction tycoon. Although Susan rejects Larry when he refuses to join his father's business, he quickly attracts another woman. Gwen makes love with Larry's former college friend, Bob, who, realizing that she is seriously attached to him, remorsefully abandons his playboy pursuits. Converted by one of Larry's songs, Charles Devon adopts his son's lifestyle. *Students. Composers. Band leaders. Tycoons. Playboys. Virginity. Filial relations. Flirtation. Sexual initiation. Vacations. San Juan (Puerto Rico).*

Note: Filmed in 1964 in Puerto Rico as *The Fun Lovers*.

SEX AND THE SINGLE GAY   **F6.4394**
Bizarre Productions. 13 Aug **1970** [San Francisco showing]. Sd; col. 35mm. 126 min.

Prod-Writ Pat Rocco. *Photog* Pat Rocco. *Film Ed* Pat Rocco. *Song:* "Changes" Pat Rocco.

Cast: Ross Judd, Jr., Larry Lynn, Chico Rodriguez, William King, Jimmie Michaels, Gerald Strickland, Chris Markham, Judy Coleman, Ron Dilly, Paul Bach, John Marino.

Compilation film. Segments of short films on male homosexuality with scenes of men making love, an interview with a man who discusses his pending sex-change operation and then runs through the woods dressed in feminine clothing, and a card game in which the players' clothing disappears and the players themselves disappear after a group orgy. *Male homosexuality. Transvestism. Orgies. Sex change operations.*

SEX AND THE SINGLE GIRL
F6.4395

Reynard Productions. *Dist* Warner Bros. Pictures. 25 Dec **1964** [New York opening; c26 Dec 1964; LP32383]. Sd; col (Technicolor). 35mm (Panavision). 114 min.

Prod William T. Orr. *Dir* Richard Quine. *2d Unit Dir* Carter De Haven, Jr. *Screenplay* Joseph Heller, David R. Schwartz. *Story* Joseph Hoffman. *Dir Photog* Charles Lang. *Art Dir* Cary O'Dell. *Set Decor* Edward G. Boyle. *Titl Created by* DePatie-Freleng. *Film Ed* David Wages. *Mus Comp & Cond* Neal Hefti. *Orch* Arthur Morton. *Titl Song* Richard Quine. *Sd* M. A. Merrick. *Asst Dir* Charles L. Hansen, Mickey McCardle. *Cost Dsgn* Edith Head. *Cost* Norman Norell. *Makeup Supv* Gordon Bau. *Supv Hair Stylist* Jean Burt Reilly. *Hairstyles for Natalie Wood* Sydney Guilaroff. *Dial Supv* Benno Schneider.

Cast: Tony Curtis *(Bob Weston)*, Natalie Wood *(Helen Brown)*, Henry Fonda *(Frank Broderick)*, Lauren Bacall *(Sylvia Broderick)*, Mel Ferrer *(Rudy DeMeyer)*, Fran Jeffries *(Gretchen)*, Leslie Parrish *(Susan)*, Edward Everett Horton *(The Chief)*, Larry Storch *(motorcycle cop)*, Stubby Kaye *(Helen's cabbie)*, Howard St. John *(George Randall)*, Otto Kruger *(Dr. Anderson)*, Max Showalter *(Holmes)*, William Lanteau *(Sylvester)*, Helen Kleeb *(Hilda)*, Curly Klein, Count Basie and His Orchestra.

Comedy. Inspired by: Helen Gurley Brown, *Sex and the Single Girl* (New York, 1962). Bob Weston, managing editor of scandal magazine *Dirt*, writes a sensational and highly successful article on research psychologist Helen Gurley Brown, whose recently published book, *Sex and the Single Girl*, has become a national bestseller. Bob is assigned to interview Dr. Brown, but she refuses to see him. In order to meet her, Bob impersonates one of his neighbors, Frank Broderick, and goes to Helen for marriage counsel. After several meetings, during which Bob suggests to Helen that they commence an affair, he telephones her and threatens to drown himself unless she capitulates. She rushes to him and accidentally causes them to tumble into a boat basin. They go to Helen's apartment to dry out; Bob mixes a potent batch of martinis and attempts to seduce her. Helen confesses her love for Bob, and he replies that all is well; he is not legally married. Helen doesn't believe him and asks to see Sylvia, his wife. The next day, Bob inadvertently sends both his secretary, Susan, and his former girl friend, Gretchen, to Helen to impersonate Sylvia and convince Helen of his claim. Helen summons the real Sylvia, and the three women all turn up for the appointment. Sylvia has Frank jailed for bigamy; Helen deduces Bob's ruse and decides to leave town with colleague Rudy DeMeyer; Bob is fired from *Dirt* when he refuses to slander the innocent doctor by his article. He follows Helen onto the San Diego Freeway where they encounter both Frank, who is trying to escape to Hawaii, and Sylvia, who is pursuing him in a cab. After a wild chase and a hectic mix-up at the airport, the couples all get sorted out: Frank and Sylvia become reconciled, Bob and Helen get together at last, and Rudy and Gretchen unexpectedly enplane for Hawaii. *Editors. Psychologists. Neighbors. Imposture. Seduction. Marriage counsel. Jealousy. Bigamy. Suicide. Hoaxes. Magazines (periodicals). Los Angeles. Helen Gurley Brown. Chases.*

Note: Locations filmed in and around Los Angeles, including the San Diego Freeway and Malibu.

SEX AND THE SINGLE SAILOR (Canada)
F6.4396

Ernest Reid Films. *Dist* William Mishkin. 18 Jan **1967** [Boston opening]. Sd; b&w. 35mm. 88 min.

Prod-Dir-Writ Ernest Reid. *Photog* Herb Taylor. *Prod Mgr* Nick Moraitis.

Cast: Theo Roubanis *(Jim)*, Keti Papanika *(Tina)*, Keti Chloe *(Aleka)*, Dimitri Karystinos *(Monk)*, Jane Galani *(Jane)*, Triana *(belly dancer)*, Rita Dalton, Sue Michaels, Hank Smith, actor, Bob Green, Eleni Anousaki, Nikos Vandoros, May Gravly, Rena Cresta, Christina Nikolakopoulos, Panos Nikolakopoulos.

Melodrama. An American merchant marine ship docks at Athens, and the sex-starved crew are given 6 days shore leave. Some try to pick up women at a bar; others visit Madam Calypso's international whorehouse; and a third contingent invent elaborate plans for meeting glamorous women. By chance Jim meets Tina, a beautiful Greek woman. Though they nearly lose track of each other, they are finally reunited, and their platonic relationship develops into a love affair. Meanwhile, Tina's friend Aleka is kidnaped to an island castle by her former boyfriend, Monk, a wrestler. All ends well, however. By the time the sailors leave the harbor, all have had memorable experiences, but Jim alone will return to Athens to establish a permanent relationship with Tina. *Sailors. Madams. Americans in foreign countries. Greeks. Abduction. Pickups. Bars. Whorehouses. Merchant marine. Athens.*

Note: Filmed in Greece in 1965 as *How To Pick Up a Girl*. Released in Canada in 1970 as *Erotikos*. Alternative title: *Love and the Single Sailor*. Also advertised as *Single Sailor* and *Girls and the Single Sailor*.

SEX AT NIGHT *see* **LOVE AT NIGHT**

S—X BY ADVERTISEMENT
F6.4397

Instant Attraction, Inc. *Dist* Provocative Films. ca **1969**. Sd; b&w. 35mm. 82 min.

Prod William Samek, Elliott R. Reed. *Dir-Writ* Joel M. Reed. *Dir Photog* Gale McCarty. *2d Unit Camera* Michael Becker. *Sets* Arthur Jacob. *Titl* Joan MacKenzie. *Sd* Elliott R. Reed. *Cont* Barbara Mehroff. *Sp Eff* Arthur Jacob. *Stills* Michael Reed, still photog. *Casting* Robert Grimaldi, casting.

Cast—Featuring: Liza Duran, Vic Quaranta, Ann Harris, Barry Schreiber, Farida Fouhoudy, Nicole Cuffori, George Cord, Rose Berman, Teresa Reynolds, Cherri Lane, Howard Leof, Shiela Cronan, Barbara Myers, Geri Miller, Frank Sater, Sheri Lee Able, Randolph Carter, Bill Cames, Robert Fellatia, Jeff Reed, Cathy Lay, Mary Lewis, Joan MacKenzie, Mitchel Barry, Arnold Jay, Ginger March, Elaine Andrews, Sean Lemay, Bernie Goldberg, Harlow Berman, Dee Vane, Carroll Cromwell.

Documentary(?). A hidden camera exposes the truth behind "personal" advertisements placed in urban newspapers: a want-ad from a New Jersey establishment catering to sadomasochists reads: "Obedience counselor available—supplies own equipment"; a New York marriage broker preys on physically deformed clients; a procurer poses as a theatrical producer to lure young women into prostitution; "employment agencies" advertise around the world for "domestics" destined to become sexual playthings for their employers. Advertisers include a manufacturer of fetish and torture devices; a pornography club; a voyeur society; figure model studios; an establishment for mud fetishists; suburban orgy clubs; young couples seeking to exchange erotic photographs of themselves; couples who abuse unsuspecting babysitters; and purveyors of "medical" sex aids. A successful businessman who can achieve satisfaction only with extremely ugly women advertises for partners; business leaders dress as women after working hours and seek out male prostitutes; a sex exploitation filmmaker works on a project. A demented sadist who roams New York's Central Park delights in whipping nude teenage girls; he belongs to an organization whose membership includes many famous people. At one of their "marathons," young society women, models, and starlets find satisfaction in being sadistically abused. The film also chronicles the disappointments of the sincere lonely hearts who advertise in the personal columns. *Marriage brokers. Pimps. Domestics. Cripples. Theatrical producers. Models. Babysitters. Businessmen. Actors. Socialites. Sadomasochism. Fetishism. Prostitution. Pornography. Male homosexuality. Voyeurism. Sadism. Torture. Eroticism. Employer-employee relations. Transvestism. Flagellation. Classified advertisements. Employment agencies. Sex aids. Sex clubs. Sex exploitation films. New Jersey. New York City. New York City—Central Park.*

Note: Also known as *Sex by Advertisement*.

THE SEX CANNIBAL
F6.4398

Gaiety Theatre. Jul **1969** [San Francisco showing]. Sd; b&w. 16mm? 70 min.
Dir Ed Hunt.

Cast: Jan Fox.

Sex film. No information about the precise nature of this film has been found. *Sexuality.*

SEX CIRCUS
F6.4399

Kirt Films International. *Dist* Distribpix, Inc. 11 Apr **1969** [Champaign, Illinois, showing]. Sd; b&w. 35mm. 75 min.

Prod Leonard Kirtman. *Dir* Tommy Goetz. *Supv* Tommy Goetz.

Cast: Jane Russel *(Erika)*, Lois Lane, Rita Joyce, Mary Aster.

Melodrama. Erika, a former lion tamer for a circus in Sweden, comes to New York City in order to create an exotic sex club styled on the circus. She recruits prostitutes, seduces them, selects among them for beauty and cooperativeness, and then instructs them in a variety of sexual practices. One woman, Annie, refuses to cooperate with Erika and is mercilessly whipped. When Erika stages one of her famous orgies, a regular customer, fancying himself a lion tamer who likes to whip girls, takes on three of Erika's "lion girls." Another customer indulges his passion for corrupting innocent young women, while a third partygoer mounts leather-clad women as if they were motorcycles. Seeing an opportunity to humiliate Erika, Annie takes a whip, and, ripping off Erika's clothes, beats and drags her into the center of the party where everyone at the orgy violates her. *Swedes. Lion tamers. Prostitutes. Madams. Seduction. Sexual practices. Sadism. Lesbianism. Flagellation. Revenge. Rape. Circus. Sex clubs.*

SEX CLUB INTERNATIONAL
F6.4400

Barry Mahon Productions. 29 Mar **1967** [Champaign, Illinois, showing]. Sd; b&w. 35mm. 62 min.

A Barry Mahon Production. *Prod-Dir* Barry Mahon.

Cast: Lucky Kargo.

Crime drama. Lucky Bang Bang is hired by the state department of a foreign government to retrieve embarrassing photos and tapes implicating top-level diplomats in the activities of one of the international sex clubs run by a woman named Carol. His mission threatens the lucrative racket of a gang of blackmailers who have muscled in on the thriving business of the clubs. Lucky has many amorous adventures while trying to retrieve the material, and the gang nearly succeeds in killing him. He finally outwits Carol, blasts the racketeers, and exposes the ring from Hong Kong to New York City. *Government agents. Racketeers. Diplomats. Blackmail. Murder. Sex clubs. Documentation.*

Note: Also known as *Lucky Bang Bang's Sex Club International.*

SEX CURES THE CRAZY   **F6.4401**
Century Cinema Corp. *Dist* Chancellor Films. ca **1968.** Sd; col. 35mm. 55 min.

Drama. Samantha's ideology is simple: sex can promote world peace. Carrying her philosophy personally forward, she first converts Animal, a spry, bearded, older man who becomes her devoted student. Samantha next makes love to Fawn, and Animal joins the two women for a love session. Animal introduces Diane, a lost innocent searching for fulfillment, to this new form of emotional therapy, and he makes love to her. The small band of sensualists grows as Samantha inspires them to carry forth to suffering people everywhere her message of love. *Peacemakers. Sensualists. Innocents. Sexuality. Lesbianism. Troilism. Cults.*

THE SEX CYCLE   **F6.4402**
Leo-Todd Productions. *Dist* Haven International Pictures, Leo-Todd Motion Picture Producing and Distributing Ltd. ca **1966.** Sd; b&w. 35mm. 80 min.

Prod Paul Leonardi, Phil Todaro. *Dir-Writ* Joe Sarno.

Cast: Nick Linkov, Joanna Mills, Tony King, Sonya Valli, Cleo Nova, Vick Parisi, Pat Barrett, Carla Desmond, Sandy Jason, Jennie Jorgan, Michael Lawrence, Bob Davis.

Melodrama. Tanya Fall, a professional sketch artist, lives in a suburban ranch house with Janet, a young woman whom she employs as a figure model. Janet grows increasingly resentful of Tanya's arrogance until one day she meets Rose, a young fortune-teller who gives her the power to dominate others. Corrupted by her newfound power, Janet attracts men and women and leads them to destruction. *Models. Artists. Fortune-tellers. Suburbanites. Moral corruption. Employer-employee relations.*

Note: May also be known as *The Sex Cycles.*

SEX FAMILY ROBINSON   **F6.4403**
Boss Productions. *Dist* Distribpix, Inc. 27 Nov **1968** [Champaign, Illinois, showing]. Sd; b&w. 35mm. 64 min.

Pres by Enrico Alexandros. *Prod* Jack Bravman. *Dir* Linda Vair. *Camera* Paul Glickman.

Cast: Linda Vair (*narrator*), Lisa St. Shaw, Vinny Pappy.

Sex film. A young girl travels to the New Jersey shore to visit relatives. During her visit, they engage in various forms of sexual stimulation, including lesbianism. *Lesbianism. Incest. New Jersey.*

SEX FAMILY ROBINSON ON THE FARM   **F6.4404**
Boss Productions. *Dist* Boss Distributors. Aug **1969** [periodical notice]. Sd; b&w. 35mm. 73 min.

Pres by Enrico Alexandros. *Dir* Linda Vair. *Screenplay* Steven Fox.

Cast: Linda Vair (*narrator*), Sheba Swengire, Sandra Sture, Bill Farmer.

Sex film. The blonde heroine narrates a day's adventures down on the farm with "America's most intimate family." Appropriately attired in black lace underthings, she arrives at the farm, and there she is greeted fondly by her Aunt Alice, Uncle Dick, cousins Lem and Sandy, and their buxom maid. The heroine explores the farm, pauses to caress a horse, and then makes love with Lem in the barn. Sandy arrives to take her brother's place in the hay, and Lem discovers the maid peering lasciviously down from the loft at the goings-on below. He berates her, whips her naked body with his belt, and then allows her to join him and the others in an orgy. The heroine decides to take a nap before dinner, but Aunt Alice interrupts her, and they make love. After dinner, Sandy goes into the bathroom and finds her father hiding behind the door. He blindfolds her, and they seat themselves on the toilet, she on his lap, and play amorously in the nude. Meanwhile, brother Lem is making love with his mother; then Dick entertains their visitor from the city before passing her on to the maid. Finally, the Robinson family, their maid, and the city cousin have an orgy before arising to dress for church. *Cousins. Uncles. Aunts. Housemaids. Incest. Troilism. Voyeurism. Flagellation. Sadism. Lesbianism. Rural life. Orgies.*

Note: Also advertised as *Family Robinson on the Farm.*

SEX IS A WOMAN *see* **LOVE IS A WOMAN**

SEX IS THE GAME PEOPLE PLAY *see* **THE GAME PEOPLE PLAY**

SEX KILLER *see* **THE GIRL KILLER**

THE SEX LIFE OF ROMEO AND JULIET *see* **THE SECRET SEX LIVES OF ROMEO AND JULIET**

SEX ODYSSEY   **F6.4405**
Dist Distribpix, Inc. ca **1970.** Sd; col. 35mm. 60 min.

Science fiction drama. Victor Denning is kidnaped from Earth and transported through space to Meliad, a planet whose inhabitants—bodiless minds—are engaged in a study of human sexual activity. The Meliadians introduce Victor to Sheila, another Earthling whose beautiful body and lustful psyche they have used as the model for a series of artificially created, oversexed women. Sheila and Victor have sexual intercourse, and, because Victor responds well, the Meliadians use him as the model for making male bodies who have the same sexual drive that they observe in Victor. He tries to escape and fails. He then decides that life on the strange planet is quite agreeable—insatiable women, orgies, unearthly pleasures; and he refuses to leave when the Meliadians propose to send him back to Earth. *Space creatures. Nymphomania. Satyriasis. Sex research. Disembodiment. Imaginary planets. Orgies.*

THE SEX OF ANGELS (Italy/West Germany)   **F6.4406**
Filmes Cinematografica–Franz Seitz Filmproduktion. *Dist* Lopert Pictures. 2 Dec **1969** [New York opening]. Sd; col (Technicolor). 35mm (Techniscope). 104 min. *MPAA rating* X.

Prod Giorgio Venturini. *Dir-Writ* Ugo Liberatore. *Dir Photog* Leonida Barboni. *Art Dir* Massimo Tavazzi. *Film Ed* Franco Fraticelli. *Mus* Giovanni Fusco. *Sd* Pietro Spadoni. *Asst Dir* Luigi Perelli, Robert Azderbal. *Prod Mgr* Cecilia Bigazzi. *Cost* Nadia Vitali. *Makeup* Raoul Ranieri. *Hairdresser* Galileo Mandini.

Cast: Bernard De Vries (*Marco*), Rosemarie Dexter (*Nancy*), Doris Kunstmann (*Nora*), Laura Troschel (*Carla*), Giovanni Petrucci (*Luca*), Efisio Cabras (*Sergio*), Brizio Montinaro (*Pietro*), Silvana Bacci (*Karel*), Hans Jurgen Neuman (*sailor*).

Melodrama. Three wealthy young women—Nancy, Nora, and Carla—bored with the normal pleasures of life—seek new thrills and decide to take Nora's father's cruiser on a weekend trip to the nearby Dalmatian coast to experiment with LSD, tape-recording the action that takes place. Nancy invites Marco, a medical student who is a total stranger, to join them. After a lazy day of swimming and skin diving, they gather in the lounge and take LSD. They then throw overboard all possibly harmful items but overlook a small pistol. When Marco comes down from his LSD trip he is bleeding internally from having been shot in the spleen and knows that he must be hospitalized immediately. Upon entering one of the cabins, he discovers Nancy, whose latent lesbianism has been brought out by the drug, in bed with Carla. He urges them to take him to the nearest port in Yugoslavia, and though they promise to do so, they become afraid of the consequences and, believing that Marco has exaggerated his condition, continue their leisurely cruise. Soon, however, Carla realizes Marco's danger and pleads with the others to allow her to go to a pharmacist in a small Yugoslavian port to get morphine. Carla obtains the drug by offering the pharmacist her virginity; but her sacrifice is in vain, for Marco dies. Nora and Nancy coldly dispose of the body and once back in the resort of Caorle go ashore as if nothing has happened. Carla, realizing she was in love with Marco, rushes to the sea and waits to be swept away by the waves. *Medical students. Pharmacists. Wealth. Lesbianism. Self-sacrifice. Virginity. Suicide. Yachts. LSD. Recorders. Caorle.*

Note: Filmed largely on the Adriatic coast of Yugoslavia. Rome opening: Feb 1968 as *Il sesso degli angeli;* released in West Germany as *Das Geschlecht der Engel;* running time: 89 min.

THE SEX PERILS OF PAULETTE   **F6.4407**
Juri Productions. *Dist* J. E. R. Pictures. 21 Jul **1965** [New York showing]. Sd; b&w. 35mm. 72 min.

Prod-Dir Doris Wishman. *Screenplay-Narr* Dawn Whitman. *Dir Photog* C. Davis Smith. *Film Ed* C. Davis Smith. *Mus* Music Sound Recorders. *Sd* Titra Sound Corp. *Optical Eff* B & O Film Specialists.

Cast: Mari Hara (*narrator*), Anna Karol, Anthony Greco, Darlene Bennett, S. Stewart, Pamela Fields, Bob Oran, Marlene Starr, Barry Lane, Darlene Cotton, Alan Yorke.

Melodrama. Paulette Moore arrives in New York City from Ohio in the hopes of becoming an actress and finds a room in Tracy Kane's apartment. Tracy advises Paulette to attend a party where she will meet theatrical agent Sam Biller. Paulette discovers an orgy in progress and, breaking away from Sam she leaves. Tracy refuses to return her rent money, and Paulette begins a frantic round of job hunting. Meanwhile, she meets Allen Martin and they begin to date. Gradually, Paulette realizes that Tracy is a prostitute, and by accident she walks into the apartment while Tracy and Sam are making love. Desperate, Paulette takes a job as a waitress but is soon fired for inefficiency. Now penniless, Paulette embarks on a life of prostitution in spite of her love for Allen. One day after Paulette has been brutally beaten by a client, she meets Allen in a park. He forces the truth from her but still wishes to marry her. Paulette refuses, believing that she would not be a worthy wife. *Actors. Innocents. Roommates. Waitresses. Theatrical agents. Courtship. Prostitution. Group sex. Sadism. Moral corruption. New York City.*

Note: Also known as *Sex Perils of Pauline*, and *Paulette*.

SEX RITUALS OF THE OCCULT   F6.4408
Fine Products. *Dist* Studio West Film Distributors, Sam Lake Enterprises. Oct **1970**. Sd; col. 35mm. 82 min.

Cast: Vincent Stephens *(narrator)*.

Documentary(?). The secret erotic rituals of the occult are brought to light. The rites of witchcraft, voodoo, the black mass, devil worship, and animal worship come under scrutiny. One couple makes love in a coffin. Others are chained and shackled in their lovemaking. Celebrants participate in ritualistic orgies. *Witchcraft. Voodoo. Demonology. Sadomasochism. Occult. Orgies. Rites and ceremonies. Cults.*

THE SEX SEEKERS   F6.4409
American Film Production Co. ca **1969**. Sd; col. 16mm. [Feature length assumed.]

Farce. This film satirizes the Masters and Johnson study of American sexual behavior. *Sex researchers. Sexuality. William Howell Masters. Virginia Eshelman Johnson.*

THE SEX SHUFFLE   F6.4410
Sun Art Enterprises. 27 Mar **1968** [Boston opening]. Sd; col. 35mm. 71 min.
Prod Whit Boyd. *Dir* Ron Scott. *Screenplay* William E. Hamelman. *Photog* Ludwig Moner. *Camera* N. F. Manfred. *Art Dir* X. O. Von Gam. *Mus* The LSD Psychedelic Marching Band.

Cast: Beverly Brent *(Beverly)*, Byron Lord *(Craig)*, Chuck Bowers *(Chuck)*, Dianne Davis *(Dianne)*, Peggy Christian *(Peggy)*, Linda Lang *(Linda)*, Barbara Bolyn *(Barbara)*, Bonnie Carson *(Bonnie)*, Jimmie Raye *(Sergeant Shaffer)*, James Hawke *(Officer Becker)*, Don Prince *(John)*.

Melodrama. Innocent young girls who leave home to seek thrills in the hippie community are introduced to a world of narcotics and sexual depravity by the masterminds of a gigantic vice ring. The group's activities range from mere body painting to incest, lesbianism, and group sex. The police intervene to capture the ring leaders when one of the girls dies tragically. *Hippies. Gangsters. Police. Innocents. Lesbianism. Group sex. Incest. Prostitution. Moral corruption. Body painting. Narcotics.*

Note: Also known as *The Love Shuffle*.

THE SEX TRIP   F6.4411
Cherry Productions. ca **1969**. Sd; col (Eastmancolor). 16mm. [Feature length assumed.]
Orig Screenplay Woodrow Olivetti.

Sex film. No information about the precise nature of this film has been found. *Sexuality.*

LE SEXE DES ANGES *see* WHITE VOICES

THE SEXIEST STORY EVER TOLD   F6.4412
Dist All American Films. ca **1970**. Sd; col (Eastman Color). 35mm. 70 min.
Dir Ren-Mart. *Camera* Dick Mark. *Film Ed* Molcar Falcon. *Mus* Grace Winters. *Makeup* Sergi Castello.

Cast: Steve Hawkes, Minnie the Mermaid, Bonnie Key, John McLaughlin, Baby Mermaid, Bill Roger.

Comedy. Hugh Bangergood, playboy publisher of the men's magazine *Laygirl*, gives free-lance writer Royal Underwood one day to write an article on the history of the nudie movie. Bangergood sends along a sample film and his beautiful though frigid secretary, Penelope Honipantz, to take dictation. The two sit on the couch and begin to watch the film. Underwood becomes so engrossed in the film that he fails to notice Miss Honipantz, who, aroused by the film, begins to disrobe. Completely nude, she throws herself on Underwood, and he responds in kind. *Playboys. Publishers. Authors. Secretaries. Frigidity. Sex exploitation films. Magazines (periodicals).*

THE SEXPERTS—TOUCHED BY TEMPTATION   F6.4413
Extraordinary Films. *Dist* William Mishkin. 4 Aug **1965** [New York showing]. Sd; b&w with col sequences (Eastman Color). 35mm. 77 min.
Pres by William Mishkin. *Dir* J. Nehemiah. *Scen* Charles Ross. *Dir Photog* Ekmek Kedayeef.

Cast: Lana Lynn *(Liz Adams)*, Rusty Allen *(Connie Mason)*, Ken Curtin *(Barry Coleman)*, John Lyon *(Douglas Baines)*, Lonnie Maggio *(Leslie Carter)*, Anthony Ford *(Baxter Standish)*, Dori Davis *(Mimi)*, Yvonne Curtis, Audrey Campbell, Dixie Lester, Cary Marshall, Henry Grant, Joyce Jennifer.

Melodrama. A producer, a director, and a writer plan a film about a group of people who are obsessed with sex. Seduced and abandoned by an actor, *Liz Adams* comes to New York City to seek revenge on men, using her body to make her way in the theatrical world. To further her career, she has affairs with actor *Baxter Standish*, director *Douglas Baines*, and producer *Leslie Carter*. Liz's roommate, *Connie*, quarrels with her photographer boyfriend *Barry Coleman* when she catches him in a compromising situation with a nude model. Connie joins Liz for a round of parties that takes them from Leslie's Park Avenue penthouse to his Fire Island beach house where they borrow his yacht to sunbathe in the nude. Connie refuses Barry's phone calls and attends a Greenwich Village party with Liz. As the evening progresses, the guests shed their inhibitions, and Connie is nearly raped. She finds Liz embracing two men at once and leaves, returning home to Barry's waiting arms. As the party degenerates into an orgy, Leslie arrives to drive the women home; disgusted by Liz's behavior, he leaves alone. The filmmakers cannot decide between two alternative endings. In the first, Leslie overcomes his displeasure and maintains Liz in a Park Avenue apartment. In the second, Liz, a prostitute in a run-down hotel, sells herself to a dock worker for $5. *Actors. Man-haters. Roommates. Photographers. Theatrical directors. Theatrical producers. Mistresses. Prostitutes. Promiscuity. Seduction. Revenge. Jealousy. Orgies. Sex exploitation films. New York City—Park Avenue. New York City—Greenwich Village. Fire Island.*

Note: Also known as *Touched by Temptation*. May also be known as *The Love Experts*.

THE SEXPLOITERS   F6.4414
Esquire Pictures. *Dist* Olympic International Films. 2 Jul **1965** [Champaign, Illinois, showing]. Sd; b&w. 35mm (see note). 69 min.
Prod Jerry Denby, R. W. Cresse. *Dir* Al C. Ruban. *Mus* Steve Karmen.

Sex film. Lynn Merrick, a thrill-seeking suburban housewife, goes to New York City and becomes involved in a call girl syndicate operating within a model agency. Posing in the nude, the "models" excite desires that they later satisfy at a price. The women find their own pleasure in lesbian relationships, competing for each other's attentions. In the course of her work, Lynn meets a man who lies in a coffin pretending to be a corpse as he awaits the women who have been sent to gratify his desire. Another client delights in sadomasochistic rituals. One woman attempts to seduce a man by asking him to pose in the nude. Lynn takes part in an orgy where wild, exotic dances stimulate the senses. *Housewives. Suburbanites. Models. Prostitution. Lesbianism. Fetishism. Sadomasochism. Nudity. Orgies. New York City.*

Note: Contains sequences filmed in 8mm and blown up to 35mm. Also known as *The Exploiters*. Al C. Ruban is a pseudonym for S. N. Johnsen.

THE SEXTERMINATORS   F6.4415
John A. Grant Productions. *Dist* Emerson Film Enterprises. 29 Apr **1970** [Champaign, Illinois, showing]. Sd; col. 35mm. 78 min.
Prod Lou Martin, John A. Grant. *Dir* John A. Grant.

Cast: Charles Cashmere *(Danny Stewart)*, Jeanette Blake *(Sandy)*, Rita Kaye, Dardanella, Joe Miller, Antoinette Maynard.

Melodrama. Danny Stewart is the prime target for the "Federation," a self-appointed group of executioners of over-sexed people. After receiving money for his services from one woman, he picks up his girl friend, Sandy, and escapes to Canada. Danny is pursued and finally caught by the Federation, but instead of killing him, they castrate him. *Vigilantes. Castration. Satyriasis. Canada.*

Note: Also known as *The Six Terminators*.

SEXTET   F6.4416
International Films. *Dist* Thunderbird International Pictures. 9 Dec **1964** [New York showing]. Sd; col (Eastman Color). 35mm. 67 min.
Pres by Joseph Fink, Juan Hidalgo-Gato. *Prod* Harvey Berman.

Cast: Pauly Dash, Judy Mason.

Comedy. Pauly Dash, a slight, timid businessman, suppresses his romantic feelings toward his secretary, bookkeeper, and receptionist and rushes home at the end of each day in order to escape the thoughts which trouble him. As he drives through traffic, his persistent fantasies bring him into conflict with a policeman. His browbeating wife awaits him at home with a list of household chores, and Pauly escapes into an Oriental dream world: *On a lavish houseboat, six beautiful, scantily-clad women devote themselves to fulfilling the desires of their demanding master, Pauly.* He soon discovers that too much feminine attention can be worse than too little. Pauly happily returns to the real world but finds that his wife has transformed herself into a glamorous seductress in order to compete with the women of his dreams. Erantic, Pauly flees the clutches of his impassioned wife. *Businessmen. Orientals. Shrews. Timidity. Marriage. Reckless driving. Nudity. Houseboats. Harems. Fantasy.*

Note: Filmed in Miami. Also known as *Six Women & a Man* and *Sixtet*.

SEXUAL ENCOUNTER GROUP   F6.4417
Alex de Renzy Productions. *Dist* Sherpix, Inc. 30 Oct **1970** [San Francisco opening]. Sd; col. 35mm. 82 min.
Prod-Dir Alex De Renzy. *Photog* Alex De Renzy. *2d Camera* Michael Martin. *Film Ed* Alex De Renzy. *Sd* Bob Gravner. *Prod Mgr* Jack Teach.
Documentary. The film documents an "encounter session" in which several wealthy suburban couples hope to learn to relate sensitively to one another. Prolonged discussion culminates in group sexual activity. *Suburbanites. Encounter groups. Group sex.*
Note: Working title: *Group Encounter.*

SEXUAL FREEDOM IN DENMARK   F6.4418
Horizon Productions. *Dist* Art Films International. Mar **1970** [Los Angeles showing; c27 Mar 1970; MP20392]. Sd; col (Eastman Color). 35mm. 75 min.
Prod-Dir M. C. Von Hellen. *Camera* Finn Thomsen. *Sd* Niels Hoffman.
Cast: Ole Lassen, Karen Biller, Dorrit Frantzen, Elizabeth Bundgaard, Ruth Dymore, Age O. Lundin.
Documentary. The film argues that sexual repression is unhealthy and that all censorship should be eliminated. The film opens with a man and a woman running through a forest completely nude. There follows a comparison of primitive erotic art and contemporary erotic art in Denmark and Los Angeles. Footage is included of a nudist beauty contest. Segments of a sex education film that demonstrate various positions of sexual intercourse and give a brief survey of human sexual biology are also contained. The film closes with more of the naked couple making love in the forest. *Censorship. Nudity. Eroticism. Nudism. Sexual techniques. Sex instruction. Art. Beauty contests. Denmark. Los Angeles.*
Note: Also known as *Dansk Sexualitet.* Filmed in Denmark by Alex de Renzy, who may be the same as M. C. Von Hellen.

SEXUAL FREEDOM IN MARRIAGE   F6.4419
Dist Distribpix, Inc. ca **1970**. Sd; col. 35mm. 64 min.
Instructional film. Human sexual response is investigated. *Sexual techniques. Sex instruction.*

SEXUAL INADEQUACIES see SESSO

SEXUAL PRACTICES IN SWEDEN (Sweden)   F6.4420
Svenska Institut of Sexual Response. *Dist* William Mishkin. 5 Nov **1970** [New York opening]. Sd; col. 35mm. 79 min.
Prod William P. Martinson. *Dir-Writ* Karl Hansen. *Photog* Bertil Johanssen. *Film Ed* Sven Jungsen. *Asst Dir* Lars Mikelssen. *Prod Mgr* Chris Swenson.
Sex instruction film. Three couples demonstrate methods of foreplay and sexual intercourse, including oral sex. There is a descriptive narration by a Swedish physician. *Physicians. Sexual techniques. Oral sex.*

SEXUALITÄT IN DER EHE see THE MIRACLE OF LOVE

SEXUALITY IN MARRIAGE see THE MIRACLE OF LOVE

THE SEXUALLY LIBERATED FEMALE see THE SENSUALLY LIBERATED FEMALE

THE SEXUOUS FEMALE see THE SENSUALLY LIBERATED FEMALE

SEXUS (France)   F6.4421
Productions du Chêne. *Dist* Audubon Films. 19 Mar **1965** [Los Angeles showing]. Sd; b&w. 35mm. 77 min.
Pres by Radley H. Metzger. *Dir-Writ* José Bénazéraf. *Photog* Alain Derobe. *Asst Photog* André Debreuil. *Film Ed* Georges Marschalk. *Mus* Chet Baker.
Cast: Virginia de Solen *(Virginia [see note])*, Alain Tissier *(Blackie)*, Willy Braque *(Carl)*, Yves Duffaut *(Frankie)*, Annie Josse *(Danielle)*.
Crime melodrama. Virginia, a young Parisian, is kidnaped by a gang of criminals and taken to a deserted farmhouse. The criminals hope to receive a large ransom from her father, a wealthy banker. Virginia tries to escape, but she is caught by Carl, who tries to rape her. Blackie, another gang member who is attracted to Virginia, discovers the struggle and kills Carl. A short time later, the boss of the gang telephones from Paris and informs the kidnapers that the police are on the way, and Virginia must be killed. Instead, Blackie returns her to her father and drives back to the farm to meet his fate. [The film begins with a sequence of a lesbian nightclub act.] *Gangsters. Lesbianism. Kidnaping. Rape. Nightclubs. Paris. Crazy Horse Saloon (Paris).*
Note: Opened in Paris in Jul 1965 as *L'enfer dans la peau;* original title: *La nuit la plus longue;* running time: 85 min. The opening nightclub sequence, filmed at The Crazy Horse Saloon in Paris, was added to the U. S. version; the same footage is included in *Night of Lust,* q. v. One French source credits the leading actress as Virginie de Salem.

SEXY GANG see MICHELLE

SEXY MAGICO (Italy)   F6.4422
Eridania Cinematografica–Italian International Film. *Dist* American International Pictures. 8 Jul **1967** [Maryland license]. Sd; col (Eastmancolor). 35mm (CinemaScope). 89 min.
Prod Enrico C. Putatto, Fulvio Lucisano. *Dir* Mino Loy, Luigi Scattini. *Photog* Benito Frattari, Floriano Trenker. *Mus* Marcello Gigante.
Featuring: Black Eva, Nana Pilou, Leila Sohl, Rosetta, Esperanza, Barbara Won, Jessica Rubicon, Belinda, Monty Landis, Marlene, Fernando Rego.
Documentary. Elements of obscure sexual rites of different tribal communities are linked to the symbolic dances and acts included in various cabarets throughout the world. Sequences include: magic rites in the tropics; the dance of Scarlet and the Devil from the Sombrero Club of Nairobi; striptease acts at the Crazy Horse Saloon in Paris; striptease and exotic dance acts at Le Sexy of Paris and Eve de Paris cabarets; and an Arabian dance at the El Dyazair cabaret. *Exotic dancers. Rites and ceremonies. Tribal life. Striptease. Magic. Cabarets. Nairobi. Paris. Crazy Horse Saloon (Paris). Nouvelle Eve (Paris). Le Sexy, (Paris). Sombrero Club (Nairobi).*
Note: Opened in Rome in Oct 1963; running time: 105 min.

SEXY PROIBITISSIMO (Italy)   F6.4423
Gino Mordini Produzione Cinematografiche. *Dist* Olympic International Films. 16 Sep **1964** [Maryland license]. Sd; col (Eastman Color). 35mm. 63 min.
Prod Gino Mordini. *Dir-Comm* Marcello Martinelli. *Photog* Adalberto Albertini. *Mus* Lallo Gori. *Choreog* Wilbert Bradley.
Cast: Karmela, Lilli de Saigon, Monique, Joan Clair, Nadia Victor, Helen Mary, Corinne Fontaine, Nicole Verger, Michèle Liz, Buddy Thompson, Carol Karter, Gerry Sammer, Maureen Verrich, Violetta Montenegro, Chillian Hobart, Pamela Wellman, Leonor Rainer, George Corner, Joanna Negulesco, Diana West, Poppy Scott, Rosy Peters, Brian Jones, actor, Irene Michele, Karin Mayer, Ann Sally Pain, Hercules, Les Ciranos, Paul Steffen Ballet, Kanoi Brothers, Wilbert Bradley Ballet, Archie Savage and the Royal Ballet of the Fiji Islands, Copacabana Girls of Rio, French Can-Can of the Moulin-Rouge, La Bamba of Mexico.
Burlesque film. A tour through history supports the hypothesis that the nude female form has been instrumental in molding civilization: a cavewoman performs a striptease to arouse her mate; Phryne, a beautiful Greek courtesan, displays her nude body to judges and wins an acquittal; Cleopatra bathes in milk before Caesar; Salome's dance of seven veils brings Herod to subjugation; a woman saves herself from the guillotine in the French Revolution by stripping for the executioner; sleeping in a scanty nightgown, a woman awakens to find a vampire in her bedroom; the seductive poses of Dr. Frankenstein's nurse bring his monster to life; at the modern day Crazy Horse Saloon in Paris, the Spider Girl strips before her web; a female astronaut strips to win over the Martians; at the Club Delon in Pigalle, two lesbians perform a striptease in which they undress each other. *Cave dwellers. Vampires. Nurses. Nudity. Striptease. Lesbianism. Paris. Cleopatra. Phryne. Gaius Julius Caesar. Herod Antipas. Salome. Crazy Horse Saloon (Paris). Club Delon (Pigalle). Frankenstein.*
Note: Rome opening: Nov 1963; running time: ca100 min. Also known as *Proibitissimo, The Most Prohibited Sex,* and *Prohibited Sex.* Cast names are drawn from European sources; some roles may have been cut from U. S. version. Not to be confused with the earlier Gino Mordini production *Sexy Proibito,* which opened in Rome in Feb 1963.

SFIDA A RIO BRAVO see GUNMEN OF THE RIO GRANDE

LA SFINGE D'ORO see THE GLASS SPHINX

UNA SFINGE TUTTA D'ORO see THE GLASS SPHINX

UNO SGUARDO DAL PONTE see A VIEW FROM THE BRIDGE

THE SHABBY TIGER see MASQUERADE

SHACHO DOCHUKI see PLAYBOY PRESIDENT

SHACHO NINPOCHO see FIVE GENTS' TRICK BOOK

SHADOW OF EVIL (France/Italy)   F6.4424
P. A. C.–C. I. C. C.–DA. MA. Film. *Dist* Seven Arts Pictures. 25 Jan **1967** [Boston opening]. Sd; col (Eastmancolor). 35mm (Franscope). 92 min.
Prod Paul Cadéac. *Dir* André Hunebelle. *2d Unit Dir* Jacques Besnard. *Screenplay* Pierre Foucaud, Richard Caron, Raymond Borel, Patrice Rondard, André Hunebelle, Michel Lebrun. *Photog* Raymond Lemoigne. *Art Dir* René Moulaert. *Film Ed* Jean Feyte. *Mus* Michel Magne. *Sd* René Forget. *Prod Mgr* Cyril Grize.
Cast: Kerwin Mathews *(OSS 117)*, Robert Hossein *(Dr. Sinn)*, Pier Angeli *(Lila)*, Dominique Wilms *(Eva Davidson)*, Akom Mokranond *(Sonsak)*, Sing Milintrasai *(Prasit)*, Henri Virlojeux *(Leasock)*, Jacques Mauclair, Gamil Ratib.

Action melodrama. Source: Jean Bruce, *Lila de Calcutta* (Paris, 1960). Secret agent OSS 117 is sent to Bangkok to investigate a series of mysterious epidemics in Southeast Asia. While attending a garden party at the United States Embassy, he meets the sinister Dr. Sinn and his beautiful sister Lila. The next day, 117 is drugged, kidnaped, and taken to Sinn's house on a nearby island where Lila is also imprisoned. After learning that Sinn is the head of a secret group which plans to conquer the world by unleashing a deadly virus to exterminate "inferior" races, 117 manages to escape with Lila. Further investigation leads him to a laboratory where the virus is being developed on rats. After being captured again, 117 is saved by Lila and by his secretary Eva. Aided by faithful Oriental assistants, 117 and Lila set fire to the laboratory and escape. Eva is killed during the flight, but the threat to the world's safety ends as Dr. Sinn falls into a pit filled with thousands of contaminated rats. *Secret agents. Secretaries. Scientists. Orientals. Epidemics. Abduction. Racism. Megalomania. Microorganisms. Laboratories. Southeast Asia. Bangkok. Rats.*

Note: Location scenes filmed in Bangkok. Opened in Paris in Jun 1964 as *Banco à Bangkok*; in Italy as *OSS 117 minaccia Bangkok*. Original running time: 118 min. Alternative French title: *Banco à Bangkok pour OSS 117.*

THE SHADOW OF THE CAT (Great Britain)   F6.4425

B. H. P. Films. *Dist* Universal-International Films. 7 Jun **1961** [New York opening; c26 Apr 1961; LP24725]. Sd; b&w. 35mm. 79 min.

Prod Jon Penington. *Dir* John Gilling. *Screenplay* George Baxt. *Dir Photog* Arthur Grant. *Camera Op* Len Harris. *Art Dir* Don Mingaye. *Prod Dsgn* Bernard Robinson. *Supv Film Ed* James Needs. *Ed* John Pomeroy. *Mus Comp & Cond* Mikis Theodorakis. *Sd* Jock May, Ken Cameron. *Sd Ed* Alban Streeter. *1st & 2d Asst Dir* John Peverall, Dominic Fulford. *Prod Mgr* Don Weeks. *Cont* Tilly Day. *Wardrobe* Molly Arbuthnot. *Makeup* Roy Ashton. *Hairdresser* Frieda Steiger. *Sp Eff* Les Bowie. *Casting Dir* Stuart Lyons. *Stills Camera* Tom Edwards. *Cat Trainer* John Holmes.

Cast: Andre Morell *(Walter Venable)*, Barbara Shelley *(Beth Venable)*, William Lucas *(Jacob)*, Freda Jackson *(Clara)*, Conrad Phillips *(Michael Latimer)*, Alan Wheatley *(Inspector Rowles)*, Andrew Crawford *(Andrew)*, Henry Kendall *(doctor)*, Catherine Lacey *(Ella Venable)*, Vanda Godsell *(Louise)*, Richard Warner *(Edgar)*, Kynaston Reeves *(grandfather)*, John Dearth *(Constable Hamer)*, Fred Stone, George Doonan *(ambulance men)*, Charles Stanley *(Dobbins)*, Vera Cook *(mother)*, Rodney Burke *(workman)*, Howard Knight *(boy)*, Kevin Stoney *(father)*, Angela Crow *(daughter)*.

Horror film. Wealthy Ella Venable is murdered and buried by her husband, Walter, and their servants, Clara and Andrew, all of whom want her inheritance. Ella's pet cat witnesses the crime, and when the victim's niece Beth visits the family's Victorian mansion with newspaperman Michael Latimer, she discovers that the formerly placid animal is now a ferocious beast. As the cat's behavior becomes increasingly ominous, the murderers decide the animal must be destroyed; however, the crafty beast forces Andrew into some quicksand and so terrifies Clara that she plunges to her death down a long flight of stairs. In desperation, Walter attempts to coerce some relatives into killing the cat and destroying Ella's will, which names Beth as sole beneficiary; but they, too, are eliminated by the animal. A heart attack brought on by panic confines Walter to bed, but the hissing cat continues menacing him until he dies. The animal then leads Beth and Michael to Ella's body. *Domestics. Aunts. Newspapermen. Murder. Revenge. Inheritance. Heart disease. Convalescence. Wills. Quicksand. Cats.*

Note: Opened in London in Apr 1961.

THE SHADOW VS. THE 1,000 EYES OF DR. MABUSE *see* THE 1000 EYES OF DR. MABUSE

SHADOWS (Reissue)   F6.4426

Gena Productions. *Dist* Lion International Films. 21 Mar **1961** [New York opening]. Sd; b&w. 35mm. 87 min.

Note: Filmed in 16mm. First shown in New York City in 1959; running time: ca60 min.

THE SHADOWS GROW LONGER (Switzerland/West Germany)   F6.4427

Praesens-Film-CCC-Filmkunst. *Dist* Times Film Corp. 10 Jun **1962** [New York opening]. Sd; b&w. 35mm. 91 min.

Prod Lazar Wechsler, Artur Brauner. *Dir* Ladislao Vajda. *Screenplay* Ladislao Vajda, Heinz Pauck, Istvan Békeffi. *Photog* Enrique Gaertner. *Art Dir* Max Röthlisberger. *Film Ed* Hermann Haller. *Mus* Robert Blum. *Sd* Paul Wartman. *Prod Mgr* Uors van Planta.

Cast: Luise Ullrich *(Frau Diethelm)*, Barbara Rütting *(Christa Andres)*, Hansjörg Felmy *(Max)*, Loni von Friedl *(Erika Schoner)*, Fred Tanner *(Doctor Barner)*, Helga Sommerfeld *(Helene)*, Renja Gill *(Anni)*, Margot Philipp *(Barbara)*, Carola Rasch *(Bessie)*, Iris Erdmann *(Hilde)*, Heidi Pawellek *(Paula)*, Brit von Thiesenhausen *(Ruth)*, Elizabeth Roth *(Steffie)*, Erika Wolf *(Susanne)*, Gabriele Adam *(Vera)*, Bella Neri *(Yvette)*, Michael Paryla, Anneliese

Betschart, Hans Gaugler, Max Haufler.

Melodrama. Christa Andres, the house mistress in a reform school for delinquent girls, guards the secret of her past: as a young girl who was corrupted by Max, a procurer, she served a prison term for prostitution. Now Christa volunteers for the task of rehabilitating 16-year-old Erika Schoner, a rebellious youngster known as a troublemaker at the school. The product of a broken home, Erika wants only to return to her boyfriend Fritz, a young pimp who led her into prostitution. Reminded of her own youth, Christa makes every effort to break down the girl's hostility. Tensions at the school culminate in a riot, and Erika escapes. As Christa sets out to find Erika, Max reappears and threatens to reveal Christa's past unless she provides him with information he can use to blackmail the well-to-do parents of some of the girls in the reform school. Rather than betray her young charges, Christa kills Max. As she is being led away by police, she spots Erika in the crowd of onlookers. Erika perceives the meaning of Christa's sacrifice. *Juvenile delinquents. Prostitutes. Pimps. Prison matrons. Blackmail. Murder. Loyalty. Moral corruption. Riots. Self-sacrifice. Reformatories.*

Note: Location scenes filmed in Zurich. Released in Switzerland in 1961 and in West Germany in Aug 1961 as *Die Schatten werden länger*. Also known as *Defiant Daughters.*

SHADOWS OF FORGOTTEN ANCESTORS (U.S.S.R.)   F6.4428

Dovzhenko Film Studio. *Dist* Artkino Pictures. 16 Mar **1967** [New York opening]. Sd; col (Sovcolor) with b&w seq. 35mm. 100 min. [Also reviewed at 90 min.]

Dir Sergey Paradzhanov. *Screenplay* Sergey Paradzhanov, Ivan Chendey. *Photog* V. Ilyenko. *Art Dir* M. Rakovskiy, G. Yakutovich. *Film Ed* M. Ponomarenko. *Mus* M. Skorik. *Sd* S. Sergiyenko. *Asst Dir* V. Lugovskiy.

Cast: Ivan Mikolaychuk *(Ivan)*, Larisa Kadochnikova *(Marichka)*, Tatyana Bestayeva *(Palagna)*, Spartak Bagashvili *(Yurko)*, N. Grinko *(Batag)*, L. Yengibarov *(Miko)*, Nina Alisova, A. Gay *(Paliychuks)*, N. Gnepovskaya, A. Raydanov *(Gutenyuks)*, I. Dzyura *(Ivan as a child)*, V. Glyanko *(Marichka as a child)*.

Costume drama. Source: Mikhaylo Mikhaylovich Kotsyubinskiy, *Tini zabutykh predkiv* (Kiev?, 1911). In the early 1900's in a small Carpathian village, Ivan is saved from a falling tree by his brother, who is killed as a result. A short time later, Ivan's father is murdered in a fight, and afterwards the boy and his mother are forced to subsist in poverty. From childhood Ivan grows close to Marichka, whose father was responsible for his father's death. As they grow up, they fall in love, though his poverty and the feud separating their families make it impossible for them to marry. One day while Ivan tends his sheep, Marichka, attempting to rescue a lamb, falls from a cliff and drowns in the river below. Ivan is overwhelmed by grief and grows apathetic toward all about him. Eventually, he is persuaded to marry the sensual Palagna, but he remains haunted by memories of Marichka. Palagna visits the village sorcerer for help in reclaiming Ivan from the past, but she eventually yields to his charms. As Ivan tries to defend his family honor, the sorcerer strikes him with an axe. Dying, Ivan makes his way to the river where Marichka died and reaches out to her vision as it appears before him. The entire village mourns his death in a traditional pagan ritual. *Shepherds. Sorcerers. Ghosts. Feuds. Murder. Poverty. Death. Marriage. Memory. Rites and ceremonies. Paganism. Funerals. Carpathian Mountains. Ukraine. Visions.*

Note: Released in the U.S.S.R. in 1965 as *Tini zabutykh predkiv*. Also known as *Shadows of Our Ancestors* and *Shadows of Our Forgotten Ancestors*.

SHAKA *see* BUDDHA

SHAKESPEARE WALLAH (India)   F6.4429

Merchant-Ivory Productions. *Dist* Continental Distributing, Inc. 22 Mar **1966** [New York opening]. Sd; b&w. 35mm. 115 min.

Prod Ismail Merchant. *Dir* James Ivory. *Screenplay* Ruth Prawer Jhabvala, James Ivory. *Story* Ruth Prawer Jhabvala. *Photog* Subrata Mitra. *Film Ed* Amit Bose. *Mus* Satyajit Ray. *Sd* D. L. Vagal. *Asst Dir* Mohamed Shafi, R. Subla.

Cast: Shashi Kapoor *(Sanju)*, Felicity Kendal *(Lizzie Buckingham)*, Madhur Jaffrey *(Manjula)*, Geoffrey Kendal *(Tony Buckingham)*, Laura Liddell *(Carla Buckingham)*, Utpal Dutt *(maharaja)*, Praveen Paul *(Didi)*, Jim D. Tytler *(Bobby)*, Prayag Raaj *(Sharmaji)*, Pincho Kapoor *(Guptaji)*, Partap Sharma *(Aslam)*, Hamid Sayani *(headmaster's brother)*, Sudershan *(director)*, Jennifer Kapoor *(Mrs. Bowen)*.

Drama. A British Shakespearean acting troupe led by Mr. and Mrs. Buckingham travels through India. One day, after a performance for a maharaja, the troupe's car breaks down on a desolate road. A wealthy young Indian, Sanju, comes to their aid and lodges them at his uncle's estate for the night. When the troupe leaves the following day, Sanju follows them, for he has fallen in love with Lizzie, the Buckingham's daughter. Life for the British in India is hard, and the troupe finds it increasingly difficult to obtain engagements. Sanju's former girl friend, Manjula, a film star, is jealous of

Sanju's love for Lizzie and persuades him to take her to see Lizzie perform. Manjula's arrival excites the audience and stops the play. At another performance, Sanju starts a fight because the audience catcalls Lizzie, and the performance comes to an abrupt end. Sanju finally decides that he could not adjust himself to marriage to an actress from the West. Their romance ends, and the Buckinghams send Lizzie back to England. *British. Actors. Theatrical troupes. Royalty. Filial relations. Jealousy. England. William Shakespeare.*

Note: Filmed on location in Kasauli, Simla, Alwar, Rajasthan, Lucknow, and Bombay. Released in India in 1966. New York Film Festival (1965) version opens with the troupe performing Richard Sheridan's *The Critic*, which was deleted for U. S. commercial release. Jennifer Bragg is also known as Jennifer Kendal.

THE SHAKIEST GUN IN THE WEST   F6.4430

Universal Pictures. May **1968** [c11 May 1967; LP38822]. Sd (Westrex); col (Technicolor). 35mm (Techniscope). 101 min.

Prod Edward J. Montagne. *Dir* Alan Rafkin. *Screenplay* Jim Fritzell, Everett Greenbaum. *Dir Photog* Andrew Jackson. *Art Dir* Alexander Golitzen, Henry Larrecq. *Set Decor* John McCarthy, Perry Murdock. *Main Titl* Phill Norman, Cinefx. *Film Ed* Tony Martinelli. *Mus Comp* Vic Mizzy. *Mus Supv* Joseph Gershenson. *Titl Song* Dave Blume, Jerry Keller. *Sung by* The Wilburn Brothers. *Sd* Waldon O. Watson, David H. Moriarty. *Asst Dir* Joseph Kenny. *Asst to the Prod* Billy Sands. *Unit Prod Mgr* Jim Paisley. *Cost* Grady Hunt. *Makeup* Bud Westmore. *Hairstyles* Larry Germain. *Matte Supv* Albert Whitlock.

Cast: Don Knotts *(Jesse W. Heywood)*, Barbara Rhoades *(Penelope Cushings)*, Jackie Coogan *(Matthew Basch)*, Donald Barry *(Reverend Zachary Grant)*, Ruth McDevitt *(Olive)*, Frank McGrath *(Mr. Remington)*, Terry Wilson *(Welsh)*, Carl Ballantine *(Swanson)*, Pat Morita *(Wong)*, Robert Yuro *(Arnold the Kid)*, Herbert Voland *(Dr. Friedlander)*, Fay DeWitt *(Violet)*, Dub Taylor *(Pop McGovern)*, Hope Summers *(Celia)*, Dick Wilson *(Indian chief)*, Vaughn Taylor *(Reverend Longbaugh)*, Ed Peck *(sheriff)*, Edward Faulkner *(Huggins)*, Arthur Space *(Sheriff Tolliver)*, Gregory Mullavy *(Phelps)*, Benny Rubin, Dorothy Neumann, E. J. Andre.

Western comedy. *Source:* Edmund Hartmann and Frank Tashlin, screenplay for the film *The Paleface*, 1948. In the 19th century, Jesse W. Heywood graduates from a Pennsylvania dental college and heads west to set up a frontier practice. En route, the stagecoach on which he is riding is robbed by two masked bandits, one of whom is pretty Penelope Cushings, alias Bad Penny Cushings. She is caught by a sheriff's posse and agrees, in exchange for a full pardon, to help the government learn who is smuggling guns to renegade Sioux Indians. Then, in order to board a wagon train that does not accommodate single women, Penelope dupes Jesse into marrying her. The marriage is not consummated, however, because of a Sioux attack on the wagon train, much to Penelope's relief and Jesse's gawky chagrin. During the attack, Jesse believes he is responsible for killing more than a dozen braves, when in fact it was Penelope who scored the kills. Soon Jesse is known as the fastest gunman in the West, and the formerly timid dentist begins wearing elaborate outfits to reflect his fearsome reputation. Shattered when he learns the truth, he confesses his incompetence to the townspeople, who immediately shun him. Jesse finally proves his mettle when Penelope is captured by the Indians: disguising himself as a squaw, he rescues Penelope, helps her uncover the gun smugglers, and even shoots fairly well. *Dentists. Gunrunners. Sheriffs. Gunfighters. Sioux Indians. Frontier and pioneer life. Stagecoach robberies. Marriage of convenience. Female impersonation. Courage.*

Note: Previously filmed as *The Paleface* in 1948 by Paramount Pictures.

SHALAKO (Great Britain)   F6.4431

Kingston Films-Palomar Pictures International. *Dist* Cinerama Releasing Corp. 7 Oct **1968** [San Francisco opening]. Sd; col (Technicolor). 35mm (Franscope). 113 min.

A Dimitri De Grunwald Production. *Prod* Euan Lloyd. *Exec Prod* Dimitri De Grunwald. *Assoc Prod* Hal Mason. *Dir* Edward Dmytryk. *Action Seq Dir* Bob Simmons. *Screenplay* J. J. Griffith, Hal Hopper, Scot Finch. *Screen Story* Clarke Reynolds. *Photog* Ted Moore. *2d Unit Photog* John Cabrera. *Art Dir* Herbert Smith. *Film Ed* Bill Blunden. *Mus Comp* Robert Farnon. *Cond* Muir Mathieson. *Titl Song* Jim Dale, mus. Robert Farnon. *Sd* Keith Palmer, George Stephenson. *Asst Dir* Peter Price, Joe Ochoa. *Prod Mgr* Ronnie Bear. *Cost* Cynthia Tingey. *Makeup* Trevor Crole-Rees, Pierre Berroyer. *Sp Eff* Michael Collins. *Tech Adv* Chief Elmer Smith, Rodd Redwing.

Cast: Sean Connery *(Shalako)*, Brigitte Bardot *(Countess Irina Lazaar)*, Stephen Boyd *(Bosky Fulton)*, Jack Hawkins *(Sir Charles Daggett)*, Peter Van Eyck *(Frederick von Hallstatt)*, Honor Blackman *(Lady Julia Daggett)*, Woody Strode *(Chato)*, Eric Sykes *(Mako)*, Alexander Knox *(Henry Clarke)*, Valerie French *(Elena Clarke)*, Julian Mateos *(Rojas)*, Donald Barry *(Buffalo)*, Rodd Redwing *(Chato's father)*, "Chief" Tug Smith *(Loco)*, Hans De Vries *(Hans)*, Walter Brown *(Pete Wells)*, Charles Stalnaker *(Marker)*, Bob Cunningham

(Luther), John Clarke *(Hockett)*, Bob Hall *(Johnson)*.

Western drama. *Source:* Louis L'Amour, *Shalako* (New York, 1962). In 1880, a party of European aristocrats on a hunting expedition arrives at an Apache reservation in New Mexico. Their "white hunter" guide, Bosky Fulton, knows that their presence violates a territorial treaty with the Indians. French Countess Irina Lazaar separates from the group to hunt for bigger game, is threatened by Indians, and is saved only by the appearance of Shalako, a former cavalry officer turned guide who has been sent by the Army to oust the intruders. The party's leader, Frederick von Hallstatt, refuses to heed the warning, a decision that results in an Apache raid. Shalako sends up smoke signals, and the Indians retreat before killing the Europeans; but Fulton takes off in the last remaining stagecoach with the ammunition, the supplies, and Lady Julia, the adulterous wife of Englishman Sir Charles Daggett. Shalako returns and rounds up the survivors, hoping to get them to the safety of the nearest fort. Meanwhile, the Apaches, led by Chato, the chief's son, attack the stagecoach and kill Lady Julia by forcing her to swallow her own diamonds. Fulton escapes and makes his way to Shalako's group, but he is shot dead by Daggett. Eventually, Chato demands a final test of strength by challenging Shalako to single combat with spears; but when Shalako gets the upper hand, the chief intervenes and orders his men to retreat in exchange for his son's life. Later, when the Europeans finally leave the reservation, Irina chooses to ride off with Shalako. *French. Aristocrats. Apache Indians. Guides. Infidelity. Survival. Murder. Filial relations. Treaties. Jewels. New Mexico. United States Army—Cavalry.*

Note: Location scenes filmed in Almería, Spain. Opened in London in Dec 1968.

SHAME (Sweden)   F6.4432

Svensk Filmindustri. *Dist* Lopert Pictures. 23 Dec **1968** [New York opening; c29 Sep 1968; LF58]. Sd; b&w. 35mm. 103 min. *MPAA rating* R.

Dir-Writ Ingmar Bergman. *Photog* Sven Nykvist. *Asst Photog* Roland Lundin, Nils Fogeby. *Art Dir* P. A. Lundgren, Lennart Blomkvist. *Film Ed* Ulla Ryghe. *Sd* Lennart Engholm, Bernth Frithiof. *Prod Supv* Lars-Owe Carlberg. *Cost* Mago. *Hairstyles & Wigs* Börje Lundh. *Sp Eff* Evald Andersson. *Military Adv* Stig Lindberg. *Prop* Karl-Arne Bergman.

Cast: Liv Ullmann *(Eva Rosenberg)*, Max von Sydow *(Jan Rosenberg)*, Gunnar Björnstrand *(Colonel Jacobi)*, Sigge Fürst *(Filip)*, Birgitta Valberg *(Mrs. Jacobi)*, Hans Alfredson *(Lobelius)*, Ingvar Kjellson *(Oswald)*, Raymond Lundberg *(Jacobi's son)*, Frank Sundström *(chief interrogator)*, Willy Peters *(elder officer)*, Ulf Johansson *(doctor)*, Axel Düberg *(pilot)*, Rune Lindström *(stout man)*, Bengt Eklund *(guard)*, Vilgot Sjöman *(interviewer)*, Lars Amble *(officer)*, Åke Jörnfalk *(condemned man)*, Björn Thambert *(Johan)*, Karl-Axel Forssberg *(secretary)*, Gösta Prüzelius *(rector)*, Brita Öberg *(woman in interrogation room)*, Agda Helin *(shopkeeper)*, Ellika Mann *(woman guard)*, Frej Lindqvist *(stooping man)*, Barbro Hiort af Ornäs *(woman on boat)*, Gregor Dahlman, Nils Whiten, Per Berglund, Stig Lindberg, Jan Bergman, Nils Fogeby, Brian Wikström, Börje Lundh, Georg Skarstedt, Lilian Carlsson, Eivor Kullberg, Karl-Arne Bergman, Monica Lindberg.

Drama. In 1971, Eva and Jan Rosenberg, concert violinists, take refuge on a remote island in the hope of avoiding the civil war raging across the bay on the mainland. Jan is exempt from military service because of a bad heart; and he and Eva are indifferent to the war's outcome. They earn a living by raising and selling lingonberries. A plane is shot down near the couple's farm, and hordes of soldiers from both armies overrun the island. After making a futile attempt to leave in their car, Jan and Eva are arrested on suspicion of collaboration and are subjected to an interview filmed for television, which is later dubbed over with political propaganda. Through the intervention of Colonel Jacobi, an old friend of the Rosenbergs who is a member of the army defending the island, they are eventually released. In return for his help, Jacobi, without Jan's knowledge, exacts a heavy price—sexual intimacy with Eva. By now almost repulsed by what she considers her husband's cowardice, Eva gives herself to Jacobi and in return receives a large sum of money. The next morning, after Jan has learned of Eva's unfaithfulness, a new squad of soldiers arrives and arrests Jacobi. He asks Jan to speak in his behalf; Jan refuses and puts up little resistance when ordered to shoot Jacobi. Taking flight following the destruction of their home, Jan and Eva encounter a trusting young soldier who tells them of a boat that is leaving for another island. In his determination to survive, Jan kills the soldier for his boots and forces Eva to accompany him to the boat landing. After paying their passage with the money Jacobi gave Eva, they join a group of passengers in the small craft and set out to sea. Scores of dead soldiers float in the water around the drifting boat, and as Eva looks at them, she recalls a dream in which, holding the child she never had, she saw a high wall covered with burning roses. On awakening, she kept thinking that she ought to remember something someone had once said—but she had forgotten what it was. *Violinists. Soldiers. Farmers. War victims. Combat zone life. Marriage. Infidelity. Cowardice. Perfidy. Survival. Murder. Childlessness. Death. Islands.*

Dreams.

Note: Opened in Stockholm in Sep 1968 as *Skammen.*

SHAME *see* THE INTRUDER

THE SHAME OF PATTY SMITH *see* THE CASE OF PATTY SMITH

THE SHAME OF THE SABINE WOMEN (Mexico)   F6.4433

Constelación. *Dist* United Producers Releasing Organization. 5 Sep **1962** [Hartford, Connecticut, opening]. Sd; col (Eastman Color). 35mm. 80 min.

Prod-Dir-Writ Alberto Gout. *Exec Prod* Frank Oliver. *Photog* Alex Phillips. *Art Dir* John Albert. *Film Ed* Jorge Bustos, John F. Link. *Mus* Gustavo César Carrión. *Unit Mgr* Luis Urquidi.

Cast: Lex Johnson (*Hostes*), Lorena Doudé (*Hersilia*), Teresa Doudé (*Rhea*), William Wolf (*Romulus*), Luis Induni (*Titus Tatius*), John Monfort (*Acron*), Joan Crespi (*Egea*), C. Jimerson (*rebel woman*), Leandro Vizcaino.

Action melodrama. Romulus and his twin brother, Remus, compete for the leadership of Rome. After murdering his brother, Romulus assumes complete control of the city and promises the citizens a happy life. Since the entire population of the new city is male, Romulus sends Hostes to ask the neighboring Sabine women to become Roman wives. The offer is rejected, however, and Romulus devises a plan to trick the women into coming to Rome; they are invited to a fair and, upon arriving, are forced into marrying the Romans. Romulus marries the Sabine king's daughter Hersilia, and Hostes marries Hersilia's younger sister, Rhea. Titus Tatius, king of the Sabines, plots revenge, and after 2 years of building an army, the Sabines march into Rome. The bloody battle is stopped by the Sabine women, who reveal that they have grown to love their Roman captors and now fight along with their husbands to repel the onslaught. *Brothers. Royalty. Sabines. Sisters. Fratricide. Perfidy. Abduction. Marriage. Revenge. Rome. Romulus. Remus.*

Note: Produced in 1958 as *El rapto de las sabinas.* Alternative title: *The Mating of the Sabine Women.* Also known as *The Rape of the Sabines*; an Italian film of the same title was not released in the United States during the 1960's. Frank Oliver is a pseudonym for Francisco Olivos del Valle.

SHAME, SHAME, EVERYBODY KNOWS HER NAME   F6.4434

Dist Distribpix, Inc., J. E. R. Pictures. 7 Oct **1969.** Sd; b&w. 35mm. 79 min. *MPAA rating* R.

Prod-Dir-Orig Story Joseph Jacoby. *Screenplay* William Dorsey Blake. *Cinematog* Stephen R. Winsten. *Adtl Photog* Paul Goldsmith. *Asst Camera Op* James Hudson. *Film Ed* Kemper Peacock. *Mus* George Craig. *Sd Rec* John Fodor. *Prod Mgr* Gary Posner. *Asst to the Prod* John Fowler. *Cont* Susan Riva.

Cast: Karen Carlson (*Susan Barton*), Getti Miller (*Diane Rogers*), Augustus Sultatos (*Vic Keller*), Tony Seville (*Tony Martinelli*), Rita Bennett (*Go-go dancer*), Dennis Johnson (*Roy Davenport*), Tyrus Cheney (*General Motley*), John Harrison, actor (*George Michaels*), Vic Vallaro (*Jim Norton*), Karil Daniels (*Carol Taggart*), John Cardoza (*photographer*), Stuart Coffee (*Marvin Witherspoon*).

Melodrama. Susan Barton arrives in New York City from Dayton, finds work as a go-go dancer, and takes an apartment with Diane Rogers. To meet eligible men, Susan joins a dating service operated by Vic Keller. Diane, a lesbian, arranges with Keller to introduce Susan to a number of undesirable men, hoping thereby to persuade Susan to come to her for affection. Susan's first date, public relations man Roy Davenport, treats her to an evening out, and later he easily seduces her in his apartment. But Susan quickly changes her mood when Davenport tries to switch places with his client, General Motley, to whom he has promised a night's entertainment. George Michaels, Susan's second date, approaches her without revealing that he came by way of Keller; he seduces her and is rejected when he brings in a friend to photograph their lovemaking. Distraught, Susan retreats to Diane for solace, still ignorant of Diane's intention that Susan give up men. Diane and Keller arrange another date for Susan. Their plans go awry, however, when Susan leaves a wild party with antique dealer Jim Norton. Keller knows that Norton is dangerously disturbed, and he and Diane search for Susan. They find her, chained to a chair, the object of Norton's sadism. Norton is killed in the struggle, and it appears that Susan will finally be receptive to Diane's sexual offer. *Innocents. Roommates. Go-go dancers. Seduction. Lesbianism. Voyeurism. Sadism. Murder. Computer dating services. Photography. New York City.*

SHAMEFUL *see* BLACK ON WHITE

THE SHAMELESS   F6.4435

Jay Martin Productions. *Dist* Joseph Brenner Associates. 17 May **1962.** Sd; col. 35mm. 66 min.

Overall Production Staff: *Prod-Dir* Jay Martin. *Assoc Prod* George Rodman. *Story-Screenplay* William L. Rose. *Camera* Phillip Rossi. *Set Dsgn* Ken Sugiura. *Film Ed* Lawrence Mosher. *Mus Score* Cinemascores. *Rec* Jonathon Robert. *Asst Dir* Michael James. *Prod Mgr* Armand Dussault. *Prop Mgr* Charles Connolly.

Danish Production Staff: *Dir Photog* I. Shacke-Moller. *Asst Camera* Carl Lund. *Prod Mgr* Nils Sorenson.

German Production Staff: *Dir Photog* Heinz Koestler. *Asst Camera* Lester Berman. *Prod Mgr* Otto Schell.

French Production Staff: *Dir Photog* Charles Bernet. *Asst Camera* Paul Levin. *Prod Mgr* Henry Weyman.

Cast: Dori Davis, Sheila Gilliam, Jay Martin, Elga Jensen, Heidi Lottman, Marie Buchner.

Drama. Dashing private detective Robert Sanford undertakes a missing persons case he calls "The Naked Search." Commissioned by Barbara Whiting, Sanford must locate Barbara's sister Geraldine within a month's time; otherwise, their father's legacy will go to the "Solar Research Society." Sanford learns that the two were separated as youngsters when their parents divorced, and that Geraldine may have been influenced by her mother's interest in nudism. He follows the postmark on some recent correspondence to nudist camp Sunny Forest Park in rural Pennsylvania, and there he interviews owner Marilyn Crane, who remembers "Gerri" and shows Sanford a letter from the missing woman in which she registered her intention to tour nudist camps in Europe and Japan. Sanford departs for the Continent and travels from one nudist camp to another, through Denmark, Germany, and France, but he finds no information concerning Geraldine's whereabouts. Arriving at the famous Île du Levant, he finds a hotel owner who has a letter in Geraldine's handwriting but the letter bears Marilyn Crane's signature. He returns and confronts Marilyn, who explains that she hoped to obtain the entire inheritance for the Solar Research Society, actually a nudist group. Barbara, however, also reveals herself to be a nudist, and together the sisters fashion a nudists' paradise at Sunny Forest. *Detectives. Missing persons. Sisters. Nudism. Inheritance. Impersonation. Nudist camps. Documentation. Denmark. Federal Republic of Germany. France. Île du Levant.*

Note: Filmed on location at nudist parks in Denmark; Hamburg, Germany; the Île du Levant, Pampelonne, and St. Tropez, France. Sunny Forest Park sequences filmed at Sunny Rest Lodge, Palmerton, Pennsylvania. Film may also be known as *The Naked Search.* It was rereleased as *The Barest Heiress* in 1964.

SHAMELESS DESIRE   F6.4436

Midas Films. *Dist* Sack Amusement Enterprises, Trans-oceanic Films. 20 Jun **1967** [Maryland license; Fresno, California, showing: 1 Nov]. Sd; b&w. 35mm. 74 min.

Prod James Sadim. *Dir* Serge Bronislau. *Screenplay* Glenda A. Smythe. *Dir Photog* Ken Woods. *Camera* Ralph Alcott. *Ed* Jerry Carroway. *Orig Mus* Gay Fellowman. *Cont* Phyllis Jones. *Wardrobe* Idel Leon. *Makeup* Jan Woodard. *Dial Dir* Burton Ames.

Cast: Marty Kim, Bill Thurman, Laurel Lynn, Douglas Mann, Trey Howard, Ron Scott, Pat Adams, Byron Lord, Tiffany Sawyer, Barry Hope, Anne MacAdams.

Melodrama. Chris, a licentious exotic dancer, and her lovely roommate, Cathy, spend a weekend at Cal's fishing lodge in the Louisiana bayou. Chris hopes to patch up her relationship with Cal, who left her because of her participation in an orgy. To her dismay, Cal orders her to leave the next day. That night in the lodge bar, Chris picks up two men in the hopes of making Cal jealous, and when he does not react, she performs an erotic dance. Cal stops the dance and a brawl ensues. Cal then goes to Chris's room to force her to leave, but she succeeds in arousing his desire, and they make love. Their passion is secretly observed by Bruno, who is Cal's moronic and voyeuristic handyman. The next day the women persuade Bruno to take them for a ride through the swamps, and when they stop on an isolated island, Chris plies Bruno with liquor and entices him until he rapes and murders her. He then abducts the terrified Cathy. Cal rounds up a posse to find the demented Bruno and the two missing women. *Exotic dancers. Roommates. Handymen. Teases. Halfwits. Murder. Rape. Voyeurism. Exhibitionism. Abduction. Drunkenness. Swamps. Louisiana.*

Note: Also known as *Shameless Desires.*

THE SHAMELESS OLD LADY (France)   F6.4437

S. P. A. C.–Cinéma. *Dist* Continental Distributing, Inc. 26 Sep **1966** [New York opening]. Sd; b&w. 35mm. 95 min.

Prod Claude Nedjar. *Dir-Screenplay-Adapt-Dial* René Allio. *Photog* Denys Clerval. *Camera Op* Raymond Sauvaire. *Art Dir* Hubert Monloup. *Film Ed* Sophie Coussein. *Songs:* "On ne voit pas le temps passer," "Loin," "Tu m'as jamais quitté" *writ & sung by* Jean Ferrat. *Sd* Antoine Bonfanti. *Asst Dir* Jean Michaud. *Prod Mgr* Maurice Urbain. *Tech Adv* Jean Ravel.

Cast: Sylvie (*Madame Berthe*), Malka Ribovska (*Rosalie*), Victor Lanoux (*Pierre*), Étienne Bierry (*Albert*), François Maistre (*Gaston*), Pascale de Boysson (*Simone*), Léna Delanne (*Victoire*), Jeanne Hardeyn (*Rose*), Jean-Louis Lamande (*Charles*), Robert Bousquet (*Robert*), André Jourdan (*Lucien*), Armand Meffre (*Ernest*), Pierre Decazes (*Charlot*), Jean Bouise (*Alphonse*),

André Thorent (*Dufour*), Max Amyl, Emmanuelle Drey.

Comedy-drama. Source: Bertolt Brecht, "Die unwürdige Greisin," in *Kalendergeschichten* (Berlin, 1948). Madame Berthe is 70 years old when her husband dies. All of her life has been spent in a small village on the outskirts of Marseilles where she has raised her five children and helped her husband run his modest business. Following their father's funeral, the children hold a meeting to decide what to do with the old woman. To their surprise, Madame Berthe decides to live alone on a small pension to be provided by her children. She salvages what she can from her husband's bankrupt business but soon finds that she is no longer content with the routine of her drab and uneventful life. Filled with curiosity about the world she has never known, she sells what few valuables she owns and delights in visiting department stores, where she discovers ice cream sundaes. Although her behavior irritates and baffles her family, it wins her the affection and friendship of Rosalie, a young waitress and part-time prostitute, and Alphonse, an anarchistic shoemaker who dreams of owning his own shop. Madame Berthe's grandson Pierre visits her on behalf of his scandalized father but grows sympathetic to the old woman; he, too, would like to break away from the family business to play guitar in a band. Soon, Pierre embarks on an affair with Rosalie. One day, to the astonishment of all, Madame Berthe takes the last of her meager inheritance, buys a second-hand car, and goes off on a vacation with Rosalie. Shortly after their return, she buys a small shop for Alphonse and gives the car to Rosalie, who leaves Pierre with photographs of the trip. Having lived a whole new life in 18 months, the old woman then peacefully dies. *Widows. Waitresses. Prostitutes. Cobblers. Anarchists. Nonconformists. Grandmothers. Old age. Village life. Finance—Personal. Inheritance. Filial relations. Funerals. Automobiles. Vacations. Marseilles.*

Note: Opened in Paris in Mar 1965 as *La vieille dame indigne*; running time: 90 min.

SHAN-KO LIEN *see* THE SHEPHERD GIRL

SHANGRI-LA   F6.4438

Shangri-La Productions. *Dist* Joseph Brenner Associates. Mar **1961** [Los Angeles showing: 1 Sep]. Sd; col (Eastmancolor). 35mm. 63 min.

Prod Dick Randall. *Sp Photog* Weegee.

Cast: Sammy Petrillo, Pamela Perry, Harold Gary.

Comedy. Sammy, a zoo keeper, tells his pal, Jim, about his vacation when he followed two young women to a resort; to Washington, D. C.; to Silver Springs, Florida; and finally to a nature park called Camp Shangri-La. There he serves as a master of ceremonies in a beauty competition before being expelled from the camp for violating rules. Sammy's story of his vacation convinces Jim to embark on a similar trek. *Zoo keepers. Vacations. Resorts. Nudist camps. Beauty contests. Washington (District of Columbia). Silver Springs (Florida).*

SHANNON'S WOMEN   F6.4439

Voyage Productions. *Dist* Lima Productions, Distribpix, Inc. 17 Sep **1969** [New York showing]. Sd; b&w. 35mm. 85 min.

Exec Prod Frank Franz. *Dir* William Rotsler. *Dir Photog* Dwayne Rayven. *Asst Camera* Orrin Sackett. *Lighting* Art Grennell. *Art Dir* Brill Wilson. *Film Ed* William Rotsler. *Sd* Commercial Sound Recorders. *Location Rec* Paul Turner. *Prod Mgr* James Brand. *Cont* Lora Collins. *Cost* Earl Sheriff. *Opticals* Neuron Illusions Inc. *Head Grip* Travis MacDonald.

Cast: Kathleen Williams, Shannon Carse, Pat Barrington, Christine Thomas, Mary Warner, Cher Carr, James Brand, Orlando Fenwick, Owen Hannifen, Vic Lance, Paul Kimball, Dee Howard, Pat Davis, John Seville, Karen Swanson, Susan Webbert.

Drama. Shannon, a Hollywood sex exploitation film director who uses his position to exploit actresses sexually, falls in love with Kathy, the star of his current film. Kathy reciprocates his affection, but she leaves in a rage when she finds him seducing another actress in precisely the same manner as he seduced her. Shannon recalls former love affairs, but he is unable to forget Kathy, and he finally realizes that he truly loves her. *Motion picture directors. Actors. Employer-employee relations. Seduction. Jealousy. Group sex. Sex exploitation films. Hollywood.*

Note: Also known as *Love, Hollywood Style.*

SHANTY TRAMP   F6.4440

Dist Trans-International Films. 21 Jun **1967** [Buffalo, New York, opening]. Sd; b&w. 35mm. 72 min.

Prod K. Gordon Murray. *Dir* Joseph Prieto. *Screenplay* Reuben Guberman. *Photog* J. R. Remy.

Cast: Lee Holland, Bill Rogers, Lawrence Tobin.

Melodrama. A sharecropper's daughter who makes herself available to the male citizens of a southern town tries to add a revival preacher to her conquests. She subsequently becomes attracted to the leader of a motorcycle gang, but he threatens to disfigure her when she rejects him for refusing to pay for her favors.

A black youth saves her from the motorcyclist, and her father accuses the youth of raping his daughter. The sheriff's posse sets out to find him; he steals a car from a moonshiner in an attempt to escape and dies in a crash. The father and daughter argue, and the daughter stabs her father to death. Afterwards, she goes to the preacher and asks him to take her with him to the next town. *Farmers. Prostitutes. Preachers. Motorcycle gangs. Negroes. Sheriffs. Moonshiners. Filial relations. Frameup. Rape. Patricide. United States—South. Automobile accidents.*

Note: Filmed in Florida.

THE SHARE OUT (Great Britain)   F6.4441

Merton Park Studios. *Dist* Schoenfeld Film Distributing Corp. 13 Apr **1966** [Bay Shore, New York, opening]. Sd; b&w. 35mm. 61 min.

Prod Jack Greenwood. *Dir* Gerard Glaister. *Screenplay* Philip Mackie. *Dir Photog* Bert Mason. *Camera Op* Herbert R. Smith. *1st Camera Asst* Alan Rowland. *Art Dir* Peter Mullins. *Film Ed* Bernard Gribble. *Mus Dir* Bernard Ebbinghouse. *Sd Rec* Sidney Rider. *Boom Op* Tom Otter. *Sd Camera Op* Robin Clare. *1st, 2d & 3d Asst Dir* Ted Lewis, Al Burgess, Deh-Ta Hsiung. *Unit Prod Mgr* Joe Levy. *Prod Sec* Ann Stanborough. *Cont* Marjorie Owens. *Wardrobe Mistress* Eileen Welch. *Makeup* Aldo Manganaro. *Hairdresser* Hilda Fox. *Still Photog* Eddie Orton. *Casting Dir* Ronald Curtis. *Ch Electrn* Jim Axtell. *Prop Master* Ted Waters. *Constr Mgr* Eddie Turner. *Grip* Bert Habicht.

Cast: Bernard Lee (*Detective Superintendent Meredith*), Alexander Knox (*Colonel Calderwood*), Moira Redmond (*Diana Marsh*), William Russell, British (*Mike Stafford*), Richard Vernon (*John Crewe*), Richard Warner (*Mark Speller*), John Gabriel (*Monet*), Jack Rodney (*Gregory*), Stanley Morgan (*Detective Sergeant Anson*), Robert Percival (*Britton*), Ann Harriman (*receptionist*), Julie Shearing (*Judy*), Fanny Carby (*Mrs. Wall*), Ian Hamilton (*waiter*), Walter Horsbrugh (*registrar*).

Crime melodrama. Source: Edgar Wallace, *Jack o' Judgment* (London, 1920). To clear his police record, private detective Mike Stafford agrees to help Scotland Yard's Detective Superintendent Meredith with a murder probe. Mike infiltrates a property company used by archvillain Colonel Calderwood as a front for blackmail. Calderwood hires the private investigator to spy on Diana, the racket's secretary. Another gang member is murdered, and the others are suspect. Mike becomes infatuated with Diana. Calderwood shoots his associate, John Crewe, whereupon Mike kills Calderwood. The blackmail ring is exposed, and Diana and Mike plan to marry and leave the country, but police find diamonds in their luggage. Meredith arrests them for plotting the murders and attempting to abscond with the gang's cache of diamonds. *Detectives. Police. Racketeers. Secretaries. Murder. Blackmail. Duplicity. Conspiracy. Theft. Diamonds. Scotland Yard.*

Note: Released in Great Britain in Apr 1962. Also known as *The Shareout*.

SHARK! (United States/Mexico)   F6.4442

Heritage Enterprises–Cinematográfica Calderón. *Dist* Excelsior Distributing Co. 8 Oct **1969** [San Francisco opening]. Sd; col (Eastman Color). 35mm. 92 min. *MPAA rating* M.

Prod Skip Steloff, Marc Cooper, José Luis Calderón. *Dir* Samuel Fuller, Rafael Portillo. *Screenplay* Samuel Fuller, John Kingsbridge. *Photog* Raúl Martínez Solares. *Art Dir* Manuel Fontanals. *Film Ed* Carlos Savage. *Mus* Carlos Moroyoqui. *Sd* Manuel Topete.

Cast: Burt Reynolds (*Caine*), Barry Sullivan (*Mallare*), Arthur Kennedy (*Doc*), Silvia Pinal (*Anna*), Enrique Lucero (*Barok*), Carlos Berriochoa (*Smoky*), Manuel Alvarado (*Latalla*), Emilia Stuart (*Asha*).

Action drama. Source: Victor Canning, *His Bones Are Coral* (London, 1955). Caine, an American, arrives in a small town in the Sudan after fleeing from Sudanese soldiers who almost caught him with a truckload of illegal arms. Caine meets Doc, an American alcoholic, who informs him that he is being closely watched by police chief Barok and that his only means of escape is by boat. Anna and Dr. Mallare, owners of a boat, enlist Caine's help in what is purported to be an expedition to collect fish specimens. When Caine learns of their interest in a sunken merchant ship which holds $2 million worth of gold bullion, he forcefully informs Mallare that they are now partners. The next day Caine and Mallare cut through the ship's hull. While transferring the bullion to the boat, Anna baits the sharks with bloody pieces of fish. Mallare is killed, but Caine escapes and knocks Anna unconscious. Police chief Barok arrives and attempts to steal the gold from Caine, but Caine hurls him into the shark-infested waters. Anna revives, orders Caine onto the police launch, and takes off in her boat without knowing that the ballast valves are open and the ship will sink. *Americans in foreign countries. Soldiers. Police. Fortune hunters. Divers. Murder. Greed. Perfidy. Merchant ships. Gold. Sudan. Sharks.*

Note: Location scenes filmed in Veracruz, Manzanillo, Mexico City, Acapulco, and the Sudan. Released in Mexico as *Un arma de dos filos* in Oct 1969. Working title: *Caine*.

SHATTERHAND (France/Italy/West Germany/Yugoslavia)   **F6.4443**
CCC-Filmkunst–Avala Film–Critérion Film–Serena Film. *Dist* Goldstone
Film Enterprises. Oct **1967** [Los Angeles showing]. Sd; col (Eastmancolor).
35mm (CinemaScope [see note]). 89 min.
   Pres by Don Kay Associates. *Exec Prod* Georg M. Reuther. *Dir* Hugo
Fregonese. *Screenplay* Robert A. Stemmle, Ladislaus Fodor. *Photog* Siegfried
Hold. *Camera Op* Richard Reuven Rimmel. *Art Dir* Otto Pischinger. *Film Ed*
Alfred Srp. *Mus* Riz Ortolani. *Asst Dir* Hertha Friedl. *Prod Supv* Artur
Brauner. *Prod Mgr* Manfred Korytowski, Manfred Dölle. *Makeup* Raimund
Stangl.
   Cast: Lex Barker (*Old Shatterhand*), Pierre Brice (*Winnetou*), Daliah Lavi
(*Paloma*), Guy Madison (*Captain Bradley*), Ralf Wolter (*Sam Hawkins*),
Gustavo Rojo (*Bush*), Rick Battaglia (*Dixon*), Kitti Mattern (*Rosemary*), Alain
Tissier (*Tujunga*), Charles Fawcett (*General Taylor*), Nikola Popović (*Sheriff
Brandon*), Mirko Ellis (*Joe Barker*), Bill Ramsey (*Timpe*), Burschi Putzgruber
(*Tom*), James Burk.
   Western drama. Based on the characters created by: Karl Friedrich May.
Following General Taylor's departure for Washington, white renegades and
their Comanche minions, posing as Apaches, attack small ranches. By such
means the whites hope to discredit the Apaches and secure for themselves the
rich Indian pastures. Tom, a witness to the bogus raids, and Paloma, a halfbreed,
are escorted by Old Shatterhand to a wagon train commanded by cavalry
Captain Bradley. The train is later attacked, and two Apaches are killed.
Sensing treachery, Shatterhand consults Apache chief Winnetou, his blood
brother. When Tom is slain, Shatterhand concludes that Bradley has instigated
the hoax. Tujunga, Winnetou's son, is imprisoned as a murder suspect by
Bradley. Despite his son's presence, Winnetou attacks the fort when
Shatterhand is taken prisoner. During the battle, many die, including Tujunga,
who explodes the store of ammunition. The fighting is interrupted by the return
of General Taylor, who arrests Captain Bradley and announces conclusion of
a peace treaty between the Apaches and the federal government. *Halfcastes.
Apache Indians. Comanche Indians. Blood brothers. Perfidy. Abduction.
Frameup. Wagon trains. Forts. Treaties. United States Army—Cavalry.
Explosions. Winnetou.*
   Note: Location scenes filmed in Yugoslavia. Released in West Germany in
1964 as *Old Shatterhand* at 122 min; in Yugoslavia in 1965 as *Old Šeterhend*
at 117 min; in Italy as *La battaglia di Fort Apache*; in France in 1965 as *Les
cavaliers rouges* at 112 min. Filmed in 70mm Superpanorama.

SHE (Great Britain)   **F6.4444**
Hammer Film Productions—Seven Arts Productions. *For* Associated
British-Pathé, Ltd. *Dist* Metro-Goldwyn-Mayer, Inc. 9 Jun **1965** [Chicago
opening; c24 Mar 1965; LP31101]. Sd; col (Technicolor). 35mm
(CinemaScope). 106 min.
   Prod Michael Carreras. *Assoc Prod* Aida Young. *Dir* Robert Day.
Screenplay David T. Chantler. *Photog* Harry Waxman. *Art Dir* Robert Jones,
Don Mingaye. *Ed Supv* James Needs. *Film Ed* Eric Boyd-Perkins. *Mus Supv*
Philip Martell. *Mus Comp* James Bernard. *Choreog* Christine Lawson. *Sd* Jim
Groom, Vernon Messenger. *Sd Rec* Claude Hitchcock. *Asst Dir* Bruce
Sharman. *Cost* Carl Toms. Roy Ashton. *Sp Eff* George Blackwell, Bowie Films.
   Cast: Ursula Andress (*Ayesha*), John Richardson (*Leo Vincey*), Peter
Cushing (*Major Holly*), Bernard Cribbins (*Job*), Rosenda Monteros (*Ustane*),
Christopher Lee (*Billali*), André Morell (*Haumeid*), John Maxim (*captain of
the guard*).
   Costume melodrama. Source: H. Rider Haggard, *She, a History of
Adventure* (London, 1887). While celebrating the end of World War I in a
Jerusalem nightclub, Leo meets Ustane, a halfcaste slave who lures him into a
meeting with the beautiful Ayesha. Ayesha promises him wealth and power if
he will come with her to the mountain city of Kuma, and she gives him a map
and a ring. Major Holly, Leo's friend, identifies the ring as a 2,000-year-old
Egyptian relic, and the map is revealed to be the key to the lost city of Kuma.
Leo, Holly, and their orderly Job set out into the desert in search of the
Mountains of the Moon. Ustane, who has fallen in love with Leo, leads him to
the village of the Amahaggers where Ayesha's slaves are ruled by Ustane's
father, Haumeid. When the white men are about to be sacrificed, Billali, the
high priest, intervenes and brings Leo to Queen Ayesha. Ayesha explains that
she has ruled for 2,000 years and claims that Leo is the reincarnation of her
lover, Killikrates, whom she murdered out of jealousy. Unable to resist her, Leo
follows her into the flame of eternal youth, but because the flame can only be
entered once, Ayesha disintegrates into ash. Holly and Job depart, knowing that
Leo will have to wait another 2,000 years before the blue flame reappears and
releases him from immortality. *Halfcastes. Priests. Royalty. Slavery. Wealth.
Human sacrifice. Reincarnation. Murder. Jealousy. Immortality. Nightclubs.
Deserts. Jerusalem. Documentation. Fires.*
   Note: Location scenes filmed in Israel. Opened in London in Apr 1965.
Haggard's novel has been filmed several times, and this version is followed by
a sequel, *Vengeance of She*, q. v.

SHE AND HE (Japan)   **F6.4445**
Iwanami Productions–Eizo–Sha Co. *Dist* Brandon Films. Jun **1967**. Sd;
b&w. 35mm. 110 min.
   Dir Susumu Hani. *Screenplay* Susumu Hani, Kunio Shimizu. *Photog* Juichi
Nagano. *Mus* Toru Takemitsu. *Sd* Tetsuo Yasuda.
   Cast: Sachiko Hidari (*Naoko*), Eiji Okada (*Eiichi*), Kikuji Yamashita
(*Ikona*), Mariko Igarashi (*Hanako*), Akio Hasegawa (*laundry boy*), Takanobu
Hobuzi (*doctor*), Kuma (*himself, a dog*).
   Melodrama. Naoko and her husband, Eiichi, live in a modern housing
development near Tokyo. One night they are awakened by a nearby fire which
destroys some of the shacks inhabited by a group of ragpickers. The next
morning Naoko explores the ruins and finds herself fascinated by the poverty
that is so different from her own lifestyle. She discovers that Ikona, a ragpicker,
was one of her husband's college classmates, and she invites him to her home.
The following day a trophy belonging to Eiichi is missing, and it is apparent that
it was stolen by Ikona. Although Eiichi is angry, he yields to his wife's pleas
and offers the ragpicker a job, which he refuses. A short time later, while Eiichi
is away on business, Naoko learns that Ikona's friend Hanako, a little blind girl,
is ill, and she takes the child home to look after her. When Eiichi returns, he
berates his wife for jeopardizing their social position and sends the little girl to
a charity hospital. As the shacks are being torn down to make room for a golf
course, a group of boys from the development steal Ikona's dog. Naoko joins
Ikona in the search for his pet, and they find it dying at the bottom of a dry
well. Ikona picks up the dog and walks away. After learning that Ikona has
taken the blind girl out of the hospital, Naoko lies awake at night, imagining
that she still hears the sound of Ikona's dog barking. *Middle classes. Poverty.
Charity. Blindness. Theft. Social consciousness. Slums. Tokyo. Fires. Dogs.*
   Note: Released in Japan in 1963 as *Kanojo to kare*; running time: 115 min.

THE SHE BEAST (Great Britain/Italy)   **F6.4446**
Leith Productions. *Dist* Europix-Consolidated Corp. 2 May **1966** [Atlanta
opening]. Sd; col (Eastmancolor). 35mm (Cromoscope). 74 min.
   Prod Paul Maslansky. *Dir* Michael Reeves. *2d Unit Dir* Charles Griffith.
Screenplay Michael Byron, writ. *Photog* Amerigo Gengarelli. *Film Ed* Nira
Omri. *Mus* Ralph Ferraro. *Sd* Lars Bloch.
   Cast: Barbara Steele (*Veronica/Vardella*), Ian Ogilvy (*Philip*), John Karlsen
(*Count von Helsing*), Mel Welles, Jay Riley, Richard Watson, Ed Randolph.
   Horror film. While honeymooning near a village in Transylvania, Philip and
Veronica, a young English couple, have an accident which plunges their car into
a lake. Veronica is rescued, but she has been possessed by the spirit of Vardella,
a witch who was impaled on a stake and dropped into the lake 200 years before.
Count von Helsing explains to the distraught Philip that the only way to get
his wife back is to exorcise the vengeful witch. Although Vardella escapes and
rampages through the village, she is eventually captured, exorcised, and thrown
back into the lake. After her death Veronica reappears, apparently unaware of
the terrible experience. *Witches. Nobility. Exorcism. Revenge. Murder.
Reviviscence. Honeymoons. Transylvania. Automobile accidents.*
   Note: Opened in Rome in Jul 1967 as *Il lago di Satana*; running time: 100
min; released in Great Britain in 1966 as *The Revenge of the Blood Beast*;
running time: 76 min. Alternative Italian title: *La sorella di Satana*. Sources
conflict in crediting country of origin.

SHE CAME ON THE BUS   **F6.4447**
Dist American Film Distributing Corp. 2 Jul **1969** [Boston opening]. Sd;
b&w. 35mm. 63 min.
   Dir-Writ Curt Ledger.
   Cast: Jackie Richards, Kim Lewis.
   Crime melodrama. A sadistic group of toughs and their sex-hungry female
companions invade a suburban home and attack, torture, and rob a young
housewife. They then hitch a ride on a large cross-country bus. After killing the
driver, they proceed to terrorize and abuse the passengers. Two young women
who unwittingly board the bus for a short trip to town become victims of the
group's sadistic sexual practices. *Gangs. Housewives. Hitchhikers. Sadism.
Torture. Robbery. Murder. Rape. Buses.*
   Note: Also known as *She Came by Bus* and *The Sick Ones*.

SHE-DEVILS ON WHEELS   **F6.4448**
Creative Film Enterprises. *Dist* Mayflower Pictures. 7 May **1968** [Maryland
license; c29 May 1968; LP35737]. Sd; col (Eastmancolor). 35mm. 83 min.
   Prod-Dir Herschell Gordon Lewis. *Exec Prod* Fred M. Sandy. *Orig
Screenplay* Louise Downe. *Camera Op* Roy Collodi. *2d Unit Camera* Eskandar
Ameripoor. *Set Dsgn* Robert Enrietto. *Ed Supv* Richard Brinkman.
Background Mus Larry Wellington. *Song:* "Get Off the Road" Sheldon
Seymour. *Mus* Robert Lewis. *Sd Rec* Spyridon Horiatis. *Asst to Prod* J. G.
Patterson, Jr.

Cast: Betty Connell *(Queen)*, Pat Poston *(Whitey)*, Nancy Lee Noble *(Honey-Pot)*, Christie Wagner *(Karen)*, Rodney Bedell *(Ted)*, Ruby Tuesday *(Terry)*, Joani Kramer *(Russian)*, David Harris *(Bill)*, Donna Testa *(Poodle)*, Laura Platz *(Supergirl)*, John Weymer *(Joe-Boy)*, Steve White *(Doodie)*, Roy Collodi *(bartender)*, Rick Williams *(outlaw)*, Donna Stelzer *(Mac)*, John Shackleford, John Chaffin *(police)*.

Melodrama. A gang of female motorcyclists known as the Man-Eaters stage their weekly cycle race on an abandoned airport runway. Karen, whose demeanor away from the group is quiet and reserved, wins the race, defeating Queen, the group's leader, and Whitey, an immense, brutal woman. The women choose sexual playthings from among a group of male followers, the "stud-line," and Karen, who generally wins the right to choose first, inevitably selects Bill. Queen becomes resentful and presents Karen with an ultimatum: she must either drag Bill, who has been tied and beaten, around the track behind her cycle, or be expelled from the gang. Karen, in tears, chooses the first alternative, and Bill is killed. After the orgy initiation of Honey-Pot, the favorite among the gang members, the women go to the airstrip and find a group of hot rodders encroaching on their territory. A bloody battle ensues; the Man-Eaters emerge victorious, and Joe-Boy, the leader of the men's gang, vows revenge. Karen's decent boyfriend, Ted, tries to persuade her to leave the gang before it is too late, but she refuses. Joe-Boy and his gang initiate their revenge by kidnaping and beating Honey-Pot, whom they then return to her companions with a threatening note attached to a ring through her nose. Queen and Whitey launch a counterattack which culminates in the decapitation of Joe-Boy. The gang members are arrested for the murder, but they are released because of a lack of evidence and continue on their path of terror and destruction. *Motorcycle gangs. Gangs. Motorcycle racing. Automobile racing. Revenge. Kidnaping. Sadism. Murder. Group sex. Decapitation.*

SHE DID IT HIS WAY!　　　　　　　　　　　F6.4449
Dist Art Films International. 18 Sep **1968** [Baltimore opening]. Sd; col. 35mm. 70 min.

Prod John Lamb. *Dir* Ronald Graham. *Writ* Joseph Webber.

Cast: Kellie Everts.

Documentary(?). The intimate life of Kellie Everts, "Miss Nude Universe," is revealed by hidden cameras that capture the close physical examinations to which the contestants must submit; actual footage of the "Miss Nude Universe" contest; the uninhibited victory celebration; and scenes of Kellie's secret love life. *Nudity. Beauty contests.*

SHE DIDN'T SAY NO! *(Great Britain)*　　　F6.4450
Associated British-Pathé, Ltd. *Dist* Seven Arts Associated Corp. 28 Mar **1962** [Philadelphia opening]. Sd; col (Technicolor). 35mm. 96 min.

A Sergei Nolbandov Production. *Prod* Sergei Nolbandov. *Exec Prod* Josef Somlo. *Dir* Cyril Frankel. *Screenplay* T. J. Morrison, Una Troy. *Scen Ed* Frederick Gotfurt. *Dir Photog* Gilbert Taylor. *Prod Dsgn* William Kellner. *Film Ed* Charles Hasse. *Mus* Tristram Cary. *Sd Rec* Len Shilton, Leslie Hammond. *Prod Mgr* Victor Peck. *Casting Dir* Robert Lennard.

Cast: Eileen Herlie *(Bridget Monaghan)*, Perlita Nielson *(Mary Monaghan)*, Wilfred Downing *(Tommy Monaghan)*, Ann Dickins *(Poppy Monaghan)*, Teresa Scobie, Leslie Scobie *(The Twins)*, Raymond Manthorpe *(Toughy Monaghan)*, Niall MacGinnis *(Jamesy Casey)*, Patrick McAlinney *(Matthew Hogan)*, Jack MacGowran *(William Bates)*, Joan O'Hara *(Mrs. Bates)*, Ray McAnally *(Jim Power)*, Betty McDowall *(Mrs. Power)*, Ian Bannen *(Peter Howard)*, Eithne Dunne *(Miss Hogan)*, Hilton Edwards *(The Film Director)*, Maureen Halligan *(Miss Kelly)*, Harry Hutchinson *(The Judge)*, Paul Farrell *(Darmody)*, Shirley Joy *(Maybella Merton)*, Viola Keats *(Mrs. Merton)*, Anna Manahan *(Maggie Murphy)*, Michael O'Briain *(The Sergeant)*, Liam Redmond *(Doctor Cassidy)*, John Welsh *(The Inspector)*.

Comedy. Source: Una Troy, *We Are Seven* (New York, 1957). Bridget Monaghan, a dressmaker, is the mother of six illegitimate children and an embarrassment to the small Irish farming district where she lives. Provoked by his wife into doing something about Bridget, William Bates, the father of Bridget's twins, calls a meeting of the other fathers of the village who were Bridget's lovers: Jamesy Casey, father of Tommy, Bridget's eldest son; Matthew, whose daughter Poppy is the film-struck beauty of the family; and Jim Power, father of Toughy, the youngest of Bridget's children. First they try to have the children removed from Bridget's care by a magistrate, but she is proved to be a fit mother. Then they decide to buy Bridget a farm and install the family away from the village where they will no longer be an embarrassment. The farm is bought, and Bridget is informed that she must move. Then things start going wrong: Mrs. Power, unable to have children of her own, asks to adopt Toughy. Refusing at first, Bridget later consents when she sees that the young couple love the child. Then Poppy leaves for London with a movie contract, and Mary, Bridget's eldest daughter, becomes engaged to artist Peter Howard. Jamesy Casey, the only bachelor in the group, discovers that he has grown fond of his son Tommy, who is working for him on his derelict

farm, and he devises a plan for helping Bridget and the worried fathers and, at the same time, improving his own lot. He proposes marriage to Bridget; she accepts, and together they start life anew on the prosperous little farm. *Irish. Farmers. Dressmakers. Artists. Bachelors. Motion picture directors. Twins. Family life. Illegitimacy. Reputation. Rural life. Adoption. Filial relations. Courtship. Ireland.*

Note: Released in Great Britain in 1958.

SHE DIDN'T STAY IN BED *see* **SHE SHOULD HAVE STAYED IN BED**

SHE FREAK　　　　　　　　　　　　　　F6.4451
Sonney-Friedman Pictures. 3 May **1967** [Minneapolis opening]. Sd; col. 35mm. 87 min.

Prod-Writ David F. Friedman. *Assoc Prod* Dan Sonney, D. I. Long. *Dir* Byron Mabe. *Dir Photog* William Troiano. *Film Ed* Byron Mabe. *Orig Mus Comp* Billy Allen. *Sd Rec* Ken Carlson. *Prod Mgr* Don Hallstrom. *Makeup* Harry Thomas. *Tech Dir* Bobby Cohn.

Cast: Claire Brennen *(Jade Cochran)*, Lee Raymond *(Blackie Fleming)*, Lynn Courtney *(Pat Mullins)*, Bill McKinney *(Steve St. John)*, Van Teen *(Mr. Babcock)*, Felix Silla *(Shortie)*, Marsha Drake *(Olga)*, Claude Smith *(Greasy)*, Bobby Matthews *(Max)*, William Bagdad *("Pretty Boy")*, Ben Moore *(advance man)*, David Boudrot *(customer in cage)*, Madame Lee *(snake charmer)*, Sandra Holcomb.

Horror film. Jade Cochran, a cynical woman who works as a waitress in a sleazy roadside cafe, is determined to improve her lot by any means. She takes a job waiting on tables in the meal tent of a carnival that comes to town, makes the acquaintance of Pat, a stripper, and Steve St. John, the wealthy owner of the carnival's freak show, and immediately decides that she wants to marry him. But Blackie Fleming, the sadistic operator of the ferris wheel, also appeals to her. Jade marries Steve and at the same time embarks on an affair with Blackie. Steve learns of the affair, confronts Blackie, and is stabbed to death in a fight. Blackie is sent to prison, and after Jade inherits her husband's enterprise, she fires Shortie, the carnival freak who informed Steve about her affair with Blackie, despite warnings from her friend Pat, one of the carnival strippers. That night all of the freaks attack Jade and transform her into a sideshow attraction. *Waitresses. Stripteasers. Freaks. Entrepreneurs. Greed. Marriage. Infidelity. Murder. Revenge. Inheritance. Frameup. Carnivals.*

Note: Working title: *Freaks!* Also known as *Alley of Nightmares.*

SHE LET HIM CONTINUE *see* **PRETTY POISON**

THE SHE MAN　　　　　　　　　　　　F6.4452
Southeastern Pictures. Sep **1967**. Sd; b&w. 35mm. 68 min. [Also reviewed at 74 min.]

Prod Charles W. Broun, Jr. *Exec Prod* David B. Putnam. *Assoc Prod* Harry C. Anderson. *Dir* Bob Clark, dir. *Screenplay* Bob Clark, dir, Jeff Gillen. *Story* Harris Anders. *Introduction* Louis M. Pessolano. *Photog* Gerhard Maser. *Film Ed* Holt Gurnstein. *Mus* George Backahle. *Sd* Hack Swain.

Cast: Dorian Wayne *(Dominique)*, Leslie Marlow *(lieutenant)*, Wendy Roberts *(secretary)*, Crystal Hans, Diane O'Donnell, Jeff Gillen.

Drama. Dominique Festro becomes a female impersonator to escape detection as a United States Army deserter. He uses the name of Dominita and soon exploits his new position by building up a lucrative extortion racket. Drawing Albert Rose, his former lieutenant, into the game, Dominita forces him to take female hormone pills and become the impersonator's personal maid. After realizing that a colonel is oblivious to Dominita's masquerade, Albert and Dominita's secretary Ruth reveal the true identity of the deserter to Army officials. *Deserters—Military. Secretaries. Housemaids. Female impersonation. Extortion. United States Army.*

Note: Working title: *Fixation.*

SHE MOB　　　　　　　　　　　　　　F6.4453
Dist Sack Amusement Enterprises. 17 May **1968** [Champaign, Illinois, showing]. Sd; b&w. 35mm. 82 min.

Pres by Alfred N. Sack. *Prod* Maurice Levy, prod. *Writ* Diana Paschal. *Photog* Hal Williams. *Ed* Rex Cromwell. *Rec* Rex Cromwell. *Wardrobe* Robins of Dallas. *Makeup* Jeff Berns. *Sp Eff* George Andersen.

Cast: Marni Castle *(Big Shim/Brenda)*, Monique Duvall *(Sweetie East)*, Adam Clyde *(Tony)*, Twig *(Twig)*, Eve Laurie *(Baby)*, Ann Adams *(Lorenz)*, Joy Dale *(Harry)*, Bill Bags *(Jeff)*, Peaches Chapman *(Teeny)*, Robert Beam *(sheriff)*, Raymond Smith *(deputy)*.

Melodrama. Big Shim leads the "She Mob," a gang of lesbian prison escapees who have tired of female companionship. Shim kidnaps her old boyfriend, Tony, who is currently employed as a gigolo to wealthy, middle-aged department store owner Brenda McClain. Tony is held for $100,000 ransom and informed that he will be required to sexually satisfy the women. To prevent it from becoming known that she has a gigolo, Brenda hires Sweetie East, a female private eye, to rescue Tony. In the meantime, he meets with trouble when he tries to help Baby, Shim's favorite, escape from the mob. The jealous Shim gives chase, killing Baby and recapturing Tony, who is then dressed in Baby's lingerie and tortured. Sweetie, disguised as Brenda, delivers the ransom money and is knocked unconscious by Shim, but she revives in time to single-handedly subdue the mob. Sweetie is wounded by Shim, but the police intervene and kill the gang leader. Sweetie then tests Tony's lovemaking ability and informs Brenda that she will return the ransom money but keep Tony. *Prison escapees. Gigolos. Businesswomen. Detectives. Lesbianism. Torture. Jealousy. Sadism. Kidnaping. Ransom.*

SHE SHOULD HAVE STAYED IN BED   F6.4454

Barry Mahon Productions. *Dist* Cinema Syndicate, Inc. 19 Sep **1963** [San Francisco showing]. Sd; col (Eastman Color). 35mm. 65 min.

A Barry Mahon Production. *Prod-Dir* Barry Mahon. *Script* Clelle Mahon. *Camera* Barry Mahon. *Asst Dir* Sande N. Johnsen. *Prod Mgr* Maurice McEndree. *Makeup* Richard Kereszi.

Cast: Mike Baron *(The Photographer)*, Terry More, Peri G. France, Jack Marina, Davee Decker, Jane Day, Mary Will, Gigi Darlene, Linda Woont, Nell Murray, Faith Gilbert, Irene Charles, Mary Hall, Linda Bell, Alice Stabb.

Comedy. A photographer of nudes waits for a woman he hopes to hire for a magazine layout. He is standing in front of a fashionable East Side apartment building inhabited by a group of beautiful, aspiring young actresses and models. When the woman returns and the photographer approaches her, she thinks he is trying to molest her, and she flees into the building. The photographer follows in pursuit. Inside the building, the tenants prepare for the day's activities, dressing and undressing. The photographer is slowed in his pursuit by a delivery boy carrying a wedding cake. The fleeing girl calls a policeman, and the chase is reversed. Cornered, the photographer explains that he only wants to make a job offer. The girl accepts and poses nude in the photographer's studio. *Models. Photographers. Actors. Nudity. Mistaken identity. New York City— East Side. Chases.*

Note: The plot originally centered on a movie director filming in an apartment building. He allows his camera to stray into various apartments. The censors took exception to the peeping tom aspect of the film, and its format was changed for release. Also known as *She Didn't Stay in Bed*.

THE SHE-WOLF (U.S.S.R.)   F6.4455

Gorky Film Studio. *Dist* Artkino Pictures. 31 Aug **1963** [New York opening]. Sd; b&w. 35mm. 50 min.

Dir-Writ Kira Muratov, A. Muratov. *Story Ed* V. Pogozheva. *Photog* A. Maslennikov. *Art Dir* I. Zakharova, M. Khablenko. *Film Ed* R. Skoretskaya. *Mus Comp & Cond* O. Karavaychuk. *Sd* S. Yurtsev. *Artistic Supv* Sergey Gerasimov. *Prod Mgr* G. Rimalis. *Sp Eff* A. Petukhov.

Cast: Valeriy Isakov *(Senya)*, M. Chebotarenko *(Masha)*, V. Markin *(Kostya)*, G. Svetlani-Penkovskiy *(Gurey)*, P. Lyubeshkin *(Aleksey Stepanovich)*, V. Ivanov *(Korney Petrovich)*, A. Titov, T. Savich, V. Nosik, L. Burkova.

Drama. Source: G. Troyepolskiy, "U krutogo yara," in *U krutogo yara* (Moscow, 1956). Senya, a young hunter, is called to hunt two wolves that have been raiding the flocks of a collective farm. Guided by his sympathetic understanding of wildlife, he tracks the wolves to the vicinity of their lair and mows hay nearby so that they will become accustomed to his presence. His unusual methods earn distrust and mockery from some of the other farmers. On the day of the hunt, he finds the lair while the adult wolves are away, captures a cub, and, hiding in the lair, kills the adults when they return. *Hunters. Collective farming. Animal life. Wolves.*

Note: Released in the U.S.S.R. in Aug 1962 as *U krutogo yara*; running time: 45 min. Produced with the participation of senior students at the Soviet Institute of Cinematography.

SHÉHÉRAZADE *see* SCHEHERAZADE

SHE'LL HAVE TO GO *see* MAID FOR MURDER

SHELL SHOCK   F6.4456

Canyon Productions. *Dist* Parade Releasing Organization. Jan **1964**. Sd; b&w. 35mm. 84 min.

Pres by Riley Jackson, Robert Patrick. *Prod* Charles Beach Dickerson. *Dir* John Hayes. *Screenplay* Randy Fields, John Hayes. *Photog* Vilis Lapenieks. *Art Dir* Jaime Mendoza-Nava. *Film Ed* Thomas Conrad. *Mus* Jaime Mendoza-Nava. *Sd* Frank Murphy. *Sp Eff* Ross Hahn, Sam Altonian.

Cast: Beach Dickerson *(Rance)*, Carl Crow *(Johnny Wade)*, Frank Leo *(Gil Evans)*, Pamela Grey *(Maria)*, Bill Guhl *(Wrigley)*, Max Huber *(Major)*, Dolores Faith *(American girl)*, Martin Brady, Roland Roberts, Bill Roblin.

War melodrama. Johnny Wade, a decorated American soldier serving in Italy in 1943, suffers from shell shock. His sergeant, Rance, jealous of Wade's medal, thinks he is faking, but Gil Evans, an old friend of Johnny's from his

youth in an orphanage, persuades an officer to send Johnny for medical treatment. Rance, planning to kill Johnny, encourages him to escape and then volunteers to capture him. Evans and Sergeant Wrigley are detailed to go with Rance, and after they leave their base is destroyed. The three men, heading for the American lines, encounter Johnny and rescue him from the Germans. But after Rance mistreats him, Johnny runs away and takes refuge with Maria, an Italian. Wrigley is killed, but after meeting an Italian-American woman, Rance changes heart and helps Johnny and Maria escape from the Germans. Maria mistakes Rance for a German and kills him, but she is taken with Evans and Johnny to safety by an American patrol. Johnny soon recovers from his shell shock. *Orphans. Escapees. Italians. Shell shock. Jealousy. Courage. Friendship. Combat zone life. World War II. Italy. United States Army. Germany—Army.*

SHENANDOAH   F6.4457

Universal Pictures. 3 Jun **1965** [Houston opening; c24 Jul 1965; LP33414]. Sd (Westrex); col (Technicolor). 35mm. 105 min.

Prod Robert Arthur. *In Charge of Prod* Edward Muhl. *Dir* Andrew V. McLaglen. *Screenplay* James Lee Barrett. *Dir Photog* William H. Clothier. *Camera Op* William Dodds. *Asst Camera* William Reisbord, William Brown. *Art Dir* Alexander Golitzen, Alfred Sweeney. *Set Decor* John McCarthy, Oliver Emert. *Set Coörd* Fred Knoth. *Main Titl* Pacific Title. *Film Ed* Otho Lovering. *Mus* Frank Skinner. *Mus Supv* Joseph Gershenson. *Sd* Waldon O. Watson, William Russell, James Alexander, Don Cunliffe. *Asst Dir* Terence Nelson, William S. Gilmore, Jr., Terry Morse, Jr. *Unit Prod Mgr* Frank Parmenter. *Script Supv* Luanna Poole. *Cost* Rosemary Odell. *Wardrobe* Norman Mayreis, Tom Dawson, Olive Koenitz. *Makeup* Bud Westmore, Frank Westmore, Rolf Miller, Hank Edds. *Hairstyles* Larry Germain. *Matte Supv* Albert Whitlock. *Tech Adv* D. R. O. Hatswell. *Dial Coach* Michael Audley. *Still Photog* Jack Geraghty. *Gaffer* Ralph Owen.

Cast: James Stewart *(Charlie Anderson)*, Doug McClure *(Sam)*, Glenn Corbett *(Jacob)*, Patrick Wayne *(James)*, Phillip Alford *(Boy)*, Katharine Ross *(Ann)*, Rosemary Forsyth *(Jennie)*, Charles Robinson *(Nathan)*, James McMullan *(John)*, Tim McIntire *(Henry)*, Eugene Jackson, Jr. *(Gabriel)*, Paul Fix *(Dr. Witherspoon)*, Denver Pyle *(Pastor Bjoerling)*, George Kennedy *(Colonel Fairchild)*, James Best *(Carter)*, Tom Simcox *(Lieutenant Johnson)*, Berkeley Harris *(Captain Richards)*, Harry Carey, Jr. *(Jenkins)*, Kevin Hagen *(Mule)*, Dabbs Greer *(Abernathy)*, Strother Martin *(engineer)*, Kelly Thordsen *(Carroll)*.

War drama. Prosperous Virginia farmer Charlie Anderson, who believes that the Civil War is of no concern to him, lives with his six sons, his daughter, his daughter-in-law, and his infant granddaughter. Though they occasionally have to fight off soldiers who want their animals or supplies, they try to remain neutral. His daughter, Jennie, falls in love with and marries Sam, a Confederate officer who is called to duty on their wedding day. Charlie's youngest son, Boy, picks up and wears a discarded Confederate cap, and he is taken prisoner by Union soldiers. Leaving James, James's wife, and their baby behind to watch the farm, the others set out to find Boy and bring him back. Instead, they find Sam in a Union prison camp; and returning to the farm, they find that James and Ann have been murdered by Confederate looters, though the baby has been spared. Then another son, Jacob, is accidentally killed by a Confederate sentry. One Sunday, in the middle of church services, Boy comes limping into church to join his family. *Farmers. Soldiers. Prisoners of war. Family life. Mistaken identity. Churches. United States—History—Civil War. Virginia.*

Note: Location scenes filmed near Eugene, Oregon. Working titles: *Fields of Honor* and *Shenandoah Crossing*.

THE SHEPHERD GIRL (Hong Kong)   F6.4458

Shaw Brothers (H. K.) Ltd. *Dist* Frank Lee International. 1 Sep **1965** [New York opening]. Sd; col (Eastmancolor). 35mm. 105 min.

Prod Run Run Shaw. *Dir-Writ* Lo Chen. *Photog* Liu Chi. *Film Ed* Chiang Hsing-lung. *Mus* Wang Fu-ling. *Lyr* Li Lo-young. *Sd* Wang Yung-hua.

Cast: Julie Yeh Feng *(Hsiu Hsiu)*, Kwan Shan *(Liu Ta-lung)*, Yang Chi-ching *(Ku)*, Chu Mu *(Tiger Tseng)*, Chiang Kuang-chao *(Yao Teh-pao)*, Li Ting *(Hsiao Tsui)*, Ouyang Sh-fei *(Widow Chu)*, Lin Feng *(Wei)*.

Musical melodrama. Hsiu Hsiu, a young shepherdess, falls in love with Liu Ta-lung, a boatman. Hsiu's father is a compulsive gambler, and when he falls into debt, Tiger Tseng, a hunter who also wants Hsiu, offers to pay off the debt. Hsiu rejects his advances until she mistakes Liu's helpful gestures toward a local widow for romantic advances. To make the boatman jealous, she becomes more friendly toward Tiger, but the widow explains the circumstances to Hsiu, and once again she spurns the hunter. Liu takes on a dangerous assignment through pirate-infested waters in order to pay off Hsiu's father's debt, but when he fails to return after many days, Hsiu gives up hope and agrees to marry Tiger. On the wedding day, Liu appears and, after a fierce fight with Tiger, wins back his sweetheart. *Shepherds. Boatmen. Hunters. Gamblers. Widows. Jealousy. Debt. Weddings.*

Note: Location scenes filmed in Hong Kong. Released in Hong Kong in 1964 as *Shan-ko lien.*

THE SHEPHERD OF THE HILLS   F6.4459

Macco Productions. *Dist* Howco International. 15 Apr **1964** [Springfield, Missouri, opening; c15 Apr 1963; LP28697]. Sd; col (Eastman Color). 35mm. 110 min.

Prod Jim McCullough. *Dir-Screenplay-Dial* Ben Parker. *Dir Photog* Ted Saizis, Vincent Saizis. *2d Unit Photog* Henry Kokojan. *Art Dir* Sterling Merritt. *Film Ed* Marcell Greco. *Mus* Marlin Skiles. *Song:* "Fair Is My Lover" Marlin Skiles. *Song:* "The Buggy Ride Song" Marlin Skiles, Gregg Hunter. *Sd* LeRoy Robbins. *Sd Eff Ed* Gene Corso. *Prod Mgr* H. B. McCullough. *Script Supv* Nancy Maurer. *Wardrobe* Don Mitchell. *Coöp* Shepherd of the Hills Farm (Branson, Missouri), Silver Dollar City (Branson, Missouri). *Prop Master* Cap Middleton.

Cast: Richard Arlen (*Old Matt*), James W. Middleton (*Daniel Howitt*), Sherry Lynn (*Sammy Lane*), James Collie (*Wash Gibbs*), Lloyd Durre (*Doc Coughlan*), Hal Meadows (*Young Matt*), James Bradford (*sheriff*), Joy N. Houck, Jr. (*Ollie Stewart*), Gilbert Elmore (*Jess Lane*), George Jackson (*Jed Holland*), Delores James (*Aunt Mollie*), Danny Spurlock (*Pete*), Reubin Egan (*Howard*), Tom Pope, Roy Idom, Jim Teague, Roger Nash, Jim Greene (*The Baldknobbers*).

Rural drama. Source: Harold Bell Wright, *The Shepherd of the Hills* (New York, 1907). Daniel Howitt, a kind and gentle stranger among the mountain folk of the Missouri hills, is befriended by the Matthewses, an Ozark family. Years earlier, his son Howard deserted Old Matt Matthews' daughter, Maggie, who died in childbirth. Daniel now hopes to expiate his son's betrayal. Sammy Lane, a backwoods girl, and Young Matt Matthews are in love, but Sammy is pledged by the code of the hills to marry Ollie Stewart, a country boy turned city sophisticate. At a party celebrating his return, Ollie overhears Wash Gibbs and Jess Lane, members of the Bald Mountain gang, drunkenly brag about robbing the Roark County Bank; in the course of the crime Wash killed a teller. The sheriff, alerted by Ollie, forms a posse and surrounds the gang at their hideout. Although wounded in a shoot-out, Wash escapes and stumbles upon Pete Matthews, Daniel's young runaway grandson. As Wash holds Pete hostage, Howard emerges from the darkness and kills Wash. Fatally wounded during the confrontation, Howard tells Pete to show Daniel the gold he has mined during his years in seclusion. After confessing his son's guilt, Daniel is forgiven by Old Matt. The gold is used to help the drought-stricken community, while Young Matt and Sammy prepare to marry, having learned from Daniel that the only code that binds is love. *Strangers. Hostages. Thieves. Sheriffs. Mountain life. Desertion. Childbirth. Manslaughter. Family life. Marriage—Arranged. Guilt. Bank robberies. Posses. Gold. Drought. Missouri. Ozarks.*

Note: Filmed in and around Branson, Missouri. Earlier screen versions of Wright's novel released in 1928 and 1941. Rereleased as *Thunder Mountain*; running time: 108 min.

EL SHERIFF DEL O. K. CORRAL *see* GUNMEN OF THE RIO GRANDE

SHERLOCK HOLMES GRÖSSTER FALL *see* A STUDY IN TERROR

SHERRY'S HOUSE OF NUDES *see* CHERRY'S HOUSE OF NUDES

SHE'S DOING IT AGAIN   F6.4460

Dist Chellee Films, Abrams & Parisi, Inc. Jan **1969**. Sd; b&w. 35mm. 62 min. A Leo–Todd Production. *Prod* Paul Leonardi, Phil Todaro. *Dir-Writ* (*see note*) Victor Bertini, Victor Burton. *Dir Photog* Ralph Laube. *Ed* Kemper Peacock. *Sd Engr* Fred Kamiel. *Asst Dir* John Vidette.

Cast: Bob February (*Ben Farrow*), Jennie Reeves (*Evelyn Kruger*), Kirk Garfield (*Ron Kruger*), Marty Elson (*Barney Dixon*), Carol Menson (*Lisa Dixon*), Susan Marlowe (*Margaret Farrow*).

Drama. Ben Farrow, inventor of a valuable device, invites his friends Ron Kruger and Barney Dixon, representatives for competing automotive manufacturers, to join him with their wives for a weekend at his country retreat. Ron, anxious to secure the rights to Ben's invention, encourages his wife Evelyn to be generous with her sexual favors. Barney's scheming, ambitious wife, Lisa, equally intent on aiding her husband to the rights, hits on the same strategy. ... *Inventors. Automobile manufacture. Business competition. Ambition. Marriage. Prostitution. Business ethics. Inventions.*

Note: Conflicting sources credit two names for director-writer; one may be a pseudonym of the other.

SHE'S MONIQUE MY LOVE *see* MONIQUE MY LOVE

SHESHET HAYAMIM *see* SIX DAYS TO ETERNITY

SHIN NO SHIKOTEI *see* THE GREAT WALL

SHIN ONNA ONNA ONNA MONOGATARI *see* IT'S A WOMAN'S WORLD

SHINEL *see* THE OVERCOAT

SHINJU TEN NO AMIJIMA *see* DOUBLE SUICIDE

SHINSENGUMI *see* BAND OF ASSASSINS

THE SHIP OF CONDEMNED WOMEN (Italy)   F6.4461

Excelsa Film. *Dist* Globe Pictures, President Films. Nov **1963**. Sd; col (Gevacolor, see note). 35mm. 95 min.

Prod Alfredo De Laurentiis. *Dir* Raffaello Matarazzo. *Screenplay* Ennio De Concini, Raffaello Matarazzo. *Photog* Aldo Tonti. *Song:* "Malasierra" *Sung by* Flo Sandons.

Cast: Kerima (*Rosario*), Giorgio Capecchi (*captain of police*), Ettore Manni (*Da Silva*), Olga Solbelli (*Anita*), May Britt (*Consuelo*), Gualtiero Tumiati (*Pietro Silveris*), Tania Weber (*Isabella*), Elvy Lissiak (*Carmen*), Luigi Tosi (*Fernandez, captain of the ship*), Marcella Rovena (*Nora*), Romolo Costa (*Manuel De Haviland*), Eduardo Ciannelli (*Michele*), Flo Sandons.

Action melodrama. A sailing ship heads for the Portuguese colonies carrying a group of 100 women sentenced to deportation for theft, murder, and prostitution. Some of these hardened criminals bully Consuelo, an innocent young woman who has been falsely convicted of killing her illegitimate child. Da Silva, the corrupt lawyer who secured Consuelo's conviction, is haunted by this injustice. He stows away on the ship in an attempt to correct this wrong and thereby regain his dignity. Also on the ship is Isabella, the cousin of Consuelo, who allowed the innocent girl to be convicted of infanticide in her place. Isabella is traveling first class, having married an elderly gentleman of means. She allows her husband to die on the voyage so that she may inherit his property, and Da Silva and Consuelo publicly accuse Isabella of her crimes. Isabella responds by having the captain flog them together. Consuelo's cries stir the captive women to seize the ship. The rampaging women disfigure and then murder Isabella and the captain. A storm threatens the ship and the situation becomes desperate. The ship's cook remembers a prayer and the women turn their hopes to God, but only Consuelo and Da Silva escape the storm's fury. *Convicts. Lawyers. Sea captains. Prostitutes. Cousins. Thieves. Stowaways. Deportation. Infanticide. Frameup. Flogging. Guilt. Injustice. Inheritance. Disfiguration. Murder. Ships. Storms.*

Note: Released in Italy in 1953 as *La nave delle donne maledette* in color at 97 min. May have been released in the United States in black and white.

SHIP OF FOOLS   F6.4462

Columbia Pictures. 28 Jul **1965** [New York opening; c1 Aug 1965; LP31095]. Sd; b&w. 35mm. 149 min.

A Stanley Kramer Production. *Prod-Dir* Stanley Kramer. *Screenplay* Abby Mann. *Dir Photog* Ernest Laszlo. *Camera Op* Richard Johnson, photog. *Set Decor* Joseph Kish. *Prod Dsgn* Robert Clatworthy. *Main Titl* Pacific Title. *Film Ed* Robert C. Jones. *Mus* Ernest Gold. *Songs:* "Heute Abend geh'n wir bummeln auf der Reeperbahn," "Irgendwie, Irgendwo, Irgendwann" Ernest Gold, Jack Lloyd. *Sd Supv* Charles J. Rice. *Sd* James Z. Flaster. *Re-rec* Clem Portman. *Sd Eff* James A. Richard. *Mus Ed* Maury Winetrobe. *Asst Dir* John Veitch. *Prod Supv* Ivan Volkman. *Unit Location Mgr* Norman August. *Script Supv* Marshall Schlom. *Cost Supv* Joe King. *Cost Dsgn* Bill Thomas. *Miss Leigh's Clothes* Jean Louis. *Makeup Supv* Ben Lane. *Hairstyles* Virginia Jones. *Sp Photog Eff* Albert Whitlock. *Proc Photog* Farciot Edouart. *Sp Eff* John Burke. *Constr Coörd* Bud Pine. *Prop Master* Ernest Graber. *Grip* Marty Kashuk. *Ch Electrn* Seldon White.

Cast: Vivien Leigh (*Mary Treadwell*), Simone Signoret (*La Condesa*), Jose Ferrer (*Rieber*), Lee Marvin (*Tenny*), Oskar Werner (*Dr. Schumann*), Elizabeth Ashley (*Jenny*), George Segal (*David*), Jose Greco (*Pepe*), Michael Dunn (*Glocken*), Charles Korvin (*Captain Thiele*), Heinz Rühmann (*Lowenthal*), Lilia Skala (*Frau Hutten*), Barbara Luna (*Amparo*), Christiane Schmidtmer (*Lizzi*), Alf Kjellin (*Freytag*), Werner Klemperer (*Lieutenant Heebner*), John Wengraf (*Graf*), Olga Fabian (*Frau Schmitt*), Gila Golan (*Elsa*), Oscar Beregi (*Lutz*), Stanley Adams (*Hutten*), Karen Verne (*Frau Lutz*), Charles DeVries (*Johann*), Lydia Torea (*Pastora*), Henry Calvin (*fat man*), Paul Daniel (*Carlos*), David Renard (*woodcarver*), Rudy Carrella (*Ric*), Silvia Marino (*Rac*), Anthony Brand (*guitarist*), Peter Mamakos (*religious man #1*), Walter Friedel (*waiter*), Bert Rumsey (*2d officer*), Jon Alvar (*student*), Charles H. Radilac (*headwaiter*), Steven Geray (*steward*), Justo Robles Quintero, Maribel DeCirez Garcia, José Santiago Martínez.

Drama. Source: Katherine Anne Porter, *Ship of Fools* (Boston, 1962). In 1933, a German ocean liner bound for Bremerhaven leaves Vera Cruz with a variety of well-off passengers and a group of Spanish laborers who are being repatriated. The Germans, including the anti-Semite Rieber, are privileged to sit at the captain's table, except for Lowenthal, a Jew, and Glocken, a dwarf.

Later, the two outcasts are joined by Freytag, when he is found to be married to a Jewess. Dr. Schumann, the ship's doctor, who is suffering from a fatal heart condition, is tending La Condesa, a drug-addicted Spanish noblewoman being shipped to prison on charges of agitating for social reform, and they fall in love. Bill Tenny, an ex-baseball player, feels that his life is a failure because he could not hit an outside curve. David and Jenny, a young unmarried American couple, quarrel because David, a painter, is unhappy living on his wife's income. Mrs. Treadwell, an aging divorcée, flirts and drinks in a desperate attempt to forget her loneliness. Graf, an evangelist, causes a riot among the laborers when he preaches. Graf's nephew, Johann, has an abbreviated affair with a young prostitute who is traveling with a Spanish dance group led by her pimp, Pepe. Jenny consoles Elsa, a Swiss girl who despairs of ever being found attractive, and Lowenthal assures her of her desirability. All disembark at Bremerhaven, except for La Condesa, who had landed earlier at an island prison, and Dr. Schumann, who died of a heart attack after La Condesa's departure. *Spanish. Germans. Laborers. Jews. Dwarfs. Physicians. Drug addicts. Convicts. Athletes. Americans in foreign countries. Painters. Evangelists. Prostitutes. Pimps. Swiss. Dancers. Nobility. Repatriation. Anti-Semitism. Heart disease. Pride. Middle age. Loneliness. Riots. Drunkenness. Marriage. Ocean liners. Bremerhaven. Vera Cruz.*

SHIRIKURAE MAGOICHI see **THE MAGOICHI SAGA**

SHIRO TO KURO see **PRESSURE OF GUILT**

THE SHIRT OFF HER BACK · F6.4463

Steven Edward. *Dist* Chars International Pictures, Triangle Releasing Organization. 22 Nov **1961** [Dallas opening]. Sd; col. 35mm. 70 min.

Prod Jay Sayer. *Songs:* "Shirt Off Her Back," "He's Shy," "Mary Goody-Two-Boots" Jay Sayer.

Cast: Marli Renfro, Tommy Moe Raft, Jay Sayer, Cynthia Lane.

Comedy. No information about the precise nature of this film has been found, but press material indicates it is a burlesque comedy featuring two comedians. *Burlesque.*

SHLOSHA YAMIN VE' YELED see **NOT MINE TO LOVE**

SHNEI KUNI LEMEL see **THE FLYING MATCHMAKER**

SHOCK CORRIDOR · F6.4464

F & F Productions. *Dist* Allied Artists. 11 Sep **1963** [New York opening; c12 Sep 1963; LP26350]. Sd; b&w with col seq (Technicolor). 35mm. 101 min.

A Leon Fromkess-Sam Firks Production. *Prod-Dir-Writ* Samuel Fuller. *Dir Photog* Stanley Cortez. *Photog Col Seq* Samuel Fuller. *Art Dir* Eugene Lourie. *Set Decor* Charles Thompson. *Titl* Ray Mercer. *Film Ed* Jerome Thoms. *Mus* Paul Dunlap. *Choreog* Jon Gregory. *Rec Supv* Phil Mitchell. *Mus & Sd Eff Supv* Gordon Zahler. *Sd Eff Ed* Joseph Von Stroheim. *Mus Ed* Jack Lowry. *Sd* Ryder Sound Service. *Asst Dir* Floyd Joyer. *Prod Mgr* Rudolph Flothow. *Asst to Leon Fromkess* Herbert G. Luft. *Script Supv* Mary Chaffee. *Cost* Einar Bourman. *Makeup Supv* Dan Greenway. *Sp Optical Eff* Lynn Dunn. *Sp Eff* Charles Duncan.

Cast: Peter Breck (*Johnny Barrett*), Constance Towers (*Cathy*), Gene Evans (*Boden*), James Best (*Stuart*), Hari Rhodes (*Trent*), Larry Tucker (*Pagliacci*), William Zuckert (*Swanee*), Philip Ahn (*Dr. Fong*), Neyle Morrow (*psycho*), John Matthews (*Dr. Cristo*), Chuck Roberson (*Wilkes*), John Craig (*Lloyd*), Frank Gerstle (*police lieutenant*), Paul Dubov (*Dr. Menkin*), Rachel Romen (*singing nympho*), Linda Randolph (*dance teacher*), Barbara Perry, Marlene Manners, Lucille Curtis, Jeanette Dana, Marie Devereux, Karen Conrad, Allyson Daniell, Chuck Hicks, Wally Campo, Ray Baxter, Linda Barnett, Harry Fleer.

Melodrama. An ambitious newspaperman, Johnny Barrett, induces his stripper girl friend, Cathy, to pose as his sister and have him committed to a mental institution so he can investigate the unsolved knife murder of one of the patients. Three inmates witnessed the crime: Stuart, a former soldier brainwashed in Korea who now believes he is a Civil War general; Trent, a Negro broken by the ordeal of having been the first nonwhite to enroll at a southern university; and Boden, a former nuclear scientist whose mind has deteriorated to that of a 6-year-old child. While pretending to be a patient, Barrett is attacked by a group of nymphomaniacs, placed in a straitjacket after a riot, and forced to undergo shock therapy. Eventually he learns from Boden that the murderer is a hospital attendant, Wilkes, whose motivation arose from the need to suppress the revelation that he was having sexual relations with some of the female patients. After extracting a confession from Wilkes, Barrett is released and goes on to write an exposé, which is awarded a Pulitzer Prize. But the experience has been too much for him: he suffers a mental collapse and is returned to the institution. *Reporters. Orderlies (hospital). Veterans. Negroes. Nymphomania. Stripteasers. Scientists. Impersonation. Mental illness. Murder. Shock therapy. Brainwashing. Imposture. Hospitals. Pulitzer Prize.*

Note: Working title: *Straitjacket.* Original title: *Long Corridor.*

SHOCK TREATMENT · F6.4465

Arcola Pictures. *Dist* Twentieth Century-Fox Film Corp. 26 Feb **1964** [Los Angeles opening; c19 Feb 1964; LP27600]. Sd (Westrex); b&w. 35mm (CinemaScope). 94 min.

Prod Aaron Rosenberg. *Dir* Denis Sanders. *Screenplay* Sydney Boehm. *Dir Photog* Sam Leavitt. *Art Dir* Jack Martin Smith, Hilyard Brown. *Set Decor* Walter M. Scott, Paul S. Fox. *Film Ed* Louis R. Loeffler. *Mus* Jerry Goldsmith. *Sd* Robert O'Brien, Elmer Raguse. *Asst Dir* Joseph E. Rickards, Ad Schaumer. *Script Supv* Teresa Brachetto. *Cost Dsgn* Moss Mabry. *Wardrobe* Wesley Trist, Ollie Hughes. *Makeup Supv* Ben Nye. *Makeup* Harry Maret. *Hairstyles* Margaret Donovan, Mary Westmoreland. *Sp Photog Eff* L. B. Abbott, Emil Kosa, Jr. *Dial Coach* Herold Goodwin. *Prop* Ed Jones. *Key Grip* Lou Pazelli. *Gaffer* Ken Lang. *Still Photog* Frank Powolny.

Cast: Stuart Whitman (*Dale Nelson*), Carol Lynley (*Cynthia*), Roddy McDowall (*Martin Ashley*), Lauren Bacall (*Dr. Edwina Beighley*), Olive Deering (*Mrs. Mellon*), Ossie Davis (*Capshaw*), Donald Buka (*psychologist*), Pauline Myers (*Dr. Walden*), Evadne Baker (*intern*), Robert J. Wilke (*technician Newton*), Bert Freed (*Josephson*), Judith DeHart (*matron*), Judson Laire (*Harley Manning*), Lili Clark (*Alice*), Douglass Dumbrille (*judge*).

Mystery drama. Source: Winfred Van Atta, *Shock Treatment* (New York, 1961). Gardener Martin Ashley kills his wealthy employer and surrenders to police. Psychiatrist Edwina Beighley testifies at his trial and through her testimony Ashley is committed to a mental hospital for observation. The estate's executor, Manning, believes that Ashley is faking insanity and that he had hidden the million dollars the dead woman kept at the mansion. Manning hires actor Dale Nelson to get himself committed and find out from Ashley the location of the money. Nelson obtains admission to the hospital, eventually making friends with Ashley and falling in love with Cynthia, a young manic-depressive. Dr. Beighley, however, is suspicious of Nelson, and she orders an investigation of his background. Under hypnosis Ashley has told Dr. Beighley that he has a great deal of money. The doctor, desperate for research funds, tries to extract from him information as to the money's whereabouts, but she is unsuccessful. As Nelson's true purpose becomes known, Dr. Beighley subjects him to experimental injections which delay his impending discharge by putting him in catatonic states. He finally escapes, however, and, after finding that Manning has died, rushes to the burned mansion where he comes across Ashley and Dr. Beighley digging up the money. The discovery that the cache contains the ashes of burned currency unhinges the doctor's mind and provokes Ashley into an attempt on her life. In the ensuing fight Ashley is killed. The doctor is then committed to her own institution as Cynthia is discharged. *Gardeners. Psychiatrists. Actors. Lawyers. Murder. Insanity. Imposture. Hypnotism. Catalepsy. Theft. Trials. Hospitals.*

SHOCK TROOPS (France/Italy) · F6.4466

Terra Films—Les Productions Artistes Associés—Compagnia Cinematografica Montoro—Sol Produzioni. *Dist* United Artists. Sep **1968** [c5 Apr 1967; LF50]. Sd; col (Technicolor). 35mm (Techniscope). 106 min.

Pres by Harry Saltzman. *Prod* Raymond Froment. *Dir-Writ* Costa-Gavras. *Dial* Daniel Boulanger. *Photog* Jean Tournier. *Art Dir* Maurice Colasson. *Film Ed* Christian Gaudin. *Mus* Michel Magne. *Asst Dir* Bernard Paul. *Prod Mgr* Louis Daquin. *Sp Eff* René Albouze, Georges Iaconelli.

Cast: Jean-Claude Brialy (*Jean*), Bruno Cremer (*Cazal*), Jacques Perrin (*Kerk*), Gérard Blain (*Thomas*), Claude Brasseur (*Groubac*), Michel Piccoli (*The Extra Man*), Pierre Clementi (*Lucien*), François Périer (*Moujon*), Charles Vanel (*Passevin*), Paolo Fratini (*Philippe*), Michel Creton (*Solin*), Claude Brosset (*Ouf*), Nino Segurini (*Paco*), Med Hondo (*Lecocq*), Julie Dassin (*girl*).

War drama. Source: Jean-Pierre Chabrol, *Un homme de trop* (Paris, 1958). During World War II, a group of French resistance fighters, under the leadership of Cazal, stage a lightning raid on a German prison fortress in France to rescue 12 prisoners condemned to death. Following the success of their mission, the men discover that they have liberated an extra man. Unable to decide whether the extra man is a spy planted by the Nazis or merely a civilian prisoner, the men take him to their hideout in the hills. Upon discovering that he wears German boots and has no identification card, most of the men—particularly the outspoken Jean—decide that he should be killed. When they raid the local tax bureau, the men take the stranger along, and during the shooting, he saves the life of a child who wanders into the line of fire. Nevertheless, Cazal orders his loyal aide Thomas to take the man to the river and execute him; but when the stranger talks for the first time and honestly admits that he is a pacificist deserter, Thomas allows him to escape. During the night, he returns to warn the men that they are surrounded by the Germans. After Cazal has left to warn other resistance groups, the Germans close in and take several captives, including the extra man, to be hanged. All the other men are killed, but the stranger manages to escape. *Maquis. Prisoners of war. Germans. Strangers. Deserters—Military. Pacifists. Escapees. World War II.*

France—History—German occupation 1940–45.

Note: Opened in Paris in Apr 1967 as *Un homme de trop;* running time: 115 min.

SHOCKER *see* **TOWN WITHOUT PITY**

THE SHOCKING SEX   **F6.4467**

Dist William Mishkin. 20 Jul **1964** [New York State license]. Sd; b&w. 35mm. 57 min.

Sex film. Although no information about the precise nature of this film has been found, press material suggests that it concerns promiscuity. *Promiscuity. Sexuality.*

Note: Alternative title: *Rehearsal for Sin.*

THE SHOEMAKER AND THE ELVES (West Germany)   **F6.4468**

Schongerfilm. *Dist* K. Gordon Murray Productions, Trans–International Films. Dec **1967** [Saint Louis showing]. Sd; col (Eastman Color). 35mm (Colorscope). 75 min.

Prod-Writ Hubert Schonger. *Dir* Erich Kobler. *Photog* Wolf Schwan. *Mus* Carl Stueber.

Cast: Nora Minor, Ado Reigler, Heini Göbel, Toni Strassmeir, Bobby Todd, Rudolf Reif, Elisabeth Göbel.

Fantasy. Source: Jakob Grimm and Wilhelm Grimm, "Die Wichtelmänner". Elves return to a village one night every 100 years to do the work of the townspeople. They make shoes while the shoemaker sleeps and build toys in a large workshop; they also chase a robber and hold him captive in a barrel of tar. When the tailor's wife tries to capture the little laborers, their evening of work ends. *Elves. Cobblers. Robbers. Tailors. Village life. Toys.*

Note: Released in West Germany in 1956 as *Heinzelmännchen;* running time: 75 min.

THE SHOES OF THE FISHERMAN   **F6.4469**

Metro-Goldwyn-Mayer, Inc. 14 Nov **1968** [New York opening; c14 Nov 1968; LP36296]. Sd; col (Metrocolor). 35mm (Panavision). 155 min. [Also reviewed at 162 min.] *MPAA rating* G.

A George Englund Production. *Prod* George Englund. *Dir* Michael Anderson. *Screenplay* John Patrick, James Kennaway. *Dir Photog* Erwin Hillier. *2d Unit Camera* Ernest Day. *Art Dir* George W. Davis, Edward Carfagno. *Set Decor* Arrigo Breschi. *Film Ed* Ernest Walter. *Mus Comp & Cond* Alex North. *Rec Supv* Franklin Milton. *Sd Mix* Kurt Doubravsky. *Asst Dir* Tony Brandt, Victor Tourjansky. *Prop Supv* Stanley Goldsmith. *Prod Mgr* Danilo Sabatini. *Unit Prod Mgr* Fritz Mueller. *Cost Dsgn* Orietta Nasalli-Rocca. *Makeup* Amato Garbini. *Hairstyles* Gabriella Brozelli. *Tech Adv* Antonio Petrucci, Adone Terzariol. *Dial Coach* Margaret Anderson.

Cast: Anthony Quinn (*Kiril Lakota*), Laurence Olivier (*Piotr Lylich Kamenev*), Oskar Werner (*Father David Telemond*), David Janssen (*George Faber*), Vittorio De Sica (*Cardinal Rinaldi*), Leo McKern (*Cardinal Leone*), John Gielgud (*The Elder Pope*), Barbara Jefford (*Dr. Ruth Faber*), Rosemarie Dexter (*Chiara*), Frank Finlay (*Igor Bounin*), Burt Kwouk (*Peng*), Arnoldo Foà (*Gelasio*), Paul Rogers (*Augustinian*), George Pravda (*Gorshenin*), Clive Revill (*Vucovich*), Niall MacGinnis (*Capuchin monk*), Marne Maitland (*Cardinal Rahamani*), Isa Miranda (*The Marchesa*), Gerald Harper (*Brian*), Leopoldo Trieste (*dying man's friend*), Peter Copley, Arthur Howard (*English cardinals*), Jean Rougeul (*Dominican*), Al Thomas (*Negro cardinal*), Dom Moore (*Polish cardinal*), John Frederick (*American cardinal*).

Drama. Source: Morris L. West, *The Shoes of the Fisherman* (New York, 1963). Hoping to establish a Russian sphere of influence in Rome, Soviet Premier Piotr Lylich Kamenev arranges for the release of political prisoner Kiril Lakota, an archbishop of the Russian Catholic Church who has been held in a Siberian prison camp for 20 years. Before he leaves for Rome, Lakota is briefed by Kamenev on the world situation, particularly the extreme famine in Red China which has brought the world to the brink of atomic war. After the briefing, Lakota is escorted to Rome by Father Telemond, an ailing Jesuit priest whose nonconformist philosophical writings on evolution are under examination by a Pontifical Commission. Upon arriving at the Rome airport, Lakota is interviewed by George Faber, an American television newscaster whose extramarital activities are threatening to destroy his marriage. Lakota is made a cardinal by the pope, who, like Kamenev, sees him as a bridge between East and West. A short time later, while Father Telemond is answering the charges of the Pontifical Commission headed by the staunchly conservative Cardinal Leone, the pope collapses and dies. Coincidental with the pope's death, the Chinese begin to mobilize along the Indian and Mongolian borders. The cardinals go into conclave to elect a new pope, and a deadlock in the consistory of the sacred college results in Lakota's being chosen pope against his will. The first non-Italian pope in 400 years, Lakota chooses the name of Pope Kiril I, in memory of the saint who carried the Gospel to Russia. Almost immediately, Premier Kamenev asks the new pope to mediate the Chinese crisis. That night, feeling a need to be with the people, Kiril dresses in plain priestly clothes, wanders through the streets of Rome, and accidentally encounters Faber's wife, Ruth, a physician. After he has helped her to understand that love is missing from her marriage, Kiril is brought back to the Vatican by his emissaries. He then travels to Outer Mongolia for a meeting with Kamenev and the Red Chinese leader, Chairman Peng. Following his pledge that he will try to find a solution to the famine in China, Kiril returns to Rome and asks Father Telemond to share his problems. Before the young Jesuit can offer advice, however, he is stricken by a cerebral hemorrhage and dies in Kiril's arms. Alone with the magnitude of his papal office, Kiril makes peace with his old enemy, Cardinal Leone, and then makes his decision. On the day of his coronation, as he stands on the balcony of St. Peter's Cathedral, Pope Kiril I removes the papal crown from his head and pledges all of the vast wealth of the Catholic Church "for the relief of our hungry brothers." If necessary, the Church will "strip itself down to poverty." *Political prisoners. Clergymen. Nonconformists. Americans in foreign countries. Reporters. Physicians. Russians. Chinese. Italians. Papacy. Heresy. Famine. Infidelity. Marriage. Strokes. Coronations. Union of Soviet Socialist Republics. Rome. Siberia. People's Republic of China. Vatican. Catholic Church.*

Note: Film blown up to 70mm for roadshow presentations; location scenes filmed in Rome.

SHONEN *see* **BOY**

SHONEN SARUTOBI SASUKE *see* **MAGIC BOY**

SHOOT LOUD, LOUDER ... I DON'T UNDERSTAND (Italy)   **F6.4470**

Master Film. *Dist* Embassy Pictures. Dec **1966** [Los Angeles showing]. Sd; col (Eastmancolor, print by Pathé). 35mm. 100 min.

Prod Pietro Notarianni. *Exec Prod* Joseph E. Levine. *Dir* Eduardo De Filippo. *Screenplay* Eduardo De Filippo, Suso Cecchi D'Amico. *Photog* Aiace Parolin, Danilo Desideri. *Art Dir* Gianni Polidori. *Set Decor* Ennio Michettoni. *Film Ed* Ruggero Mastroianni. *Mus* Nino Rota. *Sd* Umberto Picistrelli. *Asst Dir* Francesco Massaro. *Cost* Enrico Job.

Cast: Marcello Mastroianni (*Alberto Saporito*), Raquel Welch (*Tania Mottini*), Guido Alberti (*Pasquale Cimmaruta*), Leopoldo Trieste (*Carlo Saporito*), Tecla Scarano (*Aunt Rosa Cimmaruta*), Eduardo De Filippo (*Uncle Nicola*), Rosalba Grottesi (*Elvira Cimmaruta*), Paolo Ricci (*Aniello Amitrano*), Regina Bianchi (*Mrs. Amitrano*), Franco Parenti (*chief police inspector*), Angela Luce (*beautiful woman*), Silvano Tranquilli (*Lieutenant Bertolucci*), Pina D'Amato (*Matilde Cimmaruta*), Carlo Bagno (*Marshal Bagnacavallo*), Pia Morra (*maid*), Gino Minopoli (*Luigi Cimmaruta*), Alberto Bugli (*deputy police inspector*), Ignazio Spalla (*Carmelo Vitiello*).

Comedy. Source: Eduardo De Filippo, *Le voci di dentro* (Milan opening: 11 Dec 1948). Alberto Saporito, a Neapolitan sculptor and antique dealer, is a dreamer who frequently finds it difficult to separate his fantasies from reality. He shares a ramshackle home with his Uncle Nicola, an eccentric so disgusted by mankind that he hasn't spoken in over 50 years; instead, he communicates by setting off homemade firecrackers. One night, after a meeting with the voluptuous Tania, Alberto dreams that a wealthy neighbor, Amitrano, has been murdered by his family. Awakening, Alberto races to the police to report the killing. Later, he confesses that the "murder" may have been only a nightmare, but the police refuse to believe him since they know Amitrano to be a notorious gangster. The Amitranos are arrested, and confusion reigns as Alberto walks around in a daze, never certain whether he is awake or dreaming. Then Amitrano appears and demands Alberto's passport so that he may use it to escape to South America. On the pretext of having to go for his papers, Alberto once more races to the police. As he tries to explain that he has found Amitrano, a gigantic explosion takes place. Uncle Nicola has set off his biggest—and last—pyrotechnics display. Fearing reprisals from just about everyone, Alberto, joined by Tania, flees from the city. *Sculptors. Antique dealers. Eccentrics. Uncles. Gangsters. Police. Murder. Fireworks. Passports. Naples. Fantasy. Dreams.*

Note: Location scenes filmed in Naples, Rome, and on the Amalfi coast. Released in Italy in 1966 as *Spara forte, più forte ... non capisco.*

SHOOT-OUT AT BEAVER FALLS   **F6.4471**

August–Knight Productions. *Dist* Chellee Films. Aug **1970** [periodical notice]. Sd; col. 35mm. 77 min.

Prod-Writ Gustave M. Knight. *Dir* Harry August.

Cast: Tanya O'Rourke, Sheba Stalion.

Western melodrama. Hank Caswell returns home to the family ranch in Montana after having been away for 5 years tracking down one of several men who brutally murdered his parents. During Caswell's absence, Slade (one of the killers) has been running the ranch. Caswell announces his intention of seeking out his brother, Sam, to find out if Sam has any new leads on the slayers. Slade, in hopes of stalling Caswell, forces two women, Sally and Sue, to detain Caswell by making love with him. Then Slade goes to Sam's cabin and kills him; he rapes and scalps Tamachi, a halfbreed with whom Caswell had been romantically involved; and finally he returns to the ranch, and while Sally and Sue are making love, he confronts Caswell, and guns him down. *Brothers. Ranch foremen. Halfcastes. Murder. Revenge. Seduction. Rape. Mutilation. Lesbianism. Ranches. Montana.*

Note: Also known as *Show Down at Beaver Falls.*

SHOOT OUT AT BIG SAG   F6.4472

Brennan Productions. *Dist* Parallel Film Distributors. Jun **1962** [c11 Apr 1960, 21 Feb 1962; LU3168, LP25627]. Sd; b&w. 35mm. 64 min.

Prod Walter A. Brennan, Jr., Bud S. Isaacs. *Dir-Writ* Roger Kay. *Dir Photog* Lothrop Worth. *Art Dir* Archie Bacon. *Film Ed* Bud S. Isaacs. *Asst Film Ed* Ruth Blythe. *Mus* William Loose, Jack Cookerly. *Mus Supv* Richard Berres. *Rec Ed* Don V. Isaacs. *Sd Mix* Earl Walcott. *Asst Dir* Frank Mayer. *Prod Supv* Stanley Frazen. *Script Girl* Mai Mohr. *Cost Ed* Lossman. *Makeup* Lee Greenway. *Hairstyles* Carmen Dirigo. *Sp Photog Eff* Howard A. Anderson Co. *Ch Set Electrn* Cliff Hutchinson. *Key Grip* Carl Noren. *Prop Master* Charles Chichetti.

Cast: Walter Brennan (*Preacher Hawker*), Leif Erickson (*Sam Barbee*), Luana Patten (*Hannah Hawker*), Chris Robinson (*Lee Barbee*), Constance Ford (*Goldie Bartholomew*), Virginia Gregg (*Sarah Hawker*), Les Tremayne (*Chan Bartholomew*), Don O'Kelly (*Fargo*), Andy Brennan, William Foster, Robert Beecher, Lennie Geer.

Western melodrama. Source: Walt Coburn, *Barb Wire* (New York, 1931). Self-appointed Preacher Hawker and family, claiming the region of Montana known as Big Sag as their own, try to run Sam Barbee and his son Lee, newly arrived from Texas, out of the territory. Knowing that her husband is a coward, Mrs. Hawker takes over and secures Big Sag by sending her daughter Hannah into town with a note begging the assistance of Chan Bartholomew, owner of the First and Last Chance Saloon; but Hannah is delayed by a violent storm and meets Lee, with whom she falls in love. She finally arrives in town, and Chan tries to make love to her; but his alcoholic wife, Goldie, breaks up the affair by killing him. Preacher Hawker shoots Fargo, a killer hired by Chan, then performs a marriage ceremony for Hannah and Lee, resolving never to touch a gun again. *Preachers. Saloon keepers. Hired killers. Land claims. Family life. Cowardice. Alcoholism. Murder. Weddings. Montana. Storms.*

Note: Filmed in 1960 as *The Rawhide Halo*, a pilot for "Barbed Wire," an unproduced television series. Also known as *Shootout at Big Sag*. Registered for copyright in 1960 as *Barb Wire (The Rawhide Halo)*.

SHOOT THE PIANO PLAYER (France)   F6.4473

Films de la Pléiade. *Dist* Astor Pictures. 23 Jul **1962** [New York opening]. Sd; b&w. 35mm (Dyaliscope). 92 min. [Also 84 min.]

Prod Pierre Braunberger. *Dir-Screenplay-Dial* François Truffaut. *Adapt* François Truffaut, Marcel Moussy. *Dir Photog* Raoul Coutard. *Camera Op* Claude Beausoleil. *Art Dir* Jacques Mely. *Film Ed* Cécile Decugis, Claudine Bouché. *Mus & Piano for Charles Aznavour* Georges Delerue. *Song:* "Dialogues d'amoureaux" Félix Leclerc. *Sung by* Félix Leclerc, Lucienne Vernay. *Song:* "Vanille et framboise" *comp & sung by* Boby Lapointe. *Sd* Jacques Gallois. *Asst Dir* Francis Cognani, Robert Bober, Björn Johansen. *Prod Supv* Serge Komor. *Prod Mgr* Roger Fleytoux. *Prod Sec* Luce Deuss. *Script Girl* Suzanne Schiffman. *English Subtitl* Noelle Gillmor.

Cast: Charles Aznavour (*Charlie Kohler/Edouard Saroyan*), Marie Dubois (*Léna*), Nicole Berger (*Théresa*), Michèle Mercier (*Clarisse*), Albert Rémy (*Chico Saroyan*), Jacques Aslanian (*Richard*), Richard Kanayan (*Fido Saroyan*), Claude Mansard (*Momo*), Daniel Boulanger (*Ernest*), Serge Davri (*Plyne*), Claude Heymann (*Lars Schmeel*), Alex Joffé (*passerby*), Boby Lapointe (*singer*), Catherine Lutz (*Mammy*).

Drama. Source: David Goodis, *Down There* (New York, 1956). Charlie Kohler, a retiring piano player in a cheap Parisian dance bar, rears his youngest brother, Fido, with the help of a prostitute neighbor, Clarisse, who has also been Charlie's mistress. Two other brothers, Chico and Richard, seek help from Charlie in escaping from Momo and Ernest, two gangsters whom they have doublecrossed over some stolen money. To avoid the gangsters, Charlie takes refuge at the apartment of Léna, a waitress at the cafe, who has fallen in love with him and discovered his hidden past. Years before, he had been a brilliant concert pianist, Edouard Saroyan. His obsession with his career prompted his wife, Théresa, to reveal that she had given him his first chance at fame by submitting to the sexual demands of an impresario. Edouard walked out on her, but returned to the apartment on a premonition and found that Théresa had committed suicide. Shattered, he abandoned his career, changed his name, and became a haunted man with a single aim—to avoid trouble. Charlie now embarks on a second chance at love with Léna, who encourages him to make a comeback as a concert pianist. They give their notice at the cafe, but Charlie is forced to fight over Léna with Plyne, the jealous bartender, and accidentally kills him. Meanwhile, Momo and Ernest kidnap Fido. Charlie and Léna attempt to cover up Plyne's death and hoping to intercept the gangsters, they drive to Charlie's family villa in Savoie, where Chico and Richard are hiding. Momo and

Ernest finally arrive with Fido. In the ensuing gunplay between Charlie's brothers and the gangsters, Léna is killed by a stray bullet. Cleared by police in Plyne's death, Charlie returns to his old job as a piano player at the cafe. *Pianists. Impresari. Brothers. Hoodlums. Waitresses. Bartenders. Prostitutes. Marriage. Self-sacrifice. Suicide. Robbery. Death. Cafes. Paris. Savoie.*

Note: Location scenes filmed in Paris and near Grenoble. Paris opening: Nov 1960 as *Tirez sur le pianiste*; running time: 80 min.

THE SHOP ON HIGH STREET *see* THE SHOP ON MAIN STREET

THE SHOP ON MAIN STREET (Czechoslovakia)   F6.4474

Barrandov Film Studio. *For* Československý Film. *Dist* Prominent Films. 24 Jan **1966** [New York opening; c1 Jan 1966; LF18]. Sd; b&w. 35mm. 128 min.

Pres by Marie Desmarais, Eurofilm Ltd. *Head of Prod* Ladislav Hanuš. *Assoc Prod* Jaromír Lukáš, Jordan Balurov. *Dir* Ján Kadár, Elmar Klos. *Screenplay* Ladislav Grosman, Ján Kadár, Elmar Klos. *Photog* Vladimír Novotný. *2d Photog* Miloš Petrolín. *Camera Op* Jaroslav Prokop. *Art Dir* Karel Škvor. *Film Ed* Jaromír Janáček, Diana Heringová. *Mus* Zdeněk Liška. *Sd* Dobroslav Šrámek. *1st & 2d Asst Dir* Juraj Herz, René Mattes, Tomás Škrdlant, Jana Štroblová. *English Subtitl* Lindsay Anderson.

Cast: Jozef Króner (*Tono Brtko*), Ida Kaminska (*Rozálie Lautmannová [Rosalie Lautmann]*), Hana Slivková (*Evelyna Brtková [Evelina Brtko]*), František Zvarík (*Markus Kolkocký [Marcus Kolktsky]*), Elena Zvaríková (*Růžena Kolkocka [Rose Kolkotsky]*), Martin Hollý (*Imro Kuchar*), Martin Gregor (*Katz, the barber*), Adam Matejka (*Piti Báci*), Mikuláš Ladižinský (*Marian Peter*), Eugen Senaj (*Blau, the printer*), František Papp (*Andorič*), Gita Mišurová (*Andoričová*), Luise Grossová (*Eliášova*), Alojz Kramár (*Balko Báci*), Tibor Vadaš (*tobacconist*).

Drama. Source: Ladislav Grosman, *Obchod na korze* (Prague, 1965). In Slovakia during World War II, Tono Brtko, a simple, good-natured carpenter, is nagged by his wife, Evelina, who wants him to improve their social standing, and also by his Fascist brother-in-law, Kolkotsky, who wants him to join the occupying regime. In the hope of satisfying both, Tono agrees to become "Aryan comptroller" of a Jewish button shop on Main Street. His dreams of attaining prestige and wealth are shattered, however, when he discovers that all the button boxes are empty and that the shop is bankrupt. Furthermore, its owner, Mrs. Lautmann, is so old and deaf that communication with her is virtually impossible. Unaware of the war, Mrs. Lautmann is being supported by the local Jews, who persuade Tono to accept a generous salary in return for pretending to be Mrs. Lautmann's new assistant. As time passes, a deep affection develops between them. This happy situation ends, however, when an order is given for the deportation of all Jews. By an accident, Mrs. Lautmann's name is omitted from the list, and Tono is torn between his wish to protect the old woman and his fear that he may be accused of harboring a Jew. As the deportation victims are herded together in front of the shop, Tono suddenly panics and tries to force Mrs. Lautmann into the street, but she slowly realizes the truth and attempts to run away. Tono pushes her into a cupboard, locks the door, and waits for the deportation to end. When it is over, he unlocks the cupboard only to find Mrs. Lautmann dead inside. Overcome by guilt and remorse, he hangs himself. *Jews. Carpenters. Storekeepers. Brothers-in-law. Old age. Anti-Semitism. Military occupation. Nazism. Friendship. Conscience. Guilt. Suicide. World War II. Slovakia.*

Note: Location scenes filmed in Sabinov in eastern Slovakia. Released in Czechoslovakia in Oct 1965 as *Obchod na korze*. U. S. prerelease title: *The Shop on High Street*. Role names in brackets have been anglicized for U. S. release.

SHORT IS THE SUMMER (Sweden)   F6.4475

Sandrews. *Dist* Shaw Film Distributors. Oct **1968**. Sd; col (Eastman Color). 35mm (AgaScope). 109 min.

Exec Prod Rune Waldekranz. *Dir* Bjarne Henning-Jensen. *Screenplay* Bjarne Henning-Jensen, Astrid Henning-Jensen. *Photog* Gunnar Fischer. *Set Dsgn* Jan Boleslaw. *Film Ed* Lennart Wallén. *Mus* Hilding Rosenberg. *Sd* Lars Lalin. *Unit Mgr* Karl-Erik Svensson.

Cast: Jarl Kulle (*Thomas Glahn*), Bibi Andersson (*Edvarda Mack*), Claes Gill (*Merchant Mack*), Liv Ullmann (*Eva*), Allan Edwall (*doctor*), Ingvar Kjellson (*baron*), Jens Bolling (*smith*), Marie Göranzon (*vicar's daughter*), Carl Johan Seth (*Jacob*), Britt-Marie Eklund (*Edvarda's girl friend*), Bjørg Vatle (*Henriette*).

Romantic melodrama. Source: Knut Hamsun, *Pan* (Kristiania, 1894). Thomas Glahn, a young Swedish lieutenant, comes to a desolate island off the coast of Lapland for the summer to escape from modern society. He rents a hunting lodge from Merchant Mack, whose daughter Edvarda finds the newcomer attractive. Her distrust of men leads her to rebuff his initial advances, however. Later, Glahn introduces her to the physical pleasures of love and her fears are abated. Meanwhile, Edvarda becomes jealous of her father's mistress, Eva, whose sensuality has attracted the young Swede. Mack soon begins to notice that both Edvarda and Eva are less tolerant of his brutality; in retaliation, he reintroduces a Finnish baron, previously unsuccessful in pursuing Edvarda, and also tells her that Glahn and Eva are having an affair. Edvarda refuses to believe him and rebuffs the baron as well. At a ball honoring the baron near the end of the summer, Edvarda finds Glahn and Eva embracing in a back room; she breaks up the party and announces that she will marry the baron. Mack goes after Eva and tries to seduce her in the forest, but she flees and runs up the mountainside. When Glahn fires a volley of shots as a signal to Edvarda, an avalanche of rocks kills Eva. In a vengeful rage, Mack then sets fire to the hunting lodge and watches as it burns to the ground. Before leaving the island, Glahn pays a farewell visit to Edvarda in an attempt at reconciliation, but Edvarda's pride will not allow her to accept him. *Soldiers. Innkeepers. Mistresses. Nobility. Finns. Vacations. Filial relations. Sexual initiation. Jealousy. Revenge. Pride. Islands. Lodges (inns). Balls (formal gatherings). Summer. Lapland. Avalanches. Fires.*

Note: Filmed on location in northern Norway. Opened in Stockholm in Dec 1962 as *Kort är sommaren*; running time: 104 min. Working title: *Det kom en sommar.*

A SHOT IN THE DARK (United States/Great Britain)   **F6.4476**
Mirisch-Geoffrey Productions. *Dist* United Artists. 23 Jun **1964** [New York opening; c23 Jun 1964; LP28602]. Sd; col (De Luxe). 35mm (Panavision). 101 min.

A Blake Edwards Production. *Prod-Dir* Blake Edwards. *Assoc Prod* Cecil F. Ford. *Screenplay* Blake Edwards, William Peter Blatty. *Anim Prod* George Dunning, Ltd. *Dir Photog* Christopher Challis. *Camera Op* Austin Dempster. *Prod Dsgn* Michael Stringer. *Titl Created by* DePatie-Freleng. *Supv Film Ed* Ralph E. Winters. *Film Ed* Bert Bates. *Mus* Henry Mancini. *Song:* "Shadow of Paris" Henry Mancini, Robert Wells. *Sd Rec* John Bramall, J. B. Smith. *Sd Ed* Ted Mason. *Asst Dir* Derek Cracknell. *Prod Mgr* Denis Johnson. *Cont* Connie Willis. *Cost Dsgn* Margaret Furse.

Cast: Peter Sellers (*Inspector Jacques Clouseau*), Elke Sommer (*Maria Gambrelli*), George Sanders (*Benjamin Ballon*), Herbert Lom (*Chief Inspector Charles Dreyfus*), Tracy Reed (*Dominique Ballon*), Graham Stark (*Hercule Lajoy*), Andre Maranne (*François, Dreyfus' assistant*), Douglas Wilmer (*Henri Lafarge*), Martin Benson (*Maurice, 1st butler*), Burt Kwouk (*Kato*), Vanda Godsell (*Madame Lafarge*), Maurice Kaufmann (*Pierre, 2d chauffeur*), Ann Lynn (*Dudu, 1st maid*), David Lodge (*Georges, gardener*), Moira Redmond (*Simone, 3rd maid*), Reginald Beckwith (*receptionist at Camp Sunshine*), Turk Thrust (*Charlie, locker attendant at Camp Sunshine*), John Herrington (*doctor*), Jack Melford (*psychoanalyst*).

Mystery farce. Source: Harry Kurnitz, *A Shot in the Dark* (New York opening: 18 Oct 1961). Marcel Achard, *L'idiote* (Paris opening: 23 Sep 1960). In Paris Maria Gambrelli, Mr. and Mrs. Benjamin Ballon's French parlormaid, is accused of killing her Spanish lover. Inspector Jacques Clouseau, accidentally assigned to the case, believes her innocent despite all the facts indicating that she is guilty. Dreyfus, Clouseau's superior, removes him from the case and arrests Maria; but, on the following day, Dreyfus learns that certain influential people wish Clouseau back on the case. Reassigned, Clouseau releases Maria and before long finds her with the gardener's dead body. Again arrested for murder, Maria is quickly released by Clouseau, who still believes in her innocence. He follows her to a nudist camp where Dudu, the Ballon's first maid, is found murdered and Maria again comes under suspicion. Lafarge, the Ballon's majordomo, is then murdered; Maria is once more arrested, and Clouseau is again removed from the case. Dreyfus reassigns the case to Clouseau, who releases Maria and takes her nightclubbing. In the course of the evening, four innocent people are killed, around the oblivious Clouseau, as a result of unsuccessful attempts on his life. The inspector gathers the six remaining suspects together in the Ballon house. They begin to accuse one another until the lights go out, and Maria and Clouseau find themselves alone. All six attempt to flee in Clouseau's car, which has been wired with a bomb intended for him. The car explodes and Clouseau has, in his own way, solved the case by the elimination of the suspects. Dreyfus goes insane because he is the real murderer, having committed the crimes to discredit the bumbling detective and thereby remove him from his staff—only to have him emerge a hero. *Detectives. French. Housemaids. Gardeners. Chauffeurs. Butlers. Majordomos. Police. Murder. Frameup. Insanity. Nudist camps. Bombs. Nightclubs. Paris. Inspector Clouseau.*

Note: Locations filmed in Paris. Released in Great Britain in 1965.

THE SHOTGUN WEDDING   **F6.4477**
Arkota Productions. 6 Nov **1963** [Phoenix, Arizona, opening; c25 Mar 1965; LP25021]. Sd; col (Eastmancolor). 35mm. 64 min.

A Pat Patterson Production. *Prod-Dir* Boris L. Petroff.

Cast: Jenny Maxwell, Valerie Allen, Nan Peterson, J. Pat O'Malley, Peter Colt.

Rural comedy-drama. Buford Ankers is the head of a family that has lived for 30 years in a riverboat stuck in the mud. The Ankers family is sheltering Mellonie, an ex-carnival worker hiding from the police. Mellonie agrees to marry Buford, but only for money; she is really in love with a fake preacher. Buford's son, Rafe, is in love with Honey Bee Heller, daughter of a family of moonshining hillbillies who have a longstanding feud with the Ankers. After a series of complications, love triumphs and the two couples are able to get married. *Moonshiners. Preachers. Fugitives. Rural life. Feuds. Marriage. Riverboats.*

SHOW DOWN AT BEAVER FALLS *see* **SHOOT-OUT AT BEAVER FALLS**

SHOW OF THE YEAR   **F6.4478**
21 Dec **1966** [Fresno, California, showing]. Sd; b&w. 35mm. [Feature film, length unknown.]

Sex film. No information about the precise nature of this film has been found.

SHOWA NO INOCHI *see* **STORMY ERA**

SHOWDOWN   **F6.4479**
Universal Pictures. 1 May **1963** [Denver, Colorado, opening; c1 Jun 1963; LP32703]. Sd (Westrex); b&w. 35mm. 79 min.

Prod Gordon Kay. *In Charge of Prod* Edward Muhl. *Dir* R. G. Springsteen. *Screenplay* Bronson Howitzer. *Dir Photog* Ellis W. Carter. *Art Dir* Alexander Golitzen, Alfred Sweeney. *Set Decor* Oliver Emert. *Main Titl* Pacific Title. *Film Ed* Jerome Thoms. *Mus* Hans J. Salter. *Mus Supv* Joseph Gershenson. *Sd* Waldon O. Watson, Frank H. Wilkinson. *Asst Dir* Terence Nelson, Carl Beringer. *Unit Prod Mgr* Bob Larson. *Asst to the Prod* Willard Willingham. *Script Supv* Cliff Bole. *Cost* Rosemary Odell. *Makeup* Bud Westmore. *Hairstyles* Larry Germain.

Cast: Audie Murphy (*Chris Foster*), Kathleen Crowley (*Estelle*), Charles Drake (*Bert Pickett*), Harold J. Stone (*Lavalle*), Skip Homeier (*Caslon*), L. Q. Jones (*Foray*), Strother Martin (*Charlie Reeder*), John McKee (*Marshal Beaudine*), Henry Wills (*Chaca*), Joe Haworth (*guard*), Kevin Brodie (*Buster*), Carol Thurston (*Smithy's wife*), Dabbs Greer (*express man*), Charles Horvath (*Hebron*), E. J. Andre.

Western melodrama. Chris Foster and Bert Pickett, shackled to a post after a brawl in the Mexican border town of Adonde, escape along with the other prisoners, outlaws led by Lavalle. Taking with them $12,000 worth of stolen securities, Chris and Bert flee the town, but Lavalle soon finds the two men. Chris is held hostage while Bert is sent to town to convert the securities into cash. Instead, he gives the securities to his former girl friend, Estelle, who is now a dancehall girl, and he returns empty-handed. Enraged, Lavalle allows Chris to go after Estelle and recover the money. Estelle, who reveals that Bert's gambling had reduced her to poverty, reluctantly turns the money over to Chris but follows him to Lavalle. In an attempt to save both his partner and Estelle as they arrive, Bert is killed by Lavalle. Chris and Estelle ride away unharmed; Lavalle tracks them back to Adonde, where Chris finally kills the outlaw, returns the securities, and looks forward to a new life with Estelle. *Outlaws. Hostages. Dancehall girls. Theft. Mexican border.*

Note: Working title: *The Iron Collar.*

SHOWDOWN FOR ZATOICHI (Japan)   **F6.4480**
Daiei Motion Picture Co. 4 Oct **1968** [New York opening]. Sd; col (Eastman Color). 35mm. 87 min.

Dir Kenji Misumi. *Screenplay* Daisuke Ito. *Story* Kan Shimozawa. *Photog* Chishi Makiura. *Mus* Akira Ifukube.

Cast: Shintaro Katsu (*Zatoichi*), Mikio Narita (*Tadasu Jumonji*), Chizu Hayashi (*Enoshimeya*), Kaneko Iwasaki (*Otane*), Gaku Yamamoto (*Tomonoshin Sagawa*).

Adventure drama. On the way to Mount Fuji to celebrate Japanese New Year, Zatoichi, the blind master swordsman, is attacked by five bandits who prove to be no match for his skill. Continuing his journey by ship, Zatoichi wins a large sum of money from amateur gamblers who are part of a gang led by Enoshimeya; he also meets Jumonji, an excellent chess player and swordsman who leaves the ship with him at the island dock. There Enoshimeya lures Zatoichi into a trap, but the latter wins the ensuing battle, although a little girl is wounded in the process. To appease his guilt, Zatoichi gambles for money to buy medicine for her but loses; Jumonji comes to the rescue, however, and provides the money. Otane, the girl's mother and widow of a man whom Zatoichi had killed in self-defense, has been sent by the bandits to spy on Zatoichi, but she falls in love with him instead. Meanwhile, Zatoichi is disturbed to learn that Jumonji enjoys killing; when a young samurai and his sister come looking for the man who wantonly killed their father, Zatoichi realizes that Jumonji is the murderer. Sensing a showdown, Jumonji decides to kill his friend, but the brother and sister slay him and avenge their father's death. *Samurai.*

Bandits. Widows. Spics. Blindness. Gambling. Guilt. Brother-sister relationship. Revenge. Murder. Zatoichi.

Note: Released in Japan in 1967 as *Zato Ichi jigokutabi.*

SHUBUN *see* **SCANDAL**

SHUT UP AND DEAL   **F6.4481**
Unit Ten Productions. *Dist* Bernhard Films. 19 Nov **1969** [New York showing]. Sd; b&w. 35mm. [Feature length assumed.]
Exec Prod Charles H. Leonard. *Dir* John Donne. *Photog* Jon Ericson. *Prod Asst* Bill Swenson.

Sex film. Tom Hansen learns the facts of life at a stag party thrown for him on the eve of his wedding when Chuck, his older brother, invites a group of prostitutes, some "turned-on" hippies, and a lingerie saleslady to his plush bachelor's apartment for an evening of card games and other diversions. *Prostitutes. Hippies. Saleswomen. Brothers. Sexual initiation.*

THE SHUTTERED ROOM (Great Britain)   **F6.4482**
Seven Arts Productions–Troy-Schenck Productions. *Dist* Warner Bros.-Seven Arts, Inc. 17 Jan **1968** [Providence, Rhode Island, opening]. Sd; col (Technicolor). 35mm. 100 min.
Prod Phillip Hazelton. *Exec Prod* Bernard Schwartz. *Assoc Prod* Alexander Jacobs. *Dir* David Greene. *Screenplay* D. B. Ledrov, Nathaniel Tanchuck. *Photog* Ken Hodges. *Art Dir* Brian Eatwell. *Titl Dsgn* Derek Nice. *Film Ed* Brian Smedley-Aston. *Mus Comp & Arr* Basil Kirchin. *Mus Cond* Jack Nathan. *Sd* Kevin Sutton, Kenneth Osborne. *Sd Rec* Gerry Humphreys. *Asst Dir* Stuart Freeman. *Prod Mgr* David Anderson. *Wardrobe* Caroline Mott, Hylan Baker. *Makeup* Harry Frampton. *Hairstyles* Eileen Warwick.
Cast: Gig Young *(Mike Kelton)*, Carol Lynley *(Susannah Kelton/Sarah)*, Oliver Reed *(Ethan)*, Flora Robson *(Aunt Agatha)*, William Devlin *(Zebulon Whateley)*, Bernard Kay *(Tait)*, Judith Arthy *(Emma)*, Robert Cawdron *(Luther Whateley)*, Celia Hewitt *(Aunt Sarah)*, Ingrid Bower *(village girl)*, Anita Anderson *(Susannah as a child)*, Charles Lloyd Pack *(Bargee)*, Peter Porteous, Clifford Diggins.

Melodrama. Source: H. P. Lovecraft and August Derleth, "The Shuttered Room," in *The Shuttered Room, and Other Pieces* (Sauk City, Wisconsin, 1959). Susannah Kelton returns with her husband, Mike, to her childhood home on an isolated island off the New England coast to inspect an old mill she has inherited. She has not been there since she was sent to New York City after both her parents died. The islanders, openly hostile to the couple, are aghast at their plans to use the millhouse, which has an ominous history, as a summer house. Mike and Susannah ignore the warnings of her brutish cousin Ethan and her morose Aunt Agatha. Curious about the shuttered room on the top floor of the millhouse, Susannah conducts an investigation. She does not know that Mike has been waylaid and beaten up by Ethan's gang of wastrels. Frightened by the dark old building, Susannah is about to leave when she is suddenly confronted and nearly assaulted by the lecherous Ethan. She takes refuge in the shuttered room, but Ethan follows her with a lighted torch. As he pursues Susannah, a strange figure lunges at him from out of the shadows, causing him to fall to his death. Mike, meanwhile, has learned the truth about the millhouse from Aunt Agatha, whose silence has been broken by the murder of Emma, Ethan's sluttish girl friend. The strange figure in the shuttered room is Sarah, Susannah's insane and physically malformed sister, who, chained in the room, has been sustained through the years by the devoted Agatha. Racing back to the millhouse, Mike arrives in time to drag Susannah from a fire started by the lighted torch Ethan dropped when he fell. Agatha then appears and locks herself in the shuttered room, choosing to perish in the flames with Susannah's terrified and bewildered sister. *Cousins. Aunts. Wastrels. Sisters. Inheritance. Village life. Lechery. Murder. Insanity. Mills. Islands. New England. Fires.*

Note: Filmed on location in Cornwall, England. Released in Great Britain in Jul 1967.

SIAVASH IN PERSEPOLIS (Iran)   **F6.4483**
Djame Djam–Iran Film–Ashna Film. Dec **1966** [New York showing]. Sd; b&w. 16mm. ca100 min.
Dir Ferydoun Rahnema. *Photog* Palan.
Cast: Minou Farjad *(Siavash)*, Marva Nabili *(Soudabeh)*, Abbas Moayeri *(Kaous)*, Nader Kouklani *(Garsivaz)*, Amir Farid *(Afrasiab)*, Ashgar Zolfaghari *(Rustam)*.

Drama. Based on the epic by: Ferdowsī, *Shāhnāmeh* (ca1010). Siavash, the son of Kai Kaous, the sovereign of Iran, is beloved by Soudabeh, his father's first wife, but, bound by his honor as a knight, he refuses her advances. Having been spurned, she relates to Kaous that Siavash is her lover and, further, that she has given birth to his children, who have been murdered. The council of priests debates the matter and elects to subject the prince to trial by fire. He is exonerated when he passes through the flames, and he gains command of the forces now drawn into battle with Turan, an enemy neighbor. Meanwhile, Soudabeh is pardoned, and Siavash forgives her. As he prepares his forces for battle, Afrasiab, the sovereign of Turan, has a dream in which he foresees his country in ruins if he engages in war with Iran. Anxious to make peace as a result, Afrasiab complies with Siavash's demand for 100 hostages. Kaous, skeptical of Afrasiab's intentions, orders Siavash to kill the hostages, but the prince again refuses by reason of honor. He is granted safe passage through Turan to a neutral country, but instead he remains in Turan, marries Afrasiab's daughter, and builds a new town in which they will live and rule. Afrasiab's brother Garsivaz opposes the new union between Iran and his country, and he devises a complicated intrigue which results in the execution of Siavash as a traitor. From the blood of the prince, the legend is told, grew an herb, the "blood of Siavash." *Royalty. Mothers-in-law. Brothers. Hostages. Peacemakers. Legendary characters. Politics. Ethics. Trials. Perfidy. Persia. Persepolis. Dreams. Siavash.*

Note: U. S. distributor is undetermined. Released in Iran in 1965(?); may have been titled *Khun-e Siaavash.*

THE SICILIAN CLAN (France)   **F6.4484**
Fox–Europa–Les Films du Siècle. *Dist* Twentieth Century-Fox Film Corp. 29 Mar **1970** [New York opening; c5 Dec 1969; LF70]. Sd; col (De Luxe). 35mm (Panavision). 121 min. *MPAA rating* GP.
Prod Jacques Strauss. *Dir* Henri Verneuil. *Screenplay* Henri Verneuil, José Giovanni, Pierre Pelegri. *Dial* José Giovanni. *Dir Photog* Henri Decaë. *Camera Op* Charles-Henry Montel. *Art Dir* Jacques Saulnier. *Set Decor* Charles Mérangel. *Film Ed* Albert Jurgenson, Pierre Gillette, Jean-Michel Gautier. *Mus* Ennio Morricone. *Mus Dir* Bruno Nicolai. *Sd* Jean Rieul. *Asst Dir* Marc Grunebaum, Bernard Stora. *Prod Mgr* Jacques Juranville. *Unit Mgr* Gérard Crosnier. *Cont* Lucile Costa. *Cost* Hélène Nourry. *Makeup* Michel Deruelle. *Hairstyles* Simone Knapp. *Prop Master* René Albouze.
Cast: Jean Gabin *(Vittorio Manalese)*, Alain Delon *(Roger Sartet)*, Lino Ventura *(Inspector Le Goff)*, Irina Demick *(Jeanne Manalese)*, Amedeo Nazzari *(Tony Nicosia)*, Sydney Chaplin *(Jack)*, Elisa Cegani *(Maria Manalese)*, Karen Blanguernon *(Thérèse)*, Marc Porel *(Sergio Manalese)*, Yves Lefebvre *(Aldo Manalese)*, Philippe Baronnet *(Luigi)*, Leopoldo Trieste *(stamp expert)*, César Chauveau *(Roberto)*, Danielle Volle *(Monique Sartet)*, Edward Meeks *(pilot)*, Jacques Duby *(Rovel)*, Yves Brainville, Gérard Buhr, Raoul Delfosse, Sally Nesbitt, André Dumas, André Thorent.

Crime melodrama. Source: Auguste Le Breton, *Le clan des Siciliens* (Paris, 1967). Condemned murderer Roger Sartet escapes from prison and locates Vittorio Manalese, a Sicilian gangster who gives the convict refuge. Sartet, a Corsican, tells Manalese of a foolproof plan to rob a fortune in jewels from a Venice exhibition. Manalese, hoping to retire after this last robbery, submits the plan to Tony Nicosia, an American gangster who suggests that they hijack the plane that is transporting the jewels from Venice to New York. Manalese's entire family takes part in the robbery, which comes off without a flaw, and they all return to Europe to hide until the loot is divided. However, Manalese learns that Sartet has been making love to his daughter-in-law, Jeanne, and he withholds Sartet's share of the money to lure him back to Paris. Sartet arrives in Paris earlier than expected and witnesses the arrest of Manalese's sons, who were sent to kill him. To avenge the shame brought on the family, Manalese kills both Sartet and Jeanne. He then returns home to find Inspector Le Goff of the Paris police waiting for him. *Gangsters. Sicilians. Corsicans. Americans in foreign countries. Hijackers. Police. Murder. Prison escapes. Robbery. Family life. Revenge. Jewels. Airplanes. Paris. New York City.*

Note: Opened in Paris in Dec 1969 as *Le clan des Siciliens*; running time: 124 min.

THE SICK ONES *see* **SHE CAME ON THE BUS**

SICK, SICK WORLD *see* **IT'S A SICK, SICK, SICK WORLD**

THE SIDEHACKERS *see* **FIVE THE HARD WAY**

THE SIDELONG GLANCES OF A PIGEON KICKER   **F6.4485**
Saturn Pictures. *Dist* Metro-Goldwyn-Mayer, Inc., Plaza Pictures. 21 Oct **1970** [San Francisco opening]. Sd; col (print by Movielab). 35mm. 106 min. [See note.] *MPAA rating* R.
Pres by Lois Holland Callaway. *Prod* Richard Lewis. *Exec Prod* William P. Wilson. *Assoc Prod* Tom Sternberg, James Signorelli. *Dir* John Dexter. *Screenplay* Ron Whyte. *Photog* Urs Furrer. *Art Dir* Manny Gerard. *Set Decor* Bob Drumheller. *Film Ed* John Oettinger. *Mus* Pat Williams, Lee Holdridge, Edd Kaleroff, Chris Dedrick, Warren Marley. *Mus Supv* Phillip Ramone. *Songs:* "Freedom Song," "Faces of You" sung by Warren Marley. *Played by* Gasmask and Great Jones. *Sd Rec* Charles Federmack, Richard Vorisek. *Asst Dir* Stanley Panesoff. *Prod Mgr* George Goodman. *Cost* Domingo Rodriguez. *Makeup* John Alese. *Hairstyles* Phil Leto. *Casting* Vic Ramos.
Cast: Jordan Christopher *(Jonathan)*, Jill O'Hara *(Jennifer)*, Robert Walden *(Winslow Smith)*, Kate Reid *(Jonathan's mother)*, William Redfield *(Jonathan's father)*, Lois Nettleton *(Mildred)*, Boni Enten *(Naomi)*, Elaine Stritch *(tough*

lady), Melba Moore (model at party), Peter Link (Oliver), Kristoffer Tabori (Oliver's boyfriend), Don Warfield (young stutterer), Jean Shevlin (Mrs. Abelman), Matt Warner (Mr. Abelman), Ethel Smith (blowsy lady at pinball machine), Mary Orr (saleslady), Nancy Andrews (passenger with crying child), Tony Capodilupo (van man), Christian Ericson (Gordon), Maria Cellario (pretty girl in laundromat), Pat Ast (fat girl at party), Sara Wilson (lesbian at party), Helen Ludlam (old lady on train), Paul Norman (orderly), Richard Clarke (Englishman), Janet Maria Burtis (cranky lady passenger), Bert Bertram (doorman), Ellis Richardson, Buddy Butler (Negro passersby), Adam Reed (little redhaired boy), Sean Campbell (boy on crutches), Margaret Brewster (pigeon lady), Arthur Anderson (floorwalker), Steve Dawson (desk sergeant), Bonnie Paul (crying girl), Bill Herndon (cop at the pier), Anne Shropshire (mother at department store), Esther Bussler (Christmas shopper in cab), Salo Douday (sad bum), Frank Hamilton (gallstone man in hospital), Wyman Pendleton (doctor), David Doyle (Mr. Seigbert), Edward Dunne (skinny fag), Sean Bersell (little boy in cab).

Comedy. Source: David Boyer, *The Sidelong Glances of a Pigeon Kicker* (New York, 1968). Three years after graduating from Princeton, disillusioned Jonathan is driving a Manhattan taxicab and expressing his disgust with the world by insulting his obnoxious passengers and kicking pigeons in Riverside Park. His circle of acquaintances includes Winslow Smith, a motorcycle-riding, leather-jacketed, self-styled rebel, whose image is undermined by the fact that at 24 he is still a virgin; Oliver, a homosexual interior decorator who stages elaborate parties and tries, unsuccessfully, to seduce his male guests; and Jennifer, a 21-year-old tenant in Jonathan's building, whose sojourn in New York City to "find herself" is being subsidized by her parents. While attending one of Oliver's wild soirees, Jonathan is accosted by a nymphomaniacal former bedmate, Naomi, who drags him into the bathroom, strips off her clothes, and invites him to join her in the fur-lined tub. Instead, he returns to his apartment, visits Jennifer, and explains why he must maintain emotional detachment. Jennifer, however, is such an understanding listener that she and Jonathan are soon making love. At Christmas, Jonathan takes Jennifer to spend the holidays in Darien, Connecticut, with his suburbanite parents—a possessive and petulant mother and a potentially alcoholic stepfather. But his mother angrily discovers Jonathan and Jennifer nude in the bed, and after a seasonal party leads to further generation gap warfare Jonathan and Jennifer abruptly return to the city. Although drawn to Jennifer, Jonathan is soured by the prospects of married life and is even becoming increasingly apathetic toward his friends. One night, attempting to explain his disenchantment to Jennifer, he enters her apartment and finds her in bed with Winslow. Shattered, Jonathan dazedly drives his cab through the city until finally, in a rage, he plunges off the docks into the river. Recovering in the intensive care unit of a hospital, Jonathan is visited by his friends as well as by Jennifer, who pleads for a second chance to demonstrate her love. Instead Jonathan slips out of the hospital, packs his bags, and boards a train for Des Moines, Iowa. There he plans to drive a truck and continue his isolated existence of thumbing his nose at the world. *Taxi drivers. Motorcyclists. Interior decorators. Disillusionment. Virginity. Male homosexuality. Seduction. Filial relations. Suburban life. Alcoholism. Jealousy. Christmas. New York City. Darien (Connecticut). Des Moines. New York City—Waterfront. New York City—Riverside Park. Automobile accidents. Pigeons.*

Note: Filmed in New York City. Actor Peter Link is also known as Riggs O'Hara. Shortly after the film's initial 1970 showings, distribution rights were sold by M-G-M to Plaza Pictures, who shortened the running length to 87 min and changed its title to *Pigeons.*

THE SIDEWALK COWBOY   F6.4486

Dist Sam Lake Enterprises. **1968.** Sd; col (Eastman Color). 35mm. 75 min.
Pres by Sam Lake.

Cast: Sietir Olsun (*Carl Talbot*), Lois Boyd (*Susie*).

Melodrama. Carl Talbot, a quiet, good-looking young man, finds himself in New York City with no money. He pawns his beloved guitar and quickly spends the small amount of money it brings him. Just when it appears that Carl will soon be destitute, his best friend's ex-wife, Susie, invites him to stay in her apartment. Carl soon realizes that Susie's generosity is motivated by lust. His idea of a satisfying sexual relationship is very different from hers. Carl cannot cope with her strange passions and becomes obsessed with raising enough money to escape. In desperation, he makes the rounds of pool halls and cruises the streets looking for older women and homosexuals, without much success. The tensions of his own sexual difficulties, his frustration at being unable to raise the money he needs, and Susie's continual sexual demands push Carl to the breaking point. *Lust. Seduction. Prostitution. Finance—Personal. Male homosexuality. New York City.*

Note: May also be known as *Matinee Cowboy.*

SIEBZEHN JAHR, BLONDES HAAR *see* **THE BATTLE OF THE MODS**

SIEDMA PEVNINA *see* **THE SEVENTH CONTINENT**

LE SIÈGE DE SYRACUSE *see* **SIEGE OF SYRACUSE**

SIEGE OF FORT BISMARCK (Japan)   F6.4487

Toho Co. 12 Mar **1968** [Los Angeles showing]. Sd; col (Eastmancolor). 35mm (Tohoscope). 98 min.

Exec Prod Tomoyuki Tanaka. *Dir* Kengo Furusawa. *Screenplay* Katsuya Suzaki. *Photog* Fukuzo Koizumi. *Mus* Hachiro Matsui. *Sp Eff* Eiji Tsuburaya.

Cast: Makoto Sato, Yosuke Natsuki, Yuzo Kayama, Ryo Ikebe, Mie Hama, Toru Ibuki.

War drama. Just prior to World War I, Germany builds a fortress at Tsingtao, to further its colonial policies in Asia. In 1914 Japan joins the Allies against Germany and one of the first Japanese goals is the capture of the powerful Fort Bismarck. The Japanese air force, which consists of two Farman biplanes purchased from France, encounters a German monoplane on its first reconnaissance mission and in the confusion, none of the Japanese photographs come out. On a second flight, the Japanese pilots drop various objects on the Germans, but they inflict little damage and one of the planes is shot down. An all-out assault by the Japanese Navy is now ordered on the fort, and the second biplane contributes to the success of the attack by scoring a direct hit, this time with real bombs, on a supply train headed for the fort. *Air pilots. Germans. Reconnaissance. Forts. Airplanes. Trains. World War I. Tsingtao. Japan—Navy.*

Note: Released in Japan in 1963 as *Chintao Yosai bakugeki meirei.*

THE SIEGE OF HELL STREET *see* **THE SIEGE OF SIDNEY STREET**

THE SIEGE OF SIDNEY STREET (Great Britain)   F6.4488

Mid–Century Film Productions. *Dist* United Producers Releasing Organization. 6 Dec **1961** [Los Angeles opening; c7 Nov 1960; LP22341]. Sd; b&w. 35mm (Dyaliscope). 93 min.

Prod-Dir Robert S. Baker, Monty Berman. *Screenplay* Jimmy Sangster, Alexander Baron. *Story* Jimmy Sangster. *Photog* Robert S. Baker, Monty Berman. *Camera Op* Chic Waterson. *Focus* Robin Vidgeon. *Art Dir* William Kellner. *Set Dresser* Freda Pearson. *Ch Draughtsman* Dick Byrne. *Film Ed* Peter Bezencenet. *Asst Film Ed* Jeanne Henderson. *Mus Comp & Cond* Stanley Black. *Song:* "Ya Vas Lyu-Blyu" David Palmer, Robert Musel, Stanley Black. *Sung by* Nicole Berger. *Sd Mix* Syd Wiles. *Boom Op* Brendan Redmond. *Sd Camera Op* Liam Saurin. *1st, 2d & 3d Asst Dir* Peter Manley, Charles Blair, Grania O'Shannon. *Prod Mgr* Ronald Liles. *Cont* Phyllis Crocker. *Prod Sec* Shileen O'Rourke. *Wardrobe Master* Jim Dunlevy. *Makeup* Jill Carpenter. *Hairstyles* Betty Sherriff. *Sp Eff* Cliff Richardson. *Grip* William Robinson. *Still Photog* Roy Byrne. *Prop Buyer* Maureen Roche. *Constr Mgr* Bill Greene. *Studio Constr Mgr* Peter McGoldrick. *Prop Master* Noel Coade. *Ch Electrn* Tom Chapman. *Studio Mgr* P. L. Kendrick.

Cast: Donald Sinden (*Insp. John Mannering*), Nicole Berger (*Sara*), Kieron Moore (*Yoska*), Peter Wyngarde (*Peter*), Godfrey Quigley (*Blakey*), Leonard Sachs (*Svaars*), Tutte Lemkow (*Dmitrieff*), George Pastell (*Brodsky*), Angela Newman (*Nina*), T. P. McKenna (*Lapidos*), Maurice Good (*Gardstein*), James Caffrey (*Hefeld*), Harold Goldblatt (*Hersh*), Christopher Casson (*police commissioner*), Harry Brogan (*Old Harry*), Alan Simpson (*police inspector*), Robert Lepler (*jeweler*), Margaret D'Arcy (*nurse*), Joe Lynch (*Sergeant Todd*), Stanley Illsley (*doctor*), Anne Sharpe (*woman on estate*), Bart Bastable (*Sergeant Tucker*), Paul Farrell (*barman*), Bill Foley (*1st detective*), Aiden Grennell (*2d detective*), Jimmy Sangster (*Winston Churchill*).

Historical drama. Peter heads a gang of militant Russian exiles living in London who have terrorized the city with robbery and murder in order to acquire funds needed for their anarchist ends. Sara, a young orphaned Russian refugee, meets Peter in the club where she sings and is drawn to him. When she learns that Peter, along with members of his gang including Yoska, Svaars, and Dmitrieff, participated in a bank robbery in which a man was murdered, she is horrified, but Peter justifies his crimes as fighting oppression. Meanwhile, Inspector Mannering, posing as a wanted man frequenting the East End dives, finally tracks down the gang. During this time he gets to know and understand Sara and the reasons for her complicity. However, further acts of crime and butchery by the gang arouse the entire nation and the anarchists flee to a hideout at 100 Sidney Street. On January 3, 1911, the police surround the neighborhood and close in for the siege. *Russians. Anarchists. Orphans. Refugees. Singers. Police. Exile. Bank robberies. Murder. Gangs. Nightclubs. Winston Leonard Spencer Churchill. Sidney Street Siege. London—East End.*

Note: Released in London in Oct 1960. Also known as *The Siege of Hell Street.*

SIEGE OF SYRACUSE (France/Italy)   **F6.4489**
Glomer Film–Galatea–Société Cinématographique Lyre. *Dist* Paramount Pictures. 31 Jan **1962** [Detroit opening; c1 Dec 1960; LP21190]. Sd; col (Eastman Color). 35mm (Dyaliscope). 97 min.

Prod Enzo Merolle. *Dir* Pietro Francisci. *Screenplay* Pietro Francisci, Giorgio Graziosi, Ennio De Concini. *Photog* Carlo Carlini. *Art Dir* Ottavio Scotti. *Mus* Angelo Francesco Lavagnino.

Cast: Rossano Brazzi *(Archimedes)*, Tina Louise *(Diana)*, Sylva Koscina *(Clio)*, Enrico Maria Salerno *(Gorgia)*, Gino Cervi *(Gerone)*, Alberto Farnese, Luciano Marin, Alfredo Varelli.

Action melodrama. Both the Romans and the Carthaginians are laying siege to Syracuse, and defense preparations have been entrusted to Archimedes. When his beloved Diana becomes pregnant by him, her evil stepbrother, Gorgia, who is in league with Rome, delivers her to some Roman soldiers, a shock that causes her to lose her memory. Eventually she marries Marcello, a Roman consul, while Archimedes obeys his father's wishes and weds the beautiful Clio. Several years later, Archimedes goes to Rome to arrange a new alliance. When Diana sees him, her memory returns, but they decide to sacrifice their love so that their child will not learn of his true parentage. The Romans attack Syracuse, and Archimedes turns back their fleet by using "burning glasses," which magnify the sun's rays and destroy whatever they are turned upon. In the final fighting, both Marcello and Gorgia are killed. With Syracuse still free, Archimedes, whose wife has died, is reunited with Diana, but they vow to maintain the secret of their son. *Mathematicians. Carthaginians. Stepbrothers. Pregnancy. Brother-sister relationship. Amnesia. Illegitimacy. Filial relations. Parentage. Inventions. Rome—History—Monarchy & Republic. Punic Wars. Syracuse. Archimedes.*

Note: Opened in Rome in Apr 1960 as *L'assedio di Siracusa;* running time: 115 min (also known as *Archimede);* in France as *Le siège de Syracuse.*

SIEGE OF THE SAXONS (Great Britain)   **F6.4490**
Ameran Films. *Dist* Columbia Pictures. Aug **1963** [c1 Aug 1963; LP26842]. Sd (RCA); col (Technicolor). 35mm. 85 min.

A Charles H. Schneer Production. *Prod* Jud Kinberg. *Dir* Nathan Juran. *Screenplay* John Kohn, Jud Kinberg. *Photog* Wilkie Cooper, Jack Mills, photog. *Art Dir* Bill Constable. *Film Ed* Maurice Rootes. *Mus* Laurie Johnson. *Sd Rec* Ken Rawkins, Ken Cameron. *Asst Dir* George Pollard. *Prod Mgr* Ted Wallis. *Cont* Pauline Wise.

Cast: Ronald Lewis *(Robert Marshall)*, Janette Scott *(Katherine)*, Ronald Howard *(Edmund of Cornwall)*, Mark Dignam *(King Arthur)*, John Laurie *(Merlin)*, Jerome Willis *(limping man)*, Richard Clarke *(Saxon Prince)*, Charles Lloyd Pack *(doctor)*, Francis De Wolff *(blacksmith)*, John Gabriel *(Earl of Chatham)*, Peter Mason *(young monk)*, Michael Mellinger *(thief)*, Gordon Boyd *(captain)*, Robert Gillespie, Kenneth Cowan *(soldiers).*

Adventure melodrama. King Arthur of England becomes ill in the 20th year of his reign, and he decides to recuperate discreetly in the castle of Edmund of Cornwall. Arthur is unaware that Edmund is in league with the Saxons, who plan to seize the kingdom and put Arthur to death. Outlaw Robert Marshall stops the first assassination attempt, but the second murder plot succeeds. Edmund then tries to legitimize his claim to the throne by forcing Arthur's daughter, Katherine, to marry him. She escapes with Marshall, and Edmund spreads the news that she is dead and proclaims himself king. Robert and Katherine find the ancient magician Merlin, and the three of them break into and halt the coronation ceremony. Merlin challenges Edmund to draw Arthur's sword, Excalibur, from its scabbard; Edmund fails, but Katherine easily draws the sword and takes her place as rightful heir to the throne. Edmund escapes to join the Saxons and signals an invasion which fails when the combined English forces crush their attack. Katherine then knights Robert and makes him her consort. *Outlaws. Royalty. Saxons. Regicide. Convalescence. Knighthood. Magic. Castles. Swords. King Arthur. Merlin: Legendary characters.*

Note: Released in Great Britain in 1963; running time: 85 min.

LOS SIETE ESPARTANOS see **GLADIATORS SEVEN**

SIETE HOMBRES DE ORO see **SEVEN GOLDEN MEN**

LAS SIETE MAGNIFICAS see **THE TALL WOMEN**

SIETE MUJERES PARA LOS MACGREGOR see **UP THE MACGREGORS**

SIETE PISTOLAS PARA LOS MACGREGOR see **SEVEN GUNS FOR THE MACGREGORS**

IL SIGILLO DI PECHINO see **THE CORRUPT ONES**

SIGN OF AQUARIUS   **F6.4491**
Cinar Productions. 10 Jun **1970** [Cleveland opening]. Sd; col. 35mm. 95 min. *MPAA rating* R.

Pres by George B. Roberts, Paul Rubenstein. *Prod* George B. Roberts, Paul Rubenstein. *Co-prod* Oscar Zimmerman. *Exec Prod* John Pappas. *Dir* Robert J. Emery. *Screenplay* John Pappas, Robert J. Emery. *Dir Photog* Paul Rubenstein. *Dir Lighting* Nick Boris. *Mus Dir* Thomas Baker. *Orig Songs* Al Zbacnic, Thomas Baker. *Choreog* Jeff Kutash. *Sd Rec* Mike Chamoon.

Cast: Paul Elliot, Gabe Lewis, Mickey Shiff, Jim Coursar, Nick Kleinholtz, III, Thomas Baker, Toni Ceo, Virginia Morris.

Musical melodrama. A group of hippies who live together in a communal apartment are arrested during a peace demonstration. Upon their release, they return home to discuss plans for another demonstration. That evening in a nightclub, the hippies watch as the mother of a young patron, Donna, arrives to take her home, in an effort to remove her from bad company. Sonny, one of the hippie group, passes Donna a note with the address of the communal apartment. Later at the apartment, a young woman experiences a bad LSD trip in which she "gives birth" to a huge egg. Donna arrives and is introduced to LSD during a musical ritual called "Om Pax Om." The next morning the hippies sell newspapers on a street corner. That evening Sonny and Donna go walking and encounter a gangster drug dealer and his friends, who proceed to beat up Sonny for refusing to become a dealer. The next day, after the second peace demonstration, the pushers wait in the alley for Sonny, and when he appears, they shoot at him but accidentally hit Donna instead. The group conducts a solemn procession through the streets carrying Donna's body. Additional songs include "The Aquarians" (title song), and "I'm Gonna Dodge the Draft." *Hippies. Drug dealers. Filial relations. Murder. Demonstrations. Communal living. Psychedelic states. LSD. Nightclubs.*

Note: Also known as *Ghetto Freaks.*

SIGN OF THE VIRGIN (Czechoslovakia)   **F6.4492**
Barrandov Film Studio. *For* Československý Film. *Dist* Brandon Films. 3 Nov **1969** [New York opening]. Sd; b&w. 35mm (CinemaScope). 83 min.

Dir Zbyněk Brynych. *Screenplay* Milan Uhde, Zbyněk Brynych. *Story* Milan Uhde. *Photog* Jan Kališ. *Camera* Alexandr Rašilov. *Art Dir* Milan Nejedlý. *Film Ed* Miroslav Hájek. *Mus* Jiří Sternwald. *Song:* "Stairway to Heaven" Karel Kopecký, Jindřich Faktor. *Sung by* Karel Kopecký. *Sd* Miloš Alster. *Asst Dir* Ota Koval. *In Charge of Prod* Václav Rouha. *Prod Assoc* Ladislav Dražan. *Adv* František Říčka, Václav Pospíšil.

Cast: Josef Čáp *(Standa)*, Jaroslava Obermayerová *(Jana)*, Vladimír Pucholt *(Veleba)*, Jiří Wimmer *(Beiman [Rejman])*, Ilja Prachař *(Captain Pazourek)*, Jiří Adamíra *(Lieutenant Březina)*, Rudolf Jelínek *(Lieutenant Toneiser)*, Ivan Vyskočil *(Vyskočil)*, Jan Kotva *(Samek)*, Jaroslava Pokorná *(chambermaid)*, Jan Libíček *(Augustin).*

Romantic comedy. Jana, a young woman living in Prague, and her fiancé, Standa, a soldier in the Czechoslovakian Army, are eager to begin sexual relations, but Standa is not permitted to have female visitors on the military post. Nevertheless, Jana leaves Prague and goes to the base. Standa fears that the officers in his unit will penalize him if he is found with Jana; in addition, they have no place with sufficient privacy to make love. Eventually they are aided by a medical officer who permits them to use a bed in the infirmary. *Sexual initiation. Military life. Hospitals. Prague. Czechoslovakia—Army.*

Note: Location scenes filmed in Žatec. Released in Czechoslovakia in Oct 1966 as *Souhvězdí Panny.* Working title: *Ošetřovna.* U. S. prerelease title: *Constellation: Virgo.*

SIGNORE E SIGNORI see **THE BIRDS, THE BEES, AND THE ITALIANS**

SIGNPOST TO MURDER   **F6.4493**
Marten Productions. *Dist* Metro-Goldwyn-Mayer, Inc. 10 Feb **1965** [Denver, Colorado, opening; c21 Jul 1964; LP29361]. Sd (Westrex); b&w. 35mm (Panavision). 74 min. [Also 77 min.]

A Lawrence Weingarten Production. *Dir* George Englund. *Screenplay* Sally Benson. *Dir Photog* Paul C. Vogel. *Art Dir* George W. Davis, Edward Carfagno. *Set Decor* Henry Grace, Frank McKelvy. *Film Ed* John McSweeney, Jr. *Mus* Lyn Murray. *Rec Supv* Franklin Milton. *Asst Dir* Wallace Worsley. *Miss Woodward's Gowns by* Travilla. *Makeup Supv* William Tuttle. *Hairstyles* Sydney Guilaroff. *Sp Vis Eff* J. McMillan Johnson.

Cast: Joanne Woodward *(Molly Thomas)*, Stuart Whitman *(Alex Forrester)*, Edward Mulhare *(Dr. Mark Fleming)*, Alan Napier *(The Vicar)*, Joyce Worsley *(Mrs. Barnes)*, Leslie Denison *(Superintendent Bickley)*, Murray Matheson *(Dr. Graham)*, Hedley Mattingly *(Officer Rogers)*, Carol Veazie *(Auntie).*

Mystery melodrama. Source: Monte Doyle, *Signpost to Murder* (London opening: 9 Feb 1962). Alex Forrester, convicted of murdering his wife, fails to gain his release after spending 10 years in a British asylum for the criminally insane. Dr. Mark Fleming, Forrester's psychiatrist, informs him of an old law which provides for the reopening of a trial if the prisoner escapes and remains at large for 14 days. Forrester escapes and takes refuge in the home of Molly Thomas, who claims that she is awaiting the return of her husband from a trip to The Hague. Molly tells him of her unhappy marriage, and the two become attracted to each other. In the evening, Forrester discovers a man's body by the mill wheel of Molly's house. After stumbling down a flight of steps, he regains consciousness and finds that the body is missing. The corpse is later found by the police, and Molly identifies the dead man as her husband. She accuses Forrester of the murder but later breaks down and informs the police that she and Fleming are lovers and that they arranged Forrester's escape in order to frame him for the murder. *Psychiatrists. Prison escapees. Police. Murder. Infidelity. Frameup. Insane asylums. England.*

Note: Some location scenes filmed in England.

SIGNS OF LIFE (West Germany)   **F6.4494**
Werner Herzog Filmproduktion. *Dist* Werner Herzog. Nov **1968**. Sd; b&w. 35mm. 91 min.
Prod-Dir-Writ Werner Herzog. *Photog* Thomas Mauch. *Ed* Beate Mainka-Jellinghaus, Maxi Mainka. *Mus* Stavros Xarhakos. *Sd* Herbert Prasch. *Collab* Florian Fricke, Nicos Triandafyllidis, Ina Fritsche, Tasos Karabelas, Mike Piller, Thomas Hartwig, Dieter Lohmann, Bettina von Waldthausen, Friederike Pezold, Martje Grohmann.
Cast: Peter Brogle *(Stroszek)*, Wolfgang Reichmann *(Meinhard)*, Athina Zacharopoulou *(Nora)*, Wolfgang von Ungern-Sternberg *(Becker)*, Wolfgang Stumpf *(captain)*, Henry van Lyck *(lieutenant)*, Julie Pinheiro *(Gypsy)*, Florian Fricke *(pianist)*, Heinz Usener *(doctor)*, Achmed Hafiz *(Greek resident)*, Jannakis Frasakis, Katerinaki.
Drama. Stroszek, a German soldier wounded in combat, is sent in 1944 to a Nazi-occupied Greek island to guard an old fortress, accompanied by his wife, Nora, and two other soldiers, Meinhard and Becker. With nothing to do, they are forced to find ways to occupy their time. They paint their living quarters, acquire some chickens and a goat, and, discovering an ammunition depot full of explosives, make rockets. Becker begins to translate the ancient Greek texts carved in stone around the castle and learns that it was once occupied by pirates who were all hanged; Meinhard devises an elaborate contraption for catching cockroaches, which he executes in military fashion. A mysterious Gypsy appears and gives them a wooden owl whose eyes and ears are agitated by flies imprisoned inside. But the general tedium causes Stroszek to show signs of insanity, and he becomes visibly disturbed after hearing a pianist play Chopin. He then appeals to his commanding officer, who assigns him to patrol a nearby ridge with Meinhard. When they come to a field of windmills, Stroszek goes berserk, firing at the windmills; and Meinhard subdues him. Nora and Meinhard report the incident to the commanding officer, who decides to send Stroszek back to Germany. Feeling betrayed, Stroszek forces Nora, Meinhard, and Becker to leave the fortress and begins firing on the town, even threatening to blow it up. Though his rebellion ends in failure, his descent into madness has produced some "signs of life." *Gypsies. Pianists. Insanity. Military occupation. Ammunition. Windmills. Islands. Rockets. Greek language—Attic. World War II. Greece. Frédéric François Chopin. Germany—Army. Cockroaches. Chickens. Goats.*

Note: Inspired by a newspaper report of an apparently actual incident of the Seven Years' War. Released in West Germany in 1968 as *Lebenszeichen.*

THE SILENCE (Sweden)   **F6.4495**
Svensk Filmindustri. *Dist* Janus Films. 3 Feb **1964** [New York opening]. Sd (AGA-Baltic); b&w. 35mm. 95 min.
Prod Allan Ekelund. *Dir-Writ* Ingmar Bergman. *Photog* Sven Nykvist. *Asst Photog* Rolf Holmqvist, Peter Wester. *Art Dir* P. A. Lundgren. *Film Ed* Ulla Ryghe. *Mus* Bo Nilsson. *Mus:* "Goldberg Variations" (25th Variation) Johann Sebastian Bach. *Sd Engr* Stig Flodin. *Sd Asst* Bo Leveren, Tage Sjöberg. *Sd Eff* Evald Andersson. *Sd Mix* Olle Jakobsson. *Asst Dir* Lenn Hjörtzberg, Lars-Erik Liedholm. *Prod Mgr* Lars-Owe Carlberg. *Script Girl* Katherina Farago. *Cost* Marik Vos-Lundh. *Makeup & Hairstyles* Börje Lundh. *Asst Makeup & Hairstyles* Gullan Westfelt. *Prop* Karl-Arne Bergman. *Still Photog* Harry Kampf.
Cast: Ingrid Thulin *(Ester)*, Gunnel Lindblom *(Anna)*, Jörgen Lindström *(Johan)*, Håkan Jahnberg *(hotel waiter)*, Birger Malmsten *(restaurant waiter)*, The Eduardini *(the seven dwarfs)*, Eduardo Gutiérrez *(dwarf manager)*, Lissi Alandh *(girl in cabaret)*, Leif Forstenberg *(man in cabaret)*, Nils Waldt *(cashier in cinema)*, Birger Lensander *(usher in cinema)*, Eskil Kalling, Karl-Arne Bergman, Olof Widgren *(shadows)*.
Drama. Two women, Ester, a translator and intellectual, and her younger sister, Anna, and Anna's young son, Johan, who are returning by train to Sweden after a vacation, stop in Timuku, a town in the foreign country they are passing through, and check into an old, elegant hotel. The language that is spoken is foreign to the visitors; the streets are narrow, and people are hurrying around. Ester, a lonely spinster who is suffering from a terminal lung disease, is dominating and protective toward Anna, for whom she represses a lesbian desire. Anna, sensual and less sensitive, is repulsed by Ester's attitude and annoyed at being tied to her ailing sister. In the hotel suite Ester works on her

translating between coughing spasms and consoles herself by chain-smoking and drinking. Anna leaves the hotel and goes to a local variety theater where she witnesses a couple openly making love. She immediately picks up a waiter in a cafe. Meanwhile, Johan wanders about the hotel and meets a group of dwarfs, a theatrical troupe who dress him in women's clothes. An old gentleman, the hotel waiter, reminisces to Johan about his past. Sirens wail, and a tank rumbles by beneath the hotel window, suggesting that this country is at war. Returning to the hotel, Anna tells her sister about the couple in the theater and relates the details of her pickup, then goes off into an empty room to make love with him again; the story arouses Ester and she masturbates. Ester learns from Johan where her sister is and leads her to the room. Anna begins making love for a third time in front of her sister but stops and has a violent quarrel with her. The next morning Anna and Johan depart, leaving Ester alone and near death with only the old waiter to care for her. On the train Johan puzzles over a note from Ester written in the strange language of the country. *Sisters. Translators. Intellectuals. Dwarfs. Waiters. Children. Pickups. Lust. Lesbianism. Autoeroticism. Incest. Death. Trains. Hotels. Tuberculosis. Tanks (armored cars).*

Note: Opened in Stockholm in Sep 1963 as *Tystnaden;* running time: 105 min.

SILENCE HAS NO WINGS (Japan)   **F6.4496**
Nippon Eiga Shinsha. *Dist* Toho Co. Jan **1967**. Sd; b&w. 35mm. 103 min.
Prod Yasuo Matsukawa. *Dir* Kazuo Kuroki. *Screenplay* Yasuo Matsukawa, Hisaya Iwasa, Kazuo Kuroki. *Photog* Tatsuo Suzuki. *Mus* Teizo Matsumura.
Cast: Mariko Kaga, Fumio Watanabe, Hiroyuki Nagato, Toshie Kimura, Kunie Tanaka, Minoru Nakahira, Takeshi Kusaka, Yukio Shirukaya, Katamasa Komatsu, Shoichi Ozawa.
Allegory. A schoolboy in Hokkaido captures a rare butterfly and shows it to his teacher, who refuses to believe that the boy caught it nearby, since the variety is found only in the extreme southern region of Japan. Suspected of lying, the boy tearfully destroys the insect. The film then traces what might have been the butterfly's journey from the south. Through the eyes of the butterfly, which becomes a symbol of love, the dehumanizing aspects of contemporary urban life in cities such as Nagasaki, Hiroshima, Kyoto, Osaka, Hong Kong, and Yokohama are shown. *Students. Urban life. Hokkaido. Nagasaki. Hiroshima. Kyoto. Osaka. Hong Kong. Yokohama. Butterflies.*

Note: Released in Japan in 1966 as *Tobenai chinmoku.*

THE SILENCERS   **F6.4497**
Meadway–Claude Productions. *Dist* Columbia Pictures. 18 Feb **1966** [Chicago opening; cl Mar 1966; LP32469]. Sd; col (Pathé). 35mm. 105 min.
Prod Irving Allen. *Assoc Prod* Jim Schmerer. *Dir* Phil Karlson. *2d Unit Dir* James Havens. *Screenplay* Oscar Saul. *Dir Photog* Burnett Guffey. *Art Dir* Joe Wright. *Set Decor* George R. Nelson. *Main Titl* Pacific Title. *Film Ed* Charles Nelson. *Mus & Orig Songs* Elmer Bernstein. *Orig Songs* Mack David. *Songs Sung by* Cyd Charisse, Vikki Carr, Dean Martin. *Titl Song Sung by* Cyd Charisse. *Choreog* Robert Sidney. *Sd* Charles J. Rice, Lambert Day. *Asst Dir* Clark Paylow. *Unit Prod Mgr* Sergei Petschnikoff, Ralph Black. *Cost* Moss Mabry. *Makeup* Ben Lane. *Hairstyles* Virginia Jones. *Parodies* Herbert Baker.
Cast: Dean Martin *(Matt Helm)*, Stella Stevens *(Gail)*, Daliah Lavi *(Tina Batori)*, Victor Buono *(Tung-Tze)*, Arthur O'Connell *(Wigman)*, Robert Webber *(Sam Gunther)*, James Gregory *(MacDonald)*, Nancy Kovack *(Barbara)*, Roger C. Carmel *(Andreyev)*, Cyd Charisse *(Sarita)*, Beverly Adams *(Lovey Kravezit)*, Richard Devon *(Domino)*, David Bond *(Dr. Naldi)*, John Reach *(Traynor)*, Robert Phillips *(1st armed man)*, John Willis *(m.c.)*, Frank Gerstle *(Frazer)*, Grant Woods *(radio man)*, Patrick Waltz *(hotel clerk)*.
Action comedy. Source: Donald Hamilton, *The Silencers* (New York, 1961). Donald Hamilton, *Death of a Citizen* (New York, 1960). When American Intelligence learns that an enemy ring led by Tung-Tze is planning to divert an American missile so that it will destroy a vital atomic testing base in the United States, retired secret agent Matt Helm is persuaded to take the case. Clues lead Helm and Tina Batori, his former colleague, to Phoenix, where they witness the murder of Sarita, a strip tease dancer, by a man named Sam Gunther. Before she dies, Sarita gives an American scientist's computer tape to Gail, a woman who had been with Gunther. Helm forces Gail to take them to Tung-Tze's hideout, and there they meet "The Cowboy," a double agent who is the real leader of the spy ring. Helm destroys the equipment designed to divert the missile, kills the members of the spy ring, and goes back into retirement. *Secret agents. Stripteasers. Orientals. Murder. Espionage. Sabotage. Missiles. Nuclear weapons. Phoenix (Arizona). Matt Helm.*

THE SILENT CALL   **F6.4498**
Associated Producers, Inc. *Dist* Twentieth Century–Fox Film Corp. May **1961** [c28 Apr 1961; LP20238]. Sd; b&w. 35mm (CinemaScope). 63 min.
Prod Leonard A. Schwartz. *Dir* John Bushelman. *Writ* Tom Maruzzi. *Dir Photog* Kay Norton. *Art Dir* John Mansbridge. *Set Decor* Harry Reif. *Film Ed*

Carl Pierson. *Mus Comp & Cond* Richard D. Aurandt. *Sd* Larry Gannon. *Supv Sd Ed* Jack Cornall. *Sd Facilities* Continental Sound Corp. *Asst Dir* Frank Parmenter. *Prod Supv* Frank Parmenter. *Script Supv* Sandra Nelson. *Cost* Joseph Dimmitt. *Makeup* John Sylvester. *Prop Master* Leigh Carson.

Cast: Gail Russell (*Flore Brancato*), David McLean (*Joe Brancato*), Roger Mobley (*Guy Brancato*), Roscoe Ates (*Sid*), Milton Parsons (*Mohammed*), Dal McKennon (*old man*), Sherwood Keith (*Johnny*), Jack Younger (*Muscles*), Rusty Wescoatt (*Moose*), Pete—The Dog of Flanders (*himself*), H. Tom Hart, Joe Besser.

Drama. When Joe and Flore Brancato move from Nevada to Los Angeles, their young son, Guy, is heartbroken because there is not enough room in the small family car for his huge pet dog, Pete. The animal is left behind with a somewhat unsavory neighbor, but Guy's parents promise that Pete will be sent for as soon as possible. The dog breaks away, however, tries to follow the car, and becomes lost. Guy blames his parents and becomes sullen and embittered; but the resourceful animal continues his 1,000-mile journey, hitchhiking rides and making progress despite bad weather, until eventually he arrives in Los Angeles. After creating a traffic jam, Pete is reunited with the overjoyed Guy. *Children. Filial relations. Los Angeles. Nevada. Pets. Dogs.*

SILENT DEATH (Reissue)   **F6.4499**
Bel-Air Productions. *Dist* Cari Releasing Corp. 14 Apr **1963** [New York showing]. Sd; b&w. 35mm. 76 min.
Note: Originally released as *Voodoo Island* by United Artists in 1957; c8 Mar 1957; LP8146.

THE SILENT WITNESS   **F6.4500**
Ken Kennedy Productions. *Dist* Emerson Film Enterprises. 17 Oct **1962** [Los Angeles opening]. Sd; b&w. 35mm. 70 min.
A John C. Mullins-Ken Kennedy Production. *Prod-Dir* Ken Kennedy. *Exec Prod* John C. Mullins. *Assoc Prod* Tom Corradine. *Orig Story-Screenplay* Frank Jessy. *Photog* Richard E. Cunha. *Camera Op* Jack McCoskey. *Lighting* Don Carstensen. *Film Ed* Herbert L. Strock. *Orig Mus Score* Gene Kauer, Douglas Lackey. *Sd Engr* Herman Lewis. *Prod Supv* Gil Lee.

Cast: Tris Coffin (*Lieutenant Williams*), Marjorie Reynolds (*Mary*), George Kennedy (*Gus Jordan*), Andrea Lane (*Lola*), Billy Shanley (*Danny*), Dick Haynes, Dick Kruse, Ora Keller, George Salem, Teddy Keller, George Dunn, Steve Pavlisin, John Hill, Ben Avery, Jon Moxley, Vern Porter, R. James Straley, King Byrne, John Waschak, Stephanie Watts, Paul Moore, actor, Patricia Lasky.

Crime melodrama. Mary, a police officer's widow, lives with her 14-year-old son, Danny, a delivery boy for the *Denver Post*. Lieutenant Williams, Danny's father's best friend, loves Mary, but she is determined not to remarry a policeman. Meanwhile, Gus Jordan, a wrestler with a heart condition, steals a fur for Lola, a nightclub performer. After learning the gift is stolen property, Lola is accidentally killed in a struggle with Gus. Danny, delivering papers on his route, witnesses the incident and flees. While investigating the fur theft, Lieutenant Williams realizes the connection with Lola's death. The officer locates Gus's hotel room, but the wrestler, having learned where Danny lives, breaks into the boy's home. Danny escapes through a back door and is chased to the Lakeside Amusement Park, not yet opened for the day. A watchman alerts the police after he notices Gus cornering Danny atop the framework of the roller coaster. Gus explains to the boy that he doesn't want to hurt him, but needs him to tell the police that Lola's death was accidental. Although Danny tries to save Gus when he suffers a heart seizure, Gus, realizing his weight will plunge both he and the boy to their deaths, releases Danny's hand and falls to his death. Lieutenant Williams rescues Danny, and Mary decides to marry him. *Widows. Police. Wrestlers. Hoodlums. Entertainers. Delivery boys. Adolescence. Heart disease. Theft. Manslaughter. Self-sacrifice. Rescue. Marriage. Amusement parks. Denver. "Denver Post". Chases.*
Note: Filmed in Denver.

THE SILICATES see **ISLAND OF TERROR**

THE SILKEN TRAP see **THE MONEY JUNGLE**

THE SIMCHON FAMILY (Israel)   **F6.4501**
Noy Films. *Dist* Israel Films. ca **1969**. Sd; b&w. 35mm. 88 min.
Prod Shlomo Nouman, Yair Pecker. *Dir-Writ* Yoel Zilberg. *Screenplay* (see note) Moshe Ben-Ephraim, Leo Filler, Yoel Zilberg. *Photog* Marco Ya'acobi. *Film Ed* Helga Cranston. *Mus & Song:* "Speak to Me With Flowers" Dov Seltzer.

Cast: Meir Margalit (*Noah Simchon*), Shoshana Barnea (*Zfira*), Oded Kotler (*Gabi*), Rina Ganor (*Na'ava*), Tikva Mor (*Orna*), Zalman Leviush (*Zwirn*), Shraga Friedman, Elisheva Michaeli, Eddie Calvert and Band.

Domestic comedy. Israeli diplomat Noah Simchon lives beyond his means, hoping to impress members of high society. He buys a penthouse and furnishes it ostentatiously. While his daughter prefers telephone conversation to study, his son plans imaginary wars, and his bemused wife endures all. *Social climbers. Diplomats. Family life. Fantasy. Telephone.*
Note: Released in Israel Apr 1964 as *Mishpachat Simchon*. Sources conflict as to screenplay credit. Marco Ya'acobi is also credited as Marco Yocovlevitz. Based upon an Israeli radio series.

SIMEON DEL DESIERTO see **SIMON OF THE DESERT**

SIMÓN DEL DESIERTO see **SIMON OF THE DESERT**

SIMON OF THE DESERT (Mexico)   **F6.4502**
Gustavo Alatriste. *Dist* Fleetwood Films, Altura Films International. 11 Feb **1969** [New York opening]. Sd; b&w. 35mm. 45 min.
A Gustavo Alatriste Production. *Prod* Gustavo Alatriste. *Dir-Story* Luis Buñuel. *Screenplay* Luis Buñuel, Julio Alejandro. *Photog* Gabriel Figueroa. *Asst Camera* Sigfrido Garcia. *Film Ed* Carlos Savage. *Mus:* "Hymn of the Pilgrims" Raúl Lavista. *Perf by* Saeta y Tambores de la Semana Santa de Calanda (Aragon). *Sd* James L. Fields. *Asst Dir* Ignacio Villarreal.

Cast: Claudio Brook (*Simon*), Silvia Pinal (*The Temptress*), Hortensia Santoveña (*The Mother*), Enrique Alvarez Félix (*Brother Matias*), Enrique del Castillo (*mutilated one*), Jesús Fernández Martínez (*dwarf shepherd*), Francisco Reiguera, Luis Aceves Castañeda, Antonio Bravo, Enrique García Alvarez, Eduardo MacGregor (*priests*).

Allegory. Simon, a bearded ascetic, has withdrawn from the world in order to commune with God from atop a pillar in the desert. After 6 years, 6 months, and 6 days of prayer and physical deprivation, he is rewarded with a taller pillar by a powerful and wealthy family. Simon dismisses the solicitude of his mother, who lives in a shack in the desert to be near him, declares himself unworthy of the honor of the priesthood which his bishop wants to bestow upon him, and mounts his new pillar to continue his prayers in penance for all humanity. By prayer he restores the severed hands of a thief who has been unable to work as a result of his punishment, but the miracle is accepted with total indifference. Existing on a small number of lettuce leaves brought to him by an order of priests who see to his care, Simon steadfastly refuses to succumb to the world's evils. He sends an adolescent lay brother away from the order because the youth's pleasure in the priest's life is not of a spiritual nature; converses with a superstitious dwarf shepherd who enjoys his goats sexually; and confronts a demonically possessed priest who places rich foods in Simon's food sack and accuses him of hypocrisy in his asceticism. Simon must also withstand assaults from his own personal devil. She appears to him as an innocent girl wearing a sailor dress and bares her thighs and breasts. Simon defends himself by prayer, and she is transformed into a hideous, naked hag. Later she appears with a flock of lambs as the "good shepherd," exhorting Simon to leave his column and surfeit himself on worldly pleasures. Simon again banishes her and vows to stand on one leg in penance for his weakness. Another priest, Daniel, climbs a ladder to tell Simon of the ongoing wars engendered by ownership, and when Simon fails to comprehend the meaning of "thine and mine," Daniel declares that his sanctity is irrelevant to man. The Devil at last removes Simon from his pillar to a noisy discotheque in New York City. Simon remains detached in the midst of a frantic, swirling horde. The Devil informs him that his pillar is now occupied by another and that he must remain here until the end. *Priests. Temptresses. Dwarfs. Shepherds. Meditation. Asceticism. Moral corruption. Lust. Disguise. Hypocrisy. Motherhood. Deserts. Discotheques. New York City. Catholic Church. Saint Simeon Stylites. The Devil. Miracles.*
Note: Location scenes filmed in Mexico. Screened to the press in Mexico City in May 1965; running time: 42 min. Spanish title: *Simón del desierto*; also reviewed as *Simeon del desierto* and *San Simeon del desierto*.

UNE SIMPLE HISTOIRE (France)   **F6.4503**
Marcel Hanoun-R. T. F. *Dist* New Yorker Films. 26 Dec **1970** [New York opening]. Sd; b&w. 16mm. 60 min.
Prod-Dir-Writ Marcel Hanoun. *Photog* Marcel Hanoun. *Mus Selections* Antonio Vivaldi, Domenico Cimarosa.

Cast: Micheline Bezançon (*The Mother*), Elizabeth Huart (*Sylvie*).

Drama. Armed with their meager savings, a provincial mother and her small daughter move to Paris. Unable to afford a hotel, they spend a night in a vacant lot and are later taken in by an old woman who lives nearby. Prompted by her benefactress, the mother describes her futile search for employment. *Lower classes. Children. Unemployment. Filial relations. Poverty. Charity. Paris.*
Note: Produced in France in 1957. Opened in Paris in Apr 1959. May also be known as *A Simple Story*.

A SIMPLE STORY see **UNE SIMPLE HISTOIRE**

SIN ALLEY (Denmark)   **F6.4504**
ASA Film. *Dist* Manhattan Films International. 30 Aug **1961** [Los Angeles opening]. Sd; b&w. 35mm. [Feature film, length unknown.]
Dir Palle Kjaerulff-Schmidt, Robert Saaskin. *Screenplay* Palle Kjaerulff-Schmidt. *Photog* Rudolf Frederiksen. *Art Dir* Steini Sveinbjørnsson. *Film Ed*

Wera Iwanouw. *Mus* Sven Gyldmark. *Sd* Bent Høyer.

Cast: Birgitte Bruun, Ib Mossin, Ghita Nørby, Bent Christensen, Lone Hertz, Preben Kaas, Jakob Nielsen, Christian Brochorst, Jørn Jeppesen, Poul Müller, Poul Wøldike, Bendt Rothe, Jørgen Buckhøj, Ove Rud.

Melodrama? No information about the precise nature of this film has been found, but press material suggests that it concerns an exposé of vice in the city. *Urban life. Organized crime.*

Note: Opened in Copenhagen in Aug 1957 as *Bundfald.* Also known as *The Gentle Sex.*

SIN IN THE CITY   F6.4505
Dist Associated Film Distributors of California. 6 Jul 1966 [Fresno, California, showing]. Sd; b&w? 35mm. [Feature length assumed.]Although no information about the precise nature of this film has been found, press material suggests that it deals with a bar, nude dancing, and lesbianism. *Lesbianism. Nudity. Bars.*

SIN IN THE SUBURBS   F6.4506
Lojeare Productions. *Dist* Lojeare Productions, Seymour Borde & Associates. 21 Feb **1964** [Scottsdale, Arizona, opening]. Sd; b&w. 35mm. 82 min.

Prod Burton Bradley. *Assoc Prod* Harold Bradley. *Dir-Writ* Joe Sarno. *Dir Photog* Jim Markos. *Film Ed* Jim Markos. *Mus* Sam Feidel. *Cost* Florence Ryan. *Makeup* Vincent Lo Scalzo.

Cast: Alice Linville (*Kathi Lewis*), W. B. Parker (*Louis Muse*), Audrey Campbell (*Geraldine Lewis*), Lahna Monroe (*Yvette Talman*), Marla Ellis (*Lisa Francis*), Richard Tatro (*Roy Minton*), Derek Crane (*Scott Lewis*), Ella Daphni (*Peggy Thomas*), Charles Clements (*Cliff Haddison*), Wayne Roberts (*Jimmy Reed*), John Aristedes (*Tad Benton*), William Donaldson (*Larry Harket*), Joseph Garri (*Henry Francis*), Mari Kiselle (*Pam*), Carla Conners (*teenage girl*).

Melodrama. Kathi Lewis, a 16-year-old high school girl living in a suburban community, resists the advances of her boyfriend, and he slaps her. She runs home and finds Geraldine, her mother, involved in a love affair. Shattered by the experience, Kathi flees from her home and runs into Yvette Talman, a kind but immoral neighbor. Yvette and her lover, Louis Muse, are planning to organize a sex club for bored, pleasure-seeking wives and willing men. Kathi shares confidences with Yvette, and as time passes, their relationship becomes intimate. Louis calls upon Geraldine to help solicit women for the club. Kathi is among the participants when the group assembles for the first time, but Geraldine is unaware of her presence because everyone arrives in cloaks and masks. The club becomes a financial success, although Lisa Francis, one of the members, is driven by guilt to the brink of insanity, and Peggy Thomas, already an excessive drinker, becomes more sodden with her own burden of guilt. Louis, aware of the relationship between Yvette and Kathi, demands that Yvette give up Kathi. Yvette concedes, but Kathi continues to attend the meetings. One night Geraldine discovers that Kathi is a club member and is confronted with the results of her neglect of her daughter. *Housewives. Neighbors. Adolescence. Suburban life. Filial relations. Moral corruption. Infidelity. Lesbianism. Guilt. Alcoholism. Sex clubs.*

SIN MAGAZINE   F6.4507
Dist Ridges of Autumn, Inc. 19 Feb **1965** [Champaign, Illinois, showing]. Sd; b&w. 35mm. 64 min.

Cast: Jed Hudson, Turina Hayes.

Melodrama. Three brothers live on a secluded farm, where they publish a thriving sex magazine. Ross, a schizophrenic whose wife, Pam, is unable to respond sexually, becomes involved in an affair with Beth, whose sexual appetite is insatiable. Bill, a con man, takes charge of business matters and romances a succession of New York City secretaries to win their influence. Otis, the magazine's lustful photographer, has lascivious designs on Bill's naive European wife, Lisa, and he persuades her to pose for him in a secluded part of the woods. Ross spies on the models who pose for the magazine, and during periodic lapses of sanity he is subject to rages that end in violence. A prostitute becomes one of the victims of his madness. [Press material suggests that the film contains scenes of murder, attempted rape, lesbianism, seduction, and a nightmarish surgical operation.] *Brothers. Photographers. Models. Prostitutes. Secretaries. Pornography. Schizophrenia. Frigidity. Nymphomania. Voyeurism. Lesbianism. Seduction. Rape. Murder. Magazines (periodicals).*

SIN NOW ... PAY LATER see **LOVE NOW ... PAY LATER**

THE SIN OF MONA KENT   F6.4508
Mermaid Productions. *Dist* Astor Pictures. Aug **1961**. Sd; col (DeLuxe). 35mm. 75 min.

Prod-Dir Charles J. Hundt. *Assoc Prod* Paul Fanning. *Screenplay & Orig Story* Dick Brighton. *Dir Photog* James Lillis. *Film Ed* Eric Albertson.

Background Mus Corelli Jacobs. *Song:* "Mona" Michael Merlo, Patrick Welch. *Sd Engr* William Swift.

Cast: Johnny Olsen (*himself*), Sandra Donat (*Elvira Kowalski/Mona Kent*), Vic Ramos (*Eddie Logan*), Gil Brandsen (*Jerry Roberts*), Joy Violette (*Janice Lane*), Allan Frank (*Stephan Gregory*), Sam Alfredo (*bartender*).

Melodrama. New York City radio and television interviewer Johnny Olsen tracks down the true story of Mona Kent, a glamorous Broadway star, by contacting people who knew her before she achieved success: Elvira Kowalski, a midwestern farm girl, comes to New York after winning a phony talent contest. Though disillusioned, she stays on, determined to make good. While living in Greenwich Village with Janice, another disappointed actress, she becomes friendly with a painter, Eddie, who finds her a job as a hatcheck girl. Aging gossip columnist Stephan Gregory invents the name Mona Kent for her and invites her to a party at his Long Island estate, where she attracts attention by diving, clad in her undergarments, into the swimming pool. As a result, she obtains a part in summer stock. Later, as she swims naked at a deserted beach, young photographer Jerry takes pictures of her, and they become friends after he promises not to make the photos public. Mona's blossoming acting career suffers a setback, and she returns to her job as a hatcheck girl, meanwhile agreeing to pose for Eddie. She is incredulous when Stephan proposes marriage, but when she learns that both Eddie and Jerry have sold the nude pictures of her, she agrees to marry the columnist who promises to make her a star. *Television personalities. Actors. Roommates. Columnists. Painters. Photographers. Checkgirls. Fraud. Publicity. Marriage of convenience. Disillusionment. Ambition. Nudity. Talent contests. New York City— Broadway. New York City—Greenwich Village.*

Note: Also known as *The Sins of Mona Kent.*

SIN ON THE BEACH (France)   F6.4509
Les Films Univers. *Dist* American Film Distributing Corp. 9 Mar **1964** [New York State license]. Sd; b&w. 35mm (Dyaliscope). 75 min.

Pres by Stan Borden. A José Bénazéraf Production. *Prod-Dir* José Bénazéraf. *Screenplay* Grisha M. Dabat, Yves-Claude Denaux. *Dial* Yves-Claude Denaux. *Dir Photog* Marcel Combes. *Art Dir* Claude Bouxin. *Film Ed* Georges Marchalk. *Mus* Louiguy. *Prod Mgr* Yves-Claude Denaux, Guy Fanelli.

Cast: Monique Just (*Maria*), Sylvia Sorente (*Brigitte*), Michel Lemoine (*Jean-Marc*), Gisèle Gallois (*Françoise*).

Melodrama. Source: G.-J. Arnaud, *L'éternité pour nous* (Paris, 1960). Jean-Marc and Brigitte, partners in an unhappy love affair, arrive at an isolated French seaside resort managed by Maria Barneir, whose elderly husband is in poor health. Gradually, Maria falls in love with Jean-Marc. Suddenly her husband dies, and Jean-Marc threatens to tell the police that she hastened his death unless she will let the couple remain at the hotel free of charge; Maria agrees. Bored with the solitude Jean-Marc enjoys, Brigitte performs a striptease for Paul, the bartender. Maria finds them together and seduces Brigitte, hoping to anger Jean-Marc into breaking off the romance, but the plan backfires and Maria is left alone. Resuming their former existence, the lovers soon quarrel and Brigitte leaves. Jean-Marc returns to the resort and makes love with Maria on the beach, but their happiness is short-lived. Brigitte appears with a blackmail scheme of her own, and Maria reveals that she actually did murder her husband. Jean-Marc leaves with Brigitte, and Maria is again left alone. *Hotelkeepers. Bartenders. Murder. Blackmail. Seduction. Lesbianism. Striptease. Resorts. Hotels.*

Note: Opened in Paris in 1963 as *Le cri de la chair*; running time: 92 min or 85 min. Pre-release title: *L'éternité pour nous.* Alternative title: *Romance on the Beach.*

THE SIN SYNDICATE see **ZERO GIRLS**

SIN YOU SINNERS   F6.4510
Farno Productions. *Dist* Joseph Brenner Associates. 13 Feb **1963** [Maryland license]. Sd; b&w. 35mm. 73 min.

Dir Anthony Farrar. *Screenplay* Joe Sarno.

Cast: June Colbourne (*Bobbi*), Dian Lloyd (*Jule*), Derek Murcott (*Dave*), Beverly Nazarow (*Gloria*), Charles Clements (*Ben*), Douglas Gregory.

Melodrama. A middle-aged striptease dancer exerts a powerful influence over those near her. She assigns her extraordinary abilities to her belief in the supernatural powers of a golden, coin-like amulet she wears around her neck. The owner of the cabaret in which she works plots with a prostitute to steal the amulet and thereby acquire the woman's power; simultaneously, the woman's daughter sets out to steal the talisman. The cunning woman senses the plot against her, and she hypnotizes the cabaret owner, causing him to murder the prostitute. The man commits suicide when he realizes what he has done. The woman loses the amulet, and it is found by the daughter, who inherits its secret power. Bereaved of the amulet, the woman loses her confidence and her youthful appearance; she runs out into the street and is struck and killed by a truck. *Stripteasers. Cabaret owners. Prostitutes. Supernatural. Theft. Murder.*

Suicide. Hypnotism. Filial relations. Superstition. Talismans. Automobile accidents.

SINAI COMMANDOS (Israel/West Germany)   F6.4511

Aero Film–Ran Films. *Dist* Gillman Film Corp. 24 Nov **1968** [Los Angeles opening]. Sd; col (Eastman Color). 35mm. 99 min.

Prod Raphael Nussbaum. *Asst Prod* R. Weiser, Naftali Scheinberg. *Exec Prod* Aric Dichner. *Dir-Story* Raphael Nussbaum. *Screenplay* Jack Jacobs. *Dir Photog* Benno Bellenbaum. *Asst Camera* Yaacov Kallach. *Film Ed* Ursula Möhrle, Erika Stegman. *Mus* Horst A. Haas, Rolf Bauer. *Titl Theme* Roy Etzel. *Song:* "Sharm Al-Sheikh" Ron Eliran. *Sd* Harry Rausch, Naftali Scheinberg.

Cast: Robert Fuller *(Capt. Uri Litman)*, John Hudson *(General Golan)*, Esther Ullman *(Nira)*, Avram Mor, Rolf Eden *(Lieut. Moshe Kramer [see note])*, Eli Sinai *(Sgt. Zwi Neumann)*, Gabi Amrani *(Nissim)*, Avram Hefner *(Elihu Goldfarb)*, Reuven Bar-Yotam *(Bulgaro)*, Raffi Nathan *(Yigal)*, Boris Rosenberg *(Nathan)*, Ziona Tukterman *(Ellen Neumann)*, Aviva Marks *(Sylvia Litman)*, Joseph Shiloach *(Captain Halill)*, Ammon Berenson *(air force pilot)*.

War drama. During the 1967 Israeli-Arab War, Capt. Uri Litman, commander of a small Israeli task force, is assigned to knock out a vital Arab radar installation just before a major Israeli offensive. Nira, an Israeli, finds herself drawn into the conflict when she uses her father's small boat to land Litman's men on a deserted coast of the Sinai Peninsula. She is forced to sink the boat and join the patrol to avoid being captured by the Egyptians. Though caught under enemy fire, Litman and his remaining men infiltrate the radar station. The mission is successful, allowing Israeli airplanes to proceed to their target of Sharm al-Sheikh. *Commandos. Rowboats. Radar. Israeli-Arab War 1967. Sinai Peninsula. Sharm al-Sheikh.*

Note: Filmed entirely on location in the Sinai Desert. Includes black and white footage of the 1967 Israeli-Arab War. Jerusalem opening: May 1968 as *Ha'matarah Tiran*; released in West Germany as *Schatten über Tiran— Kommando Sinai*; running time: 105 min. Alternative German title: *Der 6-Tage-Krieg.* U. S. subtitle: *The Story of the Six Day War.* Sources conflict in crediting the role of Lieutenant Kramer.

SINAIA see CLOUDS OVER ISRAEL

SINDERELLA AND THE GOLDEN BRA   F6.4512

Paul Mart Productions. *Dist* Manson Distributing Corp. 16 Dec **1964** [trade review; Maryland license: 24 Feb 1965]. Sd; col (Eastman Color). 35mm. 81 min.

Prod Paul Mart. *Assoc Prod* Ed Ludlum, Sy De Bardas. *Dir* Loel Minardi. *Screenplay* Frank Squires. *Story Idea* Paul Mart. *Story* Loel Minardi, Frank Squires, Les Szarvas. *1st Camera* Fou. *2d Camera* Mario Tosi. *Set Dsgn & Art* Tod Jonson. *Ed* Karl Von. *Orig Mus & Lyr* Les Szarvas. *Mus Dir* Jacques Montreaux. *Mus Arr* Paul Sorenson. *Asst Dir* Ron Terry. *Prod Mgr* Lawrence Jason. *Cost Dsgn* Bert Bliss. *Men's Hair* Bruce Hein, Beryl Bleeden. *Stills* Glenn Otto. *Set Constr* Harry Woolman.

Cast: Suzanne Sybele *(Sinderella)*, Bill Gaskin, actor *(Prince David)*, David Duffield *(king)*, Sid Lassick *(godfather)*, Patricia Mayfield *(stepmother)*, Joan Lemmo *(Fanny)*, June Faith *(Flossy)*, Gerald Strickland *(adviser)*, John Bradley *(first page)*, Kay Hall *(matron)*, Althea Currier, Jackie De Witt, Justine Scott, Lisa Carole, Beverly Frankell, Donna Anderson *(village maidens)*.

Fantasy. Sinderella works as a scullery maid for her stepmother and stepsisters, who constantly scold her and keep her dressed in rags. Sinderella hopes to meet the man of her dreams, unaware that the man she has been dreaming of is the heir to the throne, Prince David. The Prince likewise dreams of Sinderella. The King holds a ball to choose a wife for the Prince, and Sinderella is forced to remain at home; but an intoxicated fairy godfather appears and changes her rags into fine clothes to wear to the ball; and she and the Prince instantly fall in love. In her haste to leave the ball before midnight lest her finery change back into rags, Sinderella loses her golden bra, and the Prince hunts throughout the kingdom to find the garment's rightful owner. Many maidens attempt unsuccessfully to fit into the bra before the Prince is finally reunited with Sinderella and they live happily ever after. *Royalty. Stepmothers. Stepsisters. Domestics. Nudity. Magic. Lingerie. Balls (formal gatherings). Fairies. Cinderella.*

Note: Also known as *CINderella and the Golden——.* Also advertised as *Sinderella, Cindy and Her Golden Dress,* and *Cinderella and the Golden Dress.* A version with less nudity was also available.

SINFONIA PER DUE SPIE see SERENADE FOR TWO SPIES

SINFONIA PER UN MASSACRO see SYMPHONY FOR A MASSACRE

THE SINFUL ADVENTURES OF DAVEY HAGGART see SINFUL DAVEY

SINFUL DAVEY (Great Britain)   F6.4513

Mirisch–Webb Productions. *Dist* United Artists. 7 May **1969** [Baltimore opening; c5 Mar 1969; LP36950]. Sd; col (Eastman Color, print by De Luxe). 35mm (Panavision). 95 min. *MPAA rating* M.

A John Huston–Walter Mirisch Production. *Prod* William N. Graf. *Exec Prod* Walter Mirisch. *Assoc Prod* William Kirby. *Dir* John Huston. *Writ* James R. Webb. *Dir Photog* Freddie Young, Edward Scaife. *Art Dir* Carmen Dillon. *Set Decor* Josie MacAvin. *Prod Dsgn* Stephen Grimes. *Film Ed* Russell Lloyd. *Mus Comp & Cond* Ken Thorne. *Titl Song* Don Black, Ken Thorne. *Sung by* Esther Ofarim. *Choreog* Alice Dalgarno. *Sd* Basil Fenton-Smith, Leslie Hodgson. *Asst Dir (see note)* Tom Pevsner, John O'Connor, Jim Brennan. *Prod Mgr* Ernest Holding. *Pers Asst to the Dir* Gladys Hill. *Cost* Margaret Furse. *Makeup* Neville Smallwood. *Hairstyles* Joan Smallwood. *Sp Eff* Richard Parker. *Master of the Horse* Frank Hayden.

Cast: John Hurt *(Davey Haggart)*, Pamela Franklin *(Annie)*, Nigel Davenport *(Constable Richardson)*, Ronald Fraser *(MacNab)*, Robert Morley *(Duke of Argyll)*, Fidelma Murphy *(Jean Carlisle)*, Maxine Audley *(Duchess of Argyll)*, Fionnuala Flanagan *(Penelope)*, Donal McCann *(Sir James Graham)*, Allan Cuthbertson *(Captain Douglas)*, Eddie Byrne *(Yorkshire Bill)*, Niall MacGinnis *(Boots Simpson)*, Noel Purcell *(Jock)*, Judith Furse *(Mary)*, Francis De Wolff *(Andrew)*, Paul Farrell *(Bailiff of Stirling)*, Geoffrey Golden *(Warden McEwan)*, Leon Collins *(Dr. Gresham)*, Mickser Reid *(Billy the Goat)*, Derek Young *(Bobby Rae)*, John Franklin *(George Bagrie)*, Eileen Murphy *(Mary Kidd)*.

Adventure comedy. Source: David Haggart, *The Life of David Haggart* (1821). In Scotland in the early 1820's young Davey Haggart vows to follow in the footsteps of his late father, a would-be highwayman who was hanged at the age of 21 for an ill-fated robbery attempt on the Duke of Argyll. Deserting from the King's Army, Davey joins forces with MacNab, a grubby pickpocket, but their efforts at thievery (including the filching of a corpse for medical research) succeed only in landing them in jail. Unable to escape, Davey breaks into the women's quarters and cavorts with Jean Carlisle, trollop to a band of roving criminals. Once he has been bailed out by Annie, a childhood friend from his orphanage days, Davey helps MacNab escape and then robs a stagecoach on his own. When word of the holdup reaches Constable Richardson, he solicits Annie's help, warning her that Davey's efforts to follow in his father's footsteps will eventually lead to the gallows. Although she, too, wants Davey to reform, Annie refuses to cooperate and does what she can to foil the constable's pursuit. Davey, meanwhile, is residing in the Scottish highlands and matching wits with Jock, a dastardly innkeeper. While fleeing from the irate father of a girl he has seduced, Davey rescues Sir James Graham from four young ruffians. Unaware that his savior has pocketed his money, Sir James invites Davey to visit the home of his uncle, the Duke of Argyll. Delighted at this opportunity to meet his father's nemesis, Davey accompanies Sir James on his journey, followed by MacNab and Jean, who in turn are followed by Annie and the constable. Using a false name, Davey endears himself to the duke and his niece Penelope and plots with MacNab and Jean to rob the guests the duchess has invited to her grand ball. Everything goes as planned until Annie, still determined to reform Davey, returns all the stolen jewels. The constable discovers Davey's identity and goes after him. Eluding the constable's hounds, Davey mounts a horse, becomes embroiled in a fox hunt, gallops across a golf course, and is knocked flat by a low flying tee shot. Arrested, tried, and sentenced to be hanged, he sits in his cell writing his memoirs as the duke, now his loyal friend, plays the bagpipes for his pleasure. On the day of execution, however, Annie and MacNab rig the gallows, fake Davey's hanging, and whisk him away. After dancing in a graveyard, Davey and Annie ride off together into the hills. *Highwaymen. Pickpockets. Nobility. Fox hunts. Prostitutes. Constables. Innkeepers. Uncles. Criminals—Rehabilitation. Capital punishment. Robbery. Personal identity. Prison escapes. Jails. Scotland. Chases.*

Note: Location scenes filmed in Ireland. Opened in London in May 1969. British sources credit Pevsner and Brennan as assistant directors; U. S. sources credit Pevsner and O'Connor. Working title: *The Sinful Adventures of Davey Haggart.*

SING A SONG, FOR HEAVEN'S SAKE   F6.4514

Victor Lewis Associates. *Dist* Marathon Pictures. 21 Oct **1966** [Memphis, Tennessee, opening]. Sd; col (Eastmancolor). 35mm. 95 min.

Pres by Nashville Film & Sound Commission, Victor Lewis. *Dir* Ulf Van Court.

With: Merle Kilgore *(Reverend Todd)*, Red Foley, The Statesmen, Blackwood Brothers, The Stamps, Chuck Wagon Gang, The Imperials, Oak Ridge Boys, The Lewis Family, Blue Ridge Quartette, Billy Grammer, The Rangers, The Gospel Echoes, Klaudt Indian Family, Doris Akers, Los Quatros Latinos, Swanee River Boys, Gospel Chorale Singers, Marilyn Lewis, Lee Clayton, Ron Page, Sam Tarpley, Mindy Clayton, Martin Clayton, III.

Musical revue. Over 30 songs, sung by more than 50 artists, proclaim that attending a gospel singing lightens one's worldly burdens. A subplot to the musical revue concerns a 12-year-old youth who is encouraged to sing gospel rather than rock and roll songs. *Singers. Gospel music. Religion.*

Note: Filmed in Nashville.

SING AND SWING (Great Britain) F6.4515

Three Kings Films. *Dist* Universal Pictures. 4 Nov **1964** [New York opening]. Sd; b&w. 35mm. 75 min.

Prod-Dir Lance Comfort. *Orig Story & Screenplay* Lyn Fairhurst. *Based on an Idea by* Harold Shampan. *Photog* Basil Emmott. *Art Dir* Jack Shampan. *Film Ed* John Trumper. *Mus Arr* Norrie Paramor, Kenny Ball. *Songs:* "Rondo," "Hand Me Down My Walkin' Shoes," "Live It Up!" "Temptation Baby," "Please Let It Happen to Me," "Keep It Moving," "Law and Order," "Loving Me This Way," "Don't Take You From Me," "Don't You Understand," "Sometimes I Wish" Joe Meek, Norrie Paramor, Kenny Ball. *Song:* "Accidents Will Happen" Norrie Paramor, Bob Barratt. *Sung by* Patsy Ann Noble. *Sd Rec* Robert MacPhee, Colin Le Mesurier. *Dub Ed* Roy Taylor. *Asst Dir* John Stoneman. *Prod Mgr* Roy Baird. "The Smart Alecs" *Band Cost Dsgn by* John Stephen. *Model Cost* Mary Quant. *Makeup* George Blackler. *Hairdresser* Helen Bevan.

Cast: David Hemmings (*Dave Martin*), Jennifer Moss (*Jill*), John Pike (*Phil*), Heinz Burt (*Ron*), Steven Marriott (*Ricky*), Joan Newell (*Margaret Martin*), Ed Devereaux (*Herbert Martin*), Veronica Hurst (*Kay Miller*), Penny Lambirth (*Barbara*), Peter Glaze (*Mike Moss*), David Bauer (*Mark Watson*), Anthony Ashdown (*Bob*), Douglas Ives (*Bingo*), Paul Hansard (*film director*), Geoffrey L'Oise (*assistant*), Nancy Spain (*columnist*), Peter Haigh (*announcer*), Peter Noble (*interviewer*), Trevor Maskell (*Aldo*), John Mitchell, actor (*Andrews*), Anthony Shepard (*commissionaire*), David Clark (*recording man*), Pat Gilbert (*housekeeper*), Kenny Ball and His Jazzmen, Gene Vincent, Patsy Ann Noble, Kim Roberts, The Outlaws, Sounds Incorporated, Andy Cavell and the Saints (*guest artists*).

Comedy with music. Post office messenger boy Dave Martin has promised his father that within a month he will abandon his obsession with rock and roll if the tape recording that his group, "The Smart Alecs," has made is unsuccessful. After several frantic attempts to get an audition, Dave loses the tape recording when he is hit on the head while delivering a package to a film studio. Mark Watson, an American film producer, discovers the tape and is enchanted with it. He searches for the boys, who finally make a successful audition by playing over the intercom of the taxicab in which Watson is a passenger. *Mail carriers. Musicians. Motion picture producers. Americans in foreign countries. Rock and roll. Show business. Adolescence. Recorders. Taxicabs.*

Note: Released in Great Britain in Dec 1963 as *Live It Up*; running time: 74 min.

SINGAPORE, SINGAPORE (France/Italy) F6.4516

Les Films Number One–Poste Parisien–Franco Riganti. *Dist* Ben Barry & Associates. **1969.** Sd; col (Eastmancolor). 35mm. 95 min.

Prod Pierre Kalfon. *Dir* Bernard Toublanc-Michel. *Screenplay* Bernard Toublanc-Michel, Pierre Kalfon. *Italian Version Screenplay* Sergio Amidei. *Photog* Jean Charvein. *Art Dir* Gilbert Margerie. *Film Ed* Gabriel Rongier. *Mus* Antoine Duhamel, Ward Swingle. *Asst Dir* Philippe d'Argila. *Prod Mgr* G. S. Heng, Georges Chappedelaine.

Cast: Sean Flynn (*Capt. Art Smith*), Marika Green (*Monica*), Terry Downes (*Sergeant Gruber*), Marc Michel (*Capt. Kevin Grey*), Peter Grayford (*Mr. Brown*), Denis Berry (*Dan*), Bernard Meusnier (*Angel*), Andrew Ray, pseud (*Ta-tchouen*), Jessy Greek (*Ten-sin*), Trudy Connor (*Tchin-saw*), William Brix (*captain*).

Action melodrama. Source: Jean Bruce, *Cinq gars pour Singapour* (Paris, 1959). In Singapore, CIA agent Art Smith, after meeting with Mr. Brown of the British Secret Service, joins four volunteer U. S. Marines in a mission to capture the men responsible for the disappearance of 17 fellow soldiers. They learn that Ta-tchouen, a mad scientist, is preparing to conduct brainwashing experiments on the missing Marines, who are currently being kept alive in frozen hibernation, and then to exchange them for money and weapons. Art and Sergeant Gruber, one of the volunteers, sneak into the doctor's secret laboratory aboard a freighter. British secret agent Monica, Mr. Brown, the other volunteers, and the local police rescue Art and the Marines and destroy the ship. *Americans in foreign countries. Secret agents. Scientists. Insanity. Kidnaping. Brainwashing. Cryogenics. Rescue. Experiments. Laboratories. Freighters. Singapore. United States—Central Intelligence Agency. Great Britain—Intelligence service. United States Marines.*

Note: Opened in Paris in Mar 1967 as *Cinq gars pour Singapour*; running time: 105 min; in Rome in Aug 1967 as *Cinque Marines per Singapore*; running time: 105 min. Andrew Ray is a pseudonym for Andrea Aureli.

UN SINGE EN HIVER *see* **A MONKEY IN WINTER**

THE SINGER NOT THE SONG (Great Britain) F6.4517

Rank Organisation. *Dist* Warner Bros. Pictures. 20 Jan **1962** [New York opening: 2 May; c27 Dec 1961; LP27114]. Sd; col (Technicolor). 35mm (CinemaScope). 129 min.

A Roy [Ward] Baker Production. *Exec Prod* Earl St. John. *Prod-Dir* Roy [Ward] Baker. *Assoc Prod* Jack Hanbury. *Screenplay* Nigel Balchin. *Photog* Otto Heller. *Camera Op* David Harcourt. *Focus Op* John Alcott. *Art Dir* Alex Vetchinsky. *Set Decor* Arthur Taksen. *Draughtsman* Terence Marsh. *Film Ed* Roger Cherrill. *Mus* Philip Green. *Sd* Dudley Messenger, Gordon K. McCallum. *Boom Op* J. W. N. Daniel. *Sd Camera Op* Peter Lacey. *1st, 2d & 3d Asst Dir* Stanley Hosgood, Donald Toms, Anthony Waye. *Prod Mgr* Denis Holt. *Cont* Penny Daniels. *Prod Sec* Maureen Hensby. *Cost Dsgn* Yvonne Caffin. *Women's Wardrobe* Maggie Lewin. *Men's Wardrobe* John Hilling. *Makeup* George Blackler. *Hairdresser* Stella Rivers. *Still Photog* George Ward, Norman Gryspeerdt. *Ch Electrn* Vic Smith. *Grip* Bill Bannister. *Chargehand Prop* George Ball. *Rigger* E. Lyons.

Cast: Dirk Bogarde (*Anacleto*), John Mills (*Father Keogh*), Mylene Demongeot (*Locha*), Laurence Naismith (*old uncle*), John Bentley (*chief of police*), Leslie French (*Father Gomez*), Eric Pohlmann (*presidente*), Nyall Florenz (*Vito*), Roger Delgado (*De Cortinez*), Philip Gilbert (*Phil Brown*), Selma Vaz Dias (*Chela*), Laurence Payne (*Pablo*), Jacqueline Evans (*Dona Marian*), Lee Montague (*Pepe*), Serafina Di Leo (*Josefa*).

Drama. Source: Audrey Erskine Lindop, *The Singer Not the Song* (London, 1953). Father Keogh, a dedicated Roman Catholic priest from Ireland, arrives in Quantano, an isolated Mexican village cowering under the atheistic and tyrannical rule of bandit Anacleto. Father Keogh replaces the aging and broken-in-spirit Father Gomez. Despite threats and several attempts upon his life, Father Keogh openly defies the bandit and persuades some of the villagers to start attending church again, among them Locha, the daughter of the leading landowner. In retaliation, Anacleto tries to intimidate the priest by murdering the villagers in alphabetical order. Gradually, however, he begins to feel reluctant admiration for his adversary (he even kills one of his own men for attempting to shoot the priest). Eventually Anacleto asks if he may live with Father Keogh to determine whether it is the "song" (the religion) or the "singer" (the priest) that inspires good. During his stay Anacleto learns that Locha has fallen in love with Father Keogh, and when her family tries to force her into a loveless marriage, Anacleto hides her at his mountain stronghold. He then tells Father Keogh that unless he announces from the pulpit that he is a failure as a priest, Locha will be killed. Father Keogh agrees, but as he begins his sermon he spies Locha safely seated far back in the congregation. Tricked by Anacleto into breaking a vow to defeat evil, Father Keogh launches into a violent denunciation of the bandit. Authorities arrest Anacleto, and his gang attempts to rescue him on the way to prison. During the ensuing gunfire both Anacleto and the priest are fatally wounded. As the two men die side by side, Anacleto murmurs "the singer, not the song." *Priests. Outlaws. Gangs. Murder. Atheism. Religion. Self-sacrifice. Mexico. Catholic Church.*

Note: Location scenes filmed in Spain. Released in Great Britain in 1961; running time: 132 min.

SINGING IN THE SUN *see* **GOLDILOCKS AND THE THREE BARES**

THE SINGING NUN F6.4518

Metro-Goldwyn-Mayer, Inc. 17 Mar **1965** [New York opening; c3 Feb 1966; LP32216]. Sd (Westrex); col (Metrocolor). 35mm (Panavision). 98 min.

A John Beck Production. *Prod* John Beck. *Co-prod* Hayes Goetz. *Assoc Prod* Hank Moonjean. *Dir* Henry Koster. *Screenplay* Sally Benson, John Furia, Jr. *Story* John Furia, Jr. *Dir Photog* Milton Krasner. *Art Dir* George W. Davis, Urie McCleary. *Set Decor* Henry Grace, Jerry Wunderlich. *Film Ed* Rita Roland. *Mus Score* Harry Sukman. *Mus Supv* Harold Gelman. *Song:* "Dominique" Soeur Sourire. *English Lyr* Randy Sparks. *Songs:* "Sister Adele (Soeur Adèle)," "It's a Miracle (Une fleur)," "Beyond the Stars (Entre les étoiles)," "A Pied Piper's Song (Petit Pierrot)" Soeur Sourire. *Lyr* Randy Sparks. *Songs:* "Brother John," "Lovely" Randy Sparks. *Song:* "Raindrops" (*Inspired by "Chante rivière" by Soeur Sourire*) Randy Sparks. *Songs:* "Je voudrais," "Mets ton joli jupon," "Avec toi," "Alleluia" Soeur Sourire. *Songs Sung by* Debbie Reynolds. *Choreog* Robert Sidney. *Rec Supv* Franklin Milton. *Asst Dir* Kevin Donnelly. *Makeup* William Tuttle.

Cast: Debbie Reynolds (*Sister Ann*), Ricardo Montalban (*Father Clementi*), Greer Garson (*Mother Prioress*), Agnes Moorehead (*Sister Cluny*), Chad Everett (*Robert Gerarde*), Katharine Ross (*Nicole Arlien*), Juanita Moore (*Sister Mary*), Ricky Cordell (*Dominic Arlien*), Michael Pate (*Mr. Arlien*), Tom Drake (*Fitzpatrick*), Larry D. Mann (*Mr. Duvries*), Charles Robinson (*Marauder*), Monique Montaigne (*Sister Michele*), Joyce Vanderveen (*Sister Elise*), Anne Wakefield (*Sister Brigitte*), Pam Peterson (*Sister Gertrude*),

Marina Koshetz (Sister Marthe), Nancy Walters (Sister Therese), Violet Rensing (Sister Elizabeth), Inez Pedroza (Sister Consuella), Ed Sullivan (himself).

Drama with music. Sister Ann leaves the Dominican convent near Antwerp for her assignment at Samaritan House in a depressed area of Brussels. Sister Ann loves to play the guitar and sing, and when she joins in the traditional evensong at Samaritan House, she impresses the other nuns and Father Clementi. She becomes fond of Dominic Arlien, a motherless child whose father is an unemployed drunkard and who is loved only by his 17-year-old sister, Nicole. Sister Ann composes the song *Dominique* for the boy. Father Clementi persuades Robert Gerarde, a partner in a recording firm, to listen to Sister Ann's music in the hope of having it recorded. When Robert meets Sister Ann, he discovers that she was his classmate at the Paris Conservatory of Music 5 years ago. Later, while visiting the Arlien house, Sister Ann discovers pictures of Nicole in provocative poses; the girl defiantly tells the nun that she posed to get food and rent money for her family. Her father overhears them, strikes Nicole, and orders the nun out of the house. The Mother Prioress later admonishes Sister Ann for allowing the young girl's secret to be made known to the father. Robert, whose attraction to Sister Ann has been rekindled, obtains permission from church authorities to have her record an album; *Dominique* becomes a worldwide hit, and Ed Sullivan brings a television crew to Brussels to film Sister Ann for his show. Sister Ann becomes confused by her success and by Robert's personal interest in her, and she seeks counsel from Father Clementi. Her decision is made for her when Dominic is seriously injured in an accident; she prays for him, promising to give up her music and care for others if he recovers. The boy recovers, and the Arlien family, shaken by the incident, decide to move to the country. Sister Ann gives Nicole her guitar and goes to an African village to work among the natives. *Dominicans. Nuns. Priests. Guitarists. Singers. Children. Models. Alcoholism. Brother-sister relationship. Television. Recording. Antwerp. Brussels. Africa. Ed Sullivan Show.*

THE SINGING PRINCESS (Italy)   F6.4519

Ima Film. *Dist* Trans-National Film Corp. 11 Nov **1967** [New York showing]. Sd; col (Technicolor). 35mm. 76 min.

Pres by Larry Joachim Productions. *Prod-Dir* Anton Gino Domeneghini. *English Dial* Nina Maguire, Tony Maguire. *Photog* Cesare Pelizzari. *Mus* Riccardo Pick Mangiagalli. *English Lyr:* "Song for the Bee," "Sunset Prayer," "The Flower Song" Nina Maguire, Tony Maguire. *Sung by* Julie Andrews.

Cast—Voices: Julie Andrews (Princess Zeila), Howard Marion-Crawford (narrator).

Animated fantasy. In Bagdad Caliph Oman is preparing to greet three suitors for the hand of Princess Zeila, his lovely niece. The cruel Sheik Jafar, assisted by the evil sorcerer Boork, schemes to marry Zeila and gain her kingdom. Amin, a young minstrel, discovers the plot but is imprisoned by Boork on the top of a mountain. Eventually, he escapes. An old woman presents him with Aladdin's lamp, whose genie helps Amin vanquish Boork and Jafar. All of Bagdad celebrates Zeila and Amin's engagement. *Royalty. Uncles. Sheiks. Sorcerers. Minstrels. Genii. Marriage. Magic. Imprisonment. Bagdad. Aladdin.*

Note: Opened in Rome in Dec 1949 as *La rosa di Bagdad;* running time: ca85 min. English version produced in Great Britain in 1952.

SINGLE ROOM FURNISHED   F6.4520

Unifilm Productions. *Dist* Crown International Pictures. 21 Aug **1968** [Phoenix, Arizona, opening]. Sd; col (DeLuxe). 35mm. 93 min.

Exec Prod Michael Musto. *Assoc Prod* Hugo Grimaldi. *Dir* Matteo Ottaviano. *Screenplay* Michael Musto. *Photog* Leslie Kovacs. *Art Dir* Mike McCloskey. *Film Ed* Hugo Grimaldi. *Mus* James Sheldon. *Titl Song Sung by* The Paris Sisters. *Introductory Comments in Memory of Jayne Mansfield* Walter Winchell.

Cast: Jayne Mansfield (Johnnie/Mae/Eilene), Dorothy Keller (Flo), Fabian Dean (Charley), Billy M. Greene (Pop), Terri Messina (Maria Adamo), Martin Horsey (Frankie), Walter Gregg (Billy), Bruno Ve Sota (Mr. Duck), Velia Del Greco (Mrs. Adamo), Isabelle Dwan (Grandmother), Jean London, Nancy Brock (girls), Margie Duncan, Ava Sheara (dancers), Michael Rich, Elisa Rich (grandchildren), Erie MacGruder (girl at window), Robert Van Strawder (grocery boy).

Drama. Based on an unidentified play by: Gerald Sanford. Teenaged Maria wants to emulate her voluptuous neighbor, Eilene, but Maria's mother and the old janitor, Pop, tell her a story that they hope will end the idolatry. *Johnnie and her husband, Frankie, move into the apartment building. Frankie does not want to settle down, and upon discovering that she is pregnant, he deserts her. Johnnie loses the baby, but she overcomes her depression when she starts a new life. She dyes her hair, takes a job as a waitress, and changes her name to Mae. After a brief romance with a Mr. Duck, she is again impregnated and abandoned. She finds consolation with her neighbor, Charley, who is so sympathetic that he proposes to her. He breaks the engagement, however; and*

Mae, left in despair, gives her baby away for adoption. She becomes a prostitute and changes her name to Eilene. Marie is shocked to realize that the story is about the neighbor she admires. Meanwhile, Billy, a young sailor, falls in love with Eilene and proposes to her, but he accidentally breaks a doll that she has kept since her marriage to Frankie. Angrily, she turns Billy away; he leaves and shoots himself. Time passes, and Eilene realizes that her fate will never change. *Janitors. Waitresses. Neighbors. Prostitutes. Sailors. Infants. Adolescence. Filial relations. Marriage. Pregnancy. Desertion. Adoption. Suicide. Dolls.*

Note: Director Ottaviano is also known as Matt Cimber.

SINGLE SAILOR *see* **SEX AND THE SINGLE SAILOR**

SINGLE SWINGERS ONLY *see* **FOR SINGLE SWINGERS ONLY**

THE SINGLES   F6.4521

Associates Productions. *Dist* Chellee Films. 29 Nov **1967** [New York showing]. Sd; b&w. 35mm. 74 min.

Prod-Dir S. N. Johnsen. *Writ* Eugene Price. *Story Ed* Al Rosati. *Cinematog* Harry August. *Prod Mgr* Philip Dross. *Cont* Dossie. *Stills* Bob Jardine.

Cast: Steve Harris, Sean Martin, Linda Scott, actress, Bob Jardine, Doris Rhinhold, Betty Lynn.

Sex film. In an interview with a writer, the head of a computer dating service reveals the hidden sexual desires of his clients and discusses the often incongruous matches made by the computer. Press photographs indicate that the film contains scenes of lesbianism, troilism, and male impersonation. *Reporters. Computer dating services. Troilism. Lesbianism. Male impersonation.*

Note: Also known as *Singles Only.*

SINGLES ONLY *see* **THE SINGLES**

THE SINISTER MAN (Great Britain)   F6.4522

Merton Park Studios. *Dist* Schoenfeld Film Distributing Corp. 6 Oct **1965** [Newark, New Jersey, opening]. Sd; b&w. 35mm. 61 min.

Prod Jack Greenwood. *Assoc Prod* Jim O'Connolly. *Dir* Clive Donner. *Screenplay* Robert Stewart. *Dir Photog* Bert Mason. *Art Dir* Peter Mullins. *Film Ed* Derek Holding. *Mus Dir* Charles Blackwell. *Sd Rec* Sidney Rider.

Cast: John Bentley (Superintendent Wills), Patrick Allen (Dr. Nelson Pollard), Jacqueline Ellis (Elsa Marlowe), Eric Young (Johnny Choto), Arnold Lee (Soyoki), John Glyn-Jones (Dr. Maurice Tarn), Brian McDermott (Detective Sergeant Stillman), Gerald Andersen (Maj. Paul Amery), Yvonne Buckingham (Miss Russell), William Gaunt (Mitch Hallam), Michael Deacon (Angus), Leslie Nunnerley (Vera Martin), Malcolm Russell (Joe Martin), Yvonne Shima (Tamaya), Robert Lee (Nam Lee), Burt Kwouk (Captain Feng), John Horsley (pathologist), Wilfrid Brambell (lock-keeper), Keith Faulkner (his assistant), Edward Atienza (clerk).

Crime melodrama. Source: Edgar Wallace, *The Sinister Man* (London, 1924). Oxford scholar Neil Raeburn is found murdered and the Kytang Wafers, the subject of his archeological investigation, are missing. Among the victim's colleagues at the Oriental Research Institute are American physician Nelson Pollard, Oriental fellow Johnny Choto, and Englishwoman Elsa Marlowe. Although Scotland Yard Superintendent Wills first suspects the Oriental, he later learns from Elsa that Korean War veteran Pollard is secretly allied with the Kytang ambassador in London. When the diplomat attempts to slay his American associate in a judo club, Wills intervenes, arresting both. *Archeologists. Detectives. Researchers. Americans in foreign countries. Orientals. Veterans. Diplomats. Murder. Theft. Conspiracy. Perfidy. London. Oxford University. Scotland Yard. Imaginary republics.*

Note: Released in Great Britain caDec 1961.

THE SINISTER URGE   F6.4523

Headliner Productions. 27 Dec **1961** [New York showing; c8 Dec 1960; LP26631]. Sd; b&w. 35mm. 75 min.

Dir Edward Davis Wood, Jr.

Cast: Kenne Duncan (Lieut. Matt Carson), James Moore (Sgt. Randy Stone), Jean Fontaine (Gloria Henderson), Carl Anthony (Johnny Ryde), Dino Fantini (Dirk Williams), Jeanne Willardson (Mary Smith), Harry Keatan (Jaffe), Reed Howes (police inspector), Harvey Dunne (Mr. Romaine), Kenneth Willardson (theatrical agent), Vic McGee (syndicate man), Judy Berares (Frances), Vonnie Starr (secretary), Oma Soffian (nurse), Toni Costello, Kathy Randall, Sylvia Marenco, April Lynn (models), Fred Mason, Jean Baree, Clayton Peca (policemen).

Crime melodrama. Police Lieut. Matt Carson and his assistant Sgt. Randy Stone are searching for the murderer of three pornography models. The officers link the crimes to a syndicate that produces and sells sex films directed by Johnny Ryde and financed by Gloria Henderson. Dirk Williams sees explicit photographs of Mary Smith, an innocent young woman, who was manipulated by Ryde to pose. Seeing the photographs, Williams loses control and, upon finding Mary in the park, rapes and murders her. The police officers track down the murderer and smash the smut racket. *Police. Models. Murder. Pornography. Rape. Syndicates. Photographs.*

Note: Also known as *The Young and Immoral.*

THE SINNERS see **5 SINNERS**

SINNERS À LA CARTE see **NUDE IN CHARCOAL**

SINNERS GO TO HELL see **NO EXIT**

SINS OF KITTY see **URSULA**

THE SINS OF LOLA MONTES see **LOLA MONTÈS**

THE SINS OF MONA KENT see **THE SIN OF MONA KENT**

THE SINS OF RACHEL CADE F6.4524

Warner Bros. Pictures. 29 Mar **1961** [Philadelphia opening; c1 Apr 1960; LP25361]. Sd; col (Technicolor). 35mm. 123 min.

Prod Henry Blanke. *Dir* Gordon Douglas. *Screenplay* Edward Anhalt. *Photog* J. Peverell Marley. *Art Dir* Leo K. Kuter. *Set Decor* Ralph S. Hurst. *Film Ed* Owen Marks. *Mus* Max Steiner. *Orch* Murray Cutter. *Native Dances Choreog* James Truitte. *Sd* Francis M. Stahl. *Asst Dir* Russell Saunders, William Kissel. *Makeup* Gordon Bau.

Cast: Angie Dickinson (*Rachel Cade*), Peter Finch (*Col. Henri Derode*), Roger Moore (*Paul Wilton*), Errol John (*Kulu*), Woody Strode (*Muwango*), Juano Hernandez (*Kalanumu*), Frederick O'Neal (*Buderga*), Mary Wickes (*Marie Grieux*), Scatman Crothers (*Musinga*), Rafer Johnson (*Kosongo*), Chuck Wood (*Mzimba*), Douglas Spencer (*Dr. Bikel*).

Melodrama. Source: Charles E. Mercer, *Rachel Cade* (New York, 1956). During World War II, Rachel Cade, a young missionary nurse, arrives at a dilapidated hospital mission in a remote part of the Congo. The inept, defeated head of the hospital dies, but Rachel decides to stay on despite the advice of the cynical Belgian administrator, Col. Henri Derode. With patience and sympathy, she works among the natives and tries to get them to accept the Christian way of life. After successfully performing an appendectomy on a native child, she wins the trust of some of the villagers, and her little hospital is soon filled with patients. One night, after watching a sensuous fertility dance, Rachel almost succumbs to the advances of Derode. Then an RAF plane crashes in the vicinity; and the pilot, an American named Paul Wilton, is brought to the mission. During his long convalescence they fall in love; and as his departure grows near, Rachel, unable to restrain her desires, submits to his lovemaking. After Paul has left, Derode learns that Rachel is pregnant. Sensing that she never told Paul about the baby, Derode wires the information to Boston, where Paul has become an established society doctor. Derode then asks to be transferred to the battle front. Paul returns to the Congo and offers to take Rachel and the baby back with him; but Rachel perceives that it is pride rather than love that motivates his actions, and she sends him away. Remaining in the Congo to continue her missionary work, she prays with the natives for the safe return of the combat troops, realizing that Derode's love for her is selfless. *Nurses. Physicians. Air pilots. Missionaries. Americans in foreign countries. Belgians. Pregnancy. Christianity. Rites and ceremonies. Hospitals. World War II. Congo. Great Britain—Royal Air Force.*

Note: Also known as *Rachel Cade.*

SINS OF SODOM see **ALL THE SINS OF SODOM**

SINS OF THE FLESHAPOIDS F6.4525

Dist Film-Makers' Cooperative, Film-Makers' Distribution Center. 20 Aug **1965** [New York opening]. Sd; col. 16mm. 45 min. [Also 50 min.]

Prod-Dir Mike Kuchar. *Narr* Bob Cowan. *Photog* Mike Kuchar. *Sets* Mike Kuchar. *Soundtrack* Mike Kuchar, Bob Cowan.

Cast: Bob Cowan (*Mister Robot*), Donna Kerness (*Voluptuous Princess*), George Kuchar (*Evil Prince*), Julius Mittleman (*Voluptuous Tarzan*), Maren Thomas (*Lady Robot*).

Satire. A million years in the future, an atomic war has nearly devastated the world. In recovering from the disaster, people have abandoned the pursuit of knowledge and have rejected all that has been learned over the preceding millennia, becoming totally preoccupied with sexuality. The robots, who have begun to assume human characteristics, are likewise dominated by carnal instincts. The machines are hampered in their sexual pursuits, however, by their physical limitations and by the "pagan" humans, who treat them cruelly. Consequently, a disastrous confrontation takes place between the robots, or Fleshapoids, and the humans. The robots emerge triumphant, and their joy is punctuated by a remarkable event: Lady Robot gives birth to a 2-pound baby machine with blinking red and green eyes. *Human race. Sexuality. Nuclear warfare. Childbirth. Robots. The Future.*

Note: Filmed on location in the Bronx.

SINTHIA F6.4526

Gentlemen II Productions. *Dist* Sack Amusement Enterprises. 20 May **1970** [Oklahoma City opening]. Sd; col. 35mm. 61 min.

Prod Robert L. McCore. *Dir* Kendall S. Rose. *Screenplay* Bonnie Lee. *Dir Photog* Stan Slate. *Camera* Ted Ford. *2d Camera* Bill Coors. *Lighting* Ken Stewart. *Film Ed* Kendall S. Rose. *Rec* Robert B. Lee. *Makeup* Harry Hash. *Hairstyles* Dian Stewart. *Key Grip* Robert Rubio.

Cast: Barbara Caron (*Sinthia*), Robert Cole (*Stephan*), Mai Ling (*Sue Ann*), Bridget (*Belinda*).

Drama. Stephan devotes all his energies to entertaining his secretary, leaving his wife, Sinthia, to find companionship with a girl friend. The friendship develops into a lesbian relationship, an affair that ends when Sinthia discovers that her friend is bisexual. *Secretaries. Infidelity. Lesbianism. Bisexuality.*

SINTHIA, THE DEVIL'S DOLL F6.4527

Sun Art Enterprises. 10 Jun **1970** [Atlanta opening]. Sd; col. 35mm. 80 min.

Exec Prod Dorothy K. Sonney. *Dir (see note)* Sven Christian. *Screenplay* Herb Robins. *Photog* Sven Christian. *Art Dir* David Miles. *Mus* Henri Price.

Cast: Shula Roan (*Sinthia*), Boris Balachoff, Diane Webber, Maria Lease.

Melodrama. Sinthia becomes possessed by the Devil and engages in orgies but is unable to satisfy her sexual desires. *Orgies. The Devil.*

Note: Sven Christian is a pseudonym for Ray Dennis Steckler.

LA SIRÈNE DU MISSISSIPPI see **MISSISSIPPI MERMAID**

SIROCCO D'HIVER see **WINTER WIND**

SIROKKÓ see **WINTER WIND**

SISSI see **FOREVER MY LOVE**

SISSI—DIE JUNGE KAISERIN see **FOREVER MY LOVE**

SISSI—SCHICKSALSJAHRE EINER KAISERIN see **FOREVER MY LOVE**

DE SISTA STEGEN see **A MATTER OF MORALS**

THE SISTERS (Greece) F6.4528

Th. A. Damaskinos–V. G. Michaelides, A. E. *Dist* Joseph Brenner Associates. 19 Mar **1969** [San Francisco opening; c19 Mar 1969; LP36760]. Sd; b&w. 35mm. 96 min.

Prod Theophanis A. Damaskinos, Viktor G. Michaelides. *Dir* Errikos Andreou. *Script* Panos Kontellis, Irene Vardoulaki. *Cinematog* Demetris Papakonstantis. *Mus Score* Yannis Markopoulos. *English Subtitl* Peter Fernandez.

Cast: Petros Fissoun (*Constantis*), Elli Fotiou (*Thalia*), Nikos Rizos (*Yorghis*), Despo Diamantidou ("*The Lady*"), Vangelis Kazan (*Yorghis' mother*), Niki Shellby (*English bar girl*).

Melodrama. Constantis and Yorghis, two close friends in a poverty-ridden Greek village on the isle of Lesbos, find that sponge diving is the only occupation open in the area to men of their background. Constantis owns his own ships, but they are rendered useless when the town's only rich citizen, a powerful matriarch known as "The Lady," seizes them until he can pay his debts. "The Lady" has three daughters, one of whom, Thalia, is pursued by Yorghis, whose mother wants him to settle down with a wife. Thalia does not love Yorghis but finds the affections of any man preferable to the incestuous sex life of her two spinster sisters. When diving season begins, the men visit "The Lady" to discuss ship rental terms, but she raises their rental fees. Thalia meets Constantis, who is living with an English barmaid; and during the negotiations, she becomes so attracted to him that she seduces him and supplies him with enough money to reclaim his boats. Constantis finally rejects her, however, out of loyalty to Yorghis. In spite of "The Lady"'s strong disapproval of any courtship on the part of her daughters, Thalia becomes engaged to Yorghis, but she finds her desire for Constantis overpowering, and she runs off with him during her engagement party. *Divers. Sisters. Spinsters. Village life. Debt. Filial relations. Incest. Lesbianism. Loyalty. Seduction. Ships. Lesbos.*

Note: Produced in Greece in 1965. Also known as *Make Me a Woman.*

SISTERS IN LEATHER F6.4529

Satyr IX productions. *Dist* Sack Amusement Enterprises. Feb **1969** [periodical notice; San Francisco showing: 26 Jun]. Sd; b&w. 35mm. 64 min.

Prod-Dir (see note) Spence Crilly, Zoltan G. Spencer. *Photog* Manuel S. Conde. *Film Ed* W. C. Meadows. *Sd* W. C. Meadows. *Prod Mgr* Wallace Dare.

Cast: Kathy Williams (*Mary*), Pat Barrington.

Melodrama. A gang of lesbian motorcyclists send their youngest member to seduce Joe, a young, married executive, in order to set a trap for blackmail. The women demand $2,000 from Joe in exchange for photographs of the encounter, and they lure his wife, Mary, to a picnic where they reveal Joe's infidelity in an attempt to seduce her. Two of the gang members ride their motorcycles in the nude and then make love while their leader, Butch, caresses Mary. That night Joe finds a note from Mary that leads him to Butch's house, and he watches through a window as the women hold a champagne orgy to celebrate Mary's forthcoming initiation into the group. He then enlists the aid of a gang of male motorcyclists in rescuing his wife. The men interrupt the initiation ceremony, in which Mary is forced to submit to the embraces of the entire group, and they overcome the lesbians in a rough-and-tumble sexual encounter. *Executives. Motorcycle gangs. Blackmail. Lesbianism. Infidelity. Rape. Seduction. Bisexuality. Orgies. Photographs.*

Note: Also known as *Sisters in Leatherette.* Sources conflict in crediting the producer-director; one name is a pseudonym for the other.

DER SITTLICHKEITSVERBRECHER see **THE MOLESTERS**

SITUATION HOPELESS—BUT NOT SERIOUS   **F6.4530**
Castle Productions. *Dist* Paramount Pictures. 13 Oct **1965** [New York opening; c29 Sep 1965; LP31681]. Sd; b&w. 35mm. 97 min.
Prod-Dir Gottfried Reinhardt. *Asst Prod* Jose de Villaverde. *Prod Exec* Kurt Hartmann. *2d Unit Dir* Walter Boos. *Screenplay* Silvia Reinhardt. *Adapt* Jan Lustig. *Dir Cinematog* Kurt Hasse. *Art Dir* Rolf Zehetbauer. *Film Ed* Walter Boos. *Mus* Harold Byrns. *Sd* Walter Ruhland. *Asst Dir* Henri Sokal. *Prod Mgr* Michael Bittins. *Cost* Ilse Dubois. *Makeup Artist* Arthur Schramm, Albert Nagel.
Cast: Alec Guinness *(Herr Frick)*, Michael Connors *(Lucky)*, Robert Redford *(Hank)*, Anita Hoefer *(Edeltraud)*, Mady Rahl *(Lissie)*, Paul Dahlke *(Herr Neusel)*, Frank Wolff *(quartermaster master sergeant)*, John Briley *(sergeant)*, Elisabeth Von Molo *(Wanda)*, Carola Regnier *(Senta)*.
Comedy. Source: Robert Shaw, *The Hiding Place* (London, 1959). Near the end of World War II, American flyers Lucky and Hank are forced to parachute into a town in Germany. They are captured by Herr Frick, a shy, lonely clerk, who hides them in the cellar of his house. Frick treats the men very well but does not tell them when the war ends and instead keeps them prisoner for 7 years by fabricating stories of German victories. The village is occupied by American troops while the men are being held captive. Frick's fellow worker Edeltraud, a former Hitler Youth, has become the girl friend of an American master sergeant. Frick tries to secure a prostitute for Lucky as a Christmas present, but Lissie, the madam, thinks he is insane and has him thrown into the streets. Frick suffers a heart attack and is taken to a hospital; but, worried about Lucky and Hank, he breaks out with two policemen in close pursuit. Frick releases his prisoners but does not tell them the truth, and it is only after they blunder into a film crew making a war movie that they realize what has transpired. All three men are reunited in America, and Hank hires Frick as his butler. *Air pilots. Clerks. Germans. Butlers. Madams. Police. Loneliness. Timidity. Friendship. Insanity. Hoaxes. Heart disease. Motion pictures. World War II. Germany. United States Army—Air Force. Hitler Youth.*
Note: Filmed in West Germany.

SIX BLACK HORSES   **F6.4531**
Universal Pictures. *Dist* Universal-International. 28 Mar **1962** [San Francisco opening; c26 Dec 1961; LP24132]. Sd; col (Eastman Color by Pathé). 35mm. 80 min.
Prod Gordon Kay. *Dir* Harry Keller. *Screenplay* Burt Kennedy. *Dir Photog* Maury Gertsman. *Art Dir* Alexander Golitzen, Robert Luthardt. *Set Decor* Oliver Emert. *Film Ed* Aaron Stell. *Mus Supv* Joseph Gershenson. *Sd* Waldon O. Watson, Frank H. Wilkinson. *Asst Dir* Ivan Volkman, Charles Scott, Jr., Fred Hartsook. *Unit Prod Mgr* Foster Thompson. *Makeup* Bud Westmore. *Hair Stylist* Larry German.
Cast: Audie Murphy *(Ben Lane)*, Dan Duryea *(Frank Jesse)*, Joan O'Brien *(Kelly)*, George Wallace *(Boone)*, Roy Barcroft *(mustanger)*, Bob Steele *(puncher)*, Henry Wills *(Indian leader)*, Phil Chambers *(undertaker)*, Charlita Regis *(Mexican girl)*, Dale Van Sickel *(man)*, Richard Pasco *(Charlie)*.
Western melodrama. Professional wrangler Ben Lane lassos a wild horse in the desert to replace his lost mount and is stopped by a group of toughs, who prepare to hang him as a horsethief. He is rescued by gunman Frank Jesse, and the two men ride into Perdido, where they are confronted by an attractive blonde, Kelly. She hires them to escort her through dangerous Indian territory to rejoin her husband in Santa Rita del Cobre. En route the party is forced to take refuge in a ruined mission and fight off marauding Indians. During the gunplay, Kelly is on the point of shooting Jesse in the back when she is wounded by an Indian spear. She then reveals to Ben that her husband is dead, having been murdered by hired-killer Jesse, and she confesses her determination to take revenge. When Ben suggests they turn back, Jesse refuses. (Secretly he plans to gain possession of the money Kelly has in the Santa Rita bank.) He knocks Ben unconscious and kidnaps Kelly. Ben follows them, kills Jesse in a showdown, and rides off with Kelly. *Wranglers. Horsethieves. Indians of North America. Hired killers. Revenge. Lynching. Abduction. Deserts.*
Note: Location scenes filmed in southern Utah.

SIX DAYS A WEEK (France/Italy/Spain)   **F6.4532**
Ultra Film–Consortium Pathé–Tecisa. *Dist* Atlantic Pictures. **1966**. Sd; b&w. 35mm. 91 min.
Dir Luigi Comencini. *Screenplay* Marcello Fondato, Luigi Comencini, José G. Maesso. *Photog* Armando Nannuzzi. *Set Decor* Luigi Scaccianoce, Francisco Canet. *Mus* Benedetto Ghiglia.
Cast: Catherine Spaak *(Maria/Silvana/Caterina)*, Enrico Maria Salerno *(Count Adriano Silveri)*, Marc Michel *(Arturo Santini)*, Manuel Miranda *(Gianni Moraldi)*, Pepe Calvo, Riccardo Cucciolla, Nando Angelini, Didi Perego, Mara Fernández, Janine Reynaud, Daina Saronni, Grazia Martini, Giuseppe Ranieri, Mario de Gual, Guadalupe Muñoz Sampedro, María Fernanda Ladrón de Guevara.
Comedy. Source: Diego Fabbri, *La bugiarda* (Milan opening: 21 Jan 1956). Maria masquerades as Silvana, her French roommate who is an airline hostess, in order to meet with her friend's lovers. For 3 days each week, she becomes the mistress of a Vatican official, Count Adriano Silveri; the next 3 days she spends with Roman dentist Arturo Santini, who wishes to marry her. On the last day of the week, she works as a typist in her own apartment and is visited by a third lover, Gianni Moraldi, who knew her as Caterina when they were students together. Eventually, the three men discover Maria's ruse, but she manages to convince each of them that he is the one she loves. *Roommates. Airline stewardesses. Mistresses. Dentists. Typists. Nobility. Imposture. Rome.*
Note: Released in Italy in 1965 as *La bugiarda* at 95 min; in Paris in Aug 1965 as *Le partage de Catherine*; and in Spain as *La mentirosa* at 102 min.

SIX DAYS TO ETERNITY (Israel)   **F6.4533**
Brummer Film Production. *Dist* Peppercorn–Wormser, Inc. 30 Oct **1968** [New York opening]. Sd; b&w. 35mm. 88 min.
Prod (see note) Michael Shvily, Yigal Efrati, Avraham Shalev. *Dir* Yaacov Hameiri, Itzhak Herbst. *English Narr* Uri Sella. *Hebrew Narr* Haim Hefer. *Ed (see note)* Nelly Gilad, Yaacov Hameiri, Tova Biram. *Asst Ed* Frida Gabai. *Mus* Yochannan Arai. *Sd Rec* Elisha Birnbaum. *Unit Prod Mgr* M. Kadesh. *Asst Prod Mgr* Moshe Gez, Shlomo Gavriel. *Tech Adv* A. Roet. *Coöp* Israeli Prime Minister's Office.
Narrators: Illy Gorlitzky, Zaharira Harifai *(English)*, Yossi Banai *(Hebrew)*.
Documentary. The official film on the Six-Day Israeli-Arab War that began on 5 June 1967, two days after Israel's 19th anniversary as an independent state. Compiled from 300,000 feet of footage (part of which was reportedly taken from Arab archives), the film includes scenes of anti-Israel demonstrations instituted by Egypt's President Nasser; scenes photographed from Israeli planes while bombing Arab airports; re-creations of battles in which Israeli soldiers repeat their movements step by step; and shots of Israeli generals explaining the military strategy that was victorious in the Sinai Peninsula, Jordan, and Syria. *Militarism. Demonstrations. Aerial bombardment. Israeli-Arab War 1967. Egypt. Sinai Peninsula. Jordan. Gamal Abdel Nasser.*
Note: Released in Tel Aviv in Mar 1968 as *Sheshet hayamim*; running time: 105 min. U. S. sources credit Michael Shvily as producer; a review from Tel Aviv lists only Yigal Efrati and Avraham Shalev. U. S. sources conflict in crediting editor. Also known as *Follow Me ....*

SIX FEMMES POUR L'ASSASSIN see **BLOOD AND BLACK LACE**

SIX IN PARIS (France)   **F6.4534**
Les Films du Losange–Barbet Schroeder. *Dist* New Yorker Films. Oct **1968** [Los Angeles showing]. Sd; col (Ektachrome). 35mm (see note). 96 min.
Overall Production Credits: *Prod* Barbet Schroeder. *Assoc Prod* Patrick Bauchau. *Art Dir* Eliane Bonneau. *Film Ed* Jackie Reynal. *Asst to the Prod* Pierre-Richard Bré, Pierre Cottrell.
Production Credits—"Saint-Germain-des-Prés": *Dir* Jean Douchet. *Screenplay* Jean Douchet, Georges Keller. *Photog* Nestor Almendros.
Production Credits—"Gare du Nord": *Dir-Writ* Jean Rouch. *Photog* Etienne Becker. *Sd* Bernard Ortion.
Production Credits—"Rue Saint-Denis": *Dir-Writ* Jean-Daniel Pollet. *Photog* Alain Levent.
Production Credits—"Place de l'Etoile": *Dir-Writ* Eric Rohmer. *Photog* Alain Levent, Nestor Almendros.
Production Credits—"Montparnasse-Levallois": *Dir-Writ* Jean-Luc Godard. *Photog* Albert Maysles. *Sd* René Levert.
Production Credits—"La Muette": *Dir-Writ* Claude Chabrol. *Photog* Jean Rabier.
Cast—"Saint-Germain-des-Prés": Barbara Wilkin *(Katherine)*, Jean-François Chappey *(Jean)*, Jean-Pierre Andréani *(Raymond)*.
Cast—"Gare du Nord": Nadine Ballot *(Odile)*, Barbet Schroeder *(Jean-Pierre)*, Gilles Quéant *(stranger)*.
Cast—"Rue Saint-Denis": Micheline Dax *(prostitute)*, Claude Melki *(Léon)*.

Cast—"Place de l'Etoile": Jean-Michel Rouzière (Jean-Marc), Marcel Gallon (victim).

Cast—"Montparnasse-Levallois": Joanna Shimkus (Monica), Philippe Hiquilly (Roger), Serge Davri (Ivan).

Cast—"La Muette": Stéphane Audran (wife), Claude Chabrol (husband), Gilles Chusseau (boy), Dinah Saril (maid).

Drama. SAINT-GERMAIN-DES-PRES: Jean brings Katherine, an American student, to an apartment in the Saint-Germain district of Paris and then gets rid of her the next morning by announcing that he is going to join his father in Mexico. Later, Katherine attends her art class and discovers that Jean is one of the male models. Disillusioned, she allows herself to be picked up by another man, Raymond, only to be taken back to the same flat; Raymond had loaned both his car and his apartment to Jean. GARE DU NORD: While her husband eats his breakfast, Odile complains bitterly that her life lacks both romance and adventure. As tempers flare, Odile storms out of the house and is nearly run down by a well-dressed man in an expensive car. After making his apologies, the man tells Odile that he had decided to kill himself, but he will give up the idea if she will go away with him. When Odile rejects his offer, the stranger leaps from a railway bridge. RUE SAINT-DENIS: Léon, a shy dishwasher on the Rue Saint-Denis, finally finds the courage to bring a prostitute to his room, but he talks so incessantly that the prostitute decides to stay for dinner before taking care of business. PLACE DE L'ETOILE: On his way to work, salesman Jean-Marc collides with a derelict on the Place de l'Etoile and, during the ensuing altercation, strikes the man with his umbrella. The man falls to the ground, and Jean-Marc flees, certain that he has committed murder. For weeks he searches the papers for news of the incident, until one day he sees his victim having a similar argument with another commuter. MONTPARNASSE-LEVALLOIS: Monica mails a letter to each of her two lovers—Ivan, a sculptor, and Roger, a coachbuilder—confirming the time and place of their next meetings. Certain that she has mixed up the envelopes, she visits the two men and tries to cover her mistake. Both men throw her out, however, and Monica realizes that she did not mix up the envelopes. LA MUETTE: Tired of his parents' quarreling about money, his mother's health, and his father's flirtations with the maid, a young boy buys earplugs to blot out the noise of their arguments. The earplugs are so effective that when his mother falls down the stairs, the son is unable to hear her cries for help. *Students. Americans in foreign countries. Models. Dishwashers. Prostitutes. Salesmen. Derelicts. Duplicity. Marriage. Suicide. Guilt. Family life. Paris—Saint-Germain. Paris—Gare du Nord. Paris—Rue Saint-Denis. Paris—Place de l'Etoile. Paris—La Muette. Documentation.*

Note: Filmed on location in Paris in 16mm. Opened in Paris in Oct 1965 as *Paris vu par ....*

6-9 THE DAILY DOUBLE   F6.4535

Kirt Films International. *Dist* Distribpix, Inc. ca **1970**. Sd; col. 35mm. 63 min.

Melodrama. A young actress who has achieved stardom in sex exploitation films discovers that the director of her latest assignment demands her services offscreen as well. A veteran of hundreds of sex films, she soon realizes that her employer is a sexual pervert—he amuses himself by depriving his partner of the pleasure of orgasm, thus driving her to tear in distress at her own body. The actress submits to her employer's method of torture until she can no longer bear it, and she kills both the director and herself. *Actors. Motion picture directors. Sadism. Murder. Suicide. Employer-employee relations. Sex exploitation films.*

Note: Also known as *The Daily Double*.

SIX SHES AND A HE   F6.4536

Associated Producers Studio. *Dist* Dominant Pictures, Wheeler Film Co. **1964**. Sd; col. 35mm. 72 min.

Pres by Richard S. Flink. A Richard S. Flink Production. *Prod* Frank M. Malagon.

Cast: Joel Hamilton, Dolores Hodges.

Science fiction drama. Returning to earth after a space exploration, astronaut Bill Rogers makes a forced landing off an uncharted Pacific island. Having lost consciousness, Bill awakens to find himself the captive of six sex-starved goddesses. Expected to work as a slave by day and function as a lover at night, Bill finds relief only during the ritual bath. Bill and the goddess Helenia fall in love and plan their escape. During primitive rites in which the goddesses intend to torture Bill, Helenia defeats the queen in battle and flees the island with her lover. *Astronauts. Sexuality. Slavery. Rites and ceremonies. Torture. Islands. Pacific Ocean.*

Note: Filmed in Miami. Working title: *Love Goddesses of Blood Island.*

SIX SUSPECTS (Japan)   F6.4537

Takarazuka Motion Picture Co. *Dist* Toho Co. 21 Apr **1961** [Los Angeles opening]. Sd; col? 35mm. 107 min.

Dir Umeji Inoue.

Cast: Tatsuya Mihashi, Akira Takarada, Shin Morikawa, Minoru Takada, Yumi Shirakawa, Chiaki Tsukioka, Yasuko Nakada, Hisaya Ito, Hideo Takamatsu, Masumi Okada.

Action drama. No information about the precise nature of this film has been found.

Note: Released in Japan in Nov 1960 as *Dairoku no yogisha.*

THE SIX TERMINATORS see THE SEXTERMINATORS

633 SQUADRON (United States/Great Britain)   F6.4538

Mirisch Corp. *Dist* United Artists. 24 Jun **1964** [New York opening; c5 Jun 1964; LP28321]. Sd; col (De Luxe). 35mm (Panavision). 101 min. [Copyright length: 94 min.]

Prod Cecil F. Ford. *Exec Prod* Lewis J. Rachmil. *Dir* Walter Grauman. *2d Unit Dir* Roy Stevens. *Screenplay* James Clavell, Howard Koch. *Photog* Edward Scaife. *Adtl Photog* John Wilcox. *Prod Dsgn* Michael Stringer. *Film Ed* Bert Bates. *Mus* Ron Goodwin. *Sd Supv* A. W. Watkins. *Sd Rec* John Bramall, J. B. Smith. *Asst Dir* Ted Sturgis. *Prod Mgr* Albert Becket. *Sp Eff* Tom Howard. *Adv* Hamish Mahaddie, (Group Capt.). *Stunt Flying* John Crewdson.

Cast: Cliff Robertson (Wing Comdr. Roy Grant), George Chakiris (Lieut. Erik Bergman), Maria Perschy (Hilde Bergman), Harry Andrews (Air Marshal Davis), Donald Houston (Wing Comdr. Tom Barrett), Michael Goodliffe (Squadron Leader Bill Adams), John Meillon (Flight Lieutenant Gillibrand), John Bonney (Flight Lieutenant Scott), Angus Lennie (Flight Lieut. Hoppy Hopkinson), Scot Finch (Flight Lieutenant Bissel), Barbara Archer (Rosie, the barmaid), Julian Sherrier (Flight Lieutenant Singh), Suzan Farmer (Mary, W.A.F. sergeant), John Church (Flight Lieutenant Evans), Jeremy Wagg (Flight Lieutenant Reynolds), Johnny Briggs (Flight Lieutenant Jones), Sean Kelly (Flight Lieutenant Nigel), Edward Brayshaw (Flight Lieutenant Greiner), Arnold Locke (Kearns), Peter Kriss (Flight Lieutenant Milner), Geoffrey Frederick (Flight Lieutenant Frank), Richard Shaw (Johansen), Anne Ridler (SS woman), Cavan Malone (Ericsen), Drewe Henley (Thor), John Dray (Henrik), Chris Williams (Goth).

War melodrama. Source: Frederick E. Smith, *633 Squadron* (London, 1958). During World War II, Norwegian underground leader Erik Bergman informs the British of the location of a German V2 fuel manufacturing plant. Situated beneath an overhanging cliff at the end of an easily defended fjord, the factory can be destroyed only by collapsing the cliff on top of it, using light Mosquito aircraft. Wing Comdr. Roy Grant's 633 squadron is assigned the task, and Bergman plans a ground attack to coincide with the air strike, but he is captured and tortured by the Gestapo. Gestapo headquarters is destroyed by the 633 squadron, and Bergman is killed, but not before he reveals the plans for the attack. Underground resistance is destroyed, and Mosquito pilots, unaware that the ground attack will not take place, fly to the factory, and the entire squadron is wiped out. However, the last bomb dropped makes the mission a success. Only Grant and his navigator survive. *Norwegians. Informers. Air pilots. Nazis. Resistance (political). Torture. Aerial bombardment. Fjords. Factories. Airplanes. World War II. Norway. Great Britain—Royal Air Force. Gestapo.*

Note: Released in Great Britain in 1964. Filmed in England, with exteriors shot on west coast of Scotland.

SIX WOMEN & A MAN see SEXTET

SIXTET see SEXTET

THE SIXTH MAN see THE OUTSIDER

SKAMMEN see SHAME

SKAZKA O KONKE-GORBUNKE see THE LITTLE HUMPBACKED HORSE

SKEZAG   F6.4539

Cinnamon Productions. *Dist* Soho Cinema, Ltd. Dec **1970** [New York showing]. Sd; col. 16mm. 73 min.

Dir-Writ Joel Freedman, Philip F. Messina. *Photog* Joel Freedman, Philip F. Messina.

Cast: Wayne Shirley, Louis "Sonny" Berrios, Angel Sanchez.

Documentary. New York filmmakers Joel L. Freedman and Philip F. Messina interview Wayne Shirley, a black Vietnam veteran who earns his living as a prostitute and admits to using drugs, although he maintains that he is not "hooked." The interview moves from the street to Shirley's East Village apartment, where "Sonny" Berrios and Angel Sanchez, his two Puerto Rican friends, discuss social philosophy. After injecting heroin into their veins, the three men continue the discussion until they lose consciousness. Four months later, the filmmakers again encounter Shirley, but this time he is transformed: his eyes are dull, his speech is thick, and his face is scarred and sagging. He confesses that he fooled himself about drugs and that he is now addicted. Despite the filmmakers' efforts to get Wayne into a drug rehabilitation program, the next time they see him he is totally dependent on heroin and is planning to leave New York City for his home in Indiana. *Filmmakers. Negroes. Prostitutes. Veterans. Puerto Ricans. Drug addicts. Race relations. Heroin. New York City—East Village. Vietnam War 1964–73.*

SKI FEVER (United States/Austria/Czechoslovakia)   **F6.4540**
   Gaumont International-Parnass-Film–Československý Film. *Dist* Allied Artists. 5 Mar **1969** [Boston opening]. Sd; col (Eastman Color). 35mm. 98 min. *MPAA rating* M.
   Prod Wolfgang Schmidt, Mark Cooper. *Dir* Curt Siodmak. *Screenplay* Curt Siodmak, Robert L. Joseph. *Orig Story* Frank Agrama, Edward Zatlyn. *Dir Photog* Jan Stallich. *Art Dir* Karel Černý. *Film Ed* Antonín Zelenka. *Songs Comp & Arr* Guy Hemric, Jerry Styner. *Song:* "Ski Fever" sung by Jerry Styner. *Asst Dir* Vladimír Zelenka. *Prod Mgr* Rudolf Wolf.
   Cast: Martin Milner *(Brian Davis)*, Claudia Martin *(Susan Halsey)*, Vivi Bach *(Karen Sloan)*, Dietmar Schönherr *(Toni Brandt)*, Toni Sailor *(Franz Gruber)*, Dorith Dom *(Dominique Leseur)*, Kurt Grosskurth *(Max)*, Curt Bock *(MacDoodle)*, Karla Chadimová, Lenka Fišerová, Jana Nováková, Rajmund Gabriel, Vladimír Pospíšil, Miloš Zavadil.
   Romantic comedy-drama. Brian Davis, an American music student enrolled at a European university, teaches skiing at an Austrian resort to pay for his studies. Max, the lodge manager, stipulates in the instructors' contracts that they must entertain the female guests during the evenings. The employees have wired a bed in one of the guest rooms to a pinball machine, and while one of the group tries to seduce the occupant of the room, the others place bets on the amount of time that will elapse before the machine registers a "tilt." Susan Halsey, a Californian, arrives at the lodge and becomes the center of the game. Brian, who has not joined in the competition, falls in love with her. He and Toni Brandt, the head instructor, wager their season's pay on who will win her affections. Susan, repelled by Brian's aggressive attitude, becomes attracted to Toni, but eventually she learns of the game and discovers that Toni is merely interested in winning the bet. Brian and Toni agree on a ski jumping contest to determine the winner. Brian competes using inferior equipment and is injured when he jumps. Susan becomes convinced of his sincerity and realizes that she loves him. *Americans in foreign countries. Students. Ski instructors. Skiing. Seduction. Wagers. Ski resorts. Pinball machines.*
   Note: Location scenes filmed in Austria. Released in Austria caJan 1967 as *Liebesspiele im Schnee*; running time: 87 min.

SKI ON THE WILD SIDE   **F6.4541**
   Warren Miller Productions. *Dist* Sigma III Corp. 1 Aug **1967** [New York opening]. Sd; col. 35mm. 104 min.
   Prod-Dir-Narr Warren Miller. *Photog* Warren Miller, Don Brolin, Rod Allin. *Mus* Billy Allen.
   Cast—Narrator: Warren Miller.
   Featured skiers: Jean-Claude Killy, Marielle Goitschel, Stan Tomlinson, Annie Famose, Jimmy Huega, Art Furrer, Nancy Greene, Sue Chaffee, Joan Hannah, Roger Staub, Karl Schranz, Alf Engan, Junior Bounous, Warren Miller.
   Sports documentary. Warren Miller, a former ski instructor and veteran lecturer on the sport of skiing, narrates this documentary. Both champion and beginning skiers are shown on the slopes of Squaw Valley, California; Vail and Aspen, Colorado; Mount Snow, Vermont; Jackson Hole, Wyoming; Val d'Isère and Courchevel, France; Itkul, Russia; Planica, Yugoslavia; the Tasman Glacier in New Zealand; and Mount Zoa, Japan. Coverage of competitive events, such as ski jumping, features well-known international skiers. *Skiers. Skiing. Squaw Valley. Vail (Colorado). Aspen. Mount Snow. Jackson Hole (Wyoming). Val d'Isère (France). Courchevel (France). Itkul (U.S.S.R.). Planica (Yugoslavia). Tasman Glacier (New Zealand). Mount Zoa (Japan).*

SKI PARTY   **F6.4542**
   American International Pictures. 30 Jun **1965** [Boston opening; c16 Jun 1965; LP31196]. Sd; col (PathéColor). 35mm (Panavision). 90 min.
   A Gene Corman Production. *Prod* Gene Corman. *Exec Prod* James H. Nicholson, Samuel Z. Arkoff. *Dir* Alan Rafkin. *Screenplay* Robert Kaufman. *Dir Photog* Arthur E. Arling. *Camera Op* John C. Stevens. *Art Dir* Howard Campbell. *Set Decor* George R. Nelson. *Film Ed* Mort Tubor. *Mus* Gary Usher. *Titl Song* Gary Usher, Roger Christian. *Song:* "Lots, Lots More" Ritchie Adams, Larry Kusik. *Song:* "Paintin' the Town" Bob Gaudio. *Song:* "We'll Never Change Them" Guy Hemric. *Sung by* Deborah Walley, Jerry Styner. *Other Songs* Marvin Hamlisch, Howard Liebling, Ted Wright. *Sd* Bob Post. *Asst Dir* Dale Hutchinson. *Prod Supv* Jack Bohrer. *Cost* Richard Bruno. *Makeup* Ted Coodley.
   Cast: Frankie Avalon *(Todd Armstrong/Jane)*, Dwayne Hickman *(Craig Gamble/Nora)*, Deborah Walley *(Linda Hughes)*, Yvonne Craig *(Barbara Norris)*, Robert Q. Lewis *(Donald Pevney)*, Bobbi Shaw *(Nita)*, Aron Kincaid *(Freddie Carter)*, Steve Rogers *(Gene)*, Mike Nader *(Bobby)*, Jo Collins *(Jo)*,

Mickey Dora *(Mickey)*, John Boyer, Ronnie Dayton *(ski boys)*, Bill Sampson *(Arthur)*, Patti Chandler *(Janet)*, Salli Sachse *(Indian)*, Sigi Engl *(ski instructor)*, Mikki Jamison, Mary Hughes, Luree Holmes *(ski girls)*, The Hondells, James Brown and the Flames, Lesley Gore *(themselves)*, Annette Funicello *(uncredited appearance)*.
   Comedy with music. Handsome athletes Todd Armstrong and Craig Gamble pursue co-eds Linda Hughes and Barbara Norris at a Los Angeles college, but the girls prefer stuffy, unathletic Freddie Carter. When the gang takes a ski holiday at a Sun Valley lodge run by social director Donald Pevney, Todd and Craig decide to pose as females and flirt with Freddie to discover why the girls find him irresistible. Masquerading as Jane and Nora, the boys join the ladies' ski lessons where Freddie takes notice of the two newcomers. While the enamoured Freddie flirts with them, Todd becomes involved with a Swedish girl, and Craig courts his buxom ski instructor. Pevney provides the group with a show of ski stunts and music. Freddie makes an advance toward Craig disguised as Nora, and he chases the gang through Sawtooth National Forest and back to the heated pools of Los Angeles. Once home, the co-eds realize the joke Todd and Craig have played on Freddie. No longer prey to Freddie's flirtations, the girls find romance with Todd and Craig. *Students. Social directors. Flirts. Athletes. Swedes. College life. Female impersonation. Skiing. Sun Valley. Sawtooth National Forest. Los Angeles. Chases.*

SKIDOO   **F6.4543**
   Sigma Productions. *Dist* Paramount Pictures. 19 Dec **1968** [Miami, Florida, opening; c31 Oct 1968; LP36994]. Sd; col (Technicolor). 35mm (Panavision). 98 min. *MPAA rating* M.
   An Otto Preminger Production. *Prod-Dir* Otto Preminger. *Screenplay* Doran William Cannon. *Story* Erik Kirkland. *Dir Photog* Leon Shamroy. *Camera Op* Irving Rosenberg, Dewey Wrigley. *Art Dir* Robert E. Smith. *Asst Art Dir* John M. Elliott. *Set Decor* Fred Price. *Vis Cons* Sandy Dvore. *Titl* Sandy Dvore, Pacific Title. *Film Ed* George Rohrs. *Asst Ed* Dean O. Ball. *Neg Cutter* Connie Roese. *Mus & Lyr* Harry Nilsson. *Mus Arr & Cond* George Tipton. *Titl Song Sung by* Carol Channing. *Choreog* Tom Hansen. *Sd* Glenn Anderson, Franklin Milton, Lloyd Hanks. *Sd Eff Ed* Donn Higgins. *Mus Ed* Fred Prior. *Asst Dir* Eric Von Stroheim, Jr., Wallace Jones, Al Murphy, Steven North. *Exec Asst to the Prod* Nat Rudich. *Prod Mgr* Kenneth DeLand, Howard Joslin. *Script Supv* Kathleen Fagan. *Prod Sec* Joyce Lilley. *Cost Coörd* Hope Bryce. *Cost Dsgn* Rudi Gernreich. *Wardrobe* Ted Parvin, Phyllis Garr, George Thompson, John Perry. *Makeup* Web Overlander. *Hairdressing* Vivian Thompson. *Sp Eff* Charles Spurgeon. *Casting* Erik Kirkland. *Dial Coach* Max Slater. *Ch Electrn* Fred Hall. *Key Grip* Leo McCreary. *Prop Man* Ken Westcott.
   Cast: Jackie Gleason *(Tony Banks)*, Carol Channing *(Flo Banks)*, Frankie Avalon *(Angie)*, Fred Clark *(tower guard)*, Michael Constantine *(Leech)*, Frank Gorshin *(The Man)*, John Phillip Law *(Stash)*, Peter Lawford *(The Senator)*, Burgess Meredith *(The Warden)*, George Raft *(Captain Garbaldo)*, Cesar Romero *(Hechy)*, Mickey Rooney *("Blue Chips" Packard)*, Groucho Marx *("God")*, Austin Pendleton *(The Professor [Fred])*, Alexandra Hay *(Darlene Banks)*, Luna *("God"'s mistress)*, Arnold Stang *(Harry)*, Doro Merande *(The Mayor)*, Phil Arnold *(The Mayor's husband)*, Slim Pickens, Robert Donner *(switchboard operators)*, Richard Kiel *(Beany)*, Tom Law *(Geronimo)*, Jaik Rosenstein *("Eggs" Benedict)*, Stacy King *(The Amazon)*, Renny Roker, Roman Gabriel *(prison guards)*, Harry Nilsson *(tower guard)*, William Cannon *(convict)*, Stone Country *(themselves)*, Orange County Ramblers *(Green Bay Packers)*.
   Comedy. Former mobster Tony Banks now operates a carwash and lives with his wife, Flo, in an affluent San Francisco suburb. His peaceful existence is disrupted, however, when his teenaged daughter, Darlene, falls in love with Stash, a long-haired hippie, and two underworld cronies, Hechy and his son Angie, arrive with word that their gangland boss—"God"—wants Tony to do one last job by rubbing out "Blue Chips" Packard, an imprisoned mobster who is planning to tell all to a Senate crime committee in return for a life of luxurious solitary confinement. At first Tony balks at "God"'s suggestion, but he changes his mind when his best friend, Harry, is shot through the head. Once Tony's imprisonment has been arranged, Flo permits Stash and his flower friends to camp on the front lawn and take over the household. While in jail Tony ingests some LSD-soaked stationery belonging to his draft-dodging cellmate, the "professor," and goes on an acid trip that convinces him that violence is evil. To avoid killing "Blue Chips," Tony and the professor get the entire prison high on LSD-spiked soup and then make a getaway in garbage cans attached to balloons made from plastic food bags. As they make an aerial landing on "God"'s yacht, where Darlene is being held prisoner, Flo and Stash arrive by water with a flotilla of hippies. Outwitted and outnumbered, "God" (dressed in hippie clothes) sails off on a raft with the professor, and Tony is happily reunited with Flo, Darlene, and Stash—his new son-in-law. *Criminals—Rehabilitation. Gangsters. Draft dodgers. Hippies. Murder. Prison escapes. Abduction. LSD. Balloons (ascent). Yachts. Carwashes. San Francisco. United*

States Congress. Hallucinations.

Note: Location scenes filmed in the Haight-Ashbury section of San Francisco and at the Lincoln Heights Jail in Los Angeles.

SKIN DEEP IN LOVE   F6.4544

H. F. Number 3 Inc. *Dist* Distribpix, Inc. caSep **1967**. Sd; b&w. 35mm. 80 min.

Pres by Howard Farber. *Exec Prod* Howard Farber, Arthur Morowitz. *Dir-Writ* Joe Sarno. *Dir Photog* Bruce Sparks. *Asst Camera* Robert Bailin. *Film Ed* Kemper Peacock. *Mus* Burton Greene. *Sd Engr* James Lynch. *Ch Electrn* Myron Odegaard.

Cast: Joanna Mills *(Nancy),* Judson Todd *(Mark),* Carla Desmond *(Tanya),* Chris Koersen *(Penny),* Nick Linkov *(Rick),* Cherie Winters *(Paulette),* Randy Jason *(Zina),* Michael Lawrence *(Al),* Cleo Nova *(Bobbi),* David C. Stone *(Lou),* Pete Hall *(Les),* Ava Martin *(Christine),* Pat Barrett *(Janet).*

Melodrama. Magician Mark Hess, a dark, handsome man who has little trouble attracting female admirers, becomes sexually excited by any resistance to his charms. Tanya Korak, Mark's assistant, offers herself to Mark, and he takes her as his occasional mistress, but he soon becomes fascinated by Nancy Sample, a cocktail waitress in the High Seas Bar where Mark and Tanya perform their magic act. One night, Mark lures Nancy to his room where his brash suggestions provoke her scorn, and he becomes enslaved by her resistance. Tanya then hypnotizes Nancy into submitting to Mark in the hope that he will lose his desire for Nancy, but the magician continues his courtship. Meanwhile, Rick MacLeod, a small-time hoodlum who has spent one memorable night with Nancy, becomes jealous of Mark. Rick learns of Tanya's abilities as a hypnotist and deduces the reason for Nancy's submission to Mark. Rick and Nancy are reunited when Tanya breaks the hypnotic spell she has over Nancy, while Mark, crushed by the realization that he is the victim of his own carnal desires, looks on in disbelief. *Magicians. Mistresses. Waitresses. Hoodlums. Hypnotism. Jealousy. Bars.*

Note: Also known as *Deep in Love.*

THE SKIN GAME (Great Britain)   F6.4545

Searchlight Productions. *Dist* William Mishkin. 8 Apr **1965** [San Francisco showing]. Sd; b&w. 35mm. 61-71 min.

Prod Stanley A. Long, Arnold Louis Miller. *Dir* Arnold Louis Miller. *Screenplay* Bob Kesten. *Photog* Stanley A. Long. *Film Ed* John Dunsford. *Mus Comp* De Wolfe. *Sd* Robert Allen.

Cast: Ronald Howard *(Inspector Gordon),* Jess Conrad *(Ted-o),* Melody O'Brian *(Marlene),* Peter Gray *(Hon John [Edgar]),* David Graham *(Alvero Belda),* Peter Hager *(Sergeant Phelan),* Larry Taylor *(Sammy),* Anne Martin *(Mrs. Markham),* Jane Wilde *(Laura),* John Scott *(Superintendent Train),* Headley Colson *(Sergeant Brown),* Peter Evans *(Mr. Lethbridge),* Michael Lee *(Q car driver),* Ivor Phillips *(Ian Lethbridge),* Pauline Wingfield *(Lucy).*

Melodrama. Inspector Gordon and Sergeant Phelan of Scotland Yard are alerted to a wave of fraudulent checks given to people who sell their cars. Junk yard owner Alvero Belda, his assistant Sammy, and American John Edgar operate a nearly foolproof car racket. After Ian Lethbridge dies in a car crash, Belda obtains the wreckage, gives a woman a bad check for the same model car, exchanges the plates, paints it the same color as the wrecked car, and puts the car, with its corresponding papers, up for sale. A member of the mob, mechanic Ted-o, is caught with Belda's mistress and beaten. For revenge, Ted-o kills Belda and witness Edgar. Ted-o uses the prepared car for a weekend trip with his girl friend, Laura, but Lethbridge's father spots what he thinks is his son's car—using the unusual license plate number KIL 1 (the initials of his son)—and reports it to Gordon, now aware of the operation. Trying to evade a police roadblock, Ted-o and Laura are killed when the car goes over a cliff. *Detectives. Fraud. Revenge. Murder. Automobiles. Scotland Yard.*

Note: Released in Great Britain in 1964 in a 61 min version under the title *KIL 1.* Also known as *Skin Games.*

THE SKIN OF OUR TEETH *see* CIVILISATION: THE SKIN OF OUR TEETH

DIE SKLAVEN ROMS *see* THE REVOLT OF THE SLAVES

SKOOL DAZE   F6.4546

Dist Stacey Distributors. ca **1970**. Sd; col. 16mm. 61-81 min.

Sex film. No information about the precise nature of this film has been found. *Sexuality.*

THE SKULL (Great Britain)   F6.4547

Amicus Productions. *Dist* Paramount Pictures. 25 Aug **1965** [Los Angeles opening; c25 Aug 1965; LP31461]. Sd; col (Technicolor). 35mm (Techniscope). 83 min. [Also 90 min.]

Prod Milton Subotsky, Max J. Rosenberg. *Dir* Freddie Francis. *Screenplay* Milton Subotsky. *Dir Photog* John Wilcox. *Camera Op* David Harcourt. *Art Dir* Bill Constable. *Set Decor* Scott Slimon. *Film Ed* Oswald Hafenrichter. *Mus*

Comp Elisabeth Lutyens. *Mus Dir* Philip Martell. *Sd Supv* John Cox. *Sd Rec* Buster Ambler. *Sd Ed* Tom Priestley. *Asst Dir* Anthony Waye. *Prod Mgr* Ted Lloyd. *Cont* Pamela Davies. *Cost* Jackie Cummins. *Makeup* Jill Carpenter. *Hairdresser* Henry Montsash. *Sp Eff* Ted Samuels. *Constr Mgr* Bill Waldron.

Cast: Peter Cushing *(Prof. Christopher Maitland),* Patrick Wymark *(Marco),* Christopher Lee *(Sir Matthew Phillips),* Jill Bennett *(Jane Maitland),* Nigel Green *(Wilson),* Michael Gough *(auctioneer),* George Coulouris *(Dr. Londe),* Patrick Magee *(police doctor),* Peter Woodthorpe *(Travers),* April Olrich *(girl),* Maurice Good *(man in cloak),* Frank Forsyth *(judge),* Anna Palk *(maid),* Paul Stockman, Geoffrey Cheshire, George Hillsden.

Horror film. Source: Robert Bloch, "The Skull of the Marquis de Sade," in *The Skull of the Marquis de Sade* (New York, 1965). Sir Matthew Phillips, seized by an unknown force, outbids his friend Professor Maitland at an auction for some items dealing with witchcraft. Marco, a dealer in the occult, visits Professor Maitland and offers him a biography of the Marquis de Sade. He also returns with a skull, allegedly de Sade's, stolen from the grave. Maitland refuses to buy it, even though Marco offers to sell it cheaply. That night, Maitland reads the book, has a nightmare, and awakens in Marco's apartment. He visits Sir Matthew, who is also interested in the occult, and learns that the skull was stolen from him; Sir Matthew warns Maitland not to touch the skull, relating how he had been seized by a spiritual force. Disregarding this advice, Maitland goes to Marco's apartment, finds Marco dead, and takes the skull. He becomes possessed by the skull and tries to kill his wife, but she is saved by her crucifix. Maitland dies in his own bedroom, his throat slit. *Professors. Collectors. Grave robbers. Occult. Witchcraft. Evil spirits. Auctions. Skulls. Donatien Alphonse François [Marquis de] Sade. Dreams.*

Note: Released in Great Britain in Nov 1966.

SKULLDUGGERY   F6.4548

Universal Pictures. 11 Mar **1970** [New York opening; c11 Mar 1970; LP38937]. Sd (Westrex); col (Technicolor). 35mm (Panavision). 105 min. *MPAA rating* GP.

A Saul David Production. *Prod* Saul David. *Assoc Prod* Martin Fink. *Dir* (see note) Gordon Douglas, Richard Wilson. *2d Unit Dir* Robert Buzz Henry. *Screenplay* Nelson Gidding. *Dir Photog* Robert Moreno. *2nd Unit Photog* John McLean. *Set Decor* George Milo. *Prod Dsgn* Hilyard Brown. *Optical & Titl Dsgn* Richard Kuhn. *Film Ed* John Woodcock. *Mus* Oliver Nelson. *Mus Supv* Stanley Wilson. *Sd* Waldon O. Watson, Frank H. Wilkinson, Ronald Pierce. *Asst Dir* William Lukather, Newt Arnold. *Prod Mgr* Lee Lukather. *Asst to the Prod* John Wallace Hyde. *Miss Clark's Cost* Edith Head. *Makeup* Bud Westmore, Jack Young. *Miss Clark's Hairstyles* Evelyn Coffey. *Sp Photog Eff* Albert Whitlock. *Titl & Optical Eff* Universal Title. *2d Unit Tech Adv* John Keith McCarthy.

Cast: Burt Reynolds *(Douglas Temple),* Susan Clark *(Dr. Sybil Greame),* Roger C. Carmel *(Otto Kreps),* Paul Hubschmid *(Vancruysen),* Chips Rafferty *(Father "Pop" Dillingham),* Alexander Knox *(Buffington),* Pat Suzuki *(Topazia),* Edward Fox *(Bruce Spofford),* Wilfrid Hyde-White *(Eaton),* William Marshall *(attorney general),* Rhys Williams *(Judge Draper),* Mort Marshall *(Dr. Figgins),* Michael St. Clair *(Tee Hee Lawrence),* Booker Bradshaw *(Smoot),* John Kimberley *(Epstein),* James Henry Eldridge *(district officer),* Totty Ames *(motel manager),* James Bacon *(commentator),* Gilbert Senior *(Kauni),* Clarence Harris *(Siria),* Burnal "Custus" Smith *(chief),* John Woodcock *(Spigget),* Newt Arnold *(Inspector Mimms),* Wendell Baggett *(Reverend Holzapple),* Michael Preece *(Naylor),* Charles Washburn *(Papuan),* Cliff Bell, Jr. *(worker),* Alex Gradussov *(Russian delegate),* Jim Alexander *(reporter),* Saul David *(Berle Tanen),* Bernard Pike *(associate judge),* Eddie Fuchs *(Israeli delegate),* Students of University of Djakarta *(The Tropis).*

Adventure drama. Source: Vercors, *Les animaux dénaturés* (Paris, 1952). Douglas Temple, a young adventurer searching for phosphorous deposits in New Guinea, persuades attractive archeologist Dr. Sybil Greame to allow him to join her expedition. She reluctantly grants permission to Douglas and his associate, Otto Kreps, who accompany her and Father "Pop" Dillingham, a Catholic missionary, to the interior of the island. Upon arrival, Douglas and Otto scatter some old bones around the area to retain Sybil's interest. Later, she finds a skull that she believes may be the missing link between man and ape; the group then discovers an ape-man tribe, which they name the Tropis. They befriend the ape-people, and Otto becomes attracted to Topazia, a young female. Sybil radios news of their discovery to Vancruysen, the financier of the expedition, who flies in immediately to see the newly discovered species. Douglas is horrified to learn that Vancruysen intends to breed the Tropis and sell them as slaves. The two adventurers then take Topazia away from the interior, in the hope of persuading the world that the Tropis are more human than animal. Upon arriving at Sydney, Australia, Douglas discovers that Topazia has been impregnated by Otto. When she delivers a stillborn child, a doctor is summoned to sign a death certificate, and Douglas asserts that he murdered the infant to gain publicity. The resulting trial becomes a political circus, with testimony coming both from black power advocates and white supremacists. When Topazia is brought into court as a caged exhibit, she escapes in panic and is killed. The judge, stating that society rather than the court must decide whether the ape-men are animal or human, frees Douglas. *Adventurers. Archeologists. Catholics. Missionaries. Ape-men. Judges. Evolution. Slavery. Pregnancy. Stillbirth. Confession (law). Racism. Trials. New Guinea. Sydney (Australia).*

Note: Location scenes filmed in New Guinea and Jamaica. Douglas replaced Wilson as director one week into production; Wilson receives no screen credit.

SKUPLJAČI PERJA see **I EVEN MET HAPPY GYPSIES**

THE SKY ABOVE—THE MUD BELOW (Belgium/France/Netherlands)
F6.4549
Ardennes-Films–Société Parisienne de Cinéma–Michael Arthur Films. *Dist* Embassy Pictures. 19 Jun **1962** [New York opening]. Sd; col (Agfacolor). 35mm. 90 min.

Pres by Joseph E. Levine. *Prod* Arthur Cohn, René Lafuite. *Dir-Writ* Pierre-Dominique Gaisseau. *Photog* Gilbert Sarthre. *Asst Camera* Jean Bordes-Pages. *Film Ed* Georges Arnstam. *Mus* Jacques Lasry. *Asst Dir* Gérard Delloye. *Still Photog* Tony Saulnier.

Cast: William Peacock (narrator), Pierre-Dominique Gaisseau (leader of expedition), Gérard Delloye (assistant director), Hervé de Maigret (radio engineer), John Sneep (patrol officer), Gilbert Sarthre (photographer), Jean Bordes-Pages (assistant photographer), Tony Saulnier (still photographer).

Documentary. In 1959 adventurer Pierre-Dominique Gaisseau organizes a 7-month Franco-Dutch expedition 1,000 miles into New Guinea. Accompanied by six fellow explorers, four soldiers, and 60 bearers, Gaisseau travels on foot and by raft and canoe. The company crosses mountain ranges, descends into valleys, and charts the Princess Marijke River; its members are introduced to the rituals of cannibals, pygmies, and headhunters and plagued by leeches and swarms of insects. At the journey's end three escorts are dead; eight men have been wounded; and 22 have fallen ill. *Explorers. Pygmies. Cannibals. Headhunters. Exploration. Primitive life. Rites and ceremonies. New Guinea. Princess Marijke River. Leeches.*

Note: Opened in Paris in May 1961 as *Le ciel et la boue*; running time: 85 min. Ardennes Films receives credit as principal production company; made in cooperation with Michael Arthur Films. Only a French source credits the Société Parisienne de Cinéma as a production company.

THE SKY PIRATE   **F6.4550**
Andrew Meyer. *Dist* Film-Makers' Distribution Center. 23 Jan **1970** [Los Angeles showing]. Sd; col. 16mm. 105 min.

Prod-Dir-Writ Andrew Meyer. *Film Ed* Andrew Meyer, Suki Poor. *Mus* Brian Trentham. *Sp Sd Eff* Brian Trentham. *Asst Dir* Suki Poor.

Cast: Michael McClanathan (Joe), Claudia Leacock (Charlie), Frank Meyer (Norman), Margaret Kramer (shy lady), Lorenzo Mans (Pepe), Zelda Keiser (Sarah), Francesca Annis (uptight girl), Rainy Michaelyan (Carmen), Joy Bang (Lynn Beasy).

Drama. Charlie hears on the car radio that her Uncle Joe, with whom she has a very close relationship, has just hijacked a jet to Cuba. In a series of flashbacks, the development of the hijacking is related. *Charlie is living with Norman, an ineffectual, would-be reporter for an underground newspaper, while Joe occasionally stays with Sarah, his fat, neurotic ex-wife, whom he left to join the Navy. Meeting in a park, Joe and Norman mull over their thoughts and memories of Cuba: Norman dreams of the revolutionary Cuban society emerging there, and Joe reminisces about a Cuban prostitute whom he picked up while he was in the Navy. The idea of returning to Cuba thus resulted in Joe's plan for the hijacking. Hijackers. Reporters. Revolutionaries. Uncles. Prostitutes. Cubans. Newspapers—Underground. New York City. Cuba. United States Navy.*

SKY SCRAPER! (Japan)   **F6.4551**
Toho Co. Sep **1970** [Los Angeles showing]. Sd; col? 35mm. [Feature film, length unknown.]

Dir Hideo Sekigawa.

Cast: Ryo Ikebe, Yoshiko Sakuma, Michiyo Aratama, Koshiro Matsuomoro.

Drama. No information about the precise nature of this film has been found.

Note: Released in Japan in 1969 as *Chokoso no akebono*.

SKY WEST AND CROOKED see **GYPSY GIRL**

THE SKYDIVERS   **F6.4552**
Cardoza-Francis Productions. *Dist* Crown International Pictures. 13 Nov **1963** [San Francisco opening]. Sd; b&w. 35mm. 75 min.

Prod Anthony Cardoza. *Exec Prod* George Buckner, Helen Buckner. *Dir-Writ* Coleman Francis. *Photog* Austin McKinney, Lee Strosnider. *Aerial Photog* Jack Kupp. *Film Ed* Bob Lusby. *Mus Dir* John Bath. Songs: "Ha-So," "Tobacco Worm," "Stratosphere Boogie" *Perf by* Jimmy Bryant and the Night

Jumpers. *Dance Dir* Robert Banas. *Sd* Brandon Kellogg. *Sd Rec & Mix* TV Recorders. *Asst Dir* Anthony M. Lanza.

Cast: Kevin Casey (Beth), Marcia Knight (Suzy Belmont), Eric Tomlin (Joe), Tony Cardoza (Harry Rowe), Titus Moede (Frankie Bonner), Michael Rae (Red), Bob Carrano (Bob), Paul Francis, actor (Peter), Jimmy Bryant and the Night Jumpers, Monty McRae, Marilyn McRae, Jack Kupp.

Melodrama. Recently married, ex-paratrooper Harry Rowe and his wife, Beth, run a skydiving school in California, assisted by Casey's Army buddy, Joe. Wealthy young Suzy Belmont threatens to destroy the school after Harry discourages her flirtations, and tensions increase as Joe becomes attracted to Beth. Suzy loosens some wires on Beth's plane and nearly causes a crash. The school is temporarily closed by the authorities after a daredevil free fall enthusiast waits too long to open his parachute and is killed. As Harry prepares for a night jump, Suzy and Frankie Bonner, an accomplice, pour acid into his parachute, and he falls 16,000 feet to his death. Suzy and Frankie are pursued by police and meet a violent end. *Newlyweds. Police. Veterans. Skydiving. Murder. Revenge. Airplane accidents. Infidelity. Airplanes. California. Chases.*

SLÅ FØRST, FREDE! see **OPERATION LOVEBIRDS**

THE SLAUGHTER OF THE VAMPIRES see **CURSE OF THE BLOOD-GHOULS**

THE SLAVE (Italy)   **F6.4553**
Titanus–Arta Cinematografica. *Dist* Metro-Goldwyn-Mayer, Inc. 29 May **1963** [New York opening; c31 Dec 1962; LP24720]. Sd (Westrex); col (Eastmancolor). 35mm (CinemaScope). 110 min. [Copyright length: 102 min.]

Dir Sergio Corbucci. *2d Unit Dir* Franco Giraldi. *Screenplay* Adriano Bolzoni, Bruno Corbucci, Giovanni Grimaldi. *Orig Story* Adriano Bolzoni. *Dir Photog* Enzo Barboni. *Camera* Stelvio Massi. *Art Dir* Ottavio Scotti. *Set Decor* Riccardo Domenici. *Film Ed* Ruggero Mastroianni. *Mus* Piero Piccioni. *Mus Cond* Pierluigi Urbini. *Asst Dir* Franco Rossellini, Mimmola Girosi. *Prod Mgr* Franco Palaggi. *Prod Supv* Sergio Borelli. *Cost* A. Antonelli, Mario Giorsi. *Footwear* Pompei. *Makeup* Piero Mecacci, Franco Di Girolamo. *Wigs* R. Rocchetti. *Arms* L. Tani and Brothers. *Fencing Master* Benito Stefanelli.

Cast: Steve Reeves (The Son of Spartacus), Jacques Sernas (Vezio), Gianna Maria Canale (Clodia), Claudio Gora (Caesar Grassus), Ivo Garrani (Julius Caesar), Enzo Fiermonte (Giular), Ombretta Colli (slave girl), Roland Bartrop, Franco Balducci, Renato Baldini, Gloria Parri, Benito Stefanelli, Ahmed Ramzy.

Action melodrama. In 48 B.C., Julius Caesar sends a young centurion named Randus to investigate the rule of the corrupt Grassus in the province of Lydia. En route by sea, Randus' ship runs aground, and he is captured by a band of slave drivers. But he leads a revolt, and the slaves defeat and destroy their captors. By means of a talisman he wears, Randus is then identified as the son of Spartacus, the gladiator-slave who was crucified 20 years earlier for warring against Rome. Arriving in Lydia, Randus is met by Grassus, his wily mistress Clodia, and her warrior brother Vezio. Outwardly pretending friendship, Randus secretly carries on his father's work by leading the enslaved Lydians in a revolt against the tyrannical Grassus. Randus terrorizes the tyrants by slashing "S" as a signature. Although he is unmasked by Clodia and imprisoned, Randus is rescued by his followers, who kill Grassus by pouring molten gold over his face. Clodia is exiled to the desert, and Vezio is slain in combat by Randus. Caesar then arrives and decrees that the rebellious Randus be crucified. But the entire populace pleads for his life, and Caesar, a diplomat as well as a warrior, grants Randus a pardon. *Royalty. Centurions. Despots. Slavery. Revolts. Exile. Murder. Crucifixion. Talismans. Rome—History—Empire. Lydia. Gaius Julius Caesar. Spartacus.*

Note: Released in Italy as *Il figlio di Spartacus* in 1962.

THE SLAVE (France)   **F6.4554**
Les Films du Griffon–Unicité. *Dist* Olympic International Films. 7 Apr **1967** [San Francisco showing]. Sd; b&w. 35mm. 67 min.

A Max Pecas Production. *Dir* Max Pecas.

Cast: Claude Cerval, Véra Valmont, Pierre Tissot, Marie-Christine Weill, Sylvie Coste, Alain Chevallier, Milarka Nerri.

Melodrama. Carol's marriage is suddenly threatened by the appearance of some pornographic photographs taken 9 years earlier, when she was 19 years old and desperate for money. Eric Colar and his girl friend blackmail Carol into satisfying their various sexual desires and giving them enough money to escape from the police. A confrontation with William Verner, who had been unjustly imprisoned for a crime committed by Eric, puts a violent end to the scheme. *Blackmail. Sexual practices. Lesbianism. Pornography. Photographs.*

Note: Opened in Paris in Jul 1967 as *Une femme aux abois*; running time: 75 min.

SLAVE GIRLS *see* **PREHISTORIC WOMEN**

SLAVE TRADE IN THE WORLD TODAY (France/Italy)   **F6.4555**
GE. SI. Cinematografica–C. I. S. A.–Agiman. *Dist* Continental Distributing, Inc. 23 Nov 1964 [New York opening]. Sd; col with b&w seq (Eastman Color). 35mm. 87 min.
Prod Maleno Malenotti. *Dir* Roberto Malenotti, Folco Quilici. *Screenplay* Baccio Bandini, Gianfranco Calderoni. *English Narr* Elihu Winer. *Photog* Adalberto Albertini, Aldo Nascimbene, Giuseppe Pinori, Giovanni Scarpellini, Aldo Tonti. *Film Ed* Eraldo Da Roma. *U. S. Vers Ed* Stephen Billings. *Mus* Teo Usuelli. *Asst Dir* Piero Nelli.
Narrator: Allen Swift.
With: Robin Maugham, Eve Kenneth.
Documentary. Source: Sean O'Callaghan, *The Slave Trade* (London, 1961). Robin Maugham, *The Slaves of Timbuktu* (London, 1961). Lord Robin Maugham, campaigning against the practice of slavery, states that the illegal traffic in human life is thriving in violation of the United Nations Declaration of Human Rights because the American and British governments are unwilling to challenge Arab oil potentates who favor the slave trade. Throughout Africa, India, and the Middle East, hidden cameras are used to collect evidence of outlawed practices: young boys and girls are traded openly in a marketplace; harems flourish along the Arabian peninsula; in a slave market near Khartum, elderly sheiks examine nude women; police raid a caravan smuggling enslaved children from Chad to Saudi Arabia; a woman with shackles on her feet hobbles around a market; Arab herdsmen whip African natives in order to select the strongest for sale; Eve Kenneth, a British prostitute who spent 2 years in a sultan's harem, produces a film depicting her experiences; and giant land crabs are seen dragging skeletons of escaped slaves on an island in the Red Sea. The investigators explain that the Africans were driven to slavery by poverty, preferring bondage to starvation. *British. Slavers. Oil magnates. Arabs. Sheiks. Prostitutes. Royalty. Africans. Slavery. Torture. Flogging. Poverty. Starvation. Markets. Harems. Motion pictures. Africa. Arabia. India. Middle East. Khartum. Chad. Red Sea. United Nations. Crabs.*
Note: Filmed on location in Africa, the Arabian peninsula, India, the Middle East, and London. Released in Italy in 1964 as *Le schiave esistono ancora;* running time: 90 min; opened in Paris in Jul 1966 as *Les esclaves existent toujours;* running time: 85 min.

SLAVES   **F6.4556**
Theatre Guild Films–Slaves Co.–Walter Reade Organization. *Dist* Continental Distributing, Inc. 6 May 1969 [Baltimore opening]. Sd; col (Eastman Color, print by Movielab). 35mm. 110 min.
Prod Philip Langner. *Assoc Prod* Marshall Young. *Dir* Herbert J. Biberman. *2d Unit Dir* Dan Eriksen. *Screenplay* Herbert J. Biberman, John O. Killens, Alida Sherman. *Photog* Joseph Brun. *Art Dir* Burr Smidt. *Film Ed* Sidney Meyers. *Mus & Songs* Bobby Scott. *Songs:* "Slaves," "Lullaby," "Another Mornin'" sung by Dionne Warwick. *Sd* Albert Gramaglia. *Asst Dir* Janet Mokarzel. *Prod Mgr* Preston Collins. *Cost* Robert Magahay, Laurence Gross.
Cast: Stephen Boyd (*Nathan MacKay*), Dionne Warwick (*Cassy*), Ossie Davis (*Luke*), Robert Kya-Hill (*Jericho*), Barbara Ann Teer (*Esther*), Marilyn Clark (*Mrs. Bennett*), Gale Sondergaard (*New Orleans lady*), Nancy Coleman (*Mrs. Stillwell*), Shepperd Strudwick (*Arthur Stillwell*), Julius Harris (*Shadrach*), David Huddleston (*Holland*), Eva Jessye (*Julia*), James Heath (*Luther*), Aldine King (*Emmeline*), Oscar Paul Jones (*Zacharious*).
Drama. Arthur Stillwell, a Kentucky rancher in the 1850's, is forced by debt to sell his favorite slaves, Luke and Jericho. Nathan MacKay, a former slaveship captain and Mississippi plantation owner, buys Luke and Jericho, in addition to a 16-year-old girl named Emmeline. MacKay's home is filled with African art, and although he showers his slave-mistress, Cassy, with clothing and jewelry, he enjoys humiliating her and treating his other slaves cruelly. One night a slave woman dies during childbirth because of MacKay's refusal to call a doctor; Luke adopts the child and vows that she will never grow up to be a slave. Cassy comes to respect Luke's strength and begins to defy MacKay. One night when he is drunk, she threatens to stab him, but she is dissuaded by Luke who promises to arrange an escape. With the help of Jericho, Luke hides Cassy, Emmeline, and the infant in an attic, but MacKay discovers their plot. He tortures Jericho to try to discover Cassy's whereabouts but is unsuccessful. When MacKay offers Luke his freedom in exchange for knowledge of Cassy's whereabouts, Luke is silent, and MacKay flogs him to death. His death unites the rest of the slaves, and the housekeeper sets the cotton sheds on fire to divert MacKay's attention from Cassy, Jericho, Emmeline, and the infant, who make their escape with the help of a sympathetic neighbor. *Negroes. Mistresses. Infants. Slaves—Runaway. Housekeepers. Slavery. Finance—Personal. Sadism. Miscegenation. Childbirth. Drunkenness. Torture. Murder. Plantations. Kentucky. Mississippi. Fires.*
Note: Location scenes filmed in Shreveport, Louisiana.

SLAVES OF CHINATOWN *see* **WHITE SLAVES OF CHINATOWN**

SLAVES OF LOVE   **F6.4557**
Green Dolphin Productions. *Dist* Sack Amusement Enterprises, Manson Distributing Corp. Jan 1969. Sd; col (Eastman Color). 35mm. 76 min.
Prod Dave Ackerman. *Assoc Prod* Ian Nitz. *Dir* Charles Nizet. *Camera* Peter Iofolice. *Script Girl* Ebby Rhodes.
Cast: Peter Owen (*Joe*), Lloyd Davish (*Troy*), Tina Brown (*leader*), Sallie Blair (*dancer*), Lynn Hayes, Cary St. Clair, Tina Vienna, Mary Horton (*love slaves*).
Melodrama. Joe and Troy mysteriously lose control of their private plane while on a business trip and land on an island inhabited by a group of sex-starved women. The women have devised a magnetic force which forces down all planes flying within a certain radius of the island. Joe and Troy are taken to the group's underground headquarters where the leader announces that they must satisfy all of the women or die. During an unsuccessful escape attempt, Troy kills one of the women, and as punishment he is sentenced to 1,000 lashes. Joe is given a love potion, and the women perform erotic dances to excite him. He makes love to each woman in turn, but is unable to satisfy them, and he is sentenced to death. One of the women, unhappy with her life on the island, helps the men to escape, but during the ensuing chase she and Troy are killed. Just in time, Joe reaches a boat which takes him to safety. *Businessmen. Flagellation. Magnetism. Airplanes. Aphrodisiacs. Islands.*

SLAVES OF THE SIN-DICATE   **F6.4558**
Mitam Productions. 4 Oct 1967 [Fresno, California, showing]. Sd; b&w. 35mm. 62 min.
Melodrama. Chuck Andrews and his wife arrive in the "Big Town" and move in with Gail, who works for the syndicate. Gail gets Chuck a job with the organization, and he soon rises to an important position. A jealous co-worker murders Chuck's wife, and Chuck, now in charge of prostitution, works harder to forget his sorrow. His boss, thinking Chuck has overworked, gives him one of the women, and with her Chuck releases all his pent-up emotions. Chuck then seduces the boss's girl, and the organization, as well as the police, pursue him. He finally surrenders to the syndicate. *Racketeers. Murder. Prostitution. Syndicates.*
Note: Also known as *Slaves of the Syndicate.*

SLEEP   **F6.4559**
Dist Film-Makers' Cooperative. 17 Jan 1964 [New York opening]. Si; b&w. 16mm. ca360 min.
Prod-Dir Andy Warhol.
Cast: John Giorno.
Experimental film. In 10-minute segments, each shown twice, a man is shown sleeping on a bed. The camera focuses on different parts of his body. *Sleep.*
Note: The frame remains fixed throughout each reel.

SLEEPING BEAUTY (West Germany)   **F6.4560**
Fritz Genschow-Film. *Dist* Childhood Productions. Oct 1965. Sd; col (Agfacolor). 35mm. 70 min.
Prod-Dir Fritz Genschow. *Screenplay* Fritz Genschow, Renée Stobrawa, Helga Weichert. *English Adapt* Childhood Productions. *Photog* Gerhard Huttula. *Art Dir* Otto Reysser, Waldemar Volkmer. *Mus* Hans-Joachim Wunderlich. *English Vers Mus Dir* Lehman Engel. *English Vers Mus Arr* George Brackman. *English Vers Songs* Anne Delugg, Milton Delugg. *Choreog* Carola Krauskopf.
Cast: Karin Hardt (*The Queen*), Fritz Genschow (*The King*), Angela von Leitner (*Sleeping Beauty*), Gert Reinholm (*Prince Charming*), Paul Tripp (*narrator*), Renée Stobrawa, Gustav Bertram, Elfe Schneider, Wulf Rittscher, Gisela Schauroth, Rudolf Stör, Anni Marlé, Theodor Vogeler, Walter Bluhm.
Fantasy. Source: Jakob Grimm and Wilhelm Grimm, "Dornröschen". The classic fairy tale is told against a real background of Bavarian forests. *Royalty. Fairies. Infants. Curses. Magic. Sleep. Forests. Birthdays. Bavaria. Imaginary kingdoms. Prince Charming.*
Note: Released in West Germany in Nov 1955 as *Dornröschen;* running time: 82 min. Rescored and dubbed for U. S. release.

THE SLEEPING BEAUTY (U.S.S.R.)   **F6.4561**
Lenfilm. *Dist* Royal Films International. 4 May 1966 [New York opening]. Sd; col (Sovcolor, print by Technicolor). 35mm & 70mm (Techniscope). 90 min.
Pres by J. Jay Frankel, Douglas Netter. *Dir* Apollinariy Dudko, Konstantin Sergeyev. *Screenplay* Konstantin Sergeyev, Iosif Shapiro. *Photog* Anatoliy Nazarov. *Art Dir* T. Vasilkovskaya, V. Ulitko. *Set Decor* Ye. Yakuba. *Mus Comp* Pëtr Ilich Tchaikovsky. *Mus Cond* B. Khaykin, V. Gamaliya. *Played by* Kirov State Academic Theatre Orchestra. *Choreog Adapted From* Marius Petipa. *Choreog* Konstantin Sergeyev. *Sd* A. Bekker. *Asst Dir* A. Sokolov. *Sp*

Eff N. Pokoptsev, M. Krotkin.

Cast: Alla Sizova *(Princess Aurora)*, Yuriy Solovyov, dancer *(Prince Désiré)*, Natalya Dudinskaya *(The Wicked Fairy)*, Irina Bazhenova *(The Lilac Fairy)*, Vsevolod Ukhov *(The King)*, O. Zabotkina *(The Queen)*, Natalya Makarova *(Princess Florina)*, Valeriy Panov *(Blue Bird)*, V. Ryazanov *(master of ceremonies)*, E. Minchenok *(Tenderness)*, I. Korneyeva *(Playfulness)*, L. Kovalyova *(Generosity)*, K. Fedicheva *(Courage)*, N. Sakhnovskaya *(Lightheartedness)*, G. Kekisheva *(White Pussy)*, S. Kuznetsov *(Puss in Boots)*, Sergey Vykulov, Kirov State Academic Theatre Corps de Ballet, Students of the Vaganova Dancing School.

Ballet film. Source: Charles Perrault, "La belle au bois dormant," in *Mercure galant* (Feb 1696). Pëtr Ilich Tchaikovsky, *Spyashchaya krasavitsa* (St. Petersburg opening: 15 Jan 1890). Palace rejoicing at the christening of the infant Princess Aurora is disrupted by the unannounced appearance of Carabosse, The Wicked Fairy. She utters a curse over the cradle and predicts that the princess will die from a wound caused by pricking her finger. Fortunately, The Lilac Fairy has not yet made her gift, and she alters Aurora's fate by promising that instead of dying she will fall into a deep slumber. The Wicked Fairy again appears on the princess' 16th birthday, disguised as a kindly old woman, and causes Aurora to prick her finger on a knitting needle concealed in a bouquet. As Aurora falls asleep, The Lilac Fairy waves her magic wand and puts the entire kingdom to sleep. A hundred years later the kingdom has been overgrown by a black forest. Handsome Prince Désiré encounters The Lilac Fairy and receives through her a vision of the princess and of the palace where she lies sleeping. The Lilac Fairy summons her magic boat to carry the prince to the palace, and there he awakens the princess with a kiss. The entire kingdom stirs from its deep slumber and prepares the celebration of the royal wedding. *Royalty. Fairies. Infants. Curses. Magic. Weddings. Sleep. Forests. Birthdays. Imaginary kingdoms.*

Note: Released in the U.S.S.R. in 1964 in Kinopanorama as *Spyashchaya krasavitsa*; running time: ca97 min.

THE SLEEPING CAR MURDER (France)   F6.4562

P. E. C. F. *Dist* Seven Arts Associated Corp. 7 Mar **1966** [New York opening]. Sd; b&w. 35mm (CinemaScope). 92 min.

Prod Julien Derode. *Dir-Writ* Costa-Gavras. *Dial* Sébastien Japrisot. *Photog* Jean Tournier. *Art Dir* Rino Mondellini. *Film Ed* Christian Gaudin. *Mus* Michel Magne. *Sd* Joseph de Bretagne. *Asst Dir* Bernard Paul. *Prod Mgr* Jean-Paul Delamotte.

Cast: Yves Montand *(Inspector Grazzi)*, Simone Signoret *(Eliane Darrès)*, Pierre Mondy *(commissioner)*, Catherine Allégret *(Bambi)*, Pascale Roberts *(Georgette Thomas)*, Jacques Perrin *(Daniel)*, Michel Piccoli *(Cabourg)*, Jean-Louis Trintignant *(Eric)*, Charles Denner *(Bob)*, Claude Mann *(Jean-Lou)*, Nadine Alari *(Madame Grazzi)*, Georges Géret, Claude Dauphin, Daniel Gélin, Marcel Bozzufi, Tanya Lopert, Bernadette Lafont, Françoise Arnoul, André Valmy, Maurice Chevit, Jacques Dynam, Jean Lefebvre, Jean-Pierre Périer, Christian Marin, Serge Rousseau, Paul Pavel, Albert Michel, Jenny Orléans, Clément Harari, B. Paul, R. Sabatier, J. Steiner.

Crime drama. Source: Sébastien Japrisot, *Compartiment tueurs* (Paris, 1962). Daniel, a young runaway riding the overnight train from Marseilles to Paris without a ticket, is aided in avoiding the conductor by Bambi, a young woman on her way to a job in Paris. She arranges for him to spend the night in an unoccupied berth in her compartment. He leaves early the next morning but returns when he realizes that he has forgotten his suitcase. He finds Georgette Thomas, a perfume saleswoman who had a lower berth, murdered in the compartment. Inspector Grazzi and his assistant, Jean-Lou, are assigned to the case. Through the newspapers, Grazzi asks the other occupants of the compartment that night to contact the police. Cabourg, an office worker, is the first to come forward, but he is soon found dead. Daniel and Bambi remain together, but they avoid the police because they fear discovery by their parents. Daniel finds the wallet of Eliane Darrès, a fading actress who had been in the compartment, but when he and Bambi return it, they find Eliane being interrogated by Grazzi. They hide and see a young man, Eric, slipping out of Eliane's back door. Eliane tells Grazzi that Daniel had occupied the sixth berth. Shortly thereafter, Eliane is murdered, as is Rivolani, a truckdriver who also had been in the compartment. Eric, who had been Eliane's lover, is questioned but has an alibi. Daniel overhears two men planning to kill Bambi, and after telling her to hide in a hotel room, he calls Grazzi to tell all he knows. The police prevent Eric from killing Bambi, but Eric is only an accomplice; the real murderer, Jean-Lou, is now after Daniel. Jean-Lou knew of Eliane's large bank account and her passion for young men and had plotted with his friend Eric to kill her. Grazzi manages to save Daniel, and, after a wild chase through Paris, Jean-Lou is apprehended. *Runaways. Saleswomen. Police. Actors. Truckdrivers. Murder. Conspiracy. Trains. Marseilles. Paris. Chases.*

Note: Opened in Paris in Nov 1965 as *Compartiment tueurs*; running time: 95 min.

THE SLEEPING PARTNER *see* THE SECRET PARTNER

SLEEPING PARTNERS *see* CARNIVAL OF CRIME

THE SLENDER THREAD   F6.4563

Athene Productions. *Dist* Paramount Pictures. 15 Dec **1965** [Los Angeles opening; c15 Dec 1965; LP32171]. Sd; b&w. 35mm. 98 min.

Prod Stephen Alexander. *Dir* Sydney Pollack. *Screenplay* Stirling Silliphant. *Dir Photog* Loyal Griggs. *Art Dir* Hal Pereira, Jack Poplin. *Set Decor* Robert R. Benton, Joseph Kish. *Film Ed* Thomas Stanford. *Mus* Quincy Jones. *Sd* John Carter, Charles Grenzbach. *Asst Dir* Donald Roberts, William R. Poole. *Unit Prod Mgr* William C. Davidson. *Cost* Edith Head. *Makeup* Wally Westmore.

Cast: Sidney Poitier *(Alan Newell)*, Anne Bancroft *(Inga Dyson)*, Telly Savalas *(Dr. Coburn)*, Steven Hill *(Mark Dyson)*, Indus Arthur *(Marion)*, Greg Jarvis *(Chris Dyson)*, Robert Hoy *(Patrolman Steve Peters)*, John Benson *(Patrolman Bert Enyard)*, Paul Newlan *(Sgt. Harry Ward)*, Edward Asner *(Det. Judd Ridley)*, Jason Wingreen *(medical technician)*, Dabney Coleman *(Charlie)*, Janet Dudley *(Edna)*, Lane Bradford *(Al McCardle)*, John Napier *(Dr. Alden Van)*, Marjorie Nelson *(Mrs. Thomas)*, H. M. Wynant *(doctor)*, Thomas Hill *(liquor salesman)*, Steve Marlo *(Arthur Foss)*, Stephen Pellegrini, Jerome R. Brand, Kay Doubleday, Jo Helton, Richard Doorish, Charlotte Stewart, Viola Harris, George Savalas, O. L. Haavik, Nicholas Prebezac, Drew Eskenazi, Erin Almond, Pam Bagby, William R. Rhodes, Charles C. Andrews, Melody Greer, Sons of Adam, Walter Mazlow, Allen Emerson, Lou Clark, David Harris, Phillip Browne, Archie Smith, Joseph R. Denini.

Drama. Source: Shana Alexander, "Decision To Die," in *Life* (29 May 1964). Psychology student Alan Newell, a black volunteer worker at Seattle's Crisis Clinic, receives a phone call from Inga Dyson, a housewife and mother who has taken an overdose of sleeping pills but will not reveal where she can be reached. Through a series of flashbacks, Mrs. Dyson explains that she wants to kill herself to solve marital problems precipitated when her husband, Mark, a fishing captain, discovered that their son is the product of a premarital affair. Newell and Dr. Coburn, a psychologist, arrange for the police to put an emergency trace on the call while Mrs. Dyson continues to talk about her feelings. Under the guidance of Sgt. Harry Ward, Patrolmen Steve Peters and Bert Enyard search for the woman while Mrs. Dyson recounts to Newell the coldness of her husband and a previous suicide attempt that resulted in her hospitalization. The police notify Mark of his wife's circumstances, search her home, and call the Coast Guard to transport her husband from his fleet to Seattle. Sergeant Ward enters the motel room where he has traced Mrs. Dyson just as she drops into a coma. A doctor notifies Newell that Mrs. Dyson can be saved, and, accompanied by her husband, she is placed in an ambulance. *Students. Negroes. Psychologists. Police. Fishermen. Suicide. Marriage. Parentage. Motels. Seattle Crisis Clinic. United States Coast Guard.*

Note: Location scenes filmed in Seattle.

SLEPOY MUZYKANT *see* SOUND OF LIFE

THE SLIME PEOPLE   F6.4564

Hutton–Robertson Productions. *Dist* Hansen Pictures. 18 Sep **1963** [Boston opening]. Sd; b&w. 35mm. 60 min.

Prod Joseph F. Robertson. *Dir* Robert Hutton. *Screenplay* Vance Skarstedt. *Photog* William Troiano. *Film Ed* Donald Henderson. *Mus* Lou Froman. *Sd* Rod Sutton. *Asst Dir* Herbert Willis.

Cast: Robert Hutton *(aviator)*, Robert Burton *(professor)*, Susan Hart *(his daughter)*, William Boyce *(Marine)*, Les Tremayne, Judee Morton, John Close.

Science fiction melodrama. Prehistoric creatures, disturbed by nuclear tests, invade Los Angeles and take over the city. To overpower the remaining population, they create a dome of fog above the city and attempt to lower the temperature. Six people—including a professor and his daughter—who are trapped behind discover the machine that creates the dome and destroy it with salt. Because the slime people cannot exist in a normal temperature, they are annihilated. *Prehistoric creatures. Professors. Radiation. Nuclear energy. Los Angeles. Fog.*

SLIP OF THE TONGUE   F6.4565

Dist Distribpix, Inc. ca **1970**. Sd; col. 35mm. 61 min.

Drama. Four women and two men in an encounter group reveal to one another their problems of sexual adjustment. The group leader, Rosalyn, tells of her experience as a secretary in a modeling agency: she became extremely aroused by the physique of an applicant for a male nude modeling study, induced him to take off his clothes, and made love with him. The graphic detail with which Rosalyn relates this incident prompts Andrea, a housewife, to tell of her own difficulties. She is able to stimulate her husband only when she makes love to another woman. He then becomes sufficiently excited to accommodate both of them. A third woman has been traumatized after a rape at knifepoint by a sadistic criminal. Sexually aroused by these stories, the members of the encounter group strip and engage in an orgy. *Secretaries.*

Models. Housewives. Seduction. Voyeurism. Troilism. Lesbianism. Rape. Sadism. Encounter groups. Orgies.

SLOGAN (France)   **F6.4566**

Orphée Productions-Hamster Films. *Dist* Royal Films International. 16 Mar **1970** [New York opening]. Sd; col (Eastman Color). 35mm. 90 min. [Also reviewed at 94 min.] *MPAA rating* GP.

Dir-Writ Pierre Grimblat. *Photog* Jean-Louis Maligne, Claude Beausoleil. *Art Dir* Jean-Daniel Vignat. *Film Ed* Françoise Garnault. *Asst Ed* Jacques Witta. *Mus* Serge Gainsbourg. *Asst Dir* Jean-Patrick Lebel.

Cast: Serge Gainsbourg *(Serge)*, Jane Birkin *(Evelyne)*, Andréa Parisy *(wife)*, Daniel Gélin *(father)*, Juliette Berto *(secretary)*, James Mitchell, actor *(Hugh)*, Gilles Millinaire *(Dado)*, Henri-Jacques Huet, Pierre Doris.

Drama. Serge, a successful television commercials producer in his early 40's, travels to Venice to enter his films in a festival. Dissatisfied with his life and his marriage, Serge meets Evelyne, a pretty 18-year-old English girl, and makes her his mistress. He rents an apartment and lives with her while waiting for his divorce. Evelyne soon tires of him, however, and abandons him for a Venetian speedboat driver. In search of companionship and consolation, Serge picks up another young woman. *Television producers. English. Mistresses. Middle age. Infidelity. Divorce. Film festivals. Venice.*

Note: Opened in Paris in Aug 1969; running time: 90 min.

SLOW RUN   **F6.4567**

Larry Kardish. *Dist* Film-Makers' Distribution Center. 10 Oct **1968** [New York opening]. Sd; b&w. 16mm. 78 min.

Prod-Dir-Writ Larry Kardish. *Photog* Larry Kardish. *Main Titl* Joseph Ryder. *Film Ed* Larry Kardish. *Orig Mus* Saul Rubinek.

Cast: Saul Rubinek *(narrator)*, Bruce Gordon, David Flower, Heather Sim, Jane Amsten, Pat Jones, Rita Stein, Melvyn Green.

Drama. After 14 months of living a Bohemian life in New York City, a young Canadian becomes anxious that he is "settling down." To quell this fear, he impulsively buys a plane ticket for an unspecified destination. About a week before his scheduled departure, he wakes up musing as to whether or not he will inform his friends and his landlord. When he suddenly becomes nostalgic about the city, he is angered by his own sentimentality. Nevertheless, he lapses into a reverie in which he recalls his stay in Manhattan—working at an unspecified job, establishing a relationship with a long-haired intellectual, and having brief affairs with a number of women. *Canadians. Intellectuals. Bohemianism. Nostalgia. New York City.*

Note: Filmed on location in New York City.

SLUMBER PARTY IN A HAUNTED HOUSE *see* **THE GHOST IN THE INVISIBLE BIKINI**

SLUMBER PARTY IN HORROR HOUSE *see* **THE GHOST IN THE INVISIBLE BIKINI**

THE SLUT   **F6.4568**

Montgomery Productions-C. I. T. Films. *Dist* T & S Films, I. R. M. I. Films, Distribpix, Inc. 23 Dec **1965** [San Francisco showing]. Sd; b&w. 35mm. 61 min.

Prod H. A. Tilb. *Assoc Prod* Sam Sloss. *Dir* Nicholas Milor. *Screenplay* Bob Gree. *Dir Photog* Bill Simpson, photog. *Film Ed* Bob Clar. *Sd* Ken Rik. *Prod Mgr* Lee Aims.

Cast: Gaby Sims *(Ursula)*, Don Rowe *(stranger)*, Felicia Mills, David Rich, Monique Lamiue, Arnold Dole, Chantel Simon, Linda Rosten, Julia Morgan, Sylva Hanson.

Drama. A man obsessed by sexual fantasies encounters women who indulge in various sexual practices. One woman gains pleasure from the power she holds over a boot fetishist. Another's suppressed sensuality is released when she dons a pair of long black gloves. A third finds that wearing a black mask enables her to enjoy all forms of sexual gratification. [Sources suggest that the film deals with voyeurism, impotence, various forms of fetishism, and troilism.] *Fetishism. Impotence. Voyeurism. Sadomasochism. Troilism. Masks.*

Note: Retitled *Ursula the Slut;* also known as *Ursula* and *Ursula the Hussy.*

THE SMALL HOURS   **F6.4569**

Norman C. Chaitin. *Dist* Bell Film Exchange, Thunderbird International Pictures. 13 Aug **1962** [New York opening]. Sd; b&w. 35mm. 95 min.

Pres by Norman C. Chaitin. *Prod-Dir-Writ* Norman C. Chaitin. *Photog* Sheldon Rochlin. *Ed* Norman C. Chaitin. *Mus* Daniel Hart. *Sd* Titra Sound Corp. *Sd Ed* Fred De Croce, Edwin Picker. *Sd Eff* Jeff Dell.

Cast: Michael Ryan *(Tom Anderson)*, Lorraine Avins *(Laurie)*, Henry Madden *(Easton)*, Bryce Holman *(Martin)*, Tony Madden *(Gomez)*, Marilyn Thorson *(Kit Anderson)*, Jewel Walker *(preacher)*, Lynn Norris *(Cindy)*.

Melodrama. Depressed by the news of his partner's suicide, New York advertising executive Tom Anderson leaves home to supervise the filming of a commercial. On the set, Tom is attracted to Laurie, a young actress whose attention is occupied by the director, Easton, with whom she once had an affair.

Tom learns of a party to be held later that day at Martin's Greenwich Village apartment, and he decides to attend in the hopes of becoming better acquainted with Laurie. He soon becomes depressed and leaves to walk by the river. In the meantime, Laurie is rebuffed in her attempt to rekindle the affair with Easton, who is preoccupied with his career and plans to marry Tom's secretary, Cindy. Laurie leaves the party and meets Tom near the river. He confesses his love, but she remains indifferent and returns to Martin's house to join the few remaining guests in a desperate attempt to have an orgy. Once more rejected by Easton, Laurie fights off the drunken Martin and goes to a nearby tavern. She fails to notice Easton, who is waiting outside for her, and by chance she meets Tom again. She accepts his invitation to go with him to a hotel room, but after they make love she makes it clear that she has no interest in his problems. His depression intensified, Tom returns home and quarrels with his wife, Kit, who reveals her own infidelity. His marriage in ruins, Tom goes to a neighborhood bar. Through the haze of too many drinks, he thinks he sees his late business partner outside. He runs into the street and is struck and killed by a passing car. *Advertising executives. Actors. Television directors. Secretaries. Marriage. Infidelity. Suicide. Ambition. Hotels. Television. New York City. Hallucinations. Automobile accidents.*

Note: Cut to 76 min and released in 1965 by Thunderbird International Pictures as *Flaming Desire.*

THE SMALL WORLD OF SAMMY LEE (Great Britain)   **F6.4570**

Bryanston–Seven Arts Productions-Elgin Films. *For* British Lion Films. *Dist* Seven Arts Associated Corp. 13 Aug **1963** [New York opening]. Sd; b&w. 35mm. 105 min.

Prod Frank Godwin. *Exec Prod* Kenneth Hyman. *Dir-Screenplay* Ken Hughes. *Photog* Wolfgang Suschitzky. *Art Dir* Seamus Flannery. *Film Ed* Henry Richardson. *Mus Comp* Kenny Graham. *Mus Cond* Philip Martell. *Choreog* Lili Berde. *Sd Ed* Jim Roddan. *Sd Rec* Leslie Hammond, Hugh Strain. *Asst Dir* Christopher Dryhurst. *Prod Mgr* Robert Sterne. *Wardrobe* Eileen Sullivan, Ray Beck. *Makeup* Jimmy Evans. *Hairstyles* Joyce James.

Cast: Anthony Newley *(Sammy Lee)*, Julia Foster *(Patsy)*, Robert Stephens *(Gerry)*, Wilfrid Brambell *(Harry)*, Warren Mitchell *(Lou)*, Miriam Karlin *(Milly)*, Kenneth J. Warren *(Fred)*, Clive Colin Bowler *(Johnny)*, Toni Palmer *(Joan)*, Harry Locke *(stage manager)*, Al Mulock *(dealer)*, Cyril Shaps *(Morrie)*, Roy Kinnear *(Lucky Dave)*, Harry Baird *(Buddy Shine)*, Alfred Burke *(Big Eddie)*, June Cunningham *(Rita)*, Ronald Radd *(Big Alf)*, Elmer, Lynda Baron, Ken Wayne.

Comedy-drama. Source: Ken Hughes, *Sammy* (a teleplay; BBC, 1958). Sammy Lee is the quick-witted master of ceremonies at the Peepshow Club, a sleazy striptease joint in Soho. In debt to a gangster-bookie, he has just 5 hours to raise £300 or face a brutal beating. Turned down by Lou, his hard-working, delicatessen-owner brother, because Lou's unsympathetic wife, Milly, will not let Lou help, Sammy tries to raise cash through shady deals in American whisky, Swiss watches, and marijuana. A naive North Country girl, Patsy, who came to London because Sammy promised her a career in show business, tries to help get money by agreeing to do a striptease for his lecherous employer, Gerry. Disgusted, Sammy puts her on a bus and sends her home, hoping to join her later. As time runs out, Sammy's schemes pay off but, because part of the money is in the form of a check, his frantic efforts have been to no avail. It is with relief that he turns to face the hoodlums. After the beating, however, he makes the ironic discovery that much of the money has been left in his wallet. *Entertainers. Innocents. Gangsters. Bookies. Brothers. Debt. Smuggling. Lechery. Striptease. Liquor. Marijuana. Watches. Nightclubs. London—Soho. England—North.*

Note: Location scenes filmed in the Soho and East End districts of London. Opened in London in Apr 1963; running time: 107 min. Ken Hughes's original teleplay was also produced for U. S. television and presented as *Eddie* on the 10 Nov 1958 segment of "Award Theatre."

LA SMANIA ADDOSSO *see* **THE EYE OF THE NEEDLE**

SMASHING OF THE REICH (United States/France)   **F6.4571**

Le Film d'Art–Irja Film Productions–C. B. S. Europe. *Dist* Brigadier Film Associates. 2 Oct **1962** [New York opening]. Sd; b&w. 35mm. 84 min.

Prod-Dir-Writ Perry Wolff. *Film Ed* Françoise Diot, James B. Faichney, Peter Poor, Leo Zochling. *Mus* Norman Dello Joio. *Sd* Pierre Calvet.

Narrators: Jim Stephens, Duncan Elliott.

Documentary. Highlights of newsreel footage depicting the fall of Nazi Germany include scenes from the Normandy Beach landings, the battle for Paris, the battering of Bastogne, and the U. S.-Russian combined assault at the Elbe River. Particular emphasis is placed on the repeated Allied bombings of German industrial and oil centers. Also shown are the ultimate liberation of Paris and the freeing of concentration camp survivors. *Aerial bombardment. Concentration camps. World War II. Germany—History—Third Reich. Normandy. Paris. Elbe River. Bastogne. United States Army. Union of Soviet*

Socialist Republics—Army. Germany—Army.
Note: Opened in Paris in May 1961 as *La guerre inconnue.*

SMASHING TIME (Great Britain)   F6.4572

Partisan Film Productions. *Dist* Paramount Pictures. 20 Dec **1967** [New York opening; c20 Dec 1967; LP35320]. Sd; col (Eastman Color). 35mm. 96 min.

Pres by Selmur Productions, Carlo Ponti. *Prod* Roy Millichip, Carlo Ponti. *Exec Prod* Selig J. Seligman. *Dir* Desmond Davis. *Orig Screenplay* George Melly. *Dir Photog* Manny Wynn. *Camera Op* Ray Parslow. *Art Dir* Ken Bridgeman. *Titl Drawn by* Trog. *Film Ed* Barry Vince. *Mus Comp & Cond* John Addison. *Orch* Raymond Jones, Charles Blackwell. *Skip Bifferty Group Mus Comp* Victor Smith, mus. *Songs:* "Baby, Don't Go," "Carnaby Street," "Day Out," "While I'm Still Young," "It's Always Your Fault," "New Clothes," "Smashing Time," "Trouble," "Waiting for My Friend" John Addison, George Melly. *Sd Rec* Robin Gregory. *Dub Ed* Alan Pattillo. *Asst Dir* Jake Wright. *Prod Mgr* Bruce Sharman. *Prod Asst* Jane Moscrop. *Cont* Betty Harley. *Cost* Ruth Myers. *Sp Wigs Created for Miss Redgrave* Evansky. *Makeup* Richard Mills. *Hairdresser* Stephanie Kaye. *Casting Dir* Paul Lee Lander. *Prop Supv* John Leuenberger. *Jabberwock Machine Sculpture* Bruce Lacey.

Cast: Rita Tushingham *(Brenda)*, Lynn Redgrave *(Yvonne)*, Michael York *(Tom Wabe)*, Anna Quayle *(Charlotte Brilling)*, Irene Handl *(Mrs. Gimble)*, Ian Carmichael *(Bobbi Mome-Rath)*, Toni Palmer *(Toni)*, Jeremy Lloyd *(Jeremy Tove)*, Arthur Mullard *(cafe boss)*, Sydney Bromley *(tramp)*, Howard Marion-Crawford *(hall porter)*, Murray Melvin *(1st exquisite)*, Paul Danquah *(2d exquisite)*, Valery Leon *(Tove's secretary)*, Adele Strong *(gossiping customer)*, Jerold Wells *(man in cafe no. 6)*, Peter Jones *(Dominic)*, George A. Cooper *(Irishman)*, Ronnie Stevens *(1st waiter)*, John Clive *(Sweenie Todd manager)*, Mike Lennox *(disc jockey)*, Bruce Lacey *(Clive Sword)*, Cardew Robinson *(custard-pie vicar)*, David Lodge *(The Caretaker)*, Ray Mackin *(2d waiter)*, Amy Dalby *(demolished old lady)*, The Tomorrow *(The Snarks)*, Bart Allison, Gabor Baraker, Eve Belton, Kate Binchy, Yuri Borienko, Teresa Buckingham, Veronica Carlson, Golda Casimir, Richard Coe, Julian Curry, Desmond Davies, Jonathon Elsom, Olivia Farjeon, Tom Gill, Danny Green, Luanshiya Greer, Geoffrey Hughes, Brenda Kempner, Leigh Kostelanetz, Sam Kydd, Valerie Leon, Arthur Lovegrove, George O'Gorman, Stuart Saunders, Frank Sieman, Will Stampe, Bernard Stone, Michael Ward, Susan Whitman.

Comedy with music. Two North Country young women, plain Brenda and flamboyant Yvonne, arrive in London and head immediately for the mod scene on Carnaby Street to find fame and fortune. They are misdirected and end up eating at a workman's cafe. Their money is stolen, and Yvonne runs off, leaving Brenda to wash a mountain of dishes. On the street, Yvonne's picture is taken by a successful fashion photographer, Tom Wabe, who uses her "look" as an illustration of what *not* to do. Taking jobs at the Menagerie Club, Yvonne, as a seductively-dressed hostess, is pursued by a lecherous member, Bobbi Mome-Rath, while Brenda, as a pussycat waitress, looks on worriedly. When Mome-Rath entices Yvonne to his apartment, Brenda goes along and creates enough mood-destroying havoc to "save" Yvonne. When the women lose their jobs, Brenda goes to work for the Honorable Charlotte Brilling, who owns a boutique frequented primarily by freeloading friends. Brenda changes this state of affairs, however, and when Charlotte returns one day, with Tom Wabe in tow, she finds her entire stock sold. Wabe then takes Brenda to a restaurant where Yvonne has become a waitress. When Yvonne sees them together, she begins throwing pies; and soon everyone is engaged in a free-for-all. Both out of jobs again, the girls return home and find their apartment demolished, the result of a practical joke perpetrated by a TV station, for which they are given £10,000 compensation. Yvonne spends the money on a manager, Jeremy Tove, and moves to Chelsea. Tove promotes her into a wildly successful recording star and "now" personality, and Brenda becomes little more than Yvonne's body servant. Wabe eventually woos Brenda away, ensconces her in a luxurious houseboat, and publicizes her, through modeling, as "the face of the Seventies." As Yvonne's career begins to wane, Tove throws a publicity party in the Post Office Tower's revolving restaurant. Brenda arrives with Tom and, appalled by what she and Yvonne have become, short circuits the tower and sets the restaurant spinning so fast that the generator explodes and blacks out an entire section of London. Reunited, Yvonne and Brenda sneak out and wander the darkened streets, knowing they are now ready to return to the North Country. *Nightclub hostesses. Waitresses. Photographers. Models. Playboys. Singers. Ambition. Seduction. Publicity. Practical jokes. Blackout. Boutiques. Cafes. Nightclubs. Television. Houseboats. London. England—North. London—Chelsea. London—Carnaby Street. Post Office Tower (London).*
Note: Filmed on location in London. Opened in London in Dec 1967.

A SMELL OF HONEY, A SWALLOW OF BRINE!   F6.4573

Essaneff. *Dist* Sonney Amusement Enterprises. 10 Jun **1966** [Los Angeles opening]. Sd; b&w. 35mm. 71 min.

Prod-Writ David F. Friedman. *Dir* B. Ron Elliott. *Photog* Art Radford. *Asst Camera* Myron Griffin. *Film Ed* Byron Mabe. *Mus Comp* Mark Wayne. *Played by* "et cetra". *Sd Rec* Bill Markey. *Prod Mgr* Don Hallstrom.

Cast: Stacey Walker *(Sharon Winters)*, Neville Coward *(Lowell Carter)*, Sharon Carr *(Paula)*, Bob Todd *(Tony)*, Michael Wright *(Mr. Gordon)*, Michael O'Kelly *(Roy)*, Tom Hughes *(Dick Owens)*.

Melodrama. Sharon Winters sends men to passionate heights and then cries "rape." Of three of her victims, one is sent to jail, another loses his job, and the third is shot while attempting to rape another woman. Even Sharon's mannishly attractive roomate, Paula, is subjected to the teasing and is repulsed by it. Eventually Sharon meets Tony, who scorns her cries and, in anger, beats her. Once beautiful, Sharon now bears scars of Tony's brutality, and she ends up working for him as a prostitute. *Teases. Pimps. Prostitutes. Rape. Lesbianism. Disfiguration.*
Note: Also known as *The Smell of Honey!* and *A Taste of Honey, a Swallow of Brine!*

THE SMILE OF REASON see CIVILISATION: THE SMILE OF REASON

SMITH!   F6.4574

Walt Disney Productions. *Dist* Buena Vista Distribution Co. Apr **1969** [c11 Mar 1969; LP36580]. Sd (RCA); col (Technicolor). 35mm. 102 min.

A Walt Disney Production. *Prod* Bill Anderson, prod. *Assoc Prod* Tom Leetch. *Dir* Michael O'Herlihy. *Dir Indian Actors Workshop* Jay Silverheels. *Screenplay* Louis Pelletier. *Dir Photog* Robert Moreno. *Art Dir* John B. Mansbridge, Robert E. Smith. *Set Decor* Emile Kuri, Hal Gausman. *Titl Dsgn* Alan Maley. *Film Ed* Robert Stafford. *Mus* Robert F. Brunner. *Orch* Walter Sheets. *Song:* "The Ballad of Smith and Gabriel Jimmyboy" *Writ & Sung by* Bob Russell. *Sd Supv* Robert O. Cook. *Sd Mix* Roger Parish. *Mus Ed* Evelyn Kennedy. *Asst Dir* Russell Llewellyn. *Cost* Chuck Keehne, Emily Sundby. *Makeup* Otis Malcolm. *Hairstylist* La Rue Matheron.

Cast: Glenn Ford *(Smith)*, Nancy Olson *(Norah)*, Dean Jagger *(judge)*, Keenan Wynn *(Vince Heber)*, Warren Oates *(Walter Charlie)*, Chief Dan George *(Ol' Antoine)*, Frank Ramirez *(Gabriel Jimmyboy)*, John Randolph *(Mr. Edwards)*, Christopher Shea *(Albie)*, Roger Ewing *(Donald Maxwell)*, Jay Silverheels *(McDonald Lasheway)*, James Westerfield *(sheriff)*, Indian Actors Workshop of Hollywood.

Western comedy-drama. Source: Paul St. Pierre, *Breaking Smith's Quarter Horse* (Chicago, 1966). Smith lives on a small ranch with Norah, his wife, and their 10-year-old son, Albie. Upon returning from a 3-day trip, Smith learns that Gabriel Jimmyboy, a young Indian suspected of murder, has taken refuge on his property in the shack belonging to Smith's Indian blood brother, Ol' Antoine. Smith, who believes that Jimmyboy is innocent and will get a fair trial, tries to persuade Antoine to turn in Jimmyboy and use the reward money to hire a good lawyer, but the young Indian does not believe Smith and sends him away. Albie and his Indian friend Peterpaul find Jimmyboy hiding in the woods, and they bring him food. They are forced to reveal Jimmyboy's whereabouts to Smith when they learn that Vince, the Indian-hating deputy sheriff and Eddie, his assistant, along with some tracking dogs, are on his trail. Smith and Albie rush to warn Jimmyboy, but Antoine has already turned him in to the sheriff and collected the reward. The Indian haying crew the Smiths are relying on to cut their hay arrive but only to say that they are leaving to attend Jimmyboy's trial. Smith goes, too, when he learns that Antoine is also in jail. Smith gets Antoine freed and replaces Walter Charlie, a conniving Indian, as interpreter at the trial. Antoine's testimony describing the injustices done to the Indians in the past impresses the judge and jury, and Jimmyboy is freed. After the trial, Smith returns home to cut the hay alone, but the Indians soon come to help, and Antoine, after many months of promise, begins breaking Albie's prize Appaloosa. *Ranchers. Indians of North America. Blood brothers. Sheriffs. Interpreters. Farm workers. Murder. Friendship. Racial prejudice. Trials.*
Note: Location scenes filmed in Washington and Oregon.

SMOKE AND FLESH   F6.4575

Imperial Pictures. *Dist* Imperial Pictures. 23 Aug **1968** [Champaign, Illinois, showing]. Sd; b&w. 35mm. 70 min.

Dir-Writ Joe Mangine.

Cast: Richard Howell, Lee Parker, Ed Sansone.

Drama. Turk, a "cool swinger," throws a pot and sex party at his house. Hoodlums Skif, Babe, and Chick crash the party, but to forestall trouble Turk slips Skif a cube of LSD as the party gets into full swing. Skif has a bad trip and loses control; and his companions carry him from the house while the other guests proceed uninterrupted with the party. *Hoodlums. Marijuana. LSD. Orgies.*

SMOKE OF EVIL   F6.4576
   Dist Inter-American Film Distributors. 17 May **1967** [New York showing].
Sd; b&w. 35mm. [Feature film, length unknown.]
   Sex film. No information about the precise nature of this film has been
found, but press material suggests that it concerns a club where marijuana and
other drugs are used. Included are scenes of lesbianism, sadomasochism, and
group sex. *Marijuana. Drugs. Group sex. Sadomasochism. Lesbianism. Sex
clubs.*

SMOKY   F6.4577
   Arcola Pictures. *Dist* Twentieth Century-Fox Film Corp. 3 Aug **1966** [Saint
Louis opening; c3 Aug 1966; LP33000]. Sd (Westrex); col (DeLuxe). 35mm.
103 min.
   An Aaron Rosenberg Production. *Prod* Aaron Rosenberg. *Assoc Prod* David
Silver. *Dir* George Sherman. *Screenplay* Harold Medford. *Dir Photog* Jack
Swain. *Art Dir* Jack Martin Smith, John M. Elliott. *Film Ed* Joseph Silver. *Mus*
Leith Stevens. *Orch* Herbert Spencer. *Titl Song* Ernie Sheldon, Leith Stevens.
Sung by Hank Thompson. *Songs:* "Five Dollar Bill," "Smile As You Go By,"
"Trouble and Misery," "Queen of the Rockin' R" comp & sung by Hoyt Axton.
Sd Luis Fernandez, Harry M. Leonard. *Asst Dir* Ted Schilz. *Unit Prod Mgr*
David Silver. *Makeup* Ben Nye. *Hairstyles* Margaret Donovan. *Tech Adv*
Carlos Reyes. *Horse Trained by* Les Hilton.
   Cast: Fess Parker *(Clint)*, Diana Hyland *(Julie)*, Katy Jurado *(Maria)*, Hoyt
Axton *(Fred)*, Robert J. Wilke *(Jeff)*, Armando Silvestre *(Gordon)*, Jose Hector
Galindo *(Manuel)*, Jorge Martinez de Hoyos *(Pepe)*, Ted White *(Abbott)*,
Chuck Roberson, Robert Terhune, Jack Williams *(cowboys)*, Diamond Jet
(Smoky).
   Western melodrama. Source: Will James, *Smoky, the Cowhorse* (New York,
1926). Lillie Hayward, Dwight Cummins and Dorothy Yost, screenplay for the
film *Smoky*, 1946. Clint, a lone cowboy, aids in rounding up a pack of wild
horses and bringing them in to the Rocking R ranch. The ranch owner, Julie,
employs Clint as a wrangler, and he sets about breaking in the pack's leader,
a beautiful stallion given the name Smoky. One day a youngster on the ranch
inadvertently allows the horse to escape, forcing Clint to ride out to capture
him. After saving the animal from quicksand, Clint returns to the ranch and
discovers that his brother Fred also has been hired by Julie. Longtime enemies,
the two brothers conceal their relationship until Fred signs Clint's name on a
gambling debt IOU. After a bitter fight, the beaten Fred whips Smoky and tries
to exchange him for the IOU. But the animal breaks loose, tramples Fred to
death, and bolts off into the hills. Clint searches for Smoky for days but finally
gives up and enlists for service in World War II. During his absence, Smoky
is captured and traded to a rodeo, where he performs until he is injured. Then
he is sold to a junk dealer. After the war Clint returns to Albuquerque on the
day a rodeo is in town. As he watches the parade, he spies a lame, half-starved
horse pulling a driverless wagon. Clint seeks out the junkman and is reunited
with his beloved horse. *Broncobusters. Wranglers. Ranchers. Brothers. Junk
dealers. Forgery. Gambling. Quicksand. Rodeos. World War II. Albuquerque.
Horses.*
   Note: Location scenes filmed in Mexico. Filmed twice previously by Fox
(1933, 1946).

SMORGASBROAD *see* **INTERNATIONAL SMORGASBROAD**

THE SMUGGLERS (France)   F6.4578
   Luc Moullet. *Dist* New Yorker Films. 20 Apr **1969** [New York opening]. Sd;
b&w. 35mm. 80 min.
   Prod-Dir-Writ Luc Moullet. *Photog* Philippe Theaudière. *Film Ed* Cécile
Decugis.
   Cast: Françoise Vatel *(Brigitte)*, Monique Thiriet *(Francesca)*, Johnny
Monteilhet *(customs officer)*, Albert Juross *(poacher)*, Paul Martin, actor
(official), Bernard Cazassua *(nomad)*, Luc Moullet *("Connard")*, Gérard
Tanguy, Patrick Huber *(syndicate members)*.
   Drama. Disillusioned with city life, Brigitte, a student, takes up smuggling
in a mountainous border region and becomes the lover of a customs officer who
is also involved in the smuggling racket. Another young woman, Francesca,
lives on the other side of the border and is also a lover of the customs officer
as well as a smuggler. Her reason for dealing in contraband goods is to cut down
on her country's revenue because she disapproves of its war-waging policy. For
a time the customs officer manages to divide his time evenly between Brigitte
and Francesca; but when an armistice is signed, the border is removed and the
two women meet. Since they have broken with middle-class conventions, they
decide that they can all live happily together; jealousy eventually erupts,
however, and Brigitte confronts Francesca with a loaded revolver. At the same
time, they are the target of gunfire from members of the smugglers union in
helicopters and are hunted down by members of the customs patrol. United by
their common plight, Brigitte and Francesca escape and return to city life.
Though they try to readjust to urban living, they are defeated by the new social

order when technology turns them out of their jobs. Not knowing what else to
do, they return to smuggling. *Students. Customs officers. Smuggling. Jealousy.
Mountain life. Urban life.*
   Note: Opened in Paris in Dec 1968 as *Les contrebandières*.

THE SMUT PEDDLER   F6.4579
   Biolane Corp. *Dist* American Film Distributing Corp. 26 Nov **1965**
[Champaign, Illinois, showing]. Sd; b&w. 35mm. 60-75 min.
   Prod Herbert Lannard. *Dir* Warner Rose.
   Cast: Woody Parker, Tommy Spencer, Liselotte Fugger, Roy Drurden,
Jackie Miller, Renate Vogt, Hedi John, Roberta Evans.
   Sex film. D. G. (DeGenerate) Rawlins, the vicious, deviant publisher of
Dream Girl magazine, has an insatiable appetite for oysters, women, and
increasing his magazine's circulation. He spares no expense in creating his lush
"nudie" features; "Girls of Vienna" and "Paris Mademoiselles" are among his
classic issues. Surrounded by beautiful young women, D. G. seduces one after
another, while his trusted feature editor, a lesbian, picks up where he leaves off,
using her job to force the women into compliance. At last a Broadway columnist
puts the spotlight on the perverts and brings the operation to a close.
Pornographers. Models. Columnists. Pornography. Lesbianism. Seduction.
   Note: May also be known as *The Smut Peddlars*.

THE SNAKE WOMAN (Great Britain)   F6.4580
   Caralan Productions. *Dist* United Artists. 26 Apr **1961** [Los Angeles
opening]. Sd; b&w. 35mm. 68 min.
   Prod George Fowler. *Exec Prod* David E. Rose. *Dir* Sidney J. Furie.
Screenplay Orville H. Hampton. *Photog* Stephen Dade. *Art Dir* John Earl. *Film
Ed* Anthony Gibbs. *Mus Comp* Buxton Orr. *Mus Cond* Philip Martell. *Sd*
Robert Winter, H. C. Pearson. *Asst Dir* Douglas Hickox. *Prod Mgr* Buddy
Booth. *Wardrobe* Dulcie Midwinter. *Makeup* Freddie Williamson. *Hairstyles*
Helen Penfold.
   Cast: John McCarthy, actor *(Charles Prentice)*, Susan Travers *(Atheris
Adderson)*, Geoffrey Danton *(Colonel Wynborn)*, Arnold Marle *(Dr. Murton)*,
Elsie Wagstaff *(Aggie)*, John Cazabon *(Dr. Adderson)*, Frances Bennett
(Polly), Jack Cunningham, actor *(constable)*, Hugh Moxey *(inspector)*, Michael
Logan *(Barkis)*, Dorothy Frere *(Martha Adderson)*, Stevenson Lang
(shepherd).
   Horror film. Late in the 19th century, on the lonely Northumberland moors,
herpetologist Dr. Adderson restores his wife's sanity by injecting her with
venom from the snakes he uses in his experiments. A short time later she dies
giving birth to a daughter, Atheris. Aggie, the midwife, runs to warn the
villagers that the child has the evil eye, forcing Dr. Adderson to hide his infant
daughter in a shepherd's hut. That night the villagers burn down the doctor's
house, and he is fatally bitten by one of his snakes. Years later, a young Scotland
Yard inspector, Charles Prentice, is sent to Northumberland to investigate
several deaths from snakebite. While strolling in the woods, he encounters the
beautiful Atheris. Though she responds to the music of a snake charmer's flute,
Prentice, unaware that she is Adderson's daughter, at first does not connect her
with the mysterious deaths; but eventually, following several more killings, he
realizes that Atheris is both snake and woman, capable of transforming herself
at will. Confronted with the truth, she turns into a cobra and attacks him. As
he fires three bullets at her, the writhing serpent turns into the corpse of Atheris.
Hoping that all mention of this incident will die with the case report, the police
destroy it. *Herpetologists. Midwives. Infants. Detectives. Insanity. Childbirth.
Village life. Metamorphosis. Snakebites. Incendiarism. Moorlands. Serums.
Northumberland. Scotland yard. Snakes.*
   Note: Released in Great Britain in 1962.

SNIPER'S RIDGE   F6.4581
   Associated Producers, Inc. *Dist* Twentieth Century-Fox Film Corp. Feb
1961 [Los Angeles opening: 15 Mar; c27 Jan 1961; LP18692]. Sd; b&w. 35mm
(CinemaScope). 61 min.
   Prod-Dir John Bushelman. *Writ* Tom Maruzzi. *Dir Photog* Kenneth Peach.
Art Dir John Mansbridge. *Set Decor* Harry Reif. *Film Ed* Carl Pierson. *Mus*
Richard La Salle. *Sd* Carl Zint. *Supv Sd Ed* Jack Cornall. *Sd Facilities*
Continental Sound Corp. *Asst Dir* Ira Stewart. *Prod Supv* Harold E. Knox.
Script Supv Mel Marshall. *Cost* Robert Olivas. *Makeup* Ernie Park. *Prop
Master* Monroe Liebgold.
   Cast: Jack Ging *(Private Scharack)*, Stanley Clements *(Corporal Pumphrey)*,
John Goddard *(Captain Tombolo)*, Douglas Henderson *(Sergeant Sweatish)*,
Gabe Castle *(Lieutenant Peer)*, Allan Marvin *(Wardy)*, Anton Van Stralen
(Bear), Mason Curry *(David)*, Mark Douglas *(Bo-Bo)*, Scott Randall *(soldier)*,
George Yoshinaga *(Mongolian)*, Albert C. Freeman, Jr. *(Gwathney)*, Henry
Delgado *(Tonto)*, Joe Cawthon *(young soldier)*, Richard Jeffries *(soldier)*.
   War drama. Shortly before the end of the Korean War, a courageous but
battle-weary soldier, Private Scharack, learns that his long-overdue rotation
home has been suppressed by his tough but cowardly superior, Captain

Tombolo. Enraged, Scharack hitches a ride to a field hospital, pretending severe headaches, but is humiliated by the equally war-weary doctor. When Scharack returns to his outfit, Tombolo punishes him by giving him latrine duty. Scharack becomes even more embittered when Tombolo orders a patrol into enemy territory on the very night that the "cease fire" is expected. Before the patrol sets out, however, Tombolo accidentally steps on a "bouncing Betty"—a mine that explodes when one steps *off* the plunger. Though none of the other men come to Tombolo's aid, Scharack wraps the captain in flack jackets and tells him to leap off the bomb. But the terrified Tombolo is unable to move, and Scharack is forced to push him off. Tombolo is unharmed but Scharack is seriously wounded and sent to a hospital. At 10 p.m., when the "cease fire" is sounded, Tombolo's clumsy attempt at an apology is flatly rejected by his men. *Soldiers. Battle fatigue. Courage. Cowardice. Mines (war explosives). Korean War 1950-53.*

Note: Location scenes filmed in California.

THE SNOUT *see* **UNDERWORLD INFORMERS**

SNOVA K ZVYOZDAM *see* **FLIGHT TO THE STARS**

SNOW COUNTRY (Japan)   F6.4582
Shochiku Co. *Dist* Shochiku Films of America. Mar **1969** [Los Angeles showing]. Sd; col (Fuji Color). 35mm (Shochiku GrandScope). 115 min.

Prod Shizuo Yamanouchi. *Dir* Hideo Oba. *Screenplay* Ryosuke Saito, Hideo Oba. *Photog* Toichiro Narushima. *Art Dir* Inko Yoshino. *Prod Dsgn* Ryotaro Kuwata. *Mus* Naozumi Yamamoto.

Cast: Shima Iwashita *(Komako)*, Isao Kimura *(Shimamura)*, Mariko Kaga *(Yoko)*, Tamotsu Hayakawa *(Yukio)*, Chieko Naniwa *(The Masseuse)*, Sadako Sawamura *(The Dance Teacher)*, Mineko Bandai *(The Landlady)*, Shinichi Yanagisawa *(The Banto)*, Mutsuko Sakura *(The Maid)*, Kakuko Chino *(Kikuyu)*, Kyomi Sakura *(Kintaro)*, Takanobu Hozumi *(The Drunk Guest)*, Ushio Akashi *(The Stationmaster)*, Kaneko Iwasaki *(Mrs. Shimamura)*, Taketoshi Naito *(Koizumi)*, Michisumi Sugawara *(Komako's patron)*, Nijiko Kiyokawa *(mistress of geisha house)*.

Romantic drama. Source: Yasunari Kawabata, *Yukiguni* (Tokyo; segments published 1935-37, final installment 1947). In the spring of 1935 Shimamura, a writer and critic, visits a small hot springs resort town in northern Japan and meets Komako, a 19-year-old girl who helps the geishas to entertain the tourists. Shimamura is attracted to her, but when he asks her to send him a geisha, she throws a tantrum and leaves his room, only to return later, drunk from a party, to spend the night with him. As the two become more intimate over the next few days, Shimamura learns that Komako is the adopted daughter of a local dance teacher who wishes her to marry her son. Shimamura returns to his wife and child in Tokyo, but the following winter finds him on the way to the same town. On the train, he spots a young girl, Yoko, caring for a sick young man, Yukio. Later he finds out from Komako that Yoko also was adopted by the dance teacher and Yukio is the teacher's son. The blind masseuse of the village tells Shimamura that Komako has had to become a geisha to support her family after her step-mother fell ill and was unable to work. Komako reveals that Yukio contracted intestinal tuberculosis while studying in Tokyo and Yoko brought him back from there to care for him. Shimamura senses that Yoko loves Yukio, who loves Komako, and Yoko is bitter toward her step-sister for not reciprocating Yukio's love. After a short stay Shimamura is about to leave for Tokyo when Yoko comes to the train station with news that Yukio's condition has suddenly deteriorated. Komako refuses to leave the station, however, without seeing off her lover. In the autumn of the following year Shimamura revisits the town, which is already covered with snow. The dance teacher and Yukio have died; Komako has left Yoko to live alone in the family house. By now Komako is so in love with Shimamura that she claims she would be happy if he came to see her only once a year. Realizing that he cannot reciprocate such passionate devotion, Shimamura decides to leave the town for good. Before he can announce his intentions, however, Yoko is badly burned in a fire. Shimamura leaves town without telling Komako that he will not be back. *Authors. Geishas. Dance teachers. Masseurs. Students. Drunkenness. Infidelity. Adoption. Tuberculosis. Resorts. Tokyo. Fires.*

Note: Released in Japan in 1965 as *Yukiguni.*

SNOW IN THE SOUTH SEAS (Japan)   F6.4583
Toho Co. Apr **1963** [Los Angeles showing]. Sd; col (Eastmancolor). 35mm (Tohoscope). 103 min.

Exec Prod Ichiro Sato, Fumio Kinbara. *Dir* Seiji Hisamatsu. *Screenplay* Ryozo Kasahara. *Story* Daisuke Kato. *Photog* Tokuzo Kuroda. *Mus* Kenjiro Hirose.

Cast: Daisuke Kato, Hisaya Morishige, Tatsuya Mihashi, Franky Sakai, Junzaburo Ban.

War drama. During the last days of World War II, troop morale begins to lag. In New Guinea, a staff officer asks Sergeant Kato, an actor and scriptwriter in civilian life, for suggestions on entertaining the troops. Kato produces a play

with soldiers volunteering their services as actors and stagehands, and the performance is such a success that the garrison commander orders a modest theater be constructed for future performances. Dubbed the "Monoquari," the theater presents entertainment to enthusiastic military audiences. As the Allies threaten to invade New Guinea, the Monoquari's final performance features a snow fall evoking memories of Japan. *Actors. Combat zone life. Theater. World War II. New Guinea. Japan—Army.*

Note: Released in Japan in 1961 as *Minami no shima ni yuki ga fura.*

SNOW JOB   F6.4584
Dist Distribpix, Inc. 4 Jul **1969** [Champaign, Illinois, showing]. Sd; col. 35mm. 63 min.

A Norman Norman Production. *Prod-Dir-Writ* Arlo Shiffen.

Cast: Cindy Sugar, Lena Jacobson.

Comedy-drama. Three young secretaries who decide to explore the world of ski weekending go to a local ski shop to rent some equipment, and there they meet Eric, a pro who encourages them to go to a resort operated by his friend Alan. When Eric calls Alan to tell him of the impending visit, Alan's homely and awkward assistant, Elvin, listens on an extension and figures that one of the young women will be his. The secretaries arrive, and after a welcoming round of drinks, they spend the weekend skiing and making love with Eric and Alan. Elvin, however, fails to score. He fumbles at every chance and finally passes out from too much to drink. As the women leave for the city, Elvin exacts a kind of revenge when Eric and Alan fall on the ice. *Secretaries. Innkeepers. Storekeepers. Skiing. Sexuality. Ski resorts.*

SNOW TREASURE   F6.4585
Sagittarius Productions. *Dist* Allied Artists. Oct **1968** [c1 Dec 1967; LP35404]. Sd; col (Eastman Color). 35mm. 95 min.

Prod-Dir Irving Jacoby. *Exec Prod* Claude Giroux. *Screenplay* Irving Jacoby, Peter Hansen. *Photog* Sverre Bergli. *Art Dir* Grethe Hejil. *Film Ed* Ralph Sheldon. *Mus* Egil Monn-Iversen. *Sd* Noel Cantrill. *Asst Dir* Remo Caprino. *Prod Mgr* Peter Hansen.

Cast: James Franciscus *(Lieutenant Kalasch)*, Ilona Rodgers *(Bente Nielsen)*, Paul Austad *(Peter Lundstrom)*, Raoul Oyen *(Victor Lundstrom)*, Randi Borch *(Inger Lundstrom)*, Tor Stokke *(Lars Lundstrom)*, Wilfred Breistrand *(Captain Kantzeler)*.

Adventure drama. Source: Marie McSwigan, *Snow Treasure* (New York, 1942). In April 1940, at the start of the Nazi invasion of Norway, Peter, a 14-year-old Norwegian boy, witnesses the secret arrival of a shipment in his village. The next day Peter explores the countryside on his skis, discovers the shipment hidden in a snow-covered cave, and learns of its contents—a vast quantity of gold placed there for safekeeping by the Norwegian underground. He tells no one about his discovery and secretly evolves a plan to use a group of children to transport the gold in their knapsacks to a concealed fishing boat, the hideout of his Uncle Victor, a member of the Norwegian underground. The need for the removal of the gold becomes urgent when all of the men in the village are captured, and Peter reveals his plan to Victor. Lieutenant Kalasch, a German officer who is attracted to Bente, Victor's fiancée, also finds out about the plan, but he is sympathetic to the Norwegians and offers to help. He proves himself worthy of their trust when he rescues Peter, who after 6 weeks of helping to smuggle the gold, is captured by the Germans. During the escape Kalasch is shot. Mortally wounded, he dies in the boat, but Peter safely reaches the boat before it puts out to sea. *Nazis. Children. Traitors. Escapees. Uncles. Skiing. Resistance (political). Smuggling. Self-sacrifice. Caves. Gold. Fishing boats. Fishing villages. World War II. Norway.*

Note: Filmed in Norway.

SNOW WHITE (West Germany)   F6.4586
Schongerfilm. *Dist* Childhood Productions. 23 Oct **1965** [New York opening]. Sd; col (Eastman Color). 35mm. 74 min.

Prod Hubert Schonger. *Dir* Erich Kobler. *Screenplay* Konrad Lustig, Walter Oehmichen. *Photog* Wolf Schwan. *Art Dir* Günther Strupp. *Film Ed* Horst Rossgerber. *Mus Comp* Carl Stueber, Franz Miller. *Mus Dir* Lehman Engel. *Mus Arr* George Brackman. *English Vers Songs* Anne Delugg, Milton Delugg. *Sd* Winicke. *Prod Mgr* Laci Martin. *Cost* W. Pechanz.

Cast: Paul Tripp *(narrator)*, Elke Arendt *(Snow White)*, Addi Adametz *(evil queen)*, Renate Eichholz *(good queen)*, Nils Clausnitzer *(prince)*, Dietrich Thomas *(huntsman)*, Zita Hitz *(chambermaid)*, Erwin Platzer, Susi Bohm Dance School.

Fantasy. Source: Jakob Grimm and Wilhelm Grimm, "Schneewittchen und die sieben Zwerge". The film is a screen adaptation of the Grimm Brothers' fairy tale. *Dwarfs. Hunters. Jealousy. Friendship. Poisoning. Imaginary kingdoms. Snow White. Prince Charming.*

Note: Released in West Germany in Nov 1956 as *Schneewittchen und die sieben Zwerge*; running time: 77 min.

SNOW WHITE AND ROSE RED (West Germany)   **F6.4587**

Schongerfilm. *Dist* Childhood Productions. Jan **1966**. Sd; col (Eastmancolor). 35mm. 55 min.

Dir Erich Kobler. *Screenplay* Walter Oemichen, Konrad Lustig. *Photog* Wolf Schwan. *Mus* Oskar Sala.

Cast: Rosemarie Seehofer *(Snow White)*, Ursula Herion *(Rose Red)*, Heini Göbel *(prince)*, Ruth von Zerboni, Nils Clausnitzer, Dieter Wieland, Richard Krüger.

Narrator: Paul Tripp.

Fantasy. Source: Jakob Grimm and Wilhelm Grimm, "Schneeweisschen und Rosenrot". Snow White and Rose Red live with their mother in a cottage in the woods near a castle owned by two princes. In the same forest lives a wicked dwarf with magical powers who steals jewels from the castle. One day the princes see the dwarf stealing a load of jewels, and they chase him into the woods, where the dwarf turns one of the princes into a big brown bear. Snow White and Rose Red find the bear and shelter him from the winter and the hunters. A short time later, the enchanted prince again sees the dwarf carrying another sack of stolen treasures and chases him to the top of a high cliff. Unwilling to abandon the jewels, the wicked dwarf loses his balance and falls from the cliff. His death releases the evil spell, and the prince and his brother bring Snow White and Rose Red to their castle as their brides. *Royalty. Brothers. Sisters. Dwarfs. Magic. Theft. Marriage. Jewels. Spells. Bears.*

Note: Filmed in Bavaria. Released in West Germany in 1955 as *Schneeweisschen und Rosenrot*; running time: 62 min.

SNOW WHITE AND THE THREE STOOGES   **F6.4588**

Chanford Productions. *Dist* Twentieth Century–Fox Film Corp. 21 Jun **1961** [Philadelphia opening; c26 May 1961; LP19570]. Sd (Westrex); col (De Luxe). 35mm (CinemaScope). 107 min.

Prod-Story Charles Wick. *Dir* Walter Lang. *Screenplay* Noel Langley, Elwood Ullman. *Dir Photog* Leon Shamroy. *Art Dir* Jack Martin Smith, Maurice Ransford. *Set Decor* Walter M. Scott, Paul S. Fox. *Main Titl* Pacific Title. *Film Ed* Jack W. Holmes. *Mus Supv & Cond* Lyn Murray. *Orch* Arthur Morton, Edward B. Powell. *Songs:* "A Place Called Happiness," "I Said It Then, I Say It Now," "Because I'm in Love" Harry Harris. *Song:* "Once in a Million Years" Earl Brent. *Sp Material* Ivan Lane. *Ice Choreog* Ron Fletcher. *Sd* Arthur Kirbach, Frank W. Moran. *Asst Dir* Eli Dunn. *Cost Dsgn* Renie. *Makeup* Ben Nye. *Hairstyles* Helen Turpin. *Sp Photog Eff* L. B. Abbott, Emil Kosa, Jr.

Cast: Carol Heiss *(Snow White)*, The Three Stooges *(themselves)*, Edson Stroll *(Prince Charming)*, Patricia Medina *(The Queen)*, Guy Rolfe *(Count Oga)*, Michael David *(Rolf)*, Buddy Baer *(Mordred)*, Edgar Barrier *(King Augustus)*, Peter Coe *(captain)*, Lisa Mitchell *(Linda)*, Chuck Lacy *(Frederick)*, Owen McGivney *(physician)*, Sam Flint *(chamberlain)*, Blossom Rock *(servant)*, Robbi LaLonde *(Snow White, as a child)*.

Fantasy. Source: Jakob Grimm and Wilhelm Grimm, "Schneewittchen und die sieben Zwerge". In the faraway kingdom of Fortunia lives beautiful Princess Snow White, betrothed to the handsome Prince Charming of the neighboring land of Bravuria. As Snow White skates around the ice rink on her 17th birthday, her father, King Augustus, dies, and the princess is left at the mercy of her wicked stepmother, who is determined that Snow White will never replace her as queen. Encouraged by Oga, her sinister adviser, the queen orders her chief executioner to murder Snow White, but he allows her to escape into the forest. (Years before he also failed to carry out orders to kill Prince Charming.) Snow White happens upon the cottage of the Seven Dwarfs, which is occupied by the Three Stooges while the dwarfs are gold-prospecting in King Solomon's mines. The Three Stooges, traveling puppeteers, have adopted the prince and, unaware of his royal blood, have made him part of their medicine show. When the queen learns from her magic mirror that Snow White still lives, she transforms herself into a witch, flies to the cottage, and gets Snow White to take a bite from a poisoned apple that induces a sleep of death. As the queen rides homeward on her broom, the Three Stooges destroy her life forever by making a wish upon a magic sword they have taken from Oga. All ends happily as Prince Charming, after many perilous journeys, finds the sleeping princess and restores her to life with a magic kiss of love. *Royalty. Stepmothers. Executioners. Dwarfs. Puppeteers. Witches. Magic. Personal identity. Adoption. Ice skating. Medicine shows. Swords. Imaginary kingdoms. Snow White. Prince Charming.*

SO YOUNG SO BRIGHT (Japan)   **F6.4589**

Toho Co. *Dist* Topaz Film Corp. Mar **1963** [Los Angeles showing]. Sd; col (Eastmancolor). 35mm. 91 min.

Dir Toshio Sugie.

Cast: Hibari Misora, Chiemi Eri, Izumi Yukimura.

Musical drama. No information about the precise nature of this film has been found.

Note: Released in Japan in Nov 1955 as *Janken musume*.

SOCK IT TO ME BABY   **F6.4590**

Cinex Film Industries. 23 Oct **1968** [Boston opening]. Sd; b&w. 35mm. 87 min.

Prod Les Baker. *Exec Prod* Lou Campa. *Dir* Lou Campa. *Story & Screenplay* Ronald Edwards. *Dir Photog* Dave McKenna. *Asst Camera* Michael Rousch. *Film Ed* Lou Campa. *Songs:* "Sock It to Me Baby," "Waltz," "Blues Line" Darlene Cotton Quartet. *Incidental Mus & Songs:* "Cheetah," "Perfect Love" Year 2000. *Sd Rec* W. W. Lister. *Locations* Ron Vitello. *Coöp* John Liggio. *Grip* Gerard Damiano. *Stills* David Gerard.

Cast: Ileen Wreffer *(Tina)*, Larry Hunter *(Ron)*, Rosina Martin *(Betty)*, Dina St. Helena *(June)*, Gillian Martine *(Susan)*, Illya Souvern, Ron Wreffer, Bob Niles, Richard Bennett, actor, Patrice Dinehart, Richard Kennedy, Linda Herb, Theresa Faiello, Dotty Kaly, Jeanne Sarta, Alice Bozy, Carolyn Barbato, Tony La Rocca, Dom Conte.

Drama. For 15 years, Ron and June Baker have been man and wife in name only. Ron has never stopped seeing his sweetheart, Betty, and June has carried on lesbian affairs with every woman she could interest. Ron discovers that his wife has taken her blonde sexpot niece, Susan, as a lover. Later, returning home, he finds a teenage record club meeting in their living room. He discovers that his wife has been using the club to seduce young girls. Wandering over to a neighbor's house, he watches through a window as three boys take turns making love with Tina, the 15-year-old babysitter. He fights his desire to seduce the girl, but he succumbs to her aggressive advances a few days later. Their 2-week love affair comes to an end when Tina's three boyfriends return. Ron tries to throw them out; they threaten him, and he returns to his room to get drunk. Awakening, he calls Betty and blurts out a confession, asking her to marry him if he can get a divorce. She accepts. Ron surprises June and Tina naked together, and he departs to inform the police. *Aunts. Neighbors. Babysitters. Marriage. Infidelity. Lesbianism. Seduction. Group sex. Voyeurism. Promiscuity. Adolescence.*

Note: Also known as *Hot Blooded Gals*.

SOCK IT TO ME WITH FLESH *see* **I WANT MORE**

LE SOCRATE (France/West Germany)   **F6.4591**

C. E. C. R. T.–Bayerischer Rundfunk Telepool–O. R. T. F.–Jacques Pollet–Pierre Domec. *Dist* New Yorker Films. 9 Mar **1969** [New York opening]. Sd; col (Eastmancolor). 35mm. 90 min.

Prod Claude Nedjar. *Dir-Writ* Robert Lapoujade. *Adtl Dial* Colette Audry, Jean-Patrick Manchette. *Photog* Jean-Jacques Renon. *Film Ed* Jean Ravel. *Mus* Bernard Parmeggiani.

Cast: Pierre Luzan *(Le Socrate)*, R. J. Chauffard *(Lemay)*, Martine Brochard *(Sylvie)*, Stéphane Fay *(Pierre)*, Jean-Pierre Sentier *(Adam)*.

Satire. The eccentricities of Le Socrate, a philosopher who has divorced himself from materialistic society, attract attention, and a police officer is assigned to trail him. In due course, the policeman becomes a disciple, albeit unwilling, of the philosopher. Alarmed by her father's conversion, the policeman's daughter, aided by her nihilist lover, attracts the attention of the press to Le Socrate. The confrontation with public notoriety, however, destroys the visionary's peace of mind. *Philosophers. Police. Journalists. Middle classes. Publicity. Filial relations. Socrates.*

Note: Paris opening: Oct 1968.

SOD SISTERS   **F6.4592**

Popular Productions. Sep **1969** [c7 Mar 1969; LU3579]. Sd; b&w. 35mm. 74 min.

Prod J. T. Urishin, Rod Witmer. *Dir* Lester Williams. *Screenplay* Stan Potosky. *Photog* Rod Witmer. *Film Ed* J. T. Urishin. *Sd* Stan Potosky.

Cast: Genie Palmer *(Jeannie)*, Breege McCoy *(Lil)*, Hank Harrigan *(Zeb)*, Tim E. Lane *(Tom)*, James Schacht *(Hood)*, Glen Stannel *(Moose)*, Joseph Mikel, Lou Tu, Pat McLamry.

Crime melodrama. Tom, Hood, and Moose are involved in a robbery, and Tom is knocked unconscious and left by a mountain road. Hillbilly Zeb picks up Tom and takes him to his cabin. Tom revives but has completely forgotten his past life. Jeannie and Lil, Zeb's daughters, find the stranger attractive and take turns having sex with him, while Zeb spends his time protecting his moonshine stills from federal agents. When Hood and Moose finally discover Tom's mountain retreat, they refuse to believe that he cannot recall where the stolen money was hidden. One of the sisters finds the money, throws it into the river, and watches as the greedy men dive for it. *Robbers. Moonshiners. Sisters. Amnesia. Filial relations. Mountain life.*

Note: Alternative title: *Head for the Hills*.

SODOM AND GOMORRAH (United States/France/Italy)   **F6.4593**

Titanus–Pathé Cinéma–S. G. C. *Dist* Twentieth Century–Fox Film Corp. 23 Jan **1963** [New York opening; c31 Dec 1962; LP23723]. Sd; col (DeLuxe).

35mm. 154 min.

Pres by Goffredo Lombardo, Joseph E. Levine. *Prod* Goffredo Lombardo. *Exec Prod* Maurizio Lodi-Fe. *Dir* Robert Aldrich, Sergio Leone. *2d Unit Dir* Oscar Rudolph. *Screenplay* Hugo Butler, Giorgio Prosperi. *Photog* Silvano Ippoliti, Mario Montuori, Cyril Knowles. *Camera Op* Leonardo Bedini, Aldo DeRobertis. *Art Dir* Ken Adam. *Set Decor* Gino Brosio, Emilio D'Andria. *Prologue & Main Titl Dsgn* Maurice Binder. *Film Ed* Peter Tanner. *Mus* Miklos Rozsa. *Choreog* Archie Savage. *Sd* Kurt Doubravsky. *Eff Ed* Leslie Hodgson. *Asst Dir (see note)* Gus Agosti, Giorgio Contili, Franco Cirino, Benchekroun Larbi. *Prod Mgr* Giorgio Adriani, Giorgio Zambon, Mario Del Papa. *Cost* Giancarlo Bartolini Salimbeni. *Makeup* Euclide Santoli. *Hairstyles* Amalia Paoletti. *Sp Eff* Lee Zavitz, Serse Urbisaglia, Wally Veevers. *Dial Dir* Michael Audley.

Cast: Stewart Granger *(Lot)*, Pier Angeli *(Ildith)*, Stanley Baker *(Astaroth)*, Rossana Podestà *(Shuah)*, Anouk Aimée *(Queen Bera)*, Claudia Mori *(Maleb)*, Rik Battaglia *(Melchir)*, Giacomo Rossi Stuart *(Ishmael)*, Feodor Chaliapin *(Alabias)*, Aldo Silvani *(Nacor)*, Enzo Fiermonte *(Eber)*, Scilla Gabel *(Tamar)*, Antonio De Teffé *(captain)*, Gabriele Tinti *(lieutenant)*, Daniele Vargas *(Segur)*, Massimo Pietrobon *(Isaac)*, Andrea Tagliabue *(Eber's son)*, Francesco Tensi *(1st old man)*, Mitsuko Takara *(Orpha, the dancer)*, Liana Del Balzo *(Hebrew woman)*, Mimmo Palmara *(Arno)*, Ellen Kessler, Alice Kessler *(The Dancers)*, Giovanna Galletti *(Malik)*, Aldo Silvani *(Nacor)*, Vittorio Artesi *(Eber's other son)*, Primo Moroni *(2d old man)*.

Biblical epic. A group of Hebrews searching for a new home approach Sodom and Gomorrah, twin cities ruled by the ruthless Queen Bera. Bera permits the Hebrews to remain outside the cities and farm the land along the Jordan River, in the hopes that they will serve as a buffer against the fierce, nomadic Helamites, who have enlisted the aid of Bera's vice-ridden brother, Astaroth, in plotting to take control of the two cities. On the night of Lot's wedding to a former slave, Ildith, the Helamites attack the Hebrew camp; but Lot orders the destruction of a dam, and the Helamites are drowned in a raging flood. The Hebrews' lands are destroyed by the flood, and the grateful Bera allows the homeless people to move into Sodom, where they become enterprising salt sellers. Though Lot prospers, he gradually sees the corrupting influence of life in the city. Lot kills Astaroth, who has violated both of his daughters, and Bera has him imprisoned. Two angels appear before Lot and instruct him to lead his people away from the wickedness of the cities before sunset, when Jehovah will destroy both Sodom and Gomorrah. Lot, miraculously freed from his chains, assembles those who will heed his warning and leads them into the mountains. At sunset, the earth splits apart and the two cities burn to ashes. Ildith ignores the Lord's warning that "he who looks back upon the destruction of this place, does so in regret." As she turns her head toward her former home, a bolt of lightning cracks across the sky, and she turns into a pillar of salt. *Settlers. Royalty. Jews. Moral corruption. Rape. Revenge. Dams. Mines. Sodom and Gomorrah. Jordan River. Earthquakes. Floods. Prison escapes. Fires. Miracles. Lot. Ildith. Biblical characters.*

Note: Released in Italy in 1961 as *Sodoma e Gomorra*. Released in France in 1962 as *Sodome et Gomorrhe*. Gus Agosti is credited as 1st assistant director; Giorgio Contili is credited as 2d unit assistant director; Franco Cirino and Benchekroun Larbi are credited as assistant directors. One Italian source credits Dimitri Tiomkin with music.

SODOMA E GOMORRA *see* **SODOM AND GOMORRAH**

SODOME ET GOMORRHE *see* **SODOM AND GOMORRAH**

SOFI   **F6.4594**

Robert Carlisle Productions. *Dist* Golden Bear Films. 13 Dec **1967** [Los Angeles opening]. Sd; b&w. 35mm. 96 min. [Cut to 92 min.]

Prod-Dir Robert Carlisle. *Assoc Prod* John F. Meyers. *Screenplay* Don Eitner, Tom Troupe. *Photog* Alfred Taylor. *Art Dir* Michael Haller. *Main Titl* Vaccaro Associates, S. Hayaski. *Film Ed* Robert Grant, ed. *Mus* Allyn Ferguson. *Asst to the Prod* Sperry MacNaughton, Ruth Foster. *Makeup* Harry Thomas.

Cast: Tom Troupe *(The Clerk)*.

Drama. Source: Nikolay Vasilyevich Gogol, "Zapiski sumasshedshego," in *Arabeski* (1835). Don Eitner and Tom Troupe, *Diary of a Madman* (Los Angeles opening: caDec 1966). In 19th-century Russia an impoverished clerk lapses with increasing frequency into periods of paranoiac melancholia. Depressed by his lowly station in life and his frustrated love for the beautiful Sofi, his office director's daughter, he retreats from the world and seeks companionship only with his small wooden puppet. But even this in time depresses him, and he hurls the puppet into his stove. As the disintegration of his mind progresses, he becomes convinced that Sofi's dog will talk to him and reveal the secrets of its mistress' life. In a fit of dementia he constructs letters he imagines the dog has written. Eventually, when he learns that Sofi has married an Army officer, the clerk loses all touch with reality and believes

himself to be Ferdinand VIII, the fugitive king of Spain. Through the intervention of his landlady and his office co-workers, the clerk is declared insane and committed to an asylum. The ill treatment he receives there only increases his paronoiac belief that he is a man against the world. *Clerks. Landladies. Paranoia. Mental illness. Puppets. Insane asylums. Russia. Dogs.*

THE SOFT BODY OF DEBORAH *see* **THE SWEET BODY OF DEBORAH**

THE SOFT SKIN (France)   **F6.4595**

Films du Carrosse–S. E. D. I. F. *Dist* Cinema V Distributing, Inc. 12 Oct **1964** [New York opening; c20 May 1964; LP31860]. Sd; b&w. 35mm. 120 min.

Dir-Dial François Truffaut. *Orig Screenplay* François Truffaut, Jean-Louis Richard. *Dir Photog* Raoul Coutard. *Camera Op* Claude Beausoleil. *1st Asst Op* Georges Liron. *2d Asst Op* Denis Mornet. *Film Ed* Claudine Bouché. *Asst Film Ed* Lila Biro. *Mus* Georges Delerue. *1st & 2d Asst Dir* Jean-François Adam, Claude Othnin-Girard. *Prod Supv* Marcel Berbert. *Prod Mgr* Gérard Poirot. *Script Girl* Suzanne Schiffman. *Prod Sec* Lucette Desmouceaux, Yvonne Goldstein. *Wardrobe Mistress* Renée Rouzot. *Makeup* Nicole Félix. *Apprentice* Jean-Pierre Léaud. *Still Photog* Raymond Cauchetier. *Ch Electrn* Fernand Coquet. *Prop Master* Jean-Claude Dolbert. *Ch Engr* Bernard Largemains.

Cast: Jean Desailly *(Pierre Lachenay)*, Françoise Dorléac *(Nicole Chomette)*, Nelly Bénédetti *(Franca Lachenay)*, Daniel Ceccaldi *(Clément)*, Laurence Badie *(Ingrid)*, Jean Lanier *(Michel)*, Paule Emanuele *(Odile)*, Philippe Dumat *(Reims cinema manager)*, Pierre Risch *(canon)*, Dominique Lacarrière *(Pierre's secretary)*, Sabine Haudepin *(Sabine)*, Maurice Garrel *(bookseller)*, Gérard Poirot *(Franck)*, Georges de Givray *(Nicole's father)*, Charles Lavialle *(night porter at Hotel Michelet)*, Carnero *(Lisbon organizer)*, Catherine Duport *(young girl at Reims dinner)*, Maximilienne Harlaut *(Madame Leloix)*, Olivia Poli *(Madame Bontemps)*, Thérésa Renouard *(cashier)*, Brigitte Zhendre-Laforest *(linen deliverywoman)*, Jean-Louis Richard *(man in street)*.

Drama. Pierre Lachenay, successful literary magazine editor and family man, meets Nicole Chomette, an airline stewardess, while traveling to a lecture engagement in Lisbon; and they begin an affair that continues after their return to Paris. Because meetings are difficult, Pierre arranges a lecture trip to Reims so that they can be together; but the difficulties arising from his attempts to keep the affair secret from his lecture sponsors result in an awkward and unsuccessful time for the lovers. Upon his return to Paris, his suspicious wife, Franca, quarrels with him, and he leaves her, determined upon divorce and marriage to Nicole. But Nicole rejects his proposal, and Pierre fails to reach his wife by telephone to plan a reconciliation. Franca, having had her suspicion of his infidelity confirmed, goes to the restaurant where she knows she will find him and shoots him. *Editors. Lecturers. Airline stewardesses. Infidelity. Murder. Divorce. Marriage. Paris. Lisbon. Reims.*

Note: Exteriors filmed in Paris, Orly, and Lisbon. Opened in Paris in May 1964 as *La peau douce*; running time: 115 min.

SOFT SKIN AND BLACK LACE *see* **SOFT SKIN ON BLACK SILK**

SOFT SKIN ON BLACK SILK (France/Spain)   **F6.4596**

Pecsa Films–Contact Organisation–Sopadec–P. I. P.–Petrus. *Dist* Audubon Films. 13 Mar **1964** [Los Angeles showing]. Sd; b&w. 35mm. 90 min.

Pres by Radley H. Metzger. *Prod* René Thevenet. *Assoc Prod* Valentin Sallent, Jacques Garcia. *Dir* José Antonio de la Loma, Louis Duchesne. *Adtl Dir (see note)* Radley H. Metzger. *Orig Screenplay* José Antonio de la Loma, L. S. Poveda. *French Dial* Frédéric Dard. *English Dial* LaVerne Owens. *Dir Photog* Alfredo Fraile. *Art Dir* Alfonso de Lucas. *Film Ed (see note)* Louis Devaivre, Teresa Alcocer. *Mus (see note)* Daniel White, Federico Martinez Tudo. *Prod Mgr* Tony Belletier.

Cast: Agnès Laurent *(Theresa)*, Armand Mestral *(Don)*, Barbara Laage *(Isabelle)*, Vincent Parra *(André)*, Sandrine, José Marco Davó *(Mr. Michel)*, Maria Valence, Marujita Bustos, Queti Clavijo.

Players in domestically-filmed sequences: Edie Burke *(Nicole)*, Ira Lewis *(Roger)*.

Melodrama. Nicole meets Roger on a deserted Mediterranean beach and takes him to her villa, where he reveals his plan to kill Nicole's neighbor for seducing his fiancée. Nicole relates a story, hoping to discourage him: *André Michel, heir to his father's lucrative textile business, decides to become a priest. Mr. Michel contracts his debauched nephew Don to persuade André to abandon his plan. At a cabaret, André is attracted to Don's mistress, Theresa, an exotic dancer who agrees to encourage André's naive interest. When André learns of the plotting, he jealously hits Don and kills him.* Moved by this account, Roger nonetheless will not abandon his plan, claiming that his fiancée's seducer robbed him of the only woman he could love. Nicole seduces Roger and convinces him that his future is not so desolate. They part and promise to meet again. *Exotic dancers. Heirs. Priests. Cousins. Mistresses.*

Filial relations. Seduction. Jealousy. Revenge. Murder.

Note: Opened in Madrid in Jun 1959 as *Un mundo para mí;* opened in Paris in Mar 1960 as *Tentations.* Spanish and French sources credit various functions differently: Louis Devaivre is credited as editor by French source, while Spanish source credits Teresa Alcocer; Daniel White is credited with music by French source, while Spanish source credits Federico Martinez Tudo; Louis Duchesne is given co-director credit by French source only. Maria Valence may be a pseudonym for Marujita Bustos. It is reported that Radley Metzger cut 42 min from the original film and shot 40 min of footage to replace it; the original, abbreviated film becomes the story Nicole tells Roger on the beach. Tony Belletier is credited as production manager only by pressbook for U. S. version. American locations filmed at Montauk Beach, Long Island. May also be known as *Soft Skin and Black Lace.* Footage also included in *Dictionary of Sex,* q. v.

SOFT TOUCH OF NIGHT (Japan)   F6.4597

Tokyo Eiga Co. *Dist* Toho Co. 9 Aug **1961** [Los Angeles opening]. Sd; col (Eastmancolor). 35mm (Tohoscope). 106 min.

Dir Yuzo Kawashima.

Cast: Chikage Awashima, Michiyo Aratama, Tomoko Kawaguchi, Yunosuke Ito, Jun Tazaki, Frankie Sakai, Tatsuya Mihashi, Asami Kuji.

Drama. Although no information about the precise nature of this film has been found, sources indicate that the story concerns three sisters living in the Akasaka entertainment district of Tokyo. *Sisters. Tokyo.*

Note: Released in Japan in Nov 1960 as *Yoru no hada.*

A SOFT WARM EXPERIENCE *see* **THE SATIN MUSHROOM**

SOGEKI *see* **SUN ABOVE, DEATH BELOW**

SOL MADRID   F6.4598

Gershwin-Kastner Productions–Hall Bartlett Productions. *Dist* Metro-Goldwyn-Mayer, Inc. 7 Feb **1968** [San Francisco opening; c27 Dec 1967; LP35086]. Sd; col (Metrocolor). 35mm (Panavision). 90 min.

A Jerry Gershwin–Elliott Kastner Production. *Prod* Hall Bartlett. *Dir* Brian G. Hutton. *Screenplay* David Karp. *Dir Photog* Fred Koenekamp. *Art Dir* George W. Davis, Carl Anderson. *Set Decor* Henry Grace, Hugh Hunt. *Film Ed* John McSweeney. *Mus* Lalo Schifrin. *Rec Supv* Franklin Milton. *Asst Dir* William R. Finnegan. *Unit Prod Mgr* Robert Vreeland. *Miss Stevens' Cost Dsgn* Moss Mabry. *Makeup* William Tuttle. *Hairstyles* Sydney Guilaroff.

Cast: David McCallum *(Sol Madrid),* Stella Stevens *(Stacey Woodward),* Telly Savalas *(Emil Dietrich),* Ricardo Montalban *(Jalisco),* Rip Torn *(Dano Villanova),* Pat Hingle *(Harry Mitchell),* Paul Lukas *(Capo Riccione),* Michael Ansara *(Captain Ortega),* Perry Lopez *(hood #1),* Michael Conrad *(Scarpi),* Robert Rockwell *(Chief Danvers),* Merritt Bohn *(refinery engineer),* Madge Cameron *(woman in cantina),* Shepherd Sanders *(cantina operator),* Henry Escalante *(2d Dietrich gunman),* George Sawaya *(3d Dietrich gunman),* Ken Del Conte *(Joe Brighton),* Robert McNamara *(oilfield foreman),* Tony Barbario *(Stacey's dance partner).*

Action melodrama. Source: Robert Wilder, *Fruit of the Poppy* (New York, 1965). Harry Mitchell has absconded with $500,000 of Mafia leader Riccione's money, and Dano Villanova is assigned to kill him before he reveals any organization secrets to the police. At the same time, Sol Madrid, an undercover narcotics agent, begins a search for Mitchell, hoping to persuade him to testify against the Mafia. Madrid finds Villanova's former mistress, Stacey Woodward, who has half the stolen money, and learns from her that Mitchell is in Acapulco. Threatening to inform Villanova of her whereabouts, Madrid forces Stacey to accompany him to Mexico and there she introduces him to both Mitchell and Emil Dietrich, a leading supplier of heroin who has also recently broken with the Mafia. Posing as a border runner, Madrid works his way into Dietrich's confidence despite Mitchell's skeptical objections. With the assistance of Mexican agent Jalisco, Madrid spirits Stacey away in a yacht while he baits the final trap for the narcotics smugglers. But, before he can execute his final plan, she is kidnaped by Villanova and forcibly turned into a dope addict. Then, after Mitchell has been murdered, Madrid enlists local police assistance and learns that Jalisco is a Mafia payoff man. After shooting Dietrich, Madrid corners Jalisco, forces him to reveal Villanova's hiding place, and then kills him. Finally, Madrid tracks down Villanova in a dense jungle and disposes of him also; and in a hospital bed Stacey slowly recovers from her addiction. *Gangsters. Secret agents. Mistresses. Drug dealers. Drug addicts. Hired killers. Mexicans. Police. Murder. Theft. Extortion. Kidnaping. Imposture. Heroin. Acapulco. Mexico. Mafia.*

Note: Location scenes filmed in and around Acapulco.

SOLDATERKAMMERATER PÅ VAGT *see* **OPERATION CAMEL**

SOLDIER BLUE   F6.4599

Katzka-Berne Productions. *Dist* Avco Embassy Pictures. 12 Aug **1970** [New York opening]. Sd; col (Technicolor, print by Movielab). 35mm (Panavision). 112 min. *MPAA rating* R.

Prod Gabriel Katzka, Harold Loeb. *Exec Prod* Joseph E. Levine. *Assoc Prod* William S. Gilmore, Jr. *Dir* Ralph Nelson. *2d Unit Dir* Everett Creach. *Screenplay* John Gay. *Dir Photog (see note)* Robert Hauser, Arthur J. Ornitz. *Art Dir* Frank Arrigo. *Set Decor* Carlos Grandjean. *Film Ed* Alex Beaton. *Mus* Roy Budd. *Songs:* "Soldier Blue," "No One Told Me" *comp & sung by* Buffy Sainte-Marie. *Sd Effects* Barry Thomas. *Asst Dir* Terry Morse, Jr. *Prod Mgr* Antonio Guerrero, Jr. *Cost* Ted Parvin. *Makeup* Del Armstrong. *Hairstyles* Naomi Cavin. *Sp Eff* Herman Townsley. *Tech Adv* Eddie Little Sky.

Cast: Candice Bergen *(Cresta Marybelle Lee),* Peter Strauss *(Pvt. Honus Gant),* Donald Pleasence *(Isaac Q. Cumber),* Bob Carraway *(Lieut. John McNair),* Jorge Rivero *(Spotted Wolf),* Dana Elcar *(Captain Battles),* John Anderson *(Colonel Iverson),* Martin West *(Lieutenant Spingarn),* Jorge Russek *(Running Fox),* Marco Antonio Arzate *(Kiowa brave),* Ron Fletcher *(Lieutenant Mitchell),* Barbara Turner *(Mrs. Long),* James Hampton *(Private Menzies),* Mort Mills *(Sergeant O'Hearn),* Ralph Nelson *(Indian agent),* Aurora Clavel *(Indian woman).*

Western drama. Source: Theodore V. Olsen, *Arrow in the Sun* (New York, 1969). Cresta Marybelle Lee and Pvt. Honus Gant, the sole survivors of a Cheyenne massacre, set out for Fort Reunion. As they travel, the foulmouthed Cresta reveals that during two years of captivity she was the wife of Spotted Wolf, head of the raiding party, and that she now intends to marry Lieut. John McNair, her wealthy fiancé. Although menaced by a Kiowa band, the pair is allowed to proceed when Gant bests the Indian leader in a fight. When they encounter gunrunner Isaac Q. Cumber, however, Gant sets the saleman's store afire, and the infuriated Cumber shoots Gant in retaliation. In a secluded cave Cresta binds the soldier's wounds and the couple make love. Anxious for Gant's recovery, Cresta rushes to Fort Reunion. As she arrives, she learns that the cavalry is bound on a reprisal raid against the Cheyenne. Alarmed, she warns the tribe and discovers Spotted Wolf eager to make peace. Gant reaches the regiment as it, ignoring Spotted Wolf's white flag, massacres, mutilates, rapes, and pillages the Indian encampment. Horrified, he protests and is promptly arrested. Cresta chooses to remain among the survivors. *Cheyenne Indians. Kiowa Indians. Gunrunners. Massacres. Rape. Miscegenation. Forts. Caves. United States—History—Indian campaigns. United States Army—Cavalry.*

Note: Exterior scenes filmed in Mexico. Arthur Ornitz was replaced as photographer several weeks into production; Robert Hauser receives screen credit.

SOLDIER IN THE RAIN   F6.4600

Allied Artists–Cedar Productions–Solar Productions. *Dist* Allied Artists. 27 Nov **1963** [New York opening]. Sd; b&w. 35mm. 88 min.

A Blake Edwards Production. *Prod* Martin Jurow. *Assoc Prod* Dick Crockett. *Dir* Ralph Nelson. *Screenplay* Maurice Richlin, Blake Edwards. *Photog* Philip Lathrop. *Camera Op* Kyme Meade. *Asst Camera Op* Cliff King. *Art Dir* Phil Barber. James W. Payne. *Film Ed* Ralph Winters. *Mus Comp & Cond* Henry Mancini. *Sd* Carlton W. Faulkner, Al Cuesta. *Boom Op* Bill Hamilton. *Asst Dir* Austen Jewell. *Prod Mgr* J. Paul Popkin. *Script Supv* Meta Rebner. *Prod Sec* Doris Turner. *Wardrobe* Jerry Alpert, Shirlee Strahm. *Makeup* Bud Bashaw. *Hairstyles* Maryce Bates. *Sp Eff* Lawrence A. Hampton. *Dial Coach* Dan Frazer. *Prop* Robert Eaton, Stephen Ferry. *Grip* Murray Young. *Gaffer* Joe Edesa.

Cast: Jackie Gleason *(M/Sgt. Maxwell Slaughter),* Steve McQueen *(Supply Sgt. Eustis Clay),* Tuesday Weld *(Bobby Jo Pepperdine),* Tony Bill *(Pfc. Jerry Meltzner),* Tom Poston *(Lieutenant Magee),* Chris Noel *(Frances McCoy),* Ed Nelson *(MP Sergeant Priest),* Lew Gallo *(MP Sergeant Lenahan),* Rockne Tarkington *(1st Sergeant Booth),* Lewis Charles *(Sergeant Tozzi),* Sam Flint *(old man),* Paul Hartman *(chief of police),* Adam West *(Captain Blekeley),* John Hubbard *(battalion major).*

Comedy-drama. Source: William Goldman, *Soldier in the Rain* (New York, 1960). In a southern army camp, Sgt. Eustis Clay hopes that M/Sgt. Maxwell Slaughter will leave the service with him and become his business partner. However, Slaughter, who has his own air conditioner and a free soft drink machine, is content with army life and afraid to venture into the civilian world. Sergeant Clay introduces him to Bobby Jo Pepperdine, and together with Clay's girl, they double date. MP Sergeant Lenahan berates Bobby Jo for standing him up, and Bobby Jo is charmed when Slaughter forces the soldier to apologize to her. Later, when Clay gets into a brutal fight with his arch enemies, MP Sergeants Priest and Lenahan, Slaughter comes to his rescue but collapses from the exertion and is taken to the hospital. The next morning Slaughter talks to Clay of his dream of retiring to a Pacific island to relax and dream. But he dies and Clay reenlists, drinking a silent toast to his former pal. *Friendship. Military life. United States—South. United States Army.*

A SOLDIER'S PRAYER (Japan)   F6.4601

Ninjin Club–Shochiku Co. *Dist* Shochiku Films of America. 5 Aug **1970** [Los Angeles opening]. Sd; b&w. 35mm (Shochiku Grandscope). 190 min.

Prod Shigeru Wakatsuki, Masaki Kobayashi. *Dir* Masaki Kobayashi. *Screenplay* Masaki Kobayashi, Zenzo Matsuyama, Koichi Inagaki. *Photog* Yoshio Miyajima. *Art Dir* Kazue Hirataka. *Film Ed* Keiichi Uraoka. *Mus* Chuji Kinoshita.

Cast: Tatsuya Nakadai *(Kaji)*, Michiyo Aratama *(Michiko)*, Taketoshi Naito *(Private Tange)*, Keijiro Morozumi *(Corporal Hironaka)*, Yusuke Kawazu *(Private Terada)*, Kyoko Kishida *(Ryuko)*, Reiko Hitomi *(Umeko)*, Fijio Suga *(Captain Nagata)*, Nobuo Kaneko *(Corporal Kirahara)*, Tamao Nakamura *(female refugee)*, Hideko Takamine *(woman in settlers' village)*, Chishu Ryu *(village elder)*.

War drama. Source: Jumpei Gomigawa, *Ningen no joken*, vol 5 & 6 (Kyoto, 1958). Kaji, a Japanese soldier, faces the Russian invasion of Manchuria at the end of World War II. After his unit has been destroyed by Russian tanks, he surrenders to the advancing Russians, naively believing that they will treat prisoners of war in a more civilized manner than his own people have treated them. He soon learns, however, that he is again under the strict discipline of Japanese officers in the prison camp. At first Kaji believes that conditions would be better if he could communicate with the Russian soldiers, but he finally realizes that all captors are alike. His idealism shattered, he murders a man to avenge the death of a friend and then escapes from the camp. Hoping to be reunited with his wife, he attempts to cross the vast wastelands of Manchuria to reach her. In the end, his strength fails as he struggles through a blizzard, and he falls dead in the snow. *Russians. Idealists. Prisoners of war. Prison escapes. Revenge. Murder. World War II. Manchuria. Japan—Army. Union of Soviet Socialist Republics—Army. Blizzards.*

Note: Released in Japan in 1961 as *Ningen no joken III*. Film is the third part of the trilogy entitled *The Human Condition*, released in its entirety in Los Angeles in 1970. The other parts are *The Human Condition* (1959) and *Road to Eternity* (1961), q. v.

SOLDIERS 3 *see* **SERGEANTS 3**

SOLDIER'S WIFE *see* **I FEEL IT COMING**

LE SOLEIL DES VOYOUS *see* **ACTION MAN**

SOLEIL NOIR *see* **BLACK SUN**

SOLIMANO IL CONQUISTATORE *see* **SULEIMAN THE CONQUEROR**

SOLNTSE SVETIT VSEM *see* **THE SUN SHINES FOR ALL**

SOLO CONTRO ROMA *see* **ALONE AGAINST ROME**

SOLO FOR SPARROW (Great Britain)   **F6.4602**
Merton Park Studios. *Dist* Schoenfeld Film Distributing Corp. 11 May **1966** [Bay Shore, New York, opening]. Sd; b&w. 35mm. 56 min.

Prod Jack Greenwood. *Dir* Gordon Flemyng. *Screenplay* Roger Marshall. *Photog* Bert Mason. *Camera Op* Noel Rowland. *1st Camera Asst* Alan Rowland. *Art Dir* Peter Mullins. *Film Ed* Derek Holding. *Mus Dir* Bernard Ebbinghouse. *Sd Rec* Sidney Rider. *Boom Op* Tom Otter. *Sd Camera Op* Robin Clare. *1st, 2d & 3d Asst Dir* Ted Lewis, Al Burgess, Deh-Ta Hsiung. *Prod Mgr* Bill Shore. *Cont* Phyllis Townshend. *Wardrobe Mistress* Eileen Welch. *Makeup* Michael Morris. *Hairdresser* Hilda Fox. *Still Photog* Eddie Orton. *Casting Dir* Ronald Curtis. *Ch Electrn* Jim Axtell. *Prop Master* Ted Waters. *Constr Mgr* Eddie Turner. *Grip* Bert Habicht.

Cast: Anthony Newlands *(Mr. Reynolds)*, Glyn Houston *(Inspector Sparrow)*, Nadja Regin *(Mrs. Reynolds)*, Michael Coles *(Pin Norman)*, Allan Cuthbertson *(Chief Superintendent Symington)*, Ken Wayne *(Baker)*, Jerry Stovin *(Lewis)*, Jack May *(Inspector Hudson)*, Murray Melvin *(Larkin)*, Peter Thomas, actor *(Bell)*, Michael Caine *(Mooney)*, Neil McCarthy *(Dusty)*, Susan Maryott *(Sue Warren)*, Nancy O'Neil *(Miss Martin)*.

Crime melodrama. Source: Edgar Wallace, *The Gunner* (London, 1928). A gang of thieves led by Pin Norman abducts an elderly cashier for her keys to a jewelry store. The woman dies from suffocation, and the local police discover her corpse. Inspector Sparrow resents Scotland Yard's being called in on the case and takes leave unofficially to continue investigating on his own. Acting on a suspicion that Reynolds, the jewelry store owner, conspired with Norman, Sparrow is captured by Norman's gang. Sparrow's sergeant learns of the inspector's predicament from Sue, Sparrow's girl friend, and arrives in time to help apprehend the crooks after a shoot-out. *Thieves. Cashiers. Police. Jewelers. Abduction. Murder. Conspiracy. Scotland Yard.*

Note: Released in Great Britain in 1962.

SOM HAVETS NAKNA VIND *see* **ONE SWEDISH SUMMER**

SOME GIRLS DO *see* **THE GIRLS THAT DO**

SOME KIND OF A NUT (Reissue) (Great Britain)   **F6.4603**
E. J. Fancey Productions. *Dist* Albex Films, Jacon Film Distributors. ca **1963**. Sd; b&w. 35mm. 71 min.

Note: Released in Great Britain in 1952 as *Down Among the Z Men*. Released in the United States in 1959 by Albex Films as *Stand Easy*. Released by Jacon Film Distributors in 1965.

SOME KIND OF A NUT   **F6.4604**
Mirisch–DFI–T. F. T. Productions. *Dist* United Artists. 25 Sep **1969** [Denver, Colorado, opening; c24 Sep 1969; LP38113]. Sd; col (DeLuxe). 35mm. 89 min. *MPAA rating* M.

A Garson Kanin–Walter Mirisch Production. *Prod* Walter Mirisch. *Assoc Prod* Allen K. Wood. *Dir-Writ* Garson Kanin. *Dir Photog* Burnett Guffey, Gerald Hirschfeld. *Camera Op* Al Cline. *Art Dir* Albert Brenner. *Set Dsgn* Ward Preston. *Set Decor* Marvin March. *Film Ed* Richard Farrell. *Mus* Johnny Mandel. *Sd* Robert Martin. *Asst Dir* John C. Chulay, Chris Seitz. *Prod Supv* Edward Morey, Jr. *Prod Mgr* Terry Nelson. *Cost* Anthea Sylbert. *Makeup* Tom Tuttle. *Hairstyles* Cherie Huffman. *Sp Photog Eff* Jerome Rosenfeld. *Sp Eff* Justus Gibbs.

Cast: Dick Van Dyke *(Fred Amidon)*, Angie Dickinson *(Rachel Amidon)*, Rosemary Forsyth *(Pamela Anders)*, Zohra Lampert *(Bunny Erickson)*, Elliott Reid *(Gardner Anders)*, Steve Roland *(Baxter Anders)*, Dennis King, actor *(Otis Havemeyer)*, Pippa Scott *(Dr. Sara)*, Peter Brocco *(Mr. Suzuki)*, Robert Ito *(George Toyota)*, Peter Turgeon *(Mr. Defoe)*, Harry Davis *(Dr. Ball)*, Benny Baker *(cab driver)*, Lucy Saroyan *(Samantha)*, Roy Roberts *(1st vice president)*, Jonathan Hole *(2d vice president)*, Ned Wertimer *(Larry)*, Danny Crystal *(Dr. Abrams)*, Connie Gilchrist *(Mrs. Boland)*, Heywood Hale Broun *(himself)*, Milo Boulton *(bank guard)*, David Doyle, Carole Shelley.

Comedy. Bank teller Fred Amidon, who has 3 weeks before receiving the final divorce papers from his bossy wife, Rachel, is stung on the chin by a bee while having a picnic in Central Park with co-worker and fianceé, Pamela Anders. As a result, Fred is unable to shave during a cross-country vacation trip they take. Upon his return to the office, Fred decides, despite Pamela's objections, to keep his now fully-grown beard; and when his boss orders him to shave it off, Fred, who has been a lifelong conformist, refuses. He is promply fired, but he becomes a *cause célèbre*, for his fellow workers, who support him by growing beards and calling a sympathy strike. They are joined in the picket line by a group of hippies and a jazz band. Before long their demonstration attracts the attention of the news media and Fred becomes an overnight television celebrity. Though Rachel is impressed by her husband's new-found independence, Pamela is not, and she schemes to get rid of the beard and restore Fred's position. One night, she drugs Fred's champagne, waits for him to pass out, and enlists her two brothers in giving Fred a shave. Fred wakes up when the job is only half done; he flees, attired only in shoes, socks, and undershorts; is chased through the streets; and is eventually arrested in Central Park and taken to a psychiatric ward. Rachel bails him out and effects a reconciliation before their divorce decree becomes final. Once back in his apartment, Fred shaves off his beard—he never liked it anyway. *Bank clerks. Nonconformists. Hippies. Brothers. Divorce. Employer-employee relations. Marriage. Picnics. Beards. Strikes. Drugs. Television. Vacations. New York City. New York City—Central Park. Chases. Bees.*

Note: Location scenes filmed in New York City. Prerelease title: *The One With the Fuzz.*

SOME LIKE IT COOL (Great Britain)   **F6.4605**
S. F. Films. *Dist* Janus Films. 11 Aug **1961** [Los Angeles showing]. Sd; col (Eastman Color). 35mm. 61 min.

Prod Adrienne Fancey. *Exec Prod* B. C. Fancey. *Assoc Prod* Michael Winner. *Asst Prod* Malcolm Fancey. *Dir-Writ* Michael Winner. *Photog* Alex Sheridan. *Film Ed* Peter Austen-Hunt, Roy Smith, ed, Edna Dangerfield. *Mus Comp* Jackie Brown, Cy Payne. *Sd Rec* Peter Birch. *Asst Dir* Cino Bassi, Gerry Arbeid. *Coöp* The British Sunbathing Association, The Thames Sun Club, The Bristol Solarians Sun Club, The Minerva Sun Club, South Devon Naturist Hotel.

Cast: Julie Wilson *(Nancy)*, Wendy Smith *(Joy)*, Thalia Vickers *(Jill Clark)*, Brian Jackson *(Mike Hall)*, Mark Roland *(Roger)*, Douglas Muir *(Colonel Willoughby-Muir)*.

Melodrama. Jill Clark likes to sunbathe in the nude despite the disapproval of her fiancé, Roger. Jill's friends persuade her to join a nudist colony on an island in the Thames where she will be undisturbed. Roger and Jill get married; and at their wedding, Mike Hall, an American tourist, meets one of Jill's friends, Joy. Joy persuades Mike to go with her to a nudist camp in Devonshire. Jill, anxious to persuade Roger of the joys of nudism, takes her husband on a honeymoon near the island nudist camp. One day, their canoe overturns, and they swim to safety on the island. The next day Jill convinces Roger that he should become a nudist. Jill's parents arrive, suspicious that Jill is being corrupted, but they too become nudists in a short time. The proprietor of a nearby hotel is forced to close because of the competition of the nudist camp. The nudists throw a farewell party for him. He sees the free and open life of the nudists and decides to join the colony. *Tourists. Hotelkeepers. Nudism. Honeymoons. Filial relations. Islands. Nudist camps. Weddings. Hotels. Thames River. Devonshire (England).*

Note: Opened in London in May 1961.

SOME LIKE IT VIOLENT   **F6.4606**

Barry Mahon Productions. *Dist* W. G. B. ca **1968**. Sd; b&w. 35mm. 72 min.

A Barry Mahon Production. *Prod-Dir* Kemal Horulu.

Cast: Bob O'Connell.

Crime melodrama. Johnny Scaro, a sadistic, big-time hoodlum, searches for a way to put his call girls back to work in the wake of police department raids on his houses of prostitution. With the help of his lawyer, Dapper Dan, he takes over a lonely-hearts computer "dating club." The client pays a fee to join the club, and he is matched with a woman by computer, so that no money changes hands. Scott, a young vice squad lieutenant, sets out to destroy Scaro with the aid of Dolores, the embittered daughter of another detective murdered by Scaro. She joins the club and finds that Scaro is trying to enlarge his collection of women by recruiting legitimate club members as high-priced computer call girls. To help resolve the case, she agrees to let Scaro approach her, and she fills out her computer card so as to attract his attention. He takes her out, offers her work with his prostitution ring, and rapes her. She passes on all she knows to the police, who place her under protective guard. Scaro tries to murder Dolores in her home and is killed by Scott. He and Dolores discover that they have fallen in love. *Detectives. Hoodlums. Lawyers. Prostitution. Rape. Murder. Sadism. Imposture. Computer dating services.*

SOME PEOPLE (Great Britain)   **F6.4607**

Vic Films. *Dist* American International Pictures. Jun **1964**. Sd; col (Eastmancolor). 35mm. 93 min.

Prod James Archibald. *Assoc Prod* Michael Birkett. *Dir* Clive Donner. *Screenplay* John Eldridge. *Photog* John Wilcox. *Art Dir* Reece Pemberton. *Film Ed* Fergus McDonell. *Mus* Ron Grainer. *Songs* Ron Grainer, Johnny Worth. *Rock Numbers Played by* The Eagles, British. *Sd* Robert Allen.

Cast: Kenneth More (*Mr. Smith*), Ray Brooks (*Johnnie*), Annika Wills (*Anne*), David Andrews (*Bill*), Angela Douglas (*Terry*), David Hemmings (*Bert*), Timothy Nightingale (*Tim*), Frankie Dymon, Jr. (*Jimmy*), Harry H. Corbett (*Johnnie's father*), Fanny Carby (*Johnnie's mother*), Michael Gwynn (*vicar*), Cyril Luckham (*magistrate*), Fred Ferris (*clerk of the court*), Richard David (*Harper*), Dean Webb (*Mike*).

Melodrama. Johnnie, Bill, and Bert, three teenaged factory workers, enjoy their motorcycles until a dangerous incident causes them to lose their licenses. After being thrown out of a youth club for opening up a locked piano, they go to a church where the vicar catches them playing rock and roll music on the organ. Mr. Smith, the organist and choirmaster, is sympathetic, however, and offers them the choir hall to practice their music. Smith, who is working on a secret aircraft project, is also in charge of the Duke of Edinburgh's Award Scheme, in which all of the choir members are participating. After Johnnie has a brief romance with Smith's daughter Anne, Bill breaks away from the group and leads a gang attack on the church hall. Johnnie, ashamed of his former friend, is reluctant to return to his new friends, but Smith convinces him to come back and he receives a hearty welcome. *Motorcyclists. Clergymen. Organists. Gangs. Adolescence. Vandalism. Rock and roll. Duke of Edinburgh's Award Scheme.*

Note: Released in Great Britain in Aug 1962.

SOMEONE   **F6.4608**

Bizarre Productions. *Dist* Continental Theatres. Dec **1968**. Sd; col (Eastmancolor). 16mm. 80 min.

Prod-Dir Pat Rocco. *Screenplay* Edward Middleton. *Photog* Pat Rocco. *Film Ed* Pat Rocco.

Cast: Joe Adair (*model*), Bambi Allen (*young girl*), David Russell (*hustler*), Joe Caruso (*photographer*), Kay Hall (*pianist*).

Melodrama. The film focuses on a male fashion model and his search for sexual identity. Working for a lecherous photographer who wants more from his subject than professional work, the model seeks the affection of a young woman only to discover that he cannot relate sexually to women. Frustrated and insecure, the model at first runs to a street-hustling homosexual but finds the change too drastic and instead returns to accept the advances of the photographer. *Models. Photographers. Male homosexuality. Prostitution. Impotence.*

SOMETHING FOR EVERYONE   **F6.4609**

Media Productions. *Dist* National General Pictures. 22 Jul **1970** [New York opening; c15 Jul 1970; LP39820]. Sd; col (Eastman Color). 35mm. 110 min. *MPAA rating* R.

Pres by Cinema Center Films. *Prod* John P. Flaxman. *Dir* Harold Prince. *2d Unit Dir* George Tyne. *Screenplay* Hugh Wheeler. *Cinematog* Walter Lassally. *Art Dir* Otto Pischinger. *Set Dsgn* Herta Pischinger. *Titl Paintings* Tom Morrow. *Film Ed* Ralph Rosenblum. *European Ed* Barry Peters. *Mus* John Kander. *Mus Dir* Harold Hastings. *Song:* "Weil du so schön tanzen kannst" Hans Otter. *Song:* "Das kleine Rendezvous" Karl Schachinger, Max Schachinger. *Song:* "Geh' alte Schau mi net so teppart an" Friedl Szalat, Bert Ull, Ernst Geiger. *Sd Ed* Robin Gregory. *Sd Mix* John Strauss. *Asst Dir* Eberhard Schröder. *Prod Supv* Michael F. Johnson. *Prod Mgr* Georg M. Reuther. *Unit Mgr* Wolfram Kohtz. *Asst to the Prod* Bud Rosenthal. *Prod Sec* Arlene Caruso, Johanna Haass. *Script Supv* Trudy von Trotha. *Cost Dsgn* Florence Klotz. *Wardrobe Supv* Irms Pauli. *Makeup* Raimund Stangl. *Hairdresser* Susanne Krause. *Hairstyles* Gordon Bond. *Prop Master* Georg Attlfellner.

Cast: Angela Lansbury (*Countess Herthe von Ornstein*), Michael York (*Conrad Ludwig*), Anthony Corlan (*Helmuth von Ornstein*), Heidelinde Weis (*Annaliese Pleschke*), Eva-Maria Meineke (*Mrs. Pleschke*), John Gill (*Mr. Pleschke*), Jane Carr (*Lotte von Ornstein*), Despo (*Bobby*), Wolfried Lier (*Klaus*), Walter Janssen (*Father Georg*), Klaus Havenstein (*Rudolph*), Enzi Fuchs (*waitress*), Erland Erlandson (*Schoenfeld*), Hans Possenbacher (*Carl*), Hilde Weisner (*Princess Palamir*), Hela Gruel (*cook*), Marius Aicher (*scullery boy*), Mogens von Gadow (*station master*), James F. Hurley (*general*), Ernst Zeigler (*elderly man*), Erik Jelde.

Comedy-drama. Source: Harry Kressing, *The Cook* (New York, 1965). Young Conrad Ludwig, bicycling through the Bavarian Alps, comes upon the Castle Ornstein. Conrad, who longs to live in a castle, immediately sets out to ingratiate himself with the Countess von Ornstein, whose noble title belies her dwindling finances. He becomes acquainted with Rudolf, the von Ornstein's footman, and after getting him thoroughly drunk, pushes him in front of a train; the enterprising young man is soon hired as Rudolf's replacement. Three obstacles remain in his path: the countess's son Helmuth, her obese daughter Lotte, and Klaus, the faithful butler. Conrad seduces Helmuth, but they are observed by Klaus, who threatens to inform the countess. When Conrad denounces him as a neo-Nazi, Klaus is exiled from the town, and Conrad replaces him as butler. For his next move, Conrad arranges a marriage between Helmuth and Annaliese Pleschke, the daughter of wealthy American tourists. After the marriage Annaliese discovers Conrad and Helmuth embracing and threatens to expose her husband and his lover. While taking the Pleschke family for a scenic drive, Conrad drives the car over a cliff, leaping to safety at the last moment. Lotte, who has observed Conrad's intrigues, blackmails him into marrying her, thus blocking his final move toward the countess. *Opportunists. Nobility. Butlers. Americans in foreign countries. Murder. Male homosexuality. Slander. Marriage—Arranged. Blackmail. Castles. Bavaria. Alps. Drunkenness. Automobile accidents.*

Note: Location scenes filmed in Füssen, Bavaria, and Salzburg, Austria. Formerly titled: *The Rook.*

SOMETHING OF VALUE *see* **AFRICA ABLAZE**

SOMETHING WEIRD   **F6.4610**

Hur-Lew Productions. *Dist* Mayflower Pictures. **1967** [San Antonio, Texas, opening: 27 Mar 1968]. Sd; col. 35mm. 83 min.

Prod-Writ James F. Hurley. *Dir* Herschell Gordon Lewis. *Photog (see note)* Herschell Gordon Lewis, Andy Romanoff.

Cast: Tony McCabe, Elizabeth Lee, William Brooker, Mudite Arums, Ted Heil, Lawrence J. Aberwood, Stan Dale, Ione.

Horror film. Horribly disfigured when burned by a high-tension wire, electrical engineer Cronin Mitchell discovers that he has acquired powers which allow him to read minds and move objects. As a masked fortune-teller, he enters into a bargain with Ellen Parker, an ugly witch, becoming her lover in return for her giving him a handsome face. The combination of beauty and extrasensory power brings Mitchell fame. Accompanied by Ellen—who is beautiful to all but her lover—Mitchell is called to a Midwestern town to help the police solve a series of bewildering crimes. There, Ellen is wooed by playboy Dr. Alex Jordan, an ESP expert sent by federal authorities to observe Mitchell. Alerted by Ellen, Mitchell telekinetically causes Jordan's bedclothes to strangle him, but Jordan escapes. Mitchell predicts an attempt on his life by Maddox, a local police detective responsible for the crimes, but he is killed nonetheless when Jordan delays the police. After killing Maddox, Jordan sees Ellen as she really is and flees. She causes him to fall and burn his face, then offers to restore it in exchange for his love. *Engineers—Electrical. Fortune-tellers. Witches. Playboys. Detectives. Disfiguration. Magic. Telekinesis. Murder. Extrasensory perception. Masks. United States—Midwest.*

Note: Filmed in Chicago in 1966; working title: *The Eerie World of Dr. Jordan.* Sources conflict in crediting photographer.

SOMETHING WILD F6.4611

Prometheus Enterprises. *Dist* United Artists. 23 Dec **1961** [New York opening; c20 Dec 1961; LP21508]. Sd; b&w. 35mm. 112 min.

Prod George Justin. *Dir* Jack Garfein. *Screenplay* Jack Garfein, Alex Karmel. *Camera* Eugen Shuftan. *Art Dir* Richard Day. *Titl* Saul Bass. *Film Ed* Carl Lerner. *Mus Comp & Cond* Aaron Copland. *Asst Dir* Jim Di Gangi, Angelo Laiacona. *Prod Asst* Warren Lyons. *Cost* Frank Thompson.

Cast: Carroll Baker (*Mary Ann*), Ralph Meeker (*Mike*), Mildred Dunnock (*Mrs. Gates*), Charles Watts (*Warren Gates*), Jean Stapleton (*Shirley Johnson*), Martin Kosleck (*landlord*), Ken Chapin (*manager of 5 & 10*), Clifton James (*Detective Bogarde*), George L. Smith (*policeman*), Warren Lyons (*college student*), Duke Howard (*young boy*), Tanya Lopert, Peg Shirley, Virginia Baker, Doris Roberts, Anita Cooper (*girls in 5 & 10*), Jane MacArthur, Roger Dekoven, Logan Ramsey, William Hickey, Nancy Baker, Diane Ladd, Reid Cruickshanks, Evelyn Wall.

Melodrama. Source: Alex Karmel, *Mary Ann* (New York, 1958). One spring evening a young, innocent girl named Mary Ann is savagely raped by an unknown assailant in a New York City park. When she regains consciousness, she returns home and sneaks past her prudish mother. She then destroys her soiled, torn clothes, scrubs herself with hard laundry soap, and, wrapped in a blanket, goes to sleep on the floor of her room. The next morning she attempts to go on living her routine life as though nothing had happened. But, overcome by physical weakness and repulsed by the crowding flesh around her, she collapses on a subway platform. Still haunted by her ordeal, she leaves home, moves into a shabby room on the Lower East Side, and takes a job in a five-and-ten-cent store. Eventually, after a series of sleepless nights, she wanders onto a suspension bridge and attempts suicide. She is rescued by a lonely garage mechanic, Mike, who takes her back to his basement flat. Almost as desperate as she, he keeps her prisoner, explaining that she is his "last chance" for happiness. She fights him off when he drunkenly attempts to make love to her, and, in a hysterical effort to escape, she kicks out his eye. Fleeing from the apartment, she spends the night sleeping on the grass in Central Park. With the coming of morning, she wanders through the city, reviewing her life. At the end of the day, she returns to Mike's two basement rooms and offers to marry him. A few months later she is reconciled with her mother and tells her that she is going to have a baby. *Mechanics. Hostages. Adolescence. Rape. Innocents. Filial relations. Suicide. Marriage. Drunkenness. New York City—Lower East Side. New York City—Central Park.*

Note: Filmed in New York City.

SOMETHING WORTH REMEMBERING see FULFILLMENT, SOMETHING WORTH REMEMBERING

SOMETHING'S HAPPENING see THE HIPPIE REVOLT

ETT SOMMARÄVENTYR see ANNA, MY DARLING

SOMMERSPROSSEN see BEYOND CONTROL

SON OF A GUNFIGHTER (United States/Spain) F6.4612

Lester Welch–Zurbano Films. *Dist* Metro-Goldwyn-Mayer, Inc. 31 Mar **1966** [San Antonio, Texas, opening; c31 Dec 1964; LP31994]. Sd (RCA); col (Metrocolor). 35mm (CinemaScope). 92 min.

Prod Lester Welch. *Assoc Prod* Sam X. Abarbanel, Gregorio Sacristan. *Dir* Paul Landres. *Screenplay* Clarke Reynolds. *Photog* Manuel Berenguer. *Camera Op* Manuel Berenguer, Jr. *Art Dir* Julio Molina. *Set Decor* José María Tapiador. *Film Ed* Sherman Rose. *Mus Theme* Robert Mellin. *Mus Arr & Dir* Frank Barber. *Sd Ed* Kurt Herrnfeld. *Sd Rec* Ben Winkler. *Asst Dir* Joe Ochoa. *Cont* Isabel Ruiz Capillas. *Wardrobe* Flora Salamero. *Makeup* Carmen Martín. *Hairdresser* Josefa Rubio Martos.

Cast: Russ Tamblyn (*Johnny*), Kieron Moore (*Deputy Fenton*), James Philbrook (*Ketchum*), Fernando Rey (*Don Fortuna*), Maria Granada (*Pilar*), Aldo Sambrell (*Morales*), Antonio Casas (*Pecos*), Barta Barri (*Esteban*), Ralph Browne (*sheriff*), Andy Anza (*Fuentes*), Fernando Hilbeck (*Joaquin*), Hector Quiroga (*stagecoach guard*), Carmen Tarrazo (*Maria*), Maria José Collado (*Sarita*), Julio Pérez Tabernero.

Western melodrama. In 1877, the Mexican-American border country is terrorized both by a gang of outlaws headed by Ketchum and by Mexican bandits led by Morales. The local sheriff and his half-Mexican, half-Texan deputy, Fenton, accompany a stagecoach carrying a shipment of gold and pick up a young sharpshooter, Johnny. Ketchum's gang attacks the coach, but Johnny, whose hatred of the outlaw is apparent, helps the lawmen to drive away the robbers. Later, Morales' bandits attack a cattle ranch belonging to Don Fortuna, and Johnny is wounded in the shoulder as he saves the rancher's life. Don Fortuna's daughter, Pilar, nurses him back to health and falls in love with him, but he leaves her to pursue Ketchum, whom he blames for his mother's death. Deputy Fenton accompanies him to obtain the reward offered for Ketchum. Eventually they find the outlaw, but he refuses to draw his gun

against Johnny, revealing that the young sharpshooter is his son. Fenton, who has joined forces with Morales in his eagerness to collect the reward money, wounds Ketchum as the Mexicans attack. Johnny rescues his father, and the two men ride back to Don Fortuna's hacienda. Johnny evolves a plan for outwitting the Mexicans. The bandits are driven off, but Ketchum and Morales meet their deaths in the final shootout. Now able to settle down, Johnny obtains Don Fortuna's permission to marry Pilar. *Gunfighters. Outlaws. Bandits. Sheriffs. Ranchers. Mexicans. Halfcastes. Filial relations. Murder. Stagecoach robberies. Revenge. Rewards. Mexican border.*

Note: Opened in Madrid in Aug 1965 as *El hijo del pistolero*.

THE SON OF CAPTAIN BLOOD (United States/Italy/Spain) F6.4613

C. C. M.-Producciones Benito Perojo. *Dist* Paramount Pictures. 18 Mar **1964** [Los Angeles opening; c31 Dec 1963; LP27747]. Sd; col (Technicolor). 35mm (CinemaScope). 88 min. [Copyright length: 95 min.]

A Harry Joe Brown Production. *Prod* Harry Joe Brown. *Exec Prod* Benito Perojo. *Dir* Tulio Demicheli. *Story-Orig Screenplay* (see note) Casey Robinson, Mario Caiano. *Script* Giuseppe Masini. *Dir Photog* Alejandro Ulloa. *2d Unit Photog* Yakima Canutt. *Art Dir* Piero Filippone, Enrique Alarcón. *Film Ed* Renato Cinquini, Antonio Ramirez. *Mus* Gregorio García Segura, Angelo Francesco Lavagnino. *Asst Dir* Yakima Canutt.

Cast: Sean Flynn (*Robert Blood*), Alessandra Panaro (*Abbigail*), José Nieto (*de Malagon*), Ann Todd (*Arabella Blood*), John Kitzmiller (*Moses*), Raffaele Baldassarre (*Bruno*), Fernando Sancho (*Timothy*), Roberto Camardiel (*Orguelthorpe*), Carlos Casaravilla, Luisa De Cordoba, Ray Martino, Simonetta Simeoni, Ettore Ribotta, Angeles Macua.

Adventure melodrama. Based on characters created by: Rafael Sabatini. Young Robert Blood and his mother, Ann, live in Port Royal in the Caribbean. The young Blood is inspired by the legend of his late father, the notorious Peter Blood, a surgeon who was sold into slavery and became a pirate. Robert wants to follow in his father's footsteps and go to sea, but Ann has encouraged him to become a doctor. She finally grants permission, and Robert signs on as navigator aboard a small ship bound for England. On board he meets Abbigail, and they fall in love. The ship is captured by de Malagon, a pirate who was an enemy of Robert's father, and who delights in discovering Robert's identity. Robert and Abbigail are rescued by a group of pirates who once sailed under his father, and together they become involved in a series of battles and adventures. They return to Port Royal in time to rescue Mrs. Blood and the islanders from a severe earthquake and tidal wave. Robert and his pirates are granted pardons because of their bravery, as his father also was pardoned for turning on the enemies of England. A free man who has had an adventuresome excursion into piracy, Robert decides to settle down with Abbigail and become a doctor. *Pirates. Physicians. Sailors. Filial relations. Seafaring life. Piracy. Caribbean. England. Earthquakes. Tidal waves.*

Note: Filmed in Spain and released there as *El hijo del Capitán Blood*. Released in Italy in 1962 as *Il figlio del Capitano Blood* at 95 min. Most sources credit only Casey Robinson with screenplay, but one foreign source adds Mario Caiano; one Italian source credits Giuseppe Masini with script.

SON OF FLUBBER F6.4614

Walt Disney Productions. *Dist* Buena Vista Distribution Co. 16 Jan **1963** [Los Angeles opening; c1 Dec 1962; LP23502]. Sd (RCA); b&w. 35mm. 100 min.

Pres by Walt Disney. A Walt Disney Production. *Assoc Prod* Ron Miller. *Co-prod* Bill Walsh. *Dir* Robert Stevenson. *2d Unit Dir* Arthur J. Vitarelli. *Screenplay* Bill Walsh, Don DaGradi. *Dir Photog* Edward Colman. *Art Dir* Carroll Clark, William H. Tuntke. *Set Decor* Emile Kuri, Hal Gausman. *Film Ed* Cotton Warburton. *Mus* George Bruns. *Orch* (see note) Walter Sheets, Franklyn Marks. *Sd Supv* Robert O. Cook. *Sd Mix* Dean Thomas. *Mus Ed* Evelyn Kennedy. *Asst Dir* Joseph L. McEveety. *Cost Dsgn* Bill Thomas. *Cost* Chuck Keehne, Gertrude Casey. *Makeup* Pat McNalley. *Hairstylist* Ruth Sandifer. *Sp Eff* Eustace Lycett, Peter Ellenshaw, Robert A. Mattey, Jack Boyd, Jim Fetherolf.

Cast: Fred MacMurray (*Prof. Ned Brainard*), Nancy Olson (*Betsy Brainard*), Keenan Wynn (*Alonzo Hawk*), Tommy Kirk (*Biff Hawk*), Elliott Reid (*Shelby Ashton*), Joanna Moore (*Desiree de la Roche*), Leon Ames (*Pres. Rufus Daggett*), Ed Wynn (*A. J. Allen*), Ken Murray (*Mr. Hurley*), Charlie Ruggles (*Judge Murdock*), William Demarest (*Mr. Hummel*), Bob Sweeney (*Mr. Harker*), Paul Lynde (*sportscaster*), Stuart Erwin (*coach*), Edward Andrews (*defense secretary*), Alan Hewitt (*prosecutor*), Leon Tyler (*Humphrey*), Forrest Lewis (*Officer Kelly*), James Westerfield (*Officer Hanson*), Alan Carney (*referee*), Lee Giroux (*newscaster*), Jack Albertson (*Mr. Barley*), Eddie Ryder (*Mr. Osborne*), Harriet MacGibbon (*Mrs. Daggett*), Beverly Wills (*mother*), Wally Boag (*father*), Wed Miller (*Baby Walter*), Robert Shayne (*assistant to defense secretary*), Henry Hunter (*admiral*), Hal Smith (*bartender*), J. Pat O'Malley (*sign painter*), Norman Grabowski (*Rutland football player #33*), Gordon Jones (*Rutland coach*), Lindy Davis (*newsboy*

Joey Marriano), Hope Sansberry (secretary), Byron Foulger (proprietor), Jack Rice, Dal McKennon (jurors), Burt Mustin (#1 bailiff), Ned Wynn (Rutland student manager).

Comedy. Source: Jay Williams and Raymond Abrashkin, "Danny Dunn" books. Samuel W. Taylor, "A Situation of Gravity," in *Liberty Magazine* (22 May 1943). Prof. Ned Brainard of Medfield College goes to Washington, D.C., to sell to the Defense Department his anti-gravitation invention, flying rubber, or "flubber." He hopes the government will purchase his invention so that he may help Medfield pay off its mortgage owed to loan shark Alonzo Hawk, who is eager to foreclose and use the school property for a business enterprise. Congress refuses to approve the expenditure, and Ned returns to Medfield emptyhanded and unable, for national security reasons, to sell flubber privately. Undaunted, the professor continues to experiment with other inventions, including a weather gun (a machine to promote rainfall) and a flubbergas suit for football players. Domestic strife further complicates Ned's life when his wife, Betsy, becomes jealous of the attentions paid to him by his ex-sweetheart, Desiree de la Roche, and she leaves him. Moreover, Ned's experiments with the weather gun cause all the glass in town to shatter. Alonzo, whose insurance company must pay the claims for the broken glass, traces the damage to Ned and threatens legal action. By this time, though, Ned is busy perfecting a flubbergassed football suit invented by his student Bill Hawk, Alonzo's son. The invention works, helping Medfield win the game, but the victory is clouded by Ned's trial. County agricultural agent A. J. Allen testifies that a beneficial effect of Ned's weather gun, which he calls "dry rain," has resulted in bumper crops. To prove his claim, Allen exhibits mammoth vegetables and an enormous chicken egg. The judge dismisses the case, and Ned, now a hero, is reunited with Betsy. *Professors. Loan sharks. Students. Judges. College life. Insurance. Weather. Jealousy. Gravitation. Inventions. Mortgages. Football. Trials. Rubber. Washington (District of Columbia). United States Congress. United States—Defense Department.*

Note: A sequel to *The Absent-Minded Professor*, q. v. Published sources credit Marks with orchestration; the studio continuity names Sheets.

SON OF GREETINGS *see* HI, MOM!

SON OF SAMSON (France/Italy/Yugoslavia)   F6.4615
Jolly Film–Gallus Films–C. I. C. C.–Dubrava Film. *Dist* Medallion Pictures. 2 Jun **1962** [New York opening]. Sd; col (Eastmancolor). 35mm (TotalScope). 89 min.

Pres by Samuel Schneider. *Prod* Ermanno Donati, Luigi Carpentieri. *Dir* Carlo Campogalliani. *Screenplay* Oreste Biancoli, Ennio De Concini. *Photog* Riccardo Pallottini. *Art Dir* Oscar D'Amico. *Film Ed* Roberto Cinquini. *Mus Comp* Carlo Innocenzi. *Mus Cond* Carlo Franci. *Choreog* Tito LeDuc. *Sd* Leopoldo Rosi. *Asst Dir* Mate Relja, Romolo Girolami. *Cost* Maria De Matteis.

Cast: Mark Forest (*Maciste*), Chelo Alonso (*Queen Smedes*), Angelo Zanolli (*Kenamun*), Vira Silenti (*Tekaet*), Federica Ranchi (*Nofret*), Carlo Tamberlani (*Armitec*), Petar Dobrić (*vizier*), Nino Musco (*Nenneka*), Ignazio Dolce, Zvonimir Rogož, Andrea Fantasia, Mario Girotti, Ada Ruggeri.

Adventure melodrama. A wave of terror sweeps across Egypt when the aged Pharaoh Armitec is murdered; his young Persian wife, Queen Smedes, has entire villages burned and sells the survivors into slavery to the Persians. As part of her plan to turn Egypt over to the Persians, she has also captured her stepson Kenamun and, by keeping him drugged, has forced him to consent to their marriage. Then Maciste, the legendary son of Samson, arrives and performs great feats of strength and courage, constantly routing the queen's slavedrivers. Maciste goes to the capital city of Tanis to find his long-time friend Kenamun, and Smedes tries to seduce him, but when he rejects her, she has him thrown into the dungeons. He escapes and leads the slaves in a mass revolt. In the ensuing battle, Smedes is killed when she falls into a crocodile pit. With the queen's evil spell broken, Kenamun assumes the throne, peace returns to Egypt, and Maciste rides off to the mountains. *Royalty. Persians. Stepmothers. Slavery. Feats of strength. Revolts. Drugs. Egypt—Ancient. Maciste. Crocodiles.*

Note: Opened in Paris in Mar 1961 as *Le géant de la vallée des rois*; in Rome in Dec 1960 as *Maciste nella valle dei re*; running time: 95 min.

SON OF THE RED CORSAIR (Italy)   F6.4616
Panda Film. *Dist* Medallion Pictures. 11 Dec **1963** [New York showing]. Sd; col (Eastman Color). 35mm (Totalscope). 97 min.

Prod Ermanno Donati, Luigi Carpentieri. *Dir* Primo Zeglio. *Screenplay* Alberto Liberati, Fede Arnaud, Primo Zeglio. *Photog* Carlo Carlini. *Art Dir* Mario Chiari, Alfredo Montori. *Mus* Roman Vlad. *Cost* Maria De Matteis.

Cast: Lex Barker (*Enrico di Ventimiglia*), Sylvia Lopez (*Carmen di Montelimar*), Vira Silenti (*Neala*), Luciano Marin, Luigi Visconti, Saro Urzì, Antonio Crast, Vicki Lagos, Elio Pandolfi, Franco Fantasia, Diego Michelotti, Livio Lorenzon, Nietta Zocchi.

Adventure melodrama. Source: Emilio Salgari, *Il figlio del Corsaro Rosso* (Florence, 1920). Enrico di Ventimiglia, son of the famous "Red Corsair" who was killed by the governor of Panama, leads his band of pirates in capturing a Spanish galleon carrying Van Hais, who betrayed Enrico's father to the governor. To save his life, Van Hais reveals that Neala, Enrico's wealthy sister, believed to be dead, is alive and serving as a governess to Carmen di Montelimar, the governor's sister-in-law. Soon after arriving at Carmen's palace in Cartagena, Enrico is accused of kidnaping Neala; Carmen, who has loved Enrico, believes the story and turns against him. Neala is actually a prisoner of the governor, who wants to marry her for her money. He orders the execution of her fiancé, who is Carmen's brother, and then tortures Carmen until Neala agrees to marry him. The wedding is interrupted by Enrico, who defeats the governor in a duel and rescues Carmen and Neala. *Pirates. Traitors. Territorial governors. Governesses. Sisters-in-law. Revenge. Abduction. Brother-sister relationship. Torture. Murder. Weddings. Panama. Cartagena. Duels.*

Note: Opened in Rome in Aug 1960 as *Il figlio del Corsaro Rosso*.

THE SONG AND THE SILENCE   F6.4617
Cloverhouse Films. 2 Feb **1969** [New York opening]. Sd; b&w. 35mm. 80 min.

Pres by Nathan Silberberg. *Prod-Dir-Writ* Nathan Cohen. *Photog* Nathan Cohen. *Mus* Nathan Cohen.

Cast: Annita Koutsouveli (*Rivkeh Shlomo*), Harry Rubin (*Rabbi Shlomo*), Jim Murphy, actor (*Fievel*), Nana Austin (*Mrs. Shlomo*), Mary Antoianette (*Channaleh*), Jonathan Scott (*David Shlomo*), Harry Leshner (*principal*), Felix Fiebich (*matchmaker*).

Drama. A group of Hasidic Jews live in peace in a small Polish community in 1939. While Rabbi Shlomo is somewhat apprehensive about his son David's unritualistic interpretation of the Torah, his concern is offset by his delight in the love his daughter Rivkeh has for Fievel, a rabbinical student. At first Fievel resists the efforts of a matchmaker to arrange a wedding, maintaining that he must first complete his studies, but eventually he consents to the marriage. Then, without warning, the Nazis arrive, round up the members of the community, and shoot them. After the execution has been carried out and the soldiers have left, the Aryans in the village pick up the routine of their daily lives, apparently indifferent to the tragedy that has taken place. *Hasidim. Rabbis. Ministerial students. Matchmakers. Nazis. Village life. Filial relations. Genocide. World War II. Poland. The Torah.*

Note: Location scenes filmed at Kiamesha Lake in the Catskill Mountains.

SONG XV *see* XV SONG TRAITS

THE SONG FROM MY HEART (Japan)   F6.4618
Shochiku Co. *Dist* Shochiku Films of America. Jan **1970** [Los Angeles showing]. Sd; col (Eastmancolor). 35mm (Shochiku GrandScope). 99 min.

Assoc Prod Koichi Enatsu, Saburo Muto. *Dir* Noboru Nakamura. *Screenplay* Sakae Hirosawa, Noboru Nakamura. *Story* Hitomi Yamaguchi, Soji Yoshino. *Photog* Hiroshi Takemura. *Art Dir* Chiyoo Umeda. *Mus* Masaru Sato.

Cast: Kanzaburo Nakamura (*Hideo Yoshino*), Shima Iwashita (*Tomiko*), Kaoru Yachigusa (*Hatsuko*), Katsuo Nakamura (*Koichi*), Muga Takewaki (*Kenji*), Sanae Kitabayashi (*Motoko*), Ken Ogata (*Hitomi Yamaguchi*), Mitsuyo Kamei (*Mitsuyo*), Sadako Sawamura (*Hitomi's mother*), Norihei Miki (*Kasui Wakabayashi*), Anna Losen, Hideko Okiyama, Kankuro Nakamura, Seitaro Okamura, Ushio Akashi, Jun Kojima, Nobuo Takagi, Reijiro Osugi, Kosaku Mizuno, Keiko Sawai, Kosaku Yamayoshi, Yoji Toki, Hideaki Komori, Sanzaemon Nakamura, Koyu Tsuruta, Takashi Suga, Noriyuki Watanabe, Eriko Wada, Nobuko Suzuki, Naoki Izumi, Reiko Mizuki.

Biographical drama. Lisa Jacobsen, a Swedish student studying in Japan, learns that one of her classmates, Kenji, is the son of the famous poet, Hideo Yoshino, whom she is eager to meet. The interview begins badly when Lisa frankly asks Yoshino if he writes about sex. Yoshino's first marriage, with Hatsuko, was a happy one, producing three children, Motoko, Koichi, and Kenji. Although the family was poor, Hatsuko managed the home well, while Yoshino wrote much of his best poetry. Hatsuko died, however, and after World War II, Yoshino spent more time taking care of the family and less time writing. Finally, he married Tomiko, his housekeeper, and he was able to concentrate once again on his art. Motoko is now married, but because of her fierce loyalty to her mother, she rarely visits her home. Koichi, with only one lung, lives in a sanatorium, and Kenji lives at home. The two sons both get along with Tomiko, but they feel inadequate in the shadow of their father's talent. Kenji leaves home to become more independent, and Koichi runs away from the sanatorium to try painting. On his deathbed, Yoshino is reconciled with Kenji and leaves one last poem. *Poets. Students. Swedes. Housekeepers. Invalids. Family life. Marriage. Fatherhood. World War II. Hideo Yoshino.*

Note: Released in Japan in Oct 1969 as *Waga Koi waga uta*. Japanese sources indicate that Hideo Yoshino either collaborated on the original story or wrote an autobiographical novel; but because he died in 1967 and publication is unconfirmed, Yoshino's participation in the film is questionable.

SONG OF NORWAY F6.4619

ABC Pictures. *Dist* Cinerama Releasing Corp. 4 Nov **1970** [New York opening]. Sd; col (De Luxe). 35mm & 70mm (Super Panavision). 142 min. *MPAA rating* G.

An Andrew L. Stone-Virginia Stone Production. *Prod* Andrew L. Stone, Virginia Stone. *Dir-Screen Story-Screenplay* Andrew L. Stone. *2d Unit Dir* Yakima Canutt. *Anim Dir* Jack Kinney. *Photog* Davis Boulton. *2d Unit Photog* Terry Gould. *Art Dir* William Albert Havemeyer. *Film Ed* Virginia Stone. *Mus* Robert Wright, George Forrest. *Based on the Work of* Edvard Grieg. *Mus Supv, Orch & Cond* Roland Shaw. *Piano Concerto played by* London Symphony Orchestra. *London Symphony Orchestra Cond* Oivin Fjeldstad. *Piano Soloist* John Ogdon, Brenda Lucas. *Violin Soloist* Manoug Parikian. *Choreog* Lee Theodore. *Sd Ed* Virginia Stone. *Sd Rec* John Purchese. *Asst Dir* John O'Connor. *2d Unit Asst Dir* Leif Jul. *Prod Mgr* Peter Crowhurst, Ted Wallis. *2d Unit Prod Mgr* Fred Slark. *Cost* David Walker, Fiorella Mariani. *Museum Coöp* Old Town (Aarhus, Denmark), Funen Village (Odense, Denmark), Old Bergen (Bergen, Norway), De Sandvigske Semlinger (Lillehammer, Norway), Transportation Museum (Hammer, Norway), Folk Museum (Oslo, Norway).

Cast: Toralv Maurstad *(Edvard Grieg)*, Florence Henderson *(Nina Grieg)*, Christina Schollin *(Therese Berg)*, Frank Porretta *(Rikard Nordraak)*, Harry Secombe *(Bjørnsterne Bjørnson)*, Robert Morley *(Berg)*, Edward G. Robinson *(Krogstad)*, Elizabeth Larner *(Mrs. Bjørnson)*, Oscar Homolka *(Engstrand)*, Frederick Jaeger *(Henrik Ibsen)*, Henry Gilbert *(Franz Liszt)*, Richard Wordsworth *(Hans Christian Andersen)*, Bernard Archard *(George Nordraak)*, Susan Richards Chitty *(Aunt Aline)*, John Barrie *(Hagerup)*, Wenke Foss *(Mrs. Hagerup)*, Ronald Adam *(Gade)*, Carl Rigg *(Captain Hansen)*, Aline Towne *(Mrs. Thoresen)*, Nan Munro *(irate woman)*, James Hayter *(Berg's butler)*, Avind Harum *(Freddie)*, Rolf Berntzen *(doctor)*, Tordis Maurstad *(Mrs. Schmidt)*, Erik Chitty *(Helsted)*, Charles Lloyd Pack *(Chevalier)*, Robert Rietty *(Winding)*, Rosalind Speight, Ros Drinkwater *(Liszt's friends)*, Tracey Crisp *(Scandinavian Club receptionist)*, Cyril Renison *(Therese's Rome butler)*, Manoug Parikian *(violinist)*, Richard Vernon *(1st councilman)*, Ernest Clark *(2d councilman)*, Eli Lindtner *(Bjørnson's secretary)*, Ilse Tromm *(girl's mother)*, Jeffrey Taylor, Peter Salmon, Roy Jones, Gordon Coster, Paddy McIntyre, Barrie Wilkinson, Rupert Lupone, Stephen Reinhardt, Jane Darling, Barbara von der Heyde, Hermione Farthingale, Jennie Walton, Michele Hardy, Susan Claire, Denise O'Brien, Jane Kells *(dancers)*.

Musical drama. Source: Milton Lazarus, Robert Wright and George Forrest, *Song of Norway* (New York opening: 21 Aug 1944). Homer Curran, *Song of Norway* (an unpublished play). A concert by composer Edvard Grieg is arranged by the wealthy Therese Berg. Therese's father, however, opposes her infatuation and exacts a promise that she will not see the musician again. His recital a success, Grieg travels to Copenhagen, where he marries his cousin Nina and is influenced by the works of Rikard Nordraak. News of the death of Therese's father reaches Grieg on his wedding day. The couple moves to Kristiania, where the composer hopes to be appointed conductor at the national theater. His disappointment at the loss of this appointment is intensified by the failure of a concert series secretly sponsored by Therese. Winning a stipend for foreign travel, Grieg moves to Rome. There he meets Franz Liszt and collaborates with Henrik Ibsen on *Peer Gynt*. Learning of Nordraak's death, Grieg returns to Kristiania and Nina. *Songs:* "Opening Piano Concerto—'The Life of a Wife of a Sailor'" (Orchestra & Chorus), "Freddie & His Fiddle" (Children & Chorus), "Strange Music" (Grieg), "The Song of Norway" (Nordraak), "A Rhyme & a Reason" (Nina), "The Little House" (Nordraak), "Hill of Dreams" (Nina, Nordraak & Grieg), "I Love You" (Nina), "Hymn of Betrothal" (Chorus), "Be a Boy Again" (Nordraak), "Midsummer's Eve, Hand in Hand" (Chorus), "Three There Were" (Nordraak), "The Solitary Wanderer" (Nina), "A Welcome Toast" (Bjørnson), "Wrong To Dream" (Nina), "Solvejg's Song—Norwegian National Anthem" (Chorus), "Grieg's Piano Concerto" (Orchestra), "At Christmas Time," "John Heggerstrom," "When We Wed," "Ribbons and Wrappings." *Composers. Cousins. Patrons. Ambition. Marriage. Rome. Copenhagen. Kristiania. Edvard Hagerup Grieg. Franz Liszt. Henrik Ibsen. "Peer Gynt".*

Note: Location scenes filmed in Norway.

SONG OF THE FOREST (U.S.S.R.) F6.4620

Dovzhenko Film Studio. *Dist* Artkino Pictures. **1963**. Sd; col. 35mm. 95 min. [Soviet running time.]

Dir-Writ Viktor Ivchenko. *Story Ed* N. Orlova. *Photog* A. Prokopenko. *Asst Camera* N. Andreychuk, O. Glushchuk. *Art Dir* V. Agranov. *Asst Art Dir* M. Tereshchenko. *Film Ed* L. Mkhitaryants. *Mus* I. Shamo. *Mus Arr* I. Klyucharyov. *Cond* V. Tolba. *Ballet Dir* Ye. Vislotskaya. *Sd* R. Bisnovataya. *Asst Dir* V. Konarskiy. *Prod Mgr* M. Rotleyder. *Cost* Ya. Dobrovolskaya. *Makeup* Ya. Grinberg. *Sp Eff* V. Kurach, V. Deminskiy. *Pyrotechnics* N. Suprun.

Cast: Raisa Nedashkovskaya *(Mavka)*, V. Sidorchuk *(Lukash)*, P. Vesklyarov *(Uncle Lev)*, V. Rudin *(Spirit of the Forest)*, V. Kvitka *(Forest Fire)*, V. Gubenko *(Lukashi's mother)*, R. Pirozhenko *(Kilina)*, R. Doroshenko, A. Rogovtseva *(nymphs)*, Lyudmila Marchenko *(Kuts)*, N. Tayenko *(water sprite)*, Ye. Kharchenko *("fever")*, V. Maksimenko *("one who sits on the rocks")*, Borya Voblyy, Yura Barantsev *(Kilina's children)*, Ira Semko, Seryozha Shiman.

Fantasy. Source: Lesya Ukrainka, *Lisova pisnya: drama-feeriya* (Kiev? 1911). Mavka, a water nymph, loves Lukash, a country youth. Their brief happiness ends when Lukash is forced to marry the shrewish Kilina. The Spirit of the Forest turns Lukash into a wolf as punishment for his infidelity. The strength of Mavka's love breaks the spell, but Kilina curses the nymph, transforming her into a weeping willow. Lukash is ordered to cut down the tree, but the Forest Fire, who also loves Mavka, embraces her; and she is consumed in a bright flame. *Fairies. Shrews. Marriage—Arranged. Infidelity. Spells. Magic. Curses. Forests. Trees. Forest fires. Wolves.*

Note: Released in the U.S.S.R. in Aug 1961 as *Lesnaya pesnyá*.

SONG OF THE LOON F6.4621

Sawyer Productions. *Dist* Hollywood Cinema Associates. 11 Mar **1970** [Los Angeles opening]. Sd; col (Eastman Color). 35mm. 79 min.

Prod Richard Amory. *Dir* Andrew Herbert. *Dir Photog* Robert Maxwell. *Film Ed* Andrew Herbert. *Coöp* United States Forest Service.

Cast: Jon Iverson *(Cyrus Wheelwright)*, Morgan Royce *(Ephraim MacIver)*, Lancer Ward *(John)*, Jon Evans *(Montgomery)*, Brad Fredericks *(Mr. Calvin)*, John Kalfas *(Singing Heron)*, Martin Valez *(Acomas)*, Michael Traxon *(Tiasholah)*, Lucky Manning *(Bear-Who-Dreams)*, Brad Della Valle *(Tsi-Nokha)*, John Drake *(Luke)*, Robert Vilardi *(Plum-of-the-Night)*.

Drama. Source: Richard Amory, *Song of the Loon* (New York, 1966). A romantic story of homosexuality takes place in the 1870's in the mountains of northern California. An old trapper, Calvin, tells how his lost lover, Ephraim, became upset by promiscuity among homosexuals, and how he, Calvin, sent Ephraim to visit an Indian medicine man who convinced him that sexual love should not necessarily be restricted to one partnership. With his views thus liberalized, Ephraim moved on to find further fulfillment. *Trappers. Medicine men. Indians of North America. Male homosexuality. Mountain life. California.*

Note: Location scenes filmed in California's Trinity Alps and the Big Pines National Reserve.

SONG OVER MOSCOW (U.S.S.R.) F6.4622

Lenfilm. *Dist* Artkino Pictures. 21 Nov **1964** [New York opening]. Sd; col. 35mm. 92 min.

Dir Gerbert Rappaport. *Libretto* Vladimir Zakharovich Mass, Mikhail Abramovich Chervinskiy. *Story Ed* I. Glikman. *Photog* Anatoliy Nazarov. *Camera* K. Solovyov, A. Chirov. *Art Dir* M. Gaukhman-Sverdlov. *Film Ed* K. Kozyreva. *Mus* Dmitriy Dmitriyevich Shostakovich. *Cond* N. Rabinovich. *Ballet Master* K. Boyarskiy. *Sd* G. Elbert. *1st & 2d Asst Dir* L. Makhtin, N. Okuntseva, A. Matusov. *Prod Mgr* A. Arshanskiy. *Cost* L. Shildknekht. *Makeup* M. Matusova, N. Elenbogen. *Sp Eff* M. Shamkovich, M. Krotkin.

Cast: Olga Zabotkina *(Lida)*, Vladimir Vasilyev *(Boris)*, M. Khotuntseva *(Masha)*, Grigoriy Bortnikov *(Sasha)*, Svetlana Zhivankova *(Lyusya)*, V. Zemlyanikin *(Sergey)*, Vasiliy Merkuryev *(Drebednev)*, Marya Polbentseva *(Vava)*, Ye. Leonov *(Barabashkin)*, Fyodor Nikitin *(Baburov)*, Konstantin Sorokin *(Kurochkin)*, R. Zelyonaya *(Kurochkina)*, S. Filippov *(Mylkin)*, E. Treyvas *(Mylkina)*, M. Pugovkin *(Kovalyov)*.

Vocalists: A. Aleksandrovich, A. Zilbert, Z. Rogozikova, T. Glinkina, G. Mnatsakanova, E. Khil.

Operetta. Source: Dmitriy Dmitriyevich Shostakovich, Vladimir Zakharovich Mass and Mikhail Abramovich Chervinskiy, *Moskva, Cheryomushki* (Moscow opening: 24 Jan 1959). Lida Baburova, a lecturer at the Museum of the History and Reconstruction of Moscow, lives with her father in an old, cramped apartment. One day they are delighted to learn that they are to receive a large new apartment in the housing development of Cheryomushki. Sergey, the chauffeur friend of Lida's admirer Boris, drives them to visit their new quarters. Another of the new tenants is Lyusya, a crane operator with whom Sergey has long been in love without daring to declare himself. Newlyweds Masha and Sasha also await the move eagerly. The tenants are forced to reckon with the hard-hearted superintendent Barabashkin, who holds them at his mercy and refuses to turn over the keys. When at last they are able to enter the new apartments, Lida and her father discover that Drebednev, a minor official, has been permitted by Barabashkin to expand his quarters to include the Baburovs' apartment. Lida and her father are helped by their friends to regain their rightful home; and Sergey's romance with Lyusya also prospers. *Lecturers. Newlyweds. Chauffeurs. Apartment house managers. Housing. Urban life. Bureaucracy. Museums. Moscow. Museum of the History*

and Reconstruction of Moscow.
Note: Released in the U.S.S.R. in Apr 1963 as *Cheryomushki.*

SONG 27 *see* **MY MOUNTAIN, SONG 27**

SONG XXIII *see* **23RD PSALM BRANCH**

EL SONIDO DE LA MUERTE *see* **SOUND OF HORROR**

EL SONIDO PREHISTÓRICO *see* **SOUND OF HORROR**

LA SONRISA DE LA VIRGEN *see* **LITTLE ANGEL**

SONS AND DAUGHTERS   **F6.4623**
American Documentary Films. 21 Apr **1967** [San Francisco showing]. Sd;
b&w. 35mm. 98 min.
   Dir-Writ Jerry Stoll. *Narr* David Castro. *Photog* Stephen Lighthill. *Film Ed*
Sally Pugh, Jerry Stoll, Stephen Lighthill. *Mus Comp & Perf by* Jon Hendricks,
Virgil Gonsalves, The Grateful Dead.
   Narrator: Janet Pugh.
   Documentary. The Vietnam War protest movement from the student point
of view is the basis for this documentary shot in the San Francisco Bay area
and dealing mainly with a protest march from the University of California to
the Oakland Army Terminal in 1966. *Students. Demonstrations. Vietnam War
1964–73. San Francisco. Oakland (California). University of California.*

SONS AND MOTHERS (U.S.S.R.)   **F6.4624**
Gorky Film Studio. *Dist* Brandon Films, Artkino Pictures. 30 Oct **1967**
[New York opening]. Sd; b&w. 35mm (Sovscope). 95 min.
   Dir Mark Donskoy. *Screenplay* Zoya Voskresenskaya, Irina Donskaya.
Photog Mikhail Yakovich. *Art Dir* Boris Dulenkov. *Mus* R. Khozak. *Sd*
Anatoliy Dikan. *Asst Dir* Ye. Lunina.
   Cast: Yelena Fadeyeva (*The Mother, Mariya Aleksandrovna Ulyanova*),
Daniil Sagal (*The Father, Ilya Nikolayevich Ulyanov*), Nina Menshikova
(*Anna*), Gennadiy Chertov (*Aleksandr*), Rodion Nakhapetov (*Vladimir Ilich*),
Nina Vilvovskaya (*Olga*), Andrey Bogoslovskiy, Yuriy Solomin (*Dmitriy*),
Olya Izgorodina, Svetlana Balashova (*Mariya*), Georgiy Yepifantsev
(*Yelizarov*), V. Safonov (*Ishcherskiy*), Fyodor Nikitin (*Neklyudov*), V. Mizin
(*Gorchilin*), N. Ashikhmyan (*Pashka*), V. Churkin (*Fedka*), V. Salin (*Lenka*).
   Biographical drama. In the small town of Simbirsk in 1886, Mariya
Aleksandrovna Ulyanova is left a widow at an early age. With four children
remaining at home and two others away at university in St. Petersburg, Mariya
Aleksandrovna guides the family. Her husband, Ilya Nikolayevich, a school
inspector, had been concerned with the welfare of the oppressed peasants, and
the children, too, are concerned with social issues. The oldest son, Aleksandr,
and a daughter, Anna, are arrested in St. Petersburg as participants in a plot to
assassinate Tsar Aleksandr III, and although their mother journeys to the city
in an attempt to save them, Aleksandr refuses to voice remorse and is executed;
and Anna is sent into exile. The family moves to Samara to join her, while the
youngest son, Vladimir, deeply affected by his brother's death, studies law. He
is placed under surveillance for participating in university disturbances and,
through his mother's efforts, joins the family in Samara. He begins his law
practice here but longs to return to St. Petersburg to be in the midst of social-
democratic activities. Fully aware of the dangers that lie ahead, Mariya
Aleksandrovna sends the other children to Moscow and accompanies her son
on the beginning of a long journey that will ultimately lead to his renown
throughout the world as Nikolai Lenin. *Widows. School inspectors.
Revolutionaries. Lawyers. Motherhood. Family life. Capital punishment. Exile.
Simbirsk. Saint Petersburg. Samara. Mariya Aleksandrovna Ulyanova. Ilya
Nikolayevich Ulyanov. Nikolai Lenin. Aleksandr Ilich Ulyanov. Anna
Ilinichna Yelizarova-Ulyanova.*
   Note: Released in the U.S.S.R. in 1966 as *Serdtse materi.*

SONS OF GOOD EARTH (Hong Kong)   **F6.4625**
Shaw Brothers (H. K.) Ltd. *Dist* Frank Lee International. 15 Sep **1967** [New
York opening]. Sd; b&w. 35mm. 120 min.
   Prod Run Run Shaw. *Dir-Writ* Hu Chin-chuan.
   Cast: Peter Chen Ho (*Yu Jui*), Betty Loh Tih (*Lotus*), King Chuan (*Tiger
Ting*), Julia Hsia (*Mrs. Li Meng-shih*), Chen Yen Yen (*Mrs. Tien*).
   War drama. During the Japanese occupation of Manchuria, Yu Jui, his wife,
Lotus, and their friend Tiger Ting are Chinese patriots who wage guerrilla
warfare against the invaders, finally driving them out of the Manchurian village
they had taken over. *Guerrillas. Japanese. Sino-Japanese Conflict 1937–45.
Manchuria.*
   Note: No information on the original title or release of this film has been
found.

THE SONS OF KATIE ELDER   **F6.4626**
Hal Wallis Productions. *Dist* Paramount Pictures. 23 Jun **1965** [Chicago
opening; c24 Jun 1965; LP30968]. Sd; col (Technicolor). 35mm (Panavision).

122 min.
   Prod Hal B. Wallis. *Assoc Prod* Paul Nathan. *Dir* Henry Hathaway.
Screenplay William H. Wright, Allan Weiss, Harry Essex. *Story* Talbot
Jennings. *Cinematog* Lucien Ballard. *Art Dir* Hal Pereira, Walter Tyler. *Set
Decor* Sam Comer, Ray Moyer. *Film Ed* Warren Low. *Mus* Elmer Bernstein.
Sd Harold Lewis. *Asst Dir* D. Michael Moore. *Prod Mgr* Frank Caffey. *Cost*
Edith Head. *Sp Eff* Bob Peterson.
   Cast: John Wayne (*John Elder*), Dean Martin (*Tom Elder*), Martha Hyer
(*Mary Gordon*), Michael Anderson, Jr. (*Bud Elder*), Earl Holliman (*Matt
Elder*), Jeremy Slate (*Deputy Sheriff Ben Latta*), James Gregory (*Morgan
Hastings*), Paul Fix (*Sheriff Billy Wilson*), George Kennedy (*Curley*), Dennis
Hopper (*Dave Hastings*), Sheldon Allman (*Judge Harry Eyers*), John Litel
(*minister*), John Doucette (*undertaker Hyselman*), James Westerfield (*banker
Vannar*), Rhys Williams (*Charlie Bob Striker*), John Qualen (*Charlie Biller*),
Rodolfo Acosta (*Blondie Adams*), Strother Martin (*Jeb Ross*), Percy Helton
(*storekeeper Peevey*), Karl Swenson (*Doc Isdell*), Harvey Grant (*Jeb*), Jerry
Gatlin (*Amboy*), Loren Janes (*Ned Reese*), Red Morgan (*Burr Sandeman*),
Chuck Roberson (*townsman*), Ralph Volkie (*bit man*), Jack Williams (*Andy
Sharp*), Henry Wills (*Gus Dolly*), Joseph Yrigoyen (*Buck Mason*).
   Western drama. Katie Elder's four sons return to Clearwater, Texas, for her
funeral. John, the eldest, is a notorious gunslinger, and of the four, only Bud,
who has been going to college, shows signs of being responsible. The brothers
learn that Pa Elder supposedly got drunk and gambled away the family ranch
and was killed on the same night. They decide to investigate the peculiar
circumstances and unearth the truth, despite warnings from the sheriff to stay
out of trouble. Morgan Hastings and his son Dave had been the only witnesses
to the events. In order to protect themselves, the Hastings kill the sheriff, and
the Elder brothers, whose reputations were poor to begin with, are blamed. The
deputy sheriff swears in a group of Hastings' men to take the Elders to Laredo,
unaware that they have been ordered to slaughter the Elders. In the gunfight
that ensues, Matt Elder and the deputy sheriff are killed; and those of Hastings'
men who escape return to tell that they were ambushed by John Elder's gang.
The Elders return to town to get medical attention for Bud; John tells the judge
what really happened; and the judge consents to his request that the brothers
surrender to a U. S. marshal. Meanwhile, Tom sneaks away and captures Dave
Hastings to force from him a confession. When Morgan Hastings goes to rescue
Dave, he shoots his son by mistake. Before he dies, Dave reveals that his father
shot Pa Elder. Tom, who is mortally wounded, makes John responsible for
Bud's upbringing. John engages Morgan Hastings in a gun duel and kills him.
Mary, who was a friend of Katie Elder and a close observer of the recent events,
assures John that Bud will survive. *Gunfighters. Students. Brothers. Sheriffs.
Judges. Gambling. Murder. Frameup. Ranches. Funerals. Texas. Laredo.
Mexico.*
   Note: Partly filmed in Mexico on the northern plateau and in the Sierra
Madre Occidental.

SOPHIE'S PLACE (United States/Great Britain)   **F6.4627**
Herman Cohen Productions. *Dist* Warner Bros.–Seven Arts, Inc. 4 Nov
1970 [Los Angeles opening; c2 Apr 1969; LP42913]. Sd; col (Technicolor).
35mm. 106 min. MPAA rating GP.
   A Herman Cohen Production. *Prod* Herman Cohen. *Assoc Prod* Clifford
Parkes. *Dir-Writ* Jim O'Connolly. *Photog* Desmond Dickinson. *Art Dir* Alex
Vetchinsky. *Set Decor* Freda Pearson. *Film Ed* Martin Charles. *Mus* Patrick
John Scott. *Sd* Mike Le Mare, Sydney Squires. *Asst Dir* Christopher Dryhurst,
Malcolm Stamp, Richard Dobson. *Prod Mgr* Bryan Coates.
   Cast: Telly Savalas (*Herbie Hassler*), Edith Evans (*Lady Sophie Fitzmore*),
Warren Oates (*Marty Miller*), Cesar Romero (*Nick Marco*), Harry H. Corbett
(*Frank Finley*), Nicky Henson (*Lord Freddie Fitzmore*), Hattie Jacques
(*Mabel*), Vickery Turner (*Annie*), Arthur Mullard (*Perce*), Frank Thornton
(*Cyril*), Thorley Walters (*Hubbard*), Jeremy Young (*Reilly*), Leslie Dwyer
(*Henry*), Will Leighton (*Bowers*), Clive Dunn (*Basil*), David Lodge
(*policeman*), David Bauer (*Jack*), Ivor Dean (*Bellows*), Joan Crane (*Sally*),
Herman Cohen, Jim O'Connolly.
   Crime comedy. While in prison, Herbie Hassler, a small-time American
gangster, devises a scheme to rob an English mansion called Great Friars. After
his release Herbie and his friend Marty Miller persuade Nick Marco, a powerful
gang leader, to back their plan. They immediately fly to England to complete
the preparations. Herbie, posing as a tourist, takes a guided tour of the house
and meets the owner, Lady Sophie Fitzmore, and her nephew Freddie. Herbie
and Freddie become friends, and when Herbie claims to be an expert in security
systems, Freddie invites him to stay on at the house. Freddie explains that the
family has become financially unstable and is concerned about the safety of
their heirlooms. Herbie helps plan tourist attractions and completely forgets
about the robbery, until Nick arrives and orders them to proceed. Unable to
persuade Nick that Great Friars has tight security, Herbie himself successfully
defends the mansion against the gangster. Meanwhile, Lady Fitzmore has gone

to a London gambling casino and recouped the family fortune. She returns to Great Friars with the intention of transforming the mansion into her own casino. *Gangsters. Americans in foreign countries. Tourists. Aristocrats. Conspiracy. Robbery. Gambling. Casinos. London.*

Note: Location scenes filmed in London and at Cliveden, Lord Astor's estate near Maidenhead, England. Opened in London in Apr 1969 as *Crooks and Coronets.*

THE SORCERERS (Great Britain)   **F6.4628**
Tigon British Film Productions–Curtwel–Global Productions. *Dist* Allied Artists. Nov **1967**. Sd; col (Eastmancolor). 35mm. 87 min.
Prod Patrick Curtis, Tony Tenser. *Exec Prod* Arnold Louis Miller. *Dir* Michael Reeves. *Screenplay* Michael Reeves, Tom Baker, writ. *Orig Idea* John Burke, writ. *Photog* Stanley Long. *Art Dir* Tony Curtis, art dir. *Film Ed* David Woodward. *Mus Comp & Cond* Paul Ferris. *Songs Sung by* Toni Daly, Lee Grant & The Capitals. *Sd* Kenneth Osborne. *Asst Dir* Keith Wilkinson.
Cast: Boris Karloff *(Professor Monserrat)*, Catherine Lacey *(Estelle Monserrat)*, Ian Ogilvy *(Mike)*, Elizabeth Ercy *(Nicole)*, Victor Henry *(Alan)*, Susan George *(Audrey)*, Dani Sheridan *(Laura)*, Ivor Dean *(Inspector Matalon)*, Peter Fraser *(detective)*, Meier Tzelniker *(snack bar owner)*, Bill Barnsley *(constable)*, Martin Terry *(tobacconist)*, Gerald Campion *(customer)*, Alf Joint *(Ron)*.
Science fiction melodrama. After suffering years of poverty and ridicule because of their experiments in medical hypnosis, Professor Monserrat and his wife, Estelle, perfect a method of obtaining control over the mind through use of a mesmeric light machine. Anxious to test the invention, Estelle persuades her husband to find a suitable subject. At a nearby coffee bar, he meets a bored young man, Mike, who has quarreled with his friend Alan over the affections of Nicole, the woman they both love. By promising Mike a psychedelic experience, the professor is able to lure him to his house, where the experiment proves more successful than Monserrat and his wife had hoped. Monserrat intends to use his discovery to help elderly people relive the experiences of youth, but Estelle sees more selfish opportunities in her husband's invention and persuades him to make Mike steal a fur coat for her. To satisfy her craving for excitement, she makes Mike beat up Alan and then brutally murder two girls. When the police set out to find him, Mike tries to escape in an automobile. Summoning what little will power he still possesses, Monserrat causes Mike's car to crash, killing not only the young man but himself and his wife as well. [One source indicates that Professor Monserrat survives the crash.] *Professors. Hypnotism. Psychedelic states. Robbery. Murder. Experiments. Automobile accidents.*
Note: Filmed on location in London. Released in Great Britain in 1967; running time: 85 min.

SORCERERS' VILLAGE see **VOODOO VILLAGE**

LES SORCIÈRES see **THE WITCHES**

LA SORELLA DI SATANA see **THE SHE BEAST**

49 DNEY see **FORTY-NINE DAYS**

IL SORPASSO see **THE EASY LIFE**

SORYU HIKEN see **SECRET SCROLLS (PART II)**

SOTTO IL TALLONE see **CLOPORTES**

SOUHVĚZDÍ PANNY see **SIGN OF THE VIRGIN**

SOUL LOVER   **F6.4629**
Dist Stacey Distributors. ca **1970**. Sd; col. 16mm. 61-81 min.
Sex film. No information about the precise nature of this film has been found. *Sexuality.*

THE SOUL SNATCHER   **F6.4630**
Dist American Film Distributing Corp. **1965**. Sd; col (Eastman Color). 35mm. 68 min.
Prod Laurence Abel. *Assoc Prod* Jacqueline Pierce. *Dir* H. L. Zimmer. *Camera* Harry Schmidt. *Asst Camera* Jack Lupert. *Lighting* Pete Sears. *Film Ed* Len Rosen. *Asst Ed* Jean Lewis. *Prod Mgr* Al Gordon. *Prop* Horace Fuller.
Cast: Dan Hughs *(narrator)*, Diane Webster, Hilda Goring, Valerie-Ann, Fred Dennie, Jo Ann March, Lou Johnson, Gloria Prince, Scott Peters.
Melodrama. The devil secretly manipulates three beautiful young women in order to gain control of their souls. He appears to Kathy as a mysterious stranger, promising romance, happiness, and prosperity if she will agree to wear a pair of golden shoes. Driven to despair by frustration, she accepts; soon, however, she begins to feel that her life is controlled by some evil force. The devil returns to claim her soul; he guides her in a weekend of lovemaking with her boyfriend, and leads all three women on a path of unrestrained sexuality. *Sexuality. The Devil. The Soul.*
Note: Filmed in New York in 16mm.

SOULS FOR SALE see **CONFESSIONS OF AN OPIUM EATER**

SOULS OF SIN see **MALE AND FEMALE SINCE ADAM AND EVE**

SOUND OF HORROR (Spain)   **F6.4631**
Zurbano Films. *Dist* Europix–Consolidated Corp. Oct **1966** [Pittsburgh showing]. Sd; b&w. 35mm. 85 min.
Prod Gregorio Sacristan. *Dir* José Antonio Nieves-Conde. *Screenplay* Sam X. Abarbanel, Gregorio Sacristan. *Photog* Manuel Berenguer. *Art Dir* Luis Pérez Espinosa, Gil Parrondo. *Set Decor* Julio Molina. *Film Ed* Margarita Ochoa. *Mus* Luis de Pablo. *Prod Mgr* Fernando Navarro Correcher.
Cast: James Philbrook *(Pete)*, Arturo Fernández *(Professor Andre)*, Soledad Miranda *(Maria)*, Ingrid Pitt *(Sofia)*, Antonio Casas, José Bódalo, Lola Gaos, Francisco Piquer.
Horror film. Professor Andre, his daughter Maria, and his assistant Stavres, are searching for buried treasure with the aid of half a map in a Greek cave that is considered taboo by the local peasants. Using an explosive, they unearth two pods, actually the eggs of brontosaurus-like creatures that become invisible and make horrifying noises when in motion. The group takes one of the two eggs home for examination; the other cracks open and rolls away. Months later, driver-guide Pete and an Italian woman named Sofia join the expedition, bringing with them the missing half of the map. When the treasure's exact location is found and more dynamite is needed, Stavres is left behind in the cave and is slashed to death by the now-hatched creature. After the professor is also killed, Pete devises a plan to maim the monster but succeeds only in wounding it. An assistant then sacrifices his life by setting himself and the creature on fire, thereby saving the others. *Professors. Italians. Chauffeurs. Self-sacrifice. Caves. Treasure. Eggs. Greece. Explosions. Documentation. Dinosaurs.*
Note: Opened in Madrid in Aug 1966 as *El sonido de la muerte*; running time: 91 min. Alternative Spanish title: *El sonido prehistórico.*

SOUND OF LAUGHTER   **F6.4632**
Dist Union Film Distributors. 17 Dec **1963** [New York opening]. Sd; b&w. 35mm. 75 min.
Prod Barry B. Yellen, Irvin S. Dorfman. *Dir* John O'Shaughnessy. *Narr* Fred Saidy. *Mus* Robert Waldman. *Cont* Fred Saidy.
Narrator: Ed Wynn.
Compilation film. The film is a compilation of clips from the early talkies. Sequences include: Danny Kaye trying to get married by a deadline to avoid losing his inheritance; Bob Hope, in a grocery store, singing a duet with his girl; Bing Crosby attempting to elope and getting involved in a wild chase with a lion; Milton Berle singing a production number with chorus girls; Buster Keaton competing on Major Bowes' Amateur Hour and, in another excerpt, playing on a local baseball team; diapered Shirley Temple performing as a sultry nightclub singer; Imogene Coca as a prima ballerina; Bert Lahr, a floorwalker, trying to break into the movies; Harry Langdon hitchhiking by airplane; and the Ritz Brothers as irresponsible employees of a hotel. *Singers. Entertainers. Chorus girls. Dancers. Actors. Motion pictures. Motion pictures—History. Major Bowes' Amateur Hour.*
Note: Copyright claimant: Film Copy.

SOUND OF LIFE (U.S.S.R.)   **F6.4633**
Mosfilm. *Dist* Artkino Pictures. 10 Feb **1962** [New York opening]. Sd; col (Sovcolor). 35mm. 78 min.
Dir Tatyana Lukashevich. *Screenplay* Iosif Manevich. *Story Ed* A. Repina. *Photog* V. Masevich. *Asst Camera* A. Priyezzhev. *Art Dir* B. Tsaryov. *Film Ed* A. Medvedeva. *Mus* Yuriy Levitin. *Mus Selections* Felix Mendelssohn, Frédéric François Chopin. *Cond* V. Dudarova. *Sd* Ye. Kashkevich. *1st & 2d Asst Dir* G. Komarovskiy, V. Sevastyanova. *Prod Mgr* V. Gvozdeva. *Cost* V. Kiselyova. *Makeup* M. Agafonova. *Cons* O. Grinshteyn, P. Krasnousov, F. Shoyev.
Cast: Boris Livanov *(Uncle Maksim Yatsenko)*, Vasiliy Livanov *(Pyotr)*, Marina Strizhenova *(Anna Mikhaylovna)*, L. Kurdyumova *(Evelina)*, Yu. Puzyryov *(Iokhim)*, Aleksey Gribov *(Fyodor Kandyba)*, S. Blinnikov *(Stavruchenko)*, V. Murganov *(Ilya)*, V. Grachyov *(Andrey)*, N. Kondratyev *(Kuzma)*, N. Kozinin *(bell-ringer)*, A. Smirnov *(Popelskiy)*, Seryozha Shestopalov *(Pyotr as a child)*, Marina Kurakova *(Evelina as a child)*, Leonid Zolotukhin, N. Valandina, V. Yakovlev.
Drama. Source: Vladimir Galaktionovich Korolenko, *Slepoy musykant* (Moscow, 1888). Pyotr, the blind, sheltered child of a wealthy 19th-century Russian noble family, shows great promise as a pianist. When he grows older, his family decide that he should enroll in the Kiev conservatory to finish his formal music training. However, counseled by his Uncle Maksim, who in years past had fought for Garibaldi, he dresses in peasant's clothing and travels around the countryside with two blind bandurists. He encounters many misfortunes greater than his own and learns the "sound of life" from the people he meets. He returns to give a triumphant concert with his friends by his side.

Pianists. Beggars. Children. Uncles. Musicians. Nobility. Blindness. Education. Adolescence. Wealth. Family life. Kiev.

Note: Released in the U.S.S.R. in Mar 1961 as *Slepoy muzykant.* U. S. sources indicate that the film was produced by Gorky Film Studio, while Soviet sources credit Mosfilm.

THE SOUND OF MUSIC   **F6.4634**

Argyle Enterprises. *Dist* Twentieth Century-Fox Film Corp. 2 Mar **1965** [New York opening; c2 Mar 1965; LP30289]. Sd (Westrex); col (De Luxe). 35 & 70mm (Todd-AO). 174 min.

A Robert Wise Production. *Prod-Dir* Robert Wise. *Assoc Prod* Saul Chaplin. *Screenplay* Ernest Lehman. *Adtl Photog* Paul Beeson. *Camera Op* Paul Lockwood. *Asst Art Dir* Harry Kemm. *Set Decor* Walter M. Scott, Ruby Levitt. *Prod Dsgn* Boris Leven. *Film Ed* William Reynolds. *Asst Ed* Larry Allen. *Songs* Richard Rodgers, Oscar Hammerstein, II. *Adtl Mus & Lyr* Richard Rodgers. *Mus Supv, Arr & Cond* Irwin Kostal. *Vocal Supv* Robert Tucker. *Choreog* Marc Breaux, Dee Dee Wood. *Sd* Murray Spivack, Bernard Freericks. *Rec* William Buffinger. *Mus Ed* Robert Mayer. *Sd Rec Supv* Fred Hynes, James Corcoran. *Asst Dir* Ridgeway Callow, Richard Lang. *Unit Prod Mgr* Saul Wurtzel. *2d Unit Supv* Maurice Zuberano. *Script Supv* Betty Levin. *Cost Dsgn* Dorothy Jeakins. *Cost* Dick James, Josephine Brown, cost. *Makeup* Ben Nye, Willard Buell. *Hairstyles* Margaret Donovan, Ray Foreman. *Sp Photog Eff* L. B. Abbott, Emil Kosa, Jr. *Puppeteers* Bill Baird, Cora Baird. *Dial Coach* Pamela Danova. *Still Photog* James Mitchell. *Grip* Walter Fitchman. *Gaffer* Jack Brown. *Prop* Ed Jones.

Cast: Julie Andrews *(Maria)*, Christopher Plummer *(Captain von Trapp)*, Eleanor Parker *(The Baroness)*, Richard Haydn *(Max Detweiler)*, Peggy Wood *(Mother Abbess)*, Charmian Carr *(Liesl)*, Heather Menzies *(Louisa)*, Nicholas Hammond *(Friedrich)*, Duane Chase *(Kurt)*, Angela Cartwright *(Brigitta)*, Debbie Turner *(Marta)*, Kym Karath *(Gretl)*, Anna Lee *(Sister Margaretta)*, Portia Nelson *(Sister Berthe)*, Ben Wright *(Herr Zeller)*, Daniel Truhitte *(Rolfe)*, Norma Varden *(Frau Schmidt)*, Gilchrist Stuart *(Franz)*, Marni Nixon *(Sister Sophia)*, Evadne Baker *(Sister Bernice)*, Doris Lloyd *(Baroness Ebberfeld)*.

Musical melodrama. Source: Richard Rodgers, Oscar Hammerstein, II, Howard Lindsay and Russel Crouse, *The Sound of Music* (New York opening: 16 Nov 1959). The antics of tomboyish Maria, a novice at the abbey in Salzburg, concern the Mother Abbess, who is unsure whether Maria wants to become a nun. To allow the girl to test her feelings, the Mother Abbess sends Maria to be the governess for the seven children of the widowed Baron von Trapp, a retired naval officer. The children are at first hostile to Maria, but she soon wins them over. The baron, who is a strict disciplinarian, leaves to visit Baroness Schraeder, and while he is gone, Maria allows them greater freedom and teaches them to sing. The children become so excited when the baron returns that they fall out of a rowboat in the lake. The accident precipitates an argument between Maria and the baron, and he orders her to leave; but when he goes into the house and finds the children entertaining his friend Max and the baroness with a song, he asks Maria to stay. Max later suggests that they enter the Salzburg Festival as a singing group, but the baron refuses. Maria becomes aware that she is falling in love with the baron and returns to the abbey. The children follow her there and try to persuade her to return; when the Mother Abbess learns of their visit, she sends Maria back to the Trapp home. Maria again decides to leave when she hears that the baron plans to marry the baroness, but the baroness realizes that he loves Maria and releases him. He then marries Maria, and while they are away on their honeymoon, the Nazis take over Austria. Max, taking advantage of the baron's absence, enters the children in the Salzburg Festival. When Maria and the baron return, he forbids the children to appear at the festival. The baron learns that the Nazis, to whom he is violently opposed, have ordered him to take command of a ship. The Trapps plan an escape but are stopped by Storm Troopers. Max convinces them that they are on their way to the festival and that the baron is leaving for his ship immediately after the performance. The Trapps win first place and, using their exit song to escape, they take refuge in the abbey. The Nazis learn their whereabouts and surround the building, but the family escape through a secret tunnel to the nearby mountains. *Musical numbers:* Prelude, "The Sound of Music" (Maria); Overture, "Preludium (Dixit Dominus)" (orchestra and nun's chorus); "Morning Hymn," "Alleluia" (nun's chorus); "Maria" (nun's chorus); "I Have Confidence" (Maria); "Sixteen Going on Seventeen" (Rolf and Liesl); "My Favorite Things" (Maria); "Climb Every Mountain" (Mother Abbess); "The Lonely Goatherd" (Maria and children); "The Sound of Music" (children and baron); "Do-Re-Mi" (Maria and children); "Something Good" (Maria and baron); Processional, "Maria" (organ, orchestra, and nun's chorus); "Edelweiss" (captain, Maria, and children); "So Long, Farewell" (children). *Tomboys. Novices. Nuns. Governesses. Nobility. Widowers. Nazis. Escapees. Children. Music. Courtship. Marriage. Family life. Abbeys. World War II. Salzburg. SA. Trapp Family Singers. Salzburg Music Festival.*

Note: Filmed in the Austrian Alps and near Salzburg; scenes at the von Trapp home were shot at the Frohnburg Castle. A similar story based on the same characters was filmed as *The Trapp Family,* q. v.

THE SOUND OF TRUMPETS (Italy)   **F6.4635**

Twenty-Four Horses–Titanus. *Dist* Janus Films. 22 Oct **1963** [New York opening]. Sd; b&w. 35mm. 90 min.

Prod Alberto Soffientini. *Dir-Writ-Story* Ermanno Olmi. *Photog* Lamberto Caimi. *Art Dir* Ettore Lombardi. *Film Ed* Carla Colombo. *Mus* Pier Emilio Bassi. *Prod Mgr* Giuseppe Donata.

Cast: Sandro Panzeri *(Domenico Cantoni)*, Loredana Detto *(Antonietta Masetti)*, Tullio Kezich *(psychologist)*, Mara Revel *(old woman)*.

Drama. Domenico, the teenaged son of working-class villagers, comes to Milan to take a test for a job with a large industrial company. During the day-long examination, Domenico becomes attracted to Antonietta, another applicant; they bid each other goodby, hoping to meet again if they are hired. Both pass their tests but are assigned to positions in different buildings, Antonietta as a typist and Domenico as a messenger because there are no clerical positions available. Although they rarely meet at work, Domenico looks forward to seeing Antonietta at the company's New Year's Eve dance, but she never arrives at the party. After the holidays, a clerk dies, and Domenico replaces him. The other clerks move one desk forward, and Domenico proudly settles down at the last desk in line, accepting the security of a dull lifetime position with the company. *Typists. Office clerks. Messengers. Employment. Adolescence. New Year's Eve. Milan.*

Note: Opened in Rome in Oct 1961 as *Il posto;* 1961 Venice Film Festival running time: 98 min.

LE SOUPIRANT see **THE SUITOR**

SOUTH SEAS FURY (Reissue)   **F6.4636**

Paramount Pictures. *Dist* Citation Films. 20 Nov **1961** [Maryland license]. Sd; col (Technicolor). 35mm (VistaVision). 84 min.

Note: Originally released by Paramount Pictures in 1955 as *Hell's Island;* c12 May 1955; LP4680.

THE SOUTHERN STAR (France/Great Britain)   **F6.4637**

Euro France Films–Capitole Films–Columbia (British) Productions. *Dist* Columbia Pictures. 28 May **1969** [New York opening; c1 May 1969; LP37145]. Sd; col (Technicolor). 35mm (Techniscope). 104 min. *MPAA rating* M.

A Nat Wachsberger Production. *Prod* Roger Duchet. *Dir* Sidney Hayers. *Screenplay* David Pursall, Jack Seddon. *French Screenplay* Jean Giono. *Dir Photog* Raoul Coutard. *Asst Camera* Georges Liron, Jean Garcenot. *Set Dsgn* Pierre Thévenet. *Film Ed* Tristam Cones. *Asst Ed* Glenn Hyde. *Mus Comp* Georges Garvarentz. *Titl Song Lyr* Don Black. *Sung by* Matt Monro. *Orch* George Martin. *Sd* Ken Heeley-Ray, Jean Jak. *Asst Dir* Jacques Bourdon. *Prod Supv* Andrée Debar. *Dress Dsgn* Yvonne Caffin. *Wardrobe* Marie Feldwick. *Makeup* Hugh Richards. *Sp Makeup for Miss Andress* John O'Gorman. *Hairdresser* Maud Onslow. *Sp Eff* F. Sune, A. Trielli.

Cast: George Segal *(Dan Rockland)*, Ursula Andress *(Erica Kramer)*, Orson Welles *(Plankett)*, Ian Hendry *(Karl Ludwig)*, Johnny Sekka *(Matakit)*, Michel Constantin *(José)*, Georges Géret *(André)*, Sylvain *(Louis)*, Charles Lamb *(Todd)*, Guy Delorme *(Michel)*, Harry Andrews *(Kramer)*, Van Dooren *(man in bar)*, National Ballet of Senegal.

Adventure comedy. Source: Jules Verne, *L'étoile du sud, le pays des diamants* (Paris, 1884). In French West Africa in 1912, Dan Rockland, a penniless American fortune hunter posing as a geologist, works for Kramer, a diamond tycoon and entrepreneur. Kramer's native employees find a huge diamond along the coastline, and Rockland, accompanied by his African companion, Matakit, proceeds by train to bring the gem to Kramer. Along the way they survive a dynamite explosion arranged by Capt. Karl Ludwig, Kramer's villainous security chief who is jealous of Rockland's good fortune and his courtship of Kramer's daughter, Erica. At a garden party given by Kramer to celebrate his acquisition, which is christened the "Southern Star," the lights suddenly go out. The diamond disappears, and Matakit is seen riding away on Kramer's pet ostrich. Because Rockland is suspected of complicity in the theft, Erica insists that he give chase and, furthermore, that he take her along since she is familiar with the bush country. Karl and his men follow close behind, intent on stealing the diamond themselves. Word of the theft quickly reaches the sinister Plankett, Kramer's former security chief who lost his position to Karl and swears revenge. Plankett captures Matakit and uses him as bait to trap Karl. The plan backfires, however; Karl gains the upper hand and uses Matakit to lure Rockland into a trap. With Erica's help, Rockland outwits his opponents and rescues Matakit as Karl is killed in a shootout. With the diamond returned, Kramer greets Rockland as an ideal prospective son-in-law. In the midst of the congratulations, Kramer's pet suddenly swallows a large object and bolts off to join a herd of other ostriches. Persuaded that the bulge in the bird's throat is the diamond, Kramer and Erica give chase on horseback—as Matakit opens his hand and shows Rockland the Southern Star. *Fortune hunters. Geologists. Tycoons. Guards. Americans in foreign countries. Jealousy. Theft. Revenge. Imposture. Filial relations. Gems. Diamond mines. Jungles. French West Africa. Chases. Explosions. Train wrecks. Ostriches.*

Note: Location scenes filmed in Senegal. Opened in London in May 1969; Paris opening: Feb 1969 as *L'étoile du sud.* Filmed in French and English versions.

SOUTHWEST TO SONORA *see* **THE APPALOOSA**

SPACE   F6.4638
Dist Andy Warhol. 17 Sep **1965** [New York opening]. Sd; b&w. 16mm. 70 min.
Prod-Dir Andy Warhol. *Writ* Ronald Tavel. *Prod Asst* Paul Morrissey.
Cast: Edie Sedgwick, Eric Anderson. No information about the precise nature of this film has been found.

SPACE INVASION OF LAPLAND *see* **INVASION OF THE ANIMAL PEOPLE**

SPACE MEN *see* **ASSIGNMENT—OUTER SPACE**

A SPACE ODYSSEY *see* **2001: A SPACE ODYSSEY**

SPACE STATION-X *see* **MUTINY IN OUTER SPACE**

SPACE STATION X-14 *see* **MUTINY IN OUTER SPACE**

SPACE THING   F6.4639
B & B Productions. *Dist* FPS Ventures, Entertainment Ventures, Inc. 20 Sep **1968** [Champaign, Illinois, showing]. Sd; col. 35mm. 69 min.
Prod-Dir B. Ron Elliott. *Screenplay* Cosmo Politan. *Camera* Sy Klops. *Lighting* A. C. Powers. *Sets* Don Hallstrom. *Sd* Sam Kopetzky. *Script Girl* Kara Kooze. *Cost* Daisy Designer. *Key Grip* Allus Dropsit.
Cast: Paula Pleasure, Steve Stunning.
Science fiction comedy-drama. James Granilla, a Kansas City science fiction enthusiast, reads about the theory of an infinite number of inhabited worlds as he lies in bed. His wife, lying next to him, awakens and complains that he pays more attention to his books than to her. They make love, and Granilla's wife returns to sleep and he resumes reading. He falls asleep and dreams of life in the future: The year is 2069. Col. James Granilla of the Royal Planetarian Navy, thrown from his spaceship by a mutinous crew, is picked up by the Terranian Spaceship Supreme Erection, staffed by a crew of five and commanded by Captain Mother, a sadistic lesbian. Granilla discovers that the ship is en route to his native world, Planetaria, to bring captives back to Earth. Granilla decides that he must destroy the ship. The three crewwomen fall in love with him and two of them seduce him as Captain Mother watches in jealous rage through a television intercom. Captain Mother beats the girls for their heterosexual trespasses. Granilla then forces the ship to land on an uncharted asteroid. Jealous of Granilla's sexual success, crewman Cadet tries to kill him but Granilla disintegrates his rival. The other male crew member, Willie, an idiot, remains on the asteroid when the ship departs. Captain Mother decides to investigate Granilla's power over women and asks him to make love to her. Granilla leaves with the four women, but, obedient to his conscience, he destroys the ship and returns to Planetaria and his loving wife. *Spaceship crews. Marriage. Space travel. Mutiny. Jealousy. Lesbianism. Murder. Sadism. Seduction. Spaceships. Imaginary planets. Eavesdropping. Asteroids. Kansas City (Missouri). Dreams. The Future.*

SPACEFLIGHT IC-1 (Great Britain)   F6.4640
Lippert Films. *Dist* Twentieth Century-Fox Film Corp. Oct **1965** [c31 Dec 1965; LP32874]. Sd (Westrex); b&w. 35mm. 65 min.
Prod Robert L. Lippert, Jack Parsons. *Dir* Bernard Knowles. *Story & Screenplay* (see note) Harry Spalding. *Dir Photog* Geoffrey Faithfull. *Camera Op* Len Harris. *Art Dir* Harry White. *Supv Film Ed* Robert Winter. *Asst Ed* Colin Miller. *Mus Comp* Elisabeth Lutyens. *Mus Dir* Philip Martell. *Sd Rec* Jock May. *Sd Ed* Clive Smith. *Asst Dir* Gordon Gilbert. *Prod Mgr* Clifton Brandon. *Prod Sec* Angela Cockill. *Wardrobe Supv* Jean Fairlie. *Makeup* Harold Fletcher. *Hairdresser* Pearl Tipaldi.
Cast: Bill Williams (*Capt. Mead Ralston*), Kathleen Breck (*Kate Saunders*), John Cairney (*Steven "Doc" Thomas*), Donald Churchill (*Carl Walcott*), Jeremy Longhurst (*John Saunders*), Linda Marlowe (*Helen Thomas*), Margo Mayne (*Joyce Walcott*), Norma West (*Jan Ralston*), Tony Doonan (*Griffith*), James Terry, Andrew Downie (*Captain Burnett* [see note]), John Lee (*Dr. Garth*), Chuck Julian (*Webster*), Max Kirby (*Clown*), Mark Lester (*Don*), Stuart Middleton (*Michael*), Anthony Honour (*Robert*).
Science fiction melodrama. In the year 2015, spaceship *IC-1* travels toward a planet with an atmosphere similar to Earth's to explore the possibility that the population problem on Earth can eventually be solved there. *IC-1*'s crew consists of Capt. Mead Ralston, his wife Jan, Drs. Steven and Helen Thomas,

two other married couples, and four people in suspended animation. Helen is found to have an incurable pancreatic infection, but Ralston refuses to turn back; and when he denies her permission to have another child, she commits suicide. Steven and the other crew members mutiny and imprison Captain Ralston, but they are forced to succumb to Ralston when he threatens to destroy the ship. Ralston plans to execute Steven. Ignoring the warnings of the crew, he releases one of the "animates" by raising the temperature of the compartment in which it is suspended, and the "animate" kills him before dying. The ship goes on under Steven's leadership. *Astronauts. Physicians. Overpopulation. Cryogenics. Space exploration. Suicide. Mutiny. Murder. Spaceships. Incurable illness. The Future.*

Note: Released in Great Britain in Jun 1967. Spalding may have received screenplay credit under his pseudonym, Henry Cross. Sources disagree in crediting the role of Captain Burnett.

SPACERAID 63 *see* **THE DAY MARS INVADED EARTH**

SPACESHIP TO VENUS *see* **FIRST SPACESHIP ON VENUS**

LA SPADA DEL CID *see* **THE SWORD OF EL CID**

UNA SPADA PER DUE BANDIERE *see* **LAFAYETTE**

LO SPADACCINO DI SIENA *see* **SWORDSMAN OF SIENA**

SPARA FORTE, PIÙ FORTE ... NON CAPISCO *see* **SHOOT LOUD, LOUDER ... I DON'T UNDERSTAND**

SPARROWS CAN'T SING (Great Britain)   F6.4641
Carthage Productions. *Dist* Janus Films. 6 May **1963** [New York opening]. Sd; b&w. 35mm. 93 min.
Prod Donald Taylor. *Dir* Joan Littlewood. *Screenplay* Stephen Lewis, Joan Littlewood. *Photog* Max Greene, Desmond Dickinson. *Art Dir* Bernard Sarron. *Film Ed* Oswald Hafenrichter. *Mus Comp* James Stevens. *Background Score & Mus Dir* Stanley Black. *Titl Song* Lionel Bart. *Sung by* Barbara Windsor. *Sd* Kevin Sutton. *Asst Dir* Peter Medak. *Asst to the Dir* Daniel Farson. *Prod Mgr* Clifford Parkes. *Makeup* Bill Lodge. *Hairstyles* Polly Young.
Cast: James Booth (*Charlie Gooding*), Barbara Windsor (*Maggie Gooding*), Roy Kinnear (*Fred Gooding*), George Sewell (*Bert*), Avis Bunnage (*Bridgie Gooding*), Barbara Ferris (*Nellie Gooding*), Murray Melvin (*Georgie*), Griffith Davies (*Chunky*), Arthur Mullard (*Ted*), Bob Grant (*Perce*), Stephen Lewis (*caretaker*), Fanny Carby (*Lil*), Brian Murphy, British (*Jack*), Wally Patch (*watchman*), May Scagnelli (*Gran*), Jenny Sontag (*Momma*), Victor Spinetti (*Arnold*), Yootha Joyce (*Paddy [Yootha?]*), Marjie Lawrence (*girl*), Peggy Ann Clifford (*Ted's wife*), Janet Howse (*Janet*), Queenie Watts (*Queenie*), Glynn Edwards (*Charlie's friend*), Harry H. Corbett (*stall-holder*), Gerry Raffles (*lorry-driver*).
Domestic comedy-drama. Source: Stephen Lewis, *Sparrers Can't Sing* (Stratford-upon-Avon opening: 24 Aug 1960). After 2 years at sea, hard-drinking merchant sailor Charlie Gooding returns to London and discovers that his East End home has been replaced by a block of new apartments and his wife, Maggie, is missing. Because of his explosive temper, his mother and neighbors are afraid to tell him that Maggie is living with Bert, a bus driver. Furious, Charlie holds his brother, Fred, hostage in the Red Lion, a local pub, until the latter's wife sends for Maggie. Charlie finally does meet his wife in the park, where she is wheeling a baby carriage, but Charlie doubts that the child is his. However, after confessing their mutual infidelities, Charlie accepts Christabel, the infant, as his daughter and takes immediate steps to move his family into his mother's home. That evening all concerned are celebrating the reunion at the Red Lion when Bert suddenly appears. The inevitable brawl follows, but Maggie thrashes Bert with her handbag. Peace is restored, and Bert philosophically decides to return to his estranged wife as Charlie and Maggie bicker, a longstanding practice of theirs. *Sailors. Bus drivers. Brothers. Infants. Infidelity. Family life. Marriage. Parentage. Housing. Alcoholism. Pubs. Parks. Merchant marine. London—East End.*

Note: Filmed in London's East End. Opened in London in Mar 1963; running time: 94 min. Subtitles were added to some American release prints to ensure that the dialog, spoken in a Cockney dialect, would be understood.

THE SPECIALISTS   F6.4642
C. I. T. Films. *Dist* I. R. M. I. Films. 31 Jul **1968** [New York showing]. Sd; b&w. 35mm. 60 min.
Dir Clem Moser.
Cast: Ina Albrecht, Sylvia Koerner, Janice Kelly.
Sex film. A bored young woman in Munich becomes a prostitute and visits a nightclub where two women perform a lesbian act. The young woman subsequently has an affair with a lesbian, gets drunk, and commits suicide. *Prostitutes. Entertainers. Lesbianism. Suicide. Drunkenness. Munich.*
Note: Country of origin undetermined.

SPEED LOVERS F6.4643

Associates & Wilmac Productions. *Dist* Jemco Pictures. 14 Feb **1968** [Atlanta opening]. Sd; col (Eastman Color). 35mm. 102 min.

Prod-Dir-Writ William McGaha. *2d Unit Dir* Fred Tuch. *Orig Script* Elaine Wilkerson. *Story* William McGaha, Fred Tuch. *Dir Photog* Joe Shelton. *Prod Dsgn* Fred Tuch. *Film Ed* John Fitzstephens, David Moscovitz, William Freda. *Mus Score* Carleton Palmer. *Titl Song Sung by* Billy Lee Riley. *Script Girl* Shelly Charles.

Cast: Fred Lorenzen (*himself*), William McGaha, Peggy O'Hara, David Marcus, Carol Street, Glenda Brunson.

Action drama. Inspired by the exploits of driver Fred Lorenzen, the son of a mechanic aspires to be a great stock car racer. *Stock car drivers. Automobile racing.*

Note: Location scenes filmed in Atlanta. Racing footage shot at Atlanta International Raceway and at speedways in Riverside, California; Hampton, Georgia; Asheville, Charlotte, North Wilkesboro, and Rockingham, North Carolina; Daytona Beach, Florida; Darlington, South Carolina; and Martinsville, Virginia.

SPEEDWAY F6.4644

Metro-Goldwyn-Mayer, Inc. 12 Jun **1968** [Charlotte, North Carolina, opening; c4 Apr 1968; LP35454]. Sd; col (Metrocolor). 35mm (Panavision). 95 min. [Also 90 min.]

Prod Douglas Laurence. *Dir* Norman Taurog. *Writ* Phillip Shuken. *Dir Photog* Joseph Ruttenberg. *Art Dir* George W. Davis, Leroy Coleman. *Set Decor* Henry Grace, Don Greenwood, Jr. *Film Ed* Richard Farrell. *Mus Score* Jeff Alexander. *Song:* "Your Groovy Self" Lee Hazlewood. *Sung by* Nancy Sinatra. *Songs:* "Speedway," "He's Your Uncle, Not Your Dad," "Who Are You? (Who Am I?)," "Let Yourself Go," "Your Time Hasn't Come Yet, Baby," "There Ain't Nothing Like a Song," "Five Sleepy Heads," "Western Union," "Mine," "Goin' Home," "Suppose" Mel Glazer, Stephen Schlaks. *Sung by* Elvis Presley. *Vocal Backgrounds* The Jordanaires. *Sd* Larry Jost. *Rec Supv* Franklin Milton. *Asst Dir* Dale Hutchinson. *Unit Prod Mgr* G. Rex Bailey. *Makeup* William Tuttle. *Hairstyles* Sydney Guilaroff. *Sp Vis Eff* Carroll L. Shepphird. *Dial Coach* Michael A. Hoey.

Cast: Elvis Presley (*Steve Grayson*), Nancy Sinatra (*Susan Jacks*), Bill Bixby (*Kenny Donford*), Gale Gordon (*R. W. Hepworth*), William Schallert (*Abel Esterlake*), Victoria Meyerink (*Ellie Esterlake*), Ross Hagen (*Paul Dado*), Carl Ballantine (*Birdie Kebner*), Poncie Ponce (*Juan Medala*), Harry Hickox (*cook*), Christopher West (*Billie Jo*), Miss Beverly Hills (*Mary Ann*), Harper Carter (*Ted Simmons*), Bob Harris (*Lloyd Meadows*), Michele Newman (*Debbie Esterlake*), Courtney Brown (*Carrie Esterlake*), Dana Brown (*Billie Esterlake*), Pattie Jean Keith (*Annie Esterlake*), Carl Reindel (*Mike*), Gari Hardy (*dumb blonde*), Charlotte Considine (*Lori*), Sandy Reed (*race announcer*), Ward Ramsey, Robert James, Gary LittleJohn, Ralph Adano, Tom McCauley (*Dado's crew*).

Melodrama with music. Stock car racer Steve Grayson spends most of his earnings helping Abel Esterlake, a poverty-stricken father of several little girls, though he still has enough left over to support a lavish lifestyle. Unknown to him, his manager, Kenny Donford, has lost the remainder of Steve's prize money by gambling on horses. To recover $145,000 in back taxes, Internal Revenue Service chief R. W. Hepworth assigns Susan Jacks to investigate the racer's finances and manage his affairs until the government debt is paid. Susan and Steve soon fall in love, despite initial antagonism, and together they try to obtain the money he owes. While qualifying for a high-paying race, Steve has an accident that seriously damages his car. His friends repair the car, and at the last minute Steve enters the race. Though he places third, he wins enough laps to pay most of his debt, leaving him free to continue his romance with Susan. *Stock car drivers. Investigators. Automobile racing. Gambling. Finance—Personal. Income tax. United States—Internal Revenue Service. Automobile accidents.*

Note: Location scenes filmed at the Charlotte Speedway in North Carolina.

SPENCER'S MOUNTAIN F6.4645

Warner Bros. Pictures. 16 May **1963** [New York opening; c6 Jul 1963; LP29446]. Sd; col (Technicolor). 35mm (Panavision). 119 min. [Also reviewed at 123 min.]

A Delmer Daves Production. *Prod-Dir-Writ* Delmer Daves. *2d Unit Dir* Robert Totten. *Photog* Charles Lawton. *2d Unit Photog* H. F. Koenekamp. *Art Dir* Carl Anderson. *Set Decor* Ralph S. Hurst. *Film Ed* David Wages. *Mus* Max Steiner. *Orch* Murray Cutter. *Sd* M. A. Merrick. *Rec* Russell Ashley. *Boom Op* John Jensen. *Asst Dir* Gil Kissel, William F. Sheehan, Monty Masters. *Unit Location Mgr* Joseph Barry. *Cost Dsgn* Marjorie Best. *Cost* Norma Brown, Geoffrey Alan. *Makeup* Gordon Bau, James Barker. *Hairstyles* Jean Burt Reilly, Fae Smith. *Sp Eff* Wellington Honn. *Still Photog* Jack Woods, still photog. *Prop* Weldon H. Patterson. *Gaffer* Charles O'Bannon. *Grip* Louis Maschmeyer.

Cast: Henry Fonda (*Clay Spencer*), Maureen O'Hara (*Olivia Spencer*), James MacArthur (*Clayboy Spencer*), Donald Crisp (*Grandpa Spencer*), Wally Cox (*Preacher Goodson*), Mimsy Farmer (*Claris Coleman*), Virginia Gregg (*Miss Parker*), Lillian Bronson (*Grandma Spencer*), Whit Bissell (*Dr. Campbell*), Hayden Rorke (*Colonel Coleman*), Kathy Bennett (*Minnie-Cora Cook*), Dub Taylor (*Percy Cook*), Hope Summers (*Mother Ida*), Ken Mayer (*Mr. John*), Bronwyn Fitzsimmons (*college secretary*), Barbara McNair (*graduation singer*), Buzz Henry, Larry D. Mann, Jim O'Hara, Victor French, Michael Greene, Med Flory, Ray Savage, Mike Henry (*Spencer brothers*), Veronica Cartwright, Susan Young, Michele Daves, Rocky Young, Michael Young, Gary Young, Ricky Young, Kym Karrath (*Spencer children*).

Rural comedy-drama. Source: Earl Hamner, Jr., *Spencer's Mountain* (New York, 1961). Three generations ago, Grandpa Spencer homesteaded a mountain in the Grand Tetons of Wyoming and left the land to his heirs, but eight of his nine grandsons eventually sold their inheritance. The exception, Clay Spencer, a quarry worker, lives in the valley with his wife, Olivia, and their nine children. The oldest son, Clayboy, is about to graduate from high school, a feat no other Spencer has ever accomplished. Because of the boy's intense desire to learn, his teacher, Miss Parker, nominates him for a scholarship at the state university, but the only opening turns out to be a divinity scholarship, which the church-shunning Clay opposes. When Clayboy's application is rejected because he lacks knowledge of Latin, he agrees to attend church every Sunday in return for Preacher Goodson's service as a Latin tutor. While studying at the new town library, Clayboy falls in love with Claris Coleman, the wealthy daughter of Clay's employer. Meanwhile, tragedy strikes the Spencer family when Grandpa is crushed to death by a fallen tree. The university finally accepts Clayboy's application, but there is no scholarship money available. Realizing that he must sacrifice for the good of future Spencers, Clay sells the piece of land on which he had been building a "dreamhouse" for Olivia for 20 years. In September, the family gathers to bid farewell to Clayboy as he leaves for college. *Homesteaders. Grandparents. Students. Schoolteachers. Preachers. Family life. Mountain life. Inheritance. Adolescence. Education. Poverty. Scholarships. Libraries. Latin language. Teton Range. Wyoming.*

Note: Filmed on location in the Grand Tetons.

THE SPESSART INN (West Germany) F6.4646

Georg Witt. *Dist* Casino Films, United Film Enterprises. 17 Feb **1961** [New York opening]. Sd; col (AgfaColor). 35mm. 99 min.

Prod Georg Witt. *Asst Prod* Hans Krause. *Dir* Kurt Hoffmann. *Screenplay* Heinz Pauck, Liselotte Enderle. *Story* Günter Neumann. *Dir Photog* Richard Angst. *Camera Asst* Alfred Westphal. *Art Dir* Robert Herlth, Kurt Herlth. *Film Ed* Claus von Boro. *Mus* Franz Grothe. *Songs* Günter Neumann. *Sd* Walter Rühland. *Asst Dir* Wolfgang Kühnlenz. *Prod Mgr* Frank Roell, Waldemar Albert. *Cost* Elisabeth Urbanic. *Wardrobe* Josef Dorrer, Josefine Franz. *Makeup* Georg Jauss, Charlotte Müller. *Prop* Werner Wappler, Rolf Taute.

Cast: Liselotte Pulver (*Countess Franziska*), Carlos Thompson (*robber captain*), Günther Lüders (*Baron Sperling*), Rudolf Vogel (*Buffon Parucchio*), Ina Peters (*Maid Barbara*), Veronika Fitz (*Maid Luise*), Herbert Hübner (*Count Sandau*), Hubert von Meyerinck (*police major*), Helmut Lohner (*Felix*), Hans Clarin (*Peter*), Paul Esser (*corporal*), Otto Storr (*reverend*), Karl Hanft (*farmhand Jacob*), Vera Complojer (*landlady*), Ernst Braasch (*servant Anton*), Annette Karman (*kitchen maid Adele*), Wolfgang Neuss (*robber Knoll*), Wolfgang Müller, actor (*robber Funzel*), Kai Fischer.

Musical comedy. Source: Wilhelm Hauff, "Das Wirtshaus im Spessart" (adapted by C. H. Gutbrod, 1828). En route to Würzburg the Countess Franziska's coach is intercepted by a robber band and brought to the Spessart Inn. Learning that she is to be held for ransom, the countess changes clothes with fellow traveler Felix and returns to her father's castle. When the miserly count refuses to ransom the other captives, however, she returns to the Spessart Inn disguised as a man. All but the robber captain fail to recognize her. Having fallen in love with the countess, the chieftain remains silent. Rebelling against him, the band attacks its prisoners, an assault interrupted by the arrival of soldiers, who arrest the brigands. Aided by Franziska, the captain takes refuge in the castle. Following his departure, the countess reluctantly prepares for her marriage to the fop, Baron Sperling. The ceremony is stopped by the bandit chieftain, who reveals himself to be an Italian nobleman, the patron of Franziska's father, and claims the countess as his own. *Nobility. Highwaymen. Misers. Italians. Kidnaping. Marriage—Arranged. Filial relations. Imposture. Male impersonation. Inns. Castles. Weddings. Spessart. Würzburg.*

Note: Released in West Germany in Jan 1958 as *Das Wirtshaus im Spessart*; running time: 100 min.

LO SPETTRO see THE GHOST

SPIDER BABY F6.4647

Lasky-Monka Productions. *Dist* American General Pictures, Distributors International. 18 Jan **1968** [New Orleans opening]. Sd; b&w. 35mm. 80 min.

Pres by David L. Hewitt. *Prod* Gil Lasky, Paul Monka. *Dir-Writ* Jack Hill. *Photog* Alfred Taylor. *Art Dir* Ray Storey. *Film Ed* Elliot Fayad. *Mus* Ronald Stein. *Sd* Austin McKinney. *Prod Mgr* Bart Patton.

Cast: Lon Chaney, Jr., Carol Ohmart, Quinn Redeker, Mantan Moreland, Beverly Washburn, Mary Mitchell, Karl Schanzer, Sid Haig, Jill Banner *(uncredited roles)*, Carolyn Cooper, Joan Keller *(gal ghouls)*.

Horror film. A caretaker devotes himself to three demented adults after their father's death. When a telegram announces the arrival of heirs, the guardian suspects that his wards are to be confined in an asylum and detonates the paternal estate, destroying himself and his charges. *Caretakers. Heirs. Insanity. Suicide. Murder. Fires.*

Note: Location scenes filmed in and around Los Angeles. Produced in 1964 as *Cannibal Orgy, or The Maddest Story Ever Told.* Also known as *Spider Baby, or The Maddest Story Ever Told* and *The Liver Eaters.*

THE SPIDER'S WEB see **IT'S HOT IN PARADISE**

LE SPIE UCCIDONO A BEIRUT see **SECRET AGENT FIREBALL**

LE SPIE VENGONO DAL SEMIFREDDO see **DR. GOLDFOOT AND THE GIRL BOMBS**

SPIES-A-GO-GO see **THE NASTY RABBIT**

SPIKED HEELS AND BLACK NYLONS   **F6.4648**
Dist Crescent International Pictures. 19 Jan **1967** [Minneapolis opening]. Sd; col. 35mm. 74 min.
Prod-Dir Whit Boyd. *Screenplay* Wolf Larkin. *Photog* Ludwig Moner. *Asst Camera* James Finley. *Art Dir* R. C. Anderson. *Mus Comp & Dir* Roger Stevens and the Realistics. *Sd* Forest Duval. *Wardrobe* Rosemarie McKay. *Makeup* Rosemarie McKay.

Cast: Cherry James *(Gina)*, Bill Thurman *(Abel)*, Shirley Boyd *(Sybil)*, Ron Scott *(Glenn)*, Rosemarie McKay *(Myrna)*, Ann Ruthers *(Reba)*, Cher Lamait *(Dienna)*, Ann Phillips *(dope addict)*.

Melodrama. Under Reba's supervision, a variety of women cater to the strange desires of Club Lesbo's clientele: Myrna turns to prostitution to support her costly drug habit; Sybil enjoys sex with men but prefers the forbidden company of women; Dienna performs a topless dance under the erotic influence of marijuana; and Gina, a suburban housewife blackmailed into entertaining, enjoys being degraded in spite of herself. Gina's policeman husband raids the club and finds her making love to another man; overwhelmed by shame, she pleads with him to kill her. *Prostitutes. Drug addicts. Go-go dancers. Housewives. Madams. Lesbianism. Blackmail. Infidelity. Masochism. Marijuana. Nightclubs. Whorehouses.*

Note: May also be known as *Black Nylons.*

SPINOUT   **F6.4649**
Euterpe, Inc. *Dist* Metro-Goldwyn-Mayer, Inc. 23 Nov **1966** [Los Angeles opening; c27 Jul 1966; LP33273]. Sd (Westrex); col (Metrocolor). 35mm (Panavision). 93 min.
Prod Joe Pasternak. *Assoc Prod* Hank Moonjean. *Dir* Norman Taurog. *Screenplay* Theodore J. Flicker, George Kirgo. *Dir Photog* Daniel L. Fapp. *Camera Op* James King. *Camera Asst* Hugh Crawford. *Art Dir* George W. Davis, Edward Carfagno. *Set Decor* Henry Grace, Hugh Hunt. *Film Ed* Rita Roland. *Asst Ed* Frank Urioste. *Mus* George Stoll. *Mus Assoc* Robert Van Eps. *Titl Song* Sid Wayne, Ben Weisman, Darrell Fuller. *Song:* "Stop, Look, Listen" Joy Byers. *Song:* "Adam and Evil" Fred Wise, Randy Starr. *Songs:* "All That I Am," "Am I Ready," "Smorgasbord" Sid Tepper, Roy C. Bennett. *Song:* "Never Say Yes" Doc Pomus, Mort Shuman. *Song:* "Beach Shack" Bill Giant, Florence Kaye, Bernie Baum. *Song:* "I'll Be Back" Sid Wayne, Ben Weisman. *Songs Sung by* Elvis Presley. *Vocal Backgrounds* The Jordanaires. *Mus Numbers Staged* Jack Baker. *Rec Supv* Franklin Milton. *Mix* Larry Jost. *Rec* Frank Antunez. *Boom Op* Barry Thomas. *Asst Dir* Claude Binyon, Jr., Donald Verk, James Westman. *Unit Prod Mgr* Al Shenberg. *Script Supv* Cleo Anton. *Wardrobe* Lambert Marks, Margo Weintz. *Makeup* William Tuttle, Roy Stork. *Hairstyles* Sydney Guilaroff, Josephine Ardigo. *Sp Vis Eff* J. McMillan Johnson, Carroll L. Shepphird. *Tech Adv* Col. Tom Parker. *Dial Supv* Michael A. Hoey. *Still Photog* Virgil Apger. *Gaffer* George Lasher. *Key Grip* Howard Bradner. *Prop Master* Robert Schultz.

Cast: Elvis Presley *(Mike McCoy)*, Shelley Fabares *(Cynthia Foxhugh)*, Diane McBain *(Diana St. Clair)*, Deborah Walley *(Les)*, Dodie Marshall *(Susan)*, Jack Mullaney *(Curly)*, Will Hutchins *(Lieut. Tracy Richards)*, Warren Berlinger *(Philip Short)*, Jimmy Hawkins *(Larry)*, Carl Betz *(Howard Foxhugh)*, Cecil Kellaway *(Bernard Ranley)*, Una Merkel *(Violet Ranley)*, Frederic Worlock *(Blodgett)*, Dave Barry *(Harry)*.

Comedy with music. Singer Mike McCoy is head of a touring combo, which suits him perfectly since he has no intention of marrying. In Santa Barbara, however, he becomes involved with three females eager to change his single status. First, there is his drummer Les, who resents his treating her as "one of

the boys." Then there is Cynthia Foxhugh, the daughter of a millionaire car manufacturer who wants Mike to drive for him in the Santa Fe Road Race. Finally there is Diana St. Clair, who has selected Mike as the model for a book she is writing on the perfect American male. Annoyed by Cynthia's overbearing father, Mike wins the Santa Fe race by driving his own sports car. At the party following the event, he learns that all three girls are tired of waiting for him to marry; Les is in love with a young policeman, Cynthia has decided to marry her father's assistant, and Diana announces that she soon will be Cynthia's stepmother. Mike remains free of romantic entanglements, except for Susan, his new drummer. *Singers. Drummers. Bachelors. Millionaires. Authors. Police. Marriage. Automobile racing. Bands. Sports cars. Santa Barbara.*

Note: Auto racing scenes filmed at Dodger Stadium.

THE SPINSTER see **TWO LOVES**

LO SPIONE see **DOULOS—THE FINGER MAN**

SPIONE UNTER SICH see **THE DIRTY GAME**

THE SPIRAL ROAD   **F6.4650**
Universal Pictures. 3 Aug **1962** [New York opening; c1 Jun 1962; LP24329]. Sd; col (Eastman Color by Pathé). 35mm. 145 min. [Copyright length: 139 min.]
Prod Robert Arthur. *Dir* Robert Mulligan. *Screenplay* John Lee Mahin, Neil Paterson. *Photog* Russell Harlan. *Art Dir* Alexander Golitzen, Henry Bumstead. *Set Decor* Oliver Emert. *Titl Executed by* Pacific Title. *Film Ed* Russell F. Schoengarth. *Mus Supv* Joseph Gershenson. *Mus* Jerry Goldsmith. *Sd* Waldon O. Watson, Joe Lapis. *Asst Dir* Joseph Kenny. *Unit Prod Mgr* Richard McWhorter. *Gowns* Rosemary Odell. *Makeup* Bud Westmore. *Hair Stylist* Larry Germain. *Tech Adv* John Datu Arensma.

Cast: Rock Hudson *(Dr. Anton Drager)*, Burl Ives *(Dr. Brits Jansen)*, Gena Rowlands *(Els)*, Geoffrey Keen *(Willem Wattereus)*, Neva Patterson *(Louis Kramer)*, Will Kuluva *(Dr. Sordjano)*, Philip Abbott *(Frolick)*, Larry Gates *(Dr. Kramer)*, Karl Swenson *(Inspector Bevers)*, Edgar Stehli *(The Sultan)*, Judy Dan *(Laja)*, Robert F. Simon *(Dr. Martens)*, Ibrahim Bin Hassan *(Stegomyia)*, Reggie Nalder *(Burubi)*, Leon Lontoc *(Dr. Hatta)*, David Lewis *(Major Vlormans)*, Parley Baer *(Mr. Boosmans)*, Fredd Wayne *(Van Bloor)*, Leslie Bradley *(Krasser)*, Barbara Morrison *(Mrs. Boosmans)*, Martin Brandt *(Dr. Sander)*.

Melodrama. Source: Jan de Hartog, *The Spiral Road* (New York, 1957). In 1936, a young atheistic doctor, Anton Drager, arrives in Java to learn from Dr. Brits Jansen, the world's leading authority on leprosy, all he can about the dread disease and then return home to profit from his knowledge. Although Drager wins the old man's grudging respect, he antagonizes him by his lack of religious faith and his indifferent attitude toward humanity. Furthermore, Drager's wife, Els, finds herself neglected because of her husband's immersion in his work. One day Drager goes into the jungle to search for Frolick, an alcoholic river master who has been driven mad by the voodoo of a medicine man, Burubi. After being forced to kill Frolick in self-defense, Drager vows to fight the vicious Burubi. But he is tricked by Burubi and becomes lost in the jungle. Harassed by witchcraft horrors, he finds himself following the same crazed pattern that demented Frolick, who also lived without spiritual guidance. When Drager is at last found by a rescue party, he has lapsed into a coma. But Jansen's fight to save his life and Els's ceaseless devotion finally restore him to normalcy. And Drager now knows that one cannot live without thought for man, wife, or God. *Physicians. Boatmen. Medicine men. Atheists. Voodoo. Leprosy. Jungles. Religion. Alcoholism. Plague. Witchcraft. Java.*

Note: Location scenes filmed in Dutch Guiana.

THE SPIRIT IS WILLING   **F6.4651**
William Castle Enterprises. *Dist* Paramount Pictures. Jul **1967** [c31 Dec 1966; LP34615]. Sd; col (Technicolor). 35mm. 94 min. [Copyright length: 100 min.]
A William Castle Production. *Prod-Dir* William Castle. *Assoc Prod* Dona Holloway. *Screenplay* Ben Starr. *Dir Photog* Hal Stine. *Art Dir* Hal Pereira, Walter Tyler. *Set Decor* Robert R. Benton, Don Greenwood. *Film Ed* Edwin H. Bryant. *Mus Comp & Cond* Vic Mizzy. *Sd* Garry Harris, Charles Grenzbach. *Asst Dir* Daniel J. McCauley, Nat Holt, Jr. *Prod Mgr* Frank Caffey. *Makeup* Wally Westmore, Monte Westmore. *Hairstyles* Nellie Manley. *Sp Photog Eff* Paul K. Lerpae. *Proc Photog* Farciot Edouart. *Sp Eff* Lee Vasque.

Cast: Sid Caesar *(Ben Powell)*, Vera Miles *(Kate Powell)*, Barry Gordon *(Steve Powell)*, John McGiver *(Uncle George)*, Cass Daley *(Felicity Twitchell)*, Ricky Cordell *(Miles Thorpe)*, Mary Wickes *(Gloria Tritt)*, Jesse White *(Fess Dorple)*, Harvey Lembeck *(Captain Pederson)*, Robert Donner *(Ebenezer Twitchell)*, Nestor Paiva *(Felicity's father)*, Mickey Deems *(Rabbit Warren)*, Doodles Weaver *(Booper Mellish)*, Jay C. Flippen *("Mother")*, Jill Townsend *(Jenny/Priscilla Weems/Carol Weems)*, John Astin *(Dr. Frieden)*.

Mystery comedy. Source: Nathaniel Benchley, *The Visitors* (New York, 1964). Ben Powell, his wife Kate, and their teenaged son Steve rent a New England seaside house for their summer vacation. Unknown to them, the house has been haunted ever since the day, 100 years before, that Felicity Twitchell accidentally met her death while axing her unfaithful bridegroom Ebenezer and their servant girl Jenny. The three ghosts, infuriated that their private domain is being invaded, go on a spree of destruction, for which young Steve is blamed. Although the spirits eventually materialize before Steve, his parents and his millionaire Uncle George persist in believing that he is a troublemaker. The situation becomes desperate when the ghosts sink Uncle George's yacht and Steve once more is held responsible. Frantic, he seeks the aid of two local sisters, Priscilla and Carol, direct descendants of Jenny, who advise him to bribe the ghosts with gifts. After the unearthly trio has sunk a second yacht belonging to Uncle George, Steve purchases cosmetics and lingerie for Felicity and Jenny, an act which prompts his uncle to call in a psychiatrist, Dr. Frieden. Priscilla then suggests that Steve give a costume party so that the ghosts may materialize in their 19th-century clothes. The party, however, turns into a shambles when Felicity becomes so enamored of Uncle George that she pushes him off a cliff in order to make him her ghost-husband. Finally, as one of Uncle George's yachts rises miraculously from the depths and Dr. Frieden races off to seek the aid of a psychiatrist himself, the Powells decide to leave their summer home. And the old Twitchell place is left to the spirits of Ebenezer and Jenny: the ghosts of Felicity and Uncle George are sitting in the rumble seat of the Powell car as it heads back to the city. *Millionaires. Psychiatrists. Uncles. Sisters. Adolescence. Vacations. Murder. Ghosts. Haunted houses. Masquerades. Yachts. New England.*

Note: Location scenes filmed at Fort Bragg, California.

SPIRITISM (Mexico)   **F6.4652**
Cinematográfica Calderón. *Dist* K. Gordon Murray Productions, Trans-International Films. ca *1965.* Sd; b&w. 35mm. 85 min.
Pres by K. Gordon Murray. *Prod* Guillermo Calderón. *Dir* Benito Alazraki. *Screenplay* Rafael García Travesi. *Story* Rafael García Travesi, Guillermo Calderón. *Photog* Enrique Wallace. *Art Dir* José Rodríguez Granada. *Film Ed* Jorge Bustos. *Mus* Antonio Díaz Conde. *Sd* Eduardo Arjona.
Cast: Nora Veyrán, José Luis Jiménez, Jorge Mondragón, René Cardona, Jr., María Eugenia San Martín, Miguel Manzano, Rita Macedo, Antonio Bravo, Beatriz Aguirre, Carmel González.
Horror film. Source: W. W. Jacobs, "The Monkey's Paw," in *Harper's* (Sep 1902). Granted three wishes, a mother asks that her dead son return to life. A severed hand moves as if attached to a body, ghosts appear, and a midnight seance is held. *Death. Reviviscence. Mutilation. Seances. Ghosts.*
Note: Produced in Mexico in 1961 as *Espiritismo.*

SPIRITS OF THE DEAD (France/Italy)   **F6.4653**
Les Films Marceau-Cocinor-P. E. A. *Dist* American International Pictures. 6 Aug *1969* [Washington, D. C., opening; c23 Jul 1969; LP37270]. Sd; col (Berkey Pathé). 35mm. 117 min. *MPAA rating* R.
Production Credits--English Vers: *English Narr* Clement Biddle Wood. *Song:* "Ruby" sung by Ray Charles.
Production Credits for "Metzengerstein": *Dir* Roger Vadim. *Screenplay* Roger Vadim, Pascal Cousin. *Photog* Claude Renoir. *Art Dir* Jean Forestier. *Set Decor* Jean André. *Film Ed* Hélène Plemiannikov. *Mus* Jean Prodromidès. *Asst Dir* Jean-Michel Lacor, Michel Clément, Serge Vallin. *Prod Mgr* Ludmilla Goulian, André Cultet. *Cost* Jacques Fonteray.
Production Credits for "William Wilson": *Dir-Writ* Louis Malle. *Dial* Daniel Boulanger. *Photog* Tonino Delli Colli. *Art Dir* Ghislain Uhry, Carlo Leva. *Film Ed* Franco Arcalli, Suzanne Garon. *Mus* Diego Masson. *Asst Dir* Vana Caruso. *Prod Mgr* Tommaso Sagone. *Cost* Ghislain Uhry, Carlo Leva.
Production Credits for "Never Bet the Devil Your Head" or "Toby Dammit": *Dir* Federico Fellini. *Screenplay* Federico Fellini, Bernardino Zapponi. *Photog* Giuseppe Rotunno. *Art Dir* Piero Tosi. *Film Ed* Ruggero Mastroianni. *Mus* Nino Rota. *Asst Dir* Eschilo Tarquini. *Prod Mgr* Tommaso Sagone. *Cost* Piero Tosi. *Sp Eff* Joseph Natanson.
Narrator: Vincent Price.
Cast—"Metzengerstein": Jane Fonda (*Countess Frederica*), Peter Fonda (*Baron Wilhelm*), Carla Marlier (*Claude*), Françoise Prévost (*friend of countess*), James Robertson-Justice (*countess' advisor*), Anny Duperey (*1st guest*), Philippe Lemaire (*Philippe*), Serge Marquand (*Hugues*), Andreas Voutsinas (*2d guest*), Audoin de Bardot (*page*), Douking (*du Lissier*).
Cast—"William Wilson": Brigitte Bardot (*Giuseppina*), Alain Christina (*Wilson*), Katia Christina (*young girl*), Umberto D'Orsi (*Hans*), Daniele Vargas (*professor*), Renzo Palmer (*priest*).
Cast—"Never Bet the Devil Your Head" or "Toby Dammit": Terence Stamp (*Toby Dammit*), Salvo Randone (*priest*), Fabrizio Angeli (*1st director*), Ernesto Colli (*2d director*), Marina Yaru (*child*), Anne Tonietti (*television commentator*), Aleardo Ward (*1st interviewer*), Paul Cooper (*2d interviewer*),

Antonia Pietrosi, Rick Boyd, Polidor.
Drama. Source: Edgar Allan Poe, "Metzengerstein," in *Saturday Courier* (14 Jan 1832). Edgar Allan Poe, "William Wilson," in *The Gift: A Christmas and New Year's Present for 1840* (Philadelphia, 1839). Edgar Allan Poe, "Never Bet Your Head," in *Graham's Magazine* (Sep 1841). METZENGERSTEIN: Dissolute Countess Frederica fancies a distant relative, Baron Wilhelm; but, spurned by the nobleman, she sets his stable afire. While attempting to save his favorite stallion, the baron dies. Thereafter, the countess is mesmerized by the steed, which has survived the blaze. She mounts the horse, which rushes into a blazing heath. WILLIAM WILSON: An Austrian officer confesses the murder of his "double" to a naive country priest. Wilson describes the shadow's persistent intrusion into his life and his own sadistic activities in school, including lowering a schoolmate into a tub of rats, performing surgery on an unwilling young girl, and flogging Giuseppina, his card partner. Unable to find solace in the sacrament, Wilson despairs and throws himself from the steeple of the church. TOBY DAMMIT: When a cynical, liquor-soaked English superstar is lured to Rome to make a film by the promise of a Maserati automobile, he is haunted by a lewdly smiling, small, blonde girl, who bounces a large white ball. Upon completion of the first Catholic western, Toby receives the car during a grotesque film award party. He gets drunk and leaves the party, roaring off in the Maserati; attempting to jump over a ruined bridge and muttering, "Let the Devil take my head off if I don't make the jump," Toby is decapitated by a wire strung across his path. The girl nonchalantly picks up his head. *Nobility. Austrians. Soldiers. Doubles. Priests. Students. English. Actors. Children. Supernatural. Revenge. Arson. Obsession. Suicide. Murder. Conscience. Confession. Decapitation. Sadism. Drunkenness. Rome. The Devil. Fires. Horses.*
Note: Opened in Paris in Jun 1968 as *Histoires extraordinaires;* running time: 123 min; in Rome in 1968 as *Tre passi nel delirio.*

SPLENDOR IN THE GRASS   **F6.4654**
NBI Productions–Newton Productions. *Dist* Warner Bros. Pictures. 10 Oct *1961* [New York opening; c14 Oct 1961; LP29395]. Sd; col (Technicolor). 35mm. 124 min.
Prod-Dir Elia Kazan. *Assoc Prod* William Inge, Charles H. Maguire. *Orig Story & Screenplay* William Inge. *Photog* Boris Kaufman. *Art Dir* Richard Sylbert. *Set Decor* Gene Callahan. *Film Ed* Gene Milford. *Mus Comp & Cond* David Amram. *Choreog* George Tapps. *Sd* Edward Johnstone. *Asst Dir* Don Kranze. *Script & Cont* Marguerite James. *Cost* Anna Hill Johnstone. *Makeup* Robert Jiras. *Hairstyles* Willis Hanchett.
Cast: Natalie Wood (*Wilma Dean Loomis*), Warren Beatty (*Bud Stamper*), Pat Hingle (*Ace Stamper*), Audrey Christie (*Mrs. Loomis*), Barbara Loden (*Ginny Stamper*), Zohra Lampert (*Angelina*), Fred Stewart (*Del Loomis*), Joanna Roos (*Mrs. Stamper*), Jan Norris (*Juanita Howard*), Gary Lockwood (*Toots*), Sandy Dennis (*Kay*), Crystal Field (*Hazel*), Marla Adams (*June*), Lynn Loring (*Carolyn*), John McGovern (*Doc Smiley*), Martine Bartlett (*Miss Metcalf*), Sean Garrison (*Glenn*), Charles Robinson (*Johnny Masterson*), Phyllis Diller (*Texas Guinan*), William Inge (*Reverend Whitman*), Phoebe Mackay (*Stamper maid*).
Drama. In a small Kansas town during the late 1920's, two high school students, Wilma Dean Loomis and Bud Stamper, fall in love. Frightened by their physical desires but unwilling to have a sexual relationship, their time together is filled with confusion and frustration. Furthermore, their well-intentioned parents are of little help. Wilma's mother is a domineering woman who boasts of her aversion to men and warns her daughter that nice girls do not have sexual feelings. Bud's father, Ace, is an arrogant self-made millionaire who advises his son to forget marriage until he graduates from Yale. Unable to consummate their love, either sexually or through marriage, the youngsters end their relationship. For Bud, it means both physical and emotional collapse, and, after a bout with pneumonia, he takes up with Juanita, the most permissive girl in school. Following an attempted suicide, Wilma suffers a mental breakdown and is sent away for psychiatric care. As the years pass, additional tragedy strikes Bud. His promiscuous sister, Ginny, dies in an automobile accident; and his father, whose oil holdings were wiped out by the 1929 stock market crash, commits suicide. Bud leaves Yale after failing almost all of his courses and marries a poor Italian waitress, Angelina. When Wilma is released from the sanitarium, fellow patient Johnny Masterson proposes to her and offers her the chance for a new life. Before she can accept, however, Wilma feels that she must see Bud once more. She visits him at his little farm, and they realize that they are almost strangers and that the past must be buried. *Students. Millionaires. Waitresses. Italians. Smalltown life. High school life. Adolescence. Filial relations. Sexual initiation. Promiscuity. Mental illness. Suicide. Marriage. Sanitariums. The Great Depression (1929–34). Yale University.*
Note: Location scenes filmed in Staten Island and High Falls, New York. Wordsworth's "Ode on Intimations of Immortality" is the source of the film title.

THE SPLIT   F6.4655
Spectrum Productions. *Dist* Metro-Goldwyn-Mayer, Inc. 8 Oct **1968** [Chicago opening; c30 Aug 1968; LP36034]. Sd; col (Metrocolor). 35mm (Panavision). 90 min.
Prod Irwin Winkler, Robert Chartoff. *Dir* Gordon Flemyng. *Screenplay* Robert Sabaroff. *Dir Photog* Burnett Guffey. *Art Dir* George W. Davis, Urie McCleary. *Set Decor* Henry Grace, Keogh Gleason. *Film Ed* Rita Roland. *Mus* Quincy Jones. *Titl Song* Quincy Jones, Ernie Shelby. *Sung by* Billy Preston. *Song: "A Good Woman's Love"* Quincy Jones, Sheb Wooley. *Sung by* Sheb Wooley. *Song: "It's Just a Game, Love"* Quincy Jones, Ernie Shelby. *Sung by* Arthur Prysock, Clydic King, Billy Preston. *Sd* Larry Jost. *Rec Supv* Franklin Milton. *Asst Dir* Al Jennings. *Unit Prod Mgr* Jim Henderling. *Makeup* William Tuttle. *Hairstyles* Sydney Guilaroff.
Cast: Jim Brown *(McClain)*, Diahann Carroll *(Ellie)*, Ernest Borgnine *(Bert Clinger)*, Julie Harris *(Gladys)*, Gene Hackman *(Lieut. Walter Brill)*, Jack Klugman *(Harry Kifka)*, Warren Oates *(Marty Gough)*, James Whitmore *(Herb Sutro)*, Donald Sutherland *(Dave Negli)*, Joyce Jameson *(Jenifer)*, Harry Hickox *(1st detective)*, Jackie Joseph *(Jackie)*, Warren Vanders *(Mason)*.
Crime melodrama. Source: Richard Stark, *The Seventh* (New York, 1966). McClain, an accomplished thief, returns to California after several years' absence and joins an old friend, Gladys, in masterminding a plan for robbing half a million dollars in receipts from the Los Angeles Coliseum while a sell-out football game is in progress. In organizing his gang, McClain subjects possible candidates to a brutal initiation test and comes up with four suitable recruits: gym instructor Bert Clinger, driver Harry Kifka, safecracker Marty Gough, and professional killer Dave Negli. Following weeks of careful preparation, the heist goes as scheduled and the money is hidden in the apartment of McClain's ex-wife, Ellie, who has consented to keep it on the condition that this be McClain's last job. But the next morning, while McClain is out, Ellie's psychotic landlord, Herb Sutro, attempts to assault her and actually kills her, then makes off with the money. A crooked police lieutenant, Walter Brill, investigates the murder and connects it with the stadium robbery; McClain is tortured by the other gang members and accused of stealing the money himself; and in the violent argument that follows, both Gladys and Kifka are killed, though McClain escapes. When Sutro is shot by Detective Brill while resisting arrest, McClain realizes that Brill now has the money and offers to share it with him if he will help eliminate the remaining gang members. Though Brill accepts the proposal and assists McClain in killing his former accomplices, the detective plans to turn a portion of his share over to the authorities and earn a promotion while making it appear that McClain has made off with the rest of the money. As McClain prepares to board a plane for Mexico, however, he recalls his promise to Ellie. Troubled, he must decide whether to escape with the money or turn himself over to the police. *Thieves. Athletic coaches. Safecrackers. Hired killers. Psychopaths. Landlords. Police. Chauffeurs. Gangs. Robbery. Divorce. Murder. Torture. Duplicity. Ambition. Los Angeles Coliseum.*
Note: Location scenes filmed in Los Angeles and San Pedro, California.

SPLIT COMMISSION   F6.4656
Dist Stacey Distributors. ca **1970**. Sd; col. 16mm. 61-81 min.
Sex film. No information about the precise nature of this film has been found. *Sexuality.*

SPLIT LOVERS   F6.4657
Mitam Productions. 23 Jul **1969** [Champaign, Illinois, showing]. Sd; b&w. 35mm. 63 min.
Story Idea Fred Hermann.
Cast: Arthur Hermann.
Melodrama. High school dropout Rick and his girl friend, Lily, break into a vacant house and use it to stage group sex parties. Lily becomes jealous of Rick's interest in Cindy and asks Bob to take her to the house. Bob breaks into the house, and Rick, thinking that the intruder is either the owner or the police, clubs his friend to death. Rick is arrested. *Adolescence. Burglary. Group sex. Jealousy. Murder.*

SPOILED DARLING   F6.4658
C. I. T. Films. *Dist* I. R. M. I. Films. 2 May **1968** [New York showing]. Sd; b&w. 35mm? 75 min.
Sex film. After an opening sequence in which two lesbians make love, the "spoiled darling" seduces her brother-in-law. She then convinces him to drug and seduce her sister. At the end of the film a striptease is performed. *Brothers-in-law. Sisters. Lesbianism. Seduction. Striptease. Drugs.*
Note: Also released as *Spoiled Darlings*.

SPOILED ROTTEN (Greece)   F6.4659
Finos Films. *Dist* Chancellor Films. Mar **1968**. Sd; b&w. 35mm. 89 min. [Also 97 min.]

Pres by Chellee Wilson. *Dir* Yannis Dalianidis.
Cast: Zoe Laskari *(Rhea)*, Nikos Kourkoulos.
Melodrama. Costas, a violent young teenager, grows bored with his willful mistress Rhea, and she, consequently, decides to have an affair with another boy to make Costas jealous. Costas bitterly sets out to ruin Rhea. He invites her out on the pretext of winning her back and abandons her naked on a country road. Still wounded in his pride, Costas seduces Rhea's younger sister. Rhea finds them in bed together and kills Costas. *Mistresses. Sisters. Adolescence. Jealousy. Revenge. Infidelity. Reputation. Seduction. Murder.*
Note: Alternative title: *Prized as a Mate!*

SPOILS OF THE NIGHT (Japan)   F6.4660
Toei Co. *Dist* William Mishkin. 14 Aug **1969** [New York opening]. Sd; b&w. 35mm. 84 min.
Dir Shinji Murayama. *Screenplay* Masashige Narusawa. *Photog* Hanjiro Nakazawa. *English Subtitl* Lewis Mishkin.
Cast: Tatsuo Umemiya *(Toru Matoba)*, Mako Midori *(Kazuko Uehara)*, Reiko Ohara *(Hatsue Uehara)*, Akiyo Kubo *(older woman)*.
Melodrama. Toru Matoba is a bartender at a singles bar in Tokyo. Besides his regular duties, he is a pimp and a gigolo, constantly seducing and using the women customers in the bar. Kazuko Uehara and her younger sister, Hatsue, are two of his victims; when he finds himself in trouble, Toru forces Kazuko to become a prostitute. A group of professional prostitute dealers resent Toru's efforts and give him a beating that sends him to the hospital. Meanwhile, Kazuko is arrested for prostitution and discovers that Toru denies any knowledge of her and that her parents have disowned her. The younger sister, Hatsue, seeks revenge and murders Toru. *Bartenders. Gigolos. Pimps. Seduction. Prostitution. Filial relations. Revenge. Murder. Singles bars. Tokyo.*
Note: Released in Japan in 1966 as *Iro*.

SPORTING HOUSE *see* **THIS SPORTING HOUSE**

SPORTORAMA   F6.4661
Paramount Pictures. May **1963**. Sd; col. 35mm. 64 min.
Anthology. Six short films about sports are featured: "Boats A-Poppin," "A Sport Is Born," "Kings of the Keys," "Speedway," "The Big A," and "Ten Pin Tour." *Sports.*
Note: All the films except "Boats A-Poppin" were featured in Paramount Pictures' *Sports Illustrated* series.

SPORTSMAN'S WORLD   F6.4662
Outdoor Film Productions. *Dist* Northwest Cinema Corp. 12 Feb **1969** [Minneapolis opening]. Sd; col. 35mm. 90 min.
Prod-Writ Bill Bryant. *Camera* Ebb Warren. *Film Ed* Bill Bryant.
Narrator: Gary Short.
Documentary. The film centers on hunting and fishing and includes scenes from hunting expeditions in New Zealand, India, and Africa. Unusual methods for hunting tigers in India and elephants in Africa are depicted. *Hunting. Fishing. India. New Zealand. Africa. Tigers. Elephants.*

LA SPOSA IN NERO *see* **THE BRIDE WORE BLACK**

SPREAD EAGLE (Reissue)   F6.4663
Paramount Pictures. *Dist* Citation Films. 15 Nov **1961** [Maryland license]. Sd; col. 35mm. 104 min.
Note: Originally released by Paramount Pictures in 1950 as *The Eagle and the Hawk*; c30 May 1950; LP142.

SPREAD EAGLES   F6.4664
Kirt Films International. *Dist* Distribpix, Inc. 18 Jul **1968** [San Francisco showing]. Sd; col. 35mm. 63 min.
Sex film. Two overworked airline stewardesses seeking rest and relaxation participate in a group sex activity. One of the men feels that he is being slighted; he goes berserk and stabs everyone else with a kitchen knife. *Airline stewardesses. Group sex. Murder.*

SPREAD IT AROUND   F6.4665
Dist Stacey Distributors. ca **1970**. Sd; col. 16mm. 61-81 min.
Sex film. No information about the precise nature of this film has been found. *Sexuality.*

SPREE   F6.4666
Producers Equity Corp. *Dist* United Producers Releasing Organization, Trans American Films. 21 Jun **1967** [Los Angeles opening; c15 Feb 1967; LP34887]. Sd; col (Pathé Color). 35mm. 84 min.
Prod Carroll Case, Hal Roach, Jr. *Dir* Mitchell Leisen, Walon Green. *Screenplay & Narr* Sydney Field. *Photog* Alan Stensvold. *Art Dir* Cajado. *Film Ed* (see note) Roy Livingston, Edward A. Biery, Otho Lovering. *Mus* Remo Usai. *Sd* Dick Peck. *Asst Dir* Bill Forsyth.

With: Vic Damone, Jayne Mansfield, Juliet Prowse, Mickey Hargitay, Constance Moore, Rozana Tapajos, Clara Ward Singers, Barklay Shaw.

Documentary. Highlighted in this journalistic view of Las Vegas are various cabaret acts at The Tropicana and at The Dunes. Included are a striptease number by Jayne Mansfield, a take-off on *Cleopatra* by Juliet Prowse, scenes of Vic Damone performing in one of the large club rooms, Constance Moore singing in the more intimate lounges, and the Clara Ward Singers performing. There are also miscellaneous shots of legitimate gambling, along with closed-door cockfights and bare-fisted boxing matches. *Entertainers. Singers. Chorus girls. Striptease. Gambling. Boxing. Cockfighting. Casinos. Nightclubs. Cabarets. Las Vegas. The Dunes. Tropicana (Las Vegas).*

Note: Filmed in 1962–63 in Las Vegas as *Las Vegas by Night.* Sources disagree in crediting film editor.

SPRING NIGHT, SUMMER NIGHT see MISS JESSICA IS PREGNANT

SPRINGTIME IN VIENNA (West Germany)   F6.4667
Dist Hoffberg Productions. Feb **1966**. Sd; col? 35mm. 90 min.

Opera film. No information about the precise nature of this film has been found.

Note: Original title and release undetermined.

SPRINGTIME ON THE VOLGA (U.S.S.R.)   F6.4668
Gorky Film Studio. *Dist* Artkino Pictures. 23 Dec **1961** [New York opening]. Sd; col (Sovcolor). 35mm. 75 min.

Dir Veniamin Dorman, Genrikh Oganisyan. *Screenplay* Mikhail Dolgopolov, Iosif Prut, Nadya Nadezhdina. *Photog* Vyacheslav Shumskiy. *Art Dir* Mark Gorelik, Sergey Serebrenikov. *Film Ed* R. Shor. *Mus* Aleksandr Flyarkovskiy. *Dance Mus:* "Devichya vesna" Ye. Kuznetsov. *Cond* D. Shtilman, A. Ilin. *Choreog* Nadya Nadezhdina. *Sd* A. Izbutskiy. *Creative Supv* Sergey Gerasimov. *Prod Mgr* V. Maron. *Cost* L. Silich.

Featuring: Beryozka Ensemble.

Cast: Mira Koltsova (*Galya*), D. Agafonova (*Vera*), G. Petrova (*Lena*), Garen Zhukovskaya (*Lugovaya*), Lyudmila Ovchinnikova (*Nastya*), E. Treyvas (*Angelina*), Anna Bogdanova (*grandmother*), Lev Barashkov (*Volodya*), Vladimir Lepko (*Gamba*), Georgiy Tusuzov (*cook*), Aleksandr Denisov (*mechanic*), Georgiy Slabinyak (*captain*), Vladimir Dorofeyev (*grandfather*), A. Vanin (*Lyosha*), I. Ryzhov (*porter*), L. Krauzova, M. Kutakhova, M. Grigoryeva (*girls on deck*).

Comedy-drama. Volodya, a Moscow optician, falls in love from a distance with Galya, a dancer with the Beryozka Ensemble. To be close to her, he signs on as a cook on the boat which is to carry the troupe on a tour along the Volga. Another member of the kitchen staff, Nastya, becomes attracted to Volodya, arousing Galya's jealousy. In spite of comical misunderstandings, however, Volodya and Galya find romance. *Opticians. Dancers. Cooks. Theatrical troupes. Jealousy. Ships. Moscow. Volga River.*

Note: Released in the U.S.S.R. in May 1960 as *Devichya vesna;* running time: 97 min.

SPY IN YOUR EYE (Italy)   F6.4669
Italian International Film–Publi Italia. *Dist* American International Pictures. 12 Jan **1966** [Boston opening; c29 Dec 1965; LP32303]. Sd; col (Eastman Color by Pathé). 35mm. 88 min. [Copyright length: 84 min.]

Prod Fulvio Lucisano, Lucio Marcuzzo. *Dir* Vittorio Sala. *Screenplay* Romano Ferrara, Adriano Baracco, Adriano Bolzoni. *Story* Lucio Marcuzzo. *Photog* Fausto Zuccoli. *Art Dir* Luciano Del Greco. *Film Ed* Renato Cinquini, Roberto Cinquini. *Mus* Riz Ortolani. *Asst Dir* Stefano Rolla.

Cast: Brett Halsey (*Bert Morris*), Pier Angeli (*Paula Krauss*), Dana Andrews (*Colonel Lancaster*), Gastone Moschin (*Boris*), Tania Beryl, Alessandro Sperli, Mario Valdemarin, Tino Bianchi, Aldo De Francesco, Renato Baldini, Marco Guglielmi, Luciana Angiolillo, George Wang, Luciano Pigozzi, Massimo Righi, Franco Baltimor, Giulio Mecale, Aghul Rain Bozan.

Melodrama. In Berlin, both U. S. and Russian agents are trying to discover the formula for a death ray perfected by a now deceased Nobel Prize winning scientist. Both sides have reason to believe the secret lies with his daughter Paula, though she insists she knows nothing. When she is abducted by the Russians, American agent Bert Morris is ordered to find her. The American chief of intelligence is unwittingly supplying the Soviets with information, for in the course of surgery for the replacement of his blinded eye, the Russians succeeded in placing a minute transmitting telecamera in the false eye and therefore are able to follow his every movement. Meanwhile, Bert has rescued Paula but loses her to the enemy again. American intelligence uncovers "the eye spy" and through it feeds false information to the Russians; and in the resulting confusion Morris and Paula make their way to safety. It is discovered that Paula's father had the death ray formula tattooed on her head, where it has been hidden by her hair. *Secret agents. Scientists. Americans in foreign countries. Russians. Abduction. Filial relations. Eye surgery. Secret formulas.*

Death rays. Tattoos. United States Army—Intelligence. Berlin.

Note: Rome opening: Oct 1965 as *Berlino, appuntamento per le spie;* running time: 105 min.

THE SPY WHO CAME   F6.4670
Cinex Film Industries. 22 Jan **1969** [New York showing]. Sd; b&w. 35mm. 71 min.

Prod R. Rawley Easton. *Dir* Ron Wertheim. *Writ* Bruce Marcus. *Photog* Joao Fernandes. *Lighting* Ron Sullivan. *Ed* Ron Wertheim. *Mus Comp & Cond* Dave Herman. *Sd* Arthur Marks. *Asst Dir* Don Walters. *Script Girl* Virginia Ruffalo.

Cast: Louis Waldon, William Countryman, James Vinci, Illya Souvern, Grace Young, Marilyn Walters, Gary Maxwell, Don Izzo, Pepper Stone, Debby Ryan, Ultra Blue, Philipa Reed.

Crime drama. A woman trained in the art of blackmail seduces detective Sgt. Harry Harris a week before his wedding. Harry's predicament becomes painfully clear as the closet door of their hotel room opens to reveal two thugs and a beautiful blonde woman holding a movie camera. They drive their victim to an abandoned castle, where an Arab presides, surrounded by beautiful women. The blonde cameraman, a lesbian, is ordered to make love with the detective for the voyeuristic pleasure of the Arab. Reluctantly she complies, and renders Harry powerless with her sensuous embraces. The next day, Harry's chief introduces him to a Frenchman from Interpol, who has been gathering evidence through the window slots at the castle. A huge programming operation is in progress: electronic devices, audio-visual equipment, and drugs are used to condition women with the perfect sexual response for the task of blackmail. The Frenchman exposes the sinister operation, and the beautiful lesbian meets with a violent end as the carefully engineered scheme is exploded. *Detectives. Arabs. French. Seduction. Blackmail. Lesbianism. Abduction. Brainwashing. Electronics. Narcotics. Motion pictures. Castles. INTERPOL.*

THE SPY WHO CAME IN FROM THE COLD (Great Britain)   F6.4671
Salem Films. *Dist* Paramount Pictures. 16 Dec **1965** [Miami Beach, Florida, opening; c16 Dec 1965; LP32193]. Sd; b&w. 35mm. 112 min.

A Martin Ritt Production. *Prod-Dir* Martin Ritt. *Screenplay* Paul Dehn, Guy Trosper. *Dir Photog* Oswald Morris. *Camera Op* Brian West. *Art Dir* Edward Marshall. *Set Dresser* Josie MacAvin. *Scenic Artist* Peter Melrose. *Prod Dsgn* Tambi Larsen. *Film Ed* Anthony Harvey. *Mus* Sol Kaplan. *Sd Mix* John W. Mitchell, John Cox. *Asst Dir* Colin Brewer. *Prod Supv* James Ware. *Asst to the Prod* Richard McWhorter. *Cont* Angela Martelli. *Wardrobe Mistress* Barbara Gillett. *Cost* Motley. *Makeup Supv* George Frost. *Hairdresser* Joan Smallwood.

Cast: Richard Burton (*Alec Leamas*), Claire Bloom (*Nan Perry*), Oskar Werner (*Fiedler*), Peter Van Eyck (*Hans-Dieter Mundt*), Sam Wanamaker (*Peters*), George Voskovec (*East German defense attorney*), Rupert Davies (*Smiley*), Cyril Cusack (*Control*), Michael Hordern (*Ashe*), Robert Hardy (*Carlton*), Bernard Lee (*Patmore*), Beatrix Lehmann (*president of tribunal*), Esmond Knight (*old judge*), Walter Gotell (*Holten*), Tom Stern (*CIA agent*), Niall MacGinnis, George Mikell (*German checkpoint guards*), Scot Finch (*German guide*), Katherine Keeton (*stripper*), Richard Caldicot (*Mr. Pitt*), Marianne Deeming (*Frau Floerdke*), Michael Ripper (*Lofthouse*), Henk Mobenberg (*passport officer*), Richard Marner (*Vopo captain*), David Bauer (*young judge*), Steve Plytas (*East German judge*), Anne Blake (*Miss Crail*), Michael Ritterman (*security officer*), Edward Harvey (*man in the shop*), Nancy Nevinson (*Mrs. Zanfrello*), Warren Mitchell (*Mr. Zanfrello*), Philip Badoc (*young German officer*).

Drama. Source: John Le Carré, *The Spy Who Came In From the Cold* (London, 1963). Alec Leamas, the British intelligence officer in charge of espionage in Germany, is sent home after another British agent is killed at the Berlin Wall. The British service, led by Control, wants to eliminate Hans-Dieter Mundt, head of the East German organization. Leamas acts as an alcoholic to undertake the assignment. He obtains a job as an assistant librarian and slowly becomes involved with librarian Nan Perry, a Communist. Sent to jail for fighting, he is released and offered a sum of money to reveal his secrets. Leamas accepts and meets Fiedler, Mundt's assistant. Fiedler, a brilliant Jew who is eager to frame Mundt as a double agent, arranges a secret trubunal with Leamas as the star witness. At the tribunal, Nan Perry is called as a surprise witness, and Leamas realizes that the purpose of the plot was to eliminate Fiedler and strengthen Mundt, who is really a British agent. Mundt arranges for Nan and Leamas to escape over the Berlin Wall, but when Nan, a security risk, has to be shot, Leamas stays behind and is also killed. *Germans. Spies. Secret agents. Communists. Jews. Librarians. Bribery. Frameup. Perfidy. Trials. German Democratic Republic. Great Britain—Intelligence service. Berlin Wall.*

Note: Filmed in England, Ireland, Holland, and West Germany. Opened in London in Jan 1966.

THE SPY WITH A COLD NOSE (Great Britain)   F6.4672

Associated London Films. *For* Paramount Pictures/Embassy Pictures. *Dist* Embassy Pictures. 19 Dec **1966** [New York opening]. Sd; col (Eastman Color by Pathé). 35mm. 93 min.

Prod Leonard Lightstone. *Exec Prod* Joseph E. Levine. *Assoc Prod* Robert Porter. *Dir* Daniel Petrie. *Orig Story & Screenplay* Ray Galton, Alan Simpson. *Photog* Ken Higgins. *Art Dir* Peter Mullins. *Titl* Richard Williams. *Film Ed* Jack Slade. *Mus Comp & Cond* Riz Ortolani. *Sd (see note)* Rusty Coppleman, Leslie Hammond, John Aldred. *Asst Dir* Colin Brewer. *Prod Assoc* Beryl Vertue. *Prod Mgr* Geoffrey Helman. *Cost* Yvonne Blake. *Makeup* Philip Leakey. *Hairstyles* Gladys Leakey.

Cast: Laurence Harvey *(Dr. Francis Trevellyan)*, Daliah Lavi *(Princess Natasha Romanova)*, Lionel Jeffries *(Stanley Farquhar)*, Eric Sykes *(Wrigley)*, Eric Portman *(British ambassador)*, Denholm Elliott *(Pond-Jones)*, Colin Blakely *(Russian premier)*, June Whitfield *(Elsie Farquhar)*, Nai Bonet *(belly dancer)*, Paul Ford *(American general)*, Peter Bayliss *(professor)*, Robert Flemyng *(chief of M.I. 5)*, Genevieve *(nightclub hostess)*, Norma Foster *("Ark" nurse)*, Renee Houston *(Lady Blanchflower)*, Robin Bailey *(M.I. 5 commander)*, Michael Trubshawe *(Braithwaite)*, Amy Dalby *(Miss Marchbanks)*, Bernard Archard *(Russian intelligence chief)*, Ronald Brittain *(commissionaire)*, Bruce Carstairs *(butler)*, Glen Mason *("Ark" assistant)*, Perry Brooks, Trevor Delaney, Steven Morley *(Farquhar's children)*, Gillian Lewis *(Lady Warburton)*, Tricia De Dulin *(air hostess)*, Virginia Lyon *(lift attendant)*, Julian Orchard *(policeman)*, John Forbes-Robertson *(M.I. 5 workshop director)*, Arnold Diamond *(agent in water wagon)*, Wanda Ventham *(Mrs. Winters)*, Disraeli *(himself, an English bulldog)*, Marianne Stone, Sally Low.

Comedy. In a rare moment of inspiration Stanley Farquhar, a bumbling British Intelligence man, conceives the idea of bugging a dog with a tiny microphone-transmitter and then presenting the animal to the Russian prime minister. Dr. Francis Trevellyan, a playboy veterinarian, is coerced into implanting the delicate instrument just underneath the skin of Disraeli, an English bulldog. The prime minister delightedly accepts the gift and takes his new pet everywhere. The plan is an enormous success, and British Intelligence is alerted to every Communist move and strategy, but complications develop when the dog develops a respiratory ailment. Terrified that a Russian veterinarian may detect the hidden transmitter, Farquhar and Francis fly to Moscow and enlist the aid of Natasha Romanova, a mercenary Russian princess whose political affiliation vacilates between the East and West. Natasha has already been assigned to the case by the Russians, but she is bribed by the British and helps them lure Disraeli away from the prime minister with a female dog. Although the deception works and Francis is able to extract the transmitter from the dog, Farquhar is knocked over by a truck and taken to a Russian hospital. He quickly recovers and triumphantly returns to England—unaware that the Russians planted a bug in his stomach during his stay in the Moscow hospital. *Spies. Prime ministers. Veterinarians. Russians. Royalty. Espionage. Electronic surveillance. Bribery. Moscow. Great Britain—Intelligence service. Dogs.*

Note: Kremlin scenes filmed on location at Castle Howard, England. Released in Great Britain in 1967. Sources conflict in crediting sound recorder.

THE SPY WITH MY FACE   F6.4673

Arena Productions. *Dist* Metro-Goldwyn-Mayer, Inc. 19 Jan **1966** [Boston opening]. Sd; col (Metrocolor). 35mm. 86 min.

Prod Sam Rolfe. *Exec Prod* Norman Felton. *Assoc Prod* Joseph Calvelli. *Dir* John Newland. *2d Unit Dir* E. Darrell Hallenbeck. *Screenplay* Clyde Ware, Joseph Calvelli. *Story* Clyde Ware. *Dir Photog* Fred Koenekamp. *Art Dir* George W. Davis, Merrill Pye. *Set Decor* Henry Grace, Robert R. Benton. *Film Ed* Joseph Dervin. *Mus* Morton Stevens. *Titl Theme* Jerry Goldsmith. *Sd* Franklin Milton. *Asst Dir* E. Darrell Hallenbeck.

Cast: Robert Vaughn *(Napoleon Solo)*, Senta Berger *(Serena)*, David McCallum *(Illya Kuryakin)*, Leo G. Carroll *(Alexander Waverly)*, Michael Evans *(Darius Two)*, Sharon Farrell *(Sandy Wister)*, Fabrizio Mioni *(Arsene Coria)*, Donald Harron *(Kitt Kittridge)*, Bill Gunn *(Namana)*, Jennifer Billingsley *(Taffy)*, Paula Raymond *(director)*, Donna Michelle *(Nina)*, Harold Gould *(doctor)*, Nancy Hsueh *(Wanda)*, Michele Carey *(Maggie)*, Paul Siemion *(clerk)*, Jan Arvan *(waiter)*.

Action comedy-drama. UNCLE agents Napoleon Solo, an American, and Illya Kuryakin, a Russian, are assigned to fly to Switzerland while guarding the combination to a vault in the Swiss Alps which holds the secret of a nuclear weapon powerful enough to destroy the world. Before the flight, THRUSH agent Serena lures Solo to her apartment, and there he is overpowered and his place on the plane is taken by a THRUSH agent who has been transformed by plastic surgery to look exactly like Solo. The impostor fools Illya but is nearly discovered when he does not recognize UNCLE agent Kittridge, whom he kills. He then obtains the combination to the vault. Arriving in Switzerland, Illya begins to be suspicious, and he makes his way to THRUSH headquarters. Meanwhile, Solo, who is being held prisoner in THRUSH headquarters, escapes after shooting THRUSH's leader Darius Two. Darius Two then pushes an "auto-destruct" button which blows up THRUSH headquarters, killing himself and most of the gang. The two Solos have a confrontation, and the real Solo is saved when Serena, taking sympathy on him, comes to his aid and shoots the impostor. *Secret agents. Doubles. Russians. Imposture. Murder. Organized crime. Theft. Suicide. Nuclear weapons. Airplanes. Plastic surgery. Vaults. Switzerland. Documentation. Explosions.*

Note: First shown on television 17 Nov 1964 as a 60-min episode of NBC's "Man From U.N.C.L.E." series as *The Double Affair;* c17 Nov 1964; LP33335.

SPYASHCHAYA KRASAVITSA *see* **THE SLEEPING BEAUTY**

SQUARE OF VIOLENCE (United States/Yugoslavia)   F6.4674

Lovćen Film. *Dist* Metro-Goldwyn-Mayer, Inc. May **1963** [c31 Dec 1962; LP25387]. Sd; b&w. 35mm. 98 min. [Copyright length: 94 min.]

Prod Aleksandar Sekulović. *Prod-Dir* Leonardo Bercovici. *Assoc Prod* Nikola Popović. *Story-Screenplay* Eric Bercovici, Leonardo Bercovici. *Photog* Aleksandar Sekulović. *Art Dir* Zoran Zorčić. *Film Ed* Roberto Cinquini, Olga Skrigin. *Mus Comp* Dušan Radić. *Mus Cond* Franco Ferrara. *Asst Dir* Stevo Petrović.

Cast: Broderick Crawford *(Dr. Stefan Bernardi)*, Valentina Cortese *(Erica Bernardi)*, Branko Pleša *(Major Kohler)*, Bibi Andersson *(Maria)*, Anita Björk *(Sophia)*, Bert Sotlar *(partisan leader)*, Dragomir Felba *(Serafin)*, Viktor Starčić *(German commandant)*, Nikola Simić *(radio operator)*.

War melodrama. In 1944, partisans in a German-occupied city plan to attack the Nazi forces in coordination with an Allied air offensive. The air attack is called off without their knowledge, however, and Dr. Stefan Bernardi throws a bomb, killing 30 German officers. Nazi Major Kohler demands 300 male hostages to be shot at 9 o'clock the following morning unless the man who threw the bomb surrenders. Dr. Bernardi is torn between protecting the partisans and saving the hostages. After a haunted night, he visits Major Kohler to receive assurance that the prisoners will be freed if the man responsible gives himself up. Upon receiving further promises, Bernardi decides to confess, but, upon returning home, he is restrained by the partisan leader, who reasons that under torture Bernardi may endanger the lives of thousands. He escapes, however, and while running to confess is shot by another member of the underground. Before he dies, he tells Major Kohler that it was he who committed the act, but the fanatical officer screams the order for execution of the hostages. *Hostages. Nazis. Military occupation. Resistance (political). Massacres. Bombs. World War II. Germany—Army.*

Note: Produced in Yugoslavia in 1961 as *Nasilje na trgu;* running time: 120 min.

THE SQUARE ROOT OF ZERO   F6.4675

Mark-L Enterprises. *Dist* Grooviemoovies, Pat Patterson Productions. **1964**. Sd; b&w. 16mm & 35mm. 80 min.

Prod-Dir-Writ William Cannon. *Cinematog* Sheldon Rochlin. *Asst Camera* Ed Ivins. *Titl* Al Stahl, Otis Maclay. *Film Ed* Sheldon Rochlin, Otis Maclay, William Cannon. *Orig Mus Comp, Arr & Cond* Elliot Kaplan. *Sd* Otis Maclay, Mark Dichter. *Asst Dir* George Jones, asst dir. *Prod Mgr* Ted Delot. *Script Supv* Veronica Bellach. *Makeup & Cost* Vincent Loscalzo. *Sp Eff* Al Stahl, Otis Maclay. *1st Grip* Bill Landis. *Props* Jerry Jenkins.

Cast: Michael Egan *(Zero)*, Jimmy Gavin *(Alan)*, Leslie Davis *(Jane Liggett)*, Don Woodbury *(Arch Liggett)*, Mary Bauer *(May Liggett)*, Jeri Archer *(Nell)*, George Quinn *(Garfield, the chauffeur)*, Roberta Longhi *(Agnes, the housemaid)*, Bob Spivak *(Hank)*, Barbara Krauthamer *(Dorrie)*, Dan Broyles *(The Indian)*, K. T. Daggott *(Mrs. Harrison)*.

Comedy. Zero, a beatnik who makes up true-confession stories but never writes them down, imagines that he and his friend Alan, a painter, go camping on an island in Maine. Alan makes the acquaintance of Jane, a young woman who with her wealthy parents is also camping on the island. Zero is left to a dull, platonic relationship with Jane's mother May, a writer of squalid dramas. Her husband Arch spends his time on his yacht with Nell, a vacationing prostitute. Alan becomes frightened when he learns that Jane might be pregnant, and he and Zero depart after staging a mock drowning and funeral. *Authors. Beatniks. Painters. Businessmen. Playwrights. Prostitutes. Camping. Pregnancy. Hoaxes. Wealth. Funerals. Maine. Fantasy.*

Note: Released by Signature Films as *This Immoral Age.*

SREDI DOBRYKH LYUDEY *see* **MOTHER AND DAUGHTER**

SREO SAM ČAK I SREĆNE CIGANE *see* **I EVEN MET HAPPY GYPSIES**

STACHKA *see* **STRIKE**

DIE STADT IST VOLLER GEHEIMNISSE *see* **CITY OF SECRETS**

STADT OHNE MITLEID *see* **TOWN WITHOUT PITY**

STAGE TO THUNDER ROCK   **F6.4676**

A. C. Lyles Productions. *Dist* Paramount Pictures. 17 Jun **1964** [Seattle, Washington, opening; c31 Dec 1963; LP28084]. Sd; col (Technicolor). 35mm (Techniscope). 82 min.

Prod A. C. Lyles. *Dir* William F. Claxton. *Screenplay* Charles A. Wallace. *Dir Photog* W. Wallace Kelley. *Art Dir* Hal Pereira, Robert Smith. *Set Decor* Sam Comer, James Roach. *Film Ed* Jodie Copelan. *Mus* Paul Dunlap. *Sd* Harold Lewis. *Asst Dir* Russ Haverick. *Makeup Supv* Wally Westmore.

Cast: Barry Sullivan (*Sheriff Horne*), Marilyn Maxwell (*Leah Parker*), Scott Brady (*Sam Swope*), Lon Chaney, [Jr.] (*Henry Parker*), John Agar (*Dan Carrouthers*), Wanda Hendrix (*Mrs. Swope*), Anne Seymour (*Myra Parker*), Keenan Wynn (*Ross Sawyer*), Allan Jones (*Mayor Ted Dollar*), Ralph Taeger (*Reese Sawyer*), Laurel Goodwin (*Julie Parker*), Robert Strauss (*Judge Bates*), Robert Lowery (*Seth Barrington*), Argentina Brunetti (*Sarita*), Rex Bell, Jr. (*"Shotgun"*), Suzanne Cupito (*Sandy Swope*), Wayne Peters (*Toby Sawyer*), Paul E. Burns, Roy Jenson.

Western melodrama. Sheriff Horne, in his last job before retirement, tracks down the Sawyer brothers, who have robbed the town bank of $50,000. Horne kills one of the brothers and captures the other, Reese, who taunts him with threats that his father, Ross Sawyer, who adopted and reared Horne, will soon be coming after him. Horne takes Reese to the nearby stagecoach depot to await the next stage to town. There Henry Parker, the dispirited owner of the station, along with his nagging wife, Myra, and daughter Julie, are celebrating the return of eldest daughter Leah, a former sweetheart of Horne's whom they believe to be a schoolteacher but who is in fact a woman with a shady reputation. The Parkers, in danger of losing their land, hope that Leah can provide them with the needed funds. Meanwhile, Judge Bates and Mayor Dollar, aware of Horne's personal involvement with the Sawyers, have hired Sam Swope, a friend of Horne, to hunt the brothers. Swope, desperately in need of money for his blind daughter, goes out to intercept Ross, who has a price on his head, but he is killed. Reese manages to bribe Mrs. Parker into helping him escape, but her family refuses to assist him, and his escape attempt fails. Ross arrives at the station, and in the showdown Horne kills him. The Parkers determine to keep their land, and Horne rides to town with Reese and the stolen money, knowing that Leah will be awaiting his return. *Sheriffs. Outlaws. Brothers. Mayors. Judges. Bounty hunters. Retirement. Bank robberies. Filial relations. Eviction. Bribery. Reputation. Adoption. Stagecoach depots.*

Note: Working title: *Stagecoach to Hell.*

STAGECOACH   **F6.4677**

Martin Rackin Productions. *Dist* Twentieth Century–Fox Film Corp. 18 May **1966** [Denver, Colorado, opening; c18 May 1966; LP32929]. Sd (Westrex); col (DeLuxe). 35mm (CinemaScope). 114 min.

A Martin Rackin Production. *Prod* Martin Rackin. *Assoc Prod* Alvin G. Manuel. *Dir* Gordon Douglas. *2d Unit Dir* Ray Kellogg. *Screenplay* Joseph Landon. *Dir Photog* William H. Clothier. *Art Dir* Jack Martin Smith, Herman A. Blumenthal. *Set Decor* Walter M. Scott, Stuart A. Reiss. *Film Ed* Hugh S. Fowler. *Mus* Jerry Goldsmith. *Song:* "Stagecoach to Cheyenne" Lee Pockriss, Paul Vance. *Sung by* Wayne Newton. *Orch* Arthur Morton. *Sd* Bernard Freericks, Elmer Raguse. *Asst Dir* Joseph E. Rickards. *Unit Prod Mgr* Harry Caplan. *Prod Asst* Arthur Steloff. *Makeup* Ben Nye. *Supv Hairstylist* Margaret Donovan. *Hairstyles for Ann-Margret Created by* Sydney Guilaroff. *Sp Photog Eff* L. B. Abbott, Emil Kosa, Jr. *Coöp* Caribou Country Club Ranch (Nederland, Colorado), Colorado Game, Fish & Parks Department. *Cast Paintings* Norman Rockwell. *Stunt Coörd* Dick Hudkins.

Cast: Ann-Margret (*Dallas*), Red Buttons (*Mr. Peacock*), Michael Connors (*Hatfield*), Alex Cord (*Ringo*), Bing Crosby (*Doc Boone*), Bob Cummings (*Mr. Gatewood*), Van Heflin (*Curly*), Slim Pickens (*Buck*), Stefanie Powers (*Mrs. Lucy Mallory*), Keenan Wynn (*Luke Plummer*), Brad Weston (*Matt Plummer*), Joseph Hoover (*Lieutenant Blanchard*), Oliver McGowan (*Mr. Haines*), David Humphreys Miller (*Billy Picket*), Bruce Mars (*trooper*), Brett Pearson (*sergeant*), Muriel Davidson (*woman*), Ned Wynn (*Ike Plummer*), Norman Rockwell (*townsman*), Edwin Mills (*sergeant major*), Hal Lynch (*bartender*), Walker Edmiston (*Wells Fargo agent*), Barbara Wilkin (*Susan*), John Gabriel.

Western drama. Sources: Ernest Haycox, "Stage to Lordsburg," in *Collier's* (10 Apr 1937). Dudley Nichols, screenplay for the film *Stagecoach*, 1939. Shortly after a band of Sioux Indians have slaughtered a detachment of the U. S. Cavalry, a stagecoach passes through the area of the massacre. The occupants of the stagecoach are: Dallas, a dancehall girl being run out of town; Doc Boone, an alcoholic medic; Mr. Peacock, a liquor salesman who dresses like a preacher; Lucy Mallory, a pregnant Army wife en route to join her husband in Cheyenne; Hatfield, a hardened gambler who served in the Civil

War under Mrs. Mallory's father; and Henry Gatewood, a banker absconding with $10,000 of his father-in-law's money. Riding atop alongside the jittery driver, Buck, is Marshal Curly. The coach is stopped by the Ringo Kid, an outlaw tracking down the Plummer family, who killed his father and brother. The marshal takes away Ringo's rifle and orders him into the coach. During the long journey Doc Boone and Peacock become fast friends, Ringo romances the fiery Dallas, Hatfield comforts Mrs. Mallory as her labor begins, and the nervous Gatewood endlessly complains about time being wasted. At Horseshoe Bend, Mrs. Mallory, attended by Doc and Dallas, gives birth to her baby. Gatewood makes an unsuccessful attempt to steal one of the stage horses, and Ringo tries to escape from the marshal. Once the coach is again under way, Apaches attack. In the furious battle that follows, Hatfield is killed before the Indians are finally driven off. When the battered coach reaches Cheyenne, the marshal handcuffs Ringo to a wheel to prevent him from going after the Plummer family. The marshal learns about Gatewood's crime from the local stage agent. He enters the saloon to arrest Gatewood and is wounded by the Plummer boys. Luke Plummer, the boys' father, kills Gatewood for the $10,000; and Ringo is set free. In the final shoot-out, Ringo guns down his three enemies as a fire breaks out in the saloon. The marshal forfeits the reward for Ringo's capture and allows the outlaw to ride off with Dallas during the confusion caused by the fire. *Sioux Indians. Stagecoach drivers. Dancehall girls. Physicians. Salesmen. Gamblers. United States marshals. Outlaws. Apache Indians. Bankers. Alcoholism. Childbirth. Theft. Impersonation. Murder. Revenge. Massacres. Stagecoaches. Cheyenne. United States Army—Cavalry. Fires.*

Note: Location scenes filmed in Colorado. The film is a remake of John Ford's *Stagecoach*, released in 1939 by United Artists.

STAGECOACH TO DANCERS' ROCK   **F6.4678**

Gray-Mac Productions. *Dist* Universal-International. caOct **1962** [c15 Oct 1962; LP24451]. Sd; b&w. 35mm. 72 min.

Prod-Dir Earl Bellamy. *Story-Screenplay* Kenneth Darling. *Dir Photog* Ed Fitzgerald. *Mus* Franz Steininger. *Asst Dir* Daniel J. McCauley.

Cast: Warren Stevens (*Jess Dollard*), Martin Landau (*Dade Coleman*), Jody Lawrence (*Ann Thompson*), Judy Dan (*Loi Yan Wu*), Del Moore (*Hiram Best*), Don Wilbanks (*John Southern*), Bob Anderson (*Carl "Whip" Mott*), Rand Brooks (*Quint Rucker*), Gene Roth (*Jude*), Charles Tannen (*sheriff*), Mike Ragan (*Ben Wade*), Mauritz Hugo (*Roy*), Tim Bolton (*1st holster*), Milan Smith (*2d holster*), Alicia Li (*Mai Lei*), Cherylene Lee (*Ah Ling*).

Western melodrama. In 1873, the driver and guard of an Arizona-bound stagecoach abandon five passengers in the desert because one of them, Loi Yan Wu, is feared to have smallpox. A sixth passenger, Indian agent Hiram Best, inadvertently remains inside the stage. Besides the stricken young woman, the forsaken group includes gunslinger Jess Dollard, gambler Dade Coleman, U. S. Cavalry Maj. John Southern, and Dr. Ann Thompson, who has diagnosed the young woman's disease as chickenpox. [According, to one source, Coleman is the gunman and Dollard, the gambler.] Setting out on foot, the passengers find the stage with the bodies of the three men, victims of an Indian attack. Coleman hoards a canteen of water and steals Dollard's gun, thereby gaining power over the others. Dollard is bitten by a rattlesnake, but he is nursed back to health. Coleman, distraught, forces him out of the camp along with Loi Yan Wu, the object of anti-Chinese sentiments, and then murders both Major Southern and Dr. Thompson. The driver of an arriving stage, however, mistakes him for an attacking Indian and shoots him, leaving only Loi Yan Wu and Dollard as survivors. *Chinese. Gamblers. Physicians. Indians of North America. Indian agents. Snakebites. Murder. Racial prejudice. Survival. Stagecoaches. Smallpox. Deserts. Arizona. United States Army—Cavalry.*

Note: Working title: *Ballad at Dancers' Rock.*

STAGECOACH TO HELL *see* **STAGE TO THUNDER ROCK**

STAIRCASE   **F6.4679**

Stanley Donen Films. *Dist* Twentieth Century–Fox Film Corp. 20 Aug **1969** [New York opening; c20 Aug 1969; LP37507]. Sd; col (DeLuxe). 35mm (Panavision). 98 min. *MPAA rating* R.

A Stanley Donen Production. *Prod-Dir* Stanley Donen. *Screenplay* Charles Dyer. *Dir Photog* Christopher Challis. Philippe Brun. *Camera Op* Freddie Cooper. *Art Dir* Willy Holt. *Main Titl* Maurice Binder. *Film Ed* Richard Marden. *Mus* Dudley Moore. *Song Sung by* Ray Charles. *Sd Mix* Alex Pront, Jean-Louis Ducarme. *Dub Ed* Kenout Peltier. *Asst Dir* Marc Grunebaum, Pierre Roubaud. *Prod Exec* Arthur Carroll. *Prod Supv* Marc Maurette. *Wardrobe Supv* Clare Rendlesham. *Mr. Burton's Makeup* Ron Berkeley. *Mr. Harrison's Makeup* Alberto De Rossi. *Casting Dir* Maude Spector.

Cast: Rex Harrison (*Charlie Dyer*), Richard Burton (*Harry Leeds*), Cathleen Nesbitt (*Harry's mother*), Beatrix Lehmann (*Charlie's mother*), Stephen Lewis (*Jack*), Neil Wilson (*policeman*), Gordon Heath (*postman*), Avril Angers (*Miss Ricard*), Shelagh Fraser (*cub mistress*), Gwen Nelson (*matron*), Pat Heywood (*nurse*), Dermot Kelly (*gravedigger*), Jake Kavanagh (*choirboy*), Rogers and

Starr *(drag singers).*

Drama. Source: Charles Dyer, *Staircase* (London opening: 2 Nov 1966). For 30 years homosexuals Charlie Dyer and Harry Leeds have lived together over a barber shop they run in London; Harry now suffers from a scalp condition so aggravated that he keeps his head wrapped in towels, and Charlie is nervously awaiting a court summons for having been caught by the police for being dressed in drag. Although the two men have stung each other with insults for years, with Charlie usually the aggressor, the tension increases when Charlie receives a letter from his ex-wife informing him that their daughter is coming for a visit. Therefore he tries to get Harry out of the house by suggesting that his roommate take his mother for a drive in the country, whereupon Harry accuses Charlie of selfishness since the old woman is an arthritic cripple unable to move from her bedroom above the barber shop. That evening Charlie's summons arrives, and he asks Harry to lend him the money for his defense, but Harry refuses. Harry visits his own mother in an old age home, but she curses him and calls him "a sodomite." The fights between Charlie and Harry reach a peak when Charlie returns home with Jack, a casual pick-up, and when he hears Charlie order Jack to undress, Harry locks himself in the bathroom. Charlie later finds him unconscious and attempts to revive him, pleading with his roommate never to leave him alone. Harry eventually comes round and explains that he had not attempted suicide but was merely suffering from an attack of high blood pressure. On the day of his court appearance, Charlie prays for help, promising to be kinder to Harry in the future, but the promise is forgotten as soon as Harry appears wearing a cheap black wig. Ignoring Charlie's jibes, Harry offers to accompany him to court. Charlie refuses but realizes by the time he reaches the corner that he cannot go it alone, and he calls out for Harry to accompany him. *Barbers. Roommates. Invalids. Pickups. Police. Male homosexuality. Middle age. Old age. Filial relations. Jealousy. Female impersonation. Barbershops. Old age homes. Baldness. London.*

Note: Location scenes filmed in Paris and London.

STAKEOUT!　　　　　　　　　　　　　　　　　　　　　　　　　　**F6.4680**

Hughes Productions. *Dist* Crown International Pictures. Oct **1962.** Sd; b&w. 35mm. 81 min.

Prod Robert Hughes, William Hughes, Joe R. Gentile. *Dir-Writ* James Landis. *Cinematog* Jack Specht. *Asst Camera* Fred Lawrence. *Art Dir* Emogene Chapman. *Mus* Tom Downing. *Sd* William M. Andrews. *Asst Dir* C. M. Florance.

Cast: Bing Russell *(Joe),* Billy Hughes *(Joey),* Bill Hale *(Stoddard),* Jack Harris, actor *(Gus),* Bernie Thomas *(Greer),* William Foster *(Benny),* Eve Brent *(Susie),* Chris Wayne *(Jimmy Stoddard),* Whitey Hughes *(Sautu).*

Drama. Upon being released from prison, Joe is reunited with his 10-year-old son, Joey, and gets a job; but his employer's wife, who knows of his record, has him fired. Joe and Joey go to Wichita Falls, where Joe becomes a driller in the Stoddard oil fields. They are befriended by the foreman, Gus, but Joe is again fired because of his past history. Unemployed and desperate, Joe calls upon Benny, a former prison pal, to help him kidnap the Stoddard boy and hold him for ransom. They carry out the crime and hide out in a shack to await the ransom payment. They are discovered by a low-flying plane; and as the police close in, Joe saves the little boy from being killed by the other kidnaper at the cost of his own life. Joey, a witness to his father's heroism, is adopted by their friend, Gus. *Ex-convicts. Oilmen. Police. Fatherhood. Criminals—Rehabilitation. Unemployment. Kidnaping. Self-sacrifice. Adoption. Prisons. Oil fields. Wichita Falls.*

Note: Filmed in Texas. Producer Robert Hughes also acts in the film as Whitey Hughes.

THE STALKING MOON　　　　　　　　　　　　　　　　　　　　**F6.4681**

Pakula-Mulligan Productions-Stalking Moon Co. *Dist* National General Pictures. 25 Dec **1968** [Los Angeles opening]. Sd (Westrex); col (Technicolor). 35mm (Panavision). 109 min. *MPAA rating* G.

Prod Alan J. Pakula. *Dir* Robert Mulligan. *Screenplay* Alvin Sargent. *Adapt* Wendell Mayes. *Dir Photog* Charles Lang. *Art Dir* Roland Anderson, Jack Poplin. *Set Decor* Frank Tuttle. *Titl* National Screen Service. *Film Ed* Aaron Stell. *Mus* Fred Karlin. *Sd* Jack Solomon. *Mus Ed* John Mick. *Asst Dir* Don Kranze. *Unit Prod Mgr* Russ Saunders. *Exec Prod Mgr* Harry A. Caplan. *Script Supv* Meta Rebner. *Post Prod Supv* Jack Kirschner. *Cost* Dorothy Jeakins. *Miss Saint's Cost* Seth Banks. *Ladies' Cost* Grace Harris. *Makeup Supv* Del Armstrong, Frank Prehoda. *Hairstyles* Naomi Cavin. *Casting* Lynn Stalmaster.

Cast: Gregory Peck *(Sam Varner),* Eva Marie Saint *(Sarah Carter),* Robert Forster *(Nick Tana),* Noland Clay *(boy),* Russell Thorson *(Ned),* Frank Silvera *(major),* Lonny Chapman *(Purdue),* Lou Frizzell *(stationmaster),* Henry Beckman *(Sergeant Rudabaugh),* Charles Tyner *(Dace),* Richard Bull *(doctor),* Sandy Wyeth *(Rachel),* Joaquin Martinez *(Julio),* Red Morgan *(Shelby, stage driver),* Nathaniel Narcisco *(Salvaje),* Rolf *(a dog).*

Western melodrama. Source: Theodore V. Olsen, *The Stalking Moon* (Garden City, N. Y., 1965). In the Arizona of 1881, veteran scout Sam Varner

is present when a detachment of Army troopers rounds up a group of Apaches who have escaped from nearby reservations. Among the Indians is a white woman, Sarah Carver, who has been a captive of the Apaches for 10 years. Explaining that her 9-year-old halfbreed son is endangered by the Indians, Sarah wants permission to leave the area immediately. Since Sam is preparing to retire as a scout and settle down on a ranch he has bought in New Mexico, he consents to accompany Sarah and the boy to a railway depot. Salvaje, a renegade Apache, goes on a murderous rampage in order to get his hands on the boy, and when Sarah confesses that Salvaje is the child's father, Sam offers to take the woman and child with him. After traveling many miles by train and buckboard, they safely reach the ranch and settle down to a silent, peaceful existence. They are eventually joined by Nick, a halfbreed friend of Sam's, who warns that Salvaje has been tracking them all the way from Arizona. After Sam has discovered the mutilated bodies of a nearby Mexican family, he returns to his ranch and finds that Salvaje has kidnaped Sarah. Accompanied by his hired hand Ned, Sam finds Sarah's bleeding and unconscious body on a trail, where the Apache has left her to die. They bring her back to the farmhouse, and Salvaje continues to stalk his prey, boldly pitting his cunning against Sam's. First the Indian kills Ned's dog, then Ned himself, and finally Nick. Sam wounds him and chases him into the hills when he attempts to sneak into the cabin. Although Sam is wounded in the leg, he pursues his quarry until he finally manages to shoot and kill him. As Sam crawls back to the cabin, Sarah is waiting inside to help him. *Scouts—Frontier. Apache Indians. Halfcastes. Retirement. Kidnaping. Murder. Mutilation. Motherhood. Ranches. Arizona. New Mexico. United States Army—Cavalry. Dogs.*

Note: Location scenes filmed in Nevada. Stalking Moon Co. unconfirmed as production company.

STAND EASY see SOME KIND OF A NUT

STAR!　　　　　　　　　　　　　　　　　　　　　　　　　　　　**F6.4682**

Robert Wise Productions. *Dist* Twentieth Century–Fox Film Corp. 22 Oct **1968** [New York opening; c22 Oct 1968; LP36587]. Sd (Westrex); col (De Luxe) with b&w seq. 35mm & 70mm (Todd-AO). 175 min.

Prod Saul Chaplin. *Prod Assoc* Maurice Zuberano. *Dir* Robert Wise. *Screenplay* William Fairchild. *Narr* Peter Church. *Dir Photog* Ernest Laszlo. *Set Decor* Walter M. Scott, Howard Bristol. *Prod Dsgn* Boris Leven. *Film Ed* William Reynolds. *Mus Arr & Cond* Lennie Hayton. *Dance Mus Comp* Jay Thompson. *Titl Song* Sammy Cahn, James Van Heusen. *Sung by* Julie Andrews. *Song:* "In My Garden of Joy" Saul Chaplin. *Song:* "Down at the Old Bull and Bush" Harry Von Tilzer, Andrew B. Sterling, Russell Hunting, P. Krone. *Song:* "Piccadilly" Paul Morande, Walter Williams, mus, Bruce Seiver. *Song:* "Oh, It's a Lovely War" J. P. Long, Maurice Scott. *Songs:* "Forbidden Fruit," "Parisian Pierrot," "Someday, I'll Find You," "Has Anybody Seen Our Ship?" Noel Coward. *Song:* " 'N' Everything" Bud G. De Sylva, Al Jolson, Gus Kahn. *Song:* "Burlington Bertie From Bow" William Hargreaves. *Song:* "Limehouse Blues" Philip Brahm, Douglas Furber. *Songs:* "Someone To Watch Over Me," "Dear Little Boy," "Do, Do, Do" George Gershwin, Ira Gershwin. *Song:* "The Physician" Cole Porter. *Songs:* "My Ship," "Jenny" Kurt Weill, Ira Gershwin. *Dances & Mus Numbers Staged by* Michael Kidd. *Sd* Murray Spivack, Douglas O. Williams, Bernard Freericks. *Mus Ed* Robert Tracy. *Asst Dir* Ridgeway Callow. *Unit Prod Mgr* Saul Wurtzel. *Cost* Donald Brooks. *Wardrobe* Ed Wynigear, Adele Balkan. *Makeup* Willard Buell, William Turner. *Hairstyles for Miss Andrews* Hal Saunders. *Sp Photog Eff* L. B. Abbott, Art Cruickshank, Emil Kosa, Jr. *Dance Asst* Shelah Hackett.

Cast: Julie Andrews *(Gertrude Lawrence),* Richard Crenna *(Richard Aldrich),* Michael Craig *(Sir Anthony Spencer),* Daniel Massey *(Noel Coward),* Robert Reed *(Charles Fraser),* Bruce Forsyth *(Arthur Lawrence),* Beryl Reid *(Rose),* John Collin *(Jack Roper),* Alan Oppenheimer *(André Charlot),* Richard Karlan *(David Holtzman),* Lynley Laurence *(Billie Carleton),* Garrett Lewis *(Jack Buchanan),* Elizabeth St. Clair *(Jeannie Banks),* Jenny Agutter *(Pamela),* Anthony Eisley *(Ben Mitchell),* Jock Livingston *(Alexander Woollcott),* J. Pat O'Malley *(Dan),* Harvey Jason *(Bert),* Damian London *(Jerry Paul),* Richard Angarola *(Cesare),* Matilda Calnan *(Dorothy),* Lester Matthews *(Lord Chamberlain),* Bernard Fox *(assistant to Lord Chamberlain),* Murray Matheson *(bankruptcy judge),* Robin Hughes *(Hyde Park speaker),* Anna Lee *(hostess),* Don Crichton *(Gertrude's "Limehouse Blues" dance partner),* Peter Church *(newsreel narrator),* Jan Gernat *(stage manager),* Conrad Bain *(salesman at Cartier's).*

Cast—The Daffodil Girls: Jeanette Landis *(Eph),* Dinah Anne Rogers *(Molly),* Barbara Sandland *(Mavis),* Ellen Plasschaert *(Moo),* Ann Hubbell *(Beryl).*

Biographical drama with music. In the early 1940's Gertrude Lawrence, while starring in the Broadway musical *Lady in the Dark,* watches a newsreel summary of her career and recalls her past: In 1915 as a young woman, Gertrude leaves her mother's home in Bermondsey and goes to Brixton to join her father, Arthur, and his partner Rose, who are performing at a seedy music hall. Deciding that she also wants a career on the stage, Gertrude eventually lands a chorus job in London in an André Charlot revue. There her deliberate attempts to steal the limelight nearly lose her job, but the company's stage manager, Jack Roper, intervenes. Gertrude marries Jack, but his idea of marriage conflicts with her professional ambitions, and they divorce shortly after the birth of their daughter, Pamela. Helped by childhood friend and confidant Noel Coward, Gertrude stars in Charlot's first New York revue and receives instant acclaim. Each success makes it more difficult for her to choose among her suitors, however, and she juggles diplomat Sir Anthony Spencer, American actor Charles Fraser, and New York stockbroker Ben Mitchell, without committing herself to any of them. Similarly, her preoccupation with her career has also led to estrangement from her rapidly-maturing daughter, Pamela. Eventually, Gertrude's increasingly extravagant lifestyle leads her to bankruptcy, and she collapses from overworking to pay off her sizable debts. Following an enormous success with Noel Coward in his *Tonight at 8:30*, Gertrude goes on to do her first dramatic role in *Susan and God*. After a long run, Gertrude sees Richard Aldrich, a New England banker whom she had met earlier while playing *Private Lives* in London. Though initially hostile toward him, Gertrude agrees to appear in *Skylark* at Aldrich's Cape Cod playhouse; and after scoring a personal triumph in *Lady in the Dark* Gertrude marries Aldrich. *Songs*: "Down at the Old Bull and Bush" (Ensemble); "Piccadilly" (Gertrude Lawrence, Arthur Lawrence, Rose); "Oh, It's a Lovely War," "In My Garden of Joy" (Gertrude and the Daffodil Girls); "Forbidden Fruit" (Noel Coward); "'N' Everything" (Jack Buchanan, Billie Carleton, Gertrude, and the Charlot Revue Ensemble); "Burlington Bertie From Bow" (Gertrude); "Parisian Pierrot," "Limehouse Blues" (Gertrude and the Dance Ensemble); "Someone To Watch Over Me" (Gertrude); "Dear Little Boy" (Gertrude and Noel); "Do, Do, Do" (Gertrude); "Someday I'll Find You" (Gertrude and Noel); "The Physician" (Gertrude and the Dance Ensemble); "Has Anyone Seen Our Ship?" (Gertrude and Noel); "My Ship" (Gertrude); "Jenny" (Gertrude, Circus Performers, and the Entire Company). *Careerwomen. Chorus girls. Actors. Singers. Stage managers. Theatrical producers. Playwrights. Diplomats. Stockbrokers. Bankers. Theater. Fame. Vaudeville. Marriage. Divorce. Bankruptcy. Motherhood. Music halls. New York City—Broadway. London. Cape Cod. Riviera. Gertrude Lawrence. Noel Coward. Alexander Woollcott. Richard Aldrich. André Charlot. "Lady in the Dark". "Tonight at 8:30". "Susan and God". "Private Lives". "Skylark".*

Note: Location scenes filmed in New York City, London, Cape Cod, and the French Riviera. After its initial release, the film was withdrawn from circulation and reissued in Oct 1969 as *Those Were the Happy Times*; running time: 120 min. Film contains portions of Noel Coward's *Tonight at 8:30* and *Private Lives* and Rachel Crothers' *Susan and God*.

STAR IN THE WEST see THE SECOND TIME AROUND

STAR OF HONG KONG (Japan)   F6.4683
Toho Co.-The Cathay Organization. *Dist* Toho Co. Dec **1962** [Los Angeles showing]. Sd; col (Eastmancolor). 35mm (Tohoscope). 109 min.
Exec Prod Sanezumi Fujimoto, Robert Chung. *Dir* Yasuki Chiba. *Screenplay* Ryozo Kasahara. *Photog* Rokuro Nishigaki. *Mus* Hachiro Matsui.
Cast: Yu Ming, Wang Ing, Reiko Dan, Akira Takarada, Rin Tsuong, Mitsuko Kusabue, Wong Yen, So Yamamura, Sadako Sawamura, Lin Chong, Hiroshi Koizumi, Yu Fujiki, Daisuke Kato, Asami Kuji.
Romantic melodrama. Hsin Lien, the only daughter of Dr. Wang, chief of Hong Kong's refugee clinic, is studying in Tokyo when she meets Toru, whom she had known previously in Hong Kong. Although Toru is attracted to her, Hsin Lien decides to discourage his advances because she believes Kanako, a girl with whose family she is living, is in love with him. Toru informs Hsin Lien that he is being transferred to Hong Kong, and she replies that she is engaged to Ing Ming, a pupil of her father's. In Hong Kong, Kanako reveals to Toru that no such engagement exists, and Toru rushes off to Singapore, where Hsin Lien has gone to ease the pain of her decision. Hsin Lien accepts Toru's proposal of marriage, but her father dies before they can marry. Hsin Lien cancels the wedding to take over his work, and Toru is transferred to San Francisco. *Students. Physicians. Courtship. Marriage. Tokyo. Hong Kong. Singapore.*
Note: Released in Japan in 1962 as *Honkon no hoshi*.

THE STARFIGHTERS   F6.4684
Riviera Productions. *Dist* Parade Pictures. 25 Mar **1964** [California opening]. Sd; col (Technicolor). 35mm. 78 min. [Original length: 84 min.]
Pres by Robert Patrick. A Will Zens Production. *Prod-Dir-Writ* Will Zens. *Assoc Prod* Richard Bertea. *Photog* Leif Rise. *Film Ed* Michael David, ed. *Mus* Stephen Paul. *Sd Eff* Mark Thomas. *Prod Mgr* Robert Sands. *Tech Adv* B. A. Whitaker, (Maj. USAF), Brooks Morris, (Capt.).
Cast: Robert Dornan (*Lieut. John Witkowski*), Richard Jordahl (*Major Stevens*), Shirley Olmstead (*Mary Davidson*), Richard Masters (*Colonel Hunt*), Steve Early (*Lieutenant York*), Robert Winston (*Lieutenant Lyons*), Carl

Rogers (*Congressman Witkowski*), Ralph Thomas, actor (*Captain O'Brien*), Joan Lougee (*Betty Lyon*).
Melodrama. Three Air Force pilots, Lieutenants York, Lyons, and Witkowski, are assigned to Major Stevens' F-104 Starfighter training program. Witkowski's father, a famed World War II bomber pilot and now a prominent congressman, expresses his displeasure with his son's assignment to the Tactical Air Command and attempts to have him transferred to a B-58 bomber squadron. Nevertheless, Witkowski continues to train with the other men and becomes an expert pilot; meanwhile, he meets Mary Davidson, and a romance develops between them. The three trainees are sent by Major Stevens on a cross-country mission during a storm, and they are forced to separate. Lyons' plane is downed in the mountains, and Witkowski is feared lost; but it is later learned that Lyons has made a successful parachute landing, and Witkowski has brought his plane to safety at an alternate base. Witkowski, who has won his father's admiration, bids a temporary good-by to Mary and leaves for Europe with the rest of the squadron. *Air pilots. Filial relations. Parachuting. Airplanes—Jet. United States Air Force. United States Congress.*

STARK FEAR   F6.4685
B. H. S. Productions. *Dist* Ellis Films. Jan **1963** [c10 Jan 1963; LP26811]. Sd; b&w. 35mm. 86 min.
Pres by Burke-Hockman-Swain Productions. *Prod* Joe E. Burke, Ned Hockman, Dwight V. Swain. *Assoc Prod* Carl G. Stevenson. *Dir* Ned Hockman. *Screenplay* Dwight V. Swain. *Photog* Robert E. Bethard. *Camera Op* George Peters, photog, Laney Duck. *Art Dir & Set Decor* Marcus Fuller. *Mus Comp & Cond* Lawrence V. Fisher. *Perf by* Oklahoma City Symphony Orchestra. *Party Mus* Johnny Williams. *Sd* John Pierce. *Asst Dir* Robert E. Rogers. *Script Supv* Daniel Chichester. *Wardrobe* Joan McCrary. *Makeup* Melvin Parlow. *Hairstyles* Roy Long. *Psychological Cons* Charlyce King. *Dial Coach* Charles Suggs. *Gaffer* Les Tannehill. *Key Grip* Cloy Webb.
Cast: Beverly Garland (*Ellen Winslow*), Skip Homeier (*Gerald Winslow*), Kenneth Tobey (*Cliff Kane*), Hannah Stone, Paul Scovil, Edna Neuman, Bruce Palmer, Cortez Ewing, Barbara Freeman, George Clow, Darlene Dana Reno, John Arville, Carey Mount, Bob Stone, actor, Joseph Benton.
Melodrama. Ellen Winslow, in an attempt to get out of debt and help her unemployed husband, Gerald, finds a job for herself working for Cliff Kane. Instead of being pleased, Gerald flies into a jealous, sadistic rage and leaves her. Ellen finds Gerald in his Texas hometown, and there she is subjected to more abuse from him and then assaulted by his best friend, Harvey Suggett. She returns home to work and falls in love with Kane, but even after Gerald divorces her she cannot totally discard the emotional ties to her ex-husband. However, when she learns from a friend that Gerald secretly witnessed her run-in with Suggett and had done nothing about it, Ellen is freed of her guilt feelings and joins Kane in Mexico, where he has accepted a new job. *Marriage. Employment—Women. Unemployment. Jealousy. Divorce. Guilt. Employer-employee relations. Desertion. Debt. Texas.*
Note: Filmed in 1961 in Norman and Lexington, Oklahoma, and in Eureka Springs, Arkansas. Working titles: *Brink of Love* and *The Hate Within*.

STARLET   F6.4686
Ado Productions. *Dist* Entertainment Ventures, Inc. 10 Sep **1969** [Champaign, Illinois, showing]. Sd; col. 35mm. 100 min.
Prod David F. Friedman, William Allen Castleman. *Dir* Richard Kanter. *Orig Story-Screenplay* David F. Friedman. *Dir Photog* Paul Hipp. *Asst Camera* Sid Brownlee, Henning Schellerup. *Film Ed* Robert Freemantle. *Mus Supv* Billy Allen. *Sd* Sam Kopetsky. *Asst Dir* Don Brodie. *Prod Asst* Richard Jaloff. *Head Grip* Paul Wilmoth. *Ch Electrn* Rod Wilmoth.
Cast: Shari Mann (*Allison Jordan*), Deirdre Nelson (*Carol Yates*), Chris Mathis (*Linda Ford*), Stuart Lancaster (*Kenyon Adler*), John Alderman (*Phil Latio*), Kathi Cole (*Maxine Henning*), Vincent Brian (*Forrest Barker*), Jay Donohue (*Jerry*), Joe Gardner (*Doug Davis*), Karen Nichols (*Miss Scott*), Clark Twelvetrees (*cameraman*), Paul Wilmoth (*motorcycle gang leader*), Dave Friedman (*himself*), Billy Allen (*himself*), Heaven's Devils (*themselves*).
Drama. Young starlet Carol Yates appears with Doug Davis in a stag film directed by Phil Latio. Studio boss Kenyon Adler sees the film and asks that Carol and her roommates, Allison, a bisexual hippie, and Linda, a 23-year-old virgin, come to his party. There they meet the reigning sex star, Maxine, a bisexual who is attracted to Allison. Carol, after a good performance on Adler's couch, gets the lead in the new sex film *A Youth in Babylon*. Maxine is tossed aside for Carol and swears revenge; with the help of her new lover, Allison, she steals Carol's first stag film. Allison is chased through the EVI lot and runs into the generator room where she is accidentally electrocuted and the film destroyed. Carol, as "Starliss Knight," rockets to stardom and surprises everyone by marrying Doug Davis, now "Rick Arnold," a rising actor under contract to a competitive studio. *Actors. Motion picture producers. Motion picture directors. Hippies. Revenge. Bisexuality. Lesbianism. Electrocution—Accidental. Sex exploitation films. Motion picture studios.*
Note: Deirdre Nelson may be a pseudonym for Dee Lockwood.

STARS IN YOUR BACKYARD see **PARADISE ALLEY**

START THE REVOLUTION WITHOUT ME   F6.4687
Norbud Films. *Dist* Warner Bros.–Seven Arts, Inc. 4 Feb **1970** [New York opening]. Sd; col (Technicolor). 35mm. 90 min. [Also reviewed at 98 min.] *MPAA rating* GP.

Prod-Dir Bud Yorkin. *Exec Prod* Norman Lear. *Assoc Prod* Edward Stephenson. *Screenplay* Fred Freeman, Lawrence J. Cohen. *Photog* Jean Tournier. *Art Dir* François de Lamothe. *Set Decor* Gabriel Bechir. *Main Titl* Unicorn Inc. *Film Ed* Ferris Webster. *Mus & Mus Dir* John Addison. *Sd* Julien Coutellier. *Asst Dir* Georges Grodzenczyk. *Prod Mgr* Roger Debelmas. *Cost* Alan Barrett.

Cast: Gene Wilder *(Claude Coupé/Philippe Di Sisi)*, Donald Sutherland *(Charles Coupé/Pierre Di Sisi)*, Hugh Griffith *(Louis XVI)*, Jack MacGowran *(Jacques Cabriolet)*, Billie Whitelaw *(Marie Antoinette)*, Victor Spinetti *(Duke d'Escargot)*, Ewa Aulin *(Princess Christina)*, Helen Fraser *(Mimi Montage)*, Rosalind Knight *(Helene Di Sisi)*, Maxwell Shaw *(Comte Di Sisi)*, George A. Cooper *(Dr. Duval)*, Graham Stark *(Coupé father)*, Harry Fowler *(Jacques' lieutenant)*, Murray Melvin *(blind man)*, Ken Parry *(Dr. Boileau)*, Jacques Maury *(Lieutenant Sorel)*, Denise Coffey *(Anne Duval)*, Barry Lowe *(Sergeant)*, Michael Rothwell *(Paul Duval)*, Orson Welles *(narrator)*.

Farce. In 18th-century France a doctor confuses two sets of twins born to the Corsican Duke Di Sisi and to Coupé, a peasant; to ensure that each father will get at least one of his natural sons, he gives both men one baby from each set. By 1789 the Di Sisi brothers, Philippe and Pierre, have become notorious for their swordplay, and when King Louis XVI begins to fear that revolution is imminent, he sends a note asking for their help. The message is intercepted, however, by the Duke d'Escargot who, with Queen Marie Antoinette, is the chief conspirator against the throne; he invites the Di Sisis to join him in overthrowing the king, and they tentatively accept. Meanwhile, as the Di Sisis depart on a barge for Paris disguised as peasants, the simple-minded Coupé brothers, Claude and Charles, have joined Jacques Cabriolet's band of revolutionaries. When Cabriolet's men attack the barge, the Coupé brothers are mistaken for the Di Sisis and taken to the palace, while the Di Sisis are taken back to the revolutionaries' hideout and committed to an insane asylum when Cabriolet finds their behavior to be radically different. At the palace, the king asks the Coupés to assassinate the Duke d'Escargot to prevent him from marrying Princess Christina of Belgium and thus acquiring the power to conquer France; in addition, the unfaithful queen conspires with Claude, whom she still believes to be one of the Di Sisis, to kill d'Escargot so that they can rule France together. As the duke and a group of his men disguised as monks attempt unsuccessfully to assassinate the Coupés, the Di Sisi brothers escape from the asylum and rush to the palace, where great confusion results concerning the men's true identity. Cabriolet and his band march on the palace to depose the king, while the Coupé brothers hurriedly extract a reform proclamation from him; the reforms come too late, however, and the peasants attack the palace. At this point, narrator Orson Welles, in a 20th-century setting, attempts to complete the story by reading from a history book, but two look-alikes (descendants of Charles and Pierre) appear and shoot Welles; two more look-alikes (descendants of Claude and Philippe) appear, and one shoots both Charles/Pierre descendants. One of the Claude/Philippe descendants then shoots the other, and the survivor himself is shot by the "Man in the Iron Mask," who has finally been freed from the Tower by the insurgents. *Physicians. Corsicans. French. Twins. Brothers. Nobility. Royalty. Peasants. Revolutionaries. Belgians. Doubles. Childbirth. Conspiracy. Disguise. Mistaken identity. Infidelity. Ambition. Assassination. Murder. Insane asylums. France—History—Revolution 1789–93. France. Paris. Louis XVI (France). Marie Antoinette. Versailles Palace.*

Note: Location scenes filmed in France around the Château de Rochefort and the Cathedral of Notre Dame. Working title: *Two Times Two.* Prerelease title: *Louie, There's a Crowd Downstairs!*

ŠŤASTNÝ KONEC see **HAPPY END**

STATE FAIR   F6.4688
Twentieth Century-Fox Film Corp. 4 Apr **1962** [Dallas opening; c1 Apr 1962; LP21691]. Sd (Westrex); col (De Luxe). 35mm (CinemaScope). 118 min.

Prod Charles Brackett. *Dir* Jose Ferrer. *Screenplay* Richard Breen. *Adapt* Oscar Hammerstein, II, Sonya Levien, Paul Eliot Green. *Dir Photog* William C. Mellor. *Art Dir* Jack Martin Smith, Walter M. Simonds. *Set Decor* Walter M. Scott, Lou Hafley. *Film Ed* David Bretherton. *Mus* Richard Rodgers. *Lyr* Oscar Hammerstein, II. *Adtl Songs* Richard Rodgers. *Mus Supv & Cond* Alfred Newman. *Assoc* Ken Darby. *Orch* George Bassman, Henry Beau, Benny Carter, Pete King, Gus Levene, Bernard Mayers. *Choreog* Nick Castle. *Sd* Alfred Bruzlin, Warren B. Delaplain. *Asst Dir* Ad Schaumer. *Cost* Marjorie Best. *Makeup* Ben Nye. *Hairstyles* Helen Turpin. *Sp Photog Eff* L. B. Abbott,

Emil Kosa, Jr. *Location Casting Dir* Bob Palmer.

Cast: Pat Boone *(Wayne Frake)*, Bobby Darin *(Jerry Dundee)*, Pamela Tiffin *(Margie Frake)*, Ann-Margret *(Emily Porter)*, Tom Ewell *(Abel Frake)*, Alice Faye *(Melissa Frake)*, Wally Cox *(Hipplewaite)*, David Brandon *(Harry)*, Clem Harvey *(Doc Cramer)*, Robert Foulk *(squat judge)*, Linda Henrich *(Betty Jean)*, Edward "Tap" Canutt *(Red Hoerter)*, Margaret Deramee *(Lilya)*, Albert Harris *(Jim)*, Bebe Allan *(usherette)*, George Russell *(George Hoffer)*, Edwin McClure *(announcer)*, Walter Beilbey *(swine judge)*, Tom Loughney *(Dick Burdick)*, Claude Hall *(Sime)*, Tony Zoppi *(The Masher)*, Mary Durant *(woman judge)*, Sheila Mathews *(Hipplewaite's girl)*, Kay Sutton, Ken Hudgins, Dan Terrell, Louis Roussel, Milton Stolz, Bob Larkin, Tommy Allen, Carl Princi, Jack Carr, Mamie Harris, Paul Rhone, Freeman Morse.

Musical comedy. Source: Philip Stong, *State Fair* (New York, 1932). Expectations are high as the Frake family arrives at the annual Texas State Fair: Abel is entering his prize hog, Blue Boy, in the grand championship; Melissa hopes to win the mincemeat competition; young Wayne is planning to enter the sports car racing event; and 17-year-old Margie dreams of romance and adventure. Almost immediately Wayne becomes enamored of Emily Porter, a sexy showgirl, and Margie falls for Jerry Dundee, a brash and cocky television interviewer. Although Blue Boy is triumphant and Melissa's brandy-spiked mincemeat creates a sensation when the judge becomes drunk, the younger Frakes suffer disappointments. Wayne allows another competitor to win the auto race, and Emily, certain the Frakes will think her a tramp, walks out on him; Margie is heartbroken when Jerry suddenly disappears. Once back on the family farm, however, Wayne quickly forgets his first big romantic experience and runs off to visit his old girl friend. Later Margie is radiant when Jerry phones, explains he was called out of town, and asks her to marry him. *Songs:* "It Might As Well Be Spring" (Margie); "Our State Fair" (Wayne, Abel, Margie, & Melissa); "It's a Grand Night for Singing" (entire cast); "That's for Me" (Wayne); "Isn't It Kind of Fun" (Emily & chorus); "It's the Little Things in Texas" (Abel & Melissa); "More Than Just a Friend" (Abel); "Willing and Eager" (Wayne & Emily); "Never Say 'No' " (Melissa); "This Isn't Heaven" (Jerry). *Farmers. Showgirls. Television personalities. Family life. Farm life. Automobile racing. Drunkenness. Contests. Texas State Fair. Pigs.*

Note: Location scenes filmed in Dallas and Oklahoma City. Previously filmed and released under the same title by Twentieth Century–Fox in 1933 and 1945.

STATION SIX–SAHARA (Great Britain/West Germany)   F6.4689
CCC-Filmkunst–CCC Films. *Dist* Allied Artists. 26 Aug **1964** [Philadelphia opening]. Sd; b&w. 35mm. 99 min.

A CCC Films–Artur Brauner Production. *Prod* Victor Lyndon. *Exec Prod* Gene Gutowski. *Dir* Seth Holt. *Screenplay* Bryan Forbes, Brian Clemens. *Dir Photog* Gerald Gibbs. *Camera Op* Ray Sturgess. *Focus Op* Michael Sarafian. *Camera Grip* Jack Roche. *Art Dir* Jack Stephens. *Asst Art Dir* Geoffrey Tozer. *Draughtsman* Nigel Curzon. *Film Ed* Alastair McIntyre. *1st Asst Ed* Jonathan Bates. *2d Asst Ed* John Jeremy. *Mus* Ron Grainer. *Sd* Norman Bolland, Jonathan Bates. *Boom Op* John Salter. *Sd Camera Op* Barbara Hopkins. *Dub Ed* Keith Palmer. *1st, 2d & 3d Asst Dir* David Bracknell, Richard Dalton, Cliff Castle. *Prod Mgr* Clifton Brandon. *Cont* Pamela Carlton. *Wardrobe Mistress* Bridget Sellers. *Makeup Artist* Gerry Fletcher. *Hairstyles* Joan Smallwood. *Still Photog* Norman Hargood. *Chargehand Prop* Sidney Leggett. *Chargehand Electrn* Edward Haste.

Cast: Carroll Baker *(Catherine)*, Peter Van Eyck *(Kramer)*, Ian Bannen *(Fletcher)*, Denholm Elliott *(Macey)*, Hansjörg Felmy *(Martin)*, Mario Adorf *(Santos)*, Biff McGuire *(Jimmy)*, Harry Baird *(sailor)*.

Melodrama. Source: Jacques Maret, *Men Without a Past* (a play; publication undetermined). Five men at an isolated oil-pumping station in the Sahara share in the blistering heat of the desert a mutual contempt for one another and a deep hunger for women. Kramer, the German in charge, is cool, sadistic, and mechanical, brooding alone in his quarters. His deputy, Macey, is a spineless Englishman living in memories of the desert war that somehow made him a major. Fletcher, a sex-starved Scot with a warped sense of humor, delights in teasing the snobbish Macey, while Martin, a new arrival from Germany, refuses to submit to the domination of Kramer. Santos, a chunky Spaniard, quietly and glumly remains in his own silent world. One evening their tense poker game is interrupted when an American car crashes into their encampment. The men lift from the wreckage a passenger, Catherine, who explains that the injured driver, Jimmy, is her jealous ex-husband and that he tried to kill them both. Catherine's presence exacerbates the taut atmosphere as she sleeps first with Kramer and then with Martin. Unable to bear her seemingly flagrant infidelity, the crazed Jimmy stabs her to death and then kills himself. An ambulance removes the corpses, and the station returns to strained and bitter normality. *Laborers. Americans in foreign countries. Spanish. Scotch. Veterans. Infidelity. Sexuality. Snobbery. Poker. Murder. Suicide. Jealousy. Sadism. Promiscuity. Oil. Sahara. Automobile accidents.*

Note: Location scenes filmed in the Libyan Desert. Released in West Germany in Jan 1963 as *Endstation 13 Sahara*; running time: 100 min. Opened in London in Sep 1963; running time: 101 min. A nude sequence of Miss Baker was cut from the U. S. print.

THE STATUE *see* **THE LOVE STATUE**

STAY AWAY, JOE   F6.4690

Metro-Goldwyn-Mayer, Inc. 8 Mar **1968** [Birmingham, Alabama, opening; c27 Mar 1968; LP35457]. Sd; col (Metrocolor). 35mm (Panavision). 101 min. [Copyright length: 95 min.]

Prod Douglas Laurence. *Dir* Peter Tewksbury. *Screenplay* Michael A. Hoey. *Orig Treatment* Burt Kennedy. *Dir Photog* Fred Koenekamp. *Art Dir* George W. Davis, Carl Anderson. *Set Decor* Henry Grace, Don Greenwood, Jr. *Film Ed* George W. Brooks. *Mus Score* Jack Marshall. *Song:* "Stay Away" Sid Tepper, Roy C. Bennett. *Sung by* Elvis Presley. *Song:* "U. S. Male" Jerry Reed. *Vocal Backgrounds* The Jordanaires. *Rec Supv* Franklin Milton. *Sd* Larry Jost. *Asst Dir* Dale Hutchinson. *Unit Prod Mgr* William R. Finnegan. *Asst to the Prod* Michael A. Hoey. *Wardrobe* Lambert Marks, Elva Martien. *Makeup* William Tuttle. *Hairstyles* Sydney Guilaroff.

Cast: Elvis Presley *(Joe Lightcloud)*, Burgess Meredith *(Charlie Lightcloud)*, Joan Blondell *(Glenda Callahan)*, Katy Jurado *(Annie Lightcloud)*, Thomas Gomez *(Grandpa)*, Henry Jones *(Hy Slager)*, L. Q. Jones *(Bronc Hoverty)*, Quentin Dean *(Mamie Callahan)*, Anne Seymour *(Mrs. Hawkins)*, Douglas Henderson *(Congressman Morrissey)*, Angus Duncan *(Lorne Hawkins)*, Michael Lane *(Frank Hawk)*, Susan Trustman *(Mary Lightcloud)*, Warren Vanders *(Hike Bowers)*, Buck Kartalian *(Bull Shortgun)*, Maurishka *(Connie Shortgun)*, Caitlin Wyles *(Marlene Standing Rattle)*, Marya Christen *(Billie-Jo Hump)*, Sonny West *(Jackson He-Crow)*, Jennifer Peak *(Little Dear)*, Brett Parker *(Deputy Sheriff Hank Matson)*, Michael Keller *(Orville Witt)*.

Comedy-drama. Source: Dan Cushman, *Stay Away, Joe* (New York, 1953). Joe Lightcloud, a brawling, half-Navajo rodeo champion, persuades an Arizona congressman to give Charlie, his father, 20 heifers and a young bull with which to build a herd on the Indian reservation. But at a party given by Joe for his Navajo neighbors, the bull, mistaken for a cow, is killed and barbecued by the drunken revelers, thus confirming the belief of Joe's stepmother, Annie, that anything initiated by Joe leads to trouble. Searching for another bull, Joe is sidetracked by Glenda Callahan, a lusty, gun-toting older woman with whom he was once involved. When he meets Glenda's daughter, Mamie, who has been kept in strict social isolation, Joe arranges to get Glenda out of town, then to give another party and romance Mamie. Though Joe does manage to borrow a second bull, a rodeo animal, it is definitely not interested in breeding. Meanwhile, Joe's half sister, Mary, has met a young white man whose mother is coming to call, and Annie is eager to redecorate the house before the visit. Gradually the heifers are all sold by Annie to subsidize the renovation, and Charlie is in danger of being jailed for selling government property. At the last minute, however, Joe saves the day by taking the borrowed bull to a rodeo, using the animal to win a big stake, and investing the money in a new herd. *Halfcastes. Navajo Indians. Stepmothers. Broncobusters. Filial relations. Brother-sister relationship. Rodeos. Arizona. United States Congress. Cows. Bulls.*

Note: Location scenes filmed in Sedona, Arizona.

STEAM HEAT   F6.4691

Pad Productions. *Dist* William Mishkin. 15 Feb **1963** [San Francisco opening]. Sd; col (Eastman Color). 35mm. 68 min.

Prod-Dir Russ Meyer.

Cast: Bill Teas, Brandy Long, Enrico Banducci.

Comedy. Crooks Enrico and Bill become involved with murder when they hide from the police in a ladies' reducing salon where Brandy has been killed in the Turkish bath. The police chase them through rooms filled with disrobed women until the right man is apprehended. *Hoodlums. Police. Murder. Turkish baths. Chases.*

Note: Title changed to *Mr. Tease and His Playthings*.

THE STEEL CLAW   F6.4692

Ponderey Productions. *Dist* Warner Bros. Pictures. 10 May **1961** [San Francisco opening; c27 May 1961; LP25368]. Sd; col (Technicolor). 35mm. 96 min.

Prod-Dir George Montgomery. *Assoc Prod* Al Wyatt, Ferde Grofé, Jr. *Screenplay* Ferde Grofé, Jr., Malvin Wald, George Montgomery. *Photog* Manuel Rojas. *Film Ed* Jack Murray. *Mus Comp & Cond* Harry Zimmerman. *Sd* Jack Milner. *Asst Dir* Mario Barri, Vicente Nayve, Jairo Mullin.

Cast: George Montgomery *(Capt. John Larsen)*, Charito Luna *(Lolita)*, Mario Barri *(Santana)*, Carmen Austin *(Rosa)*, Ben Perez *(Dolph Rodríguez)*, Paul Sorensen *(Frank Powers)*, Amelia de la Rama *(Christina)*, John MacGloan *(commander)*, Joe Sison *(himself)*, Pedro Faustino *(a father)*, Oscar Keesee, Jr. *(a child)*, Al Wyatt *(sergeant)*.

War melodrama. In Manila in World War II, Capt. John Larsen, USMC, loses his right hand in a drunken accident. Following his release from a hospital, he joins a rescue party sent to find a marine general believed to be held for ransom by Filipino guerrillas. The expedition, however, is turned back by the Japanese, and Larsen decides to undertake the mission alone. When he learns the general is in the hands of the Japanese, he recruits guerrillas to assist in the rescue by offering them the ransom money. After fashioning a steel hook to replace his missing hand, Larsen leads his guerrillas in a successful raid on the enemy camp; and the general is rescued. In the fighting, Lolita, a native with whom Larsen has become passionately involved, is seriously wounded. On the trek back Larsen discovers that the general is actually dead, and the man he rescued is a cowardly sergeant, Frank Powers, who assumed the dead officer's identity in the hope of receiving preferential treatment from the enemy. Following a Japanese raid in which Powers is killed, the little group masquerades as a sea-going funeral party and safely reaches a naval rescue vessel. Larsen and Lolita go aboard, and the guerrillas return to continue fighting the enemy. *Guerrillas. Filipinos. Prisoners of war. Drunkenness. Ransom. Impersonation. Cowardice. Artificial limbs. World War II. Manila. Philippines. United States Marines. Japan—Army.*

Note: Filmed on location in the Philippines.

STEFANIA (Greece)   F6.4693

Finos Films. *Dist* Chancellor Films. Jul **1968.** Sd; b&w. 35mm. 92 min.

Pres by Chellee Wilson. *Prod* Filopimin Finos. *Dir-Screenplay* Yannis Dalianidis. *Screenplay (see note)* Nelle Theodorou. *Dir Photog* Nikos Kavoudikis. *Set Decor* Markos Zervas. *Mus* Mimis Plessas. *English Subtitl* Herman G. Weinberg.

Cast: Zoe Laskari *(Stefania)*, Spiros Focas *(Dr. Georges)*, Spyros Kalogyrou *(guard)*, Tasso Kavadia *(directress)*, Viron Pallis *(stepfather)*, Nora Valsami *(Esther)*, Despo Diamantidou *(woman guard)*, Kakia Panayotou *(Stefania's mother)*, Lefteris Vournas *(delivery boy)*, Dimitrios Bislanis *(student)*.

Melodrama. Source: Nelle Theodorou, *Hē Stephania sto anamorphotērio* (Athens, 1960). Guilty of prostitution and sent to a reformatory, a young woman named Stefania is so shocked by the degeneracy and cruelty she witnesses that she makes an ill-fated attempt to escape. Later, she is somewhat heartened to discover that the reformatory doctor, Georges, is a man whom she had loved before being sent to prison. Although Georges' concern for the imprisoned women reawakens Stefania's love for him, Georges himself is blocked at every turn by an obstinate superintendent. As all of Georges' attempts to institute reforms fail, conditions become so bad that the women stage a rebellion, only to have it end in failure and the death of one of the inmates. Wanting Georges to know the story that led to her imprisonment, Stefania writes him a letter telling how, after being raped by her stepfather, she ran away from home and eventually drifted into prostitution out of desperation. Appalled by the confession, Georges leaves the reformatory, but later returns, forgives Stefania, and asks her to marry him. When she is finally released from the reformatory, Stefania is seized by Armagos, a sex-starved guard who, in trying to commit rape, strangles her. *Prostitutes. Physicians. Prison guards. Stepfathers. Prison reform. Prison revolts. Rape. Murder. Lust. Reformatories. Criminals—Rehabilitation.*

Note: Released in Greece in 1967 as *Stephania*. Sources conflict in crediting screenplay.

STEPCHILDREN (U.S.S.R.)   F6.4694

Gruziya-Film. *Dist* Artkino Pictures. 30 Jun **1962** [New York opening]. Sd; b&w. 35mm. 75 min.

Dir Tengiz Abuladze. *Screenplay* Revas Dzhaparidze, Tengiz Abuladze. *Screenplay Adapt From a Sketch by* N. Aleksandrova. *Photog* Levan Paatashvili. *Art Dir* Givi Gigauri, Kakhi Khutsishvili. *Film Ed* Vasiliy Dolenko. *Mus* Archil Kereselidze. *Sd* R. Kezeli. *1st & 2d Asst Dir* O. Andronikashvili, M. Eristavi. *Prod Mgr* G. Darsavelidze, S. Sikharulidze.

Cast: Tsitsino Tsitsishvili *(Nato)*, Otar Koberidze *(Data)*, Asmat Kandaurishvili *(Teo)*, Nani Chikvinidze *(Liya)*, Mikho Borashvili *(Giya)*, S. Takayshvili *([Elisabed])*.

Melodrama. Left a widower, Data, a train engineer, is forced to leave his two young children without a caretaker. Anxious to remarry, he proposes to his girl friend, Teo, but she turns down his proposal because she is unwilling to care for another woman's children. Later, Nato, a student, brings home the children after Giya, Data's son, is nearly struck by a truck. Nato and Data grow to love each other and marry, and the children begin to enjoy a family life again. Giya's upbringing poses certain problems, but Nato gradually gains his trust. The family's happiness is disturbed by the return of Teo, who rekindles Data's former feelings. He eventually runs off with Teo, and Nato in turn decides to leave the house. As her train begins to leave the station, however, she sees her stepchildren running down the tracks after her; and she jumps down to join them. The family is reunited, stronger than before. *Railroad engineers. Widowers. Children. Students. Stepmothers. Parenthood. Infidelity. Family* *life. Desertion. Trains.*

Note: Released in the U.S.S.R. in May 1959 as *Chuzhiye deti*.

STEPHANIA *see* **STEFANIA**

LA STEPPA *see* **THE STEPPE**

THE STEPPE (France/Italy)   **F6.4695**
Zebra Film–Aera Films. *Dist* Royal Films International. 30 Sep **1963** [New York opening]. Sd; col (Eastmancolor, print by Pathé). 35mm (Totalscope). 100 min.
   Prod Moris Ergas. *Dir* Alberto Lattuada. *Screenplay* Alberto Lattuada, Enzo Currelli, Tullio Pinelli. *Photog* Enzo Serafin. *Art Dir* Luigi Scaccianoce. *Film Ed* Leo Catozzo. *Mus Comp* Guido Turchi. *Mus Cond* Franco Ferrara. *Sd* Federico Savina, Renato Cadueri, Emilio Ciaffarini. *Asst Dir* Mile Pascucci, Stevo Petrović. *Prod Mgr* Antonio Sarno. *Prod Supv* Bianca Lattuada. *Wardrobe* Danilo Donati. *Makeup* Goffredo Rocchetti.
   Cast: Daniele Spallone *(Jegoruska)*, Pavle Vujisić *(Kuzmiciov)*, Charles Vanel *(Father Christopher)*, Milan Bosiljčić *(Dimov)*, Marina Vlady *(Countess Dranitsky)*, Pero Kvrgić *(Mossei)*, Hermina Pipinić *(Olga Ivanovna)*, Marianna Leibl *(grandmother)*, Cristina Gajoni *(girl of the river)*, Milan Djurdjević *(Daniska)*, Ljuba Tadić *(Jamelian)*, Michèle Bally *(Gypsy)*, Milorad Majić *(Pantalei)*, Fernando Cicero.
   Drama. Source: Anton Pavlovich Chekhov, *Istoriya odnoy poyezdki* (1888). Young Jegoruska leaves his home in the Russian steppe, accompanied by his Uncle Kuzmiciov and the aged Father Christopher, to travel to the city where he will begin school. During his journey, many unfamiliar sights and new experiences contribute to his growing awareness: gay celebrations at village feasts, farm workers in the fields, an adventure at a lonely inn, meeting and falling in love with the beautiful Countess Dranitsky, and seeing a dying man abandoned by the roadside. Jegoruska becomes ill during a storm, and his dreams turn to nightmares of the recent experiences. When he recovers, however, he is no longer a frightened little boy but well on his way to being a man. *Uncles. Priests. Nobility. Adolescence. Manhood. Travel. Steppes. Inns. Russia. Dreams.*
   Note: Location scenes filmed in Yugoslavia. Released in Italy in Jan 1963 as *La steppa*; French title: *La steppe*; original running time: 110 min.

THE STERILE CUCKOO   **F6.4696**
Boardwalk Productions. *Dist* Paramount Pictures. 22 Oct **1969** [New York opening; c11 Aug 1969; LP37237]. Sd; col (Technicolor). 35mm. 107 min. *MPAA rating* M.
   An Alan J. Pakula Production. *Prod-Dir* Alan J. Pakula. *Assoc Prod* David Lange. *Screenplay* Alvin Sargent. *Dir Photog* Milton Krasner. *Camera Op* Alfred Lebovitz. *1st Asst Camera* George Hollister. *Art Dir* Roland Anderson. *Set Decor* Chuck Pierce. *Ed Supv* Sam O'Steen. *Asst Ed* John W. Wheeler. *Mus Score* Fred Karlin. *Theme Song:* "Come Saturday Morning" Fred Karlin, Dory Previn. *Perf by* The Sandpipers. *Sd Mix* Ben Winkler, John Wilkinson. *Sd Boom Op* John K. Nelson. *Sd Rec* John Muchmore. *1st & 2d Asst Dir* Don Kranze, Newt Arnold, Steve Marvin. *Prod Mgr* Kenneth DeLand. *Prod Asst* Mary Hughes. *Script Supv* Marie Kenney. *Ladies' Cost* Jennifer Parsons. *Men's Cost* John A. Anderson. *Makeup* Mike Moschella. *Hairstylist* Cherie. *Sp Eff* Charles Spurgeon. *Dramatic Coach* Robert McAndrew. *Prop Master* William Wainess. *Ch Electrn* James Field. *Key Grip* Martin Kashuk.
   Cast: Liza Minnelli *(Pookie)*, Wendell Burton *(Jerry)*, Tim McIntire *(Charlie Schumacher)*, Elizabeth Harrower *(landlady)*, Austin Green *(Pookie's father)*, Sandra Faison *(Nancy Putnam)*, Chris Bugbee *(Roe)*, Jawn McKinley *(Helen Upshaw)*, Fred M. Lerner, A. Frederick Gooseen, Mark P. Fish, Philip S. Derfler, John A. Hussey, Toni Shorrock, Eric Best, Becky Davis, Towyna Thomas, Frances Tobin, Tim Laurie, Margaret Markov, Anita Alberts, Warren Peterson, Paul McConnell, Adele Wynn, Cynthia Hull.
   Comedy-drama. Source: John Treadwell Nichols, *The Sterile Cuckoo* (New York, 1965). Pookie Adams and Jerry Payne meet while traveling by bus to their respective colleges in upstate New York. The outspoken behavior of Pookie overwhelms the reserved Jerry, and he is relieved when she departs. No sooner has Jerry settled down to sharing a dormitory room with the athletic, beer-drinking Charlie Shumacher, than Pookie arrives in a dilapidated old car and announces that she has come to visit him for the weekend. Shocked by her brashness, but unable to ask her to leave, Jerry finds Pookie accomodations at a boardinghouse and devotes all of his time to her. Before long, Jerry is visiting Pookie at her school 70 miles away; and, as friendship turns to romance, they awkwardly and nervously make love in a motel cabin. Trouble erupts when Jerry accepts Charlie's offer to spend Christmas skiing at his parents' mountain cabin. Offended by this, Pookie tells Jerry that she is pregnant. Alarmed at the news, Jerry asks Pookie to marry him, but she refuses. After Christmas, Pookie tells him that the baby "went away." When Jerry takes her to a college party, she gets drunk and insults all the students. Later, Jerry telephones Pookie, and she is contrite, but he announces that he will be staying at school over the Easter

vacation to study. Tearfully pleading that she will be quiet if Jerry lets her stay with him, Pookie wins his consent. Their week together at Jerry's dorm is sometimes fun and loving, but mostly strained. As a result, Jerry decides that they should not see each other for a few weeks. When he finally calls her, he learns that she has left college. Some time later, Jerry finds Pookie, alone and subdued, staying at the boardinghouse. Jerry suggests to Pookie that she return home to visit her father. Reluctantly, Pookie says goodbye and leaves. *Students. Roommates. College life. Sexual initiation. Pregnancy. Vacations. Drunkenness. Boardinghouses. Motels. New York State.*
   Note: Location scenes filmed at Hamilton College and Rome, New York.

THE STEWARDESSES   **F6.4697**
Louis K. Sher. *Dist* Sherpix, Inc. 25 Jul **1969** [San Francisco opening]. Sd; col (Eastmancolor). 35mm (see note). 93 min. [Also reviewed at 75 min.] *MPAA rating* X.
   Exec Prod Louis K. Sher. *Dir-Writ* Alf Silliman, Jr. *Dir Stereo Photog* Christopher Bell.
   The Stewardesses: Christina Hart *(Samantha)*, Paula Erikson *(Tina)*, Angelique De Moline *(Jo)*, Kathy Ferrick *(Kathy)*, Janet Wass *(Wendy)*, Donna Stanley *(Horney Annie)*, Patricia Fein *(Karen)*, Beth Shields *(Cindy)*, Monica Gayle *(Ursula)*.
   Their Men: Michael Garrett *(Colin Winthrop)*, William Basil *(Captain Masters)*, Jerry Litvinoff *(Cappy)*, Robert Keller *(Charles)*, Andy Roth *(the soldier)*, John Barcado *(a pilot)*, Gordon White *(Loren Hatcher)*, Barry Schoenborn *(Steve Smith)*.
   And: Alicia Taggart, Linda Francis, Cindy Hopkins, Barbara Caron, Lynn Harris, Candy Stokes, Brenda Morrison, Mindy Baker, Phyllis Stangel, Ann Reynolds, Nancy O'Gorman, Karen Sherman, Nancy Ison, Babbette Cartier.
   Drama. During an 18-hour stopover at the end of the Los Angeles-Honolulu run, the crew of a 747 pursue their separate activities: Bachelor pilot Brad Masters takes Tina, a new stewardess, home to make another in a long line of conquests. Tina gives in and later feels victimized, but Brad, suddenly compassionate, restores her sense of decency. Passenger Colin Winthrop, an advertising executive, picks up the beautiful, ambitious Samantha, who hopes to entice him into signing her as "the beautiful mouth" for his new publicity campaign. The jaded young businessman confesses that although his success began with a homosexual affair with the president of the company, he would like to divest himself of his corrupt life. Samantha nonetheless tries to secure the promotional job, and Colin forces her to pay for her ambition by submitting to his abuse. Stewardess Wendy picks up a soldier on leave from Viet Nam, while most of the remainder of the flight crew go to a nightclub restricted to airline personnel. Karen leaves for home and an LSD trip while Horney Annie goes off with a pilot. During the celebration, Annie slips out with Cappy, a pilot friend of Brad, and when her date discovers her indiscretion, he brutally beats Cappy. Jo Peters, the head stewardess and a lesbian, manages to lure an unsuspecting woman home with her. Cappy calls Brad, who is consoling Tina, and asks his friend to take the upcoming flight. When Samantha awakes, the memory of the night's horror provokes her to take revenge on Colin by beating him to death with a heavy statuette, after which she leaps off his 28th-floor balcony. The men and women re-convene at the airport for the flight. *Airline stewardesses. Air pilots. Bachelors. Advertising executives. Soldiers. Seduction. Male homosexuality. Sadism. Promiscuity. Lesbianism. Murder. Suicide. Revenge. Nightclubs. LSD. Los Angeles. Honolulu.*
   Note: Screen process credited as "3 Dimensional Stereo-Vision as developed by Magnavision." After initial release, some 70mm prints were prepared. Originally a string of six hard-core shorts, *The Stewardesses* assumed a more cohesive story line when additional footage was filmed and inserted. During the re-shooting, 56 women were used to enact the roles of the several characters in the film. Also reviewed as *Airline Stewardess*. Filmed in California.

STICKS AND STONES   **F6.4698**
Filmteam–Toktee-O'Kay–M. B. P. 12 Jan **1970** [New York opening]. Sd; col (Eastmancolor) by Movielab). 35mm. 85 min. *MPAA rating* X.
   Prod Stan LoPresto, Tom O'Keefe, Miro Bartonik. *Dir* Stan LoPresto. *Screenplay* Tom O'Keefe. *Photog* Miro Bartonik. *Film Ed* Ivar Rushevic. *Mus* Mary Jo Frontiera. *Song:* "Let It Always Be Summer" Mary Jo Frontiera, David Newburge. *Sung by* Jim Pompeii.
   Cast: Craig Dudley *(Peter)*, J. Will Deane *(Buddy)*, Jimmy Foster *(Jimmy)*, Robert Case *(The Guru)*, Daniel Landau *(Danny)*, Maureen Sadusk *(Lou)*, Wyn Shaw *(Irving)*, Kim Pope *(June)*, Robert Nero *(Bobby)*, Fernando Ascencio *(Fernando)*, Gene Edwards *(George)*, Gary Bennet *(Gary)*.
   Melodrama. Peter and Buddy, two homosexual lovers whose relationship is faltering, give a party at their Fire Island home. Guests include a nervous newcomer and his leather-clad partner, a loquacious guru and his muscle-bound companion, and two lesbians. Some of the partygoers take off their clothes and indulge in various sexual activities. *Gurus. Male homosexuality. Lesbianism. Jealousy. Fire Island.*
   Note: Photographed in 16mm.

STILETTO   **F6.4699**

Harold Robbins Co. *Dist* Avco Embassy Pictures. 30 Jul **1969** [Los Angeles opening]. Sd; col (Berkey-Pathé). 35mm. 98 min. *MPAA rating* R.

Prod Norman Rosemont. *Exec Prod* Joseph E. Levine. *Dir* Bernard L. Kowalski. *Screenplay* A. J. Russell. *Photog* Jack Priestley. *Art Dir* Jan Scott. *Set Decor* Bob Drumheller. *Film Ed* Frank Mazzola, Stuart Chasmar. *Mus* Sid Ramin. *Song:* "Sugar in the Rain" Marilyn Bergman, Alan Bergman. *Sd* Jack C. Jacobsen. *Asst Dir* Peter Scoppa. *Prod Supv* Roger Michael Rothstein. *Prod Mgr* Sal Scoppa. *Cost* Alvin Colt. *Makeup* John Alese. *Hairstyles* William Farley. *Casting* Alan Shayne Associates.

Cast: Alex Cord (*Count Cesare Cardinali*), Britt Ekland (*Illeana*), Patrick O'Neal (*George Baker*), Joseph Wiseman (*Emilio Matteo*), Barbara McNair (*Ahn Dessje*), John Dehner (*Frank Simpson*), Titos Vandis (*Tonio*), Eduardo Ciannelli (*Don Andrea*), Roy Scheider (*Bennett*), Lincoln Kilpatrick (*Hannibal Smith*), Louis Elias (*Mann*), Luke Andreas (*Macy*), Dominic T. Barto (*Franchini*), James Tolkan (*Edwards*), Amaru (*Rosa*), Michaelina Martel (*blonde at casino*), Fat Thomas (*Dutch Wehrman*), Leonardo Cimino (*Allie Fargo*), Luis Antonio Martinez (*John Vanicola*).

Crime melodrama. Source: Harold Robbins, *Stiletto* (New York, 1969). Cesare Cardinali, a playboy and prosperous foreign car dealer, also serves as the "stiletto man," or contracted assassin, for the New York Mafia headed by Emilio Matteo, who, years before in Italy, saved Cardinali's life. Cesare is in a posh nightclub disposing of a Mafia enemy while Manhattan District Attorney Frank Simpson is in court losing a battle to indict Matteo and two other Mafia members. Matteo is released and orders Cesare to kill two possible witnesses who could prove damaging to the Mafia. Cesare does as he is told, but he then goes to Italy (where Matteo has been deported) to announce that he has fulfilled his obligation to the organization. His request to withdraw is refused because, he is told, he is indispensible. Meanwhile, Assistant District Attorney George Baker finds evidence linking Cesare to the killings, and Baker resigns his official position to conduct a private investigation. Cesare returns to the States; he learns that the New York Mafia has marked him for death; and realizing that Matteo is still his only hope, Cesare persuades his mistress Illeana to intercede on his behalf. Illeana heads for the airport to catch a plane to Italy, but she is detained by Baker and forced to reveal her mission before being permitted to leave the country. She persuades Matteo to agree to a meeting with Cesare in Puerto Rico, whereupon the Mafia's patriarch, Don Andrea, decrees that Cesare has outlived his usefulness and must be killed. Cesare is sheltered in the Harlem apartment of another girl friend, Ahn Dessje, while awaiting the go-ahead to meet Matteo. Following a Mafia attack which costs Ahn her life, Cesare leaves for Puerto Rico. Baker, who has learned of the meeting by tapping Illeana's telephone, follows and arrives in time to witness the meeting between Cesare and Matteo. Baker is too late to stop a rifleman perched atop a wall from fatally shooting Cesare; and though Baker kills Matteo, he himself is gunned down by the hidden marksman. *Playboys. Gangsters. Hired killers. Mistresses. District attorneys. Deportation. Murder. Electronic surveillance. Interrogation. Nightclubs. Automobile agencies. Airfields. New York City. New York City—Harlem. Puerto Rico. Italy. Mafia.*

Note: Location scenes filmed in New York City and Puerto Rico.

STILL ROOM IN HELL see **THERE IS STILL ROOM IN HELL**

STILLE DAGE I CLICHY see **QUIET DAYS IN CLICHY**

STING OF DEATH   **F6.4700**

Essen Productions. *Dist* Thunderbird International Pictures. 27 Nov **1966** [Maryland license; c14 Sep 1966; LP33141]. Sd; col (Eastman Color). 35mm. 76 min. [Copyright length: 81 min.]

Pres by Joseph Fink, Juan Hidalgo-Gato. *Prod* Joseph Fink, Juan Hidalgo-Gato, Richard S. Flink. *Dir* William Grefé. *Screenplay* Al Dempsey. *Dir Photog Unit #1* Julio C. Chavez. *Dir Photog Unit #2* Julio Roldan. *Film Ed* Julio C. Chavez. *Mus* Al Jacobs, Lon Norman. *Song Sung by* Neil Sedaka. *Sd Engr* Manuel Sole. *Script Clerk* Doris Bernhardt. *Wardrobe* Irene Velton. *Sp Makeup Eff* Harry Kerwin. *Exec Script Cons* Ben Lithman.

Cast: Joe Morrison (*John Hoyt*), Valerie Hawkins (*Karen Richardson*), John Vella (*Egon*), Jack Nagle (*Dr. Richardson*), Sandy Lee Kane (*Louise*), Deanna Lund (*Jessica*), Barbara Paridon (*1st girl*), Lois Etelman (*Donna*), Judy Lee (*Ruth*), Blanche Devreaux (*Susan*), Doug Hobart (*The Monster*), Robert Stanton (*sheriff*), Tony Gulliver (*1st boy*), Ron Pinchbeck (*2d boy*), John Castle (*3d boy*), Neil Sedaka (*singer*).

Horror film. In the Florida Everglades, marine biologist Dr. Richardson and his two aides, John Hoyt and Egon, are conducting experiments with Portuguese men-of-war. Unknown to his associates, Egon, who suffers from a persecution complex because of his horribly disfigured face, has built an underwater cave laboratory in the hope that secrets learned from his studies of the Portuguese men-of-war might help to erase the scars that are driving him

to madness. Shortly after the arrival of Richardson's daughter, Karen, and four of her college friends, Egon's tests produce disastrous results, and he is transformed into a vengeful half human, half Portuguese man-of-war. Because he has learned to communicate with the men-of-war, he amasses a host of them and systematically attacks boats and their passengers; and he murders all the students except Karen, whom he loves. Eventually he kidnaps Karen and takes her to his underwater laboratory. John follows but is overpowered by Egon. Before Egon can complete his task, however, he dies tragically as a result of an explosion of his laboratory apparatus. *Marine biologists. Students. Disfiguration. Murder. Insanity. Abduction. Transmutation. Experiments. Florida Everglades. Jellyfish.*

Note: Filmed on location in the Florida Everglades.

A STITCH IN TIME (Great Britain)   **F6.4701**

Rank Organisation. *Dist* Zenith International Film Corp. 23 Jun **1967** [Los Angeles opening; c29 Dec 1963; LF172]. Sd; b&w. 35mm. 94 min.

A J. Arthur Rank Production. *Prod* Hugh Stewart. *Exec Prod* Earl St. John. *Dir* Robert Asher. *Screenplay* Jack Davies, Norman Wisdom, Henry Blyth, Eddie Leslie. *Photog* Jack Asher. *Camera Op* James Bawden. *Art Dir* Bert Davey. *Set Dresser* Arthur Taksen. *Film Ed* Gerry Hambling. *Mus* Philip Green. *Sd Ed* Jim Sibley. *Sd Rec* Dudley Messenger, Colin Le Mesurier. *Asst Dir* Anthony Waye. *Prod Mgr* L. C. Rudkin. *Cont* Splinters Deason. *Cost Dsgn* Joan Ellacott. *Makeup* George Blackler. *Hairdressing* Biddy Chrystal. *Still Photog* Ian Jeayes.

Cast: Norman Wisdom (*Norman Pitkin*), Edward Chapman (*Grimsdale*), Jeannette Sterke (*Janet Haskell*), Jerry Desmonde (*Sir Hector Hardcastle*), Jill Melford (*Lady Brinkley*), Glyn Houston (*Welsh*), Hazel Hughes (*matron*), Patsy Rowlands (*Amy*), Peter Jones (*Russell*), Ernest Clark (*Professor Cranshaw*), Lucy Appleby (*Lindy*), Vera Day (*Betty*), Frank Williams (*Nuttall*), Penny Morrell (*Nurse Rudkin*), Patrick Cargill (*Dr. Meadows*), Francis Matthews (*Benson*), Pamela Conway (*woman patient*), Danny Green (*Ticehurst*), Johnny Briggs (*Teddy Boy*), John Blythe (*Dale*).

Comedy. Hapless butcher's assistant Norman Pitkin visits the hospital where his employer, Mr. Grimsdale, is being treated after swallowing his gold watch and chain. After twice humiliating Lady Brinkley, the hospital's rich patron, Norman is chased through the institution by Sir Hector Hardcastle, the pompous hospital director. Taking refuge in a children's ward, Norman brings a smile to the face of Lindy, a girl who, having lost both her parents in a plane crash, has been in shock until now. He promises nurse Janet that he will see Lindy again, but Sir Hector bans him from the building. Attempting to return as a patient, he tries not only to catch pneumonia but also to make himself the victim of a hit-and-run accident; but once he returns to the hospital, he disguises himself as a nurse to avoid an operation planned for him. Subsequently, he and Grimsdale, dressed in ambulance uniforms, purposely become entangled in a televised charity ball. Although Lindy is watching the ball on television, she is sent back to bed before Norman appears on the screen. Janet soon discovers Lindy's empty bed and follows her to the ball, where Norman is making an emotional appeal to the guests to contribute money and valuables for a children's seaside home. Sir Hector apologizes to Norman and Grimsdale, who mistake the director's purpose and run out of the hotel into the path of an automobile. Now recovered, Lindy visits the two men in the hospital as they recuperate from their injuries. *Butchers. Orphans. Nurses. Disguise. Charity. Hospitals. Shock. Television. Balls (formal gatherings). Chases. Automobile accidents.*

Note: Opened in London in Dec 1963.

THE STOLEN AIRLINER (Great Britain)   **F6.4702**

Associated British–Pathé Ltd. *For* Children's Film Foundation. *Dist* Continental Distributing, Inc. 15 May **1962** [Maryland license]. Sd; b&w. 35mm. 60 min.

Prod Howard Thomas. *Dir-Writ* Don Sharp. *Photog* Jo Jago. *Art Dir* Bertram Tyrer. *Film Ed* Eily Boland. *Mus* Philip Green. *Coöp* Royal Air Force, Vickers-Armstrong Co.

Cast: Fella Edmunds (*Fred*), Diana Day (*Anne*), Peter Dyneley (*Uncle George*), Michael MacGuire, British (*John*), Nicola Braithwaite (*Kitty*), Ballard Berkeley (*Mr. Head*), Iris Russell (*Mrs. Head*), David King-Wood (*controller*).

Action melodrama. Source: John Pudney, *Thursday Adventure* (London, 1955). A group of crooks kidnap a delegation from Francovinia who are in Britain to buy the airliner *Z09*. Impersonating the delegation members, the crooks go to the air field where Anne, the daughter of the field's superintendent, and Fred and John, two air cadets, are standing guard over the plane. The crooks overpower the youngsters and make off with them and the airplane. Anne and Fred manage to bail out over Elba, and upon landing they notify the Royal Air Force of the plane's position. John and his Uncle George, also captive on the airliner, free themselves, overpower the crooks, and aid the air force in recovering the plane. *Cadets. Kidnaping. Impersonation. Airplanes. Airfields.*

Elba. Great Britain—Royal Air Force.
Note: Released in Great Britain in 1955.

STOLEN HOURS   **F6.4703**
Mirisch Films–Barbican Films–Millar/Turman Productions. *Dist* United Artists. 2 Oct **1963** [Chicago opening; c9 Oct 1963; LP29366]. Sd; col (DeLuxe). 35mm. 100 min. [Copyright length: 97 min.]

Prod Denis Holt. *Exec Prod* Stuart Millar, Lawrence Turman. *Dir* Daniel Petrie. *Screenplay* Jessamyn West. *Story Adapt* Joseph Hayes. *Dir Photog* Harry Waxman. *Camera Op* Gerry Turpin. *Focus Op* Gerry Anstiss. *Art Dir* Tony Woollard. *Set Decor* John Hoesli. *Scenic Artist* Peter Melrose. *Draughtsmen* Fred Carter, Brian Ackland-Snow. *Prod Dsgn* Wilfred Shingleton. *Main Titl* Maurice Binder. *Film Ed* Geoffrey Foot. *1st Asst Film Ed* Graham Shipham. *2d Asst Film Ed* Roy Deverall. *Mus* Mort Lindsey. *Song Lyr* Marilyn Keith, Alan Bergman. *Sd Mixer* Cecil Mason. *Boom Op* Charles Wheeler, sd. *Sd Camera Op* Desmond Edwards. *Dub Ed* Gordon Daniel. *1st, 2d & 3d Asst Dir* Colin Brewer, Scott Wodehouse, Barry Langley, Kit Lambert. *Prod Supv* Teddy Joseph. *Unit Mgr* John Peverall. *Cont* Pamela Davies. *Asst to the Prod* Rose Tobias Shaw. *Prod Asst* Marion Rosenberg. *Wardrobe Mistress* Beatrice Dawson. *Miss Hayward's Cost* Fabiani. *Makeup* George Partleton, Tony Sforzini. *Hairstyles* Joan Smallwood. *Prop Buyer* George Durant. *Still Photog* Ted Reed. *Constr Mgr* Leon Davis. *Grip* Frank Howard. *Prop* J. Hayward. *Elec Supv* Maurice Gillett.

Cast: Susan Hayward *(Laura Pember)*, Michael Craig *(Dr. John Carmody)*, Diane Baker *(Ellen Pember)*, Edward Judd *(Mike Bannerman)*, Paul Rogers *(Dr. Eric McKenzie)*, Robert Bacon *(Peter)*, Paul Stassino *(Dalporto)*, Jerry Desmonde *(colonel)*, Ellen McIntosh *(Miss Kendall)*, Gwen Nelson *(hospital sister)*, Peter Madden *(Reynolds)*, Joan Newell *(Mrs. Hewitt)*, Chet Baker *(himself)*.

Drama. Source: George Emerson Brewer, Jr. and Bertram Block, *Dark Victory* (New York opening: 7 Nov 1934). Wealthy, twice-divorced playgirl Laura Pember, while driving to the London airport to meet her younger sister Ellen, has a sudden attack of vertigo. Recovering and going on to meet Ellen, she brings her sister home to find a lavish party in progress. In the course of the evening, Laura's current lover, race car driver Mike Bannerman, arranges for his friend John Carmody, a physician, to see Laura about her headaches, dizziness, and periodic loss of vision. John, in turn, persuades her to consult a brain specialist, Eric McKenzie; and Laura undergoes an apparently successful operation. By this time Laura and John have fallen deeply in love; but confused and bitter upon learning that she has less than a year to live, Laura runs away to Italy to be with Bannerman when he competes in the Grand Prix. John finds her, however; and they marry and settle down in a Cornish village where Laura discovers the rewards of simple living and for the first time is able to give and receive love. No longer afraid, she lies down alone to die while John is visiting one of his patients. *Sisters. Playgirls. Physicians. Vertigo. Brain surgery. Automobile racing. Marriage. Hospitals. London. Cornwall (England). Italy.*
Note: Filmed in England. Working title: *Summer Flight.* Copyright claimants: The Mirisch Co., Millar/Turman Productions, and Carrollton of Panama. Previously filmed in 1939 as *Dark Victory.*

STOLEN KISSES (France)   **F6.4704**
Films du Carrosse–Les Productions Artistes Associés. *Dist* Lopert Pictures. 21 Feb **1969** [Los Angeles opening; c6 Sep 1968; LF53]. Sd; col (Eastman Color, print by De Luxe). 35mm. 90 min. *MPAA rating* R.

Prod Marcel Berbert. *Dir* François Truffaut. *Orig Story & Screenplay* François Truffaut, Bernard Revon, Claude de Givray. *Dir Photog* Denys Clerval. *Camera Op* Jean Chiabaut. *Art Dir* Claude Pignot. *Film Ed* Agnès Guillemot. *Mus* Antoine Duhamel. *Song:* "Que reste t'il de nos amours?" comp & sung by Charles Trenet. *Sd* René Levert. *Asst Dir* Jean-José Richer, Alain Deschamps. *Prod Mgr* Claude Miler. *Script Girl* Suzanne Schiffman. *Tech Adv* L'Agence de Détectives Privés Dubly. *English Subtitl* Mary Louise Gradwohl.

Cast: Jean-Pierre Léaud *(Antoine Doinel)*, Delphine Seyrig *(Fabienne Tabard)*, Michel Lonsdale *(Monsieur Tabard)*, Claude Jade *(Christine Darbon)*, Harry-Max *(Monsieur Henri)*, Daniel Ceccaldi *(Monsieur Darbon)*, Claire Duhamel *(Madame Darbon)*, Catherine Lutz *(Catherine)*, André Falcon *(Monsieur Blady)*, Paul Pavel *(Julien)*, Serge Rousseau *(stranger)*, Marie-France Pisier *(Colette Tazzi)*, Jean-François Adam *(Albert Tazzi)*, Jacques Robiolles *(writer)*, Martine Ferrière *(manageress of shoe shop)*, Simono *(conjurer's friend)*, Roger Trapp *(hotel manager)*, Jacques Delord *(conjurer)*, Jacques Rispal *(deceived husband)*, Martine Brochard *(unfaithful wife)*, Robert Cambourakis *(lover)*, Karine Jeantet, François Darbon.

Comedy. Discharged from the army for mental instability, Antoine Doinel visits a prostitute. He then goes to the home of his girl friend, Christine Darbon. Although Christine is away on a skiing trip, Antoine stays for dinner and later takes a job as a night clerk in a Montmartre hotel. While on the job, Antoine is tricked by private detective Monsieur Henri into opening a room where the wife of one of Henri's clients is in bed with her lover. Antoine is promptly fired,

and feeling sorry for him, Henri finds him a job with the Blady Detective Agency. Antoine loses the trail of a nanny who spends her afternoons working as a stripteaser, bungles the case of a homosexual who suspects his magician friend of having a clandestine affair, and then is assigned to the case of Monsieur Tabard, an obnoxious man obsessed with the idea that everyone hates him. Antoine is told to work in Tabard's shoe salon and spy on the employees. Depressed by the lack of interest Christine shows in him, Antoine becomes enamored of Tabard's beautiful wife, Fabienne. She invites him to lunch, and he is so overwhelmed by her that he spills a cup of coffee, and bolts out of the house. She sends him a kind note, and he responds with a passionate letter of farewell inspired by a Balzac novel. The next morning Fabienne comes to his room and persuades him to make love for the first and last time before parting. A short time later Monsieur Henri dies, and Antoine ends his career as a private detective. He goes to work as a television repairman, and Christine takes advantage of her parents' absence by pulling out wires from her television and then calling for service. Antoine makes a shambles of the set and stays the night. The following day as they are discussing their marriage plans in the park, a stranger appears before them. Dismissing Antoine's presence, he declares his love for Christine and announces that someday she will marry him. After the stranger has left, Antoine and Christine question the man's sanity and walk off hand in hand. *Shoeclerks. Prostitutes. Hotel clerks. Detectives. Stripteasers. Magicians. Storekeepers. Television repairmen. Strangers. Students. Infidelity. Male homosexuality. Unemployment. Hotels. Shoeshops. Paris. France—Army. Documentation. Honoré de Balzac.*
Note: Filmed on location in Paris. Opened in Paris in Sep 1968 as *Baisers volés.* Registered for copyright under French title. The film is dedicated to Henri Langlois' Cinémathèque Française.

THE STOLEN PLANS (Great Britain)   **F6.4705**
Gaumont–British Picture Corp. *For* Children's Film Foundation. *Dist* Continental Distributing, Inc. 2 May **1962** [Maryland license]. Sd; b&w. 35mm. 57 min.

Prod Frank Wells. *Dir-Writ* James Hill. *Story* Michael Poole. *Photog* Frank North, Gerry Massy-Collier. *Art Dir* Don Chaffey. *Film Ed* Arthur Stevens. *Mus* Jack Beaver.

Cast: Mavis Sage *(Nicolette Renaud)*, Lance Secretan *(Michael Foster)*, Peter Neil *(Tony Burton)*, Pamela Edmunds *(Mrs. Foster)*, Peter Burton *(Dr. Foster)*, Patrick Boxill *(Mr. Palmer)*, Len Sharp *(Tod)*, Geoffrey Goodheart *(The Boss)*, Larry Burns *(Alf)*, Ludmilla Tchakalova *(Meg)*.

Adventure drama. A London boy, Michael Foster, and his pen pal from France, Nicolette Renaud, meet aircraft designer Tony Burton, and he invites them to his house. On their first visit, they become involved with a thief who steals some top secret aircraft designs. After a series of adventures, the children foil the plans of a group of international crooks, who are arrested by the police. *Children. Engineers. Thieves. French. Documentation.*
Note: Location scenes filmed in South Kensington. Released in Great Britain in 1952.

STOP ME BEFORE I KILL! (Great Britain)   **F6.4706**
Hammer Film Productions–Falcon Films–Hilary Productions. *Dist* Columbia Pictures. 17 May **1961** [Baltimore opening; c1 May 1961; LP20543]. Sd (RCA); b&w. 35mm (Megascope). 93 min. [Cut from 110 min.]

A Val Guest Production. *Prod-Dir* Val Guest. *Assoc Prod* Victor Lyndon. *Screenplay* Val Guest, Ronald Scott Thorn. *Dir Photog* Gilbert Taylor. *Camera Op* Moray Grant. *Art Dir* Tony Masters. *Set Decor* Scott Slimon. *Film Ed* Bill Lenny. *Mus Comp & Cond* Stanley Black. *Sd Rec* Bert Ross. *Asst Dir* Kip Gowans. *Prod Mgr* Clifton Brandon. *Cont* Doreen Dearnaley. *Cost* Beatrice Dawson. *Makeup* Tony Sforzini. *Hairstyles* Ivy Emmerton.

Cast: Claude Dauphin *(Dr. David Prade)*, Diane Cilento *(Denise Colby)*, Ronald Lewis *(Alan Colby)*, Françoise Rosay *(Madame Prade)*, Bernard Braden *(Harry Stonehouse)*, Katya Douglas *(Connie Stonehouse)*, Barbara Chilcott *(Baroness de la Vaillon)*, Ann Tirard *(Nicole)*, Edwin Styles *(Dr. Roberts)*, George Merritt *(Dr. Manfield)*.

Mystery drama. Source: Ronald Scott Thorn, *The Full Treatment* (London, 1959). Only hours after his wedding, British international racing driver Alan Colby is injured in an automobile crash. The accident leaves him emotionally disturbed, and during a delayed honeymoon in the south of France, he finds himself attempting to strangle his Italian wife, Denise, whenever they make love. Dr. Prade, a psychiatrist vacationing on the Riviera with his mother, persuades Denise that Alan is in desperate need of help, but Alan scoffs at the idea and returns to London. Prade, now in love with Denise, follows and eventually succeeds in getting Alan to submit to treatment; he uses drugs, autosuggestion, and his own persuasive personality to convince Alan that he has murdered his wife. Panic-stricken, Alan flees to friends on the Riviera. There, one morning, he catches sight of Denise with Prade and confronts them at gunpoint. Prade almost succeeds in convincing Alan that he has hallucinated; but Alan turns the tables on Prade, who himself begins to behave irrationally.

Running away, Prade tries to escape by cable car but falls to his death, leaving Alan and Denise free to resume their honeymoon. *Italians. Psychiatrists. Automobile racing. Mental illness. Murder. Hypnotism. Honeymoons. Drugs. Cable cars. Riviera. London. Automobile accidents.*

Note: Location scenes filmed in the south of France. Opened in London in Feb 1961 as *The Full Treatment*; running time: 109 min. U. S. prerelease title: *The Treatment.*

STOP THE WORLD—I WANT TO GET OFF (Great Britain)   F6.4707
Warner Bros. Pictures. 13 Apr **1966** [Los Angeles opening; c16 May 1966; LP32704]. Sd (RCA); col (Technicolor). 35mm (Mitchell Camera System 35). 98 min.

Prod Bill Sargent. *Dir* Philip Saville. *Tech Dir* Gordon Hesketh. *Stage Dir* Michael Lindsay-Hogg. *Screenplay* Leslie Bricusse, Anthony Newley. *Adtl Material* David Donabie, Al Ham, Marilyn Bergman, Alan Bergman. *Dir Photog* Oswald Morris. *Camera Op* James Bawden, Derek Browne, Jimmy Turrell, Ron Francis, Barry Bergthorson. *Asst Art Dir* Maurice Fowler, Michael Knight. *Prod Dsgn* Sean Kenny. *Film Ed* Jim Sibley. *Asst Ed* David Grimsdale. *Mus & Lyr* Anthony Newley, Leslie Bricusse. *Mus Supv & Songs:* "I Believed It All," "The New York Scene" Al Ham. *Perf by* Al Ham Orchestra. *Songs:* "A, B, C Song," "I Wanna Be Rich," "Gonna Build a Mountain," "Mumbo Jumbo," "Once in a Lifetime," "What Kind of Fool Am I" sung by Tony Tanner. *Songs:* "Glorious Russian," "Typically Japanese," "All American" sung by Millicent Martin. *Songs:* "Typically English," "Lumbered," "Malinki Meilchick," "Family Fugue," "Nag Nag Nag," "Someone Nice Like You" sung by Tony Tanner, Millicent Martin. *Mime & Movement Dir* Tutte Lemkow. *Sd Supv* Cyril Crowhurst. *Sd Mix* Dudley Messenger. *Mus Sd Mix* Len Abbott. *Mus Sd Supv* A. W. Lumkin. *Asst Dir* Robert Lynn. *Prod Supv* Ted Lloyd. *Prod Asst* Gillian Morgan. *Asst to the Prod* Marilyn Schlossberg. *Cont* Joy Mercer. *Cost Dsgn* Gina Fratini, Kiki Byrne. *Makeup* George Claff. *Hairdresser* Daphne Martin. *Casting* Robert Lennard.

Cast: Tony Tanner (*Littlechap*), Millicent Martin (*Evie/Anya/Ara/Ginnie*), Leila Croft (*Susan*), Valerie Croft (*Jane*), Neil Hawley (*Little Littlechap*), Graham Lyons (*father-in-law*), Georgina Allen, Natasha Ashton, Sandra Burville, Carlotta Barrow, Vyvyan Dunbar, Katerina Holden, Margaret Frost, Ann Holloway, Liz Gold, Derina House, Marion Horton, Carolyn Irving, Pamela Hart, Pam Jones, Sarah Hardenburg, Kay Korda, Rosemary Philips, Judith McGilligan, Jo Anna Short, Julie Pitcher, Liz White, Heather Simms.

Musical comedy-drama. Source: Anthony Newley and Leslie Bricusse, *Stop the World—I Want To Get Off* (London opening: 20 Jul 1961). In the presence of fellow performers in an empty circus tent, a clown creates a character: Littlechap, the eternal opportunist. Littlechap's driving ambition is to climb the ladder of success, the first rung of which is marriage to the boss's daughter, Evie. Despite Littlechap's arrogance, Evie succumbs to his charm and soon becomes pregnant. Following their wedding, Littlechap's father-in-law makes him manager of one of his less productive factories in Sludgepool. Quickly turning it into a huge enterprise, Littlechap goes from success to success as Evie bears him two more children. In Moscow on business, he captivates a beautiful Russian "comrade" and makes her his mistress. Once back home, his star continues to ascend; he becomes managing director of the factory and acquires membership in Snobb's Club, a seat in Parliament, and two more beautiful mistresses (his Japanese housemaid and an American showgirl). His social and financial success continues until he is elevated to the peerage. Now exhausted and eager for retirement, he feels it is time to write his memoirs. But with time for reflection, Lord Littlechap finally realizes that he has never stopped to love anyone other than himself. *Clowns. Opportunists. Social climbers. Egotists. Fathers-in-law. Mistresses. Russians. Japanese. Housemaids. Americans in foreign countries. Showgirls. Ambition. Employer-employee relations. Marriage. Pregnancy. Factory management. Infidelity. Circus. Moscow. Great Britain—Parliament.*

Note: Opened in London in Apr 1966; running time: 100 min.

STOP TRAIN 349 (France/Italy/West Germany)   F6.4708
Da. Ma. Film-Hoche Productions-Hans Oppenheimer Film-P. C. M. *Dist* Allied Artists. Jul **1964**. Sd; b&w. 35mm. 95 min. [Also reviewed at 91 min.]

Pres by Hans Oppenheimer, Ray Ventura. *Prod* Hans Oppenheimer, Ray Ventura. *Dir* Rolf Haedrich. *Screenplay* Victor Vicas. *Collab* Jim Henaghan. *Dial* Norman Borisoff. *Story* Will Tremper. *Photog* Roger Fellous. *Set Decor* Dieter Bartels, Albrecht Hennings. *Film Ed* Georges Arnstam, Margot Jahn. *Mus* Peter Thomas. *Sd* Gunther Kortwich. *Asst Dir* Uschi Baumann, Marc Maurette. *Prod Dir* Willy Pickardt. *Prod Mgr* Jochen Graubner. *Makeup* Ruth Mohr.

Cast: Jose Ferrer (*Cowan*), Sean Flynn (*Lieutenant Novak*), Nicole Courcel (*Nurse Kathy*), Jess Hahn (*Sergeant Torre*), Joseph Yadin (*Major Menschikov*), Hans Joachim Schmiedel (*Banner*), Christiane Schmidtmer (*Karin*), Joy Aston (*Mrs. Abramson*), Art Brauss (*IMP*), Fred Dürr (*Major*

Finnegan*), Wolfgang Georgi (*Russian Officer Gorski*), Annie Gorassini (*Abramson's daughter*), Charles Hickman (*Corporal Williams*), Carlo Hintermann (*Russian officer*), Hjordis Hume (*Mrs. Watts*), Margaret Jahnen (*Mrs. Stein*), Maria Pia Luzi (*teenager*), Lothar Mann (*East German conductor*), Edward Meeks (*U. S. Captain Kolski*), Len Monroe (*U. S. soldier*), Antonella Murgia (*teenager*), Robert Shankland (*U. S. diplomat*), Narziss Sokatscheff (*Russian officer*), Ted Turner (*Colonel Abramson*), Konrad Thoms, Egon Vogel (*East German conductors*).

Drama. As an American train sealed for security travels through East Germany toward Frankfurt, Kathy, a nurse, sees Banner, a young East German, clinging to the outside of a window and helps him inside. The East German authorities are aware that the refugee, whose family has escaped to West Germany, is aboard, and they phone the border control station to order the train stopped. A reporter named Cowan discovers Banner and plans to expose the escape attempt in a big story since he feels no pity for the German people. The train's commanding officer, Lieutenant Novak, at first denies that the escapee is aboard and refuses to allow the compartments to be searched. When he learns the true situation, however, he wires his colonel for instructions. At Marienborn the train is halted, and the stalemate continues with U. S. and Russian authorities taking opposite sides. Novak risks a possible court martial by promising the refugee that he will not be relinquished. Banner forces the issue when he makes another abortive escape attempt in front of the Russians. The carefully guarded secrecy surrounding the story leaks out, and West Berlin radios carry the news. With the incident reaching international proportions, Novak is forced to turn the young man over to Russian authorities. *Political refugees. Nurses. Russians. Reporters. Cold war. Trains. German Democratic Republic. Marienborn. United States Army. Union of Soviet Socialist Republics—Army.*

Note: Opened in Paris in Jun 1964 as *Le train de Berlin est arrêté* at 92 min; in Rome in Mar 1965 as *Un treno è fermo a Berlino* at 95 min; in West Germany as *Verspätung in Marienborn* at 105 min.

STORIA DI UNA DONNA see **STORY OF A WOMAN**

UNA STORIA LOMBARDA see **THE LADY OF MONZA**

UNA STORIA MODERNA (L'APE REGINA) see **THE CONJUGAL BED**

STORK TALK (Great Britain)   F6.4709
Unifilms (Feature Productions). *Dist* Parade Pictures. Aug **1964**. Sd; b&w. 35mm. 85 min.

Prod Charles Bruce Newbery. *Exec Prod* Lionel Clyne. *Assoc Prod* Paul J. Sellwyn. *Dir* Michael Forlong. *Screenplay* Donald Ford. *Adtl Dial* Peter Rosser, William Hepper. *Photog* Norman Warwick. *Camera Op* Eric Besche. *Camera Focus* Stuart Hetherington. *Art Dir* Norman Arnold. *Set Decor* Andrew Low. *Draughtsman* Arden Gantley. *Scenic Artist* Paul Shliamin. *Film Ed* John Jympson. *Asst Ed* Jennifer Thompson. *Mus* Tony Hatch. *Titl Song Sung by* Mike Sammes Singers. *Sd Rec* Bill Bulkley. *Sd* Archie Ludski. *Boom Op* Michael Francis. *Sd Camera Op* Liam Saurin. *1st, 2d & 3d Asst Dir* Harry Kratz, Ernie Lewis, Jeremy Swan. *Prod Mgr* Ronald Liles. *Prod Sec* Jane Moscrop. *Cont* Splinters Deason. *Wardrobe Mistress* Eileen Long. *Makeup* Gerry Fletcher. *Hairdresser* Kevin Hudson. *Instruction Mgr* Peter McGoldrick. *Prop Buyer* Maureen Roche. *Still Photog* Roy Byrne. *Prop Master* Noel Coade. *Ch Electrn* Tom Chapman.

Cast: Tony Britton (*Dr. Paul Vernon*), Anne Heywood (*Lisa Vernon*), John Turner (*Dr. Robert Sterne*), Nicole Perrault (*Tina Monet*), Daphne Anderson (*Dr. Mary Willis*), Marie Kean (*Mrs. Webster*), Gladys Henson (*matron*), John Sharp (*Papa Pierre*), John Molloy (*pram salesman*), Gerry Sullivan (*Dr. Sefton*), Marie Conmee (*Mrs. Jeffries*), George Hill, actor (*Henry*), Pamela Mant (*Mrs. Stanton*), Genevieve Lyons, Ann Mulvey (*receptionists*), Jimmy Gaffrey (*booking office clerk*), Denise Hirst, Annest Williams (*sisters*).

Romantic comedy. Source: Gloria Russell, *The Night Life of a Virile Potato* (London opening: 8 Feb 1960). Lisa Vernon walks out on her husband, Paul, a fashionable gynecologist. Shortly afterwards, Paul is taken to a party by his partner, Robert Sterne; gets drunk; and spends the night with an attractive Frenchwoman, Tina Monet. Tina is evicted from her lodgings for staying out all night, whereupon Paul has his housekeeper, Mrs. Webster, employ her as a maid. Having discovered that she is pregnant, Lisa soon arrives at the house, anxious to effect a reconciliation with Paul, and she meets Tina, who has also learned that she is pregnant. Since both babies are expected at the same time, Lisa asks Robert to register both infants as her twins by altering the birth certificates. Both Lisa and Tina give birth to twins, however, making the scheme impossible. Robert resolves the problem by marrying Tina, and Lisa and Paul are reunited. *French. Gynecologists. Twins. Housemaids. Pregnancy. Infidelity. Marriage. Drunkenness.*

Note: Opened in London in Mar 1962; running time: 97 min.

THE STORM OVER THE PACIFIC *see* **I BOMBED PEARL HARBOR**

STORMY ERA (Japan)   **F6.4710**
Nikkatsu Corp. *Dist* Toho Co. Mar **1969** [Los Angeles showing]. Sd; col. 35mm. 165 min.
Dir Toshio Masuda.
Cast: Yujiro Ishihara, Ryutaro Tatsumi, Hideki Takahashi, Mie Hama, Katsuo Nakamura, Ruriko Asaoka, Mitsuo Hamada, Eiji Okada, Shogo Shimada.
Historical drama. Although no information about the precise nature of this film has been found, sources indicate that the story concerns a young patriot active between 1920 and 1930. *Patriotism.*
Note: Released in Japan in Jun 1968 as *Showa no inochi.*

THE STORY OF A DRAFT DODGER *see* **WINDFLOWERS; THE STORY OF A DRAFT DODGER**

THE STORY OF A MAN AND HIS WOMAN *see* **FREUDUS SEXUALIS**

THE STORY OF A THREE DAY PASS (France)   **F6.4711**
O. P. E. R. A. *Dist* Sigma III Corp. 8 Jul **1968** [New York opening]. Sd; b&w. 35mm. 87 min.
Prod Guy Belfond. *Dir-Writ* Melvin Van Peebles. *Photog* Michel Kelber. *Settings* Yves Decaux. *Film Ed* Liliane Korb. *Mus* Mickey Baker, Melvin Van Peebles.
Cast: Harry Baird *(Turner)*, Nicole Berger *(Miriam)*, Christian Marin *(hotelman)*, Pierre Doris *(peasant)*, Hal Brav, Tria French.
Drama. Source: Melvin Van Peebles, *La permission* (Paris, 1967). While stationed in France, Turner, a black American GI, is promoted and given a 3-day pass to Paris. On his first day there, he wanders the streets alone, feeling uncomfortable and lonely. At night he visits a nightclub, hoping the atmosphere will enliven him, but a curt rejection from a beautiful young woman increases his dejection. His spirits brighten, however, when another woman, Miriam, dances and talks with him and, after some coaxing, agrees to accompany him to the seashore the following day. Miriam leaves her job, claiming she is ill, and spends a pleasant day with Turner. They drive in the country, have dinner in a Chinese restaurant, and spend the night together. Only a skirmish in the restaurant, when Turner feels he has been racially insulted by an entertainer, mars their idyll, and even that unpleasantness is short-lived. The following day, however, Turner runs into three buddies from his Army post, and he fears that they will report his having dated a white girl to their captain. Choosing to ignore their presence, Turner spends another day with Miriam, and they vow their love for each other before parting. As Turner feared, he is instantly demoted upon his return to the camp by his bigoted captain. Nevertheless, Turner still has Miriam, or so he thinks, until he calls her at her office and is told that she is "ill," the same excuse she used for her 3 days with Turner. *Americans in foreign countries. Negroes. Military life. Miscegenation. Racial prejudice. Paris. United States Army.*
Note: Filmed on location in Paris. Paris opening: Apr 1968 as *La permission;* running time: 86 min. Original running time: 90 min.

STORY OF A WOMAN (United States/Italy)   **F6.4712**
Westward Productions. *Dist* Universal Pictures. 13 Feb **1970** [Dallas opening; c11 Feb 1970; LP38936]. Sd; col (Technicolor). 35mm. 90 min. *MPAA rating* R.
Prod-Dir-Writ Leonardo Bercovici. *Cons to the Prod* Dede Allen. *Dir Photog* Piero Portalupi. *Camera Op* Cesare Allione. *Art Dir* Alexander Golitzen, Aurelio Crugnola. *Set Decor* John McCarthy, Franco Fumagalli. *Titl* Universal Title. *Film Ed* Milton Shifman. *Film Cons* Renzo Lucidi. *Mus Score* Johnny Williams. *Mus Supv* Stanley Wilson. *Song:* "Uno di qua, l'altra di la" Johnny Williams, A. Amurri. *Sung by* Ornella Vanoni. *Sd* Waldon O. Watson, Luciano Welisch. *Asst Dir* Roberto Malenotti. *Prod Supv* Milton Feldman. *Unit Prod Mgr* Luciano Piperno. *Prod Mgr* Fred S. Wallach. *Script Supv* Marion Mertes. *Cost Dsgn* Edith Head. *Wardrobe Dsgn* Itala Scandariato. *Makeup* Bud Westmore, Giuseppe Banchelli, Cesare Gambarelli. *Hairstyles* Larry Germain, Vasco Reggiani.
Cast: Bibi Andersson *(Karin Ullman)*, Robert Stack *(David Frasier)*, James Farentino *(Bruno Cardini)*, Annie Girardot *(Liliana Cardini)*, Frank Sundström *(Karin's father)*, Didi Perego *(Bruno's girl friend)*, Francesco Mulè *(Manzetti)*, Birgitta Valberg *(Karin's mother)*, Cathy Riney *(Cathy)*, Beppe Wolgers *(Mr. Fahlen)*, Ingella Rossell *(Mrs. Fahlen)*, Toivo Pawlo *(Mr. Rushenkov)*, Elsa Vazzoler *(Luisa)*, Pippo Starnazza *(Mario)*, Gisella Sofio *(Mrs. Curtis)*, Diana Lante *(ambassador's wife)*, Anna Liotti *(Nadia)*, Mario Nascimbene *(music professor)*, Erika Rossell *(Sissi)*, Marco Raviart *(TV announcer)*.
Romantic melodrama. Rome, 1953. Aspiring Swedish pianist Karin Ullman has an affair with Bruno Cardini, a brash Italian medical student, until Bruno's wife, Liliana, drives Karin away. Returning to Stockholm, Karin meets American diplomat David Frasier; they eventually marry and move to Washington, D. C. At the same time, Liliana and Bruno are involved in a car crash, which takes her life and maims Bruno's right hand, ending his medical career. Four years later, after the birth of a daughter, David is assigned to Rome, and Karin again meets Bruno, who is now that city's most popular soccer player. Though Karin rebuffs Bruno's advances, she visits him at a hospital when he is injured in a match. She grows increasingly colder toward David, who finally guesses the truth and accuses her of betraying his trust. Karin retreats to the ski resort at Cortina, and Bruno follows; however, both realize they cannot resume their former love. In despair Bruno drives his car off a mountain road. Learning of the tragedy, David reconciles himself with Karin. *Swedes. Pianists. Medical students. Americans in foreign countries. Diplomats. Athletes. Infidelity. Mutilation. Suicide. Soccer. Ski resorts. Rome. Cortina d'Ampezzo. Stockholm. Washington (District of Columbia). Automobile accidents.*
Note: Location scenes filmed in Rome, Cortina, and Stockholm. Produced in 1968; Italian title: *Storia di una donna.*

THE STORY OF AN ARTIST'S STUDIO SECRETS *see* **ARTIST'S STUDIO SECRETS**

THE STORY OF ARNOLD ROTHSTEIN *see* **KING OF THE ROARING 20'S—THE STORY OF ARNOLD ROTHSTEIN**

THE STORY OF BIRTH *see* **BIRTH OF TRIPLETS**

THE STORY OF DINAH EAST *see* **DINAH EAST**

THE STORY OF 8 GIRLS   **F6.4713**
Barry Mahon Productions. *Dist* Cinema Syndicate, Inc. 13 Aug **1965** [Los Angeles showing]. Sd; col. 35mm. 65 min.
A Barry Mahon Production. *Prod-Dir* Barry Mahon. *Photog* Barry Mahon. *Sd* Magno Sound. *Asst Dir* Byron Mabe. *Opticals* Eastern Effects.
Cast: Rick Bolan *(The Photographer)*.
Comedy. A photographer of nudes reveals the secrets of his career, reminiscing about his models: He convinces a beautiful German girl to pose in the nude after he meets her in a park. A sculptor friend recruits a voluptuous saleswoman as a model. One pinup loves skydiving. Two of the models pose for a man they think is an artist, only to find that he is a housepainter. A group of models enjoys a nude picnic in the country. *Photographers. Models. Sculptors. Salesmen. Germans. Painters. Nudity. Mistaken identity.*
Note: Also known as *The Story of 8 Models.*

THE STORY OF F   **F6.4714**
Jim Babb. *Dist* Sherpix, Inc. 15 Oct **1970** [San Francisco showing]. Sd; col (Eastmancolor). 35mm. 67 min. *MPAA rating* X.
Prod-Dir-Writ Jim Babb. *Photog* Jim Babb. *Sd* Jon Graham.
Narrators: Ed Louis, Judy Koller.
Documentary. In an attempt to document the history of pornography, the participants in the film perform various sexual acts depicted by classical drawings and sculpture. Also included is *The Nun's Story*, a stag movie of the late 1950's. *Sexual practices. Sex exploitation films. Drawings. Sculpture.*

THE STORY OF JOSEPH AND HIS BRETHREN (Italy)   **F6.4715**
Ermanno Donati–Luigi Carpentieri–Cosmopolis Film–Jolly Film. *Dist* Colorama Features, Capitol Films. 30 Nov **1962** [New York opening]. Sd; col (Eastman Color). 35mm (CineScope). 103 min.
Prod Ermanno Donati, Luigi Carpentieri. *English Vers Dir* Irving Rapper. *Italian Vers Dir* Luciano Ricci. *Screenplay* Guglielmo Santangelo, Oreste Biancoli, Ennio De Concini. *English Vers Screenplay* Guy Elmes. *Story* Guglielmo Santangelo. *Photog* Riccardo Pallottini. *Art Dir* Oscar D'Amico. *Film Ed* Mario Serandrei. *Mus* Mario Nascimbene. *Cost* Maria De Matteis.
Cast: Geoffrey Horne *(Joseph)*, Robert Morley *(Potiphar)*, Belinda Lee *(Henet)*, Vira Silenti *(Asenath)*, Mario Girotti *(Benjamin)*, Carlo Giustini *(Reuben)*, Finlay Currie *(Jacob)*, Arturo Dominici *(Rekmira)*, Robert Rietty *(Pharaoh)*, Julian Brooks *(chief baker)*, Mimo Billi *(chief butler)*, Marietto *(Benjamin, as a child)*, Marco Guglielmi *(Judah)*, Dante Di Paolo *(Simeon)*, Charles Borromel *(Dan)*, Helmut Schneider *(Zebulun)*, Loris Bazzocchi *(Issachar)*, Marin Marija *(Asher)*, Antonio Segurini *(Gad)*, Tonko Sarcevic *(Levi)*.
Biblical drama. In Canaan, Joseph is the favorite among the 12 sons of the patriarch Jacob. Jealous of his favored position and his ability to interpret dreams, Joseph's older brothers are angered when he is entrusted by their father with selling a flock of sheep. The brothers beat him and sell him to an Egyptian slave trader, duping Jacob into believing that he has been killed. Bought by Potiphar, the pharaoh's superintendent of prisons, Joseph saves his master's life and gains his trust. However, Potiphar's young wife, Henet, repulsed in her advances toward Joseph, falsely accuses him of attacking her, and he is imprisoned. While in prison, he correctly foresees from the dreams of the

pharaoh's disgraced chief baker and chief butler that the first will die and the second regain his position. Word of Joseph's power reaches the pharaoh, who summons the young man to interpret a dream that has puzzled his advisors. Joseph prophesies that Egypt will enjoy 7 prosperous years followed by 7 years of famine. Appointed to prepare for the famine, Joseph saves Egypt by storing grain. Meanwhile, Potiphar learns of Henet's treachery, kills her, and commits suicide over her body. Rekmira, a noble jealous of Joseph's success, encourages an attack from the King of Syria, but Joseph opens a great dam, and Egypt's enemies are swept away. Joseph, now a powerful official, takes Asenath for his bride. During the years of famine, Egypt is able to sell grain to its starving neighbors. Among those who arrive seeking grain are Joseph's older brothers, one of whom he takes hostage to summon his father and younger brother, Benjamin. Their arrival occasions a tender reunion as Joseph reveals his identity and forgives his older brothers. *Brothers. Patriarchs. Prophets. Royalty. Shepherds. Traitors. Slavery. Seduction. Murder. Suicide. Famine. Perfidy. Jealousy. Prisons. Canaan. Egypt. Dreams. Biblical characters. Joseph.*

Note: Corporations involved in production are unconfirmed. Opened in Rome in Sep 1960 as *Giuseppe venduto dai fratelli*. Also known as *Joseph and His Brethren*.

THE STORY OF MONTE CRISTO *see* **THE STORY OF THE COUNT OF MONTE CRISTO**

THE STORY OF THE COUNT OF MONTE CRISTO (France/Italy)   F6.4716

Les Films J.-J. Vital–Les Productions René Modiano–S. N. E. Gaumont–Cineriz—Royal Film. *Dist* Warner Bros. Pictures. 13 Jun 1962 [Washington D. C., opening; c1 Jan 1962: LP29390]. Sd; col (Technicolor). 35mm (Dyaliscope). 132 min.

Pres by Seven Arts Associated Corp. *Prod* Jean-Jacques Vital, René Modiano. *Dir* Claude Autant-Lara. *Adapt & Dial* Jean Halain. *Photog* Jacques Natteau, Jean Isnard. *Art Dir* Max Douy. *Film Ed* Madeleine Gug. *Mus* René Cloerec. *Sd* René Forget. *Asst Dir* Ghislaine Autant-Lara. *Prod Mgr* Georges Charlot. *Cost* Rosine Delamare.

Cast: Louis Jourdan (*Edmond Dantès*), Yvonne Furneaux (*Mercedes*), Pierre Mondy (*Caderousse*), Franco Silva (*Mario*), Bernard Dhéran (*Villefort*), Jean-Claude Michel (*Fernand de Mortcerf*), Jean Martinelli (*Vidocq*), Claudine Coster (*Haydée*), Henri Guisol (*Abbé Faria*), Marie Mergey (*Madame Caderousse*), Yves Renier (*Albert de Mortcerf*), Alain Ferral (*Benedetto*), Lupi Roldano (*Morel*), Henri Vilbert (*Dantès' father*), Jean-Jacques Delbo.

Adventure drama. Source: Alexandre Dumas, père, *Le Comte de Monte-Cristo* (Paris, 1844–45). In 19th-century Marseilles, seaman Edmond Dantès is condemned to life imprisonment for conspiring with Bonapartists to return the exiled Napoleon from Elba. This false accusation and unjust sentence are brought about through the maneuvers of Caderousse, a man envious of Dantès' position; Fernand de Mortcerf, who is in love with Dantès' fiancée, Mercedes; and Villefort, an ambitious magistrate who must eliminate Dantès in order to advance his own career. After being imprisoned in the Château d'If for 17 years, Dantès escapes and, with the map of a dead prisoner, recovers a vast treasure buried on the island of Monte Cristo. Returning to Marseilles as the Count of Monte Cristo, he takes revenge on Caderousse, Villefort, and de Mortcerf, who married Mercedes after she became convinced of Dantès' death. Dantès then sails off alone to erase the unhappy memories of his past. *Nobility. Seamen. Adventurers. Magistrates. Injustice. Treason. Envy. Ambition. Prison escapes. Revenge. Treasure. Marseilles. Montecristo. Duels.*

Note: Opened in Paris in Dec 1961 as *Le comte de Monte Cristo*; running time: 180 min; in Rome in Apr 1962 as *Il conte di Montecristo*; running time: 120 min. Also reviewed as *The Count of Monte Cristo* and *The Story of Monte Cristo*.

THE STORY OF THE PERVERTED *see* **FILE X FOR SEX**

STOWAWAY IN THE SKY (France)   F6.4717

Filmsonor–Films Montsouris. *Dist* Lopert Pictures. 18 Jun 1962 [New York opening; c18 Jun 1962; LP27772]. Sd; col (Eastmancolor, print by Technicolor). 35mm (Dyaliscope). 82 min. [Also reviewed at 100 min.]

Pres by Jalem Productions. *Dir-Writ* Albert Lamorisse. *English Narr* S. N. Behrman. *Photog* Maurice Fellous, Guy Tabary. *Aerial Photog* Albert Lamorisse. *Art Dir* Pierre Thévenet. *Film Ed* Pierre Gillette. *Mus* Jean Prodromidès. *Sd* Pierre Vuillemin. *Asst Dir* Michel Wyn, Jean Flechet. *Prod Mgr* Jean Velter. *Artistic Adv* Marthe de Sels.

Cast: Pascal Lamorisse (*Pascal*), André Gille (*Grandfather*), Maurice Baquet (*Tou-Tou*), Jack Lemmon (*narrator*).

Adventure drama. In early 20th-century France little Pascal stows away in a 60-foot-tall orange balloon his grandfather has invented. Although he is discovered shortly after the balloon has left the ground, his grandfather not only lets him remain aboard but makes him first mate. By controlling their flight via pipes and levers they float over Alsace and Paris and along the Loire Valley,

and they watch a stag hunt and a Breton wedding party. After stretching their legs on the ground with their mechanic, Tou-Tou, they go aloft again and fly over a forest fire. The heat of the blaze explodes the balloon, and they are forced to make a landing. Tou-Tou puts on a new balloon and they take off again. After flying over the Alps and Provence, they once more make a landing. Alone in the balloon, little Pascal is accidentally sent aloft but, as the balloon dips toward the sea, the boy jumps onto the sand before the balloon drifts away. *Grandfathers. Children. Mechanics. Stowaways. Inventors. Travel. Balloons (ascent). Forest fires. Weddings. Alsace. Loire River. Provence. Brittany. Alps.*

Note: Location filming in and over Paris, Brittany, the French Riviera, the French Alps, La Camargue, and the Loire Valley. Opened in Paris in Sep 1960 as *Le voyage en ballon*; running time: 85 min. Filmed in Hélivision, a system of low-altitude aerial photography.

LA STRADA PER FORT ALAMO *see* **THE ROAD TO FORT ALAMO**

LA STRAGE DEI VAMPIRI *see* **CURSE OF THE BLOOD-GHOULS**

STRAIGHT BANANA   F6.4718

Leo Productions. 19 Nov 1970 [San Francisco showing]. Sd; col? 35mm? [Feature length assumed.]

Dir Lowell Pickett.

Sex film. No information about the precise nature of this film has been found. *Sexuality.*

STRAIT-JACKET   F6.4719

William Castle Pictures. *Dist* Columbia Pictures. 22 Jan 1964 [New York opening; c1 Dec 1963; LP26783]. Sd (RCA). b&w. 35mm. 89 min.

A William Castle Production. *Prod-Dir* William Castle. *Assoc Prod* Dona Holloway. *Writ* Robert Bloch. *Dir Photog* Arthur Arling. *Set Decor* Frank Tuttle. *Prod Dsgn* Boris Leven. *Film Ed* Edwin Bryant. *Mus* Van Alexander. *Sd* Charles J. Rice, Lambert Day. *Asst Dir* Herbert S. Greene. *Makeup* Ben Lane. *Miss Crawford's Makeup* Monte Westmore. *Miss Crawford's Hairstyles* Peggy Shannon. *Hairstyles* Virginia Jones. *Sp Eff* Richard Albain.

Cast: Joan Crawford (*Lucy Harbin*), Diane Baker (*Carol*), Leif Erickson (*Bill Cutler*), Howard St. John (*Raymond Fields*), John Anthony Hayes (*Michael Fields*), Rochelle Hudson (*Emily Cutler*), George Kennedy (*Leo Krause*), Edith Atwater (*Mrs. Fields*), Mitchell Cox (*Dr. Anderson*), Lee Yeary (*Frank Hardin*), Patricia Krest (*Stella Fulton*), Vickie Cos (*Carol, 3 years*), Patty Lee (*1st little girl*), Laura Hess (*2d little girl*), Robert Ward, actor (*shoe clerk*), Lyn Lundgren (*beauty operator*).

Mystery melodrama. Lucy Harbin returns unexpectedly to her farm after a trip out of town and discovers her husband in bed with another woman. Crazed, she grabs an ax and hacks the lovers to death in full view of her 3-year-old daughter, Carol. Lucy is committed to an asylum and her brother and sister-in-law take Carol and move west to another farm. Twenty years later Lucy is released from the asylum and comes to find her family. Carol, now a talented sculptress, is in love with wealthy young Michael Fields. The girl is anxious for her dowdy mother to look as she did 20 years earlier and persuades her to wear makeup, a black wig, youthful clothing, and jangling jewelry. Lucy behaves badly when she meets Michael; and the arrival of Dr. Anderson, the psychiatrist who treated her at the asylum, upsets her further. The doctor tells Carol that he thinks Lucy should return to the asylum and he is about to tell Lucy when he is hacked to death in a farm building. Later, Lucy tells Carol that the doctor left, but the girl finds the doctor's car and, suspecting that Lucy has reverted to violence, she hides the car. A hired hand sees her, and the next day Carol finds him repainting the car, which he says is his. She fires him but he refuses to leave, threatening to reveal that he discovered Dr. Anderson's body in the meat refrigerator. Lucy overhears the conversation, and the hired hand is later found axed to death. That night Lucy meets Michael's parents and she nervously reveals the couple's plan to wed. Mrs. Fields objects and is rude to Lucy, who flies into a rage, vows that nothing will stop the marriage, and rushes from the house. Later that night, Mr. Fields is chopped to death and, when his wife investigates the noise, a woman who appears to be Lucy attempts to kill her, but Lucy walks in and stops her. The look-alikes grapple until Lucy strips a mask and wig from the other woman, revealing her own daughter, who had planned the deaths of her beau's parents even before Lucy's release. Carol has a complete breakdown and is committed to an asylum. Realizing that her own crime led to Carol's insanity, Lucy goes to care for her at the asylum. *Psychopaths. Farmers. Sculptors. Psychiatrists. Handymen. Infidelity. Insanity. Murder. Disguise. Filial relations. Axes. Insane asylums.*

STRAITJACKET *see* **SHOCK CORRIDOR**

STRANDED *see* **VALLEY OF MYSTERY**

THE STRANGE AFFAIR (Great Britain)   F6.4720

Paramount Pictures. 24 Jul 1968 [New York opening; c17 Jun 1968: LP36949]. Sd; col (Technicolor). 35mm (Techniscope). 106 min.

A Howard Harrison-Stanley Mann Production. *Prod* Howard Harrison. *Assoc Prod* Rene Dupont. *Dir* David Greene. *Screenplay* Stanley Mann. *Photog* Alex Thomson. *Camera Op* Herbert R. Smith. *Focus Puller* Harvey Harrison. *Art Dir* Nicholas Pollock. *Set Dresser* Peta Button. *Prod Dsgn* Brian Eatwell. *Film Ed* Brian Smedley-Aston. *1st Asst Ed* Brian Mann. *Mus* Basil Kirchin. *Mus Supv* Jack Nathan, John A. Coleman. *Sd Rec* H. L. Bird. *Sd* Doug Turner. *Sd Camera Op* Michael Silverlock. *Boom Op* William Burgess. *Dub Ed* Keith Palmer. *1st & 2d Asst Dir* Jack Causey, Ariel Levy. *Prod Mgr* Derek Kavanagh. *Location Mgr* Robert Simmonds. *Cont* Eileen Head. *Dress Dsgn* Sue Yelland. *Wardrobe Supv* Ray Beck. *Ch Makeup* George Blackler. *Hairdresser* Betty Glasow. *Police Liaison Officer* James Dunham. *Casting Dir* James Liggat. *Still Photog* Barry Payne.

Cast: Michael York (*Peter Strange*), Jeremy Kemp (*Detective Sergeant Pierce*), Susan George (*Frederika March*), Jack Watson (*Daddy Quince*), George A. Cooper (*Superintendent Kingley*), Barry Fantoni (*Charley Small*), Artro Morris (*Inspector Evans*), Nigel Davenport (*defense attorney*), Madge Ryan (*Aunt Mary*), George Benson (*Uncle Bertrand*), George Selway (*Sergeant Clancy*), Michael Gover (*Detective Chief Superintendent Bryan*), Terence De Marney (*Mahon*), Jeremy Wilkin (*P. C. Wills*), Richard Pearson (*constable*), Patrick Connor (*Sergeant Mac*), George Ghent (*Sergeant Perry*), David Glaisyer (*Roddy Quince*), Richard Vanstone (*Arthur Quince*), Robin Tolhurst (*air hostess*), Rita Webb (*bedraggled woman*), Patrick Newell (*victim*), Richard Warner (*magistrate*), Philip Ryan, Dave Carter (*building site workmen*), Bernard Stone, Janet Lees Price, Toba Laurence (*neighbors*), John Paul, The Blue Mountain Boys (*pub group*).

Melodrama. Source: Bernard Toms, *The Strange Affair* (London, 1966). Peter Strange fails his university examinations in philosophy and joins the London Metropolitan Police Force. Serving in the same district is Detective Sergeant Pierce, an embittered man obsessed with obtaining the conviction of Quince, a former policeman now involved in drug peddling. On a tip from informer Charley Small, Pierce goes to the heliport where Quince and his two sons are scheduled to receive a consignment of stolen drugs. Pierce is astonished to observe one of his superiors, Inspector Evans, warning the Quinces that the police are present. Despite Pierce's efforts to catch Evans receiving a pay-off, Evans is cleared after an investigation, and Charley is killed by Quince. Meanwhile, Peter has become involved with a wild teenaged girl who calls herself Fred and is unaware that their lovemaking is being secretly filmed by her aunt and uncle, who deal in pornographic photographs. The next day, the Quinces brutally attack Peter and drive an electric drill through his cheeks. Pierce's frustration at Peter's inability to identify his assailants multiplies when the Quinces use bribed witnesses to absolve themselves of Charley's murder. Consequently, when the pornographic pictures of Peter and Fred accidentally fall into Pierce's hands, he uses them to blackmail Peter into planting drugs on Quince. At the resulting trial, however, Pierce's method of obtaining the Quinces' arrest is exposed, the case against the criminals is dropped, and Peter is sentenced to 2 years imprisonment for conspiring to obstruct justice and corrupt public morals. *Police. Drug dealers. Informers. Obsession. Murder. Pornography. Bribery. Blackmail. Frameup. Trials. London.*

Note: Location scenes filmed in London. Opened in London in Aug 1968.

STRANGE BEDFELLOWS   F6.4721

Fernwood Productions. *Dist* Universal Pictures. 10 Feb **1965** [Miami, Florida, opening; c13 Mar 1965; LP33023]. Sd (Westrex); col (Technicolor). 35mm. 99 min.

A Norman Panama-Melvin Frank Production. *Prod-Dir* Melvin Frank. *In Charge of Prod* Edward Muhl. *Assoc Prod* Hal C. Kern. *Screenplay* Melvin Frank, Michael Pertwee. *Story* Norman Panama, Melvin Frank. *Dir Photog* Leo Tover. *Art Dir* Alexander Golitzen, Joseph Wright. *Set Decor* John McCarthy, John Austin. *Main Titl* Pacific Title. *Film Ed* Gene Milford. *Mus* Leigh Harline. *Mus Supv* Joseph Gershenson. *Sd* Waldon O. Watson, Corson Jowett. *Asst Dir* Joseph Kenny, Paul Cameron. *Unit Prod Mgr* Bob Larson. *Cost* Peter Saldutti, Sally Wood. *Gina Lollobrigida's Gowns Dsgn* Jean Louis. *Makeup* Bud Westmore. *Hairstyles* Larry Germain. *Dial Coach* Lyle Moraine.

Cast: Rock Hudson (*Carter Harrison*), Gina Lollobrigida (*Toni*), Gig Young (*Richard Bramwell*), Edward Judd (*Harry Jones*), Terry-Thomas (*assistant mortician*), Arthur Haynes (*Carter's taxi driver*), Howard St. John (*J. L. Stevens*), Nancy Kulp (*aggressive woman*), David King (*Toni's taxi driver*), Peggy Rea (*Mavis*), Joseph Sirola (*Petracini*), Lucy Landau (*jolly woman*), Bernard Fox (*policeman*), Edith Atwater (*Mrs. Stevens*), James McCallion (*old man*), Hedley Mattingly (*Bagshott*), John Orchard (*radio dispatcher*).

Comedy. Richard Bramwell, an American public relations ace for a U. S. oil company, comes to London to clean up the "corporate image" of Carter Harrison, a young executive destined to become president of the firm's international branch. Carter has been separated for 7 years from his Italian wife, Toni, whom he married after a whirlwind courtship. Toni now spends her time

championing an assortment of bizarre minority causes. At first interested in divorce, Carter and Toni rekindle the old flame; but he is angered when he discovers that she is still attached to "nutty" causes and that she plans to picket the U. S. Embassy. Toni's current boyfriend, Harry Jones, advises her to leave for Reno immediately. Another breakup is followed by another reconciliation, with Carter promising to allow Toni anything in the way of causes. He and Bramwell then propose a plan to make her think Carter is about to accept a dangerous assignment—in reality, a scheme to prevent her from leading a protest march dressed as Lady Godiva astride a horse. At first Toni agrees to go to Nassau with Carter, but when she discovers the ruse she rushes off to Soho to take her place as Godiva. Chasing after her, Carter purposely causes a traffic disturbance, and the ensuing brawl lands everybody in court. When Bramwell is unable to shield Carter from the shocked attention of J. L. Stevens, his boss, an oil company lawyer makes a clever plea in Carter's defense. But Carter repudiates the defense, declaring he did everything for the love of Toni, who promptly melts into his arms. Stevens, aware of the "corporate image," fires Carter and Bramwell—but, mindful of the tender feelings of Mrs. Stevens, also promises to rehire them. *Americans in foreign countries. Executives. Lawyers. Italians. Separation (marital). Divorce. Oil business. Public relations. Appearances. Demonstrations. Traffic. London. London—Soho. Godiva.*

THE STRANGE CASE OF ...! # & % ? see **THE MALTESE BIPPY**

STRANGE COMPULSION   F6.4722

Irvmar Productions. *Dist* Manson Distributing Corp. Dec **1964**. Sd; b&w. 35mm. 81 min.

Prod-Dir Irvin Berwick. *Screenplay* Jason Johnson. *Photog* Joseph V. Mascelli. *Camera Op* Robert C. Jessup. *Asst Camera* Robert E. Bethard. *Art Dir* David Towbin. *Film Ed* Gerard Wilson. *Mus* Mutel Co. *Sd* S. F. Brownrigg. *Unit Mgr* John Harmon, prod mgr. *Script Cont* Betty Sooter. *Prod Coörd* Denis Adams. *Prod Asst* Joseph Cavalier. *Key Grip* James Finley. *Still Photog* Ralph K. Johnson.

Cast: Preston Sturges, Jr. (*The Young Man*), Jason Johnson (*The Psychiatric Counsellor*), Helen Melene, Shirlee Garner, June Oliver, Patricia King, Jane Hall, Anne MacAdams, Bob French, Frank Page, Jonathan Ledford, Mitzie Dickey, Dale Berry, Anita Harrison, Mamie Carroll, Barbara Tomlin, William Peck.

Drama. A young medical student who is afflicted with compulsive voyeurism goes to a psychiatrist and, in analysis, reveals the origin and nature of his illness. *Students. Psychiatrists. Voyeurism. Obsession. Mental illness.*

Note: Also known as *The Strange Compulsion.*

THE STRANGE FETISHES   F6.4723

Americana Entertainment Association. 29 Nov **1967** [Maryland license]. Sd; b&w. 35mm. ca66 min.

Pres by G. B. Roberts. *Prod-Dir* Enrico Blancocello.

Cast: Sammy Arena (*Bill Shawn*), Sandy O'Hara, Taylor March.

Horror film. Bill Shawn, the arrogant and widely-hated emcee of a midnight television horror show, disappears and is believed murdered. Only Dirk Johnson, the television station manager and Bill's worst enemy, knows for certain that Bill is dead, because he accidentally killed him during a fight. Dirk returns to the room where the fight took place and finds only a pool of acid where Bill's body had been. Horrible crimes begin to occur around the studio and in the town, and Bill's enemies, all guilty of having wished him dead, are threatened by a phantom whose face is horribly scarred. Several go-go dancers are strangled, and Dirk is thrown by the phantom from the station roof. Banner pursues the phantom and finds only Bill's decomposing body. ... *Television personalities. Detectives. Go-go dancers. Murder. Guilt. Disfiguration. Television.*

Note: Also known as *The Strange Fetishes of the Go-Go Girls.*

STRANGE HOLIDAY (Australia)   F6.4724

Mass-Brown Pictures. 20 Dec **1969** [Charlotte, North Carolina, opening; c18 Dec 1969; LP38133]. Sd; col (Eastman Color). 35mm. 75 min.

Pres by Golden Record Film Library. *Prod-Dir-Screenplay* Mende Brown.

Cast: Jaeme Hamilton (*Briant*), Mark Healey (*Doniphan*), Jaime Messang (*Moco*), Van Alexander, actor (*Gordon*), Carmen Duncan (*Kate*), Tony Allyn.

Adventure drama. Source: Jules Verne, *Deux ans en vacance* (Paris, 1888). Caught in a storm at sea, 10 boys and a dog are shipwrecked on a seemingly deserted island. Several months later, another storm shipwrecks four men, whom the boys mistakenly assume to be dead. Near their cave, the boys discover Kate, a nurse, who tells of the events during a recent storm. Aboard a ship bound for Sydney, a group of British prisoners escaped, killed most of the crew, and were forced to abandon ship when caught in a typhoon. Evans, the ship's carpenter, Kate, and three convicts were the only apparent survivors. Evans, badly wounded and feverish, is rescued and brought back to camp by Moco, a Polynesian youth. That night, the boys hide in the bush and frighten the escapees into a state of panic. In the confusion, two of the men die by their own hands, while the third is captured alive. After Evans realizes that the island is part of the Australian archipelago, the dory of the second wreck is repaired. At sea again, all are rescued. *Children. Nurses. British. Convicts. Carpenters. Polynesians. Survival. Murder. Rescue. Sea rescue. Islands. Caves. Shipwrecks. Storms. Typhoons.*

Note: Filmed in Australia.

STRANGE LOVERS F6.4725

Mast Productions. *Dist* Gillman Film Corp. 5 Jul **1963** [Los Angeles showing]. Sd; b&w. 35mm. 73 min.

Prod Robert Stambler, William Mahan. *Dir* Robert Stambler. *Screenplay* Robert Stambler, William Mahan, Nick Boretz, Alex Beaton. *Dir Photog* Fouad Said. *Mus Score* Warren Barker. *Asst Dir* Kamzi Thomas.

Cast—"End of the Path": Walter Koenig *(Bob Fuller)*, Sally le Cuyer *(Jackie Hart)*, Elaine Kaye *(Mrs. Hart)*.

Cast—"Homo Means Man": Joe D'Agosta *(George Lynn)*, Mark Bradley *(assailant)*, Jennifer Boles *(Ann)*.

Cast—"Segue": Arlene Hedrick *(Yvonne Martin)*, Sylvia Brenner *(Anita Rochland)*, Steve Hollister *(photographer)*.

Drama. A drama in three parts. END OF THE PATH—Bob is picked up by Jackie while he is walking along a California highway. They are attracted to each other, and she takes him to a deserted lake. There he mentally relives a traumatic experience in which as a child he was forced by a sadistic homosexual to commit a perverted act. Jackie calms him and takes him to her home. That night Bob has a nightmare about being assaulted when a teenager by a nymphomaniac. He awakes and goes to the swimming pool. There Jackie's mother, who has been watching Bob, attempts to seduce him. He forces her to her knees and strangles her. Tried and convicted of murder, Bob is put into a prison cell with a sex-starved criminal. HOMO MEANS MAN—George goes to a notorious bar, rejects the advances of a woman, and makes the acquaintance of a handsome, blond man. They leave together, intending to return to George's apartment. On a back road, George's companion beats him up and steals his money and his car. George is picked up by Ann, a woman from the bar who takes him to her apartment. George resists her sexual advances and explains to her that before his marriage he had been involved in homosexual relationships. He tells Ann about his estranged wife and his inability to confess to her his past involvements. After the birth of their first child, George and his wife separated and he returned to perversion. Having unburdened himself, George falls asleep, and Ann telephones his wife, who takes him home and gives him love and understanding. SEGUE—Newly-arrived in Los Angeles, Yvonne, alone and out of work, finds a job as a fashion model and attracts the attention of Anita, a department head. Yvonne tells Anita of her fear of men, and Anita schemes to gain Yvonne's affection. Anita tells the company photographer, a lecherous man, that Yvonne is "on the make," thus provoking him to attack her. Hysterical, Yvonne, reminded of an event in which she was raped in the back seat of a car, is propelled into the waiting arms of Anita. *Pickups. Models. Photographers. Sadism. Male homosexuality. Seduction. Murder. Marriage. Guilt. Lesbianism. Nymphomania. Rape. Bars. Prisons. California. Los Angeles. Dreams.*

Note: Location scenes filmed in Arizona, New Mexico, and Southern California. Working title: *Stranger Than Love.*

STRANGE PATTERNS F6.4726

Dist Chancellor Films. Dec **1969**. Sd; col. 35mm. 61 min.

Sex film. Several women who work in a city's garment district gang up on their employer and rape him. After exhausting him, the women turn to one another for sexual gratification. One woman makes love to a stockboy behind the dress racks. *Seamstresses. Rape. Lesbianism. Employer-employee relations.*

STRANGE RAMPAGE F6.4727

Monique Productions. 6 Jul **1967** [New York showing]. Sd; b&w. 35mm. 65 min.

Prod Harry Niwrek. *Dir* Ignatius Volpe. *Screenplay* Mel Carto. *Dir Photog* Wayne Wright. *Asst Camera* Merrill Terrance. *Film Ed* Harry Niwrek, Wayne Wright. *Mus* Agnes Strokin. *Sd Rec* Claude Pounds. *Asst Dir* Sam Kerry. *Unit Mgr* Raymond Kane. *Script Supv* Betty Svatos. *Makeup* Mel Van Toule. *Head Gaffer* John Duke, gaffer.

Cast: Ann Howe *(Ann Rowe)*, Bunny Ware *(Sally Lane)*, Duke Moberly *(Dr. Nathan Sarbone)*, Teri Sims *(Elaine Martin)*, Linda Miller *(Janis Payne)*, Cheri La Strapes *(Sara)*, Dina Darlene *(Jean)*, Dawn Walters *(Kathy)*, Maria Cola *(Marie)*, Boris Hume *(Captain Terane)*, Todd Walters *(Joe)*, Miki McGee *(Ralph)*, Bob Morris *(neighbor)*, Al Valenzano *(TV repairman)*, Katherine Preston, Bill Tyler *(couple on beach)*.

Drama. Dr. Nathan Sarbone, a psychiatrist who specializes in the sexual disorders of women, narrates three case histories: Janis Payne and Elaine Martin are daydreamers who share an identical fantasy—a trip to Miami that culminates in an orgy. Dr. Sarbone solves exhibitionist Ann Rowe's problem by getting her a job as a nightclub stripper. Sally Lane, who is looking for the perfect husband, lavishes her affection on a department store dummy. During her analysis, Dr. Sarbone becomes personally involved with Sally, and he brings her back into touch with reality. *Psychiatrists. Exhibitionism. Fantasy. Striptease. Orgies. Dummies. Miami.*

Note: Filmed in Miami.

STRANGE VICTORY (Reissue) F6.4728

Target Films. *Dist* Brandon Films. ca **1964**. Sd; b&w. 35mm. 77 min.

Voices added for 1964 epilog: Martin Luther King, Jr., John L. Lewis, Walter Reuther, Joachim Prinz, Eugene Carson Blake, Matthew Ahman, Roy Wilkins, A. Philip Randolph, Bayard Rustin.

Note: Originally released in 1948 by Target Films. An epilog was added for the reissue.

THE STRANGER (Algeria/France/Italy) F6.4729

Dino De Laurentiis Cinematografica–Master Film–Marianne Productions–Casbah Films. *Dist* Paramount Pictures. 18 Dec **1967** [New York opening]. Sd; col (Technicolor). 35mm. 104 min.

A Dino De Laurentiis Production. *Assoc Prod* Pietro Notarianni. *Dir* Luchino Visconti. *Screenplay* Suso Cecchi D'Amico, Georges Conchon, Emmanuel Robles, Luchino Visconti. *Photog* Giuseppe Rotunno. *Art Dir* Mario Garbuglia. *Film Ed* Ruggero Mastroianni. *Mus* Piero Piccioni. *Mus Cond* Bruno Nicolai. *Sd* Vittorio Trentino. *Asst Dir* Rinaldo Ricci, Albino Cocco. *Prod Mgr* Mario Lupi. *Cost* Piero Tosi. *Makeup* Mario Banchelli, Giuseppe Banchelli. *Hairstyles* Salvatore Cotroneo.

Cast: Marcello Mastroianni *(Arthur Meursault)*, Anna Karina *(Marie Cardona)*, Bernard Blier *(defense counsel)*, Georges Wilson *(examining magistrate)*, Bruno Crémer *(priest)*, Pierre Bertin *(judge)*, Jacques Herlin *(director of home)*, Marc Laurent *(Emmanuel)*, Georges Géret *(Raymond)*, Alfred Adam *(prosecutor)*, Jean-Pierre Zola *(employer)*, Mimmo Palmara *(Masson)*, Angela Luce *(Madame Masson)*, Saada Cheritel, Mohamed Ralem, Brahim Hadjadj *(Arabs)*, Vittorio Duse *(lawyer)*, Joseph Maréchal *(Salamano)*, Jacques Monod, Valentino Macchi, Paolo Herzl.

Drama. Source: Albert Camus, *L'étranger* (Paris, 1942). In pre-World War II Algiers, Arthur Meursault, a French clerk, learns of his mother's death; he attends the funeral but feels removed from grief, conscious only of the blinding sun. Upon returning to Algiers after the burial, he resumes the drab ritual of his daily life. He meets and spends the day with Marie Cardona; he testifies for a procurer, Raymond, who has been arrested for beating a young Arab girl; and he spends a weekend with Marie, Raymond, and a married couple. None of these relationships impinge on Meursault's solitude or his devotion to simple pleasures. One day he sets out for a walk alone on the beach and is startled by the Arab girl's brother, who earlier that day stabbed Raymond. Gradually Meursault becomes hypnotized by the sun's rays and fires five bullets into the boy. Brought to trial, Meursault slowly realizes that his refusal to indulge in social hypocrisy has condemned him, and he is sentenced to be guillotined. Back in his cell, Meursault rejects the consoling last words of a priest and accepts the inevitability of death. *Clerks. Arabs. Pimps. Priests. Death. Murder. Hedonism. Existentialism. Capital punishment. Funerals. Trials. Algiers.*

Note: Filmed on location in and around Algiers. Opened in Rome in Oct 1967 as *Lo straniero*; in Paris in Oct 1967 as *L'étranger*; running time: 100 min.

STRANGER IN HOLLYWOOD F6.4730

Roda Productions. *Dist* Emerson Film Enterprises, Roda Productions. caSep **1968**. Sd; col (Eastman Color). 35mm. 96 min. *MPAA rating* GP.

Prod Anne Slipyj. *Dir-Writ* Rodion Slipyj. *Photog* Steve Salamandro. *Art Dir* Ruth Brande. *Film Ed* Norm Vizents. *Sd* Gregory Valtierra.

Cast: Sue Bernard *(woman)*, Scott Every *(fiancé)*, Guy Mecoli, Mario Arezney, Grace Burnard, Phyllis Janus, Victor Smith, Anne Slipyj, Mary Clarke.

Melodrama. A young woman discovers crude oil in her residential backyard along Los Angeles' "Miracle Mile." She runs away from her new-found wealth and her fiancé and becomes involved with some sordid people and situations in Hollywood before she returns home. *Runaways. Oil. Urban life. Los Angeles. Hollywood.*

Note: Location scenes filmed in Los Angeles.

STRANGER IN THE HOUSE *see* **COP-OUT**

A STRANGER IN TOWN (United States/Italy) F6.4731

Primex Italiana–Taka Productions. *Dist* Metro-Goldwyn-Mayer, Inc. 24 Apr **1968** [New York opening; c29 Dec 1967; LP35855]. Sd; col (Eastman Color). 35mm. 86 min. [Cut from 96 min(?).]

An Allen V. Klein Production. *Prod* Carlo Infascelli. *Exec Prod* James Hagen. *Dir* Vance Lewis. *Story & Screenplay* Warren Garfield, Jone Mang. *Photog* Marcello Masciocchi. *Art Dir* Carmelo Patrono. *Film Ed* Maurizio Lucidi. *Mus Comp & Cond* Benedetto Ghiglia. *Asst Dir* Antonio Segurini.

Cast: Tony Anthony (*The Stranger*), Frank Wolff (*Aguila*), Iolanda Modio (*Cica*), Gia Sandri (*Maruka*), Raf Baldassarre, Aldo Berti, Enrico Capoleoni, Antonio Marsina, Arturo Corso, Salvatore Puntillo, Ivan Scratt, Rossella Bergamonti, Fortunato Arena, Ugo Carbone, Loris Bazzocchi, Angela Minervini, Lars Bloch.

Western melodrama. The Stranger, a wandering adventurer, rides into a Mexican village ruled by the bandit Aguila. As The Stranger looks on, Aguila captures and shoots a detachment of Mexican soldiers sent to receive a shipment of U. S. gold and dresses his outlaws in the dead soldiers' uniforms to await the arrival of the U. S. troops bringing the gold. Posing as a U. S. Army captain, The Stranger offers his assistance to Aguila in exchange for a promise of half the gold, but the bandit reneges on the agreement once the troops have departed. The Stranger escapes with two bags of gold and takes refuge with Cica, a young widow whose husband was killed by Aguila. To save Cica and her baby, The Stranger gives up the gold and flees when the house is besieged by Aguila, but the bandit abducts Cica. The Stranger is captured as he attempts to recover the gold, and he is brutally beaten by Aguila and his men. Aguila's sadistic mistress, Maruka, assumes charge of his torture, but he escapes with Cica and the gold. Aguila follows The Stranger to Cica's house, and a final gun battle ensues. The Stranger guns down the bandits one by one and then kills Aguila, who is armed with a machine gun. The American troops return to recover the gold, but The Stranger is permitted to keep half the loot as a reward. *Adventurers. Bandits. Soldiers. Widows. Strangers. Impersonation. Murder. Perfidy. Robbery. Abduction. Torture. Gold. Rewards. Mexico. United States Army—Cavalry.*

Note: Rome opening: Jun 1967 as *Un dollaro tra i denti*; running time: 90 min. The following are credited under pseudonyms: Luigi Vanzi (Vance Lewis), Giuseppe Mangione (Jone Mang), and Ivan Scratuglia (Ivan Scratt).

A STRANGER KNOCKS (Denmark)　　　　　　　F6.4732
Flamingo Productions. *Dist* Trans-Lux Distributing Corp. 31 Oct **1963** [San Francisco showing]. Sd; b&w. 35mm. 81 min.
Prod Annelise Hovmand, Johan Jacobsen. *Dir* Johan Jacobsen. *Screenplay* Finn Methling. *Camera* Åke Borglund, Johan Jacobsen. *Sets* Annelise Hovmand. *Mus Comp* Erik Fiehn. *Sd* Erik Rasmussen.
Cast: Birgitte Federspiel (*[The Woman]*), Preben Lerdorff Rye (*[The Stranger]*), Victor Montell (*[man from village]*).
Melodrama. In August, 1947, a hunted man seeks refuge at a cottage on a lonely stretch of land along the North Sea. The sole occupant of the cottage is a stoic woman who feeds the stranger and allows him to sleep by the hearth. The stranger, taking note of the woman's lonely isolation, stays on the next day, and the woman tells him of her life alone in the cottage ever since the day 3 years earlier when her husband, a member of the Danish resistance, was murdered by collaborators. As the man prolongs his stay at the cottage, the woman awakens to his physical presence, and they become lovers. Then one night as they consummate their passion, the woman notices that the man bears a scar shaped like an animal's mouth on his arm. It is a mark that could belong to only one man—the quisling responsible for torturing and executing her husband. Horrified, she taunts the stranger, wrings a confession of guilt from him, and shoots him as he tries to escape. Now aware that she has erased the man's guilt by slaying him, she bears within herself the even greater guilt of murder. *Widows. Strangers. Fugitives. Traitors. War crimes. Murder. Resistance (political). Personal identity. Revenge. Sexuality. Guilt. World War II. North Sea.*
Note: Released in Denmark in 1959 as *En fremmed banker på*; running time: 87 min.

STRANGER ON MY BED　　　　　　　　　　　F6.4733
Dist Inter-American Film Distributors. 5 Jun **1968** [New York opening]. Sd; b&w. 35mm. [Feature film, length unknown.]
Dir Frank Bryan.
Crime melodrama. After burglarizing an apartment and raping the two female inhabitants, a pair of hoodlums enter a nightclub and force the entertainers to perform an impromptu striptease. They later rape two lesbian roommates and compel an inexperienced teenaged boy to have sex with their moll. After shooting the adolescent, the gangsters are slain. *Hoodlums. Innocents. Entertainers. Molls. Rape. Striptease. Sexual initiation. Murder. Lesbianism. Burglary. Nightclubs.*

THE STRANGER RETURNS (United States/Italy/West Germany)
　　　　　　　　　　　　　　　　　　　　　　　　F6.4734
Primex Italiana-Juventus-Reverse Productions. *Dist* Metro-Goldwyn-Mayer, Inc. 21 Aug **1968** [Detroit opening; c14 Aug 1968; LP36022]. Sd; col (Metrocolor). 35mm. 90 min.
An Allen V. Klein Production. *Prod* Roberto Infascelli, Massimo Gualdi. *Exec Prod* Allen V. Klein. *Dir* Vance Lewis. *Screenplay* Bob Ensescalle, Jr., Jone Mang. *Orig Story* Tony Anthony. *Dir Photog* Marcello Masciocchi. *Art*

Dir Franco Bottari. *Film Ed* Renzo Lucidi. *Mus Comp & Cond* Stelvio Cipriani. *Asst Dir* Gaetano Scala. *Sp Eff* Stacchini.
Cast: Tony Anthony (*The Stranger*), Dan Vadis (*En Plein*), Daniele Vargas (*Good Jim*), Marco Guglielmi (*The Preacher*), Jill Banner (*Caroline*), Ettore Manni (*Stafford*), Marina Berti (*Ethel*), Raf Baldassarre, Anthony Freeman, Renato Mambor, Mario Dionisi, Armando Mangolini, Silvana Fiorini, Arturo Danesi, Filippo Antonelli.
Western melodrama. A conniving postal inspector tells a gang of Mexican bandits about an expected stagecoach shipment of gold and is immediately shot to death by the gang. The Stranger, a sarape-draped wanderer who carries a pink parasol, finds the man's body, takes his identification card, kills several of the bandits, and rides into Moon Village. En Plein, the gang leader, seizes the designated stagecoach, killing the driver and passengers, but discovers that it is a decoy. The Stranger, masquerading as the dead postal inspector, attempts to gain entrance to En Plein's hideout but is ambushed and captured. He learns that Good Jim, a local official, is in league with En Plein to steal the real stagecoach, whose solid gold framework is concealed by wooden panels painted red. The Stranger is tortured by the gang but manages to free himself by cutting his bonds with a piece of broken glass. Good Jim tries to double-cross En Plein by switching coaches, but his ruse is discovered, and he is murdered after revealing that the real coach is hidden in a cemetery. The Stranger arrives on the scene in time to prevent the rape of Good Jim's daughter, Caroline. Then, aided by a preacher known as The Prophet who sets off fireworks at opportune moments, The Stranger guns down the gang members with a sawed-off shotgun. The Stranger and The Prophet take the bandits' corpses into town and collect a $10,000 reward. Since The Stranger plans to keep the disguised gold coach for himself, he magnanimously gives The Prophet the entire reward. As The Stranger drives out of town, however, fireworks left inside the coach explode and expose the gold framework. Relinquishing the coach to the U. S. Cavalry, The Stranger seeks out The Prophet and reclaims his share of the reward. *Strangers. Postal clerks. Mexicans. Bandits. Wanderers. Preachers. Stagecoach robberies. Murder. Impersonation. Torture. Perfidy. Rape. Gold. Rewards. Mexican border. United States Army—Cavalry.*
Note: Rome opening: 1968 as *Un uomo, un cavallo, una pistola*. The following are pseudonyms: Vance Lewis (Luigi Vanzi), Jone Mang (Giuseppe Mangione), Anthony Freeman (Mario Novelli).

STRANGER THAN LOVE see **STRANGE LOVERS**

STRANGERS see **I NEVER SANG FOR MY FATHER**

STRANGERS IN THE CITY　　　　　　　　　　F6.4735
Rick Carrier Productions. *Dist* Embassy Pictures. 16 Jul **1962** [New York opening]. Sd; b&w. 35mm. 83 min.
Pres by Joseph E. Levine. *Prod-Dir-Writ* Rick Carrier. *Exec Prod-Story Collab* Elgin Ciampi. *Assoc Prod* James Geallis. *Photog* Rick Carrier. *Film Ed* Stan Russell. *Mus Comp & Cond* Robert Prince. "Strangers" Theme Rick Carrier. *Sd* Elgin Ciampi. *Asst Dir* Elgin Ciampi. *Prod Mgr* James Geallis.
Cast: Robert Gentile (*Felipe Alvarez*), Camilo Delgado (*José Alvarez*), Rosita de Triana (*Antonia Alvarez*), Creta Margos (*Elena Alvarez*), Robert Corso (*caddy*), Bob O'Connell (*Dan*), John Roeburt (*grocer*), Ruth Kuzab (*Jo*), Kenny Delmar (*Mr. Lou*).
Domestic melodrama. Puerto Rican immigrants José Alvarez and his family live in one room in a tenement on Manhattan's upper East Side. José, an unemployed guitar player, refuses to take menial jobs that would hamper his guitar playing, and as a consequence his wife, Antonia, is forced to find work, despite his protestations. Felipe, their teenaged son, is fired from his job as delivery boy when hoodlums steal a large grocery order from him. Felipe, criticized by his father for not fighting back, seeks out the gang leader and challenges him to a fight, but the brawl is broken up by police, and the two boys become friends. The teenaged daughter, Elena, allows her shop foreman to take advantage of her in hopes of bettering herself. The foreman passes Elena on to Mr. Lou, the leader of a vice ring, and she becomes a prostitute. Antonia learns about Elena's experiences with the foreman. She goes to the factory and in a scuffle stabs him to death. She returns home to her husband; he accuses her of infidelity and pushes her into the bathtub. As she falls she drags an electric cord into the water and is electrocuted. Horrified by what he has done, José takes poison. Felipe finds Elena with a strange man in a parked car. After persuading her that she is doing wrong, Felipe takes her home, unaware of the tragedy that awaits them. *Puerto Ricans. Immigrants. Guitarists. Delivery boys. Hoodlums. Police. Shop foremen. Factory workers. Urban life. Family life. Adolescence. Poverty. Employment. Employment—Women. Theft. Prostitution. Murder. Jealousy. Manslaughter. Suicide. Poisoning. Electrocution—Accidental. Tenements. New York City.*
Note: Filmed on location in Harlem, Manhattan, and Coney Island, New York City.

THE STRANGLER
F6.4736

Allied Artists. 8 Apr **1964** [Boston opening]. Sd; b&w. 35mm. 89 min.

Prod Samuel Bischoff, David Diamond. *Dir* Burt Topper. *Screenplay* Bill S. Ballinger. *Photog* Jacques Marquette. *Art Dir* Hal Pereira, Eugene Lourie. *Set Decor* Sam Comer, James Payne. *Film Ed* Robert S. Eisen. *Mus* Marlin Skiles. *Sd* Hugo Grenzbach, Charles Grenzbach. *Asst Dir* Clark Paylow. *Prod Mgr* Edward Morey, Jr. *Script Supv* Robert Gary. *Makeup* Wally Westmore. *Hairstyles* Nellie Manley.

Cast: Victor Buono (*Leo Kroll*), David McLean (*Lieutenant Benson*), Diane Sayer (*Barbara*), Davey Davison (*Tally*), Ellen Corby (*Mrs. Kroll*), Michael Ryan (*Posner*), Baynes Barron (*Sergeant Clyde*), Russ Bender (*Dr. Sanford*), Jeanne Bates (*Clara*), Wally Campo (*Eggerton*), Mimi Dillard (*Thelma*), Byron Morrow (*Dr. Morton*), John Yates (*intern*), James Sikking (*artist*), Selette Cole (*Helen*), Robert Cranford (*Jack Rosten*), Victor Masi (*attendant*).

Crime melodrama. Leo Kroll, an obese hospital laboratory technician, is questioned by police after the strangulation of a nurse, the eighth in a string of similar murders. After his release, he visits his possessive mother, who has survived a recent heart attack largely with the aid of her nurse, Clara. Leo hates Clara for her devotion to his mother and on the following night, after winning a doll at the amusement park stand operated by Tally and Barbara, he strangles Clara in her apartment and smashes the doll against the wall. Questioned by the police again, he voluntarily takes and passes a lie detector test. Warned about his mother's condition, Leo deliberately tells her about Clara's murder, and she suffers a fatal heart attack. At the amusement stand he sees Barbara talking to a detective. When Leo learns she was questioned about dolls, he strangles her. Aware that he is now a prime suspect, Leo desperately proposes to Tally and becomes furious when she rejects him. Later, as he is about to strangle Tally, the police rush into her apartment and Leo plunges through a window to his death. *Psychopaths. Nurses. Police. Insanity. Murder. Momism. Heart disease. Dolls. Amusement parks.*

LO STRANIERO *see* THE STRANGER

STRATEGY OF TERROR
F6.4737

Roncom Films. *Dist* Universal Pictures. Feb **1969**. Sd; col (Pathé). 35mm. 90 min. *MPAA rating* M.

Prod Arthur H. Nadel. *Exec Prod* Frank P. Rosenberg. *Dir* Jack Smight. *Screenplay* Robert L. Joseph. *Photog* Bud Thackery. *Film Ed* Sam E. Waxman. *Mus Score* Lyn Murray.

Cast: Hugh O'Brian (*Matt Lacey*), Barbara Rush (*Karen Lownes*), Neil Hamilton (*Mr. Harkin*), Frederick O'Neal (*Jacques Serrac*), Will Corry (*Wally Pitt*), Harry Townes (*Richard*), Jan Merlin (*Jon*), Eric Morris (*Tippo*), Mort Mills (*Victor Pelling*).

Mystery drama. Karen Lownes, a newspaper reporter, receives a phone call from a childhood classmate who urgently requests a meeting. When she arrives, Karen finds the man has been shot, but before he dies he tells her of a right-wing plot that is underway to assassinate three United Nations undersecretaries. Karen tells the story to a police lieutenant, Matt Lacey, but Lacey believes that the dead man was only a petty gangster and assumes that he was killed by his own associates. After Karen is attacked by a hoodlum anonymously hired to follow her, Lacey becomes convinced that the matter is to be taken seriously, and he doubles his efforts to uncover the plot. Karen follows a lead to a freight company office, where she inadvertently uncovers the identity of the assassins. The assassination is to take place at a diplomatic reception attended by the three undersecretaries, but Karen recognizes one of the men from the freight company, and Lacey arrests the would-be assassins. *Reporters. Diplomats. Police. Assassination. Conspiracy. Murder. United Nations.*

Note: Originally presented on ABC's "Kraft Suspense Theatre" as a 2-part episode titled *In Darkness Waiting*; c14 Jan, 21 Jan 1965; LP32345, LP32346; telecast on the same days as registered for copyright.

A STRAVINSKY PORTRAIT
F6.4738

Rolf Liebermann–Leacock Pennebaker, Inc. *For* Norddeutscher Rundfunk. *Dist* Leacock Pennebaker, Inc. 31 Jan **1968** [Los Angeles opening]. Sd; b&w. 16mm. 57 min.

A Film by Richard Leacock, Rolf Liebermann. *Photog* Richard Leacock. *Film Ed* Richard Leacock. *Sd Rec* Sarah Hudson.

Interviewer: Rolf Liebermann.

With [In Order of Appearance]: Igor Stravinsky, Vera Stravinsky, Robert Craft, Pierre Boulez, Nicolas Nabokov, George Balanchine, Suzanne Farrell, Jacques D'Amboise, Gloria Govrin, Gerald Heard, Christopher Isherwood, West German Symphony Orchestra.

Documentary. This tribute to composer Igor Stravinsky shows the artist relaxing at home in Beverly Hills with his wife and friends, conducting a recording session of his tribute to Aldous Huxley with the West German Symphony Orchestra, discussing work with his colleagues, and being interviewed by filmmaker Liebermann. *Composers. Orchestra conductors. Los Angeles—Beverly Hills. Igor Fyodorovich Stravinsky.*

THE STRAWBERRY STATEMENT
F6.4739

Metro-Goldwyn-Mayer, Inc. 15 Jun **1970** [New York opening; c6 May 1970; LP38101]. Sd; col (Metrocolor). 35mm. 103 min. [Cut from 109 min.] *MPAA rating* R.

Prod Irwin Winkler, Robert Chartoff. *Dir* Stuart Hagmann. *Screenplay* Israel Horovitz. *Dir Photog* Ralph Woolsey. *Camera Op* Mike Margulies. *Camera Asst* Roger Smith, photog. *Art Dir* George W. Davis, Preston Ames. *Set Decor* Robert R. Benton, Chuck Pierce. *Film Ed* Marjorie Fowler, Fredric Steinkamp, Roger J. Roth. *Mus Score* Ian Freebairn-Smith. *Song:* "The Circle Game" Joni Mitchell. *Sung by* Buffy Sainte-Marie. *Song:* "Something in the Air" John Keene. *Perf by* Thunderclap Newman. *Song:* "Helpless" Neil Young. *Perf by* Crosby, Stills, Nash & Young. *Song:* "Our House" Graham Nash. *Perf by* Crosby, Stills, Nash & Young. *Song:* "Suite Judy Blue Eyes" Stephen Stills. *Perf by* Crosby, Stills, Nash & Young. *Song:* "Long Time Gone" David Crosby. *Perf by* Crosby, Stills & Nash. *Songs:* "The Loner," "Down by the River" comp & perf by Neil Young. *Song:* "Give Peace a Chance" John Lennon, Paul McCartney. *Concerto in D minor* Alessandro Marcello. *Mus:* "Thus Spake Zarathustra" Richard Strauss. *Sd* Jerry Jost, Franklin Milton, Harry W. Tetrick. *Boom Op* Robert Crosby. *Rec* Bill Manooch. *Asst Dir* Al Jennings, John Behm, Robert Steinhauer. *Unit Prod Mgr* John W. Rogers. *Script Supv* H. Bud Otto. *Cost* Norman Burza, Ricky Roberts. *Makeup* Jerry Cash. *Hairstyles* Faith Schmehr. *Sp Eff* J. D. Day. *Action Coörd* Cliff Coleman. *Stunt Coörd* Dick Ziker. *Still Photog* Lee Sporkin. *Gaffer* George Lasher. *Prop* Bill Bates, John Leishman. *Grip* Leo Monlon, Lloyd Isbell.

Cast: Bruce Davison (*Simon*), Kim Darby (*Linda*), Bud Cort (*Elliot, the coxswain*), Murray MacLeod (*George*), Tom Foral (*coach*), Danny Goldman (*Charlie*), Kristina Holland (*Irma*), Bob Balaban (*Elliot, the organizer*), Kristin Van Buren (*filing room girl*), Israel Horovitz (*Dr. Benton*), James Simon Kunen (*chairman*), James Coco (*grocer*), Eddra Gale (*dean's secretary*), Michael Margotta (*Swatch*), Bob Benjamin (*man*), Jeannie Berlin (*clipboard girl*), Carol Bagdasarian (*telephone girl*), Jon Hill, Jess Walton, Andrew Parks (*students*), Booker Bradshaw (*Lucas*), Drew Eshelman (*Tim*), Greta Pope (*song leader*), David Dukes (*guard*), Ed Greenberg (*bearded leader*), Kertia Thomas, Debbie Muller, Bruce Neckels (*student speakers*), Larry Canaga, Justin Christopher, Diann Henrichsen, Robin Menken, Christopher Pray, John R. Pray, Paul Willson (*guerrilla theater troupe*), Henry Leff (*police inspector*), Bert Remsen (*policeman*), Joe Quinn (*professor*), Pat May, Bill Boelk, Randy Thornally, Pat Rooney (*Red Mountain Jug Band*), Jack Schmidt (*university president*), King Moody (*television newscaster*), Bill Striglos (*televison technician*), Joseph Reale (*Jock*), Nancy Burnett, Margo Winkler, Ruth Silveira, Julie Payne (*women*).

Comedy-drama. Source: James Simon Kunen, *The Strawberry Statement: Notes of a College Revolutionary* (New York, 1969). Simon, a somewhat apolitical Western University student, goes to a sit-in so that he can take pictures and meet some girls. As he passes the demonstration, he is attracted by the sight of one girl, but his attention is diverted by the prodding of a policeman who calls him a communist. As a gesture of protest, he goes to the university president's office where another sit-in is taking place, and he is once again charmed by the girl, whose name is Linda. Moved by her political enthusiasm, he volunteers to go with her on a food patrol, but at the store the grocer, believing he is being robbed, points to the expensive items and calmly yells for the police as Simon and Linda leave. Early the next morning, Simon goes to crew practice and recruits the coxswain, Elliot, for the protest movement. After practice, he meets Linda at a playground where they demonstrate until the police arrest them. Linda later learns that Simon is a crew member, and her antipathy toward the sport (and athletes in general) causes him to involve himself more strongly in politics, although he continues with the crew team. In a scuffle over politics with his friend George, Simon is hit in the mouth, and when he returns to school, he allows everyone to believe that he has been hit by the police. Finally, all the demonstrators gather at the gymnasium where another rally is held. Outside, amidst television interviews, the National Guardsmen take their positions and the students brace for the attack, singing "Give Peace a Chance." The soldiers charge the building, attacking the students with tear gas; as the police try to drag Linda away, Simon, now totally committed to the movement, lunges to protect her. *Students. Grocers. Athletes. Police. Demonstrations. Sit-ins. College life. Student activism. Rowing. Police brutality. Tear gas. National Guard.*

Note: Location scenes filmed in San Francisco.

STRAY DOG (Japan)
F6.4740

Shin Toho Co. *Dist* Toho International, Inc. Aug **1963** [Los Angeles showing]. Sd; b&w. 35mm. 122 min.

Prod Sojiro Motoki. *Dir* Akira Kurosawa. *Screenplay* Ryuzo Kikushima, Akira Kurosawa. *Photog* Asakazu Nakai. *Camera* H. Kusada. *Art Dir* So

Matsuyama. *Film Ed* Yoshi Sugihara. *Mus* Fumio Hayasaka.

Cast: Toshiro Mifune *(Murakami)*, Takashi Shimura *(Sato)*, Ko Kimura *(Yuro)*, Keiko Awaji *(Harumi)*, Reisaburo Yamamoto *(Hondo)*, Noriko Sengoku *(girl)*.

Melodrama. Based on an unpublished novel by: Akira Kurosawa. In Tokyo just after World War II, Murakami, a recently appointed detective, has his gun stolen by a woman on a bus. Because pistols are scarce in postwar Japan, Murakami, afraid of losing his job, begins to hunt for the gun. He later finds the woman, but she has sold the gun to a fence who in turn has passed it on to a young hoodlum. The gun, loaded with seven bullets, is first used in a stickup in which a girl is wounded. Murakami, with the help of Sato, an older detective, finds Harumi, the hoodlum's girl friend, and when the second bullet is used to kill a young housewife, Harumi gives the detectives the hoodlum's former address. With this information Sato traces the criminal to his current address, but the hoodlum uses the third and fourth bullets to shoot and seriously wound Sato as he is telephoning Murakami. Harumi tells Murakami that the hoodlum is to meet her at a train station, and he goes in her place. The criminal wounds the detective with the fifth bullet, but when he misses with the sixth and seventh Murakami overpowers and arrests him. *Detectives. Hoodlums. Molls. Fences (for stolen goods). Murder. Robbery. Guns. Tokyo.*

Note: Released in Japan in Oct 1949 as *Nora inu.*

THE STREET IS MY BEAT   F6.4741

Harann Productions. *Dist* Emerson Film Enterprises. 9 Nov **1966** [San Francisco opening]. Sd; b&w. 35mm. 93 min.

Prod Alan P. Magerman, Jack Paller, Irvin Berwick. *Dir* Irvin Berwick. *Screenplay* Harold Livingston, Irvin Berwick. *Orig Story* Jack Kevan, Irvin Berwick. *Photog* Joseph V. Mascelli. *Art Dir* David Towbin. *Film Ed* Gerard Wilson. *Mus* Harrose. *Titl Song Sung by* Marilyn Michaels. *Sd* Ernie Reed.

Cast: Shary Marshall *(Della Martinson)*, Todd Lasswell *(Phil Demarest)*, John Harmon *(Mr. Martinson)*, Anne MacAdams *(Mr. Martinson)*, Tom Irish *(Johnny Gibson)*, Beverly Oliver *(Sally)*, Bob Brown *(McGruber)*, Susan Cummings *(Cora)*, J. Edward McKinley *(Danby)*.

Melodrama. Seventeen-year-old Della Martinson leads an unhappy home life with her shiftless father, a night watchman, and domineering mother. Phil Demarest, 10 years older than Della, easily charms her into accepting his marriage proposal and gives her parents $200 to ensure their approval. The marriage begins happily, but Della soon learns that Phil is a professional procurer for out-of-town businessmen. One night he tricks her into going into a man's hotel room and notifies the police, who arrest her. Upon her release from prison, Della attempts to find a legitimate job, but her prison record follows her, and she is finally forced to capitulate to Phil, who trains her as a high-priced call girl. After three years, Della discovers another woman in Phil's apartment and is forced to leave, avowing that she no longer needs to pay Phil a commission. She informs on Phil and, embittered by her parents' earlier rejection, refuses their help. She quickly deteriorates through drink and becomes a common streetwalker living in cheap hotel rooms. Following a struggle with a drunk, Della steps into the path of a passing automobile. She is rushed to the hospital where her parents, who have been brought closer together by their suffering, visit her and promise to help her begin a new life. *Watchmen. Pimps. Ex-convicts. Police. Prostitution. Alcoholism. Parenthood. Marriage. Frameup. Conscience.*

STREET/RACK *see* MEAT/RACK

STREETS OF SIN (Reissue)   F6.4742

Emerald Productions. *Dist* Alexander Enterprises. 29 Jun **1961** [Maryland license]. Sd; b&w. 35mm. 94 min.

Note: Originally released by Film Classics in 1949 as *Not Wanted.*

LA STREGA IN AMORE *see* THE WITCH

LE STREGHE *see* THE WITCHES

STRIKE (U.S.S.R.)   F6.4743

Goskino-Proletkult. *Dist* Brandon Films. 4 Jan **1962** [New York opening]. Si; b&w. 35mm. 6458 ft.

Dir Sergei Eisenstein. *Screenplay* Valeriy Pletnyov, Sergei Eisenstein, I. Kravchunovskiy, Grigoriy Aleksandrov. *Photog* Eduard Tisse, Vasiliy Khvatov. *Asst Camera* V. Popov. *Art Dir* Vasiliy Rakhals. *Asst Dir* Grigoriy Aleksandrov, I. Kravchunovskiy, A. Levshin.

Cast: Grigoriy Aleksandrov *(foreman)*, Maksim Shtraukh *(detective)*, Mikhail Gomorov *(worker)*, Yudit Glizer *(woman)*, Boris Yurtsev *(king of the underworld)*, Aleksandr Antonov *(member of the strike committee)*, I. Klyukvin *(activist)*, I. Ivanov *(chief of police)*, V. Uralskiy, A. Kuznetsov, actor 1, V. Yanukova, Misha Mamin, V. Poltoratskiy, P. Belyayev, V. Zhuravlyov.

Drama. Intolerable working conditions, including wage reductions and extended work loads, precipitate labor agitation in a factory. The ranks of labor are infiltrated, however, by company provocateurs, among them "Monkey,"

"Owl," "Bulldog," "Tailor," "Slyboots," "Peasant," "Fox," and "Shepherd." When a company agent steals a micrometer, its loss is blamed on an honest workman. Overwhelmed by the injustice, the laborer hangs himself. His death touches off a general strike, during which company representatives are dunked in a muddy pond. In response to demands for an 8-hour day, wage increases, and restrictions on child labor, the industrialist wipes his shoes with the workers' petition. An activist, photographed by "Owl," is arrested and tortured. Though a dwarf provocateur sets fire to a warehouse, the workers discover his treachery and summon the fire department. The firemen maliciously turn their hoses on the strikers, however, drowning one man in the mud. Frustrated by labor unity and by their inability to incite the strikers to violence, the police slaughter the workers, trampling an infant with their horses, dropping a child from a high building, and firing into the crowd. *Informers. Factory management. Factory workers. Police. Firemen. Strikes. Torture. Arson. Murder. Capitalism. Factories.*

Note: Released in the U.S.S.R. in Apr 1925 as *Stachka.*

STRIKE ME DEADLY *see* THE CRAWLING HAND

STRIP POKER *see* THE BIG SWITCH

STRIP-TEASE *see* SWEET SKIN

THE STRIPPER   F6.4744

Jerry Wald Productions. *Dist* Twentieth Century–Fox Film Corp. 19 Jun **1963** [New York opening; c15 May 1963; LP24886]. Sd (Westrex); b&w. 35mm (CinemaScope). 95 min.

A Jerry Wald Production. *Prod* Jerry Wald. *Assoc Prod* Curtis Harrington. *Dir* Franklin J. Schaffner. *Screenplay* Meade Roberts. *Dir Photog* Ellsworth Fredricks. *Art Dir* Jack Martin Smith, Walter M. Simonds. *Set Decor* Walter M. Scott, Stuart A. Reiss, Norman Rockett. *Film Ed* Robert Simpson. *Mus* Jerry Goldsmith. *Dance Dir* Alex Romero. *Sd* W. D. Flick, Warren B. Delaplain. *Asst Dir* Eli Dunn. *Gowns Dsgn* Travilla. *Makeup* Ben Nye. *Miss Woodward's Hair Styles Dsgn* George Masters. *Hair Styles Supv by* Margaret Donovan.

Cast: Joanne Woodward *(Lila Green)*, Richard Beymer *(Kenny Baird)*, Claire Trevor *(Helen Baird)*, Carol Lynley *(Miriam Caswell)*, Robert Webber *(Ricky Powers)*, Louis Nye *(Ronnie Cavendish)*, Gypsy Rose Lee *(Madame Olga)*, Michael J. Pollard *(Jelly)*, Sondra Kerr *(Edwina)*, Susan Brown *(Mrs. Mulvaney)*, Marlene De Lamater *(Sandra Mulvaney)*, Gary Pagett *(Dizzy)*, Ralph Lee *(Sonny)*, Bing Russell *(Mr. Mulvaney)*.

Melodrama. Source: William Inge, *A Loss of Roses* (New York opening: 28 Nov 1959). After failing to make a successful career as a dancer in movies, Lila Green joins a second-rate vaudeville act. When the show arrives in the small Kansas town where Lila spent part of her childhood, Ricky Powers, the troupe's manager and Lila's lover, skips town with her money, and Lila moves in with an old friend, Helen Baird, and her young son, Kenny. The ardent but inexperienced Kenny becomes so attracted to Lila that he breaks off with his teenaged girl friend and asks Lila to marry him. Lila's happiness is shattered when she realizes that Kenny's promises are a result of youthful infatuation. Ricky returns to offer Lila a job—performing a striptease at a stag show—and she reluctantly agrees to do the act. Kenny watches the performance and becomes so disgusted with what Lila has been reduced to that he once more proposes. She refuses, however, knowing that their marriage would never work, and she decides also to forego her career to make a new life for herself. *Dancers. Theatrical managers. Striptease. Vaudeville. Stag shows. Smalltown life. Adolescence. Kansas.*

Note: Working titles: *Celebration* and *A Woman in July.*

STRIPPING WIVES *see* THE CASE OF THE STRIPPING WIVES

STROKE OF NINE   F6.4745

Dist Distribpix, Inc. ca **1970**. Sd; col. 35mm. 64 min.

Melodrama. A young, unemployed woman takes work at a massage parlor, believing it to be legitimate. She soon discovers that the clients expect considerably more than a massage, and she finds herself under the tutelage of the women who specialize in providing sex for their customers. When the boss of the establishment throws a party for his closest friends, the women entertain them. In the ensuing orgy, the young woman is sexually mistreated and subjected to acts of lesbianism and group sex. *Masseurs. Prostitutes. Sexual techniques. Lesbianism. Massage parlors. Orgies.*

STRONGROOM (Great Britain)   F6.4746

Theatrecraft Ltd.–Bryanston Films. *Dist* Union Film Distributors. Dec **1962** [Los Angeles showing: Mar 1963]. Sd; b&w. 35mm. 80 min.

Prod Guido Coen. *Dir* Vernon Sewell. *Screenplay* Max Marquis, Richard Harris, writ. *Idea* Richard Harris, writ. *Photog* Basil Emmott. *Art Dir* Duncan Sutherland. *Film Ed* John Trumper. *Mus* Johnny Gregory. *Sd* Stephen Dalby. *Sd Rec* George Adams. *Asst Dir* Jan Saunders. *Prod Mgr* Douglas Hermes.

Cast: Derren Nesbitt *(Griff)*, Colin Gordon *(Mr. Spencer)*, Ann Lynn *(Rose Taylor)*, Keith Faulkner *(Len)*, Morgan Sheppard *(Alec)*, John Chappell *(John Musgrove)*, Hilda Fenemore, Diana Chesney *(charladies)*, Ian Colin *(Creighton)*, Kevin Stoney *(police sergeant)*, Duncan Lewis *(mortuary attendant)*, Lockwood West *(police inspector)*, Pamela Conway *(secretary)*, Colin Tapley *(Haynes)*, John Dearth *(Hopkins)*, Frank Seton *(gatekeeper)*, Anna Turner *(Mrs. Snape)*, Keith Campbell *(Snape)*, Duncan McIntyre *(duty sergeant)*, Jack Stewart, British *(Sergeant McIntyre)*, Colin Rix *(P. C. Harper)*, Michael Peake *(Inspector Gregg)*.

Crime melodrama. Three petty criminals—Griff, Alec and Len—carefully plan the robbery of a bank in a small inland city. In the execution of the crime, they lock the manager, Mr. Spencer, and his secretary, Rose, in an airtight vault. As they escape, they realize that the two people will suffocate unless released in a few hours, thus adding murder to robbery. They agree that Alec should inform the authorities anonymously, but before he can do so, he is killed in an automobile accident. While the police are trying to identify the vault keys found on Alec's body, Griff and Len decide to return to the bank to rescue the two captives. They succeed as the police close in, but Rose is already dead, and they find themselves facing a murder charge. *Secretaries. Bankers. Police. Bank robberies. Murder. Vaults. Automobile accidents.*

Note: Released in London in Jun 1962.

THE STUD   F6.4747

Fleetan Films. *Dist* Able Film Co. ca **1969**. Sd; col. 16mm. 60 min.

Cast: Randy Gilman, Sylvia Summers.

Melodrama. Josh Lyle, lead singer for the rock and roll group "Rubber Carburetor" can have any girl he wants. Jenny, his devoted partner, has learned that Josh can never love anyone. Josh's agent tries out an aspiring vocalist by seducing her. Josh finally meets his match in Lynn, whose sex drive is even stronger than his own. *Singers. Talent agents. Sexuality. Seduction. Rock and roll.*

THE STUD FARM   F6.4748

Dist McAbee Pictures. Jun **1969**. Sd; col (Eastman Color). 35mm (see note). 58 min.

Prod-Story Ian Ogilvie, M. J. Margolis. *Dir-Screenplay* Jac Zacha. *Photog* Manuel S. Conde. *Film Ed* Manuel S. Conde. *Mus* David Hayward.

Cast: Gary Yuma *(Gary)*, Wayne Douglas *(Wayne)*, Paul Daniel *(Sam)*, Joe Dante *(Clarence)*, Ken Craig *(house manager)*, Jac Zacha *(Sheldon Bryant)*.

Melodrama. Gary leaves home to join his brother, a successful fashion model on the West Coast. Along the way he meets Sam, a young hippie who enjoys relaxing without any clothes, and Clarence, a transvestite. Hitchhiking, Gary is picked up by Sheldon Bryant, who offers friendship and $200 to help him on his way. When he arrives in Venice, California, Gary learns that his brother is not a fashion model, but a male prostitute at the "Farm." Disillusioned, he joins the Farm's male sex show in a flagellation act. His first client, as he follows in his brother's footsteps, is his benefactor, Sheldon Bryant. *Brothers. Hippies. Hitchhikers. Models. Nudity. Prostitution. Transvestism. Male homosexuality. Flagellation. Stag shows. Venice (California).*

Note: Filmed in 16mm and blown up to 35mm. Also advertised as *Study Farm* and *The Male Farm*.

THE STUDENT NURSES   F6.4749

New World Pictures. 27 Aug **1970** [New Orleans opening]. Sd; col (Movielab). 35mm. 85 min. *MPAA rating* R.

Prod Charles S. Swartz. *Prod-Dir* Stephanie Rothman. *Exec Prod* Roger Corman. *Assoc Prod* Paul Rapp. *Screenplay* Don Spencer. *Story* Charles S. Swartz, Stephanie Rothman. *Photog* Stefan Larner. *Art Dir* David Nichols. *Film Ed* Stephen Judson. *Mus Supv* Clancy B. Grass, III. *Sd* Sunshine Meyer.

Cast: Elaine Giftos *(Sharon)*, Karen Carlson *(Phred)*, Brioni Farrell *(Lynn)*, Barbara Leigh *(Priscilla)*, Reni Santoni *(Victor Charlie)*, Richard Rust *(Les)*, Lawrence Casey *(Jim Caspar)*, Darrell Larson *(Greg)*, Paul Camen *(Mark)*, Richard Stahl *(Dr. Warshaw)*, Scottie MacGregor *(Miss Boswell)*, Pepe Serna *(Luis)*, John Pearce *(patient)*, Mario Aniouv *(Ralpho)*, Ron Gans *(psychiatrist)*, El Teatro Popular *(themselves)*.

Melodrama. Sharon, Lynn, Phred, and Priscilla are in their last year of nursing school. Sharon falls in love with a patient who is dying. Lynn becomes involved with a Chicano revolutionary and runs away with him after he and his friends shoot a policeman. Phred administers an overdose of drugs, but a young doctor, Jim, saves her from punishment. Phred and Jim's romance is shattered, however, when she learns that he has performed an abortion on her roommate, Priscilla, who has had an affair with a drug addict. All four women eventually graduate and go their separate ways. *Nurses. Physicians. Students. Mexicans. Revolutionaries. Police. Roommates. Murder. Abortion. Drug overdose. Hospitals.*

Note: Filmed on location in Los Angeles.

STUDY FARM *see* **THE STUD FARM**

A STUDY IN TERROR (Great Britain/West Germany)   F6.4750

Compton-Tekli Film Productions-Sir Nigel Films-Planet Film Productions. *Dist* Columbia Pictures. 20 Apr **1966** [Waco, Texas, opening; c31 Dec 1965; LP32835]. Sd (Westrex); col (Eastman Color, print by Pathé). 35mm. 94 min.

Pres by Herman Cohen. *Prod* Henry E. Lester. *Exec Prod* Herman Cohen. *Dir* James Hill. *Screenplay* Donald Ford, Derek Ford. *Dir Photog* Desmond Dickinson. *Camera Op* Norman Jones. *Set Dresser* Helen Thomas. *Prod Dsgn* Alex Vetchinsky. *Film Ed* Henry Richardson. *Mus Comp & Cond* Johnny Scott. *Sd Ed* Jim Roddan. *Sd Mix* H. L. Bird. *Sd Supv* John Cox. *Asst Dir* Barry Langley. *Prod Mgr* Robert Sterne. *Cont* Gladys Goldsmith. *Cost* Motley. *Wardrobe* Laurel Staffell, Larry Stewart. *Makeup* Tom Smith. *Hairdresser* Gladys Leakey. *Sp Eff* Wally Veevers. *Casting* Maude Spector.

Cast: John Neville *(Sherlock Holmes)*, Donald Houston *(Dr. John Watson)*, John Fraser *(Lord Edward Carfax)*, Anthony Quayle *(Dr. Murray)*, Robert Morley *(Mycroft Holmes)*, Barbara Windsor *(Annie Chapman)*, Adrienne Corri *(Angela)*, Frank Finlay *(Inspector Lestrade)*, Judi Dench *(Sally)*, Cecil Parker *(prime minister)*, Georgia Brown *(singer)*, Barry Jones *(Duke of Shires)*, Kay Walsh *(Cathy Eddowes)*, Edina Ronay *(Mary Kelly)*, Terry Downes *(Chunky)*, Peter Carsten *(Max Steiner)*, Charles Regnier *(Joseph Beck)*, Dudley Foster *(home secretary)*, John Cairney *(Michael Osborne)*, Christiane Maybach *(Polly Nichols)*, Avis Bunnage *(landlady)*, Barbara Leake *(Mrs. Hudson)*, Patrick Newell *(P. C. Benson)*, Norma Foster *(Liz Stride)*.

Mystery melodrama. Based on characters created by: Arthur Conan Doyle. In the 1880's, three prostitutes are brutally murdered in the Whitechapel section of London. After the press has dubbed the unknown killer "Jack the Ripper," Sherlock Holmes receives a package containing a box of surgical instruments from which a scalpel is missing. Aided by his friend Dr. Watson, Holmes traces the instruments to the home of the Duke of Shires and learns that they were once the property of the duke's elder son, Michael, who was disowned for marrying a prostitute, Angela. Holmes also learns that the duke's younger son, Lord Carfax, has been paying blackmail to Max Steiner, the local pub owner, to conceal Michael's marriage and preserve the family honor. Also implicated in the killings is Dr. Murray, the owner of a Whitechapel clinic, who confesses that his assistant is Michael, who went berserk when he spilled acid on his wife's face upon discovering her with a lover. When Holmes learns that Steiner is Angela's lover and that she is the blackmailer, he takes Michael home to his father and sets a trap for the killer in Angela's room. "The Ripper" is revealed to be Lord Carfax; he killed the other prostitutes only to obscure his intention of murdering Angela. As Holmes struggles with Lord Carfax, a lamp is knocked over and flames sweep the room. Lord Carfax, Angela, and Steiner perish in the fire; and Holmes decides to spare the feelings of the Duke of Shires by allowing the identity of "Jack the Ripper" to remain a mystery. *Physicians. Prostitutes. Detectives. Nobility. Murder. Blackmail. Infidelity. Filial relations. Pubs. Clinics. London—Whitechapel. Fires. Sherlock Holmes. Dr. Watson. Jack the Ripper.*

Note: Location scenes filmed in London. Opened in London in Nov 1965; running time: 95 min; in West Germany in Jan 1966 as *Sherlock Holmes grösster Fall*; running time: 94 min. Co-production status of West Germany is unconfirmed. Also known as *Fog.*

THE SUBJECT WAS ROSES   F6.4751

Edgar Lansbury Productions-T. D. J. Productions-Delos Productions. *Dist* Metro-Goldwyn-Mayer, Inc. 13 Oct **1968** [New York opening; c17 Sep 1968; LP36115]. Sd; col (Metrocolor). 35mm. 107 min.

Prod Edgar Lansbury. *Assoc Prod* Kenneth Utt. *Dir* Ulu Grosbard. *2d Unit Dir* Burtt Harris. *Screenplay* Frank D. Gilroy. *Dir Photog* Jack Priestley. *Camera Op* Dick Kratina. *Art Dir* George Jenkins. *Set Decor* John Godfrey. *Master Scenic Artist* Stanley Cappiello. *Film Ed* Jerry Greenberg. *Mus Comp & Cond* Lee Pockriss. *Song:* "Who Knows Where the Time Goes" Sandy Denny. *Sung by* Judy Collins. *Song:* "Albatross" *writ & sung by* Judy Collins. *Sd* Jack C. Jacobsen. *Sd Ed* Sanford Rackow. *Sd Mix* Richard Vorisek. *Asst Dir* Paul Ganapoler, Terence A. Donnelly. *Script Supv* Maggie James. *Cost Dsgn* Anna Hill Johnstone. *Wardrobe* Flo Transfield, George Newman. *Makeup Supv* Mike Maggi. *Hairdresser* Vern Caruso. *Head Carpenter* Jules Wollock. *Ch Electrn* Willie Meyerhoff. *Key Grip* Jack Kennedy, Robert Volpe. *Prop Master* Tom Tonery.

Cast: Patricia Neal *(Nettie Cleary)*, Jack Albertson *(John Cleary)*, Martin Sheen *(Timmy Cleary)*, Don Saxon *(nightclub m. c.)*, Elaine Williams *(woman in club)*, Grant Gordon *(man in restaurant)*.

Domestic drama. Source: Frank D. Gilroy, *The Subject Was Roses* (New York opening: 25 May 1964). Young veteran Timmy Cleary returns to his Bronx home at the end of World War II and is soon disillusioned to find his parents' marriage filled with discord, quarreling, and recriminations. Previously his mother Nettie's pride and joy, Timmy now establishes rapport with his salesman father, John, and attempts to reconcile his parents without taking sides. While returning to the apartment after a day with his father at the family's summer cottage, Timmy picks up a bouquet of roses for Nettie and suggests that John take credit for the idea. Nettie is deeply touched by the gift and joins her men for a nightclub tour of Broadway; later, however, John's drunken attempts at lovemaking disgust her, and she smashes the vase of roses, whereupon he tells her that it was Timmy who bought them. The next morning, John is angered to learn that Timmy no longer attends Sunday mass and leaves for church alone. After Timmy accuses Nettie of trying to make him side with her against John, she disappears for awhile to collect her thoughts but later returns home to find a worried and accusing John quarreling with their half-drunk son. Aware that everyone shares blame for their domestic situation, Timmy decides the next morning that he must leave home to make a life of his own. Although saddened by his announcement, both parents realize it is best for him, and when he changes his mind at the last minute, John insists that he go. United at least temporarily by Timmy's parting, the family has breakfast together. *Veterans. Irish. Catholics. Salesmen. Family life. Parenthood. Marriage. Disillusionment. Drunkenness. Flowers. Nightclubs. New York City—Bronx. New York City—Broadway.*

Note: Filmed in New York City and Spring Lake, New Jersey.

SUBMARINE X-1 (Great Britain)   F6.4752
Mirisch Films-Oakmont Productions. *Dist* United Artists. Jul **1969** [Los Angeles opening; c1 Oct 1968; LP36699]. Sd; col (DeLuxe). 35mm. 89 min. *MPAA rating* G.
A John C. Champion Production. *Prod* John C. Champion. *Exec Prod* Irving Temaner. *Assoc Prod* Ted Lloyd. *Dir* William Graham. *Screenplay* Donald S. Sanford, Guy Elmes. *Story* John C. Champion, Edmund H. North. *Dir Photog* Paul Beeson. *Art Dir* Bill Andrews. *Film Ed* John S. Smith. *Mus Score* Ron Goodwin. *Sd Mix* Cyril Swern. *Asst Dir* Anthony Waye. *Prod Mgr* Tom Sachs. *Wardrobe* John Briggs. *Makeup* George Blackler. *Sp Eff* Bowie Films.

Cast: James Caan (*Commander Bolton*), Rupert Davies (*Vice-Admiral Redmayne*), David Sumner (*Lieutenant Davies*), William Dysart (*Lieutenant Gogan*), Norman Bowler (*Sub-Lieutenant Pennington*), Brian Grellis (*Chief Petty Officer Barquist*), Paul Young (*Leading Seaman Quentin*), John Kelland (*Sub-Lieutenant Willis*), Kenneth Farrington (*Chief Petty Officer Knowles*), George Roubicek (*Redmayne's flag officer*), Keith Alexander (*sub-lieutenant*), Carl Rigg (*Chief Petty Officer Kennedy*), Nicholas Tate (*leading seaman on X-1*), Steve Kirby (*leading seaman on X-2*), Dennis Mayers (*sub-lieutenant*), Diana Beevers (*W.R.N.S. officer*), Paul Hansard (*Commander Steiner*), Hans De Vries (*German lieutenant*), Richard Steele (*captain in Redmayne's office*), Desmond Jordan (*naval doctor*), George Pravda (*Captain Erlich*).

War drama. In 1943, a British naval officer from Canada, Lieut.-Comdr. John Bolton, loses his submarine and most of his crew in a raid on the "invincible" German battleship Lindendorf. Although Bolton is cleared of charges in a court of inquiry, the few survivors from the encounter hold him responsible for the deaths of their shipmates. A short time later, Bolton is assigned by Vice-Admiral Redmayne to train three 4-man crews along the northern coast of Scotland for a trio of midget submarines equipped with side cargoes of amatol explosives. Because the exact nature of the mission is kept secret, and because four of the men are survivors from the previous expedition, Bolton's rigid disciplinary measures are met with open hostility. However, the men unite when a German reconnaissance plane is sighted over the camouflaged training base, and German paratroopers land in the area. The Admiralty reveals that the midget subs are to attack the Lindendorf while she is undergoing repairs inside a Norwegian fjord. The subs make their way through heavily mined waters to reach the fjord, and crew members battle German frogmen underwater. One of the subs, the X-2, is sunk by a German E-boat's depth charges, and a second, the X-1, is scuttled by its crew before they are captured and taken aboard the Lindendorf. Before the men from the X-1 can be subjected to forced interrogation, however, the X-3 fires its explosives and destroys the Lindendorf. *Ship crews. Canadians. Naval bombardment. Submarines. Explosives. Mines (war explosives). World War II. Norway. Scotland. Great Britain—Royal Navy. Germany—Navy.*

Note: Location scenes filmed in Scotland. Produced in 1967. According to one source, director William Graham collaborated on original story with John C. Champion but did not receive screen credit.

SUBMISSION   F6.4753
S & J Films. *Dist* Chancellor Films. **1969** [Champaign, Illinois, showing: 29 May 1970]. Sd; b&w. 35mm. 73 min.
Prod Arthur Savage. *Dir* Allen Savage. *Screenplay* Donald Stanley. *Camera, Unit 1* Norris Eisenbrey. *Camera, Unit 2* Fred Murphy. *Film Ed* Kemper Peacock. *Mus* 91.

Cast from Pressbook: Jenny Wells, Gary Judis, Sheba Britt, Samantha Sigal, Gloria and Ivan, Joao Fernandes.
Cast from Review: Lisa Puran, June Adams, Sheba Britt, Natalie Shilvers, Christine Stein.

Melodrama. Two degenerates, Barry and Vickie, visit the home of wealthy Linda Staples. Barry attempts to seduce Linda, but she rejects him. Linda goes out one evening, and Barry and Vickie find a film revealing Linda's past as a prostitute and a lesbian. Barry forces Vickie to have sex with Linda; the women find they are attracted to each other, and they trick Barry to his death. *Houseguests. Wealth. Seduction. Prostitution. Lesbianism. Murder. Motion pictures.*

SUBSTITUTION   F6.4754
Dist Boxoffice International Film Distributors. Oct **1970**. Sd; col. 35mm. 73 min.
Prod-Dir Walt Davis. *Assoc Prod* Louise Duran. *Mus* Jonathan. *Asst Dir* Carl Ray. *Wardrobe* Valli. *Makeup* Valli.

Cast: Chuck Sailor (*Henry Hedon*), Patrice Nastasia (*Alice Hedon*), James Paulin (*Fred Letcher*), Marnie Kay (*Dottie Letcher*), Pam Collins, Kevin Johnston, Pat Duran, Leslie Schootz, Bernie Schootz, Fran Briggs, Jim Muntz, Carol Shiada, Diane Hunter, Renee Ray, Dana Schootz, Mary Bauer.

Comedy-drama. Timid Henry Hedon and his wife, Alice, no longer excite each other sexually. A business associate suggests to Henry that he visit the mystic Mahar"iji. Henry undergoes the prescribed treatment and returns home to see the results. While he waits in bed for his wife to join him, he begins to lose faith in the cure. Suddenly, a voluptuous, seductive stranger steps out of the bathroom to provide the most erotic night of Henry's life. Each night Alice disappears only to reappear as another ravishing beauty. With the help of the Mahariji, Henry has learned to imagine his wife in a wide variety of seductive guises. Alice, who has visited the same Mahariji, shares Henry's new enthusiasm. *Gurus. Marriage. Eroticism.*

SUBTERFUGE (United States/Great Britain)   F6.4755
Intertel Production Services, Ltd. (VTR)-Commonwealth United Productions. *Dist* Commonwealth United Entertainment, Inc. 27 Dec **1968** [Baltimore opening]. Sd; col (Eastmancolor). 35mm. 89 min.
Pres by Commonwealth United Corp. *Prod* Peter Snell. *Exec Prod* Trevor Wallace. *Dir* Peter Graham Scott. *Screenplay* David Whitaker, writ. *Camera* Roy Garner, Albert Tolley, Peter Lamb. *Lighting* Horst Wenzel. *Art Dir* Ron Fouracre. *Film Ed* Bill Lewthwaite. *Mus & Mus Dir* Cyril Ornadel. *Song:* "No Escape" Cyril Ornadel, Norman Newell. *Sung by* Malcolm Roberts. *Song:* "Love Looks Good on You" Cyril Ornadel, Peter Callander. *Sung by* Marmalade. *Sd* David Ashley Smith, Don Warren, Nigel Hanley. *Asst Dir* Andrew Grieve. *Prod Mgr* Nigel Warwick. *Miss Collins' Wardrobe Coörd* Joan Collins. *Vision Mix* Judy Dearden.

Cast: Gene Barry (*Donovan*), Joan Collins (*Anne Langley*), Richard Todd (*Col. Victor Redmayne*), Tom Adams (*Peter Langley*), Suzanna Leigh (*Donetta*), Michael Rennie (*Goldsmith*), Marius Goring (*Shevik*), Scott Forbes (*Pannell*), Colin Gordon (*Kitteridge*), Guy Deghy (*Dr. Lundgren*), Dermot Kelly (*van driver*), Stuart Cooper (*Dubrossman*), John Welsh (*Heiner*), Clifford Earl (*policeman*), Ron Pember (*photographer*), Gary Clifford (*Michael Langley*), Jane Blackburn (*Aunt Mary*), Harry Locke, Fred Peisley (*tramps*), Sidney Vivian (*taxi driver*), Robert Raglan (*Fennimore*), Graham Lines (*immigration officer*), Bill Nagy (*embassy attaché*), John Clifford (*government chauffeur*), Freda Dowie (*waitress*), Charles Lamb (*caretaker*), Marian Diamond (*schoolteacher*), Carmen Dene, Lyn Marshall, Donna Reading, Valerie Hudson (*club waitresses*), Stella Sands (*nude*).

Drama. CIA agent Donovan, in England trying to discover the identity of a double agent, is unaware that his contact Schoener has been murdered. Donovan is kidnaped by a Russian organization headed by Shevik but is rescued by Peter Langley, who is impersonating a Dr. Lundgren. Langley takes Donovan to his headquarters, and there Col. Victor Redmayne informs Donovan that he is being returned to the United States because his activities embarrass the British Secret Service. Actually Redmayne intends to send a substitute, but his plan is foiled by Pannell, one of Shevik's men. Donovan receives instructions from Goldsmith, the CIA agent stationed in London, to meet Langley's wife, Anne, and their child, Michael. The Langley marriage is failing, and Anne becomes attracted to Donovan, unaware that he is investigating her husband. When Michael is kidnaped by Shevik's men, Anne discovers Donovan's connection with the CIA; and when Langley disappears, she agrees to help Donovan, believing that Langley will lead them to her son. Donovan discovers that Langley is preparing to flee the country with Shevik, taking Michael with him, but he averts the flight and rescues Michael. *Americans in foreign countries. Secret agents. Russians. Abduction. Marriage. Espionage. Murder. Impersonation. London. Great Britain—Intelligence service. United States—Central Intelligence Agency.*

Note: Filmed on location in London and in the Home Counties. Released in Great Britain in Mar 1971; running time: 86 min.

SUBURBAN GIRLS CLUB　　　　　　　　　　F6.4756

Mitam Productions. 8 May 1968 [periodical notice]. Sd; b&w. 35mm. 63 min. [Also reviewed at ca50 min.]

Cast: Capri.

Drama. A woman describes the activites of a sex club to an enquiring reporter. At a weekly meeting of the Suburban Girls Club, the members decide to have a raffle, the winner of which may do anything she wants with the male "prize." The idea is a great success, and there is an orgy involving the weekly winners. Kate, a social climber, joins the club and wins the raffle. She refuses to engage in sex acts, and the man she is with brutally rapes her. Kate goes to the police, and the club is broken up. *Reporters. Group sex. Rape. Suburban life. Sex clubs. Contests.*

SUBURBAN PAGANS　　　　　　　　　　F6.4757

Boxoffice International Pictures. *Dist* Boxoffice International Film Distributors. Sep 1968. Sd; b&w. 35mm. 75 min.

Prod Harry H. Novak. *Dir-Writ* Shannon Carse. *Dir Photog* Sam Rayven. *Ed* Shannon Carse. *Sd* Rayven Productions.

Cast: Vincent Stephens (*Lieut. Art Grennell*), James Brand (*George Ferris*), Cara Peters, Carol Saunders, Christine Thomas, Karen Richards, Carol Turner, Elaine Teff, Clint Randall, Bob Penn, Art Wesley, Stan Logan, Morton Smith.

Drama. Lieutenant Art Grennell of the Los Angeles Police Department talks to television interviewer George Ferris about the activities of a suburban mate swapping club that has just been exposed after the attempted blackmail of one of its members. He reveals how informal groups, bored with traditional monogamous relationships, meet to search for pleasure. They may cut cards, flip coins, or fish for house keys from a bowl to choose partners. New members are usually recruited through the efforts of the wives, who are especially dissatisfied with their sex lives. Orgies of group sex and lesbian relationships between housewives all form part of the group's sexual explorations. Fear of exposure in the community makes the members highly susceptible to blackmail. Lieutenant Grennell believes that such clubs are multiplying at an alarming rate, and he doesn't know whether the cause lies with the tensions of war, the lack of strong religious convictions, or the approach of a new age of hedonism. Although he has succeeded in breaking up one group, he is sure that others are thriving. *Housewives. Police. Reporters. Hedonism. Suburban life. Mate swapping. Blackmail. Group sex. Lesbianism. Orgies. Television. Sex clubs. Los Angeles.*

SUBURBAN ROULETTE　　　　　　　　　　F6.4758

Unusual Films International. *Dist* Argent Film Productions. Jun 1968. Sd; col (Eastman Color). 35mm. 83 min. [May have been cut from 96 min.]

Prod David Chudnow. *Dir* Herschell Gordon Lewis. *Screenplay* James Thomas. *Photog* Roy Collodi.

Cast: Elizabeth Wilkinson (*Ilene Fisher*), Ben Moore (*Ron Elston*), Ione Rolnick, Tony McCabe, Vickie Miles, Thomas Wood.

Melodrama. Ilene Fisher's promiscuity has driven her husband to a state of near-alcoholism. Shortly after moving into a quiet suburban neighborhood, they attend a swimming pool party at the home of wealthy Ron Elston. Ignoring the presence of the other guests and Mrs. Elston, Ilene succumbs to the advances of Ron and makes love to him. In the weeks that follow, the Fishers and the Elstons join with a third couple in drunken parties that eventually lead to their playing a form of roulette in which the prize is someone else's marital partner. Outraged by everyone's immorality, including his own, Ilene's husband demands that they move out of the area; but Ilene, confident that Ron will divorce his wife and marry her, refuses. Ron, however, makes it clear that his only interest in Ilene is physical and that he has no intention of breaking up his family. Ilene takes an overdose of sleeping pills but is saved from death by her husband and daughter. As the Fishers resolve to save their marriage, Ron and their other neighbors look for new participants in their game of suburban roulette. *Suburban life. Marriage. Promiscuity. Alcoholism. Mate swapping. Group sex.*

SUBURBIA CONFIDENTIAL　　　　　　　　　　F6.4759

A. F. P. I. Productions. *Dist* SCA Distributors, Sack Amusement Enterprises. 28 Nov 1966 [Maryland license]. Sd; b&w. 35mm (Astravision). 82 min.

Prod-Dir A. C. Stephen. *Assoc Prod* Don Nagel. *Screenplay* Jason Underwood. *Dir Photog* Robert Wilson. *Art Dir* Bud Costello. *Post Prod* Herr Freed. *Mus Score* Igor Gigagusky.

Cast: George Cooper, actor (*Dr. H. Legrand*), John Andrews (*Howard Arnold*), John Bealy (*Ralph Harris*), James Jeans (*Paul Reynolds*), Eastman Price (*Hugh Randall*), Louis Ojena (*Robert Wood*), Phil Brian (*Pat Garrity*), Mark Crowe (*bellboy*), Don Jones (*waiter*), Helena Clayton (*Helena Fox*), Didi Seider (*Patsi Palmer*), Barbara Corey (*Sally Dane*), Brandi (*Mona Carter*), Patti Hahn (*Lesley Crane*), Lolita Williams (*Meylang Hensen*), Jade Green (*Joy Graham*).

Sex film. Psychiatrist Henri Legrand opens his files on the unhappy suburban housewives who come to him for treatment: Annoyed by her husband's absences, Helena Fox joined the milkman in an illicit affair and then seduced the T.V. repairman. Patsi Palmer became involved with a transvestite who made passionate love to her while wearing her own undergarments. Sally Dane tried to seduce a meek carpet salesman who was unable to enjoy normal lovemaking; instead he tied her to the bed and ravaged her. Mona Carter, ashamed of having been seduced by a lesbian cosmetic saleswoman, sought a normal relationship with lingerie salesman Robert Wood, only to discover that he was a shoe fetishist. Korean war bride Meylang Hensen needed psychiatric help to abandon sexual customs considered shocking in the United States. Joy Graham, Dr. Legrand's last case, is a nymphomaniac. Left alone by her husband at their hotel, she made desperate advances to the homosexual bellboy, and then seduced a young room service attendant. Dr. Legrand fears that Mrs. Graham cannot be cured without surgery. *Psychiatrists. Suburbanites. Housewives. Salesmen. Saleswomen. Milkmen. Television repairmen. Koreans. Bellboys. Waiters. Seduction. Infidelity. Lesbianism. Rape. Fetishism. Sexual techniques. Psychiatry. Nymphomania. Transvestism.*

IL SUCCESSO (France/Italy)　　　　　　　　　　F6.4760

Fair Film–Incei Film–Mountfluor Films–Cinétel. *Dist* Embassy Pictures. 28 Apr 1965 [New York opening]. Sd; b&w. 35mm. 103 min.

Prod Mario Cecchi Gori. *Dir* Mauro Morassi. *Story & Screenplay* Ettore Scola, Ruggero Maccari. *Photog* Alessandro D'Eva. *Film Ed* Maurizio Lucidi. *Mus Comp & Cond* Ennio Morricone. *Asst Dir* Vana Caruso. *Cost* Ugo Pericoli.

Cast: Vittorio Gassman (*Giulio Ceriani*), Anouk Aimée (*Laura Ceriani*), Jean-Louis Trintignant (*Sergio*), Leopoldo Trieste (*Grassi*), Cristina Gajoni (*maid*), Umberto D'Orsi (*fascist-capitalist*), Filippo Scelzo (*Giulio's father*), Gastone Moschin (*Giulio's brother-in-law*), Maria Grazia Spina (*Diana*), Annie Gorassini (*Marisa*), Franca Polesello (*Carla*), Riccardo Garrone, Armando Bandini, Daniele Vargas, Mino Doro, Elisabetta Velinsky, Mary Welles, Carlo Ragno, Ugo Attanasio.

Drama. Restless since the end of the war, Giulio Ceriana has gone from job to job consumed by his quest for success; neither his attractive and devoted wife, Laura, nor his friend Sergio can detract him from his goal. While employed by a real estate firm, he finds plans for a residential development on Sardinia. Realizing that a fortune could be made through land speculation, he goes to the island and purchases a large tract of land with a post-dated check and a promissory note. To raise the money, he turns to a bank, a private lender, his brother-in-law, a government official, and a cardinal; finally he persuades his aged father to sell the family's farm. Meanwhile, his employer learns of Giulio's underhanded dealings, and he is dismissed from his job. Undaunted, he adds his severance pay to the money from the sale of the farm and continues his frantic search for more capital. Aware of the disintegration of Giulio's character, Laura and Sergio eventually end their relationships with him. By the end of 2 years, Giulio is a successful and wealthy man, but his life of luxury has resulted in loneliness, a broken marriage, an ended friendship, and the broken heart of his father. *Real estate agents. Ambition. Obsession. Land speculation. Marriage. Divorce. Loneliness. Sardinia.*

Note: Opened in Rome in Sep 1963; running time: 110 min.

SUCCUBUS (West Germany)　　　　　　　　　　F6.4761

Aquila Film Enterprises. *Dist* Trans American Films. 25 Apr 1969 [New York opening; c25 Apr 1969; LP37878]. Sd; col (Eastman Color, print by Berkey Pathé). 35mm. 83 min. *MPAA rating* X.

Prod Pier A. Caminneci, Adrian Hoven. *Assoc Prod* Robert Gaffron. *Dir* Jess Franco. *Screenplay* Pier A. Caminneci. *Photog* Franz Lederle, Georg Herrero. *Art Dir* H. Peter Krause, Carlos Viudes. *Film Ed* Fritzi Schmidt. *Mus:* "Music for Four Soloists and Band" Friedrich Gulda. *Arr & Orch* Jerry van Rooyen. *Sd* Fritz Schwarz. *Prod Supv* K. H. Mannchen. *Cost* Karl Lacerfeld. *Makeup* Irmgard Förster. *Masks* Irmgard Förster.

Cast: Janine Reynaud (*Lorna*), Jack Taylor (*Bill*), Howard Vernon (*Kapp*), Michel Lemoine (*Pierce*), Nathalie Nort (*Bella*), Pier A. Caminneci (*Herman*), Adrian Hoven (*psychiatrist*), Americo Coimbra, Linda de Wolf, Eva Brauner.

Melodrama. For her Lisbon nightclub act, Lorna performs a sadomasochistic ritual in which she alternately tortures and fondles her "victim" before pretending to kill him. Lorna is influenced by a demonic stranger who goads her into committing erotic acts; and though she is counseled by her psychiatrist and comforted by her lover, nightclub owner Bill Mulligan, Lorna becomes less able to distinguish reality from fantasy. She attends an orgiastic party where the guests call her countess and attack her, and she murders a woman whom she has taken as a lover. Finally, Lorna kills her fellow nightclub actors; stabs Bill to death during an embrace in his apartment; and walks off with the demonic stranger. *Entertainers. Psychiatrists. Nightclub owners. Sadomasochism. Murder. Eroticism. Lesbianism. Mental illness. Nightclubs. Sex shows. Hallucinations. Orgies. Lisbon. The Devil.*

Note: Location scenes filmed in Lisbon and West Berlin. Opened in West Berlin in Apr 1968 as *Necronomicon—geträumte Sünden*; running time: 82 min; cut from 91 min.

SUCCUBUS *see* **THE SATANIST**

THE SUCKER (France/Italy)   F6.4762

Les Films Corona-Explorer Film. *Dist* Royal Films International. 11 May **1966** [Cleveland opening]. Sd; col (Eastmancolor). 35mm (Franscope). 101 min. [Also 112 min.]

Prod Yves Laplanche, Enzo Provenzale. *Assoc Prod* Robert Dorfmann. *Dir-Story* Gérard Oury. *Screenplay* Gérard Oury, Marcel Jullian, Georges Tabet, André Tabet. *Photog* Henri Decaë. *Art Dir* Robert Giordani, Francesco Ciarletta. *Film Ed* Albert Jurgenson. *Mus* Georges Delerue. *Sd* Antoine Bonfanti. *Asst Dir* Serge Vallin. *Prod Mgr* Jean Pieuchot.

Cast: Bourvil (*Antoine Maréchal*), Louis de Funès (*Leopold Saroyan*), Walter Chiari (*La Souris*), Venantino Venantini (*stutterer*), Beba Loncar (*Ursula*), Daniela Rocca (*Gina*), Lando Buzzanca (*Lino*), José-Luis de Vilallonga (*Maurel*), Saro Urzi (*Tagliella*), Pierre Roussel (*Mario Costa*), Michel Galabru (*Martial*), Jean Lefebvre (*storekeeper*), Henri Genès, Henri Virlogeux, Jacques Eyser, Jacques Ary, Guy Delorme, Yvon Jeanclaude, Alida Chelli, Bernard Meusnier, Jean Meyer, Jean Droze, Jean-Marie Bon, Jacques Ferrière, Bob Lerick, Louis Viret.

Comedy. As good-natured but befuddled Antoine Maréchal leaves Paris for a holiday, his car is demolished in a collision with a Bentley that belongs to wealthy Leopold Saroyan. Next day Saroyan offers to make amends by flying Antoine to Naples and arranging for him to drive a friend's Cadillac to Bordeaux. Delighted to have a paid vacation, Antoine readily agrees. Unknown to him, however, a fortune in contraband goods has been concealed on the car: the bumpers are solid gold coated with chrome plating, the tailfins are packed with heroin, and stolen jewels are immersed in the battery fluid. Oblivious to the fact that he is being tailed by Saroyan and his henchmen and also by a trio of hijackers led by the notorious La Souris, Antoine thoroughly enjoys his trip, stopping to offer a ride to a seductive hitchhiking manicurist and, later, a beautiful German girl en route to a nudist colony. As the two rival gangs take potshots at each other, the guileless Antoine rolls merrily along, unaware that bit by bit his precious cargo is either being stolen by garage mechanics or lost on the road. Eventually Antoine realizes that he has been duped; incensed, he cleverly outwits his pursuers by luring them into a police trap. His joy at being still alive is enhanced when he accidentally discovers the world's largest diamond hidden on the Cadillac's steering wheel. *Gangsters. Mechanics. Smugglers. Hijackers. Hitchhikers. Duplicity. Vacations. Jewels. Heroin. Gold. Paris. Bordeaux. Cadillac automobiles. Bentley automobiles. Automobile accidents.*

Note: Location scenes filmed in Naples, Rome, Pisa, and Carcassonne. Opened in Paris in Mar 1965 as *Le corniaud*; running time: 105 min; in Italy in 1965 as *Colpo grosso ma non troppo*. Alternative title: *The Sucker ... or How To Be Glad When You've Been Had!*

SUDBA CHELOVEKA *see* **FATE OF A MAN**

SUDDEN DEATH *see* **ONCE YOU KISS A STRANGER**

SUDDENLY, A WOMAN! (Denmark)   F6.4763

Morten Schyberg Productions. *Dist* PMK Productions. 11 Oct **1967** [Albany, New York, opening]. Sd; col (Eastmancolor, print by Technicolor). 35mm. 91 min.

Pres by Marion Gering. A Marion Gering-Morten Schyberg Production. *Prod* Morten Schyberg. *Dir-Writ* Anker. *Adtl Dial* Mette Budtz-Jørgensen. *Photog* Henning Bendtsen. *Art Dir* Kai Rasch. *Mus Comp* Ib Glindemann. *Sd* Erik Jensen, Niels Ishøy. *English Dial* Tom Rowe.

Cast: Laila Andersson (*Gudrun*), Jørgen Buckhøj (*Manne*), Poul Reichhardt (*Mr. Hollund*), Nils Asther (*Mr. Rossen*), Birgitte Federspiel (*Mrs. Brunn*), Elsa Kourani (*Mrs. Hollund*), Yvonne Ingdal (*office girl*), Constance (*dancer*), Albert Watson.

Melodrama. Source: Johannes Vilhelm Jensen, *Gudrun* (Copenhagen, 1936). Gudrun arouses both the normal and abnormal desires of those around her as she makes the transition from adolescence to womanhood. Though she cares only for Manne, her childhood sweetheart, Gudrun finds herself pursued by Mr. Hollund (her employer), Mr. Rossen (an industrial tycoon), and Mrs. Brunn (a lesbian landlady). Rossen, a lonely widower, hopes to recapture his lost youth with Gudrun but is rejected. Hollund assaults Gudrun and then begs her to marry him. Mrs. Brunn futilely tries to turn Gudrun against men. In an attempt to get rid of the persistent Hollund, Gudrun goes for a drive with him and tries to explain that she loves Manne. Unable to control his anguish, Hollund loses control of his car and runs off the highway. Reviving in a hospital, Gudrun discovers Manne by her side and realizes that her future is secure. *Employers. Tycoons. Landladies. Widowers. Sexual initiation. Lesbianism.*

Hospitals. Automobile accidents.

Note: Filmed in Copenhagen and released there in Nov 1963 as *Gudrun*; running time: 95 min.

SUGAR DADDY   F6.4764

Lark Film Productions. *Dist* Cinex Film Industries. 12 Jun **1968** [New York showing]. Sd; b&w. 35mm. 75 min.

Prod Lou Campa. *Dir* Larry Crane. *Screenplay* Walter M. Berger. *Cinematog* Lew Waldeck. *Camera Asst* Gerard Damiano. *2d Unit* Dave McKenna. *Freehand Camera* Lou Campa. *Sets* Donald Purdy, Thomas D. Trovato, Frank Wakula. *Titl* Frank Wakula. *Ed* Dennis Daniels. *Songs:* "Marriage Is a Wonderful Institution," "Two of a Kind," "Change My Name" Larry Crane. *Songs Arr* Lorenzo Fuller. *Songs:* "Polka Dot," "Down to the River" Larry Crane. *Songs Arr* Darlene Cotton. *Songs:* "Nobody Cares," "That Girl Julie" Larry Crane. *Songs Arr* Sticks Evans. *Songs:* "Give Me a Kiss for My Birthday," "Stand Up Blues" Larry Crane. *Songs Arr* Al Greiner. *Sd Rec* Michael Rauch.

Cast: Jon Elder ("*Gumdrop*" *Sweet*). Danielle Roberts (*Taffy Touraine*), Everett Ensley (*Robin Ellsworth*), Darlene Cotton (*Linda*), Linda Boyce (*Honey*), Louise Brent (*Candy*), Carin Russell (*Meg*), Ella Bussman (*Nellie*), Joe Kugel (*Mr. Keister*), Donny Lee (*Ernie*), Ileen Wreffer (*Sylvia*), Paul Brancato (*Jeff*), Lou Champion (*The Intruder*), Paul Sindab (*Paul Duncan*), The Thomas Sisters, Manzini the Great, Christine, Jay Green, Darlene Cotton Quartet.

Musical comedy-drama. Taffy Touraine, a naive young woman, sets out to establish herself in the world of New York show business. Her equally naive boyfriend Jeff, determined to succeed in the field of public relations, becomes Taffy's agent and pushes her forward for an opening as a singer with a trio. Taffy discovers to her dismay that the act involves a striptease, but she finds the nudity quite tasteful. Jeff invents a publicity stunt that puts Taffy's name on the front page of the newspapers. G. D. "Gumdrop" Sweet, a sex exploitation film producer, spots Taffy's picture and invites her out for dinner. She arrives with Jeff, but he soon disappears with a stripper who is furnishing the dinner entertainment. Mr. Sweet, five times divorced, offers to marry Taffy, but she turns him down and returns to the rehearsal hall. She is unwittingly drawn into a hippie pot party which grows increasingly licentious. The next morning, unable to remember what went on and overwhelmed by shame, Taffy rushes off to accept Mr. Sweet's proposition. As the wedding ceremony is about to begin, a messenger arrives with the news that another young singer has been gravely injured in a motorcycle accident. A group of performers organize a television benefit to pay his medical bills. Taffy finds a bicycle and rushes off to take part in the show. She arrives just in time to join the trio onstage. As the show comes to a close, Mr. Sweet arrives to find Taffy and Jeff embracing in the wings. *Innocents. Singers. Publicists. Motion picture producers. Entertainers. Hippies. Ambition. Striptease. Marriage. Guilt. Marijuana. Sex exploitation films. New York City.*

Note: Pressbook photographs suggest that portions of the footage of *Sugar Daddy* and *Private Relations* are identical. Also known as *Games and Variations*.

SUGATA SANSHIRO *see* **JUDO SAGA**

A SUITABLE CASE FOR TREATMENT *see* **MORGAN!**

THE SUITOR (France)   F6.4765

C. A. P. A. C.-Cocinor. *Dist* Atlantic Pictures. 17 Sep **1963** [New York opening]. Sd; b&w. 35mm. 83 min.

Pres by Wilshire International Pictures. *Prod* Paul Claudon. *Dir* Pierre Etaix. *Screenplay & Dial* Pierre Etaix, Jean-Claude Carrière. *Photog* Pierre Levent. *Film Ed* Pierre Gillette. *Mus* Jean Paillaud. *Sd* Jean Bertrand.

Cast: Pierre Etaix (*Pierre, the suitor*), Laurence Lignères (*Laurence*), Claude Massot (*father*), Denise Péronne (*mother*), Karin Vesely (*Ilka*), France Arnell (*Stella*), Lucien Fregis (*painter*), Brigitte Juslin, Petit Bobo.

Comedy. Pierre, a 30-year-old bachelor, lives with his parents and devotes all of his time to studying science and the astronomical charts. His strong-willed mother, vexed by Pierre's lack of interest in women, goads her husband into persuading him that it is time he took a wife. Pierre dutifully proposes to Ilka, the family's Swedish au pair girl, but she does not understand French and fails to comprehend his offer, so Pierre continues his search, learning what he can from experienced men-about-town. After several disastrous efforts to meet prospective brides, he encounters Laurence, a young woman who spends all of his money getting drunk on champagne. Several days later, she attempts to seduce him at her apartment, but he is distracted by the television performance of a sensuous singer, Stella. Suddenly hopelessly in love with the singer, he throws away all of his astronomical paraphernalia and covers the walls of his room with photographs of her. Bearing an engagement ring, he makes his way into her dressing room, but his matrimonial intentions are shattered when he discovers that Stella is a married woman with a son his own age. Completely disillusioned, he returns home as Ilka is leaving to return to Sweden. By now she has learned enough French to understand Pierre's proposal, and she accepts; ecstatically happy, he follows her to the railroad station. *Bachelors. Au pair girls. Swedes. Singers. Courtship. Filial relations. Marriage. Astronomy.*

Note: Opened in Paris in Feb 1963 as *Le soupirant*; running time: 85 min.

SULEIMAN THE CONQUEROR (Italy) F6.4766

Produzioni Astor. *Dist* Medallion Pictures. 1963. Sd; col (Eastman Color). 35mm (Totalscope). 99 min.

A Vatroslav Mimica Production. *Dir* Vatroslav Mimica. *Screenplay* Vatroslav Mimica, Mario Caiano, Michelangelo Frieri, Stipe Delić. *Dir Photog* Giuseppe La Torre. *Mus* Francesco De Masi.

Cast: Edmund Purdom *(Ibrahim Pasha)*, Georgia Moll *(Vesna)*, Alberto Farnese *(Gaspar)*, Luciano Marin *(Ivan)*, Loris Gizzi *(Suleiman)*, Stane Potokar *(Nicholas Orlovic)*, Evi Maltagliati *(Anna)*, Raf Baldassarre *(Boris)*, Nando Tamberlani *(Viennese chancellor)*, John MacDouglas, Silvio Bagolini, Amedeo Trilli.

Historical melodrama. In the mid 1500's, Ottoman Sultan Suleiman's army advances toward Central Europe, spreading ruin and death. His grand vizier, Ibrahim Pasha, suggests that the troops march on Vienna, but Suleiman's vanity leads him to attack Szigetvar, an isolated Christian fortress defiantly commanded by Nicholas Orlovic. During the battle, Suleiman dies of a stroke; Ibrahim hides the news from the soldiers, however, by killing all of the witnesses. Inside the swamp-bound outpost, Ivan, a young officer who is in love with Orlovic's daughter Vesna, is ordered by the jealous Gaspar, Orlovic's second-in-command, to bring reinforcements from Vienna. The renegade Gaspar deserts when Vesna repulses his advances. Returning from Vienna, Ivan is attacked by Gaspar, who drowns in the marshland. Ivan arrives at Szigetvar and informs Orlovic of the Viennese court's indifference toward their struggle. The commander orders the evacuation of all women and children, then leads his garrison in a hopeless counterattack against the Turkish forces. Orlovic's heroic sacrifice succeeds in halting the fatigued Turkish army, which, hampered by the beginning of the rainy season, retreats from Austria. Ivan and Vesna lead the children back to safety. *Royalty. Viziers. Soldiers. Traitors. War heroes. Deserters—Military. Jealousy. Military invasion. Evacuation. Forts. Strokes. Swamps. Ottoman Empire. Austria. Vienna. Szigetvár. Suleiman I. Ibrahim Pasha.*

Note: Filmed in Yugoslavia. Released in Italy in 1961 as *Solimano il conquistatore*; running time: 106 min. John MacDouglas is a pseudonym for Giuseppe Addobbati.

SULLIVAN'S EMPIRE F6.4767

Universal Pictures. Aug 1967 [Los Angeles showing; c2 Sep 1967; LP40551]. Sd (Westrex); col (Technicolor). 35mm. 85 min. [Also reviewed at 91 min.]

Prod Frank Price. *Dir* Harvey Hart, Thomas Carr. *Screenplay* Frank Chase. *Dir Photog* Hal McAlpin. *Col Coörd* Robert Brower. *Art Dir* Russell Kimball. *Set Decor* John McCarthy, Ralph Sylos. *Film Ed* Robert F. Shugrue. *Mus* Lalo Schifrin. *Mus Supv* Stanley Wilson. James T. Porter. *Asst Dir* Thomas J. Schmidt, Rowe Wallerstein. *Unit Prod Mgr* Abby Singer. *Cost* Burton Miller. *Makeup* Bud Westmore. *Hairstyles* Larry Germain.

Cast: Martin Milner *(John Sullivan, Jr.)*, Linden Chiles *(Patrick Sullivan)*, Don Quine *(Kevin Sullivan)*, Clu Gulager *(Juan Clemente)*, Arch Johnson *(John Sullivan, Sr.)*, Karen Jensen *(Doris Wheeler)*, Bernie Hamilton *(Amando)*, Lee Bergere *(Rudi Andujar)*, Than Wyenn *(Inspector Huante)*, Jeanette Nolan *(Miss Wingate)*, Miguel de Anda *(driver)*, Ken Renard *(clerk)*, Marianne Gordon *(2d girl)*, Eileen Wesson *(3d girl)*, Mark Miranda *(boy)*, Ruben Moreno *(Carlos)*, Nadine Nardi *(Ramona)*, Robert de Coy *(Chico)*, Pepe Callahan *(bartender)*, Peter Pascal *(pilot)*, Sergio Mendes and Brasil '66.

Adventure drama. Wealthy John Sullivan, Sr., disappears after a crash landing near his ranch in the Amazon River territory, and his three sons—racing driver John, Jr., playboy-gambler Patrick, and surfer-student Kevin—journey to South America to form a search party. After meeting at Kiva, they travel upstream to the Izos Indian country where they rescue a young boy about to be sacrificed by headhunters. They also encounter Miss Wingate, an eccentric retired schoolteacher, and Doris Wheeler, a young woman who had made arrangements with their father for a safari. As the three sons continue their search, they are confronted by Juan Clemente, a revolutionary guerrilla, who tells them he is holding their father for $100,000 ransom. Lacking the necessary funds, the boys appeal to their father's business partner, Rudi Andujar, for help. But he will lend them the money only if he is given control of the Sullivan empire should their father be dead. Once the offer has been rejected, the boys are kidnaped by rebels and taken to Clemente's camp where they are reunited with their captive father. Andujar also appears, announces he is in league with Clemente, and threatens to kill the boys unless Mr. Sullivan signs over his estate to the revolutionaries. But unexpected help comes when Miss Wingate arrives in a helicopter firing a machine gun. During the diversion,

John, Jr., throws a grenade into the artillery supply house, Clemente is shot, and Andujar falls victim to piranhas. When they return to the Sullivan ranch, the three sons spot three attractive young tourists and decide to remain a while longer in South America. And Mr. Sullivan is already romancing the spunky Miss Wingate. *Playboys. Students. Partnerships. Revolutionaries. Headhunters. Kidnaping. Extortion. Jungles. Helicopters. Brazil.*

SULT *see* **HUNGER**

THE SULTAN F6.4768

Dist Able Film Co. ca 1970. Sd; col. 16mm. [Feature length assumed.] *Prod-Dir* Jimmy DeKnight.

Sex film. No information about the precise nature of this film has been found, but press material indicates there are scenes of fellatio and cunnilingus. *Sexuality. Oral sex.*

SUMMER AND SMOKE F6.4769

Hal Wallis Productions. *Dist* Paramount Pictures. 16 Nov 1961 [New York opening; c16 Nov 1961; LP21509]. Sd; col (Technicolor). 35mm (Panavision). 118 min.

A Hal Wallis Production. *Prod* Hal B. Wallis. *Assoc Prod* Paul Nathan. *Dir* Peter Glenville. *Screenplay* James Poe, Meade Roberts. *Cinematog* Charles Lang, Jr. *Col Cons* Richard Mueller. *Art Dir* Hal Pereira. *Unit Art Dir* Walter Tyler. *Set Decor* Sam Comer, Arthur Krams. *Film Ed* Warren Low. *Mus* Elmer Bernstein. *Sd* Phil Mitchell, Charles Grenzbach. *Asst Dir* Mickey Moore, James Rosenberger. *Unit Prod Mgr* Richard Blaydon. *Cost* Edith Head. *Makeup* Wally Westmore. *Hairstyles* Nellie Manley. *Sp Photog Eff* John P. Fulton.

Cast: Laurence Harvey *(John Buchanan)*, Geraldine Page *(Alma Winemiller)*, Rita Moreno *(Rosa Zacharias)*, Una Merkel *(Mrs. Winemiller)*. John McIntire *(Dr. Buchanan)*, Malcolm Atterbury *(Reverend Winemiller)*, Pamela Tiffin *(Nellie Ewell)*, Casey Adams *(Roger Doremus)*, Thomas Gomez *(Zacharias)*, Earl Holliman *(Archie Kramer)*, Lee Patrick *(Mrs. Ewell)*. Marjorie Bennett *(saleslady)*, Harry Shannon, Pattee Chapman, Jester Hairston, Pepe Hern, Elektra Rozanska, Dick Ryan, Winnie Chandler, Linda Knutson, Robert Slade, Rico Alaniz, John Frank, Susan Roberts, Pamela Duncan, Margaret Blye, Charles Watts, Cheryl Anderson, Almira Sessions.

Drama. Source: Tennessee Williams, *Summer and Smoke* (New York opening: 9 Oct 1948). Alma Winemiller is the fragile, lonely, and oversensitive daughter of a minister in a small Mississippi town shortly before the first World War. From childhood she has harbored an almost spiritual love for John Buchanan, who, though a physician like his father, resents being forced to follow in his father's footsteps. But the unruly John prefers livelier company than the timid Alma; in particular, he is attracted by Rosa Zacharias, the tigerish daughter of the owner of Moon Lake Casino. One night, John becomes intrigued by Alma's shy, inhibited gropings toward love, and he takes her to the casino. When he tries to seduce her, the horrified Alma hysterically denounces him and runs away. A short time later, the elder Dr. Buchanan is called out of town, and John uses the occasion to throw a wild party celebrating his betrothal to Rosa. Alma frantically telephones Dr. Buchanan, who quickly returns, quarrels with Zacharias, and is accidentally shot and killed. Shattered by the tragedy caused by his carousing, John reforms and takes over his father's practice. As the months pass, Alma's brooding love erupts into passion; and she goes to John and offers herself to him. But it is too late; it is John who now regards their relationship as a spiritual one. After learning that John plans to marry Nellie Ewell, a young girl, the heartbroken and frustrated Alma wanders down to the park. There she strikes up an acquaintance with a lonely traveling salesman, Archie Kramer. When he asks what excitement can be found in the town, Alma smiles at him and suggests they take a taxi to Moon Lake Casino. As they drive off, Alma watches the dying leaves of summer blowing across the pavement. *Clergymen. Physicians. Traveling salesmen. Inhibition. Filial relations. Seduction. Smalltown life. Loneliness. Death. Casinos. Mississippi.*

Note: Copyright claimants: Hal B. Wallis and Joseph H. Hazen.

SUMMER FIRES *see* **MADEMOISELLE**

SUMMER FLIGHT *see* **STOLEN HOURS**

SUMMER HOLIDAY (Great Britain) F6.4770

Ivy Productions-Elstree Distributors. *Dist* American International Pictures. 23 Oct 1963 [Oklahoma City, Oklahoma, opening]. Sd; col (Technicolor). 35mm (CinemaScope). 100 min.

Prod Kenneth Harper. *Assoc Prod* Andrew Mitchell. *Exec Prod* James H. Nicholson, Samuel Z. Arkoff. *Dir* Peter Yates. *Screenplay* Peter Myers, Ronald Cass. *Photog* John Wilcox. *Camera Op* Tony White. *Focus* Geoffrey Glover. Brian Ellis. *Camera Grip* Sid Payne. *Art Dir* Syd Cain. *Asst Art Dir* John Graysmark. *Ch Draughtsman* Alan Tomkins. *Film Ed* Jack Slade. *Asst Film Ed* Lois Gray. *Mus Comp & Cond* Stanley Black. *Songs:* "All at Once," "A Stranger in Town," "A Swinging Affair," "Yugoslav Wedding" Peter Myers,

Ronald Cass. *Song:* "*Bachelor Boy*" Bruce Welch, Cliff Richard. *Songs:* "*Dancing Shoes*," "*Foot Tapper*" Bruce Welch, Hank B. Marvin. *Song:* "*Summer Holiday*" Bruce Welch, Brian Bennett. *Songs:* "*Les Girls*," "*Round and Round*" Bruce Welch, Hank B. Marvin, Brian Bennett. *Song:* "*The Next Time*" Buddy Kaye, Philip Springer. *Song:* "*Big News*" Mike Conlin, Cliff Richard, Ronald Cass. *Mus Supv of Cliff Richard and the Shadows* Norrie Paramor. *Mus Numbers Stgd* Herbert Ross. *Sd* Wally Milner, Len Shilton. *Boom Op* Don Wortham. *Sd Camera Op* Francis Fahy. *Playback Op* Ron Conley. *Mus Ed* Roy Nevill. *1st, 2d & 3d Asst Dir* Frank Ernst, Bill Cartlidge, Roger Simons. *Prod Mgr* John Wilcox. *Prod Sec* Valerie Cort. *Cont* Helen Whitson. *Wardrobe Mistress* Jackie Breed. *Makeup* John O'Gorman. *Hairstyles* Eileen Warwick. *Sp Eff* George Blackwell. *Still Photog* Ronnie Pilgrim. *Prop Buyer* Arthur Howe. *Casting Dir* Robert Lennard. *Supv Chargehand Electrn* Stephen Birtles.

Cast: Cliff Richard *(Don)*, Lauri Peters *(Barbara)*, Melvyn Hayes *(Cyril)*, Una Stubbs *(Sandy)*, Teddy Green *(Steve)*, Pamela Hart *(Angie)*, Jeremy Bulloch *(Edwin)*, Jacqueline Daryl *(Mimsie)*, Madge Ryan *(Stella)*, Lionel Murton *(Jerry)*, Christine Lawson *(Annie)*, Ron Moody *(Orlando)*, David Kossoff *(magistrate)*, Wendy Barry *(shepherdess/dancer)*, Nicholas Phipps *(Wrightmore)*, The Shadows *(themselves)*, Lindsay Dolan, Richard Farley, Terry Gilbert, Ian Kaye, Vincent Logan, John MacDonald, Paddy McIntyre, Leon Pomerantz, Ben Stevenson, Anne Briley, Leander Gilbert, Sarah Hardenberg, Derina House, Eithne Milne, Sheila O'Neill, Joan Palethorpe *(dancers)*.

Musical comedy. Don, Cyril, Edwin, and Steve, four young London mechanics who hope to operate a vacation travel service by bus in Europe, make a trial run in a borrowed double-decker bus that is outfitted with living facilities. Outside Paris they crash into an old car carrying Sandy, Angie, and Mimsie, three young English singers on their way to Athens. Because their automobile is demolished, the boys take the girls along with them in the bus. Later, they add another boy to their number, but the boy is really a young American girl singer, Barbara, who ran away from her ambitious mother, Stella, and her agent, Jerry, when they reneged on their promise to give her a vacation. The others agree to help Barbara, but Stella and Jerry learn her whereabouts and decide to use the situation for publicity purposes. They cause the youngsters on the bus to be subjected to a variety of difficulties newsworthy enough to make headlines. After traveling through France, Switzerland, Austria, and Yugoslavia, the bus finally arrives in Athens, and there Stella calls a press interview and accuses Don, the boys' leader, of abducting her daughter, whereupon Don and Barbara announce their engagement. A London bus company announces that the boys will receive 200 buses for their travel service, and the mother, realizing that her publicity scheme is running wild, gives the young couple her blessing. *Mechanics. Entrepreneurs. Americans in foreign countries. Singers. Booking agents. Travel. Disguise. Abduction. Ambition. Publicity. Buses. Vacations. Summer. France. Greece. Athens. Yugoslavia. Austria. Switzerland. Paris. Automobile accidents.*

Note: Location scenes filmed in France and Greece. Opened in London in Jan 1963; running time: 109 min.

SUMMER MAGIC　　　　　　　　　　　　　　　　　　　**F6.4771**

Walt Disney Productions. *Dist* Buena Vista Distribution Co. Jul **1963** [New York opening: 21 Aug 1963; c2 Apr 1963; LP25495]. Sd (RCA); col (Technicolor). 35mm. 109 min. [Also reviewed at 100 min.]

Pres by Walt Disney. *Prod* Walt Disney. *Assoc Prod* Ron Miller. *Dir* James Neilson. *Screenplay* Sally Benson. *Dir Photog* William Snyder. *Art Dir* Carroll Clark, Robert Clatworthy. *Set Decor* Emile Kuri, Frank R. McKelvy. *Film Ed* Robert Stafford. *Mus* Buddy Baker. *Songs* Richard M. Sherman, Robert B. Sherman. *Orch* Walter Sheets, Bobby Hammack. *Vocal Supv* Camarata. *Sd Supv* Robert O. Cook. *Sd Mix* Dean Thomas. *Mus Ed* Evelyn Kennedy. *Asst Dir* Austen Jewell. *Cost Dsgn* Bill Thomas. *Cost* Chuck Keehne, Gertrude Casey. *Makeup* Pat McNalley. *Hairstyles* Ruth Sandifer. *Sp Photog Eff* Peter Ellenshaw. *Sp Eff* Eustace Lycett.

Cast: Hayley Mills *(Nancy Carey)*, Burl Ives *(Osh Popham)*, Dorothy McGuire *(Margaret Carey)*, Deborah Walley *(Cousin Julia)*, Eddie Hodges *(Gilly Carey)*, Jimmy Mathers *(Peter Carey)*, Michael J. Pollard *(Digby Popham)*, Wendy Turner *(Lallie Joy Popham)*, Una Merkel *(Maria Popham)*, Peter Brown *(Tom Hamilton)*, James Stacy *(Charles Bryant)*, O. Z. Whitehead *(Mr. Perkins)*, Harry Holcombe *(Henry Lord)*, Jan Stine *(Mr. Perkins' son)*, Hilda Plowright *(Mary)*, Marcy McGuire *(Ellen)*.

Comedy with music. Source: Kate Douglas Wiggin, *Mother Carey's Chickens* (Boston, 1911). Recently widowed Margaret Carey must move her family from their large house in Boston in order to economize. Osh Popham, the Beulah, Maine, postmaster, constable, and representative of an absentee landlord, receives a letter from Nancy, Margaret's teenage daughter, explaining the family's plight and asking about the availability of a large, yellow house in Beulah. Touched by the letter, in which Nancy describes their rickets-ridden

brothers' need for country life, Osh allows them to move into the house practically rent-free, unbeknownst to the owner of the house, Tom Hamilton, who is abroad and is not expected to return. Osh's one condition is that the Careys enshrine a portrait of Tom's allegedly dead mother in the living room. Osh searches for the picture while the Careys set out to clean and paint the house, assisted by Osh's teenage children, Lallie Joy and Digby. Just as things begin to roll smoothly, Julia, the Careys' orphaned but haughty cousin, reluctantly comes to live with the Careys, and friction arises between her and Nancy. Osh finds Mrs. Hamilton's picture, and a great celebration is planned. All the preparations are made when on the day of the party Nancy realizes that she does not have an escort. Tom Hamilton suddenly arrives home, and he and Nancy are immediately attracted to each other. Without realizing who he is, Nancy reveals her fear that the owner of the house, "Old Tom Hamilton," will return and evict her family. Nancy later discovers Tom's identity, and it becomes clear that he does not intend to take the house from them and that he is seriously interested in Nancy. *Songs:* "Flitterin'," "Beautiful Beulah," "The Pink of Perfection" (Nancy & Gary); "Summer Magic" (Margaret); "The Ugly Bug Ball" (Osh); "On the Front Porch" (Osh & entire cast); "Femininity" (Nancy, Cousin Julia & Lallie Joy). *Widows. Postmasters. Constables. Cousins. Orphans. Housing. Finance—Personal. Family life. Adolescence. Smalltown life. Personal identity. Portraits (paintings). Boston. Maine.*

Note: Remake of *Mother Carey's Chickens*, filmed by RKO in 1938.

SUMMER OF THE SEVENTEENTH DOLL *see* **SEASON OF PASSION**

SUMMER TALES *see* **LOVE ON THE RIVIERA**

A SUMMER TO REMEMBER (U.S.S.R.)　　　　　　　**F6.4772**

Mosfilm. *Dist* Kingsley International Pictures, M. J. P. Enterprises. 6 Nov **1961** [New York opening]. Sd; b&w. 35mm. 80 min.

Pres by J. Jay Frankel. *Dir* Georgiy Daneliya, Igor Talankin. *Screenplay* Vera Panova, Georgiy Daneliya, Igor Talankin. *Story Ed* M. Kachalova. *Photog* Anatoliy Nitochkin. *Photog Adv* Leonid Kosmatov. *Art Dir* V. Nisskaya. *Film Ed* P. Chechyotkina. *Mus* Boris Chaykovskiy. *Cond* A. Roytman. *Sd* L. Trakhtenberg. *Asst Dir* D. Tambiyeva. *Prod Mgr* Viktor Tsirgiladze. *Makeup* K. Yarmolyuk. *Sp Eff* B. Pluzhnikov, N. Spiridonova.

Cast: Borya Barkhatov *(Seryozha)*, Sergey Bondarchuk *(Korostelyov)*, Irina Skobtseva *(Maryana)*, Natasha Chechyotkina *(Lidka)*, Seryozha Metelitsyn *(Vaska)*, Yura Kozlov *(Zhenka)*, Alyosha Dotsenko *(Shurik)*, L. Sokolova *(Vaska's mother)*, Vasiliy Merkuryev *(Uncle Kostya)*, A. Panova *(Aunt Pasha)*, K. Frolova *(Zhenka's aunt)*, Nikolay Sergeyev *(Lukyanych)*, Valentin Bryleyev, V. Brovkin, Ye. Gulyayeva, P. Vinnik, M. Zharova, Ye. Zhdanova, P. Kiryutkin, Ye. Kudryashov.

Comedy-drama. Source: Vera Fyodorovna Panova, *Seryozha* (Leningrad, 1955). Five-year-old Seryozha lives with his widowed mother, Maryana, in a small provincial town. Suddenly the happy routine of the youngster's life is disrupted by the news that his mother has remarried to an imposing stranger, Korostelyov. Seryozha's doubts and misgivings are allayed, however, as he discovers that Korostelyov is a kind and understanding man. On his first day off from work as a collective farm director, Korostelyov buys Seryozha a bicycle, which the child and his playmates quickly demolish. Seryozha timidly returns home with his present, but his stepfather quietly assures him that the damage can be repaired. Seryozha is completely won over when Korostelyov defends him for insulting a foolish uncle. A short time later Seryozha's mother gives birth to another child, whom the youngster greets with mixed feelings of wonder and jealousy. With the coming of winter, Korostelyov is transferred to another farm in a more rugged and less populated region. Because Seryozha's health is fragile, it is decided that he should be left behind with an aunt until the following summer. But as the parents prepare to leave, Korostelyov decides to take the heartbroken child along. *Children. Stepfathers. Widows. Farmers. Brothers. Family life. Collective farming. Summer.*

Note: Released in the U.S.S.R. in Aug 1960 as *Seryozha.*

SUMMERSKIN (Argentina)　　　　　　　　　　　　　**F6.4773**

Producciones Angel. *Dist* Angel Productions. 28 May **1962** [New York opening]. Sd; b&w. 35mm. 96 min.

Prod-Dir Leopoldo Torre-Nilsson. *Exec Prod (see note)* Juan Sires. *Assoc Prod* Nestor R. Gaffet, J. A. Ciancaglini. *Screenplay* Beatriz Guido, Leopoldo Torre-Nilsson. *Photog* Oscar Melli. *Sets* Oscar Lagomarsino. *Film Ed* Jacinto Cascales. *Mus Selections* Robert Schumann, Claudio Monteverdi. *Jazz Perf by* Lopez Furst. *English Subtitl* Travers Clement.

Cast: Alfredo Alcón *(Martin)*, Graciela Borges *(Marcela)*, Franca Boni *(Joujou)*, Luciana Possamay *(Adela)*, Juan Jones *(Marcos)*, Pedro Laxalt, Rafael Salzano, Juan Carlos, Carrasco, Rosita Miranda.

Drama. Source: Beatriz Guido, "Convalecencia" (publication undetermined). Marcela, a bored student living an idle life in the Uruguayan summer resort of Punta del Este, receives an unexpected visit from her grandmother, Joujou, a once-famous courtesan, and Joujou's wealthy lover, Albert. The old woman tells Marcela that if she will consent to brighten up the last days of Albert's young son Martin, who is dying of an incurable disease, she will be rewarded with a year in Paris and a new Dior wardrobe. Marcela consents, although she feels an aversion for Martin and has rejected his advances in the past. Weak and gaunt, Martin arrives with his domineering servants, Adela and Marcos. As time passes, Martin begins to forget his weakness and gains strength with the growing love he feels for Marcela. On the morning Marcela has planned to take Martin shopping with her, Adela seduces him. Later, with renewed vigor, Martin persuades Marcela to make love, and the following weeks are spent in idyllic romps on the beach. Towards the end of the summer, Martin returns from a medical examination with the news that he has been miraculously cured by Marcela's love and now wishes to marry her. Confused by this unexpected turn of events, Marcela tells Martin bluntly that she does not love him and confesses the pact she made with her grandmother. Shattered, Martin commits suicide. Although she is rewarded for keeping her part of the bargain, Marcela feels depressed by Martin's death, and she breaks down and weeps. *Students. Grandmothers. Domestics. Duplicity. Seduction. Incurable illness. Suicide. Resorts. Beaches. Summer. Punta del Este (Uruguay).*

Note: Filmed in Punta del Este and other coastal locations in Uruguay. Produced in Argentina as *Piel de verano*; running time: 100 min. Juan Sires may have been producer or co-producer.

SUMURU *see* **THE MILLION EYES OF SU-MURU**

SUN ABOVE, DEATH BELOW (Japan)   F6.4774
Toho Co. Mar **1969** [Los Angeles showing]. Sd; col (Eastmancolor). 35mm. 87 min.
Dir Hiromichi Horikawa. *Screenplay* Hidekazu Nagahara. *Photog* Kiyoshi Hasegawa. *Art Dir* Shinobu Muraki. *Mus* Riichiro Manabe.
Cast: Yuzo Kayama *(Toru Matsushita),* Ruriko Asaoka *(Akiko),* Masayuki Mori *(Katakura).*
Crime melodrama. Toru Matsushita, a hired killer, is commissioned to break up a gang of gold smugglers. Just as he thinks his job is completed, he hears of another killer, Katakura, who has been given a contract on the lives of both Toru and his employer. Akiko, a model who loves Toru, urges him to leave the country, but he realizes he cannot escape with Katakura still alive. Katakura kills Toru's boss and Akiko, but in the final showdown, Toru wins, only to realize he has lost everything. *Hired killers. Models. Smugglers.*
Note: Released in Japan in Nov 1968 as *Sogeki.*

THE SUN IS UP *see* **A BOY ... A GIRL**

THE SUN SHINES FOR ALL (U.S.S.R.)   F6.4775
Mosfilm. *Dist* Artkino Pictures. 8 Jul **1961** [New York opening]. Sd; b&w. 35mm. 91 min.
Dir Konstantin Voinov. *Screenplay* Semyon Freylikh. *Story Ed* Yu. Vinokurova. *Photog* Anatoliy Kuznetsov. *Art Dir* Boris Chebotaryov, F. Yasyukevich. *Film Ed* Z. Veryovkina. *Mus* Veniamin Basner. *Song Lyr* M. Matusovskiy. *Choirmaster* F. Koslov. *Mus Cond* K. Eliasberg. *Sd* S. Litvinov. *Asst Dir* N. Moskalenko. *Prod Mgr* I. Gurman. *Cost* T. Kasparova. *Makeup* B. Baldin, L. Goremykina.
Cast: Valentin Zubkov *(Nikolay Savelyev),* Liliya Aleshnikova *(Svetlana),* Tatyana Konyukhova *(Tasya),* Yevgeniy Burenkov *(Koren),* Nikolay Sergeyev *(Maksim Petrovich),* Yelena Maksimova *(Pelageya Ivanovna),* Viktor Koltsov *(school director),* Olya Narovchatova *(Katya),* Vitya Lobzov *(Yevsikov),* Lyudmila Ovchinnikova, R. Rakitin, A. Lebedev, I. Ryabinin, O. Dolgova, M. Zharova, N. Pogodin, N. Smirnov, actor, V. Seleznyov, S. Korenev, V. Pitsek, L. Chubarov, S. Gorokhova, N. Burenkova, P. Dolzhanov.
Melodrama. Nikolay Savelyev, a Soviet soldier, is seriously wounded and blinded in one of the final skirmishes with the Germans in World War II. Svetlana, his nurse, who is in love with him, takes him home to his wife and family in the town where he had been a schoolteacher before the war. Nikolay learns braille at the school where he formerly taught, but his return to civilian life is beset with problems. His marriage is now unhappy, and although he resumes his job, he leaves his class when a student takes advantage of his blindness to cheat. Despairing, Nikolay discovers that Koren, the new school principal, who calls for his dismissal, is the cowardly deserter responsible for his wartime disability. Nikolay feels a renewed responsibility to his students and pursues his idealistic commitment to teaching. Having parted from his wife, he is reunited with Svetlana, who has remained in the town to be near him. *Veterans. Schoolteachers. Idealists. Deserters—Military. School principals. Blindness. Marriage. Cowardice. Cheating. Braille. World War II.*
Note: Released in the U.S.S.R. in Oct 1959 as *Solntse svetit vsem.* Also known as *The Sun Shines for Everybody.*

SUN TAI SIL YEN YIN *see* **BETWEEN TEARS AND SMILES**

THE SUN, THE PLACE & THE GIRLS *see* **NUDES OF ALL NATIONS**

SUNA NO KAORI *see* **THE NIGHT OF THE SEAGULL**

SUNA NO ONNA *see* **WOMAN IN THE DUNES**

SUNBURST *see* **BOOM!**

SUNDAY IN NEW YORK   F6.4776
Seven Arts Productions. *Dist* Metro-Goldwyn-Mayer, Inc. 5 Feb **1964** [Boston opening; c13 Nov 1963; LP26595]. Sd (Westrex); col (Metrocolor). 35mm. 105 min.
Prod Everett Freeman. *Dir* Peter Tewksbury. *Screenplay* Norman Krasna. *Dir Photog* Leo Tover. *Camera Op* Til Gabani. *Asst Camera Op* Hugh Crawford, George Hollister. *Art Dir* George W. Davis, Edward Carfagno. *Set Decor* Henry Grace, George R. Nelson. *Film Ed* Fredric Steinkamp. *Asst Ed* Allan Jacobs. *Mus* Peter Nero. *Mus Supv* Robert Van Eps. *Mus Cond* Robert Armbruster. *Titl Song* Carroll Coates, Peter Nero. *Sung by* Mel Torme. *Song:* "Hello" Roland Everett, Peter Nero. *Rec Supv* Franklin Milton. *Mix* Bob Oshier. *Rec* Howard Voss. *Boom Op* Dean Hodges. *Asst Dir* Eli Dunn, Herb Hirst. *Prod Supv* Abe Steinberg. *Unit Prod Mgr* Clarence Eurist. *Script Supv* Cleo Anton. *Wardrobe Dsgn* Orry-Kelly. *Wardrobe* Norman Burza, Florence Hackett. *Makeup Supv* William Tuttle. *Makeup* John Truwe. *Hairstyles* Sydney Guilaroff, Shirley Althouse. *Still Photog* Virgil Apger. *Gaffer* Milford Cline. *Head Grip* Leo Monlon. *Prop* Dick Neblett, Andy Martinez. *Casting* Warren Mace.
Cast: Rod Taylor *(Mike Mitchell),* Jane Fonda *(Eileen Tyler),* Cliff Robertson *(Adam Tyler),* Robert Culp *(Russ Wilson),* Jo Morrow *(Mona Harris),* Jim Backus *(flight dispatcher),* Peter Nero *(himself).*
Romantic comedy. Source: Norman Krasna, *Sunday in New York* (New York opening: 29 Nov 1961). Airline pilot Adam Tyler's plans to spend a romantic weekend in his New York apartment with Mona Harris are interrupted by the unexpected arrival of his sister Eileen, who has just quarreled with her fiancé, Russ Wilson, because she refuses to sleep with him before marriage. After assuring Eileen that she has done the proper thing and advising her to remain a virgin, Adam persuades Mona to accompany him on his next flight. His assignment is changed at the last minute, however, and he is unable to reach Mona, who is stranded in a strange city. Meanwhile, Eileen finds evidence of her brother's double standard, and when she meets Philadelphia newspaperman Mike Mitchell on a Fifth Avenue bus, she becomes determined to seduce him. Mike respects her virtue and is reluctant to comply, even though both of them soon realize they are falling in love. After getting caught in a downpour, they take refuge in Adam's apartment and are surprised by the arrival of a forgiving Russ, who mistakes Mike for Eileen's brother. Upon his return Adam is introduced as his own co-pilot but goes along with the masquerade, even though he suspects the truth. The situation is resolved later that evening: Mike and Eileen admit their love; Russ, believing that Eileen has been unfaithful to him, admits defeat; and Adam decides it will be easier to marry Mona than to arrange illicit meetings with her. *Air pilots. Newspapermen. Virginity. Double standard. Brother-sister relationship. Mistaken identity. Seduction. Airplanes. Airfields. New York City.*
Note: Location scenes filmed in New York City.

SUNDAY SUITOR   F6.4777
MJ Productions. *Dist* MarJon Film Distributors. ca **1970.** Sd; col. 16mm. [Feature film, length unknown]
Sex film. No information about the precise nature of this film has been found. *Sexuality.*

SUNDAYS AND CYBÈLE (France)   F6.4778
Terra Films–Fidès–Orsay Films–Les Films du Trocadéro. *Dist* Davis–Royal Films International, Columbia Pictures. 12 Nov **1962** [New York opening]. Sd; b&w. 35mm (Franscope). 110 min.
Prod Romain Pinès. *Assoc Prod* Raymond Froment, Gérard Ducaux-Rupp. *Dir* Serge Bourguignon. *Screenplay-Adapt* Serge Bourguignon, Antoine Tudal. *Scen-Dial* Serge Bourguignon, Bernard Eschassériaux. *Dir Photog* Henri Decaë. *Art Dir* Bernard Evein. *Film Ed* Léonide Azar. *Mus* Maurice Jarre. *Sd* Robert Teisseire, Jean Nény. *Prod Mgr* Jacques Planté.
Cast: Hardy Krüger *(Pierre),* Patricia Gozzi *(Françoise [Cybèle]),* Nicole Courcel *(Madeleine),* Daniel Ivernel *(Carlos),* Michel de Ré *(Bernard),* André Oumansky *(nurse),* Anne-Marie Coffinet, Alain Bouvette, René Clermont, Malka Ribovska, Jocelyne Loiseau, Renée Duchâteau, Raymond Pélissier, Martine Ferrière, Maurice Garrel, France Anglade, Albert Hugues, Florence Blot, Gilbert Edard, Antoine Tudal, Paul Bonifas, Serge Bourguignon, Dominique Maurin, Jacques Prévot, Jacques Robiolles, Jacques Tessier, Roger Trapp, Lisette Le Bon, Denise Péronne, Bibiane Stern.

Drama. Source: Bernard Eschassériaux, *Les dimanches de Ville d'Avray* (Paris, 1958). Pierre, a pilot during the French-Indochina War, develops amnesia as a result of his fear that he killed a young girl on a bombing mission. He returns to France, moves in with Madeleine, a nurse whom he had met while hospitalized, and begins a pointless life of wandering around the small town of Ville d'Avray. One day he meets Françoise, a 12-year-old girl who has been left by her father at the local convent school. The nuns, assuming Pierre to be her father, allow the two to spend each Sunday together, and a warm relationship develops. The child makes Pierre vow to bring her the weathercock from a church steeple, and in return, Françoise promises to tell him her real name. Eventually, a friend of Madeleine's becomes suspicious of the relationship between the man and child and notifies the police. While they celebrate Christmas together near a lake, the child tells Pierre that her name is Cybèle (the goddess of the earth). Their idyl is interrupted by the arrival of the police, who assume that Pierre intends to assault the child. After killing Pierre, they ask Françoise her name, but she replies that she no longer has one. *Air pilots. Veterans. Nurses. Children. Nuns. Police. Amnesia. Friendship. Manslaughter. Convents. Christmas. French-Indochina War 1945–54. Ville d'Avray.*

Note: Opened in Paris in Nov 1962 as *Les dimanches de Ville d'Avray.* Alternative French title: *Cybèle.*

SUNFLOWER (France/Italy)   **F6.4779**

C. C. Champion–Les Films Concordia. *Dist* Avco Embassy Pictures. 24 Sep 1970 [New York opening]. Sd; col (Technicolor). 35mm. 101 min. *MPAA rating* G.

Pres by Joseph E. Levine. *Prod* Carlo Ponti, Arthur Cohn. *Exec Prod* Joseph E. Levine. *Dir* Vittorio De Sica. *Screenplay* Tonino Guerra, Cesare Zavattini. *Screenplay Collab* Georgiy Mdivani. *Photog* Giuseppe Rotunno. *2d Unit Photog* David Vinitskiy. *Art Dir* Piero Poletto. *Film Ed* Adriana Novelli. *Mus* Henry Mancini. *Sd* Carlo Palmieri, Alvaro Orsini. *Asst Dir* Luisa Alessandri, Paolo Serbandini. *Prod Supv* Gianni Cecchin. *Prod Mgr* Ione Tuzi. *Cost* Enrico Sabbatini. *Coop* Mosfilm.

Cast: Sophia Loren (*Giovanna*), Marcello Mastroianni (*Antonio*), Lyudmila Savelyeva (*Mascia*), Galina Andreyeva (*Soviet woman official*), Anna Carena (*Antonio's mother*), Germano Longo (*Ettore*), Nadya Serednichenko (*woman in sunflower field*), Glauco Onorato (*returning veteran*), Silvano Tranquilli (*Russian-Italian worker*), Marisa Traversi (*prostitute*), Gunar Zilinskiy (*Russian ministry official*), Carlo Ponti, Jr. (*Giovanna's baby*), Giorgio Basso, Umberto Di Grazia, Gianni Bortolotti, Giuliano Girardi, Pippo Starnazza, Dino Peretti.

Drama. Giovanna and Antonio have been married for only 12 days when World War II breaks out. Antonio is drafted into the army, but he tries to dodge the draft by pretending to be insane; military officials see through his scheme, however, and send him to the Russian front. The Italian Army is quickly forced into retreat, and Antonio is rescued by Mascia, a young Russian woman. Antonio stays with Mascia for the duration of the war, and they marry. Despite the fact that Antonio has been declared missing in action, Giovanna travels to Russia at the end of the war and finds him there with Mascia and their son. Heartbroken, Giovanna resigns herself to Antonio's new marriage and returns to Italy, where she later marries. After many years have passed, Antonio is still obsessed with the memory of Giovanna's visit, and he goes to Italy to see her again. They meet and talk of their lives, but, realizing that they cannot recapture the past, they return to their spouses. *Deserters—Military. Missing persons. Russians. Marriage. Military draft. Bigamy. Conscience. World War II. Union of Soviet Socialist Republics. Italy—Army.*

Note: Location scenes filmed in Moscow and the Ukraine. Released in Italy in 1969 as *I girasoli*; opened in Paris in Oct 1970 as *Les fleurs du soleil*; running time: 105 min.

SUNSCORCHED (Spain/West Germany)   **F6.4780**

Balcázar P. C.–Creole Filmproduktion. *Dist* Feature Film Corp. of America. Nov 1966. Sd; col (Eastman Color). 35mm (Techniscope). 78 min.

Pres by Harold Goldman, United Pictures. *Prod* Ronald Rietti. *Dir (see note)* Mark Stevens, Jesús Jaime Balcázar. *Screenplay (see note)* Mark Stevens, Irving Dennis, Alfonso Balcázar, José Antonio de la Loma. *Orig Story* Mark Stevens. *Photog* Francisco Marín. *Art Dir* Juan Alberto Soler. *Film Ed* Steven Collins. *Mus* Michel Auzepi, Silvestre Enzo. *Prod Mgr* Valentín Sallent.

Cast: Mark Stevens (*Sheriff Jess Kinley*), Mario Adorf (*Abel Dragna*), Marianne Koch (*Anna-Lisa*), Frank Oliveras (*Luke*), Antonio Iranzo (*Charlie*), Oscar Pellicer, Julio Peña, Albert Bessler, Mario Via, Vivian Dodds, Felipe Peña, Luis Rivera, Jesús Puche.

Western melodrama. In the small Missouri town of Fraserville during post-Civil War days, Sheriff Jess Kinley is considered a coward for not taking a stand against four outlaws. Anna-Lisa, who is in love with Kinley, is the only one who remains loyal to him. Outlaw chief Abel Dragna threatens to expose Kinley's former association with his gang and to harm his family should the sheriff take action against the gunslingers. After the outlaws attack a widow and a minister

and then kill the latter's son, Kinley shoots the guilty gunman. The townspeople, however, still are displeased; Kinley's badge is removed, his past is revealed, and his wife, Lily, deserts him. Just as Kinley is about to leave town, Anna-Lisa is murdered. Heading off an angry mob, Kinley kills the other outlaws, winning back the respect of the townspeople and the love of his wife. *Sheriffs. Outlaws. Clergymen. Widows. Cowardice. Murder. Missouri.*

Note: Produced in Spain in 1965 as *Tierra de fuego*; running time: 88 min. Released in West Germany in Oct 1965 as *Vergeltung in Catano*; running time: 87 min. Only Spanish sources credit Jesús Jaime Balcázar as director and Alfonso Balcázar and José Antonio de la Loma with screenplay.

SUNSWEPT (Great Britain)   **F6.4781**

Dist Advent Film Productions, American Film Distributing Corp. 31 Jul 1963 [New York State license]. Sd; col (Eastman Color). 35mm. 63 min.

Prod-Dir Michael Keatering. *Screenplay* Antony Craven. *Photog* Michael Keatering. *Film Ed* Peter Austen-Hunt. *Mus* John Brunel.

Cast: Elizabeth, Yannick, Karen, Lita, Ingrid (*participants*), Lisa Rayne (*narrator*).

Nudist film. The camera follows a group of authentic English nudists as they travel to nudist camps in Corsica, the Isle of Levant, and Yugoslavia. Joyously devoted to the practice of nudism, members of the group bathe in the sun, swim in an underwater ballet, enjoy "natural" water skiing, dance by moonlight, and perform in a midnight piano recital. *Nudism. Nudist camps. Corsica. Île du Levant. Yugoslavia.*

Note: Originally released in Great Britain in 1962; running time: 69 min.

IL SUO MODO DI FARE see **THE GIRL WHO COULDN'T SAY NO**

SUPER DRAGON see **SECRET AGENT SUPER DRAGON**

THE SUPER FIGHT   **F6.4782**

Woroner Productions–Computer Sports, Inc. *Dist* Woroner Productions. 20 Jan 1970 [c20 Jan 1970; MP20255]. Sd; col. 35mm. 70 min.

Prod-Dir Murry Woroner. *Assoc Prod* William Hallahan. *Photog* Howard Winner, Willard Jones, photog, Oscar Barber, Richard Schwartz, Rick Anderson, Egon Stephan. *Film Ed* Oscar Barber, William Hallahan, Ralston Prince. *Sd* Ben-Scott Recording. *Master Rec* Frank Linale. *Asst Dir* Mark Harris, asst dir. *Graphics* Eric-Balir Associates.

Featuring: Rocky Marciano, Muhammad Ali (*themselves*), Chris Dundee (*referee*), Angelo Dundee, Mel Ziegler (*seconds*), Ferde Pacheco (*ring physician*), Mel Wolfe (*ring announcer*), Murry Woroner (*narrator*), Joe Louis, Jimmy Braddock, Jack Sharkey, Jersey Joe Wolcott, Max Schmeling, Jack Kearns, Jr., Nat Fleischer (*voices*), Guy LeBow (*announcer*).

Sports film. Rocky Marciano and Muhammad Ali, two undefeated heavyweight champions, are featured in a simulated fight. The film begins with scenes from the training camps of both fighters and moves to the actual fight. Off-screen interviews are conducted with Joe Louis, Jimmy Braddock, Max Schmeling, Jack Kearns, Jr., and Nat Fleischer. After 12 rounds, Marciano wins by a knockout. [Seventy one-minute rounds and seven possible endings were filmed; the results were then determined by computer and kept secret until the first showing of the film.] *Prizefighters. Prizefighting. Muhammad Ali. Rocky Marciano.*

SUPER SENSUALISTS see **SUPERSENSUAL**

SUPERARGO CONTRO DIABOLIKUS see **SUPERARGO VS. DIABOLICUS**

SUPERARGO EL HOMBRE ENMASCARADO see **SUPERARGO VS. DIABOLICUS**

SUPERARGO VS. DIABOLICUS (Italy/Spain)   **F6.4783**

Liber Film–Balcázar P. C.–S. E. C. *Dist* Columbia Pictures. May 1969 [Los Angeles showing; c1 Dec 1968; LP37130]. Sd; col (Eastmancolor). 35mm (Cromoscope). 88 min. *MPAA rating* G.

Prod Ottavio Poggi. *Exec Prod* Nino Battiferri. *Dir* Nick Nostro. *Screenplay* Jesús Jaime Balcázar. *Story* Mino Giarda. *Dir Photog* Francisco Marín. *Camera* Sandro Mancori. *Asst Camera* Giulio Battiferri. *Art Dir* Juan Alberto Soler. *Asst Art Dir* Paolo Mugani. *Set Dresser* Pierluigi Basile. *Set Furnishings* Cimino, Gabriele D'Angelo. *Main Titl* Biamonte & Grisanti. *Film Ed* Teresa Alcocer. *Orig Mus* Franco Pisano. *Sd Tech* Mario Celentano. *Asst Dir* Ferruccio Castronuovo. *Prod Mgr* Valentín Sallent. *Prod Supv* Gino Fanano. *Prod Sec* Arrigo Peri. *Script Girl* Maria Luisa Rosen. *Wardrobe* Nadia Vitali. *Makeup* Anacleto Giustini. *Hairstyles* Mara Rocchetti.

Cast: Ken Wood (*Superargo*), Gérard Tichy (*Diabolicus*), Loredana Nusciak, Monica Randal, Francisco Castillo Escalona, Emilio Messina, Valentino Macchi, Geoffrey Copleston, Giulio Battiferri.

Action melodrama. Wrestling champion Superargo's career is cut short when he accidentally kills a man during a match. An international Secret Service hires him because of his ability to withstand extreme physical hardship. While investigating mysterious shipments of uranium and mercury, he comes upon the island hideout of mastermind criminal Diabolicus, whose plan to conquer the world includes the manufacturing of artificial gold. Diabolicus captures Superargo and his fiancée, Lidia, but Superargo's strength is too much for the villain and his men, who are blown up before they can escape from the island. *Wrestlers. Masterminds. Feats of strength. Secret agents. Islands. Gold.*

Note: Opened in Rome in Dec 1966 as *Superargo contro Diabolikus;* released in Spain in 1967 as *Superargo contra Diabolicus.* Alternative Spanish title: *Superargo el hombre enmascarado.*

SUPERSENSUAL   F6.4784

Dist I. R. M. I. Films. 15 Nov **1967** [New York showing]. Sd; b&w. 35mm? 60 min.

Dir Jan Anders.

Cast: Greta Nelson.

Sex film. A bisexual woman is institutionalized because of her insatiable desires. On her release she plunges back into her life of hedonism. [Included are scenes of a stripper fondling herself and at least one lesbian sequence.] *Stripteasers. Autoeroticism. Lesbianism. Nymphomania. Bisexuality.*

Note: Also known as *Super Sensualists, Super Senses,* and *Supersens.*

SUPPORT YOUR LOCAL SHERIFF!   F6.4785

Cherokee Productions. *Dist* United Artists. 26 Mar **1969** [Detroit opening; c26 Mar 1969; LP36780]. Sd; col (Technicolor, print by DeLuxe). 35mm. 92 min. *MPAA rating* G.

Prod-Writ William Bowers. *Assoc Prod* William R. Finnegan. *Dir* Burt Kennedy. *Dir Photog* Harry Stradling, Jr. *Camera Op* Wally Meinardus. *Art Dir* Leroy Coleman. *Set Decor* Hugh Hunt. *Film Ed* George W. Brooks. *Mus* Jeff Alexander. *Sd* Bruce Wright. *Asst Dir* Ray De Camp. *Cost* Norman Burza, Florence Hackett. *Makeup* Stan Smith. *Hairstyles* Helen Parrish. *Sp Eff* Marcel Vercoutere.

Cast: James Garner (*Jason McCullough*), Joan Hackett (*Prudy Perkins*), Walter Brennan (*Pa Danby*), Harry Morgan (*Olly Perkins*), Jack Elam (*Jake*), Bruce Dern (*Joe Danby*), Henry Jones (*Henry Jackson*), Walter Burke (*Fred Johnson*), Dick Peabody (*Luke Danby*), Gene Evans (*Tom Danby*), Willis Bouchey (*Thomas Devery*), Kathleen Freeman (*Mrs. Danvers*), Gayle Rogers (*bar girl*), Richard Hoyt (*gunfighter*), Marilyn Jones (*bordello girl*).

Western comedy. While burying an itinerant stranger in the small western town of Calendar, Prudy Perkins, the daughter of the ineffectual mayor, spots gold in the open grave, leaps in to stake her claim, and turns the funeral into a scrambling riot. With that incident, the gold rush begins as hordes of prospectors, pioneers, and prostitutes swarm into Calendar. Since the only road in or out of town is blocked by a ranch belonging to the conniving Danby clan, old Pa Danby demands a levy of 20 percent of every gold shipment that passes through. After three of Mayor Perkins' sheriffs have been disposed of by the Danbys, an easy-going stranger, Jason McCullough, rides into town while en route to Australia. Jason agrees to accept the post of temporary sheriff because he cannot afford the inflationary prices in the boomtown. Quickly breaking up a street brawl by hosing down the participants, Jason makes Jake, a dimwitted drunk, his deputy and arrests Joe Danby for murder and slaps him in the new jail that does not yet have bars. While Jason settles down as a boarder in the Perkins' home Pa Danby plots ways to get his son out of jail. His schemes fail dismally, however, and Pa summons all the Danbys in the territory to help dispose of the troublesome Jason. But when they march into town, Jason tricks them into holding their fire until he has had time to take Joe and tie him across the town's Civil War cannon. By threatening to put his lighted cigar to the cannon's fuse, Jason forces the Danbys to drop their firearms. Boasting to Prudy that he bluffed the Danbys with an unloaded cannon, Jason lights the fuse—and demolishes Madame Orr's brothel. As Prudy falls into Jason's arms, he agrees to marry her and consents to remain on as sheriff. *Mayors. Prospectors. Bullies. Sheriffs. Frontier and pioneer life. Gold rushes. Greed. Extortion. Alcoholism. Funerals. Boomtowns. Ordnance. Jails. Whorehouses.*

SUPPOSE THEY GAVE A WAR AND NOBODY CAME   F6.4786

ABC Pictures. *Dist* Cinerama Releasing Corp. 20 May **1970** [Philadelphia opening]. Sd; col (De Luxe). 35mm. 113 min. *MPAA rating* GP.

A Fred Engel-Hy Averback Production. *Prod* Fred Engel. *Assoc Prod* J. Paul Popkin. *Dir* Hy Averback. *2d Unit Dir* Paul Baxley. *Screenplay* Don McGuire, Hal Captain. *Story* Hal Captain. *Dir Photog* Burnett Guffey. *Camera Op* Al Cline, Til Gabani. *Asst Camera* Jack Morrow, Felix Barlow. *Aerial Photog* Jack Willoughby, Tyler Camera Systems. *Set Decor* James W. Payne. *Prod Dsgn* Jack Poplin. *Film Ed* John F. Burnett. *Asst Ed* William Chulack. *Mus* Jerry Fielding. *Song:* "Mama Two March" Jerry Fielding, David McKechnie. *Sd* Everett Hughes. *Supv Mus & Eff Ed* Richard Carruth. *Sd Eff Ed* Frank Warner. *Mus Ed* Donald Harris. *Rec* Brandon Kellogg. *Boom Op* Ben Sad. *Asst Dir* Jack Aldworth, Joe Lauth. *Prod Supv* Joe Popkin. *Script Supv* June Sampson. *Wardrobe* Jerry Alpert. *Cost Coörd* Michael Rachmil. *Makeup*

Gary Liddiard, Robert Bau. *Sp Eff* Larry Hampton, George Peckham. *Tech Adv* Paul Lacy, (Maj.). *Stunt Coörd* Paul Baxley. *Prop Master* Arthur Friedrich. *Constr Coörd* Harold Nyby. *Casting* Harvey Clermont. *Gaffer* George Lasher. *Key Grip* Lester Kahn. *Still Photog* Lee Green.

Cast: Brian Keith (*Nace*), Tony Curtis (*Shannon Gambroni*), Ernest Borgnine (*Sheriff Harve*), Ivan Dixon (*Sergeant Jones*), Suzanne Pleshette (*Ramona*), Tom Ewell (*Billy Joe Davis*), Bradford Dillman (*Captain Myerson*), Arthur O'Connell (*Mr. Kruft*), John Fiedler (*Major Purvis*), Don Ameche (*Colonel Flanders*), Robert Emhardt (*Lester Calhoun*), Maxine Stuart (*Zelda*), Christopher Mitchum (*Alturi*), Pamela Britton (*Sergeant Graham*), Grady Sutton (*Reverend Dinwood*), Cliff Norton (*Herman Hyde*), Jeanne Bates (*Mrs. Flanders*), Eddie Firestone (*Deputy Goulash*), William Bramley (*Deputy Henry*), Sam G. Edwards (*Deputy Sam*), Buck Young (*Deputy Ron*), Paul Sorensen (*Deputy Randy*), David Cass (*Deputy Dave*), John Lasell (*Dr. Hillery*), Dorothy Green (*Mrs. Kruft*), Pamela Branch (*Mrs. Purvis*), Janet E. Clark (*Mrs. Davis*), Jean Argyle (*Mrs. Calhoun*), Monty Margetts (*Mrs. Dinwood*), Paula Stewart (*1st prostitute*), Carolyn Williamson (*2d prostitute*), John James Bannon (*1st military policeman*), Vince Howard (*2d military policeman*), Stanley W. Barrett (*Green Beret*).

Comedy. Colonel Flanders, the commander of a U. S. Army missile base in the South, plans to hold a dance to foster good relations with the nearby town of Anderson. The colonel appoints four of his subordinates, Warrant Officer Nace, Sgt. Shannon Gambroni, black Sergeant Jones, and Captain Myerson, as his community relations committee. Together with Billy Joe Davis (the town's leading citizen, a bigot, and the leader of a right-wing militia) they arrange the social event. On the night of the dance, Gambroni persuades Ramona, a bar girl and the town's loveliest citizen, to join him in the back seat of a parked car. Sheriff Harve, who considers Ramona his girl friend, arrests Gambroni for indecent conduct. Sergeant Jones, who has been refused a loan by bank official Kruft, decides to free Gambroni from jail. Jones and Nace, who is already quite drunk, commandeer an obsolete tank and storm the town. Billy Joe Davis is quick to defend his town; directing his forces from a helicopter, he orders his militia out onto a field in their jalopies. The tank devastates the private army and demolishes the jail. Colonel Flanders and the troops arrive to find Sheriff Harve holding the three sergeants captive, and Flanders forces the sheriff to release the men to him for military discipline. Billy Joe Davis is discredited, and the sheriff is fired, to the delight of practically the whole town. *Bar girls. Negroes. Southerners. Bankers. Sheriffs. Military life. Smalltown life. Bigotry. Finance—Personal. Jailbreaks. Drunkenness. Civil defense. Missile sites. Jails. Tanks (armored cars). United States Army.*

Note: Location scenes filmed at Fort Huachuca, Arizona.

SUR LA COUR *see* **THE CRIME OF MONSIEUR LANGE**

SURCOUF, LE DERNIER CORSAIRE *see* **THE SEA PIRATE**

SURCOUF, LE TIGRE DES SEPT MERS *see* **THE SEA PIRATE**

SURCOUF L'EROE DEI SETTE MARI *see* **THE SEA PIRATE**

SURF PARTY   F6.4787

Associated Producers, Inc. *Dist* Twentieth Century–Fox Film Corp. Jan **1964** [c31 Dec 1963; LP27017]. Sd; b&w. 35mm. 68 min.

Prod-Dir Maury Dexter. *Assoc Prod* "By" Dunham. *Story-Screenplay* Harry Spalding. *Dir Photog* Kay Norton. *Set Decor* Harry Reif. *Supv Film Ed* Jodie Copelan. *Mus* Jimmie Haskell. *Songs:* "If I Were an Artist," "That's What Love Is," "Surf Party" "By" Dunham, Bobby Beverly. *Titl Song Played by* The Astronauts. *Songs:* "Fire Water," "Glory Wave," "Crack-Up," "Never Comin' Back," "Great White Water" "By" Dunham, Jimmie Haskell. *Song:* "Pearly Shells" Lani Kai, Jericho Brown, "By" Dunham. *Sd* William Bernds. *Asst Dir* Harold E. Knox. *Prod Mgr* Harold E. Knox. *Script Supv* Dixie McCoy. *Wardrobe* George Herrington. *Makeup* Ted Coodley. *Prop Master* Jockey Liebgold.

Cast: Bobby Vinton (*Len Marshal*), Patricia Morrow (*Terry Wells*), Jackie DeShannon (*Junior Griffith*), Kenny Miller (*Milo Talbot*), Lory Patrick (*Sylvia Dempster*), Richard Crane (*Sgt. Wayne Neal*), Jerry Summers (*Skeet Wells*), Martha Stewart (*Pauline Lowell*), The Astronauts, The Routers (*themselves*), Mickey Dora, John Fain, Pam Colbert, Donna Russell, Lloyd Kino.

Comedy-drama with music. Terry, Sylvia, and Junior arrive in Malibu Beach from Arizona to vacation and to visit Terry's brother Skeet, a former football star whose career was ended by a skull injury. Sylvia falls in love with Skeet; Terry falls in love with Len, the operator of a local surf shop; and Junior falls in love with Milo, another surfer. Milo is injured in an accident while trying to qualify for membership in Skeet's unruly surfing club, "The Lodge." As a result of the accident, Len argues with Skeet, and they are about to fight when Terry warns Len that Skeet's football injury is still dangerous. Skeet is further humiliated when he gives a party, and Pauline, a wealthy older woman, finds him in the bedroom with Sylvia. Pauline reveals that she has been keeping

Skeet. Skeet realizes how much he loves Sylvia and decides to return to Arizona with her. The girls enjoy the rest of the vacation with their boyfriends. *Surfers. Athletes. Gigolos. Vacations. Brother-sister relationship. Clubs. Malibu (California).*

SURF TERROR *see* **THE BEACH GIRLS AND THE MONSTER**

SURFARI   **F6.4788**

American Sports Films. *Dist* Don Brown, Canyon Pictures, Excelsior Distributing Co. 18 Jul **1967** [New York opening]. Sd; col (Eastmancolor). 35mm. 90 min.

Prod-Dir Milton Blair. *Exec Prod* Don Brown. *Narr* Don Brown. *Photog* Don Brown. *Film Ed* Don Brown. *Mus* The Blazers.

With: Ricky Grigg, Greg Noll, Sue Peterson, John Teague, Mike Bennett, actor, Pam Douglas *(themselves),* Hal Buckley *(narrator).*

Documentary. The central figure in this examination of surfing is Ricky Grigg, a 29-year-old Californian who was the 1967 World Champion Surfer as well as a student of oceanography. Beginning with footage shot in California, the film describes the origins of the sport itself and its rapid development during the last decade. Included are scenes of Australia's beaches, a skiing interlude, a beach-buggy ride, and the continuing progress of a neophyte surfer from France, John Teague, who succeeds primarily in getting in everyone else's way. The concluding portion takes place in Hawaii at Oahu's famed "Banzai Pipeline" where the powerful waves rise to over 40 feet. *Surfers. French. Beaches. California. Australia. Hawaii.*

Note: Location scenes filmed in California, Australia, and Hawaii. Also known as *Blue Surfari.*

SURFSIDE LOVE *see* **SURFSIDE SEX**

SURFSIDE SEX   **F6.4789**

Movie One Productions. *Dist* Howard Farber Films, Distribpix, Inc. Nov **1967**. Sd; b&w. 35mm. 67 min.

Prod-Dir William K. Hennigar. *Writ* Jack Russell. *Camera* John Fisher. *Crew* Dodge, Dubrow. *Mus* Luristan. *Prod Supv* Dell Raley.

Cast: Verne Williams, Susan Reiner, Suzzan Landow, Fred Hamburg.

Melodrama. Two vagabond couples who are leisurely traveling across the country in a small car stop at the beach to swim in the nude and then go to a deserted seashore house where one of them once spent some time. They find that the house is occupied by an eccentric writer who spurns city life. Although the writer objects to the group's staying there, he is not forceful enough to throw them out. The two women sexually taunt the man and seduce him for money which they spend on LSD and marijuana. They induce the writer, who has gradually come to accept the four people, to take some LSD. Later, while they are having lunch, the writer's snobbish fiancée arrives unexpectedly. She attacks the group's depravity, and they depart, leaving the writer to bear the brunt of her admonitions. *Vagabonds. Authors. Teases. Seduction. Sexuality. Prostitution. Troilism. LSD. Marijuana. Beaches.*

Note: Also known as *Surfside Love.*

SURFTIDE 77   **F6.4790**

Volcan Productions. *Dist* Olympic International Films. 29 May **1962** [Los Angeles showing]. Sd; col (Eastman Color). 35mm. ca60 min.

Prod H. Duane Weaver. *Dir* R. L. Frost.

Cast: Tom Newman *(Bernard Bingbang),* Bob Cresse *(Agatha Bungworthy/ Townsend Bungworthy),* Virginia Gordon *(Vultura),* Dwayne Winton *(Lieutenant Ricketts),* Victor Tayback *(Arms Cooper).*

Comedy. Wealthy Agatha Bungworthy hires private detective Bernard Bingbang, known as "The Canary," to find her niece Cynthia Kingman, heir to a large fortune. Cynthia has a butterfly birthmark on her left breast. Bingbang is nearly killed during his search for Cynthia. He escapes Vultura, his would-be murderer, and attends a Hollywood strip party, but he turns up no leads. Bingbang learns that Agatha is actually a man, and that Bungworthy wants to kill Cynthia for her inheritance. The case comes to a frantic conclusion. *Detectives. Aunts. Heiresses. Inheritance. Nudity. Murder. Female impersonation. Birthmarks. Wealth. Hollywood.*

Note: Location scenes filmed in Hollywood. Also known as *Call Surftide 77, Call Girl 77,* and *Surftide 777.*

SURVIVAL *see* **THE GUIDE**

SURVIVAL *see* **PANIC IN YEAR ZERO!**

SURVIVAL *see* **SURVIVAL 1967**

SURVIVAL 1967   **F6.4791**

Jules Dassin–Irwin Shaw. *Dist* United Film Enterprises. 11 Jun **1968** [New York opening]. Sd; col. 35mm. 70 min.

Prod Jules Dassin, Irwin Shaw. *Dir* Jules Dassin. *Screenplay* Irwin Shaw. *Photog* Daniel Vogel, Christian Darraux. *Film Ed* Roger Dwyre, Michele

Neny. *Mus* Irwin Bazelon.

Documentary. Following the Six-Day War in 1967, this documentary was made to show part of the story of Israel's existence. There is little actual footage of the war, but much is seen of its aftermath, including the physical remains of war, the human story of the refugees, and Jews returning to the Western Wall. Interviews are held with David Ben-Gurion, Moshe Dayan, and Levi Eshkol. Talks with the faculty and students of Chaim Weizman University are shown. The growth of Israel in the past and its hopes and questions about peace in the future end the film. *Israeli-Arab War 1967. Israel. David Ben-Gurion. Moshe Dayan. Levi Eshkol. Chaim Weizman University.*

Note: Filmed on location in Israel. Also reviewed as *Survival.*

SUSAN SLADE   **F6.4792**

Warner Bros. Pictures. 8 Nov **1961** [Los Angeles opening; c24 Nov 1961: LP27098]. Sd; col (Technicolor). 35mm. 116 min.

A Delmer Daves Production. *Prod-Dir-Writ* Delmer Daves. *Photog* Lucien Ballard. *Art Dir* Leo K. Kuter. *Set Decor* William L. Kuehl. *Film Ed* William Ziegler. *Mus* Max Steiner. *Orch* Murray Cutter. *Sd* Stanley Jones. *Asst Dir* Russell Llewellyn. *Cost* Howard Shoup. *Makeup* Gordon Bau. *Hairstyles* Jean Burt Reilly.

Cast: Troy Donahue *(Hoyt Brecker),* Connie Stevens *(Susan Slade),* Dorothy McGuire *(Leah Slade),* Lloyd Nolan *(Roger Slade),* Brian Aherne *(Stanton Corbett),* Grant Williams *(Conn White),* Natalie Schafer *(Marian Corbett),* Kent Smith *(Dr. Fain),* Bert Convy *(Wells Corbett),* Guy Wilkerson *(Slim).*

Melodrama. Source: Doris Hume, *The Sin of Susan Slade* (New York, 1961). After 10 years of service as a mining engineer in Chile, Roger Slade sets sail for Carmel, California, with his wife Leah, and their 17-year-old daughter, Susan. En route, the naive and virginal Susan has an affair with Conn White, a wealthy mountain-climber. Once in Carmel, Susan meets Wells Corbett, the son of her father's employer, and Hoyt Brecker, an aspiring author. Hoyt is embittered by the suicide of his father, who had been convicted of embezzling $10,000 from the Corbett company. On the day of her parents' housewarming party, Susan learns that she is pregnant and sends a frantic wire to Conn. When word arrives that he has been killed while attempting to scale Mount McKinley, the hysterical Susan attempts suicide, but Hoyt rescues her. Susan then informs her parents of her pregnancy, and it is decided that Mr. Slade will take a post in Guatemala and that Mrs. Slade will pretend to be the child's mother. Following the birth of the baby, Mr. Slade dies of a heart attack; and Susan, her mother, and the baby return to Carmel. Tortured by frustration and her own deceit, Susan rejects the marriage proposals of both Hoyt and Wells. A short time later the baby is severely burned in an accident, and Susan breaks down and confesses that she is the child's mother. Stunned by the news, Wells withdraws his offer of marriage. However, when Susan returns home with her baby, Hoyt, who has just sold his first novel, is waiting for her. *Engineers—Mining. Ingenues. Authors. Infants. Family life. Illegitimacy. Mountain climbing. Suicide. Appearances. Conscience. Chile. Carmel (California). Mount McKinley. Guatemala.*

Note: Location scenes filmed in Carmel and San Francisco, California.

SUSPECT *see* **THE RISK**

SUSUZ YAZ *see* **DRY SUMMER**

SVÄLT *see* **HUNGER**

SVEGLIATI E UCCIDI (LUTRING) *see* **WAKE UP AND DIE**

SVENSKA FLICKOR I PARIS *see* **THE FLAMBOYANT SEX**

SVEZIA, INFERNO E PARADISO *see* **SWEDEN—HEAVEN AND HELL**

SVIRACHŬT *see* **THE CLOWN AND THE KIDS**

SWAMP COUNTRY   **F6.4793**

Patrick-Sandy Productions. caApr **1966** [Waycross, Georgia, opening]. Sd; col (Technicolor). 35mm (Techniscope). 98 min.

Prod-Dir Robert Patrick. *Assoc Prod* Jerome Sandy. *Screenplay* David DaLie. *Dir Photog* Mario Tosi. *2d Unit Photog* Jerry Wenziner. *Asst Camera* Robert Caramico, Tankred Wenziner. *Mus Score* Michael Terresco. *Songs:* "Wasted Love," "Man With a Plan," "Swamp Country," "The Misfits," "You Turn and Walk Away" *writ & sung by* Baker Knight. *Sd Eff* Magisound. *Sd Eff Supv* Jack Cornall.

Cast: Rex Allen *(sheriff),* Baker Knight *(Baker),* Carole Gilbert *(Nora Cox),* Sue Casey *(Mrs. Cox),* David DaLie *(Dave Wetzel),* Lyle Waggoner *(deputy),* Kiva Lawrence *(Mary Richmond),* Marian Patrick *(Nora's sister),* R. L. Armstrong *(Hysmith),* Vincent Barbi *(head of the bootlegging syndicate).*

Action melodrama. At a Georgia motel, Mary Richmond, a gangster's moll, is murdered. Dave Wetzel, a former big game hunter, is accused of the crime and flees the police. While the sheriff chases Wetzel through the Okefenokee Swamp, his deputy warns Nora Cox, her sister, and her mother of the danger. The sheriff temporarily abandons his search for Wetzel to save Baker Knight, a singer and the sheriff's rival for Nora, abducted by bootleggers who think he is an informer for revenue agents. After Wetzel rescues her 10-year-old sister from a panther, Nora agrees to help the fugitive prove his innocence. The hunter rescues Nora from Hysmith, the motel owner, who confesses to the murder. Later at a local dance, the sheriff realizes Nora loves Baker. *Molls. Hunters. Sheriffs. Singers. Fugitives. Bootleggers. Sisters. Murder. Abduction. Rescue. Okefenokee Swamp. Chases. Panthers.*

Note: Filmed on location in the Okefenokee Swamp.

THE SWAP AND HOW THEY MAKE IT F6.4794
General Studios. *Dist* General Studios, Cannon Releasing Corp. 27 May **1966** [Los Angeles showing]. Sd; b&w. 35mm. 97 min.
Dir-Writ Joe Sarno. *Camera* Robert Gage. *Lighting* Bruce Sparks. *Film Ed* Joe Sarno. *Sd* James Lynch. *Prod Coörd* Mel Garfinkel.
Cast: Loraine Claire *(Mona Parsons)*, Sheila Britton *(Karen Picard)*, George Wolfe *(Les Parsons)*, Jim Chisholm *(Wayne Picard)*, Crystal Snow *(Penny Craig)*, Pat Davis *(Brooke Furman)*, Joyce Knight *(Kathy)*, Judson Todd *(Pete Furman)*, Cleo Nova *(Stella Morse)*, Steve Barton *(Danny Morse)*, Rick Sheldon *(Morgan Hackett)*, Richard Sarnes *(Kent Craig)*, Rynn Marlowe *(Gene Hackett)*, Warwick Christian *(Paul)*, Alix Reed *(Dick)*, Harold Frank *(Ed)*.
Melodrama. Two couples, Mona and Les Parsons and Karen and Wayne Picard, move to a small, industrial community. There the men make elaborate plans to open a new business, and the neglected women become restless from inactivity. Karen seduces college student Dick and begins meeting him daily at Mona's house. Reluctantly following suit, Mona gives in to the sexual advances of her neighbor, Brooke Furman. The meeting with Furman leaves Mona unsatisfied, and she allows herself to be drawn into a mate swapping club. Wayne and Karen gleefully accept Furman's invitation to join the club, but Les has to be coerced into going along. As a result of the exchange, Les and Karen are paired off, and they are soon joined by Kathy, the teenaged girl friend of college student Dick. Furman becomes dissatisfied with Penny Craig, the group's "leader," and he gives a masquerade party to pair off Penny and Dick (mother and son), hoping thereby to banish her from the group. When the cruel trick is revealed, Dick leaves the party, distressed at having had sex with his mother, while Kathy remains behind to chastise Furman. When it is revealed that Kathy's uncle published a scandal magazine, Penny snaps some compromising photographs of Kathy to guard against her spilling the story to her uncle. Mona and Les leave the party in utter disgust; they pack their suitcases and plan to move away from Denton. *Entrepreneurs. Neighbors. Housewives. Students. Infidelity. Mate swapping. Group sex. Seduction. Marriage. Troilism. Incest. Moral corruption. Masquerades. Photographs.*

Note: Also known as *The Swap*.

THE SWAPPERS F6.4795
Mitam Productions. 29 Nov **1967** [New York showing]. Sd; b&w. 35mm. 63 min.
Melodrama. After 8 years of marriage, Jim and Marcie Swanson consider joining a mate swappers club. One night they meet Alphonse and Ding Ding in a bar. Ding Ding takes an immediate liking to Jim, and the foursome go back to Alphonse and Ding Ding's apartment and exchange partners for sex. Alphonse and Ding Ding tell Jim and Marcie about a mate swapping club. The next weekend, Jim and Marcie give a "get acquainted" party for some of the club members. An orgy ensues when Ding Ding begins to make love to another woman. Jim sees someone at the window and, thinking himself endangered, kills the intruder. The dead man turns out to be a mentally retarded neighbor who looks in everyone's windows. The police are called, and they begin an investigation. *Marriage. Mate swapping. Lesbianism. Group sex. Voyeurism. Murder. Mental retardation.*

THE SWAPPERS (Great Britain) F6.4796
Salon Productions. *Dist* Trans-American Films. 8 Jul **1970** [San Diego, California, opening; c24 Jun 1970; LP39861]. Sd; col (Eastmancolor, print by Movielab). 35mm. 84 min. *MPAA rating* R.
Prod Stanley Long. *Exec Prod* Barry Jacobs. *Dir* Derek Ford. *Screenplay* Derek Ford, Stanley Long. *Photog* Michael Francis, Trevor Brooker, Richard Pope, Albert Lloyd. *Film Ed* Dorak Film Services. *Mus Comp & Cond* Michael Eaton, John Fiddy. *Titl Song Sung by* Jay Dee. *Sd Supv* Tony Anscombe. *Sd* Alan Vetter, Laurie Barnett. *Res* Leslie Toye.
Cast: James Donnelly *(Paul)*, Larry Taylor *(Leonard)*, Valerie St. John *(Ellen)*, Denys Hawthorne *(Cliff)*, Bunty Garland *(Sheila)*, Sandra Satchwith *(Carol)*, Fiona Fraser *(Marion)*, Joan Hayward *(Jean)*, Stacy Harris *(psychiatrist)*, David Gell *(narrator)*.

Melodrama. A psychiatrist discusses mate swapping, warning that it is a game of increasing risk. To illustrate his point he presents several examples of the practice in documentary fashion. First, a young thrill-seeking wife receives a phone call, after which she is apparently kidnaped, taken to an isolated river bank, and ordered to swim naked to a houseboat to spend the night. In the next scene, Paul and Ellen, an outwardly happy couple, hope to solve their sexual problems with organized extra-marital sex. Once Ellen gets over her initial inhibitions, she becomes an enthusiastic participant in mate-swapping sessions. Another example shows a couple aboard a cabin cruiser for a weekend outing. They encounter difficulty when the clumsy advances of the host repel the guest's wife, and she has to fight off a rape. In an interview, a wife reveals that she became a prostitute through contacts in the mate-swapping club in order to solve her husband's financial problems. Although her husband was sent to prison for living off her earnings, she decides to continue working as a prostitute. In the final scene, Sheila, a childless wife, becomes repulsed by the mate-swapping parties, and one night she throws the guests out and suggests to her husband that a divorce might better satisfy their needs. *Psychiatrists. Prostitutes. Mate swapping. Marriage. Rape. Childlessness. Divorce. Cruisers.*

Note: Released in Great Britain in 1970 as *The Wife Swappers*; running time: 86 min.

SWEDEN—HEAVEN AND HELL (Italy) F6.4797
Produzione Atlas Cinematografica-Caravel Film. *Dist* Avco Embassy Pictures. 25 Jun **1969** [Washington, D. C., opening]. Sd; col (Eastman Color). 35mm. 90 min.
Prod Mario Bregi. *Dir-Writ* Luigi Scattini. *Photog* Claudio Racca. *Film Ed* Luigi Scattini. *Mus* Piero Umiliani.
Narrator: Edmund Purdom.
Documentary. Included in this film on Swedish manners and mores are scenes showing what the narration calls an "anything goes" attitude toward sex: contraceptive devices are readily available to girls of 15 and over; pornographic photo studios permit patrons to give the models posing instructions; access is easy to wife-swapping and lesbian clubs; and students further their sex education on chartered boats that sail around Stockholm harbor. Also depicted are the problems the Swedes have with alcoholism, drug addiction, a housing shortage that has led to communal living, the isolation of the very old, and hoodlum motorcycle gangs. The more favorable aspects of Swedish society depicted include the minimum of red tape encountered in adopting a child, the widespread abhorrence of violence, the love for the sauna, and the traditional festivities of Walpurgis Night. *Models. Students. Motorcycle gangs. Drug addicts. Birth control. Alcoholism. Adoption. Mate swapping. Pornography. Communal living. Lesbianism. Old age. Social customs. Sex clubs. Saunas. Walpurgis Night. Sweden. Stockholm.*

Note: Produced in Italy in 1968 as *Svezia, inferno e paradiso*, narrated by Enrico Maria Salerno. Also reviewed as *Sweden—Heaven or Hell*.

SWEDISH AND UNDERAGE *see* **EVA ... WAS EVERYTHING BUT LEGAL**

THE SWEDISH FANNY HILL *see* **FANNY HILL**

THE SWEDISH MISTRESS (Sweden) F6.4798
Svensk Filmindustri. *Dist* Janus Films. 19 Feb **1964** [San Francisco opening]. Sd; b&w. 35mm (AgaScope). 77 min.
Dir-Writ Vilgot Sjöman. *Photog* Lars Björne. *Sets* P. A. Lundgren. *Film Ed* Lennart Wallén. *Prod Mgr* Lars-Owe Carlberg. *Cost* Mago.
Cast: Bibi Andersson *(girl)*, Per Myrberg *(boy)*, Max von Sydow *(married man)*, Öllegård Wellton *(his wife)*, Birgitta Valberg *(elderly woman)*.
Romantic drama. A young Swedish secretary begins an affair with an older, married man whom she met at a scientific meeting in Stockholm. She is extremely tormented by their relationship, because the man refuses to divorce his wife. The young woman finally tells her boyfriend about her affair, then decides to leave both men. She accepts a job in Rome and is about to board her train when the older man stops her and tells her how much he needs her. They spend one last night together on the train, but in the morning she resolves to break off with him and begin a new life for herself. *Mistresses. Secretaries. Scientists. Infidelity. Trains. Rome. Stockholm.*

Note: Released in Sweden in Oct 1962 as *Älskarinnan*.

SWEDISH SUMMER F6.4799
1 Nov **1970** [Redwood City, California, showing]. Si; col. 35mm. 120 min. *Pres by* Explorama. *A Film by* Dick Reddy.
Travelog. A travel host describes the sights of Stockholm, Lapland, the Göta Canal, Dalecarlia, and Göteborg. *Travel. Sweden. Stockholm. Lapland. Göta Canal. Dalecarlia. Göteborg.*

Note: Narration delivered live on stage.

SWEDISH WEDDING NIGHT (Sweden) F6.4800
Minerva Film Produktion. *Dist* Royal Films International. 14 Nov **1965** [New York opening]. Sd; b&w. 35mm. 95 min.
Prod Tore Sjöberg, Lorens Marmstedt. *Dir* Åke Falck. *Screenplay* Lars Widding. *Photog* Rune Ericson. *Art Dir* Rolf Bohman. *Film Ed* Ingemar Ejve. *Mus* Georg Riedel. *Sd* Leif Hansen.
Cast: Jarl Kulle *(Hilmer Westlund)*, Lena Hansson *(Siri Westlund)*, Christina Schollin *(Hildur Palm)*, Edvin Adolphson *(Victor Palm)*, Isa Quensel *(Hilma Palm)*, Catrin Westerlund *(Irma Palm)*, Tor Isedal *(Rudolph Palm)*, Peter Thelin *(Gunnar Palm)*, Lars Ekborg *(Simon)*, Margaretha Krook *(Mary)*, Yvonne Lombard *(Svea)*, Georg Årlin *(Johan Borg)*, Ove Tjernberg *(Ivar)*, Lars Passgård *(Martin)*, Lars Lind *(Sören)*, Sigge Fischer *(Philip)*, Tommy Nilsson *(Loony-Anders)*, Ulla Edin *(Rullan)*, Claes Esphagen *(Wallinder)*, John Norrman *(Bjuhr)*, Sten Mattsson *(Hagström)*, Thor Zackrisson *(Karlsson)*, Gösta Krantz *(Nisse Johansson)*, Jessie Flaws *(Mary Lou)*, Frithiof Bjärne *(beef manager)*, Lasse Pöysti *(pedlar)*, Julia Caesar *(cafe proprietor)*, Åke Falck *(narrator)*.
Melodrama. Source: Stig Halvard Dagerman, *Bröllopsbesvär* (Stockholm, 1949). The story takes place at the wedding of Hildur Palm and Hilmer Westlund, a wealthy butcher old enough to be her father. Hildur is already pregnant by Martin, a farmhand on her father's farm; she is in love with Martin, but he has refused to marry her. At the dinner following the wedding, the villagers become drunk and reveal their secret love affairs, and Martin commits suicide by hanging himself from a tree in the yard. Hilmer takes his bride home after the party, but since he is too drunk to make love, his best friend goes to bed with Hildur. *Butchers. Farmers. Village life. Weddings. Pregnancy. Drunkenness. Suicide.*
Note: Released in Stockholm in Aug 1964 as *Bröllopsbesvär;* running time: 100 min.

SWEET AND SOUR (France/Italy) F6.4801
Compagnia Cinematografica Antonio Cervi-Les Films Number One. *Dist* Pathé Contemporary Films. 27 Dec **1964** [New York opening]. Sd; b&w. 35mm. 93 min.
Prod Pierre Kalfon. *Dir* Jacques Baratier. *Screenplay* Guy Bedos, Jacques Baratier, Eric Ollivier. *Photog* Henri Decaë. *Art Dir* Jacques Noël, Raymond Gabutti. *Film Ed* Néna Baratier. *Mus* Ward Swingle. *Lyr* Bassiak, Jacques Audiberti. *Choreog* Jean Babilée. *Sd* Pierre Calvet. *Asst Dir* Jean Léon. *Prod Mgr* Louis de Masure.
Cast: Guy Bedos *(Gérard)*, Jean-Pierre Marielle *(Rakanowski)*, Sophie Daumier *(Jackie)*, Francis Blanche *(Franz)*, Jean-Marc Bory *(reporter)*, Anna Karina *(Ginette [Giselle?])*, Simone Signoret *(Geneviève)*, Jean-Paul Belmondo *(Raymond)*, Alexandra Stewart *(Anna)*, Jacques Dufilho *(Monsieur Alphonse)*, François Périer *(Legrand)*, Jean Richard *(Lepetit)*, Monica Vitti *(She)*, Roger Vadim *(He)*, Romolo Valli *(Monsieur X)*, Françoise Brion *(striptease girl)*, Claude Brasseur *(plumber)*, Sophie Desmarets *(The Pianist)*, Anne Doat *(journalist)*, Daniel Laloux *(Gaby)*, Rita Renoir *(ethnologist [striptease girl])*, Francesca Solleville *(singer)*, Jean-Baptiste Thierrée *(Grégoire)*, Marina Vlady *(radio-taxi-girl)*, Elisabeth Wiener *(Frédérique)*, Georges Wilson *(Casimir)*, Jean Babilée *(Oscar)*, Jacques Seiler *(police officer)*, Pascale Roberts, Valérie Lagrange, Andréa Parisy *(striptease girls)*.
Satire with music. A group of film enthusiasts, overwhelmed by the style and possibilities of the hand-held camera, film life in the streets of Paris and interview a number of subjects in an effort to capture some truths about humanity. The results are screened in an old loft serving as the filmmakers' headquarters. There is film of Gérard, who beats an old pro at tennis and is then talked into regretting his victory; the same Gérard meeting a prostitute, Jackie, in the Bois de Boulogne; and Jackie escaping a police raid on the Bois. There are scenes of an effeminate man instructing women in a charm school; two new fathers discussing their infants, a giant and a midget respectively; an elderly German searching in Paris for his daughter; a striptease lesson; a tryst in an atmosphere reminiscent of *Last Year at Marienbad*; a pleading telephone conversation between Geneviève, a lovelorn prostitute, and her ex-lover Raymond, a French Legionnaire who hardly remembers her; a sequence in which a naive plumber shows more interest in the leaky faucet in a frustrated prostitute's apartment than in the woman herself; and a gang "rumble" in dance in the style of *West Side Story*. The leader of the filmmakers shows a movie in which a woman confides stories about her dull husband who has been dead for years. The final scene is an interview with a leather-jacketed Method actor *(Gérard)* who is about to leave for Hollywood. He reveals his plan to make a film about Voltaire as a teenager. *Prostitutes. Plumbers. Actors. Germans. Street gangs. Motion pictures. Tennis. Fatherhood. Effeminacy. Striptease. Charm schools. Paris. Paris—Bois de Boulogne. Hollywood. France—Army— Foreign Legion.*
Note: Opened in Paris in Sep 1963 as *Dragées au poivre;* running time: 94 min; 1963 Venice Film Festival running time: 98 min. Italian title: *Confetti al*

pepe. Apo Films is credited by one source as production company with Les Films Number One.

SWEET BEAT *see* **THE AMOROUS SEX**

SWEET BIPPY (BLUE) F6.4802
Dist Freeway Films, Cinex International Film Distributors. **1968**. Sd; b&w. 35mm. 72 min.
Dir Kevin Duffy.
Sex film. In a city, the private lives of a number of men and women are depicted as they search for sexual fulfillment. Included are scenes of violence and death, exhibitionism, lesbianism, interracial sex, bondage, oral sex, nymphomania, fetishism, sadomasochism, and doctors using their patients sexually. A pregnant woman is also featured. *Physicians. Urban life. Sadomasochism. Exhibitionism. Lesbianism. Pregnancy. Fetishism. Nymphomania. Oral sex. Miscegenation.*

SWEET BIRD OF AQUARIUS F6.4803
K & W Pictures. Dec **1970**. Sd; col. 35mm. 90 min.
Prod Earl Wainwright. *Dir* Harry E. Kerwin. *Story & Screenplay* Edmond Niwrek. *Dir Photog* Thomas Casey. *Camera* Earl Wainwright. *Asst Camera* David Lang. *Set Dsgn* Paul Moore. *Film Ed* Lee Gilmore, Martin Kahan. *Mus Dir* Lamar Talbot. *Mix-Rec* Larry Fisher. *Boom Op* George Hunt. *Asst Dir* William Kerwin. *Prod Mgr* James Carson. *Script Supv* Betty Kaye. *Wardrobe Dsgn* Barbara Stuart, cost. *Makeup Artist* Gayle Doucette. *Still Photog* Albert J. Doucette, Carl Kesser. *Ch Electrn* Duke McGrath. *Key Grip* Harold Glaze.
Cast: Suzanne Robinson *(Lori Bradford)*, Thomas Wood *(Steve Bradford)*, Jason Saturday *(George Bowman)*, Sherry Nealson *(Liz Bowman)*, Dan Roper *(Jim Bennett)*, Mimi Montel *(Jean Bennett)*, Enid Torrell *(Sally Dawson)*, Gordon Rodney *(Fred Dawson)*, Reginald Hornsby, Jr. *(Dr. Regents)*, Gayle Aymes *(Nurse Cultice)*, Steve Landers *(bellboy)*, Roger Barron *(copy boy)*.
Domestic drama. Newlywed Steve Bradford is denied his conjugal rights by Lori, his frigid bride. After several weeks of frustration, Steve relieves the tension by raping Lori. While she seeks medical advice, he confides in sports commentator George Bowman, who later introduces the couple to several swinging suburbanites. After a regimen of weekly orgies, Steve finds himself unable to meet Lori's sexual demands. *Newlyweds. Suburbanites. Television announcers. Marriage. Frigidity. Rape. Sexual initiation. Group sex. Mate swapping.*

SWEET BIRD OF YOUTH F6.4804
Roxbury Productions-Metro-Goldwyn-Mayer, Inc. *Dist* Metro-Goldwyn-Mayer, Inc. 21 Mar **1962** [Los Angeles opening; c31 Dec 1961; LP21774]. Sd (Westrex); col (Metrocolor). 35mm (CinemaScope). 120 min.
Prod Pandro S. Berman. *Assoc Prod* Kathryn Hereford. *Dir & Writ for the Screen by* Richard Brooks. *Dir Photog* Milton Krasner. *Col Cons* Charles K. Hagedon. *Art Dir* George W. Davis, Urie McCleary. *Set Decor* Henry Grace, Hugh Hunt. *Film Ed* Henry Berman. *Mus Supv* Harold Gelman. *Orch Cond* Robert Armbruster. *Rec Supv* Franklin Milton. *Asst Dir* Hank Moonjean. *Cost* Orry-Kelly. *Makeup* William Tuttle. *Hairstyles* Sydney Guilaroff. *Sp Vis Eff* Lee Le Blanc.
Cast: Paul Newman *(Chance Wayne)*, Geraldine Page *(Alexandra Del Lago)*, Shirley Knight *(Heavenly Finley)*, Ed Begley *("Boss" Finley)*, Rip Torn *(Thomas J. Finley, Jr.)*, Mildred Dunnock *(Aunt Nonnie)*, Madeleine Sherwood *(Miss Lucy)*, Philip Abbott *(Dr. George Scudder)*, Corey Allen *(Scotty)*, Barry Cahill *(Bud)*, Dub Taylor *(Dan Hatcher)*, James Douglas *(Leroy)*, Barry Atwater *(Ben Jackson)*, Charles Arnt *(Mayor Henricks)*, Dorothy Konrad *(Mrs. Maribelle Norris)*, James Chandler *(Prof. Burtus H. Smith)*, Mike Steen *(deputy)*, Kelly Thordsen *(Sheriff Clark)*, William Forrest *(Benny Taubman)*, Roy Glenn *(Charles)*, Davis Roberts *(Fly)*, Robert Burton *(director)*.
Melodrama. Source: Tennessee Williams, *Sweet Bird of Youth* (New York opening: 10 Mar 1959). Chance Wayne has youth, good looks, virility, and complete self-confidence—four qualities he feels certain will make him a Hollywood star. After drifting for several years, he goes to Florida and picks up Alexandra Del Lago, an aging film star. Convinced that her comeback picture is a failure, Alexandra has taken to drinking vodka, smoking hashish, inhaling oxygen, and keeping young lovers. She promises to help Chance in Hollywood, and he drives her to the small southern town of his birth. Here he plans a reunion with his girl friend, Heavenly, the only daughter of a corrupt and powerful politician, "Boss" Finley. Chance quickly learns, however, that he is unwelcome. (He does not know that following his last visit Heavenly became pregnant and had an abortion.) While Finley and his hoodlum son, Tom Junior, meditate their revenge, Heavenly's Aunt Nonnie arranges several meetings between the young lovers. In the meantime, Chance continues to nurture his relationship with Alexandra, and he records her drugged confessions with a view to future blackmail. Suddenly Alexandra learns from Walter Winchell that her comeback film is an unqualified triumph and that she

is once more in demand. Her old self again, she rejects Chance, ignores her promises, and prepares to leave. As she does so a giant political rally is turned into a brawl when Finley's discarded mistress, Miss Lucy, exposes his ruthless tactics and reveals Heavenly's abortion. Sensing the impending violence, Alexandra offers to take Chance away, but he refuses to leave Heavenly. A group of thugs headed by Tom Junior beat Chance into senselessness and badly disfigure his face. Chance is finally able to face the truth about himself, and he leaves with Heavenly. *Drifters. Actors. Political bosses. Mistresses. Aunts. Gigolos. Self-confidence. Alcoholism. Blackmail. Ambition. Abortion. Reputation. Disfiguration. Filial relations. Brother-sister relationship. Motion pictures. Hashish. Oxygen. Recorders. United States—South. Florida. Walter Winchell.*

THE SWEET BODY OF DEBORAH (France/Italy)   F6.4805

Zenith Cinematografica-Flora Film-C. C. F. Lux. *Dist* Warner Bros.-Seven Arts, Inc. 12 Mar **1969** [Detroit opening; c1 Mar 1969; LP37141]. Sd; col (Technicolor). 35mm (Techniscope). 95 min. [Cut from 105 min.] *MPAA rating* R.

Prod Mino Loy, Luciano Martino. *Exec Prod* Sergio Martino. *Dir* Romolo Guerrieri. *Screenplay* Ernesto Gastaldi. *Story* Ernesto Gastaldi, Luciano Martino. *Dir Photog* Marcello Masciocchi. *Camera* Antonio Schiavolena. *Art Dir* Amedeo Fago. *Film Ed* Eugenio Alabiso. *Asst Film Ed* Amedeo Moriani. *Mus Comp* Nora Orlandi. *Mus Cond* Robby Poitevin. *Sd Tech* Bruno Zanoli, Bruno Moreal. *Asst Dir* Roberto Pariante. *Prod Supv* Vittorio Galiano, William Azzella. *Script Clerk* Renato Moretti. *Wardrobe* Gaia Romanini. *Miss Baker's Gowns* Balestra. *Makeup* Mario Van Riel. *Hairstyles* Jolanda Conti.

Cast: Carroll Baker *(Deborah)*, Jean Sorel *(Marcel)*, George Hilton *(Robert)*, Evelyn Stewart *(Susan)*, Luigi Pistilli *(Philip)*, Michel Bardinet *(police commissioner)*, Renato Montalbano *(telephone man)*, Mirella Pamphili *(telephone clerk)*, Domenico Ravenna *(doctor)*, Valentino Macchi *(garage attendant)*, Giuseppe Ravenna *(maître d')*.

Drama. Deborah, a wealthy American, and her Italian husband, Marcel, are honeymooning in Geneva when they meet Marcel's friend Philip, who belligerently informs them that Susan, Marcel's former fiancée, has committed suicide. The couple stop at Susan's deserted villa, where Marcel receives a death threat over the telephone. In Nice, he continues to receive menacing phone calls, and Deborah begins taking tranquilizers; one evening she accidentally takes too many and is revived by Robert, an artist who lives in the adjacent villa. Later, Philip attempts to murder her to avenge Susan's suicide, but Marcel appears, stabs Philip, and buries his body in the garden. The next morning, when Marcel leaves to buy two plane tickets to the United States, Philip and Susan suddenly appear; when the terror-stricken Deborah faints, the couple drug her, slash her wrists to make her death look like suicide, and drive away. On the highway, they pass Marcel and exchange knowing glances with him. Marcel returns to the villa and encounters Robert, who tells Marcel that he knows of the suicide-murder plot and demands payment for his silence. Unaware that Robert has taken the phone off the hook and that the police are listening in the next room, Marcel agrees to pay, but upon seeing the receiver, he draws his gun and is shot dead by Robert. Later, Deborah and Robert meet and congratulate each other on the success of their scheme to collect Marcel's insurance money. *Americans in foreign countries. Newlyweds. Artists. Suicide. Murder. Conspiracy. Perfidy. Blackmail. Honeymoons. Telephone. Tranquilizers. Geneva. Nice.*

Note: Location scenes filmed in Nice. Released in Italy in 1968 as *Il dolce corpo di Deborah*; opened in Paris in Feb 1969 as *L'adorable corps de Deborah*. Also reviewed in the United States as *The Soft Body of Deborah* and *The Sweet Body.*

SWEET CHARITY   F6.4806

Universal Pictures. 11 Feb **1969** [Boston opening; c5 Apr 1968; LP38879]. Sd (Westrex); col (Technicolor). 35mm (Panavision, see note). 150 min. *MPAA rating* G.

Prod Robert Arthur. *Dir* Bob Fosse. *Screenplay* Peter Stone. *Dir Photog* Robert Surtees. *Art Dir* Alexander Golitzen, George C. Webb. *Set Decor* Jack D. Moore. *Titl Dsgn* Howard A. Anderson Co. *Film Ed* Stuart Gilmore. *Mus & Mus Score* Cy Coleman. *Songs* Dorothy Fields, Cy Coleman. *Mus Supv & Cond* Joseph Gershenson. *Orch* Ralph Burns. *Choreog* Bob Fosse. *Sd* Waldon O. Watson, William Russell, Ronald Pierce, Len Peterson. *Mus Ed* Arnold Schwarzwald. *Asst Dir* Douglas Green. *Prod Mgr* Ernest B. Wehmeyer. *Script Supv* Betty Abbott. *Cost Dsgn* Edith Head. *Makeup* Bud Westmore. *Miss MacLaine's Hairstyles* Sydney Guilaroff. *Hairstyles* Larry Germain. *Dial Coach* Leon Charles. *Dance Asst* Paul Glover, Ed Gasper, John Sharpe, Sonja Haney. *Vocal Coach* Jack Lee.

Cast—Principal Players: Shirley MacLaine *(Charity Hope Valentine)*, Sammy Davis, Jr. *(Big Daddy)*, Ricardo Montalban *(Vittorio Vitale)*, John McMartin *(Oscar Lindquist)*, Chita Rivera *(Nickie)*, Paula Kelly *(Helene)*, Stubby Kaye *(Herman)*, Barbara Bouchet *(Ursula)*, Alan Hewitt *(Nicholsby)*,

Dante D'Paulo *(Charlie)*, John Wheeler *(Rhythm of Life dancer)*, John Craig *(man in Fandango Ballroom)*, Dee Carroll *(woman on tandem)*, Tom Hatten *(man on tandem)*, Sharon Harvey *(young woman on bridge)*, Charles Brewer *(young man on bridge)*, Richard Angarola *(maître d')*, Henry Beckman, Jeff Burton *(policemen)*, Ceil Cabot *(married woman)*, Alfred Dennis *(waiter at Chile Hacienda)*, David Gold *(panhandler)*, Nolan Leary *(Manfred)*, Diki Lerner *(man with dog on bridge)*, Buddy Lewis *(appliance salesman)*, Joseph Mell *(man on bridge)*, Geraldine O'Brien *(lady on bridge)*, Alma Platt *(lady with hat on bridge)*, Maudie Prickett *(nurse on bridge)*, Chet Stratton *(waiter)*, Robert Terry *(doorman)*, Roger Til *(greeter at Pompeii Club)*, Buddy Hart, Bill Harrison *(baseball players)*, Suzanne Charny *(lead frug dancer)*, Bick Goss *(drummer boy)*.

Cast—Dancers, Singers & Models: Chelsea Brown, Ray Chabeau, Bryan Da Silva, Lynn Fields, Roy Fitzell, Ellen Halpin, Dick Korthaze, April Nevins, Maris O'Neill, Lee Roy Reams, Sandy Roveta, Charleen Ryan, Juleste Salve, Patrick Spohn, Jerry Trent, Ben Vereen, Bud Vest, Lorene Yarnell *(frug dancers)*, John Frayer, Dom Salinaro, Paul Shipton, Walter Stratton *(patrons at dancehall)*, Larry Billman, Herman Boden, Dick Colacino, Lynn McMurrey, Ted Monson, Ed Robinson *(waiter-dancers)*, Leon Bing, Sue Linden, Jackie Mitchell, Carroll Roebke *(models)*, Kathryn Doby, Al Lanti, Gloria Mills, Louise Quick, Victoria Scruton, Tiffni Twitchell, Renata Vaselle, Adele Yoshioka *(dancers in "Big Spender" number)*, Chuck Harrod, Charles Lunard, Jerry Mann, Frank Radcliff *(singers)*, Marie Bahruth, Toni Basil, Carol Birner, Donald Bradburn, Lonnie Burr, Cheryl Christiansen, Marguerite De Lain, Jimmy Fields, Ben Gooding, Carlton Johnson, Kirk Kirksey, Lance Le Gault, Trish Mahoney, Walter Painter, Bob Thompson, Jr., Bonnie G. West, Kay York *(dancers in "Rhythm of Life" number)*, Leon Alton, Norman Stevans *(conversions)*.

Musical comedy-drama. Source: Neil Simon, Cy Coleman and Dorothy Fields, *Sweet Charity* (New York opening: 29 Jan 1966). Charity Hope Valentine, though only a hostess in a cheap New York City dancehall called the Fandango Ballroom, refuses to be disillusioned by the disappointments life has handed her; ever the optimist, she dreams of one day meeting the true love who will bring her happiness and respectability. Charity's latest beau, Charlie, a gangster-gigolo, pushes her off a Central Park bridge and runs away with her life savings, leaving her with only his name tattooed across an arrow-pierced heart on her arm; nevertheless, she refuses to give up hope. One night Charity witnesses a sidewalk argument between Italian film star Vittorio Vitale and his elegant girl friend Ursula. Ursula drives off in a rage, whereupon Vittorio impulsively takes Charity to an exclusive nightclub and then back to his apartment for an intimate supper. But the evening is ruined when an apologetic Ursula arrives, and Charity is forced to spend the night hiding in one of Vittorio's closets. Following a disastrous attempt to better herself by registering at an employment agency, Charity becomes trapped in an elevator with Oscar Lindquist, a timid, claustrophobic insurance actuary. Believing that Charity works in a bank, he asks her for a date, and, despite the warnings of Helene and Nickie, her girl friends at the Fandango, Charity decides that this romance is the one she has been waiting for all her life. Oscar asks Charity to marry him, despite his learning that she is a dancehall hostess; but he meets her Fandango chums at the Marriage License Bureau and gets a good look at Charity's tattoo, and he is unable to go through with the wedding. Once again alone and abandoned, Charity wanders through Central Park until she finds herself at the bridge where Charlie deserted her. As she broods over her fate, a group of flower children hand her a daisy and thus renew her faith in what tomorrow will bring. *Songs:* "My Personal Property" (Charity), "Hey, Big Spender" (Ballroom Girls), "Rich Man's Frug" (instrumental), "If My Friends Could See Me Now" (Charity), "There's Gotta Be Something Better Than This" (Charity, Nickie & Helene), "It's a Nice Face" (Charity), "Rhythm of Life" (Big Daddy & Ensemble), "Sweet Charity" (Oscar), "I'm a Brass Band" (Charity), "I Love To Cry at Weddings" (Herman & Ensemble), "Where Am I Going?" (Charity). *Dancehall hostesses. Gangsters. Gigolos. Italians. Actors. Clerks. Flower children. Robbery. Marriage. Dancehalls. Nightclubs. Tattoos. New York City. New York City—Central Park.*

Note: Location scenes filmed in New York City. Filmed in 35mm and blown up to 70mm for some roadshow presentations. The play *Sweet Charity* was based on Fellini's film, *Notti di Cabiria* (1957).

SWEET ECSTASY (France)   F6.4807

Paris Inter Productions-Contact Organisation-Les Films du Griffon. *Dist* Audubon Films. 4 May **1962** [Los Angeles showing]. Sd; b&w. 35mm (CinemaScope). 75 min. [Also reviewed at 81 min.]

Prod Joël Lifschutz. *Dir* Max Pecas. *Screenplay* Jacques Aucante, Grisha M. Dabat, Max Pecas. *Photog* Marc Fossard. *Art Dir* Bob Luchaire. *Film Ed* Paul Cayatte. *Mus* Charles Aznavour. *Lyr* Georges Garvarentz, Clément Nicolas. *Songs Sung by* Johnny Hallyday. *Sd* Séverin Frankiel. *Prod Mgr* Jacques Garcia.

Cast: Elke Sommer (*Elke*), Pierre Brice (*Maddy*), Christian Pezey (*Olivier*), Claire Maurier (*Claire*), Jenny Astruc (*Mick*), Michèle Bardollet (*Chouttc*), Robert Darane (*Charlie*), Agnès Spaak (*Dominique*), Albert Dinan (*Popoff*), Robert Bar, Mitsouko.

Melodrama. Olivier, a restless young man, hesitates to become involved with Barbara, an aspiring actress who loves him. She introduces him to a group of wealthy, pleasure-mad idlers living on the Côte d'Azur. Their leader, the cynical Maddy, suggests to his mistress, Elke, that she seduce the newcomer and thereby make him an intimate member of the group. At a party aboard a yacht, Olivier resists Elke's advances, explaining that he craves more than physical satisfaction. His confession elicits a genuine feeling of warmth in Elke; this, in turn, sparks a spirit of rivalry between Olivier and Maddy. To settle the matter, the two men engage in a test of daring by jumping blind-folded from a moving crane onto the top of a building under construction. Olivier misses his footing but is unexpectedly saved by Maddy. Elke and Maddy realize the futility of their lives and decide to reform, while Olivier returns to the uncomplicated Barbara. *Actors. Mistresses. Wealth. Seduction. Hedonism. Yachts. Riviera.*

Note: Opened in Paris in Mar 1962 as *Douce violence*; running time: 88 min. Also known as *Sweet Violence*. One U. S. source lists Les Films du Griffon, Max Pecas' firm, as production company, while other sources credit Paris Inter Productions and Contact Organisation.

SWEET IS THE MEAT   F6.4808
    Dist Cine Flicks International. ca **1970**. Sd; col. 35mm. 72 min.
    Dir-Writ Robert Soukis.
    Cast: Pricilla Goodbody, Orwell Hung, Mike Hunt.
    Drama. A woman relates the explicit details of her sex life to her doctor, and he becomes sexually excited as the tale unfolds. [Press photos suggest that the film contains scenes of a sexually uninhibited party, nudity, oral sex, and a sexual threesome.] *Physicians. Sexuality. Troilism. Oral sex.*

SWEET LIGHT IN A DARK ROOM (Czechoslovakia)   F6.4809
    Barrandov Film Studio. *For* Československý Film. *Dist* Promenade Films. 29 Jun **1966** [New York opening]. Sd; b&w. 35mm. 93 min.
    Pres by Moris Ergas, Vlado Hreljanovic, CBK Film Enterprises. *Dir* Jiří Weiss. *Screenplay* Jan Otčenášek, Jiří Weiss. *Photog* Václav Hanuš. *Asst Camera* Josef Hanuš, Ivan Šlapeta, Ladislav Chroust. *Art Dir* Karel Škvor. *Asst Art Dir* Oldřich Okáč. *Film Ed* Miroslav Hájek. *Asst Film Ed* Magda Hájková. *Mus* Jiří Srnka. *Sd* Emil Poledník. *Asst Sd* Adolf Werner. *1st & 2d Asst Dir* Věra Ženíšková, Zdenek Sirový. *Prod Supv* František Milič. *Prod Assoc & Asst* Věra Kadlecová, Karel Škorpík, Eva Kučerová, Miloš Bergl. *Production Group* Kubala–Novotný.
    Cast: Ivan Mistrík (*Pavel*), Dana Smutná (*Hanka*), Jiřina Šejbalová (*Pavel's mother*), František Smolík (*grandfather*), Blanka Bohdanová (*Kubiasová*), Eva Mrázová (*Alena*), Karla Chadimová (*Josefka*), Miroslav Svoboda (*Wurm*), Karlička Svobodová (*Martička Wurmová*), Vladimír Ráž (*class master*), Miloš Nedbal (*headmaster*), Anna Melíšková (*Kubrychtová*), Václav Lohniský (*railwayman*), Josef Kozák (*janitor*), Ladislav Kazda (*Melichar*), Jiří Kodet (*Vojta*), Jindřich Narenta (*Bubi*), Josef Vorel, Ivo Gübel, Pavel Bártl (*Gestapo agents*), Věra Tichánková (*farmer's wife*), Alexandra Myšková (*Wurmová*), Marie Marešová, Ela Poznerová (*neighbors*), Věra Váchová (*Irena*), Zuzana Fišárková (*Melicharová*), Stanislav Langer (*doctor*), Ladislav Mrkvička (*Bubeník*), Ladislav Gzela (*neighbor*), Jan Pelikán (*old man*), Ruda Princ (*trash collector*), Jan Skopeček (*secret agent*), Václav Sloup (*student*).
    War drama. Source: Jan Otčenášek, *Romeo, Julie a tma* (Prague, 1960). In 1942 during the German occupation of Czechoslovakia, Hanka, a Jewish schoolgirl in Prague, escapes when her family is shipped away to the ghetto. Pavel, a university student, comes to her aid by hiding her in an attic storeroom. While Pavel struggles to keep Hanka safe, a romance blossoms between them. In addition to the danger of Hanka's discovery by the Nazis, which is heightened after the assassination of SS Gen. Reinhard Heydrich and the consequent reprisals, Pavel faces increasing pressure from his possessive mother, who has grown suspicious about the disappearance of food and his increased absence from home. Pavel searches in vain for a new hiding place. Finally, a collaborator neighbor discovers Hanka, and the tenants argue about what should be done with her. As an SS division approaches the building, Hanka is faced with the dilemma of endangering lives of others, and she decides to leave the house. Pavel tries in vain to stop her, but Hanka rushes into the street and is shot by the SS patrol. *Jews. Fugitives. Nazis. Germans. Students. Neighbors. Resistance (political). Military occupation. Self-sacrifice. Filial relations. Assassination. War crimes. Czechoslovakia—History—1938–45. World War II. Prague. Reinhard Heydrich. Gestapo. SS.*
    Note: Location scenes filmed in Prague. Released in Czechoslovakia in Apr 1960 as *Romeo, Julie a tma*; running time: 96 min.

SWEET LOVE, BITTER   F6.4810
    Film 2 Associates. *Dist* Film 2 Associates, Peppercorn-Wormser, Inc., U-M Film Distributors. 30 Jan **1967** [New York opening]. Sd; b&w. 35mm. 92 min.
    Prod Lewis Jacobs. *Exec Prod* Gerald Kleppel, Robert Ferman. *Dir* Herbert Danska. *Screenplay* Herbert Danska, Lewis Jacobs. *Photog* Victor Solow. *Film Ed* Gerald Kleppel. *Mus* Mal Waldron. *Prod Supv* Louis Kellman.
    Cast: Dick Gregory (*Richie "Eagle" Stokes*), Don Murray (*David Hillary*), Diane Varsi (*Della*), Robert Hooks (*Keel Robinson*), Jeri Archer (*Candy*), Barbara Davis (*girl in bar*), Bruce Glover, Carla Pinza.
    Drama. Source: John Alfred Williams, *Night Song* (New York, 1961). Richie "Eagle" Stokes, a distinguished jazz saxophonist, has become frustrated and embittered by his contact with white society. He attempts to find relief through liquor, drugs, and women, including his white mistress, Candy. One day he meets a down-and-out, white college teacher, David Hillary, who has left his teaching job and torments himself with blame for the death of his wife in an automobile accident. The two men go on a drinking spree that ends when they pass out in an alley. They are brought home by Eagle's devoted friend, Keel Robinson, who offers David a room and a job as a waiter in his all-night coffeehouse. Keel's relationship with his white girl friend, Della, is made difficult by racial barriers. In spite of his mistrust of whites, however, he gradually accepts David; and a warm friendship develops among the three men. At last David finds the strength to return to his teaching job. While walking on campus with the dean one day, David sees a policeman accost Eagle, who, playing a one-night stand nearby, has come to visit him. Angered by Eagle's defiant attitude, the policeman suddenly begins beating him with a club while David stands frozen, unable to speak or move to aid his friend. Some time later, on a trip to the city, David confesses his cowardice to Eagle, who reacts, characteristically, by laughing off the incident and going on a binge. This time he dies from an overdose of heroin. Realizing that they will probably never see each other again, David and Keel say goodby and go their separate ways. *Musicians. Negroes. Mistresses. Professors. Police. Race relations. Urban life. Jazz. Drug overdose. Friendship. Guilt. Cowardice. Drunkenness. Miscegenation. Heroin. Coffeehouses.*
    Note: Filmed in New York City and Philadelphia. Rereleased as *It Won't Rub Off, Baby!*; also known as *Black Love—White Love.*

SWEET NOVEMBER   F6.4811
    Gina Productions. *Dist* Warner Bros.-Seven Arts, Inc. 8 Feb **1968** [New York opening; c1 Apr 1968; LP35729]. Sd; col (Technicolor). 35mm. 114 min.
    A Jerry Gershwin-Elliott Kastner Production. *Prod* Jerry Gershwin, Elliott Kastner. *Dir* Robert Ellis Miller. *Screenplay* Herman Raucher. *Photog* Daniel L. Fapp. *Art Dir* John Robert Lloyd. *Set Dsgn* Ralph S. Hurst. *Film Ed* James Heckert. *Mus Comp & Cond* Michel Legrand. *Song:* "Sara's Theme" Michel Legrand. *Titl Song* Leslie Bricusse, Anthony Newley. *Sung by* Anthony Newley. *Sd Dsgn* Stanley Jones. *Asst Dir* Fred Gammon, Fred Giles. *Script Supv* Dorothy Aldrin. *Cost Dsgn* Ann Roth. *Makeup Supv* Gordon Bau. *Supv Hairstylist* Jean Burt Reilly. *Dial Supv* Bert Steinberger.
    Cast: Anthony Newley (*Charlie Blake*), Sandy Dennis (*Sara Deever*), Theodore Bikel (*Alonzo*), Burr DeBenning (*Clem Batchman*), Sandy Baron (*Richard*), Marj Dusay (*Carol*), Martin West (*Gordon*), Virginia Vincent (*Mrs. Schumacher*), King Moody (*Digby*), Robert Gibbons (*Sam Naylor*).
    Drama. Each month of the year, Sara Deever, a Brooklyn Heights woman who leases apartments and sublets them at a profit, shares her bohemian flat with a different man with different "conformist hang-ups." In this way, she feels that she has helped someone and, in turn, she will always be remembered. One day in October, she meets Charlie, a staid British manufacturer, and invites him to be her "November." Intrigued by the offer and the woman, Charlie accepts. As the days pass, Charlie finds himself losing his inhibitions and falling in love with Sara. But when he asks to stay beyond November, Sara tells him that he must leave, as all his predecessors have done, on the last day of the month. Then Charlie learns from a neighbor and friend, Alonzo, that Sara is dying from an incurable illness. Overcoming his grief, Charlie begs Sara to seize whatever happiness she can by letting him remain. Although she knows that for the first time she is truly in love, Sara tells Charlie that he must go. On the last night of the month, Sara packs Charlie's bags and waits for "December" to arrive. When he does, Charlie kisses Sara goodby and reminds her that she will never be forgotten. *Nonconformists. British. Manufacturers. Neighbors. Bohemianism. Inhibition. Friendship. Incurable illness. New York City—Brooklyn.*
    Note: Location scenes filmed in Manhattan and Brooklyn.

THE SWEET RIDE   F6.4812
    Twentieth Century-Fox Film Corp. 22 May **1968** [San Francisco opening; c29 Dec 1967; LP35408]. Sd (Westrex); col (De Luxe). 35mm (Panavision). 110 min.
    Prod Joe Pasternak. *Dir* Harvey Hart. *Screenplay* Tom Mankiewicz. *Dir Photog* Robert Hauser. *Art Dir* Jack Martin Smith, Richard Day. *Set Decor*

Walter M. Scott, Stuart A. Reiss. *Main Titl* Richard Kuhn. *Film Ed* Philip W. Anderson. *Mus* Pete Rugolo. *Song:* "Sweet Ride" Lee Hazlewood. *Sung by* Dusty Springfield. *Song:* "Never Again," *writ & sung by* Moby Grape. *Sd* Harry M. Lindgren, David Dockendorf. *Asst Dir* Eli Dunn, Richard Kobritz. *Unit Prod Mgr* Francisco Day. *Makeup* Dan Striepeke. *Hairstyling* Edith Lindon. *Sp Photog Eff* L. B. Abbott, Art Cruickshank, Emil Kosa, Jr. *Surfing Seq* MacGillivray/Freeman Films.

Cast: Tony Franciosa (*Collie*), Michael Sarrazin (*Denny*), Jacqueline Bisset (*Vicki*), Bob Denver (*Choo-Choo*), Michael Wilding (*Mr. Cartwright*), Michele Carey (*Thumper*), Lara Lindsay (*Martha*), Norma Crane (*Mrs. Cartwright*), Percy Rodriguez (*Lieutenant Atkins*), Warren Stevens (*Brady Caswell*), Pat Buttram (*Texan*), Michael Forest (*Barry Green*), Lloyd Gough (*Parker*), Stacy King (*Big Jane*), Corinna Tsopei (*tennis girl*), Charles Dierkop (*Mr. Clean*), Arthur Franz (*psychiatrist*), Seymour Cassel (*surfer/cyclist*), Paul Condylis (*Sergeant Solomon*), Ralph Lee (*Scratch*), Lou Procopio (*Diablo*), Linda Gamble, Sam Chew, Jr.

Melodrama. Source: William Murray, *The Sweet Ride* (New York, 1967). The near-dead body of a brutally beaten and molested young woman is dumped on a highway in the Malibu Beach area peopled by surfers and drifters. Police investigation reveals that the woman, actress Vicki Cartwright, was dating surfer Denny McGuire, a young wastrel who shares a beach house with Collie Ransom, an aging tennis hustler, and Choo-Choo Burns, an unemployed jazz pianist. At a questioning conducted by Lieutenant Atkins, Denny explains that he first met Vicki on the beach and that, from the very beginning, their love affair was unstable. Denny later learned that Vicki was trapped professionally and psychologically by Brady Caswell, the producer of her new television series. When Denny asked Vicki to marry him, she insisted that she could not and began lying about her reasons for spending time away from him. Denny's jealousy was further inflamed by the interest taken in Vicki by repugnant cyclist Mr. Clean. Denny eventually learned of her relationship with Caswell; a bitter and vindictive quarrel ensued; and Denny did not see her again until she was brought into the hospital 2 weeks later. Once the police questioning is over and Denny and Collie are released, they learn what really happened on that fateful night: after Vicki had masochistically offered herself to Mr. Clean, she was savagely beaten by Caswell. To avenge Vicki, who is recovering from the attack, Denny assaults Caswell at his home, leaving him bleeding and unconscious. At last recognizing that there must be something more to life, Denny abandons his aimless way of life to work in a Santa Monica hardware store. *Roommates. Surfers. Police. Actors. Pianists. Television producers. Motorcyclists. Jealousy. Blackmail. Masochism. Malibu (California). Santa Monica.*

Note: Location scenes filmed at Malibu, California.

A SWEET SICKNESS   **F6.4813**
Hollywood Film Studio. *Dist* FPS Ventures. 15 Nov **1968** [Champaign, Illinois, showing]. Sd; b&w. 35mm. 70 min.
Prod Don Brown. *Dir* Jon Martin.
Cast: Vincene Cradduck, Art T. Romaus.

Melodrama. Dee, an inexperienced actress from a small town, comes to Los Angeles to find a career in the theater without prostituting herself. Her disillusionment begins when the manager of the building where Dee shares an apartment with a friend, arrives to collect the rent, finds Dee naked, and rapes her. Dee is not discouraged, however, and she agrees to appear at a stag party arranged by her agent and have her clothing auctioned off. A drunk who bids $250 for her underpants later forces his way into Dee's dressing room, expecting more for his money. Dee rebuffs him and is beaten by the club's manager for insulting his patron. In her search for another apartment, Dee is attacked and chloroformed by a rental agent, and she awakens to find herself at a wild orgy. She passes out, wakes up in a telephone booth smelling of whiskey, and is unable to convince the police that she was abducted. Despondent, Dee finally acquiesces to her agent's wishes, and he forces her to have sex with him to demonstrate her willingness to cooperate. The agent arranges an appointment for Dee with a movie producer—none other than the drunk from the stag party. A more mature woman because of her recent experiences, Dee has intercourse with the producer. *Actors. Apartment house managers. Theatrical agents. Pimps. Motion picture producers. Real estate agents. Rape. Drunkenness. Moral corruption. Prostitution. Disillusionment. Stag shows. Striptease. Auctions. Orgies. Los Angeles.*

SWEET SKIN (France/Italy)   **F6.4814**
Lambor Films-Variety Film. *Dist* Times Film Corp. Oct **1965**. Sd; b&w. 35mm. 96 min.
Prod Jules Borkon. *Dir* Jacques Poitrenaud. *Screenplay* Jacques Poitrenaud, Jacques Sigurd. *Dial* Jacques Sigurd. *Idea* Alain Moury. *Photog* Raymond Lemoigne. *Ed* Gilbert Natot. *Mus* Serge Gainsbourg. *Sd* Guy Chichignoud. *Prod Mgr* Pierre Laurent.
Cast: Krista Nico (*Ariane*), Dany Saval (*Dodo Voluptuous [Berthe]*), Darry Cowl (*Paul*), Jean Sobieski (*Jean-Loup*), Renée Passeur (*The Rich Woman*),

Jean Tissier (*The Painter*), Alice Cocéa (*A Middle Class Lady [Jean-Loup's aunt]*), Umberto Orsini (*A Dancer [Ariane's dance partner]*), Yves Barsacq, Badin, Jean-Pierre Zola, Norma Dugo, Marcello Oliveto.

Comedy-drama. Ariane, a German ballet dancer, has been assigned the leading role in the "Ballets Modernes." Then the financial backer of the production decides to replace Ariane with his mistress, and Ariane is left unemployed. Despite the warnings of a Negro musician friend, she turns to a striptease club, The Crazy Horse Saloon, recommended by her friend Dodo. She is hired at this club and spends several nights watching the others perform. On her first night as a performer, she refuses to uncover her breasts. This act of modesty makes her a favorite among the audience. Jean-Loup, a millionaire playboy, attends one show and falls in love with Ariane. At first she resists his attentions but she eventually begins to accept the gifts he offers her and becomes his mistress. His parents, upset by the romance of their son and a stripteaser, threaten to disinherit him. Confronting his parents in Ariane's presence he in turn threatens that, if disinherited, he will marry Ariane. Humiliated, Ariane breaks with him and returns his gifts during one of her performances. She quits the club and returns to the ballet, her true vocation. *Dancers. Germans. Theatrical backers. Millionaires. Mistresses. Playboys. Nightclub owners. Stripteasers. Musicians. Negroes. Disinheritance. Filial relations. Ballet. Upper classes. Paris. Crazy Horse Saloon (Paris).*

Note: Released in France in 1963 as *Strip-Tease*. Filmed on location in Paris.

SWEET SMELL OF LOVE (Italy/West Germany)   **F6.4815**
La Regina Produzione–Thor Film. *Dist* William Rowland. 9 Aug **1966** [Houston opening]. Sd; b&w. 35mm. 81 min.
Prod Joseph Justman. *Dir* Edward Dein. *Screenplay* Edward Dein, Karlheinz Deikert. *Photog* Franco Delli Colli. *Film Ed* Giancarlo Cappelli. *Mus* Ugo Calise. *Sd* Domenico Luria.
Cast: Marisa Solinas (*Maria*), Dan Harrison (*Philip*), Henrik Reinkwell (*Kurt*), Georg Hauke, Gianluigi Crescenzi.

Romantic drama. Philip steals cash and jewels from a luxury yacht, sidesteps his accomplice, Kurt, and absconds with the loot to a sparsely populated island. There he meets Maria, the hostess of a rundown cantina, who has an innocent friendship with a mute named Paco. Philip tries in vain to seduce Maria, but she continues to refuse his offers of golden jewelry. Kurt arrives on the island intending to take revenge on his partner, but he is killed by Philip, who leaves the body for Maria and Paco to bury. Finally, Philip proposes marriage to Maria and she accepts. The morning after the wedding, however, Philip deserts his bride, and Maria returns to Paco for comfort. *Barroom hostesses. Mutes. Theft. Partnerships. Perfidy. Revenge. Murder. Bribery. Marriage. Desertion. Yachts. Jewels. Islands. Saloons.*

Note: Released in Italy in 1966 as *Una vergine per un bastardo* or *Vergine per un bastardo*; running time: 85 min; in West Germany in Apr 1969 as *Das Bett einer Jungfrau*. Edward Dein is a pseudonym for Ubaldo Ragona.

THE SWEET SMELL OF SEX   **F6.4816**
Barnard L. Sackett Productions. *Dist* Adelphia Pictures, Film-Makers' Cooperative, Canyon Cinema Cooperative. 30 Jun **1965** [New York showing]. Sd; b&w. 35mm. 74 min.
Prod Barnard L. Sackett. *Dir* Robert Downey. *Screenplay* Barnard L. Sackett, Charles E. Martin. *Mus* Tom O'Horgan.

Melodrama. Bebe Katsafannis arrives in New York City to celebrate Flag Day and visit her stripper friend from Indiana, Smokey La Bare, who rooms with a man who has a compulsion for picking pockets. In the hope of earning extra money, Bebe visits the apartment of the "Fat Man" and discovers that he collects stray cats, chickens, and pigeons. The "Bald Man" follows Bebe in his limousine and pays her $1,000 for posing nude while he satisfies his voyeuristic urges. Bebe next accepts a modeling job for a "photographer" without a camera who fantasizes about sex as his models parade by. Bebe rejects the advances of Joe, who has been following her, because he appears too upright and ordinary; and, preferring outlandish excitement, she goes to a masquerade party frequented by guests of every sexual preference. She leaves when the dancing degenerates into a sadistic exercise, and, raped by a cab driver, she decides to leave the city. As she is about to board a bus, Joe stops her, and although Bebe finds him a bore, she goes with him to his apartment. While they embrace, the ordinary Joe reveals his underlying perversion and strangles Bebe. *Stripteasers. Roommates. Pickpockets. Photographers. Taxi drivers. Models. Prostitution. Sadism. Rape. Murder. Voyeurism. Urban life. Masquerades. New York City.*

Note: Also known as *Sweet Smell of Perfume* and *Sweet Smell of Love.*

SWEET SUBSTITUTE *see* **CARESSED**

SWEET SWEAT (Japan)   **F6.4817**
Toho Co. Sep **1965** [Los Angeles showing]. Sd; b&w. 35mm. [122]
Dir Shiro Toyoda.

Cast: Machiko Kyo *(bar girl)*, Keiji Sada, Junko Ikeuchi, Miyuki Kuwano.

Romantic drama. A bar hostess encounters her old lover, but they eventually decide to go their separate ways. *Bar girls. Mistresses.*

Note: Released in Japan in 1964 as *Amai ase.*

SWEET TASTE OF JOY   F6.4818

Kirt Films International–Triumph Films. *Dist* Distribpix, Inc. 6 Aug **1970** [Champaign, Illinois, showing]. Sd; col 35mm. 64 min.

Prod Bob Mansy. *Dir* C. Walsh.

Cast: Janet Topaz *(Joy)*, Margaret Leigh.

Sex film. Impregnated by her boyfriend, Joy suspects that he plans to shirk his paternal obligations, and she makes her own plans to exact revenge. She enlists the aid of several of her promiscuous friends and lures her boyfriend to her apartment for a farewell supper. He is bound to the bed while Joy and her girl friends abuse him and use him to enact their wildest imaginings; Joy is somewhat distracted from her vendetta by sexual encounters with friends of both sexes, but her boyfriend is repaid unquestionably for his lack of fidelity. *Revenge. Pregnancy. Desertion. Sadism. Lesbianism. Group sex.*

SWEET TRASH   F6.4819

Dist Clover Films. **1970** [Los Angeles showing]. Sd; col 35mm. 79 min.

Prod Daniel Cady, John Hayes. *Dir-Writ* John Hayes. *Photog* Paul Hipp.

Cast: Patrick Shea, William Conners, Mary McGee.

Melodrama. Honest dockworker Michael Donovan is drawn into the loan shark racket by a group of Manhattan prostitutes and "businessmen" who easily corrupt the susceptible man. Donovan proves unable to adjust to his new role as a loan shark out to cheat his friends and co-workers, and he becomes a helpless alcoholic. *Stevedores. Prostitutes. Racketeers. Loan sharks. Moral corruption. Alcoholism. New York City.*

SWEET VENGEANCE   F6.4820

Artscope Ltd. *Dist* Europix-Consolidated Corp. 14 Oct **1970** [York, Pennsylvania, opening]. Sd; col (Movielab). 35mm. 81 min. *MPAA rating* X.

Prod-Dir Amin Chaudhri. *Story-Screenplay* Joel O'Brien. *Photog* Amin Chaudhri. *Titl Song Writ, Arr & Cond by* George Fischoff. *Mus Comp* Ernest McCarty.

Cast: Betty Harrison *(Betty)*, Art Roberts *(Mark Stevens)*, Patricia Murray *(Helen Stevens)*, Joe Moreno *(Big Mike)*, Ron Abbot *(The Bear)*, Alan Marlowe *(Gino)*, Nels Hedrick *(Sugie)*.

Melodrama. Gambler Mark Stevens is brutally beaten and murdered by "The Bear" under orders from Big Mike, a New York City gambling syndicate boss to whom Mark owes a sum of money. Betty, a woman with whom Mark has been having an affair while his wife, Helen, is away on a business trip, witnesses the killing and decides to avenge Mark's death. (Betty is a friend of Helen's who has recently arrived in New York and is living with Mark and Helen while looking for a job.) Betty learns how to use the blackjack and razor from a homosexual photographer, and she repays him by allowing him to paint her body in psychedelic colors. Betty then infiltrates Big Mike's syndicate through his procurer, a lesbian, and receives from her a date with the syndicate boss. Betty seduces Big Mike, then beats him to death with a blackjack and castrates him with a razor. Fleeing his apartment, she stumbles into The Bear, slays him, and, pursued by one of Mike's henchmen, joins Helen, waiting outside in her auto. A wild chase takes place up New York's West Side Highway, culminating on the George Washington Bridge. There the women realize they are doomed, and, turning their car around, they crash head on into their pursuer's oncoming car. *Gamblers. Gangsters. Pimps. Murder. Debt. Revenge. Infidelity. Male homosexuality. Body painting. Lesbianism. Seduction. Castration. Suicide. Syndicates. New York City. George Washington Bridge. Chases. Automobile accidents.*

SWEET VIOLENCE *see* **SWEET ECSTASY**

SWEETS   F6.4821

Dec **1970** [New York showing]. [Feature length assumed.]

Sex film. No information about the precise nature of this film has been found. *Sexuality.*

THE SWIMMER   F6.4822

Horizon Dover, Inc. *Dist* Columbia Pictures. 15 May **1968** [New York opening; c1 Jun 1968; LP36051]. Sd; col (Technicolor). 35mm. 94 min.

Prod Frank Perry, Roger Lewis. *Dir* Frank Perry. *Adtl Dir* (see note) Sydney Pollack. *Screenplay* Eleanor Perry. *Dir Photog* David Quaid. *Adtl Photog* Michael Nebbia. *Art Dir* Peter Dohanos. *Scenic Artist* Stanley Cappiello. *Film Ed* Sidney Katz, Carl Lerner, Pat Somerset. *Mus* Marvin Hamlisch. *Orch* Leo Shuken, Jack Hayes. *Sd Mix* Willard Goodman. *Asst Dir* Michael Hertzberg. *In Charge of Prod* Joseph Manduke. *Prod Asst* Florence Nerlinger. *Script Supv* Barbara Robinson. *Wardrobe Dsgn* Anna Hill Johnstone. *Swimwear* Elizabeth Stewart. *Makeup* John Jiras. *Hairstyles* Ed Callaghan. *Casting* Alan Shayne Associates. *Dial Coach* Thom Conroy. *Key Grip* Al Stetson. *Gaffer* Richard

Falk. *Prop Master* Thomas Wright.

Cast: Burt Lancaster *(Ned Merrill)*, Janet Landgard *(Julie Hooper)*, Janice Rule *(Shirley Abbott)*, Tony Bickley *(Donald Wersterhazy)*, Marge Champion *(Peggy Forsburgh)*, Nancy Cushman *(Mrs. Halloran)*, Bill Fiore *(Howie Hunsacker)*, John Garfield, Jr. *(ticket seller)*, Kim Hunter *(Betty Graham)*, Rose Gregorio *(Sylvia Finney)*, Charles Drake *(Howard Graham)*, Bernie Hamilton *(chauffeur)*, House Jameson *(Mr. Halloran)*, Jimmy Joyce *(Jack Finney)*, Michael Kearney *(Kevin Gilmartin)*, Richard McMurray *(Stu Forsburgh)*, Jan Miner *(Lillian Hunsacker)*, Diana Muldaur *(Cynthia)*, Keri Oleson *(Vernon)*, Joan Rivers *(Joan)*, Cornelia Otis Skinner *(Mrs. Hammar)*, Dolph Sweet *(Henry Biswanger)*, Louise Troy *(Grace Biswanger)*, Diana Van Der Vlis *(Helen Westerhazy)*, Alva Celauro *(Muffie)*, Lisa Daniels *(matron at the Biswangers' pool)*, John Gerstad *(guest at the Bunkers' pool)*, Marilyn Langner *(Enid Bunker)*, Ray Mason *(Bunkers' party guest)*.

Drama. Source: John Cheever, "The Swimmer," in *New Yorker* (18 Jul 1964). On a summer afternoon in suburban Connecticut, adman Ned Merrill inexplicably finds himself 8 miles from home, dressed only in swimming trunks. Partly to demonstrate his athletic vigor despite the advent of middle age, partly on an impulse, Ned decides to swim across the county, from pool to pool, until he gets home. In his odyssey from one neighbor's pool to another, he gradually confronts the sorry facts of his present existence. At Betty and Howard Graham's pool, he admits to Betty that he once loved her, but her reaction seems muted and unmoved. Mrs. Hammar bears him such a bitter grudge that she will not even allow him to cross her property. At another pool he meets Julie Hooper, a former babysitter who concedes that she had a crush on him several years before. Their encounter is ended by Ned's amorous overtures and by his insistence that she return to his home to babysit. Everywhere Ned goes, he is met by hostility and is taunted about his failures—his marriage, his unloving daughters, his inability to face reality, his recent financial troubles. As painful and puzzling as these ordeals are to Ned, it is his reunion with a former mistress, Shirley Abbott, that cuts most deeply: she claims, in a final outburst, that she never loved him. Finally, shivering in the rain and shaken by the succession of ego-shattering attacks, Ned arrives home. For the first time he seems able to face the reality of what his life has become, symbolized by the rundown house in which he used to live. *Advertising executives. Neighbors. Babysitters. Mistresses. Suburban life. Swimming. Middle age. Marriage. Connecticut.*

Note: Location scenes filmed in and around Westport, Connecticut. Pollack directed only the scene with Janice Rule.

THE SWIMMING POOL (France/Italy)   F6.4823

S. N. C.–Tritone Filmindustria. *Dist* Avco Embassy Pictures. 29 May **1970** [Hartford, Connecticut, opening]. Sd; col (Eastman Color). 35mm. 87 min. *MPAA rating* X.

Pres by Joseph E. Levine. *Prod* Gérard Beytout. *Dir* Jacques Deray. *Screenplay* Jean-Emmanuel Conil, Jean-Claude Carrière, Jacques Deray. *Dial* Jean-Claude Carrière, Jacques Deray. *Photog* Jean-Jacques Tarbès. *Film Ed* Paul Cayatte. *Mus* Michel Legrand. *Sd* René Longuet. *Asst Dir* Louis Pitzelé, Michèle Sennet. *Prod Mgr* Paul Laffargue.

Cast: Alain Delon *(Jean-Paul)*, Romy Schneider *(Marianne)*, Maurice Ronet *(Harry)*, Jane Birkin *(Penelope)*, Paul Crauchet *(Inspector Levêque)*.

Drama. Jean-Paul, an unsuccessful writer, and Marianne, a journalist, are vacationing at a friend's villa near Saint-Tropez on the Riviera when Harry, the wealthy head of a record company, and his 18-year-old daughter Penelope arrive and disturb the couple's summer. Harry, one of Marianne's former lovers, arouses Jean-Paul's envy for his obvious success and wealth; Jean-Paul also becomes suspicious of the attention Harry is paying to Marianne. At a party, Harry couples with Marianne, and Jean-Paul shows a romantic interest in Penelope, who tells him that her father could resume his affair with Marianne any time he wanted her. One night, Harry returns to the villa, where he and Jean-Claude become involved in an argument that brings out all of their suppressed animosity. When the drunken Harry tries to hit Jean-Paul, Harry falls into the swimming pool, and Jean-Paul drowns him. The police arrive the next day to investigate the drowning, and although they do not turn up evidence of foul play, Marianne realizes the circumstances of Harry's death. Penelope returns to Switzerland, leaving Jean-Claude and Marianne to share the secret of Harry's murder. *Authors. Journalists. Executives. Police. Vacations. Envy. Jealousy. Filial relations. Drunkenness. Murder. Swimming pools. Saint-Tropez.*

Note: Location scenes filmed at Saint-Tropez. Opened in Paris in Jan 1969 as *La piscine* at 120 min; released in Italy as *La piscina.*

THE SWINDLE *see* **IL BIDONE**

THE SWINGER   F6.4824

Paramount Pictures. Nov **1966** [New York opening: 14 Dec; c1 Nov 1966; LP33407]. Sd; col (Technicolor). 35mm. 81 min.

Prod-Dir George Sidney. *Screenplay* Lawrence Roman. *Dir Photog* Joseph Biroc. *Art Dir* Hal Pereira, Walter Tyler. *Set Decor* Robert R. Benton, Arthur Krams. *Titl (uncredited)* Bill Scott. *Film Ed* Frank Santillo. *Mus & Songs:* "Oh So Bad," "Once" Marty Paich. *Lyr:* "Once" Mel Torme. *Mus:* "The Swinger" Andre Previn. *Lyr* Dory Previn. *Songs Sung by* Ann-Margret. *Other Songs* Johnny Mercer, Harold Arlen, Richard Rodgers, Lorenz Hart, Billy Rose, Edward Heyman. *Choreog* David Winters. *Sd Rec* Garry Harris, Charles Grenzbach. *Asst Dir* Daniel J. McCauley. *Unit Prod Mgr* Kenneth DeLand. *Cost* Edith Head. *Makeup Supv* Wally Westmore. *Ann-Margret's Makeup* Frank McCoy. *Ann-Margret's Hairdresser* Cherie. *Hairstyle Supv* Nellie Manley. *Process Photog* Farciot Edouart. *Sp Photog Eff* Paul K. Lerpae. *Still Photog* Mel Traxel.

Cast: Ann-Margret *(Kelly Olsson)*, Tony Franciosa *(Ric Colby)*, Robert Coote *(Sir Hubert Charles)*, Yvonne Romain *(Karen Charles)*, Horace McMahon *(Detective Sergeant Hooker)*, Nydia Westman *(Aunt Cora)*, Craig Hill *(Sammy Jenkins)*, Milton Frome *(Mr. Olsson)*, Mary LaRoche *(Mrs. Olsson)*, Clete Roberts *(Clete Roberts)*, Myrna Ross *(Sally)*, Corinne Cole *(Sir Hubert's secretary)*, Bert Freed *(police captain)*, Romo Vincent *(Jack Happy)*, Steven Geray *(man with fish)*, Larry D. Mann *(John Mallory)*, Lance Le Gault *(Warren)*, Diki Lerner *(Svengali)*, Barbara Nichols *(Blossom LaTour)*.

Romantic comedy. Highly insulted when *Girl-Lure Magazine* rejects her short stories as being too naive and sugary, Kelly Olsson buys some lurid paperback books, steals lines and situations from them, and writes *The Swinger*, the saga of a depraved young lady, which Kelly claims is semi-autobiographical. *Girl-Lure's* lecherous publisher, Sir Hubert Charles, and smooth editor, Ric Colby, doubt the authenticity of the tale and decide to pay Kelly a surprise visit. Tipped off, she wins the help of some male dancers who live in her building and stages an orgy. When Sergeant Hooker of the vice squad (another of Kelly's fellow tenants) raids the apartment, the delighted Sir Hubert agrees to publish the book, but Ric takes Kelly to his Aunt Cora in Malibu for help in reforming the wayward young woman. Ric eventually learns of the deception and takes his revenge by forcing Kelly to re-create her streetwalker past for a photo layout in *Girl-Lure*. His plan backfires, however, when Sergeant Hooker arrests him for forcible abduction. After Ric explains the mix-up and obtains his release, he drives off and crashes into Kelly, who was racing to his rescue on her motorcycle. The vehicles are destroyed, but Kelly and Ric end up together. *Authors. Publishers. Editors. Dancers. Police. Aunts. Vice squads. Pornography. Hoaxes. Lechery. Plagiarism. Magazines (periodicals). Orgies. Motorcycles. Malibu (California). Automobile accidents.*

Note: Location scenes filmed in Los Angeles. Fashion montage photographed at Saks Fifth Avenue, Beverly Hills.

SWINGERS' PARADISE (Great Britain)   **F6.4825**
Ivy Productions. *Dist* American International Pictures. 5 May **1965** [Kansas City, Missouri opening; c12 May 1965; LP31154]. Sd; col (Technicolor). 35mm (Techniscope). 83 min. [Cut from 117 min.]

Prod Kenneth Harper. *Assoc Prod* Andrew Mitchell. *Dir* Sidney J. Furie. *Story & Screenplay* Peter Myers, Ronald Cass. *Camera* Ken Higgins. *Art Dir* Herbert Smith. *Prod Dsgn* Stanley Dorfman. *Film Ed* Jack Slade. *Songs* Peter Myers, Ronald Cass. *Background Score* Stanley Black. *Mus Supv (of Cliff Richard and The Shadows)* Norrie Paramor. *Adtl Songs* Cliff Richard, Hank B. Marvin, Brian Bennett, Bruce Welch. *Choreog* Gillian Lynne. *Sd* A. W. Lumkin. *Sd Rec* Les Hammond, Len Shilton. *Asst Dir* Fred Slark. *Prod Mgr* John D. Wilcox. *Cost* Cynthia Tingey. *Spanish Coörd* Roberto Roberts.

Cast: Cliff Richard *(Johnnie)*, Walter Slezak *(Lloyd Davis)*, Susan Hampshire *(Jenny)*, Hank B. Marvin, Bruce Welch, Brian Bennett, John Rostill *(mood musicians)*, Melvyn Hayes *(Jerry)*, Richard O'Sullivan *(Edward)*, Una Stubbs *(Barbara)*, Joseph Cuby *(Miguel)*, Derek Bond *(Douglas Leslie)*, Gerald Harper *(Senior Sheik/Scotsman/Harold)*.

Comedy with music. Johnnie and his friends work as rock musicians on a luxury liner. After their electric guitar amplifiers short out the ship's lights, the band and two waiters who assisted them are accused of conspiring to sink the ship and put to sea on a raft. When they reach the Canary Islands, Johnnie takes a job as stuntman for Douglas Leslie, an aging movie actor, and befriends Jenny, an inexperienced leading lady who is nervous about working with veteran filmmaker Lloyd Davis. Johnnie helps the novice rehearse her scenes, taking the part of the romantic male lead on and off the set. The gang decides that Johnnie's version is better than Davis', and, with the help of script girl Barbara, they secretly make a movie of their own with some scenes duplicated from Davis' film. Davis discovers their project and tries to sabotage the production, but both films reach completion. Since each version has good and bad scenes, Davis combines the two films; and the premiere is a critical triumph. Johnnie, now a successful director and leading man, asks Jenny to marry him and finds out that Davis, who has kept secret his relationship with Jenny, will be his father-in-law. *Actors. Stuntmen. Motion picture directors. Motion picture crews. Ship crews. Musicians. Personal identity. Ocean liners. Rafts. Motion*

pictures. *Canary Islands.*

Note: Opened in London in Jul 1964 as *Wonderful Life*; running time: 113 min.

A SWINGIN' AFFAIR   **F6.4826**
Bengal International Pictures. *Dist* Emerson Film Enterprises. 23 May **1963** [Sacramento, California, opening]. Sd; b&w. 35mm. 85 min.

Prod-Writ Gunther Collins. *Dir* Jay O. Lawrence.

Cast: William Wellman, Jr., Arline Judge, Dick Dale and the Del Tones, Sandra Gale Bettin.

Drama with music. A young man takes up prizefighting to finance his college education but never loses affection for his waitress girl friend. *Waitresses. Students. Prizefighting.*

Note: Also known as *A Swinging Affair*.

SWINGIN' ALONG   **F6.4827**
Twentieth Century-Fox Film Corp. 14 Feb **1962** [Omaha, Nebraska, opening; c26 Dec 1961; LP21146]. Sd (Westrex); col (De Luxe). 35mm (CinemaScope). 74 min.

Prod Jack Leewood. *Dir* Charles Barton. *Writ* Jameson Brewer. *Dir Photog* Arthur E. Arling. *Art Dir* Duncan Cramer, George Van Marter. *Set Decor* Walter M. Scott, Lou Hafley. *Film Ed* Betty Steinberg. *Mus* Arthur Morton. *Cond* Lionel Newman. *Song:* "Song of the City" Walter Kent, Walton Farrar. *Sd* Don McKay, Frank W. Moran. *Asst Dir* Ad Schaumer. *Makeup* Ben Nye. *Hairstyles* Helen Turpin.

Cast: Tommy Noonan *(Freddy Merkle)*, Peter L. Marshall *(Duke)*, Barbara Eden *(Carol Walker)*, Connie Gilchrist *(Aunt Sophie)*, Carol Christensen *(Ginny)*, Alan Carney *(Officer Sullivan)*, Mike Mazurki *(bookie)*, Tommy Farrell *(Georgie)*, Lennie Bremen *(Willie)*, Don Diamond *(Tony)*, Ted Knight *(priest)*, Terry Miele *(Mrs. Crenshaw)*, Frank Wilcox *(psychiatrist)*, Sandra Warner *(secretary)*, Bill Bradley, Art Baker *(TV announcer [see note])*, Ray Charles, Roger Williams, Bobby Vee *(themselves)*.

Comedy. Freddy Merkle, a simple-minded delivery boy, is incapable of finishing any of his artistic projects. His attempt at painting is half completed, his sculpture of a horse has only a rear end, and his original sonata consists of only a few opening bars. However, when his delivery motorcycle is destroyed in a collision with a circus elephant, Freddy decides to enter a song-writing contest in San Francisco. Encouraging him is Duke, a fast-talking con man who hopes to get part of the $2,500 prize money. Disaster strikes when Freddy's piano is repossessed and then sold by a finance company. Duke and Freddy retrieve the piano from the new owner by claiming that it must be removed for tuning. With the inspiration of his girl friend Ginny and the help of a cat that runs across the piano keyboard, Freddy completes his sonata; but the music is blown away by the wind. Disconsolate, he tries to commit suicide, but in typical fashion, he bungles the job. Unknown to him, a kindly priest has found his music and entered it in the contest. Freddy later learns that he is a finalist in the competition and races to Golden Gate Park to receive first prize. *Delivery boys. Confidence men. Composers. Priests. Suicide. Contests. Pianos. San Francisco. Motorcycle accidents. Elephants. Cats.*

Note: Location scenes filmed in San Francisco. Working title: *The Schnook*. Originally scheduled for release in 1961 as *Double Trouble*. Sources conflict in crediting the role of the TV announcer.

THE SWINGIN' MAIDEN (Great Britain)   **F6.4828**
G. H. W. Productions. *For* Anglo-Amalgamated Film Distributors. *Dist* Columbia Pictures. 31 Dec **1963** [New York opening]. Sd; col (Eastman Color). 35mm. 98 min. [Also 81 min.]

Prod Peter Rogers. *Assoc Prod* Frank Bevis. *Dir* Gerald Thomas. *Screenplay* Vivian A. Cox, Leslie Bricusse. *Orig Story* Harold Brooks, Kay Bannerman. *Photog* Alan Hume. *Art Dir* Carmen Dillon. *Film Ed* Archie Ludski. *Mus Comp & Cond* Eric Rogers. *Sd* Dudley Messenger, Gordon K. McCallum, Dino Di Campo. *Asst Dir* Douglas Hermes. *Unit Mgr* Donald Toms. *Cost* Joan Ellacott. *Makeup* W. T. Partleton, Basil Newall. *Hairstyles* Betty Sherriff.

Cast: Michael Craig *(Jack Hopkins)*, Anne Helm *(Kathy Fisher)*, Jeff Donnell *(Mrs. Fisher)*, Alan Hale, [Jr.] *(Paul Fisher)*, Noel Purcell *(Adm. Sir Digby Trevelyan)*, Cecil Parker *(Sir Giles Trent)*, Roland Culver *(Lord Upshott)*, Joan Sims *(Mrs. Fred)*, John Standing *(Humphrey)*, Brian Oulton *(vicar)*, Sam Kydd *(Fred)*, Judith Furse *(Mrs. Webb)*, Richard Thorp *(Harry Markham)*, Brian Rawlinson *(village policeman)*, Tom Gill *(rally official)*, Duke of Bedford *(himself)*, Jim Dale, George Woodridge, Ian Wilson, Douglas Ives, David Aylmer, Peter Burton, Michael Nightingale, Raymond Glendenning, Cyril Chamberlain, Peter Jesson, Anton Rodgers, Anthony Baird, Bill Cartwright, Peter Byrne, Middleton Woods, Peter Wells, Eric Corrie, Jonathan Kydd.

Comedy. Two British aircraft companies are competing for the business of American tycoon Paul Fisher, and in consequence airplane designer Jack Hopkins clashes with Humphrey Upshott, son of the owner of the rival firm.

Hopkins' devotion to his hobby—steam traction engines—and to his own engine, "The Iron Maiden," involves Fisher, his status-seeking wife, and his daughter Kathy in a number of unpleasant situations; and Fisher becomes furious with Hopkins though he is impressed by his airplane. With the start of the year's most important traction engine rally, at Woburn, circumstances place Fisher in "The Iron Maiden" assisting Hopkins as a stoker. Kathy takes her father's place when his back gives out and helps win the race. By the end of the race, Kathy and Hopkins have fallen in love; and as they embrace, "The Iron Maiden" blows up. Hopkins' firm gets Fisher's contract, and the first plane is christened "The Iron Maiden." *Americans in foreign countries. Tycoons. Social climbers. Stokers. Airplane manufacture. Filial relations. Employer-employee relations. Contests. Explosions. Woburn Abbey (England).*

Note: Location scenes filmed in Henley, Ascot, and at Woburn Abbey, England. Opened in London in Feb 1963 as *The Iron Maiden*; running time: 98 min.

THE SWINGIN' SET *see* **GET YOURSELF A COLLEGE GIRL**

A SWINGIN' SUMMER　　　　　　　　　　　　　　　　　**F6.4829**
Reno Carell–National Talent Consultants. *Dist* United Screen Arts. Apr **1965**. Sd; col (Technicolor). 35mm (Techniscope). 80 min.
Prod Reno Carell. *Exec Prod* Ken Raphael, Larry Goldblatt. *Dir* Robert Sparr. *Screenplay* Leigh Chapman. *Story* Reno Carell. *Dir Photog* Ray Fernstrom. *Camera Op* Ned Davenport. *Asst Camera* George Dye. *Film Ed* James Heckert, William E. Lee. *Mus* Harry Betts. *Titl Song Sung by* Jody Miller. *Choreog* Michael Blodgett. *Sd* George C. Emick. *Asst Dir* Rusty Meek. *Prod Mgr* Jack Lacey. *Key Grip* George Hill, Jr. *Gaffer* Charles Rosen, gaffer.
Cast: William Wellman, Jr. *(Rick)*, Quinn O'Hara *(Cindy)*, James Stacy *(Mickey)*, Martin West *(Turk)*, Raquel Welch *(Jeri)*, Mary Mitchell *(Shirley)*, Robert Blair *(Tony)*, Allan Jones *(Mr. Johnson)*, Lili Kardell *(Sandra)*, Diane Bond, Diane Swanson, Irene Sale, Kathy Francis, Laurie Williams *(The Girls)*, Reno Carell, Buck Holland, Glenn Stensel *(The Hoods)*, The Righteous Brothers, The Rip Chords, Donnie Brooks, Gary Lewis and the Playboys, Jody Miller *(themselves)*.
Comedy-drama with music. The California lakeside dance pavillion where Cindy, Rick, and Mickey plan to work is in danger of closing so Cindy secretly arranges for her wealthy father to finance the project. Turk, a local lifeguard, becomes jealous of Rick and Mickey and tries to ruin their plans as well as entice Cindy away from Rick. Rick, who is very proud, becomes angry when he learns that Cindy's father is financing the pavillion but forgives her later. Turk pays three men to wreck the dance hall, but they fail and then force Turk to help them steal the money from the cashbox. At the last minute, however, he helps Rick recover the money, and everyone returns to the dance. *Songs:* "Red Hot Roadster," "Justine," "Penny the Poo," "Out To Lunch," "Nitro," and "Ready To Groove." *Lifeguards. Youth. Singers. Rock and roll. Robbery. Jealousy. Pride. Dancehalls. California.*
Note: Filmed on location in Lake Arrowhead, California.

SWINGIN' SWAPPERS　　　　　　　　　　　　　　　　**F6.4830**
Fountain Films. *Dist* Astro-Jemco Film Distributors. 2 Apr **1969** [Champaign, Illinois, showing]. Sd; b&w. 35mm. 70 min.
Dir Rex Brand.
Drama. Married to Diane for two years, Tom has grown bored with her unimaginative lovemaking. Continually frustrated in his attempts to broaden her outlook, he meets Ken, the office playboy, and accepts his invitation to a "swingin' swappers" party. Ecstatic after attending two of the parties, Tom finally persuades Diane to join him and discovers that she is already an experienced "swinger." *Playboys. Marriage. Group sex. Mate swapping. Eroticism. Sexual techniques.*
Note: Also known as *Swinging Swappers*.

THE SWINGING FINK *see* **RAT FINK**

SWINGING LONDON *see* **PRIMITIVE LONDON**

SWINGING LONDON EXPOSED *see* **PRIMITIVE LONDON**

SWINGING SECRETARY *see* **OFFICE LOVE-IN, WHITE COLLAR STYLE**

SWINGTAIL　　　　　　　　　　　　　　　　　　　　**F6.4831**
Dist Cosmos Films. 10 Dec **1969** [New York showing]. Sd; b&w. 35mm (Cosmovision [see note]). 65 min.
Pres by Ted Kariofilis. A Guy King Production. *Prod* Guy King. *Dir-Writ* Dave Shane. *Photog* Stephen Bower. *Asst Camera & Lighting* Charles Teitelbaum. *Sets* Billy Cuthbert, Robert Kenner. *Film Ed* Gayle Jarocki. *Mus* J. C. Fox. *Makeup* Helcene. *Stills* Bob Davis.
Cast: Karen Park, Lisa La Shawn, Alex Mann, Gillian Hollander, Jerry Castle, Suzzan Landow, Tony Marconi, Allison Kensey, John Anthony, Lydia Terrel, Robert Lane, Anna Lee, Bertha Bigg, Art Yates, III.

Drama. A young producer dreams that he is filming a friend. He discovers that she has a secret erotic life as he follows her from one sexual adventure to another. Finally he becomes involved in the sex-play. Press photographs suggest that the film includes scenes of lesbianism, fetishism, fellatio, and interracial and group sex. *Motion picture producers. Lesbianism. Oral sex. Group sex. Miscegenation. Fetishism. Sex exploitation films. Dreams.*
Note: Cosmovision is a 3-D process using an anaglyph system of red and green filters.

SWITCHEROO!　　　　　　　　　　　　　　　　　　**F6.4832**
Unit Ten Productions. *Dist* Bernhard Films. 24 Oct **1969** [Champaign, Illinois, showing]. Sd; col. 35mm. [Feature length assumed.]
Exec Prod Charles H. Leonard. *Assoc Prod* John Donne. *Dir-Writ* John Donne. *Photog* Lew Jennings. *Mus* Music Industries. *Asst Dir* Fred Simpson.
Cast: Jan Myers, Angel Capri, Mary Minor, Sharon Cartwright, Betty Jo Sanders.
Melodrama. Five young women answer a newspaper advertisement for an all-girl crew to make a summer cruise to Tahiti aboard a lavish yacht owned by Captain Hooker, a wealthy philanthropist. Unaware that Captain Hooker is a depraved madman and that they will be forced to submit to his lustful appetite for perversion, the women all sign up for the cruise. They are given "malaria vaccinations," actually a powerful aphrodisiac intended to escalate their normal sex drives. The actual crew includes first mate Bobbie Fletcher and Hardrock, a brutal deckhand whose function is to terrorize, torture, and rape Hooker's female captives. *Sea captains. Ship crews. Rape. Torture. Sex deviates. Aphrodisiacs. Yachts. Tahiti.*

SWITZERLAND AND THE ALPS　　　　　　　　　　　**F6.4833**
VPR Ltd. 16 Feb **1967** [Atlanta opening]. Sd eff & mus score; col. 35mm. 120 min.
Pres by Burton Holmes Theatre Productions. *Prod-Dir-Writ* André De La Varre, Jr. *Photog* Kurt Jetmar, Peter Baudendistel, André De La Varre, Jr. *Film Ed* André De La Varre, Jr., Pablo Zavala. *Mus Ed* André De La Varre, Jr., Music Sound Track Service.
Travelog. Swiss sites visited by the travel host include the Alps, the Engadine in winter, the province of Ticino, Lake Lugano, Locarno, cheese and chocolate factories, Charlie Chaplin's villa at Vevey, Lake Geneva, Bern, the Rhine River, Lucerne, Basel, Zurich, and famous sports areas. *Travel. Vevey. Ticino. Engadine. Switzerland. Alps. Lake of Geneva. Locarno. Bern. Rhine River. Lucerne. Lake Lugano. Basel. Zurich.*
Note: Narration delivered live on stage.

THE SWORD IN THE STONE　　　　　　　　　　　　**F6.4834**
Walt Disney Productions. *Dist* Buena Vista Distribution Co. 25 Dec **1963** [New York opening; c9 Aug 1963; LP26593]. Sd (RCA); col (Technicolor). 35mm. 75 min. [Copyright length: 79 min.]
Pres by Walt Disney. A Walt Disney Production. *Dir* Wolfgang Reitherman. *Story-Screenplay* Bill Peet. *Dir Anim* Frank Thomas, Ollie Johnston, Milt Kahl, John Lounsbery. *Character Dsgn* Milt Kahl, Bill Peet. *Character Anim* Hal King, Eric Cleworth, Cliff Nordberg, Eric Larson, John Sibley, Hal Ambro, Dick Lucas. *Eff Anim* Dan MacManus, Jack Boyd, Jack Buckley. *Background* Walt Peregoy, Bill Layne, Anthony Rizzo, Al Dempster, Ralph Hulett, Fil Mottola. *Layout* Don Griffith, Vance Gerry, Dale Barnhart, Basil Davidovich, Sylvia Cobb, Homer Jonas. *Art Dir* Ken Anderson. *Film Ed* Donald Halliday. *Mus Dir & Arr* George Bruns. *Orch* Franklyn Marks. *Songs:* "That's What Makes the World Go 'Round," "A Most Befuddling Thing," "Higitus Figitus," "Mad Madam Mim," "Blue Oak Tree," "The Legend of the Sword in the Stone" Richard M. Sherman, Robert B. Sherman. *Titl Song Sung by* Fred Darian. *Sd Supv* Robert O. Cook. *Mus Ed* Evelyn Kennedy. *Prod Supv* Ken Peterson.
Voices: Rickie Sorenson *(Wart)*, Sebastian Cabot *(Sir Ector)*, Karl Swenson *(Merlin)*, Junious Matthews *(Archimedes)*, Alan Napier *(Sir Pelinore)*, Norman Alden *(Kay)*, Barbara Jo Allen *(scullery maid)*, Ginny Tyler *(little girl squirrel)*, The Mellomen, Richard Reitherman, Robert Reitherman.
Animated film. Source: T. H. White, *The Sword in the Stone* (London, 1938). In the Dark Ages England is without a king and will be without one until a great sword, stuck through an anvil and buried deep in a stone, is pulled out. One day Wart, a young boy learning to be the squire of his loutish foster brother Kay, enters the forest in search of an arrow and falls through the roof of the cottage where the wizard Merlin lives with his talking owl, Archimedes. Though Sir Ector, Wart's foster father, seems pessimistic, Merlin sets out to supervise the lad's education. In the process Merlin turns him successively into a fish, a squirrel, and a sparrow. In each guise the boy experiences great difficulties but learns a valuable lesson of life. After saving him in the nick of time from the evil witch Mad Madam Mim, Merlin bests the witch in a duel of magic. Meanwhile, Kay has been training for a great tournament that will

determine who shall be the new king. For the event Wart journeys to London as Kay's squire, but, having forgotten Kay's sword, he returns to the inn and finds it locked. He finds a sword in a stone in a nearby churchyard and easily pulls it out to give to Kay. No one believes that he has performed the feat, but he repeats the miraculous deed and is immediately acclaimed the rightful heir to the throne and crowned King Arthur. *Sorcerers. Witches. Foster brothers. Foster fathers. Nobility. Education. Transmutation. Personal identity. Magic. Swords. Tournaments. Middle Ages. England. London. King Arthur. Merlin. Wolves. Fish. Owls. Squirrels. Sparrows.*

THE SWORD OF ALI BABA   F6.4835

Universal Pictures. May **1965** [c29 May 1964; LP33028]. Sd (Westrex); col (Eastman Color). 35mm. 81 min.

Prod Howard Christie. *Dir* Virgil W. Vogel. *Screenplay* Edmund Hartmann, Oscar Brodney. *Story* Edmund Hartmann. *Dir Photog* William Margulies. *Art Dir* Alexander Golitzen, William D. DeCinces. *Set Decor* John McCarthy, Julia Heron. *Main Titl* Pacific Title. *Film Ed* Gene Palmer. *Mus* Frank Skinner. *Mus Supv* Joseph Gershenson. *Sd* Waldon O. Watson, Corson Jowett. *Asst Dir* Phil Bowles, Bill Gilmore. *Unit Prod Mgr* John Morrison. *Cost* Helen Colvig. *Makeup* Bud Westmore. *Hairstyles* Larry Germain.

Cast: Peter Mann *(Ali Baba)*, Jocelyn Lane *(Amara)*, Frank McGrath *(Pindar)*, Gavin MacLeod *(Hulagu Khan)*, Frank Puglia *(Prince Cassim)*, Peter Whitney *(Abou)*, Greg Morris *(Yusuf)*, Frank De Kova *(Old Baba)*, Irene Tsu *(Nalu)*, Morgan Woodward *(captain of guard)*.

Fantasy. As children in Bagdad, Amara, daughter of Prince Cassim, and Ali, son of the caliph, pledge marriage. When the Mongol Hulagu Khan invades Bagdad, the caliph is killed through Cassim's treachery; but Ali escapes and finds refuge with Old Baba and his band of 40 thieves. Fifteen years later, Ali falls in love with Amara without recognizing her. Learning that she is to be married to Hulagu Khan, he devises a plan to rescue her and stir up a revolt against the cruel Mongol at the same time. Disguised as a rich merchant, Ali enters the city with his men hidden in 40 large oil jars. The plot is discovered by Hulagu Khan, and during a celebration, he has the oil jars pierced with spears by members of a dance troupe; but the men have already left the jars. The thieves begin the revolt, and the Mongol is defeated. Ali, reunited with Amara, takes his rightful place as Bagdad's ruler. *Royalty. Mongols. Thieves. Despots. Orphans. Traitors. Disguise. Marriage—Arranged. Revolts. Bagdad. Ali Baba.*

Note: Stock footage is included from *Ali Baba and the Forty Thieves* (Universal, 1944).

THE SWORD OF DOOM (Japan)   F6.4836

Toho Co. 1 Jul **1966** [Los Angeles opening]. Sd; b&w. 35mm (Tohoscope). 122 min.

Exec Prod Sanezumi Fujimoto. *Dir* Kihachi Okamoto. *Screenplay* Shinobu Hashimoto. *Photog* Hiroshi Murai. *Mus* Masaru Sato.

Cast: Tatsuya Nakadai *(Ryunosuke Tsukue)*, Toshiro Mifune *(Toranosuke Shimada)*, Yuzo Kayama *(Hyoma Utsuki)*, Michiyo Aratama *(Ohama)*, Ichiro Nakaya *(Bunnojo Utsuki)*, Yoko Naito, Kei Sato.

Action drama. Source: Kaizan Nakazato, *Daibosatsu toge* (Tokyo, 1940). In ancient Japan, Tsukue, a brooding and violent samurai of aristocratic heritage, believes that a man can control his destiny only as well as he can handle his sword. Feeling the need for a woman, he cuts down a friend and takes the man's widow, Ohama, for himself. His action arouses the wrath of the murdered man's younger brother, Hyoma, who enrolls at a fencing school to prepare himself for the day when he will take his revenge. One day Tsukue visits the school and challenges Hyoma to a duel; Tsukue wins, and the two men part without knowing each other's true identity. When Hyoma eventually learns that Tsukue was his brother's killer, he sends him a formal note of challenge, but Tsukue kills Ohama and leaves for Kyoto. Hyoma follows him there but learns that Tsukue has been killed in a sword fight with his samurai clan. *Samurai. Brothers. Widows. Murder. Revenge. Kyoto. Duels.*

Note: Released in Japan in Feb 1966 as *Daibosatsu toge.*

THE SWORD OF EL CID (Italy/Spain)   F6.4837

Alexandra Produzione-Cintora, S. L.-Victor Torruella. *Dist* Production Releasing Corp., Eldorado Pictures International. Feb **1964** [New York showing]. Sd; col (Eastman Color). 35mm (Supercinescope). 86 min.

Pres by Eldorado Films, East-West Films. *Dir* Miguel Iglesias. *Screenplay* José Luis Navarro, Víctor Torruella, Ferdinando Baldi, Alfredo Giannetti, Antonio Navarro Linares, Miguel Iglesias. *Photog* Francisco Marín. *Camera* Herrada, Carmelo Petralia. *Art Dir* Juan Alberto Soler. *Mus* Carlo Savina. *Prod Supv* Miguel Grau. *Spanish Vers Dial* Noel Clarasó.

Cast: Roland Carey *(Bernardo)*, Sandro Moretti *(Ramón)*, Chantal Deberg *(María Sol)*, Iliana Grimaldi *(Bianca)*, José Luis Pellicena *(Félix Muñoz)*, Daniela Bianchi *(Elvira)*, Ray Miles, Jeff Russel, Luis Induni, Andrés Mejuto, Fernando Cebrián, Andrea Fantasía.

Historical melodrama. María Sol and Elvira, daughters of the Cid, are tortured and abandoned by their husbands, the brothers Fernando and Diego Carrión. King Alfonso of Castile orders the husbands to pay a fine, surrender their swords, and fight the Cid's knights to the death. The brothers seek the help of the ruthless Berenguer, who previously murdered his own brother and usurped the throne of Catalonia. The Cid's nephew, Félix Muñoz, is wounded, and a young knight, Ramón, takes his place in the battle. Diego is killed in the duel, but Ramón is captured by Berenguer when it is discovered that he is the son of the murdered king of Catalonia and therefore rightful heir to the throne. A number of Catalonian nobles and knights of the Cid storm the castle where Ramón is being held and liberate him. Berenguer is forced into exile; Ramón marries María Sol; and together they rule the land of Catalonia. *Royalty. Brothers. Sisters. Usurpers. Murder. Knighthood. Catalonia. Castile. Alfonso VI (Castile and León). El Cid. Ramón Berenguer, III. Duels.*

Note: Released in Italy in 1962 as *La spada del Cid;* in Spain in Oct 1963 as *Las hijas del Cid.*

SWORD OF LANCELOT (Great Britain)   F6.4838

Emblem Productions. *Dist* Universal-International Films. 5 Jun **1963** [Los Angeles opening; c7 Sep 1963; LP35482]. Sd; col (Eastman Color, print by Technicolor). 35mm (Panavision). 116 min.

Prod Bernard Luber. *Exec Prod-Dir* Cornel Wilde. *Assoc Prod* George Pitcher. *Screenplay* Richard Schayer, Jefferson Pascal. *Dir Photog* Harry Waxman. *Camera Op* Robert Thomson, Cecil Cooney. *Camera Focus* Steve Claydon, Kenneth Coles. *Art Dir* Maurice Carter. *Asst Art Dir* Jack Maxsted. *Set Dresser* Leonard Townsend. *1st Draughtsman* Alec Gray. *Titl Background Photog* Karsh. *Film Ed* Frederick Wilson. *1st Asst Ed* Thom Noble. *2d Asst Ed* Kevin Connor. *Mus Comp & Cond* Ron Goodwin. *Sd Rec* Bill Daniels. *Sd Ed* Don Sharpe. *Sd Camera Op* Vivian Temple-Smith. *Sd Boom Op* Charles McFadden. *1st, 2d, & 3d Asst Dir* Rene Dupont, David Anderson, Derek Cracknell. *Prod Mgr* David W. Orton. *Cont* Connie Willis. *Prod Sec* Curlie Flower. *Cost Dsgn* Terence Morgan, II. *Wardrobe Supv* Dorothy Edwards. *Wardrobe Master* Jim Dunlevy. *Makeup Artist* George Blackler. *Hairdresser* Biddy Chrystal. *Matte Artist* Les Bowie. *Sp Eff* Ron Ballanger. *Prod Buyer* Harry Hannay. *Still Photog* Albert Clarke. *Carpenter* J. Bray. *Grip* Fred Graver, M. Beauchamp. *Ch Electrn* John Swan. *Prop Master* P. Rivers.

Cast: Cornel Wilde *(Sir Lancelot)*, Jean Wallace *(Guinevere)*, Brian Aherne *(King Arthur)*, George Baker *(Sir Gawaine)*, Archie Duncan *(Sir Lamorak)*, Adrienne Corri *(Lady Vivian)*, Michael Meacham *(Sir Modred)*, Iain Gregory *(Sir Tors)*, Mark Dignam *(Merlin)*, Reginald Beckwith *(Sir Dragonet)*, John Barrie *(Sir Bedivere)*, Richard Thorp *(Sir Gareth)*, Joseph Tomelty *(Sir Kaye)*, Graham Stark *(Rian)*, Geoffrey Dunn *(Edric)*, Walter Gotell *(Sir Cedric)*, Peter Prowse *(Brandegorus)*, Christopher Rhodes *(Ulfus)*, John Longden *(King Leodogran)*, Bob Bryant *(Sir Dorjak)*, Violetta Farjeon *(serving maid)*.

Drama. Source: Thomas Malory, *Le morte d'Arthur* (1485). In order to marry Guinevere, King Leodogran's daughter, King Arthur must find a knight to defeat Leodogran's champion. Arthur chooses Lancelot, who mortally wounds his opponent. On the way back to Camelot, Lancelot foils an attempt on Guinevere's life by Sir Modred, Arthur's illegitimate son; and before the end of the journey Lancelot and Guinevere realize their love for each other. Though Lancelot is loyal to Arthur and Guinevere's marriage to the king takes place as planned, it is not long before the two become lovers. Modred spies on them and informs Arthur of his wife's infidelity. Lancelot escapes, but Guinevere is condemned to be burned at the stake. He returns in time to save her and then offers to give himself up provided there will be no retaliation. Nevertheless, Arthur banishes him and sends Guinevere to a convent. Years later, Modred murders Arthur for his throne, and Lancelot returns to defeat him, thus ending the civil war that has been raging in Britain. He then finds Guinevere about to take the vows of a nun. *Royalty. Knighthood. Illegitimacy. Infidelity. Assassination. Banishment. Capital punishment. Convents. Age of Chivalry. King Arthur. Guinevere. Lancelot. Merlin. Camelot. Round Table.*

Note: Location scenes filmed in Yugoslavia. Released in Great Britain in Jun 1963 as *Lancelot and Guinevere;* running time: 117 min.

SWORD OF SHERWOOD FOREST (Great Britain)   F6.4839

Hammer Film Productions-Yeoman Films. *Dist* Columbia Pictures. 25 Jan **1961** [New York opening; c1 Nov 1960; LP20460]. Sd (RCA); col (Eastman Color, print by Technicolor). 35mm (Megascope). 80 min. [Copyright length: 96 min.]

Prod Sidney Cole, Richard Greene. *Exec Prod* Michael Carreras. *Dir* Terence Fisher. *Screenplay* Alan Hackney. *Dir Photog* Ken Hodges. *Camera Op* Richard Bayley. *Art Dir* John Stoll. *Main Titl* Chambers & Partners. *Supv Ed* James Needs. *Ed* Lee Doig. *Mus Comp* Alun Hoddinott. *Mus Supv* John Hollingsworth. *Songs Comp by* Stanley Black. *Sung by* Dennis Lotis. *Sd Ed* Alban Streeter. *Sd Mix* John Mitchell, Harry Tate. *Asst Dir* Bob Porter. *Prod Mgr* Ronald Liles, Don Weeks. *Cont* Pauline Wise, Dot Foreman. *Cost Supv* John McCorry. *Wardrobe Mistress* Rachel Austin. *Makeup* Gerry Fletcher.

Hairdresser Hilda Fox. *Casting* Stuart Lyons. *Master of Horse* Ivor Collin. *Master of Arms* Patrick Crean. *Master of Archery* Jack Cooper.

Cast: Richard Greene (*Robin Hood*), Peter Cushing (*Sheriff of Nottingham*), Niall MacGinnis (*Friar Tuck*), Sarah Branch (*Maid Marian Fitzwalter*), Richard Pasco (*Earl of Newark*), Nigel Green (*Little John*), Jack Gwillim (*Hubert Walter, Archbishop of Canterbury*), Vanda Godsell (*prioress*), Dennis Lotis (*Alan A'Dale*), Desmond Llewelyn (*wounded traveler*), Edwin Richfield (*sheriff's lieutenant*), Brian Rawlinson (*1st falconer*), Patrick Crean (*Ollerton*), Oliver Reed (*Melton*), Derren Nesbitt (*Martin*), Reginald Hearne (*1st man of arms*), Jack Cooper (*master of archery*), Adam Kean (*Retford*), Charles Lamb (*Old Bowyer*), Aiden Grennell (*1st veteran outlaw*), James Neylin (*Roger*), Barry De Boulay (*officer*), John Hoey (*Old Jack*), Anew McMaster (*judge*), John Franklin (*archbishop's secretary*), Maureen Halligan (*portress*).

Adventure drama. In Sherwood Forest, Robin Hood and his band of outlaws continue to oppose the rule of the tyrannical Sheriff of Nottingham. One day a wounded traveler rides into the outlaw camp and before dying whispers something about danger in the town of Bawtry. The only clue to the mystery is a gold emblem found on the dead man's body. Consequently, when Robin notices the same emblem being worn by the Earl of Newark, he poses as a woodsman and joins the earl's group of hired archers. Aided by Friar Tuck and Maid Marian, Robin learns that the plot of the earl and the sheriff to take over Bawtry Castle has been foiled by Hubert Walter, the Archbishop of Canterbury. Aware that the two villains plan to murder the archbishop, who is traveling with Maid Marian, Robin rescues the travelers and takes them to the sanctuary of a monastery. The sheriff, blamed for the failure of the plan, is killed by one of the earl's men. The earl then invades the monastery, but he and his men all meet their deaths at the hands of Robin's band. The next morning, the departing archbishop gives his blessing to the forthcoming marriage of Maid Marian and Robin. *Outlaws. Despots. Sheriffs. Nobility. Woodsmen. Murder. Castles. Monasteries. Sherwood Forest. Nottingham. Hubert Walter. Robin Hood.*

Note: Filmed in Ireland. Opened in London in Dec 1960; running time: 80 min.

SWORD OF THE CONQUEROR (Italy)   **F6.4840**
Titanus. *Dist* United Artists. 5 Sep 1962 [Chicago opening; c12 Sep 1962; LP23093]. Sd; col (Eastman Color). 35mm (CinemaScope). 95 min.

Prod Gilberto Carbone. *Dir* Carlo Campogalliani. *2d Unit Dir* Romolo Girolami. *Screenplay* Roberto Gianviti, Alessandro Ferraù, Carlo Campogalliani. *Story* Paola Barbara, Primo Zeglio. *Photog* Raffaele Masciocchi. *Camera* Antonio Schiavolena, Elio Polacchi. *Art Dir* Giorgio Giovannini. *Set Decor* Massimo Tavazzi. *Film Ed* Mario Serandrei. *Mus Comp* Carlo Rustichelli. *Cond* Carlo Savina. *Sd* Giulio Tabliacozzo. *Prod Mgr* Renato Parravicini. *Cost* Giuliana Ghidini.

Cast: Jack Palance (*Alboino*), Eleonora Rossi-Drago (*Rosamunde*), Guy Madison (*Amalche*), Mirella D'Angelo (*Falisco*), Andrea Bosic (*King Cunimondo*), Edy Vessel (*Mathilde*), Ivan Palance (*Ulderico*), Vittorio Sanipoli (*Wolfango*), Raf Baldassarre, Guido Celano, Guido Manfrino, Alfredo Marchetti, Elio Folgaresi, Olga Romanelli, Vittorio Vaser, Franco Jamonte, Joe Camel, Spartaco Nale, Renato Mori, Giovanni Vari, Lamberto Antinori, Roberto Altamura, Calisto Calisti, Aldo Pini.

Costume melodrama. After defeating the Gepidae in 566 A. D., Alboino, the Lombard king, offers peace on the condition that Rosamunde, daughter of the Gepidae king, Cunimondo, marry him. She refuses because she is in love with Amalche, a Gepidae warrior whose son she has borne. Her father threatens to have Amalche killed, however, and she consents to marry Alboino. Then Alboino's brother, the peace emissary, is killed through treachery, and the Lombard king swears vengeance on the Gepidae. He attacks, defeats them in a battle in which Cunimondo is killed, and takes Rosamunde as his bride. After the celebration feast, Amalche, who has escaped from imprisonment, breaks into the nuptial chamber, rescues Rosamunde, and kills Alboino. Amalche's followers again battle the Lombards and this time defeat them. As peace is restored, Rosamunde is crowned queen and is reunited with Amalche and their son. *Royalty. Brothers. Marriage. Perfidy. Revenge. Illegitimacy. Filial relations. Alboino. Cunimund. Lombards. Gepidae.*

Note: Produced in Italy in Aug 1961 as *Rosmunda e Alboino*; running time: 105 min. Copyright claimant: Tan Film.

SWORDSMAN OF SIENA (France/Italy)   **F6.4841**
Monica Film–C. C. M.–CIPRA–Jacques Bar. *Dist* Metro-Goldwyn-Mayer, Inc. 28 Nov 1962 [Los Angeles opening; c31 Oct 1962; LP23377]. Sd; col (Metrocolor). 35mm (Cinemascope). 96 min. [Also 92 min.]

Prod Jacques Bar. *Dir (see note)* Etienne Périer, Baccio Bandini. *Screenplay (see note)* Michael Kanin, Fay Kanin, Alec Coppel, Sandro Continenza, Dominique Fabre. *English Story* Anthony Marshall. *Dir Photog* Tonino Delli Colli. *Camera Op* Franco Delli Colli. *Art Dir* Alberto Boccianti. *Film Ed* Robert Isnardon, Monique Isnardon. *Mus Comp (see note)* Mario Nascimbene. *Mus Cond* Carlo Rustichelli, Franco Ferrara. *Rec Supv* Kurt Doubravsky. *Asst*

Dir Gus Agosti. *Prod Mgr* Bianca Lattuada.

Cast: Stewart Granger (*Thomas Stanwood*), Sylva Koscina (*Orietta Arconti*), Christine Kaufmann (*Serenella Arconti*), Riccardo Garrone (*Don Carlos*), Tullio Carminati (*Father Giacomo*), Alberto Lupo (*Paresi*), Fausto Tozzi (*Hugo*), Tom Felleghi (*Spanish captain*), Carlo Rizzo (*Gino*), Claudio Gora (*Leoni*), Marina Berti (*Countess of Osta*), Fanfulla, Giulio Marchetti, Ignazio Dolce.

Adventure melodrama. In the 16th century, Thomas Stanwood, an English adventurer and mercenary, arrives in the Italian city of Siena and joins the guard of Don Carlos, the city's despised, tyrannical Spanish governor. For political reasons, Don Carlos plans to wed Orietta Arconti, a member of one of Italy's most influential families, and he assigns Stanwood as her bodyguard. Violently opposed to the match is Orietta's younger sister, Serenella, who loathes the Spanish, disapproves of her sister's complicity, and sympathizes with The Ten, an underground force of Italian patriots. She learns that Don Carlos plans to force her to marry his cousin Hugo and attempts to flee the city, but she is killed by a guardsman. Stanwood then joins the underground and discovers that Orietta is the group's secret leader. For a number of years Hugo has contrived by foul play to win the annual Siena horserace, thereby obtaining the homage of the populace. Don Carlos arrests Paresi, who is to ride for The Ten in the race, and has him tortured to death. Stanwood then enters the race in his place. Don Carlos tries to have the Englishman murdered, but a stray crossbow bolt strikes a woman bystander, and the crowd riots. Hugo is unhorsed and trampled to death as he tries to kill Stanwood; and the Englishman is victorious. The Spaniards are driven from Siena by the elated populace, and Stanwood rides off to seek new adventures. However, Orietta sends her men to bring him back, and he returns a willing prisoner. *Mercenaries. English. Sisters. Adventurers. Spanish. Bodyguards. Aristocrats. Despots. Military occupation. Resistance (political). Horseracing. Murder. Torture. Marriage—Arranged. Siena.*

Note: Filmed in Siena and other locations in Tuscany. Opened in Paris in Dec 1962 as *Le mercenaire*; running time: 92 min; alternative French running time: 100 min. Italian titles: *Lo spadaccino di Siena* and *Il mercenario*. French and Italian sources credit Bandini as director; Continenza and Fabre as screenplay writers; and Rustichelli as composer of music. U. S. sources credit Périer as director; Michael Kanin, Fay Kanin, Coppel, and Marshall as writers; and Nascimbene with music.

SYLVIA   **F6.4842**
Marpol Productions. *For* Paramount Pictures. *Dist* Paramount Pictures. 10 Feb 1965 [New York opening; c31 Dec 1964; LP29727]. Sd (Westrex); b&w. 35mm. 115 min.

A Martin Poll Production. *Prod* Martin Poll. *Assoc Prod* Shirley Mellner. *Asst Prod* Steve Shagan. *Dir* Gordon Douglas. *Screenplay* Sydney Boehm. *Dir Photog* Joseph Ruttenberg. *Camera Op* Kyme Meade. *Art Dir* Hal Pereira, Roland Anderson. *Set Decor* Sam Comer, Arthur Krams. *Titl Dsgn* Roy Besser. *Film Ed* Frank Bracht. *Mus (see note)* David Raksin, Walter Scharf. *Song: "Love and Learn"* Ira Gershwin, Harold Arlen. *Titl Song* Paul Francis Webster, David Raksin. *Sung by* Paul Anka. *Sd Rec* Harry Lindgren, John Wilkinson. *Boom Op* John K. Nelson. *Asst Dir* Dick Moder, James Rosenberger. *Unit Mgr* Kenneth Deland. *Script Supv* Claire Behnke. *Cost* Edith Head. *Makeup Supv* Wally Westmore. *Makeup* William Reynolds, makeup. *Hairstyle Supv* Nellie Manley. *Hairstyles* Gladys Witten. *Spec Photog Eff* Paul K. Lerpae. *Proc Photog* Farciot Edouart. *Dial Coach* Leon Charles. *Casting* Ed Morse. *Still Photog* Art Say.

Cast: Carroll Baker (*Sylvia West*), George Maharis (*Alan Macklin*), Joanne Dru (*Jane Philips*), Peter Lawford (*Frederic Summers*), Viveca Lindfors (*Irma Olanski*), Edmond O'Brien (*Oscar Stewart*), Aldo Ray (*Jonas Karoki*), Ann Sothern (*Mrs. Argona*), Lloyd Bochner (*Bruce Stamford III*), Paul Gilbert (*Lola Diamond*), Nancy Kovack (*Big Shirley*), Paul Wexler (*Peter Memel*), Jay Novello (*Father Gonzales*), Connie Gilchrist (*Molly Banter*), Alan Carney (*Gus*), Shirley O'Hara (*Mrs. Karoki*), Anthony Caruso (*Muscles*), Gene Lyons (*Gavin Cullen*), Val Avery (*Pudgey*), Manuel Padilla (*Pancho*), Majel Barrett (*Anne*), Bob Random.

Drama. Source: E. V. Cunningham, *Sylvia* (New York, 1960). California millionaire Frederic Summers hires private investigator Alan Macklin to uncover the mysterious past of his fiancée, Sylvia West, a cultured, well-to-do author of a book of poetry. An English professor friend of Macklin deduces from her poetry that Sylvia is from Pittsburgh. Macklin goes there and interviews people who once knew Sylvia. He learns that as a teenager Sylvia was raped by her stepfather and drifted into a life of prostitution. She blackmailed a perverted client, and the money was successfully invested for her by the banker husband of a girl friend who was also a prostitute. After she became wealthy, Sylvia left her life of prostitution; she began to write and publish her poetry. Before reporting to Summers, Macklin decides to meet Sylvia, and he is tremendously attracted by her beauty, intelligence, and charm.

He decides not to reveal her past to Summers and instead tells Sylvia that her fiancé hired him to investigate her. Angry and hurt, Sylvia tells Summers the truth about herself, and when she and Macklin meet again, they decide to remain together. *Millionaires. Poets. Prostitutes. Detectives. Stepfathers. Rape. Blackmail. Wealth. Reputation. California. Pittsburgh.*

Note: Sources conflict in crediting Raksin and Scharf for music.

SYLVIA'S GIRLS F6.4843

United Pictures Organization. *Dist* Central Film Distributors. 7 Jul **1965** [Chicago opening]. Sd; b&w. 35mm. 79 min.

Prod Harry Kerwin. *Dir* Al Dempsey. *Screenplay* J. Huntington Held. *Orig Story* Tod Sackman. *Dir Photog* Mario Di Leo. *Asst Camera* Andy Romanoff. *Set Decor* Harry Ortiz. *Film Ed* Al Dempsey, Bert Lovitt. *Orig Mus Comp* Paul J. Gillette. *Mus Cond* John Cantor. *Vocalist* Rex Marlow. *Sd Tech* Claude Pounds. *In Charge of Prod* J. Huntington Held. *Script Coörd* Anita Metzger. *Makeup Supv* Nancy Roldan. *Sp Eff* Cineffects.

Cast: Valerie Hawkins, Gene Burk, Djonald Gache, Cynthia Williams, Larry Holmes, Len Camp, Cyndi Du Val, Richard Bloom, Fred Robbins, Linda Finley, Ignacio Del Magro, Rick Powell.

Melodrama. Although Helen enjoys a chaste relationship with her boyfriend, Bob, she cannot accept his marriage proposal because she secretly enjoys being picked up by strangers. One evening in a cocktail lounge, Helen meets Clark, a procurer, who convinces her to try prostitution, arguing that she should be reimbursed for her sexual favors. Helen agrees and goes to work for Sylvia, a madam, but after a few assignments with older men, Helen begins to have doubts and accepts the advice of her roommate, Wanda, that she seek psychiatric help. Sylvia convinces Helen to try one more customer before quitting, but the man's sexual demands repulse her, and Helen leaves in disgust. Helen explains her problem to the psychiatrist and screams with frustration when he suggests they meet after hours. Later, Bob is called to the police station where he is informed of Helen's suicide. Clark and Sylvia are arrested, and Bob learns of Helen's secret life. *Pimps. Psychiatrists. Madams. Pickups. Prostitution. Suicide. Promiscuity.*

Note: Produced in Florida.

SYMPATHY FOR THE DEVIL (1 + 1) (Great Britain) F6.4844

Cupid Productions. *Dist* New Line Cinema. 22 Apr **1969** [San Francisco opening]. Sd; col (Eastman Color). 35mm. 110 min.

Prod Michael Pearson, Iain Quarrier. *Exec Prod* Eleni Collard. *Dir-Writ-Comm* Jean-Luc Godard. *Photog* Tony Richmond. *Camera Op* Colin Corby. *Film Ed* Ken Rowles. *Asst Film Ed* Agnès Guillemot. *Song:* "Sympathy for the Devil" Keith Richard, Mick Jagger. *Perf by* The Rolling Stones. *Sd* Arthur Bradburn. *Prod Mgr* Clive Freedman, Paul De Burgh.

Cast: The Rolling Stones (*themselves*), Anne Wiazemsky ("*Eve Democracy*"), Iain Quarrier (*bookman*), Frankie Dymon, Jr. (*Black Power militant*), Sean Lynch (*narrator*), Danny Daniels, Illario Pedro, Roy Stewart, Linbert Spencer, Tommy Ansah, Michael McKay, Rudi Patterson, Mark Matthew, Karl Lewis, Bernard Boston, Nike Arrighi, Françoise Pascal, Joanna David, Monica Walters, Glenna Forster-Jones, Elizabeth Long, Jeanette Wild, Harry Douglas, Colin Cunningham, Graham Peet, Matthew Know, Barbara Coleridge.

Film essay. Interspersed with sequences of a studio session of the Rolling Stones developing their song "Sympathy for the Devil" are several scenes: A group of armed Black Power advocates in a London riverside automobile graveyard prepare for the revolution, reading passages from the writings of Eldridge Cleaver and LeRoi Jones concerning revolution and the black man's lust for white women. They nonchalantly fondle and execute several white women clad in virginal white gowns. In a pornographic bookstore the fascist owner reads aloud extracts from *Mein Kampf*. A television crew wandering in an Edenic forest conducts an interview with Eve Democracy, who answers the politico-philosophical questions put to her with a simple *yes* or *no*. The film's soundtrack contains intermittent readings from a pornographic political novel. There are brief views of Eve Democracy/Anne Wiazemsky painting graffiti ("Cinemarx," "SoViet Cong," "FBI + CIA = TWA + PanAm") on various surfaces in London. She is finally shot down on a beach by black militants, after which her bloodied body is lifted up on a camera crane, with black and red flags on either side. *Militants. Negroes. Revolutionaries. Lust. Rape. Murder. Fascism. Racism. Pornography. Bookshops. Graffiti. London. LeRoi Jones. Eldridge Cleaver. "Mein Kampf".*

Note: Filmed on location in London, at the Olympic Recording Studios (Barnes), and at Camber Sands, Sussex. Released in Great Britain in 1971 as *Sympathy for the Devil*. This title represents producer Iain Quarrier's version of Godard's film *1 + 1 (One Plus One)*. Though the director left the creation of the song unfinished in the original version, shown at the 1968 London Film Festival, *Sympathy for the Devil* includes the complete version of the song with footage consisting of monochromatic shots of the film's final image. Original running time: 104 min.

SYMPHONIE POUR UN MASSACRE *see* SYMPHONY FOR A MASSACRE

SYMPHONY FOR A MASSACRE (France/Italy) F6.4845

C. I. C. C.–P. E. C. F.–Dear Film–Ultra Film. *Dist* Seven Arts Pictures, Goldstone Film Enterprises. 27 May **1965** [New York opening]. Sd; b&w. 35mm. 115 min.

Prod Julien Derode. *Dir* Jacques Deray. *Screenplay* José Giovanni, Claude Sautet, Jacques Deray. *Dial* José Giovanni, Claude Sautet. *Photog* Claude Renoir. *Art Dir* Léon Barsacq. *Film Ed* Paul Cayatte. *Mus* Michel Magne. *Sd* Jo de Bretagne. *Prod Mgr* Robert Vélin.

Cast: Michel Auclair (*Clavet*), Claude Dauphin (*Valoti*), José Giovanni (*Moreau*), Charles Vanel (*Paoli*), Jean Rochefort (*Jabeke*), Michèle Mercier (*Madeleine Clavet*), Daniela Rocca (*Hélène Valoti*).

Crime melodrama. Source: Alain Reynaud-Fourton, *Les mystifiés* (Paris, 1962). Parisian gangsters Clavet, Moreau, Valoti, Paoli, and Jabeke agree to share the purchase of a large shipment of narcotics. Moreau is chosen to make the purchase, but Jabeke plans an elaborate doublecross by providing himself with an alibi and then slipping aboard the train carrying Moreau to Marseilles. Entering Moreau's sleeping compartment in disguise, Jabeke accidentally awakens Moreau and kills him in the ensuing struggle. Back in Paris, Paoli confronts Jabeke with a newspaper account of Moreau's death; Jabeke mistakenly reveals his guilt and stabs Paoli to ensure his silence. Clavet and Valoti find Paoli's corpse, but the evidence seems to point to Valoti as the doublecrosser. Jabeke kills Clavet since further examination of the evidence would reveal his own guilt. Valoti searches Jabeke's apartment and finds the money, but Jabeke surprises him and kills him. Seemingly free now, Jabeke is about to enter his car when Clavet's widow shoots him. *Gangsters. Widows. Perfidy. Murder. Disguise. Narcotics. Trains. Paris. Marseilles.*

Note: Opened in Paris in Aug 1963 as *Symphonie pour un massacre*; running time: 110 min; in Rome in Dec 1963 as *Sinfonia per un massacro*. U. S. title later changed to *The Mystifiers*.

SYNANON F6.4846

Richard Quine Productions. *Dist* Columbia Pictures. 5 May **1965** [New York opening; c1 May 1965; LP30836]. Sd; b&w. 35mm. 107 min. [Copyright length: 104 min.]

Prod-Dir Richard Quine. *Screenplay* Ian Bernard, S. Lee Pogostin. *Story* Barry Oringer, S. Lee Pogostin. *Dir Photog* Harry Stradling. *Camera Op* Emil Oster, Jr. *Camera Asst* Gerald Finnerman. *Art Dir* Philip Jefferies. *Set Decor* William Kiernan. *Film Ed* David Wages. *Mus* Neal Hefti. *Sd Supv* Charles J. Rice. *Sd* Josh Westmoreland, Walter Goss. *Asst Dir* Carter De Haven, Jr., Roger Slater. *Unit Mgr* Sergei Petschnikoff. *Asst to the Prod-Dir* Carter De Haven, Jr. *Cost* Kathleen McCandless. *Makeup Supv* Ben Lane. *Hairstyles* Virginia Jones. *Tech Adv* Charles E. Dederich. *Dial Coach* Benno Schneider. *Prop* Jack Carter, prop. *Gaffer* James Field. *Grip* Dick Borland.

Cast: Chuck Connors (*Ben*), Stella Stevens (*Joaney*), Alex Cord (*Zankie Albo*), Richard Conte (*Reid*), Eartha Kitt (*Betty Coleman*), Edmond O'Brien (*Chuck Dederich*), Barbara Luna (*Mary*), Alejandro Rey (*Chris*), Richard Evans (*Hopper*), Gregory Morton (*Vince*), Chanin Hale (*Arline*), Casey Townsend (*Pruddy*), Larry Kert (*Bob Adamic*), Bernie Hamilton (*Pete*), Mark Sturges (*Joe Mann*), Lawrence Montaigne (*Greek*), Patricia Huston (*Carla*).

Cast—Residents of Synanon House: Arnold Ross, John Peterson, James Middleton, Anthony Daddio, Candy Latson, Dan Spaccarelli, Herb Rosen, William Crawford, Charles Haden, Matthew Notkins.

Drama. Desperate for a place of refuge until he can get back on his feet again, heroin addict Zankie Albo wanders into Synanon House, a rehabilitation center run by former alcoholic Chuck Dederich. There he is placed in the care of Joaney, a nearly rehabilitated addict who reveals during a group therapy session that she is in danger of having her child taken away by her ex-husband. As Joaney watches over Zankie during the terrible initial stages of his withdrawal from narcotics, a strong attraction develops between them. Their relationship arouses the envy of one of the "graduate" residents, Ben, a parolee whom Zankie had known previously. Ben catches Joaney and Zankie in a midnight rendezvous at a beach house, and he reports them to the Synanon authorities. Zankie sees another resident, Pete, getting high on cough syrup and forces him to share it. Eventually Zankie leaves Synanon. Joaney follows, trailed by the anxious Ben. They are too late, however, for Zankie is already dead from an overdose of heroin. Joaney voluntarily returns to Synanon to continue her cure. *Drug addicts. Group therapy. Parole. Drug overdose. Heroin. Santa Monica. Charles E. Dederich. Synanon House.*

Note: Filmed at Synanon House in Santa Monica, California.

THE SYNDICATE (Great Britain) F6.4847

Associated British–Pathé Ltd. *Dist* Schoenfeld Film Distributing Corp. 13 Nov **1968** [Newark, New Jersey, opening]. Sd; col (Technicolor). 35mm. 63 min.

Prod Harry Field. *Assoc Prod* Lionel Hoare. *Dir* Frederic Goode. *Screenplay* Geoffrey Hays. *Dir Photog* George Stevens, photog. *Supv Film Ed* John Blair. *Film Ed* Frederick Ives. *Mus* Edwin Astley. *Sd* Trevor Pyke. *Prod Mgr* Ron Holtzer.

Cast: William Sylvester *(Burt Hickey)*, June Ritchie *(Mari Brant)*, Robert Urquhart *(George Brant)*, Christian Doermer *(Kurt Hohmann)*, John Bennett *(Dr. Singh)*, John De Villiers *(Schultz)*, Omari Suleman *(Kamahru)*, Sal Davis *(Shafiq)*, Bill Dixson *(Englishman)*.

Adventure melodrama. Source: Denys Rhodes, *The Syndicate* (New York, 1960). German Kurt Hohmann is the self-appointed leader of a syndicate searching for uranium in Kenya. The other partners—alcoholic white hunter George Brant, American ex-airplane pilot Burt Hickey, and George's ambitious wife, Mari—are unaware that Kurt is really working for Dr. Singh, who wants the mineral rights for his company. After fruitless digging and an act of sabotage against the group, Burt discovers a rich uranium deposit at another site. He also discovers Kurt's perfidy, but Kurt attempts to dissociate himself from Singh. Singh, however, murders Kurt and tries to eliminate the others. As George is murdered, Mari and Burt escape in Singh's plane. *Germans. Hunters. Americans in foreign countries. Air pilots. Prospectors. Perfidy. Murder. Alcoholism. Syndicates. Uranium. Mineral rights. Kenya.*

Note: Location scenes filmed in Kenya. Released in Great Britain in Sep 1968; cut from 106 min.

SYSKONBÄDD 1782 *see* **MY SISTER, MY LOVE**

THE SYSTEM *see* **THE GIRL GETTERS**

SYTTEN *see* **ERIC SOYA'S "17"**

SZEGÉNYLEGÉNYEK *see* **THE ROUND UP**

T. P. A. (THE PRESIDENT'S ANALYST) *see* **THE PRESIDENT'S ANALYST**

TA CHI *see* **THE LAST WOMAN OF SHANG**

TABLE BAY *see* **CODE 7, VICTIM 5!**

TABOOS OF THE WORLD (Italy)   **F6.4848**
   Royal Film. *Dist* American International Pictures. Mar **1965** [c24 Mar 1965; LP31195]. Sd; col (Eastmancolor). 35mm. 86 min. [Also 97 min.]
   Prod Guido Giambartolomei. *Dir* Romolo Marcellini. *Screenplay* Romolo Marcellini, Ugo Guerra. *Story* Romolo Marcellini, Virgilio Lilli, Ettore Della Giovanna, L. De Marchi, Bonacina, Lanzmann. *Photog* Rino Filippini. *Film Ed* Otello Colangeli. *Mus* Francesco Lavagnino, Armando Trovajoli.

Narrator: Vincent Price.

Documentary. Religious rites and taboos depicted include: the Muslim 5-minute divorce; a funeral on the sacred Ganges River; Catholic mass offered for a group of lepers; scenes of East Indian gurus, sacred cows and elephants, and a Buddhist priest and his mother. Sexual and medical topics include: childbirth, atom bomb victims, Japanese public bathing, and drug addicts selling their children into slavery or prostitution to support their habits. Other topics cover a wide variety of subjects: tattooing women in Japan, Laplanders drinking blood, Malaysians fishing in the mud, and a member of a secret Japanese society amputating his little finger as part of initiation. *Muslims. Catholics. East Indians. Gurus. Buddhism. War victims. Japanese. Drug addicts. Rites and ceremonies. Divorce. Funerals. Leprosy. Childbirth. Bathing customs. Slavery. Prostitution. Fishing. Mutilation. Tattoos. Secret societies. Ganges River. Japan. Malaysia. India. Lapland. Cows. Elephants.*

Note: Filmed in India, Japan, Finland, Sweden, Lapland, and Hawaii. Opened in Rome in Dec 1963 as *I tabù*; running time: 100 min.

I TABÙ *see* **TABOOS OF THE WORLD**

TABÚ (FUGITIVOS DE LAS ISLAS DEL SUR) *see* **THE DRUMS OF TABU**

TABÙ N. 2 *see* **MACABRO**

TAFFY AND THE JUNGLE HUNTER   **F6.4849**
   Zimbalist Co. *Dist* Allied Artists. Jul **1965** [Los Angeles showing]. Sd; col (Technicolor). 35mm. 87 min.
   Prod William Faris. *Assoc Prod* Jack Warner, Jr. *Exec Prod* Byron Roberts. *Prod Supv* Alfred Zimbalist. *Dir* Terry O. Morse. *Screenplay* Arthur Hoerl. *Adtl Dial* Alfred Zimbalist. *Story* Donald Zimbalist. *Dir Photog* Brydon Baker. *Film Ed* William Faris. *Mus Comp & Cond* Shorty Rogers. *Theme Song:* "Taffy" Alfred Zimbalist, Shorty Rogers. *Sd* Dale Knight. *Asst Dir* Robert Shannon. *Script Supv* Marie Kenney. *Makeup* Louis Haszillo. *Prop Master* Ed Goldstein. *Gaffer* Robert Petzoldt.

Cast: Jacques Bergerac *(David Claveau)*, Manuel Padilla *(Beau)*, Shary Marshall *(Rosa Wynn)*, Hari Rhodes *(Kahli)*, Taffy *(herself, an elephant)*, Margo *(animal)* *(herself, a chimpanzee)*, Robert DoQui.

Comedy-drama. David Claveau, a jungle hunter in East Africa who captures wild animals for zoos, has an 8-year-old son, Beau, and together they capture a baby elephant to which the little boy becomes extremely attached. A friendly native chief, Kahli, warns David of imminent tribal warfare, and the hunter decides to send Beau and his governess, Rosa, an ex-circus performer who was wounded in an accident with a lion, to Nairobi, to sell his animal stock. Beau is so upset at the thought of being separated from his elephant, which he calls Taffy, that he runs away with the elephant and his pet chimpanzee, Margo. David and Rosa, assisted by Kahli, search for Beau in the jungle, and then separate. Rosa finds Beau as he is about to be attacked by a lion. She overcomes her fear of lions, fends off the animal, and saves the boy's life. Later, Taffy is flown to the United States along with David, Rosa, and Beau. *Hunters. Children. Tribal chiefs. Governesses. Filial relations. Zoos. Jungles. East Africa. Nairobi. Elephants. Chimpanzees. Lions.*

TAGGART   **F6.4850**
   Gordon Kay & Associates. *Dist* Universal Pictures. 24 Dec **1964** [New York opening; c13 Mar 1964; LP33020]. Sd (Westrex); col (Technicolor). 35mm. 85 min.
   Prod Gordon Kay. *Dir* R. G. Springsteen. *Screenplay* Robert Creighton Williams. *Dir Photog* William Margulies. *Art Dir* Alexander Golitzen, Raymond Beal. *Set Decor* John McCarthy, James M. Walters, Sr. *Film Ed* Tony Martinelli. *Mus* Herman Stein. *Mus Supv* Joseph Gershenson. *Sd* Waldon O. Watson, David H. Moriarty. *Asst Dir* Carl Beringer. *Unit Prod Mgr* Frank Parmenter. *Makeup* Bud Westmore. *Hairstyles* Larry Germain.

Cast: Tony Young *(Kent Taggart)*, Dan Duryea *(Jason)*, Dick Foran *(Stark)*, Elsa Cardenas *(Consuela)*, Jean Hale *(Miriam)*, Emile Meyer *(Ben Blazer)*, David Carradine *(Cal Dodge)*, Peter Duryea *(Rusty Bob)*, Tom Reese *(Vince August)*, Ray Teal *(Ralph Taggart)*, Claudia Barrett *(Lola)*, Stuart Randall *(sheriff)*, Harry Carey, [Jr.] *(Lieutenant Hudson)*, Bill Henry *(Army sergeant)*, Sarah Selby *(Maude Taggart)*, George Murdock *(Army scout)*, Arthur Space *(colonel)*, Bob Steele *(cook)*.

Western melodrama. Source: Louis L'Amour, *Taggart* (New York, 1959). Kent Taggart and his parents purchase Federal land in the West. Wealthy rancher Ben Blazer and his son Rusty Bob, who own most of the territory, attack the Taggarts in an attempt to drive them off the land. Kent is wounded and watches Rusty Bob brutally murder his parents. He follows the Blazers into town, kills Rusty Bob, and wounds Ben. Before dying, Ben hires three gunmen to track down Kent. The three men overtake him, and in an exchange of gunfire, Kent kills one and wounds another before heading into Apache country. Jason, the remaining gunman, then shoots his wounded partner, who has become a burden, and pursues Kent alone. Meanwhile, Kent comes upon a mission inhabited by an aging gold miner named Stark, his young Mexican wife, Consuela, and daughter Miriam. Kent wins the miner's friendship by helping to repel an Indian attack, and Stark locks up Jason when he arrives with legal authorization to take Kent prisoner. Consuela tries unsuccessfully to seduce Kent, and, angered by her failure, she frees Jason and helps him steal her husband's gold. They join a wagon train and Consuela tries to run away with the gold, but she is killed during an Indian attack. At a U. S. Cavalry fort, Jason encounters Kent, Miriam, and Stark just as the soldiers are preparing to face an Indian attack. Jason kills Stark, but Kent shoots Jason's horse from under him, and he is crushed by the weight of the stolen gold. The battle subsides, and Miriam and Kent are left to start a new life together. *Ranchers. Homesteaders. Hired killers. Apache Indians. Miners. Mexicans. Murder. Revenge. Greed. Theft. Desertion. Wagon trains. Forts. Gold. United States Army—Cavalry.*

TAIHEIYO HITORIBOTCHI *see* **MY ENEMY, THE SEA**

TAIHEIYO NO ARASHI *see* **I BOMBED PEARL HARBOR**

TAKE A GIRL LIKE YOU (Great Britain)   **F6.4851**
   Albion Film Corp. *Dist* Columbia Pictures. Oct **1970** [c10 Oct 1970; LP39192]. Sd (RCA); col (Technicolor). 35mm. 96 min. *MPAA rating* R.
   Prod Hal E. Chester. *Assoc Prod* L. C. Rudkin. *Dir* Jonathan Miller. *Screenplay* George Melly. *Dir Photog* Dick Bush. *Camera Op* Ken Nicholson. *Art Dir* Jack Shampan. *Set Decor* Tim Abadie. *Film Ed* Jack Harris, Rex Pyke. *Mus* Stanley Myers. *Titl Song* Bill Martin, Phil Coulter. *Sung by* The Foundations. *Song:* "It Takes a Lot of Loving" Stanley Myers, Hal Shaper. *Sung by* Harmony Grass. *Sd Rec* Ken Ritchie, Nolan Roberts. *Sd Ed* Arthur Ridout. *Asst Dir* Douglas Hermes, Joe Marks. *Prod Mgr* Denis Johnson, Jr. *Cont* Penny Daniels. *Wardrobe Supv* Bridget Sellers. *Makeup* George Partleton. *Hairdresser* Joan Carpenter. *Art Works* Brian Wall, Allen Jones, Peter Phillips, Howard Hodgkin.

Cast: Hayley Mills *(Jenny)*, Oliver Reed *(Patrick)*, Noel Harrison *(Julian)*, John Bird *(Dick)*, Sheila Hancock *(Martha)*, Aimi MacDonald *(Wendy)*, Geraldine Sherman *(Anna)*, Ronald Lacey *(Graham)*, John Fortune *(Sir Gerald)*, Imogen Hassall *(Samantha)*, Pippa Steel *(Ted)*, Penelope Keith *(Tory lady)*, Nicholas Courtney *(panel chairman)*, George Woodbridge *(publican)*,

Jimmy Gardner (voter), Nerys Hughes (teacher), Jean Marlow (mother), Howard Goorney (labor agent).

Romantic comedy-drama. Source: Kingsley Amis, *Take a Girl Like You* (London, 1960). Jenny Bunn, a conservative schoolteacher, arrives in a London suburb to begin a new teaching job. She finds a room in a boardinghouse and becomes friendly with Anna, another lodger, who introduces Jenny to her boyfriend, Patrick Standish, a callous playboy. He shows an immediate interest in Jenny and asks her for a date; she agrees to have dinner with him, but his plans also include seducing her. Jenny, however, is a virgin and resists his advances. Patrick finds her innocence charming and continues to see her, although he complains to his wealthy friend Julian of his lack of amatory success with her. When Patrick takes Jenny to a party given by Julian, she becomes convinced of his sincerity and finally agrees to have sex with him. They arrange a rendezvous for the following Saturday. Several days after the party, Jenny runs into Julian, who indicates that Patrick has confided everything to him. On Saturday night, instead of meeting Patrick, Jenny has sex with Julian. Patrick, upset because Jenny failed to show up for their rendezvous, goes to Julian's house and finds the two in bed together. Shocked by Jenny's behavior, Patrick demands an explanation, and Jenny tells him that she tired of his pretenses and wanted him to pursue her with more determination. *Schoolteachers. Playboys. Ingenues. Virginity. Seduction. Duplicity. Sexual initiation. Boardinghouses. London.*

Note: Opened in London in Jan 1971; running time: 98 min (cut from 101 min).

TAKE HER BY SURPRISE (Canada)   **F6.4852**
Somerset Motion Picture Productions. *Dist* Cannon Releasing Corp. 12 Apr 1967 [Boston opening]. Sd; b&w. 35mm. 80 min.
Prod John Somerset. *Assoc Prod* Ted Lawrence. *Dir* Rudi Dorn. *Dir Photog* Gerhard Alsen. *Adtl Photog* Robert Martin, photog, John S. Gaisford, Ted Lawrence. *Film Ed* Glenn Ludlow. *Mus* John Bath. *Sd* Edward McCormack. *Re-rec* Clarke Daprato. *Cost* Christine. *Makeup* Peggy Stevens, Marjorie Spencer.
Cast: Paul Negri (*Walter Dorland*), Nuel Beckett (*Miklos*), Joan Armstrong (*Margaret Dorland*), Peter F. Adamson (*Korba*), Solveigh Schattmann (*social worker*), Michelle Albert (*Korba's assistant*), Dara Wells (*Carla*), Marjorie Spencer (*audience volunteer*), Edward McCormack (*Mr. Kimble*), Marjorie McCormack (*Mrs. Kimble*).
Drama. Racketeer Walter Dorland plans to rid himself of his wife, Margaret, by employing Miklos, a sex offender, to murder her. Miklos, who has recently lured his caseworker into the woods and raped her, is put under a spell of obedience to Dorland by Korba, a hypnotist whom Dorland had blackmailed into helping him. While Dorland establishes an alibi in Montreal, Miklos goes to northern Ontario where Margaret is spending the weekend at a secluded cabin. Miklos, acting under hypnotic command, goes to Margaret's bedroom and attacks her, but he is so intent on gaining sexual satisfaction before killing her that she is able to knock him out and escape. She flees through the woods all night and, exhausted, falls asleep in a barn. At dawn, Miklos finds her, but in the ensuing struggle he stumbles from the hayloft and is killed. Dorland returns to the cottage expecting to find himself a widower, but he is instead greeted by his wife who is wielding the gun Dorland had given Miklos. She kills him and wanders, in a daze, toward a lake. *Racketeers. Hired killers. Murder. Insanity. Rape. Blackmail. Marriage. Hypnotism. Montreal. Ontario.*
Note: Filmed in Canada; working title: *Death Trap*. Alternative U. S. title: *Taken by Surprise*. May also be known as *Violent Love*. John Somerset and Ted Lawrence are pseudonyms for John S. Gaisford and Ted Leversuch, respectively.

TAKE HER, SHE'S MINE   **F6.4853**
Twentieth Century-Fox Film Corp. 13 Nov 1963 [New York opening; c3 Nov 1963; LP26784]. Sd (Westrex); col (De Luxe). 35mm (CinemaScope). 98 min.
Prod-Dir Henry Koster. *Screenplay* Nunnally Johnson. *Dir Photog* Lucien Ballard. *Art Dir* Jack Martin Smith, Malcolm Brown. *Set Decor* Walter M. Scott, Stuart A. Reiss. *Film Ed* Marjorie Fowler. *Mus* Jerry Goldsmith. *Orch* Arthur Morton. *Sd* W. D. Flick, Elmer Raguse. *Asst Dir* Joseph E. Rickards. *Gowns Dsgn* Travilla. *Makeup* Ben Nye. *Hairstyles* Margaret Donovan. *Sp Photog Eff* L. B. Abbott, Emil Kosa, Jr.
Cast: James Stewart (*Frank Michaelson*), Sandra Dee (*Mollie Michaelson*), Audrey Meadows (*Anne Michaelson*), Robert Morley (*Pope-Jones*), Philippe Forquet (*Henri Bonnet*), John McGiver (*Hector G. Ivor*), Bob Denver (*Alex*), Monica Moran (*Linda*), Cynthia Pepper (*Adele*), Jenny Maxwell (*Sarah*), Maurice Marsac (*Monsieur Bonnet*), Irene Tsu (*Miss Wu*), Charla Doherty (*Liz Michaelson*), Marcel Hillaire (*first policeman*), Charles Robinson (*Stanley*), Janine Grandel (*Madame Bonnet*).
Romantic comedy. Source: Phoebe Ephron and Henry Ephron, *Take Her, She's Mine* (New York opening: 21 Dec 1961). When lawyer Frank Michaelson

and his wife, Anne, send their daughter, Mollie, to college, they soon discover that boys are not the only danger to her reputation. She soon becomes involved with beatnik folksingers and "Ban the Bomb" demonstrators, and Frank finds himself in several humiliating situations when attempting to help her. Matters are made worse when Mollie goes to Paris on an art scholarship. Seeing in *Life* magazine that Henri, a young artist, is painting her in the style of Picasso, Frank flies to France, but in Paris he only causes more confusion when he is accidentally arrested in a police raid on a shady bistro. Mollie finally confesses her love for Henri and introduces him to her harassed father at a costume ball; all goes well until Frank's Daniel Boone costume disintegrates, and he falls into the Seine. But true love triumphs over petty adversities, and the young couple are married. Frank returns home to begin worrying about his younger daughter, Liz. *Lawyers. Beatniks. Artists. Singers. Police. Fatherhood. Adolescence. Atom bomb. College life. Masquerades. Scholarships. Bistros. Paris. Seine River. Pablo Picasso. "Life" (magazine).*

TAKE IT ALL (Canada)   **F6.4854**
Films Cassiopée–Orion Films. *Dist* Lopert Pictures. 25 Apr 1966 [New York opening]. Sd; b&w. 35mm. 99 min.
Prod Claude Jutra, Robert Hershorn. *Creator-Dir-Screenplay* Claude Jutra. *Adtl Dial* Johanne, Victor Désy. *English Narr?* Leonard Cohen. *Photog* Michel Brault, Jean-Claude Labrecque, Bernard Gosselin. *Film Ed* Claude Jutra, Camil Adam, Eric de Bayser, Pierre Bernard, Michel Brault, Gilles Groulx, Werner Nold. *Mus Theme* Jean Cousineau. *Choir Mus* Maurice Blackburn. *Jazz* Serge Garant. *Sd* Michel Belaieff.
Cast: Johanne (*Johanne*), Claude Jutra (*Claude*), Victor Désy (*Victor*), Tania Fédor (*The Mother*), Guy Hoffmann (*The Priest*), Monique Joly (*Monique*), Monique Mercure (*Barbara*), Patrick Straram (*Nicolas*), François Tasse (*an actor*).
Drama. Claude, a young Québecois intellectual, meets Johanne, a Negro model, at a Bohemian party in Montreal. Although married, she is evidently separated from her husband, and she and Claude have an affair. Eventually, however, Claude tires of Johanne. She discovers that she is pregnant, and Claude briefly considers then rejects marriage, refusing to accept limitations upon his freedom. Johanne loses the child [according to a Canadian source he sends her money for an abortion], and Claude, dismissing the affair as a mere interlude, returns to his former existence, dedicated to the creation of laughter, totally free. *French Canadians. Negroes. Models. Separation (marital). Pregnancy. Bohemianism. Miscegenation. Abortion. Montreal.*
Note: Filmed in 16mm on location in Montreal. Released in Canada in May 1964 as *À tout prendre*; running time: 90 min. The film is dedicated to Norman McLaren and Jean Rouch. Sources indicate that much or all of the dialog was improvised during shooting. A Canadian source credits the lead actress as Johanne Harelle.

TAKE IT OUT IN TRADE   **F6.4855**
MJ Productions. *Dist* MarJon Film Distributors. ca 1970. Sd; col. 16mm. [Feature film, length unknown.]
Sex film. No information about the precise nature of this film has been found. *Prostitution. Sexuality.*

TAKE ME see **TAKE ME NAKED**

TAKE ME AWAY, MY LOVE (Greece)   **F6.4856**
Bezant Films. *Dist* Greek Motion Pictures. 28 Jul 1962 [New York opening]. Sd; b&w. 35mm. 90 min.
Prod K. Dritsa, G. Dambakare. *Dir* E. Giannopoulou. *Screenplay* K. Dritsa.
Cast: Christina Sylba (*Lilia*), George Foundas (*Memas*), Andrew Barkoulis (*Alkis*), Betty Sabba (*Sophia*).
Melodrama. Lilia, a nightclub hostess in Athens, is forced by her boss, Memas, into prostitution and smuggling. Lilia's true love, the journalist Alkis, finally rescues her from this way of life. *Nightclub hostesses. Employers. Journalists. Employment—Women. Prostitution. Smuggling. Athens.*

TAKE ME NAKED   **F6.4857**
Nebuchadnezzar Productions. *Dist* American Film Distributing Corp. 24 Nov 1966 [San Francisco showing]. Sd; b&w. 35mm. 70 min.
A Julian Marsh–Anna Riva Production. *Prod-Dir-Writ* Julian Marsh, Anna Riva. *Photog* Michael Fenway. *Lighting* Anna Riva. *Ed* Julian Marsh. *Mus* Robin Aden. *Sd* Robert Marx. *Poetry* Pierre Louys. "*Leves Amores*" Arthur Symons.
Cast: Kevin Sullivan (*Jason*), Anna Riva, Robert West, Sally Farb, Bert Gray, Joan Ames, Bob Goon.
Crime melodrama. Jason, a frustrated writer turned Bowery alcoholic, has lost contact with reality in his quest for erotic love. Spying through his window at Elaine, who lives across the street, he imagines that she strips, poses seductively, and begins to masturbate, and he grows increasingly frustrated and disgusted. He sees himself making love with a beautiful girl in an idyllic setting,

but soon two lesbians invade his fantasy. Louis, a homosexual, interrupts Jason's reverie and makes advances, taking advantage of Jason's need for a drink. Revolted, Jason brutally clubs Louis, and falls dazed into another daydream: a stripper removes a series of veils until she is naked; then two girls strip and make love. In a trance, Jason takes a butcher knife to Elaine's apartment; he believes that he is carrying flowers. As he imagines a scene of gentle love-making, he rapes the horrified girl, murders her with the knife, and passionately embraces her lifeless body. *Authors. Alcoholism. Insanity. Voyeurism. Lesbianism. Autoeroticism. Male homosexuality. Rape. Murder. Necrophilia. New York City—Bowery. Hallucinations. Dreams.*

Note: Also known as *Take Me.* Julian Marsh and Anna Riva are pseudonyms for Michael and Roberta Findlay.

TAKE ME TO THE FAIR *see* **IT HAPPENED AT THE WORLD'S FAIR**

TAKE MY HEAD   F6.4858
Dist Distribpix, Inc. **1970**. Sd; col. 35mm. 65 min.
Prod Jack Bravman, Michael Findlay. *Dir* Roberta Findlay. *Photog* Michael Findlay. *Film Ed* Michael Findlay.
Sex film. No information about the precise nature of this film has been found. *Sexuality.*

TAKE OFF YOUR CLOTHES AND LIVE (Great Britain)   F6.4859
Searchlight Productions–Miracle Film Productions. *Dist* Seymour Borde & Associates. 17 Apr **1964** [Los Angeles showing]. Sd; col (Eastman Color). 35mm (CinemaScope). 62 min.
Prod Arnold Louis Miller, Stanley A. Long. *Dir* Arnold Louis Miller. *Photog* Stanley A. Long. *Mus Dir* Tony Kind. *Prod Mgr* Harry Green.
Cast: Ian Michael *(Tony)*, Gino Nennan *(John)*, Jenny Lane *(Lee)*, Maureen Haydon *(June)*, Susan Irwin-Clark *(Carol)*, Terry Lee *(Ingrid)*, Margaret Collins *(Mandy)*, Angela Lowe *(Pat)*, Hedy Borland *(Heidi)*, Paula Ku-Chich *(Esme)*, Ulla Thoren *(Barbara)*, Anna Silvers *(Marie)*.
Nudist film. Nine young women leave for a vacation on the Mediterranean; four travel by plane, three by car, and two hitchhike. They meet in Cannes and are joined by two young men, John and Tony. From there, the group continues on to Côte d'Azur, and they begin their nudist vacation. They travel on a luxurious yacht, stop at a millionaire's villa, and participate in a twist contest. Their journey ends at the Île du Levant, where they meet other nudists from around the world. *Nudism. Hitchhikers. Vacations. Travel. Dance contests. Mediterranean Sea. Riviera. Cannes. Île du Levant. Twist (dance).*
Note: Opened in London in Mar 1963; running time: 64 min.

TAKE THE MONEY AND RUN   F6.4860
Heywood–Hillary Productions. *For* Palomar Pictures International. *Dist* Cinerama Releasing Corp. 18 Aug **1969** [New York opening]. Sd; col. 35mm. 85 min. *MPAA rating* M.
Prod Charles H. Joffe. *Exec Prod* Sidney Glazier. *Assoc Prod* Jack Grossberg. *Dir* Woody Allen. *Screenplay* Woody Allen, Mickey Rose. *Dir Photog (see note)* Lester Shorr, Fouad Said. *Camera Op* William Mendenhall. *Art Dir* Fred Harpman. *Set Dir* Marvin March. *Supv Film Ed* Ralph Rosenblum. *Ed* James Heckert, Ron Kalish, Paul Jordan. *Mus Comp* Marvin Hamlisch. *Mus Cond* Kermit Levinsky. *Mus Supv* Felix Giglio. *Sd Mix* Bud Alper. *Sd Rec* Richard Vorisek. *Mus & Sd Eff Ed* John Strauss, Sanford Rackow. *Asst Dir* Louis A. Stroller, Walter Hill. *Prod Mgr* Jack Grossberg. *Unit Mgr* Fred Gallo. *Script Supv* Jeanetta Lewis. *Wardrobe Supv* Erick M. Hjemvik. *Makeup* Stanley R. Dufford. *Sp Eff* A. D. Flowers. *Casting* Marvin Paige. *Set Prop* Ken Phelps.
Cast: Woody Allen *(Virgil Starkwell)*, Janet Margolin *(Louise)*, Marcel Hillaire *(Fritz)*, Jacquelyn Hyde *(Miss Blaire)*, Lonny Chapman *(Jake)*, Jan Merlin *(Al)*, James Anderson *(chain gang warden)*, Howard Storm *(Fred)*, Mark Gordon *(Vince)*, Micil Murphy *(Frank)*, Minnow Moskowitz *(Joe Agneta)*, Nate Jacobson *(judge)*, Grace Bauer *(farmhouse lady)*, Ethel Sokolow *(Mother Starkwell)*, Henry Leff *(Father Starkwell)*, Dan Frazer *(psychiatrist)*, Mike O'Dowd *(Michael Sullivan)*, Jackson Beck *(narrator)*.
Crime farce. Lonely and frustrated, Virgil Starkwell decides to become a professional thief. Though moderately successful at robbing gum-ball machines, he is apprehended and sent to prison when he attempts an armored car heist. His escape by means of a pistol whittled from a bar of soap results in a 2-year increase of his sentence. But Virgil courageously consents to act as a human guinea pig in a medical experiment and then is paroled and tries to go straight. Unable to find a job, he resorts to purse-snatching, and, while cruising a park for victims, he meets and falls in love with Louise, a lovely young laundress. Determined to change the course of his life, Virgil decides to rob a bank—but the tellers involve him in a heated argument over the spelling in his illegible holdup note, and Virgil again is put in jail. Louise visits him weekly and tries to keep up his spirits, but his jail term ends abruptly when he accidentally finds himself on the outside of the walls. Free again, he marries Louise and begins

a new life by taking an office job in another state. Miss Blaire, a predatory fellow employee, learns about his criminal past and blackmails him, whereupon Virgil repeatedly attempts to murder her by stabbing her with a drumstick from the turkey dinner she has prepared. Having failed at an honest living, and with Louise now pregnant, Virgil makes plans for his future family by masterminding still another bank robbery—and once more finds himself behind bars. Undaunted, he effects a daring escape chained to five other convicts and makes his way back to Louise. Now a notorious fugitive, Virgil is recaptured and returned to jail. Sitting in his cell, he reflects on his life of crime as he picks up a bar of soap and begins to whittle. *Convicts. Thieves. Fugitives. Laundresses. Criminals—Rehabilitation. Bank robberies. Blackmail. Murder. Prison escapes. Pregnancy. Chain gangs. Prisons.*
Note: Location scenes filmed in San Francisco and San Quentin. Fouad Said was replaced as photographer several weeks into production; he receives no screen credit.

TAKEN BY SURPRISE *see* **TAKE HER BY SURPRISE**

THE TAKERS *see* **MALAGA**

TALE OF A CARPENTER (Japan)   F6.4861
Toho Co. May **1966** [Los Angeles showing]. Sd; col. 35mm (Tohoscope). 101 min.
Dir Shiro Toyoda.
Cast: Hisaya Morishige, Hajime Hana, M. Fujita, Junko Ikeuchi.
Drama. No information on the precise nature of this film has been found. *Carpenters.*
Note: Released in Japan in 1965 as *Daiku taiheiki.*

TALE OF THE COCK *see* **CHILDISH THINGS**

THE TALE OF THE DEAN'S WIFE *see* **THE DEAN'S WIFE**

TALENT COMPETITION *see* **AUDITION**

TALES FOR MALES   F6.4862
28 Aug **1970** [Los Angeles showing]. Sd; col? 35mm? [Feature film, length unknown.]
Anthology. This anthology of male homosexual films includes *Roman Tidbits, Always on Sundays, Discobolos,* and *Sabre Dance. Male homosexuality.*

TALES OF A SALESMAN   F6.4863
Lawtone Productions. *Dist* Rossmore Film Distributors. 6 Aug **1965** [Los Angeles showing]. Sd; col (DeLuxe). 35mm. [Licensed in Maryland at 53 min.]
Pres by Harry H. Novak. *Prod-Writ* John Lawrence. *Dir* Don Russell. *Photog* William Zsigmond.
Cast: David Reed *(Herman)*, Pope Hook *(sales manager)*, Terri Collins, Terri Dean, Karen Wyatt, Carol Dark, Vicki Reim.
Comedy. Impervious to his wife's attempts to wake him, Herman dreams of being warned by his manager to increase his sales. As he contemplates his predicament, a mischievous poltergeist arrives to help him out. The ghost surveys the salesman's territory for potential customers and discovers five scantily-dressed prospects: one housewife, busy with a vacuum cleaner, nearly loses the brief towel she wears for housecleaning; another plays "bust beach ball" as she swims naked in her pool; a third nude wife prepares a birthday cake for her husband; the occupant of the fourth house has sex with her milkman; and the final prospect sips a drink in the nude, sensuously relishing the cherry. Wishing that he were human, the poltergeist rushes back to Herman to assure him that his neighborhood is full of good prospects. *Salesmen. Housewives. Nudity. Voyeurism. Swimming. Dreams. Ghosts.*
Note: Also known as *Tales of a Traveling Salesman.*

TALES OF PARIS (France/Italy)   F6.4864
Francos Films–Incei Film. *Dist* Times Film Corp. 26 Aug **1962** [New York opening]. Sd; b&w. 35mm. 100 min. [Also released at 85 min.]
Overall Production Credits: A Francis Cosne Production. *Prod* Francis Cosne. *Assoc Proc* Léon Carré. *Art Dir* Jean André. *Film Ed* Léonide Azar. *Mus* Georges Garvarentz. *Songs* Charles Aznavour.
Production Credits for "The Tale of Ella": *Dir* Jacques Poitrenaud. *Screenplay* Isabelle Phat, Marc Aurian. *Dial* Jean-Loup Dabadie. *Adapt* Jean-Loup Dabadie, Jacques Poitrenaud, Francis Cosne. *Photog* Henri Alekan. *Sd* Antoine Petitjean.
Production Credits for "The Tale of Antonia": *Dir* Michel Boisrond. *Screenplay-Dial* Annette Wademant. *Adapt* Annette Wademant, Michel Boisrond, Francis Cosne. *Photog* Henri Alekan. *Sd* Antoine Petitjean.
Production Credits for "The Tale of Françoise": *Dir* Claude Barma. *Screenplay* Jacques Armand. *Dial* Claude Brulé. *Adapt* Claude Barma, Claude Brulé, Francis Cosne. *Photog* Armand Thirard. *Sd* Robert Biart.

Production Credits for "The Tale of Sophie": *Dir* Marc Allégret. *Screenplay-Dial* Roger Vadim. *Adapt* Marc Allégret, Francis Cosne. *Photog* Armand Thirard. *Sd* Robert Biart.

Cast—"The Tale of Ella": Dany Saval *(Ella)*, Darry Cowl *(Hubert)*, Henri Tisot *(Eric)*, Jacques Ary *(Pidoux)*, Françoise Giret *(Juliette)*, Serge Marquand *(taxi driver)*, Les Chaussettes Noires *(themselves, singers)*.

Cast—"The Tale of Antonia": Dany Robin *(Antonia)*, Jean Poiret *(Jean-Pierre)*, Christian Marquand *(Christian)*, Bernard Lavalette *(Richard)*.

Cast—"The Tale of Françoise": Françoise Arnoul *(Françoise)*, Françoise Brion *(Jacqueline)*, Paul Guers *(Michel)*.

Cast—"The Tale of Sophie": Catherine Deneuve *(Sophie)*, Johnny Hallyday *(Jean)*, Gillian Hills *(Theodora)*, Elina Labourdette *(The Mother)*, José-Luis de Vilallonga *(her suitor)*, Berthe Grandval *(Suzanne)*, Gisèle Sandre *(Andrée)*.

Romantic comedy. THE TALE OF ELLA: Ella, a young nightclub performer late for rehearsal, forces her way into a taxi occupied by a shy young man and charms him into accompanying her to the club. He turns out to be Hubert Parker, a famous American producer whom Ella has been trying to meet. Not only does he sign her for his new film, but he marries her as well. THE TALE OF ANTONIA: Antonia, the happily-married wife of an eminent plastic surgeon, learns that Christian, a former lover, has made disparaging remarks about her love-making ability. She decides to teach him a lesson by systematically seducing him. Once she is certain of his renewed infatuation, she calls him a bore and returns to her husband. THE TALE OF FRANÇOISE: Françoise and Jacqueline are former schoolmates who have remained close friends. Jacqueline boasts of her lover's faithfulness, while the more cynical Françoise decides to find out for herself. After easily seducing him she concludes that a woman should never take a man's devotion for granted. THE TALE OF SOPHIE: Attempting to appear worldly before her classmates, the innocent Sophie invents a passionate lover. Her friends stand watch in front of her supposed love nest (in reality, the home of her best friend), while Sophie sneaks out through a window and enters the room of a young rock-and-roll singer. They fall in love and are seen by Sophie's envious friends. The next morning Sophie tries to confess the truth, but no one will believe her. *Entertainers. Motion picture producers. Students. Singers. Revenge. Seduction. Infidelity. Nightclubs. Taxicabs. Paris.*

Note: Opened in Paris in Jan 1962 as *Les parisiennes;* running time: 100 min; in Rome in Apr 1962 as *Le parigine.* Also known in the United States as *Of Beds and Broads.*

TALES OF TERROR   F6.4865

Alta Vista Productions. *Dist* American International Pictures. 4 Jul **1962** [New York opening; c4 Jul 1962; LP23210]. Sd; col (Pathé). 35mm (Panavision). 90 min. [Copyright length: 88 min.]

Prod-Dir Roger Corman. *Exec Prod* James H. Nicholson, Samuel Z. Arkoff. *Screenplay* Richard Matheson. *Photog* Floyd Crosby. *Camera* Art Lane, Kenneth Peach, Jr., Maynard Rugg, Glenn Shanks. *Art Dir* Daniel Haller. *Set Decor* Harry Reif. *Film Ed* Anthony Carras. *Mus* Les Baxter. *Sd* Jack Woods. *Mix* John Bury. *Boom Op* Bill Clark. *Rec* Brad Trask. *Asst Dir* Jack Bohrer, Larry Powell. *Prod Supv* Robert Agnew. *Prod Mgr* Bartlett A. Carre. *Script Supv* Betty Crosby. *Wardrobe Supv* Marjorie Corso. *Wardrobe* Richard Staub. *Makeup* Louis La Cava. *Hairstyles* Ray Foreman. *Sp Eff* Pat Dinga. *Prop* Dick Rubin, John Cengia. *Grip* Charles Hannawalt, Jack Boyd, grip, Bill Santoro, Paul Gilday, Mason Sperry. *Constr* Ross Hahn. *Still Photog* Ed Jones.

Cast—"Morella": Vincent Price *(Locke)*, Maggie Pierce *(Lenora)*, Leona Gage *(Morella)*, Edmund Cobb *(driver)*.

Cast—"The Black Cat": Vincent Price *(Fortunato)*, Peter Lorre *(Montresor)*, Joyce Jameson *(Annabel)*, Lennie Weinrib *(policeman)*, Wally Campo *(bartender)*, Alan DeWitt *(chairman)*, John Hackett *(policeman)*.

Cast—"The Facts in the Case of M. Valdemar": Vincent Price *(Valdemar)*, Basil Rathbone *(Carmichael)*, Debra Paget *(Helene)*, David Frankham *(Dr. Elliot James)*, Scotty Brown *(servant)*.

Horror film. Source: Edgar Allan Poe, "Morella," in *Southern Literary Messenger* (Apr 1835). Edgar Allan Poe, "The Black Cat," in *United States Saturday Post* (19 Aug 1843). Edgar Allan Poe, "The Cask of Amontillado," in *Godey's Magazine and Lady's Book* (Nov 1846). Edgar Allan Poe, "Facts in the Case of M. Valdemar," in *American Whig Review* (Dec 1845). MORELLA: Since the death of his wife, Morella, 26 years before, Locke, an alcoholic, has lived alone in a gloomy mansion. One day he is visited by his daughter, Lenora, whom he blames for his wife's death. Upon entering Morella's bedroom, Lenora discovers her mother's mummified body lying on a bed. That night Morella's spirit rises from its corpse and possesses Lenora. Locke hears Lenora's screams, rushes to her room, and finds her dead. He sees his daughter's body twitching beneath the sheets and watches in horror as Lenora's face turns into that of Morella. His dead wife announces that she has returned to avenge herself; Locke drops a candle onto the dry bedclothes, and all three perish in flames. THE BLACK CAT: Drunken, foulmouthed Montresor

prefers alcohol to his wife, Annabel, a seamstress. The lonely Annabel falls victim to the advances of Fortunato, a fastidious winetaster who has befriended her husband. Montresor, learning of their affair, drugs Fortunato's amontillado and entombs him, along with Annabel, in the cellar wall of the house. Annabel's cat has slipped unnoticed into the tomb, however, and as police inspect the cellar at Montresor's invitation, the animal's wails betray the murderer's secret. THE FACTS IN THE CASE OF M. VALDEMAR: Monsieur Valdemar has forestalled death by allowing Carmichael, a mesmerist, to keep him in a trance halfway between life and death. Though Valdemar's young wife, Helene, has fallen in love with her husband's physician, Dr. Elliot James, she remains faithful to her husband. Valdemar is in agony, but Carmichael refuses to break the spell unless Helene agrees to marry him. She consents to the forced marriage, whereupon Valdemar rises from his bed and envelops Carmichael, who dies of fright. The spell broken, Valdemar becomes an oozing liquid surrounding the mesmerist's body. *Recluses. Widowers. Ghosts. Seamstresses. Winetasters. Police. Hypnotists. Physicians. Death. Revenge. Alcoholism. Filial relations. Infidelity. Murder. Hypnotism. Suspended animation. Corpses. Wine. Fires. Cats.*

Note: Also known as *Poe's Tales of Terror.*

THE TALISMAN   F6.4866

Dist Gillman Film Corp. 2 Nov **1966** [Los Angeles opening]. Sd; b&w. 35mm. 93 min.

Prod-Dir-Writ John Carr. *Assoc Prod* Jerald Cormier. *Mus* Jaime Mendoza-Nava.

Cast: Ned Romero *(Indian)*, Linda Hawkins *(woman)*, Richard Thies *(Buford)*, Jerald Cormier *(Jubilo)*, Raymond Brown *(Martineau)*, Raymond DeAnda *(Leveque)*, Louis Bacigalupi *(Isaac)*.

Western melodrama. After participating in the massacre of a wagon train, a Cheyenne finds himself unable to kill the sole female survivor. Concluding that the Great Spirit has directed him to protect her, the Indian escorts the woman through hostile territory. En route they fall in love and are attacked by three white men, led by a Confederate cavalry veteran. After saving the Indian's life, the woman leaves with the white men. That night they rape her. Returning, her lover finds her maddened by the assault. Enraged, he tracks down her ravishers. He buries the first in sand, exposing his head, which the Indian coats with honey to attract ants; he ties the second to two saplings, which tear the rapist asunder when sprung; and he kills the third with a rattlesnake. *Cheyenne Indians. Confederate veterans. Rape. Insanity. Revenge. Torture. Wagon trains. Massacres. Snakes.*

Note: Also known as *The Savage American.*

THE TALKING BEAR *see* THE BEAR

THE TALL WOMEN *(Austria/Italy/Spain)*   F6.4867

Danubia Films—Danny Film—L. M. Films. *Dist* Allied Artists. 8 Mar **1967** [Charlotte, North Carolina, opening]. Sd; col (Eastmancolor). 35mm (Cinemascope). 101 min. [Also reviewed at 92 and 94 min.]

Pres by Sidney Pink. A Sidney Pink Production. *Prod* Zeliko Kunkera. *Dir* Rudolf Zehetgruber. *Screenplay* Mino Roli, Jim Henaghan. *Orig Script* Mike Ashley. *Photog* Marcello Gatti. *Art Dir* Luis Argüello. *Film Ed* Antonio Ramírez. *Mus* Gregorio García Segura, Carlo Savina. *Prod Mgr* Angel Monis, Antonio López Moreno. *Prod Supv* Robert Russ.

Cast: Anne Baxter *(Mary Ann)*, Maria Perschy *(Ursula)*, Gustavo Rojo *(Gus McIntosh)*, Rossella Como *(Katy)*, Adriana Ambesi *(Betty)*, Perla Cristal *(Perla)*, María Mahor *(Dorothy)*, Christa Linder *(Bridgette)*, Luis Prendes *(Pope)*, Mara Cruz *(Blanche)*, Fernando Hilbeck *(White Cloud)*, Alejandra Nilo *(White Cloud's squaw)*, John Clarke *(Colonel Howard)*, Jorge Rigaud, Valentino Macchi.

Western drama. A wagon train traveling in 1870 toward Fort Lafayette is attacked by Apaches led by the savage warrior Pope, and the seven survivors—all women—take refuge in a cave. Led by the courageous Mary Ann, the women set out across the Arizona desert without horses, food, or weapons. At the fort, when the wagon train fails to arrive, scout Gus McIntosh suggests that the Army send troopers disguised as hunters to rescue any possible survivors. By the time the patrol reaches the women, now six in number, they are in danger of being ambushed. McIntosh leads them to the safety of an Indian burial ground and then joins the patrol for the attack. Pope's warriors kill all the men except McIntosh, who, though wounded, makes his way back to the women's hiding place. As they start once more on their journey, Pope readies his braves for the final assault. But his chief, White Cloud, prevents the attack and grants the women and McIntosh an escort in recognition of their courage. *Apache Indians. Courage. Scouts—Frontier. Survival. Massacres. Deserts. Burial grounds. Wagon trains. Caves. Forts. Arizona. United States Army—Cavalry.*

Note: Location scenes filmed in Spain and Rome. Opened in Madrid in Sep 1966 as *Las siete magníficas.* Released in Italy in 1966 as *Donne alla frontiera;* in Austria in 1967 as *Frauen, die durch die Hölle gehen.*

TAMAHINE (Great Britain)   F6.4868

Associated British Picture Corp. *Dist* Metro-Goldwyn-Mayer, Inc., Seven Arts Associated Corp. caMar **1964** [New York opening: 15 Jul; c31 Dec 1963; LP27170]. Sd; col (Metrocolor). 35mm (CinemaScope). 85 min.

Prod John Bryan. *Assoc Prod* Michael Forlong. *Dir* Philip Leacock. *Screenplay* Denis Cannan. *Photog* Geoffrey Unsworth. *Camera Op* Ron Taylor. *Focus* Maurice Arnold, John Alcott. *Art Dir* Tony Masters. *Set Dresser* Helen Thomas. *Scenic Artist* Bill Beavis. *Film Ed* Peter Tanner. *Mus Comp & Cond* Malcolm Arnold. *Sd* Len Shilton. *Sd Mix* Eric Bayman. *Boom E.* Haben. *1st Asst Dir* Ted Sturgis. *Unit Mgr* Timothy Burrill. *Cont* June Randall. *Prod Sec* Valerie Kent. *Cost Dsgn* Julie Harris, cost. *Miss Kwan's Wardrobe* Guy LaRoche. *Wardrobe Mistress* Jackie Jackson. *Ch Makeup* Neville Smallwood. *Ch Hairdresser* Bill Griffiths. *Casting Dir* Robert Lennard. *Still Photog* George Higgins, Roy Gough. *Prop Buyer* Dudley May. *Chargehand Electrn* Wally Thompson.

Cast: Nancy Kwan (*Tamahine*), John Fraser (*Richard*), Dennis Price (*Poole*), Coral Browne (*Madam Becque*), Dick Bentley (*storekeeper*), Derek Nimmo (*Clove*), Justine Lord (*Diana*), Michael Gough (*Cartwright*), Allan Cuthbertson (*housemaster*), Noel Hood (*Mrs. MacFarlane*), Derek Fowlds (*Bash*), Robin Stewart (*Fiend*), Viola Keats (*Mrs. Spruce*), Howard Marion Crawford (*Major Spruce*), Lally Bowers (*Mrs. Cartwright*), Joan Benham (*Mrs. O'Shaugnessy*), Max Kirby (*Mr. O'Shaugnessy*), William Mervyn (*Lord Birchester*), Barbara Cavan (*nun*), Ian Fleming (*manservant*), James Fox (*Oliver*), Bee Duffell (*nun*), Harry Lockhart (*2d young man*).

Comedy. Source: Thelma Nicklaus, *Tamahine* (London, 1957). Tamahine, the 17-year-old half-Polynesian daughter of an English anthropologist, travels to England when her father dies. She is to visit Charles Poole, her father's cousin and the headmaster of Hallow, a noted boys' school. Tamahine's Polynesian ways disrupt order at the school among students and teachers alike. At the sports day she wins all the races and climbs the clock tower in her underwear to place a chamber pot at the top. Poole's son Richard falls in love with and marries Tamahine. Several years pass, and Poole has been so influenced by Tamahine that he retires to her native island; Richard takes over as headmaster; and Tamahine, who has developed into a quiet, adoring wife, remains with him. *Polynesians. Headmasters. Halfcastes. Cousins. Anthropologists. Orphans. Adolescence. Social customs. Marriage. Retirement. Boarding schools. Sports. South Sea Islands.*

Note: Released in Great Britain in 1963; running time: 95 min.

THE T.A.M.I. SHOW   F6.4869

Electronovision Productions-Screen Entertainment Co. *Dist* American International Pictures. 14 Nov **1964** [Los Angeles showing]. Sd; b&w. 35mm (Electronovision). 113 min. [Also 110 min.]

Prod Lee Savin. *Exec Prod* William Sargent, Jr. *Dir* Steve Binder. *Assoc Dir* George Turpin. *Tech Dir* Charles LaForce. *Photog* Jim Kilgore. *Video Engr* Carl Hanseman. *Art Dir* Frank Swig. *Mus Dir* Jack Nitzsche. *Sp Material* Digby Wolfe. *Choreog* David Winters. *Audio Engr* Lionel St. Peter. *Sd Coörd* Dave Hassinger. *Prod Mgr* Del Jack. *Prod Coörd* John Rougeot. *Post Prod Supv* Richard Krown. *Wardrobe* Wally Harton. *Mus Cons* Al Ham. *Tech Facilities Supv* by Joseph Bluth. *Tech Supv* Robert Ringer.

Featuring: The Beach Boys, Chuck Berry, Marvin Gaye, Lesley Gore, The Rolling Stones, The Barbarians, James Brown and the Flames, Gerry and the Pacemakers, Jan and Dean, The Supremes, Billy J. Kramer and the Dakotas, Smokey Robinson and the Miracles.

Musical revue. Filmed at a rock concert in the Santa Monica Civic Auditorium on October 29, 1964, T.A.M.I. (Teenage Awards Music International) offers music sung by pop groups and individual artists. An incomplete listing of songs includes: "Maybe I Know," "It's My Party," "You Don't Own Me," "It's Judy's Turn to Cry" (Lesley Gore); "Hitchhike" (Marvin Gaye); "Time Is on My Side" (Rolling Stones); "Ferry Cross the Mersey," "I'm Telling You Now," "I Like It" (Gerry and the Pacemakers); "Little Children," "Do You Wanna Know a Secret" (Billy J. Kramer); "Maybelline," "Johnny B. Goode," "Roll Over Beethoven" (Chuck Berry); "Surfer Girl," "Fun, Fun, Fun," "I Get Around" (Beach Boys); "Little Old Lady From Pasadena," "Sidewalk Surfin'" (Jan and Dean); "Shop Around" (Smokey Robinson and the Miracles); "Baby Love," "Baby Don't Leave Me" (Supremes). *Singers. Guitarists. Musicians. Rock and roll. Santa Monica Civic Auditorium.*

Note: Subtitle(?): *Teenage Command Performance*. Also known as: *Teenage Music International, Teenage Awards Music International,* and *T.A.M.I.*

THE TAMING   F6.4870

Victoria Films. *Dist* Victoria Films, Times Film Corp. 21 Aug **1968**. Sd; b&w. 35mm (Ultrascope). 85 min.

Prod-Dir-Writ Robert Arkless. *Dir Photog* Julianna Wang. *Mus* Marcel Aimee.

Cast: Lindsey Bowen (*Tom Mannix*), Liz Stevens (*Rita*), Sharon Church (*Barbra Forrest*), Sam Stewart (*Marco*), Maria Riva.

Drama. While traveling on the subway, three strangers—Tom Mannix, Rita, and Barbra Forrest—daydream to alleviate their loneliness. Tom, longing for female companionship, sees himself as a James Bond type protecting Barbra from a gang of sexual perverts. In his efforts to subdue the assailants, he is captured, seduced and tortured by the female leader of the gang and compelled to watch as an erotic operation is performed on Barbra. In Rita's daydream, she imagines that she and the man sitting next to her, Marco, are blackmailing an eminent politician by photographing him while he abuses Rita with a perfume bottle. Barbra, in reality a naive, inexperienced girl, fantasizes that her peaceful trip to the country is interrupted by the appearance of Tom, Rita, and Marco. Barbra watches Rita and Marco make passionate love; Barbra is raped by Tom and then whipped by Rita. Arriving at their subway stop, Rita and Marco, who have sized each other up, go off together, and Tom and Barbra, though both shy, have sufficiently communicated their feelings to do likewise. *Gangs. Politicians. Innocents. Loneliness. Sex deviates. Seduction. Torture. Blackmail. Sadism. Rape. Flagellation. Surgery. Subways. Fantasy.*

THE TAMING OF THE SHREW (Reissue)   F6.4871

Pickford Corp.-Elton Corp. *Dist* Cinema Classics. 4 Nov **1966** [Los Angeles opening; c13 May 1966; LP35400]. Sd eff & mus score; b&w. 35mm. 63 min.

Prod Matty Kemp. *Titl & Opticals* Consolidated Film Industries. *Film Ed* John F. Link.

Note: Film version of Shakespeare's comedy with Mary Pickford and Douglas Fairbanks. Originally released 26 Oct 1929; c1 Nov 1929; LP825; length: 6,116 ft. Reissue contains new music score and sound effects. Copyright claimants: Mary Pickford Corp. and Douglas Fairbanks, Jr.

THE TAMING OF THE SHREW (United States/Italy)   F6.4872

Royal Films International-F. A. I. *Dist* Columbia Pictures. 8 Mar **1967** [New York opening; c1 Mar 1967; LF10]. Sd (Westrex); col (Technicolor). 35mm (Panavision). 122 min.

Prod Elizabeth Taylor, Richard Burton, Franco Zeffirelli. *Exec Prod* Richard McWhorter. *Dir* Franco Zeffirelli. *Screenplay* Paul Dehn, Suso Cecchi D'Amico, Franco Zeffirelli. *Dir Photog* Oswald Morris. *Camera* Luciano Trasatti. *Op* Nino Cristiani. *Art Dir* Elven Webb, Giuseppe Mariani. *Sketch Artist* Gianito Burchiellaro. *Set Decor* Dario Simoni, Luigi Gervasi. *Assoc Dsgn* John De Cuir. *Prod Dsgn* Renzo Mongiardino. *Main Titl Graphics* Maurice Binder. *Film Ed* Peter Taylor. *Mus Comp* Nino Rota. *Cond* Carlo Savina. *Sd Mix* David Hildyard. *Sd* Aldo De Martini, Mario Ottani. *Dub Ed* Graham Harris, Janet Davidson. *Dub Rec* John Aldred. *Ed Italian Vers* Franca Silvi, Carlo Fabianelli. *Asst Dir* Carlo Lastricati, Rinaldo Ricci, Albino Cocco. *Prod Supv* Guy Luongo. *Unit Mgr* Roberto Cocco, Daniele Micheletti. *Cont* Elaine Schreyeck. *Cost Dsgn* Danilo Donati. *Cost for Elizabeth Taylor Dsgn* Irene Sharaff. *Wardrobe* Gloria Mussetta. *Elizabeth Taylor's Cost* Sartoria S.A.F.A.S. *Cost Houses* Casa d'Arte Cerratelli, Sartoria Farani. *Wigs Furnished* Maggi and Orcchetti. *Wigs* Leclabart (Paris). *Makeup for Elizabeth Taylor* Frank LaRue. *Makeup for Richard Burton* Ron Berkeley. *Makeup* Alberto De Rossi, Giannetto De Rossi. *Elizabeth Taylor's Hairstyles* Alexandre of Paris. *Hairdressing for Elizabeth Taylor* Agnes Flanagan. *Hairdresser* Grazia De Rossi. *Sp Eff* Augie Lohman. *Prop* Ken Muggleston.

Cast: Elizabeth Taylor (*Katharina*), Richard Burton (*Petruchio*), Cyril Cusack (*Grumio*), Michael Hordern (*Baptista*), Alfred Lynch (*Tranio*), Alan Webb (*Gremio*), Giancarlo Cobelli (*The Priest*), Vernon Dobtcheff (*pedant*), Ken Parry (*tailor*), Anthony Garner (*haberdasher*), Natasha Pyne (*Bianca*), Michael York (*Lucentio*), Victor Spinetti (*Hortensio*), Roy Holder (*Biondello*), Mark Dignam (*Vincentio*), Bice Valori (*The Widow*), Gianni Magni (*Curtis*), Lino Capolicchio (*Gregory*), Roberto Antonelli (*Philip*), Alberto Bonucci (*Nathaniel*), Tina Perna, Milena Vucotich, Alfredo Bianchini, Valentino Macchi.

Costume comedy. Source: William Shakespeare, *The Taming of the Shrew*. A rich Paduan merchant named Baptista has two beautiful daughters, the unruly and vile-tempered Katharina, and the sweet and lovable Bianca. The many suitors for the hand of Bianca are greatly dismayed by Baptista's refusal of their petitions so long as the elder Katharina remains unwed. Lucentio, a young student from Pisa, is so taken by Bianca's beauty that he poses as a teacher of languages and obtains a position as a tutor in Baptista's household. As Lucentio is proceeding with his wooing, a fortune-hunting scoundrel named Petruchio arrives in Padua seeking a wealthy wife. Although he immediately falls victim to Katharina's scorn and abuse, he wards off her outraged blows until they both fall exhausted into a huge mound of sheep wool. He then calmly praises her numerous charms and announces that they will marry the following Sunday. On their wedding day, he arrives late, very drunk, and wearing indecorous clothes. But despite everyone's apprehension, the ceremony is performed, and Petruchio sets his wildly protesting bride on a broken-down horse and leads her on a muddy journey to his dilapidated country home. There, under the pretext of his great love for Katharina, he rejects all manner of comfort and luxury, maintaining they are unworthy of her. Eventually, after Lucentio has been revealed to be the son of the honored Vincentio of Padua and won permission to marry his beloved Bianca, Katharina and Petruchio are invited to the wedding feast. There Petruchio wagers that Katharina is the most devoted and obedient of wives. And to the astonishment of all, Katharina shames all the other women by giving them a lecture on the virtues of wifely obedience. *Merchants. Sisters. Tutors. Shrews. Fortune hunters. Marriage. Filial relations. Courtship. Disguise. Weddings. Honeymoons. Padua.*

Note: Released in Italy in 1967 as *La bisbetica domata.*

TAMMY AND THE DOCTOR   **F6.4873**

Ross Hunter Productions. *Dist* Universal International Films. 29 May **1963** [Dallas opening; c15 Jun 1963; LP33834]. Sd (Westrex); col (Eastman Color by Pathé). 35mm. 89 min.

Prod Ross Hunter. *In Charge of Prod* Edward Muhl. *Dir* Harry Keller. *Writ* Oscar Brodney. *Dir Photog* Russell Metty. *Camera Op* Ed Pyle. *Camera Asst* Ledger Haddow, Wilbur Gossman. *Art Dir* Alexander Golitzen, George Webb. *Set Decor* Howard Bristol. *Set Coörd* Fred Knoth. *Film Ed* Milton Carruth. *Asst Ed* Richard Bracken. *Mus Supv* Joseph Gershenson. *Mus* Frank Skinner. *Song:* "Tammy" Jay Livingston, Ray Evans. *Sung by* Sandra Dee. *Sd* Waldon O. Watson, Frank H. Wilkinson, James Swartz, Harold King, James Curtis. *Asst Dir* Phil Bowles, Carl Beringer. *Unit Prod Mgr* Bob Larson. *Script Supv* Diana Loomis. *Wardrobe Dsgn* Rosemary Odell. *Makeup* Bud Westmore, Jack Freeman, Allan Snyder, Jean Mollner. *Hairstyles* Larry Germain, Kay Reed, Le Vaughn Speer. *Dial Coach* Leon Charles. *Still Photog* Jack Geraghty. *Gaffer* Max Nippell. *Grip* Charles Cowie, Ken Smith. *Prop* Sol Martino, John Faltis, Walter Hammond.

Cast: Sandra Dee *(Tammy)*, Peter Fonda *(Dr. Mark Cheswick)*, MacDonald Carey *(Dr. Wayne Bentley)*, Beulah Bondi *(Mrs. Call)*, Margaret Lindsay *(Rachel Coleman)*, Reginald Owen *(Jason Tripp)*, Alice Pearce *(Millie)*, Adam West *(Dr. Eric Hassler)*, Joan Marshall *(Vera)*, Stanley Clements *(Wally Day)*, Doodles Weaver *(traction patient)*, Mitzi Hoag *(Pamela)*, Alex Gerry *(chief of staff)*, Robert Foulk *(surgeon)*, Jill Jackson *(assistant surgeon)*, Forrest Lewis *(Dr. Crandall)*, Sondra Rodgers *(1st nurse)*, Charles Seel *(Dr. Smithers)*, Suzie Kaye *(Dora)*, Paul Nesbitt *(David)*.

Drama. Based on characters created by: Cid Ricketts Sumner. When elderly and wealthy Mrs. Call is taken to a Los Angeles hospital for a serious operation, her young companion Tammy, a country girl from Mississippi, goes along and takes a job as an assistant to the nursing staff. Though Tammy's inexperience causes considerable confusion, she wins the support of Miss Coleman, the head nurse, and manages to pacify old Jason Tripp, the hospital's crotchety millionaire patient. She also attracts the interest of Dr. Mark Cheswick, but their romance comes to a premature end when Mark is warned by his superior, Dr. Bentley, that a romantic entanglement might jeopardize his career. Upon learning that Miss Coleman is hopelessly in love with Dr. Bentley, Tammy tries to intercede but succeeds only in getting the older woman to turn in her resignation. She returns, however, to assist at Mrs. Call's operation, which is successful. Now aware of his love for Miss Coleman, Dr. Bentley proposes, thereby opening the way for Tammy and Mark to renew their romance. *Ingenues. Physicians. Millionaires. Surgery. Nurses. Hospitals. Los Angeles.*

Note: One of a series of films based on the Tammy character.

TAMMY AND THE MILLIONAIRE   **F6.4874**

Uni-Bet Productions. *Dist* Universal Pictures. Jul **1967** [Los Angeles showing; c22 Jul 1967; LP38808]. Sd (Westrex); col (Pathé Color). 35mm. 88 min. [Copyright length: 80 min.]

Prod Dick Wesson. *Dir* Sidney Miller, Ezra Stone, Leslie Goodwins. *Screenplay* George Tibbles. *Dir Photog* John F. Warren, Robert Wyckoff, Enzo A. Martinelli, Bud Thackery. *Col Coörd* Robert Brower. *Art Dir* Henry Larrecq, Howard E. Johnson. *Set Decor* John McCarthy, Audrey Blasdel, Ralph Sylos. *Film Ed* Larry D. Lester. *Mus* Jack Marshall. *Mus Supv* Stanley Wilson. *Sd* Waldon O. Watson, Earl Martin Madery. *Asst Dir* George Bisk, John Clarke Bowman. *Unit Prod Mgr* James Hogan, Abby Singer. *Makeup* Bud Westmore. *Hairstyles* Larry Germain.

Cast: Debbie Watson *(Tammy Tarleton)*, Frank McGrath *(Uncle Lucius)*, Denver Pyle *(Grandpa)*, George Furth *(Dwayne Whitt)*, Donald Woods *(John Brent)*, Dorothy Green *(Lavinia Tate)*, David Macklin *(Peter Tate)*, Linda Marshall *(Gloria Tate)*, Jay Sheffield *(Steven Brent)*, Teddy Quinn *(Dewey Maine McKinley)*, Bella Bruck *(Sybelline Tate)*, Andy Albin *(mailman)*, Craig Hundley *(Billy Joe Morgan)*, Roy Roberts *(Governor Alden)*, Jeff York *(Grundy Tate)*.

Romantic comedy. Source: Cid Ricketts Sumner, *Tammy Out of Time* (Indianapolis, 1948). Cid Ricketts Sumner, *Tammy, Tell Me True* (Indianapolis, 1959). When Tammy is hired as secretary to millionaire John Brent, she arouses the anger of Lavinia Tate, who hoped that her daughter Gloria would get the position and be able to win the affection of Brent's

collegiate son, Steven. While home from school, Steven is attracted to Tammy, and the efforts of Gloria and her mother to discredit the young girl only succeed in bringing the couple closer together. Mrs. Tate attempts to have Tammy's home taken away from her because of unpaid taxes, but Tammy's Grandpa and Uncle Lucius find an ancient deed which establishes their ownership of much of the local property. Although they are anxious to take advantage of the situation, Tammy makes them promise to leave the Tates alone. After Mr. Brent has anonymously paid the back taxes, Tammy's relatives crash a party and reduce it to a shambles. Later, all is forgiven, and Tammy ends up in Steven's arms. *Ingenues. Secretaries. Millionaires. Uncles. Grandfathers. Jealousy. Filial relations. Taxes. Documentation.*

Note: Film is composed of four episodes of the ABC television series *Tammy* (1965-66). The fourth in a series of films based on the "Tammy" character.

TAMMY TELL ME TRUE   **F6.4875**

Ross Hunter Productions. *Dist* Universal–International. 26 Jul **1961** [New York opening; c1 Jul 1961; LP24726]. Sd; col (Eastman Color). 35mm. 97 min.

Prod Ross Hunter. *Dir* Harry Keller. *Screenplay* Oscar Brodney. *Dir Photog* Clifford Stine. *Art Dir* Alexander Golitzen, Alfred Sweeney. *Set Decor* Howard Bristol. *Film Ed* Otto Ludwig. *Mus* Percy Faith. *Mus Supv* Joseph Gershenson. *Title Song* Dorothy Squires. *Sung by* Sandra Dee. *Sd* Waldon O. Watson, Frank H. Wilkinson. *Asst Dir* Joseph Kenny, Charles Scott, Jr. *Unit Prod Mgr* Lew Leary. *Gowns* Rosemary Odell. *Miss Grey's Wardrobe* Stanley Sherman. *Makeup* Bud Westmore. *Hair Stylist* Larry Germain. *Dial Dir* Leon Charles.

Cast: Sandra Dee *(Tammy)*, John Gavin *(Tom Freeman)*, Charles Drake *(Buford Woodly)*, Virginia Grey *("Miss" Jenks)*, Julia Meade *(Suzanne Rook)*, Beulah Bondi *(Mrs. Call)*, Cecil Kellaway *(Captain Joe)*, Edgar Buchanan *(Judge Carver)*, Gigi Perreau *(Rita)*, Juanita Moore *(Della)*, Hayden Rorke *(Joshua Welling)*, Ward Ramsey *(Caleb Slade)*, Henry Corden *(Captain Armand)*, Don Dorrell *(Roger)*, Pat McNulty *(Joan)*, Taffy Paul *(Kay)*, Lowell Brown *(John)*, Bill Herrin *(Phil)*, Catherine McLeod *(Mrs. Bateman)*, Ross Elliott *(Professor Bateman)*, Ned Wever *(Dr. Stach)*.

Romantic comedy. Source: Cid Ricketts Sumner, *Tammy, Tell Me True* (Indianapolis, 1959). Heartbroken because her college boyfriend fails to answer her letters, shantyboat-bred Tammy decides to go to college herself. After moving her decrepit craft downriver to Seminola College, she gains admission as a special student and, to pay her expenses, takes a job as companion to Mrs. Call, a wealthy eccentric. Tammy's fresh and unspoiled nature so delights the old lady that she moves in with Tammy on her shantyboat and rewards the young girl with an expensive necklace. Meanwhile, Tammy has also won the affections of Tom Freeman, the handsome public speaking instructor, and "Miss" Jenks, the unhappily married dean of women. Eventually Mrs. Call's conniving niece, Suzanne Rook, launches a search for her missing aunt. When she catches a glimpse of Tammy wearing the necklace, she has the young girl arrested and arranges a sanity hearing for Mrs. Call, but the simple honesty of Tammy's testimony so impresses the judge that he dismisses Suzanne's charges. Tammy helps straighten out "Miss" Jenks's marriage to her artist husband, Buford Woodly. She then realizes that she has forgotten all about her former boyfriend—it is Tom whom she really loves. *Students. Eccentrics. Aunts. College teachers. Deans. Judges. Artists. College life. Missing persons. Theft. Insanity. Marriage. Houseboats.*

Note: The film is a sequel to *Tammy and the Bachelor* (1957) and was followed by *Tammy and the Doctor*, q. v.

TANIN NO KAO *see* **THE FACE OF ANOTHER**

TANTE ZITA *see* **ZITA**

DAS TAPFERE SCHNEIDERLEIN *see* **THE BRAVE LITTLE TAILOR**

LOS TARANTOS (Spain)   **F6.4876**

Tecisa. *Dist* Sigma III Corp. 29 Jun **1964** [New York opening]. Sd; col (Eastman Color). 35mm. 81 min.

Prod José G. Maesso, Leonard Gruenberg. *Dir* Rovira-Beleta. *Screenplay* Rovira-Beleta, Alfredo Mañas. *Photog* Massimo Dallamano. *Art Dir* Juan Alberto Soler. *Film Ed* Emilio Rodriguez Oses. *Mus* Emilio Pujol, Fernando García Morcillo, Andrés Batista, José Solá. *Still Photog* Rafael Pérez de Rozas.

Cast: Carmen Amaya *(Augustias)*, Sara Lezana *(Juana)*, Daniel Martin *(Rafael)*, Antonio Prieto *(Rosendo)*, Margarita Lozano *(Isabel)*, José Manuel Martín *(Curro)*, Antonio Gades *(Mojigongo)*, Antonia Singla *(Sole)*, Aurelio Galán *(Jero)*, Carlos Villafranca *(Salvador)*, Antonio Escudero *(Juan)*, Amapola García *(Antonia)*, Rosario Ortíz *(Aurora)*, Antonio Lavilla *(Sancho)*, Anselmo Batista, Andrés Batista *(picaos)*, Antonio Guisa *(friend of the picaos)*, Carmen Amaya Co. *(flamenco dancers)*.

Musical drama. Source: Alfredo Mañas, *La historia de los Tarantos* (a play; production undetermined). In the Gypsy quarter of Barcelona, a young man and woman meet at a wedding and fall in love, unaware that their families are sworn enemies. Rafael is a Taranto, and Juana is the daughter of Rosendo, the hotblooded leader of the Zoronga family. The beauty of Juana's flamenco dancing, however, wins over Rafael's mother, Augustias, and she accepts Juana as her daughter-in-law. But as the Gypsy quarter prepares for a fiesta, the elder Zoronga, faithful to his vow of hatred, forces Juana into the arms of Curro, an unscrupulous *picao*. Juana escapes to Rafael, and the two lovers take refuge at the beach in a small house owned by the Tarantos. To the sound of Christmas Eve celebrations, they repeat their vows of love and make plans to flee to a place where they can live without hate. Violence erupts as Curro finds their hiding place and murders them both. Rafael's brother takes revenge by slaying Curro; only then do the two families mournfully pledge a new peace. *Gypsies. Dancers. Feuds. Filial relations. Revenge. Murder. Weddings. Christmas. Barcelona.*

Note: Filmed in Barcelona. Released in Spain in 1963; running time: 92 min. Rovira-Beleta is also known as Francisco Rovira Beleta.

TARAS BULBA　　　　　　　　　　　　　　　　　　　　　　　F6.4877

Hecht-Curtleigh Productions. *Dist* United Artists. 19 Dec **1962** [Chicago opening; c21 Dec 1962; LP23669]. Sd; col (Eastman Color, print by DeLuxe). 35mm (Panavision). 122 min.

Prod Harold Hecht. *Assoc Prod* Alexander Whitelaw. *Dir* J. Lee Thompson. *2d Unit Dir* Cliff Lyons. *Screenplay* Waldo Salt, Karl Tunberg. *Photog* Joseph MacDonald. *Art Dir* Edward Carrere. *Set Decor* William Calvert. *Film Ed* William Reynolds, Gene Milford, Eda Warren, Folmar Blangsted. *Mus* Franz Waxman. *Song Lyr* Mack David. *Orch* Leonid Raab. *Sd Mix* Stan Cooley. *Sd* Bert Hallberg. *Asst Dir* Tom Shaw, Dave Silver. *Prod Mgr* Gilbert Kurland. *Cost Dsgn* Norma Koch. *Men's Cost* Israel Berne. *Ladies' Cost* Olive Koenitz. *Makeup* Frank McCoy, Emile Lavigne, Dan Striepeke. *Hairstyles* Joan St. Oegger. *Sp Eff* Fred Wolff, Barney Wolff, Butler-Glouner Inc. *Sp Photog Eff* Howard A. Anderson, Russ Lawson. *Tech Adv* Audrey Tolstoy.

Cast: Tony Curtis (*Andrei Bulba*), Yul Brynner (*Taras Bulba*), Christine Kaufmann (*Natalia Dubrov*), Sam Wanamaker (*Filipenko*), Brad Dexter (*Shilo*), Guy Rolfe (*Prince Grigory*), Perry Lopez (*Ostap Bulba*), George Macready (*governor*), Ilka Windish (*Sophia Bulba*), Vladimir Sokoloff (*Old Stepan*), Vladimir Irman (*Grisha Kubenko*), Daniel Ocko (*Ivan Mykola*), Abraham Sofaer (*abbot*), Mickey Finn (*Korzh*), Richard Rust (*Captain Alex*), Ron Weyand (*Tymoshevsky*), Vitina Marcus (*gypsy princess*), Martine Milner (*redheaded girl*), Chuck Hayward (*Dolotov*), Syl Lamont (*Kimon Kander*), Ellen Davalos (*Zina*), Marvin Goux (*Brother Bartholomew*), Jack Raine (*mayor*).

Historical drama. Source: Nikolay Vasilyevich Gogol, "Taras Bulba," in *Mirgorod* (Saint Petersburg, 1835). After centuries of fighting for possession of the Ukraine, the Cossacks aid the Polish Army in 1550 by defeating the Turks and driving their soldiers over a steep cliff. Cossack leader Taras Bulba is invited to a Polish banquet celebrating the victory, but he and his men are betrayed by their hosts and forced to flee across the steppes. Later, Taras raises two sons, Andrei and Ostap, and eventually sends them to Kiev University to learn the ways of their enemies. The headstrong Andrei falls in love with Natalia, a young Polish noblewoman, but is considered unworthy of her because of his lowly birth. Driven back to his homeland after Natalia's brother dies in a fight with him and Ostap, Andrei finds that the Cossacks have amassed an army large enough to attack the Poles at Dubno. Taras and his men lay siege to the city, causing famine and pestilence, but Andrei sneaks inside the city walls when he learns that Natalia is trapped within. After he is captured trying to rescue her, Andrei agrees to raid the Cossack camp for food to prevent Natalia from being burned at the stake. Although Andrei succeeds in getting her to safety, he is shot down as a traitor by Taras; the Cossack leader is humbled, however, by the sight of Natalia weeping over his son's body. *Cossacks. Poles. Turks. Nobility. Brothers. Traitors. Revenge. Perfidy. Filial relations. Famine. Plague. Kiev. Dubno (Ukraine). Poland—Army.*

Note: Location scenes filmed in Salta, Argentina. Avala Film is credited as a coproducer by British sources.

TARGETS　　　　　　　　　　　　　　　　　　　　　　　　　F6.4878

Saticoy Productions. *Dist* Paramount Pictures. 13 Aug **1968** [New York opening; c30 Dec 1967; LP36028]. Sd; col (Pathé). 35mm. 90 min.

Prod-Dir-Writ Peter Bogdanovich. *Assoc Prod* Daniel Selznick. *Uncredited Exec Prod* Roger Corman. *Story* Polly Platt, Peter Bogdanovich. *Photog* Laszlo Kovacs. *Prod Dsgn* Polly Platt. *Main Titl* Cinema Research Corp. *Film Ed* Peter Bogdanovich. *Asst Film Ed* Mae Woods. *Incidental Mus* Charles Greene, Brian Stone. *Sd* Sam Kopetzky. *Sd Ed* Verna Fields. *Asst Dir* Gilles De Turenne. *Prod Mgr* Paul Lewis. *Makeup* Scott Hamilton.

Cast: Boris Karloff (*Byron Orlok*), Tim O'Kelly (*Bobby Thompson*), Nancy Hsueh (*Jenny*), James Brown (*Robert Thompson, Sr.*), Sandy Baron (*Kip Larkin*), Arthur Peterson (*Ed Loughlin*), Mary Jackson (*Charlotte Thompson*), Tanya Morgan (*Ilene Thompson*), Monty Landis (*Marshall Smith*), Peter Bogdanovich (*Sammy Michaels*), Paul Condylis (*drive-in manager*), Mark Dennis, Stafford Morgan (*gunshop salesmen*), Daniel Ades (*chauffeur*),

Timothy Burns (*waiter*), Warren White (*grocery boy*), Geraldine Baron (*Larkin's girl*), Gary Kent (*gas tank worker*), Ellie Walker (*woman on freeway*), Frank Marshall (*ticket boy*), Byron Betz (*projectionist*), Mike Farrell (*man in phone booth*), Carol Samuels (*cashier*), Jay Daniel (*snack bar attendant*), James Morris (*man with pistol*), Elaine Partnow, Paul Belcher, James Bowie, Anita Poree, Robert Cleaves, Kay Douglas, Raymond Roy, Diana Ashley, Kirk Scott, Susan Douglas.

Drama. After a screening of his latest film, famous horror film star Byron Orlok announces his retirement. Despite the anger of his producer and the pleas of director-writer Sammy Michaels, Orlok is adamant. As he leaves for his limousine, he is momentarily caught in the cross-hair of a telescopic-sight rifle being tested in a gunshop across the street by young Bobby Thompson. After adding the rifle to an arsenal of weapons in his car trunk, Thompson drives to his San Fernando Valley home, where he lives with his wife, Ilene, and his parents. That evening, as Ilene prepares to leave for her night job, Thompson asks her to stay home, but she refuses. When she greets him the next morning, Thompson shoots her and then kills his mother and a delivery boy in the kitchen. After leaving behind a note stating that there will be more killing before he dies, Thompson drives to a complex of gasoline tanks overlooking a freeway, climbs atop one of the tanks, eats his lunch, and begins shooting people in the passing cars. When the police arrive, he escapes to a drive-in theater where Byron Orlok is scheduled to make a personal appearance. The previous evening, Orlok had refused to go to the drive-in and, following an argument with his secretary, remained in his hotel suite. After drinking half a bottle of Scotch, he was visited by the drunken Sammy Michaels; they talked but resolved nothing and passed out on the bed. The next day, however, Orlok agreed to appear at the drive-in. By the time Orlok and his party arrive, Thompson has poked a hole in the screen and begun firing at people in their cars. As panic breaks out, Orlok decides to confront the killer; upon seeing the real Orlok approaching (appearing simultaneously on the screen), Thompson becomes so confused that he is easily taken by the police. *Actors. Psychopaths. Motion picture producers. Motion picture directors. Motion picture scriptwriters—Drive-ins. Delivery boys. Police. Murder. Matricide. Firearms. Motion picture theaters—Drive-ins. Traffic. San Fernando Valley (California). "The Terror". "The Criminal Code".*

Note: Location scenes filmed in Los Angeles. Included are film clips from *The Terror*, q. v., and *The Criminal Code* (1931).

I TARTARI see THE TARTARS

THE TARTARS (Italy/Yugoslavia)　　　　　　　　　　　　　F6.4879

Lux Film–Dubrava Film. *Dist* Metro-Goldwyn-Mayer, Inc. 20 Jun **1962** [New York opening; c31 Dec 1961; LP23138]. Sd (Fonolux); col (Technicolor). 35mm (Totalscope). 83 min.

Dir Richard Thorpe. *Dir Italian Vers* Ferdinando Baldi. *Story-Screenplay* Emimmo Salvi, Sabatino Ciuffini, Oreste Palella, Gaio Fratini, Ambrogio Molteni. *Adtl English Dial* Julian De Kassel. *Dir Photog* Amerigo Gengarelli. *Camera Op* Carlo Fiore. *Asst Camera* Mario Cimini, Silvano Mancini. *Art Dir* Oscar D'Amico. *Set Dresser* Antonio Fratalocchi. *Set Dsgn* Pasquale D'Alpino. *Film Ed* Maurizio Lucidi. *Mus* Renzo Rossellini. *Orch Cond* Pierluigi Urbini. *Sd Rec* Kurt Doubravsky. *Asst Dir* Giorgio Gentili, Ambrogio Molteni. *Prod Supv* Alessandro Tasca. *Prod Mgr* Renato Jaboni, Elios Vercelloni. *Unit Mgr* Roberto Onorati. *Prod Asst* Carlo Bartolini, Luigi Guasco. *Script Girl* Ama Tasca. *Cost Dsgn* Giovanna Natili. *Makeup* Renato Bomarsi. *Hairdresser* Giovanni Palombi. *Sp Eff* Costel Grozea. *Master of Arms* Franco Fantasia.

Cast: Victor Mature (*Oleg*), Orson Welles (*Burandai*), Folco Lulli (*Togrul*), Liana Orfei (*Helga*), Bella Cortez (*Samia*), Luciano Marin (*Eric*), Arnoldo Foà (*Chu-Lung*), Furio Meniconi (*Sigrun*), Pietro Ceccarelli, Renato Terra, Spartaco Nale.

Action drama. In the early Middle Ages the Russian steppes are dominated by Tartars who allow only Vikings to pass through from their northern sites. The alliance is disrupted, however, when the Viking chieftain, Oleg, refuses to join Togrul the Tartar in warring against the Slavs. Oleg kills Togrul and takes his daughter, Samia, as hostage. Togrul's brother, Burandai, the new Tartar chief, retaliates by capturing Oleg's wife, Helga, drugging her, and then leaving her to the lust of his men. An exchange of prisoners is proposed, but Samia has fallen in love with Oleg's younger brother, Eric, and no longer wishes to return to her people. Furthermore, Helga is unable to face her shame and leaps to her death from a fortress tower. Oleg and Eric then quarrel over Samia's fate, but their argument is interrupted by the arrival of the Tartars. In the bloody battle between the two tribes, both Oleg and Burandai are killed, and the Viking fortress is burned to the ground. Eric and Samia escape and take refuge on a ship, which carries them to the safety of the far North. *Tartars. Vikings. Brothers. Hostages. Prisoners of war. Kidnaping. Revenge. Suicide. Rape. Ships. Middle Ages. Steppes. Russia.*

Note: Opened in Rome in Apr 1961 as *I tartari*; running time: 105 min.

THE TARTS   F6.4880

C. I. T. Films. *Dist* I. R. M. I. Films. ca **1965**. Sd; b&w. 35mm. 60 min.
Dir Joe Davis. *Photog* Bob Riko.
Cast: Marianna Bensin.
Drama. Fashion model Cynthia Lane is eventually destroyed by her indulgence in voyeurism, lesbianism, and promiscuity. *Models. Voyeurism. Lesbianism. Promiscuity.*
Note: Filmed on location in San Francisco.

THE TARTS *see* **THE WORST CRIME OF ALL!**

TARZAN AND JANE REGAINED SORT OF   F6.4881

Dist Film-Makers' Cooperative. 24 Feb **1964** [New York opening]. Si with sd-on-tape; col & b&w. 16mm. 120 min.
Prod-Dir Andy Warhol. *Film Ed* Taylor Mead. *Sd-on-tape* Taylor Mead.
Cast: Taylor Mead *(Tarzan)*, Naomi Levine *(Jane)*, Dennis Hopper, Claes Oldenburg, Pat Oldenburg, Wally Berman.
Satire. At a seaside playground, a man makes faces and strikes poses satirizing Edgar Rice Burroughs' character Tarzan; a woman ("Jane") swims in the nude. They wash each other in a bathtub. The man plays with some dogs, romps about, and dances. *Swimming. Nudity. Playgrounds. Beaches. Tarzan. Dogs.*
Note: Filmed in Los Angeles. Each scene consists of a fixed-frame image.

TARZAN AND THE GREAT RIVER   F6.4882

Banner Productions–Allfin, A. G. *Dist* Paramount Pictures. 13 Sep **1967** [Los Angeles opening; c13 Sep 1967; LP35366]. Sd; col (Eastman Color). 35mm (Panavision). 88 min.
Prod Sy Weintraub. *Assoc Prod* Steve Shagan. *Dir* Robert Day. *Screenplay* Bob Barbash. *Story* Bob Barbash, Lewis Reed. *Dir Photog* Irving Lippman. *Camera Op* Hugo Velasco. *Asst Camera* Roy Ford. *Art Dir* Herbert Smith. *Main Titl* CINEFX, Phill Norman. *Film Ed* Anthony Carras, Edward Mann, James Nelson. *Assoc Ed* Donald Wolfe. *Mus Comp & Cond* William Loose. *Mus Supv* Igo Kantor. *Sd Eff* Edit-Rite Inc. *Re-rec* Don Minkler, Bill Mumford. *Asst Dir* Mario Cisneros. *Prod Mgr* John Palmer. *Unit Mgr* Camillo Sampaio. *Cont* Barbara Rowland. *Sp Eff* Ira Anderson. *Prop Master* George Walford.
Cast: Mike Henry *(Tarzan)*, Jan Murray *(Capt. Sam Bishop)*, Manuel Padilla, Jr. *(Pepe)*, Diana Millay *(Dr. Ann Phillips)*, Rafer Johnson *(Barcuna)*, Paulo Gracindo *(professor)*.
Adventure melodrama. Based on characters created by: Edgar Rice Burroughs. Visiting his animal friends at the Rio de Janeiro zoo, Tarzan learns that a tribal chieftain known as Barcuna has revived the ancient cult of leopard men and has been raiding villages along the Amazon and forcing the natives into slave labor. When his professor friend at the zoo is murdered by the leopard men, Tarzan sets out with Cheetah, his pet chimp, and Baron, his pet lion, to find Barcuna. Upon reaching the river, he encounters Capt. Sam Bishop, the owner of a small cargo boat, and his young aide, Pepe, an orphan of the Marakeet tribe. Captain Sam agrees to take Tarzan upstream as far as Calebah; but before reaching their destination they find Dr. Ann Phillips wandering about in shock following a raid by the leopard men. After being revived, she explains that she must get medicine to the Marakeet country to check an epidemic. When they arrive, however, the chief, out of fear and superstition, refuses to allow Dr. Phillips to inoculate his people. Young Pepe volunteers for the treatment; and when the natives see that no harm has befallen him, they all agree to accept inoculation. With the epidemic under control, Tarzan makes his way to Barcuna's hideout, where the captured slaves are being forced to dig for diamonds. The two men engage in hand-to-hand combat until Tarzan emerges triumphant. With the death of its leader, the leopard cult collapses. Captain Sam, Pepe, and Ann return to civilization, but Tarzan chooses to remain in the jungle for a while longer. *Professors. Physicians. Orphans. Tribal chiefs. Seamen. Indians of South America. Slavery. Murder. Superstition. Epidemics. Cults. Medicines. Zoos. Diamond mines. Jungles. Rio de Janeiro. Brazil. Amazon River. Tarzan. Leopards. Chimpanzees. Lions.*
Note: Filmed in and around Rio de Janeiro.

TARZAN AND THE JUNGLE BOY (United States/Switzerland)   F6.4883

Banner Productions–Allfin, A. G. *Dist* Paramount Pictures. May **1968** [c31 Dec 1967; LP35691]. Sd; col (Technicolor). 35mm (Panavision). 90 min.
Prod Robert Day. *Exec Prod* Sy Weintraub. *Dir* Robert Gordon. *Screenplay* Steven Lord. *Dir Photog* Ozen Sermet. *Camera Op* Leobardo Sanchez. *Asst Camera* Johnnie Baker. *Art Dir* Herbert Smith. *Main Titl* Cinefx. *Film Ed* Milton Mann, Reg Browne. *Asst Ed* Laurette Odney. *Mus Comp & Cond* William Loose. *Mus Supv* Igo Kantor. *Sd Eff* Edit-Rite Inc. *Re-rec* Don Minkler, Bill Mumford. *Asst Dir* Claudio Petraglia. *Prod Supv* John Palmer. *Prod Mgr* Camillo Sampaio. *Wardrobe* Tereza Azevedo. *Sp Eff* Gabriel Queiroz.

Cast: Mike Henry *(Tarzan)*, Rafer Johnson *(Nagambi)*, Alizia Gur *(Myrna Claudel)*, Steven Bond *(Erik Brunik)*, Ron Gans *(Ken Matson)*, Edward Johnson *(Buhara)*.
Adventure drama. Based on the characters created by: Edgar Rice Burroughs. A famed geologist, accompanied by his infant son Erik and pet leopard cub, is drowned in a canoe accident while searching for mineral deposits in Africa. Years later, journalist Myrna Claudel and photographer Ken Matson parachute into the jungle and persuade Tarzan to help them find a wild boy believed to be the geologist's son. Upon reaching Zagunda territory, the trio persuade tribal chief Buhara to help them find the boy. During the search, Buhara is attacked and nearly killed by his brother, Nagambi, who hopes to usurp Buhara's crown. Young Erik finds the wounded chief and takes him to his cave, where Tarzan later discovers them and helps Erik nurse Buhara back to health. Meanwhile, Myrna and Ken, who have followed Tarzan into the Zagunda jungle, with the help of Tarzan's chimp, are ambushed by Nagambi's warriors, and Ken is killed. Tarzan rescues Myrna, and Buhara kills his brother. The jungle boy, now known as Jukaro, heeds Tarzan's advice and returns to civilization with Myrna. *Geologists. Journalists. Photographers. Tribal chiefs. Brothers. Filial relations. Fratricide. Jungles. Caves. Africa. Tarzan. Leopards. Chimpanzees.*
Note: Filmed in Brazil. Original production title: *Tarzan No. 22.*

TARZAN AND THE VALLEY OF GOLD (United States/Switzerland)   F6.4884

Banner Productions–Allfin, A. G. *Dist* American International Pictures. 8 Jun **1966** [Buffalo, New York, opening; c25 May 1966; LP34060]. Sd; col (Eastmancolor). 35mm (Panavision). 100 min. [Also 90 min.]
A Sy Weintraub Production. *Prod* Sy Weintraub. *Assoc Prod* Steve Shagan. *Dir* Robert Day. *Screenplay* Clair Huffaker. *Dir Photog* Irving Lippman. *Camera Op* José León Sánchez. *Asst Camera* Emilio Calori. *Art Dir* José Rodriguez Granada. *Main Titl Dsgn* Phill Norman. *Film Ed* Frank P. Keller. *Mus Comp & Cond* Van Alexander. *Sd Eff* Nelson-Corso. *Sd Producers* Sound Service. *Asst Dir* Max Stein, Mario Cisneros. *Prod Mgr* Sam Manners. *Unit Mgr* Antonio Guajardo. *Prod Asst* Nicky Blair, Manuel Vasconcelos. *Cont* John Gannon. *Asst to the Prod* Margaret Jennings. *Wardrobe Master* Alfonso Rubio. *Makeup* Roman Juarez, Elvira Oropoeza. *Hairdresser* Evelina Casas. *Sp Eff* Ira Anderson, Ira Anderson, Jr. *Prop Master* Raul Serrano. *Animals* Safari Rentals, Stewart Raffill.
Cast: Mike Henry *(Tarzan)*, Nancy Kovack *(Sophia)*, David Opatoshu *(Vinaro)*, Manuel Padilla, Jr. *(Ramel)*, Don Megowan *(Mr. Train)*, Enrique Lucero *(Perez)*, Eduardo Noriega *(Talmadge)*, John Kelly *(Voss)*, Francisco Riquerio *(Manco)*, Frank Brandstetter *(Ruiz)*, Carlos Rivas *(Romulo)*, Jorge Beirute *(Rodriquez)*, Oswald Olvera *(Antonio)*.
Adventure melodrama. Based on characters created by: Edgar Rice Burroughs. In Central America, a little native boy, Ramel, is abducted by Vinaro, a madman who believes the child to be the sole link to a lost Aztec city of gold. Vinaro uses one of his diabolical explosive mechanisms to eliminate police and army officials; and the legendary Tarzan is flown in to help locate the jungle city. After trading his civilian clothes for a leather loincloth and a knife, Tarzan sets out on his mission, aided by a chimpanzee, a jaguar, and a lion. He rescues the boy, saves the life of Sophia Renault, Vinaro's former mistress, and finds the secret caves that lead to the lost city. Once there, however, Tarzan is unable to persuade the aged chieftain, Manco, that he must resort to violence if he is to protect his city from Vinar. Consequently, when the madman arrives with troops and armored tanks, Manco offers him a fortune in gold. The insatiable Vinaro demands more, and Manco leads him into a chamber where Vinaro pulls a lever and releases a shower of gold dust that entraps and suffocates him. Simultaneously, Tarzan engages the mercenaries in battle and successfully defeats them. As Manco observes sadly that violence is sometimes necessary to preserve one's way of life, Tarzan and Sophia leave the valley of gold and return to modern civilization. *Aztec Indians. Masterminds. Mercenaries. Greed. Abduction. Gold. Jungles. Caves. Explosives. Central America. Tarzan. Chimpanzees. Lions. Jaguars.*
Note: Filmed in Mexico. Working title: *Tarzan '65*; prerelease title: *Tarzan '66*.

TARZAN GOES TO INDIA (United States/Great Britain/Switzerland)   F6.4885

Banner Productions–Allfin, A. G.–Solar Productions. *Dist* Metro-Goldwyn-Mayer, Inc. Jul **1962** [c6 Jul 1962; LP23599]. Sd; col (Metrocolor). 35mm (CinemaScope). 88 min.
A Sy Weintraub Production. *Prod* Sy Weintraub. *Assoc Prod* Jesse Corallo. *2d Unit Prod* Ellis Dungan. *Prod Exec* Robert Hardy Andrews. *Prod Assoc-Indian Prod Unit* S. Chakraverthy, Adi J. Crawford, M. Subramanya Raj Urs, Gulam Mohammed Lakhawala. *Dir* John Guillermin. *Screenplay* Robert Hardy Andrews, John Guillermin. *Dir Photog* Paul Beeson. *2d Unit Photog* Ellis Dungan. *Camera Op* Godfrey Godar. *Art Dir* George Provis. *Asst Art*

Dir–Indian Prod Unit K. P. Sankarankutty. *Film Ed* Max Benedict. *Mus* Ken Jones. *Indian Mus Comp & Arr* Ravi Shankar, Panchal Jaikishan. *Sd Rec* Bill Howell. *Dub Ed* Chris Greenham. *Asst Dir* Dennis Bertera. *Asst Dir–Indian Prod Unit* Chimankant Gandhi. *Prod Supv* Joe Levy. *Cont* Marjorie Lavelly. *Makeup* Stuart Freeborn. *Sp Eff* Roy Whybrow. *Constr Mgr* Bill Greene. *Prop Master* Joseph Cairns. *Elec Supv* Thomas Tilly.

Cast: Jock Mahoney *(Tarzan)*, Jai *(The Elephant Boy, Jai)*, Leo Gordon *(Bryce)*, Mark Dana *(O'Hara)*, Feroz Khan *(Ragu Kuma)*, Simi *(Princess Kamara)*, Murad *(maharajah)*, Jagdish Raaj *(Raaj)*, G. Raghaven *(Chakra)*, Aaron Joseph *(driver)*, Abas Khan *(pilot)*, Pehelwan Ameer *(Mooty)*, K. S. Tripathi *(conservation officer)*, Peter Cooke *(foreman)*, Denis Bastian *(servant)*, Rajendra Presade *(Dutt)*, Gajendra *(an elephant)*.

Adventure melodrama. Based on characters created by: Edgar Rice Burroughs. Summoned to India by a dying maharajah, Tarzan attempts to remove an elephant herd from a valley to be flooded upon completion of a modern dam. O'Hara, a contractor who will brook no delay to his project, and Bryce, a longtime adversary and former ivory poacher, oppose Tarzan's mission. He is assisted, however, by Princess Kamara, the maharajah's daughter; Ragu Kuma, an engineer; Jai, an orphan; and the boy's elephant, Gajendra. After Gajendra helps to kill a rogue elephant and kills Bryce to defend Jai, Tarzan and his company drive the elephants to safety through a narrow pass. During the escape the dam is damaged. Acknowledging their responsibility, Tarzan and the Indians reconstruct the project with the help of the elephants. *Royalty. Engineers. Contractors. Orphans. Wildlife— Conservation. Dams. Stampedes. Wildlife refuges. Jungles. India. Tarzan. Elephants.*

Note: Filmed on location in India, with the cooperation of the forestry departments of Mysore and Madras. Opened in London in Nov 1962.

TARZAN NO. 22 *see* **TARZAN AND THE JUNGLE BOY**

TARZAN '65 *see* **TARZAN AND THE VALLEY OF GOLD**

TARZAN '66 *see* **TARZAN AND THE VALLEY OF GOLD**

TARZAN VERSUS I.B.M. *see* **ALPHAVILLE**

TARZANOVA SMRT *see* **THE DEATH OF TARZAN**

TARZAN'S DEADLY SILENCE   F6.4886
National General Pictures. 22 Apr **1970** [Saint Louis opening]. Sd; col (DeLuxe). 35mm. 88 min. *MPAA rating* G.

Prod Leon Benson. *Exec Prod* Sy Weintraub. *Assoc Prod* Vernon E. Clark. *Prod Exec* Steve Shagan. *Dir* Robert L. Friend, Lawrence Dobkin. *Screenplay* Lee Erwin, Jack A. Robinson, John Considine, writ, Tim Considine. *Photog* Abraham Vialla, Gabriel Torres. *Art Dir* José Rodríguez Granada. *Film Ed* Edward M. Abroms. *Mus & Mus Dir* Walter Greene. *Asst Dir* William Schwartz. *Prod Mgr* Alfonso Sanchez Tello. *Sp Eff* Laurencio Cordero.

Cast: Ron Ely *(Tarzan)*, Manuel Padilla, Jr. *(Jai)*, Jock Mahoney *(The Colonel)*, Woodrow Strode *(Marshak)*, Gregorio Acosta *(Chico)*, Rudolph Charles *(officer)*, Nichelle Nichols *(Ruana)*, Robert DoQui *(Metusa)*, Kenneth Washington *(Akaba)*, Lupe Garnica *(Boru)*, José Chavez *(Okala)*, Virgil Richardson *(Tabor)*.

Adventure melodrama. Based on characters created by: Edgar Rice Burroughs. The Colonel, a former soldier with a lust for power, plans to use his private army to gain control over all the African jungle tribes. First he captures one of the tribal chiefs and holds him hostage; Jai, Tarzan's young friend, is also captured, and Tarzan is forced to fight a lion, finally subduing the beast by using mental telepathy to save the boy. Meanwhile, Metusa, the son of the hostage chief, learns that his father is dead and takes the Colonel prisoner, but Chico and Marshak, two of the Colonel's cronies, free him and set out in search of Tarzan. When they close in on him, Tarzan dives into a river, and Chico and Marshak throw hand grenades into the river. Tarzan is deafened by the blasts but escapes alive. Jai is again taken captive, and Tarzan goes after him. After Chico drowns in a pit of quicksand, the Colonel and Marshak try to overpower Tarzan, but Tarzan hurls the Colonel to the ground and his head strikes a rock, killing him; Marshak takes advantage of the momentary lull in the fighting to escape. *Soldiers. Tribal chiefs. Hostages. Abduction. Mental telepathy. Manhunts. Deafness. Quicksand. Africa. Tarzan. Lions.*

Note: First presented as "The Deadly Silence" on the NBC television series *Tarzan* in two parts on 28 Oct and 4 Nov 1966.

TARZAN'S THREE CHALLENGES   F6.4887
Banner Productions. *Dist* Metro-Goldwyn-Mayer, Inc. Jun **1963** [c25 Jun 1963; LP26844]. Sd (RCA); col (Metrocolor). 35mm (Dyaliscope). 92 min.

A Sy Weintraub Production. *Prod* Sy Weintraub. *Prod Exec* Willy Dow. *Thai Prod Assoc* Ratanaprasert. *Dir* Robert Day. *Screenplay* Berne Giler, Robert Day. *Dir Photog* Ted Scaife. *Camera Op* Ernest Day. *Thai Art Assoc* Payut Ngaokrachang. *Prod Dsgn* Wilfred Shingleton. *Film Ed* Fred Burnley.

Mus Comp Joseph Horovitz. *Orch Cond* Marcus Dods. *Dir Sd* Stephen Dalby. *Sd Ed* Chris Greenham. *Sd Mix* Wally Milner. *Asst Dir* Clive Reed. *Prod Mgr* Otto Plaschkes. *Location Mgr* Claud Hudson. *Cont* Lee Turner. *Wardrobe Master* John Brady. *Makeup* Freddie Williamson. *Sp Eff* Cliff Richardson, Roy Whybrow. *Coöp* Tourist Organization of Thailand. *Prop Master* Dave Fowlie. *Electrn Supv* Maurice Gillett. *Constr Mgr* Leon Davis.

Cast: Jock Mahoney *(Tarzan)*, Woody Strode *(Khan/Tarim)*, Tsuruko Kobayashi *(Cho-San)*, Earl Cameron *(Mang)*, Salah Jamal *(Hani)*, Anthony Chinn *(Tor)*, Robert Hu *(Nari)*, Christopher Carlos *(Sechung)*, Ricky Der *(Kashi)*, Hungry *(himself, a baby elephant)*.

Adventure melodrama. Based on characters created by: Edgar Rice Burroughs. Tarim, the spiritual leader of Sun Mai, is dying, and his brother Khan plots to take over and make his own son the successor. But the true heir, Kashi, living in a distant monastery, summons Tarzan to escort him to Sun Mai to claim his throne. When Tarzan arrives from Africa, the monks subject him to tests of skill, wisdom, and strength to prove that he really is Tarzan. With the monks satisfied, he begins his journey with Kashi and Cho-San, his nursemaid. Along the way, Khan's men attack, Tarzan is separated from the boy and his nurse, and those two are captured. Tarzan rescues them, however, and they arrive safely at their destination. Khan does not dare slay Kashi; but according to law, he can still challenge his right to rule through tests of skill. The boy passes three tests; but the fourth, a test of might in which he would be pitted against the mighty Khan himself, causes him to select a defender in his place. He chooses Tarzan. Tarzan and Khan fight with knives on a net over a pit of burning coals, and Tarzan emerges the victor. Kashi can now be crowned ruler by his people, and Tarzan returns to Africa. *Royalty. Heirs. Monks. Brothers. Nursemaids. Contests. Imaginary kingdoms. Elephants. Tarzan.*

Note: Filmed in Thailand.

A TASTE FOR WOMEN (France/Italy)   F6.4888
Les Films Number One–Francoriz–Federiz. *Dist* Comet Film Distributors. Feb **1966**. Sd; b&w. 35mm. 90 min.

Prod Pierre Kalfon. *Dir-Adapt* Jean Léon. *Screenplay* Roman Polanski. *Dial* Gérard Brach. *Photog* Sacha Vierny. *Art Dir* Bernard Evein. *Film Ed* Kenout Peltier. *Mus* Ward Swingle. *Lyr* Gérard Brach. *Sd* Guy Villette. *Prod Mgr* Louis de Masure.

Cast: Sophie Daumier *(Violette/Marguerite)*, Guy Bedos *(Jérôme Fenouic)*, Edwige Feuillère *(Aunt Flo)*, Grégoire Aslan *(Inspector Rossi)*, Guido Alberti *(Mr. Kouroulis)*, Roger Blin *(Larsen)*, Gérard Séty *(Palmer)*, Georges Adet *(Richter)*, Maria Rosa Rodrigues *(stripper)*, Colette Castel *(Jeanine Dupellier)*, Raoul Delfosse *(bargeman)*, Graziella Granata *(bargeman's wife)*, Gordon Felio *(Dr. Rotman)*.

Mystery comedy. Source: Georges Bardawil, *Aimez-vous les femmes?* (Paris, 1961). Jérôme Fenouic, a writer of children's stories, finds a corpse in the washroom of a vegetarian restaurant where he is dining with his Aunt Flo. He dons the dead man's hat and is mistaken for the man by Violette, a mysterious blonde woman. Following the murder of his neighbor, a series of promiscuous love affairs, and numerous unsuccessful attempts on his life, Jérôme gradually learns that he is involved in a gang war between Nirvana, a secret sect of cannibals run by Kouroulis, and a gang of opium smugglers led by Larsen, a cripple. Returning to the restaurant, Jérôme discovers the naked corpse of Violette—or perhaps Marguerite, her identical twin sister—who had been Larsen's mistress and is about to be eaten by Kouroulis's sect. With the timely intervention of the police, Jérôme helps subdue the fighting gangs and is reunited with Violette (or Marguerite). *Authors. Aunts. Cannibals. Cripples. Sisters. Twins. Smugglers. Police. Murder. Mistaken identity. Gang wars. Restaurants. Corpses. Opium.*

Note: Opened in Paris in May 1964 as *Aimez-vous les femmes?*; running time: 100 min.

A TASTE OF BLOOD   F6.4889
Creative Film Enterprises. *Dist* Ajay Film Co. 9 Aug **1967** [Atlanta opening]. Sd; col (Eastmancolor). 35mm. 120 min.

Prod-Dir Herschell Gordon Lewis. *Exec Prod* Sidney J. Reich. *Orig Screenplay* Donald Stanford. *Camera Op* Andy Romanoff. *Ed Supv* Richard Brinkman. *Mus Dir* Larry Wellington. *Sd Rec* Alan Tadie. *Asst Dir* Louise Downe. *Prod Mgr* William Kerwin. *Asst to Prod* J. G. Patterson, Jr. *Crew Ch* Roy Collodi.

Cast: Bill Rogers *(John Stone)*, Elizabeth Wilkinson *(Helene Stone)*, Thomas Wood *(Hank Tyson)*, Otto Schlesinger *(Howard Helsing)*, Eleanor Vaill *(Hester)*, Lawrence Tobin *(Detective Crane)*, Ted Schell *(Lord Gold)*, Sheldon Seymour *(seaman)*, Dolores Carlos *(Sherri Morris)*, Sidney Jaye *(lawyer)*, Gail Janis *(Vivacious Vivian)*.

Horror film. John Stone, an American businessman, receives a parcel marked "Of Gravest Urgency" which contains two old bottles of Slivovitz brandy with instructions to toast his mother's ancestor from whom he has inherited property in England. Despite his wife Helene's fears, John drinks the brandy and over a period of time becomes a vampire. Helene asks Dr. Hank Tyson, a family friend, to help her husband, but the doctor cannot detect the transformation. John visits England to claim his lands and to avenge the death of his ancestor Count Dracula. To recall the manner of Dracula's demise, he thrusts a pool cue through the heart of one descendant, Lord Gold. Returning home, he lives as a vampire and keeps Helene in a trance with Dracula's magic ring. He murders Vivacious Vivian, a burlesque dancer whose cut finger entices him, and Sherri Morris, a descendant of Dracula's murderers whom he meets in Houston. Dr. Howard Helsing arrives from England to end John's vengeful acts. With Dr. Tyson's aid, he forces John into his casket and drives a stake through his heart, awakening Helene from her trance. *Vampires. Physicians. Stripteasers. Businessmen. Murder. Revenge. Liquor. England. Houston. Dracula.*

Note: Filmed in Miami.

TASTE OF FEAR *see* **SCREAM OF FEAR**

A TASTE OF FLESH
F6.4890

Mostest Productions. *Dist* Jerand Film Distributors. 19 Jul **1967** [Champaign, Illinois, showing]. Sd; b&w. 35mm. 73 min.

Prod-Dir-Writ Louis Silverman. *Dir Photog* C. Davis Smith. *Ed* Louis Silverman.

Cast: Cleo Nova *(Hannah)*, Michael Lawrence *(Nick)*, Layla Peters *(Bobi)*, Buck Starr *(Frankie)*, Darlene Bennett *(Carol)*.

Melodrama. Frankie and Nick, two killers hired to assassinate a visiting European political leader, enter the apartment of lesbians Carol and Bobi so as to watch their victim's movements in a nearby hotel. The dignitary's secretary (Hannah) is a guest of Carol and Bobi, and the thugs beat her for information on her employer's whereabouts. During the night, Frankie seduces Carol and Bobi dreams of having relations with the sleeping Hannah. The assassination attempt fails when Hannah fatally stabs Nick and frames Frankie for the murder. *Hired killers. Secretaries. Politicians. Lesbianism. Imposture. Assassination. Hotels. Dreams.*

A TASTE OF HONEY (Great Britain)
F6.4891

Woodfall Film Productions. *Dist* Continental Distributing, Inc. 30 Apr **1962** [New York opening]. Sd; b&w. 35mm. 100 min.

Prod-Dir Tony Richardson. *Screenplay* Shelagh Delaney, Tony Richardson. *Dir Photog* Walter Lassally. *Camera Op* Desmond Davis. *Focus Puller* Manny Wynn. *Camera Grip* Vic Butler. *Art Dir* Ralph Brinton. *Asst Art Dir* Ted Marshall. *Film Ed* Anthony Gibbs. *Asst Ed* Michael Rabiger, Patricia Gilbert. *Mus Comp & Cond* John Addison. *Played by* The Virtuoso Ensemble. *Sd Mix* Charles Poulton. *Sd Camera Op* Derek Leather. *Dub Ed* Roy Hyde. *Asst Dub Ed* Karen Heward. *Sd* Don Challis. *Boom Op* Tom Buchanan. *1st, 2d & 3d Asst Dir* Peter Yates, Roy Millichip, Tony Wallis. *Prod Supv* Leigh Aman. *Cont* Rita Davison. *Prod Sec* Jane Moscrop, Jenny Lawton. *Prod Asst* Andrew Mollo. *Asst to the Prod* Michael Holden. *Wardrobe Dsgn* Sophie Harris. *Wardrobe Mistress* Barbara Gillett. *Makeup Artist* George Frost. *Hairdresser* Bill Griffiths. *Still Photog* Ray Hearne. *Prop Supv* Tommy Erley. *Rigger* Jack Yarker.

Cast: Dora Bryan *(Helen)*, Rita Tushingham *(Jo)*, Robert Stephens *(Peter)*, Murray Melvin *(Geoffrey)*, Paul Danquah *(Jimmy)*, David Boliver *(Bert)*, Moira Kaye *(Doris)*, Herbert Smith, actor *(shoe shop proprietor)*, Valerie Scarden *(woman in shoe shop)*, Rosalie Scase *(nurse)*, Veronica Howard *(Gladys)*, Jack Yarker *(ship's mate)*, Margo Cunningham *(landlady)*, John Harrison *(cave attendant)*, A. Goodman *(rag and bone man)*, Janet Rugg, Sonia Stephens *(girls on pier)*, Eunice Black *(school mistress)*.

Melodrama. Source: Shelagh Delaney, *A Taste of Honey* (Stratford-upon-Avon opening: 27 May 1958). During a holiday at Blackpool, Jo, the 17-year-old illegitimate daughter of impoverished and promiscuous Helen, is rejected by her mother's lecherous suitor, Peter. For solace Jo turns to Jimmy, a black sailor enjoying brief shore leave. They make love and Jimmy's ship departs. Indifferent to Jo's feelings, Helen, evicted from her Salford flat, moves in with Peter. Her deserted daughter gets a job as a shoe clerk and rents a room, which she shares with the gentle Geoffrey, a penniless homosexual. Upon discovering that she is pregnant, Jo is disconsolate, but Geoffrey is delighted. Enthusiastically preparing for the baby's arrival, he sews a layette, visits a clinic for instruction in child care, and proposes marriage to the indifferent Jo. Concerned by her depression, the homosexual visits Helen and tells her of the pregnancy. When Peter's interest wanes, Helen abruptly moves in with her pregnant daughter, promptly ousts Geoffrey, and torments Jo by bemoaning the baby's mixed race. *Mistresses. Shoeclerks. Negroes. Sailors. Poverty. Miscegenation. Filial relations. Adolescence. Promiscuity. Pregnancy. Illegitimacy. Male homosexuality. Racial prejudice. Docks. Salford. Blackpool.*

Note: Filmed on location in Salford and Blackpool, England. Opened in Great Britain in Oct 1961.

A TASTE OF HONEY, A SWALLOW OF BRINE! *see* A SMELL OF HONEY, A SWALLOW OF BRINE!

A TASTE OF HOT LEAD
F6.4892

Falcon Film Productions. *Dist* Chancellor Films. Aug **1969**. Sd; col. 35mm. 71 min.

Prod Richard A. Marlow. *Dir* William Rotsler.

Cast—Pressbook: Vincene Wallace *(Toni)*, James Brand *(Kelly)*, Dee Howard *(Joy)*, Bruce McQueen *(Eddie)*, Susan Canyon *(Mitzi)*, Rae Torres *("Baby Doll")*.

Cast—Review: Vance Wallace, Dee Howard, James Brand, Tom Tiny, Linda Jackson, Lee Sommers.

Melodrama. Kelly and Eddie, two fugitives who have committed robbery and murder, take refuge in a house inhabited by four women, all lesbians who have rather "special" sexual preferences. Kelly, an ex-convict, caresses Joy, one of the women, with his pistol—to her obvious pleasure—and then rapes her; he beats Mitzi, another roommate, who has sadomasochistic fantasies of being held captive by two men, when she hands him a whip; but Kelly is rebuffed by Toni, the leader of the group, when he tries to force "Baby Doll," Toni's current favorite, into doing a sex act. Toni, maintaining that Baby Doll prefers women, demonstrates female cunnilingus. Angry, Kelly ties Toni to the bed and rapes her. Finally, the women attempt to escape. They bash in Eddie's head and shoot and seriously wound Kelly. Toni is accidentally killed in a struggle with Joy, who interferes when Toni announces that she will emasculate Kelly with the gun. *Roommates. Hoodlums. Ex-convicts. Sadomasochism. Lesbianism. Rape. Flagellation. Revenge. Oral sex. Murder. Robbery. Guns.*

Note: Also known as *Hot Lead*. Credits differ for cast as taken from pressbook and published review.

A TASTE OF YOUTH
F6.4893

MJ Productions. *Dist* Marjon Film Distributors. **1970**. Sd; col. 16mm. 75 min.

Cast: April Hale *(Dina Sloan)*, Fredrick Louis *(Lance)*, Suzie Hart *(Jane)*.

Drama. Dina Sloan, a lonely widow, meets Lance, a naive young man. Though dazzled by her wealth and sophistication, Lance becomes fearful of Dina's desire to dominate him. Eventually, Dina is rivaled for Lance's affections by Jane, a seductive neighbor. *Widows. Neighbors. Innocents. Jealousy. Sexuality.*

TASTE THE BLOOD OF DRACULA (Great Britain)
F6.4894

Hammer Film Productions. *Dist* Warner Bros. Pictures. 16 Sep **1970** [Boston opening]. Sd; col (Technicolor). 35mm. 95 min. *MPAA rating* GP.

Prod Aida Young. *Dir* Peter Sasdy. *Screenplay* John Elder. *Photog* Arthur Grant. *Art Dir* Scott MacGregor. *Film Ed* Chris Barnes. *Mus* James Bernard. *Mus Supv* Philip Martell. *Sd* Roy Hyde. *Sd Re-rec* Denis Whitlock. *Asst Dir* Derek Whitehurst. *Makeup Supv* Gerry Fletcher. *Sp Eff* Brian Johncock.

Cast: Christopher Lee *(Dracula)*, Geoffrey Keen *(William Hargood)*, Gwen Watford *(Martha Hargood)*, Linda Hayden *(Alice Hargood)*, Peter Sallis *(Samuel Paxton)*, Anthony Corlan *(Paul Paxton)*, Isla Blair *(Lucy Paxton)*, John Carson *(Jonathan Secker)*, Martin Jarvis *(Jeremy Secker)*, Ralph Bates *(Lord Courtley)*, Roy Kinnear *(Weller)*, Michael Ripper *(Cobb)*, Russell Hunter *(Felix)*, Shirley Jaffe *(Hargood's maid)*, Keith Marsh *(father)*, Peter May *(son)*, Reginald Barratt *(vicar)*, Madeline Smith *(Dolly)*, Lai Ling *(Chinese girl)*, Malaika Martin *(snake girl)*.

Horror film. Based on the character created by: Bram Stoker. Three respectable family men—William Hargood, Samuel Paxton, and Jonathan Secker—make their monthly pilgrimage to a stylish bordello on London's East End, where they meet Lord Courtley, a depraved occultist who intrigues them with a dare to sell their souls to the devil. They purchase a black coat, ring clasp, and a phial of dried ashes from an antique dealer and take them to a desecrated chapel, where Lord Courtley revives the vampire Count Dracula in a blood-letting ceremony. The other three men flee in terror after beating Courtley to death, but Dracula materializes in the corpse of Courtley and vows revenge for the death of his servant. While under Dracula's hypnotic influence, Alice, Hargood's daughter, kills her father with a spade. She then lures Paxton's daughter, Lucy, into Dracula's grasp, and he forces her to murder her father with Alice's assistance. Lucy's boyfriend, Jeremy Secker, also becomes mesmerized by Dracula and kills his father; but before the elder Secker dies, he sends a message to Lucy's brother Paul, who is in love with Alice, and warns him of the dangerous fiend. Paul is able to destroy the vampire, thus releasing Alice from Dracula's spell. *Antique dealers. Vampires. Occult. Murder. Revenge. Spells. Patricide. Whorehouses. Rites and ceremonies. Corpses. Churches. London—East End. Dracula.*

Note: Released in Great Britain in Jun 1970.

THE TASTERS see **ODD TASTES**

TATSU (Japan)   F6.4895
Toho Co. Nov **1962** [Los Angeles showing]. Sd; col (Agfacolor). 35mm (Tohoscope). 115 min.
Exec Prod Tomoyuki Tanaka. *Dir* Hiroshi Inagaki. *Screenplay* Masato Ide, Toshio Yasumi. *Photog* Kazuo Yamada. *Mus* Kan Ishii.
Cast: Toshiro Mifune *(Tatsu)*, Tatsuya Mihashi, Chikage Awashima, Junko Ikeuchi, Ichiro Arishima, Yoshio Tsuchiya, Sonomi Nakajima, Jun Tazaki, Soji Kiyokawa, Ryosuke Kagawa, Chieko Nakakita, Yoshio Kosugi, Sachio Sakai.
Drama. A group of temporary laborers hired for a construction job in a remote forest are paid in advance, but armed guards surround the construction site to prevent anyone from escaping the backbreaking work. Among the workers is Tatsu, a brutal, powerful illiterate whose gentle qualities are unknown to his fellow workers. He becomes infatuated with a woman who works in the camp mess hall, but she rejects his clumsy advances. The foreman then forces his attentions on the woman, Tatsu intervenes, and a duel with axes ensues. The woman, who now respects Tatsu, is actually married to an ex-convict who soon arrives at the camp. The jealous foreman assigns the husband difficult work, and Tatsu postpones his own escape plans to help the couple get away. Later, having made good his escape, Tatsu learns that a rival band of workers, angered over a swindle involving the foreman and their wages, are on their way to the camp. Tatsu returns ahead of them and succeeds in saving the day. *Construction crews. Construction foremen. Ex-convicts. Escapees. Jealousy. Duels. Construction camps.*
Note: Released in Japan in 1962 as *Doburoku no Tatsu.*

THE TATTOOED POLICE HORSE   F6.4896
Walt Disney Productions. *Dist* Buena Vista Distribution Co. 16 Dec **1964** [Los Angeles opening; c7 Oct 1964; LP29213]. Sd (Todd-AO); col (Technicolor). 35mm. 48 min.
Pres by Walt Disney. *Prod-Dir-Orig Story* Larry Lansburgh., *Screenplay* Janet Lansburgh. *Dir Photog* Edward P. Hughes. *Film Ed* Herman Freedman. *Mus* William Lava. *In Charge of Prod* Robert Baron. *Coöp* The Harness Racing Institute, John Lynch, (Lieut.), Boston Police Department.
Cast: Sandy Sanders *(Capt. Martin Hanley)*, Charles Seel *(Ben)*, George Swinebroad *(J. P. Rollins)*, William Hilliard *(Bill Churchill)*, Shirley Skiles *(Pam Churchill)*, Keith Andes *(narrator)*, Stan Bergstein *(race caller)*.
Drama. Jolly Roger, a young trotting horse of good breeding handpicked at a Kentucky auction by horse fancier and trainer Pam Churchill, is entered into races before Pam can cure him of breaking stride in the homestretch. He is sold to his groom, Ben, who also fails to correct the fault, and is eventually barred from racing as a threat to the other horses and drivers. In Arizona, Ben races Jolly Roger against an old roadster driven by three Indians, but a tire blowout causes the horse to bolt, and Ben sells him to a livestock dealer who ships him to an eastern city. Capt. Martin Hanley purchases Jolly Roger for the Boston Mounted Police Force and through rigorous training finally disciplines the horse. Captain Hanley is on duty astride Jolly Roger at a local harness racing track, and when he is summoned to assist a driver who has had an accident during a race, Jolly Roger breaks into a trot, swiftly races down the track, and saves the driver. The story makes the evening newspapers. Pam Churchill, who is in Boston for the races, recognizes Jolly Roger, identifies him by a registration number tattooed on the horse's upper lip, and purchases him. She retrains Jolly Roger and enters him in an important race. The discipline given him by Hanley has paid off; he wins the race and goes on to become a champion. *Horsetrainers. Stableboys. Indians of North America. Horseracing. Racetracks. Auctions. Arizona. Boston. Kentucky. Boston Mounted Police. Horses.*
Note: Location scenes filmed in Kentucky, Boston, and Arizona.

DIE TAUSEND AUGEN DES DR. MABUSE see **THE 1000 EYES OF DR. MABUSE**

TAXI FOR TOBRUK (France/Spain/West Germany)   F6.4897
Franco London Film–S. N. E. Gaumont–Procusa–Continental Produktion Films. *Dist* Seven Arts Pictures. 29 Mar **1965** [New York opening]. Sd; b&w. 35mm (Dyaliscope). 90 min. [Also 97 min.]
Prod-Dir Denys de La Patellière. *Screenplay* René Havard. *Dial* Michel Audiard. *Adapt* René Havard, Denys de La Patellière. *Photog* Marcel Grignon. *Art Dir* Paul-Louis Boutié. *Film Ed* Jacqueline Thiédot. *Mus* Georges Garvarentz. *Sd* Georges Mardiguian. *Asst Dir* Pierre Granier-Deferre.
Cast: Hardy Krüger *(Capt. Ludwig von Stegel)*, Charles Aznavour *(Samuel Goldman)*, Lino Ventura *(Théo)*, Germán Cobos *(Paolo)*, Maurice Biraud *(François)*.
War drama. In the summer of 1942, four Free French commandos participating in a raid on Tobruk blow up a gasoline depot in the North African desert, suffering the loss of their truck and commanding officer. They set out on foot to join the Allied forces 400 miles away in El Alamein. After one day in the vast scorching desert, they capture a German patrol car, taking the sole survivor, a young Afrika Korps captain, Ludwig von Stegel, as their prisoner. Relations between the commandos and the German are naturally strained, especially because one commando, Samuel, is a Jew, but as they pass the days in a common ordeal of survival demanding trust and cooperation, hostilities fade into a reluctant but real camaraderie. After they have weathered a bombing and crossed a mine field, they approach their destination. With little of their antagonism remaining, the four commandos are tempted not to turn in their prisoner. But no decision is necessary—mistaken for Germans, they are grenaded by their own allies. Only Théo, the corporal, survives. *Commandos. Nazis. Jews. Prisoners of war. Survival. Friendship. Deserts. World War II. North Africa. El Alamein. Tobruk. Afrika Korps.*
Note: Produced in France. Opened in West Berlin in May 1961 as *Taxi nach Tobruk;* running time: 89 min; in Paris in May 1961 as *Un taxi pour Tobrouk;* running time: 132 min; in Madrid in Oct 1961 as *Un taxi para Tobrouk.*

TAXI NACH TOBRUK see **TAXI FOR TOBRUK**

UN TAXI PARA TOBROUK see **TAXI FOR TOBRUK**

UN TAXI POUR TOBROUK see **TAXI FOR TOBRUK**

TAYLOR MEAD'S ASS   F6.4898
Dist Film-Makers' Cooperative. 3 Jan **1966** [New York opening]. Si; b&w. 16mm. 70 min.
Prod-Dir Andy Warhol. *Prod Asst* Gerard Malanga, Buddy Wirtschafter.
Cast: Taylor Mead.
Experimental film. Closeup views of Taylor Mead's buttocks. At first the image appears very white and overexposed; later the subject becomes more recognizable. The man holds a book, among other objects.
Note: The frame remains fixed throughout.

TCHAIKOVSKY MUSIC FESTIVAL (U.S.S.R.)   F6.4899
Moscow Popular Science Studio. *Dist* Artkino Pictures. 13 Apr **1963** [New York showing]. Sd; 35mm. 45 min.
Documentary. A record of the 2d International Tchaikovsky Competition in Moscow in 1962. *Musicians. International Tchaikovsky Competition.*

TEA AND RICE (Japan)   F6.4900
Shochiku Co. *Dist* Shochiku Films of America. 20 Nov **1964** [Los Angeles showing]. Sd; b&w. 35mm. 115 min.
Dir Yasujiro Ozu. *Story-Screenplay* Yasujiro Ozu, Kogo Noda. *Photog* Yushun Atsuta.
Cast: Shin Saburi, Michiyo Kogure, Koji Tsuruta, Keiko Tsushima, Kuniko Miyake, Chikage Awashima, Chishu Ryu, Yuko Mochizuki.
Domestic drama. Mokichi and Taeko Satake, married for some years, met through an arranged interview in accordance with Japanese custom. Mr. Yamanouchi, Taeko's father, is a retired politician and financier who personally selected Mokichi from the offices of a Yamanouchi-owned company. With no children to care for, Taeko spends her extensive leisure time with two other wives, dining at expensive restaurants, attending the theater, and taking trips to resort hotels, while informing their husbands that they are attending alumnae meetings or visiting sick friends. Taeko's niece, Setsuko, is disappointed when her parents arrange for her to interview a prospective husband. Aware of her aunt's unhappy marriage to a near-total stranger, Setsuko openly declares her opposition to an arranged marriage. Rather than appear at the theater where her parents have arranged for her to meet her prospective husband, Setsuko spends the day with Mokichi and his friend Noboru. Mokichi refuses Taeko's demand to reprimand their niece, pointing out that for Setsuko to consent to such an arrangement could only lead to a marriage as unsatisfactory as their own. For the next two weeks the couple engage in a war of nerves, picking at each other until Mokichi finally declares that he likes a simple life, while Taeko replies that she is accustomed to traveling first-class in every way. Taeko then leaves for Kobe without saying when she will return. Mokichi is called to Uruguay on business, and he wires Taeko, asking her to return. Although Taeko fails to show up at the airport to see off Mokichi, she does arrive several hours later, claiming she was unavoidably delayed. Mokichi's plane develops engine trouble and he returns home. He asks for a simple meal of tea and rice, which Taeko has always hated. She eats with him, however, and the two are reconciled. *Aunts. Uncles. Businessmen. Idle rich. Marriage—Arranged.*
Note: Released in Japan in 1952 as *Ochazuke no aji.* Alternative title: *The Flavor of Green Tea Over Rice.*

TEACH ME HOW TO DO IT!   F6.4901
Leo–Todd Productions. *Dist* Leo–Todd Motion Picture Producing and Distributing Ltd. 30 Oct **1967** [New York opening]. Sd; b&w. 35mm. 69 min.
Prod Paul Leonardi, Phil Todaro. *Dir* Michael Meola. *Dir Photog* Mort Shuman, photog.
Cast: Ingrid Larsen, Edward Kanzar, Bob Davis, Janet Banzet, Bob February, Andy Rome.

Comedy-drama. A young married couple in search of excitement found a "love school" to teach the art of physical love, and they enroll a number of men and women. Two policemen arrive to investigate the proceedings, but they soon join in the activities. *Sex instruction. Group sex. Police.*

Note: Also known as *Teach Me.*

THE TEACHER AND THE MIRACLE (Italy/Spain)   F6.4902
Gladiator Film–Union Films. *Dist* President Films. 23 Apr **1961** [New York opening]. Sd; b&w. 35mm. 88 min.

Prod-Dir Aldo Fabrizi. *English Vers Dir* Carol Riethof, Peter Riethof. *Screenplay* Aldo Fabrizi, L. Lucas, J. Gallardo, Mario Amendola. *Photog* Antonio Macasoli, Manuel Merino. *Mus* Carlo Innocenzi.

Cast: Aldo Fabrizi *(Giovanni Merino)*, Edoardo Nevola *(Antonio)*, Marco Paoletti *(Gabriel)*, Alfredo Mayo *(principal)*, Mary Lamar *(teacher)*, Félix Fernández *(porter)*, Julio San Juan *(doctor)*, José Calvo *(chauffeur)*, Julia Caba Alba *(portress)*.

Religious drama. Aging widower Giovanni Merino is devoted to his young and talented son, Antonio. On the boy's behalf, Merino, a popular teacher, hopes to open an art school and eagerly awaits the letter of permission from the Ministry of Education. On the day of its arrival Merino is attending a baptism. Well aware of his father's eagerness, Antonio rushes to the christening. In his excitement he dashes across the street and is killed by an automobile. The grieving father finds teaching a painful reminder of his dead son and announces his resignation. Before it can be accepted, however, a new pupil enters his class. Gabriel, a carpenter's son, restores Merino's faith in life and rekindles his enthusiasm for teaching. He then announces his departure. Dismayed, Merino traces the boy to a church, where he discovers a statue of the Madonna and Child. The figure of Jesus is identical to that of Gabriel. *Schoolteachers. Children. Widowers. Students. Strangers. Fatherhood. Death. Miracles. Faith. Churches. Jesus.*

Note: Released in Italy in 1958 as *Il maestro*; running time: 100 min; in Spain in 1957 as *El maestro*.

TEARS ARE FOR TOMORROW *see* THE PAWN

TECHNIQUE D'UN MEURTRE *see* THE HIRED KILLER

THE TECHNIQUES OF LOVE   F6.4903
Dist First Amendment Inc. 1 Mar **1970** [San Francisco opening]. Sd; col. 35mm? [Feature film, length unknown.]

Sex film. No information about the precise nature of this film has been found. *Sexual techniques.*

TECNICA DI UN OMICIDIO *see* THE HIRED KILLER

THE TEDDY BEAR *see* BAMSE

TEEN-AGE STRANGLER   F6.4904
Original Six Productions. *Dist* Ajay Film Co. 9 Aug **1967** [Atlanta opening]. Sd; col. 35mm. 61 min. [Also reviewed at 67 min.]

Prod-Writ Clark Davis. *Exec Prod* Elvin Beltner. *Dir* Bill Posner. *Photog* Fred Singer.

Cast: Bill A. Bloom, Jo Canterbury, John Ensign, Jim Asp, Johnny Haymer, Bill Mills.

Horror film. No information about the precise nature of this film has been found, but press material suggests that it deals with teenagers who are chased by a "Bluebeard." *Murder. Adolescence.*

Note: Filmed in 1964 in West Virginia.

TEEN AGE TRAMP *see* THAT KIND OF GIRL

TEEN KANYA *see* TWO DAUGHTERS

TEENAGE AWARDS MUSIC INTERNATIONAL *see* THE T.A.M.I. SHOW

TEENAGE COMMAND PERFORMANCE *see* THE T.A.M.I. SHOW

TEENAGE GANG DEBS   F6.4905
Jode Productions. *Dist* CIP Ltd. 4 Nov **1966** [Charlotte, North Carolina, opening]. Sd; b&w. 35mm. [Feature length assumed.]

Prod Jerry Denby. *Dir* Sande Johnsen. *Screenplay* Hy Cahl. *Photog* Harry Petricek. *Mus* Steve Karmen. *Sd* Bill Riely. *Prod Mgr* Anthony Scaretti. *Script Supv* Fran Calley. *Makeup* Dossie.

The Debs: Diana Conti *(Terry)*, Linda Gale *(Angel)*, Eileen Scott *(Ellie)*, Sandra Kane *(Annie)*, Robin Nolan *(Maria)*, Linda Cambi *(Shirley)*, Sue McManus *(Sally)*, Geri Tyler *(Geri)*.

The Gang: Joey Naudic *(Nino)*, John Batis *(Johnny)*, Tom Yourk *(Hawkeye)*, Thomas Andrisano *(Piggie)*, George Winship *(Slats)*, Doug Mitchell *(Burt)*, Tom Eldred *(Tony)*, Frank Spinella *(Diablo)*.

And: Alec Primrose *(bartender)*, Gene Marrin *(Mr. Fiore)*, Lyn Kennedy *(Mrs. Fiore)*, Janet Banzet *(Rosie)*, RPM Motorcycle Club of Brooklyn *(The Rat Pack)*.

Action melodrama. Terry, a teenaged girl who has recently moved to the Brooklyn tenements, meets Nino, a member of a gang known as the Rebels. At the Rebel clubhouse, Johnny, the head of the Rebels, makes advances, causing his girl friend Angel to become jealous. Terry and Angel fight; Terry wins and becomes a member. A few days later, Terry tells Nino that she will be his lover if he becomes the head of the Rebels. Nino stabs Johnny, making it appear that a rival gang was responsible, and assumes the gang's leadership. Terry, the real power, arranges a rumble between the Rebels and the Warriors. The Rebels win, leaving four dead Warriors. Terry has one of the Rebels killed when he announces that he wants to quit the gang. One day, Terry is called to the Rebel clubhouse and confronted by the other girl members, who fall upon her with knives, clubs, and chains. They slash her face so that hideous scars will remain, take her to the East River and, before dumping her, carve onto her chest Johnny's initials. *Street gangs. Adolescence. Jealousy. Murder. Revenge. Disfiguration. Gang wars. New York City—Brooklyn.*

Note: Filmed on location in Brooklyn.

TEENAGE MILLIONAIRE   F6.4906
Ludlow Productions. *Dist* United Artists. 17 Aug **1961** [New Orleans opening; c17 Aug 1961; LP21953]. Sd; b&w with col seq (Musicolor). 35mm. 84 min.

Prod Howard B. Kreitsek. *Prod Exec* John E. Pommer. *Dir-Adtl Dial* Lawrence F. Doheny. *Screenplay* H. B. Cross. *Dir Photog* Gordon Avil. *Song Seq Dir Photog* Arthur J. Ornitz. *Art Dir* Rolland M. Brooks, Howard Hollander. *Song Seq Art Dir* Paul Sylbert. *Set Decor* Harry Gordon. *Film Ed* Jack Ruggiero. *Titl Song:* "Green Light" writ & sung by Jimmy Clanton. *Sd* James Thompson. *Asst Dir* Hal Klein, Bruce Bilson. *Song Seq Asst Dir* Don Kranze. *Script Supv* Kathleen Fagan. *Wardrobe* Claire Cramer, Paula Giokaris. *Makeup* David Newell. *Hairstyles* Anne Malin. *Still Photog* Jack Harris, still photog.

Cast: Jimmy Clanton *(Bobby Chalmers)*, Rocky Graziano *(Rocky)*, ZaSu Pitts *(Aunt Theodora)*, Diane Jergens *(Bambi)*, Joan Tabor *(Adrienne)*, Sid Gould *(Sheldon Vale)*, Maurice Gosfield *(Ernie)*, Eileen O'Neill *(Desidieria)*, Jackie Wilson, Chubby Checker, Dion, Bill Black's Combo, Marv Johnson, Vicki Spencer, Jack Larson *(performers)*.

Comedy with music. Following the death of his millionaire parents in a plane crash teenager Bobby Chalmers is placed in the care of his prim Aunt Theodora and bodyguard Rocky, an ex-fighter. Because the youngster is fond of music, his aunt allows him to pick out hit records to play on a family-owned radio station. One day Bobby cuts a demonstration record of a song he has written and signs a phony name to it. Bambi, a girl who works in the record-file department and with whom Bobby is in love, hears the disc, likes it, and plays it at a community dance. Bambi forces Bobby to admit being the vocalist when the record is declared a smash hit. Requests for the record pour in, and a talent scout becomes interested in Bobby; whereupon Aunt Theodora, fearful of notoriety, tells the family trustees to sell the radio station. Then Bobby learns he has been drafted and will be 21—and his own boss—by the time he is discharged. The news softens Aunt Theodora, and she gives Bobby a huge going-away party for all his friends. *Heirs. Orphans. Aunts. Singers. Disc jockeys. Bodyguards. Adolescence. Rock and roll. Military draft. Wealth. Radio.*

Note: H. B. Cross is a pseudonym for Harry Spalding. Sources indicate that 19 additional songs are performed in the film.

TEENAGE MOTHER   F6.4907
Jerry Gross Productions–Arrow Productions. *Dist* Cinemation Industries. 22 Nov **1967** [Detroit opening]. Sd; col (De Luxe). 35mm. 78 min. [Also 65 min.]

Pres by Jerry Gross, Nicholas Demetroules. *Prod-Dir-Writ* Jerry Gross. *Co-prod & Orig Story* Nicholas Demetroules. *Photog* George Zimmermann, Richard E. Brooks. *Film Ed* Israel Ortiz. *Mus* Steve Karmen. *Sd* April Pollack.

Cast: Arlene Sue Farber *(Arlene Taylor)*, Frederick Riccio *(Duke Markell)*, Julie Ange *(Erica Peterson)*, Howard Le May *(Tony Michaels)*, George Peters, Matt Reynolds *(Mr. Taylor [see note])*.

Melodrama. A new teacher from Sweden offers a sex education course in a smalltown high school. Included in her course is a film depicting the delivery of a baby. When a young girl claims to be pregnant, the teacher is blamed for corrupting her. Later it is learned that the teenager was feigning pregnancy in order to trap her boyfriend into marriage. *Schoolteachers. Swedes. Adolescence. Pregnancy. Sex instruction. Smalltown life. High school life.*

Note: Sources conflict in crediting the role of Mr. Taylor.

TEENAGE MUSIC INTERNATIONAL *see* THE T.A.M.I. SHOW

TEENAGE PSYCHO MEETS BLOODY MARY see **THE INCREDIBLY STRANGE CREATURES WHO STOPPED LIVING AND BECAME CRAZY MIXED-UP ZOMBIES**

TEENAGE REBELLION see **MONDO TEENO**

THE TEENIE SWAPPERS   F6.4908
Dist Distribpix, Inc. 18 Jun **1969** [Boston opening]. Sd; b&w. 35mm. 65 min.
Sex film. Marcia and Georgie, two nubile 18-year-olds, share an apartment on New York's East Side near singles clubs they both frequent. One evening, Marcia is making love with her boyfriend Fred when Georgie comes home with her lesbian companion, Sue. The two couples decide to switch partners for variety. Subsequently, the roommates come to each other for sexual adventure and demonstrate a variation on some standard sex play. *Roommates. Adolescence. Mate swapping. Lesbianism. Sexual techniques. Singles bars. New York City—East Side.*

TEENIE TULIP   F6.4909
Cinex Film Industries. *Dist* Cinex International Film Distributors. 8 May **1970** [Miami, Florida, showing]. Sd; col (Eastman Color). 35mm. 80 min.
Prod George DeLemos. *Dir-Writ* Gerard Damiano. *Dir Photog* Jay Ryder. *Asst Camera* Tommy Goetz, George Feinberg, Charles Carmello. *Art Dir* Charles Carmello. *Film Ed* Gerard Damiano. *Mus D & D. Sd* Stewart Troy, Tony Foresto. *Prod Mgr* Charles Carmello. *Script Cont* Barbie. *Coöp* Charles Carmello, Hank Rifkin. *Grip* Mike Haley.
Cast: Steve Dickenson (*Dr. Luv*), Peggy Simpson, U. S. actress (*Karen Stuart*), Linda Southern (*Jane Goodwill*), Don Nardo (*Jim Harrington*), Hack Rightor (*Dr. Butler*), Ron Wertheim (*Dr. Waldron*), Donny Lee (*Clyde*), Brenda Baines (*Wanda*), Richard Lipton (*Richard*), Anita Ventura (*Rita Bryant*), Lucy Rey (*Mrs. Freestone*), Larry Hunter (*Morris*), Jackie Richards (*mother*), Suzzan Landow (*girl*), Bridget.
Melodrama. Although she is very much in love with Jim, her fiancé, Karen is troubled by sexual misgivings as their marriage draws near. She confides in her friend Jane, who recommends that she visit Dr. Jason Luv, a New York psychiatrist currently treating Jane for promiscuity. Dr. Luv uses sex to treat all of his patients. Clyde, for example, loves to watch naked women in secret; Dr. Luv obliges him by sending his own mistress, Bridget, to strip before him. The understanding doctor also encourages Morris' infatuation with another man. When the patient Rita attempts to satisfy her lust with a horse, however, she is trampled to death. Karen sees Dr. Luv and reveals that an unhappy sexual experience in high school has left her emotionally scarred. Dr. Luv instructs her to make use of Richard, his assistant, who functions as a human sex machine. Cured, Karen leaves the love clinic. Later, Dr. Luv is surprised during an argument with a stranger over his unorthodox methods. His antagonist is Dr. Waldron, one of the psychiatrists who are attempting to revoke Dr. Luv's license, and Luv's own analyst since the departure of Karen. *Psychiatrists. Mistresses. Promiscuity. Bestiality. Voyeurism. Male homosexuality. Sex clinics. Horses.*
Note: Also known as *Dr. Love.*

EL TEJANO see **THE TEXICAN**

THE TELEGIAN see **SECRET OF THE TELEGIAN**

TÉLI SIROKKÓ see **WINTER WIND**

TELL ME IN THE SUNLIGHT   F6.4910
Britannia Films. *Dist* Movie-Rama Color Corp. 1 Sep **1967** [Chicago opening]. Sd; b&w. 35mm. 82 min.
Exec Prod Arnold Stoltz. *Assoc Prod* Jerald Cormier. *Dir* Steve Cochran. *Screenplay* Jo Heims. *Orig Story* Robert Stevens. *Dir Photog* Rod Yould. *Art Dir* Jerry Sjolander. *Film Ed* David Woods. *Mus* Michael Andersen. *Titl Song* Steve Cochran, Franz Steininger, Jack Ackerman. *Sung by* Darlene Paul. *Sd Engr* Joseph Keener. *Asst to the Dir* Adrian Crossett.
Cast: Steve Cochran (*Dave*), Shary Marshall (*Julie*), Jay Robinson (*barber*), Dave Bondu (*Alex*), Patricia Wolf (*Chata*), George Hopkins (*Tony*), Rockne Tarkington (*Rocky*), Harry Franklin (*Dr. Franklin*), Hamish MacKay (*airport attendant*), Lucille (*Princess Naga*), George Roberts (*pickpocket*), Jill Walden (*Carol, the girl in the park*), Oliver Nissick (*Pepe*), Joe Hardy (*driver*).
Romantic drama. Dave, a merchant seaman on a banana boat in the Caribbean, goes alone on shore leave in Nassau despite the request of his happy-go-lucky shipmates, Tony and Rocky, to join them. He befriends Carol, a pregnant, despondent young fish seller and prevents her attempt at suicide. Returning to the ship, Dave is kidded by Rocky and Tony for being a lone wolf, but he continues his Nassau leave alone. At the scene of an auto accident he meets Julie, a stripteaser, who is being romanced by the influential Dr. Franklin. Dave and Julie fall in love. Their affair is aborted, however, when Dave is shipped out. Julie comes down to the dock to see him off, but she is accompanied by Franklin. Dave eventually returns to Nassau, gets drunk, and

seduces the reluctant Julie. Their romance is then helped along by the efforts of Julie's girl friend and co-stripper, Chata, and Dave and Julie finally realize happiness with each other. *Seamen. Fishmongers. Stripteasers. Physicians. Loneliness. Pregnancy. Drunkenness. Suicide. Seduction. Nassau. Merchant marine.*
Note: Filmed in Nassau in 1964. Cut from 120 min following the death of the director in 1965.

TELL ME LIES (Great Britain)   F6.4911
Ronorus Films. *Dist* Continental Distributing, Inc. 12 Feb **1968** [New York opening]. Sd; b&w and col (Eastman Color). 35mm. 118 min.
A Peter Brook Production. *Prod-Dir* Peter Brook. *Exec Prod* Peter Sykes. *Assoc Dir* Albert Hunt, Geoffrey Reeves. *Orig Text* Denis Cannan. *Adapt of Documentary Material* Michael Kustow, Michael Scott, writ. *Photog* Ian Wilson. *Dsgn* Sally Jacobs. *Film Ed* Ralph Sheldon. *Mus Comp* Richard Peaslee. *Chorus & Mus Dir* Michael Reeves, mus. *Lyr* Adrian Mitchell. *Sd* Robert Allen.
Cast—Royal Shakespeare Company: Mark Jones (*Mark*), Pauline Munro (*Pauline*), Robert Lloyd (*Bob*), Eric Allan, Jeremy Anthony, Noel Collins, John Hussey, actor, Marjie Lawrence, Leon Lissek, Clifford Rose, Hugh Sullivan, Henry Woolf, Mary Allen, Hugh Armstrong, Ian Hogg, Glenda Jackson, Joanne Lindsay, Ursula Mohan, Morgan Sheppard, Barry Stanton, Michael Williams.
Additional Cast: Kingsley Amis, James Cameron, Peggy Ashcroft, Stokely Carmichael, Tom Driberg, Reginald Paget, Jacqueline Porcher, Ivor Richards, Hilary Rose, Steven Rose, Paul Scofield, Patrick Wymark, Peregrine Worsthorne.
Documentary drama. Source: Denis Cannan, *US* (London opening: 13 Oct 1966). Disturbed by a photograph of a mutilated Vietnamese child, three London actors—Mark, Pauline, and Bob—set out to learn the reasons for the war and what they can do to end the atrocities. Their quest takes them from protest demonstrations to a series of discussions with a group of politicians at a London cocktail party, with black power advocate Stokely Carmichael, with a Buddhist monk living in Hampstead, and with leftwing militants. Interspersed with these oral analyses is documentary footage of the Vietnam War and reenactments of several historic events, including the self-immolation of Quaker Norman Morrison on the steps of the Pentagon. Also converging on Mark's consciousness is a series of fantasies and dreams, including the constant petitioning of a Maoist woman for "class revolution" and Mark's imagining himself burning down the United States Embassy in London and touring Saigon's bars. The search for moral truth having proved fruitless, Mark, Pauline, and Bob find themselves still staring at the photograph. *Actors. War victims. Politicians. Militants. Monks. Maoists. Demonstrations. Race relations. Self-immolation. Photographs. Bars. Vietnam War 1964–73. London. Saigon. Norman Morrison. The Pentagon. Dreams.*
Note: Released in Great Britain in Feb 1968; running time: 117 min. Working title: *Make and Break.*

TELL ME THAT YOU LOVE ME, JUNIE MOON   F6.4912
Sigma Productions. *Dist* Paramount Pictures. 1 Jul **1970** [New York opening; c31 Dec 1969; LP38096]. Sd; col (Technicolor). 35mm. 113 min. *MPAA rating* GP.
An Otto Preminger Production. *Prod-Dir* Otto Preminger. *Assoc Prod* Nat Rudich. *Screenplay* Marjorie Kellogg. *Dir Photog* Boris Kaufman. *Camera Op* Alfred Lebovitz. *Titl Seq Photog* Stanley Cortez. *Set Decor* Morris Hoffman. *Prod Dsgn* Lyle Wheeler. *Main Titl* Howard A. Anderson. *Film Ed* Henry Berman, Dean O. Ball. *Mus* Philip Springer. *Adtl Mus* Johann Sebastian Bach. *Mus Coörd* Thomas Z. Shepherd. *Song:* "Old Devil Time" writ & sung by Pete Seeger. *Songs:* "The Rake," "Work Your Show" Philip Springer, Estelle Levitt. *Song:* "Elvira" writ & perf by Pacific Gas and Electric. *Sd* Ben Winkler, Franklin Milton, Stanley Gordon. *Mus Ed* Robert Tracy. *Asst Dir* Norman Cook. *Prod Mgr* Robert Vreeland. *Exec Asst to the Prod* Erik Kirkland. *Script Supv* Wallace Bennett, Cleo Anton. *Prod Asst* James D. Pasternak, Jerome Brandt. *Cost Coörd* Hope Bryce. *Wardrobe Dsgn* Ronald Talsky, Phyllis Garr. *Miss Thompson's Cost* Halston. *Makeup* Charles Schram. *Ch Electrn* Joe Edesa. *Key Grip* Martin Kashuk. *Dial Coach* Max Slater. *Prop Master* Stephen Ferry. *Still Photog* Robert Ross.
Cast: Liza Minnelli (*Junie Moon*), Ken Howard (*Arthur*), Robert Moore (*Warren*), James Coco (*Mario*), Kay Thompson (*Miss Gregory*), Fred Williamson (*beach boy*), Ben Piazza (*Jesse*), Emily Yancy (*Solana*), Leonard Frey (*Guiles*), Clarisse Taylor (*Minnie*), James Beard (*Sidney Wyner*), Julie Bovasso (*Ramona*), Gina Collens (*Lila*), Barbara Logan (*Mother Moon*), Nancy Marchand (*Nurse Oxford*), Lynn Milgrim (*Nurse Holt*), Ric O'Feldman (*Joebee*), James D. Pasternak (*artist*), Angelique Pettyjohn (*Melissa*), Anne Revere (*Miss Farber*), Elaine Shore (*Mrs. Syner*), Guy Sorel (*Dr. Gaines*), Wayne Tippett (*Dr. Miller*), Pete Seeger (*himself*), Pacific Gas & Electric (*themselves*), Ulla Bomser, Cynthia Korman, Anne Larson.

Drama. Source: Marjorie Kellogg, *Tell Me That You Love Me, Junie Moon* (New York, 1968). Junie Moon, whose face was badly scarred when her deranged boyfriend poured battery acid on her, leaves the hospital with two new friends, Arthur and Warren, who also have major physical and emotional problems. Arthur is an epileptic whose disability forced him to spend his childhood in a foster home, and Warren, raised by one of his mother's bohemian friends, is a paraplegic homosexual, crippled by a gunshot wound. The three of them rent a house from the eccentric Miss Gregory, and Junie manages to find Arthur a job with Mario, who runs a nearby fish market. Miss Gregory soon invites her three tenants to dinner at her mansion, but she spoils the evening when she tries to make Warren get out of his wheelchair and walk by offering him a $100,000 antique cross as a reward. Soon afterwards, an anonymous phone caller tells Mario that Arthur is a sodomist, and he is forced to fire his new employee. Even so, Mario, who is falling in love with Junie, lends the trio money to take a vacation at a seaside resort. While they are there, Warren is carried around by the resort's handsome black social director, and on one occasion he spends the entire night on the beach making love with Solana, the social director's girl friend. Arthur tells Junie he loves her, but she mistrusts men and is reluctant to have sex with him. They finally make love, but the next day Arthur's health begins to fail, and he dies in Junie's arms. At his funeral, Junie, Warren, and Mario are the only mourners. *Paraplegics. Landlords. Eccentrics. Fishmongers. Social directors. Negroes. Sadism. Disfiguration. Epilepsy. Male homosexuality. Friendship. Employer-employee relations. Slander. Vacations. Death. Hospitals. Beaches. Funerals.*

Note: Location scenes filmed at the Hammond Museum in Magnolia, Massachusetts; the Kona Kai Club, Shelter Island, California; Sequoia National Park, California; and the towns of Salem, Beverly Farms, Manchester, and Rockport, Massachusetts.

THE TELL-TALE HEART (Great Britain)   F6.4913
Danziger Productions. *Dist* Brigadier Film Associates, Union Film Distributors. 7 Feb **1962** [Baltimore opening]. Sd; b&w. 35mm. 81 min.
Prod Edward J. Danziger, Harry Lee Danziger. *Dir* Ernest Morris. *Screenplay* Brian Clemens, Eldon Howard. *Photog* James Wilson. *Art Dir* Norman Arnold. *Set Decor* Peter Russell. *Film Ed* Derek Parsons. *Mus* Tony Crombie, Bill Le Sage. *Sd* W. A. Howell, John S. Smith. *Prod Supv* Brian Taylor.
Cast: Laurence Payne (*Edgar Marsh*), Adrienne Corri (*Betty Clare*), Dermot Walsh (*Carl Loomis*), Selma Vaz Dias (*Mrs. Vine*), John Scott (*inspector*), John Martin (*police sergeant*), Annette Carell (*Carl's landlady*), David Lander (*jeweller*), Rosemary Rotheray (*Jackie*), Suzanne Fuller (*Dorothy*), Yvonne Buckingham (*Mina*), David Courtney, Richard Bennett, Joan Peart, Elizabeth Paget, Frank Thornton, Nada Beall, Pamela Plant, Graham Ashley, Brian Cobby, Madeline Leon, Patsy Smart.
Horror film. Source: Edgar Allan Poe, "The Tell-Tale Heart," in *The Pioneer* (Jan 1843). Edgar Allan Poe dreams that he is a crippled librarian named Edgar Marsh. Morbidly sensitive about his disability, he lives in solitude with a housekeeper in his dead mother's house. He spends his evenings in a haze of drugs and dreams lasciviously of encounters with women he ordinarily would not dare approach. A florist's attractive assistant, Betty Clare, moves across the way, and he secretly watches her from his bedroom window and becomes passionately aroused. Although he manages, through a contrived meeting, to arrange a date with her, it soon becomes apparent that she prefers the company of his best friend, Carl Loomis. Insanely jealous, Edgar kills Carl and hides the body under the floorboards of his study. Haunted by the hallucination that he can still hear Carl's heart beating, he cuts the heart from the body and buries it in the nearby woods; but the relentless hammering continues. Betty, meanwhile, has asked the police to investigate Carl's mysterious disappearance. When they question Edgar, he breaks down and confesses to the murder. At this point, Poe awakens from his dream, looks out of his window and sees a young woman—Betty Clare—moving into the house across the way. *Cripples. Librarians. Housekeepers. Florists. Police. Voyeurism. Murder. Jealousy. Mutilation. Guilt. Mental illness. Narcotics. Corpses. Edgar Allan Poe. Dreams. Hallucinations.*
Note: Released in Great Britain in Jan 1963 at 78 min. Union Film Distributors re-released the film in 1964 as *The Hidden Room of 1,000 Horrors.*

TELL THEM WILLIE BOY IS HERE   F6.4914
Universal Pictures. 18 Dec **1969** [New York opening; c18 Dec 1969; LP39050]. Sd; col (Technicolor). 35mm (Panavision). 98 min. *MPAA rating* M.
Pres by Jennings Lang. A Philip A. Waxman Production. *Prod* Philip A. Waxman. *Dir-Writ* Abraham Polonsky. *Photog* Conrad Hall. *Art Dir* Alexander Golitzen, Henry Bumstead. *Set Decor* John McCarthy, Ruby Levitt. *Film Ed* Melvin Shapiro. *Mus* Dave Grusin. *Mus Supv* Stanley Wilson. *Sd* Waldon O. Watson, David H. Moriarty. *Asst Dir* Joseph E. Kenny. *Unit Prod Mgr* Hal Polaire. *Cost Dsgn* Edith Head. *Makeup* Bud Westmore. *Hairstyles* Larry Germain. *Stunt Coord* John Daheim.

Cast: Robert Redford (*Christopher Cooper*), Katharine Ross (*Lola*), Robert Blake (*Willie Boy*), Susan Clark (*Liz Arnold*), Barry Sullivan (*Ray Calvert*), John Vernon (*Hacker*), Charles Aidman (*Benby*), Charles McGraw (*Frank Wilson*), Shelly Novack (*Finney*), Robert Lipton (*Newcombe*), Lloyd Gough (*Dexter*), Ned Romero (*Tom*), John Wheeler (*Newman*), Erik Holland (*Digger*), Garry Walberg (*Dr. Mills*), Jerry Velasco (*Chino*), George Tyne (*Le Marie*), Lee De Broux (*Meathead*), Wayne Sutherlin (*Harry*), Jerome Raphel (*salesman*), Lou Frizzell (*station agent*), John Day (*Sam Wood*), Steve Shemayne (*Johnny Hyde*), John Hudkins (*3d man*), Mikel Angel (*Old Mike*), Everett Creach (*fake Indian*), Johnny Coons (*clerk*), Stanley Torres (*1st committee man*), Kenneth Holzman (*reporter*), Spencer Lyons (*Cody*), Joseph C. Mandel (*2d reporter*), Robert Du Laine (*1st escort*).
Western drama. Source: Harry Lawton, *Willie Boy, a Desert Manhunt* (Balboa Island, California, 1960). Willie Boy, a young Paiute Indian, returns to his Banning, California, reservation in 1909 so that he may attend his tribe's annual fiesta and resume his relationship with Lola, whose father has stood between them. When Willie attempts to arrange a midnight date with Lola, her father threatens to shoot him. Concurrently, easygoing Under-Sheriff Christopher Cooper, or "Coop," comes into town to see Liz Arnold, a wealthy Bostonian who doubles as doctor and superintendent of the reservation. Their relationship is tenuous: though Liz is sexually attracted to Coop, she regards him as her social and intellectual inferior and scorns his coarse manner. Willie meets Lola in the woods at midnight as planned, but their lovemaking is interrupted by the appearance of her father and brothers. Lola's father is killed in the ensuing scuffle, and, according to tribal tradition, Lola becomes Willie's wife. Liz, however, has other ambitions for Lola, and she insists that Coop apprehend the couple so that she can be returned to the reservation. Though his sympathies are with the Indians, Coop reluctantly heads a posse of bloodthirsty ranchers, but Willie and Lola evade the group. As the pursuit through the Mojave Desert drags on, Coop abandons the posse in order to return to town so that he may serve as bodyguard to the visiting President Taft. In Coop's absence, Willie picks off the pursuers' horses and accidentally shoots Ray Calvert, a member of the posse. The hysterical fear of an Indian uprising and assassination attempt against the President sweeps the town, and Coop is forced to continue his pursuit. The chase has left Lola so exhausted that she has become a liability to Willie, but she refuses to abandon him; and when the posse finds her dead body the following day, opinion is divided on whether she died by Willie's hand or by her own. Coop soon traps Willie in the mountains, and a confrontation is forced. When the Indian raises his rifle, Coop shoots against his will, only to discover that Willie's gun contains no bullets. *Paiute Indians. Fugitives. Physicians. Indian agents. Sheriffs. Ranchers. Filial relations. Class conflict. Murder. Suicide. Race relations. Racism. Assassination. Rites and ceremonies. California. Banning. Mojave Desert. William Howard Taft. Willie Boy. Chases.*
Note: Filmed at Thousand Oaks, California. Appreciation is expressed to the Indian peoples of Pechanga, Morongo, Los Coyotes, Soboba, Agua-Caliente, and Torres-Martinez Reservations (Reservation, California).

TEMPO DI MASSACRO see **THE BRUTE AND THE BEAST**

TEMPORARY WIVES   F6.4915
Garva Productions. *Dist* Astro-Jemco Film Distributors. 28 Nov **1969** [Champaign, Illinois, showing]. Sd; col. 35mm. 70 min.
Dir Gene Shamblin. *Photog* Edward I. Miller.
Cast: Gina Quintella, Ed De Hat.
Comedy-drama. A man's three ex-wives read in the newspaper of his approaching marriage to a princess and plot their revenge. One of the women invites him to her house to pick up a forgotten item; he arrives to find all three waiting in various stages of undress. The party begins with a drinking bout, and turns into a sex marathon that lasts almost 48 hours. The ex-husband staggers away just in time to marry the princess, but he is unable to consummate the marriage. After a second failure the following night, he is forced to confess his encounter with his three ex-wives. His new bride walks out, leaving him to bemoan the premature loss of his sexual potency. *Royalty. Newlyweds. Impotence. Marriage. Divorce. Revenge. Group sex.*

LE TEMPS DES AMANTS see **A PLACE FOR LOVERS**
LE TEMPS DU GHETTO see **THE WITNESSES**

TEMPTATION (France)   F6.4916
Riviera International Films-Jean Joannon. *Dist* Cameo International Pictures. 7 Feb **1962** [Washington, D. C., opening]. Sd (Western Electric); b&w. 35mm. 94 min.
Pres by William Shelton. *Prod-Dir* Edmond T. Gréville. *Assoc Prod* François Carron. *Screenplay* Edmond T. Gréville, Henri Crouzat, Louis A. Pascal. *English Dial* Jack Andrews. *Photog* Jacques Lemare. *Camera* Gustave Raulet. *Asst Camera* Philippe Brun, Alex Tomatis. *Art Dir* Jean Douarinou.

Film Ed Jean Ravel. *Asst Film Ed* Marie-Rose Mascarello. *Mus* Charles Aznavour, Marguerite Monnot, Eddie Barclay, Jean-Pierre Landreau. *Sd* Jacques Lebreton. *Rec* Jean-Claude Evangelou. *Boom* Charles Akerman. *Asst Dir* Louis A. Pascal, Claude Desvernet. *Prod Mgr* Louis Pointet. *Script Girl* Lucie Lichtig. *Unit Mgr* Fernand Bernardi. *Prod Sec* Marthe Toti. *Wardrobe* Annie Marolt, Majo Brandley, Clo Ramoin. *Makeup* Marcel Occelli. *Hairstyles* Odette Rey. *Still Photog* Jacques Boutinot. *Prop* Aldo Spaperi, Rémy Bernardi.

Cast: Magali Noël *(Jane)*, Dawn Addams *(Victoria)*, Rossana Podestà *(Caterina)*, Christian Marquand *(Patrick)*.

Melodrama. Source: Henri Crouzat, *L'île du bout du monde* (Paris, 1954). Victoria, an English nurse, Caterina, her Italian colleague, and Jane, a secretary from Canada [France?], find themselves sharing a lifeboat with Patrick, a French war correspondent, after the Red Cross ship in which they were returning from Korea is sunk. They land on a small volcanic island in the Indian Ocean, and conflicting passions soon come into play. Rebuffed by the cold Victoria, Patrick becomes romantically involved with the innocent Caterina, who loves him but refuses to become physically intimate. The carnal Jane bids for his attentions, and they carry on a sexual relationship. After the departure of Caterina, who leaves in the patched lifeboat to find help and is drowned in a storm, it is revealed by Victoria that Jane is a psychopath whom she was escorting back to face a murder charge. Victoria, too, becomes intimate with Patrick, and the possessive Jane kills her by pushing her off a cliff. When a boat is seen on the horizon, Jane, unable to keep Patrick from signaling for help, jumps from a cliff to her death. *Castaways. English. Italians. Canadians. Journalists. Nurses. Psychopaths. Secretaries. Seduction. Jealousy. Murder. Islands. Korean War 1950–53. Indian Ocean. Shipwrecks.*

Note: Filmed on location in Théoule, Cap Ferrat, and Île de Porquerolles, France. Opened in Nice in Feb 1959 as *L'île du bout du monde*; running time: 104 min.

THE TEMPTRESS AND THE MONK (Japan)   **F6.4917**
Nikkatsu Corp. *Dist* Gaston Hakim Productions International. 27 May **1963** [New York opening]. Sd; col (Eastmancolor). 35mm (Cinemascope (see note)). 88 min.
Prod Masayuki Takaki. *Dir* Eisuke Takizawa. *Screenplay* Toshio Yasumi, Kyoka Izumi. *Photog* Minoru Yokoyama. *Art Dir* Takashi Matsuyama. *Film Ed* Masanori Tsujii. *Mus* Yutaka Makino.
Cast: Yumeji Tsukioka *(temptress)*, Ryoji Hayama *(Socho)*, Tadashi Kobayashi *(dwarf)*, Ichijiro Oya *(grandfather)*, Jun Hamamura *(criminal)*, Akitake Kono.

Horror film. Source: Kyoka Izumi, *Koya hijiri* (Tokyo, 1901). Socho, a monk in ancient Japan, loses his way on a walk through the forest and comes upon an isolated house. The inhabitants, a voluptuous woman and her husband, an imbecilic dwarf, offer him lodging for the night. The dwarf, a descendant of the Shirafuji clan, has lived in the forest for years and has married on the condition that his wife lure any traveler to their home. After she seduces each man, she transforms him into an animal so that she may be free to lure the next traveler. Socho learns of this horrible practice but finds himself falling in love with the woman; she reciprocates his love and is unable to perform the terrible transformation on him. *Monks. Dwarfs. Temptresses. Seduction. Witchcraft. Forests.*

Note: Released in Japan in 1958 as *Byakuya no yojo*. Also reviewed as *The Temptress*. Some sources list the wide-screen process as NikkatsuScope.

TEN LITTLE INDIANS (Great Britain)   **F6.4918**
Tenlit Films. *Dist* Seven Arts Pictures. 9 Feb **1966** [New York opening]. Sd; b&w. 35mm. 92 min.
Pres by Seven Arts Productions. *Prod (see note)* Harry Alan Towers, Oliver A. Unger. *Prod In Assoc With* Harry M. Popkin. *Dir* George Pollock. *Screenplay* Peter Yeldham, Peter Welbeck. *Photog* Ernest Steward. *2d Unit Photog* Robert Thomson. *Art Dir* Frank White. *Film Ed* Peter Boita. *Mus Comp & Cond* Malcolm Lockyer. *Sd* Peter Keen. *Sd Rec* John Brommage, Ken Cameron. *Asst Dir* Barrie Melrose. *Prod Mgr* John Comfort.
Cast: Hugh O'Brian *(Hugh Lombard)*, Shirley Eaton *(Ann Clyde)*, Fabian *(Mike Raven)*, Leo Genn *(General Mandrake)*, Stanley Holloway *(William Blore)*, Wilfrid Hyde-White *(Judge Cannon)*, Daliah Lavi *(Ilona Bergen)*, Dennis Price *(Dr. Armstrong)*, Marianne Hoppe *(Frau Grohmann)*, Mario Adorf *(Herr Grohmann)*.

Mystery melodrama. Source: Agatha Christie, *Ten Little Niggers* (London, 1939). Agatha Christie, *Ten Little Niggers* (London opening: 20 Sep 1943). Eight strangers are invited to spend the weekend at an Austrian castle in the Alps. At the chateau, accessible only by cable car, they are received by the Grohmanns, a servant couple who have never seen their employer. As the holiday commences the guests assemble to hear the host's recorded welcome. Among them are singer Mike Raven, Judge Cannon, private investigator William Blore, actress Ilona Bergen, alcoholic Dr. Armstrong, retired General Mandrake, secretary Ann Clyde, and the American Hugh Lombard. In his

message their host discloses that each is a murderer and will be executed over the weekend. Guests and servants are slain in rapid succession, until only Ann and Lombard remain. Although they have fallen in love, the secretary shoots the American. Returning to the castle, she finds the presumably slain jurist awaiting her. Certain of Lombard's death, Cannon proclaims himself the host. Reminding Ann that she will undoubtedly be convicted of the murders, the magistrate reveals that he has poisoned himself and will be dead upon arrival of the authorities. As the judge speaks, the American enters the room. While awaiting the police, the lovers describe their mutual defense pact and verify their common innocence. *Strangers. Americans in foreign countries. Secretaries. Singers. Detectives. Actors. Judges. Housekeepers. Murder. Suicide. Poisoning. Alcoholism. Castles. Cable cars. Austria. Alps.*

Note: Filmed in Ireland. Released in Great Britain in 1966. British sources list Towers as producer, and U. S. sources credit Unger. Christie's novel also inspired the 1945 U. S. film *And Then There Were None*. Peter Welbeck is a pseudonym for Harry Alan Towers. One source indicates that the screenplay is based on an adaptation by Welbeck of Dudley Nichols' script for the earlier film.

10:30 P.M. SUMMER (United States/Spain)   **F6.4919**
Jorilie Productions–Argos Films. *Dist* Lopert Pictures. 24 Oct **1966** [New York opening; c24 Oct 1966; MP16663]. Sd; col (Technicolor). 35mm. 85 min.
Prod Jules Dassin, Anatole Litvak. *Dir* Jules Dassin. *Screenplay* Jules Dassin, Marguerite Duras. *Photog* Gabor Pogany. *Art Dir* Enrique Alarcón. *Film Ed* Roger Dwyre. *Mus* Cristóbal Halffter. *Sd* Jean Labussière.
Cast: Melina Mercouri *(Maria)*, Romy Schneider *(Claire)*. Peter Finch *(Paul)*, Julián Mateos *(Rodrigo)*, Isabel María Pérez *(Judith)*, Beatriz Savon *(Rodrigo's wife)*.

Melodrama. Source: Marguerite Duras, *Dix heures et demie du soir en été* (Paris, 1960). During a thunderstorm, Greek alcoholic Maria, her English husband, Paul, their small daughter Judith, and traveling companion Claire seek refuge overnight in a small Spanish hotel. While drinking Maria observes Paul and Claire embracing on a balcony and is strangely excited. Simultaneously she notices crouching on the rooftop Rodrigo, a young workman who has that day surprised and killed his wife and her lover. Filled with sympathy, the alcoholic drives the murderer to a deserted spot outside the village, promising to spirit him across the border on the morrow. When she returns the next day, accompanied by her entourage, Maria discovers Rodrigo dead in a pool of blood. Frustrated by Paul's continued devotion to his wife, Claire blames Maria's intervention for the worker's death. The disconcerted wife proclaims her indifference to her husband. That evening Maria abandons Paul and Claire in a cafe; they follow but despite their repeated calls, she does not answer. *Greeks. English. Fugitives. Alcoholism. Infidelity. Marriage. Murder. Jealousy. Travel. Hotels. Cafes. Storms.*

Note: Filmed on location in Castile. Spanish coproduction status unconfirmed.

TENCHU! (Japan)   **F6.4920**
Katsu Productions–Fuji Telecasting Co. *Dist* Daiei Motion Picture Co. Feb **1970** [Los Angeles showing]. Sd; col (Eastmancolor). 35mm (Daiei Scope). 140 min.
Dir Hideo Gosha. *Screenplay* Shinobu Hashimoto. *Photog* Fujio Morita. *Art Dir* Yoshinobu Nishioka. *Mus* Masaru Sato.
Cast: Shintaro Katsu *(Izo Okada)*, Tatsuya Nakadai *(Hampeita Takechi)*, Yukio Mishima, Yujiro Ishihara, Mitsuko Baisho, Takumi Shinjo, Noboru Nakaya, Tsutomu Shimomoto, Kei Yamamoto.

Historical drama. In 1862 the Tokugawa Shogunate, under both domestic and foreign pressures, concludes treaties with the United States, Great Britain, Russia, and the Netherlands, which open Japan to foreign trade and visitors. Supporters of the Emperor see this event as a signal for them to overthrow the Shogunate and restore the Emperor to the throne. Hampeita Takechi, leader of the Tosa clan, one of the three patriotic clans working against the Shogunate, is a ruthless leader who will stop at nothing to secure his own power. To this end, he retains a killer, Izo Okada, who blindly follows his every order, to the point that he is arrested for over-zealousness in getting rid of his boss's rivals. In prison Izo reconsiders his devotion to Hampeita, and upon his release he confesses all to the authorities in the hope that justice will be served. So complete is Hampeita's power, however, that Izo is placed in an untenable position and he commits hara-kiri. *Hired killers. Royalty. Loyalty. Hara-kiri. Confession (law). Treaties. Japan—History—Tokugawa period 1600–1867.*

Note: Released in Japan in Aug 1969 as *Hitokiri*.

TENDER GRASS *see* JENNIE, WIFE/CHILD

TENDER IS THE NIGHT   **F6.4921**
Twentieth Century–Fox Film Corp. 19 Jan **1962** [New York opening; c31 Dec 1961; LP21329]. Sd (Westrex); col (DeLuxe). 35mm (CinemaScope). 146 min.

Prod Henry T. Weinstein. *Dir* Henry King. *Screenplay* Ivan Moffat. *Dir Photog* Leon Shamroy. *Art Dir* Jack Martin Smith, Malcolm Brown. *Set Decor* Walter M. Scott, Paul S. Fox. *Main Titl* Pacific Title. *Film Ed* William Reynolds. *Mus* Bernard Herrmann. *Titl Song* Sammy Fain, Paul Francis Webster. *Sd* Bernard Freericks, Warren B. Delaplain. *Asst Dir* Eli Dunn. *Cost Dsgn* Marjorie Best. *Jennifer Jones, Joan Fontaine, Jill St. John Dressed by* Pierre Balmain. *Makeup* Ben Nye. *Miss Jones' Hairstyles Created by* George Masters. *Hairstyles Supv* Helen Turpin. *Sp Photog Eff* L. B. Abbott, Emil Kosa, Jr.

Cast: Jennifer Jones *(Nicole Diver)*, Jason Robards, [Jr.] *(Dick Diver)*, Joan Fontaine *(Baby Warren)*, Tom Ewell *(Abe North)*, Cesare Danova *(Tommy Barban)*, Jill St. John *(Rosemary Hoyt)*, Paul Lukas *(Dr. Dohmler)*, Bea Benaderet *(Mrs. McKisco)*, Charles Fredericks *(Mr. McKisco)*, Sanford Meisner *(Dr. Gregorovious)*, Mac McWhorter *(Colis Clay)*, Albert Carrier *(Louis)*, Richard DeCombray *(Francisco)*, Carole Mathews *(Mrs. Hoyt)*, Alan Napier *(Pardo)*, Leslie Farrell *(Topsy Diver)*, Michael Crisalli *(Lanier Diver)*, Earl Grant *(piano player)*, Maurice Dallimore *(Sir Francis Golding)*, Carol Veazie *(Mrs. Dunphrey)*, Arlette Clark *(governess)*.

Drama. Source: F. Scott Fitzgerald, *Tender Is the Night* (New York, 1934). At a lavish party given by Dick and Nicole Diver at their villa on the French Riviera, Dick meets an American starlet, Rosemary Hoyt, and Nicole's jealousy brings on a relapse of the emotional disorder which led to her first meeting with her husband: *While serving on the staff of a Zurich psychiatric clinic in the 1920's, Dick, a brilliant young American doctor, falls in love with one of his patients, wealthy Nicole Warren, whose neuroses stem from the time she was violated by her father. Dick's superior, Dr. Dohmler, warns him that marriage to Nicole can only end in tragedy; her love will die when she realizes that her god-husband is only an ordinary, fallible human being. Dick's emotions win out, however, and he marries Nicole. Catering to her every whim, he abandons his career and embarks on an endless round of pleasure-seeking and party-giving, all of which is financed by Nicole's guardian, her arrogant older sister, Baby.* Following the senseless death in a drunken brawl of their close friend, song writer Abe North, Dick senses how empty his life has become and tries to begin anew by returning to the Zurich clinic. It is too late, however; he has helped Nicole grow strong by allowing her to sap his strength, and it is now he who is the dependent one. Failing miserably at the clinic and drinking much too heavily, Dick makes a desperate attempt to recapture the gaiety of the early days of his marriage, but he succeeds only in making headlines as a result of a public fight over Rosemary. Having gained her independence with the downfall of her idol, Nicole asks Dick for a divorce in order to marry her lover. Too weak to fight and determined not to beg, Dick quietly acquiesces and leaves for an uncertain future in the small American town of his birth. *Psychiatrists. Sisters. Guardians. Idle rich. Composers. Actors. Wealth. Neurosis. Incest. Rape. Marriage. Alcoholism. Divorce. Clinics. Roaring Twenties. France. Zurich. Riviera.*

Note: Location scenes filmed in France, Italy, and Switzerland.

TENDER SCOUNDREL (France/Italy)　　　　F6.4922

Sud Pacifique Films–Fono Film. *Dist* Embassy Pictures. Aug **1967** [Los Angeles showing]. Sd; col (Eastman Color, print by Pathé). 35mm (Techniscope). 94 min.

Prod Paul-Edmond Decharme. *Dir* Jean Becker. *Screenplay* Albert Simonin, Jean Becker, Daniel Boulanger. *Dial* Michel Audiard. *Story* Albert Simonin. *Photog* Edmond Séchan. *Art Dir* Georges Wakhevitch. *Film Ed* Monique Kirsanoff. *Mus* Michel Legrand. *Sd* Robert Biart, Antoine Petitjean.

Cast: Jean-Paul Belmondo *(Tony Maréchal)*, Nadja Tiller *(Baroness Minna von Strasshofer)*, Mylène Demongeot *(Muriel)*, Robert Morley *(Lord Swift)*, Stefania Sandrelli *(Véronique)*, Maria Pacôme *(Germaine)*, Geneviève Page *(Béatrice Dumonceaux)*, Philippe Noiret *(Dumonceaux)*, Jean-Pierre Marielle *(Bob)*, Ellen Bahl *(Josette)*, Micheline Dax *(Marjorie)*, Michèle Girardon *(stranger from the Ritz)*, Paula Dehelly *(Mademoiselle Aline)*, Peter Carsten *(Capt. Otto Hanz)*, Ivan Desny *(haberdasher)*, Marcel Dalio *(Véronique's father)*, Elisabeth Teissier.

Romantic comedy. Aware that women find him irresistible, Tony Maréchal never concerns himself with finances. After a visit to the racetrack leaves him penniless, he spends the night in the lavish apartment of the beautiful Muriel. When her wealthy benefactor, Dumonceaux, arrives early the next morning, Tony introduces himself as Muriel's cousin and accepts the gullible Dumonceaux's invitation to join them at a ski resort in Megève. Here Tony becomes the subject of a battle between Muriel and Dumonceaux's wife, Béatrice. He flees into the arms of the Baroness Minna von Strasshofer, who takes him aboard her Tahiti-bound yacht, but her sexual demands are so great that Tony seeks refuge with another guest, the naive Véronique. Upon arriving in Tahiti, Véronique informs Tony that she has inherited a tiny island that is rich in manganese. The opportunistic Tony persuades an Englishman, Lord Swift, to buy the rights to the ore deposits, but they soon learn that Véronique

and her father have swindled them. After working his way back to Paris on a freighter, Tony is run down by a chauffeur-driven car belonging to a rich American widow. Exaggerating his injury, Tony permits the woman to move him into the Ritz but discovers that she is as voracious in her demands as the baroness. Momentarily depressed by his exhausting way of life, Tony considers pursuing a less strenuous vocation. *Gigolos. Mistresses. Idle rich. Aristocrats. Opportunists. Swindlers. English. Widows. Americans in foreign countries. Imposture. Gullibility. Infidelity. Jealousy. Duplicity. Mineral rights. Ski resorts. Yachts. Inheritance. Freighters. Paris. Tahiti. Megève (France). Ritz Hotel (Paris). Automobile accidents.*

Note: Location scenes filmed in Paris, the Alps, and Tahiti. Opened in Paris in Sep 1966 as *Tendre voyou*; running time: 90 min; in Rome in 1966 as *Un avventuriero a Tahiti*.

TENDERLY *see* **THE GIRL WHO COULDN'T SAY NO**

TENDRE VOYOU *see* **TENDER SCOUNDREL**

THE TENNESSEE BEAT *see* **THAT TENNESSEE BEAT**

TENNESSEE JAMBOREE　　　　F6.4923

Colorama Roadshows. 9 Sep **1964** [Cincinnati, Ohio, opening]. Sd; col (Eastman Color). 35mm. 75 min.

Prod-Dir Albert C. Gannaway.

Cast: Jim Reeves, Webb Pierce, Marty Robbins, Little Jimmy Dickens, Ernest Tubb, Minnie Pearl, Carl Smith, Lonzo & Oscar, The Carolina Cloggers, Ray Price, Chet Atkins, The Jordanaires, Goldie Hill, June Carter, Benny Martin, Rita Faye.

Musical revue. Performances by country and western singing stars, dancers, and bands are interspersed with rural comedy routines and monologs. *Singers. Dancers. Entertainers. Musicians. Bands. Country music.*

Note: Filmed in Nashville, Tennessee.

LA TENTACIÓN DESNUDA *see* **WOMAN AND TEMPTATION**

TENTATIONS *see* **SOFT SKIN ON BLACK SILK**

LE TENTAZIONI QUOTIDIANE *see* **THE DEVIL AND THE TEN COMMANDMENTS**

THE 10TH VICTIM (France/Italy)　　　　F6.4924

C. C. Champion–Les Films Concordia. *Dist* Embassy Pictures. 20 Dec **1965** [New York opening]. Sd; col (Technicolor). 35mm. 92 min.

Pres by Joseph E. Levine. *Prod* Carlo Ponti. *Exec Prod* Joseph E. Levine. *Dir* Elio Petri. *Screenplay* Ennio Flajano, Tonino Guerra, Giorgio Salvioni, Elio Petri. *Dir Photog* Gianni Di Venanzo. *Camera* Pasquale De Santis. *Art Dir* Piero Poletto. *Set Decor* Giovanni Checchi, Dario Micheli. *Film Ed* Ruggero Mastroianni. *Mus* Piero Piccioni. *Choreog* Gino Landi. *Sd* Ennio Sensi. *Asst Dir* Berto Pelosso. *Cost Dsgn* Giulio Coltellacci. *Ursula Andress' Clothes by* Sorelle Fontana (Roma).

Cast: Marcello Mastroianni *(Marcello Polletti)*, Ursula Andress *(Caroline Meredith)*, Elsa Martinelli *(Olga)*, Salvo Randone *(professor)*, Massimo Serato *(lawyer)*, Evi Rigano *(victim)*, Milo Quesada *(Rudi)*, Luce Bonifassy *(Lidia)*, Anita Sanders *(relaxatorium girl)*, Mickey Knox *(Chet)*, Richard Armstrong *(Cole)*, Walter Williams *(Martin)*, George Wang *(Chinese assailant)*.

Science fiction drama. Source: Robert Sheckley, "Seventh Victim," in *Galaxy* (Apr 1953). In the 21st century, a system of authorized murder called the "Big Hunt" has replaced war. Caroline Meredith, a licensed hunter, shoots her 9th victim in a New York City art gallery with a sophisticated setup of guns in her brassiere. Her 10th victim, whose death will bring her wealth and fame, is computer-selected Marcello Polletti. Marcello's winnings from six kills have already been spent by his mistress, Olga, and his ex-wife, Lidia. In Rome, while Marcello awaits his unknown assailant, Caroline makes an arrangement with a television company to film her kill as part of a commercial. Impersonating a reporter whose assignment is to study the sexual preoccupations of Italian men, Caroline approaches Marcello to request an interview with him at the Temple of Venus. Wary of meeting Caroline, Marcello arranges for her to be eaten by a crocodile before the cameras of a competing television company. Undaunted, Caroline lures Marcello to the beach and convinces him of her interest in him, and Marcello, for his part, begins to be fascinated by her. At the beach, Caroline drugs Marcello and the next morning hauls him back to the Temple of Venus. Caroline reluctantly shoots Marcello in front of the television cameras, but Marcello survives because he has loaded the gun with blanks. He attempts to take his revenge, but Caroline's bulletproof armorplate saves her life. The experience has drawn the two together, and they board the Wedding Airplane to be married; but after the ceremony, the pilot pulls a gun on the newlyweds. *Hunters. Mistresses. Reporters. Air pilots. Murder. Impersonation. Revenge. Contests. Art galleries. Television commercials. Weddings. Airplanes. New York City. Rome. The Future. Crocodiles.*

Note: Filmed on location in Rome and New York City. Opened in Rome in Dec 1965 as *La decima vittima*; running time: 100 min; in Paris in Feb 1967 as *La dixième victime*; running time: 90 min.

TEOREMA (Italy)   F6.4925

Aetos Film. *Dist* Continental Distributing, Inc. 21 Apr **1969** [New York opening]. Sd (Westrex); col (Eastman Color, print by Movielab). 35mm. 93 min.

Pres by Walter Reade Organization. *Prod* Franco Rossellini, Manolo Bolognini. *Dir-Writ* Pier Paolo Pasolini. *Dir Photog* Giuseppe Ruzzolini. *Camera* Otello Spila. *Asst Camera* Luigi Conversi, Giuseppe Buonaurio. *Art Dir* Luciano Puccini. *Film Ed* Nino Baragli. *Mus Comp* Ennio Morricone. *Mus Cond* Bruno Nicolai. "Requiem" by Wolfgang Amadeus Mozart. *Perf* by Moscow Philharmonic Symphony Orchestra. *Sung* by Choirs of the Russian Academy. *Sd* Dino Fronzetti. *Sd Mix* Fausto Ancillai. *Asst Dir* Sergio Citti. *Prod Mgr* Paolo Frascà. *Script Girl* Wanda Tuzi. *Prod Sec* Sergio Galiano. *Cost* Marcella De Marchis. *Wigs* Ditta Rocchetti. *Silvana Mangano's Clothes* Roberto Capucci. *Hairstyles* Maria Teresa Corridoni. *Sp Eff* Goffredo Rocchetti. *Asst Sp Eff* Manlio Rocchetti. *Optical Eff* S. P. E. S. *Under the Direction of* Ettore Catallucci. *Pictorial Technique Adv* Giuseppe Zigaina.

Cast: Terence Stamp *(visitor)*, Silvana Mangano *(mother)*, Massimo Girotti *(father)*, Anne Wiazemsky *(daughter)*, Laura Betti *(maid)*, Andrès José Cruz Soublette *(son)*, Alfonso Gatto *(doctor)*, Ninetto Davoli *(messenger)*, Susanna Pasolini *(old peasant)*, Adele Cambria, Carlo De Mejo, Luigi Barbini, Ivan Scrataglia, Cesare Carboli.

Allegory. *Source:* Pier Paolo Pasolini, *Teorema* (Milan, 1968). A wealthy Milanese family is transformed by the visit of a mysterious stranger, an irresistibly attractive engineering student who pliantly satisfies his hosts' sexual needs, gratifying in turn maid, son, mother, daughter, and father. When a telegram arrives the guest departs in a taxi, and the abandoned family experiences a terrible vacuum. The humble housemaid returns to her native village, where she fasts, prays, levitates, and is venerated as a saint. In search of a surrogate for the guest, the proper matron sleeps with several young workers, and finally seeks solace in church. The daughter, now catatonic, is admitted to a hospital, while the son becomes an artist who, obsessed with art's own absurdity, urinates on his own paintings. The industrialist father gives his factory to the workers, divests himself of clothing publicly, and wanders naked into an arid wilderness. *Strangers. Idle rich. Industrialists. Housemaids. Students. Painters. Religious conversion. Socialism. Family life. Bisexuality. Catalepsy. Levitation. Factories. Churches. Milan. Miracles.*

Note: Opened in Rome in 1968; running time: 98 min.

TERESA ... DARLING   F6.4926

21st Century Films. *Dist* American Film Distributing Corp. 22 Oct **1969** [New York opening]. Sd; b&w. 35mm. 85 min.

Dir-Writ Michel Stylianou.

Cast: Annie Claude, Diana Alicia, Laurie Rhodes, Suzzan Landow, Sorelle Faie, La Savona, C. Seligson, Christian Lord, Earl Zirn, T. Efstathiou, Sal Christi, B. Stathis, Paul Davis, J. Minaidis, Agamemnon Verry.

Drama. Soon after her marriage to John, Teresa becomes a participant in the erotic games played by her husband and his lovers, both male and female. *Marriage. Group sex. Male homosexuality.*

Note: Filmed in New York.

TERM OF TRIAL (Great Britain)   F6.4927

Romulus Films. *Dist* Warner Bros. Pictures. 30 Jan **1963** [New York opening; c31 Dec 1962; LP29394]. Sd; b&w. 35mm. 113 min.

Prod James Woolf. *Assoc Prod* James Ware. *Dir-Writ* Peter Glenville. *Photog* Oswald Morris. *Art Dir* Tony Woollard. *Set Decor* Peter James. *Prod Dsgn* Wilfred Shingleton. *Film Ed* James Clark. *Mus Comp* Jean-Michel Damase. *Mus Cond* Lambert Williamson. *Sd* Charles Poulton, Len Shilton. *Asst Dir* Gerry O'Hara. *Prod Mgr* Charles Blair. *Cost* Beatrice Dawson. *Makeup* Ernest Gasser. *Hairstyles* Gordon Bond.

Cast: Laurence Olivier *(Graham Weir)*, Simone Signoret *(Anna Weir)*, Sarah Miles *(Shirley Taylor)*, Hugh Griffith *(O'Hara)*, Terence Stamp *(Mitchell)*, Roland Culver *(Trowman)*, Frank Pettingell *(Ferguson)*, Thora Hird *(Mrs. Taylor)*, Dudley Foster *(Detective Sergeant Kiernan)*, Norman Bird *(Mr. Taylor)*, Newton Blick *(prosecutor)*, Allan Cuthbertson *(Sylvan-Jones)*, Nicholas Hannen *(Magistrate Sharp)*, Roy Holder *(Thompson)*, Barbara Ferris *(Joan)*, Rosamund Greenwood *(Constance)*, Lloyd Lamble *(Inspector Ullyat)*, Vanda Godsell *(Mrs. Thompson)*, Earl Cameron *(Chard)*, Clive Colin Bowler *(Collins)*.

Drama. *Source:* James Barlow, *Term of Trial* (London, 1961). Graham Weir, a man of high principles and a dedicated schoolteacher in a poor section of northern England, turns to drink whenever he is taunted for his spinelessness by Anna, his French-born wife. Most of his students are unruly and uninterested in schooling; however, young Shirley Taylor asks for extra tutoring, and Graham willingly complies. She falls in love with him, and upon returning from a school trip to Paris, she goes to his room and asks him to sleep with her. When he refuses, the humiliated girl accuses him of attempted sexual assault. Brought to court by Shirley's vindictive mother, Graham is tried and convicted; but Shirley breaks down and admits to her lie when Graham makes an impassioned plea. The case is dismissed, but Anna announces that she despises Graham for not seducing the girl, because his aggression would have at least made him seem more of a man. In an effort to salvage his marriage, Graham then claims that Shirley's accusations were true. Anna believes his false confession, and their marriage is saved. *Schoolteachers. French. Students. Marriage. Alcoholism. Revenge. Rape. Injustice. Confession (law). Trials. Paris.*

Note: Opened in London in Aug 1962; running time: 130 min. Copyright claimant: Harman Pictures.

TERRA EM TRANSE *see* EARTH ENTRANCED

LA TERRA TREMA (Italy)   F6.4928

Universalia. *Dist* Mario De Vecchi. 12 Oct **1965** [New York opening]. Sd; b&w. 35mm. 160 min.

Prod Salvo D'Angelo. *Dir-Writ* Luchino Visconti. *Dir Photog* G. R. Aldo. *Camera Op* Gianni Di Venanzo. *Asst Camera* Aiace Parolin. *Film Ed* Mario Serandrei. *Mus Chosen* by Willi Ferrero, Luchino Visconti. *Mus Cond* Willi Ferrero. *Asst Cond* Micucci. *Sd* Vittorio Trentino. *Asst Dir* Francesco Rosi, Franco Zeffirelli. *Prod Mgr* Anna Davini. *Prod Mgr for Universalia* Renato Silvestri. *Unit Prod Mgr* Claudio Forges Davanzati. *Still Photog* Paul Ronald. *Key Grip* Nello Nutarelli. *Ch Electrn* Bruno Pasqualini.

Cast (see note): Luchino Visconti, Antonio Pietrangeli *(narrators)*.

Drama. *Inspired by:* Giovanni Verga, *I malavoglia* (Milan, 1881). Life in the small Sicilian fishing village of Aci-Trezza carries on as it has for many years: each night the men fish from small boats and return in the morning to sell their catch to fish dealers on the beach, while the women remain in the village performing chores and mending the nets. The Valastra family, like other families in the village, is poor but spirited in their acceptance of hard work and their dedication to each other. Antonio, the oldest son, returns home from the war with new ideas which threaten the existing social structure of the village. He courts Nedda, the daughter of a relatively wealthy family, and realizes that he must elevate the economic position of his own family if her parents are to agree to their marriage. One morning, while bargaining with the fish dealers, Antonio challenges their arrogance, and a serious argument erupts. He is arrested, but not without leaving an impact on many of the villagers; some families complain that the incident has kept men from work and created communist tendencies among them. After his release from jail, Antonio begins a concerted effort to convince the villagers that they must break away from the oppression of the fish dealers. He persuades his family to mortgage their small house in order to buy salt to preserve their catches, thereby doing away with the need for dealers. The Valastras' plight worsens, however, and the bank evicts them from their home. A series of misfortunes leaves the family destitute, and Nedda decides to reject Antonio's marriage proposal. Finally, Antonio is forced to go to the fish dealers, whom he has opposed, and ask for employment. *Fishermen. Village life. Family life. Social customs. Poverty. Courtship. Communism. Fishing villages. Aci-Trezza.*

Note: Filmed in and around Aci-Trezza, Sicily. Opened in Rome in Jun 1950; running time: 120 min. Also known in Italy as *Episodio del mare*. The cast is composed of citizens of Aci-Trezza.

THE TERRACE (Argentina)   F6.4929

Internacional Films. *Dist* Royal Films International. 24 Nov **1964** [New York opening]. Sd; b&w. 35mm. 90 min.

Prod German Szulem. *Dir* Leopoldo Torre Nilsson. *Screenplay* Beatriz Guido. *Photog* Ignacio Souto. *Art Dir (see note)* Ricardo Luna, Oscar Lagomarsino. *Film Ed (see note)* Juan Sires, Jacinto Cascales. *Mus* Jorge López Ruiz. *Sd* J. M. Paleo. *Asst Dir* Jorge Briand. *Makeup* Kurt Grun.

Cast: Belita *(Belita)*, Graciela Borges *(Claudia)*, Leonardo Favio *(Rodolfo)*, Marcela López Rey *(Vicky)*, Héctor Pellegrini *(Alberto)*, Dora Baret *(Valeria)*, Norberto Suárez *(Luis)*, Enrique Leporace *(Horacio)*, Luis Walmo *(Pablo)*, Mirtha Dubner *(Mercedes)*, Oscar Caballero *(Guille)*, Bernardo Kullock *(Gaspar)*, Fernando Vegal *(Father Alfonso)*, Maria Esther Duckse *(grandmother)*, Alfredo Tobares *(Alberto's father)*, Sergio Corona *(2d floor tenant)*, Susana Brunetti *(Cuban woman)*, Félix Robles *(porter)*.

Drama. On a hot summer day, a crisis develops at a luxurious apartment house in Buenos Aires. Ten young boys and girls take over the pool and terrace on the roof of the building and indulge in whatever sport or game momentarily affords them pleasure. The only witness to their swimming, drinking, and lovemaking is 10-year-old Belita, the precocious granddaughter of the superintendent, who obligingly runs their errands and fetches their beer and whisky. When their elders attempt to end the monopolization of the terrace, the teenagers keep them at bay by threatening, one at a time, to leap from the parapet. As the drinking and lovemaking intensify, the pointless rebellion continues into the night, and the youngsters take Belita as their hostage. In the morning, when the parents dare to defy the rules of the game and storm the terrace, one of the boys grabs Belita and tosses her off the roof. She is not killed but severely injured. Months later the lame child plays alone in the empty pool on the terrace. *Children. Hostages. Cripples. Adolescence. Hedonism. Drunkenness. Parenthood. Swimming pools. Buenos Aires.*

Note: Released in Argentina in 1963 as *La terraza*. Sources conflict in crediting art director and editor.

LA TERRAZA *see* **THE TERRACE**

LA TERREUR DES MERS *see* **GUNS OF THE BLACK WITCH**

TERRIFIED!   F6.4930
Bern-Field Productions. *Dist* Crown International Pictures. 1 May **1963** [Salt Lake City, Utah, opening; c1 May 1963; LP31425]. Sd; b&w. 35mm. 81 min.

Pres by Leon Bleiberg. *Prod-Writ* Richard Bernstein. *Exec Prod* Leslie Nacman. *Asst Prod* Edward Critchfield. *Dir* Lew Landers. *Dir Photog* Curt Fetters. *Art Dir* Rudi Feld. *Set Decor* Ted Driscoll. *Titl & Opticals* Consolidated Film Industries. *Supv Film Ed* Rex Lipton. *Mus* Michael Andersen. *Sd* Earl Snyder. *Sd Eff Ed* Henry Adams. *Mus Ed* Ed Norton. *Asst Dir* Richard Dixon. *Prod Supv* Hal Kahan. *Prod Coörd* Ben Wurtzel. *Asst to the Prod* Jack Cantor. *Prod Sec* Audrey Bernstein, Betty Critchfield. *Script Supv* Doris August. *Cost* Mickey Sherrard. *Dsgn* Leslie (cost). *Makeup* Harry Thomas. *Miss Olsen's Coiffures* Lee Chenoweth. *Sp Eff* Charles Duncan. *Gaffer* Al Ronzo. *Prop Master* Royce Finley. *Dial Dir* Don Laiffer.

Cast: Rod Lauren *(Ken)*, Steve Drexel *(David)*, Tracy Olsen *(Marge)*, Stephen Roberts *(Wesley Blake)*, Sherwood Keith *(Mr. Hawley)*, Barbara Luddy *(Mrs. Hawley)*, Denver Pyle *(sheriff)*, Lee Bradley *(Mulligan)*, Ben Frank *(Duell)*, Danny Welton *(wise guy drunk)*, Michael Fellen *(Buzzy)*, Robert Towers *(Joey)*, Angelo Rossitto.

Horror film. A series of murders, committed by a hooded man, occur in a ghost town. Marge, a young waitress whose brother Joey was driven mad by the killer, goes with her student friends Ken and David to the ghost town to help solve the crimes. After finding Crazy Bill, caretaker of the town, impaled in the cemetery, David and Marge go for the sheriff, while Ken stays behind in hope of catching the murderer. The hooded man comes out of hiding, attacks Ken, and buries him alive, causing him to die of fright. After David and Marge return, the hooded man knocks David unconscious and carries Marge to an old mine shaft. The sheriff arrives, rescues David and Marge, and kills the hooded man. He is identified by Joey as Wesley Blake, Marge's boss, an ex-ventriloquist in vaudeville, obsessed with the desire to protect Marge. *Psychopaths. Waitresses. Students. Vaudevillians. Sheriffs. Ventriloquism. Murder. Disguise. Obsession. Brother-sister relationship. Impalement. Ghost towns.*

Note: Location scenes filmed in California.

THE TERROR   F6.4931
Filmgroup, Inc. *Dist* American International Pictures. 17 Jun **1963** [Buffalo, New York, opening]. Sd; col (PathéColor). 35mm (Vistascope). 81 min.

Prod-Dir Roger Corman. *Exec Prod* Harvey Jacobson. *Assoc Prod* Francis Coppola. *Uncredited Dir Collab* Francis Coppola, Monte Hellman, Jack Hale, Dennis Jacob, Jack Nicholson. *Story & Screenplay* Leo Gordon, Jack Hill. *Photog* Jack Nickolaus. *Art Dir* Daniel Haller. *Set Decor* Harry Reif. *Main Titl* Paul Julien. *Film Ed* Stuart O'Brien. *Mus Comp & Cond* Ronald Stein. *Sd* John Bury. *Asst Dir* Monte Hellman. *Cost* Marjorie Corso.

Cast: Boris Karloff *(Baron von Leppe)*, Jack Nicholson *(Lieut. André Duvalier)*, Sandra Knight *(Helene)*, Richard Miller *(Stefan)*, Dorothy Neumann *(old woman)*, Jonathan Haze *(Gustaf)*.

Horror film. André Duvalier, an officer of Napoleon's army, is lost somewhere on the Baltic coast and collapses from exhaustion only to be awakened by a mysterious girl who then disappears into the sea. Later, he wakes in a strange hovel, attended by an old woman and her half-witted servant, Gustaf. After he sees the girl again in the forest, she vanishes and André is told by Gustaf that she can be found in the castle of Baron von Leppe. Upon his arrival there, he recognizes the elusive girl's likeness in a painting which the Baron insists is a portrait of his long dead wife. When von Leppe requests him to leave, Duvalier discovers the dying Gustaf who urges him to return to the castle and find the girl. When he does so, she agrees to leave the evil place with him, but again she mysteriously disappears. The Baron's servant, Stefan, reveals that the old woman's son, Erik, thought to be dead for 20 years, is in fact alive, having killed the Baron and taken his place. As André rescues the girl, she becomes a mouldering, decayed corpse in his arms as the crazed Erik drowns himself. *Soldiers. Nobility. Strangers. Suicide. Rescue. Castles. Corpses. France—History—Napoleonic period. Baltic Sea.*

Note: Location scenes filmed in California. Working title: *Lady of the Shadows.*

TERROR AFTER MIDNIGHT (West Germany)   F6.4932
Roxy-Film. *Dist* Parade Pictures. Jan **1965**. Sd; b&w. 35mm. 82 min.
Dir Jürgen Goslar. *Photog* Klaus von Rautenfeld. *Mus* Bert Kaempfert.

Cast: Christine Kaufmann *(Julie)*, Martin Held, Hilde Krahl, Christian Doermer, Karel Stepanek, Bruno Dietrich.

Crime melodrama. Julie quarrels with her fiancé and leaves in the company of a rival suitor. Instead of seeing Julie home, the escort telephones her father to instruct him to pay a large sum of money if he ever again wants to see his daughter alive. They agree to meet at a secluded yachting clubhouse, where the abductor is shot in an ensuing struggle. *Kidnaping. Fatherhood. Courtship. Country clubs. Ransom.*

Note: Released in West Germany in Oct 1962 as *Neunzig Minuten nach Mitternacht*; running time: 77 min.

TERROR AT BLACK FALLS   F6.4933
Meridan Productions. *Dist* Beckman Film Corp. 23 May **1962** [New York opening]. Sd; b&w. 35mm. 76 min.

Prod-Dir Richard C. Sarafian. *Photog* Floyd Crosby. *Unit Prod Mgr* John Cutts.

Cast: Peter Mamakos *(father)*, House Peters, Jr. *(sheriff)*, John Alonzo, Sandra Knight, Gary Gray, Jim Bysel, I. Stanford Jolley, Marshall Bradford, Bill Erwin, Jim Hayward.

Western melodrama. A Mexican youth is about to be hanged by a lynch mob for cattle rustling when his father, blundering an attempt to save his son, accidentally causes the hanging. This event is witnessed by a sheriff who, unknown to the father, had also come to rescue the youth. In the ensuing gunfight, the Mexican is wounded in his right hand. He serves 4 years in prison, and his hand is amputated; upon his release he seeks revenge on the sheriff who sent him to prison. He takes eight villagers as hostages and threatens to kill one every 10 minutes as long as the sheriff refuses to talk with him. After the Mexican has killed three of the eight hostages, the sheriff arrives. The Mexican tries to draw his gun with his right hand and in consequence is killed. *Mexicans. Amputees. Hostages. Sheriffs. Gunfighters. Lynching. Rustling. Fatherhood. Revenge. Murder. Prisons.*

Note: Filmed on location in Scotland, Missouri.

TERROR AT HALFDAY *see* **MONSTER A GO-GO!**

TERROR CASTLE *see* **HORROR CASTLE**

TERROR-CREATURES FROM THE GRAVE (United States/Italy)
                                                   F6.4934
M. B. S. Cinematografica–G. I. A. Cinematografica–International Entertainment Corp. *Dist* Pacemaker Pictures. 16 May **1967** [Maryland license]. Sd; col. 35mm (Cinepanoramic). 85 min.

Prod Frank Merle. *Co-prod* Massimo Pupillo. *Exec Prod* Felix C. Ziffer, J. R. Coolidge. *Dir* Ralph Zucker. *Story & Screenplay* Roberto Natale, Romano Migliorini. *Photog* Carlo Di Palma. *Film Ed* Robert Ardis. *Mus* Aldo Piga.

Cast: Barbara Steele *(Cleo Hauff)*, Richard Garret *(Joseph Morgan)*, Walter Brandt *(Albert Kovaks)*, Marilyn Mitchell *(Corinne Hauff)*, Alfred Rice *(Dr. Nemek)*, Alan Collins *(Kurt)*, Tilde Till *(Louise)*, Ennio Balbo *(paralytic)*, Steve Robinson, Edward Bell, René Wolfe.

Horror film. In turn-of-the-century Central Europe, lawyer Albert Kovaks is summoned to a small village to draw up a new will for Dr. Hauff but finds upon his arrival that the doctor died mysteriously a year before. Kovaks also learns that Hauff had interests in the occult and had contacted 12th-century "scourge-spreaders" buried in the grounds of the villa now occupied by his wife, Cleo, and his daughter, Corinne. Meanwhile, several neighbors meet horrible deaths, and Kovaks, suspecting the involvement of supernatural powers, asks his employer, Morgan, to come to the villa. Sores begin to appear on Morgan the night of his arrival, and the terrible truth is revealed: Morgan and Cleo were secret lovers who conspired with the dead neighbors to murder Hauff. With his dying breath, the doctor had summoned the medieval "terror-creatures" to avenge his death, and they now inflict their curse of doom on the last of the murderers. Corinne and Kovacs, who have fallen in love, are immunized from the plague by a sudden rain and escape the doctor's wrath. *Mediums. Lawyers. Physicians. Plague. Murder. Revenge. Infidelity. Supernatural. Occult. Curses. Wills.*

Note: Rome opening: Apr 1966 as *Cinque tombe per un medium*; running time: 90 min. English pseudonyms include Ralph Zucker (Massimo Pupillo), Richard Garret (Riccardo Garrone), Walter Brandt (Walter Brandi), Alfred Rice (Alfredo Rizzo), and Alan Collins (Luciano Pigozzi).

TERROR EN EL ESPACIO *see* **PLANET OF THE VAMPIRES**

TERROR IN THE CITY
F6.4935

Barbro Productions. *Dist* Allied Artists. Jun **1966** [c1 Jan 1963; LP33692]. Sd; b&w. 35mm. 90 min.

Pres by Bischoff-Diamond Corp. *Prod* Merrill Brody, Allen Baron, Dorothy E. Reed. *Assoc Prod* James Geallis, Joel Glickman. *Dir-Writ* Allen Baron. *Photog* Donald Malkames. *2d Unit Photog* Merrill Brody. *Art Dir* Charles Rosen. *Film Ed* Ralph Rosenblum. *Mus* Robert Mersey. *Sd* Jim Shields, Charles Federmack. *Asst Dir* Richard Wolf.

Cast: Lee Grant (*Suzy*), Richard Bray (*Brill*), Michael Higgins (*Carl*), Roberto Marsach (*Paco*), Robert Allen, actor (*Brill's father*), Sylvia Miles (*Rose*), Jaime Charlamagne (*Rick*), Robert Earl Jones (*farmer*), Ruth Attaway (*farmer's wife*), Charles Jordan (*artificial inseminator*), Roscoe Browne (*preacher*), Rick Colitti (*pickpocket*), Muriel Franklin (*Brill's sister*), Monroe Arnold (*pitchman*), Boris Marshalov (*haberdasher*), Spencer Davis, actor (*doorman*), Fred Feldt (*gas station attendant*), Bill Da Prato (*hotdog vendor*), Joseph Leberman (*delicatessen man*), Milton Luchan (*bartender*), Mel Brown (*truckdriver*), Danny Dresser (*Brill's brother*), Debby Bliss, Susie Dresser (*Brill's sisters*), Orlando Rosa, Willie Tomblin, Jon Evans, Carmelo De La Cruz, Johnny Pacyznski (*Rick's gang*), Ed Greenberg.

Melodrama. When his father scolds him for damaging the roof of his house, Brill, a young farm boy, runs away from his Pennsylvania home to make his fortune in New York City. He falls in with a gang of shoeshine boys and paper carriers working under Rick, a young hood who takes half of their earnings. On his second day in the big city, Brill wins most of Rick's money in a crap game and takes his new friend, Paco, for a night on the town. When Rick's gang beats up Brill for taking their money, he is rescued by a prostitute, Suzy, who takes him home, washes his wounds, buys him clothes and shows him the sights of Manhattan. After seeing Suzy and another prostitute arrested by the police, Brill decides to buy a bicycle and return home. En route, his bicycle is wrecked by a truck, and he spends the night with an elderly Negro couple from whom he learns the meaning of self-respect. The next day a sadder but wiser Brill arrives home and gives his father the remainder of his fortune. *Farmers. Runaways. Gangs. Bootblacks. Newsboys. Prostitutes. Police. Negroes. Urban life. Family life. Filial relations. Adolescence. Gambling. Friendship. Bicycles. Pennsylvania. New York City.*

Note: Filmed on location in New York City and in Cooperstown, New York. Working title: *The Truant;* prerelease title: *Pie in the Sky.*

TERROR IN THE JUNGLE
F6.4936

Torres International Pictures. *Dist* Crown International Pictures. Aug **1968** [Philadelphia showing]. Sd; col (Pathécolor). 35mm. 84 min.

An Enrique Torres Tudela Production. *Prod-Writ* Enrique Torres Tudela. *Assoc Prod* John M. Sher, Jr., Vlado Radovich. *Plane Seq Dir* Tom De'Simone. *Jungle Seq Dir* Andy Janzack. *Temple Seq Dir* Alexander Grattan. *Dial* Richard Ogilvie. *Dir Photog* Andy Janzack, Lewis Quinn, Mario Tosi. *Asst Camera* Jorge Vignati, Hector Diaz. *Sp Dsgn* Ofelia Mendez. *Film Ed* Alberto Soria, Tom Mosca. *Mus* Les Baxter, Stan Hofman. *Song:* "*Intr-ramy*" Robert Ojeda. *Other Songs* Rickey Torres, Jeanette Rollins, The Hypnotics. *Sd* Jean Mainferme, Rich Stephans. *Mix Ed* Jaime Mendoza. *Mix* Jim Aicholtz. *Asst Dir* Carmen Maria Romero. *Prod Mgr* Henning Bystron. *Asst to Prod* Verland Whipple. *Coörd* Jorge Torres Tudela, Chuck Angle, Fernando Geraldino, Tina Monish. *Wardrobe* Zoraida Geradino. *Makeup* John De Heven. *Sp Makeup* Robert Hunter, makeup, Art Werner. *Hairstyles* Grant Walleck. *Magicmation Eff* Jim P. Nielson. *Tech Adv* Julio Torres Tudela. *Gaffer* Foster Denker, Aggie Aguilar.

Cast: Jimmy Angle (*Henry Clayton, Jr.*), Robert Burns, Fawn Silver, Joan Addis, Ivan Stephen, Lee Childress, Jeanette Rollins, Kris Fasseas, Ben Pfeifer, Cynthia McArthur, Bob Bridges, Lizie Curtis, James C. Gates, Cholita Suray, Fernando Larranga, William Cocklin, Elaine Partnow, Henning Bystron, Chase Cordell, Wayne Douglas, Oliver Howard, actor, Herbert Fink, Mitzie Johnson, Byrd Holland, Faith Cristopher, Mario Cagnion, Tania Lish, John Johnston, Chuck Angle, Nichola Krujac, Cherleen Baxter.

Melodrama. Henry Clayton, Jr., is sent by his father to visit his estranged mother in Rio de Janeiro. The plane carrying the little boy takes off from Los Angeles and crashes in the Amazon jungles of Peru. Henry survives the crash, but he is captured by a group of Jivaro Indians, descendants of the Incas, who believe the little blonde boy is the son of their god. Riolama, chief of the Jivaro, is distrustful of the boy, however, and wants him dead. Meanwhile, news of the accident has reached Henry's parents, and they rush to Lima to search for their son. A group of Catholic missionaries join their search party in the jungle. As Riolama prepares to sacrifice Henry to the gods, the chief is attacked and killed by a jaguar. [Another source indicates that the little boy's toy tiger becomes real and kills Chief Riolama.] The boy falls into a bed of quicksand and is finally rescued by his father and the rest of the search party. *Children. Jivaro Indians. Missionaries. Parenthood. Human sacrifice. Jungles. Toys. Quicksand. Los*

Angeles. Rio de Janeiro. Peru. Lima. Amazon River. Airplane accidents. Jaguars. Tigers.

Note: Filmed on location in Peru.

TERROR IN THE MIDNIGHT SUN *see* **INVASION OF THE ANIMAL PEOPLE**

TERROR IS A MAN *see* **BLOOD CREATURE**

THE TERROR OF DR. MABUSE (West Germany)
F6.4937

CCC-Filmkunst. *Dist* Thunder Pictures. 28 Jul **1965** [New York opening]. Sd; b&w. 35mm. 88 min.

Pres by Robert Hartgrove. *Prod* Artur Brauner. *Assoc Prod* Wolf Brauner. *Dir* Werner Klingler. *Screenplay* Ladislaus Fodor, Robert A. Stemmle. *Story* Thea von Harbou. *Photog* Albert Benitz. *Camera Crew* Alex Henningsen, Thomas Kapiewicz. *Art Dir* Helmut Nentwig, Paul Markwitz. *Film Ed* Walter Wischniewsky. *Mus* Raimund Rosenberger. *Sd* Erwin Schänzle. *Asst Dir* Carl von Barany. *Prod Mgr* Heinz Götze, Manfred Korytowski. *Cost* Vera Mügge. *Makeup* Willy Stamm.

Cast: Gert Fröbe (*Inspector Lohmann*), Helmut Schmid (*Johnny Briggs*), Charles Regnier (*Mortimer*), Senta Berger (*Nelly*), Wolfgang Preiss (*Dr. Mabuse*), Walter Rilla (*Professor Polland*), Harald Juhnke (*Sergeant Kruger*), Leon Askin (*Floke*), Ann Savo (*Wabble-Heidi*), Claus Tinney (*Jack*), Zeev Berlinski (*Gulliver*), Albert Bessler (*Paragraph Joe*), Arthur Schilski (*Toni*), Alan Dijon, Alon Armand, Rolf Eden.

Crime melodrama. Based on characters created by: Norbert Jacques. Police Inspector Lohmann investigates a series of crimes that resemble the schemes of Dr. Mabuse, a notorious criminal imprisoned in an insane asylum under the care of Professor Polland. A police informer assists the inspector, but it is Johnny Briggs, a disenchanted new recruit of the gang, who informs Lohmann that Mortimer, the alleged mastermind, actually is responsible to someone at the asylum. Lohmann returns there to learn that Dr. Mabuse has died suddenly, and that, before his death, he had hypnotized the professor. Obsessed by Mabuse's mind, Polland captures Lohmann and begins to torture him with electric shock treatments until Johnny rescues him. Escaping with Dr. Mabuse's papers and pursued by police, Polland accidentally crashes his car into a deep gorge. *Police. Informers. Masterminds. Insanity. Hypnotism. Torture. Insane asylums. Automobile accidents. Chases. Doktor Mabuse.*

Note: Released in West Germany in Sep 1962 as *Das Testament des Dr. Mabuse.* Also known as *The Terror of the Mad Doctor.* Remake of a 1932 German version entitled *Das Testament von Doktor Mabuse.*

TERROR OF THE BLACK MASK (France/Italy)
F6.4938

S. N. C.-Romana Film. *Dist* Embassy Pictures. 16 Jul **1967** [New York showing]. Sd; col (Eastmancolor). 35mm. 96 min.

Pres by Joseph E. Levine. A Fortunato Misiano Production. *Exec Prod* Nino Misiano. *Dir* Umberto Lenzi. *Screenplay* Gino De Santis, Guido Malatesta, Umberto Lenzi. *Story* Gino De Santis.

Cast: Pierre Brice (*Don Diego*), Hélène Chanel (*Carmencita*), Daniele Vargas, Aldo Bufi-Landi, Carlo Latimer, Gisella Arden, Massimo Serato.

Adventure melodrama. During a plague in 17th-century Higuera the despotic Don Luis sequesters himself and his minions in his castle. A masked cavalier, however, penetrates this sanctuary and quickly dispatches the don's henchmen. His appearance coincides with the arrival of the tyrant's stepson, the timid Diego, whom the despot betroths to Carmencita, orphaned daughter of the former governor. Having gained entrance to a feast celebrating the epidemic's end, the masked swordsman kills the don during a duel. Shedding his guises of masked intruder and stepson, the cavalier reveals himself to be a Spanish officer, Captain Naderos, and he proclaims his love for Carmencita. *Spanish. Cavaliers. Territorial governors. Despots. Disguise. Impersonation. Marriage—Arranged. Murder. Masks. Epidemics. Castles. Duels. Spain. Zorro.*

Note: Original titles and release undetermined. One of a series of films based on the Zorro character.

TERROR OF THE BLOODHUNTERS
F6.4939

Warren Productions. *Dist* A. D. P. Productions. 3 May **1962** [Hartford, Connecticut, opening]. Sd; b&w. 35mm. 60 min.

Prod-Dir Jerry Warren.

Cast: Robert Clarke (*Steven Duval*), Steve Conte (*Dione*), Dorothy Haney (*Marlene*).

Action melodrama. Steven Duval, a prominent French artist and the writer of a controversial publication, is sent on false charges to the French penal colony of Devil's Island. There the commandant insists that Duval paint a portrait of his daughter Marlene. Realizing that Duval and his friend Dione were unjustly brought to the island, Marlene helps plan an escape to Brazil. Duval impersonates Captain Whorf, the prison guard engaged to be married to Marlene, and the three flee into the Amazon jungle where Dione is attacked and killed by a jaguar. In pursuit of Duval and Marlene, Captain Whorf and his men are captured by the Jivaro Indians; but Duval returns, sets fire to the Indian village, and saves Whorf. In return, Captain Whorf allows Marlene and Duval to leave safely for Brazil. *Artists. Authors. French. Prison guards. Jivaro Indians. Fugitives. Injustice. Prison escapes. Penal colonies. Jungles. Devil's Island. Amazon River. Brazil. Chases. Jaguars.*

TERROR OF THE HATCHET MEN *see* **THE TERROR OF THE TONGS**

THE TERROR OF THE MAD DOCTOR *see* **THE TERROR OF DR. MABUSE**

THE TERROR OF THE TONGS (Great Britain)   **F6.4940**
Hammer Film Productions–Merlin Film Co. *Dist* Columbia Pictures. 15 Mar **1961** [San Francisco opening; c1 Mar 1961; LP20539]. Sd (RCA); col (Eastman Color). 35mm. 80 min.

Prod Kenneth Hyman. *Exec Prod* Michael Carreras. *Assoc Prod* Anthony Nelson Keys. *Dir* Anthony Bushell. *Screenplay* Jimmy Sangster. *Dir Photog* Arthur Grant. *Camera Op* Len Harris. *Focus* Harry Oakes. *Camera Grip* Albert Cowland. *Art Dir* Thomas Goswell. *Asst Art Dir* Don Mingaye. *Prod Dsgn* Bernard Robinson. *Supv Ed* James Needs. *Film Ed* Eric Boyd-Perkins. *Asst Film Ed* Chris Barnes, Paul Smith, ed. *Mus Comp* James Bernard. *Mus Supv* John Hollingsworth. *Sd Rec* Jock May. *Sd Ed* Alban Streeter. *Boom Op* Jim Perry. *Sd Camera Op* Al Thorne, Michael Sale. *1st, 2d & 3d Asst Dir* John Peverall, Joe Levy, Dominic Fulford. *Prod Mgr* Clifford Parkes. *Prod Sec* Ann Skinner. *Cont* Tilly Day. *Wardrobe Mistress* Molly Arbuthnot. *Makeup Artist* Roy Ashton, Colin Garde. *Hairstyles* Frieda Steiger. *Still Photog* Tom Edwards. *Casting Dir* Dorothy Holloway. *Constr Mgr* Arthur Banks. *Ch Electrn* Jack Curtis, electrn. *Master Carpenter* Charles Davis. *Prop Master* Tommy Money.

Cast: Geoffrey Toone (*Captain Jackson*), Christopher Lee (*Chung King*), Yvonne Monlaur (*Lee*), Marne Maitland (*beggar*), Brian Worth (*Harcourt*), Ewen Solon (*tongman Tang How*), Burt Kwouk (*Mr. Ming*), Barbara Brown (*Helena Jackson*), Richard Leech (*Inspector Dean*), Bandana Das Gupta (*Anna*), Michael Hawkins (*priest*), Marie Burke (*Maya*), Milton Reid (*tong guardian*), Charles Lloyd Pack (*doctor*), Roger Delgado (*Tang How*), Tom Gill (*Beamish*), Eric Young (*Confucius*), Johnny Arlan (*executioner*).

Action drama. In 1910, Hong Kong is in the grips of the powerful Red Dragon tong, a secret society that extorts revenue from merchant seamen, deals in both opium and slave trades, and savagely slaughters all those who offer opposition. A merchant seaman, Captain Jackson, swears revenge on the nefarious clan after they brutally murder his first officer, his daughter, and his servant in order to obtain a list of tong leaders intended for delivery to the police. Aiding him is a young female halfcaste, Lee, who, 15 years earlier, was sold by the tongs into bonded slavery. Though Jackson is captured and tortured by tong leader Chung King, he escapes when a beggar sets him free. Unknown to Jackson, Harcourt, a district supervisor of the East India Company is a tong member. When Lee learns that Harcourt has lured Jackson to a wharf where he is to be murdered, she races to warn him. Lee is fatally wounded by a tong hatchetman but delivers her message to Jackson before she dies. Following the incident, the beggar incites the crowd to attack the tongs. Harcourt runs to Chung King, but the tong leader remains calm; after killing Harcourt, he chooses death at the hands of his own followers. *Chinese. Seamen. Sea captains. Halfcastes. Beggars. Extortion. Murder. Slavery. Torture. Riots. Suicide. Tongs. Opium. Hong Kong. Merchant marine. East India Company.*

Note: Opened in London in Sep 1961; running time: 79 min. Working title: *Terror of the Hatchet Men.*

TERROR ON BLOOD ISLAND *see* **BRIDES OF BLOOD**

IL TERRORE DEI MARE *see* **GUNS OF THE BLACK WITCH**

TERRORE NELLO SPAZIO *see* **PLANET OF THE VAMPIRES**

THE TERRORNAUTS (Great Britain)   **F6.4941**
Amicus Productions. *Dist* Embassy Pictures. 17 May **1967** [Boston opening]. Sd; col (PathéColor). 35mm. 75 min.

Prod Max J. Rosenberg, Milton Subotsky. *Dir* Montgomery Tully. *Screenplay* John Brunner. *Photog* Geoffrey Faithfull. *Art Dir* Scott Slimon. *Set Decor* Andrew Low. *Prod Dsgn* Bill Constable. *Film Ed* Peter Musgrave. *Mus Comp* Elisabeth Lutyens. *Mus Cond* Philip Martell. *Sd Ed* Stanley Smith. *Sd Rec* Laurie Clarkson. *Sd Re-rec* David Nimmo. *Asst Dir* Tom Walls. *Prod Mgr* Ted Wallis. *Cost* Eileen Welch. *Makeup* Dore Hamilton. *Hairstyles* Olive Mills. *Sp Eff* Bowie Films. *Sp Photog Eff* Ernest Fletcher.

Cast: Simon Oates (*Dr. Joe Burke*), Zena Marshall (*Sandy Lund*), Charles Hawtrey (*Joshua Yellowlees*), Patricia Hayes (*Mrs. Jones*), Stanley Meadows (*Ben Keller*), Max Adrian (*Dr. Henry Shore*), Frank Barry (*Burke as a child*), Richard Carpenter (*Danny*), Leonard Cracknell (*Nick*), Robert Jewell (*robot operator*), Frank Forsyth (*uncle*), André Maranne (*gendarme*).

Science fiction drama. Source: Murray Leinster, *The Wailing Asteroid* (New York, 1961). Dr. Joe Burke heads a British scientific project seeking to establish communication with living beings on other planets. After 4 years and thousands of pounds spent with no results, Burke and his staff members, Sandy Lund and Ben Keller, are strictly reined by Dr. Henry Shore, director of the observatory and chief opponent of the project. Although Burke eventually receives faint signals from an unidentified planet in the asteroid belt, Shore remains dubious. Suddenly all lights in the laboratory black out, caused by the descent of an alien spaceship towards Earth. The ship transports the building and its inhabitants through space to another planet where a robot tests the scientists to determine their intelligence. The robot then leads the group to another alien planet where green humanoid savages, who were once highly civilized humans, are planning to inflict a similar fate on the remaining civilized planets. Burke and his colleagues are held captive, but their scientific knowledge enables them to destroy the savages' spaceships and transport themselves back to Earth. *Scientists. Robots. Space creatures. Abduction. Space travel. Transmutation. Spaceships. Experiments. Imaginary planets.*

Note: Released in Great Britain in Aug 1971; running time: 62 min.

TERRY WHITMORE, FOR EXAMPLE (Sweden)   **F6.4942**
Bill Brodie–Hasse Seiden. *Dist* Grove Press. 14 Nov **1969** [New York opening]. Sd; b&w. 16mm. 98 min.

Prod Hasse Seiden. *Dir* Bill Brodie. *Screenplay* Hasse Seiden, Bill Brodie. *Photog* Hasse Seiden. *Film Ed* Bob O'Meara. *Sd* Tage Sjöberg. *Asst* Doon Buck, Bill Cheston, Antonina Gosling, Richard Pyatok.

Cast: Terry Whitmore (*himself*).

Documentary. Terry Whitmore, a black deserter from the U. S. Marine Corps, tells the story of his flight from the military to political asylum in Sweden where he now resides. After graduating from high school in Memphis, Tennessee, Terry enlisted in the Marines and was sent to Vietnam in June, 1967. During a mission, Terry's patrol was attacked by the North Vietnamese and several of his friends were killed; Terry was injured but managed to drag his lieutenant to safety, thus earning a Bronze Star. While convalescing in a military hospital in Japan, Terry became acquainted with a Japanese woman active in the anti-war movement. When his return to Vietnam was delayed, he deserted and, with the assistance of Japanese sympathizers, gained passage to Sweden through the Soviet Union. Terry ends his narrative by stating that he would like to return someday to the United States. *Negroes. Deserters— Military. Japanese. Combat zone life. Hospitals. Bronze Star. Vietnam War 1964–73. Japan. United States Marines.*

Note: Released in Sweden in Apr 1970 under the English title; running time: 95 min.

LA TERZA DIMENSIONE *see* **FIVE MILES TO MIDNIGHT**

TESEO CONTRO IL MINOTAURO *see* **THE MINOTAUR**

EL TESORO DE MAKUBA *see* **THE TREASURE OF MAKUBA**

IL TESORO DI ROMMEL *see* **ROMMEL'S TREASURE**

TEST TUBE BABIES *see* **THE PILL**

DAS TESTAMENT DES DR. MABUSE *see* **THE TERROR OF DR. MABUSE**

LE TESTAMENT D'ORPHÉE *see* **TESTAMENT OF ORPHEUS**

TESTAMENT OF ORPHEUS (France)   **F6.4943**
Editions Cinégraphiques. *Dist* Films Around the World, Inc., Brandon Films. 9 Apr **1962** [New York opening]. Sd; b&w with col seq. 35mm. 79 min.

Prod Jean Thuillier. *Dir-Writ* Jean Cocteau. *Photog* Roland Pontoiseau. *Camera* Eugène Raichi. *Art Dir* Pierre Guffroy. *Sculptures* Janine Janet. *Film Ed* Marie-Josèphe Yoyotte. *Mus* Georges Auric, Martial Solal. *Adtl Mus From the Works Of* Christoph Gluck, George Frederick Handel, Johann Sebastian Bach, Richard Wagner. *Arr* Jacques Metehen. *Sd* Pierre Bertrand, René Sarrazin. *Prod Mgr* Irénée Leriche. *Cost* Janine Janet. *Tech Dir* Claude Pinoteau. *English Subtitl & Comm* Charles Frank. *Still Photog* Lucien Clergue.

Cast: Jean Cocteau (*himself, the poet*), Edouard Dermit (*Cégeste*), Henri Crémieux (*scientist*), Françoise Christophe (*nurse*), Maria Casarès (*princess*), François Périer (*Heurtebise*), Yul Brynner (*doorman*), Jean-Pierre Léaud (*boy*), Daniel Gélin (*assistant*), Nicole Courcel (*young mother*), Jean Marais (*Oedipus*), Claudine Auger (*Minerva*), Georges Chretelain, Michèle Lemoigne (*lovers*), Philippe Juzau (*1st man-horse*), Daniel Moossmann (*2d man-horse*), Alice Sapritch, Marie-Josèphe Yoyotte (*gypsies*), Henry Torrès (*master of ceremonies*), Michèle Comte (*little girl*), Alec Weisweiller (*confused lady*), Philippe (*Gustave*), Guy Dute (*1st man-dog*), Jean-Claude Petit (*2d man-dog*), Alice Heyliger (*Isolde*), Brigitte Morissan (*Antigone*), Pablo Picasso, Jacqueline Roque, Luis-Miguel Dominguin, Lucia Bosè, Serge Lifar, Charles Aznavour (*themselves*), Michael Goodliffe (*English narrator*), Françoise

Arnoul, Françoise Sagan, Roger Vadim, Annette Strøyberg, Brigitte Bardot.

Allegory. In an effort to understand the world in which he lives, poet Jean Cocteau, dressed in 18th-century clothing, contacts a scientist who is working on an invention that would enable him to enter a new dimension of time and space. After several unsuccessful attempts, the scientist finally succeeds by murdering the poet; Cocteau then rises from the dead and begins his search for identity. In a mysterious wasteland, he encounters gypsies, a man-horse, and Cégeste, the dead poet from Cocteau's film *Orpheus*. Cégeste offers to serve as his guide and presents him with the Flower of Folly. Although the poet would like to give the flower to Minerva, the Goddess of Reason, he first has to stand trial before underworld judges Heurtebise and the princess, also from *Orpheus*, and they condemn him to live. Cocteau then offers the flower to Minerva, but she kills him with a lance; again arising from the dead, the poet continues his journey. He passes the Sphinx and Oedipus, but they do not recognize each other. Later, the poet hears the roar of approaching motorcycles and assumes them to be the messengers of death; the motorcyclists, however, are merely policemen who ask for his identity card. When one of the officers drops the card, it turns into the Flower of Folly as it hits the ground and is blown away by a passing car. Cocteau then follows the bidding of Cégeste and vanishes. *Poets. Scientists. Gypsies. Guides. Mythological characters. Judges. Motorcyclists. Police. Murder. Death. Reincarnation. Personal identity. Flowers. Trials. "Orpheus". Minerva. Oedipus.*

Note: Opened in Paris in Feb 1960 as *Le testament d'Orphée*; running time: 80 min. Alternative French title: *Le testament d'Orphée ou ne me demandez pas pourquoi*. Also known in the United States as *Testament of Orpheus* or *Don't Ask Me Why*. Jacqueline Roque is also known as Jacqueline Picasso.

EL TESTAMENTO DE MADIGAN see **MADIGAN'S MILLIONS**

TESTIGO PARA UN CRIMEN see **VIOLATED LOVE**

TEUFEL IN SEIDE see **DEVIL IN SILK**

TEXAS ACROSS THE RIVER   F6.4944

Universal Pictures. 26 Oct 1966 [Houston opening; c22 Oct 1966; LP34495]. Sd (Westrex); col (Technicolor). 35mm (Techniscope). 101 min.

Prod Harry Keller. *In Charge of Prod* Edward Muhl. *Dir* Michael Gordon. *Screenplay* Wells Root, Harold Greene, Ben Starr. *Uncredited Screenplay Collab* John Gay. *Story* Wells Root, Harold Greene. *Dir Photog* Russell Metty. *Camera Asst* Edwin Pyle, Ledger Haddow, William Kissel. *Art Dir* Alexander Golitzen, William D. DeCinces. *Set Decor* John McCarthy, James S. Redd. *Film Ed* Gene Milford. *Mus* DeVol. *Mus Supv* Joseph Gershenson. *Titl Song* Sammy Cahn, James Van Heusen. *Sung by* The Kingston Trio. *Sd* Waldon O. Watson, David H. Moriarty. *Asst Dir* Terry Morse, Jr., John Anderson, Jr. *Unit Prod Mgr* Wallace Worsley. *Script Supv* Betty Abbott. *Cost* Vincent Dee. *Ladies' Cost* Rosemary Odell. *Men's Cost* Helen Colvig. *Makeup* Bud Westmore. *Hairstylist* Larry Germain. *Dial Coach* Walter Kelley. *Stunt Coörd* Robert Buzz Henry.

Cast: Dean Martin (*Sam Hollis*), Alain Delon (*Don Andrea Baldasar*), Rosemary Forsyth (*Phoebe Ann Naylor*), Joey Bishop (*Kronk*), Tina Marquand (*Lonetta*), Peter Graves (*Captain Stimpson*), Michael Ansara (*Chief Iron Jacket*), Linden Chiles (*Yellow Knife*), Andrew Prine (*Lieutenant Sibley*), Stuart Anderson (*Yancy Cottle*), Roy Barcroft (*Cy Morton*), George Wallace (*Floyd Willet*), Don Beddoe (*Mr. Naylor*), Kelly Thordsen (*turkey shoot boss*), Nora Marlowe (*Emma*), John Harmon (*Gabe Hutchins*), Dick Farnsworth (*medicine man*).

Western comedy. The wedding between Southern belle Phoebe Ann Naylor and Spanish nobleman Don Andrea Baldasar is abruptly called off when one of the bride's rejected suitors, a cavalry officer, accidentally kills himself by falling through a window. The cavalry accuses Don Andrea of murder, and he flees to Texas with Sam Hollis, a brawling gunrunner, and Kronk, his Indian sidekick. En route to Texas, Don Andrea rescues an Indian girl, Lonetta, from being put to death by a Comanche medicine man. Don Andrea is reunited with his Phoebe Ann, only to discover that Sam is also attracted to her. The enraged Spaniard calls for a duel to the death, but the shootout is delayed by the arrival of the cavalry and a subsequent Indian attack. Another duel is cut short by both a hair-pulling contest between Phoebe Ann and Lonetta and the sudden spouting of an oil geyser from an open grave. During all the confusion and fighting, Don Andrea decides that it is Lonetta he truly loves, and he leaves Sam and Phoebe Ann to work out their romance. As the Texans bitterly complain about the sticky oil that has ruined their fine clothes, Sam suggests they give Texas back to the Indians. *Spanish. Nobility. Southerners. Gunrunners. Indians of North America. Comanche Indians. Fugitives. Murder. Jealousy. Courtship. Weddings. Duels. Oil. United States Army—Cavalry. Texas.*

Note: Locations filmed in Julian, California.

TEXAS KID see **THE TEXICAN**

THE TEXICAN (United States/Spain)   F6.4945

M. C. R. Productions-Balcazar, P. C. *Dist* Columbia Pictures. caOct 1966 [c1 Nov 1966; LP34402]. Sd; col (Technicolor). 35mm (Techniscope). 86 min.

Prod John C. Champion, Bruce Balaban. *Exec Prod* Paul C. Ross, Julian Ludwig. *Dir* Lesley Selander. *Story-Screenplay* John C. Champion. *Spanish Vers Screenplay* José Antonio de la Loma. *Dir Photog* Francis Marin. *Camera Op* Anthony Millán. *Photog* Max Lopez. *Art Dir* John Soler. *Film Ed* Teresa Alcocer. *Mus Comp* Nico Fidenco. *Mus Cond* Robby Poitevin. *Asst Dir* José Luis Espinosa. *Prod Supv* Eliseo Boschi. *Prod Mgr* Mario Berriatua. *Cont* Lore Meyer. *Cost Dsgn* Ralph Borque. *Makeup* Rod Gurrucharri. *Hairdresser* Lita Lopez. *Sp Eff* Tony Molina.

Cast: Audie Murphy (*Jess Carlin*), Broderick Crawford (*Luke Starr*), Diana Lorys (*Kit O'Neal*), Aldo Sambrell (*Gil*), Antonio Casas (*Frank Brady*), Anthony Molino (*Harv*), Juan Antonio Peral (*Eb*), Helga Genth (*Maria Banta*), Luz Márquez (*Sandy Adams*), Jorge Rigaud (*Mitch*), Luis Induni (*U. S. marshal*), Martha May (*Elena*), Victor Vilanova (*Roy Carlin*), Carlos Hurtado (*Tobe*), Victor Israel (*station master*), José Maria Pinillo (*Miguel*), César Osinaga (*bounty hunter*), Gérard Tichy (*Thompson*), Vicente Soler (*Dr. Miller*), Juan Carlos Torres (*townsman*), Oscar del Campo (*guitar player*), Manuel Quintana (*gunslinger*), Carlos Miguel Sola, Angel Lombardi (*poker players*), A. Malla (*Mexican boy*).

Western melodrama. Framed by saloon keeper Luke Starr, the ruthless boss of a Texas frontier town, lawman Jess Carlin takes refuge in a Mexican town and becomes known as The Texican. He breaks his vow never to return to Texas, however, when his brother, the editor of a smalltown newspaper, is murdered after exposing Starr's crooked dealings. Jess outdraws the gunfighters sent by Luke to kill him and sets about finding proof of Starr's guilt in his brother's murder. He becomes involved with Kit O'Neal, a dancehall girl to whom Luke is attracted, and with his brother's former fiancée, Sandy Adams. He finally obtains the evidence he needs and with Kit's help escapes a trap set by Luke. He guns down Luke and his henchman and goes off to clear his name while Kit awaits his return. *Outlaws. Sheriffs. Saloon keepers. Brothers. Newspapermen. Dancehall girls. Frameup. Murder. Revenge. Mexico. Texas.*

Note: Location scenes filmed in Spain. Released in Spain as *Texas Kid* or *El Tejano*. Some credits have been Anglicized.

THANK HEAVEN FOR SMALL FAVORS (France)   F6.4946

Le Film d'Art-A. T. I. L. A. *Dist* International Classics. 13 Jan 1965 [New York opening]. Sd; b&w. 35mm. 84 min.

Prod Henri Diamant-Berger, Jérôme Goulven. *Dir* Jean-Pierre Mocky. *Screenplay* Michel Servin, Jean-Pierre Mocky. *Dial* Alain Moury. *Photog* L. H. Burel. *Art Dir* Pierre Tyberghein. *Film Ed* Marguerite Renoir. *Mus* Joseph Kosma. *Sd* René Sarrazin. *Prod Mgr* Ludmilla Goulian.

Cast: Bourvil (*Georges Lachesnaye*), Francis Blanche (*Chief Inspector Cucherat*), Jean Poiret (*Raoul*), Jean Yonnel (*Lachesnaye Père*), Jean Tissier (*Inspector Bridoux*), Jean Galland (*bishop*), Véronique Nordey (*Françoise*), Marcel Pérès (*Raillargaud*), Solange Certain (*Juliette*), Denise Péronne (*Aunt Claire*), Bernard Lavalette (*prefect of police*), Roger Legris.

Comedy. Source: Michel Servin, *Deo gratias* (Paris, 1961). The Lachesnayes, an aristocratic French family, are so impoverished that they are forced to strip their apartment of doors and panelling to provide winter firewood. Nevertheless, they remain determined to follow the family tradition of not working. Georges, the most religious member of the Catholic family, goes to church and informs God of the problem and waits for a sign from heaven. He interprets the sound of coins dropping into the church alms box as the sign and helps himself to the offering. Before long, he visits some 250 churches throughout Paris and then extends his practice to the provinces. The police and church authorities are unable to apprehend him, and Georges begins to amass a considerable fortune. When he is finally caught, a new vision shows him the error of his ways. He returns half of the stolen money, invests the rest, and escapes in the family car. *Aristocrats. Police. Clergymen. Poverty. Pride. Family life. Theft. Paris. Catholic Church.*

Note: Opened in Paris in Aug 1963 as *Un drôle de paroissien*. Original French title: *Deo gratias*. Also known as *The Funny Parishioner* and *Heaven Sent*.

THANK YOU ALL VERY MUCH (Great Britain)   F6.4947

Palomar Pictures International-Amicus Productions. *Dist* Columbia Pictures. 18 Aug 1969 [New York opening; c18 Aug 1969; LP37911]. Sd (Westrex); col (Eastman Color, print by Technicolor). 35mm. 106 min. *MPAA rating* M.

Prod Max J. Rosenberg, Milton Subotsky. *Exec Prod* Edgar J. Scherick. *Dir* Waris Hussein. *Screenplay* Margaret Drabble. *Dir Photog* Peter Suschitzky. *Camera Op* Ron Robson. *Art Dir* Tony Curtis, art dir. *Prod Dsgn* Bernard Sarron. *Film Ed* Bill Blunden. *Mus Comp & Cond* Michael Dress. *Sd Ed* Ian

Fuller. *Sd Rec* Bert Ross. *Sd Re-rec* Nolan Roberts. *Asst Dir* Jake Wright. *Prod Mgr* Teresa Bolland. *Cont* Pamela Davies. *Prod Sec* Midge Warnes. *Wardrobe Supv* Evelyn Gibbs. *Makeup* Bob Lawrence. *Hairdresser* Susie Hill. *Casting Dir* Ronald Curtis.

Cast: Sandy Dennis *(Rosamund)*, Ian McKellen *(George)*, Eleanor Bron *(Lydia)*, John Standing *(Roger)*, Michael Coles *(Joe)*, Rachel Kempson *(Sister Harvey)*, Peggy Thorpe-Bates *(Mrs. Stacey)*, Kenneth Benda *(Mr. Stacey)*, Sarah Whalley *(Octavia)*, Shelagh Fraser *(Miss Guernsey)*, Deborah Stanford *(Beatrice)*, Margaret Tyzack *(Sister Bennett)*, Roger Hammond *(Mike)*, Maurice Denham *(Dr. Prothero)*.

Drama. Source: Margaret Drabble, *The Millstone* (London, 1965). Rosamund Stacey, a graduate student preparing for her doctoral degree at the British Museum, discovers that she has become pregnant from her first sexual encounter. Her socialist parents, who have always treated her in an aloof manner, are in Africa, and Rosamund feels uncomfortable in the superficial intellectual world of her best friend Lydia, and with Joe and Roger, the two men whom she has been dating. Choosing to conceal her condition from the father, George, a television announcer whom she barely knows, Rosamund first considers abortion but then decides to have the child, against the advice of Lydia and a hospital nurse. Once Lydia has moved in with her, Rosamund divides her time between her studies and receiving prenatal care. Shortly after the birth of a daughter, Rosamund learns that the baby has a congenital heart defect and must have a delicate operation, which is successfully performed by a famous surgeon who is a good friend of her father. During the next year, Rosamund receives her degree and adjusts comfortably to being an unwed mother. Then, she meets George by accident and invites him back to her flat. Startled to discover that Rosamund has a child, George indulges in some polite conversation and leaves, still unaware that he is the father. Recognizing that her nature seems to preclude marriage, Rosamund lets him walk out of her life. *Students. Socialists. Intellectuals. Television announcers. Infants. Pregnancy. Parentage. Illegitimacy. Heart disease. Surgery. Motherhood. London. British Museum.*

Note: Location scenes filmed in London. Opened in London in Oct 1969 as *A Touch of Love*; running time: 107 min.

THANOS AND DESPINA (France/Greece)   F6.4948
Lenox Films. *Dist* Grove Press. 20 Apr **1970** [New York opening]. Sd; b&w. 35mm. 96 min.

Prod Dimos Theos, A. Lappas. *Dir-Writ* Nico Papatakis. *Story* Jean Vauthier, Nico Papatakis. *Photog* Jean Boffety, Christian Guillouet. *Mus* Pierre Barbaud. *Sd* Antony Bairaktaris, Alex Pront.

Cast: Olga Carlatos *(Despina)*, George Dialegmenos *(Thanos)*, Lambros Tsangas *(Yankos)*, Elli Xanthaki *(Katina)*, Theo Karousos *(Vlahopoulos)*, Dimos Starenios *(Karavidas)*, Yannis Arghyris *(Haralambos)*, N. Naneris *(Pericles)*, Maria Kostandarou *(Loula)*, Djolly Garbi *(Madame Vlahopoulos)*, Nassos Kedrakas *(Papadimas)*.

Romantic melodrama. Katina, an impoverished Greek peasant woman, visits Vlahopoulos, a wealthy landowner, hoping to arrange the marriage of her shepherd son Thanos to his beautiful daughter Despina. Thanos' employer, Karavidas, also wants to have his son Yankos marry Despina, but Vlahopoulos decides that she will marry Papadimas, a cultured friend of Despina's brother. Angered at the loss of Despina, Yankos kills Thanos' dog, and the shepherd is blamed when the flock of sheep stray. Thanos arranges a rendezvous with Despina, and after several clandestine meetings, the couple fall in love and vow to run away together. They rob a store and take refuge in the nearby mountains. Vlahopoulos learns of the seduction of his daughter and sets out with a group of people from the village to seek revenge. The villagers discover Thanos and Despina, and Yankos challenges Thanos to a fight, in which Yankos is killed. Thanos and Despina then commit suicide by leaping from the mountain. *Peasants. Shepherds. Landowners. Marriage—Arranged. Parenthood. Revenge. Robbery. Suicide. Dogs. Sheep.*

Note: Filmed on location in Greece. Opened in Paris in Mar 1968 as *Les pâtres du désordre*; running time: 120 min (cut from 130 min).

THAR SHE BLOWS   F6.4949
Ado Productions. *Dist* Entertainment Ventures, Inc. 6 Feb **1969** [San Francisco showing]. Sd; col (Eastman Color). 35mm. 84 min.

Prod David F. Friedman, William Allen Castleman. *Dir* Richard Kanter. *Screenplay* Richard Kanter, David F. Friedman. *Cinematog* Paul Hipp. *Asst Camera* Henning Schellerup. *Film Ed* Robert Freemantle. *Mus Supv* Billy Allen. *Sd* Sam Kopetzky. *Asst Dir* Don Brodie. *Prod Supv* Paul Wilmoth.

Cast: Shari Mann *(Teddy)*, Vincent Stephens *(Bob Frigate)*, Chris Mathis *(Sally)*, Stuart Lancaster *(Kenyon Adler)*, John Alderman *(Phil Latio)*, Patrick Alain *(Ron Cochran)*, Lori Brown *(Sheri)*, Debbie Hart *(Wendy)*, Paul Wilmoth, Bill St. Pierre, James Jacks *(toughs)*, Dave Friedman *(bartender)*.

Melodrama. Captain Bob Frigate lives on his ocean-going yacht with Sally, his teen-aged sister whom he has been taking care of since their parents died,

and Ron Cochran, a French-Canadian crewman. Ron and Sally are secret lovers. Concerned over Bob's violent temper eruptions, Ron tries in vain to persuade Sally, who is devoted to her brother, to go away with him and marry. One night, Bob recalls the time 12 years earlier when, as a midshipman, he picked up prostitute Sheila. As they lay in bed, three waterfront thugs entered the room and castrated Bob with a dock hook. Ron and Sally find Bob on the deck, hysterical from reliving the experience, and they put him to bed. Wealthy industrialist Kenyon Adler charters Bob's boat, bringing aboard his pimp, Phil Latio, and three young women, Sheri, Wendy, and Teddy. Bob is shaken by Teddy's resemblance to Sheila, who he believes was the cause of his humiliation, and he repulses her advances when, during an orgy staged by Adler, she tries to seduce the moody captain. Affronted, Teddy tries to seduce Ron. Sally jealously intervenes, and she is necking with Ron when Bob appears and, enraged, knocks down Ron and spanks Sally. Teddy accidentally glimpses Bob while he is dressing and sees that he has been castrated; she runs away, and Bob chases her until he is stopped by Latio, who tells him that Sally and Ron are making love in the crew's quarters. Bob's mind snaps when he sees the young couple embracing, and he commits suicide by climbing the mast and jumping to the deck onto a dock hook. *Seamen. Shipowners. Orphans. French Canadians. Prostitutes. Industrialists. Pimps. Brother-sister relationship. Castration. Group sex. Seduction. Suicide. Yachts.*

Note: Also known as *Thar She Goes*.

THAT COLD DAY IN THE PARK (United States/Canada)   F6.4950
Factor–Altman–Mirell Films. *Dist* Commonwealth United Entertainment, Inc. 8 Jun **1969** [New York opening]. Sd; col (Eastman Color). 35mm. 112 min. *MPAA rating* R.

Prod Donald Factor, Leon Mirell. *Assoc Prod* Robert Eggenweiler. *Dir* Robert Altman. *Screenplay* Gillian Freeman. *Dir Photog* Laszlo Kovacs. *Art Dir* Leon Ericksen. *Film Ed* Danford B. Greene. *Mus* Johnny Mandel. *Sd* John Gusselle. *Asst Dir* Harold Schneider. *Prod Mgr* James Margellos.

Cast: Sandy Dennis *(Frances Austen)*, Michael Burns *(boy)*, Susanne Benton *(Nina)*, Luana Anders *(Sylvie)*, John Garfield, Jr. *(Nick)*, Edward Greenhalgh, Frank Wade, actor, Lloyd Berry, Alicia Ammon, Rae Brown, Michael Murphy.

Drama. Source: Richard Miles, *That Cold Day in the Park* (New York, 1965). Frances Austen, a wealthy spinster in her early 30's, spots a bedraggled young man huddled in the rain on a park bench across from her elegant Vancouver apartment. Strangely attracted to him, she waits until her dinner guests leave, dismisses the maid, and goes to the park to invite the young man in. Accepting wordlessly, he follows Frances into her home and allows her to pamper him as he listens to her incessant chatter. Assuming that the boy is a mute, Frances offers him the guest room for the night and serves him breakfast in the morning. Late that night, the boy sneaks away, visits his family, and then goes to see his sister Nina, who lives on a houseboat with Nick, an American draft dodger. While the three are smoking marijuana, the boy talks about his good fortune but denies Nick's contention that Frances is paying for his sexual services. Frances welcomes him when he returns and unknowingly accepts drugged cookies from him. The next day, Nina arrives while Frances is out, uses the bath, and taunts her brother with incestuous invitations. Frances, meanwhile, has become obsessed with the boy, and that night she enters his darkened room and imploringly offers herself to him only to discover that he has gone out again. Furious, she waits until the boy returns the next morning and makes him a prisoner in her apartment. The boy finally speaks to Frances, screaming that he does not want or need her. Now determined not to lose him, Frances persuades Sylvie, a prostitute, to come to the house. After locking the boy and girl in a room, Frances bursts in while they are having sex and plunges a knife into the prostitute. Terrified, the boy tries to hide, but the demented Frances finds him and passionately clutches her prisoner. *Spinsters. Mutes. Gigolos. Draft dodgers. Prostitutes. Psychopaths. Adolescence. Perfidy. Brother-sister relationship. Obsession. Murder. Imprisonment. Houseboats. Marijuana.*

Note: Location scenes filmed in Vancouver, British Columbia. Released in Canada in 1969; running time: 115 min.

THAT DARN CAT   F6.4951
Walt Disney Productions. *Dist* Buena Vista Distribution Co. 2 Dec **1965** [New York opening; c2 Aug 1965; LP31384]. Sd (RCA); col (Technicolor). 35mm. 116 min.

Pres by Walt Disney. *Co-prod* Bill Walsh, Ron Miller. *Dir* Robert Stevenson. *2d Unit Dir* Arthur J. Vitarelli. *Screenplay* Gordon Gordon, Mildred Gordon, Bill Walsh. *Dir Photog* Edward Colman. *Art Dir* Carroll Clark, William H. Tuntke. *Set Decor* Emile Kuri, Hal Gausman. *Film Ed* Cotton Warburton. *Mus* Bob Brunner. *Orch* Franklyn Marks. *Titl Song* Richard M. Sherman, Robert B. Sherman. *Sung by* Bobby Darin. *Sd Supv* Robert O. Cook. *Sd Mix* Dean Thomas. *Mus Ed* Evelyn Kennedy. *Asst Dir* Joseph L. McEveety. *Cost Dsgn* Bill Thomas. *Cost* Chuck Keehne, Gertrude Casey. *Makeup* Pat McNalley, La Rue Matheron. *Sp Eff* Eustace Lycett. *Matte Artist* Jim Fetherolf. *Animal Supv*

William R. Koehler.

Cast: Hayley Mills *(Patti Randall)*, Dean Jones *(Zeke Kelso)*, Dorothy Provine *(Ingrid Randall)*, Roddy McDowall *(Gregory Benson)*, Neville Brand *(Dan)*, Elsa Lanchester *(Mrs. MacDougall)*, William Demarest *(Mr. MacDougall)*, Frank Gorshin *(Iggy)*, Richard Eastham *(Supervisor Newton)*, Grayson Hall *(Margaret Miller)*, Ed Wynn *(Mr. Hofstedder)*, Tom Lowell *(Canoe)*, Richard Deacon *(drive-in manager)*, Iris Adrian *(landlady)*, Liam Sullivan *(Graham)*, Don Dorrell *(Spires)*, Gene Blakely *(Cahill)*, Karl Held *(Kelly)*.

Comedy. Source: Gordon Gordon and Mildred Gordon, *Undercover Cat* (Garden City, New York, 1963). Two sisters, Ingrid and Patti Randall, are temporarily alone in their suburban home with "That Darn Cat," nicknamed DC. At night, DC roams free, courting a female cat and following Iggy, who carries a piece of salmon. Iggy and Dan, two bank robbers, are holding Margaret Miller hostage while hiding from the police. Iggy decides to let DC in and feed him; and while DC is in the apartment, Margaret takes off her collar and substitutes her watch scratched with the word "Help." At the Randalls, Patti spends the evening with her boyfriend, Canoe, and Ingrid accepts a dinner invitation from Gregory Benson, an accountant whom she does not like. When DC steals the dinner, Gregory threatens to shoot him. Patti finds Margaret's watch and wants to call the police, but Ingrid forbids it, so Patti calls the FBI. Supervisor Newton assigns Zeke Kelso to the case, and Kelso assigns three agents to tail DC, but the cat eludes them. Meanwhile, all the action at the Randall house is watched by Mrs. MacDougall, a snoopy neighbor. With a bugging device implanted in his collar, DC leads Zeke into a chase at a drive-in movie and through Gregory's backyard, where Gregory shoots at them. Later Gregory finds Ingrid and Zeke alone together and breaks up with Ingrid. On the third night of being tailed, DC is followed by Zeke, Patti, Canoe, and Mrs. MacDougall. Patti and Zeke rescue Margaret, and the next day DC visits his mate and their new litter of kittens. *Sisters. Hostages. Neighbors. Accountants. Robbers. Kidnaping. Electronic surveillance. Watches. Motion picture theaters—Drive-ins. United States—Federal Bureau of Investigation. Chases. Cats.*

THAT FUNNY FEELING   F6.4952

Universal Pictures. 25 Aug **1965** [Los Angeles opening; c18 Sep 1965; LP33413]. Sd (Westrex); col (Technicolor). 35mm. 93 min.

Prod Harry Keller. *In Charge of Prod* Edward Muhl. *Dir* Richard Thorpe. *Screenplay* David R. Schwartz. *Story* Norman Barasch, Carroll Moore. *Dir Photog* Clifford Stine. *Art Dir* Alexander Golitzen, George Webb. *Set Decor* John McCarthy, Julia Heron. *Film Ed* Gene Milford. *Mus Supv* Joseph Gershenson. *Mus Comp & Titl Song Writ & Sung by* Bobby Darin. *Sd* Waldon O. Watson, Lyle Cain. *Asst Dir* Joseph Kenny, James Welch. *Unit Prod Mgr* Howard Pine. *Gowns Dsgn* Jean Louis. *Makeup* Bud Westmore. *Hairstyles* Larry Germain. *Matte Supv* Albert Whitlock. *Dial Coach* Leon Charles.

Cast: Sandra Dee *(Joan Howell)*, Bobby Darin *(Tom Milford)*, Donald O'Connor *(Harvey Granson)*, Nita Talbot *(Audrey)*, Larry Storch *(Luther)*, James Westerfield *(Officer Brokaw)*, Leo G. Carroll *(O'Shea)*, Robert Strauss, Ben Lessy *(bartenders)*, Reta Shaw, Nora Marlowe, Kathleen Greeman, Minerva Urecal *(women at phone booth)*, Arte Johnson *(Paul)*, Benny Rubin *(taxi driver)*, Aki Hara *(Hatacki)*, Don Haggerty, Larry Blake *(policemen)*, Gregory Shannon *(Lennie)*, Frank Killmond *(Mr. Scruggs)*, Herb Vigran, Jordan Whitfield.

Comedy. Aspiring actress Joan Howell, who makes a living as a maid, has a number of accidental encounters with Tom Milford, a New York City publishing company executive. After their third such meeting, she invites him to her apartment, but, ashamed of her one-room residence, she borrows the apartment of one of her employers whom she has never seen. Tom (who is the employer) cancels a trip and is surprised to see Joan in his own apartment, but he goes along with the ruse and moves in with his partner, Harvey. Eventually, each discovers the other's identity, but neither reveals the truth. Joan decides to play a trick on Tom and invites his former girl friends to a party, asking them to dress as prostitutes. The police raid the party, and as they are headed for jail, Joan accepts Tom's marriage proposal. *Actors. Housemaids. Publishers. Executives. Police. Prostitutes. Mistaken identity. Disguise. New York City.*

THAT GIRL FROM BEVERLY HILLS see THE CORPSE OF BEVERLY HILLS

THAT KIND OF GIRL (Great Britain)   F6.4953

Animated Motion Pictures—Tekli British Productions. *Dist* Topaz Film Corp., International Artists Pictures. Jun **1963**. Sd; b&w. 35mm. 78 min.

Prod Robert Hartford-Davis. *Dir* Gerry O'Hara. *Orig Story–Screenplay* Jan Read. *Dir Photog* Peter Newbrook. *Art Dir* William Brodie. *Film Ed* Derek York. *Mus Comp & Cond* Malcolm Mitchell. *Sd* Peter Birch.

Cast: Margaret-Rose Keil *(Eva)*, David Weston *(Keith Murray)*, Linda Marlowe *(Janet Bates)*, Peter Burton *(Elliot Collier)*, Frank Jarvis *(Max)*, Sylvia

Kay *(Mrs. Millar)*, David Davenport *(Mr. Millar)*, Stephen Stocker *(Nicolas)*, Charles Houston *(Ted)*, Max Faulkner *(Johnson)*, Patricia Mort *(Barbara)*, Martin Wyldeck *(Bates)*, John Wood *(doctor)*.

Melodrama. Eva, an Austrian au pair girl, lives in Kensington with Mr. and Mrs. Millar and their young son Nicolas. Eva meets Max, a pacifist librarian, and Elliot Collier, a sophisticate who seduces her. While hitchhiking in London, she encounters Keith Murray, a wealthy student engaged to working-class Janet Bates. Frustrated by Mr. Bates's insistence that he complete his education before marrying Janet, Murray turns to Eva for sexual gratification. Fearing that she will lose him, Janet makes love to her fiancé. Furious at Eva's promiscuity, Elliot rapes her. Although she refuses to name her assailant when questioned by the police, Eva submits to a medical examination which reveals that she has contracted syphilis. Alarmed, Eva warns the Millars, Max, Keith, and pregnant Janet of possible infection. Following treatment, Janet and Keith marry. Elliot, however, is arrested for making obscene telephone calls to Eva. *Austrians. Au pair girls. Pacifists. Librarians. Students. Police. Socialites. Class conflict. Venereal disease. Rape. Seduction. Jealousy. Obscenity. Pregnancy. Telephone. London—Kensington.*

Note: Filmed entirely on location in London and the Home Counties. Released in Great Britain in 1963; running time: 77 min. Cut from 82 min. Released through International Artists Pictures as *Teen Age Tramp*.

THAT MAN FROM RIO (France / Italy)   F6.4954

Ariane–Les Productions Artistes Associés–Dear Film. *Dist* Lopert Pictures. 8 Jun **1964** [New York opening]. Sd; col (Eastman Color). 35mm. 114 min.

Prod Alexandre Mnouchkine, Georges Dancigers. *Dir* Philippe de Broca. *Screenplay* Jean-Paul Rappeneau, Ariane Mnouchkine, Daniel Boulanger, Philippe de Broca. *Dial* Daniel Boulanger. *Photog* Edmond Séchan. *Film Ed* Laurence Mery, Françoise Javet. *Mus* Georges Delerue. *Sd* Jacques Maumont. *Asst Dir* Olivier Gérard. *Sp Eff* Gil Delamare.

Cast: Jean-Paul Belmondo *(Adrien Dufourquet)*, Françoise Dorléac *(Agnès)*, Jean Servais *(Professor Catalan)*, Simone Renant *(Lola)*, Milton Ribeiro *(Tupac)*, Ubiracy de Oliveira *(Sir Winston)*, Adolfo Celi *(Señor De Castro)*, Daniel Ceccaldi, Roger Dumas, Sabu do Brasil.

Crime comedy-drama. As airman Adrien Dufourquet embarks on an 8-day leave in Paris to see his fiancée, Agnès, two South American Indians steal an Amazon statuette from a museum and force Professor Catalan, the curator, into their car. Catalan was Agnès's father's companion on an Amazon expedition during which her father died. Catalan believes that the statuette is one of three which hold the secret to an Amazon treasure. Adrien arrives in time to see the Indians abducting Agnès, the only one who knows the location of the other statuettes, and he pursues them to the airport where he steals a ticket and boards the same plane. Adrien tells the pilot that his fiancée has been abducted, but Agnès has been drugged and does not recognize him. The pilot plans to have Adrien arrested when they reach Rio de Janeiro, but Adrien eludes the police upon arrival. With the help of Sir Winston, a Brazilian bootblack, Adrien rescues Agnès. They retrieve the first statuette, but the Indians steal it back again. In Sir Winston's car, Agnès and Adrien drive to Brasilia to meet Señor De Castro, a wealthy industrialist who possesses the third statuette. On the way, they come across the Indians' car with Catalan slumped inside, and after picking him up, they drive on to Brasilia. At a party in their honor, De Castro takes Catalan to his strong room to assure him of the statuette's safety, and Catalan, who planned the museum theft, murders him and steals the statuette. By the time Adrien discovers the body, Catalan and the Indians have abducted Agnès again and escaped in a seaplane. Adrien steals a plane and follows. In a floating jungle cafe run by Lola, the woman who financed Catalan, Adrien learns that Catalan murdered Agnès's father and that Agnès is being held in a boat. Rushing to the boat, Adrien hangs onto the side as it heads upstream and finally docks. While Catalan goes to the underground location of the treasure, Adrien kills all of Catalan's accomplices and rescues Agnès. Catalan finds the treasure, but an explosion set off by a nearby demolition crew causes him to be buried with it. Adrien and Agnès flee the jungle and arrive in Paris in time for Adrien to catch his train back to camp. *Indians of South America. Curators. Air pilots. Police. Brazil. Bootblacks. Industrialists. Masterminds. Cafe hostesses. Theft. Abduction. Rescue. Murder. Museums. Sculptures. Treasure. Airplanes. Drugs. Seaplanes. Jungles. Paris. Amazon River. Rio de Janeiro. Brasilia. France—Air Force. Explosions. Chases.*

Note: Filmed on location in Paris, Rio de Janeiro, Brasilia, and elsewhere in Brazil. Opened in Paris in Feb 1964 as *L'homme de Rio*; running time: 120 min; opened in Rome in 1964 as *L'uomo di Rio*.

THAT MAN GEORGE (France / Italy / Spain)   F6.4955

Europazur–Producciones Benito Perojo–Atlantis Film–Jolly Film. *Dist* Allied Artists. Sep **1967**. Sd; col (Eastman Color). 35mm. 90 min.

Prod Claude Giroux. *Dir* Jacques Deray. *Screenplay* Henri Lanoë, José Giovanni, Suzanne Arduini, Jacques Deray. *Photog* Henri Raichi. *Art Dir* Eduardo Torre de la Fuente. *Film Ed* Paul Cayatte. *Mus* Alain Goraguer. *Prod*

Mgr Ignacio Gutiérrez.

Cast: George Hamilton *(George)*, Claudine Auger *(Lila)*, Alberto de Mendoza *(Travis)*, Daniel Ivernel *(Vibert)*, Tiberio Murgia *(Jose)*, Jorge Rigaud, Giacomo Furia, Renato Baldini, Roberto Camardiel.

Action drama. Source: Robert Page Jones, *The Heisters* (New York, 1964). At the border of the desert in southern Morocco, five people are involved in the robbery of an armored van transporting gold bullion from a nearby mine. The robbers are Travis, an Argentine playboy; Lila, a young Frenchwoman; Vibert, an aging mine engineer who conceived the plan; Jose, an Italian garage mechanic; and George, an American adventurer. Once the robbery has been successfully executed, Travis murders Jose and then turns on George. Lila slips a gun to George, and he kills Travis in self-defense. Lila and George flee to Tangiers with the gold, but Vibert catches up with them and demands his share. He also accuses Lila of planning the murders and warns George that he will be the next victim. Unsure of Lila's true feelings, George asks her to give all the money to Vibert to prove her love. Lila, however, considers the request excessive and the three go their separate ways. Some time later, Vibert and Lila show up at a railroad station where the gold has been hidden in a locker. But the police are waiting, and the two thieves are shot and killed. George, the sole survivor of the ill-fated scheme, leaves town for another destination and another adventure. *Adventurers. Americans in foreign countries. Argentineans. Engineers. Greed. Robbery. Murder. Perfidy. Deserts. Gold. Morocco. Tangiers.*

Note: Location scenes filmed in Spain, Portugal, Algeria, and Morocco. Opened in Paris in Apr 1966 as *L'homme de Marrakech* at 90 min; in Italy in 1966 as *L'uomo di Casablanca*; in Madrid in Jun 1968 as *El hombre de Marrakech* at 98 min. Alternative Spanish title: *Los saqueadores del domingo*. Sources conflict in crediting Italian production company. Also known as *Our Man in Marrakesh.*

THAT MAN IN ISTANBUL (France/Italy/Spain)   **F6.4956**
E. D. I. C.–C. C. M.–Isasi Producciones Cinematograficas. *Dist* Columbia Pictures. Feb **1966** [c1 Jan 1966; LP32997]. Sd; col (Technicolor). 35mm (Techniscope). 117 min.

An Antonio Isasi Isasmendi Production. *Prod-Dir* Antonio Isasi Isasmendi. *Exec Prod* Nat Wachsberger. *Screenplay* George Simonelli, Nat Wachsberger, Antonio Isasi Isasmendi, Luis Comerón, Jorge Illa. *English Dial* Lewis Howard. *Photog* Juan Gelpi. *Art Dir* Juan Alberto. *Main Titl* Jean Fouchet. *Film Ed* Juan Pallejá. *Mus Comp* Georges Garvarentz. *Asst Dir* Luis García. *Prod Mgr* Anthony Irles, Miguel Grau. *Makeup* Praxedes Martínez, Carmen Menchaca.

Cast: Horst Buchholz *(Tony Maecenas)*, Sylva Koscina *(Kenny)*, Mario Adorf *(Bill)*, Perrette Pradier *(Elisabeth)*, Klaus Kinski *(Schenck)*, Alvaro de Luna *(Bogo)*, Gustavo Re *(Brain)*, Georges Rigaud *(CIA chief)*, Christiane Maybach *(Josette)*, Gérard Tichy *(Hansi)*, Agustín Gonzáles *(Gunther)*, Rocha *(Chinese)*, Angel Picazo *(Inspector Mallouk)*, Umberto Raho *(Professor Pendergast)*, Henri Cogan, Luis Induni, Marta Flores.

Adventure melodrama. Tony Maecenas, a nightclub owner and international playboy in Istanbul, lives a life of carefree luxury until Kenny, a beautiful FBI agent posing as an unemployed stripper, persuades him to join the hunt for a kidnaped atomic scientist. A secret power-mad organization has been paid $1 million in ransom money but has delivered up an impostor rather than the scientist. Tony is told he can keep the ransom money if he can outwit not only the secret organization but also a rival group of Chinese agents. Utilizing his knowledge of Istanbul and its denizens, Tony plunges into the adventure and has a series of narrow escapes at the city docks, at a construction site, and in a swimming pool at the Hilton Hotel. When Kenny also is kidnaped, Tony takes the law into his own hands and rescues her and the scientist. He turns him over to the FBI but keeps Kenny and the $1 million for himself. *Nightclub owners. Playboys. Stripteasers. Secret agents. Chinese. Scientists. Conspiracy. Kidnaping. Imposture. Nuclear energy. Ransom. Istanbul. United States—Federal Bureau of Investigation.*

Note: Location scenes filmed in Istanbul and Málaga (Spain). Opened in Rome in Aug 1965 as *Colpo grosso a Galata Bridge*; running time: 100 min; in Paris in Sep 1965 as *L'homme d'Istambul*; running time: 90 min; in Madrid in Oct 1965 as *Estambul 65*; running time: 115 min. Giovanni Simonelli is credited as George Simonelli; Antonio Irles as Anthony Irles; and Juan Alberto Soler as Juan Alberto.

THAT RIVIERA TOUCH (Great Britain)   **F6.4957**
Rank Organisation. *Dist* Continental Distributing, Inc. Jun **1968** [Los Angeles showing]. Sd; col (Eastman Color). 35mm. 98 min.

A Hugh Stewart Production. *Prod* Hugh Stewart. *Dir* Cliff Owen. *Screenplay* Sidney C. Green, Richard M. Hills, Peter Blackmore. *Photog* Otto Heller. *2d Unit Photog* Michel Rocca. *Art Dir* John Blezard. *Set Decor* Arthur Taksen. *Film Ed* Gerry Hambling. *Mus* Ron Goodwin. *Sd* Les Wiggins. *Sd Rec* C. C. Stevens, Len Shilton. *Asst Dir* Bert Batt. *Prod Mgr* Jack Swinburne. *Cost* Anna Duse.

Cast: Eric Morecambe *(Eric)*, Ernie Wise *(Ernie)*, Suzanne Lloyd *(Claudette)*, Paul Stassino *(Le Pirate)*, Armand Mestral *(Inspector Duval)*, George Eugeniou *(Marcel)*, George Pastell *(Ali)*, Peter Jeffrey *(Mauron)*, Gerald Lawson *(Coco)*, Michael Forest *(Pierre)*, Clive Cazes *(Renard)*, Steven Scott *(Gaston)*, Paul Danquah *(Hassim)*.

Comedy. Upon arrival at a deserted Riviera villa tourists Eric and Ernie become involved with jewel thief Le Pirate and his gang. The two vacationers mistake accomplice Marcel for a travel agent and are infatuated by moll Claudette. After murdering two rival thieves, Le Pirate conceals stolen jewels in the gas tank of the tourists' car, intending thereby to smuggle the loot through customs. Ernie, however, decides to buy a new automobile with his casino winnings. To prevent its purchase, Claudette attempts to steal his capital. Relenting, the moll befriends Eric and Ernie. Following a frantic chase by car, water skis, and helicopter, police apprehend the band. *Thieves. French. Molls. Gangs. Police. Mistaken identity. Murder. Water skiing. Gambling. Vacations. Jewels. Casinos. Helicopters. Riviera. Chases.*

Note: Location scenes filmed on the French Riviera. Opened in London in Apr 1966.

THAT TENDER AGE *see* **THE ADOLESCENTS**

THAT TENDER TOUCH   **F6.4958**
Artisan Productions. *Dist* World Premiere Distributors. Nov **1969**. Sd; col (Berkey-Pathé). 35mm. 94 min. [Also 88 min.] *MPAA rating* R.

Prod-Dir-Writ Russel Vincent. *Assoc Prod* George Moskov. *Photog* Robert Caramico. *Film Ed* Maurice Wright. *Mus & Lyr* David Saxon, mus. Hans Haller.

Cast: Sue Bernard *(Terry)*, Bee Tompkins *(Marsha Prentis)*, Rick Cooper *(Ken Manning)*, Phae Dera *(Wendy Barrett)*, Margaret Read *(Dodie)*, Victoria Hale *(Jane)*, Richard St. John *(Paul Barrett)*, Tanya Lemani *(Irene Barrett)*, Roger Helfond *(Jim)*, Joe Castagna *(Joe)*.

Melodrama. Terry, a young orphan, is befriended by Marsha Prentis, an older woman. Traumatized by a rape attempt on her, Terry is drawn into a lesbian relationship with Marsha that continues until Ken Manning, unaware of her affair with Marsha, convinces Terry that all men are not like the one who attacked her. Terry and Ken marry, but the young bride cannot bring herself to tell him about Marsha. The two women meet again at a party, and Marsha desperately tries to win back her young lover. Dodie, the maid; Jane, a neighbor; and a teenager, Wendy Barrett, all attempt to divert Marsha's attention, but she remains interested only in Terry, who refuses her advances. Desperate at the thought of losing the girl forever, Marsha drowns herself in the pool. *Orphans. Housemaids. Lesbianism. Rape. Marriage. Seduction. Jealousy. Suicide.*

THAT TENNESSEE BEAT   **F6.4959**
Robert L. Lippert Productions. *Dist* Twentieth Century-Fox Film Corp. 14 Oct **1966** [Charlotte, North Carolina, opening; c21 Sep 1966; LP34593]. Sd; col (De Luxe). 35mm. 84 min.

Pres by Robert L. Lippert. *Prod-Dir* Richard Brill. *Writ* Paul Schneider. *Dir Photog* Jack Steeley. *Lighting Dir* John Murray. *Set Decor* Bill Gernert. *Supv Film Ed* Ace Herman, Carl Pierson. *Titl Song Writ and Sung by* Merle Travis. *Song:* "I'm Sorry" writ by Merle Travis. Sung by Earl Richards. *Mus Dir* Tommy Hill. *Sd* Walter James. *Mus Ed* Lee Osborne. *Prod Mgr* Imogene Miller. *Talent Coörd* Gerard Purcell, Stan Pat.

Cast: Sharon De Bord *(Opal Nelson)*, Earl Richards *(Jim Birdsell)*, Dolores Faith *(Belle Scofield)*, Minnie Pearl *(Rev. Rose Conley)*, Merle Travis *(Larry Scofield)*, Jim Reader *(Matt Nelson)*, Cecil Scaife *(Dan Birdsell)*, Rink Hardin *(Wally Cooper)*, Lightnin' Chance *(sheriff)*, Sam Tarpley *(ticket seller)*, Buddy Mize *(hoodlum leader)*, Ed Livingston *(hoodlum)*, Ernest Keller *(announcer)*, Maurice Dembsky *(doorman)*, The Statler Brothers, Boots Randolph, Stoney Mountain Cloggers, Pete Drake *(guest stars)*.

Melodrama with music. A guitar-playing country boy steals money from a neighbor and heads for Nashville to make a name for himself. En route he is beaten up and has his guitar broken by hoodlums. Destitute, he is befriended by Opal and Matt Nelson and introduced to Rev. Rose Conley, a preacher who gives him work as a handy man and rehabilitates him. Meanwhile, under an assumed name he starts singing country music in Nashville theaters. Eventually his father and the neighbor he robbed are brought to a theater where the young singer is appearing. He publicly apologizes from the stage and dedicates a song, "I'm Sorry," to them. *Guitarists. Singers. Handymen. Clergywomen. Hoodlums. Theft. Criminals—Rehabilitation. Country music. Nashville (Tennessee). Horses.*

Note: Location scenes filmed in Nashville; scenes of Tennessee's Walking Horses shot at Worrell's Solitude Farm. Registered for copyright as *The Tennessee Beat.*

THAT TOUCH OF MINK F6.4960

Granley Co.-Arwin Productions-Nob Hill Productions. *Dist* Universal-International. 14 Jun 1962 [New York opening; c24 May 1962; LP24721]. Sd; col (Eastman Color by Pathé). 35mm (Panavision). 99 min.

Prod Stanley Shapiro, Martin Melcher. *Exec Prod* Robert Arthur. *Dir* Delbert Mann. *Screenplay* Stanley Shapiro, Nate Monaster. *Photog* Russell Metty. *Art Dir* Alexander Golitzen, Robert Clatworthy. *Set Decor* George Milo. *Titl Executed by* Pacific Title. *Film Ed* Ted J. Kent. *Mus* George Duning. *Sd* Waldon O. Watson, Corson Jowett. *Asst Dir* Phil Bowles, Carl Beringer. *Unit Prod Mgr* Norman Deming. *Gowns* Rosemary Odell. *Fashions* Norman Norell. *Makeup* Bud Westmore. *Hair Stylist* Larry Germain.

Cast: Cary Grant (*Philip Shayne*), Doris Day (*Cathy Timberlake*), Gig Young (*Roger*), Audrey Meadows (*Connie*), Alan Hewitt (*Dr. Gruber*), John Astin (*Beasley*), Dick Sargent (*young man*), Joey Faye (*short man*), Laurie Mitchell (*showgirl*), John Fiedler (*Mr. Smith*), Willard Sage (*Hodges*), Jack Livesey (*Dr. Richardson*), John McKee (*Collins*), Jan Burrell (*Miss Jones*), June Ericson (*Millie*), Russ Bender (*Williams*), Mickey Mantle, Roger Maris, Yogi Berra (*themselves, New York Yankees*), Art Passarella (*himself, umpire*), Isabella Albonico, Doris Lynn, Bette Woods, Sue Barton (*themselves, high fashion models*).

Romantic comedy. On her way to cash her unemployment check Cathy Timberlake is splattered with mud by a passing limousine belonging to tycoon Philip Shayne, a bachelor. Later, Philip spots Cathy entering an automat and sends his rebellious financial adviser, Roger, to apologize and offer her money for her ruined dress. Goaded on by both Roger and her worldly-wise roommate, Connie, Cathy decides to visit Philip personally to express her indignation. When she does meet the suave charmer, however, her wrath melts, and she agrees to accompany him on a business trip to Baltimore. Philip then takes Cathy to Philadelphia for cocktails, to Manhattan for his speech at the U. N., and then on to dinner and a baseball game. At first Cathy refuses, but later she reconsiders and ends up flying to the island with a lavish wardrobe, mink coat included, supplied by her generous host. But with the coming of night Cathy is so nervous that she develops a skin rash; and Philip spends the night playing gin rummy with another frustrated male. Back in New York, Cathy feels ashamed of herself and decides to return for a second attempt at romance. This time she takes a drink to fortify herself, gets drunk, and falls off a balcony. Disgusted, Philip returns to New York and no longer attempts to call her. To arouse his jealousy, Roger arranges for Cathy to go to a motel with a lecherous unemployment clerk, Beasley. Following a wild chase, Philip "rescues" Cathy and impulsively proposes marriage. As they arrive in Bermuda for their honeymoon, Philip suddenly realizes he is a married man; overcome by nervousness, he breaks out in a skin rash. *Bachelors. Tycoons. Clerks. Roommates. Unemployment. Drunkenness. Chastity. Lechery. Baseball. New York City. Baltimore. Philadelphia. Bermuda. United Nations. Chases.*

THAT UNCERTAIN FEELING see ONLY TWO CAN PLAY

THAT WOMAN (West Germany) F6.4961

Will Tremper Film. *Dist* Globe Pictures. 18 Jul 1968 [New York opening]. Sd; b&w. 35mm. 83 min.

Pres by Joseph Green. A Will Tremper Production. *Prod-Dir-Writ* Will Tremper. *Camera* Wolfgang Lührse. *Asst Camera* Benno Bellenbaum. *Ed* Ursula Möhrle. *Mus* Peter Thomas. *Sd Dir* Naftali Schönberg. *Prod Mgr* Felix Hock. *Wardrobe* Christine Viertel.

Cast: Eva Renzi (*Alexandra Borovski*), Harald Leipnitz (*Siegbert Lahner*), Paul Hubschmid (*Joachim Steigenwald*), Umberto Orsini (*Timo*), Elga Stass (*Hildchen Volker*), Narziss Sokatscheff (*Bogdan*), Hans-Joachim Ketzlin (*Henry*), Rudolf Schündler (*doctor*), Oestergard (*fashion designer*), Ricci (*nightclub operator*), Zellermayer (*hotelier*), Christian Doermer, Susanne Korda.

Romantic melodrama. Jet-setter Alexandra Borovski is a well-paid fashion model who drifts aimlessly from one affair to another, while secretly desiring to settle down with one man. Traveling through Europe, Alexandra is unable to establish a lasting relationship; her stay in Berlin is a typical stopover. In addition to having affairs with Siegbert Lahner, a businessman, and Timo, an Italian bisexual photographer, she becomes drawn to Lahner's employer, architect Joachim Steigenwald, whom she once met briefly in Rome. Joachim loves her and hopes he can persuade her to marry him, but they separate, Joachim returning to Hildchen, his sometime fiancée, while Alexandra moves on to her next assignment. *Jet set. Models. Businessmen. Photographers. Architects. Italians. Promiscuity. Bisexuality. Travel. Berlin. Europe.*

Note: Location scenes filmed in Berlin. Previewed in West Germany in Apr 1966 as *Berlin ist eine sünde Welt*; running time: 97 min; released in Jun 1966 as *Playgirl*; running time: 88 min.

THAT'S A DIRTY TRICK F6.4962

Dist Stacey Distributors. ca 1970. Sd; col. 16mm. 61-81 min.

Sex film. No information about the precise nature of this film has been found. *Sexuality.*

THEATRE OF DEATH see BLOOD FIEND

THEIR TOWN (TOBY SHORT) see THE CHELSEA GIRLS

THEN THERE WERE THREE F6.4963

Alexandra Films. *Dist* Parade Releasing Organization. 29 Nov 1961 [Los Angeles opening]. Sd; b&w. 35mm. 74 min. [Cut from 82 min.]

Pres by Riley Jackson, Robert Patrick. *Prod-Dir* Alex Nicol. *Screenplay* Frank Gregory, Allan Lurie. *Story* Allan Lurie. *Photog* Gastone Di Giovanni. *Film Ed* Manuel Del Campo. *Mus* Tarcisio Fusco. *Sd* Mario Celentano. *Asst Dir* Mauro Sacripanti.

Cast: Frank Latimore (*Lieutenant Willotsky*), Alex Nicol (*Sam McLease*), Barry Cahill (*Sergeant Travers*), Sidney Clute (*Ben Harvey*), Frank Gregory (*Harry Miller*), Michael Billingsley (*T. I. Ellis*), Frederick R. Clark (*Calhoun*), Paola Falchi (*Giovanna*), Brendan Fitzgerald, Gerard Herter, Kurt Polter, Richard Bull.

War melodrama. In Italy during World War II six GI's from different outfits become detached from the main body of Allied forces. As they band together, they are joined by a seventh, Sam McLease, who is actually a Nazi spy with orders to slay a certain Italian partisan leader in San Corrado. En route to the town, harassment by snipers and the treachery of McLease are responsible for the deaths of three of the Americans. When the remaining four reach San Corrado, McLease captures the partisan leader and attempts to turn him over to the Germans, but the three surviving GI's rescue the partisan. In desperation McLease breaks away and runs for the German lines, but is mistaken for one of the GI's and shot down by his own men. *Spies. Nazis. Imposture. Assassination. Resistance (political). Mistaken identity. World War II. Italy. United States Army. Germany—Army.*

Note: Filmed in Italy. Some sources indicate that Italy coproduced the film (Alexandra Produzzione).

THERE IS STILL ROOM IN HELL (West Germany) F6.4964

Theumer Filmproduktion. *Dist* Sam Lake Enterprises. 19 Jul 1963 [Los Angeles showing]. Sd; b&w. 35mm. 90 min.

Prod-Dir Ernst Ritter von Theumer. *Screenplay* Theo Gallehr. *Photog* Ali Ismir. *Mus* Frank Dallone.

Cast: Barbara Valentin (*Janet*), Paul Glawion (*Ismail*), Hermann Nehlsen (*Dexter*), Fikret Hakan (*Hassan*), Maria Vincent, Sadri Alisik.

Crime melodrama. Ismail, a Turkish narcotics dealer posing as a secondhand bookseller, contracts to deliver some heroin to a group of suppliers in the United States, but he doublecrosses them. Dexter, representing the suppliers, arrives in Istanbul with a beautiful American agent, Janet, to apprehend or possibly kill Ismail. Dexter arranges a meeting between Janet and Ismail, and Ismail falls in love with her. Ismail's collaborator, Hassan, also falls in love with Janet, and she encourages both men. When Dexter shrewdly causes a rift between Ismail and Hassan, Ismail attempts to destroy his former friend's business, further alienating him. A French singer, Juane, informs Dexter of the point of arrival of Ismail's next consignment of narcotics. There a gunfight takes place, and Hassan and Dexter corner Ismail. Dexter is killed, and Hassan and Ismail shoot each other. *Turks. French. Americans in foreign countries. Booksellers. Drug dealers. Singers. Murder. Friendship. Heroin. Istanbul.*

Note: Released in West Germany in Jul 1961 as *In der Hölle ist noch Platz*. Prerelease title: *Sex Agent*. Also known as *Still Room in Hell*.

THERE WAS A CROOKED MAN (Great Britain) F6.4965

Knightsbridge Productions. *Dist* Lopert Pictures. Jun 1962. Sd; b&w. 35mm. 107 min.

Prod John Bryan. *Exec Prod* Albert Fennell. *Dir* Stuart Burge. *Screenplay* Reuben Ship. *Photog* Arthur Ibbetson. *Camera Op* Jack Atchelor. *Camera Focus* John Morgan. *Art Dir* Charles Bishop. *Asst Art Dir* Bert Davey. *Set Dresser* Roger Ramsdell. *Draughtsman* Michael Knight. *Draughtswoman* Ann Talbot. *Film Ed* Peter Hunt. *Asst Ed* Norman Wanstall, Allan Sones. *Mus* Kenneth V. Jones. *Sd Mix* Leo Wilkins. *Dub Ed* John Glen. *Boom Op* Tony Cripps. *Sd Camera Op* Ron Butcher. *1st, 2d & 3d Asst Dir* Colin Brewer, Patrick Clayton, John Danischewsky. *Prod Mgr* Patrick Marsden. *Cont* Rita Davison. *Prod Sec* Maureen Whitty. *Wardrobe Master* Charles Guerin. *Wardrobe Mistress* Laurel Staffell. *Ch Makeup Artist* Harry Frampton. *Makeup Artist* Dick Bonnor-Moris. *Hairstyles* Barbara Ritchie. *Constr Mgr* Ron Udell. *Prop Buyer* Harry Hannay. *Still Photog* Ted Reed.

Cast: Norman Wisdom (*Davy Cooper*), Alfred Marks (*Adolf Carter*), Andrew Cruickshank (*McKillup*), Reginald Beckwith (*station master*), Susannah York (*Ellen*), Jean Clarke (*Freda*), Timothy Bateson (*Flash Dan*), Paul Whitsun-Jones (*restaurant gentleman*), Fred Griffiths (*taxi driver*), Ann

Heffernan *(hospital sister)*, Rosalind Knight *(nurse)*, Reed De Rouen *(Dutchman)*, Brian Oulton *(Ashton)*, Percy Herbert *(prison warden)*, Edna Petrie *(woman at assembly hall)*, Jack May *(police sergeant)*, Ronald Fraser *(General Cummins)*, Ed Devereaux *(American colonel)*, Sam Kydd *(foreman)*, Redmond Phillips *(padre)*, Fred Haggerty, Eddie Boyce, Totti Truman-Taylor, William Hutt, John Barrard, John Kidd.

Comedy. Source: James Bridie, *The Golden Legend of Shults* (Perth, Scotland, opening: 24 Jul 1939). Demolitions expert Davy Cooper is hired by master crook Adolf Carter to blow open a safe in a bank robbery. Carter's gang gains entry to the bank by disguising themselves as doctors and tunneling in from the hospital next door, but police raid the premises, and Davy is sent to prison for five years. Upon his release Davy vows to reform, and he is employed in a seaside factory owned by McKillup, a swindler who has cheated most of his neighbors by selling them shares in the town and falsely promising future profits. Davy recruits his old gang into posing as American army officers intent on building a rocket base in the area; McKillup buys back the land from the investors and is ruined financially when the gang blows up the town. The United States government begrudgingly promises to repair the destruction, and Davy returns to jail. *Ex-convicts. Swindlers. Demolition. Bank robberies. Fraud. Disguise. Imposture. Land speculation. Hospitals. Factories. Rocket-launching sites. United States Army. Explosions.*

Note: Released in London in Aug 1960.

THERE WAS A CROOKED MAN ...   F6.4966

Warner Bros. Pictures. 25 Dec **1970** [New York opening; c18 Sep 1970; LP42629]. Sd; col (Technicolor). 35mm (Panavision). 126 min. [Copyright length: 122 min.] *MPAA rating* R.

Prod-Dir Joseph L. Mankiewicz. *Exec Prod* C. O. Erickson. *Screenplay* David Newman, Robert Benton. *Photog* Harry Stradling, Jr. *Camera Op* Robert Morrison. *Camera Asst* Richard Meinardus, Robert Spence. *Art Dir* Edward Carrere. *Set Decor* Keogh Gleason. *Main Titl* Wayne Fitzgerald. *Film Ed* Gene Milford. *Asst Ed* Gordon Scott, ed. *Mus* Charles Strouse. *Titl Song* Charles Strouse, Lee Adams. *Sung by* Trini Lopez. *Sd* Al Overton, Jr. *Sd Rec* George Hause. *Boom Op* William Thompson. *Asst Dir* Don Kranze, Bill Green, Chris Seitz. *Asst to the Prod* Sidney Ganis. *Prod Supv* Peter V. Herald. *Script Supv* Marvin Weldon. *Location Coörd* Harry Zubrinsky. *Cost* Anna Hill Johnstone. *Men's Wardrobe* Ted Tetrick. *Women's Wardrobe* Rose Brandi. *Makeup Supv* Perc Westmore. *Makeup* Wally Westmore, George Bau, John Inzerella, Jack Dusek. *Hairstyles* Annabelle Levy. *Sp Eff* John Barton. *Still Photog* Bernard Abramson. *Prop Master* Robert Cooper. *Constr Coörd* Wally Graham. *Stunt Coörd* Roger Creed.

Cast: Kirk Douglas *(Paris Pitman, Jr.)*, Henry Fonda *(Woodward Lopeman)*, Hume Cronyn *(Dudley Whinner)*, Warren Oates *(Floyd Moon)*, Burgess Meredith *(The Missouri Kid)*, John Randolph *(Cyrus McNutt)*, Arthur O'Connell *(Mr. Lomax)*, Martin Gabel *(Warden Le Goff)*, Michael Blodgett *(Coy Cavendish)*, Claudia McNeil *(madam)*, Alan Hale, [Jr.] *(Tobaccy)*, Victor French *(Whiskey)*, Lee Grant *(Mrs. Bullard)*, C. K. Yang *(Ah-Ping Woo)*, Pamela Hensley *(Edwina)*, Bert Freed *(Skinner)*, Barbara Rhoades *(Miss Jessie Brundidge)*, J. Edward McKinley *(governor)*, Gene Evans *(Colonel Wolff)*, Jeanne Cooper *(prostitute)*, Ann Doran, Byron Foulger, Paul Newlan.

Western comedy. In 1883 Paris Pitman, the sole survivor of a $500,000 robbery staged by his gang, hides the money in a nest of rattlesnakes. While waiting for the robbery to be forgotten, Pitman is apprehended in a brothel by the diligent Sheriff Lopeman and is sent to an Arizona prison. Pitman reveals to the inmates of the prison that only he knows the location of the stolen money. Warden Le Goff summons Pitman to his office and offers to let him escape in exchange for half of the money, and Pitman agrees to the plan, but the warden is murdered by Ah-Ping, a Chinese prisoner, before their scheme can be carried out. Sheriff Lopeman is appointed the new warden, and with Pitman's help, conditions in the prison improve greatly. When Lopeman invites the governor for a tour of the prison, Pitman decides to escape. He allows three of the prisoners to be killed, and he himself kills Ah-Ping and Floyd Moon, a dim-witted gunfighter, before he makes good his escape. Lopeman, who had trusted Pitman, angrily takes pursuit. At the snakepit, Pitman unearths the money, but one of the rattlesnakes bites him on the throat and kills him. Lopeman then arrives and, following Pitman's ethics, takes the $500,000 and sets out for Mexico. *Outlaws. Sheriffs. Prison wardens. Chinese. Robbery. Bribery. Murder. Perfidy. Prison escapes. Whorehouses. Prisons. Snakebites. Snakes.*

THERE WAS AN OLD COUPLE (U.S.S.R.)   F6.4967

Mosfilm. *Dist* Artkino Pictures. 20 May **1967** [New York opening]. Sd; b&w. 35mm. 103 min.

Dir Grigoriy Chukhray. *Screenplay* Yuliy Dunskiy, Valeriy Frid. *Photog* Sergey Poluyanov. *Camera* O. Zguridi, Yu. Gantman. *Art Dir* Boris Nemechek. *Asst Art Dir* Lev Semyonov. *Mus* Aleksandra Pakhmutova. *Song Lyr* L. Oshanin, Yu. Danilovich. *Sd* S. Litvinov.

Cast: Ivan Marin *(The Old Man [Gusakov])*, Vera Kuznetsova *(The Old Woman [Gusakova])*, Lyudmila Maksakova *(Nina)*, Grigoriy Martynyuk *(Valentin)*, Galina Polskikh *(Galya)*, Anatoliy Yabbarov *(sectarian)*, V. Kolpakov *(paramedic)*, Nikolay Kryuchkov *(director of the sovkhoz)*, Nikolay Sergeyev *(accountant)*, Gyuli Chokhonelidze *(engineer)*, Lenochka Derzhavina *(Irochka)*, O. Amalina, R. Aristarkhova, N. Barmin, Yu. Volkov, V. Vyshkovskiy, M. Drozdovskaya, L. Kadrov, V. Kazanskiy, G. Krasheninnikov, M. Lukach, V. Markin, A. Fyodorinov, O. Fomichyova, N. Khlibko, O. Shtoda.

Melodrama. When their farmhouse is destroyed by fire, an elderly Russian couple decide to visit the neediest of their three children, their daughter, Nina, who lives in a small mining town beyond the polar circle. Upon their arrival, however, they learn that Nina has left with a married man, abandoning her alcoholic husband and infant daughter. Knowing they can be of help, the old couple move in and make a home in their son-in-law Valentin's cold and desolate hut. Eventually Valentin stops drinking and returns to his job. A young neighborhood woman, Galya, who loves both Valentin and the child, becomes part of the little family. The old people take an active part in the community: the old man, a retired veterinarian, is taken for his first helicopter ride, even further north, to treat a reindeer herd. One day, Nina returns, having been discarded by her lover. The old man talks tenderly to her and persuades her to leave home—though she is his daughter, her presence can bring only unhappiness. When the old man dies, he is mourned by the whole community. *Grandparents. In-laws. Veterinarians. Infants. Alcoholism. Old age. Marriage. Desertion. Parenthood. Mining towns. Helicopters. Arctic regions. Fires. Reindeer.*

Note: Released in the U.S.S.R. in 1965 as a 2-part film; combined running time: ca140 min. Cannes Festival running time: 110 min. Russian title: *Zhili-byli starik so starukhoy.* Also known as *The Couple.*

THERE'S A GIRL IN MY SOUP (Great Britain)   F6.4968

Ascot Productions. *Dist* Columbia Pictures. 15 Dec **1970** [New York opening; c1 Dec 1970; LP38734]. Sd; col (Eastman Color). 96 min. *MPAA rating* R.

An M. J. Frankovich Production. *Prod* M. J. Frankovich, John Boulting. *Exec Prod* John Dark. *Dir* Roy Boulting. *Screenplay* Terence Frisby. *Adtl Dial* Peter Kortner. *Dir Photog* Harry Waxman. *Camera Op* Gerry Anstiss. *Art Dir* John Howell. *Set Decor* Patrick McLoughlin. *Film Ed* Martin Charles. *Mus Comp and Sung by* Mike D'Abo. *Arr* Gordon Rose. Songs: "Miss Me in the Morning," "Arabella Cinderella" Mike D'Abo, Nicki Chinn. Songs: "The Lady's in Love," "It's Gotta Be Now" Mike D'Abo. *Sd Rec* David Bowen. *Sd Ed* Mike Le Mare. *Re-rec* Nolan Roberts. *Asst Dir* David Tringham. *Asst to the Asst Dir* Michael Stevenson. *Prod Mgr* John Sealey. *Location Mgr* Tim Hampton. *Cost* Vangie Harrison. *Miss Hawn's Wardrobe* Alice Pollock, Ossie Clark. *Miss Hawn's Makeup* Eric Allwright. *Mr. Seller's Makeup* John O'Gorman. *Hairstyles* Joan Carpenter.

Cast: Peter Sellers *(Robert Danvers)*, Goldie Hawn *(Marion)*, Tony Britton *(Andrew Hunter)*, Nicky Henson *(Jimmy)*, John Comer *(John)*, Diana Dors *(John's wife)*, Gabrielle Drake *(Julia Halforde-Smythe)*, Geraldine Sherman *(Caroline)*, Judy Campbell *(Lady Heather)*, Nicola Pagett *(Clare)*, Christopher Cazenove *(Nigel)*, Robin Parkinson, Roy Skelton *(reporters)*, Caroline Seymour *(Nigel's girl friend)*, Raf De La Torre *(Monsieur Le Guestier)*, Constantin De Goguel *(Michel Le Guestier)*, Thorley Walters *(manager of Carlton Hotel)*, Georges Lambert *(floor waiter)*, André Charise *(concierge)*, John Serret *(elevator operator)*, Avril Angers *(woman in elevator)*, Ruth Trouncer *(Gilly)*, Lance Percival, Mark Dignam, Eric Barker *(guests at wedding reception)*, Françoise Pascal *(Paola)*, Marianne Stone *(reporter at airport)*, Margaret Lacey *(autograph hunter)*.

Comedy. Source: Terence Frisby, *There's a Girl in My Soup* (London opening: 15 Jun 1966). Confirmed bachelor Robert Danvers, the star of a television gourmet program, makes a travesty of a wedding by seducing the bride as she changes from her wedding gown into street clothes. He then meets Marion, a 19-year-old American girl who has just quarreled with her boyfriend, Jimmy, over his infidelity. Robert invites her to his luxurious apartment and attempts to seduce her; to his shock, Marion laughs at his approach and bluntly suggests that they make love. The next day, Robert allows her to move into his apartment and later takes her on a wine-tasting trip to France, climaxed by a visit to the Riviera. Upon their return to England, Marion rejects Robert's marriage proposal and returns to Jimmy, who has promised to be faithful. The aging playboy is distraught, but he soon recovers when a pretty secretary displays an interest in him. *Bachelors. Playboys. Gourmets. Television personalities. Americans in foreign countries. Winetasters. Secretaries. Seduction. Infidelity. Weddings. France. Riviera.*

Note: Filmed on location in England, Cannes, and elsewhere on the French Riviera. Opened in London in Dec 1970.

THERE'S NO PLACE LIKE SPACE *see* **HOLD ON!**

THERE'S SOMETHING FUNNY GOING ON *see* **A MAIDEN FOR A PRINCE**

THÉRÈSE (France)　　　　　　　　　　　　　　　　　　F6.4969
Filmel. *Dist* Pathé Contemporary Films. 12 Nov **1963** [New York opening]. Sd; b&w. 35mm. 107 min.

Prod Eugène Lépicier. *Dir* Georges Franju. *Screenplay* François Mauriac, Claude Mauriac, Georges Franju. *Dial* François Mauriac. *Photog* Christian Matras. *Art Dir* Jacques Chalvet. *Film Ed* Gilbert Natot. *Mus* Maurice Jarre. *Sd* Jean Labussière. *Asst Dir* Georges Casati. *Prod Mgr* Robert Vignon.

Cast: Emmanuelle Riva (*Thérèse*), Philippe Noiret (*Bernard*), Edith Scob (*Anne de la Trave*), Sami Frey (*Jean Azévédo*), Jeanne Perez (*Balionte*), Renée Devillers (*Madame Victor de la Trave*), Richard Saint-Bris (*Hector de la Trave*), Lucien Nat (*Jérôme Larroque*), Hélène Dieudonné (*Aunt Clara*), Jacques Monod (*Duros*), Jean-Jacques Rémy (*specialist*).

Drama. Source: François Mauriac, *Thérèse Desqueyroux* (Paris, 1927). Thérèse, charged with attempting to poison her husband, Bernard, is acquitted when Bernard perjures himself for her at the trial and her politically influential father bribes a court official. On the way back to the country estate, she tries to think of an explanation to offer to Bernard. She remembers her love for Anne, Bernard's half-sister, and her fondness for his pine-tree forest, which was her primary reason for marrying him. She also recalls her increasing boredom with the provincial life and Bernard's insensitivity. On her honeymoon, she slipped away from Bernard's bed to throw away a letter from Anne in which Anne expressed her love for Jean, a Jewish student. Later, when Jean left Anne, Thérèse felt a sense of satisfaction and relief. While Anne nursed Thérèse's unwanted baby, Thérèse began to experiment with games involving Bernard's health, capitalizing on his hypochondria and forgetfulness. It was the discovery of Thérèse's forged lethal prescriptions that finally led to her arrest. Unable to give Bernard a proper explanation upon returning home, she allows him to confine her to her room where she slowly wastes away, existing on cigarettes and wine. Surprised at Thérèse's sickly appearance when the family gathers to meet Anne's new husband, Bernard moves her to Paris. Still hoping to learn the motives for her crime, he listens to her further explanations, but he cannot understand. *Sisters-in-law. Hypochondriacs. Jews. Students. Poisoning. Perjury. Bribery. Memory. Marriage. Honeymoons. Rural life. Jealousy. Forgery. Trials. Forests. Paris.*

Note: Opened in Paris in Sep 1962 as *Thérèse Desqueyroux*; running time: 109 min.

THERESE AND ISABELLE (United States/West Germany)　　F6.4970
Amsterdam Film Corp.-Berolina Films. *Dist* Audubon Films. 14 May **1968** [New York opening]. Sd; b&w. 35mm (Ultrascope). 118 min.

A Radley H. Metzger Production. *Prod-Dir* Radley H. Metzger. *Screenplay* Jesse Vogel. *Dir Photog* Hans Jura. *Camera Op* A. Guertner. *Film Ed* Humphrey Wood. *Mus* Georges Auric. *Asst Dir* Osman Ragheb. *Prod Mgr* Guy Lacourt. *Wardrobe Mistress* Roxane Vaisborg. *Makeup* Marie-Madeleine Paris.

Cast: Essy Persson (*Therese*), Anna Gael (*Isabelle*), Barbara Laage (*Therese's mother*), Anne Vernon (*Mademoiselle Le Blanc*), Maurice Teynac (*Monsieur Martin*), Remy Longa (*Pierre*), Simone Paris (*The Madame*), Suzanne Marchellier (*Mademoiselle Germaine*), Nathalie Nort (*Renée*), Darcy Pullian (*Agnes*), Martine Leclerc (*Martine*), Bernadette Stern (*Françoise*), Serge Geraert, Edith Ploquin, Alexander Kobes.

Drama. Source: Violette Leduc, *Thérèse et Isabelle* (Paris, 1966). Therese, a Frenchwoman in her mid-thirties, returns to a girls' boarding school she attended years before. As she walks among the empty buildings, closed for the summer vacation, she recalls the events that took place there so long ago: *While a young girl, she is sent to the school following her mother's remarriage to a businessman who is uninterested in children. Although her first days are lonely ones, Therese eventually finds solace in the company of Isabelle, a schoolmate as unhappy as herself. Despite the fact that neither girl seems to evince the usual interest in boys, they do occasionally date. One weekend, when Isabelle is visiting her parents, Therese goes out with a local boy, Pierre, and succumbs to his passionate and somewhat brutal lovemaking. This unpleasant experience only increases Therese's need for Isabelle, who has returned from her parents' home in a similar state of anxiety. In time the mutual dependence of the two girls leads to love, both emotional and physical. En route to visit a doctor in Paris, they rent a room in a hotel patronized by prostitutes, but Therese is repulsed by the sordid atmosphere and the noises coming from neighboring rooms, and they leave without fulfilling their purpose. That night they make love on the school grounds, but their affair ends abruptly the following morning when Isabelle's mother suddenly and inexplicably removes her daughter from the school. Therese remains haunted by the memory of the lover she has never seen again, and she turns from the old school and walks slowly back to the car where her fiancé is waiting.* *French. Students. Lesbianism. Friendship. Sexual*

initiation. *Adolescence. Boarding schools. Paris.*

Note: Filmed in France in 1968 at the Abbey of Royaumont. German release title: *Therese und Isabell*. Released in the U. S. in subtitled French language version.

THÉRÈSE DESQUEYROUX *see* **THÉRÈSE**

THERESE UND ISABELL *see* **THERESE AND ISABELLE**

THESE ARE THE DAMNED (Great Britain)　　　　　　F6.4971
Hammer Film Productions-Swallow Productions. *Dist* Columbia Pictures. 7 Jul **1965** [New York opening]. Sd; b&w. 35mm (Hammerscope). 77 min.

Prod Anthony Hinds. *Exec Prod* Michael Carreras, Anthony Nelson Keys. *Dir* Joseph Losey. *Screenplay* Evan Jones. *Dir Photog* Arthur Grant. *Camera Op* Anthony Heller. *Art Dir* Don Mingaye. *Dsgn Cons* Richard MacDonald. *Prod Dsgn* Bernard Robinson. *Supv Film Ed* James Needs. *Film Ed* Reginald Mills. *Mus* James Bernard. *Mus Dir* John Hollingsworth. *Song*: "*Black Leather Rock*" James Bernard, Evan Jones. *Sd* Jock May. *Asst Dir* John Peverall. *Prod Mgr* Don Weeks. *Cost* Molly Arbuthnot. *Sculpture* Elizabeth Frink.

Cast: MacDonald Carey (*Simon Wells*), Shirley Ann Field (*Joan*), Viveca Lindfors (*Freya Neilson*), Alexander Knox (*Bernard*), Oliver Reed (*King*), Walter Gotell (*Major Holland*), James Villiers (*Captain Gregory*), Tom Kempinski (*Ted*), Kenneth Cope (*Sid*), Brian Oulton (*Mr. Dingle*), Barbara Everest (*Miss Lamont*), Alan McClelland (*Mr. Stuart*), James Maxwell (*Mr. Talbot*), Rachel Clay (*Victoria*), Caroline Sheldon (*Elizabeth*), Rebecca Dignam (*Anne*), Siobhan Taylor (*Mary*), Nicholas Clay (*Richard*), Kit Williams (*Henry*), Christopher Witty (*William*), David Palmer (*George*), John Thompson (*Charles*), David Gregory, Anthony Valentine, Larry Martyn, Leon Garcia, Jeremy Phillips (*Teddy-boys*), Edward Harvey, Neil Wilson, Fiona Duncan, Tommy Trinder, Victor Gorf.

Science fiction drama. Source: Henry Lionel Lawrence, *The Children of Light* (London, 1960). When American Simon Wells tries to pick up an attractive woman named Joan on the promenade at Weymouth, he is robbed and beaten by a motorcycle gang. Bernard, a scientist, and his friend Freya, a sculptress, come to his assistance. Later, Simon meets Joan again and learns that she is the sister of King, the leader of the motorcycle gang. She and Simon hide from King in Freya's studio, but he finally locates them, and as they attempt to run away, all three fall from a cliff into the sea. A group of strange children rescue them and take them to a cave, where Simon and Joan discover that the children belong to Bernard's secret research project. Exposed to radiation before birth, the children are now capable of surviving in a radioactive atmosphere in case of nuclear war; they have been kept completely isolated from the outside world, cared for and educated by automation. King is antagonistic toward the children, but Simon and Joan decide to help them, not realizing until it is too late that the children are radioactive. As Simon and Joan attempt to lead the children out of the cave, they are intercepted by soldiers under Bernard's direction. King tries to escape with one of the children, but after the child is recaptured, King's car goes out of control and plummets off a bridge. Bernard then allows Simon and Joan to escape in a boat, knowing that they will soon die from exposure to the intense radiation. Meanwhile, Freya has also found out about the project, and Bernard is forced to kill her and seal the children inside the cave. *Americans in foreign countries. Motorcycle gangs. Scientists. Sculptors. Children. Robbery. Brother-sister relationship. Murder. Caves. Experiments. Radiation. Weymouth (England). Automobile accidents.*

Note: Filmed on location at Weymouth and Portland Bill, England. Opened in London in May 1963 as *The Damned*; running time: 87 min. Working title: *On the Brink*.

THEY ALL DIED LAUGHING (Great Britain)　　　　　F6.4972
Tower Films. *For* Pax Films/British Lion Films. *Dist* Continental Distributing, Inc. 15 Mar **1964** [New York opening]. Sd; b&w. 35mm. 94 min. [Also 90 min.]

A Michael Balcon Production. *Prod* Donald Taylor. *Exec Prod* Steven Pallos. *Dir* Don Chaffey. *Screenplay* Robert Hamer, Donald Taylor. *Photog* Gerald Gibbs. *Art Dir* George Provis. *Titl* Robert Ellis. *Film Ed* Peter Tanner. *Mus* John Barry. *Solo Jazz Organ Played by* Alan Haven. *Sd* H. L. Bird. *Asst Dir* Dennis Bertera. *Prod Mgr* Philip Shipway.

Cast: Leo McKern (*Professor Bowles-Ottery*), Janet Munro (*Delia Brooks*), Maxine Audley (*Clarinda Bowles-Ottery*), Duncan Macrae (*Dr. Brass*), Dennis Price (*Professor Hughes*), Miles Malleson (*Dr. Woolley*), Leonard Rossiter (*Dr. Fisher*), Alan Wheatley, Geoffrey Bayldon (*Epicene* [*see note*]), Patricia Jessel (*Mrs. Pugh-Smith*), Dinsdale Landen (*Fred*), George Benson (*Inspector Butts*), Mark Dignam (*The Master*), Jerome Willis (*Armstrong*), Ralph Michael (*Superintendent Rastleigh*), Mervyn Johns (*Willie Pugh-Smith*), Raymond Ray (*The Waiter*), Joyce Carey (*hotel receptionist*), Cliff Michelmore (*himself, a TV commentator*), Wally Patch (*landlord*).

Comedy. Source: C. E. Vulliamy, *Don Among the Dead Men* (London, 1952). Professor Bowles-Ottery, a brilliant but high-living chemist married to an actress and teaching at St. Simeon's University, discovers a poison that leaves no trace but which induces a state of hilarity in the victim shortly before death. He keeps his discovery a secret, thinking of ways it can be used in man's best interest; but when the university's senior proctor annoys him over regulations, he gets a dose of the poison and winds up dancing on the campus in his underwear and singing dirty songs before he dies. Delia Brooks, research assistant to Bowles-Ottery, decides to advance her career by compromising the professor. Mrs. Pugh-Smith, the town gossip, sees the professor lunching with Delia, tells Clarinda, his wife, and it is not long before Mrs. Pugh-Smith dies after making a public fool of herself. Hughes, his competitor for an important professorship, receives a dose when it seems likely that he will get the appointment, and he dies after disgracing himself. Delia uncovers the solution to the deaths and threatens to expose the professor unless he marries her. Ostensibly he agrees, but he gives her a poisoned cigarette from his laboratory before leaving her apartment. As Delia becomes exhilarated she realizes what he has done and telephones the police before she dies. Meanwhile, Clarinda has filled the cigarette boxes from a supply found in her husband's laboratory. The police come to arrest him, and the professor, amused because proof of the crimes is impossible, jauntily lights a cigarette. Too late he realizes the cigarette box should have been empty, and after Clarinda reveals the source of the supply, he races from the house, jumps into his car, and drives head on into a steamroller, laughing wildly all the time. *Professors. Chemists. Actors. Researchers. Police. Lunatics. Murder. Poisoning. Gossip. Blackmail. Ambition. Cigarettes. Laboratories. Automobile accidents.*

Note: Opened in London in May 1964 as *A Jolly Bad Fellow*; running time: 96 min. Also shown in the United States under the British release title. Working title: *For He's a Jolly Bad Fellow.* Sources conflict in crediting the role of Epicene.

THEY CALL ME **MISTER** TIBBS   F6.4973

Mirisch Productions. *Dist* United Artists. 8 Jul **1970** [New York opening; c8 Jul 1970; LP38114]. Sd; col (De Luxe). 35mm. 108 min. *MPAA rating* GP.

Prod Herbert Hirschman. *Exec Prod* Walter Mirisch. *Dir* Gordon Douglas. *Screenplay* Alan R. Trustman, James R. Webb. *Story* Alan R. Trustman. *Dir Photog* Gerald Finnerman. *Camera Op* Joe Jackman, Roy Clark, Brad Six, Paul Pollard, Richard Neff. *Art Dir* Addison Hehr. *Set Decor* Edward G. Boyle. *Set Dsgn* Clifford Yates, James F. McGuire. *Film Ed* Bud Molin. *Asst Ed* Irving Rosenblum. *Mus* Quincy Jones. *Sd Ed* Frank Warner. *Sd Rec* Robert Martin. *Rec* Bert Hallberg. *Boom Op* Norman Webster. *Asst Dir* Rusty Meek, Hal Washburn, Fred Brost. *Prod Supv* Edward Morey, Jr. *Prod Mgr* Terence Nelson. *Prod Sec* Ruth M. Miller. *Location Mgr* William Gallant. *Script Supv* Malcolm Atterbury, Jr. *Wardrobe Supv* John A. Anderson. *Wardrobe* Ermon Session. *Women's Wardrobe* Neva Rames. *Makeup* Mark Reedall, Al Fleming. *Hairstyles* Elizabeth Darcy. *Sp Eff* Justus Gibbs. *Tech Adv* Hal De Windt. *Still Photog* Larry Barbier. *Constr Coörd* William Maldonado. *Prop* Robert Schultz, Ed Mullay. *Gaffer* Tony Pistone. *Key Grip* George Rader. *Casting* Lynn Stalmaster.

Cast: Sidney Poitier (*Virgil Tibbs*), Martin Landau (*Rev. Logan Sharpe*), Barbara McNair (*Valerie Tibbs*), Anthony Zerbe (*Rice Weedon*), Jeff Corey (*Captain Marden*), David Sheiner (*Herbert Kenner*), Juano Hernandez (*Mealie*), Norma Crane (*Marge Garfield*), Edward Asner (*Woody Garfield*), Ted Gehring (*Sergeant Deutsch*), Beverly Todd (*Puff*), Linda Towne (*Joy Sturges*), George Spell (*Andrew Tibbs*), Wanda Spell (*Ginger Tibbs*), Garry Walberg (*medical examiner*).

Crime melodrama. Based on the character created by: John Dudley Ball. Det. Lieut. Virgil Tibbs of the San Francisco homicide squad receives an anonymous phone call accusing his close friend, community activist Rev. Logan Sharpe, of murdering a prostitute. The detective questions the clergyman, who admits having visited the victim to bestow pastoral counsel. Other suspects include Rice Weedon, a landlord and narcotics dealer whom Tibbs shoots in self-defense; black janitor Mealie; and Woody Garfield, the victim's protector. Again confronted by Tibbs, Sharpe confesses his guilt, revealing that the prostitute had mocked his sexual prowess, and begging Tibbs to defer arrest until after a referendum on a community control issue Sharpe supports. When the officer refuses, the activist throws himself under a passing truck. *Detectives. Negroes. Janitors. Police. Politicians. Drug dealers. Clergymen. Landlords. Prostitutes. Murder. Suicide. San Francisco. Automobile accidents.*

Note: Location scenes filmed in San Francisco. Film is a sequel to *In the Heat of the Night,* q. v.

THEY CAME FROM BEYOND SPACE (Great Britain)   F6.4974

Amicus Productions. *Dist* Embassy Pictures. May **1967**. Sd; col (Eastman Color by Pathé). 35mm. 85 min.

Prod Max J. Rosenberg, Milton Subotsky. *Dir* Freddie Francis. *Screenplay* Milton Subotsky. *Photog* Norman Warwick. *Art Dir* Don Mingaye, Scott Slimon. *Prod Dsgn* Bill Constable. *Titl* Francis Rodker. *Film Ed* Peter Musgrave. *Mus Comp* James Stevens. *Mus Cond* Philip Martell. *Sd* Clive

Smith, George Stephenson. *Asst Dir* Ray Corbett. *Prod Mgr* Tony Wallis. *Prod Supv* Ted Wallis. *Wardrobe* Eileen Welch. *Makeup* Bunty Phillips. *Hairstyles* Ann Rogers. *Sp Eff* Bowie Films. *Models Made & Photog by* Bowie Films.

Cast: Robert Hutton (*Dr. Curtis Temple*), Jennifer Jayne (*Lee Mason*), Zia Mohyeddin (*Farge*), Bernard Kay (*Richard Arden*), Michael Gough (*Monj*), Geoffrey Wallace (*Allan Mullane*), Maurice Good (*Stilwell*), Luanshiya Greer (*girl attendant*), John Harvey (*Bill Trethowan*), Diana King (*Mrs. Trethowan*), Paul Bacon (*Rogers*), Christopher Banks (*doctor on street*), Dermot Cathie (*Peterson*), Norman Claridge (*Dr. Andrews*), James Donnelly (*guard*), Frank Forsyth (*Blake*), Leonard Grahame (*McCabe*), Michael Hawkins (*Williams*), Jack Lambert (*doctor in office*), Robin Parkinson (*Maitland*), Edward Rees (*bank manager*), Katy Wild (*girl in street*), Kenneth Kendall (*tv commentator*).

Science fiction melodrama. Source: Joseph Millard, "The Gods Hate Kansas," in *Startling Stories* (Nov 1941). Meteorites descend onto a farm, and Dr. Curtis Temple, an astrophysicist, and Richard Arden, a government official, send their assistant, Lee Mason, to investigate. But Miss Mason and fellow scientist Allan Mullane are penetrated by the meteoritic glow and begin behaving like robots. Temple tries to learn what is happening at the farm and is attacked by Mullane, then knocked unconscious by Lee's ray-gun. Recovering, Temple discovers that Lee's body has been taken over by strange astral beings. Then a plague spreads across the town, threatening to become worldwide, though Temple and the assisting scientists escape death. Temple fires the ray-gun at Lee to destroy the creature within her, then the three scientists board a rocket headed for the moon. Once there, they learn that the creatures are disembodied intelligences from a far galaxy whose spaceship crashed on the moon. The victims of the plague are not really dead but temporarily petrified until they can be used as a labor force in building a spaceship to return the creatures to their galaxy. Farge, another scientist, leads a revolt of the slave men, and he and Temple convince their leader that they will be helped without coercion—thus beginning a new era of friendship between earthmen and the beings from beyond space. *Scientists. Physicists. Space creatures. Plague. Disembodiment. Slavery. Meteors. Rockets. The Moon.*

Note: Released in Great Britain in Sep 1968.

THEY CAME TO ROB LAS VEGAS (France/Italy/Spain/ West Germany)   F6.4975

Isasi Producciones Cinematograficas–Capitole Films–Eichberg-Film–Franca Film. *Dist* Warner Bros.-Seven Arts, Inc. 5 Feb **1969** [New York opening; c21 Dec 1968; LF121]. Sd; col (Technicolor). 35mm (Techniscope). 129 min. *MPAA rating* R.

Exec Prod Nat Wachsberger. *Dir* Antonio Isasi Isasmendi. *Screenplay* Antonio Isasi Isasmendi, Jo Eisinger, Luis Comerón, Jorge Illa, Giovanni Simonelli. *Dial* Jo Eisinger. *Photog* Juan Gelpí. *Art Dir* Antonio Cortés, Juan Alberto Soler. *Film Ed* Elena Jaumandreu, Emilio Rodriguez Oses. *Mus* Georges Garvarentz. *Asst Dir* Luis Garcia, Marcelino Riba, U. Volz. *Script Supv* Pedro Villanueva. *Prod Supv* Antonio Irlés. *Prod Mgr* Miguel Grau. *Prod Asst* Peter Goldbaum. *Cost* I. Penezis. *Sp Eff* Antonio Baquero.

Cast: Gary Lockwood (*Tony Vincenzo*), Elke Sommer (*Anne*), Lee J. Cobb (*Skorsky*), Jack Palance (*Douglas*), Georges Géret (*Leroy*), Gustavo Re (*Salvatore*), Daniel Martín (*Merino*), Jean Servais (*Gino Vincenzo*), Roger Hanin (*The Boss*), Maurizio Arena (*Clark*), Armand Mestral (*Mass*), Fabrizio Capucci (*Cooper*), Enrique Avila (*Baxter*), Rossella Bergamonti, Gérard Tichy, Rubén Rojo.

Crime melodrama. Source: André Lay, *Les hommes de Las Végas* (Paris, 1969). When his older brother is killed in San Francisco while trying to rob an armored truck owned by Skorsky, Tony Vincenzo, a Las Vegas casino dealer, vows to honor his brother's memory by successfully executing the robbery. He seduces Anne, Skorsky's secretary and mistress, and learns from her the details of a shipment coming by van from the Las Vegas casino to a California bank. Tony and his gang waylay the truck in the Nevada desert, dispose of all but one guard, and attempt to cut through the van's steel plating with blowtorches. Unknown to Tony, Skorsky has been using his company as a cover for smuggling gold ingots into Mexico for the Mafia, and the operation has aroused the suspicion of Douglas, a federal treasury agent. Meanwhile, Tony's men begin fighting among themselves; and during the mayhem, the guard inside the van, who is actually a government agent, wounds Tony and locks him in the van before dying. Tony manages to open the truck by short-circuiting the electrical lock; he then telephones Anne to meet him. She arrives, followed by Douglas' team of treasury agents, as well as Skorsky and several Mafia members. At the same time, some of Tony's men return with explosives and set off a blast which kills them and scatters the contents of the truck across the desert. As the police move in to arrest the remaining conspirators, Tony breaks into laughter, satisfied that he has avenged his brother's death. *Cardsharps. Brothers. Mistresses. Guards. Government agents. Robbery. Revenge. Seduction. Smuggling. Imposture. Armored car services. Deserts. Gold. San*

Francisco. Nevada. Las Vegas. Mafia. United States—Treasury Department. Explosions.

Note: Location scenes filmed in Almería, Spain, and in Las Vegas, Los Angeles, and San Francisco. Opened in Paris in Jan 1969 as *Les hommes de Las Végas* at 120 min; released in Italy as *Radiografia d'un colpo d'oro*; opened in Madrid in Oct 1968 as *Las Vegas, 500 millones* at 127 min; in West Germany in Mar 1969 as *An einem Freitag in Las Vegas* at 130 min.

THEY CAME TOGETHER *see* **MIDNIGHT COWGIRL**

THEY DON'T WEAR PAJAMAS AT ROSIE'S *see* **THE FIRST TIME**

THEY LOVE AS THEY PLEASE *see* **GREENWICH VILLAGE STORY**

THEY RAN FOR THEIR LIVES   **F6.4976**

Masterpiece Productions. *Dist* Color Vision International. 4 Apr **1968** [San Antonio, Texas, opening]. Sd; col (Eastmancolor). 35mm. 92 min.

Prod Samuel Ray Calabrese. *Assoc Prod* Stanley R. Caiden. *Dir* John Payne. *Screenplay* Monroe Manning. *Camera Op* Ross Kelsay. *Post Prod Supv* Igo Kantor. *Supv Film Ed* Thor Brooks. *Asst Film Ed* Sam Aanis. *Sd* Lee Strosnider. *Sd Eff* Edward Sandlin. *Asst Dir* Russell Vreeland. *Prop Master* Mike Ezzes. *Head Grip* Terry Crendoff. *Animal Trainer* Gary Gero. *Still Photog* Frank Maggio. *Stunt Coörd* Boyd Stockman.

Cast: John Payne *(Bob Martin)*, Luana Patten *(Barbara)*, John Carradine *(Laslow)*, Bravo *(Bob's dog)*, Scott Brady, Jim Davis, Anthony Eisley.

Action melodrama. Gangsters Vince Mallard, Doc Wright, and Joe, searching for a forged document that belonged to an oil geologist they killed, chase the dead man's daughter, Barbara Collins, across the desert in Nevada. Caught and drugged, Barbara is rescued by Bob Martin and his German shepherd Bravo. While they are chased by the gangsters for several days, Bob kills Doc and saves Barbara when she is temporarily recaptured by Joe. Leaving Barbara alone on the trail, Bob doubles back and rigs an explosion that kills Vince. Barbara becomes lost, stumbles upon Joe, who has been driven insane by the heat, but is again rescued by Bob and Bravo. Bob takes Joe to a nearby sheriff's office, where Laslow, Barbara's father's unscrupulous partner, overhears Bob tell a policeman of Barbara's whereabouts. Laslow confronts Barbara in the desert and attacks her in his impatience to retrieve the forged oil report. Menaced by Bravo, Laslow falls off a cliff to his death. *Gangsters. Sheriffs. Murder. Forgery. Oil. Rescue. Partnerships. Deserts. Nevada. Documentation. Chases. Dogs.*

Note: Filmed in the Valley of Fire near Las Vegas.

THEY SHOOT HORSES, DON'T THEY?   **F6.4977**

Palomar Pictures International. *Dist* Cinerama Releasing Corp. 10 Dec **1969** [New York opening]. Sd; col (DeLuxe). 35mm (Panavision). 129 min. [Also 120 min.] *MPAA rating* GP.

Pres by ABC Pictures. A Robert Chartoff–Irwin Winkler–Sydney Pollack Production. *Prod* Irwin Winkler, Robert Chartoff. *Exec Prod* Theodore B. Sills. *Assoc Prod* John Green. *Dir* Sydney Pollack. *Screenplay* James Poe, Robert E. Thompson. *Dir Photog* Philip H. Lathrop. *Camera Op* Duke Callaghan. *1st Camera Asst* Cliff King. *Set Decor* Frank McKelvy. *Sketch Artist* Mort Rabinowitz. *Prod Dsgn* Harry Horner. *Main Titl* Phill Norman. *Film Ed* Fredric Steinkamp. *Asst Film Ed* Don Guidice. *Mus* John Green. *Orch Arr* John Green, Al Woodbury. *Song:* "Easy Come, Easy Go" John Green, Edward Heyman. *Marathon Choreog & Supv* Tom Panko. *Sd* Tom Overton. *Rec* Brandon Kellogg. *Boom Op* Ora Hudson. *Asst Dir* Al Jennings, C. E. Dismukes, Lynn Guthrie. *Prod Mgr* Edward Woehler. *Script Supv* Joyce Webb. *Cost Dsgn* Donfeld. *Wardrobe* Ron Wind, Bob Scott, Joe Somaruga, Mina Mittelman, Thalia Phillips, Violet Martin, Vou Lee Giokaris. *Makeup* Frank McCoy. *Body Makeup* Maggie O'Connor. *Hairdresser* Sherry Wilson, Lenore Weaver, Carla Hadley, Shirley Kirby. *Miss York's Hairstyles* Ina Claire. *Miss Fonda's Hairstyles* Sydney Guilaroff. *Sp Eff* Blondie Anderson. *Tech Adv* Noble "Kid" Chissell. *Dial Coach* Herb Dufine. *Still Photog* Art Say. *Gaffer* Lee Wilson. *Prop* Ben L. Goodman, Danny Beneducci. *Grip* William Classen, Craig Novak. *Casting* Lynn Stalmaster, Jack Roberts, James Martell.

Cast: Jane Fonda *(Gloria Beatty)*, Michael Sarrazin *(Robert Syverton)*, Susannah York *(Alice)*, Gig Young *(Rocky)*, Red Buttons *(The Sailor)*, Bonnie Bedelia *(Ruby)*, Michael Conrad *(Rollo)*, Bruce Dern *(James)*, Al Lewis *(Turkey)*, Robert Fields *(Joel)*, Severn Darden *(Cecil)*, Allyn Ann McLerie *(Shirl)*, Jacquelyn Hyde *(Jackie)*, Felice Orlandi *(Mario)*, Art Metrano *(Max)*, Gail Billings *(Lillian)*, Maxine Greene *(Agnes)*, Paul Mantee *(Jiggs)*, Madge Kennedy *(Mrs. Layden)*, Mary Gregory *(nurse)*, Robert Dunlap *(college boy)*, Tim Herbert *(doctor)*, Tom McFadden, Noble "Kid" Chissell *(trainers)*.

Drama. Source: Horace McCoy, *They Shoot Horses, Don't They?* (New York, 1935). During the Depression, while awaiting execution for the murder of an acquaintance, Robert Syverton recalls the circumstances of the crime. *Wandering on an amusement pier beside the Pacific Ocean, he recalls when,* as a child, he witnessed the destruction of a favourite horse. Robert is then attracted to a dance marathon about to begin in the dilapidated Aragon Ballroom. As he watches, a contestant is disqualified because of an ominous cough. Pressed by the man's aggressive partner, cynical Gloria Beatty, host Rocky recruits Robert as a substitute. Among the throngs competing for the prize are a middle-aged sailor suffering from heart trouble; aspirant actress Alice and her partner, Joel; an impoverished farm worker, James, and his pregnant wife, Ruby; and other destitute couples. As the marathon continues the weaker pairs are quickly eliminated, while the vulnerabilities of the stronger contestants are observed and exploited by the master of ceremonies. The theft of Alice's alternate gown stimulates mutual suspicion. After observing Alice and Robert together, Gloria takes Joel as her partner. Joel, however, receives a job offer and quits the role. Gloria's next partner is the sailor. To rekindle the spectators' enthusiasm Rocky stages a series of derbies in which the exhausted contestants, clad in track suits, must circle the floor. In these races the last three couples are eliminated. As Gloria and the sailor participate, her partner has a heart attack. Undeterred, she lifts the man to her back and crosses the finish line. Horrified, Alice sequesters herself in the shower, where she suffers a mental breakdown. Robert and Gloria are again partners. Inspired, Rocky suggests that they marry during the marathon. When Gloria refuses, the host reveals the contest's fraudulent nature. From the prize will be deducted numerous expenses, leaving the winner with nothing. Rocky boasts that he stole Alice's dress to excite spectator interest and to stimulate the rivalrous instincts of the contestants. Disgusted with this duplicity, the couple departs. Outside Gloria attempts to shoot herself, but she cannot pull the trigger. When she requests his help Robert obliges. Questioned by the police as to the motive for the murder, Robert can only say, "They shoot horses, don't they?" Meanwhile, the marathon continues. *Entertainers. Actors. Sailors. Farm workers. Social classes. Poverty. Moral corruption. Contests. Jealousy. Theft. Murder. Suicide.*

THEY WERE TEN (Israel)   **F6.4978**

Orb Films—Scopus Productions. *Dist* George Schwartz, Arthur Sachson, Film Representations. 17 Apr **1961** [New York opening]. Sd; b&w. 35mm., 105 min.

Prod-Dir-Story Baruch Dienar. *Screenplay* Gavriel Dagan, Baruch Dienar, Menachem Shuval. *Photog* Lionel Banes. *Film Ed* Helga Cranston. *Mus* Gari Bertini.

Cast: Ninette Linar *(Manyah)*, Oded Teomi *(Yosef)*, Leo Filler *(Zalman)*, Yosef Safra *(Shimon)*, Yosef Zur *(Berl)*, Gavriel Dagan *(Mirkin)*, Israel Rubinshik *(Avraham)*, Nissim Azikri *(Asher)*, Amnon Kahanovitsh *(Shmulik)*, Itzhak Bareket *(Yoel)*, Yehuda Gabbai *(Dr. Weiss)*, Shlomit Kaplansky *(Mrs. Weiss)*, Yosef Bashi *(Jamal)*, Moshe Kedem *(Sheikh Mustafa)*, Moshe Yaari *(Turkish officer)*, Abu Attef, Eytan Priver.

Drama. At the turn of the century, 10 Jews respond to a Russian pogrom by emigrating to Galilee. In the desert the nine men and one woman battle for survival against the forces of nature, hostile Arabs, and their own human weaknesses. Despite these obstacles Yosef and Manyah marry. Although a healthy son is born of this union, Manyah dies of malaria during a drought. As the mother is buried, a rainstorm breaks the drought. This proves a good omen, for Yosef thereafter befriends Sheikh Mustafa, enabling the settlers to live in peace with their Arab and Turkish neighbors. *Jews. Immigrants. Arabs. Turks. Nationalism. Survival. Childbirth. Pogroms. Drought. Galilee. Russia.*

Note: Filmed on location in Galilee. Released in Israel in 1960 as *Hem hayu asar.*

THE THIEF OF BAGHDAD (France/Italy)   **F6.4979**

Titanus–C. C. F. Lux. *Dist* Metro-Goldwyn-Mayer, Inc. 16 Aug **1961** [New York opening; c2 May 1961; LP20384]. Sd; col (Eastman Color by Pathé). 35mm (CinemaScope). 90 min. [Also reviewed at 96 min.]

Pres by Joseph E. Levine. *Prod* Bruno Vailati. *Dir* Arthur Lubin. *Screenplay* Augusto Frassineti, Filippo Sanjust, Bruno Vailati. *Dir Photog* Tonino Delli Colli. *Camera* Franco Delli Colli. *Art Dir* Flavio Mogherini. *Set Dresser* Massimo Tavazzi. *Film Ed* Gene Ruggiero. *Mus Comp* Carlo Rustichelli. *Choreog* Paul Steffen. *Asst Dir* Robert Fiz. *Prod Mgr* Nello Meniconi. *Prod Asst* Mario De Biase, Mario Basile. *Tunisian Location Mgr* André Bessis. *Script Girl* Barbara Fuchs. *Cost Dsgn* Georges Benda. *Makeup* Romolo De Martino. *Hairdresser* Adalgisa Favella. *Sp Eff* Tom Howard.

Cast: Steve Reeves *(Karim)*, Georgia Moll *(Amina)*, Arturo Dominici *(Prince Osman)*, Edy Vessel *(Kadeejah)*, Georges Chamarat *(magician)*, Antonio Battistella, Daniele Vargas, Fanfulla, Giancarlo Zarfati, Rosario Borelli, Eduardo Bergamo, Luigi Visconti, Gina Mascetti, Antonio Rosmino, Ignazio Dolce, Mohammed Agrebi, Joudi Mohammed Jamil, Franco Cobianchi, Anita Todesco, Walter Grant, Mario Passante, Chignone.

Fantasy. In ancient Baghdad, a handsome thief, Karim, falls in love with the beautiful Amina, daughter of the sultan. Also attracted to the princess is villainous Prince Osman, who gives the young girl a magic potion to make her fall in love with him. Since Amina is already in love with Karim, however, the potion turns to poison, and she becomes gravely ill. An old magician explains that she can be cured only by an enchanted blue rose that grows beyond the mystical Seven Gates. Karim, Prince Osman, and several other suitors set out in quest of the flower, but after an encounter with trees that have serpent-like branches, only Karim continues the search. He crosses a plain of boiling lava, resists and outwits the temptress Kadeejah, survives a sudden flood, battles and kills a giant, fights a group of egg-faced men, and finally flies on a winged horse to the Seventh Gate, where he finds the blue rose. On his return to Baghdad, Karim learns that Prince Osman has taken Amina prisoner and is laying siege to the city, but with the aid of a magic diamond given him by the old magician, he creates an army of his doubles and routs the enemy forces. The blue rose is destroyed in the battle, but Karim gives a white one to Amina and tells her that if she truly loves him, the flower will turn blue. When it does so and Amina recovers, the grateful sultan makes Karim the new ruler of Baghdad. *Thieves. Royalty. Temptresses. Evildoers. Giants. Magicians. Spells. Abduction. Poisoning. Magic. Potions. Trees. Lava. Jewels. Flowers. Bagdad. Floods. Winged horses.*

Note: Location scenes filmed in Tunisia. Rome opening: Apr 1961 as *Il ladro di Bagdad*; Paris opening: Aug 1961 as *Le voleur de Bagdad*.

THE THIEF OF PARIS (France/Italy)   F6.4980

Nouvelles Editions de Films–Les Productions Artistes Associés–Compagnia Cinematografica Montoro. *Dist* Lopert Pictures. 26 Aug 1967 [New York opening; c22 Feb 1967; LF15]. Sd; col (De Luxe). 35mm. 119 min.

Prod-Dir Louis Malle. *Exec Prod* Norbert T. Auerbach. *Screenplay* Louis Malle, Jean-Claude Carrière. *Dial* Daniel Boulanger. *Dir Photog* Henri Decaë. *Camera Op* Charles-Henry Montel. *Col Cons* Ghislain Uhry. *Art Dir* Jacques Saulnier. *Film Ed* Henri Lanoe. *Sd Engr* André Hervée. *Asst Dir* Juan-Luis Buñuel, Patrick Bureau. *Prod Mgr* Hubert Mérial. *Cost Dsgn* Ghislain Uhry.

Cast: Jean-Paul Belmondo *(Georges Randal)*, Geneviève Bujold *(Charlotte)*, Marie Dubois *(Geneviève)*, Françoise Fabian *(Ida)*, Julien Guiomar *(Lamargelle)*, Paul Le Person *(Roger La Honte)*, Martine Sarcey *(Renée)*, Marlène Jobert *(Broussaille)*, Bernadette Lafont *(Marguerite)*, Madeleine Damien *(Marie Jeanne)*, Christian Lude *(Uncle Randal)*, Fernand Guiot *(Van Der Busch)*, Jacqueline Staup *(Mrs. Van Der Busch)*, Marc Dudicourt *(Antoine)*, Charles Denner *(Cannonier)*, Christian de Tilière *(Armand)*, Jacques David *(The Robbed Man)*, Roger Crouzet *(Mouratet)*, Jacques Debary *(Courbassol)*, Paul Vally *(The Solicitor)*, Nane Germon *(Mrs. Voisin)*, Jean Champion *(owner of the Hotel de la Biche)*, Odette Piquet *(his wife)*, Irène Daix *(old English maid)*, Julien Loisel *(Mr. de Montareuil)*, Dario Meschi *(owner of the Hotel du Roi Salomon)*, Maurice Auzel *(Marcel)*, Jacques Gheusi *(Professor Boileau)*, Pierre Etaix *(pickpocket)*, Monique Mélinand, Nicole Chollet, Gabriel Gobin, Duncan Elliott.

Crime drama. Source: Georges Darien, *Le voleur* (Paris, 1898). In turn-of-the-century Paris, Georges Randal, a wellborn orphan, is cheated out of his inheritance by an unscrupulous uncle and then forced to stand by helplessly while his cousin Charlotte, with whom he is in love, is forced by her uncle to become engaged to another man. He reduces Charlotte's fiancé to the status of a pauper by stealing the fiancé's family jewels, thereby causing his uncle to break the engagement. Inspired by his first taste of crime, Georges goes to Brussels and meets the Abbot Lamargelle, an underworld priest who becomes his mentor. Before long, Georges has risen to the top of his profession. By utilizing his appeal to women to gain entrance into the homes of the privileged, he quickly amasses a considerable fortune. When the rise of anarchy in France stirs police retaliation, he flees to England. There he is reunited with Charlotte, who has been disinherited by her debauched uncle. Upon learning that the old man is dying, Georges exacts the perfect revenge by destroying the uncle's will and forging a new one in Charlotte's favor. With Charlotte's fortune added to his own, Georges no longer has any need to go on stealing. But it is too late to stop; thievery has become a way of life for him. *Orphans. Uncles. Cousins. Thieves. Priests. Marriage—Arranged. Inheritance. Disinheritance. Revenge. Forgery. Jewels. Wills. Paris. Brussels. England.*

Note: Paris opening: Feb 1967 as *Le voleur*.

THIGH SPY   F6.4981

International Visual Images, Ltd. *Dist* Howard Farber Films, Distribpix, Inc. Jun 1967. Sd; b&w. 35mm. 70 min.

Prod Vera Mandelova. *Dir* William K. Hennigar. *Camera* John Fisher. *Lighting* Bruce Arceari. *Film Ed* Utopia International Visual Images. *Mus* Luristan. *Orig Score* Jeff Kanew, Gary Allen. *Sd* D'Arcy Raley. *Prod Supv* Dell Raley.

Action melodrama. Bartholomew is a struggling young artist whose patron, the incorrigible Mr. X, decides to collect the money he has loaned the painter. In lieu of payment, Bartholomew is told that he can repay Mr. X by killing Arnold, a counterspy. Temperamentally unsuited for murder, Bartholomew

despairs at his inability to raise the money. His girl friend Truska offers to work the streets to help raise the cash, but earlier efforts have been notably unsuccessful, so instead they go to a restaurant where Chrissy, one of Mr. X's agents, is detaining the unsuspecting Arnold. Bartholomew shoots at Arnold but misses. He and Truska then follow Arnold and Chrissy to a mountain cabin, and there they try once again to kill Arnold. Again off target, Bartholomew and Truska sit disconsolate in the outhouse, their body warmth waning, their bullets gone. Chrissy finally overrules Arnold and invites the two frozen agents in for food and drink, and soon, with spirits bubbling, all tumble into bed together. *Painters. Spies. Patrons. Secret agents. Hired killers. Murder. Group sex.*

Note: Also known as *High Spy*.

THIN AIR see THE BODY STEALERS

THE THIN LINE (Japan)   F6.4982

Toho Co. Jul 1967 [Los Angeles showing]. Sd; b&w. 35mm (Tohoscope). 102 min.

Exec Prod Sanezumi Fujimoto, Masakatsu Kaneko. *Dir* Mikio Naruse. *Screenplay* Toshiro Ide. *Photog* Yasumichi Fukuzawa. *Mus* Hikaru Hayashi.

Cast: Keiju Kobayashi, Michiyo Aratama, Tatsuya Mihashi, Akiko Wakabayashi, Daisuke Kato, Mitsuko Kusabue.

Melodrama. Tashiro, a middle-class businessman, is a suspect in the investigation of the murder of his best friend's wife. Eventually, he admits to his wife that he accidentally strangled the woman while making love to her. His wife agrees to keep his confession secret, but when his guilt drives him to consider giving himself up, she poisons him to protect the family name. *Businessmen. Reputation. Murder. Infidelity. Poisoning.*

Note: Released in Japan in 1966 as *Onna no nakani iru tanin*.

THE THIN RED LINE   F6.4983

Security Pictures–A. C. E. Films. *Dist* Allied Artists. 13 May 1964 [Los Angeles opening; c1 Apr 1964; LP32289]. Sd; b&w. 35mm (CinemaScope). 99 min.

A Philip Yordan Production. *Prod* Sidney Harmon. *Exec Prod* Lester A. Sansom, Bernard Glasser. *Dir* Andrew Marton. *Screenplay* Bernard Gordon. *Photog* Manuel Berenguer. *Art Dir* José Algueró. *Film Ed* Derek Parsons. *Mus Comp & Cond* Malcolm Arnold. *Sd Rec* Ronald Brown, Maurice Askew. *Sd Ed* Kurt Herrnfeld. *Asst Dir* Jose Maria Ochoa. *Prod Mgr* Gregorio Sacristan. *Script Supv* Margarita Pardo. *Wardrobe* Charles Simminger. *Makeup* Emilio Puyol. *Sp Eff* Ron Ballanger, Pat Carr.

Cast: Keir Dullea *(Private Doll)*, Jack Warden *(1st Sergeant Welsh)*, James Philbrook *(Colonel Tall)*, Ray Daley *(Captain Stone)*, Bob Kanter *(Fife)*, Merlyn Yordan *(Judy)*, Kieron Moore *(Lieutenant Band)*, Jim Gillen *(Captain Gaff)*, Steve Rowland *(Private Mazzi)*, Stephen Levy *(Staff Sergeant Stack)*, Mark Johnson *(medic)*, Edward King, Jack Gaskins, Graham Sumner, Charles Stalnaker, Gary Lasdun, Jeffrey O'Kelly, Joe Collins, Thomas Freeman, Ted Macauley, Howard Hagen, Bill Barrett, Thomas Entwhistle, Francis Deale, Gonzalo Largo, Russ Stoddard, Evaristo Falco, Ben Tatar, John Clarke, Stan Nelson, Solomon Silva, Bill Christmas, Frank Koomen, Harold Core.

War melodrama. Source: James Jones, *The Thin Red Line* (New York, 1962). As his company disembarks at Guadalcanal, young Private Doll resolves to survive, and he steals a pistol to ensure his safety. His attitude arouses the dislike of his sadistic, battle-scarred Sergeant Welsh, and a feud quickly develops between the two men. Welsh scoffs at Doll's feeling of revulsion the first time he kills a Japanese soldier. That night, Doll's dreams of his bride at home are interrupted by an enemy attack. The next day, Doll single-handedly storms and eradicates a Japanese machinegun site. Welsh dismisses the private's courage and senses that he is beginning to experience erotic pleasure when he kills. The animosity between the two men remains strong even as they collaborate to clear a mined gorge through which the company must pass. Following a surprise attack by the enemy, the small group of survivors sets out to capture a cliff dotted with caves that shelter Japanese machinegunners. Doll scales the cliff and discovers that the caves form a labyrinth. As the others join him in destroying the Japanese stronghold, Welsh dashes in front of the private to save him from enemy gunfire. Fatally wounded, Welsh dies in Doll's arms. *Combat zone life. Sadism. Courage. Self-sacrifice. Mines (war explosives). Caves. World War II. Guadalcanal. United States Marines. Japan—Army.*

Note: Filmed in Spain.

THE THING WITHOUT A FACE see PYRO

THE THINGS OF LIFE (France/Italy/Switzerland)   F6.4984

Lira Films–Fida Cinematografica–Sonocam. *Dist* Columbia Pictures. 31 Aug 1970 [New York opening; c10 May 1970; LF72]. Sd; col (Eastman Color). 35mm. 90 min. *MPAA rating* GP.

Exec Prod Raymond Danon. *Assoc Prod* Roland Girard, Jean Bolvary. *Dir* Claude Sautet. *Screenplay* Paul Guimard, Jean-Loup Dabadie, Claude Sautet. *Dial* Jean-Loup Dabadie. *Photog* Jean Boffety. *Camera* Christian Guillouet, Henry Clairon. *Asst Camera* Guy Lecouvette, François Lartigue. *Art Dir* André Pitant. *Film Ed* Jacqueline Thiedot. *Asst Film Ed (see note)* Marie-

Claude Bariset, Marie-Claude Sarnak. *Mus* Philippe Sarde. *Orch* Jean-Michel Defaye. *Sd Engr* René Longuet. *Asst Sd Engr* Pierre Davoust. *Mix* Jean Neny, Alex Pront. *Asst Dir* Claude Vital, Jean-Claude Sussfeld. *Prod Mgr* Ralph Baum. *Studio Mgr* Paul Dufour. *Asst Studio Mgr* Jean Guillaume. *Location Mgr* Louis Seuret. *Script Girl* Geneviève Cortier. *Prod Sec* Blanche Cochet. *Wardrobe Master* Jacques Cottin. *Makeup* Irène Servet. *Hairstyles* Alexandre of Paris. *Accident Seq Adv* Gérard Streiff. *Prop* Jean Catala, Frédéric Tsikinsan. *Still Photog* Claude Mathieu.

Cast: Michel Piccoli *(Pierre)*, Romy Schneider *(Hélène)*, Léa Massari *(Catherine)*, Gérard Lartigau *(Bertrand)*, Jean Bouise *(François)*, Boby Lapointe *(driver of pig truck)*, Hervé Sand *(truckdriver)*, Henri Nassiet *(Pierre's father)*, Marcelle Arnold *(Hélène's mother)*, Roger Crouzet *(promoter)*, Jean-Pierre Zola *(Hélène's father)*, Betty Beckers, Dominique Zardi *(hitchhikers)*, Gabrielle Doulcet *(Guitte)*, Jacques Richard *(nurse)*, Claude Confortes *(doctor)*, Jerry Brouer *(suitor)*, Jean Gras *(building site foreman)*, Marie-Pierre Casey *(postmistress)*, Gérard Streiff *(motorcyclist)*, Max Amyl *(priest)*, Isabelle Saroyan *(nurse)*, M. Carmet *(Paul)*, Raoul Delpard *(ambulance man)*, Loudiche *(intern)*, Christian Bertola *(surgeon)*, Beram, Luigi *(policemen)*, Karine Jeantet *(telephonist)*, Madame Blome, Madame Duval *(customers at post office)*.

Drama. Source: Paul Guimard, *Les choses de la vie* (Paris, 1967). Pierre, a middle-aged architect, is having an affair with Hélène, who is much younger than he and does not understand his reluctance to abandon everything in his past. In spite of his love for Hélène, he still has strong feelings for his estranged wife, Catherine, their son François, and his elderly father. Hélène tries to persuade him to take her on a vacation to Tunisia so that they can be alone, but he evades the issue and instead promises to take François sailing at the family resort on Île de Ré. After a party at Hélène's home, she demands that Pierre make a decision about their future. While on a business trip in Rennes, he writes her a letter explaining that their relationship must end, but he changes his mind and decides not to mail it. On the way home, however, he has an automobile accident and dies. Catherine arrives at the hospital before Hélène and destroys the letter which she finds in Pierre's coat pocket. *Architects. Mistresses. Infidelity. Marriage. Fatherhood. Rennes. Île de Ré. Automobile accidents.*

Note: Opened in Paris in Mar 1970 as *Les choses de la vie*; running time: 88 min. Sources conflict in crediting assistant editor.

THE THIRD DAY   F6.4985

Warner Bros. Pictures. 14 Jul **1965** [Salt Lake City, Utah, opening; c17 Jul 1965; LP31746]. Sd; col (Technicolor). 35mm (Panavision). 119 min.

A Warner Bros. Pictures–First National Pictures Production. *Prod-Dir* Jack Smight. *Screenplay* Burton Wohl, Robert Presnell, Jr. *Dir Photog* Robert Surtees. *Art Dir* Edward Carrere. *Set Decor* Ralph S. Hurst. *Film Ed* Stefan Arnsten. *Mus* Percy Faith. *Song:* "Love Me Now" Jay Livingston, Ray Evans, Percy Faith. *Sung by* Arte Johnson. *Sd* Francis E. Stahl. *Asst Dir* Victor Vallejo. *Unit Mgr* Russell Llewellyn. *Miss Ashley's Clothes* Donald Brooks. *Makeup Supv* Gordon Bau. *Supv Hairstylist* Jean Burt Reilly. *Dial Supv* Leon Charles.

Cast: George Peppard *(Steve Mallory)*, Elizabeth Ashley *(Alexandria Mallory)*, Roddy McDowall *(Oliver Parsons)*, Arthur O'Connell *(Dr. Wheeler)*, Mona Washbourne *(Catherine Parsons)*, Herbert Marshall *(Austin Parsons)*, Robert Webber *(Dom Guardiano)*, Charles Drake *(Lawrence Conway)*, Sally Kellerman *(Holly Mitchell)*, Arte Johnson *(Lester Aldrich)*, Bill Walker *(Logan)*, Vincent Gardenia *(Preston)*, Janine Gray *(Totti)*.

Drama. Source: Joseph Hayes, *The Third Day* (New York, 1964). Steve Mallory loses his memory as a result of an automobile accident beside a river. His Aunt Catherine Parsons picks him up and takes him to the family home. He learns that his wife, Alexandria, is planning to leave him because of his drinking and that Catherine's son Oliver expects Steve to sell him the family china manufacturing firm. During the next 3 days, Steve's past is revealed: Steve married Alexandria, daughter of Austin Parsons, the now paralyzed family patriarch. Austin planned to leave his china manufacturing firm to his nephew Oliver but changed his mind after the marriage and instead made Steve chief executive. Steve made plans to modernize the company and prevented its sale, increasing Oliver's enmity. Steve learns that Holly Mitchell, a cocktail waitress, was in the car with him when it crashed, and she dies in a hospital. Lester Aldrich, Holly's husband and a pianist at the bar where she worked, joins Oliver in attempting to frame Steve for Holly's death. Steve is arrested, and Alexandria is abducted by Aldrich, who has threatened to kill her to avenge Holly's death; but Steve, aided by Catherine, escapes in time to save Alexandria. Aldrich admits that Holly drowned herself, and he is arrested. *Manufacturers. Executives. Waitresses. Paralytics. Heirs. Pianists. Cousins. Aunts. Frameup. Amnesia. Marriage. Alcoholism. Abduction. Suicide. Family life. China (ceramic ware). Automobile accidents.*

THE THIRD LOVER (France/Italy)   F6.4986

Rome–Paris Films–Lux Film. *Dist* Atlantic Pictures. 24 Jun **1963** [New York opening]. Sd; b&w. 35mm. 85 min.

Pres by Wilshire International Pictures. *Prod* Carlo Ponti, Georges de Beauregard. *Dir-Writ* Claude Chabrol. *Literary Collab* Martial Matthieu. *Photog* Jean Rabier. *Film Ed* Jacques Gaillard. *Mus* Pierre Jansen. *Prod Mgr* Bruna Drigo.

Cast: Jacques Charrier *(Albin Mercier)*, Stéphane Audran *(Hélène Hartmann)*, Walther Reyer *(Andréas Hartmann)*, Daniel Boulanger, Badri *(policemen)*.

Drama. While in Bavaria working on a series of newspaper reports on German life, a second-rate French writer, Albin Mercier, meets Andréas Hartmann, a successful author, and his French wife, Hélène. They accept him as a friend and endeavor to make him feel at home in their luxurious villa. Instead of being grateful to them for filling his lonely hours, Albin becomes morbidly jealous of their happiness and plots to destroy them. While Andréas is away on a business trip, Albin attempts to seduce Hélène. When she rejects him, he begins spying on her and discovers that she has a lover. Albin takes pictures of them and presents them to Andréas. In the quarrel that follows, Andréas stabs his wife to death and then calls the police. Aware that he is responsible for the killing, Albin wallows in self-pity and tries to convince people of his guilt, but they refuse to believe him. *Authors. Germans. Police. Jealousy. Infidelity. Frameup. Murder. Photographs. Bavaria.*

Note: Filmed on location in Munich and elsewhere in Bavaria. Opened in Paris in May 1962 as *L'oeil du malin*; running time: 80 min. Martial Matthieu is a pseudonym for Claude Chabrol in this film.

THIRD OF A MAN   F6.4987

Phoenix Film Studios. *Dist* United Artists. caMay **1962** [c28 Jun 1962; LP22318]. Sd; b&w. 35mm. 81 min.

Prod Robert Lewin, William Redlin. *Exec Prod* Kenneth Altose, Jules Schwartz. *Dir-Writ* Robert Lewin. *Story Based on an Idea by* Robert Lewin, Allan Grant. *Dir Photog* Vilis Lapenieks. *Art Dir* Paul Mathison. *Film Ed* Frederic Knudtson. *Mus Comp & Cond* Samuel Matlovsky. *Sd* Frank Murphy. *Asst Dir* Sam Farnsworth. *Makeup* George Mitchell.

Cast: Simon Oakland *(Doon)*, James Drury *(Emmet Spile)*, Jan Shepard *(Helen)*, Whit Bissell *(Dr. Maxwell)*, Jimmy Gaines *(Leroy Spile)*, Lyda Stevens, Lee Sabinson, Marshall Reed, James Maloney, Josip Elic, Norma Connolly, Robert Fresco, Bob Roberts, actor, Stuart Nisbet, Mary Ann Dighton, Bill Stevens, Jim Cook, Robert Coogan, Sky Hixon, Phyllis Coughlin.

Melodrama. Emmet Spile is a smalltown carpenter haphazardly raising his illegitimate son, Leroy. The child's mother, Helen Detweiler, has repeatedly refused to marry Emmet because of his violent nature. Unknown to everyone in the town, Emmet has a brother, Doon, whom he has committed to a mental institution. Doon is unable to speak and is terrified of water. When a guard turns a water hose on him, he escapes from the institution. He encounters Leroy in the woods and gains confidence through the youngster's gestures of friendship. When Leroy almost drowns while swimming in a lake, Doon overcomes his fear of water and rescues the boy. But his brother has organized a posse to search for him, and, discovered carrying Leroy in his arms, he is beaten by the mob, which thinks he means to harm the boy. Helen and Dr. Maxwell, the director of the asylum, intervene to save him, and he is returned to custody. Angered by his father's treatment of Doon, Leroy runs away to find his friend. When Emmet follows him to the asylum, Leroy locks his father in a room filled with mental patients. Although terrified at first, Emmet gradually realizes that no one intends to harm him. The incident changes his mind toward the asylum and he offers to visit his brother. As he leaves, promising to return the next day, Doon says "tomorrow," the first word he has uttered in years. *Brothers. Mutes. Carpenters. Psychiatrists. Mental illness. Hydrophobia. Friendship. Smalltown life. Filial relations. Illegitimacy. Insane asylums. Posses.*

Note: Copyright claimant: Banneret Enterprises.

THE THIRD ROAD see THE 7TH DAWN

THE THIRD SECRET (Great Britain)   F6.4988

Hubris Productions. *Dist* Twentieth Century–Fox Film Corp. 28 Apr **1964** [New York opening; c28 Apr 1964; LP27975]. Sd (RCA); b&w. 35mm (CinemaScope). 103 min.

A Robert L. Joseph Production. *Prod-Screenplay* Robert L. Joseph. *Assoc Prod* Shirley Bernstein. *Dir* Charles Crichton. *Dir Photog* Douglas Slocombe. *Camera Op* Chic Waterson. *Prod Dsgn* Tom Morahan. *Film Ed* Frederick Wilson. *Mus Comp & Cond* Richard Arnell. *Rec Dir* A. W. Lumkin. *Sd Rec* Wally Milner, Len Shilton. *Sd Ed* Charles Crafford. *Asst Dir* Peter Bolton. *Unit Mgr* Rita Davison. *Cont* Joan Davis. *Asst to the Prod* Diana Hayward. *Prod Sec* Josephine Knowles. *Wardrobe* John McCorry. *Makeup* Ken MacKay. *Hairdresser* Iris Tilley.

Cast: Stephen Boyd *(Alex Stedman)*, Jack Hawkins *(Sir Frederick Belline)*, Richard Attenborough *(Alfred Price-Gorham)*, Diane Cilento *(Anne Tanner)*, Pamela Franklin *(Catherine Whitset)*, Paul Rogers *(Dr. Milton Gillen)*, Alan Webb *(Alden Hoving)*, Rachel Kempson *(Mildred Hoving)*, Peter Sallis *(Lawrence Jacks)*, Patience Collier *(Mrs. Pelton)*, Freda Jackson *(Mrs. Bales)*, Judi Dench *(Miss Humphries)*, Peter Copley *(Dr. Leo Whitset)*, Nigel Davenport *(Lew Harding)*, Charles Lloyd Pack *(Dermot McHenry)*, Barbara Hicks *(police secretary)*, Ronald Leigh-Hunt *(police officer)*, Geoffrey Adams *(floor manager)*, James Maxwell *(Mark)*, Gerald Case *(Mr. Bickes)*, Sarah Brackett *(nurse)*, Neal Arden *(Mr. Morgen)*.

Drama. Dr. Leo Whitset, an eminent London psychoanalyst, is found dying from a gunshot wound in the consulting room of his home. He is discovered by his housekeeper, and a few words whispered to her before his death leads the coroner to pronounce a verdict of suicide. Dr. Whitset had restricted his private practice to a select group of patients and devoted most of his time to teaching and research. Alex Stedman, an American TV news commentator who had been one of Dr. Whitset's patients, believes that the death was not a suicide. Catherine Whitset, the 14-year-old daughter of the dead man, visits Stedman and pleads with him to find the person responsible for her father's death. From memory, she supplies Alex with the names of the doctor's three other patients: Sir Frederick Belline, a judge; Alfred Price-Gorham, owner of a London art gallery; and Anne Tanner, a London secretary. Alex visits each of the patients in his search for the murderer and realizes that he, like the other patients, has a secret self known only to the murdered man. He accidentally learns from Catherine that there was a fifth patient, and he goes to the doctor's country home where the dead man kept his files. He learns that Catherine was the fifth patient, and she confesses that she killed her father to prevent him from sending her to an institution to be treated for schizophrenia. During a reenactment of the crime, Catherine stabs Alex. After he recovers from his wound, he visits her at the institution and promises to remain her friend. *Psychiatrists. Reporters. Americans in foreign countries. Art dealers. Judges. Secretaries. Adolescence. Schizophrenia. Suicide. Mental illness. Patricide. London.*

Note: Released in Great Britain in 1964.

13 *see* **EYE OF THE DEVIL**

13 EAST STREET *see* **13 WEST STREET**

13 FRIGHTENED GIRLS   F6.4989

William Castle Pictures. *Dist* Columbia Pictures. Jul **1963** [c1 Jun 1963; LP25418]. Sd (Westrex); col (Eastman Color by Pathé). 35mm. 89 min.

Prod-Dir William Castle. *Assoc Prod* Dona Holloway. *Screenplay* Robert Dillon. *Story* Otis L. Guernsey, Jr. *Dir Photog* Gordon Avil. *Art Dir* Don Ament. *Set Decor* William Kiernan. *Film Ed* Edwin Bryant. *Mus* Van Alexander. *Sd Supv* Charles J. Rice. *Sd* Lambert Day. *Asst Dir* Sam Nelson, Jack Roe. *Fashions* Lanz. *Wardrobe* Jack Angel, Marjorie B. Wahl. *Makeup Supv* Ben Lane. *Makeup* Joseph Di Bella.

Cast: Murray Hamilton *(Wally Sanders)*, Kathy Dunn *(Candace Hull)*, Lynne Sue Moon *(Mai-Ling)*, Joyce Taylor *(Soldier)*, Hugh Marlowe *(John Hull)*, Khigh Dhiegh *(Kang)*, Charlie Briggs *(Mike)*, Norma Varden *(Miss Pittford)*, Garth Benton *(Peter Van Hagen)*, Maria Cristina Servera *(Argentina)*, Janet Mary Prance *(Australia)*, Penny Anne Mills *(Canada)*, Alexandra Bastedo *(England)*, Ariane Glaser *(France)*, Ilona Schutze *(Germany)*, Anna Baj *(Italy)*, Aiko Sakamoto *(Japan)*, Judy Pace *(Liberia)*, Luz Gloria Hervias *(Mexico)*, Gina Trikonis *(Russia)*, Marie-Louise Bielke *(Sweden)*, Ignacia Farias Luque *(Venezuela)*, Emil Sitka *(Ludwig)*, Jon Alvar *(Fernando)*, Walter Rode *(Kagenescu)*.

Action melodrama. Candace Hull, teenaged daughter of an American diplomat working in London, arrives there on holiday from the Swiss boarding school she attends with other daughters of London-based diplomats. She visits Mai-Ling, niece of the Communist Chinese ambassador, and stumbles onto a major political secret involving a murder. To help CIA man Wally Sanders, upon whom she has a crush, she passes on this information and other espionage coups made possible by her freedom of movement at the various embassies. After a time Candace becomes known as "Kitten"—a much-hunted spy. Wally finally realizes that only Candace can be "Kitten," and the Chinese ambassador simultaneously comes to the same conclusion. Back at school in Switzerland, Candace faces assassination but, with the help of her classmates, is rescued by Wally. *Diplomats. Spies. Students. Chinese. Americans in foreign countries. Murder. Espionage. Personal identity. Boarding schools. London. Switzerland. United States—Central Intelligence Agency. United States—Diplomatic and consular service.*

Note: Working title: *The Candy Web.*

13 WEST STREET   F6.4990

Ladd Enterprises. *Dist* Columbia Pictures. 9 May **1962** [San Francisco opening; c1 Mar 1962; LP21334]. Sd (RCA); b&w. 35mm. 80 min.

Prod William Bloom. *Dir* Philip Leacock. *Screenplay* Bernard Schoenfeld, Robert Presnell, Jr. *Dir Photog* Charles Lawton, Jr. *Art Dir* Walter Holscher. *Set Decor* Darrell Silvera. *Film Ed* Al Clark. *Mus* George Duning. *Orch* Arthur Morton. *Sd Supv* Charles J. Rice. *Sd* Harry Mills. *Asst Dir* Eddie Saeta, R. Robert Rosenbaum. *Script Supv* Dorothy Hughes. *Wardrobe* Israel Berne, Pat Page. *Makeup Supv* Ben Lane. *Dial Coach* Norman Stuart.

Cast: Alan Ladd *(Walt Sherill)*, Rod Steiger *(Detective Sergeant Koleski)*, Michael Callan *(Chuck Landry)*, Dolores Dorn *(Tracey Sherill)*, Kenneth MacKenna *(Paul Logan)*, Margaret Hayes *(Mrs. Landry)*, Stanley Adams *(Finney)*, Chris Robinson *(Everett)*, Jeanne Cooper *(Mrs. Quinn)*, Arnold Merritt *(Bill)*, Mark Slade *(Tommy)*, Henry Beckman *(Joe Bradford)*, Clegg Hoyt *(Noddy)*, Jordan Gerler *(Jack)*, Robert Cleaves *(doctor)*, Bernie Hamilton *(Negro)*, Pepe Hern *(Mexican)*, Frank Gerstle *(Mr. Johnson)*.

Melodrama. Source: Leigh Brackett, *The Tiger Among Us* (Garden City, New York, 1957). Late one evening space scientist Walt Sherill is attacked and, for no apparent reason, brutally beaten by a gang of well-dressed teenagers. Brooding over his injuries, he becomes impatient with Detective Sergeant Koleski's failure to get immediate results and he decides to take the law into his own hands. Obsessed by his thirst for vengeance, he loses his job, interferes with Koleski's work, and antagonizes innocent citizens. His coercive attempts to see justice done eventually cause one of the gang members to panic and commit suicide. Chuck Landry, the wealthy psychopathic gang leader, terrorizes Walt's wife, Tracey, in revenge. Following the death of a private detective he hired to track down the boys, Walt finally catches up with Chuck at his family's home. He almost kills the boy before realizing that he is sinking to the youth's own vicious level. Coming to his senses at last, he turns Chuck over to Koleski. *Engineers. Detectives. Juvenile delinquents. Psychopaths. Revenge. Obsession. Suicide. Gangs.*

Note: Prerelease titles: *The Tiger Among Us* and *13 East Street.*

30 IS A DANGEROUS AGE, CYNTHIA (Great Britain)   F6.4991

Walter Shenson Films. *Dist* Columbia Pictures. 4 Mar **1968** [New York opening; c1 Apr 1968; LP35621]. Sd (Westrex); col (Technicolor). 35mm. 85 min.

Prod Walter Shenson. *Assoc Prod* Norman Miller. *Dir* Joseph McGrath. *Screenplay* Dudley Moore, Joseph McGrath, John Wells. *Dir Photog* Billy Williams. *Camera Op* Brian Elvin. *Art Dir* Brian Eatwell. *Graphic Eff & Titl* Richard Williams Films. *Film Ed* Bill Blunden. *Mus Comp & Cond* Dudley Moore. *Sd Rec* Charles Poulton, Maurice Askew. *Sd Ed* Keith Palmer. *Asst Dir* David Bessgrove. *Prod Mgr* Gavrik Losey. *Wardrobe* Bermans of London. *Makeup* Cliff Sharpe. *Hairdresser* Allan McKeown.

Cast: Dudley Moore *(Rupert Street)*, Eddie Foy, Jr. *(Oscar)*, Suzy Kendall *(Louise Hammond)*, John Bird *(Herbert Greenslade)*, Duncan Macrae *(Jock McCue)*, Patricia Routledge *(Mrs. Woolley)*, Peter Bayliss *(Victor)*, John Wells *(Hon. Gavin Hopton)*, Harry Towb *(Mr. Woolley)*, Jonathan Routh *(Captain Gore-Taylor)*, Ted Dicks *(Horst Cohen, Jr.)*, Nicky Henson *(Paul)*, Clive Dunn *(doctor)*, Frank Thornton *(registrar)*, Derek Farr *(television announcer)*, Michael MacLiammoir *(Irish storyteller)*, Dudley Moore Trio.

Comedy. Rupert Street has two ambitions which he hopes to fulfill in the 6 weeks remaining before his 30th birthday: to write a hit musical and to get married. His job playing piano in a nightclub owned by Jock McCue leaves him little time to compose, however, and he finds that there is a shortage of eligible women. When Louise Hammond, an art student, moves into his boardinghouse, Rupert falls in love with her. Louise visits him at the nightclub with her boyfriend Paul, and Rupert gets his arm broken in a fight with the young man. Oscar, Rupert's friend, hurries the injured musician to Dublin to work on his musical, and Louise returns to her native Birmingham. Thinking only of Louise, Rupert cannot concentrate until an Irish storyteller gives him the inspiration for his musical, which he then quickly writes. Rupert goes to Birmingham to find Louise; he is followed by Herbert Greenslade, a detective hired by Rupert's agent, Victor, to bring him back to London in time to sign a contract. Though Louise is enraged to discover that Rupert applied for a marriage license even before they met, she eventually consents to marry him; furthermore, his musical is a success—all before Rupert's birthday. *Composers. Pianists. Students. Irish. Detectives. Ambition. Courtship. Birthdays. Nightclubs. Boardinghouses. Dublin. Birmingham (England).*

Note: Opened in London in Oct 1968; running time: 84 min.

30 YEARS OF FUN   F6.4992

Robert Youngson Productions. *Dist* Twentieth Century-Fox Film Corp. 12 Feb **1963** [Cincinnati, Ohio, opening; c31 Dec 1962; LP23683]. Sd; b&w. 35mm. 85 min.

Prod-Compiler-Writ Robert Youngson. *Assoc Prod* Alfred Dahlem, John E. Allen. *Mus* Bernard Green, Jack Shaindlin. *Mus Supv & Cond* Jack Shaindlin. *Orch* Bernard Green, Milton Weinstein. *Mus Assoc* Joan Barry. *Titl Song:* "Bring Back the Laughter" Robert Youngson. *Sung by* Bernie Knee. *Sd Rec* Dick Vorisek. *Mus Ed* Angelo Ross. *Mus Rec* Phil Macy. *Prod Mgr* I. Hill

Youngson. *Opticals* Maurice Levy, Samuel Levy. *Res Supv* Jeanne Keyes. **Narrator:** Jay Jackson.

Compilation film. Spanning a period from the Gay Nineties through the Roaring Twenties, the film is a compilation of excerpts from silent screen comedies, presented chronologically and placed in historical perspective by newsreel clips of Teddy Roosevelt, the Wright brothers, World War I, the Prohibition period, etc. Included are highlights from Charlie Chaplin's *The Floorwalker* (1916), *Easy Street* (1917), *The Pawnshop* (1916), and *The Rink* (1916); Buster Keaton's *The Balloonatic* (1923), *Daydreams* (1922), and *Cops* (1922); Harry Langdon's *Smile Please* (1924); and *Lucky Dog* (1917), in which Stan Laurel and Oliver Hardy are cast together for the first time. *Motion pictures—History. Prohibition. World War I. Theodore Roosevelt. Orville Wright. Wilbur Wright. Charles Chaplin. Buster Keaton. Harry Langdon. Stan Laurel. Oliver Hardy.*

36 HOURS   F6.4993

Perlberg-Seaton Productions–Cherokee Productions. *Dist* Metro-Goldwyn-Mayer, Inc. 27 Jan **1965** [Minneapolis opening; c19 Oct 1964; LP28211]. Sd (Westrex); b&w. 35mm (Panavision). 115 min.

Prod William Perlberg. *Dir-Screenplay* George Seaton. *Story* Carl K. Hittleman, Luis H. Vance. *Dir Photog* Philip H. Lathrop. *Camera Op* William Lloyd Norton. *Asst Camera* Cliff King. *Art Dir* George W. Davis, Edward Carfagno. *Set Decor* Henry Grace, Frank McKelvy. *Film Ed* Adrienne Fazan. *Asst Ed* Alex Beaton. *Mus Comp & Cond* Dimitri Tiomkin. *Rec Supv* Franklin Milton. *Mix* Larry Jost. *Rec* Bruce Wright. *Boom Op* Larry Hadsell. *Asst Dir* Donald Roberts, Ted Schilz. *Unit Mgr* Al Shenberg. *Script Supv* Kathleen Fagan. *Wardrobe* Frank Roberts, Florence Hackett. *Makeup Supv* William Tuttle. *Makeup* Stan Smith. *Hairstyles* Sydney Guilaroff, Agnes Flanagan. *Still Photog* Ken Bell. *Gaffer* Perry O'Brien. *Grip* Hank Forrester. *Casting* Mel Ballerino.

Cast: James Garner (*Maj. Jefferson Pike*), Rod Taylor (*Maj. Walter Gerber*), Eva Marie Saint (*Anna Hedler*), Werner Peters (*Otto Schack*), Alan Napier (*Col. Peter MacLean*), Celia Lovsky (*Elsa*), John Banner (*Ernst*), Ed Gilbert (*Captain Abbott*), Russell Thorson (*General Allison*), Oscar Beregi (*Lieutenant Colonel Ostermann*), Sig Ruman (*German guard*), Karl Held (*Corporal Kenter*), Martin Kosleck (*Kraatz*), Marjorie Bennett (*charwoman*), Henry Rowland, Otto Reichow (*German soldiers*), Hilda Plowright (*German agent*), Walter Friedel (*Denker*), Joseph Mell (*Lemke*).

War drama. Source: Roald Dahl, "Beware of the Dog," in *Harper's* (Oct 1944). In 1944, while dealing with a Lisbon double agent, Maj. Jefferson Pike of U. S. Intelligence is abducted by Germans, drugged, and flown to Bavaria. He has been fully briefed on D-Day invasion operations in Normandy, and the Germans mean to pry this information from him through an elaborate trick. Pike awakens in what appears to be an American military hospital in occupied Germany: the staff speak English, newspapers are dated 1950, and the war is apparently over. Maj. Walter Gerber, seemingly an American psychiatrist but actually a Nazi, tells Pike he is an amnesia victim but can be cured by recalling the events before, during, and after D-Day. (Gerber has only 36 hours to secure this information; thereafter, it will be forced out of Pike through torture.) Pike discusses Normandy, but through a giveaway detail, he discovers the Nazi scheme. He confronts Gerber and Otto Schack, a Gestapo agent, and tries to persuade them that he has been giving false information. He is dispatched for further questioning, however, accompanied by Anna Hedler, a German nurse pretending to be his wife. Schack doubts that Normandy is the landing site, and the three men play a cat-and-mouse game utilizing this skepticism. The failure of the initial deception having put Gerber out of favor with the Gestapo, he entrusts valuable papers on his amnesia experiments to Pike, helps him and Anna escape to the Swiss frontier, and then commits suicide. The Normandy landings begin and the enraged Schack pursues Pike and Anna to the border; but he is shot down by an anti-Nazi guard who has arranged for the escapees' safe crossing. Once in Switzerland, Pike prepares to depart for London, knowing that he and Anna will meet at the end of the war. *Nazis. Psychiatrists. Nurses. Escapees. Hoaxes. Interrogation. Suicide. Abduction. Amnesia. Hospitals. World War II. D-Day (6 Jun 1944). Bavaria. Switzerland. Lisbon. United States Army—Intelligence. Gestapo.*

Note: Location scenes filmed in Yosemite National Park, in Lisbon, and elsewhere in Portugal.

36 HOURS OF TERROR *see* **OLGA'S HOUSE OF SHAME**

THIS COULD BE THE NIGHT *see* **THE BIG T.N.T. SHOW**

THIS GREEDY OLD SKIN (Japan)   F6.4994

Toho Co. Aug **1961** [Los Angeles showing]. Sd; col (Eastmancolor). 35mm (Tohoscope). 108 min.

Dir Yasuki Chiba.

Cast: Aiko Mimasu, Chinatsu Nakayama, Tadao Takashima, Chisako Hara, Hisaya Morishige, Mitsuko Kusabue, Reiko Dan, Masayuki Mori, Kyoko Anzai, Yu Fujiki, Haruko Togo.

Drama. No information about the precise nature of this film has been found.

Note: Released in Japan in Sep 1960 as *Gametsui yatsu*.

THIS GUN IS LOADED   F6.4995

Cosmos Films. *Dist* Able Film Co. ca **1970**. Sd; col. 16mm. [Feature length assumed.]

Sex film. The fingerman for a mob continuously gets himself into tight situations. Part of his job is also to set up sexual experiences for his employers, and one such experience leads to his death. *Gangsters. Hired killers. Sexuality.*

THIS IMMORAL AGE *see* **THE SQUARE ROOT OF ZERO**

THIS IS MY ALASKA   F6.4996

Alaskan Adventures, Inc. 8 Jan **1969** [Minneapolis opening; c8 Jan 1969; MP19304]. Sd; col (De Luxe). 35mm. 120 min. [Copyright length: 115 min.] *MPAA rating* G.

A Leroy Shebal Production. *Prod-Dir* Leroy Shebal. *Photog* Leroy Shebal. *Asst Camera* Charles Gray, photog. *Mus Comp* Richard LaSalle. *Sd* Ryder Sound Service. *Sd Eff* Richard Einfeld.

Cast: Leroy Shebal, Vivian Shebal, Guy Okakak.

Narrator: Leroy Shebal.

Documentary. Leroy "Buster" Shebal, an Alaskan sportsman's guide, takes off in his bush plane from Fairbanks and travels north to hunt wolves for bounty. Shebal shoots the wolves from his plane as they prey on pregnant caribou. Back at the camp, he witnesses a winter carnival of dog sled and snowmobile races; he then flies to Point Barrow and films Eskimos killing and skinning a polar bear. In the spring when flowers bloom and walruses return to their breeding ground, Shebal goes to the interior to fish for trout and salmon. When fall returns, he flies north again to hunt caribou, moose, and bear. *Guides. Hunters. Eskimos. Hunting. Fishing. Sledding. Airplanes. Snowmobiles. Alaska. Fairbanks. Point Barrow (Alaska). Wolves. Caribou. Dogs. Bears. Walruses. Trout. Salmon.*

THIS MADDING CROWD (Japan)   F6.4997

Tokyo Eiga Co. *Dist* Toho International, Inc. 16 Jun **1964** [New York opening]. Sd; col. 35mm. 101 min.

Prod Ichiro Sato, Hideyuki Shiino. *Dir* Yuzo Kawashima. *Screenplay* Kaneto Shindo. *Photog* Kozo Okazaki.

Cast: Hisaya Morishige (*professor*), Eijiro Tono (*Grandpa Yoshi*), Sachiko Hidari (*Osei*), Nobuko Otowa (*Kimino*), Frankie Sakai (*Goro*), Meiko Nakamura (*1st bride*), Junko Ikeuchi (*2d bride*).

Comedy-drama. Based on a novel by: Shugoro Yamamoto. A professor goes to a fishing town near Tokyo to write about its old-fashioned ways. The people and situations that he observes include a reformed alcoholic who takes loving care of his crippled wife; the confusion of a newly married husband, whose wife refuses to have sex; the confrontation between a neglectful mother and her beggar daughter; and an old man who lives in a boat, remembering when his sweetheart waved to him as he worked. *Professors. Authors. Cripples. Beggars. Newlyweds. Alcoholism. Marriage. Motherhood. Old age. Fishing villages.*

Note: Released in Japan as *Aobeka monogatari*.

THIS MAN CAN'T DIE (Italy)   F6.4998

Mercurio Film. *Dist* Fine Products, Capital Productions. 13 Sep **1970** [Asheville, North Carolina, opening]. Sd (RCA Italiana); col. 35mm. 90 min. [Also 95 min.] *MPAA rating* GP.

Pres by Gerald Fine. An Alborn Marucchi Production. *Prod* Gino Rossi. *Asst Prod* Rossano Moscouini. *Dir* Gianfranco Baldanello. *Screenplay* Luigi Emmanuele, Gino Mangini. *Story* Luigi Emmanuele. *Dir Photog* Claudio Cirillo. *Camera* Paola Mugnai. *Set Dsgn* Giorgio Giovannini. *Film Ed* Alberto Gallitti. *Mus* Amedeo Tommasi. *Asst Dir* Luciano Palermo. *Prod Mgr* Enrico Bologna. *Cost* Maria Luisa Panaro. *Makeup* Giuseppe Peruzzi. *Sp Eff* CI-PA-ROMA.

Cast: Guy Madison (*Martin Benson*), Peter Martell (*Tony Guy*), Rik Battaglia (*Vic Graham*), Lucienne Bridou (*Susy Benson*), Steve Merrich (*Daniel Benson*), Rosalba Neri (*Jenny Benson*), John Bartha (*Melin*).

Western drama. Posing as outlaws for the government, adventurers Tony Guy and Martin Benson infiltrate a gang of gunrunners. Martin's younger brother, Daniel, returns from town to find his parents murdered and his sister, Jenny, the mute victim of rape. Discovering one of the intruders unconscious, Daniel and his second sister, Susy, hide the wounded outlaw, hoping to save his life so that he might reveal the identity of his accomplices. Martin learns of his parents' deaths from his old girl friend Melin, the saloon owner. Arriving at the secret hiding place, he finds Susy caring for Tony Guy, the assumed outlaw, who reveals that Vic Graham, the powerful owner of the general store and Susy's rejected suitor, is the gang leader. Martin tracks down Graham and kills him in a gunfight. *Adventurers. Outlaws. Gunrunners. Saloon keepers. Storekeepers. Brothers. Family life. Murder. Rape. Imposture.*

Note: U. S. prerelease title: *Lusty Brawlers.*

THIS MAN MUST DIE (France/Italy)   F6.4999

Les Films La Boétie-Rizzoli Films. *Dist* Allied Artists. 20 Oct **1970** [New York opening]. Sd; col (Eastman Color). 35mm. 115 min. *MPAA rating* GP.

Prod André Genovès. *Dir* Claude Chabrol. *Screenplay* Paul Gégauff, Claude Chabrol. *Dial* Paul Gégauff. *Photog* Jean Rabier. *Camera Op* Claude Zidi. *Art Dir* Guy Littaye. *Film Ed* Jacques Gaillard. *Mus* Pierre Jansen. *Mus Dir* André Girard. *Song:* "Vier ernste Gesänge" Johannes Brahms. *Sung by* Kathleen Ferrier. *Sd* Guy Chichignoud. *Sd Ed* Monique Fardoux. *Asst Dir* Jacques Fansten, Michel Dupuy. *Prod Mgr* Georges Casati.

Cast: Michel Duchaussoy (*Charles Thénier*), Caroline Cellier (*Hélène Lanson*), Jean Yanne (*Paul Decourt*), Anouk Ferjac (*Jeanne [see note]*), Marc Di Napoli (*Philippe*), Maurice Pialat (*police inspector*), Guy Marly (*Jacques Ferrand*), Lorraine Rainer (*Anna Ferrand*), Stéphane Di Napoli (*Michel Thénier*), Louise Chevalier (*Madame Levenès*), Dominique Zardi (*policewoman*), Jean-Louis Maury (*peasant/Charles's friend*), Raymone, Michel Charrel, France Girard, Bernard Papineau, Robert Rondo, Jacques Masson, Georges Charrier.

Mystery melodrama. Source: Nicholas Blake, *The Beast Must Die* (London, 1938). On a rainy day in Brittany, a hit-and-run driver kills the son of Charles Thénier, a widower and an author of children's books. He swears revenge and records in his diary every step of his search for the killer. A farmer tells Charles that a damaged sportscar stopped on his land the day of the accident and that Hélène Lanson, a television celebrity, was a passenger. In Paris, Charles meets Hélène, and they begin an affair. When Charles learns that Hélène's brother-in-law, Paul Decourt, owns an automobile repair shop, he immediately suspects Paul of being the hit-and-run driver. Unaware of Charles's motives, Hélène invites him to spend a weekend with her at her brother-in-law's house. Charles becomes acquainted with Paul and finds him contemptible, but he becomes fond of Paul's son, Philippe, who confides that he is planning to kill his father. Charles buys a sailboat and takes Paul out with the intention of drowning him. Before the plan can be executed, however, Paul draws a pistol and tells him that he has read the diary and that the police will know that his death was not accidental. Unable to exact his revenge, Charles leaves for Paris with Hélène, but they learn en route that Paul has been poisoned. Upon returning to Brittany, Charles is arrested on the basis of the information in his diary, but Philippe confesses to the murder, and the police release Charles. Charles then writes a false confession and sails away in his boat. *Authors. Widowers. Hit-and-run drivers. Farmers. Television personalities. Brothers-in-law. Revenge. Murder. Patricide. Poisoning. Confession (law). Diaries. Sailboats. Brittany.*

Note: Location scenes filmed on the coast of Brittany. Opened in Paris in Sep 1969 as *Que la bête meure*. Italian title: *Ucciderò un uomo*. U. S. sources reverse the roles of Anouk Ferjac and Lorraine Rainer.

THIS PICTURE IS CENSORED *see* CENSORED

THIS PROPERTY IS CONDEMNED   F6.5000

Seven Arts Productions. *Dist* Paramount Pictures. 15 Jun **1966** [Los Angeles opening; c17 Jun 1966; LP32760]. Sd; col (Technicolor). 35mm. 110 min.

Pres by Ray Stark, Seven Arts Productions. *Prod* John Houseman. *Prod Exec* Milton Feldman. *Dir* Sydney Pollack. *Screenplay* Francis Ford Coppola, Fred Coe, Edith Sommer. *Photog* James Wong Howe. *Helicopter Shots* Nelson Tyler. *Art Dir* Hal Pereira, Stephen Grimes, Phil Jeffries. *Set Decor* William Kiernan. *Film Ed* Adrienne Fazan. *Mus Score* Kenyon Hopkins. *Song:* "Wish Me a Rainbow" Jay Livingston, Ray Evans. *Song:* "Sing You Sinners" Sam Coslow, W. Franke Harling. *Song:* "Just One More Chance" Sam Coslow, Arthur Johnston. *Sd Rec* Harry Lindgren, James E. Murphy. *Asst Dir* Eddie Saeta. *Prod Mgr* Clarence Eurist. *Cost Created by* Edith Head. *Miss Wood's Cost* Ann Landers. *Makeup* Wally Westmore. *Miss Wood's Hairstyles Dsgn & Executed* Maryce Bates. *Proc Photog* Farciot Edouart. *Sp Photog Eff* Paul K. Lerpae.

Cast: Natalie Wood (*Alva Starr*), Robert Redford (*Owen Legate*), Charles Bronson (*J. J. Nichols*), Kate Reid (*Hazel Starr*), Mary Badham (*Willie Starr*), Alan Baxter (*Knopke*), Robert Blake (*Sidney*), John Harding (*Johnson*), Dabney Coleman (*salesman*), Ray Hemphill (*Jimmy Bell*), Brett Pearson (*Charlie Steinkamp*), Jon Provost (*Tom*), Quentin Sondergaard (*Hank*), Mike Steen (*Max*), Bruce Watson (*Lindsay Tate*), Bob Random (*Tiny*), Nick Stuart (*railroad conductor*).

Drama. Source: Tennessee Williams, *This Property Is Condemned* (New York opening: 28 Oct 1956). Thirteen-year-old Willie Starr, dressed in the remnants of a once-lovely dress, sits on abandoned railroad tracks and wistfully tells her friend Tom about her dead sister, Alva. *Alva Starr is a beautiful woman living in a small town in Mississippi in the 1930's. Her mother, Hazel, the proprietor of a boardinghouse for railroad workers, insists upon steering her into the arms of a prosperous middle-aged man, Johnson, but Alva falls in love with Owen Legate, a handsome stranger from New Orleans who is in town to*

lay off a number of railroad workers as a result of the Depression. When Owen is beaten up by five of the workers, he makes plans to leave, taking Alva with him. Hazel tricks him into thinking that Alva is engaged to Johnson, however, and Owen disappears without giving Alva a chance to explain. Upon learning the truth, Alva gets drunk and spitefully marries her mother's brutish lover, J. J. Nichols. The next day she runs away and joins Owen in New Orleans. Their happiness is soon ruined by Hazel, who viciously exposes her daughter's marriage. In despair Alva runs away, becomes a cheap pickup, and eventually dies of tuberculosis. With the passing of time, Willie only recalls Alva as an enchanted creature whose life was filled with beauty and romance. Railroad workers. Sisters. Pickups. Poverty. Adolescence. Filial relations. Perfidy. Drunkenness. Revenge. Marriage. Boardinghouses. Tuberculosis. The Great Depression (1929–34). Mississippi. New Orleans.

Note: Location scenes filmed in Bay St. Louis, Mississippi, and New Orleans.

THIS REBEL BREED *see* LOLA'S MISTAKE

THIS SAVAGE LAND   F6.5001

Universal Television–National Broadcasting Corp. *Dist* Universal Pictures. 23 Jul **1969** [Saint Louis opening]. Sd; col. 35mm. 97 min. *MPAA rating* G.

Prod James McAdams. *Exec Prod* Norman MacDonnell. *Assoc Prod* Dick Nelson, Mort Zarcoff. *Dir* Vincent McEveety. *Screenplay* Richard Fielder. *Photog* Ray Flin. *Col Cons* Robert Brower. *Art Dir* Russell Kimball. *Set Decor* John McCarthy, John M. Dwyer. *Ed Supv* Richard Belding. *Mus* Leonard Rosenman. *Mus Supv* Stanley Wilson. *Sd Ed* Somers. *Asst Dir* Frank Losee. *Makeup* Bud Westmore. *Hairstyles* Larry Germain.

Cast: Barry Sullivan (*Ben Pride*), Brenda Scott (*Midge*), Andrew Prine (*Timothy*), Kelly Corcoran (*Kip*), Katherine Squire (*Grandma*), Charles Seel (*Grandpa*), Kathryn Hays (*Elizabeth*), Roy Roberts (*Elizabeth's father*), John Drew Barrymore (*Stacey*), Glenn Corbett (*Chance*), George C. Scott (*Jud Barker*).

Western melodrama. Accompanied by his parents and his children Midge, Timothy, and Kip, Ohio widower Ben Pride moves to Kansas shortly after the Civil War. Arriving in Lawrence, the homesteaders are harrassed by Confederate marauders led by Jud Barker. While Ben is away, the renegades attack the family camp outside of town, burning one of their wagons and seriously injuring Grandpa. Ben, fearing to return to the homestead, asks the help of Elizabeth Reynolds, daughter of a new doctor in town. The marauders attack the town, and Stacey Daggart, a psychopathic member of the band, murders Elizabeth's father and Grandma Pride. Having fallen in love with Elizabeth, Ben invites her to share his home. Although Elizabeth and Midge are abducted by Barker, who wants them to give medical aid to some of his wounded men, the women are rescued by Ben, Timothy, and Elizabeth's brother Chance. *Widowers. Confederate veterans. Homesteaders. Psychopaths. Physicians. Children. Murder. Family life. Revenge. United States—History— Civil War. Kansas. Abduction. Lawrence (Kansas).*

Note: Originally made for "The Road West" as a two-part episode; c12 Sep 1966, 19 Sep 1966; LP34985, LP34986; telecast on the same days as registered for copyright.

THIS SPECIAL FRIENDSHIP (France)   F6.5002

Pro Ge Fi–C. C. F. Lux. *Dist* Pathé Contemporary Films. 7 Nov **1967** [New York opening]. Sd; b&w. 35mm. 99 min.

Prod Christine Gouze-Renal. *Assoc Prod* Fred Surin. *Dir* Jean Delannoy. *Screenplay* Jean Aurenche. *Dial* Pierre Bost. *Dir Photog* Christian Matras. *Art Dir* René Renoux. *Film Ed* Louisette Hautecoeur. *Mus* Jean Prodromidès. *Sd* Jacques Lebreton.

Cast: Francis Lacombrade (*Georges de Sarre*), Didier Haudepin (*Alexandre Motier*), Lucien Nat (*The Father Superior*), Louis Seigner (*Father Lauzon*), Michel Bouquet (*Father Trennes*), François Leccia (*Lucien Rouvère*).

Drama. Source: Roger Peyrefitte, *Les amitiés particulières* (Paris, 1945). Soon after his arrival at a strict French parochial school in the early 1930's, 16-year-old Georges becomes good friends with a fellow student, Lucien. Upset at discovering a love letter to Lucien from another boy, Georges turns the note over to the Father Superior. The scandal results in the dismissal of the boy who wrote the letter, but Lucien remains in school. As the weeks pass, Georges finds himself increasingly attracted to a younger student, Alexandre. At Lucien's suggestion, Georges begins meeting Alexandre. When their regular meetings are threatened by the suspicions of Father Trennes, a young priest, Georges retaliates by telling the Father Superior that Father Trennes sometimes entertains students in his office at night. Caught one evening with a boy, Father Trennes is immediately dismissed. Before leaving, however, he warns Georges against judging others too rigidly. One afternoon Alexandre's confessor, Father Lauzon, discovers Georges and Alexandre playing and smoking together in a shed, and he threatens to expel them unless they abandon their special friendship. Georges agrees to stop seeing his young friend, but Alexandre has decided that expulsion is preferable to repudiating their relationship. Crushed by his friend's desertion, Alexandre kills himself by leaping from a train that is carrying him home. *Students. Priests. Catholics. Adolescence. Male homosexuality. Scandal. Friendship. Suicide. Boarding schools. Documentation.*

Note: Opened in Paris in Sep 1964 as *Les amitiés particulières*; running times: 90 min and 102 min.

THIS SPORTING HOUSE   F6.5003
Dist Sam Lake Enterprises. 24 Sep **1969** [Los Angeles showing]. Sd; b&w. 35mm. 73 min.

A Sam Lake Production. *Prod-Writ* Sam Lake. *Dir-Screenplay* Ron Sullivan.

Cast: Ann Wells, Laura Wood, Jessica Stuart, Rose Martin, Eric Krupnik.

Melodrama. The city crime syndicate pays off the local political machine in order to operate its high-class brothels in the open. Two syndicate men recruit new girls from the street. Picking up Laura, they take her back to the brothel before they realize that she isn't a prostitute, and then they hold her captive to protect their operation. The madam of the house, Ezmeralda, takes a special interest in Laura. She keeps the girl to satisfy her private desires. Ricky and one of the syndicate men realize that Laura doesn't belong in a brothel, and they try to help her escape. They are caught together and taken to the cellar to be murdered. Ricky catches their captors offguard. After a struggle, Ezmeralda and her henchman are left to die, while Laura and Ricky make their escape. *Racketeers. Prostitutes. Innocents. Madams. Political corruption. Abduction. Prostitution. Lesbianism. Murder. Syndicates. Whorehouses.*

Note: Also known as *Sporting House.*

THIS SPORTING LIFE (Great Britain)   F6.5004
Independent Artists. *Dist* Continental Distributing, Inc. 16 Jul **1963** [New York opening; c17 Mar 1963; LF162]. Sd; b&w. 35mm. 129 min.

A Julian Wintle–Leslie Parkyn Production. *Prod* Karel Reisz. *Exec Prod* Albert Fennell. *Dir* Lindsay Anderson. *Screenplay* David Storey. *Photog* Denys Coop. *Camera Op* John Harris. *Focus* Neil Binney. *Art Dir* Alan Withy. *Set Dresser* Peter Lamont. *Ch Draughtsman* Eric Saw. *Draughtsman* Michael Lamont. *Scenic Artist* E. Brister. *Film Ed* Peter Taylor. *Asst Film Ed* Tom Priestley. *2d Asst Ed* Philip Baker. *Mus Comp* Roberto Gerhard. *Mus Cond* Jacques-Louis Monod. *Sd Ed* Chris Greenham. *Sd Rec* John W. Mitchell, Gordon K. McCallum. *Sd Camera Op* Ron Butcher. *Boom Op* Tony Cripps. *1st, 2d & 3d Asst Dir* Ted Sturgis, Claude Watson, Ken Softley. *Prod Mgr* Geoffrey Haine. *Cont* Pamela Mann. *Pers Asst to the Prod* Miriam Brickman. *Prod Sec* Norma Garment. *Dress Dsgn* Sophie Devine. *Wardrobe Mistress* Vi Murray. *Makeup* Bob Lawrence. *Hairstyles* Ivy Emmerton. *Casting* Miriam Brickman. *Prop Buyer* Harry Parr. *Still Photog* George Ward. *Constr Mgr* Charles Hammerton. *Prop Master* Fred Eames. *Stagehand* J. Clark. *Grip* Tom Watson. *H.O.D. Elctrn* E. Gubbins. *Supv Chargehand* G. Coupe.

Cast: Richard Harris (*Frank Machin*), Rachel Roberts (*Mrs. Hammond*), Alan Badel (*Weaver*), William Hartnell (*Johnson*), Colin Blakely (*Maurice Braithwaite*), Vanda Godsell (*Mrs. Weaver*), Arthur Lowe (*Slomer*), Anne Cunningham (*Judith*), Jack Watson (*Len Miller*), Harry Markham (*Wade*), George Sewell (*Jeff*), Leonard Rossiter (*Phillips*), Frank Windsor (*dentist*), Peter Duguid (*doctor*), Wallas Eaton (*waiter*), Anthony Woodruff (*head waiter*), Katherine Parr (*Mrs. Farrer*), Bernadette Benson (*Lynda*), Andrew Nolan (*Ian*), Michael Logan (*Riley*), Murray Evans (*Hooker*), Tom Clegg (*Gower*), John Gill (*Cameron*), Ken Traill (*trainer*).

Drama. Source: David Storey, *This Sporting Life* (London, 1960). "You see something you want and you go out and get it. It's as simple as that." Armed with this philosophy and a driving ambition to attain wealth and fame, Frank Machin rejects his obscure life as a miner in northern England and battles his way to public acclaim as the most aggressive player on an English Midlands rugby team. His skill and ruthlessness on the playing field impress all but the one person he is most anxious to please—Mrs. Hammond, the lonely widow in whose home he has taken lodgings. Embittered by the death of her husband in a factory accident (which was rumored to be a suicide), Mrs. Hammond rejects Frank's romantic overtures and denounces him as a self-centered and egotistical brute. Eventually, however, she succumbs to his sexual magnetism and permits him to seduce her, but she remains emotionally isolated. As his fame increases, Frank spends his money freely and flaunts Mrs. Hammond as his mistress. At the wedding of one of Frank's teammates, Mrs. Hammond is suddenly overcome with feelings of guilt, and she savagely reproaches Frank. A series of rows follows, each more vicious than the last, until Frank is forced to leave. He returns when he can no longer stand the separation but finds the house empty. He learns that Mrs. Hammond has suffered a brain hemorrhage and is close to death. Frank visits her at the hospital, and, although she is in a coma, he makes a desperate attempt to show that he is capable of tenderness. Following her death, he returns to the rugby playing field where the crowd admires only savagery and brute force. *Miners. Widows. Landladies. Egotists. Mistresses. Athletes. Ambition. Loneliness. Seduction. Guilt. Rugby.*

Weddings. Strokes. Hospitals.

Note: Originally released in Great Britain in Jan 1963; running time: 134 min.

THIS, THAT AND THE OTHER (Great Britain)   F6.5005
Dorak Films. *Dist* Paul Mart Productions. 6 Aug **1970** [Oceanside, California, opening]. Sd; col (Eastman Color). 35mm. 85 min.

Prod Stanley Long. *Dir* Derek Ford. *Screenplay* Donald Ford, Derek Ford. *Photog* Stanley Long. *Film Ed* Glyn Byles. *Sd Rec* Tony Anscombe.

Cast: Victor Spinetti (*George*), Vanessa Howard (*Barbara*), Vanda Hudson (*Susan Stress*), John Bird (*Harold*), Peter Kinsley (*Wilbur*), Roy Brannigan (*Jeffrey*), Alexandra Bastedo (*Angie*), Christopher Mitchell (*Carl*), Sue Cole (*Jo*), Robin Courbet (*Jimmy*), Dennis Waterman (*photographer*), Gordon Sterne (*producer*), Yutte Stensgaard (*taxi girl*), Angie Grant (*flower girl*), Cleo Goldstein (*hands girl*), Michel Durant (*playboy*), Larry Taylor (*policeman*), Valerie Leon (*bath girl*), Heather Barber (*exposure girl*), Sheila Ruskin (*snake girl*), Siobhan Taylor (*party girl*), Bill Jarvis, Gregory Reid (*guests*).

Comedy. European sex star Susan Stress auditions for a London producer who wishes to test her appeal to adolescents. In compliance the actress accosts a teenaged boy she assumes to be the producer's son, seduces him, and relates her success to his supposed father, only to discover that the lad is an assistant in a camera shop. Returning from the encounter, the clerk is observed by George, an apartment tenant who is about to take his life. His suicide attempt is interrupted, however, by a phone call from a wrong number and by blonde Barbara, a party girl, who appears at his door with her entourage. Leaving George's apartment, a guest collides with a taxi. Its innocent driver, Harold, has constructed a fantasy world inspired by the cinema. Catalyzed by the collision, one such fantasy features glass-encased nude sunbathers and striptteasers. When hit on the head, Harold returns to the reality of the driver's seat. *Actors. Motion picture producers. Photographers. Taxi drivers. Seduction. Nudity. Sunbathing. Striptease. Suicide. Taxicabs. London. Fantasy.*

Note: Released in Great Britain caJan 1970 as *A Promise of Bed*; running time: 83 min.

THIS WAY OUT, PLEASE see **DOCTOR, YOU'VE GOT TO BE KIDDING**

THE THOMAS CROWN AFFAIR   F6.5006
Mirisch-Simkoe-Solar Productions. *Dist* United Artists. 19 Jun **1968** [Boston opening; c19 Jun 1968; LP35996]. Sd; col (DeLuxe). 35mm. 102 min. [Also 112 min.]

Prod-Dir Norman Jewison. *Assoc Prod* Hal Ashby. *Story-Screenplay* Alan R. Trustman. *Dir Photog* Haskell Wexler. *Camera Op* Ralph Gerling. *Art Dir* Robert Boyle. *Set Decor* Edward G. Boyle. *Titl* Pablo Ferro Films. *Supv Film Ed* Hal Ashby. *Ed* Ralph Winters, Byron Brandt. *Mus Score* Michel Legrand. *Song:* "The Windmills of Your Mind" Michel Legrand, Alan Bergman, Marilyn Bergman. *Sung by* Noel Harrison. *Sd* Walter Goss, James A. Richard, Clem Portman. *Asst Dir* Jack Reddish, Walter Hill. *Prod Supv* Allen K. Wood. *Prod Mgr* James E. Henderling. *Unit Mgr* Howard Joslin. *Faye Dunaway's Wardrobe* Theadora Van Runkle. *Steve McQueen's Wardrobe* Ron Postal. *Wardrobe* Alan Levine. *Makeup Supv* Del Armstrong. *Hairstyles* Lynn Del Kail. *Multiple Screen Seq* Pablo Ferro Films.

Cast: Steve McQueen (*Thomas Crown*), Faye Dunaway (*Vicky Anderson*), Paul Burke (*Eddy Malone*), Jack Weston (*Erwin Weaver*), Biff McGuire (*Sandy*), Yaphet Kotto (*Carl*), Todd Martin (*Benjy*), Sam Melville (*Dave*), Addison Powell (*Abe*), Sidney Armus (*Arnie*), Jon Shank (*Curley*), Allen Emerson (*Don*), Harry Cooper (*Ernie*), Johnny Silver (*Bert*), Astrid Heeren (*Gwen*), Carol Corbett (*Miss Sullivan*), John Orchard (*John*), Gordon Pinsent (*Jamie MacDonald*), Patrick Horgan (*Danny*), Peg Shirley (*Honey Weaver*), Leonard Caron (*Jimmy Weaver*), Ted Gehring (*Marvin*), Nora Marlowe (*Marcie*), Judy Pace (*pretty girl*), Tom Rosqui (*private detective*), Michael Shillo (*Swiss banker*), Carole Kelly (*motel girl*), Nikita Knatz (*sketch artist*), Charles Lampkin, James Rawley, Paul Verdier (*elevator operators*), Victor Creatore, Paul Rhone (*cash room guards*), Richard Bull (*booth guard*), Patty Regan (*girl in elevator*).

Crime drama. Self-made millionaire Thomas Crown decides to take a jab at the Establishment of which he is a part. Assisted by five accomplices previously unknown to one another, who never see him, Crown executes the daylight robbery of a Boston bank. He pays his five "employees" their share of the loot before depositing the remainder of the $2,600,000 in a Swiss bank. After reimbursing the robbed bank for its loss, the insurance company assigns its best investigator, chic Vicky Anderson, to the case. Working with police lieutenant Eddy Malone, Vicky decides that Crown is her man. Despite the fact that they openly recognize each other as antagonists, they fall in love; and Vicky attempts unsuccessfully to make a deal with Malone to exchange the returned money for her lover's amnesty. When Crown tests her loyalty by telling her that he is planning another bank job, she agrees to meet Crown after the robbery; but she brings the police with her to the cemetery where the money is hidden in a refuse basket. Crown, however, knows her better than she knows herself. When his Rolls-Royce pulls up, all that greets her is a Western Union boy with a telegram: "Left early ... You bring the money—or keep the car." And a tearful Vicky looks up as a Brazil-bound plane carries Crown away. *Gentlemen crooks. Investigators. Police. Detectives. Millionaires. Insurance. Perfidy. Rolls-Royce automobiles. Cemeteries. Boston. Switzerland.*

Note: Location scenes filmed in Boston. Split-screen techniques are used in some sequences. Working titles: *The Crown Caper* and *Thomas Crown and Company.*

THORNY HOBOES *see* **HORNY HOBO**

THOROUGHLY MODERN MILLIE   F6.5007

Ross Hunter Productions. *Dist* Universal Pictures. 21 Mar **1967** [New York opening; c6 May 1967; LP35365]. Sd (Westrex); col (Technicolor). 35mm (see note). 138 min.

Prod Ross Hunter. *Dir* George Roy Hill. *Writ* Richard Morris. *Dir Photog* Russell Metty. *Camera Op* Ed Pyle. *Asst Camera* Ledger Haddow. *Adtl Photog* (see note) Russell Harlan. *Art Dir* Alexander Golitzen, George C. Webb. *Set Decor* Howard Bristol. *Set Coörd* Virgil Clark. *Film Ed* Stuart Gilmore. *Asst Ed* Richard Bracken. *Mus Score* Elmer Bernstein. *Mus Numbers Scored by* Andre Previn. *Mus Supv* Joseph Gershenson. *Songs:* "Thoroughly Modern Millie," "The Tapioca," "The Tap-Tap-Tapioca" Sammy Cahn, James Van Heusen. *Song:* "The Jewish Wedding Song" ("Trinkt le Chaim") Sylvia Neufeld. *Song:* "Jimmy" Jay Thompson. *Song:* "Poor Butterfly" Ray Hubbell, John L. Golden. *Song:* "Do It Again" George Gershwin, Bud G. De Sylva. *Song:* "Stumbling" Zez Confrey. *Song:* "The Japanese Sandman" Richard A. Whiting, Raymond B. Egan. *Song:* "Rose of Washington Square" Ballard MacDonald, James F. Hanley. *Mus Seq Stgd & Asst* Joe Layton, Jay Thompson, Buddy Schwab. *Sd* Waldon O. Watson, William Russell, Ronald Pierce, Don Cunliffe, Perry Devore, Bruce Smith. *Asst Dir* Douglas Green, John Anderson, Jr., Joe Boston, Phil Parslow. *Unit Prod Mgr* Ernest B. Wehmeyer. *Script Supv* Dixie McCoy. *Gowns Dsgn* Jean Louis. *Makeup* Bud Westmore. *Miss Andrews' Hairstyles* Hal Saunders. *Hairstyles* Larry Germain. *Matte Supv* Albert Whitlock. *Still Photog* Larry Barbier. *Gaffer* Max Nippell. *Prop* Sol Martino, John Faltis. *Grip* Charles Cowie, Ken Smith.

Cast: Julie Andrews *(Millie Dillmount)*, Mary Tyler Moore *(Dorothy Brown)*, Carol Channing *(Muzzy Van Hossmere)*, James Fox *(Jimmy Smith)*, Beatrice Lillie *(Mrs. Meers)*, John Gavin *(Trevor Graydon)*, Jack Soo *(Oriental #1)*, Pat Morita *(Oriental #2)*, Philip Ahn *(Tea)*, Cavada Humphrey *(Miss Flannery)*, Anthony Dexter *(Juarez)*, Lou Nova *(Cruncher)*, Michael St. Clair *(Baron Richter)*, Albert Carrier *(Adrian)*, Victor Rogers *(Gregory Huntley)*, Lisabeth Hush *(Judith Tremaine)*, Herbie Faye *(taxi driver)*, Ann Dee *(singer)*, Benny Rubin *(waiter)*, Buddy Schwab *(Dorothy's dance partner)*, Jay Thompson, Todd Mason *(male pedestrian)*.

Musical comedy. In the 1920's, young Millie Dillmount comes to New York City to find herself a secretarial job with a handsome, rich, unmarried boss. After changing her image from that of a curly-haired old-fashioned girl to a modern flapper, she checks into a hotel for young ladies run by Mrs. Meers and befriends a pretty orphan, Miss Dorothy Brown. Seemingly very prim and proper, Mrs. Meers is actually a villainous white slaver who has her eye on Miss Dorothy. Though Millie does obtain a position with a handsome, eligible bachelor, Trevor Graydon, he remains indifferent to her, being in love with Miss Dorothy. Instead, Millie wins the undying devotion of Jimmy Smith, a paper clip salesman. One day Jimmy takes Millie and Miss Dorothy to a weekend party at the elegant Long Island home of Muzzy Van Hossmere, a high-living, fun-loving widow. Millie is horrified when she catches Jimmy sneaking Miss Dorothy into his room. Once back in the city, however, Millie is forced to forgive Jimmy when he scales the walls of her office building to see her. Then, Miss Dorothy suddenly vanishes. Millie and Jimmy realize the truth about Mrs. Meers when they smell opium in Miss Dorothy's room. In order to find the white slavers' hideout, Jimmy disguises himself as an orphaned young lady and registers at the hotel. The scheme backfires when the crafty Mrs. Meers manages to drug and kidnap both Jimmy and Trevor. Left to her own resources, Millie traces the white slavers to a firecracker factory in Chinatown that serves as a front for an opium den. After exploding all the factory's stock, she rescues Miss Dorothy and the other captive girls and also Jimmy and Trevor. They then all race to Muzzy's estate, with Mrs. Meers and her two henchmen in hot pursuit. After the white slavers are captured, the truth about Jimmy and Miss Dorothy is disclosed. They are brother and sister, the stepchildren of Muzzy, and fabulously wealthy. With Muzzy beaming her approval, Jimmy marries Millie and Trevor marries Miss Dorothy. *Songs:* "Thoroughly Modern Millie" (Millie), "The Tapioca" (Jimmy, Millie), "Jimmy" (Millie), "Baby Face" (Millie), "Poor Butterfly" (Millie), "Do It Again" (Muzzy), "Stumbling" (Millie, Miss Dorothy), "Jazz Baby" (Muzzy), "Rose of Washington Square" (Ann Dee), "Jewish Wedding Song" (Millie),

"The Japanese Sandman" (Oriental #1, Oriental #2). *Fortune hunters. Flappers. Secretaries. Millionaires. Orphans. Hotelkeepers. Bachelors. Salesmen. Actors. Widows. Gangsters. Stepmothers. Orientals. White slave traffic. Abduction. Disguise. Brother-sister relationship. Personal identity. Female impersonation. Hotels. Opium. Fireworks. Factories. Roaring Twenties. New York City. Long Island. New York City—Chinatown.*

Note: Blown up to 70mm for some roadshow presentations. Harlan temporarily replaced Metty as photographer during production.

THOSE CALLOWAYS   F6.5008

Walt Disney Productions. *Dist* Buena Vista Distribution Co. 28 Jan **1965** [Atlanta opening; c12 Nov 1964; LP29398]. Sd (RCA); col (Technicolor). 35mm. 131 min.

Pres by Walt Disney. A Walt Disney Production. *Co-prod* Winston Hibler. *Dir* Norman Tokar. *Screenplay* Louis Pelletier. *Dir Photog* Edward Colman. *Animal Unit Photog* Lloyd Beebe, William R. Koehler. *Wild Geese Seq* Richard Borden. *Art Dir* Carroll Clark, John B. Mansbridge. *Set Decor* Emile Kuri, Hal Gausman. *Film Ed* Grant K. Smith. *Mus* Max Steiner. *Orch* Murray Cutter. *Theme Song:* "Angel" Max Steiner, Jay Livingston, Ray Evans. *Songs:* "The Cabin Raising Song," "Rhyme-Around" Richard M. Sherman, Robert B. Sherman. *Sd Supv* Robert O. Cook. *Sd Mix* Dean Thomas. *Mus Ed* Evelyn Kennedy. *Asst Dir* Tom Leetch. *Cost Dsgn* Bill Thomas. *Cost* Chuck Keehne, Gertrude Casey. *Makeup* Pat McNalley. *Hairstyles* La Rue Matheron. *Matte Artist* Jim Fetherolf. *Sp Eff* Eustace Lycett.

Cast: Brian Keith *(Cam Calloway)*, Vera Miles *(Liddy Calloway)*, Brandon De Wilde *(Bucky Calloway)*, Walter Brennan *(Alf Simes)*, Ed Wynn *(Ed Parker)*, Linda Evans *(Bridie Mellot)*, Philip Abbott *(Dell Fraser)*, John Larkin *(Jim Mellot)*, Parley Baer *(Doane Shattuck)*, Frank De Kova *(Nigosh)*, Roy Roberts *(E. J. Fletcher)*, John Qualen *(Ernie Evans)*, Tom Skerritt *(Whit Turner)*, Paul Hartman *(Charley Evans)*, Russell Collins *(Nat Perkins)*, John Davis Chandler *(Ollie Gibbons)*, Chet Stratton *(Phil Petrie)*, Renee Godfrey *(Sarah Mellot)*.

Melodrama. *Source:* Paul Annixter, *Swiftwater* (New York, 1950). Cam Calloway, an Irish trapper and woodsman raised by the Micmac Indians, lives in Swiftwater, Maine, with his wife, Liddy, and his 19-year-old son, Bucky. His fondest hope is to establish a sanctuary for the great flocks of wild geese which fly over Swiftwater in autumn during their southward migration. In order to purchase a large tract of land for the proposed sanctuary, Cam spends all the profits from an entire season of trapping. As a result, he is unable to meet the mortgage payments on his own home, and he and his family are evicted. Forced to move to the lake, they find that many of their neighbors are willing to help them build a new home. Meanwhile, Dell Fraser, a traveling salesman, schemes to convert Swiftwater into a resort for goose hunters. Posing as a conservationist, Dell gives Cam money to plant corn which would lure the birds down during their migration. Bucky learns of the plan, and Cam has a violent argument with the profiteers. After Cam is seriously wounded by a rifle shot, the townspeople organize a petition authorizing the federal government to buy the marshland for a sanctuary. As Cam recovers from his wound, Fraser and his cohorts leave town, and the dream of the Calloways becomes a reality. *Irish. Trappers. Woodsmen. Micmac Indians. Neighbors. Traveling salesmen. Profiteers. Family life. Wildlife—Conservation. Eviction. Imposture. Hunting. Sanctuaries. Maine. Geese.*

Note: Location scenes filmed in Vermont.

THOSE DARING YOUNG MEN IN THEIR JAUNTY JALOPIES
(France/Great Britain/Italy)   F6.5009

Dino De Laurentiis Cinematografica-Marianne Productions-Basil Keys Productions. *Dist* Paramount Pictures. 28 May **1969** [New York opening; c21 May 1969; LP36761]. Sd; col (Technicolor). 35mm & 70mm (Panavision). 122 min. *MPAA rating* G.

A Ken Annakin Production. *Prod-Dir* Ken Annakin. *Assoc Prod* Basil Keys. *Paris Seq Dir* Sam Itzkovitch. *Screenplay* Jack Davies, Ken Annakin. *Dir Photog* Gabor Pogany. *Camera Op* Idelmo Simonelli. *Paris Seq Photog* Walter Wottitz. *Swedish Seq Photog* Bert Palmgren. *Art Dir* Elven Webb, Boris Juraga. *Paris Seq Art Dir* Marc Frédérix. *Swedish Seq Art Dir* Erik Björk. *Scenic Artist* Duncan Spencer. *Set Dresser* Dario Simoni. *Prod Dsgn* Ted Haworth. *Credit Titl Dsgn* Ronald Searle. *Film Ed* Peter Taylor. *Mus* Ron Goodwin. *Song:* "Monte Carlo or Bust!" Ron Goodwin. *Sung by* Jimmy Durante. *Sd Rec* John Brommage. *Sd Ed* David Hawkins. *Asst Dir* Giorgio Gentili. *Prod Supv* Baccio Bandini, Peter Manley. *Cont* Joy Mercer. *Paris Seq Prod Mgr* André Cultet. *Swedish Seq Prod Mgr* Carl-Henry Cagarp. *Cost Dsgn* John Furness. *Adtl Cost* Orietta Nasalli Rocca. *Wardrobe Supv* Bona Nasalli Rocca. *Makeup* Amato Garbini. *Hairstylist* Gabriella Borzelli. *Sp Eff* Dick Parker. *Optical Sp Eff* Giovanni Ventimiglia. *Car Constr & Tech Adv* David Watson. *Constr Mgr* Aldo Puccini. *Gaffer* Luciano Marrocchi. *Ch Grip* Romeo Governatori.

Cast: Tony Curtis *(Chester Schofield)*, Susan Hampshire *(Betty)*, Terry-Thomas *(Sir Cuthbert Ware-Armitage)*, Eric Sykes *(Perkins)*, Gert Fröbe *(Willi*

Schickel/Horst Muller, see note), Peer Schmidt (Otto), Peter Cook (Maj. Digby Dawlish), Dudley Moore (Lieut. Kit Barrington), Walter Chiari (Angelo Pincelli), Lando Buzzanca (Marcello Agosti), Jack Hawkins (Count Levinovitch), Mireille Darc (Marie-Claude), Marie Dubois (Pascale), Nicoletta Machiavelli (Dominique), Bourvil (Monsieur Vendredi [Monsieur Dupont]), Jacques Duby (motorcycle gendarme), Hattie Jacques (lady journalist), Derren Nesbitt (Waleska), Nicholas Phipps (golfer), William Rushton (John O'Groats official), Michael Trubshawe (German rally official), Richard Wattis (golf club secretary), Walter Williams (German customs official), Joe Wadham, Roy Scammel, Dinny Powell, Frank Henson, Mark Boyle, Bockie Taylor, Geoff Silk (driving team).

Comedy. In the 1920's, the contestants for the annual Monte Carlo Rally (a 1,500-mile automobile endurance race) arrive at five different starting points throughout Europe. Among those competing are Chester Schofield and Sir Cuthbert Ware-Armitage, the owners of a British auto factory. Chester, an American gambler, won his half of the factory from Cuthbert's late father during a poker game, and the two men have entered the contest on a winner-take-all basis. Other entries include Maj. Digby Dawlish and Lieut. Kit Barrington, a pair of British Army officers and would-be inventors from India; Angelo Pincelli and Marcello Agosti, two womanizing Italian policemen; Schickel and Otto, German convicts who are unaware that the owners of their car have hidden stolen jewels in a spare tire; and three French feminists led by Marie-Claude, a doctor. As the race begins and the contestants battle the elements, the hazardous roads, and each other, they run into countless calamities. Chester, due to the treachery of Cuthbert, loses his co-driver and is forced to go it alone until he meets Betty, a pretty socialite; Schickel and Otto's car becomes entangled in a series of winter sports and ends up hanging from a ski lift; all the parties converge on a French Alps resort and spend a sleepless night because of room mixups; the French feminists and the Italian policemen push each other in and out of snow drifts; the Germans discover the stolen jewels but decide to remain in the race; and Betty nearly drives herself and the sleeping Chester over a frozen waterfall. Eventually, after the feminists have dropped out to aid people injured in a snowslide, the battered cars and drivers arrive at Monte Carlo. Because they all have demerit points, however, they must now compete in a final race down a winding mountain road. Dawlish and Kit are defeated when their rocket propulsion invention blows up their car; Cuthbert is disqualified for stealing a tire; and Schickel and Otto are arrested and marched off in handcuffs. Although the Italians are declared the victors, they gallantly renounce their trophy in favor of the feminists. Chester, still asleep, is pushed over the finish line by Betty, his own personal prize. Americans in foreign countries. Automobile manufacture. Gamblers. Inventors. Great Britain—Army. Police. Germans. Convicts. Feminism. Physicians. Socialites. Automobile racing. Ski resorts. Jewels. Inventions. Monte Carlo. Alps. Automobile accidents.

Note: Filmed in Italy, France, and Sweden. Released in Great Britain in 1969 as Monte Carlo or Bust!; Italian title: Quei temerari sulle loro pazze, scatenate, scalcinate carriole. Some sources credit Gert Fröbe with two roles, Schickel and Muller.

THOSE FANTASTIC FLYING FOOLS (Great Britain)   F6.5010

Jules Verne Films. Dist American International Pictures. caJun 1967 [New York opening: 18 Oct; c21 Jun 1967; LP34527]. Sd; col (Eastman Color by Pathé). 35mm (Panavision). 95 min.

Prod Harry Alan Towers. Dir Don Sharp. Screenplay Dave Freeman. Story Peter Welbeck. Dir Photog Reg Wyer. Art Dir Frank White. Set Decor Frank Graves. Film Ed Ann Chegwidden. Mus Patrick John Scott. Song: "We Must Always Trust the Stranger" Ron Goodwin. Sd John Brommage. Asst Dir John Peverall. Prod Mgr Basil Appleby. Cost Carl Toms. Sp Eff Les Bowie, Pat Moore.

Cast: Burl Ives (Phineas T. Barnum), Troy Donahue (Gaylord Sullivan), Gert Fröbe (Professor von Bulow), Hermione Gingold (Angelica, custodian of wayward girls' home), Lionel Jeffries (Sir Charles Dillworthy), Daliah Lavi (Madelaine), Dennis Price (Duke of Barset), Stratford Johns (warrant officer), Graham Stark (Grundle), Terry-Thomas (Capt. Sir Harry Washington-Smythe), Jimmy Clitheroe (General Tom Thumb), Joachim Teege (Bulgeroff), Joan Sterndale-Bennett (The Queen), Renate von Holt (Anna), Edward De Souza (Henri), Klaus Kinski (Bulgeroff), Judy Cornwell (Electra), Derek Francis (Puddleby), Allan Cuthbertson (Scotland Yard man).

Science fiction comedy. Inspired by the writings of: Jules Verne. When his "Greatest Show on Earth" burns to the ground, the bankrupt Phineas T. Barnum, accompanied by his midget star, General Tom Thumb, heads for Victorian England. There he meets a German professor, von Bulow, who boasts that he has invented a powerful explosive capable of propelling a small projectile to the moon. Hopeful of amassing a new fortune, Barnum forms a syndicate to build a rocket for transporting the reluctant Tom Thumb into space. Although the project attracts spies from all over the world, the spaceship

designed by Sir Charles Dillworthy proves useless since it does not provide a means for returning to the earth. Also on hand are an American balloon enthusiast, Gaylord Sullivan, and his fiancée, Madelaine. Gaylord claims that he has designed a projectile equipped with round-trip rockets, whereupon his rival for the hand of Madelaine, a wealthy Frenchman named Henri, offers to finance Gaylord's missile if he agrees to take Tom Thumb's place. The enraged Dillworthy and his shady brother-in-law, Harry Washington-Smythe, who have already embezzled most of Barnum's funds, immediately plot to sabotage Gaylord's flight. When Madelaine discovers their plan, she is kidnaped and whisked off to Angelica's Home for Wayward Girls. She escapes, however, and arrives back at the launching pad, located on a mountain in Wales, just as Gaylord is being removed from the sabotaged moonship. Now Dillworthy, Washington-Smythe, and a Russian spy, Bulgeroff, sneak into the spaceship to continue their sabotage. Suddenly Bulgeroff pulls the takeoff lever, and the three men are sent soaring on a one-way trip. They land in what is presumably barren wasteland to find inhabitants singing in Russian. The befuddled Washington-Smythe can only conclude that the Russians are already on the moon. [According to British sources, the launching produces an explosion which uncovers a rich vein of coal.] Entrepreneurs. Inventors. Midgets. Spies. Balloonists. Professors. Americans in foreign countries. Germans. French. Russians. Brothers-in-law. Space travel. Embezzlement. Sabotage. Kidnaping. Finance—Personal. Explosives. Rockets. Spaceships. Reformatories. Wales. The Moon. Phineas Taylor Barnum. Charles Sherwood Stratton.

Note: Released in Great Britain in 1967 as Jules Verne's Rocket to the Moon; running time: 101 min. Alternative U. S. title: Blast-Off. Location scenes filmed in Ireland.

THOSE MAGNIFICENT MEN IN THEIR FLYING MACHINES; OR HOW I FLEW FROM LONDON TO PARIS IN 25 HOURS AND 11 MINUTES (Great Britain)   F6.5011

Twentieth Century-Fox Productions. Dist Twentieth Century-Fox Film Corp. 16 Jun 1965 [New York opening; c16 Jun 1965; LP31741]. Sd (RCA); col (DeLuxe). 35mm & 65mm (Todd-AO). 133 min. [Copyright length: 152 min.]

A Ken Annakin Production. Prod Stan Margulies. Assoc Prod Jack Davies. Dir Ken Annakin. 2d Unit Dir Don Sharp. Screenplay Jack Davies, Ken Annakin. Anim Ralph Ayres. Dir Photog Christopher Challis. Camera Op Dudley Lovell. 2d Unit Camera Skeets Kelly. Assoc Art Dir Jim Morahan. Set Dresser Arthur Taksen. Prod Dsgn Tom Morahan. Titl Dsgn Ronald Searle. Film Ed Gordon Stone, Anne V. Coates. Mus Comp & Cond Ron Goodwin. Sd John W. Mitchell, Gordon McCallum. Dub Ed Jonathan Bates. Asst Dir Clive Reed. 2d Unit Asst Dir Jake Wright. Prod Supv Denis Holt. Unit Mgr Colin Brewer, Patrick Clayton. Cont Joy Mercer. Cost Dsgn Osbert Lancaster. Assoc Cost Dsgn Dinah Greet. Makeup William Partleton, Stuart Freeborn. Hairdresser Barbara Ritchie, Biddy Chrystal. Sp Eff Supv Ron Ballanger. Sp Eff Richard Parker. Tech Adv Allen Wheeler, (Commodore). Aircraft Mech Supv Richard Parker. Casting Stuart Lyons. Titl Exec by National Screen Service Ltd.

Cast: Stuart Whitman (Orvil Newton), Sarah Miles (Patricia Rawnsley), James Fox (Richard Mays), Alberto Sordi (Count Emilio Ponticelli), Robert Morley (Lord Rawnsley), Gert Fröbe (Col. Manfred von Holstein), Jean-Pierre Cassel (Pierre Dubois), Eric Sykes (Courtney), Terry-Thomas (Sir Percival Ware-Armitage), Irina Demick (Brigitte/Ingrid/Marlene/Françoise/Yvette/Betty), Tony Hancock (Harry Popperwell, an inventor), Benny Hill (Fire Chief Perkins), Yujiro Ishihara (Yamamoto), Flora Robson (mother superior), Karl Michael Vogler (Captain Rupelstrosse), Sam Wanamaker (George Gruber), Eric Barker (French postman), Fred Emney (elderly colonel), Gordon Jackson (McDougal, a pilot), Davy Kaye (Jean, Pierre's chief mechanic), John Le Mesurier (French painter), Jeremy Lloyd (Lieutenant Parsons, a pilot), Zena Marshall (Sophia Ponticelli), Millicent Martin (airline hostess), Eric Pohlmann (Italian mayor), Marjorie Rhodes (The Waitress in Old Mill Cafe), Norman Rossington (assistant fire chief), William Rushton (Tremayne Gascoyne), Jimmy Thompson (The Photographer in Old Mill Cafe), Michael Trubshawe (Niven, Lord Rawnsley's aide), Red Skelton (The Neanderthal Man), Gerald Campion (2d fireman), Graham Stark (3d fireman), Maurice Denham (trawler skipper), Robin Chapman (postman), Ronnie Stevens (R.A.C. officer), Steve Plytas (continental journalist), Ferdy Mayne (French official), Bill Nagy (American journalist), James Robertson-Justice (narrator).

Adventure comedy. In 1910, Lord Rawnsley, a wealthy and influential newspaper publisher, sets out to prove that Britannia rules the air as well as the sea by sponsoring the first International Air Race from London to Paris. Although he invites flyers from all over the world to compete for the prize of £10,000, Lord Rawnsley clearly expects the winner to be Richard Mays, his daughter Patricia's intended bridegroom and a young Royal Navy lieutenant. Among the other entrants who converge at Brookley Airdrome with their fragile flying machines are Orvil Newton, an American barnstormer who almost immediately begins competing with Mays for Patricia's affections; Count Emilio Ponticelli, a fearless Italian who brings along his large family; Colonel Manfred von Holstein, a German cavalry officer intent upon bringing glory to the fatherland; Pierre Dubois, an amorous Frenchman bedeviled by six beautiful look-alike girls; Yamamoto, an "inscrutable" Japanese; and Sir Percy Ware-Armitage, a villainous Englishman who proves to be remarkably adept at sabotaging his rivals' aircraft. Once the race across the English Channel begins, mishaps occur with startling regularity. Inventor Harry Popperwell discovers that his plane only works in reverse, and he vanishes in a backward direction towards Scotland; Sir Percy's skulduggery causes Yamamoto's plane to crash-land upon takeoff; von Holstein plunges headlong into a drainage pond; and Sir Percy himself, after sneaking his plane across the Channel at night, lands on top of a train just as it is heading into a tunnel. Eventually the contest narrows down to three possible winners: Ponticelli, Mays, and Newton. But Ponticelli's plane catches fire (more of Sir Percy's sabotage) and Newton delays to effect a midair rescue, thereby permitting Mays to win the race. Lord Rawnsley's glee quickly turns to dismay when the ethical Mays insists upon sharing his prize with his American rival. Newton, however, has no intention of sharing his prize—the fair Patricia—with his British rival. *Publishers. Italians. French. Germans. Japanese. Americans in foreign countries. Barnstormers. Air pilots. Inventors. Nobility. Airplane racing. Courtship. Sabotage. Cheating. Rescue. English Channel. London. Paris. Great Britain—Royal Navy. Air stunts. Airplane accidents.*

Note: Filmed in Great Britain and France. London opening; 3 Jun 1965; running time: 132 min.

THOSE WERE THE HAPPY TIMES see **STAR!**

A THOUSAND CLOWNS F6.5012

Harrell, Inc. *Dist* United Artists. 13 Dec **1965** [New York opening; c13 Dec 1965; LP32309]. Sd; b&w. 35mm. 118 min.

Prod-Dir Fred Coe. *Assoc Prod* Ralph Rosenblum, Herb Gardner. *Screenplay* Herb Gardner. *Dir Photog* Arthur J. Ornitz. *Adtl Photog* Joseph Coffey. *Camera Op* Al Taffet. *Lighting* Willie Meyerhoff. *Set Dsgn* Burr Smidt. *Set Decor* Herbert Mulligan, George De Titta. *Scenic Artist* William Lucek. *Film Ed* Ralph Rosenblum. *Mus* Don Walker. *Titl Song* Judy Holliday, Gerry Mulligan. *Sung by* Rita Gardner. *Song:* "Yes Sir, That's My Baby" Walter Donaldson, Gus Kahn. *Sung by* Jason Robards, [Jr.], Barry Gordon. *Sd Mix* Jim Shields. *Sd Richard Vorisek.* 2d Asst Dir* Dan Eriksen, Tony Belletier. *Prod Mgr* Henry Spitz. *Script Supv* Betty Todd. *Prod Asst* Mel Howard. *Prod Sec* Belle Iacobellis. *Cost Dsgn* Ruth Morley. *Wardrobe* Flo Transfield. *Makeup* Irving Buchman. *Hairdresser* Charles Fialla. *Grip* Willie Meyerhoff.

Cast: Jason Robards, [Jr.] *(Murray Burns)*, Barbara Harris *(Sandra)*, Martin Balsam *(Arnold Burns)*, Barry Gordon *(Nick)*, Gene Saks *(Leo)*, William Daniels *(Albert)*.

Comedy-drama. Source: Herb Gardner, *A Thousand Clowns* (New York opening: 5 Apr 1962). Freespirited Murray Burns, unemployed for 5 months since quitting his job as a writer for the *Chuckles the Chipmunk* television show, must find a means of support for his precocious 12-year-old nephew, Nick. Nick, an illegitimate son of Murray's sister, has lived with Murray for 7 years but has never been legally adopted. One day Sandra and Albert, social workers from the New York City Child Welfare Board, visit Murray and threaten to take Nick away unless steps are taken to assure a proper home life for the boy. Albert adheres strictly to the rules, but Sandra becomes emotionally involved in the case. After informing Sandra that she is off the case, Albert leaves in a huff; but Sandra stays and spends the night with Murray. They fall in love, and at the insistence of both Sandra and Nick, Murray goes to his brother Arnold, an agent, to find a job. After some unsuccessful interviews, Murray confronts his former employer, Leo, who plays Chuckles the Chipmunk on the show. Despite Leo's dislike for Nick and his patronizing attitude toward Murray, he still offers Murray the job. Nick is offended by Leo and tries to talk Murray out of compromising his principles. Sandra, however, moves into the apartment and begins to refurbish her new home. Nick finally accepts the fact that Murray will again have to work for Leo, and the next morning Murray joins the crowd of people rushing off to their jobs. *Nonconformists. Uncles. Television scriptwriters. Children. Social workers. Brothers. Theatrical agents. Clowns. Unemployment. Illegitimacy. Child welfare. Employer-employee relations. Television. New York City.*

Note: Filmed in New York City.

THOUSAND CRANES (Japan) F6.5013

Daiei Motion Picture Co. Oct **1969** [Los Angeles showing]. Sd; col (Eastmancolor). 35mm (Daiei Scope). 97 min.

Dir Yasuzo Masumura. *Screenplay* Kaneto Shindo. *Photog* Setsuo Kobayashi. *Art Dir* Tomoo Shimogawara. *Mus* Hikaru Hayashi.

Cast: Mikijiro Hira *(Kikuji Mitani)*, Ayako Wakao *(Mrs. Ota)*, Eiko Azusa *(Fumiko)*, Machiko Kyo *(Chikako Kurimoto)*, Yoko Namikawa *(Yukiko*

Inamura), Eiji Funakoshi.

Drama. Source: Yasunari Kawabata, *Sembazuru* (Tokyo, 1958). Kikuji Mitani still recalls his father's two lovers with bitterness. When he was about 9 years old, Kikuji briefly met the first, Chikako Kurimoto, a woman with a large birthmark on her breast. That affair was brief; his father then was involved with a widow, Mrs. Ota, until his death. Kikuji's mother died a short time after his father, and he now lives alone. Out of curiosity, he accepts an invitation from Chikako to a tea ceremony, where he meets Yukiko Inamura, a girl whom Chikako intends for him to marry. He is also shocked to find Mrs. Ota and her daughter Fumiko at the ceremony, because Chikako was envious of Mrs. Ota during her affair with his father. Kikuji is embarrassed by Chikako's presumptuousness and yet is attracted to Fumiko. After the ceremony, he finds Mrs. Ota waiting for him, and as they talk, he senses that she cannot distinguish him from his father, so happy is she to see him. At a nearby inn, they make love, but Mrs. Ota is unable to believe that Kikuji does not intend to marry Yukiko, and she commits suicide. Satisfied that she has rid herself of one rival, Chikako thwarts any possibility of romance between Fumiko and Kikuji by constantly berating them until Fumiko moves away, leaving Kikuji alone. *Widows. Mistresses. Infidelity. Perfidy. Suicide. Marriage—Arranged.*

Note: Released in Japan in Apr 1969 as *Sembazuru*.

THE 1000 EYES OF DR. MABUSE (France/Italy/West Germany) F6.5014

CCC–Filmkunst–CEI Incom–Critérion Film. *Dist* Ajay Film Co. 6 Apr **1966** [Boston opening]. Sd; b&w. 35mm. 103 min.

Prod-Dir Fritz Lang. *Exec Prod* Artur Brauner. *Screenplay* Fritz Lang, Heinz Oskar Wuttig. *Based on an Idea by* Jan Fethke. *Photog* Karl Löb. *Camera* Karl-Heinz Linke, Ernst Zahrt. *Art Dir* Erich Kettelhut, Johannes Ott. *Film Ed (see note)* Walter Wischniewsky, Waltraut Wischniewsky. *Mus* Bert Grund. *Sd* Eduard Kessel. *Asst Dir (see note)* Walter Wischniewsky. *Prod Mgr* Richard Oehlers, Josef Thuis. *Prod Dir* Alfred Bittins. *Cost* Ina Stein. *Makeup* Heinz Stamm.

Cast: Dawn Addams *(Marion Menil)*, Peter Van Eyck *(Henry B. Travers)*, Gert Fröbe *(Commissioner Krauss)*, Wolfgang Preiss *(Jordan)*, Werner Peters *(Hieronymus P. Mistelzweig)*, Andrea Checchi *(Inspector Berg)*, Reinhard Kolldehoff *(Klumpfuss)*, Howard Vernon *("No. 12")*, Jean-Jacques Delbo *(servant)*, Lupo Prezzo *(Cornelius)*, Christiane Maybach *(pretty blonde)*, David Camerone *(Travers' secretary)*, Nico Pepe *(hotel manager)*, Werner Buttler *("No. 11")*, Linda Sini *(Corinna)*, Rolf Möbius *(police officer)*, Bruno W. Pantel *(reporter)*, Marie-Luise Nagel, Albert Bessler.

Crime melodrama. Based on the character created by: Norbert Jacques. The latest in a series of unsolved murders connected with the Luxor Hotel in Berlin leads the authorities to believe that a criminal gang exists headed by someone believing himself to be a reincarnation of the famous Dr. Mabuse. When Henry Travers, an American millionaire, saves Marion Menil from an attempted suicide leap from the ledge of a hotel window, both become involved in the investigation. Commissioner Krauss, meanwhile, has two suspects for the Mabuse imitator: Jordan, supposedly a blind clairvoyant, and Mistelzweig, an insurance salesman. Marion falls in love with Travers and tries to save him from Mabuse's men, even though she had been hypnotized into tricking Travers out of his fortune. Krauss's men invade the hotel and unmask Jordan as the mastermind behind the scheme. A car chase ensues, during which Jordan is killed, and, although Marion is wounded by one of Mabuse's gunmen, she and Travers are rescued by an INTERPOL agent. *Millionaires. Americans in foreign countries. Clairvoyants. Police. Insurance agents. Masterminds. Impersonation. Suicide. Murder. Blindness. Hotels. Berlin. INTERPOL. Chases. Doktor Mabuse.*

Note: Opened in Stuttgart in Sep 1960 as *Die tausend Augen des Dr. Mabuse*; in Rome in Dec 1960 as *Il diabolico Dr. Mabuse*; in Paris in Jun 1961 as *Le diabolique Docteur Mabuse*. Also known as *Eye of Evil* and *The Shadow vs. the 1,000 Eyes of Dr. Mabuse*. One German source credits Waltraut Wischniewsky as editor and Walter Wischniewsky as assistant director; other sources credit both as editors.

A THOUSAND PLEASURES F6.5015

Rivamarsh Productions. *Dist* American Film Distributing Corp. **1968**. Sd; b&w. 35mm. 70 min.

Prod Julian Marsh, Anna Riva. *Dir* Julian Marsh. *Screenplay* Berla L. Moke. *Photog* Anna Riva. *Lighting* Robert Marx. *Film Ed* Richard Jennings. *Mus* Robin Aden. *Mottle Eff* Berkey-Pathé. *Still Photog* Ellsworth Dinsmore.

Cast: Marie Brent, Linda MacTavish, Robert Wuesterwurst, Artimidia Grillet, Kim Lewid, Donna Stone, Dude Ellsworth, Anna Riva.

Sex film. Richard Davis, nagged constantly by his wife, stabs her with a bread knife and loads her body into his station wagon. On the highway, looking for a place to dispose of the body, he is forced to stop by two girls, Jackie and Maggie, one of whom performs fellatio on him. He then becomes their prisoner when they discover his wife's body. At their house, he meets a demented girl dressed as a baby and Belle, who cares for Baby. Richard forces himself on Baby, but the resentful Belle gives him a drugged drink. When he awakens, Jackie and Maggie inform him they want a baby, but because both loathe men, they manipulate him for his semen. Jackie and Maggie then make love. Richard takes a bath but is surprised by Anna, a Negro woman with huge breasts who abandons herself to him. In the living room, everyone participates in an orgy during which Jackie beats Baby and Belle masturbates while looking at lesbian magazines. Richard tries to escape to a nearby beach, but is captured by Bruno, the girls' henchman. Jackie and Maggie then beat Richard until he is unconscious. Upon awakening, he finds a straight razor, slashes Baby and Maggie, and then strangles Jackie, but Bruno ties Richard to a bed and Anna suffocates him by forcing one of her breasts into his mouth. Belle, distressed by the murder of Baby, rushes to the beach intent on committing suicide, but Anna stops her and comforts her. *Negroes. Lesbianism. Mental retardation. Torture. Sadism. Suffocation. Oral sex. Murder.*

Note: Julian Marsh and Robert Wuesterwurst are pseudonyms for Michael Findlay; Anna Riva for Roberta Findlay.

THREE (Yugoslavia)												F6.5016
Avala Film. *Dist* Impact Films. 29 Jun **1967** [New York showing]. Sd; b&w. 35mm. 79 min. [Also 70 min.]
Dir Aleksandar Petrović. *Screenplay* Antonije Isaković, Aleksandar Petrović. *Photog* Tomislav Pinter. *Film Ed* Mila Milanović.
Cast: Bata Živojinović *(Milos)*, Ali Raner *(man)*, Senka Veletanlić-Petrović *(girl)*, Voja Mirić *(partisan)*, Slobodan Perović, Mića Tomić.
War drama. Source: Antonije Isaković, *Paprat i vatra* (Belgrade, 1962). (1) In World War II, Milos, a Yugoslav partisan, is part of a crowd of refugees attempting to escape by train from the approaching Germans. Among the waiting throng is a man without identification papers who is suspected of being a fifth columnist. As the near-hysterical mob goads three soldiers into arresting the man, Milos feebly tries to intervene. But his efforts are in vain, and the man is shot to death. A few moments later, the dead man's wife appears and establishes her husband's innocence. (2) Following a resistance raid, Milos is chased by Nazis into a swamp where he encounters another man, an admitted coward, who is also in hiding. Knowing that the Germans are looking for only one fugitive, the man sacrifices himself to his pursuers and is burned to death in a small shack, thereby permitting Milos to escape to freedom. (3) As the war nears its end, Milos, now an officer in the Yugoslav Army, is forced to pass the death sentence on those of his countrymen found guilty of collaboration. Though peace is at hand, he orders the execution of a young woman to whom obviously he is attracted. *Refugees. Fugitives. Traitors. Resistance (political). Self-sacrifice. World War II. Germany—Army. Yugoslavia—Army. Swamps.*

Note: Released in Yugoslavia in 1965 as *Tri*. Bata Živojinović is also credited as Velimir Živojinović.

THREE																	F6.5017
New York State Narcotic Addiction Control Commission. 23 Jan **1969** [New York showing]. Sd; b&w. 35mm. 52 min.
Prod-Dir-Writ John J. Sughrue.
Cast: Antonio Fargas, Joseph Sirola, David Bailey.
Drama. During a group therapy session, three addicts' case histories are analyzed. The resentment of local residents toward a drug rehabilitation center is also explored. *Drug addicts. Group therapy.*

THREE BITES OF THE APPLE										F6.5018
Metro-Goldwyn-Mayer, Inc. 1 Feb **1967** [Detroit opening; c22 Dec 1966; LP33660]. Sd (Westrex); col (Metrocolor). 35mm (Panavision). 105 min. [Also reviewed at 98 min.]
An Alvin Ganzer Production. *Prod-Dir* Alvin Ganzer. *Assoc Prod* Harry Fine. *Screenplay* George Wells. *Dir Photog* Gabor Pogany. *Art Dir* Elliot Scott. *Asst Art Dir* Jonathan Barry. *Set Decor* Arrigo Breschi. *Film Ed* Norman Savage. *Mus* Eddy Manson. *Lyr & Mus:* "In the Garden—Under the Tree" Paul Francis Webster, David McCallum. *Sung by* David McCallum. *Mus:* "Carla" Mario Castellacci, Domenico Modugno. *Orch Cond* Robert Armbruster. *Sd Rec* Franklin Milton, Cyril Swern. *Asst Dir* Giuseppe Pollini. *Prod Supv* Orazio Tassara. *Cost for Miss Koscina* Pino Lancetti (Roma). *Makeup* Amato Garbini.
Cast: David McCallum *(Stanley Thrumm)*, Sylva Koscina *(Carla Moretti)*, Tammy Grimes *(Angela Sparrow)*, Harvey Korman *(Harvey Tomlinson)*, Domenico Modugno *(Remo Romano)*, Aldo Fabrizi *(The Doctor)*, Avril Angers *(Gladys Tomlinson)*, Claude Aliotti *(Teddy Farnum)*, Freda Bamford *(Gussie Hagstrom)*, Arthur Hewlett *(Alfred Guffy)*, Alison Fraser *(Peg Farnum)*, Cardew Robinson *(Bernhard Hagstrom)*, Ann Lancaster *(Winifred Batterly)*, John Sharp *(Joe Batterly)*, Maureen Pryor *(Birdie Guffy)*, Eddra Gale *(The Yodeler)*, Mirella Maravidi *(Francesca Bianchini)*, Riccardo Garrone *(croupier)*.

Comedy. Stanley Thrumm is a mild-mannered Englishman who works as a tour guide for a second-rate travel agency. While conducting a bus trip through the Italian Riviera, he enters a gambling casino to look for one of his drunken American passengers. Forced to pay admission, and handed chips instead of change, he places a bet, wins, bets again, and continues playing until he has parlayed his small wager into 30,000 lire. Unknown to him, he has been closely watched by a beautiful but scheming adventuress, Carla Moretti, who, after hastily arranging a "chance" meeting, agrees to meet him when his tour arrives in Rome. Carla then contacts her gigolo ex-husband, Remo, and awaits her innocent victim. Once there the love-struck Stanley is easily persuaded to invest his money in Switzerland where he won't have to pay any taxes on it. To avoid Italian customs, he hides his winnings in a giant stuffed dog belonging to one of his tourists, a predatory husband-hunter named Miss Sparrow. After crossing the border, Stanley accepts a worthless receipt from Remo in exchange for his money. But he soon learns of the deception and chases Remo onto a ski lift where a wild fight ensues that puts both men into a hospital. Despite his injuries, Stanley continues to beat Remo until he confesses his complicity with Carla. Sick at heart, Stanley returns to his hotel and learns that he has been fired as the result of a letter the jealous Miss Sparrow wrote to his company. All ends well as Carla brings back his money and agrees to return with him to England where he plans to open a small travel agency of his own. *English. Guides. Tourists. Adventuresses. Italians. Gigolos. Swindlers. Gambling. Buses. Casinos. Riviera. Rome. Italy. Switzerland. England.*

Note: Locations filmed in Italy, Switzerland, and England.

THREE BY JEAN-MARIE STRAUB (Monaco/West Germany)		F6.5019
Straub-Huillet-Atlas Film–Janus Film und Fernsehen-Cineropa-Film. *Dist* New Yorker Films. 23 Feb **1969** [New York opening]. Sd; b&w. 35mm. 94 min.
Dir Jean-Marie Straub.
Anthology. This program includes three films by Straub: the 1965 feature *Not Reconciled, or "Only Violence Helps Where It Rules,"* q. v.; and two shorts, *Machorka-Muff* (1963) and *The Bridegroom, the Comedienne, and the Pimp* (1968).

THREE DAYS AND A CHILD see **NOT MINE TO LOVE**

THREE DOLLS FROM HONG KONG (Japan)						F6.5020
Toho Co. 10 Mar **1966** [New York showing]. Sd; col (Eastmancolor). 35mm (Tohoscope). 98 min.
Exec Prod Sanezumi Fujimoto. *Dir* Toshio Sugie. *Screenplay* Ryozo Kasahara. *Photog* Taiichi Kankura. *Mus* Yoshiyuki Kozu.
Cast: Reiko Dan *(Punch)*, Sonomi Nakajima *(Pinch)*, Noriko Shigeyama *(Senti)*, Tatsuya Ebara *(Tatsuo Maebara)*, Akira Kubo *(Hiroshi Kubota)*, Shinji Yamada *(Hideo Kiyokawa)*.
Romantic comedy. Punch, a reporter for a weekly magazine, helps her dancer friend Senti obtain a booking for an international tour whose first stop is Hong Kong. Pinch, their wealthy and impetuous playgirl friend, reproaches them for not asking her along and, just before the boat leaves, walks into their cabin carrying a suitcase full of money, but without a ticket or passport. Enroute, the girls meet a wealthy Chinese gentleman who promises to help them in Hong Kong. Punch and Senti smuggle Pinch through customs in a suitcase, but they soon discover that the promoter of Senti's tour has absconded with all their money and their Chinese friend is only the secretary to a wealthy gentleman. Senti and her troupe make their scheduled performance, and the wealthy gentleman spots Senti from the audience. Through his secretary, he offers to make her his 13th concubine. Indignant at his suggestion, Punch threatens to publish his photograph and an article on him in her magazine, and he relents, offering the girls anything they wish. To his surprise, they insist that he allow his son to marry the woman he loves, a nightclub singer. The three return to Japan when their parents notify the Japanese Consulate of their absence. *Reporters. Dancers. Playgirls. Chinese. Entertainers. Secretaries. Wealth. Theft. Smuggling. Marriage. Imposture. Magazines (periodicals). Hong Kong.*

Note: Released in Japan in 1959 as *Oneichan makari toru*. Alternative title: *Three Dolls Go to Hong Kong.*

THREE FABLES OF LOVE (France/Italy/Spain)					F6.5021
Madeleine Films-Franco London Film-Ajace Cinematografica-Hispamer Films. *Dist* Janus Films. 20 Aug **1963** [New York opening]. Sd; b&w. 35mm. 76 min.
Overall Production Credits: *Prod* Gilbert de Goldschmidt. *Idea Conceived by* Frédéric Grendel, Hervé Bromberger. *Mus* Georges Garvarentz, Charles Aznavour.
Production Credits for "The Tortoise and the Hare": *Dir* Alessandro Blasetti. *Screenplay* Suso Cecchi D'Amico, Alessandro Blasetti. *Photog* Carlo Di Palma. *Film Ed* Nino Baragli.
Production Credits for "The Fox and the Crow": *Dir* Hervé Bromberger. *Screenplay* Hervé Bromberger, Frédéric Grendel. *Photog* Jacques Mercanton.

Film Ed Borys Lewin. *Sd* Georges Mardiguian.

Production Credits for "Two Pigeons": *Dir-Writ* René Clair. *Photog* Armand Thirard. *Art Dir* Léon Barsacq. *Film Ed* Denise Natot. *Sd* Georges Mardiguian.

Cast for "The Tortoise and the Hare": Monica Vitti *(Madeleine)*, Sylva Koscina *(Mia)*, Rossano Brazzi *(Leo)*, Alessandro Blasetti, Gianrico Tedeschi.

Cast for "The Fox and the Crow": Michel Serrault *(Mr. Crow [Albert])*, Jean Poiret *(Mr. Fox [Marcel])*, Anna Karina *(Colombe)*.

Cast for "Two Pigeons": Leslie Caron *(Annie)*, Charles Aznavour *(Charles)*, Raymond Bussières.

Romantic comedy. Based on the fables by: Jean de La Fontaine, "Le lièvre et la tortue," "Le corbeau et le renard," "Les deux pigeons," and "La mort et le bucheron". THE TORTOISE AND THE HARE: Madeleine, the unpretentious and quiet wife of Baron Leo Serpieri, joins her husband and his mistress, Mia, while they are vacationing at Positano. By various ruses, the determined Madeleine outwits her rival and wins back the love of Leo. THE FOX AND THE CROW: Mr. Fox, an unscrupulous village garage owner, covets Colombe, the beautiful wife of Mr. Crow, an extremely jealous public prosecutor. By lavishing flattery on the vain Mr. Crow, the wily Mr. Fox wins his confidence and makes love to Colombe at a picnic while her husband is demonstrating his talent with a hunting horn. TWO PIGEONS: While preparing to leave Paris for the Easter holidays, Annie, a fashion model, becomes locked in her apartment. Her neighbor Charles opens the door but locks them both inside when he attempts to demonstrate how the door jammed. By the end of the weekend, the two are in love. *Mistresses. Nobility. Garagemen. Lawyers. Models. Neighbors. Marriage. Jealousy. Infidelity. Vacations. Picnics. Positano. Paris.*

Note: Opened in Paris in Dec 1962 as *Les quatres vérités*; released in Italy in 1963 as *Le quattro verità*; in Spain in 1963 as *Las cuatro verdades*. Original running time (including a 4th episode entitled "La mort et le bucheron"): 110 min. French episode titles: "Le lièvre et la tortue," "Le corbeau et le renard," and "Les deux pigeons." Italian episode titles: "I due piccioni," "La lepre e la tartaruga," "Il corvo e la volpe."

THREE FACES OF SIN (France/Italy)   **F6.5022**
Films Caravelle–S. N. E. Gaumont–Ultra Film–Este Film. *Dist* Cameo International Pictures. 7 Aug **1963** [New York showing]. Sd; b&w. 35mm. 95 min.

Prod Irénée Leriche. *Dir* François Villiers. *Screenplay* Rémo Forlani. *Dial* Henri Jeanson. *Adapt* Henri Jeanson, Jean Canolle, François Villiers. *Dir Photog* Jacques Robin. *Art Dir* François de Lamothe. *Film Ed* Christian Gaudin. *Mus* Maurice Jarre. *Sd* Jean Bonnafoux.

Cast: Michèle Morgan *(Renée Plège)*, Jean-Claude Brialy *(Laurent)*, Catherine Spaak *(Danièle Plège)*, Scilla Gabel *(Rossana)*, Franco Fabrizi *(Guerbois)*, Michel Etcheverry *(inspector)*, Jacques-Henri Duval *(man)*, Alberto Farnese, Milton Reid, Marco Tulli.

Romantic melodrama. Source: Jean Jacques Gautier, *Le puits aux trois vérités* (Paris, 1949). Egocentric painter Laurent charms Renée Plège, a divorced Parisian antique dealer, but perversely marries her student daughter, Danièle. Tiring of both mother and daughter, the artist moves in with Rossana, a stripteaser. When Renée ransacks the couple's hotel room, Laurent assumes that his wife is responsible and violently rebukes her. Shortly thereafter she is found shot to death. Although the police conclude that Danièle's death is a suicide, Renée and Laurent bear moral responsibility for her demise. *Painters. Antique dealers. Police. Stripteasers. Students. Filial relations. Suicide. Marriage. Jealousy. Guilt. Desertion. Paris.*

Note: Opened in Paris in Sep 1961 as *Le puits aux trois vérités*; in Rome in Sep 1961 as *Il pozzo delle tre verità*. Alternative French title: *Trois vérités*. Licensed in New York State as *Three Sinners*.

THREE FOR A WEDDING *see* **DOCTOR, YOU'VE GOT TO BE KIDDING**

THREE GUNS FOR TEXAS   **F6.5023**
Universal Pictures. Jun **1968** [c6 Jul 1968; LP40552]. Sd (Westrex); col (Technicolor). 35mm. 99 min.

Prod Richard Irving. *Dir (see note)* David Lowell Rich, Paul Stanley, Earl Bellamy. *Screenplay* John D. F. Black. *Story* John D. F. Black. *Dir Photog* Andrew Jackson, Lionel Lindon. *Col Coörd* Robert Brower. *Art Dir* Howard E. Johnson, Russell Kimball, Lloyd S. Papez. *Set Decor* John McCarthy, James M. Walters, Sr., Robert C. Bradfield, Claire P. Brown. *Titl & Optical Eff* Universal Title. *Film Ed* Richard G. Wray. *Mus* Russ Garcia. *Mus Supv* Stanley Wilson. *Sd* Waldon O. Watson, David H. Moriarty, Earl Crain, Jr., Roger Parish. *Asst Dir* Jack Doran, Lester William Berke, Frank Losee. *Unit Prod Mgr* Hilton A. Green. *Makeup* Bud Westmore. *Hairstyles* Larry Germain. *Horse Provided by* Philip Carey.

Cast: Neville Brand *(Reese Bennett)*, Peter Brown *(Chad Cooper)*, William Smith *(Joe Riley)*, Martin Milner *(MacMillan)*, Philip Carey *(Captain

Parmalee)*, Albert Salmi *(Cleetus Grogan)*, Cliff Osmond *(Running Antelope)*, Michael Conrad *(Willy G. Tinney)*, Shelley Morrison *(Linda Little Trees)*, John Abbott, Richard Devon, Ralph Manza, Dub Taylor.

Western comedy-drama. The efforts of Texas Rangers to bring law and order to Laredo are endangered by Indian insurrections led by the widowed squaw Linda Little Trees. The widow falls in love with a Ranger, however, and Indians and Rangers join forces to repel a band of outlaws. *Widows. Texas Rangers. Indians of North America. Law and order. Uprisings. Laredo.*

Note: Three episodes from NBC's *Laredo* comprise this film: "Yahoo," shown 30 Sep 1965, c27 Sep 1965, LP33486, directed by Rich; "Jinx," shown 2 Dec 1965, c29 Nov 1965, LP33494, directed by Stanley; and "No Bugles, One Drum," shown 24 Feb 1966, c21 Feb 1966, LP33500, directed by Bellamy.

THE 300 SPARTANS   **F6.5024**
Twentieth Century–Fox Film Corp. 29 Aug **1962** [Philadelphia opening; c31 Dec 1961; LP22806]. Sd (Westrex); col (De Luxe). 35mm (CinemaScope). 114 min.

Prod Rudolph Maté, George St. George. *Dir* Rudolph Maté. *2d Unit Dir* Richard Talmadge. *Screenplay* George St. George. *Orig Story Material* Ugo Liberatore, Remigio Del Grosso, Giovanni D'Eramo, Gian Paolo Callegari. *Dir Photog* Geoffrey Unsworth. *2d Unit Photog* Cyril Knowles, Jerry Kalogerados. *Art Dir* Arrigo Equini. *Set Dresser* Carlo Gentili, Enzo Constantini. *Film Ed* Jerome Webb. *Mus Comp & Cond* Manos Hadjidakis. *Sd* David Hildyard. *Sd Ed* Winston Ryder, Rusty Coppleman. *Asst Dir* Fred R. Simpson, Eric Andreou. *Prod Mgr* William Eckhardt. *Asst to Prod* Ted Zarpas. *Cont* Maggie Shipway, Helen Whitson. *Cost Dsgn* Ginette Devaud. *Wardrobe Mistress* Anna Maria Fea. *Makeup* George Frost, Amato Garbini. *Hairstyles* Vasco Reggiani. *Sp Eff* Fred Etcheberry. *Historical Story Adv & Military Adv* Paul Nord, Cleanthis Damianos.

Cast: Richard Egan *(Leonidas)*, Ralph Richardson *(Themistocles)*, Diane Baker *(Ellas)*, Barry Coe *(Phylon)*, David Farrar *(Xerxes)*, Donald Houston *(Hydarnes)*, Anna Synodinou *(Gorgo)*, Kieron Moore *(Ephialtes)*, John Crawford *(Agathon)*, Robert Brown *(Pentheus)*, Laurence Naismith *(1st delegate)*, Anne Wakefield *(Artemisia)*, Ivan Triesault *(Demaratus)*, Charles Fawcett *(Megistias)*, Michael Nikolinakos *(Myron)*, Sandro Giglio *(Xenathon)*, Anna Raftopoulou *(Toris)*, Dimos Starenios *(Samos)*, George Moutsios, Nicholas Papakonstantinou, John G. Contes, Marietta Flematomas.

Historical epic. In 480 B. C. Emperor Xerxes of Persia plans a massive invasion of Greece. Themistocles of Athens calls an emergency meeting of all the Greek rulers and King Leonidas of Sparta suggests that his legions check the Persians at the narrow pass of Thermopylae, thereby giving the other Grecian states time to mobilize. But Sparta's ultimate ruling body, the Council of Euphors, decrees that there can be no fighting during the religious festival in progress; and Leonidas is left with only his personal retinue of 300 men. As they make their way to Thermopylae, they are followed by a young Spartan soldier, Phylon, who has been falsely accused of being a traitor's son, and his beloved Ellas, the niece of Leonidas. The Persians attack, and great numbers of their soldiers are slaughtered in the narrow pass. But the Spartans are betrayed by a goatherd, Ephialtes, who tells the Persians of a little-known trail by which they can traverse the mountain and attack the Spartans from the rear. Though warned of the imminent danger, Leonidas chooses to make a stand. After sending Phylon and Ellas back to Athens to warn the Greeks and tell them of the Spartans' resistance, he and his men form a wedge of shields and hold their ground until they are totally overwhelmed by the Persians. Their sacrifice serves to unite the Greeks, and a few months later the Persian army is annihilated at the Battle of Plataea. *Greeks. Persians. Royalty. Soldiers. Traitors. Goatherds. Courage. Military invasion. Self-sacrifice. Treason. Greco-Persian Wars. Greece—Ancient. Sparta. Athens. Pass of Thermopylae. Plataea. Leonidas. Themistocles. Xerxes. Ephialtes.*

Note: Filmed on location in Greece. Working title: *Lion of Sparta.*

3 IN THE ATTIC   **F6.5025**
American International Productions–Hermes Productions. *Dist* American International Pictures. 20 Dec **1968** [Chicago opening; c25 Dec 1968; LP36733]. Sd; col (Pathé). 35mm. 91 min. MPAA rating R.

Prod-Dir Richard Wilson. *Exec Prod* Samuel Z. Arkoff, James H. Nicholson. *Assoc Prod* Norman Herman. *Prod Assoc* Jack Cash. *Screenplay* Stephen H. Yafa. *Photog* J. Burgi Contner. *Prod Dsgn* William Creber. *Titl* Sandy Dvore, Pacific Title. *Film Ed* Richard C. Meyer, Eve Newman. *Mus* Chad Stuart. *Mus Supv* Al Simms. *Song:* "Paxton Quigley's Had the Course" Chad Stuart, Jeremy Clyde. *Sung by* Chad and Jeremy. *Sd* Brad Trask. *Asst Dir* Reuben Watt. *Prod Mgr* Elliot Schick. *Wardrobe* Fern Vollner. *Makeup* Ted Coodley.

Cast: Christopher Jones *(Paxton Quigley)*, Yvette Mimieux *(Tobey Clinton)*, Judy Pace *(Eulice)*, Maggie Thrett *(Jan)*, Nan Martin *(Dean Nazarin)*, Reva Rose *(Selma)*, John Beck, actor *(Jake)*, Richard Derr *(Mr. Clinton)*, Eve McVeagh *(Mrs. Clinton)*, Honey Alden *(Flo)*, Tom Ahearne *(Wilfred)*.

Comedy-drama. Source: Stephen H. Yafa, *Paxton Quigley's Had the Course* (Philadelphia, 1967). At a college dance Paxton Quigley, who likes to regale his fraternity brothers with stories of his sexual prowess, meets Tobey Clinton, a pretty student from the nearby college for women. Despite his reluctance to commit himself to any one girl, Paxton falls in love with Tobey and spends his summer vacation with her. Though their idyllic romance is cut short by the arrival of Tobey's parents, they resume their affair when classes begin again in the fall. Still unwilling to be tied down, Paxton falls victim to Eulice, an attractive black art student who seduces him and persuades him to pose for her in the nude. Before long, Paxton extends his favors to a third girl, Jan, a Jewish flower child. By adhering to an intricate time schedule, he keeps each girl convinced that she is his only love. In time, however, the girls discover his deception, and they plot to teach him a lesson. Locking him in an attic, they individually visit him daily in a combined effort to sap, and then destroy, his sexual appetite. Paxton enjoys himself at first, but he soon admits defeat and begs to be released. He goes on a hunger strike, but the girls continue to make their daily visits to the attic. Eventually, Eulice and Jan weaken in their resolve, despite Tobey's demand that he be kept a hostage until he explains his behavior. Too weak to walk when he is finally released, he collapses in the girls' dormitory and is hospitalized. While recovering, he realizes that Tobey's action was only a measure of the love she has for him; and, once he is discharged, he allows Eulice to drive him to the bus station in the hope of stopping the departing Tobey. No longer caring about his big-man-on-campus reputation, Paxton takes the willing Tobey in his arms and wins her forgiveness. *Philanderers. Braggarts. Students. Negroes. Jews. Flower children. College life. Seduction. Abduction. Vacations. Hospitals.*

Note: Locations filmed at the University of North Carolina at Chapel Hill and in Durham, North Carolina.

3 IN THE CELLAR see **UP IN THE CELLAR**

3 INTO 2 WON'T GO (Great Britain)   **F6.5026**
Julian Blaustein. *For* Ltd. Universal Pictures. *Dist* Universal Pictures. 2 Jul **1969** [New York opening; c6 Oct 1969; LP39053]. Sd; col (Technicolor). 35mm. 93 min. *MPAA rating* R.
Prod Julian Blaustein. *Dir* Peter Hall. *Screenplay* Edna O'Brien. *Dir Photog* Walter Lassally. *Art Dir* Peter Murton. *Set Decor* Bryan Graves. *Film Ed* Alan Osbiston. *Mus Comp* Francis Lai. *Mus Arr & Cond* Christian Gaubert. *Sd* Robert Allen, Garth Craven. *Asst Dir* Christopher Dryhurst. *Prod Supv* Basil Appleby. *Cost* Ruth Myers. *Makeup* Michael Morris. *Hairstyles* Joyce James.
Cast: Rod Steiger (*Steve Howard*), Claire Bloom (*Frances Howard*), Judy Geeson (*Ella Patterson*), Peggy Ashcroft (*Belle*), Paul Rogers (*Jack Roberts*), Lynn Farleigh (*Janet*), Elizabeth Spriggs (*Marcia*), Sheila Allen (*Beth*).
Drama. Source: Andrea Newman, *Three Into Two Won't Go* (London, 1967). While driving home from his office in the Midlands, Steve Howard, an English sales executive, picks up Ella Patterson, a pretty hitchhiker, and takes her to a hotel owned by his friend Jack Roberts. Steve soon discovers that she keeps a diary of the sexual prowess of her lovers and has rated him highly. The next morning Steve offers to drive Ella home, but she decides to stay and work for Jack at the hotel. Steve arrives at the new suburban home he and his schoolteacher wife, Frances, have recently purchased to bolster their childless marriage and finds her in the midst of unpacking. Despite her effort to please him by placing her mother, Belle, in a nursing home, Steve becomes restless and leaves for the Midlands again. After he has spent another night with Ella and then gone to Manchester, the young girl hitchhikes to his home and tells Frances that she was forced to quit her job because of Jack's advances. Unaware of the relationship between Ella and Steve, Frances moves the girl into the guest room. On his return trip, Steve stops at the hotel and learns from Jack that Ella took some of his money and left him only a farewell note. Flabbergasted to find Ella in his house, Steve's annoyance turns to rage when Ella tells the sympathetic Frances that she may be pregnant. Unable to cope with Ella's abortion threats, Steve finally agrees to leave his wife. Sensing that something is wrong, Frances offers to adopt the child, but Steve tells her that he is going away with Ella; however, when he goes to meet her, she fails to appear. Despondent, Steve gets drunk and returns home to find his mother-in-law chatting with Frances, as well as Ella, who has announced that she is not pregnant. After a stormy argument, Frances and Belle leave, and Ella ignores Steve. Rejected by both wife and mistress, Steve packs his suitcase and leaves. *Salesmen. Hitchhikers. Schoolteachers. Mothers-in-law. Marriage. Infidelity. Childlessness. Duplicity. Pregnancy. Drunkenness. Hotels. Diaries. The Midlands. London. Manchester (England).*
Note: Opened in London in Jul 1969.

THE THREE LIVES OF THOMASINA (United States/Great Britain)
F6.5027
Walt Disney Productions. *Dist* Buena Vista Distribution Co. 11 Dec **1963** [New York opening; c12 Dec 1963; LP27748]. Sd (RCA); col (Technicolor).

35mm. 97 min.
Overall Production Credits: *Pres by* Walt Disney. *Prod* Walt Disney. *Assoc Prod* Hugh Attwooll. *Dir* Don Chaffey. *Screenplay* Robert Westerby. *Dir Photog* Paul Beeson. *Camera Op* David Harcourt. *Focus* Alec Mills. *Art Dir* Michael Stringer. *Ch Draughtsman* Norman Dorme. *Set Dresser* Vernon Dixon. *Scenic Artist* A. Van Montagu. *Film Ed* Gordon Stone. *1st & 2d Asst Ed* Barry Peters, Tony Hunt. *Assembly Ed* Robin Clarke. *Mus* Paul Smith. *Song:* "Thomasina" Terry Gilkyson. *Orch* Walter Sheets. *Mus Cond* Eric Rogers. *Sd Ed* Jonathan Bates. *Sd Rec* C. C. Stevens, Gordon McCallum. *Boom Op* Gus Lloyd. *Sd Camera Op* Charles Arnold. *1st, 2d & 3d Asst Dir* Dennis Bertera, Terence Churcher, Terry Marcel. *Prod Mgr* Peter Manley. *Unit Mgr* Basil Appleby. *Cont* Marjorie Lavelly. *Prod Sec* Jean Walter. *Cost Dsgn* Margaret Furse. *Wardrobe Master* John Briggs. *Wardrobe Mistress* Brenda Dabbs. *Makeup* Harry Frampton. *Hairstyles* Betty Sherriff, Florence Hude. *Sp Eff* Ub Iwerks, Jim Fetherolf. *Casting* Maude Spector. *Animals* Jimmy Chipperfield. *Constr Mgr* Gus Walker. *Prod Buyer* Ron Quelch. *Still Photog* John Jay. *Chargehand Dressing Prop* Harry Townsend. *Elec Supv* Vic Smith. *Carpenter* Harry Goetz. *Stagehand* C. Manning. *Grip* Bill Bannister.
2d Unit Production Credits: *Dir* Gordon Stone. *Dir Photog* Michael Reed, Ray Sturgess. *Camera Op* Alan Hall. *Focus* Brian Bennett, photog, Michael Sarafian. *1st & 2d Asst Dir* Clive Midwinter, Richard Jenkins. *Grip* Peter Hall, photog, Ted Underwood. *Chargehand Electrn* Reg Blackburn, Curly Bradley. *Chargehand Prop* Bert Rixon, Dingle Bell.
Cast: Patrick McGoohan (*Dr. Andrew MacDhui*), Susan Hampshire (*Lori MacGregor*), Karen Dotrice (*Mary MacDhui*), Laurence Naismith (*Rev. Angus Peddie*), Jean Anderson (*Mrs. MacKenzie*), Wilfrid Brambell (*Willie Bannock*), Finlay Currie (*Grandpa Stirling*), Vincent Winter (*Hughie Stirling*), Denis Gilmore (*Jamie McNab*), Ewan Roberts (*Constable McQuarrie*), Oliver Johnston (*Mr. Dobbie*), Francis De Wolff (*Targu*), Charles Carson (*doctor*), Nora Nicholson (*old lady*), Jack Stewart, British (*Birnie*), Matthew Garber (*Geordie*), Elspeth March (*the voice of Thomasina*), Thomasina (*herself, a cat*), Alex Mackenzie, Ruth Dunning, Gwen Nelson.
Melodrama. Source: Paul Gallico, *Thomasina, the Cat Who Thought She Was God* (Garden City, New York, 1957). Andrew MacDhui, a widower and veterinarian, lives in turn-of-the-century Inveranoch, Scotland, with his young daughter, Mary, and her pet marmalade cat, Thomasina. The cat becomes injured in an accident, and MacDhui, diagnosing tetanus, orders the animal destroyed. After vowing never to speak to her father again, Mary and the other children of the village hold an elaborate funeral for the supposedly-dead Thomasina, but they are frightened away by the mysterious Lori MacGregor, a healer of animals whom the villagers regard as a sort of witch. Lori discovers that the animal is still alive and nurses it back to health, though the cat's injury has caused her to lose her memory. In time the townspeople become resentful of MacDhui, who, though he is a good doctor, shows a seeming lack of sympathy for their pets; and they begin bringing their ailing pets to Lori. MacDhui visits the young woman, and they strike up a close friendship when he saves the life of a badger. One evening Thomasina wanders near the MacDhui house and is seen by Mary, who, during a thundering rainstorm, rushes after her in vain. As a result, the child contracts pneumonia and lingers near death. Desperate, MacDhui enlists the aid of Lori in the hope that her special "medicine of love" will help Mary to recover. A sudden clap of thunder restores Thomasina's memory and causes her to return to the MacDhui house. The animal's reappearance restores Mary to health, and she recovers to be a bridesmaid at the wedding of her father and Lori. *Widowers. Veterinarians. Witches. Parenthood. Children. Village life. Animal care. Pneumonia. Funerals. Weddings. Scotland. Storms. Cats. Pets.*
Note: Location scenes filmed in Inveraray, Scotland, and Black Park in Buckinghamshire, England. Opened in London in May 1964.

THREE NIGHTS OF LOVE (Italy)   **F6.5028**
Jolly Film. *Dist* Magna Pictures Distribution Corp. Nov **1969**. Sd; col (Technicolor). 35mm (Techniscope). 112 min.
Overall Production Credits: *Prod* Silvio Clementelli. *Cost* Piero Gherardi.
Production Credits for "Fatebenefratelli": *Dir* Luigi Comencini. *Story & Screenplay* Marcello Fondato. *Photog* Mario Montuori. *Film Ed* Renato Cinquini. *Mus* Giuseppe Fusco.
Production Credits for "La vedova": *Dir* Renato Castellani. *Story & Screenplay* Franco Castellano, Pipolo. *Photog* Mario Montuori. *Film Ed* Iolanda Benvenuti. *Mus* Carlo Rustichelli.
Production Credits for "La moglie bambina": *Dir* Franco Rossi. *Story & Screenplay* Massimo Franciosa, Luigi Magni. *Photog* Roberto Gerardi. *Film Ed* Giorgio Serralonga. *Mus* Piero Piccioni.
Cast for "Fatebenefratelli": Catherine Spaak (*Ghiga*), John P. Law (*Fra Felice*).
Cast for "La vedova": Catherine Spaak (*Giselle*), Renato Salvatori (*Nicola*), Aldo Puglisi.

Cast for "La moglie bambina": Catherine Spaak (*Cirilla*), Enrico Maria Salerno (*Giuliano*), Diletta D'Andrea (*Gabriella*).

Comedy-drama. FATEBENEFRATELLI: Ghiga, a high-class call girl, is taken to a hospital run by friars after she is seriously injured in an automobile accident. Brother Felice, who is preparing to take his final vows, attempts to save Ghiga's soul while she attempts to seduce him. Later, Ghiga becomes a nun, and Felice leaves the order. LA VEDOVA: Giselle, a recently widowed Parisienne, brings her husband's body back to his hometown in Sicily without knowing that he was a Mafia kingpin. She innocently befriends several men in town, only to discover later that they have been murdered by her husband's associates. LA MOGLIE BAMBINA: Cirilla, young bride of middle-aged Giuliano, is troubled by her husband's emotional problems, most of which result from the difference in their ages, and suggests that he have an affair with another woman to ease his tension. [Sources indicate that each episode has a surprise ending.] *Prostitutes. Monks. Nuns. Widows. French. Religious conversion. Murder. Marriage. Infidelity. Monasteries. Hospitals. Sicily. Mafia. Automobile accidents.*

Note: Released in Italy in 1964 as *Tre notti d'amore*; running time: 122 min.

THREE NUTS IN SEARCH OF A BOLT   F6.5029

Harlequin International Pictures. 29 May **1964** [New York showing; c29 May 1964; LP30643]. Sd; b&w with col seq (Eastman Color). 35mm. 80 min.

A Tommy Noonan–Ian McGlashan Production. *Prod-Writ* Tommy Noonan, Ian McGlashan. *Dir* Tommy Noonan. *Photog* Fouad Said. *Art Dir* Carrol Ballard. *Supv Film Ed* William Martin. *Mus* Phil Moody. *Song:* "I Used To Be a Stripper Down on Main; Now I'm the Main Attraction on the Strip" Pony Sherrell, Phil Moody. *Choreog* Ward Ellis. *Prod Mgr* William J. Magginetti. *Prop Master* Jesse Slaughter.

Cast: Mamie Van Doren (*Saxie Symbol*), Tommy Noonan (*Tommy*), Ziva Rodann (*Dr. Myra Von*), Paul Gilbert (*Joe Lynch*), John Cronin (*Bruce Bernard*), Peter Howard (*Dr. Otis Salverson*), T. C. Jones (*Henry*), Charles Irving (*R. L. Katz*), Alvy Moore (*Sutter T. Finley*), Robert Kenneally (*Lennie*), Marjorie Bennett (*Mrs. Barkley-Kent*), Arthur Gould-Porter (*Mr. Blyth*), Pat O'Moore (*Edwards*), Jennie Lee (*Miss Griswald*), Jimmy Cross (*drunk*), Curt Mercer (*1st crook*), Richard Normoyle (*2d crook*), Frank Kreig (*bartender*), Pat Noone (*Miss Frisbee*), Kathy Waniata (*school teacher*), Phil Arnold (*television technician*).

Comedy. In search of inexpensive psychiatric treatment, three "nuts," Saxie Symbol, Joe Lynch, and Bruce Bernard, pool their limited funds and pay an unemployed actor, Tommy, to go to a leading psychiatrist, Dr. Myra Von, and act out all of their personalities. Dr. Von, after watching and listening to Tommy's antics, is convinced that he is a rare triple-personality, and she immediately sets up a secret closed-circuit telecast of their next meeting in order to share her discovery with the world's leading psychiatrists. Through an electronic error, however, Tommy's triple-personality is telecast nation-wide. A Hollywood producer, R. L. Katz, promptly buys the screen rights to their "show" for $100,000. Tommy confesses the truth to Katz but rather than being upset, he feels it improves the story even more. Tommy, now an employed actor, helps Joe and Bruce solve their problems, and he convinces Saxie that she should settle down with a good guy—like himself. *Psychiatrists. Actors. Motion picture producers. Psychiatry. Dual personality. Hoaxes. Television.*

THREE ON A COUCH   F6.5030

Jerry Lewis Productions. *Dist* Columbia Pictures. 22 Jun **1966** [Cleveland opening; c1 Jul 1966; LP32758]. Sd; col (Pathé). 35mm. 109 min.

Prod-Dir Jerry Lewis. *Assoc Prod* Joe E. Stabile. *Screenplay* Bob Ross, Samuel Taylor. *Story* Arne Sultan, Marvin Worth. *Dir Photog* W. Wallace Kelley. *Adtl Photog* Robert Bronner. *Camera Op* Richard Johnson, photog. *Art Dir* Leo K. Kuter. *Set Decor* Howard Bristol. *Film Ed* Russel Wiles. *Asst Ed* Joe Luciano. *Mus Comp & Cond* Louis Y. Brown. *Song:* "A Now and a Later Love" sung by Danny Costello. *Sd Supv* Charles J. Rice. *Sd* Walter Goss. *1st & 2d Asst Dir* Rusty Meek, Hal Bell. *Unit Prod Mgr* Howard Pine. *Script Supv* Richard Chaffee. *Cost Dsgn* Moss Mabry. *Men's Wardrobe* Sy Devore, Nat Wise. *Makeup Supv* Ben Lane. *Makeup* Jack Stone. *Hairstyles* Virginia Jones, Joyce Morrison. *Audio Vis* James Wright. *Dial Coach* Eddie Reider.

Cast: Jerry Lewis (*Christopher Pride/Warren/Ringo/Rutherford/Heather*), Janet Leigh (*Dr. Elizabeth Acord*), Mary Ann Mobley (*Susan Manning*), Gila Golan (*Anna Jacque*), Leslie Parrish (*Mary Lou Mauve*), James Best (*Dr. Ben Mizer*), Kathleen Freeman (*Murphy*), Buddy Lester (*drunk*), Renzo Cesana (*ambassador*), Fritz Feld (*attaché*), Jesslyn Fax, Renie Riano.

Comedy. Commercial artist Christopher Pride receives a $10,000 commission to design a mural in Paris and tries to persuade his fiancée, Dr. Elizabeth Acord, a psychiatrist, to marry him and honeymoon in Paris. Elizabeth refuses to leave her practice, however, because her three female patients with extreme hostility toward men should not be abandoned in analysis. Determined to marry Elizabeth, Chris decides to assume three different disguises and woo the patients. After successfully accomplishing this task, the patients are greatly improved, and Elizabeth and Chris board the ship for France, where they will marry. Unknown to Chris, Elizabeth has asked the women to come and see them off; when they each recognize Chris as their new boyfriend, Elizabeth is furious and refuses to sail. The women advise her not to make the same mistake they did, and Elizabeth rejoins Chris. *Commercial artists. Psychiatrists. Man-haters. Disguise. Neurosis. Courtship.*

Note: Location scenes filmed in San Francisco.

THREE ON A MATCH see **FOR LOVE OR MONEY**

THREE ON A SPREE (Great Britain)   F6.5031

Caralan Productions. *Dist* United Artists. 28 Jun **1961** [Los Angeles opening; c14 Jun 1961; LP21674]. Sd; b&w. 35mm. 83 min.

Prod George Fowler. *Exec Prod* David E. Rose. *Dir* Sidney J. Furie. *Screenplay* Siegfried Herzig, Charles Rogers, Wilkie Mahoney. *Adapt* James Kelly, Peter Miller. *Photog* Stephen Dade. *Camera Op* John Winbolt. *Focus Puller* Mark Hyams. *Art Dir* John Blezard. *Asst Art Dir* Donald Fisher. *Film Ed* A. H. Rule. *1st Asst Ed* Alan Bell. *2d Asst Ed* Ray Thorne. *Mus Dir* Philip Martell. *Sd Mix* Arthur Bradburn. *Boom Op* Ken Reynolds. *Sd Camera Op* Lionel Strutt. *Dub Ed* Robert Winter. *1st, 2d & 3d Asst Dir* Fred Slark, Denis Johnson, Jr., Scott Wodehouse. *Prod Mgr* Buddy Booth. *Prod Sec* Liz Charles-Williams. *Cont* Josie Fulford. *Wardrobe* Jackie Cummins. *Makeup* Scott Fletcher. *Hairdressing* Pearl Tipaldi. *Prop Buyer* George Blackburn. *Prop* Arthur Fell. *Still Photog* Freddie Williams. *Grip* Bert Habicht. *Carpenter* J. Franklin. *Rigger* W. Redmond.

Cast: Jack Watling (*Michael Brewster*), Carole Lesley (*Susan*), Renee Houston (*Mrs. Gray*), John Slater (*Sid Johnson*), Colin Gordon (*Mitchell*), John Salew (*Mr. Monkton*), Julian Orchard (*Walker*), Libby Morris (*Trixie*), Cardew Robinson (*Micki*), Ernest Clark (*Colonel Drew*), Ronald Adam (*judge*), June Cunningham (*Rosie*), Jeanne Moody (*Barbara Drew*), Marne Maitland (*Eastern gentleman*), Hugh Morton (*Grant*), Gertan Klauber (*Joe*), Ruth Lee (*receptionist*), John Vivyan (*Big Louis*).

Farce. Source: George Barr McCutcheon, *Brewster's Millions* (New York, 1902). Winchell Smith and Byron Ongley, *Brewster's Millions; a Comedy in Four Acts* (New York opening: 31 Dec 1906). A young Englishman, Michael Brewster, learns he will inherit his late uncle's fortune of £8 million provided he can spend a million within a specified time. In addition, he cannot spend the money indiscriminately, he must show receipts for every penny, and he must disavow any matrimonial intentions—a stipulation that infuriates his girl friend, Susan. After quitting his job, Michael enlists the help of two colleagues and forms a finance company, determined to make bad deals and go bankrupt, but, unhappily, everything he touches turns to gold. Increasingly desperate, he deliberately invites a breach of promise suit by proposing to a showgirl who is starring in a show he has produced and then refusing to marry her. This scheme backfires, too, and money continues to pour in from unexpected sources, but at last, he manages to give away the unspent portion of the million pounds and is reunited with Susan. *Heirs. Uncles. Millionaires. Showgirls. Theatrical producers. Breach of promise.*

Note: Released in Great Britain in Nov 1961; running time: 91 min. Working title: *Brewster's Millions.* Copyright claimant: Eldorado Pictures. Previously filmed as *Brewster's Millions* in 1921, in 1935 (Great Britain) and in 1945.

THREE PENNY OPERA (France/West Germany)   F6.5032

Kurt Ulrich Film–C. E. C. *Dist* Embassy Pictures. 14 Oct **1964** [Detroit opening]. Sd; col (Eastman Color). 35mm (Franscope). 83 min.

Prod Kurt Ulrich. *Dir* Wolfgang Staudte. *Screenplay* Wolfgang Staudte, Günter Weisenborn. *Photog* Roger Fellous. *Set Dsgn* Hein Heckroth. *Film Ed* Wolfgang Wehrum. *Mus Dir* Peter Sandloff. *Mus* Kurt Weill. *German Text* Bertolt Brecht. *English Text* Marc Blitzstein. *Mus Scoring* Karl Helmer, Erwin Dräger. *Choreog* Dick Price. *Sd* Fritz Schwarz. *Prod Mgr* Heinz Willeg. *Cost Dsgn* Hein Heckroth.

Cast: Sammy Davis, Jr. (*ballad singer*), Curd Jürgens (*Macheath*), June Ritchie (*Polly Peachum*), Hildegard Knef (*Pirate Jenny*), Marlene Warrlich (*Lucy Brown*), Lino Ventura (*Tiger Brown*), Gert Fröbe (*Peachum*), Hilde Hildebrandt (*Mrs. Peachum*), Walter Giller (*Filch*), Hans W. Hamacher, Henning Schlüter, Hans Reiser, Siegfried Wischnewski, Walter Feuchtenberg, Stanislav Ledinek, Martin Berliner, Max Strassberg, Stefan Wigger, Robert Manuel, Jürgen Feindt, Adeline Wagner, Erna Haffner, Celssia Wade, Jacqueline Pierreux.

Musical comedy. Source: John Gay, *Beggar's Opera* (London, 1728). Kurt Weill and Bertolt Brecht, *Die Dreigroschenoper* (Berlin opening: 31 Aug 1928). Macheath, chief of the London bandits, marries Polly Peachum, daughter of the beggar king. Enraged, Mr. and Mrs. Peachum arrange to have the thief arrested by his reluctant friend, police inspector Tiger Brown. Accordingly, the couple persuades Macheath's former mistress, the whore Pirate Jenny, to betray him. Although sentenced to die, Macheath is pardoned by the queen on her coronation day. *Thieves. Beggars. Prostitutes. Police. Lower classes.*

Friendship. Perfidy. Capital punishment. Weddings. Jails. London.

Note: Opened in Munich in Feb 1963 as *Die Dreigroschenoper;* running time: 124 min.

THREE PLUS THREE EQUALS SEX *see* **INSTANT NYMPHO, OR 3 + 3 = SEX**

THE THREE SEXATEERS
F6.5033

Yoni Films. *Dist* Distribpix, Inc. 5 Feb **1970** [San Francisco showing]. Sd; b&w. 35mm. 64 min.

Prod-Dir Robert Ruttenberg. *Assoc Prod* Robert Sosenko. *Camera* Robert Sosenko.

Cast: Lisa Sanders, Yolanda, Claudine DuBois, Rupert Light, Tony Dabos.

Sex film. Three young women set out for a weekend of skiing, but when their car runs out of gasoline, they meet two men. The group soon warms up, and an orgy ensues, featuring lesbian and heterosexual partnerships as well as troilism. *Troilism. Group sex. Lesbianism. Skiing.*

THREE SINNERS *see* **THREE FACES OF SIN**

THE THREE SISTERS (U.S.S.R.)
F6.5034

Mosfilm. *Dist* Brandon Films. 29 Jan **1969** [New York opening]. Sd; b&w. 35mm. 112 min. [Also reviewed at 115 min.]

Pres by Artkino Pictures. *Dir-Writ* Samson Samsonov. *Photog* Fyodor Dobronravov. *Art Dir* Sergey Voronkov, I. Novoderezhkin. *Mus* Vasiliy Dekhteryov. *Sd* Grigoriy Korenblyum. *Asst Dir* I. Bityukov.

Cast: Lyubov Sokolova *(Olga),* Margarita Volodina *(Masha),* Tatyana Malchenko *(Irina),* Leonid Gubanov *(Andrey),* Alla Larionova *(Natalya),* Lev Ivanov *(Vershinin),* Leonid Gallis *(Kulygin),* Konstantin Sorokin *(Chebutykin),* Oleg Strizhenov *(Tuzenbakh),* Vladimir Druzhnikov *(Solyonyy),* L. Konstantinova, P. Vinnik, V. Stepanov, Boris Smirnov, N. Lubko, G. Dudarev.

Drama. Source: Anton Pavlovich Chekhov, *Tri sestry* (Moscow opening: 31 Jan 1901). In the late 1890's the three Prozorov sisters are living in a provincial Russian garrison town; 11 years have passed since their father, an army officer who has since died, was transferred to the town from Moscow. Well educated, they are bored with their monotonous lives and long to return to Moscow, though they are prevented from doing so by their financial circumstances. Olga, the spinsterish eldest sister, teaches school. Masha, the middle sister, is unhappily married to the local schoolmaster, Kulygin, and secretly loves Colonel Vershinin, the new battery commander, whose home life is equally unhappy. Irina, the high-spirited youngest sister, is eventually forced to take a dull job in a telegraph office. The women's brother, Andrey, abandons his university studies when he marries a scheming and unfaithful local girl, Natalya, who takes over the management of the household. Masha enters into an illicit affair with Vershinin; and Irina and Olga gloomily face the realization that they probably will never return to Moscow. Their hopes are completely shattered when Andrey, deep in gambling debts, mortgages the family home and allows Natalya to handle the mortgage money. The following winter, after a fire has swept through the town, the army regiment is moved out of the garrison. Hoping to salvage her life, Irina agrees to marry Baron Tuzenbakh, whom she does not love, but he is killed in a duel. Once the regiment has left and Masha has bid goodby to her beloved Vershinin, the three sisters embrace as Olga wonders aloud if their suffering will ever turn to joy. *Sisters. Schoolteachers. Telegraph operators. Students. Smalltown life. Infidelity. Finance—Personal. Education. Marriage. Brother-sister relationship. Gambling. Mortgages. Moscow. Russia—Army. Fires. Duels.*

Note: Released in the U.S.S.R. in 1964 as *Tri sestry.*

THE THREE STOOGES GO AROUND THE WORLD IN A DAZE
F6.5035

Normandy Productions. *Dist* Columbia Pictures. 21 Aug **1963** [Cleveland opening; c1 Sep 1963; LP26602]. Sd (Westrex); b&w. 35mm. 94 min.

Prod-Dir-Story Norman Maurer. *Screenplay* Elwood Ullman. *Dir Photog* Irving Lippman. *Camera Op* Arnold Rich. *Camera Asst* Al Bettcher. *Art Dir* Don Ament. *Set Decor* James M. Crowe. *Film Ed* Edwin Bryant. *Mus* Paul Dunlap. *Sd Supv* Charles J. Rice. *Sd Mix* William Bernds. *Rec* Harold Lee. *Asst Dir* Eddie Saeta, Pat Corleto. *Script Supv* Charlsie Bryant. *Cost* Ted Tetrick, Grace Kuhn. *Makeup* Joe DiBella. *Hairstyles* Lillian Hokom. *Sp Eff* Richard Albain. *Still Photog* Homer Van Pelt. *Prop* Clarence Peet, Hudson Radabaugh. *Grip* Les Gaunt, W. Rose. *Gaffer* James Field.

Cast: Moe Howard *(Moe),* Larry Fine *(Larry),* Joe De Rita *(Curly),* Jay Sheffield *(Phileas Fogg III),* Joan Freeman *(Amelia),* Walter Burke *(Lory Filch),* Peter Forster *(Vickers Cavendish),* Maurice Dallimore *(Crotchet),* Richard Devon *(maharajah),* Antony Eustrel *(Kandu),* Iau Kea *(Itchi Kitchi),* Robert Kino *(Charlie Okuma),* Phil Arnold *(referee),* Murray Alper *(Gus),* Don Lamond *(Bill),* Jack Greening *(McPherson),* Emil Sitka *(butler),* Geoffrey A. Maurer *(Timmy),* Ramsay Hill *(Gatesby),* Colin Campbell *(Willoughby),* Michael St. Clair *(1st mate),* Ron Whelan *(Harry).*

Adventure farce. Loosely based on: Jules Verne, *Le tour du monde en quatre-vingts jours* (Paris, 1873). Unscrupulous crook Vickers Cavendish attains membership in London's famous Reform Club through trickery. He informs fellow member Phileas Fogg III, great-grandson of the man who made the famous 80-day trip around the world, that his own great-grandfather was one of the men financially ruined by betting against the successful completion of that journey. When Cavendish claims the feat succeeded only because Fogg I cheated, Fogg III bets him and other Reform Club members £20,000 that he can make the same trip without spending a cent. Fogg and Cavendish meet the following day to draw up a formal agreement at the bank, where the latter steals money in such a way that the theft is not discovered until Fogg and his three servants—Moe, Larry, and Curly—have stowed away on a steamer bound for Istanbul. Meanwhile, J. B. Crotchet of Scotland Yard pursues Fogg, who has been blamed for the crime, as do Cavendish and his accomplice, Lory Filch, with the latter two planning to murder Fogg to ensure their winning the bet. After wrestling toe-to-toe with a giant, dodging knives thrown by a maharajah's bodyguards, and experiencing numerous other misadventures in Calcutta, China, Tokyo, San Francisco, and Canada, the four travelers arrive back in London with Amelia, a comely American woman they have met along the way. Cavendish and Filch's guilt is established, and Fogg is able to reach the Reform Club in time to win both the bet and Amelia's hand. *Domestics. Thieves. Stowaways. Giants. Royalty. Americans in foreign countries. Travel. Ancestry. Theft. Wagers. Clubs. Banks. London. Canada. Calcutta. China. Tokyo. San Francisco. Scotland Yard. Phileas Fogg.*

THE THREE STOOGES IN ORBIT
F6.5036

Normandy Productions. *Dist* Columbia Pictures. 11 Jul **1962** [New York opening; c4 Jul 1962; LP22855]. Sd (Westrex); b&w. 35mm. 87 min.

Prod Norman Maurer. *Dir* Edward Bernds. *Screenplay* Elwood Ullman. *Story* Norman Maurer. *Dir Photog* William F. Whitley. *Camera Op* Emil Oster, Jr. *Asst Camera* Al Bettcher. *Art Dir* Don Ament. *Set Decor* Richard Mansfield. *Film Ed* Edwin Bryant. *Mus* Paul Dunlap. *Sd Supv* Charles J. Rice. *Sd* William Bernds. *Rec* Harry Foy, George Anderson. *Asst Sd* Doug Grant. *Asst Dir* Eddie Saeta, Burt Astor. *Script Supv* Eylla Jacobus. *Cost* Ted Tetrick, Pat Page. *Makeup* Frank McCoy. *Hairstyles* Peggy McDonald. *Still Photog* Homer Van Pelt. *Gaffer* James Field. *Key Grip* Les Gaunt. *Prop* Ed Goldstein, Clarence Peet.

Cast: Moe Howard *(Moe),* Larry Fine *(Larry),* Joe De Rita *(Curly Joe),* Carol Christensen *(Carol),* Edson Stroll *(Capt. Tom Andrews),* Emil Sitka *(Professor Danforth),* George Neise *(Ogg),* Rayford Barnes *(Zogg),* Norman Leavitt *(Williams),* Nestor Paiva *(chairman),* Peter Dawson *(General Bixby),* Peter Brocco *(Dr. Appleby),* Don Lamond *(Colonel Smithers),* Thomas Glynn *(George Galveston),* Maurice Manson *(Mr. Lansing),* Jean Charney *(WAF sergeant),* Duane Ament *(personnel clerk),* Bill Dyer *(Colonel Lane),* Roy Engel *(Welby),* Jane Wald *(bathing girl),* Cheerio Meredith *(tooth paste old maid).*

Comedy. Television performers Moe, Larry, and Curly Joe, known collectively as The Three Stooges, rent a room in a gloomy castle from eccentric inventor Professor Danforth, who is perfecting a combination tank-submarine-helicopter to use as an all-purpose military weapon. Unbeknown to Danforth, his servant is a Martian spy who plans to steal the machine. The professor's daughter Carol visits the castle and is present when Air Force Capt. Tom Andrews arrives to arrange a demonstration of the invention, an event the Stooges subsequently turn into a total disaster. Later, two Martians, Ogg and Zogg, steal the machine and fly away with it, but the Stooges cling to its side and are able to hang on despite all efforts to shake them loose. Both the machine and the Martians are ultimately destroyed as the Stooges crash-land in their television studio, where they are offered a new contract on the spot. Meanwhile, Carol and Tom have fallen in love. *Television personalities. Professors. Inventors. Domestics. Spies. Space creatures. Space travel. Theft. Castles. Inventions. Tanks (armored cars). Submarines. Helicopters. Television studios. United States Air Force.*

THE THREE STOOGES MEET HERCULES
F6.5037

Normandy Productions. *Dist* Columbia Pictures. 26 Jan **1962** [New York opening; c1 Feb 1962; LP21394]. Sd (RCA); b&w. 35mm. 89 min.

Prod-Story Norman Maurer. *Dir* Edward Bernds. *Screenplay* Elwood Ullman. *Dir Photog* Charles S. Welborn. *Art Dir* Don Ament. *Set Decor* William Calvert. *Film Ed* Edwin Bryant. *Mus* Paul Dunlap. *Sd Supv* Charles J. Rice. *Sd* James Z. Flaster. *Asst Dir* Herbert Wallerstein.

Cast: The Three Stooges *(themselves),* Vicki Trickett *(Diane Quigley),* Quinn Redeker *(Schuyler Davis),* George Neise *(Ralph Dimsal/Odius),* Samson Burke *(Hercules),* Mike McKeever *(Ajax [Cyclops]),* Marlin McKeever *(Argo [Cyclops]),* Emil Sitka *(shepherd),* Hal Smith *(Thesus),* John Cliff *(Ulysses),* Lewis Charles *(Achilles),* Barbara Hines *(Anita),* Terry Huntingdon *(Hecuba),* Diana Piper *(Helen),* Gregg Martell *(Simon),* Gene Roth *(captain),* Edward Foster *(Freddie),* Cecil Elliott *(matron),* Rusty

Wescoatt *(Philo)*, Don Lamond *(narrator)*.

Farce. In Ithaca, New York, the Three Stooges are working in a pharmacy run by Ralph Dimsal, an arrogant young man who is attracted to his pretty cosmetic clerk, Diane Quigley. One day the Stooges tamper with a time machine invented by Diane's boyfriend, Schuyler Davis, and transport themselves, Diane, and Schuyler to the Ithaca of 961 B. C. They discover that Ulysses has been dethroned by the arrogant Odius, who bears a remarkable resemblance to Ralph Dimsal. The Stooges and Schuyler escape from Odius' tyranny, but they are captured and made galley slaves by the King of Rhodes, who offers them their freedom if Schuyler can slay the dreaded two-headed cyclops. Aided by tranquilizers to calm his nerves, Schuyler does so and then goes on to overcome other monsters. Upon learning that Odius has designs on Diane and is forcing her into marriage, the Stooges and Schuyler hasten back to Ithaca. Odius challenges Schuyler to fight the famed but dimwitted Hercules in the arena. Schuyler gives Hercules an ignominious beating and forces him to mend his rowdy ways and live up to his future reputation by helping Ulysses regain the throne. Pursued by the enraged Odius, the five adventurers race back to the time machine and return to the present. Ralph Dimsal gets his just deserts when he becomes trapped in the time machine and narrowly escapes spending the rest of his life as a pilloried 17th-century pilgrim. *Salesclerks. Inventors. Galley slaves. Pharmacists. Royalty. Contests. Time machines. Tranquilizers. Ithaca (New York). Ithaca (Greece). Ulysses. Cyclops. Hercules. Mythological characters.*

THE THREE STOOGES MEET THE GUNSLINGERS see **THE OUTLAWS IS COMING**

THREE STRIKES AND YOU'RE ... RALPH   F6.5038
American Film Production Co. ca **1969**. Sd; col. 16mm. [Feature length assumed.]

Sex film. No information about the precise nature of this film has been found, but press sources suggest that it deals with a man who is unsuccessful in his sexual encounters with women. *Sexuality.*

THREE UNHOLY VIRGINS   F6.5039
All American Film Producers, Inc. *Dist* Empire Film Distributors. ca **1965**. Sd; col (Eastmancolor). 35mm. 60 min.

Sex film. No information about the precise nature of this film has been found, but press material indicates that it concerns three women who compare their sexual adventures with the same men. *Sexuality.*

Note: Filmed in Miami, Puerto Rico, and Venezuela.

THREE WAY MATCH see **FOR LOVE OR MONEY**

THREE-WAY SPLIT   F6.5040
Green Dolphin Productions. *Dist* Preferred Enterprises. 5 Jun **1970** [Champaign, Illinois, showing]. Sd; col. 35mm. 76 min.
Prod Dave Ackerman. *Dir* Charles Nizet.
Cast: Peter Owen, Donov Franchetti.

Action melodrama. Three psychopathic crooks attempt a daring holdup in Las Vegas, using automatic weapons and dynamite. During the adventure they seduce a number of women. *Psychopaths. Robbery. Seduction. Firearms. Dynamite. Las Vegas.*

Note: Filmed on location in Las Vegas.

THREE WAYS TO LOVE see **CHERRY, HARRY & RAQUEL**

THREE WEEKS OF LOVE   F6.5041
William E. Brusseau. *Dist* Westminster Films, Richard K. Polimer. ca **1965**. Sd; col (Eastmancolor). 35mm (CinemaScope). 75 min.
Prod-Dir-Story William E. Brusseau. *Screenplay* Harry Brown. *Photog* Junichi Segawa. *Art Dir* Totetsu Hirakawa. *Film Ed* Warren Adams. *Mus* Calvin Jackson, Ralph Carmichael. *Choreog* Don Yaka. *Sd* Gene Garvin, Russ Malmgren.
Cast: Lane Nakano *(Ken Okimura)*, Tamiko Aya *(Sumi)*, Tony Russel *(Bud)*, Tatsuo Saito *(Mr. Yasuda)*, Roland Ray *(captain)*, Joe Yue *(Joe Young)*, Miyako Morita *(Mrs. Young)*, Keiko Doi *(Sumi's sister)*, Reiko Okada *(Sumi's friend)*, Lucille Soong *(girl in Hong Kong)*, Kiyono Sasaki *(Sumi's mother)*.

Romantic melodrama. Ken Okimura, a nisei seaman who becomes a ship's officer aboard a Dutch freighter, meets Sumi, a hostess in a Tokyo nightclub, while he is on shore leave. They fall in love, but Japanese tradition prevents their marrying, and they eventually must part. *Nisei. Nightclub hostesses. Sailors. Japanese. Sea captains. Dutch. Social customs. Courtship. Freighters. Tokyo.*

Note: Location scenes filmed in Japan and Hong Kong.

THREES, MÉNAGE À TROIS   F6.5042
C. I. T. Films. *Dist* I. R. M. I. Films. 21 Feb **1968** [New York showing]. Sd; b&w. 35mm. 61 min.

Prod Sven Erikson. *Dir* Jan Anders. *Art Dir* Jack Miles. *Film Ed* Jack Miles.
Cast: Jane Lako *(Marilyn)*, John D. White, Suzanne Greco.

Melodrama. Louis and Marilyn Winston's marriage of convenience enables them to pursue separate sex lives, but Marilyn's arrangement is curtailed when her Czech lover is deported for his involvement in espionage. Marilyn seduces Louis; they quarrel; Marilyn then becomes drunk, kills Louis with a bottle, and commits suicide. *Czechoslovakians. Marriage of convenience. Deportation. Espionage. Seduction. Drunkenness. Murder. Suicide.*

THREESOME (United States/Denmark)   F6.5043
V. I. Productions. *Dist* Howard Mahler Films. 2 Oct **1970** [Los Angeles opening]. Sd; col (Technicolor). 35mm (Techniscope). 90 min. *MPAA rating* X.

A Brandon Chase Production. *Prod-Dir* Lee Beale. *Story & Screenplay* Kenneth Pressman. *Photog* Mikael Salomon. *Art Dir* The Design Group. *Set Decor* Irene Brydegaard, Aage Hansen. *Main Titl* Credit Design. *Film Ed* Lizzi Weischenfeldt. *Mus* David Whitaker. *Sd Supv* Jon Branner. *Sd Rec* Jarno Dupont. *Prod Supv* Marianne Schyberg.

Cast: Judy Brown *(Ursula)*, Marianne Tholsted *(Kirsten)*, Lotte Horne *(career woman)*, Finn Storgaard *(Peter)*, Jørgen Kiil *(Martin)*, Paul Glargaard *(playboy)*, Kjeld Norgaard *(racedriver)*, Erni Arneson *(grand hostess)*, Robert Gilston *(man from far away)*, Jørgen Weel *(psychiatrist)*, Paola Illum, Helle Louise, Ole Lassen, Vivi Olsen, Lotte Dessall, Jorn Freddie, Kate Holrick, Holger Vistisen, Jan Priiskorn Schmidt, Inger Gleerup, Leo Angart, Leif Fich, Hillary Sherrington, Avi Sagild, Kirsten Dedenroth.

Melodrama. Martin, a Danish fashion designer, marries Ursula, an American woman, in New York and returns with his bride to Denmark. Ursula is shocked by the female nudity involved in her husband's work and by the sexual freedom of her new environment. At a party, she witnesses a couple making love, and the sight of the passionate woman arouses her. She later has a series of erotic dreams and sexual affairs with both men and women. On the brink of an emotional collapse, Ursula visits a psychiatrist and is sent to a mental hospital outside of Copenhagen. There she has an affair with Peter, a narcotics addict, and watches in terror as he dies from an overdose. Afraid and alone, Ursula escapes from the hospital and finds comfort with Kirsten, a beautiful fashion model. However, upon discovering that she is pregnant by Peter, Ursula becomes disturbed by her sexual encounter with Kirsten and wanders onto a racetrack. A racing driver picks her up, and in an attempt to cure her lesbianism, he forces her to watch a stag movie. *Americans in foreign countries. Couturiers. Models. Drug addicts. Marriage. Lesbianism. Infidelity. Pregnancy. Drug overdose. Sexuality. Hospitals. Sex exploitation films. New York City. Copenhagen. Dreams.*

Note: Released in Denmark in 1969. Working title: *Ursula.* Lee Beale is a pseudonym for Brandon Chase.

THE THRILL DEVIATES see **THE THRILL KILLER**

THE THRILL KILLER   F6.5044
Dist Sack Amusement Enterprises, PAD Productions. 1 Jan **1965** [San Francisco opening]. Sd; col. 35mm. [Feature length assumed.]

Drama. A study of two sex deviates. Dale, a psychopath, follows a woman home and strangles her. Later he kills another woman and dresses in her clothes, makeup, and wig in order to avoid being detected. Glen is a rapist and child molester. He offers drugged candy to a young victim he has picked up outside a school, and when she resists his advances, he rapes her. As he is leaving, he spots his next victim, an attractive housewife. *Psychopaths. Murder. Rape. Female impersonation. Child molesting.*

Note: Also known as *Mondo Weirdo* and *The Thrill Deviates.*

THE THRILL KILLERS   F6.5045
Morgan-Steckler Productions. *Dist* Hollywood International Pictures, Hollywood Star Pictures. Jun **1965**. Sd; b&w. 35mm. 69 min.
Prod George J. Morgan. *Dir* Ray Dennis Steckler. *Screenplay* Ray Dennis Steckler, Gene Pollock. *Photog* Joseph V. Mascelli. *Art Dir* Tom Scherman. *Main Titl* Tom Scherman. *Film Ed* Austin McKinney. *Mus* Henry Price. *Sd* Lee Strosnider. *Asst Dir* Don Russell.

Cast: Cash Flagg *(Mort Click)*, Liz Renay *(Liz Saxon)*, Brick Bardo *(Joe Saxon)*, Carolyn Brandt, Ron Burr *(murdered lovers)*, Gary Kent *(Gary)*, Herb Robins *(Herbie)*, Keith O'Brien *(Keith)*, Laura Benedict *(Linda)*, Erina Enyo *(Erina Devore)*, Atlas King *(Dennis Kesdekian)*, Titus Moede *(motorcycle cop)*, George J. Morgan *(producer)*.

Melodrama. Hitchhiker Mort Click murders Dennis Kesdekian, a salesman from whom he accepted a ride. Click then stabs to death with a scissors prostitute Erina Devore. Gary, Herbie, and Keith, three psychopaths recently escaped from a mental hospital, behead a landlord and kill two lovers. In a roadhouse diner, cigar-smoking Linda poisons Herbie's coffee, and Keith is killed by Joe Saxon, an unsuccessful actor who has trailed his wife, Liz, to the country. Mort Click and Gary are finally tracked down and apprehended.

Hitchhikers. Psychopaths. Salesmen. Prostitutes. Escapees. Landlords. Actors. Murder. Poisoning. Diners (restaurants).

Note: Also known as *The Monsters Are Loose.* Cash Flagg is a pseudonym of Ray Dennis Steckler.

THE THRILL OF IT ALL   F6.5046

Ross Hunter Productions–Arwin Productions. *Dist* Universal Pictures. 17 Jul **1963** [Louisville, Kentucky, opening; c10 Aug 1963; LP32700]. Sd (Westrex); col (Eastman Color). 35mm. 108 min.

A Ross Hunter–Martin Melcher Production. *In Charge of Prod* Edward Muhl. *Dir* Norman Jewison. *Screenplay* Carl Reiner. *Story* Larry Gelbart, Carl Reiner. *Dir Photog* Russell Metty. *Art Dir* Alexander Golitzen, Robert Boyle. *Set Decor* Howard Bristol. *Main Titl* Pacific Title. *Film Ed* Milton Carruth. *Mus* De Vol. *Mus Supv* Joseph Gershenson. *Titl Song* Arnold Schwarzwald, Frederick Herbert. *Sung by* Johnny Mann Singers. *Sd* Waldon O. Watson, William Russell. *Asst Dir* Phil Bowles. *Unit Prod Mgr* Norman Deming. *Gowns Dsgn* Jean Louis. *Makeup* Bud Westmore. *Hairstyles* Larry Germain. *Rolls Royce Limousine* Peter Satori Co. *Dial Coach* Norman Stuart.

Cast: Doris Day (*Beverly Boyer*), James Garner (*Dr. Gerald Boyer*), Arlene Francis (*Mrs. Fraleigh*), Edward Andrews (*Gardiner Fraleigh*), Reginald Owen (*Old Tom Fraleigh*), ZaSu Pitts (*Olivia*), Elliott Reid (*Mike Palmer*), Alice Pearce (*woman*), Kym Karath (*Maggie Boyer*), Brian Nash (*Andy Boyer*), Lucy Landau (*Mrs. Goethe*), Paul Hartman (*Dr. Taylor*), Hayden Rorke (*Billings*), Alex Gerry (*Stokely*), Robert Gallagher (*Van Camp*), Anne Newman (*Miss Thompson*), Burt Mustin (*butler*), Hedley Mattingly (*chauffeur*), Robert Strauss (*1st truck driver*), Maurice Gosfield (*2d truck driver*), William Bramley (*driver*), Pamela Curran (*starlet*), Herbie Faye (*man*), Lenny Kent (*cabbie*), John Alderman (*Mr. Caputo*), Lennie Weinrib (*3d truck driver*), Carl Reiner.

Comedy. Beverly Boyer is a thrifty housewife living contentedly with her gynecologist husband, Gerald, and their two small children. One evening while dining at the home of Mrs. Evelyn Fraleigh, one of Gerald's patients, Beverly comments on the fine qualities of "Happy Soap," a product manufactured by Evelyn's father-in-law, Tom Fraleigh. The old man is so impressed by Beverly's enthusiasm that he hires her to do soap commercials on his television show. After an unfortunate start, Beverly's honesty and sincerity wins praise from both viewers and critics. Elated, old Fraleigh signs her to an $80,000 contract. Now a public celebrity, Beverly is forced to spend more and more time away from home; and trouble erupts at the Boyer household. The final blowup comes when Gerald accidentally drives his car into a swimming pool that had been installed in his backyard that afternoon. Outraged, he kicks cartons of "Happy Soap" into the pool and by morning the house is surrounded by soapsuds. After consulting a psychiatrist, he decides to get even with Beverly by pretending also to be too busy to spend time at home. His scheme works, and Beverly becomes so frantic that she forgets the name of the soap she advertises. The couple are reunited in the back seat of the Fraleighs' Rolls-Royce, and there Gerald delivers Evelyn's baby during a traffic jam. Beverly decides to quit her job and return to her role as wife and mother. *Housewives. Gynecologists. Manufacturers. Fathers-in-law. Psychiatrists. Marriage. Childbirth. Employment—Women. Soap. Television commercials. Swimming pools. Rolls-Royce automobiles.*

THE THRILL SEEKERS *see* GUTTER GIRLS

THRONE OF BLOOD (Japan)   F6.5047

Toho Co. *Dist* Brandon Films. 22 Nov **1961** [New York opening]. Sd; b&w. 35mm (Tohoscope). 108 min. [Also 105 min.]

Prod-Dir Akira Kurosawa. *Co-prod* Sojiro Motoki. *Screenplay* Hideo Oguni, Shinobu Hashimoto, Ryuzo Kikushima, Akira Kurosawa. *Photog* Asaichi Nakai. *Art Dir* Yoshiro Muraki, Kohei Ezaki. *Mus* Masaru Sato. *Sd* Fumio Yanoguchi. *English Adapt* Donald Richie.

Cast: Toshiro Mifune (*Taketoki Washizu*), Isuzu Yamada (*Asaji, his wife*), Takashi Shimura (*Noriyasu Odagura*), Minoru Chiaki (*Yoshiaki Miki*), Akira Kubo (*Yoshiteru, his son*), Takamaru Sasaki (*Kuniharu Tsuzuki*), Yoichi Tachikawa (*Kunimaru, his son*), Chieko Naniwa (*weird woman*).

Historical drama. Source: William Shakespeare, *Macbeth*. Returning to the Cobweb Castle after battling the warlord Inui, samurai warriors Washizu and Miki are confronted by a ghostly soothsayer, who predicts that Washizu will succeed his feudal lord, Tsuzuki, while Miki's son will inherit Washizu's throne. Fired by the prophecy and his wife Asaji's ambition, Washizu murders his sovereign, intending to make Miki's son his heir. The jealous Asaji, however, will have none of it. Insisting that she is pregnant, she commands father and son to be put to death. Although Miki is slain, his son escapes. Alarmed, Washizu again consults the oracle, who informs Washizu that he will be invincible until the surrounding forest moves against him. The next morning, Washizu is horrified to see the rival warlord Inui, his men brandishing the branches and limbs of the forest, advancing on the palace. Although he fights valiantly, Washizu is felled by a volley of arrows. *Samurai. Warlords. Seers.*

Murder. Assassination. Guilt. Insanity. Ambition. Castles. Forests. Japan—History—1333–1600.

Note: Released in Japan in Jan 1957 as *Kumonosujo*; running time: 109 min. Also known as *Kumonosu-djo.*

THROUGH A GLASS DARKLY (Sweden)   F6.5048

Svensk Filmindustri. *Dist* Janus Films. 13 Mar **1962** [New York opening]. Sd; b&w. 35mm. 91 min.

An Ingmar Bergman Production. *Prod* Allan Ekelund. *Dir-Writ* Ingmar Bergman. *Photog* Sven Nykvist. *Art Dir* P. A. Lundgren. *Film Ed* Ulla Ryghe. *Mus:* "Suite No. 2 in D Minor for Violincello" Johann Sebastian Bach. *Sd* Stig Flodin, Staffan Dalin. *Sd Eff* Evald Andersson. *Asst Dir* Lenn Hjörtzberg. *Cost* Mago.

Cast: Harriet Andersson (*Karin, the daughter*), Gunnar Björnstrand (*David, the father*), Max von Sydow (*Martin, the husband*), Lars Passgård (*Minus, the brother*).

Drama. Recently released from a mental institution, a young schizophrenic named Karin is spending the summer on an isolated island in the Baltic. With her are her father, David, a self-centered novelist who is horrified to discover that his interest in his daughter's malady is more professional than personal; her husband, Martin, who, although a doctor, is unable either to help or comfort his wife; and her 17-year-old brother, Minus, an adolescent just awakening to sex. During most of her seizures, Karin imagines that she hears voices from behind the wallpaper telling her that God will soon walk through the door and offer her salvation. After learning from her father's diary that her illness is incurable, she lapses into a fit and seduces the young Minus, an experience that leaves him shocked into silence. Karin's voices then tell her that God is about to appear. But all that comes through the door is a giant black spider. Terrified, she suffers a breakdown so violent that her father and husband are forced to restrain her until an ambulance arrives. After she has been taken back to the institution, the confused Minus turns to his father for an explanation. Realizing that each of them has failed the other by not giving completely of themselves, David tells his son that love is man's only salvation. As he leaves Minus, the boy, filled with wonder, exclaims "Father *talked* to me!" *Novelists. Physicians. Schizophrenia. Filial relations. Brother-sister relationship. Marriage. Adolescence. Seduction. Incest. Religion. Islands. Summer. Baltic Sea. Hallucinations. Spiders.*

Note: Released in Sweden in Oct 1961 as *Såsom i en spegel.*

THROUGH DAYS AND MONTHS (Japan)   F6.5049

Shochiku Co. *Dist* Shochiku Films of America. May **1969** [Los Angeles showing]. Sd; col (Eastmancolor). 35mm (Shochiku GrandScope). 98 min.

Dir Noboru Nakamura. *Screenplay* Yuzuru Hirose. *Photog* Hiroshi Takemura. *Art Dir* Yutaka Yokoyama. *Mus* Masao Yagi.

Cast: Shima Iwashita (*Matsuko*), Masayuki Mori (*her father*), Yoshiko Kuga (*her mother*), Jin Nakayama (*Munehiro*), Koji Ishizaka (*Koji*), Mayumi Ozora.

Romantic drama. Source: Yasunari Kawabata, *Hi mo tsuki mo* (Tokyo, 1953). Matsuko lives alone with her father in Kamakura, her mother having deserted them to live with a younger man. Although Matsuko has been in love only once—with Munehiro, who is now married—she is satisfied to live a quiet, solitary life. She meets Munehiro while he is convalescing from a serious illness and discovers that he is still in love with her and wishes to renew their affair, despite his jealous wife. The situation is further complicated when his younger brother, Koji, comes to care for Matsuko. However, her father dies and Munehiro, depressed over his illness, commits suicide. Although Matsuko is now drawn to Koji, her experiences have made her feel inadequate to express her emotions. *Brothers. Infidelity. Suicide. Desertion. Jealousy. Filial relations. Kamakura.*

Note: Released in Japan in Jan 1969 as *Hi mo tsuki mo.*

THUMBELINA   F6.5050

Cinetron Corp. *Dist* R & S Film Enterprises. 17 Oct **1970** [New Orleans opening]. Sd; col. 35mm. 62 min. *MPAA rating* G.

Prod-Dir Barry Mahon. *Exec Prod* Armand Cerami. *Camera* Bill Tobin. *Asst Camera* Phil Obrecht. *Scenic Dsgn* Thelma Raniero, Guy Brugger. *Mus & Lyr* George Linsenmann, Ralph Falco. *Arr by* Eugene Ventresca. *Sd* Jon Williams. *Asst Sd* Mark Tannen. *Prod Mgr* Jon Williams. *Makeup* Tom Brumberger.

Cast: Shay Garner, Pat Morell, Bob O'Connell, Heather Grinter, Mike Yuenger, Sue Cable.

Fantasy. Source: Hans Christian Andersen, "Tommelise" (1835). A live action film of the famous fairy tale. *Witches. Royalty. Motherhood. Plant life. Animal life. Magic. Kidnaping.*

THUNDER ALLEY   F6.5051

American International Pictures. 22 Mar **1967** [Baltimore opening; c1 Mar 1967; LP34386]. Sd; col (Pathé). 35mm (Panavision). 90 min. [Copyright length: 88 min.]

Prod Burt Topper. *Exec Prod* James H. Nicholson, Samuel Z. Arkoff. *Assoc Prod* Jack Cash. *Dir* Richard Rush. *Screenplay* Sy Salkowitz. *Dir Photog* Monroe Askins. *Adtl Photog* Ned Davenport. *Art Dir* Daniel Haller. *Set Decor* Harry Reif. *Film Ed* Ronald Sinclair, Kenneth Crane. *Song:* "When You Get What You Want" Guy Hemric, Jerry Styner. *Sung by* Annette Funicello. *Sd* Bob Post. *Sd Eff* Nelson-Corso. *Asst Dir* Jack Bohrer, Lew Borzage. *Prod Coörd* Al Simms. *Script Supv* Bonnie Prendergast. *Wardrobe* Richard Bruno, Ray Phelps, Connie Anderson. *Makeup* Gus Norin. *Hairstyles* Jené Bodell. *Sp Eff* Joe Zomar. *Tech Adv* Sandy Reed. *Still Photog* Art Say. *Grip* Charles Hannawalt. *Gaffer* Robert Petzoldt. *Constr Coörd* Ross Hahn. *Prop* Dick Rubin, Karl Brainard.

Cast: Annette Funicello (*Francie Madsen*), Fabian (*Tommy Callahan*), Diane McBain (*Annie Blaine*), Warren Berlinger (*Eddie Sands*), Jan Murray (*Pete Madsen*), Stanley Adams (*Mac Lunsford*), Maureen Arthur (*Babe*), Michael T. Mikler (*Harry Wise*), Michael Bell (*Leroy*), Kip King (*Dom*), Sandy Reed (*announcer*), Sammy Shore, Baynes Barron, Michael Dugan, Band Without a Name.

Action melodrama. Tommy Callahan, a fiercely competitive stock car driver, is suspended from racing when he blacks out and kills another driver. Unable to obtain a new sponsor, he goes to work for Pete Madsen's Thrill Circus and joins Madsen's daughter Francie and her boyfriend, Eddie Sands, in staging phony crashes and sideswipes. Under Tommy's coaching, Eddie trains for professional racing and is the surprise winner of his first major track event. Ecstatic over the victory, he is an easy victim for Tommy's former girl friend, thrill-hungry Annie Blaine. Meanwhile, Tommy's continued blackouts have become a matter of great concern to Francie. Despite the increasing friction between them, Tommy and Eddie are eventually sponsored as teammates in a 500-mile race. During the meet, Tommy blacks out but recovers upon realizing that his trauma is caused by guilt feelings over a childhood accident in which he ran over his brother with a go-cart. Near the end of the race, Eddie responds to Annie's goadings and attempts to take the lead, despite orders to keep his car behind Tommy's. As a result, he slams into a wall and is seriously injured. Tommy goes on to win the race and is rewarded with both the trophy and Francie's embrace. *Stock car drivers. Automobile racing. Automobile accidents. Guilt. Stunts.*

THUNDER IN DIXIE F6.5052

Willpat Productions. *Dist* MPI Inc. caMay **1965**. Sd; b&w. 35mm. 76 min.
Prod-Dir William T. Naud. *Exec Prod Supv* Irwin Nestler. *Assoc Prod* Alfred Hillman. *Writ* George Baxt. *Dir Photog* Thomas E. Spalding. *Art Dir* Chris Bottomly, Jim Johnson, Carl Hillman. *Mus Comp & Cond* Elliot Lawrence. *Song:* "Maybe Tomorrow" sung by Barry Darval. *Sd* Robert Clement, Bob Spies. *Asst Dir* Ward French. *Prod Mgr* Tom McGrath. *Script Supv* Janet French. *Casting Dir* Herb Rodgers. *Head Grip* Vincent Spangler.

Cast: Harry Millard (*Mickey Arnold*), Judy Lewis (*Lili Arnold*), Nancy Berg (*Karen Hallet*), Mike Bradford (*Ticker Welsh*), Ted Erwin (*Ben Forrest*), Richard Kuss (*Link Duggan*), Pat McAndrew (*Rachel*), Herb Rodgers (*motel manager*), Barry Darval (*himself, a singer*), Sheri Benet (*herself, a stripper*), Bob Wills (*track announcer*), Johnny Carlson (*spotter*), George Brenholtz (*bartender*), Richard Petty.

Action melodrama. In Atlanta's "Dixie 400," racer Ticker Welsh competes against his former partner Mickey Arnold. The sullen Ticker blames Mickey for the death of his fiancée, Edna, 3 months earlier, and intends to revenge himself during the race. Ticker's new girl friend, the widowed Karen Hallett, attempts to dissuade him, as does Mickey's wife, Lili, but Ticker is obdurate. Mickey discloses Edna's infidelity the night of the auto accident, further enraging his old friend. During the "Dixie 400" Ticker's anger backfires and he is injured, while Mickey wins the race. At the hospital Mickey and Ticker renew their friendship, and Karen declares her love for the injured racer. *Stock car drivers. Widows. Revenge. Automobile racing. Partnerships. Atlanta (Georgia). Atlanta International Raceway. Automobile accidents.*

Note: Racing scenes filmed at the Atlanta International Raceway. Prerelease title: *Thundering Wheels.*

THUNDER IN THE BLOOD (France) F6.5053

Florida Films–Compagnie Générale Cinématographique. *Dist* Seven Continents Film Association. ca **1962**. Sd; b&w. 35mm. 95 min.
Dir-Writ André Haguet. *Co-dir* Jean-Paul Sassy. *Photog* Lucien Joulin. *Art Dir* Jean-Roland Quignon. *Film Ed* Maurice Serein. *Mus* Marcel Stern. *Sd* Jacques Gallois. *Asst Dir* Claude Pinoteau. *Prod Mgr* Maggie Gillet.

Cast: Estella Blain (*Catherine*), Harold Kay (*Roland*), Pierre-Jean Vaillard (*Girardier*), Jean-Marie Fertey (*Alex*), Pierre Fromont (*Christian Lambert*), Liliane Brousse (*Georgina*), Michel Nastorg, Jean-Paul Thomas, Guy Henry, Jean Barrez.

Crime melodrama. To give his wife Catherine the comforts of life she demands, Alex, an alcoholic, writes crime novels and covers police stories as a reporter-photographer. Though Alex loves his neurotic wife with a morbid passion, his jealousy, as well as her boredom, drives Catherine to take a lover, playboy art collector Christian Lambert. In his dealings with the underworld, Lambert has threatened a murderer with blackmail, and when Lambert and his valet are murdered, the gangster becomes suspect. Inspector Roland, called in to investigate the case, concludes, however, that Alex was the murderer, motivated by revenge and intent on blaming the killing on his adulterous wife. Alex admits his crime and stumbles from a rooftop to his death as he tries to murder Catherine. *Reporters. Photographers. Art collectors. Playboys. Gangsters. Police. Murder. Alcoholism. Infidelity. Jealousy. Revenge.*

Note: Opened in Paris in Jun 1960 as *Colère froide;* running time: 100 min. U. S. title changed to *The Warm Body* in 1963.

THUNDER ISLAND F6.5054

Associated Producers, Inc. *Dist* Twentieth Century-Fox Film Corp. Oct **1963** [c16 Oct 1963; LP26775]. Sd; b&w. 35mm (CinemaScope). 65 min.
Prod-Dir Jack Leewood. *Assoc Prod* Frank Marrero. *Story-Screenplay* Don Devlin, Jack Nicholson. *Dir Photog* John Nickolaus, Jr. *Supv Film Ed* Jodie Copelan. *Mus* Paul Sawtell, Bert Shefter. *Sd* Jack Solomon, Harry M. Leonard. *Asst Dir* Frank Parmenter. *Prod Supv* Frank Parmenter. *Prod Mgr* Axel Anderson. *Unit Mgr* Amilcar Tirado. *Script Supv* FARE. *Makeup* Bob Mark. *Prod in Assoc With* La Coöperative de Artes Cinematograficas, Producciones del Viejo San Juan. *Prop Master* Antonio Lopez Martino.

Cast: Gene Nelson (*Billy Poole*), Fay Spain (*Helen Dodge*), Brian Kelly (*Vincent Dodge*), Miriam Colon (*Anita Chavez*), Art Bedard (*Ramon Alou*), Antonio Torres Martino (*Colonel Cepeda*), Esther Sandoval (*Rena*), José de San Anton (*Antonio Perez*), Evelyn Kaufman (*Jo Dodge*), Stephanie Rifkinson (*Linda Perez*), Axel Anderson.

Action melodrama. American Billy Poole, a professional killer, is hired by a nationalist group to assassinate exiled South American dictator Antonio Perez, who lives on a heavily guarded island in the Caribbean. Billy and his contact, Anita Chavez, force former advertising man Vincent Dodge, who regularly sails supplies to Perez, to transport Billy to the island by holding Vincent's wife, Helen, as hostage. Once on the island, Billy can only wound Perez before escaping, with both the dictator's guards and Vincent in pursuit. Billy later murders Anita in the belief that she has betrayed him but is himself killed by Vincent. Helen, free from her captors, rejoins her husband. *Hired killers. Dictators. Advertising executives. Hostages. Bodyguards. Assassination. Murder. Kidnaping. Islands. Caribbean.*

Note: Location scenes filmed at El Morro in San Juan and in other parts of Puerto Rico.

THUNDER MOUNTAIN see THE SHEPHERD OF THE HILLS

A THUNDER OF DRUMS F6.5055

Robert J. Enders, Inc. *Dist* Metro-Goldwyn-Mayer, Inc. 26 Sep **1961** [New York opening; c28 Aug 1961; LP20693]. Sd (Westrex); col (Metrocolor). 35mm (CinemaScope). 97 min.
A Robert Enders Production. *Assoc Prod* Stanley Bass. *Dir* Joseph M. Newman. *Writ* James Warner Bellah. *Dir Photog* William W. Spencer. *Col Cons* Charles K. Hagedon. *Art Dir* George W. Davis, Gabriel Scognamillo. *Set Decor* Henry Grace, Jack Mills. *Film Ed* Ferris Webster. *Mus Score* Harry Sukman. *Songs:* "Water From a Bad Well," "Ballad of Camden Yates" Duane Eddy. *Sung by* Duane Eddy. *Rec Supv* Franklin Milton. *Asst Dir* Hal Polaire. *Women's Cost* Kitty Mager. *Makeup* William Tuttle. *Hairstyles* Mary Keats.

Cast: Richard Boone (*Capt. Stephen Maddocks*), George Hamilton (*Lieut. Curtis McQuade*), Luana Patten (*Tracey Hamilton*), Arthur O'Connell (*Sergeant Rodermill*), Charles Bronson (*Trooper Hanna*), Richard Chamberlain (*Lieutenant Porter*), Duane Eddy (*Trooper Eddy*), James Douglas (*Lieutenant Gresham*), Tammy Marihugh (*Laurie*), Carole Wells (*Camden Yates*), Slim Pickens (*Trooper Erschick*), Clem Harvey (*Trooper Denton*), Casey Tibbs (*Trooper Baker*), Irene Tedrow (*Mrs. Scarborough*), Marjorie Bennett (*Mrs. Yates*), J. Edward McKinley (*Captain Scarborough*).

Western melodrama. In the 1870's, Lieut. Curtis McQuade, a headstrong, inexperienced officer, arrives at the remote cavalry post of Fort Canby in Arizona. Almost at once he is in trouble with the garrison commander, Capt. Stephen Maddocks, a hard-bitten veteran Indian-fighter who resents the younger officer's brashness. Curtis creates further trouble by rekindling his former romance with Tracey Hamilton, who is staying at the fort with her fiancé, Lieutenant Gresham. One day Gresham, who has learned of the affair between Curtis and Tracey, fails to return from a scouting party. Curtis accompanies Maddocks on the search and is horrified to discover Gresham and his men massacred by Indians. Shocked into the realization that his reckless behavior with Tracey may have caused Gresham to lose control of his wits, Curtis redeems himself by acting as the decoy with which Maddocks hopes to draw the attention of the marauding Apaches. Alone with their backs to a cliff, Curtis and a handful of his men await the onslaught. When the Indians attack at dawn, Maddocks and his troopers charge into the clearing and wipe them out. In the fighting, however, Maddocks' only close friend, Sergeant Rodermill, is killed by an Apache arrow. When Curtis returns to Fort Canby, he finds Tracey boarding the eastbound stage. As he says goodby to her, he realizes that Maddocks' credo—"Bachelors make the best soldiers, all they have to lose is their loneliness"—is the only correct philosophy for a true military man. *Bachelors. Apache Indians. Massacres. United States Army—Cavalry. Arizona. Fort Canby (Arizona).*

Note: Location scenes filmed in Arizona.

THUNDERBALL (Great Britain)   F6.5056

Eon Productions–Danjaq, S. A. *Dist* United Artists. 21 Dec **1965** [New York opening; c10 Dec 1965; LF4]. Sd; col (Technicolor). 35mm (Panavision). 132 min.

Pres by Albert R. Broccoli, Harry Saltzman. *Prod* Kevin McClory. *Dir* Terence Young. *Underwater Dir* Ricou Browning. *Stunt Dir* Bob Simmons. *Screenplay* Richard Maibaum, John Hopkins. *Orig Story* Kevin McClory, Jack Whittingham, Ian Fleming. *Dir Photog* Ted Moore. *Underwater Camera* Lamar Boren. *Art Dir* Peter Murton. *Set Decor* Freda Pearson. *Prod Dsgn* Ken Adam. *Main Titl Dsgn* Maurice Binder. *Film Ed* Peter Hunt. *Mus Comp & Dir* John Barry. *Lyr:* "Thunderball" Don Black. *Sung by* Tom Jones. *Sd* Bert Ross, Maurice Askew. *Asst Dir* Gus Agosti. *Prod Mgr* David Middlemas, Edward Haldeman. *Cost* Anthony Mendleson. *Sp Eff* John Stears. *Underwater Seq* Ivan Tors Underwater Studios. *Underwater Engr* Jordan Klein.

Cast: Sean Connery (*James Bond*), Claudine Auger (*Domino*), Adolfo Celi (*Emilio Largo*), Luciana Paluzzi (*Fiona*), Rik von Nutter (*Felix Leiter*), Bernard Lee ("*M*"), Martine Beswick (*Paula*), Guy Doleman (*Count Lippe*), Molly Peters (*Patricia*), Desmond Llewelyn ("*Q*"), Lois Maxwell (*Moneypenny*), Roland Culver (*foreign secretary*), Earl Cameron (*Pinder*), Paul Stassino (*Major Derval/Palazzi*), Rose Alba (*Madame Boitier*), Philip Locke (*Vargas*), George Pravda (*Kutze*), Michael Brennan (*Janni*), Leonard Sachs (*group captain*), Edward Underdown (*air vice marshal*), Reginald Beckwith (*Kenniston*), Bill Cummings (*Quist*), Maryse Guy Mitsouko (*Mademoiselle La Porte*), Bob Simmons (*Jacques Boitier*).

Action melodrama. Source: Ian Fleming, *Thunderball* (London, 1961). SPECTRE, an international crime syndicate, plans to hijack a Vulcan plane carrying two atomic bombs during a NATO training exercise and blackmail the Western Powers into paying £100 million ransom by threatening the destruction of two important cities. As part of the plot, Major Derval of NATO is murdered at a clinic near the NATO airfield by a bandaged assailant, Palazzi, whose features have been altered by plastic surgery to make him Derval's double. "Derval" then flies with the bombs to the Bahamas and ditches the plane under water. He is then murdered by SPECTRE official Emilio Largo, who secrets the bombs in an underwater cave. Meanwhile, British intelligence agent 007, James Bond, has been dispatched to the clinic to thwart the SPECTRE plan. After narrowly escaping death on an exercise machine, he meets Domino, Derval's sister and Largo's ward. He traces Largo to the Bahamas and, disguised as one of Largo's frogmen, approaches the underwater cave; but he is recognized and sealed into a shark-filled swimming pool adjoining the cave. CIA agent Felix Leiter, who has traced Bond's movements through a radioactive device swallowed by Bond, now saves him and takes him to Miami. Here Bond meets Fiona, a SPECTRE agent who makes love to him and then turns him over to her cohorts. He escapes with a bullet wound in the leg, and when Fiona follows his trail of blood to a dancefloor, he makes another narrow escape by maneuvering her into the path of a bullet. Meanwhile, Largo and his men hide the bombs in a sunken ship off the Florida coast, but U. S. Aquaparatroops, alerted by Bond, attack and defeat the SPECTRE forces, recovering the bombs although Largo escapes in his hydrofoil. Bond fights his way aboard the vessel and is about to be overcome by Largo and the crew when Domino appears and shoots Largo. She and Bond leap from the boat as it swerves toward the rocky shore and explodes. As they await rescue on a raft, Bond and Domino make love. *Secret agents. Guardians. Frogmen. Blackmail. Murder. Impersonation. Organized crime. Plastic surgery. Atom bomb. Airplanes. Health resorts. Hydroplanes. Yachts. Bahamas. Miami. North Atlantic Treaty Organization. United States—Central Intelligence Agency. James Bond. Sharks.*

Note: Released in Great Britain in Dec 1965. Location scenes filmed in Nassau.

THUNDERBIRDS ARE GO (Great Britain)   F6.5057

Century 21 Pictures–A. P. Films. *Dist* United Artists. Jul **1968** [c13 Dec 1966; LF90]. Sd; col (Technicolor). 35mm (Techniscope). 94 min.

Overall Production Credits: *Prod* Sylvia Anderson. *Exec Prod* Gerry Anderson. *Assoc Prod* John Read. *Dir* David Lane. *Screenplay* Gerry Anderson, Sylvia Anderson. *Supv Art Dir* Bob Bell. *Art Dir* Grenville Knott. *Film Ed* Len Walter. *Asst Ed* George Randall. *Mus Comp & Cond* Barry Gray. *Song:* "Shooting Star" *comp & perf* The Shadows. *Sung by* Cliff Richard. *Song:* "Lady Penelope" *comp & perf* The Shadows. *Sd* John Peverill. *Asst Dir* Ken

Turner, Harry Ledger. *Asst to the Exec Prod* Norman Foster, British. *Wardrobe Mistress* Elizabeth Coleman. *Coöp* Space Colonel Harris, Commander Casey, Jim Glenn, (New World Aircraft Corp.).

Visual Effects: *Dir* Derek Meddings. *Main Unit* Shawn Whittacker-Cook. *Lighting Camera* Harry Oakes. *Camera Op* Ted Cutlack, Richard Conway. *2d Unit* Peter Wragg. *2d Unit Lighting Camera* Ted Fowler. *2d Unit Camera Op* Rob Gallifant, Ron Ashdown. *Supv Model Builder* Ray Brown, sp eff. *Prop Builders* Tony Dunstenville, Plugg Shutt. *Prop Master* Arthur Cripps.

Character Animation: *Lighting Camera* Paddy Seale. *Camera Op* Alan Perry. *Character Op* Christine Glanville, Mary Turner. *Asst Character Op* Judith Shutt, Wanda Webb. *Supv Sculptor* John Brown, sculptor. *Asst Sculptor* Terry Curtis, Tim Cooksey.

Voices: Sylvia Anderson (*Lady Penelope Creighton-Ward*), Ray Barrett (*John Tracy/The Hood/controller at Glenn Field*), Alexander Davion (*Greg Martin*), Peter Dyneley (*Jeff Tracy*), Christine Finn (*Tin-Tin*), David Graham (*Brains/Gordon Tracy/Parker*), Paul Maxwell (*Paul Travers*), Neil McCallum (*Dr. Pierce*), Bob Monkhouse (*Brad Newman*), Shane Rimmer (*Scott Tracy*), Charles Tingwell (*Dr. Grant/public relations officer/angry young man*), Jeremy Wilkin (*Virgil Tracy/president of exploration center*), Matt Zimmerman (*Alan Tracy/messenger*).

Animated puppet film. In the 21st century, Zero X, the first manned spaceship to Mars, is sabotaged, and International Rescue, an organization headed by millionaire ex-astronaut Jeff Tracy and his five sons, is requested to be present for the followup launching. Assisted by London agent Lady Penelope and her Cockney servant Parker, the I. R. prevents enemy forces from causing a second disaster, and the spaceship makes a successful landing on the distant planet. Once there, the lives of the interplanetary explorers are endangered from unknown rock formations on the Martian landscape that emit spouts of flame. Their homeward voyage is jeopardized when their remote radio control unit fails, and they appear to be destined for a crash landing on Earth; but the I. R. is once more ready with help. Flying underneath the spaceship in a "Thunderbird" rescue plane, young Alan Tracy succeeds in separating the escape unit containing the astronauts from the main body of Zero X. As the spaceship crashes, the Thunderbirds guide the escape unit safely back to Earth. *Spaceship crews. Cockneys. Space rescue. Space exploration. Spaceships. Mars (planet). The Future.*

Note: Filmed in Supermarionation. Opened in London in Dec 1966.

THUNDERING WHEELS see **THUNDER IN DIXIE**

TI HO SPOSATO PER ALLEGRIA see **I MARRIED YOU FOR FUN**

TI-KOYO E IL SUO PESCECANE see **TIKO AND THE SHARK**

TI-KOYO ET SON REQUIN see **TIKO AND THE SHARK**

LA TÍA TULA (Spain)   F6.5058

Eco Films–Surco Films. *Dist* United International Films. 2 Jun **1965** [New York opening]. Sd; b&w. 35mm. 86 min.

Prod Nino Quevedo. *Dir-Writ* Miguel Picazo. *Screenplay* Luis Sánchez Enciso, José Hernández Miguel, Miguel Picazo, Manuel López Yubero. *Photog* Juan Julio Baena. *Art Dir* Luis Argüello. *Film Ed* Pedro del Rey. *Mus* Antonio Pérez Olea. *Prod Ch* Antonio López Moreno. *Prod Sec* José Luis Ruíz Marcos. *Makeup* Carmen Martín, Manuel Martín. *Hairstyles* Josefa Rubio Martos. *Still Photog* José Salvador Sanchíz.

Cast: Aurora Bautista (*Tula*), Carlos Estrada (*Ramiro*), Mari Loli Cobos (*Tulita*), Carlos Sánchez Jiménez (*Ramirín*), Chiro Bermejo (*Emilio*), José María Prada (*Padre Alvarez*), Manuel Granada (*Uncle Pedro*), Enriqueta Carballeira (*Juanita*), Irene Gutiérrez Caba (*Herminia*), Laly Soldevila (*Amalita*), Julia Delgado Caro (*Doña Cinta*), Montserrat Julió (*Paquita*), Paloma Lorena (*Milagros*), Margarita Calahorra (*Pilar*), Esmeralda Adam (*Solita*), Lola Gaos (*Jacinta*), Emilia Zambrana (*Nieves*), María Hevia (*Agueda*).

Drama. Source: Miguel de Unamuno, *La tía Tula* (Madrid, 1921). Tula, an attractive spinster, invites her brother-in-law Ramiro, a bank employee, and his children, Tulita and Ramirín, to share her home after the death of her sister Rosa. She enjoys the role of protector but gradually becomes disturbed by the jealousy that arises between Ramiro and her suitor, Emilio. Her deep-seated fear of men, conditioned by religious principles and the morality of her social class, surfaces as the widowed Ramiro becomes increasingly aware of her sexual presence and attempts physical displays of affection. She coldly rejects his marriage proposals and decides to leave the household for a vacation at the nearby home of her uncle Pedro. During this sojourn she softens and considers marrying Ramiro. In the meantime, however, Ramiro gives way to desire and seduces Pedro's teenage daughter, Juanita; he then accepts the social consequences of his action by marrying the girl. Tula bids good-by to the couple at the train station and wanders off alone. *Spinsters. Aunts. Widowers. Brothers-in-law. Uncles. Courtship. Jealousy. Seduction. Marriage. Family life.*

Note: Opened in Madrid in Sep 1964; running time: 118 min. Synopsis applies to 118 min version.

TIAO MEDONHO see TRAIN ROBBERY CONFIDENTIAL

TIARA TAHITI (Great Britain)   F6.5059

Rank Organisation–Ivan Foxwell Productions. *Dist* Zenith International Film Corp. 5 Nov **1963** [New York opening; c27 Aug 1962; LF168]. Sd; col (Eastman Color). 35mm. 100 min.

Pres by J. Arthur Rank. *Prod* Ivan Foxwell. *Exec Prod* Earl St. John. *Dir* William T. Kotcheff. *Screenplay* Geoffrey Cotterell, Ivan Foxwell. *Adtl Dial* Mordecai Richler. *Photog* Otto Heller. *Camera Op* Cecil Cooney. *Focus Op* Steve Claydon. *Art Dir* Alex Vetchinsky. *Set Dresser* Arthur Taksen. *Ch Draughtsman* Bob Laing. *Film Ed* Anthony Gibbs. *1st Asst Ed* Brian Smedley-Aston. *2d Asst Ed* Pamela Gardner. *Mus* Philip Green. *Titl Song* Philip Green, Norman Newell. *Sung by* Danny Williams. *Sd Rec* C. C. Stevens, Gordon K. McCallum. *Sd Camera Op* Simon Kaye. *Boom Op* Gus Lloyd. *Dub Ed* Harry Miller. *1st, 2d & 3d Asst Dir* Bert Batt, Terry Clegg, Michael Gray. *Prod Mgr* Harold Buck. *Cont* Joan Davis. *Prod Sec* Miriam Hart. *Dress Dsgn* Yvonne Caffin. *Women's Wardrobe* Laurel Staffell. *Men's Wardrobe* John Hilling. *Makeup* Ernest Gasser. *Hairdresser* Biddy Chrystal. *Prop Buyer* Jim Baker. *Still Photog* Norman Gryspeerdt. *Constr Mgr* Bill Surridge. *Grip* George Beavis. *Ch Floor Electrn* Vic Smith.

Cast: James Mason (*Capt. Brett Aimsley*), John Mills (*Lieut. Col. Clifford Southey*), Rosenda Monteros (*Belle Annie*), Herbert Lom (*Chong Sing*), Claude Dauphin (*Henri Farengue*), Jacques Marin (*Desmoulins*), Libby Morris (*Adele Franklin*), Madge Ryan (*Millie Brooks*), Gary Cockrell (*Joey*), Peter Barkworth (*Lieut. David Harper*), Roy Kinnear (*Capt. Tom Enderby*).

Melodrama. Source: Geoffrey Cotterell, *Tiara Tahiti* (London, 1960). When pompous British Colonel Southey discovers that Captain Aimsley has been assigned to his unit in Germany just after World War II, he attempts to conceal his pre-war employment as a clerk with the Aimsley family's firm. Aimsley's popularity with the men infuriates Southey, and he informs on Aimsley when Aimsley tries to smuggle some black-market goods into England. Court-martialed and dishonorably discharged, Aimsley sails for Tahiti and there finds an idyllic existence with a native girl, Belle Annie. Some years later, Southey, now a tycoon, comes to Tahiti to build a hotel. He and Aimsley get drunk together, and Southey confesses to informing on Aimsley. The two fight, and Aimsley is left unconscious and later nearly strangled by a thug hired by Chong Sing, a Chinese art dealer who covets Belle Annie. Southey is arrested for attempted murder and deported. Aimsley, who has learned the truth, takes revenge by saying nothing to clear Southey and returns to the happy Tahiti life with Belle Annie. *Chinese. Art dealers. Tycoons. Envy. Smuggling. Revenge. Drunkenness. Black market. Courts-martial. Deportation. Hotels. Tahiti. Germany. Great Britain—Army.*

Note: Filmed in Tahiti. Opened in London in Jul 1962.

... TICK ... TICK ... TICK ...   F6.5060

Metro-Goldwyn-Mayer, Inc. 21 Jan **1970** [Philadelphia opening; c21 Oct 1969; LP37260]. Sd; col (Metrocolor). 35mm (Panavision). 96 min. *MPAA rating G.*

Prod Ralph Nelson, James Lee Barrett. *Assoc Prod* William S. Gilmore, Jr. *Dir* Ralph Nelson. *Screenplay* James Lee Barrett. *Dir Photog* Loyal Griggs. *Art Dir* George W. Davis, William Glasgow. *Set Decor* Robert R. Benton, Don Greenwood, Jr. *Film Ed* Alex Beaton. *Mus* Jerry Styner. *Mus Supv* Mike Curb. *Song:* "Set Yourself Free" Willis Hoover. *Songs:* "All That Keeps Ya Goin'," "Walk Unashamed," "What Does It Take" Jim Glaser. *Song:* "Woman Woman" Jim Glaser, Jimmy Payne. *Songs:* "Gentle on My Mind," "Why Do You Do Me Like You Do?" John Hartford. *Song:* "California Girl and the Tennessee Square" Jack Clement. *Song:* "Where Has All the Love Gone" Chuck Glaser. *Song:* "Home's Where the Hurt Is" Arthur Owens. *Songs Sung by* Tompall and the Glaser Brothers. *Rec Supv* Franklin Milton. *Sd* Bruce Wright. *Asst Dir* Michael Glick, Newt Arnold. *Unit Prod Mgr* William S. Gilmore, Jr. *Makeup* William Tuttle. *Hairstyles* Evelyn Coffey. *Casting* Leonard Murphy.

Cast: Jim Brown (*Jimmy Price*), George Kennedy (*John Little*), Fredric March (*Mayor Jeff Parks*), Lynn Carlin (*Julia Little*), Don Stroud (*Bengy Springer*), Janet MacLachlan (*Mary Price*), Richard Elkins (*Bradford Wilkes*), Clifton James (*D. J. Rankin*), Bob Random (*John Braddock*), Mills Watson (*Deputy Joe Warren*), Bernie Casey (*George Harley*), Anthony James (*H. C. Tolbert*), Dub Taylor (*Junior*), Ernest Anderson (*Homer*), Karl Swenson (*Braddock, Sr.*), Barry Cahill (*Bob Braddock*), Ann Whitfield (*Mrs. Dawes*), Bill Walker (*John Sawyer*), Dan Frazer (*Ira Jackson*), Leonard O. Smith (*Fred Price*), Renny Roker (*shoeshine boy*), Roy Glenn (*drunk*), George Cisar (*barber*), Paulene Myers (*Mrs. Harley*), Dino Washington (*Randy Harley*), Calvin Brown (*Harrison Harley*), Beverly Taylor (*Sara Jean*).

Drama. Jim Price is elected the first black sheriff of Colusa County, Mississippi, with the help of northern organizers. A hotbed of racial prejudice, Colusa has a local chapter of the Ku Klux Klan. Retiring incumbent John Little, though he believes he was fairly defeated, offers Price no help on the new sheriff's first day. Price is greeted only by Mayor Parks, a local patriarch who admonishes Price to consult him before appealing for outside help in solving problems. Price shows his desire for moderation when he refuses to deputize a black militant. Price's first arrest, on a charge of manslaughter, is John Braddock, the son of an influential white. Driving while drunk, Braddock caused the death of a child in an automobile accident. That night Price's deputy Bradford Wilkes is beaten by a group led by Little's former deputy Bengy Springer, who had vowed to kill Price. Price next arrests black George Harley for raping a teenaged girl, and in doing so he risks alienating the black community that unanimously elected him. Braddock, Sr., arrives in Colusa and angrily demands that Price release his son, whose bail is set at $25,000. Braddock threatens to take the boy by force, whereupon Little arrives and accepts the deputy's badge. Braddock departs, but Price, knowing that he will return with a mob, makes an unsuccessful request of the mayor to call in Federal troops. As the Braddock mob approaches Colusa, Price and Little enter Junior's Place, a bar for whites only, to look for deputies. Failing to recruit any, Price and Little set up a barricade at the edge of town. Just as Braddock's men approach, however, the whites from Junior's join the sheriff and disperse the mob. *Negroes. Sheriffs. Mayors. Militants. Racial prejudice. Manslaughter. Rape. Law and order. Elections. Automobile accidents. Bars. Mississippi. Ku Klux Klan.*

TICKLE ME   F6.5061

Allied Artists. 28 May **1965** [Atlanta opening; c11 Apr 1965; LP33580]. Sd; col (DeLuxe). 35mm (Panavision). 90 min.

Prod Ben Schwalb. *Dir* Norman Taurog. *Screenplay* Elwood Ullman, Edward Bernds. *Cinematog* Loyal Griggs. *Camera Op* Kyme Meade. *Asst Camera Op* Gene Liggett. *Art Dir* Hal Pereira, Arthur Lonergan. *Set Decor* Arthur Krams. *Film Ed* Archie Marshek. *Mus Dir* Walter Scharf. *Songs:* "(It's a) Long, Lonely Highway," "Night Rider" Doc Pomus, Mort Shuman. *Song:* "It Feels So Right" Benjamin Weisman, Fred Wise. *Song:* "Dirty Dirty Feeling" (English Vers of "Si seulement!") Jerry Leiber, Mike Stoller. *Song:* "(Such an) Easy Question" Otis Blackwell, Winfield Scott. *Song:* "Put the Blame on Me" Norman Blagman, Kathleen G. Twomey, Fred Wise. *Song:* "I'm Yours" Don Robertson, Hal Blair. *Song:* "I Feel That I've Known You Forever" Doc Pomus, Alan Jeffreys. *Song:* "Slowly but Surely" Sid Wayne, Benjamin Weisman. *Songs Sung by* Elvis Presley. *Choreog* David Winters. *Sd Mix* Hugo Grenzbach, Charles Grenzbach. *Sd Rec* Jim Miller. *Asst Dir* Arthur Jacobson. *Prod Mgr* Robert Goodstein. *Script Supv* Marvin Weldon. *Cost Dsgn* Leah Rhodes. *Wardrobe* Shirlee Strahm, John A. Anderson. *Makeup* Frank Westmore, William Reynolds, makeup. *Hairdresser* Dean Cole. *Dial Coach* Michael A. Hoey. *Prop* Earl Olin, Carl Coleman. *Gaffer* Stanley Williams. *Grip* Dominic Seminerio.

Cast: Elvis Presley (*Lonnie Beale*), Jocelyn Lane (*Pam Merritt*), Julie Adams (*Vera Radford*), Jack Mullaney (*Stanley Potter*), Merry Anders (*Estelle Penfield*), Connie Gilchrist (*Hilda*), Edward Faulkner (*Brad Bentley*), Bill Williams (*Deputy Sturdivant*), Louis Elias (*Jerry*), John Dennis (*Adolf*), Laurie Burton (*Janet*), Linda Rogers (*Clair Kinnamon*), Ann Morell (*Sibyl*), Lilyan Chauvin (*Ronnie*), Jean Ingram (*Evelyn*), Francine York (*Mildred*), Eve Bruce (*Pat*), Jackie Russell (*Gloria*), Angela Greene (*Donna*), Peggy Ward (*Dot*), Dorian Brown (*Polly*), Inez Pedroza (*Ophelia*), Barbara Werle (*Barbara*), Grady Sutton (*Mr. Dabney*), Allison Hayes (*Mabel*), Robert Hoy (*Henry*), Dorothy Konrad (*Mrs. Dabney*).

Comedy-drama with music. Rodeo rider Lonnie Beale, a handsome singer, is employed by Vera Radford, proprietress of a dude ranch and beauty spa. Although he is befriended by handyman Stanley Potter, Lonnie arouses the jealousy of swimming instructor Brad Bentley. Despite her suspicion that Lonnie is a fortune hunter, physical education teacher Pam Merritt falls in love with him. Pam is the victim of repeated abduction attempts, which, she is informed by Deputy Sheriff Sturdivant, are inspired by her possession of a map of buried treasure. When she sees Lonnie kissing Vera, Pam breaks up with him, refusing to listen to his explanations. Back on the rodeo circuit, Lonnie finds himself preoccupied with Pam and is convinced by Stanley to return to her. He and Stanley locate Pam in Silverado, a restored ghost town and site of the treasure. During a night spent in a wax museum, the trio is assaulted by a procession of monsters, who are revealed to be Adolf, the ranch chef; Jerry, the groom; Henry, the gardener; and Deputy Sheriff Sturdivant. In the confrontation, the treasure is discovered. Assisted by Brad, Lonnie subdues the intruders. After a wedding at the ranch, Lonnie and Pam drive off, with Stanley trapped in a washtub he has tied to their car. *Broncobusters. Singers. Handymen. Athletic coaches. Sheriffs. Monsters. Jealousy. Rodeos. Disguise. Dude ranches. Beauty farms. Treasure. Ghost towns. Weddings. Documentation.*

TICKLED PINK see MAGIC SPECTACLES

A TICKLISH AFFAIR   F6.5062

Euterpe, Inc. *Dist* Metro-Goldwyn-Mayer, Inc. 26 Jun **1963** [Chicago opening; c7 Jun 1963; LP25419]. Sd (Westrex); col (Metrocolor). 35mm (Panavision). 88 min.

Prod Joe Pasternak. *Dir* George Sidney. *Screenplay* Ruth Brooks Flippen. *Dir Photog* Milton Krasner. *Art Dir* George W. Davis, Edward Carfagno. *Set Decor* Henry Grace, Keogh Gleason. *Film Ed* John McSweeney, Jr. *Mus* George Stoll. *Arr* Marty Paich. *Song:* "Love Is a Ticklish Affair" George Stoll, Robert Van Eps, Harold Adamson. *Sung by* Jack Jones. *Mus Assoc* Robert Van Eps. *Rec Supv* Franklin Milton. *Sd* Larry Jost. *Asst Dir* William Shanks, Jim Myers. *Asst to the Prod* Irving Aaronson. *Prod Mgr* William Kaplan. *Script Supv* Cleo Anton. *Wardrobe* Lambert Marks, Elva Martien. *Makeup* William Tuttle, Ron Berkeley. *Hairstyles* Sydney Guilaroff, Shirley Althouse. *Sp Vis Eff* J. McMillan Johnson, A. Arnold Gillespie, Robert R. Hoag. *Coöp* United States—Department of Defense, United States Navy. *Casting* Mel Ballerino, Warren Mace.

Cast: Shirley Jones *(Amy Martin)*, Gig Young *(Comdr. Key Weedon)*, Red Buttons *(Simon Shelley)*, Carolyn Jones *(Tandy Martin)*, Edgar Buchanan *(Cramps Martin)*, Eddie Applegate *(Yeoman Corker Bell)*, Edward Platt *(Capt. Haven Hitchcock)*, Billy Mumy *(Alex Martin)*, Bryan Russell *(Luke Martin)*, Robert Foulk *(policeman)*, Milton Frome *(fireman)*, Peter Robbins *(Grover Martin)*.

Romantic comedy. Source: Barbara Luther, "Moon Walk," in *Ladies Home Journal* (Feb 1962). When the crew aboard a U. S. aircraft is alerted by S.O.S. blinker light signals in the San Diego Bay area, Comdr. Key Weedon is sent to investigate. He discovers that the flashing comes from 6-year-old Grover Martin, whose Uncle Simon Shelley, a commercial flight officer, has given him a blinker light for a toy. A mutual attraction soon develops between Key and the boy's widowed mother, Amy; their romance is encouraged both by Simon and Amy's sister-in-law Tandy. Amy refuses to marry a Navy man because she wants a permanent home for Grover and his older brothers, Alex and Luke, and when Key announces he is being sent overseas, she refuses to accompany him. Simon arrives with some helium-filled weather balloons and takes his nephews "moon-walking" by tying the boys to the balloons and flying them like kites. Grover, attempting to locate Key, releases his anchoring rope and goes sailing across San Diego Bay. Helicopters, patrol boats, and many local residents attempt to rescue the child, but it is Key who saves Grover by commandeering a blimp, lowering himself on a life raft, and grabbing the boy as he floats by. When Key returns to Amy, she decides to marry him, preferring a permanent father to a permanent home. *Widows. Air pilots. Brothers. Uncles. Sisters-in-law. Family life. Marriage. Rescue. Toys. Balloons (ascent). Helicopters. Blimps. San Diego. United States Navy.*

Note: Working title: *Moon Walk*.

TIERRA BRUTAL see THE SAVAGE GUNS

TIERRA DE FUEGO see SUNSCORCHED

THE TIGER AMONG US see 13 WEST STREET

THE TIGER AND THE PUSSYCAT (United States/Italy)   F6.5063

Fair Film-Embassy Pictures. *Dist* Embassy Pictures. 6 Sep **1967** [San Francisco opening]. Sd; col (Eastman Color, print by Pathé). 35mm. 105 min.

Prod Mario Cecchi Gori. *Exec Prod* Joseph E. Levine. *Dir* Dino Risi. *Screenplay* Agenore Incrocci, Furio Scarpelli. *English Dial* John Douglas. *Story* Agenore Incrocci, Furio Scarpelli, Dino Risi. *Photog* Sandro D'Eva. *Art Dir* Luciano Ricceri. *Set Decor* Ezio Altieri. *Film Ed* Marcello Malvestiti. *Mus* Fred Bongusto. *Sd* Vittorio Massi. *Asst Dir* Mariano Laurenti. *Prod Mgr* Pio Angeletti. *Prod Supv* Mario D'Alessio. *Cost* Ezio Altieri.

Cast: Vittorio Gassman *(Francesco Vincenzini)*, Ann-Margret *(Carolina)*, Eleanor Parker *(Esperia)*, Caterina Boratto *(Delia)*, Eleonora Brown *(Luisella)*, Antonella Steni *(Pinella)*, Fiorenzo Fiorentini *(Tazio)*, Giambattista Salerno *(Luca)*, Jacques Herlin *(monsignor)*, Luigi Vannucchi *(company president)*, Ivan Scratuglia, Nino Segurini, Egidio Casolari.

Comedy-drama. Francesco Vincenzini, a handsome and dynamic 45-year-old engineer in Rome, becomes a grandfather for the first time and suffers the first emotional shock of advancing old age. He receives another shock when his teenaged son attempts suicide because he has been rejected by Carolina, a flirtatious art student. Francesco visits the girl to rebuke her for her callousness, but instead, he is seduced by her. Despite his better judgment and the advice of an old friend, Francesco plunges into an affair with Carolina, neglecting his work, reputation, and family. Eventually, Carolina demands that he abandon everything and go to Paris with her. Unable to resist, Francesco writes a farewell letter to his wife, Esperia, and goes to the train to meet Carolina. At the last minute, however, he realizes that he cannot recapture his youth. Sadly,

he returns home, and Esperia pretends that she never received his farewell letter. *Engineers. Grandfathers. Students. Middle age. Family life. Adolescence. Suicide. Seduction. Infidelity. Rome.*

Note: Location scenes filmed in Rome. Released in Italy in 1967 as *Il tigre*.

TIGER BY THE TAIL   F6.5064

United Pictures. *Dist* Commonwealth United Entertainment, Inc., American International Pictures. Jan **1970**. Sd; col (Eastman Color). 35mm. 99 min. MPAA rating GP.

Prod Francis D. Lyon. *Exec Prod* Earle Lyon. *Dir* R. G. Springsteen. *Screenplay* Charles A. Wallace. *Dir Photog* Alan Stensvold. *Film Ed* Terry O. Morse. *Mus* Joe Greene. *Song:* "Let's Drink, Friends" Xavier Cugat, Charo. *Sung by* Charo. *Sd* Robert Post. *Asst Dir* William Schwartz. *Prod Mgr* Joe Wonder. *Cont* Laura Rosser. *Cost* Frank Tauss. *Makeup* Maurice Stein.

Cast: Christopher George *(Steve Michaelis)*, Tippi Hedren *(Rita Armstrong)*, Dean Jagger *(Top Polk)*, John Dehner *(Sheriff Chancey Jones)*, Charo *(Darlita)*, Lloyd Bochner *(Del Ware)*, Glenda Farrell *(Sarah Harvey)*, Alan Hale, [Jr.] *(Billy Jack Whitehorn)*, Skip Homeier *(Deputy Sheriff Laswell)*, R. G. Armstrong *(Ben Holmes)*, Dennis Patrick *(Frank Michaelis)*, Martin Ashe *(Jimmy-San Ricketts)*, Frank Babich *(reporter)*, Marilyn Devin *(Julie Foster)*, Ray Martell *(Garcia)*, Burt Mustin *(Tom Dugger)*, Fernando Pereira *(Mendoza)*, Olga Velez *(Candita)*, Della Young, Tricia Young *(bikini girls)*, The Mescalero Apache Horn Dancers, Meredith Neal and the Boot Heel Boys.

Mystery melodrama. Vietnam War veteran Steve Michaelis returns to the United States to restore his relationship with his estranged brother Frank, who is the principal shareholder of a California racetrack. Steve arrives only to discover that his brother has been murdered by two Mexicans during a robbery. Steve believes that the robbery was merely a cover-up created by one of the other shareholders for the murder of his brother. Despite being followed by the suspicious Deputy Laswell, Steve forces shareholder Del Ware to admit that he took part in Frank's murder. Ware is murdered, however, before he can reveal the identity of his accomplices. With the assistance of Rita Armstrong, a former girl friend as well as a shareholder, Steve forces Deputy Laswell into revealing his complicity. Laswell is then shot by Sheriff Jones, who admits that it was he who planned Frank's murder; in the ensuing fight, Steve disarms and kills Jones. Now in firm control of the racetrack, Steve and Rita resume their romance. *Veterans. Brothers. Mexicans. Police. Sheriffs. Murder. Robbery. Racetracks.*

TIGER FLIGHT (Japan)   F6.5065

Toho Co. Jul **1965** [Los Angeles showing]. Sd; col (Eastmancolor). 35mm (Tohoscope). 104 min.

Exec Prod Tomoyuki Tanaka. *Dir* Kengo Furusawa.

Cast: Tatsuya Mihashi, Makoto Sato, Yosuke Natsuki, Takashi Inagaki.

Action drama. A lieutenant colonel in the Japanese Air Force is assigned to a flight group composed of pilots indifferent to regulations but passionate about defying death in their planes as they attempt to break the sound barrier. The new commander whips his men into line, and soon the flight group is concentrating on providing Japan with the best possible defense in case of attack. *Military life. Japan—Air Force.*

Note: Released in Japan in 1964 as *Kyomo ware ozorani ari*.

THE TIGER MAKES OUT   F6.5066

Elan Productions. *Dist* Columbia Pictures. 18 Sep **1967** [New York opening; c1 Oct 1967; LP34996]. Sd (RCA); col (Eastmancolor, print by Pathé). 35mm. 94 min.

A George Justin Production. *Prod* George Justin. *Assoc Prod* Claire Nichtern. *Dir* Arthur Hiller. *Screenplay* Murray Schisgal. *Dir Photog* Arthur J. Ornitz. *Camera Op* Victor Kemper. *Set Decor* John Godfrey. *Prod Dsgn* Paul Sylbert. *Film Ed* Robert C. Jones. *Mus Comp & Cond* Shorty Rogers. *Titl Song* Shorty Rogers, Diane Hilderbrand. *Sd* Dennis Maitland. *Asst Dir* Burtt Harris. *Prod Mgr* Stephen F. Kesten. *Script Supv* Marguerite James. *Cost* Anthea Sylbert. *Wardrobe* Flo Transfield, George Newman. *Makeup* Martin Bell. *Hairstyles* Robert Grimaldi. *Casting* Clifford Stevens, Vic Ramos. *Gaffer* Willie Meyerhoff. *Grip* Robert Ward. *Constr* Jules Wollock.

Cast: Eli Wallach *(Ben Harris)*, Anne Jackson *(Gloria Fiske)*, Bob Dishy *(Jerry Fiske)*, John Harkins *(Leo)*, Ruth White *(Mrs. Kelly)*, Roland Wood *(Mr. Kelly)*, Rae Allen *(Beverly)*, Sudie Bond *(Miss Lane)*, David Burns *(Mr. Ratner)*, Jack Fletcher *(pawnbroker)*, Bibi Osterwald *(Mrs. Ratner)*, Charles Nelson Reilly *(registrar)*, Frances Sternhagen *(lady on bus)*, Elizabeth Wilson *(receptionist)*, Kim August *(Toni Songbird)*, Alice Beardsley *(Kentucky neighbor)*, Mariclare Costello *(Rosi)*, David Doyle *(housing clerk)*, Dustin Hoffman *(Hap)*, Michele Kesten *(waitress)*, James Luisi *(Pete Copolla)*, Remak Ramsey *(housing guard)*, Sherman Raskin *(Red Schwartzkopf)*, John Ryan *(Toni's escort)*, Oren Stevens *(policeman)*, Edgar Stehli *(old man)*.

Comedy. Source: Murray Schisgal, *The Tiger* (New York opening: 4 Feb 1963). During a typically disaster-filled day, Ben Harris, an angry and frustrated bachelor mailman living in a cluttered Greenwich Village basement, learns he has been paying rent to a woman who hasn't owned his building in 6 years; the lady upstairs puts her leg through his ceiling; and a visit to the Housing Authority to complain about the condition of his apartment is so maddening that he nearly strangles a civil servant. No longer able to endure the injustices of society, he decides to activate the ferocious tiger within himself by abducting a helpless female and dragging her back to his lair. But Ben snares Gloria Fiske, a suburban housewife as frustrated as himself, whose middle-class husband has been ridiculing her for wanting to continue her education. As Ben and Gloria discuss their mutual disdain for society, a rapport develops between them. Gloria persuades Ben to see his former landlady, Mrs. Kelly, and demand his rent money back; she also offers to give him weekly French lessons. When Ben and Gloria go for the rent refund, the eccentric Mr. and Mrs. Kelly offer Ben a small apartment in their building to atone for taking his money. Gloria helps Ben move in and stays on for a few hours as his willing captive. When she leaves, however, Ben follows her home and, unable to resist the impulse to be near her, climbs through her bedroom window. Instead of Gloria, he finds her startled husband. Fleeing from the scene, Ben races back to the Kellys and is welcomed into their bed to watch television and eat fried chicken. He has found at least a temporary haven from the troubled world outside. *Mail carriers. Housewives. Landladies. Bureaucrats. Suburbanites. Urban life. Abduction. Fraud. Infidelity. Education. Mistaken identity. Housing. New York City— Greenwich Village.*

Note: Filmed on location in New York City.

TIGER OF THE SEVEN SEAS (France/Italy)   **F6.5067**
Liber Film–Euro International Films. *Dist* Embassy Pictures. 18 Oct **1964** [New York showing]. Sd; col (Eastman Color). 35mm (Totalscope). 90 min.
Prod Ottavio Poggi. *Dir* Luigi Capuano. *Screenplay* Arpad De Riso, Luigi Capuano, Ottavio Poggi. *Story* Nino Battiferri. *Photog* Alvaro Mancori. *Art Dir* Ernesto Kromberg, Amedeo Mellone. *Film Ed* Renato Cinquini. *Mus* Carlo Rustichelli. *Sd* Fiorenzo Magli. *Prod Mgr* Nino Battiferri. *Cost* Giancarlo Bartolini Salimbeni.
Cast: Gianna Maria Canale *(Consuelo)*, Anthony Steel *(William)*, Maria Grazia Spina *(Anna da Cordoba)*, Ernesto Calindri *(Inigo da Cordoba)*, Andrea Aureli *(Laura)*, Carlo Ninchi *(Robert)*, John Kitzmiller *(Turpentine)*, Carlo Pisacane, Pasquale De Filippo, Renato Izzo, Renato Giomini.
Adventure melodrama. Consuelo, the daughter of a retired pirate captain, wants to assume command of her father's ship, the *Santa Maria,* but the old man offers the position to the winner of a duel. After Consuelo's lover, William, defeats Robert in the contest, Consuelo takes on William herself, and he allows her to win. Later, Robert murders Consuelo's father and frames William as the killer. He is about to be executed for the crime when Spaniards attack the pirates, and William is able to escape in the *Santa Maria.* Vowing revenge, Consuelo steals a Spanish ship and apprehends William, who proclaims his innocence and promises to capture his rival. Robert, meanwhile, has joined forces with Anna da Cordoba, the wife of Porto Nuevo Governor Inigo, who is eager to find the dead captain's hidden treasure. William tries to apprehend Robert but is ambushed and tortured until Consuelo comes to the rescue and kills Robert in a duel. Anna, backed by many Spaniards, forces Consuelo to hand over the treasure before she and William are set free. *Pirates. Spanish. Territorial governors. Murder. Revenge. Filial relations. Frameup. Torture. Ships. Treasure. Duels.*
Note: Opened in Rome in 1963 as *La tigre dei sette mari;* opened in Paris in Jul 1963 as *Le tigre des mers.*

A TIGER WALKS   **F6.5068**
Walt Disney Productions. *Dist* Buena Vista Distribution Co. 11 Mar **1964** [Portland, Oregon, opening; c27 Jan 1964; LP27119]. Sd (RCA); col (Technicolor). 35mm. 91 min.
Pres by Walt Disney. A Walt Disney Production. *Co-prod* Bill Anderson, prod. *Asst Prod* Ron Miller. *Dir* Norman Tokar. *Screenplay* Lowell S. Hawley. *Dir Photog* William Snyder. *Art Dir* Carroll Clark, Marvin Aubrey Davis. *Set Decor* Emile Kuri, Frank R. McKelvy. *Film Ed* Grant K. Smith. *Mus* Buddy Baker. *Orch* Bob Brunner. *Sd* Robert O. Cook. *Mus Ed* Evelyn Kennedy. *Asst Dir* John C. Chulay. *Cost* Chuck Keehne, Gertrude Casey. *Makeup* Pat McNalley. *Hairstyles* La Rue Matheron.
Cast: Brian Keith *(Sheriff Pete Williams)*, Vera Miles *(Dorothy Williams)*, Pamela Franklin *(Julie Williams)*, Sabu *(Ram Singh)*, Edward Andrews *(The Governor)*, Una Merkel *(Mrs. Watkins)*, Peter Brown *(Vern Goodman)*, Kevin Corcoran *(Tom Hadley)*, Frank McHugh *(Bill Watkins)*, Arthur Hunnicutt *(Mr. Lewis)*, Merry Anders *(Betty Collins)*, Jack Albertson *(Sam Grotz)*, Connie Gilchrist *(Mrs. Lewis)*, Theodore Marcuse *(Josef Pietz)*, Frank Aletter *(Joe Riley)*, Donald May *(Captain Anderson)*, Doodles Weaver *(Bob Evans)*, Rajah *(himself, a Bengal tiger)*.
Drama. Source: Ian Niall, *A Tiger Walks* (London, 1960). Rajah, a tiger badly mistreated by his trainer, escapes when a circus truck breaks down in a

small town. Although Julie, the 12-year-old daughter of the local sheriff, falls down in his path, Rajah leaves her unharmed and runs for the woods. Later, the sheriff finds the sadistic trainer mauled to death in the woods. Panic seizes the town, and the governor, taking political advantage of the situation, sends in the National Guard to hunt Rajah. Julie, interviewed on television, states that Rajah had been mistreated and misunderstood and should be captured alive. Children all over the country send money to help toward this end. A fog descends, and when a farmer comes through the woods to tell the troops that the tiger is on his land, he is shot at and wounded by a guardsman. With the help of Ram Singh, a circus assistant, the sheriff captures Rajah alive, and the tiger is placed in a zoo with his mate and cubs. *Children. Animal trainers. Sheriffs. State governors. Farmers. Smalltown life. Circus. Television. National Guard. Fog. Tigers.*

TIGHT SKIRTS, LOOSE PLEASURES (France)   **F6.5069**
Comptoir Français du Film–Roal Films. *Dist* Times Film Corp. Aug **1966**. Sd; b&w. 35mm (CinemaScope). 84 min.
Dir Claude de Givray. *Screenplay* Claude de Givray, Bernard Revon. *Dial* Bernard Revon. *Cinematog* Roger Fellous. *Camera* Georges Balogh. *Film Ed* Pierre Geran, Jean-Marie Gimel. *Mus* Georges Delerue. *Asst Dir* Michel Wichard. *Prod Supv* Michel Mombailly. *Prod Mgr* Jean Lefait. *Script Girl* Suzanne Ohanessian. *Makeup* Danielle Thevenot. *Coiffures* Carita.
Cast: Valeria Ciangottini *(Catherine)*, Jean Yanne *(Pornotropos)*, Jacques Destoop *(Paul)*, Perrette Pradier *(Corinne)*, Jean-Marie Fertey *(Thanatos)*, Jean-Pierre Janssen, Jean-Paul Janssen *(twins)*, Anne-Marie Coffinet *(Juliette)*, Maria Rosa Rodrigues *(Barbara)*, Amarande *(Mélanie)*, Max Montavon *(photographer)*, Roger Fradet *(Doudou)*, Alain Raffael *(Raffa)*, Jean Dalmain *(Catherine's father)*, Hella Petri *(Thaïs)*, Lisette Le Bon *(impresario)*, Annie Duroc *(prostitute)*, Jean Roger Caussimon *(priest)*, Roger Karl *(old man)*, Jean Degrave.
Melodrama. Catherine, disillusioned by an unhappy love affair, decides to become a prostitute. She is hired by Pornotropos, an unscrupulous young hoodlum who has recently reopened several whorehouses and forced other madams to consolidate into his syndicate. After joining a new brothel managed by Corinne, Pornotropos' mistress, Catherine is brutally assaulted when she refuses the gangster's advances. She then meets Paul, a public relations representative for an elderly gentleman who died in Catherine's room; they soon fall in love and escape from the syndicate. Pornotropos, assisted by his brother Thanatos, a sadistic killer, and by a pair of murderous twins, pursues and recaptures Catherine. Paul locates her, and after Pornotropos is accidentally killed by his brother, Paul and Catherine flee to safety, while Thanatos joins Corinne in continuing his brother's enterprise. *Pimps. Madams. Mistresses. Brothers. Twins. Prostitution. Abduction. Murder. Fratricide. Whorehouses. Syndicates.*
Note: Opened in Paris in Aug 1965 as *L'amour à la chaîne.* Also known as *Tight Skirts; Chainwork Love;* and *Loose Pleasures.*

IL TIGRE *see* **THE TIGER AND THE PUSSYCAT**

EL TIGRE DE LOS SIETE MARES *see* **THE SEA PIRATE**

LA TIGRE DEI SETTE MARI *see* **TIGER OF THE SEVEN SEAS**

LE TIGRE DES MERS *see* **TIGER OF THE SEVEN SEAS**

TIKO AND THE SHARK (United States/France/Italy)   **F6.5070**
Titanus–P. C. M.–Metro-Goldwyn-Mayer Pictures–S. N. P. C.–S. G. C. *Dist* Metro-Goldwyn-Mayer, Inc. 31 Mar **1966** [San Antonio, Texas, opening; c31 Dec 1962; LP26213]. Sd (Westrex); col (Eastmancolor). 35mm. 88 min. [See note.]
Prod Goffredo Lombardo. *Dir* Folco Quilici. *Screenplay* Augusto Frassineti, Folco Quilici, Ottavio Alessi. *Dial (see note)* Giorgio Prosperi, Franco Prosperi. *Story* Italo Calvino. *Photog* Pier Ludovico Pavoni. *Underwater Photog* Masino Manunza. *Camera* Fausto Rossi. *2d Unit Camera* Giovanni Scarpellini. *Film Ed* Mario Serandrei. *Mus* Francesco De Masi. *Prod Supv* Jacques Guillerme. *Cost* Nadia Vitali.
Cast: Marlene Among *(Diana)*, Al Kauwe *(Ti-koyo)*, Denis Pouira *(Ti-koyo as child)*, Diane Samsoi *(Diana as child)*, Roau *(Cocoyo)*.
Melodrama. Source: Clément Richer, *Ti-koyo et son requin* (Paris, 1941). A young boy named Tiko, who lives on a Polynesian island of fisher-folk, finds a baby shark and, aided by his young friend Diana, raises it in a lagoon on a remote part of the island. Once the shark becomes mature, however, Tiko releases his pet and sends it into deeper waters. In the decade that follows, the simple island life is drastically altered by the emergence of organized fisheries controlled by a monopoly. Tiko resists the encroachments of civilization and earns his living by diving for mother-of-pearl. Diana, whose brother becomes a major figure in the monopoly, abandons the island to study at a school in America. Then one day the shark returns to Tiko, thus enabling him to dive in deep and dangerous water, the pet providing protection and constant vigil. But

when the business concern burns the natives' homes and attempts to kill the shark, Tiko almost loses his life protecting the pet, and he decides to seek another island, untouched by civilization. Accompanied by Diana, who has recently returned to the island, he sets sail in a small craft with the shark following close behind. *Fishermen. Businessmen. Polynesians. Divers. Social conformity. Pets. Pearl diving. Childhood. Islands. Fisheries. Trusts. Sharks.*

Note: Filmed in French Polynesia with Tuamotu Island natives in the cast. Released in Italy as *Ti-Koyo e il suo pescecane* in 1962; running time: 98 min. French release title: *Ti-Koyo et son requin.* Preview screening length: 100 min; copyright length: 107 min. The cutting continuity credits Giorgio Prosperi with dialog, while one U. S. source credits Franco Prosperi.

TILL TOMORROW COMES (Japan)   **F6.5071**
Toho Co. May **1962** [Los Angeles showing]. Sd; b&w. 35mm (Tohoscope). 113 min.
Exec Prod Ichiro Sato, Ken-ichiro Tsunoda. *Dir* Shiro Toyoda. *Screenplay* Toshio Yazumi. *Photog* Kozo Okazaki. *Mus* Hikaru Hayashi.
Cast: Kyoko Kagawa, Yuriko Hoshi, Shuji Sano, Junko Ikeuchi, Kumi Mizuno, Haruko Sugimura, Tsutomu Yamazaki, Nobuko Otowa, Takashi Inagaki.
Domestic melodrama. Natsuko's third child, Saori, is born during the summer of 1941, just before her father, Tetsuo, is drafted. A short time later, Natsuko discovers the baby girl is blind. Natsuko decides, with Tetsuo's advice, to have surgery performed on Saori, but on the day before the operation the doctor is also drafted. During the evacuation of Tokyo, Natsuko is separated from her two older children but manages to stay in touch with Saori's doctor, who finally arranges for the surgery. It proves unsuccessful and doctors predict Saori will be blind for life. Natsuko and Tetsuo, now discharged from the army, place Saori in a school for the blind. Ten years later, the family son becomes engaged to a waitress who breaks off the marriage plans when she learns she will have a blind sister-in-law. Saori, studying to become a masseuse, is nearly raped by a degenerate attracted by her innocent appearance. She finally finds happiness in a romance with a blind boy. *Surgeons. Waitresses. Blindness. Eye surgery. Family life. Motherhood. Military draft. Rape. Schools for the Blind. World War II. Tokyo.*

Note: Released in Japan in 1962 as *Asu aru kagiri* or *Ashita aru kagiri.*

TILLIE'S PUNCTURED ROMANCE see **CHARLIE'S BIG ROMANCE**

TILLSAMMANS MED GUNILLA MÅNDAG KVÄLL OCH TISDAG see **GUILT**

TIME BOMB (France/Italy)   **F6.5072**
Le Groupe des Quatre–Da. Ma. Film. *Dist* Allied Artists. Apr **1961** [c2 May 1961; LP19407]. Sd; b&w. 35mm. 92 min.
Prod Raymond Froment, Terra Films. *Assoc Prod* Julien Rivière. *Dir* Yves Ciampi. *Dial* Jacques-Laurent Bost. *Adapt* Yves Ciampi, Henri-François Rey. *Story* Jean-Charles Tacchella. *Dir Photog* Armand Thirard. *Camera Op* Louis Née. *Asst Camera* Robert Florent. *Art Dir* Roger Briaucourt. *Asst Art Dir* Yves Olivier, Jacques Mely. *Film Ed* Georges Alépée. *Asst Film Ed* Georges Deguy. *Mus* Henri Crolla, André Hodeir. *Sd* Robert Teisseire. *Sd Rec* Georges Mardiguian. *Boom* Gérard Brisseau. *Asst Dir* Jean Dewever, Bernard Deflandre. *Prod Mgr* Alain Darbon, Michel Bonnay. *Unit Mgr* Pierre Charron. *Location Mgr* Gabriel Bechir. *Prod Sec* Janine Thaon. *Set Cont* Madeleine Lefebvre. *Wardrobe* Tanine Autre. *Mylène Demongeot's Wardrobe by* Pierre Balmain. *Cost* Jeannine Germes-Vergne, Yvette Bonnay. *Makeup* Alexandre Marcus. *Hairstyles* Simone Knapp. *Still Photog* Roger Corbeau. *Props* Raymond Lemarchand, Daniel Laguille.
Cast: Curt Jurgens (*Eric Mullen*), Mylène Demongeot (*Catherine*), Alain Saury (*Michel*), Paul Mercey (*cook*), Robert Porte (*steward*), Daniel Sorano (*Mathias*), Jean Daurand (*Pépère*), Gabriel Gobin (*Aubriand*), André Dalibert (*Carminati*), Jess Hahn (*Chewing-Gum*), Raymond Loyer (*Laurent*), Jim Gérald (*drunk*), Pierre Collet, Guy Dakar, Jean-Jacques Lecot, Henri Maik, Pierre Paulet, Jean Murat, Claire Guibert (*crew*).
Melodrama. In a desperate attempt to recover a lost family fortune, orphaned brother and sister Michel and Catherine plot to defraud an insurance company of $6 million. Their plan is to wreck a family freighter captained by Catherine's middle-aged lover, Eric Mullen, so as to collect the insurance money. Before Eric leaves Hamburg he places a time bomb in the hold of his ship, setting it to explode in waters where mines are still known to exist. The ship loses 3 hours at the Kiel Canal, and Eric orders the time made up and pushes the ship toward its doom, knowing that he and his men can escape in lifeboats. As a result of the strain, one of the ship's boilers blows up, trapping a crew member in the wreckage. Suddenly repentant, Eric hurries to the hold and disconnects the bomb. He then brings the ship safely back to Hamburg, to discover that Catherine also has come to regret their dishonest scheme. *Orphans. Sea captains. Fraud. Brother-sister relationship. Finance—Personal. Insurance. Freighters. Bombs. Mines (war explosives). Hamburg. Kiel Canal.*

Ship explosions.
Note: Location scenes filmed in Hamburg and on the Kiel Canal. Paris opening: Jan 1959 as *Le vent se lève*; running time: 90 min. Rome opening: Jun 1959 as *Il vento si alza*; running time: 95 min.

A TIME FOR BURNING   **F6.5073**
Quest Productions. *For* Lutheran Film Associates. *Dist* Pathé Contemporary Films. 23 Feb **1967** [New York opening; c17 Oct 1966; MP18678]. Sd; b&w. 16mm. 58 min.
Prod William C. Jersey. *Exec Prod* Robert E. A. Lee. *Conceived & Dir* William C. Jersey, Barbara Connell. *Photog* William C. Jersey. *Asst Camera* Justus Taylor. *Film Ed* William C. Jersey, Barbara Connell. *Asst Ed* Justus Taylor. *Song* Tom Paxton. *Arr* Barry Kornfeld. *Sung by* Ronnie Gilbert. *Sd* Barbara Connell.
Participants: L. William Youngdahl, Ernie Chambers, Ted Backstrom, Ray Christensen, Gene Zimmerman, Mrs. Gene Zimmerman, Earle Persons, Mrs. Earle Persons.
Documentary. Rev. L. William Youngdahl, the new pastor of the Augustana Lutheran Church in Omaha, meets with opposition while attempting to foster improved relations between his white, middle class congregation and neighboring black churches. Youngdahl is frustrated by white indifference and black suspicion, as voiced by Ernie Chambers, an articulate barber. Nevertheless, he initiates a series of informal visits. Attorney Ted Backstrom, chairman of the church's social action committee, supports the program, while member Ray Christensen fears that forced integration will divide the church. Meanwhile, church schoolteachers Mr. and Mrs. Gene Zimmerman arrange for teenagers in their class to visit Calvin Memorial Presbyterian Church. The black youths' corresponding visit to Augustana provokes controversy within the white congregation. During a visit with Dr. and Mrs. Earle Persons, members of Hope Lutheran Church, the pastor is cautioned that predecessors advocating integration have been forced to resign their pastorates. Persons' observation is prophetic. Faced with declining attendance, Youngdahl tenders his resignation. *Clergymen. Negroes. Barbers. Youth. Dentists. Lawyers. Schoolteachers. Racial integration. Race relations. Urban life. Ghettos. Omaha. Augustana Lutheran Church (Omaha). Calvin Memorial Presbyterian Church (Omaha).*

Note: Filmed in Omaha, Nebraska. First shown on television 17 Oct 1966 on "NET Journal."

A TIME FOR GIVING see **GENERATION**

A TIME FOR HEROES see **THE HELL WITH HEROES**

A TIME FOR KILLING   **F6.5074**
Sage Western Pictures. *Dist* Columbia Pictures. Nov **1967** [c1 May 1967; LP35094]. Sd; col (Pathé). 35mm (Panavision). 88 min.
Prod (see note) Harry Joe Brown, Roger Corman. *Dir* Phil Karlson. *Screenplay* Halsted Welles. *Dir Photog* Kenneth Peach. *Art Dir* Daniel Haller. *Set Decor* Jack Ahern. *Supv Film Ed* George White. *Film Ed (see note)* Roy Livingston, Monte Hellman. *Mus* Van Alexander. *Mus Comp & Cond* Mundell Lowe. *Song:* "The Long Ride Home" Ned Washington, Van Alexander. *Sung by* Eddy Arnold. *Sd Supv* Charles J. Rice. *Sd* Philip Mitchell, Jack Haynes. *Asst Dir* Jack Bohrer, Anthony Ray. *Unit Prod Mgr* Mike Frankovich, Jr. *Asst to Prod* David Breen. *Script Supv* Wallace Bennett. *Makeup Supv* Ben Lane. *Hairstyles* Virginia Jones. *Filmed Through the Courtesy of* Department of the Interior, National Park Service—Zion National Park, Glen Canyon National Recreation Area. *Still Photog* Homer Van Pelt. *Prop* Richard Rubin, Karl Brainard. *Gaffer* Lloyd Garnell.
Cast: Inger Stevens (*Emily Biddle*).
Union Troops: Glenn Ford (*Major Charles Wolcott*), Paul Petersen (*Blue Lake*), Timothy Carey (*Billy Cat*), Kenneth Tobey (*Sergeant Cleehan*), Richard X. Slattery (*Corp. Paddy Darling*), Harrison Ford (*Lieutenant Shaffer*), Kay E. Kuter (*Owelson*), Dick Miller (*Zollicoffer*), Emile Meyer (*Colonel Harries*), Marshall Reed (*Stedner*).
Confederate Troops: George Hamilton (*Capt. Dorrit Bentley*), Max Baer (*Sgt. Luther Liskell*), Todd Armstrong (*Lieutenant Prudessing*), Duke Hobbie (*Lieutenant Frist*), Dean Stanton (*Sgt. Dan Way*), James Davidson (*Little Mo*), Charlie Briggs (*Sergeant Kettlinger*), Craig Curtis (*Bagnef*), Jay Ripley (*Lovingwood*), Dean Goodhill (*Bruce*).
Action melodrama. Source: Nelson Wolford and Shirley Wolford, *The Southern Blade* (New York, 1961). Near the end of the Civil War, a Confederate prisoner is sentenced to death for killing a Union guard while attempting to escape from Fort Hawkes, Utah. When he insults the fort's commanding officer, the military execution squad is replaced by Negro orderlies. Enraged by this humiliation, the Rebels' ranking officer, Capt. Dorrit Bentley, effects a mass escape by blowing up the fort. While on the run, he and his men kill a detail of Union soldiers and take as hostage Emily Biddle, a missionary engaged to the fort's second-in-command, Maj. Charles Wolcott. Wolcott is ordered to lead a pursuit party, and Bentley's men make their way

to a small town in the Arizona badlands, where they plan to ambush their pursuers. Bentley allows one of his men to kill a Union dispatch rider in a saloon and learns from the victim's papers that Lee has surrendered at Appomattox. Although he conceals the news from his men, Bentley divulges the information to Emily, then rapes and beats her into unconsciousness before heading toward the Mexican border with his troops. Wolcott and his men enter town, and Emily, just as Bentley intended, withholds the news about the war and demands that he track down and kill the captain. The two men finally clash in a deserted mission at the Arizona-Mexico border; Bentley is mortally wounded but has his moment of triumph by telling Wolcott both of the war's end and of Emily's knowledge of the fact. Dazed, Wolcott and the remaining survivors of the senseless conflict begin the long trek home, with Emily following behind them. *Fugitives. Missionaries. Negroes. Orderlies (military). Revenge. Prison escapes. Rape. Perfidy. Forts. Saloons. Missions. United States—History— Civil War. United States Army. Arizona. Utah. Mexican border. Explosions.*

Note: Location scenes filmed in Zion National Park, Utah, and Glen Canyon National Recreation Area, Arizona-Utah. Working title: *The Long Ride Home.* Corman withdrew as co-producer and was replaced as director by Karlson several weeks into production. Hellman was replaced as editor several weeks later.

A TIME IN THE SUN (Sweden)   **F6.5075**
Europa Film. *Dist* Universal Pictures. 27 Jan **1970** [New York opening]. Sd; b&w. 35mm. 104 min. *MPAA rating* R.
Dir Åke Falck. *Screenplay* Åke Falck, Lars Widding. *Photog* Mac Ahlberg, Ralph Evers. *Mus* Harry Arnold. *English Subtitl* Noelle Gillmor.
Cast: Grynet Molvig ("*Princess*"), Lars Passgård (*Gunnar*), Monica Nielsen (*Pirjo*), Birgitta Valberg (*doctor*), Thor Lyndthal (*obstetrician*), Heinz Spira (*chum*), Axel Duberg (*clergyman*).
Romantic melodrama. Source: Gunnar Mattsson, *Prinsessan* (Stockholm, 1960). Gunnar, a journalist, falls in love with a young nurse who is suffering from Hodgkin's disease, an affliction which her doctors tell her is incurable. "Princess," as Gunnar affectionately calls her, at first refuses to believe that he loves her, but when she is convinced of his sincerity, they marry. "Princess" soon becomes pregnant, and after the child is born, she resumes radiation treatments. Eventually, as a result of her physician's care and Gunnar's love, she is cured. *Journalists. Nurses. Physicians. Cancer. Marriage. Pregnancy. Childbirth.*
Note: Released in Sweden in Dec 1966 as *Prinsessan.* Also known as *The Princess.*

TIME LOST AND TIME REMEMBERED (Great Britain)   **F6.5076**
Partisan Film Productions. *For* J. Arthur Rank. *Dist* Continental Distributing, Inc. 29 Aug **1966** [New York opening]. Sd; b&w. 35mm. 91 min.
Prod Roy Millichip. *Dir* Desmond Davis. *Screenplay* Edna O'Brien, Desmond Davis. *Photog* Manny Wynn. *Art Dir* Tony Woollard. *Film Ed* Brian Smedley-Aston. *Mus Comp & Cond* John Addison. *Perf by* Sinfonia of London. *Sd* Don Challis, Stephen Dalby. *Sd Rec* Robin Gregory. *Asst Dir* Michael Gowans. *Prod Mgr* Bruce Sharman. *Wardrobe* Barbara Gillett. *Makeup* Richard Mills. *Hairstyles* Stephanie Kaye.
Cast: Sarah Miles (*Cass*), Cyril Cusack (*Hogan*), Julian Glover (*Dr. Matthew Langdon*), Sean Caffrey (*Colin Foley*), Marie Kean (*barkeeper*), Eve Belton (*Kate*), Cardew Robinson (*gravedigger*).
Drama. Source: Edna O'Brien, "A Woman by the Seaside" (a short story; publication undetermined). Dissatisfied with her marriage to Matthew, a medical student, Cass leaves London on Christmas Day and returns to the small fishing village of Lahinch on the west coast of Ireland. Years before, she was in love with a young fisherman named Colin and left Lahinch to go to London, certain that he would follow her. Instead, he went to sea, and Cass took a dull office job, entered into a loveless marriage, and had a miscarriage when she jumped from a bus to follow a man she thought was Colin. Now back in Lahinch, she finds everything just as it had been before. Seeking out Colin, she pleads with him to stay with her for just one night, but Colin is engaged and tells her that he can never recapture his youth. Matthew, who followed her to Lahinch, meets her on the sand dunes and asks her to come home, but Cass explains that even though Colin is lost to her, she cannot leave the only place where she once knew peace and happiness. Matthew finally says goodbye to Cass and returns to London. *Lovelorn. Irish. Fishermen. Medical students. Marriage. Miscarriage. Infidelity. Fishing villages. Christmas. London. Lahinch (Ireland).*
Note: Filmed on location in County Clare, Ireland, and London. Released in Great Britain in Jul 1966 as *I Was Happy Here.* Working title: *Passage of Love.*

TIME OF INDIFFERENCE (France/Italy)   **F6.5077**
C. C. F. Lux–Ultra Film–Vides. *Dist* Continental Distributing, Inc. 12 Oct **1965** [New York opening]. Sd; b&w. 35mm. 84 min.

Prod Franco Cristaldi. *Dir* Francesco Maselli. *Screenplay* Suso Cecchi D'Amico, Francesco Maselli. *Photog* Gianni Di Venanzo. *Art Dir* Luigi Scaccianoce. *Film Ed* Ruggero Mastroianni. *Mus* Giovanni Fusco. *Cost* Marcel Escoffier.
Cast: Rod Steiger (*Leo*), Claudia Cardinale (*Carla Ardengo*), Shelley Winters (*Lisa*), Paulette Goddard (*Maria Grazia Ardengo*), Tomas Milian (*Michele Ardengo*).
Drama. Source: Alberto Moravia, *Gli indifferenti* (Milan, 1929). In the 1920's, an impoverished widow, Maria Grazia, lives with her two grown children in the Ardengo villa. The last aristocratic remnant of her once wealthy family, Maria Grazia is blind to the fact that her ruthlessly opportunistic lover, Leo, has used their affair to gain control of her inheritance and is making advances toward her daughter Carla. Furthermore, Leo's domination has drained both Carla and her brother Michele of their self-respect and moral convictions; they now accept with indifference the decadent pattern of living surrounding them. Also present at the villa is Leo's former mistress, Lisa, who is eager to inform Michele of Leo's designs on Carla. Michele, however, has already become too ineffectual to do anything more than plead with his sister not to accept Leo's offer of marriage. Carla and Michele decide to take the easiest course of action and continue their meaningless way of life. Thus, Maria Grazia, concerned only with immediate problems, prepares for a costume ball, unaware that Carla will probably marry Leo and that Michele has already submitted to Lisa's persistent overtures of love. *Widows. Aristocrats. Idle rich. Opportunists. Mistresses. Moral corruption. Brother-sister relationship. Filial relations. Inheritance.*
Note: Opened in Rome in 1964 as *Gli indifferenti;* running time: 100 min. French title: *Les deux rivales.*

THE TIME OF RECKONING (Japan)   **F6.5078**
Daiei Motion Picture Co. Apr **1970** [Los Angeles showing]. Sd; col. 35mm. 120 min.
Dir Tadashi Imai. *Photog* Setsuo Kobayashi.
Cast: Jiro Tamiya, Wakao Ayako, Mariko Okada, Kyoko Kishida, Mariko Kaga, Masao Mishima.
Drama. No information about the precise nature of this film has been found.
Note: Released in Japan in Jun 1968 as *Fushin no taki.*

TIME OF ROSES (Finland)   **F6.5079**
Filminor. *Dist* Cinema Dimensions. 19 Oct **1970** [New York opening]. Sd; b&w. 35mm. 90 min.
Dir Risto Jarva. *Screenplay* Risto Jarva, Peter von Bagh, Jaakko Pakkasvirta. *Photog* Antti Peippo. *Mus* Otto Donner.
Cast: Ritva Vepsä (*Saara*), Arto Tuominen (*Raimo*), Tarja Markus (*Anu*).
Science fiction drama. The year is 2012 and individualism has almost vanished in Finland. Raimo, a symbol of the new classless and politically repressive society, is a successful television producer who makes influential films that reorder history to support the current ideology. He begins filming a melodrama about the 1970's, focusing on the life of a salesgirl killed in an automobile accident in 1976. A number of his employees are clandestine revolutionaries, who object to Raimo's distortion of the past. They are involved in planning a strike against an atomic power plant, but their chief hope is to expose Raimo's manipulative filmmaking techniques. Although the revolutionaries fail, Raimo is last seen celebrating the success of his movie in a drunken stupor, while his inflatable chair deflates. *Television producers. Revolutionaries. Social conformity. Propaganda. Strikes. Motion pictures. Drunkenness. The Future.*
Note: Released in Finland in 1969 as *Ruusujen aika;* running time: 105 min.

TIME OF THE HEATHEN   **F6.5080**
Emshwiller Project Co. *Dist* Lion International Films. c28 Mar **1962** [LU3204]. Sd; b&w. 35mm. 75 min. [Cut from 90 min.]
Prod Calvin Floyd. *Exec Prod* W. Ronald Lerner. *Asst Prod* Larry Adler, prod. *Dir-Writ* Peter Kass. *Photog* Ed Emshwiller. *Art work* Ed Emshwiller. *Film Ed* Ed Emshwiller, Peter Kass. *Mus & Electronic Sd* Lejaren A. Hiller, Jr. *Mus Dir* Robert Gray. *Sd* Al Gramaglia. *Asst Dir* Peg Santvoord. *Tech Adv* Albert Tompkins. *Field Coörd* James Clark, coörd, Mark Mercurio, Hannah Goulding.
Cast: John Heffernan (*Gaunt*), Stewart Heller (*Ted*), Nathaniel White (*Cal*), Ethyl Ayler (*Marie*), Orville Steward (*Link*), Barry Collins (*Jesse*), Dan Goulding.
Drama. Gaunt, a wandering stranger who carries a Bible, passes a farm at the instant Ted, the farmer's son, kills Marie, a black servant, in an attempted rape. The farmer, Link, arrives on the scene, blames the murder on the stranger, and orders Ted to shoot both Gaunt and little Jesse, Marie's mute son. When Ted hesitates, Gaunt and Jesse take flight, but Link and Cal, a sheriff, join in pursuit. Ted and Gaunt emerge face to face in the woods, and in the ensuing struggle Ted is killed. Subsequently, Link wounds Gaunt, who that night, in an

agonized delirium, relives his role as a member of the crew who dropped the atom bomb on Hiroshima. Jesse brings a doctor to tend Gaunt's wounds. When the doctor tells them that he intends to take Jesse back with him, the man and boy embrace, but Link catches sight of them and shoots Gaunt dead. The sheriff shoots Link before he can kill Jesse, and the boy sobs bitterly, uttering his first sounds. *Air pilots. Strangers. Farmers. Domestics. Negroes. Children. Physicians. Mutes. Sheriffs. Murder. Rape. Guilt. Atom bomb. Hiroshima. Chases. Dreams.*

Note: Filmed on location in Oyster Bay, New York.

TIME OUT FOR LOVE (France/Italy)   F6.5081

Films Pomereu–International Productions–PEG Produzione. *Dist* Zenith International Film Corp. 22 Apr **1963** [New York opening]. Sd; b&w. 35mm. 91 min.

Prod Bertrand Javal, Yvon Guezel. *Dir* Jean Valère. *Screenplay* Roger Nimier, Jean Valère. *Photog* Raoul Coutard. *Art Dir* Bernard Evein. *Film Ed* Léonide Azar. *Mus* Germaine Tailleferre. *Sd* Guy Villette. *Prod Mgr* Henri Jaquillard.

Cast: Jean Seberg *(Ann)*, Micheline Presle *(Michèle)*, Maurice Ronet *(Philippe)*, Françoise Prévost *(Gladys)*, Annibale Ninchi *(Dr. Séverin)*, Fernando Bruno *(Bucchieri)*.

Drama. Source: Roger Nimier, *Histoire d'un amour* (Paris, 1953). Michèle, a successful careerwoman tormented by the fickleness of her lover, Philippe, takes an overdose of drugs. After being befriended and nursed by Ann, a young American woman living in Paris, she recovers and begins meeting Philippe again. Ann is attracted to Philippe, and Michèle encourages the affair as a means of revenge on her friend Gladys, who is also involved with Philippe. Ann discovers that, in reality, he is a shy, tormented person bent on saving the family business by winning an important automobile race. As the affair deepens, Michèle is soon overcome by jealousy, and her friendship with Ann is strained. Then, Philippe's car breaks down on a trial run, and he relieves his feelings by cruelly spurning Ann and returning to Michèle for comfort. Begging her friend's forgiveness, Ann leaves Paris with her American boy friend. In the train, her thoughts turn back in despair to this period of love and disappointment. *Careerwomen. Americans in foreign countries. Infidelity. Suicide. Jealousy. Automobile racing. Revenge. Paris.*

Note: Opened in Paris in Feb 1961 as *Les grandes personnes*; running time: 96 min.

A TIME TO SING   F6.5082

Four Leaf Productions. *Dist* Metro-Goldwyn-Mayer, Inc. 15 Aug **1968** [Nashville, Tennessee, opening; c21 May 1968; LP35736]. Sd; col (Metrocolor). 35mm (Panavision). 91 min.

Prod Sam Katzman. *Assoc Prod* Jerome F. Katzman. *Dir* Arthur Dreifuss. *Screenplay* Robert E. Kent, Orville H. Hampton. *Dir Photog* John F. Warren. *Art Dir* George W. Davis, Leroy Coleman. *Set Decor* Henry Grace, Charles S. Thompson. *Film Ed* Ben Lewis. *Mus Score & Cond* Fred Karger. *Songs:* "The Humming Bird," "It's All Over but the Crying," "Rock in My Shoe" Hank Williams, Jr. *Song:* "A Man Is on His Own" John Scoggins, Hank Williams, Jr. *Songs:* "Money Can't Buy Happiness," "Old Before My Time" Steve Karliski. *Song:* "Next Time I Say Goodbye, I'm Leaving" Larry Kusik, Eddie Snyder. *Titl Song* John Scoggins. *Vocal Backgrounds* The Jordanaires. *Rec Supv* Franklin Milton. *Asst Dir* Donald C. Klune. *Unit Prod Mgr* Robert Stone. *Makeup* William Tuttle. *Hairstyles* Mary Keats.

Cast: Hank Williams, Jr. *(Grady Dodd)*, Shelley Fabares *(Amy Carter)*, Ed Begley *(Kermit Dodd)*, Charles Robinson *("Shifty" Barker)*, D'Urville Martin *(Luke Harper)*, Donald Woods *(Vernon W. Carter)*, Clara Ward *(Clara)*, Harold Ayer *(Dr. Cartright)*, Dick Haynes *(1st M. C.)*, Gene Gentry *(2d M. C.)*, The X-L's *(themselves)*.

Comedy-drama with music. Grady Dodd, a talented country and western musician, lives with his Uncle Kermit, a tobacco farmer who believes that music is no vocation for a man. Two of Grady's friends, Luke Harper, Kermit's hired hand, and Amy Carter, the daughter of the town's wealthiest man, conspire to induce Grady to perform at a jamboree. Upon seeing his nephew on a stage, Uncle Kermit has a mild heart attack and is hospitalized. When Grady is faced with a huge bill, Amy persuades her father, Vernon Carter, to cover the expense. Furious at this, and also bewildered when he notices that Uncle Kermit's hospital record lists no relatives, Grady confronts his uncle and learns that his musician mother was in a fatal accident after running away with another singer. Her dying wish was that Kermit bring up Grady as his own son. Angry at this belated disclosure, Grady leaves home to achieve success as a singer. He lands a job in a small Nashville night club and contacts Luke, who brings Kermit and Amy to the opening. Grady and Kermit are reserved with each other, but because Grady is determined to repay Mr. Carter for the hospital bill, he accepts a recording session that Carter has arranged. When Grady becomes an immediate hit, Amy and Luke devise a scheme for reconciling Grady and his uncle. Luke calls Grady to say that he is leaving Kermit's farm, and Grady,

worried over his uncle being alone, rushes out with Amy to the farm but runs his car into a ditch. At Grady's bedside, Luke confesses his part in the hoax, and Uncle Kermit, now a big fan of Grady's, is reconciled with his nephew. *Musicians. Farmers. Uncles. Farmhands. Singers. Country music. Duplicity. Hoaxes. Heart disease. Hospitals. Nightclubs. Nashville (Tennessee).*

TIME TRAP see THE TIME TRAVELERS

THE TIME TRAVELERS   F6.5083

Dobil Productions. *Dist* American International Pictures. Oct **1964** [c7 Oct 1964; LP29782]. Sd; col (Pathécolor). 35mm. 83 min.

Prod William Redlin. *Assoc Prod* Don Levy. *Dir-Writ* Ib Melchior. *Story* Ib Melchior, David L. Hewitt. *Dir Photog* William Zsigmond. *Camera Op* Leslie Kovacs. *Art Dir* Ray Storey. *Supv Film Ed* Harold J. Dennis. *Mus* Richard LaSalle. *Sd Mix* Leo Phillips, Jr. *Asst Dir* Clark Paylow, Lew Borzage. *Unit Mgr* Tom Ramsey. *Script Supv* Hannah Scheel. *Wardrobe* Phyllis Taylor, Ruth Weiss. *Makeup* Mark Snegoff. *Sp Eff* David L. Hewitt. *Gaffer* Ernie Reed.

Cast: Preston Foster *(Dr. Erik von Steiner)*, Philip Carey *(Steve Connors)*, Merry Anders *(Carol White)*, John Hoyt *(Varno)*, Dennis Patrick *(Councilman Willard)*, Joan Woodbury *(Gadra)*, Dolores Wells *(Reena)*, Steve Franken *(Danny McKee)*, Gloria Leslie *(councilwoman)*, Peter Strudwick *(deviant)*, Margaret Seldeen, Forrest J. Ackerman *(technicians)*.

Science fiction drama. A team of scientists on a university campus construct a time portal in order to view the past and the future. The scientists, headed by Dr. Erik von Steiner and including Steve Connors and Carol White, accidentally create an opening in the window portal through which they see the campus 107 years into the future. An electrician, Danny McKee, stumbles through the opening, followed by the scientists attempting to rescue him, and the portal collapses, trapping the group in a desolate countryside. Mutant creatures chase them into a cave, where they are rescued by human robots called androids. Gadra, the android leader, takes them to Council Senior Varno who explains that during the past 107 years the earth and all life forms have been dying as a result of a nuclear war. Human beings have evolved into grotesque mutations, and the land has become dry and barren. Varno tells Dr. von Steiner that the few survivors and their descendants have developed an extremely advanced technology in an underground civilization in order to construct a spaceship that will carry them to a new planet. The visitors from the past work frantically to reconstruct their time portal before the spaceship leaves, but the attacking mutants destroy the ship. Fleeing through the repaired portal into the past, the scientists and a few other survivors, including Varno, destroy the portal behind them only to discover that they have gone too far back and are frozen in time. Steve Connors opens the portal which is set for the extreme future, and they enter into a new-born earth, trapped in an endless time circle. *Scientists. Electricians. Androids. Mutation. Time travel. Evolution. Time machines. Caves. Spaceships. The Future.*

Note: Working title: *Time Trap*.

HA'TIMHONI see THE DREAMER

THE TINDER BOX (East Germany)   F6.5084

DEFA. *Dist* Childhood Productions. Oct **1968**. Sd; col (AgfaColor). 35mm. 81 min.

Prod English Vers William L. Snyder. *Dir* Siegfried Hartmann. *Screenplay* Anneliese Kocialek, Siegfried Hartmann, Fred Rodrian. *Photog* Erich Gusko. *Art Dir* Hans Poppe. *Mus* Siegfried Bethmann.

Cast: Rolf Ludwig, Bella Waldritter, Hannes Fischer, Anna-Maria Besendahl, Detlev Heinze, Barbara Mehlan, Rolf Defrank, Heinz Schubert, Hans Fiebrandt, Senta Bonacker, Fritz Schlegel.

Fantasy. Source: Hans Christian Andersen, "Fyrtøjet," in *Eventyr fortalte for Børn* (Copenhagen, 1835). A young soldier returns from war and meets a witch who promises him all the money he can carry if he will bring her a tinderbox from an underground cave. Following the witch's instructions, he comes to a passageway that leads to three rooms, each guarded by a giant dog. Keeping the dogs at bay, the soldier fills his pockets with coins of copper, silver, and gold and returns to the witch with the tinderbox. When the witch refuses to tell him why she wanted the box, he kills her and takes the box. In the city, the young soldier leads a life of luxury until his money runs out. Then he learns that the city's beautiful princess is locked up in a tower because it has been prophesied that she will marry a common soldier. He rubs the tinderbox, and the dogs reappear. The soldier orders one of the dogs to fetch the princess, and she arrives, asleep on the dog's back. He kisses her, and the dog returns her to the palace. The next day the princess tells her parents the strange story, and the queen, suspecting the truth, ties a bag of grain to her. Following another of the dog's errands, the trail of grain leads the king and queen to the soldier, who is subsequently imprisoned and condemned to death. Before he is to be executed, however, the soldier rubs the box, and the dogs appear and attack the king's men. The young soldier and the princess are declared the new king and queen, and the dogs are the guests of honor at the wedding. *Soldiers. Witches.*

Royalty. Magic. Wealth. Filial relations. Capital punishment. Weddings. Caves. Dogs.

Note: Released in East Germany in Apr 1959 as *Das Feuerzeug.* May also be known as *Tinderbox.*

TINI ZABUTYKH PREDKIV *see* **SHADOWS OF FORGOTTEN ANCESTORS**

TINY LUND: HARD CHARGER   **F6.5085**

Cinema Work. *Dist* Marathon Pictures. May **1969**. Sd; col. 35mm. 89 min. *Exec Prod* Lance Bird. *Photog* Charles Hartman. *Film Ed* Victor Kanefsky. *Sd* Michael Shrayer. *Mix* Gary Liebman. *Prod Mgr* Gordon Brown.

Documentary. The film focuses on Tiny Lund, an independent stock car racer who must compete against factory-sponsored teams. Lund lives with his wife in a community of racers, sharing the same fear of death and sense of challenge. Faced with mechanical and economic handicaps, he performs heroically on the track but never wins. *Stock car drivers. Automobile racing. Tiny Lund.*

Note: Filmed in 16mm. May also be known as *Hard Charger.*

UN TIPO CHE MI PIACE *see* **LOVE IS A FUNNY THING**

IL TIRANNO DI SIRACUSA *see* **DAMON AND PYTHIAS**

TIRE AU FLANC 62 *see* **THE ARMY GAME**

TIREZ SUR LE PIANISTE *see* **SHOOT THE PIANO PLAYER**

LES TITANS *see* **MY SON, THE HERO**

THE TITICUT FOLLIES   **F6.5086**

Bridgewater Film. *Dist* Titicut Follies Film Distributing Co. 3 Oct **1967** [New York opening]. Sd; b&w. 16mm. 87 min. *Pres by* Grove Press. *Prod-Dir* Frederick Wiseman. *Photog* John Marshall. *Film Ed* Frederick Wiseman.

Documentary. For the making of this film, Frederick Wiseman and his photographer, John Marshall, were permitted to bring their cameras into one of the three wings of the Bridgewater Hospital for the Criminally Insane in the Titicut area of Massachusetts. The film opens and closes with scenes from the annual "Titicut Follies," which is performed at the hospital by inmates and a few attendants. The middle and longer portion of the picture illustrates the living conditions, the medical care, the psychiatric treatment, and the recreational therapy of the patients. *Hospital interns. Mental illness. Prisons. Insane asylums. Theater—Amateur. Bridgewater (Massachusetts).*

Note: After the film's initial showing at the 1967 New York Film Festival, the Commonwealth of Massachusetts attempted and failed to confiscate the film. The film was then officially banned from commercial distribution in Massachusetts.

TITOV'S SPACE FLIGHT *see* **FLIGHT TO THE STARS**

TLAYUCAN *see* **THE PEARL OF TLAYUCAN**

TO BE A CROOK (France)   **F6.5087**

Films de la Pléiade-Les Films Treize. *Dist* International Entertainment Corp., Comet Film Distributors. 6 Feb **1967** [New York opening]. Sd; b&w. 35mm. 93 min. *Pres by* Felix C. Ziffer, J. R. Coolidge. *Prod-Dir* Claude Lelouch. *Screenplay* Claude Lelouch, Pierre Uytterhoeven. *Photog* Jean Collomb. *Film Ed* Claude Lelouch, Claude Barrois. *Mus* Pierre Vassilu. *Mus Arr* Yvan Julien. *Sd* Luu Than Kiem. *Prod Mgr* Roger Fleytoux.

Cast: Jean-Pierre Kalfon (*Jean-Pierre*), Amidou Ben Messoud (*Amidou*), Pierre Barouh (*Pierrot*), Jacques Portet (*Jacques*), Janine Magnan (*Martine*), Annette Karsenti (*stand-in*), Yane Barry (*cafe owner*), Gérard Sire (*reporter's voice*), Pierre Bourdon.

Crime comedy-drama. Four young men working in an automobile factory in Paris—Jean-Pierre, Amidou, Pierrot, and Jacques—decide to quit their jobs and devote themselves to crime. Influenced by the numerous gangster and western films they have seen, they begin by trying to master judo, karate, marksmanship, and horsemanship. Their only companion is Jacques' girl friend, Martine, a deafmute artist. The four begin to test their skills in stealing and shoplifting, but they fail in an effort to steal a prostitute's dog. Next, they battle with a neighborhood gang but are defeated. Finally, they plan the kidnaping from a location set of a "famous movie star," but instead they seize the star's stand-in. The film's producer conceals the mistake for the sake of the publicity and arranges to pay the ransom for the return of the actress. The money is to be paid in daylight on a main thoroughfare, but the presence of a policeman investigating the double parking causes the foursome to panic and start shooting, hitting the policeman and some bystanders. The four youths and Martine flee to an abandoned quarry, where they begin to argue about what to do. Two want to surrender, but the others are in favor of fleeing to South America. Their argument turns into a gun battle; and as Martine stares at the four apparently dead bodies, they get up and laugh. [In the original French version, the four men die.] *Factory workers. Deafmutes. Artists. Motion picture extras. Motion picture producers. Actors. Police. Kidnaping. Theft. Judo. Karate. Shoplifting. Mistaken identity. Publicity. Paris.*

Note: Paris opening in Jun 1965 as *Une fille et des fusils;* original running time: 105 min.

TO BE A MAN *see* **CRY OF BATTLE**

TO BE A WOMAN   **F6.5088**

Dist International Film Artists. 22 May **1968** [New York opening]. Sd; b&w. 35mm. 89 min. [See note.]

English Vers Supv (*see note*) Harvey Cort. *English Vers Ed* Harvey Cort. **Production Credits for "La prostitution":** *Prod-Dir-Screenplay-Dial* Maurice Boutel. *Screenplay Supv* Marcel Sicot. *Photog* Quinto Albicocco, Paul Fabian, Enzo Riccioni, Jacques Mercanton. *Film Ed* Etiennette Muse. *Mus* Roger-Roger. *Sd* Jacques Gallois. *Coöp* Interpol.

Cast—"La prostitution": Etchika Choureau (*Olga*), Evelyne Dassas (*Irène*), Alain Lionnel (*Mario*), Jean Verner (*Hans*), Alicia Gutirrez (*Concepcion*), Anne Darden (*Martha*), Rita Cadillac (*Rita*), Gabrielle Robinne (*Honorine*), Victor Guyau (*Pauwels*), Robert Dalban (*Robert*), Carl Eich (*Franck*), Raoul Dantes (*Joaquin*), Hinsing Chow (*Bangchow*), Jacques Devos.

Melodrama. *Pimps. Drug addicts. Perfidy. Prostitution. Roominghouses. Netherlands. Paris. Hamburg. Mexico. Hong Kong. INTERPOL.*

Note: Most of this film consists of footage from *La prostitution,* which was released in the United States in 1967 as *Prostitution,* q. v. Harvey Cort excised portions of the original version and added sex scenes shot in the United States. The resulting film was released in 3 versions; expurgated versions: 85 min and 81 min.

TO BED ON A BET   **F6.5089**

Crystal Productions. *Dist* Empire Film Distributors. 18 Nov **1965** [San Francisco showing]. Sd; b&w. 35mm. 60 min.

Melodrama. A little theater group rehearses a risqué drama in which there is an episode of mate swapping. Johnny and Gloria, a sexually aggressive couple, wager that they can seduce Barbara and Bob, two other performers in the play, who are married. Barbara, jealous by nature, suspects their plan, but she falls for the charming Johnny. Soon after Barbara's capitulation, the slow-witted Bob is seduced by Gloria. Bob finally realizes what has happened, and he shoots Gloria to death on the eve of the play's opening. *Actors. Seduction. Marriage. Mate swapping. Murder. Wagers. Theater—Amateur.*

TO BED OR NOT TO BED (Italy)   **F6.5090**

Dino De Laurentiis Cinematografica. *Dist* Continental Distributing, Inc. 22 Dec **1963** [New York opening]. Sd; b&w. 35mm. 103 min. *Prod* Dino De Laurentiis. *Dir* Gian Luigi Polidoro. *Story & Screenplay* Rodolfo Sonego. *Photog* Aldo Tonti. *Film Ed* Tatiana Casini. *Mus* Piero Piccioni. *Sd* Luigi Salvi, Bruno Moreal. *Asst Dir* Vana Caruso. *Dir Prod* Giorgio Morra. *Wardrobe* Marinella Giorgi. *English Subtitl* Herman G. Weinberg.

Cast: Alberto Sordi (*Amadeo Ferretti*), Bernhard Tarschys (*Professor Mayer*), Inger Sjöstrand (*Inger*), Ulf Palme (*parson*), Ulla Smidje (*parson's wife*), Gunoild Gustavson (*girl on street*), Barbro Wastenson (*Eva*), Gunilla Elm-Törnkvist (*Brigetta*), Lauritz Falk (*Peer*), Anne-Charlotte Sjöberg (*Carina*), Monica Wastenson (*Katia*), Ulla Andersson, Inger Auer, Catherina Norden-Falk.

Comedy. Amadeo Ferretti, a fur buyer, lives a quiet life with his wife and family in a small Italian town. An auction in Stockholm takes him on his first long trip away from home, and he begins to imagine that he will be overwhelmed by beautiful Swedish girls. On the ferry ride, Amadeo meets a German scientist, Professor Mayer, who is going to the Nobel Prize presentations, and Amadeo arranges to meet him there. When he first arrives, Amadeo meets a friendly girl but is dismayed to learn that she is only 13 years old. Then he meets Eva and invites her to his hotel room for a drink, but he is disappointed when she leaves after a casual chat. At the Nobel Prize presentations the next day, Amadeo becomes bored and meets another woman, Brigetta, who invites him to a party at her house, where he learns that she is happily married. Amadeo's next encounter is with Carina, who takes him to a sauna, where he faints from exhaustion after rolling naked in the snow. Finally, he meets Katia, and they enter a race riding battered cars across a frozen lake. When the ice breaks, they are rescued by helicopters, and Amadeo is happy to return to his wife and family at home. *Furriers. Germans. Scientists. Smalltown life. Adolescence. Infidelity. Family life. Automobile racing. Auctions. Saunas. Helicopters. Stockholm. Nobel Prize.*

Note: Filmed on location in Sweden. Opened in Rome in Apr 1963 as *Il diavolo;* also known as *Amore in Stockholm.*

TO COMMIT A MURDER (France/Italy/West Germany)   **F6.5091**
Gaumont International-S. N. E. Gaumont-Eichberg Film-Franca Film. *Dist* Cinerama Releasing Corp. 14 Jan **1970** [New York opening]. Sd; col (Eastman Color). 35mm. 91 min. *MPAA rating* M.

Exec Prod Alain Poiré. *Dir* Edouard Molinaro. *Screenplay* Edouard Molinaro, Jacques Robert. *Photog* Raymond LeMoigne. *Art Dir* Robert Clavel, Olivier Girard. *Film Ed* Robert Isnardon, Monique Isnardon. *Mus* José Berghmans. *Sd* Jean Labussière. *Asst Dir* Philippe Monnier. *Prod Mgr* Robert Sussfeld, Irénée Leriche.

Cast: Louis Jourdan (*Charles Beaulieu*), Senta Berger (*Gertrud*), Edmond O'Brien (*Sphax*), Bernard Blier (*Rhome*), Fabrizio Capucci (*Cecil*), Giuseppe Addobbati (*Moranez*), Maurice Garrel (*Banck*), Gamil Ratib (*Belloum*), Patricia Scott (*Scandinavian girl*), Anna Gaël (*Kiki*), Charles Millot (*poker player*), Gerhard Bohrmann, Peter Martin Urcel, Jean Rupert.

Melodrama. Source: Jacques Robert, *Peau d'espion* (Paris, 1966). Charles Beaulieu, a playboy writer, is seduced by Gertrud, a beautiful young woman who tells him that she is the wife of Sphax, a prominent art publisher. Shortly afterwards, Charles is approached by a former colleague, Commander Rhome of the Secret Service, who asks him to keep Sphax under surveillance. Rhome tells Charles that Sphax is a Communist agent planning to abduct Banck, a French nuclear scientist, and take him to China. Gertrud creates doubt in Charles's mind, however, when she tells him that he has been duped by Rhome, who actually intends to have the scientist assassinated. Charles locates Banck at the Heidelberg airport; Rhome then attempts to kill Banck but falls victim to one of Sphax's gunmen. Now convinced of Charles's sincerity, Banck turns himself over to Charles for protection. *Playboys. Authors. Publishers. Communists. Secret agents. Scientists. Seduction. Infidelity. Espionage. Cold war. Perfidy. Assassination. Airfields. Heidelberg.*

Note: Opened in Paris in Apr 1967 as *Peau d'espion*; released in Italy in 1968 as *Congiura di spie*; and in West Germany in Jan 1968 as *Der grausame Job*.

TO DIE IN MADRID (France)   **F6.5092**
Ancinex. *Dist* Altura Films International. 20 Sep **1965** [New York opening]. Sd; b&w. 35mm. 85 min.

Pres by Clem Perry. *Prod* Nicole Stephane. *Dir* Frédéric Rossif. *Dir English Vers* George Gonneau. *Orig French Text* Madeleine Chapsal. *Trans by* Helen Scott. *Photog* Georges Barsky. *Film Ed* Suzanne Baron. *Asst Film Ed* Marie-Sophie Dubus. *Mus* Maurice Jarre. *Sd* René Renault. *Asst Dir* Albert Knobler. *Prod Mgr* Monique Montivier, Guy Blanc. *English Vers* Titra Sound Corp.

Narrators: John Gielgud, Irene Worth, William Hutt, George Gonneau.

Documentary. Composed of newsreel footage from the archives of six countries, the film reviews the Spanish Civil War from its origins in 1931 to Franco's consolidation of power in 1939, with scenes of modern Spain juxtaposed. Scenes of the following events and organizations are included: the 1931 elections won by the Republicans and the formation of the Second Spanish Republic; growth of opposition to the republic by the upper class, the Roman Catholic Church, monarchists, Carlists, military cliques, and eventually the Falange; the electoral victory of the Popular Front in 1936; reforms instituted by the Popular Front causing violent reaction by many segments of Nationalists; recognition of the Nationalist government by Hitler and Mussolini; the influx of German and Italian war matériel to the Nationalists and Russian aid to the Republicans; the International Brigade of foreign sympathizers to the Loyalist (Republican) cause; the Condor Legion; Republican and Nationalist soldiers in battle; the execution of Federico García Lorca; the defense of Madrid; the silencing of philosopher Unamuno; the destruction of Guernica; Basque priests walking to their execution; the battle of Guadalajara; Hitler reviewing German troops recently returned from Spain; the demobilization of the International Brigade in Barcelona; and Franco's final victory. *Spanish. Upper classes. Monarchists. Fascists. Nazis. Italians. Germans. Russians. Communists. Basques. Priests. Nationalism. Elections. Revolts. Capital punishment. War matériel. Spain—History—Republic 1931-39. Spain—History—Civil War 1936-39. Madrid. Barcelona. Toledo (Spain). Guernica. Guadalajara (Spain). Francisco Franco. Adolf Hitler. Benito Mussolini. Federico García Lorca. Miguel Unamuno y Jugo. Catholic Church. Falange.*

Note: Opened in Paris in Apr 1963 as *Mourir à Madrid*. French version narrated by Suzanne Flon, Germaine Montero, Pierre Vaneck, Roger Mollien, and Jean Vilar.

TO HEX WITH SEX   **F6.5093**
August Films. *Dist* RAF Industries. 7 Sep **1969** [Havelock, North Carolina, opening]. Sd; col (Eastman Color). 35mm. 80-86 min.

Prod-Dir Simon Nuchtern. *Exec Prod* Murray Kaplan. *Writ* Arthur Littman, Simon Nuchtern. *Story Cons* Anoushka Kira. *Dir Photog* Kolle Frank. *Art Dir* Sidney Knight. *Film Ed* Riva Freifeld. *Mus & Eff* Dick Lavsky's Music House. *Titl Song Writ & Sung by* Michael Bolger. *Cost* Arva Littfeld.

Cast: Stefan Peters (*Marvin Swift*), Paula Shaw (*Lucibel*), Diane Goble (*Nancy*), Larry Hunter (*director*), Jack Taylor (*boss*), Harvey Green (*Burt*), Linda Boyce (*Cynthia*), Lynn Milgrim (*scriptgirl*), Kristen Steen, Donna Stine, Nicole Rude (*party girls*).

Comedy. Shy and awkward, Marvin Swift loses his job at an underwear factory and bungles lovemaking with his girl friend. He becomes locked in the boiler room of an apartment building, and there Lucibel, who says she is the devil, promises to grant him any wish. He becomes the head of a company that makes sex exploitation films. But he hasn't lost his awkwardness; he becomes excited by the simulated sex and stumbles over the equipment, wrecking the set and losing his actors and production crew. Marvin next wishes to become irresistibly attractive, and he agrees to give Lucibel, in return for granting his wish, exclusive rights to him for 6 months. He is overwhelmed by her demands upon him, and he finally trades his soul for everlasting youth—believing that his immortality will prevent her from collecting the debt. He begins to enjoy his newfound freedom and goes to a party where he is accosted at once by all the women in attendance. They follow him into the bedroom, shed their clothing, and begin to tear at his clothes. ... *Timidity. Wish fulfillment. Immortality. Sexuality. Sex exploitation films. The Devil.*

Note: May also be known as *The Hex With Sex*. Stefan Peters is also known as Sebastian Dangerfield.

TO INGRID MY LOVE, LISA (Sweden)   **F6.5094**
Cannon Productions-Omega Film. *Dist* Cannon Releasing Corp. 19 Mar **1969** [Los Angeles opening]. Sd; b&w. 35mm. 76 min. [Also reviewed at 85 and 90 min.] *MPAA rating* X.

Prod Donald C. Dennis. *Dir* Joseph W. Sarno. *Dial Dir* Börje Nyberg. *Screenplay* Joseph W. Sarno. *Dir Photog* Åke Dahlquist. *Camera Op* Anders Bodin. *Set Dsgn* Poa Sivertzen. *Film Ed* Tony Potenza. *Mus* Ken Lauber. *Sd Engr* Leif Hansen. *Script Girl* Chris Tonnert. *Prod Mgr* Mikael Ekman. *Makeup* Britt Falkemo. *English Titl* Aaron Copy.

Cast: Gun Falck (*Lisa*), Gunilla Iwansson (*Ingrid*), Heinz Hopf (*Nils*), Mimi Nelson (*The Mother*), Sten Ardenstam (*The Father*), Rex Bradhe (*Harald*), Lars Lind, Ulf Brunnberg, Pierre Lindstedt.

Melodrama. Lisa, a leading fashion designer whose reputation is declining, drinks heavily and becomes promiscuous with young men. To obtain rest and self-control, she rents a house in the country, and there she becomes involved with Ingrid, her 17-year-old neighbor. Lisa lures Ingrid away from her parents and her naive, prudish fiancé, Harald, by promising Ingrid a modeling career in Stockholm and assuring her parents that their daughter will be safe with her. In Stockholm, Ingrid indulges in a "sexual smorgasbord," unaware of Lisa's mounting desire for her. On a visit home, Ingrid brushes off Harald, pointing to the sexual freedom she enjoys, and she returns to the city and to Lisa, with whom she embarks on her first lesbian affair. *Couturiers. Models. Roommates. Promiscuity. Lesbianism. Seduction. Alcoholism. Adolescence. Bisexuality. Stockholm.*

Note: Swedish release in 1968 as *Kom i min säng*. Also known as *"Yes!" (Count the Possibilities)* and *"Yes!"*

TO KILL A MOCKINGBIRD   **F6.5095**
Pakula-Mulligan Productions-Brentwood Productions. *Dist* Universal-International Films. 25 Dec **1962** [Los Angeles opening; c16 Mar 1963; LP35477]. Sd; b&w. 35mm. 129 min.

Prod Alan J. Pakula. *Dir* Robert Mulligan. *Screenplay* Horton Foote. *Dir Photog* Russell Harlan. *Camera Op* Jack Whitman. *Asst Camera* Frank Stanley, William Egan. *Art Dir* Alexander Golitzen, Henry Bumstead. *Set Decor* Oliver Emert. *Set Coörd* Fred Knoth. *Main Titl Dsgn* Stephen Frankfurt. *Film Ed* Aaron Stell. *Asst Ed* J. Terry Williams. *Mus Comp & Cond* Elmer Bernstein. *Sd* Waldon O. Watson, Corson Jowett, Charles Cohn, James Curtis. *Dir* Joseph Kenny, Terry Morse, Jr., Charles Scott, Jr. *Prod Mgr* Ernest B. Wehmeyer. *Asst Prod Mgr* Dick Gallegly. *In Charge of Prod* Edward Muhl. *Asst to Prod* Isabel M. Halliburton. *Script Supv* Meta Rebner. *Cost* Rosemary Odell. *Men's Wardrobe* Seth Banks, John Lucas. *Women's Wardrobe* Viola Thompson. *Makeup* Bud Westmore, Frank Prehoda. *Hairstyles* Larry Germain, Le Vaughn Speer. *Still Photog* Rollie Lane. *Gaffer* Bill Neff. *Grip* Carl Gibson, Walter Woodworth. *Prop* Julius Rosenkrantz, Frank Nifong.

Cast: Gregory Peck (*Atticus Finch*), Mary Badham (*Scout Finch*), Phillip Alford (*Jem Finch*), John Megna (*Dill Harris*), Frank Overton (*Sheriff Heck Tate*), Rosemary Murphy (*Miss Maudie Atkinson*), Brock Peters (*Tom Robinson*), Ruth White (*Mrs. Dubose*), Estelle Evans (*Calpurnia*), Paul Fix (*Judge Taylor*), Collin Wilcox (*Mayella Ewell*), James Anderson (*Bob Ewell*), Alice Ghostley (*Stephanie Crawford*), Robert Duvall (*Boo Radley*), William Windom (*Gilmer*), Crahan Denton (*Walter Cunningham*), Richard Hale (*Mr. Radley*), Steve Condit (*Walter Cunningham, Jr.*), Bill Walker (*Reverend Sykes*), Hugh Sanders (*Dr. Reynolds*), Pauline Myers (*Jessie*), Jester Hairston (*Spence Robinson*), Jamie Forster (*Hiram Townsend*), Nancy Marshall (*schoolteacher*), Kim Hamilton (*Helen Robinson*), Kelly Thordsen (*burly man*),

Dan White, Tex Armstrong (men), Kim Hector (Cecil Jacobs), David Crawford (Tom Robinson, Jr.), Barry Seltzer (schoolboy), Guy Wilkerson (jury foreman), Charles Fredericks (court clerk), Jay Sullivan (court reporter).

Drama. Source: Harper Lee, To Kill a Mockingbird (Philadelphia, 1960). In a small Alabama town in 1932, Atticus Finch, a widowed lawyer, strives to create for his two children, 6-year-old Scout and her 10-year-old brother, Jem, an atmosphere free from hatred and prejudice. The youngsters lead a carefree life, racing about the town, jeering at eccentric Mrs. Dubose, and frightening themselves and their new friend, 6-year-old Dill Harris, with exaggerated stories about Boo Radley, a mentally retarded neighbor whom they have never seen. When Atticus agrees to defend Tom Robinson, a Negro accused of raping young Mayella Ewell, the children must defend themselves against the taunts of their classmates. Though Atticus is able to demonstrate Tom's innocence, forcing Mayella to admit that her father beat her when he found her making advances toward Tom, the all-white jury returns a verdict of guilty. Atticus tries to have the decision reversed, but before he can do so, Tom attempts to escape and is killed. In revenge against Atticus, Bob Ewell one day attacks Scout and Jem; but Boo Radley, who has secretly watched over the children and has left gifts for them in a tree trunk, saves them by killing Ewell. Sheriff Tate concludes that Ewell fell on his own knife and decides that there will be no trial. Widowers. Lawyers. Children. Negroes. Sheriffs. Judges. Recluses. Fatherhood. Brother-sister relationship. Smalltown life. Injustice. Friendship. Mental retardation. Rape. Racial prejudice. Flirtation. Revenge. Trials. Juries. Alabama.

TO LOVE (Sweden)   **F6.5096**
Sandrews. Dist Prominent Films, L. & N. Film Distributors. Nov **1964**. Sd; b&w. 35mm. 90 min.

Pres by Jules Levey, John Nasht. Prod Rune Waldekranz. Dir-Writ Jörn Donner. Dir Photog Sven Nykvist. Art Dir Jan Boleslaw. Main Titl Timo Sarpaneva. Film Ed Lennart Wallen. Mus Bo Nilsson, Eje Thelin's Quintet. Mus Dir Stig Westerberg, Eje Thelin. Sd Lars Lalin. Asst Dir Bertil Ohlsson, Manuel Costa e Silva. Unit Mgr Gösta Peterson. Cont Katherina Farago. Cost Mago.

Cast: Harriet Andersson (Louise), Zbigniew Cybulski (Fredrik), Isa Quensel (Marta), Thomas Svanfeldt (Jakob), Jane Friedmann (Nora), Nils Eklund (The Priest), Jan-Erik Lindqvist (The Speaker).

Comedy. At the end of 10 years of marriage, Louise has withdrawn into conformity, playing out the roles of middle-class wife and mother. Now, while still in her early thirties, she finds herself a widow. At her husband's funeral she meets Fredrik, an exuberant, open-hearted Pole working as a travel agent in Stockholm. He wants to become better acquainted; Louise agrees; and before long Fredrik moves into the apartment she shares with her mother and son. He encourages her on a path of joyful sensuality that brings a resurgence of life; her mother, Marta, and son, Jakob, find happiness in watching her solemn façade fall away. Mistrustful of binding ties, the couple abandon themselves to a celebration of physical love. Louise reveals the frustration and boredom of marriage to a man whose business left no time for pleasure, while Fredrik tells her of his past involvements and restless need to move on. Gradually the lovers reverse their roles; Louise revels in her newly-discovered sexual freedom, while Fredrik matures in the relationship and begins to take life more seriously. Eventually he proposes, and though Louise is uncertain, they agree that their shared physical joy has introduced them to love. Poles. Widows. Travel agents. Free love. Eroticism. Marriage. Filial relations. Stockholm.

Note: Released in Sweden in Aug 1964 as Att älska at 95 min.

TO SIR, WITH LOVE (Great Britain)   **F6.5097**
Columbia Pictures. 14 Jun **1967** [New York opening; c31 Dec 1966; LP34217]. Sd (Westrex); col (Technicolor). 35mm. 105 min.

A James Clavell Production. Prod-Dir-Writ James Clavell. Exec Prod John R. Sloan. Museum Montage Seq George White, British. Dir Photog Paul Beeson. Camera Op Harry Gillam. Art Dir Tony Woollard. Set Dresser Ian Whittaker. Main Titl National Screen Service Ltd. Film Ed Peter Thornton. Asst Film Ed David Campling. Mus Ron Grainer. Mus Cond Philip Martell. Titl Song Mark London, Don Black. Arr by Mike Leander. Sung by Lulu. Song: "Off and Running" Carole Bayer, Toni Wine. Song: "Stealing My Love From Me" Mark London. Song: "It's Getting Harder All the Time" Charles Albertine, Ben Raleigh. Songs Sung by The Mindbenders. Sd Ed Dino Di Campo. Sd Rec Bert Ross, Ted Karnon. Asst Dir Ted Sturgis. Prod Mgr Basil Rayburn. Cont Ivonny Richards. Wardrobe Supv John Wilson Apperson. Makeup Jill Carpenter. Hairdresser Betty Glasow. Casting Harvey Woods. Montage Stills Laurie Ridley, Dennis C. Stone.

Cast: Sidney Poitier (Mark Thackeray), Christian Roberts (Denham), Judy Geeson (Pamela Dare), Suzy Kendall (Gillian Blanchard), Lulu (Barbara Pegg), Faith Brook (Mrs. Evans), Geoffrey Bayldon (Weston), Edward Burnham (Florian), Gareth Robinson (Tich), Grahame Charles (Fernman), Roger Shepherd (Buckley), Patricia Routledge (Clinty), Mona Bruce (Jose Dawes),

Fiona Duncan (Miss Phillips), Christopher Chittell (Potter), Marianne Stone (Gert), Rita Webb (Mrs. Joseph), Cyril Shaps (Mr. Pinkus), Adrienne Posta (Moira Jackson), Peter Attard (Ingham), Anthony Villaroel (Seales), Ann Bell (Mrs. Dare), Fred Griffiths, Dervis Ward, Sally Cann, Albert Lampert, Chitra Neogy, Elna Pearl, Stewart Bevan, Carla Challoner, Joseph Cuby, Lynne Sue Moon, Jane Peach, Michael Des Barres, Margaret Heald, Ellison Kemp, Donita Shawe, Richard Willson, Sally Gosselin, Kevin Hubbard, Howard Knight, Stephen Whittaker, The Mindbenders.

Drama. Source: Edward Ricardo Braithwaite, To Sir, With Love (London, 1959). West Indian Mark Thackeray, a qualified engineer, is unable to find employment in his chosen field and takes a position as a high school teacher in London's East End slum. He finds himself confronted by a rough, unruly bunch of teenagers who have forced several of his predecessors to resign. Aware that the youngsters are basically decent and that their crude behavior and language simply reflect an indifferent upbringing, he decides to deal with their rebelliousness by treating them as adults. Discarding all the old educational rules, he throws away the class textbooks, takes the students to museums, and talks to them about marriage, rebellion, sex, and the society they will enter in a few months. Shocked by their sudden treatment as equals, they abandon their hostility toward teachers and model themselves along the standards of conduct and decency Thackeray establishes. Inevitably, the teacher suffers a few setbacks: one of the girls, Pamela Dare, imagines herself to be in love with him; the class ringleader, Denham, must be outboxed in gym class before there can be mutual respect; and the unorthodox teaching methods are sometimes ridiculed by other faculty members. Thackeray's influence is so strong that the students defy local convention by attending the funeral of a classmate's mother, even though the student previously was ostracized because of his mixed parentage. When it is time for their senior dance, the students have evolved into attractive young adults ready and eager to face the world. The dancing is interrupted when the class expresses its gratitude by having Barbara Pegg sing a song dedicated to their favorite teacher. His eyes filled with tears, Thackeray returns to his classroom and stares at a letter offering him an engineering job. As he tears it up, he meets two ill-mannered and rebellious youngsters who threaten to disrupt his class next term. Schoolteachers. Engineers. Negroes. Students. Juvenile delinquents. Mulattoes. Education. Adolescence. High school life. Boxing. Filial relations. Racial prejudice. Slums. Funerals. Gymnasiums. Museums. London—East End.

Note: Location scenes filmed in London's East End. Opened in London in Sep 1967.

TO THE SHORES OF HELL   **F6.5098**
Robert Patrick Productions. Dist Crown International Pictures. 16 Mar **1966** [San Francisco opening]. Sd; col (Technicolor). 35mm (Techniscope). 82 min. [Also reviewed at 90 min.]

A Will Zens Production. Prod-Dir Will Zens. Exec Prod Robert Patrick. Assoc Prod Richard Bertea. Screenplay Robert McFadden, Will Zens. Dir Photog Leif Rise. Camera Jerry Wenziner. Film Ed Michael David, ed. Mus William Schaefer. Sd Robert Sands. Sd Eff Capricorn Assoc. Wardrobe Lillias Haddock. Sp Eff Harry Woolman.

Cast: Marshall Thompson (Maj. Greg Donahue), Kiva Lawrence (Mary), Richard Jordahl (Father Jacques Bourget), Robert Dornan (Dr. Gary Donahue), Jeff Pearl (Mic Phin), Richard Arlen (Brig. Gen. F. W. Ramgate), Dick O'Neill (Maj. Fred Howard), Freeman Lusk (Captain Lusk), Bill Bierd (Sgt. Bill Gabreski), Marvin Yim (Major Toang).

War drama. Marine Maj. Greg Donahue anxiously awaits orders to Vietnam because his brother Gary, a physician, has been captured by the Vietcong. Donahue and his unit land in Da Nang, and there they learn that Gary will be killed unless he treats wounded Vietcong. Donahue receives permission from his superiors to help his brother; and, aided by Sgt. Bill Gabreski, French priest Jacques Bourget, and Mic Phin, a Vietnamese, Donahue makes his way through the jungle to the abandoned French garrison where his brother is being held. Gabreski is killed in an ambush, and though Mic Phin is seriously wounded by a boobytrap, he nevertheless enters the camp, helps Gary escape, and takes him to his brother and Bourget. Soon afterwards, the party is attacked by guerrillas, but a reconnaissance Marine helicopter gives Donahue and the others enough support to stage a fight. With rescue only minutes away, the party is assaulted, and both Bourget and Mic Phin are killed. As the Donahue brothers are taken away in the helicopter, they notice that friendly Vietnamese soldiers are taking precautions to ensure proper burial of their comrades. Physicians. Priests. French. Guerrillas. Vietcong. Rescue. Combat zone life. Jungles. Mines (war explosives). Helicopters. Vietnam War 1964–73. Da Nang. United States Marines.

TO TRAP A SPY   **F6.5099**
Arena Productions. Dist Metro-Goldwyn-Mayer, Inc. 19 Jan **1966** [Boston opening]. Sd; col (Metrocolor). 35mm. 92 min.

Prod-Writ Sam Rolfe. *Exec Prod* Norman Felton. *Assoc Prod* Joseph Gantman. *Dir* Don Medford. *Photog* Joseph Biroc. *Art Dir* George W. Davis, Merrill Pye. *Set Decor* Henry Grace, Frank McKelvy. *Film Ed* Henry Berman. *Mus* Jerry Goldsmith. *Sd* Franklin Milton. *Asst Dir* Maurice Vaccarino.

Cast: Robert Vaughn *(Napoleon Solo)*, David McCallum *(Illya Kuryakin)*, Luciana Paluzzi *(Angela)*, Patricia Crowley *(Elaine May Donaldson)*, Fritz Weaver *(Vulcan)*, Will Kuluva *(Mr. Allison)*, William Marshall *(Ashumen)*, Ivan Dixon *(Soumarin)*, Victoria Shaw *(Gracie Ladovan)*, Miguel Landa *(Lancer)*, Eric Berry *(Alfred Ghist)*, Mario Siletti *(Del Floria)*, Rupert Crosse *(Nobuk)*.

Action comedy-drama. UNCLE, an organization to combat international crime, learns that WASP, an international crime syndicate, plans to take over Western Natumba, a newly-independent African state, by killing its President Ashumen when he and two of his ministers visit the Vulcan Chemicals plant in the United States. UNCLE's secret agent Napoleon Solo is assigned to prevent the assassination. He enlists the aid of Elaine May Donaldson, a housewife who was Vulcan Chemicals owner Andrew Vulcan's college sweetheart. Vulcan becomes attracted to Elaine once again when Solo has her pose as a wealthy and glamorous widow. She and Solo gain admittance to the Vulcan plant, and there they discover that Vulcan and Ashumen head WASP. Alfred Ghist, an evil scientist employed by Vulcan, captures Solo and Elaine and hangs them by their wrists in a room filling up with scalding steam. In the room directly above, an explosion is set to kill Ashumen's two ministers, who are innocent of any involvement in WASP. Solo and Elaine escape, saving the two Africans; and instead, Ashumen and Vulcan are killed in the explosion. *Secret agents. Housewives. Scientists. Africans. Presidents. Industrialists. Organized crime. Assassination. Perfidy. Imposture. Factories. Explosions.*

Note: First shown on television 22 Sep 1964 as a 60-min "pilot" episode of NBC's "Man From U.N.C.L.E." series as *The Vulcan Affair*; c22 Sep 1964; LP33331.

TO TURN A TRICK   **F6.5100**
Dist Sam Lake Enterprises. Dec **1967**. Sd; b&w. 35mm. 70 min.
Cast: Inger Simonsen, Christopher Brennan.
Melodrama. Working late one night at her job as a photographer's assistant, Inger is raped by a client while two nude models force her to submit. Overwhelmed by shame, she runs away and attends a party where drugs stimulate unrestricted sexual activity. Emotionally unstable, Inger turns to lesbianism. She is drawn deeper into a life of depravity, until she is killed by an overdose of drugs. *Photographers. Models. Rape. Lesbianism. Drug overdose. Orgies. Narcotics.*

TOBACCO ROODY   **F6.5101**
Boxoffice International Pictures–Global Pictures. *Dist* Boxoffice International Pictures. 27 Jul **1970** [Champaign, Illinois, showing]. Sd; col (Movielab). 35mm. 85 min.
Pres by Harry Novak. *Prod-Dir-Writ* Buckalew. *Photog* Dwayne Rayven. *Film Ed* Dwayne Rayven. *Mus Comp* Hal Southern, Harold Hensley. *Sd Rec* Robert B. Lee. *Prod Mgr* Jim Andrian. *Prod Asst* Mike Bennett. *Script Supv* Pam Eddy. *Still Photog* Cinemagraphics.
Cast: Dixie Donovan *(Tootie)*, Johnny Rocco *(Mose)*, Debbie Osborne *(Liz)*, Wendy Winters *(Lulu)*, Gigi Perez *(Carolina)*, John Law *(sheriff)*, Joe Dunnigan, Tom A. Sipress, Clydde Stone *(farmers)*, Maxine DeVille France *(Danielle)*, Buckalew *(Harry)*, Jack Richesin *(Parker)*.
Farce. Lulu and Carolina, daughters of Mose Mason, a Neeley's Bend, Tennessee, moonshiner, are jealous of their father's voluptuous niece, Tootie. At the swimming creek, Lulu passes on to Carolina the sex education she received from Harry, a city slicker. When Tootie arrives, the sisters cover her with mud and send her home to be comforted by her uncle. The sheriff halts Mose's moonshining activities, but Liz, Mose's wife, tired of being ignored, shifts the intruder's attention to herself. The sisters continue their sex education game at home. Three farmers visit the farm and find a jug of Mose's homemade liquor. Judd Parker, the lascivious landlord, threatens to foreclose the mortgage until Liz sexually accommodates him. Tootie and her cousins fall asleep and are joined by the drunken farmers, and soon they are all making love. Danielle, a French damsel who speaks no English, passes by the farm and seeks directions of Mose, who seduces her in the barn. Liz returns just after Danielle's departure and finally agrees to try some mountain dew. Having found something to share at last, the happy couple enters the house to make love. *Moonshiners. Innocents. Sheriffs. Landlords. French. Sisters. Seduction. Mountain life. Drunkenness. Sexual initiation. Jealousy. Tennessee.*

TOBENAI CHINMOKU *see* **SILENCE HAS NO WINGS**

TOBO, THE HAPPY CLOWN   **F6.5102**
Authors Production Co.–Tobo Productions. 25 Nov **1965** [San Francisco opening]. Sd; b&w. 35mm. [Feature length assumed.]

A Jim Hope Production. *Prod* William Rowland, Edward Finney. *Dir* William Rowland. *2d Unit Dir* Gary Lindsay.
Cast: Eddie Finn *(Tobo)*. No information about the precise nature of this film has been found, but press material suggests that it features various circus performers, animals, and acts. *Clowns. Circus performers. Circus. Animals.*
Note: Also known as *The Happy Clown*.

TOBRUK   **F6.5103**
Gibraltar Productions–Corman Co. *Dist* Universal Pictures. 7 Feb **1967** [Chicago opening; c4 Mar 1967; LP35381]. Sd (Westrex); col (Technicolor). 35mm (Techniscope). 109 min.
Prod Gene Corman. *In Charge of Prod* Edward Muhl. *Dir* Arthur Hiller. *2d Unit Dir* Joe Kane. *Writ* Leo V. Gordon. *Dir Photog* Russell Harlan. *Aerial Photog* Nelson Tyler. *Art Dir* Alexander Golitzen, Henry Bumstead. *Set Decor* John McCarthy, Oliver Emert. *Main Titl* Pacific Title. *Film Ed* Robert C. Jones. *Mus* Bronislaw Kaper. *Mus Supv* Joseph Gershenson. *Sd* Waldon O. Watson, Lyle Cain. *Asst Dir* Terence Nelson, John Anderson, Jr. *Unit Prod Mgr* Robert E. Larson. *Makeup* Bud Westmore. *Hairstyles* Larry Germain. *Matte Supv* Albert Whitlock. *Tech Adv* L. J. Loughran, (Col. Royal Australian Infantry Ret.). *Coöp* California Army National Guard (40th Armored Division). *Dial Coach* Norman Stuart, Martin Kosleck. *Stunt Coörd* John Daheim.
Cast: Rock Hudson *(Maj. Donald Craig)*, George Peppard *(Capt. Kurt Bergman)*, Nigel Green *(Col. John Harker)*, Guy Stockwell *(Lieut. Max Mohnfeld)*, Jack Watson *(Sergeant Major Tyne)*, Percy Herbert *(Dolan)*, Norman Rossington *(Alfie)*, Liam Redmond *(Henry Portman)*, Heidy Hunt *(Cheryl Portman)*, Leo Gordon *(Sergeant Krug)*, Robert Wolders *(Corporal Bruckner)*, Anthony Ashdown *(Lieutenant Boyden)*, Curt Lowens *(German colonel)*, Rico Cattani *(Corporal Stuhler)*, Peter Coe *(Tuareg chieftain)*, Lawrence Montaigne *(Italian officer)*, Robert Hoy *(British corporal)*, Phil Adams *(S.I.G. Bocker)*, Ronnie Rondell *(S.I.G. Schell)*.
War drama. In 1942 Maj. Donald Craig of the British North African Army is captured by the Vichy French and then rescued by German-born Palestinian Jews working with the Allies. He is taken to the headquarters of Col. John Harker, who explains to him that because of his knowledge of desert topography he is needed for a potentially suicidal raid on the fuel bunkers at Tobruk, a Mediterranean seaport and Rommel's key supply source occupied by German and Italian troops. The plan is to proceed to Tobruk by having the Palestinian Jews, under the command of Capt. Kurt Bergman, pose as German soldiers escorting a battalion of British prisoners. In the course of their long journey across the Libyan Desert, the men trick Italian and German tank units into firing upon each other, shoot down an Allied strafing plane rather than reveal their identity, and capture two Nazi civilian spies. When the spies escape, it becomes apparent to Harker and Craig that one of their group is a traitor, and Bergman becomes the chief suspect. Upon reaching Tobruk, Craig and Harker lead the attack on the fuel depot and the surrounding gun emplacements. In the heat of battle Bergman's second in command, Lieut. Max Mohnfeld, is exposed as the traitor. The intense fighting rages until dawn, and when the mission is completed, only 4 survivors remain of the 83 who started out on the expedition. They are picked up by a small boat from one of the ships in the British task force and evacuated by sea. *Jews. Prisoners of war. Spies. Traitors. Disguise. Sabotage. World War II. Libyan Desert. Mediterranean Sea. Palestine. Tobruk. North Africa. Great Britain—Army. France—Army. Germany—Army. Italy—Army.*
Note: Location scenes filmed near Yuma, Arizona.

DER TOD RITT DIENSTAGS *see* **DAY OF ANGER**

TODAY WE LIVE *see* **THE DAY AND THE HOUR**

DER TODESKUSS DES DR. FU MAN CHU *see* **KISS & KILL**

TOGETHER IN PARIS *see* **PARIS WHEN IT SIZZLES**

TOKKYU NIPPON *see* **ROMANCE EXPRESS**

TOKYO OLYMPIAD (Japan)   **F6.5104**
Organizing Committee for the Games of the XVIII Olympiad–Toho Co. *Dist* American International Pictures, Pan–World Film Exchange, Jack Douglas Enterprises. 20 Oct **1965** [Waikiki, Hawaii, opening]. Sd; col (Eastman Color). 35mm (CinemaScope). 93 min.
Production Credits for Japanese Vers: *Prod* Suketaru Taguchi. *Dir* Kon Ichikawa. *Tech Dir* Michio Midorikawa. *Screenplay* Natto Wada, Yoshio Shirasaka, Shuntaro Tanikawa, Kon Ichikawa. *Camera Supv* Shigeo Hayashida, Kazuo Miyagawa. *Photog* Juichi Nagano, Kinji Nakamura, Tadashi Tanaka. *Art Dir* Yusaku Kamekura. *Mus* Toshiro Mayuzumi. *Sd* Toshihiko Inoue. *Prod Asst* Jun Kiyofuji, Asao Kumada, Senkichi Taniguchi.
Production Credits for English Vers: *Pres by* Jack Douglas Enterprises. *Exec Prod* Jack Douglas. *Assoc Prod* Roger Janis, Roderick Tichenor.

Screenplay Donald Richie. *Supv Film Ed* Richard L. Van Enger, Jr. *Prod Coörd* Dennis Payne.

Narrator for English Vers: Jack Douglas.

Documentary. This coverage of the 18th Olympic Games, held in Tokyo in 1964, opens in Greece with the lighting of the Olympic torch, which is then carried by runners to Tokyo and used to light the massive stationary torch that burns throughout the games. The film records events in which 5,558 athletes from 94 nations competed. Also included are spectator reactions and coverage of a marriage ceremony between two athletes. *Athletes. Olympic Games. Weddings. Greece. Tokyo.*

Note: Released in Japan in 1965 as *Tokyo Orinpikku*; running time: 132 min.

TOKYO ORINPIKKU see TOKYO OLYMPIAD

TOKYO YAWA see THE DIPLOMAT'S MANSION

DIE TOLLDREISTEN GESCHICHTEN DES HONORÉ DE BALZAC *see* **THE BRAZEN WOMEN OF BALZAC**

TOLLER HECHT AUF KRUMMER TOUR see THE PHONY AMERICAN

TOM CAT see HOW TO SUCCEED WITH SEX

TOM JONES (Great Britain)   F6.5105
Woodfall Film Productions. *Dist* Lopert Pictures. 7 Oct **1963** [New York opening; c26 Jun 1963; LP27726]. Sd; col (Eastman Color). 35mm. 131 min. [Copyright length: 127 min.]

Prod-Dir Tony Richardson. *Assoc Prod* Michael Holden, Oscar Lewenstein. *Screenplay* John Osborne. *Dir Photog* Walter Lassally. *Camera Op* Desmond Davis. *2d Unit Photog* Manny Wynn. *Col Cons & Asst* Jocelyn Herbert, Clare Jefferey. *Art Dir* Ted Marshall. *Set Decor* Josie MacAvin. *Prod Dsgn* Ralph Brinton. *Film Ed* Antony Gibbs. *Asst Film Ed* Brian Smedley-Aston. *Mus Comp & Cond* John Addison. *Played by* Sinfonia of London. *Sd Rec* Peter Handford. *Sd Ed* Don Challis. *Asst Dir* Gerry O'Hara. *Prod Exec* Alan Kaplan. *Prod Supv* Leigh Aman. *Prod Mgr* Roy Millichip. *Cont* Rita Davison. *Prod Sec* Jane Moscrop. *Script Ed* Sewell Stokes. *Personal Asst to the Dir* Jocelyn Tawse. *Wardrobe Supv* John McCorry. *Wardrobe Mistress* Barbara Gillett. *Chief Makeup* Alex Garfath. *Chief Hairdresser* Sarah Beeber. *Casting Dir* John Merrick.

Cast: Albert Finney *(Tom Jones)*, Susannah York *(Sophie Western)*, Hugh Griffith *(Squire Western)*, Edith Evans *(Miss Western)*, Joan Greenwood *(Lady Bellaston)*, Diane Cilento *(Molly Seagrim)*, George Devine *(Squire Allworthy)*, David Tomlinson *(Lord Fellamar)*, Joyce Redman *(Mrs. Waters [Jenny Jones])*, George A. Cooper *(Fitzpatrick)*, Rosalind Atkinson *(Mrs. Miller)*, Angela Baddeley *(Mrs. Wilkins)*, Peter Bull *(Thwackum)*, James Cairncross *(Parson Supple)*, Julian Glover *(Lieutenant Northerton)*, Freda Jackson *(Mrs. Seagrim)*, Rachel Kempson *(Bridget Allworthy)*, Wilfrid Lawson *(Black George)*, Rosalind Knight *(Mrs. Fitzpatrick)*, Jack MacGowran *(Partridge)*, John Moffatt *(Square)*, Patsy Rowlands *(Honour)*, David Warner *(Blifil)*, Redmond Phillips *(Lawyer Dowling)*, Mark Dignam *(lieutenant)*, Avis Bunnage *(landlady)*, Lynn Redgrave *(Susan)*, Jack Stewart, British *(MacLachlan)*, Michael Brennan *(The Jailor at Newgate)*, Michael MacLiammoir *(narrator)*.

Costume comedy. Source: Henry Fielding, *Tom Jones, a Foundling* (1749). In 18th century England, Squire Allworthy returns to his manor house to find a smiling baby boy abandoned in his bed. A serving maid, Jenny Jones, is accused of being the infant's unwed mother and Allworthy banishes her from the household. The squire then names the child Tom Jones and rears him with his legitimate heir, Blifil. Tom grows up to be an earthy but good natured boy liked by all except the envious, pimply-faced Blifil. Although Tom is in love with Sophie Western, the daughter of a neighboring squire, he falls into disgrace because of his amorous adventures with Molly, the local trollop. The two squires, goaded by Sophie's meddlesome aunt, Miss Western, arrange for a marriage between Sophie and Blifil; but when Sophie refuses because of her love for the lowly-born Tom, Squire Allworthy is pressured into sending the boy away. En route to London, Tom dallies to spend a lusty evening with Mrs. Waters, unaware that she is the former Jenny Jones. After a subsequent affair in London with the worldly Lady Bellaston, Tom is reunited with Sophie, who has left home rather than marry Blifil. Determined to be rid of Tom, Blifil has him framed for robbery and sentenced to be hanged; but at the last minute Blifil's villainy is exposed, and Tom is saved from the gallows. Further, it is revealed that Tom, although still illegitimate, is actually the son of Squire Allworthy's deceased sister. Once more reinstated in the affections of both Squire Allworthy and Squire Western, Tom is at long last granted permission to marry his beloved Sophie. *Landed gentry. Nobility. Housemaids. Aunts. Cousins. Illegitimacy. Parentage. Wealth. Lust. Frameup. Capital punishment. Courtship. Marriage—Arranged. Social classes. London. England. Tom Jones.*

Note: Released in Great Britain in 1963; running time: 128 min. Sources conflict as to whether United Artists or its subsidiary, Lopert, released the film.

TOM THUMB (Mexico)   F6.5106
Clasa Films Mundiales. *Dist* Childhood Productions. Oct **1967**. Sd; col (Eastman Color). 35mm. 79 min.

Prod Armando Orive Alba. *Dir* René Cardona. *Screenplay (see note)* René Cardona, Adolfo Torres Portillo. *Photog* José Ortiz Ramos. *Set Dsgn* Roberto Silva. *Film Ed* Jorge Bustos. *Mus* Raúl Lavista. *Sd* José de Perez.

Narrator: Paul Tripp.

Cast: María Elena Marqués *(fairy princess)*, José Elias Moreno *(ogre)*, Cesareo Quesada *(Tom Thumb)*, Paquito Fernández, Rafael Banquells, Pablo Jorge Nava, Angel Arturo Limón, Gonzalo Carmona, Eduardo Rodríguez, Manuel Dondé, Nora Veyran.

Fantasy. Source: Charles Perrault, "Le petit pouce," in *Recueil de pièces curieuses et nouvelles* (Paris, 1697). A poor, aging woodcutter lives in the forest with his wife and seven small sons. Tom Thumb, the smallest of the boys, overhears his parents talking about their poverty and persuades his brothers to go out and cut wood to help the family. In the forest they are set upon by a child-eating ogre. The boys try to escape, but their trail leads directly to the ogre's house. The ogre's wife, a former princess who lives there with her seven unkempt little daughters, shelters the boys. Tom induces the girls to bathe and put on clean clothes, and all together they persuade the ogre to give the mother the key to the chest that holds the magic wand. The wand changes the woman back into a princess; it also changes the ogre into a gentleman who gives the boys money and a magic ax to help their parents. *Brothers. Woodsmen. Royalty. Sisters. Family life. Poverty. Cannibalism. Forests. Magic. Tom Thumb.*

Note: Released in Mexico in 1958 as *Pulgarcito*; running time: 85 min.

TOM, TOM, THE PIPER'S SON   F6.5107
Dist Film-Makers' Distribution Center, Film-Makers' Cooperative. Mar **1969** [New York showing]. Si; b&w with col seq. 16mm. 86 min.

Prod-Dir-Writ Ken Jacobs. *Asst* Jordan Myers, Florence Jacobs. *Film Ed* Ken Jacobs. *Key Grip* David Hamilton.

Experimental film. A dissection and analysis of *Tom, Tom, the Piper's Son*, a 1905 film version of the nursery rhyme photographed by G. W. "Billy" Bitzer for the American Mutoscope & Biograph Company. The original film, photographed with a stationary camera on eight sets, is first presented intact. It depicts a street fair, in which acrobats and jugglers perform while a group of sailors brawl and Tom is seen stealing a pig. A dozen pursuers give chase. They search buildings, jump into haystacks, climb out of chimneys, and vault fences before capturing Tom at a well in a barnyard. In the new film, the original footage is photographed from the screen upon which it is being projected with the purpose of demonstrating the possible range in methods of depicting the same story. The filmmaker employs the freeze-frame, reverse action, slow motion, wipes, masks, superimpositions, flicker effects, split screen, rapid cutting, and changes in sequence. He photographs portions of the original frame and moves the camera around and away from the projected image, at times creating extreme, grainy close-ups. At other times, the screen is seen in long-shot: a screen-within-a-screen. Two color sequences are added to the original film, and at one point the bulb of the projector is photographed. The original film is once again presented intact, and in a coda, the original sequences appear in rapid progression. *Motion pictures. Motion pictures—History. Nursery rhymes. G. W. "Billy" Bitzer. Chases. "Tom, Tom, the Piper's Son" (1905).*

THE TOMB OF LIGEIA (Great Britain)   F6.5108
Alta Vista Film Productions. *Dist* American International Pictures. 20 Jan **1965** [Los Angeles opening; c27 Jan 1965; LP30820]. Sd; col (Eastmancolor by Pathé). 35mm. (Colorscope). 81 min.

A Roger Corman Production. *Prod* Pat Green, Roger Corman. *Asst Prod* Paul Mayersberg. *Dir* Roger Corman. *Screenplay* Robert Towne. *Photog* Arthur Grant. *Art Dir* Colin Southcott. *Main Titl* Francis Rodker. *Film Ed* Alfred Cox. *Mus Comp & Cond* Kenneth V. Jones. *Sd* Les Wiggins, Don Ranasinghe. *Sd Rec* Bert Ross, John Aldred. *Asst Dir* David Tringham. *Makeup* George Blackler. *Hairstyles* Pearl Orton. *Sp Eff* Ted Samuels.

Cast: Vincent Price *(Verden Fell)*, Elizabeth Shepherd *(Lady Ligeia/Lady Rowena)*, John Westbrook *(Christopher Gough)*, Oliver Johnston *(Kenrick)*, Derek Francis *(Lord Trevanion)*, Richard Vernon *(Dr. Vivian)*, Ronald Adam *(parson)*, Frank Thornton *(Peperel)*, Denis Gilmore *(livery boy)*, Penelope Lee.

Horror film. Source: Edgar Allan Poe, "Ligeia," in *American Museum* (Sep 1838). Verden Fell has his wife, Ligeia, buried in a churchyard in 1821 despite the parson's objections that Ligeia was not a Christian. A black cat perched atop the coffin screeches, and Ligeia's eyes open for a moment before the grave is closed. Several months later, Lady Rowena, the daughter of a local squire, is fox hunting when she is suddenly thrown from her horse near Ligeia's grave. Frightened by the surroundings and the loud wailing of a black cat, Rowena faints and is carried to safety by Fell. She finds herself strangely attracted to him in spite of his forboding manner and the gloomy Gothic abbey where he lives. The two eventually marry, but after they return from their honeymoon, Fell becomes more remote than ever and leaves Rowena alone at night. She begins to have dreams involving the black cat and Ligeia, and one night she discovers a dead fox in her bed. Christopher Gough, an admirer of Rowena, becomes suspicious, and after exhuming Ligeia's coffin, he finds a wax figure inside. Meanwhile, Rowena smashes through a mirror and finds Fell in the arms of the preserved body of Ligeia, who apparently had hypnotized Fell into believing that she would live forever. Rowena tries to help Fell, but he convinces her that she has become Ligeia. Possessed with the spirit of his dead wife, Fell sets fire to the abbey and tries to kill the cat. Christopher manages to rescue Rowena, but Fell dies in the flames, clutching the cat. *Widowers. Evil spirits. Death. Funerals. Hypnotism. Disinterment. Immortality. Corpses. Churchyards. Coffins. Dreams. Fires. Cats. Fox.*

Note: Location scenes filmed in Norfolk, England. Opened in London in Nov 1964. Working titles: *Ligeia, The Last Tomb of Ligeia, House at the End of the World.* Also released as *Tomb of the Cat.*

TOMB OF THE CAT *see* THE TOMB OF LIGEIA

TOMB OF TORTURE (Italy)   F6.5109

Virginia Cinematografica. *For* Film Development Corp. *Dist* Trans-Lux Distributing Corp. Jul **1966.** Sd; b&w. 35mm. 88 min.

Prod Frank Campitelli. *Exec Prod U. S. Vers* Richard Gordon. *Dir (see note)* Anthony Kristye. *Screenplay* Anthony Kristye, Johnny Seemonell. *Photog* William Grace, Frank Campitelli. *Film Ed* Jean-Pierre Grasset, Gaby Vital. *Mus* Armando Sciascia.

Cast: Annie Albert *(Anna Darnell/Countess Irene)*, Thony Maky *(Dr. Darnell)*, Mark Marian *(George Dickson)*, Elizabeth Queen *(Countess Elizabeth)*, William Gray, Bernard Bly, Emy Eko, Terry Thompson, Fred Pizzot, Antonio Boccacci.

Horror film. Anna, who strongly resembles Countess Irene who was murdered 20 years before, is tormented by nightmares in which she reenacts the brutal killing. In an effort to help her, Dr. Darnell, her father, takes Anna to the castle where the crime was committed. There she meets George Dickson, a journalist who has become interested in the case since the recent murder of two young women. Dickson learns that two people have motives for victimizing Anna: Erbart, a mysterious Hindu nobleman who was engaged to Irene and wants to find her body; and Countess Elizabeth, Irene's cousin who is seeking Irene's fortune in jewels. As Anna's lapses into unconsciousness increase, she finds herself wandering through a torture chamber in the cellar and encounters Irene's former butler—a horribly disfigured man who believes Anna to be the dead countess. Assisted by Erbart, George rescues Anna and solves the murder of the other women. *Doubles. Nobility. Physicians. Journalists. Hindus. Cousins. Butlers. Murder. Filial relations. Disfiguration. Mistaken identity. Castles. Dreams.*

Note: Opened in Rome in May 1963 as *Metempsyco.* Some U. S. sources credit William Grace as director. Anthony Kristye is also known as Antonio Boccacci, Johnny Seemonell as Giovanni Simonelli, Thony Maky as Adriano Micantoni, Mark Marian as Marco Mariani, and Elizabeth Queen as Flora Caroselli.

TOMBOY AND THE CHAMP   F6.5110

Signal Pictures. *Dist* Universal-International Films. 25 Jan **1961** [Houston opening]. Sd; col (Eastmancolor). 35mm. 92 min.

Prod Tommy Reynolds, William Lightfoot. *Dir* Francis D. Lyon. *Screenplay* Virginia M. Cooke. *Story* Tommy Reynolds, William Lightfoot. *Photog* William Clothier. *Film Ed* William B. Murphy. *Mus* Richard Shores. *Songs:* "Get Ready With the Ribbon, Judge," "Who Says Animals Don't Cry" Tommy Reynolds, William Lightfoot. *Sung by* Rex Allen. *Song:* "Barbecue Rock" Elsie Pierce Wilkes. *Sung by* Jerry Naill. *Sd* Dale Knight, Jerry Lightfoot. *Asst Dir* Clem Beauchamp, Hal Polaire.

Cast: Candy Moore *(Tommy Jo)*, Ben Johnson *(Uncle Jim)*, Jesse White *(Windy Skiles)*, Jess Kirkpatrick *(Model T. Parson)*, Christine Smith *(Aunt Sarah)*, Paul Bernath *(Jaspar Stockton)*, Norman Sherry *(Fowler Stockton)*, John Carpenter *(Fred Anderson)*, Wally Phillips *(hi fi club announcer)*, Ralph Fischer *(4-H club president)*, Larry Hickie *(Curley Cone)*, Rex Allen, Casey Tibbs, Jerry Naill *(themselves)*, Champy *(himself, a bull)*.

Comedy-drama. Tommy Jo, a 13-year-old Texas ranch girl, wins a calf at a county fair and names him Champy. While training the animal, Tommy Jo gets caught in a storm and develops polio. With the help of her aunt and uncle and her parson, Tommy Jo learns to walk again and discovers that the secret of training Champy is to soothe him with music. She enters her pet—now grown—in the Houston Fat Stock Show, but loses when her radio breaks down and no music is available. The parson encourages her to persevere, and with the help of the local Four-H Club, Tommy Jo is able to enter Champy in the Chicago

International Exposition. They win the grand championship when the parson sings a song to Champy. Tommy Jo's happiness is short-lived, however, as she learns that all champions are auctioned off for beef. Unable to raise the $30,000 auction price, Tommy Jo has a relapse and is rushed to the hospital with pneumonia. Fred Anderson, a kindly meatpacker, saves Champy from the slaughterhouse and reunites him with Tommy Jo at the hospital. *Tomboys. Ranchers. Clergymen. Aunts. Uncles. Adolescence. Ranch life. Poliomyelitis. Pneumonia. Music. Meatpacking. Fairs. Hospitals. Chicago. Houston. Four-H Clubs. Cattle.*

Note: Filmed on location in Chicago, Houston, and Katy, Texas.

TOMBS OF HORROR *see* CASTLE OF BLOOD

THE TOMCAT (Great Britain)   F6.5111

Tigon British Film Productions–Global Productions. *Dist* Joseph Brenner Associates. 13 Nov **1968** [Boston opening]. Sd; b&w. 35mm. 79 min.

Prod Tony Tenser. *Exec Prod* Arnold Louis Miller. *Dir* Georges Robin. *Screenplay* Georges Robin, Tony Tenser. *Photog* Stanley A. Long. *Art Dir* Tony Curtis, art dir. *Film Ed* Roy Nevill. *Mus* De Wolfe. *Sd* Dudley Plummer Services.

Cast: Anthony Trent *(Tom)*, Liza Rogers *(Sandra)*, Veronica Lang *(Jenny)*, Connie Frazer *(Tom's mother)*, Vicky Hodge *(1st dream sequence)*, Jane MacIntosh *(supermarket girl)*, Patti Bryant, Avril Gaynor *(girls in cafe sequence)*, Rosalind Elliot, Kathleen Southern *(girls in tube sequence)*, Maria Hauffer, Lucy Swain *(girls in boutique sequence)*, Eve Aubrey *(old hag)*, Anna Palk *(girl in tiles club and cinema)*, Karen Leslie *(girl in pub)*, Nina Dwyer *(girl on bus)*, Valerie Stanton *(girl in barbershop)*.

Comedy. Tom is a sex-starved young man who is harried by his old-fashioned girl friend, Sandra, and his overbearing mother. Obsessed by romantic fantasies about women, Tom spends a weekend in London's West End looking for excitement. He imagines that he is the best dressed man on Carnaby Street, and later, that he is a popular singer who is mobbed by admiring females. In a nightclub, Tom actually meets a young woman whose boyfriend has left her for the evening. She in turn ditches Tom, who then goes to a pub where he picks up a prostitute. Later, Tom visits a striptease show where he imagines saving the stripper from a gang of attacking old men. Tom decides to return home, and on the way he has a final sex fantasy in which he spends the night with a lovely woman named Jenny. *Prostitutes. Stripteasers. Singers. Fantasy. Obsession. Sexuality. Motherhood. Nightclubs. Pubs. London—West End.*

Note: Released in Great Britain in 1967 as *Mini Weekend.*

TOMORROW AT TEN (Great Britain)   F6.5112

Mancunian Film Corp. *Dist* Governor Films. May **1964.** Sd; b&w. 35mm. 80 min.

Prod Tom Blakeley. *Dir* Lance Comfort. *Screenplay* Peter Miller, James Kelly. *Dir Photog* Basil Emmott. *Art Dir* Jack Shampan. *Film Ed* John Trumper. *Mus Comp & Dir* Bernie Fenton. *Sd* Fred Turtle. *Asst Dir* George Pollard. *Prod Mgr* John Comfort.

Cast: John Gregson *(Parnell)*, Robert Shaw *(Marlow)*, Alec Clunes *(Chester)*, Alan Wheatley *(Bewley)*, Kenneth Cope *(Sergeant Grey)*, Ernest Clark *(Dr. Towers)*, Piers Bishop *(Jonathan)*, Helen Cherry *(Robbie)*, William Hartnell *(Freddy)*, Betty McDowall *(Mrs. Parnell)*, Harry Fowler *(Smiley)*, Renee Houston *(Mrs. Maddox)*, Noel Howlett *(specialist)*, Bernadette Woodman, Marguerite McCourt *(nurses)*, Ray Smith *(Briggs)*, John Dunbar *(Henry)*.

Drama. A man named Marlow poses as a chauffeur, kidnaps Jonathan, the young son of a millionaire, Chester, and takes him to a house in a remote section of London. After giving Jonathan a golliwog to keep him company, Marlow goes to Chester's house to demand a ransom of £50,000. He tells Chester that the golliwog contains a time bomb set to go off at 10 o'clock the next morning. He also says that he will depart for South America in the evening and will cable Chester the boy's whereabouts before the bomb is to explode. Chester makes plans to withdraw the ransom money, but Robbie, the boy's governess, informs the police, and Inspector Parnell arrives at the Chester house before Marlow has left. Parnell refuses to allow Chester to pay the ransom; a fight breaks out; and Chester accidentally kills Marlow before Parnell can find out from Marlow where the boy is. A rental agent recognizes a newspaper photograph of Marlow and leads the police to the house he rented to the kidnaper. Police arrive a few minutes after 10 a.m. and find Jonathan quietly playing with the golliwog: by immersing the toy in water, the boy inactivated the bomb. *Children. Chauffeurs. Millionaires. Detectives. Governesses. Real estate agents. Kidnaping. Imposture. Dolls. Bombs. Ransom. London.*

Note: Filmed in London. Opened in London in Jun 1963.

TOMORROW IS MY TURN (France/Italy/West Germany)   F6.5113

Franco London Film–Gibé–Jonia Film–UFA. *Dist* Showcorporation. 1 Feb **1962** [New York opening]. Sd; b&w. 35mm. 117 min.

Dir André Cayatte. *Screenplay* André Cayatte, Armand Jammot. *Adtl Dial* Maurice Aubergé. *Adapt* André Cayatte, Pascal Jardin. *Orig Idea* Armand Jammot. *Photog* Roger Fellous. *Camera Op* Georges Pastier. *Art Dir* Robert Clavel. *Film Ed* Borys Lewin, Alix Paturel. *Mus* Louiguy. *Sd* Georges Mardiguian. *Asst Dir* Ulrich Pickard. *Prod Mgr* Ralph Baum.

Cast: Charles Aznavour *(Roger),* Nicole Courcel *(Florence),* Georges Rivière *(Jean),* Cordula Trantow *(Helga),* Jean Marchat *(Delmas),* Betty Schneider *(Alice),* Georges Chamarat *(baker),* Michel Etcheverry *(Ludovic),* Lotte Ledl *(Lotte),* Nerio Bernardi *(Rodier),* Benno Hoffmann *(Otto),* Colette Régis *(baker's wife),* David Tonnelli *(barman),* Alfred Schieske *(Fritz Kessler),* Ruth Hausmeister *(Frau Kessler),* Oscar Albrecht *(burgomaster),* Arne Madin, Henri Lambert, Serge Frédéric, Albert Remy, Bernard Musson, Konrad Mayerhoff.

War drama. In 1940, two French soldiers—Roger, a former baker, and Jean, a former journalist—are captured and sent to work on a German farm. The wily Jean seduces Helga, the daughter of the farmer, and then tricks her into helping him escape. The more scrupulous Roger, however, remains behind to continue helping out on the farm and becomes deeply attached to Helga and her family. Jean swims the Rhine, takes part in the Resistance, and is appointed editor of a radical newspaper at the end of the war. Roger returns home to find that his wife has made a fortune during the war and is now a nagging shrew. The two men later meet in Paris, and Roger announces that he intends to leave his bakery and wife and return to Helga. Jean is so influenced by Roger's decision that he decides to resign from the newspaper and marry Florence, his mistress whom he abandoned because she was a collaborator during the German occupation of France. Unknown to Jean, Florence saved him from arrest by sleeping with a Gestapo agent, and is now unwilling to marry him. *Prisoners of war. Bakers. Journalists. Farmers. Escapees. Mistresses. Traitors. Seduction. Infidelity. Self-sacrifice. World War II. France—History—German occupation 1940–45. Paris. Rhine River. France—Army. Maquis.*

Note: Opened in Paris in Nov 1960 as *Le passage du Rhin;* running time: 124 or 130 min; in Bonn in Oct 1960 as *Jenseits des Rheins;* running time: 124 min; in Rome in Nov 1960 as *Il passaggio del Reno.*

TOMORROW YOU DIE *see* **THE CRAWLING HAND**

TON OMBRE EST LA MIENNE *see* **YOUR SHADOW IS MINE**

TONGUE TIED   F6.5114
Dist Stacey Distributors. ca 1970. Sd; col. 16mm. 61-81 min.
Sex film. No information about the precise nature of this film has been found. *Sexuality.*

TONI (France)   F6.5115
Films d'Aujourd'hui. *Dist* Pathé Contemporary Films. 18 Dec **1968** [Washington, D. C., opening]. Sd (RCA); b&w. 35mm. 90 min.
Dir Jean Renoir. *Tech Dir* Albert Ausouad. *Screenplay-Dial* Jean Renoir, Carl Einstein. *Dir Photog* Claude Renoir. *Camera* Roger Ledru. *Set Dsgn* Marius Brauquier, Léon Bourelly. *Film Ed* Marguerite Renoir, Suzanne de Troye. *Asst Film Ed* Guy Darnoux. *Mus* Paul Bozzi. *Sd* Barbishanian. *Asst Sd* Sarrazin. *Asst Dir* Georges Darnoux, Antonio Canor. *Prod Mgr* Pierre Gault. *Script Girl* Suzanne de Troye. *Apprentice* Luchino Visconti. *Mechanic* Bébert. *Admin* E. Boyer.
Cast: Charles Blavette *(Antonio Canova),* Célia Montalvan *(Josepha),* Jenny Hélia *(Marie),* Max Dalban *(Albert),* Edouard Delmont *(Fernand),* Andrex *(Gaby),* André Kovachevitch *(Sébastien),* Paul Bozzi *(Jacques Bozzi),* Jacques Levert.
Drama. Based on an incident documented by: Jacques Levert. Antonio Canova, "Toni," an Italian laborer who has arrived as part of the immigrant influx into Martigues, finds work at a local mine and begins an affair with his landlady, Marie. After several months he tires of their liaison and falls in love with Josepha, a Spanish woman who lives with her father, Sébastien, in the home of a cousin, Gaby. Toni courts Josepha, unaware that the lecherous mine foreman, Albert, is inflamed by her. Although Toni receives permission from Sébastien to marry Josepha, his hope is crushed as Albert rapes her in a ditch. Josepha subsequently marries Albert and bears his child, asking Toni to be the godfather. Following Sébastien's death, Toni leaves Marie and persuades Josepha to run away with him. Gaby persuades Josepha to steal Albert's money to finance her elopement. When Albert surprises her during the theft, she kills him. Gaby leaves for Marseilles, while Toni attempts to dispose of the corpse. Caught by a policeman while burying the body, Toni confesses to the murder and then escapes. While running away he is noticed by a hunter and killed when he refuses to halt. He dies unaware that his beloved has turned herself in to the police. *Immigrants. Miners. Italians. Spanish. Landladies. Mine foremen. Cousins. Mistresses. Godfathers. Police. Rape. Murder. Self-sacrifice. Marriage. Infidelity. Elopement. Pregnancy. Theft. Confession (law). Martigues.*

Note: Location scenes filmed in Martigues. Paris opening: Feb 1935; running time: 100 min. Jacques Levert is a pseudonym for Jacques Mortier.

TONIGHT FOR SURE!   F6.5116
Searchlight Productions. *Dist* Premier Pictures, Sam Lake Enterprises. 25 Oct **1962** [Los Angeles showing]. Sd; col (Eastman Color). 35mm. 69 min.
Prod-Dir-Writ Francis Coppola. *Photog* Jack Hill. *Op* Michele Perrult. *Scenic Dsgn* Albert Locatelli, Barbara Cooper. *Mus Comp & Cond* Carmen Coppola. *Rec* Jerry McKibben. *Asst Dir* Frank Zuniga. *Unit Mgr* Peter Good. *Master Electrn* Al Langan.
Cast: Don Kenney, Karl Schanzer, Virginia Gordon, Marli Renfro, Sandy Silver, Linda Gibson, Pat Brooks, Linda Lightfoot.
Western comedy. Ben Jabousky from the League Against Nudity visits a Hollywood burlesque house with a moralistic old miner in order to effect a plan of sabotage. Having tampered with the fuse box, they sit back to wait for midnight. The miner relates the unfortunate tale of his partner, Jamie, who was so startled by the sight of two naked women in the Nevada desert that he fell from his horse and struck his head on a rock. From that moment on, Jamie saw nude women wherever he went. Jabousky is outwardly shocked by the morally repugnant tale, though his stern exterior belies a secret fascination with nudity. His efforts have included building a telescope to spy on the proceedings at a pinup studio and attempting to tunnel through. As the intoxicated visitors move closer to the stage, the miner recounts Jamie's efforts to explain his predicament to the sheriff and the showdown that resulted. As Jamie drew his gun, his adversary turned into a nude woman before his eyes, leaving him defenseless. The moralists, reveling in their increasingly exaggerated stories, lose track of the time. At midnight, darkness strikes. A band of stone-faced women arrive bearing signs condemning nudity and chase all the sinners out of the establishment, unaware that their leader is the worst offender. *Miners. Models. Sheriffs. Hypocrisy. Voyeurism. Nudity. Drunkenness. Burlesque. Hallucinations. Hollywood.*

TONIGHT LET'S ALL MAKE LOVE IN LONDON (Great Britain)   F6.5117
Lorrimer Films. *Dist* Universal Education and Visual Arts. 19 Jul **1968** [New York opening]. Sd; col. 16mm & 35mm. 72 min.
Prod-Dir-Writ Peter Whitehead. *Photog* Peter Whitehead. *Film Ed* Peter Whitehead. *Asst Dir* John Esam, Anthony Stern.
Featuring: Michael Caine, Edna O'Brien, Genevieve, Vanessa Redgrave, Eric Burdon and the Animals, The Twice As Much, Vashti, Andrew Loog Oldham, The Rolling Stones, Mick Jagger, Julie Christie, Alan Aldridge, David Hockney, Vic Lowndes, Lee Marvin, Donyale Luna, Pink Floyd, Allen Ginsberg, The Small Faces, Chris Farlowe, Marquis of Kensington.
Documentary. This impressionistic view of 1967 London is devised as a "Pop Concerto for Film." The "overture," a montage of images set to rock music, is followed by seven "movements." The first, "Loss of the British Empire," includes scenes of traditional London: the changing of the Royal Guard, conservative clothing, a band playing. During the second movement, "Dollygirls," novelist Edna O'Brien discusses the morality of modern women, and pop singer Genevieve is interviewed. "Protest" features actress Vanessa Redgrave singing at a political demonstration in Royal Albert Hall and rock group Eric Burdon and the Animals performing. In "It's All Pop Music," record producer Andrew Loog Oldham guides two new talents, Twice As Much and Vashti, through recording sessions, while his most successful group, the Rolling Stones, perform in concert. The Stones's lead singer Mick Jagger is interviewed on the subject of modern youth. "Moviestars" features actress Julie Christie discussing her private life and the contemporary London scene and actor Michael Caine commenting on recent changes in British society. "Painting Pop" features interviews with painter and designer Alan Aldridge and painter David Hockney. In "As Scene from U.S.A.," actor Lee Marvin, London Playboy Club manager Vic Lowndes, and American model Donyale Luna are interviewed. A "postlude" features the music of experimental rock group Pink Floyd with the voice of poet Allen Ginsberg commenting optimistically on pop culture. *Novelists. Singers. Actors. Painters. Models. Poets. Nightclub managers. Americans in foreign countries. Urban life. Rock and roll. Demonstrations. London.*
Note: Released in Great Britain in 1968. First shown commercially in the U. S. with a collection of short films titled *The Kinetic Art: Series One, Program 2,* q.v.

TONIO KRÖGER (France/West Germany)   F6.5118
Mondex Films–Procinex–Thalia-Film. *Dist* Pathé Contemporary Films. 15 Jan **1968** [New York opening]. Sd; b&w. 35mm. 90 min.
Dir Rolf Thiele. *Screenplay* Erika Mann, Ennio Flajano. *Photog* Wolf Wirth. *Mus* Rolf Wilhelm. *Prod Mgr* Franz Seitz.
Cast: Jean-Claude Brialy *(Tonio Kröger),* Nadja Tiller *(Lisaweta Iwanowna),* Werner Hinz *(Consul Kröger),* Anaid Iplicjian *(Frau Kröger),* Rudolf Forster

(Herr Seehaase), Walter Giller *(merchant)*, Theo Lingen *(Knaak)*, Adeline Wagner *(woman)*, Beppo Brem *(Adalbert Prantl)*, Rosemarie Lucke *(Inge Holm)*, Elisabeth Klettenhauer *(girl)*, Mathieu Carrière *(young Tonio Kröger)*, Gert Fröbe *(Policeman Peterson)*, Günther Lüders, Valsø Holm.

Drama. Source: Thomas Mann, "Tonio Kröger," in *Tristan* (Berlin, 1903). Young author Tonio Kröger, the son of a Lübeck businessman and poetic Italian mother, roams Europe at the turn of the century. In Italy he recalls early academic inadequacies, paternal rejection, and his unrequited love for Inge Holm, who was enamored of Tonio's friend, the virile and intellectual Hans. In Munich he visits a friend, the Slavic artist Lisaweta. With her Tonio discusses the artist's isolation in the modern world. Although powerfully attracted to Lisaweta, Tonio resumes his wanderings. Upon visiting his native village the writer discovers that his ancestral home has been converted into a library. Traveling to Denmark Tonio lodges at a small seaside hotel. Although he is troubled by memories of Lisaweta during an evening dance, Tonio vows to continue his self-imposed exile, an essential condition of his creativity. *Authors. Artists. Wanderers. Businessmen. Italians. Middle classes. Personality. Alienation. Friendship. Filial relations. Travel. Beaches. Libraries. Hotels. Lübeck. Munich. Italy. Denmark.*

Note: Released in West Germany in Jun 1964.

TONNERRE SUR L'OCÉAN INDIEN *see* **THE SEA PIRATE**

TONY ROME   F6.5119
Arcola-Millfield Productions. *Dist* Twentieth Century-Fox Film Corp. 10 Nov **1967** [Miami Beach, Florida, opening; c10 Nov 1967; LP34998]. Sd (Westrex); col (De Luxe). 35mm (Panavision). 110 min.

Prod Aaron Rosenberg. *Dir* Gordon Douglas. *Action Seq Dir* Buzz Henry. *Screenplay* Richard Breen. *Dir Photog* Joseph Biroc. *Art Dir* Jack Martin Smith, James Roth. *Set Decor* Walter M. Scott, Warren Welch. *Film Ed* Robert Simpson. *Mus Comp & Cond* Billy May. *Titl Song* Lee Hazlewood. *Sung by* Nancy Sinatra. *Songs:* "Something Here Inside Me," "Hard Times" Billy May, Randy Newman. *Sd* Howard Warren, David Dockendorf. *Asst Dir* Richard Lang. *Unit Prod Mgr* David Silver. *Asst to the Prod* Michael Romanoff. *Cost Dsgn & Supv* Moss Mabry. *Women's Fashion Dsgn* Elinor Simmons, Malcolm Starr. *Makeup* Ben Nye. *Hairstyles* Edith Lindon.

Cast: Frank Sinatra *(Tony Rome)*, Jill St. John *(Ann Archer)*, Richard Conte *(Lieutenant Santini)*, Sue Lyon *(Diana Pines)*, Gena Rowlands *(Rita Kosterman)*, Simon Oakland *(Rudolph Kosterman)*, Jeffrey Lynn *(Adam Boyd)*, Lloyd Bochner *(Rood)*, Robert J. Wilke *(Ralph Turpin)*, Virginia Vincent *(Sally)*, Joan Shawlee *(Fat Candy)*, Richard Krisher *(Donald Pines)*, Lloyd Gough *(Langley)*, Babe Hart *(Oscar)*, Templeton Fox *(Mrs. Schuyler)*, Rocky Graziano *(Packy)*, Elisabeth Fraser *(Irma)*, Shecky Greene *(Catleg)*, Jeanne Cooper *(Lorna)*, Harry Davis *(Ruyter)*, Stan Ross *(Sam Boyd)*, Buzz Henry *(Nimmo)*, Deanna Lund *(Georgia McKay)*, Michael Romanoff *(maître d'hotel)*, Tiffany Bolling *(photo girl)*.

Mystery melodrama. Source: Anthony Rome, *Miami Mayhem* (New York, 1960). In return for a fee, Miami Beach private eye Tony Rome helps remove drunken, unconscious Diana Pines from a room in the motel operated by his former partner, Ralph Turpin. Tony takes Diana to her family's mansion, and the girl's millionaire father, construction magnate Rudolph Kosterman, hires him to find out what is troubling his recently married daughter; meanwhile, Diana's stepmother, Rita, offers Tony a fee if he will inform her first of his discoveries. After learning that Diana has lost a diamond pin, Tony is chloroformed and beaten by two thugs and nearly strangled by the girl's imbecilic stepuncle; later, he discovers that Turpin has been shot to death in his office. Assisted in his sleuthing by predatory divorcée Ann Archer, the detective learns that Diana has been giving large sums of money to her alcoholic mother, Lorna, and that Rita's valuable jewelry has been replaced with paste imitations. In pursuit of evidence, Tony has a series of conflicts with a stripteaser and her lesbian lover, a drug addict and her homosexual contact, the two murderers of the jeweler who was making the paste imitations for Rita, and with his old friend Lieutenant Santini of the Miami police, who wants information that Tony possesses. After an attempt is made on Kosterman's life, Tony learns that Turpin was murdered by Rita's ex-husband, Nimmo, who has been blackmailing her because their divorce was never legalized. Nimmo eventually dies from wounds inflicted by Turpin, and the case is finally solved when Lorna's second husband, Adam Boyd, a doctor who lost his license for performing abortions, confesses that he tried to kill Kosterman so that Diana could inherit the family fortune. After Santini arrests the doctor, Tony decides to take a vacation with Ann, but she chooses to return to a safer life with her former husband. *Detectives. Newlyweds. Businessmen. Millionaires. Stepmothers. Idiots. Stripteasers. Drug addicts. Jewelers. Police. Physicians. Blackmail. Inheritance. Filial relations. Murder. Divorce. Alcoholism. Drunkenness. Lesbianism. Male homosexuality. Abortion. Jewels. Motels. Miami.*

Note: Location scenes filmed in Miami, Florida.

TOO HOT TO HANDLE (Great Britain)   F6.5120
Associated British Productions-Wigmore Productions. *Dist* Topaz Film Corp. 12 Jan **1961** [Los Angeles showing]. Sd; col (Eastman Color). 35mm. 92 min.

Prod Phil C. Samuel. *Exec Prod* Selim Cattan. *Assoc Prod* Ronald Rietti, John Evans, C. P. Hamilton-Marshall. *Dir* Terence Young. *Screenplay* Herbert Kretzmer. *Story* Harry Lee. *Dir Photog* Otto Heller. *Art Dir* Alan Withy. *Film Ed* Lito Carruthers. *Mus* Eric Spear. *Choreog* Pamela Davis. *Sd* Charles Knott. *Prod Mgr* William Lang.

Cast: Jayne Mansfield *(Midnight Franklin)*, Leo Genn *(Johnny Solo)*, Karl Boehm *(Robert Jouvel)*, Danik Patisson *(Lilliane Decker)*, Christopher Lee *(Novak)*, Kai Fischer *(Cynthia)*, Patrick Holt *(Inspector West)*, Martin Boddey *(Mr. Arpels)*, Sheldon Lawrence *(Diamonds Dinelli)*, Barbara Windsor *(Pony Tail)*, John Salew *(Moeller)*, Tom Bowman *(Flash Gordon)*, Ian Fleming *(pawnbroker)*, Penny Morrell *(Terry)*, Katherine Keeton *(Melody)*, Susan Denny *(Marjorie)*, Judy Bruce *(Maureen)*, Elizabeth Wilson *(Jacky)*, Shari Khan *(Jungle)*, Bill McGuffie *(piano player)*, Michael Balfour *(tourist guide)*, Larry Taylor *(Mouth)*, June Elvin *(hostess)*, Morton Lowry *(Dinelli's driver)*, Martin Sterndale *(editor)*, Harry Lane *(Muscles)*, Robin Chapman *(priest)*, Monica Marshall, Toni Palmer, Lou Eather, Brian Tucker, Boyd McKenzie, Ken Martyne *(dancers)*.

Melodrama. French journalist Robert Jouvel, who is researching an article on the striptease clubs of London's Soho section, contacts Johnny Solo, owner of the Pink Flamingo, and his singing star girl friend, Midnight Franklin. Spending long hours at the club, Jouvel becomes attracted to Lilliane, a dancer who remains aloof, carefully guarding her past. Solo has been persuaded to team up with his rival, Diamonds Dinelli, in an effort to thwart an unknown blackmailer who has sent them both threatening letters. In reality, Dinelli himself is behind the blackmail plot, and his chief accomplice is Solo's two-timing manager, Novak. After Solo is beaten up by Dinelli's thugs, he discovers the treachery and plots his revenge. Before he can carry out his plan, however, he sends his latest recruit, 15-year-old Pony Tail, on a date with his lecherous backer Arpels, and she is found dead in his flat. Meanwhile, Jouvel, who has gradually gained Lilliane's confidence, discovers that she is a celebrated missing person whose disappearance made headlines in West German newspapers. Solo is held for police questioning in the murder case, and Midnight discovers that he has made plans to kill Novak. Although she knows that he will never forgive her, Midnight protects Solo from himself by betraying him to the police. *Journalists. Dancers. French. Nightclub owners. Singers. Hoodlums. Business managers. Germans. Missing persons. Financiers. Striptease. Blackmail. Murder. Lechery. Perfidy. Revenge. Self-sacrifice. Personal identity. Nightclubs. London—Soho.*

Note: Released in Great Britain in Dec 1960; running time: 100 min. Also known as *Playgirl After Dark*.

TOO LATE BLUES   F6.5121
Paramount Pictures. Jan **1962** [Detroit showing; c31 Dec 1961; LP21176]. Sd; b&w. 35mm. 100 min.

Prod-Dir John Cassavetes. *Screenplay* Richard Carr, John Cassavetes. *Cinematog* Lionel Lindon. *Unit Art Dir* Tambi Larsen. *Film Ed* Frank Bracht. *Mus* David Raksin. *Played by* Shelly Manne, Red Mitchell, Benny Carter, Uan Rasey, Jimmy Rowles. *Sd* Gene Merritt, John Wilkinson. *Asst Dir* Arthur Jacobson. *Unit Prod Mgr* William Mull. *Cost* Edith Head. *Dial Dir* Jud Taylor.

Cast: Bobby Darin *(John "Ghost" Wakefield)*, Stella Stevens *(Jess Polanski)*, Cliff Carnell *(Charlie)*, Seymour Cassel *(Red)*, Bill Stafford *(Shelly)*, Richard Chambers *(Pete)*, Nick Dennis *(Nick)*, Rupert Crosse *(Baby Jackson)*, Everett Chambers *(Benny Flowers)*, Vincent Edwards *(Tommy)*, Alan Hopkins *(Skipper)*, Val Avery *(Frielobe)*, James Joyce *(Reno)*, Marilyn Clark *(The Countess)*, Allyson Ames *(Billie Gray)*, June Wilkinson *(girl at bar)*, Mario Gallo.

Drama. Because he insists upon playing only what pleases him, jazz musician John "Ghost" Wakefield and his dedicated combo exist only on the outer fringes of the successful musical world. One day he meets and falls in love with Jess Polanski, a timid and uncertain vocalist, and takes her away from her fast-talking agent, Benny Flowers. Following a minor success at a recording session, Ghost, Jess, and the combo celebrate at their favorite hangout, Nick's poolhall. The party turns into a drunken free-for-all when the vindictive Benny instigates a fight between Ghost and a musician-hating bully named Tommy. Overcome by fear, Ghost is unable to fight back, a humiliation that causes him to reject Jess and his friends. His downfall is complete when he becomes the gigolo of an aging "countess" and ends up playing rank jazz for listless audiences. Only when Benny denounces him as a complete phony is Ghost able to attempt a new beginning. He seeks out Jess, now a drifter and a prostitute, and prevents her from committing suicide. Together they find the members of Ghost's combo; as Jess starts humming their old blues numbers, the antagonisms melt and the combo begins once more to play their kind of music. (Musical numbers include: "Sax Raises Its Ugly Head," "Look Inward Angel," "The Rim Shot Heard 'Round the World," "Benny Splits While Jimmy Rowles," and "Move Over.") *Musicians. Singers. Talent agents. Gigolos. Jazz. Prostitution. Suicide. Billiard parlors. Jazzbands.*

TOO LATE THE HERO

F6.5122

Associates & Aldrich Co.–Palomar Pictures International–ABC Pictures. *Dist* Cinerama Releasing Corp. 20 May **1970** [New York opening]. Sd; col (Metrocolor). 35mm. 133 min. *MPAA rating GP.*

Prod-Dir Robert Aldrich. *Assoc Prod* Walter Blake. *2d Unit Dir* Oscar Rudolph. *Screenplay* Robert Aldrich, Lukas Heller. *Story* Robert Aldrich, Robert Sherman. *Dir Photog* Joseph Biroc. *Lighting* Bill Hannah. *Camera Op* Herbert R. Smith, Joe Jackman, Orville Hallberg. *2d Unit Photog* Nonong Rasca. *Art Dir* James Dowell Vance. *Set Decor* John W. Brown. *Main Titl* Richard Kuhn. *Film Ed* Michael Luciano. *Montage Ed* Albert Nalpas. *Assoc Ed* Joseph Harrison. *Mus* Gerald Fried. *Rec Supv* Franklin Milton. *Mus Ed* William Saracino. *Sd Engr* Richard Church. *Sd Eff* Milo Lory. *2d Unit Sd Rec* Levy Principe. *1st & 2d Asst Dir* Grayson Rogers, Malcolm Harding. *2d Unit Asst Dir* Francisco MacLang. *Asst to the Prod* William Aldrich. *Unit Prod Mgr* Eddie Saeta. *Prod Supv* Fred Ahern. *Philippine Prod Supv* Vicente Nayve. *Script Supv* Ken Gilbert. *Wardrobe Supv* Charles James. *Makeup* William Turner, Jack Stone. *Sp Eff* Henry Millar, Jr. *Tech Adv* Robert C. Lefever, (Capt.), Takashi Ohashi. *Dial Supv* Robert Sherman. *Prop Master* Ygnacio Sepulveda. *Head Grip* Paul S. Schwake, Jr. *Casting* Lynn Stalmaster. *Constr Coörd* John LaSalandra.

Cast: Michael Caine *(Pvt. Tosh Hearne)*, Cliff Robertson *(Lieut. Sam Lawson)*, Henry Fonda *(Capt. John G. Nolan)*, Ian Bannen *(Private Thornton)*, Harry Andrews *(Lieutenant Colonel Thompson)*, Denholm Elliott *(Captain Hornsby)*, Ronald Fraser *(Private Campbell)*, Lance Percival *(Corporal McLean)*, Percy Herbert *(Sergeant Johnstone)*, Michael Parsons *(Private Rafferty)*, Harvey Jason *(Signalman Scott)*, William Beckley *(Private Currie)*, Don Knight *(Private Connolly)*, Sean MacDuff *(Private Rogers)*, Martin Horsey *(Private Griffiths)*, Roger Newman *(Private Riddle)*, Ken Takakura *(Major Yamaguchi)*, Sam Kydd *(sergeant-major)*, Patrick Jordan *(soldier)*, Frank Webb.

War melodrama. During World War II Japanese forces hold a crucial observation outpost on a New Hebrides island which they use to radio orders for attacks on Allied ships. U. S. Navy Lieut. Sam Lawson, an officer noted for his proficiency in speaking Japanese, is ordered to accompany a group of British commandos on a mission to destroy the radio installation. Lawson sets out with the commandos' ineffectual leader, Captain Hornsby, and soon three of the British soldiers are killed in a Japanese ambush. Lawson and Pvt. Tosh Hearne, a cynical Cockney, become increasingly distrustful of Hornsby's ability, and upon reaching the Japanese camp, Lawson refuses to go into the radio hut. Hornsby destroys the hut himself but is killed while trying to escape; the remaining five commandos retreat through the jungle with the Japanese in close pursuit. Major Yamaguchi, the Japanese commander, offers clemency to the commandos if they will surrender. Private Campbell and two of the other soldiers do so, but Yamaguchi kills Campbell for mutilating the body of a Japanese soldier in order to steal a ring. Hearne and Lawson then ambush and kill Yamaguchi and continue their flight until they reach a clearing near the British lines. They make a break across the clearing, but only Hearne survives to report Lawson's heroism. *Commandos. Linguists. Cockneys. War heroes. Combat zone life. Jungles. Islands. World War II. New Hebrides. United States Navy. Great Britain—Army. Japan—Army.*

Note: Location scenes filmed in the Philippines. Blown up to 70mm for some roadshow presentations.

TOO MUCH FOR ONE MAN *see* THE CLIMAX

TOO MUCH TOO OFTEN!

F6.5123

Mostest Productions. *Dist* Jerand Film Distributors. 26 Jun **1968** [Champaign, Illinois, showing]. Sd; b&w. 35mm. 72 min.

Prod-Dir-Writ Louis Silverman. *Dir Photog* C. Davis Smith. *Ed* Dee Ess. *Mus* Music Sound Track Service. *Sd* Titan Productions. *Mus Ed* George Craig. *Optical Eff* B. & O. Film Specialists.

Cast: Buck Starr, Sharon Kent, Lee Taylor, Michelle Fox, Sam Stewart, Bob Oran, Darlene Bennett, Stephenie Collins, Rita Bennett.

Melodrama. Sadist Mike Torsen whips masochist Gordon Dite, an advertising executive, and then blackmails Dite into offering him a job. Torsen arranges a dinner date with Dite's daughter Sara; then he visits Lita, a woman so devoted to him that she becomes a prostitute to earn money for him. Midge, a secretary, finds Torsen rifling Dite's files, and he makes love to her to ensure her silence. Lynn, a schoolgirl made pregnant by Torsen, comes to him for help, and he beats her. Dite learns that Torsen and Sara have been seeing each other, and he offers Torsen $10,000 to leave town. Torsen laughingly refuses, and Dite

warns his daughter to beware of Torsen's sadistic streak. Unafraid, Sara asks Torsen to marry her, and Torsen consents. A detective arrives, accuses Torsen of mistreating a woman, and beats him mercilessly. Sara, appalled at Torsen and ashamed at not having believed her father, leaves with Dite; and Torsen, alone, looks into the mirror at his ruined face and falls unconscious. *Advertising executives. Prostitutes. Secretaries. Detectives. Fatherhood. Sadism. Masochism. Blackmail. Seduction. Flagellation. Pregnancy.*

Note: Also known as *Too Much, Too Soon.*

TOO SOON TO LOVE *see* HIGH SCHOOL HONEYMOON

TOO YOUNG, TOO IMMORAL!

F6.5124

Raymond A. Phelan. *Dist* Rialto International Film Releasing Corp., Times Film Corp. 9 Aug **1962** [New York opening; c9 Aug 1962; LP25625]. Sd; b&w. 35mm. 89 min. [Also 77 min.]

Prod-Dir-Writ Raymond A. Phelan. *Photog* Raymond A. Phelan. *Film Ed* Raymond A. Phelan. *Mus Comp & Played by* Bob Vinas, Joe Boppo, Kenny Harris.

Cast: John Francis *(Mr. Claude)*, Larry Healey *(Joseph)*, Raymond A. Phelan *(Tony Brooks)*, Donald Shumway *(Henry)*, Taylor Mead *(Scribbles)*, Donald Ratka *(Gene Brooks)*, Susan Ashley *(Mary Boyd)*, Brenda DeNaut *(Leeta)*.

Melodrama. Gene Brooks, a drug addict and pusher, goes to Times Square to pick up a shipment of heroin and becomes trapped in a building by syndicate boss Mr. Claude, an elderly esthete confined to a wheelchair. Gene is forced to the roof and pushed to his death by members of the vice syndicate. When police inform Gene's brother Tony that the death was a suicide, Tony sets out to prove his suspicion that Gene was killed. He learns from his brother's high school friends that Gene had become an addict and dealer and that Gene's girl friend Mary, also addicted to drugs, is living in a hotel for young women who support their habits by prostitution. One of the girls at the hotel informs on the gang who killed Gene; and as Tony's quest leads him to Mr. Claude, he is himself pursued by Mr. Claude's henchmen. The chase weaves through New York City and ends at Mr. Claude's swank penthouse. There Tony, intent upon having the gang and Mr. Claude brought to justice, volunteers to dive for a cache of heroin sunk off Fire Island. When Mr. Claude orders his men to kill Tony after he has recovered the package, Tony eludes them, turns the heroin over to the police, and leads them to Claude's hideout. Tony is captured by Claude's men, but during a struggle, Claude's wheelchair topples down a flight of stairs, killing him; the police arrive and round up the rest of the gang members. *Drug addicts. Drug dealers. Gangsters. Paraplegics. Police. Suicide. Murder. Prostitution. Diving. Heroin. Syndicates. Christmas. New York City. New York City—Times Square. Fire Island. Chases.*

Note: Filmed on location in New York City—Rockefeller Center, Times Square, Central Park, Lower East Side—and on Fire Island. Script registered for copyright as *Rebels Die Young,* c13 Dec 1957. Prerelease title: *Twisted Morals.*

TOP JOB *see* GRAND SLAM

TOP SENSATION *see* THE SEDUCERS

TOPAZ

F6.5125

Universal Pictures. 19 Dec **1969** [New York opening; c19 Dec 1969; LP39052]. Sd; col (Technicolor). 35mm. 125 min. *MPAA rating M.*

Prod-Dir Alfred Hitchcock. *Assoc Prod* Herbert Coleman. *Screenplay* Samuel Taylor. *Photog* Jack Hildyard. *Camera Op* William Dodds. *Photog Cons* Hal Mohr. *Set Decor* John Austin. *Prod Dsgn* Henry Bumstead. *Film Ed* William Ziegler. *Mus & Mus Dir* Maurice Jarre. *Sd* Waldon O. Watson, Robert R. Bertrand. *Asst Dir* Douglas Green, James Westman. *Unit Prod Mgr* Wallace Worsley. *Asst to Mr. Hitchcock* Peggy Robertson. *Script Supv* Trudy von Trotha. *Cost* Edith Head. *Fashioned in Paris by* Pierre Balmain. *Men's Cost Supv* Peter Saldutti. *Makeup* Bud Westmore, Leonard Engelman. *Hairstyles* Larry Germain, Nellie Manley. *Sp Photog Eff* Albert Whitlock. *Cuban and French Tech Adv* J. P. Mathieu, Odette Perry.

Cast: John Forsythe *(Michael Nordstrom)*, Frederick Stafford *(André Devereaux)*, Dany Robin *(Nicole Devereaux)*, John Vernon *(Rico Parra)*, Karin Dor *(Juanita de Cordoba)*, Michel Piccoli *(Jacques Granville)*, Philippe Noiret *(Henri Jarre)*, Claude Jade *(Michele Picard)*, Michel Subor *(François Picard)*, Roscoe Lee Browne *(Philippe Dubois)*, Per-Axel Arosenius *(Boris Kusenov)*, Edmon Ryan *(McKittreck)*, Sonja Kolthoff *(Mrs. Kusenov)*, Tina Hedstrom *(Tamara Kusenov)*, John Van Dreelen *(Claude Martin)*, Don Randolph *(Luis Uribe)*, Roberto Contreras *(Munoz)*, Carlos Rivas *(Hernandez)*, Lewis Charles *(Mr. Mendoza)*, Anna Navarro *(Mrs. Mendoza)*, John Roper *(Thomas)*, George Skaff *(Rene D'Arcy)*, Roger Til *(Jean Chabrier)*, Sandor Szabo *(Emile Redon)*, Lew Brown.

Mystery drama. Source: Leon Uris, *Topaz* (New York, 1967). In 1962 Russian bureaucrat Boris Kusenov, his wife, and daughter, assisted by CIA agent Michael Nordstrom, escape from the Soviet embassy in Copenhagen and defect to the United States. Alarmed by Kusenov's disclosure of Soviet shipments to Cuba, Nordstrom contacts French intelligence Chief André Devereaux, who agrees to cooperate with the CIA. Consequently, Devereaux recruits Dubois, a black florist and secret agent, who infiltrates an assembly of Cuban revolutionaries housed in Harlem's Hotel Theresa and obtains photographs of important documents. Devereaux then travels to Cuba, where he is warmly received by Juanita, his counterrevolutionary mistress, who commands her loyal domestic staff to help her lover. Eagerly undertaking this assignment are Carlotta and Pablo Mendoza, who, posing as picnickers, from a knoll overlooking a harbor photograph the unloading of Soviet missiles. Their position is given away, however, by hungry seagulls which descend upon their lunch. But before being captured and tortured, the pair secrete the incriminating film in a chicken carcass. Having aroused the suspicions of Rico Parra, an important revolutionary whom Juanita has also taken as a lover, Devereaux is expelled from Cuba. As a token of their love, Juanita presents the departing Frenchman with a slim volume of poetry, in which is hidden the film. Shocked by his mistress' betrayal of the Cuban revolution, Parra shoots her to death. Upon returning to the United States, Devereaux discovers a leak in the French intelligence network. In Paris he learns that the head of Topaz, a ring of French traitors, is Jacques Granville, his friend and his wife's lover. Unmasked, Granville shoots himself to death. *Russians. Cubans. French. Florists. Intelligence agents. Mistresses. Revolutionaries. Negroes. Patriotism. Communism. Espionage. Perfidy. Infidelity. Torture. Suicide. Photographs. Copenhagen. Cuban Missile Crisis 1962. New York City. New York City—Harlem. Paris. United States—Central Intelligence Agency. Sea gulls.*

Note: Location scenes filmed in West Germany, Copenhagen, Paris, New York, and Washington, D. C. Opened in London in Nov. 1969 with an ending in which Granville escapes East; running time: 125 min.

TOPKAPI F6.5126
Filmways, Inc.-F-H Productions. *Dist* United Artists. 17 Sep **1964** [New York opening; c17 Sep 1964; LP29368]. Sd; col (Technicolor). 35mm. 120 min.
Prod-Dir Jules Dassin. *Screenplay* Monja Danischewsky. *Photog* Henri Alekan. *Camera Op* Gilbert Chain. *Asst Camera* Max Lechevallier. *Art Dir* Max Douy. *Asst Art Dir* Jacques Douy. *Set Decor* André Labussière. *Film Ed* Roger Dwyre. *Mus* Manos Hadjidakis. *Sd* William Sivel. *Asst Dir* Tom Pevsner, Joseph Dassin. *Script Supv* Lucie Lichtig. *Cost Supv* Denny Vachlioti.
Cast: Melina Mercouri *(Elizabeth Lipp)*, Peter Ustinov *(Arthur Simpson)*, Maximilian Schell *(William Walter)*, Robert Morley *(Cedric Page)*, Akim Tamiroff *(Geven)*, Gilles Segal *(Giulio)*, Jess Hahn *(Fischer)*, Titos Vandis *(Harback)*, Ege Ernart *(Major Tufan)*, Senih Orkan, Ahmet Danyal Topatan *(shadows)*, Joseph Dassin *(Josef)*, Amy Dalby *(nanny)*, Despo Diamantidou *(Voula)*.
Crime comedy-drama. Source: Eric Ambler, *The Light of Day* (London, 1962). Jewel thief Elizabeth Lipp and her lover, William Walter, plan to steal an emerald dagger from Istanbul's Topkapi Museum. Cedric Page, an eccentric British inventor; Giulio, a mute athlete; and Fischer, a strongman, are recruited. In Greece, the gang hires con man Arthur Simpson to drive a car over the border and meet them in Istanbul, but he is stopped by the Turkish police, who discover weapons hidden in the trunk. Major Tufan, one of the policemen, questions Simpson and then allows him to leave on the condition that he spy on the gang. At their villa headquarters, the gang plans the robbery: Fischer is to lower Giulio on a rope from a window near the museum's ceiling so that Giulio can steal the dagger while dangling above the sensitively wired floors of the museum. Geven, the drunken cook at the villa, believes the men are Russian spies and tells Simpson, who in turn passes the information on to Tufan. Later, Geven accidentally smashes Fischer's hands in a door, and Simpson is enlisted to take Fischer's place, although he has revealed his link to the police. The gang manages to elude Tufan, steal the dagger, and pass it to a Gypsy who will smuggle it out of Turkey. Flaunting their success, the gang goes to see Tufan, and Elizabeth explains that weapons were discovered in their car, but while they are in the major's office, a bird flies through an open window in the museum and lands on the floor, triggering the alarm. The entire gang is arrested, but the undaunted Elizabeth begins outlining plans for their next job—the theft of the Romanoff jewels from the Kremlin. *Eccentrics. Inventors. Mutes. Athletes. Strongmen. Confidence men. Spies. Border police. Cooks. Gypsies. Conspiracy. Theft. Istanbul. Turkey. Greece. Topkapi Museum. Birds.*

Note: Location scenes filmed in Istanbul and Greece.

THE TOPLESS STORY (Switzerland) F6.5127
Atlantic Film. ca **1966**. Sd; col (Eastman Color). 35mm. [U. S. release length undetermined.]
Prod Werner Kunz. *Dir-Writ* Wolfgang Selnig. *Photog* Wolfgang Anders. *Mus* Werner Kruse, Hans Moeckel. *Prod Mgr* Joachim Burgmeyer.
Cast: John Wala *(John Pearson)*, Bambi Miller *(Jo)*, Dolly Doreac *(Maya)*, Birgit Nilsen *(Birgit)*.

Nudist film. John Pearson, New York fashion designer and photographer, presents new bathing suit designs to editor Jo. Dismayed by their poor reception at a fashion show, John goes on vacation. After a visit to Athens, the couturier visits an island nudist colony. Concerned for his welfare, Jo and John's assistant Maya follow him to Bangkok, where Maya enjoys a Thai sun club. Together editor and designer sample Tokyo night life, while Maya explores a Japanese nudist camp. Refreshed, John returns to the Greek island where he creates a successful collection of topless swimwear. *Americans in foreign countries. Couturiers. Photographers. Fashion editors. Vacations. Fashion. Travel. Magazines (periodicals). Nudist camps. Bathing suits. Islands. Fashion shows. Greece. Japan. Bangkok. Tokyo.*

Note: Released in Switzerland in 1965 as *Die "Oben-ohne" Story*; running time: 70 min.

TOPSY-TURVY JOURNEY (Japan) F6.5128
Shochiku Co. *Dist* Shochiku Films of America. Apr **1970** [Los Angeles showing]. Sd; col. 35mm. 93 min.
Prod Kiyoshi Shimazu. *Dir* Shoji Segawa. *Story-Screenplay* Kazuo Funabashi. *Photog* T. Takaha. *Art Dir* Masao Kumagi. *Mus* Taku Izumi.
Cast: Frankie Sakai *(Goichi Hasegawa)*, Chieko Baisho *(Sakura)*, Kensaku Morita *(Shinsaku)*, Kumi Hayase *(Ayako)*, Tomomi Sato *(Kaori)*, Arihiro Fujimura *(Mitsui)*, Toru Yuri *(Arao)*, Chocho Miyako *(Mine)*, Junzaburo Ban *(Daikichi Yashiro)*, Utako Kyo, Keisuke Ko, Zaizu Ichiro, Hiroshi Minami, Bonta Sesshi, Harumi Miyako.
Romantic comedy. Goichi, a conductor on the Tokyo-Aomori express train, enrolls in cooking classes because he is in love with the school's manager, Kaori Hara. Sakura, who operates a barber shop and also works as a geisha, is in love with Goichi and enrolls in the same class to divert his attention from Kaori. Sakura learns that Goichi is going on a picnic with Kaori, and to further discourage their romance, she doses his food with a laxative. Just as Goichi is about to reveal his feelings for Kaori, he suffers from the effects of the laxative. Meanwhile, Ayako, a new waitress in the express diner and the daughter of the diner's manager, Daikichi, falls in love with Shinsaku, an assistant conductor. After Daikichi objects to the romance, Mine, Goichi's widowed mother, pays him a visit to intercede in behalf of the lovers, only to end up engaged to Daikichi, himself a widower. Goichi proposes to Kaori, who promises to marry him if he will quit the railroad, be adopted into her family to carry on her name, and take a job in her father's orchard. Goichi agonizes over quitting the railroad but eventually decides he can agree to Kaori's demands. He arranges to meet her at a hotel in Iizuka Spa and orders Shinsaku to give her the rail ticket for Iizuka. At the hotel, however, he finds Sakura in his room. Kaori, realizing how much Goichi loves his job, could not accept the ticket, and Sakura took it instead. *Railroad conductors. Schoolteachers. Cooks. Barbers. Geishas. Widows. Widowers. Waitresses. Matchmakers. Courtship. Jealousy. Hotels. Picnics. Iizuka.*

Note: Released in Japan in Aug 1969 as *Gyakuten ryoko*.

TORA-SAN PT. 2 (Japan) F6.5129
Shochiku Co. *Dist* Shochiku Films of America. Jul **1970** [Los Angeles showing]. Sd; col. 35mm. 93 min.
Assoc Prod Tsuguo Saito. *Dir* Yoji Yamada. *Screenplay* Yoji Yamada, Shun'ichi Kobayashi, Akira Miyazaki. *Planning by* Yukio Takashima. *Story* Yoji Yamada. *Photog* Tetsuo Takaba. *Film Ed* Iwao Ishii. *Mus* Naozumi Yamamoto.
Cast: Kiyoshi Atsumi *(Torajiro Kuruma)*, Shin Morikawa *(Ryuzo)*, Chieko Misaki *(Tsune)*, Gin Maeda *(Hiroshi Suwa)*, Chieko Baisho *(Sakura)*, Eijiro Tono *(Sampo Tsubouchi)*, Orie Sato *(Natsuko)*, Tsutomu Yamazaki *(Dr. Fujimura)*, Chocho Miyako *(Okiku)*, Shoko Kazemi, Hiroaki Tsukasa, Hisao Dadayu, Gajiro Sato, Keiroku Sato.
Comedy. Torajiro Kuruma, also known as Tora, is a fumbling but well-meaning racketeer who continually becomes involved in minor scrapes with his relatives and those who befriend him. On his way to Beppu, he stops at his uncle's house but avoids staying too long, despite the pleas of his sister, Sakura, because he is aware of the trouble he has caused his uncle in the past. He passes by the house of his teacher, Mr. Tsubouchi, and decides to visit him. The two enjoy a warm reunion and settle down to a delicious meal prepared by Natsuko, Mr. Tsubouchi's daughter and Tora's former classmate. Unused to such fine food, Tora's stomach becomes upset and he is taken to a hospital, where Natsuko must apologize to the doctors for his rambunctious behavior. After he recovers, Tora again takes to the road, this time toward Kyoto, where he believes his real mother is living. The woman turns out to be a miser who owns an inn of questionable reputation, and a very different person from that Tora had pictured. Tora returns to his uncle's house, now aware of his love for Natsuko. However, Mr. Tsubouchi suddenly dies, and at his funeral Tora learns some bitter facts. [Sources are vague regarding the end of the film.] *Racketeers. Uncles. Schoolteachers. Misers. Family life. Funerals. Inns. Hospitals. Kyoto.*

Note: Released in Japan in Nov 1969 as *Zoku otokowa tsuraiyo*, the sequel to *Otokowa tsuraiyo*, also released in Japan in 1969 but not released in the U. S. Alternative titles: *Tora—San's Cherished Mother* and *Am I Trying Part II.*

TORA–SAN'S CHERISHED MOTHER *see* **TORA-SAN PT. 2**

TORA! TORA! TORA! (United States/Japan)   **F6.5130**

Twentieth Century-Fox Film Corp. 23 Sep **1970** [New York opening; c30 Sep 1970; LP38329]. Sd (Westrex); col (DeLuxe). 35mm (Panavision). 143 min. *MPAA rating* G.

Overall Production Credits: An Elmo Williams–Richard Fleischer Production. *Prod* Elmo Williams. *Aerial Photog* Vision Photography Inc. *Main Titl* Pacific Title.

U. S. Production Credits: *Dir* Richard Fleischer. *2d Unit Dir* Ray Kellogg. *Screenplay* Larry Forrester. *Dir Photog* Charles F. Wheeler. *Art Dir* Jack Martin Smith, Richard Day. *Set Decor* Walter M. Scott, Norman Rockett. *Film Ed* James E. Newcom, Pembroke J. Herring. *Mus* Jerry Goldsmith. *Orch* Arthur Morton. *Sd Rec* James Corcoran, Murray Spivack, Douglas O. Williams, Ted Soderberg, Herman Lewis. *Asst Dir* David Hall, Elliot Schick. *Unit Prod Mgr* William Eckhardt, Jack Stubbs, Stanley Goldsmith. *Prod Coörd* Maurice Unger, Theodore Taylor. *Script Supv* Duane Toler. *Wardrobe Supv* Courtney Halsam. *Wardrobe* Ed Wynigear. *Makeup Supv* Dan Striepeke. *Makeup* Layne Britton. *Sp Photog Eff* L. B. Abbott, Art Cruickshank. *Mech Eff* A. D. Flowers. *Air Op* Arthur P. Wildern, (Lieut. Col. Ret.), George Watkins, (Capt. USN), Jack Canary. *DOD Project Officer and Naval Coörd.* E. P. Stafford, (Cmdr. USN Ret.).

Japanese Production Credits: *Assoc Prod for Japanese Seq* Otto Lang, Masayuki Takagi, Keinosuke Kubo. *Dir Japanese Seq* Toshio Masuda, Kinji Fukasaku. *Screenplay* Hideo Oguni, Ryuzo Kikushima. *Photog for Japanese Seq* Shinsaku Himeda, Masamichi Sato, Osami Furuya. *Art Dir* Yoshiro Muraki, Taizo Kawashima. *Film Ed* Inoue Chikaya. *Sd Rec* Shin Watarai. *Asst Dir* Hiroshi Nagai. *Unit Prod Mgr* Masao Namikawa. *Tech Adv* Kameo Sonokawa, Kuranoshuke Isoda, Shizuo Takada, Tsuyoshi Saka.

Cast: Martin Balsam *(Adm. Husband E. Kimmel)*, So Yamamura *(Adm. Isoroku Yamamoto)*, Jason Robards, [Jr.] *(Gen. Walter C. Short)*, Joseph Cotten *(Henry L. Stimson)*, Tatsuya Mihashi *(Comdr. Minoru Genda)*, E. G. Marshall *(Lieut. Col. Rufus S. Bratton)*, Takahiro Tamura *(Lieutenant Commander Fuchida)*, James Whitmore *(Adm. William F. Halsey)*, Eijiro Tono *(Adm. Chuichi Nagumo)*, Wesley Addy *(Lieut. Comdr. Alvin D. Kramer)*, Shogo Shimada *(Ambassador Kichisaburo Nomura)*, Frank Aletter *(Lieutenant Commander Thomas)*, Koreya Senda *(Prince Fumimaro Konoye)*, Leon Ames *(Frank Knox)*, Junya Usami *(Adm. Zengo Yoshida)*, Richard Anderson *(Capt. John Earle)*, Kazuo Kitamura *(Foreign Minister Yosuke Matsuoka)*, Keith Andes *(Gen. George C. Marshall)*, Edward Andrews *(Adm. Harold R. Stark)*, Neville Brand *(Lieutenant Kaminsky)*, Leora Dana *(Mrs. Kramer)*, Asao Uchida *(Gen. Hideki Tojo)*, George Macready *(Cordell Hull)*, Norman Alden *(Maj. Truman Landon)*, Walter Brooke *(Capt. Theodore S. Wilkinson)*, Rick Cooper *(Lieut. George Welch)*, Elven Havard *(Doris Miller)*, June Dayton *(Miss Ray Cave)*, Jeff Donnell *(Cornelia)*, Richard Erdman *(Col. Edward F. French)*, Jerry Fogel *(Lieut. Cmdr. William W. Outerbridge)*, Shunichi Nakamura *(Kameto Kurojima)*, Carl Reindel *(Lieut. Kenneth Taylor)*, Edmon Ryan *(Rear Adm. Patrick N. L. Bellinger)*, Hisao Toake *(Saburo Kurusu)*, Susumu Fujita, Bontaro Miyake, Ichiro Reuzaki, Kazuko Ichikawa, Hank Jones, Karl Lukas, Ron Masak, Kan Nihonyanagi, Toshio Hosokawa.

Historical drama. Source: Gordon W. Prange, *Tora! Tora! Tora!* (New York, 1969). Ladislas Farago, *The Broken Seal* (New York, 1967). After Japan signs the Axis Alliance with Germany in 1941, Adm. Isoroku Yamamoto, commander of the Japanese Navy, realizes that the center of United States Naval operations at Pearl Harbor must be destroyed if Japanese power is to spread in the Pacific. In Washington, Secretary of State Cordell Hull and Secretary of War Henry L. Stimson suggest the cooling of diplomatic relations with Japan after the treaty, but few in the U. S. military or diplomatic corps fear imminent attack. At Pearl Harbor, Gen. Walter C. Short, commander of U. S. ground forces, is more worried about sabotage than foreign attack and orders all planes to be placed in the middle of the runway; in addition, the radar system he has developed is rendered useless since its operators do not know how to interpret the readings. After Japan invades Indochina, Lieut. Col. Rufus S. Bratton of U. S. Army Intelligence convinces Stimson that a Japanese attack is impending, and Pearl Harbor is placed on full alert on November 30th; few preparations are actually made, however, and within a couple of days the base is back to its unprepared state. Just before the actual attack, Bratton learns from a decoded message that Japanese Adm. Chuichi Nagumo has received orders to sail for Hawaii with six aircraft carriers, but the intelligence officer is unable to locate Army Chief of Staff George C. Marshall, who is horseback riding, and President Roosevelt is warned only hours before the bombing is to begin. Japan instructs Ambassador Kichisaburo Nomura to present Hull with an ultimatum, which the Japanese expect to be refused, in order to make the attack seem retaliatory, but an inept typist in the Japanese Embassy delays the message so that its delivery coincides with the actual bombing. The Japanese attack results in the devastation of almost all Navy ships and planes based in the Pacific, but Yamamoto regards the holocaust with mixed emotions because of the anticipated American retaliation. *Military life. Combat zone life. Aerial bombardment. Treaties. Radar. Bombers. Airfields. Aircraft carriers. World War II. Pearl Harbor Attack 1941. Hawaii. Germany. Pacific Ocean. Indochina. Rufus S. Bratton. Cordell Hull. George C. Marshall. Chuichi Nagumo. Kichisaburo Nomura. Franklin Delano Roosevelt. Walter Campbell Short. Henry Lewis Stimson. Hideki Tojo. Isoroku Yamamoto. Zengo Yoshida. Japan—Navy. United States Navy. United States Army—General Staff. United States—State Department—Secretary of State. United States—War Department—Secretary of War. United States Army—Intelligence. United States—Diplomatic and consular service. Japan—Diplomatic and consular service. Explosions. Ship explosions.*

Note: Location scenes filmed in Hawaii. Subtitles are used in the Japanese sequences.

TORMENT (France)   **F6.5131**

Les Films du Griffon-Unicité. *Dist* Olympic International Films. 5 Oct **1967** [New Orleans opening]. Sd; b&w. 35mm. 66 min.

A Max Pécas Production. *Prod-Dir-Writ* Max Pécas. *Photog* Robert Lefebvre. *Mus* Louiguy.

Cast: Marie-Christine Weill *(Kim)*, Claude Cerval, Véra Valmont, Pierre Tissot, Jean-Pierre Dartois, Alain Bouvette, Agnès Datin, Patrice Fabien, Guy Kim, Pascal Leguen.

Melodrama. A model studio becomes involved in the theft of $50,000 worth of uncut gems, and as a result, the mob moves onto the scene. Kim, one of the models, innocently befriends a young mobster and inadvertently brings a reign of terror to the studio. [Press material suggests that the film contains scenes of seduction, lesbianism, autoeroticism, and sadism.] *Models. Gangsters. Theft. Organized crime. Seduction. Lesbianism. Sadism. Autoeroticism. Gems.*

Note: Opened in Paris in Jun 1967 as *La peur et l'amour*; running time: 75 min. Alternative French title: *La peur et le désir.* Also known in the U. S. as *Love + Fear = Torment* and *Fear and Love.*

TORN CURTAIN   **F6.5132**

Universal Pictures. 14 Jul **1966** [Boston opening; c6 Aug 1966; LP35396]. Sd (Westrex); col (Technicolor). 35mm. 128 min.

An Alfred Hitchcock Production. *Prod-Dir* Alfred Hitchcock. *Story-Screenplay* Brian Moore. *Dir Photog* John F. Warren. *Camera Op* Leonard South. *Art Dir* Frank Arrigo. *Set Decor* George Milo. *Pictorial Dsgn* Albert Whitlock. *Prod Dsgn* Hein Heckroth. *Film Ed* Bud Hoffman. *Mus* John Addison. *Sd* Waldon O. Watson, William Russell. *Asst Dir* Donald Baer. *Unit Prod Mgr* Jack Corrick. *Script Supv* Lois Thurman. *Asst to Mr. Hitchcock* Peggy Robertson. *Cost Supv* Grady Hunt. *Miss Andrews' Cost* Edith Head. *Makeup* Jack Barron. *Hairstylist* Lorraine Roberson. *Miss Andrews' Hairstylist* Hal Saunders.

Cast: Paul Newman *(Prof. Michael Armstrong)*, Julie Andrews *(Sarah Sherman)*, Lila Kedrova *(Countess Kuchinska)*, Hansjörg Felmy *(Heinrich Gerhard)*, Tamara Toumanova *(ballerina)*, Ludwig Donath *(Prof. Gustav Lindt)*, Wolfgang Kieling *(Hermann Gromek)*, Gunter Strack *(Prof. Karl Manfred)*, David Opatoshu *(Mr. Jacobi)*, Gisela Fischer *(Dr. Koska)*, Mort Mills *(farmer)*, Carolyn Conwell *(farmer's wife)*, Arthur Gould-Porter *(Freddy)*, Gloria Gorvin *(Fraulein Mann)*, Erik Holland *(hotel travel clerk)*, Hedley Mattingly *(airline official)*, Norbert Schiller *(Gutman)*, Peter Bourne *(Olaf Hengstrom)*, Peter Lorr *(taxi driver)*, Frank Aberschal *(factory manager)*, Charles H. Radilac.

Drama. While attending a physicists' congress in Copenhagen, U. S. nuclear scientist Michael Armstrong publicly defects to the Communist side. He flies to East Germany to confer with Russia's top physicist, Prof. Gustav Lindt of Leipzig University, followed by his assistant and fiancée, Sarah Sherman. She learns that Michael's actual plan is to gain information from the professor for furthering U. S. antimissile defense. Aided by members of the East German underground, Michael outwits the Communist security chief, Heinrich Gerhard, and tricks Professor Lindt into divulging his nuclear secrets. Before Michael and Sarah can escape, however, their deception is discovered. Once more the underground goes into action: a woman doctor smuggles them out of Leipzig, other agents transport them to East Berlin on an off-schedule bus, a countess helps them evade the police, and arrangements are made for them to be smuggled aboard a ship transporting a Russian ballet troupe to Sweden. Although the leading ballerina spots them and almost causes their capture, Michael and Sarah elude their pursuers and arrive safely in Stockholm. *Americans in foreign countries. Physicists. Defectors. Communists. Physicians. Russians. Stowaways. Nobility. Escapees. Espionage. Copenhagen. German Democratic Republic. Stockholm. Berlin—East. Leipzig. Chases.*

TORPEDO BAY (France/Italy)   F6.5133

Galatea–Panorama Cinematografica–Société Cinématographique Lyre. *Dist* American International Pictures. Feb **1964** [c26 Feb 1964; LP27908]. Sd; b&w. 35mm. 95 min.

Prod Bruno Vailati. *Dir (see note)* Charles Frend, Bruno Vailati. *2d Unit Dir* Pino Belli. *Screenplay* Charles Frend, Pino Belli, Alberto Ca'Zorzi, Augusto Frassineti, Bruno Vailati. *Photog* Gabor Pogany. *Art Dir* Giorgio Giovannini. *Film Ed* Giancarlo Cappelli. *Mus* Roberto Nicolosi. *Prod Mgr* Tommaso Sagone. *Cost* Giorgio Desideri.

Cast: James Mason *(Captain Blayne)*, Lilli Palmer *(Lygia da Silva)*, Gabriele Ferzetti *(Leonardi)*, Geoffrey Keen *(English Intelligence Officer Hodges)*, Alberto Lupo *(Magrì)*, Renato De Carmine *(Ghedini)*, Valeria Fabrizi *(Susanne)*, Daniele Vargas *(Brauzzi)*, Andrew Keir *(O'Brien)*, Andrea Checchi *(Micheluzzi)*, Gabriele Tinti, Jeremy Burnham, Davide Montemuri, Gaia Germani, Mimmo Poli, Paul Müller, Luigi Visconti, Aldo Pini.

War drama. In 1941 an Italian submarine damaged by depth charges and surrounded by mines tries to pass from the Mediterranean to the Atlantic by crossing the Straits of Gibraltar, a mission considered impossible. Submarine Commander Leonardi realizes that English spies have alerted British anti-submarine craft of his plans, and Commander Blayne waits to destroy the submarine when it reaches the mouth of the Straits. Traveling cautiously through the water, Leonardi decides to surface and fight Commander Blayne's craft when he sees no escape. He realizes upon surfacing that he has reached neutral waters in the international zone of Tangiers. A Spanish cruiser signals the two crafts to halt hostilities, and the commanders dock their ships. The Italians are ordered to remain in port for 2 weeks and then either leave or sink the ship and accept internment, while the British have orders to guard the Italian ship and blow up the harbor if it tries to leave. Onshore, Blayne and Leonardi and their crews become acquainted and develop a mutual respect for each other. Leonardi falls in love with Lygia, a doctor who urges him to accept internment rather than risk battle. He suspects Lygia is a collaborator, however, when British Intelligence Officer Hodges pressures him to surrender the submarine. Actually, Lygia had refused to cooperate with Hodges, and she manages to delay the explosion of the mines when the submarine leaves port. The two ship captains reluctantly face each other again in battle, and Leonardi defeats the British. *British. Spies. Physicians. Friendship. Submarines. World War II. Gibraltar. Atlantic Ocean. Mediterranean Sea. Tangiers. Great Britain—Intelligence service. Great Britain—Royal Navy. Italy—Navy. Explosions.*

Note: Released in Italy in 1963 as *Finchè dura la tempesta* and *Beta Som*; running time: 105 min; opened in Paris in Feb 1964 as *Défi à Gibraltar*. Some sources credit Charles Frend as director, while others credit Bruno Vailati as producer-director. French sources claim only French participation in the film.

TORTURE DUNGEON   F6.5134

Constitution Films. *Dist* William Mishkin. Jan **1970**. Sd; col. 35mm. 80 min. *MPAA rating* R.

Prod William Mishkin. *Dir* Andy Milligan. *Script* Andy Milligan, John Borske. *Photog* Andy Milligan. *Sets* James Fox, art. *Cost* Raffiné. *Makeup* Walter Terry.

Cast: Jeremy Brooks, actor *(Norman, Duke of Norwich)*, Susan Cassidy *(Heather McGregor)*, Patricia Dillon *(Lady Jane)*, Donna Whitfield *(Lady Agatha)*, Haal Borske *(Alfred)*, Maggie Rogen *(Margaret)*, Neil Flanagan, Richard Mason, George Box, Patricia Garvey, Dan Lyra, Helen Adams, Robert Fricelle.

Horror film. Norman, the evil Duke of Norwich who wants to become king, brutally murders all successors to the throne in the leaderless kingdom where he lives. He marries off his dimwitted half brother, Alfred, to local beauty Heather McGregor after killing her fiancé. Norman's half sisters, Ladies Jane and Agatha, take Heather into the dungeon and show her the mutilated bodies of their half brother's victims; then the sisters also fall prey to Norman's carnage, along with Alfred. Norman is prevented from killing Heather by Margaret, a mysterious, disfigured member of the court who spears him to death, and Heather is revealed to be the rightful heir to the throne. *Nobility. Halfwits. Murder. Torture. Brother-sister relationship. Marriage—Arranged. Imaginary kingdoms.*

TORTURE GARDEN (Great Britain)   F6.5135

Amicus Productions. *Dist* Columbia Pictures. 24 Apr **1968** [Atlanta opening; c31 Dec 1967; LP35731]. Sd (RCA); col (Technicolor). 35mm. 93 min.

Prod Max J. Rosenberg, Milton Subotsky. *Dir* Freddie Francis. *Screenplay* Robert Bloch. *Dir Photog* Norman Warwick. *Camera Op* David Harcourt. *Camera Grip* Ray Jones. *Art Dir* Don Mingaye, Scott Slimon. *Set Dresser* Andrew Low. *Prod Dsgn* Bill Constable. *Film Ed* Peter Elliott. *Mus Comp* Don Banks, James Bernard. *Mus Cond* Philip Martell. *Piano Solo Played by* Martino Tirimo. *Sd Rec* Ken Rawkins. *Sd Ed* Ken Rolls. *Asst Dir* Derek Parr. *Prod Supv* Ted Wallis. *Prod Mgr* Tony Wallis. *Cont* Barbara Rowland. *Wardrobe Mistress*

Evelyn Gibbs. *Makeup* Jill Carpenter. *Hairdresser* Ann Fordyce. *Constr Mgr* Bill Waldron.

Cast: Jack Palance *(Ronald Wyatt)*, Burgess Meredith *(Dr. Diabolo)*, Beverly Adams *(Carla Hayes)*, Peter Cushing *(Lancelot Canning)*, Barbara Ewing *(Dorothy Endicott)*, Michael Bryant *(Colin Williams)*, Maurice Denham *(Colin's uncle)*, John Standing *(Leo Winston)*, Robert Hutton *(Bruce Benton)*, John Phillips, British *(Eddie Storm)*, Michael Ripper *(Gordon Roberts)*, Bernard Kay *(Dr. Heim)*, Catherine Finn *(Nurse Parker)*, Ursula Howells *(Miss Chambers)*, Niall MacGinnis *(doctor)*, Timothy Bateson *(fairground barker)*, David Bauer *(Mike Charles)*, Nicole Shelby *(Millie)*, Clytie Jessop *(Atropos)*, Michael Hawkins *(constable)*, Hedger Wallace *(Edgar Allan Poe)*, Roy Stephens, Geoffrey Wallace, James Copeland, Norman Claridge, Roy Godfrey, Barry Lowe.

Horror film. Source: Robert Bloch, "Enoch," in *Bizarre Mystery Magazine* (Nov 1965). Robert Bloch, "The Man Who Collected Poe," in *Famous Fantastic Mysteries* (Oct 1951). Robert Bloch, "Mr. Steinway," in *Fantastic* (Apr 1954). Robert Bloch, "Terror Over Hollywood," in *Fantastic Universe Science Fiction* (Jun 1957). Five visitors to a fairground sideshow are dared to enter the inner sanctum of the mysterious Dr. Diabolo, promising them a vision of the future. Colin Williams, a young playboy, sees himself murder his miserly uncle for his money, only to fall under the spell of his uncle's cat and continue to kill in order to satisfy the animal's craving for human heads. Carla Hayes, an ambitious starlet, has an affair with actor Bruce Benton in order to further her career but discovers that he and other stars are metal automatons created by mastermind surgeon Dr. Heim. Heim, to prevent Carla from exposing him, also transforms her into an automaton, and as such she achieves stardom. Dorothy Endicott, Carla's cousin, sees herself as a reporter who falls in love with Leo Winston, a famed pianist, but is ultimately driven to her death by his grand piano, which is invested with the spirit of Leo's dead mother. Ronald Wyatt, a collector of Edgar Allan Poe relics, sees himself kill fellow collector Lancelot Canning in order to obtain an unpublished Poe manuscript; after discovering that the manuscript was actually written by the resurrected remains of the author, Wyatt is persuaded by Poe to end both their lives by setting the house on fire. The fifth visitor, Gordon Roberts, refuses to have his horrifying future revealed and stabs Diabolo to avoid taking his turn. When the others leave in panic, the sinister doctor pays off Roberts, who is his cohort in the bogus performance. *Charlatans. Playboys. Misers. Uncles. Actors. Robots. Surgeons. Cousins. Pianists. Collectors. Greed. Spells. Murder. Ambition. Theft. Hoaxes. Sideshows. Evil spirits. Edgar Allan Poe. Fires. Visions. The Future. The Devil. Cats.*

Note: Released in Great Britain in Nov 1967.

TORTURE ME KISS ME   F6.5136

Black Mercedes. *Dist* Jerand Film Distributors. ca **1970**. Sd; b&w. 35mm. 75 min.

Prod-Dir David R. Friedberg. *Selections From: "The Merry Widow Waltz"* Franz Lehar.

Cast: Linda Boyce *(Madelaine)*, Elaine Seagal *(Pepi)*, Frank MacIntosh *(Count Henri de Prave)*, Blaine Quincy *(Max von Hildebrandt)*, Christine Cybelle *(Ilsa Schneider)*, Wendy Wood *(Marianne Duval)*, Nick Dundas *(Lieutenant Jaeger)*, Alf Geisler *(The Priest)*, Jan Saint *(Erick, the torture master)*.

War melodrama. Under orders from Nazi General von Vogelbein, Colonel Max von Hildebrandt, accompanied by his secretary Ilsa Schneider, travels to France to expose a resistance leader. After taking up residence in a château, Max rapes and executes a suspect Frenchwoman and kills the priest who comes to her defense; is reunited with Count Henri de Prave, a German collaborator and master chess player; orders the Luftwaffe to destroy the village in retaliation for repeated sabotage attempts; and instructs his minion Erick to flog and torture three Frenchwomen. Discovering Ilsa and a partisan at a bistro, Max shoots his secretary, who dies proclaiming her Gestapo affiliation and absolute loyalty to General von Vogelbein. As she expires, Max is executed by Henri, who reveals himself to be a French loyalist. *Germans. French. Priests. Secret agents. Secretaries. Nazis. Rape. Espionage. Sabotage. Murder. Torture. Gestapo. Maquis. Chess. World War II. France. Germany—Army.*

TORTURED FEMALES   F6.5137

Mitam Productions. *Dist* S. I. E. International, Filmex Distributing Co. 7 Oct **1965** [San Francisco showing]. Sd; b&w. 35mm. 62 min.

Cast: Denine Dubois *(Helen)*.

Melodrama. Helen is out driving on a country road when her car runs out of gas. She decides to take a swim in a nearby creek before making the long walk back to town. While she is in the creek, a hunter spots her through his binoculars, and he offers her a ride. He takes her into the woods and rapes her. Then he leaves her at a house used as the center of a white slave ring, and there she is beaten and tortured. Another woman there is beaten to death and secretly buried on the property. During an orgy, Helen is stripped and forced to perform;

she escapes to the local sheriff's office and precipitates the end of the slave ring. *Hunters. Abduction. Rape. Torture. Sadism. Flagellation. Murder. Orgies. White slave traffic.*

DET TOSSEDE PARADIS *see* **CRAZY PARADISE**

THE TOTAL FEMALE *see* **MELISSA: THE TOTAL FEMALE**

DIE TOTE VON BEVERLY HILLS *see* **THE CORPSE OF BEVERLY HILLS**

DIE TOTEN AUGEN VON LONDON *see* **DEAD EYES OF LONDON**

EIN TOTER HING IM NETZ *see* **IT'S HOT IN PARADISE**

EIN TOTER SUCHT SEINEN MÖRDER *see* **THE BRAIN**

TOTÒ, VITTORIO E LA DOTTORESSA *see* **THE LADY DOCTOR**

A TOUCH OF HELL *see* **IMMORAL CHARGE**

THE TOUCH OF HER FLESH   F6.5138

Rivamarsh Productions. *Dist* American Film Distributing Corp. 19 Apr 1967 [New York showing]. Sd; b&w. 35mm. 78 min.

Prod Julian Marsh, Anna Riva. *Dir* Julian Marsh. *Photog* Anna Riva. *Lighting* Robert Marx. *Ed* Julian Marsh. *Mus* Robin Aden. *Asst to Miss Riva* Welchie. *Stills* Marvin Flower.

Cast: Suzanne Marre, Angelique, Robert West, Vivian Del Rio, Marie Lamont, Sally Farb, David Boxwell, Rit Dexter.

Melodrama. New York City gun collector Richard Jennings returns home to find his wife, Claudia, in bed with another man. Rushing wildly into the busy street, he is struck by a car. Blinded in one eye and temporarily crippled, he vows to kill all women, including his wife. His first victim is a go-go dancer; she receives a poisoned rose in the dressing room and dies onstage in a frenzied dance. Fearful that her husband will find her, Claudia, meanwhile, hides in an upstate New York woodworking plant with Janice, who excites her lust. Richard's next stop is a burlesque house. He watches a stripteaser from his wheelchair in the back and shoots a dart into her breast. Weeks later he sees Janice with a prostitute. Janice leaves, and Richard picks up the prostitute and terrorizes her into revealing his wife's whereabouts. Richard then murders the prostitute and takes his crossbow to the woodworking plant. Struggling to escape from her husband, Claudia accidentally flips the switch on the buzz saw, and Richard saws off her head. He then tries to rape Janice, but she clubs him with a piece of pipe, picks up the crossbow, and shoots him through the heart. *Psychopaths. Go-go dancers. Stripteasers. Prostitutes. Infidelity. Insanity. Revenge. Mutilation. Murder. Lesbianism. Rape. Poisoning. Decapitation. Blindness. Paralysis. Crossbows. Factories. Automobile accidents. New York City. New York State.*

Note: Also known as *Way Out Love* and *The Touch of Her Life.* This film has two sequels: *The Curse of Her Flesh* and *The Kiss of Her Flesh,* q. v.

TOUCH OF LEATHER (Great Britain)   F6.5139

Bachelor Films. *Dist* Olympic International Films. 8 May 1968 [Champaign, Illinois, showing]. Sd; b&w. 35mm. 65 min.

Dir Olaf Ericson.

Cast: Joyce Lee, Terry Brogan.

Melodrama. A boxer, selected by an opportunistic promoter, is brought to the point where he makes a little money and is dropped when he is no longer useful to the promoter. The boxer has a love affair with a woman who is also involved with a lesbian. *Boxers. Fight promoters. Lesbianism.*

Note: Also known as *The Death Blow.*

A TOUCH OF LOVE *see* **THANK YOU ALL VERY MUCH**

TOUCH OF SKIN *see* **THE EROTIC TOUCH OF HOT SKIN**

TOUCH WHITE—TOUCH BLACK *see* **THE VIOLENT ONES**

THE TOUCHABLES   F6.5140

Phaeton International Pictures. *Dist* Boxoffice International Pictures, Emerson Film Enterprises, Audubon Films. 4 Jul 1961 [Los Angeles opening]. Sd; col. 35mm. 63 min. [Also released at 58 min.]

Prod Jay Sheridan. *Exec Prod* John Shay. *Dir (see note)* Monte Mann, Monroe Manning, Jay Sheridan. *Writ* Monte Mann. *Dir Photog* William Hines. *Adtl Photog* Sven Walnum. *Camera Op* James A. Crabe. *Sd* Leroy Robbins. *Asst Dir* Jay O. Lawrence. *Makeup* June Gilham.

Cast: Claire Brennen *(Jessie),* Billy Holms *(Fred),* John Dennis *(Monk),* Brad Logan *(Louie),* Maureen Bryce *(Marge, Miss Golden Air Girl),* Doris Gohlke *(Timmy, Miss Germany),* Elaine Jones *(Kathy, Miss Canada),* Margo Woods *(Hilda, Miss Switzerland),* Rhea Walker *(guard),* Nancy Lewis *(Cindy).*

Comedy. Accountant Fred Barf is forced to flee for his life when he insists on filing an honest 1932 income tax return for his first clients, two gangsters. He dives for the rumble seat of the first roadster he sees and finds himself in

the company of a beautiful showgirl and her best friend, headed for the Fat Chance Health and Rejuvenation Resort. Fred's frantic attempts to get out of this stronghold of strictly female nudity are matched only by the inept gangsters' desperate attempts to get in. Before he has extricated himself from his predicament, Fred has fallen in love. Wild chases and misadventures fill the steam room, pool, gym, and sunbathing garden, but in the end the misunderstanding is ironed out to everyone's satisfaction. *Accountants. Gangsters. Showgirls. Nudity. Health resorts. Income tax. Chases.*

Note: Press material credits Monte Mann and Jay Sheridan with direction, while another source lists Sheridan and Monroe Manning. Sequences in 3-D may have been added. Alternative title: *Nude Heat Wave.*

THE TOUCHABLES (Great Britain)   F6.5141

Film Designs. *Dist* Twentieth Century-Fox Film Corp. 20 Nov 1968 [New York opening; c6 Nov 1968; LP36446]. Sd; col (De Luxe). 35mm. 97 min. [Copyright length: 94 min.] *MPAA rating* R.

A John Bryan Production. *Prod* John Bryan. *Assoc Prod* John Oldknow. *Dir-Orig Idea* Robert Freeman. *Screenplay* Ian La Frenais. *Script* David Cammell, Donald Cammell. *Photog* Alan Pudney. *Camera Op* Tony Troke. *Art Dir* Peter Hampton, Richard Rambaut. *Film Ed* Richard Bryan. *Asst Ed* Chris Burt. *Mus Comp & Cond* Ken Thorne. *Titl Song* Stevie Winwood, Jim Capaldi. *Sung by* Nirvana. *Sd Rec* John Brommage, John Aldred. *Dub Ed* Tony Lenny. *Asst Dir* Ted Morley. *Location Mgr* Jake Wright. *Cont* Annabel Davis-Goff. *Cost Adv* Sandy Moss. *Wardrobe Mistress* Klara Kerpen. *Makeup* Jill Carpenter. *Hairdresser* Pearl Tipaldi. *Constr Mgr* Jack Carter, constr. *Ch Electrn* Roy Larner.

Cast: Judy Huxtable *(Sadie),* Esther Anderson *(Melanie),* Marilyn Rickard *(Busbee),* Kathy Simmonds *(Samson),* David Anthony *(Christian),* Ricki Starr *(Ricki),* James Villiers *(Twyning),* John Ronane *(Kasher),* Harry Baird *(Lillywhite),* Michael Chow *(Denzil),* Joan Bakewell *(interviewer),* William Dexter *(Quayle),* Roy Davies *(Glubb),* Danny Lynch *(March),* Bruno Elrington *(Bruno),* Steve Veidor *(Danny),* Peter Gordeno *(Jimmy),* Simon Williams *(Nigel Bent),* Bryan Walsh *(Terry).*

Comedy. Four young mod London women named Sadie, Melanie, Busbee, and Samson, who call themselves the Touchables, decide to kidnap a pop singing idol named Christian. During a charity wrestling match featuring Melanie's wrestler boyfriend, Ricki Starr, the women dress as nuns and whisk Christian off to their pleasure dome, a huge plastic bubble located in the English countryside. The next morning, Christian's manager, Kasher, accuses a homosexual black wrestler-gangster, Lillywhite, of abducting the young singer; Lillywhite, who has fallen for Christian, accuses Kasher of hiding Christian. Meanwhile, at the pleasure dome, which is decorated with a round revolving bed, flashing lights, and pinball machines, Christian enjoys sex games with the Touchables. He tires of the amusement and tries to escape in an inflatable boat across a nearby lake, and Sadie sinks the boat with a rifle shot. Then, while getting supplies in London, Melanie is captured by Lillywhite and forced to lead him and his gang to the pleasure dome. Lillywhite takes the Touchables and their captive prisoner, but Samson escapes to London and tells Ricki of the situation. Rounding up a host of other wrestlers, Ricki invades the dome and rescues the girls and Christian. During the melee, the pleasure dome is deflated, but the undaunted Touchables are quick to realize that they can always inflate it again. *Singers. Wrestlers. Gangsters. Negroes. Abduction. Disguise. Hedonism. Rock and roll. Male homosexuality. Sexuality. London.*

Note: Released in Great Britain in Nov 1969.

TOUCHED BY TEMPTATION *see* **THE SEXPERTS—TOUCHED BY TEMPTATION**

A TOUGH GIG *see* **DIRTYMOUTH**

TOUGH GUY (Japan)   F6.5142

Daiei Motion Picture Co. Jul 1970 [Los Angeles showing]. Sd; col? 35mm. [Feature film, length unknown.]

Cast: Shintaro Katsu, Jiro Tamiya, Tamao Nakamura, Yasuko Nakada, Yoshie Mizutani, Reiko Fujiwara.

Drama. No information about the precise nature of this film has been found.

Note: Original title and release undetermined.

TOWER OF LONDON   F6.5143

Admiral Pictures. *Dist* United Artists. 24 Oct 1962 [Washington, D. C., opening; c24 Oct 1962; LP23207]. Sd; b&w. 35mm. 79 min. [Also 83 min?]

Prod Gene Corman. *Dir* Roger Corman. *Screenplay* Leo V. Gordon, Amos Powell, James B. Gordon. *Story* Leo V. Gordon, Amos Powell. *Photog* Arch R. Dalzell. *Art Dir* Daniel Haller. *Film Ed* Ronald Sinclair. *Mus Comp & Cond* Michael Andersen. *Sd* Phil Mitchell. *Asst Dir* Jack Bohrer. *Prod Mgr* Jack Bohrer. *Dial Dir* Francis Coppola.

Cast: Vincent Price *(Richard of Gloucester),* Michael Pate *(Sir Ratcliffe),* Joan Freeman *(Lady Margaret),* Robert Brown *(Sir Justin),* Justice Watson

(Edward IV), Sarah Selby *(queen)*, Richard McCauly *(Clarence)*, Eugene Martin *(Edward V)*, Sandra Knight *(Mistress Shore)*, Richard Hale *(Tyrus)*, Donald Losby *(Prince Richard)*, Bruce Gordon *(Earl of Buckingham)*, Joan Camden *(Anne)*, Sara Taft *(Richard of Gloucester's mother)*.

Historical melodrama. As King Edward IV of England lies dying, his hunchbacked brother, Richard of Gloucester, plots to do away with all who stand between him and the throne. To protect his two young sons until they are old enough to replace him, Edward appoints his other brother, Clarence, as Protector of the Realm, but Richard murders Clarence with a knife bearing the queen's crest. Now suspicious of his wife, Edward appoints Richard to Clarence's former position, and Richard, with the aid of his henchman Sir Ratcliffe, tries to get the royal nursemaid Mistress Shore to cast doubt on the boys' legitimacy; she prefers dying on the rack, however, to defaming the queen. Meanwhile, the queen has gathered her supporters and been assured by Margaret, her lady-in-waiting, that Scottish armies led by the latter's father, Lord Stanley, will offer military aid against Richard. When Richard sees the bloodied apparition of Mistress Shore, he becomes deranged and murders his wife, Anne. Maddened with fear and haunted by visions, Richard holds Margaret hostage to prevent her father from moving against him, suffocates the two young princes in the Tower of London, and proclaims himself king. Through a ruse, Margaret is released, forcing Richard into battle against Lord Stanley. The Earl of Richmond's army arrives from France to join in combat against Richard at Bosworth, where the ghosts of Richard's victims rise against him; he is thrown by a horse and lands on the battle-ax of a dead soldier, fulfilling prophecies of his violent death. *Royalty. Usurpers. Brothers. English. Scotch. French. Hunchbacks. Hostages. Soldiers. Ambition. Perfidy. Murder. Insanity. Filial relations. Fratricide. Torture. Suffocation. Visions. Ghosts. Great Britain—History—Plantagenets. London. Bosworth (England). Richard III. Edward IV. Tower of London.*

Note: Previously filmed in 1939 by Universal Pictures.

TOWN TAMER   **F6.5144**
A. C. Lyles Productions. *Dist* Paramount Pictures. 7 Jul **1965** [New York opening; c23 Jun 1965; LP31990]. Sd; col (Technicolor). 35mm (Techniscope). 89 min.

Prod A. C. Lyles. *Dir* Lesley Selander. *Screenplay* Frank Gruber. *Cinematog* W. Wallace Kelley. *Art Dir* Hal Pereira, Al Roelofs. *Set Decor* Claude Carpenter. *Film Ed* George Gittens. *Mus* Jimmie Haskell. *Titl Song* Jimmie Haskell, "By" Dunham. *Sung by* The Three D's. *Sd* Hugo Grenzbach. *Asst Dir* Howard Roessel. *Prop* Carl Coleman.

Cast: Dana Andrews *(Tom Rosser)*, Terry Moore *(Susan Tavenner)*, Pat O'Brien *(Judge Murcott)*, Lon Chaney, [Jr.] *(Mayor Leach)*, Bruce Cabot *(Riley Condor)*, Lyle Bettger *(Lee Ring)*, Coleen Gray *(Carol Rosser)*, Barton MacLane *(James Fenimore Fell)*, Richard Arlen *(Dr. Kent)*, Richard Jaeckel *(Honsiner)*, Philip Carey *(Sim Akins)*, DeForest Kelley *(Guy Tavenner)*, Sonny Tufts *(Carmichael)*, Roger Torrey *(Flon)*, James Brown *(Davis)*, Richard Webb *(Kevin)*, Jeanne Cagney *(Mary)*, Donald Barry *(deputy)*, Robert Ivers *(vagrant)*, Bob Steele *(vigilante)*, Dale Van Sickel, Dinny Powell, Frank Gruber.

Western melodrama. Source: Frank Gruber, *Town Tamer* (New York, 1958). Riley Condor, outlaw leader of White Plains, Kansas, hires gunman Lee Ring to kill Tom Rosser, a Kansas lawman of the 1880's. Ring aims poorly and instead kills Rosser's wife, Carol. Two years later, Rosser moves to White Plains under the pretext of buying property but actually intending to wipe out Condor and his gang and thus end their harassment of engineer James Fenimore Fell's railroad workers. By preventing the new railroad from entering town, Condor hopes to keep law and order out of White Plains. Condor appoints Lee Ring and Honsinger, another killer, deputy sheriffs, frames Rosser in an arranged attack, and asks corrupt Judge Murcott to have him arrested. Town leaders Mayor Leach, Dr. Kent, Fell, Davis, and Kevin form a vigilante committee to protect the town. Rosser shields Susan Tavenner from her drunken husband's brutality, and Condor's gang beats him. The vigilantes try to gun down Condor and his gang, but the gang soon surrounds them. Rosser urges the town leaders to back down from their attack and singlehandedly eliminates the desperadoes. Among the dead is Guy Tavenner, and Rosser later marries his widow Susan. *Outlaws. Judges. Sheriffs. Vigilantes. Physicians. Widows. Hired killers. Engineers. Law and order. Murder. Drunkenness. Frameup. Railroads. Kansas.*

TOWN WITHOUT PITY (United States/Switzerland/West Germany)
                                                                 F6.5145
Mirisch Corp.–Gloria–Film–Osweg Ltd. *Dist* United Artists. 10 Oct **1961** [New York opening; c21 Sep 1961; LP21203]. Sd; b&w. 35mm. 105 min.

A Gottfried Reinhardt Production. *Prod-Dir* Gottfried Reinhardt. *Screenplay* Silvia Reinhardt, Georg Hurdalek. *Adapt* Jan Lustig. *Dir Photog* Kurt Hasse. *Sets* Rolf Zehetbauer, Friedhelm Boehm, Werner Achmann. *Film Ed* Walter Boos, Hermann Haller. *Mus* Dimitri Tiomkin. *Titl Song* Dimitri Tiomkin, Ned Washington. *Sung by* Gene Pitney. *Sd* Helmut Ransch, Rolf Schmidt-Gentner, Carl Becker, George Drechsler. *Asst Dir* Eva-Ruth Ebner.

Prod Supv Eberhard Meichsner. *Prod Mgr* Kurt Hartmann. *Cost Dsgn* Lilo Hagen. *Wardrobe* Anton Lanner. *Makeup* Albert Nagel, Irmgard Förster. *Tech Adv* George B. Bronfen.

Cast: Kirk Douglas *(Maj. Steve Garrett)*, E. G. Marshall *(Maj. Jerome Pakenham)*, Christine Kaufmann *(Karin Steinhof)*, Robert Blake *(Jim)*, Richard Jaeckel *(Bidie)*, Frank Sutton *(Chuck)*, Mal Sondock *(Joey)*, Barbara Rütting *(Inge Koerner)*, Hans Nielsen *(Herr Steinhof)*, Karin Hardt *(Frau Steinhof)*, Ingrid van Bergen *(Trude)*, Gerhart Lippert *(Frank Borgmann)*, Eleanore van Hoogstraten *(Frau Borgmann)*, Max Haufler *(Dr. Urban)*, Siegfried Schürenberg *(bürgermeister)*, Rose Renee Roth *(Frau Kulig)*, Alan Gifford *(General Stafford)*, Fred Dürr, Robert Shankland, Joe Valerio, Gerd Vespermann, Gernot Duda, Dean Jackson, Ted Turner, Lynn Randall, Cecilie Gelers, Stefan Schnabel.

Drama. Source: Manfred Gregor, *Das Urteil* (Vienna, 1960). In the small German town of Neustadt, 16-year-old Karin Steinhof is brutally raped by four drunken GI's from the U. S. occupation forces. Outraged, the girl's father and the bürgermeister demand that the military impose the death penalty, a verdict possible only if Karin takes the stand to testify. The defense counsel, Maj. Steve Garrett, warns Karin's father that he will do all in his legal power to save the men's lives, even if it means subjecting Karin to vicious cross-examination and destroying her reputation. Herr Steinhof remains adamant in his determination to have revenge, however, and he insists that Karin testify. At the trial, Garrett uses the testimonies of vindictive witnesses to establish Karin as a tease who enjoyed exposing her naked body. He then calls her to the stand and ruthlessly badgers and taunts the girl with the implication that when the soldiers first saw her she was standing nude in the hope of exciting her boyfriend. Unable to bear the ordeal, Karin collapses before completing her testimony. Since the death penalty cannot now be imposed, the four men receive long prison sentences. As an ashamed Garrett prepares to leave the court, he learns that Karin has committed suicide after being ridiculed by the townspeople. Shunned by his fellow officers and the local citizenry, Garrett packs his briefcase and leaves Neustadt. *Mayors. Lawyers. Smalltown life. Adolescence. Drunkenness. Rape. Filial relations. Capital punishment. Reputation. Courts-martial. Suicide. United States Army.*

Note: Location scenes filmed on the French Riviera and in the German towns of Bamberg and Forcheim. Opened in West Germany in Mar 1961 as *Stadt ohne Mitleid*; running time: 112 min; in Switzerland as *Ville sans pitié*; running time: 109 min. Also known as *Shocker*.

THE TOY GRABBERS *see* **UP YOUR TEDDY BEAR**

TOYS IN THE ATTIC   **F6.5146**
Mirisch Co.–Claude Productions. *Dist* United Artists. 17 Jul **1963** [New Orleans opening; c17 Jun 1963; LP25502]. Sd; b&w. 35mm (Panavision). 90 min.

Prod Walter Mirisch. *Dir* George Roy Hill. *Screenplay* James Poe. *Photog* Joseph Biroc. *Art Dir* Cary Odell. *Set Decor* Victor Gangelin. *Film Ed* Stuart Gilmore, Marshall M. Borden. *Mus* George Duning. *Asst Dir* Emmett Emerson. *Prod Mgr* Allen K. Wood. *Cost* Bill Thomas. *Makeup* Frank Prehoda, Loren Cosand. *Hairstyles* Mary Westmoreland.

Cast: Dean Martin *(Julian Berniers)*, Geraldine Page *(Carrie Berniers)*, Yvette Mimieux *(Lily Prine Berniers)*, Wendy Hiller *(Anna Berniers)*, Gene Tierney *(Albertine Prine)*, Nan Martin *(Charlotte Warkins)*, Larry Gates *(Cyrus Warkins)*, Frank Silvera *(Henry)*, Charles Lampkin *(Gus)*.

Melodrama. Source: Lillian Hellman, *Toys in the Attic* (New York opening: 25 Feb 1960). When shiftless ne'er-do-well Julian Berniers returns with his child-like wife, Lily, to his shabby New Orleans home, he is greeted by his adoring spinster sisters, Carrie and Anna. He confesses that he has lost his shoe factory in Chicago but insists that he is, nevertheless, rich; and he showers them with expensive gifts, including two tickets to Europe. Carrie, possessed by an incestuous love for her brother, is incredulous, while the more skeptical Anna becomes suspicious because Julian refuses to explain the source of his sudden wealth. Furthermore, Lily suspects him of seeing another woman. Lily's wealthy mother, Albertine, and her Negro confidant, Henry, come to visit; and Carrie overhears them discussing a land deal between Julian and Charlotte Warkins, one of his ex-mistresses, in which the two swindled Charlotte's husband. Carrie, resentful of Lily, prods her into telephoning Mr. Warkins and exposing the scheme. As a result, Charlotte and Julian are waylaid by Warkins' hoodlums, beaten up, and robbed of their ill-gotten gains. When a battered and bruised Julian arrives home, he senses Carrie's happiness at his renewed dependence upon her; and realizing that it was Carrie, and not Lily, who betrayed him, he leaves in search of his wife. Anna, knowing that she can no longer live with Carrie, also departs. As the two leave the house, Carrie shouts after them, "You'll come back ... you'll come back." *Spinsters. Sisters. Ne'er-do-wells. Mistresses. Swindlers. Hoodlums. Perfidy. Real estate. Brother-sister relationship. Incest. New Orleans.*

TRACK OF THUNDER F6.5147

Ambassador Films. *Dist* United Artists. 15 Sep **1967** [Nashville, Tennessee, opening]. Sd; col (Technicolor). 35mm (Techniscope). 83 min.

Prod E. Stanley Williamson. *Assoc Prod* Neil E. Jackson, Jr. *Dir* Joe Kane. *Screenplay* Maurice J. Hill. *Photog* Alan Stensvold. *Film Ed* Verna Fields. *Mus Supv* John Caper, Jr. *Prod Mgr* Byron Roberts. *Asst to the Prod* J. Don Fields.

Cast: Tom Kirk *(Bobby Goodwin)*, Ray Stricklyn *(Gary Regal)*, H. M. Wynant *(Maxwell Carstairs)*, Brenda Benet *(Shelley Newman)*, Faith Domergue *(Mrs. Goodwin)*, Majel Barrett *(Georgia Clark)*, Chet Stratton *(Mr. Regal)*, James Dobson *(Bowser Smith)*, Paul Crabtree *(Mr. Bigelow)*, Sam Tarpley *(Colonel Lee)*, Bob Stewart, Chuck Doughty, Maurice Dembsky, Don Gregory, Leslie Jameson, Carol Doughty, Bob Smith, Horace Wood, Ed Livingston.

Action melodrama. Maxwell Carstairs is hired by a syndicate to manage a small stock car racetrack and turn the sport into a lucrative gambling venture. In order to increase attendance at the track, Carstairs and newspaperwoman Georgia Clark invent a feud between Gary Regal and Bobby Goodwin, two drivers who grew up together, and who both love the same girl, Shelley Newman. At first, they ignore the fake newspaper stories, but their rivalry eventually becomes genuine. Despite growing crowds, the syndicate is dissatisfied with the project and applies pressure to Carstairs, who starts embezzling funds. Bobby's mechanic, Bowser Smith, finally reveals the truth about the journalistic lies, despite Carstairs' threat to expose Bowser's involvement in a fatal crash that drove him out of racing. When Bobby refuses to drive Carstairs' car at the International 500, Bowser replaces him only to be killed in a crash. Bobby decides to quit racing and settle down on a farm with Shelley, while Gary goes on to become one of the most successful stock car racers in the country. In addition, Gary's father marries Bobby's mother, and everyone is happy except Carstairs, who has been arrested for embezzlement. *Stock car drivers. Journalists. Mechanics. Automobile racing. Organized crime. Friendship. Marriage. Embezzlement. Gambling.*

Note: Filmed in Nashville, Tennessee.

TRADER HORNEE F6.5148

Trader Film Ventures. *Dist* Entertainment Ventures, Inc. Jan **1970**. Sd; col (Eastman Color). 35mm. 105 min.

Prod David F. Friedman, William Allen Castleman. *Dir* Tsanusdi. *Orig Story-Screenplay* David F. Friedman. *Dir Photog* Paul Hipp. *Camera Op* Henning Schellerup. *Art Dir* Lee Fischer. *Film Ed* Bob Freeman. *Mus Supv* Billy Allen, William Loose. *Choreog* Rene Jensen. *Sd Rec* Sam Kopetsky. *Prod Mgr* Bob Freeman. *Script Supv* Donna Thorne. *Asst to the Prod* Richard Jaloff. *Cost* Lee Fischer. *Makeup* Ron Kinney. *Wild Animals* Gene Holter's Movieland Animals. *Gaffer* Ray Atwood. *Head Grip* Leo Thomas.

Cast: Buddy Pantsari *(Hamilton Hornee)*, Elisabeth Monica *(Jane Sommers)*, John Alderman *(Max Matthews)*, Christine Murray *(Doris Matthews)*, Deek Sills *(Algona)*, Lisa Grant *(Tender Lee)*, Sir Brandon Duffy *(Kenya Adler)*, Fletcher Davies *(Stanley Livingston)*, Neal Henderson *(Mr. Allen)*, Andrew Herbert *(Colin Carruthers-Carstairs)*, Debbie Douglas *(Prentice, as a child)*, Ed Rogers *(witch doctor)*, Ben Cadlett *(Ben)*, Chuck Wells *(warrior)*, The Meshpoka *(themselves)*, Bill Babcock *(barroom tough)*, Dave Friedman *(barroom bum)*.

Comedy. Private Detective Hamilton Hornee ["the e's are silent"] is hired by the Bank of Wabash to find the lost child of explorers who were slain in Africa by natives 15 years earlier. If the child is alive, she will be 21 years old and would inherit her father's multi-million-dollar estate. Hornee leads the expedition to find her, accompanied by his assistant, Jane. Also in the party are Max and Doris Matthews, cousins of the late millionaire who are next in line to inherit the fortune; Tender Lee, a newspaper columnist; and zoologist Stanley Livingston, who is attempting to prove the existence of Nabucco, a great white gorilla. Hornee engages as a guide once-famed hunter and explorer, Kenya Adler, an alcoholic who leads the party into the hands of the Meshpokas, a feared African tribe. The ruler of the Meshpokas is the lost child, Algona, and she receives her inheritance. Livingston's gorilla is in reality an escaped Nazi war criminal dressed in an ape suit. Algona releases the whole party except Hornee, whom she persuades to remain with her in the jungle. *Detectives. Orphans. Heiresses. Columnists. Zoologists. War criminals. Nazis. Africans. Guides. Cousins. Royalty. Inheritance. Disguise. Alcoholism. Jungles. Safaris. Africa. Gorillas.*

Note: Filmed in part in Africa.

TRAGEDIJA SLUŽBENICE P.T.T. see LOVE AFFAIR; OR THE CASE OF THE MISSING SWITCHBOARD OPERATOR

TRAGEDY OF THE AEGEAN SEA see THE AEGEAN TRAGEDY

TRAGODIA TOU AEGAEOU see THE AEGEAN TRAGEDY

THE TRAIL OF STANLEY AND LIVINGSTONE see GREAT EXPLORATIONS WITH JOHN GLENN—AFRICA

TRAIL OF THE HUNTER F6.5149

W. A. B. Motion Picture Productions. *Dist* Northwest Cinema Corp. 14 Jan **1970** [Minneapolis opening; c13 Jan 1970; MP21022]. Sd; col. 35mm. 91 min.

A Bill Bryant–Ned Payne Production. *Story* Bill Bryant. *Photog* Ned Payne, Bill Bryant. *Film Ed* James D. Mitchell, Bill Bryant. *Mus* Buz Fawcett. *Post Prod* Promotional Films.

Featuring: Victor Jory, George Nixon, Ned Payne.

Documentary. After a brief introduction by Victor Jory, several hunters are depicted shooting duck in southern Illinois, their dogs retrieving the fowl. In southern Missouri, George Nixon and his beagles hunt rabbit. Ned Payne deep-sea fishes for dolphin and marlin off Guayaquil, Ecuador, then fishes on the Colorado River. Jaguar, mountain lion, buffalo, sheep, and, in Wyoming, antelope, mule deer, and elk, are pursued. As Victor Jory fishes in California, his campsite is attacked by a black bear, which is killed by hunters. Wildlife conservation and the balance of nature are discussed. *Hunting. Fishing. Wildlife—Conservation. Illinois. Missouri. Ecuador. Colorado River. Wyoming. California. Ducks. Dogs. Rabbits and hares. Dolphin (fish). Marlin. Jaguars. Cougars. Buffalo. Sheep. Antelope. Deer. Bears.*

THE TRAIN (United States/France/Italy) F6.5150

Les Productions Artistes Associés–Ariane–Dear Film. *Dist* United Artists. 17 Mar **1965** [New York opening; c25 Sep 1964; LP30325]. Sd; b&w. 35mm. 133 min.

Prod Jules Bricken. *Assoc Prod* Bernard Farrel. *Dir (see note)* John Frankenheimer, Arthur Penn. *Screenplay* Franklin Coen, Frank Davis, Walter Bernstein. *Story* Franklin Coen, Frank Davis. *French Vers* Albert Husson. *Photog* Jean Tournier, Walter Wottitz. *Prod Dsgn* Willy Holt. *Asst Prod Dsgn* Marc Frédérix, Roger Volper. *Film Ed* David Bretherton, Gabriel Rongier. *Mus Comp & Cond* Maurice Jarre. *Sd Rec* Joseph de Bretagne. *Re-rec* Jacques Carrère, Jacques Maumont. *Prod Mgr* Robert Vélin. *Wardrobe* Jean Zay. *Makeup* Georges Bauban. *Optical Eff* Jean Fouchet. *Sp Eff* Lee Zavitz.

Cast: Burt Lancaster *(Labiche)*, Paul Scofield *(Colonel von Waldheim)*, Jeanne Moreau *(Christine)*, Michel Simon *(Papa Boule)*, Suzanne Flon *(Miss Villard)*, Wolfgang Preiss *(Herren)*, Richard Munch *(von Lubitz)*, Albert Rémy *(Didont)*, Charles Millot *(Pesquet)*, Jacques Marin *(Jacques)*, Paul Bonifas *(Spinet)*, Jean Bouchaud *(Schmidt)*, Donald O'Brien *(Schwartz)*, Jean-Pierre Zola *(Octave)*, Art Brauss *(Pilzer)*, Jean-Claude Bercq *(major)*, Howard Vernon *(Dietrich)*, Bernard La Jarrige *(Bernard)*, Louis Falavigna *(railroad worker)*, Daniel Lecourtois *(priest)*, Richard Bailey *(Grote)*, Christian Fuin *(Robert)*, Helmo Kindermann *(ordnance officer)*, Roger Lumont *(engineer officer)*, Gérard Buhr *(corporal)*, Christian Rémy *(Tauber)*, Max From *(Gestapo officer)*, Jean-Jacques Lecomte *(lieutenant of retreating convoy)*, Jacques Blot *(Hubert)*, Wolfgang Saure, Victor Beaumont.

War drama. Derived from: Rose Valland, *Le front de l'art; défense des collections françaises 1939–1945* (Paris, 1961). As Allied forces approach German-occupied Paris in the summer of 1944, a Wehrmacht officer, Col. Franz von Waldheim, receives orders from Göring to assemble the art treasures of the Jeu de Paume Museum and transport them to Germany. Mademoiselle Villard, curator of the museum, informs the Resistance of the plan and tries to persuade Labiche, area inspector of French railways, to intercept the priceless cargo. Labiche, however, is more concerned with saving lives than in preserving art, and he devotes his energies to sabotaging an armaments train. While Allied bombs are destroying the munitions, Papa Boule, an old railwayman, succeeds in burning out the engines of the train bearing the art treasures but pays for his act with his life. The enraged von Waldheim places Labiche in charge of moving the art train out of Paris. Labiche, now won over to the side of the Resistance mainly through the influence of a widowed hotelkeeper, Christine, arranges a complicated series of stratagems that lead the Nazis to believe the train has passed into Germany while, in reality, it has merely been shuttled around Paris and returned to its original depot. Upon discovering the deception, von Waldheim places French hostages on the train and orders it moved. As Labiche once more intervenes by having it derailed, von Waldheim has the hostages shot; but his own men panic and join the retreating Wehrmacht. Left alone, the two equally obsessed men face each other. Labiche kills von Waldheim and walks slowly away, leaving scattered paintings on the tracks. *Railroad workers. Nazis. Widows. Hotelkeepers. Hostages. Curators. War crimes. Art. Sabotage. Trains. World War II. France—History—German occupation 1940–45. Paris. Gestapo. Germany—Army. Maquis. Jeu de Paume (Paris). Train wrecks.*

Note: Opened in Paris in Sep 1964 as *Le train*; running time: 140 min; in Italy in 1965 as *Il treno*. Penn, the original director, was replaced by Frankenheimer, who receives sole screen credit.

LE TRAIN see **THE TRAIN**

LE TRAIN DE BERLIN EST ARRÊTÉ see **STOP TRAIN 349**

THE TRAIN GOES TO KIEV see **AGE OF YOUTH**

TRAIN ROBBERY CONFIDENTIAL (Brazil)   F6.5151
Produções Cinematográficas Herbert Richers. *Dist* Times Film Corp. Jun **1965**. Sd; b&w. 35mm. 105 min.
Prod Roberto Farias, Herbert Richers. *Dir* Roberto Farias. *Screenplay* Roberto Farias, Luiz Carlos Barreto. *Screenplay Collab* Alinor Azevedo. *Photog* Amleto Daissè. *Art Dir* Alexandre Horvath, Pierino Massenzi. *Film Ed* Rafael Justo. *Mus* Remo Usai. *Prod Mgr* Riva Faria.
Cast: Eliezer Gomes (*Tiao Medonho*), Reginaldo Faria (*Grilo Peru*), Grande Otelo (*Cachaça*), Átila Iório (*Tonho*), Miguel Rosemberg (*Edgar*), Kelé (*Lino*), Helena Ignez (*Marta*), Luíza Maranhão (*Zulmira*), Ruth de Souza (*Judith*), Dirce Migliaccio (*Edgar's wife*), Jorge Dória (*Delegado*), Miguel Ângelo (*Miguel Gordinho*), A. Fregolente, Oswaldo Louzada, Wilson Grey, Mozael Silveira.
Crime drama. Six armed men, led by Tiao Medonho and Grilo Peru, dynamite a pay train on the Central Brazil Railway, killing several people and escaping with over 27 million cruzeiros. To avoid suspicion, the men agree to spend less than 10% of their shares. While the police slowly uncover the robbers' identities, Tiao's sudden wealth makes him conspicuous amidst his modest Rio de Janeiro surroundings. Grilo, who develops a penchant for expensive living in Copacabana, is killed by Tiao for squandering his money. The other robbers generally abide by the gang's pact, but as the police begin to close in, the men become nervous. After Tiao is fatally wounded while running away from the police, his wife relinquishes the stolen money and then returns to her children and their life of poverty. *Robbers. Police. Train robberies. Murder. Wealth. Slums. Brazil. Copacabana (Brazil). Rio de Janeiro. Tião Medonho. Grilo Peru. Central do Brazil. Explosions.*
Note: Filmed on location in Brazil in 1962. Brazilian titles: *Assalto ao trem pagador* and *Tião Medonho*.

LA TRAITE DES BLANCHES see **FRUSTRATIONS**

THE TRAITORS (Great Britain)   F6.5152
Ello Productions. *Dist* Universal Pictures. 15 May **1963** [Boston opening; c7 Sep 1963; LP35478]. Sd (Westrex); b&w. 35mm. 71 min.
Prod-Writ Jim O'Connolly. *Dir* Robert Tronson. *Based on the Idea by* J. Levy, J. P. O'Connolly. *Lighting Camera* Michael Reed. *Camera Op* James Bawden. *Art Dir* Bert Davey. *Film Ed* Peter Boita. *Mus Comp & Cond* Johnny Douglas. *Sd Mix* Dudley Messenger. *Dub Ed* Stan Fiferman. *Dub Mix* Gordon McCallum. *Asst Dir* John Peverall. *Prod Mgr* Basil Appleby. *Cont* Gladys Goldsmith. *Prod Sec* Beti Parry. *Makeup* Geoffrey Rodway.
Cast: Patrick Allen (*John Lane*), Jacqueline Ellis (*Mary*), James Maxwell (*Ray Ellis*), Zena Walker (*Annette Lane*), Ewan Roberts (*Colonel Burlinson*), Jeffrey Segal (*Dr. Lindt*), Anne Padwick (*Mrs. Lindt*), Harold Goodwin (*Edwards*), John Brown, British (*Mason*), Sean Lynch (*Porter*), Jack May (*Burton*), Mark Singleton (*Venner*), A. J. Brown, Reed De Rouen, Michael Corcoran, Robert Raglan, Henry De Bray, Frank Wilson Taylor, Victor Platt, Anton Rodgers, Sheldon Lawrence, Fanny Carby, Arthur Barclay, Mike Martin.
Melodrama. A roll of top secret British microfilm is found in the wreckage of a civilian airliner near Munich; Major Ellis of NATO security and investigator John Lane are assigned to the case. Suspicion falls on Burton, a scientist, but he is killed in a London cinema by his contact, who turns out to be a foreign surgeon, Dr. Lindt. Mrs. Lindt is seen in a park meeting Venner, another member of the Communist cell who holds a high position in the Foreign Office; and Venner is then fed false information, which he passes to Lindt. In turn, Lindt gives the information to Porter, a man he meets at a swimming pool. Lane and Ellis close in and, after a fight, arrest both Porter and Lindt. *Secret agents. Scientists. Surgeons. Communists. Espionage. Murder. Motion picture theaters. Microfilm. Munich. London. North Atlantic Treaty Organization. Airplane accidents.*
Note: Opened in London in Aug 1962; running time: 69 min.

TRAITOR'S GATE (Great Britain/West Germany)   F6.5153
Summit Film Productions–Rialto Film. *Dist* Columbia Pictures. Mar **1966** [c31 Dec 1966; LP34062]. Sd (RCA); b&w. 35mm. 80 min.
Prod Ted Lloyd. *Exec Prod* Preben Philipsen, E. M. Smedley-Aston. *Dir* Freddie Francis. *Screenplay* John Sansom. *Photog* Denys Coop. *Camera Op* Ron Taylor. *Art Dir* Tony Inglis. *Film Ed* Oswald Hafenrichter. *Mus* Peter Thomas. *Sd Rec* Bill Bulkley. *Sd Ed* John S. Smith. *Asst Dir* Claud Hudson. *Prod Mgr* Ted Wallis, Wolfgang Kühnlenz. *Cont* Ann Besserman. *Wardrobe* Jean Fairlie. *Makeup* Jill Carpenter. *Hairdresser* Henry Montsash.
Cast: Albert Lieven (*Trayne*), Gary Raymond (*Graham/Lieut. Dick Lee-Carnaby*), Margot Trooger (*Dinah Pauling*), Catherina von Schell (*Hope Joyner*), Eddi Arent (*Hector*), Klaus Kinski (*Kinski*), Anthony James (*John*), Tim Barrett (*Lloyd*), Heinz Bernard (*Martin*), Dave Birks (*Spider*), Edward Underdown (*Inspector Gray*), Alec Ross (*Sergeant Carter*), Julie Mendez (*stripper*), Peter Porteous (*Kelly*), Katy Wild (*Mary*), Harry Baird (*mate on tramp steamer*), Joe Ritchie (*news vendor*), Frank Sieman (*yeoman warden guide*), Frank Forsyth (*chief yeoman warden*), Caron Gardner (*blonde*), Maurice Good (*King*), Robert Hunter, actor (*captain*), Marianne Stone (*cashier at Dandy Club*), Hedger Wallace (*Detective Sergeant Alexander*), Beresford Williams (*warden*).
Crime drama. Source: Edgar Wallace, *The Traitor's Gate* (London, 1927). A London businessman plans to steal the crown jewels from the Tower of London by abducting the watchman in charge and replacing him with an escaped convict who is his double. The plot works smoothly, including the businessman's planned double-cross of the convict, whom he sends with a set of fake jewels to a freighter which has a bomb set to explode before it reaches Amsterdam. The businessman's secretary alerts the police, however, and the plot is thwarted when the businessman is arrested, the convict is shot, and the Tower guard regains possession of the real gems. *Businessmen. Prison escapees. Doubles. Watchmen. Secretaries. Abduction. Impersonation. Perfidy. Bombs. London. Tower of London. Crown jewels (Great Britain).*
Note: Released in Great Britain in Jul 1965; in West Germany in Dec 1964 as *Das Verrätertor*.

THE TRAMPLERS (Italy)   F6.5154
Anna Maria Chrétien–Alvaro Mancori. *Dist* Embassy Pictures. Jul **1966**. Sd; col (Eastmancolor, print by Pathé). 35mm. 105 min.
Pres by Joseph E. Levine. *Prod* Alvaro Mancori, Albert Band. *Dir* Albert Band, Anthony Wileys. *Screenplay* Ugo Liberatore, Albert Band. *Photog* Alvaro Mancori. *2d Unit Photog* Silvano Ippoliti. *Art Dir* Peppino Ranieri. *Set Decor* Camillo Del Signore. *Film Ed* Maurizio Lucidi. *Mus* Angelo Francesco Lavagnino. *Sd* Fiorenzo Magli. *Asst Dir* Franco Prosperi, François Dupont-Midy. *Prod Mgr* Luigi Manini. *Cost* Sergio Selli. *Dial Coach* Anna Korda.
Cast: Joseph Cotten (*Temple Cordeen*), Gordon Scott (*Lon Cordeen*), James Mitchum (*Hoby Cordeen*), Ilaria Occhini (*Edith Wickett*), Franco Nero (*Charley Garvey*), Emma Vannoni (*Bess Cordeen*), Georges Lycan (*Longfellow Wiley*), Muriel Franklin (*Alice Cordeen*), Aldo Cecconi (*Jim Hennessy*), Franco Balducci (*Pete Wiley*), Claudio Gora (*Fred Wickett*), Romano Puppo (*Paine Cordeen*), Dario Michaelis (*Bert Cordeen*), Ivan Scratuglia (*Adrian Cordeen*), Carla Calò (*Mrs. Temple Cordeen*), Dino Desmond (*sheriff*), Silla Bettini (*Hogan*), Edith Peters (*Emma*), Emil Jordan, Giovanni Cianfriglia, Virgilio Ponti.
Western melodrama. Source: Will Cook, *Guns of North Texas* (New York, 1958). In Texas after the Civil War, ex-Confederate general Temple Cordeen refuses to accept the defeat of the South and organizes his own private army to keep Yankees out of his cattle empire. Unable to sanction their father's tyrannical rule, two of his sons, Lon and Hoby, aid their sister Bess in eloping with Charley Garvey and setting up a rival ranch outside of Cordeen territory. As a result of Temple's violent retaliatory measures, his wife dies from shock. Further violence occurs when Lon falls in love with Edith Wickett, the daughter of a Yankee lynched by Temple. During the final gun battle, Hoby shoots down three of his brothers before being killed himself. The senseless slaughter unhinges Temple's mind, and the feud ends. Lon and Edith take the old man back to the family ranch and make plans for a better future. *Confederate veterans. Ranchers. Family life. Feuds. Revenge. Elopement. Lynching. Marriage. Fratricide. United States—History—Reconstruction. Texas. Cattle.*
Note: Location scenes filmed in Italy and Spain. Opened in Rome in Apr 1966 as *Gli uomini dal passo pesante*; running time: 110 min. Anthony Wileys is a pseudonym for Mario Sequi.

UN TRANQUILLO POSTO DI CAMPAGNA see **A QUIET PLACE IN THE COUNTRY**

TRANS-EUROP-EXPRESS (France)   F6.5155
Como Films. *Dist* Trans American Films. 12 May **1968** [New York opening]. Sd; b&w. 35mm. 105 min. [Also reviewed at 87 min and 100 min.]
Prod Samy Halfon. *Dir-Writ* Alain Robbe-Grillet. *Photog* Willy Kurant. *Film Ed* Bob Wade. *Song Comp & Sung by* Clo Vanesco. *Mus Selections* Giuseppe Verdi. *Sd Engr* Raymond St. Martin. *Sd Ed* Michel Fano. *Asst to the Dir* Claude Him. Jean-Marie De Coninck. *Prod Mgr* Maurice Urbain. *Hairstyles* Jean-Louis Saint-Roch. *English Titl* Noelle Gillmor.
Cast: Jean-Louis Trintignant (*Elias/himself*), Marie-France Pisier (*Eva*), Charles Millot (*Franck*), Christian Barbier (*Lorentz*), Nadine Verdier (*hotel maid*), Clo Vanesco (*cabaret singer*), Daniel Emilfork (*false policeman*), Henri Lambert (*inspector*), Alain Robbe-Grillet (*Jean, the director*), Catherine Robbe-Grillet (*Lucette*), Gérard Palaprat (*le petit Mathieu*), Samy Halfon, Paul Louyet (*Marc [see note]*), Virginie Vignon (*suitcase salesgirl*), Salkin, Ariane Sapriel, Rezy Norbert, Raoul Guylad, Prima Symphony.

Drama. A film director, Jean, his producer, Marc, and his assistant, Lucette, board the Trans-Europ-Express in Paris bound for Antwerp. Once in their compartment it occurs to them that the drama of life aboard the train presents possibilities for a film, and they begin to write a script about dope smuggling. Subsequently, they see actor Jean-Louis Trintignant walking through the station. As seen through the eyes of Jean, Marc, and Lucette, Trintignant becomes Elias, the chief character in the script. Elias is going to Antwerp to pick up a suitcase of cocaine for delivery to an international organization based in Paris. As Trintignant acts out their labyrinthine plot, Jean and the others frequently change their minds, re-shooting, parodying, or eliminating entire sequences. Through it all Elias is confused both by the double-dealing of his syndicate compatriots and by the incompetent plotting of his creators, and he seeks release in sadomasochistic rape fantasies with Eva, an Antwerp prostitute planted by the organization. After delivering the suitcase to Paris, Elias learns that the mission was only a trial, designed to test his efficiency and loyalty to the organization. His second assignment is genuine, however, and Elias soon realizes that he is being followed by Lorentz, a Belgian policeman. Entangled in a network of disguises and suspicions, he learns that Eva is working for the police, and he strangles her in earnest in one of their sadomasochistic rituals. Aware of Elias' perverse inclinations, the police follow him to a cabaret featuring a nude-in-chains act. But the syndicate chief, Franck, is also there, and he kills Elias before the police can get to him. Their imagined screenplay completed, Jean, Marc, and Lucette disembark at Antwerp. They read a newspaper account of a real crime that closely resembles their story, and they decide to abandon the project. Leaving the train, Jean-Louis Trintignant is met and embraced by a girl who looks very much like Eva. *Actors. Motion picture directors. Motion picture producers. Police. Prostitutes. Belgians. Motion pictures. Smuggling. Murder. Sadomasochism. Rape. Disguise. Syndicates. Trains. Cabarets. Cocaine. Paris. Antwerp. Trans-Europ-Express. Fantasy.*

Note: Opened in Paris in Jan 1967; running time: 90 min. Sources conflict in crediting the role of Marc.

TRANSPORT FROM PARADISE (Czechoslovakia)　F6.5156

Barrandov Film Studio. *For* Československý Film. *Dist* Impact Films. 7 Feb **1967** [New York opening]. Sd; b&w. 35mm. 94 min.

Dir Zbyněk Brynych. *Screenplay* Arnošt Lustig, Zbyněk Brynych. *Photog* Jan Čuřík. *Asst Photog* František Uldrich, Jiří Pospíšil. *Art Dir* Karel Škvor. *Asst Art Dir* Jaroslav Brabenec. *Film Ed* Miroslav Hájek. *Asst Film Ed* Jitka Šulcová. *Mus* Jiří Sternwald. *Sd* Miloš Alster. *1st & 2d Asst Dir* Jiří Hartman, Juraj Herz. *Prod Supv* Jiří Pokorný. *Prod Mgr* Jaroslav Jaroš, Ludmila Venclíková, Jaroslav Solnička. *Sp Adv* Rudolf Iltis, Arnošt Lustig. *Film Unit* Šebor-Bor.

Cast: Zdeněk Štěpánek (*Löwenbach*), Čestmír Řanda (*Marmulstaub*), Ilja Prachař (*Mořic Herz*), Jaroslav Raušer (*von Holler*), Jiří Vršťala (*Binde*), Ladislav Pešek (*Roubíček*), Valtr Taub (*Spiegel*), Vlastimil Brodský (*Mukl*), Josef Abrhám (*Datel*), Josef Vinklář (*Vágus*), Jaroslav Rozsíval (*a smith*), Václav Lohniský (*man at the smithy*), Jiřina Štěpničková (*Feinerova*), Martin Gregor (*Geron*), Jindřich Narenta (*General Knecht*), Jiří Němeček (*Vlastimil Fiala*), František Němec (*Dany*), Helga Čočková (*Líza*), Vladimír Hrabánek (*Zrzek*), Juraj Herz (*mylord*), Vladimír Linka, Emanuel Kovařík, Václav Vondráček, Vladimír Navrátil, Štefan Bulejko, Zdeněk Braunschläger, Rudolf Cortéz, Zdeněk Jelínek (*SS men*), František Löring (*Dutch-speaking man*), Marta Richterová (*Anna*), Jan Šmíd (*Štěpán*), Ladislav Potměšil (*Kůzle*), Miroslav Svoboda (*Mayer*), Zlatomír Vacek, Fred Bulín, Anny Frey, Maurice Orion.

Drama. Source: Arnošt Lustig, *Noc a naděje* (Prague, 1957). During World War II, the Nazis set up a Jewish concentration camp in Terezín, a ghetto in southeast Germany. There are no gas chambers in the compound, and the prisoners handle their own administration and run small businesses. Underneath the comparative serenity, however, is the ever-present struggle of the oppressed; anti-fascist posters are secretly printed and pasted on the walls, and the chairman of the Council of Jewish Elders refuses to sign a list of Jews scheduled for transport because he knows that they are destined for Auschwitz. Consequently, the chairman is put in prison, and the Germans find a more cooperative successor. After the capture of a rebellious smithy worker, the final preparations for the transport are concluded. Hundreds of prisoners are herded together and lined up at a railroad siding. Still unaware that their stay at the camp was merely a waiting period before being sent to the gas chambers, they save places for their loved ones and remain in formation until they are placed aboard the train—bound for Auschwitz. *Jews. Nazis. Genocide. Concentration camps. Trains. World War II. Terezín. Auschwitz. SS.*

Note: Location scenes filmed in Terezín. Released in Czechoslovakia in Mar 1963 as *Transport z ráje*; running time: 100 min.

TRANSPORT Z RÁJE see TRANSPORT FROM PARADISE

THE TRAP (Canada/Great Britain)　F6.5157

Parallel Productions. *Dist* Continental Distributing, Inc. Jul **1967**. Sd; col (Eastmancolor). 35mm (Panavision). 106 min.

Prod George H. Brown. *Assoc Prod* Jan Darnley-Smith. *Dir* Sidney Hayers. *2d Unit Dir* Tristam Cones, Stanley Clish. *Screenplay–Orig Story* David Osborn. *Photog* Robert Krasker. *2d Unit Photog* O. H. Borradaile, Bill Roozeboom. *Art Dir* Harry White. *Film Ed* Tristam Cones. *Mus Comp & Cond* Ron Goodwin. *Sd Supv* Howard Tremaine. *Sd Rec* Anthony Wolf, Ken Cameron, George New. *Asst Dir* David Tringham. *Prod Mgr* Basil Keys, L. C. Rudkin. *Canadian Prod Mgr* Barrie McLean. *Cost* Margaret Furse.

Cast: Rita Tushingham (*Eve*), Oliver Reed (*Jean La Bête*), Rex Sevenoaks (*The Trader*), Barbara Chilcott (*trader's wife*), Linda Goranson (*trader's daughter*), Blain Fairman (*clerk*), Walter Marsh (*preacher*), Jo Golland (*Baptiste*), Jon Granik (*No Name*), Merv Campone (*Yellow Dog*), Reginald McReynolds (*captain*).

Adventure drama. To a pioneer settlement, in 19th-century British Columbia, Jean La Bête, after 3 years of trapping, returns with a rich haul of fur. Eager to find a wife, he is too late for the once-a-year auction of castoff women offered to settlers for cash. In exchange for money owed him by the settlement trader, however, La Bête takes the trader's mute, orphaned housekeeper, Eve, for his wife; and they proceed by canoe northward to his cabin. Eve serves him well, tends to him after his leg has been crushed in one of his traps, but cannot reconcile herself to life with La Bête or the primitive backwoods. After Eve has been forced to amputate La Bête's gangrenous leg, he awakes one morning, discovers her gone, and suddenly, he realizes his emotional dependence on the mute woman. Returning to the settlement after being rescued from rapids by Indians, Eve agrees to marry the trader's clerk. But on the wedding day she is not to be found: she has gone back to La Bête. *Trappers. Orphans. Mutes. Fur traders. Indians of North America. Frontier and pioneer life. Amputation. Marriage. British Columbia.*

Note: Location scenes filmed in British Columbia. Released in Great Britain in Sep 1966. French Canadian title: *L'aventure sauvage.*

DIE TRAPP-FAMILIE see THE TRAPP FAMILY

DIE TRAPP-FAMILIE IN AMERIKA see THE TRAPP FAMILY

THE TRAPP FAMILY (West Germany)　F6.5158

Divina Film. *Dist* Twentieth Century–Fox Film Corp. 22 Mar **1961** [Los Angeles opening; c1 Mar 1961; LP20322]. Sd; col (DeLuxe Color). 35mm. 106 min. [Copyright length: 97 min.]

Overall Production Credits: *Prod* Wolfgang Reinhardt, Utz Utermann. *Dir* Wolfgang Liebeneiner. *Screenplay:* "Die Trapp-familie" Georg Hurdalek. *Screenplay:* "Die Trapp-familie in Amerika" Herbert Reinecker. *Dir Photog* Werner Krien. *Camera* Gerhard Krüger. *Sets* Robert Herlth, Gottfried Will. *Film Ed* Margot von Schlieffen. *Mus* Franz Grothe. *Choir Dir* Rudolf Lamy. *Orch* Kurt Graunke. *Sd:* "Die Trapp-familie" Hans Endrulat. *Sd:* "Die Trapp-familie in Amerika" Martin Müller. *Asst Dir* Zlata Mehlers. *Dir Prod* Heinz Abel. *Prod Mgr* Kurt Paetz, Laci Martin, Herbert Junghans. *Cost* Brigitte Scholz. *Makeup* Charlotte Schmidt-Kersten, Franz Mayrhofer.

Production Credits for U. S. Vers: *Dir-Scen* Lee Kresel. *Film Ed* Salvatore Billitteri. *Sd* Robert Sherwood. *Prod Supv* Sid Samuels.

Cast—U. S. Vers: Ruth Leuwerik (*Maria von Trapp*), Hans Holt (*Baron von Trapp*), Josef Meinrad (*Dr. Wassner*), Maria Holst (*countess*), Friedrich Domin (*Gruber*), Hilde von Stolz (*Baroness Mathilde*), Michael Ande, Ursula Wolff, Angelika Werth, Knut Mahlke, Monika Wolf, Ursula Ettrich, Monika Ettrich (*children*), A. D. Edel.

Additional Cast—"Die Trapp-familie": Agnes Windeck, Liesl Karlstadt, Alfred Balthoff, Hans Schumm, Gretl Theimer, Karl Ehmann, Franz Muxeneder und die Kinder.

Additional Cast—"Die Trapp-familie in Amerika": Wolfgang Wahl, Adrienne Gessner, Peter Esser, Holger Hagen, Betty Jackson, Emiljosef Hunek, Till Klockow, Benton C. Lombard, Phyl Senter, Mildred Clinton, Frank Holms, Emory Richardson, Gerald Metcalfe.

Biographical comedy-drama. Source: Maria Augusta Trapp, *The Story of the Trapp Family Singers* (Philadelphia, 1949). In the 1930's, Maria, a high-spirited novice in an Austrian convent, is sent to the ancestral home of the widowed Baron von Trapp to care for his seven children. Appalled by the stern discipline the baron enforces, Maria teaches the children games and encourages them to lead the happy life of normal youngsters. Maria's violation of his orders so angers the baron that he decides to discharge her; but when he hears his children singing songs taught them by Maria, he has a change of heart. As time passes, the baron falls deeply in love with the young woman, and he asks her to become his wife. Maria returns to her convent, obtains permission from her mother superior to renounce her vows, and becomes the Baroness von Trapp. Encouraged by a neighborhood priest, Dr. Wassner, Maria and the children begin singing for charity, and before long they have a huge following. Soon after the Nazi annexation of Austria, the baron is dispossessed of his fortune, and he and his family emigrate to the United States. Their music attracts little attention at first, and disappointment follows disappointment, but critical acclaim and large audiences eventually come. Encouraged, they buy a farm in Vermont and decide to remain in their adopted country. *Novices. Governesses. Nobility. Children. Widowers. Singers. Priests. Immigrants. Nazis. Farmers. Family life. Charity. Convents. Austria. Vermont. Trapp Family Singers.*

Note: The film is a compilation of two West German features: *Die Trapp-Familie*, released in West Germany in 1956; running time: 103 min; and *Die Trapp-Familie in Amerika*, released in West Germany in Oct 1958; running time: 105 min.

LA TRAPPOLA SI CHIUDE *see* **ANY MAN'S WOMAN**

TRAQUENARDS *see* **ÉROTIQUE**

TRASH   F6.5159

Factory Films–Score Productions. *Dist* Cinema V Distributing, Inc. 5 Oct 1970 [New York opening; c5 Oct 1970; LP39043]. Sd; col. 35mm. 103 min. [Copyright length: 90min.] *MPAA rating* X.

Pres by Andy Warhol. *Prod* Andy Warhol. *Dir-Writ* Paul Morrissey. *Photog* Paul Morrissey. *Film Ed* Jed Johnson. *Song:* "Mama Look at Me Now" Joe Saggarino. *Sd* Jed Johnson.

Cast: Joe Dallesandro (*Joe*), Holly Woodlawn (*Holly*), Jane Forth (*Jane*), Michael Sklar (*welfare investigator*), Geri Miller (*go-go dancer*), Andrea Feldman (*rich girl*), Johnny Putnam (*boy from Yonkers*), Bruce Pecheur (*Jane's husband*), Diane Podlewski (*Holly's sister*), Bob Dallesandro (*boy on street*).

Comedy-drama. Joe, whose drug habit has made him impotent, has an encounter with a go-go dancer in which her attempts to arouse him end in failure, and he returns to the dirty, rundown Lower East Side apartment he shares with his sometime lover Holly, a transvestite who scavenges the city's streets for articles of value. On the street Joe is approached by Andrea, a wealthy dropout who is anxious to buy some LSD. She offers him $20; he takes it, buys some heroin, goes to Andrea's apartment to inject it, and again fails to function sexually. Joe returns to his apartment in time to greet Holly, who has brought home a high school student in search of "soft" drugs. Holly gives the boy a shot in his buttocks. Joe breaks into newlywed Jane's apartment in a wealthy section of the city and is told there is nothing to steal. Thrilled with the possibility of being raped by a junkie burglar, Jane gives him a bath and passes him off as an old school chum when her husband unexpectedly arrives home. Joe demonstrates to the couple his method of injecting heroin; he overdoses himself, passes out, and is thrown naked into the street by the husband. Joe returns home and is told by Holly that he must kick his drug habit because his pregnant sister is coming to live with them. Once more unable to make love, Joe falls asleep, and Holly sexually satisfies herself with the neck of a bottle. The next day Holly's pregnant sister arrives, but the stay is curtailed when Holly finds her and Joe naked together. She throws her sister out and tries to evict Joe, but he apologizes, promising to stop using drugs. Later a welfare investigator visits Holly, who, inspired by her sister's visit, stuffs a pillow under her sweater and pretends to be pregnant. Holly's silver shoes catch the investigator's fancy, and he offers to put the couple on the welfare roll in exchange for the shoes. Holly refuses; a violent argument ensues; and Holly's deception is revealed. The investigator runs out, and the couple are left alone to their own devices. *Drug addicts. Go-go dancers. Drug dealers. Students. Newlyweds. Sisters. Social workers. Impotence. Poverty. Transvestism. Autoeroticism. Pregnancy. Bribery. Fraud. Heroin. Slums. LSD. Public welfare. New York City—Lower East Side.*

Note: Filmed in New York City. Shot in 16mm. Copyright book credits Score Movies as production company and copyright claimant.

LA TRATTA DELLE BIANCHE *see* **FRUSTRATIONS**

TRAUMA   F6.5160

Artist XVI Productions. *Dist* Parade Pictures. 23 May 1962 [San Diego, California, opening]. Sd, b&w. 35mm. 93 min.

Prod Joseph Cranston. *Assoc Prod* Jean Ollevetti, Salvatore Mungo. *Dir-Screen Story-Screenplay* Robert Malcolm Young. *Photog* Jacques Marquette. *Film Ed* Harold J. Dennis. *Mus Comp & Cond* Buddy Collette. *Sd* Robert Post, Gene Ashbrook. *Asst Dir* Willis Osborn. *Paintings* Laura Wallace.

Cast: John Conte (*Warren Clyner*), Lynn Bari (*Helen Garrison*), Lorrie Richards (*Emmaline Garrison*), David Garner (*Craig Schoonover*), Warren Kemmerling (*Luther*), William Bissell (*Thaddeus Hall*), Bond Blackman (*Robert*), William Justine, Roy Lennert (*treasury agents*), Renee Mason (*Carla*), Robert Totten (*gas station attendant*), Alfred Chafe (*police officer*), Ruby Borner (*maid*).

Melodrama. Having witnessed her Aunt Helen's murder in the family swimming pool 6 years earlier, 21-year-old Emmaline Garrison returns home,

the amnesiac bride of Warren Clyner, her aunt's former beau. There she encounters Luther, the caretaker, and his nephew, Craig, to whom she is attracted. Together Craig and Emmaline explore the mansion. While so doing, Emmaline's memory is restored, and she recalls Everett, the mentally retarded son of Aunt Helen. Meanwhile, Warren is arrested for fraud by U. S. Treasury agents. Startled by Craig while attempting to drown Emmaline in the pool, Luther suffers a heart attack. Before expiring, he reveals that he had murdered Everett, his own homicidal son, and then killed Helen, his paramour, to insure her silence. *Aunts. Caretakers. Uncles. United States—Treasury Department. Murder. Amnesia. Mental retardation. Fraud. Memory. Swimming pools.*

Note: Location scenes filmed in Los Feliz, California.

THE TRAVELING EXECUTIONER   F6.5161

Solitaire Productions. *Dist* Metro-Goldwyn-Mayer, Inc. 1 Oct 1970 [Montgomery, Alabama, opening; c16 Oct 1970; LP38520]. Sd; col (Metrocolor). 35mm (Panavision). 95 min. *MPAA rating* R.

A Jack Smight Production. *Prod-Dir* Jack Smight. *Screenplay* Garrie Bateson. *Dir Photog* Philip Lathrop. *Camera Op* Duke Callaghan. *Asst Camera* Cliff King. *Art Dir* George W. Davis, Edward Carfagno. *Set Decor* Robert R. Benton, Keogh Gleason. *Film Ed* Neil Travis. *Asst Ed* Michael Stevenson, ed. *Mus* Jerry Goldsmith. *Sd* Jerry Jost, Hal Watkins. *Mix* Bill Manooch. *Boom Op* Michael Kohut. *Asst Dir* Michael Daves, Alan Rudolph. *Unit Prod Mgr* Harry F. Hogan. *Script Supv* Robert Forrest. *Wardrobe* Norman Burza, Edward Marks, Kitty Mager, Marilyn Matthews. *Makeup* Fred Williams. *Hairstyles* Jan Van Uchelen. *Still Photog* Ray De La Motte.

Cast: Stacy Keach (*Jonas Candide*), Marianna Hill (*Gundred Herzallerliebst*), Bud Cort (*Jimmy*), Graham Jarvis (*Doc Prittle*), James J. Sloyan (*Piquant*), M. Emmet Walsh (*Warden Brodski*), John Bottoms (*lawyer*), Ford Rainey (*Stanley Mae*), James Greene (*Gravey Combs*), Sammy Reese (*priest*), Stefan Gierasch (*Willy Herzallerliebst*), Logan Ramsey (*La Follette*), Charles Tyner (*Virgil*), William Mims (*Lynn*), Val Avery (*Jake*), Walter Barnes (*sheriff*), Charlie Briggs (*Zak*), Paul Gauntt (*Jeremy*), Claire Brennen (*woman passerby*), Scottie MacGregor (*Alice Thorn*), Tony Fraser (*1st child*), Martine Fraser (*2d child*), Lorna Thayer (*madam*), Pat Patterson (*Roscoe*).

Comedy-drama. In 1918 Jonas Candide, equipped with his own electric chair, travels from prison to prison charging $100 per execution. At Fairweather Prison in Alabama, he is hired to electrocute siblings Willy and Gundred Herzallerliebst. After he executes Willy, Jonas is seduced by Gundred and, hoping for her pardon, postpones her execution. When no pardon is forthcoming, Jonas attempts to persuade prison physician Doc Prittle to assist in simulating her execution. Prittle's price is so high, however, that the executioner gambles and pimps to get the money. Refused a supplementary bank loan, Jonas kills a guard. Although he frees Gundred, she deserts the executioner when he returns to town to retrieve his equipment. Gundred's sentence is commuted to life imprisonment, and Jonas is executed by his young assistant Jimmy, who ineptly transforms the electric chair into a funeral pyre. *Executioners. Convicts. Physicians. Murder. Seduction. Capital punishment. Bribery. Prison escapes. Prisons. Alabama.*

Note: Filmed on location at Kilby Prison near Montgomery, Alabama.

TRAVELING LADY *see* **BABY THE RAIN MUST FALL**

TRAVELING LIGHT (Great Britain)   F6.5162

E. C. Walker. *Dist* Victoria Films. 21 Dec 1962 [Los Angeles showing]. Sd; col (Eastman Color). 35mm. 53 min.

Prod-Dir Michael Keatering. *Screenplay* Antony Craven, Victor Hewitt. *Underwater Photog* Michael Keatering. *Film Ed* Peter Austen-Hunt. *Mus* John Brunel.

Cast: Lisa Rayne (*narrator*).

Nudist film. Elizabeth, a restless young woman, takes solitary walks over the moors and deserted beaches in hopes of finding peace. She enjoys sunbathing in the nude, and one day she meets a group of naturists, who persuade her to join them on a summer vacation at the famous naturist camp on the island of Corsica. Elizabeth's anxieties about the trip disappear as she and her friends engage in a variety of healthful activities such as swimming, sunbathing, and playing volleyball. The naturists come from all over the world, and Elizabeth finds them charming and attractive. She meets Yannick, a beautiful swimmer who performs an underwater ballet; a musician named Ingrid and her fiancée Robert; and Caren, a nude waterskier. Elizabeth discovers a new freedom in these surroundings and finds the peace for which she has been searching. *Nudism. Swimming. Sunbathing. Nudist camps. Summer. Vacations. Corsica.*

Note: Produced in 1959 as *Travelling Light. Sunswept*, q. v., is a sequel to *Traveling Light*. May be the same as *The Nymphs*, q. v.

LA TRAVIATA (Italy)   F6.5163

B. L. Vision–I. C. I. T. *Dist* Royal Films International. 27 Feb 1968 [New York showing]. Sd; col (Eastmancolor, print by Technicolor). 35mm. 110 min.

Exec Prod Afro Taccari. *Dir-Screen Adapt* Mario Lanfranchi. *Libretto* Francisco Maria Piave. *Photog* Leonida Barboni. *Art Dir* Andrea Taccari. *Set Decor* Alberto Verso. *Prod Dsgn* Maurizio Monteverde. *Film Ed* Gisa Levi Radicchi. *Mus Comp* Giuseppe Verdi. *Mus Cond* Giuseppe Patane. *Perf by* Rome Opera Orchestra. *Chorus Master* Gianni Lazzari. *Choreog* Gino Landi. *Sd* Paolo Ketoff, Fausto Ancillai. *Asst Dir* Mario Forges Davanzati, Paolo Taccari. *Prod Mgr* Lino Frascella.

Cast: Anna Moffo *(Violetta Valery)*, Gino Bechi *(Giorgio Germont)*, Franco Bonisolli *(Alfredo Germont)*, Mafalda Micheluzzi *(Flora Bervoix)*, Afro Poli *(Dr. Grenvil)*, Glauco Scarlini *(Gaston)*, Arturo La Porta *(Baron Douphol)*, Gianna Lollini *(Annina)*, Athos Cesarini *(Giuseppe)*, Maurizio Piacenti *(Marquis d'Obigny)*, Rome Opera Chorus.

Opera film. Source: Giuseppe Verdi and Francisco Maria Piave, *La traviata* (first performance: Venice, 6 Mar 1853). Alexandre Dumas, fils, *La dame aux camélias* (1848). The film is a screen performance of Verdi's opera. *Socialites. Prostitutes. Filial relations. Reputation. Self-sacrifice. Tuberculosis. Death. Paris.*

Note: Filmed in Rome in 1966; running time: 113 min.

I TRE AVVENTURIERI *see* **THE LAST ADVENTURE**

TRE NOTTI D'AMORE *see* **THREE NIGHTS OF LOVE**

TRE NOTTI VIOLENTE *see* **WEB OF VIOLENCE**

TRE PASSI NEL DELIRIO *see* **SPIRITS OF THE DEAD** ,

TRE SLAGS KAERLIGHED *see* **THE DAUGHTER; I, A WOMAN PART III**

I TRE VOLTI DELLA PAURA *see* **BLACK SABBATH**

THE TREASURE OF MAKUBA (United States/Spain)   **F6.5164**
P. C. Memsa–L. M. Films–F. I. S. A. *Dist* Producers Releasing Organization. Mar **1967.** Sd; col (Eastmancolor). 35mm. 84 min.

Pres by Sidney Pink. *Prod* Sidney Pink. *Dir* Joe Lacy. *Screenplay* Manuel M. Remis, José María Elorrieta. *Story* José Luis Navarro. *Photog* Alfonso Nieva, Pablo Ripoll. *Art Dir* Wolfgang Burman. *Film Ed* John Horvath. *Mus* Fernando García Morcillo.

Cast: Cameron Mitchell *(Coogan)*, Mara Cruz *(Maroa)*, Jessie Paradise *(Mary)*, Todd Martin *(Hank)*, Al Mulock *(Pat)*, Joseph Luis Lluch *(Tony)*, Pastor Serrador *(Duval)*, Felix Noble *(Chief Maola)*, Walter Zamudio *(Ling)*.

Adventure melodrama. Adventurer Coogan arrives on the Polynesian island of Makuba to search for pearls. The pearls apparently were stolen by a friend of Coogan's who was murdered after burying them. Reluctantly agreeing to cooperate with his dead friend's accomplices (Hank, Pat, and Tony), Coogan accompanies them on their jungle search. During the trek, Coogan prevents the lecherous Hank from assaulting a native girl, Maroa, and wins her slave-like devotion. The group arrive at the treasure site and find only an empty chest. Maroa confesses to Coogan that the pearls were taken by her brother for an offering to the island god. Although they recover the gems, Hank kills the native chief, shifts the blame to Coogan and Maroa, and absconds with the pearls. Coogan and Maroa are sentenced to death by the natives, but Police Commissioner Duval rescues them at the sacrificial site. Duval, Coogan, and Maroa head for the boat landing, where Pat, suspicious of both Hank and Tony, has forestalled departure. During the fight that ensues, the boat is set aflame, and Hank and Tony are killed. Duval takes the pearls for safe-keeping, and Coogan decides to stay with Maroa on the island. *Adventurers. Polynesians. Police. Murder. Theft. Rites and ceremonies. Frameup. Treasure. Pearls. Jungles. South Sea Islands. Ship explosions.*

Note: Filmed in Spain and released there in 1966 as *El tesoro de Makuba*; running time: 78 min.

THE TREASURE OF MONTE CRISTO *see* **THE SECRET OF MONTE CRISTO**

TREASURE OF SAN GENNARO (France/Italy/West Germany) **F6.5165**
Ultra Film–Société Cinématographique Lyre–Roxy Film. *Dist* Paramount Pictures. 26 Feb **1968** [New York opening]. Sd; col (Eastmancolor). 35mm. 102 min. [Also reviewed at 120 min.]

Exec Prod Turi Vasile, Luggi Waldleitner. *Dir* Dino Risi. *Screenplay* Adriano Baracco, Ennio De Concini, Dino Risi, Nino Manfredi. *Story* Ennio De Concini, Dino Risi. *Photog* Aldo Tonti. *Camera Op* Elio Polacchi. *Art Dir* Luigi Scaccianoce. *Film Ed* Franco Fraticelli, Lisbeth Neumann. *Mus* Armando Trovajoli. *Prod Mgr* Danilo Marciani, Günther Klein. *Cost* Maurizio Chiari.

Cast: Nino Manfredi *(Dudu)*, Senta Berger *(Maggie)*, Harry Guardino *(Jack)*, Claudine Auger *(Concettina)*, Totò *(Don Vincenzo)*, Mario Adorf *(Sciascillo)*, Frank Wolff *(Frank)*, Ugo Fangareggi *(Agony)*, Dante Maggio *(captain)*, Giovanni Bruti *(cardinal)*, Pinuccio Ardia *(baron)*, Vittoria Crispo *(Assunta)*, Jean Louis, Ralf Wolter, Solvi Stübing.

Crime comedy-drama. Three American thieves—Jack, Maggie, and Frank—arrive in Naples with plans to rob the Church of San Gennaro of 7 billion lire worth of jewels, gold, and trinkets. Needing inside help, they seek the advice of an old convict who recommends Dudu, a local petty thief. At first shocked by the idea of stealing from the city's patron saint, Dudu finally agrees to help Jack and Maggie (Frank has since died from overeating); he decides to use the money from the jewels to carry out a beautification plan for Naples. After the robbery, however, Maggie kills Jack and prepares to leave for the United States with the loot. She disguises herself as a nun, but Dudu and his buddy Sciascillo stop her at the airport and abscond with the treasure. Dudu has arranged for a fake cardinal to drive him to the Swiss border where he can sell the jewels, but the cardinal turns out to be genuine and returns the treasure to the church. *Americans in foreign countries. Thieves. Nuns. Clergymen. Conspiracy. Robbery. Perfidy. Murder. Disguise. Imposture. Churches. Jewels. Gold. Naples.*

Note: Location scenes filmed in Naples. Released in Italy in 1966 as *Operazione San Gennaro* at 96 min; in Paris in Sep 1967 as *Opération San Gennaro* at 100 min; in West Germany in Jan 1967 as *Unser Boss ist eine Dame* at 94 min.

THE TREASURE OF SAN TERESA *see* **HOT MONEY GIRL**

TREASURE OF SILVER LAKE (France/West Germany/Yugoslavia) **F6.5166**
S. N. C.–Rialto Film–Jadran Film. *Dist* Columbia Pictures. Nov **1965** [Los Angeles showing]. Sd; col (Eastmancolor, print by Pathé). 35mm (CinemaScope). 82 min. [Cut from 106 min.]

Prod Leif Feilberg. *Exec Prod* Horst Wendlandt. *Dir* Harald Reinl. *2d Unit Dir* Radenko Ostojić. *Screenplay* Harald G. Petersson. *Dir Photog* Ernst W. Kalinke. *Camera Op* Branko Ivatović, Everhard Dycke, Richard Bergmayer. *Art Dir* Duško Jeričević. *Film Ed* Hermann Haller. *Mus* Martin Böttcher. *Sd* Erich Molnar. *Asst Dir* Charles M. Wakefield. *Prod Mgr* Erwin Dräger. *Dir Prod* Stipe Gurdulic. *Prod Supv* Erwin Gitt. *Cost* Irms Pauli. *Makeup* Willi Nixdorf, Charlotte Schmidt-Kersten. *Sp Eff* Erwin Lange. *Scientific, Tech & Dramatic Adv* Piet ter Ulen.

Cast: Lex Barker *(Old Shatterhand)*, Götz George *(Fred Engel)*, Herbert Lom *(Colonel [Cornel?] Brinkley)*, Pierre Brice *(Winnetou)*, Karin Dor *(Ellen Patterson)*, Eddi Arent *(Duke of Glockenspiel)*, Marianne Hoppe *(Mrs. Butler)*, Jan Sid *(Patterson)*, Ralf Wolter *(Sam Hawkins)*, Mirko Boman *(Gunstick-Uncle)*, Jozo Kovačević, Slobodan Dimitrijević, Milivoj Stojanović, Branko Spoljar, Velimir Hitil, Antun Nalis, Ilija Ivezić.

Western melodrama. Source: Karl Friedrich May, *Der Schatz im Silbersee* (Stuttgart, 1890). A gang of bandits led by Colonel Brinkley ambush a stagecoach in Arkansas, murder Fred Engel's father, and steal his half of a treasure map. Old Shatterhand, a legendary hero who uses a special rifle that shoots silver bullets, and his Apache blood brother Winnetou set out, along with Fred Engel, to catch the murderers. Fred tells them that the map pinpoints the location of a fortune in gold at Silver Lake. The trio head for the farm owned by Engel's partner, Patterson, to retrieve the other half of the map, but the bandits attack, kidnap Fred's girl friend Ellen Patterson, and force Fred to lead the gang to Silver Lake. When Old Shatterhand and Winnetou are attacked by a band of hostile Indians, Winnetou converts them into allies, and they reach Silver Lake just as Brinkley is preparing to hang Fred and torture Ellen. Old Shatterhand's silver bullet cuts the noose around Fred's neck, Brinkley is killed when he falls through a trap, and the Indians help capture the rest of the gang. *Bandits. Apache Indians. Blood brothers. Stagecoach robberies. Murder. Revenge. Abduction. Documentation. Treasure. Gold. Arkansas. Winnetou.*

Note: Filmed on location in the Kras region of Yugoslavia. Opened in Paris in Aug 1963 as *Le trésor du Lac d'Argent* at 105 min; in West Germany in Dec 1962 as *Der Schatz im Silbersee* at 111 min; and in Yugoslavia as *Blago u srebrnom jezeru.*

THE TREATMENT *see* **STOP ME BEFORE I KILL!**

THE TREE   **F6.5167**
Robert Guenette. 9 Jun **1969** [New York opening]. Sd; b&w. 35mm. 92 min.

Prod-Dir-Writ Robert Guenette. *Assoc Prod* Robert Wood, prod. *Photog* Jesse Paley. *Prod Dsgn* Francis Gudemann. *Film Ed* Howard Milkin. *Mus* Kenyon Hopkins. *Sd* Harold Beiben, Al Gramaglia. *Asst Dir* Howard Rosenbloom, Robert Hillman, Paul Brockhurst. *Prod Supv* Paul Asselin.

Cast: Jordan Christopher *(Bucky Gagnon)*, Eileen Heckart *(Sally Dunning)*, George Rose *(Stuey)*, James Broderick *(Detective McCarthy)*, Ruth Ford *(Mrs. Gagnon)*, Fred J. Scollay *(Alex)*, Gale Dixon *(Lorry)*, Alan Landers *(Jim Wisiewski)*, Kathy Ryan *(Terry)*, Ed Griffith *(Detective Gorman)*, Tom Ahearne *(Joe)*, Glenn Scimonelli *(1st boy on bicycle)*, Alan Zemel *(2d boy on bicycle)*, Billy King, actor *(delivery boy)*, Ben Gerard *(waiter)*.

Melodrama. After abducting his young niece Terry, Bucky Gagnon finds refuge at the home of sympathetic Sally Dunning, his father's former girl friend. While in hiding, Bucky recalls his strained relationship with his parents and the marriage of his beloved sister Lorry to Jim Wisiewski, a fellow musician. Unknown to Bucky, Lorry has died. Although the police suggest that Jim is responsible for his daughter's abduction, Mrs. Gagnon discounts this theory. Informed by his mother of his sister's death, Bucky remembers forcing himself on Lorry and their subsequent incest beside a lake and speculates about Terry's paternity. Following an altercation with his mother, Bucky leaves Terry in an abandoned automobile; the next morning he is found hanging from a tree beside the lake. *Uncles. Children. Musicians. Police. Mistresses. Brother-sister relationship. Abduction. Mental illness. Jealousy. Incest. Infidelity. Parentage. Guilt. Suicide. Filial relations.*

Note: Location scenes filmed in Paterson, New Jersey and New York City.

13 JOURS EN FRANCE see **GRENOBLE**

IL TRENO see **THE TRAIN**

UN TRENO È FERMO A BERLINO see **STOP TRAIN 349**

TRES NOCHES VIOLENTAS see **WEB OF VIOLENCE**

LE TRÉSOR DES MONTAGNES BLEUES see **LAST OF THE RENEGADES**

LE TRÉSOR DU LAC D'ARGENT see **TREASURE OF SILVER LAKE**

TRETIY TAYM see **THE LAST GAME**

TRI see **THREE**

TRI SESTRY see **THE THREE SISTERS**

THE TRIAL (France/Italy/West Germany)   F6.5168
Paris Europa Production-Hisa-Film-FI. C. IT. *Dist* Astor Pictures. 20 Feb **1963** [New York opening]. Sd (Westrex); b&w. 35mm. 118 min.

Prod Yves Laplanche, Miguel Salkind, Alexander Salkind. *Assoc Prod* Robert Florat. *Dir-Screenplay-Dial* Orson Welles. *Pin-screen Images* Alexandre Alexeieff, Claire Parker. *Dir Photog* Edmond Richard. *Camera* Adolphe Charlet. *1st Asst Photog* Max Dulac. *2d Asst Photog* Robert Fraisse. *Art Dir* Jean Mandaroux. *Asst Art Dir* Jacques d'Ovidio, Jacques Brizzio, Pierre Tyberghein, Jean Bourlier. *Set Dresser* Jean Charpentier, Francine Coureau. *Scenic Artist* André Labussière. *Film Ed* Yvonne Martin. *Asst Film Ed* Chantal Delattre, Gérard Pollicand, Fritz Muller. *Mus Comp & Arr* Jean Ledrut. *Mus Leitmotif:* "Adagio" Tommaso Albinoni. *Sd Eng* Guy Villette. *Sd Mix* Jacques Lebreton. *Sd Asst* Urbain Loiseau, Guy Maillet. *1st & 2d Asst Dir* Marc Maurette, Paul Seban, Sophie Becker. *Prod Supv* Robert Florat. *Asst to the Prod* Paul Laffargue. *Admin* Henri Dutrannoy. *Prod Mgr* Jacques Pignier. *Asst Prod Mgr* Emile Blonde. *2d Asst Prod Mgr* Philippe Dubail. *Location Mgr* Guy Maugin. *2d Location Mgr* Louis Germain. *Script Girl* Marie-José Kling. *Prod Sec* Sonia Bunodière, Gisène Pillet-Collet. *Wardrobe* Hélène Thibault. *Wardrobe Mistress* Madame Brunet, Claudie Thary. *Makeup* Louis Dor. *Sp Eff Ed* Denise Baby. *Still Photog* Roger Corbeau. *Prop Master* Daniel Laguille, André Pierdel.

Cast: Anthony Perkins (*Joseph K*), Jeanne Moreau (*Miss Burstner*), Romy Schneider (*Leni*), Elsa Martinelli (*Hilda*), Suzanne Flon (*Pittle*), Orson Welles (*Hastler*), Akim Tamiroff (*Bloch*), Madeleine Robinson (*Mrs. Grubach*), Arnoldo Foà (*Inspector A*), Fernand Ledoux (*chief clerk*), Michel Lonsdale (*priest*), Max Buchsbaum (*examining magistrate*), Max Haufler (*Uncle Max*), Maurice Teynac (*deputy manager*), Wolfgang Reichmann (*courtroom guard*), Thomas Holtzmann (*Bert*), Billy Kearns, Jess Hahn (*assistant inspectors*), Maydra Shore (*Irmie*), Carl Studer (*man in leather*), Jean-Claude Remoleux, Raoul Delfosse (*policemen*), Titorelli (*X*).

Drama. Source: Franz Kafka, *Der Prozess* (Berlin, 1925). Joseph K, a young bank clerk, is awakened by a police inspector and two detectives who place him under arrest. Although he has committed no crime and has no idea of the charges, he finds himself being discussed and scorned by his neighbors, all of whom seem to know the details of his case. Eventually K is led through a labyrinth of corridors and taken before an examining magistrate, but he still cannot learn why he is under suspicion. His uncle, who somehow knows about his forthcoming trial, takes him to a bedridden advocate, Hastler, who agrees to act as his defense attorney. While the advocate rambles on about legal problems, K allows himself to be seduced by the man's nurse and mistress, Leni, a nymphomaniac irresistibly drawn to condemned men. After dismissing the advocate because of his delay in getting on with the case, K encounters a priest who tells him an allegorical tale of a man who waited all his life at the door of The Law but died without gaining admittance. Then, early one morning, K is accosted by two executioners who lead him to a quarry at the edge of town. When he defiantly maintains his innocence and laughs hysterically at his tormentors, they toss two sticks of dynamite into the pit. Following the

explosion, a tiny cloud rises from the quarry. *Bank clerks. Police. Detectives. Uncles. Lawyers. Priests. Nurses. Mistresses. Magistrates. Invalids. Seduction. Bureaucracy. Reputation. Law. Trials. Explosions.*

Note: Location scenes filmed in Paris and Zagreb. Opened in Paris in Dec 1962 as *Le procès*; running time: 120 min; in West Germany as *Der Prozess* in Apr 1963; running time: 118 min; in Rome in Sep 1963 as *Il processo*; running time: 100 min. Scenes featuring Van Doude and Katina Paxinou do not appear in U. S. release print.

TRIAL AND ERROR (Great Britain)   F6.5169
Anatole de Grunwald, Ltd. *For* Metro-Goldwyn-Mayer Pictures. *Dist* Metro-Goldwyn-Mayer, Inc. 16 Nov **1962** [New York opening: c31 Dec 1962; LP26843]. Sd; b&w. 35mm. 85-110 min. [Copyright length: 78 min.]

A Dimitri De Grunwald Production. *Prod* Dimitri De Grunwald. *Dir* James Hill. *Screenplay* Pierre Rouve. *Photog* Edward Scaife. *Camera Op* Herbert R. Smith. *Camera Focus* Wally Fairweather. *Art Dir* Ray Simm. *Asst Art Dir* Martin Atkinson. *Draughtsman* John Siddall. *Film Ed* Ann Chegwidden. *1st Asst Ed* Peter Weatherley. *2d Asst Ed* Patricia Gilbert. *Mus Comp & Cond* Ron Grainer. *Sd* Bert Ross, Red Law. *Boom Op* Ken Reynolds. *Sd Camera Op* Jack Smart. *1st, 2d & 3d Asst Dir* Jake Wright, Dennis Robertson, Eamonn Duffy. *Prod Mgr* Robert E. Dearing. *Prod Sec* Sheila Hawkins. *Cont* Jane Buck. *Wardroe* Jean Fairlie. *Makeup* Tom Smith. *Hairdresser* Sarah Beber. *Still Photog* Jack Dooley. *Prod Buyer* Eric Hillier. *Grip* Albert Lott. *Prop Master* Sidney Leggett. *Supv Electrn* Bert Owen.

Cast: Peter Sellers (*Morgenhall/doctor*), Richard Attenborough (*Fowle/judge/foreman of the jury/member of the public/character witness*), Beryl Reid (*Doris*), David Lodge (*Bateson*), Frank Pettingell (*Tuppy Morgan*), Eric Woodburn (*Judge Banter*), Frank Thornton (*photographer*), Tristam Jellinek (*Perkins*), Patrick Newell (*1st warder*), Audrey Nicholson (*Morganhall's girl*), John Waite (*clerk of the court*), David Drummond (*policeman*), Eric Dodson (*examiner*), Ian Curry (*doctor*), Henry Kay (*2d warder*).

Comedy-drama. Source: John Mortimer, *The Dock Brief* (London opening: 9 Apr 1958). After forty years of waiting for a case, an incompetent barrister named Morgenhall is finally given a dock brief. His client is Fowle, a timid little seed merchant accused of murdering his wife. When Morgenhall interviews Fowle, the man readily admits that he is guilty. A quiet man, he had found his wife Doris' incessant good humor and constant laughing intolerable. In desperation, he had taken in a lodger with a sense of humor equal to Doris'. But when Doris had refused to run off with the lodger, Fowle had killed her. Undaunted by the confession, Morgenhall plans what he considers to be a brilliant defense. He converts Fowle's cell into a courtroom, and the two men thoroughly rehearse the case, taking turns at acting out the various roles—judge, jury members, and witnesses. At the actual trial, however, Morgenhall becomes a bumbling fool incapable of uttering a single word in defense of his client. Consequently, Fowle is convicted and condemned. When Morgenhall goes to apologize to Fowle, he learns that his client has been acquitted on the grounds that his defense was totally inadequate. Fowle congratulates Morgenhall and points out that any other "technique" would have ended in disaster. *Merchants. Barristers. Lodgers. Murder. Timidity. Marriage. Trials. Impersonation. Juries. Confession (law).*

Note: Filmed in England; released there in 1962 as *The Dock Brief*; running time: 88 min.

TRIAL OF JOAN OF ARC (France)   F6.5170
Agnès Delahaie. *Dist* Pathé Contemporary Films. 11 Feb **1965** [New York opening]. Sd; b&w. 35mm. 65 min.

Prod Agnès Delahaie. *Dir-Writ* Robert Bresson. *Photog* Léonce-Henri Burel. *Art Dir* Pierre Charbonnier. *Film Ed* Germaine Artus. *Mus* Francis Seyrig. *Sd* Antoine Archimbaud. *Asst Dir* Serge Roullet. *Prod Mgr* Léon Sanz. *Cost* Lucilla Mussini.

Cast: Florence Carrez (*Jeanne d'Arc*), Jean-Claude Fourneau (*Bishop Cauchon*), Marc Jacquier (*Jean Lemaître, inquisitor*), Roger Honorat (*Jean Beaupère*), Jean Gillibert (*Jean de Châtillon*), André Régnier (*D'Estivet*), Michel Herubel (*Frère Isambart de la Pierre*), Philippe Dreux (*Frère Martin Ladvenu*), Jean Darbaud (*Nicolas de Houppeville*), E. R. Pratt (*Warwick*), Michael Williams (*Englishman*), Harry Sommers (*Bishop of Winchester*), Donald O'Brien (*English priest*), Gérard Zingg (*Jean Lohier*), André Maurice (*Tiphaine*), Paul-Robert Mimet (*Guillaume Erard*), Yves Leprince (*Pierre Morice*), Arthur Le Bau (*Jean Massieu*).

Historical drama. Based on *Procès de condamnation et de réhabilitation de Jeanne d'Arc*. In 1431 Jeanne, a French peasant girl, is imprisoned for heresy and brought to trial at Rouen. Despite rigorous interrogation by the judges and constant persecution from the jailers, her faith remains unshaken. The relentless theological questioning and argument in court is broken only by an ineffectual attempt at torture and an examination to prove her virginity. Jeanne's insistence that her military ventures were bidden by God is scoffed at by the English, who are anxious to destroy the legend already building around her. In a moment of weakness during the trial, Jeanne recants her faith. She is sentenced to life imprisonment, but when she retracts her earlier confession, the court decrees that she be burned at the stake as a witch. *Peasants. Judges. English. Heresy. Torture. Faith. Religious persecution. Capital punishment. Trials. Rouen. Jeanne d'Arc. Catholic Church.*

Note: Opened in Paris in Mar 1963 as *Procès de Jeanne d'Arc.*

THE TRIAL OF LEE HARVEY OSWALD   F6.5171

Falcon International Corp. 22 Apr **1964** [Milwaukee, Wisconsin, opening]. Sd; b&w. 35mm. 100 min.

Prod Harold Hoffman. *Dir* Larry Buchanan. *Tech Adv* Charles W. Tessmer.

Cast: Arthur Nations (*prosecuting attorney*), George Russell (*defense attorney*), George Edgley (*presiding judge*), Charles Mazyrack (*Lee Harvey Oswald*), Charles W. Tessmer (*himself*).

Drama. The Dallas trial of Lee Harvey Oswald, President John F. Kennedy's alleged assassin, is enacted as it might have occurred. After the defense enters pleas of "not guilty" and "not guilty by reason of insanity," 23 witnesses for the prosecution testify. No verdict is returned. *Lawyers. Juries. Judges. Assassination. Trials. Dallas. Lee Harvey Oswald. John Fitzgerald Kennedy.*

Note: Filmed on location in Dallas.

TRIBES   F6.5172

Twentieth Century-Fox Film Corp.-Marvin Schwartz Productions. *Dist* Twentieth Century-Fox Film Corp. 2 Dec **1970** [Madison, Wisconsin, opening]. Sd; col (DeLuxe). 35mm. 90 min. *MPAA rating* G.

Prod Marvin Schwartz. *Dir* Joseph Sargent. *Screenplay* Tracy Keenan Wynn, Marvin Schwartz. *Photog* Russell Metty. *Art Dir* Jack Martin Smith, Richard Day. *Set Decor* Walter M. Scott, Jerry Wunderlich. *Film Ed* Patrick Kennedy. *Mus* Al Capps, Marty Cooper. *Mus Supv* Lionel Newman. *Asst Dir* Bruce Fowler. *Prod Supv* Jack Sonntag. *Prod Mgr* David Silver.

Cast: Darren McGavin (*Sergeant Drake*), Earl Holliman (*DePayster*), Jan-Michael Vincent (*Adrian*), John Gruber (*Quentin*), Danny Goldman (*Sidney*), Richard Yniguez (*Sanchez*), Antone Curtis (*Marcellus*), Peter Hooten (*Scrunch*), David Buchanan (*Armstrong*), Rick Weaver (*Morton*).

Drama. As a busload of recruits arrives at a U. S. Marine training base, tough and seasoned drill instructor Sergeant Drake spots a long-haired youth wearing a flowing robe, beads, and sandals. Addressing the boy, Adrian, as "Lady," the sergeant makes it clear that he has no use for "hippies." To Drake's surprise, Adrian proves to be no problem: serenely accepting his G.I. haircut and military garb, he obeys all orders, fulfills all assignments, and, despite the lack of a high school diploma, scores top grades on all written tests. Drake asks the boy why he spends his rest periods either sitting in a lotus position or standing on his head, and Adrian explains that it relaxes him—just as Drake himself relaxes by making sketches of seagulls. Following a drill session, during which Adrian outlasts all the other recruits in holding buckets of sand at arm's length, Sergeant Drake develops a grudging respect for the boy and slackens up on disciplinary measures. After Adrian shows the other inductees how practicing yoga will help them endure holding buckets of sand, DePayster, a sadistic drill instructor, lashes out at Adrian during rifle practice for refusing to shoot at vital parts of a target figure. Further, DePayster goads Drake into such a fury by accusing him of having gone soft that the sergeant renews his harsh treatment of the men, so much so that one rookie attempts to slash his wrists. Depressed by the turn of events, Adrian deserts after taking his graduation exams. Drake, however, finds him at the bus depot and talks him into returning to the base. Learning that he has been denied graduation because of rifle practice, and that DePayster, who engineered the failure, will have him for "special" retraining, Adrian goes AWOL. Sergeant Drake pins up his sketch of the seagull as a reminder of the boy and goes out to face a new batch of recruits. *Hippies. Yogis. Deserters—Military. Basic military training. Military life. Sadism. Suicide. Disillusionment. Firearms. United States Marines.*

Note: Originally telecast on ABC-TV on 10 Nov 1970.

LES TRIBULATIONS D'UN CHINOIS EN CHINE *see* UP TO HIS EARS

TŘICET JEDNA VE STÍNU *see* 90 DEGREES IN THE SHADE

LES TRICHEURS *see* THE CHEATERS

TRICK AND THE TRADE   F6.5173

Nov **1970** [San Francisco showing]. Sd; col. 16mm? 80 min.

Melodrama. A male homosexual cannot solve his sexual problems with either love or money, so he continues to wander. *Male homosexuality.*

TRICKS OF THE TRADE   F6.5174

Extraordinary Films. *Dist* William Mishkin. 30 Oct **1968** [New York opening]. Sd; b&w. 35mm. 83 min.

Prod William Mishkin. *Dir* Andy Milligan. *Screenplay* Gerald Jacuzzo, Andy Milligan. *Photog* Andy Milligan.

Cast: Mary Carter (*Salina Claret*), Jonathan East (*Fred Claret*), Natalie Rogers (*Dr. Pauline Flood*), Josephine White (*Freda*), June Blake (*Marcy Perkins*), Mostifa Mond (*Stud Perkins*), Maggie Rogers (*Minnie Cry*), Keith Teak (*Misery*), Ivan Smith (*Four Eyes*), Haal Borske (*Bruce*), Miriam Levinson (*Betsy*), Diana May (*The Girl*), Maha (*The Woman*), Robert O'Connor (*bartender*), John Hoffman, actor (*Jack Foster*), Neil Flanagan (*Milburn*), Jack Hollister (*first man*), Gary Owen (*second man*).

Drama. After five years together, Fred and Salina Claret find that their marriage is foundering; Salina's interfering mother, Minnie, creates tension in the household, and Fred's sexual interest in his wife dwindles. Fred leaves and wanders into a Greenwich Village bar where he meets Marcy and Stud Perkins, an unconventional couple who invite him to their apartment. After smoking marijuana, Fred watches the couple's sex play and joins them in a threesome. Spurning Stud's homosexual advances, he makes love with Marcy. The next day, Fred visits psychiatrist Pauline Flood to discuss his marital difficulties, and he confesses that he would have welcomed Stud's advances. In the meantime, Stud and Marcy, actually members of a ring of degenerates, make plans to blackmail Fred; they have taken photos of Stud's homosexual embrace and of Fred's encounter with Marcy. Minnie insists that Salina investigate Fred's absences; Salina loses her way in the East Village and is raped by two hoodlums. When Fred next visits Dr. Flood, she offers her body in order to help him gain confidence. Hopeful that his marriage can be saved, Fred returns home and throws his mother-in-law out. Later, Stud shows Fred the incriminating photos and forces him to attend a secret orgy. Confronted by a demand for $5,000, Fred attempts to escape, but he is captured by the group and beaten beyond recognition. Six months later, Minnie suggests to Salina that Fred has run off with another woman. Meanwhile, Fred wanders aimlessly along the Bowery, a victim of amnesia. *Mothers-in-law. Psychiatrists. Hoodlums. Marriage. Troilism. Infidelity. Bisexuality. Rape. Amnesia. Male homosexuality. Extortion. Orgies. Marijuana. Photographs. New York City—Greenwich Village. New York City—East Village. New York City—Bowery.*

Note: Filmed in New York City. May also be known as *Tricks.*

TRIGGER HAPPY *see* THE DEADLY COMPANIONS

TRILOGY   F6.5175

American Broadcasting Co.-Xerox Corp. *Dist* Allied Artists. 6 Nov **1969** [New York opening]. Sd; col (Eastmancolor). 35mm. 110 min. [Also 100 min.] *MPAA rating* G.

Pres by Emanuel L. Wolf. *Prod-Dir* Frank Perry. *Screenplay* Truman Capote, Eleanor Perry. *Photog* Joseph Brun, Harry Sundby, Conrad Hall, Jordan Cronenweth. *Camera Op* Vincent Saizis, Peter Garbarini. *Set Decor* Leif Pedersen. *Prod Dsgn* Gene Callahan, Peter Dohanos. *Main Titl* S. Neil Fugita. *Film Ed* Patricia Jaffe, Ralph Rosenblum, Sheila Bakerman. *Mus Comp & Cond* Meyer Kupferman. *Song:* "For My Sake" Meyer Kupferman, Eleanor Perry. *Sung by* Maureen Stapleton. *Sd* Charles Federmack, Nat Boxer. *Sd Mix* Dick Vorisek. *Asst Dir* Stanley Ackerman, Dan Eriksen, George Goodman. *In Charge of Prod* Joel Glickman, Henry Spitz, Hubbell Robinson. *Prod Asst* Louis A. Stroller. *Script Supv* Marguerite James, Kay Chapin. *Asst to Mr. Perry* Lynn Forman. *Cost Dsgn* Anna Hill Johnstone, Frank Thompson. *Wardrobe* Marilyn Putnam.

Cast—"Miriam": Mildred Natwick (*Miss Miller*), Susan Dunfee (*Miriam*), Carol Gustafson (*Miss Lake*), Robin Ponterio (*Emily*), Beverly Ballard (*Nina*), Jane Connell (*Mrs. Connolly*), Frederic Morton (*man in theater*), Richard Hamilton (*man in automat*), Phyllis Eldridge (*woman in automat*), Brooks Rogers (*Mr. Connolly*), Niki Flacks (*clerk in shop*), Tony Ross (*dwarf*).

Cast—"Among the Paths to Eden": Maureen Stapleton (*Mary O'Meaghan*), Martin Balsam (*Ivor Belli*).

Cast—"A Christmas Memory": Geraldine Page (*woman*), Donnie Melvin (*Buddy*), Lavinia Cassels, Christine Marler (*aunts*), Josip Elic (*Haha Jones*), Lynn Forman (*woman in car*), Win Forman (*storekeeper*), Truman Capote (*narrator*).

Drama. Source: Truman Capote, "Miriam," in *Mademoiselle* (Jun 1945). Truman Capote, "Among the Paths to Eden," in *Esquire* (Jul 1960). Truman Capote, "A Christmas Memory," in *Mademoiselle* (Dec 1956). MIRIAM: Miss Miller, a governess who has spent her life in fashionable New York households, is rejected as nurse by a former charge who is expecting a baby of her own. At the movies that evening, she meets Miriam, a strange little girl who reminds Miss Miller of herself when she was young. Later that night, Miriam visits Miss Miller in her apartment, and the next day she is seen at a cafeteria. She appears at the apartment again, this time plundering Miss Miller's jewelry box; and a few days later, she arrives and announces her intention to stay. In horror, Miss Miller enlists the help of a neighbor, who searches the apartment for the little girl and finds no one. Miss Miller returns, however, to find Miriam sitting demurely in the living room. She reproves Miss Miller for the emptiness of her life—the ungrateful children she has cared for and the illusion that has sustained her. Miss Miller struggles with Miriam and pushes her out of the window, but upon returning to the bedroom, she finds Miriam there waiting. AMONG THE PATHS TO EDEN: In a Queens (New York) cemetery, middle-aged Ivor Belli visits his wife's grave. Mary O'Meaghan, a spinster who often walks in the cemetery, approaches Ivor in the hope of beginning a relationship based on their mutual loneliness. They discuss her dead father and his late wife, their shattered illusions, and their appreciation of singer Helen Morgan. Mary steps onto the grave of Ivor's wife and sings a torch song, imitating Helen Morgan. She sees that he is touched by the performance and invites him to dinner. Already involved with his secretary, he declines the invitation. Still hopeful, however, Mary walks him to the gate, explaining that she has a friend who met two husbands in a cemetery. Suddenly, she spots another man carrying flowers and begins to follow him. A CHRISTMAS MEMORY: Buddy is a young boy who lives in the South with his two aunts and an aging spinster cousin. The cousin is Buddy's best friend, and together they lovingly prepare Christmas fruitcakes to send to everyone they admire. They drink the leftover cooking whisky, chop down a Christmas tree, and wrap and mail their presents. On Christmas morning, they suddenly realize that Buddy is about to go away to military school and that she is becoming old and frail. They open their gifts cheerlessly and run to a pasture to fly the kites they gave each other. Exhausted from the activity, they fall into the grass and soak up the sun. After Buddy goes away, the two best friends never see each other again. *Governesses. Children. Spinsters. Widowers. Aunts. Cousins. Hallucinations. Loneliness. Disillusionment. Friendship. Old age. Cemeteries. Kites. Christmas. New York City. New York City—Queens. United States—South. Helen Morgan.*

Note: Filmed on location in New York City. "Christmas Memory" was originally telecast 21 Dec 1966 on *ABC Stage 67*; "Among the Paths to Eden" was telecast 17 Dec 1967; "Miriam" first appeared as part of *Trilogy* in the 1968 Cannes Film Festival.

IL TRIONFO DI ERCOLE *see* **HERCULES VS. THE GIANT WARRIORS**

THE TRIP   F6.5176
    American International Pictures. 23 Aug **1967** [New York opening; c10 Aug 1967; LP34700]. Sd; col (PathéColor). 35mm. 85 min. [Copyright length: 81 min.]
    A Roger Corman Production. *Prod-Dir* Roger Corman. *Screenplay* Jack Nicholson. *Photog* Arch R. Dalzell. *Camera Op* William Mendenhall. *Film Ed* Ronald Sinclair. *Mus Comp & Perf* The Electric Flag. *Mus Coord* Al Simms. *Sd* Phil Mitchell. *Asst Dir* Paul Rapp. *Prod Mgr* Jack Bohrer. *Script Supv* Bonnie Prendergast. *Cost* Richard Bruno. *Makeup* Ted Coodley. *Hairstyles* Ray Foreman. *Psychedelic Eff* Peter Gardiner. *Sp Eff* Roger George. *Montage Seq* Dennis Jacob. *Key Grip* Charles Hannawalt. *Prop* Richard M. Rubin, Karl Brainard.
    Cast: Peter Fonda (*Paul Groves*), Susan Strasberg (*Sally Groves*), Bruce Dern (*John*), Dennis Hopper (*Max*), Salli Sachse (*Glenn*), Katherine Walsh (*Lulu*), Barboura Morris (*Flo*), Caren Bernsen (*Alexandra*), Dick Miller (*Cash*), Luana Anders (*waitress*), Tom Signorelli (*Al*), Mitzi Hoag (*wife*), Judy Lang (*Nadine*), Barbara Renson (*Helena*), Susan Walters, Frankie Smith (*go-go girls*), Peter Bogdanovich.
    Drama. While filming on location at a California beach, TV commercial director Paul Groves is chided by his estranged wife, Sally, for failing to appear to sign their separation papers. Cracking under the pressures of his personal and professional life, Paul asks his friend John, a guru, to guide him through his first LSD trip. After stopping off at a psychedelic nightclub and attending a freak-out at the weirdly appointed pad of a pusher named Max, the two men go to John's place where Paul begins his trip. At first, it is cool and serene, full of brilliant colors and idyllic landscapes. Gradually, however, Sally and the seductive Glenn, a blonde Paul met at Max's, enter Paul's hallucinations, and his journey becomes a phantasmagoria of sexual encounters, medieval rites, and paranoic visions in which he assumes the guilt of mankind. Despite Paul's plea for an antidote, John persuades him to "go with it," and the nightmare progresses to a point where Paul attends his own funeral. Although this episode should be the breakthrough, the trip continues as Paul "sees" John, his head bashed in, slumped lifeless in a chair. Fleeing from the apartment, Paul wanders in a daze about the city until Max sends him to Glenn's beachhouse where he is taken through the final phase of his trip during a sexual experience. When it is finally over, Paul believes he has died, been reborn, and is now standing on the threshold of a new life. Glenn, however, warns him ominously—"It's easy now. Wait until tomorrow." *Television directors. Drug dealers. Businessmen. Gurus. Divorce. Paranoia. LSD. Hallucinations. Rites and ceremonies. California. Dreams. Chases.*

THE TRIP *see* **THE CHELSEA GIRLS**

A TRIP AROUND THE WORLD *see* **AROUND THE WORLD WITH NOTHING ON**

TRIP TO TERROR *see* **IS THIS TRIP REALLY NECESSARY?**

LES TRIPES AU SOLEIL *see* **CHECKERBOARD**

TRIPLE CROSS (France/Great Britain)   F6.5177
    Cineurop. *Dist* Warner Bros.–Seven Arts, Inc. 24 May **1967** [San Francisco opening; c27 Apr 1967; LP35732]. Sd (Westrex). col (Eastman Color, print by Technicolor). 35mm. 126 min. [Copyright length: 140 min.]
    A Jacques-Paul Bertrand Production. *Prod* Jacques-Paul Bertrand. *Assoc Prod* Georges Cheyko. *Exec Prod* Fred Feldkamp. *Dir* Terence Young. *Screenplay* René Hardy. *Adtl Dial* William Marchant. *Dir Photog* Henri Alekan. *Art Dir* Tony Roman. *Prod Dsgn* René Renoux. *Film Ed* Roger Dwyre. *Mus Comp* Georges Garvarentz. *Sd* Jacques Lebreton, Johnny Dwyre. *Asst Dir* Christian Raoux, Bernard Quatrehomme. *Prod Mgr* Jean Velter, Pierre Laurent. *Unit Mgr* Serge Lebeau, Dennis Hall. *Script Supv* Joan Davis. *Makeup Artist* Marie-Madeleine Paris.
    Cast: Christopher Plummer (*Eddie Chapman*), Romy Schneider (*The Countess*), Trevor Howard (*distinguished civilian*), Gert Fröbe (*Colonel Steinhager*), Yul Brynner (*Baron von Grunen*), Claudine Auger (*Paulette*), Georges Lycan (*Leo*), Jess Hahn (*Commander Braid*), Harry Meyen (*Lieutenant Keller*), Gil Barber (*Bergman*), Jean-Claude Bercq (*Major von Leeb*), Jean Claudio (*Sergeant Thomas*), Robert Favart (*General Dalrymple*), Bernard Fresson (*French resistance member*), Clément Harari (*Losch*), Howard Vernon (*Lisbon Embassy official*), Francis De Wolff (*German colonel-general*), Jean-Marc Bory (*resistance leader*), Hubert Noël (*von Runstedt's staff officer*), Jean Bertrand, actor.
    Biographical drama. *Source:* Eddie Chapman, *The Eddie Chapman Story [as told to] Frank Owen* (London, 1953). British safecracker Eddie Chapman is arrested during the early part of World War II for robbing a movie theater and imprisoned on the Isle of Jersey. When the Germans occupy the island, he contacts two members of German Intelligence, Colonel Steinhager and The Countess, and offers himself, for a price, as a spy. His offer accepted, Eddie receives espionage training from Baron von Grunen and after passing a loyalty test, he is parachuted into England. Once there, he volunteers to work for British Intelligence in exchange for a full pardon. When the British stage a fake explosion of an aircraft factory which is photographed by German reconnaissance planes, Eddie is credited for the sabotage and returned to Paris to be awarded the German Iron Cross. Then, as the Allies approach Paris, Eddie is sent back to England to report on the accuracy of Hitler's rocket attacks on London. Instead, he radios false reports and diverts the rockets into unpopulated areas. Now a hero in both countries, Eddie celebrates the war's end in a London pub. As he sips his beer, the temptations of his former life return to him and he surreptitiously eyes the tavern safe. *Safecrackers. Spies. Nazis. War heroes. Robbery. Espionage. Perfidy. Sabotage. World War II. Isle of Jersey. Paris. London. Edward Arnold Chapman. Great Britain—Intelligence service. Iron Cross.*
    Note: Location scenes filmed in France and England. Released in France as *Triple Cross* in Dec 1966; running times: 140 & 135 min; in Great Britain in Sep 1967; running time: 126 min. Alternative French title: *La fantastique histoire vraie d'Eddie Chapman.*

TRIPOLI *see* **FIRST MARINES**

TRISTANA (France/Italy/Spain)   F6.5178
    Epoca Films–Talía Films–Selenia Cinematografica–Les Films Corona. *Dist* Maron Films. 21 Sep **1970** [New York opening]. Sd; col (Eastman Color). 35mm. 95 min. *MPAA rating GP.*
    Pres by Forbes Film Ltd., United Cineworld Corp. *Dir* Luis Buñuel. *Screenplay* Luis Buñuel, Julio Alejandro. *Adapt* Luis Buñuel. *Photog* José F. Aguayo. *Camera* José F. Aguayo, Jr. *Asst Camera* Alberto Paniagua, José A. Noya. *Art Dir* Enrique Alarcón. *Asst Art Dir* Rafael P. Murcia. *Set Dsgn* Luis Argüello. *Film Ed* Pedro del Rey. *Asst Film Ed* José Salcedo. *Incidental Mus From the Works of* Frédéric François Chopin. *Sd* José Nogueira, Dino Fronzetti. *Asst Dir* José Puyol, Pierre Lary. *Prod Mgr* Juan Estelrich. *Prod Ch* Manuel Torres. *Asst Prod Mgr* Esteban Gutiérrez. *Cost* Rosa García. *Makeup* Julián Ruiz, Vicente Martínez. *Catherine Deneuve's Hairstyles* Julián Ruiz.
    Cast: Catherine Deneuve (*Tristana*), Fernando Rey (*Don Lope*), Franco Nero (*Horacio*), Lola Gaos (*Saturna*), Antonio Casas (*Don Cosme*), Jesús Fernández (*Saturno*), Vicente Soler (*Don Ambrosio*), José Calvo (*bellringer*), Fernando Cebrián (*Dr. Miquis*), Cándida Losada (*Señora Burguesa*), Mary Paz Pondal (*girl*), Juan José Menéndez (*Don Candido*), Sergio Mendizábal (*professor*), Antonio Ferrándis, José Maria Caffarel, Joaquim Pamplona, José Blanch, Alfredo Santa Cruz, Luis Aller, Luis Rico, Saturno Cerra, Jesús Combarro, Vicente Roca, Ximenez Carrillo, Adriano Domínguez, José Riesgo, Rosa Gorostegui, Antonio Cintado, Pilar Vela, Lorenzo Rodríguez.

Drama. Source: Benito Pérez Galdós, *Tristana* (Madrid, 1892). In 1929 after the death of her mother, Tristana goes to Toledo to live with her guardian, Don Lope; also in the house are his servant Saturna and her deafmute son, Saturno. Don Lope claims to be a free-thinker who despises the Catholic Church and most social conventions, but in practice he will do nothing to upset his own peace of mind. His affection for Tristana soon turns to desire, and when he attempts to seduce her, she complies without protest. Although Don Lope insists that she is entirely free, Tristana feels trapped by his increasing possessiveness. She falls in love with Horacio, a young artist, and runs away with him to Madrid, mainly to escape from Don Lope. Within 2 years, however, she develops a tumor in her leg and begs Horacio to return her to Don Lope, who has inherited a large sum of money. Her leg is amputated, and with Don Lope's care, she slowly recovers from the surgery. Don Lope, who has aged considerably, assumes the role of Tristana's father and encourages Horacio to court her, but she rejects his marriage proposal. Don Lope eventually marries her himself, at the insistence of a local priest. Tristana takes care of the now-senile Don Lope, who has turned to religion for consolation. One night he suffers a heart attack and implores her to call a doctor. Pretending to phone from the next room, Tristana opens the window to let the winter wind enter the dying man's room. *Catholics. Orphans. Guardians. Domestics. Deafmutes. Artists. Amputees. Priests. Seduction. Marriage. Old age. Death. Tumors. Inheritance. Heart disease. Toledo (Spain). Madrid.*

Note: Filmed on location in Toledo, Spain. Released in Spain in Mar 1970; opened in Paris in Apr 1970; running time: 105 min; and in Italy in Oct 1970.

TRIUMPH OVER VIOLENCE (U.S.S.R.)   **F6.5179**
Mosfilm. *Dist* Joseph Brenner Associates. 27 Jun **1968** [Denver, Colorado, opening]. Sd; b&w. 35mm. 82 min.
Original Production Credits: *Dir* Mikhail Romm. *Screenplay* Mikhail Romm, Mayya Turovskaya, Yuriy Khanyutin. *Photog* German Lavrov. *Film Ed* Mikhail Romm. *Mus* A. Karamanov. *Sd* S. Minervin, B. Vengerovskiy. *Asst Dir* L. Indenbom.
Production Credits for U. S. Release Vers: An Edward Diresta—Materprim S. A. Production. *Prod* Edward Diresta. *Film Ed* Charles Diana.
English Narrator: Duncan Elliott.
Compilation film. This analysis of fascism, its rise in Germany in the 1930's, culmination in World War II, and present day manifestations, is compiled largely from German news and archival footage. The film is divided into chapters depicting Hitler's early emotional appeal to the German people (mass rallies, Wagnerian torchlight parades, book-burnings, etc.); the conversion of "nice boys" into storm troopers (stressed by scenes of captured German soldiers with pictures of their loved ones juxtaposed with views of their atrocities); Hitler's eventual rise to absolute power (his conquests, policy of mass murder, crimes against the Jews, and the sealing of *Mein Kampf* in a vault designed to last 1000 years); and his defeat. (Deletions for the U. S. release include material from the final chapter depicting neo-Nazi movements throughout the world today and the training of U. S. Marines in a manner reminiscent of the indoctrination of Hitler's Brownshirts.) *Germans. Fascism. Genocide. Nazism. Militarism. Germany—History—Third Reich. World War II. Adolf Hitler. Germany—Army.*
Note: Produced in the U.S.S.R. in 1965 as *Obyknovennyy fashizm* and released in two parts; combined running time: 130-140 min. Shown in Great Britain in 1966, narrated in English by Duncan Elliott; running time: 128 min.

TROG (Great Britain)   **F6.5180**
Herman Cohen Productions. *Dist* Warner Bros. Pictures. 11 Sep **1970** [Chicago opening; c14 Aug 1970; LP42914]. Sd; col (Technicolor). 35mm. 91 min. *MPAA rating* GP.
Prod Herman Cohen. *Assoc Prod* Harry Woolveridge. *Dir* Freddie Francis. *Screenplay* Aben Kandel. *Orig Story* Peter Bryan, John Gilling. *Dir Photog* Desmond Dickinson. *Art Dir* Geoffrey Tozer. *Set Decor* Helen Thomas. *Film Ed* Oswald Hafenrichter. *Mus & Mus Dir* Johnny Scott. *Sd Ed* Michael Redbourn. *Sd Rec* Tony Dawe, Maurice Askew. *Asst Dir* Douglas Hermes. *Prod Mgr* Edward Dorian. *Cont* Leonora Hale. *Wardrobe Master* Ron Beck. *Makeup* Jimmy Evans. *Hairdresser* Pearl Tipaldi. *Sp Eff for "The Animal World" Seq (see note)* Willis O'Brien, Ray Harryhausen. *Trog Dsgn by* Charles Parker.
Cast: Joan Crawford (*Dr. Brockton*), Michael Gough (*Sam Murdock*), Bernard Kay (*Inspector Greenham*), David Griffin (*Malcolm Travers*), Kim Braden (*Ann Brockton*), Joe Cornelius (*Trog*), John Hamill (*Cliff*), Geoffrey Case (*Bill*), Thorley Walters (*magistrate*), Jack May (*Dr. Selbourne*), Maurice Good, Rona Newton-John (*reporters*), Paul Hansard (*Dr. Kurtlimer*), Robert Crewdson (*Dr. Pierre Duval*), Robert Hutton (*Dr. Richard Warren*), David Warbeck (*Alan Davis*), Brian Grellis (*John Dennis*), Simon Lack (*Colonel Vickers*), Chloë Franks (*little girl*), Cleo Sylvestre (*nurse*), Golda Casimir (*Professor Manoskiensky*), John Baker (*anaesthetist*), Bartlett Mullins

(*butcher*), Shirley Cooklin (*little girl's mother*).
Science fiction melodrama. While exploring a cave, students Malcolm, Cliff, and Bill are attacked by an ape-like beast. When Bill is killed, the other two report the incident to the skeptical police and anthropologist Dr. Brockton. The news media learn of the story, and a camera crew is sent into the cave to film the creature, but the beast chases them from the cave. Dr. Brockton, who persuades the police not to open fire, shoots the beast with a tranquilizer gun and takes it to her laboratory where she discovers that it is a troglodyte, the missing link between man and ape. After Trog is calmed, a transmitter is inserted in its chest, and the beast begins to communicate with Dr. Brockton. One day a dog steals one of Trog's toys, and the creature kills the dog. Consequently, Dr. Brockton is brought before a magistrate and told that the beast will have to be destroyed if it breaks loose again. Sam Murdock, a local land developer, and Dr. Selbourne, a jealous rival of Dr. Brockton, conspire to free Trog, but when Murdock opens the cage, Trog kills him, goes on a rampage in the town, and takes a child back to the cave. The British Army is called in, but Dr. Brockton requests an opportunity to try to save the child; she enters the cave and returns with the child, who had been treated kindly by Trog. The army, however, will no longer allow the potential danger, and they destroy the cave and Trog with dynamite. *Students. Police. Monsters. Ape-men. Anthropologists. Motion picture cameramen. Magistrates. Children. Abduction. Evolution. Caves. Tranquilizers. Laboratories. Experiments. Great Britain—Army. Explosions. Dogs.*
Note: Opened in London in Jun 1971. Includes scenes from *The Animal World* (1955).

TROIKA   **F6.5181**
Ica Films. *Dist* Emerson Film Enterprises. 21 Nov **1969** [New York opening]. Sd; col (DeLuxe). 35mm. 89 min. *MPAA rating* R.
Dir-Writ-Story Fredric Hobbs. *With the Collaboration of* Richard Faun, Gordon Mueller. *Photog* William Heick. *Art Work* Fredric Hobbs.
Cast: Fredric Hobbs (*Chef/Phantom/Hobbs*), Nate Thurmond (*Attenuated Man*), Gloria Rossi (*Mediterranean Woman*), Morgan Upton (*Rax*), Richard Faun (*Mr. Gordon Goodloins*), Parra O'Siochain (*warrior*), San Francisco Art Center Ensemble (*blue people, purple people*).
Experimental film. Fredric Hobbs, an unconventional artist, tries to persuade a cynical millionaire Hollywood producer, Gordon Goodloins, to provide financial backing for a projected art film project, *Troika*. Their continuing encounter provides the frame for the three parts of the film. In the first segment, Chef, a mad sculptor, creates strange plaster forms, smashes them, and throws them into a stove. Part two utilizes documentary footage of campus unrest, contrasting the rigid traditional college setting with the university of the present, and features the sound of machinegun fire as a girls' chorus chants "Let Me Entertain You." The third part centers on a world of variously pigmented young people led by Attenuated Man and invaded by Rax (an Everyman figure)—an 8-foot-high, bug-like, blind robot animated from within by a human being. *Artists. Sculptors. Millionaires. Motion picture producers. Cooks. Students. Art. Demonstrations. Robots.*

TROIS VÉRITÉS *see* **THREE FACES OF SIN**

LES TROIS VISAGES DE LA PEUR *see* **BLACK SABBATH**

LA TROISIÈME DIMENSION *see* **FIVE MILES TO MIDNIGHT**

THE TROJAN HORSE (France/Italy)   **F6.5182**
Europa Cinematografica–Les Films Modernes–Films Borderie. *Dist* Colorama Features, Capitol Films. Jul **1962**. Sd; col (Eastman Color). 35mm (Techniscope). 105 min.
Prod Gianpaolo Bigazzi. *Dir* Giorgio Ferroni. *Screenplay* Giorgio Stegani, Ugo Liberatore, Federico Zardi. *Photog* Rino Filippini. *Art Dir* Pier Vittorio Marchi. *Film Ed* Antonietta Zita. *Mus (see note)* Giovanni Fusco, Mario Ammonini. *Sd* Ovidio Del Grande.
Cast: Steve Reeves (*Aeneas*), John Drew Barrymore (*Ulysses*), Juliette Mayniel (*Creusa*), Hedy Vessel (*Helen*), Lidia Alfonsi (*Cassandra*), Warner Bentivegna (*Paris*), Luciana Angelillo (*Andromache*), Arturo Dominici (*Achilles*), Mimmo Palmara (*Ajax*), Nerio Bernardi (*Agamemnon*), Nando Tamberlani (*Menelaus*), Carlo Tamberlani (*Priam*).
Epic. In the 10th year of the Trojan War, waged by the Greeks against Troy in revenge for the abduction of Helen by the Trojan Paris, Hector, the Trojan leader, is slain by Achilles, and there is dissent in choosing a new commander. The choice of the nobility is the weak and treacherous Paris, while the soldiers favor the brave warrior Aeneas, who secretly marries Priam's daughter, Creusa. Accompanied by Aeneas, Priam visits the Greek camp to claim Hector's body, and Aeneas defeats the Greek warrior Ajax in single combat. While Aeneas is away raising new troops to fight the Greeks, Creusa, now pregnant, is taken hostage. Aeneas returns and rescues his wife, inflicting heavy losses on the enemy, but Paris refuses to support him. Meanwhile, the Greeks, following

Ulysses' inspiration, construct an enormous wooden horse and give out that it is a holy object on which their fortunes depend. As they retreat by sea from Troy, they leave the horse outside the gates with a number of warriors hidden inside. The Trojans draw the horse within their walls, and that night, while the city celebrates its victory, the Greek warriors emerge from the horse, open the city gates to the Greek force, and sack and burn Troy. Aeneas finds the body of Creusa, who has just given birth to a son, and escapes to Italy with the infant. There, with a small band of followers, he founds the city of Rome. *Greeks. Soldiers. Trojans. Hostages. Deception (military). Abduction. Perfidy. Incendiarism. Rome. Troy. Aeneas. Helen of Troy. Paris Prince of Troy. Creusa. Ulysses. Achilles. Ajax. Priam. Duels. Mythological characters.*

Note: Filmed in Italy and released in Dec 1961 in Italy as *La Guerra di Troia*; running time: 115 min; and in France as *La Guerre de Troie*; running time: 105 min. Also known as *The Trojan War* and *The Mighty Warrior*. Sources conflict in crediting music.

THE TROJAN WAR see **THE TROJAN HORSE**

TROPIC OF CANCER   **F6.5183**

Tropic Film Corp. *Dist* Paramount Pictures. 19 Feb **1970** [New York opening; c19 Feb 1970; LP38198]. Sd; col (Eastman Color, print by Technicolor). 35mm. 87 min. *MPAA rating* X.

Prod-Dir Joseph Strick. *Assoc Prod* Betty Botley, Michel Rittener. *Screenplay* Joseph Strick, Betty Botley. *Dir Photog* Alain Derobe. *Camera Op* Colin Mounier. *Film Ed* Sidney Meyers, Sylvia Sarner. *Mus Comp & Cond* Stanley Myers. *Sd Ed* Bart Kean. *Sd Engr* Jo de Bretagne. *Asst Dir* Jean-Michel Lacor, Martine Marchand. *Unit Mgr* Suzanne Wiesenfeld. *Script Supv* Catherine Prevert. *Prod Mgr* Michel Rittener. *Ch Electrn* Jacques Cherel.

Cast: Rip Torn (*Henry Miller*), James Callahan (*Fillmore*), Ellen Burstyn (*Mona*), David Bauer (*Carl*), Laurence Lignères (*Ginette*), Phil Brown (*Van Norden*), Dominique Delpierre (*Vite Chéri*), Stuart De Silva (*Ranji*), Raymond Gérôme (*headmaster*), Gisèle Grimm (*Germaine*), Ginette Leclerc (*Madame Hamilton*), Françoise Lugagne (*Irene*), Magali Noël (*The Princess*), Sheila Steafel (*Tania*), Elliott Sullivan (*Peckover*), Sabine Sun (*Elsa*), George Birt (*Sylvester*), Steve Eckardt (*Cronstadt*), Philippe Gasté (*train passenger*), Eleonore Hirt (*Yvette*), Ed Marcus (*Boris*), Henry Miller (*spectator*), Christine Oscar (*Helen*), Gladys Berry (*American lady*), Jo Lefevre (*accordionist*), Roger Lumont (*cafe patron*), Guy Marly (*dog lover*), Loryanne, Catherine d' Hugues, Nadia Vasil, Liane Saunier (*Madame Hamilton's girls*), Bernard Taine, Yves Rannou, Lionel Bejean (*Dijon schoolboys*).

Biographical drama. Source: Henry Miller, *Tropic of Cancer* (Paris, 1934). Henry Miller, an impoverished American expatriate, lives a meager existence in Paris. His wife, Mona, arrives and spends her first night in Paris in Henry's bug-ridden bed. Unable to bear his disgusting lifestyle, Mona leaves the next day. Relying on each of his friends to provide one meal a week for him, Henry soon begins to irritate his hosts, and the invitations become less frequent. When Sylvester, one of Henry's benefactors, discovers that his friend is repaying the kindness by making love to his wife, Henry's meals are abruptly curtailed. Henry then takes a job teaching school in Dijon but becomes bored with the provincial town and begins to give his boys lessons in female anatomy. As soon as he is offered a job as a proofreader for the *Paris Herald*, Henry leaves Dijon and moves in with his friend Fillmore and his Russian mistress. He helps another friend, Carl, write letters to a wealthy widow, and Carl succeeds in beginning a courtship with the older woman. Meanwhile, Fillmore has developed problems with another woman, Ginette, who is pregnant and trying to trap him into marriage. Henry sends him back to New York to escape, and as Henry bids him farewell, Fillmore gives him a large sum of money to be delivered to Ginette. With no intention of parting with the money, Henry happily walks through the streets of Paris. *Expatriates. Americans in foreign countries. Schoolteachers. Proofreaders. Russians. Mistresses. Gigolos. Widows. Bohemianism. Poverty. Infidelity. Pregnancy. Perfidy. Boarding schools. Paris. Dijon. Henry Miller. "Paris Herald".*

Note: Location scenes filmed in Paris.

TROPIC OF SCORPIO   **F6.5184**

Dist Canyon Distributing Co. 18 Dec **1968** [Champaign, Illinois, showing]. Sd; col. 35mm. 71 min.

A W. H. DePriest Production. *Prod* Sandford Wayne. *Dir-Writ* Spence Crilly. *Photog* Ed DePriest. *Camera Op* Manuel S. Conde. *Art Dir* Solomon Sturges. *Mus Score* Robin Herth. *Sd Rec* Paul Hunt. *Prod Mgr* Jim Shea. *Script Girl* Lisa Wright. *Wardrobe* Sharon of Hollywood. *Makeup Artist* Scott Hamilton. *Still Photog* Jerry W. Kisker.

Cast: Dianne Curtis (*Doris, the Sun Virgin*), Cathy Price (*Jane, the Insatiable*), Arnie Cohen (*Tiny, the Satyr*), Harvey Shane (*Diff, the Plunger*), Victor Izay (*Uncle Walter, the Depraved Pornographer*), Marsha Jordan (*Cheri, the Cruel Countess*), Yuki Tani (*Lelani, the Passionate Eurasian*), Pie Watanabe (*Pie, the Girl With the Long Black Hair*), Red Loin (*Salvadore, the

Eunuch*), Bob Black (*Lance, the Blond Warrior*), Sandy White (*Sean, the Black Warrior*), Janice Mackey (*Linda, the Human Salad*), Ralph Cartwright, Steve Smith, Jodi Johnson, Joan Pettet, Larry Shea, Bobbie Munsun, Lawrence Cob (*The Salad Eaters*).

Melodrama. Uncle Walter, a pornographer who revels in corrupting innocents, lures Jane and Doris to his island villa for a tropical holiday. Terrified by Walter and his bizarre entourage, the two women turn to local surfers Diff and Tiny. They are unable to escape from Walter, however, and Jane falls victim to a strange fertility rite. *Innocents. Pornographers. Surfers. Rites and ceremonies. Islands. Tropics.*

TROPICAL ECSTASY (Argentina)   **F6.5185**

Dist Haven International Pictures. 2 Oct **1970** [New York opening]. Sd; col (Eastmancolor). 35mm. 90 min. *MPAA rating* X.

Prod-Dir-Writ Armando Bo. *Photog* Ignacio Souto. *Mus* Luis Alberto del Paraná.

Cast: Isabel Sarli (*Monica*), Armando Bo (*José*), Egidio Eccio (*Pedro*), Bentinho, Juan C. Olmos.

Melodrama. Monica, an unhappy próstitute, flees from a bordello in the Brazilian coastal city of Santos. She falls in love with José, a simple fisherman, and settles into a life of domesticity, angering her pimp, Pedro. José beats Pedro in a violent fight and continues his happy life with Monica. *Prostitutes. Pimps. Fishermen. Whorehouses. Santos (Brazil).*

Note: Filmed in São Paulo and coastal locations in Brazil. The film is a remake of the 1964 Argentine production *Lujuria tropical.*

TROPICI see **TROPICS**

TROPICS (Italy)   **F6.5186**

Giannangelo Corte-B. B. G. Cinematografica. *For* RAI. *Dist* New Yorker Films. 16 Mar **1969** [New York opening]. Sd; b&w. 35mm. 87 min.

Prod Gianni Barcelloni. *Dir* Gianni Amico. *Screenplay* Gianni Amico, Francesco Tullio Altan. *Photog* Giorgio Pelloni. *Film Ed* Giorgio Pelloni. *Mus From the Works of* Wolfgang Amadeus Mozart. *Sd* Gianni Amico, Francesco Tullio Altan.

Cast: Joel Barcelos (*Miguel*), Janira Santiago (*Maria*), Graciele Campos (*Graciele*), Batista Campos (*Batista*), Antonio Pitanga (*black man*), Roque Aranjo (*Julio*), Maria Euridice (*Maria Euridice*), Giorgio Poppi (*doctor*).

Documentary drama. The first portion of the film is fictional and tells of an impoverished Brazilian family who leave their home in the dust-bowl northeastern section of the country in the hope of finding a better way of life in São Paulo. After an arduous journey which takes them through Recife, Miguel and Maria are forced to move into a São Paulo shantytown, and Miguel takes a low-paying job as a construction worker. The documentary portion of the film includes narration which provides information about Brazil's poor economic situation in relation to the rest of the world. Also shown are bulletins and newspaper headlines about U. S. events and roadside billboards advertising American companies and their products. *Lower classes. Construction workers. Poverty. Family life. Shantytowns. Billboards. Brazil—Northeast. São Paulo. Recife.*

Note: Filmed on location in Brazil. Italian title: *Tropici*. The musical score includes Brazilian folk music.

LE TROU see **THE NIGHT WATCH**

TROUBLE IN THE SKY (Great Britain)   **F6.5187**

Bryanston Films–Aubrey Baring Productions. *Dist* Universal–International Films. 29 Mar **1961** [San Francisco opening]. Sd; b&w. 35mm. 76 min.

Prod Aubrey Baring. *Dir* Charles Frend. *Screenplay* Robert Westerby. *Adtl Dial* Jeffrey Dell. *Photog* Arthur Grant. *Art Dir* Wilfred Shingleton. *Film Ed* Max Benedict. *Mus Comp & Cond* Gerard Schürmann. *Sd* John Cox, Peter Dukelow. *Sd Rec* Buster Ambler. *Asst Dir* Basil Rabin. *Prod Mgr* Jack Rix. *Wardrobe* William Walsh. *Makeup* Freddie Williamson. *Hairstyles* Ann Box.

Cast: Michael Craig (*Capt. Hugh Dallas*), Peter Cushing (*Capt. Clive Judd*), Bernard Lee (*Capt. George Gort*), Elizabeth Seal (*Charlotte Gort*), George Sanders (*Sir Arnold Hobbes, Queen's Counsel*), Andre Morell (*Capt. Edward Manningham*), Gordon Jackson (*Captain Bateson*), Charles Tingwell (*Captain Braddock*), Noel Willman (*Nigel Pickering*), Delphi Lawrence (*Joyce Mitchell*), Marne Maitland (*Mr. Robinson*), William Abney, Jack Hedley (*1st officers*), Simon Lack, Hedger Wallace (*navigators*), Charles Mylne, Howard Pays (*stewards*), Ballard Berkeley, Charles Lloyd Pack (*commissioners*), Homi Bode, Anthony Newlands (*controllers*).

Action drama. Source: David Beaty, *Cone of Silence* (London, 1959). Following the takeoff crash of a jet plane in India, veteran British pilot Capt. George Gort is called before a court of inquiry. Though he is found guilty of "pilot error," in recognition of his long safety record, he is not grounded. His daughter, Charlotte, refuses to believe her father was at fault and persuades an expert flying examiner, Captain Dallas, to help her prove her father's innocence. A short time later Gort fatally crashes in a takeoff from Ranjibad in conditions identical to those of the previous crash. As a second inquiry is held, Dallas proves that the jet's designer, Nigel Pickering, had withheld data concerning a defect in the plane's takeoff equipment, which he had been secretly trying to perfect. With this new information Charlotte is able to preserve her late father's good name. *Air pilots. Filial relations. Airplane accidents. Airplane manufacture. Airplanes—Jet. Courts of inquiry. India.*

Note: Opened in London in Apr 1960 as *Cone of Silence*; running time: 92 min.

THE TROUBLE WITH ANGELS F6.5188

William Frye Productions. *Dist* Columbia Pictures. 30 Mar **1966** [Saint Louis opening; c1 Apr 1966; LP32650]. Sd; col (Pathé). 35mm. 112 min.

Prod William Frye. *Dir* Ida Lupino. *Screenplay* Blanche Hanalis. *Dir Photog* Lionel Lindon. *Art Dir* John Beckman. *Set Decor* Victor Gangelin. *Main Titl* DePatie–Freleng. *Film Ed* Robert C. Jones. *Mus* Jerry Goldsmith. *Orch* Arthur Morton. *Sd Supv* Charles J. Rice. *Sd* Josh Westmoreland. *Asst Dir* Terry Nelson. *Asst to the Prod* James Wharton. *Nuns' Habit and Hayley Mills' Wardrobe* Sybil Connolly. *Cost Coörd* Helen Colvig. *Makeup Supv* Ben Lane. *Hairstyles* Virginia Jones.

Cast—The Nuns: Rosalind Russell *(Mother Superior)*, Binnie Barnes *(Sister Celestine)*, Camilla Sparv *(Sister Constance)*, Mary Wickes *(Sister Clarissa)*, Marge Redmond *(Sister Liguori)*, Dolores Sutton *(Sister Rose Marie)*, Margalo Gillmore *(Sister Barbara)*, Portia Nelson *(Sister Elizabeth)*, Marjorie Eaton *(Sister Ursula)*, Barbara Bell Wright *(Sister Margaret)*, Judith Lowry *(Sister Prudence)*.

Cast—The Girls: Hayley Mills *(Mary Clancy)*, June Harding *(Rachel Devery)*, Barbara Hunter *(Marvel-Ann)*, Bernadette Withers *(Valerie)*, Vicky Albright *(Charlotte)*, Patty Gerrity *(Sheila)*, Vicki Draves *(Kate)*, Wendy Winkelman *(Sandy)*, Jewel Jaffe *(Ginnie-Lou)*, Gail Liddle *(Priscilla)*, Michael-Marie *(Ruth)*, Betty Jane Royale *(Gladys)*, Ronnie Troup *(Helen)*, Catherine Wyles *(Brigette)*.

Cast—The Outsiders: Gypsy Rose Lee *(Mrs. Phipps)*, Jim Boles *(Mr. Gottschalk)*, Kent Smith *(Uncle George)*, Pat McCaffrie *(Mr. Devery)*, Harry Harvey, Sr. *(Mr. Grissom)*, Mary Young *(Mrs. Eldridge)*, Jim Hutton *(Mr. Petrie)*.

Comedy-drama. Source: Jane Trahey, *Life With Mother Superior* (New York, 1962). Mary Clancy and Rachel Devery reluctantly enter the convent school of St. Francis' Academy. Although the Mother Superior accurately pegs them as mischief makers and doles out punishment accordingly, she is unable to outsmart them. Running wild through the school and invading the cloisters, the girls substitute bubble bath powder for sugar at the nuns' tables, cause a fire emergency by smoking cigars in the boiler room, and disastrously attempt to make a mask by covering the face of a fellow student with quick-hardening plaster. Through it all, the determined Mother Superior remains confident that she can calm their temperamental natures. She befriends Rachel by staying up one night to teach the youngster how to make a new dress and recalls her own youthful dreams of becoming a fashion designer. Mary is deeply touched by the simple and devout service when one of the nuns dies suddenly, and she is further moved by the sisters' Christmas celebration. By graduation day, the change in Mary is complete; she decides to remain at the academy and join the Order. *Students. Nuns. Schoolteachers. Adolescence. Practical jokes. Religious conversion. Boarding schools. Convents. Funerals. Christmas.*

Note: *Where Angels Go—Trouble Follows*, q. v., is a sequel to this film. Working title: *Mother Superior.*

TROUBLE WITH EVE see IN TROUBLE WITH EVE

THE TROUBLE WITH GIRLS F6.5189

Metro-Goldwyn-Mayer, Inc. May **1969** [New York opening: 10 Dec; c8 May 1969; LP36951]. Sd (Westrex); col (Metrocolor). 35mm (Panavision). 97 min. [Also reviewed at 101 and 104 min.]

Prod Lester Welch. *Assoc Prod* Wilson McCarthy. *Dir* Peter Tewksbury. *Screenplay* Arnold Peyser, Lois Peyser. *Story* Mauri Grashin. *Dir Photog* Jacques Marquette. *Art Dir* George W. Davis, Edward Carfagno. *Set Decor* Henry Grace, Jack Mills. *Film Ed* George W. Brooks. *Mus Score* Billy Strange. *Song:* "Clean Up Your Own Back Yard" Scott Davis, Billy Strange. *Sung by* Elvis Presley. *Choreog* Jonathan Lucas. *Rec Supv* Franklin Milton. *Asst Dir* John Clarke Bowman. *Prod Mgr* Robert Vreeland. *Cost Dsgn* Bill Thomas. *Makeup* William Tuttle. *Hairstyles* Mary Keats.

Cast: Elvis Presley *(Walter Hale)*, Marilyn Mason *(Charlene)*, Nicole Jaffe *(Betty)*, Sheree North *(Nita Bix)*, Edward Andrews *(Johnny)*, John Carradine *(Mr. Drewcolt)*, Anissa Jones *(Carol)*, Vincent Price *(Mr. Morality)*, Joyce Van Patten *(Maude)*, Pepe Brown *(Willy)*, Dabney Coleman *(Harrison Wilby)*, William Zuckert *(Mayor Gilchrist)*, Pitt Herbert *(Mr. Perper)*, Anthony Teague *(Clarence)*, Med Flory *(constable)*, Robert Nichols *(Smith)*, Helene Winston *(Olga Prchlik)*, Kevin O'Neal *(Yale)*, Frank Welker *(Rutgers)*, John Rubinstein *(Princeton)*, Chuck Briles *(Amherst)*, Patsy Garrett *(Mrs. Gilchrist)*, Linda Sue

Risk *(Lily-Jeanne)*, Charles P. Thompson *(cabbie)*, Leonard Rumery *(1st farmhand)*, William Paris *(2d farmhand)*, Kathleen Rainey *(3d farmhand)*, Hal James Pederson *(soda jerk)*, Mike Wagner *(Chowderhead)*, Brett Parker *(iceman)*, Duke Snider *(cranker)*, Pacific Palisades High School Madrigals *(choral group)*.

Comedy-melodrama with music. Source: Day Keene and Dwight Babcock, *Chautauqua* (New York, 1960). In 1927, a chautauqua company comes into Radford Center, Iowa, and its new manager, Walter Hale, is attracted to Charlene, the Story Lady, despite their frequent quarrels over Charlene's attempts to form a union of the performers. Charlene, given the job of choosing a local child for the lead in the pageant, selects Carol Bix, whose mother, Nita, is an employee of the evil druggist Wilby. Local dignitaries are upset over the decision to use the Bix girl because they expected to see one of their own children selected. Wilby's body is found floating in the lake, and gambler Clarence is arrested. Walter realizes that Nita killed Wilby (he had forced her into having an affair with him), and he persuades her to confess publicly as part of the chautauqua performance. As a result of Nita's plea of self-defense against the lecherous Wilby, Clarence is cleared of the charge, and Nita is exonerated and gains enough money to realize her dream of moving to a new town with Carol and starting anew. Although Charlene is outraged at Walter's exploiting a killing for the company's financial advantage and threatens to quit, Walter manages to convince her of his integrity and persuades her to return to the company. *Songs include:* "Clean Up Your Own Back Yard," "America, the Beautiful," "A Thweet Yellow Tulip," "Toot-Toot-Tootsie," "Mademoiselle From Armantiers," "Rocked in the Cradle of the Deep." *Entertainers. Pharmacists. Gamblers. Justifiable homicide. Confession (law). Smalltown life. Chautauquas. Labor unions. Iowa.*

THE TROUBLEMAKER F6.5190

Ozymandias Productions–Seneca Productions. *Dist* Janus Films. 22 Jun **1964** [New York opening]. Sd; b&w. 35mm. 80 min.

Prod Robert Gaffney. *Dir* Theodore J. Flicker. *Screenplay* Theodore J. Flicker, Buck Henry. *Story* Buck Henry. *Photog* Gayne Rescher. *Art Dir* David Moon. *Set Dsgn* Leif Pedersen. *Film Ed* John McManus, William Austin. *Mus Comp & Cond* Cy Coleman. *Sd* Robert Maybaum. *Asst Dir* Ben Berk. *Prod Mgr* Lewis Bushnell.

Cast: Tom Aldredge *(Jack Armstrong)*, Joan Darling *(Denver James)*, Theodore J. Flicker *(crime commissioner)*, James Frawley *(Sol/Sal/Judge Kelly)*, Buck Henry *(T. R. Kingston)*, Charles White *(building inspector)*, Godfrey Cambridge *(fire inspector)*, Bernard Reed *(sanitation inspector)*, Michael Currie *(electrical inspector [see note])*, Leo Lerman *(dirty old man)*, Al Freeman, Jr. *(intern)*, Adelaide Klein *(psychiatrist)*, Joy Claussen *(Miss Simmons)*, China Lee *(hooker)*, Betty Stanton *(girl on the couch)*, Robbie Reed *(kid)*, Francis Dux *(Nazi leader)*, Calvin Ander *(Mr. Cohen)*, Graziella Narducci *(Sal's secretary)*.

Crime comedy. Jack Armstrong, a naive Midwesterner and former chicken farmer, runs into difficulties when he tries to open a coffee house in New York City without paying protection money to racketeer Sal and his associates. Armstrong's lawyer, T. R. Kingston, is also associated with Sal and is secretly paying off the mobster. Armstrong's moral indignation invokes Sal's wrath, and Jack is kidnaped and placed in a mental institution before he is finally able to obtain evidence that he is being harassed by criminals. Jack and his girl friend, Denver, discover that the crime commissioner is the real head of the graft racket, and, with the help of Kingston, they turn the tables on him. In the process, however, Jack loses his own integrity and becomes the biggest grafter of all. *Racketeers. Lawyers. Graft. Abduction. Urban life. Moral corruption. Coffeehouses. Hospitals. New York City.*

Note: Location scenes filmed in Cambridge, Massachusetts. Michael Currie may also be known as Kipp Currie.

TROUBLEMAKERS F6.5191

Alpha-60. *Dist* Film-Makers' Cooperative. 1 Dec **1966** [New York opening]. Sd; b&w. 16mm. 54 min.

Prod-Dir Robert Machover, Norman Fruchter. *Photog* Robert Machover. *Sd* Norman Fruchter. *Coöp* Newark Community Union Project. *Asst* Mike Robinson, Steve Gessner, Charlie Gillett.

Documentary. A record of a 3-month period in the history of the Newark Community Union Project, a community organizing movement in the black ghetto of Newark, New Jersey. During this time, the N.C.U.P. emerges as an adjunct of the Students for a Democratic Society; an attempt is made to obtain the enforcement of the housing code in a particular building; an effort is undertaken to move the city authorities to install a traffic light at a dangerous intersection; and the N.C.U.P. participates in a local political campaign. The frustrations of the community residents are made clear as the efforts of the N.C.U.P. meet with continual checks. *Negroes. Housing. Traffic. Political campaigns. Bureaucracy. Urban life. Ghettos. Newark (New Jersey). Newark Community Union Project. Students for a Democratic Society.*

THE TRUANT see TERROR IN THE CITY

TRUCKER'S GIRL   F6.5192
Carl R. Carter Productions. *Dist* Donald A. Davis Productions. ca **1970**. Sd; col (Eastman Color). 35mm. 65 min.

Dir-Writ Bobby Davis.

Cast: Constance Sirifem, Luann Cox, Eugene Wilkins, Lee Baker, Eddie Levine, Sterling Eilert, III, Lennie London, Angel Albright.

Sex film. The wife of a truckdriver awakens early one morning and, worried that her hippie husband might seek satisfaction elsewhere, makes passionate love to him. A second driver makes love to a prostitute who, after he leaves her, is raped by a sadistic bellhop. The third driver enjoys watching two women make love, but he is soon drawn into their loveplay. *Truckdrivers. Hippies. Prostitutes. Bellboys. Lesbianism. Troilism. Rape. Sadism.*

TRUE DIARY OF A WAHINE see MAEVA

TRUE GANG MURDERS   F6.5193
Sagittarius Films. *Dist* Teitel Film Corp. 29 Nov **1961** [Chicago opening]. Sd; b&w. 35mm. 62 min.

Prod-Writ Dan Goldberg, Harry Mantel. *Assoc Prod* Charles Teitel. *Dir* Sherman Rosenfield. *Dial* Rolf Forsberg. *Art Dir* Phil Lepinsky. *Background Percussion Mus* Gene Martin, mus.

Narrator: Don Gordon.

Documentary. A history of gang murder is traced through a series of still photographs of the outlaws and gangsters listed below. *Gangsters. Outlaws. Murder. Gang wars. Jesse Woodson James. Legs Diamond. Cole Younger. Albert Anastasia. John Dillinger. Emmet Dalton. Grattan Dalton. Frank Dalton. Robert Dalton. Victor F. Nelson. Charles "Pretty Boy" Floyd. Jim Colosimo. James Younger. John Younger. Robert Younger. Jack McGurn. Fred Barker. Kate "Ma" Barker. Dutch Schultz. Benny "Bugsy" Siegel. Willie Moretti. Roger Touhy.*

TRUE GRIT   F6.5194
Paramount Pictures. 11 Jun **1969** [Los Angeles opening; c16 Apr 1969; LP36735]. Sd; col (Technicolor). 35mm. 128 min. *MPAA rating G.*

A Hal Wallis Production. *Prod* Hal B. Wallis. *Assoc Prod* Paul Nathan. *Dir* Henry Hathaway. *Screenplay* Marguerite Roberts. *Dir Photog* Lucien Ballard. *Set Decor* Ray Moyer, John Burton. *Prod Dsgn* Walter Tyler. *Supv Film Ed* Warren Low. *Mus* Elmer Bernstein. *Song:* "True Grit" Don Black, Elmer Bernstein. *Sung by* Glen Campbell. *Hymn:* "Amazing Grace" John Newton. *Sd Rec* Roy Meadows, Elden Ruberg. *Asst Dir* William W. Gray. *Prod Mgr* Frank Beetson, Jr. *Cost* Dorothy Jeakins. *Makeup Supv* Jack Wilson, Carol Meikle. *Sp Eff* Dick Johnson, sp eff. *Greensman* Ernie Sawyer. *Transportation* George Coleman.

Cast: John Wayne (*Rooster Cogburn*), Glen Campbell (*La Boeuf*), Kim Darby (*Mattie Ross*), Jeremy Slate (*Emmett Quincy*), Robert Duvall (*Ned Pepper*), Dennis Hopper (*Moon*), Alfred Ryder (*Goudy*), Strother Martin (*Colonel Stonehill*), Jeff Corey (*Tom Chaney*), Ron Soble (*Capt. Boots Finch*), John Fiedler (*Lawyer Daggett*), James Westerfield (*Judge Parker*), John Doucette (*Sheriff*), Donald Woods (*Barlow*), Edith Atwater (*Mrs. Floyd*), Carlos Rivas (*Dirty Bob*), Isabel Boniface (*Mrs. Bagby*), H. W. Gim (*Chen Lee*), John Pickard (*Frank Ross*), Elizabeth Harrower (*Mrs. Ross*), Ken Renard (*Yarnell*), Jay Ripley (*Harold Parmalee*), Kenneth Becker (*Farrell Parmalee*).

Western melodrama. *Source:* Charles Portis, *True Grit* (New York, 1968). In 1880 in Yell County, Arkansas, 14-year-old Mattie Ross vows vengeance on her father's murderer, hired man Tom Chaney, who has fled into Indian Territory. Accordingly, she enlists the aid of one-eyed U. S. Marshal Rooster Cogburn and accepts the help of Texas Ranger La Boeuf, who is intent on the reward awaiting the man to capture Chaney for crimes committed in Texas. Despite mutual distrust, Rooster and La Boeuf unite to dissuade Mattie from accompanying them on their dangerous mission. Undeterred, she joins the manhunt. The trio tracks the assassin across the border to the refuge of outlaw Ned Pepper. During a surprise raid on Pepper's hideout, the lawmen kill four of his fellows and find a gold piece once the property of Mattie's father. Alone, Mattie encounters Chaney. Although she wounds him, Mattie is taken hostage by Pepper's band. Fearing for the girl's life, La Boeuf and Rooster pretend to retreat. Armed to the teeth, the two return unexpectedly to rescue Mattie. As Chaney bludgeons La Boeuf, Mattie shoots the fugitive a second time and falls backwards into a snakepit. After slaying Chaney, Rooster, aided by the dying ranger, pulls Mattie from the pit. Discovering that she has been bitten by a rattlesnake, the marshal, himself wounded, rushes the girl to a physician. Recovering from her injuries, the child proclaims to Rooster her wish to be buried next to him. *United States marshals. Farmhands. Texas Rangers. Outlaws. Gangs. Hostages. Adolescence. Murder. Robbery. Revenge. Snakebites. Arkansas.*

Note: Location scenes were filmed in and around Ridgway and Montrose, Colorado, and at Mammoth Lakes in California. Copyright claimants: Hal B. Wallis and Joseph H. Hazen.

TRUE STORY OF A WAHINE see MAEVA

THE TRUE STORY OF ADOLF HITLER see BLACK FOX

LE TRUFFE PIÙ BELLE DEL MONDO see THE BEAUTIFUL SWINDLERS

THE TRUNK (Great Britain)   F6.5195
Donwin Productions. *Dist* Columbia Pictures. 6 Sep **1961** [Seattle opening; c1 Oct 1961; LP20444]. Sd (Westrex); b&w. 35mm. 72 min.

Prod Lawrence Huntington. *Dir-Writ* Donovan Winter. *Story* Edward Abraham, Valerie Abraham. *Dir Photog* Norman Warwick. *Camera Op* Peter Allwork. *Art Dir* Bill Hutchinson. *Film Ed* Reginald Beck. *Mus Comp & Cond* John Fox, mus. *Sd Supv* John Cox. *Sd Rec* George Stephenson, Jack W. Davies. *Asst Dir* Harry Kratz. *Prod Mgr* Fraser Foulsham. *Cont* Eve Willson.

Cast: Philip Carey (*Stephen Dorning*), Julia Arnall (*Lisa Maitland*), Dermot Walsh (*Henry Maitland*), Vera Day (*Diane*), Peter Swanwick (*Nicholas Steiner*), John Atkinson (*Matt*), Betty Le Beau (*Maria*), Tony Quinn (*porter*), Robert Sansom (*bank manager*), Pippa Stanley (*Mrs. Stanhope*), Richard Nellor (*Sir Hubert*), Nicholas Tanner (*country policeman*).

Crime melodrama. Stephen Dorning, an American who is jealous because his former girl friend, Lisa, has married a London lawyer, tricks her into believing that she has killed her husband's former mistress, Diane. When Lisa panics, Stephen offers to dispose of the body for her for £2,000. Diane is alive, however, and she and Stephen are being observed by Nicholas Steiner, whom Diane has rejected. After receiving the money from Lisa, Stephen puts Diane in a trunk and drives to a deserted stretch of road. When he stops to release her from the trunk, he discovers that she is really dead—murdered by Steiner in such a way as to incriminate Stephen. *Mistresses. Americans in foreign countries. Lawyers. Jealousy. Murder. Blackmail. Frameup. London.*

Note: Released in Great Britain in Feb 1961.

TRUNK TO CAIRO (Israel/West Germany)   F6.5196
Noah Films—CCC-Filmkunst. *Dist* American International Pictures. 28 Dec **1966** [New York opening; c18 Jan 1967; LP33838]. Sd; col. 35mm. 80 min.

Prod-Dir Menahem Golan. *Assoc Prod* Michael Kugan. *Story-Screenplay* Marc Behm, Alexander Ramati. *Photog* Itzhak Herbst. *Art Dir* Shlomo Zafrir. *Film Ed* Dani Schick. *Mus Comp & Cond* Dov Seltzer. *Song:* "Dangerous Woman" Geula Gil. *Sd* Zalman Nachtigal. *Asst Dir* Jacques Erlich. *Prod Mgr* Yoel Noyman. *Wardrobe* Gina Rosenbach. *Makeup* Rachel Golan, Daliah Priver.

Cast: Audie Murphy (*Mike Merrick*), George Sanders (*Professor Schlieben*), Marianne Koch (*Helga Schlieben*), Hans von Borsody (*Hans Klugg*), Joseph Yadin (*Captain Gabar*), Gila Almagor (*Yasmin*), Elana Eden (*Hadassa*), Eytan Priver (*Jamil*), Zalman (*Ephraim*), Bomba Zur (*Ali*), Tikva Mor (*Christina*), Zeev Berlinski (*Benz*), Eliezer Young (*Dr. Heider*), Shlomo Vichinsky (*Jacob*), Yoel Noyman (*Egyptian colonel*), Cesar Suberi (*Old Mullah*), Shlomo Paz (*Joe*), Mona Silberstein (*hostess*), Anna Shell (*belly dancer*), Suzanna Ratoni (*Fraulein Bruckner*), Menashe Glazier (*Mahmud*), Karin (*young German girl*).

Action melodrama. International [Israeli?] agent Mike Merrick is sent under cover to Cairo for a rendezvous with German scientist Professor Schlieben. After striking up a romance with Schlieben's daughter, Helga, Mike learns that the professor is nearing completion of a nuclear-powered moon rocket which could be used as a weapon. Though the professor's operational center is closely guarded by the Egyptian army, Mike gains entry into Schlieben's private quarters and destroys the plans and blueprints for the rocket. Later he encounters the Holy Islam Freedom Fighters, who want to destroy the rocket but trust no one. Eluding a trap, Mike kidnaps Helga as a means of forcing the professor to leave Egypt. After they have escaped to Rome by submarine, however, Mike and Helga are captured by the Egyptians. Mike is placed in a trunk and rushed to an airport for shipment back to Cairo, but his Italian counterparts give chase and capture the Egyptians. When they open the trunk, however, they find one of Mike's guards. Mike has boarded the plane in which Helga is being held prisoner, and once in flight he overpowers the Egyptian pilot and returns Helga to her grateful father. *Secret agents. Egyptians. Scientists. Terrorists. Espionage. Kidnaping. Filial relations. Nuclear weapons. Submarines. Airplanes. Cairo. Rome. Egypt—Army.*

Note: Location scenes filmed in Israel and Italy. Hebrew title: *Mivtza Kahir*. Released in West Germany in Jun 1966 as *Einer spielt falsch*; running time: 99 min. Some U. S. sources indicate U. S. involvement in the production.

THE TRUTH (France/Italy)   F6.5197
Han Productions–Iéna Production–C. E. I. A. P. *Dist* Kingsley International Pictures. 26 Jun **1961** [New York opening]. Sd; b&w. 35mm. 127 min.

Prod Raoul J. Lévy. *Assoc Prod* Roger Debelmas. *Dir* Henri-Georges Clouzot. *Screenplay* Henri-Georges Clouzot, Simone Drieu, Michèle Perrein, Jérôme Geronimi, Christiane Rochefort, Simone Marescat, Véra Clouzot. *Photog* Armand Thirard. *Art Dir* Jean André. *Film Ed* Albert Jurgenson. *Mus From the Works of* Ludwig van Beethoven. *Excerpts From "The Firebird"* Igor Stravinsky. *Sd* William R. Sivel. *Prod Mgr* Louis Wipf. *English Subtitl* Noelle Gillmor.

Cast: Brigitte Bardot (*Dominique Marceau*), Charles Vanel (*Guérin*), Paul Meurisse (*Eparvier*), Sami Frey (*Gilbert*), Marie-José Nat (*Annie Marceau*), Louis Seigner (*president of the court*), Jacqueline Porel (*lawyer*), Jean-Louis Reynold (*Michel*), André Oumansky (*Ludovic*), Christian Lude (*colonel*), Suzy Willy (*Madame Marceau*), Barbara Somers (*Daisy*), René Blancard (*attorney general*), Fernand Ledoux (*court physician*), Louis Arbessier (*conservatory professor*).

Melodrama. Dominique Marceau is a young Frenchwoman on trial for the slaying of her lover. The prosecuting attorney, Eparvier, claims it was an act of premeditated murder that warrants the death penalty. The defense attorney, Guérin, maintains that it was an act of passion and not punishable by death. As the trial progresses and the various testimonies of the witnesses are heard, the tragic story unfolds. *For almost a year, Dominique has been living a wanton, bohemian life on the Paris Left Bank. One day she seduces Gilbert, a serious music student and the boyfriend of her sister Annie. Though he falls passionately in love with Dominique, she continues to have fleeting affairs with other men. Eventually her behavior so angers the jealous Gilbert that their affair ends in a violent quarrel. As the months pass, Dominique is reduced to prostitution while Gilbert becomes a well-known symphony conductor. When Dominique learns that Gilbert and Annie are officially engaged, she realizes that despite the quarrels, he was the only man she ever really loved. She rushes to his apartment and spends the night with him. In the morning, however, he throws her out and calls her a slut. Determined to prove her love, Dominique decides to commit suicide in his presence; but when he brutally insults her, she fires six bullets into his body. She then attempts suicide but is found and rescued by the police.* When all the testimony has been submitted, Dominique realizes that because of her sordid life the jury is unconvinced that her love for Gilbert was real. As her fate is being pondered, she returns to her prison cell and slashes her wrists with a piece of broken mirror. *Sisters. Lawyers. Students. Orchestra conductors. Trials. Bohemianism. Seduction. Prostitution. Jealousy. Murder. Suicide. Juries. Paris—Quartier Latin.*

Note: Opened in Paris in Nov 1960 as *La vérité*; running time: 124 min; in Rome in Jan 1961 as *La verità*; running time: 110 min. U. S. version includes a 3-min prolog which explains the differences between French and American court procedure. Iéna Production (Raoul Levy) is credited in some sources in place of Han Productions.

THE TRUTH ABOUT SPRING (Great Britain)   F6.5198

Quota Rentals. *Dist* Universal Pictures. 31 Mar **1965** [Pittsburgh opening; c1 Jan 1964; LP35003]. Sd (Westrex); col (Technicolor). 35mm. 102 min.

Prod Alan Brown. *Dir* Richard Thorpe. *Screenplay* James Lee Barrett. *Dir Photog* Edward Scaife. *Camera Op* Jack Atchelor. *Art Dir* Gil Parrondo. *Main Titl* National Screen Service Ltd. *Film Ed* Thomas Stanford. *Mus Comp & Cond* Robert Farnon. *Titl Song* Robert Farnon, David Heneker. *Sung by* Danny Street. *Rec Supv* A. W. Watkins. *Sd* Sash Fisher. *Asst Dir* Ted Sturgis, Pedro Vidal. *Prod Mgr* Douglas Twiddy. *Cont* Mickey Macpherson. *Makeup* Ernest Gasser. *Hairstyles* Maud Onslow.

Cast: Hayley Mills (*Spring Tyler*), John Mills (*Tommy Tyler*), James MacArthur (*William Ashton*), Lionel Jeffries (*Cark*), Harry Andrews (*Sellers*), Niall MacGinnis (*Cleary*), Lionel Murton (*Simmons*), David Tomlinson (*Skelton*).

Comedy-drama. Source: Henry de Vere Stacpoole, *Satan; a Romance of the Bahamas* (New York, 1921). Traveling in the Caribbean, wiley widower Tommy Tyler and his tomboy daughter, Spring, encounter millionaire Skelton and his vacationing nephew William Ashton. Tiring of life aboard his uncle's yacht, the young lawyer accepts an invitation to the Tylers' houseboat. Although the young people are immediately attracted to one another, their romance is interrupted by the visit of Tyler's disgruntled former associate, Cark. To pacify the old partner Tyler persuades Cark to invest heavily in an expedition to locate sunken treasure. A second former associate, Cleary, is also persuaded to part with a similar sum. When the vessel is found to contain only crumbling skeletons of slaves, Tyler retains the cash and eludes his angry investors. Having returned to his uncle's yacht, Ashton quickly discovers how much he loves Spring. With her father's blessing, the lawyer proposes. As Ashton and the pliant Spring board the yacht, Tyler speeds away to further adventures. *Fishermen. Widowers. Tomboys. Lawyers. Millionaires. Uncles. Confidence men. Filial relations. Courtship. Houseboats. Yachts. Treasure. Caribbean.*

Note: Filmed on location in Costa Brava, Spain. Opened in London in May 1965. Prerelease title: *Miss Jude*.

THE TRYGON FACTOR (Great Britain)   F6.5199

Rialto-Film Preben Philipsen. *Dist* Warner Bros.-Seven Arts, Inc. Jan **1969** [Los Angeles showing]. Sd; col (Technicolor). 35mm. 87 min. *MPAA rating* M.

Prod Brian Taylor. *Exec Prod* Ian Warren. *Dir* Cyril Frankel. *Screenplay* Derry Quinn, Stanley Munro. *Orig Story* Derry Quinn. *Photog* Harry Waxman. *Col Coörd* Stephen Andrews. *Art Dir* Roy Stannard. *Set Decor* Hazel Peisei. *Film Ed* Oswald Hafenrichter. *Mus* Peter Thomas. *Sd Rec* David Bowen. *Asst Dir* Stuart Freeman. *Prod Supv* Robert J. Faloon. *Prod Mgr* Pat Morton. *Cost Coörd* Stephen Andrews. *Sp Eff* Ted Samuels. *Prod Cons* Wolfgang Kühnlenz.

Cast: Stewart Granger (*Superintendent Cooper-Smith*), Susan Hampshire (*Trudy Emberday*), Robert Morley (*Hubert Hamlyn*), Cathleen Nesbitt (*Livia Emberday*), Brigitte Horney (*Sister General [Mrs. Hamlyn]*), Sophie Hardy (*Sophie*), James Robertson-Justice (*Sir John*), Eddi Arent (*Emil Clossen*), Diane Clare (*Sister Clare*), James Culliford (*Luke Emberday*), Allan Cuthbertson (*Detective Thompson*), Colin Gordon (*Dice*), Yuri Borienko (*Nailer*), Conrad Monk (*Pasco*), Russell Waters (*Sergeant Chivers*), Caroline Blakiston (*white nun*), Richardina Jackson (*black nun*), John Barrett (*guide*), Jeremy Hawk (*bank manager*), Joseph Cuby (*receptionist*), Inigo Jackson (*ballistics expert*), Tom Bowman (*security guard*), Cicely Paget-Bowman (*lady at hotel*), Hilary Wontner (*man at hotel*).

Crime melodrama. Livia Emberday and her photographer daughter Trudy resort to crime in order to save their stately English manor from financial ruin. Assisted by Livia's dim-witted son Luke, the two women have installed a bogus order of nuns on the grounds and are using the convent as a front for receiving stolen goods and shipping them to the warehouse of Hubert Hamlyn, an old friend whose wife is posing as the Sister General at the phony convent. When a man from Scotland Yard disappears while investigating the convent, Superintendent Cooper-Smith is assigned to the case. Arriving at Emberday Hall, he finds an interment underway in the family vault. Although he is unaware that the "corpse" is actually Emil Clossen, a safecracking specialist who has been smuggled into England for the next Emberday caper, Cooper-Smith is suspicious and enlists the aid of Sophie, the receptionist at the local hotel. Once the gang has stolen £1 million in gold bullion from a city bank, they ship the ingots to the convent for melting down before being smuggled abroad by Hamlyn. While Cooper-Smith is following a trail to the convent, Sophie is captured trying to investigate alone. Cooper-Smith arrives as the nuns are pouring the molten gold into pottery vases, and confusion quickly turns to panic: Hamlyn is strangled, Clossen is drowned in a coffin, Luke is shot by his mother, Trudy is killed by a crucible filled with the molten gold, and Cooper-Smith is accidentally knocked unconscious by Sophie. *Photographers. Halfwits. Nuns. Fences (for stolen goods). Detectives. Safecrackers. Receptionists. Filial relations. Imposture. Smuggling. Missing persons. Bank robberies. Murder. Convents. Gold. Scotland Yard.*

Note: Released in Great Britain in Jul 1967.

TSAR TO LENIN   F6.5200

Herman Axelbank Associates. 26 May **1966** [New York opening]. Sd; b&w. 35mm. 90 min.

Compiled & Prod Herman Axelbank. *Screenplay* William Hepper, Cyril Jones. *Film Ed* William Hepper, Cyril Jones.

Narrator: Valentine Dyall.

Documentary. Depicted in this chronicle of Russian communism are the diversions of the court of Nicholas II, the anarchy of Kropotkin, the 1917 revolution, the exile of Trotsky, the triumph and death of Lenin, and the rallies of Stalin. Also included is footage of Khrushchev and Nixon. *Royalty. Bolshevists. Anarchists. Communism. Russia—History—1917–21 Revolution. Nicholas II (Russia). Nikolai Lenin. Leon Trotsky. Pëtr Alekseevich Kropotkin. Joseph Stalin. Nikita Sergeyevich Khrushchev. Richard Milhous Nixon.*

Note: Released by Axelbank in 1937 in a 68-min version with editing and commentary by Max Eastman.

THE TSAR'S BRIDE (U.S.S.R.)   F6.5201

Riga Film Studio. *Dist* Artkino Pictures. 11 Mar **1966** [New York opening]. Sd; b&w. 35mm (Sovscope). 95 min.

Dir Vladimir Gorikker. *Screenplay* A. Donatov, Vladimir Gorikker. *Photog* Vadim Mass. *Camera* Kh. Kukels. *Art Dir* G. Balodis. *Mus*: "Tsarskaya nevesta" Nikolai Andreevich Rimski-Korsakov. *Mus Cond* Yevgeniy Svetlanov. *Perf by* Bolshoi Theater Orchestra. *Sd* V. Zorin. *Asst Dir* Yu. Tselms. *Sp Eff* E. August, V. Shildknekht.

Cast: Raisa Nedashkovskaya (*Marfa*), Natalya Rudnaya (*Lyubasha*), Otar Koberidze (*Grigoriy Gryaznoy*), G. Shevtsov (*Malyuta Skuratov*), V. Zeldin (*Bomeliy*), Nikolay Timofeyev (*Sobakin*), Viktor Nuzhnyy (*Ivan Lykov*), M. Maltseva (*Dunyasha*), T. Loginova (*Saburova*), Pyotr Glebov (*Ivan Groznyy*

[Ivan the Terrible]).

Singing Voices: Galina Oleynichenko *(Marfa)*, Larisa Avdeyeva *(Lyubasha)*, Yevgeniy Kibkalo *(Gryaznoy)*, A. Geleva *(Malyuta Skuratov)*, P. Chekin *(Bomeliy)*, A. Vedernikov *(Sobakin)*, Ye. Raykov *(Ivan Lykov)*, V. Klepatskaya *(Dunyasha)*, T. Tugarinova *(Saburova)*, Bolshoi Theater Chorus.

Opera film. Source: Nikolai Andreevich Rimski-Korsakov, *Tsarskaya nevesta* (an opera; Moscow opening: 3 Nov 1899). Lev Aleksandrovich Mey, *Tsarskaya nevesta* (a play; 1849). Marfa, a Russian girl of noble birth, is to be forced to marry Tsar Ivan the Terrible. Ivan's friend and bodyguard Gryaznoy, a man of wild and passionate nature, also loves Marfa. To captivate her, he persuades a German physician to prepare a love potion. Lyubasha, Gryaznoy's mistress, overhears his plan and substitutes poison for the philter. At the feast where Ivan is to announce his betrothal, Marfa drinks the poison and, dying, goes mad. When Ivan enters the hall, the remorseful Gryaznoy reveals that he has given Marfa a potion and is seized by the guards, whereupon Lyubasha confesses to the poisoning. Gryaznoy stabs her and then is led away to die. *Royalty. Bodyguards. Germans. Physicians. Mistresses. Marriage—Arranged. Jealousy. Poisoning. Insanity. Murder. Eavesdropping. Friendship. Potions. Ivan IV Vasilievich.*

Note: Released in the U.S.S.R. in 1965 as *Tsarskaya nevesta.*

TSARSKAYA NEVESTA *see* **THE TSAR'S BRIDE**

TSUBAKI SANJURO *see* **SANJURO**

TU PERDONAS ... YO NO *see* **GOD FORGIVES—I DON'T**

TU SERAS TERRIBLEMENT GENTILLE *see* **YOU ONLY LOVE ONCE**

TUCK ME IN   **F6.5202**
Cinema Central II Productions. *Dist* Jerand Film Distributors. Oct **1970**. Sd; b&w with col seq. 35mm. 82 min.

Prod Robert Wayne. *Dir* Michael Meola. *Dir Col Seq* Jeraldo Stuarti. *Screenplay* Robert Wayne, Michael Meola. *Story* Michael Meola. *Dir Photog* Mort Shuman, photog. *Film Ed* Hayward Waxman. *Sd* Vincent De Leo. *Sd Eff* Sound One Inc. *Asst Dir* Robert Pitts. *Cost Dsgn* Jane Brooks. *Makeup* Jane Brooks. *Casting Consult* Cinema Central I.

Cast: Kim Pope *(Tracy)*, Frank Durk *(Rod)*, Carolyn Kessler *(Karen)*, Richard Howell, Michael Aronson, Louanna Grant, Billy Longo, Sandra Loane, Mary Brent, Robert Janvier, Robert Wayne, Jorde Wolfe, Heather McCann, Mike Coquat, Walter Kirk, Philip Edwards, Charlotte Livingston.

Melodrama. Tracy Middleton, an aspiring young actress, shares an apartment with Karen in Greenwich Village. Tracy hopes to get a break without using her actor father's name, Rod Middleton, but she finally gives in and visits her father's producer and friend, Alex Menninger, who gives her a part only after she sleeps with him. Middleton comes to New York to visit Tracy; he seduces Karen, and Tracy later joins them in bed. Tracy teams with her father in Hollywood and makes a series of films after her first Broadway role is a success. Tracy then goes to Italy to represent the United States at film festivals. On her return 2 years later, she finds her father and Karen married. Tracy acts in another film with Middleton and is particularly successful in the final scene, a death scene. The work overtires her father, and he dies of a heart attack. Losing him is a shock to Tracy, and she wanders around the Village a stranger. She is picked up by a middle-aged couple who take her back to their place, strip her, and begin to make love to her. Tracy pulls away from them, reaches for the gun she acquired in Italy, and re-enacts her famous death scene. *Roommates. Actors. Theatrical producers. Filial relations. Incest. Seduction. Death. Troilism. Employment—Women. Motion pictures. New York City—Broadway. New York City—Greenwich Village. Hollywood. Italy.*

Note: Also known as *Keep Me In.*

LES TUEURS DE SAN FRANCISCO *see* **ONCE A THIEF**

TUMULT *see* **RELATIONS**

TUNNEL 28 *see* **ESCAPE FROM EAST BERLIN**

TUNNEL TO THE SUN (Japan)   **F6.5203**
Mifune-Ishihara Productions. *Dist* Toho Co. 2 Oct **1968** [Los Angeles opening]. Sd; col. 35mm. 198 min.

Prod Toshiro Mifune, Yujiro Ishihara. *Dir* Kei Kumai. *Screenplay* Masato Ide, Kei Kumai. *Story* Sojiro Motoki. *Photog* Mitsuji Kanau. *Mus* Toshiro Mayuzumi.

Cast: Toshiro Mifune *(Kitagawa)*, Yujiro Ishihara, Osamu Takizawa, Ryutaro Tatsumi, Jukichi Uno, Eijiro Yanagi, Eiji Okada, Shuji Sano, Mieko Takamine, Fumie Kashiyama, Tomoe Hiiro, Tanie Kitamura.

Drama. Kitagawa, an engineer, is assigned to build a tunnel through which construction supplies can be carried to the Kurobegawa No. 4 dam site, but he accepts the job with reluctance because the tunnel must be dug through a dangerous fault. [Apparently the film depicts the construction of the dam.] *Engineers. Construction. Tunnels. Dams. Kurobegawa No. 4 (dam).*

Note: Released in Japan in Mar 1968 as *Kurobe no taiyo.*

DIE TÜRKISCHEN GURKEN *see* **THE TURKISH CUCUMBER**

THE TURKISH CUCUMBER (West Germany)   **F6.5204**
Bavaria-Filmkunst. *Dist* K. Gordon Murray Productions, Inter-American Film Distributors, Trans-International Films. **1963**. Sd; b&w with col seq. 35mm. 96 min.

Pres by K. Gordon Murray. *Prod English Vers* K. Gordon Murray. *Dir* Rolf Olsen. *Screenplay* Rolf Olsen, Peter Loos, Gunther Philipp. *Photog* Walter Tuch. *Art Dir* Otto Pischinger, Herta Hareiter. *Mus* Werner Scharfenberger. *Sd* Erwin Jennewein.

Cast: Oskar Sima *(fruit merchant)*, Susi Nicoletti *(his wife)*, Ruth Stephan *(their daughter)*, Gunther Philipp, Walter Gross, Hubert von Meyerinck, Ernst Waldbrunn, Charly Müller, Ilse Petri, Monika Berger, Angela Monti, Brigitte Wenzel, Angela Hartmann, Edith Peters, Sergio Cosmei, Willy Schultes, Dora Carras, Harry Hertzsch, Lill Babs.

Comedy. Celebrating his daughter's wedding and his 50th year in the wholesale business, a German fruit merchant receives a harem as a gift from his oriental supplier, a Turkish sheik. The merchant is determined to hide the women from his daughter and jealous wife. *Merchants. Harems. Sheiks. Turks. Marriage. Filial relations. Jealousy. Weddings.*

Note: Released in West Germany in Mar 1962 as *Die türkischen Gurken.* Alternative titles: *Wedding Present* and *Daddy's Delectable Dozen.*

TURLIS ABENTEUER *see* **PINOCCHIO**

TURN ME ON!   **F6.5205**
Dynacom Productions. *Dist* Grads Corp. 12 Jun **1968** [New York showing]. Sd; b&w. 35mm. 64-73 min.

Assoc Prod Ramon Ponce. *Screenplay* R. Charleton Wilson.

Cast: Barbara Lynn *(Sharon)*, Kitty Doone *(Betsey)*, Janice Mackey *(Jan)*, Forman Shain *(Joe)*, William Hess *(Phil)*, James Quantia Scott *(Andy)*, Guy Nicholas *(bartender)*, Bud Kennedy *(detective)*, Sydney Talbert *(Dandy)*, Jimmy Green *(Arnold)*, Brett Scott *(Tanji)*, Martin Corrigan *(Paul)*, Capri *(Carole)*, Holly Saunders *(Milly)*, Suzanne Christie *(Marcia)*.

Drama. Joe, Phil, and Andy meet in a topless beer hall and exchange stories about their sexual experiences. *Dandy attempts to rob Joe, and he gives her a spanking. Dandy enjoys the experience and takes Joe home to meet her homosexual brother. They smoke marijuana; Joe passes out; and Dandy and her brother take his valuables. Phil picks up Marcia, a hostess in a service club, and they go to her apartment and make love. Phil then becomes involved with Tanji, the maid. Andy, celibate for 16 months, goes to a wild party and makes love with Carole, the host's wife. They later smoke marijuana.* Joe, Phil, and Andy pick up three topless dancers who work in the bar and go to the apartment of one of the girls. They smoke marijuana and are arrested during a police raid. *Braggarts. Go-go dancers. Cafe hostesses. Housemaids. Police. Sadomasochism. Theft. Male homosexuality. Infidelity. Group sex. Bars. Marijuana.*

TURN ON TO LOVE   **F6.5206**
L. T. Kurtmann. *Dist* Haven International Pictures. 19 Dec **1969** [New York opening]. Sd; b&w. 35mm. 83 min. [Also reviewed at 79 min.]

An L.T. Kurtmann Production. *Prod* L. T. Kurtmann. *Dir* John G. Avildsen. *Screenplay* Atlas Geodesic. *Adtl Dial* Fred Balachine. *Orig Story* Herman Worth. *Photog* John G. Avildsen. *Film Ed* John G. Avildsen. *Mus* Amanda Productions, Harmon Thronebury, The Ins and Outs.

Cast: Sharon Kent *(Janice)*, Richard Michaels *(Gerard)*, Luigi Mastroianni *(Rico)*, Jackie Riley *(Randee)*, Steven Wingate *(Henry)*, Elizabeth Tarrington *(Betty)*, Frank Rogers *(Roach)*.

Melodrama. Janice, a voluptuous newlywed, has grown restless since her marriage to Gerard, who does not sexually satisfy her. Alone, she attends a party in Greenwich Village; marijuana is smoked and couples openly engage in sexual intercourse. Janice meets Rico, a young Italian filmmaker, and he seduces her. She meets with Rico the next day and shows him Greenwich Village life. They again go to bed, but Rico confesses that he is happily married and has children. Upon hearing Janice's problem, Rico advises her to return to her husband and encourage him to satisfy her more fully. *Newlyweds. Italians. Motion picture directors. Infidelity. Group sex. Marijuana. New York City—Greenwich Village.*

Note: Filmed in New York City.

TURN ON, TUNE IN, DROP OUT   **F6.5207**
Benedict Pictures. *Dist* United Productions of America. 11 May **1967** [Los Angeles showing]. Sd; col. 35mm. 82 min.

Prod Henry G. Saperstein. *Dir* Robin Clark. *Film Ed* Frederic Knudtson. *Mus* Maryyvonne Giercurz, Lars Eric, Richard Bond. *Coörd by* Bob Lowe. *Sp*

Eff Conception UPA Pictures.

Documentary. Seated cross-legged on stage, drug advocate Timothy Leary addresses the audience at a New York theater. Behind him a trio plays Indian music. His subject is LSD, the effects of which are approximated in an animated sequence. Others discussing narcotics include Professor Ralph Metzner and Rosemary Woodruff, Leary's wife. *Professors. Mystics. Psychedelic states. LSD. New York City. Timothy Leary. Ralph Metzner. Rosemary Woodruff.*

TURNED-ON GIRL   **F6.5208**

Kirt Films International–Triumph Films. *Dist* Distribpix, Inc. 30 Dec **1970** [Fresno, California, showing]. Sd; col. 35mm. 63 min.

Prod Bob Mansy. *Dir* C. Walsh.

Cast: Janet Topaz, Margaret Leigh.

Sex film. Barbara falls in love for the first time only to discover that her boyfriend often turns to other women to satisfy his excessive sexual demands. She becomes a prostitute in order to prove herself more of a woman than any of his other girl friends. *Prostitutes. Jealousy. Satyriasis.*

TUTTE LE ALTRE RAGAZZE LO FANNO *see* **ALL THE OTHER GIRLS DO**

TUTTI A CASA *see* **EVERYBODY GO HOME!**

TUTTI FRUTTI *see* **CATCH AS CATCH CAN**

TUTTI PAZZI MENO IO *see* **KING OF HEARTS**

TVÅ LEVANDE OCH EN DÖD *see* **TWO LIVING, ONE DEAD**

THE TWELVE CHAIRS   **F6.5209**

Twelve Chairs Co. *Dist* UMC Pictures. 28 Oct **1970** [New York opening]. Sd; col (print by Movielab). 35mm. 94 min. *MPAA rating* GP.

Prod Michael Hertzberg. *Exec Prod* Sidney Glazier. *Dir-Writ* Mel Brooks. *Photog* Djordje Nikolić. *Art Dir* Mile Nikolić. *Film Ed* Alan Heim. *Mus* John Morris. *Sd* Peter Sutton. *Asst Dir* Bata Čengić, Peter Anderson. *Exec in Charge of Prod* William A. Berns.

Cast: Ron Moody (*Vorobyaninov*), Frank Langella (*Ostap Bender*), Dom DeLuise (*Father Fyodor*), Mel Brooks (*Tikon*), Bridget Brice (*young woman*), Robert Bernal (*curator*), David Lander (*engineer Bruns*), Andreas Voutsinas (*Nikolai Sestrin*), Vlada Petrić (*Sevitsky*), Diana Coupland (*Madame Bruns*), Elaine Garreau, Nicholas Smith, Will Stampe, Branka Veselinović, Mladja Veselinović, Rada Djuričin.

Comedy. Source: Ilya Arnoldovich Ilf and Yevgeniy Petrov, *Dvenadtsat stulyev* (Moscow, 1928; trans. by Elizabeth Hill and Doris Mudie as *Diamonds To Sit On*; London, 1930). In Russia in 1927, Vorobyaninov, an elderly license clerk who was once a nobleman, is informed by his dying mother that she hid a fortune in jewels in one of 12 matching chairs during the 1917 Revolution. He returns to his ancestral home to retrieve the inheritance, but he mistakenly reveals his secret to beggar Ostap Bender and is forced to accept the young man as a partner. Together they set out in search of the chairs and soon discover that Father Fyodor, a Russian Orthodox priest who heard Vorobyaninov's mother's last confession, is also in search of the jewels. Ostap, posing as a clerk in the Bureau of Housing, tricks Father Fyodor into traveling to Siberia to the home of engineer Bruns, who he is told is in possession of the chairs. Meanwhile, Vorobyaninov and Ostap locate several of the chairs in the Moscow Museum of Furniture, and after closing time, they sneak out of hiding, search through the chairs, but find no jewels. Ostap and Vorobyaninov then learn that several more of the chairs are being used as props by the Columbus Repertory Theatre Group; they join the troupe, search the chairs, but again find no gems. Another chair, used by a tightrope walker in a circus, is searched, also to no avail. Desperate for money, the two men perform a begging act in which Vorobyaninov feigns an epileptic seizure as Ostap passes his hat to sympathetic onlookers. Finally, they come upon the last chair in a railroad workers' clubhouse only to discover that the jewels were found by the workers and used to buy chess sets and other items for their recreation room. His dream of wealth destroyed, Ostap decides to break up his partnership with the old man, but he relents when Vorobyaninov goes into his routine of feigning epilepsy as a crowd gathers. *Russians. Clerks. Nobility. Beggars. Priests. Engineers. Tightrope walkers. Railroad workers. Confidence men. Confession. Partnerships. Greed. Imposture. Perfidy. Furniture. Jewels. Inheritance. Museums. Theatrical troupes. Russia—History—1917–21 Revolution. Union of Soviet Socialist Republics. Moscow. Siberia.*

Note: Location scenes filmed in Yugoslavia.

THE 25TH HOUR (France/Italy/Yugoslavia)   **F6.5210**

Les Films Concordia–C. C. Champion–Avala Film. *Dist* Metro-Goldwyn-Mayer, Inc. 1 Feb **1967** [Los Angeles opening; c23 Feb 1967; LP34024]. Sd (Westrex); col (Metrocolor). 35mm (Franscope). 119 min. [Also reviewed at 134 min.]

A Carlo Ponti Production. *Prod* Carlo Ponti. *Assoc Prod* Simon Schiffrin. *Dir* Henri Verneuil. *Screenplay* Henri Verneuil, François Boyer, Wolf Mankowitz. *Dir Photog* Andréas Winding. *Camera Op* Daniel Diot. *Set Dresser* Pierre Charron. *Prod Dsgn* Robert Clavel. *Main Titl* Jean Fouchet. *Film Ed* Françoise Bonnot. *Mus Comp & Cond* Georges Delerue. *Sd Rec* Antoine Petitjean. *Asst Dir* Claude Pinoteau. *Prod Mgr* Paul Joly. *Cost* Rosine Delamare. *Makeup* Monique Archambault. *Hairdresser* Alex Archambault.

Cast: Anthony Quinn (*Johann Moritz*), Virna Lisi (*Suzanna Moritz*), Michael Redgrave (*defense counsel*), Grégoire Aslan (*Nicolai Dobresco*), Marcel Dalio (*Strul*), Serge Reggiani (*Trajan Koruga*), Drewe Henley (*Captain Brunner*), Paul Maxwell (*photographer*), George Roderick (*Goldenberg*), Alexander Knox (*prosecutor*), Albert Rémy (*Joseph Grenier*), Françoise Rosay (*Madame Nagy*), Jean Desailly (*war minister's aide*), Marius Goring (*Colonel Müller*), John Le Mesurier (*magistrate*), Liam Redmond (*Father Koruga*), Kenneth J. Warren (*Varga*), Henia Suchar (*Nora*), Jan Werich (*Sgt. Apostol Constantin*), Harold Goldblatt (*Dr. Nagy*), Meier Tzelniker (*Abramovici*), Jacques Marin (*Fourrier*), Dara Milošević (*Mrs. Koruga*), Viktor Starčić (*Hurtig*), Stojan Dečermić (*Marcou*), Olga Schoberová (*Rosa*), David Sumner (*Ghitza Jon*), Raoul Delfosse (*usher*).

War melodrama. Source: Constantin Virgil Gheorghiu, *La vingt-cinquième heure* (trans. from Romanian by Monique Saint-Côme; Paris, 1949). At the time of the German invasion of Romania in 1939 Johann Moritz, a simple peasant, is falsely branded as a Jew and sent to a German labor camp. The man responsible for the deportation is Nicolai Dobresco, a district police officer who covets Johann's wife, Suzanna. Suzanna successfully wards off Dobresco's advances, but later she is forced to divorce Johann in order to save their home from being confiscated as Jewish property. Eighteen months later Johann escapes from the labor camp to Hungary, but Jewish refugee organizations refuse to help him because he insists that he is not a Jew. Eventually, he is captured and, ironically, selected by a Nazi colonel as the perfect example of "racially pure German stock." He is inducted into the SS and is forced to pose for photographs used on the covers of magazines circulated throughout occupied Europe. After the war he is brought to trial at Nuremberg, where he is shown little leniency by the prosecuting officer. However, a letter from Suzanna explaining her endless attempts to secure Johann's release, her rape by Russian soldiers, and the subsequent birth of an illegitimate child, so deeply moves the court that Johann is freed. After an 8-year separation, Johann is reunited with his family. *Peasants. Jews. Refugees. Police. Mistaken identity. Nazism. Divorce. Rape. Concentration camps. World War II. International Military Tribunal. Romania. Germany—Army. SS.*

Note: Location scenes reportedly filmed in Munich and Budapest. Opened in Paris in Apr 1967 as *La 25e heure*. Italian title: *La venticinquesima ora*.

24-HOUR LOVER (West Germany)   **F6.5217**

Rob Houwer-Film. *Dist* American International Pictures. 29 May **1970** [Dallas opening]. Sd; col (Eastman Color, print by Movielab). 35mm. 90 min. *MPAA rating* R.

Prod Rob Houwer. *Dir-Screenplay-Idea* Marran Gosov. *Photog* Hubs Hagen, Niklas Schilling. *Art Dir* Gabriel Bauer. *Film Ed* Gisela Haller. *Mus* Martin Böttcher. *Prod Supv* Jürgen Dohme. *Prod Mgr* Siegfried Wagner.

Cast: Harald Leipnitz (*George Weissborn*), Sybille Maar (*Irene*), Herbert Bötticher (*Alfred*), Brigitte Skay (*Marion*), Monika Lundi (*Lisa*), Renate Roland (*Peggy*), Marianne Wischmann (*Vera*), Claudia Wedekind (*Rosa*), Sylvie Beck (*Monika*), Isolde Bräuner (*Mia*), Werner Schwier (*doctor*), Jana Novakova (*Ulla*), Doris Kiesow (*Lenna*), Herbert Weissbach (*grandfather*), Inge Langen (*Claudia*), Sammy Drechsel, Henry van Lyck, Nino Korda.

Farce. Middle-aged bachelor George Weissborn is a Munich wine salesman whose promiscuity worries and embarrasses his family, especially his staid brother Alfred, an elementary school teacher whose chances for promotion depend on George's settling down. While he is in the hospital recuperating from overexertion, George finally consents to marry, and to his family's delight he returns from the hospital with his nurse and announces their engagement. But the family's pleasure is short-lived, because the next night George brings home a different fiancée. Several more fiancées later, George and his cousin Irene, a houseguest invited by the family in the vague hope that George and she would fall in love and marry, do fulfill the family's wish. After the wedding George slides down the banister to celebrate, injures himself, and thereby puts an end to his sexual rovings. *Philanderers. Salesmen. Bachelors. Schoolteachers. Nurses. Cousins. Newlyweds. Family life. Promiscuity. Health. Middle age. Hospitals. Munich.*

Note: Location scenes filmed in Munich. Released in West Germany in Dec 1968 as *Bengelchen liebt kreuz und quer*; running time: 88 min. Alternative German title: *Bengelchen hat's wirklich schwer*. Alternative U. S. title: *Crunch*.

THE TWENTY-FOUR HOUR MOVIE see ****

24 HOURS IN A WOMAN'S LIFE (France/West Germany)　F6.5211

Pro Gé Fi-Roxy-Film. Nov **1968**. Sd; col (Eastmancolor). 35mm. 86 min.

Prod Louis Emile Galey. *Dir* Dominique Delouche. *Screenplay* Dominique Delouche, Albert Valentin, Eberhard Keindorff, Johanna Sibelius, Paul Hengge. *Dial* Dominique Delouche, Marie-France Rivière. *Photog* Walter Wottitz. *Art Dir* François de Lamothe. *Film Ed* Geneviève Winding. *Mus Adapt* Jean Podromidès. *Mus Themes* Johannes Brahms.

Cast: Danielle Darrieux (*Alice*), Robert Hoffmann (*Thomas*), Romina Power (*Mariette*), Lena Skerla (*Mademoiselle Georges*), Marthe Alycia (*Madame Di Stefano*).

Drama. Source: Stefan Zweig, "Vierundzwanzig Stunden aus dem Leben einer Frau," in *Verwirrung der Gefühle* (Leipzig, 1926). Returning from the Italian lake region, Alice, a widow, who is accompanied by Mademoiselle Georges, Madame Di Stefano and a teenager, Mariette, recalls her vacation: After a Brahms piano recital is interrupted by a rainstorm, her friends take a boat back to their hotel, but Alice stays and accidentally takes a boat that goes to Switzerland. While waiting for the next ferry, Alice wanders into a casino and sees a young German, Thomas, lose his money and leave abruptly with a pistol. Alice follows the despondent young man, and they go to his hotel and spend the night together. In the morning, while Thomas sleeps, Alice leaves a note arranging for a rendezvous and returns to her hotel, avoiding the shocked Mademoiselle Georges and Madame Di Stefano but chatting with Mariette. Thomas is intentionally late for his meeting with Alice, but when he appears they spend the afternoon walking in the woods and boating. Thomas tells Alice that he has deserted from the German Army. He is, he says, a compulsive gambler, and Alice offers to pay his debts and provide passage for him to Zurich if he never gambles again. He agrees, and they part at the border. Alice then decides to go with him but misses his train. That night Alice wanders to the places they had shared and upon entering the casino finds it deserted except for one table where four young men, one of them Thomas, are sitting. When she approaches, Thomas forces money into her hand and, after insulting her, sends her away. *Widows. Germans. Deserters—Military. Gamblers. Vacations. Casinos. Italy. Switzerland.*

Note: Released in West Germany in Jun 1968 as *24 Stunden im Leben einer Frau*; running time: 81 min; in Paris in Dec 1968 as *24 heures de la vie d'une femme*; running time: 84 min. Also reviewed in an 80-min version. A British version of the Zweig novella, *24 Hours of a Woman's Life*, was released in 1952.

24 HOURS TO KILL (Great Britain)　F6.5212

Grixflag Films. *Dist* Seven Arts Pictures. Jan **1966** [Los Angeles showing]. Sd; col (Technicolor). 35mm (Techniscope). 94 min.

Prod Harry Alan Towers. *Exec Prod* Oliver A. Unger. *Assoc Prod* Bernard Coote. *Dir* Peter Bezencenet. *Screenplay* Peter Yeldham. *Story* Peter Welbeck. *Photog* Ernest Steward. *Art Dir* Scott MacGregor. *Film Ed* John Trumper. *Mus* Wilfred Josephs. *Mus for Nadia Gamel's dance* Sefik Hashen. *Mus Dir* Marcus Dods. *Sd* Brian Ash, Fred Hughesdon, Ken Cameron. *Prod Supv* John Comfort.

Cast: Lex Barker (*Jamie*), Mickey Rooney (*Norman Jones*), Michael Medwin (*Tommy*), Wolfgang Lukschy (*Kurt*), Helga Sommerfeld (*Louise*), France Anglade (*Françoise*), Helga Lehner (*Helga*), Walter Slezak (*Malouf*), Hans Clarin (*Elias*), Shakib Khouri (*Andronicus*), Maria Rohm (*Claudine*), Nadia Gamel (*Mimi*).

Action melodrama. An international flight develops engine trouble en route to Athens and is forced to land in Beirut, where it is immobilized for 24 hours. Purser Norman Jones, on the run from a gang of gold smugglers headed by Malouf, gains the sympathy of the flight's captain, Jamie, and other members of the crew who believe that Jones has been wrongly associated with the syndicate. The gang twice attempts to kill Jones and tries to kidnap air hostess Louise, the captain's girl friend, and Jamie learns that Jones is actually a member of Malouf's gang and has stolen £40,000 worth of bullion from the syndicate. Although the gangsters kidnap air hostess Françoise and propose an exchange, Françoise is rescued by the airline crew after a fight. Jones is captured by Malouf and then saved by Jamie and the crew, but just as the plane takes off, Jones is killed by one of Malouf's men. *Air pilots. Smugglers. Gangsters. Airline stewardesses. Theft. Abduction. Murder. Gold. Syndicates. Beirut.*

Note: Location scenes filmed in Lebanon. Released in Great Britain in Sep 1965; running time: 83 min. Peter Welbeck is a pseudonym of Harry Alan Towers.

TWENTY PLUS TWO　F6.5213

Allied Artists. Aug **1961** [c21 Aug 1961; LP20122]. Sd; b&w. 35mm. 102 min.

Prod-Screenplay Frank Gruber. *Exec Prod* Scott R. Dunlap. *Dir* Joseph M. Newman. *Photog* Carl Guthrie. *Art Dir* David Milton. *Set Decor* Joe Kish. *Film Ed* George White. *Mus* Gerald Fried. *Sd* Ralph Butler, Paul Schmutz, Jr.,

Charles Schelling. *Asst Dir* Lindsley Parsons, Jr. *Prod Mgr* Edward Morey, Jr. *Script Supv* Eylla Jacobus. *Wardrobe* Roger J. Weinberg, Gordon Murray, Norah Sharpe. *Makeup* Harry Maret. *Sp Eff* Milt Olsen. *Gaffer* George Satterfield. *Constr Supv* James West. *Prop* Ted Mossman.

Cast: David Janssen (*Tom Alder*), Jeanne Crain (*Linda*), Dina Merrill (*Nikki/Doris Delaney*), Agnes Moorehead (*Mrs. Delaney*), Brad Dexter (*Leroy Dane*), Robert Strauss (*Honsinger*), Jacques Aubuchon (*Frenchy Pleschette*), William Demarest (*Slocum*), George Neise (*Walter Collinson*), Fredd Wayne (*Harris Toomey*), Carleton Young (*colonel*), Robert H. Harris (*Stanley*), Billy Varga (*Mark*), Teri Janssen (*stewardess*), Ellie Kent (*blonde*), Mort Mills (*Harbin*), Robert Gruber (*bellboy*), Will Wright (*morgue attendant*).

Mystery melodrama. Source: Frank Gruber, *Twenty Plus Two* (New York, 1961). Private detective Tom Alder, who specializes in finding missing persons, links the murder of movie star Leroy Dane's secretary to the unsolved disappearance of heiress Doris Delaney several years before. Later, Alder meets Dane and Linda Foster, Alder's former fiancée who broke with him while he was in Korea. He also meets a young woman named Nikki Kovacs, and although he is not aware that Nikki is actually the missing heiress, he senses something familiar about her. He then is approached by Frenchy Pleschette, a man who tries to hire him to find his missing younger brother. After meeting Nikki on a plane, Alder remembers that they met in Japan while he was recuperating from a combat wound. It is then revealed that she had become involved with a man who made her pregnant and whom she thought she had killed. She had run away to Japan to avoid disgracing her family. Alder's further investigations also establish Dane as the killer of both his secretary and the man whom Doris thought she had murdered. He is also revealed to be the brother of Pleschette, and in a showdown between the two, the latter kills Dane. Alder and Doris resume the romance that started in Japan. *Detectives. Secretaries. Actors. Heiresses. Brothers. Missing persons. Murder. Personal identity. Japan.*

THE 26TH CAVALRY see ONCE BEFORE I DIE

23RD PSALM BRANCH　F6.5214

Dist Brakhage. 22 Apr **1967** [New York opening]. Si; col. 8mm. 100 min. [See note.]

Dir-Photog-Ed Stan Brakhage. *Assoc* Jane Brakhage.

Experimental film. This cinematic variation on the theme of war, inspired by television broadcasts of the Vietnamese conflict, is divided into two parts. Part I alternates representations of carnage with footage of pure primary colors, scenes of the filmmaker and his family in their Colorado home, and images of victory celebrations. Part II consists of five segments: "Peter Kubelka's Vienna," "My Vienna," "A Tribute to Freud," "Nietzsche's Lamb," and "East Berlin," and includes footage of Vienna, filmmaker Kubelka at home with his family, and Brakhage's children and pets. The coda depicts fireworks, dancing, the family donkey, and a child spinning a sparkler. *Motion picture directors. Children. Death. Television. Pets. Fireworks. Vietnam War 1964–73. Colorado. Vienna. Berlin—East. Sigmund Freud. Friedrich Nietzsche. Peter Kubelka. Donkeys.*

Note: Also known as *Song XXIII*. The film is one of a series of "Songs" by Brakhage. "Part I" (58 min) was first shown in New York City 1 Feb 1967.

20,000 EYES　F6.5215

Associated Producers, Inc. *Dist* Twentieth Century–Fox Film Corp. 14 Jun **1961** [New York opening; c10 May 1961; LP20071]. Sd; b&w. 35mm (CinemaScope). 60 min.

Prod-Dir Jack Leewood. *Assoc Prod-Writ* Jack Thomas. *Dir Photog* Brydon Baker. *Art Dir* John Mansbridge. *Set Decor* Harry Reif. *Supv Film Ed* Peter Johnson. *Mus* Albert Glasser. *Sd* Lloyd Wiler. *Sd Eff* Jack Cornall. *Asst Dir* Frank Parmenter, Doc Joos. *Prod Supv* Frank Parmenter. *Script Supv* Emile Ehrlich. *Wardrobe* Joseph Dimmitt. *Makeup* Emile La Vigne. *Prop Master* Leigh Carson.

Cast: Gene Nelson (*Dan Warren*), Merry Anders (*Karen Walker*), James Brown (*Jerry Manning*), John Banner (*Kurt Novak*), Judith Rawlins (*girl*), Robert Shayne (*police lieutenant*), Paul Maxey (*Ryan*), Rex Holman (*high school boy*), Ollie O'Toole (*Moore*), Bruno Ve Sota (*museum watchman*), Barbara Parkins (*high school girl*), William O'Connell (*appraiser*), Rusty Wescoatt (*policeman*), Vince Monroe Townsend, Jr. (*museum guard*).

Crime melodrama. To protect his interest in a South American diamond mine project, investment counselor Dan Warren embezzles $100,000 from one of his clients, retired racketeer Kurt Novak. When the deception is discovered by the gangster, Dan is granted time to raise the money on the condition that he take out a $100,000 life insurance policy naming Novak as beneficiary. A short time later Dan is informed by Novak that unless he returns the money within 5 days he will have an "accident." Desperate, Dan persuades his partner, Jerry Manning, and his secretary, Karen Walker, to help him. They steal a collection of diamonds from a poorly-guarded museum, replace them with a sack of low-grade stones, and then insure the valuable gems for $100,000. Jerry then "steals" the diamonds from Dan and replaces them in the museum, thereby leaving Dan free to collect the insurance money. After his cohorts have left town, Dan learns from the insurance company that he will not be paid for 5 or 6 weeks. When he so informs Novak, the racketeer shoots him in the back. Before dying, however, Dan manages to throw a TV set at Novak, knocking him into a nearby pool. The accident shorts the electrical connection, and the gangster is electrocuted. *Gangsters. Secretaries. Theft. Embezzlement. Murder. Insurance. Fraud. Diamonds. Museums.*

THE £20,000 KISS (Great Britain) F6.5216

Merton Park Studios. *Dist* Schoenfeld Film Distributing Corp. 20 May **1964** [Newark, New Jersey, opening]. Sd; b&w. 35mm. 57 min.

Prod Jack Greenwood. *Dir* John Moxey. *Screenplay* Philip Mackie. *Dir Photog* James Wilson. *Camera Op* Noel Rowland. *1st Camera Asst* Alan Rowland. *Art Dir* Peter Mullins. *Film Ed (see note)* Gordon Hales, Derek Holding. *Mus* Bernard Ebbinghouse. *Sd Rec* Sidney Rider. *Boom Op* Tom Otter. *Sd Camera Op* Robin Clare. *Dub Ed* Brian Blamey. *1st, 2d & 3d Asst Dir* Ted Lewis, Al Burgess, Roger Hudson. *Prod Mgr* Ron Fry. *Cont* Marjorie Owens. *Wardrobe* Eileen Welch. *Makeup* Michael Morris. *Hairstyles* Pat McDermott. *Still Photog* Eddie Orton. *Casting Dir* Ronald Curtis. *Ch Electrn* Jim Axtell. *Chargehand Prop* Roy Pembrook. *Constr Mgr* Eddie Turner. *Grip* Freddie Williams.

Cast: Dawn Addams *(Christina Hagen)*, Michael Goodliffe *(Sir Harold Trevitt)*, Richard Thorp *(John Durran)*, Anthony Newlands *(Leo Hagen)*, Alfred Burke *(Inspector Waveney)*, Mia Karam *(Paula Blair)*, Ellen McIntosh *(Ursula Clandon)*, Paul Whitsun-Jones *(Charles Pinder)*, Noël Hood *(Lady Clandon)*, John Miller *(Lord Clandon)*, Vincent Harding *(Detective Sergeant Holt)*, Susan Denny *(Susie)*, Joyce Hemson *(landlady)*.

Crime melodrama. Based on a story by: Edgar Wallace. Polish aristocrat Leo Hagen lives with his wife, Christina, in an apartment in London. When Paula, the maid, catches Christina kissing Sir Harold Trevitt, their neighbor and a prominent Member of Parliament, she threatens to tell the jealous husband unless Sir Harold gives her £5,000. Private detective John Durran is hired by Sir Harold to investigate the maid, but the detective finds both Paula and Leo dead. Inspector Waveney of Scotland Yard becomes involved with the case and eventually proves Sir Harold to be the killer, and Christina is revealed to have conspired with her husband and Paula in the blackmail plot. *Poles. Aristocrats. Neighbors. Politicians. Housemaids. Detectives. Blackmail. Scandal. Conspiracy. Murder. Jealousy. London. Great Britain—Parliament. Scotland Yard.*

Note: Released in Great Britain caFeb 1963. Sources conflict in crediting the editor.

TWICE A MAN F6.5218

Dist Film-Makers' Cooperative, Film-Makers' Distribution Center. 4 Oct **1963** [New York opening]. Sd; col (Eastman Color). 35mm & 16mm. 65 min. [Also 49 and 60 min.]

Prod-Dir-Writ Gregory J. Markopoulos. *Photog* Gregory J. Markopoulos. *Film Ed* Gregory J. Markopoulos. *Mus Selections* Pëtr Ilich Tchaikovsky.

Cast: Paul Klib *(Paul)*, Albert Torgessen *(physician)*, Olympia Dukakis *(young mother/commentary)*, Violet Roditi *(old mother)*.

Experimental film. A recreation of the myths of Hippolytus, Phaedra, and Asclepius. A young physician is crossing New York Harbor in a ferryboat. The physician (Asclepius) conjures up an image of Paul (Hippolytus) and begins imagining the story: Paul finds the atmosphere on a crowded dance floor unpleasant, avoids contact with a woman, and escapes to a roof where he comes across an old man, the physician. The old man is uplifted by his meeting with Paul and makes vague sexual advances toward him but is rebuffed. At home, Paul encounters his stepmother (Phaedra), who appears both as a beautiful young woman (her self-conception) and as a haggard older woman (Paul's conception of her). Paul rejects his stepmother's advances, and seeks to relieve his tension by stroking a cat and the leaves of a plant. The tension grows, and he and his stepmother quarrel. Paul dies from the emotional trauma of his situation but is restored to life by the physician and experiences union with him. On the ferryboat, the physician, realizing that Paul's problems are unsolved, brings to an end Paul's new life. Paul's face crumbles; he has been unable to accept the love of a woman or a man. *Stepmothers. Physicians. Bisexuality. Incest. Death. Male homosexuality. Reviviscence. Ferryboats. New York Harbor. Hippolytus. Asclepius. Phaedra.*

Note: Filmed on location in New York City in 16mm. Single frame editing is employed. Unfinished portions of the film were shown in New York in May 1962. A dual-screen version was first shown in New York in Jan 1967. Dedicated to Clara Hoover.

TWICE TOLD TALES F6.5219

Admiral Pictures. *Dist* United Artists. 30 Oct **1963** [Los Angeles opening: c1 Oct 1963; LP27743]. Sd (Westrex); col (Technicolor). 35mm. 119 min.

Prod-Writ Robert E. Kent. *Dir* Sidney Salkow. *Dir Photog* Ellis W. Carter. *Asst Camera* Bert Eason. *Camera Op* Joe Jackman. *Art Dir* Franz Bachelin. *Set Decor* Charles Thompson. *Supv Film Ed* Grant Whytock. *Eff Ed* Al Bird. *Mus* Richard La Salle. *Sd* Lambert Day. *Mus Ed* Edna Bullock. *Rec* Paul Wolfe. *Asst Dir* Al Westen, Nat Merman. *Prod Mgr* Joseph Small. *Script Supv* Jean Downing. *Cost* Marjorie Corso, Tom Welsh. *Makeup Artist* Gene Hibbs. *Hairstyles* Jane Shugrue. *Sp Eff* Milt Olsen, Pete Faga. *Prop Master* Irving Sindler. *Still Photog* Madison Lacy. *Casting Dir* Ralph Acton. *Gaffer* Lloyd Hill. *Prop* Irving Sindler, Dan Nelson. *Grip* Sam Bishop.

Cast—"Dr. Heidegger's Experiment": Vincent Price *(Alex Medbourne)*, Sebastian Cabot *(Dr. Carl Heidegger)*, Mari Blanchard *(Sylvia Ward)*.

Cast—"Rappaccini's Daughter": Vincent Price *(Dr. Rappaccini)*, Brett Halsey *(Giovanni Guastconti)*, Abraham Sofaer *(Prof. Pietro Baglioni)*, Joyce Taylor *(Beatrice Rappaccini)*, Edith Evanson *(Lisabetta)*.

Cast—"The House of the Seven Gables": Vincent Price *(Gerald Pyncheon)*, Beverly Garland *(Alice Pyncheon)*, Richard Denning *(Jonathan Maulle)*, Jacqueline De Wit *(Hannah)*, Floyd Simmons *(Mathew)*, Gene Roth *(cab driver)*.

Horror film. Source: Nathaniel Hawthorne, "Dr. Heidegger's Experiment," in *Twice Told Tales* (Boston, 1837). Nathaniel Hawthorne, "Rappaccini's Daughter," in *Mosses From an Old Manse* (New York, 1846). Nathaniel Hawthorne, *The House of the Seven Gables* (Boston, 1851). DR. HEIDEGGER'S EXPERIMENT describes the discovery of an elixir of youth, which restores the aged Heidegger, his old friend Alex Medbourne, and the corpse of Heidegger's fiancée Sylvia, who died on the eve of her wedding. When Sylvia discloses that Medbourne killed her in retaliation for her refusal to elope with him, the jealous assassin slays Heidegger. Suddenly, the potion loses its effect; Medbourne is once again aged, Sylvia a corpse. In RAPPACCINI'S DAUGHTER a Paduan physician, deserted by his wife, renders his daughter Beatrice forever inviolate by inoculating her with a deadly serum, the effect of which is to blight any living thing she touches. When she falls in love with their neighbor Giovanni, a medical student, Rappaccini attempts in vain to counter the poison's effects. After an antidote devised by Giovanni's science professor slays the lovers, Rappaccini kills himself. In THE HOUSE OF THE SEVEN GABLES newlywed Gerald Pyncheon scours his ancestral home for the family fortune. While so doing he confronts the ghost of a man burned as a warlock by his ancestors, who also had been the lover of his wife's ancestor. After murdering his sister, Pyncheon dies in the treasure vault. The estate is destroyed, and Pyncheon's widow elopes with the ghost's descendant. *Physicians. Ghosts. Medical students. Death. Reviviscence. Old age. Filial relations. Jealousy. Murder. Suicide. Greed. Brother-sister relationship. Experiments. Ancestry. Elopement.*

Note: Working title: *The Corpse Makers*. May also be known as *Nathaniel Hawthorne's "Twice Told Tales"*.

TWILIGHT AFFAIR see DOUBLE YOUR PLEASURE

THE TWILIGHT GIRLS (France) F6.5220

Safia–Sirius–Contact Organisation. *Dist* Audubon Films, Beverly Pictures. 25 Oct **1961** [Los Angeles opening]. Sd; b&w. 35mm. 80 min.

Dir André Hunebelle. *Dir U. S. Vers (see note)* Radley Metzger. *Screenplay* Jacques Lancien, Jean Lambertie. *Dial* Jacques Emmanuel. *English Dial* LaVerne Owens. *Adapt* Louis Duchesne, Jacques Emmanuel, Jean Halain. *Story* Jacques Lancien, Arlette Reinerg, Jean Lambertie. *Photog* Paul Cotteret. *Art Dir* Lucien Carré, Sidney Bettex. *Film Ed* Jean Feyte. *Mus* Jean Marion. *Sd* René Forget. *Prod Mgr* René Thévenet.

Cast: Gaby Morlay *(Madame Ancelin)*, Henri Guisol *(Christian Brenner)*, Paul Guers *(Dean [Gilles])*, Marie-Hélène Arnaud *(Catherine Royer)*, Christine Carère *(Monica [Monique])*, Estella Blain *(Martha [Marthe])*, Agnès Laurent *(Anne-Marie)*, Véronique Verlhac *(Sally)*, Picolette *(Bernadette)*, Jacqueline Corot, Betty Daumier, Anna Gaylor, Anita Treyens, Sylvie Dorléac, Olivia Chevalier, Madeleine Barbulée, Paulette Arnoux, Luce Fabiole, Made Siamé, Simone Berthier, Louisa Colpeyn, Solange Sicard, André Wasley, Elga Hymen, Fernand Fabre, René Bergeron, Raymond Carl, Georgina Spelvin *([see note])*.

Melodrama. Seeking to live down a family scandal, Catherine Royer enrolls in Valon, an exclusive boarding school. She becomes part of a school clique led by Anne-Marie and makes friends with Monica, thus arousing the jealousy of Martha, who previously enjoyed a close friendship with Monica. Catherine meets Dean, a young composer, at one of Anne-Marie's parties, and they fall in love. The couple's attempt to run off together is thwarted by Anne-Marie's stepfather, who intercepts Monica as she goes to the rendezvous. Believing that she has been forsaken by Dean, Catherine becomes despondent and falls into a critical illness. Monica, strongly attracted to Catherine and jealous of her relationship with Dean, intercepts the letters Dean sends Catherine in the hospital. Finally, on the eve of Dean's debut concert in which he will introduce a work dedicated to Catherine, Monica feels remorse and takes the letters to Catherine. Dean proposes marriage to Catherine, and Madame Ancelin, the school's understanding headmistress, explains to Monica that emotions which have raged at the dormitory find their explanation in the girls' transition from adolescence to womanhood. *Students. Composers. Stepfathers. Headmistresses. Adolescence. Friendship. High school life. Jealousy. Lesbianism. Boarding schools. Documentation.*

Note: Opened in Marseilles in Mar 1957 as *Les collégiennes*; running time: 88 min. Radley Metzger cut sequences from the original version, and added scenes involving sex and nudity, which feature Georgina Spelvin and which he filmed himself. Also known in the U. S. as *Twilite Girls*. The cast listing is derived in part from the original French version, and some cast members may not appear in the edited U. S. version. Footage also included in *Dictionary of Sex*, q. v.

TWILIGHT OF HONOR   **F6.5221**
 Perlberg-Seaton Productions. *Dist* Metro-Goldwyn-Mayer, Inc. 16 Oct 1963 [Chicago opening; c9 Sep 1963; LP26269]. Sd; b&w. 35mm (Panavision). 104 min.
 Prod William Perlberg, George Seaton. *Dir* Boris Sagal. *Screenplay* Henry Denker. *Dir Photog* Philip Lathrop. *Camera Op* Joe Jackman. *Asst Camera* Cliff King. *Art Dir* George W. Davis, Paul Groesse. *Set Decor* Henry Grace, Hugh Hunt. *Film Ed* Hugh S. Fowler. *Asst Ed* Jules Nayfack. *Mus Comp & Cond* John Green. *Rec Supv* Franklin Milton. *Mix* Larry Jost. *Rec* Bernard Hurlew. *Boom Op* Larry Hadsell. *Asst Dir* Donald Roberts, Al Shenberg, Richard Lang. *Script Supv* Betty Abbott. *Wardrobe* Jim Taylor, Sylvia Posner. *Makeup Supv* William Tuttle. *Makeup* Ron Berkeley, Agnes Flanagan. *Hairstyles* Mary Keats. *Prop* Robert Schultz.
 Cast: Richard Chamberlain *(David Mitchell)*, Joey Heatherton *(Laura Mae Brown)*, Nick Adams *(Ben Brown)*, Claude Rains *(Art Harper)*, Joan Blackman *(Susan Harper)*, James Gregory *(Norris Bixby)*, Pat Buttram *(Cole Clinton)*, Jeanette Nolan *(Amy Clinton)*, Edgar Stehli *(Judge James Tucker)*, James Bell *(Charles Crispin)*, George Mitchell *(Paul Farish)*, Donald Barry *(Judson Elliot)*, Bert Freed *(Sheriff Buck Wheeler)*, Robin Raymond *(Therese Braden)*, June Dayton *(Vera Driscoll)*, Vaughn Taylor *(Ballentine)*, Linda Evans *(Alice Clinton)*, Arch Johnson *(Mr. McWade)*.
 Drama. Source: Al Dewlen, *Twilight of Honor* (New York, 1961). Cole Clinton, the leading citizen of Durango, New Mexico, is brutally murdered, and young attorney David Mitchell is appointed by the court to defend suspect Ben Brown. Although he initially believes that Brown is guilty, Mitchell begins to have doubts about the written confession authorities have obtained because it seriously conflicts with the story Brown personally tells; Mitchell's only encouragement, however, comes from retired attorney Art Harper and his daughter, Susan. When the politically ambitious special prosecutor, Norris Bixby, refuses to call several important witnesses, including Brown's voluptuous wife, Laura Mae, Mitchell becomes convinced that his client is being railroaded. With Harper's subtle guidance, Mitchell stumbles upon the truth—that Brown shot Clinton after discovering him in bed with Laura Mae. The prosecution, in trying to protect the dead man's reputation, brings pressure to bear on Mitchell to abandon this line of defense, but the unwritten law dealing with adultery sways the jury to bring in a verdict of "not guilty." Meanwhile, Harper is pleased that his future son-in-law has proven himself to be an honest lawyer. *Lawyers. Public defenders. Murder. Guilt. Confession (law). Ambition. Infidelity. Reputation. Trials. New Mexico.*

TWILIGHT PATH (Japan)   **F6.5222**
 Shochiku Co. *Dist* Shochiku Films of America. 7 May 1965 [Los Angeles showing]. Sd; col (Eastmancolor). 35mm (Shochiku GrandScope). 107 min.
 Dir Minoru Shibuya. *Screenplay* Yoshio Shirasaka, Minoru Shibuya. *Orig Story* Yasujiro Ozu. *Photog* Hiroyuki Nagaoka. *Art Dir* Nobutaka Yoshino. *Mus* Toshiro Mayuzumi.
 Cast: Chishu Ryu *(Tokichi Yamaki)*, Nobuko Otowa *(Nobuyo Yamaki)*, Mariko Kaga *(Keiko Yamaki)*, Isao Yamagata *(Gohei Suzuka)*, Shima Iwashita *(Mie Kawano)*, Ryo Ikebe *(Kotaki)*, Mariko Okada *(Kyoko)*, Ineko Arima *(Natsuko)*, Yoko Tsukasa *(Haruko)*, Shin-ichiro Mikami *(Saburo)*, Kinzo Shin *(Akiyama)*, Hiroyuki Nagato *(Kosuke)*, Daisuke Kato.
 Comedy-drama. Tokichi Yamaki, the office manager of a large trading firm, enjoys a peaceful life with his wife, Nobuyo, and their youngest daughter, Keiko, whose three older sisters are married and who is herself engaged to Saburo, the son of her father's friend Suzuka. At a college reunion Yamaki argues with Suzuka over whether they should inform their ailing friend, Akiyama, that he has cancer. Yamaki now becomes aware that his own life has run much of its course. Kosuki, his younger brother, reveals he has embezzled 1 million yen from his company, and Yamaki sells his own stocks to raise the money and avoid a family scandal. With the money in his briefcase, Yamaki

impulsively boards a train to Osaka. Notified of their father's disappearance, the daughters meet with their mother and admit that they are unconcerned about their father, except for their concern with what little money their parents have saved. In Osaka Yamaki mistakes a brothel for a hotel, only to take delight in his error. After ten days of comic adventures, he returns home to be greeted with new-found respect. *Brothers. Family life. Embezzlement. Middle age. Whorehouses. Cancer. Osaka.*
 Note: Released in Japan in 1964 as *Daikon to ninjin*. Alternative titles: *Radishes and Carrots* and *Mr. Radish and Mr. Carrot*.

THE TWILIGHT STORY (Japan)   **F6.5223**
 Tokyo Eiga Co. *Dist* Toho Co. Apr 1962 [Los Angeles showing]. Sd; b&w. 35mm. 150 min.
 Prod Ichiro Sato. *Dir* Shiro Toyoda. *Screenplay* Toshio Yasumi.
 Cast: Hiroshi Akutagawa *(The Teacher)*, Fujiko Yamamoto *(The Prostitute)*, Masao Oda *(The Uncle)*, Michiyo Aratama, Eijiro Tono, Nobuko Otowa, Keiko Awaji, Shikaku Nakamura.
 Melodrama. Source: Kafu Nagai, *Bokuto kidan* (Tokyo, 1952). A smalltown girl, who becomes a prostitute in Tokyo to support her sick mother, hopes someday to marry a teacher who has told her that he is single. Actually, he is unhappily married to a woman whose child is not his. The teacher returns to his wife, however, and the prostitute's unhappiness deepens when her uncle squanders funds entrusted to him, her mother dies, and she falls ill herself. *Prostitutes. Schoolteachers. Uncles. Infidelity. Duplicity. Filial relations. Marriage. Tokyo.*
 Note: Released in Japan in 1960 as *Bokuto kidan*.

TWILITE GIRLS see **THE TWILIGHT GIRLS**

TWIN SISTERS OF KYOTO (Japan)   **F6.5224**
 Shochiku Co. *Dist* Shochiku Films of America. Mar 1964 [Los Angeles showing]. Sd; col (Eastmancolor). 35mm (Shochiku GrandScope). 107 min.
 Prod Ryotaro Kuwata. *Dir* Noboru Nakamura. *Screenplay* Toshihide Gondo. *Photog* Toichiro Narushima. *Art Dir* Jun-ichi Ozumi. *Film Ed* Hisashi Sagara. *Mus* Toru Takemitsu.
 Cast: Shima Iwashita *(Chieko/Naeko)*, Seiji Miyaguchi *(Takichiro Sada)*, Teruo Yoshida *(Ryusuke Mizuki)*, Tamotsu Hayakawa *(Shinichi Mizuki)*, Hiroyuki Nagato, Michiyo Tamaki.
 Domestic melodrama. Source: Yasunari Kawabata, *Koto* (Tokyo, 1962). Chieko, the daughter of a successful drygoods merchant living in Kyoto, was born a twin and abandoned as an infant along with her sister in accordance with the old superstition that twins were unlucky and unnatural. To shield her from the shame of being an abandoned twin, Chieko's parents have told her they kidnaped her from an unsuspecting mother. Chieko senses that her parents are concealing information from her, and her suspicions are confirmed when she meets an orphaned peasant girl, Naeko, who is her exact double. While both sisters are involved in love affairs, Chieko begins to feel insecure about her suitor, an educated young man whom she thinks may love the image of her sister rather than her. *Twins. Sisters. Foundlings. Orphans. Merchants. Social customs. Family life. Filial relations. Adoption. Kidnaping. Superstition. Kyoto.*
 Note: Released in Japan in 1963 as *Koto*.

TWINKLE AND SHINE (Reissue)   **F6.5225**
 Arwin Productions. *Dist* Columbia Pictures. 10 May 1961 [Buffalo, New York, showing; c1 Apr 1961; LP22243]. Sd (RCA); col (Eastman Color by Pathé). 35mm. 90 min.
 Song: "Twinkle and Shine" "By" Dunham.
 Note: Originally released in 1959 as *It Happened to Jane*; running time: 98 min; c25 Apr 1959; LP14707. The song "Twinkle and Shine" is substituted in the reissue version for "Be Prepared."

TWIST ALL NIGHT   **F6.5226**
 Keelou Production Co.-Alta Vista Productions. *Dist* American International Pictures. 12 Dec 1961 [San Francisco opening; c17 Feb 1962; LP22343]. Sd (RCA); b&w with col prolog (see note). 35mm. 76 min. [85 min with prolog.]
 Production Credits for the Prolog, "Twist Craze": An Independent Artists Production. *Prod-Dir* Allan David. *Exec Prod* Bill Rebane. *Dir Photog* Warren Lieb. *Film Ed* Art Ellis. *Sd Engr* Wally Hotz. *Talent Coörd* Larry Leverett. *Facilities* Jack Lieb Productions.
 Production Credits for "Twist All Night": *Prod* Maurice Duke. *Assoc Prod* Roy Willing. *Dir* William J. Hole, Jr. *Orig Screenplay* Berni Gould. *Dir Photog* Gene Polito. *Art Dir* Gabriel Scognamillo. *Set Decor* Armour Goetten. *Supv Ed* John Durant. *Song:* "Alright, Okay, You Win" S. Wyche, M. Watts. *Songs:* "When the Saints Go Twistin' In," "Everybody Knows," "The Saints Waltz," "Oh, Mama, Twist" Louis Prima. *Songs:* "Sam's Boogie," "Society Waltz," "International Waltz," "Better Twist Now, Baby," "Twistin' the Blues" Sam Butera, Louis Prima. *Song:* "Trombone Staccato" Louis Prima, Louis Sino. *Song:* "Chantilly Lace" J. P. Richardson. *Song:* "The Continental Twist" John

Berry, mus, Don Covay. *Song:* "*Coolin'* " Sid Kuller, Louis Prima. *Song:* "*Tag That Twistin' Dollie*" Ollie Jones, Lockie Edwards, Jr. *Song:* "*When You're Smiling*" Mark Fisher, Joe Goodwin, Larry Shay. *Song:* "*Fool Around*" Sam Butera. *Song:* "*I Can't Give You Anything But Love*" Dorothy Fields, Jimmy McHugh. *Song:* "*Mood Indigo*" Duke Ellington, Irving Mills, Albany Bigard. *Song:* "*I Can't Believe That You're in Love With Me*" Clarence Gaskill, Jimmy McHugh. *Choreog* Richard Humphrey. *Sd* Steve Bass. *Mus Ed* Walter Greene. *Sd Ed* Joseph Von Stroheim. *Asst Dir* Harry R. Sherman. *Prod Mgr* Harry R. Sherman. *Script Supv* Wallace Bennett. *Asst to the Prod* Neal Barry. *Wardrobe* Frank Beetson, Jr. *Miss Wilkinson's Clothes* Ottobre. *Makeup* Tom Miller, Jr. *Hair Styling* Fritzy LaBar. *Proc Titl–Optical Eff* CFI. *Prop Master* Charles Chichetti.

 Cast—"Twist Craze": Jim Lounsbury, Tobin Mathews and the All Stars, Joe Cavalier, The Parisian Twisters, The Manhattan Twisters, The Windy City Twisters.

 Cast—"Twist All Night": Louis Prima (*Louis Evans*), June Wilkinson (*Jenny*), Sam Butera and the Witnesses (*themselves*), Gertrude Michael (*Miss Clunker*), David Whorf (*Riffy*), Hal Torry (*The Mayor*), Ty Perry (*Arturo*), Fred Sherman (*Julius*), Dick Winslow (*Du Bois*), Gil Fry (*cop*).

 Comedy with music. In the prolog "Twist Craze," an emcee introduces the twist into a fashionable nightclub. Tobin Mathews and the All Stars play twist songs, and the clientele, clapping to the beat, soon learn the new dance. In the main body of the film, Louis Evans and Sam Butera and The Witnesses are unable to pay the rent for their nightclub because a group of teenagers fill the place every night without spending money. Evans and his girl friend, Jenny, find out that the youngsters have been hired by Mr. Arturo, the art gallery owner who lives upstairs, to force the club out of business. Evans intends to confront Mr. Arturo calmly, but he becomes angry and hits him. Fearful of losing his license, Evans returns to apologize. He is knocked out and arrested for breaking and entering. His innocence is proven, however, with the help of Jenny and Sam. He remembers seeing a stolen painting being covered before he was knocked unconscious and realizes that Mr. Arturo and his assistants are art thieves. The police are notified and the thieves are arrested. Evans throws a big twist block party that is so successful that the nightclub becomes a booming twist club. *Nightclub owners. Singers. Musicians. Dancers. Art dealers. Thieves. Youth. Rock and roll. Twist (dance). Nightclubs. Art galleries.*

 Note: Originally titled *The Continental Twist.* Prolog produced by Alta Vista Productions.

TWIST AROUND THE CLOCK   F6.5227

 Four Leaf Productions. *Dist* Columbia Pictures. 27 Dec **1961** [Los Angeles opening; c1 Jan 1962; LP21326]. Sd (Westrex); b&w. 35mm. 86 min.

 Prod Sam Katzman. *Dir* Oscar Rudolph. *Writ* James B. Gordon. *Photog* Gordon Avil. *Art Dir* George Van Marter. *Set Decor* Morris Hoffman. *Film Ed* Jerome Thoms. *Mus Supv* Fred Karger. *Songs:* "*Twist Around the Clock,*" "*Don't Twist With Anyone Else but Me*" Buddy Kaye, Philip Springer, Clay Cole. *Song:* "*The Wanderer*" E. Meresca. *Song:* "*Here, There, Everywhere*" Teddy Vann. *Song:* "*Twistin', U. S. A.*" Kal Mann. *Song:* "*Your Lips and Mine,*" "*Twist Along*" Kal Mann, Dave Appell. *Song:* "*Runaround Sue*" E. Meresca, Dion Dimucci. *Orig Ballad* Vicki Spencer. *Song:* "*The Twist Is Here To Stay*" Clay Cole, Fred Karger. *Song:* "*He's So Sweet*" Alonzo Tucker, Gwen Elias, Gordon Evans. *Song:* "*The Majestic*" B. L. Jones, Welton Young. *Song:* "*Merry Twist-mas*" Mack Wolfson, Wally Hall, Charlie Singleton. *Choreog* Earl Barton. *Sd Supv* Charles J. Rice. *Sd* Josh Westmoreland. *Asst Dir* Floyd Joyer.

 Cast: Chubby Checker (*himself*), Dion (*himself*), Vicki Spencer (*herself*), The Marcels (*themselves*), Clay Cole (*himself*), John Cronin (*Mitch Mason*), Mary Mitchell (*Tina Louden*), Maura McGiveney (*Debbie Marshall*), Tol Avery (*Joe Marshall*), Alvy Moore (*Dizzy Bellew*), Lenny Kent (*Georgie Clark*), Tom Middleton (*Jimmy Cook*), Jeff Parker (*Larry*), John Bryant (*Harry Davis*), Ernesto Morelli (*headwaiter*), Barbara Morrison (*Mrs. Vandeveer*), Ezelle Poule (*dowager*), Renee Aubry (*girl in booth*), Barry O'Hara (*Harvey*), Dal McKennon (*proprietor*).

 Musical comedy-drama. Mitch Mason, ex-manager of a once successful rock 'n' roll band, discovers the Twist being played and danced in a small mountain town. He books the band, led by Clay Cole, and dancers Tina and Larry for a Boston society benefit, and they create a sensation. They are unable to get other bookings, however, because Mitch has spurned the advances of Debbie Marshall, the daughter of New York's top agent. But a friend of Mitch's books them into a club where Chubby Checker and Dion are also appearing. They are a smash hit, and the Twist sweeps New York. When Debbie suspects that Mitch is falling in love with Tina, she gets her father to sign the group on the condition that Tina not marry for 3 years. The Twisters appear on a nationwide TV jamboree, and Mr. Marshall learns that Mitch and Tina were secretly married before signing the contracts. *Musicians. Dancers. Booking agents. Singers.*

Rock and roll. Twist (dance). Jealousy. Marriage. Contracts. Nightclubs. Television. Boston. New York City.

A TWIST OF SAND (Great Britain)   F6.5228

 Christina Films. *Dist* United Artists. Sep **1968** [c9 Nov 1968; LF31]. Sd; col (De Luxe). 35mm. 90 min.

 Prod Fred Engel. *Assoc Prod* John Merriman. *Dir* Don Chaffey. *Screenplay* Marvin H. Albert. *Photog* John Wilcox. *Underwater Photog* Stephen Halliday. *Prod Dsgn* John Stoll. *Film Ed* Alastair McIntyre. *Mus Comp & Cond* Tristram Cary. *Sd* James Shields, Norman Bolland. *Asst Dir* John Stoneman. *Prod Mgr* Barrie Melrose. *Sp Eff* Bill Warrington, Nick Adler.

 Cast: Richard Johnson (*Geoffrey Peace*), Honor Blackman (*Julie Chambois*), Jeremy Kemp (*Harry Riker*), Peter Vaughan (*Johann*), Roy Dotrice (*David Garland*), Guy Doleman (*patrol boat commander*), James Falkland (*patrol boat lieutenant*), Jack May (*Seekert*), Kenneth Cope (*flag officer*), Tony Caunter (*Elton*), Clifford Evans (*Admiral Tringham*).

 Action melodrama. Source: Geoffrey Jenkins, *A Twist of Sand* (London, 1959). While serving as a British submarine commander during World War II, Geoffrey Peace destroyed a Nazi U-boat and obeyed explicit orders to kill all survivors. Still haunted by the incident, he now operates a small smuggling operation out of Malta with former shipmate David Garland. While playing chess aboard ship, the two men are approached by Dutchman Harry Riker, another former shipmate, who has a plan to recover a cache of diamonds once hidden by a geologist on a Spanish galleon off the Skeleton Coast. Also involved in the scheme are Julie Chambois, the geologist's widow, and Johann, an imbecilic German who knows the desert terrain. In spite of a personality conflict between Riker and Garland, Peace agrees to navigate his cutter through dangerous coastal waters; later, as the group makes its way across the South African desert to the treasure site, Peace comes to realize that Johann is the one survivor of the wartime slaughter. The galleon is almost entirely buried in sand dunes, but the gems are eventually unearthed; Riker then dislodges a timber brace that kills Garland and causes the deck of the galleon to collapse on Johann. Peace divulges his true identity, forcing the German to his feet, but Riker shoots him down with his rifle. Before dying, however, Johann plunges his knife into Riker as a wave washes the diamonds he was clutching out to sea. Only Peace and Julie are left to return empty-handed. *Smugglers. Veterans. Widows. Dutch. Germans. Guilt. Massacres. Navigation. Diamonds. Deserts. Sailboats. World War II. Malta. South Africa.*

 Note: Location scenes filmed on Malta and in Almería, Spain. Opened in London in Nov 1968.

TWISTED LIVES see THE LIARS
TWISTED MORALS see TOO YOUNG, TOO IMMORAL!
TWISTED NERVE (Great Britain)   F6.5229

 Charter Film Productions. *Dist* National General Pictures. 26 Feb **1969** [New York opening]. Sd (Westrex); col (Technicolor). 35mm. 118 min. *MPAA rating* M.

 A Boulting Brothers Production. *Prod* George W. George, Frank Granat. *Exec Prod* John Boulting. *Dir* Roy Boulting. *Screenplay* Leo Marks, Roy Boulting. *Story* Roger Marshall. *Story Based on an Idea by* Roger Marshall, Jeremy Scott. *Photog* Harry Waxman. *Camera Op* Gerry Anstiss. *Art Dir* Albert Witherick. *Main Titl* Morton M. Lewis. *Film Ed* Martin Charles. *Mus Comp & Cond* Bernard Herrmann. *Sd* David Bowen, Jack W. Davies, Stanley Smith. *Asst Dir* Douglas Hermes. *Prod Mgr* Jack Rix.

 Cast: Hayley Mills (*Susan Harper*), Hywel Bennett (*Martin Durnley/ Georgie Clifford*), Billie Whitelaw (*Joan Harper*), Phyllis Calvert (*Enid Durnley*), Frank Finlay (*Henry Durnley*), Barry Foster (*Gerry Henderson*), Salmaan Peer (*Shashi Kadir*), Thorley Walters (*Sir John Forrester*), Christian Roberts (*Philip Harvey*), Timothy West (*Superintendent Dakin*), Gretchen Franklin (*Mrs. Clarke*), Clifford Cox (*Inspector Goddard*), Robin Parkinson (*shop manager*), Richard Davies (*Taffy Evans*), Brian Peck (*detective sergeant*), Russell Napier (*Professor Fuller*), Russell Waters (*hospital attendant*), Michael Cadman (*Mac*), Mary Land (*Judy*), Hazel Bainbridge (*nursing sister*), Timothy Bateson, Basil Dignam.

 Mystery melodrama. During moments of emotional stress, 21-year-old Martin Durnley assumes the identity of Georgie Clifford, a helpless 6-year-old boy. One day, when Martin steals a toy duck from a London store, he is helped by Susan Harper, a student who pays for the toy and persuades the store manager not to press charges. His overprotective mother, Enid, defends Martin against Henry, his distrustful stepfather, who is angered over the boy's failure to finish college or get a job. After telling his mother that he was going to take the duck to his institutionalized mongoloid brother, Martin has an argument with his stepfather and is thrown out of the house. He announces that he is going abroad, but instead goes to Susan's suburban home. Calling himself Georgie Clifford, Martin quickly ingratiates himself with her mother, Joan, who runs a boardinghouse, and is invited to stay. A few nights later, he returns to his home and brutally murders his stepfather with a pair of scissors. Martin's presence in the Harper home eventually results in Susan's breaking up with her boyfriend and Mrs. Harper ending her affair with Gerry Henderson, one of the boarders. Susan's curiosity is aroused by Martin's strange behavior, and after discovering his real name, she calls on his mother to learn more about him. Meanwhile, Mrs. Harper attempts to seduce Martin, but succeeds only in arousing his homicidal tendencies, and he bludgeons her to death. Upon returning home, Susan is cornered in her room by Martin, but Gerry Henderson, having found Mrs. Harper's body, has alerted the police, and they arrive in time to rescue Susan and capture Martin. *Psychopaths. Students. Stepfathers. Brothers. Landladies. Police. Schizophrenia. Theft. Filial relations. Mental retardation. Personal identity. Patricide. Seduction. Murder. Boardinghouses. London.*

Note: Filmed on location in London. Opened in London in Dec 1968.

THE TWISTED SEX   F6.5230

Jode Productions-Casebook Inc. *Dist* Chancellor Films. 30 Mar **1966** [Champaign, Illinois, showing]. Sd; b&w. 35mm. 79 min.

Sex film. Six case histories taken from the files of eminent psychiatrists reveal the sexual frustrations of the modern age: caught in a love triangle, Kelly is forced to choose between a beautiful woman and a young man; Vivian, a nymphomaniac, meets Harry, who cruelly shatters her fantasy world; Carol panics at the approach of middle age and attempts to buy the affection of men 15 years her junior, but she is betrayed for her money; Henry, a masochist, takes pleasure in being bound and punished by two women; Carlos, who spied on his naked sisters as a child, suffers from schizophrenia, and becomes first a peeping tom, then a fetishist, and finally a demented sex criminal; and Billy, a call girl, attempts to begin a new life after a client dies in her arms, but she falls victim to a rapist. *Psychiatrists. Prostitution. Bisexuality. Voyeurism. Schizophrenia. Rape. Nymphomania. Masochism. Fetishism. Sex deviates. Middle age.*

Note: Also known as *The Twisted Set* and *The Twisted Sex Set.*

TWO A PENNY (Great Britain)   F6.5231

World Wide Pictures. 14 Nov **1968** [San Diego, California, opening]. Sd; col (Eastmancolor). 35mm. 98 min.

Prod Frank R. Jacobson. *Dir* James F. Collier. *Story-Screenplay* Stella Linden. *Photog* Michael Reed. *Dir Photog 2d Unit* Dick Lederhaus. *Art Dir* Peter Williams. *Film Ed* Ann Chegwidden, Eugene Pendleton. *Mus Comp & Cond* Mike Leander. *Songs:* "Two a Penny," "Love You Forever, Today," "Questions" Cliff Richard, James F. Collier. *Sung by* Cliff Richard. *Sd* Gordon Everett. *Sd Rec* Michael Strong, sd. *Asst Dir* Gordon Gilbert. *Prod Mgr* Basil Appleby.

Cast: Cliff Richard (*Jamie Hopkins*), Dora Bryan (*Ruby Hopkins*), Avril Angers (*Mrs. Burry*), Ann Holloway (*Carol Turner*), Geoffrey Bayldon (*Alec Fitch*), Peter Barkworth (*vicar*), Donald Bisset (*Dr. Berman*), Edward Evans (*Jenkins*), Mona Washbourne (*Mrs. Duckett*), Tina Packer (*Gladys*), Earl Cameron (*verger*), Noel Davis (*Dennis Lancaster*), Nigel Goodwin (*Hubert*), Charles Lloyd Pack (*Reverend Allison*), Billy Graham (*himself*), Richard Vanstone (*David*), Warwick Sims (*Bill*), Rudi Patterson (*Sid*), John Watson (*Mr. Baker*), Jo Rowbottom (*Helen*), Daphne Riggs, Barbara Bruce (*middle-aged women*), Doreen Keogh (*Mary*), Norman Mitchell (*attendant*).

Melodrama. Jamie Hopkins, an art student, wants to make money quickly and begins to deal drugs. His mother works as a receptionist for Dr. Berman, a psychiatrist who is experimenting with psychedelic drugs. Jamie and his girl friend Carol go to a Billy Graham revivalist meeting, and Carol is immediately converted. Soon after, Jamie is caught stealing from Dr. Berman's drug supply and attempting to doublecross drug dealer Alec Fitch. As Carol continues to draw away from Jamie, he begins to see the religious light, and they are reunited. *Psychiatrists. Students. Drug dealers. Secretaries. Evangelists. Theft. Religious conversion. Psychedelic drugs. Billy Graham.*

Note: Opened in London in Jun 1968.

TWO AND TWO MAKE SIX (Great Britain)   F6.5232

Prometheus Productions. *For* British Lion/Bryanston Films. *Dist* Union Film Distributors. 21 Nov **1962** [Los Angeles opening]. Sd; b&w. 35mm. 89 min.

A Monja Danischewsky Production. *Prod-Writ* Monja Danischewsky. *Exec Prod* Norman Priggen. *Dir* Freddie Francis. *Photog* Desmond Dickinson, Ron Taylor. *2d Unit Photog* Denys Coop. *Art Dir* Ted Marshall. *Film Ed* Peter Taylor. *Mus* Norrie Paramor. *Song:* "A Change of Heart" Norrie Paramor, Bunny Lewis. *Sung by* Craig Douglas. *Sd* John Cox, Ted Mason. *Sd Rec* Dickie Bird, Red Law. *Asst Dir* Jim Brennan.

Cast: George Chakiris (*Larry Curado*), Janette Scott (*Irene*), Alfred Lynch (*Tom*), Jackie Lane (*Julie*), Athene Seyler (*Aunt Phoebe*), Bernard Braden (*Sergeant Sokolow*), Malcolm Keen (*Harry Stoneham*), Ambrosine Phillpotts (*Lady Smith-Adams*), Jack MacGowran (*night porter*), Robert Ayres (*Colonel Thompson*), Edward Evans (*Mack*), Harry Locke (*Ted*), Jeremy Lloyd (*young man*), Marianne Stone (*hotel receptionist*), Nina Parry (*Prudence*), Ken Wayne

(*Major Calhoun*), Gary Cockrell (*Leo Kober*), Bill Mitchell (*Bob Young*), Eric Woodburn (*dresser*), Bob Kanter, John Gardiner, Billy Edwards, George Sperdakos (*air policemen*), Patricia English (*club stewardess*).

Romantic comedy-drama. Larry Curado, a carefree American airman stationed in England, is a fancier of horseracing and pretty women. His uninhibited lifestyle gets him into trouble with the Air Force, and while resisting arrest on an AWOL charge, he knocks Sergeant Sokolow unconscious. Believing that he has killed the man, he flees to the coast with his girl friend, Julie, on her brother's motorbike. They meet another couple, Tom and Irene, at a transport cafe, and when the women come out of the cafe, they are deceived by the similarity of their boyfriends' clothes and mount the wrong motorbikes. The two couples do not discover the mistake until they are well on their way, and in the course of their adventures, Irene falls in love with Tom and Julie with Larry. Irene convinces Larry to return to the base and give himself up. He does so, and, finding that Sokolow is unharmed, he gets off with a light sentence when he announces that he and Irene will marry. Tom and Julie also wed, and a year later the two women are discovered wheeling identical baby carriages. *Americans in foreign countries. Mistaken identity. Marriage. Motorcycles. United States Air Force.*

Note: Opened in London in Jun 1962. May also be known as *A Change of Heart;* title later changed to *The Girl Swappers.*

TWO ARE GUILTY (France/Italy)   F6.5233

S. N. E. Gaumont-Trianon Productions-Ultra Film. *Dist* Metro-Goldwyn-Mayer, Inc. 28 Feb **1964** [New York opening; c31 Dec 1963; LP29212]. Sd; b&w. 35mm (Franscope). 131 min. [Copyright length: 117 min.]

Prod Alain Poiré. *Dir-Screenplay* André Cayatte. *Dial* Henri Jeanson. *Adapt* Charles Spaak. *Photog* Roger Fellous. *Art Dir* Rino Mondellini. *Film Ed* Paul Cayatte. *Mus* Louiguy. *Sd* Jean-Claude Marchetti. *Asst Dir* Pierre Léaud. *Prod Mgr* Robert Sussfeld, Willy Pickardt.

Cast: Anthony Perkins (*Johnny*), Jean-Claude Brialy (*Jean-Philippe*), Renato Salvatori (*François*), Pascale Audret (*Agnès*), Anne Tonietti (*Christine*), Marie Déa (*Mademoiselle Winter*), Elina Labourdette (*Mademoiselle Darbon*), Fernand Ledoux (*prosecutor*), Jacques Monod (*Pranzani*), Michèle Mercier (*Brigitte*), Henri Crémieux (*président des assises*), Camille Guerini (*judge*), Jean Ozenne (*Bernardi*), Claude Cerval (*Plouzenec*), Anne Rivière (*Marie*), Janine Darcey (*Chantal*), Gilbert Gil (*Inspector Portal*), M. Klemens (*1st police inspector*), Henri Vilbert, Robert Le Béal, Diana Lepvrier, Héléna Manson, Pierre Mirat, Maurice Nasil, Marcel Pérès, Robert Rollis, Maurice Chevit, Jean Marchat, Claudine Maugey.

Melodrama. A child is kidnaped and murdered on the French Riviera, and the police pursue two men fleeing the scene of the crime. A policeman is killed by the two during the pursuit, but when the police move in on a lighthouse where the suspects are hiding, three men dressed alike emerge, each claiming to be innocent and accusing the other two of the crime. The police break down all three alibis, and investigations of their pasts prove all three to be unsavory characters. Johnny, an American, is an aspiring artist who had almost contributed his girl friend to a fraternity house orgy back home. François is a gigolo who is cruel to the women who keep him. Jean-Philippe is a real estate agent not above offering his young sister as bait for business. Brought to trial, all three are acquitted, but they are killed by an angry crowd of demonstrators who set fire to the prison van transporting the defendants. It is never learned which of the three was the innocent man. *Children. Police. Americans in foreign countries. Gigolos. Real estate agents. Pimps. Artists. Kidnaping. Murder. Orgies. Brother-sister relationship. Lynching. Arson. Trials. Riviera.*

Note: Location scenes filmed on the French Riviera. Paris opening: Feb 1963 as *Le glaive et la balance;* running time: 120 or 135 min; released in Italy in 1962 as *Uno dei tre.* Original length: 140 min.

TWO BEFORE ZERO   F6.5234

Motion Picture Corp. of America. *Dist* Ellis Films, Maton Films. 31 Oct **1962** [New York opening; c26 Mar 1962; MU7120]. Sd; b&w. 35mm. 78 min.

Prod Fred A. Niles. *Assoc Prod* Reginald J. Holzer. *Dir* William Faralla. *Narr* Bruce Henry. *Photog* Jack Whitehead. *Supv Film Ed* Frank Romolo. *Ed* Robert Sinise. *Mus* Sid Siegel. *Sd* Robert Henning, Art Ziemke. *Res* John Janssen.

Narrators: Basil Rathbone, Mary Murphy.

Documentary. As a black-robed allegory of Marxism narrates the Communist saga, his discourse is interrupted by the questions of a white-robed modern Everywoman. Among the socialist milestones represented are the Russian Revolution, the death of Lenin, the rise of Stalin, the Spanish Civil War, the invasion of Hungary, and Castro's victory in Cuba. *Communism. Russia—History—1917-21 Revolution. Spain—History—Civil War 1936-39. Hungary—History—Revolt 1956. Russia. Cuba. Hungary. Nikolai Lenin. Joseph Stalin. Fidel Castro Ruz.*

Note: Also known as *Russian Roulette.*

TWO COLONELS (Italy)   F6.5235

Titanus. *Dist* Comet Film Distributors. Mar **1966**. Sd; b&w. 35mm. 90 min.

Prod Gianni Buffardi. *Dir* Steno. *Screenplay* Ruggero Grimaldi, Sergio Corbucci. *Photog* Tino Santoni.

Cast: Totò (*Colonel Di Maggio*), Walter Pidgeon (*Col. Timothy Henderson*), Scilla Gabel (*Iride*), Adriana Facchetti (*Penelope*), Nino Taranto (*Sergeant Quaglia*), Francis Lane (*Sergeant McIntyre*), Toni Ucci (*Mazzetta*), Roland Bartrop (*Major Kruger*), Gerard Herter (*German general*), Giorgio Bixio, Nino Terzo.

War comedy. Montegreco, a small town on the Greek-Albanian border, is captured 31 different times in 1943 by Italian troops led by Colonel Di Maggio and by British troops under Colonel Henderson. Iride, the tavern hostess, and the other townspeople are indifferent to the hostilities and fraternize with both sides. Upon returning to the tavern to retrieve his pipe during an Italian occupation, Colonel Henderson is captured, but Colonel Di Maggio exchanges him for two prisoners and two cases of whiskey. Ordered to attack the village, the British capture Di Maggio, but Henderson effects his escape. As the German Army attacks the Greek border, Major Kruger orders the destruction of Montegreco; Di Maggio promptly arrests the German, but Di Maggio is sentenced to be executed by the SS for his illegal action. Henderson rescues him, and by September 8, the two men are fighting a common enemy. *Barroom hostesses. Prisoners of war. Military occupation. Friendship. Bars. World War II. Greece. Albania. Great Britain—Army. Italy—Army. Germany—Army. SS.*

Note: Opened in Rome in Jan 1963 as *I due colonnelli*; running time: 103 min. Steno is a pseudonym for Stefano Vanzina.

TWO DAUGHTERS (India)   F6.5236

Satyajit Ray Productions. *Dist* Janus Films. 30 Apr **1963** [New York opening]. Sd; b&w. 35mm. 114 min.

Prod-Dir-Writ Satyajit Ray. *Assoc Prod* Amiyanath Mukherji. *Photog* Soumendu Roy. *Art Dir* Bansi Chandragupta. *Film Ed* Dulal Dutta. *Mus* Satyajit Ray. *Sd* Durgadas Mitra. *Prod Mgr* Anil Chowdhury.

Cast—"The Postmaster": Anil Chatterjee (*Nandalal*), Chandana Bannerjee (*Ratan*), Nripati Chatterjee (*Bishay*), Kagen Rathak (*Khagen*), Gopal Roy (*Bilas*).

Cast—"The Conclusion": Aparna Das Gupta (*Mrinmoyee*), Soumitra Chatterjee (*Amulya*), Sita Mukherji (*Jogmaya*), Gita Dey (*Nistarini*), Santosh Dutt (*Kishory*), Mihir Rakhal Chakravarty, Debi Neogy (*Haripada*).

Comedy-drama. Source: Rabindranath Tagore, "The Postmaster," in *Mashi and Other Stories* (New York, 1918). Rabindranath Tagore, "The Conclusion (Samapti)," in *The Runaway and Other Stories* (Calcutta, 1959). THE POSTMASTER: Nandalal, a young man from the city, takes the job of postmaster in a remote village. He is attended to by Ratan, an orphan girl of 10. Ratan also worked for the previous postmaster, an irritable old man who had severely mistreated her. The little sympathy that Nandalal shows the girl brings out all her love and tenderness. Unused to the loneliness of village life and unnerved by a severe attack of malaria, Nandalal is finally obliged to give up the job. It is only at the moment of departure that he realizes the depth of feeling that bound him to the girl. THE CONCLUSION: Young Amulya, a lawyer, rejects the girl of his mother's choice and decides to marry tomboy Mrinmoyee, with whom he has fallen in love. Alone with Amulya on the night of the wedding, the bride reveals that she was forced into the marriage, which she resents because of the loss of freedom it implies. Later in the night, she runs away from the bridal chamber. She is brought back a prisoner the following morning and receives the treatment that is normally meted out to such unconventional brides. A disillusioned Amulya sends his bride home and goes back to Calcutta. In his absence Mrinmoyee undergoes a change of heart, and, when at last she goes back to her husband, it is of her own free will and because she has realized that she loves him. *East Indians. Postmasters. Orphans. Housemaids. Lawyers. Tomboys. Brides. Village life. Loneliness. Weddings. Marriage—Arranged. Calcutta.*

Note: Released in India in 1962 as a trilogy entitled *Teen Kanya* (*Three Daughters*); running time: 171 min. The third story, "Monihara," was not included in the print for export.

TWO ENEMIES *see* **THE BEST OF ENEMIES**

THE TWO FACES OF DR. JEKYLL *see* **HOUSE OF FRIGHT**

TWO FOR THE ROAD (United States/Great Britain)   F6.5237

Stanley Donen Films. *Dist* Twentieth Century-Fox Film Corp. 27 Apr **1967** [New York opening; c31 Dec 1966; LP34888]. Sd; col (De Luxe). 35mm (Panavision). 112 min.

A Stanley Donen Production. *Prod-Dir* Stanley Donen. *Prod Exec* Arthur Carroll. *Assoc Prod* James Ware. *Screenplay* Frederic Raphael. *Dir Photog* Christopher Challis. *2d Unit Camera* Austin Dempster. *Camera Op* Henri Tiquet. *Aerial Camera* Guy Tabary. *Art Dir* Willy Holt. *Asst Art Dir* Marc Frederix. *Set Decor* Roger Volper. *Titl* Maurice Binder. *Film Ed* Richard

Marden, Madeleine Gug. *Mus* Henry Mancini. *Sd Mix* Jo de Bretagne. *Dub Ed* Sharpe Ludski Enterprises. *Re-Rec* C. T. S. Studios (London). *Asst Dir* Jacques Corbel. *Prod Supv* Christian Ferry. *Prod Mgr* Pierre Fivas, Paul Lemaire. *Mr. Finney's Clothes* Hardy Amies. *Miss Hepburn's Wardrobe Supv* by Clare Rendlesham. *Miss Hepburn's Clothes by* Ken Scott, cost, Michele Rosier, Paco Rabanne, Mary Quant, Foale & Tuffin. *Wardrobe Coörd* Sophie Issartel Rochas. *Makeup* Alberto De Rossi, Georges Bouban. *Hairdresser* Grazia De Rossi. *Sp Eff* Gilbert Manzon.

Cast: Audrey Hepburn (*Joanna Wallace*), Albert Finney (*Mark Wallace*), Eleanor Bron (*Cathy Manchester*), William Daniels (*Howard Manchester*), Claude Dauphin (*Maurice Dalbret*), Nadia Gray (*Françoise Dalbret*), Georges Descrières (*David*), Gabrielle Middleton (*Ruth Manchester*), Jacqueline Bisset (*Jackie*), Judy Cornwell (*Pat*), Irene Hilda (*Yvonne de Florac*), Dominique Joos (*Sylvia*), Kathy Chelimsky (*Caroline*), Carol Van Dyke (*Michelle*), Karyn Balm (*Simone*), Mario Verdon (*Palamos*), Roger Dann (*Gilbert, Comte de Florac*), Libby Morris (*American lady*), Yves Barsacq (*police inspector*), Hélène Tossy (*Madame Solange*), Jean-François Lalet (*boat officer*), Albert Michel (*customs officer*), Joanna Jones, Sofia Torkeli, Patricia Viterbo, Olga George Picot, Clarissa Hillel (*Joanna's touring girl friends*), Cathy Jones.

Comedy-drama. In their 12th year of marriage Joanna and Mark Wallace are en route to the French Riviera for a business and social meeting with Mark's benefactor, architect Maurice Dalbret. Joanna and Mark had met years before on such a trip: Mark was then a fledgling architect hitchhiking through Europe, and Joanna was a music student on tour with a group of American schoolgirls. Their first encounter blossomed into romance, and by the time they reached the Côte d'Azur they knew they were in love and ready for marriage. Soon afterward they returned to Europe, but their motor trip was spoiled by their companions, the snobbish Cathy and Howard Manchester and their obnoxious daughter Ruth. Having learned their lesson, Joanna and Mark took their next vacation alone. Then, while Joanna was pregnant, Mark made a business trip by himself and experienced his first marital infidelity. Success came fairly easy for Mark, but his affluence and sense of self-importance alienated Joanna; and eventually she drifted into an indiscreet affair of her own. Driven to the brink of divorce, they are now forced to evaluate themselves and their marriage. Mutually willing to concede that they have changed but have grown maturely dependent upon each other, they are able to save their marriage. *Architects. Americans in foreign countries. Hitchhikers. Students. Tourists. Courtship. Marriage. Infidelity. Snobbery. Vacations. France. Riviera.*

Note: Location scenes filmed at Beauvallon, Saint-Tropez, La Colle sur le Loup, Nice, and Paris. Released in Great Britain in Oct 1967.

TWO FOR THE SEESAW   F6.5238

Seesaw Pictures–Mirisch Pictures–Argyle Enterprises–Talbot Productions–Seven Arts Productions. *Dist* United Artists. 21 Nov **1962** [New York opening; c21 Nov 1962; LP23344]. Sd; b&w. 35mm (Panavision). 120 min.

Pres by Mirisch Pictures, Robert Wise. *Prod* Walter Mirisch. *Dir* Robert Wise. *Screenplay* Isobel Lennart. *Cinematog* Ted McCord. *Camera Op* Richard Batcheller. *Camera Asst* Bob Uhl, Jack Chandler. *Asst Art Dir* Harry Kemm. *Set Decor* Edward G. Boyle. *Set Coörd* William Maldonado. *Prod Dsgn* Boris Leven. *Film Ed* Stuart Gilmore. *Asst Ed* Marshall M. Borden. *Mus* Andre Previn. *Sd* Lambert Day. *Mus Ed* Richard Carruth. *Asst Dir* Jerome M. Siegel, John Flynn. *Prod Mgr* Allen K. Wood. *Script Supv* Dixie McCoy. *Cost Dsgn* Orry-Kelly. *Wardrobe* Bert Henrikson, Irene Caine. *Makeup* Frank Westmore. *Hairstyles* Alice Monte. *Dial Coach* Leon Charles, Renée Leff. *Prop* Frank Agnone, Ted Berkeley. *Still Photog* Jack Harris, still photog. *Grip* Karl Reed. *Gaffer* Don Stott.

Cast: Robert Mitchum (*Jerry Ryan*), Shirley MacLaine (*Gittel Mosca*), Edmon Ryan (*Taubman*), Elisabeth Fraser (*Sophie*), Eddie Firestone (*Oscar*), Billy Gray (*Mr. Jacoby*).

Romantic comedy-drama. Source: William Gibson, *Two for the Seesaw* (New York opening: 16 Jan 1958). Omaha lawyer Jerry Ryan arrives in Manhattan after the breakup of his marriage and the loss of his job. He is lonely and decides to go to a Greenwich Village party given by his friend Oscar. There, he meets Gittel Mosca, a dancer from the Bronx, and they begin an affair. Jerry's thoughts, however, are still in Omaha, and he is unable to give of himself. Though he gets a job with a prominent law firm and uses some of his money to set Gittel up with a little dance studio in an empty loft, she senses that he cannot forget his wife and becomes depressed. After attending a party with a friend, she quarrels with Jerry, and has to be taken to the hospital with a hemorrhaging ulcer. When she returns he devotedly takes care of her, but the time inevitably arrives when she examines their relationship and asks Jerry to marry her when he is free of his marital ties. She learns that his divorce has already become final, though he has been afraid to tell her. They realize that the affair must end, and Jerry decides to return to his wife. Gittel is alone in her apartment when Jerry phones to tell her he loves her, and to say goodby. *Dancers. Dance teachers. Lawyers. Divorce. Marriage. New York City—*

Greenwich Village. New York City—Bronx.

Note: Location scenes filmed in New York City.

TWO GENTLEMEN SHARING (Great Britain) **F6.5239**

Epstein-Kulick Productions. *For* Paramount Pictures. *Dist* American International Pictures. 17 Sep **1969** [New York opening; c8 Oct 1969; LP37605]. Sd; col (print by Movielab). 35mm. 105 min. [Copyright length: 112 min.] *MPAA rating* R.

Pres by Samuel Z. Arkoff, James H. Nicholson. *Prod* J. Barry Kulick. *Assoc Prod* Douglas Peirce. *Uncredited Co-prod* Jerome Epstein. *Dir* Ted Kotcheff. *Screenplay* Evan Jones. *Photog* Billy Williams. *Camera Op* David Harcourt. *Art Dir* Ken Bridgeman. *Set Decor* Chris Cook. *Mus* Stanley Myers. *Sd* David Price. *Asst Dir* Scott Wodehouse. *Prod Mgr* Ed Harper. *Unit Mgr* Gus Angus. *Cont* Barbara Rowland. *Cost* Gabriella Falk. *Makeup* Colin Garde. *Hairstyles* Mary Bredin.

Cast: Robin Phillips (*Roddy*), Judy Geeson (*Jane*), Hal Frederick (*Andrew*), Esther Anderson (*Caroline*), Norman Rossington (*Phil*), Hilary Dwyer (*Ethne*), Rachel Kempson (*Mrs. Ashby-Kydd*), Daisy Mae Williams (*Amanda*), Ram John Holder (*Marcus*), Earl Cameron (*Charles*), Shelagh Fraser (*Helen*), David Markham (*Mr. Pater*), Avice Landon (*Mrs. Pater*), Philip Stone (*Mr. Burrows*), Elspeth March (*Mrs. Burrows*), Thomas Baptiste (*Mutt*), Linbert Spencer (*Jeff*), Willy Payne (*Bizerte*), Thors Piers (*Eugene Valentine*), Nathan Dambuza (*Chicomo*), Robert Burnell (*O'Reilly*), Hamilton Dyce (*Dickson Senior*), John Humphrey (*Dickson Junior*), Harold Lang (*young man*), Lionel Ngakane (*Bill*), Tommy Ansah (*driver*), George Baizley (*caretaker*), Harcourt Curacao (*band leader*), Carl Adam (*Negro visitor*), Anna Wing (*neighbor*), Benny Nightingale (*elevator operator*), Charles Leno (*doorman*), Phillamore Davidson, Winston Mitchell, John Chandos, David Edwards, John Snow, Gary Sobers, Les Flambeaux Steel Band.

Melodrama. Source: David Stuart Leslie, *Two Gentlemen Sharing* (London, 1963). Roddy, a white advertising executive, places an ad in the newspaper for a roommate to share the expenses of his London flat, and Andrew, a black Jamaican lawyer, responds. At first hesitant, the two men discover that they are both Oxford graduates and decide to have a trial period. Andrew moves into the apartment, and his Jamaican girl friend, Caroline, pays him frequent visits. One evening, the two roommates and their girl friends go to a nightclub. Bored with Ethne, his aristocratic partner, Roddy turns his attention to Jane, a pretty white woman surrounded by admiring Negroes, and later escorts her home, where he is intrigued to discover that she lives in a house owned by a Negro man. The following week, Roddy and Andrew plan a trip to Roddy's stately Elizabethan mansion, and Roddy invites Jane. When Roddy's parents protest Andrew being brought to the house, Andrew and Caroline return to the apartment only to be interrupted in their lovemaking by the sudden appearance of the landlady who, in an outpouring of racial hatred, demands that they leave. Hastily leaving a note for Roddy, the couple move back to the black ghetto and decide to return to Jamaica where society accepts them. Several days later, Roddy gives a party, hoping to convince Andrew to stay, and drunkenly declares his desire to marry Jane, even though he has learned that the black man at her house is her stepfather; but Jane now sees Roddy as the weak man he really is. He collapses on the bed and rejects the advances of Marcus, a guest who recognizes Roddy's latent homosexual tendencies. The police arrive and break up the party, leaving Roddy alone and confused. *Advertising executives. Lawyers. Negroes. Jamaicans. Roommates. Landladies. Stepfathers. Police. Race relations. Racial prejudice. Eviction. Drunkenness. Male homosexuality. Nightclubs. Ghettos. London.*

Note: Location scenes filmed in London.

TWO GIRLS FOR A MADMAN **F6.5240**

Brasreit Films. *Dist* Distribpix, Inc. 7 Oct **1968** [New York opening]. Sd; b&w. 35mm. [Feature film, length unknown.]

Dir Stanley H. Brasloff.

Cast: Toni France, Lucky Kargo.

Melodrama. Frank, an insane rapist left unattended by his psychiatrist, attacks and rapes Toni and Sonya, two ballet students. *Psychopaths. Dancers. Psychiatrists. Rape.*

288 STOURNARA ST. (Greece) **F6.5241**

Dist Atlantic Pictures. Feb **1961**. Sd; b&w. 35mm. 90 min.

Dir Dinos Simopoulos.

Cast: Orestis Makris (*janitor*), Sophia Vembo (*faded singer*), Dinos Elliopoulos (*Cypriot agitator*), Smaroula Giouli (*clerk*).

Comedy. Life in an Athens apartment house is shown through the eyes of its janitor. *Janitors. Clerks. Singers. Housing. Athens.*

TWO IN A SLEEPING BAG (West Germany) **F6.5242**

Bavaria-Filmkunst. *Dist* Holt International, Fouad Said Productions. Aug **1964**. Sd; col (Agfacolor). 35mm. 75 min.

Prod U. S. Vers Fouad Said. *Exec Prod* Georg Richter. *Dir* Rainer Geis. *Screenplay* Joachim Wedekind. *Idea* Arnold Franck. *Photog* Klaus von Rautenfeld. *Art Dir* Hans Berthel. *Film Ed* Hilwa von Boro. *Mus* Franz Grothe. *Sd* Hans Wunschel. *Prod Mgr* Helmut Ringelmann. *Prod Dir* Hermann Höhn.

Cast: Susanne Cramer (*[The Heiress]*), Claus Biederstaedt, Eva Kerbler, Hans Nielsen, Dietmar Schönherr, Heinrich Gretler, Gundel Thormann, Lina Carstens, Ernst Tabe.

Comedy. A spoiled young heiress is prevented from marrying a ne'er-do-well fortune hunter by her father, who sends her to a strict boarding school. One night she runs away to rejoin her boyfriend. Along the way she meets an athletic young man who is traveling by kayak along the Rhine. He offers her a ride, and for several days they camp out and boat together. By the end of the trip, the heiress discovers that she has fallen in love with her camping companion. *Heiresses. Ne'er-do-wells. Fortune hunters. Runaways. Filial relations. Camping. Boarding schools. Kayaks. Rhine River.*

Note: Filmed in Bavaria and Switzerland. Released in West Germany in 1956 as *Kleines Zelt und grosse Liebe*; running time: 93 min.

TWO IN THE SHADOW (Japan) **F6.5243**

Toho Co. Apr **1968** [Los Angeles showing]. Sd; col. 35mm (Tohoscope). 108 min.

Exec Prod Sanezumi Fujimoto, Masakatsu Kaneko. *Dir* Mikio Naruse. *Screenplay* Nobuo Yamada. *Photog* Jo Aizawa. *Art Dir* Satoru Nakano. *Mus* Toru Takemitsu.

Cast: Yuzo Kayama (*Shiro Mishima*), Yoko Tsukasa (*Yumiko*), Mitsuko Mori, Mitsuko Kusabue, Daisuke Kato, Nobu Tsuchiya, Yumiko Iida, Naoya Kusakawa.

Drama. Shiro Mishima is involved in a traffic accident in Tokyo in which a man is killed. Shiro is officially absolved of any guilt in the death, but his company, an import-export firm, transfers him to their branch in Aomori. Wracked by guilt, Shiro offers before he leaves to pay the man's widow, Yumiko, a monthly compensation. Yumiko refuses at first, but under pressure from her in-laws she accepts the payments. Trying to forget the accident, she returns to Aomori, which is her home town. She and Shiro meet several times, but she spurns his attempts to be friendly. Respecting Yumiko's wishes, Shiro applies for a transfer to his firm's Pakistan office. Yumiko begins to feel some affection for Shiro and agrees to go out with him. Just before he is to leave for Pakistan, Shiro confesses his love for Yumiko. She turns him away, but on the day of his departure she finds herself wanting to accompany him. They witness a traffic accident which reminds her so much of her husband that they part, realizing they can never become lovers. *Widows. Guilt. Tokyo. Aomori. Automobile accidents.*

Note: Released in Japan in 1967 as *Midare-gumo*.

TWO INTO TWO—ONCE **F6.5244**

Dist Stacey Distributors. ca **1970**. Sd; col. 16mm. 61-81 min.

Sex film. No information about the precise nature of this film has been found. *Sexuality.*

THE TWO LITTLE BEARS **F6.5245**

Twentieth Century-Fox Film Corp. 1 Nov **1961** [Salt Lake City opening; c1 Nov 1961; LP20664]. Sd; b&w. 35mm (CinemaScope). 81 min.

Prod-Screenplay George W. George. *Exec Prod* Robert L. Lippert. *Dir* Randall Hood. *Story* Judy George, George W. George. *Dir Photog* Floyd Crosby. *Art Dir* John Mansbridge. *Set Decor* Chester L. Bayhi. *Titl Dsgn* George W. George, Jonathan Lucas. *Film Ed* Carl Pierson. *Mus Comp & Cond* Henry Vars. *Theme Song:* "Honey Bear" Jay Livingston, Ray Evans. *Song:* "Speak to Me Pretty" "By" Dunham, Henry Vars. *Songs Sung by* Brenda Lee. *Choreog* Jonathan Lucas. *Sd* E. Clayton Ward. *Asst Dir* Willard Kirkham. *Prod Supv* Harold E. Knox. *Script Supv* Winifred Gibson. *Men's Wardrobe* Robert Olivas. *Women's Wardrobe* Paula Giokaris. *Makeup* Hal Lierley. *Sp Eff* Cinema Research Corp. *Prop Master* Glenn "Skippy" Delfino. *Animal Trainers* George Fraser, John Welde.

Cast: Eddie Albert (*Harry Davis*), Jane Wyatt (*Anne Davis*), Brenda Lee (*Tina Davis*), Soupy Sales (*Officer Pat McGovern*), Butch Patrick (*Billy Davis*), Donnie Carter (*Timmy Davis*), Jimmy Boyd (*Tina's boy friend*), Nancy Kulp (*Miss Wilkins*), Milton Parsons (*psychiatrist*), Emory Parnell (*school board head*), Opal Euard (*fortune-teller*), Richard Alden (*Tom Provost*), Theo Marcuse (*Janos*), James Maloney (*Jefferson Stander*), Jack Finch (*psychiatrist*), Jack Lester (*Phil Wade*), Charlene Brooks (*Mary Jergens*).

Fantasy. Billy and Timmy, the two young sons of grade school principal Harry Davis, follow the instructions given them by a gypsy and discover how to change themselves into bears. One day they run away from home and school to play in the woods with a mother bear who cares for them. When they return home, they perform their transformation feat before their astonished father. Stunned at first, but then filled with paternal pride, Harry races out to tell all the townspeople about the miracle. The pandemonium that ensues delights the two boys but prompts Harry's superiors to suggest that he undergo psychiatric treatment. When the school board gathers to discuss Harry's dismissal, Billy and Timmy demonstrate their prowess and vindicate their father. Harry is reinstated as principal, and everyone heaves a sigh of relief when the youngsters become more interested in football than in being bears. *School principals. Gypsies. Elementary school life. Transmutation. Mental illness. Magic. Bears.*

TWO LIVING, ONE DEAD (Great Britain/Sweden) F6.5246

Swan Productions–Wera Film. *Dist* Emerson Film Enterprises. 1 Jan **1964** [Maryland license]. Sd; b&w. 35mm. 92 min.

Prod Teddy Baird. *Assoc Prod* Lorens Marmstedt. *Exec Prod* Karl E. Mosley. *Dir* Anthony Asquith. *Screenplay* Lindsay Galloway. *Photog* Gunnar Fischer. *Set Dsgn* Bibi Lindström. *Mus Score* Erik Nordgren.

Cast: Virginia McKenna (*Helen Berger*), Bill Travers (*Anderson*), Patrick McGoohan (*Berger*), Dorothy Alison (*Esther Kester*), Alf Kjellin (*Rogers*), Noel Willman (*Inspector Johnson*), Pauline Jameson (*Miss Larsen*), Peter Vaughan (*John Kester*), Derek Francis (*Broms*), Michael Crawford (*Nils*), John Moulder-Brown (*Rolf Berger*), Isa Quensel.

Melodrama. Source: Sigurd Wesley Christiansen, *To levende og en død* (Oslo, 1925). One night in a small town, three postal clerks (Berger, Anderson, and Kester) are counting receipts when they are held up by two armed men. Kester is killed during the robbery, Anderson receives a serious head injury, and Berger turns over the cash to the robbers. Afterwards, Berger is treated with contempt for being a coward, and Anderson is considered a hero. Anderson receives a promotion previously promised to Berger, while the police, the postmaster, the newspapermen, and even his wife, Helen, suspect Berger of complicity in the crime. He learns from a man who is later revealed to be one of the robbers that Anderson was actually an accomplice in the robbery. A few nights later, Berger confronts Anderson with a gun, forces him to admit his guilt, and regains the respect of the townspeople. *Postal clerks. Police. Postmasters. Newspapermen. Robbery. Murder. Reputation. Cowardice. Smalltown life.*

Note: Filmed on location in Sweden and released there in Apr 1961 as *Två levande och en död*; in Great Britain in 1961(?).

TWO LOVES F6.5247

Julian Blaustein Productions. *Dist* Metro-Goldwyn-Mayer, Inc. 24 May **1961** [Los Angeles opening; c3 Mar 1961; LP19110]. Sd (Westrex); col (Metrocolor). 35mm (CinemaScope). 100 min.

A Julian Blaustein Production. *Prod* Julian Blaustein. *Dir* Charles Walters. *Screenplay* Ben Maddow. *Dir Photog* Joseph Ruttenberg. *Col Cons* Charles K. Hagedon. *Art Dir* George W. Davis, Urie McCleary. *Set Decor* Henry Grace, Hugh Hunt. *Film Ed* Fredric Steinkamp. *Mus* Bronislau Kaper. *Orch Cond* Robert Armbruster. *Rec Supv* Franklin Milton. *Asst Dir* William Shanks. *Makeup* William Tuttle. *Hairstyles* Mary Keats. *Sp Eff* Robert R. Hoag, Lee Le Blanc.

Cast: Shirley MacLaine (*Anna Vorontosov*), Laurence Harvey (*Paul Lathrope*), Jack Hawkins (*W. W. J. Abercrombie*), Nobu McCarthy (*Whareparita*), Ronald Long (*Headmaster Reardon*), Norah Howard (*Mrs. Cutter*), Juano Hernandez (*Rauhuia*), Edmund Vargas (*Matawhero*), Neil Woodward (*Mark Cutter*), Lisa Sitjar (*Hinewaka*), Alan Roberts, actor (*Seven*).

Drama. Source: Sylvia Ashton-Warner, *Spinster* (London, 1958). American-born Anna Vorontosov teaches school in a remote, primitive section of northern New Zealand. Her experimental teaching methods have won her the love and affection of her pupils and their parents and the admiration of the unhappily married school inspector, Abercrombie. Her personal life, however, is less secure; frightened of love and sexually inhibited, she has always been aloof with men. Eager to break down this barrier is Englishman Paul Lathrope, a somewhat irrational and immature fellow teacher who aspires to be a singer. Though Anna is attracted to him, she refuses to submit to his advances. One day she is shocked to learn that one of her helpers, Whareparita, a 15-year-old unmarried Maori girl, is expecting a child. Equally devastating to Anna is the discovery that both the young girl and her relatives are eagerly awaiting the baby. This calm acceptance of nature so disturbs Anna that she begins to question her own way of life. Then Whareparita's baby dies at birth, and Paul is killed in a motorcycle accident—possibly suicidal. Shortly before the funeral Anna learns that it was Paul who fathered Whareparita's dead infant. Overcome with guilt, Anna blames her frigidity for the tragic turn of events. It is only when Abercrombie convinces her that no one is directly responsible for the actions of another person that Anna is able to absolve herself of guilt. Encouraged by the gentle and tender love offered by Abercrombie, she at last realizes that she has nothing to fear from life. *Spinsters. Americans in foreign countries. English. Schoolteachers. School inspectors. Singers. Frigidity. Illegitimacy. Suicide. Guilt. Maori. New Zealand. Motorcycle accidents.*

Note: Location scenes filmed in California. Prerelease titles: *The Spinster* and *I'll Save My Love.*

TWO MULES FOR SISTER SARA (United States/Mexico) F6.5248

Malpaso Co.-Universal Pictures–Sanen Productions. *Dist* Universal Pictures. 28 May **1970** [Dallas opening; c29 May 1970; LP38934]. Sd (Westrex); col (Technicolor). 35mm (Panavision). 114 min. [Copyright length: 105 min.] *MPAA rating* GP.

A Martin Rackin Production. *Prod* Martin Rackin, Carroll Case. *Dir* Don Siegel. *2d Unit Dir* Joseph Cavalier, René Cardona. *Screenplay* Albert Maltz. *Story* Budd Boetticher. *Dir Photog* Gabriel Figueroa. *2d Unit Camera* Gabriel Torres. *Camera Op* Bruce Surtees. *Art Dir* José Rodriguez Granada. *Set Decor* Pablo Galvan. *Film Ed* Robert F. Shugrue. *Film Ed Mexico* Juan José Marino. *Mus* Ennio Morricone. *Mus Supv* Stanley Wilson. *Sd* Waldon O. Watson, Jesús González Gancy, Ronald Pierce. *Asst Dir* Joseph Cavalier, Manuel Muñoz. *Unit Prod Mgr* William C. Davidson, Alfonso Sánchez Tello. *Cost* Helen Colvig, Carlos Chavez. *Makeup* Frank Westmore, Margarita Ortega. *Hairstyles* Evelina Casas. *Sp Eff* Frank Brendel, Leon Ortega. *Dial Coach* Leon Charles. *Stunt Coörd* Buddy Van Horn.

Cast: Shirley MacLaine (*Sister Sara*), Clint Eastwood (*Hogan*), Manolo Fabregas (*Colonel Beltran*), Alberto Morin (*General LeClaire*), Armando Silvestre (*1st American*), John Kelly (*2d American*), Enrique Lucero (*3d American*), David Estuardo (*Juan*), Ada Carrasco (*Juan's mother*), Pancho Córdova (*Juan's father*), José Chavez (*Horacio*), Pedro Galvan, José Angel Espinosa, Enrique Lucero, Aurora Muñoz, Xavier Marc, Hortensia Santoveña, Rosa Furman, José Torvay, Margarito Luna, Javier Masse.

Western drama. While three men in the Mexican desert strip the clothes off a woman and attempt to rape her, Hogan, a gunfighter, arrives on horseback and shoots the trio to death. Hogan himself finds the disrobed victim attractive, but he is shocked to learn that she is Sister Sara, a nun involved in the Mexican revolutionary movement against the French. He agrees to take her to the revolutionaries' camp and promises to help them attack the French garrison at Chihuahua if they offer him enough money. En route Hogan is surprised to find Sara smoking a cigar and sneaking a drink of whiskey. Later, near the revolutionaries' camp in Santa María, Hogan attempts to dynamite a French ammunition train, but he is hit in the shoulder by a Yaqui Indian's arrow. After Sara bandages his wound, she climbs a high train trestle to place the dynamite and then sets off the explosion by firing a rifle into the charge. When they arrive at the rebel camp, Sara astonishes Hogan by disclosing that she is actually a prostitute with an intimate knowledge of the French fort, the revolutionaries' major military objective. They devise a plan for Hogan to take Sara to the fort as a prisoner in order to gain the confidence of the French soldiers so that the gates will be opened for the Mexicans. The plan succeeds, and the fort is captured after a bloody battle; Hogan and Sara take their share of the spoils and depart. *Gunfighters. Nuns. Revolutionaries. Mercenaries. Yaqui Indians. Prostitutes. French. Soldiers. Rape. Imposture. Deserts. Forts. Trains. Mexico—History—European intervention. Chihuahua. Explosions.*

Note: Location scenes filmed in Mexico.

TWO NIGHTS WITH CLEOPATRA (Italy) F6.5249

Excelsa Film–Rosa Film. *Dist* Ultra Pictures. May **1963**. Sd; col (Ferraniacolor, U. S. print by Movielab). 35mm. 80 min. [Also 90 min.]

Dir Mario Mattoli. *Screenplay* (see note) Nino Maccari, Ettore Scola. *Photog* Karl Struss, Riccardo Pallottini. *Mus* Armando Trovajoli. *Dir Prod* Giuseppe Colizzi.

Cast: Sophia Loren (*Cleopatra/Cleopatra's double*), Ettore Manni (*Mark Antony*), Alberto Sordi, Rolf Tasna, Gianni Cavalieri, Paul Muller, Fernando Bruno, Riccardo Garrone, Carlo Dale, Alberto Talegalli.

Comedy. Queen Cleopatra is determined to spend a night with Antony before he goes into battle, although she has been advised against leaving the palace. A blonde double found at the slave market poses as the queen while Cleopatra slips out to meet Antony. Meanwhile, a new guard, who is determined to spend the night with Cleopatra, enters the palace with a scarab ring—the twin of which is owned by Cleopatra. He gains entrance to Cleopatra's bedroom, and, mistaking the double for the queen, he makes love to her. The queen returns soon after the guard's departure and hides the slave in the dungeon to conceal her secret. Antony warns Cleopatra about a conspiracy against her and promises to send the leader to her the following night. Handing her scarab ring to Antony, she tells him to make the conspirator wear it so that she can identify him. When the guard returns to the palace, his ring causes him to be mistaken for the conspirator. In an attempt to seduce him and learn his secrets, Cleopatra gets drunk and the guard learns of the double. The real conspirator is apprehended and brought to the palace, while the guard rescues the slave girl from the dungeon and the two escape. *Royalty. Guards. Doubles. Impersonation. Mistaken identity. Conspiracy. Slavery. Seduction. Drunkenness. Dungeons. Cleopatra. Mark Antony.*

Note: Opened in Rome in Feb 1954 as *Due notti con Cleopatra*. Nino Maccari is also known as Ruggero Maccari.

THE TWO OF US (France)   **F6.5250**

Valoria Films–P. A. C.–Renn Productions. *Dist* Cinema V Distributing, Inc. 19 Feb **1968** [New York opening]. Sd; b&w. 35mm. 86 min.

Prod Paul Cadéac. *Dir-Writ* Claude Berri. *Adapt* Gérard Brach, Claude Berri, Michel Rivelin. *Photog* Jean Penzer. *Art Dir* Georges Lévy, Maurice Petri. *Film Ed* Sophie Coussein, Denise Charvein. *Mus* Georges Delerue. *Sd* Jean Labussière, Julien Coutellier. *Asst Dir* Pierre Grunstein, Claude Confortes. *Prod Mgr* Jean Darvey. *English Subtitl* Noelle Gillmor.

Cast: Michel Simon (*Gramps [Pépé]*), Alain Cohen (*Claude*), Luce Fabiole (*Granny [Mémé]*), Roger Carel (*Victor*), Paul Préboist (*Maxime*), Charles Denner (*Claude's father*), Zorica Lozic (*Claude's mother*), Jacqueline Rouillard (*teacher*), Aline Bertrand (*Raymonde*), Sylvine Delannoy (*Suzanne*), Marco Perrin (*The Priest*), Elisabeth Rey (*Dinou*), Denise Péronne (*landlady*), Didier Perret (*Dinou's brother*), Kinou (*himself, a dog*).

Comedy-drama. In 1944, during the German occupation of France, a young Parisian Jewish couple represent themselves as Alsatians in the hope of avoiding deportation to a concentration camp. As a further precaution, they send their mischievous 8-year-old son, Claude, to live in the country with the elderly parents of one of their Catholic friends. Because the old man follows the Vichy line of propaganda and hates the Jews, English, Bolsheviks, and Freemasons, Claude's parents give him a Christian surname, teach him the Lord's Prayer, and instruct him always to bathe in private. After a few days on the farm the youngster succeeds in penetrating the crusty exterior of old Gramps and becomes his constant companion, usually accompanied by the old man's beloved dog, Kinou. Claude even baits Gramps about his prejudices, claiming that the old man looks Jewish. Gramps encourages Claude to write a love note to one of his classmates at the local school. When the letter is discovered and Claude's head is shaved as punishment, the old man gives the humiliated child a hat to wear and promises that he will not have to return to school until the incident is forgotten. As the war nears its end, Gramps suffers two heartbreaks in succession. First Marshal Pétain is openly vilified as a collaborationist; then the old, bronchitis-stricken Kinou dies. The happiness of the old man and the boy at the liberation of France is mixed with sadness because it means their friendship must now end. Claude leaves with his parents, and the old couple silently watch the departing bus. *Jews. Catholics. Anti-Semitism. Childhood. Old age. Bigotry. Friendship. Imposture. Rural life. Elementary school life. France—History—German occupation 1940–45. World War II. Paris. Henri Philippe Pétain. Dogs.*

Note: Paris opening: Mar 1967 as *Le vieil homme et l'enfant*; running time: 90 min. Also reviewed as *Claude*.

TWO ON A GUILLOTINE   **F6.5251**

Warner Bros. Pictures. 13 Jan **1965** [New York opening; c31 Dec 1964; LP29865]. Sd; b&w. 35mm (Panavision). 107 min.

Prod-Dir William Conrad. *Screenplay* Henry Slesar, John Kneubuhl. *Story* Henry Slesar. *Dir Photog* Sam Leavitt. *Art Dir* Art Loel. *Set Decor* William Wallace. *Film Ed* William Ziegler. *Mus* Max Steiner. *Orch Cond* Murray Cutter. *Sd* Francis E. Stahl. *Asst Dir* Phil Rawlins. *Makeup Supv* Gordon Bau. *Supv Hairstyles* Jean Burt Reilly.

Cast: Connie Stevens (*Melinda Duquesne/Cassie Duquesne*), Dean Jones (*Val Henderson*), Cesar Romero ("*Duke*" *Duquesne*), Parley Baer ("*Buzz*" *Sheridan*), Virginia Gregg (*Dolly Bast*), Connie Gilchrist (*Ramona Ryerdon*), John Hoyt (*Carl Vickers*), Russell Thorson (*Carmichael*).

Mystery drama. Cassie Duquesne, daughter of magician "Duke" Duquesne, whose wife, Melinda, was accidentally beheaded during their act in 1944, returns to Los Angeles 20 years later to attend her father's funeral. She learns that his will stipulates that, in order to receive her inheritance, she must spend seven consecutive nights in his old mansion. Duquesne claimed that he would make his presence known to her on one of those nights. Reporter Val Henderson arrives and is allowed to stay at the old house with her until Cassie learns that he is planning a story on her vigil. That night, after Val has left, Duquesne appears, alive and insane, and attempts his guillotine routine on her. Val returns with the police, however, in time to save her. *Magicians. Reporters. Decapitation. Funerals. Inheritance. Murder. Filial relations. Insanity. Los Angeles.*

TWO OR THREE THINGS I KNOW ABOUT HER (France) **F6.5252**

Anouchka Films–Argos Films–Films du Carrosse–Parc Film. *Dist* New Yorker Films. 30 Apr **1970** [New York opening]. Sd; col (Eastman Color). 35mm (Techniscope). 90 min.

Prod Raoul Lévy. *Dir-Writ* Jean-Luc Godard. *Dir Photog* Raoul Coutard. *Camera Op* Georges Liron. *Asst Camera Op* Jean Garcenot. *Film Ed* Françoise Collin, Chantal Delattre. *Mus Selections* Ludwig van Beethoven. *Sd* Antoine Bonfanti, René Levert. *Boom Op* Robert Cambourakis. *1st & 2d Asst Dir* Charles Bitsch, Isabelle Pons. *Prod Supv* Philippe Senné. *Prod Mgr* Claude Miler. *Script Girl* Suzanne Schiffman. *Cost* Gitt Marrini. *Wardrobe Mistress* Dora Balabanow. *Makeup* Jackie Reynal. *Hairstyles* Renée Guidet. *Res*

Catherine Vimenet. *Still Photog* Marilou Parolini.

Cast: Marina Vlady (*Juliette Janson*), Anny Duperey (*Marianne*), Roger Montsoret (*Robert Janson*), Jean Narboni (*Roger*), Christophe Bourseiller (*Christophe*), Marie Bourseiller (*Solange*), Raoul Lévy (*The American*), Joseph Gehrard (*Monsieur Gérard*), Helena Bielicic (*girl in bath*), Robert Chevassu (*meter-reader*), Yves Beneyton (*long-haired youth*), Jean-Pierre Laverne (*writer*), Blandine Jeanson (*student*), Claude Miler (*Bouvard*), Jean-Patrick Lebel (*Pécuchet*), Juliette Berto (*girl who talks to Robert*), Anna Manga (*woman in basement*), Benjamin Rosette (*man in basement*), Helen Scott (*woman at pinball machine*), Jean-Luc Godard (*narrator*).

Drama. Suggested by: Catherine Vimenet, "Les étoiles filantes," in *Le nouvel observateur* (23 Mar 1966). Juliette Janson, a young housewife living in a modern high-rise building in suburban Paris, works part-time as a prostitute to help maintain the middle-class lifestyle which she and her husband have achieved. One morning after she has sent her son, Christophe, to school and left her daughter, Solange, with a babysitter, Juliette goes shopping and waits in a cafe for her first customer. After spending a short time with a construction worker, she goes to the hairdresser and leaves with her manicurist, Marianne; they meet an American journalist at a luxury hotel and engage in group sex. Later, she and her husband go home together. When the children are in bed, Juliette contemplates the futility of her life. *Middle classes. Housewives. Manicurists. Construction workers. Americans in foreign countries. Journalists. Suburban life. Marriage. Materialism. Prostitution. Parenthood. Group sex. Paris.*

Note: Filmed in and around Paris. Opened in Paris in Mar 1967 as *Deux ou trois choses que je sais d'elle*; running time: 95 min.

TWO RODE TOGETHER   **F6.5253**

John Ford Productions–Shpetner Productions. *Dist* Columbia Pictures. 26 Jul **1961** [New York opening; c1 Jul 1961; LP20449]. Sd; col (Eastman Color). 35mm. 109 min.

A John Ford Production. *Prod* Stan Shpetner. *Dir* John Ford. *Screenplay* Frank Nugent. *Dir Photog* Charles Lawton, Jr. *Art Dir* Robert Peterson. *Set Decor* James M. Crowe. *Film Ed* Jack Murray. *Mus* George Duning. *Orch* Arthur Morton. *Sd Supv* Charles J. Rice. *Sd Rec* Harry Mills. *Asst Dir* Wingate Smith. *Makeup Supv* Ben Lane.

Cast: James Stewart (*Guthrie McCabe*), Richard Widmark (*Lieut. Jim Gary*), Shirley Jones (*Marty Purcell*), Linda Cristal (*Elena de la Madriaga*), Andy Devine (*Sgt. Darius P. Posey*), John McIntire (*Major Frazer*), Paul Birch (*Edward Purcell*), Willis Bouchey (*Mr. Wringle*), Henry Brandon (*Quanah Parker*), Harry Carey, Jr. (*Jackson Clay*), Olive Carey (*Abby Frazer*), Ken Curtis (*Boone Clay*), Chet Douglas (*Ward Corbey*), Annelle Hayes (*Belle Aragon*), David Kent (*Running Wolf*), Anna Lee (*Mrs. Malaprop*), Jeanette Nolan (*Mrs. McCandless*), John Qualen (*Ole Knudsen*), Ford Rainey (*Henry Clay*), Woody Strode (*Stone Calf*), O. Z. Whitehead (*officer*), Cliff Lyons (*William McCandless*), Mae Marsh (*Hanna Clay*), Frank Baker (*Captain Malaprop*), Ruth Clifford (*woman*), Ted Knight (*Lieutenant Chase*), Major Sam Harris (*post doctor*), Jack Pennick (*sergeant*), Chuck Roberson (*Comanche*), Dan Borzage, Bill Henry, Chuck Hayward, Edward Brophy.

Western drama. Source: Will Cook, *Comanche Captives* (New York, 1960). In the 1880's, Guthrie McCabe, a cynical, mercenary Texas marshal, is asked to join cavalry officer Jim Gary in rescuing some white prisoners long held captive by the Comanches. McCabe is reluctant to accept but allows himself to be persuaded by a combination of Army pressure, the offer of a salary, the promise of a fee for each captive returned, and the opportunity to take a vacation from Belle Aragon, a saloon owner who has marriage on her mind. In exchange for two rifles, McCabe and Gary obtain the release of Running Wolf, a white boy raised as an Indian, and Elena, a young Mexican woman who has been forced to become the squaw of Comanche warrior Stone Calf. As the little group leaves the Indian camp, Stone Calf tries to reclaim his woman, and McCabe kills him. Back at the fort, none of the families who anxiously awaited the return of their relatives recognize Running Wolf, and he is claimed only by the mentally deranged Mrs. McCandless, who insists the wild boy is her son. However, as she frees him of his bonds, he murders her. The inflamed settlers capture and lynch the youth, but before he dies it is discovered that he is actually the brother of Marty Purcell, a young settler with whom Gary has fallen in love. Meanwhile, Elena has been shunned by the narrow-minded officers' wives. McCabe leaves the fort to resume his marshal's job and discovers that he has been replaced by his inept deputy in the interim. Disenchanted, he rides off with Elena in search of a better life. *United States marshals. Comanche Indians. Mexicans. Settlers. Saloon keepers. Marriage. Kidnaping. Insanity. Murder. Lynching. Brother-sister relationship. Racial prejudice. Firearms. Forts. Texas. United States Army—Cavalry.*

Note: Filmed on location in southwestern Texas.

TWO ROSES AND A GOLDEN-ROD   F6.5254

Company of Artists Productions. *Dist* International Film Organization. 27 Aug **1969** [Buffalo, New York, opening]. Sd; col (Eastman Color). 35mm. 82 min.

Prcs by M. A. Ripps, Donald E. Leon. *Prod* Hal Senter. *Exec Prod* Donald E. Leon. *Dir-Writ* Albert Zugsmith. *Photog* Robert Caramico. *Film Ed* Hugo Grimaldi. *Mus* Igo Kantor. *Prod Mgr* Carol Caruso.

Cast: John Alderman, Lois Ursone, Lisa Grant, Ann Pailey.

Melodrama. A screenwriter [John Alderman] and his 16-year-old daughter [Ann Pailey] are sexually attracted to each other. The daughter sunbathes in the nude by their pool, encouraging her father's advances. The writer's wife [Lisa Grant] is torn between her attraction for her husband and her lesbian tendencies and has a sexual relationship with a close family friend [Lois Ursone]. *Motion picture scriptwriters. Incest. Lesbianism. Filial relations.*

TWO SOLDIERS—EAST AND WEST see HELL IN THE PACIFIC

2001: A SPACE ODYSSEY (United States/Great Britain)   F6.5255

Metro-Goldwyn-Mayer, Inc. 2 Apr **1968** [Washington, D. C., opening; c3 Apr 1968; LP36136]. Sd; col (Technicolor & Metrocolor). 35mm & 70mm (Super Panavision). 160 min. [Cut to 141 min.]

A Stanley Kubrick Production. *Prod-Dir* Stanley Kubrick. *Assoc Prod* Victor Lyndon. *Screenplay* Stanley Kubrick, Arthur C. Clarke. *Dir Photog* Geoffrey Unsworth. *Adtl Photog* John Alcott. *Camera Op* Kelvin Pike. *Art Dir* John Hoesli. *Prod Dsgn* Tony Masters, Harry Lange, Ernest Archer. *Film Ed* Ray Lovejoy. *Ed Asst* David De Wilde. *Mus:* "Gayane Ballet Suite" Aram Ilich Khachaturyan. *Perf by* Leningrad Philharmonic Orchestra. *Cond* Gennadiy Rozhdestvenskiy. *Mus:* "Atmosphères," "Lux Aeterna," "Requiem" György Ligeti. "Atmosphères" *perf by* South West German Radio Orchestra. *Cond* Ernest Bour. "Lux Aeterna" *perf by* Schola Cantorum of Stuttgart. *Cond* Clytus Gottwald. "Requiem" *perf by* Bavarian Radio Orchestra. *Cond* Francis Travis. *Mus:* "The Blue Danube" Johann Strauss. *Perf by* The Berlin Philharmonic Orchestra. *Cond* Herbert von Karajan. *Mus:* "Thus Spake Zarathustra" Richard Strauss. *Perf by* The Berlin Philharmonic Orchestra. *Cond* Karl Böhm. *Sd Supv* A. W. Watkins. *Sd Mix* H. L. Bird. *Ch Dub Mix* J. B. Smith. *Sd Ed* Winston Ryder. *1st Asst Dir* Derek Cracknell. *Wardrobe* Hardy Amies. *Makeup* Stuart Freeborn. *Sp Photog Eff Dsgn & Dir* Stanley Kubrick. *Supv Sp Photog Eff* Wally Veevers, Douglas Trumbull, Con Pederson, Tom Howard. *Sp Photog Eff Unit* Colin J. Cantwell, Bryan Loftus, Frederick Martin, Bruce Logan, David Osborne, John Jack Malick. *Scientific Cons* Frederick I. Ordway, III.

Cast: Keir Dullea (*David Bowman*), Gary Lockwood (*Frank Poole*), William Sylvester (*Dr. Heywood Floyd*), Daniel Richter (*Moonwatcher*), Leonard Rossiter (*Smyslov*), Margaret Tyzack (*Elena*), Robert Beatty (*Halvorsen*), Sean Sullivan (*Michaels*), Douglas Rain (*voice of Hal 9000*), Frank Miller (*mission controller*), Alan Gifford (*Poole's father*), Penny Brahms, Edwina Carroll (*stewardesses*), Vivian Kubrick ("*Squirt*," *Dr. Floyd's daughter*), Bill Weston, Mike Lovell, Edward Bishop, Ann Gillis, Heather Downham, John Ashley, Jimmy Bell, David Charkham, Simon Davis, Jonathan Daw, Peter Delmar, Terry Duggan, David Fleetwood, Danny Grover, Brian Hawley, David Hines, Tony Jackson, actor, John Jordan, actor, Scott Mackee, Laurence Marchant, Darryl Paes, Joe Refalo, Andy Wallace, Bob Wilyman, Richard Wood, Glenn Beck.

Science fiction allegory. Source: Arthur C. Clarke, "Sentinel of Eternity" ("The Sentinel"), in *Ten Story Fantasy* (Spring 1951). At the dawn of mankind, a colony of peaceful vegetarian apes awaken to find a glowing black monolith standing in their midst. After tentatively reaching out to touch the mysterious object, the apes become carnivores, with enough intelligence to employ bones for weapons and tools. Four million years later, in the year 2001, Dr. Heywood Floyd, an American scientist, travels to the moon to investigate a monolith that has been discovered below the lunar surface. Knowing only that the slab emits a deafening sound directed toward the planet Jupiter, the United States sends a huge spaceship, the *Discovery*, on a 9-month, half billion-mile journey to the distant planet. Aboard are astronauts David Bowman and Frank Poole, plus three others in frozen hibernation, and a computer called Hal. During the voyage, Hal predicts the failure of a component on one of the spacecraft's antennae. Bowman leaves the ship in a one-man space pod to replace the crucial part; the prediction proves incorrect, however, and when Poole ventures out to replace the original part, Hal severs his lifeline. Bowman goes to rescue him, but Hal closes the pod entry doors and terminates the life functions of the three hibernating astronauts. Forced to abandon Poole, who is already dead, Bowman reenters the *Discovery* through the emergency hatch and reduces Hal to manual control by performing a mechanical lobotomy on the computer's logic and memory circuits. Now alone, Bowman continues his flight until he encounters a third monolith among Jupiter's moons. Suddenly hurtled into a new dimension of time and space, he is swept into a maelstrom of swirling colors, erupting landscapes, and exploding galaxies. At last coming to rest in a pale green bedroom, Bowman emerges from the nonfunctioning space capsule. A witness to the final stages of his life, the withered Bowman looks up from his deathbed at the giant black monolith standing in the center of the room. As he reaches toward it, he is perhaps reborn, perhaps evolved, perhaps transcended, into a new "child of the universe," a fetus floating above the Earth. *Ape-men. Scientists. Astronauts. Evolution. Space exploration. Cryogenics. Death. Time travel. Monoliths. Spaceships. Computers. Space capsules. The Moon. Jupiter (planet). The Universe. The Future. Apes.*

Note: Opened in London in May 1968; running time: 141 min. Presented in Cinerama for roadshow engagements.

TWO THOUSAND MANIACS!   F6.5256

Dist Box Office Spectaculars. caMar **1964**. Sd; col (Eastmancolor). 35mm. 88 min.

A David F. Friedman–Herschell G. Lewis Production. *Prod* David F. Friedman. *Dir-Screenplay-Orig Story* Herschell G. Lewis. *Photog* Herschell G. Lewis. *Prod Dsgn* David F. Friedman. *Film Ed* Robert Sinise. *Orig Mus* Herschell G. Lewis. *Mus Arr* Larry Wellington. *Mus Cond* Chuck Scott. *Sd Rec* David F. Friedman. *Prod Mgr* Andy Romanoff. *Unit Mgr* Jerome Eden. *Unit Asst* David Guilbert. *Script Supv* Gretchen Blank. *Crew Ch* Harry Kerwin.

Cast: Connie Mason (*Terry Adams*), Thomas Wood (*Tom White*), Jeffrey Allen (*Mayor Buckman*), Ben Moore (*Lester*), Shelby Livingston (*Bea Miller*), Gary Bakeman (*Rufe*), Jerome Eden (*John Miller*), Michael Korb (*David Wells*), Yvonne Gilbert (*Beverly Wells*), Mark Douglas (*Harper*), Linda Cochran (*Betsy*), Vincent Santo (*Billy*), Andy Wilson (*policeman*), The Pleasant Valley Boys (*themselves*).

Horror film. Two vacationing Illinois couples, John and Bea Miller and David and Beverly Wells, follow a detour down a backwoods road in a southern state. Terry Adams, a wealthy playgirl from Pennsylvania, drives down the same road, accompanied by schoolteacher Tom White. The cars arrive in the secluded hamlet of Pleasant Valley (pop. 2,000) where the townspeople are celebrating a centennial. Confederate flags are flying everywhere. Mayor Earl Buckman and centennial co-chairmen Lester and Rufe insist that the six Northerners remain as guests of the town. Bea is taken by a local tough, Harper, into the woods where he cuts off her finger. He then takes her to Buckman's office where she is held down by several Confederates and murdered with an ax. Bea's husband John, escorted by a local belle, Betsy, becomes so drunk that he does not notice his wife's absence. That evening, he is executed at a town barbecue. Meanwhile, Terry and John discover a memorial plaque revealing that 100 years before, the town's citizens had been massacred by renegade Union troops. The next day David Wells is murdered by a mob of townspeople, and Beverly is crushed to death by a huge boulder while a crowd cheers. Terry and John run from the town, pursued by Harper, who falls into a pit of quicksand and dies. A local boy, Billy, divulges the hiding place of their car, and they make their escape, using Billy as a hostage. Later, they return with the incredulous police, who can find no trace of the road, the detour, or even the town. The police inform the Northerners that Pleasant Valley was wiped out during the Civil War. Back in Pleasant Valley, the decorations come down and the citizens begin to dismantle the celebration trappings, while Rufe and Lester discuss plans for the next centennial, to be held in 2065. *Playgirls. Schoolteachers. Mayors. Hostages. Police. Sadism. Torture. Murder. Drunkenness. Revenge. Mutilation. Supernatural. Vacations. Centennial celebrations. Massacres. United States—History—Civil War. United States—South.*

Note: Filmed in St. Cloud, Florida.

2069 A.D.: A SENSATION ODYSSEY   F6.5257

Hollywood Picture Recorders. *Dist* Republic Amusements Corp. 28 Mar **1969** [Champaign, Illinois, showing]. Sd; b&w. 35mm. [Feature length assumed.]

Dir Sam Kopetsky. *Dir Photog* Vic Goss. *Lighting* Russ Nannarello. *Set Dir* Darwin Swan. *Rec* Jan-Jan. *Asst Dir* Mike Shall. *Key Grip* Rocky.

Cast: Harvey Foster, Barbara Lynn, Sharon Matt, Marsha Kopete, Harry Kay, Charlotte White, Linda Marr, Mike Shadow.

Science fiction comedy. Citizen 3X47 is accused and convicted of the crime of violence in his nonviolent society in the year 2069 and is sentenced to travel back in time to learn about lovemaking in the past. He is given a ring which is programmed to convey him to the selected times and places. If he loses the ring, he will be banished to infinity. In a college dormitory in the 1960's, 3X47 shows the ring to a student, and without any hesitation they make love. 3X47 drops the ring and is sent to infinity; the student picks it up and is transported 100 years into the past to the tent of a Civil War captain. While they are making love, the captain and the ring are delivered to a Russian czarina. She seduces him, and he is sent to the next stop on the sex tour, a sultan's palace. The captain makes love with a slave girl; she receives the ring, pops up in a Roman garden, and makes love with a woman who is waiting there for her lover. This woman takes the ring and finds herself in the cell of a condemned warrior during the time of Genghis Khan. Taking the ring, the warrior travels back to prehistoric times, meets a cavewoman, and makes love with her. The woman's mate destroys the ring and is inexplicably transported to the year 2069. *Students. Soldiers. Royalty. Cave dwellers. Criminals—Rehabilitation. Seduction. Lesbianism. Prehistory. Nonviolence. Time travel. Harems. United States— History—Civil War. Rome—History—Empire. Russia. Genghis Khan. The Future.*

Note: Harvey Foster may be a pseudonym for Forman Shane, and Marsha Kopete a pseudonym for Marsha Jordan.

2,000 WEEKS (Australia)　　　　　　　　　　　**F6.5258**
Eltham Film Productions-Senior Film Productions. *Dist* Boxoffice International Film Distributors. Jun 1970. Sd; b&w. 35mm. 90 min.

Prod Patrick Ryan, David Bilcock, Sr. *Assoc Prod* John B. Murray. *Dir* Tim Burstall. *Story-Screenplay* Tim Burstall, Patrick Ryan. *Dir Photog* Robin Copping. *Camera Op* Harold Koch. *Lighting Gaffer* Noel Arden. *Asst Camera* Ron Johanson. *Art Dir* Rosemary Ryan. *Film Ed* David Bilcock, Jr. *Asst Ed* Evelyn Cronk. *Mus Comp & Cond* Don Burrows. *Sd Rec* Russell Hurley. *Boom Op* Rod Stebbing. *Sd Transfer* Jim Davies. *Sd Mix* Paul Ennis, Lloyd Coleman. *Prod Mgr* George Kischowski. *Unit Mgr* James Oastler. *Cont* Jean Frankel. *Wardrobe* Magg Calder, Bob Calder. *Makeup* Joan Cooly. *Hairdresser* Christa Mayke. *Set Constr* George Hurst. *Still Photog* Mark Strizic.

Cast: Mark McManus (*Will Gardiner*), Jeanie Drynan (*Jacky Lewis*), Eileen Chapman (*Sarah Gardiner*), David Turnbull (*Noel Oakshot*), Michael Duffield (*Will's father*), Stephen Dattner (*Sir George Turnbull*), Bruce Anderson (*Rex Stapleton*), Dominic Ryan (*Will as a boy*), Nicholas McCallum (*Noel as a boy*), Anne Charleston (*Will's mother*).

Drama. Will Gardiner, a Melbourne journalist, and Jacky Lewis, his mistress, talk about themselves and about the reasons why Will, a married man, will not leave his family to marry Jacky. For a moment, he remembers the time in his boyhood when he saw his mother go away on a ship, leaving him and his father alone. Later, Will goes to the airport to meet Noel Oakshot, a childhood friend who left Australia for England and is now returning to produce a television series. At a party that night, Noel, in the presence of Sarah, Will's wife, bluntly asks Jacky if she is Will's mistress. Though it is Jacky's last night in Melbourne, she admits the truth but spends the night with Noel. Will goes to the hospital to be with his dying father and then bids farewell to Jacky on board ship. When Noel calls Jacky a whore, the two men fight, and Will returns to tell Jacky that he loves her before he is ordered off the ship. *Journalists. Mistresses. Television producers. Expatriates. Infidelity. Death. Fatherhood. Ocean liners. Melbourne (Australia).*

Note: Filmed on location in and around Melbourne. Opened in Melbourne in Mar 1969.

2000 YEARS LATER　　　　　　　　　　　　　　**F6.5259**
The Bert Tenzer Organization. *Dist* Warner Bros.-Seven Arts, Inc. 11 Mar 1969 [New York opening; c1 Apr 1969; LP40876]. Sd; col (Technicolor). 35mm. 80 min. MPAA rating R.

Prod-Dir-Writ Bert Tenzer. *Asst Prod* Woodrow Wilson, Bob Waldron. *Dir Photog* Mario Di Leo. *Camera Op* Charles Rosher, Jr. *Art Dir* Michael Haller. *Set Decor* Harry Reif. *Film Ed* Donn Cambern. *Assoc Film Ed* Robert Lewis. *Mus Supv* Igo Kantor. *Mus Comp & Cond* Stu Phillips. *Songs* Stu Phillips, Chuck Sedacca. *Perf by* Kin Vassy, Jay Paul Kane, The Yellow Crusaders. *Sd* Earl Schwartz. *Re-rec* Bill Mumford, Don Minkler. *Sd Eff* Edit-Rite Inc. *Prod Mgr* Paul Lewis. *Prod Coörd* Monica Payne. *Script Supv* Gana Jones. *Assoc to Prod* Joel Tenzer. *Prod Asst* Fred Buckley. *Cost* Jerry Alpert. *Roman Discotheque Wardrobe* Rudi Gernreich. *Makeup* Bob Dawn. *Casting* Marvin Paige. *Prop* Ross Burke.

Cast: Terry-Thomas (*Charles Goodwyn*), Edward Everett Horton (*Evermore*), Pat Harrington (*Franchot*), Lisa Seagram (*Cindy*), John Abbott (*Gregorius*), John Myhers (*Air Force general*), Tom Melody (*senator*), Myrna Ross (*Miss Forever*), Monti Rock, III (*Tomorrow's Leader*), Murray Roman (*Superdude*), Michael Christian (*The Piston Kid*), Casey Kasem (*disc jockey*), Bert Tenzer (*Mercury's voice*), Rudi Gernreich (*himself*), Milton Parsons, Buddy Lewis, Tony Gardner.

Comedy. During the fall of Rome the god Mercury transforms citizen Gregorius into a ball of fire. Centuries later Mercury, alarmed by contemporary trends, dispatches the Roman to Hollywood. Horrified by American hedonism, Gregorius is unable to speak. The Roman's silence, however, does not prevent his discovery and exploitation by Goodwyn and Evermore, hosts of the televised "International Culture Hour." Soon the pair has packaged a Roman fad popularized by hippie idol Tomorrow's Leader and cyclist Superdude. The craze culminates in a televised Roman orgy, during which Gregorius is seduced by the Zap Pow girl, star of the show's commercials. *Television announcers. Hedonism. Advertising. Suspended animation. Orgies. Television commercials. Rome—History—Empire. Hollywood. Mercury (god).*

Note: Produced in 1966.

TWO TICKETS TO PARIS　　　　　　　　　　　　**F6.5260**
Harry Romm Productions. *Dist* Columbia Pictures. 3 Oct 1962 [Providence, Rhode Island, opening; c15 Sep 1962; LP22999]. Sd; b&w. 35mm. 78 min. [Also reviewed at 90 min.]

A Harry Romm Production. *Prod* Harry Romm. *Assoc Prod* Martha Vera Romm. *Dir* Greg Garrison. *Orig Story & Screenplay* Hal Hackady. *Photog* William O. Steiner, Sr. *Art Dir* Albert Brenner. *Film Ed* Ralph Rosenblum. *Orig Score & Mus Dir* Henry Glover. *Titl Song* Hal Hackady, Don Gohman. *Song:* "Instant Men" Hal Hackady, Don Gohman. *Perf by* Kay Medford. *Song:* "Teenage Vamp" Albert Seigal. *Perf by* Jeri Lynne Fraser. *Song:* "Baby Won't You Please Come Home" Charles Warfield, Clarence Williams. *Perf by* Jeri Lynne Fraser. *Song:* "The Lady Wants To Twist" Jerry Leiber, Mike Stoller. *Perf by* Gary Crosby. *Song:* "C'est la vie" Edward R. White, Mack Wolfson. *Perf by* Gary Crosby. *Song:* "C'est si bon" Jerry Sielen, Henry Betti. *Perf by* Joey Dee and the Starliters. *Song:* "Willy Willy" Henry Glover, Joey Dee, Morris Levy. *Perf by* The Starliters. *Song:* "This Boat" Henry Glover, Joey Dee, Morris Levy. *Perf by* Joey Dee and The Starliters. *Songs:* "Twistin' on a Liner," "Everytime" Henry Glover, Joey Dee, Morris Levy. *Perf by* Joey Dee. *Instrumentals:* "Open Sea," "Left Bank Blues" Henry Glover, Joey Dee, Morris Levy. *Song:* "Swingin' Shepherd Blues" Rhoda Roberts, Kenny Jacobson, Moe Koffman. *Perf by* The Starliters. *Song:* "What Kind of Love Is This?" Johnny Nash. *Perf by* Joey Dee. *Sd* Jim Shields. *Asst Dir* Michael Phillips. *Prod Mgr* Edgar H. Fay. *Cost Dsgn* Natalie Walker. *Makeup* Robert Jiras. *Hairstyles* Irene Hamalein.

Cast: Joey Dee (*Joey*), Gary Crosby (*Gary*), Kay Medford (*Aggie*), Jeri Lynne Fraser (*Piper*), Lisa James (*Coco*), Charles Nelson Reilly (*Claypoole*), Richard Dickens (*Tony*), Nina Paige (*dumb blonde*), Sal Lombardo (*Marmaduke*), Jeri Archer (*Mrs. Patten*), Michele Moinot (*Le Claire*), Jay Burton (*Charles*), The Starliters.

Comedy with music. Joey and Piper, betrothed teenagers, sail for France, where Joey has a Parisian singing engagement. In compliance with the wishes of Piper's mother, they are chaperoned by Aggie, a former hatcheck girl. Aboard the S. S. France, Joey attracts the attention of Coco, a French dancer, while Piper flirts with Gary, a singer. Despite jealousy and recrimination, the pair's problems are resolved before debarkation. *Singers. Chaperons. Checkgirls. Dancers. French. Jealousy. Flirtation. S. S. "France".*

Note: Filmed in New York City aboard the S.S. France.

TWO TIMES TWO see **START THE REVOLUTION WITHOUT ME**

TWO VOICES see **DEUX VOIX**

TWO-WAY STRETCH (Great Britain)　　　　　　**F6.5261**
British Lion Films. *Dist* Lion International Films, Showcorporation. 23 Jan 1961 [New York opening]. Sd; b&w. 35mm. 87 min.

A George Black-Alfred Black Production. *Prod* E. M. Smedley-Aston. *Dir* Robert Day. *Orig Screenplay* John Warren, Len Heath. *Adtl Dial* Alan Hackney. *Photog* Geoffrey Faithfull. *Camera Op* Frank Drake. *Focus* Denis Lewiston. *Art Dir* John Box. *Asst Art Dir* Roger Gain. *Set Dresser* Roy Rossotti. *Ch Draughtsman* Wallis Smith. *Scenic Artist* Ted Barnes. *Film Ed* Bert Rule. *Assembly Ed* Alan Bell. *Mus Comp & Cond* Ken Jones. *Sd* Maurice Askew. *Sd Mix* Paddy Cunningham. *Sd Boom Op* Charles Wheeler. *Sd Camera Op* Jack Smart. *Dub Ed* Ted Mason. *1st & 2d Asst Dir* Kip Gowans, John Danischewsky. *Prod Supv* Harold Buck. *Prod Mgr* Jacques De Lane Lea. *Cont* Lee Turner. *Wardrobe Master* Bob Rayner. *Makeup Ch* Jimmy Evans. *Hairdresser* Joyce James. *Casting Dir* Paul Sheridan. *Prod Buyer* Margery Whittington. *Still Photog* Norman Hargood.

Cast: Peter Sellers (*Dodger Lane*), Wilfrid Hyde-White (*Rev. Basil "Soapy" Fowler*), David Lodge (*Jelly Knight*), Bernard Cribbins (*Lennie Price*), Maurice Denham (*Cmdr. Horatio Bennet, the prison governor*), Lionel Jeffries (*Sidney Crout*), Irene Handl (*Mrs. Price*), Liz Fraser (*Ethel*), George Woodbridge (*Warder Jenkins*), Cyril Chamberlain (*Warder George*), Edwin Brown (*Warder Charlie*), John Glyn-Jones (*The Lawyer*), Beryl Reid (*Miss Pringle*), Noel Hood (*Miss Meakin*), Myrette Morven (*Miss Prescott*), Thorley Walters (*Colonel Arkwright*), Walter Hudd (*Reverend Butterworth*), Olga Dickie (*woman in pub*), Joe Gibbons (*dustman*), John Wood (*captain*), Robert James, British (*police superintendent*), Warren Mitchell (*tailor*), Ian Wilson (*milkman*), Eynon Evans (*solicitor*), Wallas Eaton (*night warder*), Larry Taylor (*warder at Rockhampton*), Andrew Downie (*warder in prison garden*), William Abney (*visiting room warder*), John Vivyan (*little prisoner*), Mario Fabrizi (*Jones*), John Harvey.

Comedy. The inmates at Huntleigh Prison enjoy a pleasant life: milk and newspapers are delivered each morning at 7, the cells resemble luxurious bed-sitting rooms, and classes are held on subjects ranging from basketweaving to safecracking. Cellmates Dodger Lane, Jelly Knight, and Lennie Price are visited by Soapy Stevens, an old crony who, posing as a clergyman, has a plan for stealing a large number of jewels from a visiting maharajah scheduled to match his weight in diamonds on his natal day. The men agree that it should be relatively easy for them to break out, pull off the job, and sneak back into prison with the gems. Just as their plans are being made final, however, the easygoing warder is replaced by the vicious, ever-suspicious Sidney Court. In spite of the setback, Soapy sneaks them out in a paddy wagon, and aided by Dodger's girl friend Ethel and Lennie's mother, they successfully execute the robbery. The diamonds are brought into prison in a dust cart and are hidden in the governor's safe. The next day the men are officially released, and they brazenly walk out with the diamonds, but Dodger's fumbling causes them to lose the jewels on a train, and Soapy is recognized by Crout and arrested. Though disheartened, they are not defeated, and with hope gleaming in their eyes, they attend the maharajah's "weighing" ceremony. *Convicts. Prison wardens. Clergymen. Royalty. Prison escapes. Disguise. Theft. Prisons. Jewels. Trains. Rites and ceremonies.*

Note: Location scenes filmed in Aldershot, Maidstone, Windsor, Pirbright, and London, England. Opened in London in Feb 1960. Working title: *Nothing Barred.*

TWO WEEKS IN ANOTHER TOWN   F6.5262

John Houseman Productions. *Dist* Metro-Goldwyn-Mayer, Inc. 17 Aug **1962** [New York opening; c22 Aug 1962; LP22805]. Sd (Westrex); col (Metrocolor). 35mm (CinemaScope). 107 min.

Prod John Houseman. *Assoc Prod* Ethel Winant. *Dir* Vincente Minnelli. *Screenplay* Charles Schnee. *Dir Photog* Milton Krasner. *Col Cons* Charles K. Hagedon. *Art Dir* George W. Davis, Urie McCleary. *Set Decor* Henry Grace, Keogh Gleason. *Film Ed* Adrienne Fazan, Robert J. Kern, Jr. *Mus Score* David Raksin. *Rec Supv* Franklin Milton. *Asst Dir* Eric Von Stroheim, Jr. *Wardrobe* Walter Plunkett. *Miss Charisse's Wardrobe* Pierre Balmain. *Makeup* William Tuttle. *Hairstyles* Sydney Guilaroff. *Sp Vis Eff* Robert R. Hoag. *Coöp* Academy of Motion Picture Arts and Sciences.

Cast: Kirk Douglas *(Jack Andrus)*, Edward G. Robinson *(Maurice Kruger)*, Cyd Charisse *(Carlotta)*, George Hamilton *(Davie Drew)*, Dahlia Lavi *(Veronica)*, Claire Trevor *(Clara)*, James Gregory *(Brad Byrd)*, Rosanna Schiaffino *(Barzelli)*, Joanna Roos *(Janet Bark)*, George Macready *(Lew Jordan)*, Mino Doro *(Tucino)*, Stefan Schnabel *(Zeno)*, Vito Scotti *(assistant director)*, Tom Palmer *(Dr. Cold Eyes)*, Eric Von Stroheim, Jr. *(Ravinski)*, Leslie Uggams *(chanteuse)*.

Melodrama. Source: Irwin Shaw, *Two Weeks in Another Town* (New York, 1960). Jack Andrus, a onetime Hollywood star whose sudden fall from stardom has led to alcoholism, divorce, a near-fatal automobile accident, and a nervous breakdown, spends 3 years in a New England sanatarium. Finally his doctors permit him to accept a small comeback role in a costume spectacle being directed by Maurice Kruger at Rome's Cinecitta Studios. Years before, Kruger had been the man responsible for Andrus' great success, but he too is now a Hollywood has-been, desperately trying to regain his lost reputation. Andrus arrives in Rome and learns that the part is no longer available, and, finding that the production is in serious trouble, reluctantly agrees to supervise the dubbing of the picture. In the evenings he soothes his wounded ego by relaxing in the company of an Italian woman named Veronica, who, unknown to Andrus, is in love with Kruger's young leading man, the rebellious Davie Drew. One night, following a fight with his shrewish wife Clara, Kruger suffers a heart attack and is hospitalized. Andrus offers to finish the film and, by working night and day, completes it ahead of schedule and under the budget. Simultaneously, he helps Davie sort out his confused life. Kruger, bitterly aware of his own failure, attacks Andrus and publicly accuses him of trying to steal the picture. Stricken, Andrus turns to his ex-wife, Carlotta, and goes on an orgiastic binge. Their night ends with a wild car ride that shocks Andrus into the realization that he cannot place his fate in the hands of others. Now strong and independent, he says goodby to Veronica and Davie and boards a plane for Hollywood. *Actors. Motion picture directors. Americans in foreign countries. Italians. Ambition. Alcoholism. Mental illness. Jealousy. Motion pictures. Heart disease. Hollywood. Rome. Cinecitta (Rome). Automobile accidents. "The Bad and the Beautiful".*

Note: Locations filmed in Rome. Scenes from *The Bad and the Beautiful* (M-G-M, 1952) are included.

TWO WEEKS IN SEPTEMBER (France/Great Britain)   F6.5263

Francos Films-Les Films du Quadrangle-Films Pomereu-Kenwood Films. *Dist* Paramount Pictures. Sep **1967**. Sd; col (Eastman Color). 35mm (Franscope). 95 min.

Prod Francis Cosne, Kenneth Harper. *Dir* Serge Bourguignon. *Screenplay* Vahé Katcha, Pascal Jardin, Serge Bourguignon. *English Adapt* Sean Graham. *Photog* Edmond Séchan. *Art Dir* Rino Mondellini. *Film Ed* Jean Ravel. *Mus* Michel Magne. *Sd* William Sivel. *Asst Dir* Georges Lussan, Ernest Morris. *Prod Mgr* Ludmilla Goulian, Jack Hanbury. *Cost* Tanine Autre. *Makeup* Odette Berroyer.

Cast: Brigitte Bardot *(Cécile)*, Laurent Terzieff *(Vincent)*, Jean Rochefort *(Philippe)*, James Robertson Justice *(McClintock)*, Michael Sarne *(Dickinson)*, Georgina Ward *(Patricia)*, Carole Lebel *(Monique)*, Annie Nicolas *(Chantal)*, Murray Head *(Dickinson's assistant)*.

Drama. Cécile, a young French model, lives in Paris with Philippe, a wealthy older man, but in spite of their deep love, romance and excitement are absent from their relationship. Hoping for time to assess her emotions, Cécile goes to London on a 6-day assignment with Dickinson, an amorous photographer. At their hotel she runs into Vincent, a carefree French geologist whom she met once in France; he follows her everywhere and wears down her resistance until she consents to go away with him on a motor trip. Dressed in a wedding gown from one of her posing sessions, Cécile pretends that their vacation to Scotland is a honeymoon, particularly when McClintock, a genial laird, lends them his castle. After a week's idyll, they return to London, where Cécile receives a telephone call from Philippe. Torn between the mature concern of her former lover and the impulsive romanticism of Vincent, who now insists that she join him on a Far Eastern jaunt, Cécile delays her decision until the last minute. She finally chooses Vincent but arrives at the airport too late to catch the plane that is taking him away from her. After an objective look at herself, Cécile accepts the fact that her recent affair was merely an interlude and that Philippe offers her a more stable life and love. *Models. Photographers. Geologists. Vacations. Hotels. Castles. Airfields. Paris. London. Scotland.*

Note: Location scenes filmed in Scotland and London. Opened in Paris in Jun 1967 as *À coeur joie*; running time: 100 min; released in Great Britain in 1967.

TWO WOMEN (France/Italy)   F6.5264

C. C. Champion-Les Films Marceau-Cocinor-S. G. C. *Dist* Embassy Pictures. 9 May **1961** [New York opening]. Sd; b&w. 35mm. 105 min.

Pres by Joseph E. Levine. *Prod* Carlo Ponti. *Dir* Vittorio De Sica. *Screenplay* Cesare Zavattini, Vittorio De Sica. *Photog* Gabor Pogany. *Camera* Mario Capriotti, Giuseppe Ruzzolini. *Art Dir* Gastone Medin. *Set Dsgn* Elio Costanzi. *Film Ed* Adriana Novelli. *Mus* Armando Trovajoli. *Sd* Giovanni Rossi. *Sd Eff* Philippe Arthuys. *Asst Dir* Luisa Alessandri. *Prod Mgr* Ione Tuzi. *Cost* Elio Costanzi. *Makeup* Giuseppe Annunziata. *Hairstyles* Maria Angelini.

Cast: Sophia Loren *(Cesira)*, Jean-Paul Belmondo *(Michele)*, Eleonora Brown *(Rosetta)*, Raf Vallone *(Giovanni)*, Renato Salvatori *(Florindo)*, Carlo Ninchi *(Michele's father)*, Andrea Checchi *(Fascist)*, Pupella Maggio, Emma Baron, Bruna Cealti, Mario Frera, Luciana Coltellesi, Toni Calio, Elsa Mancini, Luigi Terribile, Antonio Gastaldi, Antonella De La Porta, Franco Balducci, Curt Lowens, Remo Galavotti, Giuseppina Ruggeri, Luciano Igozzi, Carolina Carbonare.

War drama. Source: Alberto Moravia, *La Ciociara* (Milan, 1957). Cesira, a widow in her early 30's, lives in Rome during World War II. Terrified by the Allied bombings, she decides to leave her small grocery store and take Rosetta, her 13-year-old daughter, back to her home village in the district of Ciociaria. Before she departs, Cesira makes love to Giovanni, a neighboring coal dealer who agrees to look after the store during her absence. When Cesira and Rosetta reach the village, they settle down to a quiet life, removed from the anxieties of the war. Eventually Cesira becomes involved with Michele, a disillusioned intellectual, but their romance is complicated by Rosetta, who is infatuated with him. One day, a group of retreating Germans arrive at the village and force Michele to guide them across the mountains. Cesira then decides to return to Rome, but during the journey, she and Rosetta are brutally raped by some Moroccan soldiers in the ruins of a bombed church. The horrifying experience leaves Rosetta in a state of shock; conscious only of the ordeal, she prostitutes herself for a pair of nylon stockings. When word arrives that Michele has been killed by the Germans, Rosetta's bitterness is dissolved, and she is reunited with her mother by a common bond of grief and suffering. *Widows. Intellectuals. Soldiers. Filial relations. Adolescence. Rape. Shock. World War II. Rome. Ciociaria.*

Note: Opened in Rome in Dec 1960 as *La Ciociara*; running time: 105 min; and in Paris in May 1961; running time: 100 min.

THE TWO WORLDS OF CHARLY GORDON see CHARLY

TYSTNADEN see THE SILENCE

LE TZAREVITCH see DER ZAREWITSCH

U–47 LT. COMMANDER PRIEN (West Germany)   F6.5265

Arca-Film. *Dist* United Film Enterprises. 29 Apr **1967** [New York opening]. Sd; b&w. 35mm. 91 min.

Dir Harald Reinl. *Screenplay* Joachim Bartsch. *Story* Udo Wolter. *Photog* Ernst W. Kalinke. *Camera Op* Dieter Liphardt. *Art Dir* Erich Kettelhut, Hans Auffenberg. *Mus* Norbert Schultze. *Sd* Herbert Karwahne. *Asst Dir* Lothar Gündisch. *Prod Dir* Helmut Volmer. *Prod Asst* Mohr von Chamier. *Prod Mgr* Fritz Anton, Willi Schöne. *Wardrobe* Edith Dahlke, Ernst Erdmann. *Makeup*

Ludwig Ziegler. *Prop* Fritz Moritz, Erwin Hübenthal.

Cast: Dieter Eppler *(Günther Prien)*, Sabina Sesselmann *(his wife)*, Joachim Fuchsberger *(1st lieutenant)*, Dieter Borsche *(preacher)*, Joachim Mock *(Kaleu Schopf)*, Richard Häussler *(German U-boat fleet commander)*, Harald Juhnke, Ute Hallant, Olga Tschechowa, Ernst Reinhold, Raidar Müller, Mathias Fuchs, Rolf Möbius, Michael Cramer, Peter Carsten, Heinz Engelmann, Rolf Weih.

War drama. Based on the war experiences of Günther Prien. On 14 October 1939, Lieut. Comdr. Günther Prien, a German war hero commanding a U-47, infiltrates Scapa Flow, a Scottish bay housing the British Home Fleet. He destroys the battleship *Royal Oak* and safely brings his submarine out of the harbor. Within 2 years, his U-boat is sunk by a British destroyer. Prien and the vessel's cook are taken aboard a hostile freighter, which itself is torpedoed by a German submarine commanded by Prien's close friend, who is horrified to find Prien's cap amidst the debris. The friend's U-boat is in turn attacked by a British aircraft and sunk. *War heroes. Cooks. Submarines. Battleships. Freighters. World War II. Scapa Flow. Günther Prien. Germany—Navy. Great Britain—Royal Navy. H. M. S. "Royal Oak".*

Note: Opened in Stuttgart in Sep 1958 as *U 47—Kapitänleutnant Prien.* Working title: *Kapitänleutnant Prien—Der Stier von Scapa Flow.*

U KRUTOGO YARA *see* **THE SHE-WOLF**

U 47—KAPITÄNLEUTNANT PRIEN *see* **U–47 LT. COMMANDER PRIEN**

UCCELLACCI E UCCELLINI *see* **THE HAWKS AND THE SPARROWS**

L'UCCELLO DALLE PIUME DI CRISTALLO *see* **THE BIRD WITH THE CRYSTAL PLUMAGE**

UCCIDERÒ UN UOMO *see* **THIS MAN MUST DIE**

UCCIDI O MUORI *see* **KILL OR BE KILLED**

UDEN EN TRAEVL *see* **WITHOUT A STITCH**

THE UGLY AMERICAN   F6.5266

Universal Pictures. ca2 Apr **1963** [Los Angeles opening; c5 May 1963; LP32702]. Sd (Westrex); col (Eastman Color by Pathé). 35mm. 120 min.

Prod-Dir George Englund. *In Charge of Prod* Edward Muhl. *Story & Screenplay* Stewart Stern. *Dir Photog* Clifford Stine. *Art Dir* Alexander Golitzen, Alfred Sweeney. *Set Decor* Oliver Emert. *Film Ed* Ted J. Kent. *Mus* Frank Skinner. *Mus Supv* Joseph Gershenson. *Sd* Waldon O. Watson, Joe Lapis. *Asst Dir* Terence Nelson, James Welch, Bill Gilmore. *Prod Mgr* Marshall Green. *Script Supv* Robert Forrest. *Gowns* Rosemary Odell. *Makeup* Bud Westmore. *Hairstyles* Larry Germain. *Tech Adv* Kukrit Pramoj, Sasidhorn Bunnag.

Cast: Marlon Brando *(Harrison Carter MacWhite)*, Eiji Okada *(Deong)*, Sandra Church *(Marion MacWhite)*, Pat Hingle *(Homer Atkins)*, Arthur Hill *(Grainger)*, Jocelyn Brando *(Emma Atkins)*, Kukrit Pramoj *(Prime Minister Kwen Sai)*, Judson Pratt *(Joe Bing)*, Reiko Sato *(Rachani)*, George Shibata *(Munsang)*, Judson Laire *(Senator Brenner)*, Philip Ober *(Sears)*, Yee Tak Yip *(Sawad)*, Stefan Schnabel *(Andrei Krupitzyn)*, Pock Rock Ann *(Colonel Chee)*, Carl Benton Reid, Simon Scott, Frances Helm, James Yagi, John Day, Leon Lontoc, Bill Stout.

Drama. Source: William J. Lederer and Eugene Burdick, *The Ugly American* (New York, 1958). Harrison Carter MacWhite is appointed ambassador to the new nation of Sarkhan in Southeast Asia, despite objections from several members of the Senate Foreign Relations Committee. A former newsman, MacWhite is a longtime friend of Deong, revolutionary leader of the government opposition who led the struggle for his country's independence. MacWhite and his wife, Marion, arrive in Sarkhan and fight off a rioting crowd which greets them at the airport. MacWhite contacts Deong and tries to persuade him to end his opposition to Freedom Road, a U. S.-built highway which the rebel leader considers to be an example of Western imperialism. Deong refuses, mouthing propaganda, and MacWhite brands him a Communist and terminates their relationship. He then ignores the advice of Homer Atkins, supervising engineer of the road project, by suggesting to Prime Minister Kwen Sai that they shift the path of the road northward, thereby driving a wedge into the heart of the Communist stronghold. In return, MacWhite assures Kwen Sai of U. S. military support should there be intervention by foreign Communist troops. Deong learns of the plan, aligns himself with the local Communists, and leads a revolt. He succeeds in forcing Kwen Sai to admit defeat, but he is betrayed by the Communists when they bring in outside troops, take over the northern part of the country, and then assassinate him. Before dying, he urges his followers to form a coalition with Kwen Sai and the local government. Realizing that despite his good intentions he has bungled his assignment, MacWhite resigns from his post. He explains in an interview with the press that to help the countries of Southeast Asia, Americans must understand their internal problems before inflicting a way of life upon them. As his words are carried to the United States by television, an uninterested viewer switches off his set. *Newspapermen. Americans in foreign countries. Asians. Revolutionaries. Communists. Engineers. Prime ministers. Friendship. Riots. Imperialism. Assassination. Cold war. Road construction. Revolts. Southeast Asia. United States Congress. United States—Diplomatic and consular service.*

Note: Location scenes filmed in Thailand.

THE UGLY DACHSHUND   F6.5267

Walt Disney Productions. *Dist* Buena Vista Distribution Co. 16 Feb **1966** [Los Angeles opening; c16 Dec 1965; LP32136]. Sd; col (Technicolor). 35mm. 93 min.

Prod Walt Disney. *Co-prod* Winston Hibler. *Dir* Norman Tokar. *2d Unit Dir* Arthur J. Vitarelli. *Screenplay* Albert Aley. *Dir Photog* Edward Colman. *Art Dir* Carroll Clark, Marvin Aubrey Davis. *Set Decor* Emile Kuri, Frank R. McKelvy. *Film Ed* Robert Stafford. *Mus* George Bruns. *Orch* Franklyn Marks. *Sd Supv* Robert O. Cook. *Mus Ed* Evelyn Kennedy. *Asst Dir* Tom Leetch. *Cost* Chuck Keehne, Gertrude Casey. *Makeup* Pat McNalley, La Rue Matheron. *Sp Eff* Eustace Lycett. *Dogs Trained by* William R. Koehler, Glenn Randall, Jr.

Cast: Dean Jones *(Mark Garrison)*, Suzanne Pleshette *(Fran Garrison)*, Charlie Ruggles *(Dr. Pruitt)*, Kelly Thordsen *(Officer Carmody)*, Parley Baer *(Mel Chadwick)*, Robert Kino *(Mr. Toyama)*, Mako *(Kenji)*, Charles Lane *(judge)*.

Comedy. Source: Gladys Bronwyn Stern, *Dogs in an Omnibus* (London, 1942). When Mark and Fran Garrison's dachshund, Danke, gives birth to puppies, Dr. Pruitt, the veterinarian, persuades Mark also to take home Brutus, a Great Dane puppy that has been abandoned. Brutus grows up thinking that he is a dachshund, but his size causes problems for the Garrisons; he trees policemen, wrecks Mark's studio, and wreaks havoc at a garden party. Fran finally insists that Brutus must go, but the Great Dane redeems himself when he saves Chloe, Fran's favorite puppy, from the garbage heap. Fran trains Chloe for a dog show, and Mark secretly trains Brutus for the same show. His main objective is to convince the dog to behave like a Great Dane. At the show, Brutus almost disqualifies himself when he sees a dachshund and begins acting like one. A female Great Dane passes by, however, and Brutus assumes a proud stance and wins the blue ribbon. *Veterinarians. Police. Family life. Pet shows. Dogs.*

THE UGLY ONES (Italy/Spain)   F6.5268

Tecisa–Discobolo Film. *Dist* United Artists. 28 Aug **1968** [Baltimore opening; c 28 Aug 1968; LP36700]. Sd; col (DeLuxe). 35mm. 96 min.

Prod Giuliano Simonetti. *Asst Prod* Eduardo Esquide. *Dir* Eugenio Martín. *Screenplay* Don Prindle, Eugenio Martín, José G. Maesso, Biancini. *Photog (see note)* Enzo Barboni, José Herrero. *Art Dir* Francisco Canet. *Ed (see note)* José Rocco, Gisa Levi Radicchi. *Mus* Stelvio Cipriani. *Asst Dir* Fabrizio Gianni, Sinesio Isla. *Prod Mgr* Faustino Ocaña.

Cast: Richard Wyler *(Luke Chilson)*, Tomás Milián *(Jose Gomez)*, Ella Karin *(Eden)*, Mario Brega, Hugo Blanco, Glenn Foster, Ricardo Canales, Lola Gaos, Saturno Cerra, Manuel Zarzo, Tito Garcia, Antonio Iranzo, Fernando Sánchez Polack, Chiro Bermejo, Antonio Cintado, Ricardo Palacios, Gonzalo Esquiroz, Enrique Navarro, Rafael Vaquero.

Western melodrama. Source: Marvin H. Albert, *The Bounty Killer* (Greenwich, Connecticut, 1958). In 1850 Texas, the notorious Mexican outlaw Jose Gomez escapes with the help of his childhood sweetheart, Eden, while being transported from one prison to another. As he returns to the town of his birth, he is pursued by Luke Chilson, a renowned bounty hunter. A band of outlaws also flock to the little town and form a gang under the leadership of Jose. The townspeople, led by Eden, also rally to his support, refusing to believe that the young man they knew as a boy is anything worse than a victim of circumstance. When Chilson arrives, he is captured, tied up in a stable, and sadistically tortured by Jose. After Jose has robbed some of the townspeople and committed cold-blooded murder, however, Eden finally realizes that her sympathy is being wasted on the wrong man, and she cuts Chilson free. Faster on the draw than his adversaries, Chilson shoots down Jose and his gang one by one and then rides off to collect his bounty fee. *Outlaws. Mexicans. Prison escapees. Bounty hunters. Torture. Sadism. Robbery. Murder. Smalltown life. Texas.*

Note: Filmed in Almería, Spain in 1966 under the title *El precio de un hombre.* Italian production title: *The Bounty Killer.* Enzo Barboni and José Rocco are generally credited as photographer and editor respectively; however, a single source credits José Herrero and Gisa Levi Radicchi.

UKIGUSA *see* **FLOATING WEEDS**

L'ULTIMA PREDA DEL VAMPIRO *see* **THE PLAYGIRLS AND THE VAMPIRE**

THE ULTIMATE DEGENERATE   F6.5269

Dist American Film Distributing Corp. 1969. Sd; b&w. 35mm. [Feature film, length unknown.]

Prod-Dir-Writ Julian Marsh, Anna Riva. *Photog* Anna Riva. *Lighting* Robert Marx. *Film Ed* Julian Marsh. *Mus* Robin Aden. *Sd* Chico Buck. *Still Photog* Earl Windmin.

Cast: Artimidia Grillet, Robert Wuest, Leo Heinz, Donna Stone, Marie Brent, Rita Ford, Tinker Toy, Kym Crandall, Susan Lane, Joe Heller.

Melodrama. Responding to a newspaper advertisement, Maria Curtis meets a stranger, Bruno, at Coney Island. They drive to a palatial estate in Vermont, where they are received by Spencer, its crippled owner. Spencer injects his guest with an aphrodisiac, after which she has sex with Lola, a cigar-smoking lesbian, and performs cunnilingus with Dora, another guest. As they perform, they are photographed by Carla, whom Spencer has savagely whipped. Interrupting the women, Bruno informs Maria that she is in grave danger from Spencer. Bruno describes Spencer's torture of her predecessor with clothespins and electricity. Having substituted a powerful drug causing paranoia for the aphrodisiac, Bruno brings Maria to the cripple. Spencer unknowingly injects her with Bruno's narcotic, and Maria stabs her host. As the police escort Maria from the house, Bruno phones Helen, his male lover, who is overjoyed to hear that Spencer's mansion will now be their love nest. *Cripples. Police. Lesbianism. Oral sex. Voyeurism. Sadism. Paranoia. Murder. Male homosexuality. Aphrodisiacs. Photographs. Drugs. Coney Island. Vermont.*

Note: Julian Marsh is a pseudonym for Michael Findlay, who also appears in the cast as Robert Wuest; Anna Riva is a pseudonym for Roberta Findlay.

THE ULTIMATE VOYEUR   F6.5270

Chellee Films. 23 Jul 1969 [New York showing]. Sd; b&w. 35mm. 69 min.

Melodrama. Mr. Rich, a wealthy voyeur accustomed to paying people to perform sex acts (lesbian, male homosexual, and heterosexual) while he watches passively, finds himself attracted to Kim, a pickup. Kim, however, repulsed by what she has done for money, lashes out at Mr. Rich when he makes a pass at her and stabs him to death. *Pickups. Voyeurism. Wealth. Male homosexuality. Lesbianism.*

L'ULTIMO DEI VICHINGHI *see* **LAST OF THE VIKINGS**

EL ÚLTIMO DÍA DE LA GUERRA *see* **THE LAST DAY OF THE WAR**

L'ULTIMO GIORNO DELLA GUERRA *see* **THE LAST DAY OF THE WAR**

L'ULTIMO MERCENARIO *see* **THE LAST MERCENARY**

EL ÚLTIMO REBELDE *see* **THE LAST REBEL**

L'ULTIMO UOMO DELLA TERRA *see* **THE LAST MAN ON EARTH**

L'ULTIMO ZAR *see* **THE NIGHT THEY KILLED RASPUTIN**

ULYSSES (United States/Great Britain)   F6.5271

Ulysses Film Production. *Dist* Continental Distributing, Inc. 14 Mar 1967 [New York opening]. Sd; b&w. 35mm (Panavision). 140 min. [Also reviewed at 123 and 135 min.]

A Walter Reade, Jr.–Joseph Strick Production. *Prod-Dir* Joseph Strick. *Exec Prod* Walter Reade, Jr.. *Assoc Prod* Wilfred Eades, Fred Haines. *Screenplay* Joseph Strick, Fred Haines. *Photog* Wolfgang Suschitzky. *Camera Op* Seamus Corcoran. *Art Dir* Graham Probst. *Film Ed* Reginald Mills. *Mus Comp & Cond* Stanley Myers. *Sd* Christian Wangler. *Asst Dir* Dennis Robertson. *Prod Mgr* Pat Green.

Cast: Barbara Jefford (*Molly Bloom*), Milo O'Shea (*Leopold Bloom*), Maurice Roeves (*Stephen Dedalus*), T. P. McKenna (*Buck Mulligan*), Martin Dempsey (*Simon Dedalus*), Sheila O'Sullivan (*May Goulding Dedalus*), Graham Lines (*Haines*), Peter Mayock (*Jack Power*), Fionnuala Flanagan (*Gerty MacDowell*), Anna Manahan (*Bella Cohen*), Maureen Toal (*Zoe Higgins*), Maureen Potter (*Josie Breen*), Chris Curran (*Myles Crawford*), Maire Hastings (*Mary Driscoll*), Eddie Golden (*Martin Cunningham*), Joe Lynch (*Blazes Boylan*), Ruadhan Neeson (*Cyril Sargent*), Biddie White-Lennon (*Cissy Caffrey*), Meryl Gourley (*Mrs. Mervyn Talboys*), Ann Rowan (*Mrs. Bellingham*), Rosaleen Linehan (*Nurse Callan*), Robert Carlisle, Jr. (*Dr. Dixon*), O. Z. Whitehead (*Alexander J. Dowie*), Cecil Sheridan (*John Henry Manton*), Tony Doyle (*Lieutenant Gardner*), James Bartley (*Private Carr*), Colin Bird (*Private Compton*), Jack Plant (*Denis Breen*), Dave Kelly (*Garrett Deasy*), Des Keogh (*Joe Hynes*), Leon Collins (*Lynch*), Robert Somerset (*Lenehan*), May Cluskey (*Mrs. Yelverton Barry*), Desmond Perry (*Bantam Lyons*), John Molloy (*Corny Kelleher*), Clare Mullen (*Florry*), Pamela Mant (*Kitty*), Paddy Roche (*Madden*), Brendan Cauldwell (*Bob Doran*), Eugene Lambert (*Costello*), Danny Cummins (*The Drinker*), Geoffrey Golden (*The Citizen*), Frank Bailey, Brenda Doyle, Barry Cassin, Don Irwin, Thomas

MacAnna, Pauline Melville, Maire Ni Ghrainne, Derry Power, Lillian Rapple, Charlie Roberts, Cecil Sheehan, Ritchie Stewart.

Epic. Source: James Joyce, *Ulysses* (Paris, 1922). A warm spring day stimulates the memories of Dublin citizens, among them Stephen Dedalus, a young poet and schoolteacher, and Leopold Bloom, a Jewish advertising agent. Wracked by guilt, Dedalus recalls his intensely Catholic childhood and his mother's funeral; Bloom mourns his son Rudy. Since the child's death 11 years earlier Bloom has been impotent. His wife, Molly, has responded to this withdrawal by cuckolding him numerous times; her current lover is the virile boxing promoter, Blazes Boylan. Traveling in a funeral cortege, Bloom observes Dedalus strolling on the beach and is strongly attracted to the youth. While lunching in a pub, Bloom is taunted by a one-eyed anti-Semite. In a hospital lounge the Jew encounters the drunken poet, whom he follows to the brothel of Bella Cohen. There both men are beset by terrifying fantasies, Bloom envisioning himself an Oriental potentate, the mayor of Dublin, a culprit tried by a Jew-hating judge, and a woman. In the street Bloom invites Dedalus to his home, where the two spend the night conversing. As day breaks Bloom offers his friend lodging, but the poet refuses. Her husband asleep beside her, Molly considers her youthful courtship by Bloom, her present relationship with Boylan, and the possibility of a future affair with Dedalus. *Irish. Schoolteachers. Poets. Catholics. Jews. Cuckolds. Mistresses. Madams. Memory. Impotence. Drunkenness. Anti-Semitism. Death. Marriage. Infidelity. Friendship. Guilt. Filial relations. Whorehouses. Funerals. Pubs. Hospitals. Spring. Dublin. Fantasy.*

Note: Filmed on location in Dublin. Opened in London in Jun 1967; running time: 132 min.

THE UMBRELLAS OF CHERBOURG (France/West Germany) F6.5272

Madeleine Films—Parc Film—Beta-Film. *Dist* Landau Releasing Organization. 16 Dec 1964 [New York opening]. Sd; col (Eastman Color). 35mm. 90 min.

Prod Mag Bodard. *Dir-Writ* Jacques Demy. *Photog* Jean Rabier. *Asst Camera* Pierre Willemin, Jean-Paul Lemaître. *Art Dir* Bernard Evein. *Asst Art Dir* Claude Pignot, Jean Didenot. *Film Ed* Anne-Marie Cotret. *Asst Film Ed* Monique Teisseire, Gisèle Chezeau. *Mus Comp & Cond* Michel Legrand. *Lyr* Jacques Demy. *Asst Dir* Jean-Paul Savignac, Klaus Müller-Laue. *Prod Mgr* Philippe Dussart. *Unit Mgr* Maurice Urbain. *Script Girl* Annie Maurel. *Miss Deneuve's Wardrobe* Réal. *Cost* Jacqueline Moreau. *Hairstyles* Carita. *Still Photog* Léo Weisse.

Cast: Catherine Deneuve (*Geneviève Emery*), Nino Castelnuovo (*Guy*), Anne Vernon (*Madame Emery*), Ellen Farner (*Madeleine*), Marc Michel (*Roland Cassard*), Mireille Perrey (*Aunt Elise*), Jean Champion (*Aubin*), Harald Wolff (*Dubourg*), Dorothée Blank (*girl in the cafe*).

Comedy-drama in song. Geneviève, a 16-year-old girl whose mother, Madame Emery, operates an umbrella shop in Cherbourg, is in love with Guy, a 21-year-old auto mechanic who lives with his sickly Aunt Elise and young Madeleine, her companion. Guy and Geneviève want to marry, but he is about to begin 2 years of military service; before he departs, Geneviève has sex with him to prove her love. Guy has been away several months, and Geneviève has received only one letter when her mother learns that Geneviève is pregnant. Roland Cassard, a wealthy diamond merchant, proposes to Geneviève, declaring his willingness to raise Guy's child as his own. Geneviève is at first shocked by the idea, but as time passes, she becomes convinced that Guy has forgotten her. Won over by Cassard's tenderness and her mother's arguments, she marries Cassard. Guy returns home, learns of Geneviève's marriage, and disconsolately goes back to his old job. When Aunt Elise dies and Madeleine prepares to leave, Guy realizes that they are in love with each other. They marry and Guy buys a gas station with the money inherited from Aunt Elise; 3 years later, Guy and Madeleine are a happy family with their young son. On Christmas Eve when Guy is alone, Geneviève drives into the gas station. Aside from noting that their daughter strongly resembles Guy, the former lovers have little to say to each other, and they go their separate ways. *Mechanics. Aunts. Diamond merchants. Adolescence. Military draft. Pregnancy. Illegitimacy. Filial relations. Marriage. Inheritance. Filling stations. Christmas. Cherbourg. Umbrellas.*

Note: Location scenes filmed in Cherbourg. Opened in Paris in Feb 1964 as *Les parapluies de Cherbourg*; released in West Germany in Nov 1965 as *Die Regenschirme von Cherbourg*. Original running time: 95 min. One German source lists Ultrascope as widescreen process.

UN, DEUX, TROIS, QUATRE! *see* **BLACK TIGHTS**

THE UNADORNED WEST *see* **THE UNDRESSED WEST**

UNAKRSNA VATRA *see* **OPERATION CROSS EAGLES**

UNCHAINED *see* **ANGEL UNCHAINED**

THE UNCLE (Great Britain)   F6.5273
 Play-Pix Films. *For* British Lion Films. *Dist* Lenart Productions. 18 Jul **1966** [New York opening]. Sd; b&w. 35mm. 87 min.
 Prod Robert Goldston. *Exec Prod* Leonard Davis. *Assoc Prod* Roy Millichip, Nancy W. Green. *Dir* Desmond Davis. *Screenplay* Desmond Davis, Margaret Abrams. *Photog* Manny Wynn. *Art Dir* Edward Marshall. *Film Ed* Brian Smedley-Aston. *Makeup* Michael Morris. *Hairstyles* Olga Angelinetta.
 Cast: Rupert Davies *(David)*, Brenda Bruce *(Addie)*, Robert Duncan *(Gus)*, William Marlowe *(Wayne)*, Ann Lynn *(Sally)*, Christopher Arris *(Tom)*, Maurice Denham *(Mr. Ream)*, Helen Fraser *(Mary Ream)*, Barbara Leake *(Emma)*, John Moulder-Brown *(Jamie)*, Jane Ratcliffe *(Susie)*.
 Drama. Source: Margaret Abrams, *The Uncle* (Boston, 1962). Gus, a 7-year-old boy, is faced with a serious dilemma, when his sister's child Tom, who is the same age, comes to visit for the summer. Gus's status as an uncle quickly separates him from other children and alienates him from his parents, David and Addie, who fail to realize the seriousness of the situation. Increasingly, Gus withdraws into an old, decaying house nearby, where he feels more secure. Seeking companionship beyond that of his playmates, he purchases a parakeet, names him Charlie, and tries to teach him to speak. Gus learns much about sex, love, and death during his lonely summer: shopkeeper Mr. Ream, his best friend, dies suddenly; and his brother-in-law, Wayne, castrates the summer's herd of calves. He is angered that his father helped force him into his situation by having a son so late in life. Gradually, Gus begins to side with his nephew against the other children, and the two youngsters experience a sense of mutual understanding. From that breakthrough comes a strengthened relationship between Gus and his playmates, who suddenly find the idea of his being an uncle unique. *Children. Uncles. Storekeepers. Childhood. Loneliness. Family life. Castration. Summer. Pets. Birds. Cattle.*
 Note: Filmed on location in Plymouth, England, in 1964.

UNCLE TOMCAT'S HOUSE OF KITTENS   F6.5274
 Gunther Purdue. *Dist* Sack Amusement Enterprises. 8 Nov **1967** [Fresno, California, showing]. Sd; b&w. 35mm. 72 min.
 Pres by Alfred N. Sack. *Prod-Dir* Gunther Purdue. *Assoc Prod* Hal DeBeau. *Screenplay* Alan Michaels. *Dir Photog* Henri Marshall. *Mus Score* Herb C. Davis.
 Cast: George Cooper, actor *("Uncle Tomcat" Schultz)*, Marin Kelly *(Kitten Lucie)*, Anne Besant *(Kitten Monique)*, Teresa Jollie *(Kitten Annabelle)*, Rene West *(Kitten Mamie Lou)*, Stephanie Jones *(Kitten Rosabelle)*, Irene Gray *(Kitten Frou-Frou)*.
 Comedy. "Uncle Tomcat" Schultz, a plainclothes police detective on the trail of some counterfeiters who are operating out of an old hut, decides to spend the night in an abandoned house across from the counterfeiters' hut. Unknown to Schultz, the house is inhabited by seven unemployed chorus girls and stripteasers known as "The Krazy Kittens and the Purring Pussycats." Schultz sets up his observation post on the second floor and one by one the girls come home and happily discover him. Schultz has sex with each of the women, then stumbles into bed with all of them for an orgy. Exhausted, Schultz leaves the girls and goes across the street to arrest the counterfeiters. On his return he finds that the girls have disappeared. *Detectives. Chorus girls. Stripteasers. Counterfeiters. Group sex.*
 Note: Also known as *Uncle Tomcat and His House of Kittens*.

UNCLE TOM'S CABIN (France/Italy/West Germany/Yugoslavia)
                                                                   F6.5275
 Melodie-Film–CCC–Filmkunst–Avala Film–S. I. P. R. O.–Debora Film. *Dist* Kroger Babb & Associates. 1 Jan **1969** [Savannah, Georgia, opening]. Sd; col (Eastman Color). 35mm (CinemaScope, see note). 118 min.
 Prod Aldo von Pinelli. *U. S. Vers Supv* Kroger Babb. *Dir* Geza Radvanyi. *Screenplay* Geza Radvanyi, Fred Denger. *Photog* Heinz Hölscher. *Art Dir* Willi Schatz. *Film Ed* Victor Palfi. *U. S. Vers Ed* Will Williams. *Mus* Peter Thomas. *Dub Voice* Ella Fitzgerald. *Sd* Michele Neny. *Prod Mgr* Georg M. Reuther. *Cost* Herbert Ploberger.
 Cast: John Kitzmiller *(Uncle Tom)*, O. W. Fischer *(Saint-Claire)*, Herbert Lom *(Simon Legree)*, Eleonora Rossi-Drago *(Mrs. Saint-Claire)*, Gertraud Mittermayr *(Little Eva)*, Mylène Demongeot *(Harriet)*, Juliette Greco *(Dinah)*, Olive Moorefield *(Cassy)*, Catana Cayetano *(Eliza)*, Rhet Kirby *(Topsy)*, Eartha Kitt *(singer)*, Charles Fawcett *(Mr. Shelby)*, Thomas Fritsch *(George Shelby)*, Bibi Jelinek *(Virginia)*, Aziz Saad *(Napoleon)*, Harry Tamekloe *(Andy)*, George Goodman *(Sambo)*, Harold Bradley, actor *(Harris)*, Erika von Thellmann *(Aunt Ophelia)*, Dorothee Ellison *(Uncle Tom's mama)*, Felix White *(Dolph)*, Vilma Degischer *(Mrs. Shelby)*, Claudio Gora.
 Drama. Source: Harriet Beecher Stowe, *Uncle Tom's Cabin, or Life Among the Lowly* (Boston, 1852). Mr. Shelby, a southern plantation owner, goes into debt, and slave trader Simon Legree demands in payment 10 slaves including

Eliza, Uncle Tom, and Cassy for his mistress. Eliza escapes with her child, but Legree takes the others in chains to his Natchez estate. En route, Uncle Tom is befriended by ailing Little Eva, who induces her father, Mr. Saint-Claire, to buy Uncle Tom and free him when she dies. Mr. Saint-Claire fulfills Little Eva's dying request and also frees the rest of his slaves. Legree kills Mr. Saint-Claire for his benevolence and accuses a black man of the murder; as a result, the slave is lynched. When Legree tires of Cassy and tries to kill her, Uncle Tom sacrifices himself to save her. After Abraham Lincoln is elected President of the United States, the slaves revolt and are sheltered in a monastery. A gun battle ensues, and Cassy is killed by Sambo, an overseer, as the encircled slaves flood the cotton fields and escape to safety. *Slavers. Slaves—Runaway. Children. Mistresses. Slavery. Debt. Murder. Frameup. Lynching. Revolts. Plantations. Monasteries. United States—South. Natchez. Abraham Lincoln.*
 Note: Released in West Germany in Apr 1965 as *Onkel Toms Hütte*; running times: 170 min, 160 min, 151 min; in Paris in Sep 1965 as *La case de l'Oncle Tom*; running time: 125 min; in Italy as *Cento dollari d'odio*; in Yugoslavia as *Čiča Tomina Koliba*. Originally released in 70mm (Superpanorama).

THE UNCLEAN   F6.5276
 Dist Film-Makers' Cooperative. 12 Aug **1967** [New York opening]. Sd; b&w and col. 16mm. 90 min.
 Dir Andrew Noren.
 Cast: George Kuchar, Mike Kuchar.
 Satire. Various men and women take baths, scrubbing constantly. Filmmakers George and Mike Kuchar take a bath together. *Bathing customs.*
 Note: Comprised of three parts, each 30 min in length and also distributed separately.

AN UNCOMMON THIEF (U.S.S.R.)   F6.5277
 Mosfilm. *Dist* Artkino Pictures. 12 Nov **1967** [New York opening]. Sd; b&w. 35mm. 93 min.
 Dir Eldar Ryazanov. *Screenplay* Emil Veniaminovich Braginskiy, Eldar Ryazanov. *Photog* Anatoliy Mukasey, Vladimir Nakhabtsev. *Art Dir* Boris Nemechek, Lev Semyonov. *Mus* Andrey Petrov. *Sd* Valeriy Popov. *Asst Dir* A. Korenev.
 Cast: Innokentiy Smoktunovskiy *(Detochkin)*, Oleg Yefremov *(Maksim Podberyozovikov)*, Anatoliy Papanov *(Sokol-Kruzhkin)*, Lyubov Dobrzhanskaya, Olga Aroseva, Andrey Mironov, Tatyana Gavrilova, Georgiy Zhzhyonov, Yevgeniy Yevstigneyev, Sergey Kulagin, Viktoria Radunskaya, G. Roninson, B. Runge, Ya. Lents, V. Nevinnyy, D. Banionis, G. Volchek, L. Sokolova, A. Maksimova.
 Comedy-drama. Detochkin, a modest insurance agent, becomes incensed at the thought of crooks going unpunished, and he begins a retribution campaign by stealing offenders' automobiles, selling them, and donating the profits to an orphanage. Maksim, the police detective assigned to investigate the mysterious thefts, coincidentally is performing with Detochkin in an amateur production of *Hamlet*. Detochkin steals the car of a black marketeer after several unsuccessful attempts. Maksim arrests him, but, upon hearing Detochkin's story, he lets off his friend with a warning. However, Detochkin cannot resist stealing still another car, and he is once more arrested, though he is permitted to go on with his performance as Hamlet. At the trial, Maksim speaks on his friend's behalf, and although Detochkin is found guilty, he soon returns to his former life. *Insurance agents. Vigilantes. Thieves. Detectives. Theater—Amateur. Trials. Automobiles. Black market. Orphanages. "Hamlet".*
 Note: Released in the U.S.S.R. in 1966 as *Beregis avtomobilya!*

... UND IMMER RUFT DAS HERZ *see* **MOONWOLF**

...UND MORGEN FAHRT IHR ZUR HÖLLE *see* **DIRTY HEROES**

THE UNDEFEATED   F6.5278
 Twentieth Century-Fox Film Corp. 4 Oct **1969** [New Orleans opening; c4 Oct 1969; LP37506]. Sd (Westrex); col (De Luxe). 35mm (Panavision). 119 min. *MPAA rating* G.
 Prod Robert L. Jacks. *Dir* Andrew V. McLaglen. *Screenplay* James Lee Barrett. *Story* Stanley L. Hough. *Dir Photog* William Clothier. *Camera Op* Alfred Lebowitz, Al Myers. *Art Dir* Carl Anderson. *Set Decor* Walter M. Scott, Chester L. Bayhi. *Film Ed* Robert Simpson. *Mus Comp & Cond* Hugo Montenegro. *Orch* Herbert Spencer. *Sd* Richard Overton, David Dockendorf. *Rec* Chuck King. *Asst Dir* Jack Cunningham. *Unit Prod Mgr* Clarence Eurist. *Prod Asst* Cary Eurist. *Script Supv* Robert Forrest. *Cost Dsgn* Bill Thomas. *Cost* Frank Balchus, Diane Jones, Robert Mathews, Luster Bayless. *Makeup Supv* Dan Striepeke. *Makeup Artist* Leo Lotito, Mark Reedall, David Grayson. *Hairstyles* Edith Lindon, Sheral Ross. *Sp Photog Eff* L. B. Abbott, Art Cruickshank. *Stunt Coörd* Hal Needham. *Constr Coörd* Hank Wynands. *Gaffer* James Vaiana. *Prop* Ray Thompson.

Cast: John Wayne (*Col. John Henry Thomas*), Rock Hudson (*Col. James Langdon*), Tony Aguilar (*General Rojas*), Roman Gabriel (*Blue Boy*), Marian McCargo (*Ann Langdon*), Lee Meriwether (*Margaret Langdon*), Merlin Olsen (*Little George*), Melissa Newman (*Charlotte Langdon*), Bruce Cabot (*Jeff Newby*), Michael Vincent (*Bubba Wilkes*), Ben Johnson (*Short Grub*), Edward Faulkner (*Anderson*), Harry Carey, [Jr.] (*Webster*), Paul Fix (*Gen. Joe Masters*), Royal Dano (*Major Sanders*), Richard Mulligan (*Dan Morse*), Carlos Rivas (*Diaz*), John Agar (*Christian*), Guy Raymond (*Giles*), Don Collier (*Goodyear*), Big John Hamilton (*Mudlow*), Dub Taylor (*McCartney*), Henry Beckman (*Thad Benedict*), Victor Junco (*Major Tapia*), Robert Donner (*Judd Mailer*), Pedro Armendariz, Jr. (*Escalante*), James Dobson (*Jamison*), Rudy Diaz (*Sanchez*), Richard Angarola (*Petain*), James McEachin (*Jimmy Collins*), Gregg Palmer (*Parker*), Juan García, actor (*Colonel Gomez*), Kiel Martin (*Union runner*), Bob Gravage (*Joe Hicks*).

Western drama. At the end of the Civil War, Union Col. John Henry Thomas, his adopted son Blue Boy, a Cheyenne Indian, and 10 of his command travel to Oklahoma, intending to sell horses to the United States Cavalry. Offered a poor price by the government, the indignant Thomas decides to transport the herd to Durango, Mexico, for sale to the beleaguered Emperor Maximilian. While crossing the Rio Grande the Yankees encounter Confederate Col. James Langdon who, having destroyed his Louisiana plantation, intends with family and friends to reestablish the Confederacy in Mexico. Together the Americans repel a group of Mexican bandits who have attacked the Confederate wagon train. In gratitude Langdon arranges a Fourth of July celebration attended by his widowed sister-in-law Ann and daughter Charlotte. At the festivity Charlotte and Blue Boy fall in love, while the men enjoy a free-for-all. When Blue Boy later warns the Southerners that Maximilian's emissary has been murdered, they refuse to believe him and beat him in retaliation for his advances to Charlotte. Langdon's party proceeds to Durango, where they are promptly captured by General Rojas, a follower of Maximilian's nemesis, Juárez. Rojas informs the Yankees that he will kill his hostages unless the herd is given to the Juaristas. Complying with his request, Thomas saves his former adversary. Together again, Confederates and Yankees return to the United States. *Mexicans. Cheyenne Indians. Bandits. Confederate veterans. Foster fathers. Revolutionaries. Hostages. Racism. Filial relations. Wagon trains. Fires. Fourth of July. United States—History—Civil War. Rio Grande. Oklahoma. Durango (Mexico). Mexico. Maximilian Emperor of Mexico. Benito Pablo Juárez. United States Army—Cavalry. Horses.*

Note: Filmed on location in Mexico and in Baton Rouge, Louisiana.

UNDER AGE   **F6.5279**
Falcon International Corp. *Dist* American International Pictures. Jun **1964** [New York showing: 21 Dec 1966; c4 Mar 1964; LP28695]. Sd; b&w. 35mm. 90 min.

Prod Harold Hoffman. *Dir* Larry Buchanan. *Screenplay* Larry Buchanan, Harold Hoffman. *Dir Photog* Henry Kokojan. *Camera Op* James R. Davidson. *Asst Camera* Jack Specht. *Set Dresser* William Mitchell. *Film Ed* Larry Buchanan. *Titl Song* Harold Hoffman, Larry Buchanan. *Mus Arr* Peter Frank Organization. *Song:* "Boil Them Cabbage Down" The Alpine Trio. *Song:* "Turtledove Song" The Lost River Trio. *Sd Mix* Bruce Howard. *Sd Rec* Lee Swann. *Script Supv* Betty Sooter. *Gaffer* R. H. Christensen, Sr. *Key Grip* J. H. Beall.

Cast: Anne MacAdams (*Ruby Jenkins*), Judy Adler (*Linda Jenkins*), Roland Royter (*George Gomez*), George Russell (*Defense Attorney Tyler*), John Hicks (*Prosecuting Attorney Adkins*), George Edgley (*The Judge*), Tommie Russell (*Mrs. Sybel Riley*), Regina Cassidy (*Dr. Vivian Scott*), Joseph Patrick Cranshaw (*W. J. Earnhardt, Justice of the Peace*), Raymond Bradford (*Wilbur Neal*), Jonathan Ledford (*Barney Jenkins*), Howard Ware (*bailiff*), Joretta Cherry (*court reporter*), Robert Alcott (*assistant district attorney*), William Peck (*news photographer*), Barnett Shaw (*news reporter*).

Melodrama. Ruby Jenkins, a divorced parent, stands trial for the rape of her 14-year-old daughter, Linda, under a Texas law which states that a person who encourages an unlawful act may be held accountable as a principal offender. George Gomez, a 16-year-old of Mexican descent, takes the stand and relates how he and Linda fell in love. He claims that Mrs. Jenkins encouraged him to have sexual intercourse with Linda, stating that Mrs. Jenkins gave her daughter a contraceptive and sent them into a bedroom to have sexual relations. Linda takes the stand and testifies that her mother encouraged her to have sexual relations with George so that they might achieve lasting happiness. Further, when Linda attempted to break off with George, her mother told her that it was impossible: they were married in the eyes of God. Sybel Riley, Linda's aunt, claims that Linda came to her for shelter after the event and had refused to return home, but Mrs. Jenkins attests that Sybel kidnaped the girl and held her by force. At this point, the local justice of the peace corroborates Sybel's testimony and calls the situation nothing more than a family squabble. The judge calls in Wilbur Neal, a local minister, to testify as a character witness for

George, Linda, and Mrs. Jenkins. After announcing that the relationship between the teenagers seemed innocent enough, Neal claims that Mrs. Jenkins had consulted him when she felt that George and Linda were becoming too intimate. Barney Jenkins, Linda's father, tells that he suspected that Linda and George were having sexual relations, and, as a result, he had considered filing a statutory rape charge against the boy. Mrs. Jenkins takes the stand and fervently denies the charge, saying that the couple had voluntarily and surreptitiously begun to have sex. The jury deliberates ... *Judges. Lawyers. Clergymen. Aunts. Mexicans. Parenthood. Rape. Adolescence. Filial relations. Sexual initiation. Divorce. Trials. Law. Texas.*

Note: Filmed in Dallas, Texas.

UNDER COVER ROGUE *see* **WHITE VOICES**

UNDER THE BANNER OF SAMURAI (Japan)   **F6.5280**
Mifune Productions. *Dist* Toho Co. 25 Jun **1969** [Los Angeles showing]. Sd; col (Eastmancolor). 35mm. 166 min.

Dir Hiroshi Inagaki. *Screenplay* Shinobu Hashimoto. *Photog* Kazuo Yamada. *Art Dir* Hiroshi Ueda. *Mus* Masaru Sato.

Cast: Toshiro Mifune (*Kansuke Yamamoto*), Kinnosuke Nakamura (*Shingen Takeda*), Yoshiko Sakuma (*Princess Yufu*), Kankuro Nakamura (*Katsuyori Takeda*), Mayumi Ozora (*Princess Okoto*), Ganemon Nakamura (*Mobukata Itagaki*), Katsuo Nakamura (*Nobusato Itagaki*), Masakazu Tamura (*Nobushige Takeda*), Yujiro Ishihara (*Kenshin Uesugi*), Ken Ogata.

Action melodrama. Source: Yasushi Inoue, *Furin kazan* (Tokyo, 1955). In 16th-century Japan, during a period of civil wars, Shingen Takeda, the strongest of all warlords, hires veteran warrior Kansuke Yamamoto as his advisor. Despite Yamamoto's advice, Takeda hesitates to attack a rival, Lord Suwa, as he considers Suwa his brother-in-law. At first Yamamoto rejects this rationale, for Suwa's wife is dead, but the advisor eventually effects a peaceful reconciliation between the rivals. Then, when least expected, Yamamoto has Suwa murdered. Takeda reacts to the assassination with reluctant approval, while Princess Yufu, Suwa's daughter, attempts suicide. Yamamoto saves her and falls in love with the woman who now hates him. Takeda also becomes enamored of the princess, however, and she finally submits to his advances; she marries him and bears him a son but dies 4 years later. Takeda's reign continues until he is challenged by Kenshin Uesugi, and in Aug 1561 armies under the two rivals meet in a titanic battle during which Yamamoto is killed. *Samurai. Warlords. Royalty. Brothers-in-law. Assassination. Perfidy. Japan—History— Period of civil wars 1480–1568.*

Note: Released in Japan in Mar 1969 as *Furin Kazan*. Alternative title: *Samurai Banners*.

UNDER THE YUM YUM TREE   **F6.5281**
Sonnis-Swift Productions. *Dist* Columbia Pictures. 23 Oct **1963** [Los Angeles opening; c1 Nov 1963; LP26603]. Sd (RCA); col (Eastman Color by Pathé). 35mm. 110 min.

A Frederick Brisson-David Swift Production. *Prod* Frederick Brisson. *Dir* David Swift. *Screenplay* Lawrence Roman, David Swift. *Dir Photog* Joseph Biroc. *Camera Op* Andrew McIntyre. *Set Decor* William Kiernan. *Prod Dsgn* Dale Hennesy. *Film Ed* Charles Nelson. *Mus* Frank De Vol. *Titl Song* Sammy Cahn, James Van Heusen. *Sung by* James Darren. *Main Titl Choreog* Robert Tucker. *Sd Supv* Charles J. Rice. *Sd* James Z. Flaster. *Asst Dir* Carter De Haven, Jr., Pat Corleto. *Cost Dsgn* Don Feld. *Wardrobe* Israel Berne, Edna Taylor. *Makeup Supv* Ben Lane. *Makeup* Harry Ray. *Hairstyles* Mary Westmoreland. *Hairstyles for Miss Lynley & Miss Adams* George Masters. *Vis Material* Roy Williams. *Still Photog* Homer Van Pelt. *Dial Coach* Norman Stuart.

Cast: Jack Lemmon (*Hogan*), Carol Lynley (*Robin*), Dean Jones (*David*), Edie Adams (*Irene*), Imogene Coca (*Dorkus*), Paul Lynde (*Murphy*), Robert Lansing (*Charles*), James Millhollin (*thin man*), Pamela Curran (*Dolores*), Asa Maynor (*Cheryl*), Jane Wald (*Liz*), Bill Bixby (*boy track team*), Vera Stough (*girl in class*), Bill Erwin (*teacher*), Maryesther Denver (*woman in bus*), Erskine Johnson, Army Archerd (*writers*), Lyn Edgington (*Peggy*), Patty Joy Harmon (*Ardice*), Phil Arnold (*deliveryman*), Almira Sessions (*woman*), Gary Waynesmith (*Josh*), Irene Tsu (*Suzy*), Gloria Calomee (*Sandy*), Cliff Carnell (*athletic instructor*), Matty Jordan (*maitre d'*), John Indrisano (*boxing instructor*), Laurie Sibbald (*Eve*), Jerry Antes (*Adam*).

Comedy. Source: Lawrence Roman, *Under the Yum Yum Tree* (New York opening: 16 Nov 1960). Collegian Robin Austin persuades her boyfriend, David, to live with her platonically to discover whether they are psychologically compatible. She takes an apartment recently vacated by Dr. Irene Wilson, her instructor in marriage counseling. Her new landlord is Hogan, an unabashed, incorrigible Casanova; he has just had an affair with Irene, who now has a new beau, Charles Howard, an associate professor. Not realizing that David is his new tenant's "roommate," Hogan plans to seduce her; then, discovering the true state of affairs, he employs every stratagem to keep David and Robin apart. At a crucial moment, Irene, accustomed to Hogan's antics, arrives in time to save Robin's virtue. By this time, David, thunderously angry, decides to plan a quiet night with Robin with soft lights, music, drink, and poetry and let nature take its course; but when Robin has reached a stage of acquiescence, David remorsefully runs from the apartment. Finally, David and Robin decide to elope, and Irene becomes completely involved with Charles, leaving Hogan alone—until he rents the apartment to a new beauty. Hogan is back in business. *Marriage counsel. Students. Landlords. Professors. College life. Seduction. Platonic love. Jealousy.*

THE UNDERCOVER SCANDALS OF HENRY VIII see ROYAL FLESH

UNDERGROUND F6.5282

Brighton Pictures. *Dist* United Artists. 23 Sep **1970** [San Francisco opening; c9 Sep 1970; LP38230]. Sd; col (De Luxe). 35mm. 100 min. *MPAA rating* GP.

Prod Jules Levy, Arthur Gardner, Arnold Laven. *Dir* Arthur H. Nadel. *Screenplay* Ron Bishop, Andy Lewis. *Story* Marc L. Roberts, Ron Bishop. *Dir Photog* Kenneth Talbot. *Art Dir* Frank White. *Film Ed* Tom Rolf. *Mus* Stanley Myers. *Sd Mix* Laurie Clarkson. *Asst Dir* Richard Dalton. *Prod Mgr* Derek Kavanagh. *Location Mgr* Jack Phelan. *Sp Eff* Thomas "Knobby" Clark. *Casting Dir* Maude Spector.

Cast: Robert Goulet *(Dawson)*, Danièle Gaubert *(Yvonne)*, Lawrence Dobkin *(Boule)*, Carl Duering *(Stryker)*, Joachim Hansen *(Hessler)*, Roger Delgado *(Xavier)*, Alexander Peleg *(Moravin)*, George Pravda *(Menke)*, Leon Lissek *(sergeant in bistro)*, Harry Brooks, Jr. *(panzer sergeant)*, Sebastian Breaks *(Condon)*, Nicole Croisille *(bistro singer)*, Derry Power *(Pommard)*, Paul Murphy *(Jean)*, Gerry Sullivan *(Fosse)*, Eamonn Keane *(Emile)*, André Charise *(Gerrard)*, Martin Crosbie *(R.A.F. sergeant)*, Andreas Malandrinos *(Jacquard)*, Liam O'Callaghan *(Imhoff)*, David Leland *(Paul)*, Vincent Smith *(sentry)*, James Bartley *(1st maquis)*, Gerry Alexander *(2d maquis)*, Chris O'Neill *(aid man)*, Bill Golding *(German staff sergeant)*, Fred Meany *(enlisted man)*, Stephen Follett *(boy in church)*, Maura Keely *(mother)*, Frank Hayden *(motorcycle lieutenant)*, Robert Carlisle, Jr. *(corporal)*, Conor Evans *(German officer in church)*, Brendan Mathews *(German officer)*, Joe Pilkington *(enlisted man)*, Barry Cowan *(1st radarman)*, Jeremy Jones *(2d radarman)*.

War drama. During World War II, American intelligence agent Maj. Joe Dawson is determined to kidnap the high-ranking Nazi General Stryker, who is being recalled to Berlin because the Gestapo questions his loyalty to Hitler. Dawson manages to parachute into occupied France and secures the aid of the maquis. Boule, leader of the guerrilla group, is distrustful of Dawson because of his coldblooded manner. Yvonne, another member of the group, shares this feeling but is assigned to play the role of Dawson's wife in the scheme to kidnap Stryker. Yvonne and the others eventually learn of Dawson's earlier attempt to capture Stryker, which resulted in the brutal killing of Dawson's wife, also an agent, and Dawson's confinement to a mental hospital in England. Having escaped from the hospital, Dawson is determined to complete his mission. Yvonne gradually becomes more sympathetic and falls in love with him. Stryker is captured at a railroad station, but in a battle with the Nazis, most members of the maquis are killed, including Boule. Dawson makes sure that Stryker is aboard the British rescue plane to London, and he remains in France with Yvonne. *Intelligence agents. Nazis. Parachuting. Kidnaping. Impersonation. Hospitals. Railroad stations. World War II. France. England. Adolf Hitler. Maquis.*

Note: Filmed in Ireland.

THE UNDERTAKER AND HIS PALS F6.5283

Eola Productions. *Dist* Geneni Film Distributing Co., Howco International. 30 Nov **1966** [Birmingham, Alabama, opening]. Sd; col (Eastman Color). 35mm. 60 min.

Pres by Ted V. Mikels. *Prod* Alexander Grattan. *Exec Prod (see note)* David C. Graham. *Dir-Writ* T. L. P. Swicegood. *Dir Photog* Andrew Janczak. *Art Dir* Mike McCloskey. *Mus* Johnny White. *Sd* Jean Mainferme.

Cast: Ray Dannis *(The Undertaker)*, Warrene Ott, Rad Fulton, Robert Lowery, Marty Friedman, Sally Frei, Rick Cooper, Ryck Rydon, Charles Fox, actor, Karen Ciral.

Horror film. During a slack period, an undertaker and his two hoodlum friends go out on their motorcycles to drum up business. Selecting their victims at random from the telephone directory, they commit brutal murders and then provide the bereaved families with cheap, showy funerals at outrageous prices. A sign outside the funeral parlor advertises trading stamps. Prior to the funeral, one of the hoodlums, a medical school dropout, chops up a body in order to continue his medical studies. A detective whose two secretaries have come under the psychopaths' knife becomes involved in the pursuit of the killers and is himself killed by a bomb the undertaker has set for him, but the police intervene and save two other women from death. *Undertakers. Motorcyclists. Hoodlums. Detectives. Murder. Mutilation. Funerals. Bombs.*

Note: Location scenes filmed in Los Angeles and Glendale, California. Some sources credit David C. Graham as producer-director and T. L. P. Swicegood as screenwriter.

THE UNDERWATER CITY F6.5284

Neptune Productions. *Dist* Columbia Pictures. 10 Jan **1962** [Seattle opening; c1 Feb 1962; LP21327]. Sd (RCA); b&w. 35mm (FantaScope). 78 min.

Prod Alex Gordon. *Dir* Frank McDonald. *Screenplay* Owen Harris. *Conceived by* Alex Gordon, Ruth Alexander. *Dir Photog* Gordon Avil. *Art Dir* Don Ament. *Film Ed* Al Clark, Don Starling. *Mus* Ronald Stein. *Sd Supv* Charles J. Rice. *Sd* George Cooper. *Asst Dir* Robert Agnew. *Prod Asst* Jack Cash. *Makeup Supv* Ben Lane. *FantaScope Eff* Howard A. Anderson Co. *Sp Eff Coörd* Howard Lydecker.

Cast: William Lundigan *(Bob Gage)*, Julie Adams *(Dr. Monica Powers)*, Roy Roberts *(Tim Graham)*, Carl Benton Reid *(Dr. Halstead)*, Chet Douglas *(Chuck "Cowboy" Marlow)*, Paul Dubov *(George Burnett)*, Karen Norris *(Phyllis Gatewood)*, Kathie Browne *(Dotty)*, Edward Mallory *(Lieut. Wally Steele)*, George De Normand *(Dr. Carl Wendt)*, Edmund Cobb *(Meade)*, Roy Damron *(Winchell)*, Paul Power *(civilian)*.

Science fiction melodrama. Marine engineer Bob Gage is hired to supervise the construction of an underwater city being built by Dr. Halstead of the Institute of Oceanography. Gage would prefer to devote his energies to the conquest of outer space and is at first skeptical that the project might eventually provide a haven in the event of an atomic war. Nevertheless, he gradually becomes more enthusiastic over the underwater effort, largely because of his growing love for Dr. Halstead's niece, Dr. Monica Powers. When frogmen have completed assembling the prefabricated parts and cells of the city, Gage, Monica, and several others prepare for the arrival of an inspection team from Washington. Gage then learns that the city has been built at the edge of a subterranean chasm that is slowly being washed away, and he orders an immediate evacuation. Although Dr. Halstead and several others lose their lives when the city collapses, Gage discovers that one of the city's cells has survived the disaster. Now convinced that a new underwater city can be satisfactorily built, he makes plans with Monica to begin another project. *Marine engineers. Frogmen. Scientists. Uncles. Nuclear warfare. Oceanographers. Underwater cities.*

Note: Filmed in Eastman Color by Pathé.

UNDERWORLD INFORMERS (Great Britain) F6.5285

Rank Organisation. *Dist* Continental Distributing, Inc. 13 Oct **1965** [New York opening]. Sd; b&w. 35mm. 105 min.

Prod William MacQuitty. *Exec Prod* Earl St. John. *Dir* Ken Annakin. *Screenplay* Alun Falconer. *Adtl Dial* Paul Durst. *Photog* Reginald Wyer. *Art Dir* Alex Vetchinsky. *Film Ed* Alfred Roome. *Mus Comp* Clifton Parker. *Mus Cond* Muir Mathieson. *Sd* Don Sharpe. *Sd Rec* Dudley Messenger, Colin Le Mesurier. *Asst Dir* Jake Wright. *Prod Mgr* Charles Orme. *Tech Adv* John Gosling.

Cast: Nigel Patrick *(Chief Inspector Johnnoe)*, Margaret Whiting *(Maisie)*, Colin Blakely *(Charlie Ruskin)*, Derren Nesbitt *(Bertie Hoyle)*, Frank Finlay *(Leon Sale)*, Catherine Woodville *(Mary Johnnoe)*, Harry Andrews *(Superintendent Bestwick)*, John Cowley *(Jim Ruskin)*, Michael Coles *(Ben)*, Allan Cuthbertson *(Smythe)*, Roy Kinnear *(Shorty)*, Ronald Hines *(Lewis)*, Peter Prowse *(Lonergan)*, George Sewell *(Hill)*, Kenneth J. Warren *(Lou Waites)*, Brian Wilde *(Lipson)*.

Crime melodrama. Source: Douglas Warner, *Death of a Snout* (London, 1961). Inspector Johnnoe is ordered by Superintendent Bestwick to end his use of underworld informers to solve cases because the practice reflects badly on Scotland Yard. Johnnoe disregards the order, however, and obtains information from Jim Ruskin regarding a series of London bank robberies. Shortly after the tip-off, Ruskin is murdered, and Johnnoe goes after the suspects, Bertie Hoyle and his gangster friend Leon Sale. Hoyle and Sale decide that Johnnoe poses a threat to them, and they frame him for accepting bribes from prostitute Maisie. Johnnoe is suspended from his duties at Scotland Yard and jailed until he is set free on bail. Charlie Ruskin, the informer's brother, learns from Mary Johnnoe that Hoyle's gang was responsible for his brother's death, and, in a battle between the gangsters and the informers, Hoyle and Ruskin are killed. As the police arrive, Johnnoe catches Sale attempting to escape with two suitcases full of stolen money. *Detectives. Gangsters. Informers. Prostitutes. Bank robberies. Organized crime. Frameup. Murder. Bribery. London. Scotland Yard.*

Note: Filmed in London and released there in 1963 as *The Informers*. British alternative or working title: *The Snout.*

UNDERWORLD U. S. A. F6.5286

Globe Enterprises. *Dist* Columbia Pictures. Mar **1961** [c1 Mar 1961; LP18986]. Sd (Westrex); b&w. 35mm. 98 min.

Prod-Dir-Writ Samuel Fuller. *Dir Photog* Hal Mohr. *Art Dir* Robert Peterson. *Set Decor* William Calvert. *Film Ed* Jerome Thoms. *Mus* Harry Sukman. *Orch* Leo Shuken, Jack Hayes. *Rec Supv* Charles J. Rice. *Sd* Josh Westmoreland. *Asst Dir* Floyd Joyer. *Cost Dsgn* Beatrice Pontrelli. *Makeup* Ben Lane. *Hairstyles* Helen Hunt.

Cast: Cliff Robertson *(Tolly Devlin)*, Dolores Dorn *(Cuddles)*, Beatrice Kay *(Sandy)*, Paul Dubov *(Gela)*, Robert Emhardt *(Connors)*, Larry Gates *(Driscoll)*, Richard Rust *(Gus)*, Gerald Milton *(Gunther)*, Allan Gruener *(Smith)*, David Kent *(Tolly, 12 years)*, Tina Rome *(woman)*, Sally Mills *(Connie)*, Robert Lieb *(officer)*, Neyle Morrow *(Barney)*, Henry Norell *(prison doctor)*, Peter Brocco *(Vic Farrar)*.

Crime melodrama. Based on articles by: Joseph F. Dineen. At the age of 12, Tolly Devlin witnesses the brutal gangland murder of his father. As he matures Tolly becomes a petty criminal consumed by his vow to have revenge on the four murderers. He finds one of the four dying in a prison hospital ward and learns that the other three are now in the heirarchy of the local crime syndicate. Gradually Tolly insinuates himself into the underworld gang; at the same time he cooperates with a Federal crime commission. As he plots his revenge, he falls in love with an attractive young woman, Cuddles, whom he saves from being killed by a member of the syndicate. By playing both sides of the law, he eventually succeeds in bringing about the death of his archenemies. But he himself is mortally wounded when he kills the syndicate head rather than obey an order to kill Cuddles. *Children. Gangsters. Murder. Revenge. Filial relations. Syndicates.*

THE UNDRESSED WEST F6.5287

Dist J. M. Nercesian Productions. 12 Jun **1964** [Los Angeles opening]. Sd; col. 35mm. [Feature film, length unknown.]

Pres by Carl Pehlman.

Cast: Tawny Angel, Rick Van Diddle, Windy Street, Kelly Greene, Sunny Hills, Neda Mann, Frosty Knight, Ima Blimp.

Comedy. No information about the precise nature of this film has been found, but press material suggests that it includes scenes of modern day gold diggers shedding their clothes while in the Rockies on a hunting trip. *Gold diggers. Nudity. Hunting. Rocky Mountains.*

Note: Location scenes filmed in Colorado. Also known as *The Unadorned West*; may also be known as *Everybody Likes Mountain Women.*

THE UNEARTHLY STRANGER (Great Britain) F6.5288

Independent Artists. *Dist* American International Pictures. Apr **1964.** Sd; b&w. 35mm. 68 min.

A Julian Wintle–Leslie Parkyn Production. *Prod* Albert Fennell. *Dir* John Krish. *Screenplay* Rex Carlton. *Photog* Reg Wyer. *Art Dir* Harry Pottle. *Film Ed* Tom Priestley. *Mus Comp* Edward Williams. *Mus Cond* Marcus Dods.

Cast: John Neville *(Dr. Mark Davidson)*, Gabriella Licudi *(Julie Davidson)*, Philip Stone *(Prof. John Lancaster)*, Patrick Newell *(Major Clarke)*, Jean Marsh *(Miss Ballard)*, Warren Mitchell *(Dr. Munro)*.

Science fiction drama. Munro, chief of a team of British scientists working on a project to enable man to move through space and time by mental powers, is found dead with his brain exploded. Major Clarke, in charge of security, investigates the death and finds that Americans and Russians working on a similar project have met the same kind of death. Dr. Mark Davidson is appointed to replace Munro, but when Clarke learns that Davidson's wife, Julie, cannot blink her eyes, has no pulse, and cannot feel the difference between hot and cold, the scientist is removed from the project. At the research institute, Clarke is killed and the space travel formula destroyed. Julie confesses that she is an alien from another planet that has already discovered the secret of mind travel; originally sent to kill Davidson, she failed because of her love for him. Following her confession, Julie is killed by her people and only her clothes remain. Davidson runs to the institute and is about to be killed by Miss Ballard, a secretary, when Lancaster saves him. Miss Ballard jumps out of a window, and like Julie, all that remains of her is her clothes. As Davidson and Lancaster walk into the street, they are surrounded by alien women with unblinking eyes. *Scientists. Spacemen. Secretaries. Space travel. Teleportation. Murder.*

Note: Opened in London in Sep 1963 as *Unearthly Stranger;* running time: 75 min. Working title: *Beyond the Stars.*

UNFAITHFUL WIFE *see* **LA FEMME INFIDÈLE**

THE UNFINISHED WAR *see* **IT BEGAN ON THE VISTULA**

DAS UNGEHEUER VON LONDON CITY *see* **THE MONSTER OF LONDON CITY**

UNHOLY DESIRE (Japan) F6.5289

Nikkatsu Corp. *Dist* Toho Co. 17 Nov **1964** [New York opening]. Sd; b&w. 35mm (Nikkatsu Scope). 150 min.

Dir Shohei Imamura. *Screenplay* Keiji Hasebe, Shohei Imamura. *Orig Story* Shinji Fujiwara. *Photog* Masahisa Himeda. *Mus* Toshiro Mayuzumi.

Cast: Masumi Harukawa *(Sadako Takahashi)*, Akira Nishimura *(Koichi Takahashi)*, Shigeru Tsuyuguchi *(Hiraoko)*, Yuko Kusonoki *(Yoshiko Masuda)*, Haruo Itoga *(Yasuo Tamura)*.

Drama. Sadako Takahashi, a slow-witted housewife, lives with her husband, Koichi, in a northeastern province of Japan. One night while alone she is awakened by Hiraoko, an itinerant musician, who is robbing her house to pay for medicine for his bad heart. Instead of taking any money, however, he rapes her. The next day, Sadako finds she is unable to tell her husband of the attack, and when Hiraoko returns she resists him less than she had expected. Soon she is wandering the streets, half-searching for Hiraoko, who has fallen in love with her and wants her to leave her husband for him. Though Sadako attempts to buy Hiraoko off, she finds herself becoming even more emotionally involved with him. Yoshiko, Koichi's mistress, learns of the relationship, but she is killed before she can gather evidence to show Koichi. Though Sadako finally decides to poison Hiraoko, he dies of a heart attack, and Sadako returns to her mundane home life. *Housewives. Musicians. Mistresses. Rape. Theft. Infidelity. Murder. Heart disease. Poisoning.*

Note: Released in Japan in 1964 as *Akai satsui.*

UNHOLY MATRIMONY F6.5290

Arcanum Productions. *Dist* Arcanum Productions, Chancellor Films. 28 Dec **1966** [Champaign, Illinois, showing]. Sd; b&w. 35mm. 78 min.

Dir Arthur John. *Songs:* "Suddenly, You Find Love," "Hard, Hard Girl" *Sung by* The Warmest Spring.

Drama. Magazine editor Jim Bremmer is beaten up while researching a story about mate swapping, but this only increases his interest. Believing that there is more to the story than simple mate swapping, he assigns reporter Al Gentry to continue the research with the help of Janice, who will pose as his wife. On their first meeting with swingers Mr. and Mrs. M., Janice is nearly raped, and she asks to be taken off the assignment. Instead, Al takes her to a beach resort in order to regain her cooperation. Back on the job, they meet several couples who practice voyeurism and play an adult version of "spin-the-bottle." Al and Janice watch while mixed couples are photographed cavorting in and around a swimming pool. At last, one of the men, a victim of blackmail, gives them a lead on a blackmail ring. Bremmer follows the lead while Al and Janice rendezvous with a couple who spike the drinks with LSD and stage a weird sex "trip." Acting on Bremmer's instructions, Al and Janice find the blackmail ring, but they walk into a trap and are almost killed before the police arrive. The gang's ringleader tries to escape, and he meets his fate in a slaughterhouse. *Editors. Reporters. Blackmail. Voyeurism. Mate swapping. Rape. LSD. Photographs. Magazines (periodicals).*

THE UNINHIBITED (France/Italy/Spain) F6.5291

C. I. C. C.–Terra Films–Cesáreo Gonzáles, P. C.–Films Borderie–Francos Films–Explorer Film–Precitel–Standard Films. *Dist* Peppercorn-Wormser, Inc. 12 Jun **1968** [New York opening]. Sd; col (Eastmancolor). 35mm. 104 min.

Pres by Fiore Agnello, Stephen Vali, Gene Wesson, Peter Savage. *Dir-Adapt* Juan Antonio Bardem. *Dial* Henri François Rey. *Photog* Gabor Pogany. *Art Dir* Enrique Alarcón. *Mus* Georges Delerue.

Cast: Melina Mercouri *(Jenny)*, James Mason *(Pascal Regnier)*, Hardy Kruger *(Vincent)*, Didier Haudepin *(Daniel Regnier)*, Renaud Verley *(Serge)*, Sophie Dares, Martine Ziguel *(Nadine, see note)*, Keiko Kishi *(Nora)*, Maurice Teynac *(Reginald)*, Karin Mossberg *(Orange, the mistress)*, José Maria Mompin *(Tom)*, Luis Induni *(Bryant)*, Rafael Luis Calvo, María Albaicín.

Melodrama. Source: Henri François Rey, *Les pianos mécaniques* (Paris, 1962). After suffering a nervous breakdown in Paris, Vincent, a young painter, motors to the small fishing village of Caldeya on the Spanish Costa Brava. Badly in need of rest, he has been given the use of a home belonging to his older companion and "patron," Reginald. In Caldeya, Vincent meets Pascal Regnier, a novelist preoccupied with drinking and love affairs who spends his summers in the town with his teenage son, Daniel. Daniel's friends include Serge and Nadine, models of young love. Most of the wealthy bohemians who summer in Caldeya gravitate to a cafe belonging to Jenny, a worldly woman who has already received a letter from Reginald urging her to look after Vincent. Her attentions prove to be more than Reginald had counted on, however, as Vincent, who is uncertain of his masculinity, falls in love with the older woman. Meanwhile, Regnier meets Orange and convinces her to move into his house, to the displeasure of Daniel. Reginald suddenly arrives on the scene, but Vincent nevertheless persuades Jenny to take a trip with him to Barcelona. The older man's hold proves too strong, however, and Vincent eventually leaves Caldeya to return to Paris and Reginald. As the summer season nears its end, Serge and Nadine make plans to run away from their decadent surroundings. Daniel brings them money, but Nadine, fearful of her parents' reaction, refuses to go through with the plan. The affair ends tragically with the death of Serge, and Regnier accompanies his son home after the tragedy. Daniel then engineers Orange's departure and pleads with his father to remain in the village through the winter. Regnier agrees and, embarking on a relationship with Jenny, begins to write again. *Painters. Novelists. Nightclub owners. Mistresses. Male homosexuality. Bohemianism. Adolescence. Village life. Neurosis. Wealth. Cafes. Fishing villages. Costa Brava.*

Note: Opened in Paris in Jun 1965 as *Les pianos mécaniques;* running time: 100 min. Spanish title: *Los pianos mecánicos.* Italian title: *Amori di una calda estate.* Working title: *Los organillos.* Filmed in Cadaqués, Spain. One source gives Cesareo Gonzalez joint credit for adaptation with Bardem, but this is unconfirmed. Sources conflict in crediting the role of Nadine.

THE UNKILLABLES see **DARING GAME**

UNKISSED BRIDE see **MOTHER GOOSE À GO-GO**

THE UNKNOWN BATTLE see **THE HEROES OF TELEMARK**

UNO DEI TRE see **TWO ARE GUILTY**

UNRECONCILED see **NOT RECONCILED, OR "ONLY VIOLENCE HELPS WHERE IT RULES"**

UNRUHIGE NACHT see **THE RESTLESS NIGHT**

THE UNSATISFIED (Spain)   F6.5292
I. F. I. España. *Dist* Cambist Films. Dec **1964.** Sd; b&w. 35mm. 89 min.
Prod-Dir Ignacio F. Iquino. *Exec Prod U. S. Version* Lee Hessel. *Story-Screenplay* Federico de Urrutia. *Dir Photog* Ricardo Albiñana. *Camera* Juan Gelpi. *Art Dir* Manuel Infiesta. *Film Ed* Juan Luis Oliver. *Ed U. S. Version* Jack Curtis. *Mus* Enrique Escobar. *Sd* Miguel Sitges. *Prod Mgr* Julia San José della Fuente. *English Edition* Bellucci Productions.
Cast: Rita Cadillac *(Wilma),* Colette Descombes *(Suzanne),* Maria del Sol, Angela Tamayo, Fernando León, Julián Mateos, Adriano Rimoldi, Luis Induni, Juan Capri, Manolo Gil, José Thelman.
Melodrama. Alberto, the son of a police commissioner, falls in love with Suzanne, a young woman who, desperate for money, lures wealthy, unsuspecting men to parties at Bernardo's castle. Bernardo is a cardsharp who uses drugs and liquor to dull the skills of those whom he lures into crooked games of chance. Suzanne falls in love with Fernando, a rich playboy to whom she becomes secretly engaged. Bernardo learns from the evil Wilma that Suzanne plans to tell Fernando that he was cheated at cards, and, at Wilma's instigation, Suzanne is killed. Alberto, the prime suspect, is arrested and taken to the police station. Alberto's father believes in his innocence and conducts a special investigation of the crime. Alberto escapes from jail and searches out Tony, a wastrel member of Bernardo's gang. Alberto confronts Tony and goads him into confessing to the crime. The police raid the castle, and Tony, Wilma, and Bernardo are arrested. *Police. Cardsharps. Gangsters. Playboys. Murder. Gambling. Cheating. Castles.*
Note: Opened in Madrid in Oct 1961 as *Juventud a la intemperie.*

UNSATISFIED LOVE see **LOVE AFTER DEATH**

THE UNSENT LETTER see **THE LETTER THAT WAS NEVER SENT**

UNSER BOSS IST EINE DAME see **TREASURE OF SAN GENNARO**

DIE UNSICHTBAREN KRALLEN DES DR. MABUSE see **THE INVISIBLE DR. MABUSE**

THE UNSINKABLE MOLLY BROWN   F6.5293
Marten Productions. *Dist* Metro-Goldwyn-Mayer, Inc. 11 Jun **1964** [Denver, Colorado, opening; c20 Apr 1964; LP28121]. Sd (Westrex); col (Metrocolor). 35mm (Panavision). 128 min.
A Lawrence Weingarten Production. *Assoc Prod* Roger Edens. *Dir* Charles Walters. *Screenplay* Helen Deutsch. *Dir Photog* Daniel L. Fapp. *Art Dir* George W. Davis, Preston Ames. *Set Decor* Henry Grace, Hugh Hunt. *Film Ed* Fredric Steinkamp. *Mus Cond & Supv* Robert Armbruster. *Orch* Calvin Jackson, Leo Arnaud, Jack Elliott, Alexander Courage. *Mus Arr* Roger Edens. *Songs* Meredith Willson. *Instrumentals:* "Dolce far niente," "Up Where the People Are" Meredith Willson. *Choreog* Peter Gennaro. *Rec Supv* Franklin Milton. *Sd* Larry Jost. *Asst Dir* Hank Moonjean. *Cost Dsgn* Morton Haack. *Makeup Supv* William Tuttle. *Hairstyles* Sydney Guilaroff. *Sp Vis Eff* A. Arnold Gillespie, Robert R. Hoag, J. McMillan Johnson. *Coöp* National Park Service.
Cast: Debbie Reynolds *(Molly Brown),* Harve Presnell *(Johnny Brown),* Ed Begley *(Shamus Tobin),* Jack Kruschen *(Christmas Morgan),* Hermione Baddeley *(Mrs. Grogan),* Vassili Lambrinos *(Prince Louis de Lanière),* Fred Essler *(Baron Karl Ludwig von Ettenburg),* Harvey Lembeck *(Polak),* Lauren Gilbert *(Mr. Fitzgerald),* Kathryn Card *(Mrs. Wadlington),* Hayden Rorke *(Broderick),* Harry Holcombe *(Mr. Wadlington),* Amy Douglass *(Mrs. Fitzgerald),* George Mitchell *(Monsignor Ryan),* Martita Hunt *(Grand Duchess Elise Lupovinova),* Vaughn Taylor *(Mr. Cartwright),* Antony Eustrel *(Roberts),* Audrey Christie *(Mrs. McGraw),* Grover Dale *(Jam),* Brendan Dillon *(Murphy),* Maria Karnilova *(Daphne),* Gus Trikonis *(Joe),* Mary Ann

Niles *(dancehall girl),* Anna Lee *(passenger),* George Nicholson *(Hotchkiss),* Ramsay Hill *(Lord Simon Primdale),* Moyna Macgill *(Lady Primdale),* Pat Benedetto *(Count Feranti),* Mary Andre *(Countess Feranti),* Pat Moran *(vicar),* Herb Vigran *(Spieler),* Eleanor Audley *(Mrs. Cartwright).*
Musical comedy. *Source:* Meredith Willson and Richard Morris, *The Unsinkable Molly Brown* (New York opening: 3 Nov 1960). Molly, a tomboy orphan rescued from the Colorado River and brought up by Shamus Tobin, sets out to find a rich husband. Arriving in Leadville, she gets a job singing in Christmas Morgan's saloon. En route she has met Johnny Brown, and when he refurbishes her cabin, she marries him. Johnny, wishing to satisfy Molly's hunger for money, sells her silver mine for $300,000, but the paper currency is burned accidentally after Molly hides it in the stove. Comforting her, Johnny tosses his pickax in the air, and it cracks open the richest gold vein in Colorado history. The Browns and Shamus move into a mansion in Denver, where the unpolished Molly hopes to break into society but is thoroughly snubbed by the elite. The Browns then go to Europe, where Molly becomes the toast of royalty. They return to Denver, bringing along their royal friends, and Molly's party to introduce them to Denver society is a success until Johnny's Leadville friends show up and turn it into a free-for-all. Rejected once more, Molly returns to Europe despite Johnny's warning that the separation will end their marriage. He returns to Leadville. In Europe, Prince of Lanière falls in love with Molly, but she decides to go back to Johnny. She sails on the *Titanic,* and when the ship sinks, Molly saves the lives of the people in an overcrowded lifeboat. Her courage and selflessness make worldwide headlines, and all Denver at last welcomes her home with open arms. And Johnny, too, is on hand to welcome Molly. *Songs:* "I Ain't Down Yet" (Molly), "Colorado Is My Home" (Johnny), "Belly Up to the Bar, Boys" (Molly), "I'll Never Say No" (Molly), "Leadville Johnny Brown [Soliloquy]" (Johnny), "He's My Friend" (Molly & Cast). *Tomboys. Orphans. Singers. Royalty. Socialites. Sea rescue. Snobbery. Gold. Saloons. Silver mines. Colorado River. Denver. S. S. "Titanic". Shipwrecks.*
Note: Location scenes filmed at Black Canyon, in the Gunniston National Monument Park in Colorado.

THE UNSTOPPABLE MAN (Great Britain)   F6.5294
Argo Film Productions. *Dist* Sutton Pictures. 21 Jun **1961** [Saint Louis opening]. Sd; b&w. 35mm. 68 min.
Pres by Jack O. Lamont. *Prod* John Pellatt. *Exec Prod* Jack O. Lamont. *Dir & Dial* Terry Bishop. *Screenplay* Alun Falconer, Paddy Manning O'Brien. *Photog* Arthur Grant. *Art Dir* Tony Masters. *Film Ed* Anthony Gibbs. *Mus* Bill McGuffie. *Sd* Charles Knott, Roy Hyde. *Prod Mgr* Jacques De Lane Lea.
Cast: Cameron Mitchell *(James Kennedy),* Marius Goring *(Inspector Hazelrigg),* Harry H. Corbett *(Feist),* Lois Maxwell *(Helen Kennedy),* Denis Gilmore *(Jimmy Kennedy),* Humphrey Lestocq *(Sergeant Plummer),* Ann Sears *(Pat Delaney),* Timothy Bateson *(Rocky),* Kenneth Cope *(Benny),* Brian Rawlinson *(Moonlight Jackson),* Tony Quinn *(Casey),* Tony Doonan *(Alan),* Susan Denny *(Milly),* Jean Marlow *(May),* Edward Harvey *(Lewis),* Emrys Leyshon *(lab assistant),* Tony Hawes *(TV interviewer),* Alan Edwards *(station constable),* John Baker *(reporter),* Liza Page *(club girl),* Donald Auld *(doorman),* Graham Stewart *(taxi driver).*
Crime melodrama. *Source:* Michael Francis Gilbert, "Amateur in Violence" (publication undetermined). James Kennedy, a hard-driving American who is the executive officer in a London chemical firm, decides to use his business acumen in dealing with the international criminals who have kidnaped his son. Ignoring the assistance of Scotland Yard's Inspector Hazelrigg, Kennedy sends twice the amount of money demanded in the ransom note in the expectation that the abductors will quarrel over the division of the money. The plan works, for one of the gang is found murdered, and clues on the body lead Kennedy and the police to a house in Hampstead where the ringleader, Feist, is hiding with Kennedy's son. Hazelrigg agrees to allow Kennedy to go in alone, but says that he will wait only 3 minutes before following. As Kennedy approaches, Feist attacks; but Kennedy fights him off with a homemade flamethrower and then locks himself in a room with his son as the police break in and apprehend the gang. *Americans in foreign countries. Executives. Gangsters. Fatherhood. Kidnaping. Murder. Ransom. Flamethrowers. London. London—Hampstead. Scotland Yard.*
Note: Released in Great Britain in 1960.

UNSTRAP ME   F6.5295
Hawk Serpent Productions. 20 Nov **1968** [New York opening]. Sd; col. 16mm. 78 min.
Prod Hawk Serpent. *Dir-Writ* George Kuchar. *Mus: Piano* Michael Snow. *Mus: Sony* Bob Cowan. *Song:* "The End of the World" Dorian West. *Miss Kerness' Formal Wear Dsgn by* Hope Morris.
Cast: Walter Gutman *(Uncle Bojo),* George Segal, sculptor *(himself),* Janine Soderhjelm, Donna Kerness, Lucinda Love, Frank Meyer, Dorian West, Hanne Weaver, Corky Cristians, Floraine Connors, Doris Zeitlen, Iris Holtzman, Francis Leibowitz, Helen Segal, Hope Morris, Lucien Boujema, Lea Bobey,

Inga Nyrod.

Drama. Source: Walter Gutman, "The Trip to Chicago" (publication undetermined). Exhausted by a sexually frustrating home life in the Bronx, portly, 65-year-old Uncle Bojo tosses aside all responsibilities, leaves his wife, Stella, and sets out in search of adventures. Traveling to Provincetown, Massachusetts, he romances a shapely blonde but loses her, at least in his imagination, to younger and more attractive men. Returning to New York, he becomes involved with a free-wheeling brunette, makes love to her in her apartment, and then accompanies her on a visit to the New Jersey home of sculptor George Segal. Finally, he travels south and meets a woman in Sarasota, Florida, who agrees to spend a few hours with him in a motel. Later, they explore the deserted winter headquarters of the Ringling Bros. and Barnum & Bailey Circus. As Uncle Bojo stares at his bleak surroundings, he ponders his empty existence, wondering what will happen now. *Sculptors. Old age. Sexuality. Marriage. Motels. New York City—Bronx. New Jersey. Sarasota. Provincetown. Ringling Bros. and Barnum & Bailey Circus. Fantasy.*

Note: Location scenes filmed in New York City, Massachusetts, New Jersey, and Florida.

UNTAMED WEST (Reissue)   F6.5296

Paramount Pictures. *Dist* Citation Films. 20 Nov **1961** [Maryland license]. Sd; col. 35mm (VistaVision). 108 min.

Note: Originally released by Paramount Pictures in 1955 as *The Far Horizons*; c1 Jun 1955; LP4799.

UNTER GEIERN *see* FRONTIER HELLCAT

UNTITLED *see* HEAD

THE UNTOUCHABLES *see* THE SCARFACE MOB

UNUSUAL REQUESTS   F6.5297

Dist I. R. M. I. Films. Aug **1968**. Sd; b&w. 35mm. 60 min.
Prod John Erikson. *Dir* Jan Anders.
Cast: Silvi Walter, Gary Boyd.

Sex film. No information about the precise nature of this film has been found, but press material suggests that it explores a woman's psyche and involves people who look for unusual pleasures. *Sexuality. Sexual practices.*

UNWILLING AGENT (West Germany)   F6.5298

Filmaufbau–I. F. C.–Bavaria-Filmkunst. *Dist* United Film Enterprises. 31 Jan **1968** [Union, New Jersey, opening]. Sd; b&w. 35mm. 95 min.

Dir Franz Peter Wirth. *Screenplay* Herbert Reinecker. *Photog* Günter Senftleben. *Camera Op* Franz Hofer. *Art Dir* Franz Bi, Max Seefelder. *Film Ed* Claus von Boro. *Mus* Hans-Martin Majewski. *Sd* Walter Rühland. *Asst Dir* Horst Rainer Erler. *Prod Mgr* Kurt Paetz. *Prod Dir* Gottfried Wegeleben. *Prod Asst* Kurt Zeimert. *Cost* Ilse Dubois. *Makeup* Max Rauffer, Gertrud Weinz-Werner.

Cast: Hansjörg Felmy (*Klaus Martens*), Johanna von Koczian (*Gitta Martens*), Hannes Messemer (*Braun*), Ingeborg Schöner, Rosl Schäfer, Olga von Togni, Max Mairich, Hanns Lothar, Peter Lühr, Alexander Hunzinger, Paul Verhoeven, Helmut Brasch, Ettore Cella, Gernot Duda, Klaus Havenstein, Gerhard Just, Rolf Kralowitz, Franziska Liebing, Anton Reimer, Willy Semmelrogge.

Action melodrama. Based on newspaper reports by Will Tremper and on the work by: Erich Kern, *Menschen im Netz* (Munich, 1957). Klaus Martens, an innocent West German incarcerated in East Germany, is mysteriously released after serving 5 years of a 25-year sentence. Rejoining his wife Gitta, he learns that she has collaborated with a powerful East German espionage network in exchange for his freedom. Jealousy destroys their marriage, and Gitta, attempting to leave the secret organization, is killed by its agents. Klaus, helped by several clues, undertakes a personal investigation into his wife's murder. Police Commissioner Braun trails the distraught husband, saves him from certain death, and breaks up the spy ring. *Secret agents. Police. Ex-convicts. Traitors. Imprisonment. Espionage. Jealousy. Murder. Rescue. German Democratic Republic.*

Note: Opened in Munich in Jul 1959 as *Menschen im Netz*; running time: 95 min; cut from 100 min.

GLI UOMINI DAL PASSO PESANTE *see* THE TRAMPLERS

L'UOMO DAI CINQUE PALLONI *see* THE MAN WITH THE BALLOONS

L'UOMO DAI PALLONCINI *see* THE MAN WITH THE BALLOONS

L'UOMO DI CASABLANCA *see* THAT MAN GEORGE

L'UOMO DI HONG KONG *see* UP TO HIS EARS

L'UOMO DI RIO *see* THAT MAN FROM RIO

UN UOMO, UN CAVALLO, UNA PISTOLA *see* THE STRANGER RETURNS

UP FROM THE BEACH   F6.5299

Panoramic Productions. *Dist* Twentieth Century-Fox Film Corp. 2 Jun **1965** [Detroit opening; c23 Jun 1965; LP31263]. Sd (Westrex); b&w. 35mm (CinemaScope). 98 min.

Prod Christian Ferry. *Dir* Robert Parrish. *Screenplay (see note)* Stanley Mann, Claude Brule. *Adapt* Howard Clewes. *Dir Photog* Walter Wottitz. *Art Dir* Willy Holt. *Dsgn* Albert Rajau. *Film Ed* Samuel E. Beetley. *Mus Comp & Cond* Edgar Cosma. *Sd* Jacques Carrère. *Sd Rec* Max Olivier. *Asst Dir* Michel Wyn, George Gradzenczyk, Andre Frederick. *Prod Mgr* Louis Wipf, Lucien Lippens. *Sp Eff* Georges Iaconelli, Karl Baumgartner, Daniel Braunschweig.

Cast: Cliff Robertson (*Sgt. Edward Baxter*), Red Buttons (*P.f.c. Harry Devine*), Irina Demick (*Lili Rolland*), Marius Goring (*German commandant*), Slim Pickens (*artillery colonel*), James Robertson-Justice (*British beachmaster*), Broderick Crawford (*U. S. MP major*), Georges Chamarat (*mayor*), Françoise Rosay (*Lili's grandmother*), Raymond Bussières (*Dupré*), Fernand Ledoux (*barrelmaker*), Louise Chevalier (*Marie*), Germaine Delbat (*seamstress*), Paula Dehelly (*widow Clarisse*), Gabriel Gobin (*trombonist*), Charles Bouillaud (*French horn player*), Georges Adet (*drummer*), Pierre Moncorbier (*field-keeper*), Nicole Chollet (*post office clerk*), Raoul Marco (*cobbler*), Charlotte Eizlini (*cobbler's wife*), Pierval (*grocer*), Renée Gardes (*grocer's wife*), Paul Maxwell (*U. S. Corporal Evans*), Ken Wayne (*U. S. Private 1st Class Solly*), Brian Davies (*U. S. Private 1st Class Dinbo*), Robert Hoffmann (*SS captain*), Michael Munzer (*SS sergeant*), Henri Kuhn (*SS corporal*), Jean-Claude Berva (*resistance fighter*), Bibi Morat (*Picot*), Frawley Becker (*grocer's assistant*), Roy Stephens (*colonel's driver*), Jo Warfield (*medic driver*), Rod Calvert (*other medic*), Alexandre Grecq (*German pilot*), Tracy Wynn (*soldier in truck*), Billy Kearns (*colonel in bunker*), Thomas Farnsworth (*major in bunker*).

War drama. Source: George Barr, *Epitaph for an Enemy* (New York, 1959). On the day after D-Day, Sgt. Edward Baxter and a U. S. Army squadron overtake a group of German soldiers who are holding hostage French civilians in a Normandy farmhouse at Verville. The American soldiers kill all but the German town commandant and free the French villagers—among them, Lili, a resistance worker in love with the commandant, who has treated the townspeople with kindness and consideration during the occupation. Upon receiving orders from a U. S. artillery colonel, Sergeant Baxter rounds up the villagers and marches them to the beach for evacuation to England. When they reach the beach, the U. S. Navy and the British beachmaster refuse to accept responsibility for the group, and the tired townspeople return to their homes. They attempt the trip from the village to the beach twice again, but no evacuation occurs. German troops fire on Verville, and the German commandant suggests that the villagers take refuge in the vault of an old church. While inspecting the vault, the commandant steps into a booby trap and dies. The bombardment ends, and the liberated townspeople sing the *Marseillaise* to Baxter and his troops as they join an American column on its way to the front. *Maquis. Hostages. Military occupation. Aerial bombardment. Evacuation. Churches. Mines (war explosives). World War II. D-Day (6 Jun 1944). Normandy. United States Army—Infantry. United States Navy. Germany--Army. "Marseillaise".*

Note: Filmed in Normandy. Screen credits list Clewes as scriptwriter with Mann credited for additional dialog. Working title: *The Day After.*

UP IN THE CELLAR   F6.5300

American International Productions. *Dist* American International Pictures. 11 Aug **1970** [Las Cruces, New Mexico, opening; c12 Aug 1970; LP39824]. Sd; col (Movielab Color). 35mm. 92 min. [Copyright length: 94 min.] *MPAA rating* R.

Prod James H. Nicholson, Samuel Z. Arkoff. *Assoc Prod* Norman Herman. *Exec Prod* William J. Immerman. *Dir-Writ* Theodore J. Flicker. *Dir Photog* Earl Rath. *Camera Op* Til Gabani. *1st Asst Camera* Rick Nervick. *2d Asst Camera* Roy Hogstedt. *Titl* Pacific Title. *Film Ed* Richard Halsey. *Asst Ed* Chuck McClelland. *Mus* Don Randi. *Mus Supv* Al Simms. *Song:* "Didn't I Turn Out Nice" Dory Previn. *Perf by* Hamilton Camp. *Song:* "Ted's Tune" Don Randi. *Song:* "Three Loves" Don Randi, Bob Silver. *Sd Rec* Robert Post. *Boom Op* Alan Boyle. *1st & 2d Asst Dir* Gary Grillo, Reuben Watt. *Prod Mgr* Elliot Schick. *Prod Asst* Bill Svanoe. *Script Supv* June Sampson. *Wardrobe Master* Thomas Costich. *Makeup* Beau Wilson. *Dial Coach* Joan Darling. *Still Photog* Wynn Hammer. *Prop Master* Robert J. Visciglia. *Gaffer* Ross Maehl. *Key Grip* Mason Sperry.

Cast: Wes Stern (*Colin Slade*), Joan Collins (*Pat Camber*), Larry Hagman (*Maurice Camber*), Nira Barab (*Tracy Camber*), Judy Pace (*Harlene Jones*), David Arkin (*Hugo Cain*), Joan Darling (*Madame Krigo*), Bill Svanoe (*campus* *policeman).* Charles Pinney, David Cargo.

Comedy. Source: Angus Hall, *The Late Boy Wonder* (London, 1969). College student Colin Slade loses his scholarship when a computer judges his poetry harshly, and the politically ambitious college president, Maurice Camber, backs the machine's decision. Colin meets Hugo Cain, the leader of a campus group who believe that opposing extremists will destroy each other, leaving the path open for the "Ultimate Revolution." Hugo persuades Colin to take revenge against Camber by committing suicide at a gathering to announce Camber's candidacy for the Senate. However, as Colin prepares to jump from the college radio tower, he is rescued by Camber. Furious, Colin sets out to create a scandal by seducing Camber's wife, Pat, his daughter, Tracy, and his black secretary and sweetheart, Harlene. He discovers each woman's weakness: Pat is a secret believer in astrology; Tracy believes herself to be ugly; and Harlene believes that white men have inflated expectations of black sexual prowess and therefore refuses to have sex with Camber. Colin films Tracy in the nude, persuading her of her own beauty. At a decency rally held by Camber, Colin substitutes his home movie of Tracy for the scheduled film, *The Sound of Music.* He next seduces Pat by posing as an astrology enthusiast. Pat then interrupts Camber's press conference to urge students to embrace free, "astral" love. However, Colin's revenge is again foiled when Camber gains sympathy as a result of his public embarrassments. Pretending to be black, Colin at last seduces Harlene. He then reveals that he is white, to the delight of Harlene and Camber, who can now consummate their relationship. When Camber divorces Pat, Colin joins mother and daughter. *Students. Poets. Revolutionaries. Mistresses. Negroes. College life. Revenge. Seduction. Filial relations. Astrology. Suicide. Scandal. Nudity. Infidelity. Ambition. Imposture. Free love. Computers. Censorship. Political campaigns.*

Note: Filmed in Las Cruces, New Mexico. Working title: *Hi in the Cellar;* alternative title: *3 in the Cellar.*

UP THE DOWN STAIRCASE   F6.5301

Park Place Productions. *Dist* Warner Bros. Pictures. 19 Jul **1967** [Los Angeles opening; c1 Jul 1967; LP35722]. Sd; col (Technicolor). 35mm. 123 min.

An Alan J. Pakula-Robert Mulligan Production. *Prod* Alan J. Pakula. *Dir* Robert Mulligan. *Screenplay* Tad Mosel. *Dir Photog* Joseph Coffey. *Camera Op* Edward Brown. *Asst Camera* Jeff Hand. *Art Dir* George Jenkins. *Film Ed* Folmar Blangsted. *Mus Comp* Fred Karlin. *Mus Supv* Score Productions. *Sd* Dennis Maitland, John Bolz. *Boom Op* Vito Ilardi. *Asst Dir* Don Kranze, Tom Christy. *Prod Supv* George Justin. *Prod Asst* Tony Major. *Script Supv* Roberta Hodes. *Cost Dsgn* Ann Roth. *Wardrobe* Beatrice Leon, Max Solomon. *Sandy Dennis' Makeup* Warner Bros. Cosmetics. *Makeup* Irving Buchman. *Hairstyles* Robert Grimaldi. *Casting* Alixe Gordin. *Still Photog* Dan Reuben, Josh Weiner. *Prop* Jack Wright, III, Jack Wright, Jr. *Grip* Larry Barr. *Gaffer* Willie Meyerhoff.

Cast: Sandy Dennis *(Sylvia Barrett),* Patrick Bedford *(Paul Barringer),* Eileen Heckart *(Henrietta Pastorfield),* Ruth White *(Beatrice Schracter),* Jean Stapleton *(Sadie Finch),* Sorrell Booke *(Dr. Bester),* Roy Poole *(Mr. McHabe),* Florence Stanley *(Ella Friedenberg),* Vinette Carroll *(mother),* Salvatore Rasa *(Harry A. Kagan),* John Fantauzzi *(Eddie Williams),* Maria Landa *(Carole Blanca),* Lewis Wallach *(Lou Martin),* Jose Rodriguez *(Jose Rodriguez),* Ellen O'Mara *(Alice Blake),* Jeff Howard *(Joe Ferone),* Loretta Leversee *(social studies teacher),* Robert Levine *(Mr. Osborne),* Elena Karam *(Nurse Eagen),* Frances Sternhagen *(Charlotte Wolf),* Candace Culkin *(Linda Rosen),* Janice Mars *(Miss Gordon).*

Drama. Source: Bel Kaufman, *Up the Down Staircase* (Englewood Cliffs, New Jersey, 1965). Armed with only a college degree and her youthful idealism, Sylvia Barrett arrives at Calvin Coolidge High School to begin her career as an English teacher. The school is located in a New York City slum area where the overcrowded classes are filled with unruly and often hostile teenagers from underprivileged families. Further, Sylvia must contend with seemingly endless paperwork and fellow teachers whose experience has made them either indifferent or cynical. Sylvia initially retains her optimism; but as the school year progresses, she finds herself unable to cope with the needs of her students. The delinquent but highly intelligent Joe Ferone misinterprets her interest in him and tries to seduce her; love-sick Alice Blake writes a love letter to one of the male teachers, Paul Barringer, and then attempts suicide when he callously corrects the grammar in her letter; and Ed Williams, an embittered black youth, drops out of school because he feels that no amount of education will enable him to overcome white prejudice. Toward the end of the school year, Sylvia believes that she is a failure and submits her resignation. However, during a mock trial in her classroom, Jose Rodriguez, a previously shy and reticent Puerto Rican boy, suddenly assumes the authority and confidence of a court judge and handles himself with new self-assurance. Realizing that despite all the frustration and heartbreak she has reached at least one of her students, Sylvia decides to remain at Coolidge High. *Idealists. Schoolteachers.*

Juvenile delinquents. Lovelorn. Negroes. Puerto Ricans. High school life. Seduction. Suicide. Racial prejudice. Slums. New York City.

Note: Location scenes filmed in New York City.

UP THE JUNCTION (Great Britain)   F6.5302

B. H. E. Productions-Collinson/Crasto Productions. *Dist* Paramount Pictures. 13 Mar **1968** [New York opening; c25 Jan 1968; LF25]. Sd; col (Technicolor). 35mm (Techniscope). 119 min.

Prod Anthony Havelock-Allan, John Brabourne. *Assoc Prod* Harry Fine. *Dir* Peter Collinson. *Screenplay* Roger Smith. *Dir Photog* Arthur Lavis. *Camera Op* Ron Robson. *Camera Focus* Brian Bennett, photog. *Art Dir* Ken Jones, art. *Film Ed* John Trumper. *Mus* Mike Hugg, Manfred Mann. *Songs Sung by* Manfred Mann. *Accomp by* The Delacardos. *Sd* Gerry Humphreys. *Sd Mix* George Stephenson. *Sd Boom Op* Harry Fairbairn. *Sd Camera Op* John Twine. *Dub Ed* Roy Taylor. *Asst Dir* Michael Dryhurst. *Prod Mgr* David Griffith. *Location Mgr* Richard Gill. *Cont* Doreen Dearnaley. *Wardrobe Supv* Ray Beck. *Makeup Artist* Dore Hamilton. *Ch Hairdresser* Carol Beckett.

Cast: Suzy Kendall *(Polly),* Dennis Waterman *(Peter),* Adrienne Posta *(Rube McCarthy),* Maureen Lipman *(Sylvie McCarthy),* Michael Gothard *(Terry),* Liz Fraser *(Mrs. McCarthy),* Hylda Baker *(Winny),* Alfie Bass *(Charlie),* Linda Cole *(Pauline),* Doreen Herrington *(Rita),* Jessie Robins *(Lil),* Ruby Head *(Edith),* Barbara Archer *(May),* Susan George *(Joyce),* Sandra Williams *(Sheilah),* Aubrey Morris *(Creely),* Michael Robbins *(Figgins),* Billy Murray *(Ray),* Michael Standing *(John),* Stephen Whittaker *(Alf),* Shaun Curry *(Ted),* Leslie Meadows *(Ron),* Anthony Sharman *(Tom),* Peter Attard *(Bert),* Douglas Sheldon *(villain),* Queenie Watts *(Mrs. Hardy),* Olwen Griffith *(Fat Lil),* Lockwood West *(magistrate),* Mark Moss *(policeman),* Michael Barrington *(barrister),* Yvonne Manners *(hotel receptionist),* Harry Hutchinson *(hotel porter),* Larry Martyn *(barrow boy),* Mike Martin *(police inspector),* Ronald Clarke *(mate),* Jack Phillips *(old man),* Gladys Dawson *(woman),* Derek Ware *(Ted's friend),* The Delacardos *(pop group).*

Drama. Source: Nell Dunn, *Up the Junction* (London, 1963). Bored by the comfortable life in Chelsea, Polly is chauffered in her Rolls-Royce to the drab working-class district of Battersea in London's Clapham Junction section. She takes a job in a candy factory where she makes friends with two sisters, Rube and Sylvie. After moving into a dingy flat, Polly goes shopping for furniture at a junk shop and meets Peter, a young employee there. He blurts out an invitation for a date, and Polly accepts. Although Polly is entranced by her new environment, Peter sees only the poverty and ugliness. He takes her to his dilapidated childhood home, and they make love in Peter's old bedroom. Some time later, Polly learns that Rube is pregnant by her boyfriend Terry and accompanies her to a disreputable abortionist. Rube eventually announces her engagement to Terry, but on the night of their rowdy celebration, Terry is killed in a motorcycle accident. Upset by her friends' problems, Polly accepts Peter's invitation to spend a weekend at a fashionable seaside resort hotel. Peter declares his love for her and surprises her by proposing marriage, but after discussing the subject and bitterly quarreling, they realize the extent of the differences between them. While driving back to Battersea, he is arrested for stealing the car that he supposedly rented for the weekend. He is ultimately sentenced to 6 months in jail, and Polly watches as a police van takes him away. *Factory workers. Sisters. Class conflict. Pregnancy. Abortion. Marriage. Theft. Rolls-Royce automobiles. Resorts. London. London—Battersea. Motorcycle accidents.*

Note: Location scenes filmed in the Battersea section of London. Opened in London in Jan 1968. Dunn's novel was originally adapted for British television in 1965.

UP THE MACGREGORS (Italy/Spain)   F6.5303

Produzione D. S.-Jolly Film-Talía Films. *Dist* Columbia Pictures. Nov **1967** [c1 Apr 1968; LP35528]. Sd; col (Technicolor). 35mm (Techniscope). 93 min.

Prod Dario Sabatello. *Dir* Frank Grafield. *Screenplay* Fernand Lion, Vincent Eagle, Paul Levy, José María Rodríguez, Franco Giraldi. *Script* Fernand Lion, Vincent Eagle. *Story* Fernando Di Leo, Enzo Dell'Aquila. *Dir Photog* Alejandro Ulloa. *Camera Op* Gaetano Valle, Salvador Gil. *Asst Camera Op* Franco Lecca. *Scenic Artist* Adolfo Cofiño, Ottavio Scotti, Augusto Lega. *Film Ed* Nino Baragli. *Mus* Ennio Morricone. *Sd* Guido Ortensi, Antonio Capitan. *Asst Dir* Carlo Moscovini, Jaime D'Or. *Prod Mgr* George Bold. *Prod Supv* José María Rodríguez. *Prod Unit Mgr* Mario Berriatua, Francisco Ruiz. *Wardrobe* Itala Scandariato.

Cast: David Bailey *(Gregor MacGregor),* Agatha Flory *(Rosita Carson),* Leo Anchoriz *(Maldonado),* Roberto Camardiel *(Donovan),* Cole Kitosh *(Dick MacGregor),* Nick Anderson *(Peter MacGregor),* Paul Carter *(Kenneth MacGregor),* Julio Pérez Tabernero *(Mark MacGregor),* Hugo Blanco *(David MacGregor),* Saturnino Cerra *(Johnny MacGregor),* Georges Rigaud *(Alastair MacGregor),* Roy Bosier *(Apache),* Victor Israel *(dentist),* Ana Casares *(Dolly),* Francesco Tensi *(Harold),* Jesus Guzman *(priest),* King Black *(Tom),* Antonio Vico *(Frank James),* Elena Montoya *(child from San Raphael),* Tito

García *(Miguelito)*, Anne-Marie Noé *(Mamie)*, Margaret Horowitz *(Annie)*, Margaret Merrit *(Dublin)*, Kathleen Parker *(Belfast)*, Ana María Mendoza *(Kilkenny)*, Julie Fair *(Galway)*, Fern Water *(Tralee)*, Judith Shepard *(Dundalks)*, Joe Hamlin *(Tipperary)*, Catherine Hamlin *(Kilarny)*, Nino Scariofolo, Riccardo Pizzuti, Rinaldo Zamperla, Alberto Cevenini *(bandits)*, Harry Cotton.

Western comedy. In the border country of Texas, celebrating the engagement of Gregor MacGregor to Rosita, the Scottish MacGregors get into a friendly brawl with the Irish Donovans. The melee is interrupted when Maldonado's bandits raid the party and carry off a trunk containing all the wealth of the MacGregors. Saying goodby to their fiancées (Gregor's six brothers are engaged to the six Donovan daughters), the seven MacGregor sons split up and go after Maldonado's gang. Though they succeed in preventing the bandits from robbing a bank, the brothers are unable to find Maldonado's hideout until they encounter a dentist, accompanied by his daughter Dolly, who has been summoned by the outlaw chief. From their concealment in the dentist's wagon, the MacGregors infiltrate the hideout and succeed in absconding with the bandit's treasure. When the jealous Rosita learns that Gregor is in the company of the flirtatious Dolly, she sets out after her fiancé and is captured by the bandits. Gregor goes to her rescue but is captured and held with Rosita as hostage pending the restoration of Maldonado's treasury. Outraged, Gregor's brothers storm the bandit's camp and rescue the young couple. Though the family is forced to take shelter in an abandoned railway car, they are saved when the remaining MacGregors, assisted by the Donovans and a tribe of friendly Indians, arrive to put an end to Maldonado and his gang. *Ranchers. Scotch. Irish. Bandits. Dentists. Hostages. Indians of North America. Flirts. Brothers. Courtship. Bank robberies. Jealousy. Texas. Mexican border.*

Note: Opened in Rome in 1967 as *Sette donne per i MacGregor*; in Madrid in Jul 1967 as *Siete mujeres para los MacGregor*. The film is a sequel to *Seven Guns for the MacGregors*, q. v. The following are pseudonyms: Frank Grafield (Franco Giraldi), Fernand Lion (Fernando Di Leo), Paul Levy (Paolo Levi), Agatha Flory (Agata Flori), Margaret Horowitz (Margherita Orowitz), Nick Anderson (Nazareno Zamperla), Cole Kitosh (Alberto Dell'Acqua), Vincent Eagle (Enzo Dell'Aquila), Alexander Ulloa (Alejandro Ulloa), Anne-Marie Noé (Ana María Noé), and Paul Carter (Paolo Magalotti).

UP THE NAUGHTY STAIRCASE see **INDISCREET STAIRWAY**

UP TO HIS EARS (France/Italy)   F6.5304

Ariane–Les Productions Artistes Associés–Vides. *Dist* Lopert Pictures. 17 May **1966** [New York opening; c28 Oct 1965; LF6]. Sd; col (Eastman Color). 35mm. 94 min.

Prod Alexandre Mnouchkine, Georges Dancigers. *Dir* Philippe de Broca. *Screenplay* Daniel Boulanger, Philippe de Broca. *Scen* Daniel Boulanger. *Photog* Edmond Séchan. *Art Dir* François de Lamothe. *Film Ed* Françoise Javet. *Mus* Georges Delerue. *Sd* Antoine Bonfanti. *Asst Dir* Claude Pinoteau. *Prod Mgr* Philippe Modave. *Script Supv* Patrick Aubrée. *Cost* Jacqueline Moreau. *Sp Eff* Gil Delamare, Georges Lagonelli. *Stunts* Gil Delamare.

Cast: Jean-Paul Belmondo *(Arthur Lempereur)*, Ursula Andress *(Alexandrine Pinardel)*, Maria Pacôme *(Suzy)*, Valérie Lagrange *(Alice Ponchabert)*, Jess Hahn *(Cornélius)*, Valéry Inkijinoff *(Mr. Goh)*, Jean Rochefort *(Léon)*, Darry Cowl *(Biscoton)*, Joe Said *(Charlie Fallinster)*, Paul Préboist *(Cornac)*, Mario David *(Roquentin)*, Boris Lenissevitch *(Russian professor)*.

Adventure comedy. Source: Jules Verne, *Les tribulations d'un Chinois en Chine* (Paris, 1879). Arthur Lempereur, young heir to a fabulous fortune, and literally bored to death, has unsuccessfully attempted suicide nine times in one week. Sitting aboard his yacht in Hong Kong with his fiancée, Alice, her mother, Suzy, his faithful valet, Léon, and his Chinese guardian, Mr. Goh, Arthur is informed by his business manager that he has just lost all of his money in a stock market crash. This gives Arthur good reason to attempt suicide again; however, the wise Mr. Goh suggests that Arthur put his death to a good cause and tells Arthur to insure himself for $2,000,000 making Alice and himself the beneficiaries. Arthur agrees, and since the insurance policy becomes invalid when death is caused by suicide, Mr. Goh assures Arthur he will have him murdered quickly and painlessly. There ensues a wild chase which leads from the waterfronts of Hong Kong to New Delhi to Nepal in the Himalayas and back to Hong Kong as the killers attempt to catch Arthur, who has changed his mind and now wants desperately to live because he has fallen madly in love with a stripper named Alexandrine. She strips by night and is a student of archeology by day. Finally, back on his yacht with Alexandrine, Arthur learns that Mr. Goh never meant to kill him; that the real intended killer was hired by his future mother-in-law, Suzy, who wanted to protect her daughter's insurance claim; and that the two men tailing him so closely were from the insurance company; and that his stocks did not crash—they doubled! *Heirs. Chinese. Guardians. Striptseasers. Students. Hired killers. Suicide. Murder. Insurance. Yachts.*

Finance—Personal. Stock market. Hong Kong. New Delhi. Nepal. Himalayan Mountains. Chases.

Note: Opened in Paris in Dec 1965 as *Les tribulations d'un Chinois en Chine*; running time: 110 min; in Rome in Dec 1965 as *L'uomo di Hong Kong*; running time: 110 min.

UP YOUR TEDDY BEAR   F6.5305

Don Joslyn Productions. *Dist* Geneni Film Distributing Co., Richard Organization. Jun **1970** [Los Angeles opening: 23 Dec]. Sd; col 35mm. 89 min. *MPAA rating* R.

Prod-Dir-Writ Don Joslyn. *Assoc Prod* John Joyce. *Photog* Robert Maxwell. *Art Dir* Bud Costello. *Supv Film Ed* John Joyce. *Film Ed* John Levine. *Mus* Quincy Jones, The Eyes of Blue.

Cast: Wally Cox *(Clyde)*, Julie Newmar *(director of toy company)*, Victor Buono *(Skippy)*, Claire Kelly, Angelique Pettyjohn, Thordis Brandt, Valora Noland, Amy Thomson, Vicki Ellison.

Comedy. Clyde, a shy toy salesman, has sexual fantasies about beautiful women. His hobby is carving dolls out of wood, and when the attractive director of the Mother Knows Best Toy Company learns of the dolls, she tries unsuccessfully to buy them for mass production. She orders her assisting son Skippy to send a prostitute to seduce Clyde into parting with his creations. The unscrupulous woman's plan fails, however, when the dollmaker proves to be impotent with the prostitute; he has a mother fixation on the director of the doll company, and her presence reminds him of his mother's warning that sex is dirty. *Prostitutes. Salesmen. Businesswomen. Fantasy. Seduction. Impotence. Momism. Dolls.*

Note: Also known as *The Toy Grabbers*.

THE UPPER HAND (France/Italy/West Germany)   F6.5306

Copernic Films–Fida Cinematografica–Gloria–Film. *Dist* Paramount Pictures. 26 Jul **1967** [New York opening]. Sd; col (Eastmancolor). 35mm (Franscope). 86 min.

Prod Maurice Jacquin. *Exec Prod* Raymond Danon. *Dir-Writ* Denys de La Patellière. *Dial* Alphonse Boudard. *Photog* Walter Wottitz. *Col Cons* Jacques Fonteray. *Art Dir* Robert Clavel. *Film Ed* Claude Durand. *Mus Comp & Cond* Georges Garvarentz. *Asst Dir* Roberto Bodegas. *Prod Mgr* Ralph Baum. *Cost* Jacques Fonteray.

Cast: Jean Gabin *(Paulo Berger)*, George Raft *(Charles Binaggio)*, Gert Fröbe *(Walter)*, Nadja Tiller *(Irène)*, Mireille Darc *(Lili)*, Claudio Brook *(Mike Coppolano)*, Claude Brasseur *(Giulio)*, Daniel Ceccaldi *(Commissioner Noël)*, Claude Cerval *(René)*, Dany Dauberson *(Léa)*, Marcel Bozzufi *(Marque Mal)*, Jean-Claude Bercq *(Jo le Pâle)*, Carlo Nell *(Sergio)*, Christa Lang *(girl)*, Yves Barsacq, Philippe Clair, Mino Doro, Maurice Jacquin, Jr., Franco Ressel, Tommaso Alvieri.

Crime drama. Source: Auguste Le Breton, *Du rififi à Paname* (Paris, 1965). Aging gangster Paulo Berger and his partner Walter are heads of an international gold smuggling organization with contacts in Paris, Munich, and Tokyo. Although Walter's young wife, Irène, had once been Paulo's mistress, the two men trust and admire each other. In order to pass gold bars through customs, they hire only couriers without police records. Their newest employee is Mike Coppolano, a journalist who claims to need extra money for his mistress; actually Mike is a U. S. Treasury agent investigating a possible connection between Paulo's operation and a Mafia ring supplying weapons to Cuba. Despite pressure, Paulo has managed to ward off all attempts by the Mafia to take control of his organization; but when several of his key contacts, including Walter, are killed, Paulo agrees to meet with Mafia boss Charles Binaggio. To effect his revenge, Paulo takes a time bomb with him and leaves before the explosion. Once outside, he finds the police, alerted by Mike, waiting for him. Mike apologizes for his deception and admits that he has learned to respect Paulo's unique code of honor. Paulo responds by punching Mike in the face. *Gangsters. Government agents. Smuggling. Imposture. Murder. Revenge. Gold. Mafia. Bombs. United States—Treasury Department.*

Note: Location scenes filmed in Tokyo, Munich, and London. Opened in Paris in Mar 1966 as *Du rififi à Paname*; running time: 95 min; in Rome in Sep 1966 as *Rififi internazionale*; running time: 100 min; in West Berlin in Jun 1966 as *Rififi in Paris*. Two U. S. sources credit Eddie Barclay as music composer.

THE UPSTAIRS ROOM   F6.5307

Signature Films, Inc. caOct **1970** [New York showing]. Sd; col (Eastman Color). 16mm. 70 min.

Prod-Dir Tom Desimone. *Photog* Tom Desimone. *Film Ed* Tom Desimone.

Cast: Scot Arden, Joey Latti, Pat Sauhls, Mike Sands, Brad Campbel, Christian.

Sex film. Christian, a male "madam," acquires young men for his bordello. Various sexual activities are depicted. *Male homosexuality. Whorehouses.*

Note: Filmed on location in Los Angeles. Also known as *The Beverly Hills Call Boys* and *The Boys From Beverly Hills*.

UPTIGHT　　　　　　　　　　　　　　　　　　**F6.5308**

Marlukin Productions. *Dist* Paramount Pictures. 18 Dec **1968** [New York opening; c5 Dec 1968; LP36889]. Sd; col (Technicolor). 35mm. 104 min. [Also 94 min.] *MPAA rating* M.

A Jules Dassin Production. *Prod-Dir* Jules Dassin. *Assoc Prod* Jim DiGangi. *Screenplay* Jules Dassin, Ruby Dee, Julian Mayfield. *Dir Photog* Boris Kaufman. *Camera Op* Alfred Lebovitz. *Art Dir* Phillip Bennett. *Set Decor* Ray Moyer. *Prod Dsgn* Alexandre Trauner. *Main Titl* John Hubley, Faith Hubley. *Film Ed* Robert Lawrence. *Asst Ed* Stewart Linder. *Mus Score & Cond* Booker T. Jones. *Perf by* Booker T. and the MG's. *Featuring* Judy Clay. *Mus Coörd* Earl Robinson. *Sd Rec* Terry Kellum, David Forrest. *Asst Dir* Martin Hornstein, William McGarry, Reuben Watt. *Prod Mgr* William W. Gray. *Unit Prod Mgr* Andrew J. Durkus. *Script Supv* Cleo Anton. *Cost* Theoni V. Aldredge. *Men's Wardrobe* Lambert Marks. *Women's Wardrobe* Beatrice Pontrelli. *Makeup* Bob Sidell, Bob Morley. *Hairstyles* Jené Bodell, Elizabeth Darcy. *Dial Coach* William Watts. *Prop Master* Earl Olin. *Still Photog* Floyd McCarty.

Cast: Raymond St. Jacques (*B.G.*), Ruby Dee (*Laurie*), Frank Silvera (*Kyle*), Roscoe Lee Browne (*Clarence*), Julian Mayfield (*Tank*), Janet MacLachlan (*Jeannie*), Ji-Tu Cumbuka (*Rick*), Max Julien (*Johnny*), John Wesley Rodgers (*Larry*), Richard Anthony Williams (*Corbin*), Robert DoQui (*speaker*), James McEachin (*Mello*), Michael Baseloon (*Claude*), Juanita Moore (*Johnny's mother*), Vernett Allan (*Ralph*), Ketty Lester (*Alma*), Errol Jaye (*Mr. Oakley*), Leon Bibb (*see note*), Isabelle Cooley, Alice Childress, David Moody, Kirk Kirksey, Van Kirksey, Mello Alexandria.

Drama. Loosely based on: Liam O'Flaherty, *The Informer* (London, 1925). Shattered by the assassination of Martin Luther King, Tank Williams, an unemployed Negro steelworker, gets drunk and is unable to assist his best friend, Johnny Wells, and two confederates, Rick and Larry, in the robbery of a Cleveland ammunition depot. Hampered by Tank's absence, the trio is discovered, and Johnny kills a guard while making a getaway. Tank tries to explain his actions to black militant leader B.G., but he is informed that he has been expelled from the organization, along with Negro moderates and all whites. Convinced that the death of Martin Luther King has demonstrated the ineffectiveness of non-violence, the militants advocate the use of guns as their only means of liberation from white oppression. Later, Tank is approached by Clarence, a homosexual police informer, who reveals that there is a $1,000 reward offered for information leading to Johnny's capture. After a depressing visit with his girl friend Laurie, who has become a prostitute in order to support her children, Tank is once more rejected by his fellow blacks, including Johnny. Filled with despair, he gets drunk and betrays Johnny's whereabouts to the police. They immediately surround the black ghetto and gun down the fugitive. The next day, Tank is seen recklessly buying drinks at a local bar and making a large donation at Johnny's funeral; and the militants quickly deduce that he is the informer. After futilely trying to pass the blame onto Clarence, Tank takes refuge in a cheap hotel room and telephones Laurie. Although she consoles him briefly, Tank is forced to accept the fact that he is doomed. Pursued by Rick and Larry, he races to the steel mills where he once knew security, climbs to the top of a steel bridge, and signals to his former friends until he is finally killed by a rifle shot. *Negroes. Mill workers. Informers. Militants. Prostitutes. Police. Assassination. Race relations. Unemployment. Disillusionment. Robbery. Drunkenness. Murder. Ghettos. Cleveland. Martin Luther King, Jr.*

Note: Location scenes filmed in Cleveland. Though Errol Jaye receives screen credit for the role of Mr. Oakley, some sources credit Leon Bibb. Actor John Wesley Rodgers is also known as John Wesley. *The Informer* was first filmed by RKO-Radio in 1935. Working title: *Betrayal.*

AN URBAN AFFAIR (Japan)　　　　　　　　　**F6.5309**

Tokyo Eiga Co. *Dist* Toho Co. Apr **1962** [Los Angeles showing]. Sd; col? 35mm. 88 min.

Dir Seiji Hisamatsu.

Cast: Hisaya Morishige, Junzaburo Ban.

Comedy. No information about the precise nature of this film has been found.

Note: Released in Japan in Aug 1961 as *Eskimae danchi.*

URSULA　　　　　　　　　　　　　　　　　　**F6.5310**

Dist Interoceanic Productions. 3 Apr **1967** [Maryland license]. Sd; col. 35mm. 69 min.

Prod Laurence Abel. *Dir* H. L. Zimmer.

Cast: Diane Webster, Valerie-Ann, Fred Dennie. No information about the precise nature of this film has been found. *Sexuality.*

Note: Also known as *Sins of Kitty.*

URSULA see **THE SLUT**

URSULA see **THREESOME**

URSULA THE HUSSY see **THE SLUT**

URSULA THE SLUT see **THE SLUT**

URSUS see **MIGHTY URSUS**

URSUS GLADIATORE RIBELLE see **THE REBEL GLADIATORS**

URSUS, IL GLADIATORE RIBELLE see **THE REBEL GLADIATORS**

USE THE BACK DOOR　　　　　　　　　　　**F6.5311**

Kirt Films International. *Dist* Distribpix, Inc. ca **1970**. Sd; col. 63 min.

Drama. A high school graduate takes a job delivering groceries. He is excited by having a "man's job" and driving the delivery truck. His first customer, a sex-starved housewife, demonstrates that she expects him to deliver more than just the groceries. From then on, each delivery that he makes furthers the boy's sex education, and he carefully selects his customers so as to leave enough time for each "lesson." *Delivery boys. Housewives. Seduction. Sexual initiation.*

UTA　　　　　　　　　　　　　　　　　　　　**F6.5312**

Dist I. R. M. I. Films. **1969** [New York showing]. Sd; b&w. 35mm. 57 min.

Melodrama. Uta, a prostitute, begins to masturbate as she watches a stripteaser perform. Later Uta torments one of her middle-aged clients, and she has sexual relations with a lesbian friend. The film ends with Uta's death. *Prostitutes. Stripteasers. Autoeroticism. Lesbianism.*

V. D.　　　　　　　　　　　　　　　　　　　　**F6.5313**

Donna Productions–Big Ten Productions. *Dist* MY Films. 11 Jan **1961** [San Diego, California, opening; c11 Jan 1961; LP19505]. Sd; col (Eastman Color). 35mm. 91 min.

A Sid Davis Production. *Prod* Sid Davis. *Dir-Writ* Haile Chace. *Photog* Vilis Lapenieks. *Film Ed* Warren Brown.

Cast: Charlotte Stewart (*Judy Jackson*), Mory Schoolhouse (*Jim Radman*), Dolores Faith (*Kathy Durham*), Michael Bell (*Monk Monahan*), Joan Yarborough (*Mary Jackson*), Terry Reagan (*Fred Jackson*), George Martin, U. S. actor (*singer*).

Melodrama. High school students Judy and Jim are very much in love, but their relationship is disturbed when Jim's friend Monk introduces the couple to Kathy, a new student who makes no pretense of her interest in Jim. The group spends a lot of time together, and Kathy manages to create friction between Judy and Jim, but the two are reconciled and decide to marry. Judy's parents consider her too young for marriage, however, and they take her away for a weekend to try to change her mind. That same weekend, Jim, Monk, and two other boys visit a seaside town, get drunk at a striptease bar, and take advantage of the services of some local prostitutes. Monk tells Judy what happened, and she breaks up with Jim. Kathy seizes the opportunity to confess her love for Jim, but the affair is short-lived. Jim, who was the school's star athlete, begins to feel tired and listless and finally visits his doctor; he is told that he has venereal disease. The doctor shows him a 5-minute film made by the U. S. Public Health Service, which stresses early treatment of the disease and the importance of finding anyone who may have had sexual intercourse with the infected person. Jim declines to tell the doctor of his affair with Kathy until he learns she is going with Monk. The doctor is able to treat everyone in time to stop the infection; Judy realizes that Jim is sorry for what has occurred; and once more the two are united. *Students. Prostitutes. Physicians. High school life. Drunkenness. Venereal disease. Bars. United States—Public Health Service.*

Note: Also known as *Damaged Goods.*

THE V.I.P.S (Great Britain)　　　　　　　　　**F6.5374**

Metro–Goldwyn–Mayer Pictures–Taylor Productions. *Dist* Metro–Goldwyn-Mayer, Inc. 19 Sep **1963** [New York opening; c18 Dec 1963; LP26786]. Sd (Westrex); col (Metrocolor). 35mm (Panavision). 119 min.

Prod Anatole De Grunwald. *Assoc Prod* Roy Parkinson. *Dir* Anthony Asquith. *Crowd Dir* Jimmy Komisarjevsky. *Screenplay* Terence Rattigan. *Dir Photog* Jack Hildyard. *Camera Op* Gerry Fisher. *2d Unit Photog* Douglas Adamson. *Art Dir* William Kellner. *Asst Art Dir* Ivor Beddoes. *Set Decor* Pamela Cornell. *Ed* Frank Clarke. *Assembly Ed* Philip Barnikel. *Mus* Miklos Rozsa. *Rec Supv* A. W. Watkins. *Sd Rec* Cyril Swern. *Sd Ed* Bill Creed. *Dub Mix* J. B. Smith. *Boom Op* Bill Baldwin. *Sd Camera Op* Ron Matthews. *1st & 2d Asst Dir* Kip Gowans, Carl Mannin. *Unit Mgr* Elizabeth Woodthorpe. *Cont* June Faithfull. *Prod Sec* Valerie Cort. *Miss Taylor's Wardrobe* Givenchy. *Wardrobe Supv* Felix Evans. *Gowns* Pierre Cardin. *Wardrobe Master* Ben Foster. *Wardrobe Mistress* Gladys James, May Walding. *Makeup* Tom Smith, Eric Allwright. *Elizabeth Taylor's Makeup* Dave Aylott. *Miss Taylor's Hairstyles* Vivienne Walker. *Hairdresser* Bernadette Ibbetson. *Sp Eff* Tom Howard. *Prod Adv* Margaret Booth. *Prop Buyer* Bill Isaacs. *Still Photog* Joe Pearce.

Cast: Elizabeth Taylor *(Frances Andros)*, Richard Burton *(Paul Andros)*, Louis Jourdan *(Marc Champselle)*, Elsa Martinelli *(Gloria Gritti)*, Margaret Rutherford *(The Duchess of Brighton)*, Maggie Smith *(Miss Mead)*, Rod Taylor *(Les Mangrum)*, Orson Welles *(Max Buda)*, Linda Christian *(Miriam Marshall)*, Dennis Price *(Commander Millbank)*, Richard Wattis *(Sanders)*, David Frost *(reporter)*, Ronald Fraser *(Joslin)*, Robert Coote *(John Coburn)*, Michael Hordern *(airport director)*, Martin Miller *(Schwutzbacher)*, Lance Percival *(B.O.A.C. official)*, Joan Benham *(Miss Potter)*, Peter Sallis *(doctor)*, Stringer Davis *(hotel waiter)*, Clifton Jones *(Jamaican passenger)*, Moyra Fraser *(air hostess)*, Joyce Carey *(Mrs. Damer)*, Peter Illing *(Mr. Damer)*, Brook Williams, Alan Howard, Lewis Fiander, Barry Steele, Arthur Howard, Griffith Davies, Maggie McGrath, Frank Williams, Angus Lennie, Ray Austin, Rosemary Dorken, Pamela Buckley, Duncan Lewis, Reginald Beckwith.

Drama. A group of passengers en route to New York assemble in the V.I.P. lounge when a heavy fog delays the takeoff of planes from London Airport. All of them have reasons for wanting to depart as quickly as possible. Frances Andros is leaving her millionaire husband to run off with Marc Champselle, an international playboy. Les Mangrum, a self-made Australian industrialist, must be in New York the following day to arrange for a loan which will enable him to prevent a giant industrial combine from taking over his tractor firm. Max Buda, a film magnate traveling with his "protégé" Gloria Gritti, must be out of the country by midnight or pay a ruinous income tax. The featherbrained Duchess of Brighton has taken a job in America in order to raise the money to maintain the family estate. The flight is cancelled until morning, and all are forced to stay at the airport hotel. Frances' husband, Paul, arrives after finding the farewell note left by his wife. He convinces her of his deep need for her, and she decides to remain with him. Mangrum's company is saved when his faithful and adoring secretary, Miss Mead, persuades Paul to lend Mangrum the money he needs. Buda's accountant rescues his client by arranging for him to turn over all of his financial assets to the foreign-born Gloria, and then marry her. The Duchess is able to return happily home when Buda rents her estate for location filming on his next picture. *Playboys. Nobility. Industrialists. Australians. Motion picture producers. Actors. Mistresses. Marriage. Wealth. Infidelity. Loans. Income tax. Finance—Personal. Employment—Women. Airfields. Fog. London.*

Note: Opened in London in Sep 1963.

LA VACCA E IL PRIGIONIERO see **THE COW AND I**

LA VACHE ET LE PRISONNIER see **THE COW AND I**

VADO ... L'AMMAZZO E TORNO see **ANY GUN CAN PLAY**

VAGHE STELLE DELL'ORSA see **SANDRA**

VALI   F6.5314
Dist Film-Makers' Distribution Center, New Line Cinema. 1 Jun **1967** [New York opening]. Sd; col with b&w sequences. 16mm. 65 min.

Prod-Dir Sheldon Rochlin. *Collab Prod* George Plimpton, Mark Lawrence. *Orig Commentary* Vali Myers, Rudi Rappold. *Photog* Sheldon Rochlin. *Film Ed* Sheldon Rochlin, Diane Rochlin. *Sd* Mark Dichter. *Asst Dir* Diane Rochlin, Vali Myers, Rudi Rappold.

Cast: Vali Myers, Rudi Rappold *(themselves/commentators)*, Diane Rochlin, Caroline Thompson *(themselves)*.

Documentary. Vali Myers, the Australian dancer, artist, and self-proclaimed witch, whose bohemian life on the Left Bank in Paris during the 1950's virtually launched the "beat" era, is the subject of this *cinema verité* study. Since 1956, Vali had been living near Positano, on the coast of Italy, with her husband, Rudi Rappold, an Austrian architect, in a cabin without electricity or plumbing. The film records her mode of life, which for 9 years was one of withdrawal and rustic simplicity. Clothed in tattered, brightly-colored costumes, she climbs over craggy coastal rocks; makes love to Rudi; paints in her Black Book of "inner mysteries"; takes a trip to Rosina and Naples, where crowds follow her through the streets; visits a nearby cave where Caroline, a protégée from New Zealand, is living; chants incantations of the occult; and, as a witch, administers love potions to a friend. She reminisces about the past, when the new postwar intelligentsia and artistic community in Paris rallied around her improvisational spirit. Photographs of her and old films of this period are included. *Dancers. Painters. Expatriates. Architects. Australians. Austrians. New Zealanders. Witchcraft. Occult. Bohemianism. Aphrodisiacs. Positano. Paris—Left Bank. Vali Myers. Naples.*

Note: Also known as *Vali—The Witch of Positano.*

THE VALIANT (Great Britain/Italy)   F6.5315
B. H. P. Films-Euro International Films. *Dist* United Artists. 13 Jun **1962** [New York opening; c13 Jun 1962; LP22967]. Sd; b&w. 35mm (CinemaScope). 89 min. [Also reviewed at 80 min.]

A Jon Penington Production. *Prod* Jon Penington. *Dir* Roy [Ward] Baker, Giorgio Capitani. *Screenplay* Willis Hall, Keith Waterhouse, Giorgio Capitani,

Caprino. *Dir Photog* Wilkie Cooper. *Underwater Photog* Egil Woxholt. *Chief Camera* Amerigo Gengarelli. *Art Dir* Arthur Lawson. *Film Ed* John Pomeroy. *Mus Dir* Christopher Whelen. *Prod Supv* Harold Buck. *Sp Eff* Wally Veevers.

Cast: John Mills *(Captain Morgan)*, Ettore Manni *(Luigi Durand de la Penne)*, Roberto Risso *(Emilio Bianchi)*, Robert Shaw *(Lieutenant Field)*, Liam Redmond *(Surgeon Commander Reilly)*, Ralph Michael *(Commander Clark)*, Colin Douglas *(chief gunner's mate)*, Dinsdale Landen *(Norris)*, John Meillon *(Bedford)*, Moray Watson *(Turnbull)*, Charles Houston *(medical orderly)*, Gordon Rollings *(Payne)*, Laurence Naismith *(admiral)*, Patrick Barr *(Reverend Ellis)*, Leonardo Cortese.

War drama. Source: Robert Mallet, *L'équipage au complet* (Paris opening: 1957). In December of 1941, the British Mediterranean Fleet has at its disposal only two battleships, the *Valiant* and the *Queen Elizabeth*, both of which are anchored in Alexandria Harbor. Late one night two Italian frogmen, Luigi Durand de la Penne and Emilio Bianchi, are captured in the water near the *Valiant* and taken prisoner. When the ship's commander, Captain Morgan, is unable to learn from them whether or not they succeeded in planting a mine beneath his ship, he has them placed in the below deck. So great is Morgan's concern for the welfare of his ship that he violates the Geneva conventions and loses the respect of some of his men by refusing to give medical aid to the badly wounded Bianchi; Lieutenant Field feels particular pressure because he has married an Italian woman. Nevertheless, the two Italians refuse to talk. Eventually Bianchi does admit that the ship has been mined, but he refuses to give any information as to the time of the explosion. Morgan orders the immediate evacuation of his crew, and he remains on board with the two frogmen and a few of his officers. Thinking themselves to be alone on the battleship, the Italians discuss the time of the explosion and are overheard through a voice tube. But it is too late for action, and the bomb blast rips a 40-foot hole in the *Valiant*'s bow. Morgan, however, manages to conceal the damage from reconnaissance planes by making a show of normal activity on deck while repairs are hastily made below the water level. For the Englishmen and the Italians, it is a moment of both victory and defeat. *Fascists. Prisoners of war. Frogmen. Demolition—Underwater. Ethics. Battleships. World War II. Alexandria (Egypt). Great Britain—Royal Navy. Ship explosions.*

Note: Released in Great Britain in 1962. Released in Italy in 1962 as *L'affondamento della Valiant*. Original running time: 100 min.

EL VALLE DE LAS ESPADAS see **THE CASTILIAN**

LA VALLE DEI LUNGHI COLTELLI see **APACHE GOLD**

LA VALLÉE DES PHARAONS see **CLEOPATRA'S DAUGHTER**

THE VALLEY OF GWANGI   F6.5316
Morningside Pictures. *Dist* Warner Bros.-Seven Arts, Inc. 11 Jun **1969** [Detroit opening; c1 Jun 1969; LP38136]. Sd (Westrex); col (Technicolor). 35mm (Dynamation). 95 min. *MPAA rating* G.

A Charles H. Schneer Production. *Prod* Charles H. Schneer. *Assoc Prod* Ray Harryhausen. *Dir* Jim O'Connolly. *Screenplay* William E. Bast. *Adtl Material* Julian More. *Dir Photog* Erwin Hillier. *Camera Op* Alec Mills. *Art Dir* Gil Parrondo. *Titl Dsgn* Antonio Saura. *Film Ed* Henry Richardson. *Mus Comp & Cond* Jerome Moross. *Sd* Malcolm Stewart. *Dub Ed* Philip Bottamley, Selwyn Petterson. *Asst Dir* Pedro Vidal. *Prod Mgr* Miguel Gil. *Cont* Gladys Goldsmith. *Prod Supv* Luis Roberts. *Wardrobe Dsgn* John Furness. *Wardrobe Supv* Antonio Pueo. *Vis Eff* Ray Harryhausen. *Horsemaster* Juan Majan.

Cast: James Franciscus *(Tuck Kirby)*, Gila Golan *(T. J. Breckenridge)*, Richard Carlson *(Champ Connors)*, Laurence Naismith *(Prof. Horace Bromley)*, Freda Jackson *(Tia Zorina)*, Gustavo Rojo *(Carlos dos Orsos)*, Dennis Kilbane *(Rowdy)*, Mario de Barros *(Bean)*, Curtis Arden *(Lope)*, José Burgos *(dwarf)*.

Science fiction melodrama. Promotor Tuck Kirby arrives in a small Mexican town to visit T. J. Breckenridge, his ex-partner and girl friend who now owns a financially troubled Wild West show. Tuck suggests that she sell the show and marry him, but T. J. boasts of a new attaction that promises to make her wealthy. She shows Tuck a miniature horse which she obtained from Carlos, a gypsy who defied native superstition by removing the creature from the nearby Forbidden Valley. Baffled, Tuck takes the tiny animal to British paleontologist Prof. Horace Bromley who claims that it belongs to a species believed to have been extinct for over 50 million years. Before the horse can be put on display, however, it is stolen by gypsies and returned to the Forbidden Valley. Despite warnings about Gwangi, the monstrous 14-foot reptile that rules the valley, Tuck, T. J., and several cowboys enter the area and find themselves in a prehistoric world. After one of the cowboys is carried off by a giant prehistoric creature, the men manage to capture Gwangi, and T. J. makes plans to put the monster on exhibition in her show. The gypsies intervene again, this time by setting the monster free. Gwangi kills the professor and rampages through the town until it traps Tuck and T. J. inside a cathedral. Tuck pierces the monster's skull with a lance, and Gwangi, after knocking over a burning lamp, dies in the fire as the two lovers escape. *Gypsies. Professors. British. Cowboys. Superstition. Paleontology. Theft. Time travel. Wild West shows. Monsters. Prehistory. Mexico. Fires. Horses. Reptiles. Prehistoric creatures.*

Note: Produced in Spain. Prerelease title: *The Valley—Where Time Stood Still.*

VALLEY OF MYSTERY   F6.5317

Universal Pictures. 21 Apr **1967** [Cleveland opening; c1 Jul 1967; LP36857]. Sd (Westrex); col (Technicolor). 35mm. 94 min.

Prod Harry Tatelman. *Dir* Josef Leytes. *Screenplay* Richard Neal, Lowell Barrington. *Story* Richard Neal, Lawrence B. Marcus. *Dir Photog* Walter Strenge. *Col Coörd* Robert Brower. *Art Dir* Russell Kimball, Howard E. Johnson. *Set Decor* John McCarthy, John M. Dwyer. *Film Ed* Gene Milford. *Mus* Jack Elliott. *Mus Supv* Stanley Wilson. *Sd* Corson Jowett, David H. Moriarty. *Asst Dir* Edward K. Dodds, George Bisk. *Unit Prod Mgr* Abby Singer. *Cost* Burton Miller. *Makeup* Bud Westmore. *Hairstyles* Larry Germain.

Cast: Richard Egan (*Wade Cochran*), Peter Graves (*Ben Barstow*), Joby Baker (*Pete Patton*), Lois Nettleton (*Rita Brown*), Harry Guardino (*Danny O'Neill*), Julie Adams (*Joan Simon*), Fernando Lamas (*Francisco Rivera*), Alfred Ryder (*Dr. Weatherly*), Karen Sharpe (*Connie Lane*), Barbara Werle (*Ann Dickson*), Lee Patterson (*Dino Doretti*), Rodolfo Acosta (*Manuel Sanchez*), Douglas Kennedy (*Charles Kiley*), Don Stewart (*Jim Walker*), Leonard Nimoy (*Spence Atherton*), Tony Patino (*Juan Hidalgo*), Otis Young (*Dr. John Quincy*), Lisa Gaye (*Margalo York*), George Tyne (*Forest Hart*), Larry Domasin (*Indian boy*), Eddie Little Sky (*M'Tu*), William Phipps (*immigration inspector*).

Melodrama. An international jetliner is blown off course during a typhoon and forced to land in the trackless jungles of equatorial South America. Thanks to the skills of pilots Wade Cochran and Dino Doretti, no one is injured, but they are unable to summon help because the plane's radio has been badly damaged. Among the passengers are Ben Barstow, a writer-explorer in search of his lost sister; Rita Brown, an attractive liquor saleswoman; Joan Simon, a neurotic schoolteacher; Pete Patton, a pop singer; Danny O'Neill, an alcoholic comedian; and Francisco Rivera, a convicted murderer being transported back to his native country for execution. Rivera kills his police escort, but he himself is mortally wounded by Cochran while trying to escape. Meanwhile, Barstow learns that the crash took place in the area where his sister and brother-in-law, Dr. Weatherly, disappeared. He and Rita set out in the hope of finding them, but they are captured by natives who bring them before the tribal witch doctor—the now insane Dr. Weatherly. After informing Barstow that his sister is dead, Weatherly prepares to offer Rita and Barstow as human sacrifices to Lokiti, the god of evil. But a friendly tribe rescues them, and Barstow slays Weatherly with a machete. By this time the radio has been repaired and helicopters are arriving to return the stranded group to civilization. *Air pilots. Authors. Explorers. Saleswomen. Schoolteachers. Singers. Entertainers. Convicts. Police. Brothers-in-law. Witch doctors. Missing persons. Alcoholism. Murder. Insanity. Human sacrifice. Radio. Brother-sister relationship. Airplanes—Jet. Jungles. South America. Typhoons. Airplane accidents.*

Note: Expanded from a 43-min television pilot (not broadcast) entitled *Stranded.*

VALLEY OF THE DOLLS   F6.5318

Red Lion Productions. *Dist* Twentieth Century–Fox Film Corp. 15 Dec **1967** [New York opening; c15 Dec 1967; LP35182]. Sd; col (De Luxe). 35mm (Panavision). 123 min.

A Mark Robson–David Weisbart Production. *Prod* David Weisbart. *Dir* Mark Robson. *Screenplay* Helen Deutsch, Dorothy Kingsley. *Dir Photog* William H. Daniels. *Art Dir* Jack Martin Smith, Richard Day. *Set Decor* Walter M. Scott, Raphael Bretton. *Film Ed* Dorothy Spencer. *Mus Adapt & Cond* Johnny Williams. *Orch* Herbert Spencer. Song: "Theme from *Valley of the Dolls*" Andre Previn, Dory Previn. Sung by Dionne Warwick. Songs: "Give a Little More," "It's Impossible," Andre Previn, Dory Previn. Sung by Patty Duke. Song: "Come Live With Me" Andre Previn, Dory Previn. Sung by Tony Scotti. Song: "I'll Plant My Own Tree" Andre Previn, Dory Previn. Sung by Margaret Whiting. *Choreog* Robert Sidney. *Sd* Don Bassman, David Dockendorf. *Mus Ed* Kenneth Wannberg. *Asst Dir* Eli Dunn, Richard Lang. *Unit Prod Mgr* Francisco Day. *Prod Mgr* Dave Silver. *Gowns Dsgn* Travilla. *Makeup* Ben Nye. *Miss Parkins' Hairstyles* Kenneth. *Hairstyles Supv* Edith Lindon. *Sp Photog Eff* L. B. Abbott, Art Cruickshank, Emil Kosa, Jr.

Cast: Barbara Parkins (*Anne Welles*), Patty Duke (*Neely O'Hara*), Paul Burke (*Lyon Burke*), Sharon Tate (*Jennifer North*), Tony Scotti (*Tony Polar*), Martin Milner (*Mel Anderson*), Charles Drake (*Kevin Gillmore*), Alexander Davion (*Ted Casablanca*), Lee Grant (*Miriam*), Naomi Stevens (*Miss Steinberg*), Robert H. Harris (*Henry Bellamy*), Jacqueline Susann (*reporter*), Robert Viharo (*director*), Mikel Angel (*man in hotel room*), Barry Cahill (*man in bar*), Richard Angarola (*Claude Chardot*), Joey Bishop (*mc at telethon*),

George Jessel (*mc at Grammy Awards*), Susan Hayward (*Helen Lawson*).

Melodrama. Source: Jacqueline Susann, *Valley of the Dolls* (New York, 1966). New Englander Anne Welles arrives in New York City and accepts a secretarial job with a leading theatrical law firm. On her first day, she is present at a Broadway rehearsal when hard-boiled musical comedy star Helen Lawson discharges a talented newcomer, Neely O'Hara, because she threatens to steal the show. Lyon Burke, an associate in the law firm, gets Neely a spot on a TV show that leads to stardom in Hollywood. At the same time beautiful but untalented Jennifer North falls in love with nightclub singer Tony Polar and marries him despite the objections of his sister, Miriam. Eventually Anne and Lyon quarrel over his refusal to marry; Lyon quits the law firm to resume his writing; and Anne appears in a series of TV commercials. As time passes, Neely finds herself incapable of adjusting to fame: two unsuccessful marriages (to press agent Mel Anderson and costume designer Ted Casablanca) have led to both alcoholism and drug addiction. Neely is persuaded to enter the same sanitarium where Tony is dying of an incurable disease. Jennifer, who has been paying Tony's bills by making nudist films in Europe, learns she has breast cancer and commits suicide. After Anne and Lyon have reconciled their differences and then broken up again, Neely gets the chance for a comeback on Broadway; but she is still emotionally incapable of facing an audience. Too drunk to go on, she collapses in the theater alley after her understudy has scored an opening night triumph. By now Anne is back at her New England home. One day Lyon pays her a visit and pleads with her to marry him. Anne can only kiss him affectionately and reject his offer. *New Englanders. Secretaries. Authors. Lawyers. Showgirls. Singers. Press agents. Actors. Couturiers. Drug addicts. Marriage. Divorce. Fame. Brother-sister relationship. Infidelity. Cancer. Suicide. Alcoholism. Incurable illness. Television. Nightclubs. Motion pictures. Theater. Sanitariums. New York City. Hollywood. New England. New York City—Broadway.*

Note: Location scenes filmed in New York, New England, and Hollywood.

VALLEY OF THE DRAGONS   F6.5319

Z. R. B. Productions. *Dist* Columbia Pictures. 25 Oct **1961** [Kansas City, Missouri, opening: c1 Nov 1961; LP20440]. Sd; b&w. 35mm. 79 min.

Prod Byron Roberts. *Exec Prod* Alfred Zimbalist. *Dir-Writ* Edward Bernds. *Story* Donald Zimbalist. *Dir Photog* Brydon Baker. *Art Dir* Don Ament. *Film Ed* Edwin Bryant. *Mus* Ruby Raksin. *Sd Supv* Charles J. Rice. *Sd* Lambert Day. *Asst Dir* George Rhein. *Makeup Supv* Ben Lane. *Sp Eff* Richard Albain.

Cast: Cesare Danova (*Hector Servadac*), Sean McClory (*Denning*), Joan Staley (*Deena*), Danielle De Metz (*Nateeta*), Gregg Martell (*Od-Loo*), Gil Perkins (*Tarn/doctor*), I. Stanford Jolley (*Patoo*), Michael Lane (*Anoka*), Roger Til (*Vidal*), Mark Dempsey (*Andrews*), Jerry Sunshine (*LeClerc*), Dolly Gray (*Mara*).

Science fiction melodrama. Loosely based on: Jules Verne, *Hector Servadac: voyages et aventures à travers le monde solaire* (Paris, 1877). In 1881, a duel between two adventurers, Servadac and Denning, is halted by a tremendous windstorm that sweeps the two men onto a passing comet inhabited by prehistoric beasts and men. An attacking mammoth separates them; Servadac retreats to the River People and a beautiful blonde, Deena, while Denning finds his way to the Cave People and a brunette, Nateeta. After battles with dinosaurs and less-than-humans, the two men are reunited in rescuing the Cave People from attacking dragons. They also persuade the two peoples to end their constant warring and live in harmony. Servadac and Denning then settle down with Deena and Nateeta to wait for the time when the comet will again pass close to the earth. *Adventurers. Duels. Prehistory. Comets. Dinosaurs. Storms. Prehistoric creatures. Dragons.*

Note: Footage from *One Million B. C.* (1940) and *The Lost World* (1960) may have been used.

VALLEY OF THE SWORDS *see* THE CASTILIAN

VALLEY OF THE WHITE WOLVES *see* MARA OF THE WILDERNESS

THE VALLEY—WHERE TIME STOOD STILL *see* THE VALLEY OF GWANGI

THE VAMPIRE (Mexico)   F6.5320

Cinematográfica A. B. S. A. *Dist* K. Gordon Murray Productions, Trans-International Films. 2 Mar **1968** [Jacksonville, Florida, opening]. Sd; b&w. 35mm. 84 min.

Pres by K. Gordon Murray. *Prod* Abel Salazar. *Dir* Fernando Méndez. *Dir English Vers* Paul Nagle. *Screenplay* Henrich Rodríguez, Ramón Obón. *Story* Ramón Obón. *Photog* Rosalío Solano. *Art Dir* Günther Gerszo. *Film Ed* José Bustos. *Mus* Gustavo César Carrión. *Sd* Rafael Ruiz Esparza.

Cast: Abel Salazar (*Henry, the doctor*), Ariadne Welter (*Marta*), Germán Robles (*Count Duval/Lavud*), Carmen Montejo, José Luis Jiménez, Alicia Montoya, Mercedes Soler, Margarito Luna, Julio Daneri, José Chavez, Amado

Zumaya, Dick Barker, Edward Tucker, Lydia Mellon.

Horror film. In contemporary Mexico the vampire Count Duval and his descendants scheme to steal the beautiful Marta's fortune. The count quickly dominates Marta's aunt. Marta, although buried alive, is rescued, and a stake is driven through the vampire's heart. *Nobility. Vampires. Aunts. Theft. Rescue.*

Note: Produced in Mexico in 1957 as *El vampiro*; running time: 95 min. First released in the United States in a Spanish version in 1958.

THE VAMPIRE AND THE BALLERINA (Italy)   F6.5321

Consorzio Italiano Films. *Dist* United Artists. 31 Oct **1962** [Los Angeles opening; c24 Oct 1962; LP23301]. Sd; b&w. 35mm. 86 min.

Prod Bruno Bolognesi. *Dir* Renato Polselli. *Story & Screenplay* Renato Polselli, Giuseppe Pellegrini, Ernesto Gastaldi. *Photog* Angelo Baistrocchi. *Art Dir* Amedeo Mellone. *Mus* Aldo Piga. *Choreog* Marisa Ciampaglia. *Sd Eff* Leopoldo Rosi, Raffaele Del Monte.

Cast: Hélène Remy *(Luisa)*, Maria Luisa Rolando *(The Contessa)*, Tina Gloriani *(Francesca)*, Walter Brandi *(Luca)*, Isarco Ravaioli *(servant)*, John Turner, Pierugo Gragnani, Stefania Sabatini.

Horror film. Separated from their ballet troupe, Francesca and Luisa become lost in the dark European woods with Francesca's betrothed, Luca, and take refuge from a storm in an old castle, where they are entertained by the beautiful, sinister contessa. That night Luisa is attacked by a vampire, but in the morning she goes away with her friends. She is again ravaged by the fiend the next night, and she grows weaker, until at last she faints. Luca returns to confront the contessa and learns that she is a vampire, forced by her vampire servant to remain at the castle. Protected by her gold cross, Francesca narrowly escapes attack and is trapped with Luca deep in the woods. They manage to survive until morning, when the sun turns the vampires to dust, releasing Luisa from the spell. *Dancers. Vampires. Nobility. Castles. Forests. Storms.*

Note: Opened in Rome in Jun 1960 as *L'amante del vampiro*. Copyright claimant: Lopert Pictures.

THE VAMPIRE BEAST CRAVES BLOOD (Great Britain)   F6.5322

Tigon British Film Productions. *Dist* Pacemaker Pictures. 16 May **1969** [Maryland license]. Sd; col (Eastman Color). 35mm. 81 min. *MPAA rating* G.

Prod Arnold Louis Miller. *Exec Prod* Tony Tenser. *Dir* Vernon Sewell. *Screenplay* Peter Bryan. *Photog* Stanley A. Long. *Art Dir* Wilfred Wood. *Film Ed* Howard Lanning. *Mus Comp & Cond* Paul Ferris. *Sd* Alan Hogben. *Asst Dir* George Pollard. *Prod Mgr* Ricky Coward. *Makeup* Rosemarie McDonald-Peattie. *Sp Eff* Roger Dicken.

Cast: Peter Cushing *(Inspector Quennell)*, Robert Flemyng *(Professor Mallinger)*, Wanda Ventham *(Clare)*, Vanessa Howard *(Meg)*, David Griffin *(William)*, Kevin Stoney *(Granger)*, Glynn Edwards *(Sergeant Allan)*, William Wilde *(Britewell)*, John Paul *(Warrender)*, Roy Hudd *(morgue attendant)*, Russell Napier *(landlord)*, Simon Cain *(Clem)*, Leslie Anderson *(Joe)*, Michael Mundell, David Lyell *(students)*, Malcolm Rogers *(Dr. Elliot)*, Robin Wentworth *(Starkadder)*, John Scott Martin *(Snaflebum)*, Robert Cawdron *(chief constable)*, Drew Russell *(Smith)*, Beryl Cook *(housekeeper)*, Bill Maxwell.

Horror film. In mid-19th century England, two young entomology students of Professor Mallinger are found clawed to death and drained of blood. Soon afterwards, another scientist, Britewell, is found dead after visiting Mallinger, but the professor denies having seen Britewell when questioned by Scotland Yard Inspector Quennell. Mallinger and his "daughter" Clare, who is actually a monster of the professor's creation who can transform herself into a giant death's-head moth, travel to a fishing village so that the professor can complete his project of creating a mate for Clare. Inspector Quennell, posing as a vacationing banker, arrives in the village with his daughter Meg. Because Professor Mallinger's new creation must have human blood in order to survive, Clare captures Meg and performs a transfusion. Mallinger now realizes that his new creation must be destroyed, but Clare transforms herself into a death's-head moth and kills him in revenge. In order to rescue Meg, Quennell builds a fire, and Clare flies into the flames. *Detectives. Entomologists. Professors. Students. Vampires. Metamorphosis. Blood transfusion. Murder. Fishing villages. Scotland Yard. Moths.*

Note: Released in Great Britain in Jan 1968 as *The Blood Beast Terror*; running time: 88 min. Working titles: *Deathshead Vampire* and *Blood Beast From Hell*.

THE VAMPIRE KILLERS *see* **THE FEARLESS VAMPIRE KILLERS; OR, PARDON ME BUT YOUR TEETH ARE IN MY NECK**

THE VAMPIRE LOVERS (Great Britain)   F6.5323

Hammer Film Productions–American International Productions. *Dist* American International Pictures. 28 Oct **1970** [Chicago opening; c28 Oct 1970; LP38557]. Sd; col (Technicolor, print by Movielab). 35mm. 88 min. *MPAA rating* R.

Prod Harry Fine, Michael Style. *Exec Prod* Louis M. Heyward. *Dir* Roy Ward Baker. *Screenplay* Tudor Gates. *Adapt* Harry Fine, Tudor Gates, Michael Style. *Dir Photog* Moray Grant. *Camera Op* Neil Binney. *Art Dir* Scott MacGregor. *Film Ed* James Needs. *Mus Comp* Harry Robinson. *Mus Supv* Philip Martell. *Rec Dir* Tony Lumkin. *Sd Rec* Claude Hitchcock. *Dub Mix* Denis Whitlock. *Sd Ed* Roy Hyde. *Asst Dir* Derek Whitehurst. *Prod Mgr* Tom Sachs. *Cont* Betty Harley. *Cost Dsgn* Brian Box. *Wardrobe Mistress* Laura Nightingale. *Makeup Supv* Tom Smith. *Hairdressing Supv* Pearl Tipaldi. *Constr Mgr* Bill Greene.

Cast: Ingrid Pitt *(Carmilla/Mircalla/Marcilla)*, Pippa Steel *(Laura)*, Madeline Smith *(Emma Morton)*, Peter Cushing *(General Spielsdorf)*, George Cole *(Roger Morton)*, Dawn Addams *(The Countess)*, Kate O'Mara *(governess)*, Douglas Wilmer *(Baron Hartog)*, Jon Finch *(Carl Ebhardt)*, Kirsten Betts *(1st vampire)*, Harvey Hall *(Renton)*, Janet Key *(Gretchin)*, Charles Farrell, British *(landlord)*, John Forbes-Robertson *(man in black)*, Shelagh Wilcox *(housekeeper)*, Graham James, Tom Browne *(young men)*, Joanna Shelley *(woodman's daughter)*, Olga James *(village girl)*.

Horror film. Source: J. Sheridan Le Fanu, "Carmilla," in *In a Glass Darkly* (London, 1872). For years the populace of Styria have lived in fear of the Karnsteins, a dynasty of vampires. Baron Hartog's sister becomes the latest victim, and the baron seeks revenge. One night, he unearths the coffins in the Karnstein graveyard and drives stakes through the hearts of the living dead. Only the grave of the beautiful Mircalla Karnstein eludes the Baron's vengeance. Years later, a society ball at the home of General Spielsdorf is interrupted by the sudden appearance of a young woman called Marcilla, dressed in a red gown. The unexpected guest moves into the household and separates the general's daughter Laura from her fiancé, Carl. Laura soon becomes increasingly listless and is haunted by recurrent nightmares in which she is attacked by a giant cat. When the general returns home one evening, he discovers Laura dead, drained of all her blood, and Marcilla gone. Afterwards, an alluring young lady named Carmilla visits Emma Morton, who was Laura's best friend, and wins the confidence of Emma and her father, Roger Morton. When Morton is called away on a business trip, Carmilla seduces Emma, who subsequently becomes ill and wakes up screaming from erotic nightmares. The governess and Renton, the butler, also fall under Carmilla's spell, but Renton writes to Morton about his daughter's strange malady. When the doctor who was sent to examine Laura is found dead and bloodless, Morton enlists the aid of Baron Hartog and Carl. While Morton and the baron search for Mircalla Karnstein's grave, Carl rushes back to the house in time to prevent Carmilla from abducting Emma. As Carl lunges towards Carmilla with his sword pointed at her heart, she vanishes and then reappears in her crypt, where the baron impales and decapitates her. *Vampires. Nobility. Governesses. Butlers. Physicians. Revenge. Filial relations. Lesbianism. Murder. Seduction. Impalement. Decapitation. Coffins. Cemeteries. Dreams.*

Note: Opened in London in Sep 1970; running time: 91 min.

VAMPIRE OVER LONDON *see* **MY SON THE VAMPIRE**

VAMPIRE PEOPLE *see* **THE BLOOD DRINKERS**

VAMPIRE'S COFFIN (Mexico)   F6.5324

Cinematográfica A. B. S. A. *Dist* K. Gordon Murray Productions. 17 Nov **1965** [Cincinnati, Ohio, opening]. Sd; b&w. 35mm. 86 min.

Prod Abel Salazar. *Prod U. S. Vers* K. Gordon Murray. *Dir* Fernando Méndez. *Dir U. S. Vers* Paul Nagle. *Adapt* Ramón Obón. *Story* Raúl Zenteno. *Photog* Victor Herrera. *Art Dir* William Hayden, Gunther Gerszo. *Film Ed* Alfredo Rosas Priego. *Mus* Gustavo César Carrión. *Sd* Javier Mateos.

Cast: Abel Salazar *(Henry)*, Ariadne Welter *(Marta)*, Germán Robles *(Count Lavud)*, Alicia Rodriguez, Yerye Beirute, Guillermo Orea, Antonio Raxell, Carlos Ancira.

Horror film. Henry, a mad doctor, disinters Count Lavud, a vampire, from a cemetery. The count revives when a servant removes a wooden stake from his heart, and he terrorizes Mexico. In bat form, the vampire is destroyed when impaled by a spear. *Physicians. Grave robbers. Vampires. Nobility. Reviviscence. Impalement. Cemeteries. Bats.*

Note: Produced in Mexico in 1957 as *El ataud del vampiro*.

EL VAMPIRO *see* **THE VAMPIRE**

EL VAMPIRO SANGRIENTO *see* **THE BLOODY VAMPIRE**

IL VANGELO SECONDO MATTEO *see* **THE GOSPEL ACCORDING TO ST. MATTHEW**

VANISHING AFRICA *see* **KWAHERI**

VANISHING FRONTIER *see* **THE BROKEN LAND**

THE VANQUISHED see **GALLANT REBEL**

VARAN THE UNBELIEVABLE (United States/Japan)　　　**F6.5325**
Toho Co.–Dallas Productions–Cory Productions. *Dist* Crown International Pictures. 7 Dec **1962** [Seattle opening]. Sd; b&w. 35mm. 70 min.
　　Production Credits for U. S. Vers: *Prod-Dir* Jerry A. Baerwitz. *Screenplay* Sid Harris. *Photog* Jack Marquette. *Film Ed* Jack Ruggiero, Ralph Cushman. *Sd Rec* Vic Appel. *Mus Ed* Peter Zinner. *Asst Dir* Leonard Kunody. *Cost* Robert O'Dell. *Makeup* Robert Cowan. *Sp Eff* Howard Anderson.
　　Production Credits for Japanese Vers: *Dir* Inoshiro Honda. *Screenplay* Shinichi Sekizawa. *Idea* T. Kuronuma. *Story* Hajime Koizumi. *Photog* Hajime Koizumi. *Art Dir* K. Shimizu. *Mus* Akira Ifukube. *Sp Eff* Eiji Tsuburaya.
　　Cast: Myron Healey (*Comdr. James Bradley*), Tsuruko Kobayashi (*Anna*), Clifford Kawada (*Captain Kishi*), Derick Shimatsu (*Matsu*), Kozo Nomura, Ayumi Sonoda, Koreya Senda, Akihiko Hirata, Hideo Imamura, George Sasaki, Hiroshi Hisamune, Yoneo Iguchi, Michael Sung, Roy Ogata.
　　Science fiction melodrama. In a salt water lake located on a small Japanese island, Comdr. James Bradley conducts experiments to convert salt water to fresh. His Japanese wife, Anna, objects due to the legend that a grotesque prehistoric reptile inhabits the lake and will remain peaceful only if not disturbed. Bradley ignores the warning, and his tests arouse the monster. Total destruction follows, and all attempts to destroy the beast fail as it heads for a large city. Bradley then explodes his chemicals on the monster, and it retreats into the water, but no one knows if it will appear again. *Scientists. Americans in foreign countries. Experiments. Myths. Explosions. Dinosaurs.*
　　Note: Released in Japan in 1958 as *Daikaiju Baran*; running time: 87 min. Reedited and supplemented with additional footage for U. S. distribution.

VARELSERNA see **LES CRÉATURES**

VARGTIMMEN see **HOUR OF THE WOLF**

VARIETY LIGHTS (Italy)　　　**F6.5326**
Capitolium Film. *Dist* Pathé Contemporary Films. 6 May **1965** [New York opening]. Sd; b&w. 35mm. 93 min.
　　Prod-Dir Alberto Lattuada, Federico Fellini. *Screenplay* Federico Fellini, Alberto Lattuada, Tullio Pinelli, Ennio Flajano. *Story* Federico Fellini. *Photog* Otello Martelli. *Art Dir* Aldo Buzzi. *Mus* Felice Lattuada.
　　Cast: Peppino De Filippo (*Checco Dal Monte*), Carla Del Poggio (*Liliana*), Giulietta Masina (*Melina Amour*), Folco Lulli (*Adelmo Conti*), John Kitzmiller (*Johnny*), Dante Maggio (*Remo*), Carlo Romano, actor (*LaRosa*), Gina Mascetti (*Valeria del Sole*), Checco Durante (*theater owner*), Joe Falletta (*Bill*), Enrico Piergentili (*Melina's father*), Mario De Angelis (*maestro*), Fanny Marchiò (*soubrette*), Giacomo Furia (*The Duke*), Silvio Bagolini (*journalist*), Vanja Orico (*gypsy singer*), Franca Valeri (*designer*), Giulio Cali (*Edison Will*), Vittorio Caprioli, Alberto Bonucci.
　　Drama. Liliana, a stage-struck young woman, sees the performance of a touring variety show and follows the company to the next town. She is soon incorporated into the show as a dancer, and on the night of her first performance, she saves the evening from near disaster. Eventually Checco, the middle-aged manager of the company, falls in love with her, much to the disappointment of his mistress, Melina. The ambitious Liliana is not satisfied with the small show, however, and uses her charm to secure a part in one of the prestigious productions of impresario Conti. Sorrowful and morose, Checco returns to his forgiving mistress. The train pulls out of the station with Liliana in a first-class pullman and Checco's company in the crowded third-class compartments. *Entertainers. Mistresses. Impresari. Dancers. Ambition. Theatrical troupes. Trains.*
　　Note: Opened in Rome in 1951 as *Luci del varietà*.

VAXDOCKAN see **THE DOLL**

VECHERA NA KHUTORE BLIZ DIKANKI see **A NIGHT BEFORE CHRISTMAS**

VELIKAYA BITVA NA VOLGE see **THE GREAT BATTLE OF THE VOLGA**

VELIKAYA POBEDA SOVETSKOGO NARODA see **THE GREAT BATTLE OF EUROPE**

THE VELVET TRAP　　　**F6.5327**
Dist Gillman Film Corp. 22 Jun **1966** [Los Angeles opening]. Sd; b&w. 35mm. 80 min.
　　Prod Daniel P. Foley. *Dir-Writ* Ken Kennedy. *Camera* Sherwood Strickler, Don McIntosh, Elmer Hohnber. *Sd* Vince Orrel, Floyd Newton.
　　Cast: Jamie Karson (*Julie*), Alan Jeffory (*Brad Collins*), James F. Hurley, Bret Steel, Mike Harvey, Robert Terry, Bob Pollard, Dick Hamilton, actor, Stirling Welker, Betty Coryell, Irene Graham, John Scovern, Royce Weyers, Lorie Stark, Jerome Parentae, Ray Vegas, June Harlow.

　　Melodrama. Assaulted and raped by her employer, Julie, a waitress, elopes to Las Vegas with a photographer named Brad Collins. Collins deserts her after one night, leaving her destitute, and she pawns her wedding ring to buy a bus ticket back to Los Angeles. A pimp who has been stalking Julie steals her ticket, takes her to a brothel, and forces her into prostitution. Her first customer becomes overly excited and dies of a heart attack. Frightened, Julie runs out of the brothel and is struck and killed by a passing truck. *Waitresses. Photographers. Pimps. Rape. Employer-employee relations. Prostitution. Elopement. Desertion. Heart disease. Whorehouses. Automobile accidents. Las Vegas.*

THE VELVET UNDERGROUND AND NICO　　　**F6.5328**
Dist Film-Makers' Cooperative. 8 Feb **1966** [New York opening]. Sd; b&w. 16mm. 70 min.
　　Prod-Dir Andy Warhol. *Photog* Andy Warhol, Barbara Rubin. *Mus* The Velvet Underground, Nico.
　　Cast: The Velvet Underground, Nico.
　　Documentary. The Velvet Underground and Nico perform their electronic rock music. *Police. Rock and roll. The Velvet Underground.*
　　Note: It is unclear to what extent the footage of *The Velvet Underground and Nico* was included in the initial presentation of Andy Warhol's mixed media show in New York on 8 Feb 1966. Filming took place at each show; the episodes were known as the "Uptight" series. Footage of the New York City police breaking up a performance may be included in the film. Split-screen projection was apparently involved in the developing multi-media presentation, known as *The Exploding Plastic Inevitable* or as *Plastic Inevitables (Velvet Underground)*.

VENDETTA DELLA MASCHERA DI FERRO see **PRISONER OF THE IRON MASK**

LA VENDETTA DELLA SIGNORA see **THE VISIT**

LA VENDETTA DI SPARTACUS see **REVENGE OF THE GLADIATORS**

VENDREDI 13 HEURES see **THE WORLD IN MY POCKET**

LA VENERE DEI PIRATI see **QUEEN OF THE PIRATES**

THE VENETIAN AFFAIR　　　**F6.5329**
Jerry Thorpe Productions. *Dist* Metro-Goldwyn-Mayer, Inc. 18 Jan **1967** [New York opening; c26 Oct 1966; LP33600]. Sd (Westrex); col (Metrocolor). 35mm (Panavision). 92 min.
　　Prod Jerry Thorpe, E. Jack Neuman. *Assoc Prod* Lloyd Richards. *Dir* Jerry Thorpe. *Screenplay* E. Jack Neuman. *Dir Photog* Milton Krasner. *Locations Photog* Enzo Serafin. *Art Dir* George W. Davis, Leroy Coleman. *Set Decor* Henry Grace, Hugh Hunt. *Film Ed* Henry Berman. *Mus* Lalo Schifrin. *Song:* "Our Venetian Affair" Hal Winn, Lalo Schifrin. *Sung by* Julius La Rosa. *Rec Supv* Franklin Milton. *Asst Dir* E. Darrell Hallenbeck. *Unit Prod Mgr* Marvin Stuart. *Makeup* William Tuttle. *Hairstyles* Sydney Guilaroff. *Sp Vis Eff* Carroll L. Shepphird. *Tech Adv* Keith S. Ditman, M.D.
　　Cast: Robert Vaughn (*Bill Fenner*), Elke Sommer (*Sandra Fane*), Felicia Farr (*Claire Connor*), Karl Boehm (*Robert Wahl*), Boris Karloff (*Dr. Pierre Vaugiroud*), Roger C. Carmel (*Mike Ballard*), Edward Asner (*Frank Rosenfeld*), Joe De Santis (*Jan Aarvan*), Fabrizio Mioni (*Russo*), Wesley Lau (*Neill Carlson*), Luciana Paluzzi (*Giulia Almeranti*), Bill Weiss (*Goldsmith*).
　　Action melodrama. *Source:* Helen MacInnes, *The Venetian Affair* (New York, 1963). Reporter Bill Fenner is sent from New York to cover the case when an American diplomat blows up an international peace conference in Venice, killing all the delegates including himself. Fenner, a former CIA man who was fired when he married suspected enemy agent Sandra Fane, has been brought to Venice by the CIA. They want him to find Sandra, who is hiding from Robert Wahl, the enemy agent who hired her to befriend the American diplomat. Second, Fenner is to obtain a report written by political scientist Pierre Vaugiroud on why the explosion occurred. After he finds Sandra, Fenner contacts Wahl and accepts money in exchange for agreeing to turn over Sandra. Instead, Fenner dresses her as a nun, gives her the money, and puts her aboard a train. Before he joins her, Fenner goes to the office of Mike Ballard, his Venice colleague who has stolen the Vaugiroud report. The office is attacked by a gunman, and although Ballard and his secretary, Giulia Almeranti, are murdered, Fenner escapes with the report. Wahl is waiting when Fenner boards Sandra's train. Sandra confesses to Fenner that she betrayed him to save their lives. When it is discovered that Fenner does not have the report, Wahl kills Sandra and takes Fenner to a secret laboratory and injects him with a drug which will turn him into a robot. The drug fails to take effect; Vaugiroud, also drugged, pleads with Fenner to lead them to where the report is hidden. Although Fenner does so, he suddenly realizes that Vaugiroud's mind has been controlled by the drug, as was the mind of the American diplomat. Fenner kills

Wahl and races to the conference in time to prevent Vaugiroud from causing a second explosion. *Americans in foreign countries. Diplomats. Reporters. Secret agents. Secretaries. Disguise. Murder. Perfidy. Conferences— International. Trains. Tranquilizers. Brainwashing. Venice. United States— Diplomatic and consular service. United States—Central Intelligence Agency. Documentation. Explosions.*

Note: Locations filmed in Venice.

VENETSIANSKIY MAVR *see* **BALLET OF OTHELLO**

LA VENGANZA DEL SEXO *see* **THE CURIOUS DR. HUMPP**

VENGEANCE   F6.5330
BadAxe Productions. *Dist* Crown International Pictures. Apr **1964**. Sd; b&w. 35mm. 79 min.

Prod William Thourlby. *Dir* Dene Hilyard. *Screenplay & Orig Story* Alex Sharp, Ed Erwin. *Cinematog* Richard Kendall. *Film Ed* Ewing Brown. *Sd* Norman Houle.

Cast: William Thourlby (*Capt. Lafe Todd*), Melora Conway (*Jean Harmon*), Owen Pavitt (*Slade*), Ed Cook (*Clay*), Byrd Holland (*sheriff*), John Bliss (*Deputy Sam*), Larry Gerst (*Will Harmon*), Gordon Wynn (*Col. Carl Dorsett*), Donald Cook (*Billy Todd*), James Cavanaugh (*Uncle Ben*), Tiger Joe Marsh, The Great John L (*bullies*).

Western melodrama. Capt. Lafe Todd, a Confederate soldier released from a Union stockade at the end of the Civil War, travels to a Western town two years later to kill Col. Carl Dorsett, one of the men responsible for his brother's murder in prison. Jean Harmon, Dorsett's fiancée, her brother Will, and her Uncle Ben seek to avenge Dorsett's death by lynching Todd. The sheriff takes Todd into protective custody, but Todd and a deputy are headed off by Slade, the other man responsible for Todd's brother's murder, and brought to a hidden mountain cabin. There Todd learns that Dorsett was a rustler, and that Slade and his gang have kidnaped Jean and Will and are holding them for ransom. Uncle Ben is sent off for the ransom money, but he returns with the Harmon ranch hands. In the ensuing fight, Slade and his henchmen are killed. *Confederate veterans. Sheriffs. Rustlers. Brothers. Uncles. Revenge. Murder. Kidnaping. Rescue. Ranch life. Prisons. United States—History—Civil War.*

VENGEANCE *see* **THE BRAIN**

LA VENGEANCE DU MASQUE DE FER *see* **PRISONER OF THE IRON MASK**

LA VENGEANCE DU SARRASIN *see* **THE PIRATE AND THE SLAVE GIRL**

THE VENGEANCE OF FU MANCHU (Great Britain)   F6.5331
Babasdave Films. *Dist* Warner Bros.-Seven Arts, Inc. Jan **1968**. Sd; b&w (see note). 35mm. 91 min.

Prod Harry Alan Towers. *Dir* Jeremy Summers. *Screenplay* Peter Welbeck. *Photog* John Kotze. *Adtl Photog* Stephen Dade. *Camera Op* Tony Spratling, Neil Ginger Gemmell. *Art Dir* Scott MacGregor, Peggy Gick. *Film Ed* Allan Morrison. *Mus Comp & Cond* Malcolm Lockyer. *Songs:* "The Real Me," "Where Are the Men" Don Black, Malcolm Lockyer. *Sung by* Samantha Jones. *Sd* Brian Marshall. *Asst Dir* Anthony Waye, John Peverall. *Prod Mgr* John Comfort. *Cont* Marjorie Lavelly.

Cast: Christopher Lee (*Fu Manchu*), Tony Ferrer (*Inspector Ramos*), Tsai Chin (*Lin Tang*), Douglas Wilmer (*Nayland Smith*), Wolfgang Kieling (*Dr. Lieberson*), Suzanne Roquette (*Maria Lieberson*), Howard Marion Crawford (*Dr. Petrie*), Noel Trevarthen (*Mark Weston*), Horst Frank (*Rudy Moss*), Peter Carsten (*Kurt*), Maria Rohm (*Ingrid*), Mona Chong (*Jasmin*).

Adventure melodrama. Based on the characters created by: Sax Rohmer. Nayland Smith of Scotland Yard is in Paris helping to set up INTERPOL, an international police organization. Meanwhile, the supposedly dead Fu Manchu returns to his ancestral palace in North China with his daughter Lin Tang and plots the formation of an international crime syndicate. He begins by kidnaping a famous surgeon, Dr. Lieberson, and his daughter Maria, whom he threatens to kill unless the doctor transforms the face of a prisoner into the likeness of Smith. In Hong Kong, Mafia leader Rudy Moss is negotiating with other leading criminals to assist Fu Manchu, but his activities are being monitored by Shanghai police. When the real Smith is abducted and brought to Fu Manchu's palace, his double is shipped to London where, under a hypnotic trance, he murders Smith's Chinese servant. The double is then sentenced to the gallows, and Fu Manchu makes plans to synchronize Smith's own death with the time of the execution. The surveillance of Moss has revealed Manchu's scheme, however, and Hong Kong Inspector Ramos and FBI agent Mark Weston fight their way into Fu Manchu's palace to rescue the prisoners. The palace explodes, but from the ruins comes the voice of Fu Manchu promising that he will be heard from again. *Chinese. Surgeons. Doubles. Domestics. Police. Organized crime. Kidnaping. Plastic surgery. Murder. Filial relations.*

Hypnotism. Capital punishment. Paris. Hong Kong. London. People's Republic of China. INTERPOL. Scotland Yard. United States—Federal Bureau of Investigation. Mafia. Explosions. Fu Manchu.

Note: Location scenes filmed in Ireland and the Republic of China. Released in Great Britain in Eastman Color in 1967; running time: 89 min. Peter Welbeck is a pseudonym for Harry Alan Towers. Third in a series of Fu Manchu films produced by Towers.

THE VENGEANCE OF SHE (Great Britain)   F6.5332
Hammer Film Productions-Seven Arts Productions. *Dist* Twentieth Century-Fox Film Corp. 1 May **1968** [Portland, Oregon, opening; c31 Dec 1967; LP35829]. Sd (RCA); col (DeLuxe). 35mm. 101 min.

Prod Aida Young. *Dir* Cliff Owen. *Screenplay* Peter O'Donnell. *Dir Photog* Wolfgang Suschitzky. *Camera Op* Ray Sturgess. *Ritual Seq Dsgn* Andrew Low. *Prod Dsgn* Lionel Couch. *Supv Ed* James Needs. *Ed* Raymond Poulton. *Mus & Sp Mus Eff Comp* Mario Nascimbene. *Mus Supv* Philip Martell. *Saxophone Solo* Tubby Hayes. *Sd Rec* Bill Rowe. *Sd Ed* Roy Hyde, Jack Knight. *Asst Dir* Terry Clegg. *Prod Mgr* Dennis Bertera. *Cont* Phyllis Townshend. *Cost Dsgn* Carl Toms. *Wardrobe Mistress* Rosemary Burrows. *Makeup* Michael Morris. *Hairstyles* Mervyn Medalie. *Sp Eff* Bowie Films, Bob Cuff.

Cast: John Richardson (*Killikrates*), Olinka Berova (*Carol*), Edward Judd (*Philip*), Colin Blakely (*George*), Jill Melford (*Sheila*), George Sewell (*Harry*), Andre Morell (*Kassim*), Noel Willman (*Za-Tor*), Derek Godfrey (*Men-Hari*), Daniele Noel (*Sharna*), Gerald Lawson (*seer*), Derrick Sherwin (*No. 1*), William Lyon Brown (*magus*), Charles O'Rourke (*servant*), Zohra Segal (*Putri*), Christine Pocket (*dancer*), Dervis Ward (*lorry driver*).

Costume melodrama. Source: H. Rider Haggard, *She, a History of Adventure* (London, 1887). While dazedly wandering around the coast of southern France, a young woman, Carol, is plagued by hallucinatory voices which call her "Ayesha." After escaping from an amorous truck driver who is later fatally wounded in an accident, she arrives in Monte Carlo and stows away on a yacht bound for North Africa. On board she meets Philip Smith, a psychiatrist who senses that some compelling force is pulling the tormented woman toward the East. Upon reaching Haifa, Carol flees into the desert and falls into the clutches of a pair of Arabs. Philip, who has followed, rescues her and decides to accompany Carol to her unknown destination. They eventually reach the Lost City of Kuma, and she is greeted as the reincarnation of Queen Ayesha (She), the beloved of the immortal King Killikrates. After Philip has been imprisoned, he is visited by Za-Tor, the leader of a secret sect who reveals that Killikrates has promised his high priest, Men-Hari, the secret of immortality if he can bring back Ayesha. Hypnotized by Men-Hari into believing that she is the lost queen, Carol prepares to enter the sacred flames that will render her immortal. Philip, released by Za-Tor, persuades Killikrates that he has been betrayed, and the king kills Men-Hari. Longing to join Ayesha, Killikrates walks into the flames and perishes. As Carol and Philip escape to civilization, an explosion reduces the city of Kuma to ashes. *Truckdrivers. Hitchhikers. Psychiatrists. Stowaways. Priests. Arabs. Royalty. Immortality. Hypnotism. Perfidy. Reincarnation. Yachts. Deserts. Imaginary kingdoms. France. Monte Carlo. North Africa. Haifa. Fires.*

Note: Location scenes filmed in Spain and southern France. Released in Great Britain in Apr 1968. A sequel to *She*, q. v.

VENICE NITEMARE   F6.5333
Dist Stacey Distributors. ca **1970**. Sd; col. 16mm. 61-81 min.

Sex film. No information about the precise nature of this film has been found. *Sexuality.*

VENOM (Denmark)   F6.5334
ASA Film-Nordisk Films. *Dist* Peppercorn-Wormser, Inc., Times Film Corp. 10 Jan **1968** [New York opening]. Sd; b&w. 35mm. 96 min.

Prod Knud Leif Thomsen, Henning Karmark. *Exec Prod?* C. Bergesen. *Dir-Writ* Knud Leif Thomsen. *Photog* Claus Loof, Arne Abrahamsen. *Film Ed* Birger Lind. *Mus* Niels Viggo Bentzon, The Matadors. *Sd* Hans Sørensen. *Prod Mgr* Morten Schyberg, Bo Christensen.

Cast: Søren Strømberg (*Per*), Sisse Reingaard (*Susanne*), Poul Reichhardt (*Henrike Steen*), Astrid Villaume (*Mrs. Steen*), Judy Gringer (*Sonja*), Grethe Morgensen (*Frau Jacobsen, the secretary*), Karl Stegger (*caretaker*), Vic Salomonsen, Tine Schmedes, Per Goldschmidt, Jess Kølpin (*teenagers*).

Drama. Henrike Steen, a middle-aged real estate agent of comfortable means, looks to the family maid and secretary, Frau Jacobsen, for relief from the monotony of his marriage. His placid family life is disturbed one day by Per, an arrogant youth who invades the Steens' private beach and captivates their daughter, Susanne. Per and Susanne begin an affair, and Per invites himself to a party given for Susanne by her parents. Per offends the Steens by proclaiming his belief in hedonism, and he gives Susanne a book of pornography. Mr. Steen burns the book in the fireplace, and Per retaliates by burning the family Bible. Unable to combat Per's influence over his daughter, Mr. Steen invites him to become a houseguest so that Susanne may learn for herself that Per is a worthless boor. Per, also a fledgling pornographer, moves in with his filmmaking paraphernalia. He continues his relationship with Susanne, propositions her mother, and proceeds to make sex films. Per shows one of his films to Mrs. Steen; her interest turns to shock as she discovers her daughter fornicating on the screen. Frantic, she calls her husband, who beats up the youth and throws him out, leaving the Steen family with its ever-widening generation gap. *Real estate agents. Secretaries. Housemaids. Middle age. Infidelity. Family life. Adolescence. Hedonism. Sex exploitation films. Pornography.*

Note: Filmed in Copenhagen in 1966 and originally released under the title *Gift.*

LE VENT D'EST *see* **WIND FROM THE EAST**

LE VENT SE LÈVE *see* **TIME BOMB**

LA VENTICINQUESIMA ORA *see* **THE 25TH HOUR**

VENTO DELL'EST *see* **WIND FROM THE EAST**

IL VENTO SI ALZA *see* **TIME BOMB**

VENUS DER PIRATEN *see* **QUEEN OF THE PIRATES**

VENUS IN FURS　　　　　　　　　　　　　　　　　　　F6.5335
Cam-Scope Pictures. *Dist* Boxoffice International Film Distributors. 12 Jul **1967** [New York opening]. Sd; b&w. 35mm. 65 min.
Prod Lou Campa. *Dir* Joe Marzano. *Screenplay* Joe Marzano, "Elinore". *Dir Photog* George Cirello. *Lighting* Bill Lister, P. Brown. *2d Camera* Lou Campa. *Mus* Vito and the Vikings. *Rec* W. W. Lister. *Re-rec* Murlyn Recording. *Asst Dir* Angie Giles. *Prod Mgr* Lou Campa. *Gaffer* R. Aldous. *Locations* Cathy Starr.
Cast: "Elinore", Shep Wild, Stephanie Smyth, Pat Barnett, Bhob Stewart, Lisa Love, Ava Martin, Robert James, Joe Marzano, Gresham Law, Mary James, Sheila Fearn, Rene Spencer, Al Campa, Michael Morel, Michelle Signor, David Signorelli, Jean Fern.
Drama. Suggested by: Leopold von Sacher-Masoch, *Venus im Pelz* (1870). Young David, a salesclerk who is obsessed with sex, has fantasies of wanting to make love with Venus, although in reality David is unsure of himself, being easily intimidated by women. On his way to work, he dreams of attacking a woman on the bus, and throughout his days he imagines that the women he sees are nude. He meets Marna, a socialite, at the public library, and accepts an invitation to spend the weekend at her house. He arrives during a party but is unable to get into the mood of it. Late that night, he and another guest, Lorilie, make love on the lawn. He returns to the house and witnesses some bizarre sexual acts, including sadism and lesbianism, and discovers that Lorilie and Marna are lovers. At night, the continuing party is stimulated by drugs. Marna accuses David of sexual inadequacy; on a dawn horseback ride, she proves her superior horsemanship. As Marna and Lorilie tie David to a tree, his worst fears of inferiority are confirmed while they make love in front of him. Suddenly, he finds himself on the library steps—he has had a bad dream. As he walks away, his gaze is drawn to a woman (Marna?) smiling seductively at him from the back of a limousine. ... *Salesclerks. Socialites. Mental illness. Sadomasochism. Obsession. Self-confidence. Lesbianism. Dreams. Venus.*

VENUS IN FURS (Great Britain/Italy/West Germany)　　　F6.5336
Cineproduzioni Associate–Terra Filmkunst–Towers of London. *Dist* American International Pictures. Apr **1970**. Sd; col (Movielab). 35mm. 86 min. *MPAA rating* R.
Pres by Commonwealth United Entertainment Inc. *Prod* Harry Alan Towers. *Dir-Story (see note)* Jess Franco. *Screenplay* Malvin Wald, Jess Franco, Bruno Leder, Carlo Fadda, Milo G. Cuccia. *Dir Photog* Angelo Lotti. *Main Titl* Howard A. Anderson Co. *Film Ed* Henry Batista, Mike Pozen, Nicholas Wentworth. *Post Prod Supv* Robert S. Eisen, Harry Eisen. *Mus* Manfred Mann, Mike Hugg. *Titl Song Sung by* Barbara McNair. *Song:* "Let's Get Together" Robert B. Sherman, Richard M. Sherman. *Sung by* Barbara McNair. *Mus Supv* Synchrofilm. *Sp Eff* Howard A. Anderson Co.
Cast: James Darren *(Jimmy Logan)*, Barbara McNair *(Rita)*, Maria Rohm *(Wanda Reed/Venus)*, Klaus Kinski *(Ahmed)*, Dennis Price *(Kapp)*, Margaret Lee *(Olga)*, Adolfo Lastretti *(inspector)*, Paul Müller *(nightclub owner)*, Mirella Pamphili.
Melodrama. Suggested by: Leopold von Sacher-Masoch, *Venus im Pelz* (1870). On a beach near Istanbul Jimmy Logan, a young American jazz musician, finds the mutilated body of Wanda Reed, a beautiful woman Jimmy had earlier seen sadistically killed by Olga, a fashion photographer, Ahmed, a millionaire playboy, and Kapp, a homosexual. Jimmy leaves Istanbul for Rio de Janeiro, where he meets and has an affair with Rita, a nightclub singer. One night, a woman known as Venus enters the club, and Jimmy, struck by her resemblance to Wanda, is attracted to her. She seduces Kapp, now living in Rio, and he dies of a heart attack. She then has a lesbian encounter with Olga, who

commits suicide. Jimmy, fearful of Venus, returns with Rita to Istanbul, and Venus follows. She meets up with Ahmed, and while they enact a story about a sultan and his sadistic slave mistress, Ahmed dies. Trailed by the police, Venus disappears in a cemetery, and Jimmy finds her fur coat draped over Wanda's grave. Returning to the beach, Jimmy finds his own body washed ashore. *Musicians. Singers. Americans in foreign countries. Photographers. Playboys. Millionaires. Revenge. Lesbianism. Male homosexuality. Suicide. Murder. Mutilation. Sadomasochism. Seduction. Heart disease. Nightclubs. Cemeteries. Beaches. Istanbul. Rio de Janeiro. Ghosts.*

Note: Location scenes filmed in 1968 in Istanbul, England, Spain, West Germany, and Italy; stock footage of the Rio de Janeiro Carnival is included. Released in Italy as *Paroxismus.* Alternative Italian title: *Può una morta rivivere per amore?* Jess Franco is credited as Hans Billian in Italian sources. Writers Leder, Fadda, and Cuccia are not credited by U. S. sources.

VERBRECHEN NACH SCHULSCHLUSS *see* **THE YOUNG GO WILD**

EL VERDUGO *see* **NOT ON YOUR LIFE**

VERFÜHRUNG AM MEER *see* **SEDUCTION BY THE SEA**

VERGELTUNG IN CATANO *see* **SUNSCORCHED**

LA VERGINE DI NORIMBERGA *see* **HORROR CASTLE**

LA VERGINE DI SAMOA *see* **THE DRUMS OF TABU**

UNA VERGINE PER IL PRINCIPE *see* **A MAIDEN FOR A PRINCE**

UNA VERGINE PER UN BASTARDO *see* **THE PSYCHIC LOVER**

UNA VERGINE PER UN BASTARDO *see* **SWEET SMELL OF LOVE**

LE VERGINI DI ROMA *see* **AMAZONS OF ROME**

LA VERITÀ *see* **THE TRUTH**

LA VÉRITÉ *see* **THE TRUTH**

VERMILION DOOR (Hong Kong)　　　　　　　　　　　F6.5337
Shaw Brothers (H. K.) Ltd. Oct **1969** [Los Angeles showing]. Sd; col (Eastman Color). 35mm (Shawscope). 120 min.
Prod Run Run Shaw. *Dir* Lo Chen. *Screenplay* Chin Ko. *Photog* Liu Chi. *Film Ed* Chiang Hsing-lung. *Mus* Wang Ju-jen.
Cast: Li Li-hua *(Lo Hsiang-chi)*, Ivy Ling Po *(Mei Pao)*, Kwan Shan *(Chiu Hai-tang)*, Hsia Yi-chiu *(The Deaf Maid)*, Yang Chi-ching *(Chi Shao-shiung)*, Ching Miao *(Yuan Pao-fan)*, Tien Feng *(Shang Lao-er)*, Ho Fan *(Lo Shao-hua)*, Woo Wei *(Mrs. Meng)*, Chao Ming *(Han Shao-wen)*, Li Kuan *(Shiao K'ao-tsc)*, Ruey Ming *(Old Man Han)*, Chiang Kuang-chao *(Chao Eu-K'un)*.
Melodrama. In China during the early days of the Republic, lovers Lo Hsiang-chi and Mei Pao are forced to separate by a lecherous colonel. Their lives are wrought with tragedy as they are forced into clandestine meetings, infants are changed in their cradles, and one of the pair has his face scarred by an angry warlord. The lovers are separated for 17 years, only to be reunited on their deathbed. *Soldiers. Infants. Warlords. China—History—Republic 1912-49.*

Note: Produced in Hong Kong in 1965.

DAS VERRÄTERTOR *see* **TRAITOR'S GATE**

VERSPÄTUNG IN MARIENBORN *see* **STOP TRAIN 349**

A VERY CURIOUS GIRL (France)　　　　　　　　　　　F6.5338
Cythère Films. *Dist* Regional Film Distributors. 30 Dec **1970** [New York opening]. Sd; col (Technicolor). 35mm. 107 min. *MPAA rating* R.
Exec Prod Claude Makovski. *Dir* Nelly Kaplan. *Screenplay-Dial* Nelly Kaplan, Claude Makovski. *Adapt* Nelly Kaplan, Claude Makovski, Jacques Serguine, Michel Fabre. *Photog* Jean Badal. *Art Dir* Michel Landi, Patrick Lafarge, Jean-Claude Landi. *Film Ed* Nelly Kaplan, Gérard Pollicand, Noëlle Boisson, Suzanne Lang-Willar. *Mus* Georges Moustaki. *Song:* "Moi, je me balance" sung by Barbara (French). *Sd* Claude Jauvert. *Asst Dir* Joseph Drimal. *Prod Mgr* Moshe Mizrahi.
Cast: Bernadette Lafont *(Marie)*, Georges Géret *(Gaston Duvalier)*, Michel Constantin *(André)*, Julien Guiomar *(Le Duc)*, Jean Parédès *(Monsieur Paul)*, Francis Lax *(Emile)*, Claire Maurier *(Irène)*, Henry Czarniak *(Julien)*, Jacques Marin *(Félix Lechat)*, Pascal Mazzotti *(Father Dard)*, Marcel Pérès *(Pépé)*, Micha Bayard *(Mélanie Lechat)*, Fernand Berset *(Jeanjean)*, Gilberte Géniat *(Rose)*, Jacques Masson *(Polite)*, Renée Duncan *(Delphine)*, Claire Ollivier *(mother)*, Louis Malle *(Jesus)*, Claude Makovski *(Victor)*.
Drama. Marie lives as an outcast with her mother in a shack on the edge of the Provençal village of Tellier, working at menial tasks and sometimes accommodating the sexual desires of the village men and of her lesbian employer. Her life changes when her mother is killed in a hit-and-run accident. Taking the few hundred francs her mother possessed, Marie stages a

combination wake and party to which she invites her admirers. Unable to afford a proper burial for her mother, she waits until the men are thoroughly intoxicated and then asks them to bury the corpse in the yard, promising her sexual favors in return. Marie in broad daylight begins to fulfill her promise the following day, and an angry mob arrives at her door. The game warden retaliates against her by killing her pet goat, the sole creature she loves, and thereafter Marie swears revenge against the smug populace. She seduces each of the townsmen in turn, now charging progressively higher fees for the services she once provided free. André, an itinerant movie projectionist, is a friend to her, providing her with goods from the world outside the little village, but his attempts to persuade her to leave are unsuccessful. With a tape recorder, she collects information with which to betray and ruin her clients, who run the gamut of the village society. Then one Sunday Marie attends mass, and before leaving the church she deposits the tape recorder, playing at full volume, in the collection box. Outraged, the villagers descend on her shack, only to find that Marie has abandoned the village for a better life elsewhere. *Drudges. Prostitutes. Motion picture projectionists. Village life. Revenge. Hypocrisy. Drunkenness. Lesbianism. Seduction. Poverty. Recorders. Funerals. Provence. Automobile accidents. Goats.*

Note: Opened in Paris in Dec 1969 as *La fiancée du pirate*; running time: 105 min.

THE VERY FRIENDLY NEIGHBORS   F6.5339

Leon Film Enterprises. *Dist* International Film Organization. ca **1969**. Sd; col (Eastman Color). 35mm. 88 min.

Pres by Donald E. Leon, William Rowland. *Prod* Donald E. Leon. *Dir-Writ* Albert Zugsmith. *Camera* Bob Maxwell. *2d Unit Camera* Joe Bardo. *Art Dir* Clyde Houston. *Sd Mixer* Clark D. Will. *Prod Mgr* Carol Caruso. *Makeup* Nora Maxwell. *Prop* Dave Anderson, prop. *Boom* Chick Boom. *Key Grip* Rocky Pebbles. *Grip* Garti Pucket. *Gaffer* Ken Gibbs.

Cast: Angelia Caron, Alain Germaine, Ami Paisley, Sally Sanford, Alexander Beckett.

Sex film. Lisa, a beautiful Hollywood starlet, grows tired of her playboy husband, Charlie, and attempts to seduce her newlywed neighbor's husband. Lisa settles for a lesbian bout with the wife when her advances are spurned by the husband. Charlie likewise begins to look elsewhere for satisfaction. He goes to Hollywood swim parties with his employer and witnesses him seduce a virgin by hypnosis. Lisa and Charlie decide to engage in group sex with their neighbors, but after a short time the newlyweds' feeling of guilt forces them to withdraw. Lisa and Charlie then engage in mate swapping with Charlie's employer and his new bride, his hypnosis victim. Eventually, Lisa becomes tired of the same sex partners and begins to search for new lovers. *Playboys. Newlyweds. Actors. Neighbors. Mate swapping. Seduction. Infidelity. Hypnotism. Group sex. Employer-employee relations. Lesbianism. Swimming pools.*

Note: May also be known as *Friendly Neighbors*.

A VERY HANDY MAN (France/Italy)   F6.5340

Napoleon Film–Franco London Film–Federiz–Francinex. *Dist* Rizzoli Film Distributors. 14 Dec **1966** [New York opening]. Sd; b&w. 35mm. 95 min.

Prod Nino Crisman. *Dir* Alessandro Blasetti. *Screenplay* Sergio Amidei, Elio Bartolini, Carlo Romano, Adriano Bolzoni, Alessandro Blasetti. *Photog* Leonida Barboni, Tonino Delli Colli, Carlo Di Palma. *Mus* Carlo Savina.

Cast: Ugo Tognazzi *(Liolà)*, Giovanna Ralli *(Tuzza Azzara)*, Pierre Brasseur *(Simone Palumbo)*, Anouk Aimée *(Mita)*, Elisa Cegani *(Aunt Geas)*, Dolores Palumbo, Umberto Spadaro, Rocco D'Assunta, Carlo Pisacane, Claudio Micheli, Antonio Piretti, Stefano Maggi, Carlo Angeletti, Massimo Giuliani, Mariettino, Giulio Tomasini, Angela Lavagna, Miranda Poggi, Vera Drudi, Gian Gabella, Giuseppe Stagnitti, Solveig D'Assunta, Nino Musco, Graziella Granata, Renato Terra, Vanda Tibursi, Erina Torelli.

Comedy. Source: Luigi Pirandello, *Liolà* (Rome opening: 4 Nov 1916). Liolà, a carefree bachelor, works as a handyman in the Sicilian village of Lentini[?] where he has fathered five children born to five different women. His peaceful life is disrupted when he becomes involved in a village feud between the Azzara and the Palumbo families. Tuzza Azzara, one of Liolà's old conquests, visits him at old Simone Palumbo's house, where he is working, and by claiming to be pregnant by him, persuades him to divert some of Simone's water to her orange groves. Simone, the chief landowner of the village, forces Liolà to remedy the situation, and this time both families lose their water. The case is brought to court, and Tuzza, now genuinely pregnant by Liolà, is confident that he will take her side. When he remains indifferent, Tuzza visits Simone, whose pride has been wounded by the failure of his young wife, Mita, to bear him an heir, and she suggests that he pose as the father of the unborn child. Tuzza believes that in this way the feud will be settled, and the entire village will assume that Mita is responsible for the barrenness of her marriage with Simone. After beating and insulting Mita, Simone sends her away. Liolà visits her, and, after consoling each other for the injuries they have suffered, they make love. Mita

soon becomes pregnant, to the delight of her deceived husband, while Liolà gains the satisfaction of maintaining his freedom, gaining revenge against Simone and Tuzza, and fathering two more illegitimate children. *Bachelors. Handymen. Village life. Feuds. Illegitimacy. Water rights. Pregnancy. Lawsuits. Marriage. Sterility (sexual). Infidelity. Duplicity. Parentage. Lentini. Sicily.*

Note: Released in Italy in 1964 as *Liolà*.

VERY HAPPY ALEXANDER (France)   F6.5341

Productions de la Guéville–Madeleine Films–Films de la Colombe. *Dist* Cinema V Distributing, Inc. 17 Feb **1969** [New York opening]. Sd; col (Eastman Color). 35mm. 94 min. *MPAA rating G.*

Prod Danièle Delorme, Yves Robert. *Exec Prod* Léon Carré. *Dir-Story-Dial* Yves Robert. *Screenplay & Adapt* Yves Robert, Pierre Levy-Corti. *Photog* René Mathelin. *Art Dir & Set Dsgn* Jacques d'Ovidio. *Film Ed* Andrée Werlin. *Mus Comp & Cond* Vladimir Cosma. *Sd Dir* Guy Rophe. *English Subtitl* Noëlle Gillmor.

Cast: Philippe Noiret *(Alexander)*, Françoise Brion *(La Grande)*, Marlène Jobert *(Agathe)*, Antoinette Moya *(Angéle Sanguin)*, Paul Le Person *(Sanguin)*, Pierre Richard *(Colibert)*, Jean Carmet *(La Fringale)*, Tsilla Chelton, Léonce Corne, Jean Saudray, Kaly, Pierre Barnley, Marcel Bernier, Bernard Charlan, Madeleine Damien, Pierre Maguelon, Marie Marc, François Vibert.

Comedy. Alexander is a good-natured farmer who would love to devote all his time to sleeping and doing nothing. His shrewish wife, however, known as La Grande, keeps him working by snapping her fingers and by using a walkie-talkie. But one day Alexander becomes a widower when his wife and in-laws are killed in an automobile accident. He takes to his bed, refuses to budge from the house, and trains his faithful dog to do the marketing. Gradually, Alexander's philosophy that man was meant to relax and enjoy life wins converts; and the villagers decide that something must be done before laziness reaches epidemic proportions. But Alexander still refuses to return to work and devotes his waking hours to fishing, swimming, and drinking wine in the open fields. In time he finds a companion in Agathe, a lazy village girl who eagerly shares his happy-go-lucky life. After they have decided to marry, Agathe discovers the amount of property Alexander owns; and she is soon considering the fortune that could be made by developing the 300 acres. On the day of the wedding, Alexander is kneeling at Agathe's side when he suddenly hears his dog barking outside the church. As he turns his head, Agathe snaps her fingers in the manner of his late wife, whereupon Alexander leaps to his feet, backs out of the church, and—still a free spirit—runs off with his dog. *Idlers. Farmers. Shrews. Widowers. Marriage. Farm life. Village life. Fishing. Swimming. Automobile accidents. Dogs.*

Note: Released in France in Feb 1968 as *Alexandre le bienheureux*; running time: 96 min. Also known as *Happy Alexander* and *Alexander*.

VERY IMPORTANT PERSON see A COMING-OUT PARTY

THE VERY NAKED CANVAS   F6.5342

Stereo Productions. *Dist* Juri Productions. 22 Sep **1965** [Maryland license]. Sd; col (Eastman Color by Movielab). 35mm. 70 min.

Prod Savarino Lopez. *Dir* Jerome Jacobsen. *Screenplay* Manuel Roth. *Dir Photog* Robert Campbell, photog. *Mus* Thomas J. Valentino. *Sd* Magno Sound. *Optical Eff* B. & O. Film Specialists. *Casting* Hal Allen Associates.

Cast: Darlene Hall *(Miss Cavalier)*, Brenda De Naut, Vicki Lane, Judy Page, Lenore Rhein, Toni Stevens, Tove Pollin, Helen Eriksen, Esther Paige, Martha Dawson, Nellie De Carlo, Brigette Bidet, George Read, Dolly Burns, Natalie Rogers, Steve De Naut, Mike Arquette, John Farr, Dave Tolber, Tony Bogart, Dawn O'Day, Otto Franz Krone, Ellen Simms.

Comedy. Greenwich Village artist Otto Franz Krone receives an assignment from a popular "nudie" magazine to make a series of sketches of beautiful nudes for publication each month. After some initial difficulty—one model, Darlene Hall, is rejected because she has appeared previously on a competitive magazine; another woman disappears before Otto can finish his sketch—Otto finds a suitable first model, redheaded Ellen Simms, winner of a beauty contest at a nearby nudist camp. At the suggestion of the magazine's publisher, Ellen dyes her hair blonde, and Otto's drawing of her is accepted. The film's ending finds Otto chasing after a ravishing brunette. *Artists. Models. Drawings. Magazines (periodicals). Nudist camps. Beauty contests. New York City—Greenwich Village.*

Note: Location scenes filmed at Sunny Heights Lodge and in Greenwich Village.

A VERY PRIVATE AFFAIR (France/Italy)   F6.5343

Pro Ge Fi–CIPRA–Jacques Bar–C. C. M. *Dist* Metro-Goldwyn-Mayer, Inc. 28 Sep **1962** [New York opening; c17 Sep 1962; LP23092]. Sd (Westrex); col (Eastmancolor). 35mm. 95 min.

Prod Christine Gouze-Renal. *Dir* Louis Malle. *Screenplay* Jean-Paul Rappeneau, Louis Malle. *Adapt* Jean Ferry. *Dir Photog* Henri Decae. *Camera* Alain Douarinou. *Art Dir* Bernard Evein. *Film Ed* Kenout Peltier. *Mus*

Fiorenzo Carpi. *Song*: "*Sidonie*" Jean-Max Rivière, Jean Spanos, Charles Cros. *Sung by* Brigitte Bardot. *Rec Supv* William R. Sivel. *Asst Dir* Philippe Collin, Alain Gouze. *Prod Mgr* Fred Surin. *Miss Bardot's Dresses* Marie-Martine. *Still Photog* Paul Apoteker.

Cast: Brigitte Bardot *(Jill)*, Marcello Mastroianni *(Fabio)*, Gregor von Rezzori *(Gricha)*, Eléonore Hirt *(Cecile)*, Ursula Kubler *(Carla)*, Dirk Sanders *(Dick)*, Paul Sorèze *(Maxime)*, Jacqueline Doyen *(Juliette)*, Antoine Roblot *(Alain)*, Nicolas Bataille *(Edmond)*, Marco Naldi *(Italian grocer)*, François Marie *(François)*, Elie Presman *(Olivier)*, Gilles Quéant *(Trovar)*, Christian de Tilière *(Albert)*, Stan Kroll *(Maxime's chauffeur)*, Jeanne Allard *(charwoman)*, Gloria France *(Anna)*, Louis Malle *(journalist)*, Isarco Ravaioli, Simonetta Simeoni, Jacques Gheusi.

Drama. Jill, a wealthy 18-year-old blonde living with her mother in a luxurious villa on Lake Geneva, is hopelessly in love with Fabio, an Italian theater director, married to her friend Carla. Frustrated by her unrequited love, she moves to Paris and, after trying unsuccessfully to become a ballerina, turns to modeling. Her looks attract the attention of a film producer, who turns her into an international sex symbol by means of an elaborate publicity campaign. Then one night, after fainting while being crushed by a mob of hysterical fans, she decides to give up her career. Disguised in a black wig, she again meets Fabio and learns he is separated from his wife. They fall in love, and Jill follows him to Spoleto, where he is staging a spectacle for the arts festival. But her presence attracts hordes of fans and reporters, and Fabio is compelled to ask her to remain in her room while he is holding rehearsals at the theater. Following several violent quarrels, Jill climbs out onto a roof to watch the opening night performance. She is spotted by a photographer, who takes a flash-bulb picture. Startled by the sudden burst of light, she loses her balance and plunges to her death. *Theatrical directors. Actors. Dancers. Models. Motion picture producers. Photographers. Publicity. Fame. Disguise. Wealth. Paris. Spoleto. Lake of Geneva.*

Note: Filmed in Paris, Spoleto, and the environs of Lake of Geneva. Opened in Paris in Jan 1962 as *La vie privée*; running time: 103 min; in Rome in Apr 1962 as *Vita privata*; running time: 103 min.

A VERY SPECIAL FAVOR F6.5344

Lankershim Co. *Dist* Universal Pictures. Aug **1965** [c14 Aug 1965; LP34926]. Sd (Westrex); Col (Technicolor). 35mm. 105 min. [Copyright length: 94 min.]

Prod Stanley Shapiro. *Exec Prod* Robert Arthur. *Dir* Michael Gordon. *Story-Screenplay* Stanley Shapiro, Nate Monaster. *Photog* Leo Tover. *Art Dir* Alexander Golitzen, Walter Simonds. *Set Decor* John McCarthy, John Austin. *Titl* Pacific Title. *Film Ed* Russell F. Schoengarth. *Mus* Vic Mizzy. *Mus Supv* Joseph Gershenson. *Choreog* David Robel. *Sd* Waldon O. Watson, Corson Jowett. *Asst Dir* Phil Bowles. *In Charge of Prod* Edward Muhl. *Unit Prod Mgr* Wallace Worsley. *Miss Caron's Wardrobe* Yves Saint Laurent. *Makeup* Bud Westmore. *Hairstyles* Larry Germain. *Dial Coach* Norman Stuart.

Cast: Rock Hudson *(Paul Chadwick)*, Leslie Caron *(Lauren Boullard)*, Charles Boyer *(Michel Boullard)*, Walter Slezak *(Etienne)*, Dick Shawn *(Arnold Plum)*, Larry Storch *(Harry)*, Nita Talbot *(Mickey)*, Norma Varden *(Mother Plum)*, George Furth *(Pete)*, Marcel Hillaire *(Claude)*, Jay Novello *(Rene)*, Stafford Repp *(bartender)*, Danica D'Hondt *(Jacqueline)*, Frank De Vol, actor *(desk clerk)*, John Harding *(Dr. Lambert)*.

Comedy. Wealthy American oilman Paul Chadwick wins a court case in Paris against French attorney Michel Boullard by seducing the judge, a woman. Boullard flies to New York for a reunion with his daughter Lauren, whom he has not seen in 25 years, and on the plane he meets Chadwick, who promises a favor in compensation for the injury to Boullard's French pride. In New York, Boullard discovers that his daughter is a spinster psychologist engaged to mother-dominated Arnold Plum, and he asks Chadwick to have an affair with her. Posing as a patient, Chadwick seeks Lauren's help in fighting off sexually aggressive women. Falling for the scheme, Lauren shelters him in her apartment. He gets her drunk on champagne and takes her to his apartment when she passes out. Mickey, the switchboard operator, helps undress her while her future mother-in-law, Mrs. Plum, watches, unaware that Lauren is her son's fiancée. Upset by her indiscretion, Lauren tests herself by taking Arnold out to drink champagne; again she passes out. Chadwick sneaks her back to his apartment. This time she is recognized by Mrs. Plum. Boullard takes pity on his daughter, tells her about the plan he concocted with Chadwick, and helps her plan a counter-attack. Lauren invents a Spanish lover, and an ego-shattered Chadwick goes on a drinking spree. Boullard steps in again to change the course of events, and Lauren is tricked into accepting Chadwick's marriage proposal. *Lawyers. Judges. Oilmen. Psychologists. French. Playboys. Spinsters. Mothers-in-law. Seduction. Imposture. Filial relations. Drunkenness. Duplicity. Momism. Paris. New York City.*

VET IN THE DOGHOUSE *see* **IN THE DOGHOUSE**

LA VIA LATTEA *see* **THE MILKY WAY**

VIA MARGUTTA *see* **RUN WITH THE DEVIL**

LA VIACCIA (France/Italy) F6.5345

Titanus–Arco Film–Galatea–S. G. C. *Dist* Embassy Pictures. 20 Sep **1962** [New York opening]. Sd; col (Eastman Color). 35mm. 103 min.

Prod Alfredo Bini. *Dir* Mauro Bolognini. *Screenplay* Vasco Pratolini, Pasquale Festa Campanile, Massimo Franciosa. *Photog* Leonida Barboni. *Art Dir* Flavio Mogherini. *Set Decor* Piero Tosi. *Film Ed* Nino Baragli. *Mus* Piero Piccioni. *Mus From "Rhapsodie"* Claude Debussy. *Mus Cond* Franco Ferrara. *Sd* Mario Faraoni. *Cost* Piero Tosi.

Cast: Jean-Paul Belmondo *(Amerigo Casamonti)*, Claudia Cardinale *(Bianca)*, Pietro Germi *(Stefano Casamonti)*, Paul Frankeur *(Ferdinando Casamonti)*, Romolo Valli *(Dante)*, Gabriella Pallotta *(Carmelinda)*, Gina Sanmarco *(madam)*, Marcella Valeri *(Beppa)*, Emma Baron *(Giovanna)*, Franco Balducci *(Tognaccio)*, Claudio Biava *(Harlequin)*, Nando Angelini *(1st young man)*, Giuseppe Tosi *(Casamonti relative)*, Duilio D'Amore *(Bernardo)*, Paola Pitagora *(Anna)*, Gianna Giachetti *(girl)*, Rosita Di Vera Cruz *(Margherita)*, Olimpia Cavalli *(girl)*, Maurice Poli, Dante Posani, Rina Morelli, Renzo Palmer.

Drama. Source: Mario Pratesi, *L'eredità* (Florence, 1889). "La Viaccia" is a farm belonging to the Casamonti, an Italian family of the 1880's. One day young Amerigo Casamonti leaves the farm to work for his uncle, Ferdinando, a Florentine wine merchant who owns La Viaccia. It is hoped that the ailing Ferdinando will make Amerigo his heir and disinherit his lifelong mistress. Amerigo meets and falls in love with Bianca, a prostitute, and in order to pay for his "visits," he resorts to stealing from his uncle's till. When the theft is discovered, Ferdinando sends Amerigo back to La Viaccia. Unable to forget Bianca, Amerigo returns to Florence and takes a job in the brothel where she works. One evening, when he resents the attention other patrons are paying her, he incites a brawl and is knifed; he then is taken to a hospital but runs away before his wounds are healed. Bianca, however, refuses to see him, and he makes his way back to La Viaccia. Weak from loss of blood, he collapses and dies within a few feet of the farm. His family has just learned that Ferdinando is dead and that his mistress has inherited everything. *Farmers. Wine merchants. Mistresses. Prostitutes. Thieves. Uncles. Inheritance. Jealousy. Whorehouses. Florence.*

Note: Paris opening: Jun 1961; running time: 106 min; Rome opening: Sep 1961; running time: 100 min. Also known as *The Love Makers*.

VIBRATION (Sweden) F6.5346

Nordisk Tonefilm. *Dist* Audubon Films. 2 Apr **1969** [New York showing]. Sd; b&w. 35mm. 85 min.

Pres by Radley Metzger. *Prod-Dir* Torbjörn Axelman. *Screenplay* Bengt V. Vall, Sandro Key-Åberg, Torbjörn Axelman. *Screenplay Collab* Ardy Strüwer, Lars Åberg. *Photog* Hans Dittmer. *Asst Camera* Ulf Björck. *Film Ed* Margit Nordqvist. *Mus* Sven-Bertil Taube. *Mus Arr* Ulf Björlin, Ronnie Dunnie Quartet. *Sd* Kurt Holmberg. *Prod Mgr* Kjell Johnsson. *Script Girl* Margit Nordqvist. *Still Photog* Hans Dittmer, Lars Åberg.

Cast: Essy Persson *(Eliza)*, Margareta Sjödin *(Barbro)*, Sven-Bertil Taube *(Mauritz)*, Ulf Brunnberg *(Jonas)*, Ardy Strüwer *(Kono Tahiri [Jurgen, see note])*, Lars Åberg *(Gunnar)*, Yvonne Persson *(Annika)*, Ann-Christine Magnussen *(Mari [Britta, see note])*, Annmari Engwall *(Louise)*, Hasse Wallbom, Thyra Pettersson, William Pettersson, Inez Graaf.

Drama. Mauritz, an intellectual turned hack writer, arrives at a Gotland resort for a few weeks of work and vacation. While working on his current commission, a housewives' guide to astrology, he has several affairs, first with the hotel chambermaid, Barbro, then with a vacationing actress, Eliza; and he spends much of his time partying with a group of unrestrained artists and aspiring actors. Eliza confesses that she loves him, but Mauritz is unable to commit himself. After a moonlight beach party in which one of his group, a Japanese painter, burns his paintings, Mauritz bids Eliza good-bye at the airport and returns to his noncommittal existence. *Authors. Intellectuals. Chambermaids. Actors. Artists. Alienation. Sexuality. Vacations. Islands. Resorts. Gotland.*

Note: Released in Sweden in Jan 1968 as *Lejonsommar*; running time: 96 min. Role names in brackets refer to original Swedish version.

VIBRATIONS F6.5347

Morris Kaplan. 26 Feb **1969** [New York showing]. Sd; b&w. 35mm. 75 min.

Prod Morris Kaplan. *Assoc Prod* Peggy Steffans. *Dir-Writ* Joe Sarno. *Camera* Steve Silverman. *Mus* Sandy McVane.

Melodrama. Barbara Finch, an aspiring writer who works as a stenographer, moves away from her incestuous sister Julia, whose lesbianism Barbara no longer shares. Julia soon appears at Barbara's doorstep, however, and begins to pressure her into resuming a relationship that years earlier had led to Barbara's nervous breakdown. Julia joins a women's sex cult, and tries to lure Barbara into the group, but Barbara has found a young male friend, and she leaves her sister to her own devices. *Authors. Stenographers. Sisters. Roommates. Lesbianism. Incest. Mental illness. Cults.*

Note: May also be known as *Her "Thing" ... Vibrations.*

VICE AND VIRTUE (France/Italy)   **F6.5348**
S. N. E. Gaumont-Trianon Productions–Ultra Film. *Dist* Metro-Goldwyn-Mayer, Inc. 17 Mar **1965** [New York opening; c31 Dec 1963; LP31613]. Sd; b&w. 35mm (Franscope). 108 min.

Prod-Dir-Writ Roger Vadim. *Exec Prod* Alain Poiré. *Screenplay* Roger Vadim, Roger Vailland. *Screenplay Collab* Claude Choublier. *Dir Photog* Marcel Grignon. *Camera* Charles Henry Montel. *Sets* Jean André. *Asst Set Dsgn* Henri Morin, Marc Desages. *Film Ed* Victoria Mercanton. *Asst Film Ed* Monique Nana, Robert Christides. *Mus* Michel Magne. *Mus Dir* Jean Gitton. *Sd* Robert Biart. *1st & 2d Asst Dir* Serge Vallin, Jean-Michel Lacor, Jacques Lefèvre. *Prod Mgr* Irénée Leriche, Robert Sussfeld. *Gen Mgr* Roger Boulais, Suzanne Durrenberger. *Wardrobe* Georgette Fillon. *Wardrobe Dsgn* Marc Doelnitz. *Gowns* Louis Feraud. *Makeup* Odette Berroyer, Pierre Berroyer. *Sp Eff* Pierre Durin.

Cast: Annie Girardot *(Juliette)*, Catherine Deneuve *(Justine)*, Robert Hossein *(Schorndorf)*, O. E. Hasse *(von Bamberg)*, Philippe Lemaire *(Hans)*, Serge Marquand *(Ivan)*, Luciana Paluzzi *(Helena)*, Valeria Ciangottini *(Manuela)*, Georges Poujouly *(Hoech)*, Michel de Ré *(astrologer)*, Paul Gégauff *(SS doctor)*, Jean-Pierre Honoré *(Jean)*, Howard Vernon *(SS man)*, Lena von Martens, Henri Virlogeux, Jean-Daniel Simon, Pierre Gualdi, Jean Lévitte, Dorothée Blank, Lucien Guervil, Marianne Hardy, Juliette Hervieu, Michel Jourdan, Rudy Lenoir, Anne Libert, Monique Messine, José Qualglio, Jean-Michel Rouzière, Jacques Seiler, Henri Attal, Dominique Zardi.

Melodrama. Inspired by: Donatien Alphonse François [Marquis de] Sade, *Justine, ou les malheurs de la vertu* (Paris, 1791). Donatien Alphonse François [Marquis de] Sade, *La Nouvelle Justine, suivie de l'histoire de Juliette, sa soeur [ou les prospérités du vice]* (Paris, 1797). Two sisters, Juliette and Justine, take opposite paths during the Nazi occupation of Paris in World War II. Juliette engages in an affair with General von Bamberg, while the virtuous Justine plans to marry Jean, a resistance leader who was her childhood sweetheart. Following a civil ceremony, Justine and Jean are stopped by the Gestapo en route to church, and Jean is arrested. SS Colonel Schorndorf murders von Bamberg and takes the two sisters to a château where, along with other young women, they must satisfy the sexual appetites of high-ranking Nazis. Juliette becomes Schorndorf's mistress, while Justine joins the female prisoners. Through most of Justine's ordeal, Hans, Schorndorf's impotent aide, protects her. When the Allies finally arrive and liberate the women, Schorndorf poisons Juliette and dies in American machine gun fire. *Nazis. Mistresses. Sisters. Military occupation. Impotence. Poisoning. Murder. War crimes. Sexuality. Castles. World War II. Paris. Maquis. Gestapo. SS.*

Note: Filmed in part at the châteaux of Fénelon and Treyne. Opened in Paris in Mar 1963 as *Le vice et la vertu*; running time: 105 min; in Rome in Mar 1963 as *Il vizio e la virtù.*

VICE DOLLS (France)   **F6.5349**
Vascos Films. *Dist* William Mishkin. 30 Aug **1961** [Los Angeles showing]. Sd; b&w. 35mm. 92 min.

Prod Raymond Logeart. *Dir* Raoul André. *Adapt-Dial* Raymond Caillava. *Dir Photog* Roger Fellous. *Camera* Louis Stein. *Asst Camera* Claude Lecomte, Jean-Paul Schwartz. *Art Dir* Louis Le Barbenchon. *Asst Art Dir* Daniel Guéret. *Film Ed* Gabriel Rongier. *Asst Film Ed* Fernand Manella. *Sd* Pierre Goumy. *Sd Rec* Pierre Lauer. *Boom* Jacques Bissières. *Asst Dir* Tony Saytor, Jean Léon. *Gen Prod Mgr* Michel Mombailly. *Prod Mgr* Pierre Lefait. *Script Girl* Lily Hargous. *Prod Sec* Edith Tertza. *Cost* Henriette Ridard, Renée Rouzot. *Makeup* Louis Dor. *Hairstyles* Maud Begon. *Still Photog* Henri Thibault. *Prop Man* Fernand Hochmann.

Cast: Philippe Lemaire *(Pierre)*, Nicole Courcel *(Véronique)*, Maria Mauban, Dominique Wilms, André Roanne, Alex D'Arcy, Michèle Philippe, Paul Demange, Simone Berthier, Robert Chandeau, Yoko.

Crime melodrama. Source: Raymond Caillava, *Les clandestines* (Paris, 1954). Upon leaving prison, Pierre learns that his grandfather was victimized by swindlers who forced him out of his apartment, causing him to commit suicide. The swindlers then turned over the apartment to a crime syndicate which uses it as a front for a whorehouse. When Pierre tries to avenge his grandfather's death, the swindlers capture him, but he is saved by Véronique, an innocent young woman whose poverty has forced her into a life of prostitution. Véronique and Pierre fall in love and arrange for the arrest of the members of the syndicate. *Ex-convicts. Swindlers. Prostitutes. Suicide. Revenge. Syndicates. Whorehouses.*

Note: Opened in Paris in Oct 1954 as *Les clandestines*; running time: 93 min.

LE VICE ET LA VERTU *see* **VICE AND VIRTUE**

VICE GIRLS, LTD.   **F6.5350**
Artscope, Ltd. *Dist* Sam Lake Enterprises. 23 Sep **1964** [New York showing]. Sd; b&w. 35mm. 79 min.

A Jerry Gross-Amin Chaudhri Production. *Prod* Jerry Gross, Amin Chaudhri. *Dir* Amin Chaudhri. *Orig Screenplay* Jerry Gross. *Photog* Amin Chaudhri. *Asst Camera* Milton Keslow. *Lighting* John Delirod. *Film Ed* Amin Chaudhri. *Sd* Neil Fallon. *Asst Dir* Nicholas Demetroules. *Prod Mgr* Michael Hutzler. *Cont* Claude LeGallou.

Cast: Linda Bennet *(Christine)*, Brooks Clift *(Nolan)*, Joann Brier *(Jackie Miller)*, Richard DeHavilland *(Merlin)*, F. Kende Hart *(Mr. Lyle)*, Milton Carlyle *(Ivanoff)*, Anna Stanovich *(Gina)*, Norman Glind *(Robert Havershire)*, Tony Wade *(Tommy)*, Rick Fields *(Billy)*, Don Craig *(Thompson)*.

Melodrama. Gina, the newest recruit of a blackmail and espionage ring, is taken to Sunny Dale Lodge, a seaside estate. There she is trained to lure wealthy clients into compromising situations by indulging their every desire for the benefit of hidden cameras. She is taught how to dress and speak so that she may pass inconspicuously through the highest levels of society. Mr. Lyle, the leader of the ring, rules with an iron fist. Escape from the estate is impossible; breaches of discipline are handled by Ivanoff, a 300-pound chauffeur, and Merlin, a psychotic killer. The girls are personally supervised by Jackie Miller, a woman of long experience in the field of boudoir blackmail. All efforts are now directed toward the biggest operation of all. At a huge party, the assembled captains of industry and government are to be led under the influence of alcohol and narcotics to separate rooms, and there their sexual perversions will be recorded. On the night of the party, two young punks attempt to loot the estate and are shot by the organization strongmen. The noise brings government agents Nolan and Thompson crashing through the gates. For months the agents have been on the trail of the ring. The party provides all the evidence they need. Gina is shot by Lyle as she tries to escape. Lyle and Ivanoff speed away, followed by the government men. Involved in the chase, the racketeers see an oncoming train too late to avoid a flaming crash. *Racketeers. Diplomats. Businessmen. Government agents. Blackmail. Espionage. Prostitution. Photographs. Orgies. Narcotics. Upper classes. Chases.*

VICE VERSA!   **F6.5351**
Dist Distribpix, Inc. ca **1970**. Sd; col. 35mm. [Feature length assumed.]
Prod Jack Bravman, Michael Findlay. *Dir* Michael Findlay. *Photog* Roberta Findlay. *Film Ed* Michael Findlay.

Sex film. No information about the precise nature of this film has been found, but press material indicates that it contains scenes of sexual intercourse, lesbianism, and troilism. *Lesbianism. Troilism.*

VICIOUS BLONDE   **F6.5352**
C. I. T. Films. *Dist* I. R. M. I. Films. ca **1968**. Sd; b&w. 35mm. 78 min. [Also 81 min.]
Prod Jack Stram. *Dir* Allan Lindus.
Cast: Karla Fischer, Uta Vargas.

Sex film. No information about the precise nature of this film has been found, but press material suggests that it concerns a stripteaser who humiliates her 54-year-old "sugar daddy." *Stripteasers. Sexuality.*

Note: Filmed in Munich.

LE VICOMTE RÈGLE SES COMPTES *see* **THE VISCOUNT**

VICTIM (Great Britain)   **F6.5353**
Parkway Films–Allied Film Makers. *Dist* Pathé-America Distributing Co. 5 Feb **1962** [New York opening; c31 Jul 1961; LP21930]. Sd; b&w. 35mm. 100 min.

A Michael Relph–Basil Dearden Production. *Prod* Michael Relph. *Dir* Basil Dearden. *Screenplay* Janet Green, John McCormick. *Photog* Otto Heller. *Art Dir* Alex Vetchinsky. *Film Ed* John D. Guthridge. *Mus* Philip Green. *Sd* Leslie Wiggins. *Sd Rec* C. C. Stevens, Gordon K. McCallum. *Asst Dir* Bert Batt.

Cast: Dirk Bogarde *(Melville Farr)*, Sylvia Syms *(Laura Farr)*, Dennis Price *(Calloway)*, Anthony Nicholls *(Lord Fullbrook)*, Peter Copley *(Paul Mandrake)*, Norman Bird *(Harold Doe)*, Peter McEnery *(Jack Barrett)*, Donald Churchill *(Eddy Stone)*, Derren Nesbitt *(Sandy)*, John Barrie *(Detective Inspector Harris)*, John Cairney *(Bridie)*, Alan MacNaughtan *(Scott Hankin)*, Nigel Stock *(Phip)*, Frank Pettitt *(barman)*, Mavis Villiers *(Madge)*, Charles Lloyd Pack *(Henry)*, Hilton Edwards *(P. H.)*, David Evans *(Mickey)*, Noel Howlett *(William Patterson)*, Margaret Diamond *(Miss Benham)*, Alan Howard *(Frank)*, Dawn Beret *(Sylvie)*.

Drama. "Boy" Barrett, a young English construction worker, is arrested for stealing a large sum of money from his firm. When he learns that the police know he used the money to pay a ring of blackmailers who threatened to expose him as a homosexual, he hangs himself rather than endanger the career of

Melville Farr, a successful barrister with whom he had become emotionally, but not sexually, involved. Farr does become implicated, however, when the police discover that the blackmailers were using a photograph of them together to extort money from Barrett. Filled with remorse and angered by the existence of a law that makes homosexuals criminals, thereby making them easy prey for blackmailers, Farr decides to jeopardize both his marriage and his career by bringing those responsible for Farr's suicide to justice. Before his marriage Farr had admitted to his wife, Laura, that he had homosexual tendencies; now, forced to confess that these tendencies still exist, he offers Laura her freedom. Despite pressure from both the blackmailers and their victims, Farr cooperates with the police in tracking down the blackmailers—a sadistic young hoodlum, Sandy, and an embittered spinster, Miss Benham. Though fully aware that the scandal will ruin him, Farr insists upon prosecuting; as he prepares his case, Laura, who still loves him, realizes that her husband's need for her is stronger than any passing emotion he may feel, and she intimates that she will return to him when the trial is over. *Construction workers. Police. Barristers. Hoodlums. Spinsters. Robbery. Blackmail. Male homosexuality. Suicide. Marriage. Scandal. Photographs.*

Note: Opened in London in Aug 1961.

VICTIM FIVE see **CODE 7, VICTIM 5!**

THE VICTORS (United States/Great Britain) **F6.5354**
Highroad Productions-Open Road Films. *Dist* Columbia Pictures. 19 Dec **1963** [New York opening; c31 Dec 1963; LP27124]. Sd (Westrex); b&w. 35mm (Panavision). 175 min.
A Carl Foreman Production. *Prod-Dir-Writ* Carl Foreman. *Assoc Prod* Harold Buck. *Dir Photog* Christopher Challis. *Camera Op* Austin Dempster. *Art Dir* Maurice Fowler. *Art Cons* Eric Estorick. *Prod Dsgn* Geoffrey Drake. *Prolog & Titl Dsgn* Saul Bass, Associates of Hollywood. *Film Ed* Alan Osbiston. *Asst Ed* Joan Morduch. *Dial Ed* Don Deacon. *Mus Comp & Cond* Sol Kaplan. *Orch* Wally Stott. Songs: "March of the Victors," "Sweet Talk," "No Other Man" Sol Kaplan, Freddy Douglass. Song: "Theme From The Victors (My Special Dream)" Sol Kaplan, Freddy Douglass, Howard Greenfield. Song: "Does Goodnight Mean Goodbye?" Jack Keller, Howard Greenfield, Gerry Goffin. Song: "Have Yourself a Merry Little Christmas" Ralph Blane, Hugh Martin. Sung by Frank Sinatra. *Sd Ed* Winston Ryder. *Sd Rec* Buster Ambler, Bob Jones. *Asst Dir* Eric Rattray. *Prod Coörd* Leon Becker. *Unit Mgr* Geoffrey Helman. *Prod Supv* Sidney G. Barnsby. *Cont* Joan Davis. *Prod Sec* Miriam Hart. *Wardrobe Dsgn* Olga Lehmann. *Wardrobe Supv* Elsa Fennell. *Makeup* Ernest Gasser, Wally Schneiderman. *Hairdresser* Gordon Bond. *Sp Eff* Cliff Richardson, Wally Veevers. *Tech Adv* Nils Runelundquist, (Capt.). *Coöp* Swedish Army Ordnance Corps. *Titl* National Screen Service Ltd. *Casting* Barry Gray, casting dir.
Cast: Vincent Edwards *(Baker)*, Albert Finney *(Russian soldier)*, George Hamilton *(Corporal Trower)*, Melina Mercouri *(Magda)*, Jeanne Moreau *(Frenchwoman)*, George Peppard *(Corporal Chase)*, Maurice Ronet *(French Lieutenant Cohn)*, Rosanna Schiaffino *(Maria)*, Romy Schneider *(Regine)*, Elke Sommer *(Helga)*, Eli Wallach *(Sergeant Craig)*, Michael Callan *(Eldridge)*, Peter Fonda *(Weaver)*, Jim Mitchum *(Grogan)*, Senta Berger *(Trudi)*, Joel Flateau *(Jean-Pierre)*, Albert Lieven *(Herr Metzger)*, Mervyn Johns *(Dennis)*, Tutte Lemkow *(Sikh soldier)*, Peter Vaughan *(policeman)*, George Roubicek, George Mikell *(Russian sentries)*, Alf Kjellin *(priest)*, Alan Barnes *(Tom)*, John Rogers *(young British soldier)*, Marianne Deeming *(Frau Metzger)*, Patrick Jordan *(tank sergeant)*, Elizabeth Ercy *(young French girl)*, Milo Sperber *(concentration camp prisoner)*, Malya Nappi *(barmaid)*, Vanda Godsell *(nurse)*, Bee Duffell *(Joan)*, James Chase *(condemned soldier)*, Riggs O'Hara, Charles De Temple, Al Waxman, Tom Busby, Robert Nichols, Graydon Gould, Larry Caringi, Ian Hughes, Anthony McBride *(The Squad)*, Colin Maitland, Tony Wallace, John Crawford, Russ Titus, Sean Kelly, Mickey Knox, Peter Arne, Veite Bethke.
War epic. Source: Alexander Baron, *The Human Kind; a Sequence* (New York, 1953). Corporals Trower and Chase, Sergeant Craig, and other members of an American infantry squad in England are shipped to combat assignment in Italy following their training in Britain. After taking possession of a small town, Baker, one of the G.I.'s, finds a few hours of happiness with Maria, a young mother who has not heard from her soldier husband in many months. Later, the group arrives in France after the D-Day landing, where Craig spends the evening with a Frenchwoman terrified by the continuous bombing. Chase is tempted by the wealthy Magda to desert and join her in the enormously profitable black market; instead, he rejoins his outfit and suffers a leg wound in action. In Belgium, Trower falls in love with Regine, an opportunistic nightclub violinist, but she throws him over for a pimp. Throughout their ordeal, the men are subjected to strain beyond that brought on by combat or romantic entanglements: white Southerners in the outfit harass the black soldiers; battle-hardened G.I.'s shoot a puppy for sport; and Trower and Chase befriend an 11-year-old French boy, only to discover that he is baiting them for homosexual

relations. By the war's end, Craig is in the hospital with half his face shot away, Chase still has his leg wound, and Trower is living in the Russian zone of Berlin with Helga, a young blonde whose sister continually boasts of luxuries provided her by a Russian captain. After a disillusioning evening with Helga, Trower gets involved in a pointless squabble with a drunken Russian soldier; unable to understand each other, the two men pull knives and stab each other to death. *Combat zone life. French. Italians. Opportunists. Violinists. Germans. Sisters. Russians. Pimps. Military occupation. Racism. Male homosexuality. Drunkenness. Murder. Aerial bombardment. Black market. World War II. Italy. France. Belgium. Berlin. United States Army—Infantry. Dogs.*

Note: Filmed in Italy, France, England, and Sweden. Opened in London in Nov 1963.

VIDAS SÊCAS see **BARREN LIVES**

UNE VIE see **END OF DESIRE**

LA VIE À L'ENVERS see **LIFE UPSIDE DOWN**

LA VIE CONJUGALE see **ANATOMY OF A MARRIAGE; MY DAYS WITH JEAN-MARC**

LA VIE CONJUGALE see **ANATOMY OF A MARRIAGE; MY NIGHTS WITH FRANÇOISE**

LA VIE DE CHÂTEAU (France) **F6.5355**
Ancinex-Cobela Films-Productions de la Guéville. *Dist* Royal Films International. 20 Mar **1967** [New York opening]. Sd; b&w. 35mm. 92 min.
Prod Nicole Stéphane. *Dir* Jean-Paul Rappeneau. *Screenplay* Alain Cavalier, Claude Sautet, Jean-Paul Rappeneau. *Dial* Daniel Boulanger. *Photog* Pierre Lhomme. *Art Dir* Jacques Saulnier. *Film Ed* Pierre Gillette. *Mus* Michel Legrand. *Sd* Jacques Maumont. *Asst Dir* Olivier Gérard, Nicolas Ribowski. *Prod Mgr* Jacques Juranville.
Cast: Catherine Deneuve *(Marie)*, Philippe Noiret *(Jérôme)*, Pierre Brasseur *(Dimanche)*, Mary Marquet *(Charlotte)*, Henri Garcin *(Julien)*, Carlos Thompson *(Klopstock)*, Marc Dudicourt *(Schimmelbeck)*, Alexis Micha *(The Boy)*, Robert Moor *(Plantier, the gardener)*, Donald O'Brien *(The American Officer)*, Paul Le Person *(Roger)*, Pierre Rousseau *(German orderly)*, Marie Marc *(Dimanche's housekeeper)*, Annie Guégan *(waitress in bar)*, Niksa Stefanini *(German general)*, Christian Barbier *(French colonel)*, Jean-Pierre Moulin *(lieutenant)*, Valerie Camille *(English girl)*.
War comedy. In Normandy at the time of the German occupation, Marie becomes bored with her lackluster married life with Jérôme, a phlegmatic country squire 20 years her senior, and dreams of living in Paris. Consequently, she is delighted by the sudden unexpected arrival of a handsome parachutist, Julien, who has come to make preparations for the destruction of a German shore gun before D-Day. He makes contact with Marie's father, Dimanche, the local resistance leader, and then reluctantly returns to England. Meanwhile, Klopstock, a German officer, billets himself and his company at the dilapidated family chateau in order to pursue Marie. Julien is returned dead drunk, to Normandy, and to explain his presence to the Germans, Marie and Jérôme pretend that he is her brother. Klopstock, hopeful of winning Marie's gratitude, showers Julien with kindness. Marie and Julien run off, and Jérôme decides that it is time to assert himself if he is to keep his wife. He assumes Julien's hazardous mission of guiding the American parachutists who are to destroy the gun and becomes a hero. As Allied invasion troops arrive, Julien departs for adventures elsewhere while Marie gazes at her husband with a new look of admiration. *Maquis. Paratroops. War heroes. Military occupation. Imposture. Infidelity. Filial relations. Drunkenness. Castles. Ordnance. World War II. D-Day (6 Jun 1944). Normandy. Germany—Army. United States Army.*

Note: Paris opening: Jan 1966. Also known as *A Matter of Resistance.*

LA VIE, L'AMOUR, LA MORT see **LIFE LOVE DEATH**

LA VIE PRIVÉE see **A VERY PRIVATE AFFAIR**

LE VIEIL HOMME ET L'ENFANT see **THE TWO OF US**

LA VIEILLE DAME INDIGNE see **THE SHAMELESS OLD LADY**

VIENNA WALTZES (Austria) **F6.5356**
Vindobona Filmgesellschaft-Cordial Film. *Dist* Hoffberg Productions. **1961.** Sd; b&w. 35mm. 90 min.
Prod Karl Ehrlich. *Dir* Emile Edwin Reinert. *Screenplay* Benno Vigny, Jacques Companeez. *Story* Hans Gustl Kernmayr. *Photog* Günther Anders. *Camera* Hannes Staudinger. *Set Dsgn* Otto Niedermoser. *Mus Selections* Johann Strauss, Sr., Johann Strauss. *Mus Arr* Willy Schmidt-Gentner.
Cast: Anton Walbrook *(Johann Strauss)*, Marthe Harell *(Millie Trampusch)*, Lilly Stepanek *(Anna Strauss)*, Fritz Imhoff *(Oberstrasser)*, Eva Leiter *(Frau Reisner)*, Lotte Lang, Eric Frey, P. Czeike, Fritz Berger, H. Meixner, A. Truby, Karl Ehmann, F. Czepa.

Biographical drama. Cafe band conductor Johann Strauss develops a unique rythmic pattern for dance music. When he introduces his compositions, Millie, a milliner with whom Johann has been having an affair, ignores the initial unpopularity of the music and teaches the customers a new dance called the waltz. The Viennese become more tolerant as royalty accepts the waltz, and Johann soon becomes rich and famous. He leaves his wife and three children and tours Europe with Millie, but she is shunned for being his mistress. Upon returning, Johann is enraged to find that his son, Johann, Jr., has also achieved fame as a conductor. The aging musician overcomes his anger, however, when he hears his son perform, and a reconciliation takes place when Johann, Jr., visits his dying father. *Orchestra conductors. Composers. Milliners. Mistresses. Royalty. Infidelity. Music. Desertion. Filial relations. Envy. Cafes. Vienna. Johann Strauss, Sr. Johann Strauss. Emilie Trampusch.*

Note: Released in Austria in 1951 as *Wien tanzt*; running times: 93-102 min. Anton Walbrook is a pseudonym for Adolf Wohlbrück.

UNE VIERGE POUR LE PRINCE see A MAIDEN FOR A PRINCE

LES VIERGES DE ROME see AMAZONS OF ROME

24 STUNDEN IM LEBEN EINER FRAU see 24 HOURS IN A WOMAN'S LIFE

VIETNAM IN TURMOIL (Japan)   F6.5357
Shin Riken Eiga Co. *For* Mainichi. *Dist* Harrison Pictures, Daiei Motion Picture Co. 25 Mar **1966** [San Francisco opening]. Sd; col (Eastmancolor). 35mm (CinemaScope). 83 min.

Pres by Edward Harrison. *Dir* Masaharu Akasa. *Photog* Shinichi Ogawa, Masao Mizukami, Masayori Fukazawa, Isamu Nagayama.

Documentary. The war in Vietnam is examined, with emphasis on its brutality and futility. Included are scenes of actual combat, South Vietnamese soldiers torturing Vietcong suspects, city slum conditions, children gambling in the streets of Saigon, South Vietnamese girls engaging in prostitution, and the bombing of the U. S. Embassy. *Children. Combat zone life. Torture. Prostitution. Urban life. Slums. Vietnam War 1964–73. Saigon. Republic of Vietnam. United States—Diplomatic and consular service. Vietcong.*

Note: Released in Japan ca1965 as *Doran no Betonamu.*

A VIEW FROM THE BRIDGE (France/Italy)   F6.5358
Transcontinental Films–Produzione Intercontinentali. *Dist* Continental Distributing, Inc. 22 Jan **1962** [New York opening]. Sd; b&w. 35mm. 110 min.

Prod Paul Graetz. *Dir* Sidney Lumet. *Screenplay* Norman Rosten. *Photog* Michel Kelber. *Art Dir* Jacques Saulnier. *Film Ed* Françoise Javet. *Mus* Maurice Le Roux. *Sd* Jo de Bretagne. *Asst Dir* Dossia Mage. *Prod Mgr* Julien Rivière.

Cast: Raf Vallone (*Eddie Carbone*), Jean Sorel (*Rodolpho*), Maureen Stapleton (*Beatrice Carbone*), Carol Lawrence (*Catherine*), Raymond Pellegrin (*Marco*), Morris Carnovsky (*Mr. Alfieri*), Harvey Lembeck (*Mike*), Mickey Knox (*Louis*), Vincent Gardenia (*Lipari*), Frank Campanella (*longshoreman*).

Drama. Source: Arthur Miller, *A View From the Bridge* (New York opening: 29 Sep 1955). Eddie Carbone is an Italian-American longshoreman on the Brooklyn waterfront. The joy of his life is his 18-year-old niece, Catherine, whom he and his wife, Bea, have raised from infancy. When two of Bea's cousins from Sicily, Marco and Rodolpho, illegally enter the United States and take refuge in Eddie's home, an attraction develops between Catherine and the handsome young Rodolpho. Eddie's incestuous love for his niece drives him into cruel criticism of Rodolpho, including the accusation that he is an opportunist who plans to marry Catherine only to obtain his U. S. citizenship papers. When Eddie's efforts fail to influence Catherine, he brands Rodolpho a homosexual and degrades him in front of Catherine by kissing him on the lips. His desperation only serves to further alienate Catherine, however, and when she and Rodolpho make plans to marry, Eddie betrays both Marco and Rodolpho to the immigration authorities. As the two brothers are led away, Marco spits on Eddie, denouncing him as an informer. A waterfront lawyer succeeds in winning freedom for Rodolpho because of his pending marriage, but Marco is slated for deportation. While out on bail, Marco goes to the Carbone house and forces Eddie to his knees; humiliated before his family and neighbors, Eddie plunges a cargo hook into his chest. *Stevedores. Uncles. Sicilians. Cousins. Brothers. Informers. Lawyers. Adoption. Adolescence. Immigration. Incest. Jealousy. Perfidy. Suicide. New York City—Brooklyn.*

Note: Location scenes filmed in Brooklyn, New York. Opened in Paris in Jan 1962 as *Vu du pont*; in Rome in Jan 1962 as *Uno sguardo dal ponte.* Original running time: 117 min.

THE VIKING QUEEN (Great Britain)   F6.5359
Seven Arts Productions-Hammer Film Productions. *Dist* Twentieth Century-Fox Film Corp. 16 Aug **1967** [Detroit opening; c31 Dec 1966; LF14]. Sd (RCA); col (De Luxe). 35mm. 91 min.

Prod-Story John Temple-Smith. *Dir* Don Chaffey. *2d Unit Dir* Jack Causey. *Screenplay* Clarke Reynolds. *Photog* Stephen Dade. *Camera Op* David Harcourt. *2d Unit Camera* John Harris. *Prod Dsgn* George Provis. *Supv Ed* James Needs. *Ed* Peter Boita. *Mus Comp* Gary Hughes. *Mus Supv* Philip Martell. *Sd Ed* Stanley Smith. *Sd Mix* H. L. Bird, Bob Jones. *Asst Dir* Dennis Bertera. *Prod Mgr* Rene Dupont. *Cont* Ann Skinner. *Cost Dsgn* John Furness. *Wardrobe Supv* Hilda Geerdts. *Wardrobe Master* Jack Gallagher. *Makeup Supv* Charles Parker. *Hairstyles* Bobbie Smith. *Sp Eff* Allan Bryce. *Master of Horse* Frank Hayden. *Prod Liaison* William O'Kelly.

Cast: Don Murray (*Justinian*), Carita (actress) (*Salina*), Donald Houston (*Maelgan*), Andrew Keir (*Octavian*), Adrienne Corri (*Beatrice*), Niall MacGinnis (*Tiberion*), Wilfrid Lawson (*King Priam*), Nicola Pagett (*Talia*), Percy Herbert (*Catus*), Patrick Troughton (*Tristram*), Sean Caffrey (*Fergus*), Denis Shaw (*Osiris*), Philip O'Flynn (*merchant*), Brendan Mathews (*Nigel*), Gerry Alexander (*Fabian*), Bryan Marshall (*Dominic*), Jack Rodney (*Boniface*), Patrick Gardiner (*Benedict*), Paul Murphy (*Dalan, Maelgan's son*), Arthur O'Sullivan (*old man at tax enquiry*), Cecil Sheridan (*shopkeeper at protest gathering*), Anna Manahan (*shopkeeper's wife*), Nita Lorraine (*Nubian girl-slave*).

Costume melodrama. In Britain during the Roman period, Priam, the dying king of the Iceni tribe, names his daughter Salina as his successor because she possesses the strong qualities of her deceased mother, a Viking queen. In following her father's wish that peace be maintained, Salina's major problem is to control the rebellious Druids, who are determined to oust the Romans. Equally concerned with harmonious coexistence is the Roman military governor, Justinian, whose tolerance enrages his tyrannical second-in-command, Octavian. Salina and Justinian fall in love, but the Druids refuse to permit their marriage. At the same time, the wily Octavian arranges for a revolt in a faraway province. Once Justinian has left to crush the uprising, Octavian has Salina arrested and flogged, rapes her younger sister, and incites both the Druids and the Iceni to open rebellion. By the time Justinian returns, Salina has taken up the sword against the Romans and a full-scale revolution is underway. Justinian, left with no alternative, sends his legions into combat. In the final battle, the Britons are outmaneuvered, and the mortally wounded Salina dies in Justinian's arms. *Iceni. Royalty. Vikings. Druids. Despots. Revolts. Flogging. Rape. Great Britain—History—Roman period. Rome—History—Empire.*

Note: Location scenes filmed in the Wicklow Mountains in Ireland. Released in Great Britain in Mar 1967 in Technicolor.

VILLA RIDES   F6.5360
Paramount Pictures. 29 May **1968** [Denver, Colorado, opening; c29 May 1968; LP35845]. Sd; col (Technicolor). 35mm (Panavision). 125 min.

Prod Ted Richmond. *Dir* Buzz Kulik. *Screenplay* Robert Towne, Sam Peckinpah. *Dir Photog* Jack Hildyard. *Camera Op* Ricardo Navarrete. *Asst Camera* Fernando Perrote, Ron Drinkwater. *Unit Photog* Antonio Luengo, John Cabrera. *Art Dir* José Algueró. *Set Decor* Román Calatayud. *Prod Dsgn* Ted Haworth. *Film Ed* David Bretherton. *Mus Comp & Cond* Maurice Jarre. *Sd Rec* Roy Charman. *Asst Dir* Antonio Fuentes. *Prod Supv* Robert Goodstein. *Prod Mgr* Eduardo G. Maroto. *Asst to Prod Supv* José María Ochoa. *Script Clerk* Ricardo Huertas. *Cost Supv* Eric Seelig. *Makeup Supv* Richard Mills. *Hairstyles* Carmen Sánchez. *Sp Eff* Milt Rice. *Ch Grip* Mariano Denia. *Stunt Gaffer* Chuck Hayward. *Gaffer* Alejandro de la Fuente.

Cast: Yul Brynner (*Villa*), Robert Mitchum (*Lee*), Maria Grazia Buccella (*Fina*), Charles Bronson (*Fierro*), Robert Viharo (*Urbina*), Frank Wolff (*Ramirez*), Herbert Lom (*Huerta*), Alexander Knox (*Madero*), Diana Lorys (*Emilita*), Robert Carricart (*Don Luis*), Fernando Rey (*Fuentes*), Regina de Julian (*Lupita*), Andres Monreal (*Herrera*), Antonio Padilla Ruiz (*Juan*), John Ireland (*man in barber shop*), Jill Ireland (*girl in restaurant*), José María Prada.

Historical drama. Source: William Douglas Lansford, *Pancho Villa* (Los Angeles, 1965). In 1912 American pilot Lee Arnold is smuggling guns into Mexico and selling them for gold to Captain Ramirez and the insurrectionists. While waiting for his plane to be repaired after one such mission, Arnold witnesses a brutal attack by Ramirez and his men on a village known for its allegiance to Pancho Villa and the revolutionary government. When the town is retaken by Villa's sadistic aide, Fierro, Arnold is sentenced to execution for having helped the enemy; but he is spared at the last minute by agreeing to serve as Villa's one-man air force. As Arnold bombards Ramirez' men with homemade grenades, Villa and his followers capture first an enemy troop train and then an entire town. Villa's success infuriates revolutionary commander General Huerta, who had ordered Villa not to attack the town. To facilitate taking over the government from President Madero, Huerta sends Villa on a suicide mission by ordering him to take the city of Conejos. Although many of Villa's men die in battle, Arnold secures victory by bombarding the enemy from the air and crashing his plane into barbed wire holding back Villa's men. After Villa has killed Ramirez and forced the officials of the captured city to pay his troops, he is arrested by Huerta for allegedly disobeying orders. Arnold escapes by bribing his way across the border into El Paso. Sometime later, Villa and his lieutenants find Arnold in Texas. Having escaped from jail, they again need Arnold's help to overthrow Huerta, now installed as dictator after having assassinated Madero. Arnold finally agrees to assist in raising another army to march on Mexico City, this time against Emiliano Zapata. *Americans in foreign countries. Air pilots. Guerrillas. Revolutionaries. Mercenaries. Traitors. Smuggling. Capital punishment. Assassination. Guns. Mexico—History— 1910-17. El Paso. Texas. Mexico City. Francisco "Pancho" Villa. Victoriano Huerta. Francisco Indalecio Madero.*

Note: Filmed in Spain.

VILLA-VENNELY: HOME OF COPENHAGEN CALL GIRLS
(Denmark)   **F6.5361**
Pingvin Film. *Dist* Associated Film Distributors of California. 3 Apr **1965** [Sacramento, California, opening]. Sd; b&w. 35mm. 95 min.

Dir Poul Nyrup. *Screenplay* Poul Nyrup, Klaus Nielsen. *Photog* Søren Ingemann, Palle Schnedler-Sørensen. *Mus* Otto Brandenburg. *Arr* Jørn Adrian. *Perf by* The Sharks, Søren Strømberg, The Weedons.

Cast: Karine Smidt *(Lis)*, Preben Nicolaisen *(The Butler)*, Caren Birgith Petersen *(Sylvia)*, Erik Chris *(boss)*, Elinor Infred *(Anita)*, Ole Spenster *(Plovmand)*, Zola Johansen *(Zola)*, Henning Petersen *(Smarte Harry)*, Brigitte Ranten *(Joan)*, Birthe Conny Petersen *(Jette)*, Michel Hildesheim, Finn Andersen.

Melodrama. The Villa Vennely, the posh residence of a wealthy Copenhagen businessman, is a center of undercover prostitution, gambling, and drugs. A burly handyman-butler acts as "madam," fondly serving the six prostitutes who live in the house. Lis, one of the women, becomes hooked on drugs supplied to her by a regular customer who covers his heavy losses at the gaming tables with profits from narcotics. After a fight with another woman, Lis is taken to a hospital, where her doctor, an occasional visitor to the house, reports her addiction to the police. The police raid the house, and the butler is jailed. The women receive fines, remaining free to find similar employment elsewhere. *Businessmen. Prostitutes. Drug addicts. Physicians. Butlers. Drug dealers. Madams. Police. Gambling. Narcotics. Whorehouses. Copenhagen.*

Note: Opened in Copenhagen in May 1964 as *Villa Vennely*. Also known as *Copenhagen Call Girls* and *Call Girls of Copenhagen*. Role names correspond to Scandinavian version.

VILLAGE OF THE GIANTS
     F6.5362
Berkeley Productions-Embassy Pictures. *Dist* Embassy Pictures. 20 Oct **1965** [Boston opening]. Sd; col (PathéColor). 35mm. 80 min.

Pres by Bert I. Gordon. A Bert I. Gordon Production. *Prod-Dir-Story* Bert I. Gordon. *Screenplay* Alan Caillou. *Dir Photog* Paul C. Vogel. *Art Dir* Franz Bachelin. *Set Decor* Robert R. Benton. *Film Ed* John Bushelman. *Mus Comp & Cond* Jack Nitzsche. *Songs:* "Woman," "When It Comes to Your Love" Ron Elliott. *Sung by* The Beau Brummels. *Song:* "Little Bitty Corrine" Frank C. Slay, Frederick A. Picariello. *Sung by* Freddy Cannon. *Songs:* "Marianne," "Nothing Can Stand in My Way" Jack Nitzsche, Russ Titelman. *Sung by* Mike Clifford. *Choreog* Toni Basil. *Sd* John Carter, Charles Grenzbach. *Asst Dir* James Rosenberger. *Prod Mgr* Frank Caffey. *Script Supv* Dorothy Yutzi. *Cost* Leah Rhodes, Frank Richardson. *Makeup* Wally Westmore. *Hairstyle Supv* Nellie Manley. *Vis Eff* Bert I. Gordon, Flora Gordon. *Proc Photog* Farciot Edouart. *Still Photog* Talmadge Morrison.

Cast: Tommy Kirk *(Mike)*, Johnny Crawford *(Horsey)*, Beau Bridges *(Fred)*, Ronny Howard *(Genius)*, Joy Harmon *(Merrie)*, Bob Random *(Rick)*, Tisha Sterling *(Jean)*, Charla Doherty *(Nancy)*, Tim Rooney *(Pete)*, Kevin O'Neal *(Harry)*, Gail Gilmore *(Elsa)*, Toni Basil *(Red)*, Hank Jones *(Chuck)*, Jim Begg *(Fatso)*, Vicki London *(Georgette)*, Joseph Turkel *(sheriff)*, The Beau Brummels, Freddy Cannon, Mike Clifford *(singers)*.

Science fiction comedy-drama. Source: Herbert George Wells, *The Food of the Gods* (London, 1904). Four teenaged couples arrive in a town after their car is wrecked in an avalanche. Young lovers Mike and Nancy are interrupted by Nancy's younger brother, Genius, an amateur scientist who announces he has discovered a food-like substance which causes those who eat it to grow to enormous size. Hearing about the substance, the eight teenagers steal some, try it out, and grow into giants. They take over the town, holding the sheriff's daughter hostage; but Genius discovers a vapor which acts as an antidote, and the invaders are chased from town after they return to normal size. *Juvenile delinquents. Sheriffs. Giants. Scientists. Hostages. Adolescence. Abduction. Secret formulas. Automobile accidents.*

Note: Filmed in "Perceptovision."

VILLE SANS PITIÉ *see* TOWN WITHOUT PITY

VINETU *see* APACHE GOLD

VINETU II *see* **LAST OF THE RENEGADES**

VINETU III *see* **THE DESPERADO TRAIL**

LA 25ᵉ HEURE *see* **THE 25TH HOUR**

24 HEURES DE LA VIE D'UNE FEMME *see* **24 HOURS IN A WOMAN'S LIFE**

24 HEURES D'UN AMÉRICAIN À PARIS *see* **PARIS OOH-LA-LA!**

VINYL
     F6.5363
Dist Film-Makers' Cooperative. 19 Jun **1965** [New York opening]. Sd; b&w. 16mm. 70 min.

Prod-Dir Andy Warhol. *Writ* Ronald Tavel. *Tech Asst* Buddy Wirtschafter, Gerard Malanga.

Cast: Gerard Malanga *(Victor)*, Edie Sedgwick *(woman on trunk)*, John MacDermott *(detective)*, Ondine, Tosh Carillo, Larry Latrae, Jacques Potin.

Satire. Loosely based on: Anthony Burgess, *A Clockwork Orange* (London, 1962). Victor, a juvenile delinquent, beats up a passerby who reads books. He flexes a chain and dances sensuously. He is then bound in a chair for "reconditioning" by a detective who forces him and other delinquents to watch sadistic pornographic films. A young woman sits on a trunk throughout. In the background, a group of masochists are chained and tortured. Eventually, Victor is brought to his knees. *Juvenile delinquents. Police. Sadomasochism. Pornography. Criminals—Rehabilitation.*

Note: The frame remains fixed throughout. John MacDermott is credited by one source as A. D. MacDermott.

LE VIOL (France/Sweden)
     F6.5364
Parc Film-Argos Films-Sandrews. *Dist* Freena Films, G. G. Productions. 19 Sep **1968** [New York opening]. Sd; col (Eastmancolor). 35mm. 90 min.

Prod Göran Lindgren, Mag Bodard. *Dir-Writ* Jacques Doniol-Valcroze. *Photog* Rune Ericson. *Art Dir* Jan Boleslaw. *Film Ed* Sophie Bhaud. *Mus* Michel Portal. *Sd* Per-Olof Pettersson. *Asst Dir* Jean-José Richer. *Prod Mgr* Bo Jonsson. *Script Girl* Viveca Nordström. *Cost* Eva-Lisa Nelstedt.

Cast: Bibi Andersson *(Marianne Pescourt)*, Bruno Crémer *(Walter)*, Frédéric de Pasquale *(Henri Pescourt)*, Katerina Larsson *(Jacqueline, the maid)*.

Drama. At 7 o'clock on a Sunday morning, Henri Pescourt goes off for a day's hunting trip, leaving his wife, Marianne, asleep in their elegant apartment. The maid also leaves, promising to return by 6 to help prepare for a small dinner party that evening. Marianne is about to take a bath when the doorbell rings. Slipping into a robe, she opens the front door and is confronted by a man— Walter—holding a gun. After chloroforming Marianne, he places her on the couch and ties her arms and legs. When she regains consciousness, Walter informs her that he is keeping her incommunicado until "it's all over" and assures her that if she remains quiet nothing will happen to her. During the course of their conversations there are intimations that her husband may be in danger, but Walter remains noncommittal, averring that he is simply carrying out orders. When the phone rings every half hour, he assures the caller that everything is alright. Eventually, he unties Marianne, and she reluctantly prepares a meal for them. Although attracted by the man's intelligent and sympathetic manner, Marianne attempts to call the police, but she is stopped when Walter fires a shot and shatters a vase next to her. He leads her to the bedroom, and soon they are making passionate love. Henri calls to announce that he is on his way home, and Walter leaves, saying that his job is finished. After cleaning up the broken vase, Marianne begins preparing for the party. At 7 o'clock that evening, Walter arrives as one of the expected guests and is treated normally by both Marianne and Henri. That night, as Henri sleeps beside her, Marianne is restless. She tells him that a package arrived for him; he stirs and indicates that it can wait until morning. When the doorbell rings, she goes to answer it and finds Walter standing in the open doorway. *Hostages. Rape. Seduction. Infidelity. Fantasy.*

Note: Filmed in Stockholm. Opened in Paris in Dec 1967; also known in France as *Le viol ou un amour fou*. Opened in Stockholm in Apr 1968 as *Övergreppet*. Also known as *The Rape*.

LE VIOL OU UN AMOUR FOU *see* LE VIOL

VIOLATED LOVE (Argentina)
     F6.5365
Productores Argentinos Asociados. *Dist* CIP Ltd. 9 Nov **1966** [Champaign, Illinois, showing]. Sd; b&w. 35mm. 72 min.

Prod Orestes Trucco. *Dir* Emilio Vieyra. *Screenplay* Abel Santa Cruz, Vito de Martini. *Dir Photog* Aníbal González Paz. *Camera* Aníbal Di Salvo. *Film Ed* Oscar Esparza, Ralph Dell, Delia Manuel. *Mus* Víctor Buchino. *Sd Dir* George Castronuovo. *Rec* Mario Fezia. *Asst Dir* George Mobaied. *Prod Mgr* Rudolph Biancardi. *Prod Asst* John Camp. *Cost* Libertad de Baiza. *Makeup* Orlando Vilone, George Bruno. *Hairstyles* Haydee Aued. *Stills* Hans Ritter. *English Vers* Gerald Productions.

Cast: Libertad Leblanc *(Blondie)*, José Maria Langlais *(Martin Peña)*, Alfonso de Grazia *(Raúl Peña)*, Amadeo Novoa *(Ricci)*, Charles Carell *(Otero)*, Marion Bauza *(Loco)*, Eduardo Muñoz *(Inspector Santoni)*, Julea DeGrace *(Romero)*, Dora Baret *(Marguerite)*.

Crime melodrama. The wealthy Martin Peña arrives in Buenos Aires to find the murderer of his younger brother, Raúl. He meets Blondie, an entertainer in a nightclub owned by gang leader Otero and, posing as a criminal, agrees to finance a hijacking operation. Later, Martin takes Blondie to her apartment, and after they make love, he questions her about Otero's activities. Unaware that she is being used as an informer, Blondie provides evidence that leads Martin to believe that gangster Ricci is the guilty party. His plans for revenge are thwarted, however, when Ricci is killed by Loco, a half-wit admirer of Blondie who saves her from being raped by Ricci. Otero then tries to doublecross Martin in the hijacking plot, but Martin manages to kill the entire gang. Realizing that Blondie was the informer, Otero goes to her apartment and beats her until Loco again comes to her rescue and kills Otero. After Martin arrives, he is arrested for Otero's murder but set free when Loco is found. Meanwhile, a woman named Marguerite has confessed to Raúl's murder before taking a lethal dose of sleeping pills. *Brothers. Entertainers. Nightclub owners. Gangsters. Halfwits. Informers. Murder. Revenge. Imposture. Organized crime. Perfidy. Confession (law). Suicide. Buenos Aires.*

Note: Released in Argentina in 1964 as *Testigo para un crimen*; running time: 86 min.

VIOLATED PARADISE (Italy/Japan)   F6.5366

Dist Victoria Films, Times Film Corp. 7 Jun **1963** [New York opening]. Sd; col (Eastman Color). 35mm. 68 min.

Prod-Dir Marion Gering. *Co-dir (see note)* Robert De Leonardis. *English Narr* Tom Rowe. *Photog* Fosco Maraini, Roy M. Yaginuma. *Mus Comp* Marcello Abbado. *Adtl Score* Sergio Pagoni.

Cast: Kazuko Mine *(Tomako)*, Paulette Girard *(narrator)*.

Drama. Source: Fosco Maraini, *L'isola delle pescatrici* (Bari, 1960). Fosco Maraini, *Ore giapponesi* (Bari, 1957). Tomako, a young woman from the northernmost islands of Japan, leaves her provincial village to travel to Tokyo in the hope of finding love and excitement. On her way, she stops in a coastal village where the women dive for pearls. Tomako falls in love with a handsome fisherman to whom she would like someday to return. Arriving in Tokyo, Tomako is awed by its size and frightened by the crowds and noise. She wants to become a geisha but is repulsed by some of the duties required of her. Finally obtaining a job as a hotel maid, she is more and more upset by the seamy side of Tokyo life—the striptease acts relished by the city men, for instance. Her longing for the simple life is fulfilled when her young fisherman rescues her; they marry and return to the fishing village. *Fishermen. Chambermaids. Geishas. Pearl diving. Urban life. Striptease. Fishing villages. Hotels. Tokyo.*

Note: Filmed entirely in Japan. Japanese participation in production is unconfirmed. U. S. prerelease titles: *Diving Girls of Japan* and *The Diving Girls' Island.* Alternative titles: *Scintillating Sin* and *Sea Nymphs.* The participation of Robert de Leonardis is unconfirmed.

THE VIOLENT AND THE DAMNED (Brazil)   F6.5367

Artistas Associadas-Maristola. *Dist* A. D. P. Productions. **1962.** Sd; b&w. 35mm. 60 min.

Pres by Jerry Warren. *Prod* Gregory Wallerstein, Robert Acacio. *Dir* Carlos Hugo Christensen. *Screenplay* Carlos Hugo Christensen, Pedro Juan Vignalle. *Photog* Mario Pagés. *Mus* Ruy Alvez, Alexandre Guatalli. *Prod Mgr* A. Telesco, Atila L. da Rocha.

Cast: Arturo de Cordova *(Adriano [Rick Marson])*, Tonia Carrero *(Sangerin)*, Carlos Cotrim *("Tiger")*, Jackson de Souza *(Carioca)*, Sadi Cabral *(professor)*, Oswaldo Louzada *("Rat")*, Ramiro Magalhaes *(Bacana)*.

Melodrama. A massive prison riot in the Canal Zone leads to bloodshed as a group of convicts slaughter the guards and steal weapons from the armory. Led by Adriano, imprisoned for killing his wife, a band of prisoners escape in a boat, pursued by government forces. Adriano detours to a village to see his girl friend, but the pursuing captain is waiting for him. The troops kill some of the convicts, but Adriano flees into a jungle. The captain knows that Adriano cannot survive long, so he waits until the weak and feverish fugitive emerges and then recaptures him. [According to other sources, Adriano breaks out in order to see his son. When he finally reaches the boy, however, the frightened child does not recognize his father and is killed falling from a cliff. By the time Adriano is recaptured, he has gone mad.] *Prison escapees. Prison guards. Murder. Prison revolts. Survival. Filial relations. Insanity. Jungles. Canal Zone. Chases.*

Note: Location scenes filmed in Panama. Produced in Brazil in 1954 as *Mãos sangrentas*; running time: 90 min; retitled in 1959 as *Assassinos.*

THE VIOLENT ANGELS *see* **ANGELS DIE HARD!**

THE VIOLENT FOUR (Italy)   F6.5368

Dino De Laurentiis. *Dist* Paramount Pictures. 14 Aug **1968** [New York opening]. Sd; col (Technicolor). 35mm (Techniscope). 98 min.

Prod Dino De Laurentiis. *Exec Prod* Nino Krisman. *Dir* Carlo Lizzani. *Screenplay* Dino Maiuri, Massimo De Rita, Carlo Lizzani. *Photog* Otello Spila, Giuseppe Ruzzolini. *Film Ed* Franco Fraticelli. *Mus* Riz Ortolani. *Sd* Nello Boraso. *Asst Dir* Giorgio Gentili. *Cost* Sebastiano Soldati. *Sp Eff* Eros Bacciucchi.

Cast: Gian Maria Volontè *(Cavallero)*, Tomas Milian *(Inspector Basevi)*, Margaret Lee *(prostitute)*, Carla Gravina *(telephone victim)*, Don Backy *(Notarnicola)*, Ezio Sancrotti *(Rovoletto)*, Raymond Lovelock *(Lopez)*, Piero Mazzarella *(Piva)*, Peter Martell *("Protector")*, Carlo Lizzani, Nino Krisman *(police officials)*, Laura Solari, Enzo Fisichella, Gianni Bortolotti, Maria Rosa Sclauzero, Ida Meda, Emy Rossi Scotti, Aldo Vigorelli, Umberto Di Grazia, Enzo Consoli, Giorgio Osfuri.

Crime drama. As public outrage mounts against organized crime in modern-day Milan, four robbers meticulously plan a timed assault on several major banks within a period of 40 minutes. Led by the mastermind Cavallero, the men have pulled off other robberies in the past, keeping their identities secret by leading seemingly law-abiding lives. While making their getaway after one robbery, however, there is a slip-up, and the men must blast their way through the streets with submachine guns, killing several innocent bystanders in an effort to escape from the police. Three of the robbers escape, but a fourth, Rovoletto, is wounded and captured. The city is blockaded with the latest electronic devices, and police inspector Basevi questions Rovoletto, who finally breaks down. Lopez, the youngest gang member, is easily captured in his home, but Cavallero and Notarnicola evade the police dragnet. Before long, however, they are tracked down and cornered in an abandoned farmhouse. While being brought back to headquarters by Basevi, Cavallero boasts that his crimes have made him as famous as the Sicilian bandits of old, but he is shocked when a mob of irate citizens surround the police car, cursing and spitting at him. *Robbers. Detectives. Police. Bank robberies. Personal identity. Murder. Interrogation. Milan.*

Note: Location scenes filmed in Milan. Released in Italy in 1968 as *Banditi a Milano*; running time: 120 min.

VIOLENT LOVE *see* **TAKE HER BY SURPRISE**

VIOLENT MIDNIGHT   F6.5369

Del Tenney. *Dist* Victoria Films, Emerson Film Enterprises. May **1963** [New York opening]. Sd; b&w. 35mm. 93 min. [Also reviewed at 90 min.]

Dir Richard Hilliard. *Screenplay* Robin Miller. *Dir Photog* Louis McMahon. *Film Ed* Robert Q. Lovett. *Mus* Wilford Holcombe. *Coöp* Stamford (Conn.) Police Department.

Cast: Lee Philips *(Elliot Freeman)*, Shepperd Strudwick *(Adrian Benedict)*, Jean Hale *(Carol Bishop)*, Lorraine Rogers *(Alice St. Clair)*, Margot Hartman *(Lynn Freeman)*, Kaye Elhardt *(Dolores Martello)*, James Farentino *(Charlie Perone)*, Dick Van Patten *(Palmer)*, Sheila Forbes *(Janet "Lolita" Terhune)*, Sylvia Miles *(Silvia)*, Day Tuttle *(Mr. Melbourne)*, Mike Keene *(Inspector Grey)*, Mike O'Dowd *(Max)*.

Mystery melodrama. Because his family has a history of mental illness, Elliot Freeman, a war hero turned portrait painter, is suspected of sadistically murdering two beautiful young women. Freeman knew both of the victims— Dolores Martello, an artist's model, and Alice St. Clair, a student at a nearby college—and he sets out to find the killer. At different times during his unofficial investigation, Freeman comes to suspect four men: Professor Melbourne, a peeping tom; Charles Perone, a motorcycle hoodlum; Adrian Benedict, a sophisticated lawyer; and a deafmute chauffeur. Freeman finally learns that his own sister, Lynn, jealous of the attentions that he paid to other women, committed the murders. *Painters. War heroes. Models. Students. Lawyers. Motorcyclists. Chauffeurs. Hoodlums. Deafmutes. Murder. Brother-sister relationship. Jealousy. Voyeurism. Mental illness.*

Note: Filmed in Connecticut. Working title: *Black Autumn.* Title changed to *Psychomania.*

VIOLENT MOMENT (Great Britain)   F6.5370

Independent Artists. *Dist* Schoenfeld Film Distributing Corp. 29 Jun **1966** [Copiague, New York, opening]. Sd; b&w. 35mm. 61 min.

Prod Bernard Coote. *Dir* Sidney Hayers. *Screenplay* Peter Barnes. *Photog* Phil Grindrod. *Art Dir* Eric Saw. *Film Ed* Sidney Hayes. *Mus* Stanley Black. *Sd Rec* Len Page.

Cast: Lyndon Brook *(Douglas Baines)*, Jane Hylton *(Daisy Hacker)*, Jill Browne *(Janet Greenway)*, John Paul *(Sergeant Ranson)*, Rupert Davies *(Bert Glennon)*, Moira Redmond *(Kate Glennon)*, Bruce Seton *(Inspector Davis)*, Martin Miller *(Hendricks)*.

Mystery melodrama. Douglas Baines, an army deserter employed at a garage, lives with Daisy Hacker and their son Jiffy. Baines buys his son a doll, only to find that Daisy has given the boy up for adoption. He strangles her when she refuses to tell him where the boy is and runs, taking the doll as a reminder of his son. The police cannot catch him, but they do learn about the doll. Five years later, Baines is the manager of a garage and is planning to marry his secretary, Janet Greenway. Janet discovers his obsession for the doll and asks him for it. While she is on vacation, Baines, needing the doll again, breaks into her apartment, unaware that the place has already been burgled. During questioning about the burglary, Detective Ranson mentions Jiffy; and Baines is caught for the murder he committed years before. *Deserters—Military. Garagemen. Secretaries. Police. Fatherhood. Adoption. Murder. Obsession. Theft. Dolls.*

Note: Released in Great Britain in Apr 1959. One source claims film was based on an Edgar Wallace mystery.

THE VIOLENT ONES   F6.5371

Madison Productions—Harold Goldman Associates. *Dist* Feature Film Corp. of America. 2 Nov **1967** [San Antonio, Texas, opening]. Sd; col (Eastman Color). 35mm. 84 min. [Trade review length: 89 min.]

Prod Robert W. Stabler. *Dir* Fernando Lamas. *Screenplay* Doug Wilson, Charles Davis, writ. *Story* Fred Freiberger, Herman Miller. *Dir Photog* Fleet Southcott. *Art Dir* Paul Sylos, Jr. *Film Ed* Fred W. Berger. *Mus* Marlin Skiles. *Sd* Ryder Sound Service, John Bury. *Asst Dir* George Fenaja. *Prod Supv* Glenn N. Cook.

Cast: Fernando Lamas (*Manuel Vega*), Aldo Ray (*Joe Vorzyck*), Tommy Sands (*Mike Marain*), David Carradine (*Lucas Barnes*), Lisa Gaye (*Dolores*), Melinda Marx (*Juanita*).

Melodrama. A local girl, raped and beaten in a small New Mexico town, identifies her assailant to Deputy Sheriff Manuel Vega as a "gringo." Vega promptly arrests three drifters, the only white Americans found near the town, but each professes innocence. The girl dies, and the three suspects—Joe Vorzyck, Mike Marain, and Lucas Barnes—become the objects of a lynch mob headed by the victim's father. Suppressing his dislike for the white Americans, Vega smuggles them out of the jail and drives them to a neighboring city where they will be safely guarded by a white sheriff. En route, the group is attacked by the pursuing mob. The prisoners attempt to escape, and Vega is wounded, but he finally forces a confession from Lucas Barnes. Vorzyck and Marain then offer to help Vega escort the murderer to safety. *Mexicans. Sheriffs. Drifters. Racial prejudice. Rape. Murder. Lynching. Confession (law). Vigilantes. Jails. New Mexico.*

Note: Location scenes filmed in Lone Pine, California, and in the Mojave Desert. Working titles: *Touch White—Touch Black* and *The Chain.*

VIOLENT SEX AFFAIR *see* **MYRA'S BED**

VIOLENT SUMMER (France/Italy)   F6.5372

Titanus–S. G. C. *Dist* Films Around the World, Inc., Don Kay Associates. 19 May **1961** [New York opening]. Sd; b&w. 35mm. 95 min.

Prod Silvio Clementelli. *Dir* Valerio Zurlini. *Screenplay* Valerio Zurlini, Suso Cecchi D'Amico, Giorgio Prosperi. *Photog* Tino Santoni. *Sets* Dario Cecchi, Massimiliano Capriccioli. *Film Ed* Mario Serandrei. *Mus Score* Mario Nascimbene. *Mus Cond* Franco Ferrara.

Cast: Eleonora Rossi Drago (*Roberta*), Jean-Louis Trintignant (*Carlo*), Jacqueline Sassard (*Rossanna*), Lilla Brignone (*Signorina Raluisa*), Federica Ranchi (*Maddalena*), Raf Mattioli (*Giulio*), Enrico Maria Salerno (*Carlo's father*), Cathia Caro (*Gemma*), Bruno Carotenuto, Giampiero Littera, Xenia Valderi, Tina Gloriani, Nadia Gray.

War drama. For the wealthy young people vacationing at the Italian seaside resort of Riccione in the summer of 1943, the war is far away; all that concerns them are the carefree pleasures of sunbathing, partying, and romancing. Included in this little group is Carlo Romanazzi, the son of a fanatical Fascist leader. One day Carlo meets Roberta Parmesa, the widow of a naval hero and the mother of a 4-year-old daughter. He abruptly ends his romance with the young Rossana and relentlessly pursues the older, more sophisticated woman. Despite the age difference and the obvious disapproval of her mother-in-law, Roberta enters into a passionate affair with Carlo. Their happiness is suddenly disrupted when Allied forces approach the town, and the anti-Fascist population overthrows the local government. Carlo, who has evaded military service through graft and his father's influence, realizes that he is now in grave danger. Roberta agrees to accompany him to the comparative safety of southern Italy. En route, their train is bombed at the railroad station at Bologna, and for the first time Carlo is confronted with the horror of war. No longer able to ignore his conscience, he insists that Roberta return home alone, and he remains behind to join the rescue workers caring for the wounded and dying in the railway yard. *Fascists. Widows. Mothers-in-law. Draft dodgers. Wealth. Youth. Bombardment. Conscience. Resorts. Trains. Vacations. World War II.*

Riccione. Bologna.

Note: Released in Italy in 1959 as *Estate violenta;* running time: 107 min. Released in France as *Été violent.* Released by Don Kay Associates in Feb 1965 as *The Widow Is Willing;* running time: 97 min.

THE VIOLENT YEARS *see* **FEMALE**

LA VIOLENZA E L'AMORE *see* **THE MYTH**

VIOLENZA PER UNA MONACA *see* **A NUN AT THE CROSSROADS**

VIOLIN AND ROLLER (U.S.S.R.)   F6.5373

Mosfilm. *Dist* Artkino Pictures. 18 Aug **1962** [New York opening]. Sd; col (Sovcolor). 35mm. 55 min.

Dir Andrey Tarkovskiy. *Screenplay* A. Konchalovskiy, Andrey Tarkovskiy. *Story Ed* S. Bakhmetyeva. *Photog* Vadim Yusov. *Art Dir* S. Agoyan. *Film Ed* L. Butuzova. *Mus* Vyacheslav Ovchinnikov. *Cond* E. Khachaturyan. *Sd* V. Krachkovskiy. *Asst Dir* O. Gerts. *Prod Mgr* A. Karetin. *Cost* A. Martinson. *Makeup* A. Makasheva. *Sp Eff* B. Pluzhnikov, V. Sevostyanov, A. Rudachenko.

Cast: Igor Fomchenko (*Sasha*), V. Zamanskiy (*Sergey*), Nina Arkhangelskaya (*The Girl*), Marina Adzhubey, Yura Brusser, Slava Borisov, Sasha Vitoslavskiy, Sasha Ilin, Kolya Kozarev, Gena Klyachkovskiy, Igor Korovikov, Zhenya Fedchenko, Tanya Prokhorova, A. Maksimova, L. Semyonova, G. Zhdanova, M. Figner.

Comedy-drama. In Moscow, Sergey, a truck [road roller?] driver, defends Sasha, a lonely 7-year-old violin student, from a group of heckling boys, and a friendship develops between them. Sergey allows Sasha to ride on his truck and invites him for lunch. The boy learns from his friend the importance of defending the weak, while Sergey is touched by Sasha's love of music. The boy plays his violin for Sergey, and although his mother refuses to allow him out for the evening with his friend, the two look forward to a continuing friendship. *Children. Violinists. Students. Truckdrivers. Friendship. Moscow.*

Note: Released in the U.S.S.R. in Dec 1961 as *Katok i skripka;* running time: 46 min. Also known as *The Violin and the Roller.*

THE VIRGIN AND THE GYPSY (Great Britain)   F6.5375

Kenwood Films. *For* London Screenplays. *Dist* Chevron Pictures. 30 Jun **1970** [New York opening]. Sd; col (Movielab). 35mm. 92 min. *MPAA rating* R.

Pres by Dimitri De Grunwald. *Prod* Kenneth Harper. *Dir* Christopher Miles. *Screenplay* Alan Plater. *Photog* Bob Huke. *Art Dir* David Brockhurst. *Prod Dsgn* Terence Knight. *Film Ed* Paul Davies. *Mus Comp & Cond* Patrick Gowers. *Song:* "Keep Your Hand on Your Halfpenny" Alex Glasgow. *Song:* "My Latest Millionaire" Ronald Cass. *Song:* "The Charleston Hop" Peter Myers. *Sd Ed* Michael Johns. *Sd Rec* John Brommage, Bob Cox. *Asst Dir* Derek Whitehurst. *Prod Mgr* John D. Wilcox. *Cost Adv* Deirdre Clancy.

Cast: Joanna Shimkus (*Yvette*), Franco Nero (*gypsy*), Honor Blackman (*Mrs. Fawcett*), Mark Burns (*Major Eastwood*), Maurice Denham (*The Rector*), Fay Compton (*Grandma*), Kay Walsh (*Aunt Cissie*), Harriet Harper (*Lucille*), Norman Bird (*Uncle Fred*), Imogen Hassall (*gypsy's wife*), Jeremy Bulloch (*Leo*), Roy Holder (*Bob*), Margo Andrew (*Ella*), Janet Chappell (*Mary*), Helen Booth (*cook*), Laurie Dale (*Thomas*), Lulu Davies (*gypsy grandmother*).

Drama. Source: David Herbert Lawrence, *The Virgin and the Gypsy* (London, 1930). Yvette and her sister Lucille return to northern England in the early 1920's after attending finishing school in France. Their father, a village rector, runs a very restrictive household which the sisters share with their demanding grandmother, spinster Aunt Cissie, and Uncle Fred. Lucille finds a job, but Yvette becomes restless in the rectory atmosphere. The rector's wife, who ran away with a lover many years ago, is held to blame for Yvette's independent behavior. The sisters go driving one day with Leo, the son of a village businessman, and they meet a handsome gypsy who tells their fortunes. Yvette becomes infatuated with the gypsy and later visits his camp. There she meets Mrs. Fawcett, a divorcée, and Major Eastwood, who defy the scorn of the townspeople by openly living together. Her visits continue, and she finds that she can freely discuss her dawning sexual feelings with the couple. Meanwhile, to enliven her life at the rectory, Yvette has promised her father to stage a revue for the benefit of the church, but she is dismayed when he bars the unmarried couple from attendance. Later, while she is at home with her grandmother, a dam bursts and sends a flood sweeping through the rectory. The grandmother is killed, but the gypsy arrives in time to rescue Yvette, and he carries her upstairs where they make love. The next morning the waters have receded and the gypsy has gone, but Yvette has freed herself of her inhibitions and leaves the village with Mrs. Fawcett and Major Eastwood. *Gypsies. Clergymen. Grandmothers. Uncles. Aunts. Spinsters. Fortune-tellers. Filial relations. Virginity. Puritanism. Inhibition. Sexual initiation. Floods.*

Note: Opened in London in Jun 1970.

THE VIRGIN AQUA SEX see **THE AQUA SEX**

A VIRGIN FOR THE PRINCE see **A MAIDEN FOR A PRINCE**

THE VIRGIN PRESIDENT   **F6.5376**
Dist New Line Cinema. 18 Nov **1968** [Raleigh, North Carolina, opening]. Sd; b&w. 35mm. 71 min.
    Prod Severn Darden, Graeme Ferguson, Jim Hubbard. *Dir* Graeme Ferguson. *Story* Severn Darden, Graeme Ferguson. *Photog* Graeme Ferguson. *Film Ed* Mark Rappaport, Burt Rashby, Thelma Schoonmaker. *Mus* Teiji Ito. *Sd* Fred Wardenburg.
    Cast: Severn Darden (*Henry F. Millmore/Fillard Millmore/The Narrator/Millmore's Ghost*), Richard Neuweiler (*Secretary of State Schuyler Colfax*), Andrew Duncan (*Secretary of Defense William Salvo*), Louis Waldon (*C.I.A. Chief Jock Steel*), Richard Schaal (*Hugh Mugababy*), Paul Benedict (*Rutherford Melon*), Sudie Bond (*Mom Millmore*), Anthony Holland (*Machiavelli von Clausewitz*), Conrad Yama (*The Chinese Prime Minister*), L'nelle Hamanaka (*Prime Minister's daughter*), Sabrina Scharf (*President's girl friend*), Peter Boyle (*General Heath*), Charlotte Baumgartner (*White House courtesan*).
    Satire. Sometime in the future, the President of the United States dies and is succeeded by his 35-year-old son, Fillard Millmore, the 43rd president. Millmore is absolutely incompetent, and his cabinet seeks to exploit his naiveté. They devise a scheme to drop an atomic bomb on New York City and blame it on the Communist Chinese, hoping their plot will boost the stock market. Millmore manages to outwit his advisers, however, even in their plans for him to marry the daughter of the Chinese Prime Minister. *Presidents of the United States. Presidents of the United States—Cabinet. Conspiracy. Cold war. Atom bomb. New York City. People's Republic of China. The Future.*
    Note: Dialog for the film was improvised.

THE VIRGIN SOLDIERS (Great Britain)   **F6.5377**
Open Road Films–Highroad Productions. *Dist* Columbia Pictures. 5 Feb **1970** [New York opening; cl Feb 1970; LP37501]. Sd; col (Technicolor). 35mm. 96 min. *MPAA rating* R.
    Pres by Carl Foreman. *Prod* Leslie Gilliat, Ned Sherrin. *Exec Prod* Carl Foreman. *Dir* John Dexter. *Screenplay* John Hopkins. *Adtl Dial* Ian La Frenais. *Adapt* John McGrath. *Photog* Ken Higgins. *Camera Op* Alan Hall. *Art Dir* Frank White. *Film Ed* Thelma Connell. *Mus Comp, Arr & Cond* Peter Greenwell. *Comp:* "The Virgin Soldiers March" Raymond Douglas Davies. *Sd Rec* Brian Marshall, Nolan Roberts. *Sd Ed* Roy Hyde. *Asst Dir* Claude Watson. *Prod Mgr* Eddie Pike, Derek Parr. *Location Mgr* Ray Corbett. *Cont* Kay Rawlings. *Wardrobe* Jean Fairlie, Charles Guerin. *Makeup* Philip Leakey. *Hairdresser* Gladys Leakey. *Supv Electrn* Roy Larner.
    Cast: Lynn Redgrave (*Phillipa Raskin*), Hywel Bennett (*Brigg*), Nigel Davenport (*Sergeant Driscoll*), Nigel Patrick (*R. S. M. Raskin*), Rachel Kempson (*Mrs. Raskin*), Jack Shepherd (*Sergeant Wellbeloved*), Michael Gwynn (*Lieutenant Colonel Bromley-Pickering*), Tsai Chin (*Juicy Lucy*), Christopher Timothy (*Corporal Brook*), Don Hawkins (*Tasker*), Geoffrey Hughes (*Lantry*), Roy Holder (*Fenwick*), Riggs O'Hara (*Sinclair*), Gregory Phillips (*Foster*), Wayne Sleep (*Villiers*), Peter Kelly (*Sandy Jacobs*), Mark Nicholl (*Cutler*), Alan Shatsman (*Longley*), Jonty Miller (*Forsyth*), Jolyon Jackley (*Lieut. Col. "Gravy" Browning*), Robert Bridges (*Sgt. Fred Organ*), James Cosmo (*Waller*), Graham Crowden (*medical officer*), Dudley Jones (*doctor*), Mathew Guinness (*Major Cusper*), Naranjan Singh (*Sikh*), F. Yew ("*Hallelujah*"), Brenda Bruce (*nursing sister*), Barbara Keogh (*W.R.A.C.*).
    War comedy-drama. Source: Leslie Thomas, *The Virgin Soldiers* (London, 1966). Private Brigg, a young recruit stationed in Malaya in 1951, tries to court Phillipa Raskin, the daughter of the company's sergeant major; both Brigg and Phillipa are inexperienced, however, and unable to take the initiative in lovemaking. When the company holds a dance, Brigg loses his virginity to Juicy Lucy, a local prostitute, and Phillipa loses hers to a sexually experienced sergeant. Rioting breaks out in Singapore, and Private Brigg takes it upon himself to defend Phillipa and her mother. They escape from the city to hide in a nearby marsh. Phillipa's mother, overcome by fright, faints, and Phillipa and Brigg take advantage of her unconsciousness to have sex. Later, when Brigg is sent into heavy fighting, he runs for reinforcements and returns to find that his sergeant, who had bragged about his heroic actions during World War II, had been hiding in a lavatory and is being beaten for his cowardice. Shortly thereafter, the young recruit's term of service ends, and he is sent back to England. *Prostitutes. Military life. Virginity. Sexual initiation. Riots. Filial relations. Cowardice. Singapore. Malaya. Great Britain—Army.*
    Note: Filmed on location in Malaya and Singapore. Opened in London in Oct 1969.

VIRGINS OF BALI see **DJANGER "LOVE RITE OF BALI"**

VIRIDIANA (Mexico/Spain)   **F6.5378**
Uninci, S. A.–Films 59–Gustavo Alatriste. *Dist* Kingsley International Pictures. 19 Mar **1962** [New York opening]. Sd; b&w. 35mm. 90 min.
    Prod Ricardo Muñoz Suay. *Dir* Luis Buñuel. *Screenplay* Luis Buñuel, Julio Alejandro. *Photog* José F. Aguayo. *Art Dir* Francisco Canet. *Film Ed* Pedro del Rey. *Mus Dir* Gustavo Pitaluga. *Selections from* "The Messiah" George Frederick Handel. *Selections from* "Requiem" Wolfgang Amadeus Mozart. *Asst Dir* Juan Luis Buñuel, José Puyol. *Prod Mgr* Gustavo Quintana.
    Cast: Silvia Pinal (*Viridiana*), Francisco Rabal (*Jorge*), Fernando Rey (*Don Jaime*), Margarita Lozano (*Ramona*), Victoria Zinny (*Lucía*), Teresa Rabal (*Rita*), José Calvo, Joaquín Roa, Luis Heredia, José Manuel Martín, Lola Gaos, Juan García Tienda, Maruja Isbert, Joaquín Mayol, Sergio Mendizábal, Palmira Guerra, Milagros Tomás, Alicia Jorge Barriga (*The Beggars*).
    Drama. Shortly before taking her final vows, Viridiana, a young novitiate, is sent unwillingly to visit her uncle, Don Jaime, whose wife died on their wedding night 30 years earlier. One evening, the old man, struck by Viridiana's resemblance to his dead bride, persuades her to don his wife's bridal gown. Helped by his devoted housekeeper, Ramona, who has lived alone with her little daughter and Jaime, he drugs Viridiana and carries her to her room. Although he does not go through with his planned seduction, he tells her that he has done so, hopeful that she will remain with him. Instead she flees from the house, and Don Jaime hangs himself in despair. Half of the estate falls to Viridiana, the other half to Jorge, Don Jaime's illegitimate son, who arrives with a mistress. Feeling that she is to blame for her uncle's death, Viridiana takes in the beggars of the village and offers them a haven. Jorge, on the other hand, has only contempt for her charity, and he devotes his time to modernizing the hacienda and restoring the farmlands. On a day when Viridiana and Jorge are in town, the beggars take over the house and organize a huge feast that becomes a wild and drunken orgy. By the time Viridiana and Jorge return, the beggars have ruined all the finery they have touched. Two of them seize Jorge, tie him up, and attempt to rape Viridiana, but Jorge saves her by paying one of the derelicts to kill the would-be rapist. Once the beggars have fled, the humiliated and disillusioned Viridiana abandons her life of sacrifice and prayer and goes to Jorge's room. Triumphant, he smiles and invites her to join him and Ramona, his new mistress, in a game of cards. *Widowers. Nobility. Uncles. Novices. Beggars. Housekeepers. Mistresses. Guilt. Illegitimacy. Inheritance. Suicide. Rape. Charity. Disillusionment. Death. Fetishism. Moral corruption. Orgies. Catholic Church.*
    Note: Location scenes filmed in Spain; banned from exhibition there.

VISA TO CANTON see **PASSPORT TO CHINA**

THE VISCOUNT (France/Italy/Spain)   **F6.5379**
Criterion Film–Producciones Cinematografica D. I. A.–Franca Film–C. C. M.–Senior Cinematografica. *Dist* Warner Bros. Pictures. 10 May **1967** [New York opening; cl May 1967; LP35726]. Sd; col (Eastmancolor, print by Technicolor). 35mm (Techniscope). 98 min.
    Exec Prod Nat Wachsberger. *Dir* Maurice Cloche. *English Vers Screenplay* Clarke Reynolds. *French Vers Screenplay* Georges Farrel. *Spanish Vers Screenplay* Luis Marquina. *Dir Photog* Henri Raichi. *Art Dir* Jean Douarinou. *Film Ed* Ray Leboursier. *Song:* "The Investigator" Georges Garvarentz, Bill Martin, Philips Coulper. *Sung by* Tony Allen. *Sd* Jean Bertrand. *Asst Dir* Fabien Collin. *Prod Mgr* Louis de Masure. *Asst Prod Mgr* Juan Campos. *Cost Dsgn* Antonio Cortés.
    Cast: Kerwin Mathews (*Clint de la Roche, the Viscount*), Edmond O'Brien, Folco Lulli (*Ricco Barone [see note]*), Jane Fleming (*Lili Dumond*), Yvette Lebon (*Claudia*), Jean Yanne (*Billette*), Fernando Rey (*Marco Demoigne*), Maria Latour (*Tania*), José Manuel Martín (*Manuel*), Alain Saury (*Vincento*), Luis Dávila (*Steve Heller*), Franco Fabrizi (*Ramon*), Pierre Massimi (*Louis*), Christian Ferville (*Paul*), Alvaro de Luna (*Jean*), Emilio Rodriguez (*bank director*), Armand Mestral (*Claude Peroux*).
    Melodrama. Source: Jean Bruce, *Bonne mesure* (Paris, 1953). Viscount Clint de la Roche, a playboy insurance detective vacationing in Spain with his assistant, Billette, is called to Paris to investigate a $2 million bank robbery. Also taken in the robbery was a large quantity of opium stored in safe deposit boxes by Ricco Barone, a deported New Jersey gangster. The Viscount discovers that shortly before the robbery the bank president had spent a weekend with a stripteaser, Tania, who has since been murdered. The Viscount visits her roommate, Lili, and confirms his suspicions that the man responsible for the robbery is Tania's lover, international thief Marco Demoigne. Eventually, Barone contacts the Viscount in an attempt to recover the opium. With the cooperation of the American and French narcotics bureaus, the Viscount arranges a meeting between the rival gangs of Barone and Marco. The encounter explodes into violence as the two leaders attempt to double-cross each other, and all the gangsters are either gunned down or arrested. The

Viscount collects his reward money and resumes his vacation—this time with Lili. *Detectives. Nobility. Thieves. Gangsters. Stripteasers. Roommates. Narcotics agents. Bank robberies. Murder. Gang wars. Deportation. Perfidy. Vacations. Insurance. Opium. Spain. Paris.*

Note: Opened in Paris in Mar 1967 as *Le Vicomte règle ses comptes* at 90 and 100 min (also *Les aventures du Vicomte*); in Madrid in Aug 1967 as *Atraco al hampa* at 93 min (also *Las aventuras del Vizconde*); in Italy as *The Viscount, furto alla banca mondiale*. Edmond O'Brien plays Ricco Barone in the English version; Folco Lulli plays the role in the foreign language version. Jane Fleming is a pseudonym for Silvia Sorente. Registered for copyright by Omnia Deutsche Film Export and Waterview Productions.

THE VISIT (United States/France/Italy/West Germany)   **F6.5380**
Les Films du Siècle–P. E. C. F.–Dear Film–Deutsche Fox Film. *Dist* Twentieth Century-Fox Film Corp. 23 Sep **1964** [Los Angeles opening; c23 Sep 1964; LP29236]. Sd; b&w. 35mm (CinemaScope). 100 min.
Prod Julien Derode, Anthony Quinn. *Dir* Bernhard Wicki. *Screenplay* Ben Barzman. *Camera Op* Claudio Cirillo. *Dir Photog* Armando Nannuzzi. *Art Dir* Léon Barsacq. *Set Decor* Robert Christides. *Film Ed* Samuel E. Beetley, Françoise Diot. *Mus Comp & Cond* Hans-Martin Majewski, Richard Arnell. *Sd* Jacques Maumont, Umberto Picistrelli. *Asst Dir* Wieland Liebske, Ottavio Oppo. *Prod Mgr* Christian Ferry, Attilio D'Onofrio. *Miss Bergman's Wardrobe Dsgn* René Hubert. *Executed by* Nina Ricci. *Makeup* John O'Gorman. *Hairstyles* Giorgio di Roma.
Cast: Ingrid Bergman *(Karla Zachanassian)*, Anthony Quinn *(Serge Miller)*, Paolo Stoppa *(doctor)*, Romolo Valli *(town painter)*, Claude Dauphin *(Bardrick)*, Jacques Dufilho *(Fisch)*, Hans-Christian Blech *(Dobrik)*, Richard Münch *(teacher)*, Ernst Schröder *(mayor)*, Leonard Steckel *(priest)*, Valentina Cortese *(Mathilda Miller)*, Irina Demick *(Anya)*, Eduardo Ciannelli *(innkeeper)*, Marco Guglielmi *(Chesco)*, Lelio Luttazzi *(1st idler)*, Dante Maggio *(Cadek)*, Renzo Palmer *(conductor)*, Fausto Tozzi *(Darvis)*.
Drama. Source: Friedrich Dürrenmatt, *Der Besuch der alten Dame; eine tragische Komödie* (Zurich opening: 29 Jan 1956; adapted as *The Visit; a Play in Three Acts* by Maurice Valency; New York opening: 5 May 1958). Karla Zachanassian, reportedly the world's richest woman, returns to her birthplace, the small European town of Guellen. The people of the economically depressed town prepare for her visit, hoping that she will give them financial aid. She arrives in her Rolls-Royce, accompanied by bodyguards and a pet leopard. During a banquet in her honor, Karla shocks the townspeople by offering them $2 million to kill Serge Miller, the owner of the general store, who was once her lover. She explains that when she was about to bear his child, Miller bribed other men to testify that she was a whore, and she was run out of town. The child died, and Karla became a prostitute before marrying her wealthy husband. The townspeople are shocked by what they hear, but they refuse her offer. Later, trucks begin bringing valuable merchandise into Guellen, and soon the affluent townspeople come to regard Karla with more sympathy. When Karla's leopard escapes, the townspeople arm themselves for the hunt, but they are really hunting for Miller, who hides until the animal is killed. He begs Karla to put an end to her vengeful scheme, but she refuses. Miller tries to leave town, but the citizens prevent him. The town councilmen ask Karla to stop her persecution of Miller and invest in Guellen, but she informs them that she already owns all the town property. Finally, Miller is forced to stand trial, and he is sentenced to death. Karla announces that Miller will be freed if one man thinks his sentence is unjust, but no one speaks out. Then Karla instructs the court to free Miller, saying that her revenge will be Miller's living among the people who have killed him for money. Announcing that the visit is over, Karla leaves Guellen, taking with her Anya, a young woman whose life Karla fears may be damaged like her own. *Bodyguards. Storekeepers. Prostitutes. Wealth. Revenge. Illegitimacy. Poverty. Bribery. Trials. Capital punishment. Rolls-Royce automobiles. Leopards.*
Note: Location scenes filmed in Italy. Opened in Paris in Jul 1964 as *La rancune* at 120 min; in West Germany in Sep 1964 as *Der Besuch* at 100 min; and in Italy in 1964 as *La vendetta della signora*.

LA VISITA (Italy)   **F6.5381**
Zebra Film–Aera Films. *Dist* Promenade Films. 9 Aug **1966** [New York opening]. Sd; b&w. 35mm. 115 min.
Prod Moris Ergas. *Dir* Antonio Pietrangeli. *Screenplay* Ettore Scola, Ruggero Maccari, Antonio Pietrangeli. *Photog* Armando Nannuzzi. *Art Dir* Luigi Scaccianoce. *Film Ed* Eraldo Da Roma. *Mus* Armando Trovajoli.
Cast: Sandra Milo *(Pina)*, François Périer *(Adolfo)*, Mario Adorf *(Cucaracha)*, Angela Minervini *(Chiaretta)*, Gastone Moschin *(Renato)*, Didi Perego *(Nella)*.
Drama. Source: Carlo Cassola, "La visita," in *Il taglio del bosco* (Pisa, 1955). Pina, a 37-year-old self-supporting spinster, tiring of the admiration of the village idiot, Cucaracha, and of her affair with the married truck driver, Renato, places an ad in a lonely hearts column. It is answered by Adolfo, an indolent

bookstore clerk. During a visit to her home in the Po Valley, Adolfo torments Pina's pets, insults her friends, flirts with adolescents, and drinks himself into a stupor at the tavern. Despite her furor at his behavior and his interest in her dowry and real estate, Pina is touched by Adolfo's apology and permits the clerk to seduce her. The next morning the spinster drives her guest to the railroad station, where they part, each considering continued correspondence. *Salesclerks. Truckdrivers. Lovelorn. Spinsters. Drunkenness. Loneliness. Seduction. Courtship. Po River. Pets.*
Note: Opened in Rome in 1963.

UNA VITA *see* **END OF DESIRE**

LA VITA CONIUGALE *see* **ANATOMY OF A MARRIAGE; MY DAYS WITH JEAN-MARC**

LA VITA CONIUGALE *see* **ANATOMY OF A MARRIAGE; MY NIGHTS WITH FRANÇOISE**

VITA PRIVATA *see* **A VERY PRIVATE AFFAIR**

VITE PERDUTE *see* **LOST SOULS**

VIVA LAS VEGAS   **F6.5382**
Jack Cummings Productions. *Dist* Metro-Goldwyn-Mayer, Inc. 20 May **1964** [New York opening; c20 Dec 1963; LP26846]. Sd (Westrex); col (Metrocolor). 35mm (Panavision). 86 min.
A Jack Cummings–George Sidney Production. *Dir* George Sidney. *Writ* Sally Benson. *Dir Photog* Joseph Biroc. *Art Dir* George W. Davis, Edward Carfagno. *Set Decor* Henry Grace, George R. Nelson. *Film Ed* John McSweeney, Jr. *Mus* George Stoll. Songs: "Viva Las Vegas," "I Need Somebody To Lean On" Doc Pomus. Song: "The Lady Loves Me" Sid Tepper, Roy C. Bennett. Song: "Come On, Everybody" Stanley Chianese. Song: "Today, Tomorrow, and Forever" Bill Giant, Bernie Baum, Florence Kaye. Song: "If You Think I Don't Need You" Bob "Red" West. Songs: "Appreciation," "My Rival" Marvin More, Bernie Wayne. *Choreog* David Winters. *Rec Supv* Franklin Milton. *Asst Dir* Milton Feldman. *Cost Dsgn* Don Feld. *Makeup Supv* William Tuttle. *Hairstyles* Sydney Guilaroff. "Folies Bergère" seq by arr with Hotel Tropicana (Las Vegas).
Cast: Elvis Presley *(Lucky Jackson)*, Ann-Margret *(Rusty Martin)*, Cesare Danova *(Count Elmo Mancini)*, William Demarest *(Mr. Martin)*, Nicky Blair *(Shorty Farnsworth)*.
Comedy-drama with music. Sports car enthusiast Lucky Jackson defeats Italian champion Count Elmo Mancini, who then asks Lucky to drive for him. Lucky refuses and plans to get a new engine and race his own car in the Las Vegas Grand Prix. When Lucky and Mancini arrive in Las Vegas, they are both attracted to Rusty Martin, a hotel swimming instructor. Lucky loses his money when he is pushed into a pool, and he takes a job as a waiter in order to pay his bills. Rusty, falling in love with Lucky, tries to persuade him to give up racing, and she flirts with Mancini to make Lucky jealous. Lucky enters the hotel talent contest but only ties with Rusty. Instead of the necessary cash, Rusty receives a pool table and Lucky, a honeymoon. Hours before the Grand Prix, Rusty's father, who has always been interested in racing, secretly borrows the money for Lucky. Mancini's car crashes, and Lucky goes on to win the race and marry Rusty. *Performers and additional songs:* "Yellow Rose of Texas," "What'd I Say," "I Need Somebody To Lean On" (Lucky); "My Rival" (Rusty); "The Lady Loves Me" (Lucky and Rusty); "The Eyes of Texas Are Upon You" (Lucky and chorus); "The Climb" (quartet). *Singers. Italians. Waiters. Jealousy. Automobile racing. Finance—Personal. Hotels. Nightclubs. Talent contests. Las Vegas. Automobile accidents.*
Note: Locations filmed in Las Vegas and at Boulder Dam Lake.

VIVA MARIA (France/Italy)   **F6.5383**
Nouvelles Editions de Films–Les Productions Artistes Associés–Vides. *Dist* United Artists. 18 Dec **1965** [New York opening; c10 Dec 1965; LF3]. Sd; col (Eastman Color). 35mm (Panavision). 119 min.
Prod Louis Malle, Oscar Dancigers. *Dir* Louis Malle. *Screenplay, Adapt & Dial* Louis Malle, Jean-Claude Carrière. *Dir Photog* Henri Decaë. *Camera Op* Alain Douarinou. *Col Cons* Ghislain Uhry. *Art Dir* Bernard Evein. *Film Ed* Kenout Peltier, Suzanne Baron. *Orig Mus Comp* Georges Delerue. *Lyr* Louis Malle, Jean-Claude Carrière. *Sd Engr* José B. Carles. *Asst Dir* Volker Schlöndorff, Juan Luis Buñuel, Manuel Muñoz. *Prod Mgr* Alain Queffelean, Pascual Aragones. *Script Supv* Jacqueline Parey. *Cost Dsgn* Ghislain Uhry. *Miss Bardot's Makeup* Odette Berroyer. *Miss Moreau's Makeup & Hairstyles* Simone Knapp. *Miss Bardot's Hairstyles* Jean Pierre Berroyer. *Sp Eff* Lee Zavitz.
Cast: Jeanne Moreau *(Maria I)*, Brigitte Bardot *(Maria Fitzgerald O'Malley; Maria II)*, George Hamilton *(Florès)*, Paulette Dubost *(Madame Diogène)*, Gregor von Rezzori *(Diogène)*, Poldo Bendandi *(Werther)*, Claudio Brook *(Rodolfo)*, Carlos López Moctezuma *(Don Rodriguez)*, Jonathan Eden

(Juanito), Francisco Reiguera *(Father Superior),* Adriana Roel *(Janine),* José Baviera *(Don Alvaro),* José Angel Espinosa *(El Presidente),* Fernando Wagner *(father of Maria II),* José Luis Campa, Roberto Ca¤pa, Eduardo Murillo, José Esqueda *(The "Turcos"),* Luis Rizo *(strongman).*

Adventure comedy. Maria O'Malley (Maria II), daughter of a Frenchwoman and an Irish anarchist, is left alone in Central America in 1910 when her father is killed during a revolution. Skilled in guerrilla tactics, she escapes being captured and joins up with a French circus performer, also named Maria, whose partner in their song-and-dance act has killed herself over an unhappy love affair. An accident during one of the performances, in which Maria II's skirt tears, turns the act into a successful striptease routine. As the company passes through the country of San Miguel, the women are horrified at the treatment of the people by the powerful Don Rodriguez. In anger, Maria II shoots one of the soldiers who are looting a small village. The troupe is rounded up and taken to Rodriguez' hacienda. There the Marias meet the revolutionist Florès, who has been captured and tied and bound; and the elder Maria falls in love with Florès. Florès is shot, but upon his death, Maria I promises to take up his cause. The two women lead the peasants on attacks on various government strongholds until they are captured and sentenced to death by Father Superior, who is jealous of the women's power. As both Marias face the firing squad, their colleagues and fellow revolutionaries save them, hailing the women as heroines. *Anarchists. Entertainers. Irish. Police. Revolutionaries. Peasants. Priests. Striptease. Heroism. Capital punishment. Circus. Imaginary republics. Central America.*

Note: Released in France and Italy in 1965. Locations filmed in Mexico.

VIVA MAX!   F6.5384

Mark Carliner Productions. *Dist* Commonwealth United Entertainment, Inc. 18 Dec **1969** [San Antonio, Texas, opening; c18 Dec 1969; LP40002]. Sd; col (Eastman Color). 35mm. 96 min. [Also 92 min.] *MPAA rating* G.

Prod Mark Carliner. *Assoc Prod* Wally Samson. *Dir* Jerry Paris. *Screenplay* Elliott Baker. *Dir Photog* Henri Persin. *2d Unit Photog* Jack Richards. *Art Dir* Carl Braunger. *Prod Dsgn* James Hulsey. *Film Ed* Bud Molin, David Berlatsky. *Post Prod Supv* Robert S. Eisen, Harry Eisen. *Mus* Hugo Montenegro, Ralph Dino, John Sembello. *Perf* Al Hirt. *Mus Cond* Charles Koppleman. *Mus Supv* Donald Rubin. *Mus Coörd* Igo Kantor. *Sd Ed* Jim Bullock, Del Harris, Joseph G. Sorokin. *Sd* Bill Pellak, Wally Milner. *Mus Ed* James Henrikson. *Asst Dir* Claude Binyon, Jr., Neil T. Maffeo. *Prod Supv* Henri Jaquillard. *Prod Mgr* Terence A. Donnelly. *Script Supv* Marge Mullen. *Wardrobe Supv* Annalisa Nasalli-Rocca. *Makeup Supv* Monique Archambault. *Dial Coach* Robert Hoffman. *Dial Cons* Tony Palk. *Prop Master* Stephen Ferry. *Gaffer* Enzo Zocchi. *Casting* Lynn Stalmaster. *Stunt* Frank Orsatti.

Cast: Peter Ustinov *(Gen. Maximilian Rodrigues de Santos),* Pamela Tiffin *(Paula Whitland),* Jonathan Winters *(Gen. Billy Joe Hallson),* John Astin *(Sergeant Valdez),* Keenan Wynn *(Gen. Barney LaComber),* Harry Morgan *(Police Chief George Sylvester),* Alice Ghostley *(Hattie Longstreet Daniel),* Kenneth Mars *(Dr. Sam Gillison),* Ann Morgan Guilbert *(Edna Miller),* Bill McCutcheon *(Desmond Miller),* Gino Conforti *(Contreras),* Christopher Ross *(Gomez),* Larry Hankin *(Romero),* Paul Sand *(Moreno),* Don Diamond *(Hernandez),* Jack Colvin *(Garcia),* Jessica Myerson *(Mrs. Dodd),* Ted Gehring *(Customs Guard Collins),* Jim B. Smith *(Customs Guard Michaels),* Eldon Quick *(Quincy),* Jack Wakefield *(Policeman Milton),* Glenn Tucker *(Captain Harris),* Lee Brandt *(sentry bus driver),* King Cotton *(himself, a horse).*

Comedy. Source: James Lehrer, *Viva Max!* (New York, 1966). Gen. Maximilian Rodrigues de Santos leads his motley band of Mexican soldiers across the United States border on the pretext of marching in the Washington's Birthday parade; instead, the men advance to San Antonio and capture the Alamo. Max telephones Police Chief George Sylvester and proclaims his triumph, and Sylvester calls in a local National Guard unit, led by Gen. Billy Joe Hallson. The Mexicans refuse to leave the fort, however, and Max outwits the Guard when he learns that they have not been issued ammunition. During the ensuing siege, Max captures Hattie Longstreet Daniel, a right-wing fanatic who was visiting the fort, and Paula Whitland, a young woman who operates the souvenir stand. Paula becomes sympathetic to the Mexican's revolutionary cause, but Hattie secretly sends a message for help to her nephew, Sam Gillison, the leader of the Sentries, a para-military organization pledged to the defense of the United States. Max is wounded in the confrontation with the Sentries but courageously leads his unarmed soldiers to victory and then orders the army back to Mexico. *Mexicans. Revolutionaries. Police. Hostages. Vigilantes. George Washington's Birthday. San Antonio. Mexican border. The Alamo. National Guard.*

Note: Location scenes filmed in San Antonio, Texas, and Rome.

VIXEN   F6.5385

Eve Productions. 22 Oct **1968** [Los Angeles opening; c15 Oct 1968; LP36116]. Sd; col (Eastmancolor). 35mm. 71 min.

Pres by Cold Stream Films. *Prod-Dir* Russ Meyer. *Assoc Prod* Eve Meyer, Anthony James Ryan, Richard Brummer, George Costello. *Screenplay* Robert Rudelson. *Adtl Dial* Russ Meyer. *Story* Russ Meyer, Anthony James Ryan. *Photog* Russ Meyer. *Art Dir* Wilfred Kues. *Film Ed* Richard Brummer, Russ Meyer. *Mus* Igo Kantor. *Sd* Richard Brummer, John Koester. *Asst Dir* George Costello.

Cast: Erica Gavin *(Vixen),* Harrison Page *(Niles),* Jon Evans *(Jud),* Michael Donovan O'Donnell *(O'Banion),* Garth Pillsbury *(Tom),* Vincene Wallace *(Janet King),* Robert Aiken *(Dave King),* Peter Carpenter *(Mountie),* Jackie Illman *(girl),* John Furlong *(gas attendant).*

Drama. Vixen is the nymphomaniacal spouse of a bush pilot who owns a fishing lodge in British Columbia. While her husband, Tom, is away, Vixen frolics in the woods with a Canadian Mountie and then returns to the lodge to tease her motorcyclist brother Jud and insult his black friend Niles, a draft dodger from the States. When Tom flies in with a young married couple, Dave and Janet King, Vixen takes immediate advantage of the situation by seducing Dave, midstream, during a fishing expedition. At the same time, Janet attempts to arouse Tom, but she meets with no success. Her frustration is assuaged the next day, however, when Vixen recommends "a change of pace" and takes her to bed. Their lovemaking is interrupted when Dave appears, but, rather than being upset, he merely takes over where Vixen has left off. After the apparently happier couple has left, Vixen contents herself with her husband until he is once more forced to leave. She then corners her brother in the shower, unaware that they are being observed through a window by Niles. Sensing that his friend has been stimulated, Jud encourages Niles to pursue Vixen, a feat he undertakes with such zealousness that Vixen is saved from rape only by the unexpected return of Tom. This time he has brought back a bearded Irishman, O'Banion, who has hired Tom to fly him to San Francisco. O'Banion's dealings, however, are only a pretense, for he is actually a Communist who intends to hijack the plane to Cuba—and quickly sensing that the young draft dodger might be a willing accomplice, he persuades Niles to join Tom and Vixen on the flight. Once aloft, Vixen has a heated argument with Niles and is instrumental in getting him to help thwart O'Banion's hijacking scheme. When the plane lands in the States, O'Banion is turned over to the authorities, and Niles decides to remain there as it is "the lesser of two evils." *Air pilots. Motorcyclists. Draft dodgers. Irish. Hijackers. Negroes. Communists. Nymphomania. Brother-sister relationship. Incest. Seduction. Rape. Lesbianism. Racial prejudice. Lodges (inns). Fishing. British Columbia. Cuba. Royal Canadian Mounted Police.*

Note: Also known as *Russ Meyer's Vixen.* Vincene Wallace is a pseudonym for Vincene Cradduck.

VIXEN (Japan)   F6.5386

Daiei Motion Picture Co. May **1970** [Los Angeles showing]. Sd; col (Fuji Color). 35mm (Daiei Scope). 95 min.

Dir Yasuzo Masumura. *Screenplay* Yasuzo Masumura, Ichiro Ikeda. *Photog* Setsuo Kobayashi. *Art Dir* Takesaburo Watanabe. *Mus* Hikaru Hayashi.

Cast: Ruriko Asaoka *(Michi),* Eiji Okada *(Nobuyuki Ishido),* Kyoko Kishida *(Akie),* Eiko Azusa *(Ishido's sister),* Takao Ito *(Akizuki),* Yusuke Kawazu *(Goro),* Eitaro Ozawa.

Melodrama. Michi demands 2 million yen from Nobuyuki Ishido in exchange for silence about his son's alleged rape of her. Ishido pays her the full amount, despite the insistence of his wife, Akie, that he pay only 1 million yen. Michi develops an obsession with Ishido and pursues him until he gives in and begins an affair with her, disgracing himself to the point that he is only momentarily angered when Michi tells Akie of the affair. Ishido becomes jealous of Goro, a young painter who occasionally sleeps with Michi and accepts money from her. Goro tells Ishido that for 5 million yen he will leave Michi alone, but he keeps visiting her even after Ishido pays him. Ishido accidentally kills Goro, and after being acquitted of criminal charges, he buys Michi a bar and begins a new life with her. Michi, however, becomes attracted to Akizuki, an engineer who is engaged to Ishido's sister. Despite Ishido's pleas, Michi goes out driving with Akizuki. She intentionally wrecks the car, seriously injuring Akizuki, and she discovers that she is excited by the idea of the engineer's death. Ishido begs Michi to be faithful, but she is sexually insatiable, and he finally decides to leave her. After his departure, Michi falls asleep in her bath and dies, overcome by leaking gas. *Engineers. Painters. Promiscuity. Extortion. Infidelity. Jealousy. Rape. Automobile accidents.*

Note: Released in Japan in Oct 1969 as *Jotai.*

THE VIXENS F6.5387

Trio Films–International Film Artists. *Dist* International Film Artists, Stratford Pictures, Charles S. Tratler. 25 Feb **1969** [New York opening]. Sd; b&w. 35mm. 82 min. [Also 80 min.]

A Cort-Johnsen Production. *Prod* Sande N. Johnsen. *Dir* Harvey Cort. *Screenplay* Al Rosati, Harvey Cort. *Writ* Al Rosati. *Photog* Harry Petricek. *Film Ed* Pat Follmer. *Cont* Alice Schoenfeld.

Cast: Anne Linden *(Betty)*, Mary Kahn *(Ann)*, Peter Burns *(Bob)*, Steven Harrison *(Alan)*, Claudia Bach *(Judy)*, Robert Raymond *(Harold)*, Hector Elizondo *(inspector)*.

Melodrama. A man and a woman run onto a high bridge that spans a dam. On a bet the man begins to walk on the edge of the narrow wall. He slips—or is pushed—and plunges to his death. In a police station later, Betty, the man's wife, reconstructs the events of the few weeks before the tragedy: *Her childless marriage to Bob, held together paradoxically by infidelities, is further aggravated when an equally disillusioned couple, Ann and Alan, move into their suburban neighborhood. The quartet enter into a series of mate-swapping episodes and the arrangement holds their respective marriages together. Soon a third couple, Judy and Harold, who had a similar arrangement with Bob and Betty some years earlier, arrive on the scene. In a drinking spree one afternoon, Harold dares Bob to walk the wall of the bridge over the dam. Bob accepts the bet, wagering Betty against Harold's $50. Though Harold wins, he faints before collecting his prize. Bob, taunted by Betty for losing his courage, persuades Alan to join him and Judy for a garden party. As intended by Bob, Ann and Betty stumble upon the threesome's lovemaking and their revulsion awakens in them a closeness that they have never experienced with any man. After listening to Betty's story, the inspector tells her what he believes happened: She and Bob have a drunken quarrel in their car over her emasculating behavior and her feelings for Ann. Already resentful of Betty's repeated references to his lack of manhood, Bob tries to walk across the dam but in the process falls to his death.* The inspector points out to Betty that, since there is no mud on her shoes, she obviously never left the car; her guilt, if there is any, is moral, not legal. Leaving the police station, Betty is met by Ann. Upon noticing there is mud on Ann's shoes, Betty suddenly realizes what actually happened on the bridge. Ann suggests she will keep the shoes, and Betty realizes that her tie to Ann is the knowledge of their mutual implication in Bob's death. *Police. Neighbors. Suburbanites. Disillusionment. Infidelity. Mate swapping. Drunkenness. Troilism. Childlessness. Revenge. Lesbianism. Manhood. Murder. Bridges. Wagers.*

Note: Filmed on location in Candlewood Lake, Stamford, and Darien, Connecticut; and in Manhattan, Queens, and Croton, New York; additional scenes filmed on the Croton Falls Dam. Following its New York release, the title was changed to *Friends and Lovers.* Also known as *The Women.*

IL VIZIO E LA VIRTÙ *see* **VICE AND VIRTUE**

LE VOCI BIANCHE *see* **WHITE VOICES**

LA VOGLIA MATTA *see* **CRAZY DESIRE**

THE VOICE F6.5388

Dist José Soltero. 3 Jun **1967** [New York opening]. Sd; col. 16mm. 45 min. *Dir* José Soltero.

Cast: Medea Reid *(voice)*.

Experimental film. Text from the one-act play by: Jean Cocteau, *La voix humaine* (Paris opening: 17 Feb 1930). As Cocteau's monolog *La voix humaine* is read on the soundtrack, images appear in non-narrative fashion.

Note: Subsequently known as *The Human Voice.*

VOICE OF THE HURRICANE F6.5389

RAM Productions–Moral Re-Armament. *Dist* Selected Pictures. 2 Jun **1964** [New York opening; c2 Jun 1964; LP28750]. Sd; col (Technicolor). 35mm. 80 min.

Prod Scoville Wishard. *Dir* George Fraser. *Screenplay* Alan Thornhill. *Photog* Rickard Tegstrom. *Lighting* Don Carstensen. *Art Dir* W. Cameron Johnson. *Film Ed* Harry Marker. *Mus Comp & Cond* Ian Freebairn-Smith. *Adtl Mus Arr* Paul Dunlap. *Sd* Fred Hendriksz. *Cost* Athena. *Sp Eff* Thol O. Simonson.

Cast: Muriel Smith *(Mary)*, Phyllis Konstam *(Janet Lord)*, Reginald Owen *(Nigel Charter)*, William Close *(Mark Pearce)*, Jane Wax *(Dolly Charter)*, David Cole *(Richard Lord)*, William Pawley, Jr. *(Humphrey Lord)*.

Drama. Source: Peter Howard and Alan Thornhill, *The Hurricane* (London, 1960). Young journalist Richard Lord returns home from school in London to his family's farm in British East Africa, and there his liberal attitudes and championship of the African cause clash with his father's rigid and imperious stance toward the natives. With Richard is Mark Pearce, an open-minded British Member of Parliament who is in Africa to gain insight on human relations problems in the British protectorate. While the Lords are entertaining bigoted District Officer Nigel Charter and his wife, a secret rebellion led by Mbali erupts into open turmoil. The farm's staff disappear, taking with them arms from the house gun cabinet, and the Lord family prepares for an attack that never comes. Mark discovers that Mary, the family's faithful cook, is rebel leader Mbali, who, because of her affection for Richard, ordered the Lord household spared. Richard is killed, however, while returning from a hospital where he took an injured African girl, thereby saving her life. The tragedy has a profound effect on Mark, and in a speech he pleads for Christian tolerance and understanding between blacks and whites. *Journalists. Farmers. Cooks. British. Africans. Filial relations. Nationalism. Colonialism. Revolts. Murder. Race relations. Christianity. British East Africa. Kenya—History. Great Britain—Parliament.*

Note: Some exterior scenes filmed in Kenya. RAM Productions is a subsidiary of Moral Re-Armament. Working title: *The Hurricane.*

LA VOIE LACTÉE *see* **THE MILKY WAY**

LE VOLEUR *see* **THE THIEF OF PARIS**

LE VOLEUR DE BAGDAD *see* **THE THIEF OF BAGHDAD**

VOLSHEBNAYA LAMPA ALADDINA *see* **ALADDIN AND HIS MAGIC LAMP**

VOM WERDEN DES MENSCHLICHEN LEBENS *see* **HELGA**

VON RYAN'S EXPRESS F6.5390

P–R Productions. *Dist* Twentieth Century–Fox Film Corp. 23 Jun **1965** [New York opening; c23 Jun 1965; LP31265]. Sd (Westrex); col (DeLuxe). 35mm (CinemaScope). 117 min.

A Mark Robson Production. *Prod* Saul David. *Dir* Mark Robson. *2d Unit Dir* William Kaplan. *Screenplay* Wendell Mayes, Joseph Landon. *Photog* William H. Daniels. *Dir Photog 2d Unit* Harold Lipstein. *Camera Op* Al Lane. *Asst Camera* William Johnson. *Art Dir* Jack Martin Smith, Hilyard Brown. *Asst Art Dir* Ed Graves, Lou Korn. *Set Decor* Walter M. Scott, Raphael Bretton. *Film Ed* Dorothy Spencer. *Mus* Jerry Goldsmith. *Orch* Gould Morton. *Sd* Carlton W. Faulkner, Elmer Raguse. *Rec* William Buffinger. *Asst Dir* Eli Dunn. *Unit Prod Mgr* Harry A. Caplan. *Wardrobe* Mickey Sherrard. *Makeup* Ben Nye, Roy Stork. *Hairstyles* Margaret Donovan, Helen Turpin. *Sp Photog Eff* L. B. Abbott, Emil Kosa, Jr. *Coöp* Ferrovie dello Stato. *Prop Master* Tom Coleman. *Grip* Lou Pazelli. *Still Photog* Ted Allan.

Cast: Frank Sinatra *(Col. Joseph L. Ryan)*, Trevor Howard *(Maj. Eric Fincham)*, Raffaella Carra *(Gabriella)*, Brad Dexter *(Sergeant Bostick)*, Sergio Fantoni *(Captain Oriani)*, John Leyton *(Orde)*, Edward Mulhare *(Constanzo)*, Wolfgang Preiss *(Major von Klemment)*, James Brolin *(Private Ames)*, John Van Dreelen *(Colonel Gortz)*, Adolfo Celi *(Battaglia)*, Vito Scotti *(Italian train engineer)*, Richard Bakalyan *(Corporal Giannini)*, Michael Goodliffe *(Captain Stein)*, Michael St. Clair *(Sergeant Dunbar)*, Ivan Triesault *(Von Kleist)*, Jacques Stanislavski *(Gortz's aide)*, Al Wyatt, Buzz Henry, John Day, James Sikking *(American soldiers)*, Eric Micklewood *(Ransom)*, John Mitory *(Oriani's aide)*, Benito Prezia *(Italian corporal)*, Dominick Delgarde *(Italian soldier)*, Barry Ford *(Ransom's batman)*, Gino Gottarelli *(Gortz's aide #2)*, Peter Hellman *(pilot)*, Michael Romanoff *(Italian nobleman)*, Walter Linden *(German captain)*, Bard Stevens *(German sergeant)*, Ernesto Melinari *(Italian tailor)*, Bob Rosen *(POW who opens sweatbox)*.

War drama. Source: David Westheimer, *Von Ryan's Express* (Garden City, New York, 1964). In August 1943, Maj. Eric Fincham, a professional British soldier, is the ranking Allied officer in an Italian prisoner-of-war camp. He has tried to lead escapes but has always failed, and now he must relinquish his leadership to American Col. Joseph L. Ryan. Ryan's hard manner wins him the nickname "Von Ryan," and though he obtains better living conditions for his fellow prisoners, he is not popular among them. Ryan renews the plans for escape, and with Italian cooperation the prisoners take over a freight train transporting them into Germany and flee across Italy toward Switzerland. They are chased by a German troop train, attacked by German aircraft, and pursued by another Nazi train. Ryan kills Gabriella, an Italian collaborator, and he himself is killed, though most of the men arrive safely in Switzerland. *Prisoners of war. Nazis. Traitors. Prison escapes. Aerial bombardment. Railroads. Trains. World War II. Italy. Switzerland. United States Army. Great Britain—Army. Chases.*

Note: Filmed in Italy.

VOODOO ISLAND *see* **SILENT DEATH**

VOODOO VILLAGE (Reissue)   **F6.5391**
Grand Prize Films. *Dist* Continental Distributing, Inc. 3 Apr **1963** [Boston opening]. Sd; col (Pathé). 35mm. 70 min.
Note: Originally released in Jul 1958 as *Sorcerers' Village*; running time: 75 min.

VOR SONNENUNTERGANG (West Germany)   **F6.5392**
CCC-Filmkunst. *Dist* Casino Films. 2 Jun **1961** [Chicago opening]. Sd; b&w. 35mm. 102 min.
Prod Artur Brauner. *Dir* Gottfried Reinhardt. *Screenplay* Jochen Huth. *Photog* Kurt Hasse. *Mus* Werner Eisbrenner.
Cast: Hans Albers *(Mathias Clausen)*, Annemarie Düringer *(Inken Peters)*, Martin Held *(Erich Klamroth)*, Hannelore Schroth *(Ottilie Klamroth)*, Claus Biederstaedt *(Egert Clausen)*, Maria Becker *(Bettina Clausen)*, Erich Schellow *(Wolfgang Clausen)*, Inge Langen *(Paula Clausen)*, Wolfgang Preiss *(Dr. Hahnefield)*, Hans Nielsen *(Dr. Steynity)*, Johanna Hofer *(Frau Peters)*.
Melodrama. Source: Gerhart Hauptmann, *Vor Sonnenuntergang* (Berlin opening: 18 Apr 1932). After the death of his beloved wife, aging industrialist Mathias Clausen rejects his four children, whose preoccupations seem to him superficial. Although the widower is later turned from thoughts of suicide and revitalized by his love for the youthful Inken Peters, his family opposes the romance, and the relationship results in heartbreak for the young woman. *Industrialists. Widowers. Suicide. Filial relations.*
Note: Released in West Germany in 1956. Previously filmed in Germany in 1937 as *Der Herrscher*.

VOSKRESENIYE *see* **RESURRECTION**

LE VOYAGE DU SILENCE *see* **VOYAGE OF SILENCE**

LE VOYAGE EN BALLON *see* **STOWAWAY IN THE SKY**

VOYAGE OF SILENCE (France)   **F6.5393**
Fildebroc–Les Productions Artistes Associés. *Dist* Lopert Pictures. 11 Sep **1968** [New York opening]. Sd; b&w. 35mm. 89 min.
Prod Philippe de Broca. *Dir* Christian de Chalonges. *Screenplay* Christian de Chalonges, Roberto Bodegas. *Dir Photog* Alain Derobe. *Camera Op* Charles-Henry Montel. *Asst Camera* Colin Mounier. *Art Dir* Claude Pignot. *Film Ed* Hélène Arnal. *Asst Film Ed* Annie Charvein. *Mus* Luis Cilia. *Sd* Guy Villette. *1st & 2d Asst Dir* Roberto Bodegas, Pierre Roubaud. *Prod Supv* Georges Casati. *Prod Mgr* Alain Belmondo. *Script Girl* Colette Crochot. *Makeup* Simone Knapp. *Hairstyles* Simone Knapp. *Still Photog* Jean Magis.
Cast: Marco Pico *(Antonio Ferreira)*, Henrique de Sousa *(Alberto)*, Americo Trindade *(Americo)*, Antonio Passalia *(Carlos)*, Ludmila Mikael *(Dominique, the nurse)*, Heitor Fernandes, João Neto, Alfredo Neto, Antonio Gonzalves, José Belchior, José Borges, Antonio Lopez, Luis Oliveira.
Drama. Antonio Ferreira, a young Portuguese carpenter, dreams of going to Paris where his friend Carlos lives and has promised to help him find a job. Because of strict passport regulations, Antonio agrees to pay an underground network to smuggle him into Spain and across the border to France. En route, he and his colleagues are abandoned and forced to continue their journey on foot. Discouraged by the cold and hardships, Antonio's companions return to Portugal, and he is left to continue the journey alone. Confident that Carlos will help him, Antonio makes his way to Paris, only to discover that Carlos has been away for some time. Not knowing where to turn, Antonio goes to Dominique, a young French nurse whom he had met in Portugal. Though she can be of little help to an illegal immigrant who speaks almost no French, she arranges for him to earn some money by helping move a doctor's family into a new home. When Carlos finally appears, Antonio is disappointed to discover that he will have to pay his friend a high price to procure working papers and continue to pay him a portion of his salary for 5 years. Realizing that Carlos has betrayed him, Antonio downheartedly moves into a muddy shantytown that is worse than the Portuguese village he left behind. *Portuguese. Carpenters. Immigrants. Nurses. Immigration. Smuggling. Perfidy. Extortion. Poverty. Passports. Slums. Portugal. Spain. Paris.*
Note: Opened in Paris in Nov 1967 as *O salto*; running time: 88 min; also shown in France as *Le saut* at 95 min. Working title: *Le voyage du silence.* Filmed in collaboration with Portuguese immigrants who appear in many roles.

VOYAGE OF THE LEHI IV *see* **LEHI**

VOYAGE TO THE BOTTOM OF THE SEA   **F6.5394**
Windsor Productions. *Dist* Twentieth Century–Fox Film Corp. 12 Jul **1961** [Washington, D. C., opening; c12 Jul 1961; LP20072]. Sd (Westrex); col (DeLuxe). 35mm (CinemaScope). 105 min.
An Irwin Allen Production. *Prod-Dir-Story* Irwin Allen. *Screenplay* Irwin Allen, Charles Bennett. *Dir Photog* Winton Hoch. *Underwater Photog* John Lamb. *Art Dir* Jack Martin Smith, Herman A. Blumenthal. *Set Decor* Walter M. Scott, John Sturtevant. *Film Ed* George Boemler. *Mus* Paul Sawtell, Bert

Shefter. *Orch* Max Reese. *Titl Song* Russell Faith. *Sung by* Frankie Avalon. *Sd* Alfred Bruzlin, Warren B. Delaplain. *Asst Dir* Ad Schaumer. *Asst to the Prod* Albert Gail. *Cost Dsgn* Paul Zastupnevich. *Makeup* Ben Nye. *Hairstyles* Helen Turpin. *Sp Photog Eff* L. B. Abbott. *Tech Adv* Fred Zendar.
Cast: Walter Pidgeon *(Adm. Harriman Nelson)*, Joan Fontaine *(Dr. Susan Hiller)*, Barbara Eden *(Cathy Connors)*, Peter Lorre *(Commodore Lucius Emery)*, Robert Sterling *(Capt. Lee Crane)*, Michael Ansara *(Miguel Alvarez)*, Frankie Avalon *(Chip Romano)*, Regis Toomey *(Dr. Jamieson)*, John Litel *(Admiral Crawford)*, Howard McNear *(Congressman Parker)*, Henry Daniell *(Dr. Zucco)*, Mark Slade *(Smith)*, Charles Tannen *(Gleason)*, Delbert Monroe *(Kowski)*, Anthony Monaco *(Cookie)*, Robert Easton *(Sparks)*, Jonathan Gilmore *(Young)*, David McLean *(Ned Thompson)*, Larry Gray *(Dr. Newmar)*, George Diestel *(Lieutenant Hodges)*, Skip Ward, Michael Ford *(crew members)*.
Science fiction melodrama. As the U. S. O. S. *Seaview*, a mammoth glass-nosed atomic submarine designed by scientist Harriman Nelson, makes its trial run near the polar icecap, the Van Allen radiation belt suddenly bursts into flame and threatens to destroy the Earth. Nelson is convinced that the only hope for survival is to shoot a Polaris missile into the belt and thereby cause it to explode backward into space. When the United Nations rejects his proposal as being too dangerous, Nelson commandeers the *Seaview* and heads for the Marianas, where he plans to launch the missile. Also aboard the submarine are Susan Hiller, a psychiatrist studying the effects of prolonged confinement on human behavior; Cathy Connors, Nelson's devoted secretary; Lucius Emery, a noted physicist who concurs with Nelson's theory; Capt. Lee Crane, the *Seaview*'s skipper; Miguel Alvarez, a civilian scientist; and Chip Romano, a brash young officer. Once the vessel is underway, several of the personnel begin to question Nelson's sanity; and there are repeated attempts at sabotage. After a run-in with a giant squid and a passage through a World War II mine field, the *Seaview* is attacked by U. N. submarines sent to prevent the launching of the missile. But Nelson, knowing that the *Seaview* can withstand depths far greater than any other undersea vessel, takes his craft down deeper and deeper until the tremendous pressure causes the pursuing submarines to explode. When the *Seaview* reaches its destination, Susan is revealed to be the saboteur. Convinced Nelson's actions will destroy the world, she makes a last effort to prevent the launching; but she is accidentally killed. Crane then sets the detonator, and the Polaris is sent into space. The wild experiment proves successful as a shattering explosion restores the burning sky to a tropical stillness. *Scientists. Psychiatrists. Secretaries. Physicists. Saboteurs. Nuclear energy. Submarines. Missiles. Mines (war explosives). Mariana Islands. United Nations. United States Navy. Van Allen radiation belt. Squids.*

VOYAGE TO THE END OF THE UNIVERSE (Czechoslovakia) **F6.5395**
Barrandov Film Studio. *For* Československý Film. *Dist* American International Pictures. 2 Sep **1964** [Detroit opening; c2 Sep 1964; LP29678]. Sd; b&w. 35mm (CinemaScope). 81 min.
Prod Rudolph Wohl. *Assoc Prod* Ludmila Tikovská, František Jaderník, Ferdinand Zelenka, Eliška Doubková. *Dir* Jack Pollack. *Screenplay* Jack Pollack, Pavel Juráček. *Photog* Jan Kališ. *2d Unit Photog* Saša Rašilov. *Asst Photog* Oldřich Hubáček. *Art Dir* John Zaav, Bohumil Dudař. *Stage Dsgn* Carl Lukas. *Film Ed* Joe Derby, Helena Lehovcová, Růžena Hejsková. *Mus Comp* Danny List. *Played by* The Film Symphony Orchestra. *Mus Cond* František Belfín. *Choreog* Frank Haller. *Sd Ed* Kay Rose. *Sd Eff* Jaromír Svoboda, Bohumír Brunclík. *Asst Dir* Hynek Bočan, Jiří Růžička. *Cost Dsgn* Esther Smith, John Scales, Don Demore. *Wardrobe* Dena Rova. *Makeup* Rudolph Hammer. *Sp Eff* Jan Kališ, Milan Nejedlý, Jiří Hlupý, Pavel Nečesal, Karel Císařovský, František Žemlička. *Tech Adv* Rudolph Pele, Milton Karas, Mildred Kauders, Vladimír Guth, Milan Morávek, Jan Hospodář.
Cast: Dennis Stephans *(Expedition Commander Vladimir Abajev)*, Francis Smolen *(astronomer Anthony Hopkins)*, Dana Meredith *(Nina Kirova)*, Irene Kova *(Brigit)*, Rodney Lucas *(MacDonald)*, Otto Lack *(Michael)*, Myron March *(Marcel Bernard)*, Joseph Adams *(Zdenek Lorenc)*, Rudolph Dial *(Ervin Herold)*, John Rose *(doctor)*, Martin Tapin *(Peter Kubes)*, Jerry Tullis *(Erik Svensson)*, John Mares *(Milek Wertbowsky)*, Marcella Martin *(Stefa)*, Svatava Hubeňáková *(MacDonald's wife)*, Renza Nova, Jan Morris, Joe Irwin, Ludek Munzar, Emilie Vasayova.
Science fiction drama. Spaceship *Icarus*, a flying city of the 25th century, speeds its crew of 50 men and women toward distant planets. After 4 months of travel, astronomer Hopkins pinpoints a mysterious spacecraft in the path of *Icarus*. Pilots of an expeditionary rocket find that the craft is a wreck peopled by the dead; evidence of poison gas indicates foul play. The expedition commander discovers that the craft is charged with atomic energy and calls the pilots back. The pilots find unexploded bombs on the craft and attempt to return, but their rocket explodes in an enormous atomic blast. Resuming its course, *Icarus* approaches a dark star whose radiation retards the biochemical

processes of living organisms and induces a deep sleep. According to Hopkins' calculations, the ship must run on automatic pilot for 60 hours to pass the danger zone, but the crew mysteriously awakens after 25 hours. The scientists must now devote their attentions to Svensson and Michael, who have been poisoned by radiation while repairing *Icarus*. Michael has lost his ability to reason and wants only to return home; he locks himself behind armored doors, and MacDonald crawls through air ducts to subdue him. The crisis past, Brigit discovers a strange nebula moving at the same speed as the ship. Hopkins determines that the cloud is a magnetic field beamed from the Green Planet to protect them from the dark star's radiation; this phenonemon accounts for their premature awakening. Convinced that they have at last found a planet inhabited by intelligent and friendly creatures, the crew prepares to land on the Green Planet—Earth. *Spacemen. Astronomers. Scientists. Space exploration. Radiation. Nuclear energy. Sleep. Magnetism. Spaceships. Rockets. Bombs.*

Note: Released in Czechoslovakia in Agfacolor in Jul 1963 as *Ikarie XB 1*; running time: 90 min. Original Czech credit and cast names include: Rudolf Wolf (Rudolph Wohl), Jindřich Polák (Jack Pollack), Jan Zázvorka (John Zaav), Josef Dobřichovský (Joe Derby), Zdeněk Liška (Danny List), František Halmazňa (Frank Haller), Rudolf Pešek (Rudolph Pele), Milan Kauders (Mildred Kauders), Zdeněk Štěpánek (Dennis Stephans), František Smolík (Francis Smolen), Dana Medřická (Dana Meredith), Irena Kačírková (Irene Kova), Radovan Lukavský (Rodney Lucas), Otto Lackovič (Otto Lack), Miroslav Macháček (Myron March), Jozef Adamovič (Joseph Adams), Rudolf Deyl (Rudolph Dial), Jaroslav Rozsíval (John Rose), Martin Tapák (Martin Tapin), Jiří Vršťala (Jerry Tullis), Jaroslav Mareš (John Mares), Marcela Martínková (Marcella Martin), Růžena Urbanová (Renza Nova), Jan Cmíral (Jan Morris), and Vjačeslav Irmanov (Joe Irwin). U. S. copyright claimant: Alta Vista Productions.

THE VOYEUR   F6.5396
Feb **1970** [periodical review]. Sd; col. 16mm. [Feature film, length unknown.]

Sex film. A blonde, a brunette, and a black woman engage in autoerotic and lesbian activities for a peeping tom, later inviting him to their room, where they tease and torture him. *Negroes. Voyeurism. Lesbianism. Autoeroticism. Miscegenation.*

VOYNA I MIR see **WAR AND PEACE**

VRAŽDA PO ČESKU see **MURDER CZECH STYLE**

VRAŽDA PO NAŠEM see **MURDER CZECH STYLE**

VU DU PONT see **A VIEW FROM THE BRIDGE**

THE VULCAN AFFAIR see **TO TRAP A SPY**

THE VULTURE (United States/Canada/Great Britain)   F6.5397
Homeric Films–Iliad Films–Film Financial Co. *Dist* Paramount Pictures. 3 May **1967** [Portland, Oregon, opening; c31 Dec 1966; LP34357]. Sd; b&w (see note). 35mm. 91 min.

Prod-Dir-Writ Lawrence Huntington. *Exec Prod* Jack O. Lamont. *Dir Photog* Stephen Dade. *Art Dir* Duncan Sutherland. *Film Ed* John S. Smith. *Mus* Eric Spear. *Sd* Edgar Vetter. *Asst Dir* Bill Snaith. *Prod Mgr* Philip Shipway. *Wardrobe* Dulcie Midwinter. *Makeup* Geoffrey Rodway. *Hairstyles* Gordon Bond.

Cast: Robert Hutton (*Eric Lutyens*), Akim Tamiroff (*Professor Koniglich*), Broderick Crawford (*Brian Stroud*), Diane Clare (*Trudy Lutyens*), Philip Friend (*The Vicar*), Patrick Holt (*Jarvis*), Annette Carell (*Ellen West*), Edward Caddick (*The Sexton*), Gordon Sterne (*Edward Stroud*), Keith McConnell (*Police Superintendent Wendell*), Margaret Robertson (*nurse*), Monty Landis (*bus driver*), Gordon Tanner, Arnold Diamond, Murray Hayne, Roy Hanlon, Peter Elliott, actor, George Tovey.

Horror film. One stormy night in Cornwall, schoolteacher Ellen West becomes hysterical when she sees a gigantic bird with a human face fly out of the open grave of Francis Real, an 18th-century seaman. Real, buried alive with a huge, murderous bird he had found in the South Pacific, had sworn vengeance on all descendants of Squire Stroud, the man who ordered his interment; nevertheless, Brian Stroud, the present squire, is unconcerned by the prophecy of doom. American scientist Eric Lutyens, husband of Brian's sister Trudy, is troubled when he finds the mutilated body of a sheep in what appears to be a vulture's nest. He visits Professor Koniglich, a scientist friend of Brian who believes himself to be a descendant of Real, and correctly surmises that Koniglich had attempted to disintegrate his own body in the grave and reassemble it through nuclear energy; unfortunately, the professor had failed to consider the bird buried there, and a mutation resulted. Before Eric can warn the Strouds, Brian and his brother Edward are found dead on a cliffside, and Trudy is carried away to the same site by the bird after she is lured to Koniglich's house. At the cliff, Eric finds his wife threatened by the beast with

Koniglich's head and screams at her to use the gun he had given her. Trudy shoots the bird and it crashes to death on the rocks below; Eric then weights it with an anchor, tows it out to sea, and sinks it. *Landed gentry. Monsters. Professors. Germans. Scientists. Schoolteachers. Curses. Mutation. Revenge. Ancestry. Nuclear energy. Cemeteries. Cornwall (England). Birds. Sheep.*

Note: Location scenes filmed in Cornwall, England. Released in Canada in 1967 and in Great Britain in 1968. Filmed in color, with U. S. prints in black-and-white.

VYNÁLEZ ZKÁZY see **THE FABULOUS WORLD OF JULES VERNE**

VZROSLYYE DETI see **GROWN-UP CHILDREN**

W. C. FIELDS see **A NIGHT WITH THE GREAT ONE**

W. C. FIELDS FILM FESTIVAL see **THE BEST OF W. C. FIELDS**

W. I. A. (WOUNDED IN ACTION)   F6.5398
Myriad Productions. Mar **1966**. Sd; b&w. 35mm. 87 min.

Prod Irving Sunasky, Samuel Zerinksy. *Assoc Prod* Leopoldo Salcedo. *Dir-Writ* Irving Sunasky. *Photog* Enrique Rogales. *Film Ed* Gregorio Caraballo. *Mus* Leopold Silos.

Cast: Steve Marlo (*Pvt. Joe Goodman*), Maura McGiveney (*Lieut. Marietta Dodd*), Leopoldo Salcedo (*Maj. Armando De León*), Mary Humphrey (*Lieut. Joan Marsh*), Albert Quinton (*Major Slater*), Victor Izay (*Sergeant Roman*), Bella Flores (*Carmen*), John Horn (*Corporal Bliss*), Peter Deuel (*Private Myers*), Joe Sison (*Sanchez*), Brennan Wood (*Capt. Ed Bill*), Romy Brion (*Ruther*).

War drama. In the Philippines during World War II, U. S. and Filipino soldiers who have been wounded in action against the invading Japanese are taken to a military evacuation hospital. One patient, Filipino Major Armando De León, nearly begins an affair with nurse Joan Marsh, but she is transferred from the hospital. U. S. Pvt. Joe Goodman also falls in love with a nurse, Marietta Dodd, but he is returned to the United States when the officers learn of their romance. Before he leaves, however, Joe pledges to marry Marietta when they can be reunited. *Nurses. Military life. Military occupation. Hospitals. World War II. United States Army. Japan—Army. Philippines—Army.*

Note: Location scenes filmed in the Philippines. Newsreel and combat footage of World War II is included.

WUSA   F6.5399
Stuart Rosenberg Productions–Coleytown Productions–Mirror Productions. *Dist* Paramount Pictures. 1 Nov **1970** [New York opening; c19 Aug 1970; LP38418]. Sd; col (Technicolor). 35mm (Panavision). 115 min. *MPAA rating* GP.

A Stuart Rosenberg–Paul Newman–John Foreman Production. *Prod* Paul Newman, John Foreman. *Assoc Prod* Hank Moonjean. *Dir* Stuart Rosenberg. *Screenplay* Robert Stone, writ. *Ch Cinematog* Richard Moore. *Camera Op* Roger Sherman. *Asst Camera* William Clark. *Art Dir* Philip Jefferies. *Set Decor* William Kiernan. *Film Ed* Robert Wyman. *Mus Supv* Al Mack. *Mus Comp & Cond* Lalo Schifrin. *Song:* "Glory Road" writ & sung by Neil Diamond. *Sd* Jerry Jost, Richard Portman. *Sd Rec* Bill Hanks. *Boom Op* Dean Hodges. *Asst Dir* Nat Holt, Jr., Hank Moonjean, Howard W. Koch, Jr., Les Gorall, Clancy Herne. *Unit Prod Mgr* Arthur S. Newman, Jr., Austen Jewell. *Script Supv* Betty Crosby. *Miss Woodward's Cost* Travilla. *Wardrobe* Nat Tolmach, Norma Brown. *Makeup Artist* Lynn Reynolds, Jack Wilson. *Hairstyles* Sydney Guilaroff, Lorraine Roberson. *Dial Coach* James Arnett. *Prop Master* Anthony Bavero. *Gaffer* Bob Banks. *Constr Mgr* Jim Orendorff. *Grip* Lloyd Isbell. *Casting Dir* Hoyt Bowers.

Cast: Paul Newman (*Rheinhardt*), Joanne Woodward (*Geraldine*), Anthony Perkins (*Rainey*), Laurence Harvey (*Farley*), Pat Hingle (*Bingamon*), Cloris Leachman (*Philomene*), Don Gordon (*Bogdanovich*), Michael Anderson, Jr. (*Marvin*), Leigh French (*girl*), Moses Gunn (*Clotho*), Bruce Cabot (*King Wolyoe*), B. J. Mason (*Roosevelt Berry*), Robert Quarry (*Noonan*), Wayne Rogers (*Calvin Minter*), Hal Baylor (*Shorty*), Jim Boles (*hot dog vendor*), Diane Ladd (*barmaid at railroad station*), Sahdji (*Hollywood*), Skip Young (*Jimmy Snipe*), Geoff Edwards (*Irving*), Clifton James (*Speed*), Tol Avery (*senator*), Paul Hampton (*Rusty Fargo*), Jerry Catron (*Sidewinder Bates*), Geraldine West, Lucille Benson (*matrons*), Susan Batson (*teenaged girl*), Zara Cully (*white-haired woman*), The Preservation Hall Jazz Band of New Orleans.

Drama. Source: Robert Stone, *A Hall of Mirrors* (Boston, 1966). Rheinhardt, a drunken drifter, collects a debt from his old friend Farley, a con man currently posing as a revivalist preacher in New Orleans, and learns from him that right-wing radio station WUSA is looking for an announcer. Later that night in a waterfront bar he meets Geraldine, who is trying to hustle a drunken sailor into buying her dinner; after Rheinhardt buys her a steak, she takes him to her roominghouse where they spend the night together. The next day he meets Bingamon, the radio station's owner, and is hired on the stipulation that he read reactionary editorials on the air. Soon he meets the naive and liberal Rainey, who has been unknowingly duped by Bingamon into taking part in a phony welfare investigation actually intended to create a backlash among whites. Rheinhardt, disturbed because he, too, is being manipulated, gets drunk, quarrels with Rainey, and then walks out on Geraldine. Later, after Rainey has learned the truth of the situation from black newspaperman Roosevelt Berry, WUSA sponsors a large political hate rally with gospel singers, a guest appearance by an aging cowboy star, and a demonstration by black militants outside the stadium. Rainey, now completely disillusioned, tries to assassinate Bingamon in front of the audience, but he hits one of the demagogue's assistants. As Rainey tries to escape, the hysterical crowd stomps him to death. Meanwhile, the gospel group, which is made up of Geraldine's hippie neighbors, fears that the riot will lead to drug arrests, and they give Geraldine their stash of marijuana. When the police discover the drugs and arrest her, Geraldine hangs herself in the jail cell. Rheinhardt learns the news from Geraldine's crippled friend, Philomene; after visiting the grave, he packs his bags and leaves the city. *Drifters. Confidence men. Radio announcers. Sailors. Neighbors. Hippies. Negroes. Newspapermen. Militants. Cripples. Politics. Propaganda. Racism. Fraud. Duplicity. Drunkenness. Frameup. Assassination. Riots. Imprisonment. Suicide. Roominghouses. Bars. Demonstrations. Marijuana. New Orleans.*

Note: Location scenes filmed in the French Quarter and other parts of New Orleans. Working Title: *A Hall of Mirrors.*

THE WACKY PLAYBOY!   F6.5400

Dist Futuramic Releasing Organization. 19 Feb 1964 [trade review]. Sd; b&w. 35mm. 71 min. [Also reviewed at 63 min.]

Prod Ken Gary. *Dir* Steven Edward. *Screenplay* Jay Sayer.

Cast: Tommy Moe Raft *(Junior)*, Cindy Layne, Jay Sayer.

Western comedy. Junior, a girl-shy young man, will inherit a fortune if he marries by a specific date. He enlists the help of his secretary, who invites six women to spend the weekend at his isolated ranch. Junior remains hidden and spies on the women as they compete with each other to become his bride by performing various ranch chores in various states of undress. As the final hour approaches, none has passed Junior's test, but a Texas cowgirl arrives, and Junior meets his deadline. *Secretaries. Texans. Contests. Timidity. Marriage. Voyeurism. Nudity. Inheritance. Ranches.*

THE WACKY WORLD OF DR. MORGUS   F6.5401

Eugene T. Calongne–Jules Sevin. 1 Nov 1962 [New Orleans opening]. Sd; b&w. 35mm. [Feature length assumed.]

Dir Roul Haig. *Screenplay* Noel Haig, Roul Haig. *Mus* Corelli Jacobs.

Cast: Sid Noel *(Dr. Alexander Morgus)*, Dana Barton *(Pencils McCane)*, Jeanne Teslof *(Mona Speekla)*, David Kleinberger *(Bruno)*, Thomas George *(Chopsley)*, Bob Nelson, actor, Marshall Pearce, Chris Owens, Wayne Mack.

Horror film. In his New Orleans French Quarter laboratory, Dr. Alexander Morgus invents an "instant people" machine, capable of turning people into sand and then restoring them. Bruno, unscrupulous ruler of Microvania, uses the machine to place 300 spies in the United States, hoping to steal American secrets and sell them on the world espionage market, thereby enriching his country. Top spy Mona Speekla, responsible for obtaining the services of Morgus and utilizing his invention for Bruno, falls in love with reporter Pencils McCane, who helps to thwart the evil ruler's plans. *Inventors. Reporters. Spies. Transmutation. Espionage. Laboratories. New Orleans.*

Note: Filmed in New Orleans, with additional shooting in Kiln, Mississippi, and Kenner, Louisiana. Sid Noel is also known as Noel Rideau.

THE WACKY WORLD OF MOTHER GOOSE   F6.5402

Videocraft International Productions. *Dist* Embassy Pictures. 2 Dec 1967 [Yonkers, New York, opening]. Sd; col (PatheColor). 35mm. [Feature film, length unknown.]

Prod Arthur Rankin, Jr. *Exec Prod* Joseph E. Levine. *Dir* Jules Bass. *Story* Romeo Muller. *Mus & Lyr* Jules Bass, George Wilkins.

Voice: Margaret Rutherford *(Mother Goose)*.

Musical comedy with animated sequences. Mother Goose and her friends enjoy a series of adventures in Never-Never Land. *Imaginary kingdoms. Mother Goose.*

WACO   F6.5403

A. C. Lyles Productions. *Dist* Paramount Pictures. 25 Jun 1966 [Reno, Nevada, opening; c22 Jun 1966; LP32927]. Sd; col (Technicolor). 35mm (Techniscope). 85 min.

Prod A. C. Lyles. *Dir* R. G. Springsteen. *Screenplay* Steve Fisher. *Dir Photog* Robert Pittack. *Art Dir* Hal Pereira, Al Roelofs. *Set Decor* Robert R. Benton, Chuck Pierce. *Film Ed* Bernard Matis. *Mus Comp* Jimmie Haskell. *Titl Song* Jimmie Haskell, Hal Blair. *Sung by* Lorne Greene. *Sd* Terry Kellum, John Wilkinson. *Asst Dir* James Rosenberger. *Prod Mgr* Howard Roessel. *Jane Russell's Wardrobe* Edith Head.

Cast: Howard Keel *(Waco)*, Jane Russell *(Jill Stone)*, Brian Donlevy *(Ace Ross)*, Wendell Corey *(Preacher Sam Stone)*, Terry Moore *(Dolly)*, John Smith *(Joe Gore)*, John Agar *(George Gates)*, Gene Evans *(Deputy Sheriff O'Neill)*, Richard Arlen *(Sheriff Billy Kelly)*, Ben Cooper *(Scotty Moore)*, Tracy Olsen *(Patricia West)*, DeForest Kelley *(Bill Rile)*, Anne Seymour *(Ma Jenner)*, Robert Lowery *(Mayor Ned West)*, Willard Parker *(Pete Jenner)*, Jeff Richards *(Kallen)*, Reg Parton *(Ike Jenner)*, Fuzzy Knight *(telegraph operator)*, Russ McCubbin, Dan White, Red Morgan, King Johnson, Barbara Latell.

Western melodrama. Source: Harry Sanford and Max Lamb, *Emporia* (New York, 1961). Sheriff Billy Kelly is shot down in Emporia, Wyoming, and the mayor and the local preacher send for a gunfighter, Waco, to help restore law and order. The preacher's wife, Jill Stone, is apprehensive lest Waco, unaware of her marriage, attempt to resume their former romance. Upon his arrival, Waco guns down the killers hired by the town boss, Joe Gore, fires the drunken deputy sheriff, cleans up the gambling saloon operated by Gore, and calls in his old saddle companion, Ace Ross, to assist him further in bringing peace to Emporia. After he evades a trap set for him by rancher Ma Jenner, the embittered mother of a man he killed, Waco prepares for the final showdown on the main street. Though Ross backs out, Waco is supported by both the preacher and the mayor. Gore, his henchmen, and the Jenner hands are all killed; and the preacher also dies, appealing that the bloodshed be stopped. With peace restored to Emporia, Waco decides to remain as sheriff. *Sheriffs. Mayors. Preachers. Gunfighters. Ranchers. Law and order. Gambling. Drunkenness. Motherhood. Saloons. Wyoming.*

WAGA KOI WAGA UTA *see* **THE SONG FROM MY HEART**

WAHINE *see* **MAEVA**

WAIT UNTIL DARK   F6.5404

Warner Bros.–Seven Arts, Inc. 26 Oct 1967 [New York opening; c30 Dec 1967; LP35798]. Sd; col (Technicolor). 35mm. 107 min.

Prod Mel Ferrer. *Exec Prod* Walter MacEwan. *Dir* Terence Young. *Screenplay* Robert Carrington, Jane-Howard Carrington. *Dir Photog* Charles Lang. *Art Dir* George Jenkins. *Set Decor* George James Hopkins. *Film Ed* Gene Milford. *Mus* Henry Mancini. *Titl Song* Henry Mancini, Jay Livingston, Ray Evans. *Sung by* Bobby Darin. *Sd* Everett Hughes. *Asst Dir* Jack Aldworth. *Unit Mgr* Russell Llewellyn. *Makeup Supv* Gordon Bau. *Miss Hepburn's Makeup* Warner Bros. Cosmetics. *Supv Hairstylist* Jean Burt Reilly.

Cast: Audrey Hepburn *(Susy Hendrix)*, Alan Arkin *(Roat)*, Richard Crenna *(Mike Talman)*, Efrem Zimbalist, Jr. *(Sam Hendrix)*, Jack Weston *(Carlino)*, Samantha Jones *(Lisa)*, Julie Herrod *(Gloria)*, Frank O'Brien *(Shatner)*, Gary Morgan *(boy)*.

Mystery drama. Source: Frederick Knott, *Wait Until Dark* (New York opening: 2 Feb 1966). As a flight from Montreal lands at Kennedy Airport, Lisa, a fashion model asks commercial artist Sam Hendrix to hold a toy doll for her. When the woman disappears, Sam takes the doll to his Greenwich Village apartment. A short time later, hoodlums Mike Talman and Carlino arrive at Sam's empty apartment to keep what they think is an appointment with Lisa. Instead, they are met by Roat, a master criminal skilled in disguise, who informs them that he has murdered Lisa for attempting a doublecross and that they must now dispose of her body and find the missing doll, which contains a fortune in heroin. The following day, after Lisa's corpse has been removed to a nearby lot, the three man trick Sam into going to New Jersey, leaving his blind wife, Susy, alone. One by one the three hoodlums call at the house under false pretenses. Finally, Carlino, in the guise of a detective, announces that he is investigating the murder of a young woman found in the neighborhood; by insinuation Susy is led to suspect that Sam is involved in the killing and the missing doll is the link. Gradually, however, Susy begins to suspect that Roat and Carlino are imposters, and she appeals to Mike for help. After he has left, Gloria, a little girl from upstairs who had taken the doll, returns it. Believing Mike to be her husband's friend, Susy telephones him the good news; but with the help of Gloria, Susy learns that the number Mike gave her is for a telephone booth across the street. Realizing that all three men are involved in the plot to get the doll, Susy sends Gloria to meet Sam, returning from New Jersey, at the terminal. After the child has left, Susy discovers that her telephone line has been cut. Mike arrives and, touched by Susy's plight, tells her the truth about Sam's innocence. Roat, who has already killed Carlino, bursts into the apartment and murders Mike. Terrified, Susy smashes all the light fixtures in a desperate attempt to even her chances against Roat. When he opens the refrigerator door and turns on the small bulb, Susy grabs a kitchen knife and stabs him. As he lunges after her, she hides behind the refrigerator and pulls the plug. Clutching the knife he was stabbed with, Roat inches toward her in the dark. A few seconds later, Sam and the police arrive and find Susy in a corner with Roat lying dead at her feet. *Models. Commercial artists. Hoodlums. Neighbors. Police. Children. Blindness. Smuggling. Perfidy. Murder. Impersonation. Disguise. Dolls. Heroin. Customs (tariff). New York*

City—*Greenwich Village. John Fitzgerald Kennedy International Airport.*
Note: Location scenes filmed in Montreal and Greenwich Village.

WAITING FOR CAROLINE (Canada)   **F6.5405**
National Film Board of Canada–Canadian Broadcasting Corp. *Dist* Lopert Pictures. 4 Jun **1969** [Saint Louis opening; c23 Oct 1968; LP37145]. Sd; col (DeLuxe). 35mm. 83 min.
Prod Walford Hewitson. *Exec Prod* Robert Allen, prod. *Dir* Ron Kelly. *Screenplay* George C. Robertson, Ron Kelly. *Dir Photog* Denis Gillson. *Camera Op* Tony Ianzelo. *Adtl Photog* Paul Leach. *Art Dir* Earl Preston. *Film Ed* Barnie Howells. *Mus Comp* Eldon Rathburn. *Party Mus* The Jaybees. *Sd Rec* Joseph Champagne. *Sd* Jack Knight. *Sd Re-rec* Ron Alexander, Roger Lamoureux. *Asst Dir* Frank Phillips, asst dir, Michael Scott, asst dir.
Cast: Alexandra Stewart (*Caroline*), François Tasse (*Marc*), Robert Howay (*Peter*), Sharon Acker (*Emily*), William Needles (*Stephen*), Aileen Seaton (*Lally*), Paul Guevremont (*Monsieur Simard*), Daniel Gadouas (*Jean-Pierre*), Lucie Poitras (*Madame Simard*), Monique Mercure (*Yvette*), Reginald McReynolds (*Hagan*), Paul Buissoneau (*Louis*).
Drama. Caroline, the daughter of a wealthy Vancouver businessman, moves to Quebec after completing university studies in French and pursues an affair with Marc, a French-Canadian actor. Peter, her ex-lover, arrives in the hopes of persuading Caroline to marry him. The three spend Christmas with Marc's family, and upon their return to Quebec Caroline learns that her father, Stephen, to whom she is greatly attached, plans to marry a college friend of hers. Peter, Caroline, and Marc fly to Vancouver for the engagement party, and it becomes apparent to the two men that Caroline's attachment to her father prevents her from loving either of them. Caroline's continued vacillation causes both men to leave her, and she rejects her father's offer of sympathy and walks off alone. *Businessmen. French Canadians. Actors. Filial relations. Courtship. Jealousy. Vancouver (British Columbia). Quebec.*
Note: Location scenes filmed in Quebec. Originally presented on Canadian television on 30 Nov 1967.

WAKAMONO TACHI see LIVE YOUR OWN WAY

WAKARE see FAREWELL, MY BELOVED

WAKARETE IKIRU TOKI MO see ETERNITY OF LOVE

WAKE UP AND DIE (France/Italy)   **F6.5406**
Sanson Film–Castoro Film–CIPRA. *Dist* Rizzoli Film Distributors. **1967** [Los Angeles showing]. Sd; col (Eastmancolor). 35mm. 102 min.
Prod Joseph Fryd, Carlo Lizzani. *Dir* Carlo Lizzani. *Screenplay* Ugo Pirro. *Story* Carlo Lizzani, Ugo Pirro. *Photog* Armando Nannuzzi. *Film Ed* Franco Fraticelli. *Mus* Ennio Morricone.
Cast: Robert Hoffmann (*Luciano Lutring*), Lisa Gastoni (*Yvonne Lutring*), Gian Maria Volontè (*Inspector Moroni*), Claudio Camaso, Renato Nicolai, Ottavio Fanfani, Giovanni De Luca, Corrado Olmi, Aldo Suligoi, Augusto Bonardi.
Crime drama. Luciano Lutring, a petty Italian thief, jumps from a window to escape from a police roundup, leaving behind a stolen machine gun he had planned to sell in the black market. A Milan newspaper picks up the minor incident under a banner headline, and Lutring suddenly gains the reputation of a major criminal. Crimes he never committed are blamed on him and he becomes known as "The Elusive Shadow." While the police cooperate with the newspapers to dupe more dangerous criminals into believing that all police efforts are directed toward capturing the thief, Lutring himself begins to believe his own publicity and, for the first time in his life, starts shooting to kill. His wife, Yvonne, a former stripteaser, realizes that the only way to save Lutring is to turn informer, so she offers to help the police capture him. Lutring, now as crafty as his myth purports him to be, eludes the trap that is set for him and escapes to France. As both the Milan and Paris police chiefs compete in their attempts to capture Lutring, Yvonne crosses the border secretly in the hope of saving her husband; but Lutring, now an irrational, bloodthirsty criminal, is shot and captured. *Thieves. Police. Newspapermen. Informers. Manhunts. Yellow journalism. Reputation. Milan. Paris.*
Note: Opened in Rome in Apr 1966 as *Svegliati e uccidi* (*Lutring*); running time: 118 min; in Paris in Mar 1968 as *Lutring ... Réveille-toi et meurs*; running time: 124 min.

WALDEN: REEL ONE; ... REEL TWO; ... REEL THREE; ... REEL FOUR see DIARIES, NOTES AND SKETCHES

WALK A TIGHTROPE (United States/Great Britain)   **F6.5407**
Parroch-McCallum Productions—Associated Producers, Inc. *Dist* Paramount Pictures. Jun **1964** [c31 Dec 1963; LP28527]. Sd; b&w. 35mm. 69 min.
Prod Neil McCallum, Jack Parsons. *Dir* Frank Nesbitt. *Screenplay-Story* Mann Rubin. *Dir Photog* Basil Emmott. *Art Dir* Harry White. *Film Ed* Robert

Winter. *Mus Score* Buxton Orr. *Sd* Steve Stephenson. *Asst Dir* David Tringham. *Prod Mgr* Clifford Parkes.
Cast: Dan Duryea (*Lutcher*), Patricia Owens (*Ellen*), Terence Cooper (*Jason*), Richard Leech (*Doug*), Neil McCallum (*counsel*), Trevor Reid (*Inspector MacMitchell*), A. J. Brown (*magistrate*), David Bauer (*Ed*), Jack Melford.
Mystery melodrama. Based on a teleplay by: Mann Rubin. Ellen, an American happily married to an English businessman, Jason, confides to him her fear that she is being followed. Later Ellen runs into Jason and his partner, Doug, at a pub; shaken, she faints, and the two men take her home. Doug goes upstairs to make a phone call, and Jason is shot dead by the man who has been following Ellen, Lutcher. The killer leaves signs to indicate that his motive was robbery, but Doug overhears him demanding payment for the crime from Ellen. Lutcher is later arrested and insists that Ellen had hired him, but it is revealed that he was recently released from an insane asylum, and his claim of a frameup is discounted. Doug remains friendly to Ellen, and he later discovers that she is being blackmailed by her first husband, an American, on the grounds that their marriage was never legally annulled. Doug realizes that Ellen was actually trying to murder the blackmailer, and he regretfully calls Scotland Yard. *Hired killers. Americans in foreign countries. Expatriates. Businessmen. Lunatics. Murder. Blackmail. Marriage—Annulment. Mistaken identity. Bigamy. Pubs. Scotland Yard.*
Note: Produced in Great Britain in 1963 and released there in 1967; running time: 78 min.

WALK, DON'T RUN   **F6.5408**
Walk Co. *Dist* Columbia Pictures. 29 Jun **1966** [Los Angeles opening; c1 Jul 1966; LP32867]. Sd; col (Technicolor). 35mm (Panavision). 114 min.
Pres by Granley Co. A Sol C. Siegel Production. *Prod* Sol C. Siegel. *Dir* Charles Walters. *Screenplay* Sol Saks. *Story* Robert Russell, writ. Frank Ross. *Dir Photog* Harry Stradling. *Camera Op* Gerald Finnerman. *Set Decor* George R. Nelson, Robert Priestley. *Prod Dsgn* Joe Wright. *Film Ed* Walter Thompson, James Wells. *Mus* Quincy Jones. *Sd* James Z. Flaster, Jack Haynes. *Asst Dir* Jim Myers. *Unit Prod Mgr* Russell Saunders, Rusty Meek. *Cost Dsgn* Morton Haack. *Makeup Supv* Ben Lane. *Hairstyles* Virginia Jones.
Cast: Cary Grant (*William Rutland*), Samantha Eggar (*Christine Easton*), Jim Hutton (*Steve Davis*), John Standing (*Julius D. Haversack*), Miiko Taka (*Aiko Kurawa*), Ted Hartley (*Yuri Andreyovitch*), Ben Astar (*Dimitri*), George Takei (*police captain*), Teru Shimada (*Mr. Kurawa*), Lois Kiuchi (*Mrs. Kurawa*), Bob Okazaki (*plant manager*).
Comedy. British industrialist Sir William Rutland arrives in Tokyo 2 days earlier than expected during the Olympic Games and finds it impossible to get hotel accommodations. Desperate, he answers an "apartment to share" advertisement and persuades the occupant, Christine Easton, to rent his sitting room. The following day he meets Steve Davis, a member of the United States Olympic walking team. Steve has arrived early in order to study Japan's architecture, and he also needs a room. After persuading Christine to take on a second lodger, Rutland puts his matchmaking talents into action—particularly after he meets Christine's pompous and boring fiancé, Julius D. Haversack. Everything goes according to Rutland's plans until Christine overhears the two lodgers candidly discuss her virtue. When she orders them out, Rutland persuades her that it is her patriotic duty to allow Steve to remain until the games are over. Meanwhile, a Soviet security agent has become convinced that Steve and Christine are spies; and he has them arrested. Rutland bails them out, but Haversack feels certain his diplomatic career will be ruined unless the information about Steve sharing Christine's apartment can be struck from the official police records. The resourceful Rutland not only makes the necessary arrangements (he negotiates a marriage of convenience for Steve and Christine) but also sees that the couple are left alone long enough to admit they love each other. Content that he has completed his job as Cupid, Rutland returns to London to celebrate his 25th wedding anniversary. *British. Industrialists. Lodgers. Americans in foreign countries. Athletes. Matchmakers. Russians. Police. Spies. Mistaken identity. Reputation. Marriage of convenience. Olympic Games. Tokyo. Great Britain—Diplomatic and consular service.*
Note: Location scenes filmed in Japan. The film is a remake of *The More the Merrier* (1943, Columbia).

WALK IN THE SHADOW (Great Britain)   **F6.5409**
Michael Relph–Basil Dearden. *For* Allied Film Makers. *Dist* Continental Distributing, Inc. Jan **1966**. Sd; b&w. 35mm. 93 min.
Prod Michael Relph. *Dir* Basil Dearden. *Screenplay* Janet Green, John McCormick. *Dir Photog* Otto Heller. *Camera Op* H. A. R. Thomson. *Camera Focus* John Morgan. *Art Dir* Alex Vetchinsky. *Set Dresser* Arthur Taksen. *Ch Draughtsman* Bert Davey. *Film Ed* John D. Guthridge. *1st Asst Ed* Marcel Durham. *Mus* William Alwyn. *Mus Cond* Muir Mathieson. *Sd* C. C. Stevens, Gordon K. McCallum, Leslie Wiggins. *Boom Op* Gus Lloyd. *Sd Rec* Simon

Kaye. 1st, 2d & 3d Asst Dir Anthony Waye, Donald Toms, Bob Howard. *Prod Mgr* Charles Orme. *Prod Sec* Jean Hall. *Cont* Sue Dyson. *Wardrobe Supv* Dorothy Edwards. *Men's Wardrobe* John Hilling. *Makeup* Harry Frampton. *Hairdresser* Barbara Ritchie. *2d Asst Dir (Location)* Terry Clegg. *Prop Buyer* Jim Baker. *Still Photog* George Courtney Ward. *Constr Mgr* Ron Udell. *Grip* Fred Graver. *Ch Floor Electrn* Vic Smith.

Cast: Michael Craig *(John Harris)*, Janet Munro *(Pat Harris)*, Patrick McGoohan *(Dr. James Brown)*, Paul Rogers *(Hart Jacobs)*, Megs Jenkins *(Mrs. Gordon)*, Maureen Pryor *(Teddy's mother)*, John Barrie *(Mr. Gordon)*, Basil Dignam *(Mapleton)*, Leslie Sands *(Clyde)*, Ellen McIntosh *(duty sister)*, Frank Finlay *(Teddy's father)*, Michael Aldridge *(Howard)*, Malcolm Keen *(John's father)*, Lynne Taylor *(Ruth Harris)*, Freddy Ramsey *(Teddy)*, Michael Bryant *(John's counsel)*, Norman Woolland *(Crown counsel)*, Maurice Colbourne *(vicar)*, John Welsh *(marshal)*, Walter Hudd *(judge)*.

Drama. Based on a play by: Janet Green. When little Ruth Harris is injured in a boating accident and taken to a hospital, Dr. James Brown informs her distraught parents that only a blood transfusion can save her life. Because of his religious convictions, Mr. Harris refuses to give his consent. Mrs. Harris, who had superficially accepted her husband's faith when they were married, later returns to the hospital to authorize the transfusion; but it is too late, and the child is already dead. Dr. Brown, a self-professed agnostic, considers Mr. Harris' part in the girl's death tantamount to murder, and he arranges for him to be arrested and tried for manslaughter. With everyone apparently against him (even his wife has left), Harris accepts the volunteer services of a Jewish lawyer who offers a simple defense: John Harris chose to risk Ruth's temporal life rather than sacrifice her eternal one. Harris is acquitted, but he breaks under emotional strain and, realizing that he had expected God to perform a miracle to save his daughter's life, attempts suicide. Dr. Brown, however, persuades him that a man must face life. Realizing that her husband needs her, Mrs. Harris returns to him, hopeful that the memory of their dead child will not always stand between them. *Children. Physicians. Agnostics. Lawyers. Jews. Parenthood. Religion. Death. Manslaughter. Suicide. Blood transfusion. Boating accidents.*

Note: Opened in London in Sep 1962 as *Life for Ruth* at 91 min.

A WALK IN THE SPRING RAIN   F6.5410

Pingree Productions. *Dist* Columbia Pictures. 9 Apr **1970** [Knoxville, Tennessee, opening; c1 Apr 1970; LP37908]. Sd; col (Eastman Color). 35mm (Panavision). 98 min. *MPAA rating* GP.

A Stirling Silliphant–Guy Green Production. *Prod-Writ* Stirling Silliphant. *Dir* Guy Green. *Dir Photog* Charles Lang. *Camera Op* Chris Schwiebert. *Asst Camera* Kenneth Peach, Jr. *Art Dir* Malcolm C. Bert. *Set Decor* Morris Hoffman. *Film Ed* Ferris Webster. *Mus* Elmer Bernstein. *Titl Song* Elmer Bernstein, Don Black. *Sung by* Michael Dees. *Song: "Shenandoah"* sung by Janet Nelson. *Sd* Les Fresholtz, Arthur Piantadosi. *Rec* Harold Lee. *Boom Op* Doug Grant. *Asst Dir* Phil Parslow, Robert Gilmore. *Unit Prod Mgr* Herbert Wallerstein. *Script Supv* Marshall Wolins. *Asst to the Prod* Mark Silliphant. *Miss Bergman's Wardrobe* Donfeld. *Wardrobe* Guy Verhille, Edna Taylor, Alex D'Alessio. *Miss Bergman's Makeup* John O'Gorman. *Makeup Supv* Ben Lane. *Hairstyles* Virginia Jones. *Sp Eff* Ira Anderson, Jr. *Coöp* United States Department of the Interior—National Park Service. *Prop* Tom Coleman, Ronald De Waay. *Still Photog* John Monte.

Cast: Anthony Quinn *(Will Cade)*, Ingrid Bergman *(Libby Meredith)*, Fritz Weaver *(Roger Meredith)*, Katherine Crawford *(Ellen Meredith)*, Tom Fielding *(Boy Cade)*, Virginia Gregg *(Ann Cade)*, Mitchell Silberman *(Bucky)*.

Drama. Source: Rachel Maddux, *A Walk in the Spring Rain* (New York, 1966). Professor Roger Meredith and his wife, Libby, journey to rural Tennessee, where Roger hopes to spend his sabbatical writing a law text. Arriving on a snowy winter night, the middle-aged couple stops for the key to their rented house at the home of farmer-mechanic Will Cade, Cade's loquacious wife, and their profligate son, Boy. The earthy Will is attracted to the reserved Libby and courts her, offering blunt compliments and a gift of baby goats. The romance, however, is aborted by Will's and Libby's respective progeny. The Merediths' daughter, Ellen, arrives unexpectedly, announcing her acceptance by Harvard Law School and demanding that Libby return to care for grandson Bucky. Shortly after Libby's refusal, she is molested by drunken Boy Cade but rescued by Will, who accidentally kills his son. The disillusioned Merediths return to the city, Libby having abandoned her romantic hopes, Roger his literary ambitions. *Authors. Professors. Grandparents. Law students. Farmers. Mechanics. Infidelity. Rape. Filial relations. Manslaughter. Rural life. Middle age. Tennessee. Harvard Law School. Goats.*

Note: Location scenes filmed in the Great Smoky Mountains National Park.

WALK ON THE WILD SIDE   F6.5411

Famous Artists Productions. *Dist* Columbia Pictures. 21 Feb **1962** [New York opening; c1 Feb 1962; LP21333]. Sd (Westrex); b&w. 35mm. 114 min.

Pres by Charles K. Feldman. *Prod* Charles K. Feldman. *Assoc Prod* Joseph Lebworth. *Dir* Edward Dmytryk. *Screenplay* John Fante, Edmund Morris. *Dir Photog* Joseph MacDonald. *Set Decor* William Kiernan. *Prod Dsgn* Richard Sylbert. *Titl Dsgn* Saul Bass. *Film Ed* Harry Gerstad. *Mus* Elmer Bernstein. *Orch* Leo Shuken, Jack Hayes. *Songs* Mack David, Elmer Bernstein. *Vocals* Brook Benton. *Sd Supv* Charles J. Rice. *Sd* George Cooper. *Asst Dir* Floyd Joyer. *Cost* Charles Le Maire. *Makeup Supv* Ben Lane.

Cast: Laurence Harvey *(Dove Linkhorn)*, Capucine *(Hallie)*, Jane Fonda *(Kitty Twist)*, Anne Baxter *(Teresina Vidaverri)*, Barbara Stanwyck *(Jo Courtney)*, Joanna Moore *(Miss Precious)*, Richard Rust *(Oliver)*, Karl Swenson *(Schmidt)*, Donald Barry *(Dockery)*, Juanita Moore *(Mama)*, John Anderson *(preacher)*, Ken Lynch *(Frank Bonito)*, Todd Armstrong *(Lieut. Omar Stroud)*, Kathryn Card *(landlady)*, Lillian Bronson *(Amy Gerard)*, Adrienne Marden *(Eva Gerard)*, Sherry O'Neil *(Reba)*, John Bryant *(Spence)*, Paul Maxey *(auctioneer)*, Virginia Holden, Barbara Hines, Elaine Martone, Pat Tiernan, Florence Wyatt *(Doll's House girls)*.

Drama. Source: Nelson Algren, *A Walk on the Wild Side* (New York, 1956). In the 1930's Texas farmer Dove Linkhorn travels to Louisiana in search of his lost love, Hallie Gerard. Along the way he meets Kitty Twist, a saucy young tramp, and Teresina Vidaverri, a sex-starved Mexican widow who operates a cafe. Eventually Dove finds Hallie in the Doll's House, a bordello in the French Quarter of New Orleans. Although he learns she is a prostitute being kept by Jo Courtney, the lesbian madame of the Doll's House, Dove tries to persuade Hallie to come back to him. At first she refuses but the warmth and sincerity of Dove's love gradually win her over. Infuriated by the turn of events, Jo has Dove savagely beaten into unconsciousness. He is found by Kitty, who is now also working in the Doll's House. She takes him to Teresina's cafe and then tells Hallie what has happened. When Hallie goes to the cafe, she is followed by Jo and her bodyguard, Oliver. In the ensuing melee, Oliver shoots at Dove but hits Hallie by mistake. The still-bandaged Dove crawls across the room to her and takes her in his arms as she dies. [Another version has Schmidt, an amputee and Jo's spurned husband, beating Dove and killing Hallie.] *Texans. Farmers. Prostitutes. Bodyguards. Widows. Mexicans. Restaurateurs. Amputees. Jealousy. Lesbianism. Murder. Whorehouses. New Orleans.*

WALK THE WALK   F6.5412

H Q Z Productions. *Dist* Hallmark of Hollywood, Inc. 1 Jul **1970** [Norfolk, Virginia, opening]. Sd; col (Movielab). 35mm. 95 min. *MPAA rating* R.

Pres by Kroger Babb. *Prod-Dir-Writ* Jac Zacha. *Assoc Prod* Sterling Franck. *Camera* Stu Stallsmith.

Cast: Bernie Hamilton *(Mike)*, Honor Lawrence *(pusher)*, David Steinbuck, Bert Hoffman, Eric Weston, Steve Lavigne.

Melodrama. Mike, a black theological student, is addicted to heroin. He meets a very attractive pusher but resists her continuous sexual advances. Though fighting to break his habit, Mike becomes involved in the world of junkies and pushers. He wins his battle, but when, after an injury, a doctor gives him sedatives to ease his pain, Mike again becomes addicted to drugs. The torture is too much to bear, and Mike hangs himself. *Drug addicts. Ministerial students. Negroes. Drug dealers. Suicide. Heroin.*

Note: Location scenes filmed in Santa Monica, California.

A WALK WITH LOVE AND DEATH   F6.5413

Twentieth Century–Fox Film Corp. 5 Oct **1969** [New York opening; c1 Oct 1969; LP37417]. Sd (Westrex); col (DeLuxe). 35mm. 90 min. *MPAA rating* M.

A John Huston–Carter De Haven, [III] Production. *Prod* Carter De Haven, [III]. *Assoc Prod* Dale Wasserman. *Dir* John Huston. *Assoc to John Huston* Gladys Hill. *Screenplay* Dale Wasserman. *Adapt* Hans Koningsberger. *Dir Photog* Ted Scaife. *Camera Op* Ken Withers. *Art Dir* Wolf Witzemann. *Set Decor* Josie Macavin. *Prod Dsgn* Stephen Grimes. *Film Ed* Russell Lloyd. *Asst Ed* Eunice Mountjoy-Beharrel. *Mus Comp & Cond* Georges Delerue. *English Lyr* Gladys Hill. *Sd* Basil Fenton-Smith, Renato Cadueri. *Sd Ed* Leslie Hodgson. *Asst Dir* Richard Overstreet, Wolfgang Glattes. *Prod Mgr* Laci von Ronay. *Script Supv* Lucie Lichtig. *Unit Mgr* Wolfgang Odelga. *Cost* Leonor Fini. *Wardrobe Supv* Annalisa Nasalli-Rocca. *Cost Executed by* Rotislav Duboujinsky. *Makeup* Neville Smallwood. *Hairdresser* Margarete Pitter. *Casting Dir* Robert Lennard.

Cast: Anjelica Huston *(Lady Claudia)*, Assaf Dayan *(Heron of Foix)*, Anthony Corlan *(Robert)*, John Hallam *(Sir Meles)*, Robert Lang *(pilgrim leader)*, Guy Deghy *(priest)*, Michael Gough *(mad monk)*, George Murcell *(captain)*, Eileen Murphy *(gypsy girl)*, Anthony Nicholls *(father superior)*, Joseph O'Connor *(St. Jean)*, John Huston *(Robert the Elder)*, John Franklin *(whoremaster)*, Francis Heim *(knight lieutenant)*, Melvyn Hayes *(1st entertainer)*, Barry Keegan *(peasant leader)*, Nicholas Smith *(pilgrim)*, Antoinette Reuss *(charcoal woman)*, Gilles Ségal, Med Hondo, Luis Masson *(entertainers)*, Eugen Ledebur *(goldsmith)*, Otto Dworak *(innkeeper)*, Max Sulz *(peasant)*, John Veenenbos *(monk)*, Dieter Tressler *(major-domo)*, Paul Hoer *(peasant boy)*, Myra Malik *(peasant girl)*, Michael Baronne, Yvan

Strogoff *(soldiers)*.

Historical drama. Source: Hans Koningsberger, *A Walk With Love and Death* (New York, 1961). Heron of Foix leaves his university in Paris to seek adventure. Traveling across France during the chaos of the Hundred Years War, he sees the French fighting the English and the peasants in revolt against the landowners. He meets Claudia, a wealthy lord's daughter whose home has been overrun by peasants, and he takes her to her uncle, Robert the Elder, a nobleman who has joined the peasants' cause. Claudia wants revenge, but Heron, remembering the ravages of war and death, urges peace. Eventually, they find shelter in a monastery that is about to be attacked by soldiers. The monks flee as the soldiers approach, but Heron and Claudia perform a wedding ceremony for themselves and await death. *Soldiers. Peasants. Nobility. Feudalism. Revolts. Weddings. Death. Monasteries. Hundred Years War 1339–1453. Paris. France.*

Note: Filmed in Austria and Italy.

THE WALKING STICK (Great Britain)   **F6.5414**
Winkast Film Productions. *Dist* Metro-Goldwyn-Mayer, Inc. 15 Apr **1970** [San Francisco opening; c19 Feb 1970; LP38131]. Sd; col (Metrocolor). 35mm (Panavision). 101 min. *MPAA rating* GP.

A Jerry Gershwin–Elliott Kastner Production. *Prod* Alan Ladd, Jr. *Assoc Prod* Denis Holt. *Dir* Eric Till. *Screenplay* George Bluestone. *Dir Photog* Arthur Ibbetson. *2d Unit Photog* H. A. R. Thomson. *Camera Op* Ron Taylor. *Art Dir* John Graysmark. *Set Decor* Pamela Cornell. *Prod Dsgn* John Howell. *Film Ed* John Jympson. *Asst Ed* Alan Strachan. *Mus Comp & Cond* Stanley Myers. *Sd Ed* Don Sharpe. *Sd Rec* Gerry Turner. *Dub Mix* J. B. Smith. *Asst Dir* Colin Brewer, Ben Harrison. *Prod Supv* Ted Lloyd. *Location Mgr* Tom Sachs. *Asst to the Prod* Marion Rosenberg. *Cont* Gladys Goldsmith. *Cost Dsgn* Sue Yelland. *Miss Eggar's Cost* Mia Fonssagrives, Vicki Tiel. *Dial Coach* Alfredo Lettieri.

Cast: David Hemmings *(Leigh Hartley)*, Samantha Eggar *(Deborah Dainton)*, Emlyn Williams *(Jack Foil)*, Phyllis Calvert *(Erica Dainton)*, Ferdy Mayne *(Douglas Dainton)*, Francesca Annis *(Arabella Dainton)*, Bridget Turner *(Sarah Dainton)*, Dudley Sutton *(Ted Sandymount)*, John Woodvine *(Bertie Irons)*, David Savile *(David Talbot)*, Derek Cox *(1st guard)*, Harvey Sambrook *(2d guard)*, Gwen Cherrel *(Mrs. Hartley)*, Walter Horsbrugh *(Maitland)*, Basil Henson *(Inspector Malcolm)*, Anthony Nicholls *(Lewis Maude)*, Nan Munro *(Mrs. Stevenson)*, Donald Sumpter *(Max)*, David Griffin *(Benjy)*, Susan Payne *(Deborah as a child)*.

Drama. Source: Winston Graham, *The Walking Stick* (London, 1967). Leigh Hartley, an untalented young painter, meets polio victim Deborah Dainton, a cripple since childhood. Deborah, an appraiser for an antique dealer, at first spurns Leigh's attempts to date her, but finally, with the encouragement of her parents, she begins to go out with him. She agrees to sit for a portrait, and their relationship develops into love, but Deborah is puzzled by Leigh's relationship with Jack Foil, an art collector who is his patron. Leigh persuades Deborah to move into his London apartment, despite the fact that he is married, and then tells her that he and Jack need her help in robbing the auction gallery where she works. Aware that the money might enable them to start an antique shop of their own, Deborah hides in a closet, although she suffers from claustrophobia, and when the gallery is closed for the night, she opens the door for Jack and Leigh. The robbery is successful, but Deborah realizes that Leigh's courtship was just part of a plan for the robbery, and she writes a full confession to Scotland Yard, exposing all three of them. *Painters. Cripples. Antique dealers. Art collectors. Patrons. Filial relations. Perfidy. Robbery. Claustrophobia. Confession (law). Antiques. London.*

Note: Filmed on location in London. Released in Great Britain in Jun 1970.

WALKOVER (Poland)   **F6.5415**
Syrena Film Unit. *For* Film Polski. *Dist* New Yorker Films. 13 Apr **1969** [New York opening]. Sd; b&w. 35mm. 77 min.

Dir-Writ Jerzy Skolimowski. *Photog* Antoni Nurzyński. *Art Dir* Zdzisław Kielanowski. *Film Ed* Barbara Krzyczmonik. *Mus* Andrzej Trzaskowski. *Sd* Mikolaj Kompan-Altman. *Asst Dir* Henryk Kluba, Daniel Szylit, Mieczysława Taraszkiewicz. *Prod Mgr* Jerzy Nitecki.

Cast: Aleksandra Zawieruszanka *(Teresa)*, Jerzy Skolimowski *(Andrzej Leszczyc)*, Krzysztof Chamiec *(director)*, Franciszek Pieczka *(activist)*, Elżbieta Czyżewska *(girl at train station)*, Andrzej Herder *(Pawlak)*, Joanna Jedlewska *([projektantka])*, Tadeusz Kondrat *(old man)*, Stanisław Zaczyk *("priest")*, Henryk Kluba *(trainer Rogala)*, Teresa Belczyńska *(director's secretary)*, Krzysztof Litwin *(Miecio)*, Janusz Kłosiński, B. Dec, S. Przedwojewski, A. Turcewicz, J. Fedorowicz, S. Kaminska, M. Waskowski, S. Tym.

Drama. The train on which 30-year-old Andrzej Leszczyc is traveling stops at the Płock station after a suicide has taken place. On the platform Andrzej sees Teresa, the woman who caused his expulsion from the university a few years before, and he decides to interrupt his trip to see her. Teresa is in Płock

---

to submit her student design for the new cathedral. Until now, Andrzej's only income has been from the prize money won in boxing matches. Teresa introduces him to the director of the new industrial complex in Płock, and he offers him a job as supervising engineer. Andrzej hesitates to accept, but when he meets the boxing trainer of the complex, he consents to participate in the local tournament. On the evening of his first victory, he sleeps with Teresa, but since her design has been rejected and Andrzej's next match promises to be too tough, they decide to leave Płock. The boy whom Andrzej knocked out in the first round of the tournament pursues their train on a motorcycle and persuades Andrzej to return. As he reaches the ring, however, he is announced the winner in a "walkover," because the young boy failed to appear. The opponent eventually arrives and demands half of the prize, claiming that his trainer had bribed him to forfeit the bout. Andrzej refuses and challenges the boy to another fight; the challenge is taken, and Andrzej is soundly defeated. *Boxers. Students. Architects. Industrialists. Athletic coaches. Boxing. Bribery. Trains. Płock.*

Note: Released in Poland in 1965 as *Walkower*.

WALKOWER *see* **WALKOVER**

WALL-EYED NIPPON (Japan)   **F6.5416**
Toho Co. 2 Sep **1963** [New York opening]. Sd; col (Eastmancolor). 35mm (Tohoscope). 90 min.

Prod Seitan Kaneko. *Dir* Hideo Suzuki. *Screenplay* Nagaharu Okuyama. *Photog* Taiichi Kankura.

Cast: Akira Takarada *(Shin Moriyama)*, Yumi Shirakawa *(Momoko)*, Jerry Ito *(John Machihei)*, Muza Kemanai *(Meery Sweett)*, E. H. Eric *(Lafcadio Yearn)*, Akiko Wakabayashi *(Nashiko)*.

Satire. John Machihei, a nuclear scientist of American and Japanese parentage, arrives in Japan from the United States, anxious to see the sights and to find a subservient Japanese bride. Momoko, his guide, tips off her boyfriend, journalist Shin Moriyama, about John, and he tries to get an exclusive story on the scientist. Momoko introduces John to Meery Sweett, a Westernized woman, and Shin falls in love with her. Following a tour of Tokyo during which John witnesses a striking contrast between the traditional and the Westernized aspects of Japanese life, he and Momoko become attracted to one another. Momoko returns to Shin, however, and John decides to wed Meery. *Americans in foreign countries. Halfcastes. Scientists. Reporters. Guides. Marriage. Tokyo.*

Note: Released in Japan in 1964 as *Yabunirami Nippon*; running time: 97 min.

WALL FOR SAN SEBASTIAN *see* **GUNS FOR SAN SEBASTIAN**

WALL OF FLESH   **F6.5417**
Monorax–Provocative Films. *Dist* Provocative Films. 30 Oct **1968** [Champaign, Illinois, showing]. Sd; b&w. 35mm. 88 min.

Prod K. David Dietz. *Dir-Writ* Joe Sarno. *Dir Photog* Steve Silverman. *Mus* Pir Marini. *Asst to the Prod* Peggy Steffans.

Cast: Dan Machuen *(Art)*, Lita Coleman *(Vera)*, Marianne Provost *(Lauri)*, Nina Forster *(Nan)*.

Melodrama. Vera, a working woman, punishes her husband Art, a struggling writer who lives on her income, by denying him sexual satisfaction. While Vera is away at work, Art becomes involved with two sisters, Nan and Lauri. Aware of the strong physical attraction between her sister and Art, Lauri suppresses her own desire for the writer and arranges for her sister to be with Art by persuading Vera, apparently frigid, to attend group therapy sessions run by her ex-school friend Jennifer, a lesbian. Art, however, rejects Nan's obvious advances, unaware that by this time his wife, seemingly happier, has been drawn into lesbianism. In a weak moment though, Art gives in to Lauri (also a participant in Jennifer's group); but, still in love with his wife, he resists her proposal to run away together. Lauri senses that her sister is heading for a breakdown over Art, and she sacrifices her own ambivalent feelings for him to bring the two together. Art and Nan are finally united when Art lands a job in Chicago and finds that his wife prefers to remain with Jennifer, Lauri, and the group rather than go with him. *Authors. Teases. Sisters. Frigidity. Group therapy. Lesbianism. Seduction. Infidelity. Bisexuality.*

WALL OF NOISE   **F6.5418**
Warner Bros. Pictures. 28 Aug **1963** [Washington, D. C., opening; c7 Sep 1963; LP29448]. Sd; b&w. 35mm. 112 min.

Prod-Writ Joseph Landon. *Dir* Richard Wilson. *Photog* Lucien Ballard. *Camera Op* Wally Meinardus. *Asst Camera* Burdell Schweibert. *Art Dir* Hilyard Brown. *Set Decor* John P. Austin. *Film Ed* William Ziegler. *Asst Ed* Sam O'Steen. *Mus* William Lava. *Sd* Francis E. Stahl. *Rec* Edwin Harman. *Boom Op* Ora Hudson. *Asst Dir* Sergei Petschnikoff, Ed Bernoudy, Jack Stubbs. *Script Supv* Jules Miliman. *Cost* Howard Shoup. *Wardrobe* Robert Richards, Ruth Hancock. *Makeup* Gordon Bau. *Gaffer* Lee Wilson. *Dial Coach* Clark Gordon. *Grip* Charles Harris. *Prop* Pat Patterson, prop, Harry

Blackledge.

Cast: Suzanne Pleshette *(Laura Rubio)*, Ty Hardin *(Joel Tarrant)*, Dorothy Provine *(Ann Conroy)*, Ralph Meeker *(Matt Rubio)*, Simon Oakland *(Johnny Papadakis)*, Jimmy Murphy *(Bud Kelsey)*, Murray Matheson *(Jack Matlock)*, Robert F. Simon *(David McRaab)*, George Petrie *(Mr. Harrington)*, Jean Byron *(Mrs. Harrington)*, Fred Carson *(Adam Kasper)*, Bill Walker *(Money)*, Napoleon Whiting *(preacher)*, Kitty White *(singer)*, Jim Murray *(sportswriter)*.

Action melodrama. Source: Daniel Michael Stein, *Wall of Noise* (New York, 1960). After an argument with his girl friend, Ann, racehorse trainer Joel Tarrant joins the stables of Matthew Rubio, a wealthy but vulgar building contractor. Rubio's wife, Laura, immediately makes a play for Joel and, in order to please him, makes an auction bid for a horse Joel believes to be a potential champion. When Rubio learns of his wife's intentions, he fires Joel, and Joel is forced to borrow money from Ann's employer, Johnny Papadakis, to purchase the horse. Rubio offers to buy the horse (Escudero) after he wins a preliminary race, but Joel refuses to sell. Escudero loses his big contest however, and Joel is unable to repay Papadakis. Ann offers Papadakis all of her savings—plus herself—if he will cancel Joel's debt. Papadakis agrees but dies of a heart attack when he and Ann are caught in a traffic jam. After learning that the Rubios have gone to New York, Ann returns to Joel, who is keeping a constant vigil over the injured horse. *Horsetrainers. Contractors. Horseracing. Infidelity. Employer-employee relations. Debt. Heart disease. Racetracks. Auctions. Horses.*

Note: Location scenes filmed in and around Hollywood Park Racetrack, Inglewood, California.

WALL STREET WALKER   F6.5419

Kirt Films International. *Dist* Distribpix, Inc. ca **1970**. Sd; col. 35mm. 64 min.

Melodrama. A young woman looking for an exciting career answers an advertisement for an executive secretary to a Wall Street stockbroker. She gets the job, and upon arriving for work, her first function is to undress him in his office. He makes a date with her for that evening, but when she arrives at his apartment, she finds only his lesbian maid, who seduces her while the broker, unseen, watches the proceedings from an adjoining room. He apologizes to her the next day and issues a second invitation. She accepts, and arrives at his apartment to find a wild orgy in progress; her boss is nowhere to be found, for he is again a spectator in the adjacent room. She attempts to leave, but the revelers force her into a series of degrading sexual acts. *Secretaries. Stockbrokers. Housemaids. Employment—Women. Lesbianism. Voyeurism. Sexual practices. Employer-employee relations. Orgies. New York City—Wall Street.*

THE WALLS HAVE EYES   F6.5420

Dist Astro–Jemco Film Distributors, Unique Film Distributors. 15 Feb **1969** [Boston opening]. Sd; b&w. 35mm. 60 min.

Melodrama. A motel owner who rents rooms for brief sexual encounters installs one-way mirrors in the rooms so that he can secretly film the participants' activities, including group sex, wild lovemaking, and lesbianism. He tries to blackmail a woman into buying a film exposing her evening at his motel, but her boyfriend intervenes and kills him. *Voyeurism. Photography. Group sex. Lesbianism. Blackmail. Murder. Motels. Motion pictures.*

THE WALLS OF HELL (United States/Philippines)   F6.5421

Filipinas Productions–Hemisphere Pictures. *Dist* Hemisphere Pictures. Aug **1964** [cl Jul 1964; LP31907]. Sd; b&w. 35mm. 88 min.

Prod Eddie Romero. *Exec Prod* Kane W. Lynn. *Dir* Gerardo de Leon, Eddie Romero. *Screenplay* Ferde Grofe, Jr., Cesar Amigo, Eddie Romero. *Photog* Felipe Sacdalan. *Mus* Tito Arevalo.

Cast: Jock Mahoney *(Lieutenant Sorenson)*, Fernando Poe, Jr. *(Nardo)*, Michael Parsons *(Papa)*, Cecilia Lopez *(Tina)*, Oscar Roncal *(Joker)*, Vance Skarstedt *(The Captain)*, Paul Edwards, Jr. *(Murray)*, Claude Wilson *(The Major)*, Ely Ramos, Jr., Angel Buenaventura, Carpi Asturias, Arsenio Alonso, Pedro Navarro, Tommy Romulo, Fred Galang, Alex Swanbeck, Jess Montalban, Ben Sanchez, Reynaldo Sibal *(The Guerrillas)*.

War melodrama. In the final days of the battle of Manila during World War II, fanatical Japanese naval forces barricade themselves inside the walls of Intramuros, the ancient Spanish walled city of Manila. In a suicidal last stand, the Japanese hold many thousand Filipinos captive within the fortress, despite the incessant bombardment of United States artillery. An American war correspondent, Murray, arrives at the front line where a guerrilla unit led by American Lieutenant Sorenson makes contact with a young Filipino fighter, Nardo, who has escaped the fortress through a sewer passage. Nardo proposes a plan to rescue the prisoners through the tunnel. Sorenson learns that his Filipina wife, Tina, whom he had believed to be dead, is among the prisoners. The rescue operation, timed to coincide with an intensive attack against the fortress, is accomplished under fire as American howitzers breach the city

walls. Sorenson, after a brief reunion with Tina, rejoins Nardo and follows the main body of American troops as they enter the burning city. *Guerrillas. Reporters. Hostages. Military invasion. Bombardment. World War II. Manila. Japan—Navy. United States Army.*

Note: Also known as *Intramuros*, this film was filmed on location in Manila.

WALTZ OF THE TOREADORS (Great Britain)   F6.5422

Independent Artists. *Dist* Continental Distributing, Inc. 13 Aug **1962** [New York opening; c14 May 1962; LF160]. Sd; col (Eastman Color). 35mm. 105 min.

A Julian Wintle–Leslie Parkyn Production. *Prod* Peter De Sarigny. *Assoc Prod* Geoffrey Haine. *Dir* John Guillermin. *Screenplay* Wolf Mankowitz. *Photog* John Wilcox. *Camera Op* James Bawden. *Focus Puller* Geoffrey Glover. *Art Dir* Harry Pottle. *Asst Art Dir* Tony Woollard. *Set Dresser* Peter James. *Draughtsman* Peter Lamont. *Prod Dsgn* Wilfrid Shingleton. *Film Ed* Peter Taylor. *Asst Ed* Tom Priestley. *2d Asst Ed* Paul Smith. ed. *Mus Comp* Richard Addinsell. *Mus Cond* Muir Mathieson. *Sd* Peter Musgrave. *Sd Rec* John W. Mitchell, Bill Daniels. *Sd Camera Op* Roy Charman. *Boom Op* Tony Cripps. *1st, 2d & 3d Asst Dir* Rene Dupont, Stuart Freeman, Derek Cracknell. *Prod Supv* Arthur Alcott. *Unit Mgr* Geoffrey Haine. *Cont* Penny Daniels. *Prod Sec* Norma Garment. *Cost Dsgn* Beatrice Dawson. *Wardrobe Mistress* Betty Adamson. *Wardrobe Master* Jim Dunlevy. *Makeup Artist* William Partleton, Stuart Freeborn. *Hairdresser* Sarah Beber. *Still Photog* George Ward. *Constr Mgr* Bert Mansell. *Chargehand Prop* P. Rivers. *Prop Asst* Ken Wilkes, Tommy Gleed. *Chargehand Electrn* John Swan. *Grip* Reg Hall.

Cast: Peter Sellers *(Gen. Leo Fitzjohn)*, Dany Robin *(Ghislaine)*, Margaret Leighton *(Emily Fitzjohn)*, John Fraser *(Robert)*, Cyril Cusack *(Dr. Grogan)*, Prunella Scales *(Estella)*, Denise Coffey *(Sidonia)*, Jean Anderson *(Agnes)*, Raymond Huntley *(court-martial president)*, Cardew Robinson *(undertaker)*, John Glyn-Jones *(innkeeper)*, John Le Mesurier *(vicar)*, Vanda Godsell *(Mrs. Bulstrode)*, Catherine Feller *(Rosemary)*, Guy Middleton, Humphrey Lestocq *(huntsmen)*.

Domestic comedy. Source: Jean Anouilh, *La valse des toréadors* (Paris opening: 9 Jan 1952). Newly-retired Gen. Leo Fitzjohn lives in a turn-of-the-century English manor house with his wife, Emily, a nagging, whining woman whose supposed inability to walk is merely a pathetic way of keeping her husband from leaving her. Aside from pinching giggling housemaids, the general's only real pleasure in life is his love for Ghislaine, a Frenchwoman with whom he fell in love 17 years earlier, while dancing the waltz of the toreadors. Although they have never consummated their love, Ghislaine has remained faithful to the general through all the intervening years. One day she arrives unexpected at the manor house, produces two passionate love letters Emily has written to her physician, Dr. Grogan, and insists that the general is now free to elope with her. Before he can do so, however, Emily vanishes from the manor house, apparently bent on suicide. The general races after her, and Ghislaine retaliates by attempting her own suicide in a nearby pond and allowing the general's aide, Robert, to rescue her. Following a disastrously unromantic tryst with Ghislaine at the local inn, the general goes to Emily and demands that she grant him a divorce. She violently rebukes him, boasts of her own infidelities, and taunts him with the knowledge that, like her furniture and jewels, he belongs to her. Returning to Ghislaine, the general discovers that Robert has accomplished in 2 days what he himself has failed to do. Outraged, he orders the young man court-martialed but then halts the proceedings by disclosing that Robert is his illegitimate son. Later, after Robert and Ghislaine have married, he reacts to Emily's whines by deciding he should shoot himself. But a new housemaid suddenly appears, and the old general puts aside his pistol to embrace her. *Veterans. Invalids. French. Lovelorn. Physicians. Housemaids. Marriage. Infidelity. Suicide. Divorce. Illegitimacy. Fatherhood. Manors. Courts-martial. Documentation.*

Note: Opened in London in Apr 1962 at 102-104 min. Location scenes filmed in Sussex and Kent. Rereleased in the United States in 1967 as *The Amorous General*.

WANDA (THE SADISTIC HYPNOTIST)   F6.5423

Falu Productions. *Dist* Ciao Productions, Crest Film Distributors. **1969**. Sd; col (Eastmancolor). 35mm. 75 min.

Prod-Dir-Writ Greg Corarito. *Dir Photog* Bruce Scott, photog. *Lighting* David Selkink. *Film Ed* Gary Graver. *Orig Mus* Al Quick. *Re-Rec* Sam Kopetzky, Hollywood Picture Recorders. *Asst Dir* Richard Compton. *Prod Mgr* Harry Swartz. *Script Supv* Lynne Cole. *Wardrobe* Ree Fox. *Prop Master* Ken Fox.

Cast: Katharine Shubeck, Dick Dangerfield, Janine Sweet, Estelle Murphy, Robert Luisi, Laurie Davis, Jean Rodgers, Jacque Lee, Patty Roberts, Lindy Birde, Mary Weatler, Lisa Cunning, Lynn Harris, Sheri Jackson, Linda Stiles, Iris Dawne, Daryl Colinot.

Drama. Source: Greg Corarito, *The Sadistic Hypnotist* (publication undetermined). A man spends a Saturday afternoon watching two sex exploitation films. The first film, a nudist camp feature, leaves the man cold, but he quickly becomes absorbed in the second film: *Sylvester, a conservative young man, loses control of his car and it crashes. He is rescued from the wreckage by two women and taken to a nearby mansion owned by Wanda. The following morning Sylvester realizes that he has been hypnotized and is Wanda's prisoner. Forcing him to don a leather bikini, Wanda humiliates him in her swimming pool. A group of Wanda's lesbian friends pay her a visit; they are hypnotized and are also subjected to Wanda's sadism. A sex-crazed inmate from a nearby insane asylum crashes the party, usurps Wanda's control over the group, and frees Sylvester, and they both begin to flagellate the women. The two men force-feed the women LSD and promote a riotous sex party before Wanda can regain her control. The film ends; the man leaves the theater, and as he drives off, his car swerves and crashes. Before long, a mysterious brunette comes by offering aid, introducing herself as Wanda. Hypnotists. Lesbianism. Sadism. Insanity. Flagellation. Group sex. LSD. Sex exploitation films. Motion picture theaters. Automobile accidents.*

WANDER LOVE STORY see **WANDERLOVE**

THE WANDERER (France)   F6.5424

Madeleine Films–Awa Films. *Dist* Leacock Pennebaker, Inc. 9 Apr **1969** [New York opening]. Sd; col (Eastman Color). 35mm (Techniscope). 103 min. *MPAA rating* G.

Prod Gilbert de Goldschmidt. *Dir* Jean-Gabriel Albicocco. *Screenplay* Jean-Gabriel Albicocco, Isabelle Rivière. *Photog* Quinto Albicocco. *Art Dir* Daniel Louradour. *Film Ed* Georges Klotz. *Mus* Jean-Pierre Bourtayre. *Sd* Gérard Barra. *Asst Dir* Michel Leroy. *Prod Mgr* Jacques Garcia. *Cost* Sylvie Poulet.

Cast: Brigitte Fossey *(Yvonne de Galais)*, Jean Blaise *(Augustin Meaulnes)*, Alain Libolt *(François Seurel)*, Alain Noury *(Frantz de Galais)*, Juliette Villard *(Valentine Blondeau)*, Christian de Tilière *(Ganache)*, Marcel Cuvelier *(Monsieur Seurel)*, Thérèse Quentin *(Madame Seurel)*, Serge Spira *(Mouche Boeuf)*, Bruno Castan *(Delouche)*, Elizabeth Guy, Henri Alain Dmurtal.

Romantic drama. Source: Alain Fournier, "Le grand Meaulnes," in *Nouvelle revue française* (Jul-Nov 1913). At the turn of the century in rural Sologne, 18-year-old Augustin Meaulnes unexpectedly comes upon an old chateau where a masquerade celebrating the betrothal of Frantz de Galais and Valentine Blondeau is in progress. Meaulnes immediately falls in love with Frantz's sister Yvonne, but the ball ends abruptly when Frantz attempts suicide after Valentine fails to appear. The disconsolate Meaulnes returns to school and confides his loss to François Seurel, the schoolmaster's retiring son. Meaulnes attempts in vain to find the castle and celebrants again, but by chance discovers Frantz, now a member of a traveling circus. The youths vow eternal friendship, and Meaulnes renews his quest for Yvonne. In Paris he consults Valentine, who falsely informs the student of Yvonne's marriage and attempts to supplant her. François, however, reports that Yvonne is single and waiting for Meaulnes. The lovers marry, but their happiness is brief. Frantz begs Meaulnes to accompany him on a search for Valentine. Honoring his youthful vow, the bridegroom acquiesces. Although the prolonged journey is successful, upon his return Meaulnes discovers that Yvonne has died in childbirth. *Students. Lovelorn. Youth. Courtship. Friendship. Brother-sister relationship. Marriage. Childbirth. Castles. Masquerades. Circus. Weddings. Boarding schools. Paris. Sologne.*

Note: Filmed on location in Sologne. Paris opening: Sep 1967 as *Le grand Meaulnes*; running time: 110 min.

WANDERLOVE   F6.5425

Dist Fine Products. ca Feb **1970**. Sd; col (Eastman Color). 35mm. 95 min. *MPAA rating* R.

Pres by Gerald Fine. *Prod* Fletcher Fist, Gerald Fine. *Exec Prod* Jerry Jackson. *Dir-Orig Story-Screenplay* Fletcher Fist. *Dir Photog* Robert Maxwell. *Song:* "Archie's Theme" Jeff Barry. *Song:* "Gettin' in My Way Again" Frank Carillo. *Songs:* "Baby's Wearing Blue," "Farewell, Sweet Papa," "Groovy Feelin'," "Oh No, Not Again," "Once Before" Mario Castellanos. *Featuring* Adam Wade, The Hot Soup, Year 2000, The Runaway Pancake.

Cast: Jamie Michaels *(Judy)*, Fletcher Fist *(P. G.)*, Norman Cole, Gerrie Grant, Lisa Tennele.

Romantic drama. Arriving in Hollywood from the Midwest, aspiring actress Judy meets playboy film director P.G. Finding his lifestyle too demanding, she abandons her career. P.G. pursues her departing bus, proclaiming his love. *Actors. Motion picture directors. Playboys. Ambition. Disillusionment. Hollywood. United States—Midwest. Chases.*

Note: Additional song: "I'm Working So Hard." Alternative title: *Wander Love Story.*

WANTING HOUR see **THE LUSTING HOURS**

THE WANTON CONTESSA see **SENSO**

WANTON JOURNEY (Japan)   F6.5426

Toho Co. Dec **1961** [Los Angeles showing]. Sd; col? 35mm. [Feature film, length unknown.]

Cast: Hisaya Morishige, Asami Kuji, Keiju Kobayashi, Daisuke Kato, Michiyo Aratama, Keiko Awaji, Norihei Miki, Reiko Dan, Kyu Sazanka, Tatsuya Mihashi, Mie Hama, Choko Iida.

Drama. No information about the precise nature of this film has been found. **Note:** Original title and release undetermined.

WAR AND PEACE (U.S.S.R.)   F6.5427

Mosfilm. *Dist* Continental Distributing, Inc. 28 Apr **1968** [New York opening]. Sd; col (Sovcolor, U. S. print by Movielab and DeLuxe). 35mm & 70mm. 373 min. [Part 1, 195 min; Part 2, 178 min.]

Production Credits: *Dir* Sergey Bondarchuk. *Screenplay* Sergey Bondarchuk, Vasiliy Solovyov. *Story Ed* S. Yermolinskiy. *Photog* Anatoliy Petritskiy. *Camera* Dmitriy Korzhikhin. *Photog Seq:* "Battle of Schöngrabern," "Battle of Austerlitz," "Duel" Aleksandr Shelenkov, Chen Yu-lan. *Art Dir* Mikhail Bogdanov, Gennadiy Myasnikov. *Asst Art Dir* Semyon Valyushyok, Aleksandr Menyalshchikov, Aleksandr Dikhtyar. *Set Decor* G. Koshelyov, V. Uvarov. *Film Ed* Tatyana Likhachyova. *Mus Comp & Cond* Vyacheslav Ovchinnikov. *Choreog* Vladimir Burmeyster. *Sd* Yuriy Mikhaylov, Igor Urvantsev. *Asst Dir* Anatoliy Golovanov, Anatoliy Chemodurov, Adiba Shir-Akhmedova, A. Alyoshin, asst dir, A. Petrov. *Ch Prod Mgr* Viktor Tsirgiladze. *Prod Mgr* Nikolay Ivanov, G. Meyerovich, V. Krivonoshenko. *Cost* Mikhail Chikovani. *Uniform Dsgn* V. Vavra, N. Buzina. *Makeup* Mikhail Chikiryov. *Sp Eff Photog* G. Ayzenberg. *Sp Eff Art Dir* F. Krasnyy, M. Semyonov. *Pyrotechnician* Vladimir Likhachyov. *Adv* N. K. Gudziy. *Military Adv* V. V. Kurasov, (Gen.).

Production Credits for English Vers: *Pres by* Walter Reade Organization, Satra Corp. *Dub Vers* Titan Productions. *Dial Adapt & Dir* Lee Kresel. *Narr Writ* Andrew Witwer. *Titl & Introduction Created by* Elinor Bunin. *Supv Ed* Sidney Katz. *Sd* Fine Recording Inc. *Lip Sync Ed* Eli Haviv. *Project Coord* Andrew L. Sager.

Cast: Lyudmila Savelyeva *(Natasha Rostova)*, Sergey Bondarchuk *(Pierre Bezukhov)*, Vyacheslav Tikhonov *(Andrey Bolkonskiy)*, Viktor Stanitsyn *(Ilya Andreyevich Rostov)*, Kira Golovko *(Countess Rostova)*, Oleg Tabakov *(Nikolay Rostov)*, Nikolay Kodin, Seryozha Yermilov *(Petya Rostov)*, Irina Gubanova *(Sonya)*, Anatoliy Ktorov *(Nikolay Andreyevich Bolkonskiy)*, Antonina Shuranova *(Princess Marya)*, Anastasiya Vertinskaya *(Liza Bolkonskaya)*, Boris Smirnov *(Prince Vasiliy Kuragin)*, Irina Skobtseva *(Hélène Kuragina)*, Vasiliy Lanovoy *(Anatole Kuragin)*, Oleg Yefremov *(Dolokhov)*, N. Tolkachyov *(Count Bezukhov)*, Yelena Tyapkina *(Marya Akhrosimova)*, K. Polovikova *(Princess Anna Drubetskaya)*, Eduard Martsevich *(Drubetskoy)*, A. Stepanova *(Anna Schérer)*, D. Firsova *(Catiche)*, G. Kravchenko *(Julie Karagina)*, Boris Zakhava *(Kutuzov)*, Nikolay Trofimov *(Tushin)*, Gyuli Chokhonelidze *(Bagration)*, Nikolay Rybnikov *(Denisov)*, V. Murganov *(Aleksandr I)*, Vladislav Strzhelchik *(Napoleon Bonaparte)*, V. Sofronov *(Emperor Franz)*, N. Bubnov *(General Mack)*, I. Solovyov *(Shinshin)*, Yu. Chekulayev *(Nesvitskiy)*, Pyotr Savin *(Timokhin)*, A. Smirnov *(staff officer)*, V. Badayev *(regiment commander)*, Aleksandr Borisov *(Uncle Mikhail)*, Nonna Mordyukova *(Anisya Fyodorovna)*, A. Syomin *(Nikolushka)*, G. Zommer *(Bennigsen)*, Ya. Grantinsh *(Woltzogen)*, D. Eysentals *(Clausewitz)*, Mikhail Khrabrov *(Karatayev)*, Stanislav Chekan *(Tikhon Shcherbatyy)*, Jean-Claude Balard *(Ramballe)*, Georgiy Millyar *(Morel)*, Boris Molchanov *(Davout)*, L. Polyakov *(Lauriston)*, G. Shapovalov, N. Smorchkov, I. Turchenkov, A. Boldyrev, N. Khryashchikov, A. Degtyar, A. Lebedev, D. Sivakov, N. Sorokin, V. Prikhodko, D. Netrebin, A. Bakhar, Ye. Shalamov, M. Vorobyov *(Russian soldiers)*, Ye. Stroyeva, S. Uspenskaya, M. Dobrovolskaya, N. Fogel, L. Borisenko, V. Matissen, Ye. Yelina, N. Lebedev, A. Fadeyev, N. Kollen, V. Renin, Z. Smirnova-Nemirovich, A. Rebane, Yu. Ovsyannikov, Yu. Dioshi, E. Knausmyuller, A. Barushnoy, G. Kurovskiy, V. Maslatsov, P. Alekseyev, Yu. Rossinol, V. Lutsekovich, A. Ponomarenko, A. Kin, V. Mashchenko, V. Smirnov, actor, Z. Dvizhkova, V. Polonskaya, L. Kramarevskiy, Yelena Vanke, A. Begak, D. Begak, A. Sezemann, N. Sibeykin, G. Ivanov, V. Vagina, Yu. Chuveleva, S. Makovskaya, V. Yermilov, Yu. Grigoryev, actor, Ye. Khovanskaya, O. Mikhaylova, G. Rybakov, V. Lapin, Ye. Lyutsau, N. Grinko, Sergey Nikonenko, L. Vidavskiy, A. Gruzinskiy, A. Mombelli, G. Svetlani, T. Makhova, Yu. Vetrov, V. Matov, A. Glazyrin, L. Nedovich, T. Kazankova, R. Aleksandrov, V. Islavin, Yu. Kryuchkov, I. Vasilenko, B. Batashov, V. Fromgoldt, G. Shostko, Z. Zaks, G. Mityakov, G. Edzhubov, A. Komissarov, V. Levchenko, Vladimir Likhachyov, A. Yachnitskiy, S. Konovalova, V. Kosarikhin, I. Labina, N. Afrikyants, N. Avetisova, V. Alakhverdova, N. Aparin, V. Seleznyov, P. Kiryutkin, R. Chumak.

English Narr Spoken by: Norman Rose.

Epic. Source: Leo Nikolaevich Tolstoy, *Voyna i mir* (1865–69). By 1805, Russia is being drawn irrevocably into a struggle for survival against Napoleon.

Although Prince Andrey Bolkonskiy, discontented with his life and marriage, willingly goes to war, his friend Pierre Bezukhov, the illegitimate son of a wealthy count, remains behind in Saint Petersburg. Pierre's father dies, leaving the young man his title and wealth. Later, Pierre naively marries the scheming Hélène Kuragina, who is subsequently unfaithful to him. Pierre is goaded into a duel in which he severely wounds his wife's lover, Dolokhov, and he separates from Hélène. Misfortune also plagues Andrey, who is injured and captured by the French at Austerlitz. Upon his release, he returns home to find his wife, Liza, dying in childbirth. During the uneasy alliance of Russia and France, Andrey attends a lavish ball at the Rostov estate in Otradnoye and falls in love with Natasha, the 17-year-old daughter of Count Ilya Rostov. Respecting his father's wishes, Andrey agrees to postpone marriage to Natasha for a year and go abroad. Left alone, the romantic Natasha goes to Moscow with her father and is swept off her feet by the dashing young Anatole Kuragin, Hélène's brother. Natasha attempts to elope with Anatole, but Pierre, a longtime family friend, learns of the plan and prevents their departure, informing Natasha that Anatole is married. Natasha has already broken her engagement, however, and Andrey cannot forgive her. Despondent over the unhappy affair and the loss of Andrey's love, Natasha falls ill and finds comfort only in the attentions of the devoted Pierre. Then the shaky peace collapses, and Napoleon leads his armies across the Russian frontier. No longer able to ignore political events, Pierre visits the front and is witness to the Battle of Borodino, after which Kutuzov, the Russian commander-in-chief, is forced to order a retreat from Moscow. The city, quickly engulfed in flames, is left to the mercy of the French. Pierre, deeply moved by what he has seen, refuses to evacuate the city, foolishly hoping to find the opportunity to assassinate Napoleon. As the French triumphantly march into Moscow, Andrey, wounded at Borodino, is evacuated and later dies after being reunited with Natasha. Despite Napoleon's victory, he is unable to negotiate a peace treaty with Kutuzov, and, without supplies and reinforcements, French morale quickly disintegrates. Left with no alternative, Napoleon orders a retreat from Moscow, taking along the Russian prisoners, among them Pierre. But Napoleon has not reckoned with the bitter Russian winter, and his troops fall by the hundreds on the vast frozen expanse. Seizing the opportunity, Kutuzov attacks at Berezina and routs the remnants of the French Army. Pierre is freed and learns that Hélène has died. With the momentous 8-year conflict at an end, Pierre seeks out Natasha, whom he has long loved, and asks her to become his wife. *Royalty. Nobility. Aristocrats. Prisoners of war. French. Marriage. Inheritance. Infidelity. Family life. Military invasion. Combat zone life. Death. Assassination. Patriotism. Incendiarism. Hunting. Childbirth. Balls (formal gatherings). Napoleonic Wars. Russia—History—19th Century. Europe—History—1789–1815. Saint Petersburg. Moscow. Austerlitz. Borodino. Berezina River. Otradnoye. Schöngrabern. Smolensk. Mikhail Ilarionovich Kutuzov. Napoleon I. Alexander I (Russia). Francis II (Holy Roman Emperor). Pyotr Ivanovich Bagration. Karl Mack von Leiberich. Russia—Army. France—Army. Austria—Army. Duels.*

Note: Produced in the U.S.S.R. 1962–67 as *Voyna i mir*. Filmed in 70mm, partially on location in 168 localities: the Borodino battle was filmed near Smolensk; the "Moscow on Fire" episode in Volokolamsk; the "Hunting in Otradnoye" scene in the village of Boguslavskiy near Kashira. Released in the U.S.S.R. in four sections: *Andrey Bolkonskiy* (16 reels, 2 parts, released 1966), *Natasha Rostova* (12 reels, released 1966), *1812 god* (10 reels, released 1967), and *Pyer Bezukhov* (10 reels, released 1967); combined running time: ca480 min. The Soviet government assisted in providing extras and material. Walter Reade, Jr., Sergey Bondarchuk, and Sovexportfilm cooperated in fashioning 2-part U. S. release version. Theatrically released in the U. S. only in English language version.

WAR AND PIECE *see* **THE HAREM BUNCH; OR WAR AND PIECE**

THE WAR GAME (Great Britain)   F6.5428
British Broadcasting Corp.–British Film Institute. *Dist* Pathé Contemporary Films. 19 Mar **1967** [New York opening]. Sd; b&w. 35mm (see note). 47 min.
Prod-Dir-Writ Peter Watkins. *Dir Action Seq* Derek Ware. *Photog* Peter Bartlett, photog. *Dsgn* Tony Cornell, Anne Davey. *Film Ed* Michael Bradsell. *Sd* Derek Williams, Lou Hanks, Stanley Morcom. *Cost* Vanessa Clarke. *Makeup* Lilias Munro.
Cast: Michael Aspel, Dick Graham (*commentators*).
Documentary drama. During a Communist Chinese campaign in Vietnam, a new crisis develops over the Berlin question. The United States attacks Russia, and Russia retaliates. Nuclear warheads are dropped on Great Britain, and a single megaton bomb lands 27 miles from the city of Kent. All defense measures prove useless as homes are destroyed, the populace burned and blinded, and an uncontrollable fire rages throughout the city. Medical facilities are inadequate; the dying are shot; and there are mass burnings of corpses. Despite the presence of heavily armed police and firing squads, looting and violence are widespread. Interviews with various political and religious leaders on the causes and consequences of nuclear war are interspersed with scenes of

the holocaust. The film concludes with an evaluation of the nuclear arsenals of the great powers and a warning that "within 15 years, another six to 12 nations are sure to have a bomb of some kind." *Police. Politicians. Nuclear warfare. Civil defense. Holocausts. Looting. Nuclear weapons. Kent (England). Great Britain—Army. Fires. The Future.*
Note: Filmed on location in Kent, England, with local residents in the cast. Opened in London in Apr 1966. Intended for release on British television but not shown because the subject matter was considered unsuitable for mass audiences. 1966 New York Film Festival running time: 50 min.

WAR-GODS OF THE DEEP (United States/Great Britain)   F6.5429
Bruton Film Productions–American International Pictures. *Dist* American International Pictures. May **1965** [c26 May 1965; LP31197]. Sd; col (PathéColor). 35mm (Colorscope). 85 min.
Pres by James H. Nicholson, Samuel Z. Arkoff. *Prod* Daniel Haller. *Exec Prod* George Willoughby. *Assoc Exec Prod* James H. Nicholson, Samuel Z. Arkoff. *Dir* Jacques Tourneur. *Screenplay* Charles Bennett, Louis M. Heyward. *Adtl Dial* David Whitaker, writ. *Photog* Stephen Dade. *Dir Underwater Photog* John Lamb. *Underwater Photog* John Lane, Neil Ginger Gemmell. *Art Dir* Frank White. *Set Decor* Colin Southcott. *Scenic Artist* Peter Wood. *Film Ed* Gordon Hales. *Mus* Stanley Black. *Sd* Ken Rawkins, Colin Le Mesurier. *Asst Dir* David Tringham. *Prod Mgr* Pat Green. *Makeup* Geoffrey Rodway, W. T. Partleton. *Sp Eff* Frank George, Les Bowie.
Cast: Vincent Price (*The Captain [Sir Hugh Tregathion]*), Tab Hunter (*Ben Harris*), David Tomlinson (*Harold Tiffin-Jones*), Susan Hart (*Jill Tregellis*), John Le Mesurier (*Rev. Jonathan Ives*), Henry Oscar (*Mumford*), Derek Newark (*Dan*), Roy Patrick (*Simon*), Tony Selby (*George*), Michael Heyland (*Bill*), Steven Brooke (*Ted*), William Hurndell (*Tom*), Jim Spearman (*Jack*), Dennis Blake (*Harry*), Arthur Hewlett, Walter Sparrow, John Barrett (*fishermen*), Barbara Bruce, Hilda Campbell Russell (*women guests*), Bart Allison, George Richarde (*men guests*), Herbert (*himself, a rooster*).
Science fiction drama. Source: Edgar Allan Poe, "The Doomed City" ("City in the Sea"), in *Poems* (1831). Edgar Allan Poe, "A Descent Into the Maelstrom," in *Graham's Magazine* (May 1841). Jill Tregellis, a young American, owns a converted manor house hotel on the Cornish coast. The body of a guest washes up on shore, its face contorted by fear, and is discovered by another American, Ben Harris. Ben informs Jill and her eccentric artist friend, Harold Tiffin-Jones, about the body. They discover a strange creature, a gillman, in the hotel. It escapes, and Jill disappears that night leaving a trail of seaweed. Ben, Harold, and Herbert (Harold's pet rooster) follow the trail and discover a passage to Lyonesse, an underwater city surrounded by volcanoes. Lyonesse is ruled by The Captain, who, searching for a seismologist, captured the hotel guest and kidnaped Jill because he believes her to be the reincarnation of his dead wife. Life in Lyonesse is eternal except for those found guilty of crime; such people are thrown to the gillman. As Ben and Harold arrive, a Mr. Ives is being tried. Together he, Jill, Ben, Harold, and Herbert escape, and Lyonesse is destroyed by erupting volcanoes. The Captain also escapes but is destroyed when exposed to air. *Americans in foreign countries. Sea monsters. Eccentrics. Hotelkeepers. Artists. Immortality. Reincarnation. Kidnaping. Hotels. Trials. Underwater cities. Volcanoes. Cornwall (England). Roosters.*
Note: Underwater scenes filmed in the Bahamas. Released in Great Britain in Oct 1965 as *City Under the Sea*. Working titles: *City in the Sea* and *Warlords of the Deep*.

WAR HEAD *see* **OPERATION SNAFU**

WAR HERO *see* **WAR IS HELL**

WAR HUNT   F6.5430
T-D Enterprises. *Dist* United Artists. Jul **1962** [Los Angeles showing: c9 Feb 1962; LP21772]. Sd; b&w. 35mm. 81 min.
Prod Terry Sanders. *Dir* Denis Sanders. *Screenplay* Stanford Whitmore. *Cinematog* Ted McCord. *Background Titl Photog* Terry Sanders. *Art Dir* Edgar Lansbury. *Titl Dsgn* Vance Johnson. *Film Ed* John Hoffman, Edward Dutko. *Mus* Bud Shank. *Sd* Roy Meadows. *Asst Dir* Jack Bohrer.
Cast: John Saxon (*Pvt. Raymond Endore*), Robert Redford (*Pvt. Roy Loomis*), Charles Aidman (*Capt. Wallace Pratt*), Sydney Pollack (*Sergeant Van Horn*), Gavin MacLeod (*Private Crotty*), Tommy Matsuda (*Charlie*), Tom Skerritt (*Corporal Showalter*), Tony Ray (*Private Fresno*).
War drama. Each night during the fighting in Korea, U. S. A. Pvt. Raymond Endore blackens his face, sneaks into enemy territory, kills a Chinese Communist guard with his stiletto, and then performs a mock Indian war dance over the corpse. A loner among the other members of his platoon, Endore has as his only companion Charlie, an 8-year-old Korean war orphan. Endore's unhealthy influence on Charlie is challenged by a replacement, Pvt. Roy Loomis, and the two men engage in a bitter struggle to dominate him. When the cease-fire order arrives and the GI's start a mild celebration, Loomis sees Endore sneak away for his nightly ritual, and he notifies his superior, Captain

Pratt. Together, they go in search of the now psychopathic Endore. They find him, with Charlie, holed up in a caved-in bunker. Endore attacks Pratt and Loomis with his stiletto, and Pratt has no choice but to shoot him. Little Charlie looks at Endore's lifeless body, claps his hands to his ears, and runs off into no man's land. *Orphans. Psychopaths. Hero worship. Combat zone life. Korean War 1950-53. United States Army.*

WAR IS HELL   **F6.5431**
Burt Topper Productions. *Dist* Allied Artists. 22 Jan **1964** [New York opening; c1 May 1961; LP26587]. Sd; b&w. 35mm. 81 min.
Prod-Dir-Writ Burt Topper. *Co-prod* Ross Hahn. *Assoc Prod* Sam Altonian. *Dir Photog* Jacques Marquette. *Camera Op* Nelson Cordes. *Supv Film Ed* Ace Herman. *Mus* Ronald Stein. *Sd* Al Overton. *Prod Mgr* Willard Kirkham. *Unit Mgr* Edward Knight. *Script Supv* Fred Applegate, Sr. *Wardrobe* Marjorie Corso. *Sp Eff* Pat Dinga. *Key Grip* Frank Lambers, Richard M. Rubin. *Prop* Karl Brainard. *Gaffer* Bill Kain. *Still Man* Roger Mace.
Cast: Tony Russel (*Sergeant Keefer*), Baynes Barron (*Sergeant Garth*), Burt Topper (*Lieutenant Hallen*), Judy Dan (*Yung Chi Thomas*), Tony Rich (*Miller*), J. J. Dahner (*Koller*), Wally Campo (*Laney*), Bobby Byles (*Gresler*), Michael Bell (*Seldon*), Russ Prescott (*Bender*), Robert Howard (*Conners*), Paul Sherriff (*Thurston*), Kei Chung (*Korean lieutenant*), Audie Murphy (*narrator of introduction*).
War drama. During the Korean War, a group of soldiers is ordered to destroy a communist bunker, but Sergeant Keefer hides in terror as the others are killed while performing their duty. Keefer takes sole credit for the victory, claiming the other men were cowards. But his superior learns the truth, and Keefer shoots him to guarantee the medal he expects to receive. Assuming command, the sergeant is told that a truce has been declared, but he leads his unknowing men in gunning down defenseless enemy soldiers who have honored the agreement. Keefer is killed by retaliating communists as Sergeant Garth, who is aware of the truth, returns to United Nations lines with Yung Chi, a Korean girl rescued during their operations. Although he considers exposing Keefer's treachery, Garth fails to do so, thereby leaving the sergeant posthumously eligible for the medal he craved. *War heroes. Mendacity. Refugees. War victims. Koreans. Cowardice. Murder. Combat zone life. Korean War 1950-53. United States Army—Infantry.*
Note: Working title: *War Hero*. Prerelease title: *War Madness*.

THE WAR IS OVER see **LA GUERRE EST FINIE**

WAR ITALIAN STYLE (Italy)   **F6.5432**
Italian International Film. *Dist* American International Pictures. 18 Jan **1967** [Boston opening; c11 Jan 1967; LP34004]. Sd; col (Technicolor). 35mm (Techniscope). 74 min. [Also reviewed at 84 min.]
Prod Fulvio Lucisano. *Dir* Luigi Scattini. *Screenplay* Franco Castellano, Pipolo. *Idea* Fulvio Lucisano. *Photog* Fausto Zuccoli. *Mus* Piero Umiliani. *Sd* Lodovico Scardella, Bruno Moreal. *Re-rec Dir* Terry Vantell. *Asst Dir* (see note) Mauro Sacripanti, Romana Fortini.
Cast: Buster Keaton (*General Von Kassler*), Franco Franchi (*Frank*), Ciccio Ingrassia (*Joe*), Martha Hyer (*Lieut. Inge Schultze*), Fred Clark (*General Zacharias*), Franco Ressel, Tommaso Alvieri, Barbara Loy, Alessandro Sperli, Alfredo Adami, Ennio Antonelli.
War comedy. In May 1943, Joe and Frank, two American soldiers of Italian descent, are searching the North African desert for the famed German "Desert Fox," General Von Kassler. During a sandstorm, they stumble upon his oasis headquarters and are captured by his beautiful aide, Lieut. Inge Schultze. In an attempt to confuse the Allies, the Germans permit the two soldiers to escape with false plans for the German offensive. The Americans inadvertently take the real plans, however, and pave the way for an Allied victory. Some months later they are sent ashore in preparation for the Anzio invasion and are once again taken prisoner by Von Kassler's division. This time they assume the disguises of Adolf Hitler and an SS general and trick Von Kassler into destroying a huge gun impeding Allied progress. As a result of his blunders, Von Kassler is deprived of his rank by the SS and slated for execution, but Joe and Frank have by this time become somewhat fond of the "amiable old gentleman," and they dress him in the clothes of a scarecrow and permit him to escape as the Allies establish a beachhead at Anzio. *Escapees. Prisoners of war. Deserts. Ordnance. Disguise. World War II. North Africa. Anzio. Adolf Hitler. United States Army. Germany—Army. SS.*
Note: Rome opening: Apr 1966 as *Due marines e un generale*; running time: ca100 min. Sources conflict in crediting assistant director.

THE WAR LORD   **F6.5433**
Court Productions. *Dist* Universal Pictures. 10 Nov **1965** [Detroit opening; c4 Dec 1965; LP32632]. Sd (Westrex); col (Technicolor). 35mm (Panavision). 123 min. [Also 120-130 min.]
Prod Walter Seltzer. *In Charge of Prod* Edward Muhl. *Dir* Franklin J. Schaffner. *Screenplay* John Collier, Millard Kaufman. *Dir Photog* Russell

Metty. *Col Cons* Eliot Elisofon. *Art Dir* Alexander Golitzen, Henry Bumstead. *Set Decor* John McCarthy, Oliver Emert. *Main Titl* Pacific Title. *Film Ed* Folmar Blangsted. *Mus Supv* Joseph Gershenson. *Mus* Jerome Moross. *Fertility Routine Choreog* Kenny Williams. *Sd* Waldon O. Watson, William Russell. *Asst Dir* Douglas Green, Carl Beringer. *Unit Prod Mgr* Norman Deming. *Cost Supv* Vittorio Nino Novarese. *Makeup* Bud Westmore. *Hairstylist* Larry Germain. *Matte Supv* Albert Whitlock. *Tech Adv* Vittorio Nino Novarese. *Birds Trained by* Ray Berwick.
Cast: Charlton Heston (*Chrysagon*), Richard Boone (*Bors*), Rosemary Forsyth (*Bronwyn*), Maurice Evans (*priest*), Guy Stockwell (*Draco*), Niall MacGinnis (*Odins*), Henry Wilcoxon (*Frisian prince*), James Farentino (*Marc*), Sammy Ross (*Volc*), Woodrow Parfrey (*Piet*), John Alderson (*Holbracht*), Allen Jaffe (*Tybald*), Michael Conrad (*Rainault*), Dal Jenkins (*Dirck*), Johnny Jensen (*boy prince*), Forrest Wood (*Chrysagon man*), Belle Mitchell (*old woman*).
Costume melodrama. Source: Leslie Stevens, *The Lovers* (New York opening: 10 May 1956). In the 11th century, Chrysagon, a warlord under the Duke of Normandy, his brother Draco, and his companion Bors drive away the invading Frisians from a coastal town. Chrysagon, who is in charge of keeping order in the village, meets and becomes attracted to Bronwyn, a young woman betrothed to Marc, the son of the village leader, Odins. He takes advantage of his right to have wedding night privileges with the bride, and the two fall in love. When they refuse to part at dawn, Marc seeks revenge. He calls on the Frisians and informs them that the son of their king is being held prisoner in the village. While the Frisians prepare for the attack, Draco rides for reinforcements and returns with the news that he is taking over his brother's position. Realizing that he will not be able to maintain the support of the Normans as long as Chrysagon is still alive, Draco arranges a duel with his brother, but Draco himself is killed. Chrysagon then returns the young prince to the Frisians, and they agree to give sanctuary to Bronwyn. Suddenly Marc attacks, and the wounded warlord rides away with Bors to make peace with the duke. *Brothers. Warlords. Royalty. Brides. Social customs. Revenge. Perfidy. Normandy. Duels.*

THE WAR LOVER (Great Britain)   **F6.5434**
Columbia Pictures. 7 Nov **1962** [Chicago opening; c1 Nov 1962; LP23735]. Sd (Westrex); b&w. 35mm. 105 min.
An Arthur Hornblow, Jr. Production. *Prod* Arthur Hornblow, Jr. *Dir* Philip Leacock. *Screenplay* Howard Koch. *Dir Photog* Bob Huke. *Camera Op* Ronnie Maasz, Austin Dempster. *Focus* Dennis Lewiston. *Aerial Photog* Ron Taylor, Skeets Kelly. *Art Dir* Bill Andrews. *Asst Art Dir* Kenneth McCallum Tait. *Set Dresser* Andrew Low. *Ch Draughtsman* Bill Alexander. *Scenic Artist* Ben Healey. *Film Ed* Gordon Hales. *Asst Ed* Geoffrey Fry, Roy Benson. *Mus Comp* Richard Addinsell. *Mus Cond* Muir Mathieson. *Sd Supv* John Cox. *Sd Rec* Norman Bolland, Red Law. *Sd Ed* Christopher Lancaster. *Sd Camera Op* Desmond Edwards. *Boom Op* John Salter. *1st, 2d & 3d Asst Dir* Basil Rayburn, Timothy Burrill, John Danischewsky. *Prod Supv* Raymond Anzarut. *Prod Mgr* Robert Sterne. *Prod Sec* Joan Parcell. *Prod Supv Sec* Liz Charles-Williams. *Cont* Eileen Head. *Cost Dsgn* Julie Harris, cost. *Wardrobe Supv* Elsa Fennell. *Makeup* George Partleton. *Hairdresser* Betty Glasow. *Sp Eff* Wally Veevers, Ted Samuels. *Gen Tech Adv* Robert F. Spence, (Lieut. Col.). *Coöp* Great Britain—Royal Air Force, United States Air Force. *Flying Fortress Adv* William Tesla, (Lieut. Col. USAF). *Aerial Seq Arr by* John Crewdson, (Capt.). *Casting Dir* Barry Gray, casting dir. *Prod Buyer* Percy Godbold. *Still Photog* Norman Hargood. *Camera Grip* Albert Lott. *Chargehand Prop* Sidney Leggett.
Cast: Steve McQueen (*Buzz Rickson*), Robert Wagner (*Ed Bolland*), Shirley Ann Field (*Daphne Caldwell*), Gary Cockrell (*Lynch*), Michael Crawford (*Junior Sailen*), Billy Edwards (*Brindt*), Chuck Julian (*Lamb*), Robert Easton (*Handown*), Al Waxman (*Prien*), Tom Busby (*Farr*), George Sperdakos (*Bragliani*), Bob Kanter (*Haverstraw*), Jerry Stovin (*Emmet*), Edward Bishop (*Vogt*), Richard Leech (*Murika*), Bernard Braden (*Randall*), Sean Kelly (*Woodman*), Charles De Temple (*Braddock*), Neil McCallum (*Sully*), Viera (*singer*), Justine Lord (*street girl*), Louise Dunn (*Hazel*), Arthur Hewlett (*vicar*).
War drama. Source: John Hersey, *The War Lover* (New York, 1959). Buzz Rickson and Ed Bolland are American bomber pilots stationed in England during World War II. Buzz exults in combat and is often brilliant in his exploits against the enemy though his superiors have to censure him because of the great risks he takes. Ed is more cautious and abhors the act of killing but realizes it is a job that must be done. Eventually the two men become involved with an English girl, Daphne Caldwell, who, aware that to Buzz she is merely another potential conquest, offers her love to Ed. While Buzz and Ed are piloting a Flying Fortress on a bombing mission, their plane is crippled; and the crew bails out over the English Channel. Buzz, however, refuses to abandon the controls and, after forcing Ed to jump, attempts to reach England alone. But his luck runs out and he meets his death as he crashes into the Dover cliffs. *Air pilots. Aerial bombardment. Military life. Airplanes. World War II. English Channel.*

United States Army—Air Force. Airplane accidents.
Note: Opened in London in Jun 1963.

WAR MADNESS *see* **WAR IS HELL**

WAR OF THE BUTTONS (France)   F6.5435
Productions de la Guéville. *Dist* Bronston Distributions, Comet Film Distributors. 18 Dec **1963** [New York opening]. Sd; b&w. 35mm. 92 min.
Prod Yves Robert, Danièle Delorme. *Dir* Yves Robert. *Screenplay* François Boyer, Yves Robert. *Dial* François Boyer. *Photog* André Bac. *Art Dir* Pierre Thévenet. *Film Ed* Marie Josèphe Yoyotte. *Mus* José Berghmans. *Mus Cond* René-Pierre Chouteau. *Pianist* Jean Casadesus. *Sd* Pierre Calvet. *Prod Mgr* Léon Carré. *English Subtitl* Noelle Gillmor.
Cast: Martin Lartigue *(Tigibus)*, André Treton *(Lebrac)*, Michel Isella *(Aztec)*, Jacques Dufilho *(Aztec's father)*, Pierre Trabaud *(teacher)*, Jean Richard *(Lebrac's father)*, Yvette Etiévant *(Lebrac's mother)*, Michel Galabru *(Balatier)*, Pierre Tchernia, Michèle Meritz, Paul Crauchet, Claude Confortes, Henri Labussière, Robert Rollis, Louisette Rousseau, Yves Peneau.
Comedy-drama. Source: Louis Pergaud, *La guerre des boutons* (Paris, 1912). The boys of the provincial villages of Longeverne and Velrans are rivals; and open conflict breaks out between the two groups when two Longeverne boys are insulted by the Velrans boys, although the meaning of the insult is really not understood. Buttons become the prize of war, and each captive is stripped of all he possesses until the Longeverne boys led by Lebrac attack nude and deliver a crushing defeat. But there is a traitor among the Longeverne boys, and, as they are celebrating their victory at a feast, the Velrans boys led by Aztec attack and completely rout them. The traitor is discovered and punished, but he informs the elders, thus causing all the Longeverne boys to be punished. Lebrac, however, escapes to the woods and eludes searchers for 4 days. He is captured, and both he and the leader of the Velrans boys are sent to reform school for waging war without sanction. *Street gangs. Children. Traitors. Gang wars. Nudity. Village life. Buttons. Reformatories. Chases.*
Note: Opened in Paris in Apr 1962 as *La guerre des boutons*; running time: 90 min. Previously filmed as *Generals Without Buttons* (France, 1938).

THE WAR OF THE GARGANTUAS (United States/Japan)   F6.5436
Toho Co.-Henry G. Saperstein Enterprises. *Dist* Maron Films. 29 Jul **1970** [Houston opening]. Sd; col (Eastman Color). 35mm (Tohoscope). 93 min. *MPAA rating* G.
Released by United Productions of America. *Exec Prod* Tomoyuki Tanaka, Henry G. Saperstein, Reuben Bercovitch. *Dir* Inoshiro Honda. *Screenplay* Kaoru Mabuchi, Inoshiro Honda. *Photog* Hajime Koizumi. *Mus* Akira Ifukube. *Sp Eff* Eiji Tsuburaya.
Cast: Russ Tamblyn *(Dr. Paul Stewart)*, Kumi Mizuno *(his assistant)*, Kipp Hamilton *(singer)*, Yu Fujiki *(army commander)*, Kenji Sahara, Hiroshi Sekita, Jun Tazaki.
Science fiction melodrama. Dr. Paul Stewart, an expert on unusual marine life, arrives in Japan to investigate a series of mysterious deaths off the coast of Kyoto involving a huge green creature. Another creature is seen, and Dr. Stewart deduces that, as a result of atomic bomb testing, a small creature he once studied has mutated into two gargantuas. The green gargantua, leaving its sea lair, terrorizes Tokyo before being knocked unconscious by lasers; the brown gargantua arrives from the mountains to rescue its brother as the army prepares to attack. Dr. Stewart warns the military commander not to use conventional weapons on the beasts for fear that their flesh might regenerate. The brown creature is unable to persuade the green gargantua to lead a peaceful existence; after a violent fight in the sea, the two are engulfed by an erupting volcano. *Marine biologists. Monsters. Sea monsters. Mutation. Regeneration. Laser. Volcanoes. Tokyo. Kyoto. Japan—Army.*
Note: Released in Japan in Aug 1966 as *Furankenshutain no kaiju—Sanda tai Gailah.* Intended as a sequel to *Frankenstein Conquers the World,* q. v., but the film was reedited by Saperstein, eliminating Frankenstein references and adding new footage. This version was released in Japan as *Sanda tai Gailah*; running time: 88 min.

THE WAR OF THE ZOMBIES (Italy)   F6.5437
Galatea. *Dist* American International Pictures. Mar **1965**. Sd; col (Eastmancolor). 35mm (Colorscope). 85 min.
Prod Ferruccio De Martino, Massimo De Rita. *Dir* Giuseppe Vari. *Screenplay* Piero Pierotti, Marcello Sartarelli. *Orig Idea* Ferruccio De Martino, Massimo De Rita. *Photog* Gabor Pogany. *Art Dir* Giorgio Giovannini. *Film Ed* Giuseppe Vari. *Mus* Roberto Nicolosi. *Prod Mgr* Paolo Mercuri. *Cost* Tina Grani. *Sp Eff* Ugo Amadoro.
Cast: John Drew Barrymore *(Aderbal)*, Susy Andersen *(Tullia)*, Ettore Manni *(Gaius)*, Ida Galli *(Rhama)*, Mino Doro *(Lutetius)*, Philippe Hersent *(Azer)*, Ivano Staccioli *(Sirion)*, Matilda Calnan, Antonio Corevi, Giulio Maculani, Livia Contardi, Rosy Zichel.

Adventure melodrama. The centurion Gaius is sent to Armenia to investigate the disappearance of some treasure bound for Rome. He discovers that Aderbal, a powerful magician, has the treasure and has promised part of it to the local Roman official, Lutetius, in return for his help in bringing off a local revolt. In addition, Aderbal has under his power Lutetius' wife, Tullia, and her slave, Rhama, with whom Gaius falls in love. In following Rhama to the magician's cave, Gaius is captured by Aderbal, who plots with Tullia to frame him for the murder of her husband. Gaius, freed from Aderbal, avoids arrest and learns that Aderbal is assembling an army composed in part of Roman soldiers transformed by Aderbal's magic idol into invulnerable zombies. Gaius is arrested before he can stop Aderbal, and everyone ignores his warnings about the magician's plans for world conquest. Finally, a faithful soldier frees Gaius, who destroys the magic idol and with it Aderbal and his zombie army. *Soldiers. Magicians. Zombies. Slavery. Idolatry. Centurions. Rome—History—Empire. Murder. Frameup. Revolts. Treasure. Armenia.*
Note: Released in Italy in 1963 as *Roma contro Roma.* Also reviewed at 95 and 105 min.

WAR PARTY   F6.5438
Steve Production. *Dist* Twentieth Century-Fox Film Corp. 3 Feb **1965** [Los Angeles opening; c3 Feb 1965; LP31266]. Sd; b&w. 35mm. 72 min.
Prod Hal Klein. *Dir* Lesley Selander. *Screenplay* George Williams, William Marks. *Dir Photog* Gordon Avil. *Camera Op* John J. Jones. *Film Ed* John F. Schreyer. *Mus Comp & Cond* Richard La Salle. *Sd Mix* John Carter. *Sd Re-Rec* Mac Dalgleish. *Asst Dir* Harold M. Klein. *Script Supv* Billy Vernon. *Cost* Frank R. Budz. *Makeup Artist* Gustaf M. Norin. *Hairstyles* Edith W. Keon. *Sp Eff* Joe Lombardi. *Photog Eff* Butler-Glouner Inc. *Prop Master* Charles Chichetti. *Key Grip* Arthur Gaunt.
Cast: Michael T. Mikler *(Johnny Hawk)*, Davey Davison *(Sarah)*, Donald Barry *(Sergeant Chaney)*, Laurie Mock *(Nicoma)*, Dennis Robertson, actor, Charles Horvath, Michael Carr, Guy Wilkerson, Fred Krone.
Western drama. In the Indian wars of the 1870's, the Comanches unite to trap a Cavalry unit on the Plain of Tonopah. Because the Indians also control a pass leading to the besieged men, rescue troops must take a longer route. Then Nicoma, an Indian girl, brings word from a mission that the pass is open. A patrol headed by scout Johnny Hawk rides out to check on the story and talk to the rescue party. En route to the mission they meet a band of hostile Indians, and only Johnny Hawk, Sergeant Chaney, Nicoma, and one trooper survive. Arriving at the mission, they find the pastor slain and his daughter Sarah in shock; but she confirms that the pass is open, and Johnny Hawk and his men, after leaving Sarah in a safe place, set out to divert the rescue party. The group find a store of ammunition gathered by the Indians, and Nicoma sets the explosives but perishes in the explosion. The men continue, and once more they meet the Comanches. Johnny kills the chief, however, and makes his way across the mountains to the relief column and delivers the information that saves the trapped unit. *Comanche Indians. Scouts—Frontier. Missions. Ammunition. United States—History—Indian campaigns. United States Army—Cavalry. Explosions.*
Note: Location scenes filmed in California.

THE WAR WAGON   F6.5439
Batjac Productions. *Dist* Universal Pictures. 24 May **1967** [Chicago opening; c17 Jun 1967; LP35388]. Sd (Westrex); col (Technicolor). 35mm (Panavision). 101 min.
A Marvin Schwartz Production. *Prod* Marvin Schwartz. *Dir* Burt Kennedy. *2d Unit Dir* Cliff Lyons. *Screenplay* Clair Huffaker. *Dir Photog* William H. Clothier. *Art Dir* Alfred Sweeney. *Set Decor* Ray Moyer. *Titl Cinefx. Film Ed* Harry Gerstad. *Mus Comp & Cond* Dimitri Tiomkin. *Titl Song:* "Ballad of the War Wagon" Dimitri Tiomkin, Ned Washington. *Sung by* Ed Ames. *Sd* Waldon O. Watson, Robert R. Bertrand. *Re-rec* Clem Portman. *Sd Eff* Edit-Rite Inc. *Asst Dir* Al Jennings, H. A. Silverman. *Unit Prod Mgr* Joseph Behm. *Script Supv* Marshall Wolins. *Cost* Oscar Rodriguez. *Wardrobe* Robert Chiniquy, Donald Wolz. *Makeup* Donald W. Roberson, Dave Grayson, Bud Westmore. *Hairstyles* Larry Germain. *Mattes* Albert Whitlock. *Prop* Julius Rosenkrantz.
Cast: John Wayne *(Taw Jackson)*, Kirk Douglas *(Lomax)*, Howard Keel *(Levi Walking Bear)*, Robert Walker, [Jr.] *(Billy Hyatt)*, Keenan Wynn *(Wes Catlin)*, Bruce Cabot *(Frank Pierce)*, Joanna Barnes *(Lola)*, Valora Noland *(Kate Catlin)*, Gene Evans *(Hoag)*, Bruce Dern *(Hammond)*, Terry Wilson *(Strike)*, Don Collier *(Shack)*, Sheb Wooley *(Snyder)*, Ann McCrea *(Felicia)*, Emilio Fernandez *(Calita)*, Frank McGrath *(bartender)*, Chuck Roberson *(Brown)*, Red Morgan *(Early)*, Hal Needham *(Hite)*, Marco Antonio *(Wild Horse)*, Perla Walter *(Rosita)*.
Western drama. Source: Clair Huffaker, *Badman* (New York, 1957). In the 1870's Taw Jackson is paroled from prison after being framed and cheated out of his gold-rich land by Frank Pierce, the ruthless owner of a mining company. Determined to have his revenge, Taw devises an elaborate plan to hijack

Pierce's huge, armor-plated war wagon when it is carrying a half million dollars in gold dust. He enlists the aid of Lomax, a flamboyant gunman previously in the employ of Pierce; Wes Catlin, a supply wagon driver; alcoholic Billy Hyatt, a young demolitions expert who soon becomes attracted to Catlin's young wife, Kate; and Levi Walking Bear, a renegade Indian. Although Pierce tries to lure Lomax back into his employ by offering him $12,000 to kill Taw, the gunman sees a chance for greater profit in the heist. Assisted by Kiowa Indians, Taw puts his plan into motion. A road is blocked, nitroglycerin charges are set off, and the war wagon is blown into a steep ravine. Pierce is shot through the head by Lomax, and the sacks of gold dust are loaded into barrels of flour in Catlin's wagon; but the Kiowas suddenly turn on their companions, shoot Catlin, and attempt to steal the gold. A charge of exploding nitroglycerin kills the Indians and sends Catlin's wagon hurtling over a ledge, whereupon hordes of starving Indians gather up the gold dust, believing it to be flour, and make off with it. Enraged at losing his share of the bounty, Lomax takes Taw's horse as partial payment and rides off. Taw, unbeknownst to Lomax, has prevented the loss of some gold Lomax had hidden from the others. He gives Billy and Kate enough to live on temporarily and sends word to Lomax that he may claim his share of the recovered gold. Soon Lomax appears and angrily demands his share, but Taw insists that the gold remain in his own secret hiding place for a waiting period of 6 months. Until that time Lomax will have to guard Taw's life 24 hours a day. *Ex-convicts. Gunfighters. Indians of North America. Kiowa Indians. Traitors. Revenge. Robbery. Alcoholism. Frameup. Perfidy. Starvation. Murder. Gold. Gold mining. Mine claims. Nitroglycerin. Stagecoaches. Explosions.*

Note: Location scenes filmed in Mexico.

WARE HITOTSUBU NO MUGI NAREDO *see* COULD I BUT LIVE

WARKILL (United States/Philippines)   F6.5440
Balut Productions–Centaur Ltd. *Dist* Universal Pictures. May 1968 [Los Angeles showing; c1 Jun 1967; LP38807]. Sd; col (DeLuxe). 35mm. 100 min. [Cut from 103 min.]

Prod-Dir-Writ Ferde Grofé, Jr. *Exec Prod* Demetrio Tuason. *Assoc Prod* Stanford Tischler. *Dir Photog* Remegio Young. *Camera Op* Silvestre Carianga, Jr. *Film Ed* Phillip Innes. *Mus* Gene Kauer, Douglas Lackey. *Sd Rec* Demetrio Carrianga. *Asst Dir* Ricardo Velasco. *Prod Mgr* Louis Florentino. *Script Supv* Hernan Robles. *Asst to the Exec Prod* Johnny Gutierrez. *Sp Eff* Enrique Ledesma.

Cast: George Montgomery *(Col. John Hannegan)*, Tom Drake *(Phil Sutton)*, Conrad Parham *(Pedring)*, Eddie Infante *(Dr. Fernandez)*, Henry Duval *(Willy)*, Paul Edwards, Jr. *(Mike Harris)*, Bruno Punzalan *(Major Hashiri)*, David Michael *(Sergeant Johnson)*, Joaquin Fajardo *(Max)*, Bert La Fortesa *(Dr. Namura)*, Claude Wilson *(U. S. major)*, Ken Loring.

War drama. As World War II nears its end, American correspondent Phil Sutton arrives in the Philippines to get first-hand information on U. S. Col. John Hannegan. Sutton has written several paperback books extolling Hannegan's heroic leadership of a small band of Filipino guerrillas who are routing the remnants of Japanese troops. Sutton quickly realizes, however, that his idol is a ruthless killer who never takes prisoners, preferring to flush out the enemy and then shoot them. Sutton's revulsion at Hannegan's methods is somewhat mollified when they come across a native village where the inhabitants have been slaughtered by a fanatical Japanese officer intent upon destroying the local hospital. When the hospital's medical officer and personnel refuse to vacate their post, Hannegan reluctantly leaves some of his men behind while he takes to the hills to harass the enemy until reinforcements arrive. Sutton offers to join Hannegan and is granted permission. After delaying the attack on the hospital by hit-and-run tactics, Sutton and Hannegan return in time to help repulse the onslaught, but Hannegan is killed just before the reinforcements arrive. In spite of Hannegan's questionable methods, Sutton realizes that he will be remembered as a hero and decides to keep secret what he has learned. *War heroes. Authors. Guerrillas. War crimes. Combat zone life. Hospitals. World War II. United States Army. Japan—Army.*

Note: Filmed in the Philippine Islands.

WARLORDS OF THE DEEP *see* WAR-GODS OF THE DEEP

WARM BED *see* THE WARM, WARM BED

THE WARM BODY *see* THUNDER IN THE BLOOD

WARM IN THE BUD   F6.5441
Dist Film-Makers' Distribution Center. Jan 1970 [Los Angeles showing]. Sd; b&w. 16mm. 57 min.

Prod-Dir-Adapt Rudolph Caringi. *Photog* John Walsh, photog, Dahl Delu. *Film Ed* Rudolph Caringi. *Latin Madrigals by* Don Carlo Gesualdo. *Sd* Al Nahmias.

Cast: Robert Mont *(Mortiz)*, Dean Stricklin *(Melchior)*, Toni Hamilton *(Martha)*, Bruce Johnson *(Ernst)*, John Goetz *(Hanchen)*, Mary Rivard

(Wendla), Nuala Willis *(Ilse)*, John Carmody *(Otto)*, Barry Peterson *(George)*, David Martini *(Robert)*, Lynne Alpert *(Ina)*, Sage Cowles *(mother)*.

Drama. Based on the play: Frank Wedekind, *Frühlings Erwachen, eine Kindertragödie* (Berlin, 1890). In the late 19th century, Mortiz and Melchior, school friends, are searching for their manhood. Eventually, Mortiz commits suicide, and Melchior is tempted to do the same. Mortiz' funeral is portrayed in an interlude of "metaphorical fantasy." *Students. Adolescence. Friendship. Suicide. Fantasy. Funerals.*

WARM NIGHTS & HOT PLEASURES   F6.5442
Crossroads Productions. *Dist* Audubon Films. 3 Oct 1964 [Los Angeles showing]. Sd; b&w. 35mm. 71 min. [Original running time: 78 min.]

Pres by Radley Metzger. *Prod* Bingo Brandt. *Dir* Joe Sarno. *Photog* Jim Markos. *Lighting* Norman Contreras. *Mus* Thomas J. Valentino. *Sd* Henry Markosfeld. *Cost* Irene V. Weston. *Makeup* Vincent Loscalzo.

Cast: Marla Ellis *(Cathy)*, Eve Harris *(Marsha)*, Shelia Barnett *(Vivian)*, Carla Desmond *(Ronnie Cobb)*, Robert Richards, actor *(Paul Cobb)*, Joe Russell *(Dick)*, Anna Bodor *(dancer)*.

Melodrama. Cathy, Vivian, and Marsha—three roommates bored with studying—leave college to find show business careers in New York City. They find lodgings in a boardinghouse operated by a model who poses for nudist magazines and begin to look for work. Cathy meets and is seduced by a theatrical agent. He then passes her on to a cabaret owner who hires her as a belly dancer. Vivian and Marsha meet the Cobbs at a wild houseparty. Ronnie Cobb, willing to teach dance routines to Vivian, makes lesbian advances toward her, which Vivian rejects. Marsha falls in love with Paul, Ronnie's husband and a theatrical producer, but their affair ends when Marsha learns that Paul has offered her as sexual bait to a potential backer of his new show. Cathy and Marsha, disillusioned by failure, return to college; Vivian, in love with Dick, a New York photographer eager to make her his wife, obtains work in a musical. *Roommates. Students. Models. Theatrical agents. Theatrical producers. Cabaret owners. Exotic dancers. Photographers. Show business. Seduction. Lesbianism. Disillusionment. Nudity. Employment—Women. Infidelity. Boardinghouses. New York City.*

Note: Filmed entirely in New York City. Also known as *Warm Nights and Secret Pleasures.*

THE WARM, WARM BED   F6.5443
Barry Mahon Productions. *Dist* W. G. B. 1 Mar 1968 [New York showing]. Sd; b&w. 35mm. 63 min.

A Barry Mahon Production. *Prod-Dir* Barry Mahon.

Drama. The sexual adventures of a bored suburban couple keep their bedroom continuously occupied. The marital partners try to conceal their activities from each other, as the wife's lover, a compliant stewardess, an amorous friend, and an unsuspecting salesman follow one another into the conjugal bed. An orgy of mate swapping with the neighbors brings the day's activities to a close. *Suburbanites. Airline stewardesses. Salesmen. Neighbors. Marriage. Infidelity. Mate swapping.*

Note: Also known as *Warm Bed.*

WARNING SHOT   F6.5444
Bob Banner Associates. *Dist* Paramount Pictures. 18 Jan 1967 [Los Angeles opening; c31 Dec 1966; LP33656]. Sd; col (Technicolor). 35mm. 100 min.

Prod-Dir Buzz Kulik. *Assoc Prod* Tom Egan. *Screenplay* Mann Rubin. *Cinematog* Joseph Biroc. *Art Dir* Hal Pereira, Roland Anderson. *Set Decor* Robert R. Benton, George R. Nelson. *Film Ed* Archie Marshek. *Mus* Jerry Goldsmith. *Sd* Joe Edmondson, John Wilkinson. *Asst Dir* Howard Roessel. *Unit Prod Mgr* William C. Davidson. *Cost* Edith Head. *Makeup* Wally Westmore. *Hairstyles* Nellie Manley. *Sp Photog Eff* Paul K. Lerpae. *Proc Photog* Farciot Edouart.

Cast: David Janssen *(Sgt. Tom Valens)*, Ed Begley *(Capt. Roy Klodin)*, Keenan Wynn *(Sgt. Ed Musso)*, Sam Wanamaker *(Frank Sanderman)*, Lillian Gish *(Alice Willows)*, Stefanie Powers *(Liz Thayer)*, Eleanor Parker *(Mrs. Doris Ruston)*, George Grizzard *(Walt Cody)*, George Sanders *(Calvin York)*, Steve Allen *(Perry Knowland)*, Carroll O'Connor *(Paul Jerez)*, Joan Collins *(Joanie Valens)*, Walter Pidgeon *(Orville Ames)*, John Garfield, Jr. *(police surgeon)*, Bob Williams *(Judge Gerald Lucas)*, Jerry Dunphy *(TV newscaster)*, Romo Vincent *(Ira Garvin)*, Vito Scotti *(designer)*, Jean Carson *(cocktail waitress)*, Donald Curtis *(Dr. James Ruston)*, Brian Dunne *(Rusty)*, Norma Clark *(Shari Sherman)*.

Crime melodrama. Source: Whit Masterson, *711—Officer Needs Help* (New York, 1965). While on the lookout for a psychopathic killer, detective Sgt. Tom Valens spots a man running across the grounds of a housing development and orders him to stop. Instead, the man draws a gun, and Valens shoots him in self-defense. The dead suspect turns out to be a highly respected doctor, James B. Ruston, well-known for his philanthropic efforts on behalf of the Mexican people in Baja California. Because no trace of the slain doctor's gun can be found, Valens' story is discredited in the press, and he is accused of being a trigger-happy cop who murdered an innocent man. Suspended from field duty, he has only a short time to clear himself before being prosecuted on manslaughter charges. Desperate, Valens returns to the housing development and visits Alice Willows, an elderly patient of Dr. Ruston's, who tells him of the doctor's weekly visits and the little presents he always brought for her dog. While there Valens also encounters two other tenants—Walt Cody, a commercial airline pilot who seems sympathetic to his plight, and a dead model, the victim of an illegal abortion. Then Valens calls on Ruston's nurse, Liz Thayer, and learns that the doctor had recently been receiving large dividend checks from his broker, Calvin York. A short time later the nurse is found murdered, and an attempt is made upon Valens' life. Deducing that somehow there are connecting links between these facts, Valens recalls something Miss Willows said about burying her dog with all of Dr. Ruston's little presents. Calling upon Walt Cody for help, Valens unearths the dog's tiny coffin and finds the missing gun—a toy wooden pistol filled with heroin. Realizing that both Ruston and his broker were part of a narcotics ring, Valens accuses Cody of being the contact to fly the heroin to every large city on the Pacific coast. Trapped, Cody draws a gun and shoots. But Valens is only wounded, and he fires two rapid shots which knock Cody into the dog's open grave. *Police. Physicians. Philanthropists. Models. Air pilots. Nurses. Justifiable homicide. Injustice. Abortion. Murder. Smuggling. Guns. Heroin. Dogs.*

Note: Locations filmed in Los Angeles.

WARRENDALE (Canada) F6.5445
Allan King Associates. *For* Canadian Broadcasting Corp. *Dist* Grove Press. 16 Sep **1968** [New York opening]. Sd; b&w. 35mm. 100 min.

Prod-Dir Allan King. *CBC Exec Prod* Patrick Watson. *CBC Supv Prod* George Desmond. *Exec Dir* Patrick Watson. *Medical & Psychiatric Dir* Martin Fischer. *Photog* William Brayne. *Film Ed* Peter Moseley. *Sd* Russel Heise, Michael Billings, sd. *Prod Mgr* Gwen Gillie. *Prod Asst* Sarah Jennings.

Cast—The Staff at Warrendale: John Brown, Terry Adler, Robyn Rice, Ena Brocklehurst, Martin Fischer, Walter Gunn, Maurice Flood, Alvyn Austin.

Documentary. The film is a study of the Warrendale treatment center for emotionally disturbed children located near Toronto. The center attempts to foster a family attitude among the children by placing them, in groups of 12, in individual houses where parent-child relationships can develop between them and the trained staff. Unlike most mental institutions, Warrendale therapists believe in the expression of violence and encourage such outbreaks of emotion. Staff members physically wrap themselves around the child in a "holding" position so that the child can express his anguish without hurting himself or others. Because the children give vent to their strongest feelings, they come to know each other intimately; and hopefully with this knowledge comes acceptance of and concern for their friends. Tony, Carol, and Irene are three of the 12 children in one Warrendale house, and all of them are of normal intelligence but subject to frequent and extreme antisocial behavior. The angelic-looking Tony cannot speak without swearing; 15-year-old Carol still drinks milk from a baby bottle; and Irene, another teenager, vacillates between calm and despair in her desperate need for self-assurance. When the friendly cook in their house dies unexpectedly, the children react in diverse ways: two girls become hysterical, others are stunned into uncomprehending silence, and one boy professes total unconcern as a means of avoiding reality. Accompanied by the staff members, the children, sad but now subdued, attend the cook's funeral. *Children. Psychiatrists. Psychologists. Adolescence. Mental illness. Group therapy. Children's homes. Warrendale. Funerals. Toronto.*

Note: Filmed at the Warrendale treatment center in Feb and Mar 1966; intended for Canadian television release but not telecast because of obscene words used by some of the children. Original running time: 120 min. Opened in Montreal in Sep 1967; running time: 97 min.

WARRING CLANS (Japan) F6.5446
Toho Co. 19 Jul **1963** [Los Angeles showing]. Sd; b&w. 35mm (Tohoscope). 97 min.

Exec Prod Tomoyuki Tanaka. *Dir* Kihachi Okamoto.

Cast: Yuzo Kayama, Yuriko Hoshi, Makoto Sato.

Action melodrama. In feudal times a samurai resigns as bodyguard to a clan in protest over the rising corruption within the clan. A conflict begins between elements who wish to bring him back and those who are secretly smuggling arms to a rival army. *Samurai. Bodyguards. Smuggling. Political corruption.*

Note: Produced in Japan in 1963 as *Sengoku yaro.*

THE WARRIOR EMPRESS (France/Italy) F6.5447
Orsay Films–Documento Film. *Dist* Columbia Pictures. 17 May **1961** [Los Angeles opening; c1 May 1961; LP20414]. Sd; col (Eastman Color). 35mm (CinemaScope). 89 min. [Also 97 min; copyright length: 101 min.]

Prod Gianni Hecht Lucari. *Dir-Story* Pietro Francisci. *Screenplay* Ennio De Concini, Pietro Francisci, Luciano Martino. *Dub English Vers Dial* Paddy

Manning O'Brien. *Photog* Carlo Carlini. *Art Dir* Giulio Bongini. *Film Ed* Nino Baragli. *Mus* Angelo Francesco Lavagnino. *Sd* Oscar De Arcangelis. *Asst Dir* Pietro Nuccorini. *Prod Mgr* Marcello D'Amico. *Cost* Gaia Romanini.

Cast: Kerwin Mathews *(Phaon)*, Tina Louise *(Sappho)*, Riccardo Garrone *(Hyperbius)*, Antonio Battistella *(Paeone)*, Enrico Maria Salerno *(Melanchrus)*, Susi Golgi *(Actis)*, Alberto Farnese *(Laricus)*, Strelsa Brown *(priestess)*, Annie Gorassini *(Dyla)*, Lilly Mantovani *(Cleide)*, Aldo Fiorelli *(man with scar)*, Elda Tattoli *(Sappho's nurse)*, Isa Crescenzi *(peasant woman)*.

Costume melodrama. In ancient Mytilene, a young warrior, Phaon, leads a revolt against the rule of the despotic Melanchrus. Wounded in battle, Phaon takes refuge in the Temple of Aphrodite, where he falls in love with the beautiful Sappho; but when one of the temple maidens betrays him, he is forced to flee Mytilene by ship. After his vessel runs into a storm, he is taken by the Sirens to the undersea palace of Poseidon. When he is about to be sacrificed, Sappho saves his life by appealing to Amphitrite, Poseidon's wife. Returning to Mytilene, he masquerades as a king's guard and continues to lead his revolt against Melanchrus; but he is discovered, captured, and sentenced to death. Sappho saves him once again by agreeing to marry the villainous Hyperbius, the king's chief guard. Though Phaon is sent into exile, his men bring him back to Mytilene to carry on the rebellion. Now Phaon learns that Sappho has forsaken all men and pledged herself to Aphrodite; but once he has overthrown Melanchrus and Hyperbius, Phaon persuades her to renounce her vows and become his wife. *Royalty. Despots. Guards. Revolts. Human sacrifice. Disguise. Exile. Ships. Lesbos. Storms. Sappho. Phaon. Aphrodite. Poseidon. Amphitrite. Sirens (mythology).*

Note: Rome opening: Aug 1960 as *Saffo, venere di Lesbo*; running time: ca100 min; Paris opening: Nov 1960 as *Sapho*; running time: ca105 min.

THE WARRIORS see KELLY'S HEROES

WARRIORS 5 (France/Italy) F6.5448
Italian International Film–S. N. C. *Dist* American International Pictures. Oct **1962** [c17 Oct 1962; LP23588]. Sd; b&w. 35mm. 84 min. [Also reviewed at 91 min.]

Prod Fulvio Lucisano. *Assoc Prod* Salvatore Billitteri. *Dir* Leopoldo Savona. *Screenplay* Gino De Santis, Ugo Pirro, Leopoldo Savona. *Story* Lino Del Fra. *Photog* Claudio Racca. *Art Dir* Gastone Carsetti. *Film Ed* Gabriele Varriale. *Mus Comp & Cond* Armando Trovajoli. *Sd* Adriano Taloni. *Prod Dir* Mario Silvestri. *Prod Mgr* Mario Giannotti.

Cast: Jack Palance *(Jack)*, Giovanna Ralli *(Italia)*, Serge Reggiani *(Libero)*, Folco Lulli *(Marzi)*, Venantino Venantini *(Alberto)*, Franco Balducci *(Conti)*, Miha Baloh *(Sansone)*, Vera Murco *(Mafalda)*, Vida Levstik *(Ida)*, Ajsa Mesic *(Luisa)*, Valeria Sila *(old woman)*, Isabella Chiurco *(Carla)*, Guido Bertone *(Carlo)*, Bruno Scipioni *(Angelino)*.

War drama. Jack, an American paratrooper dropped behind the German lines in Italy for purposes of sabotage, is captured and imprisoned. He and four Italian cellmates escape. The Italians board a train for their homes, but the train is bombed, and in fleeing they again meet Jack, who asks their help in blowing up a bridge. The mission is accomplished, but the men are discovered by German troops, and in the ensuing battle, the Italian men are killed. Only Jack and Italia, a prostitute who has joined them, are left to fight. *Paratroops. Prisoners of war. Prostitutes. Prison escapes. Sabotage. Aerial bombardment. Trains. World War II. Germany—Army. United States Army. Explosions.*

Note: Filmed in Italy. Opened in Rome in 1962 as *La guerra continua*; in Paris in Sep 1962 as *La dernière attaque*; running time: 94 min. Copyright claimant: Alta Vista Productions.

WARUI YATSU HODO YOKU NEMURU see THE BAD SLEEP WELL

THE WASTREL (Italy) F6.5449
Lux Film–Tiberia Film. *Dist* Medallion Pictures. 4 Nov **1963** [New York opening]. Sd; b&w. 35mm. 84 min.

Prod Angelo Ferrara. *Exec Prod* Domenico Fazzari. *Dir* Michael Cacoyannis. *Adtl Dir* Giovanni Paolucci. *Screenplay* Michael Cacoyannis, Frederic Wakeman, Suso Cecchi D'Amico. *Photog* Piero Portalupi. *Art Dir* Arrigo Equini. *Set Decor* Ferdinando Ruffo. *Film Ed* Alberto Gallitti. *Mus* Angelo Francesco Lavagnino, Mario Zafred. *Sd* Ennio Sensi. *Asst Dir* Guido Chiola, Andrea Volpe, P. Leone. *Prod Mgr* Anis Nohra. *Cost* Gaia Romanini.

Cast: Van Heflin *(Duncan Bell)*, Ellie Lambetti *(Liana)*, Franco Fabrizi *(Rudi Veronese)*, Michael Stellman *(Cam)*, Fosco Giachetti *(Jug Hardy)*, Tiberio Mitri *(Macniff)*, Paul Muller *(Fatso)*, Clelia Matania *(Betsy)*, Aldo Pini *(Doc)*, Annie Gorassini *(Monique)*, Alix Talton.

Melodrama. Source: Frederic Wakeman, *The Wastrel* (New York, 1949). Duncan Bell, a wealthy alcoholic living in the West Indies, quarrels with his wife and leaves the cocktail party he is hosting to board his speedboat with his 10-year-old son, Cam. The boat explodes, and as the two cling to debris, Duncan reviews his past. He recalls how he met his wife, Liana, in Rome after the war and her supposed infidelity with Rudi, a playboy, in Paris. He also recalls the boredom which caused him to attempt to sail a yacht around the world before the crew abandoned ship, his subsequent acclaim as a hero, and the start of his drinking problem. In the water for 6 hours and close to death, Duncan begins to see things in perspective and determines to start his life afresh. *Alcoholism. Filial relations. Infidelity. Survival. Motorboats. Yachts. West Indies. Ship explosions.*

Note: Rome opening: Jan 1961 as *Il relitto*; running time: 90 min. Original running time: 115 min.

WATASHI GA SUTETA ONNA *see* **THE GIRL I ABANDONED**

WATCH THE BIRDIE   F6.5450

Cupid Productions. *Dist* American Film Distributing Corp. 3 Dec **1965** [Champaign, Illinois, showing]. Sd; b&w. 35mm. 74 min.

Prod-Dir Giulio Alti. *Assoc Prod* Barnett Daish. *Screenplay-Story* William L. Rose. *Dir Photog* Sean O'Reilly. *Set Dsgn* Marley Simon. *Ed* Phil Josephs. *Mus Supv* Melito Kazar. *Song:* "The Bird Is the Word" Doug Fowlkes, Rocky Roberts. *Sung by* Rocky Roberts and The Airedales. *Sd Rec* Raoul Hitchcock. *Asst Dir* Michael James. *Prod Mgr* James Johnson, prod mgr. *Makeup* Ted Bethel.

Cast: Richard B. Shull (*Cullen Lauterbach*), Wendy Wood, Susan Winters, Linda Baxter, Pamela Sears, Sam Menning, Marlene Starr, Julie Sinclair, Gina Lyons, Bill Rose, Elizabeth Ann Cooper, Vera Caw, Fred Buckley, George Carter, Herb Fogelson, Lynn Savage.

Melodrama. Four young women become trapped in Cullen Lauterbach's sordid pornography operation: Ursula, from Germany, is intrigued by the prospect of earning easy money; "jet-setter" Joanna suffers from nymphomania; Sandy, fresh from the country, longs for glamour and fame; while Marion is committed to becoming an actress. Cullen takes perverse pleasure in enslaving the women. From pin-up modelling, they are soon led to pose for photos aimed at the sadomasochist trade. He arranges an "action" session, forcing a dozen women to participate in bondage, flagellation, and fetishism. All the women are "invited" to attend Cullen's party where a stripteaser performs and sex films heighten the excitement. Ursula is forced to beg for her paycheck, and then she is terrorized into submitting to the lesbian advances of Miss Killin, Cullen's assistant. Cullen's writer indulges his necrophiliac passion by raping Sandy, who has collapsed in a drunken stupor. Attempting to escape, Joanna threatens her boss, and he drowns her in the toilet. Cullen then shoots the rapist and the party continues. Only Marion escapes to realize her goal, becoming an actress. *Pornographers. Models. Germans. Actors. Photographers. Pornography. Nymphomania. Ambition. Sadomasochism. Flagellation. Fetishism. Necrophilia. Rape. Murder. Striptease. Lesbianism. Drunkenness. Employer-employee relations. Sex exploitation films.*

WATCH THE BIRDIE ... DIE!   F6.5451

Jacques Descent Productions. *Dist* Canyon Distributing Co. ca **1968**. Sd; col. 35mm. 80 min.

Pres by Jacques Descent. A Jacques Descent Production. *Prod* Jacques Descent. *Dir* Don Doyle. *Screenplay* Peter John, writ. *Photog* "Serges". *Film Ed* John Bath. *Mus* John Bath.

Cast: Angela Carnon (*Cheryl Darwin*), Dennis Maloney (*Tom Bender*), Donna Bradley (*Rhonda Barnes*), Honor Lawrence (*Paula Sheridan*), Ron South (*Bill Sheridan*), Lynn Lyons (*Connie*), Michael Valentine (*Mr. Hunter*), Ervin Sanders (*Gary*), Kathy Ferrick (*piano player*), Harvey Shain (*Frank*), Linda Gardner (*Pearl*), Susan Gubernan (*Shirley*).

Melodrama. Bill Sheridan's mistress, playgirl Cheryl Darwin, seduces Tom Bender, head of an advertising agency, in order to become the agency's "Body Lotion Girl." Bill's wife Paula, a lesbian, obtains the commission to take the photographs for the "Body Lotion Girl" advertising campaign. Although Paula's marriage with Bill is loveless, she seeks to destroy his relationship with Cheryl by seducing the ambitious Cheryl during the photography session. Bill learns of his wife's intentions and attempts to thwart her. By the time he reaches the studio, however, Cheryl has already succumbed to Paula's advances. In a final act of desperation, Bill kills both women and commits suicide. *Mistresses. Photographers. Models. Advertising executives. Marriage. Lesbianism. Seduction. Murder. Suicide. Advertising. Photography.*

WATCH YOUR STERN (Great Britain)   F6.5452

G. H. W. Productions. *Dist* Magna Pictures. 26 Jul **1961** [Los Angeles opening]. Sd; b&w. 35mm. 88 min.

A Peter Rogers Production. *Prod* Peter Rogers. *Dir* Gerald Thomas. *Screenplay* Alan Hackney, Vivian A. Cox. *Photog* Ted Scaife. *Camera Op* Alan Hume. *Focus* Jimmy Devis. *Camera Grip* Reg Hall. *Art Dir* Carmen Dillon. *Set Dresser* Peter Lamont. *Draughtsman* Robert Laing, Alan Fraiser. *Film Ed* John Shirley. *Asst Ed* Jim Sibley. *Mus* Bruce Montgomery. *Ch Sd Engr* Cyril Crowhurst. *Sd Mix* Robert MacPhee. *Boom Op* Harry Fairbairn. *Sd Camera*

Charles Tasto. *1st, 2d & 3d Asst Dir* Jack Causey, David Tringham, Jim Brennan. *Prod Mgr* Frank Bevis. *Prod Sec* Gay Lucas. *Cont* Marjorie Lavelly. *Wardrobe Mistress* Pat Baden. *Cost Dsgn* Joan Ellacott. *Men's Wardrobe* Ben Foster. *Makeup* Alex Garfath. *Hairdresser* Biddy Chrystal. *Casting* Betty White, casting. *Still Photog* Albert Clarke. *Constr Mgr* Bert Mansell. *Prop Buyer* Ron Quelch. *Chargehand Electrn* L. Heathcoat.

Cast: Kenneth Connor (*O/S Blissworth*), Eric Barker (*Capt. David Foster*), Leslie Phillips (*Lieutenant Commander Fanshawe*), Joan Sims (*Ann Foster*), Hattie Jacques (*Agatha Potter*), Spike Milligan (*dockyard matey*), Eric Sykes (*2d dockyard matey*), Sidney James (*C.P.O. Mundy*), Ed Devereaux (*Commander Phillips*), David Lodge (*security sergeant*), Victor Maddern (*1st sailor*), Noel Purcell (*Admiral Sir Humphrey Pettigrew*), Robin Ray (*flag lieutenant*), George Street, Michael Brennan (*security guards*), Peter Howell (*admiral's secretary*), Arch Taylor (*coxswain*), Richard Bennett (*officer of the day*), Leila Williams (*wren driver*), Eric Corrie (*engineer officer*), Rory MacDermot (*3d security guard*).

Comedy. Source: Earle Couttie, *Something About a Sailor* (a play; production undetermined). Capt. David Foster is the commander of a British destroyer which has been chosen to test the firing of a new acoustic torpedo. When it misfires, the Admiralty sends a Scottish scientist to investigate. The torpedo plans, however, are not available: one copy has been burned, and another borrowed by a U. S. naval officer. To prevent Admiral Pettigrew from learning of the missing plans, Blissworth, a seaman with some knowledge of electronics, is disguised as the scientist, and copies of the ship's refrigeration system are substituted for the torpedo plans. Later, when it is learned that famous scientist Agatha Potter has also been assigned to the investigation, Blissworth is hastily dressed in women's clothes and succeeds in persuading Miss Potter to try his theories for modifying the torpedo while the real torpedo plans are being located. The results, however, are disastrous, and both Captain Foster and Blissworth are promptly returned to civilian life. *Scotch. Scientists. Female impersonation. Impersonation. Torpedoes. Great Britain—Royal Navy. Documentation.*

Note: London opening: Oct 1960.

WATERHOLE #3   F6.5453

Geoffrey Productions. *Dist* Paramount Pictures. 10 Oct **1967** [New York opening; c10 Oct 1967; LP34993]. Sd; col (Technicolor). 35mm (Techniscope). 95 min.

A Blake Edwards Production. *Prod* Joseph T. Steck. *Exec Prod* Owen Crump. *Assoc Prod* Ken Wales. *Dir* William Graham. *Screenplay* Joseph T. Steck, Robert R. Young. *Cinematog* Robert Burks. *Art Dir* Fernando Carrere. *Set Decor* Reg Allen, Jack Stevens. *Film Ed* Warren Low. *Mus* Dave Grusin. *Song:* "The Code of the West" Dave Grusin, Robert Wells. *Sung by* Roger Miller. *Sd* Joe Edmondson. *Asst Dir* Daniel J. McCauley, Mickey McCardle. *Prod Mgr* Clem Beauchamp. *Cost* Jack Bear. *Makeup* Emile Lavigne. *Hairstyles* Lorraine Roberson. *Sp Photog Eff* Paul K. Lerpae. *Sp Action Seq* Buzz Henry.

Cast: James Coburn (*Lewton Cole*), Carroll O'Connor (*Sheriff John Copperud*), Margaret Blye (*Billee Copperud*), Claude Akins (*Sgt. Henry Foggers*), Timothy Carey (*Hilb*), Bruce Dern (*deputy*), Joan Blondell (*Lavinia*), James Whitmore (*Captain Shipley*), Harry Davis (*Ben Agajanian*), Roy Jenson (*Doc Quinlen*), Robert Cornthwaite (*George, hotel clerk*), Jim Boles (*Corporal Blyth*), Stephen Whittaker (*soldier*), Ted Markland (*Army #2*), Rupert Crosse (*Prince*), Jay Ose (*bartender*), Buzz Henry (*cowpoke*).

Western farce. In the late 1880's, Cavalry Sgt. Henry Foggers and three confederates rob the Army of a fortune in gold bullion and then bury it in a waterhole in the desert. A short time later a professional gambler named Lewton Cole steals a map showing the whereabouts of the gold, kills one of the confederates, and sets out to recover the treasure. Stopping at the small town of Integrity, he locks up Sheriff Copperud and his deputy in their jailhouse, steals a horse, takes a few minutes off to seduce Copperud's pretty daughter, Billee, and once more rides off. Indignant over being so casually discarded, Billee screams that she has been raped and joins her father in pursuit of Lewton. Copperud overtakes him just as Lewton retrieves the gold. Although Lewton suggests they divide the bullion, Sergeant Foggers arrives and relieves them both of the treasure. Not to be outdone, Lewton returns to Integrity, where Foggers and his boys are enjoying themselves in the town brothel owned by Lavinia. During the wild gun battle that follows, Lavinia persuades one of Foggers' accomplices, Ben, to bury the gold in an isolated spot outside of town. But Billee also learns of the location and gets there first. Then Lewton appears and repeats his earlier seduction of the susceptible Billee. While she is standing naked behind a rock, he takes the gold and crosses the border into Mexico, leaving all concerned—but most of all Billee—furious and frustrated. *Gamblers. Adventurers. Outlaws. Sheriffs. Murder. Robbery. Seduction. Theft. Gold. Whorehouses. Jails. Deserts. United States Army—Cavalry. Chases. Documentation.*

Note: Location scenes filmed in the Mojave Desert, California.

WATERMELON MAN   **F6.5454**

Johanna Productions. *Dist* Columbia Pictures. 27 May **1970** [New York opening; c1 May 1970; LP37955]. Sd; col (Eastman Color). 35mm. 97 min. *MPAA rating* R.

Prod John B. Bennett. *Exec Prod* Leon Mirell. *Dir* Melvin Van Peebles. *Writ* Herman Raucher. *Dir Photog* W. Wallace Kelley. *Camera Op* Kyme Meade. *Asst Camera* Gene Liggett. *Art Dir* Malcolm C. Bert, Sydney Z. Litwack. *Set Decor* John Burton. *Film Ed* Carl Kress. *Mus* Melvin Van Peebles. *Orch* Robert Matthews. *Sd* Les Fresholtz. *Sd Ed* John Newman, Luke Wolfram. *Mus Ed* Ralph Hall. *Asst Dir* Sheldon Schrager, Joe Ellis. *Unit Prod Mgr* Sheldon Schrager. *Asst Prod Mgr* Joe Ellis. *Script Supv* Marshall Schlom. *Asst to the Prod* Ivan Beckoff. *Wardrobe* Gene Ashman, Edna Taylor. *Makeup Supv* Ben Lane. *Hairstyles* Virginia Jones. *Gaffer* David Curtis. *Key Grip* Carl Manoogian. *Still Photog* Ken Bell.

Cast: Godfrey Cambridge *(Jeff Gerber)*, Estelle Parsons *(Althea Gerber)*, Howard Caine *(Mr. Townsend)*, D'Urville Martin *(bus driver)*, Mantan Moreland *(counterman)*, Kay Kimberly *(Erica)*, Kay E. Kuter *(Dr. Wainwright)*, Scott Garrett *(Burton Gerber)*, Erin Moran *(Janice Gerber)*, Irving Selbst *(Mr. Johnson)*, Emil Sitka *(delivery man)*, Lawrence Parke *(1st passenger)*, Karl Lukas *(2d policeman)*, Ray Ballard *(3d passenger)*, Robert Dagny *(2d passenger)*, Paul H. Williams *(employment office clerk)*, Ralph Montgomery *(drugstore boss)*, Charles Lampkin *(Dr. Catlin)*, Vivian Rhodes *(Gladys)*, Erik Nelson *(doorman)*, Matthias Uitz *(cab driver)*, Rhodie Cogan *(Mrs. Johnson)*, Donna Dubrow *(receptionist)*, Frank Farmer *(Andy Brandon)*, Hazel Medina *(widow)*.

Farce. Bigoted suburbanite Jeff Gerber wakes up to discover that he has become black. Horrified, he indulges in an orgy of hot showers, bleaches, hair straighteners, and milk. Although his children Burton and Janice display little interest in their father's metamorphosis, his wife Althea is repelled, his physician Dr. Wainwright suggests that he consult a Negro doctor, and his neighbors pay him to leave the community. The head of his insurance agency, however, is delighted by the commercial possibilities of the transformation, and the blonde Norwegian secretary Erica is immediately enraptured. When his wife and children leave for Indianapolis Gerber rejects both the proposed exploitation of the black community and Erica's implied bigotry. Moving into the black community, he opens his own office, sheds his funereal wardrobe, and enrolls in a militant self-defense unit. *Negroes. Insurance agents. Housewives. Secretaries. Physicians. Neighbors. Norwegians. Militants. Metamorphosis. Suburban life. Race relations. Marriage. Bigotry. Indianapolis.*

Note: Working title: *The Night the Sun Came Out.*

WATUSI A-GO-GO *see* **GET YOURSELF A COLLEGE GIRL**

WAVELENGTH   **F6.5455**

Dist Film-Makers' Cooperative. 4 Jan **1968** [New York opening]. Sd and sd-on-tape; col. 16mm. 45 min.

Prod-Dir-Writ Michael Snow. *Photog* Michael Snow. *Film Ed* Michael Snow. *Mus* Tom Wolff. *Sd* Michael Snow.

Cast: Hollis Frampton *(man who dies)*, Joyce Wieland *(woman with bookcase/woman listening to radio)*, Amy Taubin *(woman on telephone/woman listening to radio)*.

Experimental film. A one-room loft, 80 feet long and having windows facing Canal Street in New York City, is shown in a continuous zoom throughout the duration of the film. At times, the image is seen in negative or burned-out white, and extreme changes in color and light intensity occur. The zoom is interrupted by four human events: two movers accompanied by a woman carry a bookcase into the room and leave; two women drink coffee and listen to a radio; the sound of breaking glass is heard, and a man staggers into the room and drops to the floor; and a woman enters, places a telephone call to "Richard," states that the man appears to be dead, and leaves. The zoom ends on a small photograph which is affixed to the far wall. The photograph, depicting waves, entirely fills the screen. In addition to the musical background and the speech of the characters, an electronic sound, a sine wave, begins shortly after the opening of the film and increases in frequency from 50 to 12,000 cycles per second in a glissando throughout the film's duration. *Death. Lofts. New York City—Canal Street.*

Note: Filmed in New York City.

WAVES OF CHANGE   **F6.5456**

MacGillivray/Freeman Films. Aug **1970**. Sd; col (Eastman Color). 16mm. 84 min. [Also 90 min.]

Prod-Dir-Writ Greg MacGillivray, Jim Freeman. *Photog* Greg MacGillivray, Jim Freeman. *Sp Photog Seq* Bud Browne. *Film Ed* Greg MacGillivray, Jim Freeman. *Mus Score* Val Johns.

Narrator: Greg MacGillivray.

With: Mark Martinson, Nat Young, Corky Carroll, Billy Hamilton, David Nuuhiwa.

Documentary. Champion surfers are shown riding the waves in Hawaii, California, France, and Portugal. The film features Mark Martinson, a young surfer who earns money making surfboards. *Surfers. Hawaii. California. France. Portugal.*

WAY OUT   **F6.5457**

Valley Forge Films. *Dist* Premiere Presentations. 4 Nov **1966** [Fort Wayne, Indiana, opening]. Sd; col (print by Movielab). 35mm. 102 min.

Prod-Dir Irvin S. Yeaworth, Jr. *Screenplay* Jean Yeaworth, Rudy Nelson, Shirley Nelson. *Photog* Thomas E. Spalding. *Lighting* Vincent Spangler. *Art Dir* Jasper Brinton. *Film Ed* John Bushelman. *Mus* Kurt Kaiser. *Mus Supv* Jean Yeaworth. *Song:* "Lament" John Giminez. *Sung by* Roy Hamilton. *Sd* Robert Clement, Fred De Croce. *Asst to the Prod* Joe Polinski.

Cast: Frank Rodriguez *(Frankie)*, James Dunleavy *(Jim)*, Sharyn Jiminez *(Anita)*, Jerry Rutkin *(Jerry)*, Starr Ruiz *(Stella)*, Gilbert Mesa *(Fats)*, Cecil White *(Che Che)*, Louis Colon *(Louie)*, Rudy Rosado *(Rudy)*, John Giminez *(Pop)*, Eddie James *(Harlem man)*, Naomi Perez *(Anita's mother)*, Eric Hutson *(Narco)*, J. R. Helton *(Snuffy)*, Norman Yager *(pusher)*, Chuck Painter *(policeman)*, Louis Sager *(guard)*.

Drama. Source: John Giminez, *The Addict* (a play; publication undetermined). Frankie, a motherless Puerto Rican who lives in a Bronx slum, finds it impossible to establish any rapport with his father, an alcoholic policeman. He becomes one of many teenaged drug addicts in his neighborhood and eventually lands in jail, where he is forced to kick his habit "cold turkey." Upon release, he learns that one of his friends has been killed by a policeman's bullet, that two others are currently in prison, and that a fourth has died of heroin overdose. In addition, his girl friend, Anita, has become a prostitute to pay for her drug habit. With this final blow, Frankie decides that his situation is hopeless and that he cannot and does not want to reform. A former pusher who has found peace through God follows Frankie when he goes for a fix and attempts to prevent him from renewing his habit. A fight ensues, the premises are raided by the police, and Frankie runs frantically through the streets, dodging bullets, until he finds sanctuary in a church. Physically and emotionally spent, he falls to his knees and prays desperately for spiritual guidance and strength. *Puerto Ricans. Police. Drug dealers. Drug addicts. Religion. Adolescence. Urban life. Filial relations. Prostitution. Slums. Jails. Heroin. Churches. New York City—Bronx.*

Note: Location scenes filmed in Bronx, New York, and Valley Forge, Pennsylvania.

WAY OUT LOVE *see* **THE TOUCH OF HER FLESH**

THE WAY-OUT SHRINE (Japan)   **F6.5458**

Toho Co. Oct **1967** [Los Angeles showing]. Sd; col? 35mm. [Feature film, length unknown.]

Cast: Hisaya Morishige.

Comedy? No information about the precise nature of this film has been found.

Note: Original title and release undetermined.

WAY OUT TOPLESS   **F6.5459**

Dist American Film Distributing Corp. 25 Jul **1967** [Maryland license]. Sd; b&w. 35mm. 66 min.

Prod Harry A. Wilson. *Dir* Lewis S. Francis.

Cast: Jenny Long, Pussy Kate, Carol Lewis, Linda Knight, Sue Johnson, Peggy Banks, Diana Peters, Evelyn Bennett, Star Lite, Rose Neal, Connie West, Ann-May Collins.

Sex film. A survey of the "topless" profession leads to some of the most famous striptease clubs in the United States, including nightclubs of Washington, D.C., and Baltimore. *Go-go dancers. Striptease. Nightclubs. Washington (District of Columbia). Baltimore.*

Note: Also known as *Way Out Top* and *Way Out Stopless.*

WAY OUT, WAY IN (Japan)   **F6.5460**

Daiei Motion Picture Co. Nov **1970** [Los Angeles showing]. Sd; col (Fuji Color). 35mm (Daiei Scope). 84 min.

Dir Michihiko Obimori. *Screenplay* Katsuya Suzaki. *Photog* Yoshihisa Nakagawa. *Art Dir* Shigeo Mano. *Mus* Harumi Ibe.

Cast: Yoko Namikawa *(Miho Sakai)*, Ichiro Ogura *(Hiroto Miyagawa)*, Saburo Shinoda *(Yuji Shibata)*, Kozaburo Onogawa *(Kenta Namiki)*, Akiko Naruse *(Yuki Nohara)*, Eiko Yanami *(Taeko)*, Sumire Mikasa.

Drama. Miho Sakai, a high school day student, wonders who occupies her desk during night classes and decides to leave a letter of encouragement for the student. Kenta Namiki, a night student who works during the day as a mechanic, finds the note, which sparks his resentment over the condescending attitude he feels the day students take toward the working class night students.

He leaves Miho an obscene note, enclosing some of his pubic hair. In retaliation, two day students, Hiroto Miyagawa and Yuji Shibata, raid the night students, barely escaping with the help of Taeko, a girl night student. Taeko seduces Hiroto, who is shocked at first but then becomes completely enslaved to sex. In revenge, Shibata rapes Yuki Nohara, Kenta's girl friend and the brightest of all the night students. Regretting his rash action, Shibata wants to marry Yuki, but he is scorned by Kenta when he asks for the night student's help. Eventually, the two boys become friends, helping to effect a reconciliation between the two student groups by staging a motorcycle race. *Students. Mechanics. Adolescence. Seduction. Rape. High school life. Revenge. Guilt. Motorcycle racing.*

Note: Released in Japan in May 1970 as *Kokosei bancho.*

WAY ... WAY OUT   F6.5461
Jerry Lewis Productions–Coldwater Productions–Way Out Co. *Dist* Twentieth Century-Fox Film Corp. 26 Oct **1966** [New York opening; c26 Oct 1966; LP33693]. Sd (Westrex); col (DeLuxe). 35mm (CinemaScope). 101 min. [Copyright length: 106 min.]

Prod Malcolm Stuart. *Dir* Gordon Douglas. *2d Unit Dir* Ray Kellogg. *Writ for the Screen* William Bowers, Laslo Vadnay. *Dir Photog* William H. Clothier. *Art Dir* Jack Martin Smith, Hilyard Brown. *Set Decor* Walter M. Scott, Stuart A. Reiss. *Film Ed* Hugh S. Fowler. *Mus Comp & Cond* Lalo Schifrin. *Lyr:* "Way ... Way Out" Hal Winn. *Sung by* Gary Lewis and the Playboys. *Sd* Al Overton, David Dockendorf. *Asst Dir* Joseph E. Rickards. *Unit Prod Mgr* Nathan R. Barragar. *Coörd for Jerry Lewis Productions* Joe E. Stabile. *Cost Dsgn* Moss Mabry. *Makeup* Ben Nye. *Hairstyles* Margaret Donovan. *Sp Photog Eff* L. B. Abbott, Emil Kosa, Jr., Howard Lydecker.

Cast: Jerry Lewis (*Peter*), Connie Stevens (*Eileen*), Robert Morley (*Quonset*), Dennis Weaver (*Hoffman*), Howard Morris (*Schmidlap*), Brian Keith (*General Hallenby*), Dick Shawn (*Igor*), Anita Ekberg (*Anna*), William O'Connell (*Ponsonby*), Bobo Lewis (*Esther Davenport*), Sig Ruman, Milton Frome (*Russian delegate, see note*), Alex D'Arcy (*Deuce*), Linda Harrison (*Linda*), James Brolin (*Ted*), Michael Jackson (*TV announcer*).

Science fiction comedy. In 1994, two U. S. weathernauts stationed on the moon are accused of attacking Anna Soblova, a Russian citizen manning the Soviet lunar station. The situation becomes critical, and the American Weather Director, Harold Quonset, decides to replace the two male weathernauts with a married couple. Peter Mattemore, the only eligible man for the job, is persuaded to marry astronomer Eileen Forbes, although she stipulates that they are to be married in name only. On the moon, Peter and Eileen find the two bewildered, half-crazed U. S. weathernauts, as well as the voluptuous Anna and her unmarried moon companion, Igor. Peter helps settle a squabble between Anna and Igor, and the two couples celebrate with "instant vodka." Later, the badly hungover Peter is informed by Earth that the two Russians are suspected of having planted a bomb in the U. S. weather station. Although the threat passes, another crisis develops when Anna discloses that she is pregnant, and Igor agrees to marry her. The Russians exult in the news that the first baby born on the moon will be a Russian. However, Eileen reveals that she persuaded Anna to feign pregnancy in order to trick Igor into marriage. Peter enthusiastically agrees with Eileen to compete with the Soviets for the distinction of becoming the first moon parents, and, with peace restored, the world awaits the results of the contest. *Astronomers. Russians. Astronauts. Marriage of convenience. Drunkenness. Pregnancy. Space travel. Duplicity. Bombs. The Future. The Moon.*

Note: Way Out Co. is credited as production company only in copyright registration information. Film continuity credits Sig Ruman with the role of Russian delegate and Milton Frome as American delegate, while Milton Frome is credited as Russian delegate by other sources, and Ruman is not credited.

THE WAY WE LIVE NOW   F6.5462
East Coker Co. *Dist* United Artists. 27 May **1970** [New York opening; c27 May 1970; LP40174]. Sd; col (De Luxe). 35mm. 110 min. *MPAA rating* R.

Prod-Dir Barry Brown. *Exec Prod* Saul Lapidus. *Screenplay* Barry Brown, Daniel Tamkus. *Dir Photog* Barry Brown. *Film Ed* Barry Brown. *Mus* Nate Sassover, Daniel Tamkus. *Sd* Chris Newman. *Asst Dir* Robert Barth.

Cast: Nicholas Pryor (*Lionel Aldridge*), Joanna Miles (*Amelia*), Lois Smith (*Jane Aldridge*), Linda Simon (*Rosalind Leopold*), Pat McAneny (*Laurie*), Rebecca Darke (*Martha*), Sydney Walker (*Lincoln*), Linda Blair (*Sara Aldridge*), Samantha Jones (*Samantha*), Eugene Wood (*Mr. Aldridge*), Miriam Phillips (*Mrs. Aldridge*), Morris Strassberg (*Mr. Leopold*), James McMurray.

Drama. Source: Warren Miller, *The Way We Live Now* (Boston, 1958). Lionel Aldridge, 33-year-old director of a Madison Avenue advertising agency, is dissatisfied with his domestic life. Leaving his wife, Jane, and 8-year-old daughter, Sara, he rents a bachelor apartment. At a party given by his old friend Martha and her husband, Lincoln, he meets Laurie, a dancer. Although they sleep together, Aldridge remains unsatisfied. Retaining his own apartment, the executive then moves in with television producer Rosalind Leopold. Aldridge's next affair is with Amelia, his old college girl friend, now a wealthy Boston matron. Although Amelia and Aldridge enjoy a 4-day idyll, the matron refuses to divorce her husband. Disgusted by Aldridge's promiscuity, Jane files for divorce. When Aldridge attempts to seek solace with Laurie, the dancer has a nervous breakdown and is committed to a sanitarium. Aldridge then plans a weekend rendezvous with Amelia, who fails to join him because of servant problems. Initially depressed, Aldridge's spirits rise when he realizes that he can start life anew. *Advertising executives. Television producers. Dancers. Promiscuity. Infidelity. Marriage. Insanity. Wealth. Family life. Divorce. Sanitariums. New York City.*

Note: Filmed in and around New York City.

THE WAY WEST   F6.5463
Harold Hecht Corp. *Dist* United Artists. 24 May **1967** [New York opening; c24 May 1967; LP34490]. Sd; col (DeLuxe). 35mm (Panavision). 122 min.

Prod Harold Hecht. *Dir* Andrew V. McLaglen. *Screenplay* Ben Maddow, Mitch Lindemann. *Dir Photog* William H. Clothier. *Art Dir* Ted Haworth. *Asst Art Dir* Edwin O'Donovan. *Set Decor* Robert Priestley. *Mus* Andre Previn. *Cond* Andre Previn. *Titl Song* Bronislaw Kaper, Mack David. *Sung by* The Serendipity Singers. *Sd* Jack Solomon, John Romness, Bud Thompson. *Asst Dir* Terry Morse, Jr., Newt Arnold, Tim Zinnemann. *Prod Mgr* Lee Lukather. *Prod Coörd* John Cutts. *Script Supv* John Franco. *Cost* Norman Koch. *Wardrobe* Gordon Dawson, Edna Taylor. *Makeup Supv* Frank McCoy. *Hairstyles* Jean Udko. *Sp Eff* Daniel W. Hays. *Dial Dir* Willie Schorr. *Prop Master* Tom Coleman. *Constr Coörd* Hank Wynands. *Stunt Coörd* Hal Needham.

Cast: Kirk Douglas (*Sen. William J. Tadlock*), Robert Mitchum (*Dick Summers*), Richard Widmark (*Lije Evans*), Lola Albright (*Rebecca Evans*), Michael Witney (*Johnnie Mack*), Stubby Kaye (*Sam Fairman*), Sally Field (*Mercy McBee*), Katherine Justice (*Amanda Mack*), Michael McGreevey (*Brownie Evans*), Connie Sawyer (*Mrs. McBee*), Harry Carey, Jr. (*McBee*), Elisabeth Fraser (*Mrs. Fairman*), William Lundigan (*Michael Moynihan*), Anne Barton (*Mrs. Moynihan*), Roy Barcroft (*Masters*), Eve McVeagh (*Mrs. Masters*), Paul Lukather (*Turley*), Peggy Stewart (*Mrs. Turley*), Stefan Arngrim (*Tadlock, Jr.*), Jack Elam (*Weatherby*), Hal Lynch (*Big Henry*), Timothy Scott (*Middle Henry*), John Mitchum (*Little Henry*), Roy Glenn (*Saunders*), Patric Knowles (*Colonel Grant*), Nick Cravat (*Calvelli*), Gary Morris (*Paw-Kee-Mah*), Michael Lane (*Sioux chief*), Eddie Little Sky, Michael Keep (*Sioux braves*), Clarke Gordon (*Caleb Greenwood*), Ken Murray (*Hank*), Paul Wexler (*barber*), Mitchell Schollars (*Indian boy*), Jack Coffer, Everett Creach, James Burk, Gary McLarty (*cattlemen*).

Western drama. Source: Alfred Bertram Guthrie, Jr., *The Way West* (New York, 1949). In 1843, a wagon train led by widowed Sen. William J. Tadlock leaves Independence, Missouri, for the long trek across the Oregon Trail. Foremost among the settlers are: Dick Summers, a seasoned trail scout with failing eyesight; farmer Lije Evans, his wife Rebecca, and their 16-year-old son, Brownie; newlyweds Johnnie and Amanda Mack; Sam Fairman and his wife, who are awaiting the birth of their child; and the slovenly McBee family. After several weeks on the trail, Johnnie, frustrated by his bride's frigidity, makes love with the flirtatious Mercy McBee during a drunken celebration; later that night, he shoots at what he thinks is a wolf and kills the son of a Sioux chief. Tadlock tries to evade the vengeful Indians by driving the wagon train into a buffalo herd, but the settlers are overtaken, and he is forced to hang Johnnie as retribution for the slaying. Mercy, pregnant with Johnnie's child, then accepts Brownie's offer of marriage. During a cattle crossing, Tadlock's son is killed in a stampede, and the senator is so disgusted by his own resulting emotional breakdown that he orders his Negro slave to whip him. In time, the settlers tire of the hardships and consider changing course from Oregon to California; to avert this, Tadlock fakes a smallpox scare, forcing the Army to order the train into the open plains. The lie is eventually exposed, and Lije attacks Tadlock savagely and assumes command. Eventually the caravan reaches its destination, with only a deep gorge remaining to be crossed. When Rebecca Evans shows the settlers Tadlock's design for a great city in Oregon, the ostracized leader is welcomed back into the group and permitted to supervise the lowering of people, animals, and dismantled wagons down the steep ravine. As the senator descends the cliff, however, Amanda Mack, driven to insanity by her husband's hanging, cuts the rope, and Tadlock plummets to his death. After his burial, the settlers journey down the Columbia River, leaving Summers behind. *Settlers. Farmers. Scouts—Frontier. Sioux Indians. Newlyweds. Teases. Widowers. Politicians. Negroes. Frontier and pioneer life. Family life. Infidelity. Frigidity. Pregnancy. Marriage. Revenge. Murder. Blindness. Flogging. Insanity. Capital punishment. Wagon trains. Smallpox. Funerals. Independence (Missouri). Oregon. Oregon Trail. Columbia River. United States Army—Cavalry. Stampedes. Cattle. Buffalo.*

WAYLAID WOMEN see **INDECENT**

THE WAYSIDE PEBBLE (Japan)   **F6.5464**
Tokyo Eiga Co. *Dist* Toho Co. Oct **1962** [Los Angeles showing].
Sd; b&w. 35mm (Tohoscope). 104 min.
Dir Seiji Hisamatsu. *Screenplay* Kaneto Shindo. *Photog* Shojiro Sugimoto.
Mus Ichiro Saito.
Cast: Hiroyuki Ota *(Goichi Aikawa)*, Setsuko Hara *(Oren Aikawa)*, Hisaya
Morishige *(Shogo Aikawa)*, Tatsuya Mihashi *(Tsugino)*, Kyu Sazanka
(Chusuke), Yusuke Takita, Masao Oda.
Drama. In a village in 1910 Japan, Goichi, a young boy, dreams of someday
attending a private school, though his parents cannot afford to send him. A
bookseller befriends Goichi, but Shogo, his father, still refuses to send him to
school and instead sells Goichi's services to a callous merchant. After Goichi's
mother, Oren, dies, he refuses to work for the merchant and sets off on a train
for Tokyo to begin a new life. *Children. Merchants. Booksellers. Indentured
servants. Runaways. Filial relations. Poverty.*
Note: Released in Japan in 1960 as *Robo no ishi.*

WAYWARD WIVES   **F6.5465**
Mitam Productions. **1968.** Sd; b&w. 35mm. 64 min.
Drama. Deserted in a strange town by her husband, Rosi seeks solace in a
local bar. Solicited by its proprietor, Rosi finds herself an inmate of a brothel
run by a gang of thieves. Chief among the prostitutes is Samantha, a lesbian who
teaches Rosi the art of love. While personally administering brutal beatings to
defiant women, the boss rewards his band with bonus orgies. Rosi is freed,
however, when police raid the house in search of the thieves. *Thieves. Police.
Saloon keepers. Prostitution. Lesbianism. Desertion. Orgies. Gangs. Bars.
Whorehouses.*

WE A FAMILY   **F6.5466**
Great Empire Films. *Dist* Hollywood Cinemart. 29 Nov **1968** [Champaign,
Illinois, showing]. Sd; col. 35mm. 70 min.
Exec Prod Elsa Singman. *Dir-Writ* J. Van Hearn.
Cast: Deborah Downey *(Baby)*, Jennie Lee *(Mom)*, Revel Quinn *(Suzy)*,
Ralph Esor *(Dad)*, Jerry Patterson *(Don)*, Erika Andrea *(Jill)*, John Hamlet
(Bob), Steve Goodwyn *(butler)*, Tanya Zhivago *(Betty)*, Cha Cha O'Brien,
Jacqueline Stokes *(sales girls)*.
Comedy-drama. Baby, the youngest member of her family, sets out to
acquire sexual experience. Her own sexual liberation causes a chain reaction:
her father follows suit by seducing the maid; her mother finds satisfaction with
the butler, an alcoholic, and the roughneck chauffeur, who loves money; and
Baby's sister Jill loses her much-professed virginity and becomes a skillful tease.
The entire family joins in a wild party in the servants' quarters. *Chauffeurs.
Butlers. Housemaids. Sisters. Teases. Family life. Group sex. Promiscuity.
Alcoholism. Infidelity. Virginity.*

WE ALL GO DOWN   **F6.5467**
Combined Films. *Dist* Cinex Film Industries. 3 Dec **1969** [New York
showing]. Sd; b&w. 35mm. 73 min.
Prod-Dir Gerard Damiano. *Dir Photog* Eric Breitbart. *Asst Photog* Tommy
Goetz, George Feinberg. *Ed* Jerry Gerard. *Mus* Horn O Plenty. *Sd* Tony
Foresto. *Stills* David Gerard.
Cast: Bill Doukas *(Pete)*, Alice Haley *(Nancy)*, Justine Simmon *(Peggy)*,
Kelly Durtis *(Judy)*, Daniel Moge *(Dick)*, Bob Shoffues *(Burt)*, James Burnette
(Jay), Ada McAllister *(Carrol)*, Jayson Troy *(pusher)*, Sylvia Brown, Marie
Hoff, Donny Lee, Xona Knodoff, Mike Hall, Merry Smith, Jayson Stone.
Melodrama. A mad whirlwind of unrestricted sexual activity and
experimentation with drugs ends in violence and death for members of today's
generation. *Sexuality. Drugs.*
Note: Also known as *We All Go.*

WE ARE ALL CHRIST see **THE YOUNG SINNER**

WE ARE ALL NAKED (Canada/France)   **F6.5468**
Citel–Canada–Eurocitel. *Dist* Citel/USA. Jan **1970.** Sd; b&w. 35mm
(Totalscope). 82 min.
Pres by Testament Films. *Prod-Dir* Claude Pierson. *Screenplay* Huguette
Boisvert. *English Dial* Jack Curtis. *Photog* Jean-Louis Picavet. *Mus* Jean-Paul
Mengeon. *Titl Song English Lyr* Arnold Drake. *Sung by* Charles Duval. *Sd*
Jean-Louis Bertucelli.
Cast: Alain Saury *(stranger)*, Jacques Normand *(father)*, Rita Maiden
(mother), Catherine Ribeiro *(niece)*, Gérard Desalles *(son)*, Isabelle *(daughter)*,
Georges Beauvilliers *(worker)*, Max Montavon *(crony)*, René Roussel *(young
seaman)*, Boniface *(old seaman)*.
Drama. An impoverished family lives in a crumbling blockhouse on the bleak
Picardy shore in northern France. The father, once a respected fisherman, is
now an alcoholic; his wife, having lost all interest in him, has casual sex with
local fishermen. The household also is comprised of a young daughter, a

retarded son, and a teenaged niece. A stranger employed at a nearby gravel
works appears and disrupts their lives. He seduces the mother; and one day,
while he and she are making love in the sand, they are observed by the retarded
son. Frightened, he runs into quicksand and is pursued by his mother; both
drown when the tide comes in. The stranger now turns his attention to the
niece, and they leave together. The father and daughter are left alone to face
their uncertain future. *Fishermen. Children. Strangers. Family life. Poverty.
Alcoholism. Seduction. Infidelity. Mental retardation. Quicksand. Picardy.*
Note: Released in Canada in 1966 as *Ils sont nus*; running time: 86 min.

WE DO IT!   **F6.5469**
Mitam Productions. 12 Aug **1970** [Champaign, Illinois, showing]. Sd; col
(Eastman Color). 35mm. 73 min.
Cast: Gay Lee *(Wilma)*.
Melodrama. Housewives Wilma and Jeanne stop at a downtown bar after
shopping, and there they are persuaded by Harry, the bartender, to throw good
luck coins into a fountain. The coins activate mesmerizing lights in a statue, and
the women immediately fall under Harry's spell and become his sex slaves,
prostituting themselves day after day for the monetary gain of Harry and his
boss, Matson, who makes films of the orgies that ensue and sells them to private
clubs for stag parties. Fear of blackmail makes the women unable to resist
Harry's demands, but eventually Wilma informs the police and brings an end
to the racket. *Housewives. Bartenders. Pimps. Hypnotism. Blackmail. Orgies.
Lesbianism. Bars.*

WE HAVE ONLY ONE LIFE (Greece)   **F6.5470**
Finos Films. *Dist* Greek Motion Pictures. 23 Jun **1963** [New York opening].
Sd; b&w. 35mm. 116 min.
Dir-Writ George Tzavellas. *Photog* Dinos Katsouridis. *Mus* Manos
Hadjidakis.
Cast: Dimitri Horn *(Kleon)*, Yvonne Sanson *(Bibi)*, Basil Avlonitis *(guard)*,
Christ Tzagneas *(bank president)*.
Melodrama. Kleon, a dull-witted and persecuted bank clerk, embezzles some
money and briefly enjoys the favors of Bibi, who leaves him when the money
runs out. Kleon serves a period of time in jail, and when he is released he is still
dreaming of large sums of money. *Bank clerks. Embezzlement. Dreams.
Wealth.*
Note: Released in Greece in 1958.

WE SHALL RETURN   **F6.5471**
United International Pictures. *Dist* Cari Releasing Corp., Cinema-Video
International, Inc. 15 Feb **1963** [Miami Beach, Florida, opening]. Sd; b&w.
35mm. 92 min.
Prod Robert M. Carson. *Dir* Philip S. Goodman. *Screenplay* Pat Frank.
Photog Ted Saizis, Vincent Saizis. *Film Ed* David Tucker. *Mus* Edgar
Summerlin. *Prod Supv* Sidney N. Berry.
Cast: Cesar Romero, Tony Ray, Linda Libera, Ramon Rodrigues, Mario
Rodrigues, Nina Ortiz, Paul Daniel.
Drama. Before the ill-fated Bay of Pigs invasion, a wealthy Cuban planter,
his younger son and the young man's fiancée flee to Miami where they meet
the elder son, a member of a "Free Cuba" political group. The younger son is
to return to Cuba and set up contact with other anti-Castro groups. Discovering
that his older son has attempted to reveal the landing place to pro-Castro forces
on the island, the planter shoots him to prevent betrayal. *Cubans. Political
refugees. Planters. Filial relations. Anti-communism. Perfidy. Cuba—History—
Invasion 1961. Miami. Fidel Castro Ruz.*
Note: Filmed in 1961 on location in Saint Augustine and Daytona Beach,
Florida. Working title: *Force of the Wind.*

WE STILL KILL THE OLD WAY (Italy)   **F6.5472**
Cemo Film. *Dist* Lopert Pictures. 28 Feb **1968** [New York opening; c8 Oct
1967; LF38]. Sd; col (Technicolor). 35mm. 92 min.
Prod Giuseppe Zaccariello. *Assoc Prod* Luigi Millozza. *Dir* Elio Petri.
Screenplay Elio Petri, Ugo Pirro. *Dir Photog* Luigi Kuveiller. *Art Dir* Sergio
Canevari. *Film Ed* Ruggero Mastroianni. *Mus* Luis Enriquez Bacalov. *Sd* Mario
Bramonti. *Asst Dir* Marcello Crescenzi. *Prod Mgr* Felice D'Alisera. *Cost*
Luciana Marinucci. *Makeup* Pier Antonio Mecacci.
Cast: Gian Maria Volontè *(Paolo Laurana)*, Irene Papas *(Luisa Roscio)*,
Gabriele Ferzetti *(Rosello)*, Salvo Randone *(Professor Roscio)*, Luigi Pistilli
(Arturo Manno), Mario Scaccia *(The Priest)*, Laura Nucci *(Paolo's mother)*,
Leopoldo Trieste *(The Member of Parliament)*, Franco Tranchina *(Dr. Antonio
Roscio)*, Luciana Scalise *(Rosina)*, Anna Rivero *(Manno's wife)*, Giovanni
Pallavicino *(Ragana)*, Orio Cannarozzo *(The Police Inspector)*, Carmelo
Oliviero *(The Archpriest)*, Tanina Zappalà.
Crime melodrama. Source: Leonardo Sciascia, *A ciascuno il suo* (Turin,
1966). The murder of two Sicilians, Arturo Manno and Dr. Antonio Roscio,
is assumed by the local townspeople and police to be a crime of honor against
Manno because of his illicit love affair with Rosina, a peasant girl. However,

Prof. Paolo Laurana, an idealistic intellectual, remains unconvinced that the murders were committed by Rosina's father and two brothers, and he begins his own investigation. After diligent inquiry, with virtually no help from the close-mouthed villagers, Paolo becomes certain that the real motive behind the killings was to silence Dr. Roscio's criticism of Mafia power and that Manno was slain only as a coverup. Aided by Roscio's widow, Luisa, the professor uncovers a diary left by Roscio in which he indicates his plan to denounce an unnamed political figure whom Paolo suspects is Luisa's cousin Rosello. After receiving anonymous letters threatening his life, Paolo is drawn into an ambush by Rosello, but he is allowed to escape when he reveals that he has Roscio's incriminating diary. Luisa, whom Paolo now loves, lures him to a deserted beach where he learns that she is Rosello's mistress. He is brutally attacked by hired killers and buried alive in a sandstone quarry. The professor's death permits Luisa and Rosello to marry and the town to keep its secret about the true motives behind the three murders. *Professors. Intellectuals. Widows. Mistresses. Hired killers. Police. Cousins. Infidelity. Murder. Political corruption. Village life. Diaries. Sicily. Mafia.*

Note: Location scenes filmed in Cefalù, Palermo, and the Villa Floria. Released in Italy in 1967 as *A ciascuno il suo;* running time: 90 min. Registered for copyright in the United States under the German title *Zwei Särge auf Bestellung.*

WE WANT TO LIVE ALONE see **FATHER CAME TOO**

WE WILL REMEMBER (Japan)   **F6.5473**
Toho Co. *Dist* Official Films. Apr **1966** [Los Angeles showing]. Sd; col (Eastmancolor). 35mm (Tohoscope). 134 min.
Prod Sanezumi Fujimoto. *Dir-Writ* Zenzo Matsuyama. *Story* Ikuma Dan. *Photog* Asaichi Nakai. *Mus* Ikuma Dan. *Sd* Akira Saito.
Cast: Hisaya Morishige *(Kiyoshi Kodama),* Chang Mei Yao *(Yoichi Mashio),* Keiju Kobayashi *(Masaya Nihei),* Daisuke Kato *(Akira Kubo),* Kon Omura, Yuzo Kayama, Kiyoshi Kodama, Yoichi Mashio, Yukihiko Gondo, Kazuo Suzuki, Chutaro Togin, Yoko Fujiyama.
War drama. Near the end of World War II a number of young Japanese, eager to stay out of combat, volunteer for an army band undergoing an accelerated training course. The methods employed include a strong measure of discipline similar to that used by the army to prepare men for combat, and the young men complain of the harassment to which they are subjected. At the end of the course, the band is sent to the Chinese front to boost the troops' morale. On the way, they witness the havoc and destruction the war has caused, and eventually they are attacked and their numbers decimated by Chinese guerrillas. The few survivors are sent to the Philippines as prisoners of war. *Chinese. Guerrillas. Prisoners of war. Combat zone life. Basic military training. Military bands. Massacres. Sino-Japanese Conflict 1937-45. China. Philippines.*
Note: Released in Japan in 1965 as *Senjo ni nagareru uta.*

WEAKER SEX (Japan)   **F6.5474**
Toho Co. 9 Aug **1961** [Los Angeles opening]. Sd; col? 35mm. 87 min.
Dir Toshio Sugie.
Cast: Franky Sakai, Hajime Hana, Yoshie Mizutani, Michiyo Yokoyama, Ichiro Arishima, Mitsuko Kusabue, Sadako Sawamura, Kuji Asami, Hara Chisako, Kiyoshi Kodama.
Comedy. No information about the precise nature of this film has been found.
Note: Released in Japan in Dec 1960 as *Ah jonan.*

WEB OF FEAR (France/Spain)   **F6.5475**
Luxor Films–Capitole Films–Balcázar P. C. *Dist* Comet Film Distributors. Aug **1966**. Sd; b&w. 35mm. 92 min.
Prod Gérard Ducaux-Rupp, Aimos Mezo. *Dir* François Villiers. *Screenplay* Jacques Sigurd, Jean-Pierre Ferrière. *Photog* Manuel Berenguer. *Art Dir* Pierre Thévenet. *Film Ed* Christian Gaudin. *Mus* Claude Bolling.
Cast: Michèle Morgan *(Constance),* Dany Saval *(Pascale),* Simón Andreu *(Hugo),* Maria Pacôme *(Marie-Cécile),* Claude Rich *(student),* Georges Rigaud *(Sartori),* Carlos Casaravilla *(detective).*
Drama. Source: Jean-Pierre Ferrière, *Constance aux enfers* (Paris, 1963). From the window of her Paris apartment, Constance, a lonely 38-year-old widow, is able to observe the promiscuous behavior of a young starlet who lives across the courtyard. One night Constance hears a violent quarrel and looks out of her window in time to see the starlet being strangled by her lover. When the man, Hugo, pleads with her for mercy, Constance allows him to hide in her apartment, and soon she becomes his mistress. She is then blackmailed by a night watchman who knows she is harboring a murderer. After being forced to pay out almost all of her savings, Constance learns that the starlet is still alive and that the murder was part of a blackmail plot conceived by Hugo, the watchman, and the starlet. Humiliated and outraged, she plans her revenge. After indicating to Hugo that she has received more blackmail letters than he

knows about, Constance convinces him that he is being doublecrossed by his accomplices. Furthermore, she uses photographs to suggest to Hugo that the starlet has another lover. Her strategy works; Hugo is driven to such jealousy that he strangles the starlet. *Widows. Actors. Watchmen. Murder. Frameup. Blackmail. Revenge. Jealousy. Paris.*
Note: Opened in Paris in Feb 1964 as *Constance aux enfers;* running time: 90 min; in Madrid in Feb 1964 as *Un balcón sobre el infierno.*

WEB OF PASSION see **LEDA**

WEB OF VIOLENCE (Italy/Spain)   **F6.5476**
Liber Film–Hesperia Films. *Dist* Governor Films. **1966**. Sd; col (Eastman Color). 35mm. 90 min.
Prod Ottavio Poggi. *Dir* Nick Nostro. *Screenplay* Fernando Cerchio, Mino Giarda, Juan Cobos, Ottavio Poggi. *Photog* Emilio Foriscot. *Art Dir* Carlos Viudes. *Film Ed* Magdalena Pulido. *Mus* Franco Pisano. *Prod Supv* Luis Laso Moreno.
Cast: Brett Halsey *(Walter),* Margaret Lee *(Cristina),* Pepe Calvo, Julio Peña, Daniele Vargas, Irán Eory, Emilio Messina, Enzo Cerusico, Mirko Ellis, Aldo Cristiani, Renato Chiantoni, Valentino Macchi, Renzo Palmer.
Crime melodrama. Source: Sergio Donati, *L'altra faccia della luna* (publication undetermined). Walter, a Roman journalist who has lost his job, witnesses the kidnaping of his former girl friend, Lisa, who left him to marry Fassi, an older man. Walter visits Fassi but is told that his relationship with Lisa ended some time ago. Walter investigates and learns that Lisa was abducted by Lo Vecchio, a drug smuggler and gangster. Lisa's corpse is discovered in the sea, and Walter is offered assistance in exposing the murderers by Cristina, an old friend. Walter is taken prisoner and tortured by Lo Vecchio, who evidently seeks to retrieve incriminating documents about which Walter knows nothing. Helped to escape by Cristina, Walter finds the evidence and uses it to force Lo Vecchio to identify the head of the smuggling ring. At a meeting with the gangsters, Fassi is revealed to be their chief, and he is killed with Lo Vecchio in the ensuing gun battle. Cristina remains with Walter and helps him to regain his confidence and his job. *Journalists. Smugglers. Gangsters. Abduction. Murder. Drugs. Torture. Blackmail. Rome. Documentation. Evidence.*
Note: Exteriors filmed in Italy. Released in Italy as *Tre notti violente;* Madrid opening: Dec 1966 as *Tres noches violentas;* running time: 92 min.

WEDDING NIGHT (Ireland)   **F6.5477**
Ardmore–Krasne Productions. *Dist* American International Pictures. May **1970** [c3 Jun 1970; LP39863]. Sd; col (Print by Movielab). 35mm. 99 min. *MPAA rating* GP.
Pres by Philip N. Krasne, Lee Davies. *Prod* Philip N. Krasne. *Dir* Piers Haggard. *Screenplay* Robert I. Holt, Lee Dunne. *Adtl Dial* Piers Haggard. *Story* Robert I. Holt. *Photog* Ray Sturgess. *Art Dir* James Weatherup. *Film Ed* Kenneth Crane. *Mus Comp & Cond* Cyril Ornadel. *Song:* "Mady" Piers Haggard. *Sung by* Scott Peters. *Sd Ed* Michael Kelleher. *Sd Rec* Liam Saurin. *Asst Dir* Tom Hayes.
Cast: Dennis Waterman *(Joe O'Reilly),* Tessa Wyatt *(Mady),* Alexandra Bastedo *(Gloria),* Eddie Byrne *(Tom),* Martin Dempsey *(Father Keegan),* Maire O'Donnell *(Kate),* Patrick Laffan *(Dr. Farnum),* Garden Odyssey Enterprise *(rock group),* Peter Mayock, Eileen Page, Trevor Bailey, Chris Curran, Vernon Hayden, Cecil Nash, Christian Lyons, Martin Lyons.
Melodrama. Following the Catholic wedding of Joe and Mady in Dublin, the bride's mother, who is bearing her eighth child, has a miscarriage and dies. Blaming her father's sexual appetite for the death of her mother, and plagued by a childhood fear of intercourse, Mady refuses to let Joe touch her on their wedding night. With patience and compassion, Joe agrees to return alone to London, where he works as a commercial artist, while Mady remains in Dublin to help her father and younger brothers and sisters. When Mady eventually joins Joe, her problems have intensified, and she invents excuses for delaying the consummation of their marriage. Motivated both by concern and frustration, Joe tries to force himself on Mady, but he succeeds only in driving her to the brink of hysteria. When Joe seeks comfort with Gloria, a former girl friend, Mady returns to Dublin. Her doctor advises the use of contraceptives to quell her fear of pregnancy, but the local priest reminds her of the church law prohibiting birth control. Unable to persuade the priest that her marriage should be annulled, Mady collapses and is hospitalized. After she attempts suicide, Joe rushes to her bedside, and Mady realizes that perhaps she can overcome her fears. *Catholics. Commercial artists. Physicians. Priests. Miscarriage. Death. Marriage. Frigidity. Suicide. Weddings. Birth control. Dublin. London.*
Note: Location scenes filmed in Dublin. Produced in Ireland in 1969 as *I Can't ... I Can't.*

THE WEDDING PARTY   **F6.5478**
Powell Productions–Ondine Presentations. *Dist* Ajay Film Co. 9 Apr **1969** [New York opening]. Sd; b&w. 35mm. 90 min.

Prod-Dir-Writ Cynthia Munroe, Brian De Palma, Wilford Leach. *Photog* Peter Powell. *Film Ed* Cynthia Munroe, Brian De Palma, Wilford Leach. *Mus* John Herbert McDowell. *Sd* Henry Felt, Betsy Powell, Jim Swan. *Sp Eff* B & O Film Specialists.

Cast: Jill Clayburgh *(Josephine Fish)*, Charles Pfluger *(Charlie)*, Valda Setterfield *(Mrs. Fish)*, Raymond McNally *(Mr. Fish)*, Jennifer Salt *(Phoebe)*, John Braswell *(Reverend Oldfield)*, Judy Thomas *(Celeste)*, Sue Ann Converse *(nanny)*, John Quinn *(Baker)*, Robert De Niro *(Cecil)*, William Finley *(Alistair)*, Richard Kollmar, Jr. *(Jean-Claude/Hindu/Klaus)*, Helmuth Pfluger *(Charlie's father)*.

Comedy. Two days before his marriage to Josephine Fish, Charlie arrives at the island estate of his fiancée's wealthy parents. He is disturbed to see that Mrs. Fish is too busy with elaborate party preparations to give him much attention, that Mr. Fish is an emasculated husband who paints a bleak picture of marriage, and that Josephine is guarded by a protective nanny who frustrates all their efforts to be alone. Despite the added presence of Josephine's relatives, Charlie tries to maintain his cheerful optimism, but he begins to balk at matrimony upon realizing that Josephine has already mapped out and restricted his future activities. After he is forced to miss his own bachelor party, Charlie tries unsuccessfully to rekindle the romance between Josephine and one of her former suitors, a Hindu. Later, he decides to try to get caught seducing Celeste, the mousy church organist, but discovers too late that she is willing to cooperate, provided their lovemaking is not discovered. As the wedding day approaches, Charlie decides to leave Josephine waiting at the altar. He makes a desperate dash for freedom by foot, bicycle, hitchhiking, and rowboat, but his friends give chase and capture him in time for the ceremony. *Bachelors. In-laws. Nursemaids. Hindus. Organists. Marriage. Weddings. Wealth. Seduction. Islands.*

Note: Location scenes filmed in Shelter Island, New York and Jim Thorpe, Pennsylvania.

WEDDING PRESENT see **THE TURKISH CUCUMBER**

WEE-GEE BROAD   **F6.5479**
Kirt Films International. *Dist* Distribpix, Inc. 6 Dec **1967** [New York showing]. Sd; col. 35mm. 65 min.

Sex film. Newlyweds Wendy and Charlie begin marriage with great gusto, but Charlie's happiness is soon marred by his obsessive nightmares. He consults a fortune-teller, and he sees in a crystal ball that Wendy has strange sexual preferences. While he is looking into the magic globe, he is entertained by several of the fortune-teller's lovely assistants, who respond to his every whim and fancy. *Newlyweds. Fortune-tellers. Prostitutes. Sexual practices. Dreams.*

Note: Also known as *Wee Gee*.

WEEK-END À ZUYDCOOTE see **WEEKEND AT DUNKIRK**

LES WEEK-ENDS DE NÉRON see **NERO'S MISTRESS**

WEEKEND (Denmark)   **F6.5480**
Bent Christensen Filmproduktion. *Dist* Cinema-Video International, Inc. 26 Apr **1964** [New York opening]. Sd; b&w. 35mm. 84 min.

Prod Bent Christensen. *Exec Prod* Preben Philipsen. *Dir* Palle Kjaerulff-Schmidt. *Screenplay* Klaus Rifbjerg. *Photog* Georg Oddner. *Asst Photog* Henrik Fog-Møller. *Art Dir* Erik Aaes. *Film Ed* Maj Soya. *Mus* Erik Moseholm. *Sd* Jon Branner. *Asst Dir* Jetter Kehlet, Allan de Waal. *Prod Mgr* Finn Aabye.

Cast: Jens Østerholm *(Lars)*, Birgit Brüel *(Tove)*, Willy Rathnov *(Kjeld)*, Elsebet Knudsen *(Bet)*, Jesper Jensen *(Knud)*, Bente Dessau *(Ilse)*, Erik Kühnau *(Jan)*, Lotte Tarp *(Birthe, the maid)*, Jørgen Beck *(innkeeper)*, Carl Johan Hviid *(Herr Cornelius)*, Inga Reim *(Fru Cornelius)*, Hugo Herrestrup *(shooting gallery attendant)*, Tove Bang *(cloakroom attendant)*, Erik Paaske *(man on the beach)*, Masja Dessau *(Tanja)*, Tine Kjaerulff-Schmidt *(Tine)*, Morten Kjaerulff-Schmidt *(Morten)*, Jens Oliver Henriksen.

Drama. Knud, a teacher, and his wife, Bet, are staying in a rented seaside cottage with their two children. They invite two other couples, Kjeld, another teacher, and Tove, his wife, and Jan, a master builder, and his wife, Ilse, and their daughter. Also along are Birthe, the teenage babysitter for the daughter, and a footloose bachelor named Lars. Throughout the afternoon they indulge in so much eating and drinking that there is a loosening of spirits and sexual inhibitions. Knud and Ilse start an affair; Lars and Tove pair off; Bet consoles Jan; and Kjeld goes off on his own. In the morning, Kjeld tries to rape Birthe as she is changing her clothes on the beach. He returns to the cottage, Jan attacks him, and they are separated by Lars and Knud. The weekend over, the couples return home. *Schoolteachers. Architects. Bachelors. Babysitters. Infidelity. Mate swapping. Drunkenness. Rape. Beaches.*

Note: Opened in Copenhagen in Oct 1962.

WEEKEND (France/Italy)   **F6.5481**
Comacico–Copernic Films–Lira Films–Ascot Cineraid. *Dist* Grove Press. 30 Sep **1968** [New York opening]. Sd; col (Eastman Color). 35mm. 103 min.

Dir-Writ Jean-Luc Godard. *Photog* Raoul Coutard. *Film Ed* Agnès Guillemot. *Mus* Antoine Duhamel. *Mus:* "Piano Sonata K. 576" Wolfgang Amadeus Mozart. *Song:* "Allô, allô, tu m'entends" Guy Béart. *Sd* René Levert. *Asst Dir* Claude Miler. *Prod Mgr* Ralph Baum, Philippe Senné. *English Subtitl* Sonya Mays Friedman.

Cast: Mireille Darc *(Corinne)*, Jean Yanne *(Roland)*, Jean-Pierre Kalfon *(leader of the FLSO)*, Valérie Lagrange *(his moll)*, Jean-Pierre Léaud *(Saint-Just/man in phone booth)*, Yves Beneyton *(member of FLSO)*, Paul Gégauff *(pianist)*, Daniel Pommereulle *(Joseph Balsamo)*, Yves Alfonso *(Gros Poncet)*, Blandine Jeanson *(Emily Brontë/girl in farmyard)*, Ernest Menzer *(cook)*, Georges Staquet *(tractor driver)*, Juliette Berto *(girl in car crash/member of FLSO)*, Anne Wiazemsky *(girl in farmyard/member of FLSO)*, Virginie Vignon *(Marie-Madeleine)*, Jean Eustache *(hitch-hiker)*, Monsieur Jojot, Isabelle Pons, Laszlo Szabo, J. C. Guilbert, Michel Cournot.

Allegory. Despite their often-expressed desire to kill each other, an upper middle-class Parisian couple, Corinne and Roland, decide to visit Corinne's wealthy mother one weekend in order to get some money. Before their departure, Corinne has a session with her analyst and describes the details of a recent orgiastic experience. Once on the road, the couple unfeelingly make their way through a seemingly endless traffic jam of battered, burning cars and mutilated bodies. They then encounter a series of real and imaginary characters: an Algerian garbage collector who speaks on behalf of black power, and his partner, an American Negro; a pianist performing Mozart in a farmyard; a hitchhiker hippie who identifies himself as Joseph Balsamo (the notorious charlatan Alessandro di Cagliostro of 18th century Europe), Saint-Just, Emily Brontë (whom the couple set afire), and Tom Thumb. When the hippie ("the son of God and Alexandre Dumas") offers to reward Corinne and Roland for giving him a lift, the couple ask for a new sports car, natural blonde hair, and a weekend with James Bond. Instead, the hippie transforms some wrecked automobiles into a flock of sheep. When the couple finally reach their destination, they brutally murder Corinne's mother because she refuses to give them any money. On their way home, they are captured by a tribe of primitive anarchists dedicated to waging guerrilla war against their natural enemy, the bourgeoisie. Although Roland is killed, Corinne joins the band and ends her first day by eating a cannibal stew—fully aware that it contains her husband's remains. *Psychiatrists. Algerians. Negroes. Pianists. Hitchhikers. Hippies. Anarchists. Trash collectors. Greed. Murder. Death. Cannibalism. Matricide. Automobiles. Automobile accidents. Louis Antoine Léon de Saint-Just. Emily Brontë. Tom Thumb. Alessandro di Cagliostro. Sheep.*

Note: Opened in Paris in Dec 1967 as *Le Week-end*; running time: 95 min.

WEEKEND AT DUNKIRK (France/Italy)   **F6.5482**
Paris-Films Production–Interopa Film. *Dist* Twentieth Century-Fox Film Corp. 18 May **1966** [New York opening; c17 Dec 1964; LF2]. Sd; col (Eastman Color, U. S. prints by DeLuxe). 35mm (Franscope). 102 min. [Copyright length: 120 min.]

Prod Robert Hakim, Raymond Hakim. *Dir* Henri Verneuil. *Screenplay* François Boyer, Robert Merle. *Adapt* François Boyer. *Photog* Henri Decaë. *Art Dir* Robert Clavel. *Set Decor* Pierre Charron. *Film Ed* Claude Durand. *Mus Comp & Cond* Maurice Jarre. *Sd* René Longuet. *Asst Dir* Claude Pinoteau. *Prod Mgr* Ralph Baum. *Cost* Jean Zay, Leon Zay. *Sp Eff* Karl Baumgartner.

Cast: Jean-Paul Belmondo *(Sergeant Maillat)*, Catherine Spaak *(Jeanne)*, Georges Géret *(Pinot)*, Jean-Pierre Marielle *(Father Pierson)*, Pierre Mondy *(Dhery)*, Marie Dubois *(Helene)*, François Périer *(Alexandre)*, Kenneth Haigh *(Atkins)*, Ronald Howard *(Robinson)*, Nigel Stock *(burnt man)*, Albert Rémy *(Virrel)*, François Guérin *(lieutenant)*, Jean-Paul Roussillon *(blackguard)*, Michel Barbey *(Cirilli)*, Christian Barbier *(Giant)*, Pierre Vernier *(happy undertaker)*, Raoul Delfosse *(infantryman)*, Marie-France Mignal *(Antoinette)*, Marie-France Boyer *(Jacqueline)*, Christian Melsen *(1st German parachutist)*, Rolf Spath *(2d German parachutist)*, Robert Bazil, Julien Verdier, Gerard Darrieu, Robert Deslandes, Dominique Zardi, Alan Adair, Donald O'Brien, Anthony Stuart, Robert Napier, Rene Penetra, Paul Préboist, Robert Rollis, Charles Bouillaud.

War drama. Source: Robert Merle, *Week-end à Zuydcoote* (Paris, 1949). In June, 1944, the beaches at Zuydcoote near Dunkirk are filled with thousands of British and French troops trapped between the sea and the advancing Germans. A vast fleet of ships and small boats are evacuating the British, but the fate of the French is uncertain. In an abandoned ambulance on the beach, four men discuss their prospects of surviving. Sergeant Maillat wants to escape on one of the boats and continue fighting the Nazis; Dhery, a cowardly opportunist, wants only to get away; Pierson, a chaplain, decides to work in a hospital; and Alexandre will take a chance on getting by on his wits. As he attempts to persuade the British to evacuate him, Maillat meets and falls in love with Jeanne, a young woman who refuses to leave her home in spite of the incessant bombing that has left her nearly hysterical with fright. Maillat returns to the ambulance and discovers that Alexandre is dead and his other friends have left; he kills two of his own men for attempting to rape Jeanne. He then manages to persuade her to try to escape with him, and they arrange to meet on the beach the next day. But Maillat is killed by an exploding shell when Jeanne reaches their rendezvous spot at the ambulance. *Chaplains. Opportunists. War heroes. Rape. Cowardice. Bombardment. Beaches. Ambulances. World War II. Dunkirk. Zuydcoote. Germany—Army. Great Britain—Army. France—Army.*

Note: Produced on location in France and released there in 1964 as *Weekend à Zuydcoote*; running time: 120 min. Italian title: *Week-end a Zuydcoote.*

WEEKEND BABYSITTER see **WEEKEND WITH THE BABYSITTER**

WEEKEND, ITALIAN STYLE (France/Italy/Spain)   F6.5483
Ultra Film–Les Films du Siècle–Altura Films. *Dist* G. G. Productions, Marvin Films. 2 Aug **1967** [Rochester, New York, opening]. Sd; col (Eastman Color). 35mm. 90 min. *MPAA rating* R.

Dir Dino Risi. *Screenplay–Orig Story* Dino Risi, Ennio De Concini. *Photog* Armando Nannuzzi. *Art Dir* Mario Chiari. *Film Ed* Franco Fraticelli. *Asst Ed* Emilio Rodríguez Oses. *Mus* Lelio Luttazzi. *Song:* "Take a Weekend Italian Style" *(English version)* Bob Swanson. *Vocalists* The Beejays. *Prod Mgr* José Manuel M. Herrero.

Cast: Enrico Maria Salerno *(Enrico Marletti)*, Sandra Milo *(Giuliana Marletti)*, Jean Sorel *(Sergio)*, Daniela Bianchi *(Signora Dominici)*, Trini Alonso *(Clelia Valdemari)*, Alicia Brandet *(Swedish vamp)*, Lelio Luttazzi *(Count Bellanca)*, Raffaele Pisu *(Pasqualino)*, Leopoldo Trieste *(Ferri)*, Ana Castor *(Signora Pellini)*, Pedro Rodríguez de Quevedo *(Gustavo Valdemari)*, Véronique Vendell, Helga Linè, Pepe Calvo, Liselotte Pulver.

Comedy. Unable to bear the sweltering heat of Rome, civil engineer Enrico Marletti decides to join his wife for a summer weekend by the sea. As soon as he arrives, however, he is caught up in a never-ending round of introductions to the many acquaintances of his wife, Giuliana. Instead of relaxing, Enrico must fight off noisy children, practical jokers, emptyheaded young women, and boring married couples. Though hoping to spend some time alone with Giuliana, he ends up following her from one loud party to another. Jealousy also adds to his problems when Enrico discovers his wife being kissed by a handsome bachelor. After Giuliana has convinced him that she could never be unfaithful to him, Enrico returns to Rome. Falling into bed, he at last finds the peace and quiet he had vainly sought in Riccione. *Engineers—Civil. Bachelors. Children. Marriage. Vacations. Jealousy. Resorts. Rome. Riccione. Adriatic Sea.*

Note: Filmed on location in Riccione, Italy. Opened in Rome in Jan 1966 as *L'ombrellone*; running time: 105 min; in Madrid in Feb 1967 as *El parasol*; running time: 87 min. Also known as *Weekend Wives.*

WEEKEND LOVER   F6.5484
Boxoffice International Pictures. *Dist* Boxoffice International Film Distributors. 2 Jul **1969** [Champaign, Illinois, showing]. Sd; col (Eastman Color). 35mm. 88 min.

Pres by Harry Novak. *Prod-Dir* Dwayne Avery. *Assoc Dir* M. K. Evans. *Writ* M. K. Evans, Dwayne Avery. *Photog* Sam Rayven. *Lighting Dir* Richard Aguilar. *Camera Asst* Ken Stewart. *Titl Art* Earl Marshall. *Ed* Sam Rayven. *Mus* Vic Lance. *Perf by* Taurus 8, The UniSouls. *Sd Rec* Robert B. Lee. *Prod Mgr* Bethel Buckalew. *Prod Asst* Stephen Tompkins. *Still Photog* CinemaGraphics.

Cast: Vic Lance *(Scott Bennett)*, Chris Mathis *(Kerry Chandler)*, Antoinette Maynard *(Ginger Bennett)*, Sydney Carlysle *(Norman Snitte)*, Elizabeth Thomas *(girl on bike)*, Jay Edwards *(truck driver)*, Deirdre Nelson *("Virgo")*, Miki MacDonald *(Candice Wellington)*, Bruce Douglas *(Phil Brooks)*, Jeri Lynn *(1st girl)*.

Drama. Each weekend, Scott Bennett walks along a California desert highway dressed as a Navy submariner, conspicuously available to attractive female drivers, who frequently join him in his reserved motel room. By this reliable method, he meets Kerry Chandler. They enjoy a weekend of romance, visiting a local fair where the carnival thrills are made even wilder by some specially-enriched homemade brownies. When Monday morning comes, Kerry awakens to find herself alone. Scott has returned to civilian life, where he works as an interviewer for a computerized dating service. Slowly realizing his love for Kerry, he returns to tell her the truth, but it is too late. Scott's sister, Ginger, who believes that his weekends are spent "rockhounding," takes note of his loneliness and checks on his computer compatibility with her roommate. Back on the desert, Scott tries to lose himself in a familiar activity. He is rescued from a burly truck driver by a motorcycle-driving nymphomaniac, who wears him to a frazzle. Ginger's college friend turns out to be Kerry, who plans revenge

when she learns that Scott is the "sailor" who jilted her in the desert, but she softens when she learns how much he cares for her. When Scott finally escapes from the man-hungry motorcyclist, he finds Ginger's car parked in front of his motel room, and Kerry waiting for him inside. *Sailors. Motorcyclists. Brother-sister relationship. Roommates. Truckdrivers. Impersonation. Seduction. Nymphomania. Computer dating services. Motels. Fairs. California.*

Note: Filmed in Hollywood. Also known as *Weekend Lovers.*

WEEKEND OF FEAR   F6.5485
JD Productions. 4 Feb **1966** [Los Angeles opening]. Sd; b&w. 35mm. 63 min.

Prod-Dir-Writ Joe Danford. *Photog* Saul N. Leyton. *Film Ed* Joe Danford. *Mus* William H. Lockwood.

Cast: Micki Malone *(Judy)*, Kenneth Washman *(young deafmute)*, Tory Alburn *(Tom)*, Ruth Trent *(Mrs. Harris)*, Dianne Danford *(Connie)*, James Vaneck *(Jack)*, Kurt Donsbach *(man in car)*, Jill Banner *(Carol)*.

Melodrama. Mrs. Harris, a middle-aged widow who is attracted to Tom, the boyfriend of young Judy, hires a deafmute to terrorize Judy and cause her seemingly accidental death. *Deafmutes. Widows. Hired killers. Jealousy. Middle age. Murder.*

Note: Filmed on location in and around Los Angeles.

WEEKEND REBELLION   F6.5486
Cinetron Corp. *Dist* CineWorld Corp. 7 May **1970** [New Orleans opening]. Sd; col. 35mm. 85 min. *MPAA rating* GP.

Prod Barry Mahon. *Song:* "Paranoia" Jerry Burchard. *Songs:* "Paranoia," "On Time" *Perf by* Grand Funk Railroad.

Cast: Grand Funk Railroad, Billy Joe Royal, The Swinging Medallions, The Tams, Mike Sharp *(themselves)*.

Documentary. Thousands of college students converge on Daytona Beach, Florida, during spring vacation. The young Northerners shed their winter clothing in favor of scanty beach costumes. They relax away from the authority of parents and professors, the local police providing the only restraint. Sunbathing, football games played with beer cans, diving from the balconies, driving on the beach, dancing, car watching, and girl watching are all part of the day's activities. At night there are parties in jam-packed motel rooms, go-go dancing in the city nightclubs, and couples making love on the beach. Northern motorcycle clubs make their own distinctive impression on the scene, dressed in black leather, with their girl friends hanging on behind. Rock music provides a continuous background to the action. *Students. Musicians. Motorcyclists. Sunbathing. Vacations. Rock and roll. Spring. Daytona Beach.*

THE WEEKEND WARRIORS   F6.5487
Jim Dempsey & Associates. *Dist* Champion Film Productions. Nov **1966**. Sd; col. 35mm. 90 min.

Prod Leonard Mishkind, Jim Dempsey, Sol Gordon, Albert B. Lefton.

Featuring: Gordon Collett, Connie Kalitta, Bill Jenkins, Don Garlits.

Sports documentary. A documentary of the two divisions of drag racing—gas and fuel racing—filmed at the National Hot Rod Association's 1964 summer nationals in Indianapolis and the 1965 winter nationals in Phoenix. Footage of a California custom car show is also shown. Racing preparations, both technical and mechanical, are shown along with action taking place in the pit. The film concludes with views of the camping facilities provided at the grounds for participants and spectators who come from all parts of the country to share in the excitement of the races. *Automobile racing. Indianapolis. Phoenix (Arizona). California. National Hot Rod Association.*

WEEKEND WITH FIFI   F6.5488
Dragon Films. 8 Oct **1969** [New York showing]. Sd; col. 35mm. [Feature film, length unknown.]

Prod Ramon Gar Len. *Camera* T. Ehrich.

Sex film. A housewife discovers that her husband plans to spend the weekend with Fifi, his secretary. She surprises the lovers, intending to kill them, but instead she is talked into joining them in bed. *Secretaries. Marriage. Infidelity. Troilism.*

A WEEKEND WITH LULU (Great Britain)   F6.5489
Hammer Film Productions. *Dist* Columbia Pictures. 1 Nov **1961** [Saint Louis opening; c1 Oct 1961; LP24051]. Sd; b&w. 35mm. 91 min. [Copyright length: 89 min.]

Prod-Writ Ted Lloyd. *Exec Prod* Michael Carreras. *Dir* John Paddy Carstairs. *Story* Ted Lloyd, Val Valentine. *Dir Photog* Ken Hodges. *Exterior Photog* Jack Mills, photog. *Camera Op* Brian West. *Focus* Wally Fairweather. *Art Dir* John Howell. *Art Dept Asst* Helen Thomas. *Supv Ed* James Needs. *Ed* Tom Simpson. *Asst Ed* Brian Smedley-Aston, Gillian Scott. *Theme Mus Comp* Trevor H. Stanford. *Adtl Mus & Orch* Tony Osborne. *Sd Rec* Bill Salter. *Sd Ed* Allan Morrison. *Boom Op* Tom Buchanan. *Sd Camera Op* Doug Barnett. *1st, 2d & 3d Asst Dir* Christopher Sutton, Richard Coward, Michael Klaw. *Prod Mgr* Jacques De Lane Lea. *Location Mgr* Colin Brewer. *Cont* Splinters Deason.

Prod Sec Jill Langley. *Wardrobe Mistress* Maude Churchill. *Makeup Artist* Dick Bonnor-Moris. *Hairstyles* Bill Griffiths. *Casting Dir* Stuart Lyons. *Prod Buyer* Charles Townsend. *Still Photog* Robert Penn. *Constr Mgr* Jack Bolam. *Grip* M. Walters.

Cast: Bob Monkhouse *(Fred Scrutton)*, Leslie Phillips *(Timothy Gray)*, Alfred Marks *(Comte de Grenoble)*, Shirley Eaton *(Dierdre Proudfoot)*, Irene Handl *(Florence Proudfoot)*, Sidney James *(café patron)*, Kenneth Connor *(British tourist)*, Sydney Tafler *(stationmaster)*, Russ Conway *(French pianist)*, Eugene Deckers *(Inspector Larue)*, Graham Stark *(Chiron)*, Harold Berens *(card seller)*, Tutte Lemkow *(Léon)*, Stuart Hillier *(Flying Corsican)*, Andreas Malandrinos *(lodge keeper)*, Ernst Walder *(count's chauffeur)*, Judith Furse *(Madame Bon-Bon)*, Denis Shaw *(bar patron)*, Keith Pyott *(count's butler)*, Gordon Rollings *(Humper)*, Edie Martin *(lodgekeeper's wife)*, Harold Kasket *(Bon Viveur)*, Alexis Bobrinskoy *(mayor)*, Heidi Erich *(Lulubelle)*, Marie Devereux, Eve Eden, Sally Douglas, Janette Rowsell.

Comedy. Tim, a young Englishman who hopes to escape the city for a holiday weekend with his girl friend, Dierdre, borrows his buddy Fred's ice cream van to help tow his trailer to the coast. His romantic expectations are dashed, however, when Dierdre's mother, Florence, decides to join the three of them for a weekend in "Lulu," as the van is called. Fred's sense of direction is found wanting the next morning when the foursome suddenly find themselves in France, having mistakenly caught the channel ferry somewhere along the way. After varied episodes with cyclists, a brothel madam, a seller of dirty postcards, and several local gendarmes, the van is rushed back to England on an air freighter when it is mistaken for an ambulance. *Bicyclists. Madams. Police. Vacations. Filial relations. Trailers. Whorehouses. France.*

Note: Opened in London in May 1961; running time: 89 min.

WEEKEND WITH THE BABYSITTER   F6.5490

Dundee Productions. *Dist* Crown International Pictures. 15 Jul **1970** [New Orleans opening]. Sd; col (Deluxe). 35mm. 93 min. *MPAA rating* R.

Prod George E. Carey. *Assoc Prod* Wesdon Bishop. *Dir* Don Henderson. *Screenplay* James E. McLarty. *Orig Story* George E. Carey, Don Henderson. *Dir Photog* Jack Steeley. *Film Ed* Dick Elliott. *Mus Comp & Cond* Robert O. Ragland. *Song* Robert O. Ragland, Marcia Waldorf. *Sung by* The Opposition. *Asst Dir* Carl Olsen. *Prod Mgr* Ellen Bailey. *Psychedelic Lighting* Castle Lighting.

Cast: George E. Carey *(Jim Carlton)*, Susan Romen *(Candy Wilson)*, James Almanzar *(Rich Harris)*, Luanne Roberts *(Mona Carlton)*, Anthony Victor *(Sancho)*, Bob Bernard *(A.K.)*, Guy Edwards *(Leon)*, Steve Vinovich *(Snitch)*, Annik Borel *(Doris)*, Gloria Hill *(Mary Mary)*, James E. McLarty *(Smitty)*, Patrick Whyte *(salesman)*, Pat Welch *(waitress)*, Ellen Bailey *(operator)*, Susan L. Stoner *(Marge)*, Easton Herd *(Michael Carlton)*.

Romantic melodrama. Film director Jim Carlton is revising the script for his new film in his Hollywood Hills home when Candy Wilson, a babysitter, arrives. Through a misunderstanding, Candy arrives just as Carlton's wife, Mona, is taking their child, Michael, to visit her mother for the weekend. Candy stays when Jim insists that he pay her for her trouble, and she reads through his script while he is out of the room. She tells Jim that the script, about the younger generation, is phony, and she offers to show Jim how youth really are. She takes him to the Sunset Strip to meet her friends A.K., Snitch, and Mary Mary. He smokes some marijuana with them, gets high, and is put to bed. Meanwhile, Mona, who is secretly a heroin addict, has left her son with her mother and gone to meet dope peddler Rich. Rich forces her to let him use her husband's boat to collect a consignment of drugs from Mexico and smuggle them back to the States. Mona goes along with Rich and his assistants Sancho and Leon. The pickup is made, but they are warned by ship-to-shore telephone to stay away for a few more hours. On Saturday morning, Candy and Jim, having spent the night together, go to a motorcycle race and fly Jim's private plane to his mountain retreat. When Jim learns on Monday that Mona is on the boat and in trouble, he and Candy fly back, and he circles the bay to find his boat. Rich, in an effort to save his drug cache, rams the boat into a pier and makes off with the dope. He is stopped by an entire motorcycle gang led by Candy, who has been alerted by Jim, and they destroy the drugs they don't want, take the rest, and leave Rich tied up. As the police close in, Jim and Mona are reunited while Candy rides away calling out "Ciao." *Motion picture directors. Babysitters. Drug addicts. Drug dealers. Hostages. Motorcycle gangs. Infidelity. Smuggling. Youth. Marijuana. Narcotics. Yachts. Airplanes. Los Angeles—Sunset Strip.*

Note: Also known as *Weekend Babysitter.* Motorcycle sequences filmed at Perris Motorcycle Recreation Center.

WEEKEND WIVES *see* WEEKEND, ITALIAN STYLE

THE WEIRD LOVE MAKERS (Japan)   F6.5491

Nikkatsu Corp. *Dist* Audubon Films. 18 Dec **1963** [Washington, D. C., opening]. Sd; b&w. 35mm (CinemaScope). 75 min.

Pres by Radley H. Metzger. *Dir* Koreyoshi Kurahara. *Screenplay* Nobuo Yamada. *Photog* Yoshio Mamiya. *Film Ed* Akira Suzuki. *Mus* Toshiro Mayuzumi.

Cast: Tamio Kawaji *(Al)*, Noriko Matsumoto *(Fumiko)*, Yuko Chiyo *(Yuki)*, Hiroyuki Nagato *(Kashi)*.

Melodrama. Al, a young Tokyo pickpocket devoted to pursuing a "cool" lifestyle, listens to modern jazz at the Bar Duet with his friend Yuki, a prostitute who caters to foreigners. Kashi, a newspaperman, and his fiancée, Fumiko, catch Al trying to pick a bar patron's pocket and turn him in to the police. While in jail Al becomes friendly with another youth, Masaru, and upon their release they go to live with Yuki, who becomes Masaru's mistress. On the beach one day, Al and Masaru meet Fumiko, and Al brutally rapes her in revenge for betraying him. Later Fumiko finds that she is pregnant, and asks Al for advice, since she is unable to face Kashi. To even the accounts, Al arranges for Yuki to have sex with Kashi, and Fumiko pays her fee. Yuki becomes pregnant by Kashi, and after Masaru is killed in a street fight, Yuki decides to go to an abortion clinic so that she can resume her trade. At the hospital, Al and Yuki meet Fumiko and Kashi, who are also there for an abortion. Al reveals to Kashi that Fumiko's child is Al's and that Kashi is the father of Yuki's child. The bewildered Fumiko and Kashi are then confronted with the cruel laughter of Al and Yuki. *Pickpockets. Mistresses. Prostitutes. Newspapermen. Abortion. Youth. Revenge. Rape. Prisons. Bars. Tokyo.*

Note: Released in Japan in 1960 under the title *Kyonetsu no kisetsu.* Also known as *Wild Love-Makers* and *The Weird Lovemakers.*

THE WEIRD ONES   F6.5492

Dist Crescent International Pictures, Colonial International Pictures. Feb **1962** [San Antonio, Texas, showing]. Sd; b&w. 35mm. 76 min.

Pres by Dale Berry, Charles Martinez. *Prod* Pat Boyette.

Cast: Mike Braden, Rudy Duran, Phyliss Warren, Lee Morgan.

Comedy. An Astronik, a creature from outer space, lands on Earth with plans to terrorize and murder women. Two press agents enlist the aid of a Cosmos-Cutie to lure the alien into a trap. *Space creatures. Press agents. Seduction. Murder.*

Note: Location scenes filmed in San Antonio. Also known as *The Weird One.*

WEIRD, WICKED WORLD *see* GO, GO, GO WORLD!

THE WEIRD WORLD OF LSD   F6.5493

Dist Americana Entertainment Association. 13 Jul **1967** [San Francisco showing]. Sd; b&w. 35mm. 76 min.

Prod George B. Roberts, Eli Jackson. *Dir* Robert Ground.

Cast: Terry Tessem, Yolanda Morino, Ann Lindsay, Robert Jackson, Ray Becker, Clif Anderson, Janet Cole, Norman Rogers, Bill Shelley, Bob Gelinas, J. Willis, L. Hale, S. Johnson.

Documentary(?). This film purports to be a graphic study of the effects of the drug LSD. A young man feels that he is being pursued by demons; a formerly reticent young woman becomes wildly passionate; another fantasizes in a room filled with dummies; two women, close friends, violently confront each other; a drag race becomes a nightmare of noise and speed; an obese man ravenously consumes a great quantity of food; another man has a fantasy about beautiful women; and two lovers become trapped in a tragic web of illicit love and violence. *Paranoia. Inhibition. Friendship. Automobile racing. Obesity. Sexuality. LSD. Dummies. Food. Hallucinations. Fantasy.*

WELCOME KOSTYA! (U.S.S.R.)   F6.5494

Mosfilm. *Dist* Artkino Pictures. 20 Nov **1965** [New York opening]. Sd; b&w. 35mm. 75 min.

Dir E. Klimov. *Screenplay* S. Lungin, I. Nusinov. *Photog* Anatoliy Kuznetsov. *Camera* M. Koroptsov. *Art Dir* V. Kamskiy, B. Blank. *Mus* Mikhail Tariverdiyev, I. Yakushenko. *Sd* V. Zorin. *Asst Dir* K. Gakkel. *Sp Eff* I. Felitsyn, N. Zvonaryov.

Cast: Vitya Kosykh *(Kostya)*, Yevgeniy Yevstigneyev *(camp director)*, Lida Smirnova *(The Informer)*, A. Aleynikova *(camp nurse)*, I. Rutberg, A. Smirnov, Yura Bondarenko, Lida Volkova, Boris Demb, Seryozha Kokorev, Igor Kryukov, Sasha Moshovets, Tanya Prokhorova, Lida Smeyan, Slava Tsaryov, T. Barysheva, A. Lagranskiy, I. Mazurova, V. Uralskiy, N. Shatskaya, Vova Bordukov, Sasha Zhiveynov, Alik Miniovich, Seryozha Shappu, Sasha Baykov.

Comedy-drama. Kostya, an independent, ebullient child, attends a Pioneer Organization summer camp. The personnel find him uncontrollable, however, and he is sent home. Undaunted, Kostya secretly returns to the camp and has himself hidden by his friends. Their mischief nearly ruins visitors' day until the kindly camp director intercedes. *Children. Summer camps. Pioneer Organization (U.S.S.R.).*

Note: Released in the U.S.S.R. in 1964 as *Dobro pozhalovat* or *Dobro pozhalovat ili Postoronnim vkhod vospreshchen.* Members of the Pioneer Organization participated in the group scenes.

WELCOME, MR. BEDDOES *see* **A MAN COULD GET KILLED**

WELCOME TO HARD TIMES   F6.5495

Metro-Goldwyn-Mayer, Inc. 1 May **1967** [New York opening; c31 Dec 1966; LP34092]. Sd; col (Metrocolor). 35mm. 103 min.

A Max E. Youngstein–David Karr Production. *Prod* Max E. Youngstein, David Karr. *Assoc Prod* Hank Moonjean. *Dir-Writ* Burt Kennedy. *Dir Photog* Harry Stradling, Jr. *Camera Op* Al Francis. *Asst Camera* Felix Barlow. *Art Dir* George W. Davis, Carl Anderson. *Set Decor* Henry Grace, Joseph J. Stone. *Film Ed* Aaron Stell. *Mus* Harry Sukman. *Rec Supv* Franklin Milton. *Mix* Phil Mitchell. *Boom Op* Charles Wilborn. *Asst Dir* Al Jennings, Dennis Donnelly, Ira Stewart. *Unit Mgr* Al Jennings. *Script Supv* Betty Crosby. *Wardrobe* Frank Roberts, Rose Rockne. *Makeup* William Tuttle, Gene Bartlett. *Hairstyles* Mary Keats, Jane Gorton. *Still Photog* Jack Albin. *Gaffer* Bill Shaw, Mel Anderson. *Grip* Hank Forrester. *Prop* Jim Luttrell, Dick Hendrickson. *Casting* Leonard Murphy.

Cast: Henry Fonda *(Will Blue)*, Janice Rule *(Molly Riordan)*, Keenan Wynn *(Zar)*, Janis Paige *(Adah)*, John Anderson *(Ezra/Isaac Maple)*, Warren Oates *(Jenks)*, Fay Spain *(Jessie)*, Edgar Buchanan *(Brown)*, Aldo Ray *("Man from Bodie")*, Denver Pyle *(Alfie)*, Michael Shea *(Jimmy Fee)*, Arlene Golonka *(Mae)*, Lon Chaney, [Jr.] *(Avery)*, Royal Dano *(John Bear)*, Alan Baxter *(Jack Millay)*, Paul Birch *(Mr. Fee)*, Dan Ferrone *(Bert Albany)*, Paul Fix *(Major Munn)*, Elisha Cook *(Hanson)*, Kalen Liu *(China)*, Ann McCrea *(Flo)*, Robert Terhune *(1st drinker)*, Ron Burke *(young miner)*.

Western drama. Source: E. L. Doctorow, *Welcome to Hard Times* (New York, 1960). Hard Times, a tiny frontier settlement consisting of a few ramshackle buildings and a stable, is terrorized one day by the "Man from Bodie," a stranger who brutally murders several people, rapes dancehall girl Molly Riordan, and burns the town to the ground before riding away. Only four of the survivors try to rebuild the town: Will Blue, lawyer and unofficial mayor; Jimmy Fee, young son of one of the murder victims; John Bear, a Pawnee Indian; and Molly. Consumed by hatred and convinced that Will is a coward, Molly teaches Jimmy how to shoot in anticipation of the stranger's inevitable return. As the survivors rebuild Hard Times, they are joined by Zar, who arrives with whiskey and women to set up a traveling saloon for neighboring miners. After a bitter winter, Hard Times begins to resemble a community once again. Finally, the stranger returns, and Molly's hysteria forces Will into taking a stand. His shot only wounds the stranger, and Molly is grabbed by the wounded man as she tries to stab him; Jimmy then tries to end the struggle by shooting the stranger, but he accidentally kills Molly instead. Aware now that bitterness can only lead to tragedy, Will decides to remain in Hard Times to ensure its safety for future residents. *Strangers. Lawyers. Dancehall girls. Pawnee Indians. Bar girls. Frontier and pioneer life. Murder. Revenge. Rape. Arson. Saloons. Winter.*

Note: Location scenes filmed in Conejo Valley, California.

WE'LL BURY YOU!   F6.5496

Contempora Productions. *Dist* Columbia Pictures. 24 Oct **1962** [New York opening; c1 Sep 1962; LP23376]. Sd; b&w. 35mm. 74 min. [Also reviewed at 77 min.]

Prod Jack Leewood, Jack Thomas. *Writ* Jack Thomas. *Film Ed* Alan Presberg, Philip R. Rosenberg, Maurice Wright. *Sd* Continental Sound Corp. *Sp Eff* Ray Mercer and Co. *Script Cons* Robert W. Lowe. *Res* Donald Armstrong, John Detra.

Narrator: William Woodson.

Documentary. This film, a compilation of still photographs and newsreel footage, traces the growth of international Communism from Karl Marx and his *Communist Manifesto* to the present day. Highlights include the early days of Lenin; the sinking of a Russian warship during the Russo-Japanese War; the fight for power between Trotsky and Stalin; Stalin's political purges, mass executions, liquidation of the Kulaks, and pacts with the Allies; the German invasion of Russia during World War II; Communism in China; the Korean War; Stalin's death; the coming to power of Khrushchev; the Soviet suppression of the Hungarian revolution; Khrushchev's famous "kitchen debate" with visiting Vice President Nixon; Khrushchev in Hollywood during his visit to the United States in 1959; and the rise of Communism in Cuba under Fidel Castro. *Communism. Russo-Japanese War 1904–05. Russia—History—1917–21 Revolution. World War II. Korean War 1950–53. Hungary—History—Revolt 1956. People's Republic of China. Cuba. Karl Marx. Nikolai Lenin. Leon Trotsky. Joseph Stalin. Nikita Sergeyevich Khrushchev. Richard Milhous Nixon. Fidel Castro Ruz. "Communist Manifesto".*

WEREWOLF IN A GIRLS' DORMITORY (Italy)   F6.5497

Royal Film. *Dist* Metro-Goldwyn-Mayer, Inc., Altura Films International. 5 Jun **1963** [New York opening; Sd; b&w. 35mm. 82 min.

Prod Jack Forrest. *Exec Prod* Guido Giambartolomei. *Dir* Richard Benson. *Story-Screenplay* Julian Berry. *Photog* George Patrick, photog. *Art Dir* Peter

Travers. *Film Ed* Julian Attenborough. *Mus* Francis Berman. *Song:* "The Ghoul in School" Marilyn Stewart, Frank Owens. *Sung by* Adam Keefe.

Cast: Barbara Lass *(Brunhilde)*, Carl Schell *(Prof. Julian Olcott)*, Curt Lowens *(Mr. Swift)*, Maurice Marsac *(Sir Alfred Whiteman)*, Maureen O'Connor *(Leonor McDonald)*, Mary McNeeran *(Mary Smith)*, Grace Neame *(Sandy)*, Alan Collins *(Walter)*, Anni Steinert *(Sheena Whiteman)*, Joseph Mercer *(porter)*, Anne Marie Avis, Elizabeth Patrick, Lucy Derleth, Patricia Meeker, Herbert Diamonds, Martha Marker.

Horror film. Shortly after Prof. Julian Olcott arrives at a school for wayward girls, the body of one of the students is found in a nearby wood, apparently the victim of some ferocious animal. Brunhilde, one of the dead girl's classmates, reveals that her friend had been blackmailing someone in the village and frequently slipped away at night. Subsequent investigations by Professor Olcott prove that the dead girl had once had an affair with Sir Alfred Whiteman, the sadistic patron of the reformatory, and that she had been blackmailing him. When confronted with the facts, Whiteman commits suicide. A short time later, Brunhilde is attacked in the woods but is saved by a watchdog. Now certain that a werewolf is in their midst, the townspeople begin to suspect Olcott, a former doctor who was once tried on a charge of lycanthropy. Following the death of the school janitor, Olcott discovers that the dead man's dog is frightened of the school superintendent, Mr. Swift. Aware that dogs are frightened of werewolves, Olcott maintains a close watch on Swift. When the werewolf attacks Brunhilde, Olcott fires three bullets, and the hideous features of the creature fade away, revealing the face of Mr. Swift. *Professors. Werewolves. Students. Headmasters. Murder. Blackmail. Suicide. Reformatories. Dogs.*

Note: Opened in Rome in Feb 1962 as *Lycanthropus*. Alternative title: *The Ghoul in School.* Richard Benson is a pseudonym for Paolo Heusch, Julian Berry for Ernesto Gastaldi, Alan Collins for Luciano Pigozzi. Austria may have been a co-producing country.

WEST END JUNGLE (Great Britain)   F6.5498

Searchlight Productions. *Dist* Wilshire International Pictures, Atlantic Pictures. 10 Jan **1962** [Maryland license]. Sd; b&w. 35mm. 60 min.

Prod Arnold Louis Miller, Stanley A. Long. *Dir* Arnold Louis Miller. *Photog* Stanley A. Long. *Film Ed* Stanley Marks.

With: David Gell *(commentator)*, Heather Russell, Tom Bowman *(voices)*.

Documentary. With the passage of the Street Offenses Bill, prostitutes were driven from London streets and into the numerous clubs that sprang up as covers for prostitution. This film depicts those clubs, including striptease clubs and clip joints, and the many chorus girls who are lured into prostitution hoping to find fame and fortune. The call girl system is depicted in all its facets: prostitutes entice passing men, massage parlors become a place for peddling vice, and luxurious nightclubs provide a "hostess service" for businessmen with large expense accounts. It becomes apparent that professional prostitutes find it difficult to change their way of life and prefer to gamble on evading the law. *Prostitutes. Chorus girls. Nightclub hostesses. Businessmen. Prostitution. Clip joints. Massage parlors. Nightclubs. Street Offenses Act 1959 (London). London—Soho.*

Note: Filmed on location in London. Released in Great Britain in 1961; running time: 55 min.

WEST SIDE STORY   F6.5499

Mirisch Pictures–Seven Arts Productions–Beta Productions. *Dist* United Artists. 18 Oct **1961** [New York opening; c18 Oct 1961; LP21934]. Sd (Westrex); col (Technicolor). 35mm & 70mm (Panavision 70). 155 min.

A Robert Wise Production. *Prod* Robert Wise. *Assoc Prod* Saul Chaplin. *Dir (see note)* Robert Wise, Jerome Robbins. *Screenplay* Ernest Lehman. *Dir Photog* Daniel L. Fapp. *Set Decor* Victor Gangelin. *Prod Artist* Maurice Zuberano. *Prod Dsgn* Boris Leven. *Titl & Vis Assoc* Saul Bass & Associates. *Film Ed* Thomas Stanford. *Asst Ed* Marshall M. Borden. *Mus* Leonard Bernstein. *Lyr* Stephen Sondheim. *Mus Cond* Johnny Green. *Orch* Sid Ramin, Irwin Kostal. *Mus Asst* Betty Walberg. *Vocal Coach* Robert Tucker. *Singing Voice for Natalie Wood–uncredited* Marni Nixon. *Singing Voice for Richard Beymer–uncredited* Jimmy Bryant. *Choreog & Choreog Asst* Jerome Robbins, Tommy Abbott, Margaret Banks, Howard Jeffrey, Tony Mordente. *Sd* Murray Spivack, Fred Lau, Vinton Vernon. *Sd Ed* Gilbert D. Marchant. *Mus Ed* Richard Carruth. *1st & 2d Asst Dir* Robert E. Relyea, Jerome M. Siegel. *Prod Mgr* Allen K. Wood. *Script Supv* Stanley Scheuer. *Cost Dsgn* Irene Sharaff. *Wardrobe* Bert Henrikson. *Makeup* Emile La Vigne. *Hairdresser* Alice Monte. *Photog Eff* Linwood Dunn, Film Effects of Hollywood. *Prop* Sam Gordon. *Casting* Stalmaster-Lister Co.

Cast—Principals: Natalie Wood *(Maria)*, Richard Beymer *(Tony)*, Russ Tamblyn *(Riff)*, Rita Moreno *(Anita)*, George Chakiris *(Bernardo)*, Simon Oakland *(Lieutenant Schrank)*, Ned Glass *(Doc)*, William Bramley *(Officer Krupke)*, John Astin *(Glad Hand, a social worker)*, Penny Santon *(Madam Lucia)*.

Cast—Jets: Tucker Smith *(Ice)*, Tony Mordente *(Action)*, David Winters *(A-Rab)*, Eliot Feld *(Baby John)*, Bert Michaels *(Snowboy)*, David Bean *(Tiger)*, Robert Banas *(Joyboy)*, Scooter Teague *(Big Deal)*, Harvey Hornecker *(Mouthpiece)*, Tommy Abbott *(Gee-Tar)*.
Cast—Their Girls: Susan Oakes *(Anybodys)*, Gina Trikonis *(Graziella)*, Carole D'Andrea *(Velma)*.
Cast—Sharks: Jose De Vega *(Chino)*, Jay Norman *(Pepe)*, Gus Trikonis *(Indio)*, Eddie Verso *(Juano)*, Jaime Rogers *(Loco)*, Larry Roquemore *(Rocco)*, Robert Thompson *(Luis)*, Nick Covacevich *(Toro)*, Rudy Del Campo *(Del Campo)*, Andre Tayir *(Chile)*.
Cast—Their Girls: Yvonne Othon *(Consuelo)*, Suzie Kaye *(Rosalia)*, Jo Anne Miya *(Francisca)*.
Musical drama. Source: Arthur Laurents, Leonard Bernstein and Stephen Sondheim, *West Side Story* (New York opening: 26 Sep 1957). The teeming slums of Manhattan's upper West Side are filled with racial tensions that frequently erupt in open warfare between the restless, embittered teenage members of rival gangs. Newly arrived in this violent atmosphere is Maria, a young Puerto Rican girl whose brother, Bernardo, is the leader of a street gang called the Sharks. Despite the warnings of Anita, Bernardo's fiery girl friend, Maria falls in love with a young Polish boy, Tony, who belongs to the Jets, the hated enemies of the Sharks. Their love affair fans the enmity between the two gangs and eventually leads to a showdown "rumble." Prodded by Maria, Tony tries to stop the bloodshed but is unsuccessful, and the Jets' leader, Riff, is stabbed to death by Bernardo. Suddenly overcome by his passions, Tony grabs a blade and fatally stabs Bernardo. In desperation, Tony runs to Maria, begs her forgiveness, and pleads with her to go away with him. But before they can escape, Tony is cornered in a neighborhood playground and killed by one of the Sharks. As Maria hysterically sobs over her dead lover, the remaining members of the two gangs wander onto the playground. The incredible waste of the triple tragedy deeply affects both sides, and they join together in carrying the dead Tony from the playground. *Musical numbers:* "Prologue" (the Jets and the Sharks); "Jet Song" (Riff & the Jets); "Something's Coming" (Tony); "Dance at the Gym" (Tony, Maria, the Jets, and the Sharks); "Maria" (Tony); "America" (Anita, Bernardo, the Sharks & Their Girls); "Tonight" (Tony and Maria); "One Hand, One Heart" (Tony and Maria); "Gee, Officer Krupke!" (Riff & the Jets); "Quintet" (Tony, Maria, Anita, the Jets, and the Sharks); "The Rumble" (the Jets and the Sharks); "Cool" (Ice & the Jets); "I Feel Pretty" (Maria, Consuelo, Rosalia, and Francisca); "Somewhere" (Tony and Maria); "A Boy Like That" and "I Have a Heart" (Maria and Anita). *Street gangs. Juvenile delinquents. Police. Poles. Puerto Ricans. Youth. Urban life. Racism. Brother-sister relationship. Murder. Slums. Playgrounds. New York City—West Side.*
Note: Filmed in part in New York City. Although Jerome Robbins received screen credit for co-direction, he left the project early in its production after choreographing "Prologue," "America," "Cool," and "I Feel Pretty."

WESTWARD DESPERADO (Japan) F6.5500
Toho Co. Jun **1961** [Los Angeles showing]. Sd; b&w. 35mm (Tohoscope). 107 min.
Dir Kihachi Okamoto. *Screenplay* Shinichi Sekizawa, Kihachi Okamoto. *Photog* Yuzuru Aizawa.
Cast: Yuzo Kayama, Makoto Sato, Kumi Mizuno, Frankie Sakai, Ichiro Nakayama, Akihiko Hirata, Sachio Sakai, Shoji Ooki, Tatsuji Ebara, Yasushi Yamamoto, Akira Kubo, Tadao Nakamaru, Mayumi Tamura, Michiyo Yokoyama, Ichiro Nakatani.
War drama. During World War II, the Independent Samonji unit of the Japanese army is ordered to regain the standard of a regiment lost on the North China front. Although accused of robbery and violations of military ethics, the unit, led by its daredevil lieutenant, accomplishes its mission against the Chinese Communists. *Chinese. Communists. Combat zone life. Robbery. Sino-Japanese Conflict 1937–45. China. Japan—Army.*
Note: Released in Japan in 1960 as *Dokuritsu gurentai nishi-e.*

WHAT! (France/Great Britain/Italy) F6.5501
Francinor-P. I. P.–Vox Film–Leone Film. *Dist* Futuramic Releasing Organization. 10 Dec **1965** [Boston opening]. Sd; col (Technicolor). 35mm. 90 min.
Pres by Richard G. Yates. *Exec Prod* John Oscar. *Dir* John M. Old. *Story & Screenplay* Julian Berry, Robert Hugo, Martin Hardy. *Photog* David Hamilton, pseud. *Art Dir* Dick Grey. *Film Ed* Bob King. *Mus* Jim Murphy. *Sd* Peter Jackson. *Asst Dir* Julian Berry. *Cost* Peg Fax.
Cast: Daliah Lavi *(Nevenka)*, Christopher Lee *(Kurt Menliff)*, Tony Kendall *(Christian Menliff)*, Isli Oberon *(Katia)*, Harriet White *(Giorgia)*, Dean Ardow *(Count Vladimir)*, Alan Collins *(manservant)*, Jacques Herlin *(priest)*.
Horror film. In the 19th century, sadistic Kurt Menliff returns to his father's castle, ending an exile imposed after his abandoned mistress Tania committed suicide. Count Menliff has recalled his wayward son at the request of Kurt's

newly married brother Christian. Upon his arrival Tania's mother, the servant Giorgia, predicts quick retribution. Encountering Christian's bride, Nevenka, on the beach, Kurt whips her into unconsciousness. Shortly thereafter Kurt is found slain, the instrument of his death being the knife used by Tania. Following Kurt's interment in the family crypt, Count Menliff's mutilated body is discovered. The weapon used in his murder is again Tania's knife. Found whipped a second time, Nevenka asserts that Kurt is still alive, citing as evidence the bloody footprints leading to the crypt. Enraged, Christian enters the crypt intending to burn his brother's body. As he does so, the sound of Kurt's laughter is heard. The corpse, however, is decomposed beyond recognition. It is later revealed that Kurt's incubus has visited Nevenka nightly. Attempting to destroy the shade, Nevenka accidentally commits suicide. Following her death, she is unmasked as the assassin of Kurt and Count Menliff. *Nobility. Housemaids. Brothers. Brothers-in-law. Newlyweds. Sadism. Suicide. Mutilation. Murder. Exile. Flogging. Castles. Fires.*
Note: Opened in Rome in Aug 1963 as *La frusta e il corpo*; in Paris in Jan 1966 as *Le corps et le fouet*; running time: 85 min; in Great Britain in 1965 as *Night Is the Phantom*; running time: 77 min. Pseudonyms include: John Oscar (Elio Scardamaglia), John M. Old (Mario Bava), Julian Berry (Ernesto Gastaldi), Robert Hugo (Ugo Guerra), Martin Hardy (Luciano Martino), David Hamilton (Ubaldo Terzano), Dick Grey (Ottavio Scotti), Bob King (Roberto Cinquini), Jim Murphy (Carlo Rustichelli), Tony Kendall (L. Stella), and Alan Collins (Luciano Pigozzi).

WHAT A CARVE UP! (Great Britain) F6.5502
New World Pictures Ltd. *Dist* Embassy Pictures. 13 Jun **1962** [Los Angeles opening]. Sd; b&w. 35mm. 87 min.
Pres by Joseph E. Levine. *Prod* Robert S. Baker, Monty Berman. *Dir* Pat Jackson. *Screenplay* Ray Cooney, Tony Hilton. *Photog* Monty Berman. *Camera Op* Gerry Fisher. *Focus Puller* Gerry Elliott. *Camera Grip* Tommy Miller. *Art Dir* Ivan King. *Draughtsman* Alan Tomkins. *Scenic Artist* Gilbert Wood. *Film Ed* Gordon Pilkington. *1st Asst Ed* Tony West. *Mus* Muir Mathieson. *Sd* Jeanne Henderson. *Sd Mix* George Adams. *Boom Op* Fred Tomlin. *Sd Camera Op* David Hill. *1st, 2d & 3d Asst Dir* Geoffrey Helman, Bill Herlihy, Max Kemp. *Prod Mgr* Johnny Goodman. *Prod Sec* Beti Parry. *Cont* Pamela Carlton. *Wardrobe Mistress* Jean Fairlie. *Makeup* Alex Garfath. *Hairdresser* Joyce Wood. *Prod Buyer* George Blackburn. *Constr Mgr* Bill Greene. *Casting Dir* Betty White, casting. *Still Photog* Laurie Turner.
Cast: Kenneth Connor *(Ernie Broughton)*, Sidney James *(Syd Butler)*, Shirley Eaton *(Linda Dickson)*, Donald Pleasence *(Mr. Sloane)*, Dennis Price *(Guy Broughton)*, Michael Gough *(Fisk)*, Valerie Taylor *(Janet Broughton)*, Esma Cannon *(Aunt Emily)*, George Woodbridge *(Dr. Edward Broughton)*, Michael Gwynn *(Malcolm Broughton)*, Philip O'Flynn *(Arkwright/Gabriel)*, Timothy Bateson *(porter)*, Frederick Piper *(hearse driver)*, Adam Faith *(himself)*.
Comedy. Source: Frank King, *The Ghoul* (London, 1928). Upon the death of his Uncle Gabriel, Ernie Broughton, a proofreader of horror and sex novels, is summoned by sinister solicitor Sloane to attend the reading of the will. Accompanied by his bookie roommate, Syd Butler, Ernie arrives at Gabriel's gloomy mansion on the Yorkshire moors and encounters the somewhat mad members of the Broughton clan. Also on hand are Fisk, the clubfooted butler, and the uncle's nurse, Linda Dickson. The will is read, and the family learns that it has been disinherited. A violent electric storm then causes a power shortage, and the house is plunged into darkness. During the night, several members of the family are murdered by a masked killer, and in the morning it is discovered that the killer is Gabriel himself. (He has pretended to be dead in order to watch his greedy relatives squabble over his money.) Ernie prepares to take Linda back to London, but his plans are frustrated by the unexpected appearance of her boyfriend, pop singer Adam Faith. *Proofreaders. Bookies. Uncles. Singers. Nurses. Butlers. Lawyers. Murder. Greed. Family life. Perfidy. Wills. Inheritance. Moorlands. Yorkshire. London.*
Note: Opened in London in Jul 1961. Title changed to *No Place Like Homicide.*

WHAT A CHASSIS! see LA BELLE AMÉRICAINE

WHAT A WAY TO GO! F6.5503
APJAC Productions–Orchard Productions. *Dist* Twentieth Century-Fox Film Corp. 14 May **1964** [New York opening; c14 May 1964; LP27976]. Sd (Westrex); col (De Luxe). 35mm (CinemaScope). 111 min.
A J. Lee Thompson Production. *Prod* Arthur P. Jacobs. *Dir* J. Lee Thompson. *Screenplay* Betty Comden, Adolph Green. *Story* Gwen Davis. *Dir Photog* Leon Shamroy. *Camera Op* Don Anderson, Red Crawford. *Art Dir* Jack Martin Smith, Ted Haworth. *Set Decor* Walter M. Scott, Stuart A. Reiss. *Film Ed* Marjorie Fowler. *Asst Ed* Pat Shade. *Mus* Nelson Riddle. *Songs:* "I Think That You and I Should Get Acquainted," "Musical Extravaganza" Betty Comden, Adolph Green, Jule Styne. *Orch* Arthur Morton. *Choreog & Asst*

Gene Kelly, Richard Humphrey. *Sd* Bernard Freericks, Elmer Raguse. *Rec* Bill Wells. *Boom Op* Anthony Samaniego. *Asst Dir* Fred R. Simpson, Les Warner, John Flynn. *Unit Prod Mgr* William Eckhardt. *Asst to the Prod* William Mahan. *Script Supv* John Franco. *Miss MacLaine's Gowns Dsgn* Edith Head. *Men's Wardrobe* Moss Mabry. *Makeup Supv* Ben Nye. *Makeup* Frank Westmore, Dick Smith, Toby Skarstedt. *Hairstyles for Miss MacLaine Created by* Sydney Guilaroff. *Supv Hairstyles* Margaret Donovan. *Sp Photog Eff* L. B. Abbott, Emil Kosa, Jr. *Dial Coach* Leon Charles. *Still Photog* James Mitchell, Mark Kaufman. *Prop* M. Abrahams. *Gaffer* Fred Hall. *Grip* Leo McCreary, Lloyd Phillips.

Cast: Shirley MacLaine (*Louisa*), Paul Newman (*Larry Flint*), Robert Mitchum (*Rod Anderson*), Dean Martin (*Leonard Crawley*), Gene Kelly (*Jerry Benson*), Bob Cummings (*Dr. Stephanson*), Dick Van Dyke (*Edgar Hopper*), Reginald Gardiner (*painter*), Margaret Dumont (*Mrs. Foster*), Lou Nova (*Trentino*), Fifi D'Orsay (*baroness*), Maurice Marsac (*René*), Wally Vernon (*agent*), Jane Wald (*Polly*), Lenny Kent (*Hollywood lawyer*), Marjorie Bennett (*Mrs. Freeman*), Christopher Connelly (*Ned*), Barbara Bouchet (*girl on plane*), Tom Conway (*Lord Kensington*), Queenie Leonard (*Lady Kensington*), Antony Eustrel (*Willard*), Sid Gould (*movie executive*), Paula Lane (*movie executive's girl*), Army Archerd (*tv announcer*), Tracy Butler (*movie star*), Anton Arnold (*Mr. Foster*), Roy Gordon (*minister*), Burt Mustin (*Crawleyville lawyer*), Billy Corcoran (*Leonard Crawley, age 7*), Jeff Fithian (*Jonathan Crawley, age 5*), Pamelyn Ferdin (*Geraldine Crawley, age 4*), Helene Winston (*Doris*), Jack Greening (*Chester*), Phil Arnold (*publicity and press agent*), Dick Wilson (*Driscoll*).

Comedy. Louisa Benson's offer to give the U. S. Government all of her wealth, amounting to more than $200 million, is refused because the gift is made in the form of a personal check. Distressed, Louisa consults psychiatrist Victor Stephanson and tells him the story of her life, in which every man she married died shortly after the wedding. *Rebelling against her money-hungry mother, Louisa, who wants a simple life, rejects Leonard Crawley, her hometown's richest boy, to marry Edgar Hopper, a carefree storekeeper with little interest in money. Their marriage is happy until Leonard ridicules the threadbare manner in which Edgar supports his wife. Stung, Edgar becomes a successful merchant—ruining Crawley in the process—and literally works himself to death, leaving Louisa a rich young widow. She goes to Paris and meets and marries taxi driver Larry Flint, who is also an unsuccessful modern artist and the inventor of a machine that converts sound into oil paintings. Their union is idyllic until Louisa feeds classical music into the machine and creates a very successful painting. By building more machines and using music, Larry becomes an enormously rich artist until he gets entangled in his machines and is killed, leaving Louisa even wealthier. For her next husband she chooses millionaire-industrialist Rod Anderson on the premise that an already wealthy man would change her luck. Rod's neglect of his empire for Louisa perversely triples his fortune. She persuades him to retire to a farm, and Rod is killed by an angry bull while mistakenly attempts to milk. Louisa's fourth husband is song-and-dance man Jerry "Pinky" Benson, who has worked in the same dingy nightclub for years performing a clown act so corny that customers never look up from their food or drink. All is perfect until Pinky, at Louisa's suggestion, goes on without costume or makeup; he does his number as a ballad and is a sensation. He rapidly becomes a top movie star but he is trampled to death by his adoring fans at a premiere.* As Louisa finishes her story, the Internal Revenue Service calls Dr. Stephanson to tell him Louisa's check is good, and he faints, having thought her wealth a fantasy. A janitor who shuffles in as Louisa is trying to revive Stephanson turns out to be Leonard Crawley, her first beau, who never regained his wealth. Louisa marries him, and they go to live on a rundown farm. There they are ecstatically poor until a hole in their field threatens their happiness when it begins to spout oil. To Louisa's relief, they learn it is merely a break in an oil company pipeline. Widows. Philanthropists. Psychiatrists. Merchants. Taxi drivers. Artists. Inventors. Industrialists. Entertainers. Janitors. Actors. Marriage. Death. Wealth. Smalltown life. Greed. Sound. Music. Retirement. Disguise. Farming. Weddings. Taxicabs. Paintings. Nightclubs. Oil. Paris. United States—Internal Revenue Service. Bulls.

WHAT A WOMAN! (Reissue) (France/Italy)   **F6.5504**
Documento Film–Le Louvre Films. *Dist* Films Around the World, Inc., Don Kay Associates. ca **1963**. Sd; b&w. 35mm. 90 min.
Note: Released in 1960 by Films Around the World as *Lucky To Be a Woman*; rereleased in 1965 by Don Kay Associates as *Mating Modern Style*. French title: *La chance d'être femme*; Italian title: *La fortuna di essere donna*.

WHAT A WONDERFUL LIFE *see* **FOLLOW THAT DREAM**

WHAT AM I BID?   **F6.5505**
Liberty International Productions. *Dist* Emerson Film Enterprises. 26 Jul **1967** [Dallas opening]. Sd; col (Technicolor). 35mm (Techniscope). 92 min.

Prod Wendell Niles, Jr. *Assoc Prod* Phil Paladino. *Dir-Writ* Gene Nash. *Photog* Ralph Woolsey. *Art Dir* Archie Bacon. *Set Decor* Harry Reif. *Film Ed* Terry O. Morse. *Mus Arr & Cond* Ernie Freeman. *Songs*: "What Am I Bid?" "I Don't Know," "Life Gets a Little More Mixed Up Ev'ry Day," "Don't Look Back," "Big Wide Wonderful World of Country Music," "When a Boy Becomes a Man," "I'll Make It Up to You," "We've Got the Best There Is," "Time Is the Only Thing," "I Never Got To Kiss the Girl," "Too Late, Too Soon," "I Didn't Know," "Mike's Theme" Gene Nash. *Song*: "Auctioneer" LeRoy Van Dyke, Buddy Black. *Songs*: "Auctioneer," "What Am I Bid?" "I Didn't Know," "Life Gets a Little More Mixed Up Ev'ry Day," "Don't Look Back," "Big Wide Wonderful World of Country Music," "I'll Make It Up to You," "We've Got the Best There Is" *sung by* LeRoy Van Dyke. *Song*: "Time Is the Only Thing" *sung by* Faron Young. *Song*: "I Never Got To Kiss the Girl" *sung by* Tex Ritter. *Song*: "When a Boy Becomes a Man," "My Searching Heart" *sung by* Johnny Sea. *Song*: "Too Late, Too Soon" *perf by* Al Hirt. *Dance Staged by* George Jack. *Sd* Barry Thomas, Frank Webster, Jr. *Asst Dir* Jim Myers.

Cast: LeRoy Van Dyke (*Pat Hubbard*), Kristin Nelson (*Beth Hubbard*), Stephanie Hill (*Maggie Hendricks*), Bill Craig (*Mike Evans*), Leland Murray (*bus ticket clerk*), Billy Benedict (*Clem*), Robert Boylan (*Captain Harrigan*), Andy Davis (*tractor salesman*), Muriel Landers (*concert fan*), Sid Rushakoff (*Fenster*), J. B. Towner (*publisher*), Jack McCall (*Hal Cook*), Darrell McCall (*Darrell*), Lea Marmer (*secretary*), Al Hirt, Tex Ritter, Johnny Sea, Faron Young (*themselves*).

Comedy-drama with music. Following his discharge from the Navy, Pat Hubbard, the son of a once-famous country music singer, stops off in Hollywood en route to his Arizona ranch. While there, he attends a Hollywood Bowl performance by Faron Young and is induced to play a country and western number. His singing attracts the attention of agent Mike Evans and fan magazine writer Maggie Hendricks, who follow him to Arizona in the hope of persuading him to become a professional singer. Pat is reluctant to enter show business because of the ruinous effect it had upon his father's personal life. During their stay at the ranch, Maggie falls in love with Pat, and Mike becomes romantically involved with Pat's sister Beth. Eventually, under the protective guidance of Tex Ritter and Al Hirt, Pat is launched into a promising career. Complications arise when an article Maggie has written on Pat's father appears in a national magazine. Furious, Pat breaks up with Maggie and decides to return to being a cattle auctioneer. Pat feels obligated to perform, however, when he is asked to do a show for the Navy aboard the aircraft carrier U.S.S. Kitty Hawk. Maggie and Mike learn about the special performance, and the two couples are reconciled as Pat sings a patriotic number on the carrier's flight deck. Veterans. Singers. Talent agents. Columnists. Auctioneers. Country music. Ranches. Hollywood. Arizona. United States Navy. Hollywood Bowl. U.S.S. "Kitty Hawk".

WHAT DID YOU DO IN THE WAR, DADDY?   **F6.5506**
Mirisch-Geoffrey Productions. *Dist* United Artists. 29 Jun **1966** [Boston opening; c29 Jun 1966; LP32949]. Sd; col (DeLuxe). 35mm (Panavision). 119 min. Copyright length: 116 min.

Prod-Dir Blake Edwards. *Exec Prod* Owen Crump. *Assoc Prod* Dick Crockett. *Screenplay* William Peter Blatty. *Story* Blake Edwards, Maurice Richlin. *Dir Photog* Philip Lathrop. *2d Unit Photog* Harold Wellman. *Set Decor* Reg Allen, Jack Stevens. *Prod Dsgn* Fernando Carrere. *Film Ed* Ralph E. Winters. *Mus* Henry Mancini. *Song*: "In the Arms of Love" Henry Mancini, Jay Livingston, Ray Evans. *Choreog* Carey Leverett. *Sd* Frank Sarver, Chuck Overhulser. *Asst Dir* Mickey McCardle, Tim Zinnemann, Charles Scott, Jr. *Prod Supv* Allen K. Wood. *Prod Mgr* Clem Beauchamp. *Unit Mgr* Jack McEdward. *Cost* Jack Bear. *Makeup* Allan Snyder. *Hairstyles* Suzanne Germaine. *Sp Eff* Danny Lee. *Photog Eff* Linwood Dunn, James Gordon.

Cast: James Coburn (*Lieutenant Christian*), Dick Shawn (*Captain Cash*), Sergio Fantoni (*Captain Oppo*), Giovanna Ralli (*Gina Romano*), Aldo Ray (*Sergeant Rizzo*), Harry Morgan (*Major Pott*), Carroll O'Connor (*General Bolt*), Leon Askin (*Kastorp*), Rico Cattani (*Benedetto*), Jay Novello (*Romano*), Kurt Kreuger (*German captain*), Vito Scotti (*Federico*), Johnny Seven (*Vittorio*), Art Lewis (*Pfc. Needleman*), William Bryant (*Captain Minow*), Robert Carricart (*cook*), Ralph Manza (*waiter*), Danny Francis (*bus boy*), Herb Ellis (*Sergeant Lumpe*), Ken Wales (*Blair*), Rex Morhan (*American general*), Carl Ekberg (*Adolf Hitler*), Richard Niles (*jeep driver*), Karla Most, Ivana Kislinger (*Italian girls*), Mina Darno (*madame*), Giovanna Coppola, Louise DeCarlo, Sondra Farrell, Emily La Rue, Jeanne Ranier (*village women employed by madame*), Eric Anderson, Ken Del Conte, Thomas Hunter, Kelly Johnson (*American soldiers*), Hern Andreas (*German lieutenant*), Horst Graf (*German officer*), Vincent Barbi, Joe Lo Presti, Benito Prezia, Cosimo Renna, Neil Rosso, Philip Garris (*Italian soldiers*), Mario Cimino, James Lanphier, Jerry Martin, Joe Polina (*Italian villagers*).

War comedy. In the World War II Allied invasion of Sicily, a battle-weary American company is assigned to capture a small village. Led by Captain Cash, a "by-the-book" West Point graduate, the company finds that its advance is interrupting a soccer game. The Americans have long been expected, however, and Captain Oppo, the Italian officer responsible for the village, explains that he is perfectly willing to surrender—with honor. In other words, the soccer game must be allowed to finish and the annual wine festival must be held before the town will yield to the occupying forces. Captain Cash has some misgivings about the unorthodox arrangement, but his second in command, Lieutenant Christian, persuades him to acquiesce. Italians and Americans join for an all-day, all-night orgy of drunken revelry and lovemaking. Reconnaissance planes from both U. S. and German headquarters mistake the frolicking in the streets for resistance fighting, and the Nazis decide to aid their Italian allies. When they arrive, however, they find the American flag unfurled above the village and American soldiers, in all manner of dress including German uniforms, holding the town. U. S. forces also arrive to rescue what they believe to be a battalion of battle-fatigued GI's; but by popping in and out of the catacombs under the town, Cash's company captures the whole of the German unit. A victory celebration is in order. *Village life. Drunkenness. Military occupation. Soccer. World War II. Sicily. Adolf Hitler. United States Army. Italy—Army. Germany—Army. United States Military Academy. Catacombs.*

WHAT DO YOU SAY TO A NAKED LADY?   F6.5507

Allen Funt Productions. *Dist* United Artists. 18 Feb **1970** [New York opening; c18 Feb 1970; LP37899]. Sd; col with b&w seq (DeLuxe). 35mm. 92 min. [See note.] *MPAA rating* X.

A Film by Allen Funt. *Prod-Dir-Writ* Allen Funt. *Asst Prod* Richard Briglia. *Dir Photog* Urs Furrer, Tom Mangravite, Gil Geller, George Silano. *Titl Dsgn* Joan Schwartzberg. *Film Ed* Allen Funt, Irving Winter, Arnold Freedman. *Mus & Lyr* Steve Karmen. *Sd Dir* Harold Beiben, Bernie Zuck, Murray Rosenbloom. *Rec Engr* Frank Kulaga. *Prod Mgr* Richard Felber. *Ed Cons* Barton Kaitz.

Cast: Joie Addison *(girl in elevator)*, Laura Huston *(girl on ladder)*, Martin Meyers *(tailor)*, Karil Daniels *(girl who is not raped)*, Donna Whitfield, Richard Roundtree *(interracial couple)*, Susanna Clemm *(girl in keyhole)*, Norman Manzon *(male model)*, Jean Bell *(lecturer)*, Allen Funt *(himself)*.

Comedy. The hidden camera of Allen Funt records the expressions of people confronted by nude members of the opposite sex, as naked women step off crowded elevators, hitchhike rides on country roads, and teach sex education in the college classroom. While a clothed female begs the man on the street for kisses, an unclad male model converses with two perplexed dowagers, and Funt interviews a prostitute. As a black man and white woman kiss passionately in a bus terminal, passengers in transit are asked their reaction. Three elderly ladies view a pornographic film, and audience reaction to the Funt feature is tested in a private screening. *Motion picture producers. Motion picture cameramen. Hitchhikers. Nudity. Miscegenation. Sex instruction. Interviewers. Elevators. Allen Funt.*

Note: Production began in 1968. Copyright length: 90 min; also reviewed at 86 min.

WHAT EVER HAPPENED TO AUNT ALICE?   F6.5508

Associates & Aldrich Co. *Dist* Cinerama Releasing Corp. 23 Jul **1969** [New York opening]. Sd; col (Metrocolor). 35mm. 101 min. *MPAA rating* M.

Pres by Palomar Pictures International. *Prod* Robert Aldrich. *Exec Prod* Peter Nelson. *Dir* Lee H. Katzin. *Screenplay* Theodore Apstein. *Dir Photog* Joseph Biroc. *Art Dir* William Glasgow. *Set Decor* John W. Brown. *Main Titl* Don Record & Associates. *Supv Film Ed* Michael Luciano. *Film Ed* Frank Urioste. *Mus* Gerald Fried. *Sd Mix* Richard Church. *Asst Dir* Daisy Gerber. *Prod Supv* Fred Ahern. *Unit Mgr* Eddie Saeta. *Script Supv* Richard Chaffee. *Cost* Renie. *Makeup* Bill Turner. *Hairstyles* Jean Austin. *Casting* Lynn Stalmaster. *Prop Master* Ygnacio Sepulveda. *Dial Supv* Michael Audley.

Cast: Geraldine Page *(Mrs. Claire Marrable)*, Ruth Gordon *(Mrs. Alice Dimmock)*, Rosemary Forsyth *(Harriet Vaughn)*, Robert Fuller *(Mike Darrah)*, Mildred Dunnock *(Miss Tinsley)*, Joan Huntington *(Julia Lawson)*, Peter Brandon *(George Lawson)*, Michael Barbera *(Jim Vaughn)*, Peter Bonerz *(Mr. Bentley)*, Richard Angarola *(Sheriff Armijo)*, Claire Kelly *(Elva)*, Valerie Allen *(Dottie)*, Martin Garralaga *(Juan)*, Jack Bannon *(Olin)*, Seth Riggs *(Warren)*, Lou Kane *(telephone man)*, Howard Wright *(mourner)*.

Mystery melodrama. Source: Ursula (Reilly) Curtiss, *The Forbidden Garden* (New York, 1962). After learning that her late husband's estate consists of little more than a stamp album, Claire Marrable moves to a remote desert section of Arizona and begins hiring a series of housekeepers, all of whom have considerable savings and no immediate family. She then fleeces them of their money, murders them, and buries them in her garden. Her latest employee is Mrs. Alice Dimmock, who is posing as a housekeeper in an attempt to locate her friend Miss Tinsley, who disappeared after going to work for Mrs. Marrable. Aiding the investigation is Alice's nephew, racing car builder Mike Darrah. Mike is attracted to Mrs. Marrable's neighbor, widow Harriet Vaughn, who

lives with her nephew Jim and a dog that often digs in the Marrable garden. When Mike learns that Miss Tinsley withdrew her savings before disappearing, he warns Alice of imminent danger, but it is too late; Mrs. Marrable beats the housekeeper into unconsciousness during a furious struggle and puts her in a car, which she sinks in a nearby lake. The body is found just as Mrs. Marrable begins to suspect that Harriet has some knowledge of the murder; to protect herself, she drugs both the young widow and her nephew, then sets fire to their home. The next morning, however, Mrs. Marrable awakens to find the Vaughns rescued and her garden of corpses unearthed. Unable to cope with the final blow—that her husband's stamp album was actually worth $100,000—she smiles insanely at Mike and asks him to drive her to Tucson so she can look for work as a housekeeper. *Psychopaths. Widows. Housekeepers. Missing persons. Aunts. Employer-employee relations. Murder. Imposture. Arson. Philately. Inheritance. Gardens. Drugs. Arizona. Deserts. Tucson (Arizona). Dogs.*

Note: Location scenes filmed in and around Tucson, Arizona.

WHAT EVER HAPPENED TO BABY JANE?   F6.5509

Associates & Aldrich Co. For Seven Arts Productions. *Dist* Warner Bros. Pictures. 31 Oct **1962** [Cincinnati, Ohio, opening; c3 Nov 1962; LP29392]. Sd; b&w. 35mm. 132 min.

Prod-Dir Robert Aldrich. *Exec Prod* Kenneth Hyman. *Screenplay* Lukas Heller. *Photog* Ernest Haller. *Camera Op* Til Gabani. *Art Dir* William Glasgow. *Set Decor* George Sawley. *Film Ed* Michael Luciano. *Mus* Frank DeVol. *Song: "I've Written a Letter to Daddy"* Frank DeVol. *Choreog* Alex Romero. *Sd* Jack Solomon. *1st & 2d Asst Dir* Tom Connors, Harry Slott. *Prod Supv* Jack R. Berne. *Asst to the Prod* Walter Blake. *Script Supv* Robert Gary. *Cost Dsgn* Norma Koch. *Wardrobe* Angela Alexander, Kathleen McCandless, Vou Lee Giokaris, Eric Seelig. *Makeup* Jack Obringer, Monte Westmore. *Hairstyles* Florence Guernsey, Peggy Shannon. *Sp Eff* Don Steward. *Dial Coach* Robert Sherman. *Still Photog* Don Christie. *Prop* John Orlando. *Grip* Dick Borland.

Cast: Bette Davis *(Jane Hudson)*, Joan Crawford *(Blanche Hudson)*, Victor Buono *(Edwin Flagg)*, Anna Lee *(Mrs. Bates)*, Maidie Norman *(Elvira Stitt)*, Marjorie Bennett *(Mrs. Flagg)*, Dave Willock *(Ray Hudson)*, Anne Barton *(Cora Hudson)*, Barbara D. Merrill *(Liza Bates)*, Julie Allred *(young Jane)*, Gina Gillespie *(young Blanche)*, Bert Freed *(producer)*, Wesley Addy *(director)*, Debbie Burton *(singing voice)*, William Aldrich, Ernest Anderson, Don Ross, Russ Conway, James Seay, Maxine Cooper, John Shay, Robert Cornthwaite, Jon Shepodd, Michael Fox, Peter Virgo, Jr., Bobs Watson.

Melodrama. Source: Henry Farrell, *What Ever Happened to Baby Jane?* (New York, 1960). In the 1920's, 6-year-old Baby Jane Hudson becomes an enormously successful child star in vaudeville while her older sister, Blanche, is forced to remain quietly in the background. As the two reach maturity, however, Jane loses both her appeal and her talent, and Blanche develops into a beautiful and renowned film actress. Then, at the height of her career, Blanche is crippled in an automobile accident for which the alcoholic Jane is held responsible. As the years pass, the two sisters become virtual recluses in an old mansion, where the slatternly and guilt-ridden Jane cares for the helpless Blanche. When she learns Blanche is planning to sell the house and perhaps place her in a home, Jane plots a diabolical revenge. She serves her sister trays of dead rats and parakeets, tears out her phone, and keeps her a prisoner in her bedroom. She even resorts to killing their black maid, Elvira, with a hammer when the woman becomes suspicious and threatens to go to the police. Jane is also planning to make a comeback and has hired the obese pianist Edwin Flagg to accompany her. But when Edwin discovers Blanche gagged and bound to her bed, he runs hysterically from the house. Realizing he will go to the police, Jane drags Blanche into a car and drives to a nearby beach. There Blanche confesses that she had arranged the automobile accident and had intended to kill her sister to avenge herself for the years of humiliation she had spent in the shadow of Baby Jane. As the police arrive upon the scene, the now totally deranged Jane goes into her song-and-dance routine of long ago. *Sisters. Actors. Children. Cripples. Recluses. Housemaids. Negroes. Pianists. Police. Jealousy. Alcoholism. Starvation. Guilt. Revenge. Murder. Insanity. Motion pictures. Beaches. Automobile accidents.*

Note: Included are film clips from *Parachute Jumper* (1933) and *Sadie McKee* (1934).

WHAT EVER HAPPENED TO COUSIN CHARLOTTE? see HUSH ... HUSH, SWEET CHARLOTTE

WHAT NEXT? (Sweden)   F6.5510

Omega Film. *Dist* Cannon Releasing Corp. 4 Nov **1970** [Chicago opening]. Sd; b&w. 35mm. 81 min. *MPAA rating* X.

Prod Christopher Dennis. *Exec Prod* Bert Sundberg. *Dir* Claes Fellbom. *Screenplay* Yvonne Andersson, Claes Fellbom. *Dir Photog* Åke Dahlquist. *Camera* Lasse Dahlqvist. *Sets* Poa Sivertzen. *Film Ed* Filmmakarna. *Mus* Guy Öhrström, Claes Fellbom. *Songs* Majilen Bergstrom, Cal Floyd. *Sd* Lars

Nordberg. *Mix* Filmmakarna. *Prod Mgr* Bert Sundberg. *Supv* Mikael Ekman. *Script Girl* Chris Tonnert. *Still Photog* Pierre Bjorklund.

Cast: Monica Nordqvist *(Carmilla Wahlström)*, Birger Malmsten *(Per Ek)*, Öllegård Wellton *(Vera)*, Lissi Alandh *(Maria Ek)*, Erik Hell *(Gunnar Wahlström)*.

Melodrama. For several years since she left home, Carmilla has lived with Vera, a lesbian who runs a high-class brothel for businessmen. After learning of her mother's death, Carmilla attends the funeral and meets her stepfather, who suggests that she visit him. Carmilla does so on several occasions, until one evening her stepfather makes advances toward her. Escaping into the street, Carmilla causes him to stumble and be killed by a car driven by Dr. and Mrs. Ek, who have been drinking and do not stop the car. Bent on revenge, Carmilla identifies the culprits, and they take her in to avoid blackmail. Dr. Ek soon develops a passion for Carmilla, while Maria, his wife, takes to drink. One evening, becoming suspicious of their relationship, Maria follows them to their rendezvous, a boathouse. While they make love, Maria bolts the door and sets fire to the building. Carmilla and Dr. Ek burn to death as Maria watches. *Physicians. Stepfathers. Hit-and-run drivers. Lesbianism. Alcoholism. Incendiarism. Infidelity. Incest. Revenge. Murder. Blackmail. Whorehouses. Automobile accidents.*

Note: Released in Sweden in Dec 1968 as *Carmilla*; running time: 92 min. U. S. prerelease title: *Incest*.

WHAT'S GOOD FOR THE GOOSE (Great Britain) **F6.5511**

Tigon British Film Productions. *Dist* National Showmanship Films. Dec **1969**. Sd; col (Eastman Color). 35mm. 104 min. *MPAA rating* R.

Prod Tony Tenser. *Assoc Prod* Norman Wisdom. *Dir-Screenplay-Story* Menahem Golan. *Script* Norman Wisdom. *Dial* Christopher Gilmore. *Photog* William Brayne. *Art Dir* Hayden Pearce. *Film Ed* Dennis Lanning. *Mus Reg* Tilsley. *Titl Song* Reg Tilsley, Howard Blaikley. *Sung by* Norman Wisdom. *Other Songs* The Pretty Things. *Sd* Hugh Strain. *Asst Dir* Gordon Gilbert, Dennis Gilbert, Peter Cotton. *Prod Mgr* George Mills.

Cast: Norman Wisdom *(Timothy Bartlett)*, Sally Geeson *(Nikki)*, Sarah Atkinson *(Meg)*, Terence Alexander *(Frisby)*, Sally Bazely *(Margaret Bartlett)*, Derek Francis *(Harrington)*, David Lodge *(hotel porter)*, Paul Whitsun-Jones *(Clark)*, Stuart Nichol *(bank manager)*, Hilary Pritchard *(cashier in discotheque)*, H. H. Goldsmith *(policeman)*, Thelma Falls-Hand *(bank clerk)*, Duncan Taylor *(other banker)*, Jonathan Cox, Patrick Goggin *(sons)*, Sally Beglin *(daughter)*, George Meaton *(3d speaker)*, Karl Lanchbury *(Peter)*, The Pretty Things.

Comedy. Timothy Bartlett, a middle-aged assistant bank manager on his way to a bankers' convention in the resort town of Southport, picks up teenaged hitchhikers Nikki and Meg. Bored by the convention, Timothy leaves and looks for the girls. He finds Nikki in a discotheque and spends the night with her in his hotel room. Timothy begins dressing in youthful, hippie-like clothing and appears at the convention in a flowered shirt. After giving a speech, he returns to Nikki, and they spend the day racing through the sand dunes and sunbathing in the nude. Timothy rents an apartment for Nikki, but he comes in one night to find an orgy in progress and Nikki in bed with a young man. Disillusioned, Timothy calls his wife, Margaret, and asks her to fly to Southport. When she arrives, he tries to introduce her to his new lifestyle, dressing her in youthful attire and teaching her to dance. Finally, both Margaret and Timothy realize the foolishness of their behavior and return home. *Hitchhikers. Bankers. Hippies. Middle age. Adolescence. Orgies. Infidelity. Conventions. Discotheques. Resorts. Southport (England).*

Note: Released in London in Mar 1969. Also reviewed as *What's Good for the Gander.*

WHAT'S HAPPENING **F6.5512**

Maysles Films. 1 Jan **1970** [Berkeley, California, opening]. Sd; b&w. 35mm. 53 min.

Prod-Dir Albert Maysles, David Maysles. *Photog* Albert Maysles.

Featuring: The Beatles, Ed Sullivan, Murray the K.

Documentary. This film records the Beatles' first visit to the United States in February 1964. They are met on their arrival in New York by an enthusiastic crowd of adolescent fans. During a press conference, the group answers unimaginative questions facetiously. In New York City, they are interviewed by disc jockey Murray the K and appear on Ed Sullivan's television show. After riding by train to a Washington, D. C., concert, the Beatles return to Great Britain. They are met at the London airport by another group of adolescent zealots. *Singers. Disc jockeys. Interviewers. Rock and roll. Adolescence. New York City. Washington (District of Columbia). The Beatles. Ed Sullivan Show.*

Note: Also known as *What's Happening!—The Beatles in the U. S. A.*

WHAT'S IN IT FOR HARRY? *see* **HOW TO MAKE IT**

WHAT'S NEW PUSSYCAT? (United States/France) **F6.5513**

Famous Artists Productions–Famartists Productions. *Dist* United Artists. 22 Jun **1965** [New York opening; c22 Jun 1965; LP30967]. Sd (Westrex); col (Technicolor). 35mm. 108 min.

Pres by Charles K. Feldman. *Prod* Charles K. Feldman. *Assoc Prod* Richard Sylbert. *Exec Prod* John C. Shepridge. *Dir* Clive Donner. *Karting Seq & 2d Unit Dir* Richard Talmadge. *Writ* Woody Allen. *Dir Photog* Jean Badal. *2d Unit Dir Photog* Henri Persin. *Camera Op* Philippe Brun. *Art Dir* Jacques Saulnier. *Set Dresser* Charles Mérangel. *Titl* Richard Williams. *Ed Fergus* McDonell. *Mus Comp* Burt Bacharach. *Songs* Burt Bacharach, Hal David. *Arr & Cond* Charles Blackwell. *Song:* "What's New Pussycat" sung by Tom Jones. *Song:* "Here I Am" sung by Dionne Warwick. *Song:* "Little Red Book" played by Manfred Mann. *Sung by* Paul Jones, singer. *Choreog* Jean Guelis. *Sd Engr* William R. Sivel, Antoine Petitjean. *Sd Rec* Jacques Gérardot, Hugh Strain. *Sd Ed* Dino Di Campo. *1st Asst Dir* Enrico Isacco. *Prod Mgr* Henri Jaquillard. *Prod Asst* Paul Lemaire, Richard Talmadge. *Cost* Gladys de Segonzac. *Miss Prentiss' Clothes Dsgn* Mia Fonssagrives, Vicki Tiel. *Ch Makeup* Charles Parker. *Hairstyles* Jacqueline Juillard. *Sp Eff* M. MacDonald.

Cast: Peter Sellers *(Dr. Fritz Fassbender)*, Peter O'Toole *(Michael James)*, Romy Schneider *(Carole Werner)*, Capucine *(Renée Lefèbvre)*, Paula Prentiss *(Liz)*, Woody Allen *(Victor Shakapopulis)*, Ursula Andress *(Rita)*, Eddra Gale *(Anna Fassbender)*, Katrin Schaake *(Jacqueline)*, Eléonore Hirt *(Mrs. Sylvia Werner)*, Jean Parédès *(Marcel)*, Jacques Balutin *(Etienne)*, Jess Hahn *(Perry Werner)*, Howard Vernon *(doctor)*, Michel Subor *(Philippe)*, Sabine Sun *(nurse)*, Nicole Karen *(Tempest O'Brien)*, Jacqueline Fogt *(Charlotte)*, Daniel Emilfork *(gas station man)*, Tanya Lopert *(Miss Lewis)*, Barbara Somers *(Miss Marks)*, Robert Rollis *(car renter)*, Annette Poivre *(Emma)*, Richard Saint-Bris *(Le Maire)*, Marion Conrad *(1st stripteaser)*, Maggie Wright *(2d stripteaser)*, Louis Falavigna *(Jean)*, Jean-Yves Autrey, Pascal Wolf, Nadine Papin *(Fassbender's children)*, Colin Drake *(Durell)*, Norbert Terry *(Kelly)*, Gordon Felio *(fat man)*, Louise Lasser *(The Nutcracker)*, F. Medard *(Nash)*, Françoise Hardy *(secretary)*, Douking *(concierge at Renée's apartment)*, Richard Burton.

Comedy. Paris fashion magazine editor Michael James is involved in a relationship with Carole Werner, but the beautiful women he encounters in his work continually distract him. He consults psychiatrist Fritz Fassbender about his problem, but the doctor's own unfulfilled desires are compounded when he hears of Michael's conquests. Fassbender's overpowering wife, Anna, intends to keep him from extramarital lapses, however. Michael's friend Victor, who is also attracted to Carole, is concerned because he can't attract women, even though he is an "undresser" at a striptease club. When Carole learns that her parents are about to arrive for a visit, she tells Michael that they will either have to get married or break off the romance. Determined to have a final fling, Michael visits Victor at the club and falls for Liz, a beautiful stripper given to casual suicide attempts, but she is only interested in reading her poetry to him. Meanwhile, through Fassbender, Michael becomes involved with Renée, whose cold exterior conceals her passionate disposition. At the same time, Carole attempts to make Michael jealous by captivating Victor. Furthermore, Michael tries to entangle Renée with the adoring Fassbender in order to get rid of her. Michael then begins a third involvement with a mad parachutist, Rita. Declaring a temporary truce, Michael and Carole spend an enjoyable evening with Carole's parents, and he decides at last to marry and settle down. In a discreet country hotel, however, everyone takes part in a climactic chase in and out of the bedrooms before the marriage question is affirmatively resolved. *Fashion editors. Psychiatrists. Stripteasers. Poets. Marriage. Jealousy. Suicide. Sexuality. Parachuting. Hotels. Nightclubs. Paris. Chases.*

Note: Filmed in and around Paris. Opened in Paris in Jan 1966 as *Quoi de neuf, Pussycat?*; running time: 105 min. French coproduction status unconfirmed.

WHAT'S SO BAD ABOUT FEELING GOOD? **F6.5514**

Universal Pictures. 24 May **1968** [New York opening; c6 Jul 1968; LP38821]. Sd (Westrex); col (Technicolor). 35mm (Techniscope). 94 min. [Copyright length: 103 min.]

Prod-Dir George Seaton. *Story & Screenplay* George Seaton, Robert Pirosh. *Dir Photog* Ernesto Caparros. *Art Dir* Alexander Golitzen, Henry Bumstead. *Set Decor* John McCarthy. *Main Titl & Art Eff* Pacific Title. *Film Ed* Alma Macrorie. *Mus De* Vol. *Songs:* "Blue, Black and Gray," "I'm Bubbling Over," "What's So Bad About Feeling Good?" Jerry Keller, Dave Blume. *Mus Supv* Joseph Gershenson. *Choreog* Michael Bennett. *Sd* Waldon O. Watson, Jim Shields. *Asst Dir* Donald Roberts, Paul Ganapoler, Phil Parslow. *Unit Prod Mgr* Wallace Worsley. *Cost Dsgn* Edith Head. *Makeup* Bud Westmore. *Hairstyles* Larry Germain. *Bird Trainer* Ray Berwick.

Cast: George Peppard *(Pete)*, Mary Tyler Moore *(Liz)*, Dom DeLuise *(J. Gardner Monroe)*, John McMartin *(the mayor)*, Nathaniel Frey *(Conrad)*, Charles Lane *(Dr. Shapiro)*, Jeanne Arnold *(Gertrude)*, George Furth *(Murgatroyd)*, Susan Saint James *(Aida)*, Don Stroud *(Barney)*, Morty Gunty

(*Sergeant Gunty*), Joe Ponazecki (*Officer Ponazecki*), Frank Campanella (*Captain Wallace*), Arny Freeman (*1st mate*), Martin O'Hara (*TV newscaster*), John Ryan (*Roger*), Cleavon Little (*Phil*), Emily Yancy (*Sybil*), Gillian Spencer (*The Sack*), Donald Hotten (*Sam*), Robert Moore (*board member*), Thelma Ritter (*Mrs. Schwartz*), Joey Faye (*zoo keeper*), Marc Seaton, Victoria Racimo, Mina Kolb, Peter Turgeon, Kay Turner, Moses Gunn, Bob Kaliban, Ira Lewis, George Petrie, Hugh Franklin, Hy Anzell, Peter Gumeny, Eda Reiss Merin, Jara Kohout, Nat Polan, Barbara Minkus, Salem Ludwig, Franklin Cover, Louis Zorich, George Sperdakos, Albert Henderson, Lincoln Kilpatrick, Tom Ahearne.

Comedy. Suggested by: Vincent McHugh, *I Am Thinking of My Darling* (New York, 1943). A brightly plumed tropical bird, infected with a rare virus that causes instant happiness, arrives in Manhattan on a Greek freighter and immediately spreads the "disease" to normally irritable New Yorkers. Among the first to be infected are Pete, a Madison Avenue drop-out who has become an East Village artist, and his hippie girl friend, Liz. They soon become well-dressed disseminators of good will; they adopt the bird, name it Amigo, and protect it from city officials who are disturbed by the alarming drop in liquor, cigarette, and tranquilizer sales. Fearing a collapse of the city's financial structure, the mayor enlists the assistance of presidential aide J. Gardner Monroe. When germ masks are distributed to the populace, Pete and his new friends thwart the government's plan by infecting the masks. Eventually, Amigo is captured, and an antidote is found for the mass euphoria. Soon New Yorkers are again snarling at each other, and Pete returns to his former bearded, shiftless self. Liz, who never actually contracted the virus, remains the same since she was only responding to the kindness of others. After Amigo has escaped from his Central Park aviary, Pete finally realizes that Liz is all that he really wants, and the two are reunited. *Artists. Hippies. Mayors. Utopia. Epidemics. New York City. New York City—East Village. New York City—Central Park. Birds.*

Note: Location scenes filmed in New York City.

WHAT'S UP FRONT   F6.5515

Delta Productions. *Dist* Fairway-International Films. 29 Apr **1964** [Maryland license]. Sd; col (Technicolor). 35mm. 83 min.

Prod Anthony M. Lanza. *Exec Prod* Nicholas Merriwether. *Dir* Bob Wehling. *Screenplay* Bob Wehling, Arch Hall, Sr. *Orig Story* Arch Hall, Sr. *Dir Photog* William Zsigmond. *Art Dir* David Reed, III. *Film Ed* Anthony M. Lanza. *Asst to the Prod* L. Steven Snyder. *Bras* Fredericks of Hollywood.

Cast: Tommy Holden (*Homer L. Pettigrew*), Marilyn Manning (*Candy Cotton*), Carolyn Walker (*Pamela Johnson*), William Watters (*Cash Johnson*), Carmen Bonacci (*August Poe*), Mary Jane Neese (*Joan*), Barbara Ballar (*Mable*), Jack Sword (*Alf*), Robert Wheeler (*General Smythe*), Nancy Czar (*Mrs. Smythe*), Joan Howard, David Reed, Rick Dennis, Addalyn Fay, Sam Chiodi.

Comedy. Looking for work, salesman Homer Pettigrew goes from his Indiana home to Los Angeles and answers a newspaper want-ad at the Johnson Bra Company. He interrupts a business meeting and suggests that he can bolster the company's dwindling sales by selling bras door-to-door. Millionaire owner Cash Johnson is impressed, but sales manager August Poe takes exception to the plan. Aided by Cash's secretary, Candy Cotton, Poe plots to take over the company by courting Cash's daughter, Pamela. Homer falls in love with Pamela, and with this incentive, he sells 300 bras the first day. Poe tries to get rid of Homer by sending him to West Virginia, but Homer wastes no time, selling bras to the airline stewardesses on board his flight. He makes customers of all the farmers' wives and daughters and receives an order for a million bras from the Women's Army Corps. Poe discredits Homer and takes credit for the sales. Homesick for Pamela, Homer sends word that he is returning to Los Angeles, but Poe reports him to the FBI as a mad bomber, and he is arrested as he boards the plane. Homer's true identity is discovered, and the federal agents arrest Poe in Las Vegas as he is about to marry Pamela. Homer takes Poe's place in the ceremony, and Cash takes advantage of the situation by marrying Candy. *Traveling salesmen. Executives. Sales managers. Secretaries. Airline stewardesses. Salesmanship. Fraud. Lingerie. Los Angeles. West Virginia. Las Vegas. United States—Federal Bureau of Investigation.*

Note: William Watters and Nicholas Merriwether are pseudonyms for Arch Hall, Sr.

WHAT'S UP TIGER LILY? (United States/Japan)   F6.5516

Toho Co.-Benedict Pictures. *Dist* American International Pictures. 2 Nov **1966** [Baltimore opening]. Sd; col (Eastmancolor). 35mm (Tohoscope, see note). 80 min.

Pres by James H. Nicholson, Samuel Z. Arkoff. A Henry G. Saperstein-Reuben Bercovitch Production. *Exec Prod American Vers* Henry G. Saperstein. *Exec Prod Japanese Vers* Tomoyuki Tanaka. *Assoc Prod* Woody Allen. *Dir Japanese Vers* Senkichi Taniguchi. *Screenplay English Vers* Woody Allen, Frank Buxton, Len Maxwell, Louise Lasser, Mickey Rose, Bryna

Wilson, Julie Bennett. *Screenplay Japanese Vers* Kazuo Yamada. *Photog Japanese Vers* Kazuo Yamada. *Titl Seq* Murakami-Wolf, Phill Norman, UPA Pictures. *Film Ed* Richard Krown. *Mus* Jack Lewis, mus. *Theme Songs:* "Pow," "Pow Revisited" John Sebastian, Joe Butler, Steve Boone, Zalman Yanovsky, Skip Boone. *Sung by* The Lovin' Spoonful. *Songs:* "Gray Prison Blues," "Unconscious Minuet," "A Cool Million," "Lookin' To Spy," "Phil's Love Theme" John Sebastian, Joe Butler, Steve Boone, Zalman Yanovsky. *Sung by* The Lovin' Spoonful. *Traditional Song:* "Fishin' Blues" arr & adapt by John Sebastian. *Sung by* The Lovin' Spoonful. *Song:* "Respoken" comp & sung by John Sebastian. *Song:* "Speakin' of Spoken" John Sebastian. *Sung by* The Lovin' Spoonful. *Sd* Glen Glenn Sound. *Prod Mgr* Jerry Goldstein. *Prod Conception* Ben Shapiro.

Cast: Tatsuya Mihashi (*Phil Moscowitz*), Mie Hama (*Terri Yaki*), Akiko Wakabayashi (*Suki Yaki*), Tadao Nakamaru (*Shepherd Wong*), Susumu Kurobe (*Wing Fat*), Woody Allen (*narrator/host/voice*), Frank Buxton, Len Maxwell, Louise Lasser, Mickey Rose, Julie Bennett, Bryna Wilson (*voices*), The Lovin' Spoonful (*themselves*), China Lee (*herself*), Kumi Mizuno.

Action farce. After a brief prolog in which Woody Allen explains that his film concoction is a sort of "bottled-in-Bond spy drama," the story relates the adventures of Phil Moscowitz, a young Japanese who is kidnaped by oriental beauties and whisked off to an unidentified Asian country to help foil an international plot to steal the best egg-salad recipe in the world. Despite numerous assassination attempts, the hero always manages to escape narrowly with his life. Brief intermissions show the Lovin' Spoonful singing "Pow" and other songs. Moscowitz discovers that the mastermind behind the theft is Shepherd Wong, a connoisseur of eggs and cigars. The blazing showdown has Moscowitz killing four villains with three bullets. As the day is saved for egg-salad, Woody Allen again appears, accompanied by China Lee. Explaining that he had promised to give her something to do in the picture, Allen munches on an apple while China Lee removes some of her clothing, and the film ends. *Spies. Masterminds. Gourmets. Espionage. Kidnaping. Eggs. Asia.*

Note: Originally released in Japan by Toho Co. in 1964 as *Kagi no kagi*; running time: 94 min. Sold to Henry G. Saperstein and Ben Shapiro, who gave the film to Woody Allen. Allen erased the soundtrack, reedited the film, added several sequences, and dubbed in a new English dialog, commentary, and music (original Japanese score was by Sadao Bekku). Only Japanese sequences were shot in Tohoscope. Title also rendered as *What's Up, Tiger Lily?*

WHEEL OF ASHES (France)   F6.5517

PBN Productions. *Dist* Film-Makers' Distribution Center. 2 Jun **1970** [New York opening]. Sd; b&w. 16mm & 35mm. 96 min. [See note.]

Dir-Writ Peter Emanuel Goldman. *Photog* Peter Emanuel Goldman. *Ed* Joele Bleton.

Cast: Pierre Clementi (*Pierre*), Katinka Bo (*Anka*), Pierre Besancon (*David*). Members of the Living Theatre.

Drama. Pierre, a young Parisian, is looking for spiritual contact with God, and in the process he has tried to cut himself off from external pursuits and temptations. His past unfolds: as a penniless youth he wandered through Paris—along the boulevards between La Bastille and the Place de la République; around Les Halles; through St. Germain; near the Place St. Michel. He also explored elements of Western religion and Eastern mysticism, meanwhile seeking meaning in sexual experiences. He now becomes involved with Anka, a Danish woman, but though Anka becomes pregnant Pierre leaves her to isolate himself in a room where he pursues his Karma and explores the concept of reincarnation. He experiences hallucinations during this period and finally is led to accept a compromise that allows him to embrace life and love. His belief in reincarnation remains while he looks forward with Anka to the birth of a child. *Danes. Mysticism. Sexuality. Reincarnation. Alienation. Pregnancy. Youth. Paris. Hallucinations.*

Note: Filmed on location in Paris in 16mm. Venice Film Festival (1968) running time: 110 min. The 16mm release runs 92 min.

THE WHEELER DEALERS   F6.5518

Filmways, Inc. *Dist* Metro-Goldwyn-Mayer, Inc. 14 Nov **1963** [New York opening; c24 Jul 1963; LP26162]. Sd (Westrex); col (Metrocolor). 35mm (Panavision). 106 min.

A Martin Ransohoff Production. *Prod* Martin Ransohoff. *Assoc Prod* John Calley. *Dir* Arthur Hiller. *Screenplay* George J. W. Goodman, Ira Wallach. *Dir Photog* Charles Lang. *Col Cons* Charles K. Hagedon. *Art Dir* George W. Davis, Addison Hehr. *Set Dsgn* Henry Grace, Keogh Gleason. *Titl Dsgn* Richard Kuhn, James S. Pollak. *Film Ed* Tom McAdoo. *Mus De Vol. *Titl Song* Randy Sparks. *Sung by* New Christy Minstrels. *Rec Supv* Franklin Milton. *Asst Dir* Al Westen. *Prod Mgr* Ivan Volkman. *Miss Remick's Wardrobe Dsgn* Norman Norell. *Makeup* William Tuttle. *Hairstyles* Sydney Guilaroff.

Cast: James Garner (*Henry Tyroon*), Lee Remick (*Molly Thatcher*), Phil Harris (*Ray Jay*), Chill Wills (*Jay Ray*), Louis Nye (*Stanislas*), John Astin (*Hector Vanson*), Jim Backus (*Bullard Bear*), Elliott Reid (*Leonard*), Patricia

Crowley (Eloise), Pat Harrington, Jr. (Buddy Zack), Joey Forman (Buster Yarrow), Charles Watts (J. R.), Vaughn Taylor (Thaddeus Whipple), Howard McNear (Mr. Wilson), Robert Strauss (Fineberg), Marcel Hillaire (Giuseppe), John Marley (Achilles Dimitrios), Don Briggs (Len Fink), Peter Leeds (Arthur Watkins), William Fawcett, Percy Kelton, Dal McKennon (The Whipples), H. M. Wynant (Bo Bluedog), Walter Burke (Billy Joe).

Comedy. Source: George J. W. Goodman, *The Wheeler Dealers* (Garden City, N. Y., 1959). "Wheeler-Dealer" Henry Tyroon comes to New York to raise more than a million dollars to finance a business scheme. He meets Molly Thatcher, a Wall Street stock analyst, whose boss, Bullard Bear, has assigned her to boost a stock (Universal Widget) that—though not to her knowledge—is apparently worthless. Molly's salary is an expense the firm can no longer afford, and they wish to be rid of her. Henry decides to help Molly with Universal Widget, maneuvering her boyfriend out of the way and dating her himself. Among the other side interests that Henry buys while in the city are a taxicab and driver, a chic restaurant, an art collection, and an abstract artist named Stanislas. In Massachusetts, Molly and Henry discover that Widgets went out of production in 1854, but they create an advertising campaign to promote the stock. They meet the Whipples, laconic New Englanders who own the hidden assets of Universal Widget, now a booming concern, and Henry strikes oil on Widget property. As Widget stock soars, a suspicious SEC investigates; and Henry, Molly, the Whipples, and assorted other characters are taken to court. Henry is revealed as a Yale man, not a Texan, and the Widget oil is discovered to stem from a pipeline. Molly, eased out of her job at this point, believes Henry responsible. A judge throws the confusing case out of court, ruling that the manipulation of Universal Widget is not against public interest. The Whipples own 48 percent, a group of Henry's Texas cronies own 48 percent, and Henry owns the controlling 4 percent of the stock. He sells his shares to the Whipples for the money he needs to support his business scheme, and he and Molly patch up their quarrel and decide to marry. *Businessmen. Millionaires. Texans. Stockbrokers. Art collectors. Restaurateurs. Taxi drivers. Artists. Judges. New Englanders. Employment—Women. Advertising. Business ethics. Oil wells. New York City—Wall Street. Massachusetts. United States—Securities and Exchange Commission.*

WHEN A WOMAN ASCENDS THE STAIRS (Japan)　　　F6.5519
Toho Co. 25 Jun **1963** [New York opening]. Sd; b&w. 35mm (Tohoscope). 111 min.
Exec Prod Ryuzo Kikushima. *Dir* Mikio Naruse. *Screenplay* Ryuzo Kikushima. *Photog* Masao Tamai. *Film Ed* H. Ito. *Cost* Hideko Takamine.
Cast: Hideko Takamine (*Keiko Yashiro*), Masayuki Mori (*Nobuhiko Fujisaki*), Daisuke Kato (*Matsukichi Sekine*), Tatsuya Nakadai (*Kenichi Komatsu*), Reiko Dan (*Junko Ichihashi*), Keiko Awaji (*Yuri*).
Drama. Keiko Yashiro, an impoverished young widow, takes a job as a hostess in a dingy bar in Tokyo's Ginza district. Though encouraged by her employer to do more than just drink with the customers, Keiko prefers to remain poor rather than become a prostitute. After working for 5 years, she attempts to open her own bar, but this venture ends in failure. A short time after she has gone back to her old job, another hostess, Yuri, commits suicide because of her financial difficulties. Foreseeing what might be her own future, Keiko becomes friendly with Sekine, a factory owner who has hinted of his desire to marry her. After having sex with him, she discovers that he already has a wife and children. Filled with despair, Keiko drowns her sorrow in whiskey and spends the night with Fujisake, a banker. When he too is gone in the morning, she realizes that it is her fate to be a prostitute, and she walks up the steps to the bar to greet the customers. *Widows. Barroom hostesses. Bankers. Employer-employee relations. Finance—Personal. Prostitution. Suicide. Disillusionment. Drunkenness. Bars. Tokyo—Ginza District.*
Note: Released in Japan in 1960 as *Onna ga kaidan o agarutoki.*

WHEN MEN ARE BEASTS (Reissue)　　　F6.5520
Southern California Pictures. *Dist* Waldorf Pictures. 27 Feb **1963** [Maryland license]. Sd; b&w. 35mm. 91 min.
Note: Originally released by Film Classics in 1948 as *Women in the Night;* c30 Dec 1947; LP1548.

WHEN THE BOYS MEET THE GIRLS　　　F6.5521
Four Leaf Productions. *Dist* Metro-Goldwyn-Mayer, Inc. 22 Dec **1965** [Los Angeles opening; c10 Oct 1965; LP31867]. Sd (Westrex); col (Metrocolor). 35mm (Panavision). 102 min. [Copyright length: 97 min; also reviewed at 110 min.]
Prod Sam Katzman. *Dir* Alvin Ganzer. *Screenplay* Robert E. Kent. *Dir Photog* Paul C. Vogel. *Art Dir* George W. Davis, Eddie Imazu. *Set Decor* Henry Grace, Keogh Gleason. *Film Ed* Ben Lewis. *Mus Score & Cond* Fred Karger. *Songs:* "But Not for Me," "I Got Rhythm," "Embraceable You," "Bidin' My Time," "Treat Me Rough" George Gershwin, Ira Gershwin. "But Not for Me," "I Got Rhythm" sung by Harve Presnell, Connie Francis.

"Embraceable You" sung by Harve Presnell. "Bidin' My Time" sung by Herman's Hermits. "Treat Me Rough" sung by Sue Ane Langdon. *Song:* "Listen People" Graham Gouldman. *Sung by* Herman's Hermits. *Song:* "Throw It Out Your Mind" Louis Armstrong, Billy Kyle. *Perf & Sung by* Louis Armstrong. *Song:* "Monkey See, Monkey Do" Johnny Farrow. *Sung by* Sam the Sham & the Pharoahs. *Songs* Fred Karger, Ben Weisman, Sid Wayne. *Sung by* Connie Francis. "It's All in Your Mind" sung by The Standells. *Titl Song* Jack Keller, Howard Greenfield. *Sung by* Connie Francis. *Song:* "Aruba Liberace" *writ & played by* Liberace. *Choreog* Earl Barton. *Rec Supv* Franklin Milton. *Sd* Larry Hadsell. *Asst Dir* Eddie Saeta. *Unit Prod Mgr* Robert Stone. *Asst to the Prod* F. Katzman. *Makeup* William Tuttle. *Hairstyles* Sydney Guilaroff. *Sp Vis Eff* J. McMillan Johnson, Carroll L. Shepphird.
Cast: Connie Francis (*Ginger*), Harve Presnell (*Danny*), Herman's Hermits (*themselves*), Louis Armstrong (*himself*), Sam the Sham & The Pharoahs (*themselves*), Liberace (*himself*), Sue Ane Langdon (*Tess*), Fred Clark (*Bill*), Frank Faylen (*Phin*), Joby Baker (*Sam*), Hortense Petra (*Kate*), Stanley Adams (*Lank*), Romo Vincent (*Pete*), Susan Holloway (*Delilah*), Russell Collins (*Stokes*), William Quinn (*dean of Cody*), Pepper Davis, Tony Reese (*themselves*), Patti Moore (*divorcée*).
Comedy with music. Source: Guy Bolton and John McGowan, *Girl Crazy* (New York opening: 14 Oct 1930). To escape from the mercenary clutches of a blackmailing showgirl who is suing him for breach of promise, Danny, a wealthy playboy, enrolls at Cody College, a remote school in Nevada. There he meets Ginger, the daughter of local mailman, Phin, whose unlucky penchant for gambling has almost forced him to sell his ranch. As romance develops between the two young people, Danny hits upon the idea of converting the ramshackle property into a luxurious dude ranch for divorcees. The opening, launched by a host of professional entertainers and the entire student body, is a huge success. Complications arise when the showgirl, Tess, joins forces with gamblers out to make a killing. But virtue triumphs: Phin's debts are paid and Danny finds true love with Ginger. *Playboys. Showgirls. Mail carriers. Entertainers. College life. Blackmail. Wealth. Debt. Gambling. Divorce. Ranches. Dude ranches. Nevada.*
Note: Shorter version(s) may not contain a sequence with the Standells. Also known as *Girl Crazy,* this film is a remake of Metro-Goldwyn-Mayer's 1943 film of that title. RKO released an earlier version of *Girl Crazy* in 1932.

WHEN THE CLOCK STRIKES　　　F6.5522
Harvard Film Corp. *Dist* United Artists. 24 May **1961** [Los Angeles opening; c13 May 1961; LP20545]. Sd; b&w. 35mm. 72 min.
Prod Robert E. Kent. *Dir* Edward L. Cahn. *Writ* Dallas Gaultois. *Dir Photog* Kenneth Peach. *Film Ed* Grant Whytock. *Mus* Richard La Salle. *Mus Dir* Lloyd Young. *Sd* Dean Thomas. *Asst Dir* Herbert S. Greene. *Prod Mgr* Joseph Small. *Wardrobe* Einar Bourman, Barbara Maxwell. *Makeup* Harry Thomas. *Hairstyles* Frances Sperry.
Cast: James Brown (*Sam Morgan*), Merry Anders (*Ellie*), Henry Corden (*Cady*), Roy Barcroft (*sheriff*), Peggy Stewart (*Mrs. Pierce*), Jorge Moreno (*Martinez*), Francis De Sales (*warden*), Max Mellinger (*postman*), Eden Hartford (*waitress*), Jack Kenny (*cafe proprietor*).
Crime melodrama. After helping to convict a man of murder, Sam Morgan is troubled, and he races through a blinding storm to the prison where the man, Frank Pierce, is scheduled to be executed at midnight. En route, he picks up a young woman named Ellie and gives her a lift to a nearby lodge. When he is unable to stop the execution, Sam returns to the lodge and joins Ellie for a drink. As the hour of execution nears, she tells him she is Pierce's wife. At midnight, a man named Martinez rushes into the lodge and confesses to the crime for which Pierce is being executed. The next day, after Martinez has been taken into custody by the police, Sam and Ellie go through the last of Pierce's belongings and find a key to a post office box in New Mexico. Certain the box contains money Pierce had stolen 2 years before, they decide to have the money sent to the lodge and divide it. Then, suddenly, the real Mrs. Pierce arrives at the lodge and announces that Frank Pierce had murdered her father. Meanwhile, the lodge owner, Cady, has also learned about the money, and he makes plans to obtain it for himself. But as he tries to shoot Sam, Mrs. Pierce sees him and he is forced to kill her. Sam and Ellie are about to leave when the money arrives. Cady warns them that if they take it, he will inform the sheriff that Sam killed Mrs. Pierce. Realizing that he must tell the truth, Sam calls the police and has Cady arrested for murder. *Innkeepers. Sheriffs. Prison wardens. Greed. Murder. Robbery. Impersonation. Capital punishment. Lodges (inns).*
Note: Working title: *You Can't Run Far.* May also be known as *The Clock Strikes Three.*

WHEN THE GIRLS TAKE OVER　　　F6.5523
Trans-Oceanic Productions. *Dist* Parade Releasing Organization. May **1962.** Sd; col (Technicolor). 35mm. 80 min.
Prod-Dir Russell Hayden. *Assoc Prod* S. A. Sanford. *Screenplay* Samuel Roeca. *Photog* Arthur Arling. *Film Ed* Reg Browne, Maurice Max. *Mus Comp*

Ben Oakland. *Mus Cond* Howard Jackson. *Sd* Dale Knight. *Hairstyles* Lydia Rodriguez.

Cast: Robert Lowery *(Maximo Toro)*, Marvin Miller *(Henri Degiere)*, Jackie Coogan *(Captain Toussaint)*, Jimmy Ellison *(Axel "Longhorn" Gates)*, Ingeborg Kjeldsen *(Françoise Degiere)*, Jeff Stone *(Steve Harding)*, Don Durrell *("Stoney" Jackson)*, Tommy Cook *(Razmo)*, True Ellison *(Melesa)*, Gabe Dell *(Henderson)*, Paul Bailey *(Clutch)*.

Comedy. The little Caribbean republic of Hondo-Rica, beset with financial problems, is also being threatened by revolutionist Maximo Toro. First Minister Henri Degiere, in New York City to raise funds for Hondo-Rica's proposed sugar by-products program, is notified that Toro has enticed his daughter, Françoise, to the revolutionist's camp and is holding her for a ransom of rifles. Degiere returns and sets out to pretend to deliver the rifles, thereby finding Toro's hideout. When this strategy fails, help arrives from New York, and, according to a plan suggested by the Hondo-Rican women, a task force led by American oil millionaire Axel "Longhorn" Gates, consisting of 26 pink jeeps filled with food, wine, and women, "invades" Toro's camp. The women charm everyone, including Toro, and they all return to town. All ends well as Hondo-Rica acquires the aid to develop its sugar program. *Revolutionaries. Prime ministers. Millionaires. Sugar. Capitalism. Trade agreements. Imaginary republics. Ransom. Firearms. Caribbean.*

Note: Filmed in 1960 in Puerto Rico; working title: *Caribe.*

WHEN THE TREES WERE TALL (U.S.S.R.) F6.5524

Gorky Film Studio. *Dist* Artkino Pictures. 20 Feb **1965** [New York opening]. Sd; b&w. 35mm. 100 min.

Dir Lev Kulidzhanov. *Screenplay* Nikolay Figurovskiy. *Story Ed* V. Pogozheva. *Photog* Valeriy Ginzburg. *Camera* B. Gokke, I. Zarafyan. *Art Dir* P. Galadzhev. *Film Ed* N. Loginova. *Mus* Leonid Afanasyev. *Song Lyr* A. Fatyanov. *Cond* G. Gamburg. *Sd* D. Belevich. *Asst Dir* I. Magiton. *Prod Mgr* B. Krakovskiy. *Cost* N. Baburina. *Makeup* A. Ivanov.

Cast: Inna Gulaya *(Natasha)*, Yuriy Nikulin *(Kuzma Kuzmich Iordanov)*, Lev Kuravlev *(Lenka)*, Ye. Mazurova *(Anastasiya Borisovna)*, Vasiliy Shukshin *(chairman of the kolkhoz)*, Lea Churdina *(Zoya)*, Ye. Korolyova *(Nyurka)*, Ye. Melnikova, V. Trusov, P. Shalnov, V. Lebedev, O. Yakushev, G. Shapovalov, M. Gavrilko, I. Marks, D. Stolyarskaya, V. Orlova, A. Pashukhina, G. Shmovanov, T. Tishura, G. Binevskaya, Olya Petrova.

Melodrama. Alone in life, Kuzma Kuzmich, a war hero and skilled mechanic living in post-war Moscow, cannot adjust to civilian life but becomes an idler and drinks excessively. Hospitalized after a fall, he learns while recuperating of Natasha, a teenaged girl living on a kolkhoz, who has been searching for her missing father. Upon leaving the hospital, Kuzma visits the kolkhoz and passes himself off as Natasha's father. His idleness and drinking initially bring him into conflict with the farm director, but he meanwhile develops a genuine attachment for the kind and sincere Natasha. He eventually confesses his deception to her, but she refuses to believe him. He remains on the farm and, heartened by Natasha's love, begins to take part in the work of the community, once more utilizing his skill as a mechanic. Meanwhile, Natasha becomes romantically involved with Lenka. The two young people decide to marry, and Kuzma, who at last has regained a meaningful place in society, remains on the kolkhoz. *War heroes. Mechanics. Veterans. Idlers. Adolescence. Fatherhood. Impersonation. Collective farming. Alcoholism. Hospitals. World War II. Moscow.*

Note: Released in the U.S.S.R. in Mar 1962 as *Kogda derevya byli bolshimi*; running time: 94 min.

WHERE ANGELS GO ... TROUBLE FOLLOWS! F6.5525

William Frye Productions. *Dist* Columbia Pictures. 3 Apr **1968** [Houston opening; c31 Dec 1967; LP35871]. Sd; col (Pathé). 35mm. 95 min.

Prod William Frye. *Assoc Prod* James Wharton. *Dir* James Neilson. *Writ* Blanche Hanalis. *Dir Photog* Sam Leavitt. *Set Decor* Frank Tuttle. *Prod Dsgn* Lyle Wheeler. *Main Titl* Wayne Fitzgerald. *Film Ed* Adrienne Fazan. *Mus* Lalo Schifrin. *Titl Song* Lalo Schifrin, Tommy Boyce, Bobby Hart. *Sung by* Tommy Boyce, Bobby Hart. *Choreog* Hannah Reiner. *Sd Supv* Charles J. Rice. *Sd* Bill Ford, Jack Haynes. *Asst Dir* Carl Beringer, John Anderson, Jr. *Prod Cons* William O'Sullivan. *Asst to the Prod* Rita Kohler. *Script Supv* Charlsie Bryant. *Cost Supv* Moss Mabry. *Makeup* Ben Lane. *Hairstyles* Virginia Jones.

Cast: Rosalind Russell *(Mother Simplicia)*, Stella Stevens *(Sister George)*, Binnie Barnes *(Sister Celestine)*, Mary Wickes *(Sister Clarissa)*, Dolores Sutton *(Sister Rose Marie)*, Milton Berle *(film director)*, Arthur Godfrey *(bishop)*, Van Johnson *(Father Chase)*, Robert Taylor *(Mr. Farriday)*, Susan Saint James *(Rosabelle)*, Barbara Hunter *(Marvel Ann Clancy)*, Alice Rawlings *(Patty)*, Hilarie Thompson *(Hilarie)*, Devon Douglas *(Devon)*, Ellen Moss *(Tanya)*, Cherie Lamour *(Cherie)*, June Fairchild *(June)*, Michael Christian *(motorcycle gang leader)*, Jon Hill *(cyclist)*, John Findlater *(Jud Farriday)*, Tom Logan *(Tom)*, William Lundigan *(Mr. Clancy)*, Mary Jo Begley *(Miss Ohio)*, Barbara Boman *(Miss Missouri)*, Janis Eaton *(Miss Oklahoma)*, Patricia Eaves *(Miss*

New Mexico), Betsy Gindele *(Miss Pennsylvania)*, Vivian Gradin *(Miss Texas)*, Suelen Helland *(Miss Illinois)*, Cindy Lu Rumple *(Miss Indiana)*.

Comedy. Based on characters created by: Jane Trahey. Despite misgivings, conservative Mother Superior Simplicia accompanies progressive Sister George and the girls of St. Francis Academy in Pennsylvania to an ecumenical rally in California. En route they encounter a gang of motorcyclists, intent on rape; spend a night at a Catholic boys' school administered by Father Chase, during which the girls demonstrate bomb manufacture and attend a rock dance; are hosted in New Mexico by Mr. Farriday and his six sons; and are attacked in Arizona by Indian extras enraged at the film director employing them. During the California rally, the nuns, inspired by the spirit of Christian fellowship, resolve their differences, changing their former habits for short skirts and ebony hose. *Nuns. Schoolteachers. Students. Motorcycle gangs. Catholics. Motion picture extras. Indians of North America. Priests. Motion picture directors. Adolescence. Boarding schools. Bombs. Pennsylvania. Arizona. New Mexico. California.*

Note: A sequel to *The Trouble With Angels*, q. v.

WHERE EAGLES DARE (Great Britain) F6.5526

Winkast Film Productions. *Dist* Metro-Goldwyn-Mayer, Inc. 12 Mar **1969** [New York opening; c31 Dec 1968; LP36545]. Sd; col (Metrocolor). 35mm (Panavision). 158 min.

A Jerry Gershwin–Elliott Kastner Production. *Prod* Elliott Kastner. *Assoc Prod* Denis Holt, Richard McWhorter. *Dir* Brian G. Hutton. *2d Unit Dir* Yakima Canutt. *Screenplay* Alistair MacLean. *Photog* Arthur Ibbetson. *Camera Op* Paul Wilson. *2d Unit Photog* H. A. R. Thomson. *Art Dir* Peter Mullins. *Set Dresser* Arthur Taksen. *Film Ed* John Jympson. *Asst Ed* Alan Strachan. *Mus Comp & Cond* Ron Goodwin. *Sd Ed* Jonathan Bates. *Sd Rec* John Bramall. *Dub Ed* J. B. Smith. *Asst Dir* Colin Brewer, Patrick Clayton, Ben Harrison, Chris Kenny. *Prod Supv* Ted Lloyd. *2d Unit Prod Mgr* Tom Sachs. *Cont* Penny Daniels. *Asst to the Prod* Marion Rosenberg. *Photog Eff* Tom Howard. *Sp Eff* Richard Parker, Fred Hellenburgh. *2d Unit Asst Dir* Anthony Waye. *Dial Coach* Alfredo Lettieri.

Cast: Richard Burton *(Smith)*, Clint Eastwood *(Schaffer)*, Mary Ure *(Mary Ellison)*, Patrick Wymark *(Colonel Wyatt-Turner)*, Michael Hordern *(Vice-Admiral Rolland)*, Donald Houston *(Christiansen)*, Peter Barkworth *(Berkeley)*, William Squire *(Thomas)*, Robert Beatty *(Cartwright-Jones)*, Brook Williams *(Harrod)*, Neil McCarthy *(Macpherson)*, Vincent Ball *(Carpenter)*, Anton Diffring *(Colonel Kramer)*, Ferdy Mayne *(Rosemeyer)*, Derren Nesbitt *(von Hapen)*, Victor Beaumont *(Weissner)*, Ingrid Pitt *(Heidi)*, Richard Beale *(telephone orderly)*, Ivor Dean *(German officer)*, Lyn Kennington *(German woman)*, Nigel Lambert *(young German soldier)*, Michael Rooney *(radio operator)*, Ernst Walder *(airport control officer)*.

War drama. Source: Alistair MacLean, *Where Eagles Dare* (London, 1966). Under the command of British Major John Smith, an international commando unit dressed in Nazi uniforms parachutes into the Bavarian Alps with the objective of rescuing a World War II Allied officer from a German castle-fortress known as the Castle of the Eagle. After one of the commandos is found with his neck broken, Smith first rendezvouses with agent Mary Ellison and then with another agent, Heidi, who, by posing as a local barmaid, succeeds in getting Mary into the fortress by introducing her as a cousin. Following the murder of a second commando and the capture of three other men, Smith and his second-in-command, American Ranger Morris Schaffer, are forced to surrender. But they escape and gain entry into the fortress by crouching on the roof of a cable car. Once there, Smith reveals to Schaffer that the Allied officer is really an actor, and that the real purpose of the mission is to discover the identity of German spies in England. After the actor-imposter has been rescued, Smith tricks the three "captured" commandos into exposing themselves as German agents. Now that they have the vital information they were sent for, Smith, Schaffer, Mary, and the imposter must face the problem of escaping. Having wired the fortress as well as certain sites in the village to explode at intervals, they make their way to a cable car. Once aboard, they outwit the Germans, reach the village, leap off the cable car, and, with the enemy still in hot pursuit, make their way through a canal to a garage. There they commandeer a bus and drive to an airfield where a plane is arriving to take them back to England. Once they are in flight, Major Smith forces one of the mission's organizers, Colonel Turner, into confessing that he is a German agent. To prevent humiliation to Turner and his family, as well as a national scandal, Smith permits Turner to meet a more honorable death by allowing him to leap from the plane. *Secret agents. Nazis. Barmaids. Commandos. Actors. Espionage. Disguise. Imposture. Suicide. Chases. Castles. Cable cars. Airplanes. Explosions. World War II. Germany—Army. Germany—Intelligence service. Great Britain—Army. Great Britain—Intelligence service. Bavaria.*

Note: Location scenes filmed in the Austrian Alps; released in Great Britain in 1968.

WHERE IT'S AT   F6.5527

Frank Ross–T. F. T. Productions. *Dist* United Artists. 7 May **1969** [New York opening; c7 May 1969; LP36849]. Sd; col (DeLuxe). 35mm. 104 min. *MPAA rating* R.

Prod Frank Ross. *Assoc Prod* Dick Ross. *Dir-Writ* Garson Kanin. *Photog* Burnett Guffey. *Art Dir* Albert Brenner. *Set Decor* Ralph S. Hurst. *Film Ed* Stefan Arnsten. *Mus* Benny Golson. *Titl Song Comp & Sung by* Jeff Barry. *Sd Mix* Everett A. Hughes. *Sd Rec* Brandon Kellogg. *Asst Dir* John C. Chulay, David Hawks, Richard C. Bennett. *Prod Mgr* William R. Finnegan. *Wardrobe* Anthea Sylbert. *Makeup* Emile La Vigne. *Hairstyles* Dorothy White. *Illus* John Jensen.

Cast: David Janssen (*A. C. Smith*), Robert Drivas (*Andy Smith*), Rosemary Forsyth (*Diana Mayhew*), Brenda Vaccaro (*Molly Hirsch*), Don Rickles (*Willie*), Warrene Ott (*Betty Avery*), Edy Williams (*Phyllis Horrigan*), Vince Howard (*Ralph*), The Committee (*voices*), Debbie Wickstrom.

Comedy-drama. Upon graduating from Princeton University, Andy Smith arrives in Las Vegas to visit his father, A. C., the owner-operator of Caesars Palace, one of the most successful of Vegas' ornate gambling hotels. Not having seen his son in some years, A. C. is disturbed by what he considers to be Andy's unmasculine appearance and unbusinesslike attitude. To prevent Andy from going to Europe, A. C. challenges him to a cut of the cards, beats him, and then forces him to work at the hotel for the summer. After A. C. has tested his son's interest in women by sending a voluptuous chorus girl named Phyllis Horrigan to his room, Andy enters into mild flirtations with his father's mistress-turned-wife, Diana Mayhew, as well as with his secretary, Molly Hirsch. Andy is sent to Zurich on business matters, and he demonstrates, almost overnight, that he has his father's talent for wheeling and dealing; and by the time he returns to Las Vegas he is adept enough to negotiate a deal whereby he gains control of Caesars Palace. Furthermore, he has become wise enough in the ways of love to decide in favor of Molly over Diana. Although A. C. is furious at being bested by his son, he is nevertheless delighted to discover that the boy has apparently inherited some of his own shrewd business acumen. Andy, however, was only interested in proving that he could do whatever he pleased, and once his father has been taught this lesson he arranges for A. C. to win back the hotel during a game of cards. With a new rapport established between father and son, Andy leaves Las Vegas with Molly to pursue graduate studies at Princeton. *Businessmen. Students. Secretaries. Chorus girls. Filial relations. Wagers. Gambling. Hotel management. Hotels. Effeminacy. Zurich. Las Vegas. Princeton University. Caesars Palace.*

Note: Location scenes filmed in and around Caesars Palace in Las Vegas.

WHERE LOVE HAS GONE   F6.5528

Embassy Pictures–Paramount Pictures. *Dist* Paramount Pictures. 9 Oct **1964** [Los Angeles opening; c9 Oct 1964; LP28980]. Sd; col (Technicolor). 35mm (Techniscope). 114 min.

Pres by Joseph E. Levine. *Prod* Joseph E. Levine. *Dir* Edward Dmytryk. *Screenplay* John Michael Hayes. *Cinematog* Joseph MacDonald. *Art Dir* Hal Pereira, Walter Tyler. *Set Decor* Sam Comer, Arthur Krams. *Film Ed* Frank Bracht. *Mus* Walter Scharf. *Titl Song* Sammy Cahn, James Van Heusen. *Sung by* Jack Jones. *Sd* John Carter, Charles Grenzbach. *Asst Dir* D. Michael Moore. *Prod Mgr* Frank Caffey. *Cost* Edith Head. *Makeup* Wally Westmore, Gene Hibbs. *Sp Photog Eff* Paul K. Lerpae. *Proc Photog* Farciot Edouart. *Dial Dir* Frank London.

Cast: Susan Hayward (*Valerie Hayden Miller*), Bette Davis (*Mrs. Gerald Hayden*), Michael Connors (*Luke Miller*), Joey Heatherton (*Danielle Valerie [Dani] Miller*), Jane Greer (*Marian Spicer*), DeForest Kelley (*Sam Corwin*), George Macready (*Gordon Harris*), Anne Seymour (*Dr. Sally Jennings*), Willis Bouchey (*Judge Murphy*), Walter Reed (*George Babson*), Ann Doran (*Mrs. Geraghty*), Bartlett Robinson (*Mr. Coleman*), Whit Bissell (*Professor Bell*), Anthony Caruso (*Rafael*).

Melodrama. Source: Harold Robbins, *Where Love Has Gone* (New York, 1962). Contractor Luke Miller returns to the San Francisco home of his ex-wife, sculptress Valerie Hayden, after learning that their 15-year-old daughter, Dani, has been arrested for the murder of Valerie's lover. His plane is met by lawyer Gordon Harris, who callously engineered Luke's divorce and deprived him of the right to visit his daughter. Now, however, Harris asks Luke's help in providing a favorable family setting for the juvenile court hearing but discourages any hopes of gaining Dani's custody once the case is resolved. Luke's return revives memories of his former life with Valerie and her domineering mother, Mrs. Gerald Hayden. *When Luke and Valerie are married, he aspires to become an independent architect, but Mrs. Hayden forces him into a business partnership with her. Valerie, ignorant of her mother's underhanded ways, blames Luke for being weak; his subsequent drinking problem and her adultery combine to destroy the marriage.* Terrified that her mother might be awarded custody of the child, Valerie takes moral responsibility for the murder at the hearing; in addition, she blames her failure as a mother on her own sorry upbringing, a disclosure that both discredits and

humiliates Mrs. Hayden. Freed at last from her mother's domination, Valerie commits suicide, making possible a reunion between Dani and Luke. *Contractors. Sculptors. Architects. Lawyers. Mothers-in-law. Parenthood. Murder. Filial relations. Guilt. Wealth. Marriage. Alcoholism. Infidelity. Divorce. Adolescence. Suicide. Trials. San Francisco.*

Note: Location scenes filmed in San Francisco.

WHERE SIN LIVES *see* **THE PINK PUSSY (WHERE SIN LIVES)**

WHERE THE BLOOD FLOWS *see* **HORROR CASTLE**

WHERE THE BULLETS FLY (Great Britain)   F6.5529

Puck Films. *Dist* Embassy Pictures. 22 Nov **1966** [Dallas opening]. Sd; col (Eastman Color, U. S. print by Pathé). 35mm. 88 min.

Prod S. J. H. Ward. *Assoc Prod* George Fowler. *Dir* John Gilling. *Screenplay* Michael Pittock. *Photog* David Holmes. *Art Dir* George Lack. *Film Ed* Ron Pope. *Mus Comp* Kenny Graham. *Mus Dir* Philip Martell. *Titl Song* Bob Kingston, Ronald Bridges. *Sung by* Susan Maughan. *Sd* Bill Bulkley. *Asst Dir* Ray Frift. *Prod Mgr* Pat Green. *Wardrobe* Joanna Wright. *Makeup* Aldo Manganaro. *Hairstyles* Blanche Arden. *Sp Eff* Pat Moore, Bowie Films.

Cast: Tom Adams (*Charles Vine*), Dawn Addams (*Felicity "Fiz" Moonlight*), Sidney James (*mortuary attendant*), Wilfrid Brambell (*train guard*), Joe Baker (*minister*), Tim Barrett (*Seraph*), Michael Ripper (*Angel*), John Arnatt (*Rockwell*), Ronald Leigh-Hunt (*Thursby*), Marcus Hammond (*O'Neil*), Maurice Browning (*Cherub*), Michael Ward (*Michael*), Bryan Mosley (*Connolly*), Terence Sewards (*minister's press agent*), Heidi Erich (*Carruthers*), Suzan Farmer (*Caron*), Maggie Kimberley (*Jacqueline*), Sue Donovan (*Celia*), Julie Martin (*Verity*), Tom Bowman (*Russian colonel*), Patrick Jordan (*Russian*), Gerard Heinz (*Venstram*), James Ellis (*Flight Lieutenant Fotheringham*), Charles Houston (*co-pilot*), Tony Alpino (*butler*), Michael Balfour (*bandleader*), Garry Marsh (*major*), Michael Graham Cox (*Lieutenant Guyfawkes*), Peter Ducrow (*Professor Harding*), Barbara French (*Harding's secretary*), John Horsley (*air marshal*), Michael Goldie (*laborer*), Joe Ritchie (*truck driver*), John Watson (*controller*), David Gregory (*R. A. F. sergeant*), Roy Stephens (*staff officer*).

Action melodrama. Secret agent Charles Vine saves England from disaster by disguising himself as a woman and eliminating enemy agents bent on launching a guided missile against the Houses of Parliament. His next assignment is to prevent a spy ring from stealing a sample of Spurium, a lightweight metal alloy used to build nuclear-powered aircraft. Under the leadership of Angel, a Russian agent, the spy organization hijacks a plane made of Spurium, but the Royal Air Force shoots it down over the English Channel. Quick to change his tactics, Angel has Vine abducted and drugged into revealing the location of the Spurium factory. Angel is thwarted once again when his henchman Seraph, after obtaining a sample of the precious metal, is blown up by the Russians, who mistakenly believe they are being double-crossed. Meanwhile, Vine escapes his captors and recovers the Spurium sample. Angel, furious with the Russians, hijacks a plane for the Chinese, but Vine boards the aircraft as it takes off from the landing field. In the ensuing battle Vine kills his opponents but is left alone in a plane he cannot pilot. Fortunately, Women's Royal Air Force officer "Fiz" Moonlight, an old girl friend, is nearby in a helicopter; she lowers herself into Vine's plane, switches the controls to automatic, and makes love with him. *Secret agents. Russians. Hijackers. Nuclear energy. Espionage. Abduction. Disguise. Drugs. Airplanes. Missiles. Helicopters. English Channel. Great Britain—Royal Air Force. Great Britain—Women's Royal Air Force.*

Note: Released in Great Britain in 1966; running time: 90 min. Sequel to *The Second Best Secret Agent in the Whole Wide World*, q. v.

WHERE THE HOT WIND BLOWS! *see* **THE LAW**

WHERE THE SPIES ARE (Great Britain)   F6.5530

Metro-Goldwyn-Mayer Pictures. *Dist* Metro-Goldwyn-Mayer, Inc. 5 Jan **1966** [Detroit opening; c2 Nov 1965; LP31869]. Sd (Westrex); col (Metrocolor). 35mm (Panavision). 110 min. [Copyright length: 113 min.]

A Val Guest Production. *Prod* Val Guest, Steven Pallos. *Assoc Prod* Frank Sherwin Green. *Dir* Val Guest. *Screenplay* Wolf Mankowitz, Val Guest. *Adtl Scenes* James Leasor. *Dir Photog* Arthur Grant. *Camera Op* Moray Grant. *Art Dir* John Howell. *Titl Dsgn* Robert Brownjohn. *Film Ed* Bill Lenny. *Orig Score Comp & Orch* Mario Nascimbene. *Cond* Alfredo Antonini. *Organ Soloist* Jimmy Smith. *Mus* (see note) Brian Fahey. *Rec Supv* A. W. Watkins. *Sd Rec* Cyril Swern. *Dub Mix* J. B. Smith. *Sd Ed* James Shields. *Asst Dir* Eric Rattray. *Prod Mgr* George Fowler. *Cont* Pamela Carlton. *Cost Dsgn* Beatrice Dawson. *Makeup* Tony Sforzini. *Hairdressing* Daphne Martin.

Cast: David Niven (*Dr. Jason Love*), Françoise Dorléac (*Vikki*), John Le Mesurier (*Col. Douglas MacGillivray*), Cyril Cusack (*Peter Rosser*), Eric Pohlmann (*Farouk*), Paul Marner (*Josef*), Paul Stassino (*Simmias*), George Pravda (*1st agent*), Noel Harrison (*Jackson*), Ronald Radd (*Stanislaus*), Alan

Gifford *(security)*, Bill Nagy *(aeradio)*, George Mikell *(assassin)*, Nigel Davenport *(Parkington)*, Reginald Beckwith *(Mr. Kahn)*, Gabor Baraker *(2d agent)*, Geoffrey Bayldon *(lecturer)*, Derek Partridge *(duty officer)*, Robert Raglan *(Sir Robert)*, Riyad Gholmieh *(1st taxi driver)*, Muhsen Samrani *(2d taxi driver)*, Basil Dignam *(Major Harding)*, Gordon Tanner *(inspector)*.

Action comedy-melodrama. Source: James Leasor, *Passport to Oblivion* (London, 1964). Rosser, a British intelligence agent, is murdered by communists in Beirut, whereupon Intelligence Chief MacGillivray persuades mild-mannered country doctor Jason Love to go to the Middle East and learn what information Rosser had discovered. Having done a bit of undercover work during World War II, Jason eagerly anticipates a little adventure in the sunshine. En route to Lebanon, he meets a beautiful model, Vikki, and decides to catch a later flight. After watching his scheduled plane explode shortly after takeoff, Jason realizes the seriousness of his mission. Once in Beirut, he and another British agent learn that communists plan to assassinate the pro-British Prince of Zahlouf, thereby threatening Britain's Eastern oil treaties. Although Jason thwarts the assassination attempt, he is forced to climb to the top of a castle to avoid an angry mob. He is snatched from his perch by a Russian helicopter, the "Dove of Peace," which ostensibly is on a global goodwill mission. Jason finds that Vikki is also aboard. Upon learning of Jason's plight, MacGillivray arranges for the craft to be sidetracked to Canada. As the plane sets down, Vikki tries to push Jason to safety but is shot. Jason tumbles out of the emergency exit, however, just as the helicopter takes off again. A message from MacGillivray asks Jason to take another little trip, but he intends to have no part of it. *Physicians. Spies. Communists. Models. Royalty. Arabs. Assassination. Cold war. Helicopters. Airplanes. Beirut. Canada. Great Britain—Intelligence service. Explosions.*

Note: Location scenes filmed in Beirut and Jubayl, Lebanon. Opened in London in Mar 1966; running time: 113 min. Working titles: *Passport to Oblivion* and *One Spy Too Many*. Brian Fahey's music credit is unconfirmed.

WHERE THE TRUTH LIES (France)   F6.5531

Marianne Productions–S. N. E. Gaumont. *Dist* Paramount Pictures. Nov **1962** [c3 Oct 1962; LP23596]. Sd; b&w. 35mm (Dyaliscope). 83 min. [Copyright length: 90 min.]

Exec Prod Alain Poiré, Michel Bernheim. *Dir* Henri Decoin. *Dial* Albert Husson. *Adapt* Henri Decoin, Claude Accursi. *Photog* Marcel Grignon. *Settings* Paul-Louis Boutié. *Film Ed* Robert Isnardon, Monique Isnardon. *Mus* Pierre Henry. *Sd* Robert Teisseire. *Asst Dir* Gérard Dreyfus. *Prod Dir* Robert Sussfeld, Irénée Leriche.

Cast: Juliette Greco *(Myriam Heller)*, Jean-Marc Bory *(François Rauchelle)*, Liselotte Pulver *(Catherine Rauchelle)*, Mathé Mansoura *(Ronga)*, Jacques Dacqmine *(Vial)*, Jeanne Perez *(Mère Capitaine)*, Georges Chamarat *(Malet)*, Marcel Pérès.

Drama. Source: Pierre Boileau and Thomas Narcejac, *Maléfices* (Paris, 1961). François Rauchelle, a young veterinarian in a French seacoast village, is called out to care for a sick cheetah belonging to Myriam Heller, a former African explorer who practices voodoo. François finds himself strangely attracted to Myriam and eventually becomes her lover, but he refuses to abandon his wife and return to Africa with Myriam. Catherine then has a series of mysterious accidents; and François, concluding that Myriam's sorcery is responsible, agrees to go away with her to save his wife's life. As they are departing, their car stalls on a flooding causeway. They make their way through the water to a lighthouse shelter, where Myriam realizes she has taken the wrong suitcase and insists upon returning to the car. The current pulls her under, providing François with the opportunity to free his wife of Myriam's spell, and he lets her drown. Sometime later, Catherine confesses to François that it was she who arranged the mysterious accidents to influence his decision not to leave her. With feelings of guilt and remorse, François walks out on Catherine and goes to inform the police that he could have prevented Myriam's death. *Veterinarians. Explorers. Marriage. Voodoo. Infidelity. Lighthouses. Floods. Cheetahs.*

Note: Filmed on the Île de Noirmoutier. Opened in Paris in Mar 1962 as *Maléfices*; running time: 104 min. Prerelease title: *Evil Spell*.

WHERE THE WILD GOOSE GOES see COUGAR COUNTRY

WHERE WERE YOU WHEN THE LIGHTS WENT OUT?   F6.5532

Metro-Goldwyn-Mayer, Inc. 19 Jun **1968** [Boston opening; c20 Feb 1968; LP35495]. Sd; col (Metrocolor). 35mm (Panavision). 94 min. [Copyright length: 91 min.]

An Everett Freeman Production. *Prod* Everett Freeman, Martin Melcher. *Dir* Hy Averback. *Screenplay* Everett Freeman, Karl Tunberg. *Dir Photog* Ellsworth Fredricks. *Camera Op* William Dodds. *Asst Camera* Harry Young. *Art Dir* George W. Davis, Urie McCleary. *Set Decor* Henry Grace, Dick Pefferle. *Film Ed* Rita Roland. *Asst Ed* Pete Denenberg. *Mus Comp* Dave Grusin. *Titl Song* Dave Grusin, Kelly Gordon. *Sung by* The Lettermen. *Song:*

"Showtime" Joe Lubin. *Rec Supv* Franklin Milton. *Mix* Jules Strausser, Jr. *Boom Op* Clint Althouse, Jules Strausser, III. *Asst Dir* Al Jennings, Lynn Guthrie, Kevin Donnelly. *Unit Prod Mgr* Robert Vreeland. *Script Supv* June Sampson. *Miss Day's Cost Dsgn* Glenn Connelly. *Wardrobe* Bill Jobe, Anne Laune. *Makeup* William Tuttle. *Miss Day's Makeup* Harry Maret. *Hairstyles* Sydney Guilaroff, Vivian Thompson. *Sp Vis Eff* J. McMillan Johnson, Carroll L. Shepphird. *Still Photog* Virgil Apger. *Gaffer* Bill Shaw. *Grip* Mervyn Price. *Prop* Bob Murdock, Ken Crawford. *Casting* Leonard Murphy.

Cast: Doris Day *(Margaret Garrison)*, Robert Morse *(Waldo Zane)*, Terry-Thomas *(Ladislau Walichek)*, Patrick O'Neal *(Peter Garrison)*, Lola Albright *(Roberta Lane)*, Steve Allen *(radio announcer)*, Jim Backus *(Tru-Blue Lou)*, Ben Blue *(man with a razor)*, Pat Paulsen *(conductor)*, Dale Malone *(Otis J. Hendershot, Jr.)*, Robert Emhardt *(Otis J. Hendershot, Sr.)*, Harry Hickox *(Det. Capt. Percy Watson)*, Parley Baer *(Dr. Dudley Caldwell)*, Randy Whipple *(Marvin Reinholtz)*, Earl Wilson *(himself)*.

Comedy. Source: Claude Magnier, *Monsieur Masure* (Paris opening: 11 May 1956). Executive Waldo Zane is planning to abscond with $2.4 million in company funds following a stockholders' meeting; Broadway star Margaret Garrison and her architect husband, Peter, are being interviewed by magazine reporter Roberta Lane; and Margaret's Hungarian director, Ladislau Walichek, is ensconced on a psychiatrist's couch, driven there by Margaret's threat to leave the theater and become a housewife. One hour later New York City is plunged into darkness by a power failure. Returning home early, Margaret finds Peter with Roberta in their Manhattan apartment. Furious, she storms out in a jealous rage, drives to their Connecticut cottage, drinks a glass of water containing a sleeping potion, and falls asleep. A few minutes later, Waldo's getaway car breaks down outside Margaret's cottage. Finding the door open, he enters the house to use the phone, sees the glass of water, and drinks from it. Then a contrite Peter arrives at the cottage and finds his wife and Waldo asleep together on the sofa; Ladislau also arrives and encourages Peter's suspicions. Once Waldo awakens, he agrees to anything in his haste to get away; but on the road, he is arrested with the stolen money then released when he convinces his employer that he took the money to protect it during the blackout. As a reward, Waldo is made president of the company, but must watch helplessly as the boss's son absconds with the money before it can be returned to the bank. *Executives. Actors. Architects. Reporters. Theatrical directors. Psychiatrists. Hungarians. Marriage. Theft. Blackout. Jealousy. Tranquilizers. New York City. Connecticut.*

Note: Location scenes filmed in New York City.

WHERE'S JACK? (Great Britain)   F6.5533

Oakhurst Productions. *Dist* Paramount Pictures. May **1969** [c20 Mar 1969; LP36933]. Sd; col (Eastman Color). 35mm. 120 min. *MPAA rating* G.

Prod Stanley Baker. *Exec Prod* Michael Deeley. *Assoc Prod* Robert Porter. *Dir* James Clavell. *Screenplay* Rafe Newhouse, David Newhouse. *Dir Photog* John Wilcox. *Camera Op* Ernest Day. *Asst Art Dir* Bill Bennison. *Set Dresser* Dorothy Elliott. *Scenic Artist* Ferdie Bellan. *Prod Dsgn* Cedric Dawe. *Film Ed* Peter Thornton. *Mus* Elmer Bernstein. *Titl Song* Elmer Bernstein, Don Black. *Sung by* Mary Hopkin. *Song:* "The Jack Sheppard Ballad" Elmer Bernstein, Don Black. *Sung by* Danny Doyle. *Choreog* Malcolm Goddard. *Sd* Brian Johnson. *Sd Mix* Laurie Clarkson. *Asst Dir* Patrick Clayton. *Prod Mgr* Ron Carr. *Wardrobe* James Smith, cost. *Cost* Cynthia Tingey. *Makeup* Wally Schneiderman, Jill Carpenter. *Hairdresser* Gordon Bond, Daphne Vollmer. *Hist Adv* Alan Dent.

Cast: Tommy Steele *(Jack Sheppard)*, Stanley Baker *(Jonathan Wild)*, Fiona Lewis *(Edgworth Bess)*, Alan Badel *(The Lord Chancellor)*, Dudley Foster *(Blueskin)*, Noel Purcell *(Leatherchest)*, William Marlowe *(Tom Sheppard)*, Sue Lloyd *(Lady Darlington)*, Harold Kasket *(The King)*, Cardew Robinson *(Lord Mayor)*, Esmond Knight *(ballad singer)*, Eddie Byrne *(Reverend Wagstaff)*, John Hallam *(The Captain)*, Leon Lissek *(Deeley)*, Iole Marinelli *(Lady Clarissa)*, Carolyn Montagu *(Mistress Barrow)*, Carla Challoner *(Emma)*, Jack Woolgar *(Mr. Woods)*, Roy Evans *(Mr. Hind)*, Michael Elphick *(Hogarth)*, Caroline Munro *(Madame Vendonne)*, Rona Newton-John *(Countess Bethune)*, Bernadette Brady *(ballad singer's guide)*, Dafydd Havard *(clerk)*, Roc Brynner *(drunk)*, Skip Martin *(dwarf)*, Vernon Hayden *(deputy marshall)*, Norman Smythe *(bosun)*, Cecil Nash *(storyteller)*, Howard Goorney *(surgeon)*, George Woodbridge *(hangman)*, Clare Mullen *(dwarf's girl friend)*, Ivan Dixon *(naval officer)*, Danny Cummins *(barker)*, Fred Johnson *(merchant)*, Loretta Clarke *(lady mayoress)*, Danny Holland, Michael Douglas, Terry Plummer *(constables)*, Liam Sweeney *(Austin)*, John Kelly *(proprietor)*, Mary Willoughby *(Poll Maggott)*, John Morley *(judge)*, Paschal Perry *(guard)*.

Biographical drama. Jack Sheppard, an apprentice locksmith in London in the 18th century, becomes a jewel thief in order to save his brother Tom from the gallows. To accomplish his robberies, he must join forces with underworld figure Jonathan Wild, a notorious "thief-taker" who turns in robbers for rewards and who captured Tom. As part of the agreement, Jack joins two of Wild's men,

Blueskin and Leatherchest, in stealing a precious jeweled tiara from a count, but he is doublecrossed when Wild ships Tom off to America as a prisoner. Since the deportation will leave his brother's wife and children penniless, Jack swears to get even with Wild but is deceived by the master criminal when Wild plants the tiara in Jack's room. "Edgworth Bess" Lyon, a pretty barmaid who loves Jack, finds the tiara and thinks it is a present for her. Wild's men rush into the room, spot the tiara, and arrest Jack for theft; but he soon escapes from prison and begins a well-publicized career as a highwayman. Meanwhile, Wild's men kidnap Bess and use her as bait to recapture Jack, who is once again sent to prison and locked in an escape-proof cell. When Lady Darlington, formerly a willing victim of Jack's escapades, sends him an invitation to dinner, Jack miraculously breaks out of jail again, to the delight of London citizens who have by now elevated him to legendary status. Interest is so strong, in fact, that King George I bets the Lord Chancellor 1,000 guineas that Jack can steal the Chancellor's chain of office. The robbery is a success, and Jack plans to trade the chain of office for his freedom. Instead, he uses it to free Blueskin and Leatherchest when he learns that they are about to be hanged by Wild. Against the protests of the Lord Chancellor, Jack is given the death sentence by his old nemesis, but the execution draws so many people that Jack is able to make his escape and return to Bess once again. *Thieves. Brothers. Royalty. Barmaids. Highwaymen. Theft. Perfidy. Prison escapes. Kidnaping. Wagers. Frameup. Capital punishment. Jewels. London. Jack Sheppard. George I (England).*

Note: Location scenes filmed in Ireland. Opened in London in Mar 1969.

WHERE'S POPPA?   F6.5534

Where's Poppa Co. *Dist* United Artists. 10 Nov **1970** [New York opening; c10 Nov 1970; LP38932]. Sd; col (DeLuxe). 35mm. 84 min. [Cut from 87 min.] *MPAA rating* R.

A Jerry Tokofsky-Marvin Worth Production. *Prod* Jerry Tokofsky, Marvin Worth. *Dir* Carl Reiner. *2d Unit Dir* Burtt Harris. *Screenplay* Robert Klane. *Dir Photog* Jack Priestley. *Art Dir* Warren Clymer. *Set Decor* Herbert Mulligan. *Titl Dsgn* Dan McLaughlin. *Film Ed* Bud Molin, Chic Ciccolini. *Mus & Songs* Jack Elliott. *Lyr* Norman Gimbel. *Titl Song Sung by* Clydie King. *Songs:* "Freedom," "Move It!" *sung by* Bright Cheerstrap. *Song:* "Pleasure Palace" *sung by* June Jackson. *Song:* "The Goodbye Song" *sung by* Harry "Sweets" Edison. *Sd* Dennis Maitland. *Asst Dir* Norman Cohen. *Prod Supv* Robert Greenhut. *Prod Mgr* Fred Gallo. *Cost Dsgn* Albert Wolsky.

Cast: George Segal *(Gordon Hocheiser)*, Ruth Gordon *(Mrs. Hocheiser)*, Trish Van Devere *(Louise Callan)*, Ron Leibman *(Sidney Hocheiser)*, Rae Allen *(Gladys Hocheiser)*, Vincent Gardenia *(Coach Williams)*, Joe Keyes, Jr. *(gang leader)*, Alice Drummond *(woman in elevator)*, Tom Atkins *(policeman in apartment)*, Florence Tarlow *(Miss Morgiani)*, Jane Hoffman, Helen Martin *(job applicants)*, Barnard Hughes *(Colonel Hendriks)*, Paul Sorvino *(owner of "Gus & Grace's Home")*, William Le Massena *(judge)*, Michael McGuire *(army lawyer)*, Rob Reiner *(Roger)*, Israel Lang *(Muthafucka)*, Garrett Morris *(Garrett)*, Arnold Williams *(Arnold)*, Buddy Butler *(Buddy)*, Martha Greenhouse *(owner of "Happytime Farms")*, Jack Manning *(lawyer for Memphis Maulers)*, John Gilliar *(policeman in courthouse)*, Rehn Scofield *(bailiff)*, John McCurry *(policeman in jail cell)*, April Geleta *(taxi lady)*, Edward Brooks *(Sheldon Hocheiser)*, W. Benson Terry *(cab driver)*, Fuddles *(shoeshine man)*.

Comedy. Source: Robert Klane, *Where's Poppa?* (New York, 1970). Gordon Hocheiser, a New York City lawyer whose love life is being ruined by his widowed mother, awakens one morning, puts on a gorilla costume, and leaps on her bed, hoping to scare her to death; the 87-year-old woman merely responds by hitting him in the groin with her cane. At his office, Gordon interviews for a nurse to take care of his senile and eccentric mother and hires Louise Callan, a pretty nurse with a long list of patients who died while under her care. He takes her home and immediately falls in love with her, but his attempts at seduction fail miserably. In desperation, he calls his brother Sidney and pleads with him to take their mother away. Sidney runs across Central Park, where he is such a frequent victim of a group of muggers that he willingly hands them his wallet; this time, however, they also strip him of his clothes. At Gordon's apartment, Sidney explains that his wife hates the mother as much as they do and that their father's dying wish was that she never be put in a rest home. Sidney borrows the gorilla suit for his return trip; once at home, he is called back by the half-crazed Gordon. Running through the park, Sidney is again stopped by the muggers who want him to rape a woman in his costume, but Sidney is arrested when the woman turns out to be a policeman. His brother arrives to bail him out, and Sidney discovers that the policeman not only refused to press charges, but has sent him a bouquet of flowers and a thank you note as well. Meanwhile, Louise threatens to return to her home in Waukegan unless Gordon succeeds in getting rid of his mother. He rushes home, packs all of her belongings, lures her into the car, goes to a succession of rest homes, finally dumps her in front of one with an old man standing in front, and introduces him to her as "Poppa." [In the uncut version, Gordon returns home

with Louise, receives a call from his mother, and rushes back to her.] *Lawyers. Widows. Eccentrics. Nurses. Brothers. Muggers. Police. Disguise. Old age. Filial relations. Rape. Female impersonation. Duplicity. Old age homes. New York City. New York City—Central Park. Apes.*

Note: Location scenes filmed in New York City.

WHEREVER LOVE TAKES ME *see* THE 7TH DAWN

WHICH WAY TO THE FRONT?   F6.5535

Jerry Lewis Films. *Dist* Warner Bros. Pictures. 22 Jul **1970** [Los Angeles opening; c24 Jun 1970; LP40893]. Sd; col (Technicolor). 35mm. 96 min. *MPAA rating* G.

Prod-Dir Jerry Lewis. *Assoc Prod* Joe E. Stabile. *Screenplay* Gerald Gardner, Dee Caruso. *Story* Gerald Gardner, Dee Caruso, Richard Miller, writ. *Photog* W. Wallace Kelley. *Camera Op* Richard Johnson, photog, Kyme Meade. *Camera Asst* Gene Liggett, Arthur Gerstle, Will C. King. *Art Dir* John Beckman. *Set Decor* Ralph S. Hurst. *Main Titl* Don Record. *Film Ed* Russel Wiles. *Mus & Mus Dir* Louis Y. Brown. *Mus Supv* Sonny Burke. *Sd* Al Overton, Sr. *Boom* Frank Regula. *Rec* George Hause. *Asst Dir* Hal Bell, Robert Steinhauer. *Asst to the Prod* Bob Harvey, Mike Romersa. *Prod Mgr* Russ Saunders. *Script Supv* Hazel Hall. *Cost Dsgn* Guy Verhille. *Cost* Tye Oswald, Dick Butz, Bob Grimm. *Makeup* Jack Stone, Fred Williams. *Sp Eff* Ralph Webb. *Still Photog* Bernard Abramson. *Prop* Richard M. Rubin, Robert Cooper. *Gaffer* Lee Wilson. *Grip* Carl Manoogian. *Dial Coach* Dick Walters.

Cast: Jerry Lewis *(Brendan Byers III)*, Jan Murray *(Sid Hackle)*, Willie Davis *(Lincoln)*, John Wood *(Finkel)*, Steve Franken *(Peter Bland)*, Dack Rambo *(Terry Love)*, Paul Winchell *(Schroeder)*, Sidney Miller *(Adolf Hitler)*, Robert Middleton *(Colonico)*, Kaye Ballard *(mayor's wife)*, Harold J. Stone *(Gen. Luther Buck)*, Joe Besser *(dock master)*, Gary Crosby, Artie Lewis, Mickey Manners *(SS guards)*, Danny Dayton *(man in car)*, Kathleen Freeman *(Bland's mother)*, Neil Hamilton *(chief of staff)*, Milton Frome *(executive)*, Bob Lauher *(sergeant)*, Bobo Lewis *(Bland's wife)*, George Takei *(Yamashita)*, Martin Kosleck *(German submarine commander)*, Fritz Feld *(Von Runstadt)*, Ronald Lewis, Benny Rubin, William Wellman, Jr.

War comedy. Brendan Byers III is a patriotic millionaire who, after being rejected in 1943 by the United States Army as physically unfit, forms his own militia to end the stalemated war in Italy. Brendan and three other draft rejects sail to Italy in Brendan's yacht and kidnap German Field Marshal Kesselring. Disguised as Kesselring, Brendan orders a wide-scale German retreat but then finds himself involved in the "Generals' Plot" to assassinate Hitler. When Brendan is captured by the Allied forces, he is unable to convince his captors that he is an American. Finally, he bribes a guard and escapes with his cronies, who immediately head for Japan to continue their war effort. *Millionaires. Prisoners of war. Patriotism. Combat zone life. Abduction. Impersonation. Assassination. Bribery. Prison escapes. Yachts. World War II. Italy. Adolf Hitler. Albert Kesselring. United States Army. Germany—Army.*

Note: Newsreel footage from World War II is included.

WHIP'S WOMEN   F6.5536

Jode Productions. *Dist* CIP Ltd., Chellee Films. 28 Feb **1968** [Champaign, Illinois, showing]. Sd; col. 35mm. [Feature length assumed.]

Dir Jerry Denby. *Screenplay* Perry Berg. *Mus* The Duvals.

Cast: Forman Shane *(Johnny Whipley)*, Robin Flynn *(Ellen)*, Cara Loren *(Louise)*, San Gie *(Kate)*, Capri *(Sally)*, Lawrence Adams *(Inspector Parker)*, Rubin Atkins *(tattoo artist)*, Suzie Wong.

Melodrama. Four women are suspected when wealthy nightclub owner Johnny Whipley is found dead in his swimming pool after a wild party. All four women lived with "Whip" in his home: Sally, an exotic dancer in Whip's nightclub, bore the mark of Whip's sadism in the form of a tattoo on her stomach reading "Property of John Whip." Ellen loved Whip, and the party was held to announce their engagement. Louise, another employee at the nightclub, does not try to conceal her hatred for the dead man, whom she describes as a sadomasochist. Finally, Kate, secretly married to Whip, confesses to the murder. The night of the party was their 5th anniversary, and Kate, having found out about Ellen, killed Whip because she could not bear to lose him. After confessing, Kate breaks away from the police, makes a mad dash along the edge of the pool, and trips. In her fall, she grabs a string of electric lights hung above the pool, pulls them down into the water, and is electrocuted. *Nightclub owners. Exotic dancers. Mistresses. Murder. Marriage. Jealousy. Sadomasochism. Electrocution—Accidental. Tattoos. Confession (law). Swimming pools.*

WHIRLPOOL (Denmark)   F6.5537

Athena Film. *Dist* Cinemation Industries. 19 Aug **1970** [New York opening]. Sd (CDS System); col (DeLuxe). 35mm. 92 min. [Also reviewed at 75 min.] *MPAA rating* X.

Pres by Jerry Gross. *Prod* Sam Lomberg. *Dir-Writ* J. R. Larrath. *Photog* Charles Childs. *Art Dir* M. B. Greene. *Film Ed* Carlo Reali. *Mus* Steven

Cipriani. *Asst Dir* Thomas Colliers. *Prod Mgr* Mogens Nielsen.

Cast: Karl Lanchbury *(Theo)*, Vivian Neves *(Tulia)*, Pia Anderson *(Sara)*, Johanna Hegger, Andren Grant, Edwin Brown, Ernest Jenning, Larry Dann, Alan Charles, Barrie Craine, John Davenport.

Melodrama. Sara, a London fashion model, meets Tulia, a young and inexperienced Danish model who complains that she needs more photographs for her portfolio. Sara invites Tulia to come to the cottage that she shares with her "nephew" Theo, an avid photographer. The first evening at the cottage, they play strip poker, and Theo wins the game and seduces Tulia, whom the couple have plied with drink and "special" cigarettes. Later, Sara and Theo compare Tulia to Tina, an Italian model with whom the pair formed a ménage à trois; Theo predicts that Tulia will become warmer once she has experienced the ecstasy of sexual pleasure with both a man and a woman. While Tulia and Theo are walking in the woods, a man named Field suddenly appears and asks of Tina's whereabouts; Theo's unclear explanation leaves Tulia apprehensive. Later that afternoon, Theo's friend Tommy joins them for a country drive. Away from any possible onlookers Tommy rips off Tulia's clothes so that Theo can take nude pictures of her. Frightened but later convinced by Theo's explanation that the violence was merely for photographic effect, Tulia returns to the cottage and is drawn once again into the sensual atmosphere surrounding Sara and Theo. She makes love with Sara while Theo photographs them; he then joins them. Hearing a noise outside, Theo finds Field spying on the cottage, stabs him, and sets fire to his car. The next morning, having discovered Tina's suitcase and passport, Tulia enters Theo's darkroom and discovers large photographs of the murdered Tina. Terrified, Tulia tries to run away but is taken to the woods by Theo, who asks her to kiss him; and as she does, he stabs her. *Italians. Models. Aunts. Photographers. Missing persons. Troilism. Seduction. Sadism. Murder. Lesbianism. Photographs. Poker. London.*

Note: Location scenes filmed in England; original title and release are undetermined. J. R. Larrath is a pseudonym for José R. Larraz, Charles Childs for Julio Pérez de Rozas, and Steven Cipriani for Stelvio Cipriani.

WHIRLPOOL OF WOMAN (Japan)   F6.5538

Nikkatsu Corp. *Dist* Toho Co. 14 Dec **1966** [Los Angeles opening]. Sd; b&w. 35mm (Nikkatsu Scope). 116 min.

Dir Ko Nakahira. *Screenplay* Masashige Narusawa. *Photog* Yoshihiro Yamazaki.

Cast: Kazuko Inano *(Sugako)*, Noboru Nakaya *(husband)*, Sadako Sawamura, Tamio Kawaji.

Melodrama. During World War II, Sugako becomes the bride of a young professor. Although her husband is completely preoccupied with his work, Sugako remains faithful. During the occupation, Sugako opens a restaurant, supplied by the black market, and takes up with a series of men. Discovering her infidelity, the husband forces her to reveal that she was raped by an elderly uncle in her youth, which resulted in an obsession with death that surfaces every time she makes love. The couple start life over, but the obsessed Sugako soon dies, hoping that her husband may find a better woman. *Professors. Uncles. Restaurateurs. Marriage. Infidelity. Rape. Obsession. Incest. Self-sacrifice. Military occupation. Death. Black market. World War II.*

Note: Released in Japan in 1964 as *Onna no uzu to fuchi to nagare.* Alternative title: *Whirlpool of Flesh.*

WHIRLWIND (Japan)   F6.5539

Toho Co. 26 Jul **1968** [New York opening]. Sd; col (Eastmancolor). 35mm (Tohoscope). 107 min.

Dir Hiroshi Inagaki. *Screenplay* Hiroshi Inagaki, Takeshi Kimura. *Photog* Kazuo Yamada. *Sp Eff* Eiji Tsuburaya.

Cast: Toshiro Mifune *(Lord Akashi)*, Somegoro Ichikawa *(Jubei)*, Yuriko Hoshi *(Kozato)*, Kumi Mizuno *(The Witch)*, Yosuke Natsuki, Yoshiko Kuga, Makoto Sato.

Action melodrama. As a series of violent feudal wars erupt throughout 17th-century Japan, Jubei, a samurai follower of a defeated warlord, is ordered to escort a young prince and a lady-in-waiting, Kozato, to safety. En route they are constantly set upon by robbers and enemies of Jubei's dethroned lord. They are aided by the intervention of Akashi, a legendary former warlord, who almost single-handedly defeats the enemy with his sword. During the journey, the trio also encounters a beautiful young witch and her brother. Although the witch uses her magical powers to aid Jubei and his charges, she deeply resents the growing love between the samurai and Kozato and periodically threatens to destroy Jubei if he refuses to accept her as his chosen mate. During a final battle between Jubei and the enemies, a giant whirlwind suddenly materializes and scatters the two opposing sides, thereby clearing the way for Jubei to fulfill his mission. *Samurai. Royalty. Robbers. Witches. Warlords. Feudalism. Magic. Jealousy. Tornadoes.*

Note: Released in Japan in 1964 as *Dai tatsumaki.*

WHISKEY'S RENEGADES *see* SAM WHISKEY

THE WHISPERERS (Great Britain)   F6.5540

Seven Pines Productions. *Dist* Lopert Pictures, United Artists. 31 Jul **1967** [New York opening]. Sd; b&w. 35mm. 105 min.

Prod Michael S. Laughlin, Ronald Shedlo. *Assoc Prod* Jack Rix. *Asst Prod* John L. Hargreaves. *Dir-Writ* Bryan Forbes. *Photog* Gerry Turpin. *Art Dir* Ray Simm. *Set Decor* Peter James. *Main Titl* Robert Ellis. *Film Ed* Anthony Harvey. *Mus Comp & Cond* John Barry. *Sd Rec* Bill Daniels, Ken Barker. *Asst Dir* Christopher Dryhurst. *Wardrobe* Dorothy Edwards, Ben Foster. *Makeup* Basil Newall. *Hairstyles* Barbara Ritchie.

Cast: Edith Evans *(Mrs. Ross)*, Eric Portman *(Archie)*, Nanette Newman *(girl upstairs)*, Gerald Sim *(Mr. Conrad)*, Avis Bunnage *(Mrs. Noonan)*, Ronald Fraser *(Charlie)*, Leonard Rossiter *(National Assistance official)*, Kenneth Griffith *(Mr. Weaver)*, Harry Baird *(Earl)*, Margaret Tyzack *(Almoner)*, Clare Kelly *(prostitute)*, Robert Russell *(Andy)*, Michael Robbins *(Mr. Noonan)*, Penny Spencer, Kaplan Kaye *(Noonan children)*, Robin Bailey *(psychiatrist)*, Max Bacon *(Mr. Fish)*, Sarah Forbes *(Mrs. Ross as a child)*, Peter Thompson *(publican)*, Tom Kempinski, George Spence, Terry Eliot, Roy Maxwell, Michael Lees.

Drama. Source: Robert Nicolson, *Mrs. Ross* (London, 1961). Mrs. Ross is a lonely old woman who lives by herself in a dingy 2-room flat. Abandoned years before by her no-good husband, she exists on a small government pension which, she proudly maintains, is not charity but merely a loan until she receives the inheritance from her late father's imaginary estate. When she is not warming her feet at the library, singing hymns in the soup kitchen, or visiting the National Assistance Board, she sits in her newspaper-cluttered rooms listening to the whispering voices—the water tap, the pipes, the walls—that are her only companions. Then one day Charlie, her son, a petty thief, comes to see her and secretly stores a parcel in one of her closets. When the old woman finds and opens it, she discovers that it is full of pound notes, about 800 in all. In her confused state, she believes the money to be her long-overdue inheritance, and she hastens to the welfare board to tell of her good fortune. She boasts to conniving Mrs. Noonan, who invites her to her home. There Mrs. Ross is drugged, robbed, and then left for the night in an alley by her home. She is found suffering from pneumonia by the girl upstairs. Sending her first to a general hospital and later to a psychiatric unit, the authorities try to figure out what is best for her. They track down her husband, Archie, and persuade him to attempt some sort of reconciliation with his wife. But their joint effort to resume their former life together is pathetically unhappy, and before long Archie takes off with some stolen money. Alone again, Mrs. Ross sits in her rooms and listens for the whispering voices. *Ne'er-do-wells. Social workers. Thieves. Loneliness. Old age. Desertion. Public welfare. Poverty. Hallucinations. Inheritance. Theft. Psychiatry. Marriage. Libraries. Hospitals. Pneumonia. Great Britain—National Assistance Board.*

Note: Released in Great Britain in 1967 at 106 min.

WHISPERING JOE (Japan)   F6.5541

Saito Productions. *Dist* Shochiku Films of America. Apr **1969** [Los Angeles showing]. Sd; b&w. 35mm (Shochiku GrandScope). 90 min.

Prod-Dir-Writ Koichi Saito. *Photog* Koichi Saito. *Art Dir* Kuninobu Yasuda. *Mus* Koichi Saito.

Cast: Jin Nakayama *(Joe)*, Reiko Asoo *(Kanako)*, Manami Fuji *(woman)*, Akira Nishimura *(her husband)*, Kinzo Shin *(tramp)*.

Melodrama. Joe, a drifter who dreams of emigrating to Brazil, lives with Kanako, a fashion model who supports him. Kanako has sex with the son of a business tycoon after he promises to give Joe a good job. Bored and desperate, Joe picks up a married woman when she flirts with him in a nightclub and, at the woman's request, kills her husband. Pursued by the police, Joe takes as hostage a beggar who witnessed the murder. Together they build a raft for Joe to sail to Brazil. Joe telephones Kanako, asking her to join him; and she rushes to him, unaware that she has been followed by the police. In anger Joe shoots her, and, realizing later that she did not betray him, he takes her aboard the raft. Knowing that Kanako is dying and that he may not be able to leave the harbor, he nevertheless launches the flimsy raft. *Drifters. Models. Beggars. Hostages. Police. Unemployment. Infidelity. Murder. Rafts. Brazil.*

Note: Released in Japan in Dec 1967 as *Sasayashi no Joe.*

WHISTLE DOWN THE WIND (Great Britain)   F6.5542

Beaver Films–Allied Film Makers. *Dist* Pathé-America Distributing Co. 21 Apr **1962** [New York opening; c21 Aug 1961; LP21929]. Sd; b&w. 35mm. 98 min.

A Richard Attenborough–Bryan Forbes Production. *Prod* Richard Attenborough. *Assoc Prod* Jack Rix. *Dir* Bryan Forbes. *Screenplay* Keith Waterhouse, Willis Hall. *Dir Photog* Arthur Ibbetson. *Camera Op* David Harcourt. *Focus* John Alcott. *Art Dir* Ray Simm. *Asst Art Dir* Leonard Townsend. *Film Ed* Max Benedict. *Asst Ed* Tom Priestley, Paul Smith, ed. *Mus*

Comp & Cond Malcolm Arnold. *Dub Ed* Alastair McIntyre. *Sd Rec* Bill Daniels. *Boom Op* Gus Lloyd. *Sd Camera* Ted Karnon. *1st, 2d & 3d Asst Dir* Basil Rayburn, Charles Blair, Henry Emery, Stephen Christian. *Cont* Penny Daniels. *Prod Sec* Ann Skinner. *Wardrobe Mistress* Laurel Staffell. *Makeup* Geoffrey Rodway. *Hairdressing* Stella Rivers. *Location Adv* John L. Hargreaves. *Casting* Maureen Goldner. *Still Photog* Harry Gillard. *Constr Mgr* Frank Trussel. *Chargehand Props* George Ball. *Grip* Ted Lockhart. *Ch Electrn* Vic Smith.

Cast: Hayley Mills *(Kathy Bostock)*, Bernard Lee *(Mr. Bostock)*, Alan Bates *(The Man)*, Diane Holgate *(Nan Bostock)*, Alan Barnes *(Charles Bostock)*, Norman Bird *(Eddie)*, Diane Clare *(Miss Lodge)*, Patricia Heneghan *(Salvation Army girl)*, Elsie Wagstaff *(Auntie Dorothy)*, John Arnatt *(Teesdale)*, Hamilton Dyce *(Reeves)*, Howard Douglas *(Weaver)*, Roy Holder *(Jackie)*, Gerald Sim *(Wilcox)*, Ronald Hines *(P. C. Thurstow)*, Michael Lees, Michael Raghan *(civil defense workers)*, Barry Dean *(Raymond)*, May Barton *(villager)*, Christine Ashworth, John Boden, Doreena Clark, Keith Clement, Pamela Lonsdale, Judy Ollerenshaw, Robert Palmer, Lois Read, Nigel Stafford *(The Disciples)*, Anne Newby, Julie Jackson *(The Latecomers)*.

Drama. Source: Mary Hayley Bell, *Whistle Down the Wind* (London, 1958). On a lonely farm in Lancashire, the three Bostock children—15-year-old Kathy, 10-year-old Nan, and 6-year-old Charles—rescue three kittens from drowning and hide them in their barn. When Charles wonders who will care for the animals, a Salvation Army woman tells him that Jesus will look after them. That night Kathy sneaks into the barn to see if the kittens are safe and stumbles upon a haggard, bearded man. When she asks him who he is, the stranger mutters "Jesus Christ" and collapses. The stunned child takes the man's words literally and races home to tell her sister. In the morning the children bring bread and wine to the man, unaware that he is actually a murderer on the run. Though the wondrous news of the Saviour's return reaches all the other children in the village, the secret is kept from the adults lest they take him away. At Charles's birthday party, Nan inadvertently betrays the man's presence to her Aunt Dorothy, and the police are quickly called. Fearful of hurting an innocent child, the murderer surrenders without a struggle and is quietly led away, as children from all over the countryside watch. *Fugitives. Children. Aunts. Police. Farm life. Murder. Brother-sister relationship. Mistaken identity. Birthdays. Lancashire. Jesus. Salvation Army. Cats.*

Note: Location scenes filmed in Burnley, Lancashire. Opened in London in Jul 1961.

WHISTLE YOUR WAY BACK HOME *see* **HEY THERE, IT'S YOGI BEAR**

THE WHITE COLT *see* **RUN WILD, RUN FREE**

WHITE FURY   **F6.5543**
A. R. Dubs Productions–Alaskan Shows. *Dist* American National Enterprises. 12 Mar **1969** [Dayton, Ohio, opening]. Sd; col. 35mm. 100 min.
Prod-Dir-Writ Arthur R. Dubs. *Photog* Arthur R. Dubs.
Narrator: Arthur R. Dubs.
Documentary. Three short films—"White Fury" (20 min), "Baja Big Horn" (55 min), and "High Desert" (25 min)—focus on big game hunting in Alaska. The last segment climaxes with the killing of a polar bear, reputed to be the largest in the world. *Hunting. Alaska. Big game. Bears.*
Note: Filmed in 16mm. A sequel to *Safari in Alaska,* q. v.

WHITE HUNTER   **F6.5544**
Signal International Productions. *Dist* Herts-Lion International Corp. 13 May **1965** [Dallas opening]. Sd; col (Eastmancolor). 35mm. 86 min.
Prod-Dir-Writ George Michael. *Photog* Tim Spring, John B. Kennard.
Cast: George Michael *(narrator)*, David Georgiades, June Michael, John Haddad, Carole Michael, Roger Blake, Jack Hutcheson, Emile Georgiades.
Adventure drama. Described by its producer-director-writer-narrator as a "semi-documentary," this combination of animal footage and dramatic story concerns the stalking of big game by hunters in Africa. Included are shots of lions, giraffes, leopards, baboons, and elephants. *Hunters. Hunting. Africa. Big game. Lions. Giraffes. Leopards. Apes. Elephants.*
Note: Filmed in Africa.

WHITE LIGHTNIN' ROAD   **F6.5545**
J. R. T. Films. *Dist* The Ormond Organization. 24 Feb **1967** [Maryland license]. Sd; col. 35mm. 95 min.
Prod June Ormond, Ron Ormond. *Dir* Ron Ormond.
Cast: Arline Hunter, Tim Ormond. No information about the precise nature of this film has been found. *Moonshiners.*

WHITE NIGHTS (France/Italy)   **F6.5546**
Cl. AS.—Vides—Intermondia Films. *Dist* United Motion Picture Organization. 28 May **1961** [New York opening]. Sd; b&w. 35mm. 105 min.

Prod Franco Cristaldi. *Dir* Luchino Visconti. *Screenplay* Suso Cecchi D'Amico, Luchino Visconti. *Dir Photog* Giuseppe Rotunno. *Camera Op* Silvano Ippoliti. *Art Dir* Mario Chiari. *Asst Art Dir* Mario Garbuglia. *Set Decor* Enzo Eusepi. *Film Ed* Mario Serandrei. *Mus* Nino Rota. *Mus Cond* Franco Ferrara. *Choreog* Dirk Sanders. *Sd* Vittorio Trentino. *Asst Dir* Fernando Cicero, Albino Cocco. *Prod Mgr* Pietro Notarianni. *Unit Mgr* Guglielmo Colonna. *Script Girl* Wanda Tuzi. *Prod Sec* Lucio Orlandini, Renato Jaboni. *Asst to the Dir* Rinaldo Ricci. *Cost* Piero Tosi. *Makeup* Alberto De Rossi. *Hairstyles* Renata Magnanti. *Still Photog* Paul Ronald.

Cast: Maria Schell *(Natalia)*, Marcello Mastroianni *(Mario)*, Jean Marais *(lodger)*, Clara Calamai *(prostitute)*, Marcella Rovena *(housewife)*, Maria Zanoli *(housekeeper)*, Dirk Sanders *(dancer)*, Giorgio Listuzzi *(policeman)*, Elena Fancera, Lanfranco Ceccarelli, Angelo Galassi, Renato Terra, Corrado Pani.

Drama. From the story by: Fëdor Mikhailovich Dostoevski, *Belyye nochi* (St. Petersburg, 1848). On a winter night in Livorno, a small city of winding canals, Mario, a shy clerk, passes a sobbing young woman, Natalia, standing on a bridge. He learns that she is a prisoner of her own romantic imagination; she has promised to wait one year for the return of her lover, a mysterious sailor who had stayed at the home of her blind grandmother. Mario falls in love with the woman and tries in vain to make her accept reality and return his love. When he fails, a prostitute offers herself to him, but he refuses, for he also has become a prisoner of an impossible love. Finally, one night after a lively cafe dance, he succeeds in arousing Natalia's emotions. As he leads Natalia away, talking happily of their future, the silhouette of a man appears standing by the bridge; it is Natalia's lover fulfilling his promise to return. Natalia runs to him, turns to Mario for a last goodby, and walks away. Mario is left standing alone and forlorn in the deserted street. *Clerks. Sailors. Prostitutes. Lovelorn. Bridges. Cafes. Winter. Livorno.*

Note: Filmed on location in Rome. Opened in Rome in Nov 1957 as *Le notti bianche;* running time: 95 min; in Paris in May 1958 as *Nuits blanches;* running time: 99 min.

WHITE, RED, YELLOW, AND PINK *see* **LOVE FACTORY**

WHITE ROSE OF HONG KONG (Japan)   **F6.5547**
Toho Co. 21 Dec **1965** [Los Angeles showing]. Sd; col (Eastmancolor). 35mm (Tohoscope). 110 min.
Prod Masumi Fujimoto. *Dir* Jun Fukuda. *Screenplay* Ichiro Okeda. *Story* Shinobu Hashimoto. *Photog* Shinsaku Uno. *Mus* Sadao Bekku.
Cast: Chang Mei Yao *(Yuli Rin)*, Tsutomu Yamazaki *(Shiro Matsumoto)*, Akira Takarada *(Susumu Uzuki)*, Kumi Mizuno *(Yoshiko Nakao)*, Kenjiro Ishiyama *(Syozo Tabe)*, Mar Chi *(Eidatsu Ki)*, Yu Fujiki *(Chief of Police Jin)*, Eijiro Yanagi *(Kiyoaki Hayashi)*.
Crime melodrama. A detective attempts to break up a morphine-smuggling operation in Hong Kong, and in the process he meets a Chinese woman whose family is involved in the smuggling. *Detectives. Chinese. Smuggling. Morphine. Hong Kong.*
Note: Released in Japan in 1965 as *Honkon no shiroibara.*

WHITE SAVAGE *see* **BIKINI PARADISE**

WHITE SLAVE SHIP (France/Italy)   **F6.5548**
Giorgio Agliani Cinematografica–Illiria Film–Gladiator Film–Champs-Elysées Productions. *Dist* American International Pictures. 17 Oct **1962** [Portland, Oregon, opening; c12 Sep 1962; LP23209]. Sd; col (Eastman Color, print by Pathé). 35mm (Colorscope). 92 min.
Prod Giorgio Agliani, Rodolphe Solmsen. *Dir* Silvio Amadio. *Screenplay* Sandro Continenza, Marcello Coscia, Ruggero Jacobbi. *Photog* Aldo Giordani. *Art Dir* Gianni Polidori. *Film Ed* Nella Nannuzzi. *Mus Italian Vers* Angelo Francesco Lavagnino. *Mus English Vers* Les Baxter. *Prod Dir* Bruno Amadio. *Makeup* Otello Fava.
Cast: Pier Angeli *(Polly)*, Edmund Purdom *(Dr. Bradley)*, Armand Mestral *(Calico Jack)*, Ivan Desny *(Captain Cooper)*, Michèle Girardon *(Anna)*, Franca Parisi Strahl, Mirko Ellis, Maria Pia Luzi, Paola Petrini, Ruth von Hagen, Ivy Holsen, Renato Speziali, Franco Capucci, Germana Francioli, Fiorella Ferrero, Letitia Bollante, Charles Borromel.
Adventure melodrama. In 1675, Polly is sent from a British prison with 12 other women prisoners to be sold into slavery in the New World. They are herded aboard the *Albatross* along with a secret load of convicts, including Dr. Bradley, a political prisoner. Also on board as passengers are Lord and Lady Gaveston, and a young brother and sister, Anna and Dick. En route to America, Polly and the other women prisoners free the convicts, and Dr. Bradley and a cutthroat, Calico Jack, assume leadership of the vessel. The prisoners murder many of the crew, and Calico Jack forces his attentions on Lady Gaveston, who afterwards kills herself. Meanwhile Dr. Bradley becomes attracted to Anna and shelters her. Encountering a storm, the ship founders, and Dr. Bradley is instrumental in restoring Captain Cooper to the helm. As mutiny is punishable

by death in America, the convicts decide to change the ship's course, imprisoning the captain and Dr. Bradley when they resist. Calico Jack plans to throw the women prisoners overboard to conserve dwindling rations, but Polly and the other women free Captain Cooper and Dr. Bradley and battle the convicts. Polly signals a passing English warship in spite of the punishment she faces. As the British board the ship, the captain helps Polly and Dr. Bradley to regain their freedom in return for their aid, and Dr. Bradley looks forward to a new life with Anna. [Publicity material refers to Anna as Lord and Lady Gaveston's daughter and omits mention of a romance between Anna and Dr. Bradley.] *Convicts. Sea captains. British. Political prisoners. Nobility. Mutiny. Rape. Suicide. Slavery. Criminals—Rehabilitation. Ships. England. Atlantic Ocean. Storms.*

Note: Rome opening: Feb 1962 in Totalscope as *L'ammutinamento*; running time: 103 min. Paris opening: Jun 1963 as *Les révoltées de l'Albatros*; running time: 98 min. Copyright claimant: Alta Vista Productions. U. S. prerelease title: *Wild Cargo.*

WHITE SLAVES OF CHINATOWN   F6.5549
Dist American Film Distributing Corp. 7 Jul **1964** [New York State license]. Sd; b&w. 35mm. 70 min.

Pres by Stan Borden. *Prod* George Weiss. *Dir* Joseph P. Mawra. *Photog* Chung Lo. *Lighting* Richard E. Brooks. *Ed* Joe Nelson. *Sd* Magno Sound.

Cast: Audrey Campbell *(Olga)*, Marlaina Abbie *(Elaine)*, Lenore Rhein *(Frenchy)*, Veronica Bellach *(Vivki)*, Jim Lyons *(Jimmy)*, Mitzi Meer *(Lola)*, Rickey Bell *(Collette)*, Lisa Vohn *(Greta)*, Amy Eden *(Jackie)*, Miss Chinatown *(Lotus)*.

Melodrama. Backed by a crime syndicate, Olga Petroff deals in narcotics and white slavery, luring young women newly released from prison to her headquarters in New York's Chinatown. Her basement is a dungeon, filled with medieval torture devices designed to destroy the resistance of the most hardened captives. She uses her sadistic techniques to brainwash Frenchy into becoming a pusher and prostitute, and to bend her rival, Collette, to the will of the mob. To ensnare additional victims, Olga stages a marijuana party. Seeking excitement, Elaine accepts Jimmy's invitation to the party, and is soon hooked on drugs. For 72 hours, she is conditioned to total slavery. In the days that follow, she gains experience in the routines of prostitution and the drug trade; soon she will be sent to do the bidding of the syndicate in cities around the country. *Madams. Drug dealers. Ex-convicts. Prostitutes. White slave traffic. Sadism. Torture. Brainwashing. Organized crime. Narcotics. Marijuana. New York City—Chinatown.*

Note: *Olga's Girls,* q. v., may be a sequel to this film. Also known as *Slaves of Chinatown* and *White Slaves.*

WHITE TIGER TATOO (Japan)   F6.5550
Toho Co. 7 Oct **1966** [Los Angeles showing]. Sd; col? 35mm. [Feature film, length unknown.]

Cast: Hideki Takahashi.No information about the nature of this film has been found. *Tattoos.*

Note: Japanese title: *Irezumi ichidai.* Original release undetermined.

WHITE TRASH ON MOONSHINE MOUNTAIN see MOONSHINE MOUNTAIN

WHITE VOICES (France/Italy)   F6.5551
Franca Film–Federiz–Francoriz. *Dist* Rizzoli Film Distributors. 12 Apr **1965** [New York opening]. Sd; col (Technicolor). 35mm (Techniscope). 93 min.

Prod Luciano Perugia, Nello Meniconi. *Dir* Pasquale Festa Campanile, Massimo Franciosa. *Screenplay* Pasquale Festa Campanile, Massimo Franciosa, Luigi Magni. *Dir Photog* Ennio Guarnieri. *Scenery* Pier Luigi Pizzi. *Film Ed* Ruggero Mastroianni. *Mus* Gino Marinuzzi, Jr. *Cost* Pier Luigi Pizzi.

Cast: Paolo Ferrari *(Meo)*, Sandra Milo *(Carolina)*, Graziella Granata *(Teresa)*, Anouk Aimée *(Lorenza)*, Vittorio Caprioli *(Matteuccio)*, Jeanne Valérie *(Maria)*, Philippe Leroy *(Ascanio)*, Barbara Steele *(Giulia)*, Leopoldo Trieste *(Oroprcenobbi)*, Jacqueline Sassard *(Eugenia)*, Claudio Gora *(Marchionne)*, Jean Tissier *(Savello)*, Alfredo Bianchini, Francesco Mulè, Luigi Basagaluppi, Giulio Battiferri, Anita Durante, Jacques Herlin, Guglielmo Spoletini, Filippo Spoletini, Ugo Carbone, Rosalba Neri.

Costume comedy. In 18th-century Rome, Meo sets out to save his family's failing chamber pot business by selling his younger brother to the Vatican choir, a common practice among impoverished Italian families during the vogue of the male soprano (castrato) voice. The brother escapes, and Meo is trapped into taking his place, but he bribes the surgeon not to perform the castration. Before joining the training program given castrated recruits, he talks his girl friend, Teresa, into submitting to him without benefit of clergy. Frustrated and unhappy in his hoax, Meo soon discovers that his position allows him entry into the homes of the wealthy and aristocratic. Since he is considered harmless by the husbands, Meo proceeds to take full advantage of the situation with their wives. Ultimately, Meo once again encounters Teresa, now the wife of an octogenarian nobleman. She becomes pregnant, and her husband threatens to have Meo beheaded if it is found that he is a castrate in name only. Resignedly, Meo departs for the conservatory to undergo the fatal operation, as his brothers follow in hot pursuit to rescue him. [In the original ending, Meo undergoes the operation rather than face beheading.] *Castrati. Singers. Aristocrats. Brothers. Cuckolds. Surgeons. Family life. Fraud. Castration. Seduction. Pregnancy. Poverty. Impersonation. Bribery. Choirs. Rome. Vatican.*

Note: Released in Italy in 1964 under the title *Le voci bianche*; running time: 100 min. Alternative Italian title: *I castrati.* Paris opening: Aug 1965 as *Le sexe des anges.* Also known as *Under Cover Rogue.*

THE WHITE WARRIOR (Italy/Yugoslavia)   F6.5552
Lovćen Film–Majestic Film. *Dist* Warner Bros. Pictures. 10 Mar **1961** [New York opening; c11 Mar 1960; LP25366]. Sd; col (Technicolor). 35mm (Dyaliscope). 86 min.

Dir Riccardo Freda. *2d Unit Dir* Leopoldo Savona. *Screenplay* Gino De Santis, Akos Tolnay. *Photog* Mario Bava, Frano Vodopivec. *Art Dir* Aleksandar Milović. *Mus* Roberto Nicolosi. *Mus Cond* Pierluigi Urbini. *Asst Dir* Leopoldo Savona. *Cost* Filippo Sanjust.

Cast: Steve Reeves *(Hadji Murad)*, Georgia Moll *(Sultanet)*, Renato Baldini *(Akmet Khan)*, Scilla Gabel *(Princess Maria)*, Gerard Herter *(Prince Sergei [General Vorontzov])*, Nikola Popović *(King Shamyl)*, Milivoje Živanović, Nikša Stefanini.

Historical melodrama. Source: Leo Nikolaevich Tolstoy, *Khadzhi-Murat* (1896–1904). In the middle of the 19th century, the tyrannical Czar Nicholas I of Russia struggles to bring the rebellious mountain tribes of the Caucasus under his domain. Strongest of the hostile tribal chieftains is Hadji Murad, "The White Warrior" [or "The White Devil" according to foreign sources] who proposes to lead his warriors against the Czar's troops. Opposing his plan is the villainous Akmet Khan, a rival chieftain who covets Hadji's betrothed, Sultanet. Betrayed by Akmet, Hadji is captured and turned over to Prince Sergei, commander of the Russian garrison. Hadji refuses to sign a peace treaty, and Sergei has him tortured, despite the pleas of his own wife, Princess Maria, who has fallen in love with Hadji. Meanwhile, Akmet captures Hadji's motherless son and threatens to have him beheaded unless Sultanet agrees to a forced marriage. Hadji, aided by a faithful lieutenant, escapes from his captors, however, and rescues both his son and Sultanet. After slaying Akmet in a hand-to-hand battle, Hadji continues the struggle for freedom. *Russians. Tribal chiefs. Royalty. Resistance (political). Perfidy. Torture. Mountain life. Fatherhood. Caucasus. Russia—History—19th Century. Hadji Murat. Nicholas I (Russia). Duels.*

Note: Produced in Italy in 1959 as *Agi Murad, il diavolo bianco*; running time: 91 min. Yugoslavian release title: *Beli djavo.*

WHO KILLED COCK ROBBIN?   F6.5553
Dist Able Film Co. Oct **1970**. Sd; col. 16mm. [Feature film, length unknown.]

Dir Harry Flynn. *Photog* Roy Lim.

Sex film. No information about the precise nature of this film has been found. *Sexuality.*

WHO KILLED TEDDY BEAR?   F6.5554
Phillips Productions. *Dist* Magna Pictures Distribution Corp. 6 Oct **1965** [New York opening]. Sd; b&w. 35mm. 90 min.

Pres by Marshall Naify. A Joseph Cates Production. *Prod* Everett Rosenthal. *Dir* Joseph Cates. *Screenplay* Leon Tokatyan, Arnold Drake. *Story* Arnold Drake. *Dir Photog* Joseph Brun. *Art Dir* Hank Aldrich. *Film Ed* Angelo Ross. *Mus Comp & Cond* Charlie Calello. *Titl & Discotheque Songs* Al Kasha, Bob Gaudio. *Sd* Charles Federmack. *Asst Dir* Sidney Kupferschmid.

Cast: Sal Mineo *(Lawrence)*, Juliet Prowse *(Norah)*, Jan Murray *(Bill Madden)*, Elaine Stritch *(Billie)*, Margot Bennett, Dan Travanty, Diane Moore, Frank Campanella, Bruce Glover, Tom Aldredge, Rex Everhart, Alex Fisher, Stanley Beck, Casey Townsend.

Mystery melodrama. Norah, a discotheque hostess living in New York City, receives a number of obscene phone calls. A vice squad detective, Bill Madden, takes a special interest in the case, and the hostess begins to suspect that he is the culprit. Norah befriends Lawrence, the busboy at the club, unaware that he is the sexually disturbed caller. He begins to watch her apartment through binoculars; the calls begin to come more frequently; and the terrified Norah is persuaded to move in with Bill and his daughter. One night, Billie, the club's owner, visits Norah, and Lawrence, mistaking her for the other woman, brutally rapes and murders her as she leaves the building. Bill, whose wife was murdered by a sex maniac some years earlier, tries desperately to track down the caller. One night while Norah is giving Lawrence dancing lessons at the club, he assaults her, thus identifying himself as the psychopath. He flees from the discotheque and is shot by police. *Nightclub hostesses. Busboys. Detectives. Nightclub owners. Psychopaths. Vice squads. Telephone. Rape. Murder.*

Mistaken identity. Voyeurism. Discotheques. New York City.
   Note: Filmed in New York City.

WHO RIDES WITH KANE? *see* **YOUNG BILLY YOUNG**

WHO'S AFRAID OF VIRGINIA WOOLF?   F6.5555

Warner Bros. Pictures-Chenault Productions. *Dist* Warner Bros. Pictures. 22 Jun **1966** [Los Angeles opening; c2 Jul 1966; LP33596]. Sd; b&w. 35mm. 131 min.

Prod-Writ Ernest Lehman. *Dir* Mike Nichols. *Dir Photog (see note)* Haskell Wexler, Harry Stradling. *Set Decor* George James Hopkins. *Prod Dsgn* Richard Sylbert. *Film Ed* Sam O'Steen. *Mus Comp & Cond* Alex North. *Sd* M. A. Merrick. *Asst Dir* Bud Grace, David Hall, Michael Daves. *Asst to the Prod* Hal Polaire. *Script Supv* Meta Rebner. *Cost Dsgn* Irene Sharaff. *Miss Taylor's Makeup* Gordon Bau. *Mr. Burton's Makeup* Ron Berkeley. *Hairstyles for Miss Taylor* Sydney Guilaroff. *Supv Hairstylist* Jean Burt Reilly. *Prod Adv* Doane Harrison.

Cast: Elizabeth Taylor *(Martha)*, Richard Burton *(George)*, George Segal *(Nick)*, Sandy Dennis *(Honey)*.

Drama. Source: Edward Albee, *Who's Afraid of Virginia Woolf?* (New York opening: 13 Oct 1962). At 2 a.m. on the campus of a New England college, a middle-aged professor of history and his wife return home from a party. Their life together, after 20 years of marriage, is dominated by violent arguments tempered by occasional moments of tenderness. George, the husband, is a victim of lost idealism—a fact that his wife, Martha, eagerly points out by constantly comparing him to her father, the president of the college. Martha conceals her own vulnerability and frustration behind a show of loud vulgarity. She has created an imaginary son, and George has indulged her in the pretense, partially for his own sake as well. Earlier in the evening, Martha invited a faculty couple, Nick and Honey, to drop by for a drink; as soon as they arrive, Martha begins making flagrant advances toward the younger man. Honey, embarrassed by Martha's behavior and unaccustomed to so much liquor, becomes ill. Intoxicated, Nick confides to George that he married Honey because she falsely told him that she was pregnant. The long night of drinking and quarreling wears on, and Martha eventually lures the opportunistic and drunken Nick to her bedroom upstairs, while George watches their shadows from the yard below. When he learns that Martha has told Honey about their son, George brutally destroys his wife's fantasy by announcing that the son is dead. He then reduces her to hysteria by conducting a mock funeral service in Latin. With the coming of dawn, the guests depart. Physically and emotionally exhausted, George and Martha share a moment of silence. *Professors. Idealists. Opportunists. Marriage. Middle age. Childlessness. Fantasy. Drunkenness. Infidelity. New England.*

Note: Location scenes filmed in Northampton, Massachusetts. Stradling was replaced during production by Wexler.

WHO'S BEEN SLEEPING IN MY BED?   F6.5556

Claude Productions-Amro Productions-Mea Productions. *Dist* Paramount Pictures. 25 Dec **1963** [New York opening; c17 Oct 1963; LP26841]. Sd; col (Technicolor). 35mm (Panavision). 103 min.

A Jack Rose Production. *Prod-Writ* Jack Rose. *Dir* Daniel Mann. *Cinematog* Joseph Ruttenberg. *Art Dir* Hal Pereira, Arthur Lonergan. *Set Decor* Sam Comer, Arthur Krams. *Film Ed* George Tomasini. *Mus Score* George Duning. *Choreog* Stephen Peck. *Sd* Harry Lindgren. *Asst Dir* Arthur Jacobson. *Prod Mgr* Robert Goodstein. *Cost* Edith Head. *Makeup* Frank Westmore.

Cast: Dean Martin *(Jason Steel)*, Elizabeth Montgomery *(Melissa Morris)*, Carol Burnett *(Stella Irving)*, Martin Balsam *(Sanford Kaufman)*, Jill St. John *(Toby Tobler)*, Richard Conte *(Leonard Ashley)*, Macha Meril *(Jacqueline Edwards)*, Louis Nye *(Harry Tobler)*, Yoko Tani *(Isami Hiroti)*, Jack Soo *(Yoshimi Hiroti)*, Dianne Foster *(Mona Kaufman)*, Elliott Reid *(Tom Edwards)*, Johnny Silver *(Charley)*, Elisabeth Fraser *(Dora Ashley)*, Steve Clinton *(Sam Jones)*, Daniel Ocko *(lawyer)*, Allison Hayes *(Mrs. Grayson)*, James O'Rear *(policeman)*.

Comedy. Actor Jason Steel, hero of a successful TV medical series with a huge female audience, is engaged to Melissa Morris, who is tiring of the delay of their wedding plans. Each Wednesday night Jason plays poker with five cronies, but he is always interrupted early in the game by a telephone call that causes him to leave. The caller is always one of his five friends' neglected wives; each of them in turn appeals to Jason for marital advice and comfort. Jason's efforts to cope with each wife's advances lead him to become disenchanted with the idea of marriage for himself, and he breaks his engagement. Melissa turns for help to her friend Stella, the secretary to an analyst who is one of Jason's poker-playing friends. Stella arranges a phony marriage for Melissa, hoping the news will prompt Jason to propose again. Jason does become upset but turns to the analyst for help and, under the influence of sodium amytal, reveals the truth about his relations with four of the wives. The eavesdropping Stella is

discovered and thrown out of the office, and she immediately rushes to reveal the details of the session to Melissa. Freed from guilt by the analyst, Jason attends Melissa's phony wedding reception, but soon thereafter Melissa makes a Wednesday night visit to Jason's apartment as the other wives have done. Jason proposes again, and Stella, having arranged a fake wedding, now has to falsify a Mexican divorce to extricate Melissa. Jason, however, makes a last-minute decision to accompany Stella and Melissa to Mexico and thus discovers the entire plot. Once more he breaks the engagement and once more Stella bumblingly attempts to reunite the pair. Analysis begins to make Jason think logically, and he finally solves his problems by putting an end to Stella's interference and marrying Melissa. *Actors. Secretaries. Psychiatrists. Television. Marriage—Fake. Marriage counsel. Jealousy. Divorce. Eavesdropping. Seduction. Poker. Truth serum. Mexico.*

WHO'S GOT THE ACTION?   F6.5557

Amro Productions-Claude Productions-Mea Productions. *Dist* Paramount Pictures. 19 Dec **1962** [Chicago opening; c21 Dec 1962; LP23597]. Sd; col (Technicolor). 35mm (Panavision). 93 min.

Prod-Writ Jack Rose. *Dir* Daniel Mann. *Camera* Joseph Ruttenberg. *Camera Op* Tom Morris. *Asst Op* Gene Liggett. *Art Dir* Arthur Lonergan. *Set Decor* Darrell Silvera. *Film Ed* Howard Smith. *Mus Comp & Cond* George Duning. *Titl Song Sung by* Nita Talbot. *Sd* Hugo Grenzbach. *Rec* Al Cuesta. *Boom Op* Al Marsh. *Asst Dir* Arthur Jacobson, Henry E. Brill, Donald Roberts. *Prod Mgr* Frank Caffey. *Asst Prod Mgr* Curtis Mick. *Unit Prod Mgr* Don Robb. *Script Supv* Eylla Jacobus. *Cost* Edith Head. *Wardrobe* Ruth Stella, Robert Magahay. *Makeup* Del Armstrong, Loren Cosand. *Body Makeup* Mary Hadley. *Hairstyles* Helen Young, Virginia Darcy. *Still Photog* G. E. Richardson. *Prop* Martin Pendleton, Wally Oliver. *Grip* Darrell Turnmire. *Gaffer* Chet Stafford. *Dialog Coach* Arno Tanney.

Cast: Dean Martin *(Steve Flood)*, Lana Turner *(Melanie Flood)*, Eddie Albert *(Clint Morgan)*, Nita Talbot *(Saturday Knight)*, Walter Matthau *(Tony Gagoots)*, Margo *(Roza)*, Paul Ford *(Judge Boatwright)*, Lewis Charles *(Clutch)*, John McGiver *(Judge Fogel)*, Dan Tobin *(Mr. Sanford)*, Alexander Rose *(Mr. Goody)*, Jack Albertson *(Officer Hodges)*, Hillary Yates *(Hoxie)*, Mack Gray, John Indrisano *(hoods)*, Ned Glass *(Baldy)*.

Comedy. Source: Alexander Rose, *Four Horse-players Are Missing* (New York, 1960). Melanie Flood learns that her husband Steve's lack of attention is attributable to his heavy losses in racetrack betting, and she persuades his law partner, Clint Morgan, to help her become Steve's bookie. (Under that arrangement the money will at least remain in the family.) The plan backfires, however, when Steve's luck changes; and Melanie is forced to sell her diamonds and antiques in order to pay his winnings. Steve then persuades his friends to place their bets through him, and Melanie's losses mount. The mysterious appearance of this new bookie arouses the curiosity of both Steve and his pals and also of Tony Gagoots, the syndicate boss. All trails lead to the Floods' apartment, and Melanie is forced to confess. When Steve discovers that Tony's singer girl friend, Saturday Knight, could turn the gangster over to the authorities, Steve suggests that Tony marry her to prevent her from testifying against him. Tony agrees, and Steve charges him $18,000 for legal advice—the exact amount needed to cover Melanie's bookie debts. *Gamblers. Lawyers. Bookies. Gangsters. Singers. Syndicates. Horseracing. Marriage. Duplicity. Debt.*

Note: Location scenes filmed in southern California.

WHO'S GOT THE BLACK BOX? (France/Greece/Italy)   F6.5558

Les Films La Boétie-Compagnia Generale Finanziaria Cinematografica-Orion Films. *Dist* RAF Industries. 17 Apr **1970** [Warren, Ohio, opening]. Sd; col (Eastman Color). 35mm. 85 min. [Unconfirmed.] *MPAA rating* M.

Prod André Génovès. *Dir* Claude Chabrol. *Screenplay* Claude Brulé, Daniel Boulanger. *Dial* Daniel Boulanger. *Photog* Jean Rabier. *Camera* Claude Zidi. *Art Dir* Marilena Aravantinou. *Film Ed* Jacques Gaillard, Monique Fardoulis. *Mus* Pierre Jansen. *Sd* Guy Chichignoud. *Asst Dir* Pierre Gauchet, Michel Gregoriou. *Prod Mgr* Alain Quéfféléan, Stefanos Vlachos.

Cast: Jean Seberg *(Shanny)*, Maurice Ronet *(Dex)*, Christian Marquand *(Robert Ford)*, Michel Bouquet *(Sharps)*, Saro Urzi *(Kalhides [Skolikides])*, Antonio Passalia *(killer)*, Paulo Justi *(Josio)*, Claude Chabrol *(Alcibiades)*.

Crime melodrama. Source: Claude Rank, *La route de Corinthe* (Paris, 1966). After U. S. radar installations in Greece have been jammed, N.A.T.O. security officer Robert Ford is gunned down while investigating the sudden appearance of some unusual black boxes containing electronic equipment. Ford's wife, Shanny, is blamed for the murder, and N.A.T.O. chief Sharps, who had previously made advances toward Shanny, orders her to leave Corinth. Knowing that Shanny will seek out her husband's killer, Sharps assigns Dex, another N.A.T.O. officer, to follow her. Shanny finally eludes Dex and contacts Alcibiades, Ford's informer, who tells her that Kalhides, a marble cutter, is behind the plot. That night Shanny enters Kalhides' marble quarry, where she is captured and then rescued from torture by a truckdriver who is himself murdered. Desperate for help, Shanny convinces Dex to accompany her on a return visit to the quarry, and they learn that the black boxes are being distributed in the heads of statues. When Sharps scoffs at their theory, Shanny escapes again but is abducted by Kalhides' men and taken to an island hideaway to be murdered. Dex arrives on the island by helicopter, kills Kalhides, and rescues Shanny. Later he decides to join Shanny on her return trip to the United States. *Americans in foreign countries. Widows. Informers. Truckdrivers. Murder. Frameup. Conspiracy. Radar. Quarries. Islands. Corinth. North Atlantic Treaty Organization.*

Note: Filmed on location on the Corinth Canal and Nafplion Bay in Greece. Opened in Paris in Oct 1967 as *La route de Corinthe;* running time: 90 min.

WHO'S MINDING THE MINT?　　　　　　　　　　F6.5559

Norman Maurer Productions. *Dist* Columbia Pictures. 26 Sep **1967** [Richmond, Virginia, opening; c10 Oct 1967; LP34961]. Sd; col (Technicolor by Pathé). 35mm. 97 min.

A Norman Maurer Production. *Prod* Norman Maurer. *Dir* Howard Morris. *Writ* R. S. Allen, Harvey Bullock. *Dir Photog* Joseph Biroc. *Aerial Photog* Nelson Tyler. *Art Dir* John Beckman. *Set Decor* Morris Hoffman, Budd S. Friend. *Film Ed* Adrienne Fazan. *Mus* Lalo Schifrin. *Sd Supv* Charles J. Rice. *Sd* Robert Martin, Jack Haynes. *Asst Dir* Bud Grace. *Unit Prod Mgr* Andrew J. Durkus. *Makeup Supv* Ben Lane. *Hairstyles* Virginia Jones. *Sp Eff* Richard Albain. *Tech Adv* Addressograph Multigraph Corp.

Cast: Jim Hutton (*Harry Lucas*), Dorothy Provine (*Verna Baxter*), Milton Berle (*Luther Burton*), Joey Bishop (*Ralph Randazzo*), Bob Denver (*Willie Owens*), Walter Brennan (*Pop Gillis*), Victor Buono (*Captain*), Jack Gilford (*Avery Dugan*), Jamie Farr (*Mario*), Peanuts (dog) (*Inky*), David Stewart (*Samson Link*), Corinne Cole (*Doris Miller*), Jackie Joseph (*Imogene Harris*), Bryan O'Byrne (*Maxwell*), Robert Ball (*Grayson*), Dodo Denney (*Bertha*), Luther James (*Jess*), Mickey Deems (*drunk*), Lennie Bremen (*man in window*), Cordy Clark (*woman in window*), Thom Carney (*1st guard*), Khalil Bezaleel (*2d guard*).

Comedy. Harry Lucas, a money checker at the United States Mint, lives like a millionaire—not by taking home "samples" but by getting luxury items on 60-day trial and then switching his accounts to other stores. Although his extravagance raises suspicions, an audit clears him. One day Verna Baxter, an attractive money cutter enamored of Harry, gives him a bag of fudge, and he mistakenly stuffs $50,000 worth of new bills into it, takes it home and—since Verna's fudge is terrible—dumps the bag's contents in the garbage disposal. Upon realizing his mistake, Harry convinces Pop Gillis, a retired member of the printing staff, that they could sneak into the mint at night and print duplicate bills. They will need safe-cracker Avery Dugan to get the essential engraved plates; Dugan is deaf, however, and needs a hearing aid to do the job. When they go to Luther Burton's pawnshop for one, he forces them to hire him as their manager for a $2,000 cut. Since their access to the mint must be through the sewer system, they next hire sewer expert Ralph Randazzo; and then they engage the services of "The Captain," whose job is to design a boat. Furthermore, because the best manhole to enter is opposite Imogene Harris' apartment, ice cream–truck driver Willie Owens is brought in to keep her out of the way. Finally, Pop realizes that they still need someone to cut the bills, and Harry persuades Verna to do this service. Luther keeps arguing for more money until finally each individual's cut comes to $1 million. Then Harry learns that automation is imminent and all presses are to be removed the following day. Frantic, he alerts the gang that the job must be done that night. When they converge in outlandish get-ups, it is obvious that they came as they were—and Pop even brings his pregnant beagle, who proceeds to deliver her litter. Although the boat collapses, they manage to get the money and escape. While they are celebrating, however, their incompetent lookout, Ralph's cousin Mario, allows garbage collectors to pick up the money, which eventually gets tossed into the sea. Only enough of the bills are recovered to correct Harry's mistake, but he has at least found true love with Verna. And the rest of the gang skin-dive for the missing money. *Safecrackers. Counterfeiters. Pawnbrokers. Sewer workers. Truckdrivers. Currency. Theft. Deafness. Retirement. United States—Printing and Engraving Bureau. United States Mint. Dogs.*

Note: Exteriors filmed in Washington, D. C.

WHO'S MINDING THE STORE?　　　　　　　　　F6.5560

York Pictures–Jerry Lewis Pictures. *Dist* Paramount Pictures. 28 Nov **1963** [New York opening; c27 Nov 1963; LP26777]. Sd; col (Technicolor). 35mm. 90 min.

A York–Jerry Lewis Production. *Prod* Paul Jones. *Assoc Prod* Arthur P. Schmidt. *Dir* Frank Tashlin. *Screenplay* Frank Tashlin, Harry Tugend. *Story* Harry Tugend. *Dir Photog* W. Wallace Kelley. *Col Cons* Richard Mueller. *Art Dir* Hal Pereira, Al Roelofs, Roland Anderson. *Set Decor* James Payne. *Film Ed* John Woodcock. *Mus Comp* Joseph J. Lilley. *Mus Cond* Irvin Talbot. *Sd* Lyle Figland. *Asst Dir* Ralph Axness. *Prod Mgr* Frank Caffey. *Cost* Edith Head. *Makeup* Wally Westmore. *Hairstyles* Nellie Manley. *Sp Eff* Paul K.

Lerpae. *Proc Photog* Farciot Edouart.

Cast: Jerry Lewis (*Raymond Phiffier*), Jill St. John (*Barbara Tuttle*), Agnes Moorehead (*Phoebe Tuttle*), John McGiver (*Mr. Tuttle*), Ray Walston (*Mr. Quimby*), Francesca Bellini (*Shirley*), Nancy Kulp (*Mrs. Rothgraber*), John Abbott (*Roberts*), Jerry Hausner (*Smith*), Peggy Mondo (*lady wrestler*), Mary Treen (*mattress customer*), Isobel Elsom (*Hazel, a dowager*), Richard Wessel (*cop*), Fritz Feld (*Irving Cahastrophe, gourmet manager*), Kathleen Freeman (*Mrs. Glucksman*), Milton Frome (*François, the driver*), Richard Deacon (*tie salesman*), Barbara Pepper (*client at sale*), Sheila Rogers (*nurse*), Mike Ross, Jerry Gordet (*caretakers*), Fifi, Bosley (*themselves, poodles*).

Comedy. Determined to break up the romance between her daughter Barbara and Raymond Phiffier, a rather unstable poodle-sitter, Mrs. Phoebe Tuttle has Raymond hired as a jack-of-all-trades at one of the department stores she owns. Although the store manager, Mr. Quimby, gives Raymond numerous impossible tasks, he not only somehow comes through but even strikes up a friendship with Barbara's father, the titular head of the store. After Barbara warns her mother not to cause Raymond further trouble, he disgraces himself when a vacuum cleaner he is demonstrating runs amok, nearly causing a riot. Mrs. Tuttle fires him, but henpecked Mr. Tuttle does an about-face by telling off his wife. The entire family apologizes to Raymond as they join his poodle-walking rounds. *Floorwalkers. Dog sitters. Salesmen. Timidity. Employment. Courtship. Department stores. Vacuum cleaners. Dogs.*

WHO'S THAT KNOCKING AT MY DOOR?　　　F6.5561

Trimod Films. *Dist* Joseph Brenner Associates. 8 Sep **1968** [New York opening]. Sd; b&w. 35mm. 90 min. *MPAA rating* R.

Prod Joseph Weill, Betzi Manoogian, Haig Manoogian. *Dir-Writ* Martin Scorsese. *Adtl Dial* Betzi Manoogian. *Camera* Michael Wadley, Richard Coll. *Art Dir* Vic Magnotta. *Film Ed* Thelma Schoonmaker. *Sd* John Binder, F. James Datri, Jr. *Unit Mgr* Barbara Battle. *Asst to the Dir* Mardik Martin.

Cast: Zina Bethune (*The Girl*), Harvey Keitel (*J.R.*), Lennard Kuras (*Joey*), Ann Colette (*girl in dream*), Michael Scala (*Sally*), Wendy Russell (*Sally's girl friend*), Philip Carlson (*mountain guide*), Robert Uricola ("*gunman*" at stag party), Bill Minkin (*Iggy/radio announcer*), Marissa Joffrey (*Rosie*), Harry Northrup (*rapist*), Saskia Holleman, Tsuai Yu-Lan, Marieka (*other girls in dream fantasy*), Susan Wood.

Cast—The Prologue: Catherine Scorsese (*J.R.'s mother*), Vic Magnotta, Paul Di Biondi (*boys in street fight*).

Drama. J.R. grew up in New York's "Little Italy" under the dual influence of a rigid Catholic upbringing and the tough law-of-the-jungle rule of the city streets. Rarely straying beyond the limits of his neighborhood, he spends his time drinking with his buddies, playing cards, and horsin' around with "broads" until the time when he will marry a "nice girl." Then, while riding on the Staten Island ferry, he meets and falls in love with a young girl unlike anyone he has ever known. She speaks French, reads F. Scott Fitzgerald, lives alone, and doesn't own a television set. As their relationship deepens, the girl offers herself to J.R. but, believing her chaste, he refuses. Following an invigorating day in the country with one of his buddies, J.R.'s high spirits are deflated when the girl tells him that she was once attacked and raped by a former boyfriend. Feeling betrayed, J.R. walks out on the girl and attempts to resume his former life. However, a wild party leaves him disgusted with both himself and his world and he returns to the girl in the early morning hours. Awkwardly trying for a reconciliation, he tells her that he is willing to forgive her and that he will try to overlook her loss of virginity. The girl, however, realizes that J.R.'s forgiveness is proof that he is incapable of accepting her for what she is, and that they could never find happiness together. When she rejects him, J.R. flies into a rage and, from years of conditioning, returns to his Church. But the present has intruded upon the past and he finds no solace. *Italians. Catholics. Braggarts. Adolescence. Rape. Urban life. Double standard. Virginity. Disillusionment. Catholic Church. New York City—Little Italy. Staten Island Ferry.*

Note: Produced in 1967, the film premiered at the Chicago Film Festival under its original title, *I Call First.* A nude fantasy sequence was then added, and the film was released theatrically under the title, *Who's That Knocking at My Door?* In 1970 it was released in Los Angeles as *J. R.* Locations filmed in New York City and Copake, N.Y.

WHY ANNA? *see* DIARY OF A SCHIZOPHRENIC GIRL

WHY BOTHER TO KNOCK (Great Britain)　　　　F6.5562

Haileywood Films–Associated British Picture Corp. *Dist* Seven Arts Pictures. 20 Nov **1964** [Los Angeles opening]. Sd; col (Technicolor). 35mm (CinemaScope). 88 min.

Prod Frank Godwin. *Exec Prod* Richard Todd. *Dir* Cyril Frankel. *Screenplay* Denis Cannan, Frederick Gotfurt, Frederic Raphael. *Photog* Geoffrey Unsworth. *1st Asst* Freddie Goode. *Camera Op* Jack Atcheler. *Art Dir* Tony Masters. *Film Ed* Anne V. Coates. *Mus* Elisabeth Lutyens. *Mus Dir*

John Hollingsworth. *Sd* Charles Crafford. *Sd Rec* H. L. Bird, Len Shilton. *Sd Mix* Les Hammond. *Prod Mgr* Leigh Aman. *Cont* June Randall. *Wardrobe* Jackie Jackson. *Makeup* Bob Clark. *Hairdresser* Gordon Bond. *Still Photog* Ronnie Pilgrim.

Cast: Richard Todd *(Bill Ferguson)*, Nicole Maurey *(Lucille)*, Elke Sommer *(Ingrid)*, June Thorburn *(Stella)*, Rik Battaglia *(Giulio)*, Judith Anderson *(Maggie Shoemaker)*, Dawn Beret *(Harry)*, Scot Finch *(Perry)*, Eleanor Summerfield *(mother)*, John Le Mesurier *(father)*, Colin Gordon *(Rolsom)*, Kenneth Fortescue *(Ian)*, Ronald Fraser *(Fred)*, Tom Duggan *(Al)*, Michael Shepley *(colonel)*, Joan Sterndale-Bennett *(spinster)*, Kynaston Reeves *(neighbor)*, John Laurie *(taxi driver)*, Warren Mitchell *(waiter)*, Robert Nichols, Jerry Stovin, Gary Cockrell *(United States sailors)*, Sara Luzita, Pirmin Trecu *(Flamenco dancers)*.

Comedy. Source: Clifford Hanley, *Love From Everybody* (London, 1959). Bill Ferguson, an Edinburgh travel agent, has a quarrel with his fiancée, Stella, when she refuses to spend the night in his apartment. He leaves on a tour of Europe and has affairs with Lucille in Austria, with Ingrid in the Alps, and with a married Englishwoman in Italy. As mementos, he gives each of them a key to his Edinburgh apartment. After returning home, he makes up with Stella and finally lures her to his flat; but Lucille, Ingrid, the Englishwoman, and her teenaged daughter all arrive at the same time. Stella storms out, Ingrid leaves with her Italian lover Giulio, and Bill is left with the adoring teenager. Assisted by Maggie Shoemaker, an American vacationing in Scotland, Bill manages to get out of his predicament and win Stella's hand. *Travel agents. Scotch. Tourists. Italians. Americans in foreign countries. Infidelity. Adolescence. Vacations. Edinburgh. Austria. Alps. Italy.*

Note: Released in Great Britain in Jul 1961 as *Don't Bother To Knock;* running time: 89 min.

WHY RUSSIANS ARE REVOLTING   F6.5563

Dist Mutual Releasing Co. Aug **1970**. Sd; b&w. 35mm (UniScope). 91 min.
Prod-Dir-Writ Neil Sullivan. *Assoc Prod* Lawrence Casey. *Photog* William Glass, James Cozart. *Film Ed* Jay Fitzgerald. *Songs:* "Those S.O.B.'s Upstairs" and "Shall My Soul Pass Through Old Ireland" Robert Hennessy, Neil Sullivan. *Sd* Sy Lubin. *Sp Eff* EFX Unlimited.

Cast: Neil Sullivan *(Cyrus Barnwhistle Diner)*, Ed Maywood *(Vladimir Flynn)*, George Badera *(Henry Sabotage)*, Seneca Ames *(Tootsie Fahrenheit)*, D. F. Barry *(Leon Trotsky)*, Herbert Boland *(Peter Tobashin)*, Ralph Hebel *(conductor)*, Saul Katz *(Stalin)*, Wes Carter *(Rasputin)*, Cookie Vazzana, Janet Wood *(girls in bar)*, Frank Walker, actor *(man in bar)*, John Connelly, Don Nevene *(high rollers)*, Andy "Slugger" Loremus, Larry O'Dea *(saloon singers)*, Edward Walsh, Robert Hennessy, Joseph Marchese *(other singers)*.

Comedy. Cyrus Barnwhistle Diner, an American salesman, travels back in time to pre-revolutionary Russia. During his travels, he meets such historical figures as Trotsky, Stalin, Rasputin, and Hitler. *Americans in foreign countries. Salesmen. Russia—History—1917-21 Revolution. Leon Trotsky. Joseph Stalin. Grigori Efimovich Rasputin. Adolf Hitler.*

Note: Location scenes filmed in New York City. Includes footage from *Dr. Jekyll and Mr. Hyde* (1920).

WHY SPY? *see* A MAN CALLED DAGGER

THE WICKED DIE SLOW   F6.5564

Cannon Productions. *Dist* Cannon Releasing Corp. Oct **1968**. Sd; col. 35mm. 75 min.
Prod Donald C. Dennis. *Dir* William K. Hennigar. *Writ* Gary Allen, Jeff Kanew. *Camera* Amin Chaudhri. *Asst Camera* John Fisher. *Film Ed* George Thomas. *Orig Score* Robert Schwartz. *Sd Eff* Robert Prescott. *Asst to Dir* Gillian Mills. *Ch Electrn* Martin Andrews.

Cast: Gary Allen *(The Kid)*, Steve Rivard *(Bart Lenoir)*, Jeff Kanew *(Armadillo)*, Sussanah Campbell *(The Kid's girl)*, Yolanda *(herself)*, Richard Palenske *(her father)*, Helen Stewart *(Bart's girl)*, Samantha Worthington *(bar girl)*, Racine *(Indian maiden)*.

Western melodrama. "The Kid," a notorious gunfighter, and his Mexican sidekick Armadillo ride through the post-Civil War West looking for four Indians who raped the Kid's girl friend. They come upon a band of outlaws beating up an old man and his daughter, rescue them, rescue another woman who is being raped by the same gang, and destroy the assailants. The Kid and Armadillo avenge the rape of the Kid's girl friend, and, finally, the Kid defeats the outlaw leader to prove that "the wicked die slow." *Outlaws. Indians of North America. Mexicans. Rape. Murder. Revenge.*

Note: Location scenes filmed in New Jersey.

THE WICKED DREAMS OF PAULA SCHULTZ   F6.5565

Edward Small Productions—Theme Pictures. *Dist* United Artists. 3 Jan **1968** [New York opening; c4 Jan 1968; LP35531]. Sd; col (DeLuxe). 35mm. 113 min.

Prod Edward Small. *Assoc Prod* Grant Whytock. *Dir* George Marshall. *Screenplay* Burt Styler, Albert E. Lewin, Nat Perrin. *Story* Ken Englund. *Dir Photog* Jacques Marquette. *Camera* Roger Sherman, Jim Weston. *Art Dir* Edward L. Ilou. *Set Decor* Raymond Paul. *Supv Film Ed* Grant Whytock. *Mus* Jimmie Haskell. *Sd* John Kean, Clyde Sorenson. *Mus Ed* Sid Sidney. *Asst Dir* Dink Templeton, Robert M. Jones. *Prod Supv* Harold E. Knox. *Script Supv* Winifred Gibson. *Fashion Dsgn* Marjorie Corso. *Wardrobe* Oscar Rodriguez. *Makeup* Hal Lierley. *Hairstyles* Jane Chabra. *Sp Eff* Robert Overbeck. *Still Photog* Bernard Abramson.

Cast: Elke Sommer *(Paula Schultz)*, Bob Crane *(Bill Mason)*, Werner Klemperer *(Klaus)*, Joey Forman *(Herbert Sweeney)*, John Banner *(Weber)*, Leon Askin *(Oscar)*, Maureen Arthur *(Barbara Sweeney)*, Robert Carricart *(Rocco)*, Theo Marcuse *(Owl)*, Larry D. Mann *(Grossmeyer)*, John Myhers *(boss)*, Chanin Hale *(Hilda)*, Barbara Morrison *(Kalbfus)*, Benny Baker *(cabdriver)*, Fritz Feld *(Kessel)*, Adele Claire *(coach)*.

Comedy. Paula Schultz, a leading East German athlete preparing to take part in the Olympic Games, rebels at the dowdy uniform she is supposed to wear and instead models her own miniskirt. Instead of punishing her, Propaganda Minister Klaus makes her his special aide in the hope of setting her up in his luxury apartment. To escape his lechery, she defects to the West by pole-vaulting over the Berlin Wall. Bill Mason, a black marketeer with his own contacts in East Berlin, agrees to assist the Communists in getting her back in exchange for money to pay a debt. Bill hides her in the home of Herbert Sweeney, an old Army friend now with the CIA, planning to turn her over to the East Germans the following morning; but he falls in love with Paula and at the last minute reneges on the deal. Still fond of money, though, Bill tries to set up a deal whereby the CIA will pay him for Paula's defection. When Paula learns how he intends to use her, she refuses asylum and sadly returns with Klaus and his agents to the East. Intent on making amends, Bill uses a secret underground entrance to East Berlin and disguises himself as a female athlete to get near Paula. Paula realizes she is in love with Bill, and the two escape to the West. *Women athletes. Government agents. Defectors. Communists. Lechery. Debt. Disguise. Pole-vaulting. Black market. Berlin—East. Berlin Wall. Olympic Games. United States—Central Intelligence Agency.*

WICKED WORLD *see* GO, GO, GO WORLD!

WIDE-OPEN COPENHAGEN 70 *see* PORNOGRAPHY: COPENHAGEN 1970

WIDE POINT   F6.5566

Dist Hardrock Movies. 6 Feb **1969** [New York showing]. Sd; col. 16mm (see note). 65 min.
Prod Alan Power. *Dir* John Chamberlain.

Cast: Taylor Mead.

Experimental film. Groups of people, many in the nude, sitting, talking, walking around, and taking baths, and a teenaged girl, dressed in blue and playing a violin, appear in the film. *Violinists. Nudity. Adolescence.*

Note: At its New York showing the film was projected simultaneously on seven screens.

THE WIDOW AND THE GIGOLO *see* THE ROMAN SPRING OF MRS. STONE

THE WIDOW IS WILLING *see* VIOLENT SUMMER

THE WIDOWER *see* AN AUTUMN AFTERNOON

WIEN TANZT *see* VIENNA WALTZES

THE WIFE OF SEISHU HANAOKA (Japan)   F6.5567

Daiei Motion Picture Co. Oct **1970** [Los Angeles showing]. Sd; col? 35mm. [Feature film, length unknown.]
Dir Yasuzo Masumura. *Photog* Setsuo Kobayashi.

Cast: Raizo Ichikawa, Ayako Wakao, Hideko Takamine, Yunosuke Ito, Misako Watanabe, Chisako Hara. No information about the nature of this film has been found.

Note: Released in Japan in 1967 as *Hanaoka Seishu no tsuma.*

WIFE SWAPPERS   F6.5568

Lawrence Productions. *Dist* Emerson Film Enterprises. 26 Feb **1965** [Champaign, Illinois, showing]. Sd; b&w. 35mm. 60 min.
Prod Ron Lawrence. *Assoc Prod* Harry Frank. *Dir* Richard W. Bomont. *Narr* Frank Woody. *Story* Terrance Michaels. *Dir Photog* Karl Prince. *Lighting Supv* Kenny Marks. *Set Decor* Lonny Davis. *Film Ed* Donald Franklin. *Mus Dir* Raynard Whittle. *Asst Dir* Don McFarlan. *Prod Mgr* Harry Samuals. *Wardrobe* Rod Rudolph. *Prop Master* Tom Harris, prop.

Cast: Judette Banket *(Margie)*, Robert Chambers *(narrator)*, Margaret MacPherson, Ken McDonald, Rudy Gome, Rosalie Saunders, Debbie Gilbert, Theresa Cauwels, Allen Moltinam.

Drama. Margie, the wife of a young up-and-coming lawyer, reluctantly joins a wife-swapping club and finds that she is to be the hostess for the next party. Margie complies because of her husband's position but remains on the sidelines at the party and begins to drink while the other women enjoy sex play in the bedrooms and encourage her to join in. Soon, Margie finds herself the center of attention as she performs a belly dance and striptease. While Margie is dressing in a bedroom, Rudy approaches her and tries to rape her. Margie defends herself with a pair of scissors, and Rudy falls dead on the bed. *Lawyers. Housewives. Mate swapping. Rape. Drunkenness. Sex clubs. Striptease.*

THE WIFE SWAPPERS see **THE SWAPPERS**

WILBUR AND THE BABY FACTORY   F6.5569

Boxoffice International Pictures. Aug **1970** [Los Angeles showing]. Sd (Audioscope); col (De Luxe). 35mm. 91 min.

Pres by Harry Novak. *Prod* Alec McCombie. *Exec Prod* Harry Novak. *Assoc Prod* Roger Russell, Grant Hoag. *Dir-Writ* Tom Wolfe. *Dir Photog* Lloyd Knechtel. *Dream Seq Photog* Barry Dukoff. *Art Dir* Michael Minor. *Film Ed* Grant Hoag. *Mus* Michael Terresco. *Protest Song* Ronee Blakley. *Asst Dir* Terry Swann, Renaud Tourneaux. *Script Supv* Pat Shea. *Sp Cost* Ruth Glunt. *Tech Dir* James A. Ryan.

Cast: Tom Shea *(Wilbur Steele)*, Keith McConnell *(Dr. Wednesday)*, Larisa Schebert *(Karen Kristine)*, Stuart Lancaster *(W.W.)*, Lisa Grant *(Mona Brigstick)*, Patrick M. Legrand *(Mawson)*, Catherine Phillippe *(Angelique)*, James Antony *(The Bull)*, Sue Silla *(W.W.'s girl friend)*, Frank Belt *(hunter)*, Edward Murphy *(listener)*, Larry Verdugo *(young lawyer)*, Candy Nash *(Suzy Polo)*, Lewis Clark *(Mr. Thermometer)*, Diane Cope *(Miss Thermometer)*, Susan Bergdahl, Jeannie Anderson, Neola Graef, Jane Tsentas, Zerrin Arbesh *(conception room girls)*, Shelley Mynatt *(Flip)*.

Comedy. Wilbur Steele, an amiable college protester trying to avoid the draft, is tricked into signing a 2-year contract with The Baby Factory, a secret organization dedicated to sterilizing the world's population and creating a genetically perfect race. Under Dr. Wednesday's direction, Wilbur is physically and chemically conditioned for the task of fathering some 2,000 children over a 2-year period. His initial shock at being informed of his mission turns to bitter resentment as he is forced to apply himself to the enormous task. Wilbur's sullen predecessor, "The Bull," kept locked in a secret room, useless as a breeder, commits suicide. To deal with Wilbur's growing hostility, Dr. Wednesday prescribes ever-increasing doses of dangerous drugs, until Wilbur breaks down completely during an attempt at conception. Wilbur finally manages to escape through an elevator shaft, and he wanders through the woods in delirium. He is shot trying to enter a hunter's cabin and taken to a mountain hospital to recuperate. Confronted by Dr. Wednesday, Wilbur decides to put an end to the whole horrendous project. As he is led to an ambulance, he grabs the sheriff's gun and shoots the doctor. *Draft dodgers. Physicians. Brainwashing. Sterilization (sexual). Eugenics. Murder. Suicide. Hospitals. Drugs.*

THE WILD AFFAIR (Great Britain)   F6.5570

Seven Arts Productions. *For* Bryanston Films. *Dist* Goldstone Film Enterprises. 20 May **1966** [Miami Beach, Florida, opening]. Sd; b&w. 35mm. 88 min.

Prod Richard L. Patterson. *Assoc Prod* William Kirby. *Dir-Writ* John Krish. *Photog* Arthur Ibbetson. *Art Dir* Terence Marsh, Wallis Smith. *Prod Dsgn* John Box. *Film Ed* Russell Lloyd, Norman Savage. *Mus & Mus Dir* Martin Slavin. *Sd Rec* Stephen Dalby, George Adams. *Asst Dir* Frank Ernst.

Cast: Nancy Kwan *(Marjorie Lee)*, Terry-Thomas *(Godfrey Deane)*, Jimmy Logan *(Craig)*, Bud Flanagan *(Sergeant Bletch)*, Gladys Morgan *(Mrs. Tovey)*, Betty Marsden *(Mavis Cook)*, Paul Whitsun-Jones *(Tiny Hearst)*, Donald Churchill *(Andy)*, David Sumner *(Ralph)*, Joyce Blair *(Monica)*, Victor Spinetti *(Quentin)*, Bessie Love *(Marjorie's mother)*, Joan Benham *(assistant)*, Bernard Adams *(Bone)*, Diane Aubrey *(Jill)*, Sheila Bernette *(tea trolly girl)*, Sidonie Bond *(Sue Blair)*, Patience Collier *(woman in travel agency)*, Paul Curran *(father)*, Frank Finlay *(drunk)*, Penny Morrell *(tart)*, Claire Neilsen *(blond assistant)*, Fred Stone *(head waiter)*, Frank Thornton *(manager)*.

Comedy-drama. Source: William Sansom, *The Last Hours of Sandra Lee* (London, 1961). Marjorie, an office clerk for a large cosmetics firm, decides to have a last fling before her wedding. At the office Christmas party, she wears a provocative dress that draws the attention of all the men. Notable for their interest are her boss, Godfrey Deane, and the visiting overseas sales manager, Craig. Her confidence bolstered by the new "vampire look" in makeup, Marjorie accepts a new dress from Craig and joins him for lunch in his hotel suite, but she runs from him when he makes advances. She returns to the office with liquor to enliven the party and ejects her fiancé, Andy, when he arrives to meet her. The group becomes sloppily amorous, and Marjorie, thoroughly dismayed, switches on the sprinkler system. However, spirits are once again lifted when one of the workers, Ralph, receives word that his wife has just had a baby. Marjorie leaves the party and is happily reconciled with Andy. *Office*

clerks. Sales managers. Employer-employee relations. Drunkenness. Lechery. Cosmetics. Christmas.

Note: Opened in London in Dec 1965.

THE WILD AND THE NAKED   F6.5571

Marsho Pictures. *Dist* Marsho Pictures, Sack Amusement Enterprises. 21 Nov **1962** [Los Angeles showing]. Sd; b&w. 35mm. 68 min.

Prod Charles Martinez. *Dir* Stan Roberts. *Orig Story* Enrique Madariaga. **Cast:** Tana French *(Paulette).*

Melodrama. Paulette, a model, poses for photographs for a sun bathers magazine and, during a break in the shooting, falls asleep in the sun and has a dream. *She dances in an exotic club and, leaving there, hitchhikes into the country. She is picked up by a handsome stranger who takes her into the wilderness and attempts to rape her. She gets away from him and comes upon a raging river. She removes her dirty clothes to wash them and is seen by the "hermit of the Brazos." He ties her to a stake and performs weird rituals. A fisherman hears her screams and kills the hermit. She falls in love with the fisherman, and they make love. A gorilla threatens them, and they elude the animal after a long chase.* There is a surprise ending. *Models. Artists. Hermits. Fishermen. Nudity. Rape. Kidnaping. Murder. Sunbathing. Dreams. Gorillas.*

THE WILD AND THE WILLING see **YOUNG AND WILLING**

WILD AND WILLING see **RAT FINK**

WILD AND WONDERFUL   F6.5572

Harold Hecht–Universal Pictures–Reynard Productions. *Dist* Universal Pictures. 27 May **1964** [Philadelphia opening]. Sd; col (Eastmancolor). 35mm. 88 min.

A Harold Hecht Production. *Prod* Harold Hecht. *Dir* Michael Anderson. *Screenplay* Larry Markes, Michael Morris, writ. Waldo Salt. *Screen Story* Richard M. Powell, Phillip Rapp. *Photog* Joseph LaShelle. *Camera Op* Robert Johannes. *Asst Camera* Bob Hosler, Jack Chandler. *Art Dir* Alexander Golitzen, Edward S. Haworth. *Set Decor* Ruby Levitt. *Set Coörd* Wes Thompson. *Film Ed* Gene Milford. *Asst Ed* Jerome F. Brady. *Mus* Morton Stevens. *Mus Supv* Joseph Gershenson. *Sd* Waldon O. Watson, Joe Lapis, Don Cunliffe, James Alexander, Victor Goode. *Asst Dir* L. V. McCardle, Jr., James Welch. *Unit Prod Mgr* Bob Larson. *Script Supv* Lew Jarrard. *Miss Kaufmann's Gowns* Valentino of Rome. *Cost Dsgn* Rosemary Odell. *Wardrobe* Norman Mayreis, Truman Eli, Olive Koenitz. *Makeup Supv* Bud Westmore. *Makeup* Nick Marcellino, Frank McCoy. *Hairstyles* Larry Germain, Joan St. Oegger. *Sp Eff* Whitey McMahon. *Dog Trainer* Sam Williamson. *Poodle Trainer* Frank Weatherwax. *Still Photog* Jack Geraghty. *Gaffer* Don Stott. *Grip* Dean Paup, George Hudder. *Prop* Bill Nunley, Fay Frame.

Cast: Tony Curtis *(Terry Williams)*, Christine Kaufmann *(Giselle Ponchon)*, Larry Storch *(Rufus Gibbs)*, Marty Ingels *(Doc Bailey)*, Jacques Aubuchon *(Papa Ponchon)*, Pierre Olaf *(Jacquot)*, Cliff Osmond *(Hercule)*, Fifi D'Orsay *(Simone)*, Marcel Hillaire *(Inspector Duvivier)*, Jules Munshin *(Rousseleau)*, Sarah Marshall *(Pamela)*, Marcel Dalio *(Dr. Reynard)*, Vito Scotti *(André)*, Steven Geray *(bartender)*, Stanley Adams *(mayor)*, Shelly Manne *(musician)*, Maurice Marsac *(announcer)*, Louis Mercier *(LeBeque)*, Dante Caesari *(butler)*, Danica D'Hondt *(Monique)*, Guy De Vestel *(Gustav)*, Monsieur Cognac *(himself, a poodle)*.

Comedy. Source: Dorothy Crider, "I Married a Dog" ["Monsieur Cognac"] (unpublished short story). Monsieur Cognac, a poodle star of French films, runs away from his owner, Giselle Ponchon, also a film star, and meets Terry Williams, an American musician working in Paris. Terry and the dog, who loves liquor, engage in an all-night drinking spree, and when Giselle and her father finally find the poodle with Terry, Giselle and Terry fall in love. They marry despite the objections of her father, but Cognac becomes jealous of Terry, and the clever dog's scheming makes a shambles of the wedding night as Terry drinks a sleeping potion intended for Cognac. Giselle refuses to leave the dog behind for a honeymoon, and she and Terry part. Terry solves their problem by arranging a romance between Cognac and Pink Poupée, a female poodle, and he and Giselle are reconciled. *Actors. Americans in foreign countries. Musicians. Marriage. Drunkenness. Bars. Weddings. Tranquilizers. Paris. Dogs.*

Note: Working title: *Monsieur Cognac.*

THE WILD ANGELS   F6.5573

American International Pictures. 20 Jul **1966** [c20 Jul 1966: LP32873]. Sd; col (Pathé). 35mm (Panavision). 90 min. [See note.]

Prod-Dir Roger Corman. *Assoc Prod* Laurence Cruikshank. *Screenplay* Charles Griffith. *Dir Photog* Richard Moore. *Camera Op* Richard C. Glouner. *Asst Camera* Glenn Shanks, Gary Boren. *Prod Dsgn* Rick Beck-Meyer. *Film Ed* Monte Hellman. *Mus* Mike Curb. *Sd Mix* Phil Mitchell. *Rec* Dick Ryan, sd. *Boom Op* Charles Wilborn. *Asst Dir* Paul Rapp. *Prod Mgr* Jack Bohrer. *Prod Asst* Barboura Freed. *Script Supv* Bonnie Prendergast. *Asst to the Dir*

Peter Bogdanovich. *Wardrobe* Glen Wright. *Makeup* Jack Obringer. *Prop Master* Richard Rubin. *Still Photog* Jack Geraghty, Lloyd Garnell.

Cast: Peter Fonda *(Heavenly Blues)*, Nancy Sinatra *(Mike)*, Bruce Dern *(Loser)*, Lou Procopio *(Joint)*, Coby Denton *(Bull Puckey)*, Marc Cavell *(Frankenstein)*, Buck Taylor *(Dear John)*, Norman Alden *(Medic)*, Michael J. Pollard *(Pigmy)*, Diane Ladd *(Gaysh)*, Joan Shawlee *(Mama Monahan)*, Gayle Hunnicutt *(Suzie)*, Art Baker *(Thomas)*, Frank Maxwell *(preacher)*, Frank Gerstle *(hospital policeman)*, Kim Hamilton *(nurse)*, Members of Hell's Angels of Venice (California), Peter Bogdanovich.

Action melodrama. Heavenly Blues is the leader of the Hell's Angels, a group of California motorcyclists intent on living lives free of all social responsibility. Trouble begins when the motorcycle of one member, Loser, is stolen by another gang. Loser then loses his construction job because of the Nazi emblems he wears. His group retaliates by raiding a rival Mexican club, inciting a rumble, and stealing one of the rivals' motorcycles. But as Loser is making his getaway, he is seriously wounded by a policeman and taken to a hospital. At the height of one of their orgies, Loser's friends decide to "rescue" him. They raid the hospital, pause long enough for one member to assault a Negro nurse, and kidnap their buddy. When Loser eventually dies from his wounds, his body is sent home for burial. His friends get drunk at the funeral service, attack and tie up the minister, rape Loser's young widow in church, and remove his body from its coffin and wrap it in a Nazi flag. The outraged local citizens break up the funeral procession and engage the cyclists in a graveside brawl. As the police arrive, the gang ride off on their motorcycles. But Heavenly Blues remains behind, throwing dirt on Loser's grave and muttering "There's nowhere to go." *Motorcycle gangs. Mexicans. Police. Clergymen. Widows. Negroes. Theft. Drunkenness. Rape. Hospitals. Orgies. Funerals. Churches. California. Hell's Angels.*

Note: Location scenes filmed in Palm Springs, California. Registered for copyright at 85 min; also reviewed at 82, 83, and 93 min. Working title: *All the Fallen Angels.*

WILD ARCTIC see THE SAVAGE WILD

THE WILD BUNCH   F6.5574
Warner Bros.–Seven Arts, Inc. 18 Jun **1969** [Los Angeles opening; c18 Jun 1969; LP40894]. Sd; col (Technicolor). 35mm (Panavision). 148 min. [See note.] *MPAA rating* R.
A Phil Feldman Production. *Prod* Phil Feldman. *Assoc Prod* Roy N. Sickner. *Dir* Sam Peckinpah. *2d Unit Dir* Buzz Henry. *Screenplay* Walon Green, Sam Peckinpah. *Story* Walon Green, Roy N. Sickner. *Dir Photog* Lucien Ballard. *Art Dir* Edward Carrere. *Film Ed* Louis Lombardo. *Mus* Jerry Fielding. *Mus Supv* Sonny Burke. *Sd* Robert J. Miller. *Asst Dir* Cliff Coleman, Fred Gammon. *Prod Mgr* William Faralla. *Wardrobe* Gordon Dawson. *Makeup* Al Greenway. *Sp Eff* Bud Hulburd.

Cast: William Holden *(Pike Bishop)*, Ernest Borgnine *(Dutch Engstrom)*, Robert Ryan *(Deke Thornton)*, Edmond O'Brien *(Sykes)*, Warren Oates *(Lyle Gorch)*, Jaime Sanchez *(Angel)*, Ben Johnson *(Tector Gorch)*, Emilio Fernandez *(Mapache)*, Strother Martin *(Coffer)*, L. Q. Jones *(T. C.)*, Albert Dekker *(Pat Harrigan)*, Bo Hopkins *(Crazy Lee)*, Dub Taylor *(Mayor Wainscoat)*, Jorge Russek *(Lieutenant Zamorra)*, Alfonso Arau *(Herrera)*, Chano Urueta *(Don José)*, Sonia Amelio *(Teresa)*, Aurora Clavel *(Aurora)*, Elsa Cardenas *(Elsa)*, Fernando Wagner *(German Army officer)*, Paul Harper, Constance White, Lilia Richards.

Western drama. By 1913, the outlaw gangs of the Old West are rapidly disappearing. Under the leadership of aging Pike Bishop, one such gang rides into San Rafael, Texas, to rob the local railway office. Though dressed in U. S. Cavalry uniforms, Bishop and his men—Dutch Engstrom, brothers Lyle and Tector Gorch, and a young Mexican—Angel—are ambushed by bounty hunters led by ex-convict Deke Thornton, a former member of Bishop's gang who must pursue his old friend or return to prison. When a group of temperance marchers are caught in the crossfire, the ambush turns into a massacre that ends when Bishop's men escape into Mexico and the bounty hunters stop to loot the corpses. At a rendezvous in Mexico with Sykes, an old broken-down gunslinger, the gang discovers that the stolen railway bags contain iron washers instead of money. Accepting their bad luck, they ride to Angel's home village, where they learn that the bandit general Mapache, a sadistic opponent of Pancho Villa, has killed Angel's father and ridden off with the youth's sweetheart, Teresa. Though Angel kills Teresa in public when he finds her with the general, Bishop intervenes on behalf of the boy and makes a deal with Mapache whereby Bishop's gang will rob an army munitions train and sell its load of rifles to the bandits for $10,000. In spite of the presence of Thornton's bounty hunters on the train, Bishop's gang hijacks the vehicle and escapes with the army rifles. Angel, who has given a carton of munitions to the people of his village, is seized and held prisoner by the bandits. Since loyalty to one another is all that remains, the "wild bunch" demands Angel's release; but when the demand is made during a drunken celebration, Mapache slashes the boy's throat. Bishop kills the

bandit chief in retaliation, thereby setting off a slaughter in which the entire gang, as well as hundreds of Mexicans, are killed. Thornton and his bounty hunters arrive to collect the bodies of the ransomed outlaws; but when all except Thornton ride out of town, they are shot down by Sykes and the peasants from Angel's village. As the Mexicans tie the sacks of gold to their horses, Sykes and the weary Thornton decide to become a team. *Outlaws. Gangs. Bounty hunters. Brothers. Mexicans. Ex-convicts. Peasants. Sadism. Robbery. Temperance. Massacres. Looting. Revenge. Murder. Jealousy. Train robberies. Drunkenness. Loyalty. Gold. Texas. Mexico. United States Army—Cavalry.*

Note: Location scenes filmed in Parras, Mexico. Four scenes were cut by the studio after release: Sykes's confession that his grandson was killed in the robbery; a flashback in which Pike is shot and crippled; a flashback in which Thornton and Pike are trapped in a brothel during an ambush; and Mapache's army fighting Pancho Villa's forces. Consequently, the running time varies between 134 and 148 min.

WILD CARGO see WHITE SLAVE SHIP

THE WILD CHILD (France)   F6.5575
Films du Carrosse-Les Productions Artistes Associés. *Dist* United Artists. 11 Sep **1970** [New York opening; c26 Feb 1970; LF80]. Sd; b&w. 35mm. 90 min. *MPAA rating* G.
Prod Marcel Berbert. *Assoc Prod* Christian Lentretien. *Dir* François Truffaut. *Screenplay* François Truffaut, Jean Gruault. *Dir Photog* Nestor Almendros. *Camera Op* Philippe Théaudière. *Asst Camera* Jean-Claude Rivière. *Art Dir* Jean Mandaroux. *Film Ed* Agnès Guillemot. *Asst Film Ed* Yann Dedet. *Mus:* "Concerto for Mandolin," "Concerto for Flautino" Antonio Vivaldi. *Recorder Solo* Michel Sanvoisin. *Mandolin Solo* André Saint-Clivier. *Mus Adv* Antoine Duhamel. *Sd* René Levert. *Sd Mix* Alex Pront. *1st & 2d Asst Dir* Suzanne Schiffman, Jean-François Stevenin. *Prod Supv* Claude Miler. *Prod Mgr* Roland Thénot. *Script Girl* Christine Pelle. *Cost* Gitt Magrini. *Makeup* Nicole Félix. *Prop Master* Jean-Claude Dolbert. *Still Photog* Pierre Zucca.

Cast: Jean-Pierre Cargol *(Victor, the boy)*, François Truffaut *(Dr. Jean Itard)*, Jean Dasté *(Prof. Philippe Pinel)*, Françoise Seigner *(Madame Guérin)*, Paul Villé *(Rémy)*, Claude Miler *(Monsieur Lémeri)*, Annie Miler *(Madame Lémeri)*, Pierre Fabre *(orderly at institute)*, René Levert *(police official)*, Jean Mandaroux *(Itard's doctor)*, Nathan Miler *(Lémeri baby)*, Mathieu Schiffman *(Mathieu)*, Jean Gruault *(visitor at institute)*, Robert Cambourakis, Gitt Magrini, Jean-François Stevenin *(peasants)*, Laura Truffaut, Eva Truffaut, Guillaume Schiffman, Frédérique Dolbert, Eric Dolbert, Tounet Cargol, Dominique Levert, Mademoiselle Théaudière *(children at farm)*.

Drama. Source: Jean Itard, *Mémoire et rapport sur Victor de l'Aveyron* (Paris; published in two parts: 1801, 1807). In late 18th-century France in the district of Aveyron, villagers capture a young boy who has been seen living wild in nearby woods. A farmer houses the boy in his barn until Dr. Jean Itard, who has read of the case in the local papers, takes the boy to the Institute for the Deaf and Dumb in Paris. There, the boy becomes a freak attraction for wealthy Parisians and a source of taunting for the other boys housed at the Institute. Itard and a colleague, Professor Pinel, examine the boy and estimate his age to be about 12; in addition, they find his body covered with small scars and one long scar across his throat, which they surmise was a result of his parents slitting his throat before abandoning him. Pinel believes the boy is a deafmute idiot, but Itard dissuades him from sending the boy to an asylum and instead takes the boy to his own country home. Placing the child under the care of his housekeeper, Madame Guérin, Itard names him Victor and proceeds with his plan to educate and civilize the boy. Carefully documenting Victor's progress, Itard tries to teach him to speak but meets with limited success. Victor develops an emotional attachment to both Madame Guérin and Itard and learns to associate some words with objects, but his powers of speech seem genuinely blocked. To test the boy's moral sense, Itard deliberately inflicts an unjust punishment on Victor, and when the boy responds with a fit of tears, Itard concludes that the experiment is a success. Shortly thereafter, Victor runs away to the woods, but after a night spent outdoors, he returns to Itard, who receives him with optimism for the boy's future. *Orphans. Farmers. Mutes. Physicians. Housekeepers. Childhood. Education. Forests. Paris. Aveyron. Jean Itard.*

Note: Location scenes filmed in Auvergne. Opened in Paris in Feb 1970 as *L'enfant sauvage;* running time: 85 min.

THE WILD EYE (Italy)   F6.5576
Georges Marci. *For* Cavara Film. *Dist* American International Pictures. 21 Aug **1968** [New York opening; c14 Aug 1968; LP36163]. Sd; col (Technicolor, print by Perfect). 35mm (Techniscope). 91 min.
Prod Georges Marci. *Dir* Paolo Cavara. *Screenplay* Paolo Cavara, Tonino Guerra. *Screenplay Collab* Alberto Moravia. *Story* Paolo Cavara, Fabio Carpi, Ugo Pirro. *Photog (see note)* Raffaele Masciocchi, Marcello Masciocchi. *2d Unit Photog* George Russo. *Art Dir* Pier Luigi Pizzi. *Film Ed* Sergio Montanari. *Mus* Gianni Marchetti.

Cast: Philippe Leroy *(Paolo)*, Delia Boccardo *(Barbara Bates)*, Gabriele Tinti *(Valentino)*, Giorgio Gargiullo *(Rossi)*, Lars Bloch *(John Bates)*, Luciana Angelillo *(Mrs. Davis)*, Gianni Bongioanni *(The Hunter)*, Tullio Marini *(Ruggero)*.

Drama. Paolo, an amoral documentary filmmaker, searches for the bizarre and the sensual. While shooting a gazelle chase in the Sahara with his cameraman assistant, Valentino, Paolo records the reactions of the other members of his party as they suffer exposure and near-starvation after their truck breaks down. After being rescued as planned, Paolo follows two of the guests, John Bates and his wife, Barbara, aboard a liner bound for Bombay. He easily seduces the bored Mrs. Bates and persuades her to become his leading lady. Once in Bombay, Paolo films opium addicts undergoing a "cure" in which they are beaten with huge paddles. When only six "patients" appear, he recruits additional phony participants to make the footage more vivid and then records Barbara's horrified reactions. In Bali, he films deafmute prostitutes. Following an unsuccessful attempt to persuade a Buddhist priest to immolate himself while he and Barbara make love, Paolo persuades a senile and starving maharajah to participate in a butterfly-eating sequence in exchange for a tin of beef. Shocked, Barbara rebukes Paolo for being the instrument of a producer who makes money from the suffering and shame of others. Later, the group goes on to Saigon for scenes of the war in Vietnam, and Barbara witnesses the execution of a young Vietcong suspect and Paolo's brutal beating by the Vietcong. She considers going back to her husband, but, feeling for the first time that Paolo may really need her, she remains. When Paolo learns that Vietcong terrorists will bomb a local bar, he sets up an automatic camera and hides in a back room, without warning the patrons of the danger. He is elated to capture footage of the blast, which kills most of those inside. Then Paolo discovers the lifeless body of Barbara; and despite his grief he asks Valentino to keep the camera focused on his face as the tears flow down his cheeks. *Motion picture directors. Motion picture cameramen. Drug addicts. Deafmutes. Prostitutes. Priests. Royalty. Sadism. Travel. Seduction. Infidelity. Hunger. Capital punishment. Motion pictures. Vietnam War 1964–73. Sahara. Bali. Bombay. Saigon. Vietcong. Explosions.*

Note: Location scenes filmed in Aden, Algiers, Bali, Bangkok, Bombay, Ceylon, Karachi, Singapore, and North and South Vietnam, including Saigon. Rome opening: Aug 1967 as *L'occhio selvaggio*; running time: 98 min. Sources conflict in crediting photographer.

THE WILD FEMALES   **F6.5577**
Dist Sack Amusement Enterprises, Paul Mart Productions, Manson Distributing Corp. 6 Dec **1968** [Champaign, Illinois, showing]. Sd; b&w. 35mm. 82 min.

Prod-Writ W. L. Schmidt. *Dir* Carlos Samoya.

Cast: Amber Arnett *(Lonnie)*, Marsha Jordan *(Rella)*, Moe Martin *(Shep)*, Fern Holbrook *(Nettie)*, Nick Titles *(Hal)*, Ron Rocco *(Tad)*, Damon Sorenson *(father)*, Juni Reynolds *(mother)*, Buckie Buck *(Tom)*.

Drama. Teenager Lonnie arrives home early one afternoon and finds her mother having sex with a stranger on the living room floor. The confused youngster flees her midwestern home and begins a hitchhiking journey to visit her sister, who she believes is a Hollywood star. Her first ride drives her to a lonely spot, knocks her unconscious, and rapes her. She soon discovers the pleasures of the flesh and uses sex to facilitate her journey to Hollywood. Rella, Lonnie's sister, is happily surprised to see her. Lonnie soon realizes that her sister's lavish lifestyle is supported by her career as a prostitute catering to the diverse sexual demands of her clientele. The older, sadder, and wiser woman arranges a date for Lonnie with an attorney and maneuvers the two into marriage so that her sister will be spared the sordid life of a prostitute. [Press photographs suggest that the film contains scenes of group sex, lesbianism, and interracial sex.] *Hitchhikers. Sisters. Lawyers. Adolescence. Prostitution. Filial relations. Rape. Sexual initiation. Group sex. Lesbianism. Miscegenation. Hollywood.*

Note: Also known as *Flocking Together*, and possibly as *Birds of a Feather ... Flocking Together*.

WILD FOR KICKS (Great Britain)   **F6.5578**
Renown Pictures. *Dist* Victoria Films, Times Film Corp. 20 Oct **1961** [New York opening]. Sd; b&w. 35mm. 91 min.

A George Minter Production. *Prod* George Willoughby. *Exec Prod* George Minter. *Dir* Edmond T. Gréville. *Screenplay-Dial* Dail Ambler. *Story* Dail Ambler, Edmond T. Gréville. *Photog* Walter Lassally. *Art Dir* Elven Webb. *Film Ed* Gordon Pilkington. *Mus Comp & Arr* John Barry. *Featuring* John Barry Seven. *Songs:* "Beat Girl," "I Did What You Told Me," "Made You" John Barry, Trevor Peacock. *Sung by* Adam Faith. *Sd* Cyril Swern.

Cast: David Farrar *(Paul Linden)*, Noëlle Adam *(Nichole)*, Christopher Lee *(Kenny)*, Gillian Hills *(Jennifer)*, Adam Faith *(Dave)*, Shirley Ann Field *(Dodo)*, Peter McEnery *(Tony)*, Claire Gordon *(Honey)*, Delphi Lawrence *(Greta)*, Oliver Reed *(Plaid Shirt)*, Michael Kane *(Duffle Coat)*, Anthony

Singleton *(Green Pants)*, Robert Raglan *(F. O. official)*, Nada Beall *(official's wife)*, Margot Bryant *(Martha)*, Nigel Green *(Simon)*, Norman Mitchell *(club doorman)*, Pascaline *(exotic strip dancer)*.

Melodrama. When Paul Linden, a wealthy British widower, returns to London with a young French bride, his rebellious teenage daughter, Jennifer, openly shows her dislike for a stepmother only a few years older than herself. Though the Frenchwoman, Nichole, makes friendly overtures, Jennifer remains hostile and spends her time dancing with her friends Dave, Tony, and Dodo in a beatnik dive across the street from a Soho burlesque club. One day Jennifer accidentally discovers that Nichole was once a stripteaser, and she warns her stepmother that if she is not left alone she will reveal this information to her father. When Jennifer invades the burlesque club to learn more about Nichole's past, she is accosted by the club's owner, Kenny. Later she gives a wild teenage party and performs a striptease just as Paul and Nichole return home. Enraged, Jennifer blurts out the truth about Nichole's past and then runs off to join Kenny. His jealous mistress, Greta, finds them together and stabs him to death. Paul and Nichole arrive in time to comfort the shocked and disillusioned young girl and then lead her home. *Widowers. French. Stepmothers. Beatniks. Stripteasers. Nightclub owners. Mistresses. Filial relations. Murder. Jealousy. Adolescence. Nightclubs. London. London—Soho.*

Note: Released in Great Britain in 1960 as *Beat Girl*; running time: 85 min.

WILD, FREE AND HUNGRY   **F6.5579**
Dist Boxoffice International Film Distributors. Jul **1970**. Sd; col (Eastman Color). 35mm. 88 min.

Pres by Harry Novak. *Prod* Gary Graver. *Dir* H. P. Edwards. *Cinematog* Rahn Vickery. *Prod Sd* Sam Kopetsky. *Boom* Bob Ford. *Prod Mgr* Ken Gibson. *Gaffer* Rocky Bisso. *Key Grip* Henry Mann. *Grip* Mike Snow.

Cast: Gary Graver *(Dave)*, Barbara Caron *(Cinthia)*, Jane Tsentas *(Evelyn)*, Jon Stone *(Frank)*, Monica Gayle *(Diane)*, George Todd *(Don)*, Michael Downing *(1st gangster)*, Rene Leeland *(2d gangster)*, Butch Griswald *(Hugo)*.

Melodrama. On his way to a motorboat race, Dave picks up Cindy on his motorcycle. The motorboat belongs to Frank, a carnival owner who is in debt to Don, a syndicate man who has pressured Frank into betting heavily on Dave to win the race. Frank's wife has fallen in love with Don, and Diane, one of the carnival girls, is in love with Frank. Dave has been pressured to withdraw from the race by Hugo, who purposely crashes into Dave's boat to prevent him from winning. Hugo is killed, and Dave is injured in the accident. Now Frank has lost everything, including his wife, his money, and his carnival to Don. His only consolation is Diane, the carnival girl whom he loves. However, two hoodlums from the syndicate. finally catch up with Don and force him to return the carnival to Frank and to give up any claims to Frank's money. *Hoodlums. Carnivals. Boat racing. Wagers. Syndicates. Debt. Infidelity. Motorboats.*

WILD GALS OF THE NAKED WEST *see* **THE IMMORAL WEST— AND HOW IT WAS LOST**

WILD GIRL *see* **WILD, WILD GIRL**

WILD GUITAR   **F6.5580**
Fairway Productions. *Dist* Fairway-International Films. 6 Nov **1962** [New Orleans opening]. Sd; b&w. 35mm. 87 min.

Prod Nicholas Merriwether. *Dir* Ray Dennis Steckler. *Screenplay* Nicholas Merriwether, Bob Wehling. *Adtl Dial* Joe Thomas. *Camera* Joseph V. Mascelli. *Film Ed* Anthony M. Lanza. *Mus* Alan O'Day. *Songs Writ by* Arch Hall, Jr., Alan O'Day. *Sd* Sam Kopetzky.

Cast: Arch Hall, Jr. *(Bud)*, Nancy Czar *(Vicky)*, William Watters, Cash Flagg, Marie Denn, Bob Crumb, Bill Lloyd, Mike Kannon, Hal Kenton, Jonathan Karle, Al Scott, Virginia Broderick, Paul Voorhees, Rick Dennis, Tony Flynn, Carol Flynn.

Melodrama. Bud, a guitar-playing, motorcycle-riding hipster, travels to Hollywood in hopes of becoming a rock and roll star. He spends the last of his money in a cafe, where he meets Vicky, a dancer who persuades a recording company agent [Hal Kenton] to enter Bud in a television talent show when one of the contestants falls ill. An ambitious record company promoter [William Watters] "discovers" Bud and begins to exploit him by cheating him out of his rightful income. Bud eventually learns from a former protégé of the promoter [Bob Crumb] that he has been cheated, and he returns to the cafe to work as a dishwasher. He is abducted, brainwashed, and tricked, but Vicky and her younger brother rescue Bud and assist him in obtaining a fair contract. *Guitarists. Motorcyclists. Singers. Dancers. Talent agents. Opportunists. Dishwashers. Rock and roll. Ambition. Cheating. Brainwashing. Abduction. Cafes. Talent contests. Television. Contracts. Hollywood.*

Note: Actor Cash Flagg is a pseudonym for Ray Dennis Steckler; Nicholas Merriwether and William Watters for Arch Hall, Sr.

WILD GYPSIES   F6.5581

Paul Mart Productions. *Dist* Manson Distributing Corp. 15 Oct **1969** [Champaign, Illinois, showing]. Sd; col. 35mm. 85 min.

A Paul Mart Production. Prod Paul Mart. *Exec Prod* Edmund Goldman. *Dir-Writ* Marc B. Ray. *Camera* Steve Burum. *Art Dir* Ektor Carranza. *Set Dsgn* Tod Jonson. *Mus Cond* Andre Brunner. *Mus Coörd* Richard La Salle. *Mus by* Hollywood String Orchestra. *Choreog* Joe Cassini. *Sd* Mike Perry. *Prod Mgr* Gilles De Turenne. *Prod Asst* Lore Goldman. *Cost* John Brandt, cost. *Makeup* Scott Hamilton. *Hairstyles* Manny Walters. *Still Photog* Robert Heinz.

Cast: Todd Grange *(Anton)*, Wayne Lundy *(Juan)*, Gayle Clarke *(Maria)*, Ray Rappa *(Armendero)*, Laura Welcome *(Julia)*, Winn Geary *(Helena)*, Carmen Filpe *(Felipe)*, Eli Hadash *(Victor)*, Kay Dahlquist *(Anna)*, Demian Oliver *(Paula)*, Samantha Scott *(Marguerite)*, Glen Jackobson *(Erik)*, Ruth Marcus *(Mama)*, Barry Michlin *(Amos)*.

Melodrama. A band of gypsies encamped in a forest remain unaware that one of their former kinsmen, Anton, is stealthily keeping a rendezvous with his lover, Marguerite. After making love to her, Anton murders her. The gypsies discover her body, and it is revealed that Anton was refused Marguerite's hand in marriage by the tribe, but that he continued to pursue her. Discovered together in violation of the gypsy code, he was tortured and scarred by the superstitious gypsies. The tribe now pursues him, in search of vengeance. They ransack a nearby farm and kidnap a pair of travelers who are brother and sister. Maria entices the brother out into the woods to make love. The sister becomes attracted to Juan, and they swim naked in the moonlit lake. The two return to camp and come across the murdered bodies of Maria and the brother. Juan sets out in pursuit of Anton, who he believes is the culprit. Anton steals into the camp just as Juan leaves on horseback to trail him. Anton kills Juan's brother and kidnaps the sister, but Juan returns, kills Anton, and rescues his love. *Gypsies. Murder. Torture. Banishment. Revenge. Kidnaping. Seduction. Brother-sister relationship.*

WILD HARVEST   F6.5582

Hollywood Artists Productions. *Dist* Sutton Pictures. 7 Nov **1961** [Maryland license]. Sd; b&w. 35mm. 80 min.

Prod Aubrey Schenck. *Exec Prod* Irving Mandell. *Dir* Jerry A. Baerwitz. *Screenplay* Sid Harris. *Photog* Gordon Avil. *Film Ed* Peter Zinner. *Mus* Bert Shefter, Paul Sawtell. *Titl Song* Bert Shefter, Paul Sawtell, Jack Ackerman. *Sung by* Tommy Cooper. *Sd* Robert Post. *Asst Dir* Bruce Bilson. *Prod Mgr* Hal Klein. *Cost* Oscar Rodriguez. *Makeup* Rudolph Liszt. *Photog Eff* Howard Anderson.

Cast: Dolores Faith *(Rose)*, Dean Fredericks *(Whitey)*, Susan Kelly *(Madge)*, Robert Harrow *(Tom Ludlow)*, Arlynn Greer *(Julie)*, Ralph Camargo *(Sam Ludlow)*, Kathleen Freeman *(Goldie)*, Walter Winchell *(narrator)*, Ivy Thayer, Gordon Casell, Dave Dundon, Annette Foosamer, Echoe Jordan, L. Michelle Marx, Ramona Fulmore, Lynda Lee Harrison.

Melodrama. Source: Stephen Longstreet, *Wild Harvest* (New York, 1960). During the grape harvest season, migratory workers gather at a San Joaquin Valley vineyard owned by Sam Ludlow and his son, Tom. The manager of the ranch is Whitey, a brutish man who treats the workers like animals, forces the women to bathe in the irrigation canals, beats up Mexican drunks, and uses the women sexually. He is secretly planning to seize control of the vineyard from young Tom Ludlow, who resents his father's excusing Whitey on the grounds he gets the work done. One day Whitey goads Tom into a fight and savagely beats him into unconsciousness. Eventually the women workers draw up a petition against Whitey and Madge, a young woman, is selected to deliver it to Ludlow. Before she can do so, she is intercepted by Whitey who has been warned by Rose, his mistress, and he attempts to rape her. During the struggle, the girl falls to her death through a broken floor shaft. Whitey races to his cabin and locks himself inside. But Rose gives the women workers a key and they pin him to the floor and attack him with razor-sharp pruning shears. He survives his mutilation as the women leave the cabin silently. *Vineyardists. Migratory workers. Mistresses. Mexicans. Employment—Women. Employer-employee relations. Rape. Castration. San Joaquin (California).*

Note: Filmed on location in Homestead, Florida.

WILD IN THE COUNTRY   F6.5583

Company of Artists. *Dist* Twentieth Century–Fox Film Corp. 8 Jun **1961** [Memphis, Tennessee, opening; c8 Jun 1961; LP19481]. Sd (Westrex); col (De Luxe). 35mm (CinemaScope). 114 min.

A Jerry Wald Production. Prod Jerry Wald. *Assoc Prod* Peter Nelson. *Dir* Philip Dunne. *Screenplay* Clifford Odets. *Dir Photog* William C. Mellor. *Art Dir* Jack Martin Smith, Preston Ames. *Set Decor* Walter M. Scott, Stuart A. Reiss. *Film Ed* Dorothy Spencer. *Mus* Kenyon Hopkins. *Orch* Edward B. Powell. *Titl Song* Hugo Peretti, Luigi Creatore, George David Weiss. *Songs:* "I Slipped, I Stumbled, I Fell," "In My Way" Fred Weiss, Ben Weidman. *Song:* "Lonely Man" Bennie Benjamin, Sol Marcus. *Songs Sung by* Elvis Presley. *Sd* Alfred Bruzlin, Warren B. Delaplain. *Asst Dir* Joseph E. Rickards, Harry Slott.

Prod Mgr Edward Woehler. *Cost Dsgn* Don Feld. *Makeup* Ben Nye. *Hairstyles* Helen Turpin.

Cast: Elvis Presley *(Glenn Tyler)*, Hope Lange *(Irene Sperry)*, Tuesday Weld *(Noreen)*, Millie Perkins *(Betty Lee Parsons)*, Rafer Johnson *(Davis)*, John Ireland *(Phil Macy)*, Gary Lockwood *(Cliff Macy)*, William Mims *(Uncle Rolfe)*, Raymond Greenleaf *(Dr. Underwood)*, Christina Crawford *(Monica George)*, Robin Raymond *(Flossie)*, Doreen Lang *(Mrs. Parsons)*, Charles Arnt *(Mr. Parsons)*, Ruby Goodwin *(Sarah)*, Will Corry *(Willie Dace)*, Alan Napier *(Professor Larson)*, Jason Robards *(Judge Parker)*, Harry Carter *(bartender)*, Harry Shannon *(Sam Tyler)*, Bob "Red" West *(Hank Tyler)*.

Rural melodrama. Source: J. R. Salamanca, *The Lost Country* (New York, 1958). Following a violent fight with his brother, Glenn Tyler, a moody, rebellious Shenandoah Valley farmboy, is paroled into the custody of his Uncle Rolfe, a conniving tonic manufacturer who hopes to find a husband for his daughter Noreen, the mother of an illegitimate child. Glenn is instructed by the court to pay weekly visits to psychiatric consultant Irene Sperry, a widow and the former fiancée of the town's wealthiest citizen, Phil Macy. Irene eventually succeeds in winning his trust and confidence by encouraging his efforts to become a writer and sends one of his stories to a college professor, hoping that Glenn will win a scholarship. Meanwhile, Glenn has rejected his former girl friend, Betty Lee, and entered into an affair with the wanton Noreen. Following a dispute with his uncle, Glenn leaves home and stops visiting Irene. She seeks him out, however, and takes him to the nearby university. Returning home, they are caught in a sudden storm and forced to spend the night at a motel. They take separate rooms, but Glenn's enemy, Cliff Macy, spreads vicious rumors among the townspeople. Furious, Glenn attacks him, unaware that Cliff has a weak heart. Cliff dies, and Glenn is arrested on charge of manslaughter. Macy takes the stand and refutes Irene's testimony that young Cliff was chronically ill. Blaming herself for the tragic turn of events, Irene attempts suicide. Only then does Macy admit the truth about his son's poor health, thus clearing Glenn. When Irene recovers completely, Glenn says goodby and leaves for college. *Farmers. Uncles. Widows. Psychiatrists. Authors. Manslaughter. Suicide. Illegitimacy. Parole. Heart disease. Perjury. Trials. Shenandoah Valley.*

Note: Location scenes filmed in Napa Valley, California.

WILD IN THE STREETS   F6.5584

American International Pictures. 29 May **1968** [New York opening; c29 May 1968; LP35944]. Sd; col (Pathé). 35mm. 97 min. [Copyright length: 86 min.]

Prod James H. Nicholson, Samuel Z. Arkoff. *Exec Prod* Burt Topper. *Assoc Prod* William J. Immerman. *Prod Assoc* Jack Cash. *Dir* Barry Shear. *Screenplay* Robert Thom. *Photog* Richard Moore. *Camera Op* Jules Brenner. *1st Asst Camera* John Viazanko. *Art Dir* Paul Sylos. *Set Decor* Harry Reif. *Main Titl* Pacific Title, Cinefx. *Film Ed* Fred Feitshans, Eve Newman. *Mus Score* Les Baxter. *Mus Supv* Al Simms. *Songs:* "The Shape of Things To Come," "Fifty-Two Per Cent," "Sally LeRoy," "Listen to the Music," "Fourteen or Fight" Barry Mann, Cynthia Weil. *Songs Sung by* Christopher Jones, Paul Wieler, The Thirteenth Power. *Sd* Al Overton. *Rec* Clyde Sorenson. *Boom Op* Charles Knight. *Asst Dir* Chuck Colean, Lew Borzage. *Prod Mgr* Jack Bohrer. *Script Supv* Bonnie Prendergast. *Cost Supv* Richard Bruno. *Wardrobe* Laurie Riley, Pat Zinn. *Makeup* Fred Williams. *Hairstyles* Myrl Stoltz. *Gaffer* Lloyd Garnell. *Key Grip* Frank Lambers. *Prop* Karl Brainard, Al Joyce. *Still Photog* Art Say. *Constr Coörd* Ross Hahn. *Dial Coach* Donald Buka.

Cast: Shelley Winters *(Mrs. Flatow)*, Christopher Jones *(Max Frost)*, Diane Varsi *(Sally LeRoy)*, Ed Begley *(Senator Allbright)*, Hal Holbrook *(John Fergus)*, Millie Perkins *(Mary Fergus)*, Richard Pryor *(Stanley X)*, Bert Freed *(Max Jacob Flatow, Sr.)*, Kevin Coughlin *(Billy Cage)*, Larry Bishop *(Abraham)*, May Ishihara *(Fuji Ellie)*, Michael Margotta *(Jimmy Fergus)*, Don Wyndham *(Joseph Fergus)*, Kellie Flanagan *(young Mary Fergus)*, Salli Sachse *(hippie mother)*, Paul Frees *(narrator)*, Walter Winchell, Melvin Belli, Kenneth Banghart, Louis Lomax, Dick Clark, Jack Latham, Pamela Mason, Allan J. Moll, Army Archerd, Gene Shacove *(themselves)*.

Drama. Source: Robert Thom, "The Day It All Happened, Baby," in *Esquire* (Dec 1966). After destroying the family car with a homemade bomb, 15-year-old Max Flatow takes the $800 he has made selling LSD and sets out on his own. Within 7 years, Max, who has changed his surname to Frost, has become the world's most idolized entertainer; a millionaire, he lives in a lavish Beverly Hills mansion with his girl friend, Sally LeRoy, a former child movie star, and an entourage of young associates. One day the opportunistic Mrs. Flatow sees her lost son on television and forces her husband to join her in attempting a family reunion. When she accidentally kills a child in an automobile accident, however, Max once more completely rejects her. Meanwhile, John Fergus, a liberal California congressman, has decided to ignore the advice of his political mentor, Senator Allbright, and run for the United States Senate by appealing to youth. Although Max consents to perform at a Fergus rally, he doublecrosses the politician by publicly demanding that the voting age be lowered to 14. The demonstrations that follow are so successful that within a month 18 states have given the vote to teenagers. Now determined to gain control of the nation, Max engineers Sally's election to Congress and then, by drugging the legislators with LSD, assures the passage of a bill to eliminate age requirements for office holders. Max runs for president and wins by a landslide. His first official act is to send all citizens over 35 to retirement camps where they are kept on a diet of hallucinogens. Although Max is now apparently all-powerful, there is a hint of things to come when he callously kills a crawfish belonging to two 7-year-old children. As the youngsters look at their dead pet, they vow to put everyone over 10 out of business. *Actors. Entertainers. Millionaires. Hippies. Opportunists. Presidents of the United States. Politicians. Children. Filial relations. Adolescence. Ambition. Youth. Perfidy. Suicide. Bombs. LSD. Beverly Hills. California. United States Congress. Automobile accidents. Crawfish.*

WILD IN THE WOODS   F6.5585
Janus II Productions–Academy Productions. *Dist* Stacey Distributors, Exhibitors Distributing, Ltd. ca **1970**. Sd; col. 16mm. 61-81 min.

Sex film. Two families, one with a sexy teenaged daughter, go on a camping trip. The daughter is ravaged by the husband of the childless couple, and a family war ensues. *Campers. Rape. Feuds.*

Note: Filmed on location in the mountains of southern California.

WILD IS MY LOVE   F6.5586
General Films. *Dist* William Mishkin. 6 Feb **1963** [trade review]. Sd; b&w. 35mm. 74 min.

Pres by William Mishkin. *Prod-Dir* Richard Hilliard. *Assoc Prod* George E. Wolf. *Screenplay* Otto Lemming. *Adtl Story Material* Richard Hilliard. *Photog* Emil Knebel, Louis McMahon. *Film Ed* Ray Pierce. *Mus Comp & Cond* Wilford Holcombe. *Prod Asst* Richard Forstmann.

Cast: Paul Hampton *(Ben)*, Ray Fulmer *(Aga)*, Bob Alexander *(Zero)*, Ralph Stanley *(Tony)*, Gene Courtney *(Lola)*, Carl Low *(Mr. Durrel)*, Elizabeth MacCraie *(Queenie)*, Mary Harrigan, Mike O'Dowd, Richard Forstmann, Victoria Ardiss, Jane Ross, Marge Randolph, "Jezebel".

Melodrama. Three students—Ben, Aga, and Zero—spend the summer at an eastern college to study for make-up examinations. The three are great friends, but Zero must constantly mediate conflicts between Ben and Aga. Ben attends a burlesque show and becomes infatuated with Queenie, a stripper. Tony, who owns the theater, encourages the romance, and Queenie accepts an invitation to spend a weekend at the college. Queenie leaves for the school, and Lola, Tony's former girl friend and the displaced star of the show, seduces Tony with a sensuous dance. Ben and Aga argue and play Russian roulette to prove their manhood. Tony goes to New York and attempts to blackmail Ben's wealthy father by threatening to reveal Ben's infatuation with the stripper, but Ben's father threatens to call the police, and Tony returns to the theater. Ben refuses to take his turn at Russian roulette; Aga calls him a coward, and the two fight. Ben goes to see Queenie, and she seduces him. Tony's spirits brighten when he discovers that Lola is a success as a stripper. Queenie leaves Ben, and the disappointed student renews his friendship with Aga and Zero. *Students. Stripteasers. Theatrical managers. Friendship. Blackmail. Manhood. Seduction. College life. Burlesque. Russian roulette.*

WILD LOVE-MAKERS see **THE WEIRD LOVE MAKERS**

WILD 90   F6.5587
Supreme Mix. 7 Jan **1968** [New York opening]. Sd; b&w. 16mm & 35mm. 90 min.

Prod-Dir Norman Mailer. *Photog* D. A. Pennebaker. *Main Titl* Lidia Ferrara. *Film Ed* Jan Welt, Norman Mailer. *Mus* Charlie Brown. *Sd* Robert Neuwirth.

Cast: Norman Mailer *(The Prince)*, Buzz Farbar *(Cameo)*, Mickey Knox *(20 Years)*, Beverly Bentley *(Margie)*, Jose Torres, boxer *(Kid Cha Cha)*, Mara Lynn *(Lillian)*, Dick Adler *(lieutenant)*, Harold Conrad *(Boots)*, Bryan Hamill *(2R)*, Milt Machlin *(chief inspector)*, Ramona Torres *(Carmela)*, D. A. Pennebaker *(Al)*.

Drama. Norman Mailer and two friends, Buzz Farber and Mickey Knox, pretend they are Mafia hoods holed up in a warehouse. Ad-libbing their dialogue, they pass the time by sparring with dangling light bulbs, drinking, cursing, arguing, and assaulting one another's egos. They also receive visits from their wives, their girl friends, a prizefighter and his dog, and finally the police. *Gangsters. Prizefighters. Police. Mafia.*

Note: Filmed in 35mm in New York City.

WILD ON THE BEACH   F6.5588
Lippert, Inc. *Dist* Twentieth Century-Fox Film Corp. 25 Aug **1965** [New York opening; c11 Aug 1965; LP31750]. Sd; b&w. 35mm. 77 min.

Prod-Dir Maury Dexter. *Asst Prod* Hank Tani. *Assoc Prod* "By" Dunham. *Screenplay* Harry Spalding. *Story* Hank Tani. *Dir Photog* Jack Marquette. *Supv Film Ed* Jodie Copelan. *Mus* Jimmie Haskell. *Song:* "Little Speedy Gonzales" Stan Ross, mus, Bobby Beverly. *Songs:* "House on the Beach," "Gods of Love," "Run Away From Him" "By" Dunham, Bobby Beverly. *Songs:* "Yellow Haired Woman (Tic-a-tic-a-tac)," "Rock the World," "Winter Nocturne" "By" Dunham, E. Davis. *Song:* "Pyramid Stomp" "By" Dunham, Jimmie Haskell. *Song:* "Drum Dance" Frank Warren, mus, Joe Saracino. *Song:* "It's Gonna Rain" Sonny Bono. *Song:* "Snap It" Jimmie Haskell. *Asst Dir* Willard Kirkham. *Wardrobe* Joseph Dimmitt. *Makeup* Dan Greenway.

Cast: Frankie Randall *(Adam)*, Sherry Jackson *(Lee Sullivan)*, Jackie & Gayle, The Astronauts, Sonny & Cher, Cindy Malone, Sandy Nelson, Russ Bender, Booth Colman, Justin Smith, Jerry Grayson, Marc Seaton, Robert Golden, Larry Gust.

Comedy with music. Lee Sullivan, a student at a California college, inherits a beach house from her uncle. She wants to use the building as a girls' boardinghouse, thus both alleviating the student housing shortage and financing her education. Meanwhile, Adam plans to turn the house into a boys' boardinghouse, claiming that he received permission to do so while Lee's uncle was still alive. Adam files first for an off-campus housing permit, and the boys take up residence in the house. Lee also receives a permit, and the administrative mixup makes for constant parties on the beach. A romance blossoms between Lee and Adam, and the housing problem is resolved when the boys acquire a nearby cottage. *Students. Uncles. College life. Inheritance. Housing. Beaches. Boardinghouses. California.*

Note: Working title: *Beach House Party.*

WILD ONES ON WHEELS   F6.5589
Charles Bros. Productions. *Dist* Emerson Film Enterprises. 27 Apr **1967** [New Orleans opening]. Sd; b&w. 35mm. 92 min.

Prod Fred Charles. *Dir* Rudolph Cusumano.

Cast: Francine York, Edmund Tontini, Robert Blair.

Melodrama. A group of violent young sports car enthusiasts murder an ex-convict on his way to the desert to unearth $240,000 buried there. The gang abducts the ex-con's wife and forces her to help them locate the money. An insurance investigator infiltrates the gang and puts an end to their nefarious activities. *Ex-convicts. Investigators. Murder. Abduction. Sports cars. Gangs. Deserts.*

Note: Filmed in the Mojave Desert in 1962 as *Drivers to Hell.*

WILD OUTTAKES   F6.5590
Hollywood Cinema Associates. *Dist* Crest Film Distributors. Nov **1969**. Sd; col. 35mm. 71 min.

Cast: Bambi Allen *(Constance Virtue)*.

Compilation film. In her one-woman censorship crusade, Constance Virtue views a collection of erotic outtakes she has assembled from several "sex exploitation films," including *For Love and Money, For Single Swingers Only, Odd Tastes, Acapulco Uncensored, The Muthers, Her Odd Tastes,* and *The Daisy Chain,* q. v. According to press photographs, the clips contain scenes of seduction, sexual intercourse, body painting, lesbianism, nude swimming, group sex, and oral intercourse. *Censorship. Seduction. Body painting. Lesbianism. Group sex. Oral sex. Nudity. Sex exploitation films.*

THE WILD PUSSYCAT (Greece)   F6.5591
Arista Films. *Dist* Crown International Pictures, Arista Films. 7 Oct **1969** [New York opening]. Sd; b&w. 35mm. 86 min. *MPAA rating* X.

Prod James Paris. *Dir* Dimi Dadira. *Screenplay* John Giotti. *Photog* James Costa. *Film Ed* Peter Kirk. *Mus* Nikolai Ignatoff. *Prod Mgr* Akyla Zafiri.

Cast: Gisela Dali *(Nadia)*, Dean Byron *(Nick)*, Kathy Impro *(Vera)*, Deam Klerr *(Nadia's escort)*, Vivian Virna *(Nick's girl friend)*, Jonathan Drake *(voyeur)*, Paul Dillon *(delivery boy)*.

Melodrama. Nadia arrives with her white cat to collect a diary that belonged to her dead sister, Vera. From it Nadia learns of her sister's demise. *Vera falls in love with Nick, a callous pimp who forces her to make love to an old lecher, and to satisfy a voyeur Nick has her commit sodomy. The disillusioned Vera is spurned by Nick when she discovers that she is pregnant, and, wandering the streets, she is killed by a car.* Bent on revenge, Nadia lures the unsuspecting Nick to her villa, where he is drugged and chained in a secluded cell. He is forced to watch Nadia make love to her boyfriend, a delivery boy, and Nick's girl friend. Frustrated, Nick is driven nearly mad observing the bizarre scene—until Nadia suddenly enters the cell and castrates him. *Sisters. Pimps. Revenge. Voyeurism. Bestiality. Disillusionment. Pregnancy. Abduction. Lesbianism. Castration. Diaries. Drugs. Automobile accidents. Cats.*

THE WILD RACERS   F6.5592
Alta Vista Productions–Filmakers Productions. *Dist* American International Pictures. 27 Mar **1968** [Kansas City, Missouri, opening; c20 Mar 1968; LP35524]. Sd; col (Pathé). 35mm. 79 min.

Prod Joel Rapp. *Exec Prod* Roger Corman. *Dir* Daniel Haller. *2d Unit Dir* Francis Ford Coppola. *Screenplay* Max House. *Photog* Nestor Almendros, Daniel Lacambre. *Film Ed* Verna Fields, Dennis Jacob. *Mus* Mike Curb, Sidewalk Productions. *Songs* Pierre Vassilu. *Sd* Phil Thomas. *Asst Dir* Beach Dickerson.

Cast: Fabian (*Jo-Jo Quillico*), Mimsy Farmer (*Katherine*), Alan Haufrect (*Charlie*), Judy Cornwell (*British girl*), David Landers (*manager*), Warwick Sims (*Jo-Jo's partner*), Talia Coppola, Ursule Pauly, Dick Miller, Ron Gans, Fabienne Arel, Patricia Culbert, Mary Jo Kennedy, Kurt Boon.

Melodrama. Jo-Jo Quillico, an unrestrained racing car driver, is hired by a race car tycoon to be runner-up for a more experienced driver in the year's big European trophy races. Their common mechanic, Charlie, is also Jo-Jo's close friend, sharing in his fast life. In the first race, Jo-Jo cannot help but try to win and burns out the expensive car's engine in the process. Jo-Jo then dumps his current girl friend and picks up another to see him through the next round of competitions. She too, however, is dropped when Jo-Jo gets a new car and takes up with another woman, Katherine, for whom he feels the first stirrings of real love. He is also being cooperative with his boss by supporting his racing partner's lead in several races. But his partner is injured, and Jo-Jo, given his chance, scores several spectacular victories. Now an international figure among racing drivers, he must deal with the marital aspirations of Katherine. Aware that his way of life could never include marriage, Jo-Jo coldly replaces Katherine with a woman willing to share his carefree existence. *Mechanics. Playboys. Automobile racing. Friendship.*

Note: Location scenes filmed in Spain and England.

THE WILD REBELS F6.5593

Comet Pictures (Miami). *Dist* Crown International Pictures. 30 Aug **1967** [Denver, Colorado, opening]. Sd; col (Technicolor). 35mm. 90 min.

Assoc Prod Joseph Fink. *Asst Prod* Charles W. Persons. *Dir-Writ* William Grefé. *Dir Photog* Clifford H. Poland, Jr., Harry Walsh. *Camera Op* William J. Walsh. *Camera Asst* Harry Walsh, Jr. *Lighting* Bill Swan. *Set Dsgn* Patrick Nielsen. *Film Ed* Julio C. Chavez, Robert Woodburn. *Mus* Al Jacobs. *Mus Prod* Henry Stone. *Song:* "*You Don't Know Like I Know*" Al Jacobs. *Sung by* Steve Alaimo. *Sd* John W. Barry, Bernie Bylander. *Boom* Nat Ragland. *1st & 2d Asst Dir* Ronald Walsh, Daniel Karoff. *Script Supv* Betty Kerwin. *Makeup* Marie Del Russo. *Head Grip* Jack Clark. *Prop* Charles Guanci. *Still Photog* Tony Gulliver.

Cast: Steve Alaimo (*Rod Tillman*), Willie Pastrano (*Banjo*), John Vella (*Jeeter*), Bobbie Byers (*Linda*), Jeff Gillen (*Fats*), Walter Philbin (*Lieutenant Dorn*), Robert Freund (*detective*), Seymour A. Eisenfeld (*Walt Simpson*), Phil Longo (*1st man*), Milton Smith (*bartender*), Kurt Nagler, Steve Gellar, Chris Martell, Gary Brady (*college boys*), Nora Alonzo (*Nori*), The Birdwatchers (*a band*), Dutch Holland (*driver*), Art Barker (*gunshop owner*), William P. Kelley (*bank teller*), Cosmo Lloyd (*bank guard*), Tom Frysinger, Emil Deaton (*sheriffs*), Jamie Hickson, Nick Bontempo, Edward Wanisko, Aaron Deaton, Dennis French, Bob Sparks (*policemen*).

Action drama. Rod Tillman retires from stock car racing when his car is wrecked. Four members of a motorcycle gang called Satan's Angels, who commit crimes strictly for "kicks," try to recruit him to drive the getaway car for an impending bank robbery. When he refuses, Lieutenant Dorn persuades him to join the gang as an undercover agent for the police. Rod then enters another race and again demolishes his car in order to encourage the Angels to repeat their offer. All goes according to plan, and Rod drives the car when the gang robs a gun store to obtain the weapons they need. Although he sees the store owner killed by Banjo and Fats, two gang members, Rod continues with the gang in order to ascertain details of the planned bank robbery. Banjo, the leader, catches Rod with "mama" Linda, but Rod wins their fierce fistfight. The next day, the gang robs the bank. Even though Rod signals the police, the Angels escape, killing three policemen in the ensuing chase. They take refuge in a deserted lighthouse but are killed, one by one, by the police. Although one of the gang members, Jeeter, escapes, he is killed by Linda just as he is about to shoot Rod. *Stock car drivers. Police. Motorcycle gangs. Storekeepers. Automobile racing. Bank robberies. Murder. Lighthouses. Guns. Chases.*

WILD ROOTS OF LOVE (France) F6.5594

Jad Films. *Dist* European Producers International, Gaston Hakim Productions. ca **1962**. Sd; b&w. 35mm. 90 min.

Dir Jacques R. Villa. *Photog* Armand Thirard.

Cast: Sylvianne Margolle, Geneviève Galéa, Catherine Deneuve, Maïté Andres, Renée Barell, France Beucler, Pierre Dudan.

Drama. No information about the precise nature of this film has been found, although it is known that the film deals with adolescent girls and contains scenes of lesbianism. *Adolescence. Lesbianism. Sexual initiation.*

Note: Produced in France in 1959 as *Les petits chats*.

THE WILD SCENE F6.5595

Sam Jacoby & Associates Productions. *Dist* Four Star Excelsior Releasing Co. Mar **1970**. Sd; col. 35mm. 96 min. *MPAA rating* R.

Prod Sam Jacoby. *Dir* William Rowland. *Screenplay* Michael Kraike, William Keys. *Story* William Rowland, Sam Jacoby. *Dir Photog* Robert Caramico. *Film Ed* Sergei Goncharoff. *Mus* Jaime Mendoza-Nava. *Songs:* "*The Wild Scene*," "*It's You Alone*" sung by Jimmie Reed. *Song:* "*I Just Want a Chance*" *perf by* Karnival. *Prod Mgr* William White.

Cast: Richard Tate (*Jack*), Alberta Nelson (*Dr. Virginia Grant*), Gary Pillar (*Hal*), Anita Eubank (*Diana*), Berry Kroeger (*Tim*), Nancy Czar (*Clarette*), John Craven (*Morton*), Rita Lupino (*Faith*), Wendy Stuart (*Andrea*), Charles Terhune (*Paul*), Katherine Darc (*Sandra*), Margaretta Ramsey (*Kay*), Jarl Victor (*Dr. Jennings*), Suzanne Bragg (*Kathy*), Rick Bentley (*student*), Kathie Zundel (*Janice*), Barbara Maneff (*Annabelle*), Jo Graff (*Nancy*), Anne Hershon (*Felicia*), Evanna Lynn (*Ella*), Jackie Kendall (*Alice*), Phyllis Sally (*Sally*).

Melodrama. Psychiatrist Virginia Durant discusses several case histories and how they relate to her domestic problems. *A daughter makes love to her father, who has been made impotent by his emasculating, adulterous wife. The daughter then attempts suicide. An elderly man becomes voyeuristic and masochistic after finding his mistress with another woman.* Virginia's hippie daughter Diane, a college dropout, lives with her militant boyfriend Hal, an underground newspaper publisher. To investigate Hal's dubious intentions, Virginia and her boyfriend Jack attend a campus demonstration which turns into a riot. Dr. Durant then relates another case history. *A doctor and father of a high school student gives his daughter and her friends birth control pills, essential to their jobs as afternoon prostitutes. Subsequently, the father exposes the racket by substituting placebos for the pills, and one girl becomes pregnant.* Virginia poses as an interested contributor, meets with Hal, and is invited to an orgy. In an attempt to extort money from Virginia, Hal attacks her; but Jack comes to her rescue. Later, Diane announces her intention to reenter college. *Psychiatrists. Mistresses. Hippies. Militants. Physicians. Filial relations. Incest. Impotence. Infidelity. Suicide. Voyeurism. Masochism. Lesbianism. Birth control. Prostitution. Pregnancy. Duplicity. Extortion. Demonstrations. Riots. Newspapers—Underground. Orgies.*

Note: Location scenes filmed in Los Angeles.

WILD SEASON (South Africa) F6.5596

Emil Nofal. *Dist* Universal Pictures. 2 Oct **1968** [Buffalo, New York, opening]. Sd; col. 35mm. 92 min.

Prod Jans Rautenbach. *Dir-Screenplay-Story* Emil Nofal. *Photog* Vincent Cox. *Film Ed* Peter Henkel. *Mus* Roy Martin. *Sd* Peter Usmar.

Cast: Gert Van den Bergh (*Dirk Maritz*), Marie Du Toit (*Martie Maritz*), Joe Stewardson (*Tom Sheppard*), Janis Reinhardt (*Jess Sheppard*), Anthony Thomas (*Michael Maritz*), Johan Du Plooy (*Hennie de Waal*), Ian Yule (*Andy Wilson*), Michel Spalletta (*Maria*), Freddie Van Urk, Gerrit Van Urk, Hynie Slade, Shelley Trope, Don Leonard, Karel De Wet, Johan Koegelenberg.

Melodrama. Tom Sheppard, first mate on a fishing boat, returns home with the body of Steve Maritz, son of fleet-owner Dirk Maritz, and tells the old captain that the young man died a hero's death on the high seas in a daring rescue. The saddened Maritz visits Michael, an older son by a former marriage, in the hope that Michael will be able to take Steve's place, but the father learns that his Cambridge-educated son lives by a code different from his own. Disgusted, he leaves his son's home in Johannesburg and returns to the South-West African coast, complaining about Michael's "softness" and mannered personality. The young man comes to the port on his own, however, and Sheppard gives him a job. When Michael begins an ill-fated romance with Jess, Sheppard's leukemia-stricken daughter, he sparks the jealousy of Hennie de Waal, one of the sailors in the fleet, who then divulges that Sheppard was responsible for Steve's death. The first mate admits to Maritz that he locked Steve in a room when he refused to pay heed to another ship's distress call, and that the young man was killed in an ensuing scuffle. Maritz fires Sheppard, and the sailors refuse to ship out with the fleet owner until the first mate is restored to his position. After Jess dies, Michael acts as a conciliator between his embittered father and the crew. The boat goes out on a fishing run and encounters another distress call. Old Maritz decides to ignore the signal, but Michael countermands his father's order, proving himself to be a strong-willed man, and finally wins the old man's acceptance. *Fishermen. Sea captains. Shipowners. Filial relations. Seafaring life. Jealousy. Cancer. Fishing boats. Johannesburg. South-West Africa. Sea rescue.*

Note: Filmed entirely on location in South-West Africa. Opened in Johannesburg in 1967. Afrikaans title: *Wilde seisoen*.

WILD SEED F6.5597

Pennebaker, Inc. *Dist* Universal Pictures. 5 May **1965** [Chicago opening: c31 Jul 1965; LP35002]. Sd (Westrex); b&w. 35mm. 99 min.

Prod Albert S. Ruddy. *Exec Prod* Marlon Brando, Sr., Walter Seltzer. *Dir* Brian G. Hutton. *Screenplay* Les Pine. *Story* Les Pine, Ike Jones. *Dir Photog*

Conrad Hall. *Camera Op* William A. Fraker. *Asst Camera* Tom Laughridge. *Art Dir* Alexander Golitzen, George Webb. *Set Decor* John McCarthy, James S. Redd. *Titl* Pacific Title. *Film Ed* Hugh S. Fowler. *Mus* Richard Markowitz. *Song:* "That's Why!" Brian G. Hutton, Albert S. Ruddy, Richard Markowitz. *Sd* Waldon O. Watson, Ed Somers. *Asst Dir* Tom Shaw, Mike Moder. *Unit Prod Mgr* Howard Pine. *Script Supv* Molly Kent. *Cost* Ted Parvin. *Makeup* Bud Westmore, Richard Cobos. *Hairstyles* Larry Germain, Clara Holgate. *Still Photog* Frank Shugrue. *Gaffer* Les Neal, William Record. *Grip* Ed Keyes, Frank Barbera. *Prod coöp* Elliott Kastner.

Cast: Michael Parks (*Fargo*), Celia Kaye (*Daffy [Daphne]*), Ross Elliott (*Mr. Collinge*), Woodrow Chambliss (*Mr. Simms*), Rupert Crosse (*hobo*), Eva Novak (*Mrs. Simms*), Norman Burton (*policeman*), Merritt Bohn (*constable*), Anthony Lettier (*bartender*).

Melodrama. Daffy, a teenaged girl, runs away from her foster parents in New York to find her real father, a Los Angeles businessman. On the road, she hitches a ride with a man who tries to assault her and steal her money, but she manages to escape and make her way to a roadside restaurant where she meets Fargo, a young drifter. He allows Daffy to travel with him and soon teaches her how to survive on the road without money. One night they are caught in a railroad car and arrested, but they are released when Fargo tells the police that they are married. After Fargo recovers from a fever, they arrive in Los Angeles and visit Mr. Collinge, Daffy's father, who seems glad to see her. Her foster parents arrive the next day, and Fargo learns from them that Collinge once had a brief affair with Daphne's mother, but they were never married. Daffy finally learns the truth, and although she realizes that her foster parents truly love her, she decides to stay with Fargo. *Runaways. Drifters. Foster parents. Hitchhikers. Businessmen. Adolescence. Illegitimacy. Trains. New York City. Los Angeles.*

Note: Location scenes filmed in Stockton, California. Working titles: *Daffy, Fargo,* and *The Rebellious One.*

WILD STUD   F6.5598
Dist Jo-Jo Distributors. ca **1970.** Sd; col. 16mm. 61-81 min.

Sex film. No information about the precise nature of this film has been found. *Sexuality.*

THE WILD WESTERNERS   F6.5599
Four Leaf Productions. *Dist* Columbia Pictures. Jun **1962** [c1 Jun 1962; LP22250]. Sd; col (Eastman Color by Pathé). 35mm. 70 min.

Prod Sam Katzman. *Dir* Oscar Rudolph. *Writ* Gerald Drayson Adams. *Dir Photog* Gordon Avil. *Art Dir* Robert Peterson. *Set Decor* Sidney Clifford. *Film Ed* Jerome Thoms. *Titl Song* Duane Eddy, Lee Hazlewood. *Sung by* Duane Eddy. *Mus Cond* Ross DiMaggio. *Sd Supv* Charles J. Rice. *Sd* Josh Westmoreland. *Asst Dir* Sam Nelson.

Cast: James Philbrook (*U. S. Marshal Jim McDowell*), Nancy Kovack (*Rose Sharon*), Duane Eddy (*Dep. Marshal Clint Fallon*), Guy Mitchell (*Dep. Johnny Silver*), Hugh Sanders (*Ch. Marshal Reuben Bernard*), Elizabeth MacRae (*Crystal Plummer*), Marshall Reed (*Sheriff Henry Plummer*), Nestor Paiva (*Gov. John Bullard*), Harry Lauter (*Judas*), Bob Steele (*Dep. Marshal Casey Banner*), Ilse Burkert (*Yellow Moon*), Terry Frost (*Ashley Cartwright*), Hans Wedemeyer (*Wasna*), Don Harvey (*Hanna*), Elizabeth Harrower (*Martha Bernard*), Frances Osborne (*Lulu*), Tim Sullivan (*Reverend Thomas*), Pierce Lyden (*Jake*), Joe McGuinn (*Sam Clay*), Charles Horvath (*Moose*), Marjorie Stapp (*Lily*).

Western melodrama. In the Montana Territory of 1864, U. S. marshals aid the Union cause by transporting shipments of gold to Union Army forts in the East. One of these marshals is Jim McDowell, who has recently been tricked into marriage by stranded entertainer Rose Sharon. En route to Virginia City to investigate a series of gold robberies and murders, they are attacked by Sioux, and the marshal's life is saved by his bride, who continues to win his respect through further difficulties. Arriving in Virginia City, the marshal's suspicions center on the local sheriff, Henry Plummer, and his deputy, Johnny Silver. Before any action can be taken, Silver kidnaps Rose and holds her hostage for the safe delivery of a stagecoach loaded with gold. McDowell attempts to outwit Silver by replacing the gold with explosives. His plans, however, are circumvented by the Sioux, who attack and kill Silver and his men. McDowell rescues Rose, whom he has come to love, and the couple returns safely to Virginia City. *United States marshals. Brides. Sioux Indians. Sheriffs. Robbery. Murder. Kidnaping. Gold. Explosives. United States—History—Civil War. Montana. Virginia City.*

Note: Working title: *The Broken Lariat.*

WILD WHEELS   F6.5600
Kendall & Associates. *Dist* Fanfare Films, Colby Productions. Jun **1969.** Sd; col. 35mm (see note). 92 min. [Cut to 81 min.] *MPAA rating* R.

Prod Budd Dell. *Dir* Kent Osborne. *Screenplay* Kent Osborne, Ralph Luce. *Dir Photog* Ralph Waldo. *Camera Op* Terry Forchette. *Film Ed* Ralph Luce.

Mus Harley Hatcher. *Sd Mix* Bob Dietz. *Prod Mgr* James Kelly Durgin. *Asst to the Prod* Aaron York. *Wardrobe* Gloria Betrue. *Still Photog* Hedy Dietz. *Gaffer* Al Denney. *Stunt Coörd* Bobby Clark.

Cast: Don Epperson (*Reb Smith*), Robert Dix (*King*), Casey Kasem (*Knife*), Dovie Beams (*Ann*), Terry Stafford (*Huey*), Johenne Lemont (*Cotton*), Bruce Kimball (*Boomer*), Mac McLaughlin (*Count*), Bobby Clark (*Gunner*), Nancy Brock (*Candy*), Evelyn Guerrero (*Sissy*), Gordon Zimmerman (*Bobo*), Lois Jones (*Helen*), Randee Jensen (*Joy*), Phill Bartell (*Lieutenant Ryan*), Lee Parrish (*Wright*), Byrd Holland (*Rich*), Mike Perrotta (*store owner*), Alex Eliot (*Hank*), Marsha Jo Sandidge (*bikini girl*), Willis Martin (*policeman*), Billie & Blue, Three of August, Saturday Revue, Thirteenth Committee.

Melodrama. The "Roadrunners," an outlaw motorcycle gang, invade Pismo Beach and clash with a local group of peace-loving dune buggy enthusiasts led by Reb Smith. King, the gang leader, makes an unsuccessful pass at Ann, Reb's girl friend, then returns to camp, joining the other bikers in a marijuana party. Boomer and Gunner, two cyclists, steal liquor from a local store, and the party becomes an orgy. Local youths Sissy and Huey, watching nearby, become separated in the dark dunes, and violence erupts when the buggy club learns that Sissy has been raped by Boomer. Taking the offensive, the buggy club attacks and overcomes the cyclists, who are later apprehended by the police. King and fellow biker Cotton decide to join the buggy club. *Motorcycle gangs. Police. Adolescence. Rape. Theft. Criminals—Rehabilitation. Automobiles. Clubs. Marijuana. Liquor. Pismo Beach (California).*

Note: Location scenes filmed in Pismo Beach, California. Shot in 16mm. Production company unconfirmed.

WILD, WILD GIRL   F6.5601
Crystal Productions. *Dist* Empire Film Distributors. 28 Oct **1965** [San Francisco showing]. Sd; b&w. 35mm. 61 min.

Dir-Writ Earl Cartwright.

Cast: Krystal Ball (*Beatrice*).

Melodrama. The influence of her overprotective father has caused 22-year-old Beatrice to remain childishly naive. Rocky, a young prizefighter, loves her, but she rejects him. A longtime friend, Emmy, introduces her to the experienced Joe, to whom she gives herself. She then leaves home, becomes a prostitute, and eventually succumbs to drug addiction. Emmy becomes Beatrice's roommate, and before long the two women are lovers. Caught passing a bad check, Beatrice goes to her father for financial help, which he refuses. Rocky, who is still in love with Beatrice, wins a fight and rushes to her rescue with his prize money, but he is too late. Beatrice has thrown herself in front of an oncoming train. *Innocents. Prizefighters. Prostitutes. Drug addicts. Roommates. Filial relations. Seduction. Moral corruption. Lesbianism. Finance—Personal. Suicide. Trains.*

Note: Also known as *Wild Girl.*

THE WILD, WILD PLANET (Italy)   F6.5602
Mercury Film International–Southern Cross Films. *Dist* Metro-Goldwyn-Mayer, Inc. 9 Aug **1967** [New York opening; c31 Dec 1965; LP34711]. Sd; col (Eastmancolor). 35mm. 93 min.

Prod Joseph Fryd, Antonio Margheriti. *Assoc Prod* Walter Manley, Ivan Reiner. *Dir* Anthony Dawson. *Screenplay* Ivan Reiner, Renato Moretti. *Dir Photog* Richard Pallton. *Scenery & Set Dsgn* Piero Poletto. *Ch Ed* Angel Coly. *Asst Ed* Mary Napoleon. *Mus* Angelo Francesco Lavagnino. *Choreog* Archie Savage. *Sd* Vittorio Massi. *1st & 2d Asst Dir* Roger Godet, Nino Fruscella. *Dir Prod* John Masin. *Script Asst* Eva Koltay. *Cost* Bernice Sparrow. *Makeup* Euclide Santoli. *Hairstyles* Italia Cambi. *Dial Dir* Gene Luotto. *Prop* Frank Calabrese.

Cast: Tony Russel (*Mike Halstead*), Lisa Gastoni (*Connie*), Massimo Serato (*Nels Nurmi*), Franco Nero (*Jake*), Charles Justin (*Ken*), Enzo Fiermonte (*general*), Umberto Raho (*Maitland*), Isarco Ravaioli (*hotel agent*), Moha Tahi (*A. G. chief*), Freddy Unger (*De Lauty*), Lino Desmond (*Schneider*), Franco Ressel (*Jeff*), Victoria Zinny, Kitty Swan, Rosemary Martin, Annelise Stern (*A.G. agents*), Giuliano Raffaelli (*Francini*), Rodolfo Lodi (*Claridge*), Renato Montalbano (*detective*), Aldo D'Ambrosio (*Fryd*), Carlo Kechler (*Werner*), Margherita Orowitz (*Edith Halstead*), Sandro Mondini (*Dr. Delfos*), Vittorio Bonos (*Dr. Delfos, dwarf*), Michel Lemoine, Aldo Conti, Franco Doria, Ivan Gilborne, Linda Sini.

Science fiction melodrama. In the year 2015 two planetary systems—the United Democracies (UD) and the Combined Corporations—are rivals for control of the universe. Under the supervision of Nels Nurmi, a brilliant scientist, Combined Corporations is engaged in the miniaturization of human organs and species. These biological experiments are distasteful to UD Commander Halstead, and further hostility between the two men develops when they both take a romantic interest in Connie Gomez, an officer in Nurmi's laboratory. When it is learned that a large number of people have been disappearing from Earth, including a UD general, Halstead is placed in charge of an investigating party. After discovering that robot creatures are abducting

Earth people and taking them to the planetoid of Delphos, Halstead accuses Nurmi of being the brains behind the operation. Halstead is arrested but escapes and takes off for Delphos with two companions, Ken and Jake, and a small band of space troops. There they find Connie, the missing general, and many others slated for transformation experiments. Despite capture and the threat of extermination, Halstead and his men outwit their adversaries and succeed in overpowering Nurmi and his organization. Realizing that he is doomed, Nurmi destroys Delphos and his laboratory as Halstead's group rescues Connie and the general. *Scientists. Missing persons. Robots. Miniaturization. Jealousy. Abduction. Space travel. Self-sacrifice. Imaginary planets. Experiments. The Future.*

Note: Released in Italy in 1966 as *I criminali della galassia.* Anthony Dawson is a pseudonym for Antonio Margheriti, Richard Pallton for Riccardo Pallottini, Angel Coly for Otello Colangeli, and Charles Justin for Carlo Giustini.

WILD, WILD WINTER   F6.5603
Universal Pictures. 5 Jan **1966** [New York opening; c5 Feb 1966; LP35392]. Sd; col (Technicolor). 35mm (Techniscope). 80 min.

A Bart Patton–Lennie Weinrib Production. *Prod* Bart Patton. *Assoc Prod* Harry R. Sherman. *Dir* Lennie Weinrib. *Writ* David Malcolm. *Dir Photog* Frank Phillips. *Set Decor* Victor Gangelin. *Main Titl* Pacific Title. *Film Ed* Jack Woods. *Mus* Jerry Long. *Mus Supv* Frank Wilson. *Titl Song* Chester Pipkin. *Song:* "Heartbeats" Al Capps, Mary Dean. *Sung by* Dick and Dee Dee. *Song:* "Snowball" Al Capps, Mary Dean. *Sung by* Jackie and Gayle. *Song:* "A Change of Heart" Chester Pipkin, Mark Gordon, mus. *Sung by* The Astronauts. *Song:* "Two of a Kind" Victor Millrose, Tony Bruno. *Sung by* Jay and The Americans. *Song:* "Just Wait and See" Ron Elliott. *Sung by* The Beau Brummels. *Sd* Lambert Day. *Asst Dir* Thomas J. Schmidt. *Unit Prod Mgr* Harry R. Sherman. *Cost Dsgn* Paula Giokaris. *Men's Wardrobe* Walt Hoffman. *Makeup* Rolf Miller. *Hairstyles* Eve Newing.

Cast: Gary Clarke *(Ronnie),* Chris Noel *(Susan),* Don Edmonds *(Burt),* Suzie Kaye *(Sandy),* Les Brown, Jr. *(Perry),* Vicky Albright *(Dot),* James Wellman *(dean),* Steve Franken *(John),* Steve Rogers *(Benton),* Loren Janes *(The Bear),* Paul Geary *(Larry),* Val Avery *(Fox),* James Frawley *(Stone),* Dick Miller *(Rilk),* Mark Sturges *(Danny),* Anna Lavelle *(bus bit girl),* Linda Rogers *(Trisha),* Buck Holland *(McGee),* Darryl Vaughan *(Bob),* Fred Festinger *(Jake McCloskey),* Jay and The Americans, The Beau Brummels, Dick and Dee Dee, The Astronauts, Jackie and Gayle *(guest stars).*

Comedy with music. Burt and Perry arrive at a small mountain college intent upon pursuing their major interests—romance and skiing. When they are totally ignored by Sandy and Dot, because their sorority head, Susan, is distrustful of men, the two students seek help from Ronnie, their fraternity brother. A student from Malibu, Ronnie is considered to be irresistible, but every attempt to influence Susan fails. When one of his ruses backfires, Ronnie is placed in the embarrassing position of having to compete in the championship ski contest. By accident he wins the crown and Susan's love. *Students. Musicians. Playboys. College life. Skiing. Sororities. Fraternities. Contests.*

THE WILD, WILD WOMEN *see ... AND THE WILD, WILD WOMEN*

WILD WILD WORLD (Italy)   F6.5604
Ajace Cinematografica–Euro International Films. *Dist* Sokoler Films. 4 Aug **1965** [Chicago opening]. Sd; col (Eastmancolor). 35mm (CinemaScope). 80 min.

Pres by Bob Sokoler, Dick Randall. *Prod* Alessandro Jacovoni. *English Vers Adapt & Dir* Bob Sokoler. *Photog* Alessandro Jacovoni. *Mus* Roberto Nicolosi.
Narrator: Eddie Bracken.
Documentary. A study of some bizarre customs as practiced throughout the world: opium smoking and prostitution in Kowloon; interracial lovemaking in a stag movie; showgirls performing in Los Angeles; prostitution in Hong Kong; bullfighting, flamenco dancing, and striptease dancing in Madrid; ancient tribal marriage and fertility rites practiced in Luzon; interracial lovemaking in Manhattan, as advocated by a bestselling book on love and sex; and West Indians dancing in Martinique. In Bangkok contestants engage in the Thai national sport of kabi-kong, and students of Silparken University perform a classical Thai dance; in Paris at the Lido Club a woman demonstrates the intimate relationship between herself and her Shetland pony, at the Crazy Horse Saloon an "upside down piano juggler" is shown engaged in his hazardous occupation, and elsewhere in Paris Vince Taylor and the Playboys perform a rock and roll number; in Manila the viewer is treated to cockfighting, traditional dances as performed by the Bayanihan National Troupe, and a festival and parade of Jeep taxicabs representing the spirit of the U. S. Army Motor Pool; in Yokohama one witnesses the preparation and eating of monkey brains, ants, dogs, and snakes, the swallowing of a live mouse, a rickshaw ride through crowded streets, and a snake dance; one sees a harem ruled by a sadistic chief in Arabia; and, finally, young Buddhist monks in Thailand, using swords

and staffs, engage in fierce combat to test physical strength and cleanse the soul. *Showgirls. Dancers. West Indians. Students. Jugglers. Monks. Social customs. Prostitution. Bullfighting. Striptease. Rites and ceremonies. Miscegenation. Sports. Bestiality. Rock and roll. Cockfighting. Buddhism. Opium. Sex exploitation films. Parades. Jeeps. Food. Harems. Kowloon. Los Angeles. New York City. Hong Kong. Madrid. Luzon. Martinique. Bangkok. Paris. Manila. Yokohama. Saudi Arabia. Lido (Paris). Crazy Horse Saloon (Paris). Horses. Snakes.*

THE WILD, WILD WORLD OF JAYNE MANSFIELD   F6.5605
Southeastern Pictures. *Dist* Blue Ribbon Pictures. 18 Apr **1968** [New Orleans opening]. Sd; col (Eastmancolor). 35mm. 120 min.

Prod Dick Randall. *Exec Prod* David B. Putnam, Charles W. Broun, Jr. *Dir* Arthur Knight. *Screenplay* Charles Ross.
Cast: Jayne Mansfield, Mickey Hargitay, The Lady Birds, Rocky Roberts and The Airedales, Leila Sohl *(themselves).*
Documentary. A presentation of scenes from the life and times of Jayne Mansfield: Jayne with muscleman husband Mickey Hargitay; a topless women's band in Hollywood; Jayne's home in Hollywood and a life-sized bust of her, nude to the waist; Jayne in Rome attending a bodybuilders contest and strolling along the Via Veneto amidst crowds of ogling men; on the Île du Levant, a famous nudist colony; in New York, Jayne at her bath as depicted by *Playboy* magazine; in Los Angeles, a demonstration of the art of the striptease; and finally Jayne's shocking death in an automobile accident. *Actors. Body-builders. Musicians. Nudity. Nudism. Striptease. Sculptures. Contests. Hollywood. Rome. New York City. Los Angeles. Jayne Mansfield. Mickey Hargitay. Île du Levant. "Playboy". Automobile accidents.*

THE WILD WORLD OF BATWOMAN   F6.5606
A. D. P. Productions. **1966.** Sd; b&w. 35mm. 70 min.

Prod-Dir-Writ Jerry Warren. *Mus* The Young Giants.
Cast: Katherine Victor, George Andre, Steve Brodie, Lloyd Nelson, Richard Banks, The Young Giants.
Science fiction drama. Mad scientist Dr. Neon and his masked boss, Ratfink, kidnap a member of the Bat Girl Club. In return for her release, the pair demands that Batwoman steal an atomic hearing aid from the Ayjax Development Company. After tricking Ratfink into releasing the hostage, Batwoman and the Bat Girls guard the hearing aid. Using laughter-inducing pills to disarm the guard, Ratfink and Dr. Neon steal the device, which they then convert into an atomic bomb. The hearing aid, however, explodes, demolishing Ratfink's secret headquarters, and Batwoman unmasks her adversary. *Scientists. Masterminds. Hostages. Theft. Kidnaping. Masks. Atom bomb.*

WILD YOUTH   F6.5607
Dist Cinema Associates. 8 Sep **1961** [Atlanta showing]. Sd; b&w. 35mm. 73 min.

Prod John Bushelman. *Exec Prod* Fred Ready. *Dir* John Schreyer. *Screenplay* Robert J. Black, Jr., Lester William Berke, Dean Romano. *Story* Lester William Berke, Gary Judis. *Photog* Lloyd Knechtel. *Film Ed* Dwight Caldwell. *Mus* Richard La Salle. *Song:* "Wild Youth" Steve Rowland. *Asst Dir* Charles Keane. *Prod Mgr* Gilbert Ray.
Cast: Robert Hutton *(Maddo),* John Goddard *(Revis),* Carol Ohmart *(Madge),* Jan Brooks *(Donna),* Robert Arthur, actor *(Frankie),* Steve Rowland *(Switch),* Clancy Cooper *(Erickson).*
Crime melodrama. Frankie, a basically decent youth who has gotten into trouble with the law through unfortunate circumstances, is persuaded to escape from an honor farm with a young tough nicknamed "Switch" for his prowess with a switchblade. The two escapees take refuge with Frankie's 16-year-old girl friend, Donna, and Switch soon makes advances, threatening the romance between Frankie and Donna with his jealous temper. One day the trio's dilapidated car breaks down near the Mexican border, and they are forced to hitch a ride. They find themselves in the company of Revis, a fugitive murderer and dope smuggler, and his pitifully drug-addicted gun moll, Madge. Switch discovers that Revis is carrying a fortune in heroin stuffed in a doll, and he attempts to run off with it. Madge allows Frankie and Donna to escape, but Revis pursues Switch and kills him. Treasury agent Maddo closes in with the border police, and there is a violent gun battle. On the point of knifing a police officer [MadJo?], Revis is gunned down by Madge. [Some sources make no mention of Madge's role in Revis' death.] *Juvenile delinquents. Border police. Fugitives. Escapees. Hitchhikers. Drug addicts. United States—Treasury Department. Molls. Smuggling. Adolescence. Murder. Jealousy. Reformatories. Heroin. Mexican border.*
Note: Filmed in New Mexico. Also known as *Naked Youth.*

WILDE SEISOEN *see* **WILD SEASON**

WILDERNESS CALLING   F6.5608
Aaro Films. 17 Oct **1969** [Minneapolis opening; c14 Oct 1969; MP20307]. Sd; col. 35mm. 102 min. [Copyright length: 90 min.]
A Film by Paul O. Hansen. *Photog* Paul O. Hansen.
Narrator: Art Mercier.
Documentary. A young boy from the Dakota prairies grows up heeding the "call of the wilderness." He hunts for pheasant in the Illinois cornfields; ducks and geese in the northern lakes; deer in the Dakota Bad Lands; mountain sheep, goats, caribou, moose, and mountain lions in British Columbia and the Yukon; and brown bears on the Alaskan peninsula. He fishes in British Columbia's mountain streams for grayling and along the Bering Sea coast for trout. The film includes footage of swans, eagles, and ptarmigan; a beaver colony repairing a dam; battling rams; and sheep at rest in the mountains. *Hunting. Fishing. Bad Lands of Dakota. Illinois. British Columbia. Alaska. Bering Sea. Yukon. Sheep. Goats. Cougars. Beavers. Ducks. Pheasant. Geese. Deer. Caribou. Moose. Bears. Trout. Ptarmigan. Eagles. Swans.*
Note: Location scenes filmed in the Dakota Bad Lands, British Columbia, the Yukon, and off the shores of the Bering Sea.

THE WILDEST!   F6.5609
Apollo Film Productions. *Dist* Sack Amusement Enterprises. 17 Sep **1969** [New York showing]. Sd; col (Eastmancolor). 35mm. 74 min.
Prod Lee Ronby. *Dir* Jim Sully.
Cast: Tom Forrest (*Bix Bennett*), Ciji Weill, Norell Douglas, Judy Farr, Christy Holiday, Dennis Adams, Kari Kastle, Stacy Stanley, Bobby Thorne, Adrainne, Michelle Michelle, Sandi Gram, Joy Jensen, Helen Ware, Byron Lord, Will Clark, Taylor Michaels, Cherrie LaMour, Harry Warden, Ron Shipman.
Melodrama. Syndicate-backed rock and roll performer Bix Bennett returns to his hometown and finds a group of teenage fans eager to become acquainted with their idol. Bix draws a number of the girls into sexual intimacies while his syndicate boss takes compromising photos. The girls are then blackmailed into paying large sums of money or becoming prostitutes. Suspicions are aroused in the community when Barbara, the daughter of a prominent politician, meets her death in Bix's motel room. Bix attempts to withdraw from his contract and is forced to confront the sadistic hoodlums who control the pop music racket. Bix's girl friend Kitty and her younger sister, as well as the town prostitute and the lesbian party girls employed by the syndicate, become involved in the attempt to unravel the murder mystery. *Singers. Racketeers. Groupies. Prostitution. Rock and roll. Adolescence. Blackmail. Murder. Lesbianism. Syndicates. Photographs.*
Note: Produced in Dallas. Christy Holiday may also be known as Christy Harding.

WILL PENNY   F6.5610
Paramount Pictures. 6 Mar **1968** [Philadelphia opening; c31 Dec 1967; LP35656]. Sd; col (Technicolor). 35mm. 109 min.
A Fred Engel–Tom Gries–Walter Seltzer Production. *Prod* Fred Engel, Walter Seltzer. *Dir-Writ* Tom Gries. *Dir Photog* Lucien Ballard. *Art Dir* Hal Pereira, Roland Anderson. *Set Decor* Robert R. Benton, Ray Moyer. *Film Ed* Warren Low. *Asst Ed* Jack Wheeler. *Mus* David Raksin. *Orch* Nathan Van Cleave, Ruby Raksin. *Song:* "The Lonely Rider" David Raksin, Robert Wells. *Sung by* Don Cherry. *Sd Rec* John Carter, John Wilkinson. *Asst Dir* Daniel J. McCauley. *Unit Prod Mgr* Kenneth DeLand. *Men's Cost* John A. Anderson. *Ladies' Cost* Ruth Stella. *Makeup Supv* Wally Westmore. *Makeup Artist* Charles Blackman. *Hairstylist* Hedvig Mjorud. *Hairstyles Supv* Nellie Manley. *Sp Photog Eff* Paul K. Lerpae. *Coöp* United States Forest Service—Inyo National Forest, United States Department of Agriculture—Bureau of Land Management, United States Department of the Interior—Inyo County.
Cast: Charlton Heston (*Will Penny*), Joan Hackett (*Catherine Allen*), Donald Pleasence (*Preacher Quint*), Lee Majors (*Blue*), Bruce Dern (*Rafe Quint*), Ben Johnson (*Alex*), Slim Pickens (*Ike Wallerstein*), Clifton James (*Catron*), Anthony Zerbe (*Dutchy*), Roy Jenson (*Boetius Sullivan*), G. D. Spradlin (*Anse Howard*), Quentin Dean (*Jennie*), William Schallert (*Dr. Fraker*), Lydia Clarke (*Mrs. Fraker*), Robert Luster (*Shem Bodine*), Dal Jenkins (*Sambo*), Matt Clark (*Romulus*), Luke Askew (*Foxy*), Anthony Costello (*Bigfoot*), Gene Rutherford (*Rufus Quint*), Chanin Hale (*girl*), Jon Francis (*Horace Greeley Allen*), Stephen Edwards (*town boy*).
Western drama. Will Penny, a middle-aged cowpuncher who has always been a loner, joins two younger men, Dutchy and Blue, in search of winter work after completing a long cattle drive in Montana in the 1880's. While hunting deer, the three men are attacked by the maniacal Preacher Quint and his three sons; in the ensuing gunfight Will kills one of the sons. Quint and his other two sons, Rafe and Rufus, ride off swearing vengeance on the cowboy. As soon as a doctor is found for the injured Dutchy, Will sets out on his own, gets a job as rider for a large ranch, and heads for a mountain shack to spend the winter. In the cabin he finds Catherine Allen, en route with her 10-year-old son, Horace, to join her husband in California. Obeying orders to evict squatters, he gives them 3 days to move. But when Will is ambushed by Quint and his sons, Catherine nurses him back to health; and in return he allows her to remain at the cabin with her son. The growing warmth between Will and Catherine is disrupted by Quint and his sons, who take Will prisoner and threaten Catherine with sexual assault. Will escapes, meets up with Blue and Dutchy, and with their help kills Quint and wounds his sons. Catherine wants to settle down with Will and help build a ranch, but Will realizes that he will always be a loner and rides off with Blue and Dutchy. *Cowboys. Ranchers. Squatters. Hunters. Preachers. Brothers. Frontier and pioneer life. Revenge. Filial relations. Montana.*
Note: Location scenes filmed in Bishop, California.

WILLY (United States / West Germany)   F6.5611
ABA. 18 Dec **1963** [Los Angeles opening]. Sd; b&w. 35mm. 73 min.
Pres by National General Corp. *Prod-Dir* Allan A. Buckhantz. *Screenplay* Günter Rudorf. *Adapt* Marcus Scholz. *Photog* Ludwig Berger. *Art Dir* Mathias Matthies, Ellen Schmidt. *Film Ed* Klaus Dudenhöfer. *Mus* Nicholas Carras. *Titl Song* Nicholas Carras, Ric Marlow. *Sd* Hans Ebel. *Asst Dir* Frank Guthke.
Cast: Hubert Persicke (*Willy*), Hannelore Schroth (*Klara*), Edith Schultze-Westrum (*grandmother*), Joseph Offenbach (*Herbst*), Peter Kuiper (*Scott*), Klaus Behrendt (*teacher*), Reinhard Kolldehoff (*brother*), Kurt A. Jung (*agent*), Viktoria von Campe (*secretary*), Wilhelm Fricke (*Herbert*), Arnfried Lerche (*Wolfgang*).
Drama. Source: Günter Rudorf, *The First Lesson* (a play; production undetermined). Willy, the illegitimate son of a German woman and an American Negro soldier, finds himself surrounded by prejudice in the small German town where he lives. At the age of 15, he is the only black person in town; he has trouble in school, cannot find a job, and discovers that even his grandmother's love for him is tainted by prejudice. After receiving his mother's permission, he goes to Hamburg, where there are more Negroes, to search for a better life. *Americans in foreign countries. Mulattoes. Negroes. Grandmothers. Adolescence. Illegitimacy. Smalltown life. Racial prejudice. Hamburg.*
Note: Filmed on location in Hamburg in 1963 for German television.

WILLY MCBEAN AND HIS MAGIC MACHINE (United States / Japan)
                                                                 F6.5612
Dentsu Motion Picture Co.–Videocraft International Productions. *Dist* Magna Pictures Distribution Corp. 23 Jun **1965** [San Francisco opening]. Sd; col (Eastman Color). 35mm (Animagic, see note). 94 min.
Pres by Marshall Naify. *Prod-Dir-Writ* Arthur Rankin, Jr. *Assoc Prod* Larry Roemer, Jules Bass. *Mus & Lyr* Edward Thomas, Gene Forrell, James Polack.
Voices: Larry D. Mann, Billie Richards, Alfred Scopp, Paul Kligman, Bunn Cowan, Paul Soles, Peggi Loder.
Puppet film. Professor Rasputin von Rotten builds a time machine in hopes of traveling back in time and changing history. Rotten's aim is to obtain credit for bringing fire and the wheel to the cavemen, discovering America, deposing King Arthur, and outshooting Buffalo Bill. Pablo, a monkey who has been imprisoned by Rotten, escapes with the professor's plans and takes them to Willy McBean, a young genius. Willy builds his own magic machine and manages to go back in time and thwart the professor's plans. He and Pablo visit the Wild West, meet Columbus in Spain, meet King Arthur at the Round Table, visit King Tut in Egypt, and finally, visit the cave dwellers of prehistoric times and save the professor's life. Rotten's machine is lost, but when he promises to behave, Willie and Pablo offer him a ride back in their time machine. The next day in school, Rotten turns up as a guest lecturer, and Willy realizes that the adventure in the time machine was only a dream. *Professors. Cave dwellers. Time travel. Time machines. Prehistory. Egypt. Spain. Christopher Columbus. William Frederick Cody. King Arthur. Tutankhamen. Dreams. Monkeys.*
Note: Produced in Japan. Animagic process involves stop-motion photography of hand-carved forms.

WIND FROM THE EAST (France / Italy / West Germany)   F6.5613
Polifilm–Anouchka Films–CCC–Filmkunst. *Dist* New Line Cinema. Nov **1970**. Sd; col (Eastman Color). 16mm & 35mm. 92 min.
Prod Gianni Barcelloni, Ettore Rosbach. *Dir* Jean-Luc Godard. *Screenplay* Jean-Luc Godard, Daniel Cohn-Bendit. *Dir Photog* Mario Vulpiani. *Film Ed* Jean-Luc Godard. *Sd* Zè Antonio Ventuza.
Cast: Gian Maria Volontè (*soldier*), Anne Wiazemsky (*whore*), Daniel Cohn-Bendit, Götz George, Christian Tullio, Rick Boyd, Paolo Pozzesi, Allen Midgette, Glauber Rocha, José Varella, Marco Ferreri.
Film essay. The film opens with a group of Third World filmmakers producing a Marxist Western. The actors read lines condemning a bourgeois society which parallels contemporary America. The filmmakers stop their activity and begin a discussion of political cinema, the director's own work, and

other related topics. As the filmmaking resumes, the Indians suddenly rise up from pretending to be dead and eliminate their oppressors. *Filmmakers. Actors. Indians of North America. Marxism. Motion pictures.*

Note: Location scenes filmed in Italy in 1969. French title: *Le vent d'est;* Italian title: *Vento dell'est;* German title: *Wind von Osten.* Alternative U. S. title: *East Wind.*

THE WIND IS DRIVING HIM TOWARD THE OPEN SEA F6.5614
Dist Film-Makers' Cooperative. 3 Dec 1968 [New York showing]. Sd; col. 16mm. 52 min.
Dir David Brooks. *Photog* David Brooks. *Film Ed* David Brooks.
Experimental film. A youth seeks to determine the origin of knowledge and embarks on explorations to find out about the world. *Youth. Philosophy.*

WIND VON OSTEN see **WIND FROM THE EAST**

WINDFLOWERS; THE STORY OF A DRAFT DODGER F6.5615
Windflowers Co. *Dist* Film-Makers' Distribution Center. 22 Feb 1968 [New York opening]. Sd; b&w. 16mm & 35mm. 75 min.
Dir-Writ Adolfas Mekas. *Dir Photog* Bruce Sparks. *2d Camera* Jim Hubbard. *Film Ed* Adolfas Mekas. *Orig Mus Comp* Adolfas Mekas, Pola Chapelle. *Mus Arr & Cond* Dave Blume. *Featured Instrumentalists* Kees Van Baaren, Skeeter Camera, Steve Wolfe. *Vocalist* Pola Chapelle. *Location Sd* William Reilly. *Other Assistance* Jonas Mekas, Karl Bissinger.
Cast: John Kramer *(Paul Ramsey)*, Pola Chapelle *(Julie)*, Dino Narizzano *(clergyman)*, Joy Nicholson *(mother of a war hero)*, Edward Rishon *(driver)*, Maxton Latham *(publisher)*, James Hunter *(newspaper reporter)*, Dave Tice *(police captain)*, Todd Everett *(police rookie)*, Roger Briant *(student)*, Barbara Vary, Margaret Vary *(The Twins)*, Tina Stoumen *(teen-age girl)*, Henry Calvert *(father)*, Ronnie Gilbert *(mother)*, William Traylor, Reathel Bean *(FBI agents)*, Harry Gantt *(office manager)*, Karl Bissinger *(man in the flower shop)*, The Brown Family *(family)*, Adolfas Mekas *(card player)*.
Drama. Henry Hawkins, a young draft dodger hiding under the assumed name of Paul Ramsey, is once again fleeing from FBI agents after 6 years of moving from city to city. As "Paul" hitchhikes a ride to a new town and a new job, a driver recognizes him from a photo in a local newspaper. Paul flees from the car through nearby fields into the woods, but the driver notifies the police, and a helicopter is dispatched to search the area. Paul is quickly sighted, and two FBI agents and a rookie policeman give chase on foot. As Paul tries to make his way across a stream, the stick he is using for support breaks. The policeman, mistaking the broken stick for a gun, fires, and Paul is killed. In flashback, Paul's tragic past begins to unfold. He meets and falls in love with Julie at a July 4th celebration. Their happiness is interrupted the next day, however, when FBI agents, having traced Paul's whereabouts, force him to flee the smalltown business office where he works. At this point in the film, a dramatization occurs in which a student explains that he opposes the draft because he wants neither to kill nor be killed. The flight resumes. Aided by Julie, Paul escapes from her apartment at night and takes refuge until morning in a basement. Julie is interrogated by the police. In further dramatizations, a working class family express disapproval of draft evaders, and the publisher of a local newspaper and a reporter analyze the social, political, and moral context of Paul's actions. In the morning, Paul accepts the ride that opens the film. The events leading to his death are repeated in a condensed form. *Draft dodgers. Fugitives. Hitchhikers. Police. Pacifists. Reporters. Publishers. Disguise. Smalltown life. Youth. Helicopters. Fourth of July. United States—Federal Bureau of Investigation. Chases.*
Note: Filmed in New York and New Jersey.

THE WINE AND THE MUSIC see **PIECES OF DREAMS**

WINE, WOMEN AND WOMEN F6.5616
Dist Canyon Distributing Co. 19 Nov 1969 [New York showing]. Sd; col. 16mm. [Feature film, length unknown.]
Sex film. After the bartender throws out the escort of a blonde woman because he will not buy her a drink, he shows movies to the blonde and another woman who has applied for a job at the bar. He then takes the blonde to bed, where they are later joined by the other woman. The jealous escort returns and empties his pistol at the group. [Included in the film are lesbian encounters, a nude go-go dance, and an erotic shower scene.] *Bartenders. Go-go dancers. Employment—Women. Troilism. Jealousy. Murder. Lesbianism. Bars. Motion pictures.*

WINGS OF CHANCE (Canada) F6.5617
Tiger Productions, Ltd. *Dist* Universal–International. 1 Mar 1961 [Los Angeles opening; c15 Feb 1961; LP24529]. Sd; col (Eastmancolor). 35mm. 76 min.
Prod Larry Matanski. *Assoc Prod* Jack Copeland. *Exec Prod* Lorne H. Reed. *Dir* Edward Dew. *Screenplay* Patrick Whyte. *Dir Photog* Leonard Claremont. *Camera Op* Jack McCoskey. *Camera Asst* Larry Prather. *Aerial Photog* Larry Matanski. *Film Ed* Walter Hannemann, Monty Pearce. *Mus Score* Michael Andersen. *Sd* Charles Sheid, Tom Goldrick. *Asst Dir* A. W. Mokry, John Langdon. *Script Supv* Kathleen Fagan. *Canadian-American Prod Coörd* Blake Warwick-Owensmith. *Makeup* Richard Cobos. *Sp Eff* Meredith Evans. *Optical Eff* Ray Mercer and Co. *Head Grip* Don Diggins. *Gaffer* Frank Leonetti.
Cast: James Brown *(Steve Kirby)*, Frances Rafferty *(Arlene Baker)*, Richard Tretter *(Johnny Summers)*, Patrick Whyte *(Mike Farrel)*.
Melodrama. Source: John Patrick Gillese, "Kirby's Gander," in *Kirby's Gander* (Toronto, 1957). Two Canadian bush pilots, Steve Kirby and Johnny Summers, are partners in a small flying business and are both interested in marrying Arlene Baker. Steve goes to the mountain lodge where Arlene works; the jealous Johnny flies there and violates air regulations by landing on a nearby lake. While Johnny is being held by the Royal Canadian Mounted Police, Steve is forced to fly his plane without the usual daily mechanical checkup. An oil line fails, and he crash-lands in the bush. For weeks he manages to keep himself alive until he hits upon a desperate scheme. He befriends a family of wild geese and attaches a strip of metal bearing his name to each bird. Winter approaches, and the geese head south. One of them is shot down, and, luckily, the band is turned over to the Air Force. Steve is found barely alive, and he is nursed back to health by Arlene. *Air pilots. Jealousy. Survival. Lodges (inns). Alberta. Royal Canadian Mounted Police. Airplane accidents. Geese.*
Note: Filmed in Alberta. Released in Canada in 1961.

THE WINNER (France) F6.5618
Films de la Pléïade. *Dist* Noelle Gillmor, Robert Kingsley. 30 Jun 1965 [New York opening]. Sd; b&w. 35mm. 82 min.
Prod Pierre Braunberger. *Dir-Writ* François Reichenbach. *From an Idea by* Jean-Marc Ripert. *Photog* François Reichenbach, Jean-Marc Ripert. *Film Ed* Liliane Korb, Kenout Peltier. *Mus* Michel Legrand. *Adtl Mus* Georges Delerue. *Song:* "Les poètes" *comp & sung by* Léo Ferré. *Song:* "Les mots d'amour" Michel Rivegauche. *Sung by* Charles Dumont. "Ode for Peace" George Frederick Handel. *Prelude and Fugue* Johann Sebastian Bach. "Cenerentola" Gioacchino Antonio Rossini. *Sd* Bernard Meusnier, J.-J. Campignon. *Sd Mix* René Renault. *Prod Mgr* Roger Fleytoux.
Cast: Abdoulaye Faye *(the Senegalese boxer)*, Marcel Bruchard *(man on train)*, Milou Pladner *(blind masseur)*, Luce Vidi *(fortune-teller)*, Yasumiko *(Japanese girl)*, Jean-Paul Belmondo *([see note])*.
Documentary drama. Based on the life of Abdoulaye Faye. The experiences of a young Senegalese boxer in Paris are depicted as he trains for a fight and tours the city for the first time. He visits a fortune-teller, takes a boat ride with a Japanese girl, talks to a blind masseur, and goes to a nightclub. *Senegalese. Prizefighters. Paris.*
Note: Opened in Paris in Jul 1962 as *Un coeur gros comme ça!;* running time: 80 min (cut from 90 min). Belmondo's appearance in the film is unconfirmed.

THE WINNER see **PIT STOP**

WINNETOU—I. TEIL see **APACHE GOLD**

WINNETOU—II. TEIL see **LAST OF THE RENEGADES**

WINNETOU—III. TEIL see **THE DESPERADO TRAIL**

WINNING F6.5619
Newman-Foreman Productions. *Dist* Universal Pictures. 22 May 1969 [New York opening; c14 Jun 1969; LP37947]. Sd (Westrex); col (Technicolor). 35mm (Panavision). 123 min. *MPAA rating* G.
A Jennings Lang Production. *Prod* John Foreman. *Assoc Prod* George Santoro. *Dir* James Goldstone. *Screenplay* Howard Rodman. *Dir Photog* Richard Moore. *Art Dir* Alexander Golitzen, John J. Lloyd, Joe Alves. *Set Decor* John McCarthy, George Milo. *Titl & Opticals* Universal Title. *Film Ed* Edward A. Biery, Richard C. Meyer. *Mus* Dave Grusin. *Mus Supv* Stanley Wilson. *Sd* Waldon O. Watson, James T. Porter, Ronald Pierce. *Mus Ed* Bettie Mosher. *Asst Dir* Earl J. Bellamy, Skip Cosper. *Prod Supv* Wallace Worsley. *Unit Prod Mgr* Arthur S. Newman, Jr. *Script Supv* Marie Kenney. *Cost Dsgn* Edith Head. *Makeup* Bud Westmore. *Hairstyles* Larry Germain. *Sp Eff* Frank Brendel. *Tech Adv* Bob Bondurant. *Coöp* Road America, Indianapolis Motor Speedway, Riverside International Speedway, Indianapolis Raceway Park. *Supv Race Cons* Roger Ward. *Race Mounts* Jerry Kulhawik.
Cast: Paul Newman *(Frank Capua)*, Joanne Woodward *(Elora)*, Robert Wagner *(Luther Erding)*, Richard Thomas *(Charley)*, David Sheiner *(Leo Crawford)*, Clu Gulager *(Larry Morechek)*, Barry Ford *(Les Bottineau)*, Robert Quarry *(Sam Jagin)*, Eileen Wesson *(Miss Redburne 200)*, Toni Clayton *(girl)*, Maxine Stuart *(Miss Redburne's mother)*, Karen Arthur *(Miss Dairy Queen)*, Paulene Myers *(cleaning woman)*, Ray Ballard *(trombone player)*, Charles Seel *(Eshovo)*, Alma Platt *(Mrs. Eshovo)*, Harry Basch *(stranger)*, Allen Emerson *(desk clerk)*, Marianna Case *(motorcycle girl)*, Carolyn McNichol *(party girl)*, Bobby Unser, Tony Hulman *(themselves)*, George Mason *(Indianapolis policeman)*, Mimi Littlejohn *(Indianapolis Queen)*, Pat Vidan *(starter)*, Bruce

Walkup *(driver no. 1)*, Timothy Galbraith *(driver no. 2)*, Lou Palmer, Jay Reynolds *(Indianapolis interviewers)*.

Action melodrama. While celebrating his victory in the Redburne 200, stock car driver Frank Capua persuades Avis representative Elora to accompany him on a drive. When Elora voices concern for her reputation, revealing that she is a divorcée with a teenaged son and suspicious mother, Capua suggests an idyll in California. Upon their return they marry, and Capua adopts Elora's son, Charley. In preparation for the Indianapolis 500 the racer embarks on a grueling training program, neglecting his wife. Arriving at Elora's motel room, he discovers her in bed with his rival Luther Erding. Following a wordless confrontation Capua leaves Elora. Alarmed, Charley hitchhikes to Indianapolis and joins his stepfather, voicing the hope that Capua will best Erding in the upcoming race. Capua is victorious in the Indianapolis 500, after which he assaults his antagonist and pleads with Elora for a reconciliation. *Stepfathers. Newlyweds. Automobile racing. Adoption. Infidelity. Filial relations. Marriage. Adolescence. Separation (marital). Motels. Indianapolis 500.*

Note: Location scenes filmed at the Indianapolis Speedway and at Elkhart Lake, Wisconsin. MPAA rerating: M.

THE WINNING POSITION *see* **NOBODY'S PERFECT**

THE WINSTONE AFFAIR *see* **MAN IN THE MIDDLE**

WINTER A-GO-GO   F6.5620
R. C. Productions. *Dist* Columbia Pictures. 28 Oct **1965** [New Orleans opening; c1 Jul 1965; LP31744]. Sd; col (Pathé). 35mm. 88 min.

A Reno Carell Production. *Prod-Story* Reno Carell. *Dir* Richard Benedict. *Screenplay* Bob Kanter. *Dir Photog* Jacques Marquette. *Camera Op* Al Myers. *Asst Camera* William Renaldi, Herb Estabrook. *Art Dir* Walter Holscher. *Set Decor* Morris Hoffman. *Film Ed* Irving Berlin, ed. *Mus* Harry Betts. *Titl Song:* "*Winter A-Go-Go*" & *Songs:* "*King of the Mountain,*" "*Ski City*" Howard Greenfield. *Titl Song Sung by (see note)* The Hondells, The Astronauts. "*King of the Mountain*" *sung by* Joni Lyman, Nooney Rickett Four. *Song:* "*Hip Square Dance*" Steve Venet, Tommy Boyce, Bobby Hart, Harry Betts. *Sung by* James Stacy. *Song:* "*I'm Sweet on You*" Tommy Boyce, Bobby Hart, Steve Venet. *Sung by* The Reflections. *Song:* "*Do the Ski (With Me)*" Steve Venet, Tommy Boyce, Bobby Hart, Toni Wine. *Choreog* Kay Carson. *Rec Supv* Earl Snyder. *Rec Supv* George Hansen. *Boom Op* Bill Clark. *Asst Dir* Robert Vreeland, Leonard Kunody. *Prod Mgr* Jack Lacey. *Asst to the Prod* Jan Lloyd. *Script Supv* Edward Knight. *Prod Coörd* Mike Frankovich, Jr. *Cost* Joseph Dimmitt, Angela Alexander. *Makeup Supv* Dan Greenway. *Adtl Makeup* Tom Case. *Hairstyles* Linda Trainoff. *Still Photog* Homer Van Pelt. *Prop* Tom Coleman, Ralph Harris. *Gaffer* Wilbur Kinnett. *Best Boy* Harold Kraus. *Grip* George Hill, Jr., Wayne Williams, Cliff Ralke, Fred Russell.

Cast: James Stacy *(Danny Frazer)*, William Wellman, Jr. *(Jeff Forrester)*, Beverly Adams *(Jo Ann Wallace)*, Anthony Hayes *(Burt)*, Jill Donahue *(Janine)*, Tom Nardini *(Frankie)*, Duke Hobbie *(Bob)*, Julie Parrish *(Dee Dee)*, Nancy Czar *(Jonesy)*, Linda Rogers *(Penny)*, Judy Parker *(Dori)*, Bob Kanter *(Roger)*, Walter Maslow *(Jordan)*, H. T. Tsiang *(Cholly)*, Buck Holland *(Will)*, Cherie Foster, Carey Foster, Arlene Charles, Cheryl Hurley *(Winter A-Go-Go girls)*, Nooney Rickett Four, Joni Lyman, The Reflections *(themselves)*.

Comedy-drama with music. Jeff Forrester inherits a ski lodge at Lake Tahoe. With the help of his friend and promotion director Danny Frazer and his secretary Jo Ann Wallace, he wants to renovate the lodge as a ski resort for young adults. They bring in a large number of friends to help with the renovation. Jordan, who holds a mortgage on the lodge, sends Burt, a thug, to impede the group's progress. Burt and Jeff have a ski fight in which Burt saves Jeff's life, and thereafter he stops working for Jordan. The success of the enterprise ensured, the friends are able to pay off the mortgage; Jo Ann and Jeff are married; and Burt and his estranged girl friend, Janine, are reconciled. *Secretaries. Publicists. Entrepreneurs. Skiing. Inheritance. Adolescence. Ski resorts. Mortgages. Lake Tahoe.*

Note: Filmed partially in the Eldorado National Forest and at Lake Tahoe. Sources conflict in crediting the performance of the title song.

WINTER KEPT US WARM (Canada)   F6.5621
Varsity Film Productions. *Dist* Film-Makers' Distribution Center. 8 Feb **1968** [New York opening]. Sd; b&w. 16mm. 81 min.

Prod-Dir-Writ David Secter. *Asst Prod* Ron B. Thomson. *Dial* David Secter, Ian Porter, John Clute. *Dir Photog* Bob Fresco, Ernest Meershoek. *Ed* Michael Foytenyi. *Mus* Paul Hoffert.

Cast: John Labow *(Doug)*, Henry Tarvainen *(Peter)*, Joy Tepperman *(Bev)*, Janet Amos *(Sandra)*, Iain Ewing *(Artie)*, Jack Messinger *(Nick)*, Larry Greenspan *(Larry)*, Sol Mandelsohn *(hall porter)*, George R. Appleby *(house don)*.

Drama. Peter, an awkward and sensitive young man from a small Ontario mining town, enters the University of Toronto, but he is slow to make friends because of his shyness. He is befriended by Doug, a popular senior, who prides

himself on his urban sophistication. Their tentative relationship eventually grows into a strong friendship. Doug's steady girl friend, Bev, is puzzled by the attachment, unable to understand what common bonds unite the two. Slowly gaining confidence and coming out of his inordinate dependence on Doug, Peter joins a campus drama group and strikes up a friendship with an older student, Sandra. Without knowing why, Doug resents Peter's new interest and begins to nag him, until finally, after Peter spends a night with Sandra, Doug punches him in the stomach and storms off. Doug in the end must reconcile himself to the fact that his protégé and intimate friend no longer needs him. *Students. College life. Friendship. Jealousy. Sexual initiation. Winter. Spring. University of Toronto.*

Note: Filmed in Toronto; produced by students of the University of Toronto and Ryerson Institute. Toronto opening: Dec 1965. Sources conflict in rendering the following names: Ron B. Thomson (Thompson); Ian (John) Porter; Ernest Meershoek (Meersholk); Joy Tepperman (Teperman); Sol Mandelsohn (Mendelson).

WINTER LIGHT (Sweden)   F6.5622
Svensk Filmindustri. *Dist* Janus Films. 5 Apr **1963** [Los Angeles opening]. Sd; b&w. 35mm. 80 min.

An Ingmar Bergman Production. *Dir-Screenplay* Ingmar Bergman. *Photog* Sven Nykvist. *Asst Photog* Rolf Holmqvist, Peter Wester. *Sets* P. A. Lundgren. *Film Ed* Ulla Ryghe. *Sd* Stig Flodin, Brian Wikstrom. *Sd Eff* Evald Andersson. *Asst Dir* Lenn Hjortzberg. *Prod Mgr* Lars-Owe Carlberg, Allan Ekelund. *Cont* Katherina Farago. *Cost* Mago. *Makeup* Börje Lundh. *Prop* Karl-Arne Bergman.

Cast: Ingrid Thulin *(Märta Lundberg)*, Gunnar Björnstrand *(Tomas Ericsson)*, Max von Sydow *(Jonas Persson)*, Gunnel Lindblom *(Karin Persson)*, Allan Edwall *(Algot Frövik)*, Kolbjörn Knudsen *(Knut Aronsson)*, Olof Thunberg *(Fredrik Blom)*, Elsa Ebbesen *(Magdalena Ledfors)*, Tor Borong *(Johan Åkerblom)*, Bertha Sånnell *(Hanna Appelblad)*, Helena Palmgren *(Doris Appelblad)*, Eddie Axberg *(Johan Strand)*, Lars-Owe Carlberg *(police inspector)*, Johan Olafs *(gentleman)*, Ingmarie Hjort *(Persson's daughter)*, Stefan Larsson *(Persson's son)*, Lars-Olof Andersson *(Fredriksson's boy I)*, Christer Öhman *(Fredriksson's boy II)*.

Drama. Tomas Ericsson, the pastor of a small Swedish church, finds his faith slipping away from him because of God's "terrible silence." His congregation has dwindled, and on one bleak Sunday morning only nine parishioners attend services. Among them is Märta Lundberg, a drab schoolteacher who has been the pastor's mistress since the death of his wife 5 years ago. Following communion, Ericsson is visited by Jonas Persson, a simple fisherman terrified at the thought that the Chinese will have no scruples about using the atom bomb. Although aware that Jonas is on the verge of suicide, Ericsson is incapable of comforting him, talking instead about his own doubts and despair. Following Persson's departure, Ericsson reads a long letter from the devoted Märta in which she pleads with him to marry her. Unable to return her love because he cannot erase the memory of his wife, Ericsson brutally rejects her. Word then arrives that Jonas Persson has shot himself through the head. Ericsson goes to the scene of the suicide, and then visits Persson's pregnant wife, Karin. Returning to church for vespers, he discovers that Märta is the only person in attendance, and he goes to the altar and conducts the service. *Widowers. Clergymen. Schoolteachers. Mistresses. Fishermen. Faith. Religion. Loneliness. Suicide. Atom bomb.*

Note: Released in Sweden in Feb 1963 as *Nattvardsgästerna*; running time: 83 min. The film is the second of a trilogy, preceded by *Through a Glass Darkly*, q. v., and followed by *The Silence*, q. v.

WINTER WIND (France/Hungary)   F6.5623
Marquise Film–Mafilm Studios. *Dist* Grove Press. 16 Mar **1970** [New York opening]. Sd; col (Eastman Color). 35mm (AgaScope). 80 min.

Co-prod Jacques Charrier. *Dir* Miklós Jancsó. *Screenplay* Gyula Hernádi, Miklós Jancsó, Jacques Rouffio, Francis Girod. *Photog* János Kende. *Asst Photog* Mihály Benyó. *Art Dir* Tamás Banovich. *Film Ed* Zoltán Farkas. *Mus* Tihamér Vujicsics. *Sd* György Pintér, Pierre Lenoir. *Asst Dir* Philippe Haudiquet, András Szurdi, Zsolt Kézdi Kovács, László Szabó, Ferenc Grunwalski. *Prod Mgr* Ottó Föld. *Script Supv* Yvette Biró. *Cost* Zsuzsa Vicze.

Cast: Jacques Charrier *(Lazar Marko)*, Marina Vlady *(Maria)*, Éva Swann *(Ilona)*, József Madaras *(Markovics)*, István Bujtor *(Tarro)*, György Bánffy *(Ante)*, Philippe March *(Captain Kovacs)*, András Kozák *(Farkas)*, Pascal Aubier *(Tihomir)*, Miklós Csányi, Tihamér Vujicsics, László Horváth, Géza Polgár, Tibor Orbán, György Pintér, Lajos Fazekas *(Serbian anarchists)*, László Szabó *(allied translator)*, Philippe Haudiquet, József Pecsenke *(allied officers)*, Gáborné Jakab, Ida Siménfalvy *(old women)*, Françoise Prévost, Barna Basilides, Claude Beausoleil, György Bordás, Michel Delahaye, Gáspár Ferdinándy, Géza Ferdinándy, Péter Fodor, Levente Hidvégi, Vilmos Izsóf, József Konrád, Balázs Kosztolányi, Zoltán Kovács, Márton Kulinyi, Mihály Papp, Dénes Szunyogh, Tibor Tóth, Győző Varga, D. Sztojan Vujicsics.

Historical drama. Source: Gyula Hernádi, *Sirokkó* (Budapest, 1969). In 1934, while carrying on terrorist training activities under the leadership of Ante Pavelić and preparing to assassinate King Alexander I, members of the Ustaše, an extreme Croatian nationalist group, sequester themselves in a castle in Hungary. Among them is Lazar Marko, a fiery anarchist fugitive, whose volatile presence provokes increasing mutual distrust. Informed that the Hungarian government, which has permitted the establishment of the training center, intends to extradite the terrorist fugitive, the partisans slay Marko, afterwards eulogizing him as a martyr. *Fugitives. Anarchists. Croatians. Serbians. Terrorism. Assassination. Nationalism. Hungary—History—1918–45. Alexander I (Yugoslavia). Ante Pavelić. Ustaše.*

Note: Opened in Hungary in Dec 1969 as *Sirokkó*; running time: 82 min; in Paris in Nov 1970 as *Sirocco d'hiver*. Also known as *Téli sirokkó*.

DAS WIRTSHAUS IM SPESSART see THE SPESSART INN

WISE GUYS (France/Italy)   F6.5624

Belles Rives–S. N. C.–Alexandra Produzione. *Dist* Universal Pictures. Jun **1969**. Sd; col (Technicolor). 35mm (Techniscope). 100 min. *MPAA rating* G.

A Michel Ardan Production. *Prod* Michel Ardan. *Dir* Robert Enrico. *Screenplay* Robert Enrico, José Giovanni. *Photog* Jean Boffety. *Art Dir* Jean Saussac. *Film Ed* Jacqueline Meppiel, Michel Lewin, Nicole Courtois. *Mus* François de Roubaix. *Sd* Robert Biart, Victor Revelly. *Sd Eff* Daniel Couteau. *Asst Dir* Jean-Philippe Merand, Lionel de Souza. *Unit Prod Mgr* Pierre Cosson, Antoine Jacquet. *Dressers* Annie Marolt, Elise Servet. *Dresser for Marie Dubois and Henia Suchar* VOG. *Makeup* Louis Dor. *Sp Eff* Marcel Ravel.

Cast: Bourvil *(Hector)*, Lino Ventura *(Laurent)*, Marie Dubois *(Jackie)*, Jean-Claude Rolland *(Mick)*, Jess Hahn *(Nénesse)*, Nick Stephanini *(Therraz)*, Paul Crauchet *(Pelissier)*, Roger Jacquet *(Capester)*, Henia Suchar *(Christiane)*, Reine Courtois *(Yvonne)*, Pierre Frag *(Fanfan)*, Marc Eyraud *(L'éducateur)*, Jean Constantin *(Skida)*.

Melodrama. Source: José Giovanni, *Le Haut Fer* (Paris, 1962). Fortune hunter Hector Valentin returns to the Vosges Mountains from Canada to take possession of an antiquated, water-powered sawmill left him by his father. Two of his employees, ex-convicts Laurent and Mick, suggest that Hector, who is having difficulty finding a work crew, employ other paroled prisoners and thus survive the powerful competition of his corrupt rival, Therraz. Laurent's true purpose in suggesting the plan is to facilitate the murder of Rechtman, the convict responsible for sending him to jail; but Rechtman is not among the first 10 men sent from the jail. Meanwhile, Laurent has fallen in love with a villager, Jackie, and Mick has been reunited with his beautiful wife, Christiane, who asks him to return with her to Paris. Mick realizes the sincerity of the convicts' desire to succeed, however; and he stays on to help them combat Therraz. The rival crews brawl at a fair, and Mick is killed. Laurent, disillusioned, leaves the camp, unaware that prison officials have decided to revoke the men's conditional freedom. As the truckful of prisoners passes him on the road, Laurent realizes that Hector is now all alone and rushes back, arriving just in time to save the life of his despondent ex-employer, who has set fire to the mill. Though the mill is destroyed, the two men set out together for Italy and a fresh start in life. *Fortune hunters. Convicts. Inheritance. Criminals—Rehabilitation. Business competition. Parole. Revenge. Murder. Suicide. Incendiarism. Sawmills. Fairs. Vosges Mountains.*

Note: Paris opening: Oct 1965 as *Les grandes gueules*; running time: 130 min. Also reviewed as *The Wise Guys*.

THE WISER AGE (Japan)   F6.5625

Toho Co. Nov **1962** [Los Angeles showing]. Sd; b&w. 35mm (Tohoscope). 111 min.

Exec Prod Sanezumi Fujimoto, Hidehisa Suga. *Dir* Mikio Naruse. *Screenplay* Toshiro Ide, Zenzo Matsuyama. *Photog* Atsushi Yasumoto.

Cast: Hideko Takamine, Tatsuya Mihashi, Akira Takarada, Yoko Tsukasa, Reiko Dan, Yuriko Hoshi, Chishu Ryu, Haruko Sugimura, Keiju Kobayashi, Yosuke Natsuki, Mitsuko Kusabue, Keiko Awaji, Aiko Mimasu, Daisuke Kato.

Domestic melodrama. The problems of the Ishikawa family who live in a Tokyo suburb center around the five daughters. The eldest of storekeeper Ichikawa's daughters runs an apartment house, while her husband is gone for months at a time chasing other women. The second daughter pursues a career and brings shame to the family by refusing to marry. The fourth and fifth daughters fall in love with the same man, Aoyama, a low-salaried clerk. Running the household is the widow of the family's first son. The third daughter arrives with her husband and begins working on a match between the fourth daughter and the wealthy Komiya. A salesman, the estranged son of Ishikawa's second wife, moves into the first daughter's apartment house; and the second daughter falls in love with him, denouncing her career for plans of marriage. The salesman is exposed as a philanderer, and the widow tactfully dissolves the relationship. Meanwhile, her son fails his college entrance examination and commits suicide. The fourth daughter decides to marry the wealthy Komiya.

Storekeepers. Widows. Philanderers. Salesmen. Matchmakers. Apartment house managers. Careerwomen. Clerks. In-laws. Family life. Marriage. Infidelity. Suburban life. Suicide. Tokyo.

Note: Released in Japan in 1962 as *Onna no za*.

THE WITCH (Italy)   F6.5626

Arco Film. *Dist* G. G. Productions. Aug **1969**. Sd; b&w. 35mm. 103 min.

Prod Alfredo Bini. *Dir* Damiano Damiani. *Screenplay* Ugo Liberatore, Damiano Damiani. *Photog* Leonida Barboni. *Art Dir* Luigi Scaccianoce. *Film Ed* Nino Baragli. *Mus* Luis Enriquez Bacalov. *Choreog* Robert Curtis. *Asst Dir* Fernando Morandi. *Cost* Pier Luigi Pizzi.

Cast: Rosanna Schiaffino *(Aura)*, Richard Johnson *(Sergio)*, Sarah Ferrati *(Consuelo)*, Gian Maria Volontè *(Fabrizio)*, Margherita Guzzinati *(Lorna)*.

Horror film. Source: Carlos Fuentes, *Aura* (Mexico City, 1962). Sergio, a young research historian, answers a newspaper advertisement soliciting a man with his precise qualifications. He is offered a job at a magnificent palace assembling the largely erotic memoirs of a recently deceased general but declines the offer upon learning that his duties include ridding the household of Fabrizio, who currently holds the same position. He changes his mind, however, when he sees the beautiful Aura, daughter of the late general and his elderly widow, Consuelo. Aura divides her attentions between Sergio and Fabrizio, who is her lover, and tension between the men grows until Sergio accidentally kills his rival and is forced by the two women to dispose of the body. Madly in love with Aura, he attempts to curtail her occasional disappearances by locking her in her room, but he discovers to his horror that her face has become that of Consuelo. Sergio pleads with the witch, who has reincarnated her youth in Aura, to restore his love to him; but becoming aware that another scholar is about to be engaged to replace him, he realizes that he is destined to meet Fabrizio's fate, and he destroys the witch by fire. *Researchers. Historians. Widows. Witches. Filial relations. Manslaughter. Youth. Erotica.*

Note: Released in Italy in 1966 as *La strega in amore*. Also known as *Aura*.

THE WITCH BENEATH THE SEA see MARIZINIA

THE WITCH DOCTOR AND THE VIRGIN see KWAHERI

A WITCH WITHOUT A BROOM (United States/Spain)   F6.5627

Westside International–L. M. Films–Cinemagic Inc.–Lacy International Films. *Dist* Producers Releasing Organization. May **1967**. Sd; col (Eastmancolor, print by Movielab). 35mm. 86 min.

Prod Sidney Pink. *Exec Prod* Stan Torchia. *Dir (see note)* Joe Lacy. *Screenplay (see note)* Howard Berk. *Story* José Luis Navarro, José María Elorrieta. *Photog* Alfonso Nieva. *Art Dir* Teddy Villalba. *Titl* Pablo Nuñez. *Film Ed* John Horvath. *Mus* Fernando García Morcillo. *Sp Eff* Luis Castro.

Cast: Jeffrey Hunter *(Garver Logan)*, Maria Perschy *(Marianna)*, Gustavo Rojo *(Cayo)*, Perla Cristal *(Octavia)*, Reginald Gillam *(Don Ignacio)*, Al Mulock *(Wurlitz the Wizard)*, Katherine Ellison *(Yolanda)*, Félix Dafauce *(Necio)*, Esperanza Roy *(Valeria)*, John Clarke *(chariot master)*, Carl Rapp *(proprietor)*, Susan Talbot, Lewis Gordon, May Johnson, Gillian Simpson, Hercules Cortés.

Fantasy. Garver Logan, an American professor teaching Spanish history in Madrid, keeps seeing a beautiful blonde in the front row of his classes—but no one else sees her. While consulting a doctor about this hallucination, Logan notices a 15th-century print of Toledo in the physician's office. Instantly Logan disappears, landing in the setting of the print through the sorcery of the blonde, Marianna, who turns out to be a not-very-competent witch. Logan demands that she return him to his 20th-century fiancée, only to find his modern-day sweetheart in another's arms. Marianna brings him back to the 15th century, but her bungling efforts to return him to his natural habitat land them both in the middle of a stone-age wedding ceremony. Marianna incants another spell, but they land in ancient Rome, where Logan is maneuvered by scheming bettors into entering a chariot race. Logan wins by sheer luck, only to have the petulant Marianna transport him to a desolate earth in the 21st century, where he is sought after by seven Martian maidens who have survived World War III and have never seen a man. Marianna's father, Wurlitz the Wizard, senses his daughter's unrequited love for Logan and spirits them both back to the present. Logan wakes up in a hospital, where he is assured his illness was purely hallucinatory. Saddened to learn that Marianna was only a dream, he is revived from his melancholy by a nurse who looks exactly like the enchantress who supposedly never existed. *Americans in foreign countries. Professors. Witches. Physicians. Space creatures. Time travel. Weddings. Wagers. Hospitals. The Future. Stone Age. Toledo (Spain). Rome—History—Empire. Hallucinations.*

Note: Filmed in Spain in 1966 and released there as *Una bruja sin escoba* at 88 min. Joe Lacy and Howard Berk are pseudonyms of José María Elorrieta and José Luis Navarro Basso, respectively. Spanish sources list production companies as Lacy Films and Cinemagic Inc.; a British source credits them as Westside International and L. M. Films.

WITCHCRAFT (Great Britain)   F6.5628

Lippert Films. *Dist* Twentieth Century-Fox Film Corp. 19 Aug **1964** [Phoenix, Arizona, opening; c3 Sep 1964; LP28963]. Sd (RCA); b&w. 35mm. 80 min.

Prod Robert L. Lippert, Jack Parsons. *Dir* Don Sharp. *Screenplay* Harry Spalding. *Dir Photog* Arthur Lavis. *Camera Op* Len Harris. *Art Dir* George Provis. *Film Ed* Robert Winter. *Asst Ed* Clive Smith. *Mus Comp* Carlo Martelli. *Mus Cond* Philip Martell. *Sd Ed* Spencer Reeve. *Sd Rec* Buster Ambler. *Asst Dir* Frank Nesbitt. *Prod Mgr* Clifton Brandon. *Cont* Renee Glynne. *Prod Sec* Barbara Allen. *Wardrobe* Jean Fairlie. *Makeup* Harold Fletcher. *Hairdresser* Joyce James.

Cast: Lon Chaney, [Jr.] (*Morgan Whitlock*), Jack Hedley (*Bill Lanier*), Jill Dixon (*Tracy Lanier*), Viola Keats (*Helen Lanier*), Marie Ney (*Malvina Lanier*), David Weston (*Todd Lanier*), Diane Clare (*Amy Whitlock*), Yvette Rees (*Vanessa Whitlock*), Barry Linehan (*Myles Forrester*), Victor Brooks (*Inspector Baldwin*), Marianne Stone (*Forrester's secretary*), John Dunbar (*doctor*), Hilda Fenemore (*nurse*).

Horror film. A family feud, dating back to the 17th century when the Laniers buried alive Vanessa Whitlock as a witch and confiscated the Whitlock estate, is revived when Bill Lanier's construction company bulldozes through the Whitlock cemetery. Morgan Whitlock protests the desecration, and when Myles Forrester, Bill's partner, is mysteriously murdered, Morgan is held for questioning. Amy, Morgan's niece who is engaged to marry Bill's brother Todd, stays with the Laniers until her uncle's release. Although Bill orders a halt to the bulldozing, Vanessa has already been disturbed from her grave and begins to haunt the Laniers, causing members of their family to have fatal or near-fatal accidents. While Bill and Todd are away, Tracy, Bill's wife, follows Amy into the family crypt where she discovers Morgan leading his family in supernatural rituals. The witches drug Tracy and tie her to the altar, but Bill and Todd return and learn Tracy's whereabouts from one of Vanessa's victims who survived. They rescue Tracy while the witches are away, but Todd returns to the crypt for Amy, who has recently been initiated into Satanism. He in turn is captured, and when Vanessa threatens him, Amy pours burning oil on her. In the resulting fire, Morgan and all the witches, including Amy, are killed. Todd escapes and watches the estate go up in flames, bringing to an end the 300-year-old curse. *Witches. Uncles. Brothers. Sorcerers. Feuds. Murder. Supernatural. Rites and ceremonies. Cemeteries. Curses. Fires.*

Note: Released in Great Britain caDec 1964. Working title: *Witches and Warlocks.*

WITCHCRAFT '70 (Italy)   F6.5629

P. A. C.–Caravel Film. *Dist* Trans American Films. 26 Aug **1970** [Chicago opening; c28 Aug 1970; LP38506]. Sd; col (Movielab). 35mm. 82 min. [Also reviewed at 75 min.] *MPAA rating* X.

Dir-Writ Luigi Scattini. *Adtl Seq Dir & Writ Comm* R. L. Frost. *Photog* Claudio Racca. *Adtl Seq Photog* R. L. Frost. *Film Ed* Luigi Scattini. *Mus* Piero Umiliani.

Narrator: Edmund Purdom.

Documentary. The film surveys the practice of the occult in the modern world. Included are scenes of: the drug-using cult of Krishna in California; a group of natives on the South Seas island of Bali who practice self-mutilation; voodoo worshipers in Louisiana; and an Italian woman in Salerno who communicates with the dead through her deceased nephew. There are also scenes of a black mass in San Francisco and footage of witches' covens in both the United States and England. *Witches. Occult. Mutilation. Voodoo. Spiritualism. Drugs. California. Bali. Louisiana. Salerno. San Francisco. England. London.*

Note: Location scenes filmed in California, Bali, Louisiana, Salerno, London, San Francisco, and Sweden. Produced in Italy in 1969 as *Angeli bianchi ... angeli neri*; running time: 95 min.

THE WITCHES (France/Italy)   F6.5630

Dino De Laurentiis Cinematografica–Les Productions Artistes Associés. *Dist* Lopert Pictures. May **1968** [New York opening: 12 Mar 1969]. Sd; col (Technicolor). 35mm. 100 min.

Overall Production Credits: *Prod* Dino De Laurentiis. *Exec Prod* Alfredo De Laurentiis. *Photog* Giuseppe Rotunno. *Camera* Giuseppe Maccari. *Art Dir* Mario Garbuglia, Piero Poletto. *Mus* Piero Piccioni, Ennio Morricone. *Sd* Vittorio Trentino. *Asst Dir* Rinaldo Ricci, Luisa Alessandri, Nello Vanin, Massimo Castellani, Renzo Marignano. *Unit Mgr* Giorgio Adriani, Carlo Bartolini. *Cost Dsgn* Piero Tosi. *Makeup* Goffredo Rocchetti. *Hairstyles* Maria Teresa Corridoni. *Sp Eff* Joseph Natanson.

Production Credits—"The Witch Burned Alive": *Dir* Luchino Visconti. *Story-Screenplay* Giuseppe Patroni Griffi, Cesare Zavattini. *Film Ed* Mario Serandrei.

Production Credits—"Civic Sense": *Dir* Mauro Bolognini. *Story-Screenplay* Age & Scarpelli, Bernardino Zapponi. *Film Ed* Nino Baragli.

Production Credits—"The Earth As Seen From the Moon": *Dir-Writ* Pier Paolo Pasolini. *Sculpture* Pino Zac. *Film Ed* Nino Baragli. *1st & 2d Asst Dir* Sergio Citti, Vincenzo Cerami.

Production Credits—"The Girl From Sicily": *Dir* Franco Rossi. *Screenplay* Franco Rossi, Luigi Magni. *Film Ed* Giorgio Serralonga.

Production Credits—"A Night Like Any Other": *Dir* Vittorio De Sica. *Screenplay* Cesare Zavattini, Fabio Carpi, Enzo Muzii. *Film Ed* Adriana Novelli.

Cast—"The Witch Burned Alive": Silvana Mangano (*Gloria*), Annie Girardot (*Valeria*), Francisco Rabal (*Valeria's husband*), Massimo Girotti (*sportsman*), Elsa Albani (*gossip*), Helmut Steinberger (*waiter*), Véronique Vendell (*young girl friend*), Bruno Filippini (*singer*), Leslie French (*industrialist*), Dino Mele (*waiter*), Marilù Tolo, Clara Calamai, Nora Ricci.

Cast—"Civic Sense": Silvana Mangano (*lady*), Alberto Sordi (*truckdriver*).

Cast—"The Earth As Seen From the Moon": Silvana Mangano (*Assurda Caì*), Totò (*Ciancicato Miao*), Ninetto Davoli (*Baciù Miao*), Laura Betti (*a tourist*), Luigi Leoni (*her husband*), Mario Cipriani (*priest*).

Cast—"The Girl From Sicily": Silvana Mangano (*Nuncia*), Pietro Tordi (*father*).

Cast—"A Night Like Any Other": Silvana Mangano (*Giovanna*), Clint Eastwood (*husband*), Armando Bottin (*Nembo Kid*), Gianni Gori (*Diabolik*), Paolo Gozlino (*Mandrake*), Angelo Santi (*Flash Gordon*), Piero Torrisi (*Batman*), Valentino Macchi (*man at stadium*), Franco Moruzzi (*Sadik*).

Comedy-drama. THE WITCH BURNED ALIVE: Gloria, a famous actress and sex symbol, is vacationing in her resort home in the Swiss Alps with her friend Valeria. The men among the guests leer at her, and their wives are jealous. Gloria discovers that she is pregnant and telephones her husband, a motion picture producer. When he tells her that she cannot have the child because she will miss too much work, Gloria realizes the extent of her loneliness and misery. CIVIC SENSE: A lady trapped in rush hour traffic in Rome sees a truckdriver injured in an accident. She offers to take him to the hospital and proceeds to speed through the traffic. Instead of going to the hospital, however, she drives home to keep an important appointment, and the man dies in the car outside of her house. THE EARTH AS SEEN FROM THE MOON: [Performed primarily in pantomime.] Ciancicato Miao and Baciù Miao, two tramps, invent a green-haired mute named Assurda Caì to act as their servant and companion. THE GIRL FROM SICILY: When Nuncia, a young Sicilian woman, is unable to marry the man of her choice, her father starts a civil war in their village. A NIGHT LIKE ANY OTHER: Giovanna, the bored wife of a banker, fantasizes that her husband has to compete for her favors with Batman, Flash Gordon, Diabolik, and Mandrake. *Actors. Motion picture producers. Truckdrivers. Tramps. Mutes. Bankers. Vacations. Pregnancy. Loneliness. Traffic. Perfidy. Marriage. Fatherhood. Fantasy. Resorts. Inventions. Alps. Rome. Sicily. Automobile accidents. Batman. Flash Gordon. Diabolik. Mandrake.*

Note: Opened in Rome in Apr 1967 as *Le streghe*; running time: 104 min; in Paris in Jun 1968 as *Les sorcières*. Italian episode titles: "La strega bruciata viva," "Senso civico," "La terra vista dalla luna," "La Siciliana," and "Una sera come le altre."

THE WITCHES *see* **THE DEVIL'S OWN**

WITCHES AND WARLOCKS *see* **WITCHCRAFT**

THE WITCHES CURSE *see* **THE WITCH'S CURSE**

WITCHFINDER GENERAL *see* **CONQUEROR WORM**

THE WITCHMAKER   F6.5631

Las Cruces Productions–Arrow Films. *Dist* Excelsior Distributing Co. 2 Apr **1969** [Phoenix, Arizona, opening; c2 Apr 1969; LP37370]. Sd; col (Technicolor). 35mm (Techniscope). 99 min. *MPAA rating* M.

Prod-Dir-Writ William O. Brown. *Exec Prod* L. Q. Jones. *Assoc Prod* Alvy Moore. *Photog* John Arthur Morrill. *Mus* Jaime Mendoza-Nava. *Sd* Rod Sutton.

Cast: John Lodge (*Luther*), Alvy Moore (*Dr. Ralph Hayes*), Thordis Brandt (*Tasha*), Anthony Eisley (*Victor Gordon*), Shelby Grant (*Maggie*), Robyn Millan (*Sharon*), Tony Benson (*Owen*), Helene Winston (*Jessie, the old witch*), Warrene Ott (*Jessie, the young witch*), Burt Mustin (*boatman*), Kathy Lynn (*Patty Ann*), Sue Bernard (*Felicity Johnson*), Howard Viet (*San Blas*), Nancy Crawford (*Goody Hale*), Patricia Wymer (*hag of Devon*), Carolyn Rhodimer (*Marta*), Diane Webber (*Nautch of Tangier*), Larry Vincent (*Amos Coffin*), Del Kaye (*Le Singe*), Gwen Lipscomb (*Fong Quai*), Valya Garanda (*El A Haish Ma*).

Horror film. Dr. Ralph Hayes, a professor of parapsychology, takes a research team into the Louisiana swamp where eight women have been murdered, drained of their blood, and marked with satanic symbols. The investigating party includes: Maggie, the professor's secretary; Tasha, a student whose grandmother was a witch; Victor Gordon, a magazine writer; and several students of witchcraft. Tasha's extra-sensory powers are detected by Luther, a warlock who has committed the murders in accordance with a pact made with the Devil. To gain control of Tasha, he calls forth Jessie, a 200-year-old witch who will help only if she receives enough blood to restore her youth. When Tasha aids Luther in luring two students to their death, Dr. Hayes and Victor realize the strength of Luther's hold over Tasha. During a ceremony to make Tasha a witch, Dr. Hayes and Maggie are killed trying to divert Luther's attention, while Victor substitutes pig's blood for the human blood. All in the coven are destroyed but Luther, who chases Victor and Tasha into the swamp. In the struggle, Luther falls into quicksand, and Tasha, proclaiming Satan to be her master, pushes Victor into the quicksand. *Professors. Secretaries. Students. Authors. Witches. Sorcerers. Human sacrifice. Witchcraft. Rites and ceremonies. Swamps. Quicksand. Louisiana. The Devil.*

Note: Location scenes filmed in Marksville, Louisiana.

THE WITCH'S CURSE (Italy)   F6.5632

Panda Film. *For* L'Industria Cinematografica Italiana. *Dist* Medallion Pictures. 4 Dec **1963** [Providence, Rhode Island, opening]. Sd; col (Eastmancolor). 35mm (CinemaScope). 78 min.

Pres by Palisades International Corp. *Prod* Luigi Carpentieri, Ermanno Donati. *Dir* Riccardo Freda. *Screenplay* Oreste Biancoli, Piero Pierotti, Ennio De Concini. *Story* Eddy H. Given. *Photog* Riccardo Pallottini. *Art Dir* Andrea Crisanti. *Set Decor* Luciano Spadoni. *Film Ed* Ornella Micheli. *Mus* Carlo Franci. *Prod Dir* Lucio Bompani. *Cost* Luciano Spadoni. *Sp Eff* Serse Urbisaglia.

Cast: Kirk Morris *(Maciste)*, Hélène Chanel *(Martha Gunt)*, Vira Silenti *(young Martha Gunt)*, Andrea Bosic *(Parris)*, Angelo Zanolli *(Charley Law)*, John Karlsen *(burgomaster)*, John Francis Lane *(coachman)*, Howard Nelson Rubien *(old villager)*, Neil Robinson *(villager)*, Charles Fawcett *(doctor)*, Mauro Donatella, Gina Mascetti, Antonella Della Porta, Antonio Cianci, Remo De Angelis, Evaristo Maran.

Horror film. Source: Guido Brignone, *Maciste all'inferno* (a film; Pittaluga Film, 1926). In the Scottish town of Loch Lake during the 17th century Martha Gunt, condemned as a witch and burned at the stake, leaves a curse on the village. Years later, her newly-married granddaughter, also named Martha Gunt, goes to live with her bridegroom in the witch's castle. Certain manifestations of witchcraft lead the villagers to believe that the witch has returned, and they attack the castle, holding Martha captive. Martha's husband seeks the help of a shepherd named Maciste who is exceptionally strong. Maciste uproots a tree and descends into Hell, where he searches for the witch in the hope of removing the spell she has cast on Loch Lake. Maciste encounters a series of difficulties in the burning underworld as he seeks the witch. At last he kisses her, putting an end to the curse and saving Martha and the villagers. *Witches. Shepherds. Curses. Village life. Witchcraft. Castles. Scotland. Maciste. Hell.*

Note: Filmed on location in Bracciano and in the vicinity of Bari and Rome. Opened in Rome in Aug 1962 as *Maciste all'inferno*; running time: 90 min. Also known as *The Witches Curse*.

THE WITCH'S MIRROR (Mexico)   F6.5633

Cinematográfica A. B. S. A. *Dist* K. Gordon Murray Productions, Trans-International Films. 29 May **1968** [Maryland license]. Sd; b&w. 35mm. 75 min.

Pres by K. Gordon Murray. *Prod* Abel Salazar. *Dir-Adapt* Chano Urueta. *Screenplay* Alfredo Ruanova, Carlos Enrique Taboada. *Photog* Jorge Stahl, Jr. *Art Dir* Javier Torres Torija. *Film Ed* Alfredo Rosas Priego. *Mus* Gustavo César Carrión. *Sd* Manuel Topete.

Cast: Armando Calvo *(husband)*, Rosita Arenas *(wife)*, Isabela Corona *(witch)*, Dina de Marco.

Horror film. A witch using a magic mirror is unable to prevent the murder of her godchild. When the dead woman's husband remarries, the witch uses her powers to scare the couple. The ghost of the first wife emerges from the mirror, plays the piano, and causes the husband to disfigure his second wife. Watched by the vengeful ghost, the husband grafts a new face and hands onto the second wife, using skin taken from corpses. *Witches. Ghosts. Murder. Supernatural. Disfiguration. Revenge.*

Note: Produced in Mexico in 1960 as *El espejo de la bruja*; running time: 90 min.

WITH GUNILLA MONDAY EVENING AND TUESDAY *see* GUILT

WITH SIX YOU GET EGGROLL   F6.5634

Arwin Productions–Cinema Center Films. *Dist* National General Pictures. 7 Aug **1968** [Boston opening; c26 Jul 1968; LP39150]. Sd; col (DeLuxe). 35mm (Panavision). 95 min.

Prod Martin Melcher. *Dir* Howard Morris. *Screenplay* Gwen Bagni, Paul Dubov, Harvey Bullock, R. S. Allen. *Story* Gwen Bagni, Paul Dubov. *Dir Photog* Ellsworth Fredricks, Harry Stradling, Jr. *Camera Op* William Dodds. *Asst Camera* George Hollister. *Art Dir* Cary Odell. *Set Decor* James Berkey.

Film Ed Adrienne Fazan. *Asst Film Ed* Bill Todd. *Mus Comp & Cond* Robert Mersey. Song: "You Make Me Want You" Robert Mersey, Robert Hilliard. *Sung by* The Grass Roots. *Sd Mix* Philip Mitchell. *Sd Rec* Dean Spencer. *1st & 2d Asst Dir* Bud Grace, Michael Daves. *Prod Mgr* Gilbert Kurland. *Unit Mgr* Bud Grace. *Script Supv* Marvin Weldon. *Miss Day's Wardrobe* Glenn Connelly. *Men's Wardrobe* Ray Summers. *Women's Wardrobe* Connie Edney. *Makeup* Harry Maret, Emile La Vigne. *Hairstyles* Barbara Lampson, Armiene Fields. *Sp Eff* Dave Lee. *Casting* Bill Kenney. *Animal Handler* Halleck H. Driscoll.

Cast: Doris Day *(Abby McClure)*, Brian Keith *(Jake Iverson)*, Pat Carroll *(Maxine Scott)*, Barbara Hershey *(Stacey Iverson)*, George Carlin *(Herbie Fleck)*, Alice Ghostley *(housekeeper)*, John Findlater *(Flip McClure)*, Jimmy Bracken *(Mitch McClure)*, Richard Steele *(Jason McClure)*, Herbert Voland *(Harry Scott)*, Elaine Devry *(Cleo)*, Allan Melvin *(desk sergeant)*, Peter Leeds *(Police Officer Joelson)*, Victor Tayback *(chicken truck driver)*, Jamie Farr *(JoJo)*, William Christopher *(Zip)*, Pearl Shear *(laughing lady)*, Mickey Deems *(Sam Bates)*, Milton Frome *(Bud Young)*, John Copage *(lumber yard employee)*, The Grass Roots *(themselves)*, Lord Nelson *(Calico, Abby's dog)*, Jackie Joseph.

Domestic comedy. Widower Jake Iverson is invited to a dinner party given by widow Abby McClure. Tiring of the matchmaking of Maxine and Harry Scott, Abby's in-laws, Iverson leaves the party, but later encounters his hostess in an all-night store. Embarrassed by the widow's apology for her relatives' behavior, Iverson arranges to see Abby again. Although the widow and widower fall in love and marry, Abby's sons, Flip, Mitch, and Jason, fight continuously with Iverson's possessive daughter Stacey. Even the family dogs are incompatible. For privacy the newlyweds borrow a camper, which they use as a bedroom. During a bedtime argument Abby drives off in the vehicle. Her husband falls from the camper, clad only in briefs and clutching a teddy bear. Abby, discovering her loss, speeds toward the site of Iverson's disappearance, escorted by a band of hippies. When the camper collides with a chicken truck, Abby and entourage are arrested. Hearing of the accident, Iverson and the children rush to her rescue, en route colliding with the same chicken truck. The irate driver menaces Iverson, and the children and pets unite in his defense. At the station house parents and children are joyfully reconciled. *Widows. Widowers. Newlyweds. In-laws. Matchmakers. Hippies. Truckdrivers. Police. Family life. Marriage. Camper buses. Jails. Automobile accidents. Dogs.*

WITHOUT A STITCH (Denmark)   F6.5635

Palladium. *Dist* VIP Distributors, Sherpix, Inc. 24 Dec **1969** [San Francisco opening; c26 Sep 1968; LF67]. Sd; col (De Luxe). 35mm. 96 min. *MPAA rating* X.

Pres by Jack H. Harris. *Prod* John Hilbard, Teuga Nielsen. *Dir* Annelise Meineche. *Screenplay* Annelise Meineche, John Hilbard. *Dir Photog* Aage Wiltrup. *Lighting* Ove Hansen. *Sets* Otto Lund, Herbi Gartner. *Film Ed* Edith Schlüssel. *Mus* Ole Høyer. *Sd* Preben Mortensen, Jens Grønborg. *Mus Rec* Birger Swan. *Script Girl* Eva Hammershøy. *Cost* Berit Nykjaer. *Makeup* Aase Tarp, Kirsten Guldbrandsen. *Wrestling* Simon Kurland.

Cast: Anne Grete *(Lilian)*, Ib Mossin *(Dr. Petersen)*, Niels Borksand *(Henry)*, Ki-Jo Feza *(Britta)*, Niels Dybeck *(Göran)*, Åke Engfeldt *(Bengt)*, Leif Fich *(Heini)*, John Martinus *(John)*, Søren Carlsbaek *(Åke)*, Joan Gamst *(Lise)*, Søren Strømberg *(Jan)*, Dieter Eppler *(Kurt von Asbach)*, Dale Robinson *(Freddy)*, Preben Ottesen *(Antonio)*, Jean Kress *(Pierre)*, Ingrid Langballe, Bjørn Spiro, Ann Bennett, Helena Germann.

Drama. Source: Jens Bjørneboe, *Uten en tråd* (Oslo, 1966). Following a sexual misadventure with her boyfriend Henry, high school graduate Lilian consults Dr. Petersen, hoping to cure her frigidity. Through word and deed the gynecologist helps the adolescent to discover her own sexuality. Satisfied, he equips her with a diary in which she is to record multiple sexual experiences to be acquired during a summer spent hitchhiking in Europe. According to the doctor's orders Lilian acts in a pornographic film in Sweden; attends an orgy with the lesbian Lise and the count Jan in Copenhagen; observes female wrestlers and whips an aristocratic sadomasochist in Hamburg; forms a threesome with two homosexuals in Italy; and makes love to the artisan Pierre in Paris. On the return flight to Copenhagen Lilian meets Henry and shares with him the fruits of her newly-acquired knowledge. She later presents Dr. Petersen with the diary, which he will use as source material for his doctoral dissertation. *Nobility. Hitchhikers. Gynecologists. Aristocrats. Wrestlers. Sex researchers. Germans. French. Sexual initiation. Adolescence. Frigidity. Lesbianism. Sadomasochism. Flagellation. Orgies. Male homosexuality. Diaries. Sex exploitation films. Copenhagen. Hamburg. Sweden. Italy. Paris.*

Note: Location scenes filmed in Norway, Sweden, Switzerland, Germany, Italy, France, Denmark, and England. Released in Denmark in 1968 as *Uden en traevl*; running time: 89 min.

THE WITNESSES (France)   **F6.5636**
Films de la Pléïade. *Dist* Altura Films International. 6 Nov **1967** [New York opening]. Sd; b&w. 35mm. 82 min.
Pres by Clem Perry. *Prod* Pierre Braunberger. *Dir* Frédéric Rossif. *English Vers Dir* Thomas Craven. *Text* Madeleine Chapsal, Frédéric Rossif. *English Adapt* Vince Pereira. *Adtl Photog* Marcel Fradétal. *Film Ed* Suzanne Baron. *Mus* Maurice Jarre. *Sd* Pierre Calvet, Julien Coutellier. *Asst Dir* Albert Knobler.
   English Vers Narr Viveca Lindfors, Michael Tolan.
   French Vers Narr: Nadine Alari, Jacques Perrot.
   Documentary. Nazi footage of the establishment and destruction of the Warsaw ghetto is accompanied by interviews with survivors of the holocaust. *Jews. Poles. Nazis. Genocide. War crimes. Anti-Semitism. Survival. Ghettos. World War II. Warsaw.*
   Note: Opened in Paris in Nov 1961 as *Le temps du ghetto.*

THE WIVES *see* **KEY CLUB WIVES**

WIVES AND LOVERS   **F6.5637**
Hal Wallis Productions. *Dist* Paramount Pictures. 28 Aug **1963** [New York opening; c28 Aug 1963; LP26412]. Sd; b&w. 35mm. 103 min.
   A Hal B. Wallis Production. *Prod* Hal B. Wallis. *Assoc Prod* Paul Nathan. *Asst Prod* Jack Saper. *Dir* John Rich. *Screenplay* Edward Anhalt. *Cinematog* Lucien Ballard. *Camera Op* Richard Batcheller. *Asst Camera Op* David M. Walsh. *Art Dir* Walter Tyler, Hal Pereira. *Set Decor* Arthur Krams, Sam Comer. *Film Ed* Warren Low. *Mus* Lyn Murray. *Sd* John Carter. *Boom Op* Rocky Nelson. *Rec* R. D. Cook. *Asst Dir* Danny McCauley, Bill Poole. *Unit Mgr* Richard Blaydon, Bill Gray. *Script Supv* Marvin Weldon. *Cost* Edith Head. *Wardrobe* Buddy Clark, Glenita Dineen. *Makeup* Gary Morris. *Hairstyles* Virginia Darcy. *Still Photog* Sterling Smith. *Prop* Carl Coleman, Wally Oliver. *Grip* Bud Gaunt, Norbert Haring. *Gaffer* George Satterfield.
   Cast: Janet Leigh (*Bertie Austin*), Van Johnson (*Bill Austin*), Shelley Winters (*Fran Cabrell*), Martha Hyer (*Lucinda Ford*), Ray Walston (*Wylie Driberg*), Jeremy Slate (*Gar Aldrich*), Claire Wilcox (*Julie Austin*), Lee Patrick (*Mrs. Swanson*), Richard Wessel (*Mr. Liberti*), Dave Willock (*Dr. Partridge*).
   Comedy. Source: Jay Presson Allen, *The First Wife* (a play; publication undetermined). Bill Austin, a struggling writer, works at home in his cold water flat while his wife, Bertie, cheerfully supports him and their small daughter, Julie. One day Bill's agent, Lucinda Ford, informs him that she has sold his novel and that it is going to be adapted for Broadway and later the movies. Overcome by his sudden wealth, Bill insists that Bertie give up her job and they move into a fashionable Connecticut home. While Bill works on his play with Lucinda, Bertie spends her time with Fran Cabrell, a martini-guzzling neighbor, and Fran's "companion," Wylie Driberg. Bill's visits to Lucinda become more frequent, and Bertie accuses him of having more than a business arrangement with his agent. In retaliation, she encourages the advances of Gar Aldrich, the film star who is to appear in Bill's play. The play finally opens on Broadway, where it is a huge success, but Bertie does not attend the performance. Later that night Bill drives to Connecticut to tell Bertie that there is no possibility of reconciliation. When Gar also arrives, however, Bill strikes him and throws him out of the house. After assuring one another that each has been faithful, Bertie and Bill decide to give their marriage another chance. *Novelists. Playwrights. Literary agents. Neighbors. Actors. Marriage. Jealousy. Drunkenness. Infidelity. Connecticut. New York City—Broadway.*
   Note: Prerelease title: *First Wife.*

THE WIZARD OF GORE   **F6.5638**
Mayflower Pictures. 23 Oct **1970** [Washington, D. C., opening]. Sd; col (Eastmancolor). 35mm. 96 min. MPAA rating R.
   Prod-Dir Herschell Gordon Lewis. *Exec Prod* Fred M. Sandy. *Orig Screenplay* Allen Kahn. *1st Camera Op* Alex Ameripoor. *2d Camera Op* Dan Krogh. *Color Lighting Coörd* William S. Stein, Jr. *Film Ed* Eskandar Ameripoor. *Ed Asst* Ray Szegho, Dan Krogh. *Mus Backgrounds* Larry Wellington. *Sd Rec* Robert Lewis. *Asst Dir* Allison Louise Downe. *Prod Mgr* John Sezonov. *Prod Coörd* Harry Ambroz. *Unit Mgr* Gary Isaacson. *Makeup & Hairstyles* Frank Morelli. *Tech Dsgn Unit Ch* Roger Strauss. *Prop Communications* Barry Lewis. *Still Photog* Roger Gee.
   Cast: Ray Sager (*Montag*), Judy Cler (*Sherry Carson*), Wayne Ratay (*Jack*), Phil Laurenson (*Greg*), Jim Rau (*Steve*), John Elliot (*Detective Harlan*), Don Alexander (*Detective Kramer*), Monika Blackwell, Corinne Kirkin, Karin Alexana, Sally Brody, Karen Burke (*girls*), Jack Gilbreth (*maître d'hotel*), Alex Ameripoor (*man on stage*).
   Horror film. Sherry Carson, a television show hostess, and her sportswriter fiancé, Jack, watch an obscure magician, Montag, perform in a small theater. After an unspectacular beginning, Montag calls a woman from the audience and saws her in half. The woman is apparently unharmed and returns to her seat, but an hour later, while she is sitting in a restaurant, she dies, her body severed

in two. Sherry, unaware of Montag's true powers, invites him to appear on her show. Meanwhile, his gruesome tricks continue to result in the delayed deaths of his female subjects. Appearing on the television show, Montag hypnotizes the entire audience, and a drop of blood appears on each person's hand. Jack, realizing the danger, rushes to the studio and pushes Montag into a fiery cauldron. Later at Sherry's apartment, Jack removes his face and becomes Montag. He dismembers Sherry, but she shares the magic power and transports Montag back to his initial performance. *Magicians. Sportswriters. Television personalities. Psychopaths. Murder. Mutilation. Hypnotism. Television.*

WIZARD OF MARS   **F6.5639**
Borealis Enterprises. *Dist* American General Pictures. ca **1964.** Sd; col. 35mm. 81 min.
   Prod-Dir-Writ David L. Hewitt. *Tech Adv* Forrest J. Ackerman.
   Cast: John Carradine (*Wizard of Mars*), Roger Gentry, Vic McGee, Jerry Rannow, Eve Bernhardt.
   Science fiction melodrama. Astronauts crashland on Mars and discover the remnants of an ancient civilization, including the last living Martian, the Wizard of Mars. A diminishing supply of oxygen threatens the lives of the four visitors, who experience other phenomena paralleling those in Lyman Frank Baum's *Wonderful Wizard of Oz. Astronauts. Sorcerers. Space exploration. Oxygen. Imaginary kingdoms. Mars (planet). "Wonderful Wizard of Oz".*

DER WOLF UND DIE SIEBEN JUNGEN GEISSLEIN *see* **BIG BAD WOLF**

WOLFPACK *see* **THE MCKENZIE BREAK**

WOMAN AND LOVER *see* **THE SENSUALLY LIBERATED FEMALE**

WOMAN AND TEMPTATION (Argentina)   **F6.5640**
Armando Bo. *Dist* Steve Prentoulis Films. 17 Nov **1967** [New York opening]. Sd; b&w. 35mm. 85-90 min.
   Prod-Dir-Screenplay Armando Bo. *Asst Prod* Juan Pitrau. *Photog* Alfredo Traverso. *Camera* Francisco Mirada. *Sets* Armando Bo. *Film Ed* Rosalino Caterbetti. *Mus* Eligio Ayala Moren. *Played by* Los Paraguayos. *Sung by* Luis Alberto del Paraná. *Asst Dir* Rodolfo Lago. *Cont* Rosalino Caterbetti. *Miss Sarli's Wardrobe* Paco Jamandreu.
   Cast: Isabel Sarli (*Sandra*), Armando Bo (*Joseph*), Víctor Bo (*Chuck*), Oscar Valicelli (*Shorty*), Juan José Miguez (*Fernando*), Aníbal Pardeiro.
   Melodrama. Sandra falls overboard from a yacht traveling along the Paraná River through the Argentine jungle. She swims ashore and meets Chuck, a middle-aged hermit who has renounced the pleasures of the flesh. Caressing her sensuous body, Sandra succeeds in enticing the hermit, but she also attracts the attention of four younger villagers who have been without women for some time. The four men play a game of cards to decide which of them will enjoy the woman, and, intent on rape, they follow Sandra and her new lover into the jungle. Finding the two in an embrace, the men attack and injure the hermit, but Sandra manages to escape after killing her wounded lover and again falls into the hands of the sex-starved villagers. Two of the men die fighting for her, and the third goes mad with desire. The hermit dies of his wounds as the flooding river makes escape impossible. *Castaways. Hermits. Seduction. Murder. Rape. Lust. Insanity. Floods. Jungles. Paraná River.*
   Note: Also known as *Naked Temptation,* film was originally released in Argentina in 1966 as *La tentación desnuda.*

A WOMAN FOR ALL REASONS *see* **WOMEN FOR ALL REASONS**

A WOMAN FOR CHARLIE *see* **THE COCKEYED COWBOYS OF CALICO COUNTY**

THE WOMAN GAMBLER (Japan)   **F6.5641**
Daiei Motion Picture Co. Jun **1969** [Los Angeles showing]. Sd; col? 35mm. 85 min.
   Dir Taro Yuge.
   Cast: Kyoko Enami, Sae Kawaguchi, Goichi Yamada, Kojiro Hongo, Ryohei Uchida.
   Melodrama. No information about the precise nature of this film has been found. *Gamblers.*
   Note: Released in Japan in Jul 1967 as *Onna tobakushi.*

WOMAN HUNT   **F6.5642**
Associated Producers, Inc. *Dist* Twentieth Century-Fox Film Corp. 28 Mar **1962** [New York opening; c31 Dec 1961; LP21041]. Sd; b&w. 35mm (CinemaScope). 60 min.
   Prod-Dir Maury Dexter. *Screenplay* Edward J. Lakso, Russ Bender. *Story* Harry Spalding. *Dir Photog* Floyd Crosby. *Set Decor* Harry Reif. *Supv Film Ed* Jodie Copelan. *Film Ed* Carl Pierson. *Mus Comp & Cond* Henry Vars. *Sd* Frank McWhorter. *Supv Sd Ed* Jack Cornall. *Asst Dir* Willard Kirkham. *Prod*

Supv Harold E. Knox. *Script Supv* Dixie McCoy. *Wardrobe* Patrick Cummings. *Makeup* Harry Thomas. *Prop Master* Mike Gordon.

Cast: Steven Piccaro *(Hal Weston)*, Lisa Lu *(Li Sheng)*, Berry Kroeger *(Petrie/Osgood)*, Bob Okazaki *(Dr. Sheng)*, Ann Carroll *(Janet Oberon)*, Tom Daly *(Mr. Davalos)*, Ivan Bonar *(Jacobs)*, Harold Bostwick, William O'Connell, Norman Burton, Dal McKennon, Lloyd Kino, Lee Frederick, Paule Lakis, Hideo Imamura, George Riley.

Crime melodrama. Hal Weston arrives in Los Angeles looking for his former wife, Nora, who divorced him to marry his old partner, Petrie, now reportedly dead. Weston contacts Osgood, Petrie's former employee, and persuades him to help in the search. Also aiding in the quest is Li Sheng, daughter of Dr. Sheng, a surgeon, who tells Weston that Nora was a drug addict. Eventually Weston discovers that Nora was murdered by Petrie, who bribed Dr. Sheng into falsifying his death certificate and a mortuary assistant into placing her body in Petrie's coffin. Then Petrie collected his own insurance money by having a cohort, Janet Oberon, pose as Nora. When confronted by Weston, Petrie tries to escape by having Dr. Sheng perform plastic surgery to make him look like Osgood. Realizing that Petrie also plans to eliminate him, Osgood kills Petrie, only to die during a fight with Weston. The mystery solved, Weston returns to Li Sheng. *Missing persons. Chinese. Surgeons. Drug addicts. Imposture. Divorce. Murder. Fraud. Plastic surgery. Insurance. Bribery. Los Angeles.*

Note: Location scenes filmed in Los Angeles.

A WOMAN IN JULY *see* **THE STRIPPER**

A WOMAN IN LOVE   F6.5643

New York Film Productions. ca **1970**. Sd; b&w. 35mm. 94 min.

Prod Mathias Sebald, Albert T. Viola. *Assoc Prod* Joseph Sutherin. *Dir* Albert T. Viola. *Screenplay* Jerold Brody, Joseph Sutherin, Mathias Sebald, Albert T. Viola. *Adtl Material* Richard Davidson. *Story* Mathias Sebald. *Dir Photog* Mathias Sebald. *Photog* Jack Malick. *Art Dir* Jurgen. *Film Ed* Mathias Sebald, Joseph Sutherin. *Song* "The Lorelei Theme" Robert N. Langworthy. *Sung by* Bobbi Lange. *Accomp* The Extremes. *Sd Rec* Joseph Sutherin. *Boom Op* Fred Von Bernewitz. *Prod Sec* Melynda Albrecht. *Prod Asst* Barbara Boone, John De Bella, David Grace, Julie Martin. *Cost* Jane Kip Stevens. *Tech Asst* Eugene Pererwa.

Cast: Phillip R. Allen, Audrey Campbell, Gunda Hecklau, Elke Hellman, Jon Viscounte, Vera Allik, Gary Malick, Natalie Rogers, Harold Herbstman, Melynda Albrecht, Lucy Becker, Boris P. Berest, Fred Von Bernewitz, Julie Breyer, Elaine Brandt, Tony Bell, Elaine Conte, Eugene Green, Jurgen, J. J. Malick, Joe Marshall, Barbara Montayne, John Ramsey, Evander Schley, Jane White, Kate Woodridge.

Drama. Phil and Bea, engaged to be married, are experiencing difficulty in resolving their personal conflicts. They gain insight from Eleanor and Jon, a couple with similar problems. Jon, thwarted in his attempts to seduce Eleanor, withdraws into a world of childhood fantasies. His suppressed hostility toward his domineering stepmother, Roberta, and his promiscuous stepsister Sue, whom he blames for his father's death, caused him to rape Eleanor, whom he imagines to be Sue. *Stepmothers. Stepsisters. Promiscuity. Filial relations. Seduction. Fantasy. Rape.*

WOMAN IN THE DUNES (Japan)   F6.5644

Teshigahara Productions. *Dist* Pathé Contemporary Films. 25 Oct **1964** [New York opening]. Sd; b&w. 35mm. 123 min.

Prod Kiichi Ichikawa, Tadashi Ohono. *Dir* Hiroshi Teshigahara. *Screenplay* Kobo Abe. *Photog* Hiroshi Segawa. *Film Ed* F. Susui. *Mus* Toru Takemitsu. *Prod Supv* Hiroshi Kawazoe.

Cast: Eiji Okada *(man)*, Kyoko Kishida *(woman)*, Koji Mitsui, Hiroko Ito, Sen Yano, Ginzo Sekigushi, Kiyohiko Ichiha, Tamutsu Tamura, Hiroyuki Nishimo.

Drama. Source: Kobo Abe, *Suna no onna* (Tokyo, 1952). While collecting beetle specimens on an isolated beach, a Japanese entomologist becomes so absorbed in his work that he misses the last bus home. The neighboring villagers inveigle him into spending the night in a dilapidated shack located at the bottom of a huge sand pit. The shack is owned by a young widow whose endless task is to shovel away the constantly shifting sands in order to prevent her home— and so the village as a whole—from becoming engulfed. With the coming of morning the man discovers that the rope ladder has been removed, and he is trapped at the bottom of the pit. After numerous futile attempts to escape, he becomes partially resigned to his desolate new existence, and helps in digging the sand in return for the necessities of life, which are lowered to him in a bucket. Even his initial hostility toward the woman is transformed into sexual attraction, and he becomes her lover. Still craving freedom, however, he willingly consents to make love to the woman in full view of the voyeuristic villagers in return for one brief look at the sea. One day he accidentally discovers a possible means of obtaining fresh water, not only for himself, but the entire village as well, through condensation and the maintenance of

pressure differences. Then one night the woman, who by now is undergoing an abnormal pregnancy, suffers abdominal pains, and the villagers take her away for treatment. In their haste they forget the rope ladder. Free at last, the man climbs out of the pit and walks to the sea. He pauses, contemplates his plan for securing fresh water, and slowly climbs back into the sand pit. *Entomologists. Widows. Shanghaiing. Imprisonment. Seduction. Pregnancy. Voyeurism.*

Note: Released in Japan in 1964 as *Suna no onna.*

A WOMAN IS A WOMAN (France/Italy)   F6.5645

Rome-Paris Films. *Dist* Pathé Contemporary Films. 3 Nov **1964** [New York opening]. Sd; col (Eastman Color). 35mm (FranScope). 80 min.

Prod Carlo Ponti, Georges de Beauregard. *Dir-Scen* Jean-Luc Godard. *Adapt* Jean-Luc Godard. *Based on an Idea by* Geneviève Cluny. *Dir Photog* Raoul Coutard. *Art Dir* Bernard Evein. *Ed* Agnès Guillemot, Lila Herman. *Mus* Michel Legrand. *Song:* "Chanson d'Angéla" Michel Legrand, Jean-Luc Godard. *Song:* "Tu te laisses aller" Charles Aznavour. *Sd* Guy Villette. *Asst Dir* Francis Cognani. *Prod Mgr* Philippe Dussart. *Script Girl* Suzanne Schiffman. *Cost* Bernard Evein.

Cast: Anna Karina *(Angéla)*, Jean-Claude Brialy *(Emile)*, Jean-Paul Belmondo *(Alfred Lubitsch)*, Nicole Paquin *(Suzanne)*, Marie Dubois *(1st prostitute)*, Marion Sarraut *(2d prostitute)*, Jeanne Moreau *(woman in bar)*, Catherine Demongeot.

Comedy-drama. Angéla, a stripteaser in a Parisian dive, and Emile, a bookseller in the Faubourg St. Denis section of Paris, have been living together for some time. Emile's friend, Alfred Lubitsch, a photographer, makes no secret of his admiration for Angéla but cherishes a hopeless dream, since she adores Emile. One night at dinner, Angéla announces that she wants to have a baby, and that the ideal moment for conception is at hand. Emile demurs, since he is not anxious to settle down to marriage. Angéla threatens to make a father out of the first man she sees but loses her nerve when a detective arrives to investigate a disturbance. She warns Emile that she will address herself to Alfred; he angrily proclaims his indifference and invites his friend up. Tired of being ridiculed, Angéla leads Alfred into the bathroom; she flirts with him but they do not make love. The next morning, Alfred sets out to convince Angéla that he loves her. He invites her to a cafe, offers her vermouth, plays Charles Aznavour's "Tu te laisses aller," and produces an old photo of Emile with another woman. Determined not to allow the opportunity for motherhood to pass, Angéla returns home to make lunch. Relations with Emile continue to be icy, however, and she decides to meet Alfred. Meanwhile, Emile decides to marry her. He finds that she is not at work, and he gloomily picks up a prostitute. He then sets out in despair for Alfred's, only to have his worst fears confirmed. He sends a message that he is leaving for Rio, and Angéla returns home in tears. Emile decides to forgive Angéla, and they make love so that he can be equally sure of being the father. *Stripteasers. Booksellers. Photographers. Prostitutes. Infidelity. Seduction. Pregnancy. Cafes. Paris.*

Note: Opened in Paris in Sep 1961 under the title *Une femme est une femme*; in Rome in Oct 1961 under the title *La donna è donna.*

WOMAN OF DARKNESS (Sweden)   F6.5646

Svensk Filmindustri. *Dist* Freena Films. Sep **1968** [Los Angeles showing]. Sd; b&w. 35mm. 112 min.

Prod Lorens Marmstedt. *Dir* Arne Mattsson. *Screenplay* Eva Dahlbeck. *Photog* Lars Björne. *Film Ed* Carl-Olov Skeppstedt. *Mus* Georg Riedel.

Cast: Gunnel Lindblom *(Anna Mansdotter)*, Gösta Ekman, Jr. *(Per Nilsson)*, Christina Schollin *(Hanna Johansdotter)*, Rune Lindström *(Wahlbom)*, Heinz Hopf *(Helmertz)*, Elsa Prawitz *(Hilda Persdotter)*, Isa Quensel *(Grave-Karna)*.

Historical drama. Source: Yngve Lyttkens, *Yngsjömordet* (Stockholm, 1951). In the late 19th century in the Kristianstad prison Anna Mansdotter recalls her recent past as she awaits execution for incest and murder. *At her trial Anna is accused of having had sexual relations with her son, Per, and having conspired with him to murder his wife, Hanna, whose body was found in the cellar of Per's farmhouse. The two defendants steadfastly protest their innocence, but Anna later admits to participating in the crime after Per has been tricked into making a false confession. As she waits for an appeals court to consider their case, Anna recalls that Per married Hanna only to curtail rumors about an incestuous relationship with his mother and to secure his wife's dowry. The two women disliked each other, and each paid visits to witch Grave-Karna, seeking advice to aid her desired domination of Per. Hanna eventually tired of her husband's inability to consummate their marriage and tried to force Per into sexual intercourse; instead, Per beat her into unconsciousness and Anna strangled her. Minutes later Anna is decapitated.* Mothers-in-law. Witches. *Murder. Incest. Confession (law). Marriage. Impotence. Dowries. Filial relations. Capital punishment. Decapitation. Prisons. Trials. Kristianstad. Anna Mansdotter.*

Note: Released in Sweden in Oct 1966 as *Yngsjömordet*; running time: 120 min.

WOMAN OF SIN (France) F6.5647

Films Marius Bouchet–Films Artistiques Français. *Dist* Ellis Films. 9 Aug **1961** [Chicago opening]. Sd; b&w. 35mm. 93 min. [Also reviewed at 97 min.]

Exec Prod Paul de Saint-André. *Dir* Guy Lefranc. *Scen & Adapt* Guy Lefranc, Jacques Séverac, Georges Tabet. *Dial* André Tabet. *Dir Photog* Maurice Barry. *Camera* Jean-Marie Maillols. *Asst Camera* Roland Paillas, Yvan Favreau. *Art Dir* Claude Bouxin. *Film Ed* Armand Psenny. *Asst Ed* Monique Pelletier. *Ch Sd* Séverin Frankiel. *Sd Rec* Michel Flour. *Boom* Lucien Moreau. *Asst Dir* Bernard Toublanc-Michel. *Prod Supv* Paul de Saint-André, Emile Buhot. *Prod Mgr* Georges Mahaut. *Location Mgr* Jean Nossereau. *Script Girl* Claude Levillain. *Prod Sec* Hélène de Gayffier. *Wardrobe Mistress* Lily Caudrelier. *Makeup & Hairstyles* Gisèle Jacquin. *Still Photog* Henri Carruel. *Prop* Marcel Landrain. *English Vers* Jon Wyner.

Cast: Dany Carrel (*Betty*), Pierre Vaneck (*Frédéric*), Yves Deniaud (*Parola*), Noël Roquevert (*lawyer*), André Weber (*Jeannot*), Albert Dinan (*Betty's father*), Serge Sauvion, Henri Crémieux, Paul Crauchet, Georges Chamarat, Yvonne Clech, Fernand Sardou, Paul Vandenberghe, Jean Morel.

Crime melodrama. Source: Christian Coffinet, *La fille de proie* (Paris, 1953). Betty, whose father is serving a prison term for theft, escapes from a reform school and rejoins her lover, Frédéric, a writer for a risqué magazine in Paris. In order to remain free, she becomes a police informer, meanwhile pursuing a life of luxury. The couple learn that Betty's father has hidden stolen diamonds worth a fortune, and with the help of Jeannot, they retrieve the jewels. When her father's friend Parola demands the diamonds, Betty has him arrested. The couple flees with the loot, pursued by Jeannot, who shoots Freédéric. The police arrive, and Betty is apprehended. *Prison escapees. Informers. Journalists. Police. Perfidy. Theft. Sexuality. Fatherhood. Diamonds. Reformatories. Paris.*

Note: Location scenes filmed in and around Paris. Paris opening: Aug 1958 as *La moucharde*; running time: 100 min.

WOMAN OF STRAW (Great Britain) F6.5648

Novus Films. *Dist* United Artists. 9 Sep **1964** [Chicago opening; c30 Apr 1964; LP29154]. Sd; col (Eastmancolor). 35mm. 120 min. [Also 117 min.]

A Michael Relph–Basil Dearden Production. *Prod* Michael Relph. *Dir* Basil Dearden. *Screenplay* Robert Muller, Stanley Mann, Michael Relph. *Dir Photog* Otto Heller. *Art Dir* Peter Murton. *Set Decor* Freda Pearson. *Prod Dsgn* Ken Adam. *Film Ed* John D. Guthridge. *Mus Arr & Cond* Muir Mathieson. *Titl Song* Norman Percival. *Mus From the Works of* Ludwig van Beethoven, Hector Berlioz, Wolfgang Amadeus Mozart, Nikolai Andreevich Rimski-Korsakov. *Sd Rec* C. C. Stevens. *Sd Ed* Roy Baker. *Asst Dir* Clive Reed. *Prod Mgr* Charles Orme. *Asst to the Prod* John L. Hargreaves. *Cost Dsgn* Beatrice Dawson. *Miss Lollobrigida's Clothes* Christian Dior. *Wardrobe Supv* Betty Adamson. *Makeup* Basil Newall, Paul Rabiger. *Hairstyles* Eileen Warwick.

Cast: Gina Lollobrigida (*Maria*), Sean Connery (*Anthony Richmond*), Ralph Richardson (*Charles Richmond*), Alexander Knox (*Lomer*), Johnny Sekka (*Thomas*), Laurence Hardy (*Baines*), Danny Daniels (*Fenton*), Peter Madden (*yacht captain*), Joseph Wise (*Peters*), Ronald Hatton (*mate of yacht*), Michael Goodliffe (*Penfield*), Douglas Wilmer (*Doctor Murray*), André Morell (*judge*), A. J. Brown (*3d executive*), George Zenios (*boy at island hotel*), Edward Underdown (*1st executive*), George Curzon (*2d executive*), Georgina Cookson (*1st guest at villa salon*), Gilda Dahlberg (*2d guest at villa salon*), Robert Bruce (*chauffeur*), Peggy Marshall (*wardress*), Michael Corcoran (*cook*).

Mystery drama. Source: Catherine Arley, *La femme de paille* (Paris, 1956). Maria, an Italian private nurse, is hired by Anthony Richmond to care for his uncle Charles, a ruthless and malicious crippled millionaire. Anthony is convinced that Charles drove his father to suicide, then married Anthony's mother, and, following her death, willed his riches to charity. Believing the money to be rightfully his, Anthony persuades Maria to become his accomplice in obtaining the inheritance by marrying Charles. After the wedding, however, she has a change of heart and tries to be fair with both men. She is therefore shocked when Charles suddenly dies on his yacht. Knowing that Charles had changed his will in Maria's favor, Anthony convinces the unsuspecting woman that Charles's premature death will invalidate the will and that they must take the dead man home. Maria believes the story and goes through with the plan only to be met by the police and arrested for murder. A Negro servant loyal to Maria produces a tape recording made by Charles on his death bed, however, and this evidence establishes Anthony's guilt and clears Maria. The maddened Anthony confronts the servant, but during the scuffle he falls to his death down a flight of stairs. *Nurses. Italians. Cripples. Uncles. Millionaires. Domestics. Revenge. Marriage. Murder. Frameup. Inheritance. Recorders. Yachts.*

Note: Location scenes filmed in England and Majorca. Opened in London in Apr 1964.

A WOMAN ON FIRE (Italy) F6.5649

Ferti Film. *Dist* Commonwealth United Entertainment, Inc., Ellman Enterprises. 27 May **1970** [Los Angeles opening]. Sd; col (Telecolor). 35mm. 93 min. *MPAA rating* R.

Pres by Expo '70 Films. *Prod* Tiziano Longo. *Dir* Fernando Di Leo. *Screenplay* Fernando Di Leo, Antonio Racioppi. *Photog* Franco Villa. *Art Dir* Pietro Liberati. *Film Ed* Mario Morra. *Mus* Gino Peguri. *Adtl Songs* Gino Peguri, Fernando Di Leo. *Sd* Roberto Alberghini. *Asst Dir* Franco Lo Cascio.

Cast: Françoise Prévost (*Clara*), Gianni Macchia (*Giancarlo*), Michel Bardinet (*Silvio*), Monica Strebel (*Marina*), Anna Pagano (*Monica*), Danika (*Aunt Bice*), Franca Sciutto, Miriam Alex, Maria Luisa Sala, Marco Veliante, Ettore Geri.

Drama. Silvio, a businessman, and his wife, Clara, go with their daughter and an aunt to an Italian seashore resort for a vacation. There they meet Giancarlo, a lecherous architecture student working as a beachguard for the summer. Giancarlo has sex with his young mistress, Marina, in front of Clara, and later he bursts into Clara's dressing room while she is naked. He seduces her, and they have sex a number of times—on a raft, on the beach, and in a boathouse. Clara experiences orgasm for the first time and realizes how unfulfilling her sexual relations with her husband have been. In hopes of improving their marriage, Clara tells Silvio of her experiences, but he becomes angry and threatens to leave her. By now, Giancarlo has returned to Marina, and Clara is extremely depressed. Her husband finds her in a coma from an overdose of barbiturates but allows her to die before calling a doctor. *Businessmen. Students. Lifeguards. Mistresses. Marriage. Infidelity. Seduction. Sexuality. Suicide. Vacations. Resorts.*

Note: Released in Italy in 1969 as *Brucia, ragazzo, brucia*; running time: 92 min.

WOMAN TIMES SEVEN (United States/France/Italy) F6.5650

Embassy Pictures–Twentieth Century-Fox Film Corp.–Société Nouvelle des Films Cormoran. *Dist* Embassy Pictures. 27 Jun **1967** [New York opening]. Sd; col (Pathé). 35mm. 99 min.

Pres by Joseph E. Levine. An Arthur Cohn Production. *Prod* Arthur Cohn. *Exec Prod* Joseph E. Levine. *Dir* Vittorio De Sica. *Pers Asst to Mr. De Sica* Peter Baldwin. *Screenplay* Cesare Zavattini. *Photog* Christian Matras. *Art Dir* Bernard Evein. *Set Decor* Georges Glon. *Titl* Jean Fouchet. *Film Ed* Teddy Darvas, Victoria Mercanton. *Mus Comp & Cond* Riz Ortolani. *Sd* Pierre Calvet. *Asst Dir* Marc Monnet. *Prod Mgr* Jacques Juranville. *Cost* Marcel Escoffier. *Makeup* Alberto De Rossi, Georges Bouban. *Hairstyles* Alex Archambault.

Cast—"Funeral Procession": Shirley MacLaine (*Paulette*), Peter Sellers (*Jean*), Elspeth March (*Annette*).

Cast—"Amateur Night": Shirley MacLaine (*Maria Teresc*), Rossano Brazzi (*Giorgio*), Catherine Samie (*Jeannine*), Judith Magre (*2d prostitute*).

Cast—"Two Against One": Shirley MacLaine (*Linda*), Vittorio Gassman (*Cenci*), Clinton Greyn (*MacCormick*).

Cast—"The Super-Simone": Shirley MacLaine (*Edith*), Lex Barker (*Rik*), Elsa Martinelli (*woman in market*), Robert Morley (*Dr. Xavier*).

Cast—"At the Opera": Shirley MacLaine (*Eve Minou*), Patrick Wymark (*Henri Minou*), Adrienne Corri (*Mademoiselle Lisiere*).

Cast—"The Suicides": Shirley MacLaine (*Marie*), Alan Arkin (*Fred*).

Cast—"Snow": Shirley MacLaine (*Jeanne*), Michael Caine (*handsome stranger*), Anita Ekberg (*Claudie*), Philippe Noiret (*Victor*).

Comedy-drama. FUNERAL PROCESSION: Leading the cortege behind her late husband's coffin, a young widow is consoled by family friend Jean; and as he confesses that he loves her, the widow's grief slowly disappears. So engrossed do they become in making plans for going away together that they miss a fork in the road and veer off to the left, while the shocked mourners continue to follow the hearse to the right. AMATEUR NIGHT: Discovering her husband in bed with another woman, an outraged wife storms out of the house vowing to sleep with the first man she meets. After joining a group of prostitutes and discovering that she is unable to carry out her threat, she accepts an accommodating procurer's offer to drive her home. When the hysterical husband greets them with insults, the procurer sends him sprawling with one punch. Seeing her husband lying in the street, the wife runs to comfort him. TWO AGAINST ONE: During an international cybernetics congress, a beautiful, bored interpreter explains to two amorous delegates, an Italian and a Scotsman, that her lover cares only for her mind and soul. To illustrate her point, she brings them to her flat and reads T. S. Eliot to them while in the nude. When one of them touches her, she furiously accuses them of reverting to the stone age. So repentant are they that they willingly accept cruel slaps from each other. Greatly impressed by the demonstration, the interpreter tosses her lover's picture out of the window and joins the delegates on a bed. THE SUPER-SIMONE: A plain housewife is married to a hack writer known for his fictional heroine Simone, a femme fatale who enslaves men by her wild and unpredictable nature.

In a pathetic attempt to emulate the Super-Simone, the wife behaves in such a bizarre fashion that her startled husband brings home a psychiatrist. When she realizes that they believe that she has lost her mind, the wife races out of their garret apartment onto the roof and wails, "I'm not crazy. I'm just in love." AT THE OPERA: When a wealthy Parisian socialite learns that a rival is wearing a copy of her new gown to the opening of the Opéra, she orders three of her husband's aides to bomb the rival's limousine. But a third woman, a plump and elderly matron, also appears in the same gown, and the humiliated socialite bolts out of the theater. As she does so, she spies her rival, blackened and disheveled from the bomb explosion, making a determined entrance. Anticipating her rival's reaction to the third woman, the socialite bursts into laughter. THE SUICIDES: Victims of a hopeless affair, a young wife and her married lover form a suicide pact. Dressed as a bride and groom, they plan to take their lives in a tacky hotel room. But they quarrel about the method they should use, and the woman goes into the bathroom. Once alone, the lover changes his mind and starts to sneak away. But as he opens the door he hears a window break in the bathroom. Peering out, he spots his beloved running down the fire escape to the street below. SNOW: While shopping with a friend, a faithful wife discovers that they are being eyed by a handsome stranger. And, when she leaves her friend, the wife is secretly thrilled to see that the man is following her. Arriving home, she greets her husband and then gazes out of the window at the stranger on the snowy street below. Overjoyed at the thought that men are still intrigued by her, the wife sighs with happiness. (Perhaps she will never know that the handsome stranger is a private detective hired by her suspicious husband.) *Widows. Prostitutes. Pimps. Interpreters. Scotch. Housewives. Authors. Psychiatrists. Socialites. Detectives. Infidelity. Cybernetics. Nudity. Suicide. Marriage. Funerals. Conventions. Bombs. Fashion. Paris. Thomas Stearns Eliot.*

Note: Filmed in Paris. National origin uncertain. The participation of the Société Nouvelle des Films Cormoran is unconfirmed. Paris opening: Oct 1967 as *Sept fois femme;* released in Italy in 1967 as *Sette volte donna.*

THE WOMAN WHO WOULDN'T DIE (United States/Great Britain) F6.5651

Parroch–McCallum Productions–Associated Producers, Inc. *Dist* Warner Bros. Pictures. 5 May **1965** [Denver, Colorado, opening; c15 May 1965; LP32354]. Sd; b&w. 35mm. 84 min.

Prod Neil McCallum, Jack Parsons. *Dir* Gordon Hessler. *Screenplay* Daniel Mainwaring. *Dir Photog* Arthur Lavis. *Art Dir* George Provis. *Film Ed* Robert Winter. *Mus* Carlo Martelli. *Mus Cond* Philip Martell. *Sd* George Stephenson. *Asst Dir* Frank Nesbitt. *Prod Mgr* Clifford Parkes. *Makeup* Wally Schneiderman.

Cast: Gary Merrill (*Raymond Garth*), Jane Merrow (*Alice Taylor*), Georgina Cookson (*Ellen Garth*), Neil McCallum (*Dick Corbett*), Rachel Thomas (*Christine*), Jack Train (*solicitor*), Frederick Piper (*police inspector*).

Mystery melodrama. Source: Jay Bennett, *Catacombs* (New York, 1959). Middle-aged Raymond Garth, an American, is married to possessive and domineering Ellen, the head of an English textile firm, who has been crippled in an automobile accident. She also intimidates her male secretary, Dick Corbett, and blackmails him because of his record of forging checks. Raymond becomes more dissatisfied with his wife when he takes an interest in Ellen's niece, Alice, an art student who has returned from Paris. Together, Dick and Raymond devise a plot to get rid of Ellen. Raymond murders Ellen by drowning her in a bathtub, and Dick hires an actress to impersonate Ellen during a trip to Italy. Ellen's housekeeper, Christine, who has always been antagonistic toward Raymond, is suspicious when she receives a postcard of the catacombs, for she knows that Ellen has claustrophobia and would be unlikely to go there. Raymond then receives a fake telegram announcing Ellen's death in an automobile accident. Christine remains suspicious when Alice and Raymond obtain control of the entire estate with the stipulation that Raymond live in Ellen's house for the rest of his life. One night, he hears what seems to be Ellen's footsteps, and he sees that her bed has been slept in. He runs for Dick, and together they search Ellen's gravesite and find it empty. Back in the house, Raymond enters the bedroom and sees Ellen's body on the bed. As she rises and moves toward him, he falls out of a window to his death. As Alice and Dick replace the body in the grave, the police, summoned by Christine, arrive to investigate. *Americans in foreign countries. Businesswomen. Cripples. Secretaries. Aunts. Students. Housekeepers. Actors. Marriage. Blackmail. Infidelity. Forgery. Murder. Impersonation. Claustrophobia. Inheritance. Disinterment. Italy.*

Note: Released in Great Britain in 1966 as *Catacombs;* running time: 90 min.

WOMAN WITHOUT A FACE see MISTER BUDDWING

A WOMAN'S LIFE (Japan) F6.5652

Toho Co. Jun **1964** [Los Angeles showing]. Sd; b&w. 35mm (Tohoscope). 120 min.

Dir Mikio Naruse. *Screenplay* Ryozo Kasahara. *Photog* Asaichi Nakai.

Cast: Hideko Takamine (*Nobuko*), Tatsuya Nakadai (*Akimoto*), Akira Takarada (*Koichi*), Yuriko Hoshi (*hostess*), Tsutomu Yamazaki.

Domestic melodrama. Nobuko, a gentle, delicate woman, marries a man who later proves unfaithful to her and is killed during the war. Left alone with her son, Nobuko manages to raise him only to have him killed in an automobile accident after he married a bar girl against his mother's wishes. Nobuko accepts her daughter-in-law, however, upon learning the younger woman is about to bear her a grandchild. *Widows. Bar girls. Mothers-in-law. Motherhood. Infidelity. Marriage. Filial relations. Automobile accidents.*

Note: Released in Japan in 1963 as *Onna no rekishi.*

A WOMAN'S URGE F6.5653

Artscope, Ltd. *Dist* Crest Film Distributors, Sam Lake Enterprises. 15 Oct **1965** [Fresno, California, showing]. Sd; b&w. 35mm. 83 min.

Prod Ed Hall, A. C. Qamar. *Dir* Ed Hall.

Cast: Maude Ferguson, Ed Hall, Lauree Ringham, Jack Cranston.

Melodrama. After an attempt at suicide, Laura Benton is placed under the care of Dr. Milton Goldstone, a psychiatrist. The events which have led to this desperate climax are unfolded. *Seduced in a hayloft, Laura abandons herself to a life of promiscuity. She is beaten by her drunken, incestuous stepfather and leaves home for New York City. There she becomes more and more compulsive in her search for the sexual satisfaction she can never find. Working as a nightclub waitress, she performs a torrid dance and wins a job as a featured dancer. She seduces the club manager, becomes a nude model, and seduces a photographer. She becomes his steady girl friend, vainly hoping to find satisfaction in a stable relationship. Her boyfriend returns home to find her in bed with the club manager, and she resumes her life of compulsive promiscuity. She spends a weekend making love with Bebe, a lesbian, but still remains unsatisfied. As her search grows more and more frantic, she becomes unbearably frustrated. After a wild orgy, she tries to kill herself.* The psychiatrist fears that Laura will continue on the path of unremitting promiscuity if his cure is not successful. *Stepfathers. Psychiatrists. Waitresses. Dancers. Models. Photographers. Nightclub managers. Suicide. Nymphomania. Seduction. Incest. Lesbianism. Nightclubs. Orgies. New York City.*

Note: Also known as *Nympho.*

THE WOMEN see THE VIXENS

WOMEN AND BLOODY TERROR see HIS WIFE'S HABIT

WOMEN AND WAR (France) F6.5654

Films A. de la Bourdonnaye–Compagnie Lyonnaise du Cinéma. *Dist* Parade Releasing Organization. 20 Oct **1965** [Chicago opening]. Sd; b&w. 35mm. 100 min.

Pres by Robert Patrick. *Prod-Dir* Georges Lautner. *Dial* Pierre Laroche. *Adapt* Pierre Laroche, Georges Lautner. *Photog* Maurice Fellous. *Art Dir* Louis Le Barbenchon. *Film Ed* Michèle David. *Mus* Georges Delerue. *Sd* René Bourdier. *Prod Mgr* Maurice Juven.

Cast: Bernard Blier (*Mayor Leproux*), Lucile Saint-Simon (*Catherine*), Lutz Gabor (*Major Frantz*), Anne Doat (*Dany*), Béatrice Bretty (*Germaine*), Daniel Sorano (*Toulousain*), Paulette Dubost (*widow*), Henri Virlojeux (*drummer*), Jacques Marin (*grocer*), Jacques Chabassol, Guy Dakar, Christian Melsen, Catherine Le Couey.

War drama. Source: Richard Prentout, *Le sentier* (Avignon, 1959). During the Nazi occupation of Calvados in 1944, Dr. Leproux, mayor and physician, assists a downed English aviator. Leproux is consequently arrested by the Germans, but his life is saved by humane Major Frantz, with whom the physician's daughter Catherine falls in love. Encouraged by the doctor, the lovers leave the village, Frantz in civilian dress. Because of his daughter's elopement, Leproux is sentenced to death by the French Resistance. He is also condemned by the Nazis and shot to death by their firing squad. The murder, however, coincides with the Allied invasion of Normandy, and aerial bombardment destroys the physician's executioners. *Mayors. Physicians. Nazis. British. Maquis. Air pilots. Military occupation. Military invasion. Village life. Capital punishment. Filial relations. Aerial bombardment. World War II. Normandy. Calvados. Great Britain—Royal Air Force.*

Note: Filmed on location in Normandy. Opened in Paris in Feb 1961 as *Arrêtez les tambours;* running time: 108 min. Also known as *Women in War.*

WOMEN ARE BAD see ALL WOMEN ARE BAD

WOMEN FOR ALL REASONS F6.5655

Fine-Flick-Film Productions. *Dist* Fine Products. 4 Sep **1969** [New York opening]. Sd; col. 35mm. 69 min.

Prod Jerry Jackson.

Cast: Karin Lox, Jack Strap.

Sex film. Two men are magically transported by a genie to ancient times. They find themselves on an island inhabited by many beautiful women. The women instruct the men in lovemaking and have lesbian relationships among themselves. *Genii. Time travel. Lesbianism. Sexual techniques. Bisexuality. Islands.*

Note: Also known as *A Woman for All Reasons.*

WOMEN IN LOVE (Great Britain)   F6.5656

Brandywine Productions. *Dist* United Artists. 25 Mar **1970** [New York opening; c13 Nov 1969; LF61]. Sd; col (De Luxe). 35mm. 130 min. *MPAA rating* R.

Pres by Larry Kramer, Martin Rosen. *Prod-Writ* Larry Kramer. *Co-prod* Martin Rosen. *Assoc Prod* Roy Baird. *Dir* Ken Russell. *Dir Photog* Billy Williams. *Camera Op* David Harcourt. *Asst Camera* Steve Claydon. *Art Dir* Ken Jones, art. *Set Dsgn* Luciana Arrighi. *Set Dresser* Harry Cordwell. *Film Ed* Michael Bradsell. *Mus Comp & Cond* Georges Delerue. *Mus Selections* Pëtr Ilich Tchaikovsky. *Choreog* Terry Gilbert. *Sd Rec* Brian Simmons. *Sd Ed* Terry Rawlings. *Sd Re-rec* Maurice Askew. *Asst Dir* Jonathan Benson. *Unit Mgr* Neville Thompson. *Cont* Angela Allen. *Location Mgr* Lee Bolon. *Asst to Prod* Tom Erhardt. *Cost Dsgn* Shirley Russell. *Wardrobe Supv* Shura Cohen. *Makeup* Charles Parker. *Hairstyles* A. G. Scott. *Constr Mgr* Jack Carter, constr. *Electrn Supv* George Cole, electrn. *Prop Master* George Ball.

Cast: Alan Bates *(Rupert Birkin)*, Oliver Reed *(Gerald Crich)*, Glenda Jackson *(Gudrun Brangwen)*, Jennie Linden *(Ursula Brangwen)*, Eleanor Bron *(Hermione Roddice)*, Alan Webb *(Thomas Crich)*, Vladek Sheybal *(Loerke)*, Catherine Willmer *(Mrs. Crich)*, Sarah Nicholls *(Winifred Crich)*, Sharon Gurney *(Laura Crich)*, Christopher Gable *(Tibby Lupton)*, Michael Gough *(Tom Brangwen)*, Norma Shebbeare *(Anna Brangwen)*, Nike Arrighi *(contessa)*, James Laurenson *(minister)*, Michael Graham Cox *(Palmer)*, Richard Heffer *(Leitner)*, Michael Garratt *(maestro)*, Leslie Anderson *(Barber)*, Charles Workman *(Gittens)*, Barrie Fletcher, Brian Osborne *(miners)*, Christopher Ferguson *(Basis Crich)*, Richard Fitzgerald *(Salsie)*.

Drama. Source: David Herbert Lawrence, *Women in Love* (New York, 1920). Gudrun Brangwen, an independent-minded sculptress, and her sister, Ursula, a schoolteacher, watch the wedding festivities of Laura Crich and Tibby Lupton in the British mining town of Beldover. At a luncheon given by the stiff and wealthy Hermione Roddice for the newlyweds, Gudrun meets Gerald Crich, a coal mine owner, and Ursula becomes preoccupied with Gerald's friend, school inspector Rupert Birkin. Breaking off his relationship with Hermione, Rupert finds tender and optimistic love with Ursula, but still he searches for a deeper and wider meaning of love. Gerald and Gudrun, however, pursue a stormy affair. The emotions of the four are heightened by the drowning of the newlyweds at a picnic given by the Crich family. Gerald and Rupert confront their fears and their need for friendship in a wrestling match; Rupert and Ursula marry; and all four go on a holiday to Switzerland. Growing impatient with Gerald, Gudrun becomes involved with Loerke, a bisexual German sculptor, and Ursula and Rupert seek the calmer atmosphere of warmer climes. Gerald, angry and tormented, attacks Loerke, makes a feeble attempt to strangle Gudrun, and wanders off into the snow until he collapses. Rupert grieves at the death of his friend and the inadequacy of love between man and woman. *Sculptors. Schoolteachers. School inspectors. Sisters. Newlyweds. Germans. Jealousy. Friendship. Bisexuality. Coal mining. Suicide. Weddings. Picnics. Switzerland.*

Note: Filmed on location in Nottinghamshire, Yorkshire, Derbyshire, Northumberland, County Durham, and London, England, and Zermatt, Switzerland. Opened in London in Nov 1969.

WOMEN IN THE NIGHT *see* **WHEN MEN ARE BEASTS**

WOMEN IN WAR *see* **WOMEN AND WAR**

WOMEN OF DESIRE   F6.5657

Boxoffice International Pictures. *Dist* Boxoffice International Film Distributors. 13 Mar **1968** [Champaign, Illinois, showing]. Sd; b&w. 35mm. 71 min.

Pres by Harry H. Novak. *Prod* Roger Scott. *Dir* Vincent L. Sinclair. *Screenplay* Carl Baker. *Dir Photog* Allan Jansen. *Op* Phil Frazier. *Sd Rec* David Kelly. *Wardrobe* Pat Hoffman.

Cast: Tiffany James, Harold Lasko, Bonny Allison, Nancy Brent, Jeanette Mason, Nick Sanicandro, Cindy Stewart, Angela Towers, Ronald Edwards.

Melodrama. Dan Davis is awakened at 6 a.m. by the police, who tell him that his wife, Pat, has been struck and killed by a truck. As his mind wanders back over the past, he begins to realize that his wife was not on her job as a nurse, but was actually working at a motel as a prostitute: Pat is approached by Tony at a bar where she has been drinking to forget her losses at the racetrack. He tells her that easy money is to be made at his motel just outside of town. She meets other women at work, witnesses several intimate affairs, and at last submits to Tony's advances to begin a new career. A month later she meets a neighbor on the job, who confesses their association to his wife. Realizing that she will soon be exposed, Pat tells Tony that she is quitting. They

struggle, and Pat breaks away, dashing out the door into the path of an oncoming truck. *Neighbors. Nurses. Pimps. Infidelity. Prostitution. Gambling. Motels.*

WOMEN OF NAZI GERMANY *see* **HITLER**

WOMEN OF THE PREHISTORIC PLANET   F6.5658

Standard Club of California Productions. *Dist* Realart Pictures, Standard Club of California Productions. Nov **1966** [Los Angeles showing; c15 Apr 1966; LP32415]. Sd; col (De Luxe). 35mm. 87 min. [Also reviewed at 90 min.]

A Jack Broder–Madelyn Broder Production. *Prod* George Edwards. *Dir-Writ* Arthur C. Pierce. *Photog* Arch R. Dalzell. *Art Dir* Paul Sylos. *Sets* Harry Reif. *Film Ed* George White. *Asst Dir* Jack Voglin, Dick Dixon. *Prod Mgr* Jack Voglin. *Sp Eff* Howard A. Anderson.

Cast: Wendell Corey *(Admiral King)*, Keith Larsen *(Commander Scott)*, John Agar *(Dr. Farrell)*, Irene Tsu *(Linda)*, Paul Gilbert *(Bradley)*, Merry Anders *(communications officer)*, Stuart Lasswell *(Charles)*, Bob Ito *(Tang)*, Adam Roarke, Suzie Kaye, Stuart Margolin.

Science fiction melodrama. After taking captives from a planet in the Centaurus star system, three spaceships set out for their home planet. En route, the captives on one of the ships revolt [apparently as a result of the racial prejudices of certain crew members], and the craft is forced to crash-land on an unexplored young planet. Three months later, the expedition's flagship, under the command of Admiral King, returns to the young planet to search for survivors. Owing to a time warp, 18 years have passed on the planet, which is inhabited by wild, prehistoric people and menacing creatures, including giant lizards and spiders; and a search party led by Commander Scott and Dr. Farrell finds the spaceship abandoned. The sole survivor of the crash, a Centaurian child, Tang, has grown into manhood, and when he encounters Linda, a Centaurian girl from the rescue ship, he takes her as his prisoner. Although she persuades him to return to the rescue ship, they are attacked by a group of wild inhabitants, and Tang is shot and wounded by mistake as Commander Scott comes to Linda's rescue. A threatening volcano forces the rescue ship to leave the planet, but Linda escapes to rejoin Tang. As Admiral King leaves the two young people to begin a new world, he gives the unknown planet a name—Earth. *Physicians. Space travel. Space exploration. Racism. Spaceships. Imaginary planets. Monsters. Volcanoes. Prehistory. Adam and Eve. Lizards. Spiders.*

Note: Working title: *Prehistoric Planet Women.*

WOMEN OF THE WORLD (Italy)   F6.5659

Cineriz. *Dist* Embassy Pictures. 2 Jul **1963** [New York opening]. Sd; col (Technicolor). 35mm. 107 min.

Pres by Joseph E. Levine. *Dir* Gualtiero Jacopetti. *Assoc Dir* Paolo Cavara, Franco Prosperi. *Writ* Gualtiero Jacopetti, Paolo Cavara, Franco Prosperi. *Photog* Antonio Climati, Benito Frattari. *Ed* Gualtiero Jacopetti. *Mus* Nino Oliviero, Riz Ortolani. *Mus Dir* Riz Ortolani. *Organizer of Foreign Prod* Stanis Nievo.

Cast: Peter Ustinov *(Narrator)*.

Documentary. A study of women around the world: During a military parade the attractive spectators capture the attention of the parading soldiers; Israeli women train for combat and relax by bathing nude; a harem of 84 women attend a retired Scottish colonel living on the island of Iwa; on a womanless island off the Australian coast, men enact the ritual of the siren; half-woman and half-fish; Parisians celebrate Bastille Day by kissing everyone they meet; in Ravenna, women wait in line to kiss the statue of the hero Guidarello Guidarelli; unique among women, a Swedish clergywoman celebrates mass; Parisian nightclubs cater to the lesbian and male homosexual populations; the women of a native Papuan tribe work while the men make themselves attractive; nudism is practiced universally on the Isle of Levant, while Chinese women bathe fully clad in sheer dresses to avoid sunburn; women in New Guinea take special mud baths to lighten their skins; in Sardinia, women are hired as professional mourners, while the people of Tahiti celebrate life by dancing; publicity-conscious young actresses attend the Cannes Film Festival clad in brief bikinis, while aspiring actresses in Los Angeles work as elevator operators and gas station attendants between jobs; an artist photographs hundreds of female subjects to create an ideal composite; in Tokyo, women undergo an operation to "westernize" their eyes and take paraffin injections to enlarge their breasts; the American "falsie" industry consumes enormous quantities of rubber; men in a Malayan village assume the maternal role, experiencing labor pains as their wives give birth; prostitutes in Hamburg beckon from apartment windows; promiscuity reigns in a Stockholm school dormitory, and young women take up hitchhiking; newlyweds in southern Italy consummate their marriage on the spot, and the graves of dishonored women remain unmarked; the Sporting Widows Association in Sydney uses the cemetery lawn for a game of bowls; young Americans use the automobile for sexual exploration; honeymooners in Honolulu spend their wedding night in a tree house; cowboys entertain recently divorced women at Las Vegas dude ranches; women in Japan dive for pearls and seaweed; United States Treasurer Elizabeth Rudel Smith makes daily inspections at the Bureau of Engraving; a woman bank president in New York conducts a directors' meeting; in Singapore, the "Sisterhood of the Night Butterflies" celebrates a prosperous business year, while in Hong Kong, policewomen attempt to eradicate prostitution; two missionary nuns in Kenya travel hundreds of miles to baptize members of the Masai tribe; native women attend an exhibit of European fashions; women in Borneo have themselves tattooed while European women undergo plastic surgery; Bedouin women obtain a skin cream from the camel; in New Zealand, Maori men risk their lives as their wives undergo labor pains, while painless childbirth is taught in a Swiss clinic; African women gather shrapnel from a military practice zone; the drug Thalidomide creates a worldwide tragedy; and mothers make a pilgrimage to Lourdes to pray for miraculous help in curing their afflicted children. *Soldiers. Scotch. Priests. Actors. Photographers. Students. Widows. Policewomen. Nuns. Missionaries. United States—Treasury Department. Bankers. Hitchhikers. Bedouins. Maori. Masai. Rites and ceremonies. Employment—Women. Women in public office. Nudity. Lesbianism. Male homosexuality. Nudism. Religion. Ambition. Vanity. Prostitution. Promiscuity. Virginity. Weddings. Divorce. Pearl diving. Plastic surgery. Childbirth. Motherhood. Birth defects. Surgery. Tattoos. Fashion shows. Harems. Nightclubs. Cosmetics. Cemeteries. Honeymoons. Dude ranches. Cannes Film Festival. Bastille Day. Rome. Israel. Iwa Island. Paris. Stockholm. Papua. Île du Levant. Sardinia. Tahiti. Los Angeles. Malaya. Hamburg. Italy. Sydney (Australia). Honolulu. Washington (District of Columbia). Singapore. Hong Kong. Kenya. New Zealand. New Guinea. Lourdes. Borneo. Las Vegas. Ravenna (Italy). New York City. China. Tokyo. Africa. Elizabeth (Rudel) Smith. Guidarello Guidarelli. Italy—Army. Israel—Army. Sporting Widows' Association. Sisterhood of the Night Butterflies. Mythological characters. Camels.*

Note: Opened in Rome in Feb 1963 as *La donna nel mondo.* Alternative Italian title: *Eva sconosciuta.*

WOMEN ... OH, WOMEN! (Japan)   F6.5660
Sano Art Productions. *Dist* Shochiku Co. 18 Sep **1964** [Los Angeles showing]. Sd; col (Eastmancolor). 35mm (Shochiku GrandScope). 80 min.
Dir Tetsuji Takechi. *Screenplay* Tatsuji Tsuta. *Photog* Kazutoshi Akutagawa.
Documentary. Included in this examination of Japanese night life (with a special emphasis on women) are scenes of nude performances of *Noh* plays; women wrestlers, divers, and other sportswomen; nuns; striptease dancers; fashion models; lesbians; transvestites; drug addicts; and the "Geisha of Gion." *Women athletes. Nuns. Stripteasers. Models. Geishas. Drug addicts. Transvestism. Nudity. Lesbianism. Theater.*
Note: Released in Japan in 1963 as *Onna onna onna monogatari.*

WOMEN WOMEN WOMEN MOIRA   F6.5661
Gladjac Films. *Dist* Preferred Enterprises, Cinex International Film Distributors, Clamil Productions. Nov **1970** [periodical notice]. Sd; col. 35mm. 72 min.
Prod Alan P. Mautz. *Dir-Writ* Morton Lewis. *Cinematog* Ralph Laube. *Mus* Dan Fox.
Cast: Eti Bitman *(Moira)*, William Grannell *(George)*, Francis O'Flyn, Artie Giannini, Frank Durk, Moreen Colbert, Cimone Clans, Richard Ju, Alice Emerson.
Drama. Middle-aged businessman George Banner relieves the boredom of his mundane existence by indulging in a vivid fantasy life. Moira, the woman of his dreams, assumes increasing control of his mind until he is driven nearly mad. He quits his job and his marriage to confront his vision in a passionate sexual encounter and departs, a free man, to find himself. [Includes scenes of sexual encounters between George and two women he picks up, and between George's wife and another couple.] *Businessmen. Middle age. Marriage. Troilism. Infidelity. Fantasy.*
Note: May also be known as *Moira.*

THE WONDERFUL LAND OF OZ   F6.5662
Cinetron Corp. *Dist* Childhood Productions. Oct **1969.** Sd; col (print by Movielab). 35mm. 72 min.
Prod-Dir-Writ Barry Mahon. *Songs (see note)* George Linsenmann, Ralph Falco. *Songs: "Did You Come To See the Wizard?" "How Do I Brew This Stew?" "I Lost My Heart," "The Wonderful Land of Oz," "Open Your Eyes"* Loonis McGlohon, Alec Wilder. *Songs: "I Would Like To Have a Brain," "I'm a Scaredy Cat," "Wail of the Witch"* Loonis McGlohon.
Cast: Joy Webb, Channy Mahon.
Fantasy. Source: Lyman Frank Baum, *The Marvelous Land of Oz* (Chicago, 1904). Dorothy continues her adventures in the land of Oz with her companions, the Pumpkin Man, the Purple Cow, the Tin Woodsman, the Scarecrow, Mombi the witch, and Glinda the good fairy. Dorothy also meets Ozma, the Queen of Emerald City; Jack Pumpkinhead; Tip, a little boy; General Jinjur, the girl chief of the army of Oz; a talking sawhorse; the scholarly Wogglebug; and the Gump, a huge bird made of sofas. *Witches. Royalty. Fairies. Children. Friendship. Imaginary creatures. Scarecrows. Imaginary kingdoms.*

Note: Mid-production press notice credits George Linsenmann and Ralph Falco with songs, while the music copyright source lists songs by Loonis McGlohon and Alec Wilder. Working title: *The Land of Oz.*

WONDERFUL LIFE *see* SWINGERS' PARADISE

WONDERFUL TO BE YOUNG! (Great Britain)   F6.5663
Associated British Picture Corp. *For* Elstree Distributors. *Dist* Paramount Pictures. 1 Nov **1962** [New Orleans opening]. Sd; col (Technicolor). 35mm (CinemaScope). 92 min. [Also 89 min.]
Prod Kenneth Harper. *Assoc Prod* Andrew Mitchell. *Dir* Sidney J. Furie. *Orig Story & Screenplay* Ronald Cass, Peter Myers. *Photog* Douglas Slocombe. *Camera Op* Chic Waterson. *Focus* Robin Vidgeon, Peter Hurst. *Camera Grip* W. Evans. *Art Dir* John Howell. *Asst Art Dir* Kenneth McCallum Tait. *Ch Draughtsman* Bill Alexander. *Film Ed* Jack Slade. *Mus Supv & Background Score* Stanley Black. *Titl Song* Burt Bacharach, Hal David. *Songs: "All for One," "Nothing's Impossible," "What D'You Know We've Got a Show"* Ronald Cass, Peter Myers. *Songs: "When the Boy in Your Arms Is the Boy in Your Heart," "When the Girl in Your Arms Is the Girl in Your Heart"* Sid Tepper, Roy C. Bennett. *Songs: "Peace Pipe," "The Savage"* Norrie Paramor. *Song: "Got a Funny Feeling"* Bruce Welch, Hank B. Marvin. *Song: "We Say Yeah"* Peter Gormley, Bruce Welch, Hank B. Marvin. *Song: "Lessons in Love"* Sy Soloway, Shirley Wolfe. *Choreog* Herbert Ross. *Sd* A. W. Lumkin. *Sd Mix* Claude Hitchcock. *Sd Camera Op* E. Haben. *Boom Op* David Jones. *1st, 2d & 3d Asst Dir* Fred Slark, William P. Cartlidge, Michael Gowans. *Prod Mgr* John D. Wilcox. *Prod Sec* Jean Clarkson. *Cont* Helen Whitson. *Cost Dsgn* Alan Sievewright. *Wardrobe Mistress* Jackie Breed. *Makeup* Stuart Freeborn. *Hairdresser* Ivy Emmerton. *Still Photog* Laurie Turner. *Prop Buyer* Jim Foster. *Casting Dir* Robert Lennard.
Cast: Cliff Richard *(Nicky Black)*, Robert Morley *(Hamilton Black)*, Carole Gray *(Toni)*, Richard O'Sullivan *(Ernest)*, Melvyn Hayes *(Jimmy)*, Teddy Green *(Chris)*, Annette Robertson *(Barbara)*, Sonya Cordeau *(Dorinda)*, Sean Sullivan *(Eddie)*, Harold Scott *(Dench)*, Gerald Harper *(Watts)*, Rita Webb *(woman in market)*, Robertson Hare *(chauffeur)*, The Shadows *(themselves)*.
Comedy-drama with music. Nicky Black, a talented pop singer, is the leader of a youth club in the slum section of London. Unknown to the other members of the club is the fact that Nicky is the son of a millionaire real estate tycoon who plans to buy up the slum area and erect a huge office building there. Nicky learns of this plan and encourages his friends to raise funds for purchasing the property by putting on a teenager musical in a dilapidated theater. Nicky's unscrupulous father, however, outwits them by buying the theater. Undaunted, the youngsters find another theater and start promoting their show by broadcasting samples of Nicky's singing over a pirate television channel. Mr. Black again tries to interfere. A tough member of the youth club attempts to abduct him, but Nicky rescues his father and reaches the theater in time to make the matinee a success. Now proud of his son, Mr. Black promises to finance for Nicky and his friends a new and better youth club. *Singers. Millionaires. Rock and roll. Adolescence. Filial relations. Abduction. Real estate. Finance—Personal. Slums. Clubs. Musical revues. Television. Publicity. London.*
Note: Opened in London in Dec 1961 as *The Young Ones;* running time: 108 min.

THE WONDERFUL WORLD OF GIRLS   F6.5664
G & S Productions. *Dist* G & S Productions, Boxoffice International Film Distributors, Rossmore Film Distributors. 10 Sep **1965** [Fresno, California, showing]. Sd; col (DeLuxe). 35mm. 67 min.
Pres by Harry H. Novak. *Dir* Arthur Stootsberry.
Comedy. Although Sammy, a maintenance man, is faithful to his suspicious wife, Fanny, he continually finds himself in compromising situations with nude women. As Sammy and Fanny watch a movie, an attractive exhibitionist sitting next to Sammy disrobes, placing her clothes on his lap. Jumping to conclusions, Fanny beats her husband. At work the next day, Sammy daydreams of beautiful girls who disrobe as he plays music on the mop, broom, and duster. Diving toward a waiting beauty, he collides with his wife, who has been napping as she keeps track of him. She again beats him. Sammy and Fanny then go to visit a doctor, but they stumble into a Nudist Colony Club office instead. A group of pretty applicants disrobe and attempt to initiate Sammy into the club. Sammy receives another beating from his wife. He finally takes a job as a salesman and visits a house inhabited by four scantily-dressed girls. As they try to lead him to the bedroom, the police burst in and drag all of them before a judge, who

places all the blame on Sammy. *Shrews. Janitors. Salesmen. Nudism. Judges. Marriage. Striptease. Seduction. Fantasy.*

THE WONDERFUL WORLD OF THE BROTHERS GRIMM F6.5665

Metro-Goldwyn-Mayer, Inc.–Cinerama, Inc. *Dist* Metro-Goldwyn-Mayer, Inc. 7 Aug 1962 [New York opening; c31 Dec 1962; LP26214]. Sd (Westrex); col (Metrocolor, print by Technicolor). 3X35mm (Cinerama). 129 min.

A George Pal Production. *Prod* George Pal. *Dir* Henry Levin. *Dir Fairy Tales Seq* George Pal. *Screenplay* David P. Harmon, Charles Beaumont, William Roberts. *Screen Story* David P. Harmon. *Dir Photog* Paul C. Vogel. *Col Cons* Charles K. Hagedon. *Art Dir* George W. Davis, Edward Carfagno. *Set Decor* Henry Grace, Dick Pefferle. *Film Ed* Walter Thompson. *Mus Score* Leigh Harline. *Songs & Themes:* "The Princess' Waltz," "Ah-Oom," "Christmas Land," "Dee-Are-A-Gee-O-En," "Gypsy Rhapsody," "Above the Stars," "Theme From the Wonderful World of the Brothers Grimm" Bob Merrill. *Song:* "Singing Bone" Bob Merrill, Charles Beaumont. *Choreog* Alex Romero. *Rec Supv* Franklin Milton. *Asst Dir* Al Jennings. *Prod Supv for Cinerama* Thomas Conroy. *Asst to the Prod* Gae Griffith. *European Prod Coörd* Robert Snody. *Cost* Mary Wills. *Makeup Created by* William Tuttle. *Hairstyles* Sydney Guilaroff. *Sp Vis Eff* Gene Warren, Wah Chang, Tim Barr, Robert R. Hoag.

Cast—The Book: Laurence Harvey (*Wilhelm Grimm*), Karl Boehm (*Jacob Grimm*), Claire Bloom (*Dorothea Grimm*), Walter Slezak (*Stossel*), Barbara Eden (*Greta Heinrich*), Oscar Homolka (*The Duke*), Arnold Stang (*Rumpelstiltskin*), Martita Hunt (*story teller*), Betty Garde (*Miss Bettenhausen*), Bryan Russell (*Friedrich Grimm*), Ian Wolfe (*Gruber*), Tammy Marihugh (*Pauline Grimm*), Cheerio Meredith (*Mrs. von Dittersdorf*), Walter Rilla (*priest*), Regensburg Domspatzen Choir.

Cast—"The Dancing Princess": Yvette Mimieux (*The Princess*), Russ Tamblyn (*The Woodsman*), Jim Backus (*The King*), Beulah Bondi (*The Gypsy*), Clinton Sundberg (*The Prime Minister*).

Cast—"The Cobbler and the Elves": Laurence Harvey (*The Cobbler*), Walter Brooke (*The Mayor*), Sandra Gale Bettin (*The Ballerina*), Robert Foulk (*The Hunter*), The Puppetoons.

Cast—"The Singing Bone": Terry-Thomas (*Ludwig*), Buddy Hackett (*Hans*), Otto Kruger (*The King*), Robert Crawford, Jr. (*The Shepherd*), Sydney Smith (*The Spokesman*).

Biographical drama. Source: Hermann Gerstner, *Die Brüder Grimm* (Munich, 1952). In Bavaria in the early 19th century, brothers Wilhelm and Jacob Grimm are commissioned to write a history of the local duke's family. Wilhelm finds it difficult to concentrate on the task, however, and irritates his wife Dorothea and his brother by devoting his time to collecting and writing fairy tales. One evening he tells to his children the story of "The Dancing Princess." *A king offers his daughter in marriage to any man who can discover why each night she wears out a pair of slippers. A young woodsman dons a cloak that renders him invisible, follows the princess into the woods, and watches as she joins a band of gypsies in their dancing. He also joins in, and the two fall in love. The woodsman later reveals her secret to the king, and the king commands that they marry, much to the princess' delight.* Wilhelm unsuccessfully tries to convince his bookseller friend Stossel of the value of his book of fairy tales by telling the tale of "The Cobbler and the Elves" to a group of small children. *An old shoemaker spends Christmas Eve carving toy elves for orphans and neglects to repair his customers' shoes. The elves come to life while he is sleeping and complete the unfinished work.* A short time later, the duke sends Wilhelm to another town to research a branch of his family. Wilhelm meets Anna Richter, an old woman who lives in the forest. Though many of the townspeople regard her as a witch, children flock to her cottage to hear her stories, one of which is "The Singing Bone." *A servant slays a ferocious dragon and is himself slain by his cowardly master, who takes credit for killing the beast. One of the murdered man's bones appears in the form of a musical instrument that sings of the treachery. The master confesses to his crime; the servant is magically restored to life; and the king commands the master to become his servant's servant.* Wilhelm, inspired by many more of Anna's tales, leaves the forest but loses the duke's manuscript along the way. The duke dismisses him, and Jacob decides to marry his fiancée, Greta, and work independently. Wilhelm becomes gravely ill and is near death when his fairy tale characters appear and plead for his life so that he may tell their stories. Wilhelm's miraculous recovery prompts Jacob to postpone his wedding and to support his brother's family. The two brothers' work eventually wins them recognition from the Berlin Royal Academy. Wilhelm is disappointed when the Academy cites only Jacob's scholarly work and ignores his own fairy tales, which have received wide popular acclaim. His despondency is short-lived, however; they arrive in Berlin and are greeted not only by Academy officials, but by hundreds of appreciative children anxious to hear a story. *Brothers. Historians. Nobility. Storytellers. Children. Woodsmen. Royalty. Gypsies. Cobblers. Orphans. Elves. Invisibility. Forests. Dragons. Toys. Christmas.*

Bavaria. *Wilhelm Grimm. Jakob Grimm. Akademie der Wissenschaften (Berlin).*

Note: Location scenes filmed in West Germany. Included in the cast of the book section are townspeople of Rothenburg and Dinkelsbühl and residents of the Rhine River Valley. Copyright claimant: Gallen Films.

THE WONDERS OF ALADDIN (France/Italy) F6.5666

Lux Film–C. C. F. Lux. *Dist* Metro-Goldwyn-Mayer, Inc. 13 Dec 1961 [Los Angeles opening; c31 Dec 1961; LP21325]. Sd; col (Technicolor). 35mm (CinemaScope). 93 min.

Pres by Joseph E. Levine. *Dir* Henry Levin. *2d Unit Dir* Mario Bava. *Screenplay* Luther Davis. *Adapt* Silvano Reina, Franco Prosperi, Pierre Very, Marco Vicario. *Story* Stefano Strucchi, Duccio Tessari. *Dir Photog* Tonino Delli Colli. *Art Dir* Flavio Mogherini. *Film Ed* Gene Ruggiero. *Mus* Angelo Francesco Lavagnino. *Played by* Orchestra Cinefonica Italiana. *Cond* Mario Ammonini. *Choreog* Secondino Cavallo. *Sd Rec* Fonolux-Rome. *Asst Dir* Alberto Cardone, Franco Prosperi. *Prod Mgr* Massimo Patrizi. *Cost* Giorgio Desideri. *Cost Dsgn* Rosine Delamare. *Wigs* Mike Maggi. *Weapons* Ditta Rancati.

Cast: Donald O'Connor (*Aladdin*), Noëlle Adam (*Djalma*), Vittorio De Sica (*genie*), Aldo Fabrizi (*sultan*), Michèle Mercier (*Princess Zaina*), Milton Reid (*Omar*), Mario Girotti (*Prince Moluk*), Fausto Tozzi (*grand vizier*), Marco Tulli (*fakir*), Raymond Bussières (*magician*), Alberto Farnese (*bandit chieftain*), Franco Ressel (*vizier's lieutenant*), Vittorio Bonos (*lamp merchant*), Adriana Facchetti (*Aladdin's mother*), Giovanna Galletti (*midwife*), Luigi Tosi.

Fantasy. In ancient Bagdad, Aladdin daydreams of great wealth and royal processions. One day his mother buys him a little lamp, and the lad accidentally discovers that it contains a genie who can grant him three wishes. Aladdin uses his first wish to escape from some merchants he has robbed and then sets out by caravan to attend the wedding of Princess Zaina and Prince Moluk. Accompanying him is Djalma, whose love for Aladdin is unrequited, and his loyal bodyguard, Omar. When Aladdin and Omar are captured by man-killing Amazon huntresses, the genie is once more summoned, and he transports the pair to an Arab camp near the royal city of Basora. Meanwhile, the wicked grand vizier has taken Prince Moluk prisoner and is planning to marry the princess himself; but Aladdin and his friends sneak into the palace and expose the grand vizier's scheme. He retreats with his guards and promises to return to destroy all those who oppose him, but Aladdin uses his last wish to rout the enemy and save the city. The prince and princess are wed, and Aladdin is lavishly rewarded by the sultan and reunited with Djalma. *Royalty. Bodyguards. Viziers. Traitors. Arabs. Genii. Magic. Robbery. Wish fulfillment. Bagdad. Aladdin. Amazons.*

Note: Filmed on location in Rome and Tunisia. Opened in Paris as *Les mille et une nuits* in Feb 1962; running time: 100 min; in Rome as *Le meraviglie di Aladino* in Jul 1962; running time: 100 min.

THE WONDROUS STORY OF BIRTH see BIRTH OF TRIPLETS

WOODSTOCK F6.5667

Wadleigh–Maurice Ltd. *Dist* Warner Bros. Pictures. 26 Mar 1970 [New York opening]. Sd; col (Technicolor). 35mm. 184 min. MPAA rating R.

Prod Bob Maurice. *Dir* Michael Wadleigh. *Photog* Michael Wadleigh, David Meyers, Richard Pearce, Don Lenzer, Al Wertheimer. *Adtl Photog* Michael Margetts, Ed Lynch, Richard Cheu, Charles Levy, Ted Churchill, Fred Underhill, Robert Dannemann, Stan Warnow. *Supv Film Ed* Michael Wadleigh, Thelma Schoonmaker, Martin Scorsese. *Film Ed* Robert Alvarez, Yeu-Bun Yee, B. K. Hirsh, Jere Huggins, Muffie Meyer, Stan Warnow. *Song:* "Long Time Gone" David Crosby. *Song:* "Wooden Ships" David Crosby, Stephen Stills. *Song:* "Suite: Judy Blue Eyes" Stephen Stills. *Songs Sung by* Crosby, Stills, Nash & Young. *Song:* "Going Up the Country" Alan Wilson. *Sung by* Canned Heat. *Song:* "Handsome Johnny" Richie Havens, Louis Goussett. *Sung by* Richie Havens. *Song:* "Freedom," adapt from "Sometimes I Feel Like a Motherless Child" sung by Richie Havens. *Song:* "Joe Hill" Earl Robinson, Alfred Hayes. *Sung by* Joan Baez. *Song:* "Swing Low, Sweet Chariot" sung by Joan Baez. *Song:* "We're Not Gonna Take It" Peter Townshend. *Song:* "Summertime Blues" Jerry Capehart, Eddie Cochran. *Songs Sung by* The Who. *Song:* "At the Hop" A. Siger, J. Medora, P. White. *Sung by* Sha-Na-Na. *Song:* "Rock & Soul Music" Joe McDonald, Barry Melton, Chicken Hirsch, Bruce Barthol, David Cohen. *Sung by* Country Joe & the Fish. *Songs:* "The 'Fish' Cheer," "I-Feel-Like-I'm-Fixin'-To-Die Rag" Joe McDonald. *Sung by* Country Joe & the Fish. *Song:* "With a Little Help From My Friends" John Lennon, Paul McCartney. *Sung by* Joe Cocker. *Song:* "Coming Into Los Angeles" writ & sung by Arlo Guthrie. *Song:* "I'm Goin' Home" Alvin Lee. *Sung by* Ten Years After. *Song:* "Younger Generation" writ & sung by John Sebastian. *Song:* "Soul Sacrifice" Carlos Santana, Gregg Rolie, José Areas, Mike Carabello, David Brown, Michael Schrieve. *Perf by* Santana. *Songs:* "Dance to the Music," "Music Lover," "I Want To Take You Higher" Sylvester Stewart. *Sung by* Sly and the Family Stone. *Songs:* "Star-Spangled

Banner," "Purple Haze" perf by Jimi Hendrix. Titl Song Joni Mitchell. Sung by Crosby, Stills, Nash & Young. Perf Sd Coörd Eric Blackstead. Perf Sd Rec Ed Kramer. Sd & Mus Ed Larry Johnson. Sd Charles Groesbeek, Malcolm Hart, Joe Low, Bruce Perlman, Charles Pitts. Asst Dir Martin Scorsese, Thelma Schoonmaker. Prod Supv Dale Bell. Prod Mgr Sonya Polonsky. Documentary Unit Coörd John Bindor. Asst to the Dir Larry Johnson.

Documentary. The film records the events of the Woodstock Music and Art Fair, held for 3 days near Bethel, New York, in August 1969. It features the participating performers and the reactions of residents of the community and of the 400,000 young people who attended. Crosby, Stills, Nash & Young's recordings of "Long Time Gone" and "Wooden Ships" are heard as stagehands construct the platform on which the musicians will perform; meanwhile, the audience is seen arriving by the thousands. Festival promoter Mike Lang is interviewed, and rock promoter Bill Graham is seen giving advice on how to control the crowds. The performers appear in the following order: Richie Havens, Joan Baez, The Who, Sha-Na-Na, Joe Cocker, Country Joe & The Fish, Arlo Guthrie, Crosby, Stills, Nash & Young, Ten Years After, John Sebastian, Santana, Sly and the Family Stone, and Jimi Hendrix. Interspersed are interviews with members of the counterculture as well as nearby farmers, merchants, policemen, and other local people, some of whom do not appreciate the permission their neighbor Max Yasgur has given to have the concert on his farm. Other scenes include: a storm that drenches the audience, turning the field into mud; mud-sliding contests after the rain; the smoking of marijuana and use of strong drugs; the expression of anti-Vietnam War sentiment; brief shots of Janis Joplin and Jerry Garcia; medical aid and food being supplied by the Army; and the appearance before the audience of farmer Yasgur. The film concludes with a helicopter view of the festival crowd. *Musicians. Singers. Hippies. Farmers. Merchants. Police. Rock and roll. Marijuana. Drugs. Woodstock Music and Art Fair (1969). Bethel (New York). Mike Lang. Bill Graham. United States Army.*

Note: Filmed in 16mm. Split-screen technique is used in many sequences.

WORK IS A FOUR LETTER WORD (Great Britain)   **F6.5668**
Cavalcade Films–Universal Pictures, Ltd. *Dist* Universal Pictures. 25 Sep **1968** [Los Angeles opening]. Sd; col (Technicolor). 35mm. 93 min.

Prod Thomas Clyde. *Assoc Prod* Harold Haysom. *Dir* Peter Hall. *Screenplay* Jeremy Brooks. *Photog* Gilbert Taylor. *Art Dir* Philip Harrison. *Dsgn Cons* Joe Tilton. *Film Ed* Keith Green, ed. *Mus* Guy Woolfenden. *Titl Song* Don Black. *Sung by* Cilla Black. *Sd Rec* Robert MacPhee, Gordon K. McCallum. *Asst Dir* Claude Watson. *Unit Prod Mgr* Donald Toms. *Sp Eff* Michael Stainer-Hutchins.

Cast: David Warner (*Val Brose*), Cilla Black (*Betty Dorrick*), Elizabeth Spriggs (*Mrs. Murray*), Zia Mohyeddin (*Dr. Narayana*), Joe Gladwin (*Pa Brose*), Julie May (*Mrs. Dorrick*), Alan Howard (*The Reverend Mort*), Jan Holden (*Mrs. Price*), John Steiner (*Anthony*), Roger Booth (*Pincher*), Tony Church (*Arkwright*), Derek Royle (*Briggs*), David Waller (*Mr. Price*), Cyril Cross (*commissionaire*), Gladys Dawson (*Gran*), Donegal (*Gramps*), Royston Tickner (*train guard*), Clifford Rose, Paul Dawkins, Tommy Godfrey, Peter Hutchins, Gordon Craig.

Farce. Source: Henry Livings, *Eh?* (London opening: 29 Oct 1964). Val Brose, a young man living in a highly automated future world, is interested only in growing mushrooms. His fiancée, Betty Dorrick, and her mother fear that Val will never take his place in society. When Betty insists that Val get a job, he obtains a position in the power station because he is attracted by the dark, damp working conditions which he believes will be perfect for his new strain of hallucinogenic mushrooms. Meanwhile, Betty has been anxiously making plans for their wedding. Soon after the ceremony, however, he takes her to see his mushrooms; Betty becomes disconcerted by Val's strange preoccupation with the plants and leaves her new husband. Val then decides to make certain changes in the generating operation in order for his mushrooms to have optimal conditions for growth. Dr. Narayana, an Indian in charge of the plant, learns of these unauthorized changes, but he is unable to catch Val in a mad chase around the boilers. Eventually, the entire plant grinds to a halt, and the lights of the city go out. Before he can be caught, Val tosses some of the mushrooms to his pursuers, who sample them and become so euphoric that they urge Dr. Narayana to destroy the power plant. Val and Betty, now reconciled, leave for the forest with a baby carriage full of mushrooms. *Nonconformists. Newlyweds. East Indians. Employer-employee relations. Mushrooms. Hallucinogens. Power companies. Weddings. Chases. The Future.*

Note: Opened in London in Jun 1968.

WORLD BY NIGHT (Italy)   **F6.5669**
Julia Film. *Dist* Warner Bros. Pictures. 27 Sep **1961** [Los Angeles opening]. Sd; col (Technicolor). 35mm (Technirama). 103 min. [Also reviewed at 80 and 90 min.]

Prod Francesco Mazzei. *Assoc Prod* Gianni Proia. *Dir* Luigi Vanzi. *U. S. Unit Dir* Don Kranze. *Japanese Unit Dir* Matsue Yoichi. *Chinese Unit Dir* Ehr

Kwong. *German Unit Dir* Jerry Mack. *English Unit Dir* John Comfort. *French Unit Dir* Julien Rivière. *Narr* Gualtiero Jacopetti. *Photog* Tonino Delli Colli. *Art Dir* Gianni Polidori. *Film Ed* Mario Serandrei. *English Vers Ed* Lewis Linzee. *Mus* Piero Piccioni. *Prod Mgr* Antonio Altoviti.

Narrator: Larry Cross.

Main Performers: Alfredo Alaría's Ballet, Macumba and the Bluebell Girls, The Tiller Girls, The Las Vegas Rythmettes, Chinese Opera Co. in Hong Kong, The Tahiti Ballet, Marco, Ricky Renée, The Nitwits Band, Wee Willie Harris, Bob Williams and His Dog "Louis," Rapha Temporel, Dodo from Hamburg, The Fraternity Brothers, Kiyokawa Geisha House, Jean Burton, Harue Takeda, Kimio Loda, George Lee, Kimi Yokoi, Joan Morse, Luki Rosa, Rudy Cardenas, Dora Pellettier.

Documentary. The film is a camera tour of some of the world's most famous nightspots and amusement centers. Highlights include scenes from the shows at the Paris Lido, Copenhagen's Tivoli Gardens, England's Blackpool Pleasure Beach, Tokyo's Queen Bee Cabaret, Las Vegas' Sands Hotel, Marineland of Hollywood, the Crazy Horse Saloon in Paris, Manhattan's Bowery Follies, Harlem's Apollo Theater, and a club in Hamburg where striptease artist Dodo performs. *Entertainers. Striptease. Nightclubs. Amusement parks. Paris. Copenhagen. Tokyo. Las Vegas. Hollywood. New York City. New York City—Harlem. Blackpool. Hamburg. Lido (Paris). Crazy Horse Saloon (Paris). Blackpool Pleasure Beach (England). Tivoli Gardens (Copenhagen). Queen Bee Cabaret (Tokyo). Marineland (Hollywood). Sands Hotel (Las Vegas). Apollo Theater (New York). Bowery Follies (New York).*

Note: Released in Italy in 1960 as *Il mondo di notte*; running time: 120 min.

THE WORLD IN MY POCKET (France/Italy/West Germany)   **F6.5670**
Corona Filmproduktion–Criterion Film–Erredi–Panta Cinematografica–CCC-Filmkunst. *Dist* Metro-Goldwyn-Mayer, Inc. Mar **1962** [Los Angeles opening: 2 May; c31 Dec 1961; LP21673]. Sd; b&w. 35mm. 93 min.

Prod Alexander Grüter. *Dir* Alvin Rakoff. *Screenplay* Frank Harvey. *Lighting Camera* Vaclav Vich. *Art Dir* Hanns Kuhnert, Wilhelm Vorwerg. *Film Ed* Alice Ludwig-Rasch, E. B. Jarvis. *Mus Comp & Cond* Claude Bolling. *Sd* Gerhard Müller. *Makeup* Gerda Scholz-Grosse, Günther Frank.

Cast: Rod Steiger (*Frank Morgan*), Nadja Tiller (*Ginny*), Peter Van Eyck (*Bleck*), Ian Bannen (*Kitson*), Jean Servais (*Gypo*), Marisa Merlini (*Frau Mandini*), Memmo Carotenuto (*Herr Mandini*), Edoardo Venola (*Carlo Mandini*), Carlo Giustini (*Pierre*).

Drama. Source: James Hadley Chase, *The World in My Pocket* (London, 1959). In Marseilles coldblooded adventuress Ginny masterminds a scheme for robbing an armored truck of a million-dollar payroll. On the day of the carefully planned crime, she races along a highway in a sports car and flirts with the driver and the guard of the armored truck. Then, once out of sight, she fakes an accident and lies down on the road. When the armored truck stops, Ginny's confederates—Morgan, Bleck, Kitson, and Gypo—overpower the two men and make off with the truck, though Kitson is killed in the struggle. The vehicle is then driven to a trailer camp, where Gypo tries unsuccessfully to open the lock. When a curious child notifies the police of the vehicle's whereabouts, the thieves flee to the mountains. Gypo is fatally bitten by a rattlesnake, Bleck is shot by police as he scales a cliff ledge, and Ginny and Morgan become trapped on the mountain peak. The police surround them below as a helicopter closes in from above. *Adventuresses. Guards. Police. Robbery. Snakebites. Helicopters. Armored car services. Marseilles.*

Note: Filmed on location near Marseilles. Opened in Essen in Feb 1961 as *An einem Freitag um halb zwölf*; running time 103 min; in Rome in May 1961 as *Il mondo nella mia tasca*; running time: 95 min; in Paris in Aug 1961 as *Vendredi 13 heures*. Alternative French title: *Pas de mentalité*.

THE WORLD OF ABBOTT AND COSTELLO   **F6.5671**
Vanguard Productions. *Dist* Universal Pictures. 2 Jun **1965** [Cincinnati, Ohio, opening; c5 Jun 1964; LP35384]. Sd; b&w. 35mm. 75 min.

Prod Max J. Rosenberg, Milton Subotsky. *Assoc Prod* Norman E. Gluck. *Ed Dir* Sidney Meyers. *Comm* Gene Wood. *Titl Dsgn* Gil Merit. *Ed Asst* Nina Feinberg. *Mus Supv* Joseph Gershenson.

Narrator: Jack E. Leonard.

Compilation film. Sequences from films starring Bud Abbott and Lou Costello include: *Buck Privates* (1941), *In the Navy* (1941), *Who Done It?* (1942), *Ride 'Em Cowboy* (1942), *Hit the Ice* (1943), *In Society* (1944), *The Naughty Nineties* (1945), *Little Giant* (1946), *Buck Privates Come Home* (1947), *The Wistful Widow of Wagon Gap* (1947), *Abbott and Costello Meet Frankenstein* (1948), *Mexican Hayride* (1948), *Abbott and Costello in the Foreign Legion* (1950), *Comin' Round the Mountain* (1951), *Lost in Alaska* (1952), *Abbott and Costello Go to Mars* (1953), *Abbott and Costello Meet the Keystone Kops* (1955), and *Abbott and Costello Meet the Mummy* (1955). *Actors. Motion pictures—History. Bud Abbott. Lou Costello.*

WORLD OF FLESH see **HOLLYWOOD'S WORLD OF FLESH**

THE WORLD OF FREUD see **MONDO FREUDO**

THE WORLD OF HENRY ORIENT   F6.5672

Pan Arts Co. *Dist* United Artists. 19 Mar **1964** [New York opening; c19 Mar 1964; LP29263]. Sd; col (DeLuxe). 35mm (Panavision). 106 min.

Prod Jerome Hellman. *Dir* George Roy Hill. *Screenplay* Nora Johnson, Nunnally Johnson. *Dir Photog* Boris Kaufman, Arthur J. Ornitz. *Art Dir* Jan Scott. *Set Decor* Kenneth Krausgill. *Prod Dsgn* James Sullivan. *Film Ed* Stuart Gilmore. *Mus* Elmer Bernstein. *Theme:* "Henry Orient Concerto" Ken Lauber. *Sd Mix* Robert Martin. *Asst Dir* Michael Hertzberg, Roger Rothstein. *Prod Mgr* Emmett Emerson. *Cost* Ann Roth. *Makeup* Dick Smith. *Hairstyles* Philip Naso.

Cast: Peter Sellers *(Henry Orient),* Paula Prentiss *(Stella),* Tippy Walker *(Valerie Boyd),* Merrie Spaeth *(Marian Gilbert),* Angela Lansbury *(Isabel Boyd),* Tom Bosley *(Frank Boyd),* Phyllis Thaxter *(Mrs. Gilbert),* Bibi Osterwald *(Boothy),* Peter Duchin *(Joe Byrd),* John Fiedler *(Sidney),* Al Lewis *(store owner),* Fred Stewart *(doctor),* Philippa Bevans *(Emma),* Jane Buchanan *(Kafritz).*

Comedy-drama. Source: Nora Johnson, *The World of Henry Orient* (Boston, 1958). The life of Henry Orient, a New York concert pianist with more ego than talent, becomes completely disrupted when Valerie Boyd and Marian Gilbert, two 14-year-old schoolgirls who delight in romantic flights of fancy, decide that they are in love with him. Henry's affair with Stella, a married woman, is ruined by the constant appearance of the two girls, who Stella is convinced are teenaged detectives hired by her suspicious husband. Marian's divorced mother is devoted to her child, but Valerie comes from an unhappy home dominated by her self-centered and adulterous mother, Isabel. The situation worsens when Isabel discovers a scrapbook compiled by the two youngsters in their passion for Henry. Misconstruing the situation, Isabel barges into Henry's apartment and accuses him of seducing Valerie. She is easily convinced of his innocence, however, and readily succumbs to his charm. Valerie learns of the illicit affair and, shattered, returns home only to be told by her mother that she must never see Marian again. Mr. Boyd, however, decides to leave Isabel and start a new life with Valerie. After a trip to Europe, Valerie visits the Gilbert apartment and resumes her friendship with Marian. Now the girls have a new interest in boys to replace their former taste for fantasy. *Pianists. Egotists. Adolescence. Friendship. Fantasy. Infidelity. Filial relations. New York City.*

Note: Location scenes filmed in New York City.

WORLD OF OBSCENITY see **MONDO OSCENITÁ**

WORLD OF PASSION   F6.5673

Topar Productions. *Dist* Probe Films. 17 Dec **1969** [New York showing]. [Feature film, length unknown.] No information about the precise nature of this film has been found. *Sexuality.*

WORLD OF THE DEPRAVED see **MUNDO DEPRAVADOS**

WORLD SAFARI   F6.5674

Dist Rainbow Adventures. Jan **1970** [Kansas City, Missouri, showing]. Sd; col. 35mm. 105 min. *MPAA rating* G.

Prod Dale Olson. *Photog* Ron Hayes, Bev Hayes.

Narrator: Dale Olson.

Documentary. This film surveys hunting adventures throughout the world. The sequences include: a Bengali tiger hunt; a leopard hunt in Uganda; an elephant hunt along the Nile River, with scenes of white rhinoceros and monitor lizards in the Nile region; wolf and polar bear hunting and whaling in the Arctic; and trout and salmon fishing in Alaska. Also shown are white Dahl sheep, brown bears, moose, and geese. *Hunting. Fishing. Big game. India. Uganda. Nile River. Arctic regions. Tigers. Leopards. Elephants. Bears. Rhinoceros. Wolves. Bears. Whales. Sheep. Moose. Geese. Salmon. Trout. Lizards.*

THE WORLD TEN TIMES OVER see **PUSSYCAT ALLEY**

WORLD WAR III BREAKS OUT see **THE FINAL WAR**

WORLD WITHOUT SHAME (Great Britain)   F6.5675

Mistral Productions. *Dist* Galaxy Films. 5 Oct **1962** [New York State license]. Sd; col (Eastman Color). 35mm. 72 min.

Exec Prod Russell Gay. *Assoc Prod* John E. Cross. *Dir-Writ* Donovan Winter. *Camera* Alex Sheridan. *Camera Op* Freddie Ford. *Song:* "Come What May" Ike Isaacs, Donovan Winter.

Cast: Yvonne Martell, Larry Bowen, Diane Valeri, Jean Robert, Laurel Grey, Paul Christian, Laura Beaumont, Michael Troy.

Drama. An advertising executive and his wife use their winnings from a football pool to buy an island in the Mediterranean in order to escape the tensions of modern life. With three other couples, they go to the island and become nudists. Preparing for the months ahead, they set up camp and take advantage of the natural surroundings. Andy, a writer, keeps a journal of their activities; Gavin paints; and George entertains in the evenings with his guitar while the women dance to his tunes. As word of the new life-style reaches civilization, the small island's population begins to increase. *Advertising executives. Painters. Authors. Musicians. Nudism. Contests. Islands. Diaries. Mediterranean Sea.*

Note: Opened in London in May 1962. Also known as *The Naked People.*

WORLD WITHOUT SUN (France/Italy)   F6.5676

Filmad—Les Requins Associés—Orsay Films—C. E. I. A. P. *Dist* Columbia Pictures. 22 Dec **1964** [New York opening; c31 Dec 1964; LP30038]. Sd; col (Eastman Color by Pathé). 35mm. 93min.

Prod-Dir Jacques-Yves Cousteau. *Assoc Prod* Jacques Mauger. *Assoc Dir* Simone Cousteau, Albert Falco. *English Comm* James Dugan, Al Ramrus, Jim Schmerer. *Photog* Pierre Goupil. *Camera Op* Gilbert Duhalde. *Film Ed* Georges Alépée, Anne Sarraute. *Mus* Serge Baudo. *Adtl Mus* Henri Crolla, André Hodeir. *Sd* Pierre Panier. *Maritime Adv* Christian Perrien, Frédéric Dumas, Serge Bertino, André Laban, Jean Mollard, Crew of the *Calypso. Underwater Constr* Jean Alinat.

Oceanauts: André Falco, Pierre Guilbert, Raymond Kientzy, Raymond Vaissière, André Portelatine, Pierre Vannoni, Claude Wesly, Antoine Lopez, Jacques-Yves Cousteau, Simone Cousteau.

Documentary. Jacques-Yves Cousteau and his oceanauts lived for a month in 1963 in an underwater community built on a coral shelf 40 to 80 feet below the surface of the Red Sea for the making of this documentary. The main house was a star-shaped, five-room construction containing all the comforts of land life. Another house, rocket-shaped, was especially designed for a two-man team living at a far greater depth. There were also two garages, one for the scooters that propelled individual divers, the other for housing the community submarine, *Diving Saucer.* Additionally, there was a pen where unusual sea specimens were kept for study. Never surfacing, the men devoted their time in this silent, sunless world to oceanographic research. They trapped new varieties of marine life, charted currents, examined fauna, studied the effects of color on fish and, in *Diving Saucer,* plunged to the ocean floor to discover a lake 1,000 feet below the surface. *Oceanographers. Marine life. Diving. Underwater laboratories. Submarines. Red Sea.*

Note: Opened in Paris in Sep 1964 as *Le monde sans soleil;* running time: 90 min; in Italy as *Il mondo senza sole.* Also known as *Jacques-Yves Cousteau's World Without Sun.*

THE WORLD'S GREATEST SINNER   F6.5677

Frenzy Productions, Inc. Jun **1962** [Los Angeles opening: 30 Jan 1963]. Sd; b&w with col seq (Technicolor). 35mm. 82 min.

A Timothy Carey Production. *Prod-Dir-Writ* Timothy Carey. *Asst Prod* Anthony M. Lanza, George E. Nahas, George F. Carey. *Camera* Ove H. Sehested, Robert Shelfow, Frank Grande, Raymond Steckler. *Film Ed* Carl Mahakian. *Mus* Frank Zappa. *Asst Dir* Gene Koziol.

Cast: Timothy Carey *(Clarence Hilliard),* Gil Baretto *(Alonzo),* Betty Rowland *(Edna Hilliard),* James Farley *(Devil),* Gail Griffen *(Betty Hilliard),* Grace De Carolis *(mother),* Gitta Maynard *(elderly woman),* Gene Pollock *(priest),* Whitey Jent *(guitar player),* Carolina Samario *(Nate),* Victor Floming *(office boss),* Ann Josephs *(secretary),* Jenny Sanches *(old lady in church),* Tyde Rule, Gene Koziol, Dana Madison, Titus Moede, Betty Sturm, Marty Prisco, George F. Carey, Duana Dedda, Doris Carey, Eleanor Enderle, Jerry Mobley, George Seemer, Ben Avila, Joe Powell, Bob Divorsney, Victor Corey, Don Mozee *(followers).*

Melodrama. Insurance salesman Clarence Hilliard denies the existence of any supernatural deity and proclaims himself God. Forming the Eternal Man Party, he becomes a rock and roll evangelist to gather converts to his cause, among them an elderly woman who agrees to finance his activities. He enters politics, but begins to doubt himself when his mother dies and his wife and daughter leave him. After violating a religious object he has stolen from a church, Hilliard challenges God to reveal himself. A miracle proves Hilliard's human fallibility, and he repents. *Salesmen. Agnostics. Evangelists. Politicians. Patrons. Religious conversion. Megalomania. Rock and roll. Miracles.*

Note: Partially filmed in Vancouver, British Columbia.

WORLD'S GREATEST SWINDLES see **THE BEAUTIFUL SWINDLERS**

THE WORSHIP OF NATURE see **CIVILISATION: THE WORSHIP OF NATURE**

THE WORST CRIME OF ALL!   F6.5678

Horizon Productions. *Dist* Ajay Film Co., Art Films International, Boxoffice International Film Distributors. 12 Oct **1966** [Albuquerque, New Mexico, opening; c23 Aug 1966; LP34801]. Sd; b&w. 35mm. 78 min.

A John Lamb–Ronald Graham Production. *A Film by* John Lamb, Jack Hill. *Prod* John Lamb, Ronald Graham. *Dir* John Lamb. *Mus* The Psychedelic Psymphony.

Cast: Nick Moriarty (*Howard Thorne*), Victoria Wren (*Vicki Thorne*), Cathy Crowfoot (*The Crow*), Christofer Winters (*Sidney*), Carol Baughman (*Carol*), Pluto Felix (*Dracula*), Penelope Faith (*Jenny*).

Horror film. Pornographer Howard Thorne, driven to commit savage attacks on women, can no longer distinguish between fantasy and reality. His beautiful wife, Vicki, finds him impotent. After vainly attempting to arouse his ardor she turns to narcotics for solace. One day Thorne rapes a woman whose lover, The Crow, is a vicious lesbian karate expert. During a masquerade the pornographer attempts to ravish a masked guest. To his horror Thorne discovers the victim to be his wife. Fleeing the scene he is abducted by The Crow who beats him into insensibility. Upon awakening Thorne finds himself in bondage, destined to suffer endless punishment at the hands of the two lesbians. As Vicki seeks escape through drugs she discovers herself in the midst of a nightmarish orgy, conducted by Dracula on a tour of the Inferno. Thorne and Vicki succumb to their fates, losing themselves in suffering and sensuality. *Pornographers. Rape. Impotence. Sadism. Lesbianism. Karate. Narcotics. Orgies. Masquerades. Fantasy. Dracula.*

Note: Also known as: *R---! The Worst Crime of All, Rape! The Worst Crime of All, Mondo Keyhole, The Tarts,* and *Mondo Key.* Copyrighted as *Mondo Keyhole.*

WORÜBER MAN NICHT SPRICHT *see* **FALSE SHAME**

WOUNDED IN ACTION *see* **W. I. A. (WOUNDED IN ACTION)**

WOW! *see* **MR. PEEK-A-BOO'S PLAYMATES**

WOZZECK (East Germany)   **F6.5679**

DEFA. *Dist* Brandon Films. 2 Mar **1962** [New York opening]. Sd; b&w. 35mm. 81 min.

Prod Kurt Halme. *Dir-Writ* Georg Klaren. *Photog* Bruno Mondi. *Sets* Hermann Warm, Bruno Monden. *Film Ed* Lena Neumann. *Mus* Herbert Trantow. *English Subtitl* Charles Clement.

Cast: Kurt Meisel (*Wozzeck*), Helga Zulch (*Marie*), Arno Paulsen (*captain*), Richard Haussler (*sergeant-major*), Paul Henkels (*doctor*), Max Eckard (*Georg Büchner*), Wolfgang Kuhne (*barker*), Willi Rose (*Andreas*).

Drama. Source: Georg Büchner, *Wozzeck* (Munich opening: 8 Nov 1913). A group of medical students, a doctor, and poet Georg Büchner stand around Wozzeck's body after he has been hanged. Büchner defends the young man and tells his story: In Prussia during the 1930's, Wozzeck is called to serve in the army. Uneducated and impoverished, the inarticulate youth quietly suffers abuse and humiliation at the hands of his arrogant captain. Wozzeck's only moments of pleasure are those spent with Marie, a young woman who has borne him a son. To provide them with a little extra money, he agrees to subject himself to a series of nutrition experiments. In time, the senseless tests, coupled with his brutal treatment as a soldier, result in Wozzeck's mental and physical deterioration. His spirit is completely broken when his sergeant-major publicly flaunts the news that he is having an affair with Marie. With all the townspeople jeering, Wozzeck's frustration explodes, and he murders his beloved Marie. *Medical students. Physicians. Poets. Prussians. Soldiers. Mistresses. Capital punishment. Military draft. Fatherhood. Infidelity. Mental illness. Murder. Experiments.*

Note: Released in East Germany in 1947.

THE WRECKERS *see* **FURY AT SMUGGLER'S BAY**

THE WRECKING CREW   **F6.5680**

Meadway-Claude Productions #4. *Dist* Columbia Pictures. 5 Feb **1969** [New York opening; c1 Feb 1969; LP36433]. Sd; col (Technicolor). 35mm. 105 min. *MPAA rating* M.

Prod Irving Allen. *Assoc Prod* Harold F. Kress. *Dir* Phil Karlson. *Screenplay* William McGivern. *Dir Photog* Sam Leavitt. *Helicopter Seq* Frank Tallman. *Art Dir* Joe Wright. *Set Decor* Frank Tuttle. *Titl Dsgn* Wayne Fitzgerald. *Film Ed* Maury Winetrobe. *Mus Comp & Cond* Hugo Montenegro. *Song:* "House of 7 Joys" Mack David, De Vol. *Sd Supv* Charles J. Rice. *Sd* James Z. Flaster, Arthur Piantadosi. *Asst Dir* Jerome M. Siegel. *Unit Prod Mgr* Ralph Black. *Cost Dsgn* Moss Mabry. *Dean Martin's Wardrobe Dsgn by* Sy Devore. *Makeup Supv* Ben Lane. *Dean Martin's Makeup by* Hank Edds. *Hairstyles* Virginia Jones. *Sp Eff* Paul Stewart, sp eff. *Karate Adv* Bruce Lee. *Prop Master* Max Frankel.

Cast: Dean Martin (*Matt Helm*), Elke Sommer (*Linka Karensky*), Sharon Tate (*Freya Carlson*), Nancy Kwan (*Yu-Rang*), Nigel Green (*Count Contini*), Tina Louise (*Lola Medina*), John Larch (*MacDonald*), John Brascia (*Karl*), Weaver Levy (*Kim*), Wilhelm von Homburg (*Gregor*), Bill Saito (*Ching*), Fuji (*Toki*), Ted H. Jordan (*guard*), Pepper Martin (*Frankie*), Whitney Chase (*Miss*

Natural Gas), Bill Ryusaki (*Henri*), Chuck Norris (*Garth*), David Chow (*bartender*), Jon Kowal (*Kelly*), Allen Pinson (*page*), James Lloyd (*desk clerk*), James Daris, Tony Giorgio, Brick Huston, Josephine James, Harry Fleer, Vincent Van Lynn, Dick Winslow, Harry Geldard, Noel Drayton, Rex Holman, J. B. Peck.

Action melodrama. Source: Donald Hamilton, *The Wrecking Crew* (Greenwich, Conn., 1963). Special agent Matt Helm is called upon to prevent an international catastrophe when a billion dollars in gold intended to bolster the British economy is hijacked in Denmark by a crime ring headed by Count Contini. The Count's former mistress, Lola Medina, offers to help Matt, but she is killed by a bomb-rigged Scotch bottle before she can talk. Also eager to assist is Freya Carlson, an enthusiastic but bumbling young woman who has been assigned by the Danish tourist office to help Matt. Matt and Freya gain entry to the Count's mansion by posing as journalists, but they are forced to flee when they are attacked by members of the gang. Two of the Count's seductive aides, Linka Karensky and Yu-Rang, then separately attempt to lure Matt to his death, but their plans for an intimate but lethal rendezvous are interrupted by the timely, though clumsy, intervention of Freya. Eventually, Matt's superior, MacDonald, arrives on the scene. After revealing that Freya is actually a secret agent, he forces a showdown with the Count. As a result, Linka is killed in an ambush set for Matt and Freya, while MacDonald succeeds only in getting himself wounded. Matt and Freya then trail Contini to his chateau and utilize numerous gadgets to outwit their opponents. After Yu-Rang has been killed in one of several explosions, Matt and Freya make a getaway by means of Matt's portable, folding mini-copter and board the train on which the Count is taking the gold to Luxembourg. During the melee that follows, the Count falls to his death through a trap door. With the gold saved, the villains foiled, and the train controls set on automatic, the mishap-prone Freya sets out to seduce the willing Matt. *Secret agents. Mistresses. Journalists. Nobility. Robbery. Organized crime. Murder. Imposture. Seduction. Trains. Helicopters. Explosions. Denmark. Matt Helm.*

Note: Location scenes filmed in Palm Springs, Idyllwild, and the Walt Disney Ranch, California. Working title: *House of 7 Joys.*

THE WRECKING YARD *see* **THE ROTTEN APPLE**

WRITTEN ON THE SAND *see* **PLAY DIRTY**

THE WRONG ARM OF THE LAW (Great Britain)   **F6.5681**

Romulus Films. *Dist* Continental Distributing, Inc. 2 Apr **1963** [New York opening]. Sd; b&w. 35mm. 91 min.

A Robert Velaise Production. *Prod* Aubrey Baring. *Exec Prod* Robert Velaise. *Assoc Prod* Cecil F. Ford. *Prod Assoc* E. M. Smedley-Aston. *Dir* Cliff Owen. *Screenplay* John Warren, Len Heath. *Adtl Dial* Ray Galton, Alan Simpson, John Antrobus. *Story* Ivor Jay, William Whistance Smith. *Photog* Ernest Steward. *Art Dir* Harry White. *Main Titl* Robert Ellis. *Film Ed* Tristam Cones. *Mus Comp* Richard Rodney Bennett. *Mus Cond* John Hollingsworth. *Sd* Bill Howell. *Asst Dir* Roy Baird.

Cast: Peter Sellers (*Pearly Gates*), Lionel Jeffries (*Inspector Parker*), Bernard Cribbins (*Nervous O'Toole*), Davy Kaye (*Trainer King*), Nanette Newman (*Valerie*), Bill Kerr (*Jack Coombes*), Ed Devereaux (*Bluey Max*), Reg Lye (*Reg Danton*), John Le Mesurier (*assistant commissioner*), Graham Stark (*Sid Cooper*), Martin Boddey (*Superintendent Forest*), Irene Browne (*dowager*), Arthur Mullard (*Brassknuckles*), Dermot Kelly (*Misery Martin*), Vanda Godsell (*Annette*), Tutte Lemkow (*Siggy Schmultz*), Barry Keegan (*Alf*), John Junkin (*Maurice*), Dennis Price (*Educated Ernie*), Dick Emery (*man*), John Harvey.

Comedy. Monsieur Jules, smooth operator of a plush Bond Street dress salon, uses his store as a front for his criminal dealings as Pearly Gates, head of a London syndicate of thieves. Despite an agreement with other local gangs not to work in the same area at the same time, three Australian hoodlums disguised as policemen confiscate Pearly Gates's loot. Soon realizing who the bogus officers are, Pearly Gates remains unaware that the impostors are being tipped off by his girl friend, Valerie. After a meeting with the crime syndicate, at which it is decided to befriend Scotland Yard, a 24-hour crime truce is declared so that all concerned may join forces in apprehending the IPO's (Impersonating Police Officers). An initial attempt by Inspector Parker, already in trouble with his superiors, goes awry. A second trap is more carefully planned, but Pearly Gates hijacks the come-on money from an armored car at the airport and absconds with the bait, taking along Parker, who is handcuffed to the moneybox. Though the other gangs are arrested, Pearly Gates and his friends escape by plane, with Valerie along as stowaway. It is revealed that the loot is merely play money, and upon arrival at a South Sea island, they begin life anew making grass skirts for the natives. *Couturiers. Gangsters. Police. Thieves. Stowaways. Australians. Impersonation. Duplicity. Disguise. Syndicates. Armored cars. Airfields. London. South Sea Islands. Scotland Yard.*

Note: Location scenes filmed in London. Opened in London in Mar 1963; running time: 94 min.

THE WRONG BOX (Great Britain)   F6.5682

Salamander Film Productions. *Dist* Columbia Pictures. 19 Jul 1966 [New York opening; c1 Oct 1966; LP33657]. Sd; col (Eastman Color). 35mm. 105 min. [Also 95 and 107 min.]

Prod-Dir Bryan Forbes. *Assoc Prod* Jack Rix. *Co-prod* Larry Gelbart, Burt Shevelove. *Screenplay* Larry Gelbart, Burt Shevelove. *Dir Photog* Gerry Turpin. *Camera Op* Ron Taylor. *Camera Asst* Michael Sarafian. *Art Dir* Ray Simm. *Set Dsgn* Peter James. *Titl Dsgn* Robert Ellis. *Film Ed* Alan Osbiston. *Mus Comp, Arr & Cond* John Barry. *Funeral & Military Airs Played by* The Temperance Seven. *Song:* "Light of Head" comp by Clifford Bevan. *Sd Rec* Bill Daniels, Ken Barker. *Dub Ed* Ted Mason. *Sd Asst* Gus Lloyd. *Asst Dir* Christopher Dryhurst. *Prod Mgr* Donald Toms. *Cont* Penny Daniels. *Asst to the Prod* John L. Hargreaves. *Wardrobe Mistress* Laurel Staffell. *Cost* Julie Harris, cost. *Makeup Artist* Paul Rabiger, Basil Newall. *Hairdresser* Maud Onslow. *Camera Grip* Ted Lockhart. *Stills* George Courtney Ward. *Constr Mgr* George Hill. *Props* George Ball, Alfred Waye.

Cast: John Mills (*Masterman Finsbury*), Ralph Richardson (*Joseph Finsbury*), Michael Caine (*Michael*), Peter Cook (*Morris*), Dudley Moore (*John*), Nanette Newman (*Julia*), Tony Hancock (*detective*), Peter Sellers (*Dr. Pratt*), Cicely Courtneidge (*Major Martha*), Wilfrid Lawson (*Peacock*), Thorley Walters (*Lawyer Patience*), Gerald Sim (*1st undertaker*), Peter Graves, British (*military officer*), Irene Handl (*Mrs. Hackett*), Norman Bird (*clergyman*), John Le Mesurier (*Dr. Slattery*), Hilton Edwards (*lawyer*), Norman Rossington (*1st rough*), Diane Clare (*Mercy*), Tutte Lemkow (*Bournemouth strangler*), Charles Bird (*Bonn's vanman*), Joseph Behrman (*vanman's mate*), Marianne Stone (*spinster on train*), Michael Bird (*countryman*), Thomas Gallagher (*2d rough*), Timothy Bateson (*clerk*), Reg Lye (*3d undertaker*), John Junkin (*1st engine driver*), Roy Murray (*1st stoker*), Tony Thawnton (*2d undertaker*), George Selway (*railway vanman*), Gwendolyn Watts (*maid*), Vanda Godsell (*Mrs. Goodge*), Donald Tandy (*ticket collector*), Lionel Gamlin (*2d engine driver*), Martin Terry (*2d stoker*), George Spence (*workman in road*), Jeremy Lloyd (*Brian Allen Harvey*), James Villiers (*Sydney Whitcombe Sykes*), Graham Stark (*Ian Scott Fife*), Dick Gregory, British (*Leicester Young Fielding*), Nicholas Parsons (*Alan Fraser Scrope*), Willoughby Goddard (*James White Wragg*), Valentine Dyall (*Oliver Pike Harmsworth*), Leonard Rossiter (*Vyvyan Alastair Montague*), Hamilton Dyce (*Derek Lloyd Peter Digby*), Donald Oliver (*gunner sergeant*), Totti Truman-Taylor (*lady at launching*), Jeremy Roughton (*bugler*), Frank Singuineau (*native bearer*), Michael Lees (*young Digby*), Andre Morell (*club butler*), Avis Bunnage (*Queen Victoria*), Penny Brahms, Maria Kazan (*twittering females on moors*), Freddy Clark, George Hillsden (*constables*), Alf Mangun, Norman Morris (*gravediggers*), Sarah Sandiford, Louise Noland (*mourners*), John Tateham (*Verger*), Sarah Harrison (*governess*), Peggy Raye (*child*), John Parker, British, John Fitch, Norman Hibbert, Jimmy Scott, Alistair Dick (*undertaker assistants*), Dan Cressey (*Judas*), Lindsay Hooper (*Matthew*), Dorothy Ford, Unity Greenwood (*Salvation Army girls*), John Morris, actor (*Sotheby's assistant*), The Temperance Seven (*themselves*), Denis Cowles (*Sotheby's partner*), Patsy Snell, Andrea Allen (*girls on train*), Phillip Stewart (*elderly man on train*), Rita Tobin (*elderly woman on train*).

Costume comedy. Source: Robert Louis Stevenson and Lloyd Osbourne, *The Wrong Box* (London, 1889). In Victorian London, two elderly brothers, Masterman and Joseph Finsbury, are bound together by a tontine, a financial arrangement whereby the last surviving member inherits a large fortune. With Masterman's decline in both health and wealth, he decides to dispose of his brother so that the money will pass to his grandson, Michael, an unpromising medical student. Masterman makes several attempts on Joseph's life, but the latter is too absorbed in his hobby of collecting useless information to notice. Meanwhile, Joseph's two greedy nephews, Morris and John, are also plotting to gain the inheritance. Mistakenly believing that Masterman is dead, that Michael is concealing the fact, and that Uncle Joseph was killed in a train wreck, they crate up what they think is Joseph's corpse and ship it home, hoping to hush up the death. The crate, however, contains the body of the Bournemouth strangler and is mistakenly delivered to Masterman's house. While the confused Michael frantically tries to dispose of it, the two nephews persuade the disreputable Dr. Pratt to sign a post-dated death certificate for Joseph. Confusion mounts as the police begin searching for the body of the strangler. After a wild chase, the situation is resolved when both Masterman and Joseph arrive, alive and well. The villainous cousins are exposed, and the tontine apparently is destined to benefit Michael and Julia, Joseph's ward, who have fallen in love. *Brothers. Cousins. Physicians. Wards. Uncles. Medical students. Police. Inheritance. Greed. Mistaken identity. Fraud. Coffins. London. Documentation. Chases.*

Note: Opened in London in May 1966; running time: 110 min.

WU-HOU *see* **EMPRESS WU**

WUTHERING HEIGHTS (Great Britain)   F6.5683

American International Pictures. 23 Dec 1970 [Los Angeles opening; c15 Dec 1970; LP40320]. Sd; col (print by Movielab). 35mm. 105 min. *MPAA rating* G.

Prod Samuel Z. Arkoff, James H. Nicholson. *Exec Prod* Louis M. Heyward. *Assoc Prod* John Pellatt. *Dir* Robert Fuest. *Screenplay* Patrick Tilley. *Photog* John Coquillon. *Art Dir* Philip Harrison. *Set Decor* Josie MacAvin. *Main Titl* Maurice Binder. *Supv Ed* Reginald Mills. *Ed* Ann Chegwidden. *Mus Comp & Cond* Michel Legrand. *Sd Ed* Leslie Hodgson, Gerry Hambling. *Sd Rec* Brian Marshall, Nolan Roberts. *Asst Dir* Ted Lewis. *Prod Supv* Ted Lloyd. *Wardrobe* Evelyn Gibbs. *Makeup* Bill Lodge. *Hairstyles* Maud Onslow.

Cast: Anna Calder-Marshall (*Catherine Earnshaw*), Timothy Dalton (*Heathcliff*), Harry Andrews (*Mr. Earnshaw*), Pamela Brown (*Mrs. Linton*), Judy Cornwell (*Nellie*), James Cossins (*Mr. Linton*), Rosalie Crutchley (*Mrs. Earnshaw*), Hilary Dwyer (*Isabella Linton*), Julian Glover (*Hindley Earnshaw*), Hugh Griffith (*Dr. Kenneth*), Morag Hood (*Frances*), Ian Ogilvy (*Edgar Linton*), Peter Sallis (*Mr. Shielders*), Aubrey Woods (*Joseph*), Wendy Allnutt, John Comer, Dudley Foster, Gordon Gostelow, Lois Daine, Keith Buckley, James Berwick, Patricia Doyle, Mark Wilding, Sandra Bryant, Bruce Beeby, Jonathan Brewster, Gillian Hayes, Libby Granger, Gertan Klauber.

Romantic drama. Source: Emily Brontë, *Wuthering Heights* (London, 1848). Late in the 18th century, Mr. Earnshaw returns to Wuthering Heights, his manor on the Yorkshire moors, with Heathcliff, an orphan he found starving on the streets of Liverpool. Earnshaw's two children, Catherine and Hindley, are jealous of their father's affection for the boy and treat him with contempt; after Hindley is sent away to boarding school, however, Catherine and Heathcliff fall in love and steal away to the moors. Upon the death of Earnshaw, Hindley becomes master of Wuthering Heights and treats Heathcliff like a stableboy. Later, when Heathcliff discovers Catherine's plans to marry wealthy Edgar Linton from nearby Thrushcross Grange, the distraught youth runs away before hearing Catherine explain that she plans to use Edgar's money to free Heathcliff from Hindley's mistreatment. Three years later, Heathcliff, now an affluent and well-groomed man of fortune, returns and finds Catherine married to Edgar and Hindley a widowed drunkard. Plotting his revenge, Heathcliff gambles with Hindley for the ownership of Wuthering Heights and wins. Next, he courts and subsequently marries Edgar's sister, Isabella, and humiliates Edgar by treating her like a servant. When Catherine becomes gravely ill in the early stages of pregnancy, she calls for Heathcliff; a short time later, she dies in childbirth. While mourning at her grave, Heathcliff is lured back to Wuthering Heights by the ghostly figure of Catherine but is shot at the site by Hindley, who has conspired in his murder with Isabella. Although mortally wounded, Heathcliff follows the ghost of Catherine to the moors where, in death, he is reunited with his beloved. *Orphans. Lovelorn. Heirs. Stableboys. Widowers. Courtship. Revenge. Jealousy. Wealth. Adoption. Filial relations. Brother-sister relationship. Alcoholism. Gambling. Childbirth. Murder. Manors. Moorlands. Yorkshire. Visions.*

Note: Location scenes filmed in Yorkshire, England. Opened in London in Jun 1971. Previously filmed in Great Britain (1920); and in the United States (1939, United Artists).

WYLIE *see* **EYE OF THE CAT**

X *see* **"X"—THE MAN WITH X-RAY EYES**

X-15   F6.5684

Essex Productions-E-C Productions. *Dist* United Artists. 21 Nov 1961 [Washington, D. C., opening; c21 Nov 1961; LP21773]. Sd; col (Technicolor). 35mm (Panavision). 107 min. [Copyright length: 112 min.]

Prod Henry Sanicola, Tony Lazzarino. *Exec Prod* Howard W. Koch. *Dir* Richard D. Donner. *Screenplay* Tony Lazzarino, James Warner Bellah. *Story* Tony Lazzarino. *Dir Photog* Carl Guthrie. *Aerial Photog* Jack Freeman, photog. *Art Dir* Rolland M. Brooks. *Set Decor* Kenneth Schwartz. *Film Ed* Stanley E. Rabjohn. *Asst Ed* Leonard Kwit. *Mus* Nathan Scott. *Sd Mix* Vic Appel. *Sd* Don Jones. *Asst Dir* Russ Haverick, Jay Sandrich, Terry Morse, Jr., George Walls. *Prod Mgr* John E. Pommer. *Script Supv* John Franco. *Wardrobe* Wesley V. Jefferies. *Makeup* Beans Ponedel, Jack Wilson. *Hairstyles* Mary Westmoreland. *Sp Eff* Paul Pollard. *Photog Eff* Howard Anderson. *Tech Adv* Milton Thompson, Jay Hanks, (Capt. USAF). *Still Photog* Ted Allan.

Cast: Charles Bronson (*Lieut. Col. Lee Brandon*), Brad Dexter (*Maj. Anthony Rinaldi*), James Gregory (*Torn Deparma*), Lisabeth Hush (*Diane Wilde*), David McLean (*Matt Powell*), Mary Tyler Moore (*Pamela Stewart*), Patricia Owens (*Margaret Brandon*), Kenneth Tobey (*Col. Craig Brewster*), Ralph Taeger (*Maj. Ernest Wilde*), Stanley Livingston (*Mike Brandon*), Lauren Gilbert (*Colonel Jessup*), Phil Dean (*Major McCully*), Chuck Stanford (*Lieut.*

Comdr. Joe Lacrosse), Patty McDonald (Susan Brandon), Mike MacKane (B-52 pilot), Robert Dornan (test engineer), Frank Watkins (security policeman), Barbara Kelley (secretary), Darlene Hendricks (nurse), Ed Fleming, Lee Giroux, Grant Holcomb, Lew Erwin (themselves), Ric Applewhite, Pat Renella (engineers), Jerry Lawrence, Richard Norris (operators), James Stewart (narrator).

Melodrama. While participating in the planned launch of an X-15 manned rocket from Edwards Air Force Base, test pilots Matt Powell, Lee Brandon, and Ernest Wilde experience emotional and physical problems which they share with their wives and sweethearts. After setting a world's speed record for a pilot-controlled plane, Lee is killed in a crash while saving Matt's life and guiding the X-15 to a safe landing. Matt himself takes the X-15 into outer space for the final test. Air pilots. Space exploration. Marriage. Self-sacrifice. Rockets. United States Air Force. United States—National Aeronautics and Space Administration. Edwards Air Force Base (California).

Note: Location scenes filmed at Edwards Air Force Base, California. Participation of E-C Productions is unconfirmed.

"X"—THE MAN WITH X-RAY EYES   F6.5685

Alta Vista Productions. Dist American International Pictures. 18 Sep 1963 [Miami, Florida, opening; c18 Sep 1963; LP27745]. Sd; col (Eastman Color by Pathé). 35mm (Spectarama). 80 min.

Prod-Dir Roger Corman. Exec Prod James H. Nicholson, Samuel Z. Arkoff. Assoc Prod Bartlett A. Carre. Screenplay Robert Dillon, Ray Russell. Story Ray Russell. Dir Photog Floyd Crosby. Col Cons John Howard, photog. Art Dir Daniel Haller. Set Decor Harry Reif. Film Ed Anthony Carras. Mus Les Baxter. Mus Coörd Al Simms. Sd Rec John Bury. Sd Ed Al Bird. Mus Ed Eve Newman. Asst Dir Jack Bohrer, Paul Rapp. Prod Mgr Robert Agnew. Prod Asst Jack Cash. Script Supv Betty Crosby. Cost Supv Marjorie Corso. Makeup Ted Coodley. Hairdresser Betty Pedretti. Sp Eff Butler-Glouner Inc. Constr Coörd Ross Hahn. Prop Karl Brainard.

Cast: Ray Milland (Dr. James Xavier), Diana Van Der Vlis (Dr. Diane Fairfax), Harold J. Stone (Dr. Sam Brant), John Hoyt (Dr. Willard Benson), Don Rickles (Crane), John Dierkes (preacher), Lorie Summers (party dancer), Vicki Lee (young girl patient), Kathryn Hart (Mrs. Mart), Carol Irey (woman patient).

Science fiction melodrama. While experimenting on an X-ray vision serum to expand human eyesight, Dr. James Xavier is told by his colleague, Dr. Diane Fairfax, that his funds from the research foundation will be cut unless he produces results. In desperation Xavier, with the reluctant assistance of Dr. Brant, decides to initiate the experiments on himself. The tests are successful, and soon Xavier is able to see through paper, materials, and even human tissue. When asked to help on a heart operation, Xavier is able to see that the diagnosis is wrong, and during the operation, he forcibly takes over to save the patient's life. The result is that he is dismissed and threatened with a malpractice suit. Meanwhile, his eyes have become so sensitive to light that he is forced to wear lead glasses and is subject to intense headaches. When Dr. Brant and Dr. Fairfax try to force him to stop administering the serum to his eyes, a struggle ensues, and Brant is accidentally killed. Xavier panics, flees the city, and finds refuge in a carnival where his strange power of eyesight is exploited by Crane, the owner; however, when Crane discovers Xavier's past, he threatens to expose him. Almost blind from the extreme vision and headaches, Xavier goes berserk and crashes his car; he stumbles into a revival meeting and, following the preacher's exhortation, plucks out his eyes. Physicians. Carnival workers. Eyesight. Surgery. Manslaughter. Blindness. Mutilation. Experiments. Serums. Carnivals. Revivals. Automobile accidents.

Note: Copyright title: X.

XMAS   F6.5686

Fearless Productions. Feb 1969 [San Francisco showing]. Si; col. 16mm? [Feature film, length unknown.]

Sex film. Three lesbians—two white and one black—return to their home after doing their Christmas shopping and make love to one another. Lesbianism. Group sex. Christmas.

Note: At the San Francisco showing this film was accompanied by taped music played by the theater.

... Y EL DEMONIO CREÓ A LOS HOMBRES see HEAT

YA KUPIL PAPU see DIMKA

YA SHAGAYU PO MOSKVE see MEET ME IN MOSCOW

YABU NO NAKA NO KURONEKO see KURONEKO

YABUNIRAMI NIPPON see WALL-EYED NIPPON

YAGYU BUGEICHO see SECRET SCROLLS (PART I)

YAGYU SECRET SCROLLS see SECRET SCROLLS (PART I)

YAKUZA BOZU see THE HOODLUM PRIEST

YAMAMOTO ISOROKU see ADMIRAL YAMAMOTO

YAMANEKO SAKUSEN see OPERATION ENEMY FORT

YAMBAÓ see YOUNG AND EVIL

YANCO (Mexico)   F6.5687

Producciones Yanco. Dist Jay K. Hoffman, Jerand Film Distributors. 17 Jun 1964 [New York opening]. Sd; b&w. 35mm. 85 min.

Pres by Jay K. Hoffman. Exec Prod Miguel González. Dir-Writ Servando González. Story Jesús Marín. Photog Alex Phillips, Jr. Film Ed Raúl Portillo. Mus Gustavo César Carrión.

Cast: Ricardo Ancona (Juanito), Jesús Medina (old man), Maria Bustamante (Maria).

Drama. To escape from the discordant noises that trouble his sensitive ears, Juanito, a young boy in an Indian village near Mexico City, makes visits on his raft to an island where he plays a homemade violin. Neither his mother nor the villagers understand his love of music, and he is taunted by the other children. One day at a marketplace, Juanito meets an aged, down-on-his-luck concertmaster with a beautiful violin which bears the name "Yanco," and the boy becomes his pupil. When the old man dies, and the violin is appropriated by a storekeeper, who refuses to sell it to Juanito's mother, the boy steals the instrument each night and takes it to the island to play. The sound of the music in the night frightens the villagers until during the Day of the Dead fiesta they take up arms and go in search of the source of the ghostly music. Juanito evades his pursuers but is caught in a whirlpool and drowns. Children. Violinists. Music teachers. Indians of North America. Poverty. Death. Superstition. Music. Islands. All Souls' Eve.

Note: Filmed in Mizquic in the Xochimilco area near Mexico City. Mexico City opening: caNov 1961; running time: 95 min. 1961 Venice Film Festival running time: 100 min.

YANG KWEI FEI see THE MAGNIFICENT CONCUBINE

A YANK IN VIET-NAM   F6.5688

Kingman Productions. Dist Allied Artists. Feb 1964. Sd; b&w. 35mm. 80 min.

Prod Wray Davis. Assoc Prod Vicente Nayve. Dir Marshall Thompson. Screenplay Jane Wardell, Jack Lewis. Story Jack Lewis. Photog Emmanuel Rojas. Art Dir Frank Holquist. Set Decor Ronald Witort. Film Ed Basil Wrangell, Orven Schanzer. Mus Comp & Dir Richard La Salle. Sd Tran Buuan. Asst Dir Nguyen Van Duc. Prod Supv Rhai Thuc Nhai. Wardrobe Rynol Dahlman. Sp Eff Crisanto Hilario.

Cast: Marshall Thompson (Major Benson), Enrique Magalona (Andre), Mario Barri (Houng), Kieu Chinh (herself), Urban Drew (Colonel Haggerty), Donald Seely (Kastens), Hoang Vinh Loc (Chau), My Tin (Quon), René Laporte (Father François), Doan Chau Mau (Colonel Thai), Pham Phuoc Chi (Kim), Nam Chau (Dr. The), Kieu Hanh (Madame The), Le Van (Vietcong leader), Nam Luong (Cung).

War drama. Marine Major Benson, stationed in South Vietnam, is taken prisoner by the Vietcong after his helicopter is shot down. Meanwhile, a hospital is attacked, Dr. The captured, and his wife killed. Andre, a mute whose life Dr. The has saved, and the doctor's daughter set out on a rescue mission with a small band of guerrillas. On the way they rescue Benson, who falls in love with the young woman. Eventually, the doctor is saved, but Andre is killed in a Vietcong attack. Later, when paratroopers arrive to rescue them, only Benson, Dr. The, and his daughter have survived. Air pilots. Vietcong. Physicians. Prisoners of war. Guerrillas. Paratroops. Combat zone life. Abduction. Helicopters. Vietnam War 1964–73. United States Marines.

Note: Filmed in Vietnam. Original title: The Year of the Tiger.

YATO KAZE NO NAKA O HASHIRU see BANDITS ON THE WIND

YAWARA SEMPU see THE BIRTH OF JUDO

YAWARA SEMPU DOTO NO TAIKETSU see JUDO SHOWDOWN

YEAR OF THE CRICKET see KENNER

THE YEAR OF THE HORSE   F6.5689

Myriad Productions. Dist Noel Meadow Associates. Mar 1966. Sd; col (Eastman Color). 35mm. 58 min.

Prod Mildred Dienstag, Therese Orkin. Assoc Prod Jean Cantor. Dir-Screenplay-Story Irving Sunasky. Narr Dir & Creator Faith Hubley. Story Collab Thomas Miller. Anim John Hubley. Photog Morton L. Heilig. Main Titl John Hubley. Film Ed Peggy Lawson.

Cast: Gabriel Mason *(Michael Farrow)*, Bradley Joe *(Richard Han, Jr.)*, Alvin Lum *(Richard Han, Sr.)*, Mary Mon Toy *(Mrs. Richard Han, Sr.)*, Lorraine Wong *(Tina Han)*, Mr. Thom, Mrs. Thom *(grandparents)*, Mary Hui *(stewardess)*, Peter Wong *(bachelor)*, Dick Hanover *(veterinarian)*, Burtt Harris, actor *(policeman)*, Mark Hubley *(narrator)*.

Drama. A 7 year-old Chinese American boy (played by Bradley Joe) in the New York Chinatown becomes friendly with an elderly hansom driver (played by Gabriel Mason) who owns a horse named Molly. Both of them are extremely fond of Molly, and the little boy often rides around Central Park with the hansom driver. One day Molly dies, and she is buried on Staten Island. Her owner becomes so depressed by her death that he loses his will to continue living. The little boy, his family, and the people of Chinatown join together to raise enough money to buy him another horse. *Chinese. Children. Cabbies. Friendship. Old age. New York City—Chinatown. New York City—Central Park. New York City—Staten Island. Horses.*

Note: Filmed on location in New York City.

YEAR OF THE HORSE *see* THE HORSE IN THE GRAY FLANNEL SUIT

THE YEAR OF THE TIGER *see* A YANK IN VIET-NAM

YEARNING (Japan) F6.5690

Toho Co. 23 Oct **1964** [Los Angeles showing]. Sd; b&w. 35mm. 98 min.
Prod Sanezumi Fujimoto, Mikio Naruse. *Dir* Mikio Naruse. *Screenplay* Zenzo Matsuyama. *Photog* Jun Yasumoto. *Mus* Ichiro Saito.

Cast: Hideko Takamine *(Reiko)*, Yuzo Kayama *(Koji)*.

Domestic melodrama. The owner of a small grocery store, in despair over the business he is losing to a nearby supermarket, commits suicide. Reiko, his widow, continues operating the business for 18 years, despite pressure by the family to convert the store into another supermarket. Koji, Reiko's brother-in-law, confesses his love for her, but she gently rejects him, preferring to remain faithful to her husband's memory. As Koji persists, Reiko finally gives in to his advances, but her guilt over the affair causes her to ultimately rebuff him, after which he commits suicide. *Widows. Grocers. Brothers-in-law. Family life. Suicide. Business competition. Grocery stores.*

Note: Released in Japan in 1964 as *Midareru*.

YEARS OF LIGHTNING, DAY OF DRUMS *see* JOHN F. KENNEDY: YEARS OF LIGHTNING, DAY OF DRUMS

YELLOW BIRD F6.5691

Century Cinema Corp. Apr **1969**. Sd; col. 35mm. 62 min.

Melodrama. Ellie works for Sylvia, with whom she has been having a lesbian affair. Ellie arrives at the office one morning to discover Sylvia in the arms of another. Indignant, Ellie goes to skid row and selects Howard, a middle-aged alcoholic, as her next lover. Ellie sexually dominates Howard until Sylvia discovers them together and joins them for group sex. Meanwhile, elsewhere in the building, Jock dominates his mistress Lily to the extent that he uses her to satisfy his business clients. One day Howard and Lily meet in the elevator, and they soon find mutual redemption in each other's love. *Careerwomen. Pimps. Pickups. Mistresses. Lesbianism. Alcoholism. Troilism. Employer-employee relations.*

Note: Also known as *Curious Yellow Bird*.

THE YELLOW CANARY F6.5692

Cooga Mooga Film Productions. *Dist* Twentieth Century-Fox Film Corp. 15 May **1963** [New York opening; c9 May 1963; LP26796]. Sd; b&w. 35mm (CinemaScope). 93 min.

Prod Maury Dexter. *Exec Prod* Robert L. Lippert. *Dir* Buzz Kulik. *Screenplay* Rod Serling. *Dir Photog* Floyd Crosby. *Art Dir* Walter Simonds. *Set Decor* Don Greenwood. *Supv Film Ed* Jodie Copelan. *Mus* Kenyon Hopkins. *Sd* William Bernds, Harry M. Leonard. *Asst Dir* Clarence Eurist. *Prod Mgr* Harold E. Knox. *Script Supv* Betty Crosby. *Wardrobe* Charles James. *Pat Boone's Wardrobe* Sy Devore. *Makeup* Bob Mark, Lynn Reynolds. *Drama Cons* Jeff Corey. *Prop Master* John Orlando.

Cast: Pat Boone *(Andy Paxton)*, Barbara Eden *(Lissa)*, Steve Forrest *(Hub Wiley)*, Jack Klugman *(Lieutenant Bonner)*, Jesse White *(Ed Thornburg)*, Steve Harris, actor *(Bake)*, Milton Selzer *(Vecchio)*, John Banner *(Sam Skolman)*, Jeff Corey *(Joe)*, Jo Helton *(Rene Pyle)*, Vici Raaf *(Crystal Towers)*, Harold Gould *(Ponelli)*, Joseph Turkel *(policeman)*, Charles Keane *(reporter)*.

Mystery melodrama. Source: Whit Masterson, *Evil Come, Evil Go* (New York, 1961). After a sensational appearance in Hollywood, singing idol Andy Paxton returns to his palatial home with his near-estranged wife, Lissa, and his bodyguard, Hub, and discovers that his infant son has been kidnaped and the nurse murdered. They find a ransom note bearing the code word "canary," and they reluctantly summon the police. Andy withholds from the police, however, the part of the note giving the code word because he fears that his son may be killed if it is divulged. A second message arrives demanding $200,000 ransom,

which he manages to raise, and the money is delivered to an isolated beach but nobody comes to meet him. Andy's valet, Bake, becomes a suspect in the kidnaping when manager Vecchio discovers that Bake has embezzled a great deal of money from Andy. United in common grief, Andy and Lissa try to discover the identity of the kidnaper. Hub takes Andy to a lonely inn and tortures a woman into giving them the address of a man who might have been in touch with the kidnapers. They find the man, but he is dead. After Bake is found murdered, Andy receives further instructions by telephone from the kidnaper and realizes that Hub is one of the few people who know their unlisted number. Andy and Lissa return to the inn and rescue their baby, and Andy shoots the mentally deranged Hub as police cars surround the inn. *Infants. Valets. Singers. Bodyguards. Psychopaths. Police. Torture. Murder. Kidnaping. Ransom. Embezzlement. Marriage.*

Note: Working title: *Evil Come, Evil Go*.

THE YELLOW GOLLIWOG *see* GUTTER GIRLS

THE YELLOW ROLLS-ROYCE (Great Britain) F6.5693

Anatole de Grunwald Productions–Metro-Goldwyn-Mayer, Inc. *Dist* Metro-Goldwyn-Mayer, Inc. 13 May **1965** [New York opening; c31 Dec 1964; LP29638]. Sd (Westrex); col (Metrocolor). 35mm (Panavision). 121 min.

Prod Anatole De Grunwald. *Assoc Prod* Roy Parkinson. *Dir* Anthony Asquith. *Screenplay* Terence Rattigan. *Dir Photog* Jack Hildyard. *Camera Op* Gerry Fisher, Austin Dempster. *2d Unit Photog* Douglas Adamson. *Art Dir (British Seq)* Elliot Scott. *Art Dir (European Seq)* Vincent Korda, William Kellner. *Set Decor* John Jarvis, Pamela Cornell. *Film Ed* Frank Clarke. *Mus Comp & Cond* Riz Ortolani. *Song:* "Forget Domani" Riz Ortolani, Norman Newell. *Sung by* Katyna Ranieri. *Sd Rec* Cyril Swern. *Sd Ed* Philip Barnikel. *Rec Supv* A. W. Watkins. *Dub Mix* J. B. Smith. *Asst Dir* Kip Gowans. *Prod Mgr* Timothy Burrill. *Unit Mgr* Jimmy Komisarjevsky. *Cont* Pamela Carlton. *Wardrobe Supv* Jackie Breed. *Miss Bergman's Wardrobe* Castillo. *Miss MacLaine's Wardrobe* Edith Head. *Miss Moreau's Wardrobe* Pierre Cardin. *Mr. Scott's Wardrobe* Gene Coffin. *Other Cost Dsgn* Anthony Mendleson. *Makeup* Tom Smith, John O'Gorman. *Hairdresser* Joan Johnstone. *Miss Bergman's Hairstyles* Giorgio di Roma. *Miss MacLaine's Hairstyles* Sydney Guilaroff. *Miss Moreau's Hairstyles* Carita. *Sp Eff* Tom Howard.

Cast—First Episode: Rex Harrison *(Marquess of Frinton)*, Jeanne Moreau *(Marchioness of Frinton)*, Edmund Purdom *(Fane)*, Michael Hordern *(Harmsworth)*, Lance Percival *(assistant car salesman)*, Roland Culver *(Norwood)*, Moira Lister *(Lady St. Simeon)*, Harold Scott *(Taylor)*, Richard Pearson *(Osborn)*, Isa Miranda *(Duchesse d'Angoulême)*, Grégoire Aslan *(Albanian ambassador)*, Jacques Brunius *(Duc d'Angoulême)*, Richard Vernon, Reginald Beckwith, Tom Gill, Dermot Kelly.

Cast—Second Episode: Shirley MacLaine *(Mae Jenkins)*, George C. Scott *(Paolo Maltese)*, Alain Delon *(Stefano)*, Art Carney *(Joey Friedlander)*, Riccardo Garrone *(Bomba)*.

Cast—Third Episode: Ingrid Bergman *(Gerda Millett)*, Omar Sharif *(Davich)*, Joyce Grenfell *(Hortense Astor)*, Wally Cox *(Ferguson)*, Carlo Croccolo *(chauffeur)*, Guy Deghy *(mayor)*, Martin Miller *(head waiter)*, Andreas Malandrinos *(hotel manager)*.

Melodrama. FIRST EPISODE: The Marquess of Frinton buys a yellow Rolls-Royce for his wife as an anniversary gift and presents it to her at their dinner party. At Ascot Heath, the marquess' horse wins the gold cup, but the marchioness disappears. Lady St. Simeon informs him that his wife is having an affair, and the marquess finds her with her lover in the back seat of the Rolls-Royce. Unable to divorce his wife because of his position in the Foreign Office, the marquess sells the car instead. SECOND EPISODE: The next owner of the Rolls is American gangster Paolo Maltese, who purchases the car while he and his moll, Mae Jenkins, are vacationing in Italy. Mae is bored with the trip, and when Paolo returns to the States on business, she has an affair with Stefano, a handsome young photographer. Realizing that Stefano would be in danger if Paolo should return, Mae foregoes her love for Stefano and returns to her gangster life. THIRD EPISODE: Mrs. Gerda Millett, a wealthy American widow traveling to Yugoslavia with her dowdy companion, Miss Hortense Astor, whimsically purchases the yellow Rolls-Royce, intending to drive it to a party given by royalty. En route she is stopped by Yugoslav patriot Davich, who persuades her to smuggle him across the border to escape a Nazi attack. Mrs. Millett undertakes this task without enthusiasm until the Nazis bomb her hotel; she then joins the patriots and risks her life to aid their cause. Once again, the back seat of the Rolls-Royce is the setting when Davich makes love with Mrs. Millett, but he then sends her back to Miss Hortense. *Aristocrats. Americans in foreign countries. Gangsters. Molls. Photographers. Widows. Nazis. Infidelity. Horseracing. Smuggling. Resistance (political). Aerial bombardment. Rolls-Royce automobiles. World War II. England. Ascot. Italy. Yugoslavia. Great Britain—Foreign Office.*

Note: Filmed on location in England, Italy, and Austria. Opened in London in Dec 1964; running time: 122 min.

THE YELLOW SLIPPERS (Poland)   F6.5694

Iluzjon Film Unit. *For* Film Polski. 7 May **1965** [Los Angeles showing]. Sd; col. 35mm. 83 min.

Dir Sylwester Chęciński. *Screenplay* Zdzisław Skowroński, Wanda Żółkiewska. *Story* Antonina Domanska. *Photog* Kazimierz Konrad. *Film Ed* Janina Niedzwiecka. *Mus* Zbigniew Turski.

Cast: Gustaw Holoubek *(Wit Stwosz),* Andrzej Szczepkowski *(Rafal),* Marek Kondrad *(Wawrzek),* Bronisław Pawlik *(Gregorius),* Tadeusz Białoszczyński *(The King),* Bogumił Kobiela *(Frącek),* Bogdan Niewinowski, Mieczysław Czechowicz, Bohdan Baer, Eugeniusz Szewczyk, Beata Barszczewska, Hanna Bedryńska, Aleksander Fogiel, Maria Kieszkowa, Włodzimierz Kwaskowski, Ignacy Machowski, Zygmunt Malawski, Marian Wojtczak, Zygmunt Zintel, Antoni Żukowski.

Drama. In 16th century Poland, Wawrzek, an orphan boy from the country, runs away from his master. Upon his arrival in Krakow, he witnesses a church robbery by a mysterious pilgrim who is later caught through information Wawrzek supplies to the authorities. Awarded a pair of yellow slippers by the King for his bravery, Wawrzek becomes an apprentice to the famous sculptor, Wit Stwosz. The thief, vowing revenge, returns and abducts Wawrzek, whom he trains as his assistant. However, Wawrzek is rescued in time to see the unveiling of Stwosz's masterpiece, the Altar of St. Mary's Church. *Runaways. Orphans. Sculptors. Thieves. Royalty. Revenge. Abduction. Churches. Rewards. Krakow (Poland). Wit Stwosz.*

Note: Released in Poland in 1961 as *Historia żółtej ciżemki.*

YELLOW SUBMARINE (Great Britain)   F6.5695

King Features–Subafilms. *Dist* United Artists. 13 Nov **1968** [New York opening; c18 Jul 1968; LP36362]. Sd; col (DeLuxe). 35mm. 85 min. *MPAA rating* G.

Pres by Apple Films. *Prod* Al Brodax. *Assoc Prod* Mary Ellen Stewart. *Dir* George Dunning. *Anim Dir* Jack Stokes, Robert Balser. *Live Action Seq Dir* Dennis Abey. *Screenplay* Lee Minoff, Al Brodax, Jack Mendelsohn, Erich Segal. *Orig Story* Lee Minoff. *Anim Seq Dir* Eldrick Radage. *Anim* Alan Ball, Reg Lodge, Tom Halley, Dave Livesey, Diane Crowther, Rich Cox, Pam Ford, Mike Pocock, Jeff Loynes, Mike Stewart, Malcolm Draper, Ted Percival, Lawrence Moorcroft, John Challis, Diane Jackson, Dennis Hunt, Arthur Humberstone, Anne Jolliffe, Tony Cuthbert, Paul Driessen, Hester Coblentz, Dick Horn, Jeff Collins, Jerry Potterton, Jim Hiltz, Terry Moesker. *Anim Sp Eff* Chris Cannter. *Supv Anim Clean-up* Ted Lewis, anim. *Anim Clean-up* Christopher Miles, anim, Ian Cowen, Rich Dalkin, Ray Newman. *Trace and Paint Supv* Helen Jones, Corona Mayer, Janet Hosie, Margaret Geddes, Jennie Brisbane, Susan Brown, anim, Susan Gibbons. *Background Supv* Alison DeVere, Millicent McMillan. *Dsgn* Jon Kramer, Dick Sawyer. *Layout* Gordon Harrison, Ray Aragon, Peter Arthy, Jack Daniels, Alan Gray, Ted Pettingell, Gil Potter. *Background Artists* Arthur Button, Caird Green, David Elvin, Muriel Jennings, Martina Selway, Malcolm Dakin, Clare Greenford, Jenny Aldridge, Paul Francis, Ian Gordon. *Camera Op* John Williams, photog, Richard Wodyinski, Vev Roberts, Graham Orrin, Rex Neville, Alan Foster, Malcolm Livesey, Ian Letts, Tony Haynes. *Art Dir* Heinz Edelmann. *Asst Prod Dsgn* John Cramer, Gordon Harrison. *Film Ed* Brian J. Bishop. *Asst Ed* Torquil Stewart. *Mus Dir* George Martin. *Songs:* "Yellow Submarine," "When I'm Sixty-Four," "Nowhere Man," "Lucy in the Sky With Diamonds," "Eleanor Rigby," "All You Need Is Love," "Sgt. Pepper's Lonely Hearts Club Band," "A Day in the Life," "All Together Now," "Hey, Bulldog" John Lennon, Paul McCartney. *Songs:* "It's All Too Much," "Only a Northern Song" George Harrison. *Sung by* The Beatles. *Songs:* "March of the Meanies," "Pepperland," "Pepperland Laid Waste," "Sea of Holes," "Sea of Monsters," "Sea of Time" George Martin. *Dub* Don Cohen, Ken Rolls. *Dub Mix* Hugh Strain. *Prod Supv* John Coates. *Prod Coörd* Abe Goodman. *Prod Asst* Sally Hyman. *Sp Eff* Charles Jenkins. *Admin* Peter Franklin, Norman Kauffman.

Voices: John Clive *(John),* Geoffrey Hughes *(Paul),* Peter Batten *(George),* Paul Angelus *(Ringo/Chief Blue Meanie),* Dick Emery *(Lord Mayor/Nowhere Man/Max),* Lance Percival *(Old Fred).*

Animated fantasy. Based on the song by: John Lennon and Paul McCartney, "Yellow Submarine". On a peaceful day in the happy kingdom of Pepperland, a concert by Sergeant Pepper's Lonely Hearts Club Band is interrupted by an invasion of the Blue Meanies, a horde of music-hating ogres who drain their victims of color with Splotch Guns and render them immobile by pelting them on their heads with huge green apples. Old Fred, the conductor of the band, escapes to the Lord Mayor, who sends him for help in a yellow submarine. Upon arriving in Liverpool, Old Fred encounters Ringo and recruits the other Beatles (John, Paul, and George) to help save Pepperland. Setting off in the yellow submarine, the five adventurers embark on a "modyssey" that carries them through many strange realms: the sea of time, the sea of science, the sea of monsters, the sea of green, and the sea of holes. After picking up the little Nowhere Man, they are propelled by an enormous sneeze through the sea of

holes into occupied Pepperland. Disguising themselves as one of the Meanies giant Apple Bonkers, they infiltrate a compound where all the musical instruments have been stored. Now armed with songs and love, they rout the Blue Meanies in a battle royal and convert them into peaceful citizens, thereby restoring life, color, music, and love to Pepperland. *Band leaders. Mayors. Musicians. Imaginary kingdoms. Disguise. Music. Imaginary creatures. Submarines. Monsters. Liverpool. The Beatles.*

Note: Released in Great Britain in 1968.

THE YELLOW TEDDYBEARS *see* GUTTER GIRLS

YELLOWSTONE CUBS   F6.5696

Walt Disney Productions–Charles Draper Productions. *Dist* Buena Vista Distribution Co. May **1963** [c16 May 1963; LP25497]. Sd (RCA); col (Technicolor). 35mm. 48 min.

Overall Production Credits: *Pres by* Walt Disney. A Walt Disney Production. *Co-prod* Winston Hibler. *Screenplay* Ralph Wright. *Narr* Jack Speirs. *Mus* Paul Smith. *Orch* Gene von Hallberg.

Production Credits for Charles Draper Productions: *Field Prod* Charles L. Draper. *Photog* Charles L. Draper, William W. Bacon, III. *Prod Asst* Hank Huisman, Tom Boutross, Robert Becker. *Tech Adv* Joe Way. *Coöp* National Park Service, Yellowstone National Park, Montana Fish and Game Commission, Yellowstone Park Co.

Production Credits for Walt Disney Productions: *Film Ed* George Gale. *Sd* Robert O. Cook. *Mus Ed* Evelyn Kennedy. *Prod Coörd* Robert F. Metzler. *Prod Mgr* Erwin L. Verity.

Cast: Rex Allen *(narrator),* Nokomis, Tuffy, Tubby *(Yellowstone bears).*

Adventure comedy-drama. Tuffy and Tubby, twin black bear cubs born to elderly Nokomis in Yellowstone National Park, learn from their mother how to obtain food from tourists. A vacationing family stops and, failing to heed park regulations on feeding wildlife, the children take a bag of marshmallows from the food box on the roof of their trailer. While the father is feeding Nokomis, her frisky cubs climb onto the trailer and begin to eat from the open food box. Nokomis, reaching for more tidbits, rips the father's coat. He mistakes the gesture for an attack and quickly drives off, trapping Tuffy and Tubby in the food box. At the campgrounds, the cubs escape while the father seeks a ranger to report the "attack." Meanwhile, Nokomis follows her cubs' scent to the campground; and the father identifies her to Joe, the ranger, as his attacker. Park regulations require that a "bad" bear be branded with paint on the forehead and, following a second disturbance, shot on sight. Joe, not realizing that such an old bear might have cubs, tranquilizes, brands, and banishes Nokomis to a remote section of the park. Nokomis immediately continues her search for Tuffy and Tubby, who are wreaking havoc in the park. Nokomis catches up with them at Old Faithful Inn, where they have either eaten or destroyed everything in the kitchen. The innkeeper spots Nokomis and reports her to the rangers, who arrive at the inn with loaded guns. There they witness a reunion between mother and cubs, and, confident that Nokomis will once again be the good bear she has always been, they allow her to go free. *Tourists. Forest rangers. Innkeepers. Animal life. Yellowstone National Park. Bears.*

Note: Filmed on location in Yellowstone National Park.

"YES!" (COUNT THE POSSIBILITIES) *see* TO INGRID MY LOVE, LISA

YESTERDAY, TODAY AND TOMORROW (France/Italy)   F6.5697

C. C. Champion–Les Films Concordia. *Dist* Embassy Pictures. 17 Mar **1964** [New York opening]. Sd; col (Technicolor). 35mm (Techniscope). 119 min.

Overall Production Credits: *Pres by* Joseph E. Levine. *Prod* Carlo Ponti. *Dir* Vittorio De Sica. *Photog* Giuseppe Rotunno. *Art Dir* Ezio Frigerio. *Set Decor* Ezio Altieri. *Film Ed* Adriana Novelli. *Mus Comp & Cond* Armando Trovajoli. *Choreog for "Mara"* Jacques Ruet. *Sd* Ennio Sensi. *Asst Dir* Luisa Alessandri. *Prod Mgr* Antonio Altoviti. *Cost* Piero Tosi. *Miss Loren's Dresses for "Mara"* Christian Dior.

Production Credits—"Adelina": *Screenplay* Eduardo De Filippo, Isabella Quarantotti.

Production Credits—"Anna": *Screenplay* Cesare Zavattini, Billa Billa Zanuso. *Based on the Story* "Troppo ricca" by Alberto Moravia.

Production Credits—"Mara": *Screenplay* Cesare Zavattini.

Cast—"Adelina": Sophia Loren *(Adelina),* Marcello Mastroianni *(Carmine),* Aldo Giuffrè *(Pasquale Nardella),* Agostino Salvietti *(Lawyer Verace),* Lino Mattera *(Amadeo Scapece),* Tecla Scarano *(Bianchina Verace).* Silvia Monelli *(Elvira Nardella),* Carlo Croccolo *(auctioneer),* Pasquale Cennamo *(police captain).*

Cast—"Anna": Sophia Loren *(Anna),* Marcello Mastroianni *(Renzo),* Armando Trovajoli *(other man).*

Cast—"Mara": Sophia Loren *(Mara),* Marcello Mastroianni *(Augusto Rusconi),* Tina Pica *(grandmother),* Giovanni Ridolfi *(Umberto),* Gennaro Di Gregorio *(grandfather).*

Comedy-drama. ADELINA: When the Naples police come to arrest the beautiful Adelina for selling contraband cigarettes, her unemployed husband, Carmine, discovers a legal loophole stating that no pregnant woman can be jailed until 6 months after her child is born. The plan works so well that Adelina conceives one baby after another to avoid arrest. Carmine becomes so overstrained that eventually Adelina can no longer produce a medical certificate of pregnancy, and she is sent to jail. The local citizens raise the money for her fine, however, and her sentence is commuted by the president of Italy. ANNA: Anna, the elegant wife of a prominent Milan industrialist, is having an affair with Renzo, a struggling young writer. One day she allows him to drive her expensive convertible which he wrecks in order to avoid hitting a small boy. Infuriated by the damage to her car and by Renzo's inability to handle the situation, Anna accepts a ride from an unattractive but obviously wealthy stranger. MARA: Shortly before the return of her lover Rusconi, Mara, a beautiful prostitute in Rome, discovers that a seminary student who is visiting his grandparents next door has fallen in love with her. Although attracted by the purity of the young man, Mara resists his advances. Eventually his grandmother accuses Mara of attempting to corrupt her grandson and announces that she plans to join the Foreign Legion. Mara confronts the young man, tells him the truth about herself, and persuades him to return to the seminary. In an offering to God for the soul of the young man, Mara makes a vow of chastity for one week, thereby leaving Rusconi sexually frustrated. *Fences (for stolen goods). Police. Idle rich. Authors. Prostitutes. Students. Grandmothers. Pregnancy. Infidelity. Moral corruption. Chastity. Naples. Milan. Rome. Automobile accidents.*

Note: Location scenes filmed in Naples, Milan, and Rome. Opened in Rome in Dec 1963 as *Ieri, oggi e domani*; in Paris in May 1964 as *Hier, aujourd'hui et demain*.

LES YEUX SANS VISAGE see **THE HORROR CHAMBER OF DR. FAUSTUS**

YNGSJÖMORDET see **WOMAN OF DARKNESS**

YO YO (France)   F6.5698

C. A. P. A. C. *Dist* Magna Pictures Distribution Corp. 28 Feb **1967** [New York opening]. Sd; b&w. 35mm. 92 min.

Prod Paul Claudon. *Dir* Pierre Etaix. *Screenplay* Pierre Etaix, Jean-Claude Carrière. *Dir Photog* Jean Boffety. *Camera Op* Christian Guillouet. *Asst Camera Op* Jacques Lefrançois, Guy Lecouvette. *Art Dir* Raymond Tournon, Raymond Gabutti. *Film Ed* Henri Lanoë. *Mus* Jean Paillaud. *Sd* Jean Bertrand. *Sd Asst* Lucien Moreau. *Asst Dir* André Bureau, Pierre Aubert. *Prod Mgr* Tonio Suné, Jean-Marie Bertrand. *Prod Admin* Hélène Desse. *Script Girl* Sylvie Carré. *Cost* Jacqueline Guyot. *Prop Master* Michel Suné. *Still Photog* Roger Forster.

Cast: Pierre Etaix (*The Millionaire/Yo Yo*), Philippe Dionnet (*Yo Yo as a child*), Luce Klein (*The Equestrienne*), Claudine Auger (*Isolina*), Siam, Pipo, Dario, Mimile.

Comedy. In 1925 a millionaire leads a solitary and lonely life in an enormous, sumptuous castle. Bored with his riches, he idles away the time playing yo-yo and yearning for his lost love, a circus rider who refused to share his gilded life. He hires a traveling circus to perform for him and discovers that the bareback rider is his lost love. Financially ruined by the stock market crash of 1929, the man joins the equestrienne and their son, the infant clown Yo Yo, in their circus act. Although they are happy and successful, Yo Yo dreams of someday restoring his father's castle to the splendor he vaguely recalls from his childhood. Following World War II Yo Yo resumes his career and becomes an international star of music halls, the cinema, and television. After spending a fortune on realizing his dream, he gives a huge party to welcome his father and mother back to the castle, but they refuse to accept his gift, preferring instead to remain with a touring circus. Aware that his life has become as empty and unhappy as his father's once was, Yo Yo gives up the castle and returns to his career as a circus clown. *Millionaires. Idlers. Equestrians. Clowns. Wealth. Loneliness. Lovelorn. Family life. Fame. Castles. Music halls. Motion pictures. Television. The Great Depression (1929–34). World War II.*

Note: Opened in Paris in Feb 1965 as *Yoyo*; running time: 98 min.

YOAKE MAE see **BEFORE DAWN**

YOJIMBO (Japan)   F6.5699

Toho Co.-Kurosawa Films. *Dist* Seneca International, Ltd. Sep **1961** [Los Angeles showing]. Sd; b&w. 35mm (Tohoscope). 110 min.

Exec Prod Tomoyuki Tanaka, Ryuzo Kikushima. *Dir* Akira Kurosawa. *Screenplay* Ryuzo Kikushima, Hideo Oguni, Akira Kurosawa. *Photog* Kazuo Miyagawa. *Lighting* Choshiro Ishii. *Art Dir* Yoshiro Muraki. *Mus* Masaru Sato. *Sd* Hisashi Shimonaga, Choshichiro Mikami.

Cast: Toshiro Mifune (*Sanjuro Kuwabatake*), Eijiro Tono (*Gonji*), Seizaburo Kawazu (*Seibei*), Isuzu Yamada (*Orin*), Hiroshi Tachikawa (*Yoichiro*), Kyu

Sazanka (*Ushitora*), Daisuke Kato (*Inokichi*), Tatsuya Nakadai (*Unosuke*), Kamatari Fujiwara (*Tazaemon*), Takashi Shimura (*Tokuemon*), Ikio Sawamura (*Hansuke*), Atsushi Watanabe (*coffin maker*), Yoshio Tsuchiya (*Kohei*), Yoko Tsukasa (*Nui*), Akira Nishimura (*Kuma*), Susumu Fujita (*Homma*), Yosuke Natsuki (*farmer's son*), Jerry Fujio (*Roku*).

Action melodrama. With the fall in the 19th century of Japan's feudal lords, samurai suddenly find that their services are no longer in demand. One of their number, unemployed Sanjuro, arrives in a village. Upon learning that the village is divided into two warring camps (one led by merchant Tazaemon and his henchman Seibei, the other by Tokuemon and his cohort Ushitora), Sanjuro calmly surveys the situation and concludes that neither side is worth defending. He needs money for food and lodging, however, and he considers Seibei's offer of 50 *ryo* to be his *yojimbo* (bodyguard). He turns down the offer, though, when he learns that Seibei intends to kill him after a battle they are planning, and instead Sanjuro tries to cause the two factions to destroy each other. The situation becomes more volatile when Unosuke (Ushitora's younger brother) arrives with a pistol, the only gun in town. Pretending to ally himself with Unosuke, Sanjuro secretly kills several of his men while helping a ravaged farmer, Kohei, to escape. Unosuke learns of Sanjuro's betrayal and has him captured and beaten. Gonji, the local innkeeper and sake seller, helps Sanjuro escape to a hut on the outskirts of town. Learning that Gonji has been captured, Sanjuro returns to town and finds the two factions burning homes and killing each other. In a duel with the armed Unosuke, Sanjuro prevails, and goes on to kill the rest of his enemies. After contemplating the piles of corpses strewn about, Sanjuro bids goodby to Gonji and the coffin maker and leaves town. *Samurai. Merchants. Hired killers. Bodyguards. Innkeepers. Brothers. Village life. Feuds. Employment. Perfidy. Torture. Guns. Swords. Duels.*

Note: Released in Japan in Apr 1961.

YOKOHAMA GIRL (Japan)   F6.5700

Toho Co. 14 Aug **1964** [Los Angeles opening]. Sd; col? 35mm. [Feature film, length unknown.]

Cast: Reiko Dan.No information about the nature of this film has been found. *Yokohama.*

Note: Original title and release undetermined.

YOLANTA (U.S.S.R.)   F6.5701

Riga Film Studio. *Dist* Artkino Pictures. 22 Dec **1964** [New York opening]. Sd; col (Magicolor). 35mm. 82 min.

Dir Vladimir Gorikker. *Photog* Vadim Mass. *Camera* Ya. Briyedis. *Art Dir* G. Likums. *Film Ed* M. Chardynina. *Mus Comp* Pëtr Ilich Tchaikovsky. *Mus Cond* B. Khaykin. *Mus Perf by* Bolshoi Theater Orchestra. *Mus Arr* N. Zolotonos. *Concertmasters* S. Brikker, O. Tomina, B. Moiseyev. *Choirmaster* A. Rybnov. *Sd* V. Zorin. *Asst Dir* Yu. Tselms. *Prod Mgr* Kh. Kinstler. *Cost* U. Pauzer(s). *Makeup* V. Kuznetsova. *Makeup Cons* V. Goryunov. *Sp Eff* E. August, V. Shildknekht.

Cast: Natalya Rudnaya (*Yolanta [Iolanta]*), Fyodor Nikitin (*René*), Yuriy Perov (*Vaudemont [Vodemon]*), Aleksandr Belyavskiy (*Robert*), Pyotr Glebov (*Ebn-Khakia*), Valentina Ushakova (*Marta*), V. Zandberg (*Bertran*), Ya. Filipson (*Almerik*), V. Sharykina (*Brigitta*), O. Amalina (*Laura*), T. Starova (*Matilda*), A. Milbret (*jester*).

Singing Voices: Galina Oleynichenko (*Yolanta [Iolanta]*), Ivan Petrov (*René*), Zurab Andzhaparidze (*Vaudemont [Vodemon]*), Pavel Lisitsian (*Robert*), V. Valaytis (*Ebn-Khakia*), Ye. Verbitskaya (*Marta*), V. Yaroslavtsev (*Bertran*), V. Vlasov (*Almerik*), M. Miglau (*Brigitta*), K. Leonova (*Laura*), Bolshoi Theater Chorus.

Opera film. Source: Pëtr Ilich Tchaikovsky and Modest Ilich Tchaikovsky, *Iolanta* (Saint Petersburg opening: 18 Dec 1892). Henrik Hertz, *Kong René's datter* (first production: 1843). King René of Provence has kept his daughter, Yolanta, from the knowledge of her own blindness, secluding her in his remote castle. The king fears that Robert, the Duke of Burgundy, betrothed to Yolanta in childhood, will learn of her affliction and refuse to wed her. Ebn-Khakia, a Moorish physician at the court, claims that he can cure Yolanta if only she knows that she is blind and has the will to see, but the king fears that the shock would be too great for his daughter and continues to keep the secret. Robert comes to the castle with his friend Vaudemont, a brave knight. Although René has forbidden entry on pain of death, Vaudemont meets Yolanta in the garden and falls in love with her. Seeing that she is unaware of her blindness, Vaudemont reveals the truth to her and tells her of the beauties of the world. René threatens that Vaudemont will be put to death if Ebn-Khakia's treatments fail. Robert confesses that he loves another woman, while Vaudemont vows his love for Yolanta irregardless of the success of the treatments. The king agrees to release Robert from his vows and allow Vaudemont to take his place as Yolanta's betrothed; and Yolanta's eyesight is restored. *Royalty. Moors. Physicians. French. Fatherhood. Blindness. Mysticism. Duplicity. Castles. Provence.*

Note: Released in Latvia in Apr 1963.

41 JIKAN NO KYOFU *see* **THE FINAL WAR**

YORU NO HADA *see* **SOFT TOUCH OF NIGHT**

YORU NO NETTAIGYO *see* **BGS OF GINZA**

YOSAKOI JOURNEY (Japan)   F6.5702
  Shochiku Co. *Dist* Shochiku Films of America. Jul **1970** [Los Angeles showing]. Sd; col. 35mm. 91 min.
  Prod Kiyoshi Shimazu. *Dir* Shoji Segawa. *Story-Screenplay* Kazuo Funabashi. *Photog* Sozaburo Shinomura. *Art Dir* Masao Kumagi. *Mus* Taku Izumi.
  Cast: Frankie Sakai (*Ryota Sakamoto*), Chieko Baisho (*Machiko*), Chocho Miyako (*Sei Ueda*), Junzaburo Ban (*Kichigoro Yamashita*), Aiko Nagayama (*Takako*), Shin-ichi Yanagizawa (*Rikizo*), Takuya Fujioka (*Ryotei Katsurai*), Kensaku Morita (*Shinsuke*), Yasushi Koga (*Sanpei Koga*), Yasushi Suzuki, Toshie Kusunoki, Chiharu Kuri, Hiroshi Tatehara, Pinky and the Killers.
  Melodrama. A small railway station near Kochi has three employees: stationmaster Yamashita, Ryota Sakamoto, and Sanpei Koga. Machiko, Ryota's wife, works as a tour guide and would rather play mahjong with the priest or go to the movies with the priest's son Shinsuke than perform her domestic duties. As a result, Ryota falls in love with Takako, the proprietress of a small restaurant. When Machiko goes to a nearby resort with Shinsuke, Ryota follows her, and the two quarrel; Ryota then returns and moves into the station house. Takako brings him lunch every day, and Ryota decides to marry her as soon as he can obtain a divorce from Machiko. Yamashita, who is Takako's father, is unaware that his daughter operates the restaurant and is engaged to the chef. Upon discovering the truth about Takako, Yamashita strikes her, and Ryota realizes that he has misinterpreted her feelings for him. When a landslide destroys a nearby track, the three stop their arguing and join forces to flag down a train headed for disaster. Later, on a festival day, Ryota manages to obtain the stationmaster's approval of Takako's marriage to the chef. Having learned that his wife had asked Takako to bring him his lunch, Ryota returns home to Machiko, who tells him that she is pregnant with his child. *Stationmasters. Guides. Restaurateurs. Cooks. Marriage. Infidelity. Divorce. Filial relations. Pregnancy. Railroad stations. Kochi. Landslides.*
  Note: Released in Japan in Nov **1969** as *Yosakoi ryoko*.

YOSAKOI RYOKO *see* **YOSAKOI JOURNEY**

YOSEI GORASU *see* **GORATH**

YOSEI GORATH *see* **GORATH**

YOTSUYA KAIDAN *see* **ILLUSION OF BLOOD**

"YOU"   F6.5703
  Dist Olympic International Films. 6 Nov **1968** [Champaign, Illinois, showing]. Sd; b&w. 35mm. 71 min.
  Prod Paul Hunt, R. W. Cresse. *Assoc Prod* Ronald Garcia. *Dir* Paul Hunt. *Writ* R. G. Vicry. *Cinematog* H. P. Edwards. *Sd Supv* Phil Josephs.
  Cast: Natasha Shore, Leisha Kai, Linda Reese, Joseph P. Phillips, Carolyn Ornsby, Shelley Williams, Gloria Rogers, Julia White, Maria Joplin, Guadalupe Garcia.
  Sex film. The "subjective camera" draws the viewer into a series of erotic adventures: the whipping of a young woman; an embrace with a grateful female hitchhiker; a response to a voyeur's request to gratify his wife's desires; an interlude with back-alley prostitutes; participation with two women in a cult's depraved initiation rite; a photography session with an aspiring starlet; indulgence in an Oriental massage; and fellatio with a young Mexican in return for helping her to escape the police. *Hitchhikers. Prostitutes. Actors. Models. Mexicans. Orientals. Flagellation. Voyeurism. Troilism. Oral sex. Massage parlors. Rites and ceremonies. Photography.*
  Note: R. G. Vicry and H. P. Edwards are pseudonyms for Ronald Garcia and Paul Hunt.

YOU ARE THE WORLD FOR ME (Austria)   F6.5704
  Erma Film. *Dist* Ring Film Corp. 25 Dec **1964** [New York opening]. Sd; b&w. 35mm. 107 min.
  Prod Karl Ehrlich. *Dir-Writ* Ernst Marischka. *Photog* Sepp Ketterer. *Sets* Fritz Juptner-Jonstorff. *Mus Dir* Anton Profes. *Mus Played by* Vienna Symphony Orchestra. *Cond by* Wilhelm Scheuchter.
  Cast: Rudolf Schock (*Richard Tauber*), Annemarie Düringer (*Christine*), Richard Romanowsky (*Professor Beines*), Fritz Imhoff (*Director Stapler*), Dagny Servaes (*his wife*), Helli Servi, Anni Korin, Gerda Scheyrer, Joachim Brennecke.
  Biographical drama. Tenor-composer Richard Tauber rises from obscurity to international fame, which interrupts his affair with Christine, a ballerina who quits the stage because of a heart condition. When Tauber returns to her, she

is dying. *Singers. Composers. Dancers. Heart disease. Opera. Richard Tauber.*
  Note: Released in Austria in 1953 as *Du bist die Welt für mich*. Reviewed in Austria at 100 min. Alternative U. S. title: *The Richard Tauber Story*. Most of singing soundtrack dubbed from Tauber recordings.

YOU ARE WHAT YOU EAT   F6.5705
  Natoma-Cerberus-Michael Butler-Peter Yarrow. *Dist* Commonwealth United Entertainment, Inc. 24 Sep **1968** [New York opening]. Sd; col (Eastman Color). 35mm. 75 min.
  Prod Peter Yarrow, Barry Feinstein. *Assoc Prod* A. Joseph Tandet. Phillip Ramone. *Dir* Barry Feinstein. *Photog* Barry Feinstein. *Titl* Tom Wilkes. *Film Ed* Howard Alk. *Mus Score* John Simon. *Mus Dir* Peter Yarrow. *Song:* "Memphis" Chuck Berry. *Sung by* Tiny Tim. *Song:* "Family Dog" John Simon. *Sung by* Johnny Herald. *Titl Song* John Simon, Peter Yarrow. *Sung by* Paul Butterfield. *Songs:* "Moments of Soft Persuasion," "Silly Girl," "Don't Remind Me of Time" *comp & sung by* Peter Yarrow. *Song:* "The Wabe" *adapt from* Lewis Carroll's "Alice in Wonderland" & *sung by* John Simon, Peter Yarrow. *Song:* "Nude Dance" *comp & perf by* Hamsa El Din. *Song:* "Be My Baby" Jeff Barry, Ellie Greenwich, Phil Spector. *Sung by* Tiny Tim. *Song:* "My Name Is Jack" *comp & sung by* John Simon. *Song:* "Sonny Boy" Al Jolson, Bud G. De Sylva, Lew Brown, mus, Ray Henderson. *Sung by* Tiny Tim. *Song:* "Come to the Sunshine" Van Dyke Parks. *Sung by* Harper's Bizarre. *Song:* "Teenage Fair" John Simon, Peter Yarrow. *Sung by* Rosko, Dave Dixon. *Song:* "I Got You Babe" Sonny Bono. *Sung by* Tiny Tim, Eleanor Baruchian. *Song:* "Freakout" *comp & perf by* The Electric Flag, John Simon.
  Featuring: Tiny Tim, Peter Yarrow, Paul Butterfield, Barry McGuire, Malcolm Boyd, Super Spade, Harper's Bizarre, The Electric Flag, Clarence Schmidt, Carol Wayne, Rosko, Super Crusader, John Simon, The Family Dog, Hamsa El Din, Carl Franzoni, David Crosby, Lawrence Lipton, Scott Ross, Johnny Herald, Van Dutch, Eleanor Baruchian, Vito's Group.
  Documentary. The film focuses on America's contemporary youth revolution. Plotless in format, the major portion of the film is devoted to rock and folk music performers. Also included are scenes of Father Malcolm Boyd, the Episcopal priest and author, consorting on a beach with a band of hippies; a visit to an institution for wayward boys and girls; teenagers rioting and police brutality; Super Spade, the underground hero murdered by mobsters in San Francisco in 1967 for giving away free marijuana and LSD; anti-Vietnam War demonstrations; advertisements for plastic Nazi helmets; Barry McGuire, the "prophet of doom," dancing in the sun; and shots of hippies sun-worshiping, eating flowers, riding motorcycles, climbing trees, surfing, and indulging in body-painting and love-ins. *Hippies. Musicians. Singers. Police. Priests. Youth. Adolescence. Love-ins. Rock and roll. Demonstrations. Marijuana. LSD. Vietnam War 1964-73. San Francisco.*

YOU CAME TOO LATE (Greece)   F6.5706
  Mirma Films. *Dist* Hellenic Films. 11 Nov **1962** [New York opening]. Sd; b&w. 35mm. 75 min.
  Dir D. Kapsakis. *Screenplay* Giannis Maris.
  Cast: Helen Hatziagyri (*girl*), Andrew Barkoulis (*boy*), D. Papagianopoulos (*father*), Theo Karousos (*uncle*).
  Melodrama. Source: Alexandre Dumas, fils, *La dame aux camélias* (novel: 1848; play: 1852). A young courtesan and an impetuous painter fall in love, but pressure from the painter's family forces them to separate. The courtesan contracts a disease and dies alone under a blanket of camelias. *Painters. Prostitutes.*
  Note: No information on the original title or release of this film has been found.

YOU CAN SUCCEED TOO (Japan)   F6.5707
  Toho Co. Dec **1964** [Los Angeles showing]. Sd; col. 35mm (Tohoscope). 102 min.
  Dir Eizo Sugawa.
  Cast: Franky Sakai, Tadao Takashima, Izumi Yukimura, Keaton Masuda, Mie Hama.
  Musical comedy. No information about the precise nature of this film has been found.
  Note: Released in Japan in 1964 as *Kimimo shussega dekiru*.

YOU CAN'T RUN FAR *see* **WHEN THE CLOCK STRIKES**

YOU CAN'T SPELL "SEX" WITHOUT ... X   F6.5708
  Kirt Films International. *Dist* Distribpix, Inc. ca **1970**. Sd; col. 35mm. 67 min.
  Sex film. A young man sees an old school friend while strolling through a park and accepts his invitation to meet a medium who will be able to predict his future. In reality, the old friend is the procurer for an underground sex cult, and the medium is the cult's high priestess. The young man and his fiancée arrive at the medium's house where they are surprised by the bizarre sexual rites

being performed by the nude cultists. They return that evening to participate in a wild orgy, and as the frenzied activity heightens, they are induced to be married in a "sexual black mass," the performance of which results in the destruction of all the cultists. *Pimps. Mediums. Sexual practices. Cults. Rites and ceremonies. Moral corruption. Orgies. Weddings.*

YOU CAN'T WIN 'EM ALL (Great Britain)   **F6.5709**
S. R. O. *Dist* Columbia Pictures. 24 Jul **1970** [Dallas opening; c1 Jul 1970; LP38029]. Sd (RCA); col (Technicolor). 35mm (Panavision). 97 min. *MPAA rating* GP.
A Gene Corman Production. *Prod* Gene Corman. *Assoc Prod* Harold Buck. *Assoc Prod for Turkey* Ali Cakus. *Dir* Peter Collinson. *2d Unit Dir* Skeets Kelly. *Screenplay* Leo V. Gordon. *Dir Photog* Ken Higgins. *2d Unit Photog* Frank Kingston. *Camera Op* Roy Ford. *2d Unit Camera Op* Ken Withers. *Art Dir* Seamus Flannery. *Asst Art Dir* Bruce Grimes. *Film Ed* Raymond Poulton. *Mus & Main Titl Theme* Bert Kaempfert. *Mus Arr & Main Titl Theme* Herbert Rehbein. *Mus Cond* Muir Mathieson. *Sd* Barrie Copland. *Sd Rec* Arthur Vincent. *Dub Ed* Derek Holding, Archie Ludski. *Asst Dir* Scott Wodehouse. *2d Unit Asst Dir* Tony Buck. *Prod Mgr* Derek Parr. *Location Mgr* Tony Williams. *Cont* Joan Davis. *2d Unit Cont* Kay Rawlings. *Wardrobe for Miss Mercier* Dinah Greet. *Wardrobe* Masada Wilmot. *Turkish Cost* Leyla Suren. *Makeup* Freddie Williamson. *Hairdresser* Betty Glasow. *Casting Dir* Rose Tobias Shaw. *Horsemaster* Jack Cooper.
Cast: Tony Curtis (*Adam Dyer*), Charles Bronson (*Josh Corey*), Michèle Mercier (*Aila*), Grégoire Aslan (*Osman Bey*), Fikret Hakan (*Colonel Elci*), Salih Guney (*Captain Enver*), Patrick Magee (*general*), Tony Bonner (*Reese*), John Acheson (*Davis*), John Alderson (*United States major*), Horst Janson (*Woller*), Leo Gordon (*Bolek*), Reed De Rouen (*United States chief petty officer*), Paul Stassino (*gunner major*), Suna Keskin (*girl in café*), Yuksel Gozen (*Papadopoulos*), Gonia Halil (*madam*), Howard Goorney, Erol Koskin, Ken Buckle, Terry Yorke, Mumtaz Alpaslan, Manny Michael.
Adventure comedy. In 1922, Adam Dyer and Josh Corey, two former soldiers in the U. S. Army, join a band of Turkish mercenaries. Seeking to aid the Sultan of the crumbling Ottoman Empire, they are hired by the local governor, Osman Bey, to escort his three daughters to Smyrna and to protect a gold shipment that is to accompany the three girls and their companion, Aila. Also hired to protect the gold is Colonel Elci, who instead plots to steal the shipment. Eventually Adam discovers that the gold is really lead, but he is informed by Aila that the caravan is secretly carrying a casket full of jewels. Adam, Josh, and Aila agree to share the treasure. Colonel Elci also learns of the jewels, but Aila kills him when he tries to steal them. Aila and Josh then escape with the jewels to Smyrna with Adam in pursuit, but Smyrna has been overrun by revolutionaries. The three are captured and the jewels lost, but they have unwittingly brought an ancient copy of the Koran, which the rebel general had been seeking. The grateful general releases the three to continue their adventures. *Veterans. Americans in foreign countries. Escorts. Royalty. Mercenaries. Revolutionaries. Theft. Murder. Perfidy. Amnesty. Gold. Jewels. Smyrna. Turkey. Ottoman Empire. The Koran.*
Note: Location scenes filmed in Turkey; interior of the Osman Bey Palace filmed at Said Halim Pasha Manor. Opened in London in Nov 1970; running time: 99 min. Prerelease title: *The Dubious Patriots.*

YOU CAN'T WIN 'EM ALL *see* **ONCE YOU KISS A STRANGER**

YOU DON'T NEED PAJAMAS AT ROSIE'S *see* **THE FIRST TIME**

YOU GET WHAT YOU PAY FOR *see* **GET WHAT YOU PAY FOR**

YOU HAVE TO RUN FAST   **F6.5710**
Harvard Film Corp. *Dist* United Artists. 15 May **1961** [Maryland license; c20 Jul 1961; LP20544]. Sd; b&w. 35mm. 71 min.
Prod Robert E. Kent. *Dir* Edward L. Cahn. *Writ* Orville H. Hampton. *Dir Photog* Gilbert Warrenton. *Set Decor* Harry Reif. *Film Ed* Robert Carlisle. *Mus* Richard La Salle. *Sd* Ralph Butler. *Asst Dir* Herbert S. Greene. *Prod Mgr* Joseph Small. *Wardrobe* Einar Bourman, Barbara Maxwell. *Makeup* Harry Thomas. *Hairstyles* Frances Sperry.
Cast: Craig Hill (*Dr. Roger Condon/Frank Harlow*), Elaine Edwards (*Laurie Maitland*), Grant Richards (*Big Jim Craven*), Shepherd Sanders (*Bert Klee*), John Apone (*Toothpick Stan*), Brad Trumbull (*deputy*), Ken Mayer (*Injun George*), Willis Bouchey (*Colonel Maitland*), Max Mellinger (*Doc Rayburn*), Jack Mann (*Lieut. Dan Corbo*), John Clarke (*Chuck*), Claudia Barrett (*Fran*), Ric Marlow (*Jay Rocco*), Jack Kenny (*Lou Miles*), Joel Lewinson (*small boy*).
Crime melodrama. A badly injured detective is brought to Dr. Roger Condon by two gangsters. When the patient dies, Roger identifies the men presumably responsible· for his death, and then, fearing gangland reprisal, hurriedly leaves town. He changes his name to Frank Harlow, takes a job as a sporting goods clerk, and moves into a mountain lodge run by Colonel Maitland, a paraplegic, and his daughter, Laurie. One of the two gangsters, Big

Jim Craven, still hiding from the police, tracks Roger down and devises a plan for eliminating him. But the plot fails when the deputy sheriff recognizes Craven. As a result, the deputy is shot and Roger drops his disguise in order to perform an emergency operation. Craven and his henchmen arrive on the scene; but the sharpshooting Colonel Maitland comes to the rescue, the gangsters are apprehended, and Roger is at last able to stop running away from his past. *Physicians. Gangsters. Salesclerks. Paraplegics. Sheriffs. Murder. Disguise. Lodges (inns).*
Note: May also be known as *Man Missing.*

YOU JUST KILL ME *see* **ARRIVEDERCI, BABY!**

YOU MUST BE JOKING! (Great Britain)   **F6.5711**
Ameran Films. *Dist* Columbia Pictures. 27 Oct **1965** [Cincinnati, Ohio, opening; c1 Sep 1965; LP31986]. Sd; b&w. 35mm. 100 min.
A Charles H. Schneer Production. *Prod* Charles H. Schneer. *Dir* Michael Winner. *Screenplay* Alan Hackney. *Story* Michael Winner, Alan Hackney. *Dir Photog* Geoffrey Unsworth. *Camera Op* Alex Thomson. *Art Dir* Maurice Carter. *Titl Dsgn* Bob Godfrey. *Film Ed* Bernard Gribble. *Mus Comp & Cond* Laurie Johnson. *Songs:* "I'm With You," "I'll Be True to You, Baby" Buddy Bregman, Hal Shaper. *Sd Rec* Wally Milner, Ken Cameron. *Asst Dir* Peter Price. *Prod Mgr* Ted Wallis. *Cont* Eileen Head. *Miss Licudi's Wardrobe* Tony Armstrong. *Constr Mgr* Harry Arbour.
Cast: Michael Callan (*Lieut. Tim Morton*), Lionel Jeffries (*Sergeant-Major McGregor*), Denholm Elliott (*Captain Tabasco*), Wilfrid Hyde-White (*General Lockwood*), Bernard Cribbins (*Sergeant Clegg*), Terry-Thomas (*Major Foskett*), Patricia Viterbo (*Sylvie Tarnet*), Gabriella Licudi (*Annabelle Nash*), Leslie Phillips (*young husband*), Irene Handl (*elderly woman*), Lee Montague (*Staff Sergeant Mansfield*), Gwendolyn Watts (*young wife*), James Villiers (*Bill Simpson*), Tracy Reed (*Poppy Penington*), Miles Malleson (*salesman*), Peter Bull (*ferocious man*), Lance Percival (*young man*), Richard Wattis (*Parkins*), James Robertson-Justice (*librarian*), David Jacobs (*himself, a disc jockey*), Norman Vaughan (*Joe*), Clive Dunn (*doorman*), Ronald Howard (*Cecil*), Graham Stark, Arthur Lowe.
Farce. Major Foskett, a psychological officer in the British Army Medical Corps, devises a 48-hour test of initiative and tries it out on five representative servicemen: Tim Morton, a woman-chasing United States Air Force lieutenant; Sergeant-Major McGregor, a highly disciplined Scotsman; Captain Tabasco, a British aristocrat who trades on his wealth; Staff Sergeant Mansfield of the Army Transport Corps; and Sergeant Clegg, a halfwit. General Lockwood orders these men to complete the test, which consists of finding one's way out of a maze and obtaining a rare breed of rose, an electric hare from a dog track, a Rolls-Royce hood mascot, a set of plaster flying-duck wall decorations, the Lutine Bell from Lloyd's of London, and a signed photograph and lock of hair from television singer Sylvie Tarnet. The men ask servants and girl friends to assist in the scavenger hunt; but when Lieutenant Morton meets Sylvie, he drops his girl friend, Annabelle, for the attractive songstress. All the soldiers achieve moderate success except Sergeant Clegg, who tries to tunnel his way from the maze but is repeatedly recaptured. Lieutenant Morton wins the prize, but he refuses the trophy, resigns his commission, and marries Sylvie Tarnet. Meanwhile, Major Foskett slips up on the project's paperwork, and General Lockwood, his commanding officer, loses his job. *Psychologists. Americans in foreign countries. Aristocrats. Scotch. Singers. Halfwits. Military life. Contests. Labyrinths. London. United States Air Force. Great Britain—Army.*
Note: Location scenes filmed in London. Opened in London in Aug 1965.

YOU ONLY LIVE TWICE (Great Britain)   **F6.5712**
Eon Productions–Danjaq, S. A. *Dist* United Artists. 13 Jun **1967** [New York opening; c13 Jun 1967; LP34526]. Sd; col (Technicolor). 35mm (Panavision). 116 min.
Pres by Albert R. Broccoli, Harry Saltzman. *Prod* Albert R. Broccoli, Harry Saltzman. *Dir* Lewis Gilbert. *Dir Action Seq* Bob Simmons. *2d Unit Dir* Peter Hunt. *Screenplay* Roald Dahl. *Adtl Story Material* Harry Jack Bloom. *Dir Photog* Freddie Young. *2d Unit Photog* Bob Huke. *Aerial Photog* John Jordan. *Underwater Photog* Lamar Boren. *Art Dir* Harry Pottle. *Set Decor* David Ffolkes. *Prod Dsgn* Ken Adam. *Main Titl* Maurice Binder. *Supv Ed* Peter Hunt. *Ed* Thelma Connell. *Mus Comp & Cond & Arr* John Barry. *Titl Song* John Barry, Leslie Bricusse. *Sung by* Nancy Sinatra. *Sd* John Mitchell. *Asst Dir* William P. Cartlidge. *Prod Supv* David Middlemas. *Location Mgr* Robert Watts. *Wardrobe* Eileen Sullivan. *Makeup* Basil Newall, Paul Rabiger. *Hairstyles* Eileen Warwick. *Sp Eff* John Stears. *Tech Adv* Kikumaru Okuda.
Cast: Sean Connery (*James Bond*), Akiko Wakabayashi (*Aki*), Tetsuro Tamba (*Tiger Tanaka*), Mie Hama (*Kissy Suzuki*), Teru Shimada (*Osato*), Karin Dor (*Helga Brandt*), Lois Maxwell (*Miss Moneypenny*), Desmond Llewelyn ("*Q*"), Charles Gray (*Henderson*), Tsai Chin (*Chinese girl*), Bernard Lee ("*M*"), Donald Pleasence (*Ernst Stavro Blofeld*), Alexander Knox (*U. S. President*), Robert Hutton (*president's aide*), Burt Kwouk (*SPECTRE No. 3*),

Michael Chow *(SPECTRE No. 4)*, Diane Cilento *(double)*.

Action melodrama. Source: Ian Fleming, *You Only Live Twice* (London, 1964). While orbiting the earth, a U. S. space capsule is intercepted and drawn into the nose of a mammoth spaceship. The Russians are blamed for the incident, but the real culprit is SPECTRE, an international crime syndicate engaged in provoking a third world war. When Allied missile tracking stations reveal the ship has landed somewhere in Japan, secret agent James Bond is sent to investigate. To convince the enemy he is dead, an elaborate murder and sea burial are staged, enabling Bond to sneak into Japan; despite the precaution, however, Bond's Tokyo contact is killed. Aided by Tiger Tanaka's secret service, Bond learns that Osato Engineering is somehow involved and takes along Tanaka's beautiful secretary, Aki, to investigate the company's shipping enterprises. He is captured by Osato's sadistic but seductive accomplice, Helga Brandt, and left alone in an airborne, pilotless plane, which he somehow manages to land. Bond then surveys the Japanese coastline in his miniature helicopter and pinpoints the center of enemy operations in the vicinity of an extinct volcano. After Aki is murdered by a poison intended for Bond, a Russian space capsule disappears. With the world on the brink of nuclear war, Bond disguises himself as a native fisherman with a beautiful wife, Kissy Suzuki, and moves toward the volcano while Tanaka prepares his commandos for attack. As another U. S. spaceship is launched, Bond and Kissy make their way into the volcano and discover the gigantic headquarters of SPECTRE. Quickly freeing the captured American and Russian astronauts, Bond fights his way to SPECTRE mastermind Ernst Stavro Blofeld, who has just thrown Helga into a pool of piranhas for failing to kill the secret agent. As Tanaka's commandos rush into the volcano, Blofeld sets off a series of tremendous explosions before being knocked into the pool and devoured. The crater and SPECTRE stronghold are destroyed, but Bond and Kissy escape by tunnel in a rubber dinghy and land atop a surfacing British submarine. *Secret agents. Secretaries. Astronauts. Fishermen. Masterminds. Abduction. Murder. Poisoning. Disguise. Space capsules. Syndicates. Helicopters. Nuclear warfare. Volcanoes. Submarines. Japan. Tokyo. Explosions. James Bond.*

Note: Location scenes filmed in Japan. Opened in London in Jun 1967.

YOU ONLY LOVE ONCE (France)   F6.5713

René Thévenet–Euro-Images–Les Films Modernes. *Dist* Sigma III Corp. 15 Jun **1969** [New York opening]. Sd; col (Eastmancolor). 35mm. 95 min. *MPAA rating* G.

Assoc Prod Emile Natan. *Exec Prod* René Thévenet, Louis Duchesne. *Dir* Dirk Sanders. *Screenplay* Dirk Sanders, Paul Soreze. *Photog* Roger Duculot. *Film Ed* Philippe Murcier. *Mus* Jacques Loussier. *Sd* Gérard David. *Asst Dir* Pierre Lambert. *Prod Mgr* Louis Duchesne. *Wardrobe* Pierre Cardin, Christian Dior.

Cast: Karen Blanguernon *(Clara Verly)*, Leslie Bedos *(Julie Verly)*, Frédéric de Pasquale *(Patrice Verly)*, Jean Moussy *(Roger)*, Victor Lanoux *(René)*, René Goliard *(Charles)*, Jean-Paul Moulinot, Tony Kinna, Tessa Sanders, Madeleine Lambert.

Drama. Clara and Patrice Verly live in Lyons with their 8-year-old daughter, Julie. Frustrated in his attempts to make a name for himself as a photographer, Patrice concludes that he will have to go to Paris to further his career, and Clara reluctantly agrees to a separation. The passage of 3 years finds Clara bored with her provincial life; and she also moves to Paris, taking the precocious Julie with her. Although Clara has an amicable reunion with Patrice, who has not had much luck in Paris, the long separation has driven them apart, and they decide to remain friends rather than live together. Enrolling Julie in school, Clara takes a sales job which leads to a beauty contest and ultimately to a successful modeling career. Despite the active social life she now leads, Clara remains discontent, partially because of Julie's demands on her time and the child's unwillingness to accept men other than her father. After Patrice has finally made his mark as a television photographer-director, Clara decides to try to win him back. But when she searches for him in Paris coffee shops and finds him in the company of two girls, she doesn't even stop to speak to him. Upon learning that she is to be sent to America on a modeling job, however, she once more seeks out Patrice, and for the first time since their estrangement they are able to set aside their false pride and communicate. With their love rekindled, Patrice drives his wife and daughter to Orly Airport, confident that when they return they will be a family once again. *Photographers. Models. Television directors. Salesclerks. Marriage. Ambition. Motherhood. Separation (marital). Beauty contests. Lyons. Paris.*

Note: Opened in Paris in Jun 1968 as *Tu seras terriblement gentille*.

YOUNG AMERICANS   F6.5714

The Young Americans. *Dist* Columbia Pictures. 11 Oct **1967** [Charlotte, North Carolina, opening; c1 Nov 1967; LP34868]. Sd; col (Technicolor). 35mm. 104 min.

Pres by Robert Cohn. *Prod* Robert Cohn. *Assoc Prod* Helen Taini. *Dir-Writ* Alex Grasshoff. *Dir Photog* Richard Moore. *Film Ed* David Newhouse. *Mus*

Supv Milton C. Anderson. *Vocal Arr* George Wyle. *Mus Score* Billy Byers. *Choreog* James Bates. *Sd Mix* George Hansen. *Asst Dir* George Marshall, Jr., Larry Kostroff. *Asst to the Prod* Robert Meyers, Jr. *Script Supv* Hazel Hall. *Prod Mgr* Jesse Corallo. *Post-prod Supv* George Grenville. *Wardrobe Supv* Charles Arrico. *Cost* J. W. Robinson Co. *Cinematic Cons* Vilis Lapenieks. *Ch Electrn* Robert Petzoldt. *Head Grip* Frank Lambers.

Participants: Milton C. Anderson *(music teacher)*, Diane Adams, Rod Alemania, Charlie Armstrong, Phil Aubrey, Kathy Austin, Mike Barger, Pat Barker, Janet Bingaman, Jan Bunch, Rick Clark, Ken Collins, Rich Cuilei, Steve Flanagan, Royce Gibson, Karen Graff, Gordon Harkness, Dennis Heath, Steve Henry, Sandi Hornyak, Connie Karcher, Betty Lou Kautto, Bill Kerry, Vicki Lawrence, Larry Lloyd, Katie Mulder, Nancy O'Brien, Gordon Paine, Ralph Pettiford, Ken Prymus, Judy Randel, Ernie Rettino, Barnette Ricci, Sharron Roark, Sandy Scott, Linda Sugars, Judy Thomas, Ana Teresa Vasquez.

Documentary. This documentary covers a cross-country tour made by the Young Americans, a group of teenaged singers founded in 1962 by music teacher Milton C. Anderson. During auditions in southern California, Anderson selects 36 youngsters from the hundreds of applicants who have already obtained parental permission to participate should they qualify. One of those rejected is young Judy Thomas, whom Anderson encourages to take dancing lessons so as to meet the group's standards. Following extensive rehearsals, the Young Americans set out by bus and encounter accommodations mixups, romantic interludes somewhat handicapped by chaperoning arrangements, and occasional acoustical problems. Aside from stopovers at major cities, the youngsters perform at the state prison in Menard, Illinois, where Ken Prymus sings "The Whole World in His Hands." In New York's Algonquin Hotel several of the teenagers don wigs and costumes and do imitations of some of the far-out current entertainers. When the tour concludes in Washington, D. C., Judy Thomas is on hand with news that she has not only learned to dance but has also written a song, "The Road Ahead." After hearing her composition performed on the steps of the Jefferson Memorial, Judy is informed that she has been accepted into the group, and the next stop for the Young Americans is in Europe. *Music teachers. Singers. Dancers. Composers. Adolescence. Patriotism. California. Menard (Illinois). New York City. Washington (District of Columbia). Algonquin Hotel (New York City). Jefferson Memorial (District of Columbia). Illinois State Penitentiary.*

THE YOUNG AND EROTIC FANNY HILL see THE YOUNG EROTIC FANNY HILL

YOUNG AND EVIL (Mexico)   F6.5715

Dominó Films. *Dist* John Alexander Film Associates. 1 Aug **1962** [Philadelphia opening]. Sd; col (Eastman Color). 35mm. 79 min. [Also reviewed at 84 & 90 min.]

Prod Ruben A. Calderón. *Dir* Alfredo B. Crevenna. *Adapt* Julio Alejandro de Castro. *Story* Julio Albo. *Photog* Raúl Martínez Solares. *Art Dir* Salvador Lozano Mena. *Film Ed* Gloria Schoemann. *Mus* Lan Adomián. *Choreog* Rodney. *Sd* Rodolfo Solís, James L. Fields.

Cast: Ninón Sevilla *(Yambao)*, Ramón Gay *(Jorge)*, Rosa Elena Durgel *(Beatriz)*, Ricardo Román, Luis López Puente, Olga Guillot.

Melodrama. When Yambao, a notorious witch's granddaughter, appears on Jorge's Cuban sugar plantation during an outbreak of plague, the slaves blame her for the pestilence and plan to burn her alive. Jorge, however, forbids it, causing the grateful and enamored Yambao to cast a spell binding them together. Refusing to leave the plantation despite her pregnancy, Jorge's wife, Beatriz, contracts the fever. Upon the birth of his son, Jorge begs forgiveness of Beatriz. Her jealousy aroused, the witch vows to kill both wife and son but, relenting, sacrifices herself to the new moon. *Witches. Planters. Plague. Slavery. Human sacrifice. Spells. Infidelity. Pregnancy. Childbirth. Suicide. Plantations. Cuba. The Moon.*

Note: Produced in Mexico in 1956 as *Yambaó*. Also released as *Cry of the Bewitched*.

THE YOUNG AND IMMORAL see THE SINISTER URGE

THE YOUNG AND THE BRAVE   F6.5716

A. C. Lyles Productions. *Dist* Metro-Goldwyn-Mayer, Inc. 29 May **1963** [Los Angeles opening; c6 Mar 1963; LP24117]. Sd (Westrex); b&w. 35mm. 84 min.

An A. C. Lyles Production. *Prod* A. C. Lyles. *Dir* Francis D. Lyon. *Screenplay* Beirne Lay, Jr. *Story* Ronald Davidson, Harry Slott. *Dir Photog* Emmett Bergholz. *Camera Op* Frank McDonald, camera, Rod Tolme. *Asst Camera* A. E. Cowan, Kenneth Peach, Jr., Tom Laughridge. *Art Dir* Paul Sylos, Jr. *Film Ed* Robert Leo. *Mus* Ronald Stein. *Rec Supv* Al Overton, Sr. *Boom Op* Anthony Samaniego. *Rec* Wallace R. Bearden. *Asst Dir* Harry F. Hogan, Robert Shannon. *Asst to the Prod* Harry F. Hogan. *Script Supv* Dick Michaels. *Wardrobe* Jim Taylor. *Makeup* Ted Coodley. *Sp Vis Eff* Roger George. *Prop*

George MacKinnon, William Thebodeaux. *Grip* George Fenaja, Ed Ledgerwood. *Gaffer* Orlon French.

Cast: Rory Calhoun *(Sgt. Ed Brent)*, William Bendix *(Staff Sgt. Peter L. Kane)*, Richard Jaeckel *(Cpl. John Estway)*, Manuel Padilla *(Han)*, Richard Arlen *(Col. Ralph Holbein)*, John Agar *(intelligence officer)*, Robert Ivers *(Pvt. Kirk Wilson)*, Weaver Levy *(Communist soldier)*, Dennis Richards *(stretcher bearer)*, Robert Goshen *(Lieut. Ulysses Nero)*, Willard Lee *(Han's father)*, Beirne Lay, Jr. *(Army major)*, Flame *(a dog)*.

War melodrama. Early in the Korean War, three American soldiers—Sgt. Ed Brent, Staff Sgt. Peter Kane, and Pvt. Kirk Wilson—escape from their North Korean captors, who then pursue the men as they attempt to return to the American lines. A Korean couple who give them shelter are killed by the Communists, while their young son hides in the hills. Despite Kane's objections, Brent takes along the boy, Han, and the abandoned K-9 Corps police dog he has adopted. The boy and his dog become important contributors to the survival effort. After Wilson is killed by a land mine, the group is joined by Corporal Estway, a brainwashed escapee, and he repairs a damaged radio so that they may communicate with their headquarters. They succeed in killing their pursuers, but Han is wounded and becomes separated from the others. An American helicopter lands to pick up the group, but Brent and Kane learn that the Americans plan to shell the area at dawn and refuse to leave until they have found Han. They do find the boy, but before they are rescued the dog is killed. Returning to their headquarters, the two soldiers successfully defend themselves against the charge that they resisted rescue. The wounded Brent is hospitalized and makes plans to adopt Han and take him home to the United States after the war. *Communists. Koreans. Orphans. Escapees. Prisoners of war. Adoption. Brainwashing. Helicopters. Mines (war explosives). Korean War 1950–53. United States Army. Dogs.*

Note: Filmed on location in Ventura County, California. Working title: *Attong.*

YOUNG AND WILLING (Great Britain)   **F6.5717**
Rank Organisation. *Dist* Universal Pictures. 26 Feb **1964** [New York opening; c6 Jun 1963; LP33835]. Sd; b&w. 35mm. 113 min.

A Betty E. Box-Ralph Thomas Production. *Prod* Betty E. Box. *Exec Prod* Earl St. John. *Dir* Ralph Thomas. *Screenplay* Nicholas Phipps, Mordecai Richler. *Dir Photog* Ernest Steward. *Camera Op* James Bawden. *Art Dir* Alex Vetchinsky. *Set Dresser* Arthur Taksen. *Film Ed* Alfred Roome. *Mus Comp & Cond* Norrie Paramor. *Mus:* "*Rhapsody on a Theme by Paganini*" Sergei Rachmaninoff. *Piano Solo* by Edward Rubach. *Jazz Club Seq Played* by Mike Cotton and His Jazzmen. *Sd Rec* Dudley Messenger, Gordon K. McCallum. *Sd Ed* Arthur Ridout. *Asst Dir* Anthony Waye. *Prod Mgr* Charles Orme. *Location Mgr* Donald Toms. *Cont* Gladys Goldsmith. *Cost Dsgn* Yvonne Caffin. *Makeup* W. T. Partleton. *Hairdressing* Betty Sherriff. *Coöp* Citizens of Lincoln (England).

Cast: Virginia Maskell *(Virginia)*, Paul Rogers *(Professor Chown)*, Ian McShane *(Harry)*, John Hurt *(Phil)*, Samantha Eggar *(Josie)*, Catherine Woodville *(Sarah)*, Johnny Sekka *(Reggie)*, David Sumner *(John)*, John Standing *(Arthur)*, Jeremy Brett *(Gilby)*, Johnny Briggs *(Dai)*, Charles Kay *(Tibbs)*, John Barrie *(Mr. Corbett)*, Victor Brooks *(fire chief)*, Ernest Clark *(vice chancellor)*, Denise Coffey *(Jane)*, George A. Cooper *(1st customer)*, Harry Locke *(2d customer)*, Megs Jenkins *(Mrs. Corbett)*, Richard Leech *(police inspector)*, Marianne Stone *(Clara)*, Richard Warner *(coroner)*, John Welsh *(publican)*, Jeremy Young *(policeman)*.

Melodrama. Source: Laurence Dobie and Robert Sloman, *The Tinker* (Stratford-upon-Avon opening: 8 Nov 1960). Among the students at provincial Kilminster University in England, Harry, a scholarship student from a working-class background, stands out because of his intelligence, athletic skill, and restlessness. Harry sees to it that Phil, his roommate, is treated as one of the crowd. While with Josie, his girl friend, at a cocktail party given by Professor Chown, Harry attracts the professor's bored wife, Virginia, who has been having an affair with Gilby, a wealthy student. Harry succumbs to Virginia's advances, but when he asks her to run off with him she breaks the relationship. Harry is humiliated further by Chown's bored reaction to the situation. On rag day Harry enlists the help of Phil, who idolizes him, in tying a banner to the top of the university tower; they perform the feat, but in their descent Phil falls to his death. Though defended by Chown, Harry is expelled. *Students. Lower classes. Roommates. Professors. College life. Infidelity. Practical jokes.*

Note: London opening: Oct 1962 as *The Wild and the Willing*; running time: 123 min; subsequently released at 112 min. Registered for copyright in the U. S. as *The Young and the Willing.*

THE YOUNG ANIMALS   **F6.5718**
American International Pictures. Oct **1968** [New York opening: 11 Dec; c18 Sep 1968; LP36435]. Sd; col (Perfect Color). 35mm. 100 min. [Also reviewed at 93 min; copyright length: 96 min.]

A Maury Dexter Production. *Prod-Dir* Maury Dexter. *Assoc Prod* Hank Tani. *Screenplay* James Gordon White. *Photog* Kenneth Peach. *Set Decor* Harry Reif. *Film Ed* Sidney Levin. *Mus* Les Baxter. *Song:* "*In Big Letters*" writ & sung by The Orphan Egg. *Song:* "*Love Has Got Me Down*" Harley Hatcher. Sung by The American Revolution. *Sd* Brad Trask. *Asst Dir* Robert M. Jones. *Prod Mgr* Harold E. Knox. *Makeup* John Inzerella. *Hairstyles* Wava Green.

Cast: Tom Nardini *(Tony)*, Patty McCormack *(Janet)*, David Macklin *(Bruce)*, Joanna Frank *(Raquel)*, Zooey Hall *(Paco)*, Sammy Vaughn *(Emmet)*, Michael Wood *(Jerry)*, Keith Taylor *(Din-Din)*, Adolph Martinez *(Johnny)*, Alberto Isaac *(Ramon)*, Russ Bender *(Mr. Simms)*, Arthur Peterson *(Mr. Wilson)*, The American Revolution *(themselves)*.

Melodrama. Tony, a Mexican-American teenager who has recently moved to a small border town, finds a great deal of anti-Mexican feeling in the local high school. Assuming peaceful leadership of the Mexican-American students, Tony unsuccessfully tries to get the principal to promote equality in school affairs. Among the students' aims is the dismissal of a particularly bigoted math teacher and football coach, Mr. Simms. Tensions mount as Janet, a liberal-minded student, defies her wealthy, racist boyfriend, Bruce, and becomes friendly with Tony. Bruce and his gang retaliate by raping Raquel, a popular Mexican-American student, and beating up her boyfriend, Paco. Paco seeks to avenge the assault by kidnaping Bruce's friend Din-Din, tying him to the hood of a car, and leaving him unconscious after a wild drive. [According to some sources, the rape precedes Tony's efforts to organize the Mexican-American students and his friendship with Janet. Bruce and his gang assault student picketers, and Paco reacts by kidnaping Din-Din.] Meanwhile, Tony and Janet have organized a grievance committee composed of both Anglo-American and Mexican-American student leaders; but the principal maintains his refusal to see them. During a committee meeting, Bruce and his gang set fire to the cars parked outside and later cause the deaths of Paco and Raquel by forcing their automobile off the road into a ravine. That night, Bruce chases Tony and Janet to his father's airplane junkyard and threatens to kill them with a giant steel wrecking machine; but they escape and summon the police. A few days later, the entire student body pickets the school on behalf of the Mexican-Americans, thus forcing the principal to give a hearing to student demands. *Mexicans. School principals. Schoolteachers. Athletic coaches. Police. Student activism. Racism. High school life. Adolescence. Kidnaping. Revenge. Rape. Murder. Arson. Automobile accidents. Mexican border.*

Note: Filmed in Tucson. Also known as *Born Wild.*

YOUNG APHRODITES (Greece)   **F6.5719**
Minos Films-Anzervos Studios. *Dist* Janus Films. 3 Nov **1966** [Los Angeles opening]. Sd; b&w. 35mm. 89 min.

Pres by Protelco Films. *Prod* George Zervos, Nikos Koundouros. *Dir* Nikos Koundouros. *Screenplay* Vassilis Vassilikos, Kostas Sphikas. *Dir Photog* Giovanni Variano. *Camera* Takis Georgeopoulos, Savas Kalogeras. *Film Ed* George Tsaoulis. *Mus* Yannis Markopoulos. *Sd* Tasis Palatsiolis, T. Kontos.

Cast: Takis Emmanouel *(Tsakalos)*, Eleni Prokopiou *(Arta)*, Vangelis Joannides *(Skymnos)*, Cleopatra Rota *(Chloë)*, Anestis Vlachos *(Erster Hirte)*, Yannis Jeannino *(Molassas)*, Kostas Papakonstantinou *(Stummer Hirte)*.

Drama. Inspired by: Longus, *Daphnis and Chloë.* Theocritus, *Idylls.* A band of Greek shepherds come down from the mountains in search of new pastures, but they lose their way and wander without water across desert valleys. Then Skymnos, a 10-year-old boy, discovers a small village near the sea. All the men of the village are away fishing, and the women hide in fear of the strangers wrapped in sheep hides. Little Skymnos, who has never seen the sea before, is fascinated by this new world. Even more, he is enchanted by 12-year-old Chloë, whom he devotedly follows about the village. One morning a sudden rainstorm drives the youngsters into a cave where they find a village woman, Arta, making passionate love to Tsakalos, one of the shepherds. Disturbed and confused by what they have seen, the children run away. When the rains increase, the shepherds decide to move south, and they pull the protesting Skymnos along with them; but he eventually breaks free and runs back to his beloved Chloë. He finds her on the beach, passively giving herself to a mute shepherd boy. Wild with anger, Skymnos clutches a dead bird belonging to Chloë and drags it into the surf. He stands silently in the water until a giant wave carries him to his death. *Children. Shepherds. Mutes. Rural life. Sexual initiation. Adolescence. Suicide. Chloë.*

Note: Filmed on the island of Rhodes and on the coast of Attica in 1962. Released in Greece as *Mikres Aphrodites*; running time: 98 min.

YOUNG BILLY YOUNG   **F6.5720**
Talbot-Youngstein Productions. *Dist* United Artists. 17 Sep **1969** [Denver, Colorado, opening; c9 Sep 1969; LP37274]. Sd; col (DeLuxe). 35mm. 88 min. *MPAA rating* G.

Prod Max E. Youngstein. *Assoc Prod* J. Paul Popkin. *Dir-Writ* Burt Kennedy. *Dir Photog* Harry Stradling, Jr. *Art Dir* Stan Jolley. *Set Decor* Richard Friedman. *Film Ed* Otho Lovering. *Mus* Shelly Manne. *Titl Song*

Shelly Manne, Ernie Sheldon. *Sung by* Robert Mitchum. *Sd Mix* Al Overton, Jr. *Mus Ed* Richard Carruth. *Sd Eff* Frank Warner. *Asst Dir* Maxwell O. Henry. *Prod Coörd* Harold Nyby. *Wardrobe* Jerry Alpert. *Makeup* Paul Stanhope. *Hairstyles* Judy Alexander. *Sp Photog Eff* Howard A. Anderson Co. *Prop* Richard Rubin.

Cast: Robert Mitchum *(Kane)*, Angie Dickinson *(Lily Beloit)*, Robert Walker, Jr. *(Billy Young)*, David Carradine *(Jesse Boone)*, Jack Kelly *(John Behan)*, John Anderson *(Frank Boone)*, Deana Martin *(Evvie Cushman)*, Paul Fix *(Charlie)*, Willis Bouchey *(Doc Cushman)*, Parley Baer *(Bell)*, Bob Anderson *(gambler)*, Rodolfo Acosta *(Mexican officer)*, Chris Mitchum *(Kane's son)*.

Western melodrama. Source: Will Henry, *Who Rides With Wyatt?* (New York, 1955). Hired killers Billy Young and Jesse Boone assassinate a Mexican general and flee to the Texas border. When Billy's horse stumbles, Jesse abandons him, and Billy encounters Kane, former sheriff of Dodge City who is searching for the murderer of his son. Kane offers to take Billy to New Mexico, where he has accepted the job of deputy marshal, to try and clear Billy of the murder charge. Once in town, however, Kane discovers that he has trouble of his own. The town boss, John Behan, advises him that there is no room for a lawman; later, dancehall girl Lily Beloit, whom Behan considers his private property, warns Kane that Behan and his associate Frank Boone are planning to kill him. Aware that Boone is the man who murdered his son, Kane refuses to leave town. Events come to a climax when young Jesse is imprisoned for accidentally killing old Doc Cushman while aiming for Kane. Kane discovers that Jesse is Boone's son and plans to use him to force a confrontation with Boone; but Billy, in an attempt to prevent the shooting, frees Jesse. Though Billy later offers to help when he learns from Lily about the murder of Kane's son, Kane knocks Billy unconscious and locks him in jail. When the shootout finally comes, both Behan and the elder Boone are killed. Kane takes Lily away to get married, and Billy becomes the deputy marshal. *Hired killers. Fugitives. Sheriffs. United States marshals. Dancehall girls. Murder. Revenge. Jailbreaks. New Mexico. Texas.*

Note: Location scenes filmed near Tuscon, Arizona. Working title: *Who Rides With Kane?*

YOUNG CASSIDY (United States/Great Britain)   **F6.5721**

Sextant Films. *Dist* Metro-Goldwyn-Mayer, Inc. 22 Mar **1965** [New York opening; c11 Jan 1965; LP29819]. Sd (Westrex); col (Metrocolor). 35mm. 108 min.

A John Ford Production. *Prod* Robert D. Graff, Robert Emmett Ginna. *Assoc Prod* Michael Killanin. *Dir (see note)* Jack Cardiff, John Ford. *Screenplay* John Whiting. *Dir Photog* Ted Scaife. *Camera Op* Jack Atchelor. *Art Dir* Michael Stringer. *Main Titl* Maurice Binder. *Film Ed* Anne V. Coates. *Mus Comp* Sean O'Riada. *Mus Dir* Marcus Dods. *Sd Mix* Robert Allen. *Dub Ed* Winston Ryder. *Asst Dir* John Quested. *Prod Supv* Teddy Joseph. *Cont* Phyllis Crocker. *Cost Dsgn* Margaret Furse. *Makeup* Ernest Gasser. *Hairstyles* Maud Onslow. *Casting Dir* Miriam Brickman.

Cast: Rod Taylor *(John Cassidy)*, Flora Robson *(Mrs. Cassidy)*, Jack MacGowran *(Archie)*, Sian Phillips *(Ella)*, T. P. McKenna *(Tom)*, Julie Ross *(Sara)*, Robin Sumner *(Michael)*, Philip O'Flynn *(Mick Mullen)*, Maggie Smith *(Nora)*, Julie Christie *(Daisy Battles)*, Pauline Delany *(Bessie Ballynoy)*, Edith Evans *(Lady Gregory)*, Michael Redgrave *(W. B. Yeats)*, Arthur O'Sullivan *(foreman)*, Joe Lynch, Vincent Dowling *(hurlers)*, Tom Irwin *(constable)*, John Cowley *(barman at Cat & Cage)*, Bill Foley *(publisher's clerk)*, John Franklin *(bank teller)*, Harry Brogan *(Murphy)*, Anne Dalton *(neighbor)*, Donal Donnelly, Martin Crosbie *(hearsemen)*, Fred Johnson *(cab driver)*, Eddie Golden *(Captain White)*, Chris Curran *(man in Phoenix Park)*, James Fitzgerald *(Charlie Ballynoy)*, Shivaun O'Casey *(Lady Gregory's maid)*, Harold Goldblatt *(Abbey Theatre manager)*, Ronald Ibbs *(theatre attendant)*, May Craig, May Cluskey *(women in foyer)*, Members of the Abbey Theatre Company.

Biographical drama. Source: Sean O'Casey, *Mirror in My House* (New York, 1956). In Dublin in 1911 during a period of growing protest against British rule, young John Cassidy is a laborer by day and a pamphleteer by night. Cassidy is a member of both the Irish Transport and General Workers Union and the Irish Citizens Army, which is trained for uprisings against the British. When the pamphlets he has written incite riots, Cassidy realizes that he can do more for his people with the pen than with the sword. In the course of a riot, Cassidy rescues Daisy Battles, a fiery music hall dancer, and they soon become lovers. Their affair is short-lived, however, and Cassidy becomes involved with Nora, a bookshop clerk who encourages his writing and falls in love with him. He brings a play he has written to the Abbey Theatre; and though it is rejected, another of his plays, *The Shadow of a Gunman*, is accepted and successfully produced, as are two subsequent plays. The opening of *The Plough and The Stars*, which deals with religion, sex, and patriotism in Ireland, causes the audience to riot, and he loses many friends; but he is undeterred and is soon

acclaimed as Ireland's outstanding young playwright. Nora realizes that Cassidy no longer needs her, and he departs for England and international acclaim. *Playwrights. Pamphleteers. Dancers. Salesclerks. Uprisings. Patriotism. Labor unions. Music halls. Bookshops. Ireland—History. Dublin. Sean O'Casey. Abbey Theatre.*

Note: Filmed on location in and around Dublin. Opened in London in Feb 1965; running time: 110 min. Original director John Ford was replaced by Jack Cardiff, who receives screen credit.

YOUNG DILLINGER   **F6.5722**

Zimbalist Co. *Dist* Allied Artists. Apr **1965** [c1 Mar 1965; LP31458]. Sd; b&w. 35mm. 102 min.

Prod Alfred Zimbalist. *Assoc Exec Prod* Byron Roberts. *Dir* Terry O. Morse. *Screenplay* Donald Zimbalist, Arthur Hoerl. *Orig Story* Donald Zimbalist. *Photog* Stanley Cortez. *Art Dir* Don Ament. *Film Ed* Terry O. Morse. *Mus* Shorty Rogers. *Sd* Harold Lewis. *Asst Dir* Robert Shannon.

Cast: Nick Adams *(John Dillinger)*, Robert Conrad *(Pretty Boy Floyd)*, John Ashley *(Baby Face Nelson)*, Mary Ann Mobley *(Elaine)*, Victor Buono *(Professor Hoffman)*, Dan Terranova *(Homer Van Meter)*, John Hoyt *(Dr. Wilson)*, Reed Hadley *(Federal Agent Parker)*, Robert Osterloh *(Federal Agent Baum)*, Anthony Caruso *(Rocco)*, Art Baker *(warden)*, Gene Roth *(justice of peace)*, Ayllene Gibbons *(justice of peace's wife)*, Frank Gerstle *(watchman)*, Emile Meyer *(Detective Jergins)*, Beverly Hills *(Floyd's girl)*, Harvey Gardner *(Mills)*, Helen Kay Stephens *(Van Meter's girl)*, Patty Joy Harmon *(Nelson's girl)*, Sol Gorse, Wally Rose *(guards)*, Walter Sande *(judge)*, Ted Knight *(Johnsyn)*, Mike Masters *(driver)*, Robert Raymond, Charles Sloan.

Biographical drama. John Dillinger and his girl friend, Elaine, decide to rob her father's safe. They are caught, and Mr. Johnsyn begs Dillinger to take the blame on himself. Dillinger receives a long sentence and in prison meets Baby Face Nelson, Pretty Boy Floyd, and Homer Van Meter. Dillinger gains the warden's favor in a fake jail riot and then escapes, later freeing his friends. They form a gang with their girls and with the help of Professor Hoffman become the most wanted criminals in the United States. Elaine wants to get married and leave their life of crime because she is pregnant, and when Dillinger refuses her request, she betrays him to the FBI. Armed Federal agents surround the gang, and only Dillinger escapes; but eventually he is hunted down. *Gangsters. Molls. Prison wardens. Informers. Robbery. Jailbreaks. Pregnancy. Perfidy. Prisons. John Dillinger. Charles "Pretty Boy" Floyd. George "Baby Face" Nelson. United States—Federal Bureau of Investigation.*

THE YOUNG DOCTORS   **F6.5723**

Drexel Films–Millar/Turman Productions. *Dist* United Artists. 23 Aug **1961** [New York opening; c24 Aug 1961; LP21040]. Sd; b&w. 35mm. 100 min.

Prod Stuart Millar, Lawrence Turman. *Dir* Phil Karlson. *Screenplay* Joseph Hayes. *Cinematog* Arthur J. Ornitz. *Art Dir* Angelo Laiacona. *Prod Dsgn* Richard Sylbert. *Film Ed* Robert Swink. *Mus* Elmer Bernstein. *Sd* Jim Shields. *Asst Dir* Jim Di Gangi. *Cost* Ruth Morley. *Tech Adv* Dr. Charles F. Begg, of St. Luke's Hospital. *Filmed with the assistance of* The American Medical Association.

Cast: Fredric March *(Dr. Joseph Pearson)*, Ben Gazzara *(Dr. David Coleman)*, Dick Clark *(Dr. Alexander)*, Ina Balin *(Cathy Hunt)*, Eddie Albert *(Dr. Charles Dornberger)*, Phyllis Love *(Mrs. Alexander)*, Edward Andrews *(Bannister)*, Aline MacMahon *(Dr. Lucy Grainger)*, Arthur Hill *(Tomaselli)*, Rosemary Murphy *(Miss Graves)*, Barnard Hughes *(Dr. Kent O'Donnell)*, Joseph Bova *(Dr. Shawcross)*, George Segal *(Dr. Howard)*, Matt Crowley *(Dr. Rufus)*, Dick Button *(operating intern)*, William Hansen *(x-ray technician)*, Addison Powell *(board physician)*, Ronald Reagan *(narrator)*, Dolph Sweet, Ella Smith, Nora Helen Spens, M. D.

Drama. Source: Arthur Hailey, *The Final Diagnosis* (Garden City, New York, 1959). When young Dr. David Coleman arrives at a large New York hospital to join the pathology staff, he is greeted with hostility by aging chief pathologist Dr. Joseph Pearson, who regards Coleman's arrival as a personal criticism of his competence. The two men first clash when David demands that three separate blood tests be made to determine whether an expectant mother's blood has become sensitized. Irritated by the young man's superior attitude, Pearson refuses to order the serum necessary for the third test. As the days pass, David becomes emotionally involved with Cathy Hunt, a student nurse troubled by a knee tumor. To determine whether the condition is cancerous, Pearson orders a biopsy. Following an examination, Pearson decides the tumor is malignant and that Cathy's leg must be amputated if her life is to be saved. Though David disagrees, he accepts the older man's diagnosis and persuades Cathy to submit to the operation. Meanwhile, because of Pearson's failure to order the blood test serum, the wife of a resident intern named Dr. Alexander is in danger of losing her newborn child. When the third test is finally made, it is learned that the woman's blood *had* become sensitized. After bitterly denouncing Pearson for his carelessness, Mrs. Alexander's physician, Dr. Dornberger, makes a desperate effort to save the baby's life by performing an exchange transfusion, total replacement of the infant's blood. Filled with remorse, Pearson submits his resignation. When the Alexander baby survives the transfusion, David tries to persuade Pearson, for whom he has developed a growing respect, to withdraw his resignation. But even though Pearson's diagnosis of Cathy's tumor was correct, he decides that it is time for him to leave. Confident that David is a worthy successor, the old man packs his few belongings and leaves the hospital. *Physicians. Surgeons. Pathologists. Nurses. Pregnancy. Blood transfusion. Old age. Cancer. Tumors. Hospitals. New York City.*

Note: Filmed in New York City's Women's Hospital, Manhattan General Hospital, and St. Luke's Hospital; and Vassar Brothers Hospital, Poughkeepsie, New York. Also presented on television's *Studio One,* 9 and 16 Dec 1957, under the title *No Deadly Machine.*

THE YOUNG EROTIC FANNY HILL   F6.5724
Joe Sarno. *Dist* Associated Film Distributors of California. ca **1970.** Sd; col. 35mm. 80 min.

Dir Joe Sarno.

Cast: Ginny Hamil, Nick Sales.

Melodrama. Lenore leaves her close friend Fanny and moves to a large city. Lenore and her two new roommates are hard-pressed for money, and they turn to modeling in the nude for employment. Despite their newfound financial security, the three women are not content with their sex lives. Soon they are seducing one another's boyfriends and even engaging in lesbian activities among themselves. Fanny arrives and demonstrates a more satisfying way of lovemaking to the three young women. *Models. Roommates. Nudity. Lesbianism. Seduction. Employment—Women. Sexual techniques.*

Note: Also known as *The Young and Erotic Fanny Hill.*

YOUNG FURY   F6.5725
A. C. Lyles Productions. *Dist* Paramount Pictures. Feb **1965** [c31 Dec 1964; LP29817]. Sd; col (Technicolor). 35mm (Techniscope). 80 min.

Prod A. C. Lyles. *Dir* Christian Nyby. *Screenplay* Steve Fisher. *Story* Steve Fisher, A. C. Lyles. *Dir Photog* Haskell Boggs. *Camera Op* Tom Morris. *Camera Asst* James Hawley. *Art Dir* Hal Pereira, Arthur Lonergan. *Set Dir* Sam Comer, Ralph S. Hurst. *Film Ed* Marvin Coil. *Mus* Paul Dunlap. *Sd Mix* Harold Lewis. *Rec* Ray Cossar. *Boom Op* Bud Parman. *Asst Dir* Michael Caffey, Howard Roessel. *Prod Mgr* Frank Caffey. *Asst Prod Mgr* Curtis Mick. *Unit Prod Mgr* Kenneth DeLand. *Script Supv* Marvin Weldon. *Cost* Hazel Hegarty, Buddy Clark. *Makeup* Wally Westmore, Jack Stone. *Hairstyles* Hedvig Mjorud. *Casting* Ed Morse. *Still Photog* Talmadge Morrison. *Prop* Earl Olin. *Grip* Murray Young. *Gaffer* Earl Crowell. *Wrangler* Tommy Sutton.

Cast: Rory Calhoun *(Clint McCoy),* Virginia Mayo *(Sara McCoy),* Lon Chaney, [Jr.] *(bartender),* Richard Arlen *(Sheriff Jenkins),* John Agar *(Dawson),* Preston Pierce *(Tige McCoy),* Linda Foster *(Sally Miller),* Bob Biheller *(Biff),* Merry Anders *(Alice),* Joan Huntington *(Kathy),* Marc Cavell *(Pancho),* Jody McCrea *(Stone),* Rex Bell, Jr. *(farmer),* William Wellman, Jr. *(Peters),* Reg Parton *(Jeb),* Jay Ripley *(Slim),* Kevin O'Neal *(Curly),* Jerry Summers *(Gabbo),* Fred Alexander *(Pony),* Dal Jenkins *(Sam),* William Bendix *(blacksmith),* Steve Condit, Sailor Vincent, Jorge Moreno, Bill Clark, actor, Dave Dunlop, Jesse Wayne, Robert Miles, Eddie Hice, Fred Krone, Joe Finnegan, Kent Hays.

Western drama. Tige McCoy and his friends are riding in search of excitement when they learn that Tige's father, Clint, has come back to his hometown, pursued by the ruthless Dawson gang. Years ago, Clint had left town because of his wife, Sara's, unfaithfulness, leaving her with the infant, Tige. Believing his mother dead and hating his father for deserting them, Tige returns to watch the Dawsons confront his father. Tige and his gang take over the town and encounter Sara, who is now the local saloonkeeper, but she is unrecognized by her son. Tige finally faces Clint in a showdown but is outsmarted and humiliated by his father. When the Dawson gang finally arrives, Tige refuses to help Clint; Sara grabs a gun, but she is shot. Before dying, however, she tells Tige the truth about her separation from Clint, and he and his friends save his father from the outlaws. *Gunfighters. Gangs. Saloon keepers. Infidelity. Desertion. Filial relations. Revenge.*

THE YOUNG GIRLS OF ROCHEFORT (France)   F6.5726
Parc Film–Madeleine Films. *Dist* Warner Bros.–Seven Arts, Inc. Jan **1968** [New York opening: 11 Apr; c1 Dec 1967; LP35743]. Sd; col (Technicolor). 35mm. 125 min.

A Mag Bodard–Gilbert de Goldschmidt Production. *Prod* Gilbert de Goldschmidt. *Exec Prod* Mag Bodard. *Dir* Jacques Demy. *2d Unit Dir* Charles Chieusse. *Orig Story–Screenplay* Jacques Demy. *Dir Photog* Ghislain Cloquet. *Asst Camera* Emmanuel Machuel, Jean-Paul Lemaitre. *Sets* Bernard Evein. *Asst Set Dsgn* Georges Glon, Claude Pignot. *Set Dresser* Louis Seuret. *Film Ed* Jean Hamon. *Asst Ed* Claudio Ventura. *Mus Writ & Dir* Michel Legrand. *Lyr* Jacques Demy. *English Lyr* Julian More, W. Earl Brown. *Choreog & Asst*

to Choreog Norman Maen, Pamela Hart, Maureen Bright. *Sd* Jacques Maumont. *Asst Dir* Michel Romanoff, Alain Franchet, Jacques Barratier, Claude Miler, Bernard Gilson. *Prod Mgr* Philippe Dussart. *Unit Mgr* Michel Choquet, René Pascal. *Location Unit Mgr* Charles Chieusse. *Script Girl* Annie Maurel. *Cost* Jacqueline Moreau, Marie-Claude Fouquet. *Robes* Jean-Marie Armand. *Hats* Jean Barthet. *Dresser* Odette Le Barbenchon, Laurence Clairval, Christiane Fageol. *Makeup* Aïda Carange, Janine Jarreau, Luc Durand, Christiane Sauvage. *Hairdresser* Carita-Edina Habik. *Stills* Hélène Jeanbrau. *Boom Op* Jean Gaudelet. *Props* Angelo Rizzi, Joseph Gerhardt. *Ch Rigger* Bernard Largemains.

Cast—Principals: Catherine Deneuve *(Delphine Garnier),* Françoise Dorléac *(Solange Garnier),* George Chakiris *(Etienne),* Grover Dale *(Bill),* Gene Kelly *(Andy Miller),* Danielle Darrieux *(Yvonne),* Jacques Perrin *(Maxence),* Michel Piccoli *(Simon Dame),* Pamela Hart *(Judith),* Leslie North *(Esther),* Jacques Riberolles *(Guillaume Lancien),* Henri Crémieux *(Dutrouz),* Patrick Jeantet *(Boubou),* Geneviève Thénier *(Josette),* René Bazart *(Pépé),* Dorothée Blank *(passerby),* Agnès Varda *(nun),* Daniel Mocquay *(sailor).* Bernard Fradet, Rémy Brozeck, Daniel Gall, Véronique Duval, Pierre Caden.

Cast—The Singing Voices: Anne Germain *(Delphine),* Claude Parent *(Solange),* Romuald *(Etienne),* José Bartel *(Bill),* Donald Burke *(Andy),* Jacques Revaux *(Maxence),* Georges Blaness *(Simon),* Claudine Meunier *(Esther),* Christiane Legrand *(Judith),* Jean Stout *(Guillaume),* Olivier Bonnet *(Boubou),* Alice Gerald *(Josette).*

Cast—The Dancers: Peter Ardran, Wendy Barry, Sarah Butler, Ann Chapman, Jane Darling, Tudor Davies, Lindsay Dolan, John MacDonald, Keith Drummond, Maureen Evans, Tara Fernando, Sarah Flemington, Johnny Greenland, Leo Guerard, David Hepburn, Bob Howe, Alix Kirsta, Jerry Manley, Tony Manning, Tom Merrifield, Connel Miles, Albin Pahernik, Nicky Temperton, Barrie Wilkinson, Maureen Willsher.

Cast—The Singers: Sue Allen, singer, George E. Becker, W. Earl Brown, Ronald D. Hicklin, Frank Allen Howren, Thomas D. Kenny, Judith E. Lawler, Bill Lee, Diana K. Lee, Gilda Maiken, Gene Merlino, Joseph A. Pryor, Ronald T. Reeve, Sally Stevens, Sara Jane Tallman, Robert Tebow, Jackie Ward.

Musical comedy. Boat salesmen Etienne and Bill arrive in Rochefort-sur-Mer with a dance troupe and attempt to establish an open-air fair. When their girl friends leave the company, the salesmen scour the city for replacements. In so doing, they encounter twin sisters, Delphine and Solange Garnier, music teachers and dancers. The twins' mother, Yvonne, owns a café and dreams of her old lover, Monsieur Dame, proprietor of a nearby music shop. Meanwhile, the sailor Maxence paints a portrait of the perfect female, and later discovers his ideal embodied in Delphine. Concert pianist Andy Miller discovers the manuscript of a masterful concerto penned by Solange, with whom he subsequently falls in love. The sisters perform at the fair, where they are a great success, but they resist entreaties to join the troupe. Instead, Solange finds happiness with Andy; Delphine meets the adoring Maxence; and Yvonne and Monsieur Dame are reunited. *Songs:* "Arrivée des camionneurs," "Le pont transbordeur," "Chanson de Maxence," "Chanson de Delphine à Lancien," "Marins, amis, amants ou maris," "Chanson de Simon," "La femme coupée en morceaux," "Chanson d'un jour d'été," "Andy amoureux," "Chanson des jumelles," "Chanson d'Andy," "Chanson de Solange," "Chanson de Delphine," "Nous voyageons de ville en ville," "Chanson d'Yvonne," "De Hambourg à Rochefort," "Dans le port de Hambourg," "Les rencontres," "Toujours jamais," "Kermesse," "Départ des camionneurs." *Salesmen. Dancers. Twins. Sisters. Music teachers. Sailors. Painters. Pianists. Composers. Courtship. Family life. Fairs. Cafes. Music stores. Rochefort-sur-Mer.*

Note: Location scenes filmed in Rochefort-sur-Mer. Opened in Paris in Mar 1967 in 70mm as *Les demoiselles de Rochefort;* running time: 120 min.

THE YOUNG GO WILD (West Germany)   F6.5727
Ultra Film. *Dist* Manson Distributing Corp., Paul Mart Productions. 12 Sep **1962** [Los Angeles opening]. Sd; b&w. 35mm. 88 min.

Prod Herbert Sennewald. *Dir* Alfred Vohrer. *Script* Harald G. Petersson. *Photog* Kurt Hasse. *Art Dir* Mathias Matthies, Ellen Schmidt. *Film Ed* Ira Oberberg. *Mus* Ernst Simon. *Sd* Werner Schlagge, Werner Pohl. *Prod Mgr* Heinz Karchow, Ulrich Misseling. *Prod Supv* Josef Wolf. *Legal Cons* Paul Ronge.

Cast: Peter Van Eyck *(Dr. Knittel),* Christian Wolff *(Fabian König),* Heidi Brühl *(Tonia Anders),* Corny Collins *(Florence Eikelberg),* Hans Nielsen *(Dr. Senftenberg),* Erica Beer *(Erna Kallies),* Walter Clemens *(Jules Bregulla),* Richard Münch *(Mr. König),* Alice Treff *(Mrs. König),* Wolfgang Koch *(Joachim Eikelberg),* Claus Wilcke *(Günther Steppe),* Jörg Holmer *(Roger Richter),* Bum Krüger, Joseph Offenbach.

Melodrama. Source: Walter Ebert, *Verbrechen nach Schulschluss* (Baden-Baden, 1956). Asked by a teacher to rescue a maltreated dog from a coalyard, Fabian König is caught scaling the property fence and charged with theft. The youth's teacher denies all knowledge of the incident, and his wealthy parents likewise disbelieve his story. Expelled from school, he becomes the leader of a gang of schoolmates. The group embarks on thefts, first as a test of daring and later more earnestly, using the profits to decorate their headquarters and to finance parties at which moral standards are relaxed. Fabian contacts Bregulla, a receiver of stolen goods. Bregulla is the tenant and lover of the promiscuous Erna Kallies, at whose house Fabian meets Tonia, an orphan and runaway. Fabian falls in love with Tonia, arousing the jealousy of his permissive girl friend, Florence, who claims that Tonia is Bregulla's mistress. Arriving at Erna's house, Fabian interrupts Bregulla as he is attempting to rape Tonia. The girl escapes and goes into hiding, and later that evening Bregulla is found murdered. Fabian is arrested, and, unable to find Tonia to testify on his behalf, he is convicted of manslaughter. Dr. Knittel, the prison doctor, believes in the youth's innocence, however, and conducts his own investigation, uncovering the true murderer, Erna. Tonia reappears, and Fabian, sentenced to serve a 1-year sentence for robbery, knows that she will wait for him. *Students. Schoolteachers. Juvenile delinquents. Orphans. Gangs. Physicians. Fences (for stolen goods). Mistresses. Adolescence. Injustice. Manslaughter. Theft. Rape. Jealousy. Criminals—Rehabilitation.*

Note: Exteriors filmed in Hamburg. Opened in West Berlin in Jun 1959 as *Verbrechen nach Schulschluss;* running time: 106 min.

YOUNG GUNS OF TEXAS F6.5728

Associated Producers, Inc. *Dist* Twentieth Century–Fox Film Corp. 2 Jan **1963** [Los Angeles opening; c2 Dec 1962; LP23851]. Sd; col (DeLuxe). 35mm (CinemaScope). 78 min.

Prod-Dir Maury Dexter. *Exec Prod* Robert L. Lippert. *Writ* Henry Cross. *Dir Photog* John Nickolaus, Jr. *Set Decor* Harry Reif. *Supv Film Ed* Jodie Copelan. *Film Ed* Richard Einfeld. *Mus Comp & Cond* Paul Sawtell, Bert Shefter. *Titl Song* Paul Sawtell, Bert Shefter, John Herring. *Sung by* Kenny Miller. *Sd* William Bernds, Harry M. Leonard. *Supv Sd Ed* Jack Cornall. *Asst Dir* Clarence Eurist. *Prod Supv* Harold E. Knox. *Script Supv* Dixie McCoy. *Wardrobe* Wesley Sherrard. *Makeup* Bob Mark. *Prop Master* Jockey Liebgold.

Cast: James Mitchum *(Morgan Coe),* Alana Ladd *(Lily Glendenning),* Jody McCrea *(Jeff Shelby),* Chill Wills *(Sam Shelby),* Gary Conway *(Tyler),* Barbara Mansell *(Martha Jane Canary),* Robert Lowery *(Jesse Glendenning),* Troy Melton *(Luke),* Fred Krone *(Pike),* Alex Sharp *(Red),* Robert Hinkle *(Sheriff Hubbard),* Will Wills *(cowhand).*

Western melodrama. Tyler Duane is expelled from West Point shortly after the Civil War when his brother, a Union officer, is accused of stealing Army funds. Determined to return the money, Tyler rides to a Texas town seeking his brother, who has joined a band of Confederate soldiers. In town Tyler befriends Jeff Shelby, the rowdy son of preacher Sam Shelby, and Morgan Coe, a young man who was reared by Comanches. Morgan dances with Lily Glendenning at a church dance, but Lily's father, a cattle baron who disapproves of Morgan, sends his gunman to break up the couple. In the ensuing fight, Glendenning's man is killed, and Tyler, Morgan, and Jeff flee. Lily meets Morgan out of town, and Sam Shelby marries them. All agree to help Tyler find his brother, who is headed toward Apache territory, and recover the money. En route they are joined by Martha Jane Canary, a rancher who has been rustling Glendenning's cattle. The group, pursued by Glendenning and his men, finds Tyler's brother murdered, apparently by the soldiers in a squabble over the money. By the time Tyler and his friends catch up with the soldiers, the patrol has suffered an Apache attack. Greed over the money causes tension to mount within the civilian group; and Lily and Morgan realize that they married in defiance only. Glendenning and his men arrive as the Indians are turning their attention to Tyler's group. In the melee both Lily's father and Morgan are killed. Tyler recovers the stolen money and plans to clear his name, then return to Texas to settle down with Lily. *Brothers. Soldiers. Apache Indians. Preachers. Ranchers. Rustlers. Theft. Smalltown life. Fatherhood. Reputation. Marriage. Murder. Greed. Texas. United States Military Academy. United States—History—Civil War.*

Note: Location scenes filmed in Big Bend National Park, Texas. Henry Cross is a pseudonym for Harry Spalding.

YOUNG GUY GRADUATES (Japan) F6.5729

Toho Co. May **1969** [Los Angeles showing]. Sd; col (Eastmancolor). 35mm. 90 min.

Dir Jun Fukuda. *Screenplay* Yasuo Tanami. *Photog* Yuzuru Aizawa. *Art Dir* Yoshibumi Honda. *Mus* Kenjiro Hirose.

Cast: Yuzo Kayama *(Yuichi),* Wakako Sakai *(Setsuko),* Kunie Tanaka *(Ishiyama),* Keiko Cho *(Midori),* Choko Iida, Ichiro Arishima, Machiko Naka, Tatsuyoshi Ebara.

Drama. On the first day of his job with an automobile company, Yuichi is late for work. However, the directors of the firm are pleased with his excuse: he helped an elderly man and his daughter, Setsuko, find a taxi. Yuichi meets Setsuko again, but this time she is with Ishiyama, his old school friend who works for a rival business. An important customer for Yuichi's company cancels his contract after hearing that the cars' motors are defective, and both Yuichi and Ishiyama are sent to the man's home in Hokkaido to investigate. There, Yuichi meets the customer's daughter Midori, and although not romantically attracted to her, he realizes that by seeing her often he can gain access to her father. Setsuko hears of Yuichi's scheme and grows jealous. Eventually, the reports on the defects are found to be false, and Yuichi and Ishiyama return to Tokyo with new orders. Setsuko meets them and, given a choice, decides on Yuichi. *Salesmen. Jealousy. Automobiles. Hokkaido. Tokyo.*

Note: Released in Japan in Jan 1969 as *Furesshuman wakadaisho.*

YOUNG GUY ON MT. COOK (Japan) F6.5730

Toho Co. *Dist* Toho International, Inc. Oct **1969** [Los Angeles showing]. Sd; col (Eastmancolor). 35mm. 86 min.

Dir Jun Fukuda. *Screenplay* Yasuo Tanami. *Photog* Shinsaku Uno. *Art Dir* Juichi Ikuno. *Mus* Kenjiro Hirose.

Cast: Yuzo Kayama *(Yuichi Tanuma),* Wakako Sakai *(Setsuko),* Kunie Tanaka *(Ishiyama),* Tatsuyoshi Ebara *(Enguchi),* Jessica Peters *(Elizabeth),* Choko Iida *(Riki),* Ichiro Arishima *(Kyutaro),* Midori Utsumi *(Saeko),* Machiko Naka *(Teruko),* Mari Nakayama.

Drama. Yuichi Tanuma, a sales engineer living in Sydney, Australia, is too busy to escort Ishiyama, his schoolmate visiting from Japan, so he asks Elizabeth, an Australian saleswoman, to show him around. Ishiyama falls in love with Elizabeth, but she is in love with Yuichi. The young salesman is transferred to Japan, where he is reunited with his grandmother, Riki; his father, Kyutaro; his sister, Teruko; and Enguchi, Teruko's husband. Kyutaro opens a restaurant, but he neglects his business for Saeko, the proprietress of a nearby boutique. Yuichi meets Setsuko, who works for a firm promoting industry in New Zealand, and he falls deeply in love with her. Elizabeth suddenly appears in Japan, and Setsuko stops seeing Yuichi, thinking Elizabeth is his Australian sweetheart. Yuichi helps his father obtain the family's approval of marriage to Saeko, but she spurns Kyutaro's proposal. Yuichi goes to Auckland to organize a parade of new cars, and Setsuko joins him reluctantly, because they have not made up. After the parade, however, the two meet on Mt. Cook and pledge their love for each other. *Salesmen. Storekeepers. Saleswomen. Restaurateurs. Australians. Family life. Automobiles. Sydney (Australia). Auckland. Mount Cook (New Zealand).*

Note: Released in Japan in Jul 1969 as *Nyujirando no wakadaisho.*

THE YOUNG LORD (West Germany) F6.5731

Beta Film–United Film. *Dist* International Television Trading Corp. Sep **1970.** Sd; col (Eastmancolor). 35mm. 137 min.

Dir Gustav Rudolf Sellner. *Libretto* Ingeborg Bachmann. *Photog* Ernst Wild. *Mus Comp* Hans Werner Henze. *Lyr* Ingeborg Bachmann. *Mus Cond* Christoph von Dohnanyi. *Mus Sung by* Deutsch Opera Berlin Chorus. *Mus Played by* Deutsch Opera Berlin Orchestra. *Cost* Filippo Sanjust.

Cast: Edith Mathis *(Luise),* Donald Grobe *(Wilhelm),* Loren Driscoll *(Barrat),* Barry McDaniel *(secretary),* Otto Fraf *(Sir Edgar),* Vera Little *(Begonia),* Lisa Otto *(Frau Hasentraffer),* Margrette Ast *(Baroness),* Gita Mikes *(Frau von Hufnagel),* Bella Jaspers *(Ida),* Manfred Rohrl *(mayor),* Ivan Sardi *(Hasentraffer),* Ernst Krubowski *(Scharf),* Helmut Krebs *(professor),* Günther Treptwo *(LaRocca),* Fritz Hoppe *(lamplighter),* Marina Tuerke *(chambermaid),* Leopold Clam *(Meadows).*

Opera film. Source: Hans Werner Henze and Ingeborg Bachmann, *Der junge Lord; Komische Oper in zwei Akten* (first performance: Berlin, 7 Apr 1965). Wilhelm Hauff, "Der junge Engländer," a fable in *Der Scheik von Alessandria und seine Sklaven.* In 1830 Sir Edgar, an English nobleman, arrives in a German town and, without speaking a word, astonishes and intrigues the townspeople with his strange collection of servants and animals. Playing on the townspeople's gullibility, the elderly and eccentric Englishman ultimately reveals his contempt for them by convincing them of the existence of a "young lord" who in fact does not exist. *English. Nobility. Mutes. Eccentrics. Domestics. Hoaxes. Gullibility. Smalltown life. Germany. Animals.*

Note: Produced in West Germany in 1965 as *Der junge Lord.*

THE YOUNG LOVERS F6.5732

Metro-Goldwyn-Mayer, Inc.–Tigertail Productions. *Dist* Metro-Goldwyn-Mayer, Inc. 14 Oct **1964** [Cleveland opening; c23 Jun 1964; LP28748]. Sd (Westrex); b&w. 35mm. 110 min. [Also 105 min.]

Pres by Samuel Goldwyn, Jr. *Prod-Dir* Samuel Goldwyn, Jr. *Screenplay* George Garrett. *Dir Photog* Joseph Biroc, Ellsworth Fredricks. *Set Decor* Frank Wade. *Prod Dsgn* Fernando Carrere. *Film Ed* William A. Lyon. *Asst Film Ed* Larry Allen. *Mus Comp & Cond* Sol Kaplan. *Choreog* Miriam Nelson. *Sd Rec* Lambert Day. *Sd Ed* Don Hall, Jr., Ben Smith. *Mus Ed* Richard C. Harris. *1st & 2d Asst Dir* Joseph Behm, Douglas Green. *Prod Mgr* Clem Beauchamp. *Script Supv* Charlsie Bryant. *Asst to the Prod* Sally Moore. *Wardrobe Woman* Rose Rockne. *Wardrobe Man* Wes Jeffries. *Makeup* Mark Reedall. *Hairstyles* Kay Reed. *Cons* Richard Day. *Gaffer* Bill Neff. *Prop Master*

Art Cole. *Casting* Stalmaster-Lister Co.

Cast: Peter Fonda (*Eddie Slocum*), Sharon Hugueny (*Pam Burns*), Nick Adams (*Tarragoo*), Deborah Walley (*Debbie*), Beatrice Straight (*Mrs. Burns*), Malachi Throne (*Professor Schwartz*), Joseph Campanella (*Professor Reese*), Nancy Rennick (*Mary Reese*), Kent Smith (*Dr. Shoemaker*), Jennifer Billingsley (*Karen*).

Melodrama. Source: Julian Halevy, *The Young Lovers* (New York, 1955). The casual relationship between art student Eddie Slocum and Pam Burns, a teacher trainee, begins innocently with meetings at the apartment Eddie shares with his eccentric friend Tarragoo. Gradually a deeper attachment develops, and when her widowed mother is away, the young couple spend the night together at Pam's home. Their carefree affair continues until Pam learns that she is pregnant. Eddie, who has no income, feels that marriage would jeopardize his chances for a fellowship; Pam therefore decides to get an abortion and forget Eddie, but she cannot go through with the operation. Her mother, in whom she has confided, helps her plan to go away. Meanwhile, Eddie, under the influence of Tarragoo, who has high principles beneath his zany exterior, and a kindly history professor, who gives him a chance to pass an important exam, is able to meet his problem and face it responsibly. After learning that Pam has left, Eddie goes after her, fully confident that they can work out a future together. *Students. Eccentrics. Widows. Professors. College life. Pregnancy. Abortion. Filial relations.*

THE YOUNG MAN'S BRIDE   F6.5733

Gunter Productions. 5 Jun **1968** [periodical notice]. Sd; b&w. 35mm. [Feature length assumed.]

Prod-Dir George Gunter. *Writ* Jim Turnage. *Mus* Fred Harper.

Cast: Patricia Moore (*Junie*), Ralph G. Edwards (*Ebb*).

Comedy-drama. A naive country bumpkin named Ebb Holt comes upon a men's magazine and thinks it is a mail order catalog. Ebb and his brother, Zeke, mail in their order for Junie. Junie's agent receives the letter and, thinking it is an offer of a modeling assignment, persuades Junie to take the job. She agrees, provided that her boyfriend Ron can accompany her. Junie and Ron arrive in Possum Hollow, Arkansas, and quickly sum up the situation. However, they must remain in the small town because the weekly train has already departed, and since the town has no hotel, Junie is forced to stay with the boys' sister, Dorcie, while Ron sleeps in the barn. On the first night Junie seduces Dorcie. Not completely satisfied, Dorcie goes to the barn to make love to Ron. Ebb and Zeke then find Junie a willing sex partner. Despite the attempted intervention by a drunken local preacher, Dorcie continues to have sex with Ron, who eventually agrees to remain in Possum Hollow and marry Dorcie. Junie returns to the city, promising to visit her country friends soon. *Brothers. Models. Talent agents. Rural life. Seduction. Lesbianism. Magazines (periodicals). Arkansas.*

THE YOUNG ONE (Mexico)   F6.5734

Producciones Olmeca. *Dist* Valiant Films, Vitalite Film Corp. 18 Jan **1961** [New York opening]. Sd; b&w. 35mm. 96 min.

Prod George P. Werker. *Dir-Adapt* Luis Buñuel. *Screenplay* Luis Buñuel, H. B. Addis. *Photog* Gabriel Figueroa. *Art Dir* Jesús Bracho. *Film Ed* Carlos Savage. *Mus* Jesús Zarzosa. *Song:* "Sinner Man" sung by Leon Bibb. *Sd* James L. Fields, José B. Carles, Galdino Samperio. *Asst Dir* Ignacio Villarreal, Juan Luis Buñuel. *Prod Mgr* Antonio de Salazar.

Cast: Zachary Scott (*Miller*), Key Meersman (*Evalyn*), Bernie Hamilton (*Traver*), Claudio Brook (*Reverend Fleetwood*), Crahan Denton (*Jackson*).

Drama. Source: Peter Matthiessen, "Travelin' Man," in *Harper's* (Feb 1957). Unjustly accused of raping a white woman, Traver, a Negro jazz clarinetist and laborer, flees from a Southern town to a nearby small island, the private game preserve of a group of wealthy sportsmen. The sole inhabitants of the island are game warden Miller and Evalyn, a girl in her early teens whose grandfather Pee Wee, the handyman, has just died. In Miller's temporary absence, Traver befriends Evalyn and pays her $20 for supplies. When the racist Miller learns of the incident, he hunts down the trespasser but later decides to let him remain as the new handyman. Having become aware of Evalyn's pubescence, Miller has sexual relations with her. The next day, Reverend Fleetwood and his boatman, Jackson, come to take Evalyn to a welfare home, and Miller swears the girl to secrecy. When Miller hears from them of the rape charge against Traver, he joins Jackson in hunting down and capturing him. Evalyn unwittingly reveals her relationship with Miller, and the preacher threatens to report Miller's conduct to the law. Fleetwood helps to prove Traver's innocence, knowing the doubtful character of the white woman, and instructs Miller to treat Traver fairly. Realizing that the Negro may be innocent and fearing that Fleetwood will report his affair with Evalyn, Miller helps Traver escape and suggests to the preacher his intention to marry Evalyn. *Negroes. Musicians. Handymen. Gamekeepers. Clergymen. Boatmen. Southerners. Rape. Adolescence. Racism. Game preserves. Islands.*

Note: Released in Mexico in Aug 1961 as *La joven*. H. B. Addis is a pseudonym for Hugo Butler.

THE YOUNG ONES *see* **WONDERFUL TO BE YOUNG!**

THE YOUNG RACERS   F6.5735

Alta Vista Productions. *Dist* American International Pictures. 22 May **1963** [Indianapolis, Indiana, opening; c22 May 1963; LP26001]. Sd; col (Eastman Color by Pathé). 35mm. 82 min.

Pres by James H. Nicholson, Samuel Z. Arkoff. *Prod-Dir* Roger Corman. *Assoc Prod* Barbara Boyle. *Screenplay* R. Wright Campbell. *Dir Photog* Floyd Crosby. *Art Dir* Albert Locatelli. *Film Ed* Ronald Sinclair. *Mus* Les Baxter. *Mus Coörd* Al Simms. *Sd* Francis Coppola. *Asst Dir* Charles Griffith. *Prod Mgr* Charles Hannawalt. *Makeup* Rachel Golan. *Tech Adv* Anthony Marsh. *Prop Master* Menahem Golan.

Cast: Mark Damon (*Stephen Children*), William Campbell (*Joe Machin*), Luana Anders (*Henny*), Robert Campbell (*Robert Machin*), Patrick Magee (*Sir William Dragonet*), Bruce McLaren (*Lotus team manager*), Milo Quesada (*Italian driver*), Anthony Marsh (*announcer*), Marie Versini (*Sesia Machin*), Beatrice Altariba (*Monique*), Margaret Robsahm (*Lea*), Christina Gregg (*Daphne*).

Action melodrama. Joe Machin, an American racedriver determined to win at any cost, wins the Grand Prix de Monaco through reckless driving. Wherever competition takes him, Joe becomes involved in extramarital affairs, using his unwitting brother, Robert, to divert the suspicions of his wife, Sesia. Meanwhile, racer turned writer Steve Children arrives in Monte Carlo to meet his girl friend, Monique, and sees her in an emotional scene with Joe, with whom she has had an affair. Steve decides to write a book exposing Joe and his tactics on and off the track. He arranges to meet Joe and accompany him to Belgium, where another Grand Prix is to take place. When they return to England, Steve's plan is revealed to Joe. In a race at Aintree, the two men participate in a personal grudge match, but when Steve's car swerves wildly, Joe has a change of heart and spins his car to avoid hurting Steve, thus sustaining serious injuries. At the hospital Steve meets Joe's brother, who explains that Joe's outward bravado hides a sensitive and confused personality. Later, Steve finds Joe considerably changed, and their friendship becomes a lasting one. *Brothers. Authors. Playboys. Automobile racing. Infidelity. Friendship. Monaco. France. Aintree (England). Belgium.*

Note: Racing scenes filmed in France, Belgium, England, and Monaco. Filmed with the cooperation of the Racing Committees of the Grands Prix of England, France, Belgium, and Monte Carlo.

THE YOUNG REBEL (France/Italy/Spain)   F6.5736

Prisma Film–Protor Film–Procinex. *Dist* American International Pictures, Commonwealth United Entertainment, Inc. Jan **1969** [c7 Apr 1968; LP35554]. Sd; col. 35mm (Colorscope). 111 min. *MPAA rating* M.

Pres by Commonwealth United Entertainment Inc. An Alexander Salkind Production. *Prod* Miguel Salkind, Pier Luigi Torri. *Exec Prod* Henry T. Weinstein. *Dir* Vincent Sherman. *2d Unit Dir* Isidoro Martínez Ferry, Piergiuseppe Sciume. *Screenplay* David Karp, Enrique Llovet, Enrico Bomba. *Adapt* Enrique Llovet. *Dir Photog* Edmond Richard. *Art Dir* Enrique Alarcón, Luciano De Nardi. *Film Ed* Margarita Ochoa. *Mus* Jean Ledrut, Angel Arteaga. *Sd* Gabriel Masaganas. *Asst Dir* Julio Sempere. *Prod Mgr* Teodoro Herrero. *Cost* Luis Argüello. *Historical Supv* Enrique Llovet.

Cast: Horst Buchholz (*Miguel de Cervantes*), Gina Lollobrigida (*Giulia*), José Ferrer (*Hassam Bey*), Louis Jourdan (*Cardinal Acquaviva*), Francisco Rabal (*Rodrigo*), Fernando Rey (*Philip II*), Soledad Miranda (*Nessa*), Maurice de Canonge, Antonio Casas, Angel Del Pozo, José Jaspe, Ricardo Palacios, Claudine Dalmas, José Nieto, Enzo Curcio, Guadenzio Di Pietro, Andres Mejuto, Vidal Molina, Fernando Hilbeck, Concha Humbria, Jorge Rigaud.

Historical melodrama. Source: Bruno Frank, *Cervantes* (Amsterdam, 1934). In the 16th century, Pope Pius IV sends his emissary, Cardinal Acquaviva, and an enthusiastic young assistant, Miguel de Cervantes, to gain support from Philip II of Spain against the aggressive Moors. The mission is successful, and Philip promises to provide troops to aid the Holy League. Cervantes' first duty upon returning to Rome is to serve as escort for the visiting Arab envoy, Hassam Bey; and despite their differences, Hassam and Cervantes gain respect for each other. Cervantes quits the assignment when he learns that his Arab friend is being deceived in his negotiations with Acquaviva. Meanwhile, Cervantes meets and falls in love with Giulia, a beautiful Roman courtesan, but they are separated when Pope Pius delivers an edict ordering all prostitutes to leave Rome. Disillusioned, Cervantes joins his brother Rodrigo to fight in the sea battle of Lepanto and is honored for bravery. He sees Giulia for the last time as he recovers from battle wounds at a Messina hospital. On the voyage home, Cervantes and Rodrigo are captured by Arab pirates and taken to Algiers where Rodrigo is sent to work in the quarries and Cervantes is tortured. They are released months later when Hassam becomes governor of Algiers. With Rodrigo, Cervantes plans to free the Christian slaves, but their uprising fails. The brothers are about to be executed when they are unexpectedly ransomed by the slaves and returned to Spain. *Moors. Arabs. Prostitutes. Brothers.*

Pirates. Diplomacy. Perfidy. Slavery. Torture. Uprisings. Ransom. Battle of Lepanto. Rome. Messina. Algiers. Pius IV (pope). Claudio Acquaviva. Miguel de Cervantes. Philip II (Spain). Catholic Church.

Note: Location scenes filmed in Spain. Opened in Paris in Mar 1968 as *Les aventures extraordinaires de Cervantes* at 90 min; in Madrid in Sep 1968 as *Cervantes* at 90 min; in Italy as *Le avventure e gli amori di Miguel Cervantes.* Produced in 70mm Totalscope. Copyrighted in the U. S. as *Cervantes.*

THE YOUNG RUNAWAYS   F6.5737

Four Leaf Productions. *Dist* Metro-Goldwyn-Mayer, Inc. 11 Sep **1968** [New York opening; c12 Aug 1968; LP36032]. Sd; col (Metrocolor). 35mm (Panavision). 91 min.

Prod Sam Katzman. *Assoc Prod* Jerome F. Katzman. *Dir* Arthur Dreifuss. *Writ* Orville H. Hampton. *Dir Photog* John F. Warren. *Art Dir* George W. Davis, Merrill Pye. *Set Decor* Henry Grace, Keogh Gleason. *Film Ed* Ben Lewis. *Mus Score & Cond* Fred Karger. *Titl Song* Fred Karger, Kevin Coughlin. *Sung by* Arthur Prysock. Songs: "*Ophelia's Dream,*" "*Couldn't We?*" James D. Weatherly, John D. Lobue, Leland Russell. *Sung by* The Gordian Knot. *Rec Supv* Franklin Milton. *Sd* Bruce Wright. *Asst Dir* Donald C. Klune, Lynn Guthrie. *Makeup* William Tuttle. *Hairstyles* Mary Keats. *Dial Coach* Flora Duane.

Cast: Brooke Bundy (*Shelly Allen*), Kevin Coughlin (*Dewey Norson*), Lloyd Bochner (*Raymond Marquis Allen*), Patty McCormack (*Deanie Donford*), Lynn Bari (*Mrs. Donford*), Norman Fell (*Mr. Donford*), Quentin Dean (*Joanne*), Richard Dreyfuss (*Terry*), Dick Sargent (*Freddie*), James Edwards (*Sgt. Joe Collyer*), Hortense Petra (*Mrs. Morse*), Isabell Sanford (*Sarah*), Stacey Maxwell (*Alicia*), Cynthia Hull (*Carol Mae*), Ken Del Conte (*Loch Riccano*), Lance Le Gault (*Curly*), Angus Duncan (*Dan Clark*), Romo Vincent (*club manager*), Nicholas Georgiade (*driver*), Steve Mitchell (*Marty*), Ted Gehring (*Charley*), Cully Richards (*police sergeant*), Edwin Cook (*guru*), Keith Taylor (*Claude Bradville*), The Gordian Knot (*themselves*), Army Archerd (*himself*).

Melodrama. For diverse reasons, three teenagers leave their homes and run off to Chicago's hippie district. Shelly Allen, the daughter of a well-to-do advertising executive, feels neglected by her busy father; Dewey Norson, a Nebraska farm boy, lacks the courage to face his morally-rigid father when his girl friend claims to be pregnant; and Deanie Donford, the daughter of a nagging, distrustful mother and an emasculated father, believes herself to be socially and sexually repressed. Alone in the city, Shelly accepts the offer of two apparently respectable girls, Joanne and Alicia, to share their apartment with her. She soon learns that they are prostitutes working for a call girl ring, and she is abducted and beaten when she poses a threat to the operation. Later, she meets and moves in with Dewey, who is already somewhat disenchanted because of his acquaintance with Terry, a draft-dodging slum boy who believes in taking what he wants and who uses the hippie philosophy as a cover-up for laziness. Deanie unwisely enters into an affair with Loch Riccano, a jealous musician, then transfers her affections to his roommate Curly, and she ends up in the city morgue. Terry steals a car and dies in a flaming crash; Shelly is found by her remorseful father; and Dewey learns that his father is capable of more understanding than he imagined. As the two of them return to their respective homes, they agree to keep in touch with each other. *Runaways. Hippies. Advertising executives. Farmers. Prostitutes. Draft dodgers. Musicians. Roommates. Adolescence. Filial relations. Pregnancy. Urban life. Abduction. Puritanism. Murder. Promiscuity. Chicago. Automobile accidents.*

Note: Location scenes filmed in Chicago and on the Sunset Strip in Los Angeles.

THE YOUNG SAVAGES   F6.5738

Contemporary Productions. *Dist* United Artists. 24 May **1961** [New York opening; c23 May 1961; LP20319]. Sd; b&w. 35mm. 100 min.

A Harold Hecht Production. *Prod* Pat Duggan. *Exec Prod* Harold Hecht. *Dir* John Frankenheimer. *Screenplay* Edward Anhalt, J. P. Miller. *Photog* Lionel Lindon. *Art Dir* Burr Smidt. *Set Decor* James M. Crowe. *Film Ed* Eda Warren. *Mus Comp & Cond* David Amram. *Sd* Harry Mills, Eldon Coutts. *Asst Dir* Carter DeHaven, Jr. *Prod Mgr* Gilbert Kurland. *Cost* Jack Angel, Roselle Novello. *Makeup* Robert Schiffer. *Hairstyles* Joan St. Oegger. *Dial Coach* Sydney Pollack.

Cast: Burt Lancaster (*Hank Bell*), Dina Merrill (*Karin Bell*), Shelley Winters (*Mary Di Pace*), Edward Andrews (*Dan Cole*), Vivian Nathan (*Mrs. Escalante*), Larry Gates (*Randolph*), Telly Savalas (*Lieut. Richard Gunnison*), Pilar Seurat (*Louisa Escalante*), Jody Fair (*Angela Rugiello*), Roberta Shore (*Jenny Bell*), Milton Selzer (*Walsh*), Robert Burton (*judge*), David Stewart (*Barton*), Stanley Kristien (*Danny Di Pace*), John Davis Chandler (*Arthur Reardon*), Neil Nephew (*Anthony Aposto*), Luis Arroyo (*Zorro*), Jose Perez (*Roberto Escalante*), Richard Velez (*Gargantua*), William Sargent (*Soames*), Chris Robinson (*Pretty Boy*), Stanley Adams (*Lieutenant Hardy*), William Quinn (*Captain Larsen*), Linda Danzil (*Maria Amora*), Rafael Lopez (*José*), Henry Norell (*Pierce*), Jon Carlo (*McNally*), Bob Biheller (*Turtleneck*), Mario

Roccuzzo (*Diavalo*), Harry Holcombe (*doctor*), Helen Kleeb (*Mrs. Patton*), Thom Conroy (*Mr. Abbeney*), John Walsh (*Lonnie*), Irving Steinberg (*Officer Wohlman*), Clegg Hoyt (*Whitey*), Joel Fluellen (*clerk of the court*), Robert Cleaves (*Sullivan*).

Drama. Source: Evan Hunter, *A Matter of Conviction* (New York, 1959). In New York's Spanish Harlem, a 15-year-old Puerto Rican boy is stabbed to death by three hoodlums from an Italian street gang. When the three teenagers are apprehended, Dan Cole, the politically ambitious district attorney, announces that he will demand the death penalty, but his prosecutor, Assistant D. A. Hank Bell (himself the product of a slum environment), decides to remain impartial until he has conducted a thorough investigation. His task is complicated by the fact that his former fiancée, Mary Di Pace, is the mother of one of the trio. Furthermore, Hank's wife, Karin, is a Vassar liberal staunchly opposed to capital punishment. Hank's probings prove that the murdered blind boy was actually the head of a Puerto Rican gang as well as a pimp for his 13-year-old sister. In addition, Hank suspects that young Danny Di Pace did not participate in the murder but is "ashamed" to admit his innocence. As the trial nears, Karin is threatened by youths brandishing switchblade knives, and Hank himself is beaten up in a subway. Suddenly blind with rage, he nearly kills one of the Puerto Rican youths who menaced his wife; only then does he comprehend the insane call for vengeance that motivated the youthful killers. At the trial he presents all of the conflicting evidence and gets Danny to admit that he never stabbed anyone in his life. One of the killers, Arthur Reardon, is sentenced to imprisonment for 20 years; the other, the moronic Aposto, is sent to a mental institution. Though Hank has destroyed his political career, he has remained true to his conscience and his personal integrity. *Street gangs. Juvenile delinquents. Lawyers. District attorneys. Pimps. Puerto Ricans. Italians. Adolescence. Revenge. Murder. Capital punishment. Slums. Trials. New York City—Spanish Harlem.*

Note: Location scenes filmed in New York City. Pre-release title: *A Matter of Conviction.*

THE YOUNG SINNER   F6.5739

T. C. Frank. *Dist* United Screen Arts. Aug **1965.** Sd; b&w. 35mm. 81 min. *Prod-Dir-Writ* Tom Laughlin. *Photog* (see note) Ed Martin, Sven Walnum, James A. Crabe. *Film Ed* Donald Henderson. *Mus* Shelly Manne. *Sd* Charles Cooper, Leroy Robbins. *Asst Dir* Herbert Willis. *Prod Mgr* Ellen Lafferty.

Cast: Tom Laughlin (*Chris Wotan*), Stefanie Powers (*Ginny Miller*), William Wellman, Jr. (*John*), Robert Angelo (*priest*), Linda March (*Tury Martin*), Julia Paul (*Mrs. Martin*), Clint Gunkel (*Mr. Martin*), Dorothy Downey (*Mrs. Wotan*), Charles Heard (*Mr. Wotan*), Roxanne Heard (*Joan Meyers*), John Burns (*Head Coach Ferguson*), Jack Starrett (*Football Coach Jennings*), Ed Cook (*Assistant Coach Webster*), Jane Taylor (*Tury's friend*), Harry Zumach (*principal*), A. C. Pagenkoff (*teacher*), Conny Van Dyke (*Joan's friend*), Richard A. Colla (*Ginny's date*), James Stacy (*Art*), Chris Robinson (*Bobby*), Dennis O'Flaherty (*Marty*), Bob Colonna (*Harry*), Chuck Siebert (*Lee*), Marlene Kelly, Charles Stobert, Terry Thompson.

Melodrama. Chris Wotan tells the story of his downfall to a priest at the confessional: A top athlete in high school, Chris hopes to win a football scholarship to college, which he could not otherwise afford. Although he has troubles at home with his ineffectual, alcoholic father and working mother, Chris is happy with his girl friend, Ginny. One day, he and his friends are caught by one of the coaches after hours at the school swimming pool; after arguing with the teacher Chris is put on probation. He dates the wealthy but insecure Tury in hopes that her influential father will help him to obtain a scholarship, and Ginny, believing his interest in Tury to be romantic, breaks off with him. Another disaster occurs when Tury's parents return home to find him in bed with their daughter. Chris goes for a ride with his friends in a fire truck they have bought, and he is wrongfully implicated in a raid on a drugstore and is expelled from school. Lonely and despondent, Chris takes Joan Meyers, a 14-year-old of doubtful reputation, to her special place in the church loft, intent on having sex with her, but his self-disgust is so great he rejects her. Smashing church ornaments, Chris runs from the church, only to return later for the help of the priest, who will help him remake his life. *Athletes. Priests. Confession. High school life. Alcoholism. Family life. Theft. Wealth. Churches.*

Note: Filmed in 1960 on location in and around Milwaukee, Wisconsin. Working title: *Christopher Wotan.* Previewed in 1961 as *Like Father, Like Son;* running time: ca86 min. Originally intended as the first part of a projected trilogy entitled *We Are All Christ.* Prerelease title: *Among the Thorns.* Additional footage may have been added prior to theatrical release. Crabe's participation is unconfirmed. T. C. Frank is a pseudonym for Tom Laughlin.

THE YOUNG SWINGERS   F6.5740

Associated Producers, Inc. *Dist* Twentieth Century-Fox Film Corp. 27 Nov **1963** [Los Angeles opening; c19 Sep 1963; LP26776]. Sd; b&w. 35mm. 71 min. *Prod-Dir* Maury Dexter. *Assoc Prod* "By" Dunham. *Screenplay* Harry Spalding. *Dir Photog* Jack Marquette. *Set Decor* Harry Reif. *Supv Film Ed*

Jodie Copelan. *Mus* Hank Levine. *Song:* "*Come to the Party*" "By" Dunham, Hank Levine. *Song:* "*Mad, Mad, Mad*" Susan Quickel, Bill Baker. *Songs:* "*Elijah*," "*Come A-Runnin'*," "*Watutsi Surfer*" "By" Dunham. *Song:* "*Voice on the Mountain*" "By" Dunham, Henry Vars. *Song:* "*Greenback Dollar*" Hoyt Axton, Ken Ramsey. *Song:* "*I Can't Get You Out of My Heart*" Robert Marcucci, Russell Faith. *Song:* "*You Pass Me By*" Rod McKuen. *Sd* William Bernds, Harry M. Leonard. *Asst Dir* Harold E. Knox. *Prod Mgr* Harold E. Knox. *Script Supv* Billy Vernon. *Wardrobe* Wesley Trist. *Makeup* Ray Sebastian. *Prop Master* Jockey Liebgold.

Cast: Rod Lauren (*Mel Hudson*), Molly Bee (*Vicki Crawford*), Gene McDaniels (*Fred Lewis*), Jack Larson (*Pete Mundy*), Jo Helton (*Roberta Crawford*), Justin Smith (*Bruce Webster*), Jerry Summers (*Roger Kelly*), Jack Younger (*Irving Bird*), Karen Gunderson (*Judi Sherwood*), John Merritt (*Ken Sherwood*), Ray Dannis, Dodie Warren, Elizabeth Thompson, Rusty Wescoatt, The Sherwood Singers.

Comedy-drama with music. Real estate agent Roberta Crawford wants to tear down the Vanguard, a nightclub owned and operated by a group of young performers, and replace it with an office building. Vicki, Roberta's niece, visits the club with Roger Kelly, her arrogant and spoiled boyfriend, and becomes attracted to Mel Hudson, the singer who is determined to keep the club going. On Vicki's 21st birthday, she announces her independence from her aunt and takes a job at the club. Despite Roberta's harassment, the club continues to operate until it burns down. Vickie accuses her aunt of arson, but Mel explains that faulty wiring caused the fire. Roberta then has a change of heart, offers to provide better facilities for the club, and gives a lavish birthday party for Vicki. *Aunts. Singers. Entertainers. Real estate agents. Nightclubs. Birthdays. Fires.*

Note: Working title: *Come to the Party.*

YOUNG SWORDSMAN (Japan)   **F6.5741**

Toho Co. May **1964** [Los Angeles showing]. Sd; b&w. 35mm. 108 min.

Prod Tomoyuki Tanaka. *Dir* Hiroshi Inagaki. *Screenplay* Hiroshi Inagaki, Takeshi Kimura.

Cast: Somegoro Ichikawa (*Tenzen Hayakawa*), Hiroyuki Nagato (*Chojuro*), Nami Tamura (*fiancée*), Junko Ikeuchi (*hill woman*), Ryunosuke Tsukigata.

Action drama. In 17th-century Japan, two foster brothers react differently to a law banning swordplay, even as a sport. Tenzen is proud of his swordsmanship and considers the law an injustice, while Chojuro quietly obeys the ban. Bored and restless, Tenzen develops a technique of lopping off his opponents' thumbs, disabling them for combat. His family, including his fiancée, are angered by his behavior, and he is driven from his home to a life of banditry in the hills. To rescue the family honor and see that justice is done, Chojuro goes after his brother and meets him in a duel. *Brothers. Bandits. Family life. Mutilation. Duels.*

Note: Released in Japan in 1963 as *Hiken.*

THE YOUNG, THE EVIL AND THE SAVAGE (Italy)   **F6.5742**

Super International Pictures–B. G. A. *Dist* American International Pictures. 14 Aug **1968** [New York opening; c14 Aug 1968; LP36044]. Sd; col (Perfect). 35mm (Cromoscope). 82 min.

Exec Prod Lawrence Woolner, Giuseppe De Blasio. *Dir* Anthony Dawson. *Screenplay* Anthony Dawson, Frank Bottar. *Story* John Simonelli. *Dir Photog* Frank Zuccoli. *Art Dir* Antonio Visone. *Ed* Otello Colangeli. *Mus* Carlo Savina. *Wardrobe* Annamode. *Makeup* Piero Mecacci.

Cast: Michael Rennie (*Inspector Duran*), Mark Damon (*Richard*), Eleonora Brown (*Lucille*), Sally Smith (*Jill*), Pat Valturri (*Denise*), Ludmilla Lvova (*Miss Clay*), Alan Collins (*DeBrazzi* [*Laforêt, see note*]), Gianni Di Benedetto (*DeBrazzi*), Franco DeRosa (*Detective Gabon*), Vivian Stapleton (*Miss Tranfield*), Esther Masing (*Miss Martin*), Valentino Macchi (*policeman*), Aldo De Carellis (*professor*), Sylvia Dionisio, Kathleen Parker, Paola Natale, Marisa Longo (*girls*), Umberto Papiri, John Hawkwood.

Horror film. A trunk containing the unclothed dead body of a young woman arrives at the fashionable St. Hilda's College for Girls on top of a van carrying a newly-appointed teacher, Miss Clay, and the school's riding instructor, Richard. A mixup in the baggage prompts one of the students to check the contents of her trunk in the college basement, and she is strangled by an unseen assailant. Lucille, an orphan enrolled at the school, slips out of her room for a rendezvous with Richard and finds the body of her fellow student, but the corpse disappears before Richard arrives. A second girl is mistaken for Lucille and strangled in a shower, whereupon Police Inspector Duran and his aide Gabon enter the case. The voyeuristic gardener is suspected of the crimes, but before he can be questioned he is found murdered. Lucille is detained from keeping a nighttime rendezvous with Richard at the college pool and sends her roommate, Denise, to explain. A figure in a black wet suit attempts to drown the girl, but she is saved by Jill, a student who fancies herself a detective. Inspector Duran's suspicions fall on Richard. Meanwhile, Lucille, realizing that she was the intended victim of the poolside attack, searches for Richard and finds him seriously wounded. Suddenly, she is confronted by the real killer, who

reveals himself to be her distant cousin. In order to gain Lucille's inheritance, which becomes due on her 18th birthday, he had strangled Miss Clay and had assumed her identity to kill Lucille. Before he can accomplish the murder, a walkie-talkie hidden in a davenport by Jill reveals his whereabouts, and the police arrive in time to save Lucille. *Schoolteachers. Riding instructors. Students. Police. Roommates. Detectives. Cousins. Orphans. Deans. Gardeners. Murder. College life. Inheritance. Personal identity. Female impersonation. Voyeurism. Eavesdropping. Boarding schools.*

Note: Rome opening: 1968 as *Nude ... si muore.* Sources conflict in crediting the actor who portrays DeBrazzi. The following are pseudonyms: Anthony Dawson (Antonio Margheriti), John Simonelli (Giovanni Simonelli), Frank Zuccoli (Fausto Zuccoli), Alan Collins (Luciano Pigozzi), Frank Bottar (Franco Bottari).

YOUNG TORLESS (France/West Germany)   **F6.5743**

Franz Seitz Filmproduktion–Nouvelles Editions de Films. *Dist* Kanawha Films. 22 Jul **1968** [New York opening]. Sd; b&w. 35mm. 90 min.

A Franz Seitz–Louis Malle Production. *Prod* Franz Seitz. *Dir-Writ* Volker Schlöndorff. *Photog* Franz Rath. *Art Dir* Maleen Pacha. *Film Ed* Claus von Boro. *Mus* Hans Werner Henze. *Sd* Klaus Ekelt. *Asst Dir* Herbert Rimbach. *Prod Mgr* Franz Achter.

Cast: Mathieu Carrière (*Torless*), Marian Seidowsky (*Basini*), Bernd Tischer (*Beineberg*), Alfred Dietz (*Reiting*), Barbara Steele (*Bozena*), Jean Launay (*mathematics teacher*), Hanne Axmann-Rezzori (*Frau Torless*), Herbert Asmodi (*Herr Torless*), Lotte Ledl (*innkeeper*), Fritz Gehlen (*school director*).

Drama. Source: Robert Musil, *Die Verwirrungen des zöglings Törless* (Berlin, 1906). After bidding farewell to his parents, Torless joins his friends at a fashionable boarding school on the eastern frontier of the Austro-Hungarian Empire, where he is to begin his senior year. With two classmates, Reiting and Beineberg, he visits Bozena, a waitress who provides sexual education for the boys at the school. The days at the academy progress normally until Basini, a self-destructive young boy, steals money from Beineberg's locker. Reiting learns of Basini's guilt but offers not to inform the authorities if Basini will serve as his personal slave. Reiting and Beineberg submit Basini to various forms of physical and psychological torture, while Torless silently observes, fascinated by the semblance of pleasure Basini experiences during his ordeal. Eventually his friends' sadistic excesses spur Torless to action, but Reiting and Beineberg threaten to blame him if he reports them. When Basini is hung by his heels in the gymnasium in front of the entire class, Torless runs away in horror. The incident is investigated by the schoolboard, and Torless admits to his participation in the torture of Basini, but he is unable to rationalize his complicity. The headmaster decides that the sensitive youth requires more careful attention than the school can provide, and Torless agrees to leave the academy. *Students. Waitresses. Headmasters. Sex instruction. Theft. Blackmail. Sadism. Masochism. Torture. Boarding schools. Austria-Hungary.*

Note: Opened in Berlin in Jun 1966 as *Der junge Törless*; running time: 87 min; in Paris in Jun 1966 as *Les désarrois de l'élève Törless*; running time: 85 min.

THE YOUNG WARRIORS   **F6.5744**

Universal Pictures. 26 Apr **1967** [Cincinnati, Ohio, opening; c3 Jun 1967; LP36896]. Sd (Westrex); col (Technicolor). 35mm (Panavision). 93 min.

Prod Gordon Kay. *Dir* John Peyser. *Screenplay* Richard Matheson. *Dir Photog* Loyal Griggs. *Art Dir* Alexander Golitzen, Alfred Ybarra. *Set Decor* John McCarthy, Ralph Sylos. *Main Titl* Pacific Title. *Film Ed* Russell F. Schoengarth. *Sd* Waldon O. Watson, Clarence Self. *Asst Dir* Joseph Kenny. *Unit Prod Mgr* John Morrison. *Makeup* Bud Westmore. *Tech Adv* H. L. Covington.

Cast: James Drury (*Sergeant Cooley*), Steve Carlson (*Hacker*), Jonathan Daly (*Guthrie*), Robert Pine (*Foley*), Jeff Scott (*Lippincott*), Michael Stanwood (*Riley*), Johnny Alladin (*Harris*), Hank Jones (*Fairchild*), Tom Nolan (*Tremont*), Norman Fell (*Sergeant Wadley*), Buck Young (*Schumacher*), Kent McWhirter (*The Lieutenant*), George Sawaya, Morgan Jones, Noam Pitlik, Jon Drury, Buck Kartalian.

War drama. Source: Richard Matheson, *The Beardless Warriors* (Boston, 1960). In Europe in 1944, a group of American recruits are delivered as replacements to war-weary Sergeant Cooley. As the young and inexperienced newcomers go into combat, a somewhat aloof private, Hacker, is stunned by his first exposure to death. But he quickly hardens himself to the business of war and is soon killing Germans with an almost fanatical pleasure, even gunning down a German soldier who is clearly trying to surrender. Sergeant Cooley rebukes him, and Hacker turns sullen and resentful. However, when Cooley is wounded during an attack on a German-held farmhouse, Hacker distinguishes himself by running through enemy fire and dragging Cooley to safety. At a field hospital, Cooley invites Hacker, who has never had a real home, to visit him in New Mexico. Then, after Cooley has been sent back to the United States, Hacker is promoted to sergeant and returned to the front lines to prepare other young men for battle. *Combat zone life. Death. Courage. United States Army. World War II.*

Note: Prerelease title: *The Beardless Warriors.*

YOUNG, WILLING AND EAGER (Great Britain)   F6.5745

Blakeley's Films. *Dist* Joseph Brenner Associates, Manson Distributing Corp. Oct **1962**. Sd; b&w. 35mm. 77 min.

Prod Tom Blakeley. *Dir* Lance Comfort. *Screenplay* Brock Williams, Derry Quinn. *Story* Brock Williams. *Photog* Basil Emmott. *Camera Op* Frank Drake. *Art Dir* John Earl. *Film Ed* Peter Pitt. *Mus Comp, Dir & Arr* Martin Slavin. *Song:* "Why Am I Living?" Martin Slavin, Abbe Gail. *Perf by* Mike Sammes Singers, Jess Conrad. *Sd Rec* Bill Bulkley. *Asst Dir* Frank Ernst. *Prod Mgr* Pat Green. *Cont* Marjorie Lavelly. *Wardrobe Mistress* Dulcie Midwinter. *Makeup* George Claff. *Hairdresser* Barbara Barnard.

Cast: Jess Conrad *(Shane)*, Hermione Baddeley *(Princess Sophia)*, Kenneth Griffith *(Wilson)*, Christina Gregg *(Carol)*, Patrick Magee *(Flynn)*, Patrick Jordan *(Wills)*, Michael Wynne *(Bellamy)*, Frank Forsyth *(superintendent)*, Marie Devereux *(Ann)*, Eve Eden *(Daphne)*, David Gregory *(1st youth)*, Leon Garcia *(2d youth)*, Frank Hawkins *(taxi driver)*, Linda Castle *(girl in cellar)*, John Line *(guitarist)*.

Melodrama. Having run away from her drunken stepfather's English roadside cafe, 17-year-old Carol Flynn hitches a ride to Covent Garden in Soho, where she gets a job in a restaurant through the efforts of Princess Sophia, a fortune-teller she befriended at a nearby amusement arcade. Carol repulses the advances of the proprietor, Mort Wilson, and begins to see Joe Shane, a would-be club singer. The crooner marries her when she becomes pregnant, and they decide to emigrate to Canada where they hope Joe will be able to secure an engagement. To finance this venture, Joe breaks into Wilson's house to steal some money, but when the restaurant owner awakens, a gun battle ensues during which Joe is wounded and Wilson killed. Joe steals a car and, together with Carol, drives into the country. The police trail them through the woods and watch Joe die from loss of blood as he is about to stand and fight them with his gun. Carol falls sobbing beside her dead husband's body. *Stepfathers. Singers. Fortune-tellers. Adolescence. Pregnancy. Marriage. Theft. Employer-employee relations. London—Soho. Canada.*

Note: Released in Great Britain in 1961 as *Rag Doll;* running time: 67 min. Footage may have been added for American release.

A YOUNG WORLD (France/Italy)   F6.5746

Terra Films–Les Productions Artistes Associés–Sol Produzioni–Compagnia Cinematografica Montoro. *Dist* Lopert Pictures. 16 May **1966** [New York opening]. Sd; b&w. 35mm. 83 min.

Pres by Harry Saltzman. *Prod* Raymond Froment. *Dir* Vittorio De Sica. *Orig Screenplay & Dial* Cesare Zavattini. *Photog* Jean Boffety. *Art Dir* Max Douy. *Film Ed* Paul Cayatte. *Mus* Michel Colombier. *English Subtitl* Noelle Gillmor.

Cast: Christine Delaroche *(Anne)*, Nino Castelnuovo *(Carlo)*, Tanya Lopert *(Mary)*. Madeleine Robinson *(woman)*, Georges Wilson *(doctor)*, Pierre Brasseur *(boss)*, Nadiege Ragoo *(Judith)*, Isa Miranda, Jeanne Aubert, Jean-Pierre Darras, Françoise Brion, Franco Bucceri, Arlette Gilbert, Paul Mercey, Charles Millot, Laure Paillette, Antoine de Rudder, Jacques Masson.

Romantic drama. One evening in Paris, Anne, a 20-year-old medical student, and Carlo, an Italian photographer, meet at the Medical Students Ball. Their meeting is a moment of magic, and they steal away for a night of lovemaking. In the morning Anne returns to her studies, and Carlo resumes his photography, but some time later, Anne learns that she is pregnant. When they meet again, they profess their love, although both are hesitant about the child. For Carlo its birth will mean certain entrapment in the middle-class world from which he desperately wants to escape; for Anne it means bringing another life into the wretched world that she has seen in hospital wards. An abortion is decided upon, and Carlo raises the money by sleeping with an older woman for a fee. Anne cannot go through with the operation, however, and she races back to Carlo. They go to a small movie theater and take refuge in the crowd of people. *Medical students. Photographers. Pregnancy. Prostitution. Abortion. Balls (formal gatherings). Clinics. Motion picture theaters. Paris.*

Note: Location scenes filmed in Paris. Opened in Paris in Mar 1966 as *Un monde nouveau;* in Rome in Sep 1966 as *Un mondo nuovo.* Original running time: 85 min. Ricardo Aragno is an unconfirmed screenplay collaborator.

YOUNGBLOOD HAWKE   F6.5747

Warner Bros. Pictures. 5 Nov **1964** [New York opening; c28 Nov 1964; LP32356]. Sd; b&w. 35mm. 137 min.

Prod-Dir-Writ Delmer Daves. *2d Unit Dir* Robert Totten. *Dir Photog* Charles Lawton. *Art Dir* Leo K. Kuter. *Set Decor* John P. Austin. *Film Ed* Sam O'Steen. *Mus* Max Steiner. *Orch* Murray Cutter. *Sd* Francis J. Scheid. *Asst Dir* Russell Llewellyn. *Cost Dsgn* Howard Shoup. *Makeup Supv* Gordon Bau. *Supv Hairstylist* Jean Burt Reilly. *Dial Supv* Bert Steinberger.

Cast: James Franciscus *(Youngblood Hawke)*, Suzanne Pleshette *(Jeanne Green)*, Geneviève Page *(Frieda Winter)*, Eva Gabor *(Fannie Prince)*, Mary Astor *(Irene Perry)*, Lee Bowman *(Jason Prince)*, Edward Andrews *(Quentin Judd)*, Don Porter *(Ferdie Lax)*, Mildred Dunnock *(Mrs. Sarah Hawke)*, Kent Smith *(Paul Winter, Sr.)*, John Dehner *(Scotty Hawke)*, John Emery *(Georges Feydal)*, Mark Miller *(Ross Hodge)*, Hayden Rorke *(Mr. Givney)*, Werner Klemperer *(Mr. Leffer)*, Berry Kroeger *(Jock Maas)*, Rusty Lane *(Gus Adam)*.

Drama. Source: Herman Wouk, *Youngblood Hawke* (New York, 1962). Youngblood Hawke, a Kentucky truckdriver and aspiring writer, moves to New York when his novel is accepted for publication. Publisher Jason Prince assigns Jeanne Green to work with Hawke preparing the final form of the book. She helps him rent an attic apartment in Brooklyn Heights, and in the course of their collaboration, she falls in love with him. Meanwhile, Hawke meets Frieda Winter, wife of a wealthy businessman, at a fashionable party, and they begin a tempestuous affair. Frieda persuades Hawke to move into plush living quarters in Manhattan, and Jeanne, dismayed, accepts a job with a rival publisher. Hawke's novel receives unenthusiastic notices, but he accepts a commission to dramatize it as a vehicle for aging stage star Irene Perry. He travels to Nassau to work with the actress, pursuing his affair with Frieda at the same time. Hawke's second novel, again with Jeanne as editor, is an enormous success. Frieda's husband, who has learned of her affair with Hawke and wants to ruin him, encourages him to open his own publishing house and invest in a projected Long Island shopping center. Hawke's third novel is recognized as a purely mercenary venture, and his play flops. His publishing house stands on the brink of failure, his investments fail, and he is faced with financial ruin. Frieda's young son, Paul, who idolizes Hawke, commits suicide at his private school when he is taunted by classmates over his mother's affair with his hero. To erase his debts, Hawke returns to Kentucky to work on another novel in the isolation of a mountain cabin. The strain of trying to meet a deadline brings him to exhaustion, and he is found unconscious, suffering from pneumonia. Both Frieda and Jeanne visit him in the hospital. Frieda offers to leave her husband and marry Hawke, but he sends her away, having come to the realization that he loves Jeanne. *Truckdrivers. Novelists. Publishers. Editors. Mistresses. Businessmen. Critics. Playwrights. Actors. Wealth. Finance—Personal. Infidelity. Revenge. Suicide. Pneumonia. Kentucky. New York City. New York City—Brooklyn Heights. Nassau.*

YOUR CHEATIN' HEART   F6.5748

Four Leaf Productions. *Dist* Metro-Goldwyn-Mayer, Inc. 4 Nov **1964** [Montgomery, Alabama, opening; c30 Jul 1964; LP28885]. Sd (Westrex); b&w. 35mm (Panavision). 99 min.

Prod Sam Katzman. *Dir* Gene Nelson. *Writ* Stanford Whitmore. *Dir Photog* Ellis W. Carter. *Camera Op* Joe Jackman. *Art Dir* George W. Davis, Merrill Pye. *Set Decor* Henry Grace, Don Greenwood, Jr. *Film Ed* Ben Lewis. *Asst Ed* William McMillin. *Mus Supv & Cond* Fred Karger. *Songs* Hank Williams. *Songs Sung by* Hank Williams, Jr. *Mus Coörd* Hal Belfer. *Rec Supv* Franklin Milton. *Sd* Tom Overton. *Mus Ed* Ralph Ives. *Asst Dir* Eddie Saeta, William R. Finnegan. *Prod Coörd* Robert Stone. *Script Supv* Stanley Scheuer. *Wardrobe* Norman Burza, Evelyn Rickart. *Makeup Supv* William Tuttle. *Makeup* Don Cash. *Hairstyles* Sydney Guilaroff. *Tech Adv* Audrey Williams. *Still Photog* Sterling Smith.

Cast: George Hamilton *(Hank Williams)*, Susan Oliver *(Audrey Williams)*, Red Buttons *(Shorty Younger)*, Arthur O'Connell *(Fred Rose)*, Shary Marshall *(Ann Younger)*, Rex Ingram *(Teetot)*, Chris Crosby *(Sam Priddy)*, Rex Holman *(Charley Bybee)*, Hortense Petra *(Wilma, the cashier)*, Roy Engel *(Joe Rauch)*, Donald Losby *(young Hank Williams)*, Kevin Tate *(boy fishing)*.

Biographical drama with music. In the early 1930's in Alabama, young Hank Williams learns from Teetot, an elderly Negro, to play the guitar and sing. Hank becomes a salesman in a traveling medicine show and meets Audrey Shepherd and Shorty Younger, leaders of a group of touring hillbilly singers. They hear Hank sing and invite him to join their group. Audrey, ambitious for Hank's success, secretly sends his song "Your Cheatin' Heart" to music publisher Fred Rose. At the same time, she and Hank marry. Fred Rose is impressed with Hank's talent and arranges for his audition on the Louisiana Hayride radio program. Hank's popularity begins to soar, and he is invited to join the Grand Ole Opry. He achieves fame and wealth, but his private life begins to suffer; he becomes a heavy drinker and alienates his friends. He stops performing altogether and goes on the road. Eventually, he quits drinking and Fred gets him a booking, but Hank Williams, at the age of 29, dies of heart failure while driving to the concert on January 1, 1953. *Songs:* "Long Gone Lonesome Blues," "I Saw the Light," "I Can't Help It," "Jambalaya," "Cold Cold Heart," "I'm So Lonesome I Could Cry," "Hey, Good Lookin'." *Singers. Negroes. Salesmen. Musicians. Country music. Ambition. Marriage. Wealth. Fame. Alcoholism. Heart disease. Medicine shows. Hank Williams. Audrey Williams. Fred Rose. Shorty Younger. Grand Ole Opry.*

Note: Screen title: *Your Cheatin' Heart (The Hank Williams Story).*

YOUR MONEY OR YOUR WIFE (Great Britain)   **F6.5749**
Alliance Productions–Sydney Box Associates. *Dist* Ellis Films. ca 1965. Sd; b&w. 35mm. 91 min.

Prod Norman Williams. *Dir* Anthony Simmons. *Screenplay* Ronald Jeans. *Photog* Brendan J. Stafford. *Art Dir* Tony Inglis. *Film Ed* Bernard Gribble. *Mus* Philip Green. *Sd* Marcel Durham. *Sd Rec* Dave Goghan.

Cast: Donald Sinden *(Pelham Butterworth)*, Peggy Cummins *(Gay Butterworth)*, Richard Wattis *(Hubert Fry)*, Peter Reynolds *(Theodore Malek)*, Georgina Cookson *(Thelma Cressingdon)*, Gladys Boot *(Mrs. Compton-Chamberlain)*, Barbara Steele *(Juliet Frost)*, Betty Baskcombe *(Janet Fry)*, Olive Sloane *(Mrs. Withers)*, Ian Fleming *(judge)*, Candy Scott *(maid)*, Noel Tregarthen *(chauffeur)*.

Domestic comedy. Gay and Pelham Butterworth, a young couple expecting to inherit a small fortune through a legacy, imagine they will be able to pay off their many debts and still maintain their large house. They discover, however, that the legacy stipulates that only the wife can receive a small allowance as long as her husband is alive or their marriage is intact. At first, Gay and Pelham take an odd assortment of lodgers to pay off the debts, but, because no one pays rent, a divorce is arranged with the understanding that the couple will remarry as soon as possible. A misunderstanding makes the divorce seem more permanent, but everything is resolved when Pelham becomes Gay's paying guest in the house. *Lodgers. Inheritance. Debt. Marriage. Divorce.*

Note: Released in Great Britain in Mar 1960.

YOUR SHADOW IS MINE (France/Italy)   **F6.5750**
Precitel—Da. Ma. Film—Cathay—Keris Productions—Cofilms. *Dist* Continental Distributing, Inc. 14 May 1963 [New York opening]. Sd; col. 35mm. 90 min.

Prod Pierre Courau. *Dir* André Michel. *Screenplay* Jean-René Huguenin, Diego Fabbri, Madeleine Courau. *Scen* Han Suyin. *Dial* Jean-René Huguenin. *Based on an Idea by* André Michel. *Photog* Edmond Séchan. *Art Dir* Jacques Paris. *Film Ed* Jean-Michel Gautier. *Mus Comp & Cond* Maurice Jarre.

Cast: Jill Haworth *(Sylvie "Devi" Bergerat)*, Michel Ruhl *(Philippe Bergerat)*, Ruos Vanny *(Rahit)*, Marcel Pagliero *(Dr. Rouvier)*, Clotilde Joano *(Anne Bergerat)*, Catherine Zago *(Madame Moniveau)*, Madame Pung-Peng-Cheng *(Mate)*, Philippe Forquet *(man at party)*.

Melodrama. Devi is a French girl who has been raised by a native Cambodian family since she was found wandering in the forest 12 years ago. She looks forward to marrying Rahit, the son of her foster mother, but her idyllic existence is shattered when government officials return her to her brother, Philippe Bergerat, who has been searching for her since the Japanese attacked their family's plantation in 1943. Determined to win Devi's love, Philippe excludes everything else from his life, including his unhappy wife, Anne, but his need for spiritual love soon becomes a physical desire for his sister. When Rahit arrives, the frightened Devi agrees to run away with him. As they make their way back to the village, Philippe takes pursuit in his car. The youngsters hide in the forest, and Philippe drives after them, but he is killed when his car skids off the road and crashes into some trees. *Orphans. Cambodians. Foster parents. Adolescence. Family life. Miscegenation. Brother-sister relationship. Incest. Cambodia. Automobile accidents.*

Note: Filmed on location in Cambodia. Released in France in 1962 as *Ton ombre est la mienne.*

YOUR TEETH IN MY NECK *see* **THE FEARLESS VAMPIRE KILLERS; OR, PARDON ME BUT YOUR TEETH ARE IN MY NECK**

YOU'RE A BIG BOY NOW   **F6.5751**
Phil Feldman. *For* Seven Arts Productions. *Dist* Seven Arts Pictures. 9 Dec 1966 [Los Angeles opening]. Sd; col (PathéColor). 35mm. 96 min.

Prod Phil Feldman. *Assoc Prod* William Fadiman. *Dir-Writ* Francis Ford Coppola. *Dir Photog* Andrew Laszlo. *Camera Op* Harvey Genkins. *Asst Camera* Jimmy Fitzsimmons. *Art Dir* Vassele Fotopoulos. *Set Decor* Marvin March. *Film Ed* Aram Avakian. *Mus Score* Robert Prince. *Mus Supv* Jack Lewis, mus. *Mus Arr & Cond* Arthur Schroeck. *Songs:* "Darling, Be Home Soon," "You're a Big Boy Now," "Kite Chase," "Letter to Barbara," "Lonely (Amy's Theme)," "March," "Miss Thing's Thang," "Try To Be Happy," "Wash Her Away" John Sebastian. *Perf by* The Lovin' Spoonful. *Miss Hartman's Choreog* Robert Tucker. *Sd* Jean Bagley, Sanford Rackow, Jack Jacobsen. *Asst Dir* Larry Sturhahn. *Prod Mgr* David Golden. *Cost* Theoni V. Aldredge. *Makeup* Bob Philippe. *Hairstyles* Philip Naso. *Coöp* John Vliet Lindsay, New York Public Library. *Gaffer* Lou Girolami.

Cast: Peter Kastner *(Bernard Chanticleer)*, Elizabeth Hartman *(Barbara Darling)*, Geraldine Page *(Margery Chanticleer)*, Julie Harris *(Miss Thing)*, Rip Torn *(I. H. Chanticleer)*, Michael Dunn *(Richard Mudd)*, Tony Bill *(Raef)*, Karen Black *(Amy)*, Dolph Sweet *(policeman Francis Graf)*, Michael

O'Sullivan *(Kurt Doughty)*, Ronald Colby, Rufus Harley, Frank Simpson, Nina Verella, Len De Carl.

Comedy. Source: David Benedictus, *You're a Big Boy Now* (London, 1963). Bernard Chanticleer, a 19-year-old virgin, works as a roller-skating stack boy in the New York Public Library. His mother, Margery, dotes on him and tries to spoil him, while his father, I. H., the library's curator of rare books, is in a hurry to see his son grow up. Bernard, however, is happy only with his dog, Rover, whom he calls "Dog" against his parents' wishes. To become more independent Bernard moves into a roominghouse run by the eccentric Miss Thing, but opportunity for romance is restricted by a woman-hating rooster who guards the premises and refuses to allow any females to pass. One night Bernard goes to a Greenwich Village discotheque with two library employees: Raef, who has had considerable experience with sex and drugs, and the pretty Amy, who soon develops a crush on him. Bernard, however, is more captivated by Barbara Darling, an actress who works as the nightclub's go-go dancer. Having once been assaulted by a wooden-legged albino hypnotherapist, Barbara is a confirmed man-hater who occupies her time in a crazily decorated apartment dictating her memoirs to Richard Mudd, a dwarf. After sending Barbara a love letter, Bernard spends a disastrous night with her, and upon returning to her apartment the next day, he finds that Raef has moved in with her. Filled with despair, he goes to his father's office, steals the library's Gutenberg Bible, and runs into the street with nearly all involved in pursuit. Bernard is cornered in a department store and arrested, but Amy, accompanied by "Dog," brings him bail money and offers all her love. Revitalized, Bernard joins her in a carefree fling through Manhattan. *Librarians. Landladies. Eccentrics. Go-go dancers. Man-haters. Dwarfs. Virginity. Filial relations. Theft. Roller skating. Roominghouses. Discotheques. New York City. New York City—Greenwich Village. New York Public Library. Gutenberg Bible. Dogs. Roosters.*

Note: Location scenes filmed in New York City.

YOU'RE DEAD RIGHT *see* **ARRIVEDERCI, BABY!**

YOURS, MINE, AND OURS   **F6.5752**
Desilu–Walden Productions. *Dist* United Artists. 24 Apr 1968 [New York opening; c24 Apr 1968; LP35532]. Sd; col (DeLuxe). 35mm. 111 min.

Prod Robert F. Blumofe. *Dir* Melville Shavelson. *Screenplay* Melville Shavelson, Mort Lachman. *Story* Madelyn Davis, Bob Carroll, Jr. *Dir Photog* Charles Wheeler. *Camera Op* Jordan Cronenweth. *Art Dir* Arthur Lonergan. *Set Decor* James Payne. *Main Titl* Howard A. Anderson Co. *Film Ed* Stuart Gilmore. *Mus Comp, Arr & Cond* Fred Karlin. *Sd* Pete Peterson. *Asst Dir* Dick Bremerkamp, Louis Nicoletti, James Benjamin. *Prod Supv* Joe Popkin. *Script Supv* Erika Wernher. *Cost* Renita Reachi, Frank Cardinale. *Makeup* Bill Phillips. *Hairstyles* Irma Kusely. *Coöp* United States Navy. *Gaffer* Don Stott. *Key Grip* Pete Bernard. *Prop* Ken Westcott.

Cast—Principals: Lucille Ball *(Helen North)*, Henry Fonda *(Frank Beardsley)*, Van Johnson *(Darrell Harrison)*, Tom Bosley *(doctor)*, Louise Troy *(Frank's date)*, Ben Murphy *(Larry)*.

Cast—The North Children: Jennifer Leak *(Colleen)*, Kevin Burchett *(Nicky)*, Kimberly Beck *(Janette)*, Mitch Vogel *(Tommy)*, Margot Jane *(Jean)*, Eric Shea *(Phillip)*, Gregory Atkins *(Gerald)*, Lynnell Atkins *(Teresa)*.

Cast—The Beardsley Children: Tim Matthieson *(Mike)*, Gil Rogers *(Rusty)*, Nancy Roth *(Rosemary)*, Gary Goetzman *(Greg)*, Suzanne Cupito *(Louise)*, Holly O'Brien *(Susan)*, Michele Tobin *(Veronica)*, Maralee Foster *(Mary)*, Tracy Nelson *(Germaine)*, Stephanie Oliver *(Joan)*.

Comedy-drama. Source: Helen Beardsley, *Who Gets the Drumstick* (New York, 1965). Naval officer Frank Beardsley, a widower with 10 children, takes a shore job so that he can look after his family; but he finds that they miss their mother and resent his attempts at discipline. Then he begins dating Helen North, a widow with 8 children. With the matchmaking assistance of Beardsley's bachelor friend, Darrell Harrison, Helen and Frank eventually decide to marry, despite the unnerving prospect of such a large family. At first the children resent the marriage, and jealousies among the youngsters create numerous problems in the crowded household; but when Helen's son Phillip begins to hero-worship Frank's eldest boy, Mike, family relations improve and hostilities subside. The bond between parents and children is strengthened by the expectation of Frank and Helen's first baby. When she returns home with the family's 19th child, both sets of children view the new offspring as their own; and they ask to be adopted by their respective stepparents in order that they may all share the same name. With Mike going off to war and Helen's daughter Colleen learning that love also brings responsibilities, the union of the two households is complete. *Widowers. Widows. Nurses. Bachelors. Children. Courtship. Marriage. Family life. Filial relations. Jealousy. Hero worship. Frank & Helen Beardsley.*

Note: Location scenes filmed in San Francisco. Based on the true story about the Beardsley family of California in the early 1960's. Working title: *His, Hers and Theirs.*

THE YOUTH AND HIS AMULET (Japan)   **F6.5753**

Toho Co. Mar **1963** [Los Angeles showing]. Sd; b&w with col seq. 35mm (Tohoscope). 111 min.

Exec Prod Hiroshi Inagaki. *Dir* Hiroshi Inagaki. *Screenplay* Toshiro Ide, Zenzo Matsuyama. *Story* Shizue Miyaguchi. *Photog* Kazuo Yamada. *Mus* Ikuma Dan. *Sp Eff* Eiji Tsuburaya.

Cast: Toru Koyanagi *(Gen)*, Hisako Sakabe *(his sister)*, Toshiro Mifune *(Fudo-myoh)*, Chishu Ryu, Yosuke Natsuki, Minoru Chiaki, Nobuko Otowa, Mie Hama.

Domestic melodrama. Gen, a 10-year-old boy, lives with his widowed father, a Buddhist priest, and his little sister in rural Japan. The boy's peaceful life is disrupted when his father decides to remarry; and to avoid conflicts with his new wife, whose son from a former marriage died a short time before, the father places Gen in the home of a parishioner in another village. The parishioner, an old woman who dislikes children, constantly scolds Gen and provides him a steady stream of menial tasks to perform. One day the boy discovers a small idol of Fudo-myoh, a god whose image he carries in an amulet he prizes, in the village shrine; he takes the idol home with him and when alone talks to it about his problems. His theft is discovered, and Gen is returned to his father and stepmother, who are having marital problems. Resentful of her stepson, the woman tosses his amulet aside and then leaves home when Gen accuses her of stealing it. Some months later Gen and his sister leave home in an effort to find their step-mother, but their actions are misinterpreted, and upon their return Gen is sent away for adoption. *Children. Stepmothers. Priests. Widows. Buddhism. Idolatry. Family life. Marriage. Theft. Rural life. Adoption. Brother-sister relationship. Talismans. Fudo-myoh.*

Note: Released in Japan in 1961 as *Gen to Fudo-myoh;* running time: 120 min.

YOUTH IN FURY (Japan)   **F6.5754**

Shochiku Co. *Dist* Shochiku Films of America. 25 Jul **1961** [Los Angeles showing]. Sd; col (Eastmancolor). 35mm (Shochiku GrandScope). 89 min.

Dir Masahiro Shinoda. *Screenplay* Shuji Terayama. *Story* Eiji Shimba. *Photog* Masao Kosugi. *Art Dir* Kiminobu Sato. *Film Ed* Keiichi Uraoka. *Mus* Toru Takemitsu. *Prod Supv* Tetsuo Ueno.

Cast: Shin-ichiro Mikami *(Takuya Shimojo)*, Shima Iwashita *(Yoko Katsura)*, Hizuru Takachiho *(Fumie Sono)*, Kayoko Honoo *(Setsuko Kitamura)*, Jun-ichiro Yamashita *(Michihiko Kihara)*, Kazuya Kosaka *(Seiichi Mizushima)*, Yunosuke Ito *(Oseto)*, Yachiyo Otori *(Shizue)*, Shinji Takano *(Fujimori)*, Eiko Kujo *(Miyoko Edamura)*, Yuki Tominaga *(Sakiko Ota)*, Keiko Kuni *(Takako Shinoyama)*, Teiko Sawamura.

Drama. Takuya Shimojo, a student radical, indiscriminately admires Hitler, Mussolini, Trotsky, and Castro, dreaming of some day commanding the same kind of fanatical devotion as his idols attained. Toward the end of the summer, Michihiko, an heir to a large fortune, invites a group of students that includes Takuya and his girl friend, Setsuko, to his seaside villa for sailing and parties. One of the students, Yoko Katsura, receives a call informing her of her father's suicide. According to newspaper reports, Katsura was involved in corruption in the firm which he managed and was forced to commit suicide by Oseto, a Diet member who feared that such a scandal could have adverse political effects. Takuya meets Oseto at a bar, and when Oseto begins discussing nationalism, Takuya bluntly states that he is interested in either murdering the rich or taking their place. Takuya then proposes that Oseto pay a college girl to become his mistress only to discover that Fumie, the bar's hostess, is already his mistress. Seiichi Mizushima, one of Takuya's friends on the radical student committee, asks for help in finding work, but when Takuya attempts to use his influence with Michihiko, the heir coldly turns him down. Takuya becomes attracted to Yoko, who has been humiliated by her family's financial dependence on Oseto, and he asks a boxer friend to beat up Yoko's sister's fiancé, Fujimori, who has broken off their engagement. Expelled from the committee for belonging to a political party and for his amoral conduct, Takuya attends wild parties given by his rich friends, while students protest against a security pact between Japan and the U. S. Yoko leaves home when she discovers that Oseto supports her family in exchange for her sister's sexual favors. Mizushima, unable to find work, hangs himself. As the protests continue, Takuya informs the committee that demonstrations are pointless, and he purchases explosive powders with which to make dynamite. Setsuko reveals that she is carrying his child, but he replies that he is too busy for her now. On the way out of his apartment, he is arrested by detectives in connection with the assault on Fujimori, and his plans for using the dynamite are thwarted. *Students. Heirs. Bar girls. Businessmen. Politicians. Mistresses. Boxers. Student activism. College life. Demonstrations. Suicide. Scandal. Pregnancy. Unemployment. Explosives. Treaties.*

Note: Released in Japan in 1960 as *Kawaita mizuumi.*

YOU'VE GOT TO BE SMART   **F6.5755**

World-Cine Associates–Stage 19 Productions. *Dist* Producers Releasing Organization. 28 Apr **1967** [Albuquerque, New Mexico, opening]. Sd; col. 35mm. 88 min.

Dir-Writ Ellis Kadison. *Mus* Stan Worth, Gerald Alters. *Mus Arr & Cond* Stan Worth. *Songs:* "Him Who Loves Ain't Got Time To Hate," "Time Will Tell," "Restin' Time," "Look Before You Leap," "Don't Look in Other Pastures" sung by The Bantams.

Cast: Tom Stern *(Nick Sloane)*, Roger Perry *(Jerry Harper)*, Gloria Castillo *(Connie Jackson)*, Mamie Van Doren *(Miss Hathaway)*, Preston Foster *(D. O. Griggs)*, Jeff Bantam *(Methuselah Jones)*, Mike Bantam, Fritz Bantam *(Methuselah's brothers)*.

Drama. At a west coast advertising agency Nick Sloane is fired for trying to steal the firm's biggest account from under the nose of his boss, D. O. Griggs. The only one surprised by the dismissal is Griggs's secretary, Connie Jackson, who refuses to believe that Nick is capable of anything underhanded. Later, Connie receives a phone call from a small town in Arkansas, where Nick has discovered a 9-year-old singing preacher, Methuselah Jones. Duped into believing that Nick's intentions are sincere, Connie quits her job and joins Nick in helping Methuselah and his two younger brothers achieve national prominence. While Connie is busy persuading television promotion man Jerry Harper to put the youngsters on the air, Nick spends his evenings with Miss Hathaway, a beautiful blonde, and dreams up ways to exploit his clients. Eventually, the disillusioned Jones brothers force Connie to see Nick in his true light. The youngsters return to their Ozark home, and Connie rejects Nick for Jerry's love. *Advertising executives. Secretaries. Preachers. Children. Publicists. Singers. Duplicity. Publicity. Television. Arkansas. Ozarks.*

YOYO see **YO YO**

YUKIGUNI see **SNOW COUNTRY**

YUSHA NOMI see **NONE BUT THE BRAVE**

YUSHU HEIYA see **MADAME AKI**

YVONNE FROM 6 TO 9   **F6.5756**

The Editing Place. *Dist* Distribpix, Inc. 3 Oct **1969** [Champaign, Illinois, showing]. Sd; col. 35mm. 63 min.

Mus Arlo Shiffen.

Cast: Sam Blake *(Doc)*, Esther Nash *(Jill)*, Arthur Marsh *(Cal)*, Melinda Mason *(Beenie)*, Ned Freestone *(Jake)*, Helen Tralor *(Irene)*, Millard More *(Roger)*, Chris Krane *(Natalie)*, Yvonne *(narrator)*.

Crime melodrama. Jill, a secretary in a loan office, awakens early one morning and suggests to her husband Roger that they begin the day by making love. Jill refuses to reciprocate his oral caresses, however, and he storms out of their apartment leaving her aroused and frustrated. She has a daydream where she is beaten into submission by two faceless attackers. On her way to work that morning, she is kidnaped by two men who have just robbed the office where she works. Taken to their hideout, she is drugged and tied to a bed. Doc, the leader of the gang, keeps Irene and Jake, two members of the gang, from molesting Jill, and he declares her off-limits for the night. Irene returns later, however, and arouses Jill, despite her protestations. Doc hides the loot and waits for a chance to skip out. As morning dawns, Cal and Jake torture the helpless woman, and again Doc comes to her rescue, this time taking her for himself. When the other gangsters decide to split the money, they become irate when it can't be found. Cal and Jake murder Doc before he can reveal its whereabouts. The distraught but cunning Jill accuses Jake of hiding the loot; Cal knifes him, but before he dies, Jake gets off a shot that is fatal to Cal. Irene attacks Jill, and Jill kills her with a pair of scissors. *Secretaries. Thieves. Gangs. Robbery. Kidnaping. Rape. Lesbianism. Murder.*

Z (Algeria/France)   **F6.5757**

Reggane Films–O. N. C. I. C. *Dist* Cinema V Distributing, Inc. 8 Dec **1969** [New York opening]. Sd; col (Eastman Color, print by Technicolor). 35mm. 127 min. *MPAA rating* M.

Prod Jacques Perrin, Hamed Rachedi. *Assoc Prod* Eric Schlumberger, Philippe d'Argila. *Dir* Costa-Gavras. *Screenplay* Costa-Gavras, Jorge Semprun. *Dial* Jorge Semprun. *Dir Photog* Raoul Coutard. *Camera* Georges Liron. *1st Asst Camera Op* Jean Garcenot. *Art Dir* Jacques d' Ovidio. *Film Ed* Françoise Bonnot. *Asst Film Ed* Marie-Thérèse Boiche. *Mus* Mikis Theodorakis. *Mus Arr & Cond* Bernard Gérard. *Sd* Michèle Boehm. *Asst Dir* Philippe Monnier. *Prod Supv* Hubert Mérial. *Prod Mgr* Lionel de Souza. *Asst Prod Mgr* Alexandre Popovic. *Script Girl* Annie Maurel. *Prod Sec* Yvonne Bénézech, Monique Agénor. *Stuntman* Yvan Chiffre. *Admin* F. Dupuis. *Still Photog* Georges Beutter, Félix Le Garrec, Joël Ducange.

Cast: Yves Montand *(The Deputy Z.)*, Jean-Louis Trintignant *(The Magistrate)*, Jacques Perrin *(The Journalist)*, François Périer *(The Public Prosecutor)*, Irene Papas *(Hélène)*, Georges Géret *(Nick)*, Charles Denner

(*Manuel*), Bernard Fresson (*Matt*), Jean Bouise (*Pirou*), Jean-Pierre Miquel (*Pierre*), Renato Salvatori (*Yago*), Marcel Bozzufi (*Vago*), Julien Guiomar (*The Colonel*), Pierre Dux (*The General*), Guy Mairesse (*Dumas*), Magali Noël (*Nick's sister*), Clotilde Joano (*Shoula*), Maurice Baquet (*The Bald Man*), Jean Dasté (*Coste*), Gérard Darrieu (*Baron*), José Artur (*The Newspaper Editor*), Van Doude (*The Hospital Director*), Eva Simonet (*Niki*), Hassan Hassani (*The General's Chauffeur*), Gabriel Jabbour (*Bozzini*), Jean-François Gobbi (*Jimmy the Boxer*), Andrée Tainsy (*Nick's mother*), Steeve Gadler (*English photographer*), Bob de Bragelonne (*Undersecretary of State*), Sid Ahmed Agoumi, Allel El Mouhib, Habib Reda, Georges Rouquier.

Historical drama. Source: Vassilis Vassilikos, *Z* (Athens, 1966). During a speaking engagement coinciding with an appearance of the Bolshoi Ballet, pacifist Deputy Z., the target of a right-wing military conspiracy, is assassinated by homosexual reactionaries Vago and Yago, and Z.'s supporters are brutally beaten by thugs before indifferent police. When an autopsy discloses that Z. was not killed by a hit-and-run driver, but bludgeoned to death, the deputy's supporters demand an investigation. In response, seemingly apathetic local authorities appoint as investigating magistrate a career civil servant, who, to the surprise of all, proves to be incorruptible. In his investigation the magistrate is assisted by a fiercely independent journalist and by a courageous eyewitness, the casket-maker Nick. Although Nick is offered bribes by civil authorities, he refuses to change his story. Hospitalized as a result of an assault and reproached by his sister, Nick sticks to his story. As a result, the military conspiracy is exposed, Vago and Yago are convicted, and Z.'s party is victorious in the general election. High army officials, however, are given suspended sentences, and several months later the military accomplish a coup d'état, imprison dissidents, and interdict long hair, miniskirts, the Beatles, several major authors, references to Socrates' homosexuality, and the letter "Z," which in the ancient Greek means "he lives." *Pacifists. Politicians. Journalists. Magistrates. Investigators. Secret police. Conspiracy. Assassination. Political corruption. Male homosexuality. Trials. Coups d'état. Military government. Greece.*

Note: Filmed in Algiers. Opened in Paris in Feb 1969; running time: 123 min; reviewed in Canada at 152 min; in West Germany at 145 min. Originally subtitled *L'anatomie d'un assassinat politique.*

ZA DVUMYA ZAYTSAMI *see* **A KIEV COMEDY**

ZABRISKIE POINT   **F6.5758**
Metro-Goldwyn-Mayer, Inc.–Trianon Productions. *Dist* Metro-Goldwyn-Mayer, Inc. 9 Feb **1970** [New York opening; c18 Mar 1970; LP38062]. Sd; col (Metrocolor). 35mm (Panavision). 112 min. *MPAA rating* R.
A Carlo Ponti Production. *Prod* Carlo Ponti. *Exec Prod* Harrison Starr. *Dir* Michelangelo Antonioni. *Screenplay* Michelangelo Antonioni, Fred Gardner, Sam Shepard, Tonino Guerra, Clare Peploe. *Orig Story* Michelangelo Antonioni. *Dir Photog* Alfio Contini. *Camera* William Snyder. *Set Decor* George R. Nelson. *Prod Dsgn* Dean Tavoularis. *Collab on Ed* Franco Arcalli. *Asst Ed* Jim Benson. *Orig Mus Comp & Perf:* "Heart Beat, Pig Meat," "Come In Number 51, Your Time Is Up," "Crumbling Land" Pink Floyd. *Song:* "Brother Mary" Robert Hunter, Jerry Garcia. *Perf by* Kaleidoscope. *Song:* "Dark Star" Robert Hunter, Jerry Garcia. *Perf by* The Grateful Dead. *Song:* "Mickey's Tune" David Lindley. *Perf by* Kaleidoscope. *Song:* "Love Scene" *comp & perf by* Jerry Garcia. *Song:* "You've Got the Silver" Mick Jagger, Keith Richard. *Perf by* The Rolling Stones. *Song:* "Sugar Babe" Jesse Colin Young. *Perf by* The Youngbloods. *Song:* "Dance of Death" *comp & perf by* John Fahey. *Song:* "I Wish I Was a Single Girl Again" *arr & perf by* Roscoe Holcomb. *Song:* "Tennessee Waltz" Pee Wee King, Redd Stewart. *Sung by* Patti Page. *Rec Supv* Franklin Milton. *Electronic Eff* Music Electronic Viva. *Sd Mix* Jerry Kosloff, Renato Cadueri. *Asst Dir* Robert J. Rubin. *Unit Prod Mgr* Don Guest. *Script Supv* Bonnie Prendergast. *Prod Asst* Sally Dennison. *Asst to the Dir* Rina Macrelli. *Cost Dsgn* Ray Summers. *Makeup* Joe McKenney. *Sp Eff* Earl McCoy. *Mus Adv* Don Hall, Jr.
Cast: Mark Frechette (*Mark*), Daria Halprin (*Daria*), Rod Taylor (*Lee Allen*), Paul Fix (*cafe owner*), G. D. Spradlin (*Lee Allen's associate*), Bill Garaway (*Morty*), Kathleen Cleaver (*Kathleen*), The Open Theatre of Joe Chaikin (*lovemakers in Death Valley*).
Drama. Mark, a student at a Los Angeles university, attends a meeting of radicals but leaves when he decides that they plan to take no action against political repression. He buys a revolver and goes to the campus where police are attempting to oust students from an occupied building, but he misses the chance to shoot a policeman when another bullet strikes the man first. Fleeing from the scene, Mark steals a small airplane from a private airport and flies east. From his plane, he sees a young woman, Daria, driving across the desert toward Phoenix; Mark flies over her car until she becomes amused by his attention and stops to wait for him to land. Leaving the plane behind, the two drive in her car until they reach Zabriskie Point in Death Valley, where Daria smokes marijuana, and they make love in the sand dunes. Later, at a roadside comfort station, Daria is questioned by a highway patrolman; unnoticed, Mark draws

his gun, but Daria stands in front of the policeman. After the policeman leaves, Mark realizes that he must leave Daria and return to Los Angeles. He finds the plane and flies back to the airport, where he is killed by the waiting police. Daria drives on toward Phoenix and hears the news of Mark's death on the car radio. She reaches the plush office of her employer, Lee Allen, who is negotiating to build a modern community in the desert. Suddenly repulsed by crass materialism, Daria departs, fantasizing about the destruction of the building and all it represents. *Students. Police. Radicalism. Demonstrations. Murder. Theft. Materialism. Fantasy. Firearms. Airplanes. Marijuana. Real estate. Los Angeles. Death Valley. Mojave Desert. Phoenix (Arizona). Arizona. Explosions.*

Note: Location scenes filmed in Los Angeles, Death Valley, the Mojave Desert, and in Arizona. Participation of Trianon Productions is unconfirmed.

ZACZĘŁO SIĘ NAD WISŁĄ *see* **IT BEGAN ON THE VISTULA**

ZAP-IN *see* **MISS NYMPHET'S ZAP-IN**

ZAR UND ZIMMERMANN (West Germany)   **F6.5759**
Polyphon Film & TV Productions. *Dist* Polytel International. 20 Jul **1970** [New York opening]. Sd; col. 35mm. 137 min.
Prod Rolf Liebermann. *Exec Prod* Gyula Trebitsch. *Dir* Joachim Hess. *Libretto* Albert Lortzing. *Sets* Herbert Kirchhoff. *Mus:* "Zar und Zimmermann" Albert Lortzing. *Mus Played by* Hamburg State Philharmonic Orchestra. *Sung by* Hamburg State Opera Chorus. *Orch Cond by* Charles Macherras.
Cast: Raymond Wolansky (*Peter Michaelov/Zar*), Peter Haage (*Peter Ivanov*), Hans Sotin (*Van Bett*), Lucia Popp (*Marie*), Ursula Boese (*Mistress Brown*), Horst Wilhelm (*Marquis de Chateauneuf*), Herbert Fliether (*Admiral Lefort*), Noel Mangin (*Lord Syndham*), Franz Grundheber (*an officer*), Jurgen Forster (*a council servant*).
Opera film. Source: Albert Lortzing, *Zar und Zimmermann* (first performance: Leipzig, 22 Dec 1837). Jean Toussaint Merle, Anne Honoré Joseph Duveyrier and Jean Bernard Eugène Cantiran de Boirie, *Le bourgmestre de Sardam, ou, Le prince charpentier* (Paris opening: 5 Mar 1825). A filmed performance of the opera. *Royalty. Deserters—Military. Russians. British. Diplomats. Magistrates. French. Mistaken identity. Disguise. Docks. Netherlands.*
Note: Produced for West German television; date of release unknown.

DER ZAREWITSCH (France/West Germany)   **F6.5760**
Films Roger Richebé–CCC–Filmkunst. *Dist* Casino Films. 3 Nov **1961** [Milwaukee, Wisconsin, opening]. Sd; b&w. 35mm. 95 min.
Prod Artur Brauner. *Dir* Arthur-Maria Rabenalt. *Screenplay* Roger Richebé. *Dial* Georges Neveux. *Adapt* Roger Richebé, Pierre Gaspard-Huit. *Photog* Georg Bruckbauer. *Art Dir* Friedrich Mögle. *Film Ed* Martha Dübber. *Mus* Franz Lehár. *Mus Adapt & Dir* Bert Grund. *Lyr* Francis Blanche. *Ballet Dir* Dimitrije Parlic. *Prod Mgr* Ernst Steinlechner.
Cast: Luis Mariano (*José*), Sonja Ziemann (*Sonia*), Ivan Petrovich, Paul Henkels, Ernst Waldow, Maria Sebaldt, Hans Richter, Hanne-Lore Morell, Axel Monjé, Edelweiss Malchin, Gerd Frickhöffer, Corps de Ballet of the National Theater of Belgrade.
Dance film. Source: Franz Lehár, *Der Zarewitsch* (first performance: Berlin, 21 Feb 1927). Sonia, a ballerina, is secretly in love with José, a tenor who plays the tzarevitch in an operetta of the same name. She dreams of finding herself in the tzarevitch's castle, threatened with deportation by his ministers unless she can win his love. Sonia disguises herself as a Cossack, so as to approach the prince, who has forbidden all women entrance to the palace as the result of an unhappy love affair. Discovering the ruse, the prince feigns love for Sonia. Soon, however, he becomes seriously infatuated but must abandon Sonia for the throne when his father dies. Awakening from her dream, Sonia finds at her feet the tenor, who proclaims his love. *Dancers. Lovelorn. Singers. Royalty. Cossacks. Opera. Ballet. Disguise. Castles. Dreams.*
Note: Released in West Germany in 1954; opened in Paris in Feb 1955 as *Le tzarevitch*; running time: 100 min.

ZARTE HAUT IN SCHWARZER SEIDE *see* **DANIELLA BY NIGHT**

ZATO ICHI CHIKEMURI KAIDO *see* **ZATOICHI CHALLENGED**

ZATO ICHI JIGOKUTABI *see* **SHOWDOWN FOR ZATOICHI**

ZATO ICHI KENKATABI *see* **ZATOICHI**

ZATO ICHI TO YOJINBO *see* **ZATOICHI MEETS YOJIMBO**

ZATOICHI (Japan)   **F6.5761**
Daiei Motion Picture Co. 27 Jun **1968** [New York opening]. Sd; col (Eastmancolor). 35mm (Daiei Scope). 90 min.
Prod Ikuro Kubokawa. *Dir* Kimiyoshi Yasuda. *Fight Seq Stgd by* Shohei Miyauchi. *Screenplay* Minoru Inuzuka. *Orig Story* Kan Shimozawa. *Photog*

Shozo Honda. *Art Dir* Yoshinobu Nishioka. *Mus* Akira Ifukube.

Cast: Shintaro Katsu *(Zatoichi)*, Shiho Fujimura *(Omitsu)*, Ryuzo Shimada *(Jingoro)*, Reiko Fujiwara *(Ohisa)*, Matasaburo Niwa *(Yamada)*, Yoshio Yoshida *(Tomegoro)*, Sonosuke Sawamura *(Tobei)*, Shosaku Sugiyama *(Hikozo)*, Yutaka Nakamura *(Matsu)*.

Action melodrama. In feudal Japan Zatoichi, a blind masseur-swordsman, is persuaded by a fellow samurai to sell his services to Hikozo, a warlord preparing for battle with his rival Tobei. Before Zatoichi and his companion can reach their destination, however, they are ambushed by three members of Tobei's clan. In the ensuing battle, Zatoichi kills all of the assailants but not before they have murdered his companion. Continuing alone, Zatoichi accedes to a dying man's request that he return a young woman, Omitsu, safely to her parents. At an inn en route to Omitsu's home, the girl is kidnaped. Using the supersensory perception of the blind, Zatoichi follows the kidnaper's trail and rescues Omitsu. As soon as she is at home, however, she is again kidnaped, this time by the evil Jingoro. Omitsu is being brought before Tobei as Zatoichi is fighting off the members of Tobei's clan, unaware that Hikozo is planning to murder him. Zatoichi finally learns that Tobei's clan is holding Omitsu and that members of his own clan have been plotting against him, whereupon Zatoichi slays all of his antagonists and then makes certain that Omitsu is safely returned to her parents. *Samurai. Warlords. Masseurs. Kidnaping. Blindness. Perfidy. Feuds. Zatoichi.*

Note: Released in Japan as *Zato Ichi kenkatabi.*

ZATOICHI CHALLENGED (Japan)   F6.5762

Daiei Motion Picture Co. Apr **1970** [Los Angeles showing]. Sd; col (Eastmancolor). 35mm (Daiei Scope). 87 min.

Dir Kenji Misumi. *Screenplay* Ryozo Kasahara. *Orig Story* Kan Shimozawa. *Photog* Chishi Makiura. *Art Dir* Shigenori Shimoishizaka. *Mus* Akira Ifukube.

Cast: Shintaro Katsu *(Zatoichi)*, Jushiro Konoe, Miwa Takada, Yukiji Asaoka, Mie Nakao, Mikiko Tsubouchi, Tomoo Koike.

Action melodrama. Zatoichi, the blind samurai-masseur, is transporting a young boy, Ryota, to his father in Maebara when the pair are attacked by five men. Zatoichi kills all five and continues on his way, now followed by the samurai Tajuro. Another gang sets upon Zatoichi and Ryota, and this time Tajuro staves off the thugs. In Maebara, Zatoichi learns that Ryota's father is being held captive by Gonzo, the town boss, whose black market operations violate the laws of the ruling shogunate. Tajuro reveals himself as a shogunate agent assigned to destroy the illegal operations. Zatoichi agrees to help him only if he will spare Ryota's father, who had been forced to work for Gonzo. Tajuro, believing he cannot deviate from his mission, refuses the request, thereby setting up a duel between the two friends. *Samurai. Masseurs. Hostages. Children. Blindness. Black market. Duels. Military government. Zatoichi.*

Note: Released in Japan in 1967 as *Zato Ichi chikemuri kaido.*

ZATOICHI MEETS YOJIMBO (Japan)   F6.5763

Katsu Productions. *Dist* Daiei Motion Picture Co., Bijou of Japan, Inc. 17 Jul **1970** [Los Angeles showing]. Sd; col (Eastman Color). 35mm (Daiei Scope). 116 min.

Dir Kihachi Okamoto. *Screenplay* Tetsuro Yoshida, Kihachi Okamoto. *Story* Kan Shimozawa. *Photog* Kazuo Miyagawa. *Art Dir* Yoshinobu Nishioka. *Mus* Akira Ifukube.

Cast: Shintaro Katsu *(Zatoichi)*, Toshiro Mifune *(Yojimbo)*, Mori Kishida *(Kuzuryu)*, Kanjuro Arashi *(Hyoroku)*, Osamu Takizawa *(Eboshiya)*, Ayako Wakao *(Umeno)*, Masakane Yonekura *(Boss Masagoro)*, Shigeru Kamiyama, Toshiyuki Hosokawa.

Action melodrama. Zatoichi, the blind masseur and expert swordsman, longs for the peaceful days when he was not defending himself against bandits or helping the poor and innocent fight the forces of evil. He returns to a quiet village he once visited, only to find that it has been taken over by a gangster, Boss Masagoro, while the venerable headman, Hyoroku, now does nothing but carve statues of the god Jizo. Masagoro, aware of Zatoichi's reputation, orders his bodyguard, Yojimbo, to kill him. Yojimbo is at first reluctant to attack a blind man, but the offer of a substantial reward changes his mind. The two men feel a grudging respect for each other after their first meeting, during which Yojimbo realizes Zatoichi is no ordinary swordsman. However, the two become enemies when Zatoichi is taken in by Eboshiya, Masagoro's father, who has disowned his criminal son. Yojimbo, actually a spy assigned by the Shogunate to find some gold bars hidden by Eboshiya, seems more interested in drinking at the sake shop run by the beautiful Umeno. Eboshiya's younger son arrives in town to demand the gold, and when his father refuses to hand it over, he kills both Eboshiya and Masagoro. Zatoichi eventually discovers that the gold is dust, which Hyoroku has been concealing in his statues. Before the greedy villagers can find it, however, the gold dust is blown away by a gust of wind. *Masseurs. Bodyguards. Gangsters. Mercenaries. Fatherhood. Greed. Duels. Blindness. Gold. Zatoichi. Jizo.*

Note: Released in Japan in Jan 1970 as *Zato Ichi to Yojinbo.*

ZAZIE (France)   F6.5764

Nouvelles Editions de Films. *Dist* Astor Pictures. 20 Nov **1961** [New York opening]. Sd; col (Eastmancolor). 35mm. 86 min.

Pres by Nouvelles Editions de Films. *Prod-Dir* Louis Malle. *Assoc Prod* Irénée Leriche. *Screenplay* Louis Malle, Jean-Paul Rappeneau. *Photog* Henri Raichi. *Camera* Jean Charvein. *1st Asst Camera* André Dubreuil. *Art Dir* Bernard Evein. *Asst Art Dir* Marc Frédérix. *Scenic Artist* Charles Merangel. *Film Ed* Kenout Peltier. *Asst Film Ed* Claudine Merlin, Yvette Bertrand. *Mus* André Pontin, Fiorenzo Carpi. *Mus Cond* Jacques Metehen. *Sd* André Hervée. *Asst Dir* Philippe Collin, Olivier Gérard. *Prod Mgr* Hubert Merial. *Script Girl* Sylvette Baudrot. *Cost* Marc Doelnitz. *Makeup* Aida Carange. *Sp Eff* Locafilms. *Optical Eff* Lax. *Artistic Cons* William Klein. *Still Photog* Jean-Louis Castelli.

Cast: Catherine Demongeot *(Zazie)*, Philippe Noiret *(Uncle Gabriel)*, Hubert Deschamps *(Turandot)*, Antoine Roblot *(Charles)*, Annie Fratellini *(Mado)*, Carla Marlier *(Albertine)*, Vittorio Caprioli *(Trouscaillon)*, Yvonne Clech *(Madame Mouaque)*, Nicolas Bataille *(Fedor)*, Jacques Dufilho *(Gridoux)*, Odette Picquet *(Madame Lalochere)*, Marc Doelnitz *(Monsieur Coquetti)*, Jacques Gheusi, Louis Lalanne, Little Bara, Georges Faye, Sylvine Delannoy, Jean-Marie De Coninck, Paul Vally, Jean-Yves Bouvier, Jean-Pierre Posier, Jeanne Allard, Jacqueline Doyen, Arlette Balkiss, Alegrina, Virginie Merlin, Irène Chabrier, Christine Howard.

Comedy. Source: Raymond Queneau, *Zazie dans le Métro* (Paris, 1959). While her mother is away with her latest lover, 11-year-old Zazie comes to Paris to spend 3 days with her Uncle Gabriel. The child's scandalous language and disrespectful attitude toward her elders quickly convinces Gabriel that this will not be a routine visit. When Zazie learns that she will not be able to ride the Metro because of a labor strike, she blames all adults for the situation and decides to make the best of her vacation. After a wild excursion in a taxi, she romps through the flea market and gets her uncle to take her to the Eiffel Tower. They become entangled in a group of tourists, and Zazie races down the tower steps while her uncle grabs a balloon and parachutes to the street. Together again, they get embroiled in a traffic jam and a mad chase through the streets of the city. That night her uncle takes Zazie to the nightclub where he works. Once more a brawl breaks out, and Zazie escapes with her uncle's wife, Albertine. When the Metro strike is over, Zazie's wish to ride the train is at last fulfilled, but, exhausted from the day's events, she sleeps all the way home. Returned to her mother, who asks her what she did in Paris, Zazie replies that she has grown older. *Children. Uncles. Aunts. Tourists. Vacations. Strikes. Traffic. Subways. Markets. Balloons (ascent). Nightclubs. Paris. Eiffel Tower.*

Note: Filmed on location in Paris. Opened in Paris in Oct 1960 as *Zazie dans le Métro*; running time: 90 min. Also known as *Zazie in the Underground.*

ZAZIE DANS LE MÉTRO *see* **ZAZIE**

ZAZIE IN THE UNDERGROUND *see* **ZAZIE**

ZBEHOVIA A PUTNÍCI *see* **THE DESERTER AND THE NOMADS**

ZEBRA IN THE KITCHEN   F6.5765

Ivan Tors Enterprises. *Dist* Metro-Goldwyn-Mayer, Inc. Jun **1965** [c2 Mar 1965; LP29825]. Sd (Westrex); col (Metrocolor). 35mm. 92 min.

An Ivan Tors Production. *Prod-Dir* Ivan Tors. *Assoc Prod* Ralph Helfer, Harry Redmond, Jr. *Screenplay* Art Arthur. *Story* Elgin Ciampi. *Dir Photog* Lamar Boren. *Art Dir* George W. Davis, Addison Hehr. *Set Decor* Henry Grace, Jack Mills. *Film Ed* Warren Adams. *Mus* Warren Barker. *Titl Song* Hal Hopper. *Sung by* The Standells. *Rec Supv* Franklin Milton. *Asst Dir* Eddie Saeta. *Asst to the Prod* Norman Siegel. *Makeup Supv* William Tuttle. *Wild Animals Supplied by* Africa U. S. A.

Cast: Jay North *(Chris Carlyle)*, Martin Milner *(Dr. Del Hartwood)*, Andy Devine *(Branch Hawksbill)*, Joyce Meadows *(Isabel Moon)*, Jim Davis *(Adam Carlyle)*, Dorothy Green *(Anne Carlyle)*, Karen Green *(Wilma Carlyle)*, Vaughn Taylor *(Councilman Pew)*, John Milford *(Sergeant Freebee)*, Tris Coffin *(Councilman Lawrence)*, Merritt Bohn *(chief of police)*, Robert Clarke *(sheriff)*, Percy Helton *(Mr. Richardson)*, Jimmy Stiles *(Tim)*, Dal Jenkins *(Kookie)*, Gordon Wescourt *(Ribs)*, Gary Judis *(Greenie)*, Robert Lowery *(Preston Heston)*, Wayne Thomas *(newscaster)*, Doodles Weaver *(nearsighted man)*, Jon Lormer *(judge)*, Vince Barnett *(man in man-hole)*, Phil Arnold *(man in tub)*.

Comedy. Young Chris Carlyle lives with his parents, Adam and Anne, on a ranch where he has made friends with a mountain lion cub. When the Carlyle family moves to a small town, Chris is told that he must leave his pet behind, but the lion hides in the trailer and arrives with the family. Upon discovering the stowaway, Chris's father finally persuades the boy to give the lion to a local zoo. Dr. Del Hartwood, the superintendent, and Branch Hawksbill, the zoo keeper, are friendly; but the zoo is crowded and Chris feels sorry for the animals caged there. One day Chris picks up the zoo keeper's keys and frees his lion as well as the rest of the animals. The animals run rampant with their new freedom; lions, hippos, elephants, monkeys, and zebras romp through the town and into the homes of the people. Hartwood and Hawksbill manage to round them all up before the police can shoot them, and the town finally awards the zoo much-needed funds for improvements. *Zoo keepers. Filial relations. Zoos. Pets. Lions. Hippopotami. Elephants. Monkeys. Zebras.*

Note: Filmed at Los Angeles' Griffin Park Zoo.

ZERO GIRLS
F6.5766

Dist Joseph Brenner Associates. **1965.** Sd; b&w. 35mm. 70 min.
Prod Joseph Brenner. *Dir* Michael Findlay. *Photog* Robert Arkless, Michael Findlay. *Film Ed* Ross-Gaffney Inc. *Choreog* Lem Amero.

Cast: Darlene Bennett, Madison Arnold, Yolanda Moreno, Judy Adler, Gigi Darlene.

Documentary(?). No information about the precise nature of this film has been found, but press material purports it to be a documentary about an international white slavery ring which operates in London, Havana, Germany, and New York. The film also includes scenes of prostitution and lesbianism. *Lesbianism. White slave traffic. London. Havana. Germany. New York City.*

Note: Also known as *The Sin Syndicate* and *Jazz Me Baby.*

ZERO IN THE UNIVERSE
F6.5767

Dist Film-Makers' Distribution Center, Dyle IV Productions. 11 Oct **1966** [New York opening]. Sd; b&w. 16mm. 85 min.
Prod Jock Livingston. *Dir* George Moorse. *Screenplay* Jock Livingston, George Moorse. *Photog* Gerard Vandenberg. *Film Ed* George Moorse. *Mus* Don Cherry. *Sd* Steve Malucheck.

Cast: Jock Livingston (*Zero*), George Bartenieff (*Steinmetz*), Pam Badyk (*Vivian*), George Moorse (*Peep*), Rob Du Mee (*Dubois*), Henke Raaff (*Gillomovitch Mullendorf*), Louis Lehmans (*The Major*).

Experimental film. Zero and Steinmetz are two struggling, disembodied forces floating in a timeless universe. Zero, accompanied by his secretary, Vivian, takes a variety of forms—Napoleon, an Arab, an antiquarian, or a South American dictator—and his opponent, Steinmetz, appears variously as a fascist leader, a business tycoon, a porter, or a space pioneer. Constantly at odds with each other, Zero and Steinmetz enter "our world" from time to time in "light images," but neither is ever able to defeat or destroy the other. *Arabs. Fascists. Spacemen. Tycoons. Secretaries. Porters. Dictators. The Universe. Napoleon I.*

Note: Location scenes filmed in Amsterdam and the Netherlands.

002 AGENTI SEGRETISSIMI *see* 00-2 MOST SECRET AGENTS

00-2 MOST SECRET AGENTS (Italy)
F6.5768

Mega Film. *Dist* Sherpix, Inc., Allied Artists. 2 Jul **1965** [Cleveland opening]. Sd; col (Eastmancolor). 35mm. 83 min.
Pres by Louis K. Sher, Gloria Sher. *Exec Prod* Antonio Colantuoni. *Dir* Lucio Fulci. *Screenplay* Lucio Fulci, Vittorio Metz, Amedeo Sollazzo, Mario Guerra, Vittorio Vighi. *Story* Vittorio Metz. *Photog* Adalberto Albertini. *Art Dir* Giuseppe Ranieri. *Film Ed* Ornella Micheli. *Mus* Piero Umiliani. *Prod Dir* Jacopo Comin. *Sp Eff* Sergio Canevari.

Cast: Franco Franchi (*Franco*), Ciccio Ingrassia (*Ciccio*), Ingrid Schoeller, Aroldo Tieri, Annie Gorassini, Carla Calò, Poldo Bendandi, Luca Sportelli, Enzo Andronico, Nando Angelini, Connie Jorgenson, Francesco Torrisi.

Farce. While attempting to rob a supposedly abandoned villa, Franco and Ciccio, a pair of bumbling drifters, are captured by foreign espionage agents who plant a phony formula for a secret weapon in one of the thieves' teeth. The enemy agents then leave clues for the spies of other nations which they hope will lead to the discovery of the bogus formula. But when it is learned that the drifters are carrying the real formula, agents from the world over converge upon the French Riviera to pursue the pair. Eventually, American agents manage to extract the valuable teeth, and the drifters return to a peaceful life of petty thievery. *Drifters. Thieves. Secret agents. Americans in foreign countries. Burglary. Perfidy. Espionage. Riviera.*

Note: Opened in Rome in Nov 1964 as *002 Agenti segretissimi*; running time: 90 min. Released in 1966 by Allied Artists as *Oh! Those Most Secret Agents!*

HO ZESTOS MĒNAS AUGOUSTOS *see* THE HOT MONTH OF AUGUST

ZHENITBA BALZAMINOVA *see* THE MARRIAGE OF BALZAMINOV

ZHEREBYONOK *see* THE COLT

ZHILI-BYLI STARIK SO STARUKHOY *see* THERE WAS AN OLD COUPLE

ZIGZAG
F6.5769

Metro-Goldwyn-Mayer, Inc. 27 Apr **1970** [New York opening: c24 Mar 1970; LP37792]. Sd; col (Metrocolor). 35mm (Panavision). 105 min. *MPAA rating* GP.
A Robert Enders–Everett Freeman Production. *Prod* Robert Enders, Everett Freeman. *Dir* Richard A. Colla. *Screenplay* John T. Kelley. *Story* Robert Enders. *Dir Photog* James A. Crabe. *Aerial Photog* Tyler Camera Systems. *Camera Op* Mike Margulies. *Asst Camera* Paul Koons, Alfred Baalas. *Art Dir* George W. Davis, Marvin Summerfield. *Set Decor* Robert R. Benton, Chuck Pierce. *Film Ed* Ferris Webster. *Asst Ed* Hal Davis. *Mus* Oliver Nelson. *Titl Song* Mike Curb, Robert Enders, Guy Hemric. *Sung by* Roy Orbison. *Rec Supv* Franklin Milton. *Sd* Jerry Jost. *Rec* Bill Manooch. *Boom Op* Robert Crosby, James Utterback. *Asst Dir* Arthur Jacobson, John Behm, John Light. *Unit Prod Mgr* Dale Hutchinson, Bud Grace. *Wardrobe* Gene Ostler, Florence Hackett, Edward Marks. *Makeup* William Tuttle, Jack Dumont. *Hairstyles* Lorraine Rowland. *Optical Eff* Robert R. Hoag. *Still Photog* Lee Sporkin. *Casting* Leonard Murphy. *Gaffer* Bill Hannah. *Prop Master* Carl Bionde.

Cast: George Kennedy (*Paul R. Cameron*), Anne Jackson (*Jean Cameron*), Eli Wallach (*Mario Gambretti*), Steve Ihnat (*Assistant District Attorney Gates*), William Marshall (*Morrie Bronson*), Joe Maross (*Lieut. Max Hines*), Dana Elcar (*Harold Tracey*), Walter Brooke (*Adam Mercer*), Anita O'Day (*Sheila Mangan*), Joan Tompkins (*Judge Beth Weaver*), Robert Sampson (*Burt Stennis*), Leonard Stone (*Jim Barris*), Stewart Moss (*Edgar Courtland*), Charlene Holt (*Sara Raymond*), Robert Donner (*Sgt. Mason Weber*), Pamela Murphy (*Elaine Mercer*), Abigail Shelton (*Muriel*), Douglas Henderson (*Dr. Leonard*), Robert Patten (*John Raymond*), Richard McMurray (*Dr. Sean Thompson*), Elizabeth Colla (*Camerons' daughter*).

Melodrama. Diagnosed as having a fatal brain tumor, insurance investigator Paul Cameron provides for his family by confessing to the murder of a wealthy industrialist. Carefully constructing a case for his prosecution, he negotiates under a pseudonym for the sizable reward offered by the victim's associates. Despite the defense of attorney Mario Gambretti, Cameron is convicted. After collapsing while leaving the courtroom Cameron is subjected to successful laser beam surgery. Fully recovered, Cameron faces imprisonment for a crime which he did not commit. Informed by Gambretti that a new trial is impossible without further evidence, Cameron escapes from the hospital and stalks the real killer. Successfully avoiding the police he confers with his attorney. Together they locate Elaine Mercer, daughter of the victim's business associate and the victim's companion the night of the murder. Confronted by Cameron, Elaine confesses an affair with the dead man. Alarmed by his daughter's avowal, Adam Mercer, the murderer, shoots Cameron and is himself slain by the police. *Insurance agents. Police. Lawyers. Industrialists. Mistresses. Brain surgery. Murder. Revenge. Rewards. Trials. Tumors. Confession (law). Laser. Hospitals.*

Note: Location scenes filmed in and around Los Angeles. Working title: *False Witness.*

ZITA (France)
F6.5770

S. N. C. *Dist* Regional Film Distributors. 11 Aug **1968** [New York opening]. Sd; col (Eastman Color, print by Technicolor). 35mm. 92 min.
Prod Gérard Beytout. *Dir* Robert Enrico. *Screenplay* Lucienne Hamon, Pierre Pelegri, Robert Enrico. *Story* Lucienne Hamon. *Photog* Jean Boffety. *Art Dir* Jacques Saulnier. *Film Ed* Michel Lewin. *Mus* François de Roubaix. *Sd* Christian Forget. *Asst Dir* Pierre Darcay. *Prod Mgr* Claude Hauser.

Cast: Joanna Shimkus (*Annie*), Katina Paxinou (*Aunt Zita*), Suzanne Flon (*Yvette*), José Maria Flotats (*Simon*), Paul Crauchet (*Bernard*), Bernard Fresson (*Boni*), Med Hondo (*James*), Roger Ibañez (*The Spaniard*), Jacques Rispal (*The Sergeant*), Odette Piquet (*The Day Watchman*), Solange Certain (*The Night Watchman*), Jean-Gabriel Nordmann (*Manuel*), Paul Pavel, Claude Leveque, Bernard Klein, Corinne Armand, Jean Darle, Lydie Murguet, Marie Pascale Daveau.

Drama. Annie, a Parisian teenager, is faced with the reality of death for the first time when her beloved Aunt Zita suffers a severe stroke. She leaves her home, where she has helped to nurse her aunt, and wanders through the city streets. At a club she is attracted to Simon, a jazz bassist who is preoccupied with racing his model car around the club track. She meets Boni, a farmer who buys her food and fashions bread animals, and James, a black militant Marxist classmate, but she becomes bored with them and leaves the club. In the street she sees a poor Spaniard killing a cat for food and is arrested with him. Bernard, her family doctor, obtains her release and sets out to distract her, but as they drive through the city they collide with a van in which Boni and James are riding. Boni's prize ram escapes and leads a chase. The group returns to the club, but Bernard learns that Zita has died and leaves without telling Annie. Boni drives Annie home and in vain proposes marriage; unready to go back into her house, Annie returns to the club. She again meets Simon, and eventually, they drive together to visit Zita's home in the country. Back at his Paris apartment [at the country home, according to one source], they make love, and Annie has flashbacks of her childhood in the country with Zita. The next morning, fortified by her experiences, Annie is able to face the fact of Zita's death. *Aunts. Musicians. Negroes. Students. Physicians. Spanish. Farmers. Strokes. Death. Adolescence. Poverty. Sexual initiation. Marxism. Cafes. Jazz. Paris. Chases. Automobile accidents. Sheep. Cats.*

Note: Opened in Paris in Jan 1968 as *Tante Zita*; running time: 105 min. Some U. S. sources credit Michael Lewin as producer.

THE ZODIAC COUPLES   F6.5771
S. A. E. Productions. 17 Jun **1970** [New York opening]. Sd; col (Eastman Color). 35mm. 77 min.

Prod-Dir-Writ Bob Stein, Alan Roberts. *Photog* Robert Maxwell. *Film Ed* D. W. Barry. *Mus* Rockwell. *Sd* Clark D. Will.

Cast: John Raymond (narrator).

Sex film. In a series of vignettes, beginning with Aries and ending with Pisces, male and female sexual traits for each of the 12 signs of the zodiac are first given by the narrator and then illustrated by brief scenes of sexual intercourse. *Astrology. Sexuality. Sexual techniques.*

ZOKU MIYAMOTO MUSASHI see SAMURAI (PART II)

ZOKU NINGEN NO JOKEN see ROAD TO ETERNITY

ZOKU OTOKOWA TSURAIYO see TORA-SAN PT. 2

ZOKU SHACHO GYOJOKI see 5 GENTS ON THE SPOT

ZORBA THE GREEK (United States/Greece)   F6.5772
Twentieth Century-Fox Film Corp.-Michael Cacoyannis-Rochley Productions. *Dist* International Classics. 17 Dec **1964** [New York opening; c17 Dec 1964; LP30833]. Sd; b&w. 35mm. 142 min.

A Michael Cacoyannis Production. *Prod-Dir-Writ* Michael Cacoyannis. *Assoc Prod* Anthony Quinn. *Dir Photog* Walter Lassally. *Asst Camera* George Antonakis. *Art Dir* Vassele Fotopoulos. *Asst Art Dir* Demetris Economou. *Film Ed* Michael Cacoyannis. *Asst Film Ed* Johnny Dwyre. *Mus Comp & Cond* Mikis Theodorakis. *Sd Engr* Mikes Damalas. *Sd Rec* Demetris Kasimatis. *Asst Dir* Franco Cirino, George Cosmatos, Panayis Roussos. *Prod Coörd* Anis Nohra. *Unit Mgr* Yannis Petropoulakis. *Location Mgr* Vassilis Mariolis. *Cont* May Kapsaskis. *Prod Sec* Yannoulla Wakefield. *Wardrobe* Anna Stavropoulou. *Makeup* Monique Archambault. *Hairstyles* Alex Archambault.

Cast: Anthony Quinn (*Alexis Zorba*), Alan Bates (*Basil*), Irene Papas (*widow*), Lila Kedrova (*Madame Hortense*), George Foundas (*Mavrandoni*), Eleni Anousaki (*Lola*), Sotiris Moustakas (*Mimithos*), Takis Emmanuel (*Manolakas*), Yorgo Voyagis (*Pavlo*), Anna Kyriakou (*Soul*).

Drama. Source: Nikos Kazantzakēs, *Zorba the Greek* (trans. by Carl Wildman of *Bios kai politeiatou Alexē Zormba*; London, 1952). Basil, an introverted English writer, comes to Greece to work on a lignite mine he has inherited from his Greek father. He meets an exuberant Greek peasant, Zorba, who persuades Basil to hire him to help work on the mine. They arrive on Crete and take up lodging in a hotel owned by Madame Hortense, an old French courtesan. Zorba courts Madame Hortense and persuades Basil to court another woman, a beautiful widow. Zorba goes to the city for a spree and leaves Basil to take care of Madame Hortense. Basil's shyness is overcome, and he visits the widow again. This time he makes love to her, and when her suitor, Pavlo, hears a rumor of this, he commits suicide. The townspeople turn against the widow and brutally murder her. Madame Hortense becomes ill; and while she is dying, the peasants of the village strip her of all her belongings. Work on the mine is finally completed, but a crucial cable line is destroyed as the operation begins. Basil is upset by his bad fortune, but Zorba teaches him to dance and be joyful in accepting what life has to offer. *Authors. Peasants. Prostitutes. French. Widows. English. Friendship. Murder. Hedonism. Village life. Suicide. Inheritance. Hotels. Coal mining. Crete.*

Note: Filmed in Crete. Greek title: *Zormba*.

ZORMBA see ZORBA THE GREEK

ZORNS LEMMA   F6.5773
Dist Film-Makers' Distribution Center. 14 Apr **1970** [New York opening]. Sd & si; col. 16mm. 62 min.

Dir Hollis Frampton. *Timing of Answer Print* Joe Williams. *Key Grip* David Hamilton.

Cast: Rosemarie Castoro, Ginger Michels, Marcia Steinbrecher, Twyla Tharp, Susan Weiner, Joyce Wieland (voices).

Experimental film. Section I (4 min): Over a blank screen, a didactic female voice recites alphabetic couplets from an early Bay State Primer. Section II (47 min, silent): Letters from the Roman alphabet, silver on a black ground, alternate with random images, including those of a book; an egg frying; a red ibis; cookies; a woman's face; a tree in winter; hands washing; a strolling man;

beef being ground; a newly-painted wall; a child swinging; three men excavating; dried beans; shoes; a steam vent; a child's Tinkertoy chain; rhinoceros; a flat tire; a tangerine; sidestreets at night; a bonfire; cattails; and waves. Gradually, these images replace letters in the sequence, according to a mathematical progression. Section III (11 min): As six female voices read from Robert Grosseteste's 13th-century treatise, *On Light or the Ingression of Forms*, each voice reciting in turn a single word, a couple and a dog retreat through a snowy field into a forest. As they disappear into the woods, the image of the field fades to white. *Mathematics. Cosmology. Bay State Primer.*

Note: The title refers to an axiom in set theory mathematics.

ZORRO CONTRO MACISTE see SAMSON AND THE SLAVE QUEEN

ZOTZ!   F6.5774
William Castle Pictures. *Dist* Columbia Pictures. 27 Jun **1962** [Los Angeles opening; c27 Jun 1962; LP22244]. Sd (RCA); b&w. 35mm. 85 min. [Copyright length: 87 min.]

Prod-Dir William Castle. *Assoc Prod* Dona Holloway. *Screenplay* Ray Russell. *Dir Photog* Gordon Avil. *Art Dir* Robert Peterson. *Set Decor* James M. Crowe. *Film Ed* Edwin Bryant. *Mus Comp & Cond* Bernard Green. *Sd Supv* Charles J. Rice. *Sd* Josh Westmoreland. *Asst Dir* Carter De Haven, Jr., Roger Slager. *Script Supv* Eylla Jacobus. *Wardrobe* Jack Angel, Edna Taylor. *Makeup Supv* Ben Lane. *Makeup* Joseph Di Bella. *Hairstyles* Jean Austin. *Still Photog* Mel Traxel.

Cast: Tom Poston (*Prof. Jonathan Jones*), Julia Meade (*Prof. Virginia Fenster*), Jim Backus (*Horatio Kellgore*), Fred Clark (*General Bulliver*), Cecil Kellaway (*Dean Updike*), Zeme North (*Cynthia Jones*), Margaret Dumont (*Persephone Updike*), James Millhollin (*Dr. Kroner*), Carl Don (*Josh Bates*), Mike Mazurki (*Igor*), Jimmy Hawkins (*Jimmy Kellgore*), Bart Patton (*Mr. Crane*), Judee Morton (*Miss Blakiston*), Michael Westfield (*Captain Byron*), Russ Whiteman (*Major Folger*), George Moorman (*Lieut. John G. Stefanski*), Elaine Martone (*secretary*), Susan Dorn (*nurse*), Albert Glasser ("*Khrushchev*"), Louis Nye.

Comedy. Source: Walter Karig, *Zotz!* (New York, 1947). Jonathan Jones, Professor of Ancient Eastern Languages at Saracen Valley College in California, lives with his niece, Cynthia, who receives an ancient coin from one of Jonathan's former students, now on an archeological dig. Jonathan discovers that the coin holds magic powers for its bearer. By pointing his index finger he can inflict pain; by uttering the word "Zotz!" he can create slow motion; and by employing both techniques at once he can cause death. His preoccupation with the coin brings about a number of unusual occurrences, one of which leads to meeting Virginia Fenster, a colleague of whom he becomes enamored. Dean Updike suspects that Jonathan is in need of psychiatric treatment and arranges an appointment with Dr. Kroner. Jonathan's rival for the post of Dean of Languages, Horatio Kellgore, is quick to take advantage of the situation. When Jonathan fails to convince Dr. Kroner of his sanity, he brings his magic coin to the Pentagon. He finds that the American military are also skeptical of the coin's properties, but the Russians are not. Khrushchev orders Communist agents to kidnap and threaten to kill Cynthia and Virginia if Jonathan does not reveal his secret to them. Jonathan goes along with the spies but tricks them into returning to the office building where Cynthia and Virginia are bound. He frees them and uses his powers to thwart the attempts of the spies to take the coin from him. In the struggle, the coin rolls into the street and disappears into a sewer just as help arrives. Somewhat relieved, Jonathan returns to college, where he wins both Virginia and the academic post. *Professors. Communists. Spies. Uncles. Psychiatrists. Russians. Magic. College life. Kidnaping. California. Nikita Sergeyevich Khrushchev. The Pentagon.*

ZULU (Great Britain)   F6.5775
Diamond Films. *Dist* Embassy Pictures. 17 Jun **1964** [Detroit opening]. Sd; col (Technicolor). 35mm & 70mm (Super-Technirama 70). 138 min. [Also reviewed at 130 min.]

Pres by Joseph E. Levine. *Prod* Stanley Baker, Cy Endfield. *Assoc Prod* Basil Keys. *Dir* Cy Endfield. *2d Unit Dir* Bob Porter. *Screenplay* John Prebble, Cy Endfield. *Story* John Prebble. *Photog* Stephen Dade. *Camera Op* Dudley Lovell. *Art Dir* Ernest Archer. *Film Ed* John Jympson. *Asst Film Ed* Jennifer Thompson. *Orig Mus Comp & Cond* John Barry. *Rec* Claude Hitchcock, Jack R. Smith. *Sd Ed* Rusty Coppleman. *Asst Dir* Bert Batt. *Prod Mgr* John D. Merriman. *Cont* Muirne Mathieson. *Wardrobe Supv* Arthur Newman. *Makeup* Charles Parker. *Prod Cons* Douglas Rankin. *Constr Mgr* Dick Frift. *Stunt Dir* John Sullivan.

Cast: Stanley Baker (*Lieut. John Chard*), Jack Hawkins (*Otto Witt*), Ulla Jacobsson (*Margaretta Witt*), James Booth (*Pvt. Henry Hook*), Michael Caine (*Lieut. Gonville Bromhead*), Nigel Green (*Colour-Sergeant Bourne*), Ivor Emmanuel (*Private Owen*), Paul Daneman (*Sergeant Maxfield*), Glynn Edwards (*Corporal Allen*), Neil McCarthy (*Private Thomas*), David Kernan

(Private Hitch), Gary Bond (Private Cole), Peter Gill (Private 612 Williams), Tom Gerard (lance corporal), Patrick Magee (Reynolds), Richard Davies (Private 593 Jones), Denys Graham (Private 716 Jones), Dafydd Havard (Gunner Howarth), Dickie Owen (Corporal Schiess), Larry Taylor (Hughes), Joe Powell (Sergeant Windridge), John Sullivan (Stephenson), Harvey Hall (sick man), Gert Van den Bergh (Adendorff), Dennis Folbigge (Commissary Dalton), Kerry Jordan (company cook), Ronald Hill (bugler), Chief Buthelezi (Cetewayo), Daniel Tshabalala (Jacob), Ephraim Mohele (Red Garters), Simon Sabela (dance leader), Richard Burton (foreword spoken by).

Historical drama. In Natal, South Africa, in 1879, Reverend Otto Witt and his daughter Margaretta are watching a Zulu ceremonial dance when they learn that 1,200 British soldiers have been slaughtered by Zulus and that the Zulus plan to attack their missionary station and destroy the small British garrison stationed there. The Witts rush to warn Lieutenants Chard and Bromhead, the commanding officers. Witt pleads with them to abandon the station, they refuse, and although the odds are 105 to 4,000 against them, the British begin plans for their defense. The Zulus attack in waves, battering the station and leaving nerve-shattering interludes of silence between each assualt. The Zulus break through the wall of the hospital after hours of fighting, but the dwindling garrison maintains a valiant defense. Suddenly the Zulus withdraw, saluting the valor of the British as they retire. Later, Chard, Bromhead, and nine others are awarded the Victoria Cross for their bravery. Zulus. Clergymen. Massacres. Filial relations. Courage. Missions. Natal. Great Britain—Army. Victoria Cross.

Note: Location scenes filmed in Natal National Park. Opened in London in Jan 1964; running time: 135 min.

ZVENI, NASHA YUNOST! see **A DAY WITH THE RUSSIANS**

ZVEROLOVY see **HUNTING IN SIBERIA**

ZVONYAT, OTKROYTE DVER see **THE GIRL AND THE BUGLER**

ZVYOZDNYYE BRATYA see **FROM THE KREMLIN TO THE COSMOS**

ZVYOZDY I SOLDATY see **THE RED AND THE WHITE**

ZWEI SÄRGE AUF BESTELLUNG see **WE STILL KILL THE OLD WAY**